2014

LexisNexis® Corporate Affiliations™

LexisNexis®

Content Operations:
Senior Director-Analytical Operations & Enterprise Entity Management Group (EEMG): Elinor Reinhardt
Director-Corporate Affiliations: Michael J. Browning
Manager-Content Operations: Tanya Hurst
Product & Marketing Manager: Laura Tarnofsky
Senior Content Analysts: Christopher Barrett, Elizabeth Marsh
Senior Quality Assurance Analyst: Erin Morales
Solutions & Content Consultant: Ummul Khair C. Morrison
Public Company Analyst: Benjamin Cohen
Content Analysts: Debra Ayn, Eric Eelman, Amanda Faria, Kevin Gaven, Denise M. Goffredo, Diane Phillips

Production:
Production Specialist: Joseph C. Stewart

Offshore Research & Information Services:
President & CEO: John Tilly, 365 Media, Inc.
Vice President-Information Services: Jayant Ramachandran, 365 Media, Inc.
Unit Manager-Information Services: Vinoth Kumar, 365 Media, Inc.

2014

LexisNexis®
Corporate Affiliations™
International Public & Private Companies

Volume VI
A-F

QUESTIONS ABOUT THIS PUBLICATION?

For CONTENT questions concerning this publication, please call:

Content Operations Department at 800-340-3244
FAX 908-790-5405

For CUSTOMER SERVICE ASSISTANCE concerning shipments, billing or other matters, please call:
Customer Service at 800-340-3244, press 3

For SALES ASSISTANCE, please call:
The Sales Department at 800-340-3244, press 2

Library of Congress Catalog Card Number: 67-22770

International Public & Private Companies Volume 6, ISBN: 978-1-6304-3981-1

Corporate Affiliations 8-Volume Library, ISBN: 978-1-5934-5787-7

Corporate Affiliations

Content Operations
121 Chanlon Road
New Providence, NJ 07974

www.corporateaffiliations.com
www.lexisnexis.com

CONTENTS

PREFACE

CORPORATE AFFILIATIONS

Corporate Affiliations is a logically organized business reference tool that covers major public and private businesses in the United States and throughout the world. The set consists of eight volumes:

Volume I	Master Index I
Volume II	Master Index II
Volume III	U.S. Public Companies
Volume IV	U.S. Private Companies I
Volume V	U.S. Private Companies II
Volume VI	International Public & Private Companies I
Volume VII	International Public & Private Companies II
Volume VIII	International Public & Private Companies III

The principle of organization for the set is geographical (by parent company) and hierarchical (by company reportage). Subsidiaries of a parent company, no matter where they are located, will be found in the same volume as the ultimate parent.

Please note that guidelines on the organization of the entire set for this edition can be found in the *Master Index* Volume I.

Entry criteria for the set are flexible. Generally speaking, non-U.S. based companies must demonstrate revenue in excess of $10 million. U.S. based companies must demonstrate revenues in excess of $10 million, substantial assets, a work force in excess of 300 employees, or be traded on a major stock exchange.

THE *INTERNATIONAL PUBLIC AND PRIVATE COMPANIES* VOLUME

Corporate Affiliations: International Public and Private Companies contains listings for companies with non-U.S. located headquarters or holding companies. Subsidiaries for these parent companies are included, whether or not they are located in the United States. Also included are outside service firms attached to the parent companies. These are firms that perform specialized services such as accounting, legal, pension management, etc.

Content and Coverage in Corporate Affiliations-International Public and Private Companies

Listing statistics for this edition of International are as follows:

Ultimate parent companies................................36,260
U.S. located sub companies..............................18,172
Non-U.S. located sub companies....................136,633
Total entry units listed...................................191,065

Outside service firms:.......................................43,141

Companies are arranged alphabetically by the name of the parent company. Subsidiary companies follow the parent in order of reporting hierarchy. The bold number in parentheses shows the level of corporate reportage. Each listing can contain an extensive number of informational items. Please refer to the helpful 'How to Use' section for a guide to referencing methods and comprehensive listing samples.

The *International Public and Private Companies* volume also contains several useful features in the frontmatter including 'New Listings' for this edition, 'Mergers and Acquisitions' and the 'Currency Exchange' table.

COMPILATION

Corporate Affiliations is compiled and updated from information supplied by the companies themselves, business publications, internet research and annual reports.

RELATED SERVICES

For information on the corporateaffiliations.com web site, please call (800) 340-3244.

Mailing lists compiled from information contained in *Corporate Affiliations* may be ordered from:

R. Michael Patterson, Inside Sales Representative
DM2 Decision Maker
2000 Clearwater Drive, Oak Brook, IL
Tel: (630) 288-8348
E-mail: robert.patterson@dm2decisionmaker.com

Electronic database tapes of the directory in raw data format are available for licensing. For electronic database tapes or alliance opportunities, please contact:

Michael J. Browning, Director, Corporate Affiliations
LexisNexis 121 Chanlon Road, New Providence, NJ 07974
Tel: (800) 340-3244, ext. 7760
E-mail: mike.browning@lexisnexis.com

Companies who wish to add or correct their listings can send information to:

LexisNexis, Corporate Affiliations Content Operations
121 Chanlon Road
New Providence, NJ 07974
Tel: (908) 665-3956

In addition to keeping the information in our directories as up to date as possible, we are constantly trying to improve their design, and add useful new features. Any comments or suggestions in this regard can be directed to the Managers of Operations at the above address.

HOW TO USE
INTERNATIONAL PUBLIC AND PRIVATE COMPANIES

Corporate Affiliations, International Public and Private Companies, contains a vast amount of useful information about firms whose ultimate parent companies are located outside the United States. Included in *International Public and Private Companies* are the parent companies and their subsidiaries, no matter where they are located.

This user guide is divided into three parts.

Part A, 'How to Locate a Company' gives referencing instructions and samples of indexes. It demonstrates many useful methods for getting the information you need from this volume and from the *Corporate Affiliations* set at large.

Part B, 'Sample Entries' shows the various data elements and listing style of companies in *Corporate Affiliations*.

Part C, 'Understanding Levels of Reportage' demonstrates how company reportage structures are simply and clearly presented throughout *Corporate Affiliations*.

PART A: HOW TO LOCATE A COMPANY

1. If you know the name of the company, but do not know its nationality or ownership status:

Look in the 'Master Index of Company Names' in volume I. This index will direct you to the correct volume of the set (i.e. Public, Private or International) and the correct page listing therein.

KOMAG, INCORPORATED; *U.S. Public*, pg. 1023
KOMAG MATERIAL TECHNOLOGY INC.—See
Komag, Incorporated; *U.S. Public*, pg. 1023
KOMAGANE ELECTRONICS, INC.—See Kenwood
Corporation; *Int'l*, pg. 638

2. If you know the company is a non-U.S. held parent company:

You can turn directly to the company listings in volumes VI, VII and VIII, all of which are alphabetized by the name of the parent company.

3. If you cannot find the company's name in the master index:

It may mean that the company has been acquired or changed its name. To confirm this, try looking in the 'Mergers and Acquisitions' section at the front of this volume.

Sample of Mergers Section

Distillers Corporation S.A.–acquired & absorbed by Rothmans UK Holdings Limited
Durr Beteiligungs-AG—name changed to Durr AG
Elosua S.A.—ceased operations (no longer in business)
Grand Metropolitan Plc–merged with Guinness Plc to form Diageo Plc

4. To locate companies in a given line of business:

Use the 'N.A.I.C.S. (North American Industrial Classification System) Master Index' in volume II. This index interfiles data from all six volumes of *Corporate Affiliations*, arranging companies by particular products and services according to their primary N.A.I.C.S. code. The index is preceded by two helpful compendia: one sorts the codes alphabetically by the name of the product or service, the other numerically by the code itself.

Sample of Alpha Compendium of N.A.I.C.S. Codes

Description	*N.A.I.C.S.*
Administration of Conservation Programs	924120
Administration of Education Programs	923110

Sample of Numeric Compendium of N.A.I.C.S. Codes

Code	*Description*
111150	Corn Farming
111160	Rice Farming
111191	Oilseed and Grain Combination Farming

Both parent and sub companies are covered in this index; parent companies are printed in bold type, sub companies in regular typeface, followed by the name of its ultimate parent. A sample of the N.A.I.C.S. Master Index is shown here:

337211 — WOOD OFFICE FURNITURE MANUFACTURING

ABCO—Jami, Inc.; *Int'l*, pg. 586
ANDERSON HICKEY, INC.—Haworth, Inc.; *U.S. Public*, pg. 516
BELVEDERE COMPANY—Smith Investment Company; *Int'l*, pg. 1019
BRAYTON INTERNATIONAL INC.—Steelcase Inc.; *U.S. Public*, pg. 1048
BRODART COMPANY; *U.S. Private*, pg. 172
COMMUNITY—Jasper Seating Co., Inc.; *U.S. Private*, pg. 589
CRAMER INC.; *U.S. Public*, pg. 288
EAC CORPORATION; *Int'l*, pg. 357

5. To locate a company in a given geographical area:

Look to the 'Master Geographic Index' in volume II. Arranged in two parts — U.S. locations and non-U.S. locations — this index interfiles data from all six volumes of *Corporate Affiliations* and shows the company's listing volume and page number.

UNITED KINGDOM

Milford Haven

DOWTY AUTOMOTIVE, pg. 4780 — IT

Millbank

VICKERS PLC, pg. 1249 — IT

AMWAY (U.K.) LIMITED, pg. 70 — IT
ASK COMPUTER SYSTEMS (UK) LTD., pg. 17 — IT
BUCKINGHAM FOODS LTD., pg. 179 — IT
DURCO PROCESS EQUIPMENT LTD., pg. 568 — IT
HIROSE ELECTRIC UK LTD., pg. 517 — IT

PART B: BASIC COMPONENTS OF AN INTERNATIONAL COMPANY LISTING

Following is an example of a typical parent company listing with tags to some of its basic components.

SULLIVAN GRAPHICS LTD.	**Company Name**
52 Upper Fitzwilliam Road	**Company Address**
Dublin 12, Ireland	
Tel.: (353) 1568 3332	**Telecommunications Data**
Telex: 95421	
Fax: (353) 1588 3334	
E-Mail: info@sulgrap.com	**Electronic Address**
Web Site: www.sulgrap.com	
Year Founded: 1967	
SULLI—(LSE)	**Ticker Symbol & Stock Exchange**
Sls.: $9,325,224,000	**Financial Information**
Assets: $2,700,000,000	
Liabilities: $2,038,000,000	
Net Worth: $662,000,000	
Emp.: 10,950	**No. of Employees, Including Sub-entries**
Fiscal Year End: 12/31/13	
Business Description:	
Designs, Manufactures & Markets	
Electronic Design Automation (EDA)	
Software & Systems for the PC &	
Systems Design Markets	
Import Export	
S.I.C.: 3577	**Standard Industrial Classification Code**
N.A.I.C.S.: 334119	**North American Industry Classification System Code**
Personnel:	
Joseph M. McGillivary (*Chm*)	**Key Personnel**
Stacey Luckus (*Pres & CEO*)	
Kevin B. O'Reilly (*COO*)	
Board of Directors:	
Joseph M. McGillivary	
Sean Connelly	
Stacey Luckus	
Patrick McGowan	
Seamus O'Dowd	
Legal Counsel:	**Name, Address & Phone of**
Simmons & Fitzgerald	**Outside Service Firm**
Consheagh Road	
Dublin 17, Ireland	
Tel.: (353) 1493 8970	
Transfer Agent:	
Bank of Ireland	
Baggot Street	
Dublin, Ireland	
Tel.: (353) 1564 3511	

Following each parent company listing are the entries for each of that company's divisions, subsidiaries, affiliates, joint ventures, units, etc. Though companies vary widely in their usage of these terms, some of the more common company designations can be defined as follows:

Affiliate A chartered business owned by the company at less than 50%.

Division An internal unit of a company, not incorporated.

Joint Venture A business in which two or more companies share responsibility and ownership.

Subsidiary A chartered business owned by the company at 50% or more.

PART C: UNDERSTANDING LEVELS OF REPORTAGE

Each sub-unit of the company will have a number in parentheses to the right of the company name. This number represents the level of reportage for that particular company. Any company with a level (1) reports directly to the parent company. Level (2) companies report to the level (1) company immediately above them. Level (3) companies report to the level (2) company immediately above them, etc.

Subsidiaries:

Ericsson Systems, Inc. —— **(1)** —— **Reports to the Parent Company (Sullivan Graphics, Ltd. from previous example)**
2 Wellington Road Killarney
County Kerry, Ireland
Tel.: (353) 1718 348
Telex: 96140
Sales Range: $25-49.9 Million
Computer Peripheral Equipment Mfr.
S.I.C. : 3577
N.A.I.C.S.: 334119 —— **North American Industry Classification System Code**
Thomas J. McSweeney (*Pres*)

Subsidiaries:

Kerrigan Co., Inc. —— **(2)** —— **Reports Direct to Level 1 Company Above (Ericsson Systems, Inc.)**
8 Swords Road
Dublin 17, Ireland —— (100%) —— **Percentage of Ownership**
Tel.: (353) 1611 457
KC—(ISE)
Emp.: 850
Mfr. of Computer Printers
S.I.C.: 3577
N.A.I.C.S.: 334119

U.S. Branch:

Kerrigan Co., Inc. —— **(3)** —— **Reports Direct to Level 2 Company Above (Kerrigan Co., Inc.)**
21 Reading Ave
Memphis, TN 38101
Tel.: (901) 324-8746 (100%)
Fax: (901) 324-8747
Mfr. of Computer Printers
S.I.C.: 3577
N.A.I.C.S.: 334119
Susan Havens (*CEO*)

Wellsley Technologies, Inc. ——— (2) ——— **Reports Direct to Level 1 Company Above (Ericsson Systems, Inc.)**
Crown Hill Clonskeagh
Dublin 4, Ireland
Tel.: (353) 278 743 (90%)
Fax: (353) 278 751
Mfr. of Computer Peripheral Equipment
S.I.C.: 3577
N.A.I.C.S.: 334119

Tennant & McDaniel, Inc. ——— (1) ——— **Reports Back to Parent Company (Sullivan Graphics, Ltd.)**
Greenhills Road Tallaght
Dublin 24, Ireland
Tel.: (353) 268 324 (100%)
Emp: 1,200
Mfr. of Computer Peripheral Equipment
S.I.C.: 3577
N.A.I.C.S.: 334119

Non-U.S. Subsidiary:

Padova Systems, Inc. ——— (1) ——— **Subsidiary Not in Ireland, and Not in the U.S. Reports to the Parent Company (Sullivan Graphics, Ltd.)**
Via Laurentina, 449
20097 Milan, Italy
Tel.: (39) 6 305291
Mfr. of Computer Printers
S.I.C.: 3577
N.A.I.C.S.: 334119
Anthony Macaluso *(Pres)*

ABBREVIATIONS

Acct	Account
Acctg	Accounting
Accts	Accounts
Acq	Acquisition(s)
Admin	Administration
Admin	Administrative
Adv	Advertising
Assoc	Associate
Asst	Assistant
Brdcst	Broadcast
Bus	Business
CEO	Chief Executive Officer
CFO	Chief Financial Officer
Chm	Chairman of the Board
CIO	Chief Information Officer
CMO	Chief Marketing Officer
Comm	Communication(s)
Comml	Commercial
COO	Chief Operating Officer
Coord	Coordinator
Corp	Corporate/Corporation
CTO	Chief Technology Officer
Dept	Department
Dev	Development
Dir	Director
Distr	Distribution
Div	Division
DP	Data Processing
Engr	Engineer
Engrg	Engineering
Environ	Environmental
Exec	Executive
Fin	Finance/Financial
Gen	General
Govt	Government
Grp	Group
HR	Human Resources
Indus	Industry/Industrial
Info	Information
Intl	International
IR	Investor Relations
IT	Information Technology
Jr	Junior

Matl	Material
Matls	Materials
Mdse	Merchandise
Mdsg	Merchandising
Mfg	Manufacturing
Mfr	Manufacturer
Mgmt	Management
Mgr	Manager
Mktg	Marketing
Mng	Managing
Natl	National
Ops	Operations
Org	Organization
Pkg	Packaging
Plng	Planning
Pres	President
Prof	Professional
Promo	Promotion
Promos	Promotions
Pub	Public
Pub	Rel Public Relations
Publ	Publishing
Publr	Publisher
Pur	Purchasing
R&D	Research & Development
Reg	Regional
Rep	Representative
Res	Research
Sec	Secretary
Sls	Sales
Sr	Senior
Supvr	Supervisor
Svc	Service
Svcs	Services
Sys	Systems
Tech	Technology
Tech	Technical
Telecom	Telecommunication(s)
Treas	Treasurer
Trng	Training
Vice Chm	Vice Chairman
VP	Vice President

COUNTRY ABBREVIATIONS

AF	Afghanistan
Al	Albania
DG	Algeria
AD	Andorra
AO	Angola
AI	Anguilla
AG	Antigua & Barbuda
Ar	Argentina
AM	Armenia
AW	Aruba
AU	Australia
AT	Austria
Az	Azerbaijan
BS	Bahamas
BH	Bahrain
BD	Bangladesh
BB	Barbados
BY	Belarus
BE	Belgium
BZ	Belize
BJ	Benin
BM	Bermuda
BT	Bhutan
BO	Bolivia
BA	Bosnia & Herzegovina
BW	Botswana
BR	Brazil
BN	Brunei Darussalam
BG	Bulgaria
BF	Burkina Faso
BI	Burundi
KH	Cambodia
CM	Cameroon
Ca	Canada
CV	Cape Verde
Ky	Cayman Islands
CF	Central African Republic
TD	Chad
CL	Chile
CN	China
Co	Colombia
KM	Comoros
CD	Congo, Democratic Republic of
CG	Congo, Republic of
CK	Cook Islands
CR	Costa Rica
CI	Cote d'Ivoire
HR	Croatia
CU	Cuba
CY	Cyprus
CZ	Czech Republic
DK	Denmark
DJ	Djibouti
DM	Dominica
DO	Dominican Republic
EC	Ecuador
EG	Egypt
SV	El Salvador
GQ	Equatorial Guinea
ER	Eritrea
EE	Estonia
ET	Ethiopia
FO	Faroe Islands
FJ	Fiji
FI	Finland
FR	France
GF	French Guiana
PF	French Polynesia
Ga	Gabon
GM	Gambia
GE	Georgia
De	Germany
GH	Ghana
GI	Gibraltar
GR	Greece
GL	Greenland
GD	Grenada
GP	Guadeloupe
GT	Guatemala
Gu	Guiana
GN	Guinea
GW	Guinea-Bissau
GY	Guyana
HT	Haiti
HN	Honduras
HK	Hong Kong
HU	Hungary
IS	Iceland
In	India
Id	Indonesia
IR	Iran
IQ	Iraq
IE	Ireland
Il	Israel
IT	Italy
JM	Jamaica
JP	Japan
JO	Jordan
KZ	Kazakhstan
KE	Kenya
KI	Kiribati
KN	Korea (North)
Ks	Korea (South)
KW	Kuwait
KG	Kyrgyzstan
La	Laos
LV	Latvia
LB	Lebanon
LS	Lesotho
LR	Liberia
LY	Libya
LI	Liechtenstein
LT	Lithuania
LU	Luxembourg
Mo	Macau
MK	Macedonia
MG	Madagascar
MW	Malawi
MY	Malaysia
MV	Maldives
ML	Mali
Mt	Malta
MQ	Martinique
MR	Mauritania
MU	Mauritius
MX	Mexico
Md	Moldova
MC	Monaco
Mn	Mongolia
Ms	Montserrat
Ma	Morocco
MZ	Mozambique
MM	Myanmar
NA	Namibia
NP	Nepal
NL	Netherlands
AN	Netherlands Antilles
Nc	New Caledonia
NZ	New Zealand
NI	Nicaragua
Ne	Niger
NG	Nigeria
NO	Norway
OM	Oman
PK	Pakistan
Pa	Panama
PG	Papua New Guinea
PY	Paraguay
PE	Peru
PH	Philippines
PL	Poland
PT	Portugal
QA	Qatar
RE	Reunion
RO	Romania
RU	Russia
RW	Rwanda
KN	Saint Kitts & Nevis
LC	Saint Lucia
VC	Saint Vincent & Grenadines
WS	Samoa
SA	Saudi Arabia
SN	Senegal
YU	Serbia & Montenegro
Sc	Seychelles
SL	Sierra Leone
SG	Singapore
Sk	Slovakia
SI	Slovenia
SB	Solomon Islands
SO	Somalia
ZA	South Africa
ES	Spain
LK	Sri Lanka
Sd	Sudan
SR	Suriname
SZ	Swaziland
SE	Sweden
CH	Switzerland
SY	Syria
TW	Taiwan
TJ	Tajikistan
TZ	Tanzania
TH	Thailand
TG	Togo
TO	Tonga
TT	Trinidad & Tobago
Tn	Tunisia
TR	Turkey
TM	Turkmenistan
TC	Turks & Caicos Islands
TV	Tuvalu
UG	Uganda
UA	Ukraine
AE	United Arab Emirates
UK	United Kingdom
UY	Uruguay
UZ	Uzbekistan
VU	Vanuatu
VE	Venezuela
VN	Vietnam
VG	Virgin Islands (British)
YE	Yemen
ZM	Zambia
ZW	Zimbabwe

COMPANY DESIGNATIONS

The following designations indicate the forms of business enterprise in various countries; these forms usually represent the organizations for large enterprises.

AB	Aktiebolag	Finland, Sweden
AG	Aktiengesellschaft	Austria, Germany, Switzerland, Liechtenstein
A/S	Aksjeselskap	Norway
	Aktieselskab	Denmark
B.V.	Besloten Vennootschap	Holland
C.V.	Commanditaire Vennootschap	Holland
Cie.	Compagnie	France, Luxembourg
Co.	Company	United States, France, South Africa, Luxembourg
Ets.	Etablissement(s)	France, Luxembourg
GmbH	Gesellschaft mit beschrankter Haftung	Austria, Germany, Switzerland
I/S	Interessantelskab	Denmark, Norway
KG	Kommanditgesellschaft	Austria, Germany, Switzerland
KK	Kabushiki Kaisha	Japan
K/S	Kommanditselskab	Denmark
Lda.	Limitada	Portugal
Ltd.	Limited	United Kingdom, United States, South Africa
Ltda.	Limitada	Brazil, Portugal
Ltee.	Limitee	Canada
Mij.	Maatschappij	Holland
N.V.	Naamloze Vennootschap	Belgium, Holland
OHG	Offene Handelsgesellschaft	Austria
Oy	Osakeyhtiot	Finland
PLC	Public Limited Company	United Kingdom
P.T.	Perusahaan Terbatas	Indonesia
Pte.	Private	Singapore
Pty.	Proprietary	Australia, South Africa
Pvt.	Private	India, Rhodesia
S.A.	Societe Anonyme	Belgium, France, Luxembourg, Switzerland
Sociedad	Anonima	Spain, Latin America
S.A.C.I.	Sociedad Anonima Comercial e Industrial	Latin America
S.A. de C.V.	Sociedad Anonima de Capital Variable	Mexico
S.A.E.	Sociedad Anonima Espanola	Spain
S.A.I.C.	Sociedad Anonima Industrial y Comercial	Latin America
S.A.R.L.	Sociedad Anonima de Responsabilidade Limitada	Brazil
	Sociedade a Responsabilitie Limitee	France, Luxembourg
S.A.S.	Societa in Accomandita Semplice	Italy
S.C.	Societe en Commandite	France
S.p.A.	Societa per Azioni	Italy
S.P.R.L.	Societe de Personnes a Responsabilitie Limitee	Belgium
S.R.L.	Societa a Responsabilita Limitata	Italy
Sdn. Bhd.	Sendirian Berhad	Malaysia
Ste.	Societe	France, Switzerland
Ste. Cve.	Societe Cooperative	Belgium
V.o.F.	Vennootschap onder firma	Holland

STOCK MARKET ABBREVIATIONS

ABU ....Abu Dhabi Securities Exchange
AIM ....AIM Market of the London Stock Exchange
AMM ....Amman Stock Exchange
ARM........................Armenian NASDAQ OMX Armenia
ASX ....Australian Stock Exchange
ATH ....Athens Stock Exchange
BAH ....Bahrain Bourse
BAK ....Baku Stock Exchange
BAN ....Bangalore Stock Exchange
BANJ........................Banja Luka Stock Exchange
BAR ....Barcelona Stock Exchange
BARB ....Barbados Stock Exchange
BEL ....Belgrade Stock Exchange
BER ....Borse Berlin-Bremen Stock Exchange
BERM ....Bermuda Stock Exchange
BERN........................Bern Stock Exchange
BESA ....Bond Exchange of South Africa
BEY ....Beirut Stock Exchange
BHU ....Royal Securities Exchange of Bhutan
BIL ....Bilbao Stock Exchange
BOA ....BOAG Borsen (Merger of Hannover & Hamburg Exchanges)
BOL ....Bolsa de Valores de Bolivia
BOM ....Bombay (Mumbai) Stock Exchange
BOT ....Botswana Stock Exchange
BRA ....Bratislava Stock Exchange
BRAZ ....Brazil Stock Exchange (BM&F Bovespa)
BRVM........................Bourse Regionale des Valeurs Mobilieres
BUC ....Bucharest Stock Exchange
BUD ....Budapest Stock Exchange
BUE ....Buenos Aires Stock Exchange (Mercado de Valores Buenos Aires)
BUL ....Bulgarian Stock Exchange
BVMAC ....Securities Exchange of Central Africa
BVT ....Bourse de Tunis
BX ....Boston NASDAQ OMX BXSM
CAR ....Caracas Stock Exchange
CAS ....Casablanca Stock Exchange
CAT ....Singapore Catalist
CAY........................Cayman Islands Stock Exchange
CHA ....Channel Islands Stock Exchange
CHI........................Chicago Stock Exchange
CHIN ....ChiNext (Chinese Exchange for Small & High-Tech Enterprises)
CHT ....Chittagong Stock Exchange
CNSX ....Canadian National Stock Exchange
COL ....Colombo Stock Exchange
COLO ....Colombia Bolsa de Valores
COR........................Cordoba Stock Exchange
CSE ....Copenhagen Stock Exchange
CYP ....Cyprus Stock Exchange
DAR ....Dar es Salaam Stock Exchange
DES ....Delhi Stock Exchange
DEU ....Deutsche Borse (Frankfurt Stock Exchange)
DFM........................Dubai Financial Market
DHA ....Dhaka Stock Exchange
DUS ....Dusseldorf Stock Exchange
ECA ....Eastern Caribbean Securities Exchange
EGX ....Egyptian Exchange
EMI ....Securities & Commodities Authority (d/b/a Emirates Securities Market)
EUR ....Euronext
FKA ....Fukuoka Stock Exchange
GEOR ....Georgian Stock Exchange
GHA ....Ghana Stock Exchange
GUA ....Guayaquil Stock Exchange
HEL ....Helsinki Stock Exchange
HKG ....Hong Kong Stock Exchange
HNX ....Hanoi Stock Exchange
HOSE ....Ho Chi Minh Stock Exchange (Vietnam)
HYD ....Hyderabad Stock Exchange
ICE ....Iceland Stock Exchange
INDO ....Indonesia Stock Exchange
IRAQ ....Iraq Stock Exchange
ISDX ....ICAP Securities & Derivatives Exchange Limited (formerly PLUS)
ISE ....Irish Stock Exchange
ISL ....Islamabad Stock Exchange
IST ....Istanbul Stock Exchange
ISX ....Inter-Connected Stock Exchange of India
ITA ....Italian Stock Exchange
JAI ....Jaipur Stock Exchange
JAM ....Jamaica Stock Exchange
JAS ....OSE JASDAQ
JSE ....Johannesburg Stock Exchange
KAR ....Karachi Stock Exchange
KAZ ....Kazakhstan Stock Exchange
KHAR........................Khartoum Stock Exchange
KLS ....Bursa Malaysia (Formerly Kuala Lumpur Stock Exchange)
KOL........................Kolkata Stock Exchange
KRS ....Korea Exchange
KUW ....Kuwait Stock Exchange
LAH ....Lahore Stock Exchange
LIM ....Lima Bolsa de Valores
LJU ....Ljubljana Stock Exchange
LSE ....London Stock Exchange
LUS........................Lusaka Stock Exchange
LUX........................Luxembourg Stock Exchange
MAC........................Macedonian Stock Exchange
MAD........................Madrid Stock Exchange
MAL ....Malta Stock Exchange
MALA ....Malawi Stock Exchange
MAU ....Stock Exchange of Mauritius
MDS ....Madras Stock Exchange
MEX ....Bolsa Mexicana de Valores

MIC ....MICEX Moscow Interbank Currency Exchange
MOLD ....Moldova Stock Exchange
MON ....Montreal Stock Exchange
MONG......................Mongolian Stock Exchange
MUN.........................Munich Stock Exchange
MUS ....Muscat Stock Exchange
NAI...........................Nairobi Stock Exchange
NAM ....Namibian Stock Exchange
NASDAQ...................National Association of Securities Dealers, Inc.
NASDAQDBAI ....NASDAQ Dubai
NEP ....Nepal Stock Exchange Ltd
NGO ....Nagoya Stock Exchange
NIGE ....Nigerian Stock Exchange
NSE ....National Stock Exchange of India
NSXA ....National Stock Exchange of Australia
NYSA ....New York Stock Exchange Arca Options Trading System
NYSE ....New York Stock Exchange
NYSEMKT ....NYSE MKT LLC
NZE ....New Zealand Exchange Limited
OMX ....Stockholm/Nordic Stock Exchange
OSE ....Osaka Stock Exchange
OSL ....Oslo Stock Exchange
OTC ....Over-the-Counter Pink Sheets
OTCB ....Over-the-Counter Bulletin Board
OTCI ....Over-the-Counter Exchange of India
PAL ....Palestine Securities Exchange
PAN..........................Bolsa de Valores de Panama
PET ....Saint Petersburg Stock Exchange
PHI ....Philippine Stock Exchange
PHLX ....Philadelphia - NASDAQ OMX PHLX
POM ....Port Moresby Stock Exchange Limited (Papua New Guinea)
PRA ....Prague Stock Exchange
PUN ....Pune Stock Exchange (India)
QE.............................Qatar Stock Exchange
RIO ....Rio de Janeiro, Bolsa de Valores
RSE ....Riga Stock Exchange
RUS ....Russian Trading System
SAP ....Sapporo Stock Exchange
SARE ....Sarejevo Stock Exchange
SAU ....Saudi Stock Exchange
SES ....Singapore Stock Exchange
SGO ....Santiago Stock Exchange
SHG ....Shanghai Stock Exchange
SPSE ....South Pacific Stock Exchange
SSE ....Shenzhen Stock Exchange
SSX............................Swaziland Stock Exchange
STU ....Stuttgart Stock Exchange (Baden)
SWX ....Swiss Stock Exchange
TAE ....Tel-Aviv Stock Exchange
TAI ....Taiwan Stock Exchange
TAL ....Tallinn Stock Exchange
TFE ....Tokyo Financial Exchange (Futures)
THA ....Stock Exchange of Thailand
THE ....Tehran Stock Exchange
TKS ....Tokyo Stock Exchange
TOSH ....Tashkent Republican Stock Exchange
TRI ....Trinidad & Tobago Stock Exchange
TSX ....Toronto Stock Exchange
TSXV ....Toronto Stock Venture Exchange
UGAN ....Uganda Securities Exchange
UKR ....Ukranian Stock Exchange
VAL ....Bolsa de Valencia
VIE ....Wiener Borse (Vienna Stock Exchange)
VLA ....Vladivostok Stock Exchange
VSE ....Vilnius Stock Exchange
WAR.............................Warsaw Stock Exchange
ZAG ....Zagreb Stock Exchange
ZIM ....Zimbabwe Stock Exchange

EXCHANGE RATES

Country	Currency	Rate
Afghanistan	Afghani	0.01927
Albania	Lek	0.00948
Algeria	Dinar	0.01273
Andorra	Euro	1.34617
Angola	Kwanza	0.01041
Antigua & Barbuda	Dollar	0.36807
Argentina	Peso	0.20132
Armenia	Dram	0.00248
Aruba	Guilder	0.55562
Australia	Dollar	1.04210
Austria	Euro	1.34617
Azerbaijan	Manat	1.27307
Bahamas	Dollar	0.99257
Bahrain	Dinar	2.59161
Bangladesh	Taka	0.01238
Barbados	Dollar	0.49196
Belarus	Ruble	0.00012
Belgium	Euro	1.34617
Belize	Dollar	0.49317
Benin	Franc	0.00205
Bermuda	Dollar	1
Bhutan	Ngultrum	0.01858
Bolivia	Boliviano	0.01400
Bosnia & Herzegovina	Marka	0.68820
Botswana	Pula	0.12310
Brazil	Real	0.49189
Brunei Darussalam	Dollar	0.80244
Bulgaria	Lev	0.68350
Burkina Faso	Franc	0.00205
Burundi	Franc	0.00065
Cambodia	Riel	0.00025
Cameroon	CFA Franc BEAC	0.00205
Canada	Dollar	0.99402
Cape Verde	Escudo	0.01194
Caribbean Netherlands	Dollar	1
Cayman Islands	Dollar	1.19325
Central African Republic	Franc	0.00205
Chad	Franc	0.00205
Chile	Peso	0.00212
China	Yuan Renminbi	0.15885
China (Hong Kong)	Dollar	0.12895
China (Macau)	Pataca	0.12319
Colombia	Peso	0.00056
Comoros	Franc	0.00273
Congo, Democratic Republic of	Franc	0.00105
Congo, Republic of	Franc	0.00205
Cook Islands	Dollar	0.83700
Costa Rica	Colon	0.00195
Cote d'Ivoire	Franc	0.00205
Croatia	Kuna	0.17771
Cuba	Peso	0.04320
Curacao	Guilder	0.54945
Cyprus	Euro	1.34617
Czech Republic	Koruna	0.05257
Denmark	Krone	0.18036
Djibouti	Franc	0.00553
Dominica	Dollar	0.36807
Dominican Republic	Peso	0.02446
East Timor	Dollar	1
Ecuador	Dollar	1

Country	Currency	Rate
Egypt	Pound	0.14854
El Salvador	Dollar	1
Equatorial Guinea	Franc	0.00205
Eritrea	Nakfa	0.06623
Estonia	Euro	1.34617
Ethiopia	Birr	0.05412
Falkland Islands	Pound	1.58003
Faroe Islands	Krone	0.18036
Fiji	Dollar	0.56329
Finland	Euro	1.34617
France	Euro	1.34617
French Guiana	Euro	1.34617
Gabon	Franc	0.00205
Gambia	Dalasi	0.02892
Georgia	Lari	0.60234
Germany	Euro	1.34617
Ghana	Cedi	0.52035
Gibraltar	Pound	1.58033
Greece	Euro	1.34617
Greenland	Krone	0.18036
Grenada	Dollar	0.36807
Guadeloupe	Euro	1.34617
Guatemala	Quetzal	0.12538
Guernsey	Pound	1.57929
Guinea	Franc	0.00014
Guinea-Bissau	Franc	0.00205
Guyana	Dollar	0.00500
Haiti	Gourde	0.02337
Honduras	Lempira	0.04939
Hungary	Forint	0.00452
Iceland	Krona	0.00782
India	Rupee	0.01854
Indonesia	Rupiah	0.00010
Iran	Rial	0.00008
Iraq	Dinar	0.00084
Ireland	Euro	1.34617
Isle of Man	Pound	1.57929
Israel	New Shekel	0.26868
Italy	Euro	1.34617
Jamaica	Dollar	0.01061
Japan	Yen	0.01100
Jersey	Pound	1.57929
Jordan	Dinar	1.40489
Kazakhstan	Tenge	0.00655
Kenya	Shilling	0.01123
Kiribati	Dollar	0.91406
Korea (North)	North Korean Won	0.00741
Korea (South)	South Korean Won	0.00093
Kuwait	Dinar	3.54359
Kyrgyzstan	Som	0.02096
Laos	Kip	0.00012
Latvia	Lat	1.89941
Lebanon	Pound	0.00065
Lesotho	Loti	0.10957
Liberia	Dollar	0.01342
Libya	Dinar	0.78401
Liechtenstein	Swiss Franc	1.07932
Lithuania	Litas	0.38428
Luxembourg	Euro	1.34617

Country	Currency	Rate
Macedonia	Denar	0.02108
Madagascar	Ariary	0.00045
Malawi	Kwacha	0.00284
Malaysia	Ringgit	0.32792
Maldives	Rufiyaa	0.06398
Mali	Franc	0.00205
Malta	Euro	1.34617
Marshall Islands	Dollar	1
Martinique	Euro	1.34617
Mauritania	Ouguiya	0.00327
Mauritius	Rupee	0.03148
Mexico	Peso	0.07868
Micronesia	Dollar	1
Moldolva	Leu	0.08084
Monaco	Euro	1.34617
Mongolia	Tughrik	0.00072
Montenegro	Euro	1.34617
Morocco	Dirham	0.11707
Mozambique	Metical	0.03247
Myanmar	Kyat	0.00115
Namibia	Dollar	0.10957
Nepal	Rupee	0.01150
Netherlands	Euro	1.34617
New Caledonia	Franc	0.01129
New Zealand	Dollar	0.83700
Nicaragua	Cordoba	0.04078
Niger	Franc	0.00205
Nigeria	Naira	0.00629
Norway	Kroner	0.18099
Oman	Rial	2.58772
Pakistan	Rupee	0.01013
Panama	Balboa	0.97898
Papua New Guinea	Kina	0.47154
Paraguay	Guarani	0.00023
Peru	New Sol	0.38347
Philippines	Peso	0.02449
Poland	Zloty	0.31713
Portugal	Euro	1.34617
Qatar	Riyal	0.26710
Reunion	Euro	1.34617
Romania	New Leu	0.30768
Russia	Ruble	0.03307
Rwanda	Franc	0.00159
Saint Kitts & Nevis	Dollar	0.36807
Saint Lucia	Dollar	0.36807
Saint Maarten	Guilder	0.54945
Saint Vincent & Grenadines	Dollar	0.36807

Country	Currency	Rate
Sakha	Ruble	0.03307
Samoa	Tala	0.42369
Saudi Arabia	Riyal	0.26630
Senegal	Franc	0.00205
Serbia	Dinar	0.01199
Seychelles	Rupee	0.07289
Sierra Leone	Leone	0.00023
Singapore	Dollar	0.80968
Slovakia	Euro	1.34617
Slovenia	Euro	1.34617
Solomon Islands	Dollar	0.13510
Somalia	Shilling	0.00062
South Africa	Rand	0.11170
Spain	Euro	1.34617
Sri Lanka	Rupee	0.00785
Sudan	Pound	0.22511
Sudan (South)	Pound	0.33070
Suriname	Dollar	0.30303
Swaziland	Lilangeni	0.10985
Sweden	Krona	0.15480
Switzerland	Franc	1.07932
Syria	Pound	0.01391
Taiwan	New Dollar	0.03387
Tajikistan	Somoni	0.21000
Tanzania	Shilling	0.00061
Thailand	Baht	0.03313
Togo	Franc	0.00205
Tonga	Pa'anga	0.57887
Trinidad & Tobago	Dollar	0.15415
Tunisia	Dinar	0.64350
Turkey	New Lira	0.56513
Turkmenistan	Manat	0.35088
Turks & Caico Islands	Dollar	1
Tuvalu	Dollar	1.04210
Uganda	Shilling	0.00037
Ukraine	Hryvnia	0.12179
United Arab Emirates	Dirham	0.27218
United Kingdom	Pound	1.57929
Uruguay	Peso	0.05088
Uzbekistan	Som	0.00050
Vanuatu	Vatu	0.01105
Venezuela	Bolivar	0.23257
Vietnam	Dong	0.00005
Virgin Islands (British)	Dollar	1
Wallis & Futuna	Franc	0.01129
Yemen	Rial	0.00463
Zambia	Kwacha	0.00019

NEW LISTINGS 2014

Appearing for the first time in this publication

1

151 Products Ltd.; Manchester, United Kingdom
1nkemia IUCT Group S.A.; Barcelona, Spain
1st RED AG; Hamburg, Germany

2

24/7 Gaming Group Holdings plc; Amsterdam, Netherlands

3

360 Capital Financial Services Group Inc.; Burnaby, Canada
360 VOX Corporation; Montreal, Canada
3S KOREA Co., Ltd.; Seoul, Korea (South)

4

49 North Resources Inc.; Saskatoon, Canada
4D Pharma PLC; Manchester, United Kingdom

5

500.com Limited; Shenzhen, China
524 Participacoes S.A.; Rio de Janeiro, Brazil
52 Weeks Entertainment Limited; Mumbai, India
58.com Inc.; Beijing, China
5N Plus Inc.; Montreal, Canada

9

99p Stores Ltd.; Northampton, United Kingdom
99 Wuxian Limited; Sydney, Australia

A

A2e Venture Catalysts Ltd; Manchester, United Kingdom
A4e Ltd.; Sheffield, United Kingdom
A&J Mucklow Group Plc; Halesowen, United Kingdom
Abbey Forged Products Limited; Sheffield, United Kingdom
ABCO Electronics Co., Ltd.; Seongnam, Korea (South)
AB Dynamics plc; Bradford-on-Avon, United Kingdom
Abhinav Capital Services Limited; Mumbai, India
Abist Co., Ltd.; Tokyo, Japan
AB Lietuvos Dujos; Vilnius, Lithuania
ABM Fujiya Berhad; Kuching, Malaysia
ABOV Semiconductor Co., Ltd.; Ochang, Korea (South)
Abril Educacao S.A.; Sao Paulo, Brazil
Absolut Bank ZAO; Moscow, Russia
Abu Dhabi Capital Management Ltd.; Dubai, United Arab Emirates
Acadia Resources Corp.; Vancouver, Canada
ACC Aviation Ltd.; Reigate, United Kingdom
Accelero Capital Holdings SARL Group; Paris, France
Accel Frontline Limited; Chennai, India
Accentuate Limited; Johannesburg, South Africa
Access International Education Ltd.; Calgary, Canada
ACC La Jonchere SA; Compiegne, France
Accu Holding AG; Emmenbrucke, Switzerland
ACCURATE TRANSFORMERS LIMITED; New Delhi, India
Acebed Co. Ltd.; Eumseong, Korea (South)
ACEP France; Paris, France
Acerolux SL; Barcelona, Spain
Ace Securities Co., Ltd.; Osaka, Japan
ACE Tours Worldwide Limited; Surat, India
ACE Winches Ltd.; Turriff, United Kingdom
Achilles Group Limited; Abingdon, United Kingdom
ACS Business Supplies Limited; Bingley, United Kingdom
Acta S.p.A.; Crespina, Italy
Actavis plc; Dublin, Ireland
ACT Co., Ltd.; Daegu, Korea (South)
Action Hotels Plc; Dubai, United Arab Emirates
Activ8 Distribution Ltd.; Watford, United Kingdom
Active Biotech AB; Lund, Sweden
Active Growth Capital Inc.; Val d'Or, Canada
Active With Me Inc.; Sarnia, Canada
ActivInstinct Ltd.; London, United Kingdom
ACTOM (Pty) Ltd.; Pinetown, South Africa
Actual Experience Ltd.; Bath, United Kingdom
Adamas Ventures, Inc.; Guangzhou, China
Adams Plc; Douglas, Isle of Man
ADARSH PLANT PROTECT LTD.; Anand, India
ADGS ADVISORY, INC.; Kowloon, China (Hong Kong)
Adi Finechem Limited; Ahmedabad, India
Adinath Exim Resources Ltd.; Ahmedabad, India
Adiuva Capital GmbH; Hamburg, Germany
ad pepper media International NV; Amsterdam, Netherlands
Adriana Resources Inc.; Toronto, Canada
AdServe Ltd.; Kowloon, China (Hong Kong)
Adtec Plasma Technology Co., Ltd.; Fukuyama, Japan
Advanced Energy Systems Limited; Kings Park, Australia
Advanced Manufacturing Control Systems Ltd.; Limerick, Ireland
Advance Energy Limited; Perth, Australia
Advance Lifestyles Limited; Mumbai, India
ADVANCE PETROCHEMICALS LIMITED; Ahmedabad, India
Advantaged Preferred Share Trust; Toronto, Canada
Advantech Technologies Ltd.; Bnei Brak, Israel
Advent Wireless Inc.; Richmond, Canada
Adways Inc.; Tokyo, Japan
Aegis Logistics Ltd.; Mumbai, India

Aeroplex of Central Europe Ltd.; Budapest, Hungary
AERTiCKET AG; Berlin, Germany
Aesica Pharmaceuticals Limited; Newcastle, United Kingdom
AESSEAL Plc; Rotherham, United Kingdom
AEVIS Holding SA; Fribourg, Switzerland
Aevitas, Inc.; Ayr, Canada
Afaq for Energy Co. PLC; Amman, Jordan
Affinity Education Group Limited; Southport, Australia
Africa Hydrocarbons Inc.; Calgary, Canada
African Dawn Capital Limited; Constantia, South Africa
African Gold Group, Inc.; Toronto, Canada
African Minerals Limited; London, United Kingdom
Africa Oilfield Logistics Limited; Saint Peter Port, Guernsey
Afrocentric Investment Corporation Limited; Roodepoort, South Africa
AGA Financial Group Inc.; Westmount, Canada
A-Gas International Holdings Ltd.; Bristol, United Kingdom
Agence Euro Services; Boulogne-Billancourt, France
Agence Meesters; Paris, France
Agence Schilling Communication; La Rochelle, France
Agenix Limited; Melbourne, Australia
AG Finance, Incorporated; Pasig, Philippines
Agility Inc.; Toronto, Canada
AGIO PAPER & INDUSTRIES LIMITED; Kolkata, India
AGORA Hospitality Group Co., Ltd.; Tokyo, Japan
Agra Limited; Windhoek, Namibia
Agrenco Ltd.; Sao Paulo, Brazil
Agrimony Commodities Ltd; Mumbai, India
Agroli Group; Crevedia, Romania
AH-Vest Limited; Johannesburg, South Africa
AICA Kogyo Company, Limited; Kiyosu, Japan
AI Champdany Industries Limited; Kolkata, India
Aichi Corporation; Saitama, Japan
AI Energy Public Company Limited; Samut Sakhon, Thailand
Aikang Remetech Co. Ltd; Seoul, Korea (South)
Aion Renewables S.p.A.; Milan, Italy
AIRA Capital Public Company Limited; Bangkok, Thailand
Airmate (Cayman) International Co. Limited; T'ainan, Taiwan
Airoil Flaregas Pvt. Ltd.; Mumbai, India
Airpark Ltd.; Seoul, Korea (South)
Airship & Balloon Company Ltd.; Bristol, United Kingdom
AIRTECH JAPAN, LTD.; Tokyo, Japan
a.i.s. AG; Berlin, Germany
Aisino Co., Ltd; Beijing, China
Ajanta Soya Limited; Delhi, India
Ajinextek Co., Ltd.; Daegu, Korea (South)
AJ Power Limited; Craigavon, United Kingdom
AJWA FUN WORLD & RESORT LIMITED; Vadodara, India
AKA Group Limited; London, United Kingdom
Akary For Industries & Real Estate Investments Plc; Amman, Jordan
Akasaka Diesels Limited; Tokyo, Japan
Aksa Akrilik Kimya Sanayii A.S.; Gumussuyu, Turkey
AKSHARCHEM (INDIA) LIMITED; Mehsana, India
Akyurek Tuketim Urunleri Pazarlama Dagitim ve Ticaret AS; Istanbul, Turkey
Alacrity Securities Limited; Mumbai, India
Al Ahlia Enterprises Plc; Amman, Jordan
Al-Amal Financial Investment Company; Amman, Jordan
Al Amin For Investment P.L.C.; Amman, Jordan
ALANG INDUSTRIAL GASES LIMITED; Bhavnagar, India
Alan Nuttall Ltd.; Hinckley, United Kingdom
Alberta Pension Services Corporation; Edmonton, Canada
Al-Bilad Medical Services Co.; Amman, Jordan
Albioma SA; Courbevoie, France
Albis Co., Ltd.; Toyama, Japan
Alchemy Worx Limited; London, United Kingdom
ALCO, INC.; Wanchai, China (Hong Kong)
Aldaman for Investments PLC; Amman, Jordan
Al Dawliyah for Hotels & Malls PLC; Amman, Jordan
Aleator Energy Limited; Claremont, Australia
Al Entkaeya for Investment & Real estate Development Co. PLC; Amman, Jordan
Alerion Clean Power S.p.A.; Milan, Italy
AlertMe.com Ltd; Cambridge, United Kingdom
Alessandro Rosso Group S.p.A.; Milan, Italy
Al-Faris National Company for Investment & Export Plc; Amman, Jordan
Alfresco Software Limited; Maidenhead, United Kingdom
Al Ghurair Investment LLC; Dubai, United Arab Emirates
Ali Abdullah Al Tamimi Company; Dammam, Saudi Arabia
Al Israa for Islamic Finance & Investment PLC; Amman, Jordan
Alisra For Education & Investment Co. PLC; Amman, Jordan
Al Jamil for Investment Company; Amman, Jordan
Al Jazira Takaful Ta'awuni Company; Jeddah, Saudi Arabia
ALKA DIAMOND INDUSTRIES LIMITED; Mumbai, India
All Asia Asset Capital Limited; Central, China (Hong Kong)
Allegion Plc; Dublin, Ireland
Alliance Energy Ltd.; Saskatoon, Canada
Allied Architects, Inc.; Tokyo, Japan
Allied Cement Holdings Limited; Wanchai, China (Hong Kong)
Allied Consolidated Limited; Sydney, Australia
Allied Glass Containers Ltd.; Leeds, United Kingdom
Allied Herbals Limited; New Delhi, India
Allis Participacoes S.A.; Sao Paulo, Brazil
All Metal Services Ltd.; London, United Kingdom
AllShips Ltd.; Maroussi, Greece

Almehanya for Real Estate Investments & Housing; Amman, Jordan
Almendral S.A.; Santiago, Chile
ALPHA Corporation; Yokohama, Japan
Alpha Exploration Inc.; Vancouver, Canada
ALPHA HI-TECH FUEL LTD.; Surendranagar, India
Alpha PetroVision Holding AG; Saint Gallen, Switzerland
Alpha Trust Investment Services SA; Athens, Greece
ALPINE Bau GmbH; Salzburg, Austria
Alpitour S.p.A.; Cuneo, Italy
Al-Safweh For Financial Investments Co. Plc; Amman, Jordan
Al-Shamekha For Real Estate & Financial Investments Co., Ltd.; Amman, Jordan
Al Sharq Investments Projects(Holding) P.L.C.; Amman, Jordan
Al Tahdith for Real Estate Investments Company; Amman, Jordan
Altair Semiconductor Ltd.; Hod Hasharon, Israel
Al Tajamouat For Touristic Projects Co Plc; Amman, Jordan
Altech Corporation; Yokohama, Japan
ALTERA Wealth Management Plc; Budapest, Hungary
Alternergy Limited; London, United Kingdom
Alticast Corp.; Seoul, Korea (South)
Altice S.A.; Luxembourg, Luxembourg
Altima Partners LLP; London, United Kingdom
Altimo Group Corp.; Bydgoszcz, Poland
Altona Energy Plc; London, United Kingdom
Alton Sports co., Ltd.; Seoul, Korea (South)
Altus Group Limited; Toronto, Canada
Alvopetro Energy Ltd.; Calgary, Canada
Al Yusr Industrial Contracting Company WLL; Al Jubayl, Saudi Arabia
Al-Zarqa Educational & Investment Co P.L.C; Amman, Jordan
Amad Investment & Real Estate Development Plc; Amman, Jordan
Amana Agricultural & Industrial Investment Co.; Amman, Jordan
Amana Holdings Inc.; Tokyo, Japan
AMAZE Co., Ltd.; Oita, Japan
Amazonia Mineracao LTDA; Goiania, Brazil
Ambassador Theatre Group Limited; London, United Kingdom
Amber Taverns Limited; Blackpool, United Kingdom
Ambika Cotton Mills Limited; Coimbatore, India
Ambitious Plastomac Company Limited; Mumbai, India
Ambroisie Capital Holding S.A.S.; Paris, France
Amer International Group Co., Ltd.; Shenzhen, China
Amex Exploration Inc.; Montreal, Canada
AMG Bioenergy Resources Holdings Ltd.; Singapore, Singapore
Amicogen, Inc.; Jinju, Korea (South)
Amicorp Switzerland AG; Zurich, Switzerland
AMINES & PLASTICIZERS LIMITED; Mumbai, India
Amoun International For Investment P.L.C; Amman, Jordan
AMRADEEP INDUSTRIES LIMITED; Ahmedabad, India
Amrapali Capital and Finance Services Limited; Ahmedabad, India
Amwal Invest PLC; Amman, Jordan
Anam Information Technology Co., Ltd.; Seoul, Korea (South)
ANAP Inc., Tokyo, Japan
Anatevka SA; Luxembourg, Luxembourg
Anconia Resources Corp.; Toronto, Canada
Anderson Spratt Group; Belfast, United Kingdom
Andulela Investment Holdings Limited; Sandton, South Africa
Anesco Limited; Reading, United Kingdom
Angelini ACRAF S.p.A.; Rome, Italy
Angel Yeast Company Limited; Yichang, China
Angus Mining Inc.; Toronto, Canada
Anhanguera Educacional Participacoes S.A.; Valinhos, Brazil
Anhui Heli Co., Ltd.; Hefei, China
Anhui Jianghuai Automobile Co., Ltd.; Hefei, China
Anhui Jinhe Industrial Co., Ltd.; Hefei, China
Anhui Juan Kuang Electric Co., Ltd.; Ningguo, China
Anhui Tianda Oil Pipe Company Limited; Tongcheng, China
Anisha Impex Limited; Ghaziabad, India
ANKA INDIA LIMITED; Gurgaon, India
Ankur Drugs & Pharma Limited; Mumbai, India
ANKUSH FINSTOCK LIMITED; Ahmedabad, India
ANNA INFRASTRUCTURES LIMITED; Agra, India
Annona Energy Inc.; Courtenay, Canada
Annuity Properties Limited; Sandton, South Africa
ANPULO FOOD DEVELOPMENT, INC.; Wuhan, China
Anpulo Food, Inc.; Laifenghsien, China
Antares Energy Limited; West Perth, Australia
Antaria Limited; Welshpool, Australia
Antibe Therapeutics Inc.; Toronto, Canada
Antisense Therapeutics Limited; Toorak, Australia
Anton Oilfield Services Group Limited; Beijing, China
AO World PLC; Bolton, United Kingdom
APA-Austria Presse Agentur eG; Vienna, Austria
APAC Resources Limited; Wanchai, China (Hong Kong)
APA Financial Services Limited; Brisbane, Australia
Apical Limited; London, United Kingdom
APIS INDIA LIMITED; New Delhi, India
APM Group Ltd.; High Wycombe, United Kingdom
Apollo Consolidated Limited; West Perth, Australia
Appian Capital Advisory LLP; London, United Kingdom
Applied Biology Company SAS; Evreux, France

Applied Graphene Materials plc; Redcar, United Kingdom
Apte Amalgamations Limited; Mumbai, India
APTUS INDUSTRIES LIMITED; Hyderabad, India
Aquaint Capital Holdings Limited; Singapore, Singapore
Aquarius Coatings Inc.; Woodbridge, Canada
Aquinox Pharmaceuticals, Inc.; Vancouver, Canada
Arab Aluminium Industry Co. Ltd.; Amman, Jordan
The Arab Assurers P.L.C; Amman, Jordan
Arab Center for Pharmaceutical & Chemical Industries Co.; Sahab, Jordan
Arab Company for Investment Projects; Amman, Jordan
Arab East For Real Estate Investments Co. Plc; Amman, Jordan
Arab East Investment Company; Amman, Jordan
Arab International Co. For Education & Investment Plc; Amman, Jordan
Arab International Food Factories & Investment Company; Amman, Jordan
Arab Investors Union Co. For Real Estates Developing P.L.C; Amman, Jordan
Arab Jordan Investment Bank; Amman, Jordan
Arab Life & Accident Insurance Company P.S.C.; Amman, Jordan
Aragon Holding GmbH; Wiesbaden, Germany
ARB Corporation Limited; Kilsyth, Australia
ARCHANA SOFTWARE LIMITED; Chennai, India
Architects Studio Japan Inc.; Tokyo, Japan
Archon Minerals Limited; Vancouver, Canada
Arco-Iris Gold Corporation; Plettenberg Bay, South Africa
Arcor Sociedad Anonima, Industrial y Comercial; Buenos Aires, Argentina
Arco Vara AS; Tallinn, Estonia
ARCUTTIPORE TEA COMPANY LIMITED; Kolkata, India
Ardian S.a.r.l.; Paris, France
Ardmore Construction Limited; Enfield, United Kingdom
Ardmore Shipping Corporation; Cork, Ireland
Ardor SA Limited; Pretoria, South Africa
Ardour World Limited; Wembley, United Kingdom
Arena Group; Saint Ives, United Kingdom
Arena REIT; Melbourne, Australia
Ares Life Sciences SA; Geneva, Switzerland
AREX INDUSTRIES LIMITED; Gandhinagar, India
Argan Beauty Corp.; Leipzig, Germany
Argent Group Europe Limited; London, United Kingdom
Argo Investments Limited; Adelaide, Australia
Aricent Infra Limited; Thane, India
ARION Technology Inc.; Anyang, Korea (South)
Aris International Limited; Kolkata, India
Aromasoft Corp.; Seoul, Korea (South)
Arora Hotels Limited; Crawley, United Kingdom
Arpadis Group; Manage, Belgium
ARRIA NLG plc; London, United Kingdom
Arricano Real Estate PLC; Kiev, Ukraine
Arrow Capital Management, Inc.; Toronto, Canada
Arrow Coated Products Limited; Mumbai, India
Arrowedge Ltd.; Poole, United Kingdom
Arrowhead Properties Limited; Melrose, South Africa
Artel Solutions Group Holdings Limited; Central, China (Hong Kong)
Artemis Optical Limited; Plymouth, United Kingdom
ArtGo Mining Holdings Limited; Xiamen, China
Artificial Solutions Holding ASH AB; Stockholm, Sweden
Artis Real Estate Investment Trust; Winnipeg, Canada
Artist & Entertainment Group Limited; Sydney, Australia
Artlant PTA, S.A.; Sines, Portugal
Artprice.com; Saint-Romain, France
ARUNJYOTI ENTERPRISES LIMITED; Secunderabad, India
ARUN VARUN TRADE & INVESTMENT LTD.; Mumbai, India
ARX Gold Corporation; Brisbane, Australia
ARYAMAN FINANCIAL SERVICES LTD; Mumbai, India
Asagami Corporation; Tokyo, Japan
Asahi Kogyosha Co., Ltd.; Tokyo, Japan
ASAHI Net, Inc.; Tokyo, Japan
Asahi Seiren Co., Ltd.; Yao, Japan
Ascot Lloyd Holdings Ltd.; Wokingham, United Kingdom
ASEEM GLOBAL LTD.; Delhi, India
Ash & Lacy Building Systems Ltd; West Bromwich, United Kingdom
Ashapura Intimates Fashion Ltd; Mumbai, India
Ashikaga Holdings Co., Ltd.; Utsunomiya, Japan
Ashimori Industry Co., Ltd.; Osaka, Japan
Ashirwad Capital Limited; Mumbai, India
Ashley & Holmes; Athens, Greece
ASHOK ALCO CHEM LIMITED; Mumbai, India
Ashutosh Paper Mills Limited; New Delhi, India
ASIA CARBON INDUSTRIES, INC.; Taiyuan, China
Asian Pay Television Trust; Singapore, Singapore
Asian Star Anchor Chain Co., Ltd. Jiangsu; Jingjiang, China
ASIAN TEA & EXPORTS LIMITED; Kolkata, India
Asia Pacific Telecom Co., Ltd.; Taipei, Taiwan
ASIA PACK LIMITED; Udaipur, India
AsiaPhos Limited; Singapore, Singapore
Asia Resources Holdings Limited; Central, China (Hong Kong)
Asiasons Capital Limited; Singapore, Singapore
Asiya Pearls, Inc.; Belgaum, India
AS Merko Ehitus; Tallinn, Estonia
AS Olainfarm; Olaine, Latvia
A/S SAF Tehnika; Riga, Latvia
ASSOCIATED FINLEASE LIMITED; New Delhi, India
Asta Holdings, Corp.; Kaliningrad, Russia
AS Tallinna Vesi; Tallinn, Estonia

AST GROUPE SA; Decines-Charpieu, France
ASTI Corporation; Hamamatsu, Japan
Astro Japan Property Group; Sydney, Australia
ASYA Infrastructure & Tourism Corporation Limited; Ahmedabad, India
ATCOAT GmbH; Duren, Germany
A-TECH Solution Co., Ltd.; Hwaseong, Korea (South)
Atevia AG; Karlsruhe, Germany
Atlantic Wind & Solar Inc.; Toronto, Canada
Atlantis Resources Limited; Singapore, Singapore
Atmira Espacio de Consultoria S.L.; Madrid, Spain
ATPI Limited; London, United Kingdom
Atreya Petrochem Ltd.; Vadodara, India
Atrium Ljungberg AB; Nacka, Sweden
@UK Plc; Reading, United Kingdom
Aucfan Co., Ltd.; Tokyo, Japan
Au Financiers (India) Limited; Jaipur, India
AUK Corp.; Iksan, Korea (South)
Aumento Capital IV Corporation; Toronto, Canada
AUN Consulting, Inc.; Tokyo, Japan
Aurania Resources Ltd.; Toronto, Canada
Auroma Coke Limited; Kolkata, India
Aurora Control Technologies Inc.; North Vancouver, Canada
Aurora Minerals Limited; Belmont, Australia
Auryn Resources Ltd.; Vancouver, Canada
Austin Fraser Limited; Reading, United Kingdom
Austock Group Limited; Melbourne, Australia
Austral Gold Limited; Sydney, Australia
Australian Food & Fibre Ltd.; Moree, Australia
Australian Industrial REIT; Sydney, Australia
Australian Natural Proteins Limited; Mordialloc, Australia
Australian Wool Testing Authority Ltd.; Kensington, Australia
Australia Sandstone Merchants Pty. Ltd.; Sydney, Australia
Ausy SA; Issy-les-Moulineaux, France
Autech Corporation; Yesan, Korea (South)
Automotive Holdings Group Limited; West Perth, Australia
Automotive Trim Developments; Coventry, United Kingdom
AUV Enterprises Limited; Sydney, Australia
Auxellence Health Corporation; North Vancouver, Canada
Avation PLC; Singapore, Singapore
AVC Media Enterprises Ltd; Aberdeen, United Kingdom
Avecto Limited; Cheadle, United Kingdom
AviaAm Leasing AB; Vilnius, Lithuania
AVIAREPS Marketing Garden Ltd.; Tokyo, Japan
AVIC International Holdings Limited; Shenzhen, China
AVOD Kurutulmus Gida ve Tarim Urunleri San. Tic. A.S.; Izmir, Turkey
Away Resorts Ltd.; Gwynedd, United Kingdom
Awtad for Diversified Investments PLC; Amman, Jordan
AXEL POLYMERS LIMITED; Vadodara, India
aXichem AB; Limhamn, Sweden
Axiom Mining Limited; Newstead, Australia
Axis Intermodal Limited; Long Hanborough, United Kingdom
AXTEL INDUSTRIES LIMITED; Halol, India
Ayima Limited; London, United Kingdom
Aylen Capital Inc.; Toronto, Canada
Azevedo & Travassos S.A.; Sao Paulo, Brazil
Azimut Holding Spa; Milan, Italy
Azul S.A.; Sao Paulo, Brazil
Azuma House Co., Ltd.; Wakayama, Japan

B

B2B Software Technologies Limited; Hyderabad, India
Bacil Pharma Limited; Mumbai, India
Baekkwang Mineral Products Co., Ltd.; Seoul, Korea (South)
Bahema S.A.; Sao Paulo, Brazil
Baiada Poultry Pty Limited; Pendle Hill, Australia
BAIKSAN OPC Co., Ltd.; Jincheon, Korea (South)
Baker Tilly UK Holdings Limited; London, United Kingdom
BALA TECHNO INDUSTRIES LTD.; Kolkata, India
Ballyvesey Holdings Limited; Newtownabbey, United Kingdom
Balocco S.p.A.; Cuneo, Italy
Balti Uudistetalituse AS; Tallinn, Estonia
Bama Gold Corp.; Vancouver, Canada
Bambino Agro Industries Limited; Secunderabad, India
BANARAS BEADS LIMITED; Varanasi, India
Banco Alfa De Investimento SA; Sao Paulo, Brazil
Banco Financiero y de Ahorros, S.A.U.; Madrid, Spain
Banco Modal S.A.; Rio de Janeiro, Brazil
Banco Panamericano S.A.; Sao Paulo, Brazil
B & A PACKAGING INDIA LIMITED; Kolkata, India
B&B Investment Partners LLP; London, United Kingdom
B&S Media Co., Ltd.; Seoul, Korea (South)
Bandvulc Tyres Ltd.; Devon, United Kingdom
B & W Instrumentation & Electrical Limited; Alberton, South Africa
Banestes S.A. Banco do Estado do Espirito Santo; Vitoria, Brazil
Banif Banco Internacional do Funchal SA; Funchal, Portugal
Bank of Chongqing Co., Ltd.; Chongqing, China
Bank of Georgia Holdings PLC; London, United Kingdom
Banque Publique d'Investissement; Maisons-Alfort, France
Baoshida Holding Group Co., Ltd.; Jinan, China
Baotou Beifang Chuangye Co., Ltd.; Baotou, China
Baoye Group Company Limited; Shaoxing, China
Bar 2 Limited; London, United Kingdom
Barakah Offshore Petroleum Berhad; Petaling Jaya, Malaysia
Bardella S.A. Industrias Mecanicas; Guarulhos, Brazil

BARODA EXTRUSION LIMITED; Vadodara, India
Baron InfoTech Limited; Secunderabad, India
Barrachd Ltd.; Edinburgh, United Kingdom
Barrett Steel Limited; Bradford, United Kingdom
Barrhead Travel Service Limited; Glasgow, United Kingdom
Barunson Games Corporation; Seoul, Korea (South)
Bassilichi S.p.A.; Siena, Italy
Bastei Lubbe AG; Cologne, Germany
Batla Minerals SA; Boujan-sur-Libron, France
Battistella Administracao e Participacoes S.A.; Curitiba, Brazil
Baumer S.A.; Mogi Mirim, Brazil
Bawan Company; Riyadh, Saudi Arabia
Baylin Technologies Inc.; Toronto, Canada
Bayshore Petroleum Corp.; Calgary, Canada
BC Power Controls Ltd.; New Delhi, India
Beaconsfield Footwear Limited; Skelmersdale, United Kingdom
Bearclaw Capital Corp.; Vancouver, Canada
Beauty Health Group Limited; Richmond, Australia
The Becker Milk Company Limited; Toronto, Canada
Bedford Capital Ltd.; Toronto, Canada
Beijing Aerospace Changfeng Co., Ltd.; Beijing, China
Beijing Automotive Industry Holding Co., Ltd.; Beijing, China
Beijing Capital Group Co., Ltd.; Beijing, China
Beijing Construction Engineering (Group) Co., Ltd.; Beijing, China
Beijing Dynamic Power Co., Ltd.; Beijing, China
Beijing Enterprises Water Group Limited; Wanchai, China (Hong Kong)
Beijing Properties (Holdings) Limited; Wanchai, China (Hong Kong)
Beijing Tong Ren Tang Chinese Medicine Company Limited; Tai Po, China (Hong Kong)
Beijing Vantone Real Estate Co., Ltd.; Beijing, China
Belapart S.A.; Rio de Janeiro, Brazil
Belphar Ltd.; Road Town, Virgin Islands (British)
Bematech S.A.; Sao Jose dos Pinhais, Brazil
BEMCO HYDRAULICS LTD; Belgaum, India
Benchmark Holdings Plc; Sheffield, United Kingdom
BENTLEY COMMERCIAL ENTERPRISES LIMITED; Mumbai, India
Benxi Iron & Steel Group Co. Ltd.; Benxi, China
Berge y Cia SA; Bilbao, Spain
BERICAP GmbH & Co. KG; Budenheim, Germany
Berjaya Auto Berhad; Shah Alam, Malaysia
Bermont Development Sdn. Bhd; Kelang, Malaysia
Berner SE; Kunzelsau, Germany
Bertel O. Steen AS; Lorenskog, Norway
BERVIN INVESTMENT & LEASING LIMITED; New Delhi, India
Beryl Drugs Ltd.; Indore, India
Best Bridal, Inc.; Tokyo, Japan
The Best Connection Employment Group; Halesowen, United Kingdom
Best Cut Limited; Empangeni, South Africa
Best Western Village Park Inn; Calgary, Canada
Betapart Participacoes S/A; Rio de Janeiro, Brazil
Betsson AB; Stockholm, Sweden
Better Bathrooms UK Limited; Leigh, United Kingdom
BEWI Produkter AS; Froya, Norway
BF1 Motorsport Holdings Ltd.; Diss, United Kingdom
BFW Liegenschaften AG; Frauenfeld, Switzerland
BGRIMM Magnetic Materials & Technology Co., Ltd.; Beijing, China
BG T&A Co.; Gunpo, Korea (South)
BHAGERIA DYE-CHEM LIMITED; Mumbai, India
Bhagyodaya Infrastructure Development Limited; Mumbai, India
Bhanot Construction & Housing Ltd.; New Delhi, India
Bhansali Engineering Polymers Limited; Mumbai, India
BH Co., Ltd.; Incheon, Korea (South)
Bhilwara Tex-Fin Limited; New Delhi, India
BHK Resources Inc.; Vancouver, Canada
BIA Overseas S.A.; Wavre, Belgium
Bibendum Wine Limited; London, United Kingdom
Bicicletas Monark S.A.; Indaiatuba, Brazil
BID Group Ltd; Westhoughton, United Kingdom
Big Bank Big Oil Split Corp.; Toronto, Canada
BIM Birlesik Magazalar A.S.; Istanbul, Turkey
BIMobject AB; Malmo, Sweden
BinckBank N.V.; Amsterdam, Netherlands
Bindar Trading & Investment Co. PLC; Amman, Jordan
Binggrae Co., Ltd.; Seoul, Korea (South)
Binhai Investment Company Limited; Hong Kong, China (Hong Kong)
The BIO Agency; London, United Kingdom
Bio Blast Pharma Ltd.; Tel Aviv, Israel
Bio Green Papers Limited; Hyderabad, India
Bioland co., ltd; Cheonan, Korea (South)
BioLight Israeli Life Sciences Investments Ltd.; Tel Aviv, Israel
Biological E. Limited; Hyderabad, India
Biologix Hair Inc.; Toronto, Canada
Bio Methanol Chemie Nederland BV; Delfzijl, Netherlands
Biomm S. A.; Belo Horizonte, Brazil
BioScience Brands Limited; Isando, South Africa
Biosev S.A.; Sao Paulo, Brazil
Biotechprogress Scientific Research & Production Co. ZAO; Kirishi, Russia
Birch & Prestige Investment Group Limited; Moorabbin, Australia
Bisan Limited; Melbourne, Australia
Bison Energy Services Plc; London, United Kingdom
BITS Private Limited; Pune, India

BJC Heavy Industries Public Company Limited; Rayong, Thailand
BJL Group Limited; Manchester, United Kingdom
BK One Limited; Cape Town, South Africa
Black Birch Capital Acquisition III Corp.; Brooklin, Canada
Blackbird International Corporation; Oakville, Canada
Blackfin Capital Partners SAS; Paris, France
Blackhawk Capital LLP; Fleet, United Kingdom
Black Isle Resources Corp.; Vancouver, Canada
Blackmores Limited; Warriewood, Australia
Blacksteel Energy Inc.; Calgary, Canada
Black Widow Resources, Inc.; Toronto, Canada
B.L.L. Holdings Ltd; Erith, United Kingdom
Bloom Dekor Limited; Ahmedabad, India
Bloom Industries Limited; Mahad, India
Blue Blends Finance Limited; Mumbai, India
Blue Blends (India) Limited; Mumbai, India
Blue Capital Reinsurance Holdings Ltd.; Pembroke, Bermuda
BLUE CIRCLE SERVICES LIMITED; Mumbai, India
Blue Colibri AG; Munich, Germany
BlueRock Diamonds plc; London, United Kingdom
Blue Sky Hosting Ltd; London, United Kingdom
Blue Solutions Limited; Wokingham, United Kingdom
Bluestar New Chemical Materials Co., Ltd.; Beijing, China
B-Maven, Inc.; Quezon City, Philippines
BM Polyco Ltd.; Enfield, United Kingdom
BMTC Group Inc.; Montreal, Canada
Bodegas Riojanas, S.A.; La Rioja, Spain
Bohae Brewery Co., Ltd.; Seongnam, Korea (South)
Bollin Group Ltd.; Macclesfield, United Kingdom
BOMBAY CYCLE & MOTOR AGENCY LIMITED; Mumbai, India
Bombay Oxygen Corporation Limited; Mumbai, India
Bombril S.A.; Sao Bernardo do Campo, Brazil
Bonatla Property Holdings Limited; Johannesburg, South Africa
BonitaSoft SA; Grenoble, France
Boost Capital Corp.; Toronto, Canada
Borax Morarji Limited; Mumbai, India
Boryung Pharmaceutical; Seoul, Korea (South)
Bosa Properties Inc.; Vancouver, Canada
BOSIG Holding GmbH & Co. KG; Gingen an der Fils, Germany
Bossini International Holdings Limited; Kowloon, China (Hong Kong)
Bouyer Leroux SA; La Seguiniere, France
Bowler Metcalf Limited; Cape Town, South Africa
Bowleven plc; Edinburgh, United Kingdom
Bowman Power Group Ltd; Southampton, United Kingdom
Boyaa Interactive International Ltd; Shenzhen, China
Brakes Auto (India) Limited; Mumbai, India
The Brand Agency Pty. Ltd.; Perth, Australia
Brand Development Company Limited; London, United Kingdom
Brand Marvel Worldwide Consumer Products Corporation; Vancouver, Canada
Brand Realty Services Ltd.; Noida, India
Brasil Brokers Participacoes S.A.; Rio de Janeiro, Brazil
BravenetMedia.com; Parksville, Canada
Brazilian Finance & Real Estate S.A.; Sao Paulo, Brazil
Brazil Pharma S.A.; Sao Paulo, Brazil
Brederode S.A.; Waterloo, Belgium
Bridgetec Corp.; Seoul, Korea (South)
BrightHouse Group Plc.; Watford, United Kingdom
Brikor Limited; Durban, South Africa
Brinquedos Estrela S/A; Sao Paulo, Brazil
Brionor Resources Inc.; Saint-Bruno, Canada
Brista Corp.; Mezares, Latvia
Britannia Superfine Ltd.; Lewes, United Kingdom
Brithol Michcoma Mozambique Limited; Maputo, Mozambique
British American Investment Co. (Mtius) Ltd.; Port Louis, Mauritius
British Controlled Oilfields Limited; Montreal, Canada
British Converting Solutions, Ltd.; Leighton Buzzard, United Kingdom
BR Malls Participacoes S.A.; Rio de Janeiro, Brazil
BroadGrain Commodities Inc.; Toronto, Canada
Brombergs Bokforlag; Stockholm, Sweden
Brompton Split Banc Corp.; Toronto, Canada
Brookfield Incorporacoes S.A.; Rio de Janeiro, Brazil
Brookfield Property Partners L.P.; Hamilton, Bermuda
Brookfield Real Estate Services Inc.; Toronto, Canada
Brookfield Soundvest Split Trust; Ottawa, Canada
Bruce Power, Inc.; Kincardine, Canada
Brushman (India) Limited; New Delhi, India
BSW Timber Ltd.; Berwick-upon-Tweed, United Kingdom
Bucher Leichtbau AG; Fallanden, Switzerland
Buettner S.A.; Brusque, Brazil
Builders Capital Mortgage Corp.; Calgary, Canada
Bullman Minerals Inc.; Vancouver, Canada
Bullock Construction Limited; Walsall, United Kingdom
Burger King Restaurants of Canada Inc.; Etobicoke, Canada
Burgess Architectural Products Limited; Hinckley, United Kingdom
Busan Textile Industry Co., Ltd.; Seoul, Korea (South)
Bush Pharmaceuticals Ltd.; Kawagoe, Japan

Business Centric Services Group; London, United Kingdom
Butcher's Pet Care Ltd.; Crick, United Kingdom
Butte Energy Inc.; Calgary, Canada
THE BYKE HOSPITALITY LIMITED; Mumbai, India

C

Cabbeen Fashion Limited; Guangzhou, China
CAFCA Limited; Harare, Zimbabwe
Cafe Soluvel Brasilia SA; Rio de Janeiro, Brazil
Caixa Economica Montepio Geral; Lisbon, Portugal
Calgro M3 Holdings Limited; Sandton, South Africa
Callabonna Resources Limited; Melbourne, Australia
Callista Private Equity GmbH & Co. KG; Munich, Germany
Cals Refineries Limited; New Delhi, India
Cambria Africa Plc; London, United Kingdom
Cambridge Semiconductor Limited; Cambridge, United Kingdom
Cambuci S.A.; Sao Paulo, Brazil
Camel Group Co., Ltd.; Wuhan, China
Camelot Management Consultants AG; Mannheim, Germany
CAMEX LIMITED; Ahmedabad, India
Caminos de las Sierras S.A.; Cordoba, Argentina
Campaign Monitor Pty Ltd; Sydney, Australia
Campine N.V.; Beerse, Belgium
Canadian Metals Inc.; Montreal, Canada
Canadian Resources Income Trust; Toronto, Canada
Canare Electric Co., Ltd.; Yokohama, Japan
Candmark Electroptics Co., Ltd.; Hsin-chu, Taiwan
Canexus Corporation; Calgary, Canada
Cannon Point Resources Ltd.; Vancouver, Canada
Canso Enterprises Ltd.; Mexico, Mexico
Canwealth Minerals Corporation; L'Ile Perrot, Canada
Capevin Holdings Limited; Stellenbosch, South Africa
Capillion International Pte Ltd.; Singapore, Singapore
Capital & Counties Properties PLC; London, United Kingdom
Capital for Colleagues plc; Manchester, United Kingdom
Capitalpart Participacoes S.A.; Sao Paulo, Brazil
CapitalWorks Investment Partners; Sandton, South Africa
Caplin Point Laboratories Limited; Chennai, India
Capricorn Systems Global Solutions Limited; Hyderabad, India
Caprolactam Chemicals Limited; Mahad, India
Captain Polyplast Ltd.; Rajkot, India
Capture; London, United Kingdom
Caracal Energy Inc.; Calgary, Canada
Carad SA; Piraeus, Greece
Carbios SACA; Saint-Beauzire, France
Carbon Minerals Limited; Sydney, Australia
Cardinal Energy Ltd.; Calgary, Canada
Cardio3 BioSciences SA; Mont-Saint-Guibert, Belgium
Carfinco Financial Group Inc.; Edmonton, Canada
Cargiant Ltd.; London, United Kingdom
Caribbean Diversified Investments Inc.; Markham, Canada
Caring Pharmacy Group Bhd; Kuala Lumpur, Malaysia
Carlit Holdings Co., Ltd.; Tokyo, Japan
Carlton Investments Limited; Sydney, Australia
Carpentaria Exploration Limited; Brisbane, Australia
Cartridge Save Limited; Stockport, United Kingdom
Cascadia Consumer Electronics Corp.; Vancouver, Canada
C.A. Sperati plc; London, United Kingdom
Castle Private Equity AG; Pfaffikon, Switzerland
Cataca Resources, Inc.; Makati, Philippines
Catelli Holding S.p.A.; Parma, Italy
Catenon S.A.; Madrid, Spain
Catering International & Services S.A.; Marseille, France
Cathedral Energy Services Ltd.; Calgary, Canada
Caverion Corporation; Helsinki, Finland
CavinKare Pvt. Ltd.; Chennai, India
CCA International; Paris, France
C Cheng Holdings Limited; Kowloon, China (Hong Kong)
CCL Products (India) Limited; Hyderabad, India
CCS Supply Chain Management Co., Ltd.; Zhengzhou, China
CCT Capital Ltd.; Vancouver, Canada
CEEREF S.A.; Luxembourg, Luxembourg
CEETA INDUSTRIES LIMITED; Kolkata, India
Celltrion, Inc.; Incheon, Korea (South)
Celltrion Pharm. Inc.; Seoul, Korea (South)
Cellulac Limited; Galway, Ireland
Celsius Coal Limited; West Perth, Australia
Cemacon S.A.; Cluj-Napoca, Romania
Cembra Money Bank AG; Zurich, Switzerland
CEMEDINE Co., Ltd.; Tokyo, Japan
Centrais Eletricas de Santa Catarina S.A. - Celesc; Florianopolis, Brazil
Central China Real Estate Limited; Zhengzhou, China
CentralNic Group Plc; London, United Kingdom
Central Sports Co., Ltd; Tokyo, Japan
Central West Gold N.L.; Sydney, Australia
Century Real Estate Holdings Pvt. Ltd.; Bengaluru, India
Ceramax Inc.; Montreal, Canada
Ceramica Chiarelli S.A.; Mogi-Guacu, Brazil
CERAM Research, Ltd.; Stoke-on-Trent, United Kingdom
Ceres Global Ag Corp.; Toronto, Canada
CERIC Technologies; Paris, France
Cervantes Corporation Limited; South Perth, Australia
Cevital S.p.A.; Algiers, Algeria
CFR Pharmaceuticals SA; Providencia, Chile
CFT Consulting GmbH; Bobingen, Germany

CFT Energy Limited; Melbourne, Australia
CHA BIO&DISOTECH CO., LTD.; Seoul, Korea (South)
Chain Reaction Cycles Ltd.; Ballyclare, United Kingdom
Challenger Deep Resources Corp.; Calgary, Canada
CHAMBAL BREWERIES & DISTILLERIES LIMITED; Kota, India
Chambers & Partners Media Ltd.; London, United Kingdom
Champions (UK) plc.; Loughborough, United Kingdom
Chanco International Group Limited; Kwai Chung, China (Hong Kong)
Chandler Corporation; Singapore, Singapore
Changan Minsheng APLL Logistics Co., Ltd.; Chongqing, China
Changchun Yidong Clutch Co., Ltd.; Changchun, China
The Change Group Corporation Ltd.; London, United Kingdom
The Change Organisation Ltd.; Whitstable, United Kingdom
Changhae Energeering Co., Ltd.; Seongnam, Korea (South)
Changlin Company Limited; Changzhou, China
Changmao Biochemical Engineering Company Limited; Changzhou, China
Chango Inc.; Toronto, Canada
Chapman Freeborn Airchartering Ltd.; London, United Kingdom
Chargemaster Plc; Luton, United Kingdom
Charles Tyrwhitt LLP.; London, United Kingdom
CHARMS INDUSTRIES LTD.; Ahmedabad, India
Charmwell Holdings Ltd.; Kowloon, China (Hong Kong)
Charoen Aksorn Holding Group Co. Ltd.; Bangkok, Thailand
Charter Hall Group; Sydney, Australia
Chartwell Retirement Residences; Mississauga, Canada
CHASE BRIGHT STEEL LTD.; Navi Mumbai, India
CHASYS Co., Ltd; Gyeongsan, Korea (South)
CHC Realty Capital Corp.; Toronto, Canada
Cheil Grinding Wheel Ind. Co., Ltd.; Pohang, Korea (South)
Chelsea FC plc; London, United Kingdom
Chelsfield Partners LLP; London, United Kingdom
Chemical Specialties Ltd.; Verulam, South Africa
CHEMO PHARMA LABORATORIES LTD; Mumbai, India
Chemtech Industrial Valves Limited; Mumbai, India
Chemtronics Co., Ltd.; Seongnam, Korea (South)
Chettinad Group of Companies; Chennai, India
CHI & Partners Limited; London, United Kingdom
Chicony Power Technology Co., Ltd.; Taipei, Taiwan
China Aerospace International Holdings Limited; Kowloon, China (Hong Kong)
China Aluminum Cans Holdings Limited; Sheung Wan, China (Hong Kong)
China Aoyuan Property Group Limited; Guangzhou, China
China-ASEAN Capital Advisory Company; Central, China (Hong Kong)
China Asean Resources Limited; Hong Kong, China (Hong Kong)
China Asset Management Co., Ltd.; Beijing, China
China Automobile Parts Holdings Limited; Kuala Lumpur, Malaysia
China Automotive Engineering Research Institute Co., Ltd.; Chongqing, China
China Cablecom Holdings, Ltd.; Jinan, China
CHINA CEETOP.COM, INC.; Shenzhen, China
China Cinda Asset Management Co., Ltd.; Beijing, China
China City Railway Transportation Technology Holdings Company Limited; Central, China (Hong Kong)
China Commercial Credit, Inc.; Wujiang, China
China Conch Venture Holdings Limited; Wuhu, China
China Culture Industrial Investment Fund Management Co., Ltd.; Beijing, China
China Energy Development Holdings Limited; Central, China (Hong Kong)
China Environmental Technology Holdings Limited; Wanchai, China (Hong Kong)
China Fortune Land Development Co., Ltd.; Beijing, China
China Galaxy Securities Company Limited; Beijing, China
China Gezhouba Group Corporation; Beijing, China
China Growth Opportunities Limited; Saint Peter Port, Guernsey
CHINA HEFENG RESCUE EQUIPMENT, INC.; Huludao, China
China Herb Group Holdings Corporation; Wuxi, China
China Huanchi Bearing Group Co., Ltd.; Ningbo, China
China Huishan Dairy Holdings Company Limited; Shenyang, China
China Infrastructure Investment Limited; Central, China (Hong Kong)
China Innovation Investment Limited; Sheung Wan, China (Hong Kong)
China Investment Development Limited; Central, China (Hong Kong)
China Kingho Energy Group Co., Ltd.; Beijing, China
China Ludao Technology Company Limited; Central, China (Hong Kong)
China Machinery Engineering Corporation; Beijing, China
China Mining United Fund; Beijing, China
China National Aviation Fuel Group Corporation; Beijing, China
China National Machinery Industry Corporation; Beijing, China
China Nonferrous Metal Mining (Group) Co., Ltd.; Beijing, China
China Nuclear Industry 23 International Corporation Limited; Wanchai, China (Hong Kong)
China Packaging Group Company Limited; Kowloon, China (Hong Kong)
China Packaging Holdings Development Limited; Yichun, China

China Pioneer Pharma Holdings Limited; Shanghai, China
China Polymetallic Mining Limited; Chengdu, China
China Post Group; Beijing, China
China Power Investment Corporation; Beijing, China
China Public Procurement Limited; Wanchai, China (Hong Kong)
China Railway Materials Co., Ltd.; Beijing, China
China Rerun Chemical Group Limited; Daqing, China
China Saite Group Company Limited; Central, China (Hong Kong)
China Success Finance Group Holdings Limited; Foshan, China
China Tianyi Holdings Limited; Causeway Bay, China (Hong Kong)
China Wood Optimization (Holdings) Limited; Wanchai, China (Hong Kong)
China Xibolun Technology Holdings Corporation; Wenzhou, China
China Xuefeng Environmental Engineering Inc.; Nanjing, China
China Yurun Food Group Limited; Nanjing, China
Chinhung International (Inc.); Incheon, Korea (South)
CHINO Corporation; Tokyo, Japan
Chinyang Chemical Corporation; Ulsan, Korea (South)
Chips&Media, Inc.; Seoul, Korea (South)
ChitrChatr Communications Inc.; Calgary, Canada
Chiyoda Integre Co., Ltd.; Tokyo, Japan
Chlitina Holding Limited; Taipei, Taiwan
CHL LIMITED; New Delhi, India
Choice Infra Ventures Limited; Mumbai, India
Choice Properties Real Estate Investment Trust; Toronto, Canada
CHOKSI IMAGING LTD.; Mumbai, India
Chong Kun Dang Pharmaceutical Corp.; Seoul, Korea (South)
ChoongAng Vaccine Laboratory Co., Ltd.; Daejeon, Korea (South)
Chorus Aviation Inc.; Enfield, Canada
Chosun Refractories Co., Ltd.; Kwangyang, Korea (South)
CHOSUN WELDING CO., LTD.; Pohang, Korea (South)
Chow Sang Sang Holdings International Limited; Kowloon, China (Hong Kong)
Christian Potier S.A.; Carpentras, France
Christine International Holdings Limited; Shanghai, China
Christof Holding AG; Graz, Austria
Chrometco Limited; Woodmead, South Africa
Chromogenex Technologies Ltd.; Llanelli, United Kingdom
Chrysalis Resources Limited; Subiaco, Australia
Chuang's China Investments Limited; Central, China (Hong Kong)
Chuang's Consortium International Limited; Central, China (Hong Kong)
Chuan Seng Leong Pte. Ltd.; Singapore, Singapore
Chungdahm Learning, Inc.; Seoul, Korea (South)
Chungho ComNet Co., Ltd.; Seoul, Korea (South)
ChungKwang Construction Co., Ltd.; Seoul, Korea (South)
Chuo Denki Kogyo Co., Ltd.; Tokyo, Japan
Chuo Spring Co., Ltd.; Nagoya, Japan
Churchill Mining Plc; Subiaco, Australia
Cia. Hering; Blumenau, Brazil
Cia Iguacu de Cafe Soluvel; Cornelio Procopio, Brazil
Cicada Ventures Ltd.; Vancouver, Canada
Cinderella Media Group Limited; Hong Kong, China (Hong Kong)
Cinerad Communications Limited; Kolkata, India
Cistro Telelink Limited; Indore, India
Citair Inc.; Hensall, Canada
CITIC Dameng Holdings Limited; Central, China (Hong Kong)
CITIC Securities Co., Ltd.; Beijing, China
Cititec Associates Limited; London, United Kingdom
City e-Solutions Limited; Singapore, Singapore
CityFibre Infrastructure Holdings PLC; London, United Kingdom
CITYMAN LIMITED; Bengaluru, India
City Office REIT, Inc.; Vancouver, Canada
City Refrigeration Holdings (UK) Limited; Glasgow, United Kingdom
CJ E&M Corporation; Seoul, Korea (South)
C.J.Gelatine Products Limited; Mumbai, India
CJSC Investlesprom; Moscow, Russia
CJSC Russian Standard Corporation; Moscow, Russia
Clancy Exploration Limited; Orange, Australia
Clarion S.A. Agroindustrial; Osasco, Brazil
Classic Minerals Limited; Osborne Park, Australia
CLC Group Limited; Southampton, United Kingdom
CLEAN & SCIENCE Co., Ltd.; Seoul, Korea (South)
Clean Coal Power R&D Co., Ltd.; Fukushima, Japan
Cleantech Capital Inc.; Toronto, Canada
Cleanup Corporation; Tokyo, Japan
Clear Leisure Plc; London, United Kingdom
Clear System Recycling, Inc.; Oakville, Canada
Click Travel Ltd.; Birmingham, United Kingdom
Cliffmont Resources Ltd.; Vancouver, Canada
Clinical Genomics Pty. Ltd.; North Ryde, Australia
Clipper Logistics Group Ltd.; Leeds, United Kingdom
CLIQ Energy Berhad; Shah Alam, Malaysia
Cloudyn Ltd.; Ra'anana, Israel
Cluff Natural Resources Plc; London, United Kingdom
CMP Capital Management-Partners GmbH; Berlin, Germany
CMST Development Co., Ltd.; Beijing, China
CNH Industrial N.V.; Basildon, United Kingdom
CNRP Mining Inc.; Toronto, Canada
CO2 Group Limited; Perth, Australia

Coast Wholesale Appliances Inc.; Vancouver, Canada
Cobar Consolidated Resources Limited; Melbourne, Australia
Cobepa S.A.; Brussels, Belgium
Coburn Japan Corporation; Tokyo, Japan
Coca-Cola HBC AG; Zug, Switzerland
Coca-Cola Icecek A.S.; Istanbul, Turkey
Code Agriculture (Holdings) Limited; Wanchai, China (Hong Kong)
Cofina SGPS, S.A.; Porto, Portugal
Cogent B2B Ltd.; Milton Keynes, United Kingdom
Cognita Schools Limited; Milton Keynes, United Kingdom
Coke Resources Limited; West Perth, Australia
Colina Holdings Bahamas Limited; Nassau, Bahamas
Colinz Laboratories Limited; Mumbai, India
Collection House Limited; Fortitude Valley, Australia
The Collinson Group Limited; London, United Kingdom
Color Chips (India) Limited; Hyderabad, India
ColorStars Group; New Taipei City, Taiwan
Colterra Capital Corporation; Montreal, Canada
Combat Drugs Limited; Secunderabad, India
Comcereal SA; Tulcea, Romania
Comjoyful International Company; Beijing, China
Communication and System Solution Public Company Limited; Nonthaburi, Thailand
Communication Weaver Co., Ltd.; Seoul, Korea (South)
Como Engineers Pty. Ltd.; Perth, Australia
Compagnia Immobiliare Azionaria S.p.A.; Milan, Italy
Compagnie de l'Occident pour la Finance et l'Industrie S.A.; Luxembourg, Luxembourg
Compagnie du Mont Blanc - SA; Chamonix-Mont-Blanc, France
Companhia Cacique de Cafe Soluvel; Londrina, Brazil
Companhia Celg de Participacoes - CELGPAR; Goiania, Brazil
Companhia de Fiacao e. Tecidos Cedro e Cachoeira; Belo Horizonte, Brazil
Companhia de Locacao das Americas; Belo Horizonte, Brazil
Companhia de Participacoes Alianca da Bahia; Salvador, Brazil
Companhia de Seguros Alianca da Bahia; Salvador, Brazil
Companhia Energetica de Brasilia - CEB; Brasilia, Brazil
Companhia Habitasul de Participacoes; Porto Alegre, Brazil
Companhia Industrial Cataguases; Brasilia, Brazil
Companhia Industrial Schlosser S/A.; Brusque, Brazil
Companhia Melhoramentos de Sao Paulo; Sao Paulo, Brazil
Companhia Tecidos Santanense; Montes Claros, Brazil
Compania Vinicola del Norte de Espana, S.A.; Haro, Spain
Compass Resources Limited; Sydney, Australia
Comprehensive Land Development & Investment Plc; Amman, Jordan
Comprehensive Multiple Projects Company Plc; Amman, Jordan
COMPTA - Equipamentos e Servicos de Informatica, S.A.; Alges, Portugal
Comstock Canada Ltd.; Burlington, Canada
ComTrade Group B.V.; Belgrade, Serbia
Comwave Networks, Inc.; Toronto, Canada
Concepcion Industrial Corporation; Makati, Philippines
Confidence Trading Company Limited; Mumbai, India
Congatec AG; Deggendorf, Germany
Consolidated Global Investments Limited; Leederville, Australia
Consorcio Alfa de Administracao S.A.; Sao Paulo, Brazil
Constantia Flexibles Group GmbH; Vienna, Austria
Construtora Beter S.A.; Sao Paulo, Brazil
Construtora Lix da Cunha S.A.; Campinas, Brazil
CONSTRUTORA SULTEPA S.A.; Porto Alegre, Brazil
The Consultant & Investment Group P.L.C.; Amman, Jordan
Consun Pharmaceutical Group Limited; Guangzhou, China
Contempro For Housing Projects PLC; Amman, Jordan
Continental Holdings Limited; Kowloon, China (Hong Kong)
Continental Petroleums Limited; Jaipur, India
Controladora Vuela Compania de Aviacion, S.A.B. de C.V.; Mexico, Mexico
Control and Applications Group; Abu Dhabi, United Arab Emirates
Control Risks Group Holdings Ltd.; London, United Kingdom
Conversion Capital Partners Ltd.; London, United Kingdom
Conway Marsh Garrett Technologies Limited; Woodbridge, United Kingdom
coolGiants AG; Bremen, Germany
Coop Norge SA; Oslo, Norway
Co-Prosperity Holdings Limited; Shishi, China
Cordant Group PLC.; Hillingdom, United Kingdom
Core Canadian Dividend Trust; Toronto, Canada
CoreCross, Inc.; Seoul, Korea (South)
Core Logic, Inc.; Seongnam, Korea (South)
Corep Lighting group; Begles, France
Core Services Group Limited; Mount Pleasant, Australia
Corney & Barrow Limited; London, United Kingdom
Corona Corporation; Sanjo, Japan
Correa Ribeiro S/A Comercio e Industria; Salvador, Brazil
Corum Group Limited; Sydney, Australia
Coset Inc.; Gwangju, Korea (South)
Coslight Technology International Group Limited; Harbin, China
Cosmo Communications Inc.; Tokyo, Japan
Cote Restaurants Ltd.; London, United Kingdom
The Covali Group LLC; Dublin, Ireland
Cover-More Group Limited; North Sydney, Australia
Covington Capital Corporation; Toronto, Canada

CPC Ingenieria y Construcciones SA; Buenos Aires, Argentina
CPMC Holdings Limited; Hangzhou, China
CR2 Empreendimentos Imobiliarios S.A.; Rio de Janeiro, Brazil
Crabtree of Gateshead Ltd.; Gateshead, United Kingdom
Cranes Software International Limited; Bengaluru, India
Cricket Resources Inc.; Vancouver, Canada
CRIF SpA; Bologna, Italy
CRM Company Group SA; Paris, France
Crodux Plin d.o.o.; Zagreb, Croatia
Croesus Retail Trust; Singapore, Singapore
Cromex S/A; Sao Paulo, Brazil
CROS NT SRL; Verona, Italy
Crossject SA; Chenove, France
Cross Marketing Group Inc.; Tokyo, Japan
Crown Tech Advance Public Company Limited; Samut Sakhon, Thailand
CRT - Concessionaria Rio-Teresopolis S/A; Brasilia, Brazil
Crucible Gold Limited; West Perth, Australia
Cryonic Medical; Besancon, France
Cryo-Save (India) Pvt. Ltd.; Bengaluru, India
CSG Holdings Limited; Pretoria, South Africa
CSLI Co., Ltd.; Seoul, Korea (South)
CSM Systems Corp.; Edmonton, Canada
CSU CardSystem S.A.; Barueri, Brazil
CTA Holding; Chaponost, France
CTC Aviation Group Limited; Southampton, United Kingdom
CTC Bio., Inc.; Seoul, Korea (South)
CT Environmental Group Limited; Guangzhou, China
ctnetworks Co., Ltd.; Ch'ung-Nam, Korea (South)
CT Real Estate Investment Trust; Toronto, Canada
CTS International Logistics Corporation Limited; Shanghai, China
CTS Spedition GmbH; Bremen, Germany
CTT - Correios de Portugal SA; Lisbon, Portugal
Cub Energy Inc.; Toronto, Canada
Cube System Inc.; Tokyo, Japan
CUBICAL FINANCIAL SERVICES LIMITED; Delhi, India
Cubic Korea INC.; Ansan, Korea (South)
CUP Interactive SAS; Levallois-Perret, France
Curo Holdings Co., Ltd.; Seoul, Korea (South)
CX Advisors LLP; New Delhi, India
Cybele Industries Limited; Chennai, India
Cyberdyne Inc.; Ibaraki, Japan
Cybergun SA; Bondoufle, France
Cyberlinks Co., Ltd.; Wakayama, Japan
Cypress Hills Resource Corp.; Calgary, Canada
Cypress Jade Agricultural Holdings Limited; Kowloon, China (Hong Kong)
Cyrela Brazil Realty S.A.; Sao Paulo, Brazil

D

DAEATI Co., Ltd.; Bucheon, Korea (South)
Daebong LS Co., Ltd.; Incheon, Korea (South)
DAECHANG Co., Ltd.; Siheung, Korea (South)
Daedong Korea Ginseng Co., Ltd.; Ch'ung-Nam, Korea (South)
Daehan Flour Mills co., Ltd; Seoul, Korea (South)
Daehan Steel Co., Ltd.; Busan, Korea (South)
Daejin DMP Co., Ltd.; Cheonan, Korea (South)
Daejoo Electronic Materials Co., Ltd.; Siheung, Korea (South)
DAELIM B&Co., LTD.; Changwon, Korea (South)
DAELIM TRADING Co., Ltd.; Seoul, Korea (South)
DAESUNG ELTEC Co., Ltd.; Seoul, Korea (South)
DAE SUNG MICROBIOLOGICAL LABS. Co., Ltd.; Uiwang, Korea (South)
DAEWON Chemical Co., Ltd.; Seoul, Korea (South)
Daewon Media Co., Ltd.; Seoul, Korea (South)
Daewon Pharmaceutical Co., Ltd.; Seoul, Korea (South)
DAEWON SANUP CO., LTD.; Ansan, Korea (South)
DAEWOO ELECTRONIC COMPONENTS Co, Ltd.; Jeonbuk, Korea (South)
Daewoong Pharmaceutical Co., Ltd.; Seoul, Korea (South)
Daidoh Limited; Tokyo, Japan
Daido Kogyo Co., Ltd.; Kaga, Japan
Daido Signal Co., Ltd.; Tokyo, Japan
Daiichi Chuo Kisen Kaisha; Tokyo, Japan
Dai-ichi Karkaria Limited; Mumbai, India
Daiki Aluminium Industry Co., Ltd.; Osaka, Japan
Daiki Ataka Engineering Co., Ltd; Osaka, Japan
Daiki Axis Co., Ltd.; Matsuyama, Japan
Daiko Denshi Tsushin, Ltd.; Tokyo, Japan
Daikoku Denki Co., Ltd.; Nagoya, Japan
DAIKOKUTENBUSSAN CO., LTD.; Kurashiki, Japan
Dainichi Co., Ltd.; Kani, Japan
DAISHO Co., Ltd.; Tokyo, Japan
Daiwa Associate Holdings Limited; Kowloon, China (Hong Kong)
Daiwa Heavy Industry Co,. Ltd.; Hiroshima, Japan
Daiwa House Residential Investment Corporation; Tokyo, Japan
Daiyang Metal Co., Ltd.; Seoul, Korea (South)
Dalata Hotel Group Ltd; Dublin, Ireland
Daleth Participacoes S.A.; Rio de Janeiro, Brazil
Dalet S.A.; Levallois-Perret, France
Dalian Top-Eastern Group Co., Ltd.; Dalian, China
Da-Li Construction Co., Ltd.; Taipei, Taiwan
Dallah Health Service Holding Company; Riyadh, Saudi Arabia
d'Amico International Shipping S.A.; Rome, Italy
Damodar Industries Limited; Mumbai, India
Danal Co., Ltd; Seongnam, Korea (South)
DanDrit Biotech A/S; Copenhagen, Denmark

Dan Form Holdings Company Limited; Kowloon, China (Hong Kong)
Danmagi Group ApS; Valby, Denmark
Dansk Traeemballage A/S; Faborg, Denmark
Daou Data Corp.; Yongin, Korea (South)
Daou InCube; Yongin, Korea (South)
Daou Technology, Inc.; Yongin, Korea (South)
Dar Al Dawa Development & Investment Co.; Amman, Jordan
Darkom Investment Co.; Amman, Jordan
DATA Group Inc.; Brampton, Canada
Datong Coal Mine Group Co., Ltd.; Datong, China
Day Lewis Plc.; Croydon, United Kingdom
Day's Motor Group; Swansea, United Kingdom
dB Broadcast Ltd.; Ely, United Kingdom
DCK Concessions Ltd.; Billericay, United Kingdom
DCM DECOmetal GmbH; Fuerstenfeld, Austria
DCM Shriram Industries Limited; New Delhi, India
D.C. Thomson & Co. Ltd.; Dundee, United Kingdom
DDS, Inc.; Nagoya, Japan
DecideBloom Ltd.; Scunthorpe, United Kingdom
Decisive Dividend Corporation; Kelowna, Canada
DECO-MICA LIMITED; Ahmedabad, India
DEEPAK NITRITE LIMITED; Vadodara, India
Deerns Raadgevende Ingenieurs B.V; Rijswijk, Netherlands
Dejmark Group s.r.o.; Prague, Czech Republic
Dekro Paints (Pty) Ltd; Kuils River, South Africa
DeLclima S.p.A.; Treviso, Italy
delfortgroup AG; Traun, Austria
Delivery Hero Holding GmbH; Berlin, Germany
DelMar Pharmaceuticals, Inc.; Vancouver, Canada
Delta Drone SA; Grenoble, France
Deltaform Ltd.; Bridgwater, United Kingdom
DELTA INSURANCE COMPANY LTD.; Amman, Jordan
Delta Magnets Ltd.; Nashik, India
Demos S.A.; Paris, France
Denkiro Service Co., Ltd.; Tokyo, Japan
Dentons Pension Management Ltd.; Godalming, United Kingdom
de Poel; Knutsford, United Kingdom
De Rouck Geomatics s.a.; Brussels, Belgium
Desarrollos Especiales de Sistemas de Anclaje, S.A.; Viladecans, Spain
Desenvix Energias Renovaveis S.A.; Barueri, Brazil
DESH RAKSHAK AUSHDHALAYA LIMITED; Haridwar, India
Detector Exploration Ltd.; Calgary, Canada
Devil AG; Braunschweig, Germany
Dexterity Ventures Inc.; Calgary, Canada
DEXUS Property Group; Sydney, Australia
DFL Holdings Pty Ltd; Brisbane, Australia
DFM Foods Limited; Delhi, India
Dhamecha Group, Inc.; Wembley, United Kingdom
DHANADA CORPORATION LIMITED; Pune, India
Dhanlaxmi Fabrics Ltd.; Thane, India
Dharani Finance Limited; Chennai, India
DHARANI SUGARS & CHEMICALS LIMITED; Chennai, India
DHB Industria e Comercio S.A.; Porto Alegre, Brazil
Dhenu Buildcon Infra Limited; Mumbai, India
DHOOT INDUSTRIES LIMITED; Mumbai, India
DHRUV ESTATES LIMITED; Mumbai, India
DHUNSERI INVESTMENTS LIMITED; Kolkata, India
Diagnosticos da America S.A.; Barueri, Brazil
Diamond Infosystems Ltd; Baroda, India
Diamyd Medical AB; Stockholm, Sweden
DIATEC s.r.l.; Collecorvino, Italy
Diaxonhit SA; Paris, France
DI Corp.; Seoul, Korea (South)
Dieselec Thistle Generators Limited; Glasgow, United Kingdom
Diesse SRL; Calcinato, Italy
Differ Group Holding Co., Ltd.; Xiamen, China
Digital Magics S.p.A.; Milan, Italy
Digital Multimedia Technology Co., Ltd.; Anyang, Korea (South)
Digital Online Media GmbH; Cologne, Germany
Digital Publishing Initiatives Japan Co., Ltd.; Tokyo, Japan
DIJET Industrial Co., Ltd; Osaka, Japan
Dimed S.A. Distribuidora de Medicamentos; Porto Alegre, Brazil
Dimensions Jordan & Emirates Commercial Investments Corporation; Amman, Jordan
Dinamo Corp.; Slough, United Kingdom
DIO Corporation; Busan, Korea (South)
Dip Corporation; Tokyo, Japan
Direcional Engenharia S.A.; Belo Horizonte, Brazil
Directi Group; Mumbai, India
Direct Line Insurance Group plc; Bromley, United Kingdom
Direct Nickel Limited; Sydney, Australia
DIRTT Environmental Solutions Ltd.; Calgary, Canada
Distimo Holding B.V.; Utrecht, Netherlands
Diversa Limited; Brisbane, Australia
Diversified United Investment Limited; Melbourne, Australia
Dividend Growth Split Corp.; Toronto, Canada
DIVYASHAKTI GRANITES LIMITED; Hyderabad, India
Dixie Energy Trust; Calgary, Canada
DK AZTEC Co., Ltd.; Anseong, Korea (South)
DKK-TOA Corporation; Tokyo, Japan
DKS Co. Ltd.; Kyoto, Japan
DLE Inc.; Tokyo, Japan
DLF AmbA; Roskilde, Denmark
DMI UK Ltd.; North Shields, United Kingdom

DNA Chip Research Inc.; Yokohama, Japan
DNA Oy; Helsinki, Finland
Dome Gold Mines Limited; Sydney, Australia
Donald Ward Limited; Ilkeston, United Kingdom
Dong Ah Tire & Rubber Co., Ltd.; Yangsan, Korea (South)
Dong-A Hwasung Co., Ltd.; Kimhae, Korea (South)
Dong Bang Transport Logistics Co., Ltd.; Seoul, Korea (South)
Dongbu Lightec Co., Ltd.; Bucheon, Korea (South)
Dongil Metal Co., Ltd.; Yeongcheon, Korea (South)
Dongil Technology LTD.; Hwaseong, Korea (South)
Dongnam Chemical Co., Ltd.; Incheon, Korea (South)
Dongnam Marine Crane Co., Ltd; Kimhae, Korea (South)
Dongsung Chemical Co., Ltd.; Busan, Korea (South)
Dong Sung Pharmaceutical Company Ltd.; Seoul, Korea (South)
DONGWHA HOLDINGS CO., LTD.; Seoul, Korea (South)
Dongwu Cement International Limited; Kowloon, China (Hong Kong)
Dongyang Engineering & Construction Corp.; Seoul, Korea (South)
Dongyang Gangchul Co., Ltd; Daejeon, Korea (South)
Dongyang Mechatronics; Seoul, Korea (South)
Dong Yang P&F Co., Ltd; Seoul, Korea (South)
Doric Nimrod Air One Limited; Saint Peter Port, Guernsey
Doric Nimrod Air Two Limited; Saint Peter Port, Guernsey
dorsaVi Ltd; Melbourne, Australia
Doshisha Co., Ltd.; Osaka, Japan
DoubleLine Income Solutions Trust; Toronto, Canada
Drake & Morgan Limited; London, United Kingdom
Dreams Ltd.; High Wycombe, United Kingdom
DREAM Unlimited Corp.; Toronto, Canada
Dream Vision Co., Ltd.; Osaka, Japan
Dr. Fritz Faulhaber GmbH & Co. KG; Schonaich, Germany
Drillco Metal Carbides Limited; Mumbai, India
Dron & Dickson Ltd.; Stirling, United Kingdom
DSR Corp.; Busan, Korea (South)
DSR Wire Corporation; Busan, Korea (South)
Dtcom - Direct to Company S/A; Brasilia, Brazil
Ducatt NV; Lommel, Belgium
Dujodwala Paper Chemicals Limited; Mumbai, India
DUKE OFFSHORE LIMITED; Mumbai, India
Duksung Co., Ltd.; Suwon, Korea (South)
Dunbia Group; Dungannon, United Kingdom
Duncans Industries Limited; Kolkata, India
DUOBACK KOREA Co., Ltd.; Incheon, Korea (South)
DUROPACK LTD; New Delhi, India
DV Resources Ltd.; Vancouver, Canada
DWF LLP; Leeds, United Kingdom
DX (Group) PLC; Iver, United Kingdom
Dyer Holdings Pty. Ltd.; Wacol, Australia
Dynac Sdn. Bhd.; Pasir Gudang, Malaysia
Dynagas LNG Partners LP; Glyfada, Greece
Dynapac Co., Ltd.; Nagoya, Japan
Dynaplast-Extruco Inc.; Montreal, Canada

E

E1 Corporation; Seoul, Korea (South)
EAF Supply Chain Limited; Wokingham, United Kingdom
Eagle Copters Ltd.; Calgary, Canada
Eagle Vet. Tech Co., Ltd.; Seoul, Korea (South)
East Africa Metals Inc.; Vancouver, Canada
East Buildtech Ltd; New Delhi, India
EASTERN TREADS LIMITED; Kochi, India
EastPack Limited; Auckland, New Zealand
Easyaccess Financial Services Limited; Chennai, India
EasyVista S.A.; Noisy-le-Grand, France
EBERTLANG Distribution GmbH; Wetzlar, Germany
EBIOSS Energy AD; Sofia, Bulgaria
EC-Founder (Holdings) Company Limited; Tsuen Wan, China (Hong Kong)
Echo International Holdings Group Limited; Tsuen Wan, China (Hong Kong)
Eclectic Bar Group Plc; London, United Kingdom
Eclipse Residential Mortgage Investment Corporation; Toronto, Canada
Eco (Atlantic) Oil & Gas Ltd.; Toronto, Canada
ECOBOARD INDUSTRIES LTD; Pune, India
Eco energy holdings Co., Ltd.; Seoul, Korea (South)
E.COM INFOTECH (INDIA) LIMITED; Mumbai, India
Eco Quest Limited; Armadale, Australia
EcoTec s.r.l.; Lamezia, Italy
Eco World Development Sdn Bhd; Shah Alam, Malaysia
ED Co., Ltd.; Seongnam, Korea (South)
Eden International SA; Preverenges, Switzerland
EdgeStone Capital Partners Inc.; Toronto, Canada
Edgewater Wireless Systems Incorporated; Ottawa, Canada
The Edinburgh Woollen Mill Ltd.; Langholm, United Kingdom
Edizione S.r.l.; Treviso, Italy
Edward Billington & Son Ltd.; Liverpool, United Kingdom
eDynamics Solutions Ltd; Delhi, India
Efficient Group Limited; Pretoria, South Africa
Effingo Textile & Trading Limited; New Delhi, India
eForce Holdings Limited; Central, China (Hong Kong)
EG Corporation; Chubu-myeon, Korea (South)
EGing Photovoltaic Technology Co., Ltd.; Changzhou, China
e'grand Co., Ltd.; Tokyo, Japan
Egreen Co., Ltd.; Icheon, Korea (South)
EHG Corporation Limited; Sydney, Australia

EHWA Technologies Information Co. Ltd.; Seoul, Korea (South)
Einbecker Brauhaus AG; Einbeck, Germany
Eins Eduteeh Limited; Mumbai, India
Ejada For Financial Investments Plc; Amman, Jordan
EKAM LEASING & FINANCE CO. LTD.; New Delhi, India
e-Kancelaria Grupa Prawno-Finansowa S.A.; Wroclaw, Poland
Ekinops SA; Lannion, France
e-Kong Group Limited; Central, China (Hong Kong)
Ekwienox Limited; London, United Kingdom
ELANGO INDUSTRIES LIMITED; Chennai, India
Elbrook Cash & Carry Ltd.; Mitcham, United Kingdom
Elcom Technology Pty Ltd; Sydney, Australia
EL Corporation Limited; Sydney, Australia
ELDER PROJECTS LIMITED; Khalapur, India
E-Leather Ltd.; Peterborough, United Kingdom
Electra Partners LLP; London, United Kingdom
Electro Aco Altona S.A.; Blumenau, Brazil
Electrometals Technologies Limited; Robina, Australia
Element 79 Capital Inc.; Montreal, Canada
Elemental Holding S.A.; Grodzisk Mazowiecki, Poland
Elephant Talk Communications Corp.; Schiphol, Netherlands
Elevation Capital Corp.; Vancouver, Canada
Eliance (Pty) Limited; Pretoria, South Africa
e-LITECOM CO., Ltd.; Suwon, Korea (South)
Elite Surface Technologies Pty. Ltd.; Clayton, Australia
Elkwater Resources Ltd.; Calgary, Canada
ELLENBARRIE INDUSTRIAL GASES LIMITED; Kolkata, India
Elsmore Resources Limited; Sydney, Australia
EMAE - Empresa Metropolitana de Aguas e Energia S.A.; Sao Paulo, Brazil
Emakina Group S.A.; Brussels, Belgium
Embelton Limited; Coburg, Australia
EMD Music S.A.; Brussels, Belgium
EME Capital LLP; London, United Kingdom
Emeco Holdings Limited; Osborne Park, Australia
Emed.com Technologies Limited; Hyderabad, India
Emerald Oil & Gas NL; West Perth, Australia
Emerald Plantation Holdings Limited; Wanchai, China (Hong Kong)
EMERAM Capital Partners GmbH; Munich, Germany
Emirates Integrated Telecommunication Company PJSC; Dubai, United Arab Emirates
Emirates Refreshments (P.S.C.); Dubai, United Arab Emirates
EMKAY GLOBAL FINANCIAL SERVICES LIMITED; Mumbai, India
Emlak Konut Gayrimenkul Yatirim Ortakligi AS; Istanbul, Turkey
Emmar Investments & Real Estate Development Company; Amman, Jordan
Emmegi S.p.a.; Soliera, Italy
Empica Ltd.; Bristol, United Kingdom
Emporis Projects Limited; Ahmedabad, India
Empresa Nacional de Comercio Redito e Participacoes, S.A.-ENCORPAR; Belo Horizonte, Brazil
EnBio Holdings Inc.; Tokyo, Japan
Enbridge Income Fund Holdings Inc.; Calgary, Canada
Encounter Resources Limited; West Perth, Australia
Encourage Technologies Co., Ltd.; Tokyo, Japan
Endless LLP; Leeds, United Kingdom
Endo International plc; Dublin, Ireland
Enea AB; Kista, Sweden
Enegex N.L.; Melbourne, Australia
Enegi Oil Plc; Manchester, United Kingdom
ENERES Co., Ltd.; Tokyo, Japan
Energy Earth Public Company Limited; Bangkok, Thailand
Energy International Investments Holdings Limited; Hong Kong, China (Hong Kong)
Energy One Limited; Sydney, Australia
Enertronica SpA; Frosinone, Italy
Enerxy AG; Stuttgart, Germany
Enfield Exploration Corp.; Vancouver, Canada
ENF Technology Co., Ltd.; Seoul, Korea (South)
Engineered nanoProducts Germany AG; Griesheim, Germany
ENHANCE SKIN PRODUCTS INC.; Toronto, Canada
Enjaz for Development & Multi Projects Company P.L.C.; Amman, Jordan
ENR Asset Management Inc.; Westmount, Canada
Ensa Steel Industries Limited; Mumbai, India
Enshu Limited; Hamamatsu, Japan
Entanet International Ltd.; Telford, United Kingdom
Enterprise Investment Fund slhf.; Reykjavik, Iceland
Entreprendre SA; Boulogne-Billancourt, France
Enustech, Inc.; Seoul, Korea (South)
Envestra Limited; Adelaide, Australia
Envipro Holdings Inc.; Shizuoka, Japan
Environnement S.A.; Poissy, France
Enzychem Lifesciences Corporation; Seoul, Korea (South)
Enzymotec Ltd.; Migdal Ha'Emeq, Israel
E.ON Thuringer Energie AG; Erfurt, Germany
EO Technics Co., Ltd.; Anyang, Korea (South)
EPC Groupe; Paris, France
Equal Experts UK Ltd.; London, United Kingdom
Equamineral Holdings Limited; West Perth, Australia
Equipceramic, S.A.; Vilanova del Cami, Spain
Equitorial Exploration Corp.; Vancouver, Canada
E.R. CAPITAL HOLDING GmbH & Cie. KG; Hamburg, Germany
Eren Groupe SA; Luxembourg, Luxembourg

ErgyCapital S.p.A.; Rome, Italy
Ericpol Sp. z o.o.; Lodz, Poland
ERI Holdings Co., Ltd.; Tokyo, Japan
Ermo Group; Marcille-la-Ville, France
ERPSOFT Systems Limited; Chennai, India
Errecinque S.r.l.; Turin, Italy
Eryplast SA; Herstal, Belgium
Esaote S.p.A.; Genoa, Italy
Escrow Agent Japan, Inc.; Tokyo, Japan
Eson Precision Ind. Co., Ltd.; Taipei, Taiwan
Essent Group Ltd.; Hamilton, Bermuda
Essex Services Group PLC; Romford, United Kingdom
Esstra Industries Inc.; Edmonton, Canada
EstechPharma Co., Ltd.; Hwaseong, Korea (South)
Estic Corporation; Moriguchi, Japan
Estoril Sol, SGPS, S.A.; Cascais, Portugal
Etablissements Maurel & Prom S.A.; Paris, France
Etalon Group Limited; Saint Peter Port, Guernsey
Etimex GmbH; Dietenheim, Germany
E-tivity Corp. (APAC) Pty Ltd.; Sydney, Australia
Eucatex S.A. Industria e Comercio; Sao Paulo, Brazil
Eugene Technology CO., LTD.; Yongin, Korea (South)
Eurogerm SA; Saint Apollinaire, France
Europacorp; Saint Denis, France
European Fine Wines Ltd.; Bromley, United Kingdom
European Real Estate Investment Trust Limited; Saint Peter Port, Guernsey
Eurosports Global Limited; Singapore, Singapore
EUROTEX INDUSTRIES & EXPORTS LIMITED; Mumbai, India
EU Supply PLC; London, United Kingdom
Evance Wind Turbines Ltd.; Loughborough, United Kingdom
EVATHERM Ltd.; Magenwil, Switzerland
Even Construtora e Incorporadora S.A.; Jardim America, Brazil
Eventa Entertainment Group Ltd.; Brighton, United Kingdom
Event Marketing Service GmbH; Vienna, Austria
EVERTECHNO CO., LTD.; Asan, Korea (South)
Everyman Media Group Plc; London, United Kingdom
Evolve IT Australia Pty. Ltd.; Forest Hill, Australia
Ewon Comfortech Co., Ltd.; Nonsan, Korea (South)
EXA E&C Inc.; Seoul, Korea (South)
excel co., ltd.; Tokyo, Japan
EXDON TRADING COMPANY LIMITED; Mumbai, India
Exito Energy II Inc.; Calgary, Canada
Expert System S.p.A.; Modena, Italy
EXPLICIT FINANCE LIMITED; Thane, India
Exter B.V.; Zaandam, Netherlands
Extol Commercial Limited; Mumbai, India
Eyegene Inc.; Seoul, Korea (South)
Ezeflow, Inc.; Granby, Canada
eZ Systems AS; Skien, Norway
EZTEC Empreendimentos e Participacoes S.A.; Sao Paulo, Brazil
Ezwelfare Co., Ltd.; Seoul, Korea (South)

F

Fabrica de Tecidos Carlos Renaux S.A.; Brusque, Brazil
FACT ENTERPRISE LIMITED; Mumbai, India
Faircourt Gold Income Corp.; Toronto, Canada
Faircourt Split Trust; Toronto, Canada
Fair Friend Group; Taipei, Taiwan
Fairvest Property Holdings Limited; Cape Town, South Africa
FAM Real Estate Investment Trust; Toronto, Canada
Far Glory Hotel Co., Ltd.; Hua-lien, Taiwan
Farmsecure Holdings (Pty) Ltd.; Cape Town, South Africa
Farncombe Technology Ltd.; Basingstoke, United Kingdom
FashionPartner Group SAS; Marne-la-Vallee, France
Fasoo.com Co., Ltd.; Seoul, Korea (South)
Fast Ejendom Danmark A/S; Hellerup, Denmark
Faubel & Co. Nachfolger GmbH; Melsungen, Germany
FAVA International Holdings Limited; Wanchai, China (Hong Kong)
FEELingK Co., Ltd.; Seoul, Korea (South)
FEELUX Lighting Co., Ltd.; Yangju, Korea (South)
Feerum S.A.; Chojnow, Poland
Feishang Anthracite Resources Limited; Central, China (Hong Kong)
Ferco Developpement; Saint-Montan, France
Ferguson Group Limited; Aberdeen, United Kingdom
Ferrex Plc; Cobham, United Kingdom
Ferronordic Machines AB; Stockholm, Sweden
Ferrum Americas Mining Inc.; Toronto, Canada
Fertoz Ltd.; Brisbane, Australia
Fervent Synergies Limited; Mumbai, India
Fever-Tree Limited; London, United Kingdom
FEV GmbH; Aachen, Germany
Fiacao e Tecelagem Sao Jose S.A.; Brasilia, Brazil
Fibam Companhia Industrial; Sao Bernardo do Campo, Brazil
Fibra Uno Administracion SA de CV; Mexico, Mexico
Field Fisher Waterhouse LLP; London, United Kingdom
Figeac-Aero SA; Figeac, France
Figtree Holdings Limited; Singapore, Singapore
Filter Vision Public Company Limited; Bangkok, Thailand
FIMA, Inc.; Calgary, Canada
Finalysis Credit & Guarantee Co. Ltd.; Mumbai, India
Financiere de Tubize SA; Brussels, Belgium
Finansinos S/A - Credito Financiamento e Investimento; Novo Hamburgo, Brazil
FINAVENTURE CAPITAL LIMITED; Mumbai, India
Finbond Group Limited; Pretoria, South Africa

Fincas Anzizu SL; Barcelona, Spain
Fine-Line Circuits Limited; Mumbai, India
Fine Sinter Co., Ltd.; Kasugai, Japan
Finetechnix Co., Ltd.; Anyang, Korea (South)
Finetex EnE, Inc.; Seoul, Korea (South)
FinEx Capital Management LLP; London, United Kingdom
FinnAust Mining PLC; London, United Kingdom
FircoSoft SAS; Paris, France
Firebird Energy Inc.; Emerald Park, Canada
FirstCaution SA; Nyon, Switzerland
Firstec Co., Ltd.; Changwon, Korea (South)
First Finance Co.; Amman, Jordan
FIRST FINANCIAL SERVICES LTD; Chennai, India
First National Financial Corporation; Toronto, Canada
First Oil Plc; Aberdeen, United Kingdom
First Utility Limited; Warwick, United Kingdom
fischerwerke GmbH & Co. KG; Waldachtal, Germany
Fission 3.0 Corp.; Kelowna, Canada
Fission Uranium Corp.; Kelowna, Canada
F.I.T. Investment JSC; Hanoi, Vietnam
Fjarskipti hf.; Reykjavik, Iceland
Flash Networks Ltd.; Herzliyya, Israel
FLC Global JSC; Hanoi, Vietnam
Fleet Canada Inc.; Fort Erie, Canada
Fleury S.A.; Sao Paulo, Brazil
Flex Equipos de Descanso SA; Madrid, Spain
Flipkart Internet Private Limited; Bengaluru, India
Flipside Group; Cranleigh, United Kingdom
Fluidata Ltd.; London, United Kingdom
Fluitronics GmbH; Krefeld, Germany
Flying A Petroleum Ltd.; Vancouver, Canada
FnGuide Inc.; Seoul, Korea (South)
FocalTech Corporation, Ltd.; Hsinchu, Taiwan
Focus Group; Southwick, United Kingdom
Focus Industrial Resources Limited; New Delhi, India
Focusrite Audio Engineering Ltd.; High Wycombe, United Kingdom
Fomento Resorts & Hotels Ltd; Goa, India
Fonciere des 6e et 7e arrondissements de Paris; Paris, France
FoneWorx Holdings Limited; Randburg, South Africa
Foodwell Corporation; Seongnam, Korea (South)
Foreman Capital B.V.; Amsterdam, Netherlands
Foremost Audio Sdn. Bhd.; Gurun, Malaysia
Forgame Holdings Limited; Guangzhou, China
Forge Group Ltd.; West Perth, Australia
Forges de Trie-Chateau; Trie-Chateau, France
Forjas Taurus S.A.; Porto Alegre, Brazil
Formaplex Ltd.; Havant, United Kingdom
Formation Fluid Management Inc.; Sylvan Lake, Canada
FORMETAL, INC.; Seosan, Korea (South)
Formous Corp.; Bishkek, Kyrgyzstan
Forpost-Holding ZAO; Kazan, Russia
Forward Internet Group Ltd.; London, United Kingdom
Foseco India Limited; Pune, India
Founder Holdings Limited; Hong Kong, China (Hong Kong)
Foundry Fuel Products Ltd.; Kolkata, India
Fountaine Pajot SA; Aigrefeuille-d'Aunis, France
Fountain S.A.; Braine-l'Alleud, Belgium
Foxtons Group plc.; London, United Kingdom
Foyer S.A.; Leudelange, Luxembourg
Foyle Food Group Ltd.; Londonderry, United Kingdom
Foyson Resources Limited; North Sydney, Australia
Frank's International N.V.; Amsterdam, Netherlands
Franshion Properties (China) Limited; Wanchai, China (Hong Kong)
Fraser Range Metals Group Limited; West Perth, Australia
Fras-le S.A.; Caxias do Sul, Brazil
Freelance.com SA; Levallois-Perret, France
FreeMs Corporation; Bucheon, Korea (South)
Freetech Road Recycling Technology (Holdings) Limited; Wanchai, China (Hong Kong)
Freeworld Trading Ltd.; Edinburgh, United Kingdom
Frequency Telecom; Chessington, United Kingdom
Fresca Group Limited; Paddock Wood, United Kingdom
Freshbaked PR Ltd; Cardiff, United Kingdom
Freshwater Technology; London, United Kingdom
Freyja Resources Inc.; Montreal, Canada
FriaSkog AB; Are, Sweden
Friday Capital Inc.; Toronto, Canada
Friosur Pesquera SA; Santiago, Chile
From30 co., ltd.; Seongnam, Korea (South)
Frontier Developments plc; Cambridge, United Kingdom
FRONTIER INFORMATICS LIMITED; Hyderabad, India
Frontier Oil Corporation; Makati, Philippines
FRONTLINE BUSINESS SOLUTIONS LIMITED; Mumbai, India
FRR Corporation Ltd.; Sydney, Australia
FRTEK Co., Ltd.; Anyang, Korea (South)
Fudo Tetra Corporation; Tokyo, Japan
Fuelcellpower Co., Ltd.; Songnam, Korea (South)
Fuerst Day Lawson Ltd.; London, United Kingdom
FueTrek Co., Ltd.; Osaka, Japan
Fuguiniao Co., Ltd.; Wanchai, China (Hong Kong)
Fujian Longking Co., Ltd.; Longyan, China
Fujian Minhang Electronics Co., Ltd.; Nanping, China
Fujian Nuoqi Co., Ltd.; Quanzhou, China

Fujibo Holdings, Inc.; Tokyo, Japan
FUJIKOH COMPANY., LIMITED; Tokyo, Japan
Fujikura Kasei Co., Ltd.; Tokyo, Japan
Fujikura Rubber Ltd.; Tokyo, Japan
Fujimak Corporation; Tokyo, Japan
Fujimori Kogyo Co., Ltd.; Tokyo, Japan
Fukoku Co., Ltd.; Ageo, Japan
Fukushima Industries Corporation; Osaka, Japan
Fulcrum Utility Services Limited; Sheffield, United Kingdom
Full Apex (Holdings) Limited; Wanchai, China (Hong Kong)
Fuluhashi EPO Corporation; Nagoya, Japan
Furniture Village Limited; Slough, United Kingdom
Fusebill Inc.; Kanata, Canada
Fu Shou Yuan International Group Limited; Shanghai, China
Fusion Group Ltd.; Chesterfield, United Kingdom
Fusion Retail Brands, Pty. Ltd.; Hawthorn, Australia
Future Arab Investment Co.; Amman, Jordan
Future Pipe Industries Group Ltd.; Abu Dhabi, United Arab Emirates
Futuristic Solutions Limited; New Delhi, India

G

G-7 HOLDINGS Inc.; Kobe, Japan
GAGAN POLYCOT INDIA LIMITED; Mumbai, India
Gaia Securitizadora S.A.; Sao Paulo, Brazil
Gaia-Wind Ltd.; Glasgow, United Kingdom
Gajra Bevel Gears Limited; Indore, India
Gala Coral Group Limited; London, United Kingdom
Galane Gold Limited; Toronto, Canada
GALAXY AGRICO EXPORTS LIMITED; Rajkot, India
Galaxy Entertainment Group Limited; Central, China (Hong Kong)
GALLANTT METAL LIMITED; Kolkata, India
Galmed Pharmaceuticals Ltd.; Tel Aviv, Israel
Gama Participacoes S.A.; Rio de Janeiro, Brazil
Gamma Logistics Corporation; Kwai Chung, China (Hong Kong)
Ganesh Holdings Limited; Mumbai, India
Gansu Dunhuang Seed Co., Ltd.; Jiuquan, China
GAON Cable Co., Ltd.; Seoul, Korea (South)
Gardline Shipping Limited; Norfolk, United Kingdom
GAYATRI SUGARS LIMITED; Hyderabad, India
Gaztransport Et Technigaz SA; Saint Remy-les-Chevreuse, France
GBC Scientific Equipment Pty Ltd.; Braeside, Australia
G Capital Public Company Limited; Bangkok, Thailand
GCI Telecom Group Ltd.; Basingstoke, United Kingdom
G-cluster Global Corporation; Tokyo, Japan
GCM Commodity & Derivatives Ltd.; Mumbai, India
GCS Recruitment Specialists Ltd.; London, United Kingdom
GDC Technology Limited; North Point, China (Hong Kong)
GDI Property Group; Sydney, Australia
GDL Leasing & Finance Limited; Delhi, India
GDS Global Limited; Singapore, Singapore
Gear Energy Ltd.; Calgary, Canada
GEE GEE GRANITES LIMITED; Chennai, India
GEMSTONE INVESTMENTS LIMITED; Mumbai, India
GeneMatrix Inc.; Seongnam, Korea (South)
General Agriculture Corp.; Beijing, China
General Investment Co., Ltd.; Amman, Jordan
General Lighting Company; Riyadh, Saudi Arabia
GENFIT SA; Loos, France
Genia Photonics Inc.; Laval, Canada
Genius Properties Ltd.; Montreal, Canada
Gentrack Limited; Auckland, New Zealand
The Genuine Gemstone Company Limited; Redditch, United Kingdom
Genuine Solutions Limited; Surbiton, United Kingdom
GeoCenter Touristik Medienservice GmbH; Stuttgart, Germany
GeoNovus Minerals Corp.; Vancouver, Canada
Georg Fischer Druckguss GmbH & Co KG; Herzogenburg, Austria
Gerard Perrier Industrie S.A.; Saint Priest, France
Gesco AG; Wuppertal, Germany
Gespeg Copper Resources Inc.; Saskatoon, Canada
Get Nice Holdings Limited; Central, China (Hong Kong)
GFK Resources Inc.; Upper Tantallon, Canada
The Ghana Airports Company Limited; Accra, Ghana
GIBLUE CO., LTD.; Seoul, Korea (South)
GI Engineering Solutions Limited; Mumbai, India
GigaLane Co., Ltd.; Hwaseong, Korea (South)
GIIR Inc.; Seoul, Korea (South)
Giken Kogyo Co., Ltd.; Tokyo, Japan
Ginger Oil AB; Froson, Sweden
Ginza Industries Ltd.; Mumbai, India
Giovanni Crespi S.p.A.; Legnano, Italy
GIRDHARILAL SUGAR & ALLIED INDUSTRIES LIMITED; Dewas, India
GLANCE FINANCE LIMITED; Mumbai, India
Glasgow Prestwick Airport Limited; Prestwick, United Kingdom
GLG Corp Ltd.; North Sydney, Australia
Glintt - Global Intelligent Technologies, S.A.; Sintra, Portugal
Global Asset Management Limited; Roodepoort, South Africa
Global Dining, Inc.; Tokyo, Japan
Global Diversified Investment Grade Income Trust; Montreal, Canada
Global Diversified Investment Grade Income Trust II; Montreal, Canada
Global Dividend Growers Income Fund; Calgary, Canada

Global Economic Advantage Pvt Ltd; Gurgaon, India
GLOBAL INFRATECH & FINANCE LIMITED; Mumbai, India
Global Land Masters Corporation Limited; Delhi, India
Global Met Coal Corporation; Vancouver, Canada
Global Personals Ltd.; Windsor, United Kingdom
Global Ports Investments Plc; Limassol, Cyprus
Global Real Estate Group; London, United Kingdom
Global Resources Corporation Limited; Perth, Australia
Global Steel Holdings Ltd.; Dubai, United Arab Emirates
Global Tech (Holdings) Limited; Kowloon, China (Hong Kong)
Globant S.A.; Luxembourg, Luxembourg
Globe Trade Centre S.A.; Warsaw, Poland
Globex Mining Enterprises Inc.; Rouyn-Noranda, Canada
Globo Foods Ltd.; Samut Prakan, Thailand
Globoforce Group PLC; Dublin, Ireland
Globo Technologies S.A.; Halandri, Greece
Globus Power Generation Limited; New Delhi, India
Godo Steel, Ltd.; Osaka, Japan
Gogia Capital Services Limited; New Delhi, India
Goldbell Corporation; Singapore, Singapore
Gold Crest Co., Ltd.; Tokyo, Japan
GOLDEN CARPETS LIMITED; Hyderabad, India
GOLDEN GOENKA FINCORP LIMITED; Kolkata, India
Goldenmars Technology Holdings Limited; Kowloon, China (Hong Kong)
Golden Ocean Group Limited; Hamilton, Bermuda
Golden Peak Minerals Inc.; Langley, Canada
Golden Saint Resources Limited; London, United Kingdom
Goldeye Explorations Limited; Richmond Hill, Canada
Goldin Properties Holdings Limited; Central, China (Hong Kong)
Gold Jubilee Capital Corp.; Vancouver, Canada
Goldpoly New Energy Holdings Limited; Central, China (Hong Kong)
Gold Ridge Exploration Corp.; Calgary, Canada
Goldrock Mines Corp.; Vancouver, Canada
GOLDSTONE TECHNOLOGIES LIMITED; Hyderabad, India
Golkunda Diamonds & Jewellery Limited; Mumbai, India
GOOD PEOPLE Co., Ltd; Seoul, Korea (South)
Go Outdoors Limited; Sheffield, United Kingdom
Goplee Infotech Ltd.; Ahmedabad, India
Gorani Industries Limited; Indore, India
Gordon Brothers Industries Pty. Limited; Brunswick, Australia
Gosford Quarries Pty. Ltd.; Sydney, Australia
GOS Systems plc; London, United Kingdom
GoStats; Waterloo, Canada
Gowin New Energy Group Limited; Dongguan, China
Gowra Leasing & Finance Limited; Secunderabad, India
Goyal Associates Ltd; Ahmedabad, India
GP Capital Co., Ltd.; Shanghai, China
G-Prop (Holdings) Limited; Kowloon, China (Hong Kong)
GPS Alliance Holdings Limited; Singapore, Singapore
GPT Infraprojects Limited; Kolkata, India
Gradiente Infotainment Limited; Hyderabad, India
GRAINES VOLTZ SA; Colmar, France
Grainger & Worrall Limited; Bridgnorth, United Kingdom
Grana y Montero S.A.A.; Lima, Peru
Grande West Transportation Group Inc.; Aldergrove, Canada
GRANDMA TRADING & AGENCIES LIMITED; Mumbai, India
Grand Ming Group Holdings Limited; Hong Kong, China (Hong Kong)
Granite Real Estate Investment Trust; Toronto, Canada
Grant Thornton UK LLP; London, United Kingdom
Gratisfilm Photocolor Club SA; Madrid, Spain
GRAVISS HOSPITALITY LIMITED; Mumbai, India
Gravity Media Group Limited; Watford, United Kingdom
Greek National Tourist Organization; Athens, Greece
Green Arrow Resources Inc.; Vancouver, Canada
Greenbank Capital Inc.; Toronto, Canada
Green Cross Cell Corp.; Seoul, Korea (South)
Green Cross Corporation; Yongin, Korea (South)
Greencross Limited; Brisbane, Australia
Greenhous Group Ltd.; Shrewsbury, United Kingdom
GreenItaly1 S.p.A.; Milan, Italy
Greenland Holding Group Co., Ltd.; Shanghai, China
Greenpower Energy Limited; West Perth, Australia
Greenpro, Inc.; Wanchai, China (Hong Kong)
Green Rock Energy Limited; Perth, Australia
Green Seal Holding Limited; Taipei, Taiwan
Green Standard Vanadium Resources Corp.; Vancouver, Canada
Green Swan Capital Corp.; Burlington, Canada
Green Valley Mine Incorporated; Langley, Canada
Grendene S.A.; Fortaleza, Brazil
Grey Matter Ltd.; Devon, United Kingdom
GRINM Semiconductor Materials Co., Ltd.; Beijing, China
Gritit; Uxbridge, United Kingdom
GRO-BELS Co., Ltd.; Tokyo, Japan
Groothandelsgebouwen N.V.; Rotterdam, Netherlands
Grosvenor Financial Services Group Ltd.; Wellington, New Zealand
Group7 AG; Schwaig, Germany
Group de Cloedt SA; Brussels, Belgium
Groupe FNAC S.A.; Ivry-sur-Seine, France
Groupe Primonial SAS; Paris, France

Groupe Unika; Croissy-Beaubourg, France
Group Thermote & Vanhalst; Waregem, Belgium
Grovepoint Capital LLP; London, United Kingdom
GRP Corporation Limited; West Perth, Australia
Grupo Siro S.L.; Palencia, Spain
Grupo Tavex, S.A.; Madrid, Spain
Gruppo Green Power S.p.A.; Venice, Italy
GS Instruments Co., Ltd.; Incheon, Korea (South)
GT&T Co.; Seoul, Korea (South)
Guangdong Guanhao High-Tech Co., Ltd.; Zhanjiang, China
Guangxi Fenglin Wood Industry Group Co., Ltd.; Nanning, China
Guangxi Liugong Machinery Co., Ltd.; Liuzhou, China
Guangzhou Kingmed Diagnostics Center Co., Ltd.; Guangzhou, China
Guangzhou Pearl River Industrial Development Holdings Co., Ltd; Guangzhou, China
Guangzhou Pharmaceutical Company Limited; Guangzhou, China
Guararapes Confeccoes S.A.; Natal, Brazil
Guate Tourism Inc.; San Marcos, Guatemala
GUD Filters Pty. Ltd.; Isipingo, South Africa
Gujarat Ambuja Exports Ltd.; Ahmedabad, India
GUJARAT CONTAINERS LIMITED; Vadodara, India
Gujarat Craft Industries Limited; Gandhinagar, India
GUJARAT INTRUX LIMITED; Rajkot, India
GUJARAT MEDITECH LTD; Ahmedabad, India
GUJARAT NATURAL RESOURCES LIMITED; Ahmedabad, India
GUJARAT ORGANICS LIMITED; Mumbai, India
Gujarat Petrosynthese Ltd; Mumbai, India
GUJARAT RAFFIA INDUSTRIES LIMITED; Gandhinagar, India
Gujarat Terce Laboratories Limited; Ahmedabad, India
GUJARAT TOOLROOM LIMITED; Ahmedabad, India
Gujchem Distillers India Limited; Ahmedabad, India
Gulfa Mineral Water & Processing Industries Co. PLC; Ajman, United Arab Emirates
Gulf Mines Limited; South Perth, Australia
Gulfstream Acquisition 1 Corp.; Toronto, Canada
Gulfstream Capital Corporation; Frankfurt, Germany
Gumho N.T Co., Ltd.; Gumi, Korea (South)
Gun Ei Chemical Industry Co., Ltd.; Takasaki, Japan
GuoGuang Electric Company Limited; Guangzhou, China
Guyoung Tech. Co., Ltd; Daegu, Korea (South)
Guyson International Limited; Skipton, United Kingdom
GVIC Communications Corp.; Vancouver, Canada
The Gym Limited; Guildford, United Kingdom

H

Haatz INC.; Seoul, Korea (South)
Haeng Nam Chinaware Inc.; Mokpo, Korea (South)
Haesung Optics Co., Ltd.; Hwaseong, Korea (South)
Haga S/A Industria e Comercio; Brasilia, Brazil
Hagoromo Foods Corporation; Shizuoka, Japan
Hai Phong Electrical Mechanical JSC; Haiphong, Vietnam
Haisco Pharmaceutical Group Co., Ltd.; Chengdu, China
Haitong International Securities Group Limited; Central, China (Hong Kong)
HaiVision Systems, Inc.; Montreal, Canada
Hakudo Co., Ltd.; Tokyo, Japan
Halcyon Agri Corporation Ltd; Singapore, Singapore
Haldane McCall PLC; Douglas, Isle of Man
Halifax Rack & Screw Cutting Co. Ltd.; Brighouse, United Kingdom
Hall Longmore (Proprietary) Limited; Germiston, South Africa
Halmont Properties Corporation; Toronto, Canada
Halogen Software Inc.; Ottawa, Canada
Halsnoy Dokk AS; Hoylandsbygdi, Norway
HaNa Elecom Ltd.; Incheon, Korea (South)
Hana Micron Inc.; Asan, Korea (South)
Hancom, Inc.; Seongnam, Korea (South)
Handok Inc.; Seoul, Korea (South)
Hanergy Solar Group Limited; Kowloon, China (Hong Kong)
HANEXPRESS CO, LTD.; Seoul, Korea (South)
Hangzhou Advance Gearbox Group Co., Ltd.; Hangzhou, China
Hangzhou Silan Microelectronics Co., Ltd.; Hangzhou, China
Hanil Chemical Ind. Co., Ltd.; Siheung, Korea (South)
Hanil Feed Co., Ltd.; Yongin, Korea (South)
HANJER FIBRES LIMITED; Mumbai, India
Hanjin Heavy Industries & Construction Co., Ltd.; Busan, Korea (South)
Han Kook Capital Co., Ltd.; Seoul, Korea (South)
HANKOOK Technology Inc.; Seoul, Korea (South)
HANKUK CARBON Co., Ltd.; Gyeongnam, Korea (South)
Hankuk Package Co., Ltd.; Ansan, Korea (South)
HANLA IMS CO., LTD.; Busan, Korea (South)
HanmiGlobal Co., LTD.; Seoul, Korea (South)
Hanover Acceptances Limited; London, United Kingdom
Hansol SeenTec Co., Ltd.; Changwon, Korea (South)
HANSUNGELCOMTEC Co., Ltd; Pyeongtaek, Korea (South)
Han Sung Enterprise Co., Ltd.; Seoul, Korea (South)
Hanyang Eng Co., Ltd.; Hwaseong, Korea (South)
Happinet Corporation; Tokyo, Japan
Harbin Air Conditioning Co., Ltd.; Harbin, China
Harbor Star Shipping Services Inc.; Makati, Philippines
HarbourVest Senior Loans Europe Limited; Saint Peter Port, Guernsey

Hardwoods Distribution Inc.; Langley, Canada
Hareon Solar Technology Co., Ltd.; Jiangyin, China
HARMONY CAPITAL SERVICES LIMITED; Jaipur, India
HARYANA TEXPRINTS (OVERSEAS) LTD; Faridabad, India
Hatstand Consulting; London, United Kingdom
Haulotte Group SA; L'Horme, France
Havila Shipping ASA; Fosnavag, Norway
HAWE Hydraulik SE; Munich, Germany
HB LEASING & FINANCE COMPANY LIMITED; Gurgaon, India
HB Portfolio Ltd.; Gurgaon, India
HB Technology Inc.; Asan, Korea (South)
Healthcare at Home Ltd.; Burton-on-Trent, United Kingdom
HEALTHY INVESTMENTS LIMITED; Hyderabad, India
Hear AtLast Holdings, Inc.; Burlington, Canada
Hearts United Group Co., Ltd.; Tokyo, Japan
Hebei Changshan Biochemical Pharmaceutical Co. Ltd.; Shijiazhuang, China
Heera Ispat Ltd.; Ahmedabad, India
Heijmans Sport en Groen B.V.; Veenendaal, Netherlands
Helbor Empreendimentos S.A.; Mogi das Cruzes, Brazil
Helical Technology Limited; Lytham Saint Anne's, United Kingdom
HellermannTyton Group PLC; Crawley, United Kingdom
Hellyer Mill Operations Pty Ltd.; Burnie, Australia
Helston Garages Group; Helston, United Kingdom
Hemoteq AG; Wurselen, Germany
Henan Energy & Chemical Industry Group Co., Ltd.; Zhengzhou, China
Henan Huanghe Whirlwind Co., Ltd.; Changge, China
Henan Rebecca Hair Products Co., Ltd.; Xuchang, China
Henan Yuguang Gold & Lead Co., Ltd; Jiyuan, China
Hendy Group Ltd.; Eastleigh, United Kingdom
Henex S.A.; Brussels, Belgium
Heng Xin China Holdings Limited; Wanchai, China (Hong Kong)
Hengyi International Industries Group Inc.; Tianjin, China
Henningsen Nederland B.V.; Waalwijk, Netherlands
H Erben Limited; Ipswich, United Kingdom
Hermes Financial Inc.; Canmore, Canada
Heyday5 Pty. Limited; North Ryde, Australia
HFX Holding Corp.; Vancouver, Canada
HHT Investments Inc.; Toronto, Canada
Hi Air Korea Co., Ltd.; Kimhae, Korea (South)
Hibiscus Petroleum Berhad; Kuala Lumpur, Malaysia
HICL Infrastructure Company Limited; Saint Peter Port, Guernsey
HidroCo Limited; Southport, Australia
Highbury Projects Inc.; Vancouver, Canada
HighCo S.A.; Aix-en-Provence, France
High Finance Ltd.; London, United Kingdom
Highland Fuels Ltd.; Inverness, United Kingdom
High Performance Real Estate Investments Company PLC; Amman, Jordan
HIGH STREET FILATEX LTD; Jaipur, India
HIMACS, Ltd.; Yokohama, Japan
Himile Mechanical Science & Technology Co., Ltd; Weifang, China
HIMS International Corporation; Daejeon, Korea (South)
HINDOOSTAN MILLS LIMITED; Mumbai, India
HintTech BV; Delft, Netherlands
Hiramatsu Inc.; Tokyo, Japan
Hironic Co., Ltd.; Songnam, Korea (South)
Hisense Group Co., Ltd.; Qingdao, China
HISTEEL Co., Ltd.; Seoul, Korea (South)
Hi Sun Technology (China) Limited; Wanchai, China (Hong Kong)
HITECHPROS S.A.; Montrouge, France
Hi-Tech Steel Services Ltd.; Saint Helens, United Kingdom
Hitron Systems Inc.; Anseong, Korea (South)
HK Electric Investments Limited; Hong Kong, China (Hong Kong)
HKR International Limited; Central, China (Hong Kong)
HL Thorne & Co., Ltd.; Oldbury, United Kingdom
HNK Machine Tool Co., Ltd.; Gyeongnam, Korea (South)
Hob Co., Ltd.; Hokkaido, Japan
Hodogaya Chemical Co., Ltd.; Tokyo, Japan
Hoffmeister-Leuchten GmbH; Schalksmuhle, Germany
Hogan Lovells International LLP; London, United Kingdom
Hokuto Corporation; Nagano, Japan
Holland Global Capital Corporation; Mississauga, Canada
The Holy Land Insurance Co.; Amman, Jordan
Home Invest Belgium SA; Brussels, Belgium
Home Mortgage Bank; Port of Spain, Trinidad & Tobago
Honda Tsushin Kogyo Co., Ltd.; Tokyo, Japan
Hong Kong Finance Group Limited; Hong Kong, China (Hong Kong)
Hong Wei (Asia) Holdings Company Limited; Shaoguan, China
Honshu Chemical Industry Co., Ltd.; Tokyo, Japan
Honworld Group Limited; Huzhou, China
Hoosiers Holdings; Tokyo, Japan
Hopewell Highway Infrastructure Limited; Wanchai, China (Hong Kong)
Hoteis Othon S.A.; Rio de Janeiro, Brazil
Hotel Property Investments Limited; Melbourne, Australia
Hotman Co., Ltd.; Sendai, Japan
Hotto Link Inc.; Tokyo, Japan
HRB FLORICULTURE LIMITED; Jaipur, India
H. R. Jasper & Son Ltd.; Truro, United Kingdom
HRS Co., Ltd.; Seoul, Korea (South)
HS VALVE CO., LTD; Daegu, Korea (South)

Huafang Co., Ltd.; Binzhou, China
Hubei Kaile Science & Technology Co., Ltd.; Wuhan, China
Hubei Xingfa Chemicals Group Co., Ltd.; Yichang, China
HUDLAND Real Estate Investment and Development JSC; Hanoi, Vietnam
Hudson's Bay Company; Toronto, Canada
Huge Group Limited; Woodmead, South Africa
Hughes Drilling Limited; Yatala, Australia
Huishang Bank Corporation Limited; Hefei, China
Huisheng International Holdings Limited; Central, China (Hong Kong)
Human Metabolome Technologies Inc.; Tsuruoka, Japan
Humanwell Healthcare (Group) Co., Ltd.; Wuhan, China
Hunan Er-Kang Pharmaceutical Co., Ltd.; Changsha, China
Hunan Haili Chemical Industry Co., Ltd.; Changsha, China
Hunt & Palmer plc.; Crawley, United Kingdom
Hunter Resources plc; Douglas, Isle of Man
Huntington Exploration Inc.; Calgary, Canada
Huntswood CTC Limited; Reading, United Kingdom
Huons Co., Ltd.; Seongnam, Korea (South)
Hurricane Energy plc; Godalming, United Kingdom
HUSTEEL CO., Ltd.; Seoul, Korea (South)
Hutchison Port Holdings Trust; Singapore, Singapore
Huviron Co., Ltd.; Bucheon, Korea (South)
Hwange Colliery Company Limited; Harare, Zimbabwe
Hwaseung Industries Co., Ltd.; Busan, Korea (South)
Hwashin Co., Ltd.; Yeongcheon, Korea (South)
Hwashin Tech Co., Ltd.; Daegu, Korea (South)
HyComm Wireless Limited; Central, China (Hong Kong)
Hydoo International Holdings Limited; Shenzhen, China
Hydro Exploitation SA; Sion, Switzerland
Hydro S&S Industries Limited; Chennai, India
Hygea VCT plc; Brackley, United Kingdom
HYMER Aktiengesellschaft; Bad Waldsee, Germany
Hyosung ITX CO., LTD.; Seoul, Korea (South)
Hyosung ONB Co, Ltd; Daejeon, Korea (South)
Hyperion Insurance Group Limited; London, United Kingdom
Hyundai Glovis Co, Ltd.; Seoul, Korea (South)
Hyundai IT Corp.; Icheon, Korea (South)
Hyun Woo Industrial Co., LTD; Incheon, Korea (South)
HyVISION SYSTEM INC.; Seongnam, Korea (South)

I

Ibersol S.G.P.S., S.A.; Porto, Portugal
IBISWorld Pty Ltd; Melbourne, Australia
Ibn al-Haytham Hospital; Amman, Jordan
iBuy Group Limited; Sydney, Australia
Ichibanya Co., Ltd.; Ichinomiya, Japan
ICM Limited; Hamilton, Bermuda
i-components Co., Ltd.; Pyeongtaek, Korea (South)
ICON International Communications Pty. Ltd.; Sydney, Australia
ICORR Properties International; London, Canada
Icraft Co., Ltd.; Seoul, Korea (South)
IDEIASNET S.A.; Rio de Janeiro, Brazil
IESA Pty Ltd; Paget, Australia
IFL Promoters Limited; New Delhi, India
IFM Impex Global Limited; Delhi, India
IFS Construction Services Limited; Subiaco, Australia
IGB Eletronica S.A.; Manaus, Brazil
IHAG Holding AG; Zurich, Switzerland
Ihdathiat Co-Ordinates; Amman, Jordan
Iida Group Holdings Co., Ltd.; Nishi-Tokyo, Japan
IJT Technology Holdings Co., Ltd.; Tokyo, Japan
iKang Healthcare Group, Inc.; Beijing, China
IKF FINANCE LIMITED; Hyderabad, India
IKM Consultants A/S; Sola, Norway
Ikwezi Mining Limited; Hamilton, Bermuda
iLAND Green Technologies S.A.; Bevaix, Switzerland
ILH Group Limited; Sydney, Australia
Ilim Timber Indastri OOO; Saint Petersburg, Russia
Il Jeong Industrial Co., Ltd; Ansan, Korea (South)
Iljin Display Co., Ltd.; Pyeongtaek, Korea (South)
ILJINENERGY CO., LTD.; Ulsan, Korea (South)
ILoadApp; Chisinau, Moldova
ilShinBioBase Co., Ltd.; Dongducheon, Korea (South)
Ilshin Stone Co., Ltd; Seoul, Korea (South)
Ilsung Pharmaceuticals CO., LTD; Seoul, Korea (South)
Image Systems AB; Linkoping, Sweden
Imagina Media Audiovisual SL; Barcelona, Spain
IMAQLIQ Service Ltd.; Saint Petersburg, Russia
Imasen Electric Industrial Co., Ltd.; Inuyama, Japan
Imbalie Beauty Limited; Centurion, South Africa
Im Co., Ltd.; Hwaseong, Korea (South)
IMC Pan Asia Alliance Pte. Ltd.; Singapore, Singapore
I-MED Network Limited; Sydney, Australia
IMER International S.p.A.; Poggibonsi, Italy
Impact Minerals Limited; Perth, Australia
Imperial Hotel, Ltd.; Tokyo, Japan
Implanet SA; Martillac, France
Imugene Limited; Armadale, Australia
IMW Immobilien AG; Berlin, Germany
Inaba Denki Sangyo Co., Ltd.; Osaka, Japan
Inabox Group Limited; Sydney, Australia

Inapa - Investimentos, Participacoes e Gestao, SA; Lisbon, Portugal
Inchcape Shipping Services Ltd.; Grays, United Kingdom
INCON ENGINEERS LIMITED; Hyderabad, India
IND-AGIV COMMERCE LTD.; Mumbai, India
Indegene Lifesystems Pvt. Ltd.; Bengaluru, India
Independent News & Media (South Africa) (Pty) Limited; Johannesburg, South Africa
Independent Oil & Gas PLC; London, United Kingdom
indesign Group; Badalona, Spain
India Finsec Limited; New Delhi, India
India Gelatine & Chemicals Ltd.; Mumbai, India
India Infraspace Limited; Ahmedabad, India
Indian Extractions Limited; Jamnagar, India
Indian Metals & Ferro Alloys Limited; Bhubaneswar, India
Indigo Properties Australia Limited; West Perth, Australia
Indo Asia Finance Limited; Chennai, India
INDO CREDIT CAPITAL LIMITED; Ahmedabad, India
Indoor Skydive Australia Group Limited; Chatswood, Australia
Indovation Technologies Limited; Visakhapatnam, India
INDSOYA LTD; Mumbai, India
Ind Tra Deco Limited; Mumbai, India
Indus Gas Limited; Saint Peter Port, Guernsey
Industria e Innovazione S.p.A.; Milan, Italy
The Industrial Commercial & Agricultural Co. Ltd.; Amman, Jordan
Industrial Stars of Italy S.p.A.; Milan, Italy
Industria REIT; Melbourne, Australia
Industrias JB Duarte S/A; Sao Paulo, Brazil
Industrias Romi S.A.; Santa Barbara d'Oeste, Brazil
Inenco Group Pty Ltd.; Kingsgrove, Australia
Inepar S.A Industria e Construcoes; Sao Paulo, Brazil
Inertia Steel Limited; Mumbai, India
I-Net Corporation; Yokohama, Japan
iNetVideo.com; Saint Laurent, Canada
INFAC Corporation; Ansan, Korea (South)
Infectious Media Ltd.; London, United Kingdom
Infinity Equity; Tel Aviv, Israel
Infinity SDC Limited; London, United Kingdom
Infobank Corporation; Seongnam, Korea (South)
Infomart Corporation; Tokyo, Japan
INFORMED TECHNOLOGIES INDIA LIMITED; Mumbai, India
InfraStrata plc; Richmond, United Kingdom
Infraware, Inc.; Seoul, Korea (South)
ING Diversified Floating Rate Senior Loan Fund; Toronto, Canada
Ingenieros Asesores, S.A.; Llanera, Spain
Ingenious Media Active Capital Limited; Saint Martin's, Guernsey
Ingersoll Tillage Group, Inc.; Hamilton, Canada
InkTec Co., Ltd.; Ansan, Korea (South)
The Inland Group; Burnaby, Canada
INLAND PRINTERS LIMITED; Mumbai, India
Inmobiliaria Espacio, S.A; Madrid, Spain
Innate Immunotherapeutics Limited; Sydney, Australia
Innelec Multimedia; Pantin, France
Innochips Technology Co., Ltd.; Ansan, Korea (South)
Innovation Software Exports Limited; Chennai, India
Innovative Tech Pack Limited; New Delhi, India
Innowireless Co., Ltd.; Seongnam, Korea (South)
INNOX Corporation; Anseong, Korea (South)
Inovalis Real Estate Investment Trust; Toronto, Canada
Inovent Capital Inc.; Vancouver, Canada
iNovuus Technologies Pte. Ltd.; Singapore, Singapore
Insigma Technology Co., Ltd.; Hangzhou, China
Insimbi Refractory & Alloy Supplies Limited; Germiston, South Africa
Inspearit SAS; Arcueil, France
inspec Inc.; Akita, Japan
Instarmac Group plc.; Tamworth, United Kingdom
Insung Information Co., Ltd.; Seoul, Korea (South)
Intec Capital Limited; New Delhi, India
Intec Ltd.; North Sydney, Australia
INTEGRA SWITCHGEAR LIMITED; Vadodara, India
Integrated Coil Coating Industries Sdn. Bhd.; Kelang, Malaysia
Integrated Dental Holdings Ltd.; Manchester, United Kingdom
Integrated Hitech Limited; Chennai, India
INTEGRATED PROTEINS LIMITED; Jamnagar, India
INTEGRATED TECHNOLOGIES LIMITED; New Delhi, India
Intelligent Energy Limited; Loughborough, United Kingdom
Intense Technologies Limited; Secunderabad, India
Interactive Prospect Targeting Limited; London, United Kingdom
InterCard AG Informationssysteme; Villingen-Schwenningen, Germany
Interel Holdings SA; Brussels, Belgium
INTER GLOBE FINANCE LIMITED; Kolkata, India
Interhouse Company; Bandar Seri Begawan, Brunei Darussalam
International Applications Limited; Banbury, United Kingdom
International Arabian Development & Investment Trading Co.; Amman, Jordan
International Conglomerate of Distribution for Automobile Holdings Co., Ltd.; Mie, Japan
International For Medical Investment Plc; Amman, Jordan
International Healthway Corp., Ltd.; Singapore, Singapore
International Housewares Retail Company Limited; Hong Kong, China (Hong Kong)
International Parkside Products Inc.; Vancouver, Canada

International Public Partnerships Limited; Saint Peter Port, Guernsey
Interport Limited; Croydon, United Kingdom
InterRent Real Estate Investment Trust; Ottawa, Canada
Inter-Rock Minerals Inc.; Toronto, Canada
Intersnack Group GmbH & Co. KG; Dusseldorf, Germany
Interspace Co., Ltd.; Tokyo, Japan
Interwaste Holdings Limited; Germiston, South Africa
Intesys S.r.l.; Verona, Italy
Intex Resources ASA; Oslo, Norway
Intime Retail (Group) Company Limited; Beijing, China
Intops Co., Ltd.; Anyang, Korea (South)
Intrance Co., Ltd.; Tokyo, Japan
IntroMedic Co., Ltd.; Seoul, Korea (South)
Intuition IT Solutions; London, United Kingdom
Invenio Business Solutions Limited; Reading, United Kingdom
Investimentos e Participacoes em Infraestrutura S.A.; Rio de Janeiro, Brazil
Investissement Quebec; Quebec, Canada
The Investors & Eastern Arab for Industrial & Real Estate Investments Ltd.; Amman, Jordan
Investors in Global Real Estate Limited; Saint Peter Port, Guernsey
INZI Controls Co., Ltd; Siheung, Korea (South)
IOI Properties Group Berhad; Putrajaya, Malaysia
Ionix Systems Ltd.; Leigh, United Kingdom
IPB Petroleum Limited; Hampton, Australia
IPD Group Limited; Regents Park, Australia
IP-Only Telecommunication AB; Uppsala, Sweden
IPOWorld; Zurich, Switzerland
IQNovate Ltd.; Sydney, Australia
IQX Limited; Sydney, Australia
Irbid District Electricity Co. Ltd.; Amman, Jordan
IRIS Corporation Berhad; Kuala Lumpur, Malaysia
Ironbark Asset Management Pty. Ltd.; Sydney, Australia
Ironbark Capital Limited; Sydney, Australia
Iron Force Industrial Co., Ltd.; New Taipei City, Taiwan
ISC Co., Ltd.; Seongnam, Korea (South)
IsCool Entertainment SA; Paris, France
ISHAN DYES & CHEMICALS LIMITED; Borsad, India
Ishita Drugs & Industries Limited; Ahmedabad, India
Ishizuka Glass Co., Ltd.; Iwakura, Japan
The Islamic Insurance Co. P.L.C.; Amman, Jordan
Islaz SA; Alexandria, Romania
ISL CONSULTING LTD; Ahmedabad, India
ISOTeam Ltd; Singapore, Singapore
IST LIMITED; New Delhi, India
iStreet Network Limited; Mumbai, India
ISU Chemical co., Ltd.; Seoul, Korea (South)
IsuPetasys Co., Ltd.; Daegu, Korea (South)
Itacare Capital Investments Limited; Road Town, Virgin Islands (British)
Italia Independent Group S.p.A.; Turin, Italy
Itcen Systems Co., Ltd.; Seoul, Korea (South)
ITH Pharma Ltd.; London, United Kingdom
IT Link S.A.; Paris, France
itmsoil Pty Ltd.; Uckfield, United Kingdom
Ivacon Engineering B.V.; Lijnden, Netherlands
Ivalis Group; Maurepas, France
IVEE INJECTAA LIMITED; Ahmedabad, India
Iv-Groep b.v.; Papendrecht, Netherlands
IVS Group S.A.; Luxembourg, Luxembourg
IwaiCosmo Holdings, Inc.; Osaka, Japan
Ixir Productions, Inc.; Nantes, France
IYKOT HITECH TOOLROOM LIMITED; Chennai, India
Iz Hayvancilik Tarim ve Gida Sanayi ve Ticaret AS; Istanbul, Turkey

J

Jack Wills Ltd.; Greenford, United Kingdom
Jacobs & Thompson Inc.; Toronto, Canada
JacTravel Limited; London, United Kingdom
JAGAN LAMPS LIMITED; New Delhi, India
Jager Metal Corp.; Vancouver, Canada
JAGSONPAL FINANCE & LEASING LTD; New Delhi, India
Jaguar Mining Inc.; Toronto, Canada
Jahr Top Special Verlag GmbH & Co. KG; Hamburg, Germany
JAHWA ELECTRONICS CO., LTD; Cheongwon, Korea (South)
JAINEX AAMCOL LIMITED; Mumbai, India
James Briggs Ltd.; Oldham, United Kingdom
James Durrans & Sons Limited; Sheffield, United Kingdom
Janalakshmi Financial Services Pvt. Ltd.; Bengaluru, India
Jane France SA; Saint-Die-des-Vosges, France
Japan Airport Terminal Co., Ltd.; Tokyo, Japan
Japan Display Inc.; Tokyo, Japan
Japan Electronic Materials Corporation; Amagasaki, Japan
Japan Wind Development Co., Ltd.; Tokyo, Japan
Jarvis Securities plc; Tunbridge Wells, United Kingdom
Jasch Industries Limited; New Delhi, India
Jattashankar Industries Limited; Mumbai, India
Jawon Co., Ltd.; Asan, Korea (South)
Jayant Mercantile Company Limited; Mumbai, India
JAYBHARAT TEXTILES & REAL ESTATE LIMITED; Mumbai, India
JAYSYNTH DYESTUFF (INDIA) LTD; Mumbai, India
Jb Global Ltd.; Cheltenham, United Kingdom
JC Group Holdings Ltd.; Kowloon, China (Hong Kong)

JCT600 Limited; Bradford, United Kingdom
JD.com, Inc.; Beijing, China
JD International Limited; Tsuen Wan, China (Hong Kong)
Jeco Co., Ltd.; Gyoda, Japan
Jeil Pharmaceutical Co., Ltd.; Seoul, Korea (South)
Jeju Semiconductor Co.; Jeju, Korea (South)
Jemi Fibre Corp.; Vancouver, Canada
Jereissati Telecom S.A.; Sao Paulo, Brazil
JHAVERI CREDITS & CAPITAL LIMITED; Vadodara, India
Jiahua Stores Holdings Limited; Shenzhen, China
Jia Meng Holdings Ltd.; Guangzhou, China
Jiangsu Etern Company Limited; Wujiang, China
Jiangsu Hengli HighPressure Oil Cylinder Co., Ltd.; Changzhou, China
Jiangsu Hengrui Medicine Co., Ltd.; Lianyungang, China
Jiangsu Holly Corporation; Nanjing, China
Jiangsu Jinsheng Industry Co., Ltd.; Changzhou, China
Jiangsu Lugang Science & Technology Co., Ltd.; Zhangjiagang, China
Jiangsu Nanfang Bearing Co., Ltd.; Wujin, China
Jiangsu Sanfangxiang Industrial Company Limited; Jiangyin, China
Jiangsu Transportation Research Institute Co., Ltd.; Nanjing, China
Jiangsu Yangnong Chemical Co., Ltd.; Yangzhou, China
Jiangsu Yinren Group Co., Ltd.; Wuxi, China
Jiangsu Yulong Steel Pipe Co., Ltd.; Wuxi, China
Jiangxi Lianchuang Optoelectronic Science & Technology Co., Ltd; Nanchang, China
Jih Lin Technology Co., Ltd.; Kaohsiung, Taiwan
Jilin Qifeng Chemical Fiber Co., Ltd.; Jilin, China
Jilin Sino-Microelectronics Co., Ltd.; Jilin, China
Jin Cai Holdings Company Limited; Shenzhen, China
Jin Co., Ltd.; Tokyo, Japan
JINDAL HOTELS LTD; Vadodara, India
Jinhui Shipping & Transportation Limited; Hong Kong, China (Hong Kong)
JinSung T.E.C. Inc; Pyeongtaek, Korea (South)
Jin Yang Pharmaceutical Co. Ltd; Seoul, Korea (South)
Jinzhou New China Dragon Moly Co., Ltd.; Jinzhou, China
Jiu Feng Investment Hong Kong Ltd.; Shanghai, China
J. J. Finance Corporation Limited; Kolkata, India
J. Murphy & Sons Limited; London, United Kingdom
Joao Fortes Engenharia S.A.; Rio de Janeiro, Brazil
JOEONE Co., Ltd.; Quanzhou, China
John Brown Media Group; London, United Kingdom
The John Clark Motor Group; Aberdeen, United Kingdom
John Daniel Holdings Limited; Pretoria, South Africa
Joincare Pharmaceutical Industry Group Co., Ltd; Shenzhen, China
Jokwang I.L.I Co., Ltd.; Pusan, Korea (South)
Jolly Plastic Industries Limited; Delhi, India
Jordan Ahli Bank; Amman, Jordan
Jordan Cement Factories Company PSC; Amman, Jordan
Jordan Decapolis Properties Plc; Amman, Jordan
Jordan Express Tourist Transportation Company; Amman, Jordan
Jordanian Electric Power Company Limited; Amman, Jordan
Jordanian Expatriates Investment Holding Plc; Amman, Jordan
Jordanian Management & Consultancy Company; Amman, Jordan
The Jordanian Pharmaceutical Manufacturing Co., P.L.C.; Amman, Jordan
Jordanian Realestate Company For Development Plc; Amman, Jordan
Jordan Industrial Resources Co. Ltd.; Amman, Jordan
Jordan Industries & Match Co., Ltd.; Amman, Jordan
Jordan International Trading Center Co., Ltd.; Amman, Jordan
Jordan Paper & Cardboard Factories Co. PLC; Amman, Jordan
Jordan pipes manufacturing co., ltd.; Amman, Jordan
Jordan Press Foundation Plc; Amman, Jordan
Jordan Projects for Tourism Development Company; Amman, Jordan
Jordan Worsted Mills Company; Amman, Jordan
JOSAPAR - Joaquim Oliveira S/A Participacoes; Porto Alegre, Brazil
Journey Energy Inc.; Calgary, Canada
Joyce Boutique Holdings Limited; Hong Kong, China (Hong Kong)
JoyCity Corporation; Seongnam, Korea (South)
JPT Securities Limited; Mumbai, India
JRSIS Health Care Corporation; Harbin, China
GRINDEKS AS; Riga, Latvia
JSC Latvijas Gaze; Riga, Latvia
JSC Zaliv Shipyard; Kerch, Ukraine
J.S. Johnson & Company Limited; Nassau, Bahamas
JSS Corporation; Osaka, Japan
J-Stream Inc.; Tokyo, Japan
JT Corporation; Cheonan, Korea (South)
JTL INFRA LIMITED; Chandigarh, India
Jubilee Gold Exploration Ltd.; Toronto, Canada
Jumbo Finance Ltd.; Mumbai, India
Just Dial Ltd; Mumbai, India
JW Holdings Corporation; Seoul, Korea (South)
Jyothi Infraventures Limited; Hyderabad, India
Jyoti overseas Limited; Indore, India
Jyoti Resins & Adhesives Ltd.; Ahmedabad, India
JYP ENTERTAINMENT CO., LTD.; Seoul, Korea (South)

K

Kabel Deutschland Holding AG; Unterfohring, Germany
KAHEE Co., LTD.; Seoul, Korea (South)

The KAIN Limited Partnership; Kitchener, Canada
Kaira Can Company Limited; Mumbai, India
Kaisa Group Holdings Limited; Shenzhen, China
Kai Yuan Holdings Limited; Wanchai, China (Hong Kong)
KAJO NEUKIRCHEN Management und Beteiligungs GmbH; Frankfurt am Main, Germany
KAKATIYA TEXTILES LIMITED; Coimbatore, India
Kama Co., Ltd.; Shanghai, China
Kamada Ltd.; Nes Ziyyona, Israel
KAMALAKSHI FINANCE CORPORATION LIMITED; Mumbai, India
Kam & Ronson Media Group Inc.; Richmond Hill, Canada
KAMPANI CONSULTANTS LTD; Mumbai, India
Kanaden Corporation; Tokyo, Japan
KANCO TEA & INDUSTRIES LIMITED; Kolkata, India
Kanda Holdings Co., Ltd.; Tokyo, Japan
K&O Energy Group Inc.; Tokyo, Japan
Kanel Industries Limited; Ahmedabad, India
Kanger International Berhad; Shenzhen, China
Kanglim Co., Ltd.; Cheongwon, Korea (South)
KANIKA INFRASTRUCTURE & POWER LIMITED; Kolkata, India
Kanto Denka Kogyo Co., Ltd.; Tokyo, Japan
KAONMEDIA CO, LTD.; Seongnam, Korea (South)
Kaori Heat Treatment Co., Ltd.; Taoyuan, Taiwan
Kappa Create Co., Ltd.; Saitama, Japan
Karan Woo-Sin Limited; Medak, India
Karex Berhad; Johor, Malaysia
Karma Industries Ltd.; Mumbai, India
Karnimata Cold Storage Limited; Burdwan, India
Karsten Energy Corp.; Vancouver, Canada
Ka Shui International Holdings Limited; Kowloon, China (Hong Kong)
Kashyap Tele-Medecine Ltd.; Ahmedabad, India
Katakura Industries Co., Ltd.; Tokyo, Japan
KATOMSK AS; Tallinn, Estonia
Kawasaki Kasei Chemicals Ltd.; Kawasaki, Japan
Kaycan Ltd.; Pointe-Claire, Canada
KayDav Group Limited; Cape Town, South Africa
Kay Power & Paper Limited; Satara, India
KBS INDIA LIMITED; Mumbai, India
KC Cottrell Co., Ltd.; Seoul, Korea (South)
KCentric Technologies, Inc.; Laval, Canada
KCTC CO. Ltd; Seoul, Korea (South)
K.C. Tech Co., Ltd.; Anseong, Korea (South)
KCW Corporation; Daegu, Korea (South)
Kdmedia Inc.; P'aju, Korea (South)
KDR Industrials Ltd.; Vancouver, Canada
KEDA Industrial Company Limited; Foshan, China
KEERTHI INDUSTRIES LIMITED; Hyderabad, India
The Keihin Co., Ltd.; Tokyo, Japan
Keisei Electric Railway Co., Ltd.; Tokyo, Japan
Keith, Bayley, Rogers & Co. Limited; London, United Kingdom
Kelvin Electric Trading Co., Ltd.; Causeway Bay, China (Hong Kong)
Kelway Limited; London, United Kingdom
Kemwell Biopharma Pvt Ltd; Bengaluru, India
Kenford Group Holdings Limited; Kwai Chung, China (Hong Kong)
Kenko.com Inc.; Tokyo, Japan
Kenkou Corp., Inc.; Tokyo, Japan
Kenshoo, Ltd.; Tel Aviv, Israel
Kentima AB; Staffanstorp, Sweden
Kentzu Steel Sdn Bhd; Kuala Lumpur, Malaysia
KEPCO Plant Service & Engineering Co., Ltd; Seongnam, Korea (South)
Kepler Weber S.A.; Sao Paulo, Brazil
Kernel Holding S.A.; Kiev, Ukraine
Kerry Group Limited; Quarry Bay, China (Hong Kong)
Keyeast Co., LTD; Seoul, Korea (South)
Keyrus SA; Levallois-Perret, France
Keystoneglobal Co., Ltd.; Seoul, Korea (South)
Keytree Ltd.; London, United Kingdom
Keywords Studios Plc; Dublin, Ireland
KFM BUILDERS & DEVELOPERS LTD.; Bengaluru, India
KG Eco Technology Service Co., Ltd.; Siheung, Korea (South)
KG Mobilians; Seongnam, Korea (South)
KGN Enterprises Limited; Mumbai, India
KGN INDUSTRIES LIMITED; Mumbai, India
KHANDELWAL EXTRACTIONS LIMITED; Kanpur, India
Khator Fibre & Fabrics Ltd.; Mumbai, India
Khoday India Limited; Bengaluru, India
KHVatec Co., Ltd.; Gumi, Korea (South)
Kim Heng Offshore & Marine Holdings Limited; Singapore, Singapore
Kim Kang Aquaculture Sdn Bhd; Batu Pahat, Malaysia
Kimoce; Mulhouse, France
Kimura Chemical Plants Co., Ltd.; Amagasaki, Japan
Kimura-Unity Co., Ltd.; Nagoya, Japan
Kinexia S.p.A.; Milan, Italy
Kingbo Strike Limited; Singapore, Singapore
King Digital Entertainment plc; London, United Kingdom
Kingdom Holdings Limited; Jiaxing, China
King George Financial Corporation; Vancouver, Canada
Kingslake International Limited; Milton Keynes, United Kingdom
Kingsland Energy Corporation; Regina, Canada
Kingwell Group Limited; Kowloon, China (Hong Kong)
Kin Mining NL; Osborne Park, Australia
KIRAN SYNTEX LIMITED; Surat, India

Kisan Telecom Co., Ltd.; Seoul, Korea (South)
KISWIRE LTD; Busan, Korea (South)
Kiwoom No2 Special Purpose Acquisition Company; Seoul, Korea (South)
The Kiyo Bank, Ltd.; Wakayama, Japan
KJ Pretech Co., Ltd; Hwaseong, Korea (South)
Klabin S.A.; Rio de Janeiro, Brazil
Klausner Trading International GmbH; Tirol, Austria
Kleannara; Seoul, Korea (South)
KMW Inc.; Hwaseong, Korea (South)
KnightHawk Inc.; Vernon, Canada
Knight Therapeutics Inc.; Westmount, Canada
Knill Holding GmbH; Weiz, Austria
Koatsu Gas Kogyo Co., Ltd.; Osaka, Japan
Kobmand Herman Sallings Fond; Hojbjerg, Denmark
KoBold Group Limited; Ipswich, Australia
Kocom Co., Ltd.; Gimpo, Korea (South)
KODACO Co., Ltd.; Cheonan, Korea (South)
Kodal Minerals plc; London, United Kingdom
KOHINOOR TECHNO ENGINEERS LIMITED; Surat, India
Kohnan Shoji Co., Ltd.; Sakai, Japan
Koh Young Technology Inc.; Seoul, Korea (South)
Kojima Iron Works Co., Ltd.; Takasaki, Japan
Kokusan Denki Co., Ltd.; Numazu, Japan
Kollakorn Corporation Limited; Sydney, Australia
Kolmar Korea Co., Ltd.; Seoul, Korea (South)
Komelon Corporation; Busan, Korea (South)
Komeri Co., Ltd.; Niigata, Japan
Komet Manufacturers Inc.; Blainville, Canada
KoMiCo Ltd.; Anseong, Korea (South)
KONA I Corporation; Seoul, Korea (South)
Kong Shum Union Property Management (Holding) Limited; Kowloon, China (Hong Kong)
KONICTECH CO., LTD; Seoul, Korea (South)
Koovs Marketing Consulting Pvt. Ltd; Gurgaon, India
Korea Cast Iron Pipe Ind. Co., Ltd.; Pusan, Korea (South)
Korea Flange Co., Ltd.; Ulsan, Korea (South)
KOREA FUEL-TECH CORPORATION; Anseong, Korea (South)
Korea Information Certificate Authority, Inc.; Seoul, Korea (South)
Korean Reinsurance Company; Seoul, Korea (South)
Korea Polymer Co., Ltd.; Seoul, Korea (South)
Korea Ratings Corp.; Seoul, Korea (South)
Korea Real Estate Investment & Trust Co., Ltd.; Seoul, Korea (South)
Korea Semiconductor System Co, Ltd.; Bucheon, Korea (South)
Korea Steel Shape Co., Ltd.; Busan, Korea (South)
Kore Resources, Inc.; Seoul, Korea (South)
Korian SA; Paris, France
Korvest Ltd.; Kilburn, Australia
Koryo Credit Information Co., Ltd.; Seoul, Korea (South)
KOTHARI FERMENTATION & BIOCHEM LIMITED; New Delhi, India
Kotobuki Spirits Co., Ltd.; Yonago, Japan
KOVAI MEDICAL CENTER & HOSPITAL LIMITED; Coimbatore, India
KPJ Healthcare Berhad; Kuala Lumpur, Malaysia
KPM Tech Co., Ltd; Ansan, Korea (South)
KPX Chemical Co., Ltd.; Seoul, Korea (South)
KPX Fine Chemical Co., Ltd.; Yeosu, Korea (South)
KPX Green Chemical Co., Ltd.; Seosan, Korea (South)
KrisEnergy Ltd.; Singapore, Singapore
KRISHNA FERRO PRODUCTS LIMITED; Sundergarh, India
KRISHNA VENTURES LIMITED; Mumbai, India
Kromek Group PLC; Durham, United Kingdom
Kryso Resources plc; London, United Kingdom
K'S Holdings Corporation; Mito, Japan
KSK Power Ventur plc; Douglas, Isle of Man
KSL & INDUSTRIES LIMITED; Mumbai, India
KSP Co., Ltd.; Busan, Korea (South)
KSS Limited; Mumbai, India
KSS LINE LTD.; Seoul, Korea (South)
KTC (Edibles) Limited; Wednesbury, United Kingdom
KTL Technologies Limited; Sydney, Australia
KUKBO DESIGN Co., Ltd; Seoul, Korea (South)
Kukdong Corporation; Seoul, Korea (South)
Kukdong Oil & Chemical Co., Ltd.; Yangsan, Korea (South)
Kukje Pharmaceutical Industrial Company Limited; Seongnam, Korea (South)
Kumho Electric, Inc.; Seoul, Korea (South)
Kumkang Kind; Seoul, Korea (South)
Kumyang Co., Ltd.; Busan, Korea (South)
Kunming Pharmaceutical Corporation; Kunming, China
Kunststoffe Industries Ltd.; Mumbai, India
Kunsul Chemical Industrial Co., Ltd.; Busan, Korea (South)
Kunwha Pharmaceutical Co., Ltd.; Seoul, Korea (South)
Kuok (Singapore) Limited; Singapore, Singapore
Kushal Tradelink Limited; Ahmedabad, India
KUWER INDUSTRIES LIMITED; Noida, India
KVB Kunlun Financial Group Limited; Kowloon, China (Hong Kong)
KVC Industrial Supplies Sdn. Bhd.; Bandar Baru Bangi, Malaysia
KWALITY CREDIT & LEASING LIMITED; Kolkata, India
Kwang Jin Ind. Co., Ltd.; Busan, Korea (South)
KWANG JIN WINTEC CO., LTD.; Busan, Korea (South)

Kyoei Sangyo Co., Ltd.; Tokyo, Japan
Kyoei Tanker Co., Ltd.; Tokyo, Japan
KYTO BIOPHARMA INC.; Toronto, Canada
Kyudenko Ltd.; Fukuoka, Japan
Kyung Chang Industrial Co., Ltd.; Daegu, Korea (South)
KyungDong Navien Co., Ltd.; Seoul, Korea (South)
Kyung In Electronics Co., Ltd; Seoul, Korea (South)
KYUNG NONG Corporation; Seoul, Korea (South)
Kyushu Railway Company; Fukuoka, Japan

L

Laboratorios Servimedic S.A.; Montevideo, Uruguay
LabStyle Innovations Corp.; Caesarea, Israel
LACROIX SA; Saint-Herblain, France
LAEP Investments, Ltd.; Sao Paulo, Brazil
LA Fitness Limited; Doncaster, United Kingdom
LA International Computer Consultants Ltd.; Stoke-on-Trent, United Kingdom
Lajavi Inversiones SL; Madrid, Spain
Lakeview Hotel Investment Corp.; Winnipeg, Canada
Lakewood Mining Co. Ltd.; Gabriola, Canada
Lakhotia Polyester (India) Limited; Nasik, India
Lakshmi Automatic Loom Works Limited; Coimbatore, India
Lalpir Power Ltd.; Lahore, Pakistan
Lamex Foods UK Limited; Broxbourne, United Kingdom
Lamprecht Transport AG; Basel, Switzerland
Lanco Infratech Limited; Gurgaon, India
L&K Biomed Co., Ltd.; Seoul, Korea (South)
Landolt & Cie SA; Lausanne, Switzerland
Landsea Green Properties Co., Ltd.; Central, China (Hong Kong)
Landvelar Hf; Kopavogur, Iceland
Langham Hospitality Investments Limited; Wanchai, China (Hong Kong)
LANSON-BCC; Reims, France
Lantern Hotel Group Limited; Five Dock, Australia
La Opala RG Limited; Kolkata, India
Lariat Energy Ltd.; Vancouver, Canada
Laricina Energy Ltd.; Calgary, Canada
Lateral Gold Corp.; Vancouver, Canada
The Law Debenture Corporation p.l.c.; London, United Kingdom
Lawrence Harvey Search & Selection Ltd.; London, United Kingdom
The Lawton Tube Co., Ltd.; Coventry, United Kingdom
LDT Inc.; Cheonan, Korea (South)
Leadership Development Solutions SRL; Bucharest, Romania
Learning Technologies Group plc; Brighton, United Kingdom
LEATT CORPORATION; Durbanville, South Africa
LEC, Inc.; Tokyo, Japan
Ledermann Immobilien AG; Zurich, Switzerland
LED International Holdings Limited; Kowloon, China (Hong Kong)
Leengate Valves Limited; Alfreton, United Kingdom
Leeno Industrial, Inc.; Busan, Korea (South)
Legendary Motorcar Company Ltd.; Halton Hills, Canada
Legend Strategy International Holdings Group Company Limited; Shenzhen, China
LegoChem Biosciences Inc.; Daejeon, Korea (South)
Leisure Pass Group Limited; London, United Kingdom
Lekoil Limited; Lagos, Nigeria
LENECO Co., Ltd; Goyang, Korea (South)
Leone Film Group S.p.A; Rome, Italy
Leon Fuat Berhad; Shah Alam, Malaysia
Leon Grosse; Aix-les-Bains, France
Leo Resources Inc.; Toronto, Canada
Lerado Group (Holding) Company Limited; Taipei, Taiwan
Les Laboratoires Servier SAS; Suresnes, France
Lewmar Marine Ltd.; Havant, United Kingdom
Leyshon Energy Limited; Beijing, China
Liaoning Chengda Co., Ltd.; Dalian, China
Liaoning SG Automotive Group Co., Ltd.; Dandong, China
Liberty Global plc; London, United Kingdom
The Licensing Company Limited; London, United Kingdom
Lienhard Office Group AG; Nanikon, Switzerland
Life Bond Holding GmbH & Co. KG; Hohenschaftlarn, Germany
LifeHealthcare Group Limited; North Ryde, Australia
Life Settlement Holding AG; Vienna, Austria
Lifestyle Global Enterprise, Inc.; Taipei, Taiwan
Lifestyle Properties Development Limited; Causeway Bay, China (Hong Kong)
Lifeways Community Care Limited; London, United Kingdom
Liffey Mills Ltd.; Meath, Ireland
Lifocolor Farben GmbH & Co. KG; Lichtenfels, Germany
Ligentia Group Ltd.; Leeds, United Kingdom
LightInTheBox Holding Co., Ltd.; Beijing, China
Lightron Fiber-Optic Devices, inc.; Daejeon, Korea (South)
Light S.A.; Rio de Janeiro, Brazil
LIMA Sp. z o.o.; Golub-Dobrzyn, Poland
Lingotes Especiales, S.A.; Valladolid, Spain
Link & Motivation Inc.; Tokyo, Japan
Link Mobility Group ASA; Oslo, Norway
LINK PHARMA CHEM LTD.; Baroda, India
LINPAC Group Limited; Birmingham, United Kingdom
LinQ Capital Limited; West Perth, Australia
Lintec Corporation; Tokyo, Japan
Linzhou Heavy Machinery Group Co., Ltd.; Anyang, China
Lion Chemtech Co., Ltd.; Daejeon, Korea (South)
Lion Print Corporation; L'viv, Ukraine

Lion Travel Service Co., Ltd.; Taipei, Taiwan
Litel Participacoes S.A.; Rio de Janeiro, Brazil
Little Real Estate Pty Ltd; Hawthorn, Australia
Livzon Pharmaceutical Group Inc.; Zhuhai, China
LML Limited; Kanpur, India
LOEN ENTERTAINMENT, INC.; Seoul, Korea (South)
Logaholic B.V.; Amsterdam, Netherlands
Logan Property Holdings Company Limited; Shenzhen, China
Logic Instrument S.A.; Domont, France
Log-In Logistica Intermodal S.A.; Rio de Janeiro, Brazil
The Logistics Partnership LLP; Droitwich, United Kingdom
Logoplaste Investimento, S.G.P.S., S.A.; Cascais, Portugal
Lojas Hering S/A; Blumenau, Brazil
London & Regional Properties Limited; London, United Kingdom
Longbau Group, Inc.; Hong Kong, China (Hong Kong)
LongDa Construction & Development Corporation; Kaohsiung, Taiwan
Longfield Chemicals Limited; Sutton, United Kingdom
Longreach Oil Limited; Sydney, Australia
Long Success International (Holdings) Limited; Sheung Wan, China (Hong Kong)
Longview Tea Company Limited; Kolkata, India
Lonseal Corporation; Tokyo, Japan
LOOK INCORPORATED; Tokyo, Japan
Lords Chloro Alkali Limited; New Delhi, India
Lords Ishwar Hotels Limited; Vadodara, India
Lornex Capital Inc.; Vancouver, Canada
LOT78, INC.; London, United Kingdom
LOT Vacuum Co., Ltd.; Anseong, Korea (South)
Louis Dreyfus Armateurs; Suresnes, France
LP Hill PLC; South Perth, Australia
LS Networks Corporation Limited; Seoul, Korea (South)
LTC Co., Ltd.; Anyang, Korea (South)
Luca Way S.R.L.; Bucharest, Romania
Luckycom Inc.; Central, China (Hong Kong)
Lucta, S.A.; Montornes del Valles, Spain
LUDLOW JUTE & SPECIALITIES LIMITED; Kolkata, India
Lu Hai Holding Corp.; Chang-Hua, Taiwan
Luk Fook Holdings (International) Limited; Kowloon, China (Hong Kong)
Luma Investments, Ltd.; Singapore, Singapore
LUMIMICRO CO., LTD.; Yongin, Korea (South)
Lunar Capital Management Ltd.; Shanghai, China
Luoyang Longhua Heat Transfer & Energy Conservation Co., Ltd.; Luoyang, China
Lutronic Corporation; Goyang, Korea (South)
Luxoft Holding, Inc.; Zug, Switzerland
Luxury For Less Limited; Coventry, United Kingdom
Luyan (Fujian) Pharma Co., Ltd.; Xiamen, China
Lycatel Group; London, United Kingdom
Lykis Limited; Mumbai, India
Lymington Precision Engineers Co., Ltd.; Lymington, United Kingdom
LYPSA GEMS & JEWELLERY LIMITED; Mumbai, India
Lysanda Ltd.; Kelvedon, United Kingdom

M

M247 Limited; Manchester, United Kingdom
Mabion SA; Kutno, Poland
Macau Legend Development Limited; Macau, China (Macau)
Macau Resources Group Limited; Macau, China (Macau)
Mace Limited; London, United Kingdom
Machinefabriek Goudkuil Apeldoorn B.V.; Apeldoorn, Netherlands
Mackenzie Master Limited Partnership; Toronto, Canada
Macro Kiosk Berhad; Kuala Lumpur, Malaysia
Macromac PLC; Petaling Jaya, Malaysia
MACSA ID, S.A.; Manresa, Spain
MADHUR CAPITAL & FINANCE LTD.; Ahmedabad, India
Madison Ventures Inc.; Queretaro, Mexico
Madrigall SA; Paris, France
Maeil Dairies Co., Ltd.; Seoul, Korea (South)
Maersk Broker K/S; Copenhagen, Denmark
Magazine Luiza S.A.; Franca, Brazil
Magicmicro Co., Ltd.; Ansan, Korea (South)
MagnaChip Semiconductor Corporation; Luxembourg, Luxembourg
MAGNA COLORS LIMITED; Thane, India
Magna Resources Ltd; Vancouver, Canada
Magnolia International Ltd.; Basel, Switzerland
Magnum Entertainment Group Holdings Limited; Central, China (Hong Kong)
Mahanivesh (India) Limited; New Delhi, India
MAHA RASHTRA APEX CORPORATION LIMITED; Bengaluru, India
MAHARASHTRA CORPORATION LIMITED; Mumbai, India
MAHASAGAR TRAVELS LIMITED; Junagadh, India
Mahle Metal Leve S.A.; Mogi-Guacu, Brazil
Mahogany Oy; Lohja, Finland
Mail Marketing (Scotland) Limited; Glasgow, United Kingdom
Mainoskentta Oy; Tampere, Finland
Maj Invest Holding A/S; Copenhagen, Denmark
Make it Cheaper Limited; London, United Kingdom
MAKISM 3D CORP.; Cambridge, United Kingdom
MAKUS, Inc.; Seoul, Korea (South)
Malabar Coal Limited; Sydney, Australia
MALABAR TRADING COMPANY LIMITED; Mumbai, India
Mallinckrodt plc; Dublin, Ireland
Malvaux Industries S.A.; Loulay, France

M&A Capital Partners Co., Ltd.; Tokyo, Japan
Mandriva S.A.; Paris, France
Mangels Industrial S.A.; Sao Paulo, Brazil
Mangrove Holdings Pte Ltd.; Singapore, Singapore
Manho Rope & Wire Ltd.; Busan, Korea (South)
Manitex Capital Inc.; Montreal, Canada
Mansion House Consulting Limited; London, United Kingdom
Maori S.A.; Sao Paulo, Brazil
Maple Leaf Green World Inc.; Calgary, Canada
Maple Power Capital Corporation; Richmond Hill, Canada
Marico Kaya Enterprises Limited; Mumbai, India
MARIGOLD GLASS INDUSTRIES LIMITED; Kolkata, India
Marine Harvest Rolmer S.A.S.; Challans, France
Marion Energy Limited; Hawthorn, Australia
Marisa Lojas S.A.; Sao Paulo, Brazil
Marketing V F Limited; London, United Kingdom
Marketwire L.P.; Toronto, Canada
Mark Group Limited; Leicester, United Kingdom
Markor International Furniture Co., Ltd.; Urumqi, China
Marksmen Energy Inc.; Calgary, Canada
Marquest Asset Management Inc.; Toronto, Canada
Martina Minerals Corporation; London, United Kingdom
Martindale Pharmaceuticals Ltd.; Brentwood, United Kingdom
Maruhachi Securities Co., Ltd.; Aichi, Japan
Maruwa Unyu Kiakan Co., Ltd.; Saitama, Japan
Maruyama Mfg. Co., Inc.; Tokyo, Japan
Maruzen Showa Unyu Co., Ltd.; Yokohama, Japan
Masafat Specialized Transport Company; Amman, Jordan
Mascotte Holdings Limited; Aberdeen, China (Hong Kong)
Masonite International Corporation; Concord, Canada
MAS Real Estate Inc.; Douglas, Isle of Man
Master Chemicals Limited; Mumbai, India
Master Drilling Group Limited; Fochville, South Africa
Mastrad SA; Paris, France
Matachewan Consolidated Mines, Limited; Toronto, Canada
Matas A/S; Allerod, Denmark
Match Capital Resources Corporation; Toronto, Canada
Materials Technologies; Crevecoeur-le-Grand, France
Mather & Platt Fire Systems Limited; Pune, India
Mathew Easow Research Securities Limited; Kolkata, India
Matrix Concepts Holdings Berhad; Seremban, Malaysia
MATRRIX Energy Technologies Inc; Calgary, Canada
Matsuya Foods, Co., Ltd.; Musashino, Japan
Maverick Advertising & Design; London, United Kingdom
MAX ALERT SYSTEMS LIMITED; Mumbai, India
Maxam Capital Corp.; Vancouver, Canada
MAX HEIGHTS INFRASTRUCTURE LIMITED; New Delhi, India
Maxigen Biotech Inc.; New Taipei City, Taiwan
MAXIMAA SYSTEMS LIMITED; Mumbai, India
Max's (Ermita), Inc.; Manila, Philippines
Max Weishaupt GmbH; Biberach, Germany
Maybank ATR Kim Eng Financial Corporation; Makati, Philippines
Mazor Robotics Ltd.; Caesarea, Israel
Mazu Alliance Limited; Bondi Junction, Australia
MBI & Partners U.K. Limited; London, United Kingdom
MBI Intercorp Limited; New Delhi, India
McAleese Limited; Camberwell, Australia
MCAN Mortgage Corporation; Toronto, Canada
McChip Resources Inc.; Toronto, Canada
McColl's Retail Group PLC; Brentwood, United Kingdom
MC Group Public Company Limited; Bangkok, Thailand
McLaren Construction Group; Brentwood, United Kingdom
McLaughlin & Harvey Ltd.; Newtownabbey, United Kingdom
MCM Capital One Inc.; Toronto, Canada
McPhy Energy S.A.; Valence, France
MCS et Associes, S.A.; Paris, France
M. Dias Branco S.A. Industria e Comercio de Alimentos; Eusebio, Brazil
MD Medical Group Investment Plc; Limassol, Cyprus
Meade-King Robinson & Co., Ltd.; Liverpool, United Kingdom
Meadow Foods Limited; Chester, United Kingdom
ME Construction Ltd.; London, United Kingdom
Medgold Resources Corp.; Vancouver, Canada
Media Analytics Corporation; Quarry Bay, China (Hong Kong)
Media Do Co., Ltd.; Nagoya, Japan
Media Experts; Toronto, Canada
Media Matrix Worldwide Limited; Mumbai, India
Mediana Co., Ltd.; Wonju, Korea (South)
Media one Global Entertainment Ltd; Chennai, India
MEDIASEEK, Inc.; Tokyo, Japan
Media-Vision International, Inc.; Toronto, Canada
MediBIC Group, Co., Ltd.; Tokyo, Japan
Medical Device Works; Brussels, Belgium
Medicalgorithmics S.A.; Warsaw, Poland
Medical Prognosis Institute A/S; Horsholm, Denmark
MedicAnimal Limited; London, United Kingdom
Medinet Co., Ltd.; Yokohama, Japan
MEDINOVA DIAGNOSTIC SERVICES LIMITED; Hyderabad, India
MEDIPOST Co., Ltd.; Seoul, Korea (South)
Mediterranean Tourism Investment Company; Amman, Jordan
Medivac Limited; Melbourne, Australia

Medtech SA; Castelnau-le-Lez, France
MEERE COMPANY INC.; Hwaseong, Korea (South)
Mega Expo Holdings Limited; Kowloon, China (Hong Kong)
Mega Fin (India) Limited; Mumbai, India
Mega Lifesciences Public Company Limited; Bangkok, Thailand
Mega Sprint Guard S.A; Thessaloniki, Greece
MEGLON INFRA-REAL (INDIA) LIMITED; Mumbai, India
Mehta Integrated Finance Limited; Ahmedabad, India
Mei Ah Entertainment Group Limited; Kowloon, China (Hong Kong)
Meito Sangyo Co., Ltd.; Nagoya, Japan
Meiwa Corporation; Tokyo, Japan
Melbye Skandinavia AS; Skedsmokorset, Norway
MelcoLot Limited; Central, China (Hong Kong)
Melcor Real Estate Investment Trust; Edmonton, Canada
MELFAS Inc.; Seongnam, Korea (South)
Melker Schorling AB; Stockholm, Sweden
Melrob Limited; Crawley, United Kingdom
MEP Technologies, Inc.; Laval, Canada
Mercado Abierto Electronico S.A.; Buenos Aires, Argentina
Mercantile Investment Company Ltd.; Sydney, Australia
Merchant House International Limited; Nedlands, Australia
Mercury Capital II Limited; Toronto, Canada
Meridex Software Corporation; Vancouver, Canada
Merricks Capital Pty Ltd.; South Yarra, Australia
Merry Garden Holdings Limited; Wanchai, China (Hong Kong)
Meta Biomed Co., Ltd.; Cheongwon, Korea (South)
Metafraks OJSC; Gubakha, Russia
Metal & Waste Recycling Ltd.; London, United Kingdom
METAL COATINGS (INDIA) LIMITED; New Delhi, India
Metalfrio Solutions S.A.; Sao Paulo, Brazil
Metalgrafica Iguacu S.A.; Ponta Grossa, Brazil
Metals Australia Limited; West Perth, Australia
Metalurgica Duque S.A.; Joinville, Brazil
Metalurgica Riosulense S.A.; Rio do Sul, Brazil
Metech Recycling (UK) Ltd.; Aberdare, United Kingdom
Meteoric Resources NL; West Perth, Australia
Metgasco Limited; North Sydney, Australia
Methaq Real Estate Investment P.L.C.; Amman, Jordan
METISA - Metalurgica Timboense S.A.; Sao Paulo, Brazil
Metrofile Holdings Limited; Johannesburg, South Africa
Mexan Limited; Tsing Yi, China (Hong Kong)
Mezzotin Minerals Inc.; Toronto, Canada
MFO S.A.; Sochaczew, Poland
MH Ethanol Co., Ltd.; Masan, Korea (South)
Micro Contact Solution Co., Ltd.; Cheonan, Korea (South)
Microelectronic NH GmbH; Munich, Germany
Midas Holdings Limited; Singapore, Singapore
Midas Resources Limited; Inglewood, Australia
Middle East Diversified Investment Company P.L.C; Amman, Jordan
Middle East Pharmaceutical & Chemical Industries Company; Amman, Jordan
Mid Industry Capital SpA; Milan, Italy
Midnight Sun Mining Corp.; Vancouver, Canada
Midong Electronics & Telecommunication Co., Ltd.; Seoul, Korea (South)
Midwest Gold Limited; Hyderabad, India
MILESTONE GLOBAL LIMITED; Hoskote, India
Milestone International, Corp.; Kaliningrad, Russia
Millers Oils Ltd.; Brighouse, United Kingdom
Milner Consolidated Silver Mines Ltd.; Tiny, Canada
Milton Plastics Limited; Mumbai, India
MINAL INDUSTRIES LIMITED; Mumbai, India
Minasmaquinas S.A.; Belo Horizonte, Brazil
Mincon Group PLC; Shannon, Ireland
Minco PLC; Navan, Ireland
Mindax Limited; West Perth, Australia
Mind Candy Ltd.; London, United Kingdom
Mindmancer AB; Gothenburg, Sweden
Mineral Ferrous Metallergy JSC; Phu Ly, Vietnam
Mine Restoration Investments Limited; Irene, South Africa
Mineria Y Exploraciones Olympia, Inc.; Bonao, Dominican Republic
Ming Fung Jewellery Group Limited; Central, China (Hong Kong)
Minitel - Sociedade de Fomento de Aplicacoes Informaticas, L.da.; Lisbon, Portugal
Minolta Finance Ltd.; Kolkata, India
Minsud Resources Corp.; Toronto, Canada
Mintel Group Ltd.; London, United Kingdom
Minth Group Limited; Ningbo, China
Minupar Participacoes S.A.; Sao Paulo, Brazil
Mirch Technologies Limited; Mumbai, India
Mirelis InvesTrust SA; Geneva, Switzerland
Mirrabooka Investments Limited; Melbourne, Australia
Misen Energy AB; Gothenburg, Sweden
MITACHI Co., LTD.; Nagoya, Japan
Mitani Sangyo Co., Ltd.; Ishikawa, Japan
Miyairi Valve Mfg. Co., Ltd.; Tokyo, Japan
MJP International Ltd.; Calgary, Canada
MK Electron Co., Ltd.; Yongin, Korea (South)
MK Restaurant Group Public Company Limited; Bangkok, Thailand
MLP Group S.A.; Pruszkow, Poland
MMG Canada, Ltd.; Toronto, Canada

MNtech Co, Ltd.; Cheongwon, Korea (South)
Moatech Co., Ltd.; Incheon, Korea (South)
Mobeus Equity Partners LLP; London, United Kingdom
Mobile Account Solutions Limited; Ware, United Kingdom
MobileWebAdz Ltd.; London, United Kingdom
Mobileye N.V.; Amsterdam, Netherlands
MobilityOne Limited; Kuala Lumpur, Malaysia
Mochida Pharmaceutical Co., Ltd.; Tokyo, Japan
Modella Woollens Limited; Mumbai, India
Model Restaurants Company PLC; Amman, Jordan
Modern Land (China) Co., Ltd.; Beijing, China
MODETOUR Network Inc.; Seoul, Korea (South)
MODI NATURALS LIMITED; Pilibhit, India
Mohit Paper Mills Limited; New Delhi, India
Moleskine SpA; Milan, Italy
Moncler S.p.A.; Milan, Italy
Money Masters Leasing & Finance Limited; Mumbai, India
MoneyMax Financial Services Ltd.; Singapore, Singapore
Mongolia Investment Group Limited; Kowloon, China (Hong Kong)
Montage Technology Group Limited; Shanghai, China
Montagne et Neige Developpement SA; Sainte-Helene-du-Lac, France
Montec International Limited; Sydney, Australia
Monteiro Aranha S.A.; Rio de Janeiro, Brazil
Monticiano Participacoes S.A.; Sao Paulo, Brazil
Monto Minerals Limited; West Perth, Australia
Monument Mining Limited; Vancouver, Canada
Mooncor Oil & Gas Corp.; Oakville, Canada
Moongipa Capital Finance Limited; New Delhi, India
MOO Print Limited; London, United Kingdom
MoPowered Group PLC; London, United Kingdom
MoraBanc Group; Andorra La Vella, Andorra
Morelli Group Limited; Enfield, United Kingdom
Morgan Ventures Limited; New Delhi, India
Morio Denki Co., Ltd.; Tokyo, Japan
Morro Bay Capital Ltd.; Calgary, Canada
MORYO INDUSTRIES LIMITED; Mumbai, India
MOTONIC CORPORATION; Seoul, Korea (South)
Mountain Warehouse Ltd.; London, United Kingdom
Mox Deals AG; Dusseldorf, Germany
Moxian Group Holdings, Inc.; Kowloon, China (Hong Kong)
MPHB Capital Berhad; Kuala Lumpur, Malaysia
MPK Group Inc.; Seoul, Korea (South)
Mrugesh Trading Limited; Mumbai, India
MS International plc; Doncaster, United Kingdom
MSR INDIA LIMITED; Hyderabad, India
MT EDUCARE LIMITED; Mumbai, India
MtekVision Co., Ltd; Seongnam, Korea (South)
MTG Metro Gratis KST; Budapest, Hungary
Mukat Pipes Ltd; Patiala, India
Muller & Phipps (India) Limited; Mumbai, India
MULTIBASE INDIA LIMITED; Daman, India
Multi Channel Solutions Limited; Kings Park, Australia
Multipanel UK Ltd.; Exeter, United Kingdom
Multistack International Limited; Cheltenham, Australia
MUNOTH CAPITAL MARKET LTD.; Ahmedabad, India
MUNOTH COMMUNICATION LIMITED; Chennai, India
Munoth Financial Services Limited; Chennai, India
Muvoni Technology Group Limited; Centurion, South Africa
MVL INDUSTRIES LIMITED; New Delhi, India
MVM Magyar Villamos Muvek Zrt.; Budapest, Hungary
MVP Capital Co. Ltd.; Seongnam, Korea (South)
M Winkworth Plc; London, United Kingdom
Myanmar Investments International Limited; Singapore, Singapore
M.Y Group Limited; Suva, Fiji
Myungmoon pharmaceutical Co., Ltd.; Seoul, Korea (South)

N

N1 hf; Kopavogur, Iceland
N24 Media GmbH; Berlin, Germany
Nabaltec AG; Schwandorf, Germany
Nadir Figueiredo Industria e Comercio S.A.; Sao Paulo, Brazil
NAGAHORI CORPORATION; Tokyo, Japan
Nagaileben Co., Ltd.; Tokyo, Japan
Nagano Keiki Co., Ltd.; Tokyo, Japan
Nagarjuna Oil Refinery Limited; Hyderabad, India
Nagatanien Co., Ltd.; Tokyo, Japan
NAGPUR POWER & INDUSTRIES LIMITED; Mumbai, India
Nakano Corporation; Tokyo, Japan
Nakayo Telecommunications, Inc.; Maebashi, Japan
NAKED BRAND GROUP INC.; Abbotsford, Canada
Nam Heng Oil Mill Co. Sdn. Bhd.; Batu Pahat, Malaysia
Namyang Dairy Products Co., Ltd.; Seoul, Korea (South)
Namyong Terminal Public Company Limited; Bangkok, Thailand
Nanjing Sinolife United Company Limited; Nanjing, China
Nan Liu Enterprises Co., Ltd.; Kaohsiung, Taiwan
Nanning Baling Technology Co., Ltd.; Nanning, China
Nanning Chemical Industry Co. Ltd; Nanning, China
NanoChemTech Inc.; Anseong, Korea (South)
NanoEnTek Inc.; Seoul, Korea (South)
Nanotech Security Corporation; Burnaby, Canada
Nanotronix Co., Ltd.; Seoul, Korea (South)
Nantong Metalforming Equipment Co., Ltd.; Rugao, China

Nanyang Holdings Limited; Central, China (Hong Kong)
Napatech A/S; Soborg, Denmark
NARA Mold & Die Co., Ltd.; Changwon, Korea (South)
Narbada Gems & Jewellery Ltd.; Hyderabad, India
National Accident Helpline Limited; Kettering, United Kingdom
National Aluminum Industrial Company; Amman, Jordan
National Cable & Wire Mfg. Co.; Amman, Jordan
National Chlorine Industries Co. LTD.; Amman, Jordan
National Engineering Pty Ltd; Young, Australia
National General Insurance Co. (P.S.C.); Dubai, United Arab Emirates
National Highways Authority of India; New Delhi, India
National Insurance Company (P.S.C); Amman, Jordan
National Pension Service; Seoul, Korea (South)
NATIONAL PLASTIC INDUSTRIES LIMITED; Mumbai, India
National Poultry P.L.C.; Amman, Jordan
National Steel Industry Company Limited; Amman, Jordan
National Storage REIT; Brisbane, Australia
Natronix Semiconductor Technology Ltd.; Chennai, India
Natural Capsules Limited; Bengaluru, India
Natural Dairy (NZ) Holdings Limited; Causeway Bay, China (Hong Kong)
Naturalendo Tech Co., Ltd.; Songnam, Korea (South)
NAVCOM INDUSTRIES LIMITED; Pune, India
Navigator Holdings Ltd.; London, United Kingdom
Navkar Builders Limited; Ahmedabad, India
Naylor Industries plc.; Barnsley, United Kingdom
NBTM New Materials Group Co., Ltd.; Ningbo, China
NCXX Inc.; Tokyo, Japan
ND Software Co., Ltd.; Yamagata, Japan
Neocom Multimedia SA; Marseille, France
Neoenergia S.A.; Rio de Janeiro, Brazil
NEOFIDELITY, Inc.; Seoul, Korea (South)
Neogem India Limited; Mumbai, India
NEO INFRACON LTD.; Mumbai, India
Neolife SA; Limonest, France
NEOMTEL Co., Ltd; Seoul, Korea (South)
NeoPharm Co., Ltd.; Daejeon, Korea (South)
Neptune Group Limited; Kowloon, China (Hong Kong)
Nergeco SA; Dunieres, France
Net Entertainment NE AB; Stockholm, Sweden
Net Insurance S.p.A.; Rome, Italy
NetScientific plc; Cambridge, United Kingdom
Network Value Components Ltd.; Yokosuka, Japan
Neungyule Education, Inc.; Seoul, Korea (South)
NeuroVive Pharmaceutical AB; Lund, Sweden
Newag SA; Nowy Sacz, Poland
New China Life Insurance Co., Ltd.; Beijing, China
Newever Trade Wings Limited; Kolkata, India
NewFlex Technology Co., Ltd.; Ansan, Korea (South)
New Forests Pty. Limited; Chatswood, Australia
New Hope Group Co., Ltd.; Chengdu, China
New Horizon Capital; Beijing, China
Newmark Security Plc; London, United Kingdom
Newport Exploration Limited; Vancouver, Canada
New Ray Medicine International Holdings Limited; Kowloon, China (Hong Kong)
NewSat Limited; Southbank, Australia
New Smart Energy Group Limited; Hong Kong, China (Hong Kong)
New Times Energy Corporation Limited; Central, China (Hong Kong)
Newtree Group Holdings Limited; Central, China (Hong Kong)
New West Energy Services Inc.; Calgary, Canada
New-York Hamburger Gummi-Waaren Compagnie AG; Luneburg, Germany
Nexentech Corporation; Ulsan, Korea (South)
NexG Co.,Ltd.; Seoul, Korea (South)
NEXTAGE Co., Ltd.; Aichi, Japan
NEXTCHIP Co., Ltd.; Seongnam, Korea (South)
NextRadioTV; Paris, France
NextStage SAS; Paris, France
Nexturn Co., ltd.; Yongin, Korea (South)
Nexus Bonds Limited; Sydney, Australia
Nexus Industries Ltd.; London, United Kingdom
NF Corporation; Yokohama, Japan
N Field Co., Ltd.; Osaka, Japan
Ngai Shun Holdings Limited; Kowloon, China (Hong Kong)
Ngee Ann Kongsi; Singapore, Singapore
NH Investment & Securities Co., Ltd.; Seoul, Korea (South)
Nicco Corporation Ltd.; Kolkata, India
NICE Holdings Co., Ltd.; Seoul, Korea (South)
Nice Holdings Inc.; Yokohama, Japan
NICHIREKI Co., Ltd.; Tokyo, Japan
Nicstech Co., Ltd.; Seoul, Korea (South)
Nido Petroleum Limited; Como, Australia
Nieuwenhuis Betonrenovatie B.V.; Twello, Netherlands
Niftylift Limited; Milton Keynes, United Kingdom
Nihon Kagaku Sangyo Co., Ltd., Tokyo, Japan
Nihon M&A Center Inc.; Tokyo, Japan
Nilachal Refractories Limited; Kolkata, India
NiMag (Pty) Ltd; Magaliesburg, South Africa
Nimax Theatres Limited; London, United Kingdom
Nine Entertainment Co. Holdings Limited; Willoughby, Australia
NingBo Bird Co., Ltd.; Fenghua, China
Ningbo Powerway Alloy Materials Co., Ltd.; Ningbo, China

Ningbo Sunny Electronic Co. Ltd.; Yuyao, China
NingGuo Lonch Electric Co., Ltd.; Ningguo, China
Nippon Aqua Co., Ltd.; Yokohama, Japan
Nippon Avionics Co., Ltd.; Tokyo, Japan
Nippon Carbon Co., Ltd.; Tokyo, Japan
Nippon Columbia Co., Ltd.; Tokyo, Japan
Nippon Conveyor Co., ltd; Daito, Japan
Nippon Crucible Co., Ltd.; Tokyo, Japan
Nippon Denko Co., Ltd.; Tokyo, Japan
Nippon Engineering Consultants Co., Ltd.; Tokyo, Japan
Nippon Filcon Co., Ltd.; Tokyo, Japan
Nippon Gas Co., Ltd.; Tokyo, Japan
Nippon Gear Co., Ltd.; Fujisawa, Japan
Nippon kinzoku co., Ltd.; Tokyo, Japan
Nippon Paper Industries Co., Ltd.; Tokyo, Japan
Nippon Seisen Co., Ltd.; Osaka, Japan
Nissei Plastic Industrial Co., Ltd.; Sakai, Japan
Nistec Ltd.; Petah Tiqwa, Israel
N.I STEEL Co., Ltd.; Seoul, Korea (South)
Nitin Alloys Global Limited; Thane, India
Nittoc Construction Co., Ltd.; Tokyo, Japan
NITTO KOGYO CORPORATION; Nagakute, Japan
Niuminco Group Limited; Sydney, Australia
NIVI TRADING LTD.; Mumbai, India
Noble Corporation plc; London, United Kingdom
Noble Foods Ltd.; Tring, United Kingdom
Noble Metal Group Incorporated; Kelowna, Canada
NoemaLife S.p.A.; Bologna, Italy
Nomura Co., Ltd.; Tokyo, Japan
Nongshim Co., Ltd.; Seoul, Korea (South)
Nopar for Trading & Investment Company Ltd.; Amman, Jordan
Norcon Plc; Limassol, Cyprus
Nord Anglia Education, Inc.; Central, China (Hong Kong)
Nord Gold N.V.; Amsterdam, Netherlands
Nordic American Offshore Ltd.; Hamilton, Bermuda
Nortec Quimica S.A.; Duque de Caxias, Brazil
North American Financials Capital Securities Trust; Toronto, Canada
Northam Platinum Limited; Johannesburg, South Africa
NORTH EASTERN CARRYING CORPORATION LIMITED; Delhi, India
Northern Cement Company; Amman, Jordan
North Group Finance Limited; Vancouver, Canada
North Mining Shares Company Limited; Wanchai, China (Hong Kong)
NorthWest Value Partners Inc.; Toronto, Canada
Norton Rose Fulbright LLP; London, United Kingdom
Norwest Energy NL; Perth, Australia
Nova Argent Canada Inc.; Toronto, Canada
Novabase SGPS, SA; Lisbon, Portugal
Novaday SAS; Pont-l'Eveque, France
Novae technology; Paris, France
Novarese Inc.; Tokyo, Japan
Nova Resources Limited; Singapore, Singapore
Novexco, Inc.; Laval, Canada
Novisource N.V.; Nieuwegein, Netherlands
Now Prepay Corp.; Port Coquitlam, Canada
NPR FINANCE LIMITED; Kolkata, India
NR 21; Colombes, France
NSE Industries SA; Emerainville-Malnoue, France
NSI Strategic Investments Ltd.; Vancouver, Canada
NSL Consolidated Limited; West Perth, Australia
NS Solutions Corporation; Tokyo, Japan
nTels Co., Ltd.; Seoul, Korea (South)
NTH AG; Bern, Switzerland
NuEnergy Gas Limited; Sydney, Australia
NUINTEK CO., LTD.; Asan, Korea (South)
Numericable Group SA; Champs-sur-Marne, France
NURI Telecom Co., Ltd.; Seoul, Korea (South)
Nutri-Asia Inc.; Taguig, Philippines
Nutriplant Industria e Comercio S.A.; Sao Paulo, Brazil
Nutritional Holdings Limited; Umhlanga, South Africa
Nuxeo; Paris, France
NVH Korea Inc.; Gyeongju, Korea (South)
NV Michel Van de Wiele; Kortrijk, Belgium
NVM Private Equity Limited; Newcastle upon Tyne, United Kingdom
NWM Solutions Limited; Bournemouth, United Kingdom
Nyesa Valores Corporacion, S.A.; Zaragoza, Spain
Nylofils India Limited; Rajahmundry, India

O

OAO SIBUR Holding; Moscow, Russia
Obducat AB; Lund, Sweden
Oben Holding Group SAC; Lima, Peru
OCEAN AGRO (INDIA) LIMITED; Baroda, India
Ocean Commerce Public Company Limited; Bangkok, Thailand
Ocean Outdoor UK Limited; London, United Kingdom
Oceanside Capital Corporation; Vancouver, Canada
Ochi Holdings Co., Ltd.; Fukuoka, Japan
OCI N.V.; Amsterdam, Netherlands
Octant Energy Corp.; Calgary, Canada
ODAS Elektrik Uretim ve Sanayi Ticaret AS; Istanbul, Turkey
Oddfellows Holdings Pty Ltd.; North Sydney, Australia
Odeon Film AG; Munich, Germany
Odin Energy Limited; West Perth, Australia
OE Solutions Co., Ltd.; Gwangju, Korea (South)

Offshore Oil Engineering Company Limited; Tianjin, China
Ogilvy PR Worldwide; Jakarta, Indonesia
Ohashi Technica, Inc.; Tokyo, Japan
Oiles Corporation; Tokyo, Japan
OJSC PhosAgro AG; Moscow, Russia
OJSC Rosgosstrakh Bank; Moscow, Russia
OJSC Rosneftegaz; Tver, Russia
Okamoto Machine Tool Works, Ltd.; Yokohama, Japan
OKANO VALVE MFG. CO.; Kitakyushu, Japan
Okaya Electric Industries Co., Ltd.; Tokyo, Japan
Okong Corporation; Incheon, Korea (South)
Okura Industrial Co., Ltd.; Marugame, Japan
Oldfields Holdings Limited; Campbelltown, Australia
Old Oak Holdings Limited; London, United Kingdom
Olie, Inc.; Vancouver, Canada
Olive Business Solutions Limited; Hatfield, United Kingdom
Oliver James Associates; London, United Kingdom
Oliver Schrott Kommunikation GmbH; Cologne, Germany
Oliver Valves Limited; Knutsford, United Kingdom
Olmix S.A.; Brehan, France
Olympia Financial Group Inc.; Calgary, Canada
OLYMPIC OIL INDUSTRIES LIMITED; Mumbai, India
OMEGA AG-SEEDS (PUNJAB) LIMITED; Hyderabad, India
OMNITECH PETROLEUM LIMITED; Mumbai, India
Omnitel Inc.; Seoul, Korea (South)
OMNITEX INDUSTRIES (INDIA) LIMITED; Mumbai, India
Onamba Co., Ltd.; Osaka, Japan
Oncolys BioPharma Inc.; Tokyo, Japan
OncoTherapy Science, Inc.; Kawasaki, Japan
OneE Tax Limited; Bolton, United Kingdom
OneLogix Group Limited; Kempton Park, South Africa
One Media iP Group Plc; Iver Heath, United Kingdom
Onesource Techmedia Limited; Chennai, India
OneStat International B.V.; Rijn, Netherlands
One World Investments Inc.; Vancouver, Canada
Onoken Co., Ltd.; Oita, Japan
On Q Group Limited; Melbourne, Australia
Open House Co., Ltd.; Tokyo, Japan
Opera SGR SpA; Milan, Italy
Opportunity Energia e Participacoes S.A.; Rio de Janeiro, Brazil
Optimus Fiduciaries Limited; Braddan, Isle of Man
Opto Device Technology Co., Ltd.; Bongdong-eup, Korea (South)
Opus Group AB; Molndal, Sweden
Orangebox Ltd.; Hengoed, United Kingdom
Orava Residential Real Estate Investment Trust Plc; Helsinki, Finland
Orbis Oy; Vantaa, Finland
Orbis Systems Oy; Oulu, Finland
Organizacion Corona SA; Bogota, Colombia
Oriental International Enterprise Limited; Shanghai, China
oriental precision & engineering co., ltd.; Busan, Korea (South)
Oriental Veneer Products Ltd.; Mumbai, India
ORIENT BEVERAGES LIMITED; Kolkata, India
Orient BlackSwan Private Limited; Hyderabad, India
Orient Refractories Limited; New Delhi, India
Orient Securities International Holdings Limited; Wanchai, China (Hong Kong)
Original Additions (Beauty Products) Ltd.; Hayes, United Kingdom
Orinoco Gold Ltd; Subiaco, Australia
Orion Engineering Services Limited; Inverness, United Kingdom
Orion Gold NL; Melbourne, Australia
Orion Metals Limited; Brisbane, Australia
Ormit Belgium N.V.; Brussels, Belgium
OR-NA Tarim Urunleri San. ve Tic. A.S.; Izmir, Turkey
Oronova Resource Corp.; Vancouver, Canada
Oroplata Resources, Inc.; San Felipe de Puerto Plata, Dominican Republic
Orora Limited; Hawthorn, Australia
Orosil Smiths India Limited; Noida, India
Oro Verde Limited; West Perth, Australia
Oryx Petroleum Corporation Limited; Geneva, Switzerland
Osaka Steel Co., Ltd.; Osaka, Japan
Oscar Properties AB; Stockholm, Sweden
Oscotec Inc.; Seongnam, Korea (South)
OSG Corporation; Toyokawa, Japan
Osiris Properties International Limited; Hamilton, Bermuda
OSK Property Holdings Berhad; Kuala Lumpur, Malaysia
Ostim Endustriyel Yatirimlar Ve Isletme AS; Ankara, Turkey
Oswal Agro Mills Ltd.; New Delhi, India
OSWAL OVERSEAS LIMITED; New Delhi, India
OTC Exchange of India; Mumbai, India
OTI Energy AG; Lugano, Switzerland
OT Logistics S.A.; Szczecin, Poland
O-uccino Inc.; Tokyo, Japan
OUE Commercial Real Estate Investment Trust; Singapore, Singapore
OUE Hospitality Trust; Singapore, Singapore
Outrider Energy Corp.; Vancouver, Canada
Outsourcery plc; Manchester, United Kingdom
OVAL Corporation; Tokyo, Japan
Oxbridge Re Holdings Limited; Georgetown, Cayman Islands
Oxford Immunotec Global PLC; Abingdon, United Kingdom
Oyster Oil & Gas Limited; Vancouver, Canada
Oz Brewing Limited; Perth, Australia
OzForex Group Limited; Sydney, Australia

P

Pacer Components Ltd.; Newbury, United Kingdom
Pacheli Enterprises Limited; Mumbai, India
Pacific Cotspin Limited; Kolkata, India
Pacific Net Co., Ltd.; Tokyo, Japan
Pacificorp International Hotel Management, Inc.; Meizhou, China
Pacific Radiance Ltd.; Singapore, Singapore
The Pack Corporation; Osaka, Japan
Pact Group Holdings Ltd.; South Yarra, Australia
Page Zero Media Inc.; Toronto, Canada
Palaces Real Estate & Development PLC; Amman, Jordan
palero capital GmbH; Munich, Germany
Pallinghurst Resources Limited; Saint Peter Port, Guernsey
Palm Holdings Inc.; Toronto, Canada
PALSOFT INFOSYSTEMS LIMITED; Jaipur, India
Panatlantica S.A.; Gravata, Brazil
PANCHMAHAL STEEL LIMITED; Kalol, India
Panda Fireworks Group Co., Ltd.; Luoyang, China
P&P Holdings Corp.; Tokyo, Japan
PAN ELECTRONICS (INDIA) LIMITED; Bengaluru, India
PAN ENTERTAINMENT CO., Ltd.; Seoul, Korea (South)
PangRim Co., Ltd.; Seoul, Korea (South)
Pankaj Piyush Trade & Investment Limited; Mumbai, India
PANKAJ POLYMERS LIMITED; Secunderabad, India
PANKAJ POLYPACK LIMITED; Secunderabad, India
Panoply Group Corp.; Stuttgart, Germany
Panora Gayrimenkul Yatirim Ortakligi AS; Ankara, Turkey
Panyam Cements & Mineral Industries Limited; Hyderabad, India
Papeles Bio Bio S.A.; Concepcion, Chile
PAPERCOREA CO., LTD.; Gunsan, Korea (South)
Paragon Care Limited; Nunawading, Australia
Paranapanema S.A.; Santo Andre, Brazil
Parasrampuria Credit & Investments Ltd.; Mumbai, India
Parc Logistic Transilvania SRL; Cluj-Napoca, Romania
Parfetts; Stockport, United Kingdom
Park & OPC Co., Ltd.; Cheongwon, Korea (South)
Parkanon Listatehdas Oy; Parkano, Finland
Parker Corporation; Tokyo, Japan
Park Resorts Limited; Hemel Hempstead, United Kingdom
Park's Motor Group; Hamilton, United Kingdom
Parshwanath Corporation Limited; Ahmedabad, India
Parsiena Design, Inc.; Concord, Canada
Partadialogue Inc.; Montreal, Canada
PARTH INDUSTRIES LIMITED; Ahmedabad, India
Partner Jet Corp.; Mississauga, Canada
Partron Co., Ltd.; Hwaseong, Korea (South)
PASECO Co., Ltd.; Ansan, Korea (South)
PATIDAR BUILDCON LIMITED; Surendranagar, India
Patriot Petroleum Corp.; Vancouver, Canada
Pawnee Energy Limited; Adelaide, Australia
PCH International Ltd.; Cork, Ireland
PCL Technologies Inc.; Taipei, Taiwan
P.C.S. Machine Group Holding Public Company Limited; Bangkok, Thailand
PDC Biological Health Group Corporation; Richmond, Canada
PDG Realty S.A. Empreendimentos e Participacoes; Rio de Janeiro, Brazil
PEACOCK INDUSTRIES LIMITED; Udaipur, India
Pearl River Holdings Limited; London, Canada
Pearl Sanitary Paper Converting Co PLC; Amman, Jordan
PEETI SECURITIES LIMITED; Hyderabad, India
Pegasus Sewing Machine Manufacturing Co., Ltd.; Osaka, Japan
Pegboard Software Pty Ltd; Melbourne, Australia
Peixin International Group B.V.; Quanzhou, China
Pengxin International Mining Co., Ltd; Shanghai, China
PENTOKEY ORGANY (INDIA) LIMITED; Mumbai, India
PEOPLE & TELECOMMUNICATION INC.; Seoul, Korea (South)
PeptiDream Inc.; Tokyo, Japan
Perennial China Retail Trust Management Pte. Ltd.; Singapore, Singapore
Perfect Optronics Ltd; Kowloon, China (Hong Kong)
Performance PR Ltd.; Kingston upon Thames, United Kingdom
Perrigo Company plc; Dublin, Ireland
Pesquera Jaramillo Ltda; Bogota, Colombia
Pet Plastics Limited; Mumbai, India
Petra Education Company; Amman, Jordan
Petroforte International Ltd.; Vancouver, Canada
Petrolia Inc; Rimouski, Canada
Petrolympic Ltd.; Toronto, Canada
Petro Matad Limited; Douglas, Isle of Man
Petroplan Limited; Guildford, United Kingdom
PetroVietnam Coating Joint Stock Company; Phu My, Vietnam
Pettenati S.A. Industria Texti; Caxias do Sul, Brazil
Petty Wood & Co. Ltd.; Andover, United Kingdom
P G FOILS LIMITED; Pali, India
P G Industry Limited; New Delhi, India
PGO Automobiles; Saint Christol-les-Ales, France
Pharma Foods International Co., Ltd.; Kyoto, Japan
PHARMICELL CO., LTD.; Seoul, Korea (South)
PharmswellBio Co,. Ltd.; Seoul, Korea (South)
Phase Eight (Fashion & Designs) Limited; London, United Kingdom
Philadelphia Insurance Company Ltd.; Amman, Jordan

Philadelphia International Educational Investment Company PLC; Amman, Jordan
Photocreate Co., Ltd.; Tokyo, Japan
Photon Capital Advisors Limited; Hyderabad, India
Physik Instrumente) GmbH & Co.; Karlsruhe, Germany
Physiotherm GmbH; Thaur, Austria
Picanol NV; Ieper, Belgium
Piccadily Sugar & Allied Industries Limited; Chandigarh, India
Pickstock Ashby Ltd.; Swadlincote, United Kingdom
Picton Property Income Limited; Saint Peter Port, Guernsey
Pierrel S.p.A.; Milan, Italy
Pilot Electronics Corporation; Taoyuan, Taiwan
PIMI AGRO CLEANTECH, INC.; Kiryat Tivon, Israel
Pingdom AB; Vasteras, Sweden
Pinnacle Technology Group plc; London, United Kingdom
PINOVA Capital GmbH; Munich, Germany
Piolink Inc.; Seoul, Korea (South)
Pioneer Agro Extracts Limited; Pathankot, India
Piquadro SpA; Gaggio Montano, Italy
Pitchblack Resources Ltd.; Toronto, Canada
Pizza Pizza Royalty Corp.; Toronto, Canada
PJSC Stroytransgaz; Moscow, Russia
Planter's Polysacks Limited; Navi Mumbai, India
Plant Health Care plc; Chesham, United Kingdom
Plantynet Co. Ltd.; Seongnam, Korea (South)
Plaspak Kimya Sanayi ve Ticaret AS; Istanbul, Turkey
Plate Resources Inc.; Vancouver, Canada
Plat'Home Co., Ltd.; Tokyo, Japan
Platina Partners LLP; London, United Kingdom
Platinum Properties Group S.A.; Warsaw, Poland
Platzer Fastigheter Holding AB; Gothenburg, Sweden
Plaza Centers N.V.; Amsterdam, Netherlands
PLD Corporation Limited; Subiaco, Australia
Plenus Company Limited; Fukuoka, Japan
Plexus Cotton Limited; Liverpool, United Kingdom
Plus8 Global Ventures Ltd.; Vancouver, Canada
Pluspetrol Resources Corporation BV; Amsterdam, Netherlands
Pluton Resources Limited; West Perth, Australia
Plymouth Realty Capital Corp.; Toronto, Canada
PM Capital Global Opportunities Fund Limited; Sydney, Australia
PMC Communications Co., Ltd.; Guangzhou, China
PMC Fincorp Limited; New Delhi, India
PMGC Technology Group Limited; London, United Kingdom
PNESOLUTION CO., LTD.; Gwangju, Korea (South)
PN MED GROUP INC.; Santiago, Chile
PN POONGNYUN CO. LTD.; Ansan, Korea (South)
POCHIRAJU INDUSTRIES LIMITED; Hosur, India
POCML 2 Inc.; Toronto, Canada
PODDAR DEVELOPERS LIMITED; Mumbai, India
Point-i; Seoul, Korea (South)
Point Inc.; Tokyo, Japan
Pokfulam Development Company Limited; Wanchai, China (Hong Kong)
Polimex-Mostostal S.A.; Warsaw, Poland
Politeknik Metal Sanayi ve Ticaret A.S.; Gebze, Turkey
Polpar S.A.; Sao Paulo, Brazil
POLSON LIMITED; Kolhapur, India
POLYCON International Limited; Jaipur, India
POLYGENTA TECHNOLOGIES LIMITED; Mumbai, India
Polygon AB; Stockholm, Sweden
Polymac Thermoformers Ltd.; Kolkata, India
POLYMECHPLAST MACHINES LTD.; Vadodara, India
Polymetal International plc; Saint Petersburg, Russia
Polyplank AB; Farjestaden, Sweden
POLYTEX INDIA LIMITED; Mumbai, India
POPULAR ESTATE MANAGEMENT LIMITED; Ahmedabad, India
Portland Investment Counsel Inc.; Burlington, Canada
Power Construction Corporation of China; Beijing, China
POWERLOGICS; Cheongwon, Korea (South)
PPS International (Holdings) Limited; North Point, China (Hong Kong)
Practicus Ltd.; Henley-on-Thames, United Kingdom
Prantalay Marketing Public Company Limited; Samut Sakhon, Thailand
PRASHANT INDIA LTD.; Surat, India
Precious Metals & Mining Trust; Toronto, Canada
PRECISION ELECTRONICS LIMITED; Noida, India
PreMedia Global Pvt. Ltd.; Chennai, India
Premier Business & Projects Co. Ltd.; Amman, Jordan
Premier Energy & Infrastructure Limited; Chennai, India
PREMIER PIPES LIMITED; Kanpur, India
PREMIER POLYFILM LTD.; New Delhi, India
Premier Synthetics Limited; Mumbai, India
PRERNA INFRABUILD LTD.; Ahmedabad, India
Prescient Limited; Cape Town, South Africa
Prescient Mining Corp.; Vancouver, Canada
Press Kogyo Co., Ltd.; Kawasaki, Japan
PRESSURE SENSITIVE SYSTEMS (INDIA) LIMITED; Mumbai, India
Pricecheck Toiletries Limited; Sheffield, United Kingdom
PricewaterhouseCoopers AG Wirtschaftsprufungs gesellschaft; Frankfurt am Main, Germany
PricewaterhouseCoopers Audit Azerbaijan LLC; Baku, Azerbaijan

PricewaterhouseCoopers Audit Caledonie SELARL; Noumea, New Caledonia
PricewaterhouseCoopers Audit LLC; Ulaanbaatar, Mongolia
PricewaterhouseCoopers Audit SA; Neuilly-sur-Seine, France
PricewaterhouseCoopers Audit sh.p.k.; Tirana, Albania
PricewaterhouseCoopers Australia (International) Pty. Ltd.; Sydney, Australia
PricewaterhouseCoopers Bulgaria EOOD; Sofia, Bulgaria
PricewaterhouseCoopers (Cambodia) Ltd.; Phnom Penh, Cambodia
PricewaterhouseCoopers Ceska republika, s.r.o.; Prague, Czech Republic
PricewaterhouseCoopers Consultants (Shenzhen) Limited; Tianjin, China
PricewaterhouseCoopers d.o.o.; Belgrade, Serbia
PricewaterhouseCoopers ehf; Reykjavik, Iceland
PricewaterhouseCoopers FAS Ltd.; Bangkok, Thailand
PricewaterhouseCoopers Hungary Limited Liability Company; Budapest, Hungary
PricewaterhouseCoopers Inter-america, S. de R.L.; Tegucigalpa, Honduras
PricewaterhouseCoopers Isla Lipana & Co.; Makati, Philippines
PricewaterhouseCoopers Lanka (Private) Limited; Colombo, Sri Lanka
PricewaterhouseCoopers Ltd.; Providenciales, Turks & Caicos Islands
PricewaterhouseCoopers LLP - Singapore; Singapore, Singapore
PricewaterhouseCoopers ME Limited; Manama, Bahrain
PricewaterhouseCoopers Pvt. Ltd.; Ahmedabad, India
PricewaterhouseCoopers Russia B.V.; Moscow, Russia
PricewaterhouseCoopers, S.A.; Guatemala, Guatemala
PricewaterhouseCoopers SARL; Douala, Cameroon
PricewaterhouseCoopers Slovensko, s.r.o.; Bratislava, Slovakia
PricewaterhouseCoopers S.p.A.; Milan, Italy
PricewaterhouseCoopers S.R.L.; La Paz, Bolivia
PricewaterhouseCoopers Tax & Legal SA; Dakar, Senegal
PricewaterhouseCoopers (Vietnam) Ltd.; Ho Chi Minh City, Vietnam
PricewaterhouseCoopers y Cia, S.A.; San Jose, Costa Rica
PRIMA AGRO LIMITED; Cochin, India
Prima Industries Limited; Cochin, India
Prime Advertising; North York, Canada
Prime Living AB; Stockholm, Sweden
Princess Private Equity Holding Limited; Saint Peter Port, Guernsey
Privoz; Holon, Israel
Produce Investments plc; Duns, United Kingdom
Productos Familia S.A.; Medellin, Colombia
Produtores Energeticos de Manso S.A.; Rio de Janeiro, Brazil
Profitable Developments, Inc.; Hinckley, United Kingdom
Project Informatica SRL; Stezzano, Italy
ProMedical Personnel Ltd.; Brentwood, United Kingdom
Pro Medicus Limited; Richmond, Australia
Pro Metalurgia SA; Atibaia, Brazil
Prophecy International Holdings Limited; Adelaide, Australia
Prosensa Holding B.V.; Leiden, Netherlands
Prosource.it (UK) Ltd.; Aberdeen, United Kingdom
Prospect Media Inc.; Toronto, Canada
Prospect Park Capital Corp.; Toronto, Canada
PROTO DEVELOPERS & TECHNOLOGIES LIMITED; New Delhi, India
Pro-Trans Ventures Inc.; Calgary, Canada
Provestment Services Limited; New Delhi, India
Pruksa Real Estate Public Company Limited; Bangkok, Thailand
PS&C Limited; Albert Park, Australia
PS Group Holdings Ltd; Singapore, Singapore
PT. ACSET Indonusa tbk; Jakarta, Indonesia
PT Asuransi Mitra Maparya Tbk.; Jakarta, Indonesia
PT Austindo Nusantara Jaya Tbk.; Jakarta, Indonesia
PT. Bakrieland Development, Tbk.; Jakarta, Indonesia
PT Bank Ina Perdana Tbk.; Jakarta, Indonesia
PT Bank Maspion Indonesia Tbk; Surabaya, Indonesia
PT Bank Mitraniaga Tbk; Jakarta, Indonesia
PT Bank Nationalnobu Tbk; Jakarta, Indonesia
PT Bank Panin Syariah Tbk.; Jakarta, Indonesia
PT Berau Coal Energy Tbk; Tanjung Redeb, Indonesia
PT Capitol Nusantara Indonesia Tbk.; Samarinda, Indonesia
PT Charoen Pokphand Indonesia Tbk; Jakarta, Indonesia
PT Cipaganti Citra Graha Tbk; Bandung, Indonesia
PT Citra Marga Nusaphala Persada Tbk.; Jakarta, Indonesia
PT Dharma Satya Nusantara Tbk; Jakarta, Indonesia
PT. Electronic City Indonesia Tbk; Jakarta, Indonesia
PTG Energy Public Company Limited; Bangkok, Thailand
PT Harum Energy Tbk.; Jakarta, Indonesia
PT Indomobil Multi Jasa Tbk; Jakarta, Indonesia
PT Industri Jamu dan Farmasi Sido Muncul Tbk; Jakarta, Indonesia
PT Infratech Indonesia; Jakarta, Indonesia
PT. Lippo Securities, Tbk; Tangerang, Indonesia
PT Logindo Samudramakmur Tbk; Jakarta, Indonesia
PT. Mandala Multifinance Tbk; Jakarta, Indonesia
PT. Mayora Indah Tbk; Jakarta, Indonesia
PT Mitra Pinasthika Mustika Tbk; Jakarta, Indonesia
PT Sarana Menara Nusantara Tbk; Jakarta, Indonesia
PT Sarana Tirta Rejeki; Serang, Indonesia

PT Sawit Sumbermas Sarana Tbk; Pangkalan Bun, Indonesia
PT. Sri Rejeki Isman Tbk; Semarang, Indonesia
PT Steel Pipe Industry of Indonesia Tbk; Surabaya, Indonesia
PT Sugih Energy Tbk; Jakarta, Indonesia
PT Summarecon Agung Tbk; Jakarta, Indonesia
PT Technic Engineering Sdn. Bhd.; Puchong, Malaysia
PT. Trikomsel Oke Tbk.; Jakarta, Indonesia
PT Wintermar Offshore Marine Tbk; Jakarta, Indonesia
Publicidad Causa (Compania Anunciadora Universal S.A.); Lima, Peru
Public Safety Equipment (Intl) Ltd.; Leeds, United Kingdom
Puloon Technology Inc.; Seoul, Korea (South)
Pulsant Limited; Reading, United Kingdom
Pulse Films Limited; London, United Kingdom
Puneet Resins Limited; Mumbai, India
Pungkang Co., Ltd; Hwaseong, Korea (South)
Purdicom Limited; Wantage, United Kingdom
Pure Gym Ltd.; Leeds, United Kingdom
Pure Recruitment Group Ltd.; London, United Kingdom
Purpose Investments Inc.; Toronto, Canada
Putrajaya Perdana Berhad; Putrajaya, Malaysia
PwC Asesores Empresariales Cia. Ltda.; Guayaquil, Ecuador
PW Medtech Group Limited; Beijing, China
Pyeong Hwa Automotive Co., Ltd; Daegu, Korea (South)

Q

Q Capital Partners Co., Ltd; Seoul, Korea (South)
QHD Gold Limited; Adelaide, Australia
Qiming Venture Partners; Shanghai, China
Qingdao Soda Ash Industrial Co., Ltd.; Qingdao, China
Qingdao Yellowsea Rubber Co., Ltd.; Qingdao, China
Qinhuangdao Port Co., Ltd.; Qinhuangdao, China
Qiwi plc; Nicosia, Cyprus
QMIS Finance Securities Corporation; Beijing, China
QPL International Holdings Limited; Tsuen Wan, China (Hong Kong)
Qrf Comm. VA; Antwerp, Belgium
Qualicorp S.A.; Sao Paulo, Brazil
Quality Meat Packers Limited; Toronto, Canada
Quang Anh Mineral Joint Stock Company; Hanoi, Vietnam
Quanta Resources Inc.; Vancouver, Canada
Quantum Pharmaceutical Limited; Durham, United Kingdom
Quantum Property Group Limited; Cape Town, South Africa
Quattro Exploration & Production Ltd.; Calgary, Canada
QubeGB Ltd.; Galashiels, United Kingdom
Quest Minerals Limited; Osborne Park, Australia
Qui! Group S.p.A.; Genoa, Italy
Quintessential Finance Group Limited; Macclesfield, United Kingdom
Quixant PLC; Sevenoaks, United Kingdom
Qunar Cayman Islands Limited; Beijing, China
Quotient Limited; Penicuik, United Kingdom
QurApps, Inc.; Pardis Hana, Israel

R

Radford Capital Investment Limited; North Point, China (Hong Kong)
Radford Global Limited; Mumbai, India
RAGHAVA ESTATE & PROPERTIES LIMITED; Vijayawada, India
Raghuvir Synthetics Limited; Ahmedabad, India
Raia Drogasil S.A.; Sao Paulo, Brazil
Rainmaker Mining Corp.; Vancouver, Canada
Raja Bahadur International Limited; Mumbai, India
Rajani Associates LLP; Mumbai, India
RAJASTHAN GASES LTD.; Jaipur, India
RAJASTHAN PETRO SYNTHETICS LTD.; New Delhi, India
Rajath Finance Limited; Rajkot, India
Rajesh Malleables Limited; Ahmedabad, India
RAJLAXMI INDUSTRIES LIMITED; Thane, India
Ralawise Limited; Deeside, United Kingdom
RAM Informatics Limited; Hyderabad, India
Ramsdens Financial Limited; Middlesbrough, United Kingdom
RAMSONS PROJECTS LIMITED; Gurgaon, India
Ram Technology Co., Ltd.; Yongin, Korea (South)
Randall & Quilter Investment Holdings plc; London, United Kingdom
Rand Merchant Insurance Holdings Limited; Sandton, South Africa
Randon S.A. Implementos e. Participacoes.; Caxias do Sul, Brazil
Randsburg International Gold Corporation; Toronto, Canada
Ranklin Solutions Limited; Hyderabad, India
Raonsecure Co. Ltd; Seoul, Korea (South)
Raphael Michel SA; Piolenc, France
RapidCloud International plc; Petaling Jaya, Malaysia
Rapid Investments Limited; Mumbai, India
Raptis Group Limited; Surfers Paradise, Australia
Rare Holdings Limited; Midvaal, South Africa
Rasa Industries, Ltd.; Tokyo, Japan
RATAN GLITTER INDUSTRIES LTD.; Mumbai, India
Ravenscroft Limited; Saint Peter Port, Guernsey
Rawson Resources Limited; Sydney, Australia
RAYMED LABS LIMITED; Saharanpur, India
Raymond Industrial Limited; Hong Kong, China (Hong Kong)
RBA Holdings Limited; Braamfontein, South Africa
RCI Industries & Technologies Ltd; Delhi, India
Reabold Resources Plc; London, United Kingdom

Reach4Entertainment Enterprises PLC; London, United Kingdom
Ready Mix Concrete & Construction Supplies P.L.C; Amman, Jordan
Real Energy Corporation Limited; North Sydney, Australia
Real Estate & Investment Portfolio Company; Amman, Jordan
Real Realty Management Co. Ltd.; Rajkot, India
Recall Holdings Limited; Alexandria, Australia
Reclaim Industries Limited; Perth, Australia
Reclay Holding GmbH; Cologne, Germany
RECURSOS MONTANA S.A.; San Felipe de Puerto Plata, Dominican Republic
Recursos Queliz, Inc.; San Felipe de Puerto Plata, Dominican Republic
Red Bee Media Limited; London, United Kingdom
Redcentric plc; Cambridge, United Kingdom
Redco Properties Group Limited; Shenzhen, China
Redeem Ltd.; Bathgate, United Kingdom
Rede Energia SA; Sao Paulo, Brazil
REDEX PROTECH LIMITED; Ahmedabad, India
Red River Resources Limited; Perth, Australia
Red Rock Capital Corp.; Vancouver, Canada
Red Star Capital Ventures Inc.; Vancouver, Canada
Red Tiger Mining Inc.; Toronto, Canada
Reece Australia Limited; Burwood, Australia
Reece Group Ltd.; Newcastle upon Tyne, United Kingdom
Refinaria de Petroleos de Manguinhos S.A.; Rio de Janeiro, Brazil
REFNOL RESINS & CHEMICALS LIMITED; Ahmedabad, India
ReformKontor GmbH & Co. KG; Zarrentin, Germany
Regal Entertainment & Consultants Ltd.; Mumbai, India
Regatta Ltd.; Manchester, United Kingdom
REGENCY CERAMICS LIMITED; Hyderabad, India
REGENCY HOSPITAL LIMITED; Kanpur, India
Regeneus Ltd.; Gordon, Australia
REHACT AB; Stockholm, Sweden
Reibel N.V.; Brussels, Belgium
Reiten & Co; Oslo, Norway
Reliance Resources Ltd.; Vancouver, Canada
Relish Pharmaceuticals Limited; Ahmedabad, India
The Remet Company Ltd.; London, United Kingdom
Remsons Industries Limited; Mumbai, India
Renar Macas S/A; Brasilia, Brazil
RENN Universal Growth Investment Trust PLC; Exeter, United Kingdom
Renotex Group Ltd.; Wakefield, United Kingdom
Renta 4 Banco, S.A.; Madrid, Spain
Rentabiliweb Group S.A.; Brussels, Belgium
REORIENT Group Limited; Hong Kong, China (Hong Kong)
Repatriates Co-operative Finance and Development Bank Limited; Chennai, India
ReproCELL Inc.; Yokohama, Japan
RESILUX NV; Wetteren, Belgium
Resimac Limited; Sydney, Australia
Resources & Energy Group Limited; Sydney, Australia
Resources Company for Development & Investment PLC; Amman, Jordan
Restamax Plc; Tampere, Finland
Retrocom Real Estate Investment Trust; Vaughan, Canada
Rex International Holding Ltd; Singapore, Singapore
RFsemi Technologies, Inc.; Daejeon, Korea (South)
RFTech Co., Ltd.; Yongin, Korea (South)
RGT Smart Market Intelligence Limited; Johannesburg, South Africa
Rheon Automatic Machinery Co., Ltd.; Utsunomiya, Japan
Rhodes Food Group (Pty) Ltd.; Cape Town, South Africa
Richco Investors Inc.; West Vancouver, Canada
Richland Resources Limited; Hamilton, Bermuda
Richoux Group plc; London, United Kingdom
Ride On Express Co., Ltd.; Tokyo, Japan
Ridgeway Group; Newbury, United Kingdom
Rightster Group PLC; London, United Kingdom
Rikei Corporation; Tokyo, Japan
Riken Vitamin Co., Ltd.; Tokyo, Japan
Ringnet Co., Ltd.; Seoul, Korea (South)
Rinko Corporation; Niigata, Japan
Rishab Financial Services Limited; Chennai, India
RISHIROOP RUBBER (INTERNATIONAL) LIMITED; Mumbai, India
R J Bio-Tech Limited; Aurangabad, India
RJCP Equity S.A.; Rio de Janeiro, Brazil
RJS DEVELOPMENT, INC.; Chengdu, China
RM2 International S.A.; Luxembourg, Luxembourg
RMG Limited; Subiaco, Australia
RM Group Holdings Ltd.; Kwai Chung, China (Hong Kong)
R. M. Mohite Industries Limited; Kolhapur, India
RMS Mezzanine, a.s.; Prague, Czech Republic
RN2 Technologies Co., Ltd.; Pyeongtaek, Korea (South)
RNB Industries Limited; Kolkata, India
Robinsons Motor Group; Norwich, United Kingdom
Robinsons Retail Holdings, Inc.; Quezon City, Philippines
Robix Alternative Fuels Inc.; Lethbridge, Canada
Robosoft Technologies Pvt. Ltd.; Udupi, India
Rocco Forte & Family Plc.; London, United Kingdom
Rockcastle Global Real Estate Company Limited; Ebene, Mauritius
Rocket Electric Co., Ltd.; Gwangju, Korea (South)
Rocky Mountain Liquor Inc.; Edmonton, Canada
Roc Search Ltd.; Reading, United Kingdom

Rodobens Negocios Imobiliarios S.A.; Sao Jose do Rio Pardo, Brazil
Rodrigo Tekstil Sanayi ve Ticaret AS; Istanbul, Turkey
Rolfes Holdings Limited; Midrand, South Africa
Romulus Corp.; Prague, Czech Republic
Romulus Resources Ltd.; Vancouver, Canada
The Roof Truss Company (Northern) Limited; Washington, United Kingdom
Rosa Capital Inc.; Calgary, Canada
Rosetti Marino S.p.A.; Ravenna, Italy
Rotkappchen-Mumm Sektkellereien GmbH; Freyburg, Germany
Rotzinger AG; Kaiseraugst, Switzerland
ROUSSELET Centrifugation SA; Annonay, France
Roxas Holdings, Inc.; Makati, Philippines
ROYAL CUSHION VINYL PRODUCTS LIMITED; Mumbai, India
Royal Europa Ltd.; Polkowice, Poland
Royal Hali Iplik Tekstil Mobilya Sanayi ve Ticaret A.S.; Gaziantep, Turkey
Royal Sapphire Corp.; Vancouver, Canada
R-Pharm CJSC; Moscow, Russia
RSC International Ltd.; Mumbai, India
Rudolf Haufe Verlag GmbH & Co. KG.; Freiburg, Germany
Ruia Group; Kolkata, India
Rullion Limited; Altrincham, United Kingdom
Rum-Aladdin Industries Company; Sahab, Jordan
Rum Group For Transportation & Tourism Investment P.L.C.; Amman, Jordan
RUNEECHA TEXTILES LIMITED; Noida, India
Rungta Irrigation Limited; New Delhi, India
Runtime Revolution Ltd.; Edinburgh, United Kingdom
Runway Global Holdings Co., Ltd.; Kowloon, China (Hong Kong)
Rupee Finance & Management Pvt Ltd.; Mumbai, India
Rural Funds Group; Deakin, Australia
RusForest AB; Stockholm, Sweden
Ruspetro plc; London, United Kingdom
Rutron International Limited; Mumbai, India

S

Sable Platinum Limited; Sandton, South Africa
SABOO BROTHERS LIMITED; Jodhpur, India
Saboo Sodium Chloro Ltd.; Jaipur, India
Sabvest Limited; Sandton, South Africa
Saccharum Energy Corp.; Calgary, Canada
SACHETA METALS LIMITED; Mumbai, India
Sacom SpA; Larino, Italy
Sadhana Nitro Chem Limited; Mumbai, India
SAEXPLORATION HOLDINGS, INC.; Calgary, Canada
Safe Bag S.p.A.; Gallarate, Italy
SafeGuard World International Ltd.; Sandbach, United Kingdom
Safestyle UK plc; Bradford, United Kingdom
Sagami Rubber Industries Co., Ltd.; Atsugi, Japan
SAGAR SOYA PRODUCTS LTD.; Sagar, India
SAGAR SYSTECH LIMITED; Mumbai, India
Sagar Tourist Resorts Limited; Mumbai, India
SAG GEST - Solucoes Automovel Globais, SGPS, S.A.; Amadora, Portugal
Sahara Housingfina Corporation Limited; Kolkata, India
SA HYDRAULIQUE PB; Escles, France
Saibu Gas Co. Ltd.; Fukuoka, Japan
The Sailor Pen Co., Ltd.; Tokyo, Japan
SAINIK FINANCE & INDUSTRIES LIMITED; New Delhi, India
Saisan Co., Ltd.; Saitama, Japan
Sajo Daerim Co., Ltd.; Seoul, Korea (South)
Sajo Haepyo; Seoul, Korea (South)
Sajo Industry Co., Ltd.; Seoul, Korea (South)
Sakai Chemical Industry Co., Ltd.; Sakai, Japan
Sakai Heavy Industries Ltd; Tokyo, Japan
SAKAI OVEX Co., Ltd.; Fukui, Japan
Sakthi Finance Limited; Coimbatore, India
SAKURA Rubber Company Limited; Tokyo, Japan
Sala Corporation; Toyohashi, Japan
Salam International Transport & Trading Co. PLC; Amman, Jordan
SA Les Hotels de Paris; Paris, France
Salts Healthcare Ltd.; Birmingham, United Kingdom
SALZER ELECTRONICS LIMITED; Coimbatore, India
Salzmann AG; Saint Gallen, Switzerland
Samchully Co., Ltd.; Seoul, Korea (South)
Samena Capital Management LLP; London, United Kingdom
SAMICK THK CO., Ltd.; Daegu, Korea (South)
Samil Enterprise Co., Ltd.; Seoul, Korea (South)
Samil Pharm. Co., Ltd.; Seoul, Korea (South)
Samji Electronics Co,. Ltd.; Seoul, Korea (South)
Samjin Pharmaceutical Co., Ltd.; Seoul, Korea (South)
SAMKANG M&T CO., LTD; Donghae-myeon, Korea (South)
Samkee Automotive Co., Ltd.; Pyeongtaek, Korea (South)
Sammok Kang Up Co., Ltd.; Ansan, Korea (South)
Sammok Precision & Ind. Co., Ltd., Seoul, Korea (South)
Samoth Oilfield Inc.; Saint Albert, Canada
Samrat Pharmachem Limited; Mumbai, India
Samruddhi Realty Limited; Bengaluru, India
Samryoong Co Ltd.; Ansan, Korea (South)
Samsonite International S.A.; Kowloon, China (Hong Kong)
Samsung Engineering Co., Ltd.; Seoul, Korea (South)
SAMTEX FASHIONS LIMITED; New Delhi, India

Samuel Taylor Limited; Redditch, United Kingdom
Samwhan Corporation; Seoul, Korea (South)
SAMWON-TECH CO., LTD.; Changwon, Korea (South)
Samyang Optics Co., Ltd.; Changwon, Korea (South)
SAMYANG TONGSANG Co., Ltd.; Seoul, Korea (South)
SamYoung Chemical; Seoul, Korea (South)
Samyoung Electronics Co., Ltd.; Seongnam, Korea (South)
Samyung ENC Co., Ltd.; Busan, Korea (South)
Sam Yung Holdings Co., Ltd.; Seoul, Korea (South)
Sanco Industries Limited; New Delhi, India
S&B Foods Inc.; Tokyo, Japan
THE SANDESH LIMITED; Ahmedabad, India
Sandon Capital Investments Limited; Sydney, Australia
SAND PLAST INDIA LTD.; New Delhi, India
S&S TECH Co., Ltd.; Daegu, Korea (South)
S&T Corporation Limited; Mumbai, India
SAN-EL Muhendislik Elektrik Taahhut Sanayi ve Ticaret AS; Istanbul, Turkey
San Far Property Limited; Taipei, Taiwan
SANGSIN BRAKE Co., Ltd.; Daegu, Korea (South)
SangsinEDP; Suwon, Korea (South)
Sanitar Company Ltd.; New Taipei City, Taiwan
Sanraa Media Limited; Chennai, India
Sanrhea Technical Textiles Limited; Gandhinagar, India
Sanshin Electric Co., Ltd.; Tokyo, Japan
Sanshin Electric Corporation; Tokyo, Japan
Santacruz Silver Mining Ltd.; Vancouver, Canada
Santana Minerals Limited; Milton, Australia
Sanwa Company Ltd.; Osaka, Japan
Sanyo Engineering & Construction Inc.; Tokyo, Japan
Sao Martinho S.A.; Pradopolis, Brazil
Sao Paulo Turismo S/A; Santana, Brazil
Sapec S.A.; Brussels, Belgium
Saptarishi Agro Industries Limited; Chennai, India
Saraswati Commercial (India) Limited; Mumbai, India
SATHAVAHANA ISPAT LIMITED; Hyderabad, India
Satin Creditcare Network Limited; New Delhi, India
Satkar Finlease Limited; Delhi, India
SATO Holdings Corporation; Tokyo, Japan
Satrec Initiative Co., Ltd.; Daejeon, Korea (South)
Saudi Arabian Mining Company - Ma'aden; Riyadh, Saudi Arabia
Saudi Electric Supply Company; Al Khobar, Saudi Arabia
Saudi Marketing Company; Dammam, Saudi Arabia
Sauflon Pharmaceuticals Limited; Twickenham, United Kingdom
Savant Infocomm Limited; Chennai, India
Savary Gold Corp.; Vancouver, Canada
Saville Resources Inc.; Vancouver, Canada
Savoy Ventures Inc.; Vancouver, Canada
SAYAJI HOTELS LIMITED; Indore, India
Sbaek Invest PLC; Amman, Jordan
Scarlet B.V.; Lelystad, Netherlands
Schaefer Werkzeug- und Sondermaschinenbau GmbH; Bad Schonborn, Germany
Schaffer Corporation Limited; West Perth, Australia
SCH Group Berhad; Balakong, Malaysia
SCH Group Ltd.; Romsey, United Kingdom
Schleicher Electronic GmbH & Co. KG; Berlin, Germany
Schneider Electric Infrastructure Limited; Noida, India
Schnigge Wertpapierhandelsbank AG; Dusseldorf, Germany
Scholium Group plc; London, United Kingdom
Scholz Industries Pty Ltd.; Hallam, Australia
Schulz S/A; Joinville, Brazil
Science in Sport plc; Nelson, United Kingdom
Scientech Corporation; Taipei, Taiwan
Scientific Brain Training SA; Villeurbanne, France
Sci-Tek Instruments Ltd.; Olney, United Kingdom
SciVision Biotech Inc.; Kaohsiung, Taiwan
S.C. Lacta S.A.; Giurgiu, Romania
S.C. Mercur SA; Brasov, Romania
Sco-Pak S.A.; Warsaw, Poland
Scorpio Bulkers Inc.; Monaco, Monaco
Scotts Garments Ltd.; Bengaluru, India
SCR; Barcelona, Spain
Scribblers' Club; Kitchener, Canada
S.C Serviciile Comerciale Romane S.R.L.; Cluj-Napoca, Romania
S. Culture International Holdings Limited; Kwai Chung, China (Hong Kong)
SEAC Limited; Wigston, United Kingdom
Sealink Travel Group Limited; Adelaide, Australia
Sea Oil Public Company Limited; Bangkok, Thailand
Searchlight Electric Ltd.; Manchester, United Kingdom
Second City Capital Partners; Vancouver, Canada
Section Rouge Media Inc.; Longueuil, Canada
SecureData Holdings Limited; Bryanston, South Africa
Sedlbauer AG; Grafenau, Germany
Seho Robot Co., Ltd.; Ansan, Korea (South)
Seibu Electric & Machinery Co., Ltd.; Koga, Japan
Seika Corporation; Tokyo, Japan
SEJIN TS Co., Ltd; Anseong, Korea (South)
SEKONIC HOLDINGS CORPORATION; Tokyo, Japan
Sekuro Plastik Ambalaj Sanayi AS; Kocaeli, Turkey
Selection du Reader's Digest S.A.; Bagneux, France
Selectpart Participacoes S.A.; Sao Paulo, Brazil
Selwood Group Limited; Eastleigh, United Kingdom

Semafone Limited; Guildford, United Kingdom
SEMISYSCO CO., LTD.; Suwon, Korea (South)
Sempio Foods Company; Seoul, Korea (South)
Senbo Industries Limited; Kolkata, India
S-Energy Co., Ltd.; Seongnam, Korea (South)
Senergy Holdings Limited; Aberdeen, United Kingdom
Senior Solution S.A.; Sao Paulo, Brazil
Senshu Electric Co., Ltd.; Osaka, Japan
Senthil Infotek Limited; Secunderabad, India
SEOHEE Construction Co., Ltd.; Seoul, Korea (South)
Seoho Electric Co., Ltd; Anyang, Korea (South)
Seondo Electric Co., Ltd.; Ansan, Korea (South)
Seoul Auction; Seoul, Korea (South)
Seoul Food Industrial. Co., Ltd.; Chungju, Korea (South)
Seoulin Bioscience Co., Ltd.; Seongnam, Korea (South)
Seoul Pharma Co., Ltd.; Seoul, Korea (South)
Seoul Semiconductor Co., Ltd.; Ansan, Korea (South)
Seowon Co., Ltd.; Ansan, Korea (South)
SEQUEL E ROUTERS LIMITED; Ahmedabad, India
Sergen - Servicos Gerais de Engenharia S.A.; Rio de Janeiro, Brazil
SERMA TECHNOLOGIES SA; Pessac, France
Sertec Group Holdings Ltd.; Birmingham, United Kingdom
SERT-MST Plc.; Swadlincote, United Kingdom
Servcorp Limited; Sydney, Australia
Serve All Enterprise Solutions Limited; Hyderabad, India
Service Innovation Group; London, United Kingdom
Servotech Engineering Industries Ltd.; Mumbai, India
Servotronix Motion Control Ltd.; Petah Tiqwa, Israel
SES Group GmbH; Munich, Germany
Settlements SA; Brussels, Belgium
Sevan Marine ASA; Arendal, Norway
Seven Squared; London, United Kingdom
Seven Technologies Ltd.; Lisburn, United Kingdom
Severn Glocon Ltd.; Gloucester, United Kingdom
Sewha P&C Inc.; Seoul, Korea (South)
SEWONCELLONTECH CORP.; Seoul, Korea (South)
SEWOONMEDICAL Co. Ltd; Cheonan, Korea (South)
SFR Energy Ltd.; Calgary, Canada
SG Choongnam Spinning Co., Ltd.; Nonsan, Korea (South)
SG Spirit Gold Inc.; Vancouver, Canada
Shaanxi Aerospace Power Hightech Co., Ltd.; Xi'an, China
Shaanxi Yanchang Petroleum Group Co., Ltd.; Xi'an, China
SHAH FOODS LTD; Gandhinagar, India
Shakti Press Limited; Nagpur, India
Shandong Caopu Arts & Crafts Co., Ltd.; Beijing, China
Shandong Heavy Industry Group Co., Ltd.; Linyi, China
Shandong Longlive Bio-technology Co., Ltd.; Yucheng, China
Shandong Pharmaceutical Glass Co., Ltd.; Zibo, China
Shandong Weiqiao Pioneering Group Co., Ltd.; Zouping, China
Shandong Zhangqiu Blower Co., Ltd.; Zhangqiu, China
Shanghai Belling Co., Ltd.; Shanghai, China
Shanghai Churui Energy Technology Co., Ltd.; Shanghai, China
Shanghai Construction Group; Shanghai, China
Shanghai Dragon Corporation; Shanghai, China
Shanghai Feilo Co., Ltd.; Shanghai, China
Shanghai Fudan Microelectronics Group Co., Ltd.; Shanghai, China
Shanghai Fudan-Zhangjiang Bio-Pharmaceutical Co., Ltd.; Shanghai, China
Shanghai Guangdian Electric (Group) Co., Ltd.; Shanghai, China
Shanghai Haixin Group Co., Ltd.; Shanghai, China
Shanghai Hyron Software Co., Ltd.; Shanghai, China
Shanghai Jiaoda Onlly Co., Ltd.; Shanghai, China
Shanghai Material Trading Co., Ltd.; Shanghai, China
Shanghai Prime Machinery Company Limited; Shanghai, China
Shanghai Pudong Science & Technology Investment Co., Ltd.; Shanghai, China
Shanghai Shyndec Pharmaceutical Co., Ltd.; Shanghai, China
Shanghai Sinyang Semiconductor Materials Co., Ltd.; Shanghai, China
Shanghai Tunnel Engineering Co., Ltd.; Shanghai, China
Shanghai Yaohua Pilkington Glass Group Co., Ltd.; Shanghai, China
Shanghai Yuyuan Tourist Mart Co., Ltd.; Shanghai, China
Shantou Dongfeng Printing Co., Ltd.; Shantou, China
Shanxi Coal Transportation and Sales Group Co., Ltd.; Taiyuan, China
Shanxi Jincheng Anthracite Coal Mining Group Co., Ltd.; Jincheng, China
Shanxi Lu'An Mining (Group) Co., Ltd.; Changzhi, China
shaPE Capital AG; Freienbach, Switzerland
Sharda Ispat Ltd.; Nagpur, India
Shareco Brokerage Co Plc; Amman, Jordan
Sharikat Permodalan Kebangsaan Bhd; Kuala Lumpur, Malaysia
SHC Capital Asia Limited; Singapore, Singapore
Sheel International Limited; New Delhi, India
Sheetal Diamonds Limited; Mumbai, India
SH ENERGY & CHEMICAL CO, LTD.; Gunsan, Korea (South)
Shengyi Technology, Co. Ltd.; Dongguan, China
Shenzhen ChangFang Light Emitting Diode Lighting Co., LTD.; Shenzhen, China
Shenzhen Jasic Technology Co., Ltd.; Shenzhen, China
Shenzhen Technology Industrial Co., Ltd.; Shenzhen, China

Shenzhen Zhongjin Lingnan Nonfemet Co., Ltd.; Shenzhen, China
Sheraton Properties & Finance Limited; Mumbai, India
The Shibusawa Warehouse Co., Ltd.; Tokyo, Japan
Shibuya Kogyo Co., Ltd.; Kanazawa, Japan
Shidax Corporation; Tokyo, Japan
Shikibo Ltd.; Osaka, Japan
Shima Seiki Mfg., Ltd.; Wakayama, Japan
Shimojima Co., Ltd.; Tokyo, Japan
Shine Co., Ltd.; Busan, Korea (South)
Shine Corporate Ltd.; Brisbane, Australia
Shinhan Eng. & Const. Co., Ltd.; Seoul, Korea (South)
Shinhung Co., Ltd.; Seoul, Korea (South)
Shinil Industrial Co., Ltd.; Hwaseong, Korea (South)
Shinko Music Entertainment Co., Ltd.; Tokyo, Japan
Shinko Plantech Co., Ltd.; Yokohama, Japan
Shinning Century Limited; Maseru, Lesotho
Shin Nippon Biomedical Laboratories, Ltd.; Tokyo, Japan
Shin Poong Pharmaceutical Co., Ltd.; Seoul, Korea (South)
Shin Pro Maint. Inc.; Tokyo, Japan
Shinsung Delta Tech Co., Ltd.; Changwon, Korea (South)
Shinsung Solar Energy Corporation; Seongnam, Korea (South)
Shinto Tsushin Co., Ltd.; Nagoya, Japan
Shinva Medical Instrument Company, Ltd.; Shangdong, China
Shinwa Co., Ltd.; Nagoya, Japan
Shinwha Intertek Corporation; Hwaseong, Korea (South)
Shinyang Company; Bucheon, Korea (South)
Shinyei Kaisha; Kobe, Japan
Shira Real Estate Development & Investments P.L.C; Amman, Jordan
Shiroki Corporation; Toyokawa, Japan
Shiva Cement Limited; Rourkela, India
SHIVA TEXYARN LIMITED; Coimbatore, India
Shofu Inc.; Kyoto, Japan
Shogun Capital Corp.; Vancouver, Canada
Showa Chemical Industry Co., Ltd.; Tokyo, Japan
Showa Holdings Co., Ltd.; Kashiwa, Japan
SHREEKRISHNA BIOTECH LTD.; Mumbai, India
Shree Krishna Paper Mills & Industries Limited; Kolkata, India
Shree Manufacturing Company Limited; Kolkata, India.
Shree Rajivlochan Oil Extraction Ltd.; Raipur, India
SHREE RAM URBAN INFRASTRUCTURE LIMITED; Mumbai, India
Shree Salasar Investments Ltd.; Mumbai, India
Shree Tulsi Online.Com Limited; Kolkata, India
SHREYAS INTERMEDIATES LIMITED; Mumbai, India
SHREY CHEMICALS LIMITED; Rajkot, India
Shricon Industries Limited; Kota, India
Shri Jagdamba Polymers Limited; Ahmedabad, India
Shuanghui International Holdings Ltd.; Kowloon, China (Hong Kong)
Shuangliang Eco-Energy Systems Company Limited; Jiangyin, China
Shun Tak Holdings Limited; Central, China (Hong Kong)
Shyamkamal Investments Limited; Mumbai, India
S i2i Limited; Singapore, Singapore
Sibanye Gold Limited; Westonaria, South Africa
Sibar Auto Parts Limited; Tirupati, India
Siberian Mining Group Company Limited; Central, China (Hong Kong)
Sichuan Tianyi Science & Technology co., Ltd.; Chengdu, China
SIDDHARTHA TUBES LIMITED; Sarangpur, India
Siderurgica J.L. Aliperti S.A.; Sao Paulo, Brazil
SIDETRADE S.A.; Boulogne-Billancourt, France
SIGMAXYZ Inc.; Tokyo, Japan
Signaux Girod S.A.; Morez, France
SIGNET INDUSTRIES LIMITED; Indore, India
Sigrun Holdings Limited; Mumbai, India
Sii sp. z o.o.; Warsaw, Poland
Silergy Corp.; Xinbei City, Taiwan
SILKAN; Meudon, France
Silla Co., Ltd.; Seoul, Korea (South)
Silverlake Axis Ltd.; Kuala Lumpur, Malaysia
SILVEROAK COMMERCIALS LIMITED; Mumbai, India
SilverStripe Limited; Wellington, New Zealand
Simavita Limited; North Sydney, Australia
Simmtech Co., Ltd.; Chongju, Korea (South)
Simo International; Gennevilliers, France
Simona AG; Kirn, Germany
SIMPAC Incorporation; Incheon, Korea (South)
Simplify Digital Limited; London, United Kingdom
SIMRAN FARMS LIMITED; Indore, India
Sincere Watch (Hong Kong) Limited; Causeway Bay, China (Hong Kong)
Sinclair Garages (Port Talbot) Ltd.; Port Talbot, United Kingdom
SINDHU TRADE LINKS LIMITED; New Delhi, India
Singapore Kitchen Equipment Limited; Singapore, Singapore
Singhania & Partners LLP; Noida, India
Singsong Holdings Co., Ltd.; Seoul, Korea (South)
Sinher Technology Inc.; New Taipei City, Taiwan
SINNAR BIDI UDYOG LIMITED; Mumbai, India
Sino Australia Oil & Gas Limited; Parkside, Australia
Sino Construction Limited; Singapore, Singapore
SINO GAS INTERNATIONAL HOLDINGS, INC.; Beijing, China
SinoMedia Holding Limited; Beijing, China
Sino-platinum Metals CO., Ltd.; Kunming, China
Sino Resources Group Limited; Central, China (Hong Kong)

Sinosoft Technology Group Limited; Nanjing, China
Sinotruk (Hong Kong) Limited; Jinan, China
Sinovus Mining Limited; Sydney, Australia
Sinteplast S.A.; Buenos Aires, Argentina
Siracom Ltd.; Basingstoke, United Kingdom
Sirocco Energy Limited; Perth, Australia
SITOA GLOBAL INC.; Wanchai, China (Hong Kong)
SI. VI. Shipping Corporation Ltd.; Surat, India
Six Degrees Technology Group Ltd.; London, United Kingdom
SJ Corporation Limited; Mumbai, India
SJEC Corporation; Suzhou, China
SJM CO., LTD.; Ansan, Korea (South)
Skandinavisk Logistik AS; Glostrup, Denmark
Skanem AS; Stavanger, Norway
Skanray Technologies Private Limited; Mysore, India
Skansen Brands Pty. Ltd.; Braeside, Australia
SKC Co., Ltd.; Seoul, Korea (South)
SK Chemicals; Seongnam, Korea (South)
SK Engineering & Construction Co., Ltd.; Seoul, Korea (South)
SK Gas Co., Ltd.; Seoul, Korea (South)
Skinner Engineering Pty. Ltd.; Epping, Australia
SK Innovation Co., Ltd.; Seoul, Korea (South)
Skipper Limited; Kolkata, India
SK Networks Co., Ltd.; Seoul, Korea (South)
Skoda Ventures, Inc.; Panama, Panama
SKP SECURITIES LIMITED; Kolkata, India
SK Securities Co., Ltd.; Seoul, Korea (South)
SK Telecom Co., Ltd.; Seoul, Korea (South)
S Kumars Online Limited; Mumbai, India
Skytel Co. Ltd.; Ulaanbaatar, Mongolia
Skyworth Digital Holdings Limited; Quarry Bay, China (Hong Kong)
SL Corporation; Gyeongsan, Korea (South)
SLOMAN NEPTUN Schiffahrts-Aktiengesellschaft; Bremen, Germany
SLR Consulting Ltd.; Aylesbury, United Kingdom
Smalandsstenars Mekaniska Verkstad - SMV Industrier AB; Smalandsstenar, Sweden
Smart Concrete Public Company Limited; Chon Buri, Thailand
Smart Metering Systems plc; Glasgow, United Kingdom
SMEC Co., Ltd.; Changwon, Korea (South)
SM Energy Teknik & Electronics Limited; Thane, India
S.M. Entertainment Co., Ltd.; Seoul, Korea (South)
SMI Corporation Limited; Central, China (Hong Kong)
Smiffy's UK; Gainsborough, United Kingdom
SML Corporation Limited; Melbourne, Australia
SML Group Ltd.; Sha Tin, China (Hong Kong)
Smoothwater Capital Corp.; Toronto, Canada
SMS Finance SA; Luxembourg, Luxembourg
SMS TECHSOFT (INDIA) LIMITED; Coimbatore, India
Snax 24 Ltd.; Watford, United Kingdom
SNet Systems Inc.; Seoul, Korea (South)
S.N.G.N. Romgaz S.A.; Medias, Romania
S.N. Nuclearelectrica S.A.; Bucharest, Romania
S.Norton & Co. Ltd.; Liverpool, United Kingdom
SNP Genetics Inc.; Seoul, Korea (South)
SNP Schneider-Neureither & Partner AG; Heidelberg, Germany
SNU Precision Co., Ltd.; Asan, Korea (South)
Societe anonyme belge de constructions aeronautiques; Brussels, Belgium
Societe des Eaux Minerales d'Ogeu SAS; Ogeu-les-Bains, France
Societe d'Exploration Miniere Vior Inc.; Quebec, Canada
Societe Fermiere du Casino Municipal de Cannes; Cannes, France
Societe Hospitaliere d'Assurance Mutuelle; Lyon, France
Societe Internationale de Plantations d'Heveas SA; Courbevoie, France
Societe Marsellaise du Tunnel Prado Carenage; Marseille, France
Societe Mutuelle d'Assurance du Batiment et des Travaux Publics; Paris, France
Socrep; Genas, France
SODITECH Ingenierie SA; Cannes, France
Sofa.com Ltd; London, United Kingdom
Sofina Foods Inc.; Markham, Canada
Soft99 Corporation; Osaka, Japan
Softbrain Co., Ltd.; Tokyo, Japan
Soft Computing; Paris, France
Softronic AB; Stockholm, Sweden
Softship AG; Hamburg, Germany
Soft Strategy S.p.A.; Rome, Italy
Soho Flordis International Pty Ltd.; Saint Leonards, Australia
SOHO Group; Jakarta, Indonesia
Soil Machine Dynamics Ltd.; Wallsend, United Kingdom
Soil Sub Technologies Limited; West Perth, Australia
Solarpraxis AG; Berlin, Germany
Solid Automotive Berhad; Johor Bahru, Malaysia
Solidium Oy; Helsinki, Finland
Solocal Group; Sevres, France
Solueta Co., Ltd.; Ansan, Korea (South)
Solution Advanced Technology Co., Ltd.; Siheung, Korea (South)
SOMA PAPERS & INDUSTRIES LIMITED; Mumbai, India
Somar Corporation; Tokyo, Japan
SoMedia Networks Inc.; Vancouver, Canada
Somers Limited; Hamilton, Bermuda
Sonae Sierra Brasil S.A.; Sao Paulo, Brazil
Sonal Adhesives Limited; Mumbai, India
Sona Petroleum Berhad; Kuala Lumpur, Malaysia

Sondotecnica Engenharia de Solos S.A.; Rio de Janeiro, Brazil
Songa Offshore SE; Oslo, Norway
Songwon Industrial Co., Ltd.; Ulsan, Korea (South)
SONOKONG Co., LTD.; Seoul, Korea (South)
Sonoro Metals Corp.; Vancouver, Canada
Soosan Heavy Industries Co., Ltd.; Hwaseong, Korea (South)
Sora Capital Corp.; Vancouver, Canada
Soulbrain Co., Ltd.; Seongnam, Korea (South)
soulbrain ENG Co., Ltd.; Seoul, Korea (South)
Soundstorm Digital, Inc.; Vancouver, Canada
SOURCE FINANCIAL, INC.; North Sydney, Australia
Source Natural Foods & Herbal Supplements Limited; Hyderabad, India
South Asian Enterprises Limited; New Delhi, India
Southeast Asia Cement Holdings, Inc.; Makati, Philippines
South East Group Limited; Central, China (Hong Kong)
South Electronics Company Plc; Amman, Jordan
SOUTHERN LATEX LIMITED; Tiruvallur, India
Southern States Sign Company; Rome, Italy
Southern Sun Minerals Inc.; Vancouver, Canada
The South India Paper Mills Limited; Mysore, India
South Sea Petroleum Holdings Limited; Central, China (Hong Kong)
Sowbhagya Media Limited; Hyderabad, India
Space Co., Ltd.; Tokyo, Japan
Spara Capital Partners Inc.; Oakville, Canada
Sparc Systems Limited; Navi Mumbai, India
Sparrows Offshore Group Limited; Aberdeen, United Kingdom
Sparrow Ventures Corp.; Vancouver, Canada
The Specialist Works Ltd.; London, United Kingdom
Specialized Investment Compounds Company, Plc.; Amman, Jordan
Specialized Trading Investments Co.; Amman, Jordan
Special Piping Materials Ltd.; Dukinfield, United Kingdom
SPECO Ltd.; Eumseong, Korea (South)
Specsavers Optical Group Limited; Saint Andrew's, Guernsey
SPEX Services Ltd.; Dyce, United Kingdom
SPG Co., Ltd.; Incheon, Korea (South)
Sphere Resources Inc.; Melbourne, Australia
SPH REIT; Singapore, Singapore
Spice Islands Apparels Limited; Mumbai, India
Spike Exploration Holding AS; Stavanger, Norway
SpineGuard S.A.; Saint-Mande, France
Spitfire Oil Limited; Perth, Australia
Spitfire Resources Limited; Subiaco, Australia
SPK Corporation; Osaka, Japan
Spliethoff's Bevrachtingskantoor B.V.; Amsterdam, Netherlands
SPN, Inc.; Tokyo, Japan
SPOLYTECH CO., Ltd.; Jincheon, Korea (South)
SponsorsOne Inc.; Waterloo, Canada
Sporting Clube de Portugal - Futebol, SAD; Lisbon, Portugal
Sport Lisboa e Benfica - Futebol SAD; Lisbon, Portugal
Springer, S.A.; Cotia, Brazil
Springwater Capital LLC; Geneva, Switzerland
Sprintex Limited; Malaga, Australia
Spronken Orthopedie NV; Genk, Belgium
Sprue Aegis Plc.; Coventry, United Kingdom
SPT Energy Group Inc.; Beijing, China
SPTS Technologies Ltd.; Newport, United Kingdom
S P V I Public Company Limited; Bangkok, Thailand
Spyglass Resources Corp.; Calgary, Canada
Square 1 Products Ltd.; Lymm, United Kingdom
Square Four Projects India Limited; Bollaram, India
Squarelife Lebensversicherungs Aktiengesellschaft S.A.; Ruggell, Liechtenstein
Sree Rayalaseema Hi-Strength Hypo Limited; Kurnool, India
S R G Securities Finance Limited; Udaipur, India
SRI ARUMUGA ENTERPRISE LIMITED; Coimbatore, India
S.R. Industries Limited; Mohali, India
SRI RAMAKRISHNA MILLS (COIMBATORE) LIMITED; Coimbatore, India
Sri Vajra Granites Limited; Hyderabad, India
Stadco Ltd.; Telford, United Kingdom
Staffgroup Ltd.; London, United Kingdom
Stage Electrics Partnership Ltd.; Avonmouth, United Kingdom
Stahler Suisse SA; Zofingen, Switzerland
Stalwart Tankers Inc.; Athens, Greece
Stamford Partners Limited; London, United Kingdom
STAMPEDE CAPITAL LIMITED; Hyderabad, India
STANDARD CAPITAL MARKETS LIMITED; New Delhi, India
Standard Firm Co., Ltd.; Seoul, Korea (South)
Standard Industries Limited; Mumbai, India
STANROSE MAFATLAL INVESTMENTS & FINANCE LIMITED; Ahmedabad, India
Starcom Information Technology Ltd; Mumbai, India
Star Delta Transformers Limited; Bhopal, India
StarDyne Technologies Inc.; Kelowna, Canada
Star Navigation Systems Group Ltd.; Toronto, Canada
Starrex Mining Corporation Ltd.; Toronto, Canada
Startia, Inc.; Tokyo, Japan
Starvest plc; Woking, United Kingdom
StatCounter Ltd.; Dublin, Ireland
Staysure.co.uk Limited; Northampton, United Kingdom
STCube, Inc.; Seoul, Korea (South)
Steadfast Group Limited; Sydney, Australia

Steilmann Holding AG; Bergkamen, Germany
Stella Chemifa Corporation; Osaka, Japan
Stellar Capital Services Limited; Delhi, India
Stella Vista Technologies Limited; Kyalami, South Africa
Step Two Corporation Limited; Kolkata, India
Sterling International Enterprises Limited; Mumbai, India
Sterling Spinners Ltd; Chennai, India
STERLING STRIPS LIMITED; Mumbai, India
STERLING WEBNET LTD.; New Delhi, India
STI CO. LTD.; Anseong, Korea (South)
St. Johns Packaging Ltd.; Saint-Jean-sur-Richelieu, Canada
St Neots Packaging Limited; Saint Neots, United Kingdom
Stolt-Nielsen Limited; London, United Kingdom
StorageVault Canada Inc.; Regina, Canada
Stormfront Retail Limited; Exeter, United Kingdom
St Peter Port Capital Limited; Saint Peter Port, Guernsey
StrategEco Solar SA; Paris, France
Strategem Capital Corporation; Vancouver, Canada
Strategic Equity Capital Plc; Exeter, United Kingdom
Strathallen Capital Corp.; Toronto, Canada
Stratos Resources Limited; West Perth, Australia
Straumur Investment Bank hf.; Reykjavik, Iceland
Stream Co., Ltd.; Tokyo, Japan
Streamwide S.A.; Paris, France
Stredoslovenska Energetika, A.S.; Zilina, Slovakia
The Stronach Group Inc.; Aurora, Canada
Structural Systems Limited; South Melbourne, Australia
STS Semiconductor & Telecommunications Co., Ltd.; Cheonan, Korea (South)
Styland Holdings Limited; Kowloon, China (Hong Kong)
Suavitas S.A.; Valencia, Spain
Subhash Silk Mills Ltd.; Mumbai, India
Subh Tex (India) Limited; Mumbai, India
Suburbia Advertising; Victoria, Canada
SubZero Group Limited; Muswellbrook, Australia
SUDEV INDUSTRIES LIMITED; New Delhi, India
Sudwestdeutsche Medienholding GmbH; Stuttgart, Germany
Sul 116 Participacoes S.A.; Rio de Janeiro, Brazil
Sulabh Engineers & Services Limited; Navi Mumbai, India
Suminoe Textile Co., Ltd.; Osaka, Japan
Summerset Group Holdings Limited; Wellington, New Zealand
Summit Industrial Income REIT; Brampton, Canada
Sun Biomedical Limited; West Perth, Australia
Sunbridge Group Limited; Melbourne, Australia
Sunchang Corporation; Incheon, Korea (South)
SunCorp Technologies Limited; Wanchai, China (Hong Kong)
Sun East Technology (Holdings) Limited; Kowloon, China (Hong Kong)
Sungchang Autotech Co., Ltd.; Anseong, Korea (South)
Sungdo Engineering & Construction Co., Ltd.; Seoul, Korea (South)
Sung Ho Electronics Corp.; Seoul, Korea (South)
Sungjin Geotec Co., Ltd.; Ulsan, Korea (South)
Sungmoon Electronics Co., Ltd.; Pyeongtaek, Korea (South)
Sungy Mobile Limited; Guangzhou, China
Sunil Industries Limited; Thane, India
SUNITEE CHEMICALS LIMITED; Ahmedabad, India
SUNJIN CO., LTD.; Seoul, Korea (South)
Sun Kwang Co., Ltd.; Incheon, Korea (South)
Sunlink International Holdings Limited; Wanchai, China (Hong Kong)
Sun Machinery Co., Ltd.; Hwaseong, Korea (South)
Sun Mark Limited; Greenford, United Kingdom
Sunright Limited; Singapore, Singapore
SUNRISE REAL ESTATE GROUP, INC.; Shanghai, China
Sunset Pacific Petroleum Ltd.; Vancouver, Canada
Sunshine Capital Investments S.p.A.; Bologna, Italy
SUN SOURCE (INDIA) LIMITED; Vadodara, India
Sunstone Realty Advisors Inc.; Vancouver, Canada
Sunvest Corporation Limited; Sydney, Australia
SUNWODA Electronics Co., Ltd.; Shenzhen, China
Sunyard System Engineering Co., Ltd.; Hangzhou, China
Superbag Co., Ltd.; Tokyo, Japan
SUPER CROP SAFE LIMITED; Ahmedabad, India
Superhouse Limited; Kanpur, India
Supreme Imports Ltd.; Manchester, United Kingdom
Supreme Tex Mart Limited; Ludhiana, India
Sura Development & Investment Plc; Amman, Jordan
Suraj Products Limited; Sundergarh, India
SURANA CORPORATION LIMITED; Chennai, India
Surfilm SAS; Surgeres, France
Surge Communications; London, Canada
Surrey Capital Corp.; Toronto, Canada
SUVIDHA INFRAESTATE CORPORATION LIMITED; Ahmedabad, India
Suyog Telematics Limited; Mumbai, India
Suzhou Anjie Technology Co., Ltd.; Suzhou, China
Suzuden Corp.; Tokyo, Japan
SVA INDIA LIMITED; Mumbai, India
S.V.A. Jean ROZE; Vitre, France
SVAM SOFTWARE LIMITED; New Delhi, India
Svenska Orient Linien AB; Gothenburg, Sweden
SVP Global Ventures Limited; Mumbai, India

SWAGRUHA INFRASTRUCTURE LIMITED; Hyderabad, India
Swala Energy Limited; Mount Pleasant, Australia
Swan Mill Paper Company Ltd.; Swanley, United Kingdom
Swansway Garages Ltd.; Crewe, United Kingdom
Swarna Securities Limited; Vijayawada, India
Swift Worldwide Resources; Enfield, United Kingdom
SWINGPLANE VENTURES, INC.; Santiago, Chile
Switch Concepts Limited; Southampton, United Kingdom
Sword South Africa (Pty) Ltd.; Midrand, South Africa
SWP Group Plc; Soham, United Kingdom
Sylph Technologies limited; Indore, India
SYNCOM FORMULATIONS (INDIA) LIMITED.; Indore, India
Synergis Holdings Limited; Kowloon, China (Hong Kong)
Synergize Consulting Ltd.; Crawley, United Kingdom
SyQic plc; Buckingham, United Kingdom
Syschem (India) Limited; Chandigarh, India
System Information Co., Ltd.; Tokyo, Japan
System Technology-i Co., Ltd.; Tokyo, Japan

T

Taaleritehdas Oyj; Helsinki, Finland
TAC Co., Ltd.; Tokyo, Japan
Tadbik Group; Petah Tiqwa, Israel
Taekwang Industrial Co., Ltd.; Seoul, Korea (South)
Taesan LCD Co., Ltd.; Asan, Korea (South)
Tae Won Mulsan Co., Ltd.; Seoul, Korea (South)
Taewoong Co., Ltd.; Busan, Korea (South)
Taeyang Electronics Co., Ltd.; Daegu, Korea (South)
Taeyang Metal Industrial Co., Ltd; Ansan, Korea (South)
Taihan Textile Co., Ltd.; Seoul, Korea (South)
Taihei Dengyo Kaisha Ltd.; Tokyo, Japan
Taiheiyo Kouhatsu Incorporated; Tokyo, Japan
Taihua plc; Xi'an, China
Tailim Co,. Ltd.; Siheung, Korea (South)
Taipan Resources Inc.; Vancouver, Canada
Taisei Lamick Co., Ltd.; Saitama, Japan
Tai Shing International (Holdings) Limited; Central, China (Hong Kong)
TaiSol Electronics Co., Ltd.; Taipei, Taiwan
Taiwan Mask Corporation; Baoshan, Taiwan
Taiwan Pelican Express Co., Ltd.; Taipei, Taiwan
Taiyo Co., Ltd.; Kagoshima, Japan
Takamatsu Machinery Co., Ltd.; Hakusan, Japan
Takano Co., Ltd.; Nagano, Japan
Takasago International Corporation; Tokyo, Japan
Takasago Tekko K.K.; Tokyo, Japan
Takashima & Co., Ltd.; Tokyo, Japan
Tak Shun Technology Group Limited; Tsuen Wan, China (Hong Kong)
Talence Gestion SAS; Paris, France
Ta Liang Technology Co., Ltd.; Taoyuan, Taiwan
Talkmed Group Limited; Singapore, Singapore
Tallwoods International Golf Resort Pty. Limited; Hallidays Point, Australia
Tamilnadu Jai Bharath Mills Limited; Coimbatore, India
TAMILNADU STEEL TUBES LIMITED; Chennai, India
Tamul Multimedia Inc; Anyang, Korea (South)
Tanabe Engineering Corporation; Joetsu, Japan
Tandom Metallurgical Group Ltd.; Congleton, United Kingdom
TANEJA AEROSPACE & AVIATION LIMITED; Bengaluru, India
Tangent International Group Plc.; Billericay, United Kingdom
Tanqueray Exploration Ltd.; Calgary, Canada
Tanrich Financial Holdings Limited; Wanchai, China (Hong Kong)
Taparia Tools Limited; Nasik, India
Tap Oil Limited; West Perth, Australia
TARAI FOODS LIMITED; New Delhi, India
Tarczynski S.A.; Trzebnica, Poland
Tarena International, Inc.; Beijing, China
Tarpon Investimentos S.A.; Sao Paulo, Brazil
Tasmania Mines Limited; Sydney, Australia
Tasman Resources Limited; Perth, Australia
Tas Tecnologia Avanzata Dei Sistemi Spa; Rome, Italy
Taste Holdings Limited; Sandton, South Africa
Tatra, a.s.; Koprivnice, Czech Republic
Tatsuta Electric Wire & Cable Co., Ltd.; Higashiosaka, Japan
Tau Capital Plc; Douglas, Isle of Man
Taylor Engineering & Plastics Limited; Rochdale, United Kingdom
TB Group Inc.; Tokyo, Japan
TBWA/Hakuhodo; Tokyo, Japan
TCC STEEL CORP.; Seoul, Korea (South)
T. C. Harrison Group Limited; Bakewell, United Kingdom
TCM Limited; Cochin, India
TCPL PACKAGING LIMITED; Mumbai, India
TCR Capital SAS; Paris, France
TDJ S.A.; Katowice, Poland
TD Split Inc.; Toronto, Canada
Teaching Personnel Ltd.; Welwyn, United Kingdom
TEAR Corp.; Nagoya, Japan
TECBLU Tecelagem Blumenau S.A.; Brasilia, Brazil
Tech21 Limited; Twickenham, United Kingdom
Techniche Limited; Cannon Hill, Australia
TechnoAlpin S.p.A.; Bolzano, Italy
Techno Associe Co., Ltd.; Osaka, Japan
TECHNOFLEX SA; Bidart, France
Techno Forge Ltd.; Ankleshwar, India
Techno Mathematical Co., Ltd.; Tokyo, Japan
Techno Medica Co., Ltd.; Yokohama, Japan
Tech Pro Technology Development Limited; Changzhou, China

Techtran Polylenses Limited; Hyderabad, India
Tecity Group; Singapore, Singapore
Tecnisa S.A.; Sao Paulo, Brazil
Tecnocap S.p.A.; Cava de Tirreni, Italy
Tecnomagnete SpA; Lainate, Italy
Tecnosolo Engenharia SA; Rio de Janeiro, Brazil
Tectoy S.A.; Manaus, Brazil
tedrive Steering Systems GmbH; Wulfrath, Germany
Teesta Agro Industries Limited; Jalpaiguri, India
Tejoori Limited; Dubai, United Arab Emirates
TEKA - Tecelagem Kuehnrich S.A.; Blumenau, Brazil
TEKNO S.A. - INDUSTRIA E COMERCIO; Sao Paulo, Brazil
TELDOR Cables & Systems Ltd.; Ein Dor, Israel
TELECANOR GLOBAL LIMITED; Hyderabad, India
Telechips Inc.; Seoul, Korea (South)
Telecom Design; Pessac, France
Telecom Service One Holdings Limited; Kwai Chung, China (Hong Kong)
TELEFIELD Inc.; Seongnam, Korea (South)
TeleMasters Holdings Limited; Irene, South Africa
Tele Plastic, C.A.; Caracas, Venezuela
Telepool GmbH; Munich, Germany
Telerik A.D.; Sofia, Bulgaria
Television Broadcasts Limited; Kowloon, China (Hong Kong)
Telinvest S.A.; Sao Paulo, Brazil
Tellumat (Pty) Ltd; Cape Town, South Africa
TE-MAPOL Polimer Plastik ve Insaat Ticaret Sanayi A.S.; Kayseri, Turkey
Tempo Participacoes S.A.; Barueri, Brazil
Tenma Corporation; Tokyo, Japan
Tensho Electric Industries Co., Ltd.; Machida, Japan
Tentiwal Wire Products Limited; Mathura, India
Terabyte Net Solution Public Company Limited; Bangkok, Thailand
TeraJoule Energy GmbH; Frankfurt am Main, Germany
Teratech Co., Ltd.; Anseong, Korea (South)
Terminal Garagem Menezes Cortes S.A.; Rio de Janeiro, Brazil
TerraSem Co., Ltd.; Cheongwon, Korea (South)
Terruzzi Fercalx SpA; Spirano, Italy
Tertiary Minerals plc; Macclesfield, United Kingdom
TES Co., Ltd.; Yongin, Korea (South)
Tesna Inc.; Pyeongtaek, Korea (South)
Tessi S.A.; Grenoble, France
Tethys Oil AB; Stockholm, Sweden
TE WIND S.A.; Luxembourg, Luxembourg
Tewoo Group Co., Ltd.; Tianjin, China
Texcell-NetCom Co., Ltd.; Seoul, Korea (South)
Textil Renauxview S.A.; Brusque, Brazil
TFS Corporation Limited; Nedlands, Australia
TGLT S.A.; Buenos Aires, Argentina
Thai Usui Co., Ltd.; Ayutthaya, Thailand
Thames & Hudson Ltd; London, United Kingdom
TheAll MEDIBIO Inc.; Seoul, Korea (South)
Thermo Electric Instrumentation B.V.; Waddinxveen, Netherlands
Thin Film Electronics ASA; Oslo, Norway
ThinkSmart Limited; West Perth, Australia
THINKWARE Systems Corporation; Seongnam, Korea (South)
Third Financial Software Limited; London, United Kingdom
Third Point Reinsurance Ltd.; Pembroke, Bermuda
THIRU AROORAN SUGARS LIMITED; Chennai, India
THN Corporation; Daegu, Korea (South)
Thomas & Coffey Limited; Homebush Bay, Australia
Thomson Directories Ltd.; Farnborough, United Kingdom
Thor Explorations Limited; Vancouver, Canada
THOR GROUP LIMITED; Canterbury, United Kingdom
Thundelarra Limited; Nedlands, Australia
Tianda Group Limited; Central, China (Hong Kong)
Tiangong International Company Limited; Danyang, China
Tianjin Human Resource & Education Consulting Co., Ltd.; Tianjin, China
Tidewater Investments Limited; Sydney, Australia
Tierra Grande Resources Inc.; Perth, Australia
Tifany Industries SAS; Seclin, France
TIGER JIUJIANG MINING, INC.; Kaohsiung, Taiwan
Tiger Logistics (India) Limited; New Delhi, India
Tikehau Capital Advisors SAS; Paris, France
Time Products Ltd.; London, United Kingdom
Tinci Holdings Limited; Guangzhou, China
Tinna Rubber & Infrastructure Limited; New Delhi, India
Tintina Mines Limited; Toronto, Canada
Tiong Woon Oil & Gas Services Pte Ltd; Singapore, Singapore
Tipik s.a.; Brussels, Belgium
TIRUPATI INDUSTRIES (INDIA) LIMITED; Mumbai, India
TITAN BIOTECH LIMITED; Delhi, India
Titan Kogyo, Ltd.; Ube, Japan
Titijaya Land Berhad; Subang Jaya, Malaysia
TJ media Co., Ltd.; Seoul, Korea (South)
TK Corporation; Busan, Korea (South)
TK Group (Holdings) Limited; Tsuen Wan, China (Hong Kong)
TLi Inc; Seongnam, Korea (South)
Tlou Energy Limited; Brisbane, Australia
TM Insurance hf.; Reykjavik, Iceland
TMT Finance SA; Lugano, Switzerland
TOA Holdings, Inc.; Osaka, Japan
TOA OIL Company, Ltd.; Kawasaki, Japan
Tocalo Co., Ltd.; Kobe, Japan
TOC Co., Ltd.; Tokyo, Japan
Toda Kogyo Corp.; Otake, Japan

Toenec Corporation; Nagoya, Japan
Togami Electric Mfg. Co., Ltd.; Saga, Japan
TOHEAL PHARMACHEM LIMITED; Ahmedabad, India
Toho Chemical Industry Co., Ltd.; Tokyo, Japan
TOHTO SUISAN Co., Ltd.; Tokyo, Japan
TOKAI CARBON KOREA Co., Ltd.; Anseong, Korea (South)
Tokai Tokyo Financial Holdings, Inc.; Tokyo, Japan
Tokyo Automatic Machinery Works, Ltd.; Tokyo, Japan
Tokyo Cosmos Electric Co., Ltd.; Zama, Japan
Tokyo Dome Corporation; Tokyo, Japan
Tokyo Energy & Systems Inc.; Tokyo, Japan
Tokyo Plast International Limited; Mumbai, India
Tokyu Fudosan Holdings Corporation; Tokyo, Japan
Tolima Gold Inc.; Toronto, Canada
TomaGold Corporation; Montreal, Canada
Tomen Devices Corporation; Tokyo, Japan
Tomi S.A.I.E.D.W.; Athens, Greece
Tong Ming Enterprise Co., Ltd.; Jiaxing, China
Tonly Electronics Holdings Limited; Huizhou, China
Toolux Sanding S.A.; Danyang, China
Top 10 Canadian Financial Trust; Toronto, Canada
Top 10 Split Trust; Toronto, Canada
TOPBI International Holdings Limited; Taipei, Taiwan
TOPFIELD CO., LTD.; Seongnam, Korea (South)
Topkey Corporation; Taichung, Taiwan
Toplofikatsia Rousse EAD; Ruse, Bulgaria
Top Metal Works Co., Ltd.; Incheon, Korea (South)
Topre Corporation; Tokyo, Japan
Top Taste Holding BV; 's-Gravenpolder, Netherlands
Torex Semiconductor Ltd.; Tokyo, Japan
THE TORIGOE CO., LTD.; Fukuoka, Japan
Torii Pharmaceutical Co., Ltd.; Tokyo, Japan
Torreal, S.A.; Madrid, Spain
Torre Industrial Holdings Limited; Cape Town, South Africa
Tose Co., Ltd.; Kyoto, Japan
TOTAL HOSPITALITY LIMITED; Gurgaon, India
Totally Plc; London, United Kingdom
Total Soft Bank Ltd.; Busan, Korea (South)
Totetsu Kogyo Co., Ltd.; Tokyo, Japan
Touch Holdings Limited; Melbourne, Australia
Tovis CO., Ltd; Incheon, Korea (South)
Towa Sokki Limited; Vadodara, India
Tower Resources Ltd.; Vancouver, Canada
Toyo Construction Co., Ltd.; Tokyo, Japan
Toyo Engineering Works, Ltd.; Yamato, Japan
Toyo Knife Company, Ltd; Miyagi, Japan
Toyo Machinery & Metal Co., Ltd.; Akashi, Japan
TPK Holding Co., Ltd.; Taipei, Taiwan
TPLEX Co., Ltd.; Ansan, Korea (South)
T.RAD Co., Ltd.; Tokyo, Japan
Tradehold Limited; Parow, South Africa
Trade Me Group Limited; Wellington, New Zealand
Trafalgar New Homes Plc; Edenbridge, United Kingdom
Trafford Resources Limited; West Perth, Australia
Tragus Ltd.; London, United Kingdom
Transaction Capital Limited; Sandton, South Africa
Transasia Bio-Medicals Ltd.; Mumbai, India
Trans Asia Corporation Limited; Indore, India
Transcorp International Limited; New Delhi, India
Trans Genic Inc.; Kumamoto, Japan
Transglobal Fuels Ltd.; Batley, United Kingdom
Trans Hex Group Limited; Cape Town, South Africa
Transmetro Corporation Limited; Sydney, Australia
Transmile Air Services Sdn. Bhd.; Subang Jaya, Malaysia
Transwarranty Finance Limited; Mumbai, India
Travel Counsellors Ltd.; Bolton, United Kingdom
Travelodge Lakeshore; North Bay, Canada
Travertine Company PLC; Amman, Jordan
TRC Financial Services Limited; Mumbai, India
Treasure Factory Co., Ltd.; Tokyo, Japan
Treasury Group Limited; Sydney, Australia
Tremula NAV SA; Constanta, Romania
Trevisa Investimentos SA; Porto Alegre, Brazil
Trident Performance Corp. II; Toronto, Canada
Trigger Communication & Design Ltd.; Calgary, Canada
Trilogic Digital Media Ltd.; Mumbai, India
Trilogiq SA; Cergy-Pontoise, France
TRINETHRA INFRA VENTURES LIMITED; Hyderabad, India
Trinity Industrial Corporation; Toyota, Japan
TRINITY LEAGUE INDIA LIMITED; New Delhi, India
Triox Limited; Wanchai, China (Hong Kong)
Trisul S.A.; Sao Paulo, Brazil
Triumph Ventures Corp.; Jerusalem, Israel
Tropical Sky Ltd.; East Grinstead, United Kingdom
Tropic International Inc.; Woodstock, Canada
True North Apartment Real Estate Investment Trust; Toronto, Canada
True North Commercial Real Estate Investment Trust; Toronto, Canada
Trulife Limited; Dublin, Ireland
Trunki; Bristol, United Kingdom
Trustees Australia Limited; Brisbane, Australia
Trust Holdings Inc.; Fukuoka, Japan

Trust International Transport Plc; Amman, Jordan
TSA Industries Sdn. Bhd.; Balakong, Malaysia
TSB Bank plc; Edinburgh, United Kingdom
TSC Group Holdings Pty. Ltd.; Auburn, Australia
Tsinghua Holdings Co., Ltd.; Beijing, China
TS Law Group Sdn. Bhd.; Kuala Lumpur, Malaysia
Tsubakimoto Kogyo Co., Ltd.; Osaka, Japan
Tsukiji Uoichiba Co., Ltd.; Tokyo, Japan
Tsurumi Manufacturing Co., Ltd.; Osaka, Japan
Tsuruya Co., Ltd.; Handa, Japan
Tsuzuki Denki Co., Ltd.; Tokyo, Japan
Tubacex S.A.; Llodio, Spain
TUC Resources Limited; Perth, Australia
Tudeley Holdings Limited; Tonbridge, United Kingdom
Tuhama For Financial Investment P.L.C; Amman, Jordan
TULASEE BIO-ETHANOL LIMITED; Khalapur, India
Tulive Developers Limited; Chennai, India
Tune Ins Holdings Berhad; Kuala Lumpur, Malaysia
Tungsten Corporation PLC; London, United Kingdom
Turbon AG; Hattingen, Germany
Turbotech Engineering Limited; Mumbai, India
Turner & Co. (Glasgow) Limited; Glasgow, United Kingdom
Turner & Townsend plc.; Leeds, United Kingdom
Turquoise Capital Corp.; Vancouver, Canada
Tuskerdirect Ltd.; Watford, United Kingdom
Twinstar Industries Limited; Navi Mumbai, India
Two-up Financial Services Limited; Mumbai, India
TYCHE INDUSTRIES LTD; Hyderabad, India
Type 1 Media, Inc.; Halifax, Canada
Typhoon International Limited; Redcar, United Kingdom
Tyrol Equity AG; Innsbruck, Austria
Tyroon Tea Company Limited; Kolkata, India
Tyrrells Potato Crisps Ltd.; Leominster, United Kingdom

U

U10, S.A.; Lyon, France
UAB Baltic Engineers; Vilnius, Lithuania
UACJ Corporation; Tokyo, Japan
UA Granite Corporation; Kiev, Ukraine
U&D Coal Limited; Eight Mile Plains, Australia
UANGEL Corporation; Seongnam, Korea (South)
U Banquet Group Holding Ltd.; Kwai Chung, China (Hong Kong)
Ubion Co., Ltd.; Seoul, Korea (South)
Ubiquoss Inc.; Seoul, Korea (South)
UBS Global Allocation Trust; Toronto, Canada
Ububele Holdings Limited; Bellville, South Africa
UCI HOLDINGS LIMITED; Auckland, New Zealand
UCR SA; Bucharest, Romania
UE Study Co., Ltd.; Seoul, Korea (South)
UGM Holdings Pty Ltd.; Teralba, Australia
UJU ELECTRONICS Co., Ltd.; Hwaseong, Korea (South)
UKC Systems Ltd.; Uttoxeter, United Kingdom
UK Flooring Direct Ltd.; Coventry, United Kingdom
ULTRA Construction & Engineering Co., Ltd.; Seoul, Korea (South)
UMS Technologies Limited; Coimbatore, India
UMW Oil & Gas Corporation Berhad; Kuala Lumpur, Malaysia
Underwired Limited; London, United Kingdom
Uneek Clothing Company Ltd.; London, United Kingdom
Unicasa Industria de Moveis S.A.; Bento Goncalves, Brazil
Unimicron Technology Corporation; Taoyuan, Taiwan
UNIMIN INDIA LTD; Daman, India
Union Andina de Cementos SAA; Lima, Peru
Union Corporation; Seoul, Korea (South)
Union Investment Corporation; Amman, Jordan
Union Jack Oil plc; Bath, United Kingdom
Union Land Development; Amman, Jordan
UNION QUALITY PLASTICS LIMITED; Mumbai, India
Union Tractor Ltd.; Edmonton, Canada
Unipres Corporation; Yokohama, Japan
Unipulse Corporation; Tokyo, Japan
Unique Organics Limited; Jaipur, India
UNISEM Co., Ltd.; Hwaseong, Korea (South)
Uniserve Communications Corporation; Vancouver, Canada
Unishire Urban Infra Ltd; Bengaluru, India
United Arab Investors Co. P.L.C; Amman, Jordan
United Cable Industries Company; Amman, Jordan
United Group for Land Transport Co. P.L.C.; Sahab, Jordan
United Legal Services Ltd.; Thame, United Kingdom
United Pacific Industries Limited; Central, China (Hong Kong)
United Wholesale (scotland) Ltd.; Glasgow, United Kingdom
UniTest Inc.; Yongin, Korea (South)
Unitronics (1989) (R.G.) Ltd.; Ben-Gurion Airport, Israel
UNI TUBES LIMITED; Vadodara, India
Univance Corporation; Kosai, Japan
Universal Chemical Industries, Ltd.; Amman, Jordan
Universal Modern Industries Co Plc; Amman, Jordan
Universal Movers Corporation; London, United Kingdom
Universal Starch-Chem Allied Limited; Mumbai, India
UNO&COMPANY Ltd.; Wonju, Korea (South)
UNOZAWA-GUMI IRON WORKS, LTD.; Tokyo, Japan
Upasana Finance Limited; Chennai, India
Up Energy Development Group Limited; Hong Kong, China (Hong Kong)
Urban Select Capital Corporation; Vancouver, Canada

URBAR Ingenieros, S.A.; Asteasu, Spain
Usami KK; Nagoya, Japan
USG Tech Solutions Limited; Noida, India
U-SHIN LTD.; Tokyo, Japan
U.S. Masters Holdings Limited; Sydney, Australia
UTAC Holdings Ltd.; Singapore, Singapore
UTIC Services Sdn. Bhd.; Petaling Jaya, Malaysia
UT LIMITED; Kolkata, India
UV Boards Limited; Chennai, India

V

Vaarad Ventures Limited; Mumbai, India
Vaghani Techno-Build Limited; Mumbai, India
Vaishnavi Corporate Communications Pvt. Ltd.; New Delhi, India
Valartis Group AG; Baar, Switzerland
Valence Industries Limited; Adelaide, Australia
Valencia Ventures Inc.; Toronto, Canada
Valentino Fashion Group S.p.A.; Milan, Italy
Valetron S.A.; Rio de Janeiro, Brazil
Valiant Communications Limited; New Delhi, India
Vallabh Poly Plast International Limited; Mumbai, India
Valmet Oyj; Espoo, Finland
Valneva SE; Lyon, France
Valor Co., Ltd.; Gifu, Japan
Valore Italia S.p.A.; Rome, Italy
Valsoia S.p.A.; Bologna, Italy
Value Group Limited; Isando, South Africa
Value HR Co., Ltd.; Tokyo, Japan
VALUE INDUSTRIES LIMITED; Aurangabad, India
ValueMax Group Limited; Singapore, Singapore
Valvosacco S.p.A.; Forette di Vigasio, Italy
VanCamel AG; Hamburg, Germany
VANDANA KNITWEAR LIMITED; Hyderabad, India
Vantage Corporate Services Ltd.; Mumbai, India
Vantage International (Holdings) Limited; Kowloon, China (Hong Kong)
Vardia Insurance Group ASA; Oslo, Norway
Varova BV; Utrecht, Netherlands
Vaulted Gold Bullion Trust; Toronto, Canada
VCCL LIMITED; Kanpur, India
VCK Capital Market Services Limited; Kolkata, India
V-cube, Inc.; Tokyo, Japan
VCU Data Management Limited; Mumbai, India
Vealls Limited; Toorak, Australia
Veda Group Limited; Sydney, Australia
Vedavaag Systems Limited; Hyderabad, India
Veeam Software AG; Baar, Switzerland
Veerhealth Care Limited; Mumbai, India
VEKTOR Management GmbH & Co Erste KG; Vienna, Austria
VeliQ BV; Barendrecht, Netherlands
VELJAN DENISON LIMITED; Hyderabad, India
Ventspils nafta JSC; Riga, Latvia
Ventura Textiles Limited; Mumbai, India
Venture Life Group PLC; Bracknell, United Kingdom
Venturi Ventures Inc.; North Vancouver, Canada
Verdane Capital Advisors AS; Oslo, Norway
Veripos Inc.; Westhill, United Kingdom
Verney-Carron S.A.; Saint-Etienne, France
Verona Pharma plc; London, United Kingdom
Version 1 Software Ltd.; Dublin, Ireland
Vessel Co., Ltd.; Kyongki, Korea (South)
Vesta International, Corp.; Shenyang, China
Vestel Elektronik Sanayi ve Ticaret A.S.; Istanbul, Turkey
Vesuvius plc; London, United Kingdom
Vetro, Inc.; Prague, Czech Republic
VGX International, Inc.; Seoul, Korea (South)
VHCL INDUSTRIES LIMITED; Mumbai, India
ViaGOLD Capital Limited; Macau, China (Macau)
Viber Media Ltd.; Limassol, Cyprus
Victek Co., Ltd.; Icheon, Korea (South)
Victoria-Jungfrau Collection AG; Interlaken, Switzerland
Victoria Park AB; Limhamn, Sweden
Victory Group Limited; Kowloon, China (Hong Kong)
Victory New Materials Limited Company; Jinjiang, China
Vicunha Textil S.A.; Fortaleza, Brazil
Vietnam Steel Corporation; Hanoi, Vietnam
Vignal Systems; Venissieux, France
Vijay Solvex Limited; Alwar, India
Vikas WSP Limited; Sri Ganganagar, India
Viking Gold Exploration Inc.; Markham, Canada
VIKING INVESTMENTS GROUP, INC.; Shanghai, China
Vikos S.A.; Ioannina, Greece
VinaCapital Vietnam Opportunity Fund, Ltd.; Ho Chi Minh City, Vietnam
Vinaditya Trading Company Limited; Mumbai, India
Vina Tech Co., Ltd.; Jeonju, Korea (South)
Vinayak Polycon International Limited; Jaipur, India
VINTRON INFORMATICS LIMITED; New Delhi, India
VINYOFLEX LIMITED; Rajkot, India
Viohalco SA/NV; Brussels, Belgium
VIPPY INDUSTRIES LIMITED; Dewas, India
VIPPY SPINPRO LTD.; Indore, India
Virgin Active Limited; Milton Keynes, United Kingdom
Viro-Immun Labor-Diagnostika GmbH; Oberursel, Germany
Virtual1 Ltd.; London, United Kingdom
VIRTUAL GLOBAL EDUCATION LIMITED; New Delhi, India
Virtus Health Limited; Greenwich, Australia
VISAGAR FINANCIAL SERVICES LIMITED; Mumbai, India

VISAGAR POLYTEX LTD.; Mumbai, India
Viscount Mining Corp.; Vancouver, Canada
Vishvprabha Trading Limited; Mumbai, India
Visiodent S.A.; La Plaine Saint-Denis, France
VISION CORPORATION LIMITED; Mumbai, India
Visio Nerf; Neuilly, France
Vision Group; Woodbridge, Canada
Vista Alegre Atlantis SGPS S.A.; Ilhavo, Portugal
Vistal Gdynia S.A.; Gdynia, Poland
Visu International Limited; Hyderabad, India
VITAL KSK HOLDINGS, INC.; Tokyo, Japan
Vitra AG; Birsfelden, Switzerland
Vitreous Glass Inc.; Airdrie, Canada
VITZROSYS CO.; Seoul, Korea (South)
VITZROTECH Co., Ltd.; Ansan, Korea (South)
Viver Incorporadora e Construtora S.A.; Sao Paulo, Brazil
VIVO BIOTECH LIMITED; Hyderabad, India
Vivonio Furniture GmbH; Munich, Germany
VKJ Infradevelopers Limited; New Delhi, India
V Media Group; Montreal, Canada
Vocation Limited; Melbourne, Australia
Vohkus Ltd.; Southampton, United Kingdom
Volac International Limited; Royston, United Kingdom
Volant Textile Mills Limited; Mumbai, India
Voltalia S.A.; Neuilly-sur-Seine, France
Vortec Electronics, Inc.; Pandan Indah, Malaysia
voxeljet AG; Friedberg, Germany
VPhase Plc; Chester, United Kingdom
VPS Holdings Limited; Borehamwood, United Kingdom
Vroegop Ruhe & Co. BV; Amsterdam, Netherlands
V R Woodart Limited; Mumbai, India
VS Energy International Ukraine LLC; Kiev, Ukraine
V-Technology Co., Ltd.; Yokohama, Japan
Vulcabras Azaleia S.A.; Jundiai, Brazil
Vunani Limited; Sandton, South Africa
VXL Instruments Limited; Bengaluru, India
Vyapar Industries Ltd.; Mumbai, India
VYBRA AUTOMET LIMITED; Nalgonda, India
Vynco Industries (NZ) Limited; Christchurch, New Zealand

W

W2 Energy, Inc.; Cambridge, Canada
Wafangdian Bearing Co Ltd; Wafangdian, China
WAGEND INFRA VENTURE LIMITED; Mumbai, India
Wakamoto Pharmaceutical Co., Ltd.; Tokyo, Japan
WALCHAND PEOPLEFIRST LIMITED; Mumbai, India
Wallenstam AB; Gothenburg, Sweden
WALLFORT FINANCIAL SERVICES LTD.; Mumbai, India
WAMET (Demetriades) Ltd.; Nicosia, Cyprus
W&R Barnett Ltd.; Belfast, United Kingdom
Wanguo International Mining Group Limited; Shanghai, China
Wanjia Group Holdings Limited; North Point, China (Hong Kong)
Warburtons Limited; Bolton, United Kingdom
Warderly International Holdings Limited; Central, China (Hong Kong)
Warren Tea Limited; Kolkata, India
The Waterbase Limited; Chennai, India
Waterfront Capital Corporation; West Vancouver, Canada
Waterlinks Investments Ltd.; Birmingham, United Kingdom
Waterton Global Resource Management Inc.; Toronto, Canada
Wates Group Limited; Leatherhead, United Kingdom
Watkin Jones & Son Limited; Bangor, United Kingdom
WATOS Corea Co., Ltd.; Gwangju, Korea (South)
Wave Electronics Co., Ltd.; Suwon, Korea (South)
Wavenet International Limited; Fremantle, Australia
WB III Acquisition Corp.; Toronto, Canada
We Are Social Ltd.; London, United Kingdom
Weber Investissements SAS; Paris, France
Weborama SA; Paris, France
Websolus Co., Ltd.; Seoul, Korea (South)
Weizmann Limited; Mumbai, India
WELCAST STEELS LTD.; Bengaluru, India
WELCRON HANTEC CO., LTD.; Hwaseong, Korea (South)
Wellness Foods Ltd.; Chertsey, United Kingdom
Wellnet Corporation; Tokyo, Japan
WellStar Energy Corp.; Vancouver, Canada
Welspun Investments & Commercials Limited; Mumbai, India
WELTERMAN INTERNATIONAL LIMITED; Vadodara, India
Welvic Australia Pty. Ltd.; Deer Park, Australia
Wembley Sociedade Anonima; Belo Horizonte, Brazil
Wentworth Holdings Limited; Melbourne, Australia
Wenzhou Hongfeng Electrical Alloy Co., Ltd.; Wenzhou, China
Werklund Capital Corporation; Calgary, Canada
Wesco Holdings Inc.; Okayama, Japan
WestCap Investments Corp.; Mississauga, Canada
Western Bulk ASA; Oslo, Norway
Westlife Development Limited; Mumbai, India
West Point Resources Inc.; Burnaby, Canada
Westports Holdings Berhad; Port Klang, Malaysia
Westshire Capital Corp.; Calgary, Canada
Westshore Terminals Investment Corporation; Vancouver, Canada
Weststar Group; Kuala Lumpur, Malaysia
Wetzel S.A.; Joinville, Brazil
WFV Werkzeug- Formen- und Vorrichtungsbau GmbH & Co. KG.; Lampertheim, Germany

What If Limited; London, United Kingdom
What's Next Partners SAS; Paris, France
W. H. Brady & Co. Ltd.; Mumbai, India
White Cliff Minerals Limited; West Perth, Australia
Wieland-Werke AG; Ulm, Germany
Wiest S.A.; Jaragua do Sul, Brazil
Will Group, Inc.; Tokyo, Japan
William Cook Holdings Limited; Sheffield, United Kingdom
WIM PLAST LTD.; Daman, India
Win4Net Co., Ltd.; Anyang, Korea (South)
Windhurst SAS; Paris, France
Wing Lee Property Investments Limited; Kowloon, China (Hong Kong)
WINHA International Group Limited; Zhongshan, China
WINIX CORP.; Siheung, Korea (South)
Winkworth Machinery Limited; Reading, United Kingdom
Winmar Resources Limited; Sydney, Australia
Winner Group Enterprise Public Company Limited; Bangkok, Thailand
WIN-Partners Co., Ltd.; Tokyo, Japan
WINRO COMMERCIAL (INDIA) LIMITED; Mumbai, India
WINS Technet Co., Ltd.; Seongnam, Korea (South)
WINTAC LIMITED; Bengaluru, India
Winter Valley Tourism Investment Company plc; Amman, Jordan
Wirecard AG; Aschheim, Germany
WIRES & FABRIKS (S.A.) LIMITED; Jaipur, India
WISCOM Co., Ltd; Ansan, Korea (South)
Wisdek Corp.; Richmond Hill, Canada
Wisdom Holdings Group; Beijing, China
Wisec Global Limited; New Delhi, India
Wise Oakwood Ventures Inc.; Edmonton, Canada
Witte Molen NV; Aalburg, Netherlands
Wiworld Co., Ltd.; Daejeon, Korea (South)
Wix.com Ltd.; Tel Aviv, Israel
Wizcom Technologies Ltd.; Ramat Gan, Israel
WIZIT Co., Ltd.; Incheon, Korea (South)
WLM Industria e Comercio S.A.; Rio de Janeiro, Brazil
WM Capital S.p.A.; Milan, Italy
Wogen Group; London, United Kingdom
WOLFFKRAN GmbH; Heilbronn, Germany
Wolfpack Capital Corp.; Kelowna, Canada
WolfVision Holding AG; Klaus, Austria
Wolong Electric Group Co., Ltd.; Shangyu, China
Wong's Kong King International (Holdings) Limited; Hong Kong, China (Hong Kong)
WONIK QnC Corporation; Gumi, Korea (South)
Wonil Special Steel; Siheung, Korea (South)
Wonpoong Corporation; Seoul, Korea (South)
WOOD ONE Co., Ltd.; Hatsukaichi, Japan
Woodsvilla Limited; New Delhi, India
Woogene B&G Co., Ltd.; Seoul, Korea (South)
WOOGROUP SA; Paris, France
Woorim Machinery Co., Ltd.; Changwon, Korea (South)
Woori Special Purpose Acquisition 2 Co., Ltd.; Seoul, Korea (South)
Woori Technology Inc.; Seoul, Korea (South)
WOORY Industrial Co., Ltd.; Yongin, Korea (South)
Wooshin Systems Co., Ltd.; Siheung, Korea (South)
WOOSU AMS Co., Ltd.; Changwon, Korea (South)
Woosung Feed Co., Ltd.; Daejeon, Korea (South)
Works Stores Ltd.; Sutton Coldfield, United Kingdom
World Financial Split Corp.; Toronto, Canada
World Gas (Thailand) Co., Ltd.; Bangkok, Thailand
Worldmark International Ltd.; East Kilbride, United Kingdom
World Moto, Inc.; Bangkok, Thailand
World of Books Limited; Goring, United Kingdom
WorldRemit Ltd.; London, United Kingdom
World Wide Web Ibercom, S.A.; Guipuzcoa, Spain
WPT Industrial Real Estate Investment Trust; Toronto, Canada
Wragge & Co. LLP; Birmingham, United Kingdom
W.S. Industries (India) Limited; Chennai, India
WSP Global Inc.; Montreal, Canada
WT SA; Balma, France
Wuxi Taiji Industry Co., Ltd.; Wuxi, China
Wuzhou International Holdings Limited; Wuxi, China
WW Technology Holdings Ltd.; Mumbai, India

X

Xceed Group; London, United Kingdom
XEBIO Co., Ltd.; Koriyama, Japan
Xexec Limited; London, United Kingdom
Xiamen C&D Inc.; Xiamen, China
Xiamen International Airport Co., Ltd.; Xiamen, China
Xiamen ITG Group Corp., Ltd.; Xiamen, China
XIILab Co., Ltd.; Incheon, Korea (South)
Xilam Animation S.A.; Paris, France
Xingda International Holdings Ltd; Shanghai, China
Xinhua News Media Holdings Limited; Wanchai, China (Hong Kong)
Xinxing Cathay International Group Co., Ltd.; Beijing, China
Xinyi Solar Holdings Limited; Wuhu, China
X-Legend Entertainment Co., Ltd.; Taipei, Taiwan
XLN Telecom Ltd.; London, United Kingdom
Xuzhou Handler Special Vehicle Co., Ltd.; Xuzhou, China
Xyec Holdings Co., Ltd.; Tokyo, Japan
Xylotek Solutions Inc.; Cambridge, Canada

Y

Yaizu Suisankagaku Industry Co., Ltd.; Shizuoka, Japan

Yamauchi Corp., Ltd.; Hirakata, Japan
Yamini Investments Company Limited; Mumbai, India
Yangjisa Co., Ltd.; Gimpo, Korea (South)
Yanke Holdings Ltd.; Saskatoon, Canada
Yantai Valiant Fine Chemicals Co. Ltd.; Yantai, China
The Yasuda Warehouse Co., Ltd.; Tokyo, Japan
Yatra Capital Limited; Saint Helier, Jersey
Yayla Enerji Uretim Turizm ve Insaat Ticaret A.S.; Ankara, Turkey
Yelopay Corporation; Seoul, Korea (South)
Yeong Hwa Metal Co., Ltd.; Changwon, Korea (South)
Yestar International Holdings Company Limited; Shanghai, China
Yiwu Huading Nylon Co., Ltd.; Yiwu, China
YKM INDUSTRIES LIMITED; Chennai, India
Ymagis S.A.S.; Paris, France
Yokota Manufacturing Co., Ltd.; Hiroshima, Japan
Yomiuri Land; Tokyo, Japan
Yonekyu Corporation; Numazu, Japan
YONGHYUN Base Materials Co., Ltd.; Yangsan, Korea (South)
Yooshin Engineering Corporation; Seoul, Korea (South)
York Mailing Limited; York, United Kingdom
YO! Sushi Worlds; London, United Kingdom
YoulChon Chemical Ltd.; Seoul, Korea (South)
Young Poong Paper Mfg Co., Ltd.; Pyeongtaek, Korea (South)
Young Poong Precision Corporation; Seoul, Korea (South)
YOUNGSIN METAL INDUSTRIAL COMPANY LIMITED; Pyeongtaek, Korea (South)
YOUNGWOO TELECOM CO, LTD.; Seongnam, Korea (South)
Younyi Information & Communication Co., LTD.; Cheonan, Korea (South)
YPF Gas, S.A.; Buenos Aires, Argentina
YPF S.A.; Buenos Aires, Argentina
Y. T. Realty Group Limited; Wanchai, China (Hong Kong)
Yuanda China Holdings Limited; Shenyang, China
Yuasa Trading Co., Ltd.; Tokyo, Japan
Yue Da Mining Holdings Limited; Sheung Wan, China (Hong Kong)
Yue Xiu Enterprises (Holdings) Limited; Hong Kong, China (Hong Kong)
Yuhan Corporation; Seoul, Korea (South)
Yujin Robot Co., Ltd.; Seoul, Korea (South)
Yummy Market Inc.; North York, Canada
Yunnan Chihong Zinc & Germanium Co., Ltd.; Kunming, China
Yunnan Yunwei Co., Ltd.; Kunming, China
YURATECH Co., Ltd.; Yeongi, Korea (South)
Yuzhou Properties Company Limited; Central, China (Hong Kong)

Z

Zahrat Alurdon Real Estate & Hotels Investment Plc; Amman, Jordan
Zain Participacoes SA; Rio de Janeiro, Brazil
Zalando GmbH; Berlin, Germany
Zalman Tech Co., Ltd.; Seoul, Korea (South)
ZAO Becema; Moscow, Russia
ZAO Bestrom; Moscow, Russia
ZAOH COMPANY, LTD.; Tokyo, Japan
Zebra Strategic Holdings Ltd; Wanchai, China (Hong Kong)
Zementwerk LEUBE GmbH; Salzburg, Austria
Zena Mining Corp.; Vancouver, Canada
Z Energy Limited; Wellington, New Zealand
Zenith Life S.A.; Geneva, Switzerland
Zenotech Laboratories Limited; Hyderabad, India
Zeria Pharmaceutical Co., Ltd.; Tokyo, Japan
Zerto Ltd.; Herzliyya, Israel
Zettasphere Limited; Poole, United Kingdom
ZEUS CO., Ltd; Osan, Korea (South)
Zhejiang Aokang Shoes Co., Ltd.; Hangzhou, China
Zhejiang Feida Environmental Science & Technology Co., Ltd.; Zhuji, China
Zhejiang Haers Vacuum Containers Co., Ltd.; Yongkang, China
Zhejiang Hangxiao Steel Structure Co., Ltd.; Hangzhou, China
Zhejiang Longsheng Group Co., Ltd.; Shangyu, China
Zhejiang Materials Industry Group Corporation; Hangzhou, China
Zhejiang Orient Holdings Co., Ltd.; Hangzhou, China
Zhejiang Qianjiang Biochemical Co., Ltd.; Haining, China
Zhejiang Shenghua Biok Biology Co., Ltd.; Hangzhou, China
Zhen Ding Resources Inc.; Montreal, Canada
Zhidao International (Holdings) Limited; Wanchai, China (Hong Kong)
Zhong Chang Marine Company Ltd.; Yangjiang, China
Zhongjin Gold Corporation Limited; Beijing, China
Zhuzhou Times New Material Technology Co., Ltd.; Zhuzhou, China
Zidane Capital Corp.; Vancouver, Canada
ZIGExN Co., Ltd.; Tokyo, Japan
Zingmobile Group Limited; Singapore, Singapore
Zinopy Limited; Dublin, Ireland
Zodiac Ventures Ltd.; Mumbai, India
Zoltav Resources Inc.; Saint Helier, Jersey
Zoogigant AG; Zug, Switzerland
Zoopla Property Group Ltd.; London, United Kingdom
Zuari Agro Chemicals Limited; Goa, India
Zuken Elmic, Inc.; Yokohama, Japan
Zwahlen & Mayr SA; Aigle, Switzerland

Mergers and Acquisitions March 2013 - February 2014 (Parent Companies Only)

7

7 Day Catering Ltd.—acquired by Servest Group (Pty) Ltd.

A

Acadian Mining Corporation—acquired & absorbed by LionGold Corp. Ltd.

Acer Energy Limited—acquired & absorbed by Drillsearch Energy Limited

ACIS Benzinkuttechnika Kft.—acquired by DANAHER CORPORATION & name changed to Gilbarco ACIS Kft.

Acquity Group Limited —acquired by Accenture plc

Active Risk Group Plc—acquired by Sword Group SE

Adampak Limited—acquired by Navis Management Sdn. Bhd.

Addiction Worldwide Ltd.—acquired by The Mission Marketing Group plc

Adeptra Ltd.—acquired by Fair Isaac Corporation & name changed to Fair Isaac (Adeptra) Ltd.

Adler Modemarkte AG—acquired by Steilmann Holding AG

Advanced Inflight Alliance AG—acquired by PAR Capital Management, Inc.

Adventa Berhad—acquired by Southern Capital Group Pte. Ltd.

Aeroquest International Limited—acquired by Geotech Ltd.

Aerowatt SA—acquired by JMB Energie SAS

Afferro Mining Inc.—acquired & absorbed by International Mining & Infrastructure Corporation plc

Agricultural Bank of Greece, S.A.—acquired by Piraeus Bank S.A.

AKVA Group ASA—acquired by Egersund Group AS

Alaska Milk Corporation—acquired by Zuivelcooperatie FrieslandCampina U.A.

Albidon Limited—acquired by Jinchuan Group Limited

Alesco Corporation Limited—acquired by Dulux-Group Limited

Alfacam Group N.V.—acquired & absorbed by Ackermans & van Haaren NV, Allianz SE

Allied Banking Corporation—acquired & absorbed by Philippine National Bank

Allon Therapeutics Inc.—acquired & absorbed by Paladin Labs Inc.

Alma Lasers Ltd.—acquired by Fosun International Limited, Chindex International Inc.

Alpha Minerals Inc.—acquired & absorbed by Fission Uranium Corp.

Alterra Capital Holdings Limited—acquired by Markel Corporation

Alti SA—acquired by Tata Sons Limited

Amalgamated Appliance Holdings Ltd.—acquired by The Bidvest Group Limited & name changed to Home of Living Brands Holdings Limited

Amil Participacoes SA—acquired by UnitedHealth Group Incorporated

Andean American Gold Corp.—acquired by Lupaka Gold Corp.

Andina Minerals Inc.—acquired by Hochschild Mining plc

Angoss Software Corporation—acquired by Peterson Partners, Inc.

ANT plc—acquired by Espial Group Inc.

Applied Extrusion Technologies, Inc.—acquired by Al Ghurair Group

Apprecia Technology, Inc.—acquired by Tazmo Co., Ltd.

Aquascutum International Ltd.—acquired by YGM Trading Ltd

Arbor Memorial Services Inc.—acquired by Fairfax Financial Holdings Limited, JC Clark Ltd., Scanfield Holdings Ltd.

Arena Leisure plc—acquired by Reuben Brothers SA & name changed to Arena Racing Corporation Limited

Arkoon Network Security SA—acquired by European Aeronautic Defence & Space Company EADS N.V.

Arrowhead Water Products Ltd.—acquired & absorbed by Ice River Springs Water Company Inc.

AS Eesti Krediidipank—acquired by JSC VTB Bank

Asia Papertec, Inc.—merged with Asia Paper Manufacturing Co., Ltd.

Astral Media Inc.—acquired by BCE Inc. & name changed to Bell Media Inc.

Astral Mining Corporation—acquired & absorbed by Orex Minerals Inc.

ATR Group Ltd.—acquired by National Bank of Greece S.A.

AUGUSTA Technologie AG—acquired by TKH Group N.V.

Auralog SA—acquired by Rosetta Stone Inc.

Aurelian Oil & Gas plc—acquired by San Leon Energy plc & name changed to Aurelian Oil & Gas Limited

Aureos Capital Limited—acquired & absorbed by Abraaj Capital Limited

Aurizon Mines Ltd.—acquired & absorbed by Hecla Mining Company

Avion Gold Corporation—acquired & absorbed by Endeavour Mining Corporation

Avocet Resources Limited—acquired & absorbed by Lion One Metals Limited

Avusa Limited—acquired & absorbed by Mvelaphanda Group Limited

Azimuth Resources Limited—acquired & absorbed by Troy Resources Limited

B

Banco de Valencia, S.A.—acquired & absorbed by Caja de Ahorros y Pensiones de Barcelona

Bandar Raya Developments Berhad—acquired by Ambang Sehati Sdn Bhd

Bank of Asia Nepal Limited—merged with Nepal Industrial & Commercial Bank Ltd. to form NIC Asia Bank Limited

BC Saw & Tool Inc.—acquired by Tenex Capital Management, L.P.

BCD Semiconductor Manufacturing Limited—acquired by Diodes Incorporated

Beehive Communications Pvt. Ltd.—acquired by Publicis Groupe S.A.

Benda-Lutz Werke GmbH—acquired by DIC Corporation

Bentley Leathers, Inc.—acquired by Novacap Investments Inc.

Big Country Energy Services LP—acquired by MasTec, Inc.

Big Sky Farms, Inc.—acquired by La Coop Federee

Biggart Baillie—acquired & absorbed by DWF LLP

BigWorld Pty. Limited—acquired by Wargaming Public Company Limited

BIS Limited—acquired by Six Degrees Technology Group Ltd.

Bos Advertising—acquired by Dentsu Inc. & name changed to DentsuBos

Boubyan Bank K.S.C.—acquired by National Bank of Kuwait S.A.K.

Brazilian Gold Corporation—acquired & absorbed by Brazil Resources Inc.

Breakaway Resources Limited—acquired & absorbed by Minotaur Exploration Ltd.

BrightStar Resources Limited—merged with Rift Valley Resources Limited

Brigus Gold Corp.—acquired & absorbed by Primero Mining Corp.

Buchans Minerals Corporation—acquired & absorbed by Minco PLC

Bulgarian Telecommunications Company AD—acquired by Corporate Commercial Bank AD, JSC VTB Bank

BusinessWorld Publishing Corporation—acquired by Philippine Long Distance Telephone Company

Butterfly Corporation—acquired by Sega Sammy Holdings, Inc.

C

C2C Industrial Properties Inc.—acquired by Dundee Corporation & name changed to DIR Industrial Properties Inc.

Cable & Wireless Worldwide plc—acquired by Vodafone Group Plc

CapLease, Inc.—acquired & absorbed by American Realty Capital Properties, Inc.

Casinos Poland Ltd.—acquired by Century Casinos, Inc.

Castlemaine Goldfields Limited—acquired by LionGold Corp. Ltd.

Celtic Exploration Ltd.—acquired & absorbed by Exxon Mobil Corporation

Cerro Resources NL—acquired & absorbed by Primero Mining Corp.

CGA Mining Limited—acquired & absorbed by B2Gold Corp.

Challenger International SA—acquired by Jarden Corporation

Charger Energy Corp.—merged with AvenEx Energy Corp., Pace Oil & Gas Ltd. to form Spyglass Resources Corp.

China Data Broadcasting Holdings Limited—acquired by Sichuan Changhong Electric Co., Ltd. & name changed to Changhong Jiahua Holdings Limited

China Dredging Group Co., Ltd.—acquired by China Growth Equity Investment Ltd. to form Pingtan Marine Enterprise Ltd.

China Kanghui Holdings—acquired by Medtronic, Inc.

Choseido Pharmaceutical Co., Ltd.—acquired by Nihon Chouzai Co., Ltd.

Coalworks Limited—acquired & absorbed by Whitehaven Coal Limited

Cobriza Metals Corp.—acquired & absorbed by Candente Copper Corp.

Colibrys SA—acquired by Safran SA

Collective Point of Sale Solutions Ltd.—acquired by U.S. Bancorp

Comasec SAS —acquired by Ansell Limited

Compton Petroleum Corporation—acquired by MFC Industrial Ltd.

Computer Systems Integration Limited—acquired by Blackhawk Capital LLP

Concordia Healthcare Inc.—acquired by Mercari Acquisition Corp. to form Concordia Healthcare Corp.

Consolidated Media Holdings Limited—acquired by News Corporation

Continental Farmers Group PLC—acquired by Almarai Company Ltd.

Cooper Gay Swett & Crawford Limited—acquired by Lightyear Capital LLC

Cordys B.V.—acquired & absorbed by Open Text Corporation

Cortona Resources Limited—acquired & absorbed by Unity Mining Limited

Cyber Village Sdn Bhd—acquired by Silverlake Axis Ltd.

D

Daewoo Electronics Corporation—acquired by Dongbu Group

Dailymotion S.A.—acquired by France Telecom SA

Daiyoshi Trust Co., Ltd.—acquired by Daiwa House Industry Co., Ltd.

Devgen NV—acquired & absorbed by Syngenta AG

Diamonds North Resources Ltd.—merged with Uranium North Resources Corp. to form Adamera Minerals Corp.

Diaz Resources Ltd.—acquired & absorbed by Tuscany Energy Ltd.

Discovery Offshore S.A. —acquired by Hercules Offshore, Inc.

DMN Ltd.—acquired by The Gores Group, LLC

Dockwise Ltd. —acquired by Royal Boskalis Westminster N.V.

Dream Dining Corp.—acquired by Toridoll Corporation

Dynetek Industries Ltd.—acquired by Luxfer Holdings PLC

E

Eftel Limited—acquired by M2 Telecommunications Group Limited

EKO Holding SA —acquired by Advent International Corporation

elgeba Geratebau GmbH—acquired & absorbed by Constellation Software Inc.

Elpida Memory, Inc.—acquired by Micron Technology, Inc. & name changed to Micron Memory Japan, Inc.

Endace Limited—acquired & absorbed by Emulex Corporation

Endocoal Limited—acquired & absorbed by Yima Coal Industry Group Co., Ltd., Daton Group Australia Limited

Energy Information Centre Ltd—acquired by Utilitywise plc

ENK PLC—acquired by DMCI Holdings, Inc., D&A Income Ltd.

Epic Data International Inc.—acquired by Sylogist Ltd.

Eraring Energy Pty Ltd.—acquired & absorbed by Origin Energy Ltd.

Esperanza Resources Corp.—acquired & absorbed by Alamos Gold Inc.

Essential Oils Of Tasmania Pty Ltd—acquired by Atlas South Sea Pearl Ltd.

Esterel Technologies S.A.—acquired by ANSYS, Inc.

Eurodrip S.A.—acquired by Paine & Partners, LLC

EVE S.A.—acquired by Synopsys, Inc.

Exco Resources Limited—acquired by Washington H. Soul Pattinson & Company Limited

Exile Resources Inc.—acquired by Ocean & Oil Holdings Limited & name changed to Oando Energy Resources Inc.

Expocrete Concrete Products Ltd.—acquired by CRH plc

Extorre Gold Mines Limited —acquired & absorbed by Yamana Gold Inc.

Harry's Holdings Ltd.—acquired by Everstone Capital Advisors Pvt. Ltd.

Havlik International Machinery Inc.—acquired by Mill City Capital, L.P.

Heartwood Wealth Management Limited—acquired by Svenska Handelsbanken AB

Helton Industries Ltd.—acquired by ASSA ABLOY AB

Hengli Commercial Properties (Group) Limited—acquired by Dalian Wanda Group Corporation Ltd. & name changed to Wanda Commercial Properties (Group) Co., Ltd.

Hi-Rel Alloys Ltd.—acquired by Main Street Capital Holdings, LLC to form Hi-Rel Group, LLC

Hi-Rel Lids Ltd.—acquired by Main Street Capital Holdings, LLC to form Hi-Rel Group, LLC

Highlands Prime, Inc.—acquired & absorbed by SM Investments Corporation

Himart Co., Ltd.—acquired by Lotte Co., Ltd. & name changed to Lotte Himart Co., Ltd.

Holyrood Communications Ltd.—acquired by Biteback Publishing Ltd.

HOMEQ Corporation—acquired by Birch Hill Equity Partners Management Inc.

The Hong Kong Parkview Group Limited—acquired by COFCO Limited

HSE Integrated Ltd.—acquired by DXP Enterprises, Inc.

Huga Optotech Inc.—acquired by Epistar Corporation

Hybrid Service Co., Ltd.—acquired by SAM Holdings KK

F

Faltman & Malmen AB—acquired by The Interpublic Group of Companies, Inc.

Farmers Co-operative Dairy Limited—merged with Agropur Cooperative

Fekete Associates Inc.—acquired by IHS Inc.

FFastFill plc—acquired by ION Trading Ireland Ltd.

& name changed to FFastFill Limited
Figtree Creative Services Ltd.—acquired by Prophet Brand Strategy
First Uranium Corporation—acquired & absorbed by Algold Resources Ltd.
Fisher & Paykel Appliances Holdings Ltd.—acquired by Qingdao Haier Co., Ltd.
Fission Energy Corp.—acquired & absorbed by Denison Mines Corp.
Flagstone Reinsurance Holdings, S.A.—acquired & absorbed by Validus Holdings, Ltd.
Flakeboard Company Limited—acquired by AntarChile S.A.
Flint Energy Services Ltd.—acquired by URS Corporation
Fonciere Sepric S.A.—acquired by Patrimoine et Commerce
Foodcorp (Pty) Ltd.—acquired by Remgro Limited
Fornix BioSciences N.V.—acquired by Value8 NV
Frontier Silicon Limited—acquired by Toumaz Limited
FTL Seals Technology Ltd—acquired by IDEX Corporation
Fulford (India) Ltd.—acquired by Merck & Co., Inc.
The Futura Loyalty Group Inc.—acquired by Pong Marketing & Promotions Inc.
Future Capital Holdings Ltd—acquired by Warburg Pincus LLC & name changed to Capital First Ltd.

G

GAC Changfeng Motor Co., Ltd.—acquired by Guangzhou Automobile Industry Group Co., Ltd.
Gadens Lawyers Pty Ltd—acquired by MacGillivrays Solicitors
Garda World Security Corporation—acquired by Apax Partners LLP
General Donlee Canada Inc.—acquired by Triumph Group, Inc.
Generale Mobiliare Interessenze Azionarie S.p.A.—acquired by Atlantia S.p.A.
Genesis Care Pty. Ltd.—acquired by KKR & CO. L.P.
GeoKnowledge AS—acquired by Schlumberger Limited
Geomark Exploration Limited—acquired & absorbed by Pine Cliff Energy Ltd.
Gerard Lighting Group Limited—acquired by CHAMP Private Equity Pty. Ltd.
Glamox ASA—acquired by Arendals Fossekompani ASA
GlobeOp Financial Services, S.A.—acquired by SS&C Technologies Holdings, Inc.
Golden Land Property Development Public Company Limited—acquired by Univentures Public Company Limited
Goodman Co., Ltd.—acquired by Nipro Corporation
Grenville Strategic Royalty Corp.—merged with Troon Ventures Ltd. to form Grenville Strategic Royalty Corp.
GungHo Online Entertainment, Inc.—acquired by SoftBank Corporation

H

H. Paulin & Co., Limited—acquired by Keystone Group, L.P.
Halo Resources Ltd.—acquired & absorbed by QRS Capital Corp.
Hana Mining Ltd.—acquired & absorbed by Cupric Canyon Capital LLC
Hang Ten Group Holdings Limited—acquired by Li & Fung Limited

I

i-design group plc—acquired by Cardtronics, Inc.
IAS Smarts Limited—merged with Stein + Partners Brand Activation to form SteinIAS
IBS AG—acquired by Siemens Aktiengesellschaft
IC Telecom SA—acquired by Financiere LR SARL
ILS Laboratories Scandinavia, AB—acquired by Advent International Corporation
Impregilo S.p.A.—acquired by Salini Costruttori S.p.A & name changed to Salini Impregilo S.p.A.
INDEXPLUS Dividend Fund —acquired & absorbed by Middlefield Group Limited
Indura S.A.—acquired by Air Products & Chemicals, Inc.
Industrea Limited—acquired by General Electric Company
Infrasors Holdings Limited—acquired by Afrimat Limited
Inghams Enterprises Pty. Ltd.—acquired by TPG Capital, L.P.
Inmet Mining Corporation—acquired & absorbed by First Quantum Minerals Ltd.
Insignia Energy Ltd.—acquired by Brookfield Asset Management Inc.
Inspirit Energy Limited—acquired by KleenAir Systems International Plc to form Inspirit Energy Holdings plc
Integra Mining Limited—acquired & absorbed by Silver Lake Resources Limited
Intek S.p.A.—merged with KME Group S.p.A. to form Intek Group S.p.A.
Inter-Citic Minerals Inc.—acquired by Western Mining Group Co., Ltd.
Intercell AG—merged with Vivalis SA to form Valneva SE
Intrado AG—acquired & absorbed by Bossard Holding AG
INUS Technology, Inc.—acquired by 3D Systems Corporation to form 3D Systems Korea, Inc.
Invicta Energy Corp.—acquired & absorbed by

Whitecap Resources Inc.
Invista Real Estate Investment Management Holdings plc—acquired & absorbed by Palmer Capital Partners Limited
IonBond AG—acquired by IHI Corporation
IQS Avantiq AG—acquired by Wolters Kluwer n.v.
I.R.I.S. Group SA—acquired by Canon Inc.
Irish Life Group Limited—acquired by Power Corporation of Canada
IROC Energy Services Corp.—acquired & absorbed by Western Energy Services Corp.
Iron Road Limited—acquired by The Sentient Group
ISS Group Limited—acquired by Vista Equity Partners, LLC
IVONA Software Sp. z o.o.—acquired by Amazon.com, Inc.

J

J&M Management Consulting AG—acquired by Ernst & Young GmbH Wirtschaftsprufungsgesellschaft & name changed to Ernst & Young J&M Management Consulting GmbH
Jadestone Group AB—acquired by WMS Industries Inc.
JJB Sports plc—acquired by Sports Direct International plc
JK Sugar Limited—acquired & absorbed by Dhampur Sugar Mills Limited
JNR Resources Inc.—acquired & absorbed by Denison Mines Corp.
Joh. Heinr. Bornemann GmbH—acquired by ITT Corporation
John St. Inc.—acquired by WPP plc
Juken Technology Limited—acquired by Frencken Group Limited

K

K-Swiss Inc.—acquired by E-Land World Ltd.
Kalgoorlie Mining Company Limited—acquired & absorbed by Zijin Mining Group Company Limited
Kaseya International Ltd.—acquired by Insight Venture Management, LLC
KashFlow Software Ltd—acquired by HgCapital Trust plc
Kenai Resources Ltd.—acquired & absorbed by Serabi Gold plc
Kewill plc—acquired by Francisco Partners Management, LLC
KFC Holdings (Malaysia) Bhd.—acquired & absorbed by Johor Corporation
Kian Ann Engineering Limited—acquired by Invicta Holdings Limited
Kinross + Render Ltd.—acquired & absorbed by Four Communications Group plc
Kirayaka Bank, Ltd.—merged with The Sendai Bank, Ltd. to form Jimoto Holdings, Inc.
KMD A/S—acquired by Advent International Corporation
Kraus Carpet Mills Limited —acquired by Hilco Trading, LLC
Kumarina Resources Limited—acquired by ICM Limited
KWG Kommunale Wohnen AG—acquired by Conwert Immobilien Invest SE

L

L&M Energy Limited—acquired & absorbed by New Dawn Energy Limited
LaCie S.A.—acquired by Seagate Technology Public Limited Company
Lacoste S.A.—acquired by Maus Freres S.A.
Latexx Partners Berhad—acquired by Semperit AG Holding
LCH.Clearnet Group Limited—acquired by London Stock Exchange Group plc
Legg Mason BW Investment Grade Focus Fund—acquired & absorbed by Limited Duration Investment Grade Preferred Securities Fund
LeGuide.com S.A.—acquired by Lagardere SCA
Liberty Phosphate Limited—acquired by The Murugappa Group, Ltd.
Lifebank Corp.—acquired by Insception Biosciences, Inc.
Lite-On IT Corporation—acquired by Lite-On Technology Corporation
Lithium One Inc.—acquired & absorbed by Galaxy Resources Limited
Little World Beverages Limited—acquired & absorbed by Kirin Holdings Company, Limited
LMA International N.V.—acquired & absorbed by Teleflex Incorporated
LML Payment Systems Inc.—acquired by Digital River, Inc.
LN Metals International Ltd —acquired & absorbed by PSA Corporation Pte Ltd.
Lochard Energy Group Plc—acquired & absorbed by The Parkmead Group plc
Lodestone Management Consultants AG—acquired by Infosys Limited
Lord Buddha Finance Limited—acquired by Global Bank Limited
Lorex Technology Inc.—acquired by FLIR Systems, Inc.
Lupprians Ltd.—acquired by RETHMANN AG & Co. KG

M

Magma Metals Limited—acquired & absorbed by Panoramic Resources Limited
Manceliere Logement Soc Economie Mixte—acquired by Caisse Nationale des Caisses

d'Epargne et de Prevoyance, Banque Federale des Banques Populaires
Manganese Bronze Holdings Plc—acquired & absorbed by Zhejiang Geely Holding Group Co., Ltd.
Marazzi Group S.r.l.—acquired by Mohawk Industries, Inc.
Marcolin S.p.A.—acquired by PAI Partners S.A.S.
Maxima Holdings Plc—acquired by Redstone plc
May Gurney Integrated Services plc—acquired & absorbed by Kier Group plc
MB Aerospace Holdings Limited—acquired by Arlington Capital Partners
McPherson's Printing Pty. Ltd.—acquired by Knox Investment Partners Limited
MCW Energy Group Ltd.—acquired by AXEA Capital Corp. to form MCW Enterprises Ltd.
Mecalux, S.A.—acquired by Acerolux SL
Meccano SA—acquired by Spin Master Ltd.
MEDIUM GmbH—acquired by Droege International Group AG
Melrose Resources plc—merged with Petroceltic International plc
Mere PR Ltd.—acquired & absorbed by BJL Group Limited
Messina Minerals Inc.—acquired & absorbed by Canadian Zinc Corporation
Metalrax Housewares Limited—acquired & absorbed by EveryWare Global, Inc.
Metric Property Investments plc—merged with London & Stamford Property PLC to form LondonMetric Property Plc
Metro International S.A.—acquired by Investment AB Kinnevik
Mikuni Coca-Cola Bottling Co., Ltd.—merged with Coca-Cola Central Japan Co., Ltd. to form Coca-Cola East Japan Bottling Co., Ltd.
Milk Link Limited—acquired by Arla Foods amba
Miranda Technologies Inc.—acquired by Belden, Inc.
Miyachi Corporation—acquired by Amada Co., Ltd.
MJ Gleeson Investments Ltd.—acquired by C&C Group Plc
Moby Oil & Gas Limited—acquired & absorbed by Enegex N.L.
M.O.TEC Corporation—acquired by Mitsubishi Corporation, Sojitz Corporation
Mountain Lake Resources Inc.—acquired by Marathon Gold Corporation

N

N-able Technologies Inc.—acquired by SolarWinds, Inc.
NCB Group Ltd.—acquired by Investec Limited
Nelson Thornes Ltd.—acquired by The Washington Post Company
Neptune Marine Services Limited—acquired by MTQ Corporation Limited
New Bond Capital Limited—acquired & absorbed by Blackstar Group SE
The New Zealand Wine Company Limited—acquired by Foley Family Wines, Inc. & name changed to Foley Family Wines Limited
Nexen Inc.—acquired by China National Offshore Oil Corp. & name changed to Nexen Energy ULC
Nik Software GmbH—acquired by Google Inc.
Nippon Office Systems Ltd.—acquired by Kanematsu Corporation
Nissin Servicer Co., Ltd.—acquired by Fortress Investment Group LLC & name changed to Blue Horizon Asset Management Co. Ltd.
Noble Investments (UK) plc—acquired & absorbed by The Stanley Gibbons Group Limited
Norfolier Norge A/S—acquired by Katalysator S.A.
Norfolk Group Limited—acquired by RCR Tomlinson Ltd. & name changed to RCR Infrastructure Group (xNFK) Pty Ltd
North American Tea & Coffee Inc.—acquired by Tor-Quest Partners Inc.
Northacre PLC—acquired by Abu Dhabi Capital Management Ltd.
Northstar Aerospace, Inc.—acquired by Wynnchurch Capital, Ltd.
Norton Gold Fields Limited—acquired by Zijin Mining Group Company Limited
Norton Rose LLP—acquired by Fulbright & Jaworski, LLP & name changed to Norton Rose Fulbright LLP

O

OJSC Kubanenergo—acquired by JSC Interregional Distribution Grid Companies Holding
Omega Insurance Holdings Ltd.—acquired & absorbed by COFRA Holding AG
Open EC Technologies, Inc.—acquired by QHR Technologies Inc.
Open Grid Europe GmbH—acquired by Macquarie Group Limited, British Columbia Investment Management Corporation, Munchener Ruckversicherungs AG
Open Range Energy Corp.—acquired & absorbed by Peyto Exploration & Development Corp.
Opti-Time SA—acquired by GeoConcept SA
Organic Resource Management Inc.—acquired by Walker Industries Holdings Ltd.
Oridion Medical 1987 Ltd.—acquired & absorbed by Covidien plc
Oriental Interest Berhad—acquired by Jupiter Sunrise Sdn. Bhd.
Origio A/S—acquired by The Cooper Companies, Inc.
Orko Silver Corp.—acquired & absorbed by Coeur

d'Alene Mines Corporation
Oromin Explorations Ltd.—acquired & absorbed by Teranga Gold Corporation
Orsa Ventures Corp.—acquired & absorbed by Alamos Gold Inc.
OST Japan Group Inc.—acquired by Fuji Yakuhin Co., Ltd.
The Outside Line Ltd.—acquired by Publicis Groupe S.A.

P

Pacific Rim Mining Corp.—acquired & absorbed by OceanaGold Corporation
Pakfood Public Company Limited—acquired by Thai Union Frozen Products Public Company Limited
Paragon Pharmacies Limited—acquired by Shoppers Drug Mart Corporation & name changed to PGNX CAPITAL CORPORATION
Paul Wurth S.A.—acquired by SMS Holding GmbH
PC Scale, Inc.—acquired by Advanced Manufacturing Control Systems Ltd.
Peer 1 Network Enterprises Inc.—acquired by Cogeco Inc.
Petrominerales Ltd.—acquired & absorbed by Pacific Rubiales Energy Corp.
Phatra Capital Public Company Limited—acquired by Kiatnakin Bank Public Company Limited
Phenix Systems SA—acquired by 3D Systems Corporation
Plains Exploration & Production Company—acquired by Freeport-McMoRan Copper & Gold Inc. & name changed to Freeport-McMoRan Oil & Gas LLC
Plan B Group Holdings Limited—acquired by IOOF Holdings Ltd.
Plexmar Resources Inc.—acquired & absorbed by Dia Bras Exploration Inc.
PMI Gold Corporation—acquired & absorbed by Asanko Gold Inc.
Polish Energy Partners S.A.—acquired by Kulczyk Investments S.A.
Precious Metal Resources Limited—acquired by Sovereign Gold Company Limited
Primaris Retail Real Estate Investment Trust—acquired & absorbed by H&R Real Estate Investment Trust
Pro Brand International, Inc.—acquired by Sandmartin International Holdings Limited
Progress Energy Resources Corp.—acquired by Petroliam Nasional Berhad & name changed to Progress Energy Canada Ltd
PROLOR Biotech, Inc.—acquired & absorbed by OPKO Health, Inc.
ProSep Inc.—acquired & absorbed by ABS Materials, Inc.
Proton Holdings Berhad—acquired by DRB-HICOM Berhad
Proximagen Group plc—acquired by Upsher-Smith Laboratories, Inc.
PRT Growing Services Ltd.—acquired by Mill Road Capital, L.P.
Pure Energy Services Ltd.—acquired by FMC Technologies, Inc.

Q

Q&A Corporation—acquired by NEC Corporation
Q-Cells SE—acquired by Hanwha Chemical Corporation to form Hanwha Q CELLS GmbH
QuickPlay Media Inc. —acquired by Madison Dearborn Partners, LLC

R

Rainy River Resources Ltd.—acquired by New Gold Inc.
Ras Propack Lamipack Ltd.—acquired & absorbed by Essel Corporate Resources Pvt. Ltd.
REBgold Corporation—merged with Aquila Resources Inc.
Redecard S.A.—acquired by Itau Unibanco Holding S.A.
Renaissance Capital Holdings Limited—acquired by Onexim Group Limited
Renesas Electronics Corporation—acquired by The Innovation Network Corporation of Japan
Reno de Medici S.p.A.—acquired by Cascades Inc.
Reservoir Prod SASU—acquired by Lagardere SCA
Retalix Ltd.—acquired by NCR Corporation
RGI International Ltd.—acquired by CJSC GLOBEX-BANK, AMG Group Limited
Richard Fritz GmbH & Co. KG—acquired by Trakya Cam Sanayii A.S.
Ridgemont Iron Ore Corp.—acquired & absorbed by Castillian Resources Corp.
Rieber & Son ASA—acquired by Orkla ASA
Riemser Arzneimittel AG—acquired by AXA S.A. & name changed to RIEMSER Pharma GmbH
Rio Verde Minerals Development Corp.—acquired & absorbed by BTG Pactual Holding S.A., AGN Agroindustrial, Projetos e Participacoes Ltda.
Riva Gold Corporation—acquired & absorbed by Wildcat Silver Corporation
Rochat & Partners—acquired by European Investor Relations SA
Rock Chemical Industries (Malaysia) Berhad—acquired by Mega First Corporation Berhad
Rockgate Capital Corp.—acquired & absorbed by Denison Mines Corp.
Rosen Eiskrem GmbH—acquired by DMK Deutsches Milchkontor GmbH
Rottneros AB—acquired by Arctic Paper S.A.
Routledge Modise Incorporated—acquired by Hogan

Lovells International LLP
Rubicon Diversified Investments PLC—acquired by Lonrho plc & name changed to FastJet Plc

S

SAND Technology Inc.—acquired & absorbed by Constellation Software Inc.
Satara Co-operative Group Limited—acquired & absorbed by EastPack Limited
Satyam Computer Services Ltd.—acquired & absorbed by Mahindra & Mahindra Limited
Schwing GmbH—acquired by Xuzhou Construction Machinery Group Co., Ltd.
Score Media Inc.—acquired & absorbed by Rogers Communications Inc.
Second Wave Petroleum Inc.—acquired by Brookfield Asset Management Inc.
Secuoya Grupo de Comunicacion, S.A.—acquired by N Mas Uno IBG SA
SEG International Bhd.—acquired by Navis Management Sdn. Bhd.
Selwyns Travel Ltd.—acquired by Regie Autonome des Transports Parisiens
Senmar Capital Corp.—acquired by Sprott Inc. to form Toscana Energy Income Corporation
servtag GmbH—acquired by Stroer Out-of-Home Media AG
ShangPharma Corporation—acquired by TPG Capital, L.P.
Shear Wind Inc.—acquired by Sprott Power Corp.
Sheltered Oak Resources Corp.—acquired & absorbed by Foundation Resources Inc.
Silvore Fox Minerals Corp.—merged with Golden Share Mining Corporation
SinoCom Software Group Limited—acquired by SJI Inc.
Sky High Plc—acquired by Tracsis Plc
Skywest Airlines Limited—acquired by Virgin Australia Holdings Limited
Smile Staff Co., Ltd.—acquired by Trancom Co., Ltd.
Softel Ltd.—acquired by Belden, Inc.
Sophia Capital Corp.—merged with Folkstone Capital Corp.
Spara Acquisition One Corp.—merged with Digital Shelf Space Corp.
Sparling's Propane Co. Ltd.—acquired by Parkland Fuel Corporation
Spartan Oil Corp.—acquired & absorbed by Bonterra Energy Corp.
SpectraSensors, Inc.—acquired by Endress+Hauser Consult AG
SPG Land (Holdings) Limited—acquired by Greenland Holding Group Co., Ltd. & name changed to Greenland Hong Kong Holdings Limited
Spinreact SA—acquired by Toyobo Co., Ltd.
SPiRE, Inc.—merged with motionBEAT Inc.
Sportingbet plc—acquired & absorbed by GVC Holdings PLC
Spotless Group Limited—acquired by Pacific Equity Partners Pty. Limited
Springsoft Inc.—acquired & absorbed by Synopsys, Inc.
Sprott Resource Lending Corp.—acquired by Sprott Inc.
Stonesoft Corporation—acquired by Intel Corporation
Strathmore Minerals Corp.—acquired & absorbed by Energy Fuels Inc.
Strike Media (Pty) Ltd.—acquired by WPP plc
Sturdell Industries Inc.—acquired by voestalpine AG
Success Resources Pte. Ltd.—acquired by Success Resources Global Ltd.
Sumitomo Light Metal Industries, Ltd.—merged with Furukawa-Sky Aluminum Corp. to form UACJ Corporation
Sumitomo Metal Industries, Ltd.—merged with Nippon Steel Corporation to form Nippon Steel & Sumitomo Metal Corporation
Sunshield Chemicals Ltd.—acquired by Solvay S.A.
Superior Multi-Packaging Limited—acquired by Crown Holdings, Inc.
Swissmetal Holding AG—acquired by Baoshida Holding Group Co., Ltd. & name changed to Baoshida Swissmetal Ltd.

T

Tagora France SARL—acquired by What's Next Partners SAS
Talent2 International Limited—acquired by Morgan & Banks Investments Pty. Ltd., Allegis Group, Inc.
Talison Lithium Limited—acquired by Chengdu Tianqi Industry (Group) Co., Ltd.
TAM S.A.—acquired by Lan Airlines S.A. to form LATAM Airlines Group S.A.
TEAC Corporation—acquired by Gibson Guitar Corp.
Tecco GmbH—acquired by Ilford Imaging Switzerland GmbH
Telkom Kenya Limited—acquired by France Telecom SA
Telstar, S.A.—acquired by Azbil Corporation & name changed to Azbil Telstar, S.A.
Temmler Pharma GmbH & Co. KG —acquired by BC Partners Limited
Terrex Energy Inc.—acquired & absorbed by Anterra Energy Inc.
Texon Petroleum Ltd.—acquired & absorbed by Sundance Energy Australia Limited
Thakral Holdings Ltd.—acquired by Brookfield Asset Management Inc. & name changed to Wynyard Properties Holdings Limited
Thallion Pharmaceuticals Inc.—acquired by BELLUS Health Inc.

Thermocompact SA—acquired by Banque Federale des Banques Populaires, Caisse Nationale des Caisses d'Epargne et de Prevoyance

Thompsons Limited—acquired by The Andersons Incorporated, Lansing Trade Group LLC

ThoughtCorp Systems Inc.—acquired by EPAM Systems, Inc. & name changed to EPAM Systems Canada, Ltd.

Thrane & Thrane A/S—acquired by Cobham plc

Tikit Group plc—acquired by BT Group plc

Timeweave plc—acquired by Mayfair Capital Investment Management Limited

Titan Europe Plc—acquired by Titan International, Inc.

TMST Tibbi Sistemler Pazarlama Ticaret ve Servis A.S.—acquired by Toshiba Corporation

TMX Group Inc.—acquired by Maple Group Acquisition Corporation to form TMX Group Limited

Tokyo Coca-Cola Bottling Co., Ltd.—merged with Coca-Cola Central Japan Co., Ltd. to form Coca-Cola East Japan Bottling Co., Ltd.

Tokyo Denpa Co., Ltd.—acquired by Murata Manufacturing Co., Ltd.

Tokyo Stock Exchange Group, Inc.—merged with Osaka Securities Exchange Co., Ltd. to form Japan Exchange Group, Inc.

Toledo Mining Corporation plc—acquired by DMCI Holdings, Inc.

Tonic Industries Holdings Limited—acquired by China Merchants Group Limited

Torquay Oil Corp.—acquired & absorbed by CanEra Energy Corp.

Travel Channel International Limited—acquired by Scripps Networks Interactive, Inc.

Trelawney Mining and Exploration Inc.—acquired & absorbed by IAMGOLD Corporation

TriOil Resources Ltd. —acquired by Polski Koncern Naftowy ORLEN Spolka Akcyjna

Tudou Holdings Limited —merged with Youku Inc. to form Youku Tudou Inc.

TurboSonic Technologies, Inc.—acquired by Hamilton Robinson LLC

Twenty20 Media Vision Limited—acquired by Porta Communications Plc

Tyco Valves & Controls Italia S.r.l.—acquired by Pentair Ltd. & name changed to Pentair Valves & Controls Italia S.r.l.

U

Ubika Corporation—merged with SearchGold Resources Inc. to form Gravitas Financial Inc.

Ubiquisys Ltd.—acquired by Cisco Systems, Inc.

Ultimate Finance Group plc—acquired by Renovo Group plc

Ultrasonix Medical Corporation—acquired by Analogic Corporation

Umeco plc—acquired by Cytec Industries, Inc.

Underwater Engineering Services Limited—acquired by National Bank of Greece S.A.

United Orogen Limited—acquired by Carling Capital Partners Pty Ltd. & name changed to Elysium Resources Limited

Urastar Gold Corp.—acquired & absorbed by Agnico-Eagle Mines Limited

Uster Technologies Ltd.—acquired by Toyota Industries Corporation

V

Valiant Petroleum plc—acquired & absorbed by Ithaca Energy, Inc.

VanceInfo Technologies Inc.—merged with HiSoft Technology International Limited to form Pactera Technology International Ltd.

Victhom Bionique Humaine Inc.—acquired by Ergoresearch Ltd.

Victory Gold Mines Inc.—merged with Northern Gold Mining Inc.

Video Futur Entertainment Group SA —acquired by Netgem SA

VIPA GmbH—acquired by Yaskawa Electric Corporation

VisionSky Corp.—acquired & absorbed by Dixie Energy Trust

Visualization Sciences Group SAS—acquired by FEI Company

Viterra Inc.—acquired by Glencore International AG

Volta Resources Inc.—acquired & absorbed by B2Gold Corp.

W

Waze Ltd.—acquired by Google Inc.

WBL Corporation Limited—acquired by United Engineers Limited

Wellypower Optronics Corporation—merged with Lextar Electronics Corp.

Wenzel Downhole Tools Ltd.—acquired by J Fitzgibbons LLC

Westco MultiTemp Distribution Centres Inc.—acquired by Congebec Capital Ltee.

Western Wind Energy Corporation—acquired by Brookfield Asset Management Inc.

Westgold Resources Limited—acquired & absorbed by Metals X Limited

WFCA plc—acquired & absorbed by Porta Communications plc

Wheels India Limited—acquired by Titan Europe Plc

Windarra Minerals Ltd.—acquired & absorbed by Wesdome Gold Mines Ltd.

Winstar Resources Ltd.—acquired & absorbed by Kulczyk Investments S.A.

Winteam Pharmaceutical Group Limited—acquired

by China National Pharmaceutical Group Corporation
Worldwide Group Internet Services Ltd.—acquired & absorbed by Daisy Group Plc

X

Xbridge Limited—acquired by AnaCap Financial Partners LLP
Xceed Mortgage Corporation—acquired by MCAN Mortgage Corporation

Y

Yaeyama Shokusan Co., Ltd.—acquired by euglena Co., Ltd.
Yashili International Holdings Ltd.—acquired by China Mengniu Dairy Company Limited
Yima Coal Industry Group Co., Ltd.—merged with Henan Coal & Chemical Industry Group Co., Ltd. to form Henan Energy & Chemical Industry Group Co., Ltd.
YM BioSciences Inc.—acquired & absorbed by Gilead Sciences, Inc.

Z

Zaklady Azotowe Pulawy S.A.—acquired by Grupa Azoty S.A.
Zetar plc—acquired by Zertus GmbH

INTERNATIONAL PUBLIC & PRIVATE COMPANIES

1000 ISLAND RV CENTRE
409 County Rd 2 E
Gananoque, ON, K7G 2V4, Canada
Tel.: (613) 382-4400
Fax: (613) 382-2466
Toll Free: (800) 837-6556
E-Mail: info@1000islandsrv.com
Web Site: www.1000islandsrv.com
Rev.: $11,337,726
Emp.: 28
Business Description:
New & Used Car Dealers
S.I.C.: 5511
N.A.I.C.S.: 441110
Personnel:
Richard E. Weigand *(Bus Mgr)*

1000MERCIS S.A.
28 rue de Chateaudun
75009 Paris, France
Tel.: (33) 149490660
Fax: (33) 149490661
E-Mail: investisseurs@millemercis.com
Web Site: www.1000mercis.com
Year Founded: 2000
ALMIL—(EUR)
Sls.: $49,000,588
Earnings: $10,365,509
Emp.: 130
Fiscal Year-end: 12/31/12
Business Description:
Interactive Advertising & Marketing Services
S.I.C.: 7319
N.A.I.C.S.: 541890
Personnel:
Yseulys Costes *(Chm & CEO)*
Thibaut Munier *(Dir Gen)*
Board of Directors:
Yseulys Costes
Thibaut Munier

1010 PRINTING GROUP LIMITED
26/F 625 Kings Road North Point
Hong Kong, China (Hong Kong)
Tel.: (852) 82261010
Fax: (852) 21568039
E-Mail: enquiry@1010printing.com
Web Site: www.1010printing.com
1127—(HKG)
Sls.: $90,273,382
Assets: $110,951,546
Liabilities: $52,671,691
Net Worth: $58,279,855
Earnings: $8,787,943
Emp.: 1,011
Fiscal Year-end: 12/31/12
Business Description:
Printing Services
S.I.C.: 2759
N.A.I.C.S.: 323111
Personnel:
Peter Sze Chen Yang *(Deputy Chm)*
Wing Yip Lam *(CTO)*
Chuk Kin Lau *(Compliance Officer)*
Lai Ming Tan *(Sec)*
Board of Directors:
Ka Sing Yeung
Wing Yip Lam
Chuk Kin Lau
Hau Leung Lee
David Hoi Li
Carmen Lai Man Ng
David King Chung Tsui
Peter Sze Chen Yang
Legal Counsel:
Reed Smith Richards Butler
20/F Alexandra House 18 Charter Road
Central, China (Hong Kong)
Butterfield Fulcrum Group (Bermuda) Limited
Rosebank Centre 11 Bermudiana Road
Pembroke, Bermuda

101013121 SASKATCHEWAN LTD
(d/b/a Kia of Saskatoon)
730 Brand Road
Saskatoon, SK, S7J 5J3, Canada
Tel.: (306) 955-5080
Fax: (306) 955-5081
Toll Free: (877) 526-1189
Web Site: www.kiaofsaskatoon.com
Year Founded: 2000
Rev.: $17,475,935
Emp.: 38
Business Description:
New & Used Car Dealers
S.I.C.: 5511
N.A.I.C.S.: 441110
Personnel:
Paul Loeppky *(Principal)*

1028918 ONTARIO INC
(d/b/a Burlington Toyota)
1249 Guelph Line
Burlington, ON, L7P 2T1, Canada
Tel.: (905) 335-0223
Fax: (905) 335-4048
Toll Free: (866) 980-1051
Web Site: www.burlingtontoyota.ca
Year Founded: 1993
Rev.: $28,394,289
Emp.: 60
Business Description:
New & Used Car Dealers
S.I.C.: 5511
N.A.I.C.S.: 441110
Personnel:
E. W. Scherle *(Pres)*

1035312 ONTARIO LIMITED
(d/b/a Brampton Chrysler Dodge)
190 Canam Crescent
Brampton, ON, L7A 1A9, Canada
Tel.: (905) 459-1810
Fax: (905) 459-2516
Toll Free: (888) 707-8658
Web Site: www.bramptonchryslerdodge.com
Rev.: $33,495,059
Emp.: 70
Business Description:
New & Used Car Sales & Service
S.I.C.: 5511
N.A.I.C.S.: 441110
Personnel:
Ed Lewis *(Pres)*

1042735 ONTARIO INC
(d/b/a Mazda Of Brampton)
15 Van Kirk Drive
Brampton, ON, L7A 1W4, Canada
Tel.: (905) 459-0290
Fax: (905) 459-0424
Toll Free: (866) 798-7640
E-Mail: sales@mazdaofbrampton.ca
Web Site: www.mazdaofbrampton.ca
Year Founded: 1995
Rev.: $18,867,054
Emp.: 40
Business Description:
New & Used Car Dealers
S.I.C.: 5511
N.A.I.C.S.: 441110
Personnel:
Manjinder Sandhu *(Gen Mgr)*

1053038 ONTARIO LIMITED
(d/b/a Sterling Honda)
1495 Upper James St
Hamilton, ON, L9B 1K2, Canada
Tel.: (905) 574-8200
Fax: (905) 574-0321
Toll Free: (866) 980-4668
Web Site: www.sterlinghonda.com
Year Founded: 1985
Rev.: $23,208,505
Emp.: 49
Business Description:
New & Used Car Dealers
S.I.C.: 5511
N.A.I.C.S.: 441110
Personnel:
John Lecluse *(Principal)*

1060038 ONTARIO LTD
(d/b/a Midtown Motors)
125 Bell Street
Ingersoll, ON, N5C 2N9, Canada
Tel.: (519) 485-2921
Fax: (519) 425-1753
Web Site: www.midtown1938.com
Year Founded: 1938
Rev.: $16,432,596
Emp.: 29
Business Description:
Automobile Whlsr & Retailers
S.I.C.: 5012
N.A.I.C.S.: 423110
Personnel:
Max Antony *(Founder)*
Paul Antony *(Pres)*

1092072 ONTARIO INC
(d/b/a Elfe Juvenile Products)
4500 Thimens Boulevard
Ville Saint Laurent, QC, 4HR 2P2, Canada
Tel.: (514) 344-3533
Fax: (514) 344-9295
Toll Free: (800) 667-8184
E-Mail: service@elfe.ca
Web Site: www.elfe.net
Rev.: $43,472,475
Emp.: 70
Business Description:
Infant Products Distr
S.I.C.: 5137
N.A.I.C.S.: 424330
Personnel:
Shell Bern *(Pres)*

109806 CANADA LTD
(See Under Subaru Montreal)

1101489 ONTARIO LTD
(d/b/a Perth Chrysler Jeep Eagle)
65 Dufferin Street
Perth, ON, K7H 3A5, Canada
Tel.: (613) 267-4021
Fax: (613) 267-3121
Rev.: $17,342,619
Emp.: 38
Business Description:
New & Used Car Dealers
S.I.C.: 5511
N.A.I.C.S.: 441110
Personnel:
Peter MacPhee *(VP)*

1133571 ALBERTA LTD
(d/b/a Toyota City)
4120-56 Street
Wetaskiwin, AB, T9A 1V3, Canada
Tel.: (780) 352-2225
Fax: (780) 352-5750
Toll Free: (877) 352-2234
E-Mail: toyotaab@telusplanet.net
Web Site: www.toyotacity.ca
Rev.: $11,585,000
Emp.: 27
Business Description:
New & Used Car Dealers
S.I.C.: 5511
N.A.I.C.S.: 441110
Personnel:
Geoffrey Skakun *(Owner)*

11336 NEWFOUNDLAND INC
(d/b/a Toyota Plaza)

11336 NEWFOUNDLAND INC—(Continued)

73 Kenmount Road
Saint John's, NL, A1B 3P8, Canada
Tel.: (709) 753-4051
Fax: (709) 739-8398
Toll Free: (866) 496-4051
Web Site: www.toyotaplaza.ca
Year Founded: 1977
Rev.: $20,231,200
Emp.: 100
Business Description:
New & Used Car Dealers
S.I.C.: 5511
N.A.I.C.S.: 441110
Personnel:
Janice Prim *(Controller)*

1166709 ONTARIO INC
(d/b/a Acura 2000)
2250 Queen Street East
Brampton, ON, L6T3S1, Canada
Tel.: (905) 458-7100
Fax: (905) 458-7109
Toll Free: (888) 728-7451
E-Mail: reception@acura2000.com
Web Site: www.acura2000.com
Year Founded: 1987
Rev.: $21,562,348
Emp.: 45
Business Description:
New & Used Car Dealers
S.I.C.: 5511
N.A.I.C.S.: 441110
Personnel:
Paul Policaro *(Owner)*

1170880 ONTARIO LIMITED
(d/b/a Acura of North Toronto)
7064 Yonge Street
Thornhill, ON, L4J 1V7, Canada
Tel.: (905) 882-4246
Fax: (905) 882-9661
Toll Free: (800) 961-1373
E-Mail: info@acuraofnorthtoronto.com
Web Site: www.acuraofnorthtoronto.com
Year Founded: 1996
Rev.: $39,070,709
Emp.: 86
Business Description:
New & Used Car Dealers
S.I.C.: 5511
N.A.I.C.S.: 441110
Personnel:
Ron Zamperin *(Controller)*

1211863 ONTARIO INC.
(d/b/a A&T Leasing)
113-115 Cushman Road Unit 55 & 56
Saint Catharines, ON, L2M 6S9, Canada
Tel.: (905) 988-9905
Fax: (905) 988-5019
E-Mail: info@autoexportcanada.com
Web Site: www.autoexportcanada.com
Year Founded: 1996
Rev.: $48,271,867
Emp.: 11
Business Description:
New Vehicles & Parts Exporter
S.I.C.: 5013
N.A.I.C.S.: 423120
Personnel:
Andrew Pilsworth *(Gen Mgr)*

1249270 ONTARIO INC
(d/b/a Bramwood Forest Products)
38 Taber Road
Toronto, ON, M9W 3A8, Canada
Tel.: (416) 747-7244
Fax: (416) 747-8576
Toll Free: (888) 594-9663
E-Mail: info@bramwood.com
Web Site: www.bramwood.com
Year Founded: 1990
Rev.: $11,136,682
Emp.: 30
Business Description:
Lumber Products Whslr
S.I.C.: 5031
N.A.I.C.S.: 423310
Personnel:
Arie Meltzer *(Pres)*

1260261 ONTARIO INC
(d/b/a True North Timber)
Corner of Hwy 101 & Hwy 129
Chappise Township
PO Box 507
Chapleau, ON, P0M 1K0, Canada
Tel.: (705) 864-1974
Fax: (705) 864-1039
E-Mail: generaldel@truenorthtimber.com
Web Site: www.truenorthtimber.com
Year Founded: 1997
Rev.: $10,533,600
Emp.: 86
Business Description:
Timber Logging Services
S.I.C.: 2411
N.A.I.C.S.: 113310
Personnel:
Raymond Duhaime *(Mgr-Ops)*

129157 CANADA INC
(d/b/a ADM Sport)
1831 boul Wilfrid-Hamel
Quebec, QC, G1N 3Z1, Canada
Tel.: (418) 527-4489
Fax: (418) 527-0339
Toll Free: (800) 463-4340
Web Site: www.admsport.com
Year Founded: 1981
Rev.: $11,082,095
Emp.: 30
Business Description:
Motorcycle Clothing, Parts & Accessories Retailer
S.I.C.: 5013
N.A.I.C.S.: 423120
Personnel:
Michel Matton *(Owner)*
Chantale Matton *(CEO)*

1300 SMILES LIMITED
Ground Floor 105 Denham Street
Townsville, QLD, 4810, Australia
Tel.: (61) 747201300
Fax: (61) 747715217
Web Site: www.1300smiles.com.au
ONT—(ASX)
Rev.: $37,706,304
Assets: $35,270,917
Liabilities: $6,142,137
Net Worth: $29,128,779
Earnings: $6,635,051
Emp.: 136
Fiscal Year-end: 06/30/13
Business Description:
Dentistry Services
S.I.C.: 8021
N.A.I.C.S.: 621210
Personnel:
Robert F. Jones *(Chm)*
Daryl Shane Holmes *(Mng Dir)*
William Bass *(Sec)*
Board of Directors:
Robert F. Jones
William Bass
Daryl Shane Holmes
Legal Counsel:
Thomson Lawyers
Level 16 Waterfront Place 1 Eagle Street
Brisbane, QLD, 4000, Australia
MacDonnells Law
Level 1 131 Denham Street
Townsville, QLD, 4810, Australia
Tel.: (61) 74722 0220
Fax: (61) 74772 5635

131448 CANADA INC
(d/b/a Adcogroup World)
5400 Armand-Frappier
Saint-Hubert, QC, J3Z 1G5, Canada
Tel.: (514) 382-0180
Fax: (514) 382-1132
Toll Free: (800) 361-9030
E-Mail: info@adco.ca
Web Site: www.adco.ca
Sales Range: $10-24.9 Million
Emp.: 80
Business Description:
Commercial Furnishings Retailer
S.I.C.: 5719
N.A.I.C.S.: 442299
Personnel:
Salomon Diaz *(Dir-Production)*

1390835 ONTARIO LIMITED
(d/b/a Toyota on Front)
6 Spadina Ave
Toronto, ON, M5V 2H6, Canada
Tel.: (416) 703-7700
Fax: (416) 703-5712
Web Site: www.toyotaonfront.com
Rev.: $37,310,976
Emp.: 45
Business Description:
New & Used Car Dealers
S.I.C.: 5511
N.A.I.C.S.: 441110
Personnel:
Ron Provost *(Dir-Ops)*

142258 CANADA INC
(d/b/a JCB Entrepreneurs Generaux Inc.)
3875 Isabelle Street
Brossard, QC, J4Y 2R2, Canada
Tel.: (450) 444-8151
Fax: (450) 444-8155
E-Mail: info@jcb.ca
Web Site: www.jcb.ca
Rev.: $24,320,107
Emp.: 60
Business Description:
Building Contractors
S.I.C.: 1542
N.A.I.C.S.: 236220
Personnel:
J. Carol Boutet *(Co-Founder & Pres)*
Jean-Francois Gravel *(Co-Founder, VP & Gen Mgr)*
Louis Lavigne *(Co-Founder & VP-Construction)*
Benoit Labelle *(Partner & VP-Estimation)*

147766 CANADA INC
(d/b/a Windsor Honda)
7180 Tecumseh Road East
Windsor, ON, N8T 1E6, Canada
Tel.: (519) 945-8100
Fax: (519) 945-2188
Web Site: www.windsorhonda.com
Year Founded: 1988
Rev.: $11,051,669
Emp.: 25
Business Description:
New & Used Car Dealers
S.I.C.: 5511
N.A.I.C.S.: 441110
Personnel:
Mike Labiak *(Gen Mgr)*

1507953 ONTARIO INC.
(d/b/a Grant Transport)
212 Bergey Court
New Hamburg, ON, N3A 2J5, Canada
Tel.: (519) 662-3640
Fax: (519) 662-1978
Toll Free: (800) 668-4481
E-Mail: administration@granttransport.com
Web Site: www.granttransport.com
Year Founded: 1972
Rev.: $16,672,177
Emp.: 150
Business Description:
Truck Transportation Services
S.I.C.: 4213
N.A.I.C.S.: 484121
Personnel:
Julie Jutzi *(Pres)*

151 PRODUCTS LTD.
The Old School House George Leigh Street
Manchester, M4 6AF, United Kingdom
Tel.: (44) 161 228 3939
Fax: (44) 844 412 4774
E-Mail: info@151.co.uk
Web Site: www.151.co.uk
Year Founded: 1997
Sales Range: $25-49.9 Million
Emp.: 80
Business Description:
Sanitation Goods Mfr
S.I.C.: 2842
N.A.I.C.S.: 325612
Personnel:
Ian George *(Dir-Fin)*

1511905 ONTARIO INC
(d/b/a Guelph Volkswagen)
635 Woodlawn Rd W
Guelph, ON, N1H 7K9, Canada
Tel.: (519) 824-9150
Fax: (519) 824-7746
E-Mail: reception@gvw.ca
Web Site: www.gvw.ca
Year Founded: 1986
Rev.: $11,051,669
Emp.: 25
Business Description:
New & Used Car Dealers
S.I.C.: 5511
N.A.I.C.S.: 441110
Personnel:
Jason Chow *(Pres)*

1512804 ONTARIO INC
(d/b/a Brampton Mitsubishi)
47 Bovaird Dr W
Brampton, ON, L6X 0G9, Canada
Tel.: (905) 459-2600
Fax: (905) 459-3400
Toll Free: (866) 938-0591
Web Site: www.bramptonmitsubishi.ca
Rev.: $11,476,733
Emp.: 25
Business Description:
New & Used Car Dealers
S.I.C.: 5511
N.A.I.C.S.: 441110
Personnel:
Zahid Ghaffar *(Gen Mgr)*

166606 CANADA INC
(d/b/a Lexus Gabriel)
3303 Cote de Liesse
Saint Laurent, QC, H4N 3C2, Canada
Tel.: (514) 747-7777
Fax: (514) 747-7447
E-Mail: sales@gabriel.Lexus.ca
Web Site: www.lexusgabriel.com

Rev.: $49,650,000
Emp.: 105
Business Description:
New & Used Car Dealers
S.I.C.: 5511
N.A.I.C.S.: 441110
Personnel:
Fadi Habre *(Gen Mgr)*

1855 SA

10 rue des Moulins
75001 Paris, France
Tel.: (33) 142611855
Fax: (33) 142611831
E-Mail: contact@1855.com
Web Site: www.1855.com
AL185—(EUR)
Sales Range: $10-24.9 Million
Emp.: 40
Business Description:
Wine Producer & E-Commerce Retailer
S.I.C.: 2084
N.A.I.C.S.: 312130
Personnel:
Emeric Sauty de Chalon *(Chm, Pres & CEO)*

1NKEMIA IUCT GROUP S.A.

Calle Alvarez de Castro 63
Mollet de Vales, 08100 Barcelona, Spain
Tel.: (34) 935793432
Web Site: www.inkemia.com
IKM—(MAD)
Business Description:
Biopharmaceutical Mfr
S.I.C.: 2834
N.A.I.C.S.: 325412
Personnel:
Josep Castells Boliart *(Chm)*

1PM PLC

15 St James Parade
Bath, BA1 1UL, United Kingdom
Tel.: (44) 8449670944
Fax: (44) 8444432779
E-Mail: support@1pm.co.uk
Web Site: www.1pm.co.uk
OPM—(LSE)
Rev.: $4,906,241
Assets: $20,457,132
Liabilities: $13,249,523
Net Worth: $7,207,610
Earnings: $952,419
Emp.: 11
Fiscal Year-end: 05/31/13
Business Description:
Finance Services
S.I.C.: 6141
N.A.I.C.S.: 522291
Personnel:
Maria-Louise Hampton *(CEO)*
Rodney O. Channon *(Sec)*
Board of Directors:
Ian Smith
Rodney O. Channon
Maria-Louise Hampton
Ronald Russell
Helen M. Walker
Legal Counsel:
Withy King
James Street West Green Park
Bath, BA1 2BT, United Kingdom
Roxburgh Milkins LLP
Merchants House Wapping Road
Bristol, BS1 4RW, United Kingdom

1ST HOLDINGS, INC.

14th floor Shibuya Infoss Tower 20-1 Sakuragaoka-cho
Shibuya, Tokyo, 150-0031, Japan
Tel.: (81) 359627400
Fax: (81) 359627401
Web Site: www.1st-hd.com
Sls.: $141,548,000
Assets: $157,586,000
Liabilities: $87,846,000
Net Worth: $69,740,000
Earnings: $21,142,000
Emp.: 71
Fiscal Year-end: 02/28/13
Business Description:
Holding Company; Software Developer
S.I.C.: 6719
N.A.I.C.S.: 551112
Personnel:
Hiroyuki Uchino *(Pres & CEO)*
Shigeyoshi Fukuhara *(CFO)*
Yoshihiko Inami *(Corp Officer)*
Kaoru Kojima *(Corp Officer)*
Kazuo Nimura *(Corp Officer)*
Satoshi Okuda *(Corp Officer)*
Board of Directors:
Yuichi Kimura
Jun Tanaka
Hiroyuki Uchino

1ST RED AG

Caffamacherreihe 8
20355 Hamburg, Germany
Tel.: (49) 40 35 61 3 1979
Fax: (49) 40 35 61 3 2710
E-Mail: info@1st-red.com
Web Site: www.1st-red.com
Year Founded: 1911
SXL—(DEU)
Rev.: $3,500,042
Assets: $68,923,904
Liabilities: $54,116,034
Net Worth: $14,807,870
Earnings: $3,096,191
Emp.: 1
Fiscal Year-end: 12/31/12
Business Description:
Real Estate Management Services
S.I.C.: 6531
N.A.I.C.S.: 531390
Personnel:
Bernhard Garbe *(Chm-Supervisory Bd)*
Christopher Garbe *(Deputy Chm-Supervisory Bd)*
Alexander Garbe *(Member-Exec Bd)*
Supervisory Board of Directors:
Bernhard Garbe
Christopher Garbe
Heiko Hecht

2-K PURCHASING CENTRE INC

61A Victoria Rd S
Guelph, ON, N1E 5P7, Canada
Tel.: (519) 763-4157
Fax: (519) 763-1284
Year Founded: 1995
Rev.: $16,000,000
Emp.: 6
Business Description:
Safety Equipment & Clothing
S.I.C.: 5099
N.A.I.C.S.: 423990
Personnel:
Karl Gortmaker *(Pres)*

2 UP GAMING PLC

439 King Street
Melbourne, VIC, 3003, Australia
Tel.: (61) 3 9329 3994
E-Mail: enquiries@2up.com
Web Site: www.2up.com
Year Founded: 2011
2GM—(DEU)
Business Description:
Online Gaming
S.I.C.: 7999
N.A.I.C.S.: 713290
Personnel:
Marino Robert Sussich *(Chm & CEO)*
Board of Directors:
Marino Robert Sussich
Peter Bentley
Richard Walker

20/20 TECHNOLOGY

(See Under Tryzens)

20 MICRONS LIMITED

307/308 Arundeep Complex Race Course
Baroda, Gujarat, 390 007, India
Tel.: (91) 2653057000
Fax: (91) 2652333755
E-Mail: enquiry@20microns.com
Web Site: www.20microns.com
533022—(BOM NSE)
Emp.: 600
Business Description:
White Minerals Producer
S.I.C.: 3299
N.A.I.C.S.: 327999
Personnel:
Chandresh S. Parikh *(Chm & Mng Dir)*
Subsidiary:

20 Microns Nano Minerals Ltd **(1)**
9 - 10 GIDC
Waghodia, Vadodara, Gujarat, 391760, India
Tel.: (91) 2668 264076
Fax: (91) 2668 262447
E-Mail: info@20nano.com
Web Site: www.20nano.com
Emp.: 60
Soft Mineral Mining Services
S.I.C.: 1459
N.A.I.C.S.: 212325
Chandresh S. Parikh *(Chm & Mng Dir)*
Atil C. Parikh *(Mng Dir)*
Rajesh C. Parikh *(Mng Dir)*

20 VIC MANAGEMENT INC.

One Queen St E Ste 300
PO Box 88
Toronto, ON, M5C 2W5, Canada
Tel.: (416) 955-0595
Fax: (416) 955-0569
Web Site: www.20vic.com
Year Founded: 1995
Rev.: $52,584,400
Emp.: 750
Business Description:
Real Estate Management
S.I.C.: 6513
N.A.I.C.S.: 531110
Personnel:
Chris Innes *(VP-Bus Unit-GTA Industrial Properties)*

208946 HOLDINGS LTD

(d/b/a GEM Resource Surveys)
1512 Meridian Road NE
Calgary, AB, T2A 2N9, Canada
Tel.: (403) 276-2919
Fax: (403) 276-2918
Web Site: www.gemresource.ab.ca
Year Founded: 1978
Rev.: $13,590,218
Emp.: 25
Business Description:
Geophysical Surveying Services
S.I.C.: 8713
N.A.I.C.S.: 541360
Personnel:
Garry Murphy *(Pres)*

21 INVESTIMENTI SOCIETA' DI GESTIONE DEL RISPARMIO S.P.A.

(d/b/a 21 Investimenti Group)
Via G Felissent 90
31100 Treviso, Italy
Tel.: (39) 0422316611
Fax: (39) 0 422 316600
E-Mail: info@21investimenti.it
Web Site: www.21investimenti.com
Year Founded: 1992
Business Description:
Investment Holding Company
S.I.C.: 6719
N.A.I.C.S.: 551112
Personnel:
Alessandro Benetton *(Mng Partner)*
Gerard Pluvinet *(Mng Partner)*
Cedric Abitbol *(Mng Partner)*
Francois Barbier *(Mng Partner)*
Henry Huyghues Despointes *(Mng Partner)*
Dino Furlan *(Mng Partner)*
Marco Monis *(Mng Partner)*
Stefano Tanzi *(Mng Partner)*
Subsidiary:

21 Partners S.p.A. **(1)**
Viale G Felissent 90
31100 Treviso, Italy IT
Tel.: (39) 422316611 (100%)
Fax: (39) 0422316777
E-Mail: info@21investimenti.it
Web Site: www.21investimenti.it
Emp.: 20
Private Equity Firm
S.I.C.: 6211
N.A.I.C.S.: 523999
Alessandro Benetton *(Founder & Mng Partner)*
Dino Furlan *(Mng Partner)*
Marco Monis *(Mng Partner)*
Stefano Tanzi *(Mng Partner)*
Giovanni Bonandini *(Principal)*
Matteo Chieregato *(Principal)*
Cristina David *(Principal-Fin & Investors Mgmt)*
Andrea Mazzucato *(Principal)*
Non-U.S. Subsidiary:

21 Centrale Partners **(1)**
9 Ave Hoche
F-75008 Paris, France FR
Tel.: (33) 156883300
Fax: (33) 156883320
E-Mail: info@21centralepartners.com
Web Site: www.21centralepartners.com
Private Equity Firm
S.I.C.: 6211
N.A.I.C.S.: 523999
Gerard Pluvinet *(Founder & Mng Partner)*
Cedric Abitbol *(Mng Partner)*
Francois Barbier *(Mng Partner)*
Stephane Perriquet *(Mng Partner)*
Henry Huyghues Despointes *(Sr Partner)*
Jacques Rossignol *(Partner)*
Eustache Besancon *(Principal)*
Francois Tranie *(Principal)*

Holding:

Digital Virgo **(2)**
88 rue Paul Bert
69446 Lyon, Cedex, France (63.61%)
Tel.: (33) 437482300
Fax: (33) 437482308
E-Mail: virgo-info@digitalvirgo.com
Web Site: www.digitalvirgo.com
Sales Range: $200-249.9 Million
Emp.: 400
Mobile Phone & Internet Multimedia Services
S.I.C.: 7372
N.A.I.C.S.: 511210
Gerard Pluvinet *(Chm-Supervisory Bd)*
Eric Peyre *(Pres)*
Manuel Cruz *(CEO)*
Laurent Radix *(Sec)*

Subsidiaries:

Jet Media SAS **(3)**
88 Rue Paul Dert
69003 Lyon, France
Tel.: (33) 437482300
E-Mail: regie-jetmedia@jetmultimedia.fr
Web Site: www.jetmedia.fr
Emp.: 50

21 Investimenti Societa' di Gestione del Risparmio S.p.A.—(Continued)

Media Buyer
S.I.C.: 7319
N.A.I.C.S.: 541830
Laurent Radix *(Pres)*

MEDIAPLAZZA.com SAS (3)
86 avenue des Ternes
75017 Paris, France FR
Tel.: (33) 1 56 47 57 56
Fax: (33) 1 56 47 57 58
Web Site: www.mediaplazza.com
Mobile Telephone Multimedia Services
S.I.C.: 7372
N.A.I.C.S.: 511210
Cyrille Rossetto *(CEO)*

Oxone Technologies SAS (3)
11 Avenue Victor Hugo
38170 Seyssinet-Pariset, France
Tel.: (33) 476843232
Fax: (33) 476098705
Web Site: www.oxone.fr
Emp.: 11
Telecommunications Hosting Services
S.I.C.: 4899
N.A.I.C.S.: 517919

Non-U.S. Subsidiaries:

Avantis SA (3)
Ul Krlewska 16
00 103 Warsaw, Poland
Tel.: (48) 223121000
Fax: (48) 22 312 1001
Web Site: www.avantis.pl
Mobile Phone Multimedia Services
S.I.C.: 7372
N.A.I.C.S.: 511210
Piotr Kisiel *(Chm)*

Jet Multimedia Espana SA (3)
Parque Empresarial Cristalia Via de los Poblados
n3 Edificio 5 Planta 4, 28033 Madrid, Spain
Tel.: (34) 902 01 02 01
Fax: (34) 902 01 00 00
E-Mail: comercial@jetmultimedia.es
Web Site: www.jetmultimedia.es
Mobile Telecommunications Services
S.I.C.: 4812
N.A.I.C.S.: 517210

Non-U.S. Subsidiary:

Jet Multimedia Argentina SA (4)
Juan B Justo 637 7
CABA, Buenos Aires, C1001AFB, Argentina
Tel.: (54) 41381600
Fax: (54) 41381600
Web Site: www.jetmultimedia.com.ar
Mobile Telephone Multimedia Services
S.I.C.: 7372
N.A.I.C.S.: 511210

Jet Multimedia Maroc S.A.R.L. (3)
11 rue Kadi Ilyass
Quartier Maarif, Casablanca, Morocco
Tel.: (212) 22 77 93 50
E-Mail: contact@jetmultimedia.ma
Web Site: www.jetmultimedia.ma
Mobile Telecommunications Services
S.I.C.: 4812
N.A.I.C.S.: 517210

Jet Multimedia Tunisie SA (3)
Rue du lac Turkana
Les berges du lac de Tunis, 1053 Tunis, Tunisia
Tel.: (216) 71964973
Fax: (216) 71960971
E-Mail: contact@jetmultimedia.com.tn
Web Site: www.jetmultimedia.com.tn
Emp.: 12
Mobile Telecommunications Services
S.I.C.: 4812
N.A.I.C.S.: 517210

21ST CENTURY TECHNOLOGY PLC

Units 3 & 4 ZK Park 23 Commerce Way
Croydon, CR0 4ZS, United Kingdom
Tel.: (44) 844 871 7990
Fax: (44) 870 160 1748
Web Site: www.21stplc.com
C21—(LSE)
Rev.: $22,151,122
Assets: $17,855,453
Liabilities: $5,224,292
Net Worth: $12,631,161
Earnings: $2,128,883
Emp.: 66
Fiscal Year-end: 12/31/12

Business Description:
Auto Parts & Security Products Sales
S.I.C.: 5013
N.A.I.C.S.: 423120

Personnel:
Mark W. Elliott *(Chm)*
Russ Singleton *(CEO)*

Board of Directors:
Mark W. Elliott
James Stuart Cumming

Legal Counsel:
Ashurst
Broadwalk House 5 Appold Street
London, United Kingdom

21VIANET GROUP, INC.

M5 1 Jiuxianqiao East Road
Chaoyang District, Beijing, 100016, China
Tel.: (86) 1084562121
Fax: (86) 1084564234
Web Site: www.21vianet.com
Year Founded: 1999
VNET—(NASDAQ)
Rev.: $242,112,498
Assets: $472,883,583
Liabilities: $172,767,484
Net Worth: $300,116,099
Earnings: $9,158,656
Emp.: 1,070
Fiscal Year-end: 12/31/12

Business Description:
Internet Data Center Services
S.I.C.: 7379
N.A.I.C.S.: 518210

Personnel:
Joshua Sheng Chen *(Co-Founder, Chm & CEO)*
Jun Zhang *(Co-Founder & COO)*
Frank Meng *(Pres)*
Shang-Wen Hsiao *(CFO)*
Wing-Dar Ker *(Pres-Microsoft Cloud Ops)*
Philip Lin *(Exec VP-Strategic & Bus Dev)*

Board of Directors:
Joshua Sheng Chen
Hongwei Jenny Lee
Zhonghe Tai
Yoshihisa Ueno
Terry Wang

24/7 GAMING GROUP HOLDINGS PLC

World Trade Centre B-Tower 5th Floor Strawinskylaan 527
1077 XX Amsterdam, Netherlands
Tel.: (31) 20 676 0304
Web Site: www.247gaminggroup.com
247—(AIM)

Business Description:
Holding Company; Gaming & Entertainment Media Publisher
N.A.I.C.S.: 551112

Personnel:
David Carr Mathewson *(Chm)*
Rogier Willem Smit *(COO)*

Board of Directors:
David Carr Mathewson
Marcel Wilhelmus Johannes Noordeloos
Rogier Willem Smit

Non-U.S. Subsidiary:

Playlogic Games B.V. (1)
World Trade Centre B-Tower 5th Floor
Strawinskylaan 527
1077 XX Amsterdam, Netherlands NL
Tel.: (31) 20 676 0304
Fax: (31) 20 673 1713
E-Mail: info@playlogicgames.com
Web Site: www.playlogicgames.com
Gaming & Entertainment Media Publisher
S.I.C.: 7372
N.A.I.C.S.: 511210
Rogier Willem Smit *(Founder & COO)*

24 IANUARIE S.A.

18 G-ral I Dragalina Street
Ploiesti, Romania 100157
Tel.: (40) 244521956
Fax: (40) 244510325
E-Mail: commercial@24january.ro
Web Site: www.24january.ro
IANY—(BUC)
Rev.: $9,835,163
Assets: $14,378,223
Liabilities: $5,175,064
Net Worth: $9,203,159
Earnings: $102,058
Emp.: 329
Fiscal Year-end: 12/31/12

Business Description:
Ferrous & Metallurgic Equipment Mfr
S.I.C.: 3399
N.A.I.C.S.: 331110

Personnel:
Ion Maistru *(Mng Dir)*

24 MOBILE ADVERTISING SOLUTIONS AB

(d/b/a 24 MAS)
Hastholmsvagen 28 5th Floor
131 30 Nacka, Sweden
Tel.: (46) 8 535 24 100
Fax: (46) 8 535 24 199
E-Mail: ir@24mas.com
Web Site: www.24mas.com

Business Description:
Mobile Application Developers
S.I.C.: 7372
N.A.I.C.S.: 511210

Personnel:
Tero Turunen *(CEO)*

Non-U.S. Subsidiary:

Liquid Air Lab GmbH (1)
Vaihinger Markt 28
70563 Stuttgart, Germany
Tel.: (49) 711 8494 78 30
Fax: (49) 711 508 90 83
Web Site: www.liquidairlab.com
Emp.: 18
Applications Developer for Mobile Advertising
S.I.C.: 7372
N.A.I.C.S.: 511210
Mikko Linnamaki *(Founder & CEO)*

2639-1862 QUEBEC, INC.

(d/b/a Wickham Hardwood Flooring)
1031 7th rang
Wickham, QC, J0C 1S0, Canada
Tel.: (819) 398-6303
Fax: (819) 398-5355
Toll Free: (888) 494-2542
Web Site: www.plancherswickham.com
Year Founded: 1989
Rev.: $11,000,000
Emp.: 95

Business Description:
Hardwood Flooring Products Mfr & Distr
S.I.C.: 1752
N.A.I.C.S.: 238330

Personnel:
Jean-Pierre Nittolo *(Pres)*

2ERGO GROUP PLC

2nd Floor Digital World Centre 1
Lowry Plaza The Quays
Salford, Manchester, M50 3UB, United Kingdom
Tel.: (44) 1618744222
Fax: (44) 1618744233
E-Mail: info@2ergo.com
Web Site: www.2ergo.com
RGO—(AIM)
Rev.: $5,849,930
Assets: $10,397,292
Liabilities: $2,374,198
Net Worth: $8,023,094
Earnings: ($7,705,759)
Emp.: 67
Fiscal Year-end: 08/31/13

Business Description:
Software Developer
S.I.C.: 7372
N.A.I.C.S.: 511210

Personnel:
Ian Smith *(Chm)*
James Esson *(Sec)*

Board of Directors:
Ian Smith
Jill Colligan
Simon Duckworth
Neale S. Graham

Legal Counsel:
Addleshaw Goddard LLP
100 Barbirolli Square
Manchester, United Kingdom

Subsidiaries:

2ergo Ltd. (1)
Digital World Ctr 4th Fl 1 Lowry Plz
The Quays, Salford, Manchester, M50 3UB, United Kingdom
Tel.: (44) 1618744222
Fax: (44) 1618744233
E-Mail: uk@2ergo.com
Web Site: www.2ergo.com
Emp.: 70
Mobile Messaging Solutions
S.I.C.: 4812
N.A.I.C.S.: 517210
Neale S. Graham *(Co-CEO)*
Barry Sharples *(Co-CEO)*

Activemedia Technologies Limited (1)
19 Bolsover St
Fitzrovia Dist, London, W1W 5NA, United Kingdom
Tel.: (44) 2078860820
Fax: (44) 2078860822
E-Mail: uk@2ergo.com
Web Site: www.activemediatech.com
Emp.: 30
Cellular Ticketing & Couponing Services
S.I.C.: 4812
N.A.I.C.S.: 517210
Ariya Priyasantha *(Mng Dir)*

Non-U.S. Subsidiary:

Active Media Technologies Pvt Limited (2)
A-61 Sector 57
Noida, Uttar Pradesh, 201301, India
Tel.: (91) 1204078000
Fax: (91) 1204078080
E-Mail: enquiries@activemediatech.com
Mobile Marketing Services
S.I.C.: 4812
N.A.I.C.S.: 517210
Raj Singh *(Mng Dir)*

Broca Communications Limited (1)
Digital World Ctr 4th Fl 1 Lowry Plz The Quays
Salford, Manchester, M50 3UB, United Kingdom
Tel.: (44) 7824 371 931
Fax: (44) 845 0066662
Secure Mobile Messaging Development Services
S.I.C.: 4812
N.A.I.C.S.: 517210

2G ENERGY AG

Benzstr 3
Heek, 48619 Borken, Germany
Tel.: (49) 2568 93 47 0
Fax: (49) 2568 93 47 15
E-Mail: info@2-g.de

Web Site: www.2-g.de
2GB—(DEU)
Business Description:
Heat & Power Plant Construction Services
S.I.C.: 1629
N.A.I.C.S.: 237990
Personnel:
Lukas Lenz *(Chm)*
Gerhard Temminghoff *(Deputy Chm)*
Christian Grotholt *(CEO)*
Peter J. Bergsteiner *(CFO)*
Ludger Holtkamp *(COO)*
Board of Directors:
Lukas Lenz
Wiebe Hofstra
Gerhard Temminghoff

U.S. Subsidiary:

2G CENERGY Power Systems Technologies Inc. (1)
151 College Drive Ste 15
Orange Park, FL 32065
Tel.: (904) 579-3217
Fax: (904) 406-8727
E-Mail: info@2g-cenergy.com
Web Site: www.2g-cenergy.com
Emp.: 300
Power Plant Construction & Generation Services
S.I.C.: 1629
N.A.I.C.S.: 237990
Michael J. Turwitt *(Pres & CEO)*

2GO GROUP INC.
15th Floor Times Plaza Building
United Nations Avenue Corner Taft Avenue, Manila, 1000, Philippines
Tel.: (63) 2 554 8777
E-Mail: investor_relations@2go.com.ph
Web Site: www.2go.com.ph
2GO—(PHI)
Rev.: $336,116,091
Assets: $274,663,505
Liabilities: $203,162,305
Net Worth: $71,501,200
Earnings: ($9,458,381)
Emp.: 1,005
Fiscal Year-end: 12/31/12
Business Description:
Freight & Passenger Ship Transportation Services
S.I.C.: 4481
N.A.I.C.S.: 483112
Personnel:
Francis C. Chua *(Chm)*
Sulficio O. Tagud, Jr. *(Pres & CEO)*
Jeremias E. Cruzabra *(CFO, Corp Info Officer & Treas)*
Zenaida R. Cabral *(Chief Corp Svcs Officer & Exec VP)*
Alejandro M. Diaz de Rivera *(Pres-2GO Logistics Inc)*
Fred S. Pajo *(Exec VP & COO-NENACO)*
Amado R. Santiago, III *(Sec)*
Jose Manuel L. Mapa *(Exec VP-Freight Sls)*
Norissa Eileen L. Ridgwell *(Sr VP-HR)*
Klaus Schroeder *(Sr VP)*
Board of Directors:
Francis C. Chua
Raul Ch. Rabe
Jeremias E. Cruzabra
Patrick Ip
Monico V. Jacob
Geoffrey M. Seeto
Sulficio O. Tagud, Jr.
Mark E. Williams
Nelson T. Yap
Transfer Agent:
Securities Transfer Services, Inc.
Ground Floor Benpres Building Exchange Road corner Meralco Avenue
Pasig, Philippines

Subsidiaries:

2GO Express, Inc. (1)
General Aviation Area
Manila Domestic Airport, Pasay, Philippines
Tel.: (63) 2 855 1776
Air Transportation Services
S.I.C.: 4581
N.A.I.C.S.: 488190

2GO Travel, Inc. (1)
Pier 4 North Reclamation Area
Cebu, Philippines
Tel.: (63) 32 233 7000
Web Site: www.supercat.com.ph
Passenger Transportation Services
S.I.C.: 4481
N.A.I.C.S.: 483112

MCC Transport Philippines, Inc. (1)
9th Floor One E-com Center Harbor Drive corner Sun SM Bay City, 1300 Pasay, Metro Manila, Philippines
Tel.: (63) 2 859 3401
Freight Transportation Arrangement
S.I.C.: 4731
N.A.I.C.S.: 488510

Negros Navigation Co., Inc. (1)
15 Times Plaza Building United Nations Ave corner Taft Ave
Ermita, Manila, 1000, Philippines
Tel.: (63) 2 554 8777
Shipping Services
S.I.C.: 4731
N.A.I.C.S.: 488510

ScanAsia Overseas, Inc. (1)
2nd Floor Priscilla 100 Building
2297 Don Chino Roces Avenue, 2297
Makati, Philippines
Tel.: (63) 2 815 0123
Fax: (63) 2 818 1467
Web Site: www.scanasia.ph
Food Products Distr
S.I.C.: 2099
N.A.I.C.S.: 311991

2S METAL PUBLIC COMPANY LIMITED
(Formerly Southern Steel Public Company Limited)
8/5 Moo 14 Tha-change
Bangklam District, Songkhla, 90110, Thailand
Tel.: (66) 74457161
Fax: (66) 74457165
Web Site: www.ss.co.th
2S—(THA)
Rev.: $134,461,418
Assets: $41,511,890
Liabilities: $20,759,258
Net Worth: $20,752,632
Earnings: $1,742,638
Emp.: 217
Fiscal Year-end: 12/31/12
Business Description:
Steel Mfr & Distr
S.I.C.: 3399
N.A.I.C.S.: 331110
Personnel:
Amnouy Phetsiri *(Chm)*

2X1 HOLDING CAPE MIDIA SHIPYARD
Incinta Port Nr 2
Constanta, Romania
Tel.: (40) 241 255633
Fax: (40) 241 255844
Web Site: www.2x1midiashipyard.ro
SNMN—(BUC)
Business Description:
Ship Building & Repairing Services
S.I.C.: 3731
N.A.I.C.S.: 336611
Personnel:
Aurelian Dabija *(Pres)*
Board of Directors:
Aurelian Dabija
Iulian Radu

3-D MATRIX, LTD.
3-2-4 6F Kojimachi Chiyoda-ku
Tokyo, 102-0083, Japan
Tel.: (81) 3 35113440
E-Mail: info@3d-matrix.co.jp
Web Site: www.3d-matrix.co.jp
Year Founded: 2004
7777—(JAS)
Sales Range: $1-9.9 Million
Emp.: 20
Business Description:
Medical Device Mfr
S.I.C.: 3841
N.A.I.C.S.: 339112
Personnel:
Keiji Nagano *(Chm & Dir-Rep)*
Marc G. Rioult *(Mng Dir)*
Board of Directors:
Keiji Nagano
John W. Maki
Shuguang Zhang

U.S. Subsidiary:

3-D Matrix, Inc. (1)
200 West St
Waltham, MA 02451
Tel.: (781) 373-9020
Fax: (877) 430-9595
E-Mail: info@puramatrix.com
Web Site: www.puramatrix.com
Bio Pharmaceutical Product Mfr
S.I.C.: 2834
N.A.I.C.S.: 325412
Marc G. Rioult *(Mng Dir)*

Non-U.S. Subsidiaries:

3-D Matrix Asia Pte. Ltd. (1)
1 Fullerton Road #02-01 One Fullerton
Singapore, 049213, Singapore
Tel.: (65) 6408 3858
Medical Device Mfr
S.I.C.: 3845
N.A.I.C.S.: 334510

3-D Matrix Europe SAS (1)
11 Chemin des Petites Brosses
Caluire-et-Cuire, 69300 Lyon, France
Tel.: (33) 4 72 13 05 20
Web Site: www.puramatrix.fr
Bio Pharmaceutical Product Mfr
S.I.C.: 2834
N.A.I.C.S.: 325412

3041518 NOVA SCOTIA LIMITED
(d/b/a Steele Ford Lincoln)
3773 Windsor Street
Halifax, NS, B3K5M2, Canada
Tel.: (902) 453-1130
E-Mail: inquiry@steeleford.com
Web Site: www.steelefordlincoln.dealerconnection.com
Rev.: $63,122,034
Emp.: 125
Business Description:
New & Used Car Dealers
S.I.C.: 5511
N.A.I.C.S.: 441110
Personnel:
Jim MacLellan *(Controller)*

32RED PLC
942 Europort
Gibraltar, Gibraltar
Tel.: (350) 20049357
Fax: (350) 20047408
Web Site: www.32redplc.com
TTR—(LSE)
Rev.: $50,784,763
Assets: $10,638,115
Liabilities: $4,288,798
Net Worth: $6,349,317
Earnings: $3,123,546
Emp.: 47
Fiscal Year-end: 12/31/12
Business Description:
Travel & Leisure Industry
S.I.C.: 7999
N.A.I.C.S.: 713290
Personnel:
Edward John Ware *(CEO)*
Jonathan Edward Hale *(Sec & Dir-Fin)*
Board of Directors:
David Thomas Fish
Matthew Booth
David Bowen
Jonathan Edward Hale
Patrick Joseph Harrison
John Lyndon Hodgson
Edward John Ware
Legal Counsel:
McDermott Will & Emery UK LLP
7 Bishopsgate
London, United Kingdom
Hodgson Bilton
Ground Floor 143 Main Street
Gibraltar, Gibraltar

330542 BC LTD
(d/b/a Regency Chrysler)
259 McLean St
Quesnel, BC, V2J 2N8, Canada
Tel.: (250) 992-9293
Fax: (250) 992-8275
Toll Free: (888) 726-4947
E-Mail: regencychrysler@aslinternet.com
Web Site: www.regencychrysler.com
Year Founded: 1987
Rev.: $49,464,430
Emp.: 100
Business Description:
New & Used Car Dealers
S.I.C.: 5511
N.A.I.C.S.: 441110
Personnel:
Doug Beckman *(Owner)*

3427951 CANADA INC
(d/b/a G-TEK)
180 Boul Bellerose West
Laval, QC, H7L 6A2, Canada
Tel.: (450) 628-4835
Fax: (450) 963-4835
E-Mail: administration@gtek.ca
Web Site: www.gtek.ca
Year Founded: 1997
Sales Range: $10-24.9 Million
Emp.: 100
Business Description:
Pipelines, Sewer & Utility Lines Services
S.I.C.: 1623
N.A.I.C.S.: 237110
Personnel:
Stephane Fortin *(Pres)*

3463192 CANADA INC
(d/b/a Mega Automotible)
1261 St Joseph Blvd North
Gatineau, QC, J8Z-3J6, Canada
Tel.: (819) 770-2277
Fax: (819) 770-6342
Web Site: www.megaautomobile.com
Year Founded: 1998
Rev.: $24,100,000
Emp.: 45
Business Description:
New Car Dealers
S.I.C.: 5511
N.A.I.C.S.: 441110
Personnel:
Nader Dormani *(Pres)*

360 CAPITAL FINANCIAL SERVICES GROUP INC.
2600-4720 Kingsway
Burnaby, BC, V5H 4N2, Canada
Tel.: (778) 374-1808
E-Mail: o@globalmga.com
Year Founded: 2013

360 Capital Financial Services Group Inc.—(Continued)

TSZ—(CNSX)
Business Description:
Investment Services
S.I.C.: 6211
N.A.I.C.S.: 523999
Personnel:
John Gan *(CEO)*
Bang Chiem *(CFO)*

360 CAPITAL GROUP LIMITED

(Formerly Trafalgar Corporate Group Limited)
Level 8 56 Pitt Street
Sydney, NSW, 2000, Australia
Tel.: (61) 2 8405 8860
Fax: (61) 2 9238 0354
Web Site: www.360capital.com.au
TGP—(ASX)
Rev.: $10,564,810
Assets: $65,431,375
Liabilities: $13,470,185
Net Worth: $51,961,190
Earnings: ($6,586,072)
Fiscal Year-end: 06/30/13
Business Description:
Real Estate Investment & Fund Management Services
S.I.C.: 6531
N.A.I.C.S.: 531390
Personnel:
David M. van Aanholt *(Chm)*
Tony R. Pitt *(Mng Dir)*
Emma Shipley *(CFO)*
Ben James *(Chief Investment Officer)*
Alan Sutton *(Sec)*
Board of Directors:
David M. van Aanholt
William J. Ballhausen
Graham E. Lenzner
Andrew G. Moffat
Tony R. Pitt
Subsidiary:

Trafalgar Corporate Pty. Limited **(1)**
Level 4 111 Harrington Street
Grosvenor Place, Sydney, NSW, 2000, Australia AU
Tel.: (61) 2 9252 4211 (100%)
Fax: (61) 2 9252 1585
Real Estate Investment & Fund Management Services
S.I.C.: 6531
N.A.I.C.S.: 531390

Subsidiary:

Trafalgar Managed Investments Limited **(2)**
Level 4 111 Harrington Street
Grosvenor Place, Sydney, NSW, 2000, Australia AU
Tel.: (61) 2 9252 4211 (100%)
Fax: (61) 2 9252 1585
Property Investment Management Services
S.I.C.: 6282
N.A.I.C.S.: 523920

360 VOX CORPORATION

2001 rue University bureau 400
Montreal, QC, H3A 2A6, Canada
Tel.: (514) 987-6452
Fax: (514) 987-6456
E-Mail: info@360vox.com
Web Site: www.360vox.com
LC9—(DEU TSXV)
Rev.: $14,806,301
Assets: $40,096,206
Liabilities: $20,984,332
Net Worth: $19,111,874
Earnings: ($10,422,145)
Fiscal Year-end: 12/31/12
Business Description:
Real Estate Development Services
S.I.C.: 6531
N.A.I.C.S.: 531390
Personnel:
Brahm Gelfand *(Chm)*
Robin Conners *(Pres & CEO)*
Colin Yee *(CFO)*
Ross McCredie *(COO)*
Robert Jerome *(Pres-Dev)*
Steve Laver *(Exec VP-Investments)*
Board of Directors:
Brahm Gelfand
Arnold Cader
Robin Conners
Ross McCredie
David Oliver
Ronald Singer
Transfer Agent:
Computershare Trust Company
510 Burrard Street
Vancouver, BC, Canada

361 DEGREES INTERNATIONAL LIMITED

361 Building Huli High-technology Park
Xiamen, Fujian, 361009, China
Tel.: (86) 592 2977609
Fax: (86) 592 2977613
E-Mail: 361sport@361sport.com
Web Site: www.361sport.com
1361—(HKG OTC)
Sls.: $786,399,315
Assets: $1,145,659,559
Liabilities: $394,225,511
Net Worth: $751,434,048
Earnings: $113,614,127
Emp.: 8,883
Fiscal Year-end: 12/31/12
Business Description:
Sporting Goods Mfr, Retailer & Distr
S.I.C.: 3949
N.A.I.C.S.: 339920
Personnel:
Huihuang Ding *(Chm)*
Wuhao Ding *(Pres)*
Mun Duen Choi *(CFO & Sec)*
Board of Directors:
Huihuang Ding
Huirong Ding
Wuhao Ding
Xianhong Sun
Yung Kwok Tsui
Jiabi Wang
Man Sing Yan

Computershare Hong Kong Investor Services Limited
Shops 1712-1716 17th Floor Hopewell Centre
183 Queens Road East
Wanchai, China (Hong Kong)
Transfer Agent:
Royal Bank of Canada Trust Company (Cayman) Limited
4th Floor Royal Bank House 24 Shedden Road
Georgetown, Cayman Islands

3617581 CANADA INC

(d/b/a Promenade Kia)
346 Boul Greber
Gatineau, QC, J8T 5R6, Canada
Tel.: (819) 561-6669
Fax: (819) 561-8771
Toll Free: (877) 524-5313
Web Site: www.promenadekia.com
Rev.: $11,051,669
Emp.: 25
Business Description:
New & Used Car Dealers
S.I.C.: 5511
N.A.I.C.S.: 441110
Personnel:
Vladimir Tolstoy *(Pres)*

365 HF

Sidumuli 28
108 Reykjavik, Iceland
Tel.: (354) 5999000
Fax: (354) 5999001
Web Site: www.365.is
Sales Range: $150-199.9 Million
Emp.: 1,500
Business Description:
Holding Company
S.I.C.: 6719
N.A.I.C.S.: 551112
Personnel:
Jon Asgeir Johannesson *(Chm)*
Ari Edwald *(CEO)*
Board of Directors:
Jon Asgeir Johannesson
Magnus Armann
Palmi Haraldsson
Thorsteinn Jonsson

3770818 CANADA INC

(d/b/a St-Jerome Chevrolet Buick GMC)
265 Rue John-F Kennedy
Saint-Jerome, QC, J7Y 4B5, Canada
Tel.: (450) 438-1203
Fax: (450) 438-8141
Toll Free: (877) 538-1203
E-Mail: reception@stjeromechevrolet.com
Web Site: www.stjeromechevrolet.com
Rev.: $12,665,134
Emp.: 75
Business Description:
New & Used Car Sales
S.I.C.: 5511
N.A.I.C.S.: 441110
Personnel:
Daniel Jarry *(Pres)*

3965546 CANADA INC

(d/b/a Novatek International)
4480 Cote De Liesse Suite 355
Montreal, QC, H4N 2R1, Canada
Tel.: (514) 668-2835
Fax: (514) 336-6537
Web Site: www.ntint.com
Year Founded: 1996
Rev.: $30,900,000
Emp.: 400
Business Description:
Software Development & Services
S.I.C.: 7372
N.A.I.C.S.: 511210
Personnel:
Parsa Famili *(Pres & CEO)*

3A FINANCE PLC

c/o 3A Finance AG
Schaffhauserstrasse 110
Optikon, CH-8152 Glattbrugg, Switzerland
Tel.: (41) 448104034
Fax: (41) 447326656
E-Mail: info@3a-finance.ch
Web Site: www.3a-finance.ch
3AM—(DEU)
Business Description:
Financial Investment Services
S.I.C.: 6211
N.A.I.C.S.: 523999
Personnel:
Daniel Bosshard *(CEO)*
Kacem Salah *(COO & Chief Sls Officer)*
Joseph Bourne *(Chief Strategic & Bus Dev Officer)*
Board of Directors:
Daniel Bosshard
Joseph Bourne
Subsidiary:

3A Finance AG **(1)**
Schaffhauserstrasse 110
8152 Opfikon, Switzerland
Tel.: (41) 448104034
Fax: (41) 448104035
E-Mail: info@3a-finance.ch
Web Site: www.3a-finance.ch
Financial Investment Services
S.I.C.: 6211
N.A.I.C.S.: 523999
Non-U.S. Subsidiary:

3A Finance Inc. **(1)**
96 Templegreen Dr N E
Calgary, AB, T1Y 4T9, Canada
Tel.: (403) 680-3949
Fax: (403) 285-4871
E-Mail: info@3a-finance.ch
Web Site: www.3af.3afinance.com
Financial Management Services
S.I.C.: 6211
N.A.I.C.S.: 523999

3D OIL LIMITED

Level 5 164 Finders Lane
Melbourne, VIC, 3000, Australia
Tel.: (61) 3 9650 9866
Fax: (61) 3 9639 1960
E-Mail: info@3doil.com.au
Web Site: www.3doil.com.au
Year Founded: 2003
TDO—(ASX)
Rev.: $105,773
Assets: $24,359,832
Liabilities: $1,227,069
Net Worth: $23,132,763
Earnings: ($2,118,699)
Emp.: 11
Fiscal Year-end: 06/30/13
Business Description:
Oil & Gas Production
S.I.C.: 1311
N.A.I.C.S.: 211111
Personnel:
Noel Newell *(CEO & Mng Dir)*
Melanie Jaye Leydin *(Sec)*
Board of Directors:
Campbell Horsfall
Philippa Kelly
Melanie Jaye Leydin
Noel Newell
Kenneth Pereira
Legal Counsel:
Baker & McKenzie
Level 19 181 William Street
Melbourne, Australia

3D RESOURCES LIMITED

Level 6 189 St Georges Terrace
Perth, WA, 6000, Australia
Mailing Address:
PO Box 7323
Perth, WA, 6831, Australia
Tel.: (61) 893205220
Fax: (61) 894816343
E-Mail: info@3dresources.com.au
Web Site: www.3dresources.com.au
DDD—(ASX)
Sales Range: Less than $1 Million
Business Description:
Mineral Exploration Services
S.I.C.: 1041
N.A.I.C.S.: 212221
Personnel:
Peter Mitchell *(Mng Dir)*
John J. Chegwidden *(Sec)*
Board of Directors:
Ian Hastings
John J. Chegwidden
Peter Mitchell
Legal Counsel:
Steinepreis Paganin
Level 4 The Read Buildings 16 Milligan Street
Perth, Australia

3D RESOURCES PLC

Prospect Business Centre
Technology Park
Dundee, DD2 1SW, United Kingdom
Tel.: (44) 1382598616
Fax: (44) 1382560918
E-Mail: info@3dresources.co.uk

Web Site: www.3dresources.co.uk
3DR—(AIM)
Sales Range: Less than $1 Million
Emp.: 18
Business Description:
Investment Services
S.I.C.: 6211
N.A.I.C.S.: 523999
Personnel:
Donald Strang *(Chm)*
Oliver Cooke *(CFO)*
Richard Whatley *(Pres-Sls & Mktg)*
Board of Directors:
Donald Strang
Oliver Cooke
Hamish Harris
Legal Counsel:
Marriott Harrison
Staple Court 11 Staple Inn Buildings
London, United Kingdom
Dougherty Quinn
The Chambers 5 Mount Pleasant
Douglas, Isle of Man

3I GROUP PLC

16 Palace Street
London, SW1E 5JD, United Kingdom
Tel.: (44) 20 7975 3131
Telex: 917844
Fax: (44) 20 7975 3232
E-Mail: ir@3igroup.com
Web Site: www.3i.com
Year Founded: 1945
III—(LSE)
Rev.: $862,292,340
Assets: $6,809,898,480
Liabilities: $2,176,261,620
Net Worth: $4,633,636,860
Earnings: $289,010,070
Emp.: 267
Fiscal Year-end: 03/31/13
Business Description:
Holding Company; Private Equity & Venture Capital Services
S.I.C.: 6719
N.A.I.C.S.: 551112
Personnel:
Simon Borrows *(CEO)*
Jeremy Ghose *(CEO/Mng Partner-3i Debt Mgmt)*
Menno Antal *(Mng Partner-Private Equity)*
Alan Giddins *(Mng Partner-Private Equity)*
Ben Loomes *(Co-Mng Partner-Infrastructure)*
Phil White *(Co-Mng Partner-Infrastructure)*
Kevin Dunn *(Gen Counsel, Sec & Head-HR)*
Board of Directors:
Adrian Montague
Jonathan Asquith
Simon Borrows
Alistair Cox
Richard Meddings
Martine Verluyten
Julia S. Wilson
Legal Counsel:
Slaughter & May
One Bunhill Row
London, EC1Y 8YY, United Kingdom
Tel.: (44) 20 7600 1200
Fax: (44) 20 7600 0289
Subsidiaries:

3i Debt Management Ltd. **(1)**
16 Palace Street
London, SW1E 5JD, United Kingdom
Tel.: (44) 2079753456
Fax: (44) 2079280058
Financial Investments; Debt Management
S.I.C.: 6099
N.A.I.C.S.: 522320
Jeremy Ghose *(CEO & Mng Partner)*
Andrew Bellis *(Mng Dir & Partner)*
Andrew Golding *(Partner)*
Peter Goody *(COO)*

Subsidiaries:

3i Debt Management Investments Limited **(2)**
Palace Street 16
SW1E 5JD London, United Kingdom
Tel.: (44) 2079283131
Fax: (44) 2079753232
Emp.: 150
Investment Management Services
S.I.C.: 6799
N.A.I.C.S.: 523920
Peter Goody *(COO)*

3i Investments plc **(1)**
16 Palace Street
London, SW1E 5JD, United Kingdom (100%)
Tel.: (44) 2079753456
Fax: (44) 2079280058
Web Site: www.3iplc.com
Emp.: 350
Investment Management Services
S.I.C.: 6282
N.A.I.C.S.: 523920

U.S. Subsidiaries:

3i Corporation **(2)**
400 Madison Ave 9th Floor
New York, NY 10017
Tel.: (212) 848-1400
Fax: (212) 848-1401
E-Mail:
Web Site: www.3i.com
Emp.: 20
Investment Management Services
S.I.C.: 6799
N.A.I.C.S.: 523920

Non-U.S. Subsidiaries:

3i Deutschland Gesellschaft fur Industriebeteiligungen mbH **(2)**
Bockenheimer Landstrasse 2/4
60323 Frankfurt am Main, Germany (100%)
Tel.: (49) 697100000
Fax: (49) 69710000113
E-Mail: infogermany@3i.com
Web Site: www.3i.com
Emp.: 55
Investment Management Services
S.I.C.: 6282
N.A.I.C.S.: 523920
Ulf von Haacke *(Partner & Mng Dir)*
Peter Wirtz *(Partner & Mng Dir)*

3i Gestion S.A. **(2)**
3 rue Paul Cezanne
75008 Paris, France (100%)
Tel.: (33) 173151100
Fax: (33) 173151124
E-Mail: paris@3i.com
Web Site: www.3i.com
Emp.: 30
Investment Management Services
S.I.C.: 6799
N.A.I.C.S.: 523920
Guy Zarzavhgjian *(Mng Partner-Ops Capabilities)*
Remi Carnimolla *(Partner)*

3i plc **(1)**
16 Palace St
London, SW1 E5JD, United Kingdom (100%)
Tel.: (44) 2079283131
Fax: (44) 2079280058
E-Mail: london@3i.com
Web Site: www.3i.com
Emp.: 200
Corporate Support & Administrative Services
S.I.C.: 7389
N.A.I.C.S.: 561499

Branches:

3i plc **(2)**
Trinity Pk Bicken Hill
B37 7ES Birmingham, United Kingdom (100%)
Tel.: (44) 1217823131
Fax: (44) 1217826161
Web Site: www.3i.com
Emp.: 100
Venture Capital
S.I.C.: 6799
N.A.I.C.S.: 523910

Subsidiaries:

3i Asia Pacific plc **(2)**
16 Palace St
London, SW1E 5JD, United Kingdom (100%)
Tel.: (44) 2079283131
Fax: (44) 2079280058
Web Site: www.3i.com
Emp.: 300
Investment Advisory Services
S.I.C.: 6282
N.A.I.C.S.: 523930
Joe Taylor *(Mng Partner)*
Cressida Hogg *(Mng Partner-Infrastructure)*
Jonathan Russell *(Partner & Global Head)*

Non-U.S. Branches:

3i Asia Pacific Ltd **(3)**
3 Temasek Ave # 22-03 Centenial Tower
Singapore, 039190, Singapore (100%)
Tel.: (65) 64383131
Fax: (65) 65362429
E-Mail: singapore@3i.com
Web Site: www.3i.com
Emp.: 8
Venture Capital
S.I.C.: 6799
N.A.I.C.S.: 523910
Samir Palod *(Mng Dir-India)*

3i Hong Kong **(3)**
26C Bank of China Tower 1 Garden Road
Central, China (Hong Kong)
Tel.: (852) 29018188
Fax: (852) 2537 7886
Web Site: www.3i.com
Venture Capital
S.I.C.: 6221
N.A.I.C.S.: 523130

3i Europe plc **(2)**
16 Palace St
London, SW1E5JD, United Kingdom (100%)
Tel.: (44) 2079283131
Fax: (44) 2079280058
Web Site: www.3i.com
Emp.: 370
Investment Advisory Services
S.I.C.: 6282
N.A.I.C.S.: 523930
Philip Yea *(Chm)*

Non-U.S. Branches:

3i Europe plc, Benelux **(3)**
Cornelis Schuytstraat 72
1071 JL Amsterdam, Netherlands (100%)
Tel.: (31) 203057444
Fax: (31) 203057455
E-Mail: amsterdam@3i.com
Web Site: www.3i.com
Emp.: 12
Venture Capital Services
S.I.C.: 6799
N.A.I.C.S.: 523910

3i Europe plc **(3)**
Avenida Diagonal 613 9th Floor
8028 Barcelona, Spain (100%)
Tel.: (34) 934391991
Fax: (34) 934393913
E-Mail: barcelona@31.com
Web Site: www.3i.com
Emp.: 4
Venture Capital
S.I.C.: 6799
N.A.I.C.S.: 523910
Agustin Pla Vila *(Partner)*

3i SGR **(3)**
Via Orefici 2
20123 Milan, Italy (100%)
Tel.: (39) 02880841
Fax: (39) 02720032
E-Mail: milan@3i.com
Web Site: www.3i.com
Emp.: 15
Venture Capital Business
S.I.C.: 6799
N.A.I.C.S.: 523910
Lorenzo Salieri *(Partner)*

3i Switzerland Limited **(3)**
Othmarstrasse 8
8008 Zurich, Switzerland (100%)
Tel.: (41) 12504400
Fax: (41) 12504410
E-Mail: switzerland@3i.com
Web Site: www.3i.com
Emp.: 10
Venture Capital
S.I.C.: 6221
N.A.I.C.S.: 523130

3i Nordic plc **(2)**
16 Palace Street
London, SW1E 5JD, United Kingdom UK
Tel.: (44) 2079283131 (100%)
Fax: (44) 2079280058
Web Site: www.3i.com
Emp.: 50
Investment Advisory Services
S.I.C.: 6282
N.A.I.C.S.: 523930
Philip Yea *(CEO)*

Non-U.S. Branches:

3i Sweden **(3)**
Bireer Garlscacal St 25
PO Box 7847
10399 Stockholm, Sweden (100%)
Tel.: (46) 850610100
Fax: (46) 850621100
E-Mail: stockholm@3i.com
Web Site: www.3i.com
Sls.: $88,388,104
Emp.: 12
Venture Capital
S.I.C.: 6221
N.A.I.C.S.: 523130
Mattias Eklund *(Mng Dir)*

Barclays Infrastructure Funds Management Limited **(1)**
10 The South Colonnade Canary Wharf
London, E14 4PU, United Kingdom
Tel.: (44) 20 7623 2323
Fax: (44) 20 3555 5029
Web Site: www.barclaysinfrastructurefunds.com
Fund Management Services
S.I.C.: 6282
N.A.I.C.S.: 523920
Christopher Elliott *(Mng Dir & Head-Infrastructure Investing)*
Andy Matthews *(Mng Dir)*
Robert McClatchey *(Mng Dir)*
Nigel Middleton *(Mng Dir)*

Gardens Pension Trustees Limited **(1)**
91 Finance House Waterloo Road
London, SE1 8XP, United Kingdom
Tel.: (44) 2079283131
Fax: (44) 2079280058
Pension Fund Trust Services
S.I.C.: 6371
N.A.I.C.S.: 525110

Holdings:

Bestinvest (Holdings) Limited **(1)**
6 Chesterfield Gardens
London, W1J 5BQ, United Kingdom UK
Tel.: (44) 2031 316 167
E-Mail: best@bestinvest.co.uk
Web Site: www.bestinvest.co.uk
Holding Company; Investment & Wealth Management Services
S.I.C.: 6719
N.A.I.C.S.: 551112
John Spiers *(Founder)*
Michael Covell *(Chm)*
Peter Howland *(Deputy Chm)*
Peter Hall *(CEO)*
Donald Reid *(COO)*
Gareth Lewis *(Chief Investment Officer)*

Subsidiary:

Bestinvest (Brokers) Limited **(2)**
6 Chesterfield Gardens
London, W1J 5BQ, United Kingdom UK
Tel.: (44) 2031 316 167
E-Mail: best@bestinvest.co.uk
Web Site: www.bestinvest.co.uk
Investment & Wealth Management Services
S.I.C.: 6799
N.A.I.C.S.: 523920
Peter Hall *(CEO)*
Donald Reid *(COO)*
Gareth Lewis *(Chief Investment Officer)*

Environmental Scientifics Group Ltd. **(1)**
(Formerly Inspicio Ltd.)

3i Group plc—(Continued)

ESG House Bretby Park Ashby Road
Burton-on-Trent, DE15 0YZ, United Kingdom
Tel.: (44) 1283 554400
E-Mail: sales@esg.co.uk
Web Site: www.esg.co.uk
Testing, Inspection & Compliance Services
S.I.C.: 8734
N.A.I.C.S.: 541380
Ian Sparks *(CEO)*

Subsidiary:

Environmental Services Group Ltd. (2)
Askern Rd
Carcroft, Doncaster, DN6 8DG, United Kingdom
Tel.: (44) 1302723456
Fax: (44) 1302725240
E-Mail: sm.doncaster@esg.co.uk
Web Site: www.esg.co.uk
Emp.: 900
Environmental Consulting Services
S.I.C.: 8999
N.A.I.C.S.: 541620
David Clave *(Mng Dir)*

Mayborn Group Limited (1)
Northumberland Business Park (West)
Dudley Lane, Cramlington, Northumberland, NE23 7RH, United Kingdom
Tel.: (44) 1912501864
Fax: (44) 1912501727
E-Mail: info@mayborngroup.com
Web Site: www.mayborngroup.com
Sales Range: $150-199.9 Million
Emp.: 1,602
Design, Mfr, Packaging & Distr of Baby Accessory Products to the Retail Trade
S.I.C.: 3089
N.A.I.C.S.: 326199
Paul Mason *(Chm)*
Steve Parkin *(CEO)*
Mark Stanworth *(CFO)*

Joint Venture:

Anglian Water Group Limited (1)
Anglian House Ambury Road
Huntingdon, Cambs, PE29 3NZ, United Kingdom JE
Tel.: (44) 1480323000
Fax: (44) 1480323115
E-Mail: enquiries@awg.com
Web Site: www.awg.com
Sls.: $2,203,899,195
Assets: $13,509,404,589
Liabilities: $13,347,053,577
Net Worth: $162,351,012
Earnings: ($75,805,920)
Emp.: 5,967
Fiscal Year-end: 03/31/13
Holding Company; Water Supply, Sewerage & Property Development Services
S.I.C.: 6719
N.A.I.C.S.: 551112
Claire Russell *(Sec)*

Subsidiaries:

Anglian Water Services Limited (2)
Anglian House Ambury Road
Huntingdon, Cambs, PE29 3NZ, United Kingdom UK
Tel.: (44) 1480323000
Fax: (44) 1480323115
Web Site: www.anglianwater.co.uk
Sls.: $1,836,714,270
Assets: $13,001,189,067
Liabilities: $11,435,007,174
Net Worth: $1,566,181,893
Earnings: $467,153,982
Emp.: 250
Fiscal Year-end: 03/31/13
Water Supply Distribution & Sewerage Services
S.I.C.: 4971
N.A.I.C.S.: 221310
Adrian Montague *(Chm)*
Peter Simpson *(Mng Dir & Member-Mgmt Bd)*
Claire Russell *(Member-Mgmt Bd, Sec & Dir-Legal)*
Scott Longhurst *(Member-Mgmt Bd & Mng Dir-Fin & Non Regulated Bus)*
Chris Boucher *(Member-Mgmt Bd & Dir-Info Svcs)*
Richard Boucher *(Member-Mgmt Bd & Dir-Bus Change & Strategy)*
Paul Gibbs *(Member-Mgmt Bd & Dir-Wastewater Svcs)*
Kate Kelly *(Member-Mgmt Bd & Dir-HR)*
Chris Newsome *(Member-Mgmt Bd & Dir-Asset Mgmt)*
Martyn Oakley *(Member-Mgmt Bd & Dir-Customer Svcs)*
Mark Pendlington *(Member-Mgmt Bd & Dir-Corp Affairs)*
Jean Spencer *(Member-Mgmt Bd & Dir-Regulation)*
Paul Valleley *(Member-Mgmt Bd & Dir-Water Svcs)*

AWG Property Limited (2)
47 Melville Street
Edinburgh, EH4 7HL, United Kingdom UK
Tel.: (44) 01313431000
Fax: (44) 01312004480
Web Site: www.awgproperty.co.uk
Emp.: 30
Commercial & Residential Property Investment & Development
S.I.C.: 6531
N.A.I.C.S.: 531390
Tony Donnelly *(Mng Dir)*

Non-U.S. Subsidiary:

3i Infrastructure plc (1)
Lime Grove House Green Street
Saint Helier, Jersey JE1 2ST JE
Tel.: (44) 1534 711 444
Fax: (44) 1534 609 333
Web Site: www.3i-infrastructure.com
3IN—(LSE)
Investment Management Services
S.I.C.: 6282
N.A.I.C.S.: 523920
Peter Sedgwick *(Chm)*

Non-U.S. Holdings:

Atle AB (1)
Birger Jarlsgatan 25
PO Box 7847
Stockholm, 111 99, Sweden
Tel.: (46) 8 50 61 01 00
Fax: (46) 8 50 62 11 00
Investment Management Services
S.I.C.: 6282
N.A.I.C.S.: 523920

Azelis S.A. (1)
Posthofbrug 12
PO Box 6
2600 Antwerp, Belgium (68%)
Tel.: (32) 36130120
Fax: (32) 36130121
E-Mail: info@azelis.com
Web Site: www.azelis.com
Sales Range: $1-4.9 Billion
Emp.: 1,100
Specialty Chemicals Distr
S.I.C.: 5169
N.A.I.C.S.: 424690
Alan Peterson *(Chm)*
Hans Udo Wenzel *(Deputy Chm)*
Blair Illingworth *(Pres & Dir-Europe)*
Gunther Krausser *(CFO)*
Adrian Jesinghaus *(CIO)*

Non-U.S. Subsidiaries:

Azelis A/S (2)
Lundtoftegaardsvej 95
2800 Kongens Lyngby, Denmark
Tel.: (45) 4526 3333
Fax: (45) 4526 3330
Web Site: www.broste.com
Chemicals Mfr & Distr
S.I.C.: 2899
N.A.I.C.S.: 325998
Steffen Kristensen *(Dir-Fin)*

Azelis Czech Republic, s.r.o. (2)
Eliasova 22
160 00 Prague, 6, Czech Republic
Tel.: (420) 224313303
Fax: (420) 224312385
Web Site: www.arnaud.cz
Emp.: 25
Chemicals Distr
S.I.C.: 5169
N.A.I.C.S.: 424690
Zsombor Bereczki *(Mng Dir)*

Azelis Deutschland GmbH (2)
Zum Siegblick 37-45
53757 Saint Augustin, Germany De
Tel.: (49) 224154970
Fax: (49) 2241 64177
E-Mail: info@azelis.de
Web Site: www.kum-online.de
Sales Range: $150-199.9 Million
Emp.: 120
Chemicals Distr
S.I.C.: 5169
N.A.I.C.S.: 424690
Michael Thompson *(Mng Dir)*

Azelis Deutschland Kosmetik GmbH (2)
Galmesweg 65
D 47445 Moers, Germany
Tel.: (49) 2841880360
Fax: (49) 28418854323
E-Mail: kosmetik@azelis.de
Web Site: www.azelis-kosmetik.de
Emp.: 30
Distr of Specialty Chemicals for Personal Care Applications
S.I.C.: 5169
N.A.I.C.S.: 424690
Michael Thomson *(Mng Dir)*

Azelis Espana, S.A. (2)
WTC Almeda Park Placa de la Pau s/n Edif 8 1a pl
Cornella de Llobregat, 08940 Barcelona, Spain
Tel.: (34) 934099070
Fax: (34) 933392162
E-Mail: azelis@azelis.es
Web Site: www.impexquimica.com
Chemicals Products Distr
S.I.C.: 5169
N.A.I.C.S.: 424690
Lorenzo Ceccarelli *(Mng Dir)*

Azelis France SAS (2)
23 Rue des Ardennes
75940 Paris, Cedex 19, France
Tel.: (33) 144731000
Fax: (33) 143468592
E-Mail: azelis@azelis.fr
Web Site: www.azelis.com
Emp.: 100
Compound Semiconductor Substrates Mfr
S.I.C.: 3674
N.A.I.C.S.: 334413
Laurent Nataf *(Mng Dir)*

Azelis India Private Limited (2)
206 I Oberoi Chambers 10 Abhishek New Link Road
Andheri West, Mumbai, 400 053, India
Tel.: (91) 2226736363
Fax: (91) 22 2673 0722
E-Mail: info@i-marigold.com
Web Site: www.i-marigold.com
Chemicals & Polymers Marketing
S.I.C.: 5169
N.A.I.C.S.: 424690
Manish Gupta *(Mng Dir)*

Azelis UK Life Sciences Ltd (2)
Foxholes Business Park
John Tate Road, Hertford, Herts, SG13 7YH, United Kingdom UK
Tel.: (44) 1992825555
Fax: (44) 1992825566
E-Mail: enquiries@azelis.co.uk
Web Site: www.azelis.com
Chemicals Distr
S.I.C.: 5169
N.A.I.C.S.: 424690
Stanley Black *(Pres)*
Joan Traynor *(Mng Dir-UK)*

Kompanija Finkochem d.o.o. (2)
Toplicin venac 3/2
11000 Belgrade, Serbia (100%)
Tel.: (381) 11 3283 390
Fax: (381) 11 3284 236
E-Mail: office@finkochem.com
Web Site: www.azelis.com
Emp.: 20
Distr of Chemicals for Food, Animal Feeds, Detergents, Textiles, Petrochemicals & Plastic Products
S.I.C.: 5169
N.A.I.C.S.: 424690
Dubravka Mirkovic *(Gen Mgr)*

S&D Group Ltd. (2)
Business Park Hartfort Westfield Lane
Harrow, Mddx, SG13 7YH, United Kingdom
Tel.: (44) 2089078822
Fax: (44) 9922825566
Web Site: izelis.com
Sales Range: $150-199.9 Million
Emp.: 80
Holding Company; Whslr & Distr of Raw Materials & Ingredients to Pharmaceutical, Food, Personal Care & Performance Chemicals Industries
S.I.C.: 6719
N.A.I.C.S.: 551112
Joan Traynor *(Mng Dir)*

Subsidiaries:

Chesham Specialty Ingredients Ltd. (3)
Cunningham House
Westfield Lane, Harrow, Middlesex, HA3 9ED, United Kingdom
Tel.: (44) 20 8907 8822
Fax: (44) 20 8927 0619
E-Mail: sales@chesham-ingredients.co.uk
Web Site: www.chesham-ingredients.com
Supplier of Raw Materials to Cosmetic & Toiletry Markets
S.I.C.: 5169
N.A.I.C.S.: 424690

Food Ingredient Technology Ltd. (3)
HiTec House Sand Road Industrial Estate
Great Gransden, Beds, SG19 3AH, United Kingdom
Tel.: (44) 1767 677666
Fax: (44) 1767 677966
E-Mail:
Web Site: www.azelis.co.uk
Emp.: 30
Distributes & Blends Ingredients for Food Processing Industry
S.I.C.: 2899
N.A.I.C.S.: 325998
David Gray *(Mng Dir)*

S&D Chemicals Ltd. (3)
Cunningham House Westfield Lane
Harrow, HA3 9ED, United Kingdom
Tel.: (44) 2089078822
Fax: (44) 2089270619
E-Mail: sales@sdcldn.com
Web Site: www.sd-chemicals.com
Sales Range: $125-149.9 Million
Emp.: 150
Chemicals Distr
S.I.C.: 5169
N.A.I.C.S.: 424690
Peter Strauss *(Mng Dir)*

Non-U.S. Branches:

S&D Chemicals Ltd. (4)
ul Malachowskiego 12
90 158 Lodz, Poland
Tel.: (48) 426780722
Fax: (48) 426780737
E-Mail: sdcpl@sdc.com.pl
Web Site: www.sdc.com.pl
Emp.: 2
Cosmetic, Industrial Raw Materials & Chemical Distr
S.I.C.: 5169
N.A.I.C.S.: 424690
Ziemowit Adamiec *(Mng Dir-S&D Chemicals)*

S&D Chemicals Ltd. (4)
Pisnicka 22
Kamyk, 142 00 Prague, 4, Czech Republic
Tel.: (420) 2 96 303 340
Fax: (420) 296303361
E-Mail: sdcprg@volny.cz
Web Site: www.sd-chemicals.com
Chemical Distr
S.I.C.: 5169
N.A.I.C.S.: 424690

S&D Chemicals Limited (4)
Room 1607 New Century Plaza Building A
1 South Tai Ping Road, Nanjing, Jiangsu, 210002, China
Tel.: (86) 2584723984
Fax: (86) 2584710725
E-Mail: sdcldnco@jsmail.com.cn
Web Site: www.sd-chemicals.com
Chemical Distr
S.I.C.: 5169
N.A.I.C.S.: 424690

S&D Chemicals Ltd. (4)
Dayka Gabor u 3 (Rubin Hotel)
H-1118 Budapest, Hungary
Tel.: (36) 13192683

Fax: (36) 13192675
E-Mail: agnes@sdc.datanet.hu
Web Site: www.sd-chemicals.com
Chemical Distr
S.I.C.: 5169
N.A.I.C.S.: 424690

S&D Chemicals Moscow (4)
3rd Nizhnelikhoborski pr 3
127238 Moscow, Russia
Tel.: (7) 4952322432
Fax: (7) 495 480 9955
E-Mail: info@sd-chemicals.ru
Web Site: www.sd-chemicals.com
Chemical Distr
S.I.C.: 5169
N.A.I.C.S.: 424690

Non-U.S. Subsidiaries:

Azelis Bulgaria EAD (4)
World Trade Centre - Interpred - Office 606B
36 Dragon Tzankov Blvd, 1040 Sofia, Bulgaria
Tel.: (359) 2 971 2130
Fax: (359) 2 971 3794
E-Mail: infobg@azelis.com
Web Site: www.azelis.com
Emp.: 15
Chemical Distr
S.I.C.: 5169
N.A.I.C.S.: 424690
Didi Angelova *(Sec)*

Azelis Canada Chemicals Ltd. (4)
131 Finchdene Square Unit 7
Scarborough, ON, M1X 1A6, Canada
Tel.: (416) 299-7772
Fax: (416) 299-0296
E-Mail:
Web Site: www.azelis.com
Emp.: 8
Chemical Distr
S.I.C.: 5169
N.A.I.C.S.: 424690
Kevin Allen *(VP)*

S&D Chemicals Australia Pty. Limited (4)
Level 1 75 Old Pittwater Road
Brookvale, NSW, 2100, Australia
Tel.: (61) 299392188
Fax: (61) 299392799
E-Mail: sanddchemicals@sydney.net
Emp.: 3
Chemical Distr
S.I.C.: 5169
N.A.I.C.S.: 424690

S&D Chemicals (India) Ltd. (4)
405 Great Eastern Chambers
Sector 11 CBD Belapur, Mumbai, 400 614, India
Tel.: (91) 2227574545
Fax: (91) 2227577887
E-Mail: info@sndindia.com
Web Site: www.sndchemicals.com
Emp.: 70
Chemical Distr
S.I.C.: 5169
N.A.I.C.S.: 424690
Sudhir Gautam *(CEO)*

DERPROSA, S.A. (1)
Edificio GAN C Ramirez Arellano 37
28043 Madrid, Spain ES
Tel.: (34) 953598100 (100%)
Fax: (34) 915153209
E-Mail: comercial@derprosa.es
Web Site: www.derprosa.es
Petroleum & Petrochemistry
S.I.C.: 2999
N.A.I.C.S.: 324199

Easysoft-Software e Sistemas SA (1)
Alfrapark Edificio F Piso 3
2721 801 Amadora, Portugal (100%)
Tel.: (351) 217229300
Fax: (351) 217229390
E-Mail: info@audaxys.com
Web Site: www.easysoft.pt
Emp.: 40
Produces Software for the Leasing, Consumer Credit & Car Rental Industries
S.I.C.: 3652
N.A.I.C.S.: 334614
E. Miguel Rangel *(Chm & CEO)*

Element Materials Technology B.V. (1)
Czaar Peterstraat 229
1000 AJ Amsterdam, Netherlands
Tel.: (31) 205563555
Fax: (31) 205563556
E-Mail: info.amsterdam@element.com
Web Site: www.element.com
Material Testing & Analysis Services
S.I.C.: 8734
N.A.I.C.S.: 541380
Charles Noall *(CEO)*
Jo Wetz *(CFO & Exec VP-Fin)*
Jeff Joyce *(Exec VP-HR)*
Arnout Lijesen *(Exec VP-Corp Dev)*

U.S. Subsidiaries:

Element Materials Technology (2)
18100 S Wilmington Ave
Rancho Dominguez, CA 90220
Tel.: (310) 632-8500
Fax: (310) 632-4700
Toll Free: (888) 632-8500
E-Mail: info.rd@element.com
Emp.: 60
Material Testing & Analysis Services
S.I.C.: 8734
N.A.I.C.S.: 541380
Kevin Ranta *(VP-Tech)*

Element Materials Technology (2)
5405 E Schaaf Rd
Cleveland, OH 44131-1337
Tel.: (216) 524-1450
Fax: (216) 524-1459
Web Site: www.element.com
Sales Range: $1-9.9 Million
Emp.: 50
Specialized Metals Testing
S.I.C.: 8734
N.A.I.C.S.: 541380
Michael R. Gaydos *(CEO, COO & Gen Mgr)*

ELTEL Group Corporation (1)
Komentajankatu 5
PO Box 50
02611 Espoo, Finland (100%)
Tel.: (358) 20411211
Fax: (358) 204113200
E-Mail: info@eltelnetworks.com
Web Site: www.eltelnetworks.com
Emp.: 100
Holding Company
S.I.C.: 6719
N.A.I.C.S.: 551112
Thomas Berglund *(Chm)*
Axel Hjarne *(Pres & CEO)*

Division:

ELTEL Networks Oy (2)
Komentajankatu 5
PO Box 50
02611 Espoo, Finland FI
Tel.: (358) 20411211
Fax: (358) 204113200
E-Mail: info@eltelnetworks.com
Web Site: www.eltelnetworks.com
Sales Range: $1-4.9 Billion
Emp.: 200
Electrical & Telecommunications Network Maintenance & Transmission Services
S.I.C.: 1629
N.A.I.C.S.: 237130
Thomas Berglund *(Chm)*
Axel Hjarne *(Pres & CEO)*
Juha Luusua *(Mng Dir & COO)*
Sonny Nielsen *(CEO-Denmark, COO-Central Europe & Mng Dir)*
Raija Sast *(Mng Dir)*
Marjut Ontronen *(CFO)*
Jukka Leskinen *(Gen Counsel & Head-Risk Mgmt)*
Hannu Tynkkynen *(Sr VP)*

Non-U.S. Divisions:

ELTEL Networks A/S (2)
Stationsparken 25
2600 Glostrup, Denmark
Tel.: (45) 088135000
Fax: (45) 88135013
E-Mail: info@eltelnetworks.com
Web Site: www.eltelnetworks.com
Emp.: 600
Electrical & Telecommunications Network Maintenance & Transmission Services
S.I.C.: 1623
N.A.I.C.S.: 237130
Sommy Neilson *(Mng Dir)*

ELTEL Networks AS (2)
Stanseveien 21 Alnabru
PO Box 343
NO-0614 Oslo, Norway
Tel.: (47) 93097000
Fax: (47) 22804801
E-Mail: reception@eltelnetworks.com
Web Site: www.eltelnetworks.com
Emp.: 650
Electrical & Telecommunications Network Maintenance & Transmission Services
S.I.C.: 1629
N.A.I.C.S.: 237130
Thor Egel Braathen *(Mng Dir)*

ELTEL Networks AS (2)
Tuisu 19
10117 Tallinn, Estonia
Tel.: (372) 6063100
Fax: (372) 6063101
E-Mail: info.estonia@eltelnetworks.com
Web Site: www.eltelnetworks.com
Emp.: 500
Electrical & Telecommunications Network Maintenance & Transmission Services
S.I.C.: 1629
N.A.I.C.S.: 237130
Enn Eelmets *(CEO)*

ELTEL Networks Communications GmbH (2)
Streufdorfer Strasse 124
98663 Westhausen, Germany
Tel.: (49) 368756789
Fax: (49) 0368756788
E-Mail: westhausen@eltelnetworks.com
Web Site: www.eltelnetworks.com
Emp.: 170
Electrical & Telecommunications Network Maintenance & Transmission Services
S.I.C.: 1629
N.A.I.C.S.: 237130
Oliver Knauth *(Gen Mgr)*

ELTEL Networks Infranet AB (2)
Adolfsbergsvagen 13
Bromma, SE-168 66 Stockholm, Sweden
Tel.: (46) 858537600
Fax: (46) 8298807
E-Mail: info.sweden@eltelnetworks.com
Web Site: www.eltelnetworks.se
Emp.: 400
Electrical & Telecommunications Network Maintenance & Transmission Services
S.I.C.: 1629
N.A.I.C.S.: 237130
Axel Hjarne *(Gen Mgr)*

ELTEL Networks SIA (2)
Lubanas Road 9km Stopinu parish
LV-1012 Riga, Latvia
Tel.: (371) 7317 500
Web Site: www.eltelnetworks.com
Electrical & Telecommunications Network Maintenance & Transmission Services
S.I.C.: 1629
N.A.I.C.S.: 237130

ELTEL Networks Telecom Sp. z o.o. (2)
Ul Zupnicza 17
03-821 Warsaw, Poland PL
Tel.: (48) 225189500
Fax: (48) 225189510
E-Mail: info.poland@eltelnetworks.com
Web Site: www.eltelnetworks.com
Electrical & Telecommunications Network Maintenance & Transmission Services
S.I.C.: 1623
N.A.I.C.S.: 237130
Andrzej Szawarski *(Mgr)*

UAB ELTEL Networks (2)
Vilkpedes g 4
LT-03151 Vilnius, Lithuania
Tel.: (370) 5403114340
Fax: (370) 52131139
E-Mail: info.lithuania@eltelnetworks.com
Web Site: www.eltelnetworks.lt
Emp.: 150
Operator of Telecommunication Networks
S.I.C.: 4813
N.A.I.C.S.: 517110

GEKA GmbH (1)
Waizendorf 3
91572 Bechhofen, Germany
Tel.: (49) 9822 87 01
Fax: (49) 9822 87 119
E-Mail: info@geka-world.com
Web Site: www.geka-world.com
Sales Range: $125-149.9 Million
Emp.: 65
Cosmetic Brush, Applicator & Packaging System Mfr
S.I.C.: 3089
N.A.I.C.S.: 326199
Yves Dominioni *(Pres & CEO)*

Hilite Germany GmbH (1)
Am Schlossfeld 5
97828 Marktheidenfeld, Germany
Tel.: (49) 9391 911 0
Fax: (49) 9391 911 222
E-Mail: info@hilite.com
Web Site: www.hilite.com
Sales Range: $400-449.9 Million
Emp.: 130
Motor Vehicle Transmission & Power Train Part Mfr
S.I.C.: 3714
N.A.I.C.S.: 336350
Karl Hammer *(CEO)*
Stefan Eck *(CFO)*
Jorg Feuring *(COO)*

Unit:

Hilite Germany GmbH (2)
Weberstrasse 17
72622 Nurtingen, Germany (100%)
Tel.: (49) 702292260
Fax: (49) 70229226298
Web Site: www.hilite.com
Emp.: 220
Motor Vehicle Transmission & Power Train Part Mfr
S.I.C.: 3714
N.A.I.C.S.: 336350
Karl Hammer *(Gen Mgr)*

U.S. Units:

Hilite International, Inc. - Whitehall (2)
2001 Peach St
Whitehall, MI 48461
Tel.: (231) 894-3200
Fax: (231) 894-3255
E-Mail: info@hilite-ind.com
Web Site: www.hilite-ind.com
Emp.: 200
Motor Vehicle Transmission & Power Train Part Mfr
S.I.C.: 3714
N.A.I.C.S.: 336350

MEMORA Servicios Funerarios S.L. (1)
Sancho De Avila 2
Barcelona, 50008, Spain ES
Tel.: (34) 916623554 (75%)
Fax: (34) 916623853
E-Mail: informacion@memora.es
Web Site: www.memora.es
Funeral Services
S.I.C.: 7261
N.A.I.C.S.: 812210
Ranon Lasuente *(Pres)*

OneMed Group Oy (1)
Grev Turegatan 9 1tr
114 46 Stockholm, Sweden
Mailing Address:
PO Box 11
FIN-01641 Vantaa, Finland
Tel.: (46) 7146800
Web Site: www.onemed.com
Sales Range: $500-549.9 Million
Emp.: 700
Medical Products, Laboratory Supplies & Chemicals Distr
S.I.C.: 5047
N.A.I.C.S.: 423450
Andreas Gothberg *(CEO)*
Leena Schnapp *(CFO)*

Non-U.S. Subsidiaries:

BATIST Medical a.s. (2)
Nerudova 309
549 41 Cerveny Kostelec, Czech Republic
Tel.: (420) 491431311
Fax: (420) 491 413 394
Web Site: www.batist.cz
Medical Products, Laboratory Supplies & Chemicals Distr

3i Group plc—(Continued)

S.I.C.: 5047
N.A.I.C.S.: 423450
Tomas Mertlik *(Mng Dir)*

BATIST Medical SK s.r.o. (2)
Racianska 184
831 05 Bratislava, Slovakia
Tel.: (421) 244888639
Fax: (421) 00420491413394
E-Mail: batist@baist.cz
Web Site: www.batist.cz
Medical Products, Laboratory Supplies & Chemicals Distr
S.I.C.: 5047
N.A.I.C.S.: 423450
Thomas Mertlik *(Mng Dir)*

Danpleje OneMed A/S (2)
Langebjerg 23
D 4000 Roskilde, Denmark
Mailing Address:
PO Pedersens Vej 16
8200 Arhus, Denmark
Tel.: (45) 46 740 030
Fax: (45) 46 74 00 59
E-Mail: dkinfo@onemed.com
Web Site: www.onemed.com
Emp.: 10
Medical Products, Laboratory Supplies & Chemicals Distr
S.I.C.: 3231
N.A.I.C.S.: 327215
Erik Boje *(Gen Mgr)*

Hand-Prod Sp. z o. o. (2)
ul St Leszczynskiego 40 A
Warsaw, Poland
Tel.: (48) 228678737
Fax: (48) 80228676675
Web Site: www.hand-prod.pl
Medical Products, Laboratory Supplies & Chemicals Distr
S.I.C.: 5047
N.A.I.C.S.: 423450
Boleslaw Kukolewski *(Mng Dir)*

OneMed AS (2)
Karihaugveien 89
N 1086 Oslo, Norway
Tel.: (47) 22 30 91 00
Fax: (47) 22 30 91 01
E-Mail: info@onemed.com
Emp.: 30
Medical Products, Laboratory Supplies & Chemicals Distr
S.I.C.: 5047
N.A.I.C.S.: 423450
Jan Knoph *(Mng Dir)*

OneMed OU (2)
Parnu MNT 501
76401 Harjumaa, Laagri, Estonia
Tel.: (372) 6503 630
Fax: (372) 6 503 629
E-Mail: tellimus@onemed.com
Web Site: www.onemed.ee
Emp.: 12
Medical Products, Laboratory Supplies & Chemicals Distr
S.I.C.: 5047
N.A.I.C.S.: 423450
Tonu Loog *(Mng Dir)*

OneMed SIA (2)
Ulmana Gatve 119
2167 Riga, Marupe, Latvia
Tel.: (371) 67964748
Fax: (371) 67421648
Medical Products, Laboratory Supplies & Chemicals Distr
S.I.C.: 5047
N.A.I.C.S.: 423450
Olafs Gutmanis *(Mng Dir)*

OneMed Sverige AB (2)
Tagenevagen 29
Hisings Karra, S 42537 Gothenburg, Sweden
Mailing Address:
PO Box 50
401 20 Gothenburg, Sweden
Tel.: (46) 317063000
Fax: (46) 317063009
E-Mail: kundservice@onemed.com
Web Site: www.onemed.com
Emp.: 150
Medical Products, Laboratory Supplies & Chemicals Distr
S.I.C.: 5047
N.A.I.C.S.: 423450
Ulf Swan *(Mng Dir)*

UAB OneMed (2)
Perkunkiemio g4A
LT-12128 Vilnius, Lithuania
Tel.: (370) 52462224
Fax: (370) 5 246 2225
Medical Products, Laboratory Supplies & Chemicals Distr
S.I.C.: 5047
N.A.I.C.S.: 423450
Tonu Loog *(Mng Dir)*

WL-Medical Oy (2)
Karvaamokuja 4
380 Helsinki, Finland
Tel.: (358) 467146850
Fax: (358) 206029450
Medical Products, Laboratory Supplies & Chemicals Distr
S.I.C.: 5047
N.A.I.C.S.: 423450

Trescal S.A. (1)
Parc d'affaires Silic 8 rue de l'Esterel
BP 30441
F-94593 Rungis, Cedex, France FR
Tel.: (33) 156703636
Fax: (33) 156703630
E-Mail: france@trescal.com
Web Site: www.trescal.com
Sales Range: $150-199.9 Million
Emp.: 1,500
Test & Measuring Equipment Calibration, Maintenance & Repair Services
S.I.C.: 7629
N.A.I.C.S.: 811219
Olivier Delrieu *(CEO)*

U.S. Subsidiary:

Dynamic Technology Inc. (2)
1200 N Old US 23
Hartland, MI 48353
Mailing Address:
PO Box 559
Hartland, MI 48353
Tel.: (810) 225-4601
Fax: (810) 225-4602
Web Site: www.dtical.com
Sales Range: $25-49.9 Million
Emp.: 180
Metrology Services
S.I.C.: 8711
N.A.I.C.S.: 541330
Peter Szekeres *(Pres)*

Non-U.S. Subsidiaries:

Trescal A/S (2)
Mads Clausens Vej 12
DK-8600 Silkeborg, Denmark DK
Tel.: (45) 87206969
Fax: (45) 86812654
E-Mail: dkcalib@trescal.com
Web Site: www.trescal.dk
Emp.: 45
Test & Measuring Equipment Calibration, Maintenance & Repair Services
S.I.C.: 7699
N.A.I.C.S.: 811219
Jin Wang *(Mng Dir)*

Trescal B.V. (2)
Storkstraat 2-4
2722 NN Zoetermeer, Netherlands NL
Mailing Address:
Postbus 142
2700 AC Zoetermeer, Netherlands
Tel.: (31) 793430000
Fax: (31) 793430099
E-Mail: info@trescal.nl
Web Site: www.trescal.nl
Emp.: 35
Test & Measuring Equipment Calibration, Maintenance & Repair Services
S.I.C.: 7699
N.A.I.C.S.: 811219

Trescal GmbH (2)
Borsigstrasse 11
D-64291 Darmstadt, Germany De
Tel.: (49) 615193440 (100%)
Fax: (49) 61519344444
E-Mail: germany@trescal.com
Web Site: www.trescal.de
Emp.: 30
Test & Measuring Equipment Calibration, Maintenance & Repair Services
S.I.C.: 7699
N.A.I.C.S.: 811219
Timo Grunewalder *(Chm-Mgmt Bd)*

Trescal Informacion Tecnologia y Mercado, S.A.U. (2)
Poligono Industrial Plaza Calle Bari 57
Edificio TIC XXI, ES-50197 Zaragoza, Spain ES
Tel.: (34) 976597386
Fax: (34) 976597194
E-Mail: itm@itm.es
Web Site: www.itm.es
Emp.: 23
Test & Measuring Equipment Calibration, Maintenance & Repair Services
S.I.C.: 7629
N.A.I.C.S.: 811219
Alain Wiedertiel *(Mng Dir)*

Subsidiary:

Trescal Espana de Metrologia, S.L.U. (3)
Poligono Industrial de Alcobendas
Avenida de Fuencarral 24, ES-28108 Alcobendas, Spain ES
Tel.: (34) 916250900
Fax: (34) 916250959
E-Mail: info@trescal.es
Web Site: www.trescal.com
Emp.: 35
Test & Measuring Equipment Calibration, Maintenance & Repair Services
S.I.C.: 7629
N.A.I.C.S.: 811219
Thomas Estrada *(Gen Mgr)*

Trescal Limited (2)
2 Queens Road
Teddington, Mddx, TW11 0LB, United Kingdom UK
Tel.: (44) 2086144050
Fax: (44) 20 8977 8928
E-Mail: ukcal@trescal.com
Web Site: www.trescal.co.uk
Test & Measuring Equipment Calibration, Maintenance & Repair Services
S.I.C.: 7629
N.A.I.C.S.: 811219
Steve Brown *(Gen Mgr)*

Trescal s.r.l. (2)
Via dei Metalli 1
IT-25039 Travagliato, BS, Italy IT
Tel.: (39) 03021491
Fax: (39) 0302722091
E-Mail: it.info.bs@trescal.com
Web Site: www.trescal.it
Test & Measuring Equipment Calibration, Maintenance & Repair Services
S.I.C.: 7629
N.A.I.C.S.: 811219

Trescal Sweden AB (2)
Frakgatan 6
SE-633 46 Eskilstuna, Sweden SE
Tel.: (46) 16153380
Fax: (46) 16153399
E-Mail: seinfo@trescal.com
Web Site: www.trescal.se
Test & Measuring Equipment Calibration, Maintenance & Repair Services
S.I.C.: 7699
N.A.I.C.S.: 811219

Xellia Pharmaceuticals AS (1)
Harbitzalleen 3
0212 Oslo, Norway NO
Mailing Address:
PO Box 158
0375 Skoyen, Norway
Tel.: (47) 22529000
Fax: (47) 22 50 58 60
E-Mail: info.dk@xellia.com
Web Site: www.xellia.com
Emp.: 850
Specialized Fermented APIs & Injectable Finished Products
S.I.C.: 2834
N.A.I.C.S.: 325412
Carl-Ake Carlsson *(Pres & CEO)*
Kennet Lundberg *(CFO & VP)*
Mikkel Lyager Olsen *(Gen Counsel & VP)*
Kristin Lund Myrdahl *(Sec)*

Non-U.S. Subsidiaries:

Xellia Pharmaceuticals ApS (2)
Dalslandsgade 11
2300 Copenhagen, S, Denmark (100%)
Tel.: (45) 32 64 5500
Fax: (45) 32 64 5501
E-Mail: info.dk@xellia.com
Web Site: www.xellia.com
Emp.: 372
Pharmaceuticals Mfr
S.I.C.: 2834
N.A.I.C.S.: 325412
John Stewart *(Mgr)*

Xellia Pharmaceuticals Ltd. (2)
Szallas u 3
1107 Budapest, Hungary (100%)
Mailing Address:
Pf 906
1386 Budapest, Hungary
Tel.: (36) 1 2604130
Fax: (36) 1 2624059
E-Mail: info.hu@xellia.com
Web Site: www.xellia.com
Emp.: 152
Pharmaceuticals Mfr
S.I.C.: 2834
N.A.I.C.S.: 325412
Attila Mile *(Gen Mgr)*

Xellia (Taizhou) Pharmaceuticals Co., Ltd. (2)
108 Binhai Road
Jiaojiang District, Taizhou, Zhejiang, 318000, China (100%)
Tel.: (86) 57688827026
Fax: (86) 57688827023
E-Mail: info.ch@xellia.com
Web Site: www.xellia.com
Emp.: 138
Pharmaceuticals Mfr
S.I.C.: 2834
N.A.I.C.S.: 325412
John Wang *(Gen Mgr-Ops)*

Non-U.S. Joint Venture:

LNI Verkko Holding Oy (1)
Televisiokatu 4 A
FIN 00240 Helsingfors, Finland FI
Tel.: (358) 2058611
Fax: (358) 20 586 7369
Web Site: www.vattenfall.fi
Sales Range: $400-449.9 Million
Emp.: 550
Holding Company; Energy Solutions Services
S.I.C.: 6719
N.A.I.C.S.: 551112
Lauri Virkkunen *(Gen Mgr)*

Subsidiaries:

LNI Lampo Oy (2)
Vankanlahde 7
PO Box 4
FIN 1310 Hameenlinna, Finland FI
Tel.: (358) 2058611
Fax: (358) 20 586 6558
Web Site: www.vattenfall.fi/fi/toimipaikat.htm
Heat Distr
S.I.C.: 4961
N.A.I.C.S.: 221330

LNI Verkko Oy (2)
Patamaenkatu 7
PO Box 2
FIN 33901 Tampere, Finland FI
Tel.: (358) 2058 911
Fax: (358) 20 586 4240
Web Site: www.vattenfall.fi/fi/toimipaikat.htm
Emp.: 170
Electric Power Generation & Distr
S.I.C.: 4931
N.A.I.C.S.: 221122
Tapani Liuhala *(CEO-Finland)*

3I INFOTECH LTD.

Tower 5 3rd to 6th Floors
International Infotech Park Vashi
Navi Mumbai, 400 703, India
Mailing Address:
Tower 5 3rd to 6th Fl International Infotech Park
Vashi, Mumbai, 400 703, India
Tel.: (91) 2267928000

Fax: (91) 2267928099
E-Mail: marketing@3i-infotech.com
Web Site: www.3i-infotech.com
532628—(BOM)
Rev.: $252,937,512
Assets: $699,881,292
Liabilities: $529,294,752
Net Worth: $170,586,540
Earnings: ($93,345,192)
Emp.: 9,000
Fiscal Year-end: 03/31/13

Business Description:
Software & Information Technology Solutions
S.I.C.: 7372
N.A.I.C.S.: 511210

Personnel:
Madhivanan Balakrishnan *(CEO & Mng Dir)*
Charanjit Attra *(CFO)*
Padmanabhan Iyer *(Pres-Corp Plng & Strategy)*
Ninad Kelkar *(Sec)*

Board of Directors:
Hoshang Noshirwan Sinor
Charanjit Attra
Madhivanan Balakrishnan
Ashok Jhunjhunwala
Vishakha V. Mulye
Ashok Shah
N. S. Venkatesh

Lodha & Co
6 Karim Chambers, 40, Ambalal Doshi Marg
Mumbai, India

Transfer Agent:
3i Infotech Limited
Tower #5 3rd to 6th Floors International Infotech Park Vashi
Navi Mumbai, India

Subsidiaries:

Locuz Enterprise Solutions Ltd. **(1)**
4 6th Floor Orion Tower Building 9 Mindspace
Cyberabad, 500 081 Hyderabad, Andhra Pradesh, India
Tel.: (91) 40 3050 9001
Fax: (91) 40 3050 9006
Web Site: www.locuz.com
Information Technology Management Services
S.I.C.: 8742
N.A.I.C.S.: 541611
Vijay Kumar Wadhi *(CEO & Mng Dir)*

Professional Access Software Development Pvt. Ltd. **(1)**
No 3 Level 4 & 5 Embassy Icon Infantry Rd
Bengaluru, Karanataka, 560001, India
Tel.: (91) 8041377900
Fax: (91) 8022996868
E-Mail: info@professionalaccess.com
Web Site: www.professionalaccess.com
Emp.: 500
Software Development Services
S.I.C.: 7371
N.A.I.C.S.: 541511
Babu Venkatesh *(CEO)*

U.S. Subsidiaries:

3i Infotech Financial Software Inc. **(1)**
555 Chorro St Ste B
San Luis Obispo, CA 93405
Tel.: (805) 544-8327
Fax: (805) 544-3905
E-Mail: factor.info@3i-infotech.com
Web Site: www.dissol.com
Emp.: 10
Factoring Software Distr
S.I.C.: 7372
N.A.I.C.S.: 511210
Rajesh Raman *(Mgr)*

Subsidiaries:

J&B Software Inc. **(2)**
510 E Township Line Rd Ste 100
Blue Bell, PA 19422-2721
Tel.: (215) 641-1500
Fax: (215) 641-1181
Web Site: www.tmsimage.com
Sales Range: $25-49.9 Million
Emp.: 80
Computer Software Development
S.I.C.: 7371
N.A.I.C.S.: 541511
Jim McShea *(Exec VP & Gen Mgr)*

Subsidiary:

J&B Software (Canada) Inc. **(3)**
510 E Township Line Rd
Blue Bell, PA 19422-2721
Tel.: (215) 641-1500
Fax: (215) 641-1181
E-Mail: info@jbsoftware.com
Emp.: 65
Software Development & Consulting Services
S.I.C.: 7371
N.A.I.C.S.: 541511

Regulus Integrated Solutions LLC **(2)**
860 Latour Ct
Napa, CA 94558-6258
Tel.: (707) 259-7100
Electronic Billing Services
S.I.C.: 6099
N.A.I.C.S.: 522320

3i Infotech Inc. **(1)**
450 Raritan Ctr Pkwy Ste B
Edison, NJ 08837 CT
Tel.: (732) 225-4242
Fax: (732) 346-1823
E-Mail: marketing.us@3i-infotech.com
Web Site: www.3i-infotech.com
Emp.: 100
IT Solutions
S.I.C.: 7373
N.A.I.C.S.: 541512
Kumar Ganesan *(CFO)*

Professional Access Ltd **(1)**
55 Broad St 27th Fl
New York, NY 10004 (51%)
Tel.: (212) 432-2844
Fax: (212) 432-2847
Web Site: www.professionalaccess.com
Sales Range: $25-49.9 Million
Emp.: 200
Computer Related Consulting Services
S.I.C.: 7373
N.A.I.C.S.: 541512
Babu Venkatesh *(CEO)*
Ashu Chahal *(COO & Exec VP)*

Regulus Group LLC **(1)**
860 Latour Ct
Napa, CA 94558
Tel.: (707) 254-4000
Toll Free: (866) 747-2877
E-Mail: web.mail@regulusgroup.com
Web Site: www.regulusgroup.com
Sales Range: $100-124.9 Million
Emp.: 1,000
Payment Processing & Remittance Services
S.I.C.: 6099
N.A.I.C.S.: 522320
Kathleen Hamburger *(Pres & CEO)*
Jaime Nunez *(COO & CTO)*
Doretta Morlacci *(Chief HR Officer)*

Non-U.S. Subsidiaries:

3i Infotech (Africa) Ltd. **(1)**
5th Aveneue Office Suite 4th Floor Suite 2 5th Ngong Road
Opp Traffic Head Quarters, Nairobi, Kenya
Tel.: (254) 202712477
Fax: (254) 203601100
Information Technology Services
S.I.C.: 7373
N.A.I.C.S.: 541512
Vishal Singh *(Asst VP-East Africa Reg)*

3i Infotech Framework Ltd. **(1)**
Level 35 Mail Drop CGC 35-02 25 Canada Sq
London, E14 5LQ, United Kingdom
Tel.: (44) 20 7071 3000
Fax: (44) 20 7071 3001
E-Mail: info@frameworksoftware.com
Emp.: 250
Information Technology Services
S.I.C.: 7373
N.A.I.C.S.: 541512

3i Infotech Pte Ltd. **(1)**
6 Temasek Boulevard 42-02 Suntec Tower 4
038986 Singapore, Singapore
Tel.: (65) 65111599
Fax: (65) 65111580
E-Mail: enquire@3i-infotech.com
Emp.: 25
Information Technology Services
S.I.C.: 7373
N.A.I.C.S.: 541512

Non-U.S. Subsidiary:

3i Infotech (Thailand) Ltd. **(2)**
44th Floor Empire Tower Unit 4410 195 Sathorn Road Yannawa Sathorn
Bangkok, 10120, Thailand
Tel.: (66) 26595879
Fax: (66) 26595880
Financial Administrative Software Development Services
S.I.C.: 7371
N.A.I.C.S.: 541511

3i Infotech Saudi Arabia LLC **(1)**
Office 24 2nd Floor Khurais Commercial Center
Riyadh, 11422, Saudi Arabia
Tel.: (966) 1 464 3391
Fax: (966) 1 465 5041
E-Mail: marketing@3i-infotech.com
Web Site: www.3i-infotech.com
Emp.: 45
Business Management Software Development Services
S.I.C.: 7371
N.A.I.C.S.: 541511
Arya Pratihar *(Gen Mgr)*

3i Infotech Sdn. Bhd. **(1)**
Ste 2a 7-2 L7 Block 2a
Plz Sentral, 50470 Kuala Lumpur, Federal Territory, Malaysia
Tel.: (60) 327868500
Fax: (60) 327868501
Web Site: www.3i-infotech.com
Emp.: 90
Information Technology Services
S.I.C.: 7373
N.A.I.C.S.: 541512
Sunil Mundhra *(Sr VP-Banking & Capital Markets)*

3i Infotech (UK) Ltd. **(1)**
Level 35 Mail Drop 25 Canada Square
London, E14 5LQ, United Kingdom
Tel.: (44) 2070713000
Fax: (44) 2070713001
Emp.: 200
Business Management Software Development Services
S.I.C.: 7371
N.A.I.C.S.: 541511
Elspeth Goodchild *(Mng Dir)*

Subsidiary:

3i Infotech (Western Europe) Holdings Ltd. **(2)**
Level 35 Mail Drop 25 Canada Square
London, E14 5LQ, United Kingdom
Tel.: (44) 1212603300
Fax: (44) 2070713001
E-Mail: marketing.mearc@3i-infotech.com
Web Site: www.3i-infotech.com
Investment Management Services
S.I.C.: 6211
N.A.I.C.S.: 523999
Ian Hallam *(CEO)*

Subsidiaries:

3i Infotech (Flagship-UK) Limited **(3)**
Huntingdon House
Ashby de la Zouch, LE65 1AH, United Kingdom
Tel.: (44) 1530410730
Emp.: 6
Information Technology Services
S.I.C.: 7373
N.A.I.C.S.: 541512
David McDowell *(Gen Mgr)*

3i Infotech (Western Europe) Group Ltd. **(3)**
5-7 Cranwood Street
London, EC1V 9LH, United Kingdom
Tel.: (44) 1212603300
Fax: (44) 1212603301
E-Mail: marketing@3i-infotech.eu
Web Site: www.3i-infotech.com
Emp.: 50
Information Technology Services
S.I.C.: 7373
N.A.I.C.S.: 541512
Piers Farbrother *(Mgr-Mktg & Sls)*

3i Infotech (Western Europe) Ltd. **(3)**
Level 35 Mail Drop 25 Canada Square
London, E14 5LQ, United Kingdom
Tel.: (44) 1212603300
Fax: (44) 1212603301
Emp.: 150
Software Products Distr
S.I.C.: 7372
N.A.I.C.S.: 511210
Ian Hallan *(Gen Mgr)*

Elegon Infotech Ltd. **(1)**
F2 B6 Building Tianfu Software Park Tianfu Main Road
Chengdu, Sichuan, 610041, China
Tel.: (86) 2866874168
Fax: (86) 20866874112
E-Mail: elegon@elegoninfotech.com
Web Site: www.elegoninfotech.com
Business Process Outsourcing Services
S.I.C.: 8742
N.A.I.C.S.: 541611

3LEGS RESOURCES PLC

Commerce House 1 Bowring Road
Ramsey, IM8 2LQ, Isle of Man
Tel.: (44) 1624811611
E-Mail: info@3legsresources.com
Web Site: www.3legsresources.com
Year Founded: 2007
3LEG—(AIM)
Rev.: $1,685,102
Assets: $91,996,801
Liabilities: $2,462,113
Net Worth: $89,534,688
Earnings: ($9,523,119)
Emp.: 7
Fiscal Year-end: 12/31/12

Business Description:
Oil & Gas Exploration Services
S.I.C.: 1311
N.A.I.C.S.: 211111

Personnel:
Kamlesh Rameshbhai Parmar *(CEO)*
Alexander Fraser *(CFO)*

Board of Directors:
Tim Eggar
David Bremner
Richard Hills
Kamlesh Rameshbhai Parmar
Rod Perry

Legal Counsel:
Squire Sanders & Dempsey (UK) LLP
7 Devonshire Square Cutlers Gardens
London, United Kingdom

Non-U.S. Subsidiary:

Lane Energy Poland Sp. z.o.o **(1)**
Chmielna 13/A
Warsaw, 00-021, Poland
Tel.: (48) 225059177
Fax: (48) 225059178
Oil & Gas Exploration Services
S.I.C.: 1389
N.A.I.C.S.: 213112

3MV ENERGY

250 305 10th Avenue Southeast
Calgary, AB, T2G 0W2, Canada
Tel.: (403) 234-8998
Fax: (403) 800-9317
E-Mail: bradiff@3mvenergy.com
Web Site: www.3mvenergy.com
Year Founded: 2009
TMV—(TSXV)

Business Description:
Investment Services
S.I.C.: 6211
N.A.I.C.S.: 523999

Personnel:
James P. Boyle *(Chm)*
Dallas C. Duce *(Interim CEO)*
Billy Abbey *(CFO & VP-Fin)*
Douglas McKinnon *(COO)*

3MV Energy—(Continued)

Board of Directors:
James P. Boyle
Ron Baba
Dallas C. Duce
Don Fairholm
Alex Francoeur
George Sereggela
Roderick W. Wilmer

3P SYSTEM CO., LTD.
500-35 Bukyang-Dong
Hwaseong, 445-040, Korea (South)
Tel.: (82) 31 3554087
Fax: (82) 31 3555751
E-Mail: account@3psystem.co.kr
Web Site: www.3psystem.co.kr
110500—(KRS)
Sales Range: $1-9.9 Million
Emp.: 40
Business Description:
Liquid Crystal Display (LCD) Equipment Mfr
S.I.C.: 3679
N.A.I.C.S.: 334419
Personnel:
Won Jae Lee *(CEO)*

3POWER ENERGY GROUP, INC.
Sh Rashid Building Sh Zayed Road
PO Box 50006
Dubai, United Arab Emirates
Tel.: (971) 4 3210312
E-Mail: info@3powerenergy.com
Web Site: www.3powerenergy.com
Year Founded: 2002
PSPW—(OTC)
Assets: $17,145
Liabilities: $8,538,652
Net Worth: ($8,521,507)
Earnings: ($2,220,088)
Emp.: 2
Fiscal Year-end: 03/31/13
Business Description:
Hydro, Wind & Solar Power Generation
S.I.C.: 4939
N.A.I.C.S.: 221114
Personnel:
Mohammed Falaknaz *(Chm)*
Shariff Rahman *(CEO & CFO)*
Dimitris Kazantzis *(Chief Engrg Officer)*
Board of Directors:
Mohammed Falaknaz
Dimitris Kazantzis
Shariff Rahman

3Q HOLDINGS LIMITED
Ground Floor 35 Spring Street
Bondi Junction, NSW, 2022, Australia
Tel.: (61) 293698590
Fax: (61) 293877110
Web Site: www.threeq.com.au
Rev.: $24,290,828
Assets: $48,057,987
Liabilities: $27,178,068
Net Worth: $20,879,919
Earnings: $137,298
Emp.: 193
Fiscal Year-end: 06/30/13
Business Description:
Software Publisher
S.I.C.: 7372
N.A.I.C.S.: 511210
Personnel:
Shaun Rosen *(Chm)*
Alan Treisman *(CFO & Sec)*
Andrew Bell *(CTO-Advance Retail)*
Clive Klugman *(CEO-Island Pacific Australia Pty Ltd)*
David Rosen *(CEO-Island Pacific Systems Inc)*
Board of Directors:
Shaun Rosen
Clive Klugman
Mark McGeachen
Alan Treisman
Stephe Wilks
Legal Counsel:
Freehills
MLC Centre Martin Place
Sydney, Australia

Subsidiary:

Island Pacific **(1)**
17310 Redhill Ave Ste 320
Irvine, CA 92614 NV
Tel.: (949) 476-2212
Fax: (949) 476-0177
Toll Free: (800) 99-GETIP
E-Mail: info@islandpacific.com
Web Site: www.islandpacific.com
Sales Range: $25-49.9 Million
Emp.: 185
Software & E-Commerce Business Solutions Mfr & Retailer
S.I.C.: 7372
N.A.I.C.S.: 511210
Davy Rosen *(CEO)*
Richard Gaetano *(COO)*
Jay Fisher *(CTO)*

3S KOREA CO., LTD.
112-3 Siheung 1-dong
Geumcheon-gu, Seoul, Korea (South)
Tel.: (82) 2 896 9474
Fax: (82) 2 896 9376
Web Site: www.3sref.com
Year Founded: 1989
060310—(KRS)
Business Description:
Electronic Component Mfr
S.I.C.: 3679
N.A.I.C.S.: 334419
Personnel:
Jong-Ik Park *(CEO)*

3SBIO INC.
3 A1 Road 10 Shenyang Economy & Development Zone
Shenyang, 110027, China
Tel.: (86) 24 2581 1820
E-Mail: Ir@3sbio.com
Web Site: www.3sbio.com
Year Founded: 1993
Rev.: $106,421,240
Assets: $233,514,107
Liabilities: $14,519,843
Net Worth: $218,994,264
Earnings: $16,294,039
Emp.: 891
Fiscal Year-end: 12/31/12
Business Description:
Holding Company; Biopharmaceutical Product Mfr
S.I.C.: 6719
N.A.I.C.S.: 551112
Personnel:
Jing Lou *(Founder, Chm & CEO)*
Bo Tan *(CFO)*
David Chen *(COO)*
Yingfei Wei *(VP-Bus Dev & Chief Scientific Officer)*
Ke Li *(Sec)*
Board of Directors:
Peiguo Cong
Bin Huang
Jing Lou
Tianruo Robert Pu
Moujia Qi
Dongmei Su
Mingde Yu

Subsidiary:

Shenyang Sunshine Pharmaceutical Co., Limited **(1)**
No 3 No 1a No 10 Road Economic Technology Development Zone
Shenyang, Liaoning, 110027, China
Tel.: (86) 2425811820
Fax: (86) 2425811821
Biopharmaceutical Products Mfr
S.I.C.: 2834
N.A.I.C.S.: 325412

3TIER, INC.
(Acquired by Vaisala Oyj)

3U HOLDING AG
Frauenbergstrasse 31-33
35039 Marburg, Germany
Tel.: (49) 64219991200
Fax: (49) 64219991222
E-Mail: info@3u.net
Web Site: www.3u.net
UUU—(DEU)
Sls.: $82,093,485
Assets: $82,870,225
Liabilities: $14,579,021
Net Worth: $68,291,204
Earnings: ($14,309,787)
Emp.: 188
Fiscal Year-end: 12/31/12
Business Description:
Holding Company
S.I.C.: 6719
N.A.I.C.S.: 551112
Personnel:
Ralf Thoenes *(Chm-Supervisory Bd)*
Gerd Simon *(Vice Chm-Supervisory Bd)*
Christoph Hellrung *(Member-Mgmt Bd)*
Andreas Odenbreit *(Memebr-Mgmt Bd)*
Michael Schmidt *(Member-Mgmt Bd)*
Supervisory Board of Directors:
Ralf Thoenes
Gerd Simon
Stefan Thies

3W POWER S.A.
Weerenweg 29
1161 AG Zwanenburg, Netherlands
Tel.: (31) 204077854
Fax: (31) 204077801
E-Mail: investors@aegps.com
Web Site: www.aegps.com
3W9—(DEU)
Rev.: $495,379,791
Assets: $489,969,533
Liabilities: $355,480,420
Net Worth: $134,489,114
Earnings: ($239,445,950)
Emp.: 1,522
Fiscal Year-end: 12/31/12
Business Description:
Holding Company
S.I.C.: 6719
N.A.I.C.S.: 551112
Personnel:
Bruce A. Brock *(Chm & CEO)*
Robert J. Huljak *(Pres & Gen Mgr)*
Jeffrey Casper *(CFO)*
Board of Directors:
Bruce A. Brock
Keith Baden Corbin
Robert J. Huljak
Lawrence N. Lavine
Thomas Middelhoff
Christopher P. Minnetian
Harris N. Williams
Mark Wossner

Non-U.S. Subsidiary:

AEG Power Solutions B.V. **(1)**
Weerenweg 29
1161 AH Zwanenburg, Netherlands
Mailing Address:
Postbus 82
1160AB Zwanenburg, Netherlands
Tel.: (31) 204077800
Telex: 41274 nife nl
Fax: (31) 204077801
Web Site: www.aegps.com
Emp.: 50
Electrical Power Control System Mfr
S.I.C.: 3643
N.A.I.C.S.: 335931
Bob Roos *(VP & Gen Mgr-Solar Bus Unit)*

U.S. Subsidiaries:

AEG Power Solutions USA, Inc. **(2)**
800 Klein Rd Ste 400
Plano, TX 75074 DE
Tel.: (469) 299-9600
Telex: 547-620
Fax: (469) 299-9650
Toll Free: (888) 727-7238
Web Site: www.aegps.com
Emp.: 20
Electrical Power Control System Mfr
S.I.C.: 3643
N.A.I.C.S.: 335931
Scott Everett *(VP-Sls-North America)*

Non-U.S. Subsidiaries:

AEG Power Solutions Aram. Kft **(2)**
Kondorfa utca 10
1116 Budapest, Hungary
Tel.: (36) 12099550
Fax: (36) 1 209 9555
Power Supplies Mfr & Distr
S.I.C.: 3699
N.A.I.C.S.: 335999

AEG Power Solutions Co. **(2)**
N 10 Factory of KangSheng Industrial Park
11 Kangding Street
Beijing, 100176, China
Tel.: (86) 10 6780 3466
Fax: (86) 10 6780 3819
E-Mail: sales.china@aegps.com
Power Supplies Equipment Mfr & Distr
S.I.C.: 3699
N.A.I.C.S.: 335999

AEG Power Solutions (France) S.A.S **(2)**
ZI 10 Rue Jean Perrin
37173 Chambray les Tours, France
Tel.: (33) 247808860
Fax: (33) 247280719
E-Mail: services.psf@aegps.com
Web Site: www.aeg.com
Emp.: 140
Electric Power Generation Services
S.I.C.: 4939
N.A.I.C.S.: 221118
Bruno Vilain *(Gen Mgr)*

AEG Power Solutions GmbH **(2)**
Emil Siepmann Strasse 32
D 59581 Warstein, Germany De
Tel.: (49) 29027630
Fax: (49) 2902763680
Web Site: www.aegpowercontrollers.com
Electrical Power Control System Mfr
S.I.C.: 3643
N.A.I.C.S.: 335931
Karl-Heinz Schulz *(CEO)*

AEG Power Solutions Iberica SL **(2)**
Parque Tecnologico de Alava C/Albert Einstein 31
01510 Minano, Alava, Spain
Tel.: (34) 945214110
Fax: (34) 945214111
E-Mail: servicios.iberica@aegps.com
Web Site: www.aegps.es
Emp.: 63
Power Transmission Equipment Distr
S.I.C.: 5084
N.A.I.C.S.: 423830
Maria Rodriguez *(Gen Mgr)*

AEG Power Solutions Inc. **(2)**
2680 14th Avenue Units 1 2
Markham, ON, L3R 5B2, Canada
Tel.: (888) 727-7238
Telex: 65-26167
Fax: (905) 480-9366
Web Site: www.aegps.com
Sales Range: $10-24.9 Million
Emp.: 87
Electrical Power Control System Mfr
S.I.C.: 3643
N.A.I.C.S.: 335931

AEG Power Solutions Ltd. **(2)**
Units 1 2 97 101 Peregrine Road
Hainault, Ilford, Essex, IG6 3XJ, United Kingdom

Tel.: (44) 2084981177
Fax: (44) 2085009365
E-Mail: uk.service@aegps.com
Web Site: www.aegps.com
Emp.: 50
Telecommunication Equipment Power Supply Products
Import Export
S.I.C.: 3643
N.A.I.C.S.: 335931
Michael Adams *(Mng Dir)*

AEG Power Solutions Middle East (2)
Office 5EA 225 Dubai Airport Free Zone
PO Box 54887
Dubai, United Arab Emirates
Tel.: (971) 4 6091 290
Fax: (971) 4 6091 291
Power Supplies Mfr & Distr
S.I.C.: 3699
N.A.I.C.S.: 335999
Assem Salaam *(Dir-Sls)*

AEG Power Solutions (Russia) LLC (2)
23 Novoslobodskaya Street Office 346
127055 Moscow, Russia
Tel.: (7) 4957950744
Fax: (7) 4957950743
Power Supplies Mfr & Distr
S.I.C.: 3699
N.A.I.C.S.: 335999

AEG Power Solutions S.A.S (2)
93/95 rue des Trois Fontanot
BP 404
92004 Nanterre, France
Tel.: (33) 1 55 51 10 40
Fax: (33) 1 55 51 10 41
E-Mail: commercial.france@aegps.com
Power Generation Services
S.I.C.: 4911
N.A.I.C.S.: 221118

AEG Power Solutions Sdn Bhd (2)
14th Floor Menara Safuan N 80
Jalan Ampang, Kuala Lumpur, 50450, Malaysia
Tel.: (60) 3 2078 8996
Fax: (60) 3 2078 8995
Emp.: 10
Electric Power Generation Services
S.I.C.: 4939
N.A.I.C.S.: 221118
Yahya Lattif *(Mng Dir)*

AEG Power Solutions, S.L. (2)
Parque Tecnologico De Alava
C Albert Einstein 31, 1510 Minano, Alava, Spain
Tel.: (34) 945214110
Fax: (34) 945214111
Web Site: www.spsi.es
Rev.: $24,143,100
Emp.: 200
Mfr of Batteries
S.I.C.: 3691
N.A.I.C.S.: 335911
Jesus Maria Rodriguez *(Gen Mgr)*

AEG Power Solutions S.p.A. (2)
Via Trento 30
20871 Vimercate, MB, Italy
Tel.: (39) 039 686 1
Fax: (39) 039 686 3847
E-Mail: service.it@aegps.com
Power Supplies Mfr & Distr
S.I.C.: 3699
N.A.I.C.S.: 335999
Alberto Dall'Asta *(Dir-Sls)*

AEG Power Solutions spol. s.r.o. (2)
Na Vlastni Pude 6/1368
102 00 Prague, 15, Czech Republic
Tel.: (420) 274 773 273
Fax: (420) 274 773 265
E-Mail: aeg@aeg-ups.cz
Web Site: www.aeg-ups.cz
Optical Fiber Cables Mfr
S.I.C.: 3357
N.A.I.C.S.: 335921

Harmer & Simmons (2)
Via Trento 30
Vimercate, 20059 Milan, Italy
Tel.: (39) 0396863837
Telex: 270355 nife i
Fax: (39) 0396863847
Web Site: www.aegps.com
Emp.: 40
Telecommunication Equipment Power Supply Products
S.I.C.: 3643
N.A.I.C.S.: 335931
Roberto Moro *(Gen Mgr)*

Skytron Energy GmbH (2)
Ernst-Augustin-Strasse 12
12489 Berlin, Germany
Tel.: (49) 3068831590
Fax: (49) 30688315999
E-Mail: info@skytron-energy.com
Web Site: www.skytron-energy.com
Emp.: 60
Photovoltaic System Installation Services
S.I.C.: 1629
N.A.I.C.S.: 237130
Marco Wirnsberger *(Mng Dir)*

4 OFFICE AUTOMATION LTD.
425 Superior Blvd Unit 1 & 2
Mississauga, ON, L5T 2W5, Canada
Tel.: (905) 564-0522
Fax: (905) 564-2865
Web Site: www.4office.ca
Sales Range: $10-24.9 Million
Emp.: 75
Business Description:
Digital Office Equipment Sales
S.I.C.: 5044
N.A.I.C.S.: 423420
Personnel:
Bill Norgate *(Pres)*

401 AUTO DEALERS EXCHANGE
60 Rigney St
Kingston, ON, K7K 6Z2, Canada
Tel.: (613) 536-0401
Fax: (613) 536-1044
Toll Free: (866) 315-4182
Web Site: www.401ade.com
Rev.: $28,952,668
Emp.: 50
Business Description:
Auto Auction Whslr
S.I.C.: 5012
N.A.I.C.S.: 423110
Personnel:
David Nelson *(Pres)*

401-DIXIE NISSAN
5500 Dixie Road
Mississauga, ON, L4W 4N3, Canada
Tel.: (905) 238-5500
Fax: (905) 238-5201
E-Mail: info@401dixienissan.com
Web Site: www.401dixienissan.com
Rev.: $73,592,036
Emp.: 65
Business Description:
New & Used Car Sales & Service
S.I.C.: 5511
N.A.I.C.S.: 441110
Personnel:
Keith de Podesta *(Mgr-Sls)*

407 INTERNATIONAL INC.
(d/b/a 407 ETR)
6300 Steeles Avenue West
Woodbridge, ON, L4H 1J1, Canada
Tel.: (905) 265-4070
Fax: (905) 265-4071
E-Mail: customerservice@407etr.com
Web Site: www.407etr.com
Sales Range: $300-349.9 Million
Emp.: 600
Business Description:
Toll Highway Operation, Management & Maintenance Services
S.I.C.: 4789
N.A.I.C.S.: 488490
Personnel:
Jose Tamariz *(Pres & CEO)*
Kenneth A. Walker *(CFO)*
Imad I. Nassereddine *(Chief Traffic Ops Officer)*
Murray Paton *(Gen Counsel)*

4077491 CANADA INC
(d/b/a Bois Laurentien Inc.)
395 Stinson
Saint Laurent, QC, H4N 2E1, Canada
Tel.: (514) 748-2028
Fax: (514) 748-2017
E-Mail: info@boislaurentien.com
Web Site: www.boislaurentien.com
Rev.: $10,742,517
Emp.: 100
Business Description:
Wooden Pallets Mfr & Distr
S.I.C.: 2448
N.A.I.C.S.: 321920
Personnel:
Marcel Guertin *(Pres & Gen Mgr)*

413554 ONTARIO LIMITED
(d/b/a Chouinard Bros.)
194 Earl Stewart Dr
Aurora, ON, L4G 6V7, Canada
Tel.: (905) 479-8300
Fax: (905) 479-8305
Toll Free: (800) 521-3229
E-Mail: info@chouinardbros.com
Web Site: www.chouinardbros.com
Year Founded: 1972
Rev.: $38,997,975
Emp.: 65
Business Description:
Residential Roofing Services
S.I.C.: 1761
N.A.I.C.S.: 238160
Personnel:
Lucien Chouinard *(Owner)*
Larry Slanks *(Pres)*
Catherine Chouinard *(Sec)*

4236009 MANITOBA LTD
(d/b/a Kelleher Ford Sales)
1445 - 18th Street North
Brandon, MB, R7C1A6, Canada
Tel.: (204) 728-8554
Fax: (204) 726-4365
Web Site: www.kelleherford.com
Year Founded: 1990
Rev.: $13,594,008
Emp.: 60
Business Description:
New & Used Car Dealers
S.I.C.: 5511
N.A.I.C.S.: 441110
Personnel:
Kara Burgoyne *(Controller)*

429149 B.C. LTD
(d/b/a Quilts Etc.)
4150 McConnell Drive
Burnaby, BC, V5A 3Y9, Canada
Tel.: (604) 421-5520
Fax: (604) 421-5540
Toll Free: (866) 421-5520
E-Mail: webstore@quiltsetc.com
Web Site: www.quiltsetc.com
Year Founded: 1992
Rev.: $27,213,769
Emp.: 250
Business Description:
Bed Linen Mfr & Retailer
S.I.C.: 7213
N.A.I.C.S.: 812331
Personnel:
Howard Haugom *(Pres)*

450477 ONTARIO LTD
(d/b/a Chartrand Equipment)
2401 Airport Road
Timmins, ON, P4N 7C3, Canada
Tel.: (705) 268-0510
Fax: (705) 268-3602
E-Mail: officec@chartrandequipment.com
Web Site: www.chartrandequipment.com
Year Founded: 1980
Rev.: $19,562,614
Emp.: 120
Business Description:
Construction Engineering Services
S.I.C.: 8711
N.A.I.C.S.: 541330
Personnel:
Colette Chartrand *(Co-Founder)*
Maurice Chartrand *(Co-Founder)*

477599 ALBERTA LTD
(d/b/a Cash Casino Place)
4040 Blackfoot Trail SE
Calgary, AB, T2G 4E6, Canada
Tel.: (403) 287-1635
Fax: (403) 243-4812
Year Founded: 1980
Rev.: $11,650,623
Emp.: 200
Business Description:
Casino Gaming Services
S.I.C.: 7999
N.A.I.C.S.: 713210
Personnel:
Joe Chapple *(Gen Mgr)*

487244 ALBERTA LTD
(d/b/a Autoworld Mazda)
6217 50th Street
Leduc, AB, T9E 7A9, Canada
Tel.: (780) 986-9665
Fax: (780) 986-9611
Toll Free: (888) 217-0208
E-Mail: info@autoworldmazda.com
Web Site: www.autoworldmazda.com
Rev.: $43,241,165
Emp.: 85
Business Description:
New & Used Car Dealers
S.I.C.: 5511
N.A.I.C.S.: 441110
Personnel:
Earl Reed *(Gen Mgr)*

49 NORTH RESOURCES INC.
Suite 602 - 224 4th Avenue S
Saskatoon, SK, S7K 5M5, Canada
Tel.: (306) 653-2692
Fax: (306) 664-4483
Web Site: www.fnr.ca
O49—(DEU)
Sales Range: $1-9.9 Million
Business Description:
Oil & Gas Exploration Services
S.I.C.: 1389
N.A.I.C.S.: 213112
Personnel:
Tom MacNeill *(Pres & CEO)*
Andrew Davidson *(CFO)*
Board of Directors:
Norman Betts
Jeffrey N. Green
Stephen P. Halabura
Tom MacNeill
C. Michael Ryer

4D PHARMA PLC
74 Gartside Street
Manchester, M3 3EL, United Kingdom
Tel.: (44) 161 837 6205
Fax: (44) 161 837 6201
E-Mail: info@4dpharmaplc.com
Web Site: www.4dpharmaplc.com
DDDD—(AIM)
Business Description:
Pharmaceutical Mfr
S.I.C.: 2834
N.A.I.C.S.: 325412

4D Pharma PLC—(Continued)

Personnel:
David Norwood *(Chm)*
Duncan Peyton *(CEO)*
Alex Stevenson *(Chief Scientific Officer)*
Board of Directors:
David Norwood
Thomas Engelen
Duncan Peyton
Alex Stevenson

4ENERGY INVEST N.V./S.A.

Paepsem Business Park Boulevard
Paepsemlaan 20
1070 Brussels, Belgium
Tel.: (32) 25269010
Fax: (32) 25269019
E-Mail: info@4energyinvest.com
Web Site: www.4energyinvest.com
ENIN—(EUR)
Sls.: $26,366,086
Assets: $76,088,221
Liabilities: $96,104,422
Net Worth: ($20,016,202)
Earnings: ($50,335,989)
Emp.: 29
Fiscal Year-end: 12/31/12
Business Description:
Renewable Energy Producer
S.I.C.: 4939
N.A.I.C.S.: 221118
Personnel:
Filip Lesaffer *(Chm)*
Nathalie De Ceulaer *(Interim CFO)*
Board of Directors:
Filip Lesaffer
Yves Crits
Nathalie De Ceulaer
Henri Meyers
Guido Schockaert
Philiep Van Eeckhout

Subsidiaries:

4BioFuels S.A. **(1)**
Chaussee d Ophain 181
1420 Braine-l'Alleud, Belgium
Tel.: (32) 80540151
Fax: (32) 80548683
Firewood Biomass Production Services
S.I.C.: 2499
N.A.I.C.S.: 321999
Yves Crits *(Mgr)*

Renogen S.A. **(1)**
Chaussee d Ophain 181
1420 Braine-l'Alleud, Belgium
Tel.: (32) 80540151
Fax: (32) 80 54 86 83
Firewood Biomass Production Services
S.I.C.: 2499
N.A.I.C.S.: 321999

4FUN MEDIA S.A.

ul Bobrowiecka 1A
00-728 Warsaw, Poland
Tel.: (48) 224884300
Fax: (48) 224884250
E-Mail: biuro.prasowe@4funmedia.pl
Web Site: www.4funmedia.pl
4FM—(WAR)
Rev.: $10,187,535
Assets: $12,931,549
Liabilities: $1,309,352
Net Worth: $11,622,197
Earnings: $2,647,751
Emp.: 60
Fiscal Year-end: 12/31/12
Business Description:
Television & Video Broadcasting, Production & Distribution Services
S.I.C.: 4833
N.A.I.C.S.: 515120
Personnel:
Dariusz Stokowski *(Chm-Supervisory Bd)*
Ewa Czekala *(CEO, Mng Dir & Member-Mgmt Bd)*
Aneta Parafiniuk *(CFO & Member-Mgmt Bd)*
Supervisory Board of Directors:
Dariusz Stokowski
Andrzej Karasowski
Andrzej Paluszynski
Marek Sowa

4IMPRINT GROUP PLC

7/8 Market Place
London, W1W 8AG, United Kingdom
Tel.: (44) 2072997201
Fax: (44) 2072997209
E-Mail: hq@4imprint.co.uk
Web Site: www.4imprint.co.uk
Year Founded: 1921
FOUR—(LSE)
Rev.: $288,888,465
Assets: $95,076,417
Liabilities: $73,298,007
Net Worth: $21,778,409
Earnings: $22,225,348
Emp.: 753
Fiscal Year-end: 12/31/12
Business Description:
Supplier of Promotional Products
S.I.C.: 7389
N.A.I.C.S.: 561990
Personnel:
John W. Poulter *(Chm)*
Andrew J. Scull *(Legal Counsel, Sec & Dir-Corp Svcs)*
Board of Directors:
John W. Poulter
Gillian Davies
Stephen Gray
Kevin Lyons-Tarr
Andrew J. Scull
John Warren
Legal Counsel:
Pinsent Curtis
1 Park Row
Leeds, L51 5AB, United Kingdom
Tel.: (44) 113 244 5000
Fax: (44) 113 244 8000
Transfer Agent:
Capita Registrars Limited
The Registry 34 Beckenham Road
Beckenham, Kent, BR3 4TU, United Kingdom
Tel.: (44) 20 8639 2157
Fax: (44) 20 8658 3430

U.S. Subsidiary:

4imprint Inc. **(1)**
101 Commerce St
Oshkosh, WI 54901 (100%)
Tel.: (920) 236-7272
Fax: (800) 355-5043
Web Site: www.4imprint.com
Emp.: 400
Supplier of Promotional Goods
S.I.C.: 7319
N.A.I.C.S.: 541890
Kevin Lyons-Tarr *(Pres)*

4IP MANAGEMENT AG

Feldeggstrasse 39
8008 Zurich, Switzerland
Tel.: (41) 442131400
Fax: (41) 442128477
E-Mail: info@4ip.ch
Web Site: www.4ip.ch
Business Description:
Asset Management & Investment Banking Services
S.I.C.: 6211
N.A.I.C.S.: 523110
Personnel:
Ulrich Kaluscha *(CEO, Mng Dir & Head-Non-Listed Property Funds)*
Board of Directors:
Jan Eckert
Ulrich Kaluscha
Nick van Ommen

4SC AG

Am Klopferspitz 19a Planegg
82152 Martinsried, Germany
Tel.: (49) 897007630
Fax: (49) 8970076329
Web Site: www.4sc.de
VSC—(DEU)
Rev.: $5,859,878
Assets: $39,129,123
Liabilities: $9,765,117
Net Worth: $29,364,006
Earnings: ($17,792,329)
Emp.: 86
Fiscal Year-end: 12/31/12
Business Description:
Drug Research & Development Services
S.I.C.: 8731
N.A.I.C.S.: 541711
Personnel:
Thomas Werner *(Chm-Supervisory Bd)*
Klaus Kuhn *(Deputy Chm-Supervisory Bd)*
Enno Spillner *(CEO, CFO & Member-Mgmt Bd)*
Bernd Hentsch *(Chief Dev Officer & Member-Mgmt Bd)*
Daniel Vitt *(Chief Scientific Officer & Member-Mgmt Bd)*
Supervisory Board of Directors:
Thomas Werner
Irina Antonijevic
Clemens Doppler
Helmut Jeggle
Klaus Kuhn
Manfred Rudiger

500.COM LIMITED

500.com Building Shenxianling Sports Center
Longgang District, Shenzhen, 518115, China
Tel.: (86) 755 8633 0000
Fax: (86) 755 8379 6070
Web Site: www.500.com
WBAI—(NYSE)
Rev.: $27,247,064
Assets: $60,258,636
Liabilities: $60,674,823
Net Worth: ($416,187)
Earnings: $674,001
Emp.: 353
Fiscal Year-end: 12/31/12
Business Description:
Online Sports Lottery Services
S.I.C.: 7999
N.A.I.C.S.: 713290
Personnel:
Man San Law *(Chm & CEO)*
Zhengming Pan *(CFO)*
Lei Zheng *(COO)*
Zhaofu Tian *(CTO)*
Punleung Liu *(Chief Risk Officer)*
Board of Directors:
Man San Law
Honghui Deng
Min Fan
Jiepin Fu
Qi Li
Jinping Ma
Jun Niu
Qian Sun
Yu Wei
Zhe Wei
Qin Zhang

501548 ONTARIO LTD

(d/b/a Ottawa Honda)
955 Richmond Rd
Ottawa, ON, K2B 6R1, Canada
Tel.: (613) 726-0333
Fax: (613) 728-0995
Web Site: www.ottawahonda.com
Year Founded: 1982
Rev.: $24,344,586
Emp.: 40
Business Description:
New & Used Car Dealers
S.I.C.: 5511
N.A.I.C.S.: 441110
Personnel:
M. Kewal Dilawri *(Pres)*

502386 ALBERTA LTD

(d/b/a T&T Honda)
888 Meridian Road NE
Calgary, AB, T2A 2N8, Canada
Tel.: (403) 291-1444
Fax: (403) 207-4356
Toll Free: (888) 606-4540
Web Site: www.tandthonda.ca
Year Founded: 1983
Rev.: $46,314,400
Emp.: 100
Business Description:
New & Used Car Dealers
S.I.C.: 5511
N.A.I.C.S.: 441110
Personnel:
Izzie Manji *(Pres)*

51JOB, INC.

Building 3 No 1387 Zhang Dong Road
Shanghai, 201203, China
Tel.: (86) 2161601888
Fax: (86) 21 6360 5788
E-Mail: investor.relations@51job.com
Web Site: www.51job.com
Year Founded: 1997
JOBS—(NASDAQ)
Rev.: $240,220,754
Assets: $514,890,354
Liabilities: $91,391,806
Net Worth: $423,498,548
Earnings: $74,676,338
Emp.: 4,593
Fiscal Year-end: 12/31/12
Business Description:
Human Resource & Recruitment Related Services
S.I.C.: 8999
N.A.I.C.S.: 541612
Personnel:
David K. Chao *(Chm)*
Rick Yan *(Pres & CEO)*
Kathleen Chien *(COO & Acting CFO)*
David Weimin Jin *(Sr VP)*
Board of Directors:
David K. Chao
Li-Lan Cheng
Hiroyuki Honda
James Jianzhang Liang
Kazumasa Watanabe
Legal Counsel:
Simpson Thacher & Bartlett LLP
ICBC Tower 7th Fl
3 Garden Road, Hong Kong, China (Hong Kong)

52 WEEKS ENTERTAINMENT LIMITED

Tarabai Hall 97 Shivprasad Building
Marine Drive
Mumbai, 400 002, India
Tel.: (91) 22 22842127
Fax: (91) 22 22819226
E-Mail: 52weeksentltd@gmail.com
Web Site: www.ssal.in
Year Founded: 1993
531925—(BOM)
Rev.: $98,800
Assets: $3,227,425
Liabilities: $2,214,344
Net Worth: $1,013,081
Earnings: $48,909
Fiscal Year-end: 03/31/13

Business Description:
Prawn Breeding Services
S.I.C.: 0273
N.A.I.C.S.: 112512
Personnel:
Surendra N. Morne *(Compliance Officer)*
Board of Directors:
Bharat Belose
Surendra N. Morne
Nayantara Sheorey
Shantanu Sheorey
Transfer Agent:
Universal Capital Securities Pvt. Ltd
21 Shakil Niwas Mahakali Caves Road Andheri East
Mumbai, India

524 PARTICIPACOES S.A.
Av Presidente Wilson 231 - 28 Andar/ parte
20030021 Rio de Janeiro, Brazil
Tel.: (55) 21 3804 3700
Fax: (55) 21 3804 3480
Web Site: www.524participacoes.com.br
Year Founded: 1997
QVQP3B—(BRAZ)
Business Description:
Investment Management Services
S.I.C.: 6799
N.A.I.C.S.: 523920
Personnel:
Maria Amalia Delfim de Melo Coutrim *(Dir-IR)*

530664 ALBERTA LTD
(d/b/a Northgate Honda)
13116 100 St
Grande Prairie, AB, T8V 4H9, Canada
Tel.: (780) 532-8010
Fax: (780) 532-8017
Toll Free: (888) 532-8010
E-Mail: info@northgatehonda.com
Web Site: www.northgatehonda.com
Year Founded: 1993
Rev.: $15,757,354
Emp.: 45
Business Description:
New & Used Vehicle Dealers
S.I.C.: 5571
N.A.I.C.S.: 441228
Personnel:
Marshall Shmyr *(Gen Mgr-Sls-New Vehicle)*

533438 ONTARIO LIMITED
(d/b/a Northlander Industries)
165 Thames Road East Hwy 83
Exeter, ON, N0M 1S3, Canada
Tel.: (519) 235-1530
Fax: (519) 235-2789
E-Mail: innovations@northlanderindustries.com
Web Site: www.northlanderindustries.com
Year Founded: 1964
Rev.: $14,825,611
Emp.: 140
Business Description:
Mobile Homes Designing & Building Services
S.I.C.: 5271
N.A.I.C.S.: 453930
Personnel:
Jim Gregory *(Controller)*

561870 ONTARIO LTD
(d/b/a Wallace Automobiles Inc.)
460 McArthur Avenue
Ottawa, ON, K1K 1G4, Canada
Tel.: (613) 746-9646
Fax: (613) 746-2094
E-Mail: info@wallaceautomobiles.com
Web Site: www.wallaceautomobiles.com
Year Founded: 1963
Rev.: $17,085,000
Emp.: 7
Business Description:
New & Used Car Dealers
S.I.C.: 5511
N.A.I.C.S.: 441110
Personnel:
Bruce Wallace *(Owner)*

565 CONSTRUCTION JOINT STOCK COMPANY
Quiet Street Tan Thinh Ward
Hoa Binh, Vietnam
Tel.: (84) 2183854024
Fax: (84) 2183855055
E-Mail: hoabinh@tsc565.vn
Web Site: www.tsc565.vn
NSN—(HNX)
Emp.: 320
Business Description:
Infrastructure Construction Services
S.I.C.: 1622
N.A.I.C.S.: 237310
Personnel:
Toan Manh Nguyen *(Chm)*

583455 SASKATCHEWAN LTD
(d/b/a Triple Seven Chrysler)
700 Broad Street
Regina, SK, S4R 8R8, Canada
Tel.: (306) 522-2222
Fax: (306) 525-4400
Toll Free: (888) 615-1485
Web Site: www.tripleseven.autotrader.ca
Year Founded: 1987
Rev.: $30,343,788
Emp.: 61
Business Description:
New & Used Car Sales & Service
S.I.C.: 5511
N.A.I.C.S.: 441110
Personnel:
Ram Dilawri *(Principal)*

58.COM INC.
Block E The North American International Business Center
Yi 108 Beiyuan Road
Chaoyang District, Beijing, 100101, China
Tel.: (86) 10 5139 5858
Web Site: www.58.com
Year Founded: 2005
WUBA—(NYSE)
Rev.: $87,122,000
Assets: $56,456,000
Liabilities: $208,520,000
Net Worth: ($152,064,000)
Earnings: ($30,401,000)
Emp.: 5,660
Fiscal Year-end: 12/31/12
Business Description:
Online Retailer
S.I.C.: 5961
N.A.I.C.S.: 454111
Personnel:
Jinbo Yao *(Chm, Pres & CEO)*
Hao Zhou *(CFO)*
Xiaohua Chen *(Sr VP-Product Mgmt & Website Ops)*
Jiandong Zhuang *(Sr VP-Sls)*
Board of Directors:
Jinbo Yao
Wensheng Cai
Julian Cheung Lun Cheng
Frank Lin
Dong Yang

591182 ONTARIO LIMITED
(d/b/a Wolverine Freight System)
2500 Airport Rd
Windsor, ON, N8W 5E7, Canada
Tel.: (519) 966-8970
Fax: (519) 966-2800
E-Mail: inquiries@wolverinefreight.ca
Web Site: www.wolverinefreight.ca
Year Founded: 1984
Rev.: $40,625,562
Emp.: 300
Business Description:
Truckload & Milk Run Operation Services
S.I.C.: 4213
N.A.I.C.S.: 484121
Personnel:
John LaMantia *(Principal)*

591226 SASKATCHEWAN LTD
(d/b/a Meidl Honda)
110A Circle Drive East
Saskatoon, SK, S7K 4K1, Canada
Tel.: (306) 373-7477
Fax: (306) 373-6026
Toll Free: (866) 981-3784
Web Site: www.meidlhonda.ca
Year Founded: 1989
Rev.: $20,800,000
Emp.: 40
Business Description:
New & Used Vehicle Dealers
S.I.C.: 5511
N.A.I.C.S.: 441110
Personnel:
Viola Ayres *(Controller)*

595242 BC LTD
(d/b/a Newcastle Nissan)
3612 Island Highway North
Nanaimo, BC, V9T 1W2, Canada
Tel.: (250) 756-1515
Fax: (250) 756-1555
Toll Free: (877) 740-2967
E-Mail: info@newcastlenissan.com
Web Site: www.newcastlenissan.com
Year Founded: 1975
Rev.: $13,677,000
Emp.: 19
Business Description:
New & Used Car Dealers
S.I.C.: 5511
N.A.I.C.S.: 441110
Personnel:
Stephen Laird *(Owner)*

598755 B.C. LTD
(d/b/a Acura of Langley)
19447 Langley Bypass
Surrey, BC, V3S 6K1, Canada
Tel.: (604) 539-2111
Fax: (604) 539-2841
Toll Free: (888) 319-5207
E-Mail: grd@acuraoflangley.ca
Web Site: www.acuraoflangley.com
Year Founded: 1995
Rev.: $13,292,400
Emp.: 30
Business Description:
New & Used Car Dealers
S.I.C.: 5511
N.A.I.C.S.: 441110
Personnel:
Gary Daviduk *(Gen Mgr-Sls)*

598840 SASKATCHEWAN LTD.
(d/b/a Western Dodge Chrysler Jeep)
1788 Main Street North
Moose Jaw, SK, S6J 1L4, Canada
Tel.: (306) 692-1808
Fax: (306) 692-7008
Toll Free: (877) 273-6343
E-Mail: derroch@westerndodge.ca
Web Site: www.westerndodge.ca
Rev.: $13,347,016
Emp.: 30
Business Description:
New & Used Car Dealers
S.I.C.: 5511
N.A.I.C.S.: 441110
Personnel:
Kyle Knight *(Owner)*

5N PLUS INC.
4385 Garand
Montreal, QC, H4R 2B4, Canada
Tel.: (514) 856-0644
Fax: (514) 856-9611
E-Mail: info@5nplus.com
Web Site: www.5nplus.com
Year Founded: 2000
VNP—(DEU TSX)
Rev.: $551,675,000
Assets: $383,978,000
Liabilities: $235,508,000
Net Worth: $148,470,000
Earnings: ($227,849,000)
Emp.: 719
Fiscal Year-end: 12/31/12
Business Description:
Specialty Metal & Chemical Product Mfr
S.I.C.: 3499
N.A.I.C.S.: 332999
Personnel:
Dennis Wood *(Chm)*
Jacques L'Ecuyer *(Pres & CEO)*
Richard Perron *(CFO)*
Jean Mayer *(Sec & Dir-Legal Affairs)*
Board of Directors:
Dennis Wood
Jean-Marie Bourassa
John H. Davis
Jacques L'Ecuyer
Pierre Shoiry
Transfer Agent:
Computershare Investor Services Inc
1500 University Ste 700
Montreal, QC, Canada

THE 600 GROUP PLC
600 House Landmark Court Revie Road
Leeds, LS11 8JT, United Kingdom
Tel.: (44) 113 277 6100
Fax: (44) 113 200 8487
E-Mail: info@600group.com
Web Site: www.600group.com
Year Founded: 1834
SIXH—(LSE)
Rev.: $65,995,371
Assets: $70,283,143
Liabilities: $36,080,459
Net Worth: $34,202,684
Earnings: $6,216,085
Emp.: 337
Fiscal Year-end: 03/31/13
Business Description:
Machine Tools & Accessories, Lasers & other Engineering Products Mfr & Distr
S.I.C.: 3545
N.A.I.C.S.: 333515
Personnel:
Nigel Foster Rogers *(CEO)*
Neil Richard Carrick *(Sec & Dir-Fin)*
Board of Directors:
Paul Dupee
Neil Richard Carrick
Nigel Foster Rogers
Stephen John Rutherford
Derek Zissman
Legal Counsel:
Simmons & Simmons
14 Dominion St.
London, EC2M 2RJ, United Kingdom

The 600 Group PLC—(Continued)

Subsidiaries:

The 600 Group (Overseas) Limited (1)
600 House 3 Landmark Court
Leeds, West Yorkshire, LS11 8JT, United Kingdom
Tel.: (44) 113 277 6100
Fax: (44) 113 276 5600
Machine Tools Mfr
S.I.C.: 3541
N.A.I.C.S.: 333517

600 Lathes Ltd (1)
Union St
PO Box 20
Heckmondwike, W Yorkshire, WF16 0HN, United Kingdom UK
Tel.: (44) 1924415000 (100%)
Fax: (44) 1924415015
E-Mail: mail@600lathes.co.uk
Web Site: www.600uk.com
Emp.: 200
Lathes Mfr
S.I.C.: 3542
N.A.I.C.S.: 333517
Mike Berry *(Mng Dir)*

Subsidiaries:

The 600 UK Ltd. (2)
Union St
PO Box 20
Heckmondwike, W Yorkshire, WF16 0HN, United Kingdom UK
Tel.: (44) 1924 415000 (100%)
Fax: (44) 1924 415011
E-Mail: mail@harrison.co.uk
Web Site: www.600group.com
Emp.: 100
Lathes Mfr
S.I.C.: 3541
N.A.I.C.S.: 333517
Nigel Foster Rogers *(Pres)*

Colchester Lathe Company Ltd (2)
PO Box 20
Union St, Heckmondwike, W Yorkshire, WF16 0HN, United Kingdom UK
Mailing Address: (100%)
PO Box 20
Heckmondwike, WF16 0HN, United Kingdom
Tel.: (44) 1924415005
Fax: (44) 1924415006
E-Mail: mail@600uk.com
Web Site: www.600uk.com
Emp.: 200
Lathes Mfr
S.I.C.: 3541
N.A.I.C.S.: 333517
David Norman *(CEO)*

600 Machinery International Ltd (1)
20 Grange Way Business Park Grange Way
Colchester, CO2 8HF, United Kingdom UK
Tel.: (44) 1206 796 600 (100%)
Fax: (44) 1206 793 600
E-Mail:
Web Site: www.600mac.co.uk
Emp.: 4
Machine Tool Mfr
S.I.C.: 3542
N.A.I.C.S.: 333517
Tony Sweeten *(Chm)*

600 UK (1)
Union Street
Heckmondwike, West Yorkshire, WF16 0HN, United Kingdom UK
Tel.: (44) 1924 415000 (100%)
Fax: (44) 1924 415011
E-Mail: mail@600uk.com
Web Site: www.600centre.co.uk
Emp.: 40
Machine Tool & Component Products Whslr
S.I.C.: 5084
N.A.I.C.S.: 423830
Ray Grocock *(Mng Dir)*

Gamet Bearings Ltd (1)
Hythe Station Road
Hythe, Colchester, Essex, CO2 8LD, United Kingdom UK
Tel.: (44) 1206862121 (100%)
Fax: (44) 1206868690
E-Mail: sales@gamet-bearings.co.uk
Web Site: www.gamet-bearings.co.uk
Emp.: 30
Bearings Mfr
S.I.C.: 3562
N.A.I.C.S.: 332991
Tony Tankard *(Gen Mgr)*

Pratt Burnerd International Limited (1)
Park Works Lister Ln
Halifax, West Yorkshire, HX1 5JH, United Kingdom UK
Tel.: (44) 1422366371 (100%)
Fax: (44) 1422359379
E-Mail: chucks@pratt-burnerd.co.uk
Web Site: www.pratt-burnerd.co.uk
Emp.: 55
Hand Tool Mfr
S.I.C.: 3546
N.A.I.C.S.: 333991

U.S. Subsidiary:

Clausing Industrial Inc (1)
1819 N Pitcher St
Kalamazoo, MI 49007-1886 (100%)
Tel.: (269) 345-7155
Fax: (269) 345-5945
E-Mail: info@clausing-industrial.com
Web Site: www.clausing-industrial.com
Emp.: 40
Cutting Tools Mgr
S.I.C.: 5084
N.A.I.C.S.: 423830
Don Haselton *(Pres)*

Subsidiaries:

600 Machine Tools (2)
5220 General Rd
Mississauga, ON, L4W 1G8, Canada (100%)
Tel.: (519) 250-5588
Fax: (519) 250-5589
E-Mail: sales@600mtc.com
Web Site: www.600machinetools.com
Emp.: 25
Machine Tools Whslr
S.I.C.: 5084
N.A.I.C.S.: 423830
Peter Turton *(Pres)*

Erickson Machine Tools Inc (2)
409 Market St
Story City, IA 50248 (100%)
Tel.: (515) 733-4361
Fax: (515) 733-2929
E-Mail: info@ericksonmachine.com
Web Site: www.ericksonmachine.com
Emp.: 15
Machine Tool Whslr
S.I.C.: 5084
N.A.I.C.S.: 423830
Kenneth Erickson, Jr. *(Pres)*

Lakeshore Machine Tools (2)
2015 N Pitcher St
Kalamazoo, MI 49007 (100%)
Tel.: (269) 349-6000
Fax: (269) 349-7326
Web Site: www.clausing-industrial.com
Emp.: 3
Machine Tool Whslr
S.I.C.: 5084
N.A.I.C.S.: 423830

Non-U.S. Subsidiaries:

600 International Ltd (1)
Baranova 33
130 00 Prague, Czech Republic (100%)
Tel.: (420) 22240133
Fax: (420) 222-44146
E-Mail: 600international@iol.cz
Web Site: www.the600group.com
Machine Tool Whslr
S.I.C.: 5084
N.A.I.C.S.: 423830

600 Machine Tools Pty Ltd (1)
27 Foundry Road Seven Hills
Newington, NSW, 2147, Australia (100%)
Tel.: (61) 297481964
Fax: (61) 296747641
E-Mail: tools@600machinery.com.au
Web Site: www.600machinery.com.au
Emp.: 50
Machine Tool Whslr
S.I.C.: 5084
N.A.I.C.S.: 423830

Branches:

600 Machine Tools New South Wales (2)
27 Foundry Rd
Newington Business Park, Seven Hills, NSW, 2127, Australia (100%)
Tel.: (61) 297481964
Fax: (61) 296747641
Web Site: www.600machinery.com.au
Emp.: 12
Machine Tool Whslr
S.I.C.: 5084
N.A.I.C.S.: 423830
Pliss Purser *(Mng Dir)*

600 Machine Tools New Zealand (2)
42 Allens Rd E Tamaki
Tamaki, Auckland, New Zealand (100%)
Tel.: (64) 92623025
Fax: (64) 92740360
Web Site: www.600machinery.com.au
Sales Range: $1-9.9 Million
Emp.: 2
Machine Tool Whslr
S.I.C.: 5084
N.A.I.C.S.: 423830

600 Machine Tools Queensland (2)
292 Evans Rd
Salisbury, QLD, 4107, Australia (100%)
Tel.: (61) 732774844
Fax: (61) 732779360
Web Site: www.600machinery.com.au
Emp.: 5
Machine Tool Whslr
S.I.C.: 5084
N.A.I.C.S.: 423830
Walley Nujin *(Gen Mgr)*

600 Machine Tools Victoria (2)
24 Wadhurst Dr
Boronia, VIC, 3155, Australia (100%)
Tel.: (61) 398003322
Fax: (61) 398873199
Web Site: www.600machinery.com.au
Emp.: 4
Machine Tool Whslr
S.I.C.: 5084
N.A.I.C.S.: 423830

Ambassador Machine Tools (2)
17 Prowse St
West Perth, WA, 6005, Australia (100%)
Tel.: (61) 893213611
Fax: (61) 893213511
E-Mail: amt@iprimus.com.au
Web Site: www.600machinery.com.au
Machine Tool Whslr
S.I.C.: 5084
N.A.I.C.S.: 423830

FMT Colchester z.o.o. (1)
Ul Jana Kochanowskiego 30
Tarnow, 33-100, Poland
Tel.: (48) 14 63 06 355
Fax: (48) 146306303
E-Mail: sekretariat@fmt-colchester.pl
Web Site: www.fmt-colchester.pl
Lathes & Grinding Machines Mfr
S.I.C.: 3559
N.A.I.C.S.: 333249
Mariusz Koziol *(Mng Dir)*

600956 ONTARIO LTD
(d/b/a Plasticsplus)
469 Woodward Avenue
Hamilton, ON, L8H 6N6, Canada
Tel.: (905) 549-4572
Fax: (905) 549-4580
E-Mail: lary@plasticsplus.ca
Web Site: www.plasticsplus.ca
Year Founded: 1984
Rev.: $10,433,394
Emp.: 70
Business Description:
Plastic Injection Molding Mfr & Automotive Supplier
S.I.C.: 3089
N.A.I.C.S.: 326199
Personnel:
Larry Mermuys *(Founder & Pres)*

602390 ONTARIO LIMITED
(d/b/a Ocean Seafood Company)
81 Scott Field Drive
Scarborough, ON, M1S 5R4, Canada
Tel.: (416) 740-9000
Fax: (416) 747-8082
Toll Free: (866) 722-8899
Web Site: www.oceanseafood.ca
Year Founded: 1984
Rev.: $34,680,440
Emp.: 40
Business Description:
Seafood Whslr & Distr
S.I.C.: 2092
N.A.I.C.S.: 311710
Personnel:
Patrick Lay *(Founder & Pres)*

615315 SASKATCHEWAN LTD
(d/b/a J.B.M. Logistics)
875 58th Street East
Saskatoon, SK, S7K 6X5, Canada
Tel.: (306) 653-5400
Fax: (306) 653-5422
Toll Free: (800) 764-5551
Web Site: www.jbmlogistics.com
Rev.: $12,618,568
Emp.: 75
Business Description:
Truckload Transportation & Services
S.I.C.: 4213
N.A.I.C.S.: 484121
Personnel:
Lindsay Keene *(Pres & Gen Mgr)*

658612 ONTARIO LTD
(d/b/a La Nassa Foods)
215 Industry Road
Kingsville, ON, N9Y 1K9, Canada
Tel.: (519) 733-9100
Fax: (519) 733-8924
Web Site: www.lanassafoods.com
Year Founded: 1986
Rev.: $21,475,403
Emp.: 50
Business Description:
Seafood Distr & Retailer
S.I.C.: 5146
N.A.I.C.S.: 424460
Personnel:
Tony Giacalone *(Pres)*
Vito Orlando Figliomeni *(VP, Sec & Treas)*

668824 ALBERTA LTD
(d/b/a Visions Electronics)
6009 1A St SW
Calgary, AB, T2H 0G5, Canada
Tel.: (403) 255-2270
Fax: (403) 255-6471
Toll Free: (866) 530-3363
E-Mail: help@visions.ca
Web Site: www.visions.ca
Rev.: $83,300,000
Emp.: 500
Business Description:
Electronic Stores
S.I.C.: 5734
N.A.I.C.S.: 443142
Personnel:
Richard Stewart *(Founder & Pres)*

669069 ALBERTA LTD
(d/b/a High River Toyota)
901 11th Ave SE
High River, AB, T1V 1P2, Canada
Tel.: (403) 652-1365
Fax: (403) 602-9986
Toll Free: (877) 694-1245
Web Site: www.highrivertoyota.ca
Year Founded: 1993
Rev.: $13,911,192
Emp.: 30
Business Description:
New & Used Car Dealers
S.I.C.: 5511

N.A.I.C.S.: 441110
Personnel:
Bev Murtack *(Controller)*

7 DAYS GROUP HOLDINGS LIMITED
5C-11 Creative Industry Zone 397
XinGangZhong Road
Guangzhou, Guangdong, 510310, China
Tel.: (86) 2089226577
Fax: (86) 2089226707
Web Site: www.7daysinn.cn
Year Founded: 2004
Rev.: $406,208,837
Assets: $482,430,786
Liabilities: $222,216,854
Net Worth: $260,213,932
Earnings: $25,285,425
Emp.: 28,764
Fiscal Year-end: 12/31/12
Business Description:
Hotel Owner & Operator
S.I.C.: 7011
N.A.I.C.S.: 721110
Personnel:
Alex Nanyan Zheng *(Co-Chm & CEO)*
Boquan He *(Co-Chm)*
Eric Haibing Wu *(CFO)*
Yuezhou Lin *(COO)*
Board of Directors:
Boquan He
Alex Nanyan Zheng
Bin Dai
Meng Ann Lim
Jeffrey Perlman
Tan Wee Seng
Tao Thomas Wu

7-ELEVEN STORES PTY. LTD.
357 Ferntree Gully Road
Mount Waverley, VIC, 3149, Australia
Tel.: (61) 395410711
Fax: (61) 395410849
Web Site: www.7eleven.com.au
Sales Range: $550-599.9 Million
Emp.: 183
Business Description:
Convenience Store Operator
S.I.C.: 5411
N.A.I.C.S.: 445120
Personnel:
Russell Withers *(Chm)*

714607 ONTARIO LTD.
(d/b/a Homestead Foods)
4445 Harvester Rd
Burlington, ON, L7L4X1, Canada
Tel.: (905) 681-8755
Fax: (905) 681-8762
E-Mail: homesteadfoods@on.aibn.com
Year Founded: 1985
Rev.: $17,657,452
Emp.: 12
Business Description:
Food Mfr, Whslr & Distr
S.I.C.: 2099
N.A.I.C.S.: 311999
Personnel:
John Katsiris *(Owner)*

723926 ONTARIO LIMITED
(d/b/a J.J. McGuire General Contractors)
1029 Brock Road South
Pickering, ON, L1W 3T7, Canada
Tel.: (905) 683-4463
Fax: (905) 683-4475
E-Mail: info@jjmcguire.com
Web Site: www.jjmcguire.com
Year Founded: 1987
Rev.: $14,519,807
Emp.: 50
Business Description:
Building Construction Services
S.I.C.: 1541
N.A.I.C.S.: 236210
Personnel:
Jeff Robinson *(Pres)*

733907 ONTARIO LTD
(d/b/a European Quality Meats & Sausages)
14 Westwyn Court
Brampton, ON, L6T 4T5, Canada
Tel.: (905) 453-6060
Fax: (905) 453-9733
Toll Free: (800) 387-7074
Web Site: www.europeanmeats.com
Year Founded: 1959
Rev.: $40,000,000
Emp.: 225
Business Description:
Meat Products Mfr & Distr
S.I.C.: 5147
N.A.I.C.S.: 424470
Personnel:
Morris Leider *(Founder & Pres)*

734758 ONTARIO LIMITED
(d/b/a Huntington Travel)
3100 Ridgeway Dr Unit 16
Mississauga, ON, L5L 5M5, Canada
Tel.: (905) 820-2266
Fax: (905) 820-1090
Toll Free: (800) 563-8939
E-Mail: online@huntingtontravel.net
Web Site: www.huntingtontravel.net
Year Founded: 1973
Rev.: $20,829,000
Emp.: 60
Business Description:
Tour & Travel Agency Services
S.I.C.: 4725
N.A.I.C.S.: 561520
Personnel:
Kiran Budhdev *(Pres)*

THE 77 BANK, LTD.
3-20 Chuo 3-chome
Aoba-ku, Sendai, Miyagi, 980-8777, Japan
Tel.: (81) 222671111
Web Site: www.77bank.co.jp
Year Founded: 1878
8341—(TKS)
Rev.: $1,233,221,000
Assets: $90,872,133,000
Liabilities: $86,829,270,000
Net Worth: $4,042,863,000
Earnings: $136,906,000
Emp.: 2,819
Fiscal Year-end: 03/31/13
Business Description:
Commercial Banking Services
S.I.C.: 6029
N.A.I.C.S.: 522110
Personnel:
Hiroshi Kamata *(Chm)*
Teruhiko Ujiie *(Pres)*
Yoshiaki Nagayama *(Deputy Pres)*
Masayuki Yamada *(Sr Mng Dir)*
Tetsuya Fujishiro *(Mng Dir)*
Makoto Igarashi *(Mng Dir)*
Mitsutaka Kambe *(Mng Dir)*
Isamu Suzuki *(Mng Dir)*
Board of Directors:
Hiroshi Kamata
Tetsuya Fujishiro
Toshimi Homareda
Makoto Igarashi
Mitsutaka Kambe
Kiyoshi Kanai
Hidefumi Kobayashi
Yoshiaki Nagayama
Hirofumi Sawano
Toru Sugawara
Masahiro Sugita
Isamu Suzuki
Takeshi Takahashi
Masakatsu Tsuda
Teruhiko Ujiie
Masayuki Yamada
Division:

The 77 Bank Ltd. - Treasury Administration & International Division (1)
3-20 Chuo 3-chome
Aoba-ku, Sendai, Miyagi, 980-8777, Japan
Tel.: (81) 222119914
Fax: (81) 222119916
Emp.: 40
Cash Management & Settlement Services
S.I.C.: 6029
N.A.I.C.S.: 522110
Atsushi Shitoh *(Gen Mgr)*

Subsidiaries:

77 Business Services Co., Ltd. (1)
3-20 Chuo 3-chome
Aoba-ku, Sendai, Miyagi, 980 8777, Japan (100%)
Tel.: (81) 22 267 1111
Web Site: www.77bank.co.jp
Emp.: 2,690
Management of Cash & Other Banking Clerical Operations
S.I.C.: 6011
N.A.I.C.S.: 521110
Hiroshi Kamata *(Chm)*

77 Lease Co., Ltd. (1)
2-15-1 Hon-cho
Aoba-ku, Sendai, Miyagi, 980-0014, Japan
Tel.: (81) 222624341
Fax: (81) 222624338
Web Site: www.77lease.co.jp
Emp.: 46
Equipment Finance Leasing Services
S.I.C.: 7389
N.A.I.C.S.: 561990
Nobuhiro Chiba *(Mgr)*

77 Staff Services Co., Ltd. (1)
2-1-12 Kimachi-dori
Aoba-ku, Sendai, Miyagi, 980-0801, Japan (100%)
Tel.: (81) 222613137
Fax: (81) 222247208
Employment Services
S.I.C.: 7361
N.A.I.C.S.: 561311

Affiliates:

The 77 Card Co., Ltd. (1)
2-4-22 Tsutsujigaoka Sendaihigashiguchi Building 3F
Miyagino-ku, Sendai, Miyagi, 983-0852, Japan
Tel.: (81) 222981877
Fax: (81) 222981870
Credit Card Processing Services
S.I.C.: 6099
N.A.I.C.S.: 522320

77 Computer Services Co., Ltd. (1)
2-10-1 Akedori
Izumi-ku, Sendai, Miyagi, Japan
Tel.: (81) 223778872
Fax: (81) 223778871
Emp.: 170
Data Processing Services
S.I.C.: 7374
N.A.I.C.S.: 518210
Sadahei Takahashi *(Mng Dir)*

77 Shin-Yo Hosyo Co., Ltd. (1)
Shichijushichi Ginko Jimu Center-Nai
Sendai, Japan
Tel.: (81) 227233685
Emp.: 2,690
Other Activities Related to Credit Intermediation
S.I.C.: 6099
N.A.I.C.S.: 522390

7SEAS ENTERTAINMENT LIMITED
6-3-1239/2/A 3rd Floor Koti's Court
Raj Bhavan Road Somajiguda
Hyderabad, 500 082, India
Tel.: (91) 40 30686161
Fax: (91) 40 30686163
E-Mail: info@7seasent.com
Web Site: www.7seasent.com
590116—(BOM)
Rev.: $2,317,948
Assets: $5,951,532
Liabilities: $1,284,930
Net Worth: $4,666,602
Earnings: ($32,362)
Fiscal Year-end: 03/31/13
Business Description:
Mobile Games Publisher & Distr
S.I.C.: 5945
N.A.I.C.S.: 451120
Personnel:
L. Maruti Sanker *(Mng Dir)*
S. Vivek *(Compliance Officer & Sec)*
Board of Directors:
A. S. R. Murthy
M. Rama Mohan Rao
L. Maruti Sanker
Transfer Agent:
Venture Capital & Corporate Investments Private Limited
12-10-167 Bharat Nagar
500018 Hyderabad, India

800 SUPER HOLDINGS LIMITED
No 17A Senoko Way
Singapore, 758056, Singapore
Tel.: (65) 6366 3800
Fax: (65) 6365 3800
E-Mail: enquires@800super.com.sg
Web Site: www.800super.com.sg
5TG—(CAT)
Rev.: $78,977,807
Assets: $54,263,134
Liabilities: $26,396,378
Net Worth: $27,866,757
Earnings: $4,675,902
Emp.: 2,900
Fiscal Year-end: 06/30/13
Business Description:
Waste Management Services
S.I.C.: 4959
N.A.I.C.S.: 562998
Personnel:
Koh Yong Lee *(Chm)*
Cheng Chye Lee *(CEO)*
Vincent Teck Ee Chan *(COO)*
Wei Lin Goh *(Co-Sec)*
Wei Jin Ong *(Co-Sec)*
Board of Directors:
Koh Yong Lee
Vincent Teck Ee Chan
Shiang Ping Foo
Cheng Chye Lee
Raymond Hoong Yip Lye
Tiak Soon Ng

845453 ONTARIO LTD
(d/b/a Hawkesbury Mazda)
959 McGill Street
Hawkesbury, ON, K6A 3K8, Canada
Tel.: (613) 632-4125
Fax: (613) 632-7544
Toll Free: (866) 959-3266
Web Site: www.hawkesburymazda.com
Rev.: $19,320,131
Emp.: 28
Business Description:
New & Used Car Dealers
S.I.C.: 5511
N.A.I.C.S.: 441110
Personnel:
Christian Joanisse *(Pres)*

866229 ONTARIO INC.
(d/b/a Northern Honda)
1401 Seymour St
North Bay, ON, P1B 8G4, Canada

866229 Ontario Inc.—(Continued)

Tel.: (705) 476-0206
Fax: (705) 476-5490
Toll Free: (866) 979-7134
Web Site: www.northernhonda.com
Rev.: $22,750,595
Emp.: 28
Business Description:
New & Used Car Dealers
S.I.C.: 5511
N.A.I.C.S.: 441110
Personnel:
David Barber *(Partner & Gen Mgr)*
Rex Hunter *(Sec & Treas)*

870892 ALBERTA LTD
(d/b/a Artec Construction Group Ltd.)
193 Everoak Close SW
Calgary, AB, T2Y 0C2, Canada
Tel.: (403) 242-1861
Fax: (403) 225-9550
E-Mail: info@artecgroup.net
Web Site: www.artecgroup.net
Year Founded: 2000
Rev.: $10,500,000
Emp.: 35
Business Description:
Building Construction Services
S.I.C.: 1542
N.A.I.C.S.: 236220
Personnel:
Marvin Boyko *(Owner)*

882819 ONTARIO LTD.
(d/b/a Morrice Transportation)
3049 Devon Drive
Windsor, ON, N8X 4L3, Canada
Tel.: (519) 250-8008
Fax: (519) 250-0195
Toll Free: (800) 567-3260
Web Site: www.morricetransportation.com
Year Founded: 1991
Rev.: $26,779,045
Emp.: 210
Business Description:
Trucking Transportation Service
S.I.C.: 4212
N.A.I.C.S.: 484110
Personnel:
Richard Morrice *(Founder & Pres)*

888 HOLDINGS PLC
Suite 601/701 Europort Road
Gibraltar, Gibraltar
Tel.: (350) 20049800
Fax: (350) 20048280
E-Mail: info@888holdingsplc.com
Web Site: www.888holdingsplc.com
888—(LSE OTC)
Rev.: $375,800,000
Assets: $284,600,000
Liabilities: $136,400,000
Net Worth: $148,200,000
Earnings: $35,400,000
Emp.: 1,010
Fiscal Year-end: 12/31/12
Business Description:
Online Gaming Services
S.I.C.: 7999
N.A.I.C.S.: 713290
Personnel:
Brian Mattingley *(CEO)*
Aviad Kobrine *(CFO)*
Board of Directors:
Richard Kilsby
John Anderson
Aviad Kobrine
Brian Mattingley
Amos Pickel
BDO Limited
Regal House
Gibraltar, Gibraltar
Legal Counsel:
Hassans
57/63 Line Wall Road
Gibraltar, Gibraltar
Freshfields Bruckhaus Deringer
65 Fleet St
London, United Kingdom
Transfer Agent:
Capita Registrars
The Registry 34 Beckenham Road
Beckenham, United Kingdom
Non-U.S. Subsidiary:
Virtual Marketing Services (UK) Limited (1)
20 Thayer st
London, W1U 2DD, United Kingdom
Tel.: (44) 2074878678
Fax: (44) 2079358219
Emp.: 25
Advertising Services
S.I.C.: 7311
N.A.I.C.S.: 541810

89419 BC LTD
(d/b/a Vernon Toyota)
3401 48th Street
Vernon, BC, V1T 9W1, Canada
Tel.: (250) 545-0687
Fax: (250) 545-0662
Toll Free: (877) 590-8787
E-Mail: info@vernontoyota.com
Web Site: www.vernontoyota.com
Year Founded: 1970
Rev.: $11,042,009
Emp.: 24
Business Description:
New & Used Car Dealers
S.I.C.: 5511
N.A.I.C.S.: 441110
Personnel:
Marty Steele *(Pres)*

898984 ONTARIO INC
(d/b/a Richmond Hill Fine Cars)
10427 Yonge St
Richmond Hill, ON, L4C 3C2, Canada
Tel.: (905) 883-8638
Fax: (905) 883-8639
E-Mail: sales@richmondhillfinecars.com
Web Site: www.richmondhillfinecars.com
Rev.: $12,004,500
Emp.: 27
Business Description:
Used Car Dealers
S.I.C.: 5521
N.A.I.C.S.: 441120
Personnel:
Patrick Ng *(Owner)*

9039-7571 QUEBEC INC
(d/b/a Volvo de Brossard)
9425 Boul Taschereau
Brossard, QC, J4Y 2J3, Canada
Tel.: (450) 659-6688
Fax: (450) 659-8111
E-Mail: sales@volvobrossard.net
Web Site: www.volvobrossard.net
Rev.: $11,943,690
Emp.: 35
Business Description:
New & Used Car Dealers
S.I.C.: 5511
N.A.I.C.S.: 441110
Personnel:
Felix Scotti *(Pres)*

9083-7436 QUEBEC INC.
(d/b/a Drytec Trans-Canada)
250 Henry-Bessemer
Terrebonne, QC, J6Y 1T3, Canada
Tel.: (450) 965-0200
Fax: (450) 965-0700
E-Mail: alafortune@drytec.ca
Web Site: www.drytec.ca
Year Founded: 1997
Rev.: $11,136,682
Emp.: 70
Business Description:
Metal Surface Treatment & Corrosion Protection Services
S.I.C.: 3441
N.A.I.C.S.: 332312
Personnel:
Michel Drysdale *(Gen Mgr-Sls & Mktg)*

9101-9091 QUEBEC INC.
1610 Place de Lierre
Laval, QC, H7G 4X7, Canada
Tel.: (450) 669-1311
Fax: (450) 669-9225
Toll Free: (800) 363-1311
E-Mail: bonbon@mondoux.ca
Web Site: www.mondoux.ca
Year Founded: 1967
Rev.: $20,000,000
Emp.: 100
Business Description:
Candy Importer, Mfr & Distr
S.I.C.: 2064
N.A.I.C.S.: 311351
Personnel:
Normand Mondoux *(Founder)*

9116-4509 QUEBEC INC
(d/b/a Les Plastiques TPI inc.)
271 Rue Saint-Jacques South
Coaticook, QC, J1A 2P3, Canada
Tel.: (819) 849-2786
Fax: (819) 849-9247
Web Site: www.tpiplastics.com
Rev.: $23,186,357
Emp.: 219
Business Description:
Plastic Products Mfr & Retailer
S.I.C.: 2821
N.A.I.C.S.: 325211
Personnel:
Angy Potvin *(CEO)*

9119-6832 QUEBEC INC
(d/b/a Paquet Mitsubishi)
1 Chemin des Iles
Levis, QC, G6W 8B6, Canada
Tel.: (418) 835-6161
Toll Free: (866) 950-7282
Web Site: www.paquetmitsubishi.com
Rev.: $12,751,926
Emp.: 14
Business Description:
New & Used Car Dealers
S.I.C.: 5511
N.A.I.C.S.: 441110
Personnel:
Donald Marcotte *(Mgr-New Vehicle Sls)*

941-2401 HEATING LIMITED
(d/b/a Bryan's Fuel)
400 Richardson Rd
Orangeville, ON, L9W 4W8, Canada
Tel.: (519) 941-2401
Fax: (519) 941-8462
Toll Free: (800) 637-5910
E-Mail: info@bryansfuel.on.ca
Web Site: www.bryansfuel.on.ca
Year Founded: 1956
Rev.: $13,563,412
Emp.: 45
Business Description:
Home Heating & Comfort Oil Products Distr
S.I.C.: 5989
N.A.I.C.S.: 454310
Personnel:
Glen Bryan *(Founder)*
Roy Bryan *(Owner)*

942599 ONTARIO LIMITED
(d/b/a Georgetown Honda)
316 Guelph Street
Georgetown, ON, L7G 4B5, Canada
Tel.: (905) 874-3021
Fax: (905) 873-8246
Toll Free: (877) 870-3511
E-Mail: sales@georgetownhonda.ca
Web Site: www.georgetownhonda.ca
Rev.: $12,000,000
Emp.: 21
Business Description:
New & Used Car Dealers
S.I.C.: 5511
N.A.I.C.S.: 441110
Personnel:
Tim Hoogaars *(Gen Mgr)*

957447 ALBERTA LTD
(d/b/a NWS Construction)
5104 55th Avenue NW
Edmonton, AB, T6B 3C6, Canada
Tel.: (780) 463-9939
Fax: (780) 437-9759
E-Mail: nws@nwsconstruction.com
Web Site: www.nwsconstruction.com
Year Founded: 1978
Rev.: $20,633,928
Emp.: 90
Business Description:
Pre-Engineered Building & Cladding Construction Service
S.I.C.: 3448
N.A.I.C.S.: 332311
Personnel:
Shilling Buck *(Gen Mgr)*

966850 ONTARIO INC
(d/b/a Christie Lites Inc.)
100 Carson St Unit A
Toronto, ON, M8W 3R9, Canada
Tel.: (416) 644-1010
Fax: (416) 644-0404
Web Site: www.christielites.com
Rev.: $22,800,000
Emp.: 92
Business Description:
Stage Lighting Services
S.I.C.: 7319
N.A.I.C.S.: 541890
Personnel:
Huntly Christie *(CEO)*
Michael Rawson *(Treas)*

969642 ALBERTA LIMITED
(d/b/a Fish Creek Nissan)
14750 5 St SW
Calgary, AB, T2Y 2E7, Canada
Tel.: (403) 256-6900
Fax: (403) 201-5582
E-Mail: sales@fishcreeknissan.com
Web Site: www.fishcreeknissancalgary.ca
Rev.: $15,238,630
Emp.: 35
Business Description:
New & Used Car Dealers
S.I.C.: 5511
N.A.I.C.S.: 441110
Personnel:
Ken Brown *(Pres)*

970207 ONTARIO LIMITED
(d/b/a Trent Valley Honda)
851 Highway 7 East RR 8
Peterborough, ON, K9J 6X9, Canada
Tel.: (705) 748-2777
Fax: (705) 743-7189
Toll Free: (800) 858-8585

E-Mail: information@trentvalleyhonda.com
Web Site: www.trentvalleyhonda.com
Sales Range: $10-24.9 Million
Emp.: 38
Business Description:
New & Used Car Dealers
S.I.C.: 5511
N.A.I.C.S.: 441110
Personnel:
Monika Carmichael *(Gen Mgr)*

979094 ALBERTA LTD
(d/b/a Southside Mitsubishi)
9605 34th Avenue
Edmonton, AB, T6E 5W8, Canada
Tel.: (780) 465-5252
Fax: (780) 465-0202
Toll Free: (888) 281-5180
Web Site: www.southsidemitsubishi.com
Year Founded: 2002
Rev.: $18,519,274
Emp.: 40
Business Description:
New & Used Car Dealers
S.I.C.: 5511
N.A.I.C.S.: 441110
Personnel:
Jennifer Coughlin *(Controller)*

982874 ONTARIO LTD
(d/b/a Mississauga Hyundai)
3045 Glen Erin Dr
Mississauga, ON, L5L 1J3, Canada
Tel.: (905) 607-4000
Fax: (905) 828-5190
E-Mail: sales@hyundaiofmississauga.ca
Web Site: www.mississaugahyundai.ca
Rev.: $18,447,786
Emp.: 40
Business Description:
New & Used Car Dealers
S.I.C.: 5511
N.A.I.C.S.: 441110
Personnel:
Navdeep Bhatia *(Owner)*

985178 ONTARIO INC.
(See Under Classic Honda)

988883 ONTARIO INC
(d/b/a Kawartha Chrysler)
1515 Lansdowne St W
Peterborough, ON, K9J 7M3, Canada
Tel.: (705) 741-5766
Fax: (705) 740-2292
Toll Free: (800) 263-5786
Web Site: www.kawarthachrysler.com
Rev.: $18,532,799
Emp.: 40
Business Description:
New & Used Car Dealers
S.I.C.: 5511
N.A.I.C.S.: 441110
Personnel:
Daniel St-Jean *(Pres)*

99 WUXIAN LIMITED
Level 26 56 Pitt Street
Sydney, NSW, 2000, Australia
Tel.: (61) 2 9247 9555
E-Mail: enquiries@99wuxian.com
Web Site: www.99wuxian.com
NNW—(ASX)
Business Description:
Mobile Online Platform
S.I.C.: 2741
N.A.I.C.S.: 519130
Personnel:
Ross Benson *(Chm)*
Amalisia Zhang *(CEO)*
Nathan Bartrop *(Sec)*
Board of Directors:
Ross Benson
David Chen
Yongkuan Duan
Simon Green
Tony Groth
Amalisia Zhang

99P STORES LTD.
Style Way Pineham Swan Valley
Northampton, NN4 9EX, United Kingdom
Tel.: (44) 1604 752299
Fax: (44) 1604 750899
E-Mail: info@99pstoresltd.com
Web Site: www.99pstoresltd.com
Year Founded: 2001
Sales Range: $400-449.9 Million
Emp.: 3,444
Business Description:
Grocery Store Operator
S.I.C.: 5411
N.A.I.C.S.: 445110
Personnel:
Nadir Lalani *(Founder & CEO)*

A & A CONTRACT CUSTOMS BROKERS LTD.
Suite 101 120-176th Street
Surrey, BC, V2S 9S2, Canada
Tel.: (604) 538-1042
Fax: (604) 538-3994
Toll Free: (800) 663-4270
E-Mail: clientservices@aacb.com
Web Site: www.aacb.com
Year Founded: 1979
Rev.: $44,376,702
Emp.: 150
Business Description:
Customs Brokerage, Freight Transportation, Warehousing & Shipping Services
S.I.C.: 4731
N.A.I.C.S.: 488510
Personnel:
Graham Robins, Sr. *(Founder)*
Graham Robins, Jr. *(Pres)*
Louisiana Pacific *(CEO)*

A&D COMPANY, LTD.
3-23-14 Higashi Ikebukuro Toshima Ku
Tokyo, 170-0013, Japan
Tel.: (81) 353916132
Fax: (81) 353916148
Web Site: www.aandd.jp
Year Founded: 1977
7745—(TKS)
Sls.: $377,443,000
Assets: $466,246,000
Liabilities: $305,910,000
Net Worth: $160,336,000
Earnings: $9,922,000
Emp.: 3,036
Fiscal Year-end: 03/31/13
Business Description:
Electronic DSP, Medical, Weighing, Testing & Measuring Equipment Mfr & Distr
S.I.C.: 3825
N.A.I.C.S.: 334515
Personnel:
Hikaru Furukawa *(Pres & CEO)*

Subsidiaries:

Best Instruments Co., Ltd. (1)
111 Nakatsutsumi
Kouzuya, Yawata, Kyoto, 614-8176, Japan
Tel.: (81) 759826007
Fax: (81) 759822010
Web Site: www.best-sokki.com
Measuring & Testing Equipments Mfr & Distr
S.I.C.: 3586
N.A.I.C.S.: 333913
Kotaro Takahashi *(Pres & CEO)*

Kensei Industry Co., Ltd. (1)
4210-15 Takasai
Shimotsuma, Ibaraki, 304-0031, Japan
Tel.: (81) 296437035
Fax: (81) 296436007
Electronic Balance Mfr & Sales
S.I.C.: 3829
N.A.I.C.S.: 333997

Litra Co., Ltd. (1)
7-5 Harajuku
Hidaka, Saitama, 350-1205, Japan
Tel.: (81) 429854668
Fax: (81) 4298254668
E-Mail: litra@litra.co.jp
Web Site: www.litra.co.jp
Emp.: 80
Weighing Scale Mfr
S.I.C.: 3829
N.A.I.C.S.: 333997
Hikar Furukawa *(Pres)*

Orientec Co., Ltd. (1)
3-23-14 Higashi-Ikebukuro Toshima-ku Dist
Toshima-ku, Tokyo, 170-0013, Japan
Tel.: (81) 353916123
Fax: (81) 1353916148
Web Site: www.aandd.co.jp
Testing Instruments Mfr
S.I.C.: 3825
N.A.I.C.S.: 334515

U.S. Subsidiaries:

A&D Engineering, Inc. (1)
1756 Automation Pkwy
San Jose, CA 95131 CA
Tel.: (408) 263-5333
Fax: (408) 263-0119
Web Site: www.andonline.com
Sls.: $10,400,000
Emp.: 60
Electronic DSP, Medical, Weighing, Testing & Measuring Equipment Distr
S.I.C.: 5046
N.A.I.C.S.: 423440
Teru Maria *(Pres & CEO)*
Teruhisa Moriya *(Pres & CEO)*
Frank Marrone *(Sec & Sr VP)*

A&D Technology Inc. (1)
4622 Runway Blvd
Ann Arbor, MI 48108 MI
Tel.: (734) 973-1111
Fax: (734) 973-1103
E-Mail: info@aanddtech.com
Web Site: www.aanddtech.com
Emp.: 100
Powertrain Testing & Measurement Equipment Distr & Engineering Services
S.I.C.: 5046
N.A.I.C.S.: 423440
Yoichiro Koyama *(Pres)*

Non-U.S. Subsidiaries:

A&D Australasia Pty. Ltd. (1)
32 Dow St
Thebarton, SA, 5031, Australia AU
Tel.: (61) 883018100
Fax: (61) 883527409
E-Mail: sales@andaustralasia.com.au
Web Site: www.andaustralasia.com.au
Emp.: 35
Holding Company; Electronic Medical & Weighing Equipment Mfr & Distr
S.I.C.: 6719
N.A.I.C.S.: 551112
Julian Horsley *(Mgr-Sls)*

Division:

A&D Weighing Pty. Ltd. (2)
32 Dew Street
Thebarton, SA, 5031, Australia AU
Tel.: (61) 883018100
Fax: (61) 883527409
E-Mail: info@andaustralasia.com.au
Web Site: www.andaustralasia.com.au
Emp.: 45
Electronic Scale & Balance Mfr & Distr
S.I.C.: 3829
N.A.I.C.S.: 333997
Julian Horsley *(Mgr-Natl Sls)*

A&D Electronics (Shenzhen) Co., Ltd. (1)
Datianyang Industry Area Tantou Village Songgang
Baoan District, Shenzhen, Guangdong, China CN
Tel.: (86) 75527130880
Fax: (86) 75527130640
Web Site: www.andch.cn
Electromedical Equipment Mfr & Distr
S.I.C.: 3845
N.A.I.C.S.: 334510

A&D Europe GmbH (1)
Im Leuschnerpark 4
D-64347 Griesheim, Germany De
Tel.: (49) 6155605250 (100%)
Fax: (49) 6155605100
E-Mail: info@aanddeurope.com
Web Site: www.aanddeurope.com
Emp.: 3
Electronic Weighing & Medical Equipment Distr
S.I.C.: 5046
N.A.I.C.S.: 423440
Jurgen Bredenbeck *(Mng Dir)*
Kazuhiko Shimizu *(Mng Dir)*

A&D Instruments India Pvt. Ltd. (1)
509 Udyog Vihar Phase V
Gurgaon, Haryana, 122 016, India In
Tel.: (91) 1244715555 (99%)
Fax: (91) 1244715599
E-Mail: info@aanddindia.in
Web Site: www.aanddindia.in
Emp.: 15
Electronic DSP, Medical, Weighing, Testing & Measuring Equipment Distr
S.I.C.: 5046
N.A.I.C.S.: 423440
Chikara Arai *(Mng Dir)*

A&D Instruments Ltd. (1)
Unit 24 26 Backlands Way
Abingdon Business Park, Abingdon, Oxon, OX14 1DY, United Kingdom UK
Tel.: (44) 1235550420
Fax: (44) 1235550485
E-Mail: info@aandd-eu.net
Web Site: www.aandd-eu.net
Emp.: 25
Electronic DSP, Medical, Weighing, Testing & Measuring Equipment Distr
S.I.C.: 5046
N.A.I.C.S.: 423440
Takeo Goto *(Mng Dir)*

A&D Korea Limited (1)
8th Fl Manhattan Bldg 36-2 Yoido-dong
Youngdeungpo-gu, Seoul, Korea (South) Ks
Tel.: (82) 27804101
Fax: (82) 27824264
E-Mail: ynkim@andk.co.kr
Web Site: www.andk.co.kr
Electronic Weighing Equipment Mfr & Distr
S.I.C.: 3829
N.A.I.C.S.: 333997

A&D Rus Co., Ltd. (1)
Vereyskaya Str 17
121357 Moscow, Russia
Tel.: (7) 4959373344
Fax: (7) 4959375566
Web Site: www.and-rus.ru
Electronic Medical & Weighing Device Distr
S.I.C.: 5047
N.A.I.C.S.: 423450

A&D Scales Co., Ltd. (1)
162-4 Insan-ni Deogsan-myeon
Jincheon, Chungcheongbug-do, Korea (South)
Tel.: (82) 435374101
Fax: (82) 435374109
Web Site: www.aandd.com
Industrial Scales Mfr
S.I.C.: 3829
N.A.I.C.S.: 333997

A&D Technology Trading (Shanghai) Co., Ltd. (1)
Room 101 No 1 Fu Hai Business Building
289 Zhang Jiang Bi Sheng Road,
Shanghai, 201204, China CN
Tel.: (86) 2133932340
Fax: (86) 2133932347
Web Site: www.aanddtech.cn
Wholesale Trade Agency

A&D Company, Ltd.—(Continued)

S.I.C.: 7389
N.A.I.C.S.: 425120

A&D PHARMA HOLDINGS S.R.L.

133 Ciobanului St
Mogosoaia, Ilfov, 077135, Romania
Tel.: (40) 213017474
Fax: (40) 213017475
E-Mail: office@adpharma.ro
Web Site: www.adpharma.ro
Year Founded: 1994
Sales Range: $650-699.9 Million
Emp.: 3,160
Business Description:
Holding Company; Pharmaceutical Wholesale, Retail Sales & Marketing Services
S.I.C.: 6719
N.A.I.C.S.: 551112
Personnel:
Robert Popescu *(CEO)*
Dimitris Sophocleous *(CFO)*
Board of Directors:
Walid Abboud
Roger Akoury
Roberto Musneci
Robert Popescu
Michael Tetreault Schilling

Subsidiary:

Sensiblu S.R.L. **(1)**
133 Ciobanului Street
Mogosoaia, Ilfov, 077135, Romania RO
Tel.: (40) 213017474 (100%)
Fax: (40) 213017475
E-Mail: office@adpharma.com
Web Site: www.sensiblu.com
Retail Pharmacies Operator
S.I.C.: 5912
N.A.I.C.S.: 446110
Lucian Neacsu *(Dir-Strategy & Dev)*

A&J MUCKLOW GROUP PLC

60 Whitehall Road
Halesowen, West Midlands, B63 3JS, United Kingdom
Tel.: (44) 121 550 1841
Fax: (44) 121 550 7532
Web Site: www.mucklow.com
Year Founded: 1933
OTT—(DEU LSE)
Rev.: $33,616,767
Assets: $422,670,121
Liabilities: $134,482,861
Net Worth: $288,187,260
Earnings: $25,879,825
Emp.: 15
Fiscal Year-end: 06/30/13
Business Description:
Real Estate Development Services
S.I.C.: 6531
N.A.I.C.S.: 531390
Personnel:
Rupert J. Mucklow *(Chm)*
D. Justin Parker *(Mng Dir)*
David Wooldridge *(Sec & Dir-Fin)*
Board of Directors:
Rupert J. Mucklow
Stephen Gilmore
Jock Lennox
Paul Ludlow
D. Justin Parker
David Wooldridge
Legal Counsel:
Wragge & Co. LLP
55 Colmore Row
Birmingham, United Kingdom
Pinsent Masons LLP
3 Colmore Circus
Birmingham, United Kingdom

A & M REALTY BERHAD

10th Floor Menara A&M Garden Business Center No 3 Jalan Istana
41000 Kelang, Selangor Darul Ehsan, Malaysia
Tel.: (60) 333732888
Fax: (60) 333728858
E-Mail: enquiries@amrealty.com.my
Web Site: www.amrealty.com.my
A&M—(KLS)
Rev.: $45,298,714
Assets: $214,489,790
Liabilities: $39,945,130
Net Worth: $174,544,660
Earnings: $9,284,745
Fiscal Year-end: 12/31/12
Business Description:
Property Development & Construction Services
S.I.C.: 1521
N.A.I.C.S.: 236115
Personnel:
Boon Thong Ng *(Chm)*
Abdul Halim Abdul Rauf *(Deputy Chm)*
Ambrose Leonard Kwee Heng Ng *(Mng Dir)*
Bernard Boon Siang Lim *(Co-Sec)*
Siew Peng Wong *(Co-Sec)*
Board of Directors:
Boon Thong Ng
Abdul Halim Abdul Rauf
Mat Ripen Mat Elah
Ambrose Leonard Kwee Heng Ng
Malcolm Jeremy Kwee Seng Ng
Milton Norman Kwee Leong Ng
Steven Jr. Kwee Leng Ng
Thian Kwee Ng
Hock Guan Ooi
Cheng Lum Sak
Jiu See Tan
Catherine Eng Neo Yeoh

A&W FOOD SERVICES OF CANADA INC.

171 W Esplanade Ste 300
North Vancouver, BC, V7M 3K9, Canada
Tel.: (604) 988-2141
Fax: (604) 988-5531
Web Site: www.aw.ca
Year Founded: 1956
Sales Range: $400-449.9 Million
Emp.: 100
Business Description:
Restaurant Operator
Import
S.I.C.: 5812
N.A.I.C.S.: 722511
Personnel:
Jefferson J. Mooney *(Chm)*
Paul F.B. Hollands *(Pres & CEO)*
Donald T. Leslie *(CFO)*

Subsidiary:

A&W Trade Marks Limited Partnership **(1)**
171 West Esplanade Ste 300
North Vancouver, BC, V7M 3K9, Canada
Tel.: (604) 988-2141
Web Site: www.aw.ca
Food Restaurant Business Service
S.I.C.: 5812
N.A.I.C.S.: 722513

Joint Venture:

A&W Trade Marks Inc. **(1)**
171 West Esplanade Suite 300
North Vancouver, BC, V7M 3K9, Canada
Tel.: (604) 988-2141
Fax: (604) 988-5531
E-Mail: info@aw.ca
Web Site: www.aw.ca
Trade Mark Owner
S.I.C.: 6794
N.A.I.C.S.: 533110
John R. McLernon *(Chm)*
Conrad A. Pinette *(Treas & Sec)*

A&W REVENUE ROYALTIES INCOME FUND

300 171 West Esplanade
North Vancouver, BC, V7M 3K9, Canada
Tel.: (604) 988-2141
Fax: (604) 988-5531
E-Mail: investorrelations@aw.ca
Web Site: www.awincomefund.ca
AW.UN—(TSX)
Sls.: $818,426,367
Assets: $177,432,570
Liabilities: $75,906,349
Net Worth: $101,526,221
Earnings: $14,217,468
Fiscal Year-end: 12/31/12
Business Description:
Trademark Owner & Licenser
S.I.C.: 6794
N.A.I.C.S.: 533110
Personnel:
John R. McLernon *(Chm)*
Paul F. B. Hollands *(Pres & CEO)*
Donald T. Leslie *(CFO)*
Susan D. Senecal *(CMO)*
Transfer Agent:
Computershare Investor Services Inc.
510 Burrard Street 2nd Floor
Vancouver, BC, V6C 3B9, Canada

Joint Venture:

A&W Trade Marks Inc. **(1)**
171 West Esplanade Suite 300
North Vancouver, BC, V7M 3K9, Canada
Tel.: (604) 988-2141
Fax: (604) 988-5531
E-Mail: info@aw.ca
Web Site: www.aw.ca
Trade Mark Owner
S.I.C.: 6794
N.A.I.C.S.: 533110
John R. McLernon *(Chm)*
Conrad A. Pinette *(Treas & Sec)*

A. B. C. RECYCLING LTD

8081 Meadow Ave
Burnaby, BC, V3N 2V9, Canada
Tel.: (604) 522-9727
Fax: (604) 522-9723
E-Mail: info@abcrecycling.com
Web Site: www.abcrecycling.com
Sales Range: $75-99.9 Million
Emp.: 70
Business Description:
Metal Scrap Recycling & Recovery
S.I.C.: 3369
N.A.I.C.S.: 331529
Personnel:
Harold Yochlowitz *(Pres)*
David Yochlowitz *(CEO)*

A. BELANGER, LTEE.

8500 Pl Marien
Montreal, QC, H1B 5W8, Canada
Tel.: (514) 648-5757
Fax: (514) 881-4056
E-Mail: service.clients@braultetmartineau.com
Web Site: www.braultetmartineau.com
Year Founded: 1985
Sales Range: $300-349.9 Million
Emp.: 1,800
Business Description:
Furniture Stores
S.I.C.: 5712
N.A.I.C.S.: 442110
Personnel:
Yves Des Groseillers *(Pres)*

A BENBOW HOLDING INC.

3F-B302D 185 Kewang Rd
Longtan Township, Taoyuan, 325, Taiwan
Tel.: (886) 34071938
Year Founded: 2011
Business Description:
Management Consulting
S.I.C.: 8748
N.A.I.C.S.: 541618
Personnel:
Chien Yang Yu *(Pres, CEO, CFO, Treas & Sec)*
Board of Directors:
Chien Yang Yu

A BROWN COMPANY, INC.

Suite 3301-A West Tower Philippine Stock Exchange Building
Exchange Road, Pasig, 1605, Philippines
Tel.: (63) 26333135
Fax: (63) 26386832
E-Mail: head_office@abrown.ph
Web Site: www.xavierestates.com.ph
BRN—(PHI)
Rev.: $18,133,703
Assets: $125,237,808
Liabilities: $56,465,597
Net Worth: $68,772,211
Earnings: $1,702,140
Emp.: 164
Fiscal Year-end: 12/31/12
Business Description:
Real Estate & Property Development Services
S.I.C.: 6531
N.A.I.C.S.: 531312
Personnel:
Walter W. Brown *(Chm)*
Robertino E. Pizarro *(Pres)*
Rosa Anna Duavit-Santiago *(CFO, Treas & VP)*
Jason C. Nalupta *(Sec)*
Board of Directors:
Walter W. Brown
Thomas G. Aquino
Annabelle P. Brown
Roel Z. Castro
Rosa Anna Duavit-Santiago
Gerardo Domenico V. Lanuza
Elpidio M. Paras
Robertino E. Pizarro
Antonio S. Soriano

A-CAP RESOURCES LIMITED

Level 16 AMP Building 140 St Georges Terrace
Perth, WA, 6000, Australia
Tel.: (61) 892209850
Fax: (61) 892209820
E-Mail: info@a-cap.com.au
Web Site: www.acap.com.au
ACB—(ASX)
Rev.: $98,921
Assets: $41,293,314
Liabilities: $741,717
Net Worth: $40,551,597
Earnings: ($2,282,215)
Emp.: 42
Fiscal Year-end: 06/30/13
Business Description:
Mineral Exploration Services
S.I.C.: 1041
N.A.I.C.S.: 212221
Personnel:
Robert James Pett *(Chm)*
Paul William Thomson *(CEO)*
Anthony Khama *(Chm-A-Cap Botswana Pty Ltd)*
Denis Ivan Rakich *(Sec)*
Board of Directors:
Robert James Pett
Paul Anthony Ingram
Richard Lockwood
Harry Stacpoole
Paul William Thomson
Paul Woolrich

Legal Counsel:
Minter Ellison
49 Central Park 152 158 St Georges Terrace
Perth, Australia
Mills Oakley Lawyers
St James Building Level 4th Floor 121 William Street
Melbourne, Australia

A-GAS INTERNATIONAL HOLDINGS LTD.
Clifton Heights Triangle West
Bristol, BS8 1EJ, United Kingdom
Tel.: (44) 117 906 9800
Fax: (44) 117 906 9801
E-Mail: sales.uk@agas.com
Web Site: www.agas.com
Year Founded: 1993
Sales Range: $125-149.9 Million
Emp.: 254
Business Description:
Refrigerant Whslr
S.I.C.: 5078
N.A.I.C.S.: 423740
Personnel:
John Rutley *(CEO)*

A-GAS LIMITED
Banyard Road Portbury West
Bristol, BS20 7XH, United Kingdom
Tel.: (44) 127 537 6600
Fax: (44) 127 537 6601
E-Mail: info@agas.com
Web Site: www.agas.com
Business Description:
Refrigeration & Air Conditioning Refrigerant Supplier
S.I.C.: 2899
N.A.I.C.S.: 325998
Personnel:
John Rutley *(Exec Chm)*
U.S. Subsidiary:

Reclamation Technologies, Inc. (1)
1100 Haskins Rd
Bowling Green, OH 43402 OH
Tel.: (419) 867-8990
Fax: (419) 867-3279
Toll Free: (800) 372-1301
E-Mail: info@remtec.net
Web Site: www.remtec.net
Emp.: 50
Industrial Gas Mfr
S.I.C.: 2813
N.A.I.C.S.: 325120
Richard Marcus *(Pres & CEO)*

A-LEHDET OY
Alehdet
00810 Helsinki, Finland
Tel.: (358) 975961
Fax: (358) 975983275
E-Mail: customerservice@a-lehdet.fi
Web Site: www.a-lehdet.fi
Year Founded: 1933
Emp.: 268
Business Description:
Periodicals Publisher
S.I.C.: 2721
N.A.I.C.S.: 511120
Personnel:
Olli Pekka Lyytikainen *(Mng Dir)*
Subsidiary:

Faktum Oy (1)
Hitsaajank. 7
SF-00810 Helsinki, Finland
Tel.: (358) 75961
Fax: (358) 783526
S.I.C.: 2721
N.A.I.C.S.: 511120

A M FORD SALES LTD
2795 Highway Dr
Trail, BC, V1R 2T1, Canada
Tel.: (250) 364-0202
Fax: (250) 364-0242
Toll Free: (800) 961-0202
E-Mail: amford@amford.com
Web Site: www.amford.com
Year Founded: 1982
Rev.: $10,600,000
Emp.: 32
Business Description:
New & Used Car Dealers
S.I.C.: 5511
N.A.I.C.S.: 441110
Personnel:
Dan Ashman *(Owner)*

A-MAX TECHNOLOGY LIMITED
10th Floor A-Max Technology Tower
12-16 Fui Yiu Kok Street, Tsuen Wan, NT, China (Hong Kong)
Tel.: (852) 27986699
Fax: (852) 27536226
E-Mail: info@amaxhk.com
Web Site: www.amaxhk.com
Year Founded: 1996
Sales Range: $300-349.9 Million
Emp.: 1,700
Business Description:
Portable Digital Audio Players Designer & Mfr
S.I.C.: 3651
N.A.I.C.S.: 334310
Personnel:
Victor Chan *(Chm & CEO)*
Diana Chan *(CFO)*
Yu Xiao Dong *(COO)*
Non-U.S. Subsidiary:

A-MAX Technology GmbH (1)
Helmholtzstr 2-9
10587 Berlin, Germany
Tel.: (49) 307900610
Fax: (49) 00493079006120
E-Mail: maria@amaxhk.com
Web Site: www.amaxhk.com
Emp.: 4
Audio & Video Equipment Mfr
S.I.C.: 3651
N.A.I.C.S.: 334310

A-ONE SEIMITSU INC.
2-20-5 Bubai-cho
Fuchu, TKY, 183-0033, Japan
Tel.: (81) 423631039
Fax: (81) 42 365 1710
Web Site: www.a-one-seimitsu.co.jp/top.htm
Year Founded: 1990
6156—(JAS)
Emp.: 150
Business Description:
Industrial Products Mfr; Machining Tools, Lathes & Precision Equipment & Time Piece Accessories
S.I.C.: 3559
N.A.I.C.S.: 333249
Personnel:
Tetsuya Hayashi *(Pres)*
Takeshi Murota *(Mng Dir)*
Board of Directors:
Tetsuya Hayashi
Nobuyuki Kanemaru
Katsuhiko Umehara

A PANAYIDES CONTRACTING PUBLIC LTD
PO Box 237366
1686 Nicosia, Cyprus
Tel.: (357) 22663333
Fax: (357) 22664257
E-Mail: a.panayides@cytanet.com.cy
Web Site: www.apco.com.cy
Year Founded: 1987
APC—(CYP)
Business Description:
Construction Services
S.I.C.: 1611
N.A.I.C.S.: 237310
Personnel:
Stavros Theodosiou *(Chm & Pres)*
Vangelis Georgiou *(Vice Chm)*
Board of Directors:
Stavros Theodosiou
Vangelis Georgiou
Demetris Kouvaros
Maria Panayidou
Evripides Polycarpou

A-POWER ENERGY GENERATION SYSTEMS, LTD.
No 44 Jingxing North Street
Tiexi District, Shenyang, Liaoning, 110121, China
Tel.: (86) 102485617788
Web Site: www.apowerenergy.com
Sales Range: $300-349.9 Million
Emp.: 457
Business Description:
Designer & Mfr of Power Generation & Distribution Systems
S.I.C.: 8711
N.A.I.C.S.: 541330
Personnel:
Jinxiang Lu *(Chm & CEO)*
Board of Directors:
Jinxiang Lu
Zhenyu Fan
Jiwei Wang
Yanqi Yu
Subsidiary:

Liaoning GaoKe Energy Group Company Limited (1)
NO 44 Jingxing N St
Tiexi District, Shenyang, 110021, China
Tel.: (86) 2485617888-8888
Fax: (86) 2485830606
Web Site: www.ligkny.org
Energy Generation
S.I.C.: 4911
N.A.I.C.S.: 221118
Lu Jinxiang *(CEO)*

A.R. THOMSON GROUP
7930 130th Street
Surrey, BC, V3W 0H7, Canada
Tel.: (604) 507-6050
Fax: (604) 507-6098
Web Site: www.arthomson.com
Year Founded: 1967
Rev.: $27,046,142
Emp.: 165
Business Description:
Gaskets & Other Fluid Containment Products Mfr
S.I.C.: 3053
N.A.I.C.S.: 339991
Personnel:
James E. Thomson *(Pres)*

A. RACKE GMBH
Gaustrasse 20
D 55411 Bingen, Germany
Tel.: (49) 67211880
Fax: (49) 6721188220
Web Site: www.racke.de
Year Founded: 1855
Emp.: 550
Business Description:
Wine & Spirits Mfr & Retailer
S.I.C.: 2084
N.A.I.C.S.: 312130
Personnel:
Marcus Moller-Racke *(Pres)*
U.S. Subsidiaries:

The Donum Estate, Inc (1)
PO Box 154
Sonoma, CA 95476-0154 CA
Tel.: (707) 939-2290 (100%)
Fax: (707) 939-0651
Toll Free: (800) 678-8504
E-Mail: info@thedonumestate.com
Web Site: www.thedonumestate.com
Emp.: 14
Premium Wines Producer
Import Export
S.I.C.: 2084
N.A.I.C.S.: 312130
Anne Moller-Racke *(Pres)*

Robert Stemmler Winery (1)
PO Box 154 24520 Ramal Rd
Sonoma, CA 95476-9790
Tel.: (707) 939-2293
Fax: (707) 939-0651
Toll Free: (800) 679-7355
E-Mail: tastingroom@robertstemmlerwinery.com
Web Site: www.robertstemmlerwinery.com
Emp.: 350
Wines & Spirits Mfr
Export
S.I.C.: 2084
N.A.I.C.S.: 312130

A-RANK BERHAD
Chamber E Lian Seng Courts No 275
Jalan Haruan 1
Oakland Industrial Park, 70200
Seremban, Negeri Sembilan Daru, Malaysia
Tel.: (60) 6762 3339
Fax: (60) 6762 9693
E-Mail: admin@arank.com.my
Web Site: www.arank.com.my
ARANK—(KLS)
Rev.: $141,496,887
Assets: $48,269,746
Liabilities: $23,340,013
Net Worth: $24,929,733
Earnings: $2,424,637
Fiscal Year-end: 07/31/13
Business Description:
Aluminum Billets Mfr
S.I.C.: 3399
N.A.I.C.S.: 331314
Personnel:
Wan Lay Tan *(Mng Dir)*
Bee Lian Ng *(Co-Sec)*
Enk Purn Tan *(Co-Sec)*
Board of Directors:
Shahrir Abdul Jalil
Ahmed Azhar Abdullah
Choon Sun Gan
Chik Weng Leong
Wan Lay Tan
Tze Kai Wong
Legal Counsel:
Soo Thien Ming & Nashrah
Wisma Selangor Dredging 10th Floor, South Block No. 142-A, Jalan Ampan
Kuala Lumpur, Malaysia

A. RAYMOND & CIE SCS
115 Cours Berriat
38000 Grenoble, France
Tel.: (33) 476334949
Fax: (33) 476482059
E-Mail: arrg@araymond.com
Web Site: www.araymond.com
Sales Range: $10-24.9 Million
Business Description:
Automotive Fastening & Fluid Handling Connections Mfr
S.I.C.: 7539
N.A.I.C.S.: 811118
Personnel:
Antoine Raymond *(CEO)*
U.S. Subsidiary:

A Raymond Tinnerman Manufacturing, Inc. (1)
1060 W 130th St
Brunswick, OH 44212-2316
Tel.: (330) 220-5100
Fax: (330) 220-5797
Toll Free: (800) 221-2344
E-Mail: araymond_tinnerman_industrial@araymondtinnerman.com
Web Site: www.tinnerman.com

A. Raymond & Cie SCS—(Continued)

Sales Range: $125-149.9 Million
Emp.: 425
Holding Company
S.I.C.: 6719
N.A.I.C.S.: 551112
Dan Kerr *(Pres & CEO)*
Dan Dolan *(COO)*

A/S NORRESUNDBY BANK

Torvet 4 Norresundby
9400 Aalborg, Denmark
Tel.: (45) 98703333
Fax: (45) 98703019
E-Mail: post@nrsbank.dk
Web Site: www.noerresundbybank.dk
NRSU—(CSE)
Int. Income: $67,044,862
Assets: $1,686,796,880
Liabilities: $1,444,654,382
Net Worth: $242,142,498
Earnings: $13,173,675
Emp.: 260
Fiscal Year-end: 12/31/12
Business Description:
Commercial Banking Services
S.I.C.: 6029
N.A.I.C.S.: 522110
Personnel:
Mads Hvolby *(Chm)*
Poul Soe Jeppesen *(Deputy Chm)*
Jorn Rosenmeier *(Co-Mng Dir)*
Karl Erik Thygesen *(Co-Mng Dir)*
Pia Foss Henriksen *(CFO & Mgr-Fin)*
Finn Ost Andersson *(Member-Mgmt Bd & Mgr)*
Andreas Rasmussen *(Member-Mgmt Bd & Mgr)*
Board of Directors:
Mads Hvolby
John Chr. Aasted
Bo Bojer
Poul Soe Jeppesen
Helle Rorbaek Juul Lynge
Kresten Skjodt

A/S SAF TEHNIKA

24a Ganibu Dambis
Riga, LV-1005, Latvia
Tel.: (371) 67046840
Fax: (371) 67046809
E-Mail: info@saftehnika.com
Web Site: www.saftehnika.com
Year Founded: 1999
VTZ—(DEU)
Sls.: $17,785,302
Assets: $16,435,711
Liabilities: $2,767,619
Net Worth: $13,668,092
Earnings: ($27,676)
Emp.: 165
Fiscal Year-end: 06/30/13
Business Description:
Data Transmission Equipment Mfr
S.I.C.: 3669
N.A.I.C.S.: 334290
Personnel:
Juris Ziema *(Co-Founder, Vice Chm-Supervisory Bd & Dir-Production Dept)*
Andrejs Grisans *(Co-Founder & Mgr-Production Dept)*
Vents Lacars *(Chm-Supervisory Bd & VP-Bus Dev)*
Normunds Bergs *(Chm-Mgmt Bd & CEO)*
Aira Loite *(COO & Member-Mgmt Bd)*
Didzis Liepkalns *(CTO & Member-Mgmt Bd)*
Supervisory Board of Directors:
Vents Lacars
Andrejs Grisans
Aivis Olsteins
Ivars Senbergs
Juris Ziema

A' SHARQIYA INVESTMENT HOLDING CO. SAOG

Al Harthy Complex
PO Box 47
118 Muscat, PC, Oman
Tel.: (968) 24566160
Fax: (968) 24566162
E-Mail: info@asharqiya.com
Web Site: www.asharqiya.com
SIHC—(MUS)
Rev.: $4,264,071
Assets: $52,673,983
Liabilities: $10,290,208
Net Worth: $42,383,774
Earnings: $739,617
Emp.: 27
Fiscal Year-end: 12/31/12
Business Description:
Investment Services
S.I.C.: 6211
N.A.I.C.S.: 523999
Personnel:
A. J. V. Jayachander *(CEO)*
Board of Directors:
Hamed Hashim Al Dhahab
Ahmed Ali Mohammed Al Araimi
Budoor Mohammed Rashid Al Fannah Al Araimi
Mohammed Ali Al Fannah Al Araimi
Saleh Ahmed Mohammed Al Harthy
Ishaq Zaid Khalifa Al Mawali
Roy Shantonu

A-SONIC AEROSPACE LIMITED

10 Anson Road
24-07 International Plaza
Singapore, 079903, Singapore
Tel.: (65) 62262072
Fax: (65) 62262071
E-Mail: enquiry@asonic-aerospace.com
Web Site: www.asonic-aerospace.com
Year Founded: 2003
A53—(SES)
Sales Range: $25-49.9 Million
Emp.: 26
Business Description:
Holding Company; Aerospace Components
S.I.C.: 6719
N.A.I.C.S.: 551112
Personnel:
Janet L.C. Tan *(CEO)*
Grace C.P. Chan *(Co-Sec)*
Ah Leng Oh *(Co-Sec)*

Subsidiaries:

A-Sonic Aviation Solutions Pte Ltd **(1)**
10 Anson Road 24-07 International Plaza
Singapore, 079903, Singapore
Tel.: (65) 6324 3248
Fax: (65) 6324 3249
E-Mail: enquiry@asonic-aviation.com
Web Site: www.asonic-aviation.com
Aircraft Products Sales & Leasing Services
S.I.C.: 5088
N.A.I.C.S.: 423860

Non-U.S. Subsidiary:

A-Sonic Express Logistics (India) Private Limited **(1)**
Unit 308 2nd Floor Prestige Meridain II No 30 M G Road
Bengaluru, 560001, India
Tel.: (91) 80 4090 4734
Fax: (91) 80 4090 4736
E-Mail: enquiry.blr@asonic-logistics.com
Logistics Consulting Services
S.I.C.: 4731
N.A.I.C.S.: 541614

A. SORIANO CORPORATION

7/F Pacific Star Bldg Makati Avenue corner Gil Puyat Avenue Ext
1209 Makati, Philippines
Tel.: (63) 28190251
Fax: (63) 28115068
E-Mail: info@anscor.com.ph
Web Site: www.anscor.com.ph
ANS—(PHI)
Rev.: $60,647,573
Assets: $340,993,484
Liabilities: $34,213,778
Net Worth: $306,779,706
Earnings: $36,535,322
Fiscal Year-end: 12/31/12
Business Description:
Investment Management Services
S.I.C.: 6282
N.A.I.C.S.: 523920
Personnel:
Andres Soriano III *(Chm, Pres & CEO)*
Eduardo J. Soriano *(Vice Chm & Treas)*
Ernest K. Cuyegkeng *(CFO & Exec VP)*
Lorna P. Kapunan *(Sec)*
Board of Directors:
Andres Soriano III
Ernest K. Cuyegkeng
John L. Gokongwei, Jr.
Oscar J. Hilado
Jose C. Ibazeta
Roberto R. Romulo
Eduardo J. Soriano
Transfer Agent:
Stock Transfer Service Inc
34/F Unit D Rufino Pacific Tower 6784 Ayala Avenue
Makati, Philippines

Subsidiary:

A. Soriano Air Corporation **(1)**
A Soriano Hangar Andrews Avenue
Pasay, Manila, 1300, Philippines
Tel.: (63) 28314207
Fax: (63) 28520948
E-Mail: a_sorav@prime.net.ph
Web Site: www.asai.com.ph
Aircraft Support & Ground Handling Services
S.I.C.: 4581
N.A.I.C.S.: 488190
Ernest K. Cuyegkeng *(Pres)*

Subsidiary:

Pamalican Island Holdings, Inc. **(2)**
7th Floor Pacific Star Building Sen Gil Puyat Avenue
Corner Makati Avenue, Makati, 1200, Philippines
Tel.: (63) 28190251
Business Management Services
S.I.C.: 6719
N.A.I.C.S.: 551112

Subsidiary:

Island Aviation, Inc. **(3)**
A. Soriano Hangar Andrews Avenue
Pasay, Philippines
Tel.: (63) 28333855
Fax: (63) 88520508
E-Mail: info@islandaviationph.com
Web Site: www.islandaviationph.com
Emp.: 35
Aircraft Maintenance Services
S.I.C.: 4581
N.A.I.C.S.: 488190
Ben Hur D. Gomez *(Chm & CEO)*

U.S. Subsidiary:

Cirrus Medical Staffing, Inc. **(1)**
309 E Morehead St Ste 200
Charlotte, NC 28202
Tel.: (704) 887-3900
Fax: (704) 887-3919
Toll Free: (800) 299-8132
E-Mail: travel@cirrusmedicalstaffing.com
Web Site: www.cirrusmedicalstaffing.com
Emp.: 50
Medical Staffing Services
S.I.C.: 7361
N.A.I.C.S.: 561311
William Ottiger *(Pres & CEO)*
Andrea Zveibil *(COO & Sr VP)*
Marty Goldberg *(CIO)*

Subsidiary:

Cirrus Allied, LLC **(2)**
309 E Morehead St Ste 200
Charlotte, NC 28202
Tel.: (866) 518-1750
Fax: (866) 600-4001
Toll Free: (800) 299-8132
E-Mail:
Web Site: www.cirrusmedicalstaffing.com
Emp.: 15
Rehabilitation Therapists Staffing Services
S.I.C.: 7361
N.A.I.C.S.: 561311

A-TEC INDUSTRIES AG

Wachtergasse 1-3
1010 Vienna, Austria
Tel.: (43) 1227600
Fax: (43) 12270160
E-Mail: office@a-tecindustries.com
Web Site: www.a-tecindustries.at
Year Founded: 2004
Sales Range: $1-4.9 Billion
Emp.: 11,883
Business Description:
Holding Company; Electric Motor & Machine Tool Mfr
S.I.C.: 6719
N.A.I.C.S.: 551112
Personnel:
Freimut Dobretsberger *(Chm-Supervisory Bd)*
Mirko Kovats *(Chm-Mgmt Bd)*
Johannes Edelsbacher *(Deputy Chm-Supervisory Bd)*
Christian Schmidt *(Deputy Chm-Mgmt Bd)*
Franz Fehringer *(Member-Mgmt Bd)*
Supervisory Board of Directors:
Freimut Dobretsberger
Johannes Edelsbacher
Alfred Finz
Gernot Grimm
Helmuth Palzer
Franz Struzl
Horst Wiesinger

Subsidiaries:

AE&E Group GmbH **(1)**
Bruenner Strasse 52
AT-1210 Vienna, Austria AT
Tel.: (43) 190 235 0 (100%)
Fax: (43) 190 235 1103
E-Mail: info@aee-group.com
Web Site: www.aee-group.com
Holding Company: Environmental Technology & Global Energy
S.I.C.: 6719
N.A.I.C.S.: 551112
Klaus Zink *(COO & Member-Mgmt Bd)*
Franz Killer *(Exec VP-Svc)*
Helmut Moshammer *(Exec VP-Air Pollution Control)*
Georg Silbermann *(Exec VP-Energy From Waste)*
Frank Steinhoff *(Sr VP-Sls-Western Europe & Middle East)*

Subsidiary:

AE&E Power Plant Systems GmbH **(2)**
Bruenner Strasse 52
1210 Vienna, Austria
Tel.: (43) 1 90180 0
Fax: (43) 1 90180 6666
E-Mail: office@aee-pps.at
Web Site: www.aee-pps.at
Emp.: 3
Electric Power Generation Services
S.I.C.: 4931
N.A.I.C.S.: 221118
Romen Stefan *(Gen Mgr)*

Non-U.S. Subsidiaries:

AE&E Duro Dakovic Termoenergetska postrojenja d.o.o. **(2)**
Dr Mile Budaka 1
35 000 Slavonski Brod, Croatia HR
Tel.: (385) 35445793 (100%)

Fax: (385) 35445550
E-Mail: info@aee-dd.hr
Web Site: www.aee-group.com
Emp.: 800
Thermal Power Generation
S.I.C.: 4911
N.A.I.C.S.: 221118
Danir Simunic *(Dir-Comml)*

AE&E Energy & Environment Consulting Shanghai Co. Ltd. **(2)**
Room 706-708 East Block China Merchants Plaza No
20004 Shanghai, China
Tel.: (86) 21 5298 1616
Fax: (86) 21 5298 1626
E-Mail: contact@aee-shanghai.cn
Power Generation Plant Construction & Engineering Services
S.I.C.: 1629
N.A.I.C.S.: 237130
Huang Gai *(Gen Mgr)*

AE&E Nanjing Boiler Co. Ltd. **(2)**
139 Tai Shan Road
Jianye District, 210019 Nanjing, Jiangsu, China
Tel.: (86) 25 8680 5888
Fax: (86) 25 8680 5861
E-Mail: sales@aee-nanjing.cn
Web Site: www.aee-nanjing.cn
Boiler & Heat Exchanger Mfr
S.I.C.: 3559
N.A.I.C.S.: 332410

iDream Media Services GmbH **(1)**
Karntner Strasse 17
1010 Vienna, Austria
Tel.: (43) 1 6021775 0
Fax: (43) 1 6021775 44
E-Mail: office@idream.at
Web Site: www.idream.at
Advertising Services
S.I.C.: 7311
N.A.I.C.S.: 541810
Frederick Abner *(Gen Mgr)*

Non-U.S. Subsidiary:

MEXPOL Werkzeugmaschinen GmbH **(1)**
Kleinhulsen 31
40721 Hilden, Germany De
Tel.: (49) 2103 955 0 (60%)
Fax: (49) 2103 955 180
E-Mail: info@mexpol.com
Web Site: www.mexpol.com
Industrial Machinery Mfr
S.I.C.: 3559
N.A.I.C.S.: 333249
Adam Baranski *(Mng Dir)*

A-TECH SOLUTION CO., LTD.

123-1 Goji-ri Jeongnam-myeon
Hwaseong, Gyeonggi, 445-962, Korea (South)
Tel.: (82) 31 350 8168
Fax: (82) 31 350 8190
Web Site: www.atechsolution.co.kr
Year Founded: 2001
071670—(KRS)
Sales Range: $150-199.9 Million
Business Description:
Industrial Mold Mfr
S.I.C.: 3544
N.A.I.C.S.: 333511
Personnel:
Young Mok Yoo *(CEO)*

A. TSOKKOS HOTELS PUBLIC LTD

PO Box 30221
5341 Ayia Napa, Cyprus
Tel.: (357) 77 777 444
Fax: (357) 23 831 447
E-Mail: reservations@tsokkos.com
Web Site: www.tsokkos.com
Year Founded: 1981
TSH—(CYP)
Business Description:
Hotel Management Services
S.I.C.: 7011
N.A.I.C.S.: 721110
Personnel:
Andreas Tsokkos *(Chm)*
Anastasia Tsokkou *(Gen Dir & Sec)*
Board of Directors:
Andreas Tsokkos
Antonis Andreou
Andreas Demetriou
Vassos Hadjitheodosiou
Nestoras Kyriakides
Loizos A. Loizou
Nicos Michaelas
George Pittadjis
Chryso Spyrou Stavroulli
George Tsokkos
Anastasia Tsokkou
Chryso Tsokkou

A W HAINSWORTH & SONS LTD.

Spring Valley Mills Stanningley
Pudsey, West Yorkshire, LS28 6DW, United Kingdom
Tel.: (44) 1132570391
Fax: (44) 1133955686
E-Mail: sales@hainsworth.co.uk
Web Site: www.hainsworth.co.uk
Year Founded: 1783
Rev.: $24,806,989
Emp.: 189
Business Description:
Fabric Mfr
S.I.C.: 2269
N.A.I.C.S.: 313310
Personnel:
Thomas Hainsworth *(Mng Dir)*

A. ZORBAS & SONS PUBLIC LTD.

Armenias 51
2006 Strovolos, Nicosia, Cyprus
Tel.: (357) 22 871700
Fax: (357) 22 318727
E-Mail: info@zorbas.com.cy
Web Site: www.zorbas.com.cy
Year Founded: 1975
ZPR—(CYP)
Business Description:
Baked Products Mfr
S.I.C.: 2051
N.A.I.C.S.: 311812
Personnel:
Costas Zorbas *(Chm)*
Demetris Zorbas *(Gen Dir)*
Board of Directors:
Costas Zorbas
Tasos Anastasiou
Panagiotis Athienitis
Michalis Papadopoulos
Anastasios Zorbas
Andreas Zorbas
Demetris Zorbas

A1 CONSOLIDATED GOLD LTD

c/o Herries Davidson & Co 32 Clifford Street
Goulburn, NSW, 2580, Australia
Tel.: (61) 8 9389 2111
Fax: (61) 8 9389 2199
E-Mail: info@a1consolidated.com.au
Web Site: www.a1consolidated.com.au
Year Founded: 2011
AYC—(ASX)
Business Description:
Gold Mining
S.I.C.: 1041
N.A.I.C.S.: 212221
Personnel:
Ashok Parekh *(Chm)*
Dennis Clark *(Mng Dir)*
Board of Directors:
Ashok Parekh
Dennis Clark
Morrie Goodz
Darren Russell-Croucher
Glenn Wardle
Jeffery Williams

A1 INVESTMENTS & RESOURCES LTD.

Suite 606 37 Bligh Street
Sydney, NSW, 2000, Australia
Tel.: (61) 2 9114 6888
Fax: (61) 2 9232 8883
E-Mail: info@a1investments.com.au
Web Site: www.a1investments.com.au
Year Founded: 2004
AYI—(ASX)
Rev.: $103,792
Assets: $3,514,967
Liabilities: $3,276,655
Net Worth: $238,312
Earnings: ($4,004,422)
Fiscal Year-end: 06/30/13
Business Description:
Metal Mining Investment Services
S.I.C.: 6211
N.A.I.C.S.: 523999
Personnel:
Charlie Nakamura *(CEO)*
Robert Kineavy *(Sec)*
Board of Directors:
Peter Ashcroft
Dan Kao
Charlie Nakamura

A2A S.P.A.

Via Lamarmora 230
25124 Brescia, Italy
Tel.: (39) 03035531
Fax: (39) 0303553204
E-Mail: info@a2a.eu
Web Site: www.a2a.eu
A2A—(ITA OTC)
Rev.: $8,723,181,600
Assets: $16,080,000,650
Liabilities: $11,103,210,160
Net Worth: $4,976,790,490
Earnings: $350,004,200
Emp.: 12,771
Fiscal Year-end: 12/31/12
Business Description:
Electricity & Natural Gas Producer & Distr; Fiber-Optic Network Operator
S.I.C.: 4911
N.A.I.C.S.: 221122
Personnel:
Pippo Ranci Ortigosa *(Chm-Supervisory Bd)*
Graziano Tarantini *(Chm-Mgmt Bd)*
Fausto di Mezza *(Vice Chm-Supervisory Bd)*
Francesco Silva *(Vice Chm-Mgmt Bd)*
Giuliano Zuccoli *(Pres)*
Giambattista Brivio *(Member-Mgmt Bd)*
Stefano Cao *(Member-Mgmt Bd)*
Bruno Caparini *(Member-Mgmt Bd)*
Maria Elena Cappello *(Member-Mgmt Bd)*
Renato Ravanelli *(Member-Mgmt Bd)*
Paolo Rossetti *(Member-Mgmt Bd)*
Supervisory Board of Directors:
Pippo Ranci Ortigosa
Marco Baga
Alessandro Berdini
Marina Brogi
Michaela Castelli
Mario Cocchi
Fausto di Mezza
Marco Manzoli
Enrico Giorgio Mattinzoli
Marco Miccinesi
Andrea Mina
Stefano Pareglio
Massimo Perona
Norberto Rosini
Angelo Teodoro Zanotti

Subsidiaries:

A2A Ciclo Idrico S.p.A. **(1)**
Via Lamarmora 230
25124 Brescia, Italy
Tel.: (39) 030 35531
Fax: (39) 030 3553204
E-Mail: a2acicloidrico@a2a.eu
Web Site: www.a2acicloidrico.eu
Emp.: 2,000
Water Supply & Treatment Services
S.I.C.: 4941
N.A.I.C.S.: 221310
Mario Tomasoni *(Gen Mgr)*

A2A Energia S.p.A. **(1)**
Corso Di Porta Vittoria 4
Milan, 20122, Italy
Tel.: (39) 0277201
Fax: (39) 0277203963
Web Site: www.a2aenergia.eu
Emp.: 50
Electric Power Generation & Distribution Services
S.I.C.: 4911
N.A.I.C.S.: 221118
Giuseppe Sala *(Gen Mgr)*

A2A Logistica S.p.A. **(1)**
Via Alessandro Lamarmora 230
Brescia, 25124, Italy
Tel.: (39) 03035531
Fax: (39) 030 3553204
Logistics Services
S.I.C.: 4731
N.A.I.C.S.: 541614

A2A Reti Elettriche S.p.A. **(1)**
Via Francesco Sforza 12
Milan, 20122, Italy
Tel.: (39) 0277201
Fax: (39) 0277203920
Electric Power Distribution Services
S.I.C.: 4911
N.A.I.C.S.: 221122

A2A Reti Gas S.p.A. **(1)**
Via Lamarmora 230
25124 Brescia, Italy
Tel.: (39) 030 35531
Fax: (39) 030 3555224
E-Mail: info@a2a.eu
Web Site: www.a2aretigas.eu
Emp.: 100
Natural Gas Distribution Services
S.I.C.: 4924
N.A.I.C.S.: 221210
Enzo Gerosa *(Gen Mgr)*

A2A Servizi alla Distribuzione S.p.A. **(1)**
Via Alessandro Lamarmora 230
Brescia, 25124, Italy
Tel.: (39) 03035531
Fax: (39) 0303553204
E-Mail: accessoretigas.bs@a2a.eu
Web Site: www.a2a.eu
Emp.: 3,000
Electric Power Distribution Services
S.I.C.: 4911
N.A.I.C.S.: 221122
Paolo Rossetti *(Gen Mgr)*

A2A Trading S.r.l. **(1)**
Corso di Porta Vittoria 4
Milan, 20122, Italy
Tel.: (39) 0277 20 31 61
Fax: (39) 0277 20 32 67
E-Mail: segreteria.aet@a2a.eu
Electric Power & Fuel Gas Distr
S.I.C.: 4931
N.A.I.C.S.: 221122

Abruzzoenergia S.p.A. **(1)**
Localita Selva 1/A
Gissi, Chieti, 66052, Italy
Tel.: (39) 0873943700
Fax: (39) 08733244551
Electric Power Generation Services
S.I.C.: 4911
N.A.I.C.S.: 221118

AEM Calore & Servizi S.p.A. **(1)**
Corso di Porta Vittoria 4
20122 Milan, Italy
Tel.: (39) 02 7720 1
Web Site: www.aemcaloreservizi.it
Facility Management

A2A S.p.A.—(Continued)

S.I.C.: 8744
N.A.I.C.S.: 561210

AEM Gas S.p.A. (1)
Corso di Porta Vittoria 4
20122 Milan, Italy
Tel.: (39) 0277201
E-Mail: presidenza.gestione@a2a.eu
Web Site: www.aemgas.it
Gas & Heat Distribution Networks
S.I.C.: 4924
N.A.I.C.S.: 221210
Renato Ravanelli *(Gen Mgr)*

AEM Service S.r.l. (1)
Corso di Porta Vittoria 4
20122 Milan, Italy
Tel.: (39) 0277201
E-Mail: aem@aem.it
Web Site: www.aemservice.it
Call Center Management, Meter Readings, Back Office & Invoicing Services
S.I.C.: 7389
N.A.I.C.S.: 561499
Severino Bongiolatti *(Dir)*

AEM Trading S.r.l. (1)
Corso di Porta Vittoria 4
20122 Milan, Italy
Tel.: (39) 0277201
E-Mail:
Emp.: 20
Electrical, Gaseous & Non-Gaseous Fuels Trading
S.I.C.: 7389
N.A.I.C.S.: 425120
Renato Ravanelli *(Mng Dir)*

Amsa SpA (1)
Via Olgettina 25
20132 Milan, Italy
Tel.: (39) 02272981
Fax: (39) 0227298276
Web Site: www.amsa.it
Energy Services
S.I.C.: 4924
N.A.I.C.S.: 221210
Sonia Cantoni *(Pres)*

Aprica SpA (1)
via Lamarmora 230
Brescia, Italy
Tel.: (39) 0303553505
E-Mail: info@apricaspa.it
Web Site: www.apricaspa.it
Waste Services
S.I.C.: 4212
N.A.I.C.S.: 562119

Aprica Studi S.R.L. (1)
Via Creta 56/C
25125 Brescia, Italy
Tel.: (39) 030225751
Fax: (39) 030220619
Web Site: www.apricastudi.it
Engineering Services
S.I.C.: 8711
N.A.I.C.S.: 541330
Fausto Cancelli *(CEO)*

ASM Energia e Ambiente S.r.l. (1)
Via Lamarmora 230
BS-25124 Brescia, Italy
Tel.: (39) 030 228 7821
Fax: (39) 030 355 3204
E-Mail: asmea@asm.brescia.it
Web Site: www.asmea.it
Energy Sales & Services
S.I.C.: 4939
N.A.I.C.S.: 221122
Fausto Cancelli *(CEO)*

ASM Energy Srl (1)
Via Lamarmora 230
25124 Brescia, Italy
Tel.: (39) 03035531
Fax: (39) 0303553204
E-Mail: info@a2a.eu
Web Site: www.a2a.eu/gruppo/cms/a2a/en/misc/contatti.html
Emp.: 2,000
Energy Sales & Services
S.I.C.: 4931
N.A.I.C.S.: 221122
Paolo Rossette *(CEO)*

ASM Reti (1)
Via Lamarmora 230
Brescia, Italy
Tel.: (39) 03035531
Fax: (39) 0303553204
E-Mail: accessoretigas.bs@a2a.eu
Web Site: www.a2aretigas.eu
Gas Services
S.I.C.: 1389
N.A.I.C.S.: 213112

ASMEA S.r.l. (1)
Via Lamarmora 230
25124 Brescia, Italy
Tel.: (39) 030 35531
Fax: (39) 030 3554391
E-Mail: info@asmea.it
Web Site: www.asmea.it
Electric Power Distribution Services
S.I.C.: 4931
N.A.I.C.S.: 221122
Paolo Rossetti *(Gen Mgr)*

Aspem S.p.A. (1)
Via San Giusto 6
21100 Varese, Italy
Tel.: (39) 0332 290111
Fax: (39) 0332 290220
E-Mail: comunicazione@aspem.it
Emp.: 29
Electric Power Distribution Services
S.I.C.: 4911
N.A.I.C.S.: 221122

BAS Omniservizi Srl (1)
via Suardi 26
24124 Bergamo, Italy
Tel.: (39) 0302287822
Web Site: www.basomniservizi.it
Natural Gas Distribution
S.I.C.: 4924
N.A.I.C.S.: 221210

BASSII S.p.a. (1)
Via Codussi 46
Bergamo, 24124, Italy
Tel.: (39) 35 216 162
Web Site: www.bassii.it
Gas & Power Services
S.I.C.: 1389
N.A.I.C.S.: 213112

Camuna Energia S.r.l. (1)
Piazza Roma 1
25051 Cedegolo, Brescia, Italy
Tel.: (39) 0364 770482
E-Mail: camuna.energia@pec.a2a.eu
Electric Power Distribution Services
S.I.C.: 4911
N.A.I.C.S.: 221122

Ecodeco (1)
Cassinazza di Baselica
Milan, Giussago, 27010, Italy
Tel.: (39) 03829311
Fax: (39) 0382927506
E-Mail: info@ecodeco.it
Web Site: www.ecodeco.it
Sales Range: $200-249.9 Million
Waste Systems
S.I.C.: 4212
N.A.I.C.S.: 562111
Nenette Carlo *(Gen Mgr)*

Fertilivita S.r.l. (1)
Loc. Manzola Fornace
27014 Pavia, Corteolona, Italy
Tel.: (39) 382 727 611
Fax: (39) 382 727 636
Web Site: www.fertilivita.it
Environmental Services
S.I.C.: 8999
N.A.I.C.S.: 541620

Itradeplace SpA (1)
230 A Via Lamarmora 230
25124 Brescia, Italy
Tel.: (39) 03035531
Fax: (39) 0303554602
E-Mail: info@itradeplace.com
Web Site: www.itradeplace.it
Electronic Procurement Services
S.I.C.: 6099
N.A.I.C.S.: 522320
Fausto Cancelli *(CEO)*

Retragas srl (1)
via Lamarmora 230
25124 Brescia, Italy
Tel.: (39) 0303554089
Fax: (39) 0303554338
E-Mail: info.retragas@a2a.eu
Web Site: www.retragas.it
Emp.: 6
Gas Services
S.I.C.: 1389
N.A.I.C.S.: 213112
Aldo Martira *(CEO)*

Selene Spa (1)
via Lamarmora 230
25124 Brescia, Italy
Tel.: (39) 303554929
Fax: (39) 303554522
Web Site: www.selenebs.it
Telecommunications
S.I.C.: 4899
N.A.I.C.S.: 517919

Tidonenergie Srl (1)
Via Abbondanza n 34
29100 Piacenza, Italy
Tel.: (39) 523336729
Fax: (39) 523 331 219
Web Site: www.tidonenergie.it
Energy Services
S.I.C.: 4731
N.A.I.C.S.: 541614

Varese Risorse S.p.A. (1)
Via San Giusto 6
21100 Varese, Italy
Tel.: (39) 0332 290111
Fax: (39) 0332290220
Emp.: 298
Electric Power & Gas Distr
S.I.C.: 4931
N.A.I.C.S.: 221122

Non-U.S. Subsidiaries:

A2A Coriance S.a.s. (1)
Immeuble Horizon 1 10 Allee Bienvenue
93885 Noisy-le-Grand, France
Tel.: (33) 1 49 14 79 79
Fax: (33) 1 43 04 51 42
E-Mail: commercial@coriance-a2a.fr
Industrial Heating & Cooling Network Operating Services
S.I.C.: 1711
N.A.I.C.S.: 238220

A2A Montenegro d.o.o. (1)
Bulevar Sv Petra Cetinjskog 1A
Podgorica, Montenegro
Tel.: (382) 20 201320
Fax: (382) 20 201350
E-Mail: info@a2amontenegro.me
Web Site: www.a2amontenegro.eu
Electric Power Generation & Distribution Services
S.I.C.: 4911
N.A.I.C.S.: 221118

A2E VENTURE CATALYSTS LTD

1 Marsden Street
Manchester, M2 1HW, United Kingdom
Tel.: (44) 161 923 6000
Fax: (44) 161 236 7266
Web Site: www.a2evc.com
Business Description:
Private Equity Firm
S.I.C.: 6211
N.A.I.C.S.: 523999
Personnel:
Amin Amiri *(Founder & Mng Dir)*

Holding:

BHW (Components) Limited (1)
Caxton Close
Wigan, Lancashire, WN3 6XU, United Kingdom
Tel.: (44) 1942 821205
Fax: (44) 1942 829552
E-Mail:
Aerospace Components Mfr
S.I.C.: 3728
N.A.I.C.S.: 336413

A2MICILE EUROPE SA

48 rue du Faubourg de Saverne
67000 Strasbourg, France
Tel.: (33) 3 88 60 66 30
Fax: (33) 3 88 13 75 26
E-Mail: joel.chaulet@a2micile.com
Web Site: www.a2micile.com
ALA2M—(EUR)
Sales Range: $25-49.9 Million
Emp.: 1,100
Business Description:
Cleaning, Ironing, Gardening, Handyman & Child Care Services
S.I.C.: 7299
N.A.I.C.S.: 812990
Personnel:
Joel Chaulet *(Chm & CEO)*
Yves Fritsch *(CFO)*

A2Z MAINTENANCE & ENGINEERING SERVICES LIMITED

0-116 First Floor Shopping Mall Arjun Marg DLF City
Phase - 1, Gurgaon, 122002, India
Tel.: (91) 1244300426
Fax: (91) 1242566651
E-Mail: investor.relations@a2zemail.com
Web Site: www.a2zgroup.co.in
A2ZMES—(BOM NSE)
Rev.: $174,159,293
Assets: $530,056,645
Liabilities: $316,771,637
Net Worth: $213,285,009
Earnings: ($19,628,030)
Emp.: 1,200
Fiscal Year-end: 03/31/13
Business Description:
Engineering Services
S.I.C.: 1629
N.A.I.C.S.: 237990
Personnel:
Ashok Kumar Saini *(CEO)*
Amit Mittal *(Mng Dir)*
Atul Kumar Agarwal *(Compliance Officer & Sec)*
Sujoy Kumar Mitra *(Corp Dev Officer)*
Rajesh Jain *(Pres-Corp Affairs)*
Sanjeev Sharma *(Pres-EPC Projects)*
Ajay Bajaj *(CEO-Transmission Line)*
Sunil B. Chhibar *(Sr VP-Projects)*
Board of Directors:
Surender Kumar Tuteja
Ashok Kumar
Amit Mittal
Dipali Mittal
Transfer Agent:
Alankit Assignments Limited
2E/21 Alankit House Jhandewalan Extension
New Delhi, India

Subsidiaries:

A2Z Infraservices Private Limited (1)
5th & 6th Floor Enkay Square 448 A Udyog Vihar Phase V
Gurgaon, Haryana, 122001, India
Tel.: (91) 1244517600
Fax: (91) 1244380014
E-Mail: enquiries@a2zemail.com
Web Site: www.a2zinfraservices.co.in
Rev.: $203,112,000
Emp.: 12,000
Facility Management Services
S.I.C.: 8742
N.A.I.C.S.: 541611
Anil Soni *(Mng Dir)*
Manish Puri *(CFO)*

A2Z Infrastructure Limited (1)
Plot No 38 Sec 32 Instiutional Area
Gurgaon, Haryana, 122001, India
Tel.: (91) 124 4517600
Fax: (91) 1244380010
E-Mail: info@a2zemail.com
Web Site: www.a2zgroup.co.in
Emp.: 200
Construction Engineering Services
S.I.C.: 8711
N.A.I.C.S.: 541330
Amit Mittal *(Mng Dir)*

A2Z Powercom Limited (1)
Plot 44 Sector 32 Institutional Area
Gurgaon, Haryana, 122001, India
Tel.: (91) 1244517600

Web Site: www.a2zpowercom.com
Electric Power Generation Services
S.I.C.: 4931
N.A.I.C.S.: 221118

A2Z Powertech Limited (1)
Enkay Tower Udyog Vihar Phase 5
Gurgaon, Haryana, 122016, India
Tel.: (91) 1244517600
Fax: (91) 124 4380014
Web Site: www.a2zpowertech.com
Power Transmission Line Construction & Maintenance Services
S.I.C.: 1629
N.A.I.C.S.: 237130

CNCS Facility Solutions Private Limited. (1)
B 27 3rd Floor Shreeram Industrial Estate
G D Ambedkar Road
Wadala Dadar East, Mumbai, 400031, India
Tel.: (91) 2224165962
Fax: (91) 22 24110770
Facility Management Services
S.I.C.: 8744
N.A.I.C.S.: 561210

Selligence Technologies Services Private Limited (1)
116 First Floor Arjun Marg DLF City Phase 1
Gurgaon, Haryana, 122002, India
Tel.: (91) 1244517600
Fax: (91) 124 4380014
E-Mail: enquiries@selligencetechnology.com
Web Site: www.selligencetechnology.com
Information Technology Consulting Services
S.I.C.: 7373
N.A.I.C.S.: 541512
Amit Mittal *(Chm-Mgmt Bd)*
Shailesh Jain *(COO)*

A4E LTD.

Queens House 105 Queen Street
Sheffield, S1 1GN, United Kingdom
Tel.: (44) 11 4220 3040
Fax: (44) 11 4244 4742
Web Site: www.mya4e.com
Year Founded: 1991
Sales Range: $350-399.9 Million
Emp.: 3,692

Business Description:
Human Resources Consulting Services
S.I.C.: 8999
N.A.I.C.S.: 541612

Personnel:
Andrew Dutton *(CEO)*

A8 DIGITAL MUSIC HOLDINGS LIMITED

5/F Fucheng Hi-tech Building South-1 Avenue
Nanshan District, Shenzhen, 518057, China
Tel.: (86) 75533326333
Fax: (86) 75533303333
E-Mail: ir@a8.com
Web Site: www.a8.com
0800—(HKG)
Rev.: $54,818,023
Assets: $112,757,925
Liabilities: $30,907,921
Net Worth: $81,850,004
Earnings: ($4,767,406)
Emp.: 251
Fiscal Year-end: 12/31/12

Business Description:
Digital Music Services
S.I.C.: 7379
N.A.I.C.S.: 541519

Personnel:
Xiaosong Liu *(Chm & CEO)*
Bin Lu *(CFO)*
Wei Su *(COO)*
Jimmy Jian-Ping Shi *(CTO)*
Keying Gao *(Co-Sec)*
Yip Betty Ho *(Co-Sec)*

Board of Directors:
Xiaosong Liu
Yiu Kwong Chan
Bin Lu
Shihong Wu
Liqing Zeng

Transfer Agent:
Computershare Hong Kong Investor Services Limited
46th Floor Hopewell Centre 183 Queen's Road East
Hong Kong, China (Hong Kong)

AA CLARK

(See Under Eden Bracknell)

AA GROUP HOLDINGS LTD.

Lot 148 149 Jalan PKNK 1 Sungai Petani Industrial Estate
08000 Sungai Petani, Malaysia
Tel.: (60) 44418351
Fax: (60) 44418349
E-Mail: info@allied-advantage.com
Web Site: www.allied-advantage.com
5GZ—(SES)
Rev.: $11,581,232
Assets: $22,373,079
Liabilities: $11,223,462
Net Worth: $11,149,617
Earnings: $13,263
Emp.: 152
Fiscal Year-end: 12/31/12

Business Description:
Loudspeaker Parts Mfr
S.I.C.: 3452
N.A.I.C.S.: 332722

Personnel:
Kuo-Chuan Hsieh *(Co-Founder & Chm)*
Tzu-Ju Feng *(Co-Founder & Mng Dir)*
Foon Yeow Chia *(Sec)*

Board of Directors:
Kuo-Chuan Hsieh
Tzu-Ju Feng
Choon Chiaw Loo
Lian Heng Phuah
Kuang Hui Tan

Legal Counsel:
Loo & Partners LLP
16 Gemmill Lane
Singapore, Singapore

Transfer Agent:
Boardroom Corporate & Advisory Services Pte. Ltd.
50 Raffles Place 32-01 Singapore Land Tower
Singapore, Singapore

AAA AUTO GROUP N.V.

Dopravaku 723
CZ-184 00 Prague, 8, Czech Republic
Tel.: (420) 284 022 076
Fax: (420) 283 060 286
E-Mail: investor.relations@aaaauto.cz
Web Site: www.aaaauto.cz
Year Founded: 1992
Rev.: $452,181,195
Assets: $128,382,887
Liabilities: $65,290,591
Net Worth: $63,092,296
Earnings: $29,988,629
Emp.: 1,757
Fiscal Year-end: 12/31/12

Business Description:
Holding Company; Motor Vehicle Sales & Support Services
Import
S.I.C.: 6719
N.A.I.C.S.: 551112

Personnel:
Anthony James Denny *(Chm-Mgmt Bd)*
Karolina Topolova *(CEO & Member-Mgmt Bd)*
Jiri Trnka *(CFO)*
Vratislav Kulhanek *(Member-Mgmt Bd)*

AAB HOLDINGS PTY LIMITED

Building B 1A Bessemer Street
Blacktown, NSW, 2148, Australia
Tel.: (61) 288220600
Fax: (61) 288220601
E-Mail: info@aabholdings.com
Web Site: www.aabholdings.com
Year Founded: 2000
Emp.: 250

Business Description:
Holding Company; Business Services
S.I.C.: 6719
N.A.I.C.S.: 551112

Personnel:
Wayne Finkelde *(CEO)*

Divisions:

Mailing and Print Services (1)
8 Aquatic Drive
French's Forest, NSW, 2086, Australia
Tel.: (61) 294516433
Fax: (61) 2 9451 3338
E-Mail: clientservices@mailandprint.com.au
Web Site: www.mailandprint.com.au
Printing & Mailing Services
S.I.C.: 2759
N.A.I.C.S.: 323111

Nature's Selection Foods (1)
Building 8 77-85 Roberts Road
Greenacre, NSW, 2190, Australia
Tel.: (61) 287557400
Fax: (61) 296426911
E-Mail: info@naturesselection.com
Web Site: www.naturesselection.com
Food Mfr, Packer & Distr
S.I.C.: 2099
N.A.I.C.S.: 311999
David Chales *(CEO)*

Pegasus Printing (1)
Building B 1A Bessemer Street
Blacktown, NSW, 2148, Australia
Tel.: (61) 288220600
Fax: (61) 288220700
E-Mail: info@aabholdings.com
Web Site: www.pegasusprintgroup.com.au
Emp.: 100
Printing Services & Supplies
S.I.C.: 2759
N.A.I.C.S.: 323111
Wayne Finkelde *(CEO)*

AAC CAPITAL PARTNERS HOLDING B.V.

ITO Tower 22nd Floor Gustav Mahlerplein 106
1082 MA Amsterdam, Netherlands
Tel.: (31) 203331300
Fax: (31) 3120333132
E-Mail: info@aaccapital.com
Web Site: www.aaccapital.com
Year Founded: 2007

Business Description:
Holding Company; Equity Investment Firm
S.I.C.: 6719
N.A.I.C.S.: 551112

Personnel:
Johan Bjurstrom *(Mng Partner-Nordic Reg)*
Paul Southwell *(Mng Partner-UK)*
Marc Staal *(Mng Partner)*
Maurice Bronckers *(Partner)*
Paul G. Hugenholtz *(Partner)*
Bert-Jan Rozestraten *(Partner)*
Frank Trijbels *(Partner)*
Paul van Steijn *(Partner)*

Holdings:

Baarsma Wine Group Holding B.V. (1)
Oude Enghweg 8
NL-1217 JC Hilversum, Netherlands NL
Mailing Address:
Postbus 111
NL-8440 AC Heerenveen, Netherlands
Tel.: (31) 356261270
Fax: (31) 356261271
E-Mail: holding@baarsma.com
Web Site: www.corporate.baarsma.com
Sales Range: $250-299.9 Million
Emp.: 250
Holding Company; Wine Distr
Import Export
S.I.C.: 6719
N.A.I.C.S.: 551112
Frans Barel *(Chm-Supervisory Bd)*
Tjeerd C. van der Hoek *(Chm-Mgmt Bd & CEO)*
Cees M. de Rade *(COO)*

Subsidiaries:

Baarsma Wine Group Nederland B.V. (2)
Badweg 48
NL-8401 BL Gorredijk, Netherlands NL
Tel.: (31) 513469469 (100%)
Fax: (31) 513469164
E-Mail: info@baarsma.com
Web Site: www.baarsma.com
Emp.: 40
Wine Distr
S.I.C.: 5182
N.A.I.C.S.: 424820
Joost Hagen *(Gen Mgr)*

De Wijnbeurs (2)
Amstellandlaan 84
1382 CH Weesp, Netherlands NL
Mailing Address: (100%)
Postbus 5020
1380GA Weesp, Netherlands
Tel.: (31) 294462800
Web Site: www.wijnbeurs.nl
Emp.: 40
Direct Mail Wine Distr
S.I.C.: 5182
N.A.I.C.S.: 424820
Frans Melenhorst *(Mng Dir)*

Lovian B.V. (2)
Badweg 48
8401 BL Gorredijk, Netherlands NL
Tel.: (31) 513469490 (70%)
Fax: (31) 513465164
E-Mail:
Web Site: www.lovian.nl
Emp.: 50
Wine Distr
S.I.C.: 5182
N.A.I.C.S.: 424820

Wijnhandel Leon Colaris B.V. (2)
Franklinstraat 1
NL-6003 DK Weert, Netherlands NL
Mailing Address: (93%)
Postbus 55
NL-6000 AB Weert, Netherlands
Tel.: (31) 495532462
Fax: (31) 495543470
E-Mail: info@colaris.nl
Web Site: www.colaris.nl
Wine Distr
S.I.C.: 5182
N.A.I.C.S.: 424820
Ruud Heuvelmans *(Mng Dir)*

Wine Excel B.V. (2)
Hoofdtocht 3
NL-1507 CJ Zaandam, Netherlands NL
Tel.: (31) 756429930 (100%)
Fax: (31) 756429970
E-Mail: info@wine-excel.com
Web Site: www.wine-excel.com
Emp.: 50
Wine Bottler & Distr
S.I.C.: 5182
N.A.I.C.S.: 424820
Marcel Campen *(Mng Dir)*

Non-U.S. Subsidiaries:

Baarsma South Africa Pty. Ltd. (2)
Blaauwklip Offices 1
Webersvallei Road, 7600 Stellenbosch, South Africa ZA
Tel.: (27) 218801221 (78%)
Fax: (27) 218800851
E-Mail: info@baarsma.co.za
Web Site: www.baarsma.co.za
Emp.: 12
Winery & Wine Distr

AAC Capital Partners Holding B.V.—(Continued)

S.I.C.: 2084
N.A.I.C.S.: 312130
Chris Rabie *(Mng Dir)*

New Holland Wine Company Pty. Ltd. (2)
Ground Level 26 Greenhill Road
Wayville, 5034, Australia AU
Tel.: (61) 883000990 (80%)
Fax: (61) 882728812
Web Site: www.newhollandwine.com.au
Producer & Packager of Wines
S.I.C.: 2084
N.A.I.C.S.: 312130
Lance Bradfield *(Mng Dir)*

Lucas Bols B.V. (1)
Paulus Potterstraat 12
1071 CZ Amsterdam, Netherlands NL
Tel.: (31) 205708575 (75%)
Fax: (31) 205708576
E-Mail: info@lucasbols.com
Web Site: www.lucasbols.com
Sales Range: $125-149.9 Million
Emp.: 32
Distilled & Blended Liquors Mfr & Distr
S.I.C.: 2085
N.A.I.C.S.: 312140
Huub van Doorne *(CEO)*

Subsidiary:

Distilleerderijen Erven Lucas Bols BV (2)
Watt St 61
2723 RB Zoetermeer, Netherlands (100%)
Tel.: (31) 793305305
Fax: (31) 793305555
E-Mail: info@bols.com
Web Site: www.lucasbols.com
Emp.: 40
Distillery
S.I.C.: 2085
N.A.I.C.S.: 312140

Orangefield Trust Holding BV (1)
Teleportboulevard 140
1043 EJ Amsterdam, Netherlands
Tel.: (31) 20 5405 800
Fax: (31) 20 6447 011
Web Site: www.orangefieldtrust.com
Management, Accounting, Trust, Estate Planning, Real Estate & Fund Administration Services
S.I.C.: 8741
N.A.I.C.S.: 561110
Joep Bruins *(CEO)*

Non-U.S. Subsidiary:

Waterlow Legal and Regulatory Limited (2)
6-14 Underwood Street
Shepherdess Walk, London, N1 7JQ, United Kingdom
Tel.: (44) 2075668200
Fax: (44) 2073242341
Web Site: www.waterlowlegal.com
Business Information Services
S.I.C.: 7389
N.A.I.C.S.: 519190
Gino De Antonis *(Sr Mgr-Adv Sls)*

Vetus N.V. (1)
Fokkerstraat 571
NL-3125 BD Schiedam, Netherlands NL
Tel.: (31) 104377700
Fax: (31) 104372673
E-Mail: info@vetus.nl
Web Site: www.vetus.nl
Sales Range: $75-99.9 Million
Emp.: 150
Marine Diesel Engine & Nautical Equipment Mfr
S.I.C.: 3714
N.A.I.C.S.: 336310
Marcel Borsboom *(CEO)*

Non-U.S. Branches:

AAC Capital Partners (1)
1 Carey Lane
London, EC2V 8AE, United Kingdom (100%)
Tel.: (44) 2071873000
Fax: (44) 2071873005
E-Mail: info@aaccapitaluk.com
Web Site: www.aaccapitaluk.com
Emp.: 10
Equity Investment Firm
S.I.C.: 6211
N.A.I.C.S.: 523999
Paul Southwell *(Mng Partner)*
Jonathan Bourn *(Partner)*
Patrick Bulmer *(Partner)*
Paul Moxon *(Partner)*
Andrew Moye *(Partner)*
Simon Tuttle *(Partner)*

Holdings:

Amtico International Ltd. (2)
Kingfield Rd
Coventry, CV6 5AA, United Kingdom
Tel.: (44) 2476861400
Fax: (44) 2476861552
E-Mail:
Web Site: www.amticointernational.com
Emp.: 150
Floor Tile Mfr
S.I.C.: 3297
N.A.I.C.S.: 327120
Jonathan Duck *(CEO)*

U.S. Subsidiary:

Amtico International, Inc. (3)
66 Perimter Ctr E
Atlanta, GA 30346
Tel.: (404) 267-1900
Fax: (404) 267-1901
Web Site: www.amticointernational.com
Floor Tile Mfr
S.I.C.: 3259
N.A.I.C.S.: 327120

Dunlop Aircraft Tyres Limited (2)
40 Fort Parkway
Erdington, Birmingham, B24 9HL, United Kingdom UK
Tel.: (44) 121 384 8800
Telex: 33164
Fax: (44) 1213777150
E-Mail: enquiries@dunlopatl.co.uk
Web Site: www.dunlopaircrafttyres.com
Rev.: $27,624,480
Emp.: 265
Aircraft Tires & Tire Parts Mfr
S.I.C.: 3011
N.A.I.C.S.: 326211
Ian Edmondson *(Chm)*

James Dewhurst Ltd. (2)
Altham Lane
Altham, Accrington, Lancs, BB5 5YA, United Kingdom UK
Tel.: (44) 1282775311
Fax: (44) 1282774717
E-Mail: info@jamesdewhurst.com
Web Site: www.jamesdewhurst.com
Sales Range: $75-99.9 Million
Emp.: 346
Industrial Woven & Non-Woven Textiles Mfr
S.I.C.: 2399
N.A.I.C.S.: 314999
Malcolm Blackwell *(CEO)*

Ocean Media Group Limited (2)
One Canada Square
Canary Wharf, London, E14 5AP, United Kingdom UK
Tel.: (44) 2077728300
Fax: (44) 2077728599
Web Site: www.oceanmedia.co.uk
Sales Range: $50-74.9 Million
Emp.: 130
Magazines Publisher & Exhibitions Organizer
S.I.C.: 2721
N.A.I.C.S.: 511120
Alejandra Campos *(Dir-Event-Natl Wedding Show & Luxury Wedding Show)*

OyezStraker Group Limited (2)
Unit 4 500 Purley Way
Croydon, Surrey, CR0 4NZ, United Kingdom UK
Tel.: (44) 2087743401
Fax: (44) 2087609797
Web Site: www.oyezstraker.co.uk
Sales Range: $350-399.9 Million
Emp.: 1,500
Office Supplies Distr & Business Support Services
S.I.C.: 5112
N.A.I.C.S.: 424120
Jeff Whiteway *(CEO)*

Volution Holdings Limited (2)
Fleming Way
Crawley, W Sussex, RH10 9YX, United Kingdom UK
Tel.: (44) 1293526062 (69.6%)
Fax: (44) 1293551188
Web Site: www.volutionholdings.com
Sales Range: $200-249.9 Million
Emp.: 300
Holding Company; Heating, Ventilation & Air Conditioning Equipment Mfr
S.I.C.: 6719
N.A.I.C.S.: 551112
Kevin Sargeant *(CEO)*

Holdings:

Torin-Sifan Limited (3)
Drakes Way Greenbridge
Swindon, Wilts, SN3 3JB, United Kingdom UK
Tel.: (44) 1793524291
Telex: 837241
Fax: (44) 1793486570
E-Mail: info@torin-sifan.com
Web Site: www.torin-sifan.com
Emp.: 200
Fans, Blowers & Ventilation Equipment Mfr
S.I.C.: 3564
N.A.I.C.S.: 333413
Neil Sproston *(Mng Dir)*

Vent-Axia Ltd. (3)
Fleming Way
Crawley, W Sussex, RH10 9YX, United Kingdom UK
Tel.: (44) 1293530202
Telex: 877491
Fax: (44) 1293565169
Web Site: www.vent-axia.com
Heating, Ventilation & Air Conditioning Equipment Mfr
Export
S.I.C.: 3564
N.A.I.C.S.: 333413
Kevin Sargeant *(CEO)*
Ronnie George *(Mng Dir)*

AAC Capital Partners (1)
Birger Jarlsgatan 12 1st Floor
PO Box 26124
100 41 Stockholm, Sweden (100%)
Tel.: (46) 84074440
Fax: (46) 86787220
Web Site: www.aaccapitalpartners.com
Emp.: 8
Equity Investment Firm
S.I.C.: 6211
N.A.I.C.S.: 523999
Johan Bjurstrom *(Mng Partner)*
David Holm-Ovren *(Partner)*
Kristofer Runnquist *(Partner)*
Tommy Wikstrom *(Partner)*

U.S. Holding:

Loparex Inc. (2)
1255 Cresent Green Ste 400
Cary, NC 27518
Tel.: (919) 678-7700
Fax: (630) 734-2690
Web Site: www.loparex.com
Sales Range: $350-399.9 Million
Emp.: 1,100
Siliconized-Release Papers & Films Mfr
S.I.C.: 2672
N.A.I.C.S.: 322220
Michael William Apperson *(Pres & CEO)*

Plant:

Loparex Inc. (3)
2000 Indus Pk Rd
Iowa City, IA 52240
Tel.: (319) 341-5000
Fax: (319) 351-8977
Web Site: www.loparex.com
Emp.: 200
Siliconized-Release Papers & Films Mfr
S.I.C.: 2671
N.A.I.C.S.: 322220
Jennifer Henderson *(Dir-Supply Chain-Plng & Scheduling)*

Non-U.S. Subsidiary:

Loparex B.V. (3)
Laan van Westenenk 45
PO Box 447
7300 AK Apeldoorn, Netherlands NL
Tel.: (31) 555276999
Fax: (31) 555276998
E-Mail: loparexbv@loparex.com
Web Site: www.loparex.com
Emp.: 130
Siliconized-Release Papers & Films Mfr
S.I.C.: 2671
N.A.I.C.S.: 322220
Paul van Pinxteren *(CFO)*

Non-U.S. Holdings:

Empower Oy (2)
Atomitie 2 C
FI-00370 Helsinki, Finland FI
Tel.: (358) 29 020 011 (65%)
Fax: (358) 29 020 2290
Web Site: www.empower.fi
Sales Range: $200-249.9 Million
Emp.: 2,300
Energy, Telecommunication & Industrial Support Services
S.I.C.: 7389
N.A.I.C.S.: 561990
Bo L. Elisson *(Chm)*
Eero Auranne *(CEO & Pres)*
Lars Schedin *(CFO)*
Antti Ruokonen *(COO & Pres-Info Mgmt Div)*
Heikki Hiltunen *(Chief Legal Officer)*
Stefan Eklund *(Pres-Indus Div)*
Timo Kiiveri *(Pres-Transmission Projects Div)*
Ari-Jussi Knaapila *(Pres-Network Div)*
Andres Vainola *(Pres-Baltic Div)*

Glud & Marstrand A/S (2)
Hedenstedvej 14
8723 Losning, Denmark DK
Tel.: (45) 63124200 (100%)
Fax: (45) 76757549
E-Mail: info@glud-marstrand.com
Web Site: www.glud-marstrand.com
Sales Range: $350-399.9 Million
Emp.: 1,158
Metal Can & Packaging Products Mfr
S.I.C.: 3411
N.A.I.C.S.: 332431
Johan Bjurstrom *(Chm)*
Jorgen Kjaergaard *(Mng Dir)*

Non-U.S. Joint Venture:

BabySam AmbA (2)
Egelund A27-29
DK-6200 Abenra, Denmark DK
Tel.: (45) 74632510
Fax: (45) 74632511
E-Mail: babysam@babysam.dk
Web Site: www.babysam.dk
Sales Range: $75-99.9 Million
Baby Equipment Retailer
S.I.C.: 5999
N.A.I.C.S.: 453998
Sanna Suvanto-Harsaae *(Chm)*
Claus Jensen *(CEO)*
Finn Petersen *(CFO)*

AAC TECHNOLOGIES HOLDINGS INC.

18 Xinxi Road North Hi-Tech Industrial Park
Nanshan District, Shenzhen, 518057, China
Tel.: (86) 755 33972018
Fax: (86) 755 33018531
E-Mail: info@aactechnologies.com
Web Site: www.aactechnologies.com
2018—(HKG OTC)
Rev.: $998,045,972
Assets: $1,417,864,283
Liabilities: $444,100,916
Net Worth: $973,763,367
Earnings: $279,031,621
Emp.: 26,575
Fiscal Year-end: 12/31/12

Business Description:
Holding Company; Acoustic Products Mfr
S.I.C.: 6719
N.A.I.C.S.: 551112

Personnel:
Boon Hwee Koh *(Chm)*
Benjamin Zhengmin Pan *(CEO)*

Kuang-Yang Du *(COO)*
David Plekenpol *(Chief Strategy Officer)*
Tai On Lo *(Sec)*
Board of Directors:
Boon Hwee Koh
Carmen I-Hua Chang
Richard Joe Kuen Mok
Benjamin Zhengmin Pan
Joseph Chung Yin Poon
Bian Ee Tan
Ingrid Chunyuan Wu

Bank of Bermuda (Cayman) Ltd.
Strathvale House North Church Street
PO Box 513
Georgetown, Grand Cayman, Cayman Islands
Tel.: (345) 949-9898
Fax: (345) 949-7959

Transfer Agents:
Computershare Hong Kong Investor Services Limited
Shops 1712-1716 17th Floor Hopewell Centre
183 Queens Road East
Wanchai, China (Hong Kong)

Bank of Bermuda (Cayman) Ltd.
Strathvale House North Church Street
PO Box 513
Georgetown, Grand Cayman, Cayman Islands
Tel.: (345) 949-9898
Fax: (345) 949-7959

Subsidiaries:

AAC Acoustic Technologies Limited (1)
Rm 2003 20F 100 Queens Rd
Central, China (Hong Kong)
Tel.: (852) 34700078
Fax: (852) 34700103
E-Mail: aac2018@aactechnologies.com
Emp.: 7
Audio Components Distr
S.I.C.: 5064
N.A.I.C.S.: 423620
Benjamin Zhengmin Pan *(CEO)*

YEC Electronics Limited (1)
Rm G 6F Co Tack Indus Bldg 17 Kin Fat St
Tuen Mun, New Territories, China (Hong Kong)
Tel.: (852) 27640299
Fax: (852) 23658817
Audio Components Distr
S.I.C.: 5946
N.A.I.C.S.: 443142

U.S. Subsidiary:

American Audio Component Inc. (1)
1920 Wright Ave
La Verne, CA 91750-5819
Tel.: (909) 596-3788
Fax: (909) 596-9108
E-Mail: sales@american-audio.com
Web Site: www.american-audio.com
Emp.: 5
Acoustic Product Mfr
S.I.C.: 3679
N.A.I.C.S.: 334419
Zhong L Pan *(Pres)*

Non-U.S. Subsidiaries:

AAC Acoustic Technologies (Shenzhen) Co., Ltd. (1)
AAC Technologies Bldg No 18 Xinxi Rd N
Hi-Tech Indus Pk
Nanshan Dist, Shenzhen, Guangdong, 518057, China
Tel.: (86) 75533972018
Fax: (86) 75533018531
E-Mail: aaca@aacelectr.com
Emp.: 3,000
Audio Components Distr
S.I.C.: 5731
N.A.I.C.S.: 443142
Benjamin Zhengmin Pan *(CEO)*

AAC Acoustic Technologies Sweden AB (1)
Kungsbron2 plan 12
111 22 Stockholm, Sweden
Tel.: (46) 87507130
E-Mail: sales@aacelectr.se
Electrical Products Distr
S.I.C.: 5064
N.A.I.C.S.: 423620

AAC Acoustic Technologies (1)
Lemminkaisenkatu 46a
20520 Turku, Finland
Tel.: (358) 22341005
E-Mail: saleseurope@aacelectr.eu
Web Site: www.aactechnologies.com
Emp.: 5
Electronic Products Sales
S.I.C.: 5064
N.A.I.C.S.: 423620
Eric Rudolfthi *(VP)*

AAC Microtech (Changzhou) Co., Ltd. (1)
No 3 Changcao Rd Wujin High-New Tech Indus Dev
Changzhou, Jiangsu, 213167, China
Tel.: (86) 51983052018
Fax: (86) 51986467231
Digital Cameras & Accessories Mfr & Sales
S.I.C.: 3577
N.A.I.C.S.: 334118

AAC Wireless Technologies AB (1)
Rallarvagen 41
184 40 Akersberga, Sweden
Tel.: (46) 8 540 20 000
Fax: (46) 8 540 23 950
E-Mail: info@aacwireless.se
Web Site: www.aacwireless.se
Antennas Mfr
S.I.C.: 3663
N.A.I.C.S.: 334220
Christer Sporrong *(Mng Dir)*

Camos Technologies Co.,Ltd. (1)
3F No 11 Beitou Rd Sec 2
Beitou Dist, Taipei, Taiwan
Tel.: (886) 228959088
Fax: (886) 228950666
E-Mail: pcsu@camostek.com
Camera Modules Mfr
S.I.C.: 3579
N.A.I.C.S.: 333316

AACL HOLDINGS LIMITED

(Name Changed to Applabs Technologies Limited)

AADI INDUSTRIES LTD.

320/7 Siddhivinayak Soc Hingwala Lane
Pantnagar Ghatkopar East
Mumbai, 400 075, India
Tel.: (91) 22 2501 2706
Fax: (91) 22 2501 2706
E-Mail: aadi.industries@hotmail.com
Web Site: www.aadiindustries.com
530027—(BOM)
Sales Range: $25-49.9 Million
Business Description:
Tarpaulins Mfr
S.I.C.: 2394
N.A.I.C.S.: 314910
Personnel:
Rushabh Shah *(Chm & Mng Dir)*
Board of Directors:
Rushabh Shah
Surjit Banga
Sunil Mistry
Mansi Shah
Transfer Agent:
Sharex Dynamics (India) Private Limited
Luthra Industrial Estate Andheri Kurla Rd
Mumbai, India

AALBERS TOOL & MOLD INC.

5390 Brendan Lane
Old Castle, ON, N0R 1L0, Canada
Tel.: (519) 737-1369
Fax: (519) 737-1711
Web Site: www.aalberstool.com
Rev.: $19,430,925
Emp.: 100
Business Description:
Industrial Mould Mfr
S.I.C.: 3544
N.A.I.C.S.: 333511
Personnel:
Gary Aalbers *(Owner)*
Toni Hansen *(Pres)*

AALBERTS INDUSTRIES N.V.

Sandenburgerlaan 4
3947 Langbroek, Netherlands
Mailing Address:
PO Box 11
3940 Doorn, Netherlands
Tel.: (31) 343565080
Fax: (31) 343565081
E-Mail: info@aalberts.nl
Web Site: www.aalberts.nl
AALB—(EUR)
Rev.: $2,725,295,588
Assets: $2,632,427,358
Liabilities: $1,313,155,181
Net Worth: $1,319,272,177
Earnings: $183,046,812
Emp.: 12,048
Fiscal Year-end: 12/31/12
Business Description:
Industrial Services & Flow Control System Activities
S.I.C.: 6719
N.A.I.C.S.: 551112
Personnel:
Henk Scheffers *(Chm-Supervisory Bd)*
Jan Aalberts *(Pres)*
Wim Pelsma *(CEO)*
John Eijgendaal *(CFO)*
Supervisory Board of Directors:
Henk Scheffers
Walter van de Vijver
Rene van der Bruggen
Martin van Pernis

Subsidiaries:

Adex BV (1)
Tjalkkade 2
NL 5928 PZ Venlo, Netherlands (100%)
Tel.: (31) 773898900
Fax: (31) 773871779
E-Mail: info@adex-dies.com
Web Site: www.adex-dies.com
Emp.: 85
Extrusion Die Mfr
S.I.C.: 3559
N.A.I.C.S.: 333249
Barthel Martin *(Gen Mgr)*

Dispense Systems International (1)
Oberster Kamp 20
D-59069 Hamm, Germany (100%)
Tel.: (49) 23857720
Fax: (49) 2385772199
E-Mail: info@dsi-group.net
Web Site: www.dispensegroup.com
Emp.: 30
Beverage Dispensing Equipment Mfr
S.I.C.: 3586
N.A.I.C.S.: 333913
Stein Metz *(Mng Dir)*

Fijnmechanische Industrie Venray B.V. (1)
Postbus 340
5430 AH Cuijk, Netherlands
Tel.: (31) 485 31 17 11
Fax: (31) 485 31 17 12
E-Mail: info@fivbv.nl
Web Site: www.fivbv.nl
Emp.: 3
Small Series Turned & Milled Component Mfr
S.I.C.: 3451
N.A.I.C.S.: 332721
J. Bakarbessy *(Office Mgr)*

Germefa B V (1)
Ivoorstraat 6
1812RE Alkmaar, Netherlands (100%)
Tel.: (31) 725350000
Fax: (31) 725350011
E-Mail: info@germefa.nl
Web Site: www.germefa.nl
Emp.: 40
Precision Industrial Tools Mfr
S.I.C.: 3546
N.A.I.C.S.: 333991
Jan Sander *(Gen Mgr)*

Hartman Fijnmechanische Industrie B.V. (1)
Industrieweg 25
7141 CX Groenlo, Netherlands
Tel.: (31) 544 47 50 00
Fax: (31) 544 47 50 09
E-Mail: info@hfibv.nl
Web Site: www.hfibv.nl
Emp.: 7
High Precision Turned Products Mfr
S.I.C.: 3451
N.A.I.C.S.: 332721
Fred Oreilly *(Mng Dir)*

Heat & Surface Treatment B.V. (1)
Achtseweg Noord 5 Bld AL
5651 GG Eindhoven, Netherlands
Tel.: (31) 40 2663000
Fax: (31) 40 2663003
E-Mail: info@h-st.nl
Web Site: www.h-st.nl
Emp.: 40
Heat & Surface Treatment Services
S.I.C.: 3398
N.A.I.C.S.: 332811
Steffen Schnieders *(Mng Dir)*

H.S.F. Samenwerkende Fabrieken B.V. (1)
Marketing 23
6921 RE Duiven, Netherlands
Tel.: (31) 26 319 5757
Fax: (31) 26 319 5758
E-Mail: info@hsfbv.nl
Metal Products Mfr
S.I.C.: 3499
N.A.I.C.S.: 332999
Henk Hollemans *(Gen Mgr)*

Kluin Wijhe BV (1)
Industrieweg 1
NL 8131 VZ Wijhe, Netherlands (100%)
Tel.: (31) 570521413
Fax: (31) 570523270
E-Mail: info@kluinwijhe.com
Web Site: www.kluinwijhe.com
Emp.: 60
Cylinder & Screw Mfr
S.I.C.: 3559
N.A.I.C.S.: 333249
R. Klaen *(Dir)*

Lamers High Tech Systems B.V. (1)
De Vlotkampweg 38
Nijmegen, 6545 AG, Netherlands
Tel.: (31) 243716777
E-Mail: info@lamers-hightech.com
Web Site: www.lamers-hightech.com
Semiconductor Equipment Distr
S.I.C.: 5065
N.A.I.C.S.: 423690

Leco Products B.V. (1)
Radonstraat 18
6718 WS Ede, Netherlands (100%)
Tel.: (31) 318665060
Fax: (31) 318665061
E-Mail: info@lecoproducts.nl
Web Site: www.lecoproducts.nl
Emp.: 200
Sliding Door Mfr
S.I.C.: 3442
N.A.I.C.S.: 332321
Jaap Zltman *(Mng Dir)*

Machinefabriek Dedemsvaart B.V. (1)
Nijverheidsweg 12
8084 GW 't Harde, Netherlands
Tel.: (31) 525 65 15 33
Fax: (31) 525 65 47 11
E-Mail: info@mfdbv.nl
Emp.: 120
Aluminium Precision Extrusion Services
S.I.C.: 3471
N.A.I.C.S.: 332813
Bias Haar *(Gen Mgr)*

Machinefabriek Technology Twente B.V. (1)
Granaatstraat 15
7554 TN Hengelo, Netherlands
Tel.: (31) 74 2438866
Fax: (31) 74 2438867
E-Mail: info@technologytwente.nl
Web Site: www.technologytwente.nl
Emp.: 5

Aalberts Industries N.V.—(Continued)

Precision Turned Products Mfr
S.I.C.: 3451
N.A.I.C.S.: 332721
L. J. M. Hofstede *(Mng Dir)*

Machinefabriek Van Knegsel BV (1)
De Hoefse Weg 2
NL 5512 CH Vessem, Netherlands (100%)
Tel.: (31) 497592200
Fax: (31) 497592245
E-Mail: info@vanknegsel.nl
Web Site: www.vanknegsel.nl
Emp.: 100
Custom Industrial Products Mfr
S.I.C.: 3559
N.A.I.C.S.: 333249

Mamesta B V (1)
Spikweien 27
NL 5943 AC Lomm, Netherlands (100%)
Tel.: (31) 774731551
Fax: (31) 774732409
E-Mail: info@mamesta.nl
Web Site: www.mamesta.nl
Emp.: 50
Steel Hardening Services
S.I.C.: 3398
N.A.I.C.S.: 332811
Geert Janssen *(Mgr-HR)*

Mifa Aluminium B V (1)
Deltakade 4 6
NL 5928 PX Venlo, Netherlands (100%)
Tel.: (31) 773898888
Fax: (31) 773898989
E-Mail: info@mifa.nl
Web Site: www.mifa.nl
Emp.: 220
Customized Extrusion Products Mfr
S.I.C.: 3364
N.A.I.C.S.: 331523
Eric A. Zantinge *(Mng Dir)*

Mogema B.V. (1)
Industrieweg 9
8084 GS 't Harde, Netherlands
Tel.: (31) 525 651 533
Fax: (31) 525 653 563
E-Mail: info@mogema.nl
Web Site: www.mogema.nl
Emp.: 13
General Purpose Machinery Mfr
S.I.C.: 3569
N.A.I.C.S.: 333999
Peter Zuidgeest *(Gen Mgr)*

Overeem B.V. (1)
Radon Straat 16
6718 WS Ede, Netherlands (100%)
Tel.: (31) 318697811
Fax: (31) 318697821
E-Mail: info@overeembv.nl
Web Site: www.overeembv.nl
Emp.: 80
Roll Formed Metal Products Mfr
S.I.C.: 3449
N.A.I.C.S.: 332114
T. Boks *(Mng Dir)*

VSH Fabrieken B.V. (1)
Oude Amersfoortseweg 99
PO Box 498
Hilversum, 1200 AL, Netherlands (100%)
Tel.: (31) 356884211
Fax: (31) 356884379
E-Mail: info@vsh.nl
Web Site: www.vsh-flowcontrol.eu
Emp.: 200
Industrial Valve Mfr
S.I.C.: 3491
N.A.I.C.S.: 332911

VSH Fittings B.V. (1)
Oude Amersfoortseweg 99
1212 AA Hilversum, Netherlands
Tel.: (31) 35 6884211
Fax: (31) 35 6884379
E-Mail: info@vsh.nl
Web Site: www.vsh-fittings.com
Emp.: 45
Metal Pipe Fitting Mfr
S.I.C.: 3498
N.A.I.C.S.: 332996

U.S. Subsidiaries:

Accurate Brazing Corporation (1)
36 Cote Ave
Goffstown, NH 03045
Tel.: (603) 625-1456
Fax: (603) 625-4526
E-Mail: sales@accuratebrazing.com
Web Site: www.accuratebrazing.com
Emp.: 40
Vacuum Brazing & Heat Treating Services
S.I.C.: 3398
N.A.I.C.S.: 332811
Brent Davis *(Mgr-Ops)*

Conbraco Industries, Inc. (1)
701 Matthews Mint Hill Rd
Matthews, NC 28105-1706 NC
Tel.: (704) 841-6000
Fax: (704) 841-6020
E-Mail: customer.services@conbraco.com
Web Site: www.apollovalves.com
Emp.: 1,550
Ball Valve Mfr
Import Export
S.I.C.: 3492
N.A.I.C.S.: 332912
Glenn Mosack *(Pres)*
Eric Miller *(CFO)*

Division:

Conbraco Industries, Inc. - Pageland (2)
1418 S Pearl St
Pageland, SC 29728-0125
Tel.: (843) 672-6161
Fax: (843) 672-6161
Emp.: 100
Ball Valve Mfr
S.I.C.: 3492
N.A.I.C.S.: 332912
Glenn Mosack *(Pres)*
Cal Mosack *(Exec VP)*

Elkhart Products Corporation (1)
1255 Oak St
Elkhart, IN 46515
Tel.: (574) 264-3181
Fax: (574) 264-0103
Web Site: www.elkhartproducts.com
Emp.: 275
Pipe Fitting Mfr & Distr
S.I.C.: 3494
N.A.I.C.S.: 332919
Glenn Mosack *(Pres & CEO)*

Plants:

Elkhart Products Corp.-Elkhart Plant (2)
1255 Oak St
Elkhart, IN 46514-2277 IN
Mailing Address:
1255 Oak St
Elkhart, IN 46514-2277
Tel.: (574) 264-3181
Fax: (574) 264-4835
Web Site: www.elkhartproducts.com
Emp.: 275
Wrot Copper Plumbing Fittings
S.I.C.: 3494
N.A.I.C.S.: 332919

Elkhart Products Corporation-Industrial Division (2)
700 Rainbow Rd
Geneva, IN 46740-9700 IN
Tel.: (260) 368-7246
Fax: (260) 368-7889
Emp.: 80
Produces Copper & Aluminum Machine Tubing Products
S.I.C.: 3494
N.A.I.C.S.: 332919

Ionic Technologies, Inc. (1)
207 Fairforest Way
Greenville, SC 29607-4610 (94%)
Tel.: (864) 288-9111
Fax: (864) 288-9169
E-Mail: rmahler@ionic-tech.com
Web Site: www.ionic-tech.com
Emp.: 12
Metal Surface Coatings Mfr
S.I.C.: 2851
N.A.I.C.S.: 325510
Ray Monahan *(Pres)*

Lasco Fittings Inc. (1)
414 Morgan St
Brownsville, TN 38012-0116
Tel.: (731) 772-3180
Fax: (731) 772-0835
Toll Free: (800) 776-2756
E-Mail: sales@lascofittings.com
Web Site: www.lascofittings.com
Emp.: 500
Injection Molded Fittings for Irrigation, Plumbing, Industrial, Pool/Spa & Retail Markets
S.I.C.: 3494
N.A.I.C.S.: 332919
Jack McDonald *(Pres)*

Nexus Valve, Inc. (1)
9982 E 121st St
Fishers, IN 46037
Tel.: (317) 257-6050
Fax: (800) 900-8654
Toll Free: (888) 900-0947
E-Mail: info@nexusvalve.com
Web Site: www.nexusvalve.com
Sales Range: $10-24.9 Million
Emp.: 60
Hydronic Components, Including Valves, Mfr & Whslr
S.I.C.: 5074
N.A.I.C.S.: 332912
Kurt Fazekas *(Pres)*

Taprite-Fassco Mfg., Inc. (1)
3248 Northwestern Dr
San Antonio, TX 78238-4043 (100%)
Tel.: (210) 523-0800
Fax: (210) 520-3035
E-Mail: taprite@aol.com
Web Site: www.taprite.com
Emp.: 200
Mfr. of Pressure Valves for the Beer & Soft Drink Industries
S.I.C.: 3499
N.A.I.C.S.: 332999
David Lease *(Pres)*

Non-U.S. Subsidiaries:

AHC Oberflachentechnik GmbH (1)
Boelckestrasse 25 - 57
50171 Kerpen, Germany
Tel.: (49) 22 37 5 02 0
Fax: (49) 22 37 5 02 100
E-Mail: info.kerpen@ahc-surface.com
Web Site: www.ahc-surface.com
Emp.: 700
Heat Treatment Services
S.I.C.: 3398
N.A.I.C.S.: 332811
Oliver Jaeger *(Gen Mgr)*

Subsidiary:

AHC Special Coatings GmbH (2)
Dycker Feld 43
42653 Solingen, Germany
Tel.: (49) 212 25 83 4 0
Fax: (49) 212 25 83 4 99
E-Mail: info.solingen@ahc-surface.com
Emp.: 65
Metal & Plastic Coating Mfr
S.I.C.: 2851
N.A.I.C.S.: 325510
Wilfrid Brake *(Gen Mgr)*

Non-U.S. Subsidiaries:

AHC Benelux B.V. (2)
Hurksestraat 32
5652 AL Eindhoven, Netherlands
Tel.: (31) 40 250 76 07
Fax: (31) 40 251 22 87
E-Mail: info.eindhoven@ahcbenelux.nl
Web Site: www.ahcbenelux.nl
Emp.: 50
Electroplating Electroless Nickel & Synergetic Coating Services
S.I.C.: 3471
N.A.I.C.S.: 332813
Hay Hulsman *(Mng Dir)*

AHC B.V. (2)
Hurksestraat 32
NL 5652 AL Eindhoven, Netherlands (100%)
Tel.: (31) 402507607
Fax: (31) 402512287
E-Mail: info@ahc-surface.com
Web Site: www.ahc-surface.com
Emp.: 50
Metal Coating Products Mfr
S.I.C.: 2851
N.A.I.C.S.: 325510
Rutger Peffers *(Mng Dir)*

AHC Italia S.R.L. (2)
Via Staffora 20/2
20090 Opera, Milan, Italy
Tel.: (39) 02 57 60 65 09
Fax: (39) 02 57 60 65 28
E-Mail: info.opera@ahc-surface.com
Web Site: www.ahc-surface.com
Emp.: 25
Metal & Plastic Coating Services
S.I.C.: 3479
N.A.I.C.S.: 332812
Sacchi Vittorio *(Gen Mgr)*

AHC Oberflachentechnik Ges.m.b.H. (2)
Kirchberg 48
5120 Sankt Pantaleon, Austria
Tel.: (43) 6277 74 00
Fax: (43) 6277 74 00 10
E-Mail: info.st.pantaleon@ahc-surface.com
Metal & Plastic Coating Solutions Mfr
S.I.C.: 3479
N.A.I.C.S.: 332812
Marco Hof *(Gen Mgr)*

AHC Surface Technology S.A.S. (2)
Avenue Bade Wurtemberg
57380 Faulquemont, France
Tel.: (33) 3 87 00 43 80
Fax: (33) 3 87 94 30 08
E-Mail: info.faulquemont@ahc-surface.com
Metal & Plastic Coating Solutions Mfr
S.I.C.: 3479
N.A.I.C.S.: 332812

AIMT Traterh, S.A.U. (1)
Polig Ind Aproin Alcotanes 32 Nave
ES 28320 Madrid, Spain (100%)
Tel.: (34) 916923330
Fax: (34) 916920880
E-Mail: info.pinto@aimt-group.com
Web Site: www.aimt-group.com
Emp.: 20
Thermal Products Mfr
S.I.C.: 3559
N.A.I.C.S.: 333249
Gaveir Martin *(Mng Dir)*

BROEN A/S (1)
Skovvej 30
Assens, 5610, Denmark (100%)
Tel.: (45) 64712095
Fax: (45) 64712495
E-Mail: broen@broen.com
Web Site: www.broen.com
Rev.: $80,000,000
Emp.: 230
Industrial Valve Mfr
S.I.C.: 3491
N.A.I.C.S.: 332911
Motens Laursen *(Mng Dir)*

U.S. Subsidiary:

BROEN, Inc. (2)
2820 Commerce Blvd
Birmingham, AL 35210-1544 (50%)
Tel.: (205) 956-9444
Fax: (205) 956-2537
E-Mail: information@broeninc.com
Web Site: www.broeninc.com
Emp.: 10
Industrial Valve Mfr
S.I.C.: 3491
N.A.I.C.S.: 332911
Tommy Peddycord *(Pres)*

Non-U.S. Subsidiaries:

BROEN Armaturen GmbH (2)
Haldenstrasse 27
Gelsenkirchen, 45881, Germany (100%)
Tel.: (49) 209404380
Fax: (49) 2094043496
Web Site: www.broen.de
Sales Range: $1-9.9 Million
Emp.: 5
Industrial Valve Mfr
S.I.C.: 3491
N.A.I.C.S.: 332911

BROEN Finland OY (2)
Kivenlahdenkatu 1
2320 Espoo, Finland
Tel.: (358) 9 412 8054
Fax: (358) 9 412 8055
E-Mail: broen@broen.com
Web Site: www.broen.fi
Heating Equipment Mfr
S.I.C.: 3433
N.A.I.C.S.: 333414
Jens Nurmi *(Gen Mgr)*

BROEN Ltd. (2)
8-ya Tekstilshchikov Str Building 2 11/2
109129 Moscow, Russia
Tel.: (7) 495 228 11 50
Fax: (7) 495 228 11 50, ext. 1133
E-Mail: info@broen.ru
Web Site: www.broen.ru
Heating Equipment Mfr
S.I.C.: 3433
N.A.I.C.S.: 333414

BROEN Malaysia Sdn. Bhd. (2)
11 Jalan USJ 8/2B
UEP, Subang Jaya, Selangor, 47610, Malaysia (100%)
Tel.: (60) 3 5635 8799
Fax: (60) 3 5635 8696
E-Mail: sales@broen.com.my
Industrial Valve Mfr
S.I.C.: 3491
N.A.I.C.S.: 332911

BROEN Raufoss AB (2)
Stora Badhusgatan 18-20
411 21 Gothenburg, Sweden
Tel.: (46) 31 761 02 00
Fax: (46) 31 704 86 00
E-Mail: info@broen.se
Emp.: 15
Heating Equipment Mfr
S.I.C.: 3433
N.A.I.C.S.: 333414

BROEN S.A. (2)
ul Nowowiejska 50 A
58200 Dzierzoniow, Poland (60%)
Tel.: (48) 748318455
Fax: (48) 748321920
E-Mail: marketing@broen.pl
Web Site: www.broen.pl
Emp.: 140
Industrial Valve Mfr
S.I.C.: 3491
N.A.I.C.S.: 332911

BROEN SEI Srl. (2)
Str Fabricii Nr 47 Corp X Et 4 Sector 6
Bucharest, Romania
Tel.: (40) 21 316 96 19
Fax: (40) 21 316 96 21
E-Mail: office@broen-sei.ro
Web Site: www.broen-sei.ro
Emp.: 4
Pipe Fitting & Valve Distr
S.I.C.: 5084
N.A.I.C.S.: 423830
Ana Sebastian *(Gen Mgr)*

BROEN Singapore Pte Ltd (2)
10 Pukit Cresent Dr
Singapore, 658079, Singapore (100%)
Tel.: (65) 62980662
Fax: (65) 62980468
E-Mail: cli@broen.com
Web Site: www.broen.com
Emp.: 3
Industrial Valve Mfr
S.I.C.: 3491
N.A.I.C.S.: 332911
Tony Yeo *(Country Mgr)*

BROEN Valves (Beijing) Co., Ltd. (2)
Rm 1610 Kuntai Building No B12
Chaoyangmenwai Av
Chaoyang D, Beijing, 100020, China
Tel.: (86) 1067892995
Fax: (86) 1061892996
Heating Equipment Mfr
S.I.C.: 3433
N.A.I.C.S.: 333414

BROEN Valves Ltd. (2)
Unit 7 Cleton Street Business Park
Cleton Street, Tipton, West Midlands, DY4 7TR, United Kingdom (100%)
Tel.: (44) 1215224505
Fax: (44) 1215224535
E-Mail: broenvalves@broen.co.uk
Web Site: www.broen.co.uk
Emp.: 5
Industrial Valve Mfr
S.I.C.: 3491
N.A.I.C.S.: 332911
Alison Spence *(Office Mgr)*

BROEN-Zawgaz Sp. z.o.o. (2)
ul Stara Droga 8
62-002 Suchy Las, Poznania, Poland
Tel.: (48) 61 812 55 17
Fax: (48) 61 812 55 90
E-Mail: zawgaz@broen-zawgaz.pl
Web Site: www.broen-zawgaz.pl
Emp.: 110
Heating Equipment Mfr
S.I.C.: 3433
N.A.I.C.S.: 333414
Dariusz Haraj *(Chm-Mgmt Bd)*
Olgierd Hanczewski *(Dir-Technical)*
Leszek Siennicki *(Dir-Sls)*

Clorius Controls A/S (1)
Tempovej 27
DK 2750 Ballerup, Denmark (100%)
Tel.: (45) 77323130
Fax: (45) 77323131
E-Mail: mail@cloriuscontrols.com
Web Site: www.cloriuscontrols.com
Sls.: $6,652,720
Emp.: 40
Heating, Cooling & Ventilation System Controls Mfr
S.I.C.: 3829
N.A.I.C.S.: 334519
Michael Kanstrup Jensen *(Mng Dir)*

Comap S.A. (1)
16 Ave Paul Santy
69008 Lyon, France
Tel.: (33) 478781600
Fax: (33) 478781695
E-Mail: info@comap.fr
Web Site: www.comap.fr
Sales Range: $200-249.9 Million
Emp.: 150
Industrial Fluid Control Components
S.I.C.: 3823
N.A.I.C.S.: 334513

Non-U.S. Subsidiaries:

Comap Hellas S.A. (2)
Terma Yakinthon
Lykovryssi, Athens, 14123, Greece
Tel.: (30) 2102842684
Fax: (30) 2102840700
Emp.: 10
Plumbing & Heating Equipment Distr
S.I.C.: 5074
N.A.I.C.S.: 423720
Spyros Tsakalos *(Gen Mgr)*

Comap Hungaria Kereskedelmi Kft. (2)
Gyar Utca 2
Budaors, 2040, Hungary
Tel.: (36) 23503871
Fax: (36) 23503870
E-Mail: comap@comap.hu
Building Materials Distr
S.I.C.: 5039
N.A.I.C.S.: 423390

Comap Italia S.r.l.u. (2)
Via Rassega 1
25030 Torbole Casaglia, Italy
Tel.: (39) 030 2151024
Fax: (39) 030 2151023
Web Site: www.comapitalia.com
Metal Products Mfr
S.I.C.: 3499
N.A.I.C.S.: 332999
Nicola Di Terlizzi *(Gen Mgr)*

Comap Nordic AB (2)
Carlsgatan 12A
211 20 Malmo, Sweden
Tel.: (46) 40 42 96 60
Fax: (46) 40 42 96 69
E-Mail: market@comap.se
Web Site: www.comap.se
Emp.: 3
Plumbing & Heating Equipment Distr
S.I.C.: 5084
N.A.I.C.S.: 423830
Michael Barmer *(Gen Mgr)*

Comap N.V. (2)
Alsembergsesteenweg 454
1653 Dworp, Belgium
Tel.: (32) 2 371 01 61
Fax: (32) 2 378 23 39
E-Mail: info@comap.be
Metal Products Mfr
S.I.C.: 3499
N.A.I.C.S.: 332999

Comap Polska Sp. z.o.o. (2)
ul Annopol 4A Hala C
03-236 Warsaw, Poland
Tel.: (48) 22 679 00 25
Fax: (48) 22 679 18 48
E-Mail: comap@comap.pl
Steel Pipe Mfr
S.I.C.: 3317
N.A.I.C.S.: 331210

Comap Praha s.r.o. (2)
Krajni 801
252 42 Jesenice, Czech Republic
Tel.: (420) 284 860 404
Fax: (420) 284 862 794
E-Mail: sklad.traha@comap.eu
Web Site: www.comap.cz
Emp.: 1
Metal Products Distr
S.I.C.: 5051
N.A.I.C.S.: 423510
Andreas Ende *(Gen Mgr)*

Comap (UK) Limited (2)
Unit C6 William Way Moss Industrial Estate
Saint Helens Road, Leigh, Lancs, WN7 3PT, United Kingdom
Tel.: (44) 1942 603 351
Fax: (44) 1942 607 780
Heating Equipment Distr
S.I.C.: 5074
N.A.I.C.S.: 423720

Conti Sanitararmaturen GmbH (1)
Hauptstrasse 98
Krofdorf/Gleiberg, 35435 Wettenberg, Germany
Tel.: (49) 6 41 9 82 21 0
Fax: (49) 6 41 9 82 21 50
E-Mail: info@conti-armaturen.com
Sanitary Fitting Services
S.I.C.: 1711
N.A.I.C.S.: 238220

Cotterlaz Connectors Shenzhen Ltd. (1)
1/F D Block Zhongxi Industry District Zone
Buchong Shajin Baoan, Shenzhen, China
Tel.: (86) 755 29 69 83 04
Fax: (86) 755 81 44 12 55
Web Site: www.cotterlaz.com.cn
Emp.: 150
Metal Products Mfr
S.I.C.: 3499
N.A.I.C.S.: 332999
Hong Pin *(Gen Mgr)*

Cotterlaz Jean S.A.S. (1)
250 rue de la Pointe d'orchex
Marnaz, 74460, France
Tel.: (33) 4 50 98 35 06
Fax: (33) 4 50 96 27 47
Emp.: 70
Connectors & Radio Frequency Component Mfr
S.I.C.: 3678
N.A.I.C.S.: 334417
Phierry Ployer *(Gen Mgr)*

DSI Getrankearmaturen GmbH & Co. KG (1)
Oberster Kamp 20
59069 Hamm, Germany (100%)
Tel.: (49) 23857720
Fax: (49) 23857720
E-Mail: info@dsi-group.de
Web Site: www.dsi.de
Emp.: 85
Beverage Dispensing Equipment Mfr
S.I.C.: 3586
N.A.I.C.S.: 333913
Heiko Wiebel *(Mgr-Sls)*

Duralloy AG (1)
Industriepark Altgraben
4624 Haerkingen, Switzerland
Tel.: (41) 62 38 88 00 0
Fax: (41) 62 38 88 00 8
E-Mail: admin@duralloy.ch
Metal & Plastic Coating Services
S.I.C.: 3479
N.A.I.C.S.: 332812

Duralloy Sud GmbH (1)
Eckweg 6
78048 Villingen-Schwenningen, Germany
Tel.: (49) 77214044410
Fax: (49) 77214044429
E-Mail: contact@duralloy.info
Web Site: www.duralloy.info
Emp.: 5
Metal & Plastic Coating Mfr
S.I.C.: 3479
N.A.I.C.S.: 332812

Elkhart Products Limited (1)
1175 Corp Dr
Burlington, ON, L7L 5H9, Canada
Tel.: (905) 336-6060
Fax: (905) 336-1555
Toll Free: (800) 668-6060
Emp.: 2
Plumbing & Heating Equipment Distr
S.I.C.: 5074
N.A.I.C.S.: 423720

Grupo Hidroaplicaciones y Gas, SL (1)
Calle Bronce Poligono Industriasl Aimayr 12a
28330 San Martin de la Vega, Madrid, Spain
Tel.: (34) 916920553
Fax: (34) 916434381
Water Pipe Accessories Mfr
S.I.C.: 3321
N.A.I.C.S.: 331511

Haerterei Hauck GmbH (1)
Walter Freitag Strasse 25
D 42899 Remscheid, Luttringhausen, Germany (90%)
Tel.: (49) 219156200
Fax: (49) 2191562089
E-Mail: info@haerterei-hauck.de
Web Site: www.haerterei-hauck.de
Emp.: 160
Heat Treatment Services for High-Grade Components & Tools
S.I.C.: 3398
N.A.I.C.S.: 332811

Subsidiaries:

Haerterei Hauck Gaidorf GmbH (2)
Wilhelm Bott Strasse 24
74405 Gaildorf, Germany (100%)
Tel.: (49) 797196980
Fax: (49) 7971969829
E-Mail: info@haerterei-hauck.de
Web Site: www.haerterei-hauck.de
Emp.: 20
Heat Treatment Services for High-Grade Components & Tools
S.I.C.: 3398
N.A.I.C.S.: 332811
Ingo Zegler *(Plant Mgr)*

Harterei Hauck Sud GmbH (2)
Wilhelm-Bott-Strasse 24
74405 Gaildorf, Germany
Tel.: (49) 79 71 96 98 0
Fax: (49) 79 71 96 98 29
E-Mail: info.gaildorf@haerterei-hauck.de
Metal Heat Treating Services
S.I.C.: 3398
N.A.I.C.S.: 332811

Henco Floor N.V. (1)
Toekomstlaan 27
2200 Herentals, Belgium
Tel.: (32) 14 28 56 73
Fax: (32) 14 23 33 64
E-Mail: info@hencofloor.be
Web Site: www.hencofloor.be
Emp.: 10
Plumbing Heating & Air Conditioning Equipment Mfr
S.I.C.: 3585
N.A.I.C.S.: 333415
Ken Te Velde *(Gen Mgr)*

Henco Industries N.V. (1)
Toekomstlaan 27
2200 Herentals, Belgium
Tel.: (32) 14 28 56 60
Fax: (32) 14 21 87 12
E-Mail: info@henco.be
Web Site: www.henco.be
Emp.: 20
Metal Pipe Fitting Mfr
S.I.C.: 3494
N.A.I.C.S.: 332919
Wim Paulissen *(Controller-Fin)*

Holmgrens Metall Aktiebolaget (1)
Stenblocksvagen
Box 141
335 23 Gnosjo, Sweden
Tel.: (46) 370 33 23 70
Fax: (46) 370 996 66
E-Mail: order@holmgrensmetall.se
Web Site: www.holmgrensmetall.se

Aalberts Industries N.V.—(Continued)

Emp.: 42
Metal Pipe Fitting Mfr
S.I.C.: 3494
N.A.I.C.S.: 332919
Hans Hornmark *(Gen Mgr)*

Integrated Dynamics Engineering GmbH (1)
Karl Liebknechtstrasse 30
65479 Raunheim, Germany (80%)
Tel.: (49) 614294000
Fax: (49) 6142940099
E-Mail: info@ideworld.com
Web Site: www.ideworld.com
Sales Range: $100-124.9 Million
Emp.: 100
Measuring & Control Device Mfr
S.I.C.: 3829
N.A.I.C.S.: 334519
Thomas Breser *(Mng Dir)*

U.S. Subsidiary:

Integrated Dynamics Engineering Inc. (2)
68 Mazzeo Dr
Randolph, MA 02368-3402
Tel.: (781) 326-5700
Fax: (781) 326-3004
E-Mail: info@ideworld.com
Web Site: www.ideworld.com
Emp.: 10
Semiconductor Manufacturing Machinery
S.I.C.: 3559
N.A.I.C.S.: 333242
Peter Heiland *(Pres)*

Non-U.S. Subsidiary:

Integrated Dynamics Engineering Ltd. (2)
1-2-4 Kamisuna-cho
Tachikawa, Tokyo, 190-0032, Japan
Tel.: (81) 42 535 7303
Fax: (81) 42 535 7304
E-Mail: info@ideworld.co.jp
Material Handling Equipment Mfr
S.I.C.: 3559
N.A.I.C.S.: 333249

Isiflo SAS (1)
18 Route Industrielle de la Hardt
67120 Molsheim, France
Tel.: (33) 3 88 04 59 70
Fax: (33) 3 88 04 59 75
Plumbing & Heating Equipment Distr
S.I.C.: 5074
N.A.I.C.S.: 423720

KAN S.p. z o.o. (1)
Ul Wiaczynska 8A
92 760 Lodz, Poland
Tel.: (48) 426777977
Fax: (48) 426777999
E-Mail: kan@kan.pl
Web Site: www.kan.pl
Sales Range: $25-49.9 Million
Emp.: 100
Mfr of Plumbing Products
S.I.C.: 3088
N.A.I.C.S.: 326191
Joseph Katitanczyk *(Owner)*

KAN-therm GmbH (1)
Brusseler Strasse 2
Troisdorf-Spich, 53842 Troisdorf, Germany
Tel.: (49) 2241 234 08 0
Fax: (49) 2241 234 08 21
E-Mail: info@kan-therm.de
Web Site: www.kantherm.de
Surface Heating & Cooling System Distr
S.I.C.: 5075
N.A.I.C.S.: 423730

Meibes System-Technik GmbH (1)
Ringstrasse 18
4827 Machern, Germany
Tel.: (49) 34292 7130
Fax: (49) 34 29 27 13 50
E-Mail: info@meibes.de
Web Site: www.meibes.de
Emp.: 20
Heating Equipment Mfr
S.I.C.: 3433
N.A.I.C.S.: 333414
Robert Sagstetter *(Mng Dir)*

Non-U.S. Subsidiaries:

Meibes Metall-Technik Sp. z.o.o. (2)
Miesza-I-Str 39
66-400 Gorzow, Poland
Tel.: (48) 65 529 49 89
Fax: (48) 65 529 59 69
E-Mail: info@meibes.pl
Heating Equipment Mfr
S.I.C.: 3433
N.A.I.C.S.: 333414

Meibes RUS OOO (2)
Bld 2 11 8th Tekstilshchikov St
Moscow, 109129, Russia
Tel.: (7) 495 727 20 26
Fax: (7) 495 727 20 26
E-Mail: moscow@meibes.ru
Web Site: www.meibes.ru
Emp.: 55
Heating Equipment Distr
S.I.C.: 5074
N.A.I.C.S.: 423720
Khalepa Alexey *(Gen Dir)*

Meibes SK s.r.o. (2)
Svatoplukova 18
979 01 Rimavska Sobota, Slovakia
Tel.: (421) 475 634 043
Fax: (421) 475 634 043
Heating Equipment Mfr
S.I.C.: 3433
N.A.I.C.S.: 333414

Meibes s.r.o. (2)
Bohnicka 5/28
Prague, 181 00, Czech Republic
Tel.: (420) 284 001 081
Fax: (420) 284 001 080
E-Mail: info@meibes.cz
Web Site: www.meibes.cz/kontakt/
Heating Equipment Mfr
S.I.C.: 3433
N.A.I.C.S.: 333414
Pavel Nonner *(Mng Dir)*

Melcher & Frenzen Armaturen GmbH (1)
Industriestrasse 76
42551 Velbert, Germany
Tel.: (49) 20 51 31 40 0
Fax: (49) 20 51 31 40 33
E-Mail: info@melcher-frenzen.de
Web Site: www.melcher-frenzen.de
Emp.: 10
Metal Pipe Repair Clamps & Tapping Sleeves Mfr
S.I.C.: 3499
N.A.I.C.S.: 332999
J. Aalberts *(Mng Dir)*
M. Lange *(Mng Dir)*
Georg H. Lechtenboehmer *(Mng Dir)*

Metalis HPS S.A.S. (1)
37 Boulevard des Entreprises Z I de Vaure
42600 Montbrison, France
Tel.: (33) 4 77 96 33 77
Fax: (33) 4 77 58 56 60
Metal Products Mfr
S.I.C.: 3499
N.A.I.C.S.: 332999

Metalis Polska Sp. z.o.o. (1)
Ul. Strefowa 6
58-200 Dzierzoniow, Poland
Tel.: (48) 74 832 72 40
Fax: (48) 74 815 70 70
Metal Products Mfr
S.I.C.: 3499
N.A.I.C.S.: 332999

Metalis S.A.S. (1)
Route de Pouligney
25640 Chaudefontaine, France
Tel.: (33) 3 81 48 50 70
Fax: (33) 3 81 57 90 18
Web Site: www.metalis.fr
Metal Stamping Services
S.I.C.: 3466
N.A.I.C.S.: 332119

Metatherm 74 S.A.S. (1)
Zone Industrielle Les Iles D Arve 64 Allee Des Cerisiers
74300 Thyez, France
Tel.: (33) 450346398
Fax: (33) 450340773
Web Site: www.metatherm.fr
Emp.: 3
Metal Coating Services
S.I.C.: 3479
N.A.I.C.S.: 332812
Karen Carpino *(Gen Mgr)*

Metatherm S.A.S. (1)
Rue de la Craye
25150 Pont-de-Roide, France
Tel.: (33) 3 81 96 45 85
Fax: (33) 3 81 92 27 84
Emp.: 33
Metal Heat Treatment Services
S.I.C.: 3398
N.A.I.C.S.: 332811
Roger Gauthier *(Mgr)*

Nova Comet S.r.l. (1)
Via Castel Mella 55/57
25030 Torbole Casaglia, Brescia, Italy
Tel.: (39) 0302159111
Fax: (39) 0302650717
E-Mail: info@novacomet.it
Gas Regulator Mfr
S.I.C.: 3822
N.A.I.C.S.: 334512

Nowak S.A.S. (1)
Zone Artisanale
35320 Pance, France
Tel.: (33) 2 99 43 01 97
Fax: (33) 2 99 43 04 60
E-Mail: contact@nowak.fr
Web Site: www.nowak.fr
Emp.: 120
Precision Casting Products Mfr
S.I.C.: 3365
N.A.I.C.S.: 331524
Thierry Avrons *(Gen Mgr)*

Pegler Yorkshire Group Ltd. (1)
St Catherines Ave
Doncaster, S Yorkshire, DN4 8DF, United Kingdom
Tel.: (44) 844 243 4400
Fax: (44) 844 243 4400
E-Mail: uk.sales@pegleryorkshire.co.uk
Web Site: www.pegleryorkshire.co.uk
Emp.: 800
Industrial Valves, Building Products, Industrial Rubber Components, Metal Fabrications & Computer Stationery Mfr & Distributor; Desalination Plant Services
S.I.C.: 3491
N.A.I.C.S.: 332911
Stuart Anderson *(Mng Dir)*

Prestorac SAS (1)
1 Rue Zack Dusoasne
Na Chatelle, 45380 Saint Mesmin, France (100%)
Tel.: (33) 233823333
Fax: (33) 238725477
E-Mail: prestorac-france@wanadoo.fr
Copper Tube Mfr
S.I.C.: 3351
N.A.I.C.S.: 331420

PUZ Meibes Sp. z.o.o. (1)
ul Gronowska 8
64 100 Leszno, Poland
Tel.: (48) 65 529 49 89
Fax: (48) 65 529 59 69
E-Mail: info@meibes.pl
Emp.: 38
Metal Products Mfr
S.I.C.: 3499
N.A.I.C.S.: 332999

Raufoss Metall GmbH (1)
An Der Schleuse 8
58675 Hemer, Germany
Tel.: (49) 2372 91975
Fax: (49) 2372 13577
E-Mail: info@raufoss-metall.de
Web Site: www.isiflo.com
Emp.: 13
Metal Products Mfr
S.I.C.: 3499
N.A.I.C.S.: 332999
Isamu Osa *(Gen Mgr)*

Raufoss Water & Gas AS (1)
Raufoss Industrial Park Enggata 40 Building 1
Postbox 143
2831 Raufoss, Norway
Tel.: (47) 61 15 27 00
Fax: (47) 61 15 20 62
E-Mail: info@isiflo.com
Web Site: www.isiflo.com
Emp.: 12
Gas Industry Equipment Mfr & Distr
S.I.C.: 3533
N.A.I.C.S.: 333132
Lars K. Olstad *(Mng Dir)*
Birgit Lund *(Sec)*

RIAG Oberflachentechnik AG (1)
Murgstrasse 19 a
9545 Wangi, Thurgau, Switzerland
Tel.: (41) 52 369 70 70
Fax: (41) 52 369 70 79
E-Mail: info.waengi@ahc-surface.com
Emp.: 22
Metal & Plastic Coating Services
S.I.C.: 3479
N.A.I.C.S.: 332812
Roland Ratschiller *(Gen Mgr)*

Rossweiner Armaturen Und Messgerate Gmbh & Co OHG (1)
Wehrstrasse 8
04741 Rosswein, Germany (100%)
Tel.: (49) 34322480
Fax: (49) 3432248213
E-Mail: info@rossweiner.de
Web Site: www.rossweiner.de
Emp.: 55
Armature & Measuring Device Mfr
S.I.C.: 3829
N.A.I.C.S.: 334519
Rheiner Haenfel *(Mng Dir)*

Seppelfricke Armaturen GmbH & Co., OHG (1)
Haldenstrasse 27
D 45881 Gelsenkirchen, Germany (100%)
Tel.: (49) 2094040
Fax: (49) 209404496
E-Mail: info@seppelfricke-armaturen.de
Web Site: www.seppelfricke.de
Emp.: 250
Industrial Valve Mfr
S.I.C.: 3491
N.A.I.C.S.: 332911
Hammer Burkhard *(Mng Dir)*

SGI Societe de Galvanoplastie Industrielle S.A.S. (1)
Z I Les Gatines Rue Pierre Curie 51
78370 Plaisir, France
Tel.: (33) 1 30 54 03 90
Fax: (33) 1 34 81 20 44
Surface Treatment Services
S.I.C.: 3471
N.A.I.C.S.: 332813

Simplex Armaturen & Systeme GmbH (1)
Isnyer Strasse 28
Argenbuhl - Eisenharz, 88260 Argenbuhl, Germany
Tel.: (49) 7566 9408 0
Fax: (49) 7566 9408 75
E-Mail: info@simplex-fit.de
Web Site: www.simplex-armaturen.de
Emp.: 6
Heating Equipment Mfr & Distr
S.I.C.: 3433
N.A.I.C.S.: 333414
Burkhard Haemer *(Mng Dir)*

Simplex Wilfer GmbH & Co. (1)
Isnyer Strasse 28
88260 Argenbuhl, Germany (100%)
Tel.: (49) 756694080
Fax: (49) 7566940842
E-Mail: info@simplex-set.de
Web Site: www.simplex-set.de
Emp.: 140
Armature & Measuring Device Mfr
S.I.C.: 3829
N.A.I.C.S.: 334519

Stalservice Produktion i Anderstorp AB (1)
Terassvagen 7
334 91 Anderstorp, Sweden
Tel.: (46) 371 587170
Fax: (46) 371 181 08
E-Mail: info@stalservice.se
Web Site: www.stalservice.se
Emp.: 6
Metal Heat Treating Services
S.I.C.: 3398
N.A.I.C.S.: 332811
Eric Norgosanow *(Mgr-Production)*

Standard Hidraulica, S.A.U. (1)
Avda de la Ferreria 73-75 / Pol Ind La Ferreria Apdo de Correos 67
8110 Montcada i Reixac, Barcelona, Spain

Tel.: (34) 935 641 094
Fax: (34) 935 640 499
E-Mail: info@standardhidraulica.com
Web Site: www.standardhidraulica.com
Plumbing & Heating Equipment Mfr
S.I.C.: 3432
N.A.I.C.S.: 332913

T. Termicos Metasa, S.A. (1)
Cl Benjamin Franklin 30 P I Cogullada
50014 Zaragoza, Spain
Tel.: (34) 976472741
Fax: (34) 976470595
E-Mail: info.zaragoza@trateriber.es
Metal Heat Treating Services
S.I.C.: 3398
N.A.I.C.S.: 332811

T. Termicos Sarasketa, S.L.U (1)
Cl Arriaga 5 P I Arriaga
20870 Elgoibar, Gipuzkoa, Spain
Tel.: (34) 943741550
Fax: (34) 943741458
E-Mail: info.elgoibar@trateriber.es
Emp.: 32
Metal Heat Treating Services
S.I.C.: 3398
N.A.I.C.S.: 332811
Conde Gomez Jesus *(Gen Mgr)*

T. Termicos Sohetrasa, S.A. (1)
Barrio Ibarra P I Condor II
48340 Amorebieta-Etxano, Vizcaya, Spain
Tel.: (34) 946300000
Fax: (34) 946300130
E-Mail: info.amorebieta@trateriber.es
Metal Heat Treating Services
S.I.C.: 3398
N.A.I.C.S.: 332811

T. Termicos Tey, S.L. (1)
Polig Ind Artia
48291 Atxondo, Vizcaya, Spain
Tel.: (34) 94 621 55 90
Fax: (34) 94 620 23 70
Emp.: 3
Metal Heat Treating Services
S.I.C.: 3398
N.A.I.C.S.: 332811
Roberto Granado *(Gen Mgr)*

T. Termicos Traterh, S.A.U (1)
Cl Alcotanes 32 P I Aproin
28320 Pinto, Madrid, Spain
Tel.: (34) 916923330
Fax: (34) 916920880
E-Mail: info.pinto@trateriber.es
Metal Heat Treating Services
S.I.C.: 3398
N.A.I.C.S.: 332811

TTI Group Limited (1)
39-43 Bilton Way
Luton, Bedfordshire, LU1 1UU, United Kingdom (100%)
Tel.: (44) 1582 488344
Fax: (44) 1582 488394
E-Mail: sledger@ttigroup.co.uk
Web Site: www.ttigroup.co.uk
Emp.: 10
Surface Treatment & Heat Treatment Services
S.I.C.: 3398
N.A.I.C.S.: 332811

VTI Ventil Technik GmbH (1)
Iserlohner Landstrasse 119
D 58706 Menden, Germany (100%)
Tel.: (49) 23739353
Fax: (49) 2373935444
E-Mail: info@vti.de
Web Site: www.vti.de
Emp.: 150
Industrial Valve Mfr
S.I.C.: 3491
N.A.I.C.S.: 332911
Thomas Wollschlaeger *(Mng Dir)*

Westco Flow Control Limited. (1)
Unit C6 William Way Moss Industrial Estate
Saint Helens Road, Leigh, Lancs, WN7 3PT, United Kingdom
Tel.: (44) 1942 603 351
Fax: (44) 1942 607 780
E-Mail: enquiries@westco.co.uk
Web Site: www.westco.co.uk
Plumbing & Heating Equipment Distr
S.I.C.: 5074
N.A.I.C.S.: 423720

Yorkshire Fittings Gyarto Kft (1)
Maglodi Ut 16
Budapest, 1106, Hungary
Tel.: (36) 1 4343 000
Fax: (36) 1 4343 001
E-Mail: info@yorkshirefittings.hu
Web Site: www.yorkshirefittings.hu
Emp.: 200
Metal Pipe Fitting Mfr
S.I.C.: 3494
N.A.I.C.S.: 332919
Gergely Urban *(Gen Mgr)*

AAMAL COMPANY Q.S.C.

PO Box 22477
Doha, Qatar
Tel.: (974) 44223888
Fax: (974) 417 5559
E-Mail: Info@aamal.com.qa
Web Site: www.aamal.com.qa
Year Founded: 2001
AHCS—(QE)
Rev.: $610,025,510
Assets: $2,238,053,237
Liabilities: $475,605,757
Net Worth: $1,762,447,479
Earnings: $166,807,553
Emp.: 2,300
Fiscal Year-end: 12/31/12

Business Description:
Real Estate Development Services
S.I.C.: 6531
N.A.I.C.S.: 531390

Personnel:
Faisal Qassim Al Thani *(Founder & Chm)*
Mohamed Faisal Al Thani *(Vice Chm)*
Tarek M. El Sayed *(Mng Dir)*
Mohamed Ramahi *(CFO)*
Mohamed Dobashi *(COO)*
Trevor Bailey *(Chief Bus Dev Officer)*
Amr Gohar *(CEO-ECCO Outsourcing)*
Raouf H. Metawie *(CEO-Doha Cables-Qatar)*

Board of Directors:
Faisal Qassim Al Thani
Bader A. Al Fehani
Abdullah Al Thani
Tarek M. El Sayed
Mohamed Faisal Al Thani
Yanni Jou'aneh

Subsidiaries:

Aamal Cement Industries W.L.L. (1)
St 41 Salwa Ind Area
PO Box 40632
Doha, Qatar
Tel.: (974) 44502010
Fax: (974) 44514778
E-Mail: info@aamalcement.com
Emp.: 100
Cement Mfr
S.I.C.: 3241
N.A.I.C.S.: 327310
Parveez Aslam, *(Gen Mgr)*

Aamal Readymix (1)
St 37 Industrial Area
PO Box 40557
Doha, Qatar
Tel.: (974) 4460 3939
Fax: (974) 4460 3838
E-Mail: info@aamalreadymix.com
Web Site: www.aamalreadymix.com
Emp.: 250
Readymix Concrete Mfr & Distr
S.I.C.: 3273
N.A.I.C.S.: 327320
Parveez Aslam, *(Gen Mgr)*

Good Life Chemist (1)
City Center Doha- Mezzanine Floor
Doha, Qatar
Tel.: (974) 44839100
Fax: (974) 448331245
Emp.: 15
Pharmaceutical Product Whslr
S.I.C.: 5122
N.A.I.C.S.: 424210
Zakaria Alwisi *(Reg Mgr)*

Non-U.S. Subsidiary:

Advanced Pipes and Casts Company W.L.L. (1)
Plot 40 M 35
Mussafah, Abu Dhabi, United Arab Emirates
Tel.: (971) 2 5511400
Fax: (971) 2 5511200
E-Mail: apacc1@eim.ae
Pipe Fitting Mfr
S.I.C.: 3089
N.A.I.C.S.: 326122

AANJANEYA LIFECARE LIMITED

Aanjaneya House 34 Postal Colony
Chembur, Mumbai, 400071, India
Tel.: (91) 22 25264500
Fax: (91) 22 25223251
E-Mail: info@aanlife.com
Web Site: www.aanlife.com
Year Founded: 2006
AANJANEYA—(BOM NSE)
Sales Range: $25-49.9 Million
Emp.: 220

Business Description:
Pharmaceutical Researcher, Developer & Mfr
S.I.C.: 2834
N.A.I.C.S.: 325412

Personnel:
Kashi Vishwanathan *(Chm)*
Kannan K. Vishwanath *(Vice Chm & Mng Dir)*
Bhanu Pandey *(Pres-Mktg)*
B. Ramamurthy *(Pres-R&D)*
Lalit Shukla *(Pres-Accts & Fin)*
Harleen Sahni *(Sec)*

Board of Directors:
Kashi Vishwanathan
Ullooppee S. Badade
Prabhat K. Goyal
Minhaj Khan
Balkrishna R. Parab
Kalidas S. Patel
Giridhar G. Pulleti
Shashikant B. Shinde
Kannan K. Vishwanath

AAP IMPLANTATE AG

Lorenzweg 5
D-12099 Berlin, Germany
Tel.: (49) 30750190
Fax: (49) 3075019111
Web Site: www.aap.de
AAQ—(DEU)
Sales Range: $25-49.9 Million

Business Description:
Biomaterial Implants Development & Mfr
S.I.C.: 8731
N.A.I.C.S.: 541712

Personnel:
Ronald Meersschaert *(Vice Chm-Supervisory Bd)*
Biense Visser *(CEO)*
Marek Hahn *(CFO)*
Bruke Seyoum Alemu *(COO)*

Supervisory Board of Directors:
Winfried Weigel
Marcel Boekhoorn
Uwe Ahrens
Reinhard Schnettler
Ronald Meersschaert

Non-U.S. Subsidiaries:

European Medical Contract Manufacturing B.V. (1)
Middenkampweg 17
6545 CH Nijmegen, Netherlands
Tel.: (31) 24 3715252
Fax: (31) 24 3715253
E-Mail: info@emcm.com
Web Site: www.emcm.com
Emp.: 70
Develops & Manufactures Sterile Medical Products
S.I.C.: 2834
N.A.I.C.S.: 325412
Hemreitti Calster *(Gen Mgr)*

AAP WINDOWS LTD

(d/b/a Allied Windows)
5690 268th Street
Langley, BC, V4W 3X4, Canada
Tel.: (604) 856-3311
Fax: (604) 856-8613
E-Mail: sales@alliedwindows.com
Web Site: www.alliedwindows.com
Year Founded: 1945
Rev.: $13,602,054
Emp.: 120

Business Description:
Windows & Doors Mfr
S.I.C.: 3442
N.A.I.C.S.: 332321

Personnel:
Gary Porter *(Sec)*

AAPICO HITECH PLC

99 Moo 1 Hitech Industrial Estate
Tambol Ban Lane Amphur Bang Pa-in
Ayutthaya, 13160, Thailand
Tel.: (66) 35350880
Fax: (66) 35350881
E-Mail: aapicohitech@aapico.com
Web Site: www.aapico.com
AH—(BAK THA)
Rev.: $556,951,638
Assets: $456,646,884
Liabilities: $293,318,158
Net Worth: $163,328,726
Earnings: $30,607,055
Emp.: 3,848
Fiscal Year-end: 12/31/12

Business Description:
Automotive Products Mfr
S.I.C.: 3714
N.A.I.C.S.: 336390

Personnel:
Swee Chuan Yeap *(Pres & CEO)*

Board of Directors:
Supasak Chirasavinuprapand
Yoshiaki Ichimura
Hiroto Murai
Kenneth Ng
John Parker
Porntipa Praditsuktavorn
Pipat R. Punya
Lee Ngo Teo
Swee Chuan Yeap

Legal Counsel:
Royal Advocates international Limited
29 Vanissa Buidling 22/F Suite 22A Soi Chidlom
Ploenchit Road Lumpini
Patumwan, Bangkok, 10330, Thailand

Subsidiaries:

AAPICO Amata Co., Ltd. (1)
700/483 Moo 2 Amata Nakorn Industrial Estate
Ban-Kao Phan Thong, Chon Buri, 20160, Thailand
Tel.: (66) 38717200
Fax: (66) 38717187
Web Site: www.aapico.com
Automobile Chassis Mfr
S.I.C.: 3714
N.A.I.C.S.: 336390

AAPICO Forging Public Co., Ltd. (1)
700/20 Moo 6 Amatanakorn Industrial Estate Bangna-Trad Road Km 57
Muang, Chon Buri, 20000, Thailand
Tel.: (66) 38213355
Fax: (66) 38 213360
Emp.: 586
Automotive Forging Parts Mfr
S.I.C.: 3699
N.A.I.C.S.: 335999
Yeap Swee Chuan *(Pres)*

AAPICO Forging PLC (1)
700/20 Moo 6 Tambol Nongmaidaeng
Ampor Muang, Chon Buri, Thailand
Tel.: (66) 38213357

AAPICO Hitech plc—(Continued)

Fax: (66) 38213360
Emp.: 400
Automotive Forging & Machining Parts Mfr
S.I.C.: 3463
N.A.I.C.S.: 332112

AAPICO Hitech Parts Co., Ltd (1)
99 Moo 1 Hitech Industrial Estate Tambol Ban Lane
Amphur Bangpa-in, 13160 Ayutthaya, Thailand (100%)
Tel.: (66) 35350880
Fax: (66) 35350881
Emp.: 300
Automotive Repair & Maintenance
S.I.C.: 7539
N.A.I.C.S.: 811198
Sattha Phetin *(Product Mgr)*

AAPICO Hitech Tooling Co., Ltd. (1)
99/2 Moo 1 Hitech Industrial Estate Tambol Ban Lane
Amphur Bangpa-in, Ayutthaya, 13160, Thailand
Tel.: (66) 35350880
Fax: (66) 35 350881
E-Mail: aapico@aapico.com
Emp.: 1,000
Car Assembly Jigs & Stamping Dies Mfr
S.I.C.: 3544
N.A.I.C.S.: 333514
Yeb Su Shuan *(Mng Dir)*

AAPICO Plastics Public Co., Ltd. (1)
358-358/1 Moo 17 Bangplee Industrial Estate Tambol Bangsaothong
Ban Sao Thong, Samut Prakan, 10540, Thailand
Tel.: (66) 23153456
Fax: (66) 23153334
Emp.: 500
Automotive Plastic Parts Mfr
S.I.C.: 3089
N.A.I.C.S.: 326199
Teeratath L. *(Gen Mgr)*

AAPICO Structural Products Co., Ltd. (1)
700/16 Moo 6 Tambol Nongmaidaeng
Chon Buri, Thailand
Tel.: (66) 38717200
Fax: (66) 38 717 187
Automotive Parts Mfr
S.I.C.: 3714
N.A.I.C.S.: 336390

Able Motors Co., Ltd. (1)
14/9 Moo 14 Phaholyothin Road Tambol Klong Neung Ampur
Khlong Luang, Pathumthani, 12120, Thailand
Tel.: (66) 2 908 6001
Fax: (66) 2 908 6009
Web Site: www.aapico.com
New Car Dealers
S.I.C.: 5511
N.A.I.C.S.: 441110
Teaw Lee Guo *(Mng Dir)*

Katsuya (Thailand) Co., Ltd. (1)
229/104-105 Moo 1 Teparak Rd Tambol Bangsaothong
Bangsaothong, 10540 Samut Prakan, Thailand
Tel.: (66) 27065915
Fax: (66) 27065910
E-Mail: kittipong.s@aapico.com
Web Site: www.aapico.com
Emp.: 600
Water Transfer Printing Services
S.I.C.: 2759
N.A.I.C.S.: 323111
Kittipong Sindhupiasert *(Mgr-Sls)*

New Era Sales Co., Ltd. (1)
66/24 Moo 14 Ramindra KM7 Kwang Kannayao
Bangkok, Thailand
Tel.: (66) 2 5195800
Fax: (66) 2 9465109
New Car Dealers
S.I.C.: 5511
N.A.I.C.S.: 441110

Non-U.S. Subsidiaries:

AAPICO Engineering Sdn. Bhd. (1)
Lot 8229 Jalan 222 Section 51A
46100 Petaling Jaya, Selangor, Malaysia
Tel.: (60) 379575590
Fax: (60) 379578718
Web Site: www.aapico.com
Engineering Research & Development Services
S.I.C.: 8711
N.A.I.C.S.: 541330
Tang Kim Koh *(Gen Mgr)*

AAPICO Shanghai Co., Ltd. (1)
3600 Wai Qing Song Road
Qingpu, Shanghai, 201709, China
Tel.: (86) 21 59744843
Fax: (86) 21 59744843
Web Site: www.aapico.com
Automotive Machining Parts Mfr
S.I.C.: 3714
N.A.I.C.S.: 336390

Kunshan Chaitai-Xincheng Precision Forging Co., Ltd. (1)
405 Yun Que Road Kunshan Development Zone
Kunshan, Jiangsu, 215331, China
Tel.: (86) 512 57671757
Fax: (86) 512 57870880
E-Mail: aapicokunshan@aapico.com
Web Site: www.aapico.cn
Emp.: 300
Steel & Copper Forging Parts Mfr
S.I.C.: 3399
N.A.I.C.S.: 331110

AAREAL BANK AG

Paulinenstrasse 15
65189 Wiesbaden, Germany
Tel.: (49) 6113480
Fax: (49) 6113482549
E-Mail: aareal@aareal-bank.com
Web Site: www.aareal-bank.com
Year Founded: 1823
ARL—(DEU OTC)
Int. Income: $1,305,784,900
Assets: $61,565,738,780
Liabilities: $58,399,546,940
Net Worth: $3,166,191,840
Earnings: $166,925,080
Emp.: 2,289
Fiscal Year-end: 12/31/12

Business Description:
International Property Financing Services
S.I.C.: 6159
N.A.I.C.S.: 522292

Personnel:
Marija G. Korsch *(Chm-Supervisory Bd)*
Wolf Schumacher *(Chm-Mgmt Bd & CEO)*
York-Detlef Bulow *(Deputy Chm-Supervisory Bd)*
Erwin Flieger *(Deputy Chm-Supervisory Bd)*
Dagmar Knopek *(Member-Mgmt Bd-Sls Units-Structured Property Fin Segment)*
Hermann J. Merkens *(Member-Mgmt Bd-Fin, Risk Controlling, Credit Mgmt & Workout)*
Thomas Ortmanns *(Member-Mgmt Bd-Institutional Housing Unit, Treasury, Org & IT Div)*

Supervisory Board of Directors:
Marija G. Korsch
Manfred Behrens
York-Detlef Bulow
Erwin Flieger
Thomas Hawel
Dieter Kirsch
Herbert Lohneiss
Joachim Neupel
Richard Peters
Stephan Schuller
Christian Graf von Bassewitz
Helmut Wagner

Subsidiaries:

Aareal Estate AG (1)
Paulinenstrasse 15
D 65189 Wiesbaden, Germany (100%)
Tel.: (49) 6113480
Fax: (49) 6113482549
E-Mail: estate@aareal-bank.com
Web Site: www.aareal-bank.com
Emp.: 21
Development, Management & Marketing of Commercial Properties
S.I.C.: 6519
N.A.I.C.S.: 531390
Rolf Buchholz *(Member-Mgmt Bd)*
Hans-Ulrich Kron *(Member-Mgmt Bd)*

Aareal Gesellschaft fur Beteiligungen und Grundbesitz Dritte mbH & Co. KG (1)
Paulinenstr 15
65189 Wiesbaden, Germany
Tel.: (49) 6113482950
Fax: (49) 611 348 28 33
E-Mail: aareal@aareal-bank.com
Property Management Services
S.I.C.: 6531
N.A.I.C.S.: 531312
Ronald Hoffmann *(Mng Dir)*

Aareal Gesellschaft fur Beteiligungen und Grundbesitz Erste mbH & Co. KG (1)
Paulinenstr 15
65189 Wiesbaden, Germany
Tel.: (49) 6113480
Fax: (49) 6113482549
E-Mail: aareal@aareal-bank.com
Web Site: www.aareal-bank.com
Emp.: 800
Real Estate Management Services
S.I.C.: 6531
N.A.I.C.S.: 531390

Aareal IT Beteiligungen GmbH (1)
Paulinenstr 15
65189 Wiesbaden, Germany
Tel.: (49) 6113480
Fax: (49) 611 348259
Web Site: www.aareal-bank.com
Emp.: 2,200
Investment Management Consulting Services
S.I.C.: 6211
N.A.I.C.S.: 523999
Wolf Schumacher *(Gen Mgr)*

Aareal Valuation GmbH (1)
Paulinenstrasse 15
65189 Wiesbaden, Germany (100%)
Tel.: (49) 6113482059
Fax: (49) 6113482640
E-Mail: info@aareal-valuation.com
Web Site: www.aareal-valuation.com
Emp.: 9
Property Valuation & Consulting Services
S.I.C.: 8748
N.A.I.C.S.: 541618
Wolf Schumacher *(Chm-Supervisory Bd)*
Karl-Ludwig Goeth *(Mng Dir)*

Aareon AG (1)
Isssac-Sulda Allee 6
55124 Mainz, Germany
Tel.: (49) 61313010
Fax: (49) 6131301419
E-Mail: info@aareon.com
Web Site: www.aareon.com
Emp.: 1,200
Software & IT Services for the Management of Residential & Commercial Properties
S.I.C.: 5734
N.A.I.C.S.: 443142
Manfred Alflen *(Chm)*

Non-U.S. Subsidiaries:

Aareon France S.A.S. (2)
9 Rue Jeanne Braconnier
92360 Meudon, France
Tel.: (33) 145379230
Fax: (33) 146329008
E-Mail: contact.fr@aareon.com
Web Site: www.aareon.fr
Emp.: 150
Property Management Consulting Services
S.I.C.: 6531
N.A.I.C.S.: 531312
Chantal Penelon *(Pres)*

Aareon UK Ltd. (2)
Building 500 Abbey Park
Stareton, Coventry, CV8 2LY, United Kingdom
Tel.: (44) 2476323723
Fax: (44) 2476323724
Web Site: www.aareon.co.uk
Emp.: 30
Business Management Software Development Services
S.I.C.: 7371
N.A.I.C.S.: 541511
Emma Woodward *(Mgr)*

Aareon Deutschland GmbH (1)
Im Muenchfeld 1-5
55122 Mainz, Germany
Tel.: (49) 6131 301 295
Fax: (49) 6131 301 546
E-Mail: liradmin@aareon.com
Investment Banking Services
S.I.C.: 6211
N.A.I.C.S.: 523110

Aareon Software Handelsgesellschaft mbH (1)
Isaac Fulda Allee 6
55124 Mainz, Germany
Tel.: (49) 61313010
Fax: (49) 6131 301 419
E-Mail: info@aareon.com
Web Site: www.aareon.com
Computer Peripheral Equipment Distr
S.I.C.: 5045
N.A.I.C.S.: 423430

Aareon Wodis GmbH (1)
Rheinlanddamm 199
44139 Dortmund, Germany
Tel.: (49) 23177510
Fax: (49) 231 7751 190
E-Mail: info@wodis.de
Web Site: www.aareon.com
Emp.: 100
Real Estate Management Services
S.I.C.: 6531
N.A.I.C.S.: 531390

BauContact Immobilien GmbH (1)
Paulinenstr 15
65189 Wiesbaden, Germany
Tel.: (49) 6113482953
Fax: (49) 61172953
Financial Management Consulting Services
S.I.C.: 8742
N.A.I.C.S.: 541611

Capital Funding GmbH & Co. KG (1)
Steinweg 3-5
60313 Frankfurt am Main, Germany
Tel.: (49) 69 2992 5385
Fax: (49) 69 2992 5387
Web Site: www.capital-funding.de
Financial Management Consulting Services
S.I.C.: 6211
N.A.I.C.S.: 523999
Florian Schluter *(Gen Mgr)*

Deutsche Bau- und Grundstucks-Aktiengesellschaft (1)
Chlodwigplatz 1
53119 Bonn, Germany
Tel.: (49) 2285180
Fax: (49) 228518276
E-Mail: info@baugrund.de
Emp.: 116
Real Estate Management Services
S.I.C.: 6531
N.A.I.C.S.: 531390
Hermann J. Merkens *(Chm)*
Niels Fischer *(CEO)*

Subsidiaries:

BauGrund Immobilien-Management GmbH (2)
Chlodwigplatz 1
53119 Bonn, Germany
Tel.: (49) 2285180
Fax: (49) 228518276
E-Mail: info@baugrund.de
Emp.: 60
Real Estate Management Services
S.I.C.: 6531
N.A.I.C.S.: 531390
Niels Fischer *(Pres)*
Markus Schmidt *(Mng Dir)*

BauGrund TVG GmbH (2)
Prinzregentenstr 22
Munich, Germany
Tel.: (49) 89 5 51 98 0
Fax: (49) 89 5 51 98 455

E-Mail: info@baugrund.de
Property Management Services
S.I.C.: 6531
N.A.I.C.S.: 531312

Deutsche Structured Finance GmbH & Co. Alphard KG (1)
Feuerbachstrasse 26-32
Frankfurt am Main, Germany
Tel.: (49) 699714970
E-Mail: dsf@dsf-fra.de
Web Site: www.dsf-fra.de
Emp.: 17
Financial Management Consulting Services
S.I.C.: 8742
N.A.I.C.S.: 541611

Deutsche Structured Finance GmbH & Co. Deneb KG (1)
Feuerbachstr 26- 32
60325 Frankfurt am Main, Germany
Tel.: (49) 699714970
Fax: (49) 69 91039805
Financial Management Consulting Services
S.I.C.: 8742
N.A.I.C.S.: 541611

Deutsche Structured Finance GmbH & Co. Titan KG (1)
Westendstr 24
Frankfurt am Main, 60325, Germany
Tel.: (49) 699714970
Financial Management Consulting Services
S.I.C.: 8742
N.A.I.C.S.: 541611

Deutsche Structured Finance GmbH (1)
Feuerbachstrasse 26-32
60325 Frankfurt, Germany
Tel.: (49) 699714970
Fax: (49) 69 97 14 97 510
Web Site: www.dsf-fra.de
Financial Management Consulting Services
S.I.C.: 8742
N.A.I.C.S.: 541611

GEV GmbH (1)
Robert-koch-str 3 A
82152 Planegg, Germany
Tel.: (49) 89 7455720
Fax: (49) 89 745572 83
E-Mail: order@gev-online.com
Web Site: www.gev-online.com
Catering Equipment Mfr & Whslr
S.I.C.: 3589
N.A.I.C.S.: 333318

Real Verwaltungsgesellschaft mbH (1)
Elisabeth-Schwarzkopf-Weg
65510 Idstein, Germany
Tel.: (49) 611 348 0
Fax: (49) 611 3482549
Real Estate Management Services
S.I.C.: 6531
N.A.I.C.S.: 531390

Rehabilitationsklinik Barby Besitzgesellschaft mbH (1)
Paulinenstr 15
65189 Wiesbaden, Hessen, Germany
Tel.: (49) 39298 61600
Fax: (49) 39298 299230
Health Insurance Services
S.I.C.: 6411
N.A.I.C.S.: 524298
Henner Montanus *(Gen Mgr)*

Terrain-Aktiengesellschaft Herzogpark (1)
Paulinenstr 15
65189 Wiesbaden, Hessen, Germany
Tel.: (49) 6113480
Fax: (49) 611 3482549
E-Mail: aareal@aareal-bank.com
Web Site: www.aareal-bank.com
Real Estate Management Services
S.I.C.: 6531
N.A.I.C.S.: 531390

U.S. Subsidiaries:

Aareal Bank Capital Funding Trust (1)
250 Park Ave Ste 820
New York, NY 10177
Tel.: (646) 465-8601
E-Mail: info@aareal-capital-funding.com
Web Site: www.aareal-capital-funding.com
Investment Banking Services
S.I.C.: 6211
N.A.I.C.S.: 523110

Aareal Capital Corporation (1)
250 Park Ave
New York, NY 10177
Tel.: (212) 508-4080
Fax: (907) 322-0285
E-Mail: jhenry@aareal-capital.com
Web Site: www.aareal-bank.com
Emp.: 30
Property Financing
S.I.C.: 6159
N.A.I.C.S.: 522292
James Henry *(Pres & CEO)*
Douglas Traynor *(Mng Dir)*

Non-U.S. Subsidiaries:

Aareal Bank AG (1)
5 rue Scribe
F-75009 Paris, France (100%)
Tel.: (33) 144516630
Fax: (33) 142669794
E-Mail: aareal-france@aareal-bank.com
Web Site: www.aareal-bank.com
Emp.: 25
International Real Estate Financing
S.I.C.: 6159
N.A.I.C.S.: 522292
Christine Schulze-Forsthoevel *(Mng Dir)*

Aareal Bank Asia Limited (1)
3 Church Street
Singapore, 049483, Singapore
Tel.: (65) 63729750
Fax: (65) 65368162
E-Mail: juergen.hetzler@aareal-bank.com
Web Site: www.aareal-bank.com
Real Estate Investment Services
S.I.C.: 6159
N.A.I.C.S.: 522292
Juergen Hetzler *(Mng Dir & CEO-Asia Pacific)*

Aareal-Financial Service, spol. s r.o. (1)
Vaclavske Namesti 19
11000 Prague, Czech Republic
Tel.: (420) 234656006
Fax: (420) 234656011
Web Site: www.aareal-bank.com
Financial Management Consulting Services
S.I.C.: 8742
N.A.I.C.S.: 541611
Jaroslav Sedivka *(Gen Mgr-Romania)*

Aareal Participations France S.a.r.l. (1)
29 B Rue D
75008 Paris, France
Tel.: (33) 144516630
Fax: (33) 142669794
Financial Management Consulting Services
S.I.C.: 8742
N.A.I.C.S.: 541611

IMMO Consulting S.p.A. (1)
Via Mercadante 12/14
198 Rome, Italy
Tel.: (39) 0683004400
Fax: (39) 0683004405
Financial Management Consulting Services
S.I.C.: 8742
N.A.I.C.S.: 541611

SG Facilitor B.V. (1)
Gronausestraat 710
7534 AM Enschede, Netherlands
Tel.: (31) 534800710
E-Mail: info@sgfacilitor.nl
Web Site: www.facilitor.nl
Emp.: 50
Software Development Services
S.I.C.: 7373
N.A.I.C.S.: 541512

SG Automatisering B.V. (1)
Cornelis Houtmanstraat 36
Postbus 2036
7825 VG Emmen, Netherlands
Tel.: (31) 591630111
Fax: (31) 591632368
E-Mail: info@sg.nl
Web Site: www.sg.nl
Software Development Services
S.I.C.: 7373
N.A.I.C.S.: 541512

SG Detachering B.V. (1)
Cornelis Houtmanstraat 36
Emmen, Drenthe, 7825 VG, Netherlands
Tel.: (31) 591630111
Fax: (31) 534800711
General Management Consulting Services
S.I.C.: 8748
N.A.I.C.S.: 541618

SG Professional Services B.V. (1)
Cornelis Houtmanstraat 36
Emmen, Drenthe, 7825 VG, Netherlands
Tel.: (31) 591666833
Fax: (31) 591632368
E-Mail: info@sg.nl
Software Development Services
S.I.C.: 7371
N.A.I.C.S.: 541511

AAREN SCIENTIFIC, INC.

(Acquired by Carl-Zeiss-Stiftung)

AAREY DRUGS & PHARMACEUTICALS LTD.

107 Sahakar Bhavan 340/348 Narshi Natha Street
Masjid, Mumbai, 400 009, India
Tel.: (91) 22 66154219
Fax: (91) 22 23455543
E-Mail: info@aareydrugs.com
Web Site: www.aareydrugs.com
524412—(BOM)
Sales Range: $10-24.9 Million

Business Description:
Pharmaceutical Products Mfr & Distr
S.I.C.: 2834
N.A.I.C.S.: 325412

Personnel:
Mihir R. Ghatalia *(Chm & Mng Dir)*

Board of Directors:
Mihir R. Ghatalia
Chetan K. Mehta
Jagdish Shah
Satish Sheth
Lalit R. Tulsiani

Transfer Agent:
Link Intime India Private Limited
C-13 Pannalal Silk Mills Compound LBS Marg
Mumbai, India

AARHUSKARLSHAMN AB

(d/b/a AAK)
Jungmansgatan 12
SE-211 19 Malmo, Sweden
Tel.: (46) 454 820 00
Fax: (46) 454 828 88
E-Mail: info@aak.com
Web Site: www.aak.com
AAK—(OMX)
Rev.: $2,634,541,200
Assets: $1,510,848,000
Liabilities: $903,567,600
Net Worth: $607,280,400
Earnings: $100,155,600
Emp.: 2,211
Fiscal Year-end: 12/31/12

Business Description:
Specialty Vegetable Fats Mfr
S.I.C.: 2079
N.A.I.C.S.: 311225

Personnel:
Melker Schorling *(Chm)*
Arne Frank *(Pres & CEO)*
Peter Korsholm *(CFO & VP)*
Anne Mette Olesen *(CMO & VP-HR, Comm & CSR)*
Karsten Nielsen *(CTO & VP)*
Torben Friis Lange *(Pres-Asia, Europe & Africa & VP)*
Renald Mackintosh *(Pres-Infant Nutrition & Food Service-Continental Europe & VP)*
Ian McIntosh *(Pres-Food Ingredients-UK & Americas & VP)*
David Smith *(Pres-European Supply Chain & VP)*
Bo Svensson *(Pres-Technical Products & Feed Bus Area & VP)*
Terrence Thomas *(Pres-USA & VP)*

Board of Directors:
Melker Schorling
Marit Beckeman
Arne Frank
Leif Hakansson
Marta Schorling
Ulrik Svensson
Lillie Li Valeur
Annika Westerlund

Subsidiaries:

AarhusKarlshamn Baltic Holding AB (1)
Jungmansgatan 12
211 19 Malmo, Sweden
Tel.: (46) 45482609
Investment Management Services
S.I.C.: 6211
N.A.I.C.S.: 523999

AarhusKarlshamn Sweden AB (1)
Vastra Kajen
374 82 Karlshamn, Sweden SE
Tel.: (46) 45482000
Telex: 4511 Akotra
Fax: (46) 45482888
E-Mail: info@aak.com
Web Site: www.aak.com
Emp.: 620
Specialty Vegetable Fats Mfr
Export
S.I.C.: 2079
N.A.I.C.S.: 311225
Arne Frank *(Pres & CEO)*
Bo Svensson *(CIO & VP)*

Belico Holding AB (1)
PO Box 74
Dalby, Sweden
Tel.: (46) 46205617
Investment Management Services
S.I.C.: 6282
N.A.I.C.S.: 523920

Binol AB (1)
Vastra Kajen 8
Karlshamn, Blekinge, 374 82, Sweden
Tel.: (46) 45482800
Fax: (46) 454752070
E-Mail: binol@aak.com
Web Site: www.akk.com
Emp.: 20
Lubricants Mfr
S.I.C.: 2992
N.A.I.C.S.: 324191
Lars Randahl *(Controller)*

U.S. Subsidiary:

AarhusKarlshamn USA, Inc. (1)
131 Marsh St
Newark, NJ 07114
Tel.: (973) 344-1300
Fax: (973) 344-9049
Toll Free: (800) 776-1338
Web Site: www.aak.com
Emp.: 77
Specialty Vegetable Fats Mfr
S.I.C.: 2079
N.A.I.C.S.: 311225
Terrence Thomas *(Pres)*

Subsidiary:

Oasis Foods Company (2)
635 Ramsey Ave Ste 201
Hillside, NJ 07205
Tel.: (908) 964-0477
Fax: (908) 964-1369
Toll Free: (888) 472-5237
E-Mail: info@oasisfoodsco.com
Web Site: www.oasisfoods.com
Sales Range: $125-149.9 Million
Emp.: 160
Mayonnaise, Dressings, Margarine, Vinegars, Edible Oils & Other Condiments Mfr & Distr
S.I.C.: 2035
N.A.I.C.S.: 311941
Anthony Alves *(Pres)*

Non-U.S. Subsidiaries:

Aarhus 3 A/S (1)
MP Bruuns Gade 27
8000 Arhus, Denmark

AarhusKarlshamn AB—(Continued)

Tel.: (45) 87306000
Fax: (45) 87306012
E-Mail: dk.info@aak.com
Emp.: 280
Oils & Fats Rendering Services
S.I.C.: 2079
N.A.I.C.S.: 311225
John Officer *(Gen Mgr)*

Aarhus Malaysia Sdn. Bhd. (1)
Jendarata Estate
36009 Teluk Intan, Perak, Malaysia
Tel.: (60) 56411411
Fax: (60) 56411876
Palm Oil Mfr
S.I.C.: 2079
N.A.I.C.S.: 311225

Aarhus United A/S (1)
MP Bruuns Gade 27
8000 Arhus, Denmark
Tel.: (45) 87306000
E-Mail: dk.info@aarhusunited.com
Web Site: www.aarhusunited.com
Emp.: 350
Vegetable Oils Mfr
S.I.C.: 2099
N.A.I.C.S.: 311999
John Officer *(Gen Mgr)*

AarhusKarlshamn Australia Pty. Ltd. (1)
Unit 4 10-12 Old Castle Hill Road
Castle Hill, NSW, 2154, Australia
Tel.: (61) 288503522
Fax: (61) 288503422
Web Site: www.aak.com
Emp.: 3
Vegetable Oils Mfr & Distr
S.I.C.: 2099
N.A.I.C.S.: 311999
Peter Brazel *(Mgr)*

AarhusKarlshamn Baltic Ltd. (1)
Kalvariju 125
02648 Vilnius, Lithuania
Tel.: (370) 52700061
Fax: (370) 52700440
E-Mail: karlshamns.baltic@takas.lt
Web Site: www.aak.com
Chemical Engineering Services
S.I.C.: 8711
N.A.I.C.S.: 541330

AarhusKarlshamn Canada Ltd. (1)
2275 Upper Middle Rd Ste 101
Oakville, ON, L6H 0C3, Canada
Tel.: (416) 621-4845
Emp.: 1
Vegetable Fats & Oils Distr
S.I.C.: 5149
N.A.I.C.S.: 424490

AarhusKarlshamn Czech Republic Spol.s.r.o. (1)
Na Pankraci 1618/30
140 00 Prague, Czech Republic
Tel.: (420) 222210406
Fax: (420) 246013242
E-Mail: info.cz@aak.com
Web Site: www.aak.com
Emp.: 2
Vegetable Fats Mfr
S.I.C.: 2099
N.A.I.C.S.: 311999

AarhusKarlshamn Denmark A/S (1)
Slipvej 4
8000 Arhus, Denmark
Tel.: (45) 87306000
Fax: (45) 87306011
E-Mail: dk.info@aak.com
Web Site: www.aak.com
Emp.: 240
Mfr. & Developer of Vegetable Oils & Various Other Baking Products
S.I.C.: 2079
N.A.I.C.S.: 311225
Arne Frank *(Pres & CEO)*
Bo Svensson *(CIO)*

AarhusKarlshamn do Brasil desenvolvimento de Negosios Ltda. (1)
Av Das Nacoes Unidas 12 551 - 17 Andar
Sala 1783 WTC Tower
06460-040 Sao Paulo, Brazil
Tel.: (55) 1134437862
Fax: (55) 1141952075
E-Mail: mauro.terreri@aak.com
Web Site: www.aak.com
Emp.: 10
Confectionery Products Distr
S.I.C.: 5145
N.A.I.C.S.: 424450
Edmond Borid *(Gen Mgr)*

AarhusKarlshamn Ghana Ltd. (1)
1st Floor SAGA GH Limited Building Plots
85-89 Tema Main Harbour
Tema, Ghana
Tel.: (233) 22 200647
Fax: (233) 22 200648
Web Site: www.aak.com
Emp.: 7
Shea Oil Mfr
S.I.C.: 2844
N.A.I.C.S.: 325620
Par Torstensson *(Gen Mgr)*

AarhusKarlshamn Havnen A/S (1)
MP Bruuns Gade 27
8000 Arhus, Denmark
Tel.: (45) 87306000
Fax: (45) 87306012
E-Mail: aarhus@aak.com
Emp.: 300
Vegetable Oils Mfr
S.I.C.: 2099
N.A.I.C.S.: 311999
John Officer *(Gen Mgr)*

AarhusKarlshamn Latin America S.A. (1)
Camino al Paso de la Arena 2460
12600 Montevideo, Uruguay
Tel.: (598) 23135135
Fax: (598) 23135075
E-Mail: info.uy@aak.com
Emp.: 20
Vegetable Fats & Oils Distr
S.I.C.: 5149
N.A.I.C.S.: 424490
Edmond Borit *(Gen Mgr)*

AarhusKarlshamn Mexico, S.A. de C.V. (1)
Av Heroes de Nocupetaro 1022 Col Industrial
Morelia, Michoacan, 58130, Mexico
Tel.: (52) 443 175 0400
Fax: (52) 443 175 0489
Web Site: www.aak.com
Vegetable Fats Distr
S.I.C.: 5149
N.A.I.C.S.: 424490

AarhusKarlshamn Netherlands BV (1)
Kreeftstraat 1
PO Box 17
1540 AA Zaandijk, Netherlands
Tel.: (31) 756278400
Fax: (31) 756278478
E-Mail: info@aarhus.com
Emp.: 75
Fatty Acids Mfr
S.I.C.: 2899
N.A.I.C.S.: 325199
Mieke Doll *(Mgr-Quality)*

AarhusKarlshamn Norway AS (1)
PO Box 2570
0202 Oslo, Norway
Tel.: (47) 22731900
Fax: (47) 22 73 19 01
Web Site: www.aak.com
Vegetable Fats Mfr
S.I.C.: 2099
N.A.I.C.S.: 311999

AarhusKarlshamn Poland Sp.z o.o. (1)
Ul Walecznych 44/3
03 916 Warsaw, Poland
Tel.: (48) 226164182
Fax: (48) 226160255
E-Mail: infopl@aak.com
Web Site: www.aak.com
Emp.: 5
Vegetable Fats Mfr
S.I.C.: 2099
N.A.I.C.S.: 311999
Jaroroaw Bogucs *(Gen Mgr)*

AarhusKarlshamn RU OOO (1)
Podsosenskiy per 20 Bldg 1
Moscow, 105062, Russia
Tel.: (7) 4959376001
Fax: (7) 4959376002
E-Mail: ru.info@aak.com
Emp.: 17
Vegetable Fats Mfr
S.I.C.: 2099
N.A.I.C.S.: 311999
Jakob Pedersen *(Mng Dir)*

AarhusKarlshamn UK Ltd. (1)
King George Dock
Hull, HU9 5PX, United Kingdom
Tel.: (44) 1482701271
Fax: (44) 1482709447
E-Mail: uk.info@aak.com
Web Site: www.aak.com
Emp.: 465
Specialty Vegetable Fats Mfr
S.I.C.: 2079
N.A.I.C.S.: 311225
Martin Craven *(Mng Dir)*

Division:

AarhusKarlshamn UK Ltd. - AAK Foods (2)
Davy Road Astmoor Industrial Estate
Runcorn, Cheshire, WA7 1PZ, United Kingdom
Tel.: (44) 1928565221
Fax: (44) 1928581185
E-Mail: info@aak.com
Emp.: 60
Mustards & Condiments Mfr
S.I.C.: 2035
N.A.I.C.S.: 311941
John Deine *(Gen Mgr)*

Subsidiary:

AAK Bakery Services (2)
Falcon Street
Oldham, Lancashire, OL8 1JU, United Kingdom UK
Tel.: (44) 1616526311
Fax: (44) 616272346
Web Site: www.croda-foods.co.uk
Sls.: $33,440,000
Emp.: 60
Technical Oils & Fats for Use in the Large Scale Manufacture of Various Baked Products & Products Manufactured in the Large Scale Food Processing Industry
S.I.C.: 2079
N.A.I.C.S.: 311225
John Dryden *(Mng Dir)*

Book & Claim Ltd. (1)
King George Dock
Hull, HU9 5PX, United Kingdom
Tel.: (44) 1482332013
E-Mail: info@bookandclaim.co.uk
Web Site: www.bookandclaim.co.uk
Emp.: 5
Oil Palm Trading Services
S.I.C.: 6221
N.A.I.C.S.: 523130
Bob Norman *(Mgr)*

Ceylon Trading Co. Ltd. (1)
36 Dr Wijewardena Mawatha
PO Box 161
Colombo, Sri Lanka
Tel.: (94) 112327336
Fax: (94) 112449586
Web Site: www.aak.com
Financial Management Consulting Services
S.I.C.: 8748
N.A.I.C.S.: 541618

Karlshamns International Plc (1)
King George Dock
Hull, HU9 5PX, United Kingdom
Tel.: (44) 1482701271
Fax: (44) 1482709447
E-Mail: info@aak.com
Emp.: 350
Edible Fats & Oils Mfr
S.I.C.: 2079
N.A.I.C.S.: 311225
Damian Peter Taylor *(Sec)*

AARTI DRUGS LTD.

Mahendra Industrial Estate Ground Floor Road No 29 Plot No 109 D
Sion East, Mumbai, 400 022, India
Tel.: (91) 2224019025
Fax: (91) 2224073462
E-Mail: aartidrugs@vsnl.com
Web Site: www.aartidrugs.com
Year Founded: 1984
524348—(BOM)
Rev.: $164,217,734
Assets: $133,435,862
Liabilities: $94,945,370
Net Worth: $38,490,492
Earnings: $8,387,204
Fiscal Year-end: 03/31/13

Business Description:
Pharmaceutical Developer & Mfr
S.I.C.: 2834
N.A.I.C.S.: 325412

Personnel:
Prakash M. Patil *(CEO & Co-Mng Dir)*
Harshit M. Savla *(Co-Mng Dir)*
Adhish P. Patil *(CFO)*
Sunny Pagare *(Compliance Officer & Sec)*

Board of Directors:
Rajendra V. Gogri
Krishnacharya G. Akamanchi
Sunil M. Dedhia
Vilas G. Gaikar
Ramdas M. Gandhi
Rashesh C. Gogri
Prakash M. Patil
Uday M. Patil
Harshit M. Savla
Harit P. Shah
Navin C. Shah
Bhavesh R. Vora

Legal Counsel:
M. P. Savla & Co
Bharat House 2nd Fl 104 Mumbai Samachar Marg
Mumbai, India

Transfer Agent:
Sharepro Services India Pvt Ltd
Samhita Warehousing Complex Bldg No 13 AB
Gala No 52-56
Sakinaka Telephone Exchange, Mumbai, India

Subsidiary:

Suyash Laboratories Ltd. (1)
Plot No 109 D Ground Fl
Mumbai, Maharashtra, 400022, India
Tel.: (91) 2224019025
Fax: (91) 2224073462
E-Mail: admin@aartidrugs.com
Emp.: 20
Pharmaceutical Products Mfr
S.I.C.: 2834
N.A.I.C.S.: 325412
Yogesh Padmashali *(Mgr)*

AARTI INDUSTRIES LTD.

(d/b/a Aarti Group)
Udyog Kshetra 2nd Floor Mulund
Goregaon Link Road Mulund West
Mumbai, Maharashtra, 400080, India
Tel.: (91) 2267976666
Fax: (91) 2225653234
E-Mail: info@aartigroup.com
Web Site: www.aartigroup.com
Year Founded: 1976
524208—(BOM NSE)
Rev.: $389,340,871
Assets: $403,427,767
Liabilities: $262,429,158
Net Worth: $140,998,610
Earnings: $24,920,281
Emp.: 1,200
Fiscal Year-end: 03/31/13

Business Description:
Holding Company; Chemicals, Intermediates, Allied Products, Pharmaceutical Ingredients, Pigments & Dyes Mfr
S.I.C.: 6719
N.A.I.C.S.: 551112

Personnel:
Parimal H. Desai *(Co-Founder & Dir-Technical & R&D)*
Chandrakant Gogri *(Co-Founder)*

Shantilal T. Shah *(Co-Founder)*
Rajendra V. Gogri *(Chm & Co-Mng Dir)*
Rashesh C. Gogri *(Vice Chm & Co-Mng Dir)*
Mona Patel *(Compliance Officer & Sec)*
Board of Directors:
Rajendra V. Gogri
Haresh K. Chheda
Manoj M. Chheda
Sunil M. Dedhia
Parimal H. Desai
Hetal Gogri Gala
Ramdas M. Gandhi
Rashesh C. Gogri
Renil R. Gogri
Laxmichand K. Jain
Kirit R. Mehta
Vijay H. Patil
P. A. Sathi
Shantilal T. Shah
K. V. S. Shyam Sunder
Bhavesh R. Vora
Transfer Agent:
Sharepro Services India Pvt Ltd
Samhita Warehousing Complex Bldg No 13 AB
Gala No 52 to 56 Sakinaka
Near Sakinaka Telephone Exchange Andheri
Kurla Road, Mumbai, 400072, India

Divisions:

Aarti Healthcare Ltd. (1)
Udyog Kshetra 2nd Floor LBS Marg
Mulund-Goregaon Link Road
Mulund West, Mumbai, Maharashtra, 400 080, India In
Tel.: (91) 2267976666 (51%)
Fax: (91) 2225904806
E-Mail: info@aartigroup.com
Web Site: www.aartihealthcare.com
Emp.: 200
Active Pharmaceutical Ingredients Researcher, Developer & Mfr
S.I.C.: 2833
N.A.I.C.S.: 325411
Chandrakant V. Gogri *(Chm)*
Rajendra V. Gogri *(Vice Chm)*
Parimal H. Desai *(Mng Dir)*

Aarti Industries Ltd. - AARTI CRAMS Division (1)
71 Udyog Kshetra 2nd Floor Mulund Goregaon Link Road
Mulund West, Mumbai, Maharashtra, 400080, India
Tel.: (91) 22 6797 6666
Fax: (91) 22 6797 6660
Web Site: www.aarticrams.com
Pharmaceutical Research & Development Serviecs
S.I.C.: 8731
N.A.I.C.S.: 541712
Chandrakant V. Gogri *(Chm)*
Rajendra Gogri *(Vice Chm)*
Parimal Desai *(Mng Dir)*

Non U.S. Subsidiary:

Alchemie Europe Ltd. (1)
7-9 St Marys Place
Bury, Lancashire, BL9 0DZ, United Kingdom
Tel.: (44) 1617631624
Fax: (44) 1617631621
Web Site: www.aartigroup.com
Dyes Mfr & Distr
S.I.C.: 2819
N.A.I.C.S.: 325130

AARTSENFRUIT HOLDING B.V.

Heilaar-Noordweg
4814 RR Breda, Netherlands
Tel.: (31) 765248100
Fax: (31) 765221247
E-Mail: info@aartsenfruit.nl
Web Site: www.aartsenfruit.nl
Sales Range: $25-49.9 Million
Emp.: 100
Business Description:
Holding Company; Fruits & Vegetables Importer & Exporter
S.I.C.: 6719
N.A.I.C.S.: 551112
Personnel:
Jack Aartsen *(Gen Dir)*
Subsidiaries:

Aartsenfruit Breda B.V. (1)
Heilaar Nordweg 9
4814 RR Breda, Netherlands (100%)
Mailing Address:
Postbus 9555
4801 LN Breda, Netherlands
Tel.: (31) 765248100
Fax: (31) 765221247
E-Mail: info@aartsenfruit.nl
Emp.: 55
Fruits & Vegetables Importer & Exporter
S.I.C.: 5431
N.A.I.C.S.: 445230
Jack Aartsen *(Mng Dir)*

Aartsenfruit Venlo B.V. (1)
Venrayseweg 136 A
5928 RH Venlo, Netherlands (100%)
Tel.: (31) 773241241
Fax: (31) 773241251
E-Mail: Info@aartsenfruit.nl
Sls.: $43,617,600
Emp.: 25
Fruits & Vegetables Importer & Exporter
S.I.C.: 5431
N.A.I.C.S.: 445230

Non-U.S. Subsidiaries:

Aartsenfruit Asia Ltd. (1)
Unit 1015 F/10 Rise Commercial Building
5-11 Granville Circuit Tsim Sha Tsui, Hong Kong, China (Hong Kong)
Tel.: (852) 3480 9165
E-Mail: info@aartsenfruit-asia.com
Fruit & Vegetable Import & Export Services
S.I.C.: 5148
N.A.I.C.S.: 424480

Aartsenfruit N.V. (1)
Strijbroek 14
2860 Saint-Katelijne-Waver, Belgium
Tel.: (32) 15560860
Fax: (32) 15560861
E-Mail: fougro@artsenfruit.be
Web Site: www.artsenfruit.nl
Emp.: 20
Fruits & Vegetables Importer & Exporter
S.I.C.: 5431
N.A.I.C.S.: 445230
Jack Aarthen *(Mng Dir)*

AARVEE DENIMS & EXPORTS LTD.

188/2 Ranipur Village Opp CNI Church Narol
Ahmedabad, Gujarat, 382 405, India
Tel.: (91) 7930417000
Fax: (91) 7930417070
E-Mail: info@aarvee-denims.com
Web Site: www.aarvee-denims.com
514274—(BOM)
Rev.: $134,442,958
Assets: $139,032,962
Liabilities: $91,351,697
Net Worth: $47,681,265
Earnings: $8,346,263
Fiscal Year-end: 03/31/13
Business Description:
Fabrics & Garments Mfr
S.I.C.: 2389
N.A.I.C.S.: 315280
Personnel:
Vinod P. Arora *(Chm & Co-Mng Dir)*
K. K. Mohale *(CEO)*
Ashish V. Shah *(Co-Mng Dir)*
Amish Shah *(Sec)*
Board of Directors:
Vinod P. Arora
Paramanand T. Arora
Rajesh P. Arora
Amol R. Dalal
Ashok C. Gandhi
Tilak Raj Kapoor
Sanjay S. Majmudar
Arvind D. Sanghvi
Ashish V. Shah
Kalpesh V. Shah

Deloitte Haskins & Sells
Heritage 3rd Floor Near Gujarat Vidhyapith Off Ashram Road
Ahmedabad, India
Transfer Agent:
Sharepro Services (India) Pvt. Ltd.
416-420 4th Floor Devnandan Mall Opp. Sanyash Ashram Ellisbridge
Ahmedabad, India

AASTRA TECHNOLOGIES LTD.

(Acquired by Mitel Networks Corporation)

A'AYAN LEASING AND INVESTMENT COMPANY KSCC

Alrai muhammed Bin Quasim Street
Block 1223
PO Box 1426
Safat, Kuwait, 13015, Kuwait
Mailing Address:
PO Box 1426
Safat, Kuwait, 13015, Kuwait
Tel.: (965) 1804488
Fax: (965) 22240959
Web Site: www.aayan.com
Emp.: 200
Business Description:
Leasing & Investment Services
S.I.C.: 6211
N.A.I.C.S.: 523999
Personnel:
Fahad Ali Mohammad Al Ghanim *(Chm)*
Abdulaziz Nasser Al Marzook *(Deputy Chm)*
Mansour Hamad Al-Mubarak *(Mng Dir & CEO)*
Bassam A. Abbas Othman *(Deputy CEO-Fin & Support Svcs)*
Khalid Zain Al-Tawari *(Asst CEO-Treas & Corp Fin)*
Ahmad Rasheed Al-Ayoub *(Asst CEO-Real Estate)*
Faisal J. Al Omar *(Sr VP-HR & Admin Affairs)*
Board of Directors:
Fahad Ali Mohammad Al Ghanim
Salah Abdulaziz Al Khamees
Abdulaziz Nasser Al Marzook
Khaled Bader Al Romi
Mansour Hamad Al-Mubarak
Talal Mohammed Redha Behbahani
Nasser Ibrahim Borosli

Subsidiaries:

A'ayan Real Estate Company K.S.C.C. (1)
Qeblah Al Soor Street Al Soor Tower 21 F
PO Box 2973
Safat, Kuwait, 13030, Kuwait
Tel.: (965) 2221 2121
Fax: (965) 2221 2120
E-Mail: info@aayanre.com
Web Site: www.aayanre.com
AAYANRE—(KUW)
Rev.: $18,727,873
Assets: $400,099,660
Liabilities: $132,654,292
Net Worth: $267,445,368
Earnings: $13,203,416
Emp.: 20
Fiscal Year-end: 12/31/12
Real Estate Services
S.I.C.: 6531
N.A.I.C.S.: 531390
Mansour Hamad Al-Mubarak *(Chm)*
Ahmad Duaij Al-Duaij *(Deputy Chm)*
Ibrahim Adeeb Al Awadhi *(CEO)*

Mubarrad Transport Company K.S.C.C. (1)
PO Box 42132 Shuwaikh
Kuwait, 70652, Kuwait (53.54%)
Tel.: (965) 22269777
Fax: (965) 22269778
E-Mail: info@mubarrad.com.kw
Web Site: www.mubarrad.com.kw
MUBARRAD—(KUW)
Rev.: $1,835,580
Assets: $82,204,201
Liabilities: $23,554,243
Net Worth: $58,649,958
Earnings: ($32,671,900)
Fiscal Year-end: 12/31/12
Land Transportation Services
S.I.C.: 4789
N.A.I.C.S.: 488490
Abdullah Mohammad Al-Shatti *(Chm)*
Eissa Bader Al-Mutawaa *(Vice Chm)*
Saad Bander Al-Lafi *(CEO)*

AB BANK LIMITED

BCIC Bhaban 30-31 Dilkusha C/A
Dhaka, 1000, Bangladesh
Tel.: (880) 29560312
Fax: (880) 29555098
E-Mail: info@abbl.com
Web Site: www.abbank.com.bd
ABBANK—(DHA)
Int. Income: $204,239,850
Assets: $2,172,904,323
Liabilities: $1,972,320,206
Net Worth: $200,584,117
Earnings: $18,097,196
Fiscal Year-end: 12/31/12
Business Description:
Retail & Corporate Banking Services
S.I.C.: 6029
N.A.I.C.S.: 522110
Personnel:
M. Wahidul Haque *(Chm)*
Salim Ahmed *(Vice Chm)*
Fazlur Rahman *(Pres & Mng Dir)*
Ahsan Afzal *(Deputy Mng DIr)*
Shamim Ahmed Chaudhury *(Deputy Mng Dir)*
Moshiur Rahman Chowdhury *(Deputy Mng Dir)*
Badrul H. Khan *(Deputy Mng Dir)*
Mahadev Sarker Sumon *(Sec)*
Board of Directors:
M. Wahidul Haque
Feroz Ahmed
Salim Ahmed
M. A. Awal
Shishir Ranjan Bose
Afzal Hasan Uddin
Md Mesbahul Hoque
M. Imtiaz Hossain
Faheemul Huq
Runa Zakia Shahrood Khan
Fazlur Rahman
Bipad Bihary Saha Roy
Gholam Sarwar
Md. Anwar Jamil Siddiqui

Non-U.S. Subsidiary:

AB International Finance Ltd (1)
Unit 1201-B 12 F Admiralty Centre Tower
One 18 Harcourt Road
Hong Kong, China (Hong Kong)
Tel.: (852) 28668094
Fax: (852) 25277298
E-Mail: abifl@abbank.com.bd
Web Site: www.abbank.com.bd/global-presence.html
Financial Investment Advisory Services
S.I.C.: 6282
N.A.I.C.S.: 523930

AB-BIOTICS S.A.

(d/b/a AB Biotics)
Edifici Eureka P1M1.1 Campus UAB
Bellaterra, 08193 Barcelona, Spain
Tel.: (34) 902903844
Fax: (34) 972576449
E-Mail: info@ab-biotics.com
Web Site: www.ab-biotics.com
ABB—(MAD)
Emp.: 17

AB-Biotics S.A.—(Continued)

Business Description:
Pharmaceutical & Nutraceutica Mfr
S.I.C.: 2834
N.A.I.C.S.: 325412
Personnel:
Luis Sanchez-Lafuente *(Chm)*
Miquel Angel Bonachera *(Co-CEO & CFO)*
Sergi Audivert *(Co-CEO & COO)*

AB CERBO

Verkmastarevagen 1
PO Box 905
461 29 Trollhattan, Sweden
Tel.: (46) 520409900
Fax: (46) 520409902
E-Mail: nolatocerbo@nolato.se
Web Site: www.Nolato.se/nolatocerbo
Emp.: 236
Business Description:
Plastic Packaging Mfr
S.I.C.: 3089
N.A.I.C.S.: 326199
Personnel:
Klenn Svedberg *(Pres)*

AB DYNAMICS PLC

Holt Road
Bradford-on-Avon, Wilshire, BA15 1AJ, United Kingdom
Tel.: (44) 1225 860 200
Fax: (44) 1225 860 201
E-Mail: info@abd.uk.com
Web Site: www.abd.uk.com
Year Founded: 1982
ABDP—(AIM)
Business Description:
Automotive Testing Systems Mfr
S.I.C.: 3559
N.A.I.C.S.: 333249
Personnel:
Anthony Best *(Chm)*
Timothy John Rogers *(Mng Dir)*
Board of Directors:
Anthony Best
Graham Dudley Eves
Robert Andrew Leonard Hart
Timothy John Rogers
Frederick Bryan Smart

AB ELECTROLUX

St Goransgatan 143
SE 105 45 Stockholm, Sweden
Tel.: (46) 87386000
Fax: (46) 87387461
E-Mail: ir@electrolux.se
Web Site: www.electrolux.com
Year Founded: 1912
ELUX B—(EUR OMX OTC)
Sls.: $17,027,071,200
Assets: $11,788,329,600
Liabilities: $8,719,574,400
Net Worth: $3,068,755,200
Earnings: $402,325,200
Emp.: 59,478
Fiscal Year-end: 12/31/12
Business Description:
Household & Commercial Appliances, Outdoor Products & Industrial Products Mfr
S.I.C.: 3639
N.A.I.C.S.: 335228
Personnel:
Marcus Wallenberg *(Chm)*
Ronnie Leten *(Deputy Chm)*
Keith R. McLoughlin *(Pres & CEO)*
Tomas Eliasson *(CFO & Sr VP)*
Marykay Kopf *(CMO & Sr VP)*
Jan Brockmann *(CTO & Sr VP)*
Jack Truong *(Pres/CEO-Major Appliances-North America)*
Cecilia Vieweg *(Gen Counsel & Member-Exec Mgmt)*
Henrik Bergstrom *(Exec VP & Head-Small Appliances)*
Ruy Hirschheimer *(Exec VP & Head-Major Appliances-Latin America)*
Gunilla Nordstrom *(Exec VP & Head-Major Appliances-Asia Pacific)*
Jonas Samuelson *(Exec VP & Head-Major Appliances-EMEA)*
Alberto Zanata *(Exec VP & Head-Pro Products)*
Anders Edholm *(Sr VP-Corp Comm & Head-Grp Staff Comm)*
Lars Worsoe Petersen *(Sr VP & Head-HR & Organizational Dev)*
Peter Nyquist *(Sr VP-IR & Fin Info)*
Board of Directors:
Marcus Wallenberg
Gerd Almlof
Ola Bertilsson
Gunilla Brandt
Ulf Carlsson
Lorna Davis
Hasse Johansson
Ronnie Leten
Viveca Brinkenfeldt Lever
Keith R. McLoughlin
Bert Nordberg
Fredrik Persson
Bo Rothzen
Ulrika Saxon
Torben Ballegaard Sorensen
Barbara Rose Milan Thoralfsson

Subsidiaries:

AB Hoors Plat **(1)**
Ringsjovagen 9
S 243 22 Hoor, Sweden (100%)
Mailing Address:
PO Box 76
S 243 22 Hoor, Sweden
Tel.: (46) 41329600
Fax: (46) 41329600
E-Mail: mail@husqvarna.com
Web Site: www.husqvarna.com
Sales Range: $10-24.9 Million
Emp.: 150
Sheet Metal Mfr
S.I.C.: 3444
N.A.I.C.S.: 332322
Anders Julin *(Mgr-Mktg)*

Electrolux Filter AB **(1)**
Mossevagen 6
46011 Nyland, Sweden (100%)
Tel.: (46) 520470400
Telex: 422 00 PJOHANS
Fax: (46) 520470425
E-Mail: info@electrolux.se
Web Site: www.electrolux.se
Emp.: 120
Household & Commercial Appliances, Outdoor Products & Industrial Products Mfr
S.I.C.: 3639
N.A.I.C.S.: 335228
Henrik Sundstrom *(CEO)*

Electrolux Floor Care and Small Appliances AB **(1)**
Sankt Goransgatan 143
Stockholm, 112 17, Sweden
Tel.: (46) 87386000
Fax: (46) 87386653
Home Appliances Mfr
S.I.C.: 3999
N.A.I.C.S.: 335210

Electrolux HemProdukter AB **(1)**
Sankt Goransgatan 143
112 17 Stockholm, Sweden
Tel.: (46) 8 672 53 20
Fax: (46) 8 506 394 07
E-Mail: centralabygg.es@electrolux.se
Electronic Home Appliances Distr
S.I.C.: 5064
N.A.I.C.S.: 423620
Keith R. McLoughlin *(Gen Mgr)*

Electrolux Laundry Systems Sweden AB **(1)**
PO Box 325
341 26 Ljungby, Sweden (100%)
Tel.: (46) 37266500
Telex: 52116
Fax: (46) 37286433
E-Mail: els.info.ljunby@electrolux.se
Web Site: www.electrolux.se
Emp.: 540
Semi-Industrial Laundry Equipment Mfr
S.I.C.: 3589
N.A.I.C.S.: 333318
Bo-Lennart Jonasson *(Dir-Mktg-Global)*

Electrolux Professional AB **(1)**
Metallgatan 2-4
SE-441 32 Alingsas, Sweden (100%)
Tel.: (46) 32274000
Telex: 27939
Fax: (46) 32274220
E-Mail: mats.lundblad@electrolux.se
Web Site: www.electrolux-professional.com
Emp.: 195
Laundry & Foodservice Equipment & Supplies Mfr
S.I.C.: 5087
N.A.I.C.S.: 423850
Mats Goran Lundblad *(Mng Dir)*

Non-U.S. Subsidiary:

Electrolux Professional AG **(2)**
Bleichematt Strasse 31
CH 5001 Aarau, Switzerland (100%)
Tel.: (41) 628376161
Fax: (41) 628376233
E-Mail: info.professional@electrolux.ch
Web Site: www.electrolux-professional.com
Emp.: 200
Laundry & Foodservice Equipment & Supplies Mfr
S.I.C.: 5087
N.A.I.C.S.: 423850
Andre Frommer *(Mng Dir)*

Electroservice AB **(1)**
Saint Goransgatan 143
10545 Stockholm, Sweden (100%)
Tel.: (46) 87386000
Telex: 11 600 ELHEADS
Fax: (46) 87387335
E-Mail: electroluxservice@electrolux.se
Web Site: www.electrolux.se
Emp.: 1,500
Service Division
S.I.C.: 7629
N.A.I.C.S.: 811219
Keich McLoughlin *(CEO)*

U.S. Subsidiary:

Electrolux North America, Inc. **(1)**
10200 David Taylor Dr
Charlotte, NC 28262-8060 OH
Tel.: (980) 236-2000
Web Site: www.electroluxusa.com
Holding Company; Regional Managing Office
S.I.C.: 6719
N.A.I.C.S.: 551112
Kevin D. Scott *(Pres)*
Nolan Pike *(Sr VP & Gen Mgr-Cooking Bus)*
John B. Weinstock *(Sr VP-Mktg)*

Divisions:

Electrolux Home Care Products, Inc. **(2)**
10200 David Taylor Dr
Charlotte, NC 28262-8060 DE
Tel.: (980) 236-2000 (100%)
Toll Free: (800) 282-2886
Web Site: www.eureka.com
Emp.: 200
Floor Care Products, Upright & Canister Vacuum Cleaners & Lightweight Cleaners Mfr
Export
S.I.C.: 2842
N.A.I.C.S.: 325612
Russell S. Minick *(Pres & CEO)*
Cennert Steffen *(Exec VP-Opers)*

Unit:

Electrolux Central Vacuum Systems **(3)**
1700 W 2nd St
Webster City, IA 50595-0788
Tel.: (515) 832-4620
Fax: (515) 832-6659
E-Mail: info@beamvac.com
Web Site: www.beamvac.com
Emp.: 170
Control Vacuum Systems Mfr
S.I.C.: 3639
N.A.I.C.S.: 335210
Lars Hybel *(VP-Intl)*

Non-U.S. Subsidiaries:

Electrolux Home Care Products Canada **(3)**
5855 Terry Fox Way
Mississauga, ON, L5V 3E4, Canada(100%)
Tel.: (905) 813-7700
Fax: (905) 813-2784
Web Site: www.electroluxca.com
Emp.: 120
Household & Commercial Appliances, Outdoor Products & Industrial Products Mfr
S.I.C.: 3639
N.A.I.C.S.: 335228

Electrolux Home Products, Inc. **(2)**
2715 Washington Rd
Augusta, GA 30909 DE
Tel.: (706) 651-1751 (100%)
Fax: (706) 651-7769
Toll Free: (800) 896-9756
E-Mail: info@electroluxusa.com
Web Site: www.electroluxappliances.com
Emp.: 400
Indoor Home Appliances Mfr & Distr
S.I.C.: 3639
N.A.I.C.S.: 335228
Jack Truong *(Pres & CEO)*

Branch:

Electrolux Home Products, Inc. - Webster City **(3)**
400 Des Moines St
Webster City, IA 50595
Tel.: (515) 832-5334
Fax: (515) 832-6988
Web Site: www.electroluxappliances.com
Emp.: 2,000
Home Laundry Appliances Mfr
S.I.C.: 3633
N.A.I.C.S.: 335224

Plants:

Electrolux Home Products, Inc. - Anderson **(3)**
101 Masters Blvd
Anderson, SC 29626
Tel.: (864) 224-5264
Fax: (864) 231-1510
Web Site: www.electroluxappliances.com
Emp.: 2,000
Refrigerators Mfr
S.I.C.: 3632
N.A.I.C.S.: 335222

Electrolux Home Products, Inc. - Saint Cloud **(3)**
701 33rd Ave N
Saint Cloud, MN 56303
Tel.: (320) 253-1212
Fax: (320) 240-3491
E-Mail: info@electroluxusa.com
Web Site: www.electroluxusa.com
Emp.: 1,600
Household Freezers Mfr
S.I.C.: 3632
N.A.I.C.S.: 335222
Terry Anthony *(Mgr)*

Electrolux Professional, Inc. **(2)**
10200 David Taylor Dr
Charlotte, NC 28262-8060 DE
Tel.: (980) 236-2000
Fax: (704) 547-7401
Toll Free: (866) 449-4200
E-Mail: electroluxprofessional@electroluxusa.com
Web Site: professional.electroluxusa.com
Commercial Cooking, Refrigeration, Dishwashing & Laundry Equipment Mfr & Distr
S.I.C.: 3589
N.A.I.C.S.: 333318
Alberto Zanata *(Pres)*

Subsidiaries:

White Westinghouse Puerto Rico **(2)**
F St Lot 34
Guaynabo, PR 00968

Mailing Address:
PO Box 363287
San Juan, PR 00936-3287
Tel.: (787) 753-5100
Fax: (787) 706-5234
Web Site: www.electroluxusa.com
Emp.: 85
Electrical Household Appliances Whslr
S.I.C.: 5722
N.A.I.C.S.: 443141

Non-U.S. Subsidiaries:

AEG Hausgerate GmbH (1)
Muggenhofer Strasse 135
D-90429 Nuremberg, Germany (100%)
Tel.: (49) 9113230
Fax: (49) 9113231770
E-Mail: aeg-hausgeraete.kundenservice@electrolux.de
Web Site: www.aeg.electrolux.de
Emp.: 8,200
Household & Commercial Appliances, Outdoor Products & Industrial Products Mfr
S.I.C.: 3639
N.A.I.C.S.: 335228
Claus Wuhrl *(Mng Dir)*

Electrolux AG (1)
Badenerstrasse 587
8048 Zurich, Switzerland
Tel.: (41) 44 405 81 11
Fax: (41) 44 405 82 55
E-Mail: info@electrolux.ch
Web Site: www.electrolux.ch
Household Appliances Distr
S.I.C.: 5064
N.A.I.C.S.: 423620
Peter Barandun *(CEO)*

Electrolux Appliances S.p.A. (1)
Corso Lino Zanussi 30
Porcia, Pordenone, 33080, Italy
Tel.: (39) 04343941
Fax: (39) 0434507294
Home Appliances Distr
S.I.C.: 5064
N.A.I.C.S.: 423620

Electrolux Argentina S.A. (1)
Herrera 2424
1273 Buenos Aires, Argentina
Tel.: (54) 11 4303 1580
Fax: (54) 11 4303 1220
E-Mail: info@electrolux.com.ar
Web Site: www.electrolux.com.ar
Emp.: 140
Home Appliances Mfr
S.I.C.: 3639
N.A.I.C.S.: 335228
Claudio Malaver *(Gen Mgr)*

Electrolux A.S. (1)
35 Tarlabasi Bulvari
Istanbul, 34435, Turkey
Tel.: (90) 212 293 1020
Fax: (90) 212 292 1025
Household Appliances Distr
S.I.C.: 5064
N.A.I.C.S.: 423620

Electrolux Associated Company B.V. (1)
Vennootsweg 1-5
Alphen aan den Rijn, 2404 CG, Netherlands
Tel.: (31) 172468168
Fax: (31) 172468158
Home Appliances Distr
S.I.C.: 5064
N.A.I.C.S.: 423620

Electrolux Austria GmbH (1)
Herziggasse 9
Vienna, 1230, Austria (100%)
Tel.: (43) 1866400
Telex: 1125 25 ELUX VA
Fax: (43) 186640300
Web Site: www.electrolux.co.at
Sales Range: $150-199.9 Million
Emp.: 80
Household & Commercial Appliances, Outdoor Products & Industrial Products Mfr
S.I.C.: 3639
N.A.I.C.S.: 335228
Alfred Janovsky *(Gen Mgr)*

Electrolux Belgium N.V. (1)
Raketstraat 40
1130 Brussels, Belgium
Tel.: (32) 2 716 26 00
Fax: (32) 2 716 24 00
E-Mail: beluxmarketing@electrolux.be
Emp.: 300
Home Appliances Mfr
S.I.C.: 3631
N.A.I.C.S.: 335221
Barb Crols *(Gen Mgr)*

Electrolux Canada Corp. (1)
5855 Terry Fox Wa
Mississauga, ON, L5V 3E4, Canada
Tel.: (905) 813-7700
Fax: (905) 813-2784
Toll Free: (800) 282-2886
Web Site: www.electrolux.ca
Home Appliances Distr
S.I.C.: 5064
N.A.I.C.S.: 423620

Electrolux CEE G.m.b.H. (1)
Herziggasse 9
1230 Vienna, Austria
Tel.: (43) 186640284
Fax: (43) 186640290
Home Appliance Mfr
S.I.C.: 3999
N.A.I.C.S.: 335210

Electrolux Central and Eastern Europe Ges. m.b.H. Nfg. KG. (1)
Herziggasse 9
1230 Vienna, Austria
Tel.: (43) 1 866400
Household Appliances Distr
S.I.C.: 5078
N.A.I.C.S.: 423740

Electrolux Comercial Venezuela C.A (1)
Av Ppal de Las Mercedes Entre Calle Mucuchies y Monterrey
Las Mercedes, Caracas, 1060, Venezuela
Tel.: (58) 212 993 1511
Fax: (58) 212 993 3123
Emp.: 45
Home Appliances Distr
S.I.C.: 5064
N.A.I.C.S.: 423620

Electrolux de Colombia S.A. (1)
Cl 97a 9a-34 Piso 2 Chico
Bogota, Colombia
Tel.: (57) 16189000
Fax: (57) 16189027
Household Appliances Mfr
S.I.C.: 3639
N.A.I.C.S.: 335228

Electrolux del Paraguay S.A. (1)
Casilla Postal 1550 - 1993
Asuncion, Paraguay
Tel.: (595) 21 491 907
Fax: (595) 21 491 062
Home Appliances Distr
S.I.C.: 5064
N.A.I.C.S.: 423620

Electrolux del Peru S.A. (1)
Av El Polo 214 Monterrico Surco
Lima, Peru
Tel.: (51) 16172121
Fax: (51) 14359053
Web Site: www.electrolux.com.pe
Emp.: 200
Household & Commercial Appliances, Outdoor Products & Industrial Products Mfr
S.I.C.: 3639
N.A.I.C.S.: 335228
Humberto Cardenas *(Gen Mgr)*

Electrolux Deutschland GmbH (1)
Further Str 246
Nuremberg, 90429, Germany
Tel.: (49) 9113230
Fax: (49) 9113231770
E-Mail: info@electrolux.de
Emp.: 2,000
Household Vacuum Cleaner Mfr
S.I.C.: 3639
N.A.I.C.S.: 335210
Klaus Wuhrl *(Gen Mgr)*

Electrolux Do Brasil SA (1)
360 Rua Ministro Gabriel Passos
Guabirotuba
Curitiba, PR, CEP 81520 900, Brazil
Tel.: (55) 41 3371 7000
Telex: 1122280 ELFA BR
E-Mail:
Web Site: www.electrolux.com.br
Emp.: 5,000
Household & Commercial Appliances, Outdoor Products & Industrial Products Mfr
S.I.C.: 3639
N.A.I.C.S.: 335228

Electrolux d.o.o. (1)
Slavonska Avenija 3
10000 Zagreb, Croatia
Tel.: (385) 1 6323 353
Fax: (385) 1 6323 352
E-Mail: adriatic@electrlux.hr
Web Site: www.electrolux.hr
Emp.: 25
Household Appliances Distr
S.I.C.: 5064
N.A.I.C.S.: 423620
Eduard Slunjsky *(Gen Mgr)*

Electrolux Espana S.A. (1)
Calle Albacete 3
28027 Madrid, Spain (100%)
Tel.: (34) 915865500
Telex: 22616 ELUX E
Fax: (34) 915865602
Web Site: www.electrolux.com
Sales Range: $400-449.9 Million
Emp.: 2,553
Household & Commercial Appliances, Outdoor Products & Industrial Products Mfr
S.I.C.: 3639
N.A.I.C.S.: 335228

ELECTROLUX ESTONIA LTD (1)
Parnu mnt 153
11624 Tallinn, Estonia
Tel.: (372) 665 004
Fax: (372) 6650 039
Emp.: 15
Household Appliances Distr
S.I.C.: 5064
N.A.I.C.S.: 423620
Andres Kesker *(Gen Mgr)*

Electrolux (Far East) Ltd. (1)
Room 4312 Metroplaza Tower 1
223 Hing Fong Road
Kwai Chung, Kowloon, NT, China (Hong Kong) (100%)
Tel.: (852) 24108386
Fax: (852) 2481 0123
Web Site: www.electrolux.com.cn
Sales Range: $200-249.9 Million
Emp.: 2,910
Household & Commercial Appliances, Outdoor Products & Industrial Products Mfr
S.I.C.: 3639
N.A.I.C.S.: 335228
Ren Weiguang *(Gen Mgr)*

Electrolux France S.A. (1)
43 Ave Felix Louat
Senlis, 60300, France
Tel.: (33) 344622000
Telex: 150 080 SIEGE
Fax: (33) 344622499
Web Site: www.electrolux.fr
Sales Range: $800-899.9 Million
Emp.: 400
Household & Commercial Appliances, Outdoor Products & Industrial Products Mfr
S.I.C.: 3639
N.A.I.C.S.: 335228
Denoingille Guillaume *(Mng Dir)*

Electrolux (Hangzhou) Domestic Appliances Co. Ltd (1)
No 18 Ave Economic Development Zone
Hangzhou, 310018, China
Tel.: (86) 57128085529
Fax: (86) 57128085551
Emp.: 240
Home Appliance Mfr
S.I.C.: 5722
N.A.I.C.S.: 443141

Electrolux Hausgerate G.m.b.H. (1)
Herziggasse 9
1230 Vienna, Austria
Tel.: (43) 1 86640 0
Fax: (43) 1 86640 250
E-Mail: info@electrolux.de
Home Appliances Mfr
S.I.C.: 3639
N.A.I.C.S.: 335210

Electrolux Holding AG (1)
Badenerstrasse 587
8048 Zurich, Switzerland (100%)
Tel.: (41) 444058111
Fax: (41) 444058255
E-Mail: info@electrolux.ch
Web Site: www.electrolux.ch
Emp.: 170
Household & Commercial Appliances, Outdoor Products & Industrial Products Mfr
S.I.C.: 3639
N.A.I.C.S.: 335228
Peter Parandun *(Pres)*

Subsidiaries:

A&T Hausgerate AG (2)
Badenerstrasse 587
8048 Zurich, Switzerland (100%)
Tel.: (41) 44 405 8111
Telex: 868 321 TGS CH
Fax: (41) 44 405 8255
E-Mail: info@electrolux.ch
Web Site: www.electrolux.ch
Emp.: 40
Household & Commercial Appliances, Outdoor Products & Industrial Products Mfr
S.I.C.: 3639
N.A.I.C.S.: 335228

Electrolux Home Appliances Sdn Bhd (1)
7th Floor Tower 2 Jaya 33 No 3 Jalan Semangat Seksyen 13
46100 Petaling Jaya, Selangor, Malaysia
Tel.: (60) 3 7843 5999
Fax: (60) 3 7955 5511
Home Appliances Distr
S.I.C.: 5064
N.A.I.C.S.: 423620

Electrolux Home Products AS (1)
Okern Rislokkveien 2
Box 77
Okern, 508 Oslo, Norway
Tel.: (47) 815 30 222
Fax: (47) 23 63 55 52
Household Appliances Distr
S.I.C.: 5064
N.A.I.C.S.: 423620

Electrolux Home Products Corporation N.V. (1)
Raket Straat 40
1130 Brussels, Belgium (100%)
Tel.: (32) 27162600
Fax: (32) 27162601
E-Mail: ellen.claes@electrolux.be
Web Site: www.electrolux.com
Sls.: $162,764,608
Emp.: 300
Household & Commercial Appliances, Outdoor Products & Industrial Products Mfr
S.I.C.: 3639
N.A.I.C.S.: 335228
Edmerson Guimaraes *(Mng Dir)*

Electrolux Home Products Denmark A/S (1)
Strevelinsvej 38 - 40
7000 Fredericia, Denmark
Tel.: (45) 79 22 11 00
Fax: (45) 79 22 11 67
Web Site: www.electrolux.dk
Emp.: 150
Home Appliances Distr
S.I.C.: 5064
N.A.I.C.S.: 423620
Erik Moller *(Mng Dir)*

Electrolux Home Products Espana S.A. (1)
Calle Albacete 3
28027 Madrid, Spain
Tel.: (34) 90 214 41 45
Fax: (34) 91 586 56 02
E-Mail: postventa@electrolux.es
Web Site: www.electrolux.es
Emp.: 500
Home Appliance Mfr & Distr
S.I.C.: 3639
N.A.I.C.S.: 335228
Amador Lopez *(Gen Mgr)*

Electrolux Home Products (Nederland) B.V. (1)
Vennootsweg 1 2400AC
Postbus 120
2400 Alphen aan den Rijn, Netherlands
Tel.: (31) 0172468468
Fax: (31) 172468523
E-Mail: receptie.alphen-ann-den-rijn@electrolux.nl

AB Electrolux—(Continued)

Web Site: www.electrolux.nl
Sls.: $238,870,896
Emp.: 1,000
Household & Commercial Appliances, Outdoor Products & Industrial Products Mfr
S.I.C.: 3639
N.A.I.C.S.: 335228
Charlotte Hartmann *(Mgr-Mktg Comm)*

Electrolux Home Products Pty. Ltd. (1)
163 O'Riordan St
Mascot, NSW, 2020, Australia
Tel.: (61) 293179500
Fax: (61) 293179510
Web Site: www.electrolux.com.au
Sales Range: $600-649.9 Million
Emp.: 4,018
Household & Commercial Appliances, Outdoor Products & Industrial Products Mfr
S.I.C.: 3639
N.A.I.C.S.: 335228
Lars Erikson *(Head-Design Grp)*

Electrolux Ireland Ltd (1)
Long Mile Road
Dublin, Ireland
Tel.: (353) 8185430
Fax: (353) 1 4565 097
Household Appliance Distr
S.I.C.: 5064
N.A.I.C.S.: 423620

Electrolux Italia S.p.A. (1)
Corso Lino Zanussi 30
Porcia, Pordenone, 33080, Italy
Tel.: (39) 04343951
Fax: (39) 0434395890
Emp.: 2,000
Home Appliances Mfr
S.I.C.: 3639
N.A.I.C.S.: 335228
Manuela Soffientini *(Mng Dir)*

Electrolux Japan Ltd. (1)
Yasuda Shibaura Bldg 2 3-2-12 Kaigan
Minato-ku, Tokyo, 108-0022, Japan
Tel.: (81) 3 5445 3360
Fax: (81) 3 5445 3362
Emp.: 100
Household Electronic Appliances Distr
S.I.C.: 5064
N.A.I.C.S.: 423620
Gordon Thom *(Gen Mgr)*

Electrolux-Juno Kuchentechnik GmbH (1)
Further Strasse 246
D 90429 Nuremberg, Germany
Tel.: (49) 9113230
Fax: (49) 9113231770
Web Site: www.aeg.de
Emp.: 630
Household & Commercial Appliances, Outdoor Products & Industrial Products Mfr
S.I.C.: 3639
N.A.I.C.S.: 335228
Klaus Wuehrl *(Gen Mgr)*

Electrolux Laundry Systems Denmark A/S (1)
Hammerholmen 24-28
DK-2650 Hvidovre, Denmark (100%)
Tel.: (45) 63762000
Telex: 50548
Fax: (45) 63762209
E-Mail: els.salt@electrolux.com
Web Site: www.laundrysystems.electrolux.dk
Emp.: 20
Commercial Laundry Equipment Mfr
S.I.C.: 3589
N.A.I.C.S.: 333318
Kenneth Billumsen *(Mng Dir)*

Electrolux Lda. (1)
Edificio Goncalves Zarco Q35 Quinto da Fonte
Paco d'Arcos, 2774518, Portugal
Tel.: (351) 214403900
Fax: (351) 214403999
E-Mail: electrolux.info@electrolux.pt
Web Site: www.electrolux.pt
Sls.: $77,952,896
Emp.: 45
Household & Commercial Appliances, Outdoor Products & Industrial Products Mfr
S.I.C.: 3639
N.A.I.C.S.: 335228
Amador Lopez *(Mng Dir)*

Electrolux Lehel Hutogepgyar Kft (1)
Erzsebet Kiralyne Utja 87
1142 Budapest, Hungary
Tel.: (36) 1 467 3200
Fax: (36) 1 467 3204
Electrical Household Appliances Mfr
S.I.C.: 3639
N.A.I.C.S.: 335228
Zsolt Belenyesi *(Gen Mgr)*

Electrolux Ljubljana d.o.o. (1)
110 Gerbiceva Ulica
1000 Ljubljana, Slovenia
Tel.: (386) 1 24 25 733
Fax: (386) 1 24 25 735
Emp.: 14
Household Appliance Distr
S.I.C.: 5064
N.A.I.C.S.: 423620
Matjaz Brinc *(Gen Mgr)*

Electrolux (Malaysia) Holdings SDN. BHD. (1)
7th Floor Tower 2 Jaya 33 No 3 Jalan Semangat Seksyen 13
46100 Petaling Jaya, Selangor Darul Ehsan, Malaysia
Tel.: (60) 3 7843 5999
Fax: (60) 3 7955 5511
Web Site: group.electrolux.com
Investment Management Services
S.I.C.: 6211
N.A.I.C.S.: 523999

Electrolux (NZ) Limited (1)
3 Niall Burgess Rd
Mount Wellington, 1060 Auckland, New Zealand
Tel.: (64) 95732220
Telex: 30101 ELUXWEL
Fax: (64) 95732380
Web Site: www.electrolux.co.nz
Emp.: 30
Household & Commercial Appliances, Outdoor Products & Industrial Products Mfr
S.I.C.: 3639
N.A.I.C.S.: 335228
Malcolm Bain *(Mng Dir)*
John C. Brown *(Mng Dir)*

Electrolux Outdoor Products A/S (1)
Lundtoftegardsvej 93 A
DK-2800 Lyngby, Denmark (100%)
Tel.: (45) 45877577
Telex: 371 99 ATLUX
Fax: (45) 45933308
E-Mail: husqvarna@husqvarna.dk
Web Site: www.husqvarna.dk
Emp.: 36
Household & Commercial Appliances, Outdoor Products & Industrial Products Mfr
S.I.C.: 3699
N.A.I.C.S.: 335999
Vagn Petersen *(Mng Dir & Dir-HR)*

Electrolux Phillippines, Inc. (1)
25th Fl Equitable Bank Tower
8751 Paseo de Roxas, Makati, 1226, Philippines
Tel.: (63) 28452273
Fax: (63) 28454543
Web Site: www.electrolux.com.ph
Sales Range: $1-9.9 Million
Emp.: 35
Household & Commercial Appliances, Outdoor Products & Industrial Products Mfr
S.I.C.: 3639
N.A.I.C.S.: 335228

Electrolux Poland Spolka Z.o.o. (1)
Ul Kolejowa 5/7
01-217 Warsaw, Poland
Tel.: (48) 22 568 98 67
Fax: (48) 22 434 73 03
Home Appliances Mfr
S.I.C.: 3639
N.A.I.C.S.: 335228

Electrolux Professional AS (1)
Rislokkveien 2
Postboks 115
Okern, 580 Oslo, Norway
Tel.: (47) 81530222
Fax: (47) 22635413
Emp.: 4
Laundry Equipment Distr
S.I.C.: 5064
N.A.I.C.S.: 423620

Electrolux Professional BV (1)
Wisselwerking 52
PO Box 188
1110 BD Diemen, Netherlands
Tel.: (31) 205692911
Fax: (31) 205692239
Web Site: group.electrolux.com
Emp.: 30
Cooking Appliances Distr
S.I.C.: 5074
N.A.I.C.S.: 423720
Peter Toller *(Gen Mgr)*

Electrolux Professional GmbH (1)
Herziggasse 9
1230 Vienna, Austria
Tel.: (43) 1 86 348 0
Fax: (43) 1 86 348 300
E-Mail: efs.office@electrolux.co.at
Web Site: www.electrolux.com
Emp.: 3
Kitchen Appliance Mfr
S.I.C.: 3631
N.A.I.C.S.: 335221
Thomas Pfeiffer *(Gen Mgr)*

Electrolux Professional Ltd (1)
Ashted Lock Way Aston Science Park
B7 4AZ Birmingham, United Kingdom
Tel.: (44) 844 375 3400
Fax: (44) 844 375 3405
E-Mail: foodservice.sales@electrolux.co.uk
Web Site: www.electrolux-professional.co.uk
Household Cooking Appliances Mfr
S.I.C.: 3631
N.A.I.C.S.: 335221

Electrolux Professional S.p.A. (1)
Viale Treviso 15
33170 Pordenone, Italy
Tel.: (39) 0434 380 1
Fax: (39) 0434 380 201
E-Mail: foodservice@electrolux.com
Household Cooking Appliances Mfr
S.I.C.: 3631
N.A.I.C.S.: 335221

Electrolux Professionnel SAS (1)
43 Avenues Felix Louat
60300 Senlis, France
Tel.: (33) 3 44 62 20 00
Fax: (33) 3 44 62 26 59
Emp.: 40
Home Appliances Mfr
S.I.C.: 3639
N.A.I.C.S.: 335228
Andrea Rossi *(Gen Mgr)*

Electrolux Pty. Ltd. (1)
13 Gilbert Park Drive
Knoxfield, VIC, 3180, Australia (100%)
Tel.: (61) 387567300
Telex: 31376 ELUXME
Fax: (61) 387567399
E-Mail: info.aus@electrolux.com.au
Web Site: www.electrolux.com.au
Emp.: 50
Household & Commercial Appliances, Outdoor Products & Industrial Products Mfr
S.I.C.: 3639
N.A.I.C.S.: 335228
John Mahar *(Mng Dir)*

Electrolux plc (1)
Addington Way
Luton, Bedfordshire, LU4 9QQ, United Kingdom (100%)
Tel.: (44) 8445612612
Fax: (44) 8445618920
Web Site: www.electrolux.co.uk
Sales Range: $800-899.9 Million
Emp.: 2,134
Household & Commercial Appliances, Outdoor Products & Industrial Products Mfr
S.I.C.: 3639
N.A.I.C.S.: 335228

Subsidiary:

Electrolux Home Products UK (2)
Cornwall House
55 77 High Street, Slough, Berks, SL1 1DZ, United Kingdom
Tel.: (44) 8705 950 950
Fax: (44) 1753 538 972
Web Site: www.electrolux.co.uk
Emp.: 660
Household & Commercial Appliances, Outdoor Products & Industrial Products Mfr
S.I.C.: 3639
N.A.I.C.S.: 335228

Electrolux Romania SA (1)
Bd Aviatorilor Nr 41 Sector 1
Bucharest, Romania
Tel.: (40) 21 222 97 62
Fax: (40) 21 222 97 90
E-Mail: office@electrolux.ro
Web Site: www.electrolux.ro
Household Appliances Mfr
S.I.C.: 3639
N.A.I.C.S.: 335228
Bogdan Neagu *(Gen Mgr)*

Electrolux S.E.A. Private Ltd. (1)
11 Lorong 3 Toa Payoh Blk B #01-13/14/15 Jackson Square
Singapore, 319579, Singapore (100%)
Tel.: (65) 6507 8900
Telex: RS 24768 ELUXSIN RS
Fax: (65) 65 6356 8984
Web Site: www.electrolux.com.sg
Sales Range: $10-24.9 Million
Emp.: 74
Household & Commercial Appliances, Outdoor Products & Industrial Products Mfr
S.I.C.: 3639
N.A.I.C.S.: 335228
Christelle Querry *(Head-Pro Reg 7)*

Electrolux Slovakia s.r.o. o.z. (1)
Galvaniho 17/B
821 04 Bratislava, Slovakia
Tel.: (421) 2 3214 1334
Household Appliances Mfr
S.I.C.: 3639
N.A.I.C.S.: 335228

Electrolux Thailand Co. Ltd. (1)
1910 New Petchburi Rd
Bangkok, 10310, Thailand
Tel.: (66) 27259000
Fax: (66) 27259043
Web Site: www.electrolux.co.th
Sales Range: $25-49.9 Million
Emp.: 337
Household & Commercial Appliances, Outdoor Products & Industrial Products Mfr
S.I.C.: 3639
N.A.I.C.S.: 335228
Sugsi Manoonkijthamun *(Pres)*

Electrolux Ukraine LLC (1)
2a Avtozavodskaya Str
04074 Kiev, Ukraine
Tel.: (380) 44 586 20 60
Fax: (380) 44 586 20 59
Household Appliance Mfr
S.I.C.: 3639
N.A.I.C.S.: 335228

Electrolux Zanussi Italia SpA (1)
Corso Lino Zanussi 26
33080 Pordenone, Italy
Tel.: (39) 04343961
Fax: (39) 0434395890
E-Mail: info@electrolux.it
Web Site: www.electrolux.it
Emp.: 225
Holding Company; Household & Commercial Appliances, Outdoor Products & Industrial Products Mfr
S.I.C.: 6719
N.A.I.C.S.: 551112

Subsidiary:

Vecta Vending Solutions S.p.A. (2)
Via Roma 24
24030 Valbrembo, Bergamo, Italy (100%)
Tel.: (39) 035606111
Telex: 300676
Fax: (39) 035606460
Web Site: www.electrolux.com
Emp.: 600
Vending Machines Mfr
S.I.C.: 3589
N.A.I.C.S.: 333318

Oy Electrolux AB (1)
Pattalantuaa 6
FIN-01510 Vantaa, Finland (100%)
Tel.: (358) 9859530
Fax: (358) 943981202
E-Mail: kari.hayri@electrolux.fi
Web Site: www.electrolux.fi
Emp.: 75
Household & Commercial Appliances, Outdoor Products & Industrial Products Mfr

S.I.C.: 3639
N.A.I.C.S.: 335228
Kari Hayri *(Mng Dir)*

Divisions:

Electrolux Professional Oy (2)
Lautatarhankatu 8 B
580 Helsinki, Finland
Tel.: (358) 939611
Fax: (358) 939612410
Web Site: www.electroluxprofessional.fi
Sales Range: $200-249.9 Million
Emp.: 376
Household & Commercial Appliances, Outdoor Products & Industrial Products Mfr Export
S.I.C.: 3639
N.A.I.C.S.: 335228
Mats Lundblad *(CEO)*

OY Electrolux Kotitalouskoneet AB (1)
Pakkalankuja 6
Vantaa, 01511, Finland
Tel.: (358) 30 600 5120
Fax: (358) 98 595 3304
E-Mail: teena.sakari@electrolux.com
Emp.: 100
Household Appliance Distr
S.I.C.: 5064
N.A.I.C.S.: 423620
Kari Haeyri *(Mng Dir)*

AB FAGERHULT

(d/b/a Fagerhult Group)
Avagen 1B
566 80 Habo, Sweden
Tel.: (46) 3610 8500
Fax: (46) 3610 8780
E-Mail: headoffice@fagerhult.se
Web Site: www.fagerhultgroup.com
FAG—(OMX)
Sls.: $477,573,480
Assets: $406,102,320
Liabilities: $262,463,400
Net Worth: $143,638,920
Earnings: $24,628,680
Emp.: 2,192
Fiscal Year-end: 12/31/12

Business Description:
Holding Company; Residential, Commercial & Industrial Lighting Fixture Mfr & Distr
S.I.C.: 6719
N.A.I.C.S.: 551112

Personnel:
Jan Svensson *(Chm)*
Eric Douglas *(Deputy Chm)*
Johan Hjertonsson *(Pres & CEO)*
Hakan Gabrielsson *(CFO)*

Board of Directors:
Jan Svensson
Anna Malm Bernsten
Eric Douglas
Catherina Fored
Johan Hjertonsson
Lars-Ake Johansson
Bjorn Karlsson
Magnus Nell
Lars Olsson
Fredrik Palmstierna
Per Wikstrom

Subsidiary:

Fagerhults Belysning AB (1)
Avagen 1
566 80 Habo, Sweden SE
Tel.: (46) 3610 8500
Fax: (46) 3610 8699
Web Site: www.fagerhult.se
Residential, Commercial & Industrial Lighting Fixture Mfr & Distr
S.I.C.: 3645
N.A.I.C.S.: 335121
Johan Hjertonsson *(Pres & CEO)*
Hakan Gabrielsson *(CFO)*

Subsidiaries:

Fagerhult Retail AB (2)
Rinnavagen 12
517 33 Bollebygd, Sweden SE
Tel.: (46) 3323 6600
Fax: (46) 3328 5800
Web Site: www.fagerhult.se/retail
Commercial Lighting Fixture Mfr & Distr
S.I.C.: 3646
N.A.I.C.S.: 335122
Morgan Svensson *(Ops Mgr)*

Fagerhults Belysning Sverige AB (2)
Avagen 1
566 80 Habo, Sweden SE
Tel.: (46) 3610 8500
Fax: (46) 3610 8699
Web Site: www.fagerhult.se
Indoor & Outdoor Residential Light Fixture Mfr & Distr
S.I.C.: 3645
N.A.I.C.S.: 335121
Frank Augustsson *(Mng Dir)*

Non-U.S. Subsidiary:

I-Valo Oy (2)
Tehtaantie 3 B
14500 Iittala, Finland FI
Tel.: (358) 10 446 6600 (100%)
Fax: (358) 10 446 6500
E-Mail: info@i-valo.com
Web Site: www.i-valo.com
Sales Range: $10-24.9 Million
Emp.: 60
Industrial Lighting Equipment Mfr
S.I.C.: 3646
N.A.I.C.S.: 335122
Mika Nurminen *(Mng Dir)*

AB GEVEKO

Marieholmsgatan 38
Box 2137
403 13 Gothenburg, Sweden
Tel.: (46) 31172945
Fax: (46) 317118866
E-Mail: info@gevekoindustry.se
Web Site: www.gevekoindusty.com
GVKO—(OMX)
Sls.: $151,415,453
Assets: $91,202,123
Liabilities: $85,108,111
Net Worth: $6,094,012
Earnings: ($18,234,047)
Emp.: 531
Fiscal Year-end: 12/31/12

Business Description:
Investment Services Including Industrial Operations & Securities Management Services
S.I.C.: 3559
N.A.I.C.S.: 523999

Personnel:
Finn Johnsson *(Chm)*
Goran Eklund *(CEO & CFO)*

Board of Directors:
Finn Johnsson
David Bergendahl
Klas Dunberger
Asa Soderstrom Jerring
Eva Kaijser
Christer Simren
Stefan Tilk

Subsidiaries:

Cleanosol AB (1)
Industrigatan 33
PO Box 160
29122 Kristianstad, Sweden
Tel.: (46) 44203900
Fax: (46) 44203901
E-Mail: info@cleanosol.se
Web Site: www.cleanosol.com
Emp.: 150
Highway & Street Construction
S.I.C.: 1622
N.A.I.C.S.: 237310
Anders Nordstrom *(Mng Dir)*

Non-U.S. Subsidiaries:

Cleanosol AS (2)
Solgaard Skog 116
1599 Moss, Norway
Tel.: (47) 69240650
Fax: (47) 69240626
E-Mail: norway@cleanosol.no
Web Site: www.cleanosol.com
Emp.: 35
Support Activities for Nonmetallic Minerals
S.I.C.: 1481
N.A.I.C.S.: 213115

Cleanosol Oy (2)
Karhutie 1
1900 Nurmijarvi, Finland
Tel.: (358) 931580148
E-Mail: info@cleansol.com
Emp.: 5
Road Signal Marking Contract Services
S.I.C.: 1799
N.A.I.C.S.: 238990
Anders Nordstrom *(Gen Mgr)*

Cleanosol Polska Sp. z o.o. (2)
Al Zwyciestwa 250
81-540 Gdynia, Poland PL
Tel.: (48) 586649796
Fax: (48) 586649796
E-Mail: info@cleanosol.pl
Web Site: www.cleanosol.pl
Emp.: 150
Printing & Writing Paper Merchant Whslr
S.I.C.: 5111
N.A.I.C.S.: 424110
Dominak De Marek *(Mng Dir)*

Geveko Industri Holding AB (1)
Marieholmsgatan 36
Gothenburg, Vastra Gotaland, 415 02, Sweden
Tel.: (46) 31172945
Investment Management Services
S.I.C.: 6211
N.A.I.C.S.: 523999

Subsidiary:

Geveko Industri AB (2)
Marieholmsgatan 38
402 51 Gothenburg, Sweden
Tel.: (46) 31 84 46 10
Fax: (46) 31 25 43 09
Web Site: www.geveko-industri.com
Paint & Coating Mfr & Distr
S.I.C.: 2851
N.A.I.C.S.: 325510
Jimmy Olsson *(Mng Dir)*

Non-U.S. Subsidiary:

Geveko Intelligent Transport Systems AB (2)
Longelsevej 34
5900 Rudkobing, Denmark
Tel.: (45) 63 51 71 71
Fax: (45) 63 51 71 72
E-Mail: info@gevekoits.dk
Web Site: www.gevekoits.dk
Emp.: 2
Road Safety System Distr
S.I.C.: 5063
N.A.I.C.S.: 423610
Bruno Hansen *(Gen Mgr)*

Geveko Kapital AB (1)
Marieholmsgatan 36
PO Box 2137
40313 Gothenburg, Sweden
Tel.: (46) 31172945
Fax: (46) 317118866
E-Mail: info@geveko.se
Web Site: www.geveko.com
Fund Management Services
S.I.C.: 6282
N.A.I.C.S.: 523920
Hans Ljungkvist *(Mng Dir)*

Non-U.S. Subsidiaries:

Allglass Reprocessors (UK) Ltd (1)
49 Burnbrae Road Linwood Industrial Estate
Linwood, Renfrewshire, PA3 3BD, United Kingdom
Tel.: (44) 1505 325564
Fax: (44) 1505 325872
E-Mail: info@allglass.org.uk
Web Site: www.allglass.org.uk
Emp.: 22
Glass Bead Mfr
S.I.C.: 3231
N.A.I.C.S.: 327215
John Rainey *(Mng Dir)*
David Williams *(Mng Dir)*

Geveko OY (1)
Muddaisvagen 261
PB 96
21600 Pargas, Finland
Tel.: (358) 207498770
Fax: (358) 207498771
E-Mail: info@geveko.fi
Web Site: www.geveko.fi
Emp.: 30
Chemical & Allied Products Merchant Whslr
S.I.C.: 5169
N.A.I.C.S.: 424690
Anssi Sippinen *(Mng Dir)*

LKF Vejmarkering A/S (1)
Longelsevej 34
5900 Rudkobing, Denmark
Tel.: (45) 63517171
Fax: (45) 63517172
E-Mail: admin@lkf.dk
Web Site: www.lkf.dk
Emp.: 115
Highway Street & Bridge Construction
S.I.C.: 1611
N.A.I.C.S.: 237310
Nis Ravnskjaer *(Mng Dir)*

Non-U.S. Subsidiaries:

Beijing Links & Lines Trading Co. Ltd. (2)
Room 209 Block A Rongchen Building 61 Fuxing Rd
Haidian District, Beijing, 100036, China
Tel.: (86) 10 62538156
E-Mail: linlin@linkandlines.com
Web Site: www.linkandlines.com
Logistics Consulting Services
S.I.C.: 4731
N.A.I.C.S.: 541614

Geveko Italy Srl (2)
Viale Salcone 7
20123 Milan, Italy
Tel.: (39) 02 36554036
Fax: (39) 02 99981315
Road Safety & Traffic Signal Mfr
S.I.C.: 3669
N.A.I.C.S.: 334290
Corrado Michaelides *(Mgr-Area)*

LKF France SA (2)
46 Avenue des Freres Lumiere
78190 Trappes, France
Tel.: (33) 130 131 572
Fax: (33) 130 131 723
E-Mail: lkffrance@lkf.net
Traffic Road Signal Mfr
S.I.C.: 3669
N.A.I.C.S.: 334290

LKF Nederland B.V. (2)
DeWoerd 15
6662 Elst, Netherlands NL
Tel.: (31) 481351166
Fax: (31) 481351730
E-Mail: axel@kerstenmarkeer.nl
Web Site: www.kerstenmarkeer.nl
Emp.: 2
Miscellaneous Durable Goods Whslr
S.I.C.: 5099
N.A.I.C.S.: 423990

Preformed Markings Ltd. (2)
Unit 6 Oyster Park
109 Chertsey Road, West Byfleet, KT14 7AX, United Kingdom
Tel.: (44) 1932359270
Fax: (44) 1932340936
E-Mail: sales@preformedmarkings.co.uk
Web Site: www.preformedmarkings.co.uk
Emp.: 3
Stationery & Office Supplies Whslr
S.I.C.: 5112
N.A.I.C.S.: 424120

Magyar Plastiroute Kft (1)
Gat u 4-10
Szigetszentmiklos-Lakihegy, 2310
Szigetszentmiklos, Hungary
Tel.: (36) 24 475 275
Fax: (36) 24 475 276
E-Mail: info@magyarplastiroute.hu
Web Site: www.magyarplastiroute.hu
Emp.: 45
Highways Traffic Signal Installation Services & Mfr
S.I.C.: 1731
N.A.I.C.S.: 238210
Sandor Pal *(Mng Dir)*

Subsidiary:

Plastiroute Forgalomtechnikai Kft (2)
Kulso Radi Ut
2600 Vac, Hungary

AB Geveko—(Continued)

Tel.: (36) 27 304 894
Fax: (36) 27 310 431
E-Mail: plastiroute@plastiroute-vac.hu
Emp.: 18
Road Traffic Signal Mfr
S.I.C.: 3669
N.A.I.C.S.: 334290
Zsolt Hamza *(Gen Mgr)*

Plastiroute SA **(1)**
8 Rte des Avouillons
1196 Gland, Switzerland
Tel.: (41) 223544510
Fax: (41) 223544514
E-Mail: info@plastiroute.ch
Web Site: www.plastiroute.com
Paint & Coating Mfr
S.I.C.: 2851
N.A.I.C.S.: 325510
Nes Ravnskjaer *(Gen Mgr)*

Non-U.S. Subsidiary:

Plastiroute GmbH **(2)**
Renkenrunsstrasse 16
Postfach 1348
79371 Mullheim, Germany
Tel.: (49) 763136870
Fax: (49) 7631368736
E-Mail: info@plastiroute.de
Web Site: www.plastiroute.de
Emp.: 32
Highway & Street Construction
S.I.C.: 1622
N.A.I.C.S.: 237310
Nes Raunfkjaer *(Mng Dir)*

S.C. Plastidrum S.R.L. **(1)**
Sos Alexandriei No 156
51543 Bucharest, Romania
Tel.: (40) 214202480
Fax: (40) 214201207
E-Mail: office@plastidrum.ro
Web Site: www.plastidrum.ro
Highway & Street Construction
S.I.C.: 1611
N.A.I.C.S.: 237310

Superco s.r.o. **(1)**
Tuchomerice 41
25267 Prague, Czech Republic
Tel.: (420) 220950531
Fax: (420) 220951146
E-Mail: superco@superco.cz
Web Site: www.superco.cz
Emp.: 10
Chemical & Allied Products Merchant Whslr
S.I.C.: 5169
N.A.I.C.S.: 424690

AB INDUSTRIVARDEN

Storgatan 10
114 51 Stockholm, Sweden
Mailing Address:
PO Box 5403
114 84 Stockholm, Sweden
Tel.: (46) 86666400
Fax: (46) 86614628
E-Mail: info@industrivarden.se
Web Site: www.industrivarden.se
Year Founded: 1944
INDU A—(OMX)
Rev.: $1,794,286,800
Assets: $10,619,589,600
Liabilities: $3,121,542,000
Net Worth: $7,498,047,600
Earnings: $1,704,038,400
Emp.: 23
Fiscal Year-end: 12/31/12
Business Description:
Holding Company
S.I.C.: 6719
N.A.I.C.S.: 551112
Personnel:
Sverker Martin-Lof *(Chm)*
Anders Nyren *(Pres & CEO)*
Martin Hamner *(CFO)*
Par Ostberg *(Chief Investment Officer & Exec VP)*
Board of Directors:
Sverker Martin-Lof
Par Boman
Christian Caspar
Boel Flodgren
Stuart E. Graham
Fredrik Lundberg
Anders Nyren
Subsidiary:

Industrivarden Service AB **(1)**
Storgatan 10
114 84 Stockholm, Sweden
Tel.: (46) 86666400
Investment Management Services
S.I.C.: 6211
N.A.I.C.S.: 523999

AB INTER RAO LIETUVA

A Tumno g 4 B korp
LT-01109 Vilnius, Lithuania
Tel.: (370) 5 242 11 21
E-Mail: info@interrao.lt
Web Site: www.interrao.lt
IRL—(WAR)
Business Description:
Electric Power Distr
S.I.C.: 4939
N.A.I.C.S.: 221122
Personnel:
Giedrius Balciunas *(CEO & Dir Gen)*
Supervisory Board of Directors:
Alexander Abramkov
Anton Badenkov
Jonas Garbaravicius
Michail Konstantinov
Alexander Pakhomov

AB LIETUVOS DUJOS

Aguonu g 24
03212 Vilnius, Lithuania
Tel.: (370) 5 236 0210
Fax: (370) 5 236 0200
E-Mail: ld@lietuvosdujos.lt
Web Site: www.dujos.lt
Year Founded: 1961
XLY—(DEU)
Rev.: $722,130,522
Assets: $1,125,242,163
Liabilities: $334,453,102
Net Worth: $790,789,061
Earnings: $28,631,166
Emp.: 1,700
Fiscal Year-end: 12/31/12
Business Description:
Natural Gas Transmission Services
S.I.C.: 4923
N.A.I.C.S.: 486210
Personnel:
Valery Golubev *(Chm)*
Achim Saul *(Deputy Chm)*
Giedre Glinskiene *(CFO & Deputy Gen Mgr)*
Board of Directors:
Valery Golubev
Uwe Fip
Valdas Lastauskas
Achim Saul
Kirill Seleznev

AB S.A.

ul Koscierzynska 32
51-416 Wroclaw, Poland
Tel.: (48) 71 32 40 600
Fax: (48) 71 32 40 529
E-Mail: cc@ab.pl
Web Site: www.ab.pl
ABEA—(WAR)
Rev.: $1,722,153,217
Assets: $370,216,928
Liabilities: $236,807,631
Net Worth: $133,409,297
Earnings: $13,214,173
Fiscal Year-end: 06/30/13
Business Description:
Consumer Electronics Distr
S.I.C.: 5045
N.A.I.C.S.: 423430
Personnel:
Andrzej Przybylo *(Chm-Exec Bd)*
Grzegorz Ochedzan *(CFO & Member-Exec Bd)*
Krzysztof Kucharski *(Member-Exec Bd & Dir-Corp & Legal Affairs)*
Zbigniew Madry *(Member-Exec Bd & Dir-Sls)*
Supervisory Board of Directors:
Katarzyna Jazdrzyk
Radoslaw Kielbasinski
Jacek Lapinski
Jan Lapinski
Iwona Przybylo
Subsidiary:

Alsen Sp. z o.o. **(1)**
Mikolowska 150
Katowice, Silesian, 40-592, Poland
Tel.: (48) 322055012
Fax: (48) 2045801
E-Mail: biuro@alsen.pl
Web Site: www.alsen.pl
Emp.: 20
Computer Peripheral Equipment Distr
S.I.C.: 5045
N.A.I.C.S.: 423430
Zdebel Jan Jozef *(Chm)*

Non-U.S. Subsidiary:

AT Computers Holding a.s. **(1)**
Tesinska 1970/56
Ostrava-Slezska, Ostrava, Czech Republic
Tel.: (420) 552300156
Fax: (420) 596241220
E-Mail: wanki@atcomputers.cz
Web Site: www.atcomputers.cz
Emp.: 150
Computer Peripheral Mfr & Distr
S.I.C.: 3577
N.A.I.C.S.: 334118
Martin Harazim *(Head-Pur)*

Subsidiaries:

AT Compus s.r.o. **(2)**
Uhlirska 3
71000 Ostrava, Czech Republic
Tel.: (420) 596253444
Fax: (420) 596253839
Web Site: www.atcompus.cz
Emp.: 20
Computer Peripheral Mfr
S.I.C.: 3575
N.A.I.C.S.: 334118
Ales Kilnar *(Dir-Sls)*

Comfor Stores a.s. **(2)**
Brno Bela Pazoutove 742 / 1
Brno, 62400, Czech Republic
Tel.: (420) 541420202
Fax: (420) 541420201
E-Mail: info@comfor.cz
Web Site: www.comfor.cz
Emp.: 60
Computer Peripheral Mfr
S.I.C.: 3572
N.A.I.C.S.: 334112
Stanislav Heza *(Chm)*

AB SCIENCE SA

3 Avenue George V
75008 Paris, France
Tel.: (33) 147200014
Fax: (33) 1 47 20 24 11
E-Mail: contact@ab-science.com
Web Site: www.ab-science.com
Year Founded: 2001
AB—(EUR)
Emp.: 50
Business Description:
Pharmaceutical Mfr
S.I.C.: 2834
N.A.I.C.S.: 325412
Personnel:
Alain Moussy *(CEO)*
Laurent Guy *(CFO)*

AB SVENSK EXPORTKREDIT

(d/b/a Swedish Export Credit Corporation)
Klarabergsviadukten 61-63
103 27 Stockholm, Sweden
Tel.: (46) 86138300
Fax: (46) 8203894
E-Mail: info@sek.se
Web Site: www.sek.se
Year Founded: 1962
Rev.: $636,486,984
Assets: $46,930,336,551
Liabilities: $44,635,471,524
Net Worth: $2,294,865,027
Earnings: $166,883,409
Emp.: 249
Fiscal Year-end: 12/31/13
Business Description:
Supplier of Long Term Financial Solutions
S.I.C.: 6159
N.A.I.C.S.: 522298
Personnel:
Lars Linder-Aronsson *(Chm)*
Peter Yngwe *(Pres & CEO)*
Per Akerlind *(COO)*
Per Jedefors *(Chief Risk Officer)*
Jane Lundgren Ericsson *(Pres-AB SEK Securities & Deputy COO)*
Board of Directors:
Lars Linder-Aronsson
Cecilia Ardstrom
Jan Belfrage
Lotta Mellstrom
Ulla Nilsson
Jan Roxendal
Ake Svensson
Eva Walder
Subsidiaries:

AB SEK Securities **(1)**
Klarabergsviaduktdn
PO Box 16368
111 53 Stockholm, Sweden
Tel.: (46) 86138300
Fax: (46) 8203894
E-Mail: info@sek.se
Web Site: www.sek.se
Emp.: 6
Securities Brokerage
S.I.C.: 6211
N.A.I.C.S.: 523120
Jane Lundgren Ericsson *(Pres)*

SEK Financial Advisors AB **(1)**
Vastra Tradgardsgatan 11
PO Box 16368
10327 Stockholm, Sweden
Tel.: (46) 86138313
Fax: (46) 8203894
E-Mail: info@sek.se
Emp.: 10
Other Management Consulting Services
S.I.C.: 8748
N.A.I.C.S.: 541618
Peter Livijn *(Mng Dir)*

AB TRACTION

Birger Jarlsgatan 33 3 tr
PO Box 3314
103 66 Stockholm, Sweden
Tel.: (46) 850628900
Fax: (46) 850628930
E-Mail: post@traction.se
Web Site: www.traction.se
Year Founded: 1974
TRAC B—(OMX)
Rev.: $101,595,240
Assets: $266,983,560
Liabilities: $21,563,640
Net Worth: $245,419,920
Earnings: $32,244,840
Emp.: 185
Fiscal Year-end: 12/31/12
Business Description:
Company Development Management Services
S.I.C.: 8742
N.A.I.C.S.: 541611
Personnel:
Bengt Stillstrom *(Chm)*

Petter Stillstrom *(Pres & CEO)*
Krister Magnusson *(CFO)*
Carl Ostring *(Gen Counsel)*
Board of Directors:
Bengt Stillstrom
Anders Eriksson
Jan Kjellman
Maria Linde
Petter Stillstrom
Par Sundberg
Subsidiaries:

Ankarsrum Assistent AB (1)
Bruksvagen 1
590 90 Ankarsrum, Sweden
Tel.: (46) 490 533 00
Fax: (46) 490 509 90
E-Mail: info@ankarsrum.com
Web Site: assistent.nu
Kitchen Appliances Mfr
S.I.C.: 3421
N.A.I.C.S.: 332215
Linus Palm *(Mgr-Export)*

Ankarsrum Industries AB (1)
Bruksvagen 1
S-590 90 Ankarsrum, Sweden
Tel.: (46) 49053300
Fax: (46) 49050990
E-Mail: info@ankarsrum.com
Web Site: www.ankarsrum.com
Emp.: 90
Holding Company; Medium-Sized Electrical, Universal & DC Motors Mfr, Developer & Marketer; Die Casting Services
S.I.C.: 3621
N.A.I.C.S.: 335312
Thomas Hakansson *(Pres & CEO)*
Hans Alsteryd *(Pres)*

Subsidiaries:

Ankarsrum Die Casting AB (2)
Bruksvagen 1
S-590 90 Ankarsrum, Sweden
Tel.: (46) 49053300
Fax: (46) 49050990
Web Site: www.ankarsrum.com
Die Casting Services
S.I.C.: 3544
N.A.I.C.S.: 333514
Anders Engsgtrom *(CEO)*

Ankarsrum Motors AB (2)
Bruksvagen 1
S-590 90 Ankarsrum, Sweden
Tel.: (46) 49053300
Fax: (46) 49050990
E-Mail: anders.egstrom@akarsrum.com
Web Site: www.ankarsrum.com
Emp.: 65
Motor Mfr, Developer & Marketer
S.I.C.: 3621
N.A.I.C.S.: 335312
Anders Engstrom *(Pres)*

Ankarsrum Universal Motors AB (2)
Bruksvagen 1
S-590 90 Ankarsrum, Sweden
Tel.: (46) 49053300
Fax: (46) 49050990
Web Site: www.ankarsrum.com
Emp.: 140
Motor Mfr, Developer & Marketer
S.I.C.: 3621
N.A.I.C.S.: 335312
Dan Augustini *(CEO)*

Gnosjoplast AB (1)
Spikgatan 1
Box 193
S-335 24 Gnosjo, Sweden
Tel.: (46) 370331550
Fax: (46) 37092222
E-Mail: info@gnosjoplast.se
Web Site: www.gnosjoplast.se
Plastic & Rubber Materials Processor
S.I.C.: 2821
N.A.I.C.S.: 325211
Roger Kullnan *(CEO)*

Nilorngruppen AB (1)
Alingsasvagen 6
PO Box 499
SE-503 13 Boras, Sweden SE
Tel.: (46) 337008888 (63%)
Fax: (46) 337008819
E-Mail: info@nilorn.com
Web Site: www.nilorn.com
Sales Range: $25-49.9 Million
Emp.: 260
Holding Company; Branded Labels, Packaging & Accessories Products & Services
S.I.C.: 6719
N.A.I.C.S.: 551112
Claes af Wetterstedt *(CEO & CMO)*
Krister Magnusson *(CFO)*

Subsidiary:

Nilorn AB (2)
Alingsasvagen 6
Box 499
SE-503 13 Boras, Sweden SE
Tel.: (46) 337008800 (100%)
Fax: (46) 337008819
E-Mail: info@nilorn.com
Web Site: www.nilorn.com
Emp.: 50
Lithographic, Flexographic & Textile Label Designer, Mfr & Distr
S.I.C.: 7389
N.A.I.C.S.: 561910
Claes af Wetterstedt *(Mng Dir)*

Non-U.S. Subsidiaries:

Nilorn Belgium NV (2)
Brusselsesteenweg 525
9090 Melle, Belgium BE
Tel.: (32) 53827777 (100%)
Fax: (32) 53827782
E-Mail: info@be.nilorn.com
Web Site: www.nilorn.com
Lithographic, Flexographic & Textile Label Products & Services
S.I.C.: 7389
N.A.I.C.S.: 561910
Marc Van Renne *(Mng Dir)*

Nilorn Dalle Caen S.A.R.L. (2)
1 Passage du Genie
F-75012 Paris, France FR
Tel.: (33) 153110010 (100%)
Fax: (33) 142261035
E-Mail: info@dalle.nilorn.com
Web Site: www.nilorn.com
Lithographic, Flexographic & Textile Label Products & Services
S.I.C.: 7389
N.A.I.C.S.: 561910

Nilorn Denmark A/S (2)
Nybovej 19
DK-7500 Holstebro, Denmark DK
Tel.: (45) 97420021 (100%)
Fax: (45) 97422888
E-Mail: info@dk.nilorn.com
Web Site: www.nilorn.dk
Lithographic, Flexographic & Textile Label Mfr & Distr
S.I.C.: 7389
N.A.I.C.S.: 561910
Alice Thomasen *(Mgr-Fin)*

Unit:

Nilorn Denmark - Forsaljning (3)
Tolderlundsvej 16
DK-5000 Odense, C, Denmark
Tel.: (45) 7023 1623
Fax: (45) 6613 4831
E-Mail: info@dk.nilorn.com
Web Site: www.nilorn.dk
Emp.: 20
Lithographic, Flexographic & Textile Label Whslr
S.I.C.: 5131
N.A.I.C.S.: 424310
Michael Seedorff *(Mng Dir)*

Nilorn East Asia Ltd. (2)
Unit 1701 17/F Westley Square
48 Hoi Yuen Road, Kwun Tong, Kowloon, China (Hong Kong) HK
Tel.: (852) 23712218 (100%)
Fax: (852) 23712629
E-Mail: info@hk.nilorn.com
Web Site: www.nilorn.com
Emp.: 70
Labeling Products Designer & Whslr
S.I.C.: 7389
N.A.I.C.S.: 561910
Andrew Hoppe *(Mng Dir)*

Nilorn Etiket Sa. Ve Tic. Ltd. Sti. (2)
Mimar Sinan Cad Unverdi Sok No 50 Kat 3
Gunesli, 34540 Istanbul, Turkey TR
Tel.: (90) 2126577676 (100%)
Fax: (90) 2126577510
E-Mail: info@tr.nilorn.com
Web Site: www.nilorn.com
Emp.: 15
Lithographic, Flexographic & Textile Label Products Distr
S.I.C.: 7389
N.A.I.C.S.: 561910
Bekir Gencoguz *(Mng Dir)*

Nilorn Germany GmbH (2)
Blucherstrasse 72-74
Postfach 110 120
D-58332 Schwelm, Germany De
Tel.: (49) 23364030 (100%)
Fax: (49) 233640320
E-Mail: info@de.nilorn.com
Web Site: www.nilorn.com
Emp.: 25
Lithographic, Flexographic & Textile Label Products & Services
S.I.C.: 7389
N.A.I.C.S.: 561910
Karl-Heinz Hamacher *(Mng Dir)*

Nilorn Portugal Lda. (2)
Rua D Afonso Henriques
Terronhas, PT-4585 640 Recarei, Portugal PT
Tel.: (351) 224119580 (100%)
Fax: (351) 224119599
E-Mail: info@pt.nilorn.com
Web Site: www.nilorn.com
Emp.: 50
Lithographic, Flexographic & Textile Label Products Mfr
S.I.C.: 7389
N.A.I.C.S.: 561910
Elizabeth Sampaio *(Gen Mgr)*

Nilorn UK Ltd. (2)
Acre Park Dalton Lane
Keighley, W Yorkshire, BD21 4JH, United Kingdom UK
Tel.: (44) 1535673500 (100%)
Fax: (44) 1535673519
E-Mail: info@uk.nilorn.com
Web Site: www.nilorn.co.uk
Emp.: 30
Lithographic, Flexographic & Textile Labeling Products Mfr & Distr
S.I.C.: 7389
N.A.I.C.S.: 561910
Karen Lord *(Dir-Fin)*

Non-U.S. Affiliate:

Calmon Abacus Textiles Pte. Ltd. (2)
A-370 Road No 27
Thane Wagle Industrial Area, Thane, Maharashtra, 400 604, India In
Tel.: (91) 225383881 (49%)
Fax: (91) 225823208
E-Mail: abtext@vsnl.net
Textile Labeling Products Designer & Mfr
S.I.C.: 2241
N.A.I.C.S.: 313220

Zitiz AB (1)
Sveavagen 63
Stockholm, 113 59, Sweden
Tel.: (46) 707218835
E-Mail: info@zitiz.com
Internet Publishing Services
S.I.C.: 2741
N.A.I.C.S.: 519130

AB UTENOS TRIKOTAZAS

J Basanaviciaus Str 122
28214 Utena, Lithuania
Tel.: (370) 38951445
Fax: (370) 38969358
E-Mail: n.vilunas@ut.lt
Web Site: www.utenostrikotazas.lt
Year Founded: 1967
Sales Range: $25-49.9 Million
Emp.: 800
Business Description:
Women's Hosiery Mfr
S.I.C.: 2269
N.A.I.C.S.: 313310
Personnel:
Gintautas Bareika *(Gen Mgr)*

AB VILNIAUS VINGIS

Savanoriu Av 176
03154 Vilnius, Lithuania
Tel.: (370) 52392500
Fax: (370) 52392555
E-Mail: info@vingis.lt
Web Site: www.vingis.lt
Year Founded: 1959
Sales Range: $25-49.9 Million
Emp.: 4
Business Description:
Electronic Components Mfr
S.I.C.: 3663
N.A.I.C.S.: 334220
Personnel:
Neringa MenAiuniene *(Mng Dir)*
Board of Directors:
Renaldas Baliutis
Vladislovas Cybas

AB VOLVO

(d/b/a Volvo Group)
Amazonvagen Torslanda
405 08 Gothenburg, Sweden
Tel.: (46) 31660000
Fax: (46) 31537296
E-Mail: groupinfo@volvo.com
Web Site: www.volvogroup.com
Year Founded: 1926
VOLVY—(OTC)
Sls.: $47,004,555,600
Assets: $52,437,261,600
Liabilities: $38,982,974,400
Net Worth: $13,454,287,200
Earnings: $1,742,738,400
Emp.: 98,717
Fiscal Year-end: 12/31/12
Business Description:
Holding Company; Trucks, Aircraft, Space Engines & Buses Mfr; Trading & Finance Services
Export
S.I.C.: 3711
N.A.I.C.S.: 336211
Personnel:
Carl-Henric Svanberg *(Chm)*
Olof Persson *(Pres & CEO)*
Jan Gurander *(CFO)*
Torbjorn Holmstrom *(CTO & Exec VP-Trucks Tech)*
Sofia Frandberg *(Gen Counsel & Exec VP-Corp Legal & Compliance)*
Mikael Bratt *(Exec VP-Trucks Ops)*
Magnus Carlander *(Exec VP-Corp Process & IT)*
Karin Falk *(Exec VP-Corp Strategy)*
Niklas Gustavsson *(Exec VP-Pub & Environmental Affairs)*
Hakan Karlsson *(Exec VP-Bus Areas)*
Peter Karlsten *(Exec VP-Trucks Sls & Mktg-EMEA)*
Kerstin Renard *(Exec VP-Corp HR)*
Joachim Rosenberg *(Exec VP-Trucks Sls & Mktg -APAC)*
Dennis R. Slagle *(Exec VP-Trucks Sls & Mktg-Americas)*
Marten Wikforss *(Exec VP-Corp Comm)*
Christer Johansson *(Sr VP-IR)*
Board of Directors:
Carl-Henric Svanberg
Matti Alahuhta
Lars Ask
Hanne de Mora
Jean-Baptiste Duzan
James W. Griffith
Hans Hansson
Peteris Lauberts
Kathryn V. Marinello
Anders Nyren
Olof Persson
Mikael Sallstrom
Berth Thulin
Subsidiaries:

AB Volvo Penta (1)
Gropegatan
40508 Gothenburg, Sweden (100%)

AB Volvo—(Continued)

Tel.: (46) 31668129
Fax: (46) 31545772
E-Mail: barbro.neiderj@volvo.com
Web Site: www.volvopenta.com
Emp.: 400
Supplier of Automobiles
S.I.C.: 5012
N.A.I.C.S.: 423110
Goran Gummeson *(Pres)*

Subsidiary:

Volvo Penta Norden AB (2)
Gropegardsgatan
SE 405 08 Gothenburg, Sweden (100%)
Tel.: (46) 31686400
Fax: (46) 4631664556
E-Mail: info@volvopenta.com
Web Site: www.volvopenta.com
Emp.: 3,000
S.I.C.: 7389
N.A.I.C.S.: 425120
Goran Gummeson *(Pres)*
Leif Johanson *(CEO)*

U.S. Subsidiary:

Volvo Penta of the Americas, Inc. (2)
1300 Volvo Penta Dr
Chesapeake, VA 23320 VA
Tel.: (757) 436-2800 (100%)
Fax: (757) 436-5150
Web Site: www.volvopenta.com
Emp.: 200
Distributor of Marine, Diesel & Industrial Engines
Import Export
S.I.C.: 5088
N.A.I.C.S.: 423860
Ron Huibers *(Pres)*

Non-U.S. Subsidiaries:

AB Volvo Penta Italia S.p.A. (2)
Via de Lavoratori 9
Buccinasco, 20090 Buccinasco, Italy (100%)
Tel.: (39) 02484301
Telex: 340650 penta i
Fax: (39) 0245716003
E-Mail: info.vpi@volvo.com
Web Site: www.volvopenta.it
Emp.: 25
Marine & Automotive Engines Mfr
S.I.C.: 3724
N.A.I.C.S.: 336412
Matteo Gasperetto *(Mng Dir)*

Volvo Cars S.L (2)
Paseo De La Castellana 130
28046 Madrid, Spain
Tel.: (34) 915666100
Fax: (34) 915666105
E-Mail: acceso@volvocars.com
Web Site: www.volvocars.com
Emp.: 70
S.I.C.: 3724
N.A.I.C.S.: 336412
German Lopez Madrid *(Pres)*

Volvo Penta Benelux B.V. (2)
Stationsweg 2
PO Box 48
4153 RD Beesd, 4153 ZG, Netherlands (100%)
Tel.: (31) 345688700
Fax: (31) 345688707
E-Mail: info.vpbnl@volvo.com
Web Site: www.volvopenta.com
Emp.: 25
Automobiles Mfr
S.I.C.: 5012
N.A.I.C.S.: 423110
Mariska van Selm *(Mgr)*

Volvo Penta Canada Ltd. (2)
7972 Enterprise St
Burnaby, BC, V5A 1V7, Canada (100%)
Tel.: (604) 872-7511
Fax: (604) 872-4606
E-Mail: support.ptcsales@volvo.com
Web Site: www.volvopenta.com
Emp.: 20
Distributors of Marine Engines
S.I.C.: 5088
N.A.I.C.S.: 423860
Fred Lachlan *(Mgr-Site)*

Volvo Penta Central Europe GmbH (2)
Amq Kanal 1
PO Box 9013
24151 Kiel, Germany (100%)
Tel.: (49) 43139940
Telex: 292764 pentad
Fax: (49) 4313994110
E-Mail: info@volvopenta.com
Web Site: www.volvopenta.com
Sls.: $62,904,648
Emp.: 25
S.I.C.: 3724
N.A.I.C.S.: 336412
Gunnar Fladvad *(Mng Dir)*

Volvo Penta do Brasil Ltda. (2)
Av das Americas 13443 Recreio dos Bandeirantes
22790-700 Rio de Janeiro, RJ, Brazil
Tel.: (55) 2124379544
Web Site: www.volvo.com
Aircraft Engine Parts
S.I.C.: 3724
N.A.I.C.S.: 336412

Volvo Penta France S.A. (2)
55 avenue des Champs Pierreux
92757 Nanterre, Cedex, France
Tel.: (33) 134290101
Fax: (33) 155176199
E-Mail: vpf@volvo.com
Web Site: www.volvopenta.fr
Emp.: 150
Truck & Automobile Sales
S.I.C.: 3711
N.A.I.C.S.: 336111

Volvo Penta UK Limited (2)
Imperial Park
Imperial Way, Watford, Herts, WD24 4AW, United Kingdom (100%)
Tel.: (44) 1923228544
Telex: 24768 VP UK G
Fax: (44) 1923691235
E-Mail: info@volvopenta.com
Web Site: www.volvopenta.com
Emp.: 35
Ship Building & Repairing
S.I.C.: 3731
N.A.I.C.S.: 336611

Volvo Peru S.A. (2)
Panamericana Sur km 23.88
Ate Vitarte, Lima, 3, Peru (100%)
Tel.: (51) 13171200
Telex: 25395 pervolvo pe
Fax: (51) 13171201
E-Mail: infoperu@volvo.com
Web Site: www.volvo.com.pe
Emp.: 150
Distributor of Automobiles
S.I.C.: 5012
N.A.I.C.S.: 423110
Segundo Aliaga *(CFO)*

AB Volvofinans (1)
Bohusg 15
PO Box 198
Gothenburg, 40123, Sweden (50%)
Tel.: (46) 31838800
Fax: (46) 31162826
E-Mail: info@volvofinans.se
Web Site: www.volvofinans.se
Sales Range: $200-249.9 Million
Emp.: 200
Mfr. of Aircraft Engines & Engine Parts
S.I.C.: 3724
N.A.I.C.S.: 336412
Connie Bergstrom *(Pres)*
Salvatore Mauro *(Pres)*
Bert Bjorn *(Mng Dir)*

Alviva AB (1)
Maskingatan 5 Van 4
Gothenburg, 417 64, Sweden
Tel.: (46) 3 17 44 98 00
Fax: (46) 3 17 44 99 01
E-Mail: info@alviva.se
Web Site: www.alviva.se
Health Care Services
S.I.C.: 8099
N.A.I.C.S.: 621999

EBP AB (1)
Agrasjovagen 3 5
PO Box 34
Olofstrom, 29340, Sweden (100%)
Tel.: (46) 454301700
Fax: (46) 45499630
E-Mail: mailbox@ebp.se
Web Site: www.ebp.se
Emp.: 190
S.I.C.: 3724
N.A.I.C.S.: 336412
Kenth Gustavsson *(Dir-Mfg)*

First Rent A Car AB (1)
Primusgatan 18
Stockholm, 11262, Sweden (70%)
Tel.: (46) 86573000
Fax: (46) 86573090
E-Mail: info@hertz.se
Web Site: www.hertz.se
Emp.: 50
S.I.C.: 3724
N.A.I.C.S.: 336412
Henrick Axling *(VP)*

Kommersiella Fordon Europa AB (1)
Arhk 5 Avd 5381
Gothenburg, 405 08, Sweden
Tel.: (46) 317095500
Automobile Mfr
S.I.C.: 3711
N.A.I.C.S.: 336111

Rossareds Fastighets AB (1)
Kalenderv 22
415 11 Gothenburg, Sweden
Tel.: (46) 31 46 99 11
Commercial Vehicle Mfr
S.I.C.: 3711
N.A.I.C.S.: 336111

Volvo Bus Corporation (1)
Dept 80000 VBA2
405 08 Gothenburg, Sweden (100%)
Tel.: (46) 31668000
Telex: 27000 volvos
Fax: (46) 31541372
Development, Design, Production & Marketing of Buses & Bus Chassis
S.I.C.: 3291
N.A.I.C.S.: 327910
Hakan Karlson *(Pres)*
Akash Passey *(Sr VP-Intl Bus Reg)*

Subsidiary:

Volvo-Saffle AB (2)
PO Box 59
661 22 Saffle, Sweden (100%)
Tel.: (46) 53346600
Fax: (46) 53346690
Web Site: www.volvo.se
Emp.: 350
S.I.C.: 3724
N.A.I.C.S.: 336412
Kjell Berg *(Dir-Plant)*

Non-U.S. Subsidiaries:

Nova Bus Corporation (2)
1000 Indus Blvd
Saint-Eustache, QC, J7R 5A5, Canada
Tel.: (450) 472-6410
Fax: (450) 974-3001
E-Mail: novabus.sales@volvo.com
Web Site: www.novabus.com
Emp.: 650
S.I.C.: 3724
N.A.I.C.S.: 336412
Nadine Bernard *(Dir-Mktg)*

Prevost Car, Inc. (2)
35 Gagnon Blvd
Sainte-Claire, QC, G0R 2V0, Canada (100%)
Tel.: (418) 883-3391
Fax: (418) 883-4157
Toll Free: (800) 463-8876
E-Mail: danye.roy@volvo.com
Web Site: www.prevostcar.com
Sales Range: $25-49.9 Million
Emp.: 1,000
Mfr. of Buses
S.I.C.: 3714
N.A.I.C.S.: 336340
Gaetan Bolduc *(Pres & CEO)*

U.S. Subsidiary:

Nova Bus Incorporated (3)
201 South Ave
South Plainfield, NJ 07080 DE
Tel.: (505) 347-2011
Fax: (505) 347-7504
Web Site: www.novabus.com
Sls.: $201,700,000
Emp.: 1,700
Mfr. of Buses
Import Export
S.I.C.: 3711
N.A.I.C.S.: 336112

Volvo Bus Poland Co. (2)
Medlana St 2
51 502 Wroclaw, Poland (100%)
Tel.: (48) 713021700
Fax: (48) 713021895
E-Mail: wroreception@volvo.com
Web Site: www.volvo.com
Emp.: 2,500
Bus Manufacturer
S.I.C.: 3724
N.A.I.C.S.: 336412
Bengt Lindstrom *(Gen Mgr)*

Volvo Busse Deutschland GmbH (2)
Lichtenbergerstrassen 26
74076 Heilbronn, Germany (100%)
Tel.: (49) 713115740
Fax: (49) 7131157489
E-Mail: info.vbg@volvo.com
Web Site: www.volvobusse.com
Sls.: $39,982,800
Emp.: 40
S.I.C.: 3724
N.A.I.C.S.: 336412
Karl Haynes *(Mng Dir)*
Ewa Gerc *(CFO)*

Volvo Cars Austria GmbH (2)
Am Concorde Park 1 A1
2320 Schwechat, Austria (100%)
Tel.: (43) 701280
Fax: (43) 701289990
E-Mail: caccc@volvocars.com
Web Site: www.volvocars.at
Emp.: 50
S.I.C.: 3724
N.A.I.C.S.: 336412

Volvo East Asia (Pte.) Ltd. (2)
33 Joon Koon Cir
Singapore, 629111, Singapore (100%)
Tel.: (65) 62213111
Fax: (65) 62221115
Web Site: www.volvo.com
Emp.: 110
S.I.C.: 3724
N.A.I.C.S.: 336412

Volvo Business Services AB (1)
Faestningsvaegen 1
405 08 Gothenburg, Sweden
Tel.: (46) 31660700
Fax: (46) 31666565
Web Site: www.volvogroup.com
Financial & Accounting Services
S.I.C.: 6211
N.A.I.C.S.: 523999

Volvo Bussar AB (1)
Fastningsvagen 1
Gothenburg, 405 08, Sweden
Tel.: (46) 31 66 80 00
Fax: (46) 33 25 72 25
E-Mail: info.buses@volvo.com
Commercial Vehicle Mfr
S.I.C.: 3711
N.A.I.C.S.: 336111

Volvo Financial Services AB (1)
Arch 5 N Arendals Skans 21
405 08 Gothenburg, Sweden (100%)
Tel.: (46) 31666500
Fax: (46) 31669588
Web Site: www.volvo.com
Emp.: 1,000
Financial Management Services
S.I.C.: 6211
N.A.I.C.S.: 523999

Subsidiaries:

VFS International AB (2)
Fastningsv 1
405 08 Gothenburg, Sweden
Tel.: (46) 31 66 43 69
Web Site: www.vfsco.com
Financial Management Services
S.I.C.: 6211
N.A.I.C.S.: 523999

VFS Nordic AB (2)
Arendals Skans 21
405 08 Gothenburg, Sweden

Tel.: (46) 31 666500
Fax: (46) 31 669588
Web Site: www.vfsco.com
Financial Management Services
S.I.C.: 6211
N.A.I.C.S.: 523999

Non-U.S. Subsidiaries:

VFS Canada Inc (2)
205 Industrial Parkway North Unit 5
Aurora, ON, L4G 4C4, Canada
Tel.: (905) 726-5500
Fax: (905) 726-5555
Web Site: www.vfsco.com
Financial Management Services
S.I.C.: 6211
N.A.I.C.S.: 523999
Suzanne MacPherson *(Mgr-HR)*

VFS Deutschland GmbH (2)
Hugenottenallee 175
63263 Neu-Isenburg, Germany
Tel.: (49) 610236693814
Fax: (49) 610236693100
Emp.: 70
Financial Management Services
S.I.C.: 6211
N.A.I.C.S.: 523999
Martin Liehr *(Mng Dir)*

VFS Financial Services Belgium NV (2)
Avenue Du Hunderenveld 10 Brussel-Hoofdstad
Brussels, 1082, Belgium
Tel.: (32) 24825521
Fax: (32) 24652955
Web Site: www.vfsco.com
Emp.: 18
Financial Management Services
S.I.C.: 6211
N.A.I.C.S.: 523999
Gavin Armitt *(Bus Dir-Svc)*

VFS Financial Services BV (2)
Stationsweg 2
Gelderland, Beesd, 4153 RD, Netherlands
Tel.: (31) 345688688
Fax: (31) 345 688 690
Web Site: www.vfsco.com
Financial Management Services
S.I.C.: 6211
N.A.I.C.S.: 523999

VFS Financial Services Spain EFC, SA (2)
Calle Procion Cr Coruna Km 11 500 1-3
Madrid, 28023, Spain
Tel.: (34) 913727800
Fax: (34) 913728203
Financial Management Services
S.I.C.: 6211
N.A.I.C.S.: 523999

VFS Financial Services (UK) Ltd (2)
Wedgnock Lane
Warwick, CV34 5YA, United Kingdom
Tel.: (44) 1926 401 203
Fax: (44) 1926 410 278
E-Mail: adm.vfs.uk@volvo.com
Web Site: www.vfsco.com
Emp.: 50
Automobile Financial Leasing Services
S.I.C.: 6153
N.A.I.C.S.: 522220

VFS Vostok (2)
Vladenie 19 Biznes-Tsentr K Ul Panfilova
Khimki, Russia
Tel.: (7) 4959161030
Financial Management Services
S.I.C.: 6211
N.A.I.C.S.: 523999

Volvo Finance (Suisse) SA Vaud (2)
Route De Divonne 50 A
Nyon, 1260, Switzerland
Tel.: (41) 227356830
Fax: (41) 227860116
Emp.: 16
Financial Management Services
S.I.C.: 6211
N.A.I.C.S.: 523999
Serge Hunziker *(Mgr-Ops)*

Volvo Group Finance Sweden (1)
Grutejardgatan
S 405 08 Gothenburg, Sweden (100%)
Tel.: (46) 31660000
Fax: (46) 31667810
Emp.: 2,000
S.I.C.: 3724
N.A.I.C.S.: 336412
Olof Persson *(CEO)*

Volvo Group Insurance Forsakrings AB (1)
Grutejardgatan
Gothenburg, Sweden
Tel.: (46) 3 166 0000
Fax: (46) 3 166 1375
Insurance Management Services
S.I.C.: 6411
N.A.I.C.S.: 524210

Volvo Group Real Estate AB (1)
Faestningsvaegen 16
405 08 Gothenburg, Sweden
Tel.: (46) 31 66 04 00
E-Mail: infovgre@volvo.com
Web Site: www.volvogroup.com
Real Estate Development Services
S.I.C.: 6531
N.A.I.C.S.: 531390
Johan Lindberg *(Mgr)*

Volvo Holding Sverige AB (1)
Arhk 5
Gothenburg, 405 08, Sweden
Tel.: (46) 31 660000
Fax: (46) 31 661114
Investment Management Services
S.I.C.: 6282
N.A.I.C.S.: 523920

Non-U.S. Subsidiary:

Banco Volvo (Brasil) SA (2)
Avenida Juscelino Kubitschek
Oliveira, 81170-300, Brazil
Tel.: (55) 41 3317 7711
Financial Management Services
S.I.C.: 6211
N.A.I.C.S.: 523999

Volvo Information Technology AB (1)
9000 VBA
405 08 Gothenburg, Sweden (100%)
Tel.: (46) 31660000
Fax: (46) 31661092
E-Mail: magnus.carlander@volvo.com
Web Site: www.volvoit.com
Emp.: 2,000
S.I.C.: 3724
N.A.I.C.S.: 336412
Olle Hogblom *(Pres)*

Volvo IT Eskilstuna (1)
Brunnsta Industriomrade
631 85 Eskilstuna, Sweden
Tel.: (46) 16 15 10 00
Fax: (46) 16 15 29 90
Information Technology Consulting Services
S.I.C.: 7373
N.A.I.C.S.: 541512

Volvo IT Umea (1)
Box 1416
901 24 Umea, Sweden
Tel.: (46) 90 70 70 00
Web Site: www.volvoit.com
Information Technology Consulting Services
S.I.C.: 7373
N.A.I.C.S.: 541512

Volvo Logistics AB (1)
Amazonvaegen
Gothenburg, Vaestra Goetaland, 418 78, Sweden
Tel.: (46) 31669300
Logistics Consulting Services
S.I.C.: 4731
N.A.I.C.S.: 541614

VOLVO PENTA SVERIGE (1)
Bjornhammarvagen 25
184 94 Akersberga, Sweden
Tel.: (46) 8 540 271 10
Fax: (46) 8 540 273 54
Web Site: www.volvopenta.com
Emp.: 10
Automotive Parts Mfr
S.I.C.: 3714
N.A.I.C.S.: 336390

Volvo Powertrain AB (1)
Herkulesgatan 72
Gothenburg, Vaestra Goetaland, 417 01, Sweden
Tel.: (46) 31660000
Fax: (46) 31665170
Automotive Engine & Gear Box Mfr
S.I.C.: 3714
N.A.I.C.S.: 336390

Volvo Technology Transfer AB (1)
Gotaverksgatan 2
Dept 3300 M2.7, SE 405 08 Gothenburg, Sweden (100%)
Tel.: (46) 31669165
Fax: (46) 31669169
Web Site: www.volvogroup.com
Emp.: 2,000
Automotive Research & Development Technologies
S.I.C.: 3711
N.A.I.C.S.: 336111
Johan M. Carlsson *(Pres & CEO)*
Charlotta Modig *(CFO)*

Volvo Treasury AB (1)
O4000 VGF
Gothenburg, 40508, Sweden (100%)
Tel.: (46) 31669500
Telex: 28285 fortoss
Fax: (46) 31158753
E-Mail: info@volvo.se
Web Site: www.volvo.se
Emp.: 45
Provider of Financial Services
S.I.C.: 6282
N.A.I.C.S.: 523930
Ulf Niklasson *(Gen Mgr)*

Volvo Truck Corporation (1)
Gropegardsgatan, 405 08 Gothenburg, Sweden (100%)
Tel.: (46) 31666000
Telex: 27000 volvos
Fax: (46) 31667810
E-Mail: info@volvo.com
Web Site: www.volvo.com
Development, Design, Production & Marketing of Trucks
S.I.C.: 3711
N.A.I.C.S.: 336211
Staffan Jufors *(Pres)*
Leis Hamssom *(Pres-European Div)*

Subsidiaries:

Volvo Lastvagnar Sverige AB (2)
Ravebergsvagen
Dept 20100 Bldg VLH8, 405 08 Gothenburg, Sweden (100%)
Tel.: (46) 31666000
Fax: (46) 31667810
Web Site: www.volvo.com
S.I.C.: 7389
N.A.I.C.S.: 425120
Lief Johanson *(Pres)*
Staffan Juforf *(Pres)*

Subsidiary:

Volvo Truck Center Sweden AB (3)
Knistavaegen 3
191 62 Sollentuna, Sweden
Tel.: (46) 86255500
Truck Mfr
S.I.C.: 3711
N.A.I.C.S.: 336120

Non-U.S. Division:

Volvo Group UK Ltd - Volvo Penta UK Division (3)
Imperial Park Imperial Way
Herts Watford, WD24 4AW, United Kingdom
Tel.: (44) 1923 228544
Fax: (44) 1923 691235
Engine Mfr
S.I.C.: 3519
N.A.I.C.S.: 333618

Non-U.S. Subsidiary:

Volvo Group UK Ltd (3)
Bury Road
Bury Saint Edmunds, Suffolk, IP29 4UQ, United Kingdom
Tel.: (44) 1284850418
Fax: (44) 1284850166
Emp.: 15
Truck Mfr
S.I.C.: 3711
N.A.I.C.S.: 336120
Michael Revans *(Gen Mgr)*

Volvo Parts Corporation (2)
Bldg ARH 12
405 08 Gothenburg, Sweden (100%)
Tel.: (46) 31660300
Fax: (46) 31661041
E-Mail: info@volvo.com
Web Site: www.volvo.com
Emp.: 350
Mfr. of Automobile Parts
S.I.C.: 3714
N.A.I.C.S.: 336340
Larsake Javert *(CEO)*
Kristina Rejare *(Sr VP)*

Volvo Truck Corporation Powertrain Division Engine (2)
Volvov 5
541 87 Skovde, Sweden (100%)
Tel.: (46) 500474000
Telex: 40750 VOLVO S
Fax: (46) 500475995
E-Mail: info@volvo.com
Web Site: www.volvo.com
Emp.: 3,000
Mfr. of Transmissions
S.I.C.: 3714
N.A.I.C.S.: 336350
Magnus Holm *(Gen Mgr)*

U.S. Subsidiaries:

Mack Trucks, Inc. (2)
7900 National Service Rd
Greensboro, NC 27409-9416 PA
Tel.: (610) 709-3011 (100%)
E-Mail: webmaster@macktrucks.com
Web Site: www.macktrucks.com
Emp.: 800
Heavy-Duty Truck Mfr
Import Export
S.I.C.: 3711
N.A.I.C.S.: 336120
Stephen Roy *(Pres-Sls & Mktg-North America)*
Tom Kelly *(Sr VP-Product Portfolio Mgmt)*

Subsidiaries:

Mack Leasing System (3)
2100 Mack Blvd
Allentown, PA 18103-5622 (100%)
Tel.: (610) 709-3011
Fax: (610) 709-2895
Web Site: www.macktrucks.com
Emp.: 1,000
Mfr. of Trucks & Truck Leasing Services
S.I.C.: 7513
N.A.I.C.S.: 532120

Mack Remanufacturing Center (3)
2800 Commerce Dr
Middletown, PA 17057-3204
Tel.: (717) 939-1338
Fax: (717) 939-8349
Web Site: www.macktrucks.com
Emp.: 160
S.I.C.: 3711
N.A.I.C.S.: 336111

Mack Trucks-Macungie Assembly (3)
7000 Alburtis Rd
Macungie, PA 18062-9632
Tel.: (610) 351-8800
Fax: (610) 966-8000
E-Mail: info@macktrucks.com
Web Site: www.macktrucks.com
Emp.: 1,000
Assembly of Heavy Duty Diesel Trucks
S.I.C.: 3711
N.A.I.C.S.: 336120
James Goodell *(VP & Gen Mgr)*

Non-U.S. Subsidiaries:

Mack Canada, Inc. (3)
2100 Derry Road W Ste 410
Mississauga, ON, L5N 0B3, Canada Ca
Tel.: (289) 998-0070 (100%)
Telex: 6 982 458
Fax: (289) 998-0065
E-Mail: info@macktrucks.com
Web Site: www.macktrucks.com
Sales Range: $350-399.9 Million
Emp.: 50
Heavy Duty Diesel Trucks
S.I.C.: 3711
N.A.I.C.S.: 336120
Lynn Grant *(Pres)*

Mack Trucks Australia Pty. Ltd. (3)
20 W Gate Street
PO Box 1047

AB Volvo—(Continued)

4074 Wacol, QLD, Australia AU
Tel.: (61) 737183333 (100%)
Fax: (61) 737183391
Web Site: www.macktrucks.com.au
Sls.: $117,988,000
Emp.: 300
Mfr. of Trucks & Bus Bodies
S.I.C.: 3711
N.A.I.C.S.: 336120
Tom Conlon *(CFO)*

Volvo Trucks North America, Inc. (2)
7900 National Service Rd
Greensboro, NC 27409 VA
Mailing Address: (100%)
PO Box 26115
Greensboro, NC 27402-6115
Tel.: (336) 393-2000
Telex: 6843027
Fax: (336) 393-2262
Web Site: www.volvotrucks.us.com
Emp.: 2,000
Mfr. & Distr of Trucks
Import Export
S.I.C.: 3711
N.A.I.C.S.: 336120
Lars Thoren *(CFO & Exec VP)*
Goran Nyberg *(Pres-Sls & Mktg)*

Non-U.S. Subsidiaries:

Renault Trucks S.A.S. (2)
99 Route de Lyon
69806 Saint Priest, Cedex, France
Tel.: (33) 472965111
Fax: (33) 472962388
E-Mail: info@renault-trucks.com
Web Site: www.renault-trucks.com
Emp.: 14,000
Truck Mfr
Import Export
S.I.C.: 3711
N.A.I.C.S.: 336120
Stefano Chmielewski *(CEO)*

Non-U.S. Subsidiaries:

Renault Trucks Italia Spa (3)
Via Sempione Sud 197
Pero, Milan, 20016, Italy
Tel.: (39) 02339771
Web Site: www.renault-trucks.it
Truck Mfr
S.I.C.: 3711
N.A.I.C.S.: 336120

Renault Trucks UK Ltd. (3)
Houghton Hall Business Park Porz Avenue
Dunstable, Beds, LU5 5FT, United Kingdom
Tel.: (44) 1582471122
Fax: (44) 1582479146
E-Mail: ukinfo@renault-trucks.com
Web Site: www.renault-trucks.co.uk
Emp.: 100
Truck Dealer & Customer Support Services
S.I.C.: 7389
N.A.I.C.S.: 561499
John Twitchen *(Mgr-Facility)*

UD Trucks Corporation (2)
1-1 Ageo
Saitama, 362 8523, Japan JP
Tel.: (81) 487812301
Fax: (81) 487813121
Web Site: www.udtrucks.co.jp
Sales Range: $1-4.9 Billion
Emp.: 2,858
Diesel Engines, Light-, Medium- & Heavy-Duty Diesel Trucks, Buses & Special-Purpose Vehicles Mfr
S.I.C.: 3714
N.A.I.C.S.: 336112
Par Ostberg *(Chm)*
Satoru Takeuchi *(Pres)*
Yusuke Sakaue *(Exec VP)*
Keishi Abe *(Sr VP)*
Tadamichi Harada *(Sr VP)*
Toshimitsu Kurihara *(Sr VP)*
Mikio Miyamura *(Sr VP)*
Claes Svedberg *(Sr VP)*

U.S. Affiliate:

UD Trucks North America, Inc. (3)
5930 W Campus Cir
Irving, TX 75063 (50%)
Mailing Address:
7900 National Service Rd
Greensboro, NC 27409-9416
Tel.: (972) 756-5500
Fax: (972) 550-1255
Web Site: www.udtrucksna.com
Sales Range: $50-74.9 Million
Emp.: 52
Diesel Truck Sales
S.I.C.: 5012
N.A.I.C.S.: 423110
Dayle Wetherell *(Pres)*

Volvo do Brasil Veiculos Ltda. (2)
Av Juscelino Kubitcheck de Oliveira 2600
81260 900 Curitiba, PR, Brazil (58%)
Tel.: (55) 4133178111
Telex: 415638 volvob br
Fax: (55) 413178601
E-Mail: adriana.martins@volvo.com
Web Site: www.volvo.com
Emp.: 8,000
Mfr & Exporter of Volvo Trucks & Busses
S.I.C.: 3724
N.A.I.C.S.: 336412
Roger Alm *(CEO)*

Volvo Europa Truck N.V. (2)
PO Box 10
BE 9041 Gent, Belgium (100%)
Tel.: (32) 092504211
Fax: (32) 92511994
Web Site: www.volvo.be
Emp.: 2,500
Truck Mfr & Distr
S.I.C.: 3711
N.A.I.C.S.: 336120
Jean Ohlsson *(Mng Dir & Gen Mgr-Mfg-Europe)*

Volvo India Private Ltd. (2)
Yelachahalli Tavarekere Post
Hosakote, Bengaluru, 562 122, India
Tel.: (91) 8066914000
Web Site: www.volvotrucks.com
Emp.: 600
Heavy Duty Truck & Automobile Mfr & Sales
S.I.C.: 3711
N.A.I.C.S.: 336120
Paul de Voijs *(Mng Dir-Volvo Car)*
Akash Passey *(Chm-Volvo Buses)*

Division:

Volvo India Ltd - Volvo Financial Services India Division (3)
65/2 Block A 5th Floor Parin Building
Bagmane Tech Park
CV Raman Nagar, 560093 Bengaluru, Karnataka, India
Tel.: (91) 80 66912106
Web Site: www.vfsco.com
Financial Management Services
S.I.C.: 6211
N.A.I.C.S.: 523999

Volvo Kuorma-ja Linja-autot Oy AB (2)
Dragganden 1E
01610 Vantaa, Finland (100%)
Tel.: (358) 950791
Fax: (358) 95079709
Emp.: 150
S.I.C.: 3724
N.A.I.C.S.: 336412

Volvo Lastvogne Danmark A/S (2)
Taastrupgrrisvej 32
PO Box 535
2630 Tastrup, Denmark (100%)
Tel.: (45) 44546770
Fax: (45) 44546779
E-Mail: taastrup.reception@volvo.com
Web Site: www.volvotrucks.com
Emp.: 100
S.I.C.: 3724
N.A.I.C.S.: 336412
Soren Wettergreen *(Mgr)*

Volvo Norge A/S (2)
Stroms Vien 314 Alnabru
PO Box 103
0614 Oslo, Norway
Tel.: (47) 23176600
Fax: (47) 22308527
E-Mail: volvotruckcentre@volvo.com
Web Site: www.volvo.com
Emp.: 150
S.I.C.: 3724
N.A.I.C.S.: 336412
Per Ahnr Johansson *(Mng Dir)*

Volvo Poland Sp. Z.o.o. (2)
Truck Branch
Aleja Katowicka 215, 05 831 Mlochow, Poland PL
Tel.: (48) 223834500 (100%)
Fax: (48) 22 383 45 01
Emp.: 100
Retailer of Trucks
S.I.C.: 5084
N.A.I.C.S.: 423830
Malgorzata Kulis *(Gen Mgr)*

Volvo Truck & Bus (Thailand) Co. Ltd. (2)
42 5 Moo 7 Bangna Trad Rd Km 26
Bantsao Tong
Samut Prakan, 10540, Thailand
Tel.: (66) 27071747
Fax: (66) 27071740
E-Mail: aunee.kitmun@volvo.com
Web Site: www.volvotrucks.volvo.co.th
Emp.: 225
S.I.C.: 3724
N.A.I.C.S.: 336412
Christophe Martin *(Mng Dir)*

Volvo Truck Australia Pty. Ltd. (2)
120 Hume Hwy
Chullora, NSW, 2190, Australia
Tel.: (61) 290368200
Fax: (61) 290368300
Web Site: www.volvotruckandbus.com
Emp.: 300
S.I.C.: 3724
N.A.I.C.S.: 336412
Arne Knaben *(VP)*

Volvo Truck Czech s.r.o. (2)
Obchodni 109
Cestlice, 251 01 Prague, Czech Republic (100%)
Tel.: (420) 272124111
Fax: (420) 272680033
E-Mail: info@volvotrucks.com
Web Site: www.volvotrucks.cz
Emp.: 100
S.I.C.: 3724
N.A.I.C.S.: 336412
John Muldoon *(CEO)*
Robert Grozdanovski *(Mng Dir)*

Volvo Truck en Bus Nederland B.V. (2)
Stationsweg 2
Postbus 95
4153 RD Beesd, Netherlands
Tel.: (31) 345688500
Fax: (31) 345688405
E-Mail: info.nl@volvo.com
Web Site: www.volvotrucks.nl
Emp.: 70
S.I.C.: 3724
N.A.I.C.S.: 336412
Wabe Van Solkema *(Controller)*

Volvo Truck Latvia Sia (2)
28A Granita St
1057 Riga, Latvia (100%)
Tel.: (371) 7813200
Fax: (371) 667813201
Web Site: www.volvotruck.lw
Emp.: 100
S.I.C.: 3724
N.A.I.C.S.: 336412
Gohan Kohlisr *(Pres)*

Volvo Truck Slovak, s.r.o. (2)
Dialnicna cesta 9
903 01 Senec, Slovakia (100%)
Tel.: (421) 232662424
Fax: (421) 232662467
E-Mail: andrea.ondrejikova@volvo.com
Truck Engine & Engine Parts Manufacturing
S.I.C.: 3714
N.A.I.C.S.: 336310
Andrea Ondrejikova *(Gen Mgr)*

Volvo Truck (2)
55 Ave Des Champs Pierreux
92757 Nanterre, France
Tel.: (33) 55175517
Fax: (33) 47251990
E-Mail: info@volvotrucks.fr
Web Site: www.volvotrucks.fr
Emp.: 100
S.I.C.: 3724
N.A.I.C.S.: 336412

Volvo Trucks Belgium N.V. (2)
Hunderenveld 10
1082 Brussels, Belgium (100%)
Tel.: (32) 24825111
Fax: (32) 24682130
E-Mail: reception.vob@volvo.com
Web Site: www.volvotrucks.com
Emp.: 60
S.I.C.: 3724
N.A.I.C.S.: 336412
Peter Himpe *(Mng Dir)*
Birger Asp *(CFO)*

Volvo Trucks Canada (2)
2100 Derry Rd W Ste 410
Mississauga, ON, L5N 0B3, Canada
Tel.: (289) 998-0020
Fax: (289) 998-0030
Web Site: www.volvo.com
Marketing, Sales & Distribution of Volvo Trucks
S.I.C.: 5599
N.A.I.C.S.: 441228
Carol Girard *(Mgr-Truck Mktg)*

Volvo Trucks de Mexico S.A. de C.V. (2)
Prolongacion Paseo De La Reforma 600 Fl 2 341
01210 Mexico, DF, Mexico (100%)
Tel.: (52) 5550816850
Fax: (52) 55709358
Web Site: www.volvotrucksmexico.com
Emp.: 70
S.I.C.: 3724
N.A.I.C.S.: 336412

Volvo Trucks (Deutschland) GmbH (2)
Oskar Messter Str 20
85737 Ismaning, Germany (100%)
Tel.: (49) 89800740
Telex: 4191556 vold
Fax: (49) 8980074350
Web Site: www.volvo.de
Emp.: 100
Mfr of Diesel Trucks
S.I.C.: 3711
N.A.I.C.S.: 336111
Goaeran Sinonsson *(Mng Dir)*
Tommy Kohle *(Sr VP-Corp Communications)*

Volvo Trucks Espana, S.A. (2)
Protion 113
28013 Madrid, Spain (100%)
Tel.: (34) 913727800
Fax: (34) 913728203
Web Site: www.volvospain.com
Emp.: 100
S.I.C.: 3724
N.A.I.C.S.: 336412
Stefan Decieisquer *(Mng Dir)*

Volvo Trucks (Schweiz) AG (2)
Lindenstrasse 6
8108 Dallikon, Switzerland (100%)
Tel.: (41) 448476100
Fax: (41) 448476101
Web Site: www.volvotrucks.ch
Emp.: 50
Truck Mfr
S.I.C.: 3711
N.A.I.C.S.: 336120

VPL Limited (2)
49C Jail Road
PO Box 1990
Lahore, 54000, Pakistan (100%)
Tel.: (92) 42111875875
Fax: (92) 4237599934
E-Mail: info.lhe@vpl.com.pk
Web Site: www.vpl.com.pk
Construction Equipment Marketing & After-Sales
S.I.C.: 3711
N.A.I.C.S.: 336120
Konoz Mohiuddin *(Mng Dir)*

VOLVO TRUCKS SWEDEN (1)
Affaersregion Norden ARH 4
405 08 Gothenburg, Sweden
Tel.: (46) 31 66 60 00
Fax: (46) 31 51 04 65
Web Site: www.volvotrucks.com
Heavy Duty Truck Mfr
S.I.C.: 3711
N.A.I.C.S.: 336120

U.S. Subsidiaries:

VFS US LLC (1)
7025 Albert Pick Rd Ste 105
Greensboro, NC 27402-6131

Tel.: (336) 931-4000
Fax: (336) 931-3773
Web Site: www.vfsco.com
Financial Management Services
S.I.C.: 6211
N.A.I.C.S.: 523999

VNA Holding Inc. (1)
7825 National Service Rd
Greensboro, NC 27409
Tel.: (336) 393-4890
Investment Management Services
S.I.C.: 6799
N.A.I.C.S.: 523920
Shumaker Donald *(Chief Tax Officer, Treas & VP)*

Volvo Financial Services (1)
7025 Albert Pick Rd Ste 105
Greensboro, NC 27409
Tel.: (336) 931-4000
Fax: (336) 931-4008
Web Site: www.us.vfsco.com
Sls.: $111,500,000
Emp.: 350
General & Industrial Loan Institutions
S.I.C.: 6159
N.A.I.C.S.: 522298
Tom Guse *(Pres)*
Leo Hawks *(CFO)*

Volvo Group North America Inc. (1)
570 Lexington Ave 20th Fl
New York, NY 10022-6885 (100%)
Tel.: (212) 418-7400
Fax: (212) 418-7435
E-Mail: info@volvo.com
Web Site: www.volvo.com
Emp.: 4
Mfr. of Trucks
S.I.C.: 8742
N.A.I.C.S.: 541611
Salvatore L. Mauro *(Pres)*
Dennis R. Slagle *(Exec VP-Trucks Sls & Mktg-Americas)*

Volvo Information Technology North America Inc. (1)
7821 National Service Rd
Greensboro, NC 27402-6115
Tel.: (336) 393-2000
Fax: (336) 393-3191
Web Site: www.volvoit.com
Information Technology Consulting Services
S.I.C.: 7373
N.A.I.C.S.: 541512
Helena Zackrisson *(Sr VP-Customer Rels & Sls)*

Volvo Information Technology Rockleigh (1)
6 Volvo Dr
Rockleigh, NJ 07647
Tel.: (201) 768-7300
Fax: (201) 767-4816
Information Technology Consulting Services
S.I.C.: 7373
N.A.I.C.S.: 541512

Volvo-Penta North America, Inc. (1)
7900 National Service Rd
Greensboro, NC 27409
Tel.: (336) 393-2000
Fax: (336) 393-2388
Automotive Parts Distr
S.I.C.: 3714
N.A.I.C.S.: 336390

Non-U.S. Division:

AB Volvo - Volvo de Mexico Autobuses Division (1)
Lago de Guadalupe 289 Fracc Ind
Cartagena, 54900 Tultitlan, Mexico
Tel.: (52) 55 50 90 37 00
E-Mail: servicioaclientes@volvo.com
Web Site: www.volvobuses.com
Truck Mfr
S.I.C.: 3711
N.A.I.C.S.: 336120

Non-U.S. Subsidiaries:

Al-Futtaim Auto & Machinery Company LLC (1)
Plot B-131 Al Ramoul - Rashidiya
PO Box 5502
Dubai, United Arab Emirates
Tel.: (971) 4 2135100
Fax: (971) 4 2135400
E-Mail: famco@alfuttaim.ae
Web Site: www.famcouae.com
Bus & Construction Equipment Distr
S.I.C.: 5012
N.A.I.C.S.: 423110
Paul Floyd *(Mng Dir)*

BRS Ltd (1)
Houghton Hall Business Park Porz Avenue
Dunstable, LU5 5FT, United Kingdom
Tel.: (44) 1582 479 666
Fax: (44) 1582 479 667
E-Mail: resource@brs.co.uk
Web Site: www.brs.co.uk
Automotive Truck Rental Services
S.I.C.: 7513
N.A.I.C.S.: 532120

DRD Co., Ltd (1)
1-1 Ageo City
Ageo, Saitama, 362-0046, Japan
Tel.: (81) 487264580
Web Site: www.ndrd.co.jp/english/index.html
Sales Range: $25-49.9 Million
Emp.: 520
Automobile Mfr
S.I.C.: 3711
N.A.I.C.S.: 336111
Yukihiro Kurosawa *(Pres)*

UD Trucks Japan Co (1)
1-1 Ageo
Saitama, Japan
Tel.: (81) 48 781 2301
Fax: (81) 48 726 7629
Web Site: www.ud-crossnet.co.jp
Commercial Truck Mfr
S.I.C.: 3711
N.A.I.C.S.: 336120

UD Trucks South Africa (Pty) Ltd. (1)
5 Piet Rautenbach Street
Rosslyn, 0200 Pretoria, South Africa
Tel.: (27) 12 564 9500
Fax: (27) 12 564 9532
E-Mail: info.support@udtrucks.co.za
Web Site: www.udtrucks.co.za
Emp.: 300
Truck Mfr
S.I.C.: 3711
N.A.I.C.S.: 336120
Frans Jacobs *(Gen Mgr)*

VFS Denmark AS (1)
Taastrupgardsvej 32
2630 Tastrup, Denmark
Tel.: (45) 44 54 66 26
Fax: (45) 44 54 66 29
Web Site: www.vfsco.com
Emp.: 9
Financial Management Services
S.I.C.: 6211
N.A.I.C.S.: 523999
Jacques Rossel *(Gen Mgr)*

VFS Financial Services (Austria) GmbH (1)
Volvostrasse 1
2512 Tribuswinkel, Austria
Tel.: (43) 5 7500
Fax: (43) 5 750010699
Financial Management Services
S.I.C.: 6211
N.A.I.C.S.: 523999

VFS Financial Services Czech Republic, s.r.o. (1)
Obchodni 109 Cestlice
251 01 Ricany, Czech Republic
Tel.: (420) 271 021 704
Fax: (420) 272 680 044
Web Site: www.vfsco.com
Emp.: 10
Financial Management Services
S.I.C.: 6211
N.A.I.C.S.: 523999
Michal Hlavaty *(Country Mgr)*

VFS Financial Services Slovakia, s.r.o. (1)
Dialnicna Cesta 9
903 01 Senec, Slovakia
Tel.: (421) 232 66 24 33
Fax: (421) 232 66 24 34
E-Mail: info.sk@vfsco.com
Web Site: www.vfsco.com
Emp.: 10
Financial Management Services
S.I.C.: 6211
N.A.I.C.S.: 523999
Martin Pisko *(Gen Mgr)*

VFS Finansal Kiralama A.S. (1)
Icerenkoy Mahallesi Engin Sokak No 9 Kadikoy
34752 Istanbul, Turkey
Tel.: (90) 216 655 75 00
Fax: (90) 216 469 29 70
Web Site: www.vfsco.com
Financial Management Services
S.I.C.: 6211
N.A.I.C.S.: 523999

VFS Finland AB (1)
Vetokuja 1 E
01610 Vantaa, Finland
Tel.: (358) 10 655 7500
Fax: (358) 10 655 7599
Web Site: www.vfsco.com
Financial Management Services
S.I.C.: 6211
N.A.I.C.S.: 523999

VFS France (1)
14 Rue Hoche - Kupka C
La Defense, 92039 Paris, France
Tel.: (33) 1 76 66 18 00
Fax: (33) 1 76 66 18 16
Web Site: www.vfsco.com
Financial Management Services
S.I.C.: 6211
N.A.I.C.S.: 523999

VFS Japan Co., Ltd. (1)
NBF Shibakoen Daimondori Bldg 3F 1-8-12 Shibakoen
Tokyo, 105-0011, Japan
Tel.: (81) 3 4330 0000
Fax: (81) 3 4330 7010
Web Site: www.vfsco.com
Financial Management Services
S.I.C.: 6211
N.A.I.C.S.: 523999
Brian Dumbill *(Co-Chm)*
Jun Takashima *(Co-Chm)*
Takashi Kurokawa *(Mng Dir)*

VFS Latvia SIA (1)
Granita Iela 28a
Stopini, Latvia 1057
Tel.: (371) 67813245
E-Mail: vfslatvia@vfsco.com
Financial Management Services
S.I.C.: 6211
N.A.I.C.S.: 523999

VFS LT, UAB (1)
Minsko Pl 9
02121 Vilnius, Lithuania
Tel.: (370) 5 210 5094
Fax: (370) 5 210 5095
Commercial Truck Mfr
S.I.C.: 3711
N.A.I.C.S.: 336120

VFS Penzugyi Szolgaltato Kft. (1)
Cinkotai Ut 34
1172 Budapest, Hungary
Tel.: (36) 1 254 0627
Fax: (36) 1 254 0628
E-Mail: info.2@vfsco.com
Web Site: www.vfsco.com
Emp.: 8
Financial Management Services
S.I.C.: 6211
N.A.I.C.S.: 523999
Radi Sandor *(Mng Dir)*

VFS Uslugi Finansowe Polska Sp. z o.o. (1)
Al Katowicka 215
05-831 Mlochow, Poland
Tel.: (48) 22 383 48 15
Fax: (48) 22 383 48 01
E-Mail: biuro@vfsco.com
Web Site: www.vfsco.com
Emp.: 50
Financial Management Services
S.I.C.: 6211
N.A.I.C.S.: 523999

VGFS Financial Services Estonia OU (1)
Kurekivi Tee 10 Lehmja Kuela
75306 Peetri, Harjumaa, Estonia
Tel.: (372) 671 8389
Fax: (372) 671 8370
Web Site: www.vfsco.com
Emp.: 2
Financial Management Services
S.I.C.: 6211
N.A.I.C.S.: 523999
Margus Saik *(Territory Mgr)*

Volvalb Sh.p.k (1)
Autostrada Durres - Tirane Km 4
Durres, Albania
Tel.: (355) 692044404
E-Mail: info@volvalb.com
Emp.: 7
Industrial Truck Mfr
S.I.C.: 3711
N.A.I.C.S.: 336120
Rubin Topi *(Gen Mgr)*

Volvo Automotive Finance (China) Ltd (1)
11F Tower C Office Park No 5 Jinghua Street South Chaoyang District
Beijing, 100020, China
Tel.: (86) 10 6598 2199
Fax: (86) 10 6591 1935
Web Site: www.vfsco.com
Financial Management Services
S.I.C.: 6211
N.A.I.C.S.: 523999

Volvo Bulgaria Ltd. (1)
630 Slivnitsa Blvd
1331 Sofia, Bulgaria
Tel.: (359) 28106700
Fax: (359) 32 2482 5449
Web Site: www.volvocars.com
Commercial Truck Mfr
S.I.C.: 3711
N.A.I.C.S.: 336120
Alexander Sanin *(Mng Dir)*

Volvo Bus Australia (1)
120 Hume Highway
Chullora, NSW, 2190, Australia
Tel.: (61) 2 8713 8266
E-Mail: info.buses.au@volvo.com
Web Site: www.volvobuses.com.au
Commercial Vehicle Mfr
S.I.C.: 3711
N.A.I.C.S.: 336111

Volvo Bus Hong Kong Limited (1)
Floor 36 Units 1-3 Aia Tower 183 Electric Road
North Point, China (Hong Kong)
Tel.: (852) 2827 1688
Fax: (852) 8802 815 5807
Web Site: www.volvobuses.com
Emp.: 13
Commercial Vehicle Mfr
S.I.C.: 3711
N.A.I.C.S.: 336111
Maisy Leung *(Accountant)*

Volvo Bus Nederland (1)
Stationsweg 2
4153 RD Beesd, Netherlands
Tel.: (31) 345 688 531
Fax: (31) 345 688 539
E-Mail: info@volvobus.nl
Web Site: www.volvobus.nl
Emp.: 10
Commercial Vehicle Whslr
S.I.C.: 5012
N.A.I.C.S.: 423110
Piet Tijsen *(Acct Mgr)*

Volvo Busser Danmark A/S (1)
Taastrupgardsvej 32
2630 Tastrup, Denmark
Tel.: (45) 44 54 66 00
Fax: (45) 420 272 680 033
Web Site: www.volvobuses.com
Emp.: 100
Commercial Vehicle Mfr
S.I.C.: 3711
N.A.I.C.S.: 336111

Volvo (China) Investment Co. Ltd (1)
22F Tower C Office Park No 5 Jinghua Street South Chaoyang District
Beijing, 100020, China
Tel.: (86) 10 6582 9199
Fax: (86) 10 6582 9299
Web Site: www.volvoit.com
Commercial Vehicle Mfr
S.I.C.: 3711
N.A.I.C.S.: 336111

AB Volvo—(Continued)

Subsidiary:

Shandong Lingong Construction Machinery (2)
Shuntai Square Office Building No 9
Room 902 Shunhua Road No 2000
Jinan High-Tech Industrial Pk, Jinan, China 250100
Tel.: (86) 531 66590966
Fax: (86) 531 66590959
E-Mail: export@sdlg.com.cn
Web Site: www.sdlg.cn/en
Construction Equipment Mfr
S.I.C.: 3531
N.A.I.C.S.: 333120

Volvo Construction Equipment Corporation (1)
Moorfield Road
Cambridge, CB22 4QX, United Kingdom (100%)
Tel.: (44) 1223836636
Fax: (44) 1223832357
Emp.: 95
Front End Loaders Mfr
S.I.C.: 3531
N.A.I.C.S.: 333120
Martin Weissburg *(Pres)*

U.S. Subsidiary:

Volvo Construction Equipment North America, Inc. (2)
1 Volvo Dr
Asheville, NC 28803-3447
Tel.: (828) 650-2000
Fax: (828) 650-2532
Web Site: www.volvo.com
Sales Range: $1-4.9 Billion
Emp.: 250
S.I.C.: 3724
N.A.I.C.S.: 336412
Goran Lindgren *(Pres & CEO)*
Patrick Shannon *(CFO & VP-Fin)*

Subsidiary:

ASC Construction Equipment USA, Inc. (3)
9115 Harris Corners Pkwy Ste 450
Charlotte, NC 28269
Tel.: (704) 494-8100
Fax: (704) 494-8196
Web Site: www.volvo.com
Sales Range: $250-299.9 Million
Emp.: 250
Construction Equipment Dealer
S.I.C.: 5571
N.A.I.C.S.: 441228
Brad Stimel *(Pres)*

Units:

Volvo Road Machinery (3)
312 Volva Way
Shippensburg, PA 17257-9209
Tel.: (717) 532-9181
Fax: (717) 530-3408
E-Mail: info@volvoroad.com
Web Site: www.road-development.irco.com
Emp.: 800
Sales of Vibratory Compactors, Paving Machines & Pavement Milling Machines
S.I.C.: 3531
N.A.I.C.S.: 333120
Pat Olmey *(Pres)*

Non-U.S. Subsidiaries:

ABG Allgemeine Baumaschinen-Gesellschaft mbH (2)
Kuhbruckenstrasse 18
31785 Hameln, Germany
Mailing Address:
PO Box 101303
31785 Hameln, Germany
Tel.: (49) 51512090
Telex: 92805 abgex d
Fax: (49) 5151209204
E-Mail: ir-abg_deutschland@eu.irco.com
Web Site: www.volvoce.com
Emp.: 500
Pneumatic, Hydraulic & General Machinery & Tools, Pumps, Compressors, Drilling Equipment, Locks, Bearings, Hoists, Winches & Off-Road Forklifts Mfr
Import Export
S.I.C.: 3569
N.A.I.C.S.: 333999
Udo Heukrodt *(Mng Dir)*

Volvo Articulated Haulers AB (2)
Carlslimellsveg
360 42 Braas, Sweden
Tel.: (46) 470779500
Fax: (46) 47431164
Emp.: 871
S.I.C.: 3724
N.A.I.C.S.: 336412

Volvo Construction Equipment Australia Pty. Ltd. (2)
65 Epping Road
North Ryde, NSW, 2113, Australia
Tel.: (61) 2 9903 9200
Web Site: www.volvocars.com.au
S.I.C.: 3724
N.A.I.C.S.: 336412

Volvo Construction Equipment Cabs AB (2)
Hyttjatam 2
694 82 Hallsberg, Sweden (100%)
Tel.: (46) 58283100
Fax: (46) 58283001
E-Mail: vce.international.online@volvo.com
Web Site: www.volvo.com.cn
Emp.: 800
S.I.C.: 3724
N.A.I.C.S.: 336412
Toregon Assarsson *(Mng Dir)*

Volvo Construction Equipment Components AB (2)
Bolingervagen
631 85 Eskilstuna, Sweden (100%)
Tel.: (46) 6151000
Fax: (46) 16152966
Web Site: www.volvo.com.cn/constructionequipment/europe/sk-sk/Applications/ContactUs/Europe.htm
Emp.: 1,000
S.I.C.: 3724
N.A.I.C.S.: 336412

Volvo Construction Equipment Customer Support AB (2)
Bolingervagen
SE 631 85 Eskilstuna, Sweden (100%)
Tel.: (46) 016151000
Fax: (46) 16152963
E-Mail: info@volvoce.com
Web Site: www.volvoce.com
Emp.: 2,000
S.I.C.: 3724
N.A.I.C.S.: 336412
Leif Johansson *(Pres & CEO)*

Volvo Construction Equipment East Asia (Pte.) Ltd. (2)
33 Joon Koon Cir
Singapore, 629111, Singapore (100%)
Tel.: (65) 62213111
Fax: (65) 62221115
Emp.: 120
Engine Manufacturing
S.I.C.: 3724
N.A.I.C.S.: 336412
Vincent Tan *(Pres-Sls-Asia Reg)*

Volvo Construction Equipment Europe AB (2)
Akermansv 5
PO Box 115
SE 241 22 Eslov, Sweden (100%)
Tel.: (46) 41367300
Telex: 32298
Fax: (46) 41367334
E-Mail: judith.lantz@volvo.com
Web Site: www.volvoconstruction.com
Emp.: 30
Mfr. of Excavators
Import Export
S.I.C.: 3531
N.A.I.C.S.: 333120
Anders Barreng *(Pres)*
Judith Lantz *(Sec)*

Volvo Construction Equipment Europe GmbH (2)
Max Planck Strasse 1
54329 Konz, Germany (100%)
Tel.: (49) 65018402
Fax: (49) 650184209
E-Mail: info.centeurope@volvo.com
Web Site: www.volvo.com
Emp.: 550
Heavy Construction Machinery
S.I.C.: 3531
N.A.I.C.S.: 333120
Carl Goeransson *(Pres)*

Volvo Construction Equipment Europe Holding GmbH (2)
Max Planck Str 1
54329 Konz, Germany (100%)
Tel.: (49) 65018401
Fax: (49) 650184209
Web Site: www.volvo.com
Emp.: 500
Aircraft Engine Parts Manufacturing
S.I.C.: 3724
N.A.I.C.S.: 336412
Matthias Keller *(Gen Mgr)*

Volvo Construction Equipment Europe SAS (2)
47 Ave George Poltzier
PO Box 117
78192 Trappes, Cedex, France (100%)
Tel.: (33) 130692828
Fax: (33) 130698339
Web Site: www.volvoce.com
Emp.: 100
S.I.C.: 3724
N.A.I.C.S.: 336412
Geanmarie Osgoit *(Gen Mgr)*

Volvo Construction Equipment International AB (2)
Bolingervagen
SE 631 85 Eskilstuna, Sweden (100%)
Tel.: (46) 16151000
Fax: (46) 16152990
Web Site: www.volvo.com
Emp.: 70
Construction Equipment Mfr & Sales
S.I.C.: 3711
N.A.I.C.S.: 336120

Volvo Construction Equipment Korea Ltd. (2)
Fl 5 Volvo Bldg 726 173 Hannam Dong
Yong San Ku, Seoul, 140-210, Korea (South) (100%)
Tel.: (82) 237809050
Fax: (82) 237809276
Web Site: www.volvo.com
Emp.: 80
S.I.C.: 3724
N.A.I.C.S.: 336412

Volvo Construction Equipment Ltd. (2)
Duxford
CB22 4QX Cambridge, United Kingdom (100%)
Tel.: (44) 1223836636
Fax: (44) 1223832357
Web Site: www.volvoce.co.uk
Emp.: 150
S.I.C.: 3724
N.A.I.C.S.: 336412
Val Ledden *(Mng Dir)*

Volvo Equipamentos de Construcao Ltda. (2)
Av Jucelino Kubicheck 2600
81260-900 Curitiba, PR, Brazil (100%)
Tel.: (55) 4133178111
Fax: (55) 4133178035
Emp.: 1,600
Mfr of Automotive Chassis
S.I.C.: 3724
N.A.I.C.S.: 336412
Tommy Svensson *(Pres)*

Volvo Maquinaria de Construccion Espana S.A. (2)
Parque Empresarial San Fernando Edificio Atenas Planta 2
28830 Madrid, Spain (100%)
Tel.: (34) 916559390
Fax: (34) 916777316
E-Mail: comeras@avaco.com
Web Site: www.avaco.com
Emp.: 30
S.I.C.: 3724
N.A.I.C.S.: 336412
Alessandro Martinez *(Pres)*

Volvo Wheel Loaders AB (2)
Hallsberg Verken
694 82 Hallsberg, Sweden (100%)
Tel.: (46) 16151000
Fax: (46) 58283200
Web Site: www.volvo.com
Emp.: 300
S.I.C.: 3724
N.A.I.C.S.: 336412
Lars Zilken *(Mgr-Production)*

Volvo Deutschland GmbH (1)
Ringstra 38-44
50981 Cologne, Germany (100%)
Tel.: (49) 22193930
Fax: (49) 2219393155
E-Mail: info@volvocars-services.de
Web Site: www.volvocars.com
Emp.: 300
S.I.C.: 3724
N.A.I.C.S.: 336412
Thomas Viehweg *(Mng Dir)*

Volvo do Brasil Veiculos Ltda. (1)
Caixa Postal 7981
CEP 81290-000 Curitiba, PR, Brazil (100%)
Tel.: (55) 41 3317 4255
Fax: (55) 413178601
Web Site: www.volvogroup.com
Emp.: 1,000
Automotive Mfr & Distr
S.I.C.: 3711
N.A.I.C.S.: 336111
Juarez Goss *(Mgr-Special Projects)*

VOLVO ESPANA, S.A.U. (1)
Calle Procion Edf Oficor 1-3 Ctra Coruna Km 11 5
Madrid, 28023, Spain
Tel.: (34) 913727800
Fax: (34) 913728203
E-Mail: volvov@volvocars.com
Web Site: www.volvocars.es
Commercial Vehicle Mfr
S.I.C.: 3711
N.A.I.C.S.: 336111

Volvo Finance Australia Pty Ltd. (1)
20 Westgate Street
Wacol, QLD, 4076, Australia
Tel.: (61) 737183500
Fax: (61) 737183391
E-Mail: enquiries@volvofinance.com.au
Web Site: volvofinance.com.au
Emp.: 15
Credit Information Services
S.I.C.: 6159
N.A.I.C.S.: 522298
Nicholas Harty *(Controller-Fin)*

Volvo Finance Peru S.A. (1)
Av Republica de Panama 3535 Piso 9 Ofic 901-902
Centro Empresarial San Isidro, Lima, 27, Peru
Tel.: (51) 1 222 1122
Fax: (51) 1 222 4500
Web Site: www.vfsco.com
Automobile Financial Leasing Services
S.I.C.: 6159
N.A.I.C.S.: 522220

Volvo Financial Services GmbH (1)
Hugenottenallee 175
63263 Neu-Isenburg, Germany
Tel.: (49) 6102 36693 0
Fax: (49) 6102 36693 100
E-Mail: reception.vfste@vfsco.com
Web Site: www.vfsco.com
Emp.: 50
Financial Management Services
S.I.C.: 6211
N.A.I.C.S.: 523999
Eike Jochen Koehler *(Territory Mgr)*

Volvo Finans Norge AS (1)
Stromsveien 314
Oslo, 1081, Norway
Tel.: (47) 23176600
Fax: (47) 23176780
Emp.: 11
Financial Management Services
S.I.C.: 6211
N.A.I.C.S.: 523999
Attila Sparre *(Territory Mgr)*

Volvo Group Australia Pty Ltd (1)
20 Westgate St
Wacol, QLD, 4076, Australia
Tel.: (61) 737183500
Fax: (61) 732113576
Web Site: www.volvotrucks.com
Automobile Distr
S.I.C.: 5012

N.A.I.C.S.: 423110

Volvo Group Automotive Ticaret, Ltd (1)
Icerenkoy Mah Engin Sok No 9 Volvo Is Merkezi
Istanbul, Turkey
Tel.: (90) 2166557500
Automobile Mfr
S.I.C.: 3711
N.A.I.C.S.: 336111

Volvo Group Canada Inc. (1)
2100 Derry Road West Suite 410
Mississauga, ON, L5N 0B3, Canada
Tel.: (289) 998-0020
Fax: (289) 998-0030
Web Site: www.volvotrucks.com
Truck Mfr
S.I.C.: 3711
N.A.I.C.S.: 336120

Volvo Group Mexico (1)
Prolongacion Paseo De La Reforma 600 2nd Floor
Santa Fe, 01210 Mexico, DF, Mexico (100%)
Tel.: (52) 5552593011
Fax: (52) 55709358
Web Site: www.volvotrucksmexico.com
Emp.: 37
S.I.C.: 3724
N.A.I.C.S.: 336412

Volvo Group Representation (1)
Rue Du Luxumbourg 3
BE 1000 Brussels, Belgium (100%)
Tel.: (32) 24825871
Fax: (32) 245136028
E-Mail: info.eu@volvo.com
Web Site: www.volvo.com
Emp.: 5
S.I.C.: 3724
N.A.I.C.S.: 336412
Fedrique Biston *(VP)*

Volvo Holding Danmark A/S (1)
Lyskar 3B
2730 Herlev, Denmark (100%)
Tel.: (45) 44546770
Fax: (45) 44546779
Web Site: www.volvopenta.dk
Emp.: 80
S.I.C.: 3724
N.A.I.C.S.: 336412

Volvo Holding France SA (1)
37 Avenue Georges Politzer
78190 Trappes, France
Tel.: (33) 1 30 69 28 28
Fax: (33) 1 30 69 83 39
Investment Management Services
S.I.C.: 6211
N.A.I.C.S.: 523999
Jean-Marie Osdoit *(Gen Mgr)*

Subsidiaries:

VFS Finance France s.a.s. (2)
Immeuble Kupka C Hauts De Seine 14
Puteaux, 92800, France
Tel.: (33) 176661800
Financial Management Services
S.I.C.: 6211
N.A.I.C.S.: 523999

VFS Location France s.a.s. (2)
Immeuble Kupka C Hauts De Seine
Puteaux, 92800, France
Tel.: (33) 176661800
Industrial Truck Rental Services
S.I.C.: 7513
N.A.I.C.S.: 532120

Volvo CE Europe s.a.s. (2)
37 Avenue Georges Politzer
78190 Trappes, France
Tel.: (33) 1 30 69 28 28
Fax: (33) 1 30 69 83 39
E-Mail: communication-France@volvo.com
Web Site: www.volvoce.com
Engineering Services
S.I.C.: 8711
N.A.I.C.S.: 541330

Volvo Compact Equipment s.a.s. (2)
Rue Pierre Pingon
01300 Belley, France
Tel.: (33) 4 79 81 15 09
Fax: (33) 4 79 81 63 48
Construction Equipment Mfr
S.I.C.: 3531
N.A.I.C.S.: 333120

Volvo Holding Mexico, S.A. De C.V. (1)
Calle Lago De Guadalupe No 289
Naucalpan, 54900, Mexico
Tel.: (52) 5550811700
Fax: (52) 5550891901
Emp.: 4
Investment Management Services
S.I.C.: 6211
N.A.I.C.S.: 523999
Luis Elena Hurato *(Gen Mgr)*

Volvo Hrvatska d.o.o. (1)
Karlovacka Cesta 94
Lucko', 10250 Zagreb, Croatia
Tel.: (385) 13867660
Fax: (385) 13867676
E-Mail: zagreb@volvo.com
Web Site: www.volvocars.com
Emp.: 30
Automotive Parts Mfr
S.I.C.: 3714
N.A.I.C.S.: 336390

Volvo Information Technology France (1)
402 Avenue Charles de Gaulle
69635 Venissieux, France
Tel.: (33) 4 72 96 81 11
Web Site: www.volvoit.com
Information Technology Consulting Services
S.I.C.: 7373
N.A.I.C.S.: 541512

Volvo Information Technology Malaysia (1)
Jalan Bicu 15/6
40000 Shah Alam, Malaysia
Tel.: (60) 3 5517 9000
Fax: (60) 3 5519 9091
Web Site: www.volvoit.com
Information Technology Consulting Services
S.I.C.: 7373
N.A.I.C.S.: 541512

Volvo Information Technology Mexico (1)
Lago de Guadalupe 289 Fracc Industrial Cartagena
54900 Tultitlan, Mexico
Tel.: (52) 55 50 90 37 00
Web Site: www.volvoit.com
Information Technology Consulting Services
S.I.C.: 7373
N.A.I.C.S.: 541512

Volvo Information Technology Poland (1)
Ul Mydlana 2
51 502 Wroclaw, Poland
Tel.: (48) 71 302 1700
Fax: (48) 71 302 1995
Information Technology Consulting Services
S.I.C.: 7373
N.A.I.C.S.: 541512

Volvo Information Technology (Tianjin) Co., Ltd (1)
22F Tower C Office Park No 5 Jinghua Street South
Chaoyang District, Beijing, 100020, China
Tel.: (86) 10 6582 9199
Fax: (86) 10 6582 9299
Information Technology Consulting Services
S.I.C.: 7373
N.A.I.C.S.: 541512

Volvo International Holding BV (1)
Stationsweg 2
PO Box 95
4153 RD Beesd, Netherlands (100%)
Tel.: (31) 345688500
Fax: (31) 345688429
E-Mail: info@volvotruck.nl
Web Site: www.volvotruck.nl
Emp.: 100
S.I.C.: 3724
N.A.I.C.S.: 336412
Wabe Van Solkema *(Mng Dir)*

Volvo IT Belgium (1)
Smalleheerweg 29
9041 Gent, Belgium
Tel.: (32) 9 255 60 00
Web Site: www.volvoit.com
Information Technology Consulting Services
S.I.C.: 7373
N.A.I.C.S.: 541512

Volvo IT Canada (1)
35 Boulevard Gagnon
Sainte-Claire, QC, Canada G0R 2V0
Tel.: (418) 883-2888
Fax: (418) 883-2388
Web Site: www.volvoit.com
Information Technology Consulting Services
S.I.C.: 7373
N.A.I.C.S.: 541512

Volvo IT Koping (1)
Eksaardserrjweg 188
9041 Gent, Belgium
Tel.: (32) 9 255 60 00
Information Technology Consulting Services
S.I.C.: 7373
N.A.I.C.S.: 541512

Volvo IT Korea (1)
726-173 Hannam-dong
Yongsan-ku, 140-210 Seoul, Korea (South)
Tel.: (82) 2 37809235
Information Technology Consulting Services
S.I.C.: 7373
N.A.I.C.S.: 541512

Volvo IT South Africa (1)
Cnr Jetpark Road & Saligna Street
Witfield, Gauteng, 1400, South Africa
Tel.: (27) 11 842 5052
Web Site: www.volvoit.com
Information Technology Consulting Services
S.I.C.: 7373
N.A.I.C.S.: 541512

Volvo IT Thailand (1)
42/5 Moo 7 Bang-na Trad Highway Km 26
T Bangsaothong Khing
Bangsaothong, Samut Prakan, 10540, Thailand
Tel.: (66) 2 707 1747, ext. 1179
Fax: (66) 2 707 1740
Web Site: www.volvoit.com
Emp.: 300
Information Technology Consulting Services
S.I.C.: 7373
N.A.I.C.S.: 541512
Jacques Michel *(Pres)*

Volvo Italia Spa (1)
Corso Europa 2 Boltiere
Bergamo, 24040, Italy
Tel.: (39) 035889111
Fax: (39) 035807564
E-Mail: reception.italia@volvo.com
Web Site: www.volvocars.com
Emp.: 100
Automobile Mfr
S.I.C.: 3711
N.A.I.C.S.: 336111
Manuele Bartolini *(Product Mgr)*

Volvo Logistics Corporation (1)
Smalleheerweg 31
9041 Gent, Belgium
Tel.: (32) 9 250 42 11
Fax: (32) 9 341 39 92
E-Mail: info.vet@volvo.com
Web Site: www.volvogroup.com
Emp.: 200
Logistics Consulting Services
S.I.C.: 4731
N.A.I.C.S.: 541614
Wini Vanderheyden *(Mgr-Bus Dev-Inbound)*

Volvo Makedonija Ltd. (1)
Kacanicki pat bb
1000 Skopje, Macedonia
Tel.: (389) 2 2652112
Fax: (389) 2 2653271
Web Site: www.volvobuses.com
Automobile Repair & Maintenance Services
S.I.C.: 7539
N.A.I.C.S.: 811198

Volvo Maskin AS (1)
Mellomasveien 1
Postboks 603
1411 Kolbotn, Norway
Tel.: (47) 66 81 86 86
Fax: (47) 66 81 86 66
Web Site: www.volvoce.com
Construction Equipment Mfr
S.I.C.: 3531
N.A.I.C.S.: 333120
Ton Yeslea *(Gen Mgr)*

Volvo Parts Gent NV (1)
Smalleheerweg 29
9041 Gent, Belgium
Tel.: (32) 9 341 39 11
Fax: (32) 9 259 26 03
Web Site: www.volvogroup.com
Automotive Parts Distr
S.I.C.: 5015
N.A.I.C.S.: 423140

VOLVO PENTA SINGAPORE (1)
33 Joo Koon Circle
Singapore, 629111, Singapore
Tel.: (65) 6221 3111
Fax: (65) 6339 7925
Automotive Engine Distr
S.I.C.: 5013
N.A.I.C.S.: 423120

VOLVO PENTA TURKEY (1)
Icerenkoey Mahallesi Engin Sokak No 9 Kadikoey
34752 Istanbul, Turkey
Tel.: (90) 216 655 75 00
Fax: (90) 216 469 29 73
E-Mail: vpservis@volvo.com
Web Site: www.volvopenta.com
Emp.: 10
Marine Engine Mfr
S.I.C.: 3519
N.A.I.C.S.: 333618
Mehdi Kilic *(Gen Mgr)*

Volvo (Southern Africa) Pty Ltd (1)
Cnr Jet Park Rd & Saligna Ave
Witfield, Gauteng, South Africa
Tel.: (27) 11 842 5000
Fax: (27) 11 842 5039
Emp.: 80
Truck Mfr
S.I.C.: 3711
N.A.I.C.S.: 336120
Cindy van Wyk *(Branch Mgr-Admin)*

Volvo Treasury Asia Ltd. (1)
33 Joo Koon Circle
629111 Singapore, Singapore
Tel.: (65) 68614582
Fax: (65) 63390850
E-Mail: Support.VTA.Customer@volvo.com
Web Site: www.volvogroup.com
Management Consulting Services
S.I.C.: 8748
N.A.I.C.S.: 541618
Judi Liu *(VP & Head-Treasury)*

Volvo Trucks Austria GmbH (1)
Volvostrasse 1
2512 Tribuswinkel, Austria
Tel.: (43) 5 7500 0
Fax: (43) 5 7500 10999
E-Mail: info.volvoa@volvo.com
Web Site: www.volvotrucks.com
Emp.: 130
Commercial Vehicle Sales & Repair Services
S.I.C.: 5012
N.A.I.C.S.: 423110
Herbert Spiegel *(Mng Dir)*

VOLVO TRUCKS BULGARIA EOOD (1)
Boulevard Slivnitsa
1331 Sofia, Bulgaria
Tel.: (359) 2 8106 700
Fax: (359) 2 4032 700
Commercial Vehicle Mfr
S.I.C.: 3711
N.A.I.C.S.: 336120

VOLVO TRUCKS ESTONIA (1)
Kurekivi Tee 10 Lehmja Kuela
75306 Harjumaa, Harjumaa, Estonia
Tel.: (372) 671 8360
Fax: (372) 671 8370
Web Site: www.volvotrucks.com
Commercial Vehicle Mfr
S.I.C.: 3711
N.A.I.C.S.: 336120

VOLVO TRUCKS FINLAND (1)
Vetotie 3
PL 13
01611 Vantaa, Finland
Tel.: (358) 10 655 00
Web Site: www.volvotrucks.com
Commercial Vehicle Mfr
S.I.C.: 3711
N.A.I.C.S.: 336111

Volvo Trucks India Pvt Ltd (1)
Yelachahalli Tavarekere Post Hosakote
Bengaluru, 562 122, India

AB Volvo—(Continued)

Tel.: (91) 80 6691 4000
Fax: (91) 11 2331 6702
Web Site: www.volvotrucks.com
Emp.: 600
Commercial Vehicle Mfr
S.I.C.: 3711
N.A.I.C.S.: 336111
Rathish Vijayan *(Mgr)*

Volvo Trucks Indonesia **(1)**
Sentral Senayan III 12th Floor Jl Asia Afrika No 8 Gelora Bung
Karno Senayan Jakarta Pusat, Jakarta, 10270, Indonesia
Tel.: (62) 21 2903 9216
Fax: (62) 21 2903 9215
Web Site: www.volvotrucks.com
Commercial Vehicle Mfr
S.I.C.: 3711
N.A.I.C.S.: 336111
Imelda Sitorus *(Mgr-Sls Strategy-Asia)*

VOLVO TRUCKS IRAN **(1)**
14th Karaj Special Road
PO Box 13895-141
13861-81198 Tehran, Iran
Tel.: (98) 21 44196513 15
Fax: (98) 21 44196518
E-Mail: info@saipadiesel.com
Web Site: www.volvotrucks.com
Automobile Distr
S.I.C.: 5012
N.A.I.C.S.: 423110

VOLVO TRUCKS LITHUANIA **(1)**
Minsko Pl 9
02121 Vilnius, Lithuania
Tel.: (370) 5 215 95 00
Fax: (370) 5 215 95 10
E-Mail: info.vilnius@volvo.com
Web Site: www.volvotrucks.com
Commercial Vehicle Mfr
S.I.C.: 3711
N.A.I.C.S.: 336111

VOLVO TRUCKS MACEDONIA **(1)**
Kacanicki Pat Bb
1000 Skopje, Macedonia
Tel.: (389) 2 2652 112
Fax: (389) 2 2653 271
Web Site: www.volvotrucks.com
Emp.: 13
Commercial Vehicle Distr
S.I.C.: 5012
N.A.I.C.S.: 423110
Joco Shofer *(Coord-Sls-Truck)*

VOLVO TRUCKS NETHERLANDS **(1)**
Stationsweg 2
4153 RD Beesd, Netherlands
Tel.: (31) 345 688500
Fax: (31) 345 688429
E-Mail: vtc9.nl001101@memo.volvo.se
Web Site: www.volvotrucks.com
Emp.: 75
Commercial Vehicle Mfr
S.I.C.: 3711
N.A.I.C.S.: 336120
Cynthia Vant Hoff *(Coord-Mktg Comm & PR)*

VOLVO TRUCKS NIGERIA **(1)**
322A Ikorodu Road Ikeja Mr Ade Ojuoko
Lagos, Nigeria
Tel.: (234) 70 56427174
Commercial Vehicle Mfr
S.I.C.: 3711
N.A.I.C.S.: 336120

Volvo Trucks Philippines **(1)**
77 Mindanao Avenue Pag-Asa
Metro Manila, Quezon City, Philippines 1100
Tel.: (63) 2 924 2261
Fax: (63) 2 924 2510
Web Site: www.volvotrucks.com
Commercial Vehicle Distr
S.I.C.: 5012
N.A.I.C.S.: 423110
Anthony L. Ngo *(Pres)*

VOLVO TRUCKS POLAND **(1)**
Oddzial Samochody Ciezarowae Aleja Katowica 215
05-831 Mlochow, Poland
Tel.: (48) 22 383 45 00
Fax: (48) 22 383 45 01
Web Site: www.volvotrucks.com
Commercial Vehicle Mfr
S.I.C.: 3711
N.A.I.C.S.: 336111

Volvo Trucks Region Central Europe GmbH **(1)**
Oskar-Messter-Str 20
85737 Ismaning, Germany
Tel.: (49) 89 800740
Fax: (49) 89 80074190
E-Mail: online-communications@volvo.com
Web Site: www.volvotrucks.com
Emp.: 120
Commercial Vehicle Mfr
S.I.C.: 3711
N.A.I.C.S.: 336111
Wim Keja *(CFO)*

VOLVO TRUCKS RUSSIA **(1)**
St Panfilov 19 Business Center Country Park
141407 Khimki, Russia
Tel.: (7) 495 961 1030
Fax: (7) 495 961 1032
Commercial Vehicle Mfr
S.I.C.: 3711
N.A.I.C.S.: 336120

VOLVO TRUCKS SAUDI ARABIA **(1)**
Kllo 14 Makkah Rd
PO Box 1588
Jeddah, 21441, Saudi Arabia
Tel.: (966) 2 620 9173
Fax: (966) 2 620 9429
Web Site: www.volvotrucks.com
Commercial Vehicle Mfr
S.I.C.: 3711
N.A.I.C.S.: 336111

Volvo Trucks (Suisse) SA **(1)**
Lindenstrasse 6
8108 Dallikon, Switzerland
Tel.: (41) 44 847 61 00
Fax: (41) 44 847 61 01
Web Site: www.volvotrucks.com
Emp.: 50
Commercial Vehicle Distr
S.I.C.: 5012
N.A.I.C.S.: 423110
Anders Magnusson *(CFO)*

VOLVO TRUCKS SYRIA **(1)**
Damascus Free Zone
PO Box 3050
Damascus, Syria
Tel.: (963) 11 212 97 36
Fax: (963) 11 212 98 51
E-Mail: intertrade@nahas.sy
Web Site: www.volvotrucks.com
Commercial Vehicle Distr
S.I.C.: 5012
N.A.I.C.S.: 423110
Emad Hamdan *(Mgr-After Sls)*

Volvo Trucks Taiwan **(1)**
Xinyi Rd 7th Floor
11049 Taipei, Taiwan
Tel.: (886) 2 81015288
Fax: (886) 2 81015299
Web Site: www.volvotrucks.com
Commercial Vehicle Mfr
S.I.C.: 3711
N.A.I.C.S.: 336111

Volvo Trucks Thailand **(1)**
42/5 Moo 7 Bang-na Trad Highway Km 26
Khing Amphur
Bangsaothong, Samut Prakan, 10540, Thailand
Tel.: (66) 2 707 1747
Fax: (66) 2 707 1734
Commercial Vehicle Mfr
S.I.C.: 3711
N.A.I.C.S.: 336120
Jacques Michel *(Gen Mgr)*

ZAO Volvo Vostok **(1)**
Business Centre Country Park Panfilova Str 19
Khimki, Moscow, 141407, Russia
Tel.: (7) 495 961 1030
Fax: (7) 495 961 1034
E-Mail: volvocst.msk@volvo.com
Web Site: www.volvoce.com
Construction Equipment Distr
S.I.C.: 5082
N.A.I.C.S.: 423810
Andrey Komov *(Gen Mgr-Construction Equipment)*

Non-U.S. Affiliates:

Merkavim Metal Works Ltd. **(1)**
22 Granit St The Industrial Park
Caesarea, 38900, Israel (27%)
Tel.: (972) 46176000
Fax: (972) 46176004
Web Site: www.merkavim.com
Emp.: 450
Mfr. of Bus Bodies & Sanitation Equipment
S.I.C.: 3711
N.A.I.C.S.: 336211
Micha Maixmer *(Pres)*

Transport Financial Services **(1)**
105 Bauer Place
Waterloo, ON, N2L 6B5, Canada
Tel.: (519) 886-8070
Fax: (519) 886-5214
Toll Free: (800) 461-5970
Web Site: www.tfsgroup.com
Emp.: 34
Accounting, Bookkeeping, Tax Return Preparation & Consulting Services for Transportation Industry
S.I.C.: 8721
N.A.I.C.S.: 541219
Steve Mulligan *(VP-Bus Dev)*

Xi'an Silver Bus Corporation **(1)**
Yanling Economic Development Zone
Xi'an, Shaanxi, 710089, China (50%)
Tel.: (86) 29 6801 8888
Fax: (86) 29 6857 4508
Web Site: www.silverbus.com
Bus Mfr
S.I.C.: 4111
N.A.I.C.S.: 485113

Non-U.S. Plants:

UD Financial Services - Hanyu Plant **(1)**
24-705-2 Komatsudai
Hanyu, Saitama, 348-0038, Japan
Tel.: (81) 48 563 2360
Financial Management Services
S.I.C.: 6211
N.A.I.C.S.: 523999

UD Financial Services - Konosu Plant **(1)**
3121-1 Mida Kounosu-shi
Saitama, 365-0062, Japan
Tel.: (81) 48 596 5051
Fax: (81) 485961065
Web Site: www.udtrucks.com
Emp.: 150
Financial Management Services
S.I.C.: 6211
N.A.I.C.S.: 523999
Kajita Masahiro *(Mgr-Production)*

ABA CHEMICALS CORPORATION

18 Dongfang Rd (E) Port Development Zone
Taicang, Jiangsu, 215433, China
Tel.: (86) 512 53641368
Fax: (86) 512 53642000
E-Mail: info@abachem.com
Web Site: www.abachem.com
300261—(CHIN)
Emp.: 210

Business Description:
Chemicals, Agricultural Chemicals, Advanced Intermediates & Active Pharmaceutical Ingredients Mfr
S.I.C.: 2899
N.A.I.C.S.: 325998

Personnel:
Tong Cai *(Chm)*

Subsidiary:

ABA Chemicals (Shanghai) Limited **(1)**
201 Ningxia Road Suite 18D
Shanghai, China
Tel.: (86) 21 5115 9199
Fax: (86) 21 5115 9188
E-Mail: info@abachem.com
Fine Chemicals & Pharmaceutical Ingredients Mfr
S.I.C.: 2819
N.A.I.C.S.: 325180

ABACUS MINING & EXPLORATION CORPORATION

6th Floor 800 West Pender Street
Vancouver, BC, V6C 2V6, Canada
Tel.: (604) 682-0301
Fax: (604) 682-0307
Toll Free: (866) 834-0301
E-Mail: info@amemining.com
Web Site: www.amemining.com
AME—(TSXV)
Sales Range: Less than $1 Million

Business Description:
Mineral Exploration Services
S.I.C.: 1081
N.A.I.C.S.: 213114

Personnel:
Michael McInnis *(Chm, Pres & CEO)*
Ian M. Macneily *(CFO & Exec VP)*

Board of Directors:
Michael McInnis
Victor Lazarovici
Thomas McKeever
Louis Montpellier

Transfer Agent:
Computershare Investor Services Inc.
510 Burrard Street 2nd Floor
Vancouver, BC, V6C 3B9, Canada

ABACUS PROPERTY GROUP

Level 34 Australia Square
264-278 George Street, Sydney, NSW, 2000, Australia
Tel.: (61) 292538600
Fax: (61) 292538616
E-Mail: enquiries@abacusproperty.com.au
Web Site: www.abacusproperty.com.au
ABP—(ASX)

Business Description:
Real Estate Management & Investment Services
S.I.C.: 6531
N.A.I.C.S.: 531390

Personnel:
Frank Wolf *(Mng Dir)*
Rod de Aboitiz *(CFO)*
Ellis Varejes *(COO & Sec)*

Board of Directors:
John Thame
Malcolm Irving
Myra Salkinder
Frank Wolf

Subsidiaries:

Abacus Funds Management Limited **(1)**
Level 34 Australia Square
264-278 George Street, Sydney, NSW, 2000, Australia
Tel.: (61) 292538600
Fax: (61) 292538616
E-Mail: enquiries@abacusproperty.com.au
Web Site: www.abacusproperty.com.au
Emp.: 50
Fund Management Services
S.I.C.: 6282
N.A.I.C.S.: 523920
Rod De Aboitiz *(CFO)*

Abacus Group Holdings Limited **(1)**
Level 34 Australia Square
264-278 George Street, Sydney, NSW, 2000, Australia
Tel.: (61) 292538600
Fax: (61) 292538616
E-Mail: enquires@abacusproperty.com.au
Web Site: www.abacusproperty.com.au
Emp.: 50
Investment Management Services
S.I.C.: 8741
N.A.I.C.S.: 551114

Frank Wolf *(Mng Dir)*

ABACUS SOFTWARE LIMITED
(d/b/a Abacus e-Media)
14-16 Regent Street
London, SW1Y 4PH, United Kingdom
Tel.: (44) 2077669810
Fax: (44) 2077669811
E-Mail: info@abacusemedia.com
Web Site: www.abacusemedia.com
Year Founded: 1997
Rev.: $6,600,000
Emp.: 30
Business Description:
Web Development Services
S.I.C.: 7371
N.A.I.C.S.: 541511
Personnel:
Daniel Murphy *(Mgr-Mktg)*

ABADGARAN IRAN TOURISM AND WELFARE COMPLEXES (PUBLIC LIMITED COMPANY)
Between Jahad & Tv Sq Shahid Kalantari Highway
PO Box 91775/1546
Mashhad, 9176983151, Iran
Tel.: (98) 8718005
Fax: (98) 8718006
E-Mail: info@abadgaraniran.com
Web Site: www.abadgaraniran.com
Year Founded: 1994
ABAD—(THE)
Business Description:
Tourism Bureaus
S.I.C.: 7389
N.A.I.C.S.: 561591
Personnel:
Mostafa Bateni *(Chm)*
Rasool Bagheriha *(Vice Chm & Mng Dir)*
Board of Directors:
Mostafa Bateni
Rasool Bagheriha
Mehdi Khajeh Dalooie
Mohammad Ali Dehghani
Hassan Rozbehi

ABAN OFFSHORE LIMITED
Janpriya Crest 113 Pantheon Road Egmore
Chennai, 600 008, India
Tel.: (91) 4428195555
Fax: (91) 4428195527
E-Mail: abanoffshore@aban.com
Web Site: www.abanoffshore.com
ABAN—(NSE)
Rev.: $685,862,086
Assets: $3,372,150,866
Liabilities: $2,763,347,695
Net Worth: $608,803,171
Earnings: $35,479,256
Emp.: 1,494
Fiscal Year-end: 03/31/13
Business Description:
Oil Drilling Services
S.I.C.: 1381
N.A.I.C.S.: 213111
Personnel:
P. Murari *(Chm)*
Reji Abraham *(Mng Dir)*
C. P. Gopalkrishnan *(Deputy Mng Dir & Sec)*
P. Venkateswaran *(Deputy Mng Dir)*
Board of Directors:
P. Murari
Reji Abraham
K. Bharathan
C. P. Gopalkrishnan
Ashok Kumar Rout
P. Venkateswaran
Transfer Agent:
Cameo Corporate Services Limited
Subramanian Building No 1 Club House Road 5th Floor
Chennai, India

Non-U.S. Subsidiary:

Aban Singapore Pte. Ltd. (1)
No 6 Temasek Boulevard
#28-01 to 05 Suntec Tower Four
Singapore, 038986, Singapore
Tel.: (65) 6500 1300
Fax: (65) 6294 8540
Oil Drilling Services
S.I.C.: 1381
N.A.I.C.S.: 213111

ABANKA VIPA D.D.
Slovenska cesta 58
1517 Ljubljana, Slovenia
Tel.: (386) 14718100
Telex: 31 228 abanka
Fax: (386) 14325165
E-Mail: info@abanka.si
Web Site: www.abanka.si
Year Founded: 1955
ABKN—(LJU)
Rev.: $239,565,759
Assets: $4,865,074,534
Liabilities: $4,642,089,551
Net Worth: $222,984,983
Earnings: ($109,127,271)
Emp.: 880
Fiscal Year-end: 12/31/12
Business Description:
International, Corporate & Retail Banking Services
S.I.C.: 6029
N.A.I.C.S.: 522110
Personnel:
Janko Gedrih *(Chm-Supervisory Bd)*
Joze Lenic *(Chm-Mgmt Bd)*
Andrej Slapar *(Deputy Chm-Supervisory Bd)*
Vesna Colja *(Chief Compliance Officer)*
Jesenka Licen Kuncic *(Chief Security Officer)*
Suzana Persolja Nikolvacic *(Money Laundering Prevention Officer)*
Igor Stebernak *(Member-Mgmt Bd)*
Supervisory Board of Directors:
Janko Gedrih
Ales Abersek
Andrej Andoljsek
Vladimir Miso Ceplak
Kristina Ana Dolenc
Andrej Slapar
Franci Strajnar
Snezana Sustersic
Aljosa Ursic

Subsidiaries:

Abancna DZU d.o.o. (1)
Secretariat Prazakova 8
1000 Ljubljana, Slovenia
Tel.: (386) 13078600
Fax: (386) 12302310
Web Site: www.abancna-dzu.si
Emp.: 15
Subsidiary Management Offices
S.I.C.: 8741
N.A.I.C.S.: 551114
Andrej Petek *(Mgr-Fund)*

Afaktor doo (1)
Slovenska cesta 56
1000 Ljubljana, Slovenia
Tel.: (386) 12306480
Fax: (386) 12306488
E-Mail: info@a-faktor.si
Web Site: www.afaktor.si
Emp.: 13
Trade Financing Services
S.I.C.: 6159
N.A.I.C.S.: 522293
Matjaz Kastrun *(Gen Mgr)*

Analozbe d.o.o (1)
Erjavceva ulica 2
5000 Nova Gorica, Slovenia
Tel.: (386) 0801360
Fax: (386) 53028506
Investment Management Services
S.I.C.: 8748
N.A.I.C.S.: 541618

Argolina d o o (1)
Slovenian Rd 58
1000 Ljubljana, Slovenia
Tel.: (386) 14718422
Fax: (386) 14338618
Project Financing Services
S.I.C.: 6211
N.A.I.C.S.: 523999
Uros Subar *(Gen Mgr)*

ABANO HEALTHCARE GROUP LIMITED
16 Floor West Plaza Building 3-7 Albert St
PO Box 106 514
Auckland, 1143, New Zealand
Tel.: (64) 93001410
Fax: (64) 93001419
E-Mail: enquiries@abanohealthcare.co.nz
Web Site: www.abanohealthcare.co.nz
ABA—(NZE)
Rev.: $173,288,295
Assets: $176,588,586
Liabilities: $113,528,169
Net Worth: $63,060,417
Earnings: $3,394,035
Emp.: 1,700
Fiscal Year-end: 05/31/13
Business Description:
Healthcare & Medical Services
S.I.C.: 8099
N.A.I.C.S.: 621410
Personnel:
Trevor David Janes *(Chm)*
Susan Marie Paterson *(Deputy Chm)*
Alan William Clarke *(Mng Dir)*
Richard G. Keys *(CFO & COO)*
Board of Directors:
Trevor David Janes
Danny Chan
Alan William Clarke
Pip Dunphy
Susan Marie Paterson
Eduard Koert van Arkel
Legal Counsel:
Harmos Horton Lusk
Vero Centre, 48 Shortland Street
Auckland, New Zealand

Buddle Findlay
PricewaterhouseCoopers Tower, 188 Quay St
Auckland, New Zealand

Subsidiaries:

Abano Rehabilitation Limited (1)
Level 1 No 2 Owens Road
Epsom, Auckland, 1023, New Zealand
Tel.: (64) 96321350
Fax: (64) 96231550
Web Site: www.abanorehab.co.nz
Emp.: 200
Healthcare & Medical Services
S.I.C.: 8099
N.A.I.C.S.: 621999

Aotea Pathology Limited (1)
Level 6 CMC Building 89 Courtenay Place
Wellington, 6011, New Zealand
Tel.: (64) 43815900
Fax: (64) 43815948
E-Mail: fjames@apath.co.nz
Web Site: www.apath.co.nz
Emp.: 230
Pathological Laboratory Services
S.I.C.: 8071
N.A.I.C.S.: 621511
Karen Wood *(CEO)*

Auckland Dental Group (1)
134 Remuera Road
Remuera, Auckland, New Zealand
Tel.: (64) 95206609
Fax: (64) 93617164
E-Mail: info@akldental.co.nz
Web Site: www.akldental.co.nz
Emp.: 25
Dental Services
S.I.C.: 8021
N.A.I.C.S.: 621210

Burtons Healthcare (1)
Level 6 13-15 College Hill
Ponsonby, Auckland, New Zealand
Tel.: (64) 93021522
Fax: (64) 93021528
Web Site: www.burtons.co.nz
Residential & Community Rehabilitation Services
S.I.C.: 8331
N.A.I.C.S.: 624310

Greenlane Imaging Ltd (1)
Radiology Department Building 4 Greenlane Clinical Centre
PO Box 24321
90 Greenlane West Royal Oak, Auckland, New Zealand
Tel.: (64) 96315383
Fax: (64) 96310365
E-Mail: glctb@adhb.govt.nz
Emp.: 8
Health Care Services
S.I.C.: 8099
N.A.I.C.S.: 621999
Anne Morcon *(Pres)*

Health Partners (1)
Level 1 No 2 Owens Rd
Etson, Auckland, New Zealand
Tel.: (64) 93021522
Fax: (64) 096231550
Web Site: www.abanorehab.co.nz
Emp.: 500
Residential & Community Rehabilitation Services
S.I.C.: 8331
N.A.I.C.S.: 624310
Robin Cooper *(Gen Mgr)*

Insight Radiology Limited (1)
20 Titoki St
Parnell, Auckland, New Zealand
Tel.: (64) 93735988
Fax: (64) 93735989
E-Mail: parnell@insightrad.co.nz
Web Site: www.insightrad.co.nz
Emp.: 15
Diagnostic Radiology Services
S.I.C.: 8071
N.A.I.C.S.: 621512
Alastair Roberts *(Head-Sonographer)*

Kidz Teeth Limited (1)
21 St Johns Rd
Meadowbank, Auckland, 1072, New Zealand
Tel.: (64) 95219003
Web Site: www.lumino.co.nz/dentists/auckland/meadowbank/kidz-teeth/
Dental Care Services
S.I.C.: 8099
N.A.I.C.S.: 621999

Lumino Care Dental (1)
Level 16 W Plz Bldg 3 Albert St
1143 Auckland, New Zealand
Tel.: (64) 93617100
Fax: (64) 93617110
Web Site: www.lumino.co.nz
Emp.: 400
Dental Services
S.I.C.: 8021
N.A.I.C.S.: 621210
Andrew Tappar *(Mng Dir)*

Lumino Dental Limited (1)
Level 7 Hope Gibbons Bldg 7 Dixon Street CBD
Wellington, 6011, New Zealand
Tel.: (64) 4 384 8481
Fax: (64) 4 3844744
Web Site: www.lumino.co.nz
Dental Care Services
S.I.C.: 8072
N.A.I.C.S.: 339116
Allen Baker *(Chm)*
Nick Tramoundanas *(Pres)*

Medical Laboratory Wellington (1)
CMC Building
89 Courtenay Place, Wellington, New Zealand
Tel.: (64) 48015111
Fax: (64) 48015943
Pathology Laboratory Diagnostics
S.I.C.: 8071
N.A.I.C.S.: 621511
Keiry Belton *(Branch Mgr)*

Nelson Diagnostic Laboratory (1)
1 Harley Street
Nelson, New Zealand

Abano Healthcare Group Limited—(Continued)

Tel.: (64) 35487395
Fax: (64) 35467213
Pathology Laboratory Diagnostics
S.I.C.: 8071
N.A.I.C.S.: 621511

Orthotic Centre (Midlands) Limited (1)
43 Pembroke Street
Hamilton, New Zealand
Tel.: (64) 78341281
Fax: (64) 7 834 1282
E-Mail: info@orthotics.co.nz
Healthcare Services
S.I.C.: 8099
N.A.I.C.S.: 621999

Orthotic Centre (NZ) Limited (1)
614 Great S Rd
Ellerslie, New Zealand
Tel.: (64) 95256061
Fax: (64) 695256426
E-Mail: info@orthotics.co.nz
Web Site: www.orthotics.co.nz
Emp.: 30
Orthotic Services
S.I.C.: 8099
N.A.I.C.S.: 621999
Con Balasoglou *(CEO)*

Orthotic Centre (Wellington) Limited (1)
3-5 George St
PO Box 12213
Thorndon, Wellington, 6011, New Zealand
Tel.: (64) 48158058
Fax: (64) 44996054
E-Mail: info@orthotics.co.nz
Healthcare Services
S.I.C.: 8099
N.A.I.C.S.: 621999

Ranworth Healthcare (1)
Level 6 13-15 College Hill
Ponsonby, Auckland, New Zealand
Tel.: (64) 93021522
Fax: (64) 93021528
Web Site: www.ranworth.co.nz
Emp.: 50
Residential & Community Rehabilitation Services
S.I.C.: 8331
N.A.I.C.S.: 624310

Non-U.S. Subsidiary:

Dental Partners Pty Limited (1)
Suite 30901 Southport Central 3 Level 9/9
Lawson St
Southport, QLD, 4215, Australia
Tel.: (61) 755917772
Fax: (61) 755328548
E-Mail: info@dentalpartners.com.au
Web Site: www.dentalpartners.com.au
Emp.: 25
Dental Care Services
S.I.C.: 8011
N.A.I.C.S.: 621491
Alan Clarke *(Chm & Dir)*

ABATTIS BIOCEUTICALS CORPORATION

(Formerly Abattis Biologix Corporation)
Suite 1000 355 Burrard Street
Vancouver, BC, V6C 2G8, Canada
Tel.: (604) 538-6650
Fax: (604) 888-1519
Web Site: www.abattis.com
Year Founded: 1997
FLU—(CNSX OTC)
Assets: $1,317,101
Liabilities: $697,363
Net Worth: $619,739
Earnings: ($986,455)
Fiscal Year-end: 09/30/12

Business Description:
Botanical-Based Antiviral Products Mfr
S.I.C.: 2833
N.A.I.C.S.: 325411

Personnel:
Michael Withrow *(Chm, Pres, CEO & Acting CFO)*

Board of Directors:
Michael Withrow
Nicholas G. Brusatore
Tim Fealey
Robert Hedley
Douglas J. Sorocco

Legal Counsel:
K MacInnes Law Group
Suite 1100 -736 Granville Street
Vancouver, BC, Canada

Transfer Agent:
Computershare Investor Services Inc.
3rd Floor 510 Burrard Street
Vancouver, BC, Canada

ABATTIS BIOLOGIX CORPORATION

(Name Changed to Abattis Bioceuticals Corporation)

ABB LTD.

Affolternstrasse 44
CH-8050 Zurich, Switzerland
Tel.: (41) 43 317 7111
Fax: (41) 43 317 4420
E-Mail: investor.relations@ch.abb.com
Web Site: www.abb.com
Year Founded: 1988
ABB—(LSE NYSE SWX)
Rev.: $41,848,000,000
Assets: $48,064,000,000
Liabilities: $28,856,000,000
Net Worth: $19,208,000,000
Earnings: $2,907,000,000
Emp.: 147,700
Fiscal Year-end: 12/31/13

Business Description:
Power & Automation Products Mfr, Sales, Distr, Construction & Engineering Services
Import Export
S.I.C.: 3612
N.A.I.C.S.: 335311

Personnel:
Hubertus von Grunberg *(Chm)*
Ulrich Spiesshofer *(CEO)*
Eric Elzvik *(CFO)*
Diane de Saint Victor *(Gen Counsel)*

Board of Directors:
Hubertus von Grunberg
Roger Agnelli
Michel De Rosen
Louis R. Hughes
Hans Ulrich Maerki
Michael Treschow
Jacob Wallenberg
Ying Yeh

Subsidiaries:

ABB Finanz AG (1)
Affolternstrasse 44
8050 Zurich, Switzerland
Tel.: (41) 433177111
Fax: (41) 433177478
Financial Management Services
S.I.C.: 6211
N.A.I.C.S.: 523999

ABB Information Systems Ltd. (1)
Affolternstrasse 44
8050 Zurich, Switzerland
Tel.: (41) 43317 71 11
Information Technology Consulting Services
S.I.C.: 7373
N.A.I.C.S.: 541512

ABB Intra AG (1)
Affolternstrasse 44
8050 Zurich, Switzerland
Tel.: (41) 43 317 71 11
Fax: (41) 43 317 77 80
Travel Arrangement Services
S.I.C.: 4729
N.A.I.C.S.: 561599

ABB Schweiz Holding AG (1)
Brown Boveri Strasse 6
5540 Baden, Switzerland
Tel.: (41) 585850000
Telex: 558230bbcch
Fax: (41) 585850100
E-Mail: claudia.lind@ch.abb.com
Web Site: www.abb.com
Emp.: 7,000
Holding Company
S.I.C.: 6719
N.A.I.C.S.: 551112
Remo Luetolf *(CEO)*

Subsidiaries:

ABB Immobilien AG (2)
Brown Boveri Strasse 6
5401 Baden, Switzerland CH
Tel.: (41) 585857799
Fax: (41) 585852929
E-Mail:
Web Site: www.abb.ch
Emp.: 15
Real Estate Investment & Asset Management Services
S.I.C.: 6531
N.A.I.C.S.: 531390
Axel Lehmann *(Mng Dir)*

ABB Insurance Brokers Ltd (2)
Brown Boveri Str 6
CH-5400 Baden, Switzerland
Tel.: (41) 0585857800
Fax: (41) 0585850100
E-Mail: info@abb.ch
Web Site: www.abb.ch
Emp.: 400
General Insurance Contractor
S.I.C.: 6411
N.A.I.C.S.: 524210
Moritz Kung *(Mng Dir)*

ABB Secheron Ltd. (2)
Rue des Sabli res 4-6
CH-1217 Meyrin, Switzerland CH
Tel.: (41) 585862211 (100%)
Telex: 412268 SECH CH
Fax: (41) 585862305
E-Mail: info.abbsecheron@ch.abb.com
Web Site: www.abb.ch
Emp.: 350
Energy & Power Distr & Supplier; Transformers Mfr
S.I.C.: 3612
N.A.I.C.S.: 335311
Goel Vauchel *(Mgr-Mktg)*

ABB Turbo Systems Holding Ltd. (2)
Bruggerstrasse 71a
5400 Baden, Switzerland
Tel.: (41) 58 585 77 77
Investment Management Services
S.I.C.: 6211
N.A.I.C.S.: 523999

Subsidiary:

ABB Turbo Systems Ltd (3)
Bruggerstrasse 71A
CH-5400 Baden, Switzerland
Tel.: (41) 585854037
Fax: (41) 585855144
E-Mail: info.turbochargers@ch.abb.com
Web Site: www.abb.ch
Emp.: 1,600
Turbocharging Diesel & Gas Engines Mfr
S.I.C.: 3714
N.A.I.C.S.: 336310
Daniel Arnet *(Pres)*

Consenec Ltd (2)
Im Segelhof
Daettwil, 5405 Baden, Switzerland
Tel.: (41) 585868360
Fax: (41) 585867390
E-Mail: info@consenec.ch
Web Site: www.consenec.ch
Rev.: $7,340,036
Emp.: 50
Management Consulting Services
S.I.C.: 8742
N.A.I.C.S.: 541611
Renato Merz *(Pres)*

Newave Energy Holding SA (2)
Via Luserte Sud 9
CH 6572 Quartino, Switzerland CH
Tel.: (41) 918502929
Fax: (41) 918401254
E-Mail: info@newaveenergy.com
Web Site: www.newaveenergy.com
Emp.: 120
Holding Company; Uninterruptible Power Supply Systems Designer, Mfr & Distr
S.I.C.: 6719
N.A.I.C.S.: 551112
Filippo Marbach *(Co-Founder & COO)*
Vllaznim Xhiha *(Co-Founder)*
Patrick Sertori *(CFO)*

Subsidiaries:

Newave Energy AG (3)
Industriestrasse 5
5432 Neuenhof, Switzerland
Tel.: (41) 56 416 01 01
Fax: (41) 56 416 01 00
E-Mail: info@newaveenergy.ch
Web Site: www.newaveenergy.ch
Inverter Mfr
S.I.C.: 3621
N.A.I.C.S.: 335312

Newave S.A. (3)
Via Luserte Sud 9
6572 Quartino, Ticino, Switzerland
Tel.: (41) 918502929
Fax: (41) 918401254
E-Mail: info@newaveenergy.com
Web Site: www.newaveups.com
Emp.: 100
UPS Mfr
S.I.C.: 3699
N.A.I.C.S.: 335999
Renzo Salmina *(Mgr-Bus Dev)*

Servicenet AG (3)
Industriestrasse 5
Neuenhof, 5432 Wettingen, Aargau, Switzerland
Tel.: (41) 56 416 01 01
Fax: (41) 56 416 01 00
E-Mail: info@servicenet.ch
Web Site: www.servicenet.ch
Emp.: 20
UPS Mfr & Sales
S.I.C.: 3699
N.A.I.C.S.: 335999
Jean-Paul Degrange *(Sls Mgr)*

Non-U.S. Subsidiaries:

Newave Energy India Private Ltd. (3)
818/819 Corporate Avenue Sonawala Road
Goregaon East, 400 063 Mumbai, India
Tel.: (91) 22 42665151
Fax: (91) 22 42665141
E-Mail: info@newaveenergy.in
Web Site: www.newaveenergy.com
Emp.: 7
Energy Consulting Services
S.I.C.: 8999
N.A.I.C.S.: 541690
Sandeep Arora *(Bus Mgr)*

Newave Energy (Jiangmen) Ltd. (3)
9/F Kawa House 49 Jiangshe Road
529000 Jiangmen, Guangdong, China
Tel.: (86) 750 368 0239
Fax: (86) 750 368 0229
E-Mail: sales-china@newave.com.cn
Web Site: www.newave.com.cn
Inverter Distr
S.I.C.: 5063
N.A.I.C.S.: 423610

Newave Espana S.A. (3)
Arturo Soria 329 1 D
28033 Madrid, Spain
Tel.: (34) 917682222
Fax: (34) 913832150
Web Site: www.newaveups.com
UPS Mfr
S.I.C.: 3699
N.A.I.C.S.: 335999

Newave Finland OY (3)
Lakkisepankuja 6
Niittlyantie 2, 00620 Helsinki, Finland
Tel.: (358) 104219400
E-Mail: info@newaveups.fi
Web Site: www.newaveups.fi
Emp.: 10
UPS Mfr
S.I.C.: 3699
N.A.I.C.S.: 335999
Sami Niiranen *(Mgr-Sls)*

Newave (Hong Kong) Ltd (3)
Rm 2506 W Tower Shun Tak Ctr
Connaught Rd, 168 200 Central, China (Hong Kong)

Tel.: (852) 642215512
E-Mail: sales-china@newave.com.cn
Web Site: www.newave.com.cn
Uninterruptible Power Supplies Mfr
S.I.C.: 3699
N.A.I.C.S.: 335999

Newave Italia SRL (3)
Via Vincenzo Ussani 90
00151 Rome, Italy
Tel.: (39) 06 65 31 316
Fax: (39) 06 65 31 306
E-Mail: info@newaveltalia.it
Web Site: www.newaveltalia.it
Emp.: 6
Inverter Mfr
S.I.C.: 3621
N.A.I.C.S.: 335312

Newave Osterreich GmbH (3)
Luxenburgerstrasse 252
1230 Vienna, Austria
Tel.: (43) 1710967016
Fax: (43) 1710967012
E-Mail: info@newwaveups.at
Web Site: www.newwaveups.at
Emp.: 9
Uninterruptible Power Supply Sales
S.I.C.: 3699
N.A.I.C.S.: 335999

Newave South America Elettroelettronica LTDA (3)
Rua Clodomiro Amazonas No 1422 Ste 68
Nova Conceicao, 04537 Sao Paulo, Brazil
Tel.: (55) 1130450809
Fax: (55) 1130450764
E-Mail: info@newavesam.com
Web Site: www.newaveups.com
Emp.: 3
UPS Mfr
S.I.C.: 3699
N.A.I.C.S.: 335999
Gabriel Gomen *(Gen Mgr)*

Newave UPS Systems BV (3)
Stephensonweg 9
4207 Gorinchem, South Holland, Netherlands
Tel.: (31) 183646474
Fax: (31) 183623540
E-Mail: info@newaveups.nl
Web Site: www.newaveenergy.nl
Emp.: 7
UPS Mfr
S.I.C.: 3699
N.A.I.C.S.: 335999
R. Labergar *(Gen Mgr)*

Newave USV Systeme GmbH (3)
Summerside Ave C 207
Baden Airpark Rheinmunster, 77386
Rastatt, Baden-Wurttemberg, Germany
Tel.: (49) 722918660
Fax: (49) 7229186633
E-Mail: zentrale@newave-usv.de
Web Site: www.newave-usv.de
Emp.: 20
UPS Mfr
S.I.C.: 3699
N.A.I.C.S.: 335999
Astrid Hennevogl *(Mgr)*

Units:

ABB Switzerland Ltd - CMC Low Voltage Products (2)
Fulachstrasse 150
8200 Schaffhausen, Switzerland
Tel.: (41) 585864111
Fax: (41) 585864222
E-Mail: cmc@ch.abb.com
Web Site: www.abb.ch
Emp.: 300
Low Voltage Electrical Switching & Protective Equipment
S.I.C.: 3613
N.A.I.C.S.: 335313
Frank Wentzler *(Mng Dir)*

ABB Switzerland Ltd - Corporate Research (2)
Segelhof 1K
5405 Baden, Switzerland
Tel.: (41) 585868411
Fax: (41) 433174420
E-Mail: info@abb.com
Web Site: www.abb.ch
Emp.: 150
Research Services
S.I.C.: 8731
N.A.I.C.S.: 541712

ABB Switzerland Ltd - Drives (2)
Austrasse
CH-5300 Turgi, Switzerland
Tel.: (41) 585892795
Fax: (41) 585892984
E-Mail: mvdrives@ch.abb.com
Web Site: www.abb.ch
Emp.: 200
Drive Mfr
S.I.C.: 3566
N.A.I.C.S.: 333612
Barbara Frei *(Mng Dir)*

ABB Switzerland Ltd - High Voltage Products (2)
Affolgernstrasse 44
PO Box 8131
CH-8050 Zurich, Switzerland
Tel.: (41) 585883300
Fax: (41) 585881188
Web Site: www.abb.ch
Emp.: 100
High Voltage Products Mfr
S.I.C.: 3699
N.A.I.C.S.: 335999

ABB Switzerland Ltd - Manufacturing & Robotics (2)
Unifer Mftg Industires
5242 Birr, Switzerland
Tel.: (41) 585867766
Fax: (41) 585865088
E-Mail: unifer.hotline@ch.abb.com
Web Site: www.abb.ch
Emp.: 290
Engineering, Manufacturing & Production Plant Servicing
S.I.C.: 8711
N.A.I.C.S.: 541330
Konrad Wirthensohn *(Mng Dir)*

ABB Switzerland Ltd - Minerals & Printing (2)
Segelhofstrasse
5405 Baden, Switzerland
Tel.: (41) 585867319
Fax: (41) 585868550
E-Mail: process.industries@ch.abb.com
Web Site: www.abb.ch
Electrical Equipment & Control Technology
S.I.C.: 3699
N.A.I.C.S.: 335999

ABB Switzerland Ltd - Normelec (2)
Brown Boveri Strasse 6
Baden, 5400, Switzerland
Tel.: (41) 585860000
Fax: (41) 585860699
E-Mail: info.normelec@ch.abb.com
Web Site: www.abb.ch
Emp.: 100
Electric Motors, Drives & Low Voltage Products Sales & Distr
S.I.C.: 4931
N.A.I.C.S.: 221122
Max Wuthrich *(Mng Dir)*

ABB Switzerland Ltd - Power Electronics (2)
Austrasse
CH-5300 Turgi, Switzerland
Tel.: (41) 585893809
Fax: (41) 585892090
E-Mail: pes@ch.abb.com
Web Site: www.abb.ch
Emp.: 350
Power Electronics Mfr
S.I.C.: 3612
N.A.I.C.S.: 335311
Remo Lutolf *(Mng Dir)*

ABB Switzerland Ltd - Power Systems (2)
Brown Boveri Stasse 5
CH-8057 Zurich, Switzerland
Tel.: (41) 585883886
Fax: (41) 585881877
Web Site: www.abb.ch
Substation Electrical Power Supply
S.I.C.: 3612
N.A.I.C.S.: 335311

ABB Switzerland Ltd - Semiconductors (2)
Lenzburg
CH-5600 Lenzburg, Switzerland
Tel.: (41) 85861000
Fax: (41) 85861305
Web Site: www.abb.ch
Emp.: 300
Semiconductor Mfr
S.I.C.: 3674
N.A.I.C.S.: 334413

ABB Switzerland Ltd., Micafil (2)
Badenerstrasse 780
CH-8048 Zurich, Switzerland CH
Tel.: (41) 4158586033
Telex: 822163
Fax: (41) 415860302
Web Site: www.micafil.ch
Emp.: 170
Power System Capacitors; Gas Servicing Engines; Transformers; Casting Resins; Coating Compounds; Dipping Resins; High-Voltage Laboratory Measuring Devices; Laminated Plastic Sheets; Injection Moulded Plastics; Foundry Equipment; Laminated Metal Tubes; Machinery for Edible Oil; Treatment Plants; Winding & Insulating Machines
S.I.C.: 3612
N.A.I.C.S.: 335311

ABB Verwaltungs AG (1)
Affolternstrasse 44
8050 Zurich, Switzerland
Tel.: (41) 43 317 71 11
Fax: (41) 44 317 73 21
Financial Management Services
S.I.C.: 6211
N.A.I.C.S.: 523999

PGC Powergen Consulting SA (1)
Molinazzo di Monteggio
Monteggio, 6995, Switzerland
Tel.: (41) 91 6113011
Fax: (41) 91 6082460
Electric Power Generation Services
S.I.C.: 4911
N.A.I.C.S.: 221118

Trasfor SA (1)
Molinazzo di Monteggio
6995 Monteggio, Switzerland
Tel.: (41) 91 611 30 11
Fax: (41) 91 608 24 60
E-Mail: infotrasfor@trasfor.ch
Web Site: www.trasfor.ch
Sls.: $109,675,370
Emp.: 300
Transformer & Inductor Mfr
S.I.C.: 3612
N.A.I.C.S.: 335311
Antonio Gonzalez *(CEO)*
Sebastiano Zumbino *(CFO)*

Non-U.S. Subsidiaries:

Trasfor Charoenchai Co. Ltd. (2)
9 Soi Prachaautis 21 Prachautis Road Rajburana
Bangkok, 10140, Thailand
Tel.: (66) 2427 5552
Fax: (66) 2427 3296
Power Transformer Mfr
S.I.C.: 3612
N.A.I.C.S.: 335311

Trasfor Electric Ltd. (2)
1a Belwell Lane
Sutton Coldfield, B74 4AA, United Kingdom
Tel.: (44) 121 3233339
Fax: (44) 121 3233301
Motor & Generator Mfr
S.I.C.: 3621
N.A.I.C.S.: 335312

Trasfor Engineering GmbH (2)
Hinterm Sielhof 4
28277 Bremen, Germany
Tel.: (49) 421 94409830
Fax: (49) 421 94409833
Emp.: 7
Electronic & Electrical Equipment Mfr
S.I.C.: 3699
N.A.I.C.S.: 335999

U.S. Subsidiary:

ABB Inc. (1)
501 Merrit 7
Norwalk, CT 06851-5308 DE
Mailing Address: (100%)
12040 Regency Pkwy Ste 200
Cary, NC 27518-7708
Tel.: (203) 750-2226
Telex: 965950 COMBENG STD
Fax: (203) 750-2283
Web Site: www.abb.us
Emp.: 11,250
Power & Automation Products, Systems, Solutions & Services
Import Export
S.I.C.: 3612
N.A.I.C.S.: 335311
Enrique O. Santacana *(Pres & CEO)*
Ismo Haka *(CFO & Sr VP)*
Roger A. Bailey *(Pres-Power Products-North America)*
Eugene E. Madara *(Gen Counsel, Sec & Sr VP)*
Martin W. Gross *(Sr VP & Head-Power Sys Div)*
Don Allen *(Sr VP-Operational Excellence)*

Group:

Thomas & Betts Corporation (2)
8155 T&B Blvd
Memphis, TN 38125-8888 TN
Tel.: (901) 252-8000
Fax: (800) 816-7810
Toll Free: (800) 816-7809
E-Mail: elec_custserv@tnb.com
Web Site: www.tnb.com
Emp.: 9,400
Electrical Connectors & Related Components Mfr
Import Export
S.I.C.: 3678
N.A.I.C.S.: 334417
Dominic J. Pileggi *(Chm)*
Charles L. Treadway *(Pres & CEO)*
W. David Smith, Jr. *(Chief Compliance Officer, Asst Sec & Asst Gen Counsel)*
Nathalie Pilon *(Pres-Canada & Australia)*
Fabrice Van Bell *(Pres-Europe, Middle East, Africa & Asia)*
J. N. Raines *(Gen Counsel, Sec & VP)*
Peggy Gann *(Sr VP-HR & Admin)*

Divisions:

T&B Retail Consumer Products (3)
32425 Aurora Rd Ste A
Solon, OH 44139 MI
Fax: (440) 914-8921
Toll Free: (800) 346-2646
E-Mail: consumerservice@tnb.com
Web Site: www.lamson-home.com
Sales Range: $50-74.9 Million
Emp.: 150
Conduit Products Mfr for the Electrical, Telecommunications, Utility & Sewer Industries
S.I.C.: 5063
N.A.I.C.S.: 423610
Norman Setterer *(VP)*

Thomas & Betts Reznor Division (3)
8155 T and B Blvd
Memphis, TN 38125-8888
Tel.: (901) 252-5000
Fax: (901) 252-1305
Toll Free: (800) 695-1901
Web Site: www.rezspec.com
Sales Range: $200-249.9 Million
Emp.: 500
Heating & Ventilating Products Mfr
Export
S.I.C.: 3643
N.A.I.C.S.: 335931
Hugh Windsor *(Pres)*

Subsidiaries:

Jennings Technology (3)
970 McLaughlin Ave
San Jose, CA 95122-2611 DE
Tel.: (408) 292-4025
Fax: (408) 286-1789
Web Site: www.jenningstech.com
Sales Range: $100-124.9 Million
Electrical Components Mfr
S.I.C.: 3677
N.A.I.C.S.: 334416
Susie Geiss *(Mgr-QA)*

Joslyn Hi-Voltage Company, LLC (3)
8155 T&B Boulevard
Memphis, TN 38125 OH
Tel.: (901) 252-5000
Fax: (800) 888-0690
Toll Free: (800) 326-5282

ABB Ltd.—(Continued)

Sales Range: $100-124.9 Million
Electric Power Switching Equipment Mfr
S.I.C.: 3613
N.A.I.C.S.: 335313
Dennis Rhyner *(Mgr-Production)*

JT Packard & Associates, Inc. (3)
275 Investment Ct
Verona, WI 53593 WI
Tel.: (608) 845-9900
Fax: (800) 579-5235
Toll Free: (800) 972-9778
E-Mail: mlamothe@jtpackard.com
Web Site: www.tnbpowersolutions.com
Sales Range: $50-74.9 Million
Emp.: 217
Network Power Equipment Services
S.I.C.: 5087
N.A.I.C.S.: 423850
Keith Bjelajac *(CFO)*

Thomas & Betts Caribe, Inc. (3)
Rd 686 Lot 32-34 Cabo Caribe Industrial Park
Vega Baja, PR 00693 DE
Tel.: (787) 855-3046
Fax: (787) 855-2688
Web Site: www.tnb.com
Sales Range: $150-199.9 Million
Emp.: 500
Electrical Components Mfr
S.I.C.: 3643
N.A.I.C.S.: 335931

Thomas & Betts Power Solutions, LLC (3)
5900 E Port Blvd Bldg V
Richmond, VA 23231 DE
Tel.: (804) 236-3300 (100%)
Fax: (804) 236-4040
Toll Free: (800) 238-5000
Web Site: www.tnbpowersolutions.com
Sales Range: $50-74.9 Million
Emp.: 200
Aircraft & Other Specialized Lightning Arresters, Microwave Station, Railroad Communications Systems & Telephone Station Protectors Mfr
S.I.C.: 3699
N.A.I.C.S.: 335999

Non-U.S. Subsidiaries:

Cable Management Products Ltd. (3)
Station Road
Coleshill, Birmingham, B46 1HT, United Kingdom UK
Tel.: (44) 1675468200
Fax: (44) 1675464930
E-Mail: info@cm-products.com
Web Site: www.cm-products.co.uk
Sales Range: $25-49.9 Million
Emp.: 300
Holding Company; Electrical Conduit & Energy Management Device Mfr
S.I.C.: 6719
N.A.I.C.S.: 551112

Divisions:

Adaptaflex Limited (4)
Station Road
Coleshill, Birmingham, B46 1HT, United Kingdom UK
Tel.: (44) 1675 468 200
Fax: (44) 1675 468 200
E-Mail:
Web Site: www.adaptaflex.com
Flexible Electric Conduit Systems Mfr
S.I.C.: 3357
N.A.I.C.S.: 335929

Elkay Electrical (4)
Station Rd
Coleshill, Birmingham, B46 1HT, United Kingdom
Tel.: (44) 1675468232
Fax: (44) 1675464930
E-Mail: sales@elkay.co.uk
Web Site: www.elkay.co.uk
Emp.: 150
Electrical Wiring & Energy Management Accessories Mfr
S.I.C.: 3643
N.A.I.C.S.: 335931

Kopex International Limited (4)
Station Road
Coleshill, Birmingham, B46 1HT, United Kingdom UK
Tel.: (44) 1675468213
Fax: (44) 1675468280
Web Site: www.kopex.co.uk
Emp.: 150
Electrical Conduit Systems Mfr
S.I.C.: 3357
N.A.I.C.S.: 335929
John Austin *(Mgr-Export)*

Kaufel GmbH & Co. KG (3)
Colditzstrasse 34-36
12099 Berlin, Germany DE
Tel.: (49) 30 701733 (100%)
Telex: 4 17 925 thomb d
Fax: (49) 30 70 173 3399
E-Mail: kaufel.germany@tnb.com
Web Site: www.kaufel.de
Sales Range: $25-49.9 Million
Emp.: 75
Emergency Lighting Systems Mfr
S.I.C.: 3648
N.A.I.C.S.: 335129
Bernd Horn *(Mng Dir)*

Thomas & Betts Ltd. (3)
700 Thomas Ave
Saint-Jean-sur-Richelieu, QC, J2X 2M9, Canada QC
Tel.: (450) 347-5318 (100%)
Fax: (450) 347-1976
E-Mail: info@tnb-canada.com
Web Site: www.tnb-canada.com
Sales Range: $75-99.9 Million
Emp.: 2,000
Electrical Connectors Mfr
S.I.C.: 3643
N.A.I.C.S.: 335931
Nathalie Pilon *(Pres-Canada & Australia)*

Non-U.S. Subsidiaries:

Thomas & Betts Limited Furse (4)
Wilford Rd
Nottingham, NG2 1EB, United Kingdom (100%)
Tel.: (44) 115 964 3700
Telex: 826051 TOMBET G
Fax: (44) 115 986 0538
E-Mail: enquiryuk@tnb.com
Web Site: www.furse.com
Sales Range: $25-49.9 Million
Emp.: 100
Electrical Components Mfr
S.I.C.: 3643
N.A.I.C.S.: 335931

Thomas & Betts Netherlands B.V. (4)
Oosteynde 3
2991LG Barendrecht, Netherlands NL
Tel.: (31) 180641888 (100%)
Fax: (31) 180641889
E-Mail: info@vanlien.nl
Sls.: $36,399,756
Emp.: 150
Electrical Connectors & Related Components Mfr
S.I.C.: 3643
N.A.I.C.S.: 335931
Jasper Bouma *(Gen Mgr)*

Non-U.S. Subsidiary:

Emergi-Lite Safety Systems Ltd. (5)
Bruntcliffe Ln Morley
Leeds, LS27 9LL, United Kingdom (100%)
Tel.: (44) 1132810600
Fax: (44) 1132810601
E-Mail: info@emergi-lite.co.uk
Web Site: www.emergi-lite.co.uk
Sales Range: $10-24.9 Million
Emp.: 75
Emergency Lighting Systems Mfr
S.I.C.: 3648
N.A.I.C.S.: 335129
Matt Etherington *(Mgr-Site)*

Subsidiaries:

ABB Susa Inc. (2)
1460 Livingston Ave Bldg B
North Brunswick, NJ 08902-1873
Tel.: (732) 932-6100
Fax: (732) 828-5263
Construction Engineering Services
S.I.C.: 8711
N.A.I.C.S.: 541330

APS Technology Group, Inc. (2)
3949 Ruffin Rd Ste A
San Diego, CA 92123 CA
Tel.: (858) 836-7990
Fax: (858) 836-7999
E-Mail: info@aps-technology.com
Web Site: www.aps-technology.com
Emp.: 50
Port & Terminal Automation Equipment Mfr
S.I.C.: 3559
N.A.I.C.S.: 333249
Scott Skillman *(Sr VP)*

Baldor Electric Company (2)
5711 RS Boreham Jr St
Fort Smith, AR 72901-8301 MO
Mailing Address:
PO Box 2400
Fort Smith, AR 72902-2400
Tel.: (479) 646-4711
Fax: (479) 648-5792
E-Mail: cdtechsupp@baldor.com
Web Site: www.baldor.com
Sales Range: $1-4.9 Billion
Emp.: 7,181
Energy-Efficient Electric Motors & Electronic Drives Designer, Mfr & Marketer
Export
S.I.C.: 3621
N.A.I.C.S.: 335312
Ronald E. Tucker *(Pres & CEO)*
George E. Moschner *(CFO & Sec)*
Bryant G. Dooly, Jr. *(Treas & Controller)*
Randy L. Colip *(Exec VP-Sls)*
Edward L. Ralston *(Exec VP-Bus Integration)*
William K. Ramsbey *(Exec VP-Mfg)*
Ronald Wayne Thurman *(Exec VP-Engrg)*
Randy G. Waltman *(Exec VP-Mfg)*

Subsidiaries:

Baldor Holdings Inc (3)
5711 R S Boreham Jr St
Fort Smith, AR 72901
Tel.: (479) 646-4711
Fax: (479) 648-5792
Investment Management Services
S.I.C.: 6211
N.A.I.C.S.: 523999

Dodge Manufacturing Company (3)
6040 Ponders Ct
Greenville, SC 29615 (100%)
Tel.: (864) 297-4800
Fax: (864) 281-2487
Web Site: www.dodge-pt.com
Sales Range: $125-149.9 Million
Mechanical Power Transmission Equipment Designer & Mfr
S.I.C.: 3568
N.A.I.C.S.: 333613
Jeff Moore *(VP-Mechanical Product Mktg Grp)*

Non-U.S. Subsidiary:

Dodge de Mexico S.A. de C.V. (4)
Calle A No 170
Parque Industrial El Salto, Jalisco, 45680, Mexico MX
Tel.: (52) 3332841622
Fax: (52) 3332851618
Web Site: www.dodge-pt.com
Sales Range: $25-49.9 Million
Emp.: 100
Roller Bearings & Sprockets Mfr
S.I.C.: 3562
N.A.I.C.S.: 332991

Nupar Manufacturing (3)
13902 E 530th Rd
Claremore, OK 74019 DE
Tel.: (918) 341-8000
Fax: (918) 342-7407
E-Mail: nupar-sales@baldor.com
Web Site: www.nupar.com
Sales Range: $50-74.9 Million
Emp.: 100
Metal Stamping
S.I.C.: 3469
N.A.I.C.S.: 332119
Dennis Darden *(Gen Mgr)*

Southwestern Die Casting, Inc. (3)
600 Raleigh St
Fort Smith, AR 72901-8358 AR
Tel.: (479) 441-6400
Web Site: www.baldor.com
Sales Range: $50-74.9 Million
Emp.: 130
Mfr of Aluminum Base Alloy Castings
S.I.C.: 3364
N.A.I.C.S.: 331523
Scott Wyckoff *(Plant Mgr)*

Plants:

Baldor Electric Company, Manufacturing Facility (3)
305 Ballman Rd
Westville, OK 74965-0305
Tel.: (918) 723-5451
Fax: (918) 458-2550
Web Site: www.baldor.com
Sales Range: $125-149.9 Million
Emp.: 450
Electric Motors Mfr
S.I.C.: 3621
N.A.I.C.S.: 335312
Jim Riffel *(Plant Mgr)*

Baldor Electric Company (3)
3560 Scarlet Oak Blvd
Saint Louis, MO 63122-6604
Tel.: (636) 225-5022
Fax: (636) 825-6902
Web Site: www.baldor.com
Sales Range: $75-99.9 Million
Emp.: 275
Mfr of Electric Motors & Generators
S.I.C.: 3621
N.A.I.C.S.: 335312
Yavuz Bilecan *(Plant Mgr)*

Non-U.S. Subsidiaries:

Australia Baldor Pty Ltd (3)
Unit 3 6 Stanton Road
Seven Hills, NSW, 2147, Australia AU
Tel.: (61) 296745455
Fax: (61) 2 9674 2495
E-Mail: sales.au@baldor.com
Web Site: www.baldor.com.au
Electric Motors & Electronic Drives Marketer
S.I.C.: 3621
N.A.I.C.S.: 335312
Daniel Vera *(Mng Dir)*

Baldor Electric Canada Inc. (3)
678 Erie St
Stratford, ON, N4Z 1A2, Canada
Tel.: (519) 271-3630
Fax: (519) 271-8213
Emp.: 100
Electric Motor Mfr
S.I.C.: 3621
N.A.I.C.S.: 335312
Doug Fleming *(Gen Mgr)*

Baldor Electric Company de Mexico S.A. de C.V. (3)
Km 2.0 Blvd Aeropuerto
Leon, Guanajuato, 37545, Mexico MX
Tel.: (52) 477 761 2030
Fax: (52) 477 761 2010
E-Mail: sales.mx@baldor.com
Web Site: www.baldor.com
Electric Motors & Electronic Drives Marketer
S.I.C.: 3621
N.A.I.C.S.: 335312

Baldor Electric India Pvt Ltd. (3)
19 Commerce Avenue Mahaganesh Colony Paud Road
Kothrud, Pune, Maharastra, 411038, India
Tel.: (91) 20 2545 2717
Fax: (91) 20 2545 2719
E-Mail: sales.in@baldor.com
Electric Motor Mfr
S.I.C.: 3621
N.A.I.C.S.: 335312

Baldor Electric (Shanghai) Company Ltd. (3)
160 Song Sheng Road Songjiang Industrial Zone
Shanghai, China 20016
Tel.: (86) 21 57605335
Fax: (86) 21 57605336
Web Site: www.baldor.com.cn
Electrical Product Mfr & Distr
S.I.C.: 3699
N.A.I.C.S.: 335999

Baldor Electric Switzerland AG (3)
Schutzenstrasse 59
8245 Feuerthalen, Switzerland
Tel.: (41) 52 647 47 00
Fax: (41) 52 659 23 94
Electric Motor Mfr
S.I.C.: 3621
N.A.I.C.S.: 335312

Baldor Panama S.A. (3)
Ave Ricardo J Alfaro Edificio Sun Towers Mall - Local 55 2 Piso
A Lado del Autocentro, Panama, Panama
Tel.: (507) 236 5155
Fax: (507) 236 0591
Electric Motor Mfr
S.I.C.: 3621
N.A.I.C.S.: 335312

Baldor UK Limited (3)
Mint Motion Centre
6 Hawkley Drive, Bristol, BS32 0BF, United Kingdom
Tel.: (44) 1454850000
Fax: (44) 1454859002
E-Mail: sales.uk@baldor.com
Web Site: www.baldor.co.uk
Emp.: 100
Electric Motors & Electronic Drives Distr
S.I.C.: 3621
N.A.I.C.S.: 335312
Tristin Hurst *(Product Mgr)*

Kuhlman Electric Corporation (2)
3101 Beaumont Centre Cir Ste 225
Lexington, KY 40513-1886 DE
Tel.: (859) 879-2999
Fax: (859) 873-8032
Toll Free: (800) 765-6930
E-Mail: kuhlman@kuhlman.com
Web Site: www.kuhlman.com
Emp.: 100
Designs, Manufactures & Markets Electrical Transformers for Electric Utility Use
S.I.C.: 3612
N.A.I.C.S.: 335311
John Zvolensky *(Pres)*

LMI Connectors (2)
1181 S Rogers Cir Ste 25
Boca Raton, FL 33487-2727 FL
Tel.: (561) 994-5896
Fax: (561) 994-5913
E-Mail: david@lmicorp.com
Web Site: www.lmicorp.com
Emp.: 4
Electronic Circuits Mfr
S.I.C.: 3679
N.A.I.C.S.: 334419
David Asseraf *(Pres)*

Power-One Inc. (2)
740 Calle Plano
Camarillo, CA 93012-8555 DE
Tel.: (805) 987-8741
Fax: (805) 388-0476
Toll Free: (800) 678-9445
E-Mail: investor.relations@power-one.com
Web Site: www.power-one.com
Sls.: $1,022,578,000
Assets: $798,932,000
Liabilities: $281,999,000
Net Worth: $516,933,000
Earnings: $55,662,000
Emp.: 3,231
Fiscal Year-end: 12/30/12
AC/DC & DC/DC Power Supplies Mfr Export
S.I.C.: 3676
N.A.I.C.S.: 334418
Richard J. Thompson *(Pres & CEO)*
Gary R. Larsen *(CFO)*
Michael Sheehan *(CIO)*
Steven Hogge *(Pres-Power Solutions Strategic Bus Unit)*
Alexander Levran *(Pres-Renewable Energy Solutions)*
Tina D. McKnight *(Gen Counsel, Sec & Sr VP)*

Subsidiaries:

Power-One Renewable Energy Solutions LLC. (3)
740 Calle Plano
Camarillo, CA 93012-8555
Tel.: (805) 987-8741
Electronic Component Mfr
S.I.C.: 3679
N.A.I.C.S.: 334419

Non-U.S. Subsidiaries:

Power-One Ireland Ltd. (3)
Raheen Business Park Raheen
Limerick, Ireland
Tel.: (353) 61225977
Fax: (353) 61225984
Electrical Equipment & Component Mfr
S.I.C.: 3699
N.A.I.C.S.: 335999

Power-One Italy S.p.A. (3)
Via S Giorgio 642
Terranuova Bracciolini, 52028 Arezzo, Italy
Tel.: (39) 05591951
Fax: (39) 0559195248
Electronic Component Mfr
S.I.C.: 3679
N.A.I.C.S.: 334419

Power-One Limited (3)
Chandlers Yard 24 Uppr High St
Worthing, Sussex, BN11 1DL, United Kingdom
Tel.: (44) 1903823323
Fax: (44) 1903823324
E-Mail: service.uk@power-one.com
Web Site: www.power-one.com
Emp.: 8
Electrical Apparatus & Equipment Whslr
S.I.C.: 5063
N.A.I.C.S.: 423610
Renato Guerriero *(Office Mgr)*

Power-One Pte. Ltd. (3)
03-02 Primefield-landmark Bldg
27 International Business Park, Singapore, 609924, Singapore
Tel.: (65) 68963363
Fax: (65) 68963353
Power Transmission Products Mfr
S.I.C.: 3699
N.A.I.C.S.: 335999

Tropos Networks Inc. (2)
555 Del Rey Ave
Sunnyvale, CA 94085
Tel.: (408) 331-6800
Fax: (408) 331-6801
E-Mail: info@tropos.com
Web Site: www.tropos.com
Emp.: 15,000
Internet Service Provider
S.I.C.: 4813
N.A.I.C.S.: 517110
Narasimha Chari *(Co-Founder & CTO)*
Tom Ayers *(Pres & CEO)*

Validus DC Systems Inc. (2)
50 Pocono Rd
Brookfield, CT 06804
Tel.: (203) 448-3600
Fax: (203) 740-4201
Toll Free: (866) 747-3600
E-Mail: info@validusdc.com
Web Site: www.validusdc.com
Emp.: 20
Direct Current Powered Equipment Distr
S.I.C.: 5063
N.A.I.C.S.: 423610
Rudy Kraus *(CEO)*

Ventyx, Inc. (2)
3301 Windy Ridge Pkwy
Atlanta, GA 30339 DE
Tel.: (770) 952-8444
Fax: (770) 989-4231
Toll Free: (800) 650-8444
E-Mail: sales@ventyx.com
Web Site: www.ventyx.com
Sales Range: $250-299.9 Million
Emp.: 900
Asset Management Software & Services
S.I.C.: 7372
N.A.I.C.S.: 511210
Steve Carpenter *(Pres & COO)*
Jeff Ray *(CEO)*
Will Dailey *(Exec VP)*

Branches:

Ventyx, Inc. (3)
437 Grant St 18th Fl
Pittsburgh, PA 15219
Tel.: (412) 471-6800
Fax: (412) 471-7333
Web Site: www.ventyx.com
Emp.: 50
Asset Management Software & Services
S.I.C.: 7372
N.A.I.C.S.: 511210

Subsidiaries:

Obvient Strategies, Inc. (3)
2550 Northwinds Pkwy
Alpharetta, GA 30004
Tel.: (678) 336-1472
Fax: (678) 336-1478
Web Site: www.obvient.com
Emp.: 26
Computer Systems Design Services
S.I.C.: 7373
N.A.I.C.S.: 541512
Raymond Kasten *(CEO)*

Ventyx Asia Inc. (3)
400 Perimeter Center Ter Ste 500
Atlanta, GA 30346
Tel.: (678) 830-1000
Fax: (678) 830-1010
Emp.: 200
Software Development Services
S.I.C.: 7371
N.A.I.C.S.: 541511
Jeff Ray *(CEO)*
Juerg Seiler *(CFO)*

Subsidiary:

Ventyx USA, Inc. (3)
6455 S Yosemite St Ste 800
Greenwood Village, CO 80111-4918 GA
Tel.: (303) 446-9000
Fax: (303) 379-5777
Asset Management Software & Services
S.I.C.: 7372
N.A.I.C.S.: 511210

Subsidiary:

Ventyx Managed Services, Inc. (4)
6455 S Yosemite St Ste 800
Greenwood Village, CO 80111 DE
Tel.: (303) 446-9000
Fax: (303) 379-5777
Web Site: www.ventyx.com
Software Development Services
S.I.C.: 7371
N.A.I.C.S.: 541511

Non-U.S. Subsidiaries:

Ventyx Barranquilla (3)
Cra 54 No 68-196 302 Ed Prado Office Ctr
Barranquilla, Colombia
Tel.: (57) 53686645
Fax: (57) 53686643
E-Mail:
Asset Management Software & Services
S.I.C.: 7372
N.A.I.C.S.: 511210

Ventyx Dutch Holdings B.V. (3)
Naritaweg 165 Telestone-8
1043 BW Amsterdam, Netherlands
Tel.: (31) 205722300
Fax: (31) 205722650
Investment Management Services
S.I.C.: 6211
N.A.I.C.S.: 523999

Ventyx France (3)
Immeuble Central Gare
1 Place Charles de Gaulle, 78180 Montigny-le-Bretonneux, France
Tel.: (33) 139301717
Fax: (33) 139301700
Web Site: www.ventyx.com
Emp.: 24
Asset Management Software & Services
S.I.C.: 7372
N.A.I.C.S.: 511210
Michel Vouille *(Mng Dir)*

Ventyx, Inc. (3)
10651 Shellbridge Way Building 3
Richmond, BC, V6X 2W8, Canada Ca
Tel.: (604) 207-6000
Fax: (604) 207-6060
Toll Free: (800) 294-6374
E-Mail: info@ventex.abb.com
Web Site: www.ventyx.com
Sales Range: $50-74.9 Million
Emp.: 142
Asset Management Software & Services
S.I.C.: 7372
N.A.I.C.S.: 511210
Peter Wolfe *(VP-Software)*

Branch:

Ventyx, Inc. - Ottawa (4)
610 220 Laurier Avenue West
Ottawa, ON, K1P 5Z9, Canada
Tel.: (613) 569-4470
Fax: (613) 569-4471
E-Mail:
Emp.: 100
Asset Management Software & Services
S.I.C.: 7372
N.A.I.C.S.: 511210

Ventyx Johannesburg (3)
11 Autumn Rd
2128 Rivonia, South Africa
Tel.: (27) 112604600
Fax: (27) 118074759
E-Mail: info@mincom.com
Web Site: www.mincom.com
Emp.: 20
Asset Management Software & Services
S.I.C.: 7372
N.A.I.C.S.: 511210
Pierre Landberg *(VP-Africa Reg)*

Ventyx Lima (3)
Av Argentina 3120
Lima, Peru
Tel.: (51) 14155100
E-Mail:
Emp.: 3
Asset Management Software & Services
S.I.C.: 7372
N.A.I.C.S.: 511210
Wilsretoal Faro *(Mgr)*

Ventyx Poland (3)
OddziaA w Polsce
Korfantego 79, 40160 Katowice, Poland
Tel.: (48) 322592839
Fax: (48) 322592840
E-Mail: office@ventyx.com
Web Site: www.ventyx.com
Emp.: 5
Asset Management Software & Services
S.I.C.: 7372
N.A.I.C.S.: 511210
Jeff Ray *(CEO)*

Ventyx Pty. Ltd. (3)
193 Turbot Street
Brisbane, QLD, 4000, Australia
Tel.: (61) 733033333
Fax: (61) 733033232
E-Mail:
Sales Range: $200-249.9 Million
Emp.: 1,000
Enterprise Resource Planning & Asset Management Software Developer
S.I.C.: 7372
N.A.I.C.S.: 511210
Gregory J. Clark *(CEO)*
Simon Peach *(CFO & Exec VP)*
Greg Davies *(Exec VP-HR)*
Ross Laughlan *(Exec VP-R&D)*
Howard Wilson *(Sr VP-Field Ops)*

Subsidiaries:

Ventyx International Pty. Ltd. (4)
193 Turbot Street
Brisbane, QLD, 4000, Australia AU
Tel.: (61) 7 3303 3333
Fax: (61) 7 3303 3232
Web Site: www.ventyx.com
Holding Company
S.I.C.: 6719
N.A.I.C.S.: 551112

Non-U.S. Subsidiaries:

Mincom International (Peru) S.A.C. (5)
Av Argentina
3120 Lima, Peru
Tel.: (51) 1 415 5100
Software Development Services
S.I.C.: 7371
N.A.I.C.S.: 541511

Ventyx Services Pty. Ltd. (5)
13 Bon Accord Square
Aberdeen, AB11 6DJ, United Kingdom UK
Tel.: (44) 1224 581646
Software Development Services
S.I.C.: 7371
N.A.I.C.S.: 541511

Ventyx Managed Services Pty. Ltd. (4)
193 Turbot Street
Brisbane, QLD, 4000, Australia AU
Tel.: (61) 7 3303 3333
Fax: (61) 7 3303 3232
Web Site: www.ventyx.com
Software Development Services
S.I.C.: 7371

ABB Ltd.—(Continued)

N.A.I.C.S.: 541511

Ventyx (UK) Ltd. (3)
Britannia Wharf
Monument Road, Woking, Surrey, GU21
5LW, United Kingdom
Tel.: (44) 1483722777
Fax: (44) 1483 721 166
Web Site: www.ventyx.com
Emp.: 50
Asset Management Software & Services
S.I.C.: 7372
N.A.I.C.S.: 511210

Units:

ABB Equity Ventures (2)
3 Indepence Way Ste 202
Princeton, NJ 08540-6626
Tel.: (609) 243-7575
Fax: (609) 243-9174
Web Site: www.abb.com
Emp.: 11
Power Plant Developer, Builder, Owner & Operator
S.I.C.: 4911
N.A.I.C.S.: 221118

ABB Inc. - Analytical & Advanced Solutions (2)
843 N Jefferson St
Lewisburg, WV 24901-0831
Mailing Address:
PO Box 831
Lewisburg, WV 24901-0831
Tel.: (304) 647-4358
Fax: (304) 645-4236
E-Mail: lwbspares@us.abb.com
Web Site: www.abb.us
Emp.: 220
Process Analytical Instruments Mfr
S.I.C.: 3612
N.A.I.C.S.: 335311

ABB Inc. - Automation Technologies Drives & Motors (2)
16250 W Glendale Dr
New Berlin, WI 53151-2840
Tel.: (262) 785-3200
Telex: 260045 ASEA NEW BERLIN
Fax: (262) 785-3290
Web Site: www.abb-drives.com
Emp.: 307
AC/DC Drives, Large Electric Motors, Generators, Power Electronics, Rectifier Systems, Sheet Metal Forming Presses Mfr
S.I.C.: 3612
N.A.I.C.S.: 335311
John Tisdale *(Mgr-Sls)*

ABB Inc. - Automation Technologies Instrumentation Products (2)
125 E County Line Rd
Warminster, PA 18974-4995 PA
Tel.: (215) 674-6000
Fax: (215) 674-7183
Toll Free: (800) 829-6001
Web Site: www.abb.us
Emp.: 500
Process Control Instruments & Systems Mfr
Import Export
S.I.C.: 3823
N.A.I.C.S.: 334513
Robert Mapleston *(Mgr-Mktg)*

ABB Inc. - Automation Technologies (2)
29801 Euclid Ave
Wickliffe, OH 44092
Tel.: (440) 585-8500
Fax: (440) 585-8756
Web Site: www.abb.us
Emp.: 500
Computerized Industrial Control System Mfr & Distr
S.I.C.: 3823
N.A.I.C.S.: 334513

ABB Inc. - Power Technologies Components Factory (2)
1128 Cavalier Dr
Alamo, TN 38001-9801
Tel.: (731) 696-5561
Fax: (731) 696-5269
Toll Free: (800) 955-8399
Web Site: www.abb.us
Emp.: 165
Transformer Components Mfr
S.I.C.: 3621
N.A.I.C.S.: 335312
Thomas Andersson *(Gen Mgr)*

ABB Inc. - Power Technologies Medium Voltage (2)
655 Century Pt
Lake Mary, FL 32746
Tel.: (407) 732-2000
Fax: (407) 732-2342
E-Mail: info@abb.com
Web Site: www.abb.com
Emp.: 230
Switch Gears Mfr
S.I.C.: 3612
N.A.I.C.S.: 335311

ABB Inc. - SSAC (2)
8242 Loop Rd
Baldwinsville, NY 13027
Tel.: (315) 638-1300
Fax: (315) 638-0333
Web Site: www.ssac.com
Emp.: 132
Electronic Controls Mfr
S.I.C.: 3625
N.A.I.C.S.: 335314

ABB Inc. - Turbocharging (2)
1460 Livingston Ave
North Brunswick, NJ 08902-1832
Tel.: (732) 932-6103
Fax: (732) 932-6378
E-Mail: turbo@us.abb.com
Web Site: www.abb.us
Emp.: 12
Turbocharger Mfr
S.I.C.: 5063
N.A.I.C.S.: 423610
Gabriel Petricone *(Acct Mgr)*

ABB Inc. - Power Systems (2)
2000 Day Hill Rd
Windsor, CT 06095-1580
Tel.: (860) 285-6870
Fax: (860) 285-6890
Web Site: www.abb.us
Emp.: 50
Power Control Equipment Mfr
S.I.C.: 3612
N.A.I.C.S.: 335311
Fred Kindle *(Pres & CEO)*

ABB Inc. (2)
1250 Brown Rd
Auburn Hills, MI 48326 (100%)
Tel.: (248) 391-9000
Fax: (248) 391-9270
E-Mail: info@abb.com
Web Site: www.abb.com
Emp.: 450
Automation Technologies
S.I.C.: 3699
N.A.I.C.S.: 335999
Charlie Miller *(Mgr-Sls)*

ABB Inc. (2)
940 Main Campus Dr Ste 400
Raleigh, NC 27606 NC
Tel.: (919) 856-2360 (100%)
Fax: (909) 666-1607
E-Mail: hrsmart@abb.us
Web Site: www.abb.us
Rev.: $303,900,000
Emp.: 150
Business Services
S.I.C.: 7389
N.A.I.C.S.: 561499

ABB Inc. (2)
579 Executive Campus Dr
Westerville, OH 43082 OH
Tel.: (614) 818-6300
Fax: (614) 818-6570
Web Site: www.abb.us
Emp.: 150
Measuring & Controlling Instruments Mfr
Import Export
S.I.C.: 3829
N.A.I.C.S.: 334519
Roger A. Bailey *(Pres-Power Products-North America)*

ABB Inc. (2)
575 Epsilon Dr
Pittsburgh, PA 15238-2816
Tel.: (412) 967-5858
Fax: (412) 967-5868
Emp.: 5
Semiconductor Mfr
S.I.C.: 3674
N.A.I.C.S.: 334413
Stephen Kochis *(Dir-Ops & Quality High Voltage-North America)*

ABB Inc. (2)
1601 Industrial Blvd
Sugar Land, TX 77478
Tel.: (281) 274-5000
Fax: (281) 274-5577
Web Site: www.abb.us.com
Emp.: 77
Electric Power Transmission, Distribution & Generation Control Systems
S.I.C.: 3612
N.A.I.C.S.: 335311
Allen R. Skopp *(VP-Sls & Mktg)*

ABB Inc. (2)
16250 W Glendale Dr
New Berlin, WI 53151-2840
Tel.: (940) 397-7000
Fax: (940) 397-7001
Toll Free: (888) 385-1221
E-Mail: info@abb-control.com
Web Site: www.abb-control.com
Emp.: 150
Industrial Motor Control Products, Disconnect Switches, Programmable Logic Controllers, Circuit Breakers, Capacitors Mfr
S.I.C.: 3625
N.A.I.C.S.: 335314

Non-U.S. Subsidiaries:

ABB A/S (1)
Meterbuen 33
2740 Skovlunde, Denmark DK
Tel.: (45) 44504450 (100%)
Fax: (45) 44504460
E-Mail: abb.dk@dk.abb.com
Web Site: www.abb.dk
Emp.: 700
Electrical Products Mfr & Sales
S.I.C.: 3699
N.A.I.C.S.: 335999
Claus Madsen *(Mng Dir)*

ABB A/S (1)
Bergerveien 12
1375 Billingstad, Norway NO
Tel.: (47) 22872000 (100%)
Fax: (47) 22874669
E-Mail: rune.finne@no.abb.com
Web Site: www.abb.no
Emp.: 2,000
Electrical Products Mfr
S.I.C.: 5211
N.A.I.C.S.: 444190

Subsidiary:

ABB Robotics (2)
Nordlysveien 3
PO Box 265
N 4340 Bryne, Norway
Tel.: (47) 51489000
Telex: 33179 robot n
Fax: (47) 51483725
E-Mail: nofac.robot@no.abb.com
Web Site: www.no.abb.com
Emp.: 92
Robotics Mfr
S.I.C.: 3559
N.A.I.C.S.: 333249
Veim Seglem *(Pres)*

ABB AB (1)
Kopparbergsvagen 2
SE 72183 Vasteras, Sweden
Tel.: (46) 21325000
E-Mail: contact.center@se.abb.com
Web Site: www.abb.se
Emp.: 4,500
Power & Automation Technology Products Mfr
S.I.C.: 3612
N.A.I.C.S.: 335311
Johan Soderstrom *(CEO & Country Mgr)*

Subsidiaries:

ABB Automation Technologies AB (2)
PO Box 1005
S 61129 Nykoping, Sweden (100%)
Tel.: (46) 155295000
Telex: 64017 SELFAS
Fax: (46) 155288110
Web Site: www.abb.se
Emp.: 11,000
Low-Voltage Apparatus Mfr; Boards, Heat Exchangers, Heat Pumps Distr
S.I.C.: 3585
N.A.I.C.S.: 333415

ABB Power Technologies AB (2)
PO Box 273
94126 Pitea, Sweden (100%)
Tel.: (46) 91177700
Telex: 80420 ELPLAST S
Fax: (46) 91177704
Web Site: www.abb.se
Emp.: 250
Electrical Insulating Materials & Industrial Plastics Mfr
S.I.C.: 3544
N.A.I.C.S.: 333511

ABB Power Technologies AB (2)
Valhalawagen 2
PO Box 702
S 77180 Ludvika, Sweden SE
Tel.: (46) 240782000 (100%)
Telex: 74507
Fax: (46) 240784190
E-Mail: info.selog@se.abb.com
Web Site: www.abb.se
Emp.: 2,500
Transformers & Reactors Mfr
S.I.C.: 3612
N.A.I.C.S.: 335311
Lars Hagerfors *(Controller)*

ABB Robotics AB (2)
Lunnagardsgadan 4
43187 Molndal, Sweden (100%)
Tel.: (46) 317738500
Fax: (46) 317738550
E-Mail: info@se.abb.com
Web Site: www.abb.se
Emp.: 45
Robotic Systems Mfr
S.I.C.: 7373
N.A.I.C.S.: 541512
Aoakim Askviken *(Mgr-Bus Center)*

ABB Robotics AB (2)
ABB Ab Robotics
Vastmanland, 721 68 Vasteras, Sweden (100%)
Tel.: (46) 21344000
Telex: 40980 ASEAROBS
Fax: (46) 21132592
E-Mail: anders.nulander@se.abb.com
Web Site: www.abb.se
Emp.: 1,000
Industrial Robots, Robot Systems & Vision Systems Mfr
S.I.C.: 3559
N.A.I.C.S.: 333249
Mikael Svensson *(Mng Dir)*

Lorentzen & Wettre AB (2)
Viderogatan 2
PO Box 4
S 164 93 Kista, Sweden (100%)
Tel.: (46) 84779000
Fax: (46) 84779199
E-Mail: info@lorentzen-wettre.com
Web Site: www.lorentzen-wettre.com
Sales Range: $25-49.9 Million
Emp.: 188
Mfr & Supplier of Quality Control, Measurement & Process Automation Equipment for Paper Mill Industries
S.I.C.: 3554
N.A.I.C.S.: 333243
Patrik Stolpe *(Pres)*

Subsidiaries:

Lorentzen & Waettre Skandinavien AB (3)
Viderogatan 2
Box 4
164 93 Kista, Sweden
Tel.: (46) 8 517 921 90
Fax: (46) 8 517 921 99
E-Mail: skandinavien@lorentzen-wettre.com
Web Site: www.lorentzen-wettre.com
Emp.: 100
Testing & Quality Control Instrument Mfr
S.I.C.: 3823
N.A.I.C.S.: 334513
Kent Ingvar Jansson *(CEO)*

Lorentzen & Wettre International AB (3)
Box 4
164 93 Kista, Sweden

Tel.: (46) 8 477 90 00
Fax: (46) 8 477 91 99
Web Site: www.lorentzen-wettre.com
Paper Product Testing Services
S.I.C.: 8734
N.A.I.C.S.: 541380
Patrick Arnstroem *(Area Mgr-Sls)*

U.S. Subsidiary:

Lorentzen & Wettre USA, Inc. (3)
1055 Windward Ridge Pkwy Ste 160
Alpharetta, GA 30005-1729
Tel.: (770) 442-8015
Fax: (770) 442-6792
E-Mail: usa@lorentzen-wettre.com
Web Site: www.lorentzen-wettre.com
Emp.: 15
Paper Testing Equipment Mfr
S.I.C.: 5084
N.A.I.C.S.: 423830
Philip Westmoreland *(Pres)*

Non-U.S. Subsidiaries:

ABB UK (3)
Auriga House Precedent Drive
Milton Keynes, Rooksley, MK13 8PQ,
United Kingdom (100%)
Tel.: (44) 1908 350 300
Fax: (44) 1908 350 301
E-Mail:
Web Site: www.abb.com
Sales & Service of Equipment for Pulp & Paper Industry
S.I.C.: 5084
N.A.I.C.S.: 423830
Hanspeter Faessler *(Global Head-Grid Sys)*

Kajaani Process Measurements Ltd. (3)
Kettukalliontie 9E
87100 Kajaani, Finland
Tel.: (358) 10 548 76 00
Fax: (358) 8 612 06 83
E-Mail: kpm@prokajaani.com
Web Site: www.prokajaani.com
Emp.: 10
Consistency Transmitter & Break Detection Equipment Mfr
S.I.C.: 3679
N.A.I.C.S.: 334419
Urpo Heikkinen *(Mng Dir)*

Lorentzen & Wettre Canada, Inc. (3)
4709 Louis-B Mayer
Laval, QC, H7P 6G5, Canada (100%)
Tel.: (514) 694-4522
Fax: (514) 694-0799
E-Mail: canada@l-w.com
Web Site: www.lorentzen-wettre.com
Emp.: 10
Sales & Service of Equipment for Pulp & Paper Industry
S.I.C.: 5084
N.A.I.C.S.: 423830

Lorentzen & Wettre GmbH (3)
Haidelweg 48
81248 Munich, Germany (100%)
Mailing Address:
PO Box 700740
D-81307 Munich, Germany
Tel.: (49) 897850040
Fax: (49) 8978500443
E-Mail: germany@lorentzen-wettre.com
Web Site: www.lorentzen-wettre.com
Emp.: 18
Sales & Service of Equipment for Pulp & Paper Industry
S.I.C.: 5084
N.A.I.C.S.: 423830

Lorentzen & Wettre Ltda (3)
Rua Machado Bittencourt 406 Vila Mariana
Sao Paulo, 04044-001, Brazil
Tel.: (55) 11 50844505
Fax: (55) 11 50844390
E-Mail: brazil@l-w.com
Testing & Quality Control Instrument Mfr
S.I.C.: 3291
N.A.I.C.S.: 327910

Lorentzen & Wettre s.a.r.l. (3)
91 Rue Pereire
F 78100 Saint Germain-en-Laye,
France (100%)
Tel.: (33) 130870220
Fax: (33) 130870230
E-Mail: france@l-w.com
Web Site: www.lorentzen-wettre.com
Emp.: 10
Sales & Service of Equipment for Pulp & Paper Industry
S.I.C.: 5084
N.A.I.C.S.: 423830
Edward Wallis *(Gen Mgr)*

Oy Lorentzen & Wettre AB (3)
Turvekuja 6
FI 00700 Helsinki, Finland (100%)
Tel.: (358) 753240400
Fax: (358) 9790097
E-Mail: finland@lorentzen-wettre.com
Web Site: www.lorentzenwettre.com
Emp.: 9
Sales & Service of Equipment for Pulp & Paper Industry
S.I.C.: 5084
N.A.I.C.S.: 423830
Asko Kangas *(Mgr)*

ABB AG (1)
Clemens Holzmeister Strasse 4
A 1109 Vienna, Austria AT
Tel.: (43) 1601090 (100%)
Fax: (43) 1601098910
E-Mail: office@at.abb.com
Web Site: www.abb.at
Emp.: 450
Power Generation, Power Transmission, Industrial & Building Systems Mfr
Import Export
S.I.C.: 4911
N.A.I.C.S.: 221118
Werner Zumpf *(Controller)*

ABB AG (1)
Kallstadter Strasse 1
D-68309 Mannheim, Germany De
Tel.: (49) 62143810 (100%)
Telex: 462 4110 bb d
Fax: (49) 6214381390
E-Mail: information@abb.de
Web Site: www.abb.de.com
Sls.: $3,634,800,128
Emp.: 2,000
Energy & Automation Products Mfr
S.I.C.: 3613
N.A.I.C.S.: 335313
Peter Smith *(CEO)*

Subsidiaries:

ABB Automation GmbH (2)
Kallstadter Str 1
68309 Mannheim, Germany
Tel.: (49) 621 381 0
Fax: (49) 381 5135
Industrial Automation System Mfr
S.I.C.: 3559
N.A.I.C.S.: 333249

ABB Automation Products GmbH (2)
Wallstadter Strasse 59
68526 Ladenburg, Germany
Tel.: (49) 6203 71 0
Web Site: www.abb.de/cawp/deabb201/0428ecb64493306ac125692a00437c82.aspx
Electric Equipment Mfr
S.I.C.: 3699
N.A.I.C.S.: 335999

ABB Bauprojektmanagement GmbH (2)
Ohmweg 11-15
68199 Mannheim, Germany
Tel.: (49) 621 81 01 0
Fax: (49) 621 81 01 5 05
Industrial Automation System Mfr
S.I.C.: 3559
N.A.I.C.S.: 333249

ABB Beteiligungs- und Verwaltungsges. mbH (2)
Kallstadter Str 1
68309 Mannheim, Germany
Tel.: (49) 6213810
Fax: (49) 6213818788
Financial Services
S.I.C.: 6211
N.A.I.C.S.: 523999

ABB Business Services GmbH (2)
Eppelheimer Str 82
69123 Heidelberg, Germany
Tel.: (49) 6221 70100
Fax: (49) 6221 701693
Electrical Engineering Services
S.I.C.: 8711
N.A.I.C.S.: 541330

ABB Calor Emag Mittelspannung GmbH (2)
Oberhausener Str 33
D-40472 Ratingen, Germany
Tel.: (49) 2102120
Telex: 858 5 123 cer d
Fax: (49) 2102121777
E-Mail: calor.info@de.abb.com
Web Site: www.abb.de
Emp.: 1,296
Switchgears & Control Systems Mfr
S.I.C.: 3613
N.A.I.C.S.: 335313

ABB Grundbesitz GmbH (2)
Wallstadter Str 59
68526 Ladenburg, Germany
Tel.: (49) 6203 71 6612
Fax: (49) 6203 71 6610
Web Site: new.abb.com
Property Management Services
S.I.C.: 6531
N.A.I.C.S.: 531312

ABB Logistics Center Europe GmbH (2)
Braukerweg 132
58708 Menden, Germany
Tel.: (49) 237 39 69 50
Fax: (49) 23 73 96 95 95
Logistics Consulting Services
S.I.C.: 4731
N.A.I.C.S.: 541614

ABB Service GmbH (2)
Max-Fischer-Strasse 11
86399 Bobingen, Germany
Tel.: (49) 8234 82 2630
Fax: (49) 8234 82 2127
Industrial Machinery Maintenance Services
S.I.C.: 7699
N.A.I.C.S.: 811310

ABB Stotz-Kontakt GmbH (2)
Eppelheimer Strasse 82
69123 Heidelberg, Germany
Tel.: (49) 6221 701 0
Fax: (49) 6221 701 1325
E-Mail: info.testo@de.abb.com
Web Site: new.abb.com
Electrical Equipment Mfr & Distr
S.I.C.: 3699
N.A.I.C.S.: 335999

ABB Stotz-Kontakt/Striebel & John Vertriebs-GmbH (2)
Eppelheimer Strasse 82
69123 Heidelberg, Germany
Tel.: (49) 180 569 2002
Fax: (49) 180 569 3003
E-Mail: info@de.abb.com
Emp.: 114
Electronic Product Distr
S.I.C.: 5065
N.A.I.C.S.: 423690

ABB Training Center GmbH & Co. KG (2)
Eppelheimer Strasse 82
Heidelberg, 69123, Germany
Tel.: (49) 6221 701 1494
Fax: (49) 6221 701 1491
Web Site: new.abb.com
Commercial & Technical Training Services
S.I.C.: 8299
N.A.I.C.S.: 611519

ABB Wirtschaftsbetriebe GmbH (2)
Kallstadter Strasse 1
68309 Mannheim, Germany
Tel.: (49) 621 381 2874
Fax: (49) 621 381 5999
Catering Services
S.I.C.: 5812
N.A.I.C.S.: 722310

Busch-Jaeger Elektro GmbH (2)
Freisenbergstrasse 2
58513 Ludenscheid, Germany
Tel.: (49) 2351 956 1600
Fax: (49) 2351 956 1700
E-Mail: info.bje@de.abb.com
Web Site: www.busch-jaeger.de
Emp.: 1,000
Electrical Equipment Mfr & Distr
S.I.C.: 3699
N.A.I.C.S.: 335999

JLEC Power Ventures GmbH (2)
Kallstadter Strasse 1
68309 Mannheim, Germany
Tel.: (49) 621 381 0
Fax: (49) 621 3818018
Electric Power Generation Services
S.I.C.: 4911
N.A.I.C.S.: 221118

Pucaro Elektro-Isolierstoffe GmbH (2)
Pucarostrasse 1
74255 Roigheim, Germany
Tel.: (49) 6298 27 0
Fax: (49) 6298 27 820
E-Mail: info@pucaro.de
Web Site: www.pucaro.com
Emp.: 300
Electrical Insulation System Mfr
S.I.C.: 3699
N.A.I.C.S.: 335999
Tomas Arenius *(Gen Mgr)*

Striebel & John GmbH & Co. KG (2)
Am Fuchsgraben 2-3
77880 Sasbach, Germany
Tel.: (49) 7841 609 0
Fax: (49) 7841 609 400
E-Mail: info.desuj@de.abb.com
Web Site: www.striebelundjohn.com
Emp.: 400
Electric Power Distribution System Mfr
S.I.C.: 3612
N.A.I.C.S.: 335311
Heinz Saure *(Mng Dir)*

Subsidiary:

Striebel Vermogensverwaltungs-GmbH (3)
Fuchsgraben 2
77880 Sasbach, Germany
Tel.: (49) 7841 6090
Fax: (49) 7841 609400
E-Mail: info.de@abb.com
Emp.: 400
Power Transmission Equipment Mfr
S.I.C.: 3568
N.A.I.C.S.: 333613
Heinz Saura *(Mng Dir)*

Non-U.S. Subsidiary:

Striebel & John France S.A.R.L. (3)
Zi Zone Industrielle
68470 Fellering, France
Tel.: (33) 3 89 38 27 28
Fax: (33) 3 89 82 66 74
Plastic Product Mfr
S.I.C.: 3089
N.A.I.C.S.: 326199

ABB Algeria SpA (1)
Chemin de la Madeleine Haute Site d
Hydra Zone Djemane Haroual
16405 Hydra, Algeria
Tel.: (213) 21 79 41 51
Fax: (213) 21 794062
Power & Electrical Engineering Services
S.I.C.: 8711
N.A.I.C.S.: 541330

Subsidiary:

ABB International Marketing Ltd. (2)
2 Impasse Ahmed Kara
PO Box 156
Cite Malki Ben Aknoun, DZ-16035 Hydra, Algeria
Tel.: (213) 21546099
Fax: (213) 21547569
Web Site: www.mena.abb.com
Power & Automation Products Marketer & Distr
S.I.C.: 5084
N.A.I.C.S.: 423830

ABB AS (1)
Arukula Tee 59
Juri, Harjumaa, 75301, Estonia
Tel.: (372) 6801 700
Fax: (372) 6801 710
E-Mail: info@ee.abb.com
Web Site: www.abb.ee
Electric Power Distribution Services
S.I.C.: 4931
N.A.I.C.S.: 221122

ABB Australia Pty Limited (1)
Level 19 68 Pitt St
Sydney, NSW, 2000, Australia AU
Tel.: (61) 292553999 (100%)

ABB Ltd.—(Continued)

Fax: (61) 292553988
Web Site: www.abbaustralia.com.au
Emp.: 20
Electric Motors, Switchgear & Circuit-Breaker Assembly
S.I.C.: 5063
N.A.I.C.S.: 423610
Axel Kuhr *(Country Mgr)*

Subsidiaries:

ABB Group Investment Management Pty. Ltd. (2)
L 20 Goldfields House 1 Alfred St
Sydney, NSW, 2000, Australia
Tel.: (61) 2 9255 3999
Investment Management Services
S.I.C.: 6211
N.A.I.C.S.: 523999

EAM Software Finance Pty Ltd (2)
L 7 193 Turbot St
Brisbane, QLD, 4000, Australia
Tel.: (61) 7 3303 3333
Financial Management Services
S.I.C.: 6211
N.A.I.C.S.: 523999

EAM Software Holdings Pty Ltd (2)
L 7 193 Turbot St
Brisbane, QLD, 4000, Australia
Tel.: (61) 7 3303 3333
Financial Management Services
S.I.C.: 6211
N.A.I.C.S.: 523999

EnergyPoint IRM Pty Ltd (2)
6 Abercrombie River Rd
Abercrombie River, NSW, 2795, Australia
Tel.: (61) 2 6332 9030
Electric Power Generation & Distribution Services
S.I.C.: 4939
N.A.I.C.S.: 221118

Powercorp Research and Development Pty Ltd (2)
Darwin Business Park Export Dr
Berrimah, Darwin, NT, 0828, Australia
Tel.: (61) 8 8947 0
Fax: (61) 8 8947 0
E-Mail: mail@pcorp.com.au
Web Site: www.pcorp.com.au
Electric Power Generation Services
S.I.C.: 4911
N.A.I.C.S.: 221118
Alan Langworthy *(Mng Dir)*

ABB Automation E.C. (1)
Bldg 175 Block 343 Rd 4304 Mina Salmon
Manama, Bahrain
Tel.: (973) 17725377
Fax: (973) 17725332
E-Mail: bhare@batelco.com.bh
Web Site: www.mena.abb.com
Emp.: 100
Power & Automation Products Sales & Distr
S.I.C.: 5084
N.A.I.C.S.: 423830
Basim Akkawi *(Pres)*

ABB Bulgaria EOOD (1)
9 Christoper Columbus Boulevard Floor 3
1592 Sofia, Bulgaria BG
Tel.: (359) 28075500 (100%)
Fax: (359) 28075599
E-Mail: office@bg.abb.com
Web Site: www.abb.com
Emp.: 1,000
Power & Automation Products Mfr
S.I.C.: 3612
N.A.I.C.S.: 335311
Peter Simon *(Country Mgr)*

Subsidiaries:

ABB Automation EOOD (2)
14 Industrialen put 1
Stryama, 4142 Rakovski, Bulgaria
Tel.: (359) 32 998800
Fax: (359) 32 621848
E-Mail: abb.rakovski-branch@bg.abb.com
Web Site: new.abb.com
Emp.: 800
Mfr of Components for Low & Medium Voltage Equipment
S.I.C.: 3612
N.A.I.C.S.: 335311

ABB Avangard AD (2)
32 Nikola Petkov Str
5400 Sevlievo, Bulgaria
Tel.: (359) 675 30037
Fax: (359) 675 30043
E-Mail: abb.avangard@bg.abb.com
Emp.: 100
Electrical Equipment Mfr
S.I.C.: 3699
N.A.I.C.S.: 335999
Luzi Schoeb *(Gen Mgr)*

ABB B.V. (1)
George Hintzenweg 81
PO Box 301
NL 3000 AH Rotterdam, Netherlands NL
Tel.: (31) 104078911 (100%)
Fax: (31) 104078452
E-Mail: info@nl.abb.com
Emp.: 500
Switchgear & Converters Mfr
S.I.C.: 3613
N.A.I.C.S.: 335313
A Goos *(Mng Dir)*

Subsidiaries:

ABB Group Accounting Services B.V. (2)
George Hintzenweg 81
3068 AX Rotterdam, Netherlands
Tel.: (31) 104078911
Fax: (31) 104078452
Emp.: 304
Accounting Services
S.I.C.: 8721
N.A.I.C.S.: 541219
Alfons Goos *(Gen Mgr)*

ABB Holdings BV (2)
Burgemeester Haspelslaan 65
1181 NB Amstelveen, Netherlands
Tel.: (31) 20 543 44 44
Fax: (31) 20 445 98 44
Web Site: www.abb.be
Emp.: 5
Investment Management Services
S.I.C.: 6211
N.A.I.C.S.: 523999
Brian Dir *(Mng Dir)*

Epyon B.V. (2)
Delftweg 65
Rijswijk, 2289 BA, Netherlands
Tel.: (31) 70 307 6200
Fax: (31) 70 307 6209
E-Mail: infoacc@nl.abb.com
Web Site: www.epyonpower.com
Emp.: 40
Electric Power Conversion System Mfr
S.I.C.: 3643
N.A.I.C.S.: 335931
Hans Streng *(Mng Dir)*

ABB (China) Ltd. (1)
Universal Plaza
10 Jiuxianqiao Lu, Beijing, 100015, China CN
Tel.: (86) 01084566688 (100%)
Fax: (86) 1084567613
Web Site: www.abb.com.cn
Power & Automation Products
S.I.C.: 3612
N.A.I.C.S.: 335311
Chunyuan Gu *(Head-China & North Asia)*

Subsidiaries:

ABB Bailey Beijing Engineering Co. Ltd. (2)
Universal Plaza 10 Jiuxianqiao Lu
Chaoyang District, Beijing, China
Tel.: (86) 10 8456 6688
Fax: (86) 10 6423 3324
Electrical Equipment Sales & Maintenance Services
S.I.C.: 7699
N.A.I.C.S.: 811310
Han Wei *(Pres)*

ABB Beijing Drive Systems Co. Ltd. (2)
No 1 Block D A-10 Jiuxianqiao Beilu
Chaoyang District, Beijing, 100015, China
Tel.: (86) 10 5821 7788
Fax: (86) 10 5821 7518
Emp.: 1,000
Speed Control Drive Mfr & Distr
S.I.C.: 3699
N.A.I.C.S.: 335999
Timo Salmela *(Pres)*

ABB Electrical Machines Ltd. (2)
No 380 Tianxing Rd
Minhang District, Shanghai, 200245, China
Tel.: (86) 21 6113 7688
Fax: (86) 21 6113 7788
Web Site: www.abb.co.in/cawp/cna bb051/3cec481a 074579c9482571cd001ee3fa.aspx
Electric Motor Mfr
S.I.C.: 3621
N.A.I.C.S.: 335312
John-Qiang Yin *(Pres)*

ABB Engineering (Shanghai) Ltd. (2)
No 5 Lane 369 Chuangye Rd
Pudong District, Shanghai, 201319, China
Tel.: (86) 21 6105 6666
Fax: (86) 21 6105 6677
Web Site: www.abb.com.cn/cawp/cna bb051/add0a9ef71047f78412567de 00545509.aspx
Emp.: 2,000
Flow Measurement Equipment Mfr
S.I.C.: 3823
N.A.I.C.S.: 334513

ABB Generators Ltd. (2)
3088 Ziyang Avenue High-Tech Development Zone
330096 Nanchang, Jiangxi, China
Tel.: (86) 791 8835 0800
Fax: (86) 791 8835 0814
Diesel Generator Mfr
S.I.C.: 3621
N.A.I.C.S.: 335312
Chen Chen *(Pres)*

ABB Hefei Transformer Co. Ltd. (2)
3318 Lianhua Road Hefei Economic & Technological Development Zone
Hefei, Anhui, 230601, China
Tel.: (86) 551 227 3814
Fax: (86) 551 227 3818
Web Site: www.abb.com
Emp.: 800
Power & Distribution Transformer Mfr
S.I.C.: 3612
N.A.I.C.S.: 335311
Swee Seng Lee *(Pres)*

ABB High Voltage Switchgear (Xiamen) Company Ltd. (2)
Guanghui Building 6 Chuang Xin 3rd Road
Xiamen SEZ, Xiamen, Fujian, 361006, China
Tel.: (86) 592 571 0330
Fax: (86) 592 571 0331
Web Site: www.abb.com
Emp.: 300
Electric Switchgear Mfr
S.I.C.: 3613
N.A.I.C.S.: 335313
Hans Persson *(Pres)*

ABB LV Installation Materials Co. Ltd. (2)
No 17 Kangding Street Beijing Economic-Technological Development Area
Beijing, 100176, China
Tel.: (86) 10 5808 5000
Fax: (86) 10 5808 5288
Web Site: www.abb.com.cn/cawp/cna bb051/738c383feba73594482576a 300387a7e.aspx
Low Voltage Product Mfr
S.I.C.: 3699
N.A.I.C.S.: 335999
Zhongdan Wang *(Pres)*

ABB Shanghai Motors Co. Ltd. (2)
88 Tianning Rd Minhang Economic & Technological Development Zone
Shanghai, 200245, China
Tel.: (86) 21 5472 3133
Fax: (86) 21 5472 5009
Emp.: 800
Induction Motor Mfr
S.I.C.: 3621
N.A.I.C.S.: 335312
Ko-Hein Chai *(Pres)*

ABB Shanghai Transformer Co. Ltd. (2)
2300 Shen Jiang Road
Pudong District, Shanghai, 201206, China
Tel.: (86) 21 5899 6488
Fax: (86) 21 5031 4387
Electrical Transformer Distr
S.I.C.: 5063
N.A.I.C.S.: 423610
Patrick Bai *(Pres)*

ABB Tianjin Switchgear Co., Ltd. (2)
No 76 Gaoxin Street Tianjin Beichen Hi-tech Industrial Park
Tianjin, 300409, China
Tel.: (86) 22 8688 0188
Fax: (86) 22 8688 0189
Web Site: www.abb.com.cn/cawp/cna bb051/13bfe94ed1c851e 2482575380028be2b.aspx
Switchgear Mfr & Distr
S.I.C.: 3613
N.A.I.C.S.: 335313
John-SiewJoon Quah *(Pres)*

ABB Xiamen Electrical Controlgear Co. Ltd. (2)
No 559 Weili Road Information And Photoelectricity Park
Torch Hi-Tech Industrial Devel, Xiamen, Fujian, 361009, China
Tel.: (86) 592 6303 000
Fax: (86) 592 6303 002
Switchgear Product Distr
S.I.C.: 5063
N.A.I.C.S.: 423610
David Xu *(Pres)*

ABB Xiamen Low Voltage Equipment Co. Ltd. (2)
No 12-20 3rd Chuang Xin Road High Technology Development Zone
Xiamen, Fujian, 361006, China
Tel.: (86) 592 603 8118
Fax: (86) 592 603 8110
Low Voltage Switchgear Mfr
S.I.C.: 3613
N.A.I.C.S.: 335313
Ian Lui *(Pres)*

ABB Xi'an Power Capacitor Company Limited (2)
No 158 Wenjing Road Xi'an Economic & Technological Development Zone
Xi'an, Shaanxi, 710021, China
Tel.: (86) 29 8422 1448
Fax: (86) 29 8428 7771
Electrical Component Mfr
S.I.C.: 3675
N.A.I.C.S.: 334416
Mun-Keong Moh *(Pres)*

ABB Zhongshan Transformer Company Ltd. (2)
No 1 Haicheng North Rd Hengmen
Nanlang Town, Zhongshan, Guangdong, 528449, China
Tel.: (86) 760 2339 2288
Fax: (86) 760 2339 6500
Web Site: www.abb.com
Transformer Mfr
S.I.C.: 3612
N.A.I.C.S.: 335311
Jim Huang *(Pres)*

Hangzhou Winmation Automation Company Limited (2)
No 67 Jianshe Er Road
Xiaoshan District, Hangzhou, 311215, China
Tel.: (86) 571 8387 6000
Fax: (86) 571 8387 6599
Industrial Control System Mfr & Distr
S.I.C.: 3823
N.A.I.C.S.: 334513

Maska Power Transmission (Changzhou) Co. Ltd. (2)
No 8 Bldg Zhisi Industrial Park No 18 Fengming Road
Wujin District, Changzhou, Jiangsu, 213161, China
Tel.: (86) 519 86220880
Fax: (86) 519 86220660
Web Site: www.maskachina.com
Emp.: 150
Power Transmission Equipment Mfr
S.I.C.: 3568
N.A.I.C.S.: 333613
Yves Falardeau *(Dir-Plant)*

Yangzhou SAC Switchgear Co., Ltd. (2)
No 88 Hanjianghe Lu
225000 Yangzhou, Jiangsu, China
Tel.: (86) 514 8971 1956

Fax: (86) 514 8971 1957
Web Site: www.abb.com
Switchgear Mfr
S.I.C.: 3613
N.A.I.C.S.: 335313
Allen-WenBin He *(Gen Mgr)*

ABB d.o.o. (1)
Kumodraska 235
11000 Belgrade, Serbia
Tel.: (381) 11 3094 300
Fax: (381) 11 3094 343
Emp.: 42
Electronic & Electrical Component Mfr
S.I.C.: 3679
N.A.I.C.S.: 334419
Katarina Grujic *(Asst Mgr-HR)*

ABB Ecuador S.A. (1)
Av Atahualpa 1-198 y Av 10 de Agosto
Edificio Atahualpa
Casilla 17-08-8431
Quito, Ecuador
Tel.: (593) 2 3994 100
Fax: (593) 2 3994 100, ext. 4110
Web Site: www.abb.com.ec
Emp.: 100
Industrial Machinery Distr
S.I.C.: 5084
N.A.I.C.S.: 423830
Freud Paredes Monteros *(Office Mgr)*

ABB Engineering Technologies Co. (KSCC) (1)
Al-Ghunaim Commercial Tower
Kuwait, 13043, Kuwait
Tel.: (965) 222 77 888
Fax: (965) 222 77 999
Web Site: www.mena.abb.com
Power & Automation Products Engineering, Sales & Distr
S.I.C.: 8711
N.A.I.C.S.: 541330

ABB Engineering Trading and Service Ltd. (1)
Vaci ut 152-156
PO Box 129
1558 Budapest, Hungary HU
Tel.: (36) 14432212 (100%)
Fax: (36) 14432211
E-Mail: info@abb.hu
Web Site: www.abb.hu
Emp.: 320
Power & Automation Products Sales & Distr
S.I.C.: 5084
N.A.I.C.S.: 423830
Rikard Jonsson *(Pres & CEO)*

ABB FZ-LLC (1)
Concord Tower Media City
Dubai, United Arab Emirates
Tel.: (971) 4 4241900
Fax: (971) 4 4380472
Project Management Consulting Services
S.I.C.: 8748
N.A.I.C.S.: 541618

Subsidiaries:

ABB Energy Automation S.p.A. (2)
Al Ghaith Office Tower 15th Floor Hamdan Street
PO Box 45710
Abu Dhabi, United Arab Emirates
Tel.: (971) 26264062
Fax: (971) 26263230
E-Mail: info@abb.com
Web Site: www.mena.abb.com
Emp.: 100
Engineering Services
S.I.C.: 8711
N.A.I.C.S.: 541330
Bjarte Pederfen *(Pres)*

ABB Global Marketing FZ LLC (2)
221 Bldg 8 DMC
PO Box 502376
Dubai, United Arab Emirates
Tel.: (971) 4 4464959
Fax: (971) 4 4298755
Automation Equipment Distr
S.I.C.: 5084
N.A.I.C.S.: 423830

ABB Industries LLC (2)
Al Quoz Industrial Area
PO Box 11070
Dubai, United Arab Emirates
Tel.: (971) 43147500
Fax: (971) 43401771
E-Mail: abbdubai@emirates.net.in
Web Site: www.mena.abb.com
Protection, Control & Power Communication Equipment Mfr & Engineering Services; LV Products, Speed Drives, Motors & Machines Sales
S.I.C.: 3669
N.A.I.C.S.: 334290
Naji Jreijiri *(Pres)*

ABB International Marketing Ltd. (2)
Al Quoz Industrial Area
PO Box 11070
Dubai, United Arab Emirates
Tel.: (971) 43401777
Fax: (971) 3157500
E-Mail: adddubai@emirates.net.ae
Web Site: www.mena.abb.com
Power & Automation Products Marketer & Distr
S.I.C.: 5084
N.A.I.C.S.: 423830
Carlos Pone *(CEO & Mgr-Southern Gulf & Pakistan)*

ABB Transmission & Distribution Ltd. (2)
Al Ghaith Tower 15th Floor Hamdan Street
PO Box 45710
Ste 1501, Abu Dhabi, United Arab Emirates
Tel.: (971) 24171333
Fax: (971) 26263230
Web Site: www.mena.abb.com
Engineering & Project Management Services
S.I.C.: 8711
N.A.I.C.S.: 541330

ABB Holding A.S. (1)
Organize Sanayi Bolgesi 2 Cadde 16
34776 Istanbul, Turkey TR
Tel.: (90) 2165282200 (99.95%)
Fax: (90) 2164665384
E-Mail: info@tr.abb.com
Emp.: 800
Power & Automation Products Mfr
S.I.C.: 3612
N.A.I.C.S.: 335311
Daghan Karakas *(Mgr-Fin)*

Subsidiaries:

ABB Elektrik Sanayi A.S. (2)
Organize Sanayi Bolgesi 2 Cadde No 16
Y Dudullu, 34776 Istanbul, Turkey
Tel.: (90) 216 528 2200
Fax: (90) 216 466 5385
Web Site: www.abb.com.tr
Emp.: 1,000
Power Transformer & Circuit Breaker Mfr
S.I.C.: 3699
N.A.I.C.S.: 335999
Ismail Timor *(Mgr-Fin)*

Elmek Elektromekanik Sanayi ve Ticaret Anonim Sirketi AS (2)
Istasyon Mahallesi Ibisaga Caddesi No 2
Tuzla, 34940 Istanbul, Turkey
Tel.: (90) 216 395 40 00
Fax: (90) 216 395 22 10
Web Site: www.elmek.com.tr
Emp.: 150
Electrical Product Mfr
S.I.C.: 3699
N.A.I.C.S.: 335999
Ali Yasar *(Gen Mgr)*

ABB (Hong Kong) Ltd. (1)
3 Dai Hei St
Hong Kong, China (Hong Kong) HK
Tel.: (852) 29293838 (100%)
Telex: HX 86 408
Web Site: www.abb.com
Emp.: 10
Electronic Assemblies & Systems Mfr & Sales
S.I.C.: 3679
N.A.I.C.S.: 334419

Subsidiary:

ABB Turbo Systems (Hong Kong) Limited (2)
No 3 Dai Hei St Tai Po Industrial Estate
Tai Po, New Territories, China (Hong Kong)
Tel.: (852) 2929 3630
Fax: (852) 2929 3501
E-Mail: turbo.hk@cn.abb.com
Web Site: www.abb.com
Turbocharger Mfr
S.I.C.: 3699
N.A.I.C.S.: 335999

ABB Inc. (1)
8585 TransCanada Highway South
Saint Laurent, QC, H4S 1Z6, Canada Ca
Tel.: (514) 856-6266 (100%)
Fax: (514) 856-6297
Web Site: www.abb.ca
Emp.: 2,500
Power & Automation Products Mfr
S.I.C.: 3612
N.A.I.C.S.: 335311
Jean Guay *(VP/Gen Mgr-Power & Indus Sys Bus)*

Branches:

ABB Inc. (2)
585 Blvd Charest E Ste 300
Quebec, QC, G1K 9H4, Canada QC
Tel.: (418) 877-2944 (100%)
Fax: (418) 877-2834
E-Mail: qcrfq@ca.abb.com
Web Site: www.abb.com
Emp.: 200
Analytical Instruments Mfr
S.I.C.: 3826
N.A.I.C.S.: 334516
Jean Rene Roy *(Pres)*

ABB Inc. (2)
2117 32e Ave
Lachine, QC, H8T 3J1, Canada QC
Tel.: (514) 420-3100 (100%)
Fax: (514) 420-3137
Web Site: www.abb.com
Emp.: 100
Electrical Apparatus & Equipment
S.I.C.: 5063
N.A.I.C.S.: 423610

ABB Inc. (2)
3450 Harvester Rd
Burlington, ON, L7N 3W5, Canada (100%)
Tel.: (905) 639-8840
Fax: (905) 639-8639
Emp.: 300
Process Automation Systems Mfr
S.I.C.: 3699
N.A.I.C.S.: 335999

Subsidiary:

Envitech Energy Inc. (2)
180 Brunswick Blvd
Pointe-Claire, QC, H9R 5P9, Canada
Tel.: (514) 426-4430
Fax: (514) 426-4435
Toll Free: (800) 905-0222
E-Mail: envitech@ca.abb.com
Web Site: www.envitech.com
Emp.: 50
Electrical Traction Power System Mfr & Distr
S.I.C.: 3699
N.A.I.C.S.: 335999
Steve Roy *(VP-Comml, Ops & Engrg)*

ABB Insurance Limited (1)
Suite 3 Weighbridge House Le Pollet
Saint Peter Port, GY1 1WL, Guernsey
Tel.: (44) 1481 716686
General Insurance Services
S.I.C.: 6411
N.A.I.C.S.: 524210

ABB International Finance Limited (1)
Weighbridge House Le Pollet Suite 3
Saint Peter Port, GY1 1WL, Guernsey
Tel.: (44) 1481 729 016
Financial Management Services
S.I.C.: 6211
N.A.I.C.S.: 523999

ABB K.K. (1)
26-1 Cerulean Tower
Sakuragaoka-cho Shibuya-ku, Tokyo, 150-8512, Japan JP
Tel.: (81) 357846000 (100%)
Telex: 781 29190
Fax: (81) 357846020
E-Mail: bs.communications@jp.abb.com
Web Site: www.abb.co.jp
Power & Automation Products
S.I.C.: 3612
N.A.I.C.S.: 335311

Subsidiary:

ABB Bailey Japan Limited (2)
511 Baraki
Izunokuni, Shizuoka, 410-2193, Japan
Tel.: (81) 559 49 3311
Fax: (81) 559 49 1114
Web Site: www.bailey.co.jp
Emp.: 250
Electrical Component Mfr
S.I.C.: 3699
N.A.I.C.S.: 335999

ABB Ltda. (1)
Avenida dos Autonomistas 1496
PO Box 975
06020-902 Osasco, SP, Brazil BR
Tel.: (55) 1136889111 (100%)
Fax: (55) 1136889993
E-Mail: abb.atende@br.abb.com
Web Site: www.abb.com
Emp.: 1,000
Power & Automation Products Sales & Distr
S.I.C.: 5084
N.A.I.C.S.: 423830
Rafael Paniagua *(Pres)*

Subsidiary:

ABB SACE Limitada (2)
Av Monteiro Lobato 3285
07190-904 Guarulhos, SP, Brazil
Tel.: (55) 1124648188
Telex: 11 33834 SACE BR
Fax: (55) 1124648750
E-Mail: alexandre.malveiro@br.abb.com
Web Site: www.abb.com
Emp.: 5,000
Circuit Breakers, Load Break Switches, Isolators, Fusegear, MV/LV Switchboards & Control Centers, HV/MV Bushings & Insulating Material Mfr
S.I.C.: 3613
N.A.I.C.S.: 335313
Alexandre Malveiro *(Mgr-Sls)*

ABB LLC (1)
218 Hatat House Wadi Adai
PO Box 778
Muscat, Oman
Tel.: (968) 24666500
Fax: (968) 24666590
E-Mail: abboman@omantel.net.com
Emp.: 82
Electrical Engineering Services
S.I.C.: 8711
N.A.I.C.S.: 541330
Saeed Fahim *(Country Mgr)*

ABB Ltd. (1)
4 Ivana Lepse Blvd
3680 Kiev, Ukraine UA
Tel.: (380) 444952211 (100%)
Fax: (380) 444952210
E-Mail: info@abb.com
Web Site: www.abb.com
Emp.: 185
Power & Automation Products Mfr
S.I.C.: 3612
N.A.I.C.S.: 335311
Dmytro Zhdanov *(Mgr)*

ABB Ltd. (1)
162 Mecca Street Al Khayatt Center 3rd Floor
PO Box 926 098
Amman, 11190, Jordan
Tel.: (962) 6 550 7733
Fax: (962) 6 553 5661
Industrial Automation Equipment Mfr
S.I.C.: 3559
N.A.I.C.S.: 333249

Subsidiaries:

ABB International Marketing Ltd. (2)
162 Mecca St Al Khayatt Center Pegeout Bldg 3rd Fl
PO Box 926 098
Amman, 11190, Jordan
Tel.: (962) 65507733
Fax: (962) 65535661
Web Site: www.abb.com
Emp.: 50
Power & Automation Products Marketer & Distr
S.I.C.: 5084
N.A.I.C.S.: 423830
Maroun Zakhour *(Country Mgr)*

ABB Ltd.—(Continued)

ABB Near East Trading Ltd. (2)
3rd Floor Al Khaiat Centre Street No 162
Mecca Street
11190 Amman, Jordan
Tel.: (962) 6 5507733
Fax: (962) 6 5535661
Industrial Automation Equipment Distr
S.I.C.: 5084
N.A.I.C.S.: 423830

ABB Ltd. (1)
157-33 Samsung-Dong Kangnam-Ku
Oksan Building 7th Floor, Seoul, 135-090, Korea (South) Ks
Tel.: (82) 25283131 (100%)
Fax: (82) 25283100
Web Site: www.abb.co.kr.com
Emp.: 560
Power & Automation Products
S.I.C.: 3612
N.A.I.C.S.: 335311

ABB Ltd. (1)
12F 181 Tiding Boulevard
Taipei, Taiwan
Tel.: (886) 287516090
E-Mail: vicky.yang@tw.abb.com
Web Site: www.abb.com.tw
Power & Automation Products
S.I.C.: 3612
N.A.I.C.S.: 335311

ABB Ltd. (1)
V UK Ovarfka 284
10000 Zagreb, Croatia HR
Tel.: (385) 16008500 (100%)
Fax: (385) 16195111
E-Mail: info@hr.abb.com
Web Site: www.abb.hr
Emp.: 100
Power & Automation Products Sales & Distr
S.I.C.: 5084
N.A.I.C.S.: 423830
Darqo Aesanhuth *(Gen Mgr)*

ABB Ltd. (1)
161 1 SG Tower 1st-4th Floor Soi Mahadlekluang 3 Rajdamri R
Bangkok, 10330, Thailand TH
Tel.: (66) 26651000 (100%)
Fax: (66) 26651030
E-Mail: info@abb.co.th
Web Site: www.abb.co.th
Emp.: 600
Power & Automation Sales & Services
S.I.C.: 5084
N.A.I.C.S.: 423830
Kumchai Lertdhirakul *(VP-Power Productions)*

ABB Limited (1)
Mombasa Road Clifton Park Mezzanine Floor
PO Box 39120-00623
Nairobi, 00623, Kenya
Tel.: (254) 20 357 9817
E-Mail: abbltd.Info@ke.abb.com
Industrial Machinery Distr
S.I.C.: 5084
N.A.I.C.S.: 423830

ABB Limited (1)
83 Grafton Road
Auckland, 1010, New Zealand NZ
Tel.: (64) 93562160 (100%)
Fax: (64) 93570098
E-Mail: peter.henderson@nzabb.com
Web Site: www.nzabb.co.nz
Emp.: 80
Power & Automation Technology Products
S.I.C.: 3612
N.A.I.C.S.: 335311
Grant Gellard *(CEO)*

ABB Ltd. (1)
Emilijana Josimovica 4 2nd Floor
11000 Belgrade, Serbia
Tel.: (381) 113244341
Fax: (381) 113241623
Web Site: www.abb.com
Power & Automation Products Sales & Distr
S.I.C.: 5084
N.A.I.C.S.: 423830

ABB Ltd. (1)
Belgard Rd
Tallaght, Co Dublin, 24, Ireland IE
Tel.: (353) 14057300 (100%)
Fax: (353) 14057327
E-Mail: information@ie.abb.com
Web Site: www.ie.abb.com
Emp.: 100
Power & Automation Product Sales
S.I.C.: 5085
N.A.I.C.S.: 423840
Damien Petticrew *(Mng Dir)*

ABB Ltd. (1)
49 Race Course Road 2nd Floor Khanija Bhavan 2nd Floor East Wing
Bengaluru, Karnataka, 560001, India (75%)
Tel.: (91) 8022948383
Fax: (91) 8022948373
Web Site: www.abb.co.in
500002—(BOM)
Rev.: $1,496,520,990
Assets: $1,205,917,614
Liabilities: $300,824,478
Net Worth: $905,093,136
Earnings: $26,130,276
Emp.: 6,752
Fiscal Year-end: 12/31/12
High Voltage Apparatus, Relays, Switchgear, Industrial Plants & Electronics Mfr & Sales
S.I.C.: 3613
N.A.I.C.S.: 335313
Bazmi R. Husain *(Mng Dir)*
Amlan Dutta Majumdar *(CFO)*
Giandomenico Testi *(CTO)*
B. Gururaj *(Sec)*

ABB Ltd. (1)
Koprska ulica 92
1000 Ljubljana, Slovenia
Tel.: (386) 12445440
Fax: (386) 12445490
E-Mail: elvara.bektasic@csi.abb.com
Web Site: www.abb.com
Emp.: 28
Power & Automation Products Sales & Distr
S.I.C.: 5084
N.A.I.C.S.: 423830
Mathia Kranience *(Branch Mgr)*

ABB Ltd. (1)
Daresbury Park
Warrington, Cheshire, WA4 4BT, United Kingdom UK
Tel.: (44) 1925741111 (100%)
Fax: (44) 1925741212
E-Mail: info@gb.abb.com
Web Site: www.abb.co.uk
Emp.: 300
Engineering Consulting & Services
S.I.C.: 8711
N.A.I.C.S.: 541330
Trevor Gregory *(Mng Dir)*

Branches:

ABB Ltd. (2)
Oulton Road
Stone, Staffs, ST15 0RS, United Kingdom (100%)
Tel.: (44) 1785825050
Telex: 23448 BBBTEL GB
Fax: (44) 1785819019
E-Mail: info@gb.abb.com
Web Site: www.abb.co.uk
Emp.: 400
Power Systems
S.I.C.: 3621
N.A.I.C.S.: 335312
Stephen Trotter *(Mng Dir-Power Sys Bus-UK & Ireland)*

ABB Ltd. (2)
Tower Ct Soleshill Enterprise Park
Coventry, CV6 5NX, United Kingdom (100%)
Tel.: (44) 2476368500
Fax: (44) 2476364499
E-Mail: info@abb.co.uk
Web Site: www.abb.co.uk
Rev.: $52,033,380
Emp.: 100
Industrial Motor Control Products, Disconnect Switches, Programmable Logic Controllers, Circuit Breakers, Capacitors Mfr & Distr
S.I.C.: 3613
N.A.I.C.S.: 335313
Reeve Carter *(Gen Mgr-Product)*

ABB Ltd. (2)
Oldends Lane
Stonehouse, Glos, GL10 3TA, United Kingdom UK
Tel.: (44) 1453826661 (100%)
Telex: 43127 KENTFPG
Fax: (44) 1453827856
E-Mail: info@gb.abb.com
Web Site: www.abb.co.com
Emp.: 200
Water & Gas Analysis Equipment & Flow Products Mfr
S.I.C.: 3823
N.A.I.C.S.: 334513
Brian Hull *(Gen Mgr)*

ABB Ltd. (2)
Howard Rd Eaton Socon
Saint Neots, Cambs, PE19 8EU, United Kingdom
Tel.: (44) 1480 475321
Telex: 727044
Fax: (44) 1480 217948
E-Mail:
Web Site: www.abb.co.uk
Emp.: 350
Process Controls
S.I.C.: 3823
N.A.I.C.S.: 334513
Ian Rennie *(Mng Dir)*

Subsidiaries:

ABB Combined Heat and Power Ltd. (2)
Daresbury Park Daresbury
Warrington, Cheshire, WA4 4BT, United Kingdom
Tel.: (44) 1785 825 050
Fax: (44) 1785 285 966
Electric Power Generation Services
S.I.C.: 4939
N.A.I.C.S.: 221118

ABB Holdings Limited (2)
Daresbury Park
Warrington, WA4 4BT, United Kingdom
Tel.: (44) 1925 741 111
Fax: (44) 1925 741 212
Investment Management Services
S.I.C.: 6211
N.A.I.C.S.: 523999

ABB Lutech Resources Ltd. (2)
Knowles House Cromwell Road
Redhill, Surrey, RH1 1RT, United Kingdom
Tel.: (44) 01737236500
Telex: 851312551
Fax: (44) 1737236546
E-Mail: lutech@gb.abb.com
Web Site: www.abb.lutech.lummusonline.com
Emp.: 15
Recruitment Services
S.I.C.: 8999
N.A.I.C.S.: 541612

ABB Maghreb Services S.A. (1)
Rue 101 Les Berges du Lac
Immeuble Stramica
2 eme etage, 1053 Tunis, Tunisia
Tel.: (216) 71860366
Fax: (216) 71 860255
Web Site: www.mena.abb.com
Power & Automation Products Sales & Distr
S.I.C.: 5084
N.A.I.C.S.: 423830

ABB Malaysia Sdn Bhd. (1)
Lot 608 Jalan SS13/1K
47500 Subang Jaya, Selangor Darul Ehsan, Malaysia
Tel.: (60) 3 5628 4888
Fax: (60) 3 5632 7889
Web Site: www.abb.com.my/cawp/myabb030/6c56f0936ae2af36c12575ad0034a9c0.aspx
Electric Power Generation & Distribution Services
S.I.C.: 4911
N.A.I.C.S.: 221118

Subsidiaries:

ABB Holdings Sdn. Bhd. (2)
Lot 608 Jalan SS 13/1K
47500 Subang Jaya, Selangor Darul Ehsan, Malaysia MY
Tel.: (60) 356284888 (100%)
Fax: (60) 356327889
Web Site: www.abb.com.my
Emp.: 175
Power & Automation Products Mfr
S.I.C.: 3613
N.A.I.C.S.: 335313
Bengt Andersson *(Pres & Country Mgr)*

ABB Manufacturing Sdn. Bhd. (2)
Lot 608 Jalan SS13/1K
Subang Jaya, 47500, Malaysia
Tel.: (60) 3 5628 4888
Fax: (60) 3 5632 7889
Industrial Automation System Mfr
S.I.C.: 3559
N.A.I.C.S.: 333249

ABB Mexico S.A. de C.V (1)
Paseo de las Americas No 31
53125 Tlalnepantla, DF, Mexico (100%)
Tel.: (52) 5553281400
E-Mail: communicationcoperative@mx.abb.com
Web Site: www.abb.com.mx
Emp.: 300
Electrical Equipment Mfr
S.I.C.: 3699
N.A.I.C.S.: 335999
Armando Basave *(Gen Mgr)*

Subsidiary:

Asea Brown Boveri S.A. de C.V. (2)
Paseo de las Americas No 31 Lomas Verdes 3ra Seccion
Naucalpan, 53125, Mexico
Tel.: (52) 55 3601 9500
E-Mail: abbmexico@mx.abb.com
Web Site: www.abb.com.mx
Power Transmission Equipment Distr
S.I.C.: 5063
N.A.I.C.S.: 423610

ABB NG Ltd (1)
Plot 259 Etim Inyang Crescent
Victoria Island, Lagos, Nigeria
Tel.: (234) 12705669
Fax: (234) 14937348
Web Site: www.ng.abb.com
Emp.: 150
Mfr. of Industrial Machinery
S.I.C.: 3559
N.A.I.C.S.: 333249

Branch:

ABBNG Limited (2)
No 4 Matadi Street Wuse Zone 3
Abuja, Nigeria
Tel.: (234) 9 670 6330
E-Mail: abbng@ng.abb.com
Web Site: www.ng.abb.com
Electric Power Generation & Distribution Services
S.I.C.: 4931
N.A.I.C.S.: 221118

ABB Norden Holding AB (1)
Kopparbergsvagen 2
Vasteras, 722 13, Sweden
Tel.: (46) 21325928
Fax: (46) 21134112
Investment Management Services
S.I.C.: 6211
N.A.I.C.S.: 523999
Johan Soderstrom *(Gen Mgr)*

ABB Oy (1)
PO Box 187
FIN 00381 Helsinki, Finland FI
Tel.: (358) 10222000 (100%)
Fax: (358) 102224360
E-Mail: mikko.niinvaara@fi.abb.com
Web Site: www.abb.fi
Sls.: $1,696,240,000
Emp.: 5,500
Power & Automation Products Mfr
S.I.C.: 3612
N.A.I.C.S.: 335311

ABB (Private) Ltd. (1)
Building 5 Arundel Park Norfolk Road
PO Box 2107
Mount Pleasant, Harare, Zimbabwe ZW
Tel.: (263) 4369070 (100%)
Fax: (263) 4369087
Web Site: www.abb.com
Power & Automation Products Sales & Distr
S.I.C.: 5084
N.A.I.C.S.: 423830

ABB Pte. Ltd. (1)
2 Ayer Rajah Crescent
Singapore, 139935, Singapore
Tel.: (65) 6776 5711

Fax: (65) 6778 0222
Web Site: www.abb.com.sg
Emp.: 1,200
Electrical & Automation Product Distr
S.I.C.: 5063
N.A.I.C.S.: 423610
David McVay *(CFO)*
Mahendran Nair *(CIO)*

Subsidiary:

ABB Industry Pte. Ltd. (2)
2 Ayer Rajah Crescent
Singapore, 139935, Singapore
Tel.: (65) 67765711
Telex: 786 26885
Fax: (65) 67780222
E-Mail: sgind@sg.abb.com
Web Site: www.abb.com.sg
Emp.: 1,000
Power & Automation Technology Products Mfr
S.I.C.: 3612
N.A.I.C.S.: 335311
James Foo *(Pres & Mgr)*
Boon Kiat Sim *(Pres-Malaysia & Country Mgr)*

ABB (Pty) Ltd. (1)
Unit C1 Gaborone International Commerce Pk
Gaborone, Botswana
Tel.: (267) 3180848
Fax: (267) 3180816
Emp.: 15
Electrical Engineering Services
S.I.C.: 8711
N.A.I.C.S.: 541330
Gift Nkwe *(Gen Mgr)*

ABB Romania (1)
Calea Floreasca 169A Cladirea A Floreasca Business Park
Etaj 5 Section 1, Bucharest, 014459, Romania
Tel.: (40) 372158200
Fax: (40) 213104383
E-Mail: office.abb@ro.abb.com
Web Site: www.abb.com
Emp.: 75
Power & Automation Products
S.I.C.: 3612
N.A.I.C.S.: 335311

ABB S.A. de CV (1)
Colonia Escalon 11 Cl Pte y 89 Av Nte Edif World Trade Center No 205
San Salvador, El Salvador
Tel.: (503) 22645471
Electrical Engineering Services
S.I.C.: 8711
N.A.I.C.S.: 541330

ABB S.A./N.V. (1)
Hoge Wei 27
B 1930 Zaventem, Belgium
Tel.: (32) 27186311
Telex: 846 31919
Fax: (32) 2718666
E-Mail: info@be.abb.com
Web Site: www.abb.be
Emp.: 300
Plumbing & Heating Equipment
S.I.C.: 5074
N.A.I.C.S.: 423720
Katrina Wright *(Mgr-Comm)*

ABB S.A. (1)
Avenida Balboa Torre Banco BVBA Piso 14
PO Box 5039
Panama, 5, Panama
Tel.: (507) 2255458
Fax: (507) 2250698
E-Mail: micnor.rivera@pa.abb.com
Web Site: www.abb.com
Emp.: 11
Power & Automation Products Sales & Distr
S.I.C.: 5084
N.A.I.C.S.: 423830

ABB S.A. (1)
Estrada Do Casal De Canas Edificio ABB
PO Box 7573
2720-092 Amadora, Alfragide, Portugal (100%)
Tel.: (351) 214256000
Fax: (351) 214256247
E-Mail: contactos.clientes@pt.abb.com
Web Site: www.abb.pt
Emp.: 700
Sales, Service & Assembly of Switchgear & Surge Arresters
S.I.C.: 3613
N.A.I.C.S.: 335313
Miguel Pernes *(Gen Mgr)*

Subsidiary:

ABB Stotz-Kontakt Electrica Lda. (2)
Rua Dr Eduardo Santos Silva 261
4200-283 Porto, Portugal
Tel.: (351) 225400636
Telex: via BBC Porto 25 106 sebb
Fax: (351) 225402115
Web Site: www.abb.pt
Emp.: 250
Contractors; Automatic Fuses; Overcurrent Relays
S.I.C.: 1799
N.A.I.C.S.: 238990

ABB S.A. (1)
Edificio Trilogia Torre 2 Oficina 221 Frente a PriceSmart de Escazu
Apartado 469-1260 Plaza Escazu, San Jose, Costa Rica
Tel.: (506) 22885484
Fax: (506) 22885482
E-Mail: oscar.retana@pa.abb.com
Web Site: www.abb.com
Emp.: 7
Power & Automation Products Sales & Distr
S.I.C.: 5084
N.A.I.C.S.: 423830

ABB S.A. (1)
Av Vicuna Mackenna 1602
PO Box 5813
Santiago, Chile
Tel.: (56) 24714000
Telex: 340 471 BBCHIL CK
E-Mail: roberto.dapaiva@cl.abb.com
Web Site: www.abb.com
Emp.: 119
Power & Automation Products Mfr
S.I.C.: 3613
N.A.I.C.S.: 335313
Jose Paiva *(Pres)*

ABB S.A. (1)
Avenue Leandro N Alem 822 9 Piso
C1001AAQ Buenos Aires, Argentina Ar
Tel.: (54) 1143115386 (100%)
Fax: (54) 1143134744
E-Mail: abb.argentina@ar.abb.com
Web Site: www.abb.com
Emp.: 600
Sales Company; Assembly of Switchgear & High-Voltage Apparatus
S.I.C.: 5085
N.A.I.C.S.: 423840

ABB S.A. (1)
15th km Thessaloniki N Moudania National Road
PO Box 60750
Thessaloniki, Thermi, GR-570-01, Greece
Tel.: (30) 2310 460 900
Telex: 412 281 skh gr
Fax: (30) 2310 460 999
E-Mail: abbng@gr.abb.com
Web Site: www.abb.gr
Emp.: 83
Electrical Products Sales
S.I.C.: 5063
N.A.I.C.S.: 423610

Branch:

Asea Brown Boveri S.A. (2)
13th km Lamia National Road
14452 Metamorfosis, Athens, Greece
Tel.: (30) 210 28 91 900
Fax: (30) 210 28 91 599
E-Mail: abb@gr.abb.com
Web Site: www.abb.gr
Emp.: 200
Electrical Equipment Mfr
S.I.C.: 3699
N.A.I.C.S.: 335999
Apostolos Petropoulos *(Gen Mgr)*

ABB S.A. (1)
9 Ave Edouard Belin
92566 Rueil-Malmaison, Cedex, France FR
Tel.: (33) 00141964500 (100%)
Fax: (33) 141964545
E-Mail: info@abb.fr
Web Site: www.abb.fr
Emp.: 40
Power & Automation Products
S.I.C.: 3612
N.A.I.C.S.: 335311
Pierre Desmaele *(CEO)*

Subsidiary:

L'Ebenoid S.A. (2)
8 rue des fleurs
69100 Villeurbanne, France
Tel.: (33) 4 72113990
Fax: (33) 4 72113999
Electrical Component Mfr
S.I.C.: 3699
N.A.I.C.S.: 335999

ABB Saudi Arabia (1)
ABB Building Al-Ahsa Street
PO Box 325841
11371 Riyadh, 11491, Saudi Arabia (100%)
Tel.: (966) 4762644
Fax: (966) 14769622
E-Mail: info@sa.abb.com
Web Site: www.abb.com.sa
Emp.: 15
Mfr. of Industrial Machinery
S.I.C.: 3559
N.A.I.C.S.: 333249
Mohamed Samkari *(Pres-ABB Contracting)*

Subsidiaries:

ABB Automation Co. Ltd. (2)
PO Box 251
Riyadh, 11383, Saudi Arabia
Tel.: (966) 1 265 3030
Fax: (966) 1 265 1211
Industrial Automation System Mfr
S.I.C.: 3559
N.A.I.C.S.: 333249
Mahmoud Shaban *(Pres)*

ABB Contracting Company Ltd. (2)
PO Box 91926
Riyadh, 11643, Saudi Arabia
Tel.: (966) 1 265 0090
Fax: (966) 1 265 2077
Electrical Engineering Services
S.I.C.: 8711
N.A.I.C.S.: 541330
Mohammed Samkari *(Pres)*

ABB Electrical Industries Ltd. (2)
PO Box 251
Riyadh, 11383, Saudi Arabia
Tel.: (966) 1 265 3030
Fax: (966) 1 265 1211
Electrical Engineering Services
S.I.C.: 8711
N.A.I.C.S.: 541330
Mahmoud Shaban *(Pres)*

ABB Service Co. Ltd. (2)
PO Box 2873
Al Khobar, 31952, Saudi Arabia
Tel.: (966) 3 882 9394
Fax: (966) 3 882 4603
Web Site: www.abb.com.sa/cawp/saabb301/a793d4434d03177f43256ae5003a2df7.aspx
Business Support Services
S.I.C.: 7389
N.A.I.C.S.: 561499
Mahmoud Shaban *(Pres)*

ABB SIA (1)
Tiraines St 3a
LV-1058 Riga, Latvia
Tel.: (371) 67063600
Fax: (371) 67063601
E-Mail: info@lv.abb.com
Web Site: www.abb.lv
Emp.: 150
Power & Automation Products Sales & Distr
S.I.C.: 5084
N.A.I.C.S.: 423830

ABB South Africa (Pty) Ltd. (1)
2 Lake Road Longmeadow Business Estate North
Modderfontein, Gauteng, 1609, South Africa
Tel.: (27) 10 202 5000
Fax: (27) 11 579 8000
E-Mail: info@za.abb.com
Web Site: www.abb.co.za
Emp.: 1,800
Industrial Machinery Mfr & Distr
S.I.C.: 3559
N.A.I.C.S.: 333249
Leon Viljoen *(CEO)*

Subsidiaries:

ABB Holdings (Pty) Ltd. (2)
ABB Park The Crescent 3 Eglin Rd
PO Box 37
Gauteng, 2157, South Africa ZA
Tel.: (27) 0112367000 (80%)
Telex: 4-25716 SA
Fax: (27) 112367001
E-Mail: info@za.abb.com
Web Site: www.abb.co.za
Emp.: 300
Engineering Services
S.I.C.: 8711
N.A.I.C.S.: 541330

K-TEK Instruments (PTY) Ltd. (2)
2 Lake Road Longmeadow Business Estate North
Edenvale, 1609, South Africa
Tel.: (27) 10 202 6458 9
Fax: (27) 10 579 8000
E-Mail: info@abbdimensions.com
Web Site: www.ktekcorp.co.za
Induatrial Measurement Instrument Mfr
S.I.C.: 3823
N.A.I.C.S.: 334513

Nelspruit Airport Operating Company (Pty) Ltd. (2)
Abb Park 3 Eglin Road
Johannesburg, 2191, South Africa
Tel.: (27) 13 7537500
Fax: (27) 13 7418051
Emp.: 500
Airport Management Services
S.I.C.: 4581
N.A.I.C.S.: 488119

Primkop Airport Management (Pty) Ltd. (2)
R538 Karino Rd White River-Plaston
Nelspruit, 1200, South Africa
Tel.: (27) 137537500
Fax: (27) 13 753 7555
Airport Management Services
S.I.C.: 4581
N.A.I.C.S.: 488119

ABB Sp. z o.o. (1)
Zegananska St 1
04-713 Warsaw, Poland PL
Tel.: (48) 609446023 (96.01%)
Fax: (48) 222202032
E-Mail: warszawa.recepcja@pl.abb.com
Web Site: www.abb.pl
Emp.: 2,000
Power & Automation Products
S.I.C.: 3612
N.A.I.C.S.: 335311
Krzysztof Kossak *(Gen Mgr)*

Subsidiary:

ABB Entrelec Sp. z.o.o. (2)
Ul Grunwaldzka 38
84-351 Nowa Wies Leborska, Poland
Tel.: (48) 59 86 15 800
Fax: (48) 59 86 15 802
Web Site: www.abb.pl/cawp/plabb041/9e7a775712051e68412567f60047bfd3.aspx
Emp.: 140
Electric Power Generation Services
S.I.C.: 4911
N.A.I.C.S.: 221118
Sylvain Danion *(Gen Mgr)*

ABB S.p.A. (1)
Via Luciano Lama 33
I-20099 Milan, Italy IT
Tel.: (39) 0224141 (100%)
Fax: (39) 02 2414 3892
Web Site: www.abb.it
Emp.: 67
Sales & Service of Switchgear & Converters
S.I.C.: 3613
N.A.I.C.S.: 335313
Barbara Frei *(CEO & Country Mgr)*

Subsidiaries:

ABB SACE S.p.A. (2)
Via Statale 113
I-22016 Lenno, Como, Italy IT
Tel.: (39) 034458111 (100%)
Telex: 380044 KENTIL I
Fax: (39) 034456278
E-Mail: abb.instrumentation@it.abb.com

ABB Ltd.—(Continued)

Web Site: www.abb.it
Emp.: 250
Electronic & Pneumatic Process Control & Instrumentation, Control Valves & Actuators Mfr
S.I.C.: 3823
N.A.I.C.S.: 334513
Barbara Frei *(Country Mgr)*

ABB SACE S.p.A. (2)
Via Baioni 35
24123 Bergamo, Italy (100%)
Tel.: (39) 035395111
Telex: 301 627 sacebg i
Fax: (39) 035395443
Web Site: www.abb.it
Emp.: 200
Circuit-Breakers Mfr
S.I.C.: 3613
N.A.I.C.S.: 335313

Intermagnetics Srl (2)
Via dei Mestieri 5/7 - Fraz Macchie
06060 Castiglione del Lago, Italy
Tel.: (39) 075 9525314
Fax: (39) 075 960107
E-Mail: info@intermagneticssrl.com
Web Site: www.intermagneticssrl.com
Emp.: 60
Transformer & Reactor Mfr
S.I.C.: 3612
N.A.I.C.S.: 335311

Italtrasfo Srl (2)
Piazza Fusina 2
20133 Milan, Italy
Tel.: (39) 0332 51 02 37
Fax: (39) 0332 50 10 22
E-Mail: info@italtrasfo.com
Web Site: www.italtrasfo.com
Power Transmission Equipment Mfr
S.I.C.: 3568
N.A.I.C.S.: 333613

ABB s.r.o. (1)
Stetkova 1638 18
140 00 Prague, 4, Czech Republic CZ
Tel.: (420) 234322318 (100%)
Web Site: www.abb.cz
Emp.: 120
Power & Automation Products
S.I.C.: 3612
N.A.I.C.S.: 335311
Martin Slechta *(Gen Mgr)*

ABB s.r.o. (1)
Westend Court Dubravska cesta 2
841 04 Bratislava, Slovakia
Tel.: (421) 259418801
Fax: (421) 259418766
E-Mail: info@sk.abb.com
Web Site: www.abb.sk
Emp.: 100
Power & Automation Products
S.I.C.: 3612
N.A.I.C.S.: 335311
Marcel Van Der Hoek *(Mgr)*

ABB Technologies Ltd. (1)
Nahum Hat Str 5 Topaz Bldg 2nd Fl
PO Box 15081
31905 Haifa, Israel II
Mailing Address: (99.99%)
PO Box 2053
39120 Tirat Karmel, Israel
Tel.: (972) 48502111
Fax: (972) 48502112
E-Mail: contact@il.abb.com
Web Site: www.abb.co.il
Emp.: 50
Power & Automation Products
S.I.C.: 3612
N.A.I.C.S.: 335311
Ronen Aharon *(Pres)*

ABB Technologies S.A. (1)
PO Box 2067
Dakar, Senegal
Tel.: (221) 849 3470
Fax: (221) 849 3460
Web Site: www.abb.com
Power & Automation Products Sales & Distr
S.I.C.: 5084
N.A.I.C.S.: 423830

ABB Technologies W.L.L. (1)
No 175 Road 4303 Block 343
PO Box 2774
Manama, Bahrain
Tel.: (973) 1 772 5377
Fax: (973) 1 772 5332
Web Site: www.abb.com.sa/cawp/saabb301/e7662d560517486a43256fcc0023a28a.aspx
Industrial Automation Equipment Mfr
S.I.C.: 3559
N.A.I.C.S.: 333249
Mahmoud Shaban *(Pres)*

ABB UAB (1)
Saltoniskiu 14
LT-08105 Vilnius, Lithuania
Tel.: (370) 52738300
Fax: (370) 52738333
E-Mail: info@lt.abb.com
Web Site: www.abb.lt
Emp.: 80
Power & Automation Products Sales & Distr
S.I.C.: 5084
N.A.I.C.S.: 423830
Bo Henriksson *(Pres)*

ABB Vietnam (1)
Milestone 9 National Highway 1A
Thanh Tri District, Hanoi, Vietnam
Tel.: (84) 48611010
Fax: (84) 48611009
Web Site: www.abb.com
Power & Automation Products Sales & Distr
S.I.C.: 5084
N.A.I.C.S.: 423830

Asea Brown Boveri Inc. (1)
KM 20 S Superhighway Sucat
Paranaque, Metro Manila, Philippines PH
Tel.: (63) 28244581 (100%)
Fax: (63) 28246616
E-Mail: corporate.comm@ph.abb.com
Web Site: www.abb.com
Emp.: 150
Automation & Power Technology Products Mfr
S.I.C.: 3613
N.A.I.C.S.: 335313
Mary Klang *(Dir-Mktg)*

Asea Brown Boveri Ltda. (1)
Carrera 100 No 45A 11
Bogota, Colombia Co
Mailing Address: (99.99%)
PO Box 6195/3984
Bogota, Colombia
Tel.: (57) 1 5644600
Fax: (57) 1 4156498
E-Mail: cc@co.abb.com
Web Site: www.abb.com.co
Emp.: 80
Automation & Power Technology Products Sales
S.I.C.: 5085
N.A.I.C.S.: 423840

Asea Brown Boveri Ltd. (1)
Obrucheva 30/1
117861 Moscow, Russia RU
Tel.: (7) 4959602200 (100%)
Fax: (7) 4959602201
Web Site: www.abb.ru
Emp.: 500
Power & Automation Products Sales & Distr
S.I.C.: 5084
N.A.I.C.S.: 423830

Branch:

ABB Ltd. (2)
Obrucheva 30/1
Moscow, 117997, Russia
Tel.: (7) 495 960 2200
Fax: (7) 495 960 2201
Web Site: www.abb.ru
Electric Power Generation Services
S.I.C.: 4939
N.A.I.C.S.: 221118

Subsidiary:

ABB Power and Automation Systems Ltd. (2)
Yakovleva Pr 1
Cheboksary, 428020, Russia
Tel.: (7) 8352 2561 62
Fax: (7) 8352 5605 03
E-Mail: rurelch@ru.abb.com
Emp.: 150
Industrial Automation Equipment Mfr
S.I.C.: 3559
N.A.I.C.S.: 333249
Lebedev Sergei *(VP)*

Asea Brown Boveri Ltd. (1)
A1 Royal Road
Port Louis, Mauritius
Tel.: (230) 208 7644
Fax: (230) 211 4077
Web Site: www.abb.mu
Emp.: 10
Industrial Automation & Process Control System Mfr
S.I.C.: 3823
N.A.I.C.S.: 334513
Ajay Vij *(Gen Mgr)*

Asea Brown Boveri (Pty) Ltd (1)
5 Tiene Louw St
PO Box 6037
9000 Windhoek, Namibia
Tel.: (264) 61240341
Fax: (264) 61240335
E-Mail: hagen.seiler@na.abb.com
Web Site: www.abb.com
Emp.: 5
Power & Automation Products Sales & Distr
S.I.C.: 5084
N.A.I.C.S.: 423830

Asea Brown Boveri, S.A. (1)
Ave Argentina 3120
PO Box 3846
Lima, 100, Peru PE
Tel.: (51) 15610404 (99.99%)
Telex: 21009
Fax: (51) 15613040
E-Mail: abb.peru@pe.abb.com
Web Site: www.abb.com.pe
Emp.: 150
Power & Automation Products
S.I.C.: 3612
N.A.I.C.S.: 335311
Enrique Rohde *(Country Mgr)*

Asea Brown Boveri, S.A. (1)
Av Atahualpa Oe1-198 y 10 de Agosto
Quito, Ecuador EC
Tel.: (593) 23994100 (96.87%)
Fax: (593) 22500650
E-Mail: ganeth.prieto@abb.com.ec
Web Site: www.abb.com.ec
Emp.: 45
Power & Automation Products Sales & Distr
S.I.C.: 5084
N.A.I.C.S.: 423830
Ganeth Prieto *(Gen Mgr-Admin & Fin)*

Asea Brown Boveri, S.A. (1)
Avenida Sanchez Bustamante 275 Between 8-9 St Calacopo
La Paz, Bolivia
Tel.: (591) 22788181
Fax: (591) 591222788184
Web Site: www.abb.com
Emp.: 30
Power & Automation Products Sales & Distr
S.I.C.: 5084
N.A.I.C.S.: 423830

Asea Brown Boveri, S.A. (1)
C San Romualdo No 13
28037 Madrid, Spain ES
Tel.: (34) 915819393 (100%)
Telex: 43 236/27 572 BBCM E
Fax: (34) 915819357
E-Mail: buzon.esabb@es.abb.com
Web Site: www.abb.es
Emp.: 500
Power & Automation Technology Products Mfr
S.I.C.: 3612
N.A.I.C.S.: 335311
Jaime Carvajal Urquijo *(Pres)*
Carlos Marcos Ramon *(Mng Dir)*

Subsidiaries:

ABB Sistemas Industriales AB (2)
Calle Torrent De l'Olla 220
08012 Barcelona, Spain (100%)
Tel.: (34) 934842121
Fax: (34) 934842201
E-Mail: maria.jiminez@abb.es
Web Site: www.abb.es
Industrial Robots & Converters Mfr
S.I.C.: 3559
N.A.I.C.S.: 333249

ABB Stotz-Kontakt S.A. (2)
C/ Carabanchel 35
28902 Getafe, Madrid, Spain
Tel.: (34) 916950200
Telex: 44277 stoz e
Fax: (34) 916825188
Web Site: www.abb.es
Emp.: 100
Circuit Breakers Mfr
S.I.C.: 3613
N.A.I.C.S.: 335313

Asea Brown Boveri, S.A. (1)
Avenida Don Diego Cisneros
PO Box 6640
Los Ruices, 1071 Caracas, Venezuela VE
Tel.: (58) 2122031740 (100%)
Fax: (58) 2122031910
Web Site: www.abb.com
Power & Automation Products
S.I.C.: 3612
N.A.I.C.S.: 335311

Asea Brown Boveri, S.A. (1)
46 Avenue Pasteur
20300 Casablanca, Morocco
Tel.: (212) 22246168
Fax: (212) 22246171
Web Site: www.mena.abb.com
Power & Automation Products Sales & Distr
S.I.C.: 5084
N.A.I.C.S.: 423830

Asea Brown Boveri S.A.E. (1)
7 Dr Mohamed Kamel Hussein Street
PO Box 5040
El Nozha El Gedieda, Cairo, Egypt EG
Tel.: (20) 226251320 (100%)
Fax: (20) 226222562
Web Site: www.eg.abb.com
Emp.: 1,137
Heavy Construction Services
S.I.C.: 1629
N.A.I.C.S.: 237990

Subsidiary:

ABB Transformers S.A.E. (2)
7 Dr Mohamed Kamel Hussein St El Nozha El Gedieda
Heliopolis, Cairo, Egypt
Tel.: (20) 226222665
Fax: (20) 226222664
Web Site: www.abb.com.eg/cawp/egabb102/fcc8681e74059e0642256cba0044a2d2.aspx
Transformer Mfr
S.I.C.: 3612
N.A.I.C.S.: 335311

PT ABB Sakti Industri (1)
Jl Gajah Tunggal Km 1
Jatiuwung, Tangerang, Banten, 15136, Indonesia
Tel.: (62) 2125595555
Telex: 44 380 Mega ia
Fax: (62) 2125595566
Web Site: www.abb.com
Emp.: 31
Switchgear Sales
S.I.C.: 5084
N.A.I.C.S.: 423830
Sim Boon Kiat *(Pres & Country Mgr)*

ABBASTAR RESOURCES CORP.

(Name Changed to Glenmark Capital Corp.)

ABBEY CAPITAL LIMITED

1-2 Cavendish Row
Dublin, 1, Ireland
Tel.: (353) 1 828 0400
Fax: (353) 1 828 0499
E-Mail: info@abbeycapital.com
Web Site: www.abbeycapital.com
Year Founded: 2000
ABC—(BERM)
Emp.: 58

Business Description:
Investment Management Services
S.I.C.: 6282
N.A.I.C.S.: 523930

Personnel:
Claire Gately *(Sec)*

Board of Directors:
Tim Brosnan
Tony Gannon
Claire Gately

D. McCarthy
Michael Swift

Legal Counsel:
Dillon Eustace
33 Sir John Rogerson's Quay
Dublin, 2, Ireland
Tel.: (353) 1 667 0022
Fax: (353) 1 667 0042

ABBEY FORGED PRODUCTS LIMITED

Beeley Wood Works Beeley Wood Lane
Sheffield, S6 1ND, United Kingdom
Tel.: (44) 114 231 2271
Fax: (44) 114 232 4983
E-Mail: info@abbeyfp.co.uk
Web Site: www.abbeyforgedproducts.co.uk
Year Founded: 1982
Sales Range: $50-74.9 Million
Emp.: 175
Business Description:
Steel Forging Product Mfr
S.I.C.: 3462
N.A.I.C.S.: 332111
Personnel:
Jackie Neal *(Mng Dir)*

ABBOTSFORD CHRYSLER LTD.

30285 Auto Mall Drive
Abbotsford, BC, V2T5M1, Canada
Tel.: (604) 857-8888
Fax: (604) 857-0110
Toll Free: (888) 379-8438
E-Mail: reception@abbotsfordchrysler.com
Web Site: www.abbotsfordchryslerdealer.com
Year Founded: 1971
Rev.: $20,720,528
Emp.: 44
Business Description:
New & Used Car Dealers
S.I.C.: 5511
N.A.I.C.S.: 441110
Personnel:
Mitch Trotman *(Pres)*

ABC ARBITRAGE S.A.

(d/b/a ABC Arbitrage Group)
18 Rue du Quatre Septembre
75002 Paris, France
Tel.: (33) 153005500
Fax: (33) 153005501
E-Mail: abc@abc-arbitrage.com
Web Site: www.abc-arbitrage.com
Year Founded: 1995
ABCA—(EUR)
Rev.: $48,712,704
Assets: $1,588,511,967
Liabilities: $1,102,631,245
Net Worth: $185,880,722
Earnings: $32,724,974
Emp.: 78
Fiscal Year-end: 12/31/12
Business Description:
Financial Trading Services
S.I.C.: 6726
N.A.I.C.S.: 525990
Personnel:
Dominique Ceolin *(Chm & CEO)*
David Hoey *(Vice Chm & COO)*
Laetitia Hucheloup *(Sec & Head-Compliance & Internal Control-ABC Arbitrage Asset Mgmt)*
Board of Directors:
Dominique Ceolin
Xavier Chauderlot
Jacques Chevalier
Sabine Roux de Bezieux
Jean-Francois Drouets
Didier Ribadeau Dumas
Jean-Christophe Esteve
David Hoey
Marie-Ange Verdickt

Deloitte & Associes
Paris, France

Subsidiary:

ABC Arbitrage Asset Management (1)
18 rue du 4 Septembre
75 002 Paris, France
Tel.: (33) 153005500
Fax: (33) 153005501
E-Mail: info@abc-am.com
Web Site: www.abc-arbitrage.com
Emp.: 80
Asset Management Services
S.I.C.: 8748
N.A.I.C.S.: 541618
Dominique Ceolin *(Chm & CEO-Trading)*
David Hoey *(Vice Chm & COO)*

ABC BEARINGS LIMITED

402 - B Poonam Chambers Dr A B Road
Mumbai, 400 018, India
Tel.: (91) 22 24964500
Fax: (91) 22 24950527
E-Mail: regdoff@abcbearings.com
Web Site: www.abcbearings.com
505665—(BOM)
Rev.: $30,910,945
Assets: $43,587,559
Liabilities: $21,055,637
Net Worth: $22,531,922
Earnings: $983,417
Emp.: 424
Fiscal Year-end: 03/31/13
Business Description:
Roller Bearing Mfr
S.I.C.: 3562
N.A.I.C.S.: 332991
Personnel:
S. M. Patel *(Chm)*
P. M. Patel *(Mng Dir)*
S. B. Desai *(Compliance Officer & Sec)*
Board of Directors:
S. M. Patel
S. K. Diwanji
Jal R. Patel
P. M. Patel
T. M. Patel
Transfer Agent:
Bigshare Services Pvt Ltd
E 2 Ansa Industrial Estate Sakivihar Road
Mumbai, India

ABC COMMUNICATIONS (HOLDINGS) LIMITED

2709-10 27/F China Resources Bldg
26 Harbour Road, Wanchai, China (Hong Kong)
Tel.: (852) 27100000
Fax: (852) 27807267
E-Mail: info@0030.com.hk
Web Site: www.0030hk.com
30—(HKG)
Sales Range: $10-24.9 Million
Emp.: 47
Business Description:
Mobile Communication Services
S.I.C.: 3663
N.A.I.C.S.: 334220
Personnel:
Jiasong Chen *(Chm)*
Bill Bao Long Zhao *(CEO)*
Board of Directors:
Jiasong Chen
Wai Shing Cheung
Andy Kai Chung Choy
Kevin Lau
Kwong Yiu Lee
Thomas Ho Yiu Lee
Sai Ma
Hai Jian Qiu
Gaofeng Song
Guang Hui Zhang

ABC DATA S.A.

14 Daniszewska St
03-230 Warsaw, Poland
Tel.: (48) 226760900
Fax: (48) 226141616
E-Mail: info@abcdata.com.pl
Web Site: www.abcdata.com.pl
ABC—(WAR)
Rev.: $1,171,183,923
Assets: $284,277,552
Liabilities: $192,862,292
Net Worth: $91,415,260
Earnings: ($1,313,235)
Emp.: 318
Fiscal Year-end: 12/31/12
Business Description:
Computer & Software Products Distr; IT Consulting Services
S.I.C.: 5045
N.A.I.C.S.: 423430
Personnel:
Ulrich Kottmann *(Chm-Supervisory Bd)*
Norbert Biedrzycki *(Chm-Mgmt Bd)*
Wojciech Lastowiecki *(Vice Chm-Mgmt Bd)*
Ilona Weiss *(Member-Mgmt Bd & VP-Fin & Ops)*
Dobrosaw Wereszko *(Member-Mgmt Bd)*
Supervisory Board of Directors:
Ulrich Kottmann
Nevres Erol Bilecik
Tomasz Czechowicz
Mirosaw Godlewski
Hans-Dieter Kemler
Marek Sadowski
Hans-Peter Stander

Non-U.S. Subsidiaries:

ABC Data Distributie SRL (1)
Bd Natiunile Unite nr 1 Gemenii Center bl 108A etaj 9 birourile
A9-B9 sector 5, Bucharest, 050121, Romania
Tel.: (40) 372 030 999
Fax: (40) 372 030 998
E-Mail: office.ro@abcdata.eu
Web Site: www.abcdata.com.ro
Consumer Electronics Whslr
S.I.C.: 5064
N.A.I.C.S.: 423620

ABC Data Germany GmbH (1)
Lindberghstr 5
Puchheim, Munich, 82178, Germany
Tel.: (49) 89 21548574
Fax: (49) 89 21548560
E-Mail: vertrieb@abcdata.eu
Web Site: www.abcdatagermany.de
Consumer Electronics Distr
S.I.C.: 5064
N.A.I.C.S.: 423620

ABC Data Hungary Kft. (1)
Kethly Anna ter 1
1077 Budapest, Hungary
Tel.: (36) 1 501 5319
E-Mail: kapcsolat@abcdata.eu
Web Site: www.abcdata.hu
Consumer Electronics Whslr
S.I.C.: 5064
N.A.I.C.S.: 423620
Poros Gabor, *(Mng Dir & Country Mgr)*

ABC Data s.r.o. (1)
Business Centre Na Radosti 399
Prague, Czech Republic
Tel.: (420) 233 091 611
Fax: (420) 233 091 619
Web Site: www.abcdata.cz
Consumer Electronics Whslr
S.I.C.: 5064
N.A.I.C.S.: 423620
Martin Kristian *(Key Acct Mgr)*

ABC Data s.r.o. (1)
Palisady 33
811 06 Bratislava, Slovakia
Tel.: (421) 232 144 592
Fax: (421) 232 144 592
Web Site: www.abcdata.sk
Consumer Electronics Whslr
S.I.C.: 5064
N.A.I.C.S.: 423620
Robert Kostolani *(Key Acct Mgr)*

UAB ABC Data Lietuva (1)
4 Jogailos Str
01116 Vilnius, Lithuania
Tel.: (370) 5 259 60 60
Fax: (370) 5 259 60 61
E-Mail: info@abcdata.eu
Web Site: www.abcdata.lt
Consumer Electronics Distr
S.I.C.: 5064
N.A.I.C.S.: 423620
Raimundas Bycius, *(Mng Dir)*

ABC DESIGN GMBH

Dr Rudolf-Eberle Str 29
D-79774 Albbruck, Germany
Tel.: (49) 775393930
Fax: (49) 7753939340
E-Mail: info@abc-design.de
Web Site: www.abc-design.de
Year Founded: 1989
Rev.: $10,759,320
Emp.: 26
Business Description:
Kids Products Distr
S.I.C.: 5641
N.A.I.C.S.: 448130
Personnel:
Bernd Fischer *(Mng Dir)*
Jorg Zehe *(Mng Dir)*

ABC HOLDINGS LIMITED

ABC House Tholo Park Plot 50669
Gaborone, Botswana
Tel.: (267) 3905455
Fax: (267) 3902131
E-Mail: info@bancabc.com
Web Site: www.bancabc.com
ABCH—(BOT)
Rev.: $170,249,147
Assets: $1,650,495,872
Liabilities: $1,508,181,931
Net Worth: $142,313,940
Earnings: $16,638,812
Emp.: 1,310
Fiscal Year-end: 12/31/12
Business Description:
Financial Holding Company
S.I.C.: 6712
N.A.I.C.S.: 551111
Personnel:
Douglas T. Munatsi *(CEO)*
Hashmon Matemera *(Mng Dir & Head-Ops-Zimbabwe)*
Beki Moyo *(CFO)*
Francis M. Dzanya *(COO)*
Johan Bosch *(CIO)*
Blessing Mudavanhu *(Chief Risk Officer)*
Elizabeth Georg *(Sec)*
Board of Directors:
Howard Buttery
Francis M. Dzanya
Simon Ipe
Doreen Khama
Ngoni Kudenga
Beki Moyo
Douglas T. Munatsi
Lakshmi Shyam-Sunder
Hans Wasmus

ABC Transfer & Secretarial Services (Pty) Ltd
ABC House, Tholo Office Park Plot 50669,
Fairground Office Park
Gaborone, Botswana

Subsidiary:

African Banking Corporation Botswana Limited (1)
BancABC house plot 62433
Fairground, Gaborone, Botswana

ABC Holdings Limited—(Continued)

Tel.: (267) 3905455
Fax: (267) 3902131
Web Site: www.bancabc.com
Emp.: 60
Banking Services
S.I.C.: 6211
N.A.I.C.S.: 523110
Jitto Kurian *(Mng Dir)*

Non-U.S. Subsidiaries:

African Banking Corporation Tanzania Limited **(1)**
1st Fl Barclays House Ohio St
PO Box 31
Ali Hassan Mwinyi Rd, Dar es Salaam, Tanzania
Tel.: (255) 222111990
Fax: (255) 222112402
E-Mail: abctz@africanbankingcorp.com
Web Site: www.tanzaniabankers.org
Emp.: 55
Banking Services
S.I.C.: 6211
N.A.I.C.S.: 523110
Fordson Musingarabwi *(Mgr)*

Microfin Africa Zambia Limited **(1)**
3rd Flr Alliance House Cairo Rd
PO Box 32482
Lusaka, 10101, Zambia
Tel.: (260) 211227691
Fax: (260) 211227694
Banking Services
S.I.C.: 6036
N.A.I.C.S.: 522120
Moses Vera *(Mgr-Fin)*

Tanzania Development Finance Company Limited **(1)**
TDFL Bldg Ohio Rd
PO Box 2478
Dar es Salaam, Tanzania
Tel.: (255) 5146144
Fax: (255) 5146145
Financial Investment Services
S.I.C.: 6282
N.A.I.C.S.: 523930

ABC INDIA LTD.

C-121 Bangur Avenue
Kolkata, West Bengal, India
Tel.: (91) 33 25748591
Fax: (91) 33 25748590
E-Mail: vrmd@abcindia.com
Web Site: www.abcindia.com
520123—(BOM)
Business Description:
Logistics & Freight Transportation Services
S.I.C.: 4731
N.A.I.C.S.: 541614
Personnel:
Anand Kumar Agarwal *(Chm)*
Ashish Agarwal *(Mng Dir)*
A. K. Thirani *(CFO & Sec)*
S. G. Das *(Sr VP-Kolkata)*
R. P. Shah *(Sr VP-Kolkata)*
Board of Directors:
Anand Kumar Agarwal
Ashish Agarwal
Ashok Agarwal
Padam Chand Agarwal
Prakash Agarwal
K. Arya
Ashoke Kumar Dutta
Vijay Kumar Jain
Debasis Sengupta
Ashok Surana

ABC-MART, INC.

19F Shibuya Mark City West 1-12-1
Dogenzaka Shibuya-ku
Tokyo, 150-0043, Japan
Tel.: (81) 334765452
Fax: (81) 334765462
E-Mail: m.noguchi@mart-abc.mart.co.jp
Web Site: www.abc-mart.co.jp
Year Founded: 1985
2670—(TKS)
Sls.: $1,753,599,540
Assets: $1,970,753,631
Liabilities: $708,342,096
Net Worth: $1,262,411,535
Earnings: $190,273,347
Emp.: 2,923
Fiscal Year-end: 02/28/13
Business Description:
Shoes, Apparel & General Merchandise Retailer
Import Export
S.I.C.: 5661
N.A.I.C.S.: 448210
Personnel:
Minoru Noguchi *(Pres)*
Yukie Yoshida *(Mng Dir)*
Board of Directors:
Kiyoshi Katsunuma
Takashi Kikuchi
Jo Kojima
Toru Nakao
Minoru Noguchi
Yukie Yoshida

U.S. Subsidiary:

LaCrosse Footwear, Inc. **(1)**
17634 NE Airport Way
Portland, OR 97230-4999 WI
Tel.: (503) 262-0110
Fax: (503) 262-0115
Toll Free: (800) 323-2668 (Customer Service)
E-Mail: customerservice@lacrossefootwear.com
Web Site: www.lacrossefootwear.com
Sales Range: $125-149.9 Million
Emp.: 390
Protective Footwear & Apparel Designer, Developer, Marketer & Mfr for the Sporting, Occupational & Recreational Markets
S.I.C.: 2389
N.A.I.C.S.: 316210
Yasushi Akaogi *(Chm & Pres)*
David P. Carlson *(CFO, Sec & Exec VP)*

Subsidiary:

Danner, Inc. **(2)**
17634 NE Airport Way
Portland, OR 97230-1027 WI
Mailing Address: (100%)
PO Box 30148
Portland, OR 97294-3148
Tel.: (503) 251-1100
Fax: (503) 251-1119
Toll Free: (877) 432-6637
E-Mail: info@danner.com
Web Site: www.danner.com
Sales Range: $50-74.9 Million
Leather Footwear Mfr
S.I.C.: 2389
N.A.I.C.S.: 316210
Joseph P. Schneider *(Pres)*

Non-U.S. Subsidiary:

LaCrosse Europe, ApS **(2)**
Niels Ebbesens Vej 19
1911 Frederiksberg, C, Denmark DK
Tel.: (45) 7026 1500 (100%)
E-Mail: info@lacrossefootwear.eu
Web Site: www.lacrossefootwear.eu
Rubber & Plastics Footwear Retailer
S.I.C.: 5139
N.A.I.C.S.: 424340

ABC MOTORS COMPANY LIMITED

ABC Centre Military Road
Port Louis, Mauritius
Tel.: (230) 206 9900
Fax: (230) 242 5427
E-Mail: nssw@abcmotors.intnet.mu
Web Site: www.abcmotors.mu
Year Founded: 1985
ABC—(MAU)
Sales Range: $25-49.9 Million
Business Description:
Automobile Parts Distr
S.I.C.: 5015
N.A.I.C.S.: 423140
Personnel:
Michael Lai Cheong *(Mgr-Svcs)*

ABC RECORDS MANAGEMENT AND DATA STORAGE INC.

Flat A 22F Block 11 Wonderland Villas
Kwai Chung, China (Hong Kong)
Tel.: (852) 6677 3973
Year Founded: 2010
ABCR—(OTC)
Assets: $4,315
Liabilities: $53,364
Net Worth: ($49,049)
Earnings: ($46,929)
Emp.: 1
Fiscal Year-end: 03/31/13
Business Description:
Data Storage Services
S.I.C.: 3572
N.A.I.C.S.: 334112
Personnel:
Marc S. Bayer *(Pres, CEO, CFO, Chief Acctg Officer, Treas & Sec)*

ABCAM PLC

330 Cambridge Science Park
Cambridge, CB4 0FL, United Kingdom
Tel.: (44) 1223696000
Fax: (44) 1223215215
E-Mail: corporate@abcam.com
Web Site: www.abcamplc.com
ABC—(LSE OTC)
Rev.: $192,998,714
Assets: $315,726,919
Liabilities: $46,810,156
Net Worth: $268,916,763
Earnings: $51,576,453
Emp.: 690
Fiscal Year-end: 06/30/13
Business Description:
Protein Research Tool Producer & Distr
S.I.C.: 5047
N.A.I.C.S.: 423450
Personnel:
Jonathan S. Milner *(CEO)*
Jeffrey Iliffe *(CFO & Sec)*
James Warwick *(COO)*
Ed Ralph *(CIO)*
Alan Hirzel *(CMO)*
Board of Directors:
Michael Redmond
Murray Edwin Hennessy
Alan Hirzel
Jeffrey Iliffe
Peter S. Keen
Anthony Francis Martin
Jonathan S. Milner
Michael Alexander Nunes Ross
James Warwick
Legal Counsel:
Eversheds LLP
One Wood Street
EC2V 7WS London, United Kingdom

Non-U.S. Subsidiary:

Abcam KK **(1)**
1-16-8 Nihonbashi Kakigaracho
Chuo-ku, Tokyo, 103-0012, Japan
Tel.: (81) 362310940
Fax: (81) 362310941
E-Mail: orders@abcam.co.jp
Web Site: www.abcam.co.jp
Antibodies Mfr & Distr
S.I.C.: 2834
N.A.I.C.S.: 325412
Nick Lines *(Gen Mgr)*

ABCANA CAPITAL INC.

910 1050 West Pender Street
Vancouver, BC, V6E 3S7, Canada
Tel.: (604) 689-0299
Fax: (604) 689-0288
E-Mail: smaskerine@goldenharpresources.com
Year Founded: 2010
ABQ.P—(TSXV)
Business Description:
Investment Services
S.I.C.: 6211
N.A.I.C.S.: 523999
Personnel:
Shaun Maskerine *(CEO, CFO & Sec)*
Board of Directors:
Shauna Lynn Hartman
Shaun Maskerine
S. Paul Simpson
Transfer Agent:
Computershare Investor Services Inc.
3rd Floor 510 Burrard St
V6C 3B9 Vancouver, BC, Canada

ABCO ELECTRONICS CO., LTD.

5448-4 Sangdaewon-Dong
Jungwon-Gu, Seongnam, Kyeongki-Do, Korea (South)
Tel.: (82) 31 730 5000
Fax: (82) 31 743 2824
Web Site: www.abco.co.kr
Year Founded: 1973
036010—(KRS)
Sales Range: Less than $1 Million
Emp.: 160
Business Description:
Electronic Component Mfr
S.I.C.: 3676
N.A.I.C.S.: 334416
Personnel:
Je Yeong Kim *(Chm)*

Non-U.S. Subsidiaries:

ABCO Hungary Kft **(1)**
Ganz Abraham utca 2
H-2001 Godollo, Hungary
Tel.: (36) 28 420 055
Fax: (36) 28 410 594
Electronic Component Mfr
S.I.C.: 3675
N.A.I.C.S.: 334416

ABCO Slovakia sro **(1)**
A Kodalya 767
924 01 Galanta, Slovakia
Tel.: (421) 31 780 7087
Fax: (421) 21 7010 917
Electronic Components Mfr
S.I.C.: 3677
N.A.I.C.S.: 334416

Tianjin Hana International Trading Co., Ltd. **(1)**
No 4 Jianfu Road Xiqing District
Tianjin, China
Tel.: (86) 22 2397 7103
Fax: (86) 22 2397 7482
Electronic Component Mfr
S.I.C.: 3676
N.A.I.C.S.: 334416

ABCOURT MINES INC.

506 des Falaises St
Mont-Saint-Hilaire, QC, J3H 5R7, Canada
Tel.: (450) 446-5511
Fax: (450) 446-3550
Web Site: www.abcourt.com
ABI—(TSXV)
Rev.: $62,100
Assets: $20,959,983
Liabilities: $970,699
Net Worth: $19,989,284
Earnings: ($352,197)
Fiscal Year-end: 06/30/13
Business Description:
Mining Exploration Services
S.I.C.: 1081
N.A.I.C.S.: 213114

Personnel:
Renaud Hinse *(Pres & CEO)*
Jean-Guy Courtois *(CFO)*
Julie Godard *(Sec)*
Board of Directors:
Jean-Guy Courtois
Andre DeGuise
Christian Dupont
Marc Filion
Normand Hinse
Renaud Hinse
Yves Usereau
Transfer Agent:
Computershare
1500 University Street Suite 700
Montreal, QC, Canada

ABDI COMPANY JSC
465/191 Seifullin Ave
050050 Almaty, Kazakhstan
Tel.: (7) 327 2985798
E-Mail: office@adi.kz
Web Site: www.abdi.kz
ABDI—(KAZ)
Sales Range: $500-549.9 Million
Emp.: 950
Business Description:
Office Supplies Stores
S.I.C.: 5112
N.A.I.C.S.: 453210
Personnel:
Abdibek Bimendiev *(Pres)*

ABDUL AALI AL AJMI CO. LTD.
Imam Saud Street
PO Box 86059
Riyadh, 11622, Saudi Arabia
Tel.: (966) 124 02450
Fax: (966) 124 02458
E-Mail: info@alajmicompany.com
Web Site: www.alajmicompany.com
Year Founded: 1981
Sales Range: $10-24.9 Million
Emp.: 7,000
Business Description:
Engineering & Construction Management Services
S.I.C.: 8711
N.A.I.C.S.: 541330
Personnel:
Ali Abdulali Al-Ajmi *(Chm)*

ABDUL LATIF JAMEEL GROUP OF COMPANIES
PO Box 248
Jeddah, 21411, Saudi Arabia
Tel.: (966) 26930000
Fax: (966) 26930678
E-Mail: contact@alj.com
Web Site: www.alj.com
Year Founded: 1955
Emp.: 6,300
Business Description:
Holding Company; Automobile Sales & Services; Real Estate Services; Financing; Advertising Services; Consumer Electronics; Durables; Hotels; Shipping
S.I.C.: 6719
N.A.I.C.S.: 551112
Personnel:
Saad Alghamdi *(Gen Mgr)*
Non-U.S. Joint Venture:

Toyota Turkiye Motorlu Araclar A.S. **(1)**
Gulsuyu Mevkii Ankara Asfalti
34846 Istanbul, Turkey
Tel.: (90) 2164585858
Fax: (90) 2163701947
E-Mail: musteri.iliskileri@toyotasa.com.tr
Web Site: www.toyotasa.com.tr
Emp.: 150
Automobiles Mfr; Joint Venture of Haci Omer Sabanci Holding A.S., Toyota Motor Corp. & Mitsui & Co., Ltd.
S.I.C.: 3711
N.A.I.C.S.: 336111
Ibrahim Orhon *(Gen Mgr)*

ABDULLA AHMED NASS GROUP WLL
(d/b/a The Nass Group)
Bldg 453 Rd 4308 Block 343
PO Box 669
Mina Salman Industrial Area, Manama, Bahrain
Tel.: (973) 17725522
Fax: (973) 17728184
E-Mail: nassbah@batelco.com.bh
Web Site: www.nassgroup.com
Year Founded: 1963
Emp.: 3,300
Business Description:
Holding Company; Construction, Manufacturing, Industrial & Trading Services
S.I.C.: 6719
N.A.I.C.S.: 551112
Personnel:
Abdulla Ahmed Nass *(Chm)*
Samir Abdulla Nass *(Vice Chm)*
Board of Directors:
Abdulla Ahmed Nass
Hisham S. Al Saie
Jamal A. Al-Hazeem
Hemant Joshi
Saleh Al Nashwan
Adel Abdulla Nass
Ahmed Abdulla Nass
Fawzi Abdulla Nass
Ghazi Abdulla Nass
Sami Abdulla Nass
Samir Abdulla Nass
Mustafa Al Sayed
Subsidiaries:

Gulf Development Corporation **(1)**
Building 453 Rd 4308 Block 343
PO Box 669
Mina Salman Industrial Area, Manama, Bahrain
Tel.: (973) 17725522
Fax: (973) 17728184
E-Mail: nassbah@batelco.com.bh
Web Site: www.nassgroup.com
Emp.: 20
International Marine Services
S.I.C.: 3731
N.A.I.C.S.: 336611
Nadeem Hanna Shaikh *(Mng Dir)*

Shaw Nass Middle East WLL **(1)**
Road 5136 Building 1242 Askar Village
PO Box 15545
South Alba Industrial Area, Manama, Bahrain BH
Tel.: (973) 17830988
Fax: (973) 17 830 939
E-Mail: shawnass@batelco.com.bh
Web Site: www.shawnass.com
Emp.: 300
Fabricated Piping Systems
S.I.C.: 3498
N.A.I.C.S.: 332996
Mazen Aviziah *(CEO & Gen Mgr)*

Holding:

Nass Corporation B.S.C. **(1)**
Building 453 Road 4308 Block 343 Mina Salman Industrial Area
PO Box 669
Manama, Bahrain BH
Tel.: (973) 17725522 (51%)
Fax: (973) 17728184
E-Mail: nassbah@batelco.com.bh
Web Site: www.nassgroup.com
NASS—(BAH)
Rev.: $310,083,545
Assets: $304,358,678
Liabilities: $157,536,197
Net Worth: $146,822,481
Earnings: $11,035,075
Emp.: 7,000
Fiscal Year-end: 12/31/12
Civil Engineering, Mechanical & Electrical Contracting Services
S.I.C.: 1629
N.A.I.C.S.: 237990
Abdulla Ahmed Nass *(Chm)*
Samir Abdulla Nass *(Vice Chm)*
Hemant Joshi *(Sec)*

Divisions:

Nass Commerical **(2)**
Building 989 Road 31 Block 634 Ma'ameer
PO Box 669
Manama, Bahrain
Tel.: (973) 17 703 123
Fax: (973) 17 703 090
E-Mail: info@nasscommercial.com
Emp.: 20
Agent for Equipment & Manufacturers
S.I.C.: 5046
N.A.I.C.S.: 423440
Bashar Nass *(Mgr-Comml)*

Nass Electrical **(2)**
Building 453 Road 4308 Block 343
PO Box 669
Mina Salman Industrial Area, Manama, Bahrain
Tel.: (973) 17 725 522
Fax: (973) 17 827 525
E-Mail: nasselec@batelco.com.bh
Web Site: www.nassgroup.com
Electrical & Instrumentation Contracting
S.I.C.: 1731
N.A.I.C.S.: 238210

Nass Mechanical **(2)**
Building 630 Road 102 Block 117
PO Box 669
Hidd, Manama, Bahrain
Tel.: (973) 17465477
Fax: (973) 17465485
E-Mail: nassmech@batelco.com.bh
Emp.: 600
Mechanical Engineering-Design & Fabrication
S.I.C.: 8711
N.A.I.C.S.: 541330
Gynandra Kumar Roy *(Gen Mgr)*

Nass Scafform **(2)**
PO Box 669
Manama, Bahrain
Tel.: (973) 17 701 584
Fax: (973) 17 701 351
E-Mail: info@nassscafform.com.bh
Web Site: www.nassscafform.com.bh
Scaffolding & Form Work Services
S.I.C.: 1799
N.A.I.C.S.: 238190
Brian Fox *(Gen Mgr)*

Subsidiaries:

Abdulla Ahmed Nass Contracting Company WLL **(2)**
Bldg 1 007 Rd 31Block 635
PO Box 669
Ma'ameer, Manama, Bahrain
Tel.: (973) 17725522
Fax: (973) 17701714
E-Mail: info@nasscontracting.com
Web Site: www.nassgroup.com
Sls.: $5,305,000
Emp.: 2,500
Civil Engineering & Building Projects
S.I.C.: 1629
N.A.I.C.S.: 237990
David Anthony *(Gen Mgr)*

Delmon Precast Company WLL **(2)**
PO Box 669
Manama, Bahrain BH
Tel.: (973) 17783838
Fax: (973) 17 784 467
E-Mail: info@delmonprecast.com
Web Site: www.delmonprecast.com
Emp.: 100
Precast Concrete Products Mfr
S.I.C.: 3272
N.A.I.C.S.: 327390

Delmon Ready Mixed Concrete & Products Co. WLL **(2)**
Rd 239 Block 702 Bldg 1295
PO Box 936
Salmabad, 936 Manama, Bahrain BH
Tel.: (973) 17783838
Fax: (973) 17784467
E-Mail: info@delmonreadymix.com
Web Site: www.delmonprecast.com
Emp.: 550
Ready-Mix Concrete Mfr
S.I.C.: 3273
N.A.I.C.S.: 327320
Jon Mottram *(Gen Mgr)*

ABDULLA FOUAD HOLDING CO.
Prince Muhd St
PO Box 257
Dammam, 31411, Saudi Arabia
Tel.: (966) 814114
Fax: (966) 8333792
E-Mail: info@abdulla-fouad.com
Web Site: www.abdulla-fouad.com
Year Founded: 1947
Sales Range: $150-199.9 Million
Emp.: 3,500
Business Description:
Trading, Agencies, Contracting, Import, Hospital, Computer & Educational Aids, Travel, Telecommunications & Electronics Import Export
S.I.C.: 6221
N.A.I.C.S.: 523130
Personnel:
Abdulla Fouad *(Founder & Chm)*
Yousef A. Seyadi *(Exec VP)*
Divisions:

Abdulla Fouad Medical Supplies Division **(1)**
P O Box 13539
Jeddah, 21414, Saudi Arabia (100%)
Tel.: (966) 26394455
Telex: 801027 FOUAD SJ
Fax: (966) 6396725
E-Mail: info@abdulla-fouad.com
Web Site: www.abdulla-fouad.com
Emp.: 50
Provider of Medical Supplies
S.I.C.: 5047
N.A.I.C.S.: 423450
Anas Afash *(Mgr-Natl Sls)*

Abdulla Fouad-Supply & Services Division **(1)**
PO Box 257
Dammam, 31411, Saudi Arabia (100%)
Tel.: (966) 3 810 1878
Telex: 801027 FOUAD SJ
Fax: (966) 3 810 1860
E-Mail: ssd@abdulla-fouad.com
Web Site: www.abdulla-fouad.com
Emp.: 18
Petroleum Products Distr
S.I.C.: 2999
N.A.I.C.S.: 324199
Suneil Menon *(Gen Mgr)*

Abdulla Fouad-Testrade Division **(1)**
PO Box 257
Dammam, 31411, Saudi Arabia (100%)
Tel.: (966) 38172900
Telex: 801027 FOUAD SJ
Fax: (966) 38345722
E-Mail: suneil@saudionline.com.sa
Web Site: www.abdullafouad.com
Sales Range: $1-9.9 Million
Emp.: 3
Marketer of Testing Equipment; Paint Inspection Equipment, Radiation Safety Signs & Monitors, Industrial X-Ray Films & Chemicals, Inspection Gauges, Mirrors & Thermometers
Import Export
S.I.C.: 5084
N.A.I.C.S.: 423830

Subsidiaries:

Abdulla Fouad Corporation Ltd. **(1)**
PO Box 257
Dammam, 31411, Saudi Arabia (100%)
Tel.: (966) 38324400
Fax: (966) 38345722
Web Site: www.abdulla-fouad.com
Emp.: 2,900
General Constructors; Civil, Electrical & Mechanical
S.I.C.: 1629

Abdulla Fouad Holding Co.—(Continued)

N.A.I.C.S.: 237120

Abdulla Fouad Impalloy Ltd. Co. (1)
PO Box 257
Dammam, 31411, Saudi Arabia (100%)
Tel.: (966) 38473300
Fax: (966) 38472233
E-Mail: afic@abdulla-fouad.com
Web Site: www.abdull-fouad.com
Emp.: 100
Mfr. of Cathodic Protection Systems & Equipment
S.I.C.: 3699
N.A.I.C.S.: 335999
Abdullah Fouad *(Chm)*

Abdulla Fouad Information Technology Co. Ltd. (1)
PO Box 257
Dammam, 31411, Saudi Arabia (100%)
Tel.: (966) 38324400
Fax: (966) 38345722
E-Mail: info@abdulla-fouad.com
Web Site: www.abdulla.fouad.com
Emp.: 2,000
Sale & Service of Office Machines & Computer Systems
S.I.C.: 5044
N.A.I.C.S.: 423420
Abdulla Fouad *(Mng Dir)*

Fouad Travel & Cargo Agency (1)
King Saud Street near Hyper Panda
PO Box 257
Dammam, Eastern Province, 31411, Saudi Arabia (100%)
Tel.: (966) 38352020
Fax: (966) 3 835 1515
E-Mail: fta@abdulla-fouad.com
Web Site: www.abdulla-fouad.com
Emp.: 50
Air Transportation Support Services
S.I.C.: 4581
N.A.I.C.S.: 488119

Mantech Co., Ltd. (1)
PO Box 257
Dammam, 31411, Saudi Arabia (100%)
Tel.: (966) 38572646
Fax: (966) 96638101649
E-Mail: toytown@mantech-sa.com
Web Site: www.abdullafouad.com
Emp.: 350
Sales of Toys, Educational Aids & Amusement Facilities
S.I.C.: 5945
N.A.I.C.S.: 451120
Hanie L. Dd *(Gen Mgr)*

Mantech Computer & Telecommunications Co., Ltd. (1)
Prince Mohammed St
PO Box 257
Dammam, 31411, Saudi Arabia (100%)
Tel.: (966) 38324400
Fax: (966) 38311512
E-Mail: software@mantech-sa.com
Emp.: 164
Mfr. of Computers, Electronic Games & Software Agencies
S.I.C.: 5734
N.A.I.C.S.: 443142

ABDULLAH ABDULMOHSEN AL-KHODARI SONS CO.

Mazen Al Saeed Business Tower 11th Floor Dammam Khobar Highway
PO Box 3589
Al Khobar, 31952, Saudi Arabia
Tel.: (966) 38147200
Fax: (966) 38147171
E-Mail: info@alkhodari.com
Web Site: www.alkhodari.com
Year Founded: 1955
Rev.: $405,791,961
Assets: $720,486,751
Liabilities: $514,736,240
Net Worth: $205,750,511
Earnings: $35,951,001
Emp.: 12,000
Fiscal Year-end: 12/31/12
Business Description:
General Contracting Services
S.I.C.: 1542
N.A.I.C.S.: 236220
Personnel:
Ali A. Al-Khodari *(Chm)*
Fawwaz A. Al-Khodari *(CEO)*
Kailash Sadangi *(CFO)*
Ibrahim Mahlab *(COO)*
Board of Directors:
Ali A. Al-Khodari
Mounir Al-Borno
Fawwaz A. Al-Khodari
Jamil A. Al-Khodari
Naif Al-Khodari
Ibrahim Al-Mutrif

Subsidiaries:

Al-Khodari Industrial Trading & Services (1)
PO Box 3589
31952 Al Khobar, Saudi Arabia
Tel.: (966) 38952840
Fax: (966) 38649684
E-Mail: kits@alkhodari.com
Web Site: www.kitsgulf.com
Emp.: 200
Industrial Equipment Design, Maintenance & Sales
S.I.C.: 3559
N.A.I.C.S.: 333249

MACE Saudi Arabia Co. Ltd. (1)
PO Box 4164
Al Khobar, Saudi Arabia
Tel.: (966) 3 898 2584
Fax: (966) 3 895 4382
E-Mail: saudimace@awalnet.net.sa
Emp.: 560
Oil, Gas & Water Pipelines, Petrochemical & Refinery Construction, Industrial Plants & Building Construction & Fire Fighting Systems
S.I.C.: 1623
N.A.I.C.S.: 237120

ABDULLAH AL-OTHAIM MARKETS COMPANY

(d/b/a Al-Othaim Markets Company)
Eastern Ring Road Exit 14
PO Box 41700
Riyadh, 11531, Saudi Arabia
Tel.: (966) 14919999
Fax: (966) 1493 3264
E-Mail: info@othaimmarkets.com
Web Site: www.othaimmarkets.com
Year Founded: 1956
4001—(SAU)
Rev.: $1,136,082,848
Assets: $469,600,259
Liabilities: $288,397,545
Net Worth: $181,202,714
Earnings: $45,741,347
Emp.: 5,250
Fiscal Year-end: 12/31/12
Business Description:
Consumer Wholesale Supermarkets, Retail Supermarkets & Convenience Stores Owner & Operator
S.I.C.: 5411
N.A.I.C.S.: 445110
Personnel:
Abdullah Saleh Al Othaim *(Chm)*
Youssef Mohamed Al Gafari *(CEO)*
Board of Directors:
Abdullah Saleh Al Othaim
Youssef Mohamed Al Gafari
Sabah Mohammad Al-Mutlaq
Fahad Abdullah Al-Othaim
Saleh Mohammad Al-Othaim
Abdulaziz Saleh Al-Rebdi
Abdul Salam Saleh Al Rajhi

ABEN RESOURCES LTD.

Suite 1610 - 777 Dunsmuir Street
Vancouver, BC, V7Y 1K4, Canada
Tel.: (604) 687-3376
Fax: (604) 687-3119
Toll Free: (800) 567-8181
E-Mail: info@abenresources.com
Web Site: www.abenresources.com
ABN—(OTC TSXV)
Int. Income: $2,635
Assets: $3,574,629
Liabilities: $320,504
Net Worth: $3,254,125
Earnings: ($4,955,610)
Fiscal Year-end: 09/30/13
Business Description:
Mineral Exploration Services
S.I.C.: 1081
N.A.I.C.S.: 213114
Personnel:
Ronald Netolitzky *(Chm)*
James G. Pettit *(Pres & CEO)*
Donald C. Huston *(CFO)*
Board of Directors:
Ronald Netolitzky
Amanda Chow
Donald C. Huston
James G. Pettit
Timothy Jay Termuende
Legal Counsel:
Venex Law
700-595 Howe Street
Vancouver, BC, V6C 2T5, Canada
Transfer Agent:
Computershare Trust Company of Canada
100 University Avenue 9th Floor
Toronto, ON, M5J 2Y1, Canada
Tel.: (416) 663-9097
Fax: (416) 263-9694

ABENEX CAPITAL S.A.

9 Avenue Matignon
F-75008 Paris, France
Tel.: (33) 153936900
Fax: (33) 153936925
E-Mail: contacts@abenexcapital.com
Web Site: www.abenexcapital.com
Managed Assets: $730,056,000
Emp.: 15
Business Description:
Equity Investment Firm
S.I.C.: 6211
N.A.I.C.S.: 523999
Personnel:
Herve Claquin *(Pres)*
Olivier Moatti *(Mng Partner)*
Patrice Verrier *(Mng Partner)*

Holding:

Buffalo Grill S.A. (1)
Route Nationale 20
91630 Avrainville, France
Tel.: (33) 160825400
Fax: (33) 164913801
Web Site: www.buffalo-grill.fr
Sales Range: $350-399.9 Million
Emp.: 4,132
Restaurant Operator
S.I.C.: 5812
N.A.I.C.S.: 722511
Gilles Douillard *(Mng Dir)*

ABENGOA S.A.

Campus Palmas Altas C/ Energia Solar 1
41014 Seville, Spain
Tel.: (34) 954937111
Fax: (34) 955413371
E-Mail: abengoa@abengoa.com
Web Site: www.abengoa.com
Year Founded: 1941
ABGB—(MAD NASDAQ)
Rev.: $10,103,743,722
Assets: $29,052,374,965
Liabilities: $26,452,429,995
Net Worth: $2,599,944,970
Earnings: $151,524,498
Emp.: 26,818
Fiscal Year-end: 12/31/13
Business Description:
Industrial Engineering & Construction Services
S.I.C.: 8711
N.A.I.C.S.: 541330
Personnel:
Felipe Benjumea Llorente *(Chm & Co-CEO)*
Jose Buenaventura Terceiro Lomba *(Vice Chm)*
Manuel Sanchez Ortega *(CEO)*
German Bejarano Garcia *(Asst CEO-Intl Institutional Rels)*
Javier Molina Montes *(Pres-Environ Svcs Bus Grp)*
Maarten Hoogstraate *(Legal Counsel)*
Jose Dominguez Abascal *(Gen Sec-Technical)*
Fernando Martinez Salcedo Parcela *(Gen Sec-Sustainability)*
Alfonso Gonzalez Dominguez *(Exec VP-Engrg & Indus Construction & Latin America)*
Javier Salgado Leirado *(Exec VP-Indus Recycling)*
Santiago Seage Medela *(Exec VP-Solar)*
Javier Garoz Neira *(Exec VP-Biofuels)*
Board of Directors:
Felipe Benjumea Llorente
Jose Joaquin Abaurre Llorente
Jose Luis Aya Abaurre
Maria Teresa Benjumea Llorente
Mercedes Gracia Diez
Jose Borrell Fontelles
Ignacio Solis Guardiola
Javier Benjumea Llorente
Carlos Sundheim Losada
Fernando Solis Martinez-Campos
Manuel Sanchez Ortega
Claudio Santiago Ponsa
Ricardo Martinez Rico
Jose Buenaventura Terceiro Lomba
Alicia Velarde Valiente

U.S. Subsidiary:

Abengoa Bioenergy Corp. (1)
16150 Main Cricle Dr Ste 300
Chesterfield, MO 63017 (100%)
Tel.: (636) 728-0508
Fax: (636) 728-1148
E-Mail: info@abengoabioenergy.com
Web Site: www.abengoabioenergy.com
Emp.: 200
Producer of Ethanol
Export
S.I.C.: 2869
N.A.I.C.S.: 325193
Ignacio Garcia *(CFO)*
Gerson Santos-Leon *(Exec VP-New Technologies)*
Christopher Standlee *(Exec VP-Institutional Relationships & Govt Affairs)*

Plant:

Abengoa Bioenergy Inc. (2)
523 E Union Ave
Colwich, KS 67030-9723 KS
Tel.: (316) 796-1234
Fax: (316) 796-1523
Web Site: www.abengoabioenergy.com
Emp.: 55
Ethanol Production
S.I.C.: 0721
N.A.I.C.S.: 115112

ABENTEUER RESOURCES CORP.

Two Bentall Centre Suite 900 555 Burrard St
Vancouver, BC, V7X 1M8, Canada
Tel.: (604) 893-7011
Fax: (604) 893-7081
Toll Free: (877) 893-7011
E-Mail: info@abuoil.com
Web Site: www.abuoil.com
ABU—(TSXV)
Sls.: $472,757
Assets: $2,136,389
Liabilities: $206,915
Net Worth: $1,929,474

Earnings: ($149,766)
Fiscal Year-end: 12/31/12
Business Description:
Oil & Gas Exploration Services
S.I.C.: 1081
N.A.I.C.S.: 213114
Personnel:
J. Lewis Dillman *(Pres & CEO)*
Sean McGrath *(CFO)*
Board of Directors:
J. Lewis Dillman
Sean McGrath
David Parry
Stephen Polakoff
Legal Counsel:
McCullough O'Connor Irwin LLP
Suite 2600 Oceanic Plaza 1066 West Hastings Street
Vancouver, BC, Canada
Transfer Agent:
Olympia Trust Company
Suite 1003 750 West Pender Street
Vancouver, BC, V6C 2T8, Canada

ABERDEEN ASSET MANAGEMENT PLC

10 Queen's Terrace
Aberdeen, AB10 1YG, United Kingdom
Tel.: (44) 1224631999
Fax: (44) 1224647010
E-Mail: group.info@aberdeen-asset.com
Web Site: www.aberdeen-asset.com
Year Founded: 1983
ADN—(LSE OTC)
Rev.: $1,648,965,312
Assets: $6,401,217,936
Liabilities: $4,356,519,816
Net Worth: $2,044,698,120
Earnings: $351,552,864
Emp.: 391
Fiscal Year-end: 09/30/12
Business Description:
Institutional & Private Client Asset Management Services
S.I.C.: 6799
N.A.I.C.S.: 523920
Personnel:
Roger Courtenay Cornick *(Chm)*
Martin James Gilbert *(CEO)*
Andrew Arthur Laing *(Deputy CEO)*
Ken Fry *(COO)*
Anne Helen Richards *(Chief Investment Officer)*
Gordon Brough *(Gen Counsel & Deputy Head-Risk)*
Scott E. Massie *(Sec)*
Board of Directors:
Roger Courtenay Cornick
Julie Chakraverty
Anita Margaret Frew
Martin James Gilbert
Andrew Arthur Laing
Roderick McLeod MacRae
Kenichi Miyanaga
Richard Mully
Jim Pettigrew
William John Rattray
Anne Helen Richards
Simon Troughton
Giles Weaver
Hugh Young
Subsidiaries:

Aberdeen Asset Managers Ltd. **(1)**
Bow Bells House
1 Bread Street, London, EC4M 9HH, United Kingdom
Tel.: (44) 20 7463 6000
Fax: (44) 20 7463 6001
Web Site: www.aberdeen-asset.com
Fund Management
S.I.C.: 6722
N.A.I.C.S.: 525910
Stephen Christopher Alexander Docherty *(Head-Global Equities & Portfolio Mgr)*

Branches:

Aberdeen Asset Managers Ltd. **(2)**
1 Bow Churchyard
Cheapside, London, EC4M 9HH, United Kingdom
Tel.: (44) 2074636000
Fax: (44) 2074636001
E-Mail: officeservices@aberdeen-asset.com
Web Site: www.aberdeenassetmanagres.com
Emp.: 300
Fund Management
S.I.C.: 6799
N.A.I.C.S.: 523920

Aberdeen Murray Johnstone Ltd. **(1)**
1 Albyn Pl
Aberdeen, AB10 1YG, United Kingdom
Tel.: (44) 224631999
Fax: (44) 224425916
Emp.: 100
Fund Management
S.I.C.: 6722
N.A.I.C.S.: 525910

Aberdeen Private Equity Fund Limited **(1)**
100 Brompton Road
London, SW3 1ER, United Kingdom
Tel.: (44) 2070529272
Web Site: www.aberdeenprivateequity.co.uk
APEF—(LSE)
Sales Range: $10-24.9 Million
Investment Services
S.I.C.: 6282
N.A.I.C.S.: 523920
Jonathan D. Carr *(Chm)*

Aberdeen Unit Trust Managers Ltd. **(1)**
Bow Bells House 1 Bread St
London, EC4M 9HH, United Kingdom
Tel.: (44) 2074636336
Fax: (44) 2074636507
Web Site: www.aberdeen-asset.com
Property Investment
S.I.C.: 6726
N.A.I.C.S.: 525990

Aberdeen UK Tracker Trust plc **(1)**
(Formerly Edinburgh UK Tracker Trust plc)
Bow Bells House 1 Bread Street
London, EC4M 9HH, United Kingdom
Tel.: (44) 20 7463 6000
Fax: (44) 20 7463 6001
E-Mail: katie.cowley@aberdeen-asset.com
Web Site: www.edinburghuktracker.co.uk
AUKT—(LSE)
Sales Range: $10-24.9 Million
Emp.: 360
Investment Services
S.I.C.: 6099
N.A.I.C.S.: 523991
David McCraw *(Head-Indexed Equities)*

Joint Venture:

Aberdeen SVG Private Equity Advisers Limited **(1)**
(Formerly SVG Advisers Limited)
61 Aldwych
London, WC2B 4AE, United Kingdom UK
Tel.: (44) 2070108900
Fax: (44) 2070108901
E-Mail: privateequity@aberdeensvg.com
Emp.: 100
Private Equity Investment Advisory Services
S.I.C.: 6282
N.A.I.C.S.: 523930
Lynn Fordham *(CEO)*

U.S. Subsidiary:

SVG Advisers Inc. **(2)**
1 Boston Pl Ste 3875
Boston, MA 02108-4407 DE
Tel.: (617) 292-2550
Fax: (617) 292-2560
E-Mail: privateequity@aberdeensvg.com
Web Site: www.svgcapital.com
Emp.: 4
Private Equity Investment Advisory Services
S.I.C.: 6282
N.A.I.C.S.: 523930
Maureen Lynch *(Office Mgr)*

Non-U.S. Subsidiary:

SVG Advisers (Singapore) Pte. Ltd. **(2)**
250 N Bridge Rd Raffles City Tower 11-02
Singapore, 179101, Singapore SG
Tel.: (65) 65061750
Fax: (65) 65061799
E-Mail: privateequity@aberdeensvg.com
Web Site: www.svgcapital.com
Emp.: 4
Private Equity Investment Advisory Services
S.I.C.: 6282
N.A.I.C.S.: 523930

U.S. Subsidiary:

Aberdeen Asset Management Inc. **(1)**
Mellon Bank Ctr 1735 Market St 17th Fl
Philadelphia, PA 19103
Tel.: (215) 405-2055
Fax: (215) 405-5978
E-Mail: info@aam.com
Web Site: www.aberdeen-asset.com
Emp.: 100
Investment Management Services
S.I.C.: 6211
N.A.I.C.S.: 523110
Martin James Gilbert *(CEO)*

Non-U.S. Division:

Aberdeen Asset Management Sweden AB **(1)**
Luntmakargatan 34
PO Box 3039
SE 103-63 Stockholm, Sweden SE
Tel.: (46) 84128000
Fax: (46) 84128600
E-Mail: post.sweden@aberdeen-asset.com
Web Site: www.aberdeen-asset.se
Emp.: 120
Asset Management Services
S.I.C.: 6282
N.A.I.C.S.: 523920
Jon Lekander *(Head-Property)*

Subsidiary:

Aberdeen Property Investors Sweden AB **(2)**
Luntmakargatan 34
PO Box 3039
10363 Stockholm, Sweden SE
Tel.: (46) 84128000
Fax: (46) 84128600
E-Mail: post.sweden@aberdeen-asset.com
Web Site: www.aberdeen.se
Emp.: 100
Real Estate Fund Management
S.I.C.: 6726
N.A.I.C.S.: 525990

Non-U.S. Subsidiaries:

Aberdeen Property Investors Deutschland GmbH **(2)**
Zeughausstrasse 28 38
50667 Cologne, Germany
Tel.: (49) 2216503140
Fax: (49) 221 65 03 14 11
E-Mail: post.de@aberdeenpropertyinvestors.com
Web Site: www.aberdeenpropertyinvestors.de
Real Estate Investment Trust
S.I.C.: 6726
N.A.I.C.S.: 525990
Ton van der Poel *(Mng Dir)*

Aberdeen Property Investors Finland Oy **(2)**
Mikonkatu 9
FI-00100 Helsinki, Finland FI
Tel.: (358) 103040100
Fax: (358) 103040303
E-Mail: post.fi@aberdeen.fi
Web Site: www.aberdeenpropertyinvestors.fi
Real Estate Investments & Asset Management Services
S.I.C.: 6726
N.A.I.C.S.: 525990
Pertti Vanhanen *(CEO)*
Tero Rantanen *(Gen Counsel)*

Aberdeen Property Investors SAS **(2)**
29 berri
75008 Paris, France
Tel.: (33) 153539394
Fax: (33) 173090328
E-Mail:
Emp.: 4
Real Estate Invesment Trust
S.I.C.: 6726
N.A.I.C.S.: 525990
Doir NaDon *(Mng Dir)*

Aberdeen Property Investors The Netherlands B.V. **(2)**
Strawinskylaan 303 WTC A Tower 3rd Fl
PO Box 79074
1070 NC Amsterdam, Netherlands
Tel.: (31) 206870500
Fax: (31) 206844291
E-Mail: info@aberdeen-asset.com
Web Site: www.aberdeenpropertyinvestors.com
Emp.: 28
Real Estate Investment Trust
S.I.C.: 6726
N.A.I.C.S.: 525990
Aad Jansen *(Head-Asset Mgmt & Transactions)*

Subsidiary:

Aberdeen Property Investors Europe B.V. **(3)**
123 St Vincent Street
G2 5EA Glasgow, Netherlands
Tel.: (31) 206870500
Fax: (31) 1413067706
Web Site: www.aberdeen-asset.com
Emp.: 20
Real Estate Investments
S.I.C.: 6726
N.A.I.C.S.: 525990
Martin James Gilbert *(CEO)*

Non-U.S. Subsidiaries:

Aberdeen Asset Management Asia Ltd. **(1)**
21 Church Street
Ste 01-01 Capital Square Two, Singapore, 049480, Singapore
Tel.: (65) 63952702
Fax: (65) 64380743
E-Mail: client.services.sing@aberdeen-asset.com
Web Site: www.aberdeen-asia.com
Emp.: 180
Fund Management
S.I.C.: 6722
N.A.I.C.S.: 525910
Hugh Young *(Mng Dir)*

Aberdeen Asset Management Company Limited **(1)**
28th Floor Bangkok City Tower 179 South Sathorn Road
Thungmahamek Sathorn, Bangkok, Thailand
Tel.: (66) 2352 3333
Fax: (66) 2352 3389
E-Mail: client.services.th@aberdeen-asset.com
Web Site: www.aberdeen-asset.co.th
Asset Management Services
S.I.C.: 6282
N.A.I.C.S.: 523920
Adithep Vanabriksha *(Chief Investment Officer)*

Aberdeen Asset Management Ltd. **(1)**
Level 6 201 Kent St
Sydney, 2000, Australia
Tel.: (61) 299502888
Fax: (61) 299502800
E-Mail: client.service.aust@aberdeen-asset.com.au
Web Site: www.aberdeen-asset.com.au
Emp.: 85
Fund Management
S.I.C.: 6722
N.A.I.C.S.: 525910
Brett Jollie *(Mng Dir)*

Aberdeen Global Service SA **(1)**
2b Rue Albert Borschette
1246 Luxembourg, Luxembourg
Tel.: (352) 26 43 30 00
Fax: (352) 26 43 30 97
Investment Management Services
S.I.C.: 6211
N.A.I.C.S.: 523999

Aberdeen Asset Management PLC—(Continued)

Aberdeen Global State Street Bank Luxembourg S.A (1)
49 Avenue J F Kennedy
1855 Luxembourg, Luxembourg
Tel.: (352) 46 40 10 820
Fax: (352) 245 29 056
E-Mail: aberdeen.global@aberdeen-asset.com
Commercial Banking Services
S.I.C.: 6029
N.A.I.C.S.: 522110

Aberdeen International Fund Managers Ltd. (1)
Room 2605206 26th Floor Alexander House
18 Chater Road, Central, China (Hong Kong)
Tel.: (852) 21034700
Fax: (852) 21034788
E-Mail: client.services.hk@aberdeen-asset.com
Emp.: 8
Fund Distribution
S.I.C.: 6722
N.A.I.C.S.: 525910
Alex Boggis *(Mng Dir)*

Aberdeen International (IoM) Life Assurance Ltd. (1)
St Georges House
PO Box 391
Hill Street, Douglas, IM99 2XW, Isle of Man
E-Mail: frontoffice.iom@aberdeen-asset.com
Web Site: www.aberdeen-asset.com
Emp.: 20
Life Insurance
S.I.C.: 6399
N.A.I.C.S.: 524128

Aberdeen International Securities Investment Consulting Company Ltd (1)
Exchange Square No 2 3-1 No 97 Songren Rd
Taipei, Taiwan
Tel.: (886) 2 87224500
Fax: (886) 2 87224501
E-Mail: client-services.taipei@aberdeen-asset.com
Web Site: www.aberdeen-asset.com.tw
Securities Brokerage Services
S.I.C.: 6211
N.A.I.C.S.: 523120

Aberdeen Investment Management K.K. (1)
Toranomon Seiwa Building 11F 1-2-3 Toranomon
Minato-ku, Tokyo, 105-0001, Japan
Tel.: (81) 3 4578 2200
Fax: (81) 3 4578 2300
Investment Management Services
S.I.C.: 6211
N.A.I.C.S.: 523999

Aberdeen Private Wealth Management Ltd. (1)
1 Seaton Pl
Saint Helier, Jersey
Tel.: (44) 534758847
Fax: (44) 534767052
E-Mail: offshore.solution@aberdeen-asset.com
Web Site: www.aberdeen-asset.com
Emp.: 9
Fund Management
S.I.C.: 6722
N.A.I.C.S.: 525910
Bruce Harrison *(Mng Dir)*

Subsidiary:

Aberdeen Asset Managers Jersey Ltd. (2)
1 Seaton Pl
Saint Helier, JE4 8YJ, Jersey
Tel.: (44) 534758847
Fax: (44) 1534767084
Web Site: www.aberdeen-asset.com
Fund Management
S.I.C.: 6722
N.A.I.C.S.: 525910

ABERDEEN INTERNATIONAL INC.

65 Queen Street West Suite 815
PO Box 75
Toronto, ON, M5H 2M5, Canada
Tel.: (416) 861-5875
Fax: (416) 861-8165
E-Mail: dstein@aberdeeninternational.ca
Web Site: www.aberdeeninternational.ca
AAB—(TSX)
Rev.: $1,931,136
Assets: $75,336,443
Liabilities: $10,277,776
Net Worth: $65,058,667
Earnings: ($30,447,249)
Emp.: 6
Fiscal Year-end: 01/31/13

Business Description:
Metal Mining Services
S.I.C.: 1099
N.A.I.C.S.: 212299

Personnel:
Stan Bharti *(Chm)*
George D. Faught *(Vice Chm)*
David M. Stein *(CEO)*
Nick Barton *(Interim Mng Dir)*
Ryan Ptolemy *(CFO & Sec)*

Board of Directors:
Stan Bharti
George D. Faught
Michael L. Hoffman
Jean-Guy Lambert
Pierre S. Pettigrew
David M. Stein
Bernard Wilson

Transfer Agent:
Equity Transfer & Trust Company
200 University Avenue Ste 400
Toronto, ON, M5H 4H1, Canada
Tel.: (416) 361-0152
Fax: (416) 361-0470

ABERDEEN LEADERS LIMITED

Level 6 201 Kent Street
Sydney, NSW, 2000, Australia
Tel.: (61) 299502888
Fax: (61) 299502800
E-Mail: client.services@aberdeen-asset.com
Web Site: www.aberdeenasset.com.au
ALR—(ASX)
Rev.: $4,457,062
Assets: $102,641,640
Liabilities: $34,499,763
Net Worth: $68,141,877
Earnings: $1,869,527
Fiscal Year-end: 06/30/13

Business Description:
Investment Services
S.I.C.: 6282
N.A.I.C.S.: 523920

Personnel:
Brian Michael Sherman *(Chm)*
Gil Orski *(Sec)*

Board of Directors:
Brian Michael Sherman
Augustine Mark Daniels
David Lindsay Elsum
Neville John Miles

ABERFORTH PARTNERS LLP

14 Melville St
Edinburgh, EH3 7NS, United Kingdom
Tel.: (44) 1312200733
Fax: (44) 1312200735
E-Mail: enquiries@aberforth.co.uk
Web Site: www.aberforth.co.uk
Year Founded: 1990
Sales Range: $1-4.9 Billion
Emp.: 10

Business Description:
Equity Investment Firm
S.I.C.: 6211
N.A.I.C.S.: 523999

Personnel:
Richard Newbery *(Founder & Partner)*
David Ross *(Founder & Partner)*
Alistair Whyte *(Founder & Partner)*
Andrew Bamford *(Partner)*
Euan Macdonald *(Partner)*

ABERTIS INFRAESTRUCTURAS S.A.

Avinguda del Parc Logistic 12-20
08040 Barcelona, Spain
Tel.: (34) 932305000
Fax: (34) 932305001
E-Mail: abertis@abertis.com
Web Site: www.abertis.com
ABE—(MAD)
Rev.: $5,437,709,675
Assets: $39,155,442,360
Liabilities: $29,784,969,723
Net Worth: $9,370,472,637
Earnings: $1,458,202,306
Emp.: 11,331
Fiscal Year-end: 12/31/12

Business Description:
Transport & Communications Infrastructure Management & Tollway Development & Maintenance Services
S.I.C.: 4491
N.A.I.C.S.: 488210

Personnel:
Salvador Alemany Mas *(Pres)*
Francisco Reynes Massanet *(CEO)*
Carlos del Rio Carcano *(Mng Dir-Abertis Airports)*
Jose Aljaro Navarro *(CFO & Chief Corp Dev Officer)*
David Diaz Almazan *(CEO-Arteris)*
Marta Casas Caba *(Co-Sec)*
Josep Maria Coronas Guinart *(Gen Sec)*
Miquel Roca Junyent *(Co-Sec)*

Board of Directors:
Maria Teresa Costa Campi
Isidre Faine Casas
D. Carlos Colomer Casellas
Juan Villar-Mir de Fuentes
Javier de Jaime Guijarro
Jose Antonio Torre de Silva Lopez de Letona
Monica Lopez-Monis Gallego
Carmen Godia
Santiago Ramirez Larrauri
Tomas Garcia Madrid
Salvador Alemany Mas
Francisco Reynes Massanet
Miguel Angel Gutierrez Mendez
Manuel Torreblanca Ramirez
Ricardo Fornesa Ribo
Marcelino Armenter Vidal
Juan-Miguel Villar Mir

Subsidiaries:

Abertis Airports S.A. (1)
Av del Parc Logistic 12 20
08040 Barcelona, Spain
Tel.: (34) 932305000
Fax: (34) 932305180
E-Mail: abertis@abertis.com
Web Site: www.abertisairports.com
Sales Range: $350-399.9 Million
Emp.: 2,000
Airport Operator
S.I.C.: 4581
N.A.I.C.S.: 488119
Carlos del Rio Carcano *(Mng Dir)*

Non-U.S. Subsidiary:

TBI plc (2)
72-104 TBI House Frank Lester Way
London Luton Airport, Luton, Beds, LU2 9NQ, United Kingdom UK
Tel.: (44) 1582817400
Fax: (44) 1582817444
E-Mail: abertis@abertis.com
Web Site: www.tbiairports.aero
Airport Operator
S.I.C.: 4581
N.A.I.C.S.: 488119
Carlos Delrio *(CEO)*

U.S. Subsidiaries:

TBI Airport Management Inc. (3)
3212 Red Cleveland Blvd
Sanford, FL 32773 (100%)
Tel.: (407) 585-4500
Fax: (407) 585-4545
Web Site: www.orlandosanfordairport.com
Emp.: 65
Airport Management
S.I.C.: 4581
N.A.I.C.S.: 488119
Larry Gouldthorpe *(Pres)*
John Green *(COO)*

Subsidiaries:

Orlando Sanford International Inc. (4)
Airport Authority
Sanford, FL 32773 (100%)
Tel.: (407) 585-4500
Fax: (407) 585-4545
Web Site: www.orlandosanfordairport.com
Emp.: 200
Airport Operator
S.I.C.: 4581
N.A.I.C.S.: 488119
Larry Gouldthorte *(Pres)*

TBI Cargo Inc. (4)
2971 Carrier Ave
Sanford, FL 32773 (100%)
Tel.: (407) 585-4620
Fax: (407) 585-4618
E-Mail: tbi.cargo@tbiusinc.aero
Emp.: 6
Air Cargo Transportation Services
S.I.C.: 4512
N.A.I.C.S.: 481112

Subsidiaries:

Belfast International Airport Ltd. (3)
Belfast Intl Airport
Belfast, BT29 4AB, United Kingdom UK
Tel.: (44) 2894484848 (100%)
Fax: (44) 2894452096
E-Mail: bss.aero@belfastairport.com
Web Site: www.belfastairport.com
Emp.: 180
Airport Operator
S.I.C.: 4581
N.A.I.C.S.: 488119
John Doran *(Mng Dir)*

Cardiff International Airport Ltd. (3)
Cardiff Intl Airport
Glamorgan, Cardiff, CF62 3BD, United Kingdom UK
Tel.: (44) 1446711111 (100%)
Fax: (44) 1446711675
Web Site: www.tbicardiffairport.com
Emp.: 150
Airport Operator
S.I.C.: 4581
N.A.I.C.S.: 488119
Lord Rowe-Beddoe *(Chm)*
Jon Horne *(CEO)*

London Luton Airport Group Limited (3)
Percival House Percival Way
London Luton Airport, Luton, Beds, LU2 9LY, United Kingdom
Tel.: (44) 1582405100
Air Transportation Management Services
S.I.C.: 4581
N.A.I.C.S.: 488190

Subsidiary:

London Luton Airport Operations Ltd (4)
Navigation House
Airport Way, Luton, Bedfordshire, LU2 9LY, United Kingdom UK
Tel.: (44) 1582405100
E-Mail: info@ltn.aero
Web Site: www.london-luton.co.uk
Airport Operation Services
S.I.C.: 4581
N.A.I.C.S.: 488119
Glyn Jones *(Mng Dir)*

Stockholm Skavsta Flygplats AB (3)
General Schybergs Vag 22
Box 44
SE 611 22 Nykoping, Sweden (100%)
Tel.: (46) 155280400
Fax: (46) 155280449
E-Mail: airport@skavsta.se
Web Site: www.skavsta.se
Emp.: 400
Airport Operator
S.I.C.: 4581
N.A.I.C.S.: 488119
Dot Gade *(Mgr)*

Abertis Logistica, S.A. (1)
Avinguda Parc Logistic 22-26
08040 Barcelona, Spain
Tel.: (34) 93 230 52 00
Fax: (34) 93 230 52 02
E-Mail: abertislogistica@abertislogistica.com
Web Site: www.abertislogistica.com
Logistics Services
S.I.C.: 4731
N.A.I.C.S.: 541614
Francesc Homs *(Chm-Mgmt Bd)*
Joan Font *(Mng Dir)*
Enrique Lacalle Coll *(Member-Mgmt Bd)*
Luis Rullan Colom *(Member-Mgmt Bd)*
Joaquin Gay de Montella Ferrer-Vidal *(Member-Mgmt Bd)*
Miguel Noguer Planas *(Member-Mgmt Bd)*
Maite Claville Mana *(Deputy Sec)*
Carlota Masdeu Toffoli *(Sec)*

Subsidiary:

Sevisur Logistica, S.A. (2)
Zona de Actividades Logisticas Ctra de la Esclusa 15
41011 Seville, Spain
Tel.: (34) 955 658 823
Fax: (34) 955 658 824
E-Mail: zalsevilla@zalsevilla.com
Web Site: www.zalsevilla.com
Logistics Consulting Services
S.I.C.: 4731
N.A.I.C.S.: 541614

Non-U.S. Subsidiary:

Abertis Logistica Chile (2)
El Golf 150 Piso 6
Las Condes, Santiago, Chile
Tel.: (56) 2 680 90 00
Fax: (56) 2 203 36 15
E-Mail: info@abertislogistica.cl
Web Site: www.abertislogistica.cl
Emp.: 3
Logistics Consulting Services
S.I.C.: 4731
N.A.I.C.S.: 541614
Miguel Gueydan *(Mgr-Technical)*

Abertis Telecom, S.A. (1)
Av Parc Logistic 12-20
08040 Barcelona, Spain ES
Tel.: (34) 935678910
E-Mail: abertistlc@abertistelecom.com
Web Site: www.abertistelecom.com
Emp.: 1,000
Telecommunication Infrastructure Operating Services
S.I.C.: 4899
N.A.I.C.S.: 517919
Salvador Alemany Mas *(Chm & CEO)*
Tobias Martinez Gimeno *(Mng Dir)*

Subsidiaries:

Adesal Telecom S.L. (2)
Av Ausias March 20 Bjos
46006 Valencia, Spain
Tel.: (34) 963029314
Fax: (34) 963029309
E-Mail: informacion@adesaltelecom.com
Web Site: www.adesaltelecom.com
Telecommunication Software Development Services
S.I.C.: 7371
N.A.I.C.S.: 541511

Hispasat, S.A. (2)
Gobelas 41 2nd Fl
28023 Madrid, Spain ES
Tel.: (34) 917102540 (57.05%)
Fax: (34) 913729000
Web Site: www.hispasat.com
Sales Range: $200-249.9 Million
Emp.: 120
Telecommunications Satellite Operator
S.I.C.: 4899
N.A.I.C.S.: 517410
Petra Mateos-Aparicio Morales *(Chm)*
Elena Pisonero *(Pres)*
Carlos Espinos Gomez *(CEO)*
Javier Folguera Fernandez *(Vice Sec)*
Pedro Ramon Y Cajal Agueras *(Sec)*

Non-U.S. Subsidiary:

Hispasat Brasil Ltda. (3)
Do Flamengo 200 17 Andar
Rio de Janeiro, RJ, 22210-901, Brazil
Tel.: (55) 2125554800
Fax: (55) 2138262670
Web Site: www.hispasat.com
Emp.: 50
Communication Services
S.I.C.: 4899
N.A.I.C.S.: 517410
Sebastiao Rego *(Chm)*

Retevision I, S.A. (2)
Avenida Parc Logistic 12-20
Barcelona, 08040, Spain
Tel.: (34) 932305020
Fax: (34) 932305001
Television Broadcasting Services
S.I.C.: 4833
N.A.I.C.S.: 515120

Autopistas de Leon, S.A.C.E. (1)
Carretera Leon Astorga Area De Mantenimiento S/N
Villadangos Del Paramo, Leon, 24392, Spain
Tel.: (34) 987390919
Fax: (34) 987390989
Highway Construction Services
S.I.C.: 1611
N.A.I.C.S.: 237310

Infraestructures Viaries de Catalunya, S.A. (1)
Avenida Parc Logistic 12-20
Barcelona, 08040, Spain
Tel.: (34) 932305000
Construction Engineering Services
S.I.C.: 1629
N.A.I.C.S.: 237990

Serviabertis, S.L. (1)
Av Parc Logistic 12-20
Barcelona, 08040, Spain
Tel.: (34) 932305000
Fax: (34) 932305001
Telecommunication Infrastructure Management Services
S.I.C.: 4899
N.A.I.C.S.: 517919

U.S. Subsidiary:

Orlando Sanford Domestic Inc (1)
3217 Red Cleveland Blvd
Sanford, FL 32773
Tel.: (407) 585-4500
Telecommunication Services
S.I.C.: 4899
N.A.I.C.S.: 517919

Non-U.S. Subsidiaries:

Grupo Concesionario del Oeste, S.A. (1)
Avenida Gaona Km 25 920
Ituzaingo, Buenos Aires, 1714, Argentina
Tel.: (54) 1144898200
Fax: (54) 1144898261
Highway Construction Services
S.I.C.: 1611
N.A.I.C.S.: 237310
Carlos Staino *(Gen Mgr)*

Holding d'Infrastructures de Transport SAS (1)
Le Crossing 30 boulevard Gallieni
F-92130 Issy-les-Moulineaux, France FR
Tel.: (33) 1 4190 5900
Web Site: www.sanefgroupe.com
Emp.: 3,500
Holding Company; Roadway Infrastructure Development & Toll Collection Services
S.I.C.: 6719
N.A.I.C.S.: 551112
Alain Minc *(Chm)*
Francois Gauthey *(CEO & Mng Dir)*

Subsidiary:

Sanef SA (2)
Le Crossing 30 boulevard Gallieni
F-92130 Issy-les-Moulineaux, France FR
Tel.: (33) 1 4190 5900
Web Site: www.sanef.com
Roadway Infrastructure Development & Toll Collection Services
S.I.C.: 4789
N.A.I.C.S.: 488490
Francois Gauthey *(Dir Gen)*

Subsidiaries:

Eurotoll SAS (3)
30 boulevard Gallieni
92442 Issy-les-Moulineaux, France
Tel.: (33) 825 10 10 80
E-Mail: service.client@eurotoll.fr
Web Site: www.eurotoll.fr
Electronic Toll Collection Services
S.I.C.: 7389
N.A.I.C.S.: 561990
Christophe Mahe *(Mgr-Sls & Mktg)*

Non-U.S. Subsidiary:

HIT Finance BV (2)
Prins Bernhardplein 200
Amsterdam, 1097 JB, Netherlands
Tel.: (31) 205214777
Financial Management Services
S.I.C.: 6211
N.A.I.C.S.: 523999

Rutas del Pacifico S.A. (1)
Ruta 68 Km 17 9 Al Costado de la Plaza de Peaje Lo Prado
Pudahuel, Santiago, Chile
Tel.: (56) 2 680 0000
E-Mail: soc_concesionaria@rutasdelpacifico.cl
Web Site: www.rutasdelpacifico.cl
Expressway Construction & Management Services
S.I.C.: 1622
N.A.I.C.S.: 237310

Non-U.S. Joint Venture:

Arteris S.A. (1)
(Formerly Obrascon Huarte Lain Brasil S.A.)
Rua Joaquim Floriano 913 - 6th Floor
Itaim Bibi, 04534-013 Sao Paulo, Brazil
Tel.: (55) 11 3074 2404
Fax: (55) 11 3074 2405
E-Mail:
Web Site: www.ohlbrasil.com.br
OHLB3—(RIO)
Rev.: $1,534,105,056
Assets: $2,975,157,314
Liabilities: $2,184,648,765
Net Worth: $790,508,549
Earnings: $198,510,080
Emp.: 1,302
Fiscal Year-end: 12/31/12
Toll Management Services
S.I.C.: 1611
N.A.I.C.S.: 237310
Sergio Silva de Freitas *(Chm)*
David Antonio Diaz Almazan *(CEO)*
Felipe Ezquerra Plasencia *(Deputy CEO)*
Maria de Castro Michielin *(Legal Officer)*
Luis Manuel Eusebio Inigo *(Exec Officer)*
Paulo Pacheco Fernandes *(Exec Officer)*
Alessandro Scotoni Levy *(IR Officer)*
Marcio Augusto Travain *(Admin & Fin Officer)*

ABFAR COMPANY (PUBLIC JOINT STOCK)

Lashkari Express Way Karaj Special Road Km 18
Tehran, Iran
Tel.: (98) 21 44984035
Fax: (98) 21 44984033
E-Mail: info@abfar.com
Web Site: www.abfar.com
Year Founded: 1968
ABFR—(THE)

Business Description:
Water Meter Mfr
S.I.C.: 3999
N.A.I.C.S.: 339999

Personnel:
A. MalakShahi Haddadi *(Mng Dir)*

ABG INFRALOGISTICS LIMITED

5th Floor Bhupati Chambers 13 Mathew Road
Mumbai, 400004, India
Tel.: (91) 22 6656 3000
Fax: (91) 22 2364 9236
E-Mail: hq@abginfra.com
Web Site: www.abgworld.com
Year Founded: 1983
520155—(BOM)
Rev.: $32,466,443
Assets: $208,304,878
Liabilities: $135,788,269
Net Worth: $72,516,609
Earnings: $11,242,225
Fiscal Year-end: 03/31/13

Business Description:
Logistics & Physical Distribution Services
S.I.C.: 4731
N.A.I.C.S.: 541614

Personnel:
C. Babu Rajeev *(CEO)*
Saket Agarwal *(Mng Dir)*
Ritul Parmar *(Compliance Officer & Sec)*

Board of Directors:
Kamlesh Kumar Agarwal
Saket Agarwal
Govindrajpuram Ramasubramanian Gayatrivallabhan
Ravishankar Gopalan
Haleangadi Panduranga Prabhu

Transfer Agent:
Bigshare Services Private Limited
E-2 Ansa Industrial Estate Sakivihar Road Saki Naka Andheri (E)
Mumbai, India

ABG SHIPYARD LTD

Near Magdala Port Dumas Road
Surat, Gujarat, 395 007, India
Tel.: (91) 2612725191
Fax: (91) 2612726481
E-Mail: shipyard@abgindia.com
Web Site: www.abgindia.com
ABGSHIP—(NSE)
Rev.: $398,024,136
Assets: $2,053,356,912
Liabilities: $1,752,797,556
Net Worth: $300,559,356
Earnings: $17,815,086
Emp.: 275
Fiscal Year-end: 03/31/13

Business Description:
Ship Building & Repairing Services
S.I.C.: 3731
N.A.I.C.S.: 336611

Personnel:
Syed Waheed Zafar Abdi *(CEO & Mng Dir)*
Rajesh Tulsiani *(CFO)*
Sunil Agarwal *(Compliance Officer, Sec & Sr Mgr-Legal)*

Board of Directors:
Rishi Agarwal
Ashok R. Chitnis
Shazaad Dalal
Dhananjay Datar
Ashwani Kumar
Aloke Sengupta

Transfer Agent:
Link Intime India Pvt. Ltd.
C-13 Pannalal Silk Mills Compound
LBS Marg
Bhandup, Mumbai, 400 078, India
Tel.: (91) 22 2596 3838
Fax: (91) 22 2594 6969

Subsidiary:

Western India Shipyard Ltd. (1)
Mormugao Harbour
PO Box 21
Mormugao, Goa, 403 803, India
Tel.: (91) 832 2520252

ABG Shipyard Ltd—(Continued)

Fax: (91) 832 2520258
E-Mail:
Web Site: www.wisl.co.in
531217—(BOM)
Rev.: $14,559,963
Assets: $42,001,703
Liabilities: $39,490,682
Net Worth: $2,511,021
Earnings: ($1,820,109)
Fiscal Year-end: 03/31/13
Ship & Rig Repair Services
S.I.C.: 3731
N.A.I.C.S.: 336611
S. K. Mutreja *(CEO)*
J. C. F. Sequeira *(Compliance Officer, Co-Sec & VP-Corp Affairs)*
Ashish Pandey *(Co-Sec & Gen Mgr-Fin)*

ABG SUNDAL COLLIER HOLDING ASA

Munkedamsveien 45 7th Floor
0250 Oslo, Norway
Tel.: (47) 22016000
Fax: (47) 22016060
E-Mail: compliance@abgsc.com
Web Site: www.abgsc.com
ASC—(OSL)
Rev.: $168,373,006
Assets: $412,803,078
Liabilities: $199,294,243
Net Worth: $213,508,835
Earnings: $29,539,197
Emp.: 257
Fiscal Year-end: 12/31/12

Business Description:
Investment Banking Services
S.I.C.: 6211
N.A.I.C.S.: 523110

Personnel:
Judy Lee Bollinger *(Chm)*
Knut Brundtland *(CEO)*
Geir B. Olsen *(CFO)*

Board of Directors:
Judy Lee Bollinger
Tone Bjornov
Jan Petter Collier
Anders Gruden
Jorgen C. Arentz Rostrup

Subsidiaries:

ABG Sundal Collier Asset Management AS (1)
Munkedamsveien 45 7th Fl
0250 Oslo, Norway
Tel.: (47) 22016000
Fax: (47) 22016060
Fund Management Services
S.I.C.: 6722
N.A.I.C.S.: 525910
Bjorn Petter Bjorgo *(Head-AM)*

ABG Sundal Collier Forvaltning AS (1)
Munkedamsveien 45 D
Postboks 1444
0115 Oslo, Norway
Tel.: (47) 22016055
Fax: (47) 22016060
Emp.: 150
Stock Broking Services
S.I.C.: 6211
N.A.I.C.S.: 523120
Pertha Raldsem *(Mgr-IT)*

ABG Sundal Collier Norge ASA (1)
Munkedamsveien 45 7th Floor
0250 Oslo, Norway
Tel.: (47) 22016000
Fax: (47) 22016060
Investment Banking Services
S.I.C.: 6211
N.A.I.C.S.: 523110
Arild Abel Engh *(Chm)*
Jan Petter Collier *(Mng Dir)*

U.S. Subsidiary:

ABG Sundal Collier Inc. (1)
535 Madison Ave 17th Fl
New York, NY 10022
Tel.: (212) 605-3800
Fax: (212) 605-3801
Securities Brokerage Services
S.I.C.: 6211
N.A.I.C.S.: 523120
Nick Williams *(Head-Bond Sls & Trading)*

Non-U.S. Subsidiaries:

ABG Sundal Collier AB (1)
Regeringsgatan 65 5th Floor
PO Box 7269
103 89 Stockholm, Sweden
Tel.: (46) 856628600
Fax: (46) 856628601
E-Mail: henrik.ekberg@abgsc.sc
Emp.: 91
Investment Banking Services
S.I.C.: 6211
N.A.I.C.S.: 523110
Jessica Blink *(Head-Compliance)*

ABG Sundal Collier Ltd. (1)
St Martins Court 10 Paternoster Row
London, EC4M 7EJ, United Kingdom
Tel.: (44) 2079055600
Fax: (44) 2079055601
E-Mail: info@abgsc.com
Web Site: www.abgsc.com
Emp.: 25
Investment Banking Services
S.I.C.: 6211
N.A.I.C.S.: 523110
Emily Dgebuadze *(Head-Compliance)*

ABHINAV CAPITAL SERVICES LIMITED

Athena House Row House No 4
Rajnigandha Gokuldham
Goregaon E, Mumbai, 400063, India
Tel.: (91) 22 28425907
Fax: (91) 22 28406189
E-Mail: info@abhinavcapital.com
Web Site: www.abhinavcapital.com
Year Founded: 1994
532057—(BOM)
Sls.: $89,882
Assets: $2,898,099
Liabilities: $140,366
Net Worth: $2,757,732
Earnings: ($48,723)
Fiscal Year-end: 03/31/13

Business Description:
Financial Management Services
S.I.C.: 6211
N.A.I.C.S.: 523999

Personnel:
Chetan Karia *(Compliance Officer)*

Board of Directors:
Chetan Karia
Girish Desai
Kamlesh Kotak

Transfer Agent:
Adroit Corporate Services Private Limited
19 Jaferbhoy Industrial Estate Makwana Road
Marol Naka Andheri E
Mumbai, India

ABINGDON FURNITURE GALLERY LIMITED

(Formerly AFG Kitchens UK Ltd.)
Unit 3 Eyston Way
Abingdon, Oxfordshire, OX14 1TR, United Kingdom
Tel.: (44) 1235558000
Fax: (44) 1235558027
E-Mail: info@afgk.co.uk
Web Site: www.afgk.co.uk
Year Founded: 2007
Emp.: 5

Business Description:
Kitchen Designing & Installation Services
S.I.C.: 7389
N.A.I.C.S.: 541490

Personnel:
Jim Gettings *(Mng Dir)*

ABINGTON RESOURCES LTD.

125A 1030 Denman Street
Vancouver, BC, V6G 2M6, Canada
Tel.: (604) 683-6657
Fax: (604) 684-4407
Toll Free: (877) 430-3113
E-Mail: info@abingtonresources.com
Web Site: www.abingtonresources.com
Year Founded: 1999
ABL—(TSXV)
Rev.: $396,050
Assets: $940,905
Liabilities: $605,779
Net Worth: $335,126
Earnings: ($724,115)
Emp.: 1
Fiscal Year-end: 10/31/12

Business Description:
Oil & Gas Exploration Services
S.I.C.: 1311
N.A.I.C.S.: 211111

Personnel:
Barry Underhill *(Pres & CEO)*
Zenaida Manalo *(CFO)*

Board of Directors:
J. Lewis Dillman
Philip Taneda
Barry Underhill

Legal Counsel:
Richards Buell Sutton LLP
700 401 West Georgia Street
Vancouver, BC, Canada

ABIRAMI FINANCIAL SERVICES INDIA LTD.

New No 16 South Boag Road T Nagar
Chennai, Tamil Nadu, 600-017, India
Tel.: (91) 44 2435 6224
Fax: (91) 44 2432 5643
Web Site: www.afslindia.com
511756—(BOM)
Sales Range: Less than $1 Million

Business Description:
Financial Services
S.I.C.: 6141
N.A.I.C.S.: 522220

Personnel:
K. V. Aiyappan *(Chm)*
J. Narassimhan *(Sec & Compliance Officer)*

Board of Directors:
K. V. Aiyappan
J. Narassimhan
P. Sankaran
T. V. Srinivasan
Teckchand Vaswani
J. Viswanathan

ABIRD HOLDING BV

Welplaatkade 21
3197 KR Rotterdam, Netherlands
Tel.: (31) 102952800
Fax: (31) 102952801
E-Mail: info@abird.nl
Web Site: www.abird.nl
Sales Range: $10-24.9 Million
Emp.: 50

Business Description:
Industrial Equipment Rental Services
S.I.C.: 7359
N.A.I.C.S.: 532412

Personnel:
Wichard Oorschot *(CEO)*

ABIST CO., LTD.

1-18-4 Tomigawa Shibuya-ku
Tokyo, 151-0063, Japan
Tel.: (81) 3 5942 4649
Web Site: www.abist.co.jp
6087—(TKS)
Rev.: $51,924,917
Emp.: 720
Fiscal Year-end: 09/30/13

Business Description:
Machine & Machine Parts Mfr
S.I.C.: 3599
N.A.I.C.S.: 332710

Personnel:
Katsuhiro Susumu *(Pres)*

ABITEX RESOURCES INC.

1019 Des Pins Blvd
Val d'Or, QC, J9P 4T2, Canada
Tel.: (819) 874-6200
Fax: (819) 874-6202
E-Mail: info@abitex.ca
Web Site: www.abitex.ca
ABE—(TSXV)

Business Description:
Mineral Exploration Services
S.I.C.: 1081
N.A.I.C.S.: 213114

Personnel:
Yves J. Rougerie *(Co-Chm, Pres & CEO)*
Jean-Francois Ruel *(Co-Chm)*

Board of Directors:
Yves J. Rougerie
Jean-Francois Ruel
Robert C. Bryce
Fred Burrows
Peter J. Hawley

Legal Counsel:
McMillan S.E.N.C.R.L., s.r.l. /LLP
1000 Sherbrooke West Suite 2700
Montreal, QC, Canada

Transfer Agent:
Computershare Investor Services Inc.
1500 University Street Suite 700
Montreal, QC, H3A 3SB, Canada

ABITIBI MINING CORP.

711-675 West Hastings Street
Vancouver, BC, Canada V6B 1N2
Tel.: (604) 685-2222
Fax: (604) 685-3764
E-Mail: info@abitibi-mining.com
Web Site: www.abitibi-mining.com
ABB—(TSXV)

Business Description:
Mineral Exploration Services
S.I.C.: 1081
N.A.I.C.S.: 213114

Personnel:
Richard W. Hughes *(Pres, CEO & Sec)*
Alan D. Campbell *(CFO)*

Board of Directors:
Alan D. Campbell
Richard W. Hughes

Transfer Agent:
Computershare Trust Company of Canada
510 Burrard St
Vancouver, BC, Canada

ABITIBI ROYALTIES INC.

152 Chemin de la Mine Ecole
Val d'Or, QC, J9P 7B6, Canada
Tel.: (604) 824-2808
Fax: (604) 824-3379
E-Mail: info@goldenvalleymines.com
Web Site: www.abitibiroyalties.com
Year Founded: 2010
RZZ—(TSXV)
Assets: $359,777
Liabilities: $36,558
Net Worth: $323,219
Earnings: ($214,237)
Fiscal Year-end: 12/31/12

Business Description:
Metal Mining Services
S.I.C.: 1099
N.A.I.C.S.: 212299

Personnel:
Glenn J. Mullan *(CEO)*
Daniel Poisson *(CFO)*

Board of Directors:
Glenn J. Mullan
Andrew T. Pepper

Chad Williams
C. Jens Zinke

ABL-TECHNIC ENTLACKUNG GMBH

Beim Hammerschmied 4-6
88299 Leutkirch, Germany
Tel.: (49) 756182680
Fax: (49) 7561826868
E-Mail: info@abl-technic.de
Web Site: www.abl-technic.de
Year Founded: 1973
Rev.: $23,449,800
Emp.: 130
Business Description:
Waste Management Services
S.I.C.: 4959
N.A.I.C.S.: 562998
Personnel:
Siegfried Richter *(CEO)*

ABLE C&C INC.

3Fl A Blg SK Twintech Tower 345-9
Gasan-Dong Keumcheon-Gu
Seoul, 153-773, Korea (South)
Tel.: (82) 2 62926789
Fax: (82) 2 62926922
Web Site: www.able-cnc.com
078520—(KRS)
Sales Range: $200-249.9 Million
Emp.: 200
Business Description:
Cosmetics Mfr
S.I.C.: 2844
N.A.I.C.S.: 325620
Personnel:
Yeong Pil Seo *(Chm & CEO)*

ABLE CHINTAI HOLDINGS INC.

1-5-5 Moto-Akasaka Minato-ku
Tokyo, Japan
Tel.: (81) 357702600
Web Site: www.achd.co.jp/english
Business Description:
Holding Company
S.I.C.: 6719
N.A.I.C.S.: 551112
Personnel:
Ryuji Hirata *(Pres & CEO)*

ABLEGROUP BERHAD

(Formerly Gefung Holdings Berhad)
Suite 111A Level 11 Menara Weld 76
Jalan Raja Chulan
50200 Kuala Lumpur, Malaysia
Tel.: (60) 320311988
Fax: (60) 320319788
Web Site:
ABLEGRP—(KLS)
Rev.: $1,868,816
Assets: $17,466,659
Liabilities: $1,415,631
Net Worth: $16,051,028
Earnings: ($2,773,219)
Fiscal Year-end: 12/31/12
Business Description:
Processing, Trading, Exporting & Contract Workmanship of Marble & Granite Slabs
S.I.C.: 3281
N.A.I.C.S.: 327991
Personnel:
Kim Huat Lim *(Mng Dir)*
Fei Chia Lim *(Sec)*
Board of Directors:
Chong Keat Yeoh
Marn Seng Cheong
Kim Huat Lim
Heng Sewn Loi
Heang Fine Wong

Subsidiary:

Syarikat Bukit Granite Sdn. Bhd. **(1)**
10th Floor Plaza Montkiara Blok E Jln 1/70c
50480 Kuala Lumpur, Malaysia
Tel.: (60) 362013978
Fax: (60) 362017286
Emp.: 30
Marble & Granite Mfr
S.I.C.: 3999
N.A.I.C.S.: 339999

ABLON GROUP LIMITED

Frances House Sir William Place
Saint Peter Port, GY1 4HQ, Guernsey
Tel.: (44) 2074483244
Fax: (44) 2074483245
E-Mail: ablon@ablon-group.com
Web Site: www.ablon-group.com
Sales Range: $25-49.9 Million
Business Description:
Real Estate Services
S.I.C.: 6531
N.A.I.C.S.: 531210
Personnel:
Uri Heller *(CEO)*

Non-U.S. Subsidiaries:

ABLON Kft. **(1)**
2 Dunavirag Utca
1132 Budapest, Hungary
Tel.: (36) 12256600
Fax: (36) 12256601
E-Mail: ablon@ablon.hu
Web Site: www.ablon.hu
Emp.: 50
Real Estate Property Development Services
S.I.C.: 6531
N.A.I.C.S.: 531390
Adrienn Lovro *(Mng Dir)*

ABLON Sp. z o.o. **(1)**
ul Nowy Swiat 60 Apt 2C
00-357 Warsaw, Poland
Tel.: (48) 228920610
Fax: (48) 228920611
E-Mail: ablon@ablon.pl
Web Site: www.ablon.pl
Emp.: 42
Real Estate Property Development Services
S.I.C.: 6531
N.A.I.C.S.: 531210
Eduard Quitt *(Mng Dir)*

ABLON s.r.l. **(1)**
Dacia Blvd 1st Fl Dist 2
153-155 Bucharest, Romania
Tel.: (40) 318059346
Fax: (40) 213114330
E-Mail: ablon@ablon.ro
Emp.: 5
Real Estate Development Services
S.I.C.: 6531
N.A.I.C.S.: 531311
Avi Goldenberg *(Gen Mgr)*

ABLON s.r.o. **(1)**
Sokolovska 100 94
Karlin, 186 00 Prague, Czech Republic
Tel.: (420) 227133111
Fax: (420) 227133122
E-Mail: ablon@ablon.cz
Web Site: www.ablon.cz
Emp.: 11
Real Estate Property Development Services
S.I.C.: 6531
N.A.I.C.S.: 531390
Eduard Quitt *(Mng Dir)*

CD Property s.r.o. **(1)**
Sokolovska 100 94
18600 Prague, Czech Republic
Tel.: (420) 227133111
Fax: (420) 227133122
Web Site: www.ablongroup.com
Emp.: 10
Real Estate Property Development Services
S.I.C.: 6531
N.A.I.C.S.: 531390
Lenka Matlova *(Mng Dir)*

Global Center Kft. **(1)**
Vaci 30
1132 Budapest, Hungary
Tel.: (36) 12256600
Fax: (36) 12256601
E-Mail: ablon@ablon.hu
Web Site: www.ablon.hu
Emp.: 30
Real Estate Property Development Services
S.I.C.: 6531
N.A.I.C.S.: 531390
Lovro Adrienn *(Gen Mgr)*

Global Development Kft. **(1)**
Vaci ut 30
1132 Budapest, Hungary
Tel.: (36) 12256600
Fax: (36) 12256601
E-Mail: ablon@ablon.hu
Web Site: www.ablon.hu
Emp.: 30
Real Estate Property Development Services
S.I.C.: 6531
N.A.I.C.S.: 531311
Adrienn Lovro *(Country Mgr)*

MH Bucharest Properties S.R.L **(1)**
Sector 2 B-Dul Dacia
153 155 Bucharest, Romania
Tel.: (40) 314051719
Fax: (40) 213114330
Emp.: 5
Real Estate Development Services
S.I.C.: 6531
N.A.I.C.S.: 531311
Asher Shmulevitz *(Mgr)*

RSL Real Estate Development S.R.L. **(1)**
Sector 2 B-Dul Dacia
153-155 Bucharest, Romania
Tel.: (40) 318059346
Fax: (40) 314051718
E-Mail: ablon@ablon.ro
Emp.: 8
Real Estate Property Development Services
S.I.C.: 6531
N.A.I.C.S.: 531390
Acher Chmulavitz *(Mng Dir)*

ABLYNX N.V.

Technologiepark 21 Zwijnaarde
9052 Gent, Belgium
Tel.: (32) 92620000
Fax: (32) 92620001
E-Mail: info@ablynx.com
Web Site: www.ablynx.com
Year Founded: 2001
ABLX—(EUR)
Rev.: $35,979,086
Assets: $100,956,019
Liabilities: $58,252,814
Net Worth: $42,703,205
Earnings: ($38,376,614)
Emp.: 262
Fiscal Year-end: 12/31/12
Business Description:
Biopharmaceutical Researcher & Developer
S.I.C.: 8731
N.A.I.C.S.: 541712
Personnel:
Edwin Moses *(Chm & CEO)*
Wim Ottevaere *(CFO)*
Eva-Lotta Allan *(Chief Bus Officer)*
Josefin-Beate Holz *(Chief Medical Officer)*
Board of Directors:
Edwin Moses
Stephen Bunting
Russell G. Greig
Denis Lucquin
Roger Perlmutter
Remi Vermeiren

ABM FUJIYA BERHAD

Lot 2224 Section 66 Lorong Pangkalan Off Jalan Pangkalan Pending Industrial Estate, Kuching, Sarawak, 93450, Malaysia
Tel.: (60) 82 333334
Fax: (60) 82 483603
E-Mail: enquiry@abmfujiya.com.my
Web Site: www.abmfujiya.com.my
Year Founded: 2003
5198—(KLS)
Business Description:
Automotive & Other Batteries Mfr
S.I.C.: 3692
N.A.I.C.S.: 335912
Personnel:
Ah Ching Tay *(Chm)*

ABM KNOWLEDGEWARE LTD

ABM House Plot No 268 Linking Road Bandra West
Mumbai, 400 050, India
Tel.: (91) 22 4290 9700
Fax: (91) 22 4290 9701
E-Mail: egovernance@abmindia.com
Web Site: www.abmindia.com
531161—(BOM)
Rev.: $13,797,680
Assets: $12,970,548
Liabilities: $1,988,276
Net Worth: $10,982,272
Earnings: $2,329,049
Emp.: 135
Fiscal Year-end: 03/31/13
Business Description:
E-Governance & System Integration Solutions
S.I.C.: 7379
N.A.I.C.S.: 541519
Personnel:
Prakash B. Rane *(Mng Dir)*
Sarika Ghanekar *(Compliance Officer)*
Board of Directors:
Sharad D. Abhyankar
M. N. Ahmed
Ajit C. Kulkarni
Prakash B. Rane
Supriya P. Rane
Transfer Agent:
Universal Capital Securities Pvt. Ltd
21 Shakil Niwas Mahakali Caves Road Andheri East
Mumbai, India

ABM RESOURCES NL

Level 1 141 Broadway
Nedlands, WA, 6009, Australia
Tel.: (61) 894239777
Fax: (61) 894239733
E-Mail: admin@abmresources.com.au
Web Site: www.abmresources.com.au
ABU—(ASX)
Rev.: $747,312
Assets: $32,885,731
Liabilities: $4,132,336
Net Worth: $28,753,395
Earnings: ($15,688,117)
Emp.: 13
Fiscal Year-end: 06/30/13
Business Description:
Gold Exploration Services
S.I.C.: 3356
N.A.I.C.S.: 331491
Personnel:
Darren Holden *(Mng Dir)*
Jutta Zimmermann *(CFO & Sec)*
Brad Valiukas *(COO)*
Board of Directors:
Michael Etheridge
Andrew Ferguson
Darren Holden
Graeme Sloan
Legal Counsel:
Steinepreis Paganin
Level 4 Next Building 16 Milligan Street
Perth, 6000, Australia

Subsidiary:

ABM Resources Operations Pty Ltd **(1)**
Level 1 141 Broadway
Nedlands, WA, 6009, Australia
Tel.: (61) 894239777
Fax: (61) 894239733
E-Mail: admin@abmresources.com.au
Web Site: www.abmresources.com.au
Emp.: 40

ABM Resources NL—(Continued)

Mineral Mining Services
S.I.C.: 1459
N.A.I.C.S.: 212325
Darren Holden *(Mng Dir)*

ABM SOLID S.A.
Bartla 3 Street
33-100 Tarnow, Poland
Tel.: (48) 146260207
Fax: (48) 146224551
E-Mail: office@abmsolid.eu
Web Site: www.abmsolid.eu
ABM—(WAR)
Rev.: $42,748,807
Assets: $55,591,620
Liabilities: $109,630,890
Net Worth: ($54,039,269)
Earnings: ($66,617,913)
Fiscal Year-end: 12/31/12
Business Description:
Industrial Construction Services
S.I.C.: 1542
N.A.I.C.S.: 236220
Personnel:
Wieslaw Waszkielewicz *(Chm-Supervisory Bd)*
Marek Pawlik *(Chm-Mgmt Bd & Dir-Strategy & Dev)*
Dominik Pawlik *(Vice Chm-Supervisory Bd)*
Michal Krzyzanowski *(Vice Chm-Mgmt Bd & Mng Dir)*
Slawomir Golonka *(Gen Dir)*
Supervisory Board of Directors:
Wieslaw Waszkielewicz
Jan Antonczyk
Jerzy Noworyta
Dominik Pawlik
Grzegorz Swiatlowski

Subsidiaries:

ABM INVEST TARNOW Ltd. **(1)**
Bartla 3 Street
33 100 Tarnow, Poland
Tel.: (48) 146260207
Fax: (48) 146224551
E-Mail: abminvest@abminvest.eu
Web Site: www.abminvest.eu
Property Development & Management Services
S.I.C.: 6531
N.A.I.C.S.: 531311
Agnes Syslo *(Chm)*

ABM SILESIA Ltd. **(1)**
Grunwaldzka 264 Street
43 600 Jaworzno, Poland
Tel.: (48) 327523107
Fax: (48) 32 752 31 08
Property Management Services
S.I.C.: 6531
N.A.I.C.S.: 531390

ABM WSCHOD Ltd. **(1)**
Bartla 3 Street
33 100 Tarnow, Poland
Tel.: (48) 146260207
Fax: (48) 146224551
Property Development & Management Services
S.I.C.: 6531
N.A.I.C.S.: 531311
Pawelek Marek *(CEO)*

BIO SOLID Ltd. **(1)**
ul Bartla 3 33-100
32 852 Tarnow, Poland
Tel.: (48) 146650315
Fax: (48) 146650315
E-Mail: biosolid@abmsolid.eu
Emp.: 11
Waste Management Services
S.I.C.: 4952
N.A.I.C.S.: 221320
Radoslolsaw Ladno *(Mgr)*

TRANSRES Ltd. **(1)**
Bieszczadzka 10 Street
35 082 Rzeszow, Poland
Tel.: (48) 178543568
Fax: (48) 17 854 34 63
E-Mail: transres@transres.pl
Web Site: www.transres.pl
Transportation Services
S.I.C.: 4522
N.A.I.C.S.: 481212

WPRM Sp. z o.o **(1)**
Jankowska 6 Street
62 100 Wagrowiec, Poland
Tel.: (48) 672621701
Fax: (48) 672162506
E-Mail: wprm1@o2.pl
Web Site: www.wprm.pl
Emp.: 40
Bridge Construction & Repairing Services
S.I.C.: 1611
N.A.I.C.S.: 237310
Andrew Szewk *(Mng Dir)*

ABN AMRO GROUP N.V.
Prins Bernhardplein 200
NL-1097 JB Amsterdam, Netherlands
Tel.: (31) 205279000
Web Site: www.group.abnamro.com
Year Founded: 2010
Sales Range: $15-24.9 Billion
Business Description:
Bank Holding Company
S.I.C.: 6712
N.A.I.C.S.: 551111
Personnel:
Hessel Lindenbergh *(Chm-Supervisory Bd)*
Gerrit Zalm *(Chm-Mgmt Bd)*
Jan C.M. van Rutte *(CFO & Vice Chm-Mgmt Bd)*
Johan Van Hall *(COO)*
Wietze Reehoorn *(Member-Mgmt Bd-Strategy & Chief Risk Officer)*
Caroline Princen *(Member-Mgmt Bd-HR/Comm/Compliance/Legal & Sustainability)*
Chris Vogelzang *(Member-Mgmt Bd-Retail & Private Banking)*
Joop G. Wijn *(Member-Mgmt Bd-Comml & Merchant Banking)*
Supervisory Board of Directors:
Hessel Lindenbergh
Hans de Haan
Bert Meerstadt
Marjan M. J. Oudeman
Annemieke Roobeek
Steven ten Have
Peter N. Wakkie

Subsidiaries:

ABN AMRO Bank N.V. **(1)**
Gustav Mahlerlaan 10
NL-1082 PP Amsterdam, Netherlands NL
Tel.: (31) 102820724
Web Site: www.abnamro.com
Sales Range: $15-24.9 Billion
Retail & Commercial Banking
S.I.C.: 6029
N.A.I.C.S.: 522110
Hessel Lindenbergh *(Chm-Supervisory Bd)*
Gerrit Zalm *(Chm-Mgmt Bd)*
Jan C.M. van Rutte *(CFO & Vice Chm-Mgmt Bd)*
Johan Van Hall *(COO)*
Wietze Reehoorn *(Member-Mgmt Bd-Strategy & Chief Risk Officer)*
Caroline Princen *(Member-Mgmt Bd-HR/Comm/Compliance/Legal & Sustainability)*
Chris Vogelzang *(Member-Mgmt Bd-Retail & Private Banking)*
Joop G. Wijn *(Member-Mgmt Bd-Comml & Merchant Banking)*

Subsidiaries:

ABN AMRO MeesPierson **(2)**
Prins Bernhardplein 200
NL-1097 JB Amsterdam, Netherlands
Mailing Address:
PO Box 293
NL-1000 AG Amsterdam, Netherlands
Tel.: (31) 205272516
Fax: (31) 206258164
Web Site: www.meespierson.nl
Sales Range: $500-549.9 Million
Emp.: 300
Private Banking & Wealth Management Services
S.I.C.: 6211
N.A.I.C.S.: 523110
H.P. Fred E. Bos *(CEO)*

Non-U.S. Subsidiaries:

MeesPierson (C.I.) Limited **(3)**
Martello Court Admiral Park
PO Box 253
Saint Peter Port, GY1 3QJ, Guernsey GY
Tel.: (44) 1481751000
Fax: (44) 1481 751 001
E-Mail: guernsey@gg.meespierson.com
Web Site: www.gg.meespierson.com
Emp.: 75
Private Banking & Wealth Management Services
S.I.C.: 6211
N.A.I.C.S.: 523110
Graham Thoume *(Mng Dir)*
Paul Martin *(CFO)*
Frank Moon *(Chief Investment Officer & Mng Dir-Investment Mgmt)*

MeesPierson (Curacao) N.V. **(3)**
1 Berg Arrarat
PO Box 3860
Willemstad, Curacao AN
Tel.: (599) 94639627
Fax: (599) 94615806
E-Mail: clientservices_curacao@meespierson.an
Web Site: www.meespierson.an
Emp.: 50
Private Banking & Wealth Management Services
S.I.C.: 6211
N.A.I.C.S.: 523110
Victor D'Hondt *(Mng Dir)*

Amstel Lease N.V. **(2)**
Franz Lisztplantsoen 100
3533 JG Utrecht, Netherlands (100%)
Mailing Address:
Postbus 3171
3502 GD Utrecht, Netherlands
Tel.: (31) 302906406
Fax: (31) 302966024
E-Mail: info@abnleaseamroleas.nl
Web Site: www.abnleaseamroleas.nl
Emp.: 160
Provider of Equipment Leasing
S.I.C.: 7359
N.A.I.C.S.: 532490
Frank Saienstra *(Gen Mgr)*

DEFAM B.V. **(2)**
Kosterijland 10
3980 CD Bunnik, Netherlands NL
Mailing Address:
Postbus 178
3980 CD Bunnik, Netherlands
Tel.: (31) 306596600
Fax: (31) 306596660
Web Site: www.defam.nl
Emp.: 130
Consumer Lending & Credit Services
S.I.C.: 6141
N.A.I.C.S.: 522291

Direktbank N.V. **(2)**
Prof JH Bavincklaan 3
NL-1183 AT Amstelveen, Netherlands NL
Mailing Address:
Postbus 306
1180 AH Amstelveen, Netherlands
Tel.: (31) 205970707
E-Mail: info@direktbank.nl
Web Site: www.direktbank.nl
Emp.: 150
Mortgage Brokerage Services
S.I.C.: 6163
N.A.I.C.S.: 522310

GroeiVermogen N.V. **(2)**
Burgerweeshuispad 201
NL-1076 GR Amsterdam, Netherlands NL
Mailing Address:
Postbus 71770
NL-1008 DG Amsterdam, Netherlands
Tel.: (31) 205275255
E-Mail: groeivermogen@fortis.nl
Web Site: www.groeivermogen.nl
Emp.: 30
Investment Products & Services
S.I.C.: 6282
N.A.I.C.S.: 523930

Interbank **(2)**
PO Box 12565
1100 AN Amsterdam, Netherlands (100%)
Tel.: (31) 203125125
Fax: (31) 203125115
E-Mail: service@interbank.nl
Web Site: www.interbank.nl
Emp.: 350
Trade Financing
S.I.C.: 6159
N.A.I.C.S.: 522298
Kees Droppert *(Mng Dir)*

International Card Services B.V. **(2)**
Wisselwerking 32
NL-1112 XP Diemen, Netherlands NL
Mailing Address: (100%)
Postbus 23225
1100DS Diemen, Netherlands
Tel.: (31) 206600678
Fax: (31) 206600688
E-Mail: clientenservice@icscards.nl
Web Site: www.icscards.nl
Emp.: 300
Issuer of Credit Cards
S.I.C.: 6141
N.A.I.C.S.: 522210

NeSBIC Groep B.V. **(2)**
Savannahweg 17
NL-3542 AW Utrecht, Netherlands NL
Tel.: (31) 30 248 1048
Fax: (31) 30 248 1049
E-Mail: info@fortisprivateequity.nl
Web Site: www.fortisprivateequity.nl
Emp.: 15
Private Equity Firm
S.I.C.: 6211
N.A.I.C.S.: 523999
Pierre Demaeroe *(Mng Dir)*

Affiliate:

ABN Assurantie Holding B.V. **(2)**
Prins Bernhardstraat 1
PO Box 10085
8000 GB Zwolle, Netherlands NL
Tel.: (31) 384992299
Telex: 24077
Fax: (31) 384992090
Emp.: 800
Insurance
S.I.C.: 6411
N.A.I.C.S.: 524298

Subsidiary:

ABN AMRO Verzekeringen B.V. **(3)**
Prins Bernhardstraat 1
PO Box 100085
8000 GB Zwolle, Netherlands NL
Tel.: (31) 384992299
Telex: 24077
Fax: (31) 384992090
Web Site: www.abnamro.nl/en/personal/insurance
Emp.: 800
Insurance
S.I.C.: 6411
N.A.I.C.S.: 524298

U.S. Subsidiary:

ABN AMRO Clearing Chicago LLC **(2)**
175 W Jackson Blvd Ste 400
Chicago, IL 60604 IL
Tel.: (312) 604-8000 (100%)
Fax: (312) 604-8111
Web Site: www.us.abnamroclearing.com
Emp.: 170
Security & Trade Clearing Services
S.I.C.: 6099
N.A.I.C.S.: 522320
Tom Anderson *(Chief Comml Officer)*

Non-U.S. Subsidiaries:

ABN AMRO Bank Brussels **(2)**
Kanselarijstraat 17A
B 1000 Brussels, Belgium (100%)
Tel.: (32) 25460460
Telex: 26194
Fax: (32) 25460404
E-Mail: info.belgium@be.abnamro.com
Web Site: www.abnamrobelgium.be
Emp.: 400
Private Banking Services
S.I.C.: 6029
N.A.I.C.S.: 522110

ABN AMRO Bank (Ireland) Ltd. (2)
Fortis House Park Lane
Spencer Dock, Dublin, 1, Ireland IE
Tel.: (353) 16071800 (100%)
Fax: (353) 18291177
E-Mail: funds@ie.primefundsolutions.com
Web Site: www.primefundsolutions.com
Emp.: 200
Alternative Asset Management Services
S.I.C.: 6799
N.A.I.C.S.: 523920
Brenda Euthley *(Mng Dir)*

ABN AMRO Bank (Luxembourg) S.A. (2)
46 Ave J F Kennedy
L 1855 Luxembourg, Luxembourg (100%)
Tel.: (352) 26071
Telex: 60818 FOREX
Fax: (352) 25226072999
E-Mail: contactform@lu.abnamro.com
Web Site: www.abnamroprivatebanking.com
Emp.: 180
Private Banking
S.I.C.: 6159
N.A.I.C.S.: 522298
Peter Aelbers *(Mng Dir)*

ABN International Diamond Division (2)
Pelikaan St 70 76
2018 Antwerp, Belgium (100%)
Tel.: (32) 32220401
E-Mail: vijaykgoel@be.abnamro.com
Web Site: www.abnamro.be
Emp.: 50
Diamond Sales
S.I.C.: 5944
N.A.I.C.S.: 448310
Vijay Goel *(Mgr)*

Banque de Neuflize OBC S.A. (2)
3 Ave Hoche
75008 Paris, France (99.84%)
Tel.: (33) 156217000
Fax: (33) 156218460
Web Site: www.banquedeneuflize.com
Emp.: 950
Bank Holding Company
S.I.C.: 6712
N.A.I.C.S.: 551111
P. Vayssettes *(Gen Mgr)*

Subsidiary:

Banque de Neuflize (3)
3 Ave Hoche
75410 Paris, Cedex, France (99%)
Tel.: (33) 156217000
Telex: 640653
Fax: (33) 156218460
E-Mail: info@banquedeneuflize.fr
Web Site: www.banquedeneuflize.fr
Emp.: 950
Commercial Banking
S.I.C.: 6029
N.A.I.C.S.: 522110
Hugues Aubry *(CEO)*

Bethmann Bank AG (2)
Bethmannstrsse 7 9
D-60311 Frankfurt am Main, Germany (100%)
Mailing Address:
Postfach 10 03 49
60003 Frankfurt am Main, Germany
Tel.: (49) 8001010760
Fax: (49) 13314140
E-Mail:
Web Site: www.bethmannbank.de
Emp.: 150
Private Banking Services
S.I.C.: 6211
N.A.I.C.S.: 523110
Horst Schmiet *(CEO)*

Fortis Commercial Finance Holding B.V. (1)
Hambakenwetering 2
Postbus 2036
NL-5202 CA 's-Hertogenbosch, Netherlands NL
Tel.: (31) 736467777
Fax: (31) 736467700
E-Mail: info@abnamrocomfin.com
Web Site: www.abnamrocomfin.com
Emp.: 200
Holding Company; Commercial Finance, Factoring, Credit Management, Debt Administration & Other Financial Services
S.I.C.: 6719
N.A.I.C.S.: 551112
Dirk Driessens *(CEO)*

Subsidiary:

Fortis Commercial Finance N.V. (2)
Hambakenwetering 2
Post box 2036
NL-5202 CA 's-Hertogenbosch, Netherlands NL
Tel.: (31) 736467777
Fax: (31) 736467700
E-Mail: info.nl@abnamrocomfin.com
Web Site: www.abnamrocomfin.com
Emp.: 200
Commercial Finance, Factoring, Credit Management, Debt Administration & Other Financial Services
S.I.C.: 6159
N.A.I.C.S.: 522298
Jacques Coppens *(Dir-Comml)*

ABNOVA (TAIWAN) CORPORATION

9th Fl 108 Jhouzih St
Neihu District, Taipei, 114, Taiwan
Tel.: (886) 287511888
Fax: (886) 266021218
E-Mail: sales@abnova.com
Web Site: www.abnova.com
4133—(TAI)
Sales Range: $10-24.9 Million
Emp.: 220

Business Description:
Antibodies & Proteins Mfr
S.I.C.: 2836
N.A.I.C.S.: 325414

Personnel:
Qingyang Huang *(Chm)*
Wilber Huang *(Pres & CEO)*

Non-U.S. Subsidiary:

Abnova GmbH (1)
Boxbergring 107
69126 Heidelberg, Baden-Wurttemberg, Germany
Tel.: (49) 62213632226
Fax: (49) 23819994411
E-Mail: sales@abnova.com
Emp.: 250
Antibody & Protein Mfr
S.I.C.: 2833
N.A.I.C.S.: 325411
Wilber Huang *(Mng Dir)*

ABO WIND AG

Unter den Eichen 7
65195 Wiesbaden, Germany
Tel.: (49) 611 26 765 0
Fax: (49) 611 26 765 99
E-Mail: global@abo-wind.de
Web Site: www.abowind.com
Sales Range: $25-49.9 Million
Emp.: 250

Business Description:
Wind Power Generation
S.I.C.: 4911
N.A.I.C.S.: 221118

Personnel:
Jochen Ahn *(Member-Mgmt Bd)*
Matthias Bockholt *(Member-Mgmt Bd)*
Andreas Hollinger *(Member-Mgmt Bd)*

ABOCOM SYSTEMS, INC.

21 R D Rd II Science-Based Industrial Park
Hsin-chu, Taiwan
Tel.: (886) 37580777
Fax: (886) 37580799
Web Site: www.abocom.com.tw
2444—(TAI)
Sales Range: $25-49.9 Million

Business Description:
Communication Equipment Mfr
S.I.C.: 3663
N.A.I.C.S.: 334220

Personnel:
Eric Oh-Yang *(Chm & Gen Mgr)*

Plant:

AboCom Systems, Inc. - Miao-Lih Hsuan Factory (1)
77 Yu-Yih Road
Chu-Nan Chen, Miao-li, 35059, Taiwan
Tel.: (886) 37580777
Fax: (886) 37580099
Emp.: 300
Networking Components Mfr
S.I.C.: 3571
N.A.I.C.S.: 334111
Eric Oh-Yang *(Gen Mgr)*

ABOITIZ EQUITY VENTURES, INC.

Gov Manuel A Cuenco Avenue
Cebu, Kasambagan, 6000, Philippines
Tel.: (63) 324111800
Fax: (63) 322314031
E-Mail: aev@aboitiz.com
Web Site: www.aboitiz.com
AEV—(OTC PHI)
Rev.: $1,984,125,922
Assets: $5,455,592,434
Liabilities: $2,675,897,450
Net Worth: $2,779,694,984
Earnings: $737,260,919
Emp.: 4,000
Fiscal Year-end: 12/31/12

Business Description:
Investment Services
S.I.C.: 6211
N.A.I.C.S.: 523999

Personnel:
Jon Ramon M. Aboitiz *(Chm)*
Erramon I. Aboitiz *(Pres & CEO)*
Stephen G. Paradies *(CFO, Corp Info Officer & Sr VP)*
Mikel A. Aboitiz *(CIO & Sr VP)*
Jasmine S. Oporto *(Chief Legal Officer, Compliance Officer, Sec & First VP)*
Horacio C. Elicano *(CTO & First VP)*
Patrick B. Reyes *(Chief Strategy Officer & First VP)*
Susan V. Valdez *(Chief Risk Mgmt Officer, Chief Reputation Officer & First VP)*
Xavier Jose Aboitiz *(Chief HR Officer & Sr VP)*
Gabriel T. Manalac *(Treas & Sr VP)*
Enrique M. Aboitiz, Jr. *(Sr VP)*
Juan Antonio E. Bernad *(Sr VP)*

Board of Directors:
Jon Ramon M. Aboitiz
Enrique M. Aboitiz, Jr.
Erramon I. Aboitiz
Roberto E. Aboitiz
Stephen T. CuUnjieng
Raphael Perpetuo M. Lotilla
Antonio R. Moraza
Justo A. Ortiz
Jose C. Vitug

Transfer Agent:
The Hongkong and Shanghai Banking Corporation Limited
7/F HSBC Centre 3058 Fifth Ave W
Taguig, Philippines

Subsidiaries:

Aboitiz Power Corporation (1)
Aboitiz Corporate Center Gov Manuel Cuenco Avenue Kasambagan
Cebu, 6000, Philippines
Tel.: (63) 324111800
Fax: (63) 322314037
Web Site: www.aboitizpower.com
AP—(OTC PHI)
Rev.: $1,522,131,011
Assets: $3,998,525,598
Liabilities: $1,970,541,123
Net Worth: $2,027,984,475
Earnings: $609,712,689
Emp.: 148
Fiscal Year-end: 12/31/12
Electricity Generation & Distribution Services
S.I.C.: 4911
N.A.I.C.S.: 221111
Enrique M. Aboitiz, Jr. *(Chm)*
Jon Ramon M. Aboitiz *(Vice Chm)*
Erramon I. Aboitiz *(Pres & CEO)*
Iker M. Aboitiz *(CFO, Corp Info Officer & First VP)*
Antonio R. Moraza *(COO-Power Generation Grp & Exec VP)*
Jasmine S. Oporto *(Chief Legal Officer, Chief Compliance Officer & Sec)*
Susan V. Valdez *(Chief Risk Mgmt Officer, Chief Reputation Officer & First VP)*
Jaime Jose Y. Aboitiz *(COO-Power Distr Grp & Exec VP)*
Gabriel T. Manalac *(Treas & Sr VP)*
Juan Antonio E. Bernad *(Exec VP-Strategy & Regulation)*
Luis Miguel O. Aboitiz *(Sr VP-Power Mktg & Trading)*

AboitizLand, Inc. (1)
Aboitiz Corporate Center Gov Manuel A Cuenco Avenue
Maria Luisa Rd, Cebu, Banilad, 6000, Philippines
Tel.: (63) 324111600
Fax: (63) 22381030
E-Mail: contactus@aboitizland.com
Web Site: www.aboitizland.com.ph
Emp.: 100
Real Estate Services
S.I.C.: 6531
N.A.I.C.S.: 531390
Andoni Aboitiz *(Pres & COO)*

Subsidiary:

Lima Land, Inc. (2)
3/F Solid House Building 2285 Pasong Tamo Ext
Makati, 1200, Philippines (60%)
Tel.: (63) 28132781
Fax: (63) 28403852
Web Site: www.lima.com.ph
Real Estate Management Services
S.I.C.: 6531
N.A.I.C.S.: 531210

ABOV SEMICONDUCTOR CO., LTD.

204 ChungBuk TechnoPark 685-3
Ochang, Chungcheongbuk-do, 361-763, Korea (South)
Tel.: (82) 43 219 5200
Fax: (82) 43 217 3534
Web Site: www.abov.co.kr
Year Founded: 2006
102120—(KRS)

Business Description:
Semiconductor Mfr
S.I.C.: 3674
N.A.I.C.S.: 334413

Personnel:
Won Choi *(CEO)*

ABR HOLDINGS, LTD.

41 Tampines St 92
ABR Bldg, Singapore, 528881, Singapore
Tel.: (65) 67862866
Fax: (65) 67882226
E-Mail: swensens@abr.com.sg
Web Site: www.abr.com.sg
Year Founded: 1996
Emp.: 1,000

Business Description:
Holding Company
S.I.C.: 2024
N.A.I.C.S.: 311520

Personnel:
Keith Tiang Choon Chua *(Chm)*
Yee Lim Ang *(Mng Dir)*

Board of Directors:
Keith Tiang Choon Chua
Chua Tiang Kwang Allan
Lian Seng Ang
Yee Lim Ang

ABR Holdings, Ltd.—(Continued)

Kim Seng Leck
Jen Howe Lim
Mong Hua Quek

Subsidiary:

Swensen's of Singapore Pte. Ltd. (1)
41 Tampines St 92
ABR Building, 528881 Singapore, Singapore
Tel.: (65) 67862866
Telex: rs 42089 bniol
Fax: (65) 67882226
E-Mail: swensens@abr.com.sg
Web Site: www.swensens.com.sg
Emp.: 230
Distributor of Ice Cream & Frozen Yogurt
S.I.C.: 5143
N.A.I.C.S.: 424430
Ana Lei *(Gen Mgr)*

ABRAAJ CAPITAL LIMITED

(d/b/a The Abraaj Group)
Dubai International Financial Centre
Gate Village 8 3rd Floor
Dubai, United Arab Emirates
Mailing Address:
PO Box 504905
Dubai, United Arab Emirates
Tel.: (971) 45064400
Fax: (971) 45064600
E-Mail: info@abraaj.com
Web Site: www.abraaj.com
Emp.: 300
Business Description:
Investment Holding Company
S.I.C.: 6719
N.A.I.C.S.: 551112
Personnel:
Arif Naqvi *(Founder & CEO)*
Board of Directors:
Mustafa Abdel-Wadood
Abdulrahman Ali Al Turki
Hussain Al-Nowais
Sean Cleary
Fadi Ghandour
Badr Jafar
Paul R. Judge
Arif Naqvi
Thomas Schmidheiny
Waqar Siddique

Non-U.S. Holding:

Karachi Electric Supply Company Limited (1)
KESC House 39-B Sunset Boulevard
Phase-2 Defence Housing Authority
Karachi, Pakistan PK
Tel.: (92) 2132637133
E-Mail: intranet@kesc.com.pk
Web Site: www.kesc.com.pk
KESC—(KAR)
Rev.: $1,914,556,304
Assets: $2,828,631,192
Liabilities: $2,280,379,991
Net Worth: $548,251,200
Earnings: $68,161,093
Emp.: 10,594
Fiscal Year-end: 06/30/13
Electric Power Distr
S.I.C.: 4939
N.A.I.C.S.: 221122
Tabish Gauhar *(Chm)*
Nayyer Hussain *(CEO)*
Moonis Abdullah Alvi *(CFO & Sec)*
Naveed Ahmed *(Chief Bus Dev Officer)*
Asir Manzur *(Chief HR Officer)*
Eram Hasan *(Chief Supply Chain Officer)*
Ghufran Atta Khan *(Chief Engagement Officer)*
Muhammad Taha *(Chief Distr Officer)*
Arshad Masood Zahidi *(Chief Generation & Transmission Officer)*

ABRAU-DURSO

Promyshlennaya St 19
353995 Krasnodar, Russia
Tel.: (7) 8617275855
E-Mail: office@abraudurso.ru
Web Site: www.abraudurso.ru
Business Description:
Wine Production & Sales
S.I.C.: 2084
N.A.I.C.S.: 312130
Personnel:
Boris Titov *(Owner)*

ABRIC BERHAD

Level 18 The Gardens N Twr Mid
Valley City Lingkaran Syed Putra
59200 Kuala Lumpur, Malaysia
Tel.: (60) 322648888
Fax: (60) 322822733
E-Mail: abhd@abric.com
Web Site: www.abric.com
ABRIC—(KLS)
Rev.: $24,466,441
Assets: $33,997,195
Liabilities: $16,147,595
Net Worth: $17,849,600
Earnings: $1,007,280
Emp.: 500
Fiscal Year-end: 12/31/12
Business Description:
Security Seals Mfr
S.I.C.: 3053
N.A.I.C.S.: 339991
Personnel:
Eng Lock Ong *(Chm)*
Adeline Hwey Ying Ong *(CEO)*
Hui Fang Kuan *(Co-Sec)*
Yen Hoong Ng *(Co-Sec)*
Board of Directors:
Eng Lock Ong
Abu Bakar Abdul Hamid
Hin See Hon
Adeline Hwey Ying Ong
Brian Zhong Hwey Ong
Chee Keong Soong

Subsidiaries:

Abric International Ltd. (1)
Level 15(A2) I Main Office Tower Financial Park Labuan
Jalan Merdeka, 87000 Labuan, Malaysia
Tel.: (60) 87453288
Fax: (60) 87451288
Web Site: www.tricorglobal.com
Emp.: 10
Consumer Goods Distr
S.I.C.: 5099
N.A.I.C.S.: 423990

Abric International Sdn. Bhd. (1)
Lot 196803 Hala Jati 12 Kawasan Perusahaan Taman Meru
Off Jalan Jelapang, 30020 Ipoh, Perak, Malaysia
Tel.: (60) 5 5018100
Fax: (60) 5 5018101
E-Mail: amm@abric.net
Web Site: www.a-mm.com
Precision Tooling Parts Mfr
S.I.C.: 3544
N.A.I.C.S.: 333514
Ong Eng Lock *(Mng Dir)*

Abric One Sdn. Bhd. (1)
J-8-8 2 Jalan Solaris
Solaris Mont Kiara, 50480 Kuala Lumpur, Malaysia
Tel.: (60) 362073366
Fax: (60) 362073232
E-Mail: awsv@abric.com
Security Seals Distr
S.I.C.: 5199
N.A.I.C.S.: 424990

Abric Worldwide Sdn. Bhd. (1)
J-8-8 2 Jalan Solaris
Solaris Mont' Kiara, 50480 Kuala Lumpur, Federal Territory, Malaysia
Tel.: (60) 362073333
Fax: (60) 362073232
E-Mail: awsb@abric.com
Web Site: www.abric.com
Emp.: 20
Security Seals Distr
S.I.C.: 5199
N.A.I.C.S.: 424990
Ong Eng Lock *(Mng Dir)*

U.S. Subsidiary:

Abric North America, Inc. (1)
220 Barren Springs Dr Ste 11
Houston, TX 77090
Tel.: (281) 569-7100
Fax: (281) 569-7101
E-Mail: ana@abric.com
Web Site: www.abric.com
Emp.: 7
Security Seals Mfr
S.I.C.: 3053
N.A.I.C.S.: 339991
Bouzigard Brandy *(Mgr-EDI)*

Non-U.S. Subsidiaries:

Abric Eastern International Ltd. (1)
770 Moo 6 Teparak Road
Ampher Meung, Samut Prakan, 10270, Thailand
Tel.: (66) 23836534
Fax: (66) 27597127
E-Mail: aei@abric.com
Security Seals Mfr
S.I.C.: 3053
N.A.I.C.S.: 339991

Abric (Europe) Limited (1)
Unit 5 Waterside Business Park Eastways
Witham, Essex, CM8 3YQ, United Kingdom
Tel.: (44) 1543500144
Fax: (44) 1543500252
E-Mail: ael@abric.com
Emp.: 6
Security Seals Mfr
S.I.C.: 3053
N.A.I.C.S.: 339991
Michael Szalajko *(Gen Mgr)*

Abric Shanghai Ltd. (1)
8 Furong Road Yexie Town
Songjiang District, 201609 Shanghai, China
Tel.: (86) 2167809077
Fax: (86) 2167809091
E-Mail: asl@abric.net
Web Site: www.abric.com
Emp.: 50
Security Seals Mfr
S.I.C.: 3053
N.A.I.C.S.: 339991
Mike Foo *(Mgr)*

ABRIL EDUCACAO S.A.

Av Otaviano Alves de Lima 4400 7 andar Vila Arcadia
Sao Paulo, SP, Brazil 02909-900
Tel.: (55) 113990 1443
Fax: (55) 11 3037 4028
E-Mail: ri@abrileducacao.com.br
Web Site: www.abrileducacao.com.br
Year Founded: 1950
ABRE11—(BRAZ)
Rev.: $434,596,620
Assets: $913,316,266
Liabilities: $398,940,498
Net Worth: $514,375,768
Earnings: $48,265,722
Fiscal Year-end: 12/31/12
Business Description:
Book Publishing Services
S.I.C.: 2731
N.A.I.C.S.: 511130
Personnel:
Giancarlo Francesco Civita *(Chm)*
Manoel Luiz Ferrao de Amorim *(Vice Chm & CEO)*
Guilherme Alves Melega *(CFO & IR Officer)*
Board of Directors:
Giancarlo Francesco Civita
Victor Civita
Manoel Luiz Ferrao de Amorim
Maria Helena Guimaraes de Castro
Jonas de Miranda Gomes
Douglas Duran
Paulo Roberto Nunes Guedes
Marcos Antonio Magalhaes
Arnaldo Figueiredo Tibyrica

ABS MANUFACTURING & DISTRIBUTING LIMITED

185 Magill St
Lively, ON, P3Y 1K6, Canada
Tel.: (705) 692-5445
Fax: (705) 692-1435
Toll Free: (800) 461-0155
E-Mail: sales@absmanufacturing.com
Web Site: www.absmanufacturing.com
Year Founded: 1973
Rev.: $16,400,000
Emp.: 52
Business Description:
Rubber Products Distr
S.I.C.: 3061
N.A.I.C.S.: 326291
Personnel:
John Bradley *(Pres & CEO)*
Linda Buckingham *(CFO)*

ABSOLENT AB

Kartasgatan 1
SE 531 40 Lidkoping, Sweden
Tel.: (46) 510484000
Fax: (46) 510484029
E-Mail: info@absolent.se
Web Site: www.absolent.se
Emp.: 25
Business Description:
Filter Mfr
S.I.C.: 3564
N.A.I.C.S.: 333413
Personnel:
Tony Landh *(CEO)*

U.S. Subsidiary:

Absolent Inc. (1)
8601 Six Forks Rd Ste 400
Raleigh, NC 27615
Tel.: (919) 882-2075
Fax: (919) 882-2087
E-Mail: info@absolent.com
Filter Mfr
S.I.C.: 3564
N.A.I.C.S.: 333413

ABSOLUT BANK ZAO

18 Tsvetnoy Boulevard
127051 Moscow, Russia
Tel.: (7) 495 777 71 71
Fax: (7) 495 935 00 52
E-Mail: info@absolutbank.ru
Web Site: www.absolutbank.com
Year Founded: 1993
Business Description:
Commercial Banking
S.I.C.: 6029
N.A.I.C.S.: 522110
Personnel:
Yury V. Novozhilov *(Chm)*
Nikolay Sidorov *(Chm-Mgmt Bd)*
Chuhlantsev Alexander *(Deputy Chm-Mgmt Bd)*
Anisimov Ivan *(Deputy Chm-Mgmt Bd)*
Evgeny Retyunsky *(Deputy Chm-Mgmt Bd)*
Board of Directors:
Yury V. Novozhilov
Andrey V. Degtyarev
Andrey V. Denisenkov
Vartan P. Dilanyan
Vladimir A. Kirillov
Vadim O. Korsakov
Yury S. Sizov

ABSOLUT CAPITAL MANAGEMENT HOLDING LTD

Tsvetnoy Blvd 18
127051 Moscow, Russia
Tel.: (7) 4957777171
Fax: (7) 495 777 71 49
E-Mail: info@absolutbank.ru

Web Site: www.absolutbank.com
Sales Range: $50-74.9 Million
Business Description:
Finance Investment Services
S.I.C.: 6211
N.A.I.C.S.: 523110
Personnel:
Nikolay Sidorov *(Chm)*
Mikhail Serdtsev *(Deputy Chm)*

ABSOLUTE IMPACT PUBLIC COMPANY LIMITED

1768 Thai Summit Tower 24th Floor
New Petchaburi Road
Bangkapi
Huay Khwang, Bangkok, 10310, Thailand
Tel.: (66) 2251 9988
Fax: (66) 2251 8159
E-Mail: info@absolute-impact.com
Web Site: www.absolute-impact.com
AIM—(THA)
Sales Range: $1-9.9 Million
Emp.: 45
Business Description:
Advertising Displays
S.I.C.: 7312
N.A.I.C.S.: 541850
Personnel:
Namkang Pungthong *(Chm)*
Parin Chanuntranont *(CEO)*

ABSOLUTE RETURN TRUST LIMITED

Trafalgar Court Les Banques
Saint Peter Port, Guernsey
Tel.: (44) 2070099100
Web Site: www.absolute-funds.com
ABR—(LSE)
Int. Income: $19,256
Assets: $88,638,545
Liabilities: $271,966
Net Worth: $88,366,579
Earnings: ($2,117,125)
Fiscal Year-end: 03/31/13
Business Description:
Investment Trust Services
S.I.C.: 6211
N.A.I.C.S.: 523999
Personnel:
Andrew Sykes *(Chm)*
Board of Directors:
Andrew Sykes
Nicholas Fry
Graham Harrison
Robert King
Nicholas Moss
Legal Counsel:
Mourant Ozannes
1 Le Marchant Street
186
Saint Peter Port, Guernsey
Herbert Smith
Exchange House Primrose Hill
London, United Kingdom
Transfer Agent:
Computershare Investor Services PLC
The Pavilions Bridgewater Road
PO Box 82
Bristol, BS13 8AE, United Kingdom
Tel.: (44) 870 702 0000
Fax: (44) 870 703 6119

ABSOLUTE SOFTWARE CORPORATION

1600-1055 Dunsmuir Street
Vancouver, BC, V7X 1K8, Canada
Tel.: (604) 730-9851
Fax: (604) 730-2621
Toll Free: (800) 220-0733
E-Mail: info@absolute.com
Web Site: www.absolute.com
ABT—(OTC TSX)
Rev.: $83,178,357
Assets: $126,398,352
Liabilities: $140,000,238
Net Worth: ($13,601,886)
Earnings: $1,738,452
Emp.: 384
Fiscal Year-end: 06/30/13
Business Description:
Laptop Computers Mfr
S.I.C.: 3571
N.A.I.C.S.: 334111
Personnel:
Daniel P. Ryan *(Chm)*
Errol Olsen *(Interim CEO)*
Rob Chase *(COO)*
Phil Gardner *(CTO)*
Thomas Kenny *(Exec VP & Gen Mgr-Global Sls & Mktg)*
John Sarantakes *(Sr VP & Gen Mgr-EMEA)*
Board of Directors:
Daniel P. Ryan
John Ian Giffen
Terry Libin
Gregory Rush Monahan
Ian Reid
Eric S. Rosenfeld
Salvatore Visca
Legal Counsel:
McMillan LLP
Vancouver, BC, Canada
Transfer Agent:
Canadian Stock Transfer Company, Inc
Vancouver, BC, Canada
U.S. Subsidiaries:

Absolute Software, Inc. **(1)**
11401 Century Oaks Ter Ste 430
Austin, TX 78758 WA
Tel.: (512) 600-7400
Fax: (604) 730-2621
Toll Free: (800) 220-0733
E-Mail: info@absolute.com
Web Site: www.absolute.com
Emp.: 200
Laptop Computer Security System Mfr
S.I.C.: 7382
N.A.I.C.S.: 561621
John Sarantakes *(Sr VP & Gen Mgr-Sls-EMEA)*

LiveTime Software, Inc. **(1)**
4100 Newport Place Dr
Newport Beach, CA 92660 CA
Tel.: (949) 777-5800
Fax: (949) 752-1649
Web Site: www.livetime.com
Emp.: 25
IT Support Software Developer
S.I.C.: 7372
N.A.I.C.S.: 511210
Darren Williams *(Pres)*

ABT SPORTSLINE GMBH

Daimlerstrasse 2
87437 Kempten, Germany
Tel.: (49) 831571400
Fax: (49) 83172666
E-Mail: info@abt-sportsline.de
Web Site: www.abt-sportsline.de
Year Founded: 1896
Rev.: $40,282,138
Emp.: 173
Business Description:
Automotive Product Mfr
S.I.C.: 7539
N.A.I.C.S.: 811198
Personnel:
Hans-Jurgen Abt *(Mng Dir)*

ABTERRA LTD.

7 Temasek Blvd Ste 11-05 Suntec Tower 1
Singapore, 038987, Singapore
Tel.: (65) 68859800
Fax: (65) 68859829
E-Mail: info@abterra.com.sg
Web Site: www.abterra.com.sg
L5I—(SES)
Sales Range: $100-124.9 Million
Business Description:
Iron Ore & Coal Distr
S.I.C.: 5051
N.A.I.C.S.: 423510
Personnel:
Sui Xin Cai *(Chm & Mng Dir)*
Suirong Cai *(Vice Chm)*
Xizhong Lin *(Vice Chm)*
Yu Lau *(CEO)*
Bee Leng Chew *(Sec)*
Board of Directors:
Sui Xin Cai
Suirong Cai
Ray Chun Tat Chan
Victor Mark Ban Chuan Chew
Yu Lau
Xizhong Lin
Maheskumar Shantilal Purshotam Mehta
Williamson Shiu Wah Wong

ABTEY PRODUCTIONS

BP 14 RN 466A
68990 Heimsbrunn, France
Tel.: (33) 389819210
Fax: (33) 389819857
Web Site: www.abtey.fr/
Sls.: $14,500,000
Emp.: 143
S.I.C.: 2066
N.A.I.C.S.: 311351
Personnel:
Odette Beck *(Pres)*

ABU DHABI AVIATION

PO Box 2723
Abu Dhabi, United Arab Emirates
Tel.: (971) 2 5758000
Fax: (971) 2 5757775
E-Mail: adava@abudhabiaviation.com
Web Site: www.abudhabiaviation.com
Year Founded: 1976
ADAVIATION—(EMI)
Rev.: $484,046,273
Assets: $975,917,176
Liabilities: $416,809,647
Net Worth: $559,107,529
Earnings: $71,819,864
Emp.: 900
Fiscal Year-end: 12/31/12
Business Description:
Air Freight Services
S.I.C.: 4731
N.A.I.C.S.: 488510
Personnel:
Nader Ahmed Mohammed Al Hamadi *(Chm)*
Ahmed Mohamed Sultan Al Dhaheri *(Vice Chm)*
Board of Directors:
Nader Ahmed Mohammed Al Hamadi
Ahmed Ali Khalfan Al Dhaheri
Ahmed Mohamed Sultan Al Dhaheri
Saif Saeed Mohammed Al Dhaheri
Youssef Abdel Aziz Ahmed Al Harmoudi
Saeed Ali Saleh Al Kuwaiti
Homaid Abdullah Al Shemmari
Abdullah Sedeeq Mohammed Khouri
Khalifa Yousif Abdullah Khouri
Subsidiary:

Maximus Air L.L.C. **(1)**
Maximus Air Cargo Villa Street No 25
PO Box 35367
Airport Road, Abu Dhabi, United Arab Emirates
Tel.: (971) 2 447 4900
Fax: (971) 2 447 4901
E-Mail: info@maximus.aero
Web Site: www.maximus.aero
Air Transportation Services
S.I.C.: 4512
N.A.I.C.S.: 481111
Fathi Hilal Buhazza, *(Pres & CEO)*

ABU DHABI CAPITAL MANAGEMENT LTD.

Al Bateen Towers
Bainunah Street C2 Suite 204, Dubai, United Arab Emirates
Mailing Address:
PO Box 482095
Dubai, United Arab Emirates
Tel.: (971) 2 639 0099
Fax: (971) 2 639 0700
E-Mail: info@adcm.ae
Web Site: www.adcm.ae
Business Description:
Venture Capital & Private Equity Firm
S.I.C.: 6211
N.A.I.C.S.: 523999
Personnel:
Jassim Alseddiqi *(CEO)*
Mustafa Kheriba *(COO)*
Non-U.S. Holding:

Northacre PLC **(1)**
8 Albion Riverside 8 Hester Road
London, SW11 4AX, United Kingdom **(66.8%)**
Tel.: (44) 20 7349 8000
Fax: (44) 20 7349 8001
E-Mail: enquiries@northacre.com
Web Site: www.northacre.com
NTA—(AIM)
Rev.: $47,534,979
Assets: $70,840,939
Liabilities: $7,487,532
Net Worth: $63,353,406
Earnings: $34,167,506
Emp.: 24
Fiscal Year-end: 02/28/13
Holding Company; Residential Property Development & Interior Design
S.I.C.: 6719
N.A.I.C.S.: 551112
Niccolo Barattieri di San Pietro *(CEO)*

Subsidiaries:

Intarya Limited **(2)**
8 Albion Riverside 8 Hester Road
London, SW11 4AX, United Kingdom
Tel.: (44) 20 7349 8020
Fax: (44) 20 7349 8021
E-Mail: info@intarya.com
Web Site: www.intarya.com
Emp.: 10
Interior Design Services
S.I.C.: 7389
N.A.I.C.S.: 541410
Daniel Kostiuc *(Mng Dir)*

Nilsson Architects Limited **(2)**
8 Albion Riverside 8 Hester Road
London, SW11 4AX, United Kingdom **(100%)**
Tel.: (44) 2073498030
Fax: (44) 2073498001
E-Mail: enquires@northacre.com
Web Site: www.northacre.com
Emp.: 15
Architectural Services
S.I.C.: 8712
N.A.I.C.S.: 541310
Klas Nilsson *(Founder)*

Waterloo Investments Limited **(2)**
8 Albion Riverside 8 Hester Rd
London, Battersea, SW11 4AX, United Kingdom **(100%)**
Tel.: (44) 2073498000
Fax: (44) 2073498001
E-Mail: enquires@northacre.com
Web Site: www.northacre.com
Emp.: 200
Development Management Services
S.I.C.: 8742
N.A.I.C.S.: 541611

ABU DHABI COMMERCIAL BANK PJSC

Abu Dhabi Commercial Bank Building
Salam Street Plot C-33 Sector E-11
PO Box 939
Abu Dhabi, United Arab Emirates

Abu Dhabi Commercial Bank PJSC—(Continued)

Tel.: (971) 26962222
Fax: (971) 26443384
Web Site: www.adcb.com
ADCB—(ABU)
Int. Income: $2,033,097,502
Assets: $49,208,979,886
Liabilities: $42,484,068,312
Net Worth: $6,724,911,574
Earnings: $764,916,980
Emp.: 3,000
Fiscal Year-end: 12/31/12
Business Description:
Commercial Banking Services
S.I.C.: 6029
N.A.I.C.S.: 522110
Personnel:
Eissa Mohamed Ghanem Al Suwaidi *(Chm)*
Mohamed Sultan Ghannoum Al Hameli *(Vice Chm)*
Ala'a Mohamed Atta Khalil Eraiqat *(CEO)*
Deepak Khullar *(CFO)*
Jerry Mollenkramer *(COO)*
Kishore Rao Naimpally *(Chief Risk Officer)*
Simon Copleston *(Gen Counsel & Sec)*
Board of Directors:
Eissa Mohamed Ghanem Al Suwaidi
Mohamed Ali Al Dhaheri
Aysha Ahmed Sultan Al Hallami
Mohamed Sultan Ghannoum Al Hameli
Mohamed Darwish Al Khoori
Abdulla Khalil Al Mutawa
Khalid Deemas Al Suwaidi
Ala'a Mohamed Atta Khalil Eraiqat
Khalid Khoori
Omar Liaqat
Sultan Suroor Al Dhahiri

Subsidiaries:

ADCB Finance (Cayman) Limited (1)
Al Salam St
Abu Dhabi, United Arab Emirates
Tel.: (971) 26962222
Fax: (971) 26776499
E-Mail: narvin.h@adcb.com
Investment Management & Share Trading Services
S.I.C.: 8748
N.A.I.C.S.: 541618
Eissa Mohamed Al Suaaidi *(Chm)*

Al Dhabi Brokerage Services LLC (1)
Al Salam St Abu Dhabi Commercial Bank Building 5th Floor
PO Box 939
Abu Dhabi, United Arab Emirates
Tel.: (971) 26962330
Fax: (971) 26109768
E-Mail: aldhabi@adsm.co.ae
Web Site: www.adbtrade.com
Emp.: 35
Brokerage Services
S.I.C.: 6221
N.A.I.C.S.: 523140
Hassan Al Hassani *(Gen Mgr)*

ABU DHABI GROUP

Al Naeem Tower Khalifa Street
PO Box 44222
Abu Dhabi, United Arab Emirates
Tel.: (971) 26266406
Fax: (971) 26266430
E-Mail: reception@dhabigroup.ae
Year Founded: 1997
Sales Range: $5-14.9 Billion
Emp.: 25,000
Business Description:
Investment Holding Company
S.I.C.: 6719
N.A.I.C.S.: 551112
Personnel:
Nahayan Mabarak Al Nahayan *(Chm)*

Non-U.S. Holdings:

Bank Alfalah Limited (1)
BA Building I I Chundrigar Road
75000 Karachi, Pakistan (74%)
Tel.: (92) 21111777786
Fax: (92) 2132461275
E-Mail: info@bankalfalah.com
Web Site: www.bankalfalah.com
BAFL—(KAR LAH)
Rev.: $466,789,569
Assets: $5,434,407,610
Liabilities: $5,128,001,428
Net Worth: $306,406,182
Earnings: $46,153,506
Emp.: 7,124
Fiscal Year-end: 12/31/12
Commercial & Investment Banking Services
S.I.C.: 6029
N.A.I.C.S.: 522110
Hamdan Mubarak Al Nahayan *(Chm)*
Atif Bajwa *(CEO)*
Mirza Zafar Baig *(CFO)*
Bahauddin Khan *(COO)*
Anwer Umed Ali *(CIO)*
Riaz Hussain Hamdani *(Chief Compliance Officer)*
Suhail Yaqoob Khan *(Chief Risk Officer)*
Mian Ejaz Ahmed *(Sec & Gen Mgr-Legal)*

Subsidiaries:

Alfalah GHP Investment Management Limited (2)
Saima Trade Towers 12th Fl Tower A
I I Chundrigar Road, Karachi, 74000, Pakistan PK
Tel.: (92) 21111090090 (56%)
Fax: (92) 002199217630
E-Mail: info@alfalahghp.com
Web Site: www.alfalahghp.com
Sales Range: $1-9.9 Million
Emp.: 50
Asset Management & Investment Advisory Services
S.I.C.: 6282
N.A.I.C.S.: 523920
Aqueel Hassan *(Chm)*
Abdul Aziz Anis *(CEO)*
Omer Bashir Mirza *(CFO, Sec & Sr VP)*

Alfalah Insurance Company Limited (2)
5-Saint Mary Park
Gulberg- III, Lahore, Pakistan PK
Tel.: (92) 111786234
Fax: (92) 3577432930
E-Mail: afi@alfalahinsurance.com
Web Site: www.alfalahinsurance.com
Property & Other Insurance Services
S.I.C.: 6331
N.A.I.C.S.: 524126
Nasar us Samad Qureshi *(CEO)*

Alfalah Securities (Pvt.) Ltd. (2)
Saima Trade Towers 12th Floor Tower A
I I Chundrigar Road, Karachi, Pakistan PK
Tel.: (92) 2199217810
Fax: (92) 992217835
E-Mail: info@alfalahsec.com
Web Site: www.alfalahsec.com
Emp.: 87
Equity Investment, Money Market Brokerage & Investment Banking Services
S.I.C.: 6211
N.A.I.C.S.: 523999

Standard Bank JSC (1)
3 K Tsamebuli Ave
Tbilisi, 0103, Georgia GE
Tel.: (995) 322550000 (100%)
Fax: (995) 322507707
E-Mail: info@ksb.ge
Web Site: www.ksb.ge
Sales Range: $1-9.9 Million
Commercial Banking Services
S.I.C.: 6029
N.A.I.C.S.: 522110
Ana Nicoladze *(Head-Central Outlet)*

Warid Telecom (Pvt) Limited (1)
PO Box 32214
54470 Lahore, Pakistan PK
Tel.: (92) 21111111321 (100%)
Fax: (92) 21111111322
Web Site: www.waridtel.com
Mobile Telecommunications Services
S.I.C.: 4812
N.A.I.C.S.: 517210
Marwan Zawaydeh *(CEO)*
Tariq Gulzar *(CFO & Gen Mgr-Audit, Risk & Corp Governance)*
Javed Mushtaq *(CIO)*
Muhammad Iltaf *(CTO)*
Thomas Yeo *(Chief Comml Officer)*
Shahzad Rauf *(Chief Strategy & Ops Officer)*
Adeel Bajwa *(Sec & Gen Mgr-Legal Affairs & Contracts)*

Non-U.S. Subsidiaries:

Warid Congo S.A. (2)
4eme etage Tour ARC
BP 238
Brazzaville, Congo, Republic of CG
Tel.: (242) 4000123
Web Site: www.waridtel.cg
Emp.: 135
Fixed & Mobile Telecommunications Services
S.I.C.: 4812
N.A.I.C.S.: 517210
Masud A. Zaidi *(CEO & Gen Dir)*

Warid Telecom Uganda Limited (2)
Plot 16A Clement Hill Road
PO Box 70665
Kampala, Uganda (100%)
Tel.: (256) 700100100
Fax: (256) 200221111
E-Mail: customercare@waridtel.co.ug
Web Site: www.waridtel.co.ug
Fixed, Mobile & Internet Telecommunications Services
S.I.C.: 4812
N.A.I.C.S.: 517210
Zulqarnain Javaid *(CEO)*
Atif Dar *(CFO)*
Muhamed Z. Kayani *(CTO)*
Tushar Maheshwari *(Chief Comml Officer)*

Wateen Telecom Limited (1)
PO Box 3527
Lahore, Pakistan PK
Tel.: (92) 111365111
E-Mail: customerservice@wateen.com
Web Site: www.wateen.com
Sales Range: $100-124.9 Million
Emp.: 320
Fixed, Mobile & Internet Telecommunications Services
S.I.C.: 4813
N.A.I.C.S.: 517110
Nahayan Mabarak Al Nahayan *(Chm)*
Naeem Zamindar *(CEO)*
Sajjeed Aslam *(CFO)*
Aamir Anwar Khan *(Chief Strategy Officer)*
Shoaib Nazir *(CTO)*
Syed Jibran Ali *(Chief Comml Officer)*
Adnan Mahmood *(Sec & Head-Legal)*

ABU DHABI INVESTMENT AUTHORITY

211 Corniche
PO Box 3600
Abu Dhabi, United Arab Emirates
Tel.: (971) 2 415 0000
Fax: (971) 2 415 1000
Web Site: www.adia.ae
Year Founded: 1976
Business Description:
Investment Services
S.I.C.: 6211
N.A.I.C.S.: 523999
Personnel:
Khalifa bin Zayed Al Nahyan *(Chm)*

ABU DHABI INVESTMENT COMPANY

National Bank of Abu Dhabi Building
Khalidiya Tariq Bin Ziad Street
PO Box 46309
Abu Dhabi, United Arab Emirates
Tel.: (971) 2 692 6101
Fax: (971) 2 692 6863
E-Mail: clientservices@investad.com
Web Site: www.investad.com
Business Description:
Investment Services
S.I.C.: 6211
N.A.I.C.S.: 523999
Personnel:
Nazem Fawwaz Al Kudsi *(CEO)*

ABU DHABI ISLAMIC BANK PJSC

PO Box 313
Abu Dhabi, United Arab Emirates
Tel.: (971) 26100600
Fax: (971) 2 6100306
Web Site: www.adib.ae
Year Founded: 1998
ADIB—(ABU)
Rev.: $1,191,693,587
Assets: $23,316,178,580
Liabilities: $19,872,589,337
Net Worth: $3,443,589,243
Earnings: $326,951,326
Emp.: 1,228
Fiscal Year-end: 12/31/12
Business Description:
Banking Services
S.I.C.: 6029
N.A.I.C.S.: 522110
Personnel:
Jawaan Awaidha Suhail Al Khaili *(Chm)*
Khaled Abdullah Neamat Khouri *(Vice Chm)*
Tirad Al Mahmoud *(CEO)*
N. Loutfy *(CEO/Mng Dir-Egypt)*
A. Abrahim *(Gen Legal Counsel)*
A. Qadir Khanani *(Treas & Acting Head-Treasury)*
Board of Directors:
Jawaan Awaidha Suhail Al Khaili
Sami Ali Al Amri
Juma Khamis Al Khaili
Abdulla Aqueeda Al Muhairi
Khamis Buharoon
Khaled Abdullah Neamat Khouri
Ragheed Najeeb Shanti

Subsidiary:

Kawader Services (1)
Najda St 11th Fl - Abu Dhabi Islamic Bank Bldg
PO Box 5414
Abu Dhabi, United Arab Emirates
Tel.: (971) 26100900
Fax: (971) 26100909
E-Mail: info@kawader.ae
Web Site: www.kawader.ae
Emp.: 1,000
Staffing Services
S.I.C.: 8999
N.A.I.C.S.: 541612

ABU DHABI MEDIA

PO Box 63
Abu Dhabi, United Arab Emirates
Tel.: (971) 2 414 4000
E-Mail: communications@admedia.ae
Web Site: www.admedia.ae
Business Description:
Media Holding Company
S.I.C.: 4833
N.A.I.C.S.: 515120
Personnel:
Mohamed Mubarak Al Mazrouei *(Chm)*
Ahmed Ali Al Sayegh *(Deputy Chm)*
Saif Saeed Ghobash *(Acting CEO)*
Frank Mooty *(CFO & Acting CEO)*
Abdul Nasser Saif Al Kaabi *(CTO)*
Raja Abdulah Halabi *(Chief Comml Officer)*
Abdul Hadi Al Sheikh *(CEO-Live Broadcast Productions & Facilities)*
Mohammed El-Said *(Gen Counsel)*
Board of Directors:
Mohamed Mubarak Al Mazrouei

Mohamed Omar Abdulla
Abdulla Ali Al Ahbabi
Noura Al Kaabi
Mubarak Hamad Al Muhairi
Ahmed Ali Al Sayegh
Saeed Al-Hajeri

U.S. Joint Venture:

VEVO LLC (1)
825 8th Ave 23rd Fl
New York, NY 10019
Tel.: (212) 331-1357
Web Site: www.vevo.com
Music Video Website Operator; Joint Venture of Universal Music Group, Sony Music Entertainment & Abu Dhabi Media
S.I.C.: 2741
N.A.I.C.S.: 519130
Rio D. Caraeff *(Pres & CEO)*
Alan Price *(CFO)*
Jonathan Carson *(Chief Revenue Officer)*
Julie Lee *(Exec VP-Bus Dev & Bus Affairs)*
Nic Jones *(Sr VP-Intl)*
Hal Trencher *(Sr VP-Natl Sls)*

ABU DHABI NATIONAL COMPANY FOR BUILDING MATERIAL

Salam St Al Nadi Al Seyahi Company Building
PO Box 2443
Abu Dhabi, United Arab Emirates
Tel.: (971) 2 6455500
Fax: (971) 2 6455544
E-Mail: bildco@eim.ae
Web Site: www.bildco.ae
Year Founded: 1974
BILDCO—(EMI)
Sales Range: $75-99.9 Million

Business Description:
Building Material Mfr & Whslr
S.I.C.: 3448
N.A.I.C.S.: 332311

Personnel:
Saif Darwish Al Kutbi *(Chm)*
Matar Abdulla Al Muhairi *(Vice Chm)*
Ali Rasheed Nassir Al Omaira *(Mng Dir)*

Board of Directors:
Saif Darwish Al Kutbi
Reyadh Mohamed Abdullah Al Homaidan
Mubarak Rashid Khamis Al Mansouri
Matar Abdulla Al Muhairi
Ali Rasheed Nassir Al Omaira
Hussain Ali Rasheed Al Omaira
Mohamed Sultan Rashid Aldahiri

Subsidiary:

Bildco Reinforcing Steel Services (1)
PO Box 2443
Abu Dhabi, United Arab Emirates
Tel.: (971) 2 5559183
Fax: (971) 2 5555330
E-Mail: sales@bildco.ae
Emp.: 75
Steel Reinforcement Services
S.I.C.: 1791
N.A.I.C.S.: 238120
Edward Najjar, *(Gen Mgr)*

ABU DHABI NATIONAL HOTELS PJSC

PO Box 46806
Abu Dhabi, United Arab Emirates
Tel.: (971) 024447228
Fax: (971) 024448495
E-Mail: info@adnh.com
Web Site: www.adnh.com
Year Founded: 1975
ADNH—(ABU)
Sales Range: $450-499.9 Million
Emp.: 218

Business Description:
Transportation, Tourism, Catering & Hotel Management Services
S.I.C.: 7011
N.A.I.C.S.: 721110

Personnel:
Salem Mohamed Athaith Al-Ameri *(Chm)*
Ahmed Khalaf Al Otaiba *(Vice Chm)*
Richad Wayne Riley *(CEO)*

Board of Directors:
Salem Mohamed Athaith Al-Ameri
Abdulrahman Hader Al Meraikhi
Hamad Abdullah Al Shamsi
Khamis Mohamed Buharoon
Alaa Mohamed Eraiqat
Ahmed Khalaf Al Otaiba
Khalid Khouri
Ahmed Mohammed Al Dhaheri
Mohamed Thaloob Al Darei

Subsidiary:

Al Ghazal Transport Co. (1)
PO Box 46806
Abu Dhabi, United Arab Emirates (100%)
Tel.: (971) 24447228
Fax: (971) 24444791
E-Mail: adnh@adnh.com
Web Site: www.adsh.com
Emp.: 300
Ground Transportation Services
S.I.C.: 4111
N.A.I.C.S.: 485999
Saleem Ahmed Al Amri *(Chm)*

Unit:

Sunshine Tours (1)
Abu Dhabi National Hotels
PO Box 8200
Abu Dhabi, United Arab Emirates
Tel.: (971) 4446856
E-Mail: adnh@emirates.net.ae
Emp.: 1,000
Tour Operator
S.I.C.: 4725
N.A.I.C.S.: 561520
Saif Alhjri *(Chm)*

ABU DHABI NATIONAL INSURANCE COMPANY

ADNIC Building Sh Khalifa Street
PO Box 839
Abu Dhabi, United Arab Emirates
Tel.: (971) 2 4080100
Fax: (971) 2 4080604
E-Mail: adnic@adnic.ae
Web Site: www.adnic.ae
Year Founded: 1972
ADNIC—(EMI)
Sales Range: $550-599.9 Million

Business Description:
Insurance Management Services
S.I.C.: 6411
N.A.I.C.S.: 524298

Personnel:
Khalifa Mohammed Al Kindi *(Chm)*
Mohamad Mohamad Al Nahyan *(Vice Chm)*

Board of Directors:
Khalifa Mohammed Al Kindi
Mohamad Abdul Aziz Al Rubaya Al Muhairy
Ahmad Ali Al Sayegh
Khalifa Sultan Ahmed Al-Suwaidi
Ghanim Ali Hamoodah
Diab T. M. Hamoodah
Abdullah Khalaf Al-Otaibah
Mohamad Mohamad Al Nahyan
Sultan Rashid

ABU DHABI NATIONAL OIL COMPANY

PO Box 898
Abu Dhabi, United Arab Emirates
Tel.: (971) 26020000
Fax: (971) 26023389
E-Mail: adnoc@adnoc.ae
Web Site: www.adnoc.com
Year Founded: 1971
Emp.: 14,000

Business Description:
Petroleum Exploration, Production, Transport & Refined-Product Distribution
S.I.C.: 1311
N.A.I.C.S.: 211111

Personnel:
Abdullah Nasser Al Suwaidi *(Dir Gen)*

Subsidiaries:

Abu Dhabi Company Onshore Oil Operations (1)
PO Box 270
Abu Dhabi, United Arab Emirates (60%)
Tel.: (971) 26040000
Fax: (971) 26669765
E-Mail: adnoc@adnoc.com
Web Site: www.adco.ae
Emp.: 1,450
Onshore Exploration, Development & Production of Crude Oil
S.I.C.: 1311
N.A.I.C.S.: 211111

Abu Dhabi Gas Industries Limited (1)
PO Box 665
Abu Dhabi, United Arab Emirates (68%)
Tel.: (971) 26030000
Fax: (971) 26037414
E-Mail: info@gasco.ae
Web Site: www.gasco.ae
Emp.: 3,500
Processing of Associate & Non-Associate Gas from Onshore Oil Production
S.I.C.: 2813
N.A.I.C.S.: 325120
Adel Salem Al Khaff *(VP-Comml)*

Abu Dhabi Gas Liquefaction Limited (1)
PO Box 3500
Abu Dhabi, United Arab Emirates (70%)
Tel.: (971) 26061111
Fax: (971) 26065500
E-Mail: info@adgas.com
Web Site: www.adgas.com
Emp.: 850
Production & Export of Liquefied Natural Gas & Liquefied Petroleum Gas
S.I.C.: 1321
N.A.I.C.S.: 211112
Fahim Kazim *(Gen Mgr)*

Abu Dhabi Marine Operating Company (1)
PO Box 303
Abu Dhabi, United Arab Emirates (60%)
Tel.: (971) 26060000
Fax: (971) 26064848
Web Site: www.abudhabimargroup.com
Emp.: 1,504
Ship Building & Repairing Services
S.I.C.: 3731
N.A.I.C.S.: 336611
Ali Aljarwan *(CEO)*

Abu Dhabi National Oil Company for Distribution (1)
PO Box 4188
Abu Dhabi, United Arab Emirates
Tel.: (971) 26771300
Fax: (971) 26722322
E-Mail: adnoc-dist@adnoc-dist.co.ae
Web Site: www.adnoc-dist.com.ae
Petroleum Products Marketing & Distribution
S.I.C.: 5172
N.A.I.C.S.: 424720
Abdullah Sanem *(Gen Mgr)*

Abu Dhabi National Tanker Company (1)
Sheikh Khalifa Energy Complex Takreer Tower 11th & 12th Floors
PO Box 2977
Khalifa Street, Abu Dhabi, United Arab Emirates (100%)
Tel.: (971) 26028400
Fax: (971) 26028323
E-Mail: adnatco@adnatco.co.ae
Web Site: www.adnatco.com
Emp.: 68
Transport of Crude Oil & Petroleum Products
S.I.C.: 4613
N.A.I.C.S.: 486910

Abu Dhabi Oil Refining Company (1)
PO Box 3593
Abu Dhabi, United Arab Emirates
Tel.: (971) 26027001
Fax: (971) 26027465
E-Mail: publicrelations@takreer.com
Web Site: www.takreer.com
Refining of Crude Oil, Salt, Chlorine & Petroleum Condensates, Sulphur Treatment & Mixing of Petroleum Products
S.I.C.: 2911
N.A.I.C.S.: 324110

Abu Dhabi Petroleum Ports Operating Company (1)
PO Box 61
Abu Dhabi, United Arab Emirates (60%)
Tel.: (971) 26028000
Fax: (971) 26742094
E-Mail: info@irshad.ae
Web Site: www.irshad.ae
Emp.: 338
Petroleum Terminals & Ports Maintenance Operations
S.I.C.: 5171
N.A.I.C.S.: 424710

ESNAAD (1)
PO Box 46121
Abu Dhabi, United Arab Emirates (100%)
Tel.: (971) 26029000
Fax: (971) 26029010
E-Mail: esnaad@esnaad.com
Web Site: www.esnaad.com
Emp.: 1,000
Production & Marketing of Mud Chemicals, Material Handling Services, Waste Management, Specialty Chemicals Blending, Operating, Chartering or Leasing Vessels
S.I.C.: 2899
N.A.I.C.S.: 325998
Darwish Al Qubaisi *(Gen Mgr)*

National Drilling Company (1)
PO Box 4017
Abu Dhabi, United Arab Emirates (100%)
Tel.: (971) 26776100
Fax: (971) 26779937
E-Mail: webmaster@ndc.ae
Web Site: www.ndc.ae
Emp.: 2,300
Onshore & Offshore Drilling of Oil & Gas Wells
S.I.C.: 1381
N.A.I.C.S.: 213111
Abdalla Saeed Al-Suwaidi *(Gen Mgr)*

National Gas Shipping Company Ltd. (NGSCO) (1)
Sheikh Khalifa Energy Complex
PO Box 2600
Takreer Tower, Abu Dhabi, United Arab Emirates VG
Tel.: (971) 26028600
Fax: (971) 26723999
E-Mail: Info@adnatcongsco.com
Web Site: www.adnatcongsco.com
Emp.: 250
Shipping of Liquefied Gas Products
S.I.C.: 4412
N.A.I.C.S.: 483111
Ali Al Yabhouni *(CEO)*

The National Petroleum Construction Company (1)
Zone No 6 7 71 Mustafa
PO Box 2058
Street No 7, Abu Dhabi, United Arab Emirates (70%)
Tel.: (971) 25549000
Fax: (971) 25549111
E-Mail: npccnet@emirates.net.ae
Web Site: www.npcc.ae
Emp.: 10,000
Engineering, Procurement & Construction Contracting Services for Onshore & Offshore Oil, Gas & Petrochemical Industries
S.I.C.: 1623
N.A.I.C.S.: 237120
Aqeel A. Madhi *(CEO)*

Zakum Development Company (1)
Khalifa Energy Complex Khalifa St
PO Box 46808
Abu Dhabi, United Arab Emirates (51%)
Tel.: (971) 26050000
Fax: (971) 26789448

Abu Dhabi National Oil Company—(Continued)

Web Site: www.zadco.com
Emp.: 1,200
Production & Development of Oil & Gas
S.I.C.: 1311
N.A.I.C.S.: 211111

Joint Venture:

Abu Dhabi Polymers Co. Ltd **(1)**
Borouge Tower, Shaikh Khalifa Energy Complex Corniche Road
PO Box 6925
Abu Dhabi, United Arab Emirates
Tel.: (971) 2 6070300
Fax: (971) 2 6070999
E-Mail: info@borouge.com
Web Site: www.borouge.com
Emp.: 1,700
Polymer Mfr
S.I.C.: 2821
N.A.I.C.S.: 325211
Abdulaziz Alhajri *(CEO)*

ABU DHABI NATIONAL TAKAFUL CO. P.S.C

PO Box 35335
Abu Dhabi, United Arab Emirates
Tel.: (971) 24107700
Fax: (971) 24107800
Web Site: www.takaful.ae
Year Founded: 2003
TKFL—(EMI)
Rev.: $53,137,292
Assets: $125,760,397
Liabilities: $80,719,884
Net Worth: $45,040,513
Earnings: $7,382,240
Fiscal Year-end: 12/31/12

Business Description:
Insurance Services
S.I.C.: 6411
N.A.I.C.S.: 524298

Personnel:
Khadem Abdulla Al Qubaisi *(Chm)*
Khamis Mohamed Buharoon *(Vice Chm)*
Osama Abdeen *(CEO)*
Saeid Abo Almagd *(Deputy CEO-Fin & Admin)*
Nazih Haidar *(Deputy CEO-Technical Affairs)*

Board of Directors:
Khadem Abdulla Al Qubaisi
Khalid Ali Al Mansoori
Khalifa Abdulla Khamis Al Romaithi
Khalid Deemas Al Suwaidi
Khamis Mohamed Buharoon
Dafer Farouq Luqman
Andrew Douglas Moir

ABU DHABI SECURITIES EXCHANGE

Al Ghaith Tower Ground Fl Hamdan Street
PO Box 54500
Abu Dhabi, United Arab Emirates
Tel.: (971) 26277777
Fax: (971) 26270300
E-Mail: info@adx.ae
Web Site: www.adx.ae
Year Founded: 2000

Business Description:
Securities Exchange Services
S.I.C.: 6231
N.A.I.C.S.: 523210

Personnel:
Rashed Al Baloushi *(CEO)*
Abdul Aziz Al Neaimi *(Asst CEO-Support Svcs)*

ABU DHABI SHIP BUILDING PJSC

Musafah Industrial Area
PO Box 8922
Abu Dhabi, United Arab Emirates
Tel.: (971) 2 502 8000
Fax: (971) 2 551 0455
E-Mail: finance@adsb.ae
Web Site: www.adsb.net
Year Founded: 1996
ADSB—(EMI)
Rev.: $347,504,182
Assets: $601,876,533
Liabilities: $495,389,919
Net Worth: $106,486,614
Earnings: $7,928,331
Fiscal Year-end: 12/31/12

Business Description:
Ship Building Services
S.I.C.: 3731
N.A.I.C.S.: 336611

Personnel:
Homaid Abdulla Al Shemmari *(Chm)*
Mohammed Rashid Ali Al Marzouqi *(Vice Chm)*
Khaled Al Mazrouei *(CEO)*
Richard Turner *(CFO)*
Ian S. Pike *(COO)*

Board of Directors:
Homaid Abdulla Al Shemmari
Abdulla Saeed Al Darmaki
Hussain Ibrahim Al Hammadi
Mohammed Rashid Ali Al Marzouqi
Salem Rashid Al Noaimi
Khaled Saleh Al Rashedi
Matar Ali Al Romaithi
Khaled Salem Al Shamlan
Ali Saleh Al Yafaei
Mansour Shams Khouri

ABU DHABI WATER & ELECTRICITY AUTHORITY

PO Box 8120
Abu Dhabi, United Arab Emirates
Tel.: (971) 26943333
Fax: (971) 2 694 3191
E-Mail: pr@adwea.ae
Web Site: www.adwea.ae
Year Founded: 1998
Sales Range: $1-4.9 Billion
Emp.: 15,000

Business Description:
Water & Electric Utility Administration Services
S.I.C.: 9631
N.A.I.C.S.: 926130

Personnel:
Diab Bin Zayed Al Nahyan *(Chm)*
Khalfan Ghaith Al Muheirbi *(Deputy Chm)*
Musallam Saeed Al Qubeisi *(Deputy Chm)*
Abdullah Saif Al Nuaimi *(Dir Gen)*

Board of Directors:
Diab Bin Zayed Al Nahyan
Mohammed Ahmed Al Bawardi
Hadef Joan Al Dhaheri
Mohamed Seif Al Mazroui
Khalfan Ghaith Al Muheirbi
Musallam Saeed Al Qubeisi
Ahmed Ali Al Sayegh
Nasser Ahmed Al Sowaidi
Hamad Al Hur Al Suweidi

Holdings:

Abu Dhabi National Energy Company PJSC **(1)**
Levels 23 24 25 Al Maqam Tower Tower 3 Sowwah Square Al Maryah Island
PO Box 55224
Abu Dhabi, United Arab Emirates
Tel.: (971) 26914900
Fax: (971) 26413286
E-Mail: info@taqaglobal.com
Web Site: www.taqaglobal.com
TAQA—(ABU)
Rev.: $7,562,521,300
Assets: $33,366,546,200
Liabilities: $29,730,765,760
Net Worth: $3,635,780,440
Earnings: $370,436,980
Emp.: 3,300
Fiscal Year-end: 12/31/12
Energy Investments; Owned 100% by the Government of the United Arab Emirates
S.I.C.: 6211
N.A.I.C.S.: 523999
Hamad Al-Hurr Al-Suwaidi *(Chm)*
Abdulla Saif Al-Nuaimi *(Vice Chm)*
Stephen Kersley *(CFO)*
Edward LaFehr *(COO)*
Frederic Lesage *(Chief Strategy Officer)*
Frank Perez *(Exec Officer-Power & Water)*
Carl Sheldon *(Chm-Power Bus-Morocco)*
Michael T. McGuinty *(Gen Counsel & Sec)*
Ryan Wong *(Treas & Grp VP)*

Subsidiaries:

Emirates CMS Power Company **(2)**
Taweelah Power & Water Complex
PO Box 47688
Abu Dhabi, United Arab Emirates AE
Tel.: (971) 25067100 (60%)
Fax: (971) 2 506 7157
Web Site: www.adwea.ae/priv/cms/index.html
Electric Power Generation & Water Desalination Plant Owner & Operator
S.I.C.: 4911
N.A.I.C.S.: 221112
Brian S. Jackson *(Exec Mng Dir)*

Taweelah Asia Power Company **(2)**
Taweelah Power & Water Complex
PO Box 32255
Abu Dhabi, United Arab Emirates (60%)
Tel.: (971) 25627000
Fax: (971) 25627055
E-Mail: info@tapco.ae
Web Site: www.tapco.ae
Emp.: 200
Electric Power Generation & Water Desalination Plant Owner & Operator
S.I.C.: 4911
N.A.I.C.S.: 221112
Omar Abughazaleh *(CFO)*

Non-U.S. Subsidiaries:

TAQA Energy B.V. **(2)**
Prinsenhof
Prinses Margrietplantsoen 40, 2502 AN Hague, Netherlands
Tel.: (31) 703337500
Fax: (31) 703337898
Web Site: www.taqaglobal.ae/nl
Emp.: 100
Oil & Natural Gas Drilling & Exploration
S.I.C.: 1381
N.A.I.C.S.: 213111
Gan Willem Vhooghstraten *(Mng Dir)*

TAQA North Ltd. **(2)**
308 4th Ave SW Ste 2100
Calgary, AB, T2P 0H7, Canada Ca
Tel.: (403) 724-5000
Fax: (403) 724-5001
Emp.: 500
Oil & Natural Gas Exploration & Production
S.I.C.: 4923
N.A.I.C.S.: 486210
Edward LaFehr *(Pres)*

Bainounah Power Company **(1)**
PO Box 33477
Abu Dhabi, United Arab Emirates
Tel.: (971) 26731100
Fax: (971) 26730403
Web Site: www.bpc.ae
Emp.: 750
Electric Power Generation & Water Desalination Plant Owner & Operator
S.I.C.: 4931
N.A.I.C.S.: 221112
Ahmed Hilal Al Kuwaiti *(Chm)*
Abdul Jaleel Al Khoury *(Deputy Chm & Mng Dir)*
Murad Sulaiman *(Deputy Mng Dir)*

Subsidiaries:

Abu Dhabi Distribution Company **(2)**
PO Box 219
Abu Dhabi, United Arab Emirates (100%)
Tel.: (971) 26423000
Fax: (971) 26426033
E-Mail: contactcentre@addc.ae
Web Site: www.addc.ae
Electric Power & Water Distr
S.I.C.: 4931
N.A.I.C.S.: 221122
Ahmed Saeed Al Muraikhi *(Mng Dir)*

Al Ain Distribution Company **(2)**
PO Box 1065
Al Ain, United Arab Emirates (100%)
Tel.: (971) 37636000
Fax: (971) 37629949
E-Mail: customercare@aadc.ae
Web Site: www.aadc.ae
Electric Power & Water Distr
S.I.C.: 4931
N.A.I.C.S.: 221122

ABU QIR FERTILIZERS AND CHEMICAL INDUSTRIES CO.

El Tabya Rasheed Road
Alexandria, Egypt
Tel.: (20) 35603053
Telex: 45063 ABUF UN
Fax: (20) 35603032
E-Mail: afc@abuqir.com
Web Site: www.abuqir.com
Year Founded: 1976
ABUK—(EGX)
Sales Range: $50-74.9 Million
Emp.: 2,950

Business Description:
Ammonium Nitrate, Urea & Anhydrous Liquid Ammonia Producer
S.I.C.: 2873
N.A.I.C.S.: 325311

Personnel:
Ahmed A. Al Jayar *(Chm & Mng Dir)*

ABUS LEVAGE

25 Rue Edouard Michelin
54710 Ludres, France
Tel.: (33) 383592222
Fax: (33) 383592225
E-Mail: contact@abus-levage.fr
Web Site: www.abus-levage.fr
Sls.: $17,900,000
Emp.: 60

Business Description:
Industrial Equipment Mfr
S.I.C.: 5084
N.A.I.C.S.: 423830

Personnel:
Delphine Renaud *(Dir-Fin)*

ABVI AYMOND BRUNEL VEHICULES INDUSTRIEL

Arnd Poent Rieucoulon
34434 Saint-Jean-de-Vedas, Herault, France
Tel.: (33) 467421540
Fax: (33) 467421548
E-Mail: j.fourquet@abvi.fr
Web Site: www.abvi.fr
Sales Range: $25-49.9 Million
Emp.: 71

Business Description:
Automobile Dealer
S.I.C.: 5599
N.A.I.C.S.: 441228

Personnel:
Jeanne Fourquet *(Dir-Fin)*

ABWICKLUNGSGESELLSCHAFT BIOGAS I AG

Bayernwerk 8
D-92421 Schwandorf, Germany
Tel.: (49) 94317510
Fax: (49) 9431751204
E-Mail: info@schmack-biogas.com
Web Site: www.schmack-biogas.com
Year Founded: 1995
SB1—(DEU)
Sales Range: $75-99.9 Million
Emp.: 300

Business Description:
Biogas Energy Facilities Construction, Project Development & Consulting Services
S.I.C.: 1629
N.A.I.C.S.: 237990

Personnel:
Thomas Noebels *(Chm-Supervisory Bd)*
Werner Ruberg *(Chm-Mgmt Bd)*
Ulrich Schmack *(Vice Chm-Mgmt Bd)*
Joachim Schlichtig *(Member-Mgmt Bd)*
Supervisory Board of Directors:
Thomas Noebels
Schlichtig Joachim
Fernand J. Kaufmann

Subsidiaries:

CarboTech Engineering Holding GmbH (1)
Bayernwerk 8
92421 Schwandorf, Germany
Tel.: (49) 9431751370
Fax: (49) 9431751 5370
Biogas Plant Construction Services
S.I.C.: 1629
N.A.I.C.S.: 237120
Push Moyer *(Mng Dir)*

Hese Biogas GmbH (1)
Magdeburger Strabe 16
45881 Gelsenkirchen, Germany
Tel.: (49) 20998099900
Fax: (49) 20998099901
E-Mail: info@hese-biogas.de
Web Site: www.hese-biogas.de
Emp.: 25
Biogas Production Services
S.I.C.: 1389
N.A.I.C.S.: 213112
Otto Eihhorn *(Mng Dir)*

VR-LEASING SOLIDUS Achtzehnte GmbH & Co. Immobilien KG (1)
Hauptstrasse 131-137
65760 Eschborn, Germany De
Tel.: (49) 61969940
Fax: (49) 6196993390
Investment Advisory Services
S.I.C.: 6282
N.A.I.C.S.: 523930

Non-U.S. Subsidiary:

Schmack Biogas S.r.l. (1)
Via Galileo Galilei 2/E
39100 Bolzano, Italy
Tel.: (39) 471 1955000
Fax: (39) 471 1955010
E-Mail: info@schmack-biogas.it
Web Site: www.schmack-biogas.com
Biogas Plant Construction Services
S.I.C.: 1623
N.A.I.C.S.: 237120

ABYAAR REAL ESTATE DEVELOPMENT COMPANY K.S.C.C.

Al Sour Street Al Sour Tower Floor No 6 Al Qebla Area
PO Box 4238
Safat, 13043 Kuwait, Kuwait
Tel.: (965) 22915254
Fax: (965) 22915250
E-Mail: info@abyaar.com
Web Site: www.abyaar.com
ABYAAR—(KUW)
Rev.: $11,552,103
Assets: $686,049,655
Liabilities: $350,829,584
Net Worth: $335,220,070
Earnings: ($41,949,018)
Fiscal Year-end: 12/31/12
Business Description:
Real Estate Services
S.I.C.: 6531
N.A.I.C.S.: 531390
Personnel:
Marzooq Rashed Al-Rashdan *(Chm)*
Saleh Abdelaziz Al Sarawi *(Vice Chm)*
Hussein Hassan Al-Basri *(CEO)*
Abdullah Fozan Al-Obaid *(Deputy CEO-Supporting Svcs & Investment)*
Board of Directors:
Marzooq Rashed Al-Rashdan
Saleh Abdelaziz Al Sarawi
Saeed Mohammad Al-Amiri
Hussein Hassan Al-Basri
Jassim Khalifa Al-Duaij

ABZU GOLD LTD.

1010-1130 West Pender St
Vancouver, BC, V6E 4A4, Canada
Tel.: (604) 398-5380
Fax: (604) 398-5387
E-Mail: info@abzugold.com
Web Site: www.abzugold.com
ABS—(OTC TSXV)
Assets: $5,547,183
Liabilities: $1,166,692
Net Worth: $4,380,491
Earnings: ($1,965,293)
Fiscal Year-end: 07/31/13
Business Description:
Gold Mining Services
S.I.C.: 1041
N.A.I.C.S.: 212221
Personnel:
Gordon K. Neal *(Chm)*
Robert William Baxter *(Pres & CEO)*
Wilson Soon *(CFO)*
Erin Walmesley *(Sec)*
Board of Directors:
Gordon K. Neal
Robert William Baxter
Tarek Damerji
David George Savage
Eric Wardle
Legal Counsel:
McCullough O'Connor Irwin LLP
2610 Oceanic Plaza 1066 West Hastings Street
Vancouver, BC, Canada
Transfer Agent:
Computershare Investor Services
3rd Floor, 510 Burrard Street
Vancouver, BC, Canada

Subsidiary:

Abzu Resources Ltd (1)
33610 E Broadway
Mission, BC, V2V 4M4, Canada
Tel.: (604) 820-3800
Gold Mining Services
S.I.C.: 1041
N.A.I.C.S.: 212221

A.C. DISPENSING EQUIPMENT INC.

100 Dispensing Way
Lower Sackville, NS, B4C 4H2, Canada
Tel.: (902) 865-9602
Fax: (902) 865-9604
Toll Free: (888) 777-9990
E-Mail: reception@sureshotdispensing.com
Web Site: www.sureshotdispensing.com
Year Founded: 1985
Rev.: $21,341,410
Emp.: 140
Business Description:
Dispensing Systems Mfr
S.I.C.: 3586
N.A.I.C.S.: 333913
Personnel:
Michael R. Duck *(Founder)*
David MacAulay *(Pres)*

AC S.A.

(d/b/a Autogaz)
ul 27 Lipca 64
15-182 Bialystok, Poland
Tel.: (48) 85 743 81 00
Fax: (48) 85 653 93 83
E-Mail: info@ac.com.pl
Web Site: www.ac.com.pl
ACG—(WAR)
Business Description:
Motor Vehicle Parts Mfr
S.I.C.: 3829
N.A.I.C.S.: 336310
Personnel:
Piotr Laskowski *(Chm-Supervisory Bd)*
Katarzyna Rutkowska *(Chm-Mgmt Bd & Pres)*
Anatol Timoszuk *(Vice Chm-Supervisory Bd)*
Supervisory Board of Directors:
Piotr Laskowski
Tomasz Marek Krysztofiak
Artur Jaroslaw Laskowski
Zenon Andrzej Mierzejewski
Anatol Timoszuk

ACA CO-OPERATIVE LIMITED

(d/b/a/ EdenValley Farms)
326 Main St
Berwick, NS, B0P 1E0, Canada
Tel.: (902) 678-8323
Fax: (902) 681-8914
E-Mail: contactus@edenvalleyfarms.com
Web Site: www.edenvalleyfarms.com
Year Founded: 1943
Sales Range: $50-74.9 Million
Emp.: 150
Business Description:
Chicken, Turkey & Egg Products
S.I.C.: 0252
N.A.I.C.S.: 112310
Personnel:
Ian Blenkharn *(CEO)*

Division:

ACA Co-operative Limited - Egg Division (1)
830 Belcher Street
Port Williams, NS, B0P 1T0, Canada
Tel.: (902) 679-4910
Fax: (902) 679-4912
Egg Hatching Services
S.I.C.: 0252
N.A.I.C.S.: 112310

Plants:

ACA Co-operative Limited - Feed Mill (1)
34 Highway 358
Greenwich, NS, B0P 1T0, Canada
Tel.: (902) 542-3821
Fax: (902) 542-3964
Poultry Feed Mfr
S.I.C.: 2048
N.A.I.C.S.: 311119

ACA Co-operative Limited - Primary Processing Plant (1)
64 Minas Warehouse Road
New Minas, NS, B4N 5A5, Canada
Tel.: (902) 678-8323
Fax: (902) 681-0574
Processed Meat Product Mfr
S.I.C.: 5147
N.A.I.C.S.: 311612

ACACIA CAPITAL PARTNERS LIMITED

CPC1 Capital Park
Cambridge, CB21 5XE, United Kingdom
Tel.: (44) 2072997399
Fax: (44) 2072997390
E-Mail: info@acaciacp.com
Web Site: www.acaciacp.com
Managed Assets: $2,000,000,000
Emp.: 3
Business Description:
Venture Capital Fund Management Services
S.I.C.: 6211
N.A.I.C.S.: 523110
Personnel:
Hitesh Mehta *(Partner)*
Christopher Smart *(Partner)*

ACACIA COAL LIMITED

Suite 1902 Level 19 Tower A Zenith Centre 821 Pacific Highway
PO Box 758
Chatswood, NSW, 2067, Australia
Tel.: (61) 1300 222 625
Fax: (61) 2 9475 0869
E-Mail: info@acaciacoal.com.au
Web Site: www.acaciacoal.com.au
AJC—(ASX)
Rev.: $337,485
Assets: $19,443,628
Liabilities: $679,530
Net Worth: $18,764,097
Earnings: ($716,354)
Emp.: 5
Fiscal Year-end: 06/30/13
Business Description:
Coal Exploration & Development Services
S.I.C.: 1241
N.A.I.C.S.: 213113
Personnel:
Gavin May *(Mng Dir)*
Robert Waring *(CFO & Sec)*
Graham Colliss *(Chief Projects Officer)*
Board of Directors:
Kym Livesley
Gavin May
Michael Mulroney
Amanda Ward

ACACIA INVERSION A.V., S.A.

Gran Via 40 Bis
48009 Bilbao, Spain
Tel.: (34) 944356740
Fax: (34) 944352610
E-Mail: info@acacia-inversion.com
Web Site: www.acacia-inversion.com
Emp.: 7
Business Description:
Business Management Services
S.I.C.: 7389
N.A.I.C.S.: 561499

ACADEMIA LTD.

8 Kinetic Crescent Innova Park
Enfield, EN3 7XH, United Kingdom
Tel.: (44) 8456 120 118
Fax: (44) 8456 120 119
E-Mail: sales@academia.co.uk
Web Site: www.academia.co.uk
Year Founded: 2003
Emp.: 75
Business Description:
Software Licensing Services
S.I.C.: 5045
N.A.I.C.S.: 423430
Personnel:
Mike Bacon *(Founder & Mng Dir)*

ACADEMIES AUSTRALASIA GROUP LIMITED

Level 6 505 George Street
Sydney, NSW, 2000, Australia
Tel.: (61) 2 9223 1116
Fax: (61) 2 9224 5560
E-Mail: info@academies.edu.au
Web Site: www.academies.edu.au
AKG—(ASX)
Rev.: $39,419,517
Assets: $28,851,581
Liabilities: $12,915,787
Net Worth: $15,935,793
Earnings: $3,406,625
Fiscal Year-end: 06/30/13
Business Description:
Training & Education Services
S.I.C.: 9411
N.A.I.C.S.: 923110
Personnel:
Christopher Elmore Campbell *(CEO & Mng Dir)*
Gabriela Del Carmen Rodriguez Naranjo *(COO & Gen Mgr)*

Academies Australasia Group Limited—(Continued)

Edmund Kwan *(CEO-Academies Australasia College Pte Limited)*
Esther Teo *(CEO-Academies Australasia Polytechnic Pty Limited)*
Stephanie Ann Noble *(Sec & Mgr-Fin)*
Board of Directors:
Neville Thomas Cleary
Christopher Elmore Campbell
Chiang Meng Heng
John Lewis Schlederer

Subsidiaries:

Academies Australasia Pty Limited (1)
L 6 505 George St
Sydney, NSW, Australia
Tel.: (61) 292231116
Fax: (61) 292245550
E-Mail: info@aca.nsw.edu.au
Web Site: www.aca.nsw.edu.au
Educational Training & Support Services
S.I.C.: 8299
N.A.I.C.S.: 611710
Gabriela Rodriguez *(Mng Dir)*

Subsidiary:

Academies Australasia (Management) Pty Limited (2)
L 6 505 George St
Sydney, NSW, 2000, Australia
Tel.: (61) 292245500
Fax: (61) 92245560
E-Mail: info@aca.nsw.edu.au
Web Site: www.aca.nsw.edu.au
Education Training & Support Services
S.I.C.: 8299
N.A.I.C.S.: 611710
Gabriela Rodriguez *(Gen Mgr)*

DFL Education (QLD) Pty Ltd. (1)
Upper Ground Level Queen Adelaide Bldg
90-112 Queen Street
Brisbane, QLD, 4000, Australia
Tel.: (61) 7 3229 2999
Fax: (61) 7 3221 0292
Web Site: www.brishair.com.au
Hairdressing Schools
S.I.C.: 8299
N.A.I.C.S.: 611699
Lina Wood *(Founder)*

ACADIA RESOURCES CORP.

804 - 750 West Pender Street
Vancouver, BC, V6C 2T8, Canada
Tel.: (604) 682-2928
Fax: (604) 685-6905
Year Founded: 1987
AIC—(TSXV)
Assets: $517,442
Liabilities: $201,627
Net Worth: $315,815
Earnings: ($1,064,630)
Fiscal Year-end: 08/31/13
Business Description:
Mineral Exploration Services
S.I.C.: 1499
N.A.I.C.S.: 212399
Personnel:
Peter Clutterbuck *(Pres & CEO)*
Nigel Friend *(CFO)*
Transfer Agent:
Computershare Investor Services Inc.
510 Burrard St 2nd Floor
Vancouver, BC, V6C 3B9, Canada
Tel.: (604) 661-9400

ACADIAN ENERGY INC.

20 Holly Street Suite 300
Toronto, ON, M4S 3B1, Canada
Tel.: (281) 751-7720
Fax: (281) 751-7778
E-Mail: jmcdevitt@acadianenergy.com
Web Site: acadianenergy.org
Year Founded: 2007
ACX—(TSXV)
Sales Range: Less than $1 Million
Business Description:
Oil & Natural Gas Exploration Services
S.I.C.: 1311
N.A.I.C.S.: 211111
Personnel:
John E. McDevitt *(Chm & CEO)*
Timothy C. Williams *(CFO, Sec & VP)*
Board of Directors:
John E. McDevitt
Mark Lawrence
Gilbert A. Smith
Kevin D. Stulp
Transfer Agent:
Equity Financial Trust Company
200 University Avenue Suite 400
Toronto, ON, Canada

ACADIAN MINING CORPORATION

(Acquired & Absorbed by LionGold Corp. Ltd.)

ACADIAN TIMBER CORP.

Suite 458 Bentall 5 550 Burrard Street
PO Box 51
Vancouver, BC, V6C 2B5, Canada
Tel.: (604) 661-9143
Fax: (604) 687-3419
Web Site: www.acadiantimber.com
ADN—(TSX)
Sls.: $68,426,349
Assets: $283,529,295
Liabilities: $100,627,627
Net Worth: $182,901,668
Earnings: $13,646,901
Emp.: 123
Fiscal Year-end: 12/31/12
Business Description:
Forest Products Supplier
S.I.C.: 0811
N.A.I.C.S.: 113110
Personnel:
Samuel J.B. Pollock *(Chm)*
Reid Carter *(Pres & CEO)*
Brian Banfill *(CFO & Sr VP)*
Board of Directors:
Samuel J.B. Pollock
J. W. Bud Bird
Reid Carter
David McDaniel Mann
Saul Shulman
Transfer Agent:
CIBC Mellon Trust Company
PO Box 700 Postal Station B
Montreal, QC, Canada

ACADOMIA GROUPE

7 rue de la Baume
75008 Paris, France
Tel.: (33) 173011304
Fax: (33) 173011319
E-Mail: investisseurs@acadomia.fr
Web Site: www.acadomia.fr
MLACA—(EUR)
Sales Range: $25-49.9 Million
Emp.: 360
Business Description:
Tutoring Services
S.I.C.: 8299
N.A.I.C.S.: 611691
Personnel:
Maxime Aiach *(Chm & CEO)*
Philippe Coleon *(Pres & Mng Dir)*

ACAL PLC

2 Chancellor Court Occam Road
Surrey Research Park
Guildford, GU2 7AH, United Kingdom
Tel.: (44) 1483 544 500
Fax: (44) 1483 544 550
E-Mail: info@acalplc.co.uk
Web Site: www.acalplc.co.uk
ACL—(LSE)
Rev.: $346,180,368
Assets: $177,985,983
Liabilities: $96,652,548
Net Worth: $81,333,435
Earnings: ($2,842,722)
Emp.: 719
Fiscal Year-end: 03/31/13
Business Description:
Electronic Components & Equipment Distr
S.I.C.: 5731
N.A.I.C.S.: 443142
Personnel:
Nicholas J. Jefferies *(CEO)*
Gary P. Shillinglaw *(Sec)*
Board of Directors:
Richard J. Moon
Eric A. Barton
Richard J. Brooman
Simon M. Gibbins
Nicholas J. Jefferies
Henrietta E. Marsh
Graham J. Williams

Subsidiaries:

Acal BFi UK Ltd (1)
3 Molly Millars Lane Business Centre
Wokingham, Berkshire, RG41 2EY, United Kingdom
Tel.: (44) 118 977 6161
Fax: (44) 118 977 6095
E-Mail: info.uk@bfioptilas.com
Web Site: www.bfioptilas.co.uk
Emp.: 170
Electronic & Photonic Equipment Whslr
S.I.C.: 5065
N.A.I.C.S.: 423690
Marc Lafferty *(Mng Dir)*

Acal Controls Ltd. (1)
Redfields Park Church Crookham
Fleet, Hampshire, GU52 0RD, United Kingdom (100%)
Tel.: (44) 252858062
Fax: (44) 252858023
E-Mail: sales@acalacr.co.uk
Distributor of Electronic Controls for Refrigeration & Air Conditioning
S.I.C.: 5078
N.A.I.C.S.: 423740

Acal Management Services Ltd. (1)
2 Chancellor Court Occam Rd Surrey Research Park
Guildford, GU2 7AH, United Kingdom (100%)
Tel.: (44) 1483 544 500
Fax: (44) 1483 544 550
E-Mail: info@acalplc.co.uk
Web Site: www.acalplc.co.uk
Emp.: 20
Management Services
S.I.C.: 8742
N.A.I.C.S.: 541611

Acal Technology Ltd. (1)
3 The Business Ctr Molly Millars Ln
Wokingham, RG11 2EY, United Kingdom (100%)
Tel.: (44) 89788878
Fax: (44) 89776095
Web Site: www.acaltechnology.co.uk
Emp.: 100
Distributor of Electronic Parts & Equipment
S.I.C.: 5065
N.A.I.C.S.: 423690

ATM Parts Company Ltd. (1)
Units 11-12 Admiralty Way
Camberley, Surrey, GU15 3DT, United Kingdom (100%)
Tel.: (44) 1276607200
Fax: (44) 1276609040
E-Mail: sales@atm-parts.com
Web Site: www.acal-atmparts.com
Distribution of ATM Parts
S.I.C.: 5044
N.A.I.C.S.: 423420

Computer Parts International Ltd. (1)
Head Office Parts House
Glaisdale Pkwy, Nottingham, NG8 4GP, United Kingdom (100%)
Tel.: (44) 159196000
Fax: (44) 159193900
E-Mail: callcenter@computerparts.co.uk
Web Site: www.computerparts.co.uk
Sales Range: $10-24.9 Million
Emp.: 100
Distributor of IT Parts & Equipment
S.I.C.: 5731
N.A.I.C.S.: 443142

Stortech Electronics Ltd. (1)
Unit 2 Spire Green Ctr
Pinnacles W, Harlow, CM19 5TS, United Kingdom (100%)
Tel.: (44) 279451100
Fax: (44) 279453300
E-Mail: sales@stortech.co.uk
Web Site: www.stortech.co.uk
Emp.: 22
Distributor of Electronic Components & Equipment
S.I.C.: 5065
N.A.I.C.S.: 423690

Townsend Coates Ltd. (1)
Lunsford Rd
Leicester, LE5 0HH, United Kingdom (100%)
Tel.: (44) 1162744444
Fax: (44) 1166743336
E-Mail: enquiries@acaltc.com
Web Site: www.acaltc.com
Emp.: 100
Distributor of Electrical Parts & Equipment
S.I.C.: 5065
N.A.I.C.S.: 423690

Vertec Scientific Ltd. (1)
5 Comet House
Aldermaston, Reading, RG7 8JA, United Kingdom (100%)
Tel.: (44) 189817431
Fax: (44) 118 981 7785
E-Mail: sales@vertec.co.uk
Web Site: www.vertec.co.uk
Sales & Service of Medical & Scientific Equipment
S.I.C.: 5047
N.A.I.C.S.: 423450

Non-U.S. Subsidiaries:

Acal Australia Pty. Ltd. (1)
PO Box 2406
Caulfield Junction, Melbourne, VIC, 3150, Australia (100%)
Tel.: (61) 3 9523 1895
Fax: (61) 3 9523 1295
E-Mail: sales@acal.com.au
Distributor of Electronic Components & Equipment
S.I.C.: 5065
N.A.I.C.S.: 423690

Acal Europe Holding BV (1)
Eindhoven Airport Beatrix De Rijkweg 12
5657 EG Eindhoven, Netherlands (100%)
Tel.: (31) 402507400
Fax: (31) 402507409
E-Mail: acel@acel.nl
Web Site: www.acel.nl
Emp.: 125
Holding Company
S.I.C.: 6719
N.A.I.C.S.: 551112
Simon Gibbins *(Grp Fin Dir-Tech Bus)*

Subsidiaries:

Acal BFi Netherlands BV (2)
Beatrix de Rijkweg 12
5657 EG Eindhoven, Netherlands (100%)
Tel.: (31) 402507400
Fax: (31) 402507409
Web Site: www.acaltechnology.nl
Distr of Logistics Equipment
S.I.C.: 5065
N.A.I.C.S.: 423690

Non-U.S. Subsidiaries:

EAF Computer Service Supplies GmbH (3)
Borsigstrasse 8
47574 Goch, Germany De
Tel.: (49) 282393130
Fax: (49) 282393136116
E-Mail: info@eaf-gmbh.de
Web Site: www.eaf-gmbh.de

Sls.: $30,178,876
Emp.: 50
Distributor of Logistics Equipment
S.I.C.: 5731
N.A.I.C.S.: 443142
Herbert Schiffer *(Mng Dir)*

EAF France SA (3)
36 Rue Luzene Dueuis
Fontenay Sous Bois, F94043 Creteil, Cedex, France (100%)
Tel.: (33) 145147337
Fax: (33) 148761825
E-Mail: nancym@eaf.fr
Web Site: www.acalplc.co.uk/acalplc/search.jsp?words=fax
Emp.: 50
Distributor of Logistics Equipment
S.I.C.: 5065
N.A.I.C.S.: 423690

Acal Nederland BV (2)
Eindhoven Airport Beatrix De Rijkweg 12
5657 EG Eindhoven, Netherlands (100%)
Tel.: (31) 402507400
Fax: (31) 402507409
E-Mail: acal@acal.nl
Web Site: www.acal.nl
Emp.: 40
Distributor of Electronic Components & Equipment
S.I.C.: 5065
N.A.I.C.S.: 423690
Peater Gan Rovels *(Mng Dir)*

Non-U.S. Subsidiaries:

Acal AB (2)
Solna Strandvag 21
171 54 Solna, Sweden (100%)
Tel.: (46) 854656500
Fax: (46) 854656565
E-Mail: info.se@bfiokgilas.com
Web Site: www.bfiokgilas.se
Emp.: 8
Distributor of Electronic Components & Equipment
S.I.C.: 5065
N.A.I.C.S.: 423690
Stefan Los *(Mng Dir)*

Acal BFi Denmark (2)
Jernbanegade 23b
4000 Roskilde, Denmark
Tel.: (45) 70 26 22 25
Fax: (45) 70 26 22 21
E-Mail: sales@acaltechnology.dk
Electronic Component Whslr
S.I.C.: 5065
N.A.I.C.S.: 423690

Acal BFi France SAS (2)
Zi La Petite Montagne Sud 4 Rue Du Cantal
91090 Lisses, Essonne, France
Tel.: (33) 160795900
Fax: (33) 160798901
Web Site: www.bfioptilas.com
Emp.: 18
Electronic Product Whslr
S.I.C.: 5065
N.A.I.C.S.: 423690
Vincent Courty *(Gen Mgr)*

Acal BFi Germany GmbH (2)
Assar Gabrielsson Strasse 1
63128 Dietzenbach, Germany
Tel.: (49) 6074 4098 0
Fax: (49) 6074 4098 110
E-Mail: info-de@acalbfi.de
Web Site: www.acalbfi.com
Emp.: 5
Electronic Component Distr
S.I.C.: 5065
N.A.I.C.S.: 423690
Joerg Duebener *(Gen Mgr)*

Acal BFi Italy S.r.l. (2)
Via Cascina Venina 20/A
20090 Assago, MI, Italy (100%)
Tel.: (39) 02 53 58 31
Fax: (39) 02 53 58 32 01
E-Mail: sales-it@acalbfi.it
Web Site: www.acalbfi.it
Distributor of Electronic Components & Equipment
S.I.C.: 5065
N.A.I.C.S.: 423690

Acal BFi Nordic AB (2)
Portalgatan 2B
754 23 Uppsala, Sweden
Tel.: (46) 18 56 58 30
Fax: (46) 18 69 66 66
E-Mail: info.se@bfioptilas.com
Web Site: www.bfioptilas.se
Electronic Equipment Whslr
S.I.C.: 5065
N.A.I.C.S.: 423690

Acal nv/sa (2)
Lozenberg 4
1932 Zaventem, Belgium (100%)
Tel.: (32) 27205983
Fax: (32) 27251014
E-Mail: acal@acal.be
Web Site: www.acal.be
Emp.: 25
Distributor of Electronic Components & Equipment
S.I.C.: 5065
N.A.I.C.S.: 423690
Guy Maertens *(Mng Dir)*

Acal SA (2)
ZA Des Marais 1 Ave Louison
P O Box 94122
94000 Fontenay-sous-Bois, Paris, France (100%)
Tel.: (33) 145147300
Fax: (33) 148776230
E-Mail: acal@acal.fr
Web Site: www.acal.fr
Emp.: 40
Distributor of Electronic Components & Equipment
S.I.C.: 5065
N.A.I.C.S.: 423690
Michel Rispal *(Mng Dir)*

CompoTron GmbH (2)
Sandstrasse 26
80335 Munich, Germany
Tel.: (49) 89 53 88 66 0
Fax: (49) 89 53 81 93 77
E-Mail: info@compotron.com
Web Site: www.compotron.de
Communication Fiber Wire Mfr
S.I.C.: 3357
N.A.I.C.S.: 335929
Werner Brack *(Gen Mgr)*

Vertec Scientific SA (Pty) Ltd. (1)
8 Charmaine Avenue Presidents Ridge
Randburg, 2194, South Africa
Tel.: (27) 11 789 7177
Fax: (27) 11 789 7391
E-Mail: cmccabe@vertecsa.co.za
Web Site: www.vertecsa.co.za
Emp.: 23
Medical Device Mfr
S.I.C.: 3845
N.A.I.C.S.: 334510
Cindy McCabe *(Mng Dir)*

ACANA CAPITAL CORP.

8338 120th Street
Surrey, BC, V3W 3N4, Canada
Tel.: (604) 592-6881
Fax: (604) 592-6882
APB—(CNSX)

Business Description:
Real Estate Investment & Development
S.I.C.: 6726
N.A.I.C.S.: 525990

Personnel:
Eugene Beukman *(Pres & CEO)*
Sandy Janda *(CFO)*

Board of Directors:
Eugene Beukman
Ravinder Binpal
Brian Findlay

ACANDO AB

Klarabergsviadukten 63
Box 199
101 23 Stockholm, Sweden
Tel.: (46) 86997000
Fax: (46) 86997999
E-Mail: info@acando.com
Web Site: www.acando.com
ACANB—(OMX)
Rev.: $239,921,114
Assets: $163,551,773
Liabilities: $49,037,389
Net Worth: $114,514,384
Earnings: $12,091,118
Emp.: 1,109
Fiscal Year-end: 12/31/12

Business Description:
Management & IT Consultant Services
S.I.C.: 8742
N.A.I.C.S.: 541611

Personnel:
Ulf J. Johansson *(Chm)*
Carl-Magnus Mansson *(Pres & CEO)*
Gunilla Bjerre *(Deputy Mng Dir)*
Anneli Lindblom *(CFO)*
John Karnblad *(CTO)*
Carl Linton *(PR Officer)*

Board of Directors:
Ulf J. Johansson
Magnus Groth
Mija Jelonek
Lennart Karlsson
Birgitta Klasen
Susanne Lithander
Mats O. Paulsson
Anders Skarin
Alf Svedulf

Subsidiaries:

Acando Business Intelligence AB (1)
PO Box 5528
11485 Stockholm, Sweden
Tel.: (46) 87530730
IT Consultancy Services
S.I.C.: 8742
N.A.I.C.S.: 541611

Acando Consulting AB (1)
Klarabergsviadukten 63
101 23 Stockholm, Sweden
Tel.: (46) 86997000
Fax: (46) 86997999
E-Mail: info@acando.com
Web Site: www.acando.com
Emp.: 300
Business Management Services
S.I.C.: 8742
N.A.I.C.S.: 541611
Carl Mansson *(Mng Dir)*

Acando Europe AB (publ.) (1)
St Eriksgatan 60A
SE 11234 Stockholm, Sweden
Tel.: (46) 851903000
Fax: (46) 851903200
Web Site: www.acando.se
Business Consultancy Services
S.I.C.: 8742
N.A.I.C.S.: 541611

Acando Incentive AB (1)
PO Box 5528
11485 Stockholm, Sweden
Tel.: (46) 8 4702261
Business Consultancy Services
S.I.C.: 8742
N.A.I.C.S.: 541611

Acando Management Consulting AB (1)
Jakobsgatan 6
111 52 Stockholm, Sweden
Tel.: (46) 87530730
Business Management & Consulting Services
S.I.C.: 8742
N.A.I.C.S.: 541611

Acando Sverige AB (1)
Klarabergsviadukten 63
111 64 Stockholm, Sweden
Tel.: (46) 86997000
Fax: (46) 86997999
E-Mail: info@acando.se
Web Site: www.acando.se
Emp.: 300
Business Management & Consulting Services
S.I.C.: 8742
N.A.I.C.S.: 541611
Carl Magnus Mansson *(CEO)*

Edge Consulting AB (1)
Klarabergsviadukten 63
11152 Stockholm, Sweden
Tel.: (46) 8 6997000
Fax: (46) 86997999
E-Mail: info@acando.com
Web Site: www.acando.com
Emp.: 300
Business Consultancy Services
S.I.C.: 8742
N.A.I.C.S.: 541611
Carl Mansson *(Mng Dir)*

Frontec AB (1)
Torpavallsgatan 9
SE 416 73 Gothenburg, Sweden
Tel.: (46) 317071000
Fax: (46) 317071199
Business Management & Consulting Services
S.I.C.: 8742
N.A.I.C.S.: 541611

Frontec Affarssystem AB (1)
PO Box 5528
114 85 Stockholm, Sweden
Tel.: (46) 46317071000
Business Management & Consulting Services
S.I.C.: 8742
N.A.I.C.S.: 541611

Frontec Business Integration AB (1)
PO Box 5528
114 85 Stockholm, Sweden
Tel.: (46) 8 7337400
Business Consulting Services
S.I.C.: 8742
N.A.I.C.S.: 541611

Frontec Business Solutions AB (1)
PO Box 6090
400 60 Gothenburg, Sweden
Tel.: (46) 313453000
Fax: (46) 313453999
E-Mail: info@acando.com
Emp.: 300
Business Management & Consulting Services
S.I.C.: 8742
N.A.I.C.S.: 541611
John Karnblad *(Mgr)*

Frontec Multidesign AB (1)
PO Box 5528
114 85 Stockholm, Sweden
Tel.: (46) 92075200
IT Consultancy Services
S.I.C.: 8742
N.A.I.C.S.: 541611

Non-U.S. Subsidiaries:

Acando AS (1)
Klarabergsveidukten 63
101 23 Stockholm, Sweden
Tel.: (46) 93001000
Fax: (46) 73825901
E-Mail: acando@acando.no
Web Site: www.acando.no
Emp.: 90
Business Consultancy Services
S.I.C.: 8742
N.A.I.C.S.: 541611
Aasmund Frooth *(CEO)*

Acando Denmark A/S (1)
Stationsparken 37
2600 Glostrup, Denmark
Tel.: (45) 70229015
Fax: (45) 70229016
E-Mail: denmark@acando.com
Web Site: www.acando.dk
Emp.: 30
Business Consultancy Services
S.I.C.: 8742
N.A.I.C.S.: 541611

Acando Ltd (1)
7750 Daresbury Bus Park
Daresbury, Warrington, Cheshire, WA4 4BS, United Kingdom
Tel.: (44) 8700119118
Fax: (44) 1928716025
E-Mail: info@acando.co.uk
Web Site: www.acando.co.uk
Emp.: 40
Business Consultancy Services
S.I.C.: 8742
N.A.I.C.S.: 541611
Bengt Lejdstrom *(CFO)*

ACAP ADVISORY PUBLIC COMPANY LIMITED

195 Empire Tower 2-3 22nd Floor
South Sathorn Rd YanNawa
Sathorn, Bangkok, 10120, Thailand
Tel.: (66) 2 694 4999
Fax: (66) 2 694 4977
Web Site: www.acap.co.th
Year Founded: 1998
ACAP—(THA)
Rev.: $7,748,312
Assets: $34,075,298
Liabilities: $2,045,976
Net Worth: $32,029,322
Earnings: ($2,265,429)
Emp.: 72
Fiscal Year-end: 12/31/12

Business Description:
Investment Banking Services
S.I.C.: 6211
N.A.I.C.S.: 523110

Personnel:
Vivat Vithoontien *(Chm & CEO)*
Anake Pinvanichkul *(Deputy Mng Dir-Investment Banking)*
Chalermchai Sirinopawong *(Deputy Mng Dir-Acctg & Fin)*
Saringkarn Sutaschuto *(Deputy Mng Dir-Asset Mgmt)*
Parankoon Waiyahong *(Deputy Mng Dir-Ops)*
Ithidej Chuerangsun *(Sec)*

Board of Directors:
Vivat Vithoontien
Issarachai Decharit
Anake Pinvanichkul
Suvimol Pumpaisanchai
Suraphol Sindhuvanich
Chalermchai Sirinopawong
Saringkarn Sutaschuto
Chatchawan Triamvicharnkul
Parankoon Waiyahong
Narumol Wangsatorntanakul

Subsidiary:

ACAP Asset Management Company Limited (1)
195 Empire Tower 2-3 22nd Floor
YanNawa Sathorn, Bangkok, 10120, Thailand
Tel.: (66) 2 694 4999
Fax: (66) 2 694 4977
Asset Management Services
S.I.C.: 6531
N.A.I.C.S.: 531390

Non-U.S. Subsidiary:

ACAP (Malaysia) Sdn. Bhd. (1)
Lot 24 AB 24th Floor UBN Tower No 10
Jalan P Ramlee
50250 Kuala Lumpur, Malaysia
Tel.: (60) 3 2026 4099
Fax: (60) 3 2026 4098
Mortgage Loan Brokerage Services
S.I.C.: 6163
N.A.I.C.S.: 522310

ACBEL POLYTECH INC.

No 159 Sec 3 Danjin Rd
Tanshui Dist, Taipei, 251, Taiwan
Tel.: (886) 226217672
Fax: (886) 226234156
E-Mail: headquarter@acbel.com
Web Site: www.acbel.com
6282—(TAI)
Sls.: $828,241,197
Assets: $567,671,361
Liabilities: $280,027,507
Net Worth: $287,643,854
Earnings: $35,720,047
Fiscal Year-end: 12/31/12

Business Description:
Adapters & Converters Mfr
S.I.C.: 3483
N.A.I.C.S.: 332993

Personnel:
Rock S.H. Hsu *(Chm)*
David C. S. Kao *(Pres)*

Transfer Agent:
China Trust Commercial Bank
Transfer Agency Department
15F 83 Sec 1 Chung-Ching S Rd
Taipei, Taiwan

U.S. Subsidiary:

Acbel (USA) Polytech Inc. (1)
251 Dominion Dr Ste 103
Morrisville, NC 27560-7334
Tel.: (919) 388-4316
Fax: (919) 388-4317
Computer System Storage Devices Mfr
S.I.C.: 3572
N.A.I.C.S.: 334112

Non-U.S. Subsidiaries:

AcBel Electronic (Dong Guan) Co., Ltd. (1)
No 17-28 Hong Yeh Road Hong Yeh Industrial District
Tang Xia Town, Dongguan, Guangdong, China
Tel.: (86) 76987913815
Fax: (86) 76987728464
Power Supplies Mfr
S.I.C.: 3699
N.A.I.C.S.: 335999

AcBel Polytech Japan Inc. (1)
Takashin Bldg 1F 4-18-5 Shiba
Minato-ku, Tokyo, 108-0014, Japan
Tel.: (81) 334565855
Fax: (81) 334565856
E-Mail: tokyo@acbel.com
Web Site: www.acbel.com
Power Supplies Mfr
S.I.C.: 3699
N.A.I.C.S.: 335999

Acbel Polytech (Malaysia) SDN. BHD. (1)
1-5-27 Krystal Point II Corporate Park Jalan Tun Dr Awang
11900 Sungai Nibong, Penang, Malaysia
Tel.: (60) 46437678
Fax: (60) 46465984
E-Mail: headquarter@acbel.com
Web Site: www.acbel.com
Emp.: 15
Electronic Components Whslr
S.I.C.: 5063
N.A.I.C.S.: 423610
K. F. Chong *(Mgr)*

AcBel Polytech (UK) Co. Ltd. (1)
32 Hepburn Road Hillington Business Park
Glasgow, G52 4RT, United Kingdom
Tel.: (44) 1418838631
Fax: (44) 141 883 8752
E-Mail: scotland@acbel.com
Emp.: 7
Power Supplies Mfr & Distr
S.I.C.: 3699
N.A.I.C.S.: 335999
Vincent Kong *(Mgr)*

AcTel Electronic (Dong Guan) Co., Ltd. (1)
No 10-11 Hu Pan Rd 138 Industrial District
Tang Xia Town, Dongguan, Guangdong, China
Tel.: (86) 76987913815
Fax: (86) 76987728464
Web Site: www.acbel.com
Power Supplies Mfr
S.I.C.: 3699
N.A.I.C.S.: 335999

ACC AVIATION LTD.

40-44 Church Street
Reigate, Surrey, RH2 0AJ, United Kingdom
Tel.: (44) 1737 232 230
Fax: (44) 1737 244 850
E-Mail: services@flyacc.com
Web Site: www.flyacc.com
Year Founded: 2002
Sales Range: $75-99.9 Million
Emp.: 25

Business Description:
Aircraft Leasing & Charter Services
S.I.C.: 7359
N.A.I.C.S.: 532411

Personnel:
Chris Clapham *(CEO)*

ACC COMPRESSORS SPA

11 Viale Lino Zanussi
33170 Pordenone, Italy
Tel.: (39) 0434 379911
Fax: (39) 0434 379913
E-Mail: acc.info@accomp.it
Web Site: www.the-acc-group.com
Sales Range: $800-899.9 Million
Emp.: 7,000

Business Description:
Household Refrigeration & Industrial Electrical Appliances Mfr
S.I.C.: 3632
N.A.I.C.S.: 335222

Personnel:
Ramella Luca *(Owner)*

Non-U.S. Subsidiaries:

ACC Germany GmbH (1)
Alter Postweg 75
26133 Oldenburg, Germany
Tel.: (49) 4414010
Fax: (49) 441401546
E-Mail: acc-germany@accomp.it
Web Site: www.the-acc-group.com
Emp.: 150
Appliance Motor Mfr
S.I.C.: 5065
N.A.I.C.S.: 423690
Thorsten Albrs *(Gen Mgr)*

Appliances Components Companies Spain, S.A. (1)
Antoni Forrellad 2
08912 Sant Quirze del Valles, Barcelona, Spain
Tel.: (34) 937106008
Fax: (34) 937106958
Appliance Motor Sales
S.I.C.: 5065
N.A.I.C.S.: 423690

Shanghai Zanussi Elettromeccanica Co., Ltd. (1)
160 Basheng Road
Waigaoqiao Free Trade Zone, Shanghai, 200131, China
Tel.: (86) 2150481048
Fax: (86) 2150481115
Web Site: www.highly.cc/english/company2.asp
Appliance Motor Sales
S.I.C.: 5065
N.A.I.C.S.: 423690

ACC LA JONCHERE SA

5 Rue Des Ateliers
60 200 Compiegne, Hauts De Seine, France
Tel.: (33) 3 44 38 66 66
Fax: (33) 3 44 38 66 77
E-Mail: acc@acc.fr
Web Site: www.acc.fr
Sales Range: $50-74.9 Million
Emp.: 150

Business Description:
Panels & Pipes Mfr
S.I.C.: 3444
N.A.I.C.S.: 332322

Personnel:
Charles Laubie *(Mng Dir)*

Board of Directors:
Charles Laubie
Patrick Laubie

ACC LIMITED

Cement House 121 Maharishi Karve Road
Mumbai, 400 020, India
Tel.: (91) 2233024321
Fax: (91) 2266317440
Web Site: www.acclimited.com
Year Founded: 1936
500410—(BOM NSE)
Rev.: $2,343,394,818
Assets: $2,211,484,572
Liabilities: $844,163,280
Net Worth: $1,367,321,292
Earnings: $194,653,314
Emp.: 9,769
Fiscal Year-end: 12/31/12

Business Description:
Cement Mfr
S.I.C.: 3241
N.A.I.C.S.: 327310

Personnel:
N. S. Sekhsaria *(Chm)*
Paul Hugentobler *(Deputy Chm)*
Kuldip K. Kaura *(CEO & Mng Dir)*
Sunil K. Nayak *(CFO)*
J. Datta Gupta *(Chief Comml Officer)*
Burjor D. Nariman *(Compliance Officer, Sec & Head-Compliance)*
Shakti Arora *(Chief Central Procurement Officer)*
Vivek Chawla *(CEO-East)*
P. N. Iyer *(CEO-South & West)*
Rajiv Prasad *(CEO-North)*

Board of Directors:
N. S. Sekhsaria
Naresh Chandra
Ashwin S. Dani
Bernard Fontana
Shailesh Haribhakti
Paul Hugentobler
Kuldip K. Kaura
Aidan John Lynam
M. L. Narula
S. M. Palia
Sushil Kumar Roongta
R. A. Shah
Bernard Terver

Subsidiaries:

ACC Concrete Limited (1)
Survey No 334 IDA
Qutubullapur Mandal Rangareddy, 500055
Bachupally, Andhra Pradesh, India
Tel.: (91) 9160016168
Cement Mfr
S.I.C.: 3241
N.A.I.C.S.: 327310

ACC Mineral Resources Limited (1)
Cement House 121 Maharshi Karve Road
400 020 Mumbai, Maharastra, India
Tel.: (91) 22 66654 321
Fax: (91) 22 66317 440
Web Site: www.acclimited.com
Coal Exploration Services
S.I.C.: 1241
N.A.I.C.S.: 213113

Bulk Cement Corporation (India) Limited (1)
W-7 KWC
Kalamboli, Dist Raigad, 410 218, India
Tel.: (91) 2227424285
Fax: (91) 2227422421
Web Site: www.acc.com
Emp.: 55
Cement Storage, Packaging & Shipping
S.I.C.: 3273
N.A.I.C.S.: 327320
N. S. Sekhsaria *(Chm)*

Plants:

ACC Limited - Bachupally Plant (1)
Survey No 334 IDA Bachupally
Quthbullapur Mandal
Rangareddy District, 500 055 Hyderabad, Andhra Pradesh, India
Tel.: (91) 9160016168
E-Mail: acccl.bachupally@accconcreate.com
Web Site: www.acclimited.com
Emp.: 80
Concrete Products Mfr
S.I.C.: 3273
N.A.I.C.S.: 327320
Ramchandar Rao *(Bus Mgr)*

ACC Limited - Bargarh Cement Works (1)
Cement Nagar
Bardol, 768038 Bargarh, Orissa, India

Tel.: (91) 6646 246189
Fax: (91) 6646 246430
Web Site: www.acclimited.com
Cement Mfr
S.I.C.: 3241
N.A.I.C.S.: 327310

ACC Limited - Chanda Cement Works (1)
Cementnagar
442 502 Chandrapur, Maharashtra, India
Tel.: (91) 7172 285026
Fax: (91) 7172 285165
Web Site: www.acclimited.com
Cement Mfr
S.I.C.: 3241
N.A.I.C.S.: 327310
Manoj Mishra *(Dir-Plant)*

ACC Limited - Changodar Plant (1)
Block No 259 Opp Laxminarayan Petrol Pump
Changodar, 382213 Ahmedabad, Gujarat, India
Tel.: (91) 96876 34206
Web Site: www.accconcrete.com
Emp.: 12
Ready Mixed Concrete Mfr
S.I.C.: 3273
N.A.I.C.S.: 327320
Sudhir Jain *(Mgr)*

ACC Limited - Damodhar Cement Works (1)
Madhukunda
Sunuri, 723 121 Puruliya, West Bengal, India
Tel.: (91) 3251272007
Fax: (91) 3251272202
Cement Mfr
S.I.C.: 3241
N.A.I.C.S.: 327310

ACC Limited - Ghaziabad Concrete Plant (1)
Plot No C 181 Industrial Area Site I
Bulundshahar Road
Ghaziabad, Uttar Pradesh, 2010009, India
Tel.: (91) 9582217106
E-Mail: acccl.ghaziabad@accconcrete.com
Emp.: 30
Concrete Mfr
S.I.C.: 3273
N.A.I.C.S.: 327320
Sourav Gorai *(Mgr)*

ACC Limited - Greater Noida Concrete Plant (1)
13A 1 Udyog Kendra Near Grazino Behind New Holland Tractors
201304 Noida, Uttar Pradesh, India
Tel.: (91) 95822 17114
Web Site: www.acclimited.com
Emp.: 80
Concrete Mfr
S.I.C.: 3273
N.A.I.C.S.: 327320
Hans Joseph Fuchs *(Mng Dir)*

ACC Limited - Jaipur Plant (1)
Plot No 148 C Road No 9 J Vishwakarma Industrial Area
302013 Jaipur, Rajasthan, India
Tel.: (91) 9587017100
Web Site: www.acclimited.com
Concrete Mfr
S.I.C.: 3273
N.A.I.C.S.: 327320
Ritesh Vohra *(Mgr)*

ACC Limited - Jamul Cement Works (1)
Jamul Cement Works
490 024 Durg, Chhattisgarh, India
Tel.: (91) 7882285081
Fax: (91) 7882282585
Cement Mfr
S.I.C.: 3241
N.A.I.C.S.: 327310
G.P. Tiwari *(Dir-Plant)*

ACC Limited - Kundali Plant (1)
Ready Mixed Concrete Plant Nathupur
131 029 Sonipat, Haryana, India
Tel.: (91) 9671400940
Cement Mfr
S.I.C.: 3241
N.A.I.C.S.: 327310

ACC Limited - Kymore Cement Works (1)
Kymore
483 880 Katni, Madhya Pradesh, India
Tel.: (91) 7626 272301
Fax: (91) 7626 272303
Cement Mfr
S.I.C.: 3241
N.A.I.C.S.: 327310

ACC Limited - Lakheri Cement Works (1)
Lakheri
323 603 Bundi, Rajasthan, India
Tel.: (91) 7438 261642
Fax: (91) 7438261504
Emp.: 700
Cement Mfr
S.I.C.: 3241
N.A.I.C.S.: 327310

ACC Limited - Ludhiana Plant (1)
Mouza Village Gaispura Industrial Estate C G T Rd
141010 Ludhiana, Punjab, India
Tel.: (91) 97809 28426
Web Site: www.acclimited.com
Emp.: 400
Concrete Mfr
S.I.C.: 3273
N.A.I.C.S.: 327320
Gurear Kash *(Mgr)*

ACC Limited - Mandoli Plant (1)
Mandoli Prison Complex
Mandoli, 110093 New Delhi, India
Tel.: (91) 95822 17124
Emp.: 150
Concrete Mfr
S.I.C.: 3273
N.A.I.C.S.: 327320
Anil Kulkarni *(Head-Bus)*

ACC Limited - Mohali Plant (1)
Plot No C 103 Phase 7 Industrial Area
Focal Point
160 055 Mohali, Punjab, India
Tel.: (91) 9780928414
E-Mail: acccl.mohali@accconcrete.com
Web Site: www.acclimited.com
Emp.: 12
Concrete Mfr
S.I.C.: 3273
N.A.I.C.S.: 327320
Japjit Singh *(Mgr)*

ACC Limited - Patancheru Plant (1)
Survey No 405/1 IDA Opp Srujana Steel Fabricators
Patancheru, 502 319 Medak, Andhra Pradesh, India
Tel.: (91) 91600 16169
E-Mail: sunil.kumar@accconcrete.com
Web Site: www.acclimited.com
Emp.: 7
Concrete Products Mfr
S.I.C.: 3273
N.A.I.C.S.: 327320
Sunil Kumar *(Plant Mgr)*

ACC Limited - Rajarhat Plant (1)
JL 44 Langal Pota Station Near 211
Bustand Rajarhat Bishpur District
700135 Kolkata, West Bengal, India
Tel.: (91) 96741 68717
Web Site: www.acclimited.com
Emp.: 9
Concrete Products Mfr
S.I.C.: 3273
N.A.I.C.S.: 327320
Anup Mondal *(Plant Mgr)*

ACC Limited - Ravirala Plant (1)
Survey No 300 Ravirala Village
Maheshwaram Mandal
Ranga Reddy District, 501510 Hyderabad, Andhra Pradesh, India
Tel.: (91) 9160016149
E-Mail: Srinivas.Kadrekar@accconcrete.com
Web Site: www.acclimited.com
Emp.: 6
Concrete Products Mfr
S.I.C.: 3272
N.A.I.C.S.: 327390
Srinivas Kadrekar *(Mgr)*

ACC Limited - Tikaria Cement Grinding and Packing Plant (1)
Tikaria Industrial Area Tehsil Gauriganj
227 409 Sultanpur, Uttar Pradesh, India
Tel.: (91) 5368 244096
Fax: (91) 5368 244479
Cement Mfr
S.I.C.: 1629
N.A.I.C.S.: 236210

ACC Limited - Vadodara Franchisee Plant (1)
Behind Umiya Weigh Bridge Sama-Savli Road
391740 Vadodara, Gujarat, India
Tel.: (91) 96876 24225
Web Site: www.acclimited.com
Emp.: 50
Concrete Products Mfr
S.I.C.: 3241
N.A.I.C.S.: 327310
Paresh Amin *(Mgr)*

ACCEL FRONTLINE LIMITED

75 Nelson Manickam Road
Aminjikarai, Chennai, Tamil Nadu, 600029, India
Tel.: (91) 44 4225 2000
Fax: (91) 44 2374 1271
E-Mail: info@accelfrontline.in
Web Site: www.accelfrontline.in
532774—(BOM NSE)
Rev.: $74,415,759
Assets: $66,367,990
Liabilities: $47,301,769
Net Worth: $19,066,221
Earnings: $220,014
Emp.: 3,000
Fiscal Year-end: 03/31/13

Business Description:
Integrated Information Technology Services
S.I.C.: 7376
N.A.I.C.S.: 541513

Personnel:
N. R. Panicker *(Chm & CEO)*
K. R. Chandrasekaran *(CFO)*
Maqbool Hassan *(COO)*
R. Ganesh *(Pres-Warranty Mgmt Svcs)*
Philip John *(Pres-Software Svcs)*
Sweena Nair *(Sec & Compliance Officer)*
Jayesh Ahluwalia *(Sr VP)*

Board of Directors:
N. R. Panicker
Amba Preetham Parigi
R. Ramaraj
Sam Santhosh
Alok Sharma
Steve Tuan Toon Ting

ACCEL, S.A.B. DE C.V.

Circuito No 5 Parque Industrial Las Americas
Chihuahua, CP 31220, Mexico
Tel.: (52) 614 4260024
Fax: (52) 614 4260056
E-Mail: asanchecz@accel.com.mx
Web Site: www.accel.com.mx
Year Founded: 1992
ACCELSA—(MEX)
Sales Range: $200-249.9 Million
Emp.: 1,485

Business Description:
Contract Manufacturing Services
S.I.C.: 7389
N.A.I.C.S.: 561499

Personnel:
Eloy Santiago Vallina Laguera *(Chm)*
Eloy Santiago Vallina Garza *(Co-CEO)*
Robert Jay Whetton Judd *(Co-CEO)*
Carlos Girardo Hernandez Rodarte *(Sec)*

Subsidiaries:

Accel Distribucion, S. A. de C. V. (1)
Virginia Fabregas No 80
Col San Rafael, 06470 Mexico, Mexico (98%)
Tel.: (52) 5557052788
Fax: (52) 5557054794
Warehousing & Storage
S.I.C.: 4226
N.A.I.C.S.: 493190
Ricardo Alanso *(Mng Dir)*

Accel Servicios, S. A. de C. V. (1)
Virginia Fabregas No 80
Col San Rafael, 06470 Mexico, Mexico (99.99%)
Tel.: (52) 5557052788
Management Consulting Services
S.I.C.: 8748
N.A.I.C.S.: 541618
Ricardo Alanso *(Mng Dir)*

Almacenadora Accel, S. A. (1)
Virginia Fabregas No 80
Col San Rafael, 06470 Mexico, Mexico (100%)
Tel.: (52) 5557052788
Fax: (52) 57054794
Web Site: www.accelonline.com
Warehousing & Storage
S.I.C.: 4226
N.A.I.C.S.: 493190
Ricardo Alanso *(Mng Dir)*

Corporativo de Negocios de Comercio Exterior, S.A. de C.V. (1)
Manuel J Clouthier No 1251
Ciudad Juarez, 32550, Mexico (65%)
Tel.: (52) 6563970354
Fax: (52) 6822658126
E-Mail: jcsaenz@accel.com.mx
Web Site: recintofiscalizado.com
Emp.: 18
Freight Transportation Arrangement
S.I.C.: 4731
N.A.I.C.S.: 488510
Julio C. Saenz Luna *(Dir-Ops)*

Servicios Administrativos Accel, S.A. de C.V. (1)
Virginia Fabregas No 80
Col San Rafael, 06470 Mexico, Mexico (98%)
Tel.: (52) 5557052788
Fax: (52) 53410222
Web Site: www.accel.com
Management Consulting Services
S.I.C.: 8748
N.A.I.C.S.: 541618
Ricardo Alanso *(Mng Dir)*

Servilogistics de Mexico, S.A. de C.V. (1)
Virginia Fabregas No 80
Col San Rafael, 06470 Mexico, Mexico (98%)
Tel.: (52) 5557052788
Fax: (52) 525557055559
E-Mail: ralanso@accel.com.mx
Emp.: 700
Freight Transportation Arrangement
S.I.C.: 4731
N.A.I.C.S.: 488510
Ricardo Alanso *(Mng Dir)*

U.S. Subsidiary:

Elamex, S.A. de C.V. (1)
1800 Northwest Dr
El Paso, TX 79912 (50%)
Tel.: (915) 298-3061
Fax: (915) 298-3065
Web Site: www.elamex.com
ELAMF—(OTC)
Sales Range: $75-99.9 Million
Emp.: 937
Contract Manufacturing Services
S.I.C.: 3714
N.A.I.C.S.: 336320

Division:

Accel Logistica S.A. de C.V. (1)
Virginia Fabregas 80
Col San Rafael, 06470 Mexico, Mexico
Tel.: (52) 5557052788
Fax: (52) 5557055559
Web Site: www.accellogistica.com.mx
Refrigerated Warehousing & Storage
S.I.C.: 4222
N.A.I.C.S.: 493120
Ricardo Alanso *(Mgr-Comml)*

ACCEL TRANSMATIC LTD.

75 Nelson Manickam Road
Aminjikarai, Chennai, 600029, India

Accel Transmatic Ltd.—(Continued)

Tel.: (91) 44 4225 2000
Fax: (91) 44 42252315
E-Mail: info@acceltransmatic.com
Web Site: www.acceltransmatic.com
517494—(BOM)
Rev.: $312,056
Assets: $3,748,871
Liabilities: $4,019,685
Net Worth: ($270,814)
Earnings: ($1,212,965)
Emp.: 28
Fiscal Year-end: 03/31/13
Business Description:
Information Technology Consulting Services
S.I.C.: 7373
N.A.I.C.S.: 541512
Personnel:
N. R. Panicker *(CEO)*
Birendra Sasmal *(Pres/Head-Telecom Solutions Grp)*
Philip John *(Pres-Accel Frontline Limited)*
S. T. Prabhu *(Sec)*
Maqbool Hassan *(Exec VP & Head-Ops)*
S. V. Prasad *(Sr VP & Head-Ops-Japan)*
Jayesh Ahluwalia *(Sr VP)*
Board of Directors:
N. R. Panicker
Gopalakrishnan Nair N.
M. R. Narayanan
S. T. Prabhu
A. Mohan Rao
Legal Counsel:
S Ramasubramaniam & Associates
6/1 Bishop Wallers Avenue West Mylapore
Chennai, India
Transfer Agent:
Integrated Enterprises (India) Ltd
2nd Floor Kences Towers 1 Ramakrishna Street
North Usman Road T Nagar
Chennai, India

ACCELERATED SYSTEMS, INC.

60 Northland Rd Unit 6
Waterloo, ON, N2V 2B8, Canada
Tel.: (519) 342-2507
Fax: (519) 342-2508
Toll Free: (800) 461-9338
E-Mail: info@accelerated-systems.com
Web Site: www.accelerated-systems.com
Year Founded: 1990
Sales Range: $50-74.9 Million
Emp.: 20
Business Description:
Programmable Electronic Motor Speed Control Products Mfr
S.I.C.: 3714
N.A.I.C.S.: 336320
Personnel:
Rob Lankin *(Owner)*

ACCELERO CAPITAL HOLDINGS SARL GROUP

29 rue de Berri
75008 Paris, France
Tel.: (33) 1 83 81 94 61
E-Mail: info@accelerocapital.com
Web Site: www.accelerocapital.com
Business Description:
Telecommunication, Digital Media & Technology Investment & Management Services
S.I.C.: 6211
N.A.I.C.S.: 523999
Personnel:
Naguib Sawiris *(Chm)*
Ossama Bessada *(Mng Partner)*
Khaled Bichara *(Mng Partner)*
Aldo Mareuse *(Mng Partner)*
Board of Directors:
Naguib Sawiris

ACCELEWARE LTD.

435 - 10th Ave SE
Calgary, AB, T2G 0W3, Canada
Tel.: (403) 249-9099
Fax: (403) 249-9881
E-Mail: sales@acceleware.com
Web Site: www.acceleware.com
AXE—(TSXV)
Rev.: $2,893,175
Assets: $1,497,126
Liabilities: $735,633
Net Worth: $761,493
Earnings: ($480,922)
Fiscal Year-end: 12/31/12
Business Description:
Software Development Services
S.I.C.: 7371
N.A.I.C.S.: 541511
Personnel:
Michal Okoniewski *(Founder & Chief Scientific Officer)*
Bohdan Romaniuk *(Chm)*
Geoff Clark *(CEO)*
Michael Tourigny *(CMO)*
Robert Miller *(hief Sls Officer)*
Dan Cyca *(CTO)*
Board of Directors:
Bohdan Romaniuk
Geoff Clark
Jens Horstmann
Dennis Nerland
Peter Neweduk
Michal Okoniewski
Transfer Agent:
Olympia Trust Company
Suite 2300 125 9th Ave SE
Calgary, AB, Canada

ACCELINK TECHNOLOGIES CO., LTD.

88 Youkeyuan Road
Hongshan District, Wuhan, 430074, China
Tel.: (86) 2787692533
Fax: (86) 2787691105
E-Mail: ms@accelink.com
Web Site: www.accelink.com
Sales Range: $50-74.9 Million
Emp.: 1,900
Business Description:
Fiber Optic Product Mfr
S.I.C.: 3357
N.A.I.C.S.: 335921
Personnel:
Guo Hua Tong *(Chm)*
Shuihua Liu *(CEO)*

ACCELL GROUP N.V.

Industrieweg 4
8444 AR Heerenveen, Netherlands
Mailing Address:
PO Box 435
8440 AK Heerenveen, Netherlands
Tel.: (31) 513638703
Fax: (31) 513638709
E-Mail: info@accell-group.com
Web Site: www.accell-group.com
ACCEL—(EUR)
Sls.: $1,039,978,249
Assets: $810,506,072
Liabilities: $477,046,301
Net Worth: $333,459,771
Earnings: $31,186,720
Emp.: 2,776
Fiscal Year-end: 12/31/12
Business Description:
Design, Production, Marketing & Sales of Bicycles
S.I.C.: 3751
N.A.I.C.S.: 336991
Personnel:
Ab J. Pasman *(Chm-Supervisory Bd)*
Rene J. Takens *(CEO & Member-Mgmt Bd)*
Hielke H. Sybesma *(CFO & Member-Mgmt Bd)*
Jeroen M. Snijders Blok *(COO & Member-Mgmt Bd)*
Supervisory Board of Directors:
Ab J. Pasman
P. B. Ernsting
A. Kuiper
J. van den Belt
Subsidiaries:

Accell Duitsland B.V. (1)
Industrieweg 4
8444AR Heerenveen, Netherlands (100%)
Tel.: (31) 513638254
Fax: (31) 513638262
E-Mail: info@accell-group.com
Web Site: www.accell-group.com
Emp.: 2,000
Religious Organizations
S.I.C.: 8661
N.A.I.C.S.: 813110
Jdema Renee *(CEO)*

Accell Fitness Benelux B.V. (1)
Postbus 60001
1320AA Almere, Netherlands (100%)
Tel.: (31) 365460050
Fax: (31) 365460055
E-Mail: info@tumturi.nl
Web Site: www.tumturi.com
Emp.: 60
Sporting & Recreational Goods & Supplies Whslr
S.I.C.: 5091
N.A.I.C.S.: 423910

Accell Fitness Division B.V. (1)
Purmerweg 1
1311XE Almere, Netherlands (100%)
Tel.: (31) 365397102
Fax: (31) 365460055
E-Mail: info@tunturi-fitness.com
Web Site: www.tunturi-fitness.com
Emp.: 50
Sporting & Recreational Goods & Supplies Whslr
S.I.C.: 5091
N.A.I.C.S.: 423910
Eohan Sphut *(CEO)*

Accell IT Services B.V. (1)
Jagtlustweg 5
8444 AV Heerenveen, Netherlands
Tel.: (31) 513 63 87 77
Fax: (31) 513 68 10 34
E-Mail: helpdesk@accell-it-services.com
Emp.: 4
Software Consulting Services
S.I.C.: 7373
N.A.I.C.S.: 541512
Menno Bokslag *(Mgr-IT)*

Batavus B.V. (1)
Industrieweg 4
8444AR Heerenveen, Netherlands (100%)
Tel.: (31) 513638999
Fax: (31) 513638260
E-Mail: info@batavus.com
Web Site: www.batavus.com
Emp.: 350
Motorcycle Bicycle & Parts Mfr
S.I.C.: 3751
N.A.I.C.S.: 336991
Hoop Snellen *(CEO)*

Juncker B.V. (1)
Fokkerstraat 25
3905KV Veenendaal, Netherlands (100%)
Tel.: (31) 318553030
Fax: (31) 318553211
E-Mail: info@juncker.nl
Web Site: www.juncker.nl
Emp.: 40
Sporting & Recreational Goods & Supplies Whslr
S.I.C.: 5091
N.A.I.C.S.: 423910
Manno Fisser *(CEO)*

Koga B.V. (1)
Tinweg 9
8445PD Heerenveen, Netherlands (100%)
Tel.: (31) 513630111
Fax: (31) 513633289
E-Mail: info@koga.com
Web Site: www.koga.com
Emp.: 85
Motorcycle Bicycle & Parts Mfr
S.I.C.: 3751
N.A.I.C.S.: 336991
Wouter Jager *(Mng Dir)*

Loekie B.V. (1)
Wilmersdorf 37
7327 AD Apeldoorn, Netherlands (100%)
Mailing Address:
PO Box 5
7300 AA Apeldoorn, Netherlands
Tel.: (31) 553578700
Fax: (31) 553578709
E-Mail: info@loekie.nl
Web Site: www.loekie.nl
Emp.: 50
Bicycles Whslr
S.I.C.: 5091
N.A.I.C.S.: 423910
Hyoup Snellen *(Gen Mgr)*

Sparta B.V. (1)
Wilmersdorf 37
7327AD Apeldoorn, Netherlands (100%)
Tel.: (31) 553578700
Fax: (31) 553578705
E-Mail: info@sparta.nl
Web Site: www.sparta.nl
Emp.: 200
Motorcycle Bicycle & Parts Mfr
S.I.C.: 3751
N.A.I.C.S.: 336991
Huub Snellen *(CEO)*

Webena Sport Almere B.V. (1)
De Steiger 95 -96
1351AH Almere, Netherlands (100%)
Tel.: (31) 365359050
Fax: (31) 365348156
Emp.: 40
Sporting & Recreational Goods & Supplies Merchant Wholesalers
S.I.C.: 5091
N.A.I.C.S.: 423910

Non-U.S. Subsidiaries:

Accell Fitness North America Inc (1)
130 Hayward Ave Ste 2
N2C2E4 Kitchener, ON, N2G 4B6, Canada (100%)
Tel.: (519) 578-2640
Fax: (519) 576-2521
Toll Free: (800) 667-1020
Web Site: www.accellfitnessna.com
Sporting & Recreational Goods & Supplies Whslr
S.I.C.: 5091
N.A.I.C.S.: 423910

Accell Germany GmbH (1)
Max-Planck-Strasse 4
97526 Sennfeld, Germany
Tel.: (49) 9721 675160
Fax: (49) 9721 67516 99
E-Mail:
Emp.: 2
Bicycle Mfr
S.I.C.: 3751
N.A.I.C.S.: 336991
Susanne Puello *(Gen Mgr)*

Subsidiaries:

E. Wiener Bike Parts GmbH (2)
Max-Planck-Str 8
97526 Sennfeld, Germany (100%)
Tel.: (49) 9721650188
Fax: (49) 9721650173
E-Mail: info@bike-parts.de
Web Site: www.bike-parts.de
Emp.: 100
Motorcycle Bicycle & Parts Mfr
S.I.C.: 3751
N.A.I.C.S.: 336991
Sussana Puello *(Mng Dir)*

Winora Staiger GmbH (2)
Max-Planck-Str 6
97526 Sennfeld, Germany (100%)
Tel.: (49) 972165940
Fax: (49) 9721650160
E-Mail: info@staiger-fahrrad.de
Web Site: www.staiger-fahrrad.de
Emp.: 100

Sporting & Recreational Goods & Supplies Whslr
S.I.C.: 5091
N.A.I.C.S.: 423910
Sussana Puello *(Mng Dir)*

Accell Hunland Kft (1)
Parkolo ter 1
5091 Toszeg, Hungary (100%)
Tel.: (36) 56586481
Fax: (36) 56586484
E-Mail: z.steurer@accell-group.com
Emp.: 600
Motorcycle Bicycle & Parts Mfr
S.I.C.: 3751
N.A.I.C.S.: 336991
Zfolt Fteuer *(Gen Mgr)*

Accell Suisse AG (1)
Industriestrasse 21
6055 Alpnach, Switzerland
Tel.: (41) 41 670 21 90
Fax: (41) 41 670 21 92
Emp.: 3
Bicycle Parts Distr
S.I.C.: 5013
N.A.I.C.S.: 423120
Thomas Geiser *(Gen Mgr)*

Brasseur S.A. (1)
13 rue de Steppes
4000 Liege, Belgium
Tel.: (32) 4 228 72 60
Fax: (32) 4 227 40 78
E-Mail: info@brasseur-bicycles.com
Web Site: www.brasseur-bicycles.com
Emp.: 20
Bicycle Parts Mfr & Distr
S.I.C.: 3751
N.A.I.C.S.: 336991
Stephan Brasseur *(Mng Dir)*

Cycles France-Loire S.A.S. (1)
Rue Branly
PO Box 61
42162 Andrezieux-Boutheon, France
Tel.: (33) 477 55 54 00
Fax: (33) 477 55 54 00
Bicycle Parts Mfr & Distr
S.I.C.: 3751
N.A.I.C.S.: 336991

Cycles Lapierre S.A. (1)
Rue Edmond Voisenet
Dijon, France (100%)
Tel.: (33) 380525186
Fax: (33) 0033380520851
E-Mail: contact@lapierre-bikes.com
Web Site: www.lapierre-bikes.co.uk
Emp.: 65
Motorcycle Bicycle & Parts Mfr
S.I.C.: 3751
N.A.I.C.S.: 336991
Gilles Lapierre *(Gen Mgr)*

Cycles Mercier France-Loire S.A. (1)
Ave Industrie
42160 Saint Etienne, France (100%)
Tel.: (33) 477555400
Fax: (33) 477366543
E-Mail: j.pegig@cyclesfranceloire.com
Web Site: www.cyclesfranceloire.com
Emp.: 38
Motorcycle Bicycle & Parts Mfr
S.I.C.: 3751
N.A.I.C.S.: 336991
Jeane Lapierre *(Mgr)*

Koga Trading A.G. (1)
Postfach 161
6018 Buttisholz, Switzerland (100%)
Tel.: (41) 9281841
Sporting & Recreational Goods & Supplies Whslr
S.I.C.: 5091
N.A.I.C.S.: 423910

Raleigh Cycle Co. Ltd (1)
Church Street Eastwood
Nottingham, NG16 3HT, United Kingdom UK
Tel.: (44) 1773 532 600
Fax: (44) 1773 532 601
E-Mail: sales@raleigh.co.uk
Web Site: www.raleigh-group.com
Sales Range: $250-299.9 Million
Emp.: 430
Bicycle Designer, Mfr & Marketer
S.I.C.: 3751
N.A.I.C.S.: 336991
Mark Gouldthorp *(Mng Dir)*

Subsidiary:

Raleigh UK Ltd (2)
Church Street Eastwood
Nottingham, NG16 3HT, United Kingdom
Tel.: (44) 1773 532 600
Fax: (44) 1773 532 601
Bicycle Designer, Mfr & Marketer
S.I.C.: 3751
N.A.I.C.S.: 336991
Geoff Giddings *(Mktg Dir)*

U.S. Subsidiary:

Raleigh America Inc. (2)
6004 S 190th St Ste 101
Kent, WA 98032 DE
Tel.: (253) 395-1100 (100%)
Fax: (253) 872-0257
Web Site: www.raleighusa.com
Bicycles & Parts Dist
S.I.C.: 5091
N.A.I.C.S.: 423910
Steve Meineke *(Pres)*

Non-U.S. Subsidiaries:

Raleigh Canada Ltd. (3)
2124 London Lane
Oakville, ON, L6H 5V8, Canada ON
Tel.: (905) 829-5555 (100%)
Fax: (905) 829-4567
E-Mail: bicycles@raleigh-canada.ca
Web Site: www.raleigh-canada.ca
Emp.: 22
Bicycles Mfr
S.I.C.: 3751
N.A.I.C.S.: 336991
Farid Vaiya *(Pres)*

Tunturi-Hellberg Oy Ltd. (1)
Varusmestarintie 26
PO Box 750
20361 Turku, Finland (100%)
Tel.: (358) 10 27 33 200
E-Mail: info@tunturi.com
Web Site: www.tunturi.com
Emp.: 70
Fitness Equipment & Products
S.I.C.: 3949
N.A.I.C.S.: 339920
Marcijn Nalissen *(CEO)*

ACCELONIX LIMITED

10 Anstey Rd
Alton, Hants, United Kingdom
Tel.: (44) 1420590000
E-Mail: sales@accelonix.co.uk
Web Site: www.accelonix.co.uk
Emp.: 12

Business Description:
Microelectronics Packaging, PCB Assembly & Test & Device Programming Services
S.I.C.: 3825
N.A.I.C.S.: 334515

Non-U.S. Subsidiaries:

Accelonix B.V. (1)
Troy C 7F
5653 LC Eindhoven, Noord Brabant, Netherlands
Tel.: (31) 407501650
Fax: (31) 402930722
E-Mail: info@accelonix.nl
Web Site: www.accelonix.nl
Rev.: $9,000,000
Emp.: 10
Microelectronics Packaging, PCB Assembly & Test & Device Programming Services
S.I.C.: 3825
N.A.I.C.S.: 334515
Frank Van Asberdt *(Mng Dir)*

Accelonix SARL (1)
260 Rue Clement Ader
Evreux, 27000, France
Tel.: (33) 232356480
Fax: (33) 232350066
E-Mail: info@accelonix.com
Web Site: www.accelonix.com
Emp.: 20
Microelectronics Packaging, PCB Assembly & Test & Device Programming Services
S.I.C.: 3825
N.A.I.C.S.: 334515
Patrick Legenre *(Pres)*

ACCELYA KALE SOLUTIONS LIMITED

3rd Floor Modi House Eastern Express Highway
Naupada, Thane, 400602, India
Tel.: (91) 22 6780 8888
Fax: (91) 22 6780 8899
Web Site: www.accelyakale.com
532268—(BOM NSE)
Rev.: $57,219,599
Assets: $42,671,789
Liabilities: $23,769,280
Net Worth: $18,902,509
Earnings: $15,643,287
Emp.: 1,595
Fiscal Year-end: 06/30/13

Business Description:
Information Technology Software
S.I.C.: 7371
N.A.I.C.S.: 541511

Personnel:
Philippe Lesueur *(Chm)*
Vipul Jain *(CEO & Mng Dir)*
Ninad G. Umranikar *(Compliance Officer & Sec)*

Board of Directors:
Philippe Lesueur
Vipul Jain
Nani Javeri
Sekhar Natarajan
Kewal Nohria

Transfer Agent:
Karvy Computershare Private Limited
17-24 Vittal Rao Nagar Madhapur
Hyderabad, India

Subsidiaries:

Zero Octa Recruitment And Training (India) Private Limited (1)
Excom House 7 Saki Vihar Rd
Saki Naka Andheri E, Mumbai, Maharastra, 400072, India
Tel.: (91) 2228515929
Fax: (91) 2228516430
E-Mail: traininginfo@zeroocta.com
Web Site: www.zerooctatraining.com
Emp.: 170
Airline Educational Services
S.I.C.: 8249
N.A.I.C.S.: 611512

Zero Octa Selective Sourcing India Private Limited (1)
1st Fl Excom Hse South Wing Sakivihar Junc Bhd H P Petrol Pump
7 Saki Vihar Rd, Mumbai, Maharastra, 400072, India
Tel.: (91) 2228516970
Fax: (91) 2228516430
E-Mail: zohr@zerooctagroup.com
Web Site: www.zeroocta.com
Emp.: 250
Software Services
S.I.C.: 7371
N.A.I.C.S.: 541511
Sidney Rocha *(Mng Dir)*

Non-U.S. Subsidiary:

Kale Technologies Limited (1)
100A High St
Hampton, TW12 2ST, United Kingdom
Tel.: (44) 2087832392
Fax: (44) 2087832391
Web Site: www.accelyakale.com
Emp.: 10
Airline & Travel Software Solutions
S.I.C.: 7371
N.A.I.C.S.: 541511
Peter O'Sullivan *(Mgr)*

ACCENT EQUITY PARTNERS AB

Engelbrektsgatan 7
PO Box 5784
114 87 Stockholm, Sweden
Tel.: (46) 8 545 073 00
Fax: (46) 8 545 073 29
E-Mail: info@accentequity.se
Web Site: www.accentequity.se
Emp.: 10

Business Description:
Private Equity Investment
S.I.C.: 6211
N.A.I.C.S.: 523999

Personnel:
Jan Ohlsson *(Partner & CEO)*
Niklas Sloutski *(Deputy CEO & Sr Partner)*
Hakan Soderback *(Partner & Mgr-Investment)*
Jerker Sundstrom *(Partner & Mgr-Investment)*

Holdings:

AR Packaging Group AB (1)
Adelgatan 6
SE 211 22 Malmo, Sweden
Tel.: (46) 46 287 33 00
Fax: (46) 46 287 33 04
Web Site: www.ar-carton.com
Sales Range: $600-649.9 Million
Emp.: 2,000
Packaging Mfr
S.I.C.: 2657
N.A.I.C.S.: 322212
Stig Gustavson *(Chm)*

Subsidiaries:

A&R Carton AB (2)
Adelgatan 6
SE 211 22 Malmo, Sweden
Tel.: (46) 406615660
Fax: (46) 406116605
Web Site: www.ar-carton.com
Sls.: $362,192,992
Emp.: 17
Folding Cartons & Packaging Machinery Mfr
S.I.C.: 2653
N.A.I.C.S.: 322211
Morten Ahlstrom *(Chm)*

Subsidiary:

A&R Carton Lund AB (3)
Maskinvagen 1
221 00 Lund, Sweden
Tel.: (46) 46183020
Fax: (46) 4646183295
E-Mail: lund@ar-carton.com
Web Site: www.ar-carton.com
Emp.: 80
Folding Cartons & Packaging Machinery Mfr
S.I.C.: 2653
N.A.I.C.S.: 322211
Claf Goran Wigstrand *(VP-Specialty Pkg)*

U.S. Subsidiary:

A&R Carton North America Inc. (3)
1400 N Brook Pkwy Ste 350
Suwanee, GA 30052
Tel.: (770) 623-8235
Fax: (770) 623-8236
E-Mail: atlanta@ar-carton.com
Web Site: www.ar-carton.com
Emp.: 2
Folding Cartons & Packaging Machinery Solutions
S.I.C.: 2653
N.A.I.C.S.: 322211

Non-U.S. Subsidiaries:

A&R Carton A/S (3)
Bredmyra 4 N
Box 33
Borgenhaugen, NO-1739 Sarpsborg, Norway
Tel.: (47) 69973803
Telex: 77532 ahlas n
Fax: (47) 69973801
E-Mail: skjeberg@ar-carton.com
Web Site: www.ar-carton.com
Emp.: 100
Folding Cartons & Packaging Machinery Mfr
S.I.C.: 2653
N.A.I.C.S.: 322211
Pal Wikstrom *(Gen Mgr)*

A&R Carton BV (3)
Steenhouwersstraat 4
NL-8601 WD Sneek, Netherlands

Accent Equity Partners AB—(Continued)

Tel.: (31) 515422922
Fax: (31) 515423215
E-Mail: sneek@ar-carton.com
Web Site: www.ar-carton.com
Emp.: 110
Folding Cartons & Packaging Machinery Mfr
S.I.C.: 2653
N.A.I.C.S.: 322211
Gerard De Vries *(Mng Dir)*

A&R Carton cdf SA **(3)**
Boulevard du Cormier
FR-49302 Cholet, Cedex, France
Tel.: (33) 241462940
Fax: (33) 241628046
E-Mail: cholet@ar-carton.com
Web Site: www.ar-carton.com
Folding Cartons & Packaging Machinery Mfr
S.I.C.: 2653
N.A.I.C.S.: 322211

A&R Carton Oy **(3)**
Luvalahdentie 1
PO Box 120
FI-27501 Kauttua, Finland
Tel.: (358) 10 430 500
Telex: 124518 altim sf
Fax: (358) 10 430 55 34
E-Mail: kauttua@ar-carton.com
Web Site: www.ar-carton.com
Folding Cartons & Packaging Machinery Mfr
S.I.C.: 2657
N.A.I.C.S.: 322212
Harald Schulz *(Pres & CEO)*

A&R Carton St Petersburg ZAO **(3)**
Volkhonskoye Shosse 4
Lomonosov District
Poselok Gorelovo, 198323 Saint Petersburg, Russia
Tel.: (7) 8123466167
Fax: (7) 812 3466165
E-Mail: st.petersburg@ar-carton.com
Web Site: www.ar-carton.com
Emp.: 25
Folding Cartons & Packaging Machinery Mfr
S.I.C.: 2653
N.A.I.C.S.: 322211

A&R Carton **(3)**
Romuvos str 32 C
47197 Kaunas, 21, Lithuania
Tel.: (370) 37460626
Fax: (370) 37432001
Web Site: www.ar-carton.com
Folding Cartons & Packaging Machinery Mfr
S.I.C.: 2653
N.A.I.C.S.: 322211

Flextrus AB **(2)**
Lund Business Park Maskinvagen 1
PO Box 22
SE-221 00 Lund, Sweden
Tel.: (46) 46 18 30 00
Fax: (46) 46 211 36 00
E-Mail: info@flextrus.com
Web Site: www.flextrus.com
Flexible Packaging Mfr
S.I.C.: 2672
N.A.I.C.S.: 322220
Per Nystrom *(CEO)*

Autotube AB **(1)**
Susvindsvagen 28
PO Box 1114
43215 Varberg, Sweden (100%)
Tel.: (46) 340628600
Fax: (46) 340628610
E-Mail: info@autotube.se
Web Site: www.autotube.se
Sales Range: $50-74.9 Million
Emp.: 220
Motor Vehicle Parts Mfr
S.I.C.: 3714
N.A.I.C.S.: 336390
Sven-Olov Liback *(Mng Dir)*
Madeleine Andersson *(CFO)*

Aviator Airport Alliance Europe AB **(1)**
Generatorgatan 11
Box 118
Stockholm-Arlanda, 190 46 Stockholm, Sweden
Tel.: (46) 8 58 55 42 00
Fax: (46) 8 58 55 42 01
E-Mail: excellence@aviator.eu
Web Site: www.aviator.eu
Airport Ground Handling Services
S.I.C.: 4581
N.A.I.C.S.: 488119
Paul Synnott *(CEO)*
Birgitta Andersson *(CFO)*
Per Wassberg *(COO)*
Paul Nord *(CIO)*
Catharina Redgard *(Chief Comml Officer)*

Non-U.S. Subsidiary:

Novia Danmark A/S **(2)**
Copenhagen Airport
Terminal 2, 2770 Kastrup, Denmark
Tel.: (45) 3247 4001
Fax: (45) 3251 1018
Web Site: www.novia.aero
Sales Range: $50-74.9 Million
Emp.: 825
Airport Ground Handling Services
S.I.C.: 4581
N.A.I.C.S.: 488119
Ole Brinks Andersen *(Mng Dir)*

Candyking Holding AB **(1)**
Telegrafgatan 8A
Box 729
169 27 Solna, Sweden SE
Tel.: (46) 8 795 03 00 (100%)
E-Mail: info@candyking.se
Web Site: www.candyking.com
Sales Range: $250-299.9 Million
Emp.: 800
Holding Company; Candy Whslr
S.I.C.: 6719
N.A.I.C.S.: 551112
Morthen Johannessen *(CEO)*
Krister Lindgren *(CFO)*

Subsidiary:

Candyking Sweden AB **(2)**
Telegrafgatan 8A
Box 729
169 27 Solna, Sweden
Tel.: (46) 8 795 03 00
E-Mail: info@karamellkungen.se
Web Site: www.candyking.com
Candy Whslr
S.I.C.: 5145
N.A.I.C.S.: 424450
Daniel Julin *(Mng Dir)*

Non-U.S. Subsidiaries:

Candyking Finland Oy **(2)**
Hameentie 135 A
560 Helsinki, Finland
Tel.: (358) 9 8561 5000
Fax: (358) 9 8561 5050
E-Mail: info.finland@candyking.com
Web Site: www.candyking.com
Candy Whslr
S.I.C.: 5145
N.A.I.C.S.: 424450

Candyking Norge AS **(2)**
Vanemveien 1
1599 Moss, Norway
Tel.: (47) 69 35 59 88
Fax: (47) 69 35 59 88
E-Mail: informasjon@candyking.com
Web Site: www.candyking.com
Candy Mfr
S.I.C.: 5145
N.A.I.C.S.: 424450

Candyking UK Ltd. **(2)**
Fort Southwick
James Callaghan Drive, Fareham, Hampshire, PO17 6AR, United Kingdom
Tel.: (44) 2392 630 300
Fax: (44) 2392 630 333
E-Mail: info.uk@candyking.com
Web Site: www.candyking.com
Candy Whslr
S.I.C.: 5145
N.A.I.C.S.: 424450
Graham Richardson *(Mng Dir)*

Candymix Ireland Ltd. **(2)**
First Floor Unit 12 Nort Street Business Park
Swords, Dublin, Ireland
Tel.: (353) 18700 920
Fax: (353) 18700 921
E-Mail: customerservice.ie@candyking.com
Web Site: www.candyking.com
Emp.: 15
Candy Whslr
S.I.C.: 5145
N.A.I.C.S.: 424450
Dave Spencer *(Country Mgr)*

Non-U.S. Holding:

Tastymix A/S **(2)**
Kertemindevej 58
8900 Randers, Denmark
Tel.: (45) 86 40 54 99
Fax: (45) 86 40 54 92
E-Mail: tastymix@tastymix.dk
Web Site: www.tastymix.dk
Sales Range: $25-49.9 Million
Emp.: 55
Candy Distr
S.I.C.: 5145
N.A.I.C.S.: 424450
Michael Blok *(Dir-Sls & Mktg)*

Mont Blanc Industri AB **(1)**
Toarpsdal
516 90 Dalsjofors, Sweden
Tel.: (46) 33 22 27 00
E-Mail: sales@montblanc.se
Web Site: www.montblanc.se
Sales Range: $50-74.9 Million
Emp.: 275
Mfr of Car Load Carrying Equipment, Including Roof Racks, Bicycle Holders, Roof Boxes & Other Accessories
S.I.C.: 3714
N.A.I.C.S.: 336390
Per Zaunders *(Chm)*
Per Ekholm *(CEO)*

Non-U.S. Subsidiaries:

Automaxi International **(2)**
24 Rue Claude Bernard
35400 Saint-Malo, Ille Et Vilaine, France
Tel.: (33) 299211270
Web Site: www.automaxi.fr
Sales Range: $10-24.9 Million
Emp.: 100
Designer & Mfr of Automobile Carrying Accessories, Including Roof Racks & Bike Carriers
S.I.C.: 3714
N.A.I.C.S.: 336390
Jean-Yves Letanoux *(Pres)*

Mont Blanc Industri UK Ltd **(2)**
Eden Way
Leighton Buzzard, Bedfordshire, LU7 4TZ, United Kingdom
Tel.: (44) 1525 850800
Fax: (44) 1525850808
E-Mail: uk@montblancgroup.com
Web Site: www.montblancgroup.com
Emp.: 15
Aftermarket Sales of Car Load Carrying Equipment
S.I.C.: 5013
N.A.I.C.S.: 423120

Troax AB **(1)**
Tyngel
Box 89
330 33 Hillerstorp, Sweden (100%)
Tel.: (46) 370 828 00
Fax: (46) 370 824 86
E-Mail: info@troax.com
Web Site: www.troax.com
Sales Range: $50-74.9 Million
Mfr of Mesh Panels, Machine Guard Fencing Systems & Locking Devices
S.I.C.: 3499
N.A.I.C.S.: 332999
Thomas Widstrand *(Mng Dir)*

ACCENT RESOURCES N.L.

Level 9 250 Queen Street
Melbourne, VIC, 3000, Australia
Tel.: (61) 3 9670 0888
Fax: (61) 3 9670 3883
E-Mail: admin@accentresources.com.au
Web Site: www.accentresources.com.au
ACS—(ASX)
Rev.: $270,504
Assets: $22,420,711
Liabilities: $305,689
Net Worth: $22,115,022
Earnings: ($745,247)
Emp.: 2
Fiscal Year-end: 06/30/13

Business Description:
Mineral Exploration
S.I.C.: 1041
N.A.I.C.S.: 212221

Personnel:
Ian Charles Hastings *(Chm)*
Philip Ash *(CEO)*
Robert Allen *(Sec)*

Board of Directors:
Ian Charles Hastings
Dian Zhou He
Jerry Jun Sheng Liang
Albert Yuzi Zhou

Legal Counsel:
Steinepreis Paganin
Level 4 Next Building 16 Milligan St
Perth, Australia

Allion Legal
Level 2 50 Kings Park Road
West Perth, Australia

ACCENTIA TECHNOLOGIES LIMITED

D-207 Second Floor International Infotech Centre
Belapur Railway Station Complex
CBD Belapur, Navi Mumbai, 400 614, India
Tel.: (91) 22 2757 5922
Fax: (91) 22 25276089
E-Mail: bus.dev@accentiatech.com
Web Site: www.accentiatech.com
531897—(BOM)
Sales Range: $50-74.9 Million

Business Description:
IT Products & Services
S.I.C.: 7379
N.A.I.C.S.: 541519

Personnel:
Pradeep S. Viswambharan *(Mng Dir & CEO)*
Rolita Gupta *(Sec & Compliance Officer)*

Board of Directors:
Kabir Kewalramani
Ghanshyam Krishna Mishra
S. M. Parande
Ravi Sankar
C. K. Sooraj
Pradeep S. Viswambharan

Transfer Agent:
Sharex Dynamic (India) Pvt. Ltd.
17/B, Dena Bank Building, 2nd Floor, Horniman Circle
400 001 Mumbai, India

Units:

Accentia Technologies - Cochin Unit **(1)**
39 1463-c Near S over Bridge
Valanjambalam
Cochin, Kerala, 682016, India
Tel.: (91) 4842375215
E-Mail: sojan.ts@accentiatech.com
Emp.: 50
Business Management Services
S.I.C.: 8741
N.A.I.C.S.: 561110
Santhosh K. Pillai *(Gen Mgr)*

Accentia Technologies Ltd. - Bhubaneswar Unit **(1)**
STPI Ctr C Ground Zero
Fortune Towers C S 4, Bhubaneswar, Orissa, 751023, India
Tel.: (91) 6742300412
E-Mail: hr@accentiatech.com
Web Site: www.accentiatech.com
Emp.: 120
Business Process Management Services
S.I.C.: 8741
N.A.I.C.S.: 561110
Pankaj Singh *(Mgr)*

Accentia Technologies Ltd. - Trivandrum Unit **(1)**
233 241 Nila
Techno Park Campus, Trivandrum, Kerala, 695 581, India

Tel.: (91) 4712700964
Fax: (91) 4712700250
E-Mail: info@accentiatech.com
Web Site: www.accentiatech.com
Emp.: 400
Business Process Management Services
S.I.C.: 8741
N.A.I.C.S.: 561110
Viswambharan S. Pradeep *(CEO & Mng Dir)*

Asscent Infoserve Pvt. Ltd. (1)
MKB Towers No 3802/B
7th Main HAL 2nd Stage, 56038 Bengaluru, Karnataka, India
Tel.: (91) 25275603
Information Services & Solutions
S.I.C.: 7389
N.A.I.C.S.: 519190

U.S. Subsidiaries:

GSR Physicians Billing Services Inc. (1)
10096 Griffin Rd
Cooper City, FL 33328
Tel.: (954) 680-5233
Fax: (954) 680-0663
Business Process Management Services
S.I.C.: 8741
N.A.I.C.S.: 561110

ACCENTIS SA/NV

Ter Waarde 21
8900 Ieper, Belgium
Tel.: (32) 92105853
Fax: (32) 3257221281
Web Site: www.accentis.com
ACCB—(EUR)
Sales Range: $10-24.9 Million
Business Description:
Property Management & Project Development Services
S.I.C.: 6531
N.A.I.C.S.: 531312
Personnel:
Jacques De Bliek *(Chm)*
Tim Rottger *(CEO)*
Board of Directors:
Jacques De Bliek
Wim Deblauwe
Jean-Luc Desmet
Hubert Ooghe
Wouter Vandeberg

Non-U.S. Subsidiary:

BBS Verwaltungs GmbH (1)
Hafenweg 24a
Munster, 48155, Germany
Tel.: (49) 7643933980
Fax: (49) 7836521240
Real Estate Management Services
S.I.C.: 6531
N.A.I.C.S.: 531390

ACCENTUATE LIMITED

32 Steele Street
Steeledale, Johannesburg, 2197, South Africa
Mailing Address:
PO Box 1754
Alberton, 1450, South Africa
Tel.: (27) 11 406 4100
Fax: (27) 11 406 4047
E-Mail: info@accentuateltd.co.za
Web Site: www.accentuateltd.co.za
Year Founded: 1953
ACE—(JSE)
Rev.: $31,746,592
Assets: $20,931,128
Liabilities: $5,901,893
Net Worth: $15,029,235
Earnings: $985,976
Emp.: 274
Fiscal Year-end: 06/30/13
Business Description:
Chemical & Floor Covering Product Distr
S.I.C.: 5169
N.A.I.C.S.: 424690
Personnel:
Frederick Cornelius Platt *(CEO)*
Christopher John Povall *(CFO)*
Paresh S. Dayah *(Sec)*
Board of Directors:
Malesela David Clement Motlatla
Dineo Molefe
Ralph Bruce Patmore
Donald Ernest Platt
Frederick Cornelius Platt
Christopher John Povall
N. Eric Ratshikhopha
Transfer Agent:
Computershare Investor Services Proprietary Limited
70 Marshall Street
Johannesburg, South Africa

ACCENTURE PLC

1 Grand Canal Square
Grand Canal Harbour, Dublin, 2, Ireland
Tel.: (353) 1 646 2000
Fax: (353) 1 646 2020
E-Mail: investor.relations@accenture.com
Web Site: www.accenture.com
ACN—(NYSE)
Rev.: $30,394,285,000
Assets: $16,867,049,000
Liabilities: $11,439,220,000
Net Worth: $5,427,829,000
Earnings: $3,554,519,000
Emp.: 275,000
Fiscal Year-end: 08/31/13
Business Description:
Management Consulting, Technology & Outsourcing Services
S.I.C.: 8742
N.A.I.C.S.: 541611
Personnel:
Pierre Nanterme *(Chm & CEO)*
Martin I. Cole *(Grp CEO-Tech)*
Robert E. Sell *(Grp CEO-Comm, Media & Tech)*
David P. Rowland *(CFO)*
David Thomlinson *(COO & Chief Geographic Strategy Officer)*
Johan G. Deblaere *(COO)*
Roxanne Taylor *(CMO & Chief Comm Officer)*
Julie Spellman Sweet *(Chief Compliance Officer, Gen Counsel & Sec)*
Shawn Collinson *(Chief Strategy Officer)*
Richard P. Clark *(Chief Acctg Officer & Controller)*
Ellyn J. Shook *(Chief HR Officer)*
Adrian Lajtha *(Chief Leadership Officer)*
Gianfranco Casati *(CEO-Growth Markets)*
Richard A. Lumb *(CEO-Fin Svcs)*
Jean-Marc Ollagnier *(CEO-Resources Operating Grp)*
Stephen J. Rohleder *(CEO-Health Pub Svc)*
Michael J. Salvino *(CEO-Bus Process Outsourcing)*
Alexander M. van 't Noordende *(CEO-Products)*
Board of Directors:
Pierre Nanterme
Jaime Ardila
Dina Dublon
Charles H. Giancarlo
Nobuyuki Idei
William L. Kimsey
Robert I. Lipp
Marjorie Magner
Blythe J. McGarvie
Mark Moody-Stuart
Gilles C. Pelisson
Wulf von Schimmelmann

Subsidiary:

Accenture Global Services Ltd. (1)
3 Grand Canal Plaza Upper Grand Canal St 4 Dublin, Ireland
Tel.: (353) 1 407 6000
Fax: (353) 1 407 7500
E-Mail: accenture.direct.ela@accenture.com
Business Process Outsourcing Services
S.I.C.: 7389
N.A.I.C.S.: 561499
Mark Ryan *(Country Mng Dir)*

U.S. Subsidiaries:

Accenture 2, Inc. (1)
1345 Ave
New York, NY 10105-0103
Tel.: (917) 452-4400
Business Process Outsourcing Services
S.I.C.: 7389
N.A.I.C.S.: 561499
Christine Bailey *(Deputy CFO-Federal Svcs-Arlington)*

Accenture Capital Inc. (1)
1501 S MoPac Ste 300
Austin, TX 78746
Tel.: (512) 732-5300
Fax: (512) 476-7765
Financial Investment Services
S.I.C.: 6211
N.A.I.C.S.: 523999

Accenture Financial Corporation (1)
300 Campus Dr
Florham Park, NJ 07932
Tel.: (973) 301-1000
Fax: (973) 301-1005
Financial Management Services
S.I.C.: 6211
N.A.I.C.S.: 523999

Accenture LLC (1)
900 W Trade St Ste 800
Charlotte, NC 28202-2225
Tel.: (704) 332-6411
Business Process Outsourcing Services
S.I.C.: 7389
N.A.I.C.S.: 561499
Gilbert Wootton *(Mng Dir-Seattle)*

ASM Research, Inc. (1)
4050 Legato Rd Suite 1100
Fairfax, VA 22033
Tel.: (703) 645-0420
E-Mail: info@asmr.com
Web Site: www.asmr.com
Sales Range: $50-74.9 Million
Emp.: 453
IT Services to Government Organizations
S.I.C.: 7389
N.A.I.C.S.: 519190
Jeri W. Lassiter *(Chm & CEO)*
John Fraser *(Pres & COO)*
Russell L. Frutiger *(Sr VP-Govt Solutions Grp)*
Frosty Price *(Sr VP-Health Solutions)*

Avanade Inc. (1)
818 Stewart St Ste 400
Seattle, WA 98101
Tel.: (206) 239-5600
Fax: (206) 239-5605
Web Site: www.avanade.com
Sales Range: $50-74.9 Million
Emp.: 10,000
Managed IT Services
S.I.C.: 7373
N.A.I.C.S.: 541512
Adam Warby *(CEO)*
Dennis Knapp *(CFO)*
Andrew White *(COO)*
Chris Miller *(CIO)*
Stella Goulet *(CMO)*
Tyson Hartman *(CTO)*
Adam Wengert *(CTO-Ops-Australia)*
Howard Kilman *(Chief Leadership Officer)*
Florin Rotar *(Chief Tech Innovation Officer)*
Ashish Kumar *(Pres-Europe)*
Aziz Virani *(Pres-North America)*
Ian Jordan *(Exec VP-Sls, Mktg, Innovation & Alliances)*
Mick Slattery *(Exec VP-Global Delivery)*

Subsidiary:

Azaleos Corp. (2)
18109 NE 76th St Ste 105
Redmond, WA 98052 WA
Tel.: (866) 318-8767
Fax: (206) 260-7480
E-Mail: info@azaleos.com
Web Site: www.azaleos.com
Sales Range: $10-24.9 Million
Emp.: 200
Custom Computer Programming Services
S.I.C.: 7371
N.A.I.C.S.: 541511
Phil V. Etten *(CEO)*
Scott Parrish *(CFO)*

Non-U.S. Branches:

Avanade France (2)
125 Avenue De Paris
92320 Chatillon, Hauts De Seine, France
Tel.: (33) 147466600
E-Mail: direction.achats@avanade.com
Web Site: www.avanade.com
Rev.: $15,500,000
Emp.: 79
S.I.C.: 8742
N.A.I.C.S.: 541611
Niecolal Marry *(Pres)*
Mitch Hill *(CEO)*

Avanade UK Ltd. (2)
135-141 Wardour Street
London, W1F 0UT, United Kingdom
Tel.: (44) 2070251000
Fax: (44) 2070251005
E-Mail: ukinfo@avanade.com
Web Site: www.avanade.com
Emp.: 300
Information Technology Consultants
S.I.C.: 8243
N.A.I.C.S.: 611420
Pam Maynard *(Gen Mgr)*

Avventa Worldwide, LLC (1)
1150 Hungryneck Blvd
Mount Pleasant, SC 29464
Tel.: (843) 881-3515
Toll Free: (877) 629-3682
Web Site: www.avventa.com
Sales Range: $10-24.9 Million
Emp.: 600
Motion Picture & Video Production Services
S.I.C.: 7812
N.A.I.C.S.: 512110
Jay Noce *(CEO)*
David Matt *(Chief Creative Officer)*

BABCN LLC (1)
333 S 7th St Ste 500
Minneapolis, MN 55402-2443
Tel.: (612) 317-7777
Fax: (612) 317-7575
Web Design Services
S.I.C.: 7371
N.A.I.C.S.: 541511

Navitaire Inc. (1)
333 S 7th St Ste 700
Minneapolis, MN 55402-2443
Tel.: (612) 317-7000
Fax: (612) 317-7575
Toll Free: (877) 216-6787
Web Site: www.navitaire.com
Accounting & Bookkeeping Services
S.I.C.: 8721
N.A.I.C.S.: 541219
Michael Dickoff *(CEO)*

Navitaire International Inc. (1)
333 S 7th St Ste 500
Minneapolis, MN 55402-2443
Tel.: (612) 317-7000
Fax: (612) 317-7575
Business Process Outsourcing Services
S.I.C.: 7389
N.A.I.C.S.: 561499

Octagon Research Solutions, Inc. (1)
585 E Swedesford Rd Ste 200
Wayne, PA 19087
Tel.: (610) 535-6500
Fax: (610) 535-6515
E-Mail: info@octagonresearch.com
Web Site: www.octagonresearch.com
Sales Range: $10-24.9 Million
Emp.: 150
Software Mfr
S.I.C.: 5045
N.A.I.C.S.: 423430
James C. Walker *(Chm & CEO)*
Kirk Gallion *(Pres)*
Gina L. Schmidt *(Exec VP-Global Regulatory Submission Mgmt)*

Accenture plc—(Continued)

Procurian Inc. (1)
211 S Gulph Rd Ste 500
King of Prussia, PA 19406
Tel.: (484) 690-5000
Fax: (877) 424-2339
Toll Free: (877) 935-4242
Web Site: www.procurian.com
Emp.: 780
Procurement Solutions
S.I.C.: 7372
N.A.I.C.S.: 511210
Carl Guarino *(CEO)*
Joseph Waterman *(CFO)*
Rick Bunker *(CIO)*
Michael Shim *(Sr VP-Gen Counsel & Corp Sec)*
David Clary *(Sr VP-Global Program Mgmt)*
Jason Gilroy *(Sr VP-North American Program Mgmt)*
Keith Hausmann *(Sr VP-Global Delivery)*
Bob Kothari *(Sr VP-Sls & Bus Dev)*

Non-U.S. Subsidiaries:

Accenture A.S (1)
Rolfsbuktveien 2
1360 Fornebu, Norway
Tel.: (47) 67 12 67 00
Fax: (47) 67 12 67 01
Web Site: www.accenture.com
Business Process Outsourcing Services
S.I.C.: 7389
N.A.I.C.S.: 561499

Accenture Automacao e TI Industrial Ltda (1)
Afonso Pena 4 001 9 Andar Funcionarios
30130-008 Belo Horizonte, Minas Gerais, Brazil
Tel.: (55) 3132897700
Web Site: www.accenture.com
Software Development Services
S.I.C.: 7371
N.A.I.C.S.: 541511

Accenture (Botswana) (PTY) Ltd. (1)
Plot 112 Pula Holdings Building Kgale Mews
POX 2691
Gaborone, Botswana
Tel.: (267) 365 9900
Fax: (267) 316 2224
Emp.: 30
Business Process Outsourcing Services
S.I.C.: 7389
N.A.I.C.S.: 561499
Bashi Gaetsaloe *(Mng Dir)*

Accenture BPM CVBA/SCRL (1)
Waterloolaan 16
Brussels, 1000, Belgium
Tel.: (32) 22267211
Emp.: 120
Business Process Outsourcing Services
S.I.C.: 7389
N.A.I.C.S.: 561499
Olivier Gillerod *(Mng Dir)*

Accenture BPM is Yonetimi Limited Sirketi (1)
Rbs Binasi 13 Tamburi Ali Efendi Sokak
Istanbul, 34337, Turkey
Tel.: (90) 2123493200
Fax: (90) 2123517881
Web Site: www.acccenture.com
Emp.: 30
Business Process Outsourcing Services
S.I.C.: 7389
N.A.I.C.S.: 561499
Tolga Ulutas *(Gen Mgr)*

Accenture BPM S.A. (1)
1 Arkadias
Kifissia, 14564, Greece
Tel.: (30) 2106781400
Fax: (30) 2106776405
Business Process Outsourcing Services
S.I.C.: 7389
N.A.I.C.S.: 561499

Accenture Branch Holdings B.V. (1)
Gustav Mahlerplein 90
Amsterdam, 1082 MA, Netherlands
Tel.: (31) 204938383
Investment Management Services
S.I.C.: 6211
N.A.I.C.S.: 523999

Accenture Business Services for Utilities Inc. (1)
401 West Georgia Street Suite 1400
Vancouver, BC, V6B 5A1, Canada
Tel.: (604) 663-3800
Fax: (604) 663-3801
Business Process Outsourcing Services
S.I.C.: 7389
N.A.I.C.S.: 561499

Accenture Business Services of British Columbia Limited Partnership (1)
401 Georgia St W 14th Floor
Vancouver, BC, V6B 5A1, Canada
Tel.: (604) 663-3800
Fax: (604) 663-3801
Web Site: www.accenture.com
Business Process Outsourcing Services
S.I.C.: 7389
N.A.I.C.S.: 561499

Accenture BV (1)
Gustav Mahlerplein 90
1082 MA Amsterdam, Netherlands
Tel.: (31) 20 493 8383
Fax: (31) 20 493 8080
E-Mail: marketing.nl@accenture.com
Information Technology Consulting Services
S.I.C.: 7373
N.A.I.C.S.: 541512
Sytze-Johan Bakker *(Grp CEO-Products)*
Joost A. C. N. de Haas *(Grp CEO-Mgmt Consulting)*
Tom Loozen *(Grp CEO-Comm, Media & Tech)*
Anja Montijn-Groenewoud *(Grp CEO-Resources & Country Mng Dir)*
Bas Telgenkamp *(Grp CEO-Tech)*
Jan Willem van den Bremen *(Grp CEO-Resources)*
Geert van den Goor *(Grp CEO-Health & Public Svc)*
Tom van der Spek *(Grp CEO-Fin Svcs)*
Barend van Doorn *(Grp CEO-Outsourcing)*

Accenture C.A. (1)
Centro SegurosLa Paz Piso 7 Ala Noreste
Avenida Francisco de Miranda
La California Norte, Caracas, 1070, Venezuela
Tel.: (58) 2122735000
Fax: (58) 2122735555
Web Site: www.accenture.com
Emp.: 80
Management Consulting & Technology Services
S.I.C.: 8742
N.A.I.C.S.: 541611
Beatriz Carmona *(Gen Mgr)*

Accenture Canada Holdings Inc. (1)
5450 Explorer Dr Ste 400
Mississauga, ON, L4W 5M1, Canada
Tel.: (416) 641-5000
Fax: (416) 641-5099
Emp.: 1,800
Investment Management Services
S.I.C.: 6719
N.A.I.C.S.: 551112
Dave Seibel *(Mng Dir)*

Accenture CAS GmbH (1)
Brusseler Strasse 3
67657 Kaiserslautern, Germany
Tel.: (49) 6313033700
Fax: (49) 6313033701
E-Mail: Accenture.CAS@accenture.com
Web Site: www.accenture.com
Emp.: 200
Customer Relationship Management & Mobility Software Solutions Provider
S.I.C.: 7372
N.A.I.C.S.: 511210
Henning Fromme *(Gen Mgr)*

Accenture Central Europe B.V. (1)
Versterkerstraat 6
1322 AP Almere, Netherlands
Tel.: (31) 36 546 14 70
E-Mail: marketing.nl@accenture.com
Web Site: www.accenture.com
Business Management Consulting Services
S.I.C.: 8742
N.A.I.C.S.: 541611

Accenture (China) Co Ltd. (1)
21/F West Tower World Financial Center No 1 East 3rd Ring Middle Road
Chaoyang District, Beijing, 100020, China
Tel.: (86) 1058705870
Fax: (86) 1065612077
Web Site: www.accenture.com
Management Consulting & Technology Services
S.I.C.: 8742
N.A.I.C.S.: 541611

Accenture Co Ltd. (1)
30th Floor Abdulrahim Place 990 Rama IV Road
Si Lom Bangrak, Bangkok, 10500, Thailand
Tel.: (66) 2 636 1616
Fax: (66) 2 636 1640
Emp.: 40
Business Process Outsourcing Services
S.I.C.: 7389
N.A.I.C.S.: 561499
Orapong Thien-Ngern *(Country Mng Dir)*

Accenture Consultores de Gestao S.A. (1)
Avenida Eng Duarte Pacheco Torre 1 Floor 16 Amoreiras
Lisbon, 1070-101, Portugal
Tel.: (351) 21 380 3500
Fax: (351) 21 371 3500
E-Mail: accenture.portugal@accenture.com
Web Site: www.accenture.com
Emp.: 50
Business Management Consulting Services
S.I.C.: 8742
N.A.I.C.S.: 541611
Udo Schmidt *(Mng Dir)*

Accenture Danismanlik Limited Sirketi (1)
Rbs Building Tamburi Ali Efendi Sokak No 13 Etiler
34330 Istanbul, Turkey
Tel.: (90) 2123493200
Fax: (90) 2123517881
Web Site: www.accenture.com
Emp.: 300
Management Consulting & Technology Services
S.I.C.: 8742
N.A.I.C.S.: 541611
Tolga Ulutas *(Gen Mgr)*

Accenture Denmark Holdings A/S (1)
Arne Jacobsens All 15
2100 Copenhagen, Denmark
Tel.: (45) 72288000
Fax: (45) 72288100
Web Site: www.accenture.com
Emp.: 50
Investment Management Services
S.I.C.: 6211
N.A.I.C.S.: 523999

Accenture do Brasil Ltda (1)
Rua Alexandre Dumas 2 051 Chacara Santo Antonio
Sao Paulo, 04717-004, Brazil
Tel.: (55) 11 51883000
Fax: (55) 11 51883200
Business Process Outsourcing Services
S.I.C.: 7389
N.A.I.C.S.: 561499

Accenture Equity Finance BV (1)
Gustav Mahlerplein 90
Amsterdam, 1082 MA, Netherlands
Tel.: (31) 204938383
Fax: (31) 204938080
Web Site: www.accenture.com
Financial Management Services
S.I.C.: 6211
N.A.I.C.S.: 523999

Accenture Finance and Accounting BPO Services SpA (1)
Via Strada 4 Palazzo Q
Rozzano, 20089, Italy
Tel.: (39) 0257581
Fax: (39) 0257583000
Financial Business Process Outsourcing Services
S.I.C.: 7389
N.A.I.C.S.: 561499

Accenture GmbH (1)
Borsegebaude Schottenring 16
1010 Vienna, Austria
Tel.: (43) 1205020
Fax: (43) 1205021
E-Mail: Accenture.direct.ela@accenture.com
Web Site: www.accenture.com
Management Consulting & Technology Services
S.I.C.: 8742
N.A.I.C.S.: 541611
Klaus Malle *(Mng Dir-Country)*

The Accenture Group (1)
Plantation Place 30 Fenchurch Street
London, EC3M 3BD, United Kingdom
Tel.: (44) 2078444000
Fax: (44) 2078444444
Business Process Outsourcing Services
S.I.C.: 7389
N.A.I.C.S.: 561499
Oliver Benzecry *(Gen Mgr)*

Accenture Healthcare Processing Inc. (1)
27th Floor G T Tower International Ayala Avenue Corner
H V Dela Costa Street, Makati, 1226, Philippines
Tel.: (63) 28410111
Fax: (63) 28495005
Business Process Outsourcing Services
S.I.C.: 7389
N.A.I.C.S.: 561499

Accenture Holding GmbH & Co. KG (1)
Campus Kronberg 1
61476 Kronberg, Germany
Tel.: (49) 61739499
Fax: (49) 61739498
Investment Management Services
S.I.C.: 6211
N.A.I.C.S.: 523999

Accenture Holdings B.V. (1)
Gustav Mahlerplein 90
Amsterdam, 1082 MA, Netherlands
Tel.: (31) 204938383
Fax: (31) 204938080
Web Site: www.accenture.com
Investment Management Services
S.I.C.: 6211
N.A.I.C.S.: 523999

Accenture Holdings France SAS (1)
118 Avenue De France
Paris, 75013, France
Tel.: (33) 153235555
Fax: (33) 153235323
E-Mail: direction.achats@accenture.com
Emp.: 3,000
Investment Management Services
S.I.C.: 6719
N.A.I.C.S.: 551112

Accenture Holdings (Iberia) S.L. (1)
Edificio Torre Picasso Plaza Pablo Ruiz Picasso s/n
Madrid, 28020, Spain
Tel.: (34) 915967000
Fax: (34) 915966136
Web Site: www.accenture.com
Investment Management Services
S.I.C.: 6211
N.A.I.C.S.: 523999

Accenture Human Capital Mgmt. Sol. S.L. (1)
Avinguda Diagonal 615
8028 Barcelona, Spain
Tel.: (34) 93 227 10 00
Financial Investment Services
S.I.C.: 6211
N.A.I.C.S.: 523999

Accenture Inc. (1)
Makati Stock Exchange Bldg Ayala Avenue
Makati, Philippines
Tel.: (63) 29082100
Fax: (63) 28495005
Web Site: www.accenture.com
Management Consulting & Technology Services
S.I.C.: 8742
N.A.I.C.S.: 541611

Accenture Inc. (1)
Sun Life Plaza Suite 300 140 4th Avenue SW
Calgary, AB, T2P 3N3, Canada
Tel.: (403) 476-1510
Fax: (403) 476-1511
Web Site: www.accenture.com
Emp.: 200

Management Consulting & Technology Services
S.I.C.: 8742
N.A.I.C.S.: 541611
Michael Denham *(Mng Dir)*

Accenture International Capital SCA (1)
Avenue J F Kennedy 46a
Luxembourg, 1855, Luxembourg
Tel.: (352) 26 423 1
Investment Management Services
S.I.C.: 6211
N.A.I.C.S.: 523999

Accenture International Sarl (1)
Avenue J F Kennedy 46a
Luxembourg, 1855, Luxembourg
Tel.: (352) 264231
Fax: (352) 26423233
Emp.: 6
Information Technology Consulting Services
S.I.C.: 7373
N.A.I.C.S.: 541512
Pascal Denis *(Gen Mgr)*

Accenture Ltda (1)
Carrera 7 Numero 71-52 Torre A Piso 10
Bogota, Colombia
Tel.: (57) 13266400
Fax: (57) 13130508
Emp.: 250
Business Process Outsourcing Services
S.I.C.: 7389
N.A.I.C.S.: 561499
Beatriz Carmona *(Gen Mgr)*

Accenture Ltd. (1)
11 Galgalei Haplada Street
Herzliyya, 46733, Israel
Tel.: (972) 9961 9600
Fax: (972) 9955 1317
E-Mail: info@accenture.com
Emp.: 2
Management Consulting Services
S.I.C.: 8748
N.A.I.C.S.: 541618

Accenture Mauritius Ltd. (1)
Royal Road Cassis
Port Louis, Mauritius
Tel.: (230) 2032600
Fax: (230) 2086782
Emp.: 800
Business Process Outsourcing Services
S.I.C.: 7389
N.A.I.C.S.: 561499

Accenture (Mauritius) Onshore Ltd. (1)
NexTeracom Tower 2 9th Floor
Ebene, Mauritius
Tel.: (230) 4021700
Fax: (230) 4021800
Business Process Outsourcing Services
S.I.C.: 7389
N.A.I.C.S.: 561499

Accenture Middle East B.V. (1)
Gustav Mahlerplein 90
Amsterdam, 1082 MA, Netherlands
Tel.: (31) 204938383
Fax: (31) 206748414
Business Process Outsourcing Services
S.I.C.: 7389
N.A.I.C.S.: 561499

Accenture OOO (1)
2 Str 2 Paveletskaya Pl
Moscow, 115054, Russia
Tel.: (7) 4957559770
Fax: (7) 4957559780
Web Site: www.accenture.com
Business Process Outsourcing Services
S.I.C.: 7389
N.A.I.C.S.: 561499
Vartan Dilanian *(Gen Dir)*

Accenture Outsourcing Services S.A. (1)
Paseo De La Finca Bl 2d 1
Pozuelo de Alarcon, 28223, Spain
Tel.: (34) 915966000
Fax: (34) 915967100
Business Process Outsourcing Services
S.I.C.: 7389
N.A.I.C.S.: 561499

Accenture Participations BV (1)
Gustav Mahlerplein 90
Amsterdam, 1082 MA, Netherlands
Tel.: (31) 204938383
Fax: (31) 204938080
Business Process Outsourcing Services
S.I.C.: 7389
N.A.I.C.S.: 561499

Accenture S.A. (1)
1 Arcadias Str
Kifissia, 14564 Athens, Greece
Tel.: (30) 2106781400
Fax: (30) 2106776405
E-Mail: athens@accenture.com
Emp.: 35
Business Process Outsourcing Services
S.I.C.: 7389
N.A.I.C.S.: 561499
Evangelia Pateraki *(Country Mgr)*

Accenture Sarl (1)
46A Avenue J-F Kennedy
1855 Luxembourg, Luxembourg
Tel.: (352) 26 42 31
Fax: (352) 26 42 32 33
Emp.: 10
Business Process Outsourcing Services
S.I.C.: 7389
N.A.I.C.S.: 561499
Olivier Gillerot *(Mng Dir-Belgium)*

Accenture S.C. (1)
Blvd Manuel Avila Camacho No 138 Piso 7
Lomas De Chapultepec, Mexico, 11000, Mexico
Tel.: (52) 5552847300
Fax: (52) 5552847301
Management & Technical Consulting Services
S.I.C.: 8748
N.A.I.C.S.: 541618

Accenture SCA (1)
46A Avenue J F Kennedy
L-1855 Luxembourg, Luxembourg LU
Tel.: (352) 26423500 (100%)
Fax: (352) 26423233
E-Mail: marketing.belux@accenture.com
Web Site: www.accenture.lu
Rev.: $30,394,284,000
Assets: $16,867,048,000
Liabilities: $11,439,219,000
Net Worth: $5,427,829,000
Earnings: $3,554,518,000
Emp.: 274,000
Fiscal Year-end: 08/31/13
Management & Business Consulting Services
S.I.C.: 7389
N.A.I.C.S.: 561499

U.S. Subsidiary:

Accenture, Inc. (2)
161 N Clark St 23rd Fl
Chicago, IL 60601
Tel.: (312) 693-0161
Fax: (312) 693-0507
Web Site: www.accenture.com
Emp.: 5,000
Business Management, Outsourcing & Technology Consulting Services
S.I.C.: 8742
N.A.I.C.S.: 541611
Kathy Samuels *(Dir-Bus Dev-North America)*

Division:

Accenture Duck Creek (3)
1807 Jones St
Bolivar, MO 65613-3305
Tel.: (417) 777-6970
Fax: (417) 777-3792
Toll Free: (866) DUCK-TEC
E-Mail: info@accenture.com
Web Site: www.accenture.com
Emp.: 100
Software Solutions for Property & Casualty Insurance Industry
S.I.C.: 7372
N.A.I.C.S.: 511210
Steve Hall *(Pres & CEO)*
Andrew Yohn *(CTO-Duck Creek Software)*
Sam McGuckin *(Sr VP-Pro Svcs)*
John Roller *(Sr VP-Product Mgmt)*

Subsidiaries:

Accenture National Security Services LLC (3)
11951 Freedom Dr Ste 1000
Reston, VA 20190
Tel.: (703) 947-3000
Defense Consulting Services
S.I.C.: 8748
N.A.I.C.S.: 541618
Eric S. Stange *(Mng Dir)*

Corliant, Inc. (3)
1210 Northbrook Dr Ste100
Trevose, PA 19053
Tel.: (215) 244-5000
Fax: (215) 244-5099
Toll Free: (866) CORLIANT
E-Mail: info@corliant.com
Web Site: www.corliant.com
Sales Range: $10-24.9 Million
Emp.: 150
Information Technology Consulting & Network Solution Services
S.I.C.: 7373
N.A.I.C.S.: 541512

Gestalt, LLC (3)
1040 1st Ave
King of Prussia, PA 19406
Tel.: (610) 768-0800
Management Consulting Services
S.I.C.: 8748
N.A.I.C.S.: 541618
Bill Loftus *(Pres & CEO)*
James Stogdill *(CTO)*
Lori McKaig *(Sr VP-Comm & Workforce Enrichment)*
David Turner *(Sr VP-Svcs & Product Dev-Energy Practice)*

NaviSys, Inc. (3)
499 Thornall St
Edison, NJ 08837
Tel.: (732) 549-3663
Fax: (732) 549-5445
Toll Free: (800) 775-3592
E-Mail: info@navisys.com
Web Site: www.navisys.com
Emp.: 350
Developer of Insurance Software
S.I.C.: 7372
N.A.I.C.S.: 511210
Thomas Famularo *(Sr VP-Tech & Dev)*
Ronald T. Karam *(Sr VP-Consulting Svcs)*

Origin Digital, Inc. (3)
1200 Harbor Blvd 8th Fl
Weehawken, NJ 07086 NJ
Tel.: (201) 537-8600
Fax: (201) 537-8686
Web Site: www.origindigital.com
Emp.: 50
Video Capture, Transformation & Delivery Services
S.I.C.: 7372
N.A.I.C.S.: 511210
Erik Perkins *(Pres & CFO)*
Darcy Lorincz *(CEO)*
Chris Lemire *(Exec VP)*

Joint Venture:

Xceleron Health LLC (3)
Merck Medco Office Bldg 2nd Fl 101 Paragon Dr
Montvale, NJ 07645
Tel.: (201) 269-6240
Fax: (201) 782-6678
Emp.: 500
Technology Consulting For Healthcare Industry; Joint Venture of Merck Medco Managed Care LLC (33%), UnitedHealth Group Incorporated (33%) & Accenture Ltd. (33%)
S.I.C.: 8299
N.A.I.C.S.: 611710

Non-U.S. Subsidiaries:

Accenture A.B. (2)
Alstromergatan 12
PO Box 1331
11183 Stockholm, Sweden (100%)
Tel.: (46) 84513000
Fax: (46) 84512000
E-Mail: info@accenture.com
Web Site: www.accenture.com
Emp.: 350
Various Business Services
S.I.C.: 7389
N.A.I.C.S.: 561499
Peter Meinhartt *(Mng Dir)*

Accenture AG (2)
Fraumunsterstrasse 16
8001 Zurich, Switzerland (100%)
Tel.: (41) 442199889
Fax: (41) 61739498
E-Mail: info-de@accenture.com
Web Site: www.accenture.com
Emp.: 1,000
Various Business Services
S.I.C.: 7389
N.A.I.C.S.: 561499

Accenture Argentina (2)
Maipu 1210 Fl 8
Buenos Aires, C1006ACT, Argentina (100%)
Tel.: (54) 1143188500
Fax: (54) 1143188555
E-Mail: roberto.albarez@accenture.com
Web Site: www.accenture.com
Emp.: 5,000
Business Services
S.I.C.: 7389
N.A.I.C.S.: 561499
Roberto Albarez *(Mng Dir)*

Accenture Australia (2)
180 Lonsdale Street
Melbourne, VIC, 3000, Australia (100%)
Tel.: (61) 398387000
Fax: (61) 398387100
Web Site: www.accenture.com
Emp.: 2,000
Business Services
S.I.C.: 7389
N.A.I.C.S.: 561499
Jack Percy *(Mng Dir)*

Accenture Austria (2)
Borsegebaude Schottenring 16
Vienna, A 1010, Austria (100%)
Tel.: (43) 01205020
Fax: (43) 01205021
E-Mail: klaus.malle@accenture.com
Web Site: www.accenture.at
Emp.: 500
Business Services
S.I.C.: 7389
N.A.I.C.S.: 561499
Roxanne Taylor *(Mng Partner)*
Klaus Malle *(Mng Dir)*

Accenture Belgium (2)
Waterloolaan 16
1000 Brussels, Belgium (100%)
Tel.: (32) 22267211
Fax: (32) 22267233
E-Mail: reception.belgium@accenture.com
Web Site: www.accenture.be
Emp.: 1,400
Business Services
S.I.C.: 7389
N.A.I.C.S.: 561499
Eric Lombois *(CEO)*

Subsidiary:

Accenture Technology Solutions (ATS) NV (3)
Medialaan 38
1800 Vilvoorde, Belgium
Tel.: (32) 2 226 72 11
Fax: (32) 2 226 72 33
Web Site: www.accenture.com
Information Technology Consulting Services
S.I.C.: 7373
N.A.I.C.S.: 541512
Olivier Gillerot *(Country Mgr)*

Accenture Brazil (2)
Avda Republica Do Chile 500 18 Andar Centro
Rio de Janeiro, 20031 170, Brazil
Tel.: (55) 2145019000
Fax: (55) 2145019300
Web Site: www.accenture.com
Emp.: 80
Business Services
S.I.C.: 7389
N.A.I.C.S.: 561499
Roger Imgold *(Pres)*

Accenture Canada (2)
145 King St West Ste 1401
Toronto, ON, M5H 1J8, Canada (100%)
Tel.: (416) 641-5220
Fax: (416) 641-5651
Web Site: www.accenture.com
Emp.: 130
Business Services
S.I.C.: 7389
N.A.I.C.S.: 561499
Michael Denham *(CEO)*

Accenture plc—(Continued)

Accenture Central Europe B. V. (2)
Jiraskovo Nam 6
120 00 Prague, Czech Republic (100%)
Tel.: (420) 221984545
Fax: (420) 221984646
E-Mail: prague@accenture.com
Emp.: 200
Business Services
S.I.C.: 7389
N.A.I.C.S.: 561499
Nauirzio Barini *(Mng Dir)*

Accenture Chile Asesorias y Servicios Ltda. (2)
Rosario Norte 530 Piso 6
Las Condes, 7561186 Santiago, Chile (100%)
Tel.: (56) 23377100
Fax: (56) 23377102
E-Mail: rukmini.bermudez@accenture.com
Web Site: www.accenture.com
Emp.: 600
Business Services
S.I.C.: 7389
N.A.I.C.S.: 561499
Ricardo Cerean *(Pres)*

Accenture Colombia (2)
Carrera 7 Numero 71-52
Torre A Oficina 706, Bogota, Colombia (100%)
Tel.: (57) 3131000
Fax: (57) 13130508
Web Site: www.accenture.com
Business Services
S.I.C.: 7389
N.A.I.C.S.: 561499

Accenture Co. Ltd. (Taiwan) (2)
218 Tun Hwa S Rd Sec 2 21st Fl Cathay Taipei Intl Bldg B
Taipei, 106, Taiwan (100%)
Tel.: (886) 221926030
Fax: (886) 227396015
Emp.: 50
Various Business Services
S.I.C.: 7389
N.A.I.C.S.: 561499
Gong Li *(Chm)*

Accenture Company Ltd. (2)
85/F International Commerce Ctr 1 Austin Rd W
Kowloon, China (Hong Kong)
Tel.: (852) 22492388
Fax: (852) 28508956
E-Mail: info@accenture.com
Emp.: 20
Business Services
S.I.C.: 7389
N.A.I.C.S.: 561499

Accenture Denmark (2)
Arne Jacobsen Alle 15
PO Box 2677
Copenhagen, 2300, Denmark (100%)
Tel.: (45) 72288000
Fax: (45) 72288100
E-Mail: info@accenture.com
Web Site: www.accenture.dk
Emp.: 550
Business Services
S.I.C.: 7389
N.A.I.C.S.: 561499
Philip Wiig *(Mng Dir)*

Accenture Dienstleistungen GmbH (2)
Campus Kronberg 1
Kronberg, 61476, Germany (100%)
Tel.: (49) 61739499
Fax: (49) 61739498
E-Mail: info-de@accenture.com
Emp.: 200
Business Services
S.I.C.: 7389
N.A.I.C.S.: 561499

Accenture European Service Centre Ltd. (2)
3 Grand Canal Plz
Grand Canal upper, Dublin, 4, Ireland (100%)
Tel.: (353) 14076000
Fax: (353) 14077500
Web Site: www.accenture.com
Emp.: 1,700
Business Services
S.I.C.: 7389
N.A.I.C.S.: 561499

Accenture GmbH (2)
Campus Kronberg 1
Kronberg, 61476, Germany (100%)
Tel.: (49) 61739499
Fax: (49) 61739498
E-Mail: info-de@accenture.com
Web Site: www.accenture.de
Emp.: 200
Business Services
S.I.C.: 7389
N.A.I.C.S.: 561499
Stephan Scholtissek *(CEO)*

Accenture India Private Ltd. (2)
6th Floor DLF Centre
Sansad Marg, New Delhi, 110 001, India (100%)
Tel.: (91) 1142980100
Fax: (91) 1142980101
Web Site: www.accenture.com
Emp.: 50
Business Services
S.I.C.: 7389
N.A.I.C.S.: 561499
Avinash Vashistha *(Co-Chm & Mng Dir)*
Harsh Manglik *(Co-Chm)*

Accenture (Ireland) (2)
Grand Canal Square Grand Canal Harbour
Dublin, 2, Ireland (100%)
Tel.: (353) 16462000
Fax: (353) 16462020
Emp.: 1,000
Business Services
S.I.C.: 7389
N.A.I.C.S.: 561499
Mark Ryan *(Mng Dir)*

Accenture Japan Ltd. (2)
Akasaka Intercity 1 11 44 Akasaka Minato ku
Tokyo, 107-8672, Japan
Tel.: (81) 335883000
Fax: (81) 335883001
Web Site: www.accenture.com
Emp.: 4,000
Business Services
S.I.C.: 7389
N.A.I.C.S.: 561499

Accenture (Korea) Ltd. (2)
10th Fl Kyobo Securities Bldg
Yoido Dong
Youngdeungpo Ku, 150 737 Seoul, Korea (South) (100%)
Tel.: (82) 237778888
Fax: (82) 27691900
Web Site: www.accenture.com
Emp.: 100
Various Business Services
S.I.C.: 7389
N.A.I.C.S.: 561499
Alex Geong *(Mng Dir)*

Accenture Ltd. Nigeria (2)
2nd Floor Citi Bank Building
27 Kofo Abayomi Street, Victoria Island, Lagos, 1712, Nigeria (100%)
Tel.: (234) 12707100
Fax: (234) 12707111
Business Services
S.I.C.: 7389
N.A.I.C.S.: 561499
Niyi Yusus *(Mng Dir)*

Accenture Management GmbH (2)
Campus Kronberg 1
Kronberg, 61476, Germany (100%)
Tel.: (49) 61739499
Fax: (49) 61739498
E-Mail: info-de@accenture.com
Web Site: www.accenture.com
Emp.: 2,000
Business Management Services
S.I.C.: 8741
N.A.I.C.S.: 561110
Frank Riemensperger *(Mng Dir)*

Accenture Oy (2)
Itaanrenkatu 1
PO Box 1109
Helsinki, FIN 00101, Finland (100%)
Tel.: (358) 205725000
Fax: (358) 205721000
E-Mail: finlandservicecenter@accenture.com
Web Site: www.accenture.fi
Emp.: 1,200
Business Services
S.I.C.: 7389
N.A.I.C.S.: 561499
Frank Korsstrom *(Mng Dir)*

Accenture Pte. Ltd. (2)
250 N Bridge Rd # 33-00 Raffles City Tower
Singapore, 179101, Singapore (100%)
Tel.: (65) 64108000
Fax: (65) 64108008
E-Mail: tina.dias@accenture.com
Web Site: www.accenture.com
Emp.: 1,000
Business Services
S.I.C.: 7371
N.A.I.C.S.: 541511
Ceoleylin Teo *(Pres)*
Shtheryl Chan *(CFO)*

Accenture plc (2)
1 Plantation Pl
30 Fenchurch St, London, EC3M 3BD, United Kingdom
Tel.: (44) 2078444000
Fax: (44) 2078444444
E-Mail: mark.bryant@accenture.com
Emp.: 500
Management Consulting, Technological & Outsourcing Services
S.I.C.: 8742
N.A.I.C.S.: 541611

Accenture Sdn. Bhd. (2)
Level 66 Twr 2 Petronas Twin
KLCC 50088 Kuala Lumpur, Malaysia (100%)
Tel.: (60) 327314000
Fax: (60) 320572537
Web Site: www.accenture.com
Business Services
S.I.C.: 7389
N.A.I.C.S.: 561499

Accenture Services Private Ltd. (2)
6th Fl DLF Ctr Sansad Marg
New Delhi, 110 001, India (100%)
Tel.: (91) 1142980100
Fax: (91) 1142980101
E-Mail: ico.talentscout@accenture.com
Web Site: www.accenture.com
Emp.: 100
Business Services
S.I.C.: 7389
N.A.I.C.S.: 561499
Sanjay Jain *(Mng Dir)*

Accenture, S.L. (2)
Plz Pablo Ruiz Picasso S No
28020 Madrid, Spain (100%)
Tel.: (34) 915966000
Fax: (34) 915966695
E-Mail: info@accenture.com
Web Site: www.accenture.com
Emp.: 100
Various Business Services
S.I.C.: 7389
N.A.I.C.S.: 561499
Vicente Moreno *(Mng Dir)*

Accenture Solutions Co. Ltd. (2)
30th Fl Abdulrahim Pl
990 Rama IV Rd, 10500 Bangkok, Thailand (100%)
Tel.: (66) 26361616
Fax: (66) 26361640
E-Mail: info@accenture.com
Emp.: 400
Various Business Services
S.I.C.: 7389
N.A.I.C.S.: 561499

Accenture (South Africa) Pty. Ltd. (2)
Bldg 19 Harrowdene Ofc Park
Kelvin Dr Sandton, Woodmead, 2054, South Africa (100%)
Tel.: (27) 112083000
Fax: (27) 115075400
Emp.: 1,200
Business Services
S.I.C.: 7389
N.A.I.C.S.: 561499
William Nzinda *(Country Mng Partner)*

Accenture Sp. z.o.o. (2)
Ul Sienna 39
Warsaw, 121, Poland (100%)
Tel.: (48) 225288000
Fax: (48) 224640001
E-Mail: pl.office@accenture.com
Web Site: www.accenture.pl
Emp.: 1,100
Business Services
S.I.C.: 7389
N.A.I.C.S.: 561499
Jioosoib Kroc *(Pres)*

Accenture SpA (2)
Via Maurizio Quadrio 17
20154 Milan, Italy (100%)
Tel.: (39) 02 7775 1111
Fax: (39) 02 7776 99999
E-Mail: infoitalia@accenture.com
Web Site: www.accenture.com
Emp.: 100
Management Consulting, Technology & Outsourcing Services
S.I.C.: 7389
N.A.I.C.S.: 561499
Fabio Benasso *(Mng Dir)*

Accenture s.r.o. (2)
Plynarenska 7 C
81409 Bratislava, Slovakia (100%)
Tel.: (421) 259290290
Fax: (421) 259290291
E-Mail: bratislava@accentura.com
Web Site: www.accentura.com
Emp.: 1,000
Various Business Services
S.I.C.: 7389
N.A.I.C.S.: 561499

Accenture Technology Services Ltda. (2)
Rua Alexandre Dumas 2051 Chacara Santo Antonio, Sao Paulo, 04717-004, Brazil (100%)
Tel.: (55) 1151883000
Fax: (55) 1151883200
Technology Services
S.I.C.: 7389
N.A.I.C.S.: 561499

Accenture Technology Solutions GmbH (2)
Kronberg 1 Campus
Kronberg, 61476, Germany (100%)
Tel.: (49) 61739499
Fax: (49) 61739498
E-Mail: info-de@accenture.com
Emp.: 5,000
Technology Services
S.I.C.: 7389
N.A.I.C.S.: 561499

Accenture Technology Solutions (HK) Co. Ltd. (2)
85 Fl International Commerce Center
1 Austin Rd W, Kowloon, China (Hong Kong)
Tel.: (852) 22492388
Fax: (852) 28508956
Emp.: 150
Technology Services
S.I.C.: 7389
N.A.I.C.S.: 561499

Accenture Technology Solutions, KK (2)
Akasaka Intercity 1 11 44 Akasaka Minato ku
Tokyo, 107 8672, Japan
Tel.: (81) 335883000
Fax: (81) 335883001
E-Mail: info.tokyo@accenture.co.jp
Web Site: www.accenture.co.jp
Emp.: 2,000
Business Services
S.I.C.: 7389
N.A.I.C.S.: 561499
Kenzo Maeda *(Pres)*

Accenture Technology Solutions Oy (2)
Itamerenkatu 1 Pl 1109
Helsinki, 101, Finland (100%)
Tel.: (358) 205725000
Fax: (358) 205721000
E-Mail: finlandservicecenter@accenture.com
Web Site: www.accenture.com
Emp.: 950
Technology Services
S.I.C.: 7389
N.A.I.C.S.: 561499
Pasi Koivunen *(Mng Dir)*

Accenture Technology Solutions (2)
Fraumunsterstrasse 16
Zurich, 8001, Switzerland (100%)
Tel.: (41) 442199889
Fax: (41) 442198889
E-Mail: location.zurich@accenture.com
Emp.: 507
Various Technology Services
S.I.C.: 9661
N.A.I.C.S.: 927110
Maryann Krauer *(Dir-HR)*

Accenture Turkey (2)
Is Kuleleri
Kule 2 Kat 5, Istanbul, 34330, Turkey (100%)
Tel.: (90) 2122808100
Fax: (90) 2122805100
E-Mail: sunda.derindag@accenture.com
Web Site: www.accenture.com
Emp.: 200
Various Business Services
S.I.C.: 7389
N.A.I.C.S.: 561499

Accenture UK Ltd. (2)
1 Planatation Place
30 Fenchurch Street, London, EC3M 3BD, United Kingdom UK
Tel.: (44) 2078444000
Web Site: www.accenture.com
Sales Range: $10-24.9 Million
Emp.: 14
Financial Loss Recovery Services
S.I.C.: 6726
N.A.I.C.S.: 525990

Accenture (2)
118 Avenue De France
75013 Paris, 75636, France (100%)
Tel.: (33) 153235555
Fax: (33) 153235323
Web Site: www.accenture.fr
Emp.: 4,000
Business Services
S.I.C.: 7389
N.A.I.C.S.: 561499
Nibou Rel *(Pres)*
John L. Woodward, Jr. *(Assoc Partner & Sr Exec VP-Natl Security Bus Dev)*

Accenture (2)
30 F Shanghai Central Plaza
381 Huai Hai Zhong Road, Shanghai, 200020, China
Tel.: (86) 2123053333
Fax: (86) 2163869922
Web Site: www.accenture.com
Management Consulting Services
S.I.C.: 8748
N.A.I.C.S.: 541618

P.T. Accenture (2)
Wisma 46 Kota BNI 18th Fl Jl
Jakarta, 10220, Indonesia Id (100%)
Tel.: (62) 215746575
Fax: (62) 215746575
Web Site: www.accenture.com
Emp.: 300
Business Services
S.I.C.: 7389
N.A.I.C.S.: 561499
Julianto Sidarto *(Mng Dir)*

Accenture Service Center SRL (1)
RSP Building Roque Saenz Pena 777
Capital Federal, Buenos Aires, Argentina C1035AAC
Tel.: (54) 1143188500
Fax: (54) 1143188555
Web Site: www.accenture.com
Management Consulting & Technology Services
S.I.C.: 8742
N.A.I.C.S.: 541611

Accenture Service Centre Morocco SA (1)
Park Casanearshore Shore 1100 Bd El Qods
Casablanca, 20270, Morocco
Tel.: (212) 522 461950
Fax: (212) 522783031
E-Mail: Accenture.maroc@Accenture.com
Web Site: www.Accenture.com
Emp.: 17
Business Process Outsourcing Services
S.I.C.: 7389
N.A.I.C.S.: 561499
Jose Ramon Alonso *(Gen Mgr)*

Accenture Services AG (1)
Fraumunsterstrasse 16
8001 Zurich, Switzerland
Tel.: (41) 44 2199889
Fax: (41) 442198889
E-Mail: accenture.direct.ela@accenture.com
Emp.: 700
Business Process Outsourcing Services
S.I.C.: 7389
N.A.I.C.S.: 561499
Thomas Meyer *(Mng Dir)*

Accenture Services GmbH (1)
Campus Kronberg 1
61476 Kronberg, Germany
Tel.: (49) 61739499
Fax: (49) 61739498
E-Mail: accenture.direct.ela@accenture.com
Web Site: www.accenture.com
Emp.: 100
Business Process Outsourcing Services
S.I.C.: 7389
N.A.I.C.S.: 561499
Karl Rathgeb *(Mng Dir & Gen Mgr)*

Accenture Services Ltd. (1)
1 Plantation Place 30 Fenchurch Street
London, EC3M 3BD, United Kingdom
Tel.: (44) 2078444000
Fax: (44) 2078444444
Web Site: www.accenture.com
Information Technology Consulting Services
S.I.C.: 7373
N.A.I.C.S.: 541512

Accenture Services (Mauritius) Ltd. (1)
Royal Road Cassis
Port Louis, Mauritius
Tel.: (230) 2032600
Fax: (230) 2086782
Web Site: www.accenture.com
Management Consulting & Technology Services
S.I.C.: 8742
N.A.I.C.S.: 541611

Accenture Services Oy (1)
Itamerenkatu 1
180 Helsinki, Finland
Tel.: (358) 205 7 25000
Fax: (358) 205721000
E-Mail: finlandservicecenter@accenture.co m
Web Site: www.accenture.com
Emp.: 130
Business Process Outsourcing Services
S.I.C.: 7389
N.A.I.C.S.: 561499
Stefan Damlin *(CEO)*

Accenture Services (South Africa) Pty Ltd. (1)
Bld 19 Harrowdene Office Park Kelvin Drive
Johannesburg, Gauteng, 2191, South Africa
Tel.: (27) 112083000
Fax: (27) 115475400
Web Site: www.accenture.com
Emp.: 200
Management Consulting Services
S.I.C.: 8748
N.A.I.C.S.: 541618
William Mzimba *(Mng Dir)*

Accenture Services Sp. z.o.o. (1)
ul Chocimska 17
00-791 Warsaw, Poland
Tel.: (48) 22 349 70 00
Fax: (48) 22 349 70 01
Emp.: 60
Business Process Outsourcing Services
S.I.C.: 7389
N.A.I.C.S.: 561499

Accenture Services S.r.l. (1)
24 Preciziei Bd Westgate Office Park H1 Building 1st Floor
6th district, 062204 Bucharest, Romania
Tel.: (40) 372286000
Fax: (40) 372286001
E-Mail: romania@accenture.com
Web Site: www.accenture.com
Management Consulting & Technology Services
S.I.C.: 8742
N.A.I.C.S.: 541611
Andrea Multare *(Mng Dir-Country)*

Accenture Services s.r.o (1)
Bucharova 8
158 00 Prague, Czech Republic
Tel.: (420) 225 045 000
Fax: (420) 225 045 900
Emp.: 800
Business Process Outsourcing Services
S.I.C.: 7389
N.A.I.C.S.: 561499

Accenture Services s.r.o. (1)
Plynarenska 7/C St
82109 Bratislava, Slovakia
Tel.: (421) 259290290
Fax: (421) 259290291
Web Site: www.accenture.com
Business Process Outsourcing Services
S.I.C.: 7389
N.A.I.C.S.: 561499
Peter Skodny *(Country Mng Dir)*

Accenture Solutions Sdn Bhd (1)
Level 35 The Gardens North Tower Mid Valley City
Lingkaran Syed Putra, 59200 Kuala Lumpur, Malaysia
Tel.: (60) 320884000
Fax: (60) 320887000
Web Site: www.accenture.com
Management Consulting & Technology Services
S.I.C.: 8742
N.A.I.C.S.: 541611
Aik Meng Goh *(Mng Dir-Country)*

Accenture Tanacsado Korlatolt Felelossegu Tarsasag KFT (1)
Rakoczi u 1-3
Budapest, 1088, Hungary
Tel.: (36) 1 327 3700
Fax: (36) 1 266 7709
E-Mail: info.budapest@accenture.com
Web Site: www.accenture.hu
Software Development Services
S.I.C.: 7371
N.A.I.C.S.: 541511
Peter Skodny *(Gen Mgr)*

Accenture Technolgy Solutions (Thailand) Ltd. (1)
30th Floor Abdulrahim Place 990 Rama IV Road
Silom Bangrak, Bangkok, Thailand
Tel.: (66) 2 636 1616
Fax: (66) 2 636 1640
Information Technology Consulting Services
S.I.C.: 7373
N.A.I.C.S.: 541512

Accenture Technology Solutions A/S (1)
Arne Jacobsens Alle
Orestad, Copenhagen, 2300, Denmark
Tel.: (45) 72288188
Business Process Outsourcing Services
S.I.C.: 7389
N.A.I.C.S.: 561499
Pernille Molbak *(Mgr-SAP)*

Accenture Technology Solutions BV (1)
Gustav Mahlerplein 90
1082 MA Amsterdam, Netherlands
Tel.: (31) 20 4938383
E-Mail: marketing.nl@accenture.com
Web Site: www.accenture.com
Emp.: 800
Information Technology Consulting Services
S.I.C.: 7371
N.A.I.C.S.: 541511

Accenture Technology Solutions-Canada, Inc. (1)
630 Blvd Rene-Levesque Ouest
Montreal, QC, H3B 1S6, Canada
Tel.: (514) 848-1648
Fax: (514) 848-0785
Web Site: www.accenture.com
Emp.: 30
Business Process Outsourcing Services
S.I.C.: 7389
N.A.I.C.S.: 561499

Accenture Technology Solutions (Dalian) Co Ltd. (1)
No 1 North Section Digital Road
Dalian, 116023, China
Tel.: (86) 41182147800
Fax: (86) 41184768876
Business Process Outsourcing Services
S.I.C.: 7389
N.A.I.C.S.: 561499

Accenture Technology Solutions GmbH (1)
Boersengebaeude Schottenring 16
1010 Vienna, Austria
Tel.: (43) 1 205020
Fax: (43) 1 205021
Business Process Outsourcing Services
S.I.C.: 7389
N.A.I.C.S.: 561499

Accenture Technology Solutions Ltd. (1)
10th Fl Posco P&S Tower 735-3 Yeoksam-Dong
Gangnam-Gu, Seoul, Korea (South) 135-923
Tel.: (82) 237778888
Fax: (82) 27691900
Web Site: www.accenture.com
Management Consulting & Technology Services
S.I.C.: 8742
N.A.I.C.S.: 541611

Accenture Technology Solutions Pte Ltd. (1)
250 North Bridge Road 33-00 Raffles City Tower
Singapore, 179101, Singapore
Tel.: (65) 6410 8000
Information Technology Consulting Services
S.I.C.: 7373
N.A.I.C.S.: 541512

Accenture Technology Solutions Pty Ltd. (1)
Level 24 400 George St
Brisbane, QLD, 4001, Australia
Tel.: (61) 731174001
Fax: (61) 731174455
Web Site: www.accenture.com
Management Consulting & Technology Services
S.I.C.: 8742
N.A.I.C.S.: 541611

Accenture Technology Solutions S.A. (1)
Avenida da Boavista n 1837 Edificio Torre Burgo 13 Àndar Sala 3
4100-133 Porto, Portugal
Tel.: (351) 229471430
Fax: (351) 213713500
Information Technology Consulting Services
S.I.C.: 7373
N.A.I.C.S.: 541512

Accenture Technology Solutions SAS (1)
125 Avenue de Paris
92320 Chatillon, France
Tel.: (33) 472831620
Fax: (33) 472831621
E-Mail: direction.achats@accenture.com
Web Site: www.accenture.com
Management Consulting & Technology Services
S.I.C.: 8742
N.A.I.C.S.: 541611
Pierre Nanterme *(Chm & CEO)*
David C. Thomlinson *(Chief Strategy Officer-Geographic & COO)*
Johan G. Deblaere *(COO)*
Roxanne Taylor *(CMO & Chief Comm Officer)*
Hawn Collinson *(Chief Strategy Officer)*
Adrian Lajtha *(Chief Leadership Officer)*
David P. Rowland *(Sr VP-Fin)*

Accenture Technology Solutions S.C. (1)
Blvd Manuel Avila Camacho No 138 Piso 7
Lomas de Chapultepec
Mexico, 11000, Mexico
Tel.: (52) 5552847300
Fax: (52) 5552847301
Web Site: www.accenture.com
Management Consulting & Technology Services
S.I.C.: 8742
N.A.I.C.S.: 541611

Accenture Technology Solutions Sdn Bhd (1)
Level 35 The Gardens North Tower Mid Valley City Lingkaran Syed Putra
59200 Kuala Lumpur, Malaysia

Accenture plc—(Continued)

Tel.: (60) 320884000
Fax: (60) 320887000
Web Site: www.accenturetechnologysolutions.it/my-en/
Emp.: 1,000
Information Technology Consulting Services
S.I.C.: 7373
N.A.I.C.S.: 541512
Goh Aik Meng *(Mng Dir)*

Accenture Technology Solutions-Slovakia s.r.o. (1)
Plynarenska 7/C
Bratislava, 821 09, Slovakia
Tel.: (421) 259290290
Fax: (421) 59290291
Information Technology Consulting Services
S.I.C.: 7373
N.A.I.C.S.: 541512

Accenture Technology Solutions-Solucoes Informaticas Integrados, S.A. (1)
Avenida Eng Duarte Pacheco Amoreiras Torre 1-16 Piso
1070-101 Lisbon, Portugal
Tel.: (351) 213803500
Fax: (351) 213713500
Business Process Outsourcing Services
S.I.C.: 7389
N.A.I.C.S.: 561499
Jose Galamba de Oliveira *(Mng Dir)*

Accenture Technology Solutions SRL (1)
Via Maurizio Quadrio 17
Milan, 20154, Italy
Tel.: (39) 0277751111
Fax: (39) 02777699999
Web Site: www.accenturetechnologysolutions.it
Information Technology Consulting Services
S.I.C.: 7373
N.A.I.C.S.: 541512
Lindsey Basadien *(Mgr-Mgmt Consulting)*

Accenture Technology Solutions s.r.o. (1)
The Dancing House Jiraskovo Namesti 6
120 00 Prague, Czech Republic
Tel.: (420) 221984545
Fax: (420) 221984646
Web Site: www.accenture.com
Management Consulting & Technology Services
S.I.C.: 8742
N.A.I.C.S.: 541611

Accenture Technology Ventures BV (1)
Gustav Mahlerplein 90
Amsterdam, North Holland, 1082 MA, Netherlands
Tel.: (31) 204938383
Fax: (31) 206748830
Management Consulting & Technology Services
S.I.C.: 8742
N.A.I.C.S.: 541611

Accenture Technology Ventures S.P.R.L. (1)
Rue Royale 145 Koningsstraat
Brussels, 1000, Belgium
Tel.: (32) 2 226 72 11
Fax: (32) 2 226 72 33
Information Technology Consulting Services
S.I.C.: 7373
N.A.I.C.S.: 541512

Acquity Group Limited (1)
6th Floor Alexandra House 18 Chater Road
Hong Kong, China (Hong Kong) Ky
Tel.: (852) 3106 4999
Fax: (852) 3106 4706
Web Site: www.acquitygroup.com
Rev.: $141,011,000
Assets: $110,856,000
Liabilities: $18,433,000
Net Worth: $92,423,000
Earnings: $2,537,000
Emp.: 645
Fiscal Year-end: 12/31/12
Holding Company; Brand E-Commerce & Digital Marketing
S.I.C.: 7319
N.A.I.C.S.: 541890
Jay Dettling *(Pres)*
Tim Irvine *(Chief Experience Officer)*
Adrian Chan *(Sec)*
Raymond Grady *(Exec VP & Head-Global Sls)*
Andy Peebler *(Exec VP)*
Robert Barr *(Sr VP-Tech Svcs)*
David Chang *(Sr VP-Digital Strategy, Mktg & Creative Svcs)*
Karen Jackson *(Sr VP-HR)*

U.S. Subsidiary:

Acquity Group, LLC (2)
500 W Madison St Ste 2200
Chicago, IL 60661
Tel.: (312) 427-2470
Fax: (312) 427-2471
Web Site: www.acquitygroup.com
Emp.: 300
Brand E-Commerce & Digital Marketing
S.I.C.: 7319
N.A.I.C.S.: 541890
Matthew Schmeltz *(Founder & CMO)*
Paul Weinewuth *(CFO)*
Jay Dettling *(Pres-North American Svcs)*
Ray Grady *(Exec VP-Business Dev & Expansion Strategy)*
James Newman *(Exec VP-Recruiting, HR, IT, Consultant Ops & Internal Application)*
Andrew Peebler *(Exec VP-Bus Dev)*
Mark Joseph *(Sr VP-Inside Sls & Accts)*

Alnova Technologies Corporation S.L. (1)
Ramirez de Arellano 35
Madrid, 28043, Spain
Tel.: (34) 91 596 60 76
Fax: (34) 91 596 66 95
Web Site: www.alnovatech.com
Information Technology Consulting Services
S.I.C.: 7373
N.A.I.C.S.: 541512

Avanade Asia Pte Ltd. (1)
250 North Bridge Road
No 30-03 Raffles City Tower, Singapore, 179101, Singapore
Tel.: (65) 65922133
Fax: (65) 63380943
Web Site: www.avanade.com
Application Program Development & Outsourcing Services
S.I.C.: 7371
N.A.I.C.S.: 541511
Kevin Wo *(VP & Country Mgr)*

Avanade Australia Pty Ltd. (1)
Level 24 400 George Street
Brisbane, QLD, 4000, Australia
Tel.: (61) 731174540
Fax: (61) 731174541
Web Site: www.avanade.com
Application Program Development & Outsourcing Services
S.I.C.: 7371
N.A.I.C.S.: 541511
Jeyan Jeevaratnam *(Mng Dir & Sr VP)*

Avanade Belgium SPRL (1)
Medialaan 38
1800 Vilvoorde, Belgium
Tel.: (32) 22267774
Fax: (32) 22267776
Web Site: www.avanade.com
Application Program Development & Outsourcing Services
S.I.C.: 7371
N.A.I.C.S.: 541511
Nicolas Marry *(Gen Mgr)*

Avanade Canada Inc. (1)
140 4th Avenue West Suite 300
Calgary, AB, T2P 3N3 , Canada
Tel.: (403) 774-9555
Fax: (403) 476-1511
Web Site: www.avanade.com
Application Program Development & Outsourcing Services
S.I.C.: 7371
N.A.I.C.S.: 541511
Benoit Bertrand *(VP & CTO)*

Avanade Denmark ApS (1)
Arne Jacobsens Alle 15
2300 Copenhagen, Denmark
Tel.: (45) 70107172
Fax: (45) 70137172
Emp.: 60
Management Consulting & Technology Services
S.I.C.: 8742
N.A.I.C.S.: 541611
Morten Stern *(Mng Dir)*

Avanade Deutschland GmbH (1)
Campus Kronberg 7
61476 Kronberg, Germany
Tel.: (49) 61739463800
Fax: (49) 61739463999
Web Site: www.avanade.com
Emp.: 50
Application Program Development & Outsourcing Services
S.I.C.: 7371
N.A.I.C.S.: 541511
Andrew Smith *(Mng Dir)*

Avanade do Brasil Ltda (1)
Rua Alexandre Dumas 2051 Ch Santo Antonio
Sao Paulo, 04717-007, Brazil
Tel.: (55) 1151883000
Fax: (55) 1151883200
E-Mail: avanade.brazil@avanade.com
Web Site: www.avanade.com
Emp.: 350
Application Program Development & Outsourcing Services
S.I.C.: 7371
N.A.I.C.S.: 541511
Jun Endo *(Mng Dir)*
Hamilton Berteli *(CTO)*

Avanade Finland Oy (1)
Porkkalankatu 5
00180 Helsinki, Finland
Tel.: (358) 207433380
Fax: (358) 207433381
Application Program Development & Outsourcing Services
S.I.C.: 7371
N.A.I.C.S.: 541511
Peter Lindberg *(VP-Bus Dev)*

Avanade Guangzhou (1)
Unit 7 10th Floor The Hna Tower No 8 Linhe Zhong Lu
Tianhe District, Guangzhou, Guangdong, China 510610
Tel.: (86) 2028317367
Fax: (86) 2028317268
Web Site: www.avanade.com
Application Program Development & Outsourcing Services
S.I.C.: 7371
N.A.I.C.S.: 541511

Avanade Japan KK (1)
Yagi Ark Hills 6F 1-8-7 Roppongi
Minato-ku, Tokyo, 106-0032 , Japan
Tel.: (81) 362340150
Fax: (81) 362340151
Web Site: www.avanade.com
Application Program Development & Outsourcing Services
S.I.C.: 7371
N.A.I.C.S.: 541511
Takashi Ishikawa *(Gen Mgr)*

Avanade Malaysia Sdn Bhd (1)
Suite 22 01 Level 22 The Gardens North Tower Mid Valley City
Lingkaran Syed Putra, Kuala Lumpur, 59200, Malaysia
Tel.: (60) 320887111
Fax: (60) 320887112
E-Mail: malaysiahr@avanade.com
Web Site: www.avanade.com
Emp.: 70
Application Program Development & Outsourcing Services
S.I.C.: 7371
N.A.I.C.S.: 541511
Mahmood Ghani *(Country Mgr)*

Avanade Netherlands BV (1)
Amplifier Street 6
1322 AP Almere, Netherlands
Tel.: (31) 365475100
Fax: (31) 365475156
E-Mail: info-nl@avanede.com
Web Site: www.avanade.com
Emp.: 300
Application Program Development & Outsourcing Services
S.I.C.: 7371
N.A.I.C.S.: 541511
Eric Hol *(VP-Solution Dev)*

Avanade Norway AS (1)
Snaroyveien 30 Building A
Fornebu, 1360, Norway
Tel.: (47) 67128570
Fax: (47) 67531631
Application Program Development & Outsourcing Services
S.I.C.: 7371
N.A.I.C.S.: 541511
Goran Karlsson *(Sr Dir-Bus Dev)*

Avanade Schweiz GmbH (1)
Innere Margarethenstrasse 5
4051 Basel, Switzerland
Tel.: (41) 612044545
Web Site: www.avanade.com
Application Program Development & Outsourcing Services
S.I.C.: 7371
N.A.I.C.S.: 541511
Andrew Smith *(Gen Mgr)*

Avanade Spain SL (1)
Paseo De Gracia 11 Esc C 3rd Floor
08007 Barcelona, Spain
Tel.: (34) 934459300
Fax: (34) 934459301
Web Site: www.avanade.com
Application Program Development & Outsourcing Services
S.I.C.: 7371
N.A.I.C.S.: 541511
Jordi Griful *(CEO)*
Emilio Jaraiz *(CFO)*
Ramon Miranda *(CTO)*

Avanade Sweden AB (1)
Alstromergatan 12
PO Box 12502
102 29 Stockholm, Sweden
Tel.: (46) 84021270
Fax: (46) 84513001
Application Program Development & Outsourcing Services
S.I.C.: 7371
N.A.I.C.S.: 541511

Beaumont Development Centre Holding Ltd. (1)
Royal Road Cassis
Port Louis, Mauritius
Tel.: (230) 4021700
Investment Management Services
S.I.C.: 6211
N.A.I.C.S.: 523999

Coritel S.A. (1)
Paseo de la Finca 1 Bloque 2
Pozuelo de Alarcon, 28223 Madrid, Spain
Tel.: (34) 915967000
Fax: (34) 915967100
E-Mail: atencion.clientes.coritel@accenture.com
Web Site: www.coritel.es
Emp.: 5,000
Application Program Development & Outsourcing Services
S.I.C.: 7371
N.A.I.C.S.: 541511
Antonio Moncada *(Partner)*

CustomerWorks Europe SL (1)
Poligono Teknologi Elkartegia Ed 207 A Plt -1
Zamudio, 48170, Spain
Tel.: (34) 944062200
Fax: (34) 944062205
Business Management Consulting Services
S.I.C.: 8742
N.A.I.C.S.: 541611

Digiplug SAS (1)
12 rue Godot de Mauroy
75009 Paris, France
Tel.: (33) 1 53 43 37 00
E-Mail: sales@digiplug.com
Web Site: www.digiplug.com
Emp.: 10
Digital Software Development Services
S.I.C.: 7371
N.A.I.C.S.: 541511
Rahmyn Kress *(Pres & CEO)*
Vincent Cabanel *(COO)*
Regis Allegre *(CTO)*

Insurance Services SAS (1)
40 Rue Jean Mermoz
78600 Maisons-Laffitte, France
Tel.: (33) 182040400
Fax: (33) 134 934 089

General Insurance Services
S.I.C.: 6411
N.A.I.C.S.: 524210

Operaciones Accenture S.A. de C.V. (1)
Boulevard Manuel Avila Camacho No 138
Piso 7 Lomas de Chapultepec
Miguel Hidalgo, Mexico, 11000, Mexico
Tel.: (52) 5552847300
Fax: (52) 5552847301
Business Process Outsourcing Services
S.I.C.: 7389
N.A.I.C.S.: 561499

Qi Jie (Beijing) Info Tech Co Ltd. (1)
808 8th Floor Ocean International Center A
No 56 Dong Si Huan Zhong Lu
Chaoyang District, Beijing, 100025, China
Tel.: (86) 105908 1687
Fax: (86) 105908 1723
Web Site: www.qijie-tech.com
Information Technology Consulting Services
S.I.C.: 7373
N.A.I.C.S.: 541512
Alex Yang *(Gen Mgr)*

ACCES INDUSTRIE SA

2 rue du Pont de Garonne
47400 Tonneins, France
Tel.: (33) 5 53 88 27 98
Fax: (33) 5 53 84 41 94
E-Mail: contact@acces-industrie.com
Web Site: www.acces-industrie.com
Year Founded: 1997
ALACI—(EUR)
Sales Range: $50-74.9 Million
Emp.: 453

Business Description:
Aerial Work Platforms & Telescopic Handlers Rental & Leasing Services
S.I.C.: 7359
N.A.I.C.S.: 532412

Personnel:
Pierre Costes *(Chm-Supervisory Bd)*
Daniel Duclos *(Chm-Mgmt Bd & Pres)*
Francoise Duclos *(Vice Chm-Supervisory Bd)*

Supervisory Board of Directors:
Pierre Costes
Olivier Athanase
Walter Butler
Mael de la Lande de Calan
Francoise Duclos

ACCESS BANK PLC

Plot 999c Danmole Street Off Adeola Odeku/Idejo Street Victoria Island
Lagos, Nigeria
Tel.: (234) 12805628
Fax: (234) 1 2771185
E-Mail: info@accessbankplc.com
Web Site: www.accessbankplc.com
Year Founded: 1989
ACCESS—(NIGE)
Rev.: $1,310,262,811
Assets: $10,977,165,701
Liabilities: $9,461,335,551
Net Worth: $1,515,830,151
Earnings: $241,566,091
Emp.: 10,164
Fiscal Year-end: 12/31/12

Business Description:
Banking Services
S.I.C.: 6029
N.A.I.C.S.: 522110

Personnel:
Aigboje Aig-Imoukhuede *(CEO & Mng Dir)*
Tunde Coker *(CIO)*
Greg Jobome *(Chief Risk Officer, Head-Enterprise Risk Mgmt & Gen Mgr)*
Hebert Wigwe *(Grp Deputy Mng Dir)*
Adedapo Olagunju *(Treas & Deputy Gen Mgr)*
Sunday Ekwochi *(Sec)*

Board of Directors:
Gbenga Oyebode
Aigboje Aig-Imoukhuede
Ajoritsedere Awosika
Emmanuel Ndubisi Chiejina
Victor Etuokwu
Babatunde Folawiyo
Mahmoud Isa-Dutse
Taukeme Koroye
Ernest Ndukwe
Okey Nwuke
Anthonia Olufeyikemi Ogunmefun
Mosunmola Olusoga
Ortishedere Samuel Otubu
Hebert Wigwe

Subsidiaries:

Intercontinental Homes Savings & Loans Limited (1)
26 Adeola Hopewell Street
Victoria Island, Lagos, Nigeria
Tel.: (234) 1 2771127
Mortgage Banking
S.I.C.: 6163
N.A.I.C.S.: 522310

Intercontinental Life Assurance Company Limited (1)
6 Hughes Avenue
Alagomeji, Yaba, Lagos, Nigeria
Tel.: (234) 1 4611637
Fax: (234) 1 4630754
Web Site: www.intercontinentallifeng.com
Life Insurance
S.I.C.: 6311
N.A.I.C.S.: 524113
Olajide Akinola *(CEO & Mng Dir)*

Intercontinental Properties Limited (1)
IPL Plaza 274 Murtala Mohammed Way
Herbert Macaulay Street
Alagomeji, Yaba, Lagos, Nigeria
Tel.: (234) 1 2771459
E-Mail: info@intercontinentalpropertieslimited.com
Web Site: www.intercontinentalpropertieslimited.com
Property Development & Support Services
S.I.C.: 6531
N.A.I.C.S.: 531390
O. I. Asamu *(CEO & Mng Dir)*

Wapic Insurance Plc (1)
119 Awolowo Road
Ikoyi, Lagos, Nigeria
Tel.: (234) 1 4615153
Fax: (234) 1 4613433
E-Mail: info@intercontinentalwapicinsplc.com
Web Site: www.intercontinentalwapicinsplc.com
Insurance Services
S.I.C.: 6331
N.A.I.C.S.: 524126
Segun Balogun *(Mng Dir)*

Non-U.S. Subsidiaries:

Access Bank Cote d'Ivoire (1)
Immeuble Woodin Center Avenue Nogues
BP 6928
Abidjan, Cote d'Ivoire
Tel.: (225) 20 31 58 30
Fax: (225) 20 22 56 41
E-Mail: info.cotedivoire@accessbankplc.com
Web Site: www.accessbankplc.com
Banking Services
S.I.C.: 6029
N.A.I.C.S.: 522110

Access Bank (D.R. Congo) Sarl (1)
158 Avenue de la Democratie
Kinshasa, Gombe, Congo, Democratic Republic of
Tel.: (243) 81 22 22 111
Fax: (243) 81 22 22 116
E-Mail: info.rdcongo@accessbankplc.com
Web Site: www.accessbankplc.com
Banking Services
S.I.C.: 6029
N.A.I.C.S.: 522110

Access Bank (Gambia) Limited (1)
47 Kairaba Avenue
Fajara, KMSD, Gambia
Mailing Address:
PO Box 3177
Serrekunda, Gambia
Tel.: (220) 4398227
Fax: (220) 4396640
E-Mail: info.gambia@accessbankplc.com
Web Site: www.accessbankplc.com
Banking Services
S.I.C.: 6029
N.A.I.C.S.: 522110

Access Bank (Ghana) Limited (1)
Starlets 91 Road Opposite Accra Sports Stadium
PO Box GP 353
Osu, Accra, Ghana
Tel.: (233) 302 684 860
E-Mail: info.ghana@accessbankplc.com
Web Site: www.accessbankplc.com
Banking Services
S.I.C.: 6029
N.A.I.C.S.: 522110

Access Bank (Rwanda) Limited (1)
3rd Floor UTC Building Avenue de la Paix
PO Box 2059
Kigali, Rwanda
Tel.: (250) 252 500089
Fax: (250) 252 575761
E-Mail: info.rwanda@accessbankplc.com
Web Site: www.accessbankplc.com
Banking Services
S.I.C.: 6029
N.A.I.C.S.: 522110

Access Bank (Sierra Leone) Limited (1)
30 Siaka Stevens Street
Freetown, Sierra Leone
Tel.: (232) 25 334933
Fax: (232) 22 220119
Banking Services
S.I.C.: 6029
N.A.I.C.S.: 522110

Access Bank (UK) Limited (1)
4 Royal Court Gadbrook Way
Gadbrook Park, Northwich, Cheshire, CW9 7UT, United Kingdom
Tel.: (44) 1606813020
Fax: (44) 2031786721
E-Mail: info@theaccessbankukltd.co.uk
Web Site: www.theaccessbankukltd.co.uk
Emp.: 50
Banking Services
S.I.C.: 6029
N.A.I.C.S.: 522110
Jamie Simmonds *(CEO & Mng Dir)*
Sean McLaughlin *(Dir-Fin & COO)*

Access Bank (Zambia) Limited (1)
Plot 682 Cairo Road Northend
PO Box 35273
Lusaka, Zambia
Tel.: (260) 211 227941
Fax: (260) 211 227956
E-Mail: info.zambia@accessbankplc.com
Web Site: www.accessbankplc.com
Banking Services
S.I.C.: 6029
N.A.I.C.S.: 522110

Finbank SA (1)
16 Boulevard de La Liberte
BP 2998
Place de l'Independence, Bujumbura, Burundi
Tel.: (257) 22 24 32 06
Fax: (257) 22 24 32 07
E-Mail: info@finbankburundi.com
Web Site: www.finbankburundi.com
Banking Services
S.I.C.: 6029
N.A.I.C.S.: 522110

ACCESS CO., LTD.

1-10-2 Nakase
Mihama-ku, Chiba, Chiba, 261-0023, Japan
Tel.: (81) 43 212 2111
Fax: (81) 43 212 3222
E-Mail: adinfo@access.co.jp
Web Site: gl.access-company.com
Year Founded: 1979
4813—(TKS)
Sls.: $128,832,000
Assets: $377,399,000
Liabilities: $25,597,000
Net Worth: $351,802,000
Earnings: $28,600,000
Emp.: 615
Fiscal Year-end: 01/31/13

Business Description:
Mobile Content Delivery & Internet Access Technologies
S.I.C.: 4812
N.A.I.C.S.: 517210

Personnel:
Nobuya Murofushi *(Pres & CEO)*
Koichi Narasaki *(COO & Exec VP)*
Kunihiro Ishiguro *(Co-CTO)*
Michimasa Uematsu *(Co-CTO)*
Kiyoyasu Oishi *(Chief Bus Dev Officer)*

Board of Directors:
Kunihiro Ishiguro
Yoshihiko Miyauchi
Nobuya Murofushi
Koichi Narasaki
Takeshi Niinami
Kiyoyasu Oishi

Subsidiary:

ACCESS Publishing Co. Ltd. (1)
Sarugaku-cho 2-8-16
Chiyoda-ku, 101-0064 Tokyo, Japan
Tel.: (81) 352593511
Fax: (81) 352593532
E-Mail: support@tokyo-calendar.tv
Web Site: www.tokyo-calendar.tv
Periodical Publishers
S.I.C.: 2721
N.A.I.C.S.: 511120

U.S. Subsidiaries:

ACCESS Systems Americas Inc. (1)
1188 E Arques Ave
Sunnyvale, CA 94085-4602
Tel.: (408) 400-3000
Fax: (408) 400-1500
Web Site: www.access-company.com
Emp.: 100
Computer Systems Design Services
S.I.C.: 7373
N.A.I.C.S.: 541512
Kiyoyasu Oishi *(CEO)*

ACCESS Systems USA, Inc. (1)
1188 E Arques Ave
Sunnyvale, CA 94085
Tel.: (408) 400-1900
Fax: (408) 400-1500
Web Site: www.access-company.com
Operating Systems for Handheld Computers
S.I.C.: 7371
N.A.I.C.S.: 541511
Kiyoyasu Oishi *(Chm & CEO)*

Non-U.S. Subsidiaries:

ACCESS (Beijing) Co., Ltd. (1)
3rd Fl China Data Kingdom Mansion
No 1 North Wangjing Road
Chaoyang District, 100102 Beijing, China
Tel.: (86) 1064396000
Fax: (86) 1064396001
Web Site: www.access-company.com
Emp.: 100
Other Telecommunications
S.I.C.: 4899
N.A.I.C.S.: 517919
Min Zhao *(CEO)*

ACCESS (Beijing) Media Solutions Co. Ltd (1)
3rd Fl China Data Kingdom Mansion
No 1 N Wangjing Rd Chaoy, 100102
Beijing, China
Tel.: (86) 1064396000
Fax: (86) 1064396001
Web Site: www.accessmedia.com.cn
Emp.: 30
Other Telecommunications
S.I.C.: 4899
N.A.I.C.S.: 517919
Pierre Suhandinata *(CEO)*

ACCESS (Nanjing) Co. Ltd. (1)
189 Guangzhou Road 18th Floor
Gulou District, 210009 Nanjing, China
Tel.: (86) 2583209900

Access Co., Ltd.—(Continued)
Fax: (86) 2583247799
Web Site: www.access-company.com
Internet Service Providers
S.I.C.: 4899
N.A.I.C.S.: 517919
Zhao Min *(CEO)*

ACCESS Seoul Co. Ltd (1)
402 DMC High-tech Industry Center
121-835 Seoul, Korea (South)
Tel.: (82) 231537900
Fax: (82) 231537910
E-Mail: hyeokmin.kwon@access-company.com
Web Site: www.access-company.com
Emp.: 100
Software Reproducing
S.I.C.: 3652
N.A.I.C.S.: 334614
Toru Arakawa *(Chm & CEO)*

ACCESS Europe GmbH (1)
Essener Strasse 5 TZU-IV
46047 Oberhausen, Germany
Tel.: (49) 208 8290 6464
Fax: (49) 208 8290 6465
E-Mail: obe-info@access-company.com
Web Site: eu.access-company.com
Emp.: 20
Custom Computer Programming Services
S.I.C.: 7371
N.A.I.C.S.: 541511
Raiko Funakami *(CEO)*

ACCESS Systems France SARL (1)
Parc Club du Millenaire - Batiment 24 1025 Rue Henri Becquerel BP 59, 34935
Montpellier, France
Tel.: (33) 499524300
Fax: (33) 499524399
E-Mail: micheal.teiueal@access-company.com
Web Site: www.access-company.com
Emp.: 70
Custom Computer Programming Services
S.I.C.: 7371
N.A.I.C.S.: 541511
Pick Mount *(Pres)*
Michael Teiueal *(CEO)*

ACCESS INTELLIGENCE PLC
32 Bedford Row
London, WC1R 4HE, United Kingdom
Tel.: (44) 2074000485
Fax: (44) 2078315077
E-Mail: info@accessintelligence.com
Web Site: www.accessintelligence.com
ACC—(LSE)
Rev.: $12,718,022
Assets: $24,076,276
Liabilities: $9,728,426
Net Worth: $14,347,850
Earnings: ($180,039)
Emp.: 104
Fiscal Year-end: 11/30/12

Business Description:
Software & Computer Services
S.I.C.: 7371
N.A.I.C.S.: 541511

Personnel:
Michael E. W. Jackson *(Chm)*
Kole Dhoot *(CFO)*
Joanna Arnold *(COO)*
Jeremy J. Hamer *(Sec)*

Board of Directors:
Michael E. W. Jackson
Joanna Arnold
Henrik Peter Bang
Kole Dhoot
Jeremy J. Hamer
Ray R. Jackson
David Lowe

Legal Counsel:
Wright Hassall LLP
Olympus House Olympus Avenue Leamington Spa
Warwick, United Kingdom

Subsidiaries:

Access Intelligence Media & Communications Ltd. (1)
3rd Floor Welken House 10-11 Charterhouse Square
London, EC1M 6EH, United Kingdom
Tel.: (44) 84 3659 3480
Fax: (44) 84 3659 3482
E-Mail: info@aimediacomms.com
Web Site: www.aimediacomms.com
Emp.: 20
Software Support Services
S.I.C.: 7371
N.A.I.C.S.: 541511
Charlie O'Rourke *(Mng Dir)*

Solcara Limited (1)
The Long Rm Coppermill Lock
Harefield, Middlesex, UB9 6JA, United Kingdom
Tel.: (44) 1895820950
Fax: (44) 1895820955
E-Mail: info@solcara.com
Web Site: www.solcara.com
Emp.: 15
Software Development Services
S.I.C.: 7371
N.A.I.C.S.: 541511
Rob Martin *(Mng Dir)*

ACCESS INTERNATIONAL EDUCATION LTD.
100 - B1 - 2451 Dieppe Ave SW
Calgary, AB, T3E 7K1, Canada
Tel.: (403) 217-3830
E-Mail: info@accessinternationaleducation.com
Web Site: www.accessinternationaleducation.com
Year Founded: 1967
AOE—(TSXV)

Business Description:
Education Services
S.I.C.: 8211
N.A.I.C.S.: 611110

Personnel:
Chris Gee *(Chm, Pres & CEO)*
David Chen *(Acting CFO)*
Jian Li *(COO)*
Roger Humbke *(Chief Academic Officer)*

Board of Directors:
Chris Gee
David Chen
Jian Li

Transfer Agent:
Computershare Investor Services Inc.
3rd Floor 510 Burrard St
V6C 3B9 Vancouver, BC, Canada

ACCESSKENYA GROUP LIMITED
3rd & 4th Floor Purshotam Place
Westlands Road
PO Box 43588
00100 Nairobi, Kenya
Tel.: (254) 203600000
Fax: (254) 203742107
E-Mail: info@accesskenya.com
Web Site: www.accesskenya.com
ACES—(NAI)
Sls.: $21,343,963
Assets: $25,443,968
Liabilities: $11,435,902
Net Worth: $14,008,066
Earnings: $1,699,964
Fiscal Year-end: 12/31/12

Business Description:
Internet Service Providers
S.I.C.: 4813
N.A.I.C.S.: 517110

Personnel:
Jonathan Somen *(Co-Founder & Mng Dir)*
David Somen *(Co-Founder)*
Daniel Ndonye *(Chm)*
Peter Ndirangu *(CFO)*
Raymond Macharia *(CTO)*
Conrad Nyukuri *(Sec)*

Board of Directors:
Daniel Ndonye
Titus Naikuni
Nick Reed
Paras Shah
David Somen
Jonathan Somen
Julian Sunker
Michael Turner
Derek Wilcocks

Legal Counsel:
Hamilton Harrison & Mathews
PO Box 30033
Nairobi, Kenya

Subsidiaries:

Broadband Access Limited (1)
Purshottam Pl Building Westlands Road
City Centre, Nairobi, Kenya
Tel.: (254) 203 101 64
Internet Service Provider
S.I.C.: 4899
N.A.I.C.S.: 517919

Communication Solutions Limited (1)
TSS Towers 14th Floor Nkrumah Road
PO Box 81364
Mombasa, Coast Province, Kenya
Tel.: (254) 41 222 20 54
Fax: (254) 41 222 64 78
E-Mail: info@accesskenya.com
Emp.: 20
Internet Service Provider
S.I.C.: 4899
N.A.I.C.S.: 517919
Jackline Mate *(Branch Mgr)*

ACCESSO TECHNOLOGY GROUP PLC
(Formerly Lo-Q plc)
Unit 2 The Pavilions Ruscombe Park
Twyford, Berks, RG10 9NN, United Kingdom
Tel.: (44) 1189347400
Fax: (44) 1189347410
Web Site: www.accesso.com
Year Founded: 2000
ACSO—(AIM)
Rev.: $46,016,357
Assets: $21,116,448
Liabilities: $1,600,988
Net Worth: $19,515,460
Earnings: $3,981,933
Emp.: 372
Fiscal Year-end: 11/04/12

Business Description:
Theme Park Ride Reservation & Virtual Queuing Product Mfr
S.I.C.: 3679
N.A.I.C.S.: 334419

Personnel:
Leonard Sim *(Founder)*
Tom Burnet *(CEO)*
Steve Drake *(COO)*
Chris Galley *(CTO)*
Douglas Armour *(Sec)*

Board of Directors:
John Weston
John Alder
Anthony Bone
Steve Brown
Tom Burnet
Matthew Jonathan Cooper
David Gammon
Leonard Sim

U.S. Subsidiaries:

Lo-Q Virtual Queuing Inc. (1)
351 Thornton Rd Ste 119
Lithia Springs, GA 30122
Tel.: (678) 838-6930
Fax: (678) 838-6932
Web Site: www.lo-qusa.com
Emp.: 100
Virtual Queuing Product Sales & Support
S.I.C.: 5065
N.A.I.C.S.: 423690
John Alder *(Dir-Fin)*

Siriusware, Inc. (1)
302 Camino de la Placita
Taos, NM 87571 NM
Tel.: (505) 751-4166
E-Mail: sales@siriusware.com
Web Site: www.siriusware.com
Sales Range: $1-9.9 Million
Emp.: 58
Point of Sale Software
S.I.C.: 7372
N.A.I.C.S.: 511210
Mark Danemann *(Pres & CEO)*

ACCIAIERIE VALBRUNA S.P.A.
Viale della Scienza 25 ZI
36100 Vicenza, Italy
Tel.: (39) 0444 962733
Fax: (39) 0444 963836
E-Mail: info@valbruna.it
Web Site: www.acciaierie-valbruna.com
Emp.: 1,600

Business Description:
Stainless Steel Products & Metal Alloys Supplier & Mfr
S.I.C.: 3399
N.A.I.C.S.: 331110

Personnel:
Massimo Amenduni Gresele *(Mng Dir)*
Santi Filocamo *(CIO & Dir-Info Sys)*

U.S. Subsidiaries:

Valbruna Slater Stainless, Inc. (1)
2400 Taylor St
Fort Wayne, IN 46801
Tel.: (260) 434-2800
Web Site: www.valbrunastainless.com
Emp.: 75
Stainless Steel & Nickel Alloy Long Round Bars Mfr
S.I.C.: 3399
N.A.I.C.S.: 331110
Steve Fuller *(Controller)*

Valbruna Stainless, Inc. (1)
2400 Taylor St W
Fort Wayne, IN 46801
Tel.: (260) 434-2894
Fax: (260) 434-2802
Web Site: www.valbrunastainless.com
Steel Bars & Tubing Whslr
N.A.I.C.S.: 423510
Matt Brown *(Mgr-IT)*

Branches:

Valbruna Stainless (2)
13950 Benson Ave
Chino, CA 91710
Tel.: (562) 921-9724
Fax: (562) 921-5644
Web Site: www.valbrunastainless.com
Emp.: 10
Stainless Steel Products Distr
S.I.C.: 5051
N.A.I.C.S.: 423510
Bruce Hobson *(Mgr-Branch)*

Valbruna Stainless (2)
4747 Oates Rd
Houston, TX 77013 TX
Tel.: (713) 676-1700
Fax: (713) 676-1176
Toll Free: (800) 899-3642
Web Site: www.valbrunastainless.com
Emp.: 50
Stainless Steel Products Supplier
S.I.C.: 5051
N.A.I.C.S.: 423510
Christopher Curran *(Mgr-Inside Sls)*

Non-U.S. Subsidiaries:

Valbruna AG (1)
Neuenburgstrasse 54
3282 Bargen, Switzerland
Tel.: (41) 32 391 71 81
Fax: (41) 32 391 71 89
E-Mail: info@valbruna.ch
Web Site: www.valbruna.ch
Stainless Steel, Nickel Alloys & Titanium Products Distr
N.A.I.C.S.: 423510
Maurizio Carlotto *(Gen Mgr)*

Valbruna Edel Inox GmbH (1)
Siemensstrasse 14
41542 Dormagen, Germany
Tel.: (49) 2133 2706 0
Fax: (49) 2133 2706 30
E-Mail: verkauf@valbruna.de
Web Site: www.valbruna.de
Stainless Steel Mill & Service Center
N.A.I.C.S.: 331110
Christian Pottbecker, *(Exec Dir)*

Valbruna Nederland B.V. (1)
Utrechthaven 15 Straat 55
3433 PN Nieuwegein, Netherlands
Tel.: (31) 30 60 80 100
Fax: (31) 30 60 80 020
E-Mail: info@valbruna.nl
Web Site: www.valbruna.nl
Stainless Steel, Nickel Alloys & Titanium Products Distr
N.A.I.C.S.: 423510

Valbruna Nordic AB (1)
Lovartsgatan 7
SE 652 21 Karlstad, Sweden (100%)
Tel.: (46) 54 14 45 00
Fax: (46) 54 15 44 59
E-Mail: karlstad@valbrunanordic.se
Web Site: www.valbrunanordic.se
Sls.: $41,766,928
Emp.: 28
Stainless Steel Products Distr
S.I.C.: 2999
N.A.I.C.S.: 423510
Torbjorn Nilsson *(Mng Dir)*

Valbruna Nordic Oy (1)
Lappersintie 675
02590 Lappers, Finland
Tel.: (358) 207 414 250
Fax: (358) 207 414 251
E-Mail: info@valbruna.fi
Web Site: www.valbruna.fi
Stainless Steel, Nickel Alloys & Titanium Products Importer & Whslr
N.A.I.C.S.: 423510
Seppo Jarvinen, *(Mng Dir)*

Valbruna Polska Sp. Z.o.o (1)
Ul Katowicka 11
42 530 Dabrowa Gornicza, Poland
Tel.: (48) 32 2625043
Fax: (48) 32 2625051
E-Mail: info@valbruna.pl
Web Site: www.valbruna.pl
Stainless Steel, Nickel Alloys & Titanium Products Distr
N.A.I.C.S.: 423510
Luciano Danti *(Chm)*

Valbruna UK Ltd (1)
Oldbury Road
Oldbury, West Bromwich, B70 9BT, United Kingdom UK
Tel.: (44) 121 553 5384
Fax: (44) 121 500 5095
E-Mail: sales@valbruna.co.uk
Web Site: www.valbruna.co.uk
Stainless Steel, Nickel Alloys & Titanium Products Distr
N.A.I.C.S.: 423510
Keith Underhill *(Deputy Mng Dir)*

ACCIDENT EXCHANGE GROUP PLC

Alpha 1 Canton Lane
Hams Hall, Birmingham, B46 1GA, United Kingdom
Tel.: (44) 8700116720
Fax: (44) 8700116725
E-Mail: info@accidentexchange.com
Web Site: www.accidentexchange.com
Year Founded: 2001
ACE—(LSE)
Sales Range: $150-199.9 Million
Emp.: 775

Business Description:
Vehicle Replacement Services
S.I.C.: 7549
N.A.I.C.S.: 811198

Personnel:
David Allistair Galloway *(Chm)*
Stephen Antony Evans *(CEO)*
Stephen R. Jones *(Sec)*

Board of Directors:
David Allistair Galloway
Stephen Antony Evans
David John Lees
Graham Kemble Stanley

Legal Counsel:
DLA Piper UK LLP
Victoria Square House
Birmingham, United Kingdom

Subsidiaries:

Accident Exchange Limited (1)
Alpha One Canton Ln
Hams Hall, Coleshill, Warwickshire, B46 1GA, United Kingdom
Tel.: (44) 8700116720
Fax: (44) 8700116725
E-Mail: info@accidentexchange.com
Web Site: www.accidentexchange.com
Emp.: 500
Automobile Insurance Services
S.I.C.: 6411
N.A.I.C.S.: 524298
Steve Evans *(CEO)*

DCML Limited (1)
Trinity House Bredbury Pkwy
Bredbury, Stockport, Cheshire, SK6 2SN, United Kingdom
Tel.: (44) 8444152400
Fax: (44) 8444152440
E-Mail: webenquiry@dcml.co.uk
Web Site: www.dcml.co.uk
Emp.: 25
Software Development Services
S.I.C.: 7371
N.A.I.C.S.: 541511

ACCIONA, S.A.

Avda de Europa 18 Parque Empresarial La Moraleja
28108 Alcobendas, Madrid, Spain
Tel.: (34) 916632850
Fax: (34) 916632851
E-Mail: comunicacion@acciona.es
Web Site: www.acciona.es
Year Founded: 1997
ANA—(MAD)
Rev.: $9,444,674,873
Assets: $26,680,143,042
Liabilities: $19,265,075,217
Net Worth: $7,415,067,826
Earnings: $247,940,283
Emp.: 32,905
Fiscal Year-end: 12/31/12

Business Description:
Holding Company; Infrastructure, Energy & Water Facility Construction, Real Estate Development, Environmental & Transportation Services
S.I.C.: 6719
N.A.I.C.S.: 551112

Personnel:
Jose Manuel Entrecanales Domecq *(Chm)*
Juan Ignacio Entrecanales Franco *(Vice Chm)*
Valentin Montoya Moya *(Gen Dir-Economics & Fin)*
Juan Gallerdo *(CFO)*
Pio Cabanillas *(CMO & Chief Global Brand Officer)*
Carmen Becerril *(Chief Intl Officer)*
Alfonso Callejo *(Chief Corp Resource Officer)*
Joaquin Mollinedo Chocano *(Chief Institutional Rels Officer)*
Juan Muro-Lara *(Chief Corp Dev Officer & Chief IR Officer)*
Luis Castella *(Pres-Acciona Agua)*
Pedro Martinez *(Pres-Acciona Infrastructure)*
Rafael Mateo *(CEO-Acciona Energy)*
Jorge Vega-Penichet Lopez *(Gen Counsel)*

Board of Directors:
Jose Manuel Entrecanales Domecq
Jaime Castellanos Borrego
Sol Daurella Comadran
Consuelo Crespo Bofill
Daniel Entrecanales Domecq
Miriam Gonzalez Durantez
Javier Entrecanales Franco
Juan Ignacio Entrecanales Franco
Carlos Espinosa de los Monteros Bernaldo de Quiros
Juan Carlos Garay Ibargaray
Valentin Montoya Moya
Fernando Rodes Vila
Belen Villalonga Morenes

Subsidiaries:

Acciona Agua, S.A. (1)
Avenida de Europa 22 Bajo
Parque Empresarial La Moraleja, CP 28108
Alcobendas, Madrid, Spain ES
Tel.: (34) 917907700 (100%)
Fax: (34) 917907712
E-Mail: accionaagua@acciana.es
Web Site: www.acciona-agua.es
Emp.: 1,900
Water Treatment Facilities Design, Construction, Operation & Maintenance Services
S.I.C.: 1541
N.A.I.C.S.: 236210
Luis Castilla Camara *(Mng Dir)*

Acciona Airport Services, S.A. (1)
Avenida de Europa 10
Parque Empresarial La Moraleja, CP 28108
Alcobendas, Madrid, Spain ES
Tel.: (34) 916630670 (100%)
Fax: (34) 916630738
Web Site: www.acciona-airportservices.es
Emp.: 1,000
Cargo Handling & Air Transportation Support Services
S.I.C.: 4581
N.A.I.C.S.: 488119

Acciona Aparcamientos, S.L. (1)
Avenida de Europa 20A
Parque Empresarial La Moraleja, CP 28108
Alcobendas, Madrid, Spain ES
Tel.: (34) 916630671 (100%)
Fax: (34) 916630746
Web Site: www.acciona-inmobiliaria.es
Car Park Facility Leasing Services
S.I.C.: 6512
N.A.I.C.S.: 531120

Acciona Concesiones, S.L. (1)
Avenida de Europa 18 Parque Empresarial La Moraleja
CP 28108 Alcobendas, Madrid, Spain ES
Tel.: (34) 916630677 (100%)
Fax: (34) 916231181
E-Mail: concesiones@acciona.es
Web Site: www.acciona-concesiones.es
Emp.: 35
Infrastructure Construction Projects Financing Services
S.I.C.: 6141
N.A.I.C.S.: 522220
Abal Derto *(Gen Mgr)*

Acciona Energia, S.A. (1)
Ave Ciudad de la Innovacion 5
CP 31621 Sarriguren, Navarra, Spain ES
Tel.: (34) 948006000 (100%)
Fax: (34) 948006001
E-Mail: contact@acciona.es
Web Site: www.acciona-energia.com
Sales Range: $1-4.9 Billion
Emp.: 1,309
Renewable Energy Facility Development, Construction, Operation & Maintenance Services
S.I.C.: 4939
N.A.I.C.S.: 221118
Rafael Mateo *(Gen Dir)*

Subsidiary:

Acciona Solar, S.A. (2)
Avenida Ciudad de la Innovacion 3
CP 31621 Sarriguren, Navarra, Spain ES
Tel.: (34) 948166800 (75%)
Fax: (34) 948166801
E-Mail: solar@acciona.es
Web Site: www.aesol.es
Solar Energy Panel Installation, Operation & Maintenance Services
S.I.C.: 4931
N.A.I.C.S.: 221118

Acciona Facility Services, S.A. (1)
Francesc Layret 12-14 Nave 33
08630 Barcelona, Abrera, Spain ES
Tel.: (34) 932075053 (100%)
Fax: (34) 934570178
E-Mail: info@accionafs.com
Web Site: www.acciona-fs.es
Emp.: 100
Environmental Conservation & Sustainable Development Services
S.I.C.: 8744
N.A.I.C.S.: 561210
Ignacio Casamada Lasus *(Mng Dir)*

Acciona Infraestructuras, S.A. (1)
Avenida de Europa 18
Parque Empresarial La Moraleja, CP 28108
Alcobendas, Madrid, Spain ES
Tel.: (34) 916632850 (100%)
Fax: (34) 916633099
Web Site: www.acciona-infraestructuras.es
Sales Range: $5-14.9 Billion
Emp.: 15,409
Infrastructure Construction Services
S.I.C.: 1611
N.A.I.C.S.: 237310
Pedro Martinez Martinez *(Mng Dir)*

Acciona Inmobiliaria, S.L. (1)
Avenida de Europa 20A 3a planta
Parque Empresarial La Moraleja, CP 28108
Alcobendas, Madrid, Spain ES
Tel.: (34) 916576490 (100%)
Fax: (34) 916615488
E-Mail: inmobi@acciona.es
Web Site: www.acciona-inmobiliaria.es
Sales Range: $650-699.9 Million
Emp.: 401
Real Estate Developer & Property Leasing Services
S.I.C.: 6531
N.A.I.C.S.: 531390
Isabel Antunez Cid *(Mng Dir)*

Affiliate:

Compania Urbanizadora del Coto, S.L. (2)
C/o Machupichu 89
CP 28043 Madrid, Spain ES
Tel.: (34) 914043337 (50%)
Fax: (34) 914033610
E-Mail: david@cucsa.es
Web Site: www.cucsa.es
Residential Housing Developer & Rental Services
S.I.C.: 6531
N.A.I.C.S.: 531390
Monica Rodriguez Ramon *(Mgr)*

Non-U.S. Subsidiary:

Acciona Nieruchomosci Sp. z o.o. (2)
ul Gen R Abrahama 18 lok 320
PL-03982 Warsaw, Poland PL
Tel.: (48) 225140880 (100%)
Fax: (48) 226717416
E-Mail: sekretariat@acciona.com.pl
Web Site: www.acciona-nieruchomosci.pl
Emp.: 100
Real Estate Developer
S.I.C.: 6531
N.A.I.C.S.: 531390
Santiago Mas Martinez *(Gen Mgr)*

Acciona Logistica, S.A. (1)
Avenida de Europa 10
Parque Empresarial La Moraleja, 28108
Alcobendas, Madrid, Spain ES
Tel.: (34) 914238500 (100%)
Fax: (34) 914238760
Web Site: www.acciona.com
Emp.: 150
Holding Company; Maritime Passenger & Cargo Transportation Services
S.I.C.: 6719
N.A.I.C.S.: 551112
Antonio Gravalos *(Mng Dir)*

Subsidiary:

Acciona Trasmediterranea, S.A. (2)
Avenida de Europa 10
Parque Empresarial La Moraleja, CP 28108
Alcobendas, Madrid, Spain ES
Tel.: (34) 914238500 (60.08%)

Acciona, S.A.—(Continued)

Fax: (34) 914238555
E-Mail: info@trasmediterranea.es
Web Site: www.trasmediterranea.es
Maritime Passenger & Cargo Transportation Services
S.I.C.: 4481
N.A.I.C.S.: 483114
Antonio Gravalos *(Mng Dir)*

Acciona Medio Ambiente (1)
C/ Universidad 4-4
CP 46003 Valencia, Spain ES
Tel.: (34) 963524500 (100%)
Fax: (34) 963524663
E-Mail: medioambiente@acciona.es
Web Site: www.acciona-medioambiente.es
Emp.: 180
Garden, Reforestation & Irrigation Project Planning, Construction & Maintenance Services
S.I.C.: 0851
N.A.I.C.S.: 115310
Alfonso Blanco *(Mng Dir)*

Acciona Servicios Urbanos, S.L. (1)
Avenida de Europa 18
Parque Empresarial La Moraleja, CP 28108
Alcobendas, Madrid, Spain ES
Tel.: (34) 916630669 (100%)
Fax: (34) 916332850
E-Mail: info@acciona.es
Web Site: www.acciona.es
Emp.: 100
Private & Public Sector Urban Support Services
S.I.C.: 7389
N.A.I.C.S.: 561990

Bestinver, S.A. (1)
C Juan de Mena 8 1D
CP 28014 Madrid, Spain ES
Tel.: (34) 915959110 (100%)
Fax: (34) 915959120
E-Mail: bestinver@bestinver.es
Web Site: www.bestinver.es
Pension & Mutual Funds Asset Management Services
S.I.C.: 6799
N.A.I.C.S.: 523920
Ignacio Pedrosa Taboada *(CMO)*
Francisco Garcia Parames *(Chief Investment Officer)*
Maria Caputto Barbadillo *(Deputy Mktg Officer)*

General de Producciones y Diseno, S.A. (1)
Avenida de la Borbolla 57
CP 41013 Seville, Spain ES
Tel.: (34) 954238595 (100%)
Fax: (34) 954236707
E-Mail: expo@gpdsa.es
Web Site: www.gpdsa.es
Emp.: 200
Exhibitions, Events Planning & Support Services
S.I.C.: 7389
N.A.I.C.S.: 561499
Boria Micka *(Dir-Design)*

Hijos de Antonio Barcelo, S.A. (1)
C/ Julian Camarillo 6A B
CP 28037 Madrid, Spain ES
Tel.: (34) 915006000 (100%)
Fax: (34) 915006006
E-Mail: habarcelo@habarcelo.es
Web Site: www.habarcelo.es
Emp.: 40
Wineries
S.I.C.: 2084
N.A.I.C.S.: 312130
Richer Grand *(Mng Dir)*

Terminal de Contenedores de Algeciras, S.A. (1)
Gaitan de Ayala s/n
Muelle de Isla Verde, Cadiz, Algeciras, 11207, Spain ES
Tel.: (34) 956604958 (100%)
Fax: (34) 956 58 0026
E-Mail: info@tcal.com
Web Site: www.acciona.com
Marine Cargo Terminal Operations
S.I.C.: 4491
N.A.I.C.S.: 488320
Pedro Martinez *(Pres-Acciona Infrastructure)*

ACCOR S.A.

2 rue de la Mare Neuve
91021 Evry, France
Tel.: (33) 169368080
Telex: 601852
Fax: (33) 169367900
Web Site: www.accor.com
Year Founded: 1967
AC—(EUR OTC)
Rev.: $7,604,514,330
Assets: $10,177,045,200
Liabilities: $6,153,343,070
Net Worth: $4,023,702,130
Earnings: ($786,163,280)
Emp.: 133,886
Fiscal Year-end: 12/31/12

Business Description:
Holding Company; Hotel Franchisor & Operator
S.I.C.: 6719
N.A.I.C.S.: 551112

Personnel:
Sebastien Bazin *(Chm)*
Philippe Citerne *(Vice Chm)*
Vivek Badrinath *(CEO)*
Sophie Stabile *(Global CFO)*
Gregoire Champetier *(CMO & Chief Distr Officer)*
Giller Bonnier *(Chief Investment Officer & Chief Asset Officer)*
Antoine Recher *(Chief HR Officer)*
Dominique Esnault *(Chief Partners Officer & Chief Hotel Svcs Officer)*
Michael Issenberg *(Chm/COO-Hospitality-Asia Pacific)*
Samuel Shih *(Chm/COO-Greater China)*
Pascal Quint *(Sec)*
Jean-Luc Chretien *(Exec VP-Sls, Distr & Loyalty)*
Marc Vieilledent *(Exec VP-Asset Mgmt)*
Isabelle Birem *(Sr VP-Direct Sls)*
Agnes Carade *(Sr VP-Comm & External Rels)*
Cedric Gobilliard *(Sr VP-Sls & Distr)*
Renaud Jezequel *(Sr VP-Mergers & Acq & Real Estate Transactions)*
Yves Lacheret *(Sr VP-Bus Dev-Europe)*
Carlo Olejniczak *(Sr VP-Global Sls)*
Romain Roulleau *(Sr VP-ECommerce)*
Sebastien Valentin *(Sr VP-Fin Comm & IR)*

Board of Directors:
Sebastien Bazin
Jean-Paul Bailly
Philippe Citerne
Mercedes Erra
Sophie Gasperment
Iris Knobloch
Bertrand Meheut
Virginie Morgan
Nadra Moussalem
Patrick Sayer

Deloitte & Associes
185 avenue Charles-de-Gaulle
Neuilly-sur-Seine, France

Transfer Agent:
Societe Generale
32 rue champ de Tir
Nantes, France

Subsidiaries:

Academie Accor SA (1)
1 rue de la Mare-Neuve
91021 Evry, France
Tel.: (33) 1 69 36 86 00
Fax: (33) 1 61 61 26 05
E-Mail: reception@accor.com
Web Site: www.accor.com
Hotel Management Services
S.I.C.: 7011
N.A.I.C.S.: 721110
Laurence Caron *(Gen Mgr)*

Accor Casinos (1)
35 Blvd de Capocinas Distt 2
75002 Paris, France (50%)
Tel.: (33) 142865400
Fax: (33) 142865410
E-Mail: c.hussel@lucemoeneaffeofo.com
Web Site: www.lucemoeneaffeofo.com
Emp.: 150
Casino Hotel
S.I.C.: 7011
N.A.I.C.S.: 721120
Christine Hussel *(Gen Mgr)*

Accor centre de contacts clients (1)
31 Rue du Colonel-Pierre-Avia
75904 Paris, France
Tel.: (33) 825 88 00 00
Fax: (33) 1 41 33 71 71
Web Site: www.accor.com
Hotel Management Services
S.I.C.: 7011
N.A.I.C.S.: 721110

Accor Reservation (1)
28 Rue Blaise Pascal
91025 Evry, France (99.88%)
Tel.: (33) 60879400
Fax: (33) 160879230
Web Site: www.accorhotels.com
Emp.: 50
Services
S.I.C.: 5713
N.A.I.C.S.: 442210

All Seasons Hotels (1)
Immeuble Odyssey 110 Av de France
75210 Paris, France
Tel.: (33) 1 45 38 00 00
E-Mail: info.allseasons@accor.com
Web Site: www.all-seasons-hotels.com
Hotel Management Services
S.I.C.: 7011
N.A.I.C.S.: 721110
Pierre Lagrange *(Dir-Publ)*

Developpements Immobiliers Et Commerciaux S.A. (1)
4 Rue De La Mare Neuve
91080 Courcouronnes, France (100%)
Tel.: (33) 169136361
Fax: (33) 169367900
Hotel Management
S.I.C.: 7011
N.A.I.C.S.: 721110

Etap Hotels Ltd (1)
ZI Rue Rene Dingeon
80100 Abbeville, France
Tel.: (33) 892680772
Fax: (33) 322200011
E-Mail: helping@etaphotel.com
Web Site: www.etaphotel.com
Hotel Management Services
S.I.C.: 7011
N.A.I.C.S.: 721110
Pierre Lagrange *(Dir-Publ)*

Frantour Group (1)
3 3 Bis
Villa Thoreton, 75015 Paris, France (100%)
Tel.: (33) 156826000
Fax: (33) 566827100
Toll Free: 825 0 1 2 3 4 5
E-Mail: infos@govoyages.com
Web Site: www.govoyages.com
Emp.: 100
Hotel Chain & Travel Business
S.I.C.: 7011
N.A.I.C.S.: 721110

Go Voyages (1)
14 Rue De Clery
75002 Paris, France (100%)
Tel.: (33) 153404400
Fax: (33) 153404401
E-Mail: info@govoyages.com
Web Site: www.govoyages.com
Emp.: 400
Travel Services
S.I.C.: 4724
N.A.I.C.S.: 561510
Carlos da Silva *(CEO)*
Nicolas Brumelot *(Mng Dir)*

Mercure (1)
2 Rue De La Mare Neuve
91021 Evry, France (100%)
Tel.: (33) 0169368080
Fax: (33) 161617900
Emp.: 1,200

Business & Leisure Hotels
S.I.C.: 7011
N.A.I.C.S.: 721110
Christian Achard *(Gen Mgr)*

Pradotel SAS (1)
6 Rue Du Bois Briard
91080 Courcouronnes, France
Tel.: (33) 169367500
Hotel Management Services
S.I.C.: 7011
N.A.I.C.S.: 721110

Pullman International Hotels (1)
2, rue de la Mare Neuve
91021 Evry, France (100%)
Hotels
S.I.C.: 7011
N.A.I.C.S.: 721110
Xavier Louyot *(VP-Global Mktg)*

SNC NMP France (1)
Avenue de Verdun
45800 Saint Jean de Braye, France
Tel.: (33) 238846565
Fax: (33) 238846661
Emp.: 20
Hotel Management Services
S.I.C.: 7011
N.A.I.C.S.: 721110
Pascale Laplace *(Gen Mgr)*

So luxury HMC Sarl (1)
110 Avenue de France
75013 Paris, France
Tel.: (33) 1 45 38 86 00
Hotel Management Services
S.I.C.: 7011
N.A.I.C.S.: 721110

Societe d'Exploitation d'Agences de Voyages et de Tourisme SA (1)
31 rue du Colonel Pierre Avia
75015 Paris, France (49.72%)
Tel.: (33) 1 41 33 6000
Fax: (33) 1 41 33 6047
E-Mail: info@cwt.fr
Web Site: www.carlsonwagonlit.fr
Emp.: 200
Travel Agencies
S.I.C.: 4724
N.A.I.C.S.: 561510

Societe Francaise de Promotion Touristique et Hoteliere SA (1)
31, rue du Colonel Pierre Avia
Paris, 75015, France (69.54%)
S.I.C.: 5713
N.A.I.C.S.: 442210

Societe Hoteliere 61 Quai de Grenelle (1)
61 Quai Grenelle
75015 Paris, France
Tel.: (33) 1 40 58 20 00
Hotel Management Services
S.I.C.: 7011
N.A.I.C.S.: 721110

Societe Hoteliere Paris Vanves (1)
110 rue Jean Bleuzen
92170 Vanves, France (100%)
Tel.: (33) 155950215
Hotel Operations
S.I.C.: 7011
N.A.I.C.S.: 721110

Societe Internationale des Hotels Novotel (1)
2 Rue De La Mare Neuve
91021 Evry, Cedex, France (100%)
Tel.: (33) 169368080
Fax: (33) 161617900
E-Mail: info@novotel.com
Web Site: www.novotel.com
Emp.: 1,200
Operater of Hotels
S.I.C.: 7011
N.A.I.C.S.: 721110
Fredrice Gosenhans *(Sr VP-Mktg)*

Societe Parisienne des Hotels Economiques (1)
2 Rue de la Mare Neuve
91080 Courcouronnes, France
Tel.: (33) 1 69 36 75 00
Hotel Management Services
S.I.C.: 7011
N.A.I.C.S.: 721110

Sofitel Luxury Hotels France SAS (1)
14 rue Beaujon
75008 Paris, France
Tel.: (33) 153895050
Fax: (33) 153895051
E-Mail: h1296@sofitel.com
Web Site: www.sofitel.com
Emp.: 120
Hotel Management Services
S.I.C.: 7011
N.A.I.C.S.: 721110
Francoise Parguel *(VP-Comm)*

Sofitel (1)
2 Rue De La Mare Neuve
91021 Evry, France (100%)
Tel.: (33) 145381909
Fax: (33) 0161617900
Web Site: www.sofitel.com
Business & Leisure Hotels
S.I.C.: 7011
N.A.I.C.S.: 721110

Thalamer SA (1)
2 Rue De La Mare Neuve
Courcouronnes, 91080, France
Tel.: (33) 321098500
Hotel Management Services
S.I.C.: 7011
N.A.I.C.S.: 721110

Joint Venture:

Newrest Wagons-Lits S.A.S. (1)
04 rue du 08 Mai 1945
F-75010 Paris, France FR
Tel.: (33) 140388666
Web Site: www.newrest.eu/en/services/newrestwagons-lits
Emp.: 1,500
Train Catering & Support Services
Contractor; Owned 60% by Newrest Group International S.A.S. & 40% by Accor S.A.
S.I.C.: 5812
N.A.I.C.S.: 722320
Pascale Perez *(Mng Dir)*
Didier Le Blanc *(COO)*

U.S. Subsidiaries:

Accor Business & Leisure North America Inc. (1)
223 Twin Dolphin Dr
Redwood City, CA 94065-1414
Tel.: (650) 598-9000
Fax: (650) 598-9383
Hotel Management Services
S.I.C.: 7011
N.A.I.C.S.: 721110

Accor North America, Inc. (1)
4001 International Pkwy
Carrollton, TX 75007 (100%)
Tel.: (972) 360-9000
Web Site: www.accor-na.com
Emp.: 300
Holding Company; Hotel & Restaurant Operator
S.I.C.: 7011
N.A.I.C.S.: 721110
Jeffrey Palmer *(CMO)*
Robert Moore *(Exec VP-Tech Svcs & New Construction)*

Divisions:

Motel 6 (2)
4001 International Pkwy
Carrollton, TX 75007
Tel.: (972) 360-9000
Fax: (972) 360-5821
Web Site: www.motel6.com
Emp.: 400
Motels
S.I.C.: 7011
N.A.I.C.S.: 721110
Lance Miceli *(CMO-Motel 6 & Studio 6)*
Kristin Taylor *(Exec VP-Technical Svcs, Real Estate & Dev-Motel 6 & Studio 6)*

Subsidiaries:

Workplace Options (2)
3020 HighWoods Blvd
Raleigh, NC 27604 (100%)
Fax: (919) 833-9888
Toll Free: (800) 628-5437
Web Site: www.wlb.com
Rev.: $29,800,000
Emp.: 305
Benefit Administrator for Companies Providing Pre-Tax Dependent Care Benefit to Employees
S.I.C.: 8999
N.A.I.C.S.: 541612
Alan King *(Pres & Mng Dir)*

Non-U.S. Subsidiaries:

Accor Austria AG (1)
Am Euro Platz 1
1120 Vienna, Austria
Tel.: (43) 1 81 43 46 00
Fax: (43) 1 814 34 99
Hotel Management Services
S.I.C.: 7011
N.A.I.C.S.: 721110

Accor Brasil SA (1)
Avenida Maria Coelho de Aguiar 215 Bloco F 5 andar
Sao Luis, Sao Paulo, SP, 05805 000, Brazil (99.99%)
Tel.: (55) 11 374 11500
Fax: (55) 11 3748 6562
E-Mail: recepcao@accorhotels.com.br
Web Site: www.accor.com.br
Emp.: 200
Hotel & Catering Services
S.I.C.: 7011
N.A.I.C.S.: 721199

Accor Canada Inc. (1)
3670 Hurontario St
Mississauga, ON, L5B 1P3, Canada
Tel.: (905) 896-1000
Fax: (905) 803-6726
Web Site: www.novotel.com
Hotel Management Services
S.I.C.: 7011
N.A.I.C.S.: 721110

Accor Gestion Maroc SA (1)
La Colline ii N 33 Route de Nouaceur-Sidi Maarouf
20100 Casablanca, Morocco
Tel.: (212) 522 97 78 00
Fax: (212) 22 97 48 99
Emp.: 40
Hotel Management Services
S.I.C.: 7011
N.A.I.C.S.: 721110
Christian Rousseau *(Gen Mgr)*

Accor GmbH (1)
Palmgasse 3
1150 Vienna, Austria (100%)
Tel.: (43) 1892052500
Fax: (43) 1892052585
Web Site: www.accor.com
Emp.: 20
Hotel Operator
S.I.C.: 7011
N.A.I.C.S.: 721199

ACCOR HOSPITALITY ARGENTINA SA (1)
Arroyo 841
Buenos Aires, 1007, Argentina
Tel.: (54) 1141310000
Fax: (54) 1141310044
E-Mail: sofitelbuenosaires@sofitel.com
Web Site: www.sofitel.com
Emp.: 18
Hotel Management Services
S.I.C.: 7011
N.A.I.C.S.: 721110
Fernando Mendez *(Office Mgr)*

Accor Hospitality Germany Gmbh (1)
Hanns-Schwindt-Str 2
Munich, 81829, Germany
Tel.: (49) 89 63002 447
Fax: (49) 63002224
Web Site: www.accor.com
Emp.: 25
Hotel Management Services
S.I.C.: 7011
N.A.I.C.S.: 721110
Herman Simon *(Mng Dir)*

Accor Hospitality Nederland B.V (1)
Joan Muyskenweg 10
Amsterdam, 1096 CJ, Netherlands
Tel.: (31) 206658181
Fax: (31) 206948735
Emp.: 120
Hotel Management Services
S.I.C.: 7011
N.A.I.C.S.: 721110
Willem Bleuland *(Gen Mgr)*

Accor Hoteles Espana S.A. (1)
Avda Capital de Espana 10 Campo de las Naciones
28042 Madrid, Spain ES
Tel.: (34) 917210070
Fax: (34) 917210515
E-Mail: h1606@accor.com
Web Site: www.accorhotels.com
Emp.: 100
Hotels
S.I.C.: 7011
N.A.I.C.S.: 721110
Dadaer Bellaserraere *(Gen Mgr)*

Accor Hotellerie Deutschland GmbH (1)
Hanns Schwindt Str 2
81829 Munich, Germany (98.86%)
Tel.: (49) 8963002200
Fax: (49) 8963002244
Emp.: 5,000
S.I.C.: 5713
N.A.I.C.S.: 442210
Volker Buering *(Chm & CEO)*

Accor Hotels Belgium NV (1)
Avenue des Arts 56
Brussels, 1000, Belgium
Tel.: (32) 24816965
Fax: (32) 2 481 6948
E-Mail: reception.ahb@accor.com
Web Site: www.accorhotels.com
Hotel Management Services
S.I.C.: 7011
N.A.I.C.S.: 721110
Christophe Vanswieten *(Gen Mgr)*

Accor Hotels Romania S.R.L. (1)
37b Calea Victoriei
Bucharest, 010061, Romania
Tel.: (40) 213088500
Fax: (40) 213088501
E-Mail: h555@accor.com
Hotel Management Services
S.I.C.: 7011
N.A.I.C.S.: 721110

Accor UK Economy Hotels Limited (1)
Mile Lane
Coventry, CV1 2LN, United Kingdom
Tel.: (44) 24 7625 0500
Fax: (44) 24 7655 3548
Web Site: www.accorhotels.com
Emp.: 14
Hotel Management Services
S.I.C.: 7011
N.A.I.C.S.: 721110
Joanna Torbus *(Gen Mgr)*

Accor UK (1)
255 Hammersmith Rd
London, W6 8SJ, United Kingdom (100%)
Tel.: (44) 02082377474
Fax: (44) 02082377410
Web Site: www.accorhotel.com
Emp.: 100
Holding Co. for UK Operations
S.I.C.: 6710
N.A.I.C.S.: 551112
Michael Flexmen *(CEO)*

Compagnie Internationale des Wagons Lits et du Tourisme S.A. (1)
51-53 bd Clovis
1040 Brussels, Belgium (99.44%)
S.I.C.: 5713
N.A.I.C.S.: 442210

El Gezirah Hotels Tourism (1)
El Gezirah Sofitel Hotel Bldg
Cairo, Egypt
Tel.: (20) 227363770
Hotel Management Services
S.I.C.: 7011
N.A.I.C.S.: 721110

Formula1 Pty (1)
Block B 2nd Floor Edenburg Terraces 348 Rivonia Boulevard
Rivonia, Johannesburg, 2128, South Africa
Tel.: (27) 11 807 0750
Fax: (27) 11 807 3888
Hotel Management Services
S.I.C.: 7011
N.A.I.C.S.: 721110

Hospitality Int. Thailande (1)
33/JJ6 Wall Street Tower Surawongse Road
Bangkok, Thailand (99.95%)
Business Services
S.I.C.: 7389
N.A.I.C.S.: 561499

Katerinska Hotels S.R.O (1)
Katerinska 38/1476
Prague, 120 00, Czech Republic
Tel.: (420) 222865777
Fax: (420) 224941201
E-Mail: h3195@accor.com
Web Site: www.accorhotel.com
Hotel Management Services
S.I.C.: 7011
N.A.I.C.S.: 721110
Eva Paskova *(Gen Mgr)*

Marara SA (1)
PO Box 6
98730 Vaitape, French Polynesia
Tel.: (689) 605500
Fax: (689) 410404
Emp.: 80
Hotel Management Services
S.I.C.: 7011
N.A.I.C.S.: 721110
Didier Lamoot *(Gen Mgr)*

Muranowska Sp. z o.o. (1)
Bracka 16
Warsaw, 00-028, Poland
Tel.: (48) 223101000
Fax: (48) 223101010
Hotel Management Services
S.I.C.: 7011
N.A.I.C.S.: 721110
Sebastien Deneasr *(Gen Mgr)*

Novotel Athens S.A. (1)
4 6 Michael Voda Et
10439 Athens, Greece (98.53%)
Tel.: (30) 2108200700
Fax: (30) 2108200777
E-Mail: h0866@accor.com
Web Site: www.novetel.gr
Emp.: 70
Hotel Line
S.I.C.: 7011
N.A.I.C.S.: 721110
Corrie Stathis *(Dir-Sls & Mktg-Novotel Forest Resort Creswick)*

Novotel Goteborg AB (1)
Klippan 1
S 414 51 Gothenburg, Sweden (100%)
Tel.: (46) 317202200
Fax: (46) 317202299
E-Mail: info@novotel.se
Web Site: www.novotel.se
Emp.: 40
Hotel Operator
S.I.C.: 7011
N.A.I.C.S.: 721110
Jerker Dellblad *(Gen Mgr)*

Novotel Rotterdam Brainpark BV (1)
KP Van Der Mandelelaan 150
NL 3062 MB Rotterdam, Netherlands (100%)
Tel.: (31) 0102532532
Fax: (31) 102532571
E-Mail: h1134@accor.com
Web Site: www.novotel.com
Emp.: 60
Hotel
S.I.C.: 7011
N.A.I.C.S.: 721199
Ra Hoondert *(Gen Mgr)*

Novotel (1)
3670 Hurontario St
Mississauga, ON, L5B 1P3, Canada(100%)
Tel.: (905) 896-1000
Fax: (905) 803-6726
Web Site: www.novotel.com
Emp.: 100
Business Travel Accomodations
S.I.C.: 7011
N.A.I.C.S.: 721110
Eric Buitenhuis *(VP)*

Orbis S.A. (1)
Ul Bracka 16
00028 Warsaw, Poland (50.01%)
Tel.: (48) 22 8293969
Fax: (48) 22 8273301

Accor S.A.—(Continued)

E-Mail: orbissa@orbis.pl
Web Site: www.orbis.pl
ORB—(WAR)
Sls.: $224,286,387
Assets: $672,255,345
Liabilities: $59,548,451
Net Worth: $612,706,894
Earnings: $21,623,192
Emp.: 5,111
Fiscal Year-end: 12/31/12
Hotel Owner & Operator; Hotel Construction Services; Car Rental Services
S.I.C.: 7011
N.A.I.C.S.: 721110
Laurent Picheral *(Chm-Mgmt Bd & CEO)*
Andrzej Przytula *(Deputy Chm-Supervisory Bd)*
Ireneusz Andrzej Weglowski *(Vice Chm-Mgmt Bd)*
Dorota Wierucka *(IR Officer)*
Marcin Szewczykowski *(Member-Mgmt Bd)*

Subsidiaries:

Orbis Transport Sp. z o.o. (2)
Ul Lopuszanska 47
Warsaw, 02 232, Poland
Tel.: (48) 225001680
Fax: (48) 228683586
E-Mail: info@orbis-transport.pl
Web Site: www.orbis-transport.pl
Emp.: 35
Business Services
S.I.C.: 9621
N.A.I.C.S.: 926120
Andrzej Marconi *(Mng Dir)*

Subsidiaries:

Capital Parking Sp. z o.o. (3)
Nowogrodzka 27
Warsaw, Poland
Tel.: (48) 226224312
Fax: (48) 22 622 62 78
E-Mail: biuro@capital-parking.pl
Web Site: www.capital-parking.anonser.pl/
Car Parking Services
S.I.C.: 7521
N.A.I.C.S.: 812930

PKS Tarnobrzeg Sp. z o.o. (3)
Ul Gen Wladyslaw Sikorski 86
Tarnobrzeg, Rzeszow, Podkarpackie, 39 400, Poland
Tel.: (48) 15 822 17 45
Fax: (48) 15 822 17 04
Web Site: www.pks.tarnobrzeg.pl
Bus Transportation Services
S.I.C.: 4111
N.A.I.C.S.: 485113

PBP Orbis Sp. z o.o. (2)
Ul Kremerowska 5
PL 31130 Krakow, Poland
Tel.: (48) 124221805
Fax: (48) 124222885
E-Mail: info@orbis.krakow.pl
Web Site: www.orbis.krakow.pl
Travel & Tour Services
S.I.C.: 4725
N.A.I.C.S.: 561520
Agnieszka Grzesaik *(Mgr)*

Pannonia Hotels RT (1)
Kethly Anna Ter 1
Budapest, 1075, Hungary
Tel.: (36) 14855550
Fax: (36) 14855525
E-Mail: hu-recepcio-rso@accor.com
Web Site: www.accor.com
Emp.: 5
Hotel Management Services
S.I.C.: 7011
N.A.I.C.S.: 721110
Antoine Guego *(COO)*

Premier Lodge South Africa (1)
33 Bradford Rd Bedford Gardens
Bedfordview, 2007, South Africa
Tel.: (27) 11 622 1556
Fax: (27) 11 622 8725
E-Mail: H2919@accor.com
Web Site: www.accor.com
Emp.: 25
Hotel Management Services
S.I.C.: 7011
N.A.I.C.S.: 721110
Michael Delaney *(Gen Mgr)*

Societe Abidjanaise (1)
1 Rue Des Gallions Zone Portuaire
San Pedro, 0101, Cote d'Ivoire
Tel.: (225) 21240361
Fax: (225) 21256907
Hotel Management Services
S.I.C.: 7011
N.A.I.C.S.: 721110

W.L. Tourisme (1)
51-53, bd Clovis
1040 Brussels, Belgium (42.26%)
Travel Agent
S.I.C.: 4724
N.A.I.C.S.: 561510

World Tourist Rejsebureau A/S (1)
Oerestads Blvd 35
2300 Copenhagen, Denmark (100%)
Tel.: (45) 33637878
Fax: (45) 32714875
Web Site: www.carlsonwagonlit.dk
Emp.: 100
Travel Agent
S.I.C.: 4724
N.A.I.C.S.: 561510
Sophie Hulgard *(Gen Mgr)*

ACCORD FINANCIAL CORP.

77 Bloor Street West Suite 1803
Toronto, ON, M5S 1M2, Canada
Tel.: (416) 961-0007
Fax: (416) 961-9443
Toll Free: (800) 967-0015
E-Mail: info@accordfinancial.com
Web Site: www.accordfinancial.com
ACD—(TSX)
Rev.: $25,735,702
Assets: $123,846,898
Liabilities: $76,734,833
Net Worth: $47,112,065
Earnings: $6,338,465
Emp.: 181
Fiscal Year-end: 12/31/12
Business Description:
Financial Services
S.I.C.: 6726
N.A.I.C.S.: 525990
Personnel:
Ken Hitzig *(Chm)*
Thomas L. Henderson *(Pres & CEO)*
Stuart Adair *(CFO & VP)*
Matthew Panosian *(Chief Credit Officer & Sr VP)*
Simon Hitzig *(Pres-Accord Financial Ltd & VP)*
Fred Moss *(Pres-Accord Financial Inc & VP)*
Jim Bates *(COO-Accord Financial Ltd & Sec)*
Cynthia Aboud *(Sr VP)*
Lilies Lanway *(Sr VP)*
Jason Rosenfeld *(Sr VP)*
Board of Directors:
Ken Hitzig
Robert J. Beutel
Ben Evans
Thomas L. Henderson
Robert S. Sandler
John J. Swidler
Stephen D. Warden
Legal Counsel:
Stikeman Elliott
Commerce Court West
199 Bay Street Suite 5300, Toronto, ON, M5L 1B9, Canada
Transfer Agent:
Computershare Investor Services Inc.
100 University Ave 9th Floor
Toronto, ON, Canada

Subsidiaries:

Accord Business Credit, Inc. (1)
77 Bloor St W Ste 1803
Toronto, ON, M5S 1M2, Canada (100%)
Tel.: (416) 961-0007
Fax: (416) 961-9443
Toll Free: (800) 701-9170
E-Mail: info@accordfinancial.com
Web Site: www.accordcredit.com
Emp.: 35
Financial Services
S.I.C.: 6282
N.A.I.C.S.: 523930
Simon Hitzig *(Pres)*

Montcap Financial Corp. (1)
3500 De Maisonneuve Blvd W Ste 1510
Montreal, QC, H3Z 3C1, Canada (100%)
Tel.: (514) 932-8223
Fax: (514) 932-0076
Toll Free: (800) 231-2977
E-Mail: info@accordfinancial.com
Web Site: www.accordfinancial.com
Emp.: 50
Provides Financial Services
S.I.C.: 6282
N.A.I.C.S.: 523930
Fred Moss *(Pres)*

U.S. Subsidiary:

Accord Financial, Inc. (1)
25 Woods Lake Rd Ste 102
Greenville, SC 29607
Mailing Address:
PO Box 6704
Greenville, SC 29606-6704
Tel.: (864) 271-4384
Fax: (864) 242-0863
Toll Free: (800) 231-2757
E-Mail: thenderson@accordfinancial.com
Web Site: www.accordfinancialus.com
Emp.: 20
Provider of Financial Services
S.I.C.: 6159
N.A.I.C.S.: 522298
Thomas Henderson *(Pres)*
Fred Moss *(Pres)*
Leonard Broderick *(CFO)*

ACCORD GROUP LIMITED

The Grange 100 High Street
London, N14 6EQ, United Kingdom
Tel.: (44) 2089209020
Fax: (44) 2089209090
Web Site: www.accordgroup.co.uk
Year Founded: 1999
Sls.: $182,096,210
Emp.: 70
Business Description:
Holding Company; Advertising & Direct Marketing Services
S.I.C.: 6719
N.A.I.C.S.: 551112
Personnel:
Robert J. Walton *(Chm)*
David C. Sitwell *(CEO)*
Peter C. Clark *(Sec & Dir-Fin)*
Board of Directors:
Robert J. Walton
Scot Ryan
David C. Sitwell
Vincent L. Sitwell
Sally M. Winfield

Divisions:

Artavia Advertising Ltd. (1)
Artavia House Queen St
Barnstable, Devon, EX32 8HW, United Kingdom
Tel.: (44) 1271323333
Fax: (44) 1271 323555
E-Mail: info@artavia.co.uk
Web Site: www.artavia.co.uk
Billings: $106,024,710
Emp.: 160
Advertising Agency
S.I.C.: 7311
N.A.I.C.S.: 541810
Steve Holder *(Mng Dir)*

Conrad Advertising (1)
The Grange 100 High St
London, N14 6EQ, United Kingdom
Tel.: (44) 20 8920 9000
Fax: (44) 20 8920 9090
E-Mail: info@conrad.co.uk
Web Site: www.conrad.co.uk
Emp.: 50
Advertising Agency
S.I.C.: 7311
N.A.I.C.S.: 541810
Kimio Shioiri *(Exec VP)*

MKH (1)
Castlewood House 77-91 New Oxford St
London, WC1 A 1DG, United Kingdom
Tel.: (44) 2089209173
Fax: (44) 20 7785 9245
E-Mail: london@mkh.co.uk
Web Site: www.mkh.co.uk
Emp.: 30
Advertising Agency
S.I.C.: 7311
N.A.I.C.S.: 541810
Martin Arnold *(Mng Dir)*

ACCREDITED BUSINESS CONSOLIDATORS CORP.

De La Estatua de Montoya 1 Cuadra al Sur
Casa Esquinera Apartado PA-228,
Managua, 10000, Nicaragua
Tel.: (505) 87968888
Web Site:
ACDU—(OTC)
Sales Range: Less than $1 Million
Business Description:
Business Financial Services
S.I.C.: 7389
N.A.I.C.S.: 561499
Personnel:
Joanna Chmielewska *(Pres, CEO, CFO, Treas & Sec)*
Andy William *(COO & VP)*
Board of Directors:
Joanna Chmielewska

ACCRETIVE CO., LTD.

5F 4-9-1 Minamiyawata
Ichikawa, Chiba, 272-0023, Japan
Tel.: (81) 473140654
Fax: (81) 473140621
E-Mail: info@accretive.jp
Web Site: www.accretive.jp
8423—(TKS)
Rev.: $30,877,000
Assets: $224,290,000
Liabilities: $193,226,000
Net Worth: $31,064,000
Earnings: $9,383,000
Emp.: 72
Fiscal Year-end: 03/31/13
Business Description:
Financial Services
S.I.C.: 6099
N.A.I.C.S.: 522320
Personnel:
Toru Mukai *(Pres & CEO)*
Board of Directors:
Toru Mukai
Takeshi Sugahara
Mitsuo Takahashi
Transfer Agent:
Sumitomo Mitsui Trust Bank Limited
2-4-8 Izumi Suginami-ku
Tokyo, Japan

Subsidiary:

Medical Payment Corporation (1)
5F 4-9-1 Minamiyawata
Ichikawa, Chiba, 272-0023, Japan
Tel.: (81) 473140620
Fax: (81) 473140621
E-Mail: mp-info@medicalpayment.co.jp
Web Site: www.medicalpayment.co.jp
Emp.: 5
Medical Payment Processing Services
S.I.C.: 6099
N.A.I.C.S.: 522320

ACCSYS TECHNOLOGIES PLC

Royal Albert House Sheet Street
Windsor, SL4 1BE, United Kingdom
Tel.: (44) 1753 757500
Fax: (44) 1753 854730
E-Mail: info@accsysplc.com
Web Site: www.accsysplc.com
AXS—(AIM)

Rev.: $25,337,612
Assets: $82,201,179
Liabilities: $7,464,513
Net Worth: $74,736,666
Earnings: ($14,838,832)
Emp.: 96
Fiscal Year-end: 03/31/13
Business Description:
Wood Milling & Mfr
S.I.C.: 2499
N.A.I.C.S.: 321999
Personnel:
Paul Clegg *(CEO)*
Hans Pauli *(COO)*
Angus Dodwell *(Legal Counsel & Sec)*
Board of Directors:
Gordon Campbell
Paul Clegg
Nick Meyer
Hans Pauli
William Rudge
Patrick Shanley
Legal Counsel:
Dijkstra Voermans
Winthontlaan 2
Utrecht, Netherlands

Bristows
100 Victoria Embankment
London, EC4Y 0DH, United Kingdom

Subsidiary:

Titan Wood Limited (1)
Kensington Ctr
66 Hammersmith Rd, London, W14 8UD, United Kingdom
Tel.: (44) 3338884141
E-Mail: info@titanwood.com
Web Site: www.titanwood.com
Emp.: 15
Biotechnology Research & Development Services
S.I.C.: 8731
N.A.I.C.S.: 541711
Paul Clegg *(CEO)*

U.S. Subsidiary:

Titan Wood Inc. (2)
5000 Quorum Dr Ste 620
Dallas, TX 75254
Tel.: (972) 233-6565
Fax: (972) 233-6568
Web Site: www.accoya.com
Emp.: 50
Biotechnology Research & Development Services
S.I.C.: 8731
N.A.I.C.S.: 541711

Non-U.S. Subsidiary:

Titan Wood Technology B.V. (1)
PO Box 2147
6802 Arnhem, Gelderland, Netherlands
Tel.: (31) 263664122
Fax: (31) 263665936
E-Mail: info@titanwood.com
Emp.: 50
Biotechnology Research & Development Services
S.I.C.: 8731
N.A.I.C.S.: 541711
Victor Vos *(Mgr-Sls)*

ACCTON TECHNOLOGY CORPORATION

1 Creation Rd 3rd Science-based Industrial Park
Hsin-chu, 30077, Taiwan
Tel.: (886) 35770270
Fax: (886) 35780764
Web Site: www.accton.com
Year Founded: 1997
Sls.: $428,000,000
Emp.: 900
Business Description:
Computer Networking & Communication Equipment
S.I.C.: 3577
N.A.I.C.S.: 334118
Personnel:
Samuel Chang *(VP-Sls & Mktg)*

ACCU HOLDING AG

Gerliswilstrasse 17
6021 Emmenbrucke, Switzerland
Tel.: (41) 44 318 88 00
Fax: (41) 44 318 88 02
E-Mail: info@accuholding.ch
Web Site: www.accuholding.ch
Year Founded: 1896
ACUN—(SWX)
Sales Range: $25-49.9 Million
Emp.: 113
Business Description:
Real Estate Development Services
S.I.C.: 6531
N.A.I.C.S.: 531390
Personnel:
Marco Marchetti *(Chm & CEO)*
Andreas Kratzer *(CFO & COO)*
Board of Directors:
Marco Marchetti
Matthree Goddard
Andreas Kratzer

Subsidiary:

RCT Hydraulic-Tooling AG (1)
Von Roll-Areal 2
CH-4712 Klus, Switzerland
Tel.: (41) 62 386 9020
Fax: (41) 62 386 9029
E-Mail: info@crt-cnc.ch
Industrial Machinery
S.I.C.: 3559
N.A.I.C.S.: 333249
Konrad Peter *(CEO)*

Non-U.S. Subsidiaries:

Nexis Fibers a.s. (1)
Chemlonska 1
SK-066 12 Humenne, Slovakia Sk
Tel.: (421) 57 771 3130 (100%)
Fax: (421) 57 7722 650
E-Mail: nexisinfo.hum@nexis-fibers.com
Fiber Mfr
S.I.C.: 2299
N.A.I.C.S.: 313110
Stefan Borc *(CEO)*

Nexis Fibers SIA (1)
Vishku Str 21
LV-5410 Daugavpils, Latvia LV
Tel.: (371) 654 02112 (100%)
Fax: (371) 654 23349
E-Mail: nexisinfo.dgs@nexis-fibers.com
Fiber Mfr
S.I.C.: 2299
N.A.I.C.S.: 313110

RCT Sachsen GmbH (1)
Tuchschererstrasse 15
D-09116 Chemnitz, Germany
Tel.: (49) 371 236 2059
Fax: (49) 371 236 2057
Industrial Services
S.I.C.: 3559
N.A.I.C.S.: 333249

ACCUCAPS INDUSTRIES LIMITED

2125 Ambassador Dr
Windsor, ON, N9C 3R5, Canada
Tel.: (519) 969-5404
Fax: (519) 250-3321
Web Site: www.accucaps.com
Year Founded: 1990
Sales Range: $75-99.9 Million
Emp.: 475
Business Description:
Pharmaceutical Products Mfr
S.I.C.: 2834
N.A.I.C.S.: 325412
Personnel:
Bruno Biscaro *(Pres)*

ACCUMA GROUP

City Tower Piccadilly Plz
Manchester, M1 4BT, United Kingdom
Tel.: (44) 8000434373
Fax: (44) 8700423424
Sales Range: $1-9.9 Million
Business Description:
Financial Services
S.I.C.: 8742
N.A.I.C.S.: 541611
Personnel:
A. Bland *(Sec, Dir-Fin & Ops)*
Board of Directors:
C. Taylor
L. Gregory

Subsidiaries:

Byrom & Keeley Financial Services Ltd. (1)
5th Fl Trafford Plaza 73 Seymour Grove
Manchester, M16 0LD, United Kingdom
Tel.: (44) 8000434373
Fax: (44) 8704450331
E-Mail: support@byromandkeeley.com
Web Site: www.byromandkeeley.com
Debt Management Services
S.I.C.: 6211
N.A.I.C.S.: 523999

Thomas Charles & Co. Ltd. (1)
5th Fl Trafford Plaza 73 Seymour Grove
Manchester, M16 0LD, United Kingdom
Tel.: (44) 870 141 7271
Fax: (44) 870 455 0331
Toll Free: 8000439220
E-Mail: marketing@accuma.com
Web Site: www.thomascharles.com
Debt Management & Counselling Services
S.I.C.: 8742
N.A.I.C.S.: 541611

ACCUMULI PLC

Tuscany House White Hart Lane
Basingstoke, RG21 4AF, United Kingdom
Tel.: (44) 1256 303 700
Fax: (44) 1256 303 701
E-Mail: info@accumuliplc.com
Web Site: www.accumuli.com
ACM—(AIM)
Rev.: $22,296,416
Assets: $44,076,405
Liabilities: $20,974,550
Net Worth: $23,101,854
Earnings: $5,453,288
Emp.: 55
Fiscal Year-end: 03/31/13
Business Description:
Information Security Solutions
S.I.C.: 7382
N.A.I.C.S.: 561621
Personnel:
Gavin Anthony Peter Lyons *(CEO)*
Ian David Winn *(CFO, COO, Sec & Dir-Fin)*
Andy Aplin *(CTO)*
Board of Directors:
Nick Kingsbury
Simon Duckworth
Gavin Anthony Peter Lyons
Graham Richard Norfolk
Ian David Winn
Legal Counsel:
Beachcroft LLP
100 Fetter Ln
London, United Kingdom

ACCUPIX INC.

3F Gaeyang Bldg 548-1 Anyang8-Dong
Manan-Gu, 430-730 Anyang, Kyeonggi-Do, Korea (South)
Tel.: (82) 314782377
Fax: (82) 314665608
Web Site: www.accupix.com
Year Founded: 1996
056730—(KRS)
Emp.: 55
Business Description:
Telecommunication Services
S.I.C.: 4899
N.A.I.C.S.: 517919
Personnel:
Hanil Ko *(CEO)*

ACCURATE TRANSFORMERS LIMITED

8 L S C Vardhman Sidhant Plaza 3rd Floor
Sarita Vihar, New Delhi, 110092, India
Tel.: (91) 11 32597531
Fax: (91) 11 22149456
E-Mail: accuratetransformers@yahoo.co.in
Web Site: www.accuratetransformers.com
Year Founded: 1988
530513—(BOM)
Sales Range: $25-49.9 Million
Business Description:
Electrical Equipment Mfr
S.I.C.: 3612
N.A.I.C.S.: 335311
Personnel:
C. L. Sharma *(Chm & Co-Mng Dir)*
Deepak Sharma *(Co-Mng Dir)*
Board of Directors:
C. L. Sharma
K. L. Chauhan
Deepak Sharma
Om Prakash Sharma
Bhupal Singh

ACD SYSTEMS INTERNATIONAL INC.

1312 Blanshard Street Suite 200
Victoria, BC, V8W 2J1, Canada
Tel.: (250) 419-6700
Fax: (250) 419-6745
Toll Free: (800) 579-5309
E-Mail: pr@acdsee.com
Web Site: www.acdsee.com
Year Founded: 1993
Sales Range: $10-24.9 Million
Emp.: 141
Business Description:
Digital Imaging & Communications Software Products
S.I.C.: 7371
N.A.I.C.S.: 541511
Personnel:
Douglas Vandekerkhove *(Chm & CEO)*
Frank Lin *(Gen Mgr & CTO)*
Board of Directors:
Douglas Vandekerkhove
George Mitchell
Legal Counsel:
Borden Ladner Gervais LLP
1000 Canterra Tower 400 3rd Ave SW
Calgary, AB, T2P 4H2, Canada
Transfer Agents:
Montreal Trust Company of Canada
411 8th Ave SW Ste 530
Calgary, AB, T2P 1E7, Canada
Tel.: (403) 267-6800

Computershare Trust Company of Canada
Ste 600 530 8th Ave SW
Calgary, AB, Canada T2P 3S8
Tel.: (800) 558-0046

ACE AVIATION HOLDINGS INC.

5100 de Maisonneuve Blvd West
Montreal, QC, H4A 3T2, Canada
Tel.: (514) 205-7639
Fax: (514) 205-7863
E-Mail: des.beaumont@aceaviation.com
Web Site: www.aceaviation.com
Year Founded: 1937
ACE.H—(TSXV)
Sales Range: $1-9.9 Million

ACE Aviation Holdings Inc.—(Continued)

Business Description:
International Passenger & Cargo Air Carrier
Import Export
S.I.C.: 4512
N.A.I.C.S.: 481111

Personnel:
Duncan Dee *(Chief Admin Officer & Sr VP-Corp Affairs)*
Sydney Isaacs *(Chief Legal Officer & Sr VP-Corp Dev)*
Carolyn M. Hadrovic *(Sec)*

Board of Directors:
Gregory A. Boland
Pierre Marc Johnson
David J. Kassie
David I. Richardson
Marvin Yontef

Transfer Agent:
CIBC Mellon Trust Company
2001 University Street Suite 1600
Montreal, QC, Canada

Subsidiaries:

Air Canada (1)
1601 Airport Rd NE Ste 708
Calgary, AB, T2E 6Z8, Canada AB
Fax: (866) 584-0380 (75%)
Toll Free: (888) 247-2262
Web Site: www.aircanada.com
Emp.: 14,399
Commercial Airlines
S.I.C.: 4512
N.A.I.C.S.: 481111
Calin Rovinescu *(Pres & CEO)*
Klaus Goersch *(COO & Exec VP)*
Michael Friisdahl *(Pres/CEO-Leisure Grp)*
Kevin C. Howlett *(Sr VP-Reg Markets)*

Subsidiaries:

Air Canada (2)
8050 22nd NE
Calgary, AB, T2E 7H6, Canada (100%)
Tel.: (403) 440-3200
Web Site: www.aircanada.com
S.I.C.: 4512
N.A.I.C.S.: 481111
Calin Rovinescu *(Pres & CEO)*
Duncan Dee *(COO & Exec VP)*
Lise Fournel *(CIO & Sr VP-E-Commerce)*
Sydney John Isaacs *(Chief Legal Officer & Sr VP-Corp Dev)*
Claude Morin *(CEO-Air Canada Cargo & VP)*
Benjamin Smith *(CEO-Air Canada Vacations & VP)*
David J. Shapiro *(Gen Counsel & VP)*
Carolyn M. Hadrovic *(Sec)*
David Legge *(Sr VP-Ops)*

Touram Limited Partnership (2)
1440 Saint Catherine St W Ste 600
Montreal, QC, H3G 1R8, Canada (100%)
Tel.: (514) 876-0700
Telex: 55-61594
Fax: (514) 876-4065
E-Mail: info@aircanadavacations.com
Web Site: www.aircanadavacations.com
Sls.: $135,000,000
Emp.: 354
Air Transportation Chartering, Tour Productions & Operations
S.I.C.: 4725
N.A.I.C.S.: 561520
Eamonn Ferrin *(Pres & COO)*
Zeina Gedeon *(CEO)*

Non-U.S. Subsidiary:

Air Canada UK (2)
Air Canada Complex Radius Park Hatton Cross
Feltham, Mddx, TW14 ONJ, United Kingdom
Tel.: (44) 2087508476
Fax: (44) 2087508482
E-Mail: ukleisuresales@aircanada.ca
Web Site: www.aircanada.com
Emp.: 800
Airline Services
S.I.C.: 4512
N.A.I.C.S.: 481111
Gary Cross *(Gen Mgr-Europe)*

ACE DEVELOPMENT BANK LIMITED

Narayan Chour Naxal
PO Box 13383
Kathmandu, Nepal
Tel.: (977) 14441110
Fax: (977) 14445554
E-Mail: info@ace.com.np
Web Site: www.ace.com.np
ACEDBL—(NEP)
Sales Range: $1-9.9 Million
Emp.: 70

Business Description:
Corporate Banking & Financial Services
S.I.C.: 6011
N.A.I.C.S.: 521110

Personnel:
Yogendra Sakya *(Chm)*
Siddhant Raj Pandey *(CEO)*
Rameshwar Pokharel *(Sec & Sr Mgr-Legal)*

Board of Directors:
Yogendra Sakya
Mukesh Kumar Agrawal
Rajib Raj Bhandari
Sanjib Raj Bhandari
Siddhant Raj Pandey
Shiva Bikram Shah
Binod Ratna Tuladhar

Subsidiary:

Ace Capital Ltd. (1)
Lal Colony Marg Lal Darbur
PO Box 13383
Kathmandu, Nepal
Tel.: (977) 14426161
Fax: (977) 14426133
E-Mail: acecapital@ace.com.np
Web Site: www.acecapital.com.np
Emp.: 30
Merchant Banking Services
S.I.C.: 6029
N.A.I.C.S.: 522110

ACE EDUTREND LTD.

10178/ 304A Ravindera Plaza Abdul Aziz Road
Karol Bagh, New Delhi, India 110005
Tel.: (91) 120 4633000
E-Mail: info@aceedutrend.com
Web Site: www.aceedutrend.com
530093—(BOM)
Sales Range: $1-9.9 Million

Business Description:
Educational Support Services
S.I.C.: 8299
N.A.I.C.S.: 611710

Personnel:
Sushil Aggarwal *(Chm)*

Board of Directors:
Sushil Aggarwal
Gajanand Gupta
L. K. Maheshwari
Yamuna Dhar Pande
Mahendra Sodha Sodha

Transfer Agent:
Beetal Financial & Computer Services Pvt. Ltd
Beetal House 3rd Floor 99 Madangir Behind L S C Near Dada Harsukh Dass
New Delhi, India

ACE LIMITED

Barengasse 32
Zurich, Switzerland CH-8001
Tel.: (41) 43 456 7600
E-Mail: info@acelimited.com
Web Site: www.acelimited.com
Year Founded: 1985
ACE—(NYSE)
Rev.: $19,261,000,000
Assets: $94,510,000,000
Liabilities: $65,685,000,000
Net Worth: $28,825,000,000
Earnings: $3,758,000,000
Emp.: 20,000
Fiscal Year-end: 12/31/13

Business Description:
Holding Company; Insurance & Reinsurance Products & Services
S.I.C.: 6719
N.A.I.C.S.: 551112

Personnel:
Evan G. Greenberg *(Chm, Pres & CEO)*
John W. Keogh *(Vice Chm & COO)*
Philip V. Bancroft *(CFO)*
Timothy Boroughs *(Chief Investment Officer)*
Sean Ringsted *(Chief Risk Officer & Chief Actuary)*
John J. Lupica *(Chm-Insurance-North America)*
Edward Kopp *(Country Pres-ACE American Fire and Marine Insurance Company)*
Giles R. Ward *(Pres-Eurasia & Africa)*
Joseph F. Wayland *(Gen Counsel)*
Ken Koreyva *(Treas)*
Andrew McBride *(Exec VP-Claims-Intl Bus)*

Board of Directors:
Evan G. Greenberg
Michael G. Atieh
Mary A. Cirillo-Goldberg
Michael P. Connors
Robert M. Hernandez
John W. Keogh
Peter Menikoff
Leo F. Mullin
Thomas J. Neff
Robert Ripp
Eugene B. Shanks, Jr.
Theodore E. Shasta
Olivier Steimer

Transfer Agent:
The Bank of New York
One Wall Street
New York, NY 10286
Tel.: (212) 495-1784
Fax: (212) 571-3050

Subsidiary:

ACE Insurance (Switzerland) Limited (1)
Barengasse 32
PO Box 2033
8022 Zurich, Switzerland
Tel.: (41) 43 456 7600
Fax: (41) 43 456 7601
E-Mail: info.ch@acegroup.com
Emp.: 5
Insurance Management Services
S.I.C.: 6411
N.A.I.C.S.: 524298
Florian Mueller *(Gen Mgr)*

Subsidiary:

ACE Reinsurance (Switzerland) Limited (2)
Barengasse 32
Zurich, 8001, Switzerland
Tel.: (41) 434567600
Reinsurance Services
S.I.C.: 6399
N.A.I.C.S.: 524130

U.S. Subsidiaries:

ACE American Insurance Company (1)
436 Walnut St
Philadelphia, PA 19105
Tel.: (215) 640-1000
Fax: (215) 640-5529
General Insurance Services
S.I.C.: 6411
N.A.I.C.S.: 524210
Stephen Haney *(Chief Underwriting Officer-Global Surety)*

ACE Financial Solutions, Inc. (1)
1133 Ave Of The Americas
New York, NY 10036
Tel.: (212) 642-7800
Fax: (212) 642-7889
Financial Management Services
S.I.C.: 6211
N.A.I.C.S.: 523999

ACE Group Holdings, Inc. (1)
1133 Avenue of the Americas
New York, NY 10036
Tel.: (212) 827-4400
Fax: (212) 827-4441
Insurance Brokerage Services
S.I.C.: 6411
N.A.I.C.S.: 524210
John Keogh *(Vice Chm)*
Andrew Hurley *(COO)*
Robert Courtemanche *(Chm-Private Risk Svcs)*
Mary Boyd *(Pres-Private Risk Svcs)*
Chris Maleno *(Pres-USA)*
Orazio Rossi *(Pres-Italy)*
Bror Sandas *(Pres-Nordics)*
Luc Reuter *(Sr VP & Head-Surety-Europe)*

ACE INA International Holdings, Ltd. (1)
436 Walnut St
Philadelphia, PA 19106-3703
Tel.: (215) 640-1000
Fax: (215) 640-5592
Insurance Reinsurance & Financial Services
S.I.C.: 6411
N.A.I.C.S.: 524298
David Lupica *(Pres-Comml Risk Svcs)*
Tom McGrath *(Sr VP & Head-Programs-Comml Risk Svcs)*
Bill Franchi *(Sr VP-Programs-Comml Risk Svcs)*

Non-U.S. Subsidiaries:

ACE Australia Holdings Pty Limited (2)
L 11 28 O'Connell Street
Sydney, NSW, 2000, Australia
Tel.: (61) 293353200
Fax: (61) 93353493
Web Site: www.aceinsurance.com.au
Emp.: 200
Investment Management Services
S.I.C.: 6719
N.A.I.C.S.: 551112

ACE Insurance Company Limited (2)
Saigon Finance Center 9 Dinh Tien Hoang Street 8th Floor
Da Kao Ward District 1, Ho Chi Minh City, Vietnam
Tel.: (84) 839107227
Fax: (84) 839107228
E-Mail: Inquiries.VN@acegroup.com
Web Site: www.aceinsurance.com.vn
Emp.: 20
Insurance Brokerage Services
S.I.C.: 6411
N.A.I.C.S.: 524210
Christopher Twomey *(CEO & Gen Dir)*

U.S. Subsidiary:

Agri General Insurance Company (3)
9200 Northpark Dr Ste 350
Johnston, IA 50131-3010
Tel.: (515) 559-1200
Fax: (515) 559-1201
Web Site: www.rainhail.com
Agricultural Insurance Services
S.I.C.: 6351
N.A.I.C.S.: 524126

Division:

ACE Agribusiness (4)
72 N Franklin St
Wilkes Barre, PA 18773-0016 PA
Tel.: (570) 822-8111
Fax: (570) 829-2060
Toll Free: (800) 233-8347
Web Site: www.aceagribusiness.com
Sales Range: $75-99.9 Million
Emp.: 114
Commercial Insurance Services
S.I.C.: 6331
N.A.I.C.S.: 524126
Dorrance R. Belin *(Vice Chm)*
Douglas A. Gaudet *(Pres & CEO)*

Michael O. Banks *(CFO, Chief Acctg Officer & Treas)*
Keith A. Fry *(Sr VP-Comml Bus)*

ACE INA Properties, Inc. **(1)**
436 Walnut St
Philadelphia, PA 19106-3703
Tel.: (215) 640-1000
Insurance Management Services
S.I.C.: 6411
N.A.I.C.S.: 524298

Subsidiary:

Rain and Hail Insurance Service Incorporated **(2)**
9200 Northpark Dr Ste 300
Johnston, IA 50131
Tel.: (515) 559-1000
Fax: (515) 559-1001
Toll Free: (800) 776-4045
Web Site: www.railhail.com
Emp.: 150
Agricultural Insurance Management Services
S.I.C.: 6331
N.A.I.C.S.: 524126
Michael Coleman *(Pres)*

ACE Insurance Company of the Midwest **(1)**
120 N 9th St
Richmond, IN 47374
Tel.: (215) 640-1000
Web Site: www.ace-ina.com
Property & Casualty Insurance Services
S.I.C.: 6351
N.A.I.C.S.: 524126

ACE Insurance Company **(1)**
San Juan Pr
Hato Rey, PR 00919-1249
Tel.: (787) 274-4700
Fax: (787) 758-6989
General Insurance Services
S.I.C.: 6411
N.A.I.C.S.: 524210

Subsidiary:

ACE Insurance Agency, Inc. **(2)**
2200 Kensington Ct
Oak Brook, IL 60523-2103
Tel.: (630) 990-6576
Insurance Agencies Services
S.I.C.: 6411
N.A.I.C.S.: 524210

ACE Property and Casualty Insurance Company **(1)**
436 Walnut St
Philadelphia, PA 19106
Tel.: (215) 640-1000
Property & Casualty Insurance Services
S.I.C.: 6351
N.A.I.C.S.: 524126

Atlantic Employers Insurance Company **(1)**
55 Haddonfield Rd Ste 210
Cherry Hill, NJ 08002
Tel.: (215) 640-1000
Web Site: www.ace-ina.com
General Insurance Services
S.I.C.: 6411
N.A.I.C.S.: 524210

Conference Facilities, Inc. **(1)**
800 Ridge Pike
Lafayette Hill, PA 19444
Tel.: (610) 825-8000
Fax: (610) 940-4343
Toll Free: (800) 523-3000
Web Site: www.aceconferencecenter.com
Conference Center Operating Services
S.I.C.: 6512
N.A.I.C.S.: 531120

Employee Benefit Communications, Inc. **(1)**
60 Connolly Pkwy Bldg 12 Ste 201
Hamden, CT 06514-2599
Tel.: (203) 281-5300
Fax: (203) 281-6582
Toll Free: (800) 982-5697
Web Site: www.employeebenefitcommunicationsinc.com
Life Insurance Management Services
S.I.C.: 6311
N.A.I.C.S.: 524113

David Czaplicki *(Pres)*

NewMarkets Insurance Agency, Inc. **(1)**
11575 Great Oaks Way Ste 200
Alpharetta, GA 30022
Tel.: (678) 795-4000
Fax: (215) 640-1420
Toll Free: (800) 633-3390
E-Mail: submissions@newmarketsagency.com
Web Site: www.newmarketsagency.com
Insurance Management Services
S.I.C.: 6411
N.A.I.C.S.: 524298
Jeffery M. Clark *(VP)*

Pacific Employers Insurance Company **(1)**
436 Walnut St
Philadelphia, PA 19106
Tel.: (215) 640-1000
Property & Casualty Insurance Services
S.I.C.: 6331
N.A.I.C.S.: 524126

Subsidiary:

Illinois Union Insurance Company **(2)**
525 W Monroe St Ste 400
Chicago, IL 60661
Tel.: (215) 640-1000
Fax: (215) 640-4796
Insurance Brokerage Services
S.I.C.: 6411
N.A.I.C.S.: 524210

Recovery Services International, Inc. **(1)**
436 Walnut St
Philadelphia, PA 19106
Tel.: (215) 640-4386
Fax: (215) 640-5551
Web Site: www.esis.com
Emp.: 5
Materials Recovery Services
S.I.C.: 4953
N.A.I.C.S.: 562920
Daniel D'Imperio *(Asst VP)*

Westchester Surplus Lines Insurance Company **(1)**
11575 Great Oaks Pkwy Ste 200
Alpharetta, GA 30022
Tel.: (678) 795-4000
Fax: (866) 635-5688
Insurance Agencies & Brokerage Services
S.I.C.: 6411
N.A.I.C.S.: 524210
Bruce Kessler *(Gen Mgr)*

Non-U.S. Group:

ACE Group Management & Holdings Ltd. **(1)**
17 Woodbourne Ave
Hamilton, HM 08, Bermuda BM
Tel.: (441) 295-5200 (100%)
Fax: (441) 295-5221
Web Site: www.acebermuda.com
Holding Company: Insurance Programs
S.I.C.: 6719
N.A.I.C.S.: 551112
Evan G. Greenberg *(Chm, Pres & CEO)*
John Keogh *(Vice Chm & COO)*
Philip V. Bancroft *(CFO)*
Samantha Froud *(Chief Admin Officer)*
Sean Ringsted *(Chief Actuary & Chief Risk Officer)*
Frank Lattal *(Chief Claims Officer)*
Robert F. Cusumano *(Gen Counsel)*

Group:

ACE Tempest Re Group **(2)**
The ACE Tempest Re Building
30 Woodbourne Avenue, Hamilton, HM 08, Bermuda (100%)
Mailing Address:
PO Box HM 2702
Hamilton, HM KX, Bermuda
Tel.: (441) 292-2603
Web Site: www.acedoran.com
Reinsurance Products & Services
S.I.C.: 8741
N.A.I.C.S.: 551114
Jacques Q. Bonneau *(Chm)*
Gus Hardart *(CFO)*
Giuseppe Russo *(Grp Chief Actuary)*
Claudio Ronzitti *(Asst Gen Counsel)*

Subsidiary:

ACE Tempest Life Reinsurance Limited **(3)**
ACE Building 17 Woodbourne Avenue
Hamilton, HM 08, Bermuda BM
Mailing Address: (100%)
PO Box HM 2702
Hamilton, HM KX, Bermuda
Tel.: (441) 2922603
Fax: (441) 2952888
E-Mail: acetempestre@acegroup.com
Web Site: www.acetempestre.com
Life & Annuity Reinsurance Products & Services
S.I.C.: 6399
N.A.I.C.S.: 524130
David Drury *(Pres & CEO)*

Subsidiary:

ACE Tempest Reinsurance Ltd. **(4)**
The ACE Tempest Re Bldg 17 Woodbourne Ave
Hamilton, HM 08, Bermuda BM
Mailing Address: (100%)
PO Box HM 2702
Hamilton, HM KX, Bermuda
Tel.: (441) 292-2603
Fax: (441) 2922395
E-Mail: acetempestre@acegroup.com
Web Site: www.aceltd.com
Emp.: 60
Reinsurance Products & Services
S.I.C.: 6399
N.A.I.C.S.: 524130
Evan G. Greenberg *(Chm, Pres & CEO)*
Tim Mardon *(Pres)*
David Drury *(Sr VP)*

U.S. Subsidiary:

ACE Tempest Reinsurance USA, LLC **(5)**
2 Stamford Plaza 281 Tresser Blvd Ste 500
Stamford, CT 06901-3264
Tel.: (203) 328-7000
Fax: (203) 328-7003
E-Mail: acetempestre@acegroup.com
Web Site: www.acetempestre.com
Reinsurance Products & Services
S.I.C.: 6399
N.A.I.C.S.: 524130
James E. Wixtead *(CEO)*

Unit:

ACE Tempest Life Re USA **(6)**
2 Stamford Plz 281 Tresser Blvd Ste 500
Stamford, CT 06901-3264
Tel.: (203) 328-7000
Fax: (203) 328-7003
Web Site: www.acetempestlifereusa.com
Life & Annuity Reinsurance Products & Services
S.I.C.: 6399
N.A.I.C.S.: 524130
Cristina Downey *(Chief Underwriter)*

Non-U.S. Units:

ACE Tempest RE Canada **(5)**
1800 McGill College Avenue Suite 910
Montreal, QC, H3A 3J6, Canada (100%)
Tel.: (514) 798-7275
Fax: (514) 798-8805
Web Site: www.acetempestre.com
Property & Casualty Reinsurance Underwriting Services
S.I.C.: 6411
N.A.I.C.S.: 524298
Constantin Petalas *(Pres)*

ACE Tempest Re Europe **(5)**
The ACE Building 100 Leadenhall Street
London, EC3A 3BP, United Kingdom
Tel.: (44) 2071737000
Fax: (44) 1293597233
E-Mail: info@acetempestre.com
Web Site: www.acetempestre.com
Emp.: 500
Reinsurance Products & Services
S.I.C.: 6399
N.A.I.C.S.: 524130
Andreas Lewin *(Mng Dir)*
Matthew Shaw *(Pres-Global Mktg-East Reg)*

Subsidiary:

ACE Bermuda Insurance Ltd. **(2)**
ACE Building 17 Woodbourne Avenue
Hamilton, HM 08, Bermuda BM
Mailing Address: (100%)
PO Box HM 1015
Hamilton, HMDX, Bermuda
Tel.: (441) 295 5200
Fax: (441) 296-7802
E-Mail: info@acebermuda.com
Web Site: www.acebermuda.com
Insurance
S.I.C.: 6399
N.A.I.C.S.: 524128
Rees Fletcher *(Pres & CEO)*
Gus Hardart *(CFO)*
Allison Towlson *(COO & Reg Exec VP)*
Samantha Froud *(Chief Admin Officer)*
Judy Gonsalves *(Exec VP-Mgmt & Dev-Excess Liability Dept)*
Philippe Bacon *(Sr VP-Pro Lines Dept)*
Jeffrey Jabon *(Sr VP-Pro Lines Dept)*

Subsidiaries:

Paget Reinsurance International Ltd **(3)**
17 Woodbourne Avenue
Hamilton, HM08, Bermuda
Tel.: (441) 295 5200
Fax: (441) 292 8635
General Insurance Services
S.I.C.: 6411
N.A.I.C.S.: 524210

Paget Reinsurance Ltd **(3)**
ACE Building 17 Woodbourne Avenue
Hamilton, HM08, Bermuda
Tel.: (441) 295 5200
Fax: (441) 298 9664
E-Mail: info@pagetre.com
Web Site: www.acerentacaptive.com
General Insurance Services
S.I.C.: 6411
N.A.I.C.S.: 524210
Samantha Froud *(Chief Admin Officer)*

Sovereign Risk Insurance Ltd. **(3)**
ACE Bldg 17 Woodbourne Ave 45 Reid Street
Hamilton, HM 08, Bermuda
Tel.: (441) 296 4279
Fax: (441) 296 4281
E-Mail: svninfo@ace.bm
Web Site: www.sovereignbermuda.com
Emp.: 12
Risk Insurance Services
S.I.C.: 6411
N.A.I.C.S.: 524298
Price Lowenstein *(Pres & CEO)*

U.S. Division:

ACE Overseas General **(2)**
1133 Ave of the Americas 44th Fl
New York, NY 10036 (100%)
Tel.: (212) 827-4400
Web Site: www.acelimited.com
Emp.: 60
Regional Managing Office; Property & Casualty Insurance Products & Services
S.I.C.: 8741
N.A.I.C.S.: 551114
John W. Keogh *(Chm)*
Juan Andrade *(COO)*
Michael Furgueson *(Pres-Multinational Client Grp)*
Russell Bundschuh *(Pres-Intl Life Insurance Bus)*
David M. A. Furby *(Pres-Comml Property & Casualty Div)*
Edward M. Levin *(Pres-Accident & Health Div)*
Howard S. Schrader *(Gen Counsel & Exec VP)*
Peter Murray *(Sr VP-Claims)*

Group:

ACE Latin America **(3)**
2 Datran Ctr 9130 S Dadeland Blvd Ste 1100
Miami, FL 33156
Tel.: (305) 670-9935
Fax: (305) 671-1630
E-Mail: info@acelatinamerica.com
Web Site: www.acelatinamerica.com
Emp.: 1,000

ACE Limited—(Continued)

Regional Managing Office; Insurance Products & Services
S.I.C.: 8741
N.A.I.C.S.: 551114
Jorge Luis Cazar *(Pres & CEO)*
Roberto Salcedo *(CFO)*
Marcos Gunn *(COO)*
Brent Hooker *(Gen Counsel)*

Non-U.S. Groups:

ACE Asia Pacific (3)
600 North Bridge Road 17-01 Parkview Square
Singapore, 188 778, Singapore (100%)
Tel.: (65) 6398 8000
Fax: (65) 6293 6276
Regional Managing Office; Insurance Products & Services
S.I.C.: 8741
N.A.I.C.S.: 551114
Damien M. Sullivan *(Chm)*
Juan Luis Ortega *(Pres)*
Paul McNamee *(Deputy Pres)*
Steve Crouch *(COO)*

Subsidiary:

ACE Insurance Limited (4)
600 North Bridge Road 04-02 Parkview Square
Singapore, 188778, Singapore SG
Tel.: (65) 63988000 (100%)
Fax: (65) 62981055
E-Mail: cs@aceinsurance.com.sg
Web Site: www.aceinsurance.com.sg
Premiums: $118,357,273
Assets: $211,719,648
Liabilities: $163,928,032
Net Worth: $47,791,616
Earnings: $8,151,558
Emp.: 200
Fiscal Year-end: 12/31/12
Insurance Products & Services
S.I.C.: 6411
N.A.I.C.S.: 524298
Mack Lip Chian Eng *(Pres)*
Alina Ang *(CFO)*
Jean Ong *(Chief Compliance Officer & Chief Risk Officer)*

Non-U.S. Subsidiaries:

ACE Insurance Japan (4)
Arco Tower 13F 1-8-1 Shimo-Meguro
Meguro-ku, Tokyo, 153-0064, Japan (100%)
Tel.: (81) 357400600
Fax: (81) 357400739
E-Mail: info@acefareast.com
Web Site: www.ace-insurance.co.jp
Sales Range: $550-599.9 Million
Insurance Products & Services
S.I.C.: 6311
N.A.I.C.S.: 524113
Takashi Imai *(Pres & CEO)*
Shinji Nomoto *(CFO)*
Kazuhisa Ohtani *(Exec Officer)*
Kiyoshi Okanoya *(Exec Officer)*
Kiyotaka Shimada *(Exec Officer)*
Takeshi Yamaguchi *(Exec Officer)*

ACE Insurance Limited (4)
Level 3 28-34 O'Connell St
Sydney, NSW, 2000, Australia
Tel.: (61) 293353200
Fax: (61) 293353411
E-Mail: hr.au@acegroup.com
Web Site: www.aceinsurance.com.au
Rev.: $445,612,864
Emp.: 220
Insurance Services
S.I.C.: 6311
N.A.I.C.S.: 524113
Kenneth Brown *(COO-Australia & New Zealand Ops)*

ACE Insurance Limited (4)
CU 1/3 Shed 24 Princess Wharf
Auckland, New Zealand
Tel.: (64) 93771459
Fax: (64) 93031909
E-Mail: info@acegroup.com
Web Site: www.acegroup.com
Sales Range: $75-99.9 Million
Emp.: 32
Insurance Services
S.I.C.: 6311
N.A.I.C.S.: 524113

Paul Martin *(CEO)*

ACE Synergy Insurance Berhad (4)
Wisma ACE Jerneh 38 Jalan Sultan Ismail
Jalan Raja Chulan, Kuala Lumpur, 50200, Malaysia (100%)
Tel.: (60) 320583000
Fax: (60) 320583333
E-Mail: Inquiries.MY@acegroup.com
Web Site: www.acejerneh.com.my
Sales Range: $25-49.9 Million
Emp.: 700
Insurance Services
S.I.C.: 6311
N.A.I.C.S.: 524113
Lim Joo Leong *(CFO)*

ACE European Group Limited (3)
The ACE Building 100 Leadenhall Street
London, EC3A 3BP, United Kingdom UK
Tel.: (44) 2071737000
Fax: (44) 2071737800
E-Mail: info@acegroup.com
Web Site: www.aceeuropeangroup.com
Premiums: $3,544,004,145
Assets: $9,643,241,077
Liabilities: $8,148,221,991
Net Worth: $1,495,019,086
Earnings: $200,205,014
Emp.: 1,092
Fiscal Year-end: 12/31/12
Holding Company; Regional Managing Office
S.I.C.: 6719
N.A.I.C.S.: 551112
Andrew J. Kendrick *(Chm)*
Tony Jordan *(Chief Actuary)*
Mark McCausland *(Chief Risk Officer)*
Joe S. Clabby *(Pres-Continental Europe)*
D. P. Robinson *(Pres-ACE UK)*
A. M. W. Shaw *(Pres-ACE Global Markets)*
Kenneth Underhill *(Gen Counsel)*
Pat Drinan *(Sr VP-Accident & Health-EMEA)*
Lance Grant *(Sr VP-Ops & IT)*
Sue Smith *(Sr VP-HR)*

Division:

ACE Global Markets Limited (4)
The ACE Building 100 Leadenhall St
London, EC3A 3BP, United Kingdom UK
Tel.: (44) 2071737000 (100%)
Fax: (44) 1293597233
E-Mail: matthew.shaw@acegroup.com
Web Site: www.aceglobalmarkets.com
Emp.: 500
Holding Company; Comprehensive Specialty Insurance Products & Underwriting Services
S.I.C.: 6719
N.A.I.C.S.: 551112
Richard V. Pryce *(Pres)*
Matthew Shaw *(Chief Underwriting Officer)*

Subsidiaries:

ACE Underwriting Agencies Limited (5)
The ACE Building 100 Leadenhall Street
London, EC3A 3BP, United Kingdom UK
Tel.: (44) 2071737000 (100%)
Fax: (44) 2071737800
E-Mail: michael.reynolds@aceeuropeangroup.com
Web Site: www.aceeuropeangroup.com
Sales Range: $600-649.9 Million
Emp.: 600
Insurance Underwriting Agency
S.I.C.: 6411
N.A.I.C.S.: 524210
Michael Reynolds *(CFO)*

Unit:

ACE Europe UK (4)
The ACE Building 100 Leadenhall Street
London, EC3A 3BP, United Kingdom (100%)
Tel.: (44) 2071737000
Fax: (44) 2071737800
E-Mail: info@acegroup.com
Web Site: www.aceeurope.co.uk
Emp.: 500
Insurance Products & Services
S.I.C.: 6331
N.A.I.C.S.: 524126
Richard V. Pryce *(Pres)*
Mike Reynolds *(CFO)*

Non-U.S. Units:

ACE European Group Ltd. - Ireland (4)
5 George's Dock
IFSC, Dublin, 1, Ireland (100%)
Tel.: (353) 14401700
Fax: (353) 14401701
Web Site: www.aceeurope.ie
Emp.: 20
Insurance Products & Services
S.I.C.: 6331
N.A.I.C.S.: 524126
David Furby *(Pres-Continental Europe)*

ACE European Group Ltd. - Spain (4)
Francisco Gervas 13
28020 Madrid, Spain
Tel.: (34) 918374977
Fax: (34) 918376776
Web Site: www.aceeurope.es
Emp.: 90
Insurance Products & Services
S.I.C.: 6411
N.A.I.C.S.: 524298
Angel Diaz Millan *(Dir Gen)*

U.S. Subsidiaries:

ACE INA Holdings, Inc. (2)
436 Walnut St
Philadelphia, PA 19106 DE
Mailing Address: (100%)
PO Box 1000 19105
Philadelphia, PA 19106
Tel.: (215) 640-1000
Fax: (215) 640-1133
Web Site: www.acegroup.com
Emp.: 4,000
Holding Company; Insurance Products & Services
S.I.C.: 6719
N.A.I.C.S.: 551112
Christopher Maleno *(Div Pres)*
Jamie English *(COO-Comml, Property & Casualty Insurance Bus-North America)*
John Alfieri *(Pres-Global Accts-North America)*
Joseph S. Clabby *(Pres-Reg Ops-USA)*
Doug Poetzsch *(Exec VP-Claims)*
Joe Vasquez *(Exec VP-Accident & Health)*
Karen Griswold *(Sr VP-Comml Marine)*
Katharyn Kubursi *(Sr VP-Distr Mgmt)*
Bill O'Donnell *(Sr VP-Distr Mgmt)*
Carl Sutter *(Sr VP-Distr Mgmt)*

Subsidiaries:

Combined Insurance Company of America (3)
1000 N Milwaukee Ave
Glenview, IL 60025 IL
Tel.: (847) 953-2025
Fax: (847) 953-8030
Toll Free: (800) 225-4500
Web Site: www.combined.com
Emp.: 40,000
Supplemental Accident, Disability, Health & Life Insurance
S.I.C.: 6311
N.A.I.C.S.: 524113
Brad Bennett *(Pres)*
James L. Coleman *(CMO & Sr VP)*
James P. Zils *(CMO & Sr VP)*
Steven E. Lippai *(Chief Actuary & Exec VP)*
Chris Martin *(Pres-Worksite Solutions Div)*
Clive Robinson *(Pres-Europe & Asia Pacific)*
David A. Goldberg *(Gen Counsel & Sec)*
Des Bosnic *(Exec VP-Sls)*
Jacques Thibaudeau *(Exec VP)*
Tony O'Dierno *(Sr VP & Mgr-South & Southeast)*

Branch:

Combined Insurance Company of America - Chicago (4)
5050 N Broadway St
Chicago, IL 60640-3007
Tel.: (773) 765-1000
Fax: (773) 765-1850
Toll Free: (800) 428-5466
E-Mail: info@combined.com
Web Site: www.combined.com
Emp.: 1,500
Supplemental Accident, Disability, Health & Life Insurance

S.I.C.: 6311
N.A.I.C.S.: 524113

Subsidiaries:

Combined Life Insurance Company of New York (4)
11 British American Blvd
Latham, NY 12110-1405 NY
Tel.: (518) 220-9333 (100%)
Fax: (518) 220-2939
Toll Free: (800) 951-6206
Web Site: www.combinedny.com
Emp.: 110
Supplemental Accident, Disability, Health & Life Insurance
S.I.C.: 6311
N.A.I.C.S.: 524113
Michael Hurd *(VP)*

Non-U.S. Branch:

Combined Insurance Company of America - Canada (4)
7300 Warden Ave Ste 300
Markham, ON, L3R OX3, Canada
Tel.: (905) 305-1922
Fax: (905) 305-8600
Web Site: www.combined.ca
Sales Range: $150-199.9 Million
Emp.: 200
Supplemental Accident, Disability, Health & Life Insurance
S.I.C.: 6321
N.A.I.C.S.: 524114
Guy Sauve *(Mng Dir & Exec VP)*

Non-U.S. Subsidiaries:

Combined Insurance Company of Europe Limited (4)
Merrion House Merrion Road
Dublin, 4, Ireland IE
Tel.: (353) 12696522
Fax: (353) 1 283 8585
E-Mail: csd@ie.combined.com
Web Site: www.combinedinsurance.ie
Sales Range: $1-9.9 Million
Emp.: 25
Supplemental Accident, Disability, Health & Life Insurance
S.I.C.: 6311
N.A.I.C.S.: 524113

Combined Insurance Company of New Zealand (4)
105 Great S Rd Remuera
1005 Auckland, New Zealand NZ
Tel.: (64) 95209000
Fax: (64) 95209009
E-Mail: nz.service@nz.combined.com
Web Site: www.combinedinsurance.com
Emp.: 35
Supplemental Accident, Disability, Health & Life Insurance
S.I.C.: 6311
N.A.I.C.S.: 524113

Combined Insurance (4)
Combined House
15 Wheatfield Way, Kingston upon Thames, Surrey, KT1 2PA, United Kingdom UK
Tel.: (44) 2085467733
Telex: 851-929986
Fax: (44) 2085495584
E-Mail: csd@uk.combined.com
Web Site: www.combinedinsurance.co.uk
Emp.: 400
Life Insurance Services
S.I.C.: 6311
N.A.I.C.S.: 524113

Combined Life Insurance Company of Australia (4)
51 Berry Street
North Sydney, NSW, 2060, Australia AU
Tel.: (61) 299225033
Fax: (61) 299222096
E-Mail: customer@combined.com.au
Web Site: www.combined.com.au
Emp.: 450
Supplemental Accident, Disability, Health & Life Insurance
S.I.C.: 6321
N.A.I.C.S.: 524114
Des Bosnic *(CEO)*

ESIS, Inc. (3)
436 Walnut St
Philadelphia, PA 19106 PA

Tel.: (215) 640-1000
Fax: (215) 640-2489
Toll Free: (800) 234-8223
E-Mail: info@esis.com
Web Site: www.esis.com
Emp.: 120
Workers Compensation Claims Management Services
S.I.C.: 6411
N.A.I.C.S.: 524298
David K. Patterson *(Pres)*
Jim Bond *(CFO & COO)*
Brian Dowd *(COO & Sr VP)*
Lee W. Farrow *(Sr VP-Client Svcs & Bus Dev)*
Frank Murray *(Sr VP-Claims)*
Sam Terzich *(Sr VP-Product & Pro Liability)*

Subsidiary:

Proclaim America, Inc. (4)
3100 S Gessner Rd Ste 600
Houston, TX 77063
Tel.: (713) 771-3500
Fax: (713) 771-7749
Web Site: www.proclaimamerica.com
Emp.: 20
Claims & Risk Management Services
S.I.C.: 6371
N.A.I.C.S.: 524292
Heather Roy *(Mng Dir)*

Units:

ACE USA - Mid-Atlantic Region (3)
436 Walnut St
Philadelphia, PA 19106
Mailing Address:
PO Box 1000
Philadelphia, PA 19105
Tel.: (215) 640-1000
Fax: (215) 640-1133
Web Site: www.acegroup.com
Insurance Products & Services
S.I.C.: 6411
N.A.I.C.S.: 524210
Robert Poliseno *(Sr VP)*

ACE USA - New York Region (3)
1133 Avenue of the Americas 32nd Fl
New York, NY 10036
Tel.: (212) 642-7800
Fax: (212) 642-7887
Web Site: www.aceusa.com
Emp.: 300
Insurance Products & Services
S.I.C.: 6411
N.A.I.C.S.: 524210
Andrew Hurley *(COO)*
Tim O'Donnell *(Pres-Pro Lines-North America)*
Ed Zaccaria *(Div Pres-Reg Ops)*
Suresh Krishnan *(Gen Counsel-Multinational Client Grp)*

ACE USA - Southeast Region (3)
500 Colonial Centre Pkwy Ste 200
Roswell, GA 30076-8852
Mailing Address:
500 Colonial Center Pkwy Ste 200
Roswell, GA 30076-8852
Tel.: (678) 795-4000
Fax: (678) 795-4249
Web Site: www.aceusa.com
Emp.: 400
Insurance Products & Services
S.I.C.: 6411
N.A.I.C.S.: 524210
Bruce Jervis *(Exec VP-Comml & Inland Marine)*
Rob Huber *(Sr VP & Reg Mgr)*
Stephen P. Dinsdale *(Sr VP-Aviation)*
Jim Shevlin *(Sr VP)*

Non-U.S. Subsidiary:

ACE INA Insurance (3)
25 York St Ste 1400
Toronto, ON, M5J 2V5, Canada (99.99%)
Tel.: (416) 368-2911
Fax: (416) 594-2600
E-Mail: info@ace-ina-canada.com
Web Site: www.ace-ina-canada.com
Emp.: 175
Carrier of Property & Casualty Insurance Services
S.I.C.: 6351
N.A.I.C.S.: 524126
Andy Hollenberg *(Pres & COO)*
David Brosmen *(CEO)*
Robert Campitelli *(Chief Risk Officer)*

Rain & Hail LLC (2)
9200 Northpark Dr Ste 300
Johnston, IA 50131-3006 IA
Tel.: (515) 559-1000
Fax: (515) 559-1001
Toll Free: (800) 776-4045
Web Site: www.rainhail.com
Emp.: 200
Crop Insurance Services
S.I.C.: 6411
N.A.I.C.S.: 524210
Steve Harms *(Chm & CEO)*

Westchester Fire Insurance Company (2)
500 Colonial Ctr Pkwy Ste 200
Roswell, GA 30076-8852 NY
Mailing Address: (100%)
PO Box 100005
Roswell, GA 30077-7005
Tel.: (678) 795-4000
Fax: (678) 795-4249
Toll Free: (800) 241-5161
E-Mail: wsgmarketing@acegroup.com
Web Site: www.acewestchester.com
Commercial Property & Casualty Insurance & Reinsurance Products & Services
S.I.C.: 6351
N.A.I.C.S.: 524126
Jamie English *(COO)*
John Berger *(Pres-Inland Marine)*
Barbara Deas *(Pres-Environ)*
Bruce Kessler *(Pres-Casualty & Specialty Lines)*
David Lupica *(Pres-Pro Risk & Comml Risk Svcs)*
Bob Meyer *(Pres-Property)*

Non-U.S. Subsidiaries:

ABA Seguros, S.A. de C.V. (1)
Montes Rocallosos No 505 Sur Residencial San Augustin
San Pedro, Garza Garcia, NL, Mexico MX
Tel.: (52) 81 8368 1400
Toll Free: 8007122828
E-Mail: info@abaseguros.com
Web Site: www.abaseguros.com
Emp.: 2,000
Property & Casualty Insurance Products & Services
S.I.C.: 6331
N.A.I.C.S.: 524126
Alejandro Gonzalez Davila *(Dir Gen)*

ACE Arabia Insurance Company Limited B.S.C. (C) (1)
8th Floor Southern Tower Units 801-804
King Faisal Bin
Abdulaziz Street Coastal Road, Al Khobar, Saudi Arabia
Tel.: (966) 3 849 3633
Fax: (966) 3 849 3660
General Insurance Services
S.I.C.: 6411
N.A.I.C.S.: 524210

ACE Asia Pacific Services Pte. Ltd. (1)
600 North Bridge Road No 17-01 Parkview Square
Singapore, 188778, Singapore
Tel.: (65) 6308 8000
Fax: (65) 6298 1055
Insurance Management Services
S.I.C.: 6411
N.A.I.C.S.: 524298

ACE Canada Holdings, Inc. (1)
Suite 5600 100 King Street West
Toronto, ON, M5X 1C9, Canada
Tel.: (877) 947-7922
Fax: (877) 262-0256
E-Mail: customerservice@zippycash.ca
Web Site: www.zippycash.ca
Emp.: 10
Payday Lending Services
S.I.C.: 6099
N.A.I.C.S.: 522390

ACE Canada (1)
25 York Street Suite 1400
Toronto, ON, Canada
Tel.: (416) 368-2911
Fax: (416) 594-2600
Toll Free: (877) 772-7797
E-Mail: Canada.Claims@acegroup.com
Web Site: www.ace-ina-canada.com
Emp.: 175

Property & Casualty Insurance Services
S.I.C.: 6331
N.A.I.C.S.: 524126
David J. Brosnan *(Pres)*
Bruce Walker *(CFO)*
Terri Mitchell *(COO & Exec VP-Life, Accident & Health)*

ACE Environmental Health and Safety Consulting (Shanghai) Company Limited (1)
Unit 2208 Pos Plaza 1600 Century Avenue
Shanghai, 200122, China
Tel.: (86) 21 5175 8795
Fax: (86) 21 5175 8796
E-Mail: rcsasia@esis.com
Environmental Consulting Services
S.I.C.: 8999
N.A.I.C.S.: 541620

ACE Europe Life Limited (1)
Leadenhall Street 100
London, EC3A 3BP, United Kingdom
Tel.: (44) 2071737000
Fax: (44) 1293597233
Emp.: 50
Insurance Agency & Brokerage Services
S.I.C.: 6411
N.A.I.C.S.: 524210
Andrew Kendrick *(Gen Mgr)*

ACE European Group Limited (1)
Karntner Ring 5-7
1010 Vienna, Austria
Tel.: (43) 1 710 93 55
Fax: (43) 1 710 95 20
E-Mail: info.at@acegroup.com
Web Site: www.acegroup.com
Emp.: 1
Insurance Management Services
S.I.C.: 6411
N.A.I.C.S.: 524298
Walter Lentsch *(Gen Mgr)*

ACE European Holdings Limited (1)
Ace Building 100 Leadenhall St
London, EC3A 3BP, United Kingdom
Tel.: (44) 20 7173 7000
Fax: (44) 12 9359 7246
Emp.: 60
Investment Management Services
S.I.C.: 6211
N.A.I.C.S.: 523999
Andrew Kendrick *(CEO)*

Non-U.S. Subsidiary:

ACE Insurance Management (DIFC) Limited (2)
Office 3 & 4 Currency House Office Building
Level 7 DIFC Street
PO Box 62425
Dubai, United Arab Emirates
Tel.: (971) 4 3117129
Insurance Management Services
S.I.C.: 6411
N.A.I.C.S.: 524298

Non-U.S. Subsidiaries:

ACE Insurance Limited (3)
25th Floor Shui On Centre
No 6-8 Harbour Road, Wanchai, China (Hong Kong)
Tel.: (852) 31916800
Fax: (852) 25603565
Web Site: www.aceinsurance.com.hk/Contact-ACE-Hong-Kong
Insurance Brokerage Services
S.I.C.: 6411
N.A.I.C.S.: 524210
Raimund Navakas *(VP & Reg Mgr-Asia Pacific)*

ACE Seguradora S.A. (3)
Avenida Comercial De Macau No 5
Edf FIT Centre 5 Andar, Macau, China (Macau)
Tel.: (853) 82964322
Fax: (853) 82964323
Web Site: www.acegroup.com
Insurance Brokerage Services
S.I.C.: 6411
N.A.I.C.S.: 524210

ACE Seguros S.A. (3)
Calle Amador Merino Reyna 267 Street Office 402
San Isidro, Lima, Peru
Tel.: (51) 14175000

Fax: (51) 12212943
E-Mail: atencion.seguros@acegroup.com
Web Site: www.acegroup.com
Insurance Brokerage Services
S.I.C.: 6411
N.A.I.C.S.: 524210
Juan Carlos Puyo *(Pres-Country)*

ACE Seguros S.A. (3)
Alisos No 47A Forest Floor 1 and 4 Colonia Bosques de las Lomas
Cuajimalpa de Morelos, Mexico, 05120, Mexico
Tel.: (52) 5552585800
Fax: (52) 5552585899
Web Site: www.acegroup.com
Insurance Brokerage Services
S.I.C.: 6411
N.A.I.C.S.: 524210
Roberto Flores *(Pres)*

ACE Fianzas Monterrey, S.A. (1)
(Formerly Fianzas Monterrey, S.A.)
Ruben Dario 38
11580 Mexico, Mexico (100%)
Tel.: (52) 55 57 26 3700
Fax: (52) 5552502520
Web Site: www.fianzasmonterrey.com.mx
Emp.: 300
Surety Bonding Services
S.I.C.: 6099
N.A.I.C.S.: 522390
Arturo Martinez *(Dir Gen)*

ACE Gibraltar Limited (1)
Suite 837 Europort
Gibraltar, Gibraltar
Tel.: (350) 20075122
Fax: (350) 20075129
E-Mail: acegib@gibtelecom.net
Web Site: www.acegroup.com
Insurance Brokerage Services
S.I.C.: 6411
N.A.I.C.S.: 524210
Tony Jordan *(Chief Actuary-ACE European Grp)*
Mark McCausland *(Chief Risk Officer-ACE European Grp)*
Andrew Kendrick *(Chm-ACE European Grp)*
Matthew Shaw *(Pres-Div-ACE Global Markets)*
Kenneth Underhill *(Gen Counsel)*
Peter Murray *(Dir-Claims & Sr VP-Claims)*
Lance Grant *(Sr VP-Ops & IT ACE European Grp)*

ACE INA Life Insurance (1)
25 York Street Suite 1400
Toronto, ON, M5J 2V5, Canada
Tel.: (416) 368-2911
Fax: (416) 594-2600
E-Mail: canada.claims@acegroup.com
Emp.: 175
General Insurance Services
S.I.C.: 6411
N.A.I.C.S.: 524210
David J. Brosnan *(Gen Mgr)*

ACE INA Services U.K. Limited (1)
The Ace Bldg 100 Leadenhall St
London, EC3A 3BP, United Kingdom
Tel.: (44) 2071737000
Fax: (44) 1293597233
Emp.: 500
General Insurance Services
S.I.C.: 6411
N.A.I.C.S.: 524210
Andrew Kendrick *(CEO)*

ACE Insurance Company Egypt S.A.E. (1)
3 Abou El Feda Street 5th Floor
Zamalek, Cairo, 11211, Egypt
Tel.: (20) 2 2736 0006
Fax: (20) 2 2736 0002
E-Mail: egypt@acegroup.com
Emp.: 2
Insurance Management Services
S.I.C.: 6411
N.A.I.C.S.: 524298
Alia Helmy *(Gen Mgr)*

ACE Insurance Limited (1)
Ground Floor The Bridle Hunts End Office Park 38 Wierda Road West
Wierda Valley, Sandton, 1926, South Africa
Tel.: (27) 11 722 5700
Fax: (27) 11 783 0812
Web Site: www.aceinsurance.co.za
Emp.: 4

ACE Limited—(Continued)

General Insurance Services
S.I.C.: 6411
N.A.I.C.S.: 524210
Christine Davis *(Head-Admin Property)*

ACE Insurance S.A.-N.V. **(1)**
Avenue Des Nerviens 9-31 Nervierslaan 9-31
Brussels, 1040, Belgium
Tel.: (32) 2 516 97 11
Fax: (32) 2 513 08 84
E-Mail: info.benelux@acegroup.com
Web Site: www.aceeurope.com
Emp.: 6
Insurance Management Services
S.I.C.: 6411
N.A.I.C.S.: 524298
R. Verhulsdonck *(Country Mgr)*

ACE Insurance (Thailand) Co., Ltd. **(1)**
Levels 25-30 Interchange 21 Building 399 Sukhumvit Rd399
Wattana, Bangkok, 10110, Thailand
Tel.: (66) 2611 4040
Fax: (66) 2611 4050
Web Site: www.aceinsurance.co.th
General Insurance Services
S.I.C.: 6411
N.A.I.C.S.: 524210
Rob Wilkinson *(Country Pres)*

ACE Jerneh Insurance Berhad **(1)**
Wisma ACE Jerneh 38 Jalan Sultan Ismail
50250 Kuala Lumpur, Malaysia
Tel.: (60) 3 2116 3300
Fax: (60) 3 2142 6672
E-Mail: Inquiries.MY@acegroup.com
Web Site: www.acejerneh.com.my
Emp.: 300
General Insurance Services
S.I.C.: 6411
N.A.I.C.S.: 524210
Michele Anne Minjoot *(VP & Head-Comm)*

ACE Life Assurance Co. Ltd. **(1)**
30-132 Sindhorn Building Tower 1 11th-12th Floor Wireless Road
Pathumwan, Bangkok, 10330, Thailand
Tel.: (66) 2615 6860
Fax: (66) 2615 6878
Web Site: www.acelife.co.th
Insurance Agency Services
S.I.C.: 6411
N.A.I.C.S.: 524210

ACE Life Insurance Company Limited **(1)**
21th Floor Sun Wah Tower 115 Nguyen Hue St
Dist 1, Ho Chi Minh City, Vietnam
Tel.: (84) 8 38 27 8989
Fax: (84) 8 38 21 9000
E-Mail: acelife.vietnam@acegroup.com
Web Site: www.acelife.com.vn
General Insurance Services
S.I.C.: 6411
N.A.I.C.S.: 524210
Tuan Hai Lam *(Chm-Exec Bd)*
Son Hong Nguyen *(CFO)*
Hiep Phuoc Le *(COO)*
Paul George Nguyen *(Chief Actuary & Head-Special Distr & IT)*
Kevin Goulding *(Pres-Asia Pacific)*
Allan Lam *(Pres-Hong Kong)*

ACE Resseguradora S.A. **(1)**
Edificio Eluma - Av Paulista 1 294 - 16 Andar
Sao Paulo, 01310-915, Brazil
Tel.: (55) 11 4504 4400
Fax: (55) 11 4504 4399
Insurance Management Services
S.I.C.: 6411
N.A.I.C.S.: 524298

ACE Seguros de Vida S.A. **(1)**
Miraflores No 222 Piso 17
Santiago, Chile
Tel.: (56) 225498300
Fax: (56) 226328289
Web Site: www.acegroup.com
Insurance Brokerage Services
S.I.C.: 6411
N.A.I.C.S.: 524210
Juan Manuel Merchan *(Pres)*
Jose Soler *(COO)*

ACE Seguros S.A. **(1)**
Av Amazonas 3655 y Juan Pablo Sanz Edif Antisana 5to Piso
Quito, Ecuador
Tel.: (593) 2 292 0555
Fax: (593) 2 244 5817
Web Site: www.acelatinamerica.com
General Insurance Services
S.I.C.: 6411
N.A.I.C.S.: 524210
Edwin Astudillo *(Country Pres)*
Audrey Ramirez *(CFO)*

ACE Seguros S.A. **(1)**
Calle 72 10-51 Piso 7
Bogota, 208208, Colombia
Tel.: (57) 13190300
Fax: (57) 13190408
E-Mail: ace.servicioalcliente@acegroup.com
Web Site: www.acelatinamerica.com
General Insurance Services
S.I.C.: 6411
N.A.I.C.S.: 524210
Pilar Lozano *(Pres)*
Adriana Redondo *(CFO)*

ACE Seguros S.A. **(1)**
Torre Sur Planta Baja Este Business Park Costa del Este Ave
Principal y Ave La Rotonda, Panama, Panama
Tel.: (507) 205 0400
Fax: (507) 205 0499
E-Mail: panama.recepcion@acegroup.com
Web Site: www.acelatinamerica.com
Emp.: 6
General Insurance Services
S.I.C.: 6411
N.A.I.C.S.: 524210
Oscar Perez Nation *(Country Pres)*
Silvia Cervantes *(CFO)*

ACE Seguros S.A. **(1)**
Miraflores 222 Piso 17
Santiago, Chile
Tel.: (56) 2 549 8300
Fax: (56) 2 632 8289
General Insurance Services
S.I.C.: 6411
N.A.I.C.S.: 524210
Juan Manuel Merchan *(Country Pres)*
Veronica Campos *(CFO)*

ACE Seguros S.A. **(1)**
Torre Alem Plaza Av L N Alem 855-Piso 19
Buenos Aires, C1001AAD, Argentina
Tel.: (54) 1141144000
Fax: (54) 1141144001
E-Mail: aceseguros@acegroup.com
Web Site: www.acegroup.com
Emp.: 150
Insurance Brokerage Services
S.I.C.: 6411
N.A.I.C.S.: 524210
Roberto Salcedo *(CFO)*

ACE Servicios S.A. **(1)**
Av Leandro N Alem 855 Piso 19
Buenos Aires, 1001, Argentina
Tel.: (54) 1141144000
Fax: (54) 1141144001
E-Mail: aceseguros@acegroup.com
Web Site: www.acelimited.com
Emp.: 15
General Insurance Services
S.I.C.: 6411
N.A.I.C.S.: 524210
Agnes Colhoun *(Pres & Gen Mgr)*
Roberto Hidalgo *(Pres & Gen Mgr)*

CJSC ACE Insurance Company **(1)**
Barykovskiy Pereulok 2
119034 Moscow, Russia
Tel.: (7) 495 589 22 27
Fax: (7) 495 589 22 28
Web Site: www.aceeurope.ru
General Insurance Services
S.I.C.: 6411
N.A.I.C.S.: 524210
Julia Piskulova *(CFO)*
Tatiana Ushakova *(Gen Dir)*

Combined International Services, Ltd. **(1)**
Combined House 15 Wheatfield Way
Kingston upon Thames, KT1 2PQ, United Kingdom
Tel.: (44) 20 8546 7733
Fax: (44) 20 8541 6294
E-Mail: csd@uk.combined.com
Web Site: www.combinedinsurance.co.uk
General Insurance Services
S.I.C.: 6411
N.A.I.C.S.: 524210
Christopher Michael Harrison *(Gen Mgr)*

INACAN Holdings Ltd. **(1)**
25 York St
Toronto, ON, M5J 2V5, Canada
Tel.: (416) 368-2911
Fax: (416) 594-2600
Emp.: 175
Investment Management Services
S.I.C.: 6211
N.A.I.C.S.: 523999
David Brosnan *(CEO)*

PT. ACE INA INSURANCE **(1)**
World Trade Center 13th Fl Jl Jenderal Sudirman Kav 29-31
Jakarta, 12920, Indonesia
Tel.: (62) 21 5299 8200
Fax: (62) 21 521 1801
E-Mail: CustomerService.ID@acegroup.com
Web Site: www.aceinsurance.co.id
General Insurance Services
S.I.C.: 6411
N.A.I.C.S.: 524210

PT. ACE Life Assurance **(1)**
Menara Cakrawala 5th Floor Jl M H Thamrin Kav 9
Jakarta, 10340, Indonesia
Tel.: (62) 21 2356 8888
Fax: (62) 21 2356 8889
Web Site: www.acelife.co.id
General Insurance Services
S.I.C.: 6411
N.A.I.C.S.: 524210
Chee Kong Tham *(Chm-Exec Bd)*
Susanto Halim *(Member-Exec Bd)*

Rain and Hail Insurance Service, Ltd. **(1)**
4303 Albert St Ste 200
Regina, SK, S4S 3R6, Canada
Tel.: (306) 584-8844
Fax: (306) 584-3466
Emp.: 3
General Insurance Services
S.I.C.: 6411
N.A.I.C.S.: 524210
Robert Goeres *(Gen Mgr)*

Rio Guayas, Compania de Seguros y Reaseguros, S.A. **(1)**
Rocafuerte 732 Entre Urdaneta Y Mendiburu Edificio Subsidiarias
Banco De Guayaquil Piso 2, Guayaquil, Ecuador
Tel.: (593) 43730110
Emp.: 75
Insurance Management Services
S.I.C.: 6411
N.A.I.C.S.: 524298
Martin Vilches *(Gen Mgr)*

ACE PILLAR CO., LTD.

4F 5 Lane 83 Sec 1 Guangfu Road
Taipei, Sanchong, Taiwan
Tel.: (886) 229958400
Fax: (886) 229993775
E-Mail: sf_tsai@acepillar.com.tw
Web Site: www.acepillar.com.tw
8374—(TAI)
Sales Range: $25-49.9 Million
Emp.: 450

Business Description:
Automatic Mechatronics Components
S.I.C.: 3566
N.A.I.C.S.: 333612

Personnel:
Zhicheng Lin *(Chm)*

Board of Directors:
Zhicheng Lin
Qingfeng Li
Gongquan Yang
Weimeng Yang
Zhengli Yang

Non-U.S. Subsidiaries:

Ace Pillar (S) Pte Ltd **(1)**
No 1 Kakl Bukit Ave 3 No 06-02
Singapore, 416087, Singapore
Tel.: (65) 67486586
Fax: (65) 67485613
E-Mail: sales@acepillar.com.sg
Web Site: www.acepillar.com
Emp.: 6
Automation Components Supplier
S.I.C.: 5063
N.A.I.C.S.: 423610
Chen Wen De *(CEO)*

HongKong Ace Pillar Co., Ltd **(1)**
Rm 10 12 F Shatin Galleria 18-24 Shan Mei St
Fotan, China (Hong Kong)
Tel.: (852) 26901859
Fax: (852) 26904859
E-Mail: sales@acepillar.com.hk
Web Site: www.acepillar.com.hk
Emp.: 4
Automatic Mechatronics Distr
S.I.C.: 5063
N.A.I.C.S.: 423610
Ken Chan *(Mgr)*

Tianjin Ace Pillar Enterprise Co., Ltd. **(1)**
No 3 West 10 Avenue
Tianjin Airport Economic Area, Tianjin, 300308, China
Tel.: (86) 22 2489 1997
Fax: (86) 22 2355 6368
Web Site: www.acepillar.com.cn
Sales Range: $10-24.9 Million
Emp.: 60
Automatic Mechanic Components Distr
S.I.C.: 5084
N.A.I.C.S.: 423830

ACE SECURITIES CO., LTD.

2-6-11 Honmachi Chuo-ku
541-0053 Osaka, Japan
Tel.: (81) 662672111
Fax: (81) 662530368
Web Site: www.ace-sec.co.jp
Emp.: 417

Business Description:
Securities Brokerage
S.I.C.: 6211
N.A.I.C.S.: 523120

Personnel:
Yutaka Inui *(Pres)*

ACE SOFTWARE EXPORTS LTD.

801 Everest Commercial Complex
Limda Chowk
Rajkot, 360 001, India
Tel.: (91) 281 222 6097
Fax: (91) 281 223 2918
E-Mail: Info@acesoftex.com
Web Site: www.acesoftex.com
531525—(BOM)
Rev.: $695,714
Assets: $3,219,081
Liabilities: $110,353
Net Worth: $3,108,727
Earnings: $37,877
Fiscal Year-end: 03/31/13

Business Description:
Electronic Publishing Services
S.I.C.: 2741
N.A.I.C.S.: 519130

Personnel:
Sanjay H. Dhamsania *(Co-Founder & Co-Mng Dir)*
Vikram B. Sanghani *(Co-Founder & Co-Mng Dir)*
Nellickal I. Thomas *(Compliance Officer & Sec)*

Board of Directors:
Pratik C. Dadhania
Sanjay H. Dhamsania
Vimal L. Kalaria
Vikram B. Sanghani
Dharamshibhai R. Vadaliya

Transfer Agent:
Link Intime India Private Limited
303 3rd Floor Shopper's Plaza 5 Near 5 Government Society
Opp Municipal Market C G Road, Ahmedabad, 380009, India

Subsidiary:

Speedwell Engineers Pvt. Ltd. (1)
R C Electronics Compound Opp Rajkamal Petrol Pump Outside
Octroi Naka Gondal Road, 360004 Rajkot, India
Tel.: (91) 281 2388 487
Engineering Consulting Services
S.I.C.: 8711
N.A.I.C.S.: 541330

ACE TECHNOLOGIES CORP.

24B 5L Namdong Complex 451-4
Nonhyeon-Dong
Namdong-Gu, Incheon, 405-849, Korea (South)
Tel.: (82) 32 8185500
Fax: (82) 32 8185505
Web Site: www.aceteq.co.kr
088800—(KRS)

Business Description:
Radio Frequency Products Mfr
S.I.C.: 3663
N.A.I.C.S.: 334220

Personnel:
Song Hawk Kim *(CEO)*

ACE TOURS WORLDWIDE LIMITED

F22/23 Jolly Arcade Ghod-dod Road
Surat, Gujarat, 395007, India
Tel.: (91) 261 6718888
Fax: (91) 261 2656851
E-Mail: enquiry@acetours.in
Web Site: www.ace1world.com
Year Founded: 2007
536492—(BOM)
Rev.: $3,644,000
Emp.: 34
Fiscal Year-end: 03/31/13

Business Description:
Tours, Cruises, Travel Bookings, Hotel Bookings, Car Rentals & Other Related Services
S.I.C.: 4729
N.A.I.C.S.: 561599

Personnel:
Raju Jashwantlal Choksi *(Mng Dir)*
Ankit Shukla *(Compliance Officer & Sec)*

Board of Directors:
Bharat Jashwantlal Choksi
Raju Jashwantlal Choksi
Rajendra K. Desai
Rakesh Mohinder Puri

ACE WINCHES LTD.

Towie Barclay Works
Turriff, Aberdeenshire, AB53 8EN, United Kingdom
Tel.: (44) 1888 511600
Fax: (44) 1888 511601
E-Mail: info@ace-winches.co.uk
Web Site: www.ace-winches.com
Year Founded: 1986
Sales Range: $25-49.9 Million
Emp.: 253

Business Description:
Winch Mfr
S.I.C.: 3536
N.A.I.C.S.: 333923

Personnel:
Alfie Cheyne *(Founder & CEO)*
Sam Morrison *(CFO)*
Graham Thomson *(COO)*
Valerie Cheyne *(Chief Compliance Officer)*

ACEA S.P.A.

Piazzale Ostiense 2
00154 Rome, Italy
Tel.: (39) 0657991
E-Mail: info@aceaspa.it
Web Site: www.aceaspa.it
Year Founded: 1909
ACE—(ITA)
Rev.: $4,835,337,639
Assets: $9,179,102,456
Liabilities: $7,385,453,432
Net Worth: $1,793,649,024
Earnings: $114,828,301
Emp.: 7,256
Fiscal Year-end: 12/31/12

Business Description:
Water & Electric Power Distribution & Production Services
S.I.C.: 4941
N.A.I.C.S.: 221310

Personnel:
Giancarlo Cremonesi *(Chm)*
Paolo Gallo *(CEO)*

Board of Directors:
Giancarlo Cremonesi
Francesco Caltagirone
Diane D'Arres
Paolo Di Benedetto
Paolo Gallo
Giovanni Giani
Antonella Illuminati
Maurizio Leo
Andrea Peruzy

Subsidiaries:

Acea Ato 2 S.p.A. (1)
Piazzale Ostiense 2
00154 Rome, Italy
Tel.: (39) 0657991
Fax: (39) 0657994297
E-Mail: formezione@acea.it
Web Site: www.aceaato2.it
Drinking Water Supplier
S.I.C.: 4971
N.A.I.C.S.: 221310
Alessandro Cecili *(Pres)*

Acea Distribuzione S.p.A. (1)
Piazzale Ostiense 2
00154 Rome, Italy
Tel.: (39) 0657991
Fax: (39) 0657994529
Emp.: 100
Electric Power Distribution Services
S.I.C.: 4931
N.A.I.C.S.: 221122
Giancarlo Cremonesi *(Pres)*

Acearieti S.R.L. (1)
Piazzale Ostiense 2
00154 Rome, Italy
Tel.: (39) 0657991
Fax: (39) 065758095
Drinking Water Supplier
S.I.C.: 4971
N.A.I.C.S.: 221310
Sandro Tetili *(Pres)*

Crea Gestioni S.R.L. (1)
Piazzale Ostiense 2
00154 Rome, Italy
Tel.: (39) 0657991
Drinking Water Supplier
S.I.C.: 4971
N.A.I.C.S.: 221310

LaboratoRI S.p.A. (1)
Via Vitorchiano 165/167
00189 Rome, Italy
Tel.: (39) 0657992600
Fax: (39) 0657992629
E-Mail: solution@laboratorispa.it
Web Site: www.laboratorispa.it
Emp.: 140
Water Testing Services
S.I.C.: 8734
N.A.I.C.S.: 541380
Roberto Zocchi *(Pres)*

Umbra Acque S.p.A. (1)
Via G Benucci N 162
06087 Ponte San Giovanni, Perugia, Italy
Tel.: (39) 0755978011
Fax: (39) 075398217
E-Mail: info@umbraacque.com
Web Site: www.umbraacque.it
Drinking Water Supplier
S.I.C.: 4941
N.A.I.C.S.: 221310
Angelo Zucchini *(Pres)*

Non-U.S. Subsidiary:

Acea Dominicana S.A. (1)
Autopista las Americas Esq Calle Masoneria Ens Ozama
Santo Domingo, Distrito Nacional, Dominican Republic
Tel.: (809) 5981722
Fax: (809) 5981716
Web Site: www.aceadominicana.com
Emp.: 120
Water Treatment Services
S.I.C.: 4971
N.A.I.C.S.: 221310
Andrea Leone *(Dir-Comml)*

Non-U.S. Subsidiary:

Consorcio Agua Azul S.A. (1)
Amador Merino Reyna 307 of 803
San Isidro, Lima, Peru
Tel.: (51) 14417072
Fax: (51) 14417073
E-Mail: mail@caa.com.pe
Web Site: www.caa.com.pe
Water Supply Projects Operation & Maintenance Services
S.I.C.: 4941
N.A.I.C.S.: 221310
Andres Arias Congrains *(Gen Mgr)*

ACEBED CO. LTD.

310-1 Sanggok-ri
Samseong-myeong, Eumseong, Chungcheongbuk-do, Korea (South)
Tel.: (82) 43 877 1881
Fax: (82) 43 877 1889
Web Site: www.acebed.com
Year Founded: 1963
003800—(KRS)

Business Description:
Bed Mfr
S.I.C.: 2511
N.A.I.C.S.: 337122

Personnel:
Sungho Ahn *(CEO)*

ACEGAS-APS SPA

Via Del Teatro 5
34121 Trieste, Italy
Tel.: (39) 0407793111
Fax: (39) 0407793427
E-Mail: info.ts@acegas-aps.it
Web Site: www.acegas-aps.it
Rev.: $647,267,650
Emp.: 1,000

Business Description:
Water, Electricity, Gas Distribution & Waste Collection
S.I.C.: 4939
N.A.I.C.S.: 221122

Personnel:
Massimo Paniccia *(Chm)*
Cesare Pillon *(CEO)*

Subsidiary:

APS Sinergia S.p.A. (1)
Via Monta 29
35138 Padua, Italy
Tel.: (39) 0498908111
Fax: (39) 0498908199
E-Mail: info.pd@sinergiespa.com
Web Site: www.sinergiespa.com
Facility Management & Energy Services
S.I.C.: 8744
N.A.I.C.S.: 561210
Fabrizio Granata *(Dir-Creative)*

ACEITES BORGES PONT, S.A.

Avenida Jose Trepat S N
E 25300 Tarrega, Lerida, Spain
Tel.: (34) 973501212
Fax: (34) 973500060
E-Mail: info@borges.es
Web Site: www.borges.es
Year Founded: 1896
Emp.: 800

Business Description:
Mfr. of Edible Oils & Dried Foods
S.I.C.: 2034
N.A.I.C.S.: 311423

Personnel:
Jose Pont *(Founder)*

U.S. Subsidiary:

STAR Fine Foods-Borges USA (1)
4652 E Date Ave
Fresno, CA 93725 DE
Tel.: (559) 498-2900
Fax: (559) 498-2920
E-Mail: postmaster@starfinefoods.com
Web Site: www.starfinefoods.com
Emp.: 24
Olive Oil, Wine Vinegar, Maraschino Cherries, Onions, Olives, Sundried Tomatoes, Pickle Specialties, Capers, Anchovies, Peppers, Jalapeno Peppers, Chili Peppers Importer
Import Export
S.I.C.: 5149
N.A.I.C.S.: 424490
Jeffrey Freeman *(Pres & CEO)*

ACELON CHEMICALS & FIBER CORPORATION

No 94 Fan Chin Road
Puyan, Chang Hua, Taiwan
Tel.: (886) 47638869
Fax: (886) 47626831
E-Mail: service1@acelon.com.tw
Web Site: www.acelon.com.tw
Year Founded: 1988
1466—(TAI)
Sales Range: $150-199.9 Million

Business Description:
Polyester Filaments Mfr
S.I.C.: 2823
N.A.I.C.S.: 325220

Personnel:
Weng Dong Chou *(Chm)*
Wen-Tung Chou *(Gen Mgr & Pres)*

ACEP FRANCE

15 rue de Vezelay
75008 Paris, France
Tel.: (33) 1 46 45 15 18
Fax: (33) 1 49 53 06 85
Web Site: www.smart-mirror.com
Year Founded: 1994
MLACP—(EUR)
Sales Range: $1-9.9 Million
Emp.: 14

Business Description:
Electronic Eye Care Product Mfr & Distr
S.I.C.: 3679
N.A.I.C.S.: 334419

Personnel:
Jean-Philippe Sayag *(Chm & CEO)*

ACER INCORPORATED

8F 88 Sec 1Xintai 5th Rd
Xizhi, New Taipei City, 221, Taiwan
Tel.: (800) 220901204
Telex: 26318 Acer
Fax: (886) 286911031
Toll Free: 8007332237
E-Mail: andrew_chang@acer.com.tw
Web Site: www.acer-group.com
Year Founded: 1976
2353—(TAI)
Sls.: $14,547,534,623
Assets: $7,676,940,127
Liabilities: $5,135,601,172
Net Worth: $2,541,338,954
Earnings: ($98,568,101)
Emp.: 7,967
Fiscal Year-end: 12/31/12

Business Description:
Computers & Computer Peripherals Mfr
Import Export
S.I.C.: 3571
N.A.I.C.S.: 334111

Personnel:
Stan Shih *(Founder & Chm)*

Acer Incorporated—(Continued)

Jason Chen *(Pres & CEO)*
Eva Ho *(CFO)*
Michael Birkin *(CMO)*
Jackson Lin *(Pres-Design Center & CTO)*
Oliver Ahrens *(Pres-EMEA & Sr VP)*
Scott Lin *(Pres-GC & Sr VP)*
Steve Lin *(Pres-AAP & Sr VP)*
Emmanuel Fromont *(Pres-PA & VP)*
Tiffany Huang *(Pres-Personal Computer Global Ops)*
S. T. Liew *(Pres-SPBG)*
Ben Wan *(Pres-EBBG)*
Walter Deppeler *(Sr VP)*

Board of Directors:
Stan Shih
Julian Michael Horn-Smith
Hsin-I Lin
Philip Peng
F. C. Tseng

Supervisory Board of Directors:
George Huang
Carolyn Yeh

Subsidiaries:

Acer Capital Corporation (1)
23F 88 Hsin Tai Wu Road Sec 1 Hsichih
Taipei, Taiwan
Tel.: (886) 2 2696 1234
Fax: (886) 2 2696 4747
Financial Investment Services
S.I.C.: 6211
N.A.I.C.S.: 523999

Acer Cyber Center Services Ltd (1)
No 69 Lane 368 shin-ho Rd Sanhe Village
Lungtan Shiang, Taoyuan, 325, Taiwan
Tel.: (886) 3 407 2000
Fax: (886) 3 407 2002
Web Site: www.accsi.net
Web Hosting Services
S.I.C.: 7379
N.A.I.C.S.: 518210
Ben Wan *(Gen Mgr)*

Acer Information Products Group (1)
8 Fl 88 Hsin Tai Wu Rd
Sec 1 Hsichih, Hsien, 221, Taiwan (100%)
Tel.: (886) 226961234
Fax: (886) 26963535
Web Site: www.acer.com.tw
Emp.: 2,000
Mfr & Designer of Computer Systems, Components & Consumer Electronics Products
S.I.C.: 7373
N.A.I.C.S.: 541512
Sscottl Lin *(Pres)*

Acer Internet Services Inc. (1)
5F 88 Hsin Tai Wu Rd
Hsien, 221, Taiwan
Tel.: (886) 226963131
Fax: (886) 226963535
E-Mail: webmaster@acer.net
Web Site: www.acer.net
Emp.: 1,000
Internet Communication Services
S.I.C.: 4899
N.A.I.C.S.: 517919
Jan Franco *(CEO)*

Acer Property Development, Inc. (1)
Aspire Pk Kur Wong Rd
Kao Yuan Village
Taoyuan, Hsien, 325, Taiwan (100%)
Tel.: (886) 3 407 1888
Fax: (886) 3 407 1777
E-Mail: aspire-park@aspirepark.com.tw
Web Site: www.aspirepark.com.tw
Emp.: 22
Real Estate Services
S.I.C.: 6726
N.A.I.C.S.: 525990
Jones Yu *(Pres)*

Acer Technologies Corp. (1)
16F 84 Hsin Tai Wu Rd
Sec 1, Hsien, 221, Taiwan
Tel.: (886) 226964055
Fax: (886) 226963131
Web Site: www.acer.com
Emp.: 300
Multimedia Peripherals, Information Storage Media, Computer Communications Products, Memory, Upgrade Kits, Image Process Products
S.I.C.: 3575
N.A.I.C.S.: 334118

Acer Technology, Inc. (1)
8F 88 Sec 1 Xintai 5th Rd Xizhi
Taipei, 221, Taiwan
Tel.: (886) 2 2696 1234 3131
Fax: (886) 225019162
Web Site: www.acer.com.tw
Emp.: 11
Mfr., Designer, Marketer & Retailer of Memory Modules
S.I.C.: 3577
N.A.I.C.S.: 334118

AOpen Inc. (1)
3F No 19-8 San Chung Rd
Nan Kang Area, Taipei, 115, Taiwan
Tel.: (886) 226961333
Fax: (886) 237895899
E-Mail: webmaster@aopen.com.tw
Web Site: www.aopen.com.tw
Mfr. & Designer of Motherboards, Housings, CD-ROMs, Optical Devices & Multimedia Products
S.I.C.: 3575
N.A.I.C.S.: 334118

Eten Information System Co., Ltd. (1)
No 256 Yangguang Street Neihu Chiu
Taipei, 114, Taiwan
Tel.: (886) 2 7721 0000
Fax: (886) 2 7721 0123
E-Mail: sales_inter@eten.com.tw
Web Site: www.eten.com.tw
Emp.: 150
Communication Equipment Mfr
S.I.C.: 3669
N.A.I.C.S.: 334290
Simon Hwang *(Chm & CEO)*

Vision Tech Information Technology, Inc. (1)
7F 135 Section 2 Chien Kuo North Rd
Taipei, 104, Taiwan (100%)
Tel.: (886) 225178500
Fax: (886) 2 2517 8722
Web Site: www.omnieast.com
Software Distr
S.I.C.: 5045
N.A.I.C.S.: 423430

Weblink International, Inc. (1)
2 8Fl No 39 Chung Hsiao W Rd
Sector 1, Taipei, 100, Taiwan
Tel.: (886) 223716000
Fax: (886) 223717750
E-Mail: terrylio@weblink.com.tw
Web Site: www.weblink.com.tw
Emp.: 200
Computer Services
S.I.C.: 7373
N.A.I.C.S.: 541512
Terry Lio *(Pres)*

Wistron Nexus Inc. (1)
2nd Fl 5 Hsin An Rd
Science Based Industrial Park
Hsin-chu, 300, Taiwan (100%)
Tel.: (886) 35631000
Fax: (886) 35790955
Web Site: www.wnexus.com.tw
Emp.: 80
Mfr. of ISDN, Computer Networking/Data Communications Equipment, Intergrating INternet Protocol (IP) & PSTN (Public Switched Telephone Networks) Technologies
S.I.C.: 3661
N.A.I.C.S.: 334210

U.S. Subsidiaries:

Acer America Corporation (1)
333 W San Carlos St
San Jose, CA 95110 (100%)
Tel.: (408) 533-7700
Fax: (408) 533-4555
E-Mail: webmaster@acer.com
Web Site: www.acer.com
Emp.: 180
Computer Sales & Service
Import Export
S.I.C.: 3571
N.A.I.C.S.: 334111
Ming Wang *(CFO)*

Non-U.S. Branch:

Acer America Corp. (2)
5540 McAdam Rd
Mississauga, ON, L4Z 1P1, Canada (100%)
Tel.: (905) 755-7570
Fax: (905) 755-7591
E-Mail: info@acer.ca
Web Site: www.acer.ca
Emp.: 50
Mfr. of Computers & Computer Accessories
S.I.C.: 3571
N.A.I.C.S.: 334111
Terry Tomecek *(Gen Mgr)*

Acer American Holding Corp. (1)
333 W San Carlos St 1500
San Jose, CA 95110-2726
Tel.: (408) 533-7700
Investment Management Services
S.I.C.: 6211
N.A.I.C.S.: 523999

Acer Cloud Technology Co. (1)
1200 Villa St Ste 100
Mountain View, CA 94041-2920
Tel.: (650) 810-2000
Fax: (650) 810-2001
Cloud Computing Software Developer
S.I.C.: 7372
N.A.I.C.S.: 511210
Raymond Lo *(VP-Engrg)*

Acer Latin America, Inc. (1)
3750 NW 87th Ave Ste 640
Miami, FL 33178
Tel.: (305) 392-7000
Fax: (305) 392-7020
Web Site: www.acer.com
Sales Range: $10-24.9 Million
Emp.: 9
Sales of Computers & Computer Hardware
S.I.C.: 3571
N.A.I.C.S.: 334111

Gateway, Inc. (1)
7565 Irvine Center Dr
Irvine, CA 92618 DE
Tel.: (949) 471-7000
Fax: (949) 471-7041
Web Site: www.gateway.com
Sales Range: $1-4.9 Billion
Emp.: 1,645
Personal Computer Products Mfr
Import Export
S.I.C.: 3571
N.A.I.C.S.: 334111

Subsidiaries:

Acer Service Corporation (2)
1394 Eberhardt Rd
Temple, TX 76504-8832
Tel.: (254) 298-4000
Electronic Computer Mfr
S.I.C.: 3571
N.A.I.C.S.: 334111
Keith Hogwood *(Dir-Svc Plng & Logistics)*

Gateway Manufacturing LLC (2)
7565 Irvine Ctr Dr
Irvine, CA 92618-2930
Tel.: (949) 471-7000
Computer Peripheral Equipment Mfr
S.I.C.: 3577
N.A.I.C.S.: 334118

Gateway US Retail, Inc. (2)
7565 Irvine Ctr Dr
Irvine, CA 92618
Tel.: (949) 471-7000
Fax: (949) 471-7041
Electronic Computer Mfr
S.I.C.: 3571
N.A.I.C.S.: 334111

Non-U.S. Subsidiary:

Gateway Hong Kong Ltd (2)
13 Canton Road
Harbour City, Kowloon, China (Hong Kong)
Tel.: (852) 2113 0888
Fax: (852) 2113 0022
Electronic Computers Mfr
S.I.C.: 3571
N.A.I.C.S.: 334111

Non-U.S. Subsidiaries:

Acer Africa Pty. Ltd. (1)
Acer House Naivasha Rd
Haltway House 1685, Sandton, Sunninghill, South Africa (100%)
Tel.: (27) 112336100
Fax: (27) 112336200
E-Mail: aaf_acercare@acer-euro.com
Web Site: www.acer.co.za
Emp.: 80
S.I.C.: 3571
N.A.I.C.S.: 334111
Graham Braum *(Mng Dir)*

Acer Asia Pacific Sdn Bhd (1)
Level 24 Menara Ambank No 8 Jalan Yap Kwan Seng
50450 Kuala Lumpur, Malaysia
Tel.: (60) 3 2162 1388
Fax: (60) 3 2162 4949
Web Site: www.acer-group.com
Emp.: 100
Computer Peripheral Equipment Distr
S.I.C.: 5045
N.A.I.C.S.: 423430
Steve Lin *(Pres)*

Acer Austria GmbH (1)
Europaring Floor 15
2345 Brunn am Gebirge, Austria
Tel.: (43) 22363075200
Fax: (43) 22363075250
E-Mail: vertrieb-austria@acer-euro.com
Web Site: www.acer.at
Emp.: 11
Computer & Computer Equipment Whslr
S.I.C.: 7379
N.A.I.C.S.: 541519
Gleb Mishin *(VP-Emerging Markets-EMEA)*

Acer CIS, Inc. (1)
St. Large Academic 5A Hi-Tec House
Business Ctr Ste 309, 127299 Moscow, Russia
Tel.: (7) 4956465373
Fax: (7) 4956465374
E-Mail: partners@acer.com.ru
Web Site: www.acer.com.ru
Emp.: 12
S.I.C.: 3571
N.A.I.C.S.: 334111
Mishin Gleb *(Gen Mgr)*

Acer Computec Mexico, S.A. de C.V. (1)
Avenida Ejercito Nacional 579 Piso 1
Colonia Granada, 11520 Mexico, DF, Mexico
Tel.: (52) 55 5999 9400
Fax: (52) 55 5999 9401
Web Site: www.acer.com.mx
Sales Range: $300-349.9 Million
Emp.: 420
Product Assembly, Marketing & Sales
S.I.C.: 3571
N.A.I.C.S.: 334111
Juan Jose Cordova *(CFO)*

Acer Computer Australia Pty. Ltd. (1)
5 Figtree Drive Australia Center Sydney Olympic Park
Sydney, NSW, 2127, Australia (100%)
Tel.: (61) 287623000
Fax: (61) 297642368
Web Site: www.acer.com.au
Sales Range: $200-249.9 Million
Emp.: 302
S.I.C.: 3571
N.A.I.C.S.: 334111
Charles Chung *(Mng Dir)*

Acer Computer B.V. Benelux (1)
Europalaan 89
Postbox 70576
5201 CZ 's-Hertogenbosch, 5232 BC, Netherlands (100%)
Tel.: (31) 736459645
Fax: (31) 736459699
E-Mail: webmaster@acer.nl
Web Site: www.acer.nl
Emp.: 80
Electronic Computers
S.I.C.: 3571
N.A.I.C.S.: 334111

Acer Computer Co., Ltd. (1)
191 62 63 16Th Fl CTI Tower
Rachadapised Rd
Bangkok, 10110, Thailand (100%)
Tel.: (66) 26619700
Fax: (66) 26619721
Web Site: www.acer.co.th
Emp.: 150

S.I.C.: 3571
N.A.I.C.S.: 334111
Nikipat Praweenwongwuthi *(Sr Mgr)*

Acer Computer Czech and Slovak Republics (1)
Novodvorska 1010 14B
142 00 Prague, 4, Czech Republic (100%)
Tel.: (420) 244112555
Fax: (420) 244112599
E-Mail: cz_quest@acer-euro.com
Web Site: www.acer.cz
Emp.: 10
S.I.C.: 3571
N.A.I.C.S.: 334111

Acer Computer (Far East) Limited (1)
6 F Guangdong Investment Tower
148 Connaught Road, Hong Kong, China (Hong Kong) (100%)
Tel.: (852) 25280233
Fax: (852) 28613758
E-Mail: zoe_yung@acer.com.hk
Web Site: www.acer.com.hk
Emp.: 150
Manufacturer of Computers
S.I.C.: 3571
N.A.I.C.S.: 334111

Acer Computer Finland Oy (1)
Malminkaari 21 C
0070 Helsinki, Finland (100%)
Tel.: (358) 98763574
Fax: (358) 922526916
Web Site: www.acer.fi
Emp.: 11
S.I.C.: 3571
N.A.I.C.S.: 334111

Acer Computer France S.A.R.L. (1)
Paris Nord II Ilot E 66
PO Box 40005
Rue De Vanesses, Villepinte, Cedex, 959111, France (100%)
Tel.: (33) 148174040
Fax: (33) 148174088
E-Mail: infocom_france@acer.euro.com
Web Site: www.acer.fr
Sales Range: $150-199.9 Million
Emp.: 30
S.I.C.: 3571
N.A.I.C.S.: 334111

Acer Computer GmbH (1)
Kornkamp 4
22926 Ahrensburg, Germany (100%)
Tel.: (49) 41024880
Fax: (49) 4102488101
E-Mail: info@acer.com
Web Site: www.acer-euro.com
Emp.: 300
S.I.C.: 3571
N.A.I.C.S.: 334111
Wilfried Thom *(Country Mgr)*

Acer Computer Handels GmbH (1)
Europaring F15
Brunn Am Gebirge, 2345 Vienna, Austria (100%)
Tel.: (43) 22363075200
Fax: (43) 22363075302
E-Mail: vertrieb-austria@acer-euro.com
Web Site: www.acer.at
Emp.: 10
S.I.C.: 3571
N.A.I.C.S.: 334111
Anna Ermer *(Gen Mgr)*

Acer Computer Iberica, S.A.U. (1)
Calle Samonta 25 4 planta
Sant Joan Despi, 08970 Barcelona, Spain (100%)
Tel.: (34) 902 20 23 23
Fax: (34) 902 15 89 17
E-Mail: acer_iberica@acer-euro.com
Web Site: www.acer.es
Emp.: 40
Computers & Computer Equipment Whslr
S.I.C.: 5045
N.A.I.C.S.: 423430
Walter Deppeler *(VP-Acer EMEA)*

Acer Computer International Ltd. (1)
29 International Business Park Acer Building Tower A
Singapore, 609923, Singapore
Tel.: (65) 65636563
Fax: (65) 68956419
Emp.: 100
Computer Peripheral Equipment Distr
S.I.C.: 5045
N.A.I.C.S.: 423430
Pin Mng Dir *(Mng Dir)*

Acer Magyarorszag (1)
Arpad Fejedelem utja 26-28
1023 Budapest, Hungary (100%)
Tel.: (36) 13363300
Fax: (36) 13363309
E-Mail: info@acer.hu
Web Site: www.acer.hu
Emp.: 6
Computers & Computer Equipment Distr
S.I.C.: 7379
N.A.I.C.S.: 541519
Tamas Borhi *(Country Mgr)*

Acer Computer (M.E.) Ltd. (1)
Jebel Ali Free Zone
PO Box 16951
Dubai, United Arab Emirates (100%)
Tel.: (971) 48813111
Fax: (971) 4 8812200
E-Mail: ame_feedback@acer-euro.com
Web Site: www.acer.ae
Sales Range: $200-249.9 Million
Emp.: 90
S.I.C.: 3571
N.A.I.C.S.: 334111
Walter Deppeler *(Deputy Pres-EMEA)*

Acer Computer New Zealand Ltd. (1)
Suite 2 Ground Floor Building A Millenium Phase II
600 Great South Road
Ellerslie, Auckland, 1051, New Zealand (100%)
Tel.: (64) 99695600
Fax: (64) 95265002
Web Site: www.acer.co.nz
Emp.: 11
S.I.C.: 3571
N.A.I.C.S.: 334111

Acer Computer Norway A/S (1)
Skysstasjon 5
PO Box 75
N 1371 Asker, Norway (100%)
Tel.: (47) 32843000
Fax: (47) 66901031
E-Mail: salg@acer.no
Web Site: www.acer.no
Sales Range: $10-24.9 Million
Emp.: 40
S.I.C.: 3571
N.A.I.C.S.: 334111

Acer Computer Poland (1)
Ul Domaniewska 41 Fl 9
Budynek Saturn IX p, 02-672 Warsaw, 00 028, Poland (100%)
Tel.: (48) 226062590
Fax: (48) 226062591
Web Site: www.acer.pl
Emp.: 5
Computers & Computer Equipment Distr
S.I.C.: 7379
N.A.I.C.S.: 541519

Acer Computer (Shanghai) Ltd. (1)
3F Headquarters Building No 168 Xizang Middle Rd
Shanghai, 200001, China
Tel.: (86) 21 5117 8999
Fax: (86) 21 6352 8628
E-Mail: service@acer.com.cn
Web Site: www.acer.com.cn
Emp.: 150
Consumer Peripherals Distr
S.I.C.: 5045
N.A.I.C.S.: 423430
Oliver Arhens *(Gen Mgr)*

Acer Computer (Singapore) Pte. Ltd. (1)
29 International Bus Park 01 01
Singapore, 609923, Singapore
Tel.: (65) 65636563
Fax: (65) 65676676
E-Mail:
Web Site: www.acer.com.sg
Sls.: $615,000,000
Emp.: 150
Marketer, Retailer & Assembler of Computer Products
S.I.C.: 3571
N.A.I.C.S.: 334111
Pin Gek Nea *(Mng Dir)*

Acer Computer Sweden AB (1)
Mariehallsvagen 37B
SE 16865 Bromma, Sweden (100%)
Tel.: (46) 84447910
Fax: (46) 94447920
E-Mail: info@acercomputer.se
Web Site: www.acercomputer.se
Emp.: 15
S.I.C.: 3571
N.A.I.C.S.: 334111
Hams Akae Frimark *(Controller)*

Acer Computer (Switzerland) AG (1)
Moosmattstrasse 30
8953 Dietikon, Switzerland
Tel.: (41) 447455858
Fax: (41) 447420646
E-Mail: info_ch@acer-euro.com
Web Site: www.acer.ch
Emp.: 40
Computers & Computer Equipment Whslr
S.I.C.: 5045
N.A.I.C.S.: 423430

Acer Czech Republic s.r.o. (1)
Novodvorska 1010/14B
142 00 Prague, 4, Czech Republic
Tel.: (420) 244112555
Fax: (420) 244112599
Web Site: www.acer.cz
Computer & Computer Peripheral Equipment Whslr
S.I.C.: 7379
N.A.I.C.S.: 541519
Stefan Ferdinand Engel *(Mng Dir)*

Acer Denmark A/S (1)
Linde Alle 5b
2850 Naerum, Denmark (100%)
Tel.: (45) 39168800
Fax: (45) 39168801
E-Mail: home@acer.dk
Web Site: www.acer.dk
S.I.C.: 3571
N.A.I.C.S.: 334111
Peter Kristensen *(Country Mgr)*

Acer do Brasil Limitada (1)
Rua Campos Sales 303 Pavimento Inferior Ed Centro Empresarial
Barueri, SP, 60411 150, Brazil
Tel.: (55) 11 2764 6410
E-Mail: faleconosco@cpsy.com.br
Web Site: www.acer.com
Computer Mfr & Distr
S.I.C.: 3571
N.A.I.C.S.: 334111

Acer Europe SA (1)
Via Cantonale Centro Galleria 2
6928 Manno, Switzerland
Tel.: (41) 91 261 0111
Fax: (41) 91 261 0322
Web Site: www.acer-euro.com
Computer Peripheral Equipment Distr
S.I.C.: 5045
N.A.I.C.S.: 423430
Walter Deppeler *(Gen Mgr)*

Acer Europe Services S.R.L. (1)
Via Lepetit 40
Lainate, Milano, 20020, Italy
Tel.: (39) 02939921
Fax: (39) 0293992912
Web Site: www.acer-group.com
Computer Software Development Services
S.I.C.: 7371
N.A.I.C.S.: 541511
Walter Deppeler *(Gen Mgr)*

Acer Hellas LTD (1)
Grigoriou Lambraki 54
11674 Glyfada, Athens, Greece
Tel.: (30) 210 96 06 430
Fax: (30) 210 96 06 450
Web Site: www.acer.gr
Computer Peripheral Equipment Mfr & Distr
S.I.C.: 5045
N.A.I.C.S.: 423430

Acer India (Pvt) Ltd. (1)
Embassy Heights 6th Floor
No 13 Magrath Rd, Bengaluru, 560025, India (100%)
Tel.: (91) 8025329520
Fax: (91) 8025329535
E-Mail: ail_easycare@acer.co.in
Web Site: www.acer.co.in
Sls.: $85,000,000
Emp.: 70
Computer Mfr
S.I.C.: 3571
N.A.I.C.S.: 334111
W. S. Mukund *(Mng Dir)*

Acer Information Services International (1)
Barreal, Heredia, Costa Rica
Tel.: (506) 2930942
Fax: (506) 293 0339
E-Mail: info@aisinternational.com
Web Site: www.aisinternational.com
S.I.C.: 3571
N.A.I.C.S.: 334111

Acer Italy S.r.l. (1)
Via Garbagnate 2
20020 Lainate, Milan, Italy
Tel.: (39) 0931469410
Fax: (39) 0931469431
E-Mail: alessandro_delio@acer-euro.com
Web Site: www.acer.it
S.I.C.: 3571
N.A.I.C.S.: 334111
Alessandro Deli *(Mgr-Mktg)*

Acer Japan Corporation (1)
18F Nishi Shinjuku Mitsui Building 6 24 1
Nishi Shinjuku Shinjuku ku, Tokyo, 160 0023, Japan
Tel.: (81) 3 5324 2788
Fax: (81) 3 5324 2786
E-Mail: jinfo@acer.co.jp
Web Site: www.acer.co.jp
Computer Manufacturer
S.I.C.: 3571
N.A.I.C.S.: 334111
Bob Sam *(Pres)*

Acer Philippines, Inc. (1)
Unit 3401 34F PBCom Tower 6795 Ayala Ave Corner Hirara St
Makati, 1226, Philippines (100%)
Tel.: (63) 28153388
Fax: (63) 28154940
E-Mail: info@acer.com.ph
Web Site: www.acer.com.ph
Sales Range: $1-9.9 Million
Emp.: 39
Mfr. & Marketer of Computers & Related Products
S.I.C.: 3571
N.A.I.C.S.: 334111
Manuel Wong *(Pres & Gen Mgr)*

Acer Sales & Services Sdn. Bhd. (1)
Level 24 Bangunan Am Fin 8
50450 Kuala Lumpur, Malaysia (100%)
Tel.: (60) 321621388
Fax: (60) 321624949
E-Mail: info@acer.com.my
Web Site: www.acer.com.my
Emp.: 50
S.I.C.: 3571
N.A.I.C.S.: 334111
Steve Lin *(Mng Dir)*

Subsidiaries:

Highpoint Service Network Sdn Bhd (2)
Lot 4 20 4th Floor Plaza Low Yat Off Jalan Bukit Bintang
55100 Kuala Lumpur, Malaysia
Tel.: (60) 3 2141 2942
Fax: (60) 3 2141 2942
E-Mail: supercare@highpoint.com.my
Web Site: www.highpoint.com.my
Emp.: 170
Information Technology Consulting Services
S.I.C.: 7373
N.A.I.C.S.: 541512
Gerard Ho *(Gen Mgr)*

Servex (Malaysia) Sdn Bhd (2)
No 8 Jalan Tp6 Taman Perindustrian Uep
Subang Jaya, Selangor, 47600, Malaysia
Tel.: (60) 3 80246688
Fax: (60) 3 80245155
Computer Peripheral Equipment Distr
S.I.C.: 5045
N.A.I.C.S.: 423430
Pau Chin Kar *(Gen Mgr)*

Acer Sweden AB (1)
Mariehallsvagen 37B
168 65 Bromma, Sweden
Tel.: (46) 850557300

Acer Incorporated—(Continued)

Fax: (46) 884447920
E-Mail: info@acer.computer.se
Web Site: www.acercomputer.se
Emp.: 15
Computers & Computer Equipment Distr
S.I.C.: 7379
N.A.I.C.S.: 541519
Hans-Ake Frimark *(Mgr-Fin)*

Acer UK Limited (1)
Acer House Heathrow Boulevard III
282 Bath Road, West Drayton, Middlesex, UB7 0DQ, United Kingdom
Tel.: (44) 8708531005
Fax: (44) 870 853 1004
E-Mail: support@aceruk.co.uk
Web Site: www.acer.co.uk
Emp.: 33
Computers & Computer Equipment Whslr
S.I.C.: 5045
N.A.I.C.S.: 423430

Acer Vietnam Co., Ltd. (1)
5th Floor Rosana Building
60 Nguyen Dinh Chieu Street
Da Kao Ward District 1, Ho Chi Minh City, Vietnam (100%)
Tel.: (84) 39106888
Fax: (84) 39101234
E-Mail: acervietnam@acer.com.vn
Web Site: www.acer.com.vn
Sales Range: $1-9.9 Million
Emp.: 22
S.I.C.: 3571
N.A.I.C.S.: 334111

Asplex Sp. z.o.o. (1)
Graniczna 8d/4
54-610 Wroclaw, Poland
Tel.: (48) 71 735 83 00
E-Mail: office@asplex.eu
Electronic Component Mfr
S.I.C.: 3679
N.A.I.C.S.: 334419

Gateway Europe B.V. (1)
Prins Bernhardplein
200 1097 Amsterdam, Netherlands
Tel.: (31) 20 5214777
Computer Peripheral Equipment Retailer
S.I.C.: 5731
N.A.I.C.S.: 443142

Packard Bell Belgium BVBA (1)
Senneberg Jean Monnetlaan
1804 Vilvoorde, Belgium
Tel.: (32) 22 55 30 30
Fax: (32) 22 55 30 60
Web Site: www.packardbell.be
Computer Peripheral Equipment Distr
S.I.C.: 5045
N.A.I.C.S.: 423430

Packard Bell Deutschland GmbH (1)
Kornkamp 4
22926 Ahrensburg, Germany
Tel.: (49) 4102 488 0
Fax: (49) 4102 488 101
E-Mail: info@acer.com
Web Site: www.packardbell.de
Emp.: 20
Computer Peripheral Equipment Distr
S.I.C.: 5045
N.A.I.C.S.: 423430
Wilfried Thom *(Gen Mgr)*

Packard Bell (UK) Ltd. (1)
Acer House Heathrow Boulevard III 282 Bath Road
West Drayton, Middlesex, UB7 0DQ, United Kingdom
Tel.: (44) 871 467 0008
Web Site: www.packardbell.co.uk
Computer Peripheral Equipment Maintenance Services
S.I.C.: 7378
N.A.I.C.S.: 811212

PT Acer Indonesia (1)
Wisma 46 Kota BNI 15F Ste 1508
Jl Jendral Sudirman Kav 01, Jakarta, 10220, Indonesia (100%)
Tel.: (62) 215745888
Fax: (62) 215746263
Web Site: www.acerindonesia.com
Emp.: 70
S.I.C.: 3571
N.A.I.C.S.: 334111

ACERINOX, S.A.

Santiago de Compostela Street n 100
28035 Madrid, Spain
Tel.: (34) 91 398 52 85
Fax: (34) 91 398 51 95
E-Mail: accionistas@acerinox.com
Web Site: www.acerinox.es
ACX—(BAR LSE MAD)
Rev.: $6,131,384,345
Assets: $5,674,960,022
Liabilities: $3,368,953,312
Net Worth: $2,306,006,710
Earnings: ($43,244,365)
Emp.: 7,252
Fiscal Year-end: 12/31/12

Business Description:
Steel Plates, Sheets, Strips, Rods, Bars & Tubing Mfr & Distr
S.I.C.: 3317
N.A.I.C.S.: 331210

Personnel:
Rafael Naranjo Olmedo *(Chm)*
Bernardo Velazquez Herreros *(CEO)*
Antonio Fernandez-Pacheco Martinez *(Mng Dir)*
Luis Gimeno Valledor *(Gen Counsel)*

Board of Directors:
Rafael Naranjo Olmedo
Clemente Cebrian Ara
Oscar Fanjul Martin
Luis Lobon Gayoso
Jose Ramon Guerediaga Mendiola
Manuel Conthe Gutierrez
Ryo Hattori
Santos Martinez-Conde y Gutierrez-Barquin
Braulio Medel Camara
Yukio Nariyoshi
Diego Prado Perez-Seoane
Mvuleni Geoffrey Qhena
Pedro Ballesteros Quintana
Belen Romana Garcia
Bernardo Velazquez Herreros

Subsidiaries:

ACERINOX EUROPA, S.A.U (1)
Calle Santiago De Compostela 100
Madrid, 28035, Spain
Tel.: (34) 913985102
Fax: (34) 913985197
Stainless Steel Products Mfr
S.I.C.: 3312
N.A.I.C.S.: 331110

INOXCENTER CANARIAS, S.A. (1)
Pol Ind Salinetas C/ Tornero s/n
Gran Canaria, 35214 Telde, Las Palmas, Spain
Tel.: (34) 928 13 60 15
Fax: (34) 928 13 06 48
E-Mail: inoxcanarias.laspalmas@acerinox.com
Stainless Steel Products Distr
S.I.C.: 5051
N.A.I.C.S.: 423510

INOXIDABLES DE EUSKADI S.A. (1)
Pol Ind de Jundiz C/ Lermandabide 17
01195 Vitoria, Alava, Spain
Tel.: (34) 945 18 48 00
Fax: (34) 945 18 48 19
Web Site: www.acerinox.es/Grupo_Acerinox/Mapa_de_localizacion/?__setlocale=en
Flat Steel Processing Services
S.I.C.: 5051
N.A.I.C.S.: 423510

METALINOX BILBAO, S.A. (1)
Aranaztegi Etorbidea 13
20140 Andoain, Guipuzcoa, Spain
Tel.: (34) 943 59 17 99
Fax: (34) 943 59 11 52
E-Mail: metalinox.andoain@acerinox.com
Emp.: 35
General Warehousing Services
S.I.C.: 4225
N.A.I.C.S.: 493110
Joaquin Beorlegui *(Gen Mgr)*

ROLDAN S.A. (1)
Calle Santiago De Compostela 100
Madrid, 28035, Spain
Tel.: (34) 913 98 52 33
Fax: (34) 913 98 51 93
Iron & Steel Products Mfr
S.I.C.: 3312
N.A.I.C.S.: 331110

Subsidiary:

INOXFIL S.A. (2)
Paises Bajos 11-15
Igualada, Barcelona, Spain
Tel.: (34) 93 8018200
Fax: (34) 93 8018216
E-Mail: fabrica@acxgroup.com
Emp.: 130
Stainless Steel Products Mfr
S.I.C.: 3317
N.A.I.C.S.: 331210
Angel Brunen *(Gen Mgr)*

Non-U.S. Subsidiaries:

Acerinox Argentina (1)
Av Velez Sarsfield 1535
1285 Buenos Aires, Argentina
Tel.: (54) 01143030349
Fax: (54) 11 4303 14 39
E-Mail: jcrodri@acxgroup.com
Web Site: www.acerinox.es/acerinox/ingacerinox.nsf/acerinoxgroup.html
Stainless Steel Distr
S.I.C.: 3462
N.A.I.C.S.: 332111
Jose Carlos Rodriguez *(Gen Mgr)*

Acerinox Australasia Pty Ltd (1)
Suite 502 Level 5th 781 Pacific Highway
2067 Chatswood, NSW, Australia
Tel.: (61) 294123500
Fax: (61) 294123604
E-Mail: ghale@acxgroup.com
Web Site: www.acerinox.es/acerinox/ingacerinox.nsf/acerinoxgroup.html
Emp.: 3
Stainless Steel Distr
S.I.C.: 3462
N.A.I.C.S.: 332111
Geoff Hale *(Mgr-Sls)*

Acerinox Benelux, S.A./NV (1)
Avenue Tervueren 100
B 1040 Brussels, Belgium BE (100%)
Tel.: (32) 27432200
Fax: (32) 27432201
E-Mail: ingrid.judak@acerinox.com
Web Site: www.acerinox.com
Emp.: 4
Steel Products Distr
S.I.C.: 3399
N.A.I.C.S.: 331221

Acerinox Chile (1)
Parque Industrial Valle Grande Calle Don Luis 590
Lampa, Santiago, Chile
Tel.: (56) 27385030
Fax: (56) 27386082
E-Mail: bgallego@acxgroup.com
Web Site: www.acerinox.com.es
Emp.: 22
Warehouse & Distr for Steel Products
S.I.C.: 3312
N.A.I.C.S.: 331221
Hernan Ortega *(Gen Mgr)*

Acerinox Colombia (1)
Calle 93 A No 14-17
Oficina 509
Bogota, Colombia Co (100%)
Tel.: (57) 16220599
Fax: (57) 16215276
E-Mail: juanmanuel.frutos@acerinox.com
Web Site: www.acerinox.es
Emp.: 5
Steel Products Distr
S.I.C.: 3312
N.A.I.C.S.: 331221
Juan Manuel Frutos *(Dir Gen)*

Acerinox Deutschland GmbH (1)
Berner Feld 15
D 78628 Rottweil, Germany De (100%)
Tel.: (49) 741174850
Fax: (49) 7411748550
E-Mail: Acerinox.Deutschland@acerinox.com
Web Site: www.acerinox.com
Steel Mfr Service Center
S.I.C.: 3312
N.A.I.C.S.: 331221
Fritz Oppenlaender *(Gen Mgr)*

Acerinox Deutschland GmbH (1)
Poensgenstrasse No 10
Langenfeld, D 40764 Dusseldorf, Germany De (100%)
Tel.: (49) 217327070
Fax: (49) 2173270770
E-Mail: anke.nicht@acerinox.com
Web Site: www.acerinox.es
Emp.: 65
Steel Products Distr & Servicing
S.I.C.: 3312
N.A.I.C.S.: 331221

Acerinox France (1)
5 Rue Gay Lussac
PO Box 89
Gonesse, 95503 Paris, France FR (100%)
Tel.: (33) 139876656
Fax: (33) 134538337
Web Site: www.acerinox.com
Emp.: 45
Steel Producer & Service Center
S.I.C.: 3399
N.A.I.C.S.: 331110
Philippe Audeon *(Dir Gen)*

Acerinox Italia Srl (1)
Via Chiesaccia SNC
Crespellano, 40056 Bologna, Italy
Tel.: (39) 029 50 04 01
Fax: (39) 029 50 04 050
E-Mail: gdecarli@acxgroup.com
Web Site: www.acerinox.es/Grupo_Acerinox/Mapa_de_localizacion/?__setlocale=es
Emp.: 45
Steel Products Servicing & Distr
S.I.C.: 3312
N.A.I.C.S.: 331221
Giovanni de Carli *(Gen Mgr)*

Acerinox Malaysia Sdn. Bhd. (1)
PTD 175189 Batu 11 1/2 Jalan Johor Bahru Kota Tinggi
Ulu Tiram, 81800 Johor, Malaysia
Tel.: (60) 78625230
Fax: (60) 78617377
E-Mail: bramos@acxgroup.com
Web Site: www.acerinox.es
Steel Products Whslr
S.I.C.: 3312
N.A.I.C.S.: 331221
Benjamin Ramos *(Mng Dir)*

Acerinox Norway A.S. (1)
Tollbugata 17
PO Box 819
152 Oslo, Norway
Tel.: (47) 22479660
Fax: (47) 22479666
E-Mail: bengt.lagergren@acerinox.com
Web Site: www.acerinox.com
Emp.: 8
Steel Products Distr
S.I.C.: 3312
N.A.I.C.S.: 331221
Bengt Lagergren *(Gen Mgr)*

Acerinox Pacific (1)
Ste 1102 11th Flr Chinachem Century Tower 175-180 Gloucester Rd
Wanchai, China (Hong Kong)
Tel.: (852) 28023666
Fax: (852) 28023707
Web Site: www.acerinox.es/acerinox/ingacerinox.nsf/acerinoxgroup.html
Emp.: 10
Steel Products Distr
S.I.C.: 3312
N.A.I.C.S.: 331221
Jorte Vlerraee *(Mng Dir)*

Acerinox Peru (1)
Mirtir Olaya 129 office 505 Miraflores
Lima, Peru
Tel.: (51) 014453391
Fax: (51) 5112433762
E-Mail: alferado.ieaneue@acerinox.com
Web Site: www.acerinox.es/acerinox/ingacerinox.nsf/acerinoxgroup.html
Emp.: 3
Steel Products Distr
S.I.C.: 5051
N.A.I.C.S.: 423510
Alferado Ieaneue *(Gen Mgr)*

Acerinox Polska Sp.Zo.O. (1)
Daniszewska 23.
02-230 Warsaw, Poland

Tel.: (48) 226360816
Fax: (48) 225103731
E-Mail: acerinox.polska@acerinox.com
Web Site: www.acerinox.es/acerinox/ingace rinox.nsf/acerinoxgroup.html
Emp.: 24
Steel Products Distr
S.I.C.: 3312
N.A.I.C.S.: 331221
Pilar Senise *(Gen Mgr)*

Acerinox Scandinavia A.B. (1)
Sandtagsgatan 2
PO Box 21057
211 24 Malmo, Sweden
Tel.: (46) 406919400
Fax: (46) 406919425
E-Mail:
Emp.: 40
Steel Products Servicing
S.I.C.: 3312
N.A.I.C.S.: 331221
Bengt Lagergren *(Gen Mgr)*

ACERINOX (SCHWEIZ) A.G. (1)
Weihermattstr 2
5507 Mellingen, Switzerland
Tel.: (41) 56 481 82 42
Fax: (41) 56 481 82 40
E-Mail: info@acerinox.ch
Web Site: www.acerinox.ch
Emp.: 7
Stainless Flat Rolled Products Mfr
S.I.C.: 3399
N.A.I.C.S.: 331221

Acerinox Sea Pte Ltd (1)
16 Raffles Quay 33-02 Hong Leong Building
048581 Singapore, Singapore
Tel.: (65) 62265405
Fax: (65) 62265368
E-Mail: benjamin.ramos@acerinox.com
Web Site: www.acerinox.com.sg
Emp.: 18
Steel Products Distr
S.I.C.: 3399
N.A.I.C.S.: 331221
Benjamin Ramos *(Mng Dir)*

ACERINOX SOUTH EAST ASIA PTE.LTD. (1)
16 Raffles Quay 16-02 Hong Leong Bldg
Shentonway, 48581 Singapore, Singapore
Tel.: (65) 62265405
Fax: (65) 62265368
Web Site: www.acerinox.com
Emp.: 1
Stainless Steel Products Mfr
S.I.C.: 3312
N.A.I.C.S.: 331110

Acerinox UK Ltd (1)
Heath Rd
Darlaston, West Midlands, WS10 8XL, United Kingdom
Tel.: (44) 1215268000
Fax: (44) 1215268006
E-Mail: jpcantle@acxgroup.com
Web Site: www.acerinox.co.uk
Emp.: 60
Steel Products Distr
S.I.C.: 3312
N.A.I.C.S.: 331221
Pablo Cantle *(Mng Dir)*

Acerinox Venezuela (1)
Avenida Principal de la Castellana Edificio Banco Lara Piso 3 Ofic D-1
La Castellana, Caracas, Venezuela
Tel.: (58) 2122634497
Fax: (58) 2122630051
E-Mail: gdelcampo@acxgroup.com
Emp.: 100
Steel Products Distr
S.I.C.: 3312
N.A.I.C.S.: 331221
Gonzalo del Campo *(Gen Mgr)*

Acerol Comercio E Industria De Acos Inoxidaveis, Lda. (1)
Outeiro Maia Zona Industrial da Maia I
Sector VII Apartado 6060
4476 908 Porto, Portugal
Tel.: (351) 229479280
Fax: (351) 229419175
E-Mail: acerolportugal@acxgroup.com
Web Site: www.acxgroup.com
Metals Service Center
S.I.C.: 5051
N.A.I.C.S.: 423510
Fernando Monteiro *(Gen Mgr)*

Acx Do Brasil Representacoes, Ltda. (1)
Rua Caconde 235 Apartamento 151
CEP 01425 011 Sao Paulo, Brazil
Tel.: (55) 1138858308
Fax: (55) 1138876728
E-Mail: jfrutos@acerinox.com
Web Site: www.acerinox.es/acerinox/ingace rinox.nsf/acerinoxgroup.html
Emp.: 3
Steel Products Distr
S.I.C.: 5051
N.A.I.C.S.: 423510
Joaquin Frutos *(Gen Mgr)*

Betinoks Turkey (1)
Ikitelli Organize Kucuk Sanayi Bolgesi Kisim
Turgut Ozal Caddesi 110
34670 Istanbul, Turkey
Tel.: (90) 2125490700
Fax: (90) 2125490710
E-Mail: info@betinoks.com
Web Site: www.betinoks.com
Emp.: 30
Metals Service Center & Distr
S.I.C.: 5051
N.A.I.C.S.: 423510
A. Eken *(Gen Mgr)*

Columbus Stainless (Pty) Ltd (1)
Hendrina Road
Private Bag 251844
Middelburg, 1050, South Africa (76%)
Tel.: (27) 00132479111
Fax: (27) 132472484
E-Mail: potgieter.piet@columbus.co.za
Web Site: www.columbusstainless.co.za
Emp.: 1,600
Stainless Steel Products
S.I.C.: 3462
N.A.I.C.S.: 332111
Dave Martin *(CEO)*

INOXPLATE, LTDA. (1)
Zona Industrial Maia I Sector Vii-Rua E Lt 2-A
Maia, 4470-000, Portugal
Tel.: (351) 229479280
Fax: (351) 229862022
Metal Products Mfr
S.I.C.: 3499
N.A.I.C.S.: 332999

NAS Canada (1)
740 Imperial Road North
Guelph, ON, N1K 1Z3, Canada
Tel.: (519) 767-6830
Fax: (519) 767-6840
E-Mail: rmansfield@northamericanstainless.com
Web Site: www.northamericanstainless.com
Emp.: 18
Steel Products Distr
S.I.C.: 5051
N.A.I.C.S.: 423510
Roger Mansfield *(Gen Mgr)*

NAS Mexico (1)
Priv Andres Guajardo No 360
Parque Industrial Apodaca I
66600 Apodaca, NL, Mexico
Tel.: (52) 81 1253 7700
Fax: (52) 81 1253 7701
E-Mail: bthirion@northamericanstainless.com
Web Site: www.northamericanstainless.com
Steel Products Distr
S.I.C.: 5051
N.A.I.C.S.: 423510
Barbara Thirion *(Gen Mgr)*

ACEROLUX SL

Calle Joan Guell 111
08028 Barcelona, Spain
Tel.: (34) 93 280 41 22
Business Description:
Metal Product Mfr & Whslr
S.I.C.: 3499
N.A.I.C.S.: 332999
Personnel:
Jose Luis Carrillo Rodriguez *(Chm)*

Subsidiary:

Mecalux, S.A. (1)
Silici 1
ES-08940 Cornella, Spain ES
Tel.: (34) 932616901 (53.7%)
Fax: (34) 933350098
E-Mail: info@mecalux.com
Web Site: www.mecalux.com
Sales Range: $650-699.9 Million
Emp.: 3,709
Holding Company; Steel Shelving & Storage Systems Mfr & Distr
S.I.C.: 6719
N.A.I.C.S.: 551112
Jose Luis Carrillo Rodriguez *(Pres)*
Jordi Catala Masdeu *(CEO)*
Pere Kirchner Ballu *(Sec)*

Subsidiaries:

Esmena, S.L.U. (2)
Pol Ind Los Campones Ataulfo Friera Tarfe 12
33211 Gijon, Asturias, Spain ES
Tel.: (34) 985178000 (100%)
Fax: (34) 985 178 040
E-Mail: esmena@esmena.com
Web Site: www.esmena.com
Emp.: 500
Steel Shelving & Storage Systems Designer, Mfr, Distr & Installer
S.I.C.: 3441
N.A.I.C.S.: 332312
Rafael Vallejo Polo *(CEO)*

Mecalux Servis, S.A. (2)
Calle Julio Palacios 14
Pol Ind Ntra Sra Butarque, 28914 Leganes, Spain
Tel.: (34) 916 888 333
Fax: (34) 916 860 945
Web Site: www.mecalux.es
Steel Shelving & Storage Systems Whslr
S.I.C.: 5084
N.A.I.C.S.: 423830
Julian Moreno Diaz *(Gen Mgr)*

Unit:

Logismarket (2)
Silici 1
ES-08940 Cornella, Spain
Tel.: (34) 902 121 312
Fax: (34) 933 356 090
Web Site: www.logismarket.com
Logistics, Storage, Packaging & Industrial Equipment Business-to-Business Corporate Directory Publisher
S.I.C.: 2741
N.A.I.C.S.: 511140
Miguel Davila *(Mng Dir)*

U.S. Subsidiary:

Interlake Mecalux, Inc. (2)
1600 N 25th Ave
Melrose Park, IL 60160-1868 DE
Tel.: (708) 344-9999 (100%)
Fax: (708) 343-9788
Toll Free: (877) 632-2589
Web Site: www.interlakemecalux.com
Emp.: 50
Steel Shelving & Storage Systems Mfr & Distr
S.I.C.: 3441
N.A.I.C.S.: 332312
Javier Carrillo *(Pres)*

Non-U.S. Subsidiaries:

Mecalux Argentina, S.A. (2)
Boulogne Sur Mer 2538
Villa Maipu, Buenos Aires, 1650, Argentina Ar
Tel.: (54) 11 4006 4444 (100%)
Fax: (54) 11 4006 4400
Web Site: www.mecalux.com.ar
Steel Shelving & Storage Systems Mfr & Distr
S.I.C.: 3441
N.A.I.C.S.: 332312
Angel Jimenez Pastor *(Mng Dir)*

Mecalux Belgium S.A. (2)
Boulevard Paepsem 11 A
1070 Anderlecht, Belgium BE
Tel.: (32) 2 346 90 71 (100%)
Fax: (32) 2 346 28 36
E-Mail: info@mecalux.com
Web Site: www.mecalux.be
Steel Shelving & Storage Systems Whslr
S.I.C.: 5084
N.A.I.C.S.: 423830
Daniel Joly *(Mng Dir)*

Mecalux do Brasil Sistemas de Armazenagem Ltda. (2)
Rua Eonio Moreira Diniz s/n
Jardim Nova Europa, Hortolandia, SP, 13184-861, Brazil BR
Tel.: (55) 19 3809 6800 (100%)
Fax: (55) 19 3809 6868
Web Site: www.mecalux.com.br
Steel Shelving & Storage Systems Designer, Mfr & Distr
S.I.C.: 3441
N.A.I.C.S.: 332312
Ivan Poblet Menendez *(Mng Dir)*

Mecalux France S.a.r.l. (2)
1 rue Colbert
ZAC de Montavas, 91320 Wissous, France FR
Tel.: (33) 1 60 11 92 92 (100%)
Fax: (33) 1 60 11 55 75
E-Mail: france@mecalux.com
Web Site: www.mecalux.fr
Emp.: 50
Steel Shelving & Storage Systems Whslr
S.I.C.: 5084
N.A.I.C.S.: 423830
Daniel Joly *(Gen Mgr)*

Mecalux GmbH (2)
Moselstrasse 19
D-41464 Neuss, Germany De
Tel.: (49) 2131 40 760 (100%)
Fax: (49) 2131 40 7640
E-Mail: contact@mecalux.com
Web Site: www.mecalux.de
Emp.: 10
Steel Shelving & Storage Systems Whslr
S.I.C.: 5084
N.A.I.C.S.: 423830
Juan Maria Santos Veira *(Mng Dir)*

Mecalux Milano, S.r.l. (2)
Via Benaco 14
20098 San Giuliano Milanese, MI, Italy IT
Tel.: (39) 02 98836601 (100%)
Fax: (39) 02 98287273
E-Mail: italia@mecalux.it
Web Site: www.mecalux.it
Emp.: 14
Steel Shelving & Storage Systems Whslr
S.I.C.: 5084
N.A.I.C.S.: 423830
Emmanuel Beghin *(Gen Mgr)*

Mecalux Sp. z o.o. (2)
ul Wyczolkowskiego 125
44 109 Gliwice, Poland PL
Tel.: (48) 32 331 69 66 (100%)
Fax: (48) 32 331 69 67
E-Mail: recepcion@mecalux.com
Web Site: www.mecalux.pl
Emp.: 600
Steel Shelving & Storage Systems Whslr
S.I.C.: 5084
N.A.I.C.S.: 423830
Juan Maria Santos Veira *(Mng Dir)*
Gerz Demczak *(CFO)*

Mecalux (UK) Ltd. (2)
Unit 9 Network Park Duddeston Mill Road
Saltley, Birmingham, B8 1AU, United Kingdom UK
Tel.: (44) 121 3336 602 (100%)
Fax: (44) 121 3335 622
E-Mail: info@mecalux.com
Web Site: www.mecalux.co.uk
Emp.: 15
Steel Shelving & Storage Systems Whslr
S.I.C.: 5084
N.A.I.C.S.: 423830
Emmanuel Beghin *(Mng Dir)*

ACERTEC PLC

15 Shottery Brook Timothys Bridge Road
Stratford-upon-Avon, Warks, CV37 9NR, United Kingdom
Tel.: (44) 1789 403070
Fax: (44) 1789 403079
E-Mail: info@acertec.com
Web Site: www.acertec.com
Sales Range: $600-649.9 Million

Acertec plc—(Continued)

Emp.: 48

Business Description:
Engineered Steel Products Mfr
S.I.C.: 3312
N.A.I.C.S.: 331221

Personnel:
David Hussey *(Chm)*
Steve Kynaston *(Grp Dir-Fin)*
Greg MacLeod *(Chief Restructuring Officer)*
Mick Hayhurst *(Sec)*

ACES ELECTRONIC CO., LTD.

13 Dongyuan Road
Jhongli City, Taoyuan, 320, Taiwan
Tel.: (886) 34632808
Fax: (886) 34631800
E-Mail: tinachen@acesconn.com
Web Site: www.acesconn.com
Year Founded: 1996
3605—(TAI)
Sales Range: $125-149.9 Million
Emp.: 5,412

Business Description:
Electronic Connectors Mfr
S.I.C.: 3678
N.A.I.C.S.: 334417

Personnel:
Wanding Yuan *(Chm)*

Non-U.S. Subsidiary:

Dong Guan Aces Electronic Co.,Ltd (1)
Hong San Industrial Park Xin An Community
Chang An Town, Dongguan, Guangdong, China
Tel.: (86) 76985393066
Fax: (86) 769 8539 7686
E-Mail: acesglobal@acesconn.com
Electronic Goods Mfr
S.I.C.: 3679
N.A.I.C.S.: 334419

ACEZ INSTRUMENTS PTE. LTD.

Blk 28D Penjuru Close 01 07
Singapore, 609132, Singapore
Tel.: (65) 62680100
Fax: (65) 62687286
E-Mail: sales@acez.com.sg
Web Site: www.acez.com.sg
Emp.: 75

Business Description:
Measuring & Controlling Devices; Engineering & Construction Products Distr
S.I.C.: 3823
N.A.I.C.S.: 334513

Personnel:
Ricky Yeo *(Mng Dir)*

Subsidiary:

Acez Sensing Pte Ltd. (1)
Blk 28E Penjuru Close 01-04
Singapore, 609133, Singapore
Tel.: (65) 6265 1588
Fax: (65) 6264 3992
E-Mail: contact@acezsensing.com
Web Site: www.acezsensing.com
Emp.: 27
Thermal Sensing Equipment Mfr
S.I.C.: 3559
N.A.I.C.S.: 333249
Khin Maung Myint *(Gen Mgr)*

Non-U.S. Subsidiaries:

ACEZ Instruments Philippines Corporation (1)
Unit 301-303 DMG Center Libertad cor Calbayog Street
Mandaluyong, Philippines 1553
Tel.: (63) 2 4708068
Fax: (63) 2 4708043
E-Mail: sales@acez.com.ph
Emp.: 8
Thermal Sensing Equipment Mfr
S.I.C.: 3559
N.A.I.C.S.: 333249
Sockalingam Jayabalan, *(Pres & Gen Mgr)*

Acez Instruments (Shenzhen) Co., Ltd (1)
2105B Seg Plaza Huaqiang Road
Futian, Shenzhen, China
Tel.: (86) 755 6136 2528
Fax: (86) 755 6136 2529
E-Mail: sales@acez.com.cn
Web Site: www.acez.com.cn
Thermal Sensing Equipment Mfr
S.I.C.: 3559
N.A.I.C.S.: 333249

PT Acez Instruments Indonesia (1)
Jl Mangga Besar Raya No 33B Mangga Besar Taman Sari Jakarta Barat
Jakarta, 11180, Indonesia
Tel.: (62) 21 6232 0237
Fax: (62) 21 6232 0236
E-Mail: sales@acez.co.id
Emp.: 10
Thermal Sensing Equipment Mfr
S.I.C.: 3559
N.A.I.C.S.: 333249
Nanang Suryatman, *(Engr-Sls)*

ACH, D.D.

Baragova 5
Ljubljana, 1000, Slovenia
Tel.: (386) 15883100
Fax: (386) 15883114
E-Mail: info@ach.si
Web Site: www.ach.si
Year Founded: 1952
Sales Range: $650-699.9 Million
Emp.: 2,394

Business Description:
Holding Company
S.I.C.: 6719
N.A.I.C.S.: 551112

Personnel:
Sonja Gole *(Pres)*
Herman Rigelnik *(Gen Dir)*

Supervisory Board of Directors:
Majda Rubido

ACHESON & GLOVER LTD.

127 Creevehill Rd
Fivemiletown, Dungannon, Tyrone, BT75 0SY, United Kingdom
Tel.: (44) 2889521275
Fax: (44) 2889521866
E-Mail: fmt@acheson-glover.com
Web Site: www.acheson-glover.com
Sales Range: $200-249.9 Million
Emp.: 600
Fiscal Year-end: 12/31/12

Business Description:
Stone & Concrete Products Mfr
S.I.C.: 3273
N.A.I.C.S.: 327320

Personnel:
Thomas Raymond Acheson *(Mng Dir)*

ACHIEVA LTD.

SUTL House 100J Pasir Panjang Road #05-00
118525 Singapore, Singapore
Tel.: (65) 6590 7100
Fax: (65) 6590 7101
E-Mail: apl_enquiry@achieva.com.sg
Web Site: www.achieva.com.sg
A02—(SES)
Rev.: $112,615,962
Assets: $50,335,377
Liabilities: $15,415,498
Net Worth: $34,919,879
Earnings: $525,482
Emp.: 180
Fiscal Year-end: 12/31/12

Business Description:
Electronics & IT-Related Products Distr
S.I.C.: 5045
N.A.I.C.S.: 423430

Personnel:
Arthur Teng Guan Tay *(CEO)*
Adrian Pengee Chan *(Sec)*

Board of Directors:
Syn Pau Lew
Kum Tao Chan
Colin Teck Sim Ng
Arthur Teng Guan Tay
Peter Teng Hock Tay

Subsidiaries:

Achieva Investments Pte Ltd (1)
240 Macpherson Road
02-04 Pines Industrial Bld, 348574
Singapore, Singapore (100%)
Tel.: (65) 68414898
Fax: (65) 68414896
E-Mail: yuliyani@achieva.com.sg
Web Site: www.achieva.com.sg/alcont.htm
Emp.: 55
Miscellaneous Financial Investment Activities
S.I.C.: 6211
N.A.I.C.S.: 523999
Tony Ng *(CEO)*

Achieva Technology Pte Ltd (1)
SUTL House, 100J Pasir Panjang Road #05-00, 118525 Singapore,
Singapore (100%)
Tel.: (65) 67495832
Fax: (65) 67487219
E-Mail: sales@achieva.com.sg
Web Site: www.achieva.com.sg/alcont.htm
Emp.: 100
Computer & Computer Peripheral Equipment & Software Merchant Whslr
S.I.C.: 5045
N.A.I.C.S.: 423430
Arthur Tay Teng Guan *(CEO)*

Non-U.S. Subsidiaries:

Achieva Technology Sdn. Bhd (2)
2 02 2nd Floor Wisma Academy No 4A Jalan 19/1
46300 Petaling Jaya, Selangor Darul Ehsan, Malaysia
Tel.: (60) 3 7955 1768
Fax: (60) 3 7955 1728
E-Mail: sales@achieva.com.my
Web Site: www.achieva.com.my
Emp.: 50
Computer Peripheral Products Distr
S.I.C.: 5045
N.A.I.C.S.: 423430
Thomas Teng *(Gen Mgr)*

PT Atikom Mega Protama (Indonesia) (2)
Jalan Mangga Dua Raya Komplek Ruko Dusit Orion Blok D No 17
Jakarta, 10730, Indonesia
Tel.: (62) 216123612
Fax: (62) 21 6123508
E-Mail: sales@atikom.co.id
Web Site: www.atikom.co.id
Computer Peripheral Products Distr
S.I.C.: 5045
N.A.I.C.S.: 423430

Non-U.S. Subsidiaries:

Achieva Technology Australia Pty. Ltd. (1)
U 7-8 5 Dunlop St South
Strathfield, NSW, Australia (100%)
Tel.: (61) 297423288
Fax: (61) 297423188
Web Site: www.achieva.com.au
Emp.: 20
Computer & Computer Peripheral Equipment & Software Merchant Whslr
S.I.C.: 5045
N.A.I.C.S.: 423430

Achieva Technology Philippines Pte Ltd (1)
2nd Floor Topy Main Bldg
Bagumbayan Libis, Quezon City,
Philippines (100%)
Tel.: (63) 26368069
Fax: (63) 26366027
E-Mail: mishael@achieva.com.ph
Web Site: www.verdurexchange.com
Emp.: 52
Other Computer Peripheral Equipment Manufacturing
S.I.C.: 3575
N.A.I.C.S.: 334118
Choo Kwang Bern *(CEO)*

Astone Holdings Pty Ltd (1)
Unit 7-8 5 Dunlop Street Strathfield South
Sydney, NSW, 2136, Australia (70%)
Tel.: (61) 297423288
Fax: (61) 297588074
Web Site: www.astone.com.au/index.php?show_aux_page=2
Emp.: 12
Other Computer Peripheral Equipment Mfr
S.I.C.: 3577
N.A.I.C.S.: 334118
Steven Lee *(Mng Dir)*

PT. ATIKOM Mega Pratama (1)
Jl Mangga Dua Abdad Komp
Rukan Mangga Dua Elok B/16, 10730
Jakarta, Indonesia
Tel.: (62) 216123612
Fax: (62) 216123508
Other Computer Related Services
S.I.C.: 7379
N.A.I.C.S.: 541519

ACHILLES CORPORATION

22-5 Daikyo-Cho Shinjuku-Ku
Tokyo, 160-8885, Japan
Tel.: (81) 333415111
Fax: (81) 332252281
E-Mail: achilles-group@tokyo.email.ne.jp
Web Site: www.achilles.jp
Year Founded: 1947
5142—(TKS)
Sales Range: $900-999.9 Million
Emp.: 1,496

Business Description:
Footwear, Supported & Unsupported PVC Sheeting, Polyurethane, Industrial & Insulation Products Mfr
S.I.C.: 2389
N.A.I.C.S.: 316210

Personnel:
Hiroshi Nakata *(Pres)*

Legal Counsel:
Mitsuharu Mamuro
Hinokimachi Law Ofc., Room #246
#7-1-9 Akasaka, Minato-ku
Tokyo, Japan

U.S. Subsidiary:

Achilles USA, Inc. (1)
1407 80th St SW
Everett, WA 98203-6220 (100%)
Tel.: (425) 353-7000
Fax: (425) 348-6683
Web Site: www.achillesusa.com
Emp.: 175
Plastics Products Mfr
S.I.C.: 3081
N.A.I.C.S.: 326113
Scott Bollinger *(VP-Sls)*

Non-U.S. Subsidiary:

Achilles Hong Kong Co., Ltd. (1)
Block A 5th Floor Winner Building
36 Man Yue St Hung Hom, Kowloon, China (Hong Kong)
Tel.: (852) 23628324
Fax: (852) 27641024
E-Mail: ahk@achilles.com.hk
Web Site: www.achilles.jp/english/company/08/index.html
Emp.: 5
Footwear Merchant Whslr
S.I.C.: 5139
N.A.I.C.S.: 424340
Y. Yumoto *(Mng Dir)*

Non-U.S. Division:

Kunshan Achilles Artificial Leather Co., Ltd. (1)
Yushan Economics Developing Zone No 500 Ma An Shan Middle Rd
Kunshan, Jiangsu, China
Tel.: (86) 51257519340
Fax: (86) 51257550957
Web Site: www.kunshanachilles.com

Leather Good Mfr
S.I.C.: 3199
N.A.I.C.S.: 316998

ACHILLES GROUP LIMITED

30 Western Avenue Milton Park
Abingdon, Oxfordshire, OX14 4SH, United Kingdom
Tel.: (44) 1235 861118
Fax: (44) 1235 821093
E-Mail: enquiries@achilles.com
Web Site: www.achilles.com
Year Founded: 1990
Sales Range: $10-24.9 Million
Emp.: 639
Business Description:
Supply Chain Management Services
S.I.C.: 5085
N.A.I.C.S.: 423840
Personnel:
Colin Maund *(Founder & Chm)*

ACHMEA B.V.

Handelsweg 2
3707 NH Zeist, Netherlands
Mailing Address:
PO Box 866
3700 AW Zeist, Netherlands
Tel.: (31) 30693700
Fax: (31) 306937265
E-Mail: investors@achmea.com
Web Site: www.achmea.com
Year Founded: 1992
Rev.: $34,000,215,690
Assets: $127,639,800,890
Liabilities: $113,674,633,310
Net Worth: $13,965,167,580
Earnings: $609,815,010
Emp.: 19,302
Fiscal Year-end: 12/31/12
Business Description:
Holding Company; Insurance Services
S.I.C.: 6719
N.A.I.C.S.: 551112
Personnel:
Erik A. J. van de Merwe *(Chm-Supervisory Bd)*
Willem A.J. van Duin *(Chm-Exec Bd)*
Marinus Minderhoud *(Vice Chm-Supervisory Bd)*
Huub Arendse *(CFO & Member-Exec Bd)*
Stefan Kloet *(Press Officer)*
Bert Rensen *(Press Officer)*
Marco Simmers *(Press Officer)*
Roelof Konterman *(Member-Exec Bd)*
Jeroen A. S. van Breda Vriesman *(Member-Exec Bd)*
Danny van der Eijk *(Member-Exec Bd)*
Supervisory Board of Directors:
Erik A. J. van de Merwe
Mijntje Luckerath-Rovers
Marinus Minderhoud
Paul F. M. Overmars
Lineke Sneller
Be J. van der Weg
Joke S. T. van Lonkhuijzen-Hoekstra
Aad W. Veenman
Antoon J. A. M. Vermeer

Subsidiaries:

Eureko RE N.V. **(1)**
Spoorlaan 298
5017 JZ Tilburg, Netherlands (100%)
Mailing Address:
PO Box 90106
5000LA Tilburg, Netherlands
Tel.: (31) 13 462 3822
Fax: (31) 13 462 3498
Emp.: 3
Reinsurance Services
S.I.C.: 6399
N.A.I.C.S.: 524130

Non-U.S. Subsidiaries:

Eureko Sigorta A.S. **(1)**
Altunizade Mahallesi Ord Prof Fahrettin Kerim Gokay Caddesi No 20
34662 Istanbul, Turkey (100%)
Tel.: (90) 216 400 10 00
Web Site: www.eurekosigorta.com.tr
Rev.: $385,571,055
Assets: $458,364,268
Liabilities: $266,345,869
Net Worth: $192,018,399
Earnings: $4,335,499
Emp.: 508
Fiscal Year-end: 12/31/12
Insurance Services
S.I.C.: 6411
N.A.I.C.S.: 524298
H. Okan Utkueri *(CEO)*
Mehmet Emin Alkan *(Exec VP-Sls & Mktg)*
Suha Cele *(Exec VP-Technical)*
Wieger Wagenaar *(Exec VP-Fin Affairs)*

Friends First Holdings Ltd. **(1)**
Friends First House
Cherrywood Science & Tech Park
Loughlinstown, Dublin, 18, Ireland IE (100%)
Tel.: (353) 16610600
Fax: (353) 1 661 6651
E-Mail: callcentre@friendsfirst.ie
Web Site: www.friendsfirst.ie
Assets: $5,477,770,000
Emp.: 390
Financial Services
S.I.C.: 6282
N.A.I.C.S.: 523930
Adrian Hegarty *(CEO)*

Subsidiaries:

First Life Assurance Company Ltd. **(2)**
Friends First House Cherrywood Business Park
Loughlinstown, Dublin, 18, Ireland
Tel.: (353) 16610600
Fax: (353) 016186751
E-Mail: callcenter@friendsfirst.ie
Web Site: www.friendsfirst.ie
Emp.: 300
Pension Administrator
S.I.C.: 6371
N.A.I.C.S.: 524292
Adrain Hegarty *(Gen Mgr)*

Friends First Ireland **(2)**
Cherrywood Business Park Loughlinstown
Dublin, 18, Ireland
Tel.: (353) 16610600
Fax: (353) 16616651
E-Mail: info@friendsfirst.ie
Web Site: www.friendsfirst.ie
Emp.: 450
S.I.C.: 6411
N.A.I.C.S.: 524298
Adrian Hegarty *(CEO)*
Tom Brown *(Mng Dir)*

Risk & Insurance S.A. **(1)**
1 A Ruedunord
PO Box 237
2163 Luxembourg, 2012, Luxembourg (100%)
Mailing Address:
P.O. Box 237
2012 Luxembourg, Luxembourg
Tel.: (352) 222474
Fax: (352) 221550
Emp.: 4
S.I.C.: 6411
N.A.I.C.S.: 524298
Christin Christiansen *(Dir-Risk Insurance)*

ACI ELEVATION S.A.

49 Rue De Boult
F 51110 Isles-sur-Suippes, France
Tel.: (33) 326032959
Fax: (33) 326880336
E-Mail: info@aci-elevation.com
Web Site: www.aci-elevation.com
Emp.: 65
S.I.C.: 2439
N.A.I.C.S.: 321214
Personnel:
Sylvie Owen *(Pres & CEO)*
Claude Courtin *(Mng Dir)*

A.C.I. STARCASE GROUP INC.

2616 Sheridan Garden Drive
Oakville, ON, L6J 7Z2, Canada
Tel.: (905) 829-1566
Fax: (905) 829-1766
E-Mail: info@acibrands.com
Rev.: $37,590,321
Emp.: 167
Business Description:
Accessories & Personal Care Product Mfr
S.I.C.: 2389
N.A.I.C.S.: 315990
Personnel:
Jeff Goraieb *(Pres)*

ACICO INDUSTRIES CO. K.S.C.C.

Raed Center
PO Box 24079
Safat, Kuwait, 13101, Kuwait
Tel.: (965) 1888811
Fax: (965) 22422103
E-Mail: info@acico.com.kw
Web Site: www.acicogroup.com
Year Founded: 1990
ACICO—(KUW)
Sales Range: $125-149.9 Million
Emp.: 225
Business Description:
Concrete Products Mfr; Real Estate Developer
S.I.C.: 3271
N.A.I.C.S.: 327331
Personnel:
Abdulaziz Ahmed Al-Ayuob *(Chm)*
Ghassan Ahmed Saud Al-Khaled *(Vice Chm & CEO)*
Hussam Abu-Lughod *(CFO)*
Board of Directors:
Abdulaziz Ahmed Al-Ayuob
Ahmed Ghassan Ahmad Saud Al-Khaled
Ghassan Ahmed Saud Al-Khaled
Walid Ahmed Saoud Al-Khalid
Faisal Yousuf Jasim Al-Majid
Faten Farouq Al-Naqeeb
Ahmad Faisal Al-Refaie

Abdul Rahman Al-Qaoud & Partners
PO Box 26111
Kuwait, Kuwait

ACINO HOLDING AG

Erlenstrasse 1
4058 Aesch, Switzerland
Tel.: (41) 613386000
Fax: (41) 613386080
E-Mail: info@acino-pharma.com
Web Site: www.acino-pharma.com
ACIN—(SWX)
Rev.: $346,100,307
Assets: $680,912,979
Liabilities: $304,709,618
Net Worth: $376,203,361
Earnings: $12,702,460
Emp.: 836
Fiscal Year-end: 12/31/12
Business Description:
Pharmaceutical Mfr
S.I.C.: 2834
N.A.I.C.S.: 325412
Personnel:
Luzi Andreas von Bidder *(Chm)*
Andreas Rummelt *(Vice Chm)*
Peter Burema *(CEO)*
Martin Gertsch *(CFO)*
Jurgen Betzing *(COO)*
Ruud van Anraat *(Chief Comml Officer)*
Daniel Hossli *(Gen Counsel)*
Board of Directors:
Luzi Andreas von Bidder
Anders Harfstrand
Hans Peter Hasler
Jurg Michel
Andreas Rummelt
Subsidiaries:

Acino Pharma Ltd **(1)**
Birsweg 2
4253 Liesberg, Basel, Switzerland
Tel.: (41) 617758000
Fax: (41) 617758001
E-Mail: info@acino-pharma.com
Web Site: www.acino-pharma.com
Emp.: 300
Pharmaceutical Products Mfr
S.I.C.: 2834
N.A.I.C.S.: 325412
Hans Van Nuffel *(Mng Dir)*

Acino Supply Ltd **(1)**
Erlenstrasse 1
4058 Basel, Switzerland
Tel.: (41) 613386000
Fax: (41) 613386080
E-Mail: info@acino-pharma.com
Emp.: 300
Pharmaceutical Products Distr
S.I.C.: 5122
N.A.I.C.S.: 424210

Non-U.S. Subsidiaries:

Acino AG **(1)**
Am Windfeld 35
83714 Miesbach, Germany
Tel.: (49) 802528670
Fax: (49) 8025286728
E-Mail: martin.nittnaier@acino-pharma.com
Web Site: www.acino-pharma.com
Emp.: 220
Pharmaceutical Products Mfr
S.I.C.: 2834
N.A.I.C.S.: 325412
Peter Purema *(Founder)*
Robert Schmid *(Mng Dir)*

DigiCore (UK) Limited **(1)**
Sage House 319 Pinner Rd
Harrow, Middlesex, HA1 4HF, United Kingdom
Tel.: (44) 2085152900
Fax: (44) 2088613888
E-Mail: info@digicore.co.uk
Web Site: www.digicore.co.uk
Emp.: 20
Vehicle Tracking & Fleet Management Services
S.I.C.: 4899
N.A.I.C.S.: 517919
Tom O'Connor *(Mng Dir)*

ACKERMANS & VAN HAAREN NV

Begijnenvest 113
2000 Antwerp, Belgium
Tel.: (32) 32318770
Fax: (32) 32252533
E-Mail: info@avh.be
Web Site: www.avh.be
ACKB—(EUR OTC)
Rev.: $582,215,833
Assets: $9,099,413,230
Liabilities: $5,717,197,452
Net Worth: $3,382,215,778
Earnings: $283,160,129
Emp.: 18,752
Fiscal Year-end: 12/31/12
Business Description:
Investment Company
S.I.C.: 6722
N.A.I.C.S.: 525910
Personnel:
Tom Bemelis *(CFO & Dir-Fin)*
Andre-Xavier Cooreman *(COO)*
Brigitte Adriaensens *(Legal Counsel)*
Sofie Beernaert *(Legal Counsel)*
Jean-Claude Janssens *(Treas)*
Piet Bevernage *(Sec Gen)*
Board of Directors:
Jacques Delen
Luc Jacques Leon Cesar Bertrand
Teun Jurgens
Pierre Macharis
Julien Pestiaux

Ackermans & van Haaren NV—(Continued)

Thierry van Baren
Frederic van Haaren
Pierre Willaert

Subsidiaries:

Algemene Aannemingen Van Laere NV (1)
Kattestraat 77
9150 Kruibeke, Belgium (100%)
Tel.: (32) 32522020
Fax: (32) 32522040
E-Mail: mailbox@vanlaere.be
Web Site: www.vanlaere.be
Emp.: 300
Construction & Civil Engineering
S.I.C.: 1541
N.A.I.C.S.: 236210

Anfima NV (1)
Begijnenvest 113
Antwerp, 2000, Belgium
Tel.: (32) 32318770
Fax: (32) 32252533
Investment Management Services
S.I.C.: 6211
N.A.I.C.S.: 523999
Luc Bertrand *(Gen Mgr)*

Anmeco N.V. (1)
Antwerpsesteenweg 320
Burcht, Zwijndrecht, Belgium
Tel.: (32) 32541117
Fax: (32) 32540763
E-Mail: info@anmeco.be
Web Site: www.anmeco.be
Heavy Engineering Construction Services
S.I.C.: 1629
N.A.I.C.S.: 237990
Geert Van De Velde *(Gen Mgr)*

Bank Delen N.V. (1)
Jan Van Rijswijcklaan 184
2020 Antwerp, Belgium (75%)
Tel.: (32) 445566
Fax: (32) 160491
E-Mail: info@delen.be
Web Site: www.delen.be
Emp.: 250
Banking Services
S.I.C.: 6029
N.A.I.C.S.: 522110
Jacques Delen *(Dir)*

Bank J. Van Breda & Co. N.V. (1)
Ledeganckkaai 7
2000 Antwerp, Belgium
Tel.: (32) 32175333
Fax: (32) 32961096
E-Mail: helpdesk@bankvanbreda.be
Web Site: www.bankvanbreda.be
Emp.: 200
Commercial Banking Services
S.I.C.: 6029
N.A.I.C.S.: 522110
Carlo Henriksen *(Gen Mgr)*

Brinvest NV (1)
Begijnenvest 113
2000 Antwerp, Belgium
Tel.: (32) 32318770
Fax: (32) 3 225 25 33
E-Mail: info@avh.be
Emp.: 35
Financial Management Services
S.I.C.: 6211
N.A.I.C.S.: 523999

CFE S.A. (1)
avenue Hermann Debroux 42
1160 Brussels, Belgium (60.39%)
Tel.: (32) 26611211
Fax: (32) 26607710
E-Mail: info@cfe.be
Web Site: www.cfe.be
CFEB—(EUR)
Rev.: $2,555,434,511
Earnings: $66,096,947
Emp.: 5,582
Fiscal Year-end: 12/31/12
Construction Services
S.I.C.: 1542
N.A.I.C.S.: 236220
Philippe Delaunois *(Chm)*
Renaud Bentegeat *(CEO & Mng Dir)*
Jacques Ninanne *(CFO)*

Non-U.S. Subsidiaries:

CFE Hungary Epitoipari Kft. (2)
Hercegprimas Utca 21
1051 Budapest, Hungary
Tel.: (36) 1 332 73 12
Fax: (36) 1 269 46 86
E-Mail: welcome@cfehungary.hu
Web Site: www.cfehungary.hu
Construction Engineering Services
S.I.C.: 8711
N.A.I.C.S.: 541330
Pascal Steens *(Area Mgr)*

CFE Nederland B.V. (2)
Kilkade 2
3316 BC Dordrecht, Netherlands
Tel.: (31) 78 632 10 20
Fax: (31) 78 632 10 55
E-Mail: info@cfe.nl
Web Site: www.cfe.nl
Emp.: 25
Construction Engineering Services
S.I.C.: 8711
N.A.I.C.S.: 541330
Andre de Koning *(Mgr)*

CFE Polska Sp. z o.o. (2)
Al Jerozolimskie 92 West Gate 4th floor
00-807 Warsaw, Poland
Tel.: (48) 22 456 16 00
Fax: (48) 48 22 456 16 01
E-Mail: cfe@cfe.com.pl
Web Site: www.cfe.com.pl
Emp.: 30
Construction Engineering Services
S.I.C.: 8711
N.A.I.C.S.: 541330
Lambrecht Bruno *(Gen Mgr)*

CFE Tunisia (2)
Rue du Lac de Come Res La Rose Blanche - Building B 1 G
1053 Tunis, Tunisia
Tel.: (216) 71 961 236
Fax: (216) 71 961 581
Web Site: en.cfe.be/poles/construction/cfe-tunisie.aspx
Construction Engineering Services
S.I.C.: 8711
N.A.I.C.S.: 541330

CLE S.A. (2)
19-21 Route d'Arlon
8009 Luxembourg, Luxembourg
Tel.: (352) 44 65 491
Fax: (352) 45 44 18
E-Mail: info@cle.lu
Web Site: www.cle.lu
Construction Engineering Services
S.I.C.: 8711
N.A.I.C.S.: 541330
Olivier Vanderdeelen *(Gen Mgr)*

CLI (2)
19-21 route d'Arlon
8009 Luxembourg, Luxembourg
Tel.: (352) 44 65 491
Fax: (352) 45 44 18
Emp.: 60
Real Estate Management Services
S.I.C.: 6531
N.A.I.C.S.: 531390
Olivier Van Der Deelan *(CEO)*

GEKA Bouw BV (2)
Kilkade 2 - 4
3316 BC Dordrecht, Netherlands
Tel.: (31) 78 652 48 52
Fax: (31) 78 618 18 76
E-Mail: info@gekabouw.nl
Web Site: www.gekabouw.nl
Emp.: 50
Pile Driving Services
S.I.C.: 1799
N.A.I.C.S.: 238910

Subsidiaries:

Aannemingen Van Wellen (2)
Klinkaardstraat 198
2950 Kapellen, Belgium
Tel.: (32) 3 660 21 21
Fax: (32) 3 665 39 55
E-Mail: info@vanwellen.be
Web Site: www.vanwellen.be
Emp.: 300
Construction Engineering Services
S.I.C.: 8711
N.A.I.C.S.: 541330

Yves Weyts *(Gen Mgr)*

AMART S.A. (2)
Rue du Pavillon 4
1000 Brussels, Belgium
Tel.: (32) 2 241 89 70
Fax: (32) 2 241 90 44
E-Mail: secretariat@amart.be
Web Site: www.amart.be
Construction Engineering Services
S.I.C.: 8711
N.A.I.C.S.: 541330
Ivan De Wilde *(Mng Dir)*

Bageci (2)
Parc industriel Rue des Pieds d'Alouette 12
5100 Namur, Belgium
Tel.: (32) 81 40 79 11
Fax: (32) 81 40 79 24
E-Mail: info@bageci.be
Web Site: www.bageci.be
Construction Engineering Services
S.I.C.: 8711
N.A.I.C.S.: 541330
Patrick Verswijvel *(Gen Mgr)*

be.Maintenance (2)
Humaniteitslaan 114
1070 Brussels, Belgium
Tel.: (32) 2 526 60 40
Fax: (32) 2 524 12 60
E-Mail: info@bemaintenance.be
Web Site: www.bemaintenance.be
Emp.: 40
Air Conditioning Equipment Installation Services
S.I.C.: 1731
N.A.I.C.S.: 238210
Andre Vandenbauw *(Gen Mgr)*

Benelmat sa (2)
Avenue Albert 1er 83a
1342 Limelette, Belgium
Tel.: (32) 1 043 89 11
Fax: (32) 1 041 34 94
Web Site: www.vinci.com
Construction Engineering Services
S.I.C.: 8711
N.A.I.C.S.: 541330

BPC sa/nv (2)
Chaussee de la Hulpe 166
1170 Brussels, Belgium
Tel.: (32) 2 663 60 00
Fax: (32) 2 672 42 50
E-Mail: bpc@bpc.be
Web Site: www.bpc.be
Emp.: 200
Construction Engineering Services
S.I.C.: 8711
N.A.I.C.S.: 541330
Frederic Claes *(Mng Dir)*

BPI sa/nv (2)
Avenue Herrmann-Debroux 42
1160 Brussels, Belgium
Tel.: (32) 2 663 60 10
Fax: (32) 2 673 59 25
E-Mail: info@bpisa.be
Web Site: www.bpisa.be
Construction Engineering Services
S.I.C.: 8711
N.A.I.C.S.: 541330
Jacques Lefevre *(Mng Dir)*
Fabien De Jonge *(CFO)*

CFE Brabant (2)
Avenue Herrmann-Debroux 42
1160 Brussels, Belgium
Tel.: (32) 2 661 12 11
Fax: (32) 2 661 14 32
Web Site: www.vinci.com
Construction Engineering Services
S.I.C.: 8711
N.A.I.C.S.: 541330
Christophe van Ophem *(Gen Mgr)*

Subsidiary:

Leloup Entreprise Generale SPRL (3)
Avenue Herrmann-Debroux 42
1160 Brussels, Belgium
Tel.: (32) 2 661 12 11
Fax: (32) 2 661 14 32
E-Mail: cfebrabant@cfe.be
Web Site: en.cfe.be/poles/construction/leloup.aspx
Emp.: 200
Construction Engineering Services

S.I.C.: 8711
N.A.I.C.S.: 541330
Christophe van Ophem *(Gen Mgr)*

CFE Immo (2)
Avenue Herrmann-Debroux 42
1160 Brussels, Belgium
Tel.: (32) 2 661 12 11
Fax: (32) 2 673 59 25
E-Mail: info@cfe.be
Web Site: www.cfe.be
Emp.: 28
Real Estate Management Services
S.I.C.: 6531
N.A.I.C.S.: 531390
Jacques Lefevre *(Gen Mgr)*

CFE International (2)
Avenue Herrmann-Debroux 42
1160 Brussels, Belgium
Tel.: (32) 2 661 13 67
Fax: (32) 2 661 12 36
Web Site: www.cfe.be
Emp.: 20
Construction Engineering Services
S.I.C.: 8711
N.A.I.C.S.: 541330
Youssef Merdassi *(Gen Mgr)*

Construction management sa/nv (2)
Avenue Herrmann-Debroux 42
1160 Brussels, Belgium
Tel.: (32) 2 661 16 61
Fax: (32) 2 661 16 60
E-Mail: info@constructionmanagement.be
Web Site: www.comanag.com
Construction Engineering Services
S.I.C.: 8711
N.A.I.C.S.: 541330

Dredging International NV (2)
Haven 1025 Scheldedijk 30
2070 Zwijndrecht, Antwerp, Belgium (48%)
Tel.: (32) 32505211
Fax: (32) 32505650
E-Mail: info@deme.be
Web Site: www.deme.be
Emp.: 800
Dredging Services
S.I.C.: 1623
N.A.I.C.S.: 237110
Alain Bernard *(Mng Dir)*

Divisions:

DEC N.V. (3)
Haven 1025
Scheldedijk 30, B-2070 Zwijndrecht, Belgium
Tel.: (32) 3 250 54 11
Fax: (32) 3 250 5253
Web Site: www.decnv.com
Dredging, Environmental & Marine Engineering
S.I.C.: 8711
N.A.I.C.S.: 541330
Veerle Vercruysse *(Mng Dir)*

DEME Building Materials N.V. (DBM) (3)
Haven 1025 Scheldedijk 30
2070 Zwijndrecht, Belgium
Tel.: (32) 3 250 5423
Fax: (32) 3 250 5522
E-Mail: infodbm@deme.be
Web Site: www.dbmnv.be
Dredging, Environmental & Marine Services
S.I.C.: 1623
N.A.I.C.S.: 237110
Frank Devriese *(Mng Dir)*

Ecoterres S.A. (3)
Avenue Jean Mermoz 3c
B-6041 Gosselies, Belgium
Tel.: (32) 71 256 041
Fax: (32) 71 256 044
Web Site: www.ecoterres.be
Environmental Services
S.I.C.: 8999
N.A.I.C.S.: 541620
M. Benedicte Bauduin *(Mng Dir)*

Subsidiaries:

Baggerwerken Decloedt en Zoon N.V. (3)
Slijkensesteenweg 2
8400 Oostende, Belgium
Tel.: (32) 59 242 140
Fax: (32) 59 242 180

E-Mail: infodecloedt@deme.be
Web Site: www.decloedt.be
Port Dredging & Sea Lane Maintenance
S.I.C.: 4499
N.A.I.C.S.: 488390
Bart Verboomen *(Mng Dir)*

C-Power N.V. (3)
Buskruitstraat 1
Scheldedijk 30, 2070 Oostende, Belgium
Tel.: (32) 59797980
Fax: (32) 3 250 5552
E-Mail: c-power@c-power.be
Environmental Services
S.I.C.: 8999
N.A.I.C.S.: 541620
Jaak Rutten *(CEO)*

CTow N.V. (3)
Haven 1025
Scheldedijk 30
2070 Zwijndrecht, Belgium
Tel.: (32) 3 250 5551
Fax: (32) 3 250 5552
E-Mail: info@ctow.be
Web Site: www.ctow.be
Port Terminal & Marine Services
S.I.C.: 4493
N.A.I.C.S.: 713930

DEME Blue Energy (3)
Haven 1025
Scheldedijk 30, B-2070 Zwijndrecht, Belgium
Tel.: (32) 360 52 11
Fax: (32) 3 250 5650
Environmental Services
S.I.C.: 8999
N.A.I.C.S.: 541620

GeoSea N.V. (3)
Haven 1025
Scheldedijk 30, Zwijndrecht, 2070, Belgium
Tel.: (32) 3 250 53 12
Fax: (32) 250 55 41
E-Mail: infogoc@deme.be
Web Site: www.geosea.be
Emp.: 20
Environmental Services
S.I.C.: 8999
N.A.I.C.S.: 541620
Luc Vanderbulcke *(Mng Dir)*

Grondrecyclage Centrum Kallo N.V. (GRC) (3)
Haven 1562 St Jansweg 10
9130 Kallo, Belgium
Tel.: (32) 3 570 9030
Fax: (32) 3 570 9039
E-Mail: info@GRCKallo.be
Web Site: www.grckallo.be
Emp.: 15
Soil & Waste Management Services
S.I.C.: 0711
N.A.I.C.S.: 115112
Dirk Ponnet *(Mng Dir)*

Power@Sea N.V. (3)
Haven 1025
Scheldedijk 30, B-2070 Zwijndrecht, Belgium
Tel.: (32) 3 250 5633
Fax: (32) 3 250 5665
Web Site: www.poweratc.com
Environmental Services
S.I.C.: 8999
N.A.I.C.S.: 541620
Marc Van de Perre *(Mng Dir)*

Scaldis Salvage and Marine Contractors N.V. (3)
North Trade Building
Bus 31
Noorderlaan 133, 2030 Antwerp, Belgium
Tel.: (32) 3 541 6955
Fax: (32) 3 541 8193
E-Mail: mail@scaldis-smc.com
Web Site: www.scaldis-smc.com
Emp.: 22
Dredging, Marine & Environmental Services
S.I.C.: 8999
N.A.I.C.S.: 541620
Marc Voorhuis *(Mng Dir)*

Non-U.S. Subsidiary:

Dredging International Asia Pacific (PTE) Ltd (3)
371 Beach Rd 24 08 Keypoint
199597 Singapore, Singapore (100%)
Tel.: (65) 68632108
Fax: (65) 68631108
E-Mail: info@diap-deme.com
Web Site: www.deme.be
Emp.: 20
Dredging Services
S.I.C.: 1629
N.A.I.C.S.: 237990
Daniel Kong *(Mng Dir)*

Druart S.A. (2)
Place de Spiennes 1
7032 Spiennes, Belgium
Tel.: (32) 64 310920
Fax: (32) 64 310921
E-Mail: info@druart-sa.be
Web Site: www.druart-sa.be
Rev.: $26,923,400
Heating & Air Conditioning Equipment Installation Services
S.I.C.: 1711
N.A.I.C.S.: 238220
Jean Marie Chabart *(Gen Mgr)*

Subsidiary:

Prodfroid SA (3)
Rue des Pieds d Alouette 12
5100 Namur, Belgium
Tel.: (32) 81 51 39 91
Fax: (32) 81 51 39 92
E-Mail: info@prodfroid.be
Web Site: www.prodfroid.be
Industrial Cooling System Sales & Installation Services
S.I.C.: 5075
N.A.I.C.S.: 423730
Jean Marie Chabart *(Mng Dir)*

Electronizet SA (2)
Rue Laid Burniat 2
1342 Louvain-la-Neuve, Belgium
Tel.: (32) 10 45 18 63
Fax: (32) 10 45 18 56
E-Mail: info@voltis.be
Web Site: www.voltis.be
Emp.: 25
Consumer Electronics Distr
S.I.C.: 5064
N.A.I.C.S.: 423620
Senzot Philippe *(Gen Mgr)*

Engema Lignes (2)
Route de Sainte-Ode 34 Lavacherie
6681 Sainte-Ode, Belgium
Tel.: (32) 61 68 88 52
Fax: (32) 61 68 88 53
E-Mail: lignes@engema.be
Web Site: www.en.engema.be/history-engema/lignes.aspx
Heating & Air Conditioning Equipment Installation Services
S.I.C.: 1711
N.A.I.C.S.: 238220
Bruno Lambert *(Mgr)*

Engema Montage (2)
Avenue Albert 1er 83a Limelette
Ottignies, 1342 Louvain-la-Neuve, Belgium
Tel.: (32) 10 43 89 42
Fax: (32) 10 43 89 65
E-Mail: montage@engema.be
Web Site: en.engema.be/history-engema/montage.aspx
Emp.: 40
Railway Signalling System Installation Services
S.I.C.: 1731
N.A.I.C.S.: 238210

Engema Rail (2)
Horizonpark 3 bus 14 Leuvensesteenweg 510
1930 Zaventem, Belgium
Tel.: (32) 2 717 89 80
Fax: (32) 2 717 89 89
E-Mail: rail@engema.be
Web Site: www.engema.be
Emp.: 15
Railroad Construction & Maintenance Services
S.I.C.: 1629
N.A.I.C.S.: 237990
Jean-Paul Coch *(Mng Dir)*

Engema sa/nv (2)
Horizonpark 3 bus 14 Leuvensesteenweg 510
1930 Zaventem, Belgium
Tel.: (32) 2 717 89 80
Fax: (32) 2 717 89 89
E-Mail: rail@engema.be
Web Site: www.engema.be
Railway Signaling Installation Services
S.I.C.: 1731
N.A.I.C.S.: 238210
Jean-Paul Coch *(Mng Dir)*

ETEC SA (2)
Zoning Industriel de Manage Zone D Rue Jean Perrin 2
7170 Manage, Belgium
Tel.: (32) 64 54 85 35
Fax: (32) 64 54 84 48
E-Mail: info@etec-sa.be
Web Site: en.cfe.be/poles/multitechnics/etec.aspx
Lighting Equipment Installation Services
S.I.C.: 1731
N.A.I.C.S.: 238210
Luc Dutrieux *(Mgr)*

Groep Terryn NV (2)
Nieuwstraat 8
Moorslede, 8890, Belgium
Tel.: (32) 5 177 73 14
Fax: (32) 5 177 17 43
Web Site: www.groepterryn.be
Wooden Product Mfr
S.I.C.: 2499
N.A.I.C.S.: 321999

Louis Stevens & Co n.v. (2)
Stadsbeemd 1314
3545 Halen, Belgium
Tel.: (32) 13 44 15 71
Fax: (32) 13 44 26 25
E-Mail: info@stevensco.be
Web Site: www.stevensco.be
Emp.: 150
Rail Signaling Equipment Installation Services
S.I.C.: 1731
N.A.I.C.S.: 238210
Chris Presiaux *(Gen Mgr)*

MBG Brugge (2)
Hertogenstraat 69
Sint-Andries, 8200 Brugge, Belgium
Tel.: (32) 50 39 57 64
Fax: (32) 50 39 57 63
Web Site: www.mbg.be/UK/contact.htm
Construction Engineering Services
S.I.C.: 8711
N.A.I.C.S.: 541330

MBG Wilrijk (2)
Garden Square Blok D Laarstraat 16 Bus 12
Wilrijk, 2610 Antwerp, Belgium
Tel.: (32) 3 820 40 11
Fax: (32) 3 820 40 04
E-Mail: mbg@mbg.be
Web Site: www.mbg.be
Emp.: 150
Construction Engineering Services
S.I.C.: 8711
N.A.I.C.S.: 541330

Nizet Entreprise SA (2)
Parc Scientifique Fleming Rue Laid Burniat 2
1348 Louvain-la-Neuve, Belgium
Tel.: (32) 10 45 18 67
Fax: (32) 10 45 27 82
E-Mail: nizet@nizet.be
Web Site: www.nizet.be
Emp.: 130
Electrical Equipment Installation Services
S.I.C.: 1731
N.A.I.C.S.: 238210
Hubert Lacroix *(Mng Dir)*

Remacom NV (2)
Hoogstraat 2
Beervelde, 9080 Lochristi, Belgium
Tel.: (32) 93 56 98 24
Fax: (32) 93 55 36 72
E-Mail: info@remacom.be
Railroad Construction & Maintenance Services
S.I.C.: 1629
N.A.I.C.S.: 237990
Erwin Imschoot *(Mng Dir)*

Van De Maele Multi-Techniek NV (2)
Tieltstraat 69
8760 Meulebeke, Belgium
Tel.: (32) 51 48 65 73
Fax: (32) 51 48 54 06
E-Mail: info@vandemaele.be
Web Site: www.vandemaele.be
Industrial Automation & Maintenance Services
S.I.C.: 8711
N.A.I.C.S.: 541330

Vanderhoydoncks Elektrotechnieken nv (2)
Kolmen 1108
3570 Alken, Belgium
Tel.: (32) 11 59 02 00
Fax: (32) 11 59 27 04
E-Mail: info@vdhs.be
Web Site: www.vdhs.be
Emp.: 60
Security System Installation Services
S.I.C.: 1731
N.A.I.C.S.: 238210
Eddy Schrijvers *(Mgr)*

VMA nv (2)
Kortrijksesteenweg 14B
9830 Sint-Martens-Latem, Belgium
Tel.: (32) 9 280 95 25
Fax: (32) 9 282 33 22
E-Mail: info@vma.be
Web Site: www.vma.be
Emp.: 150
Electrical Engineering Services
S.I.C.: 8711
N.A.I.C.S.: 541330
Guy Wynendaele *(Mng Dir)*

De Toekomst vzw (1)
Sint Kamielstraat 85
9300 Aalst, Belgium
Tel.: (32) 53607500
Fax: (32) 53607414
E-Mail: info@vzwdetoekomst.be
Web Site: www.vzwdetoekomst.be
Emp.: 65
Residential Services
S.I.C.: 1522
N.A.I.C.S.: 236118

Extensa Development SA (1)
Avenue Du Port 86c Internal
PO Box 316
Brussels, 1000, Belgium
Tel.: (32) 22370820
Fax: (32) 22370821
E-Mail: info@extensa.be
Web Site: www.extensa.be
Real Estate Management Services
S.I.C.: 6531
N.A.I.C.S.: 531390
Ward Van Gorp *(Gen Mgr)*

Extensa Group SA (1)
Av du Port 86c Boite 316
1000 Brussels, Belgium
Tel.: (32) 22370820
Fax: (32) 2 237 08 21
E-Mail: info@extensa.be
Web Site: www.extensa.be
Emp.: 15
Apartment Construction Services
S.I.C.: 1542
N.A.I.C.S.: 236220
Kris Verhellen *(CEO)*
Laurent Jacquemart *(CFO)*

Subsidiary:

Extensa NV (2)
Avenue Du Port 86c Bus 316
Brussels, 1000, Belgium
Tel.: (32) 22370820
Fax: (32) 22370821
E-Mail: info@extensa.be
Emp.: 15
Real Estate Management Services
S.I.C.: 6531
N.A.I.C.S.: 531390
Chris Verhellen *(Gen Mgr)*

Non-U.S. Subsidiaries:

Extensa Istanbul (2)
Maya Akar Center Kat 18
Esentepe, Turkey 34394
Tel.: (90) 212 274 2484
Fax: (90) 212 275 3070
E-Mail: info@extensa.com.tr
Web Site: www.extensa.com.tr
Emp.: 8
Real Estate Development Services
S.I.C.: 6531
N.A.I.C.S.: 531390

Ackermans & van Haaren NV—(Continued)

Ozlem Gotce *(Gen Mgr)*

Extensa Slovakia s.r.o. (2)
C/o ES Partners Zahradnicka 51
821 08 Bratislava, Slovakia
Tel.: (421) 918 625 395
Web Site: www.extensa.be/nl/contact
Emp.: 1
Real Estate Management Services
S.I.C.: 6531
N.A.I.C.S.: 531390
Stefan Harmanos *(Country Mgr)*

Extensa Land II SA (1)
Havenlaan 86c 316
Brussels, 1000, Belgium
Tel.: (32) 22370820
Fax: (32) 22370821
E-Mail: info@extensa.be
Web Site: www.extensa.be
Real Estate Management Services
S.I.C.: 6531
N.A.I.C.S.: 531390
Kris Verhellen *(Gen Mgr)*

Finaxis Nv (1)
Begijnenvest 113
2000 Antwerp, Belgium
Tel.: (32) 32318770
Fax: (32) 32252533
E-Mail: info@avh.be
Web Site: www.finaxis.be
Financial Management Services
S.I.C.: 6211
N.A.I.C.S.: 523999

FRACAV NV (1)
Ledeganckkaai 7
Antwerp, 2000, Belgium
Tel.: (32) 65346346
Office Building Leasing Services
S.I.C.: 6512
N.A.I.C.S.: 531120

GROUPE THIRAN SA. (1)
rue du Parc Industriel d Achene 2
5590 Achene, Belgium
Tel.: (32) 83230790
Fax: (32) 83 23 07 80
E-Mail: mailbox@thiran.be
Web Site: www.thiran.be
Emp.: 120
Construction Engineering Services
S.I.C.: 8711
N.A.I.C.S.: 541330
Patrick Denis *(Gen Mgr)*

Huize Philemon & Baucis WZC (1)
Zoutleeuwsesteenweg 11
Dormaal, 3440 Zoutleeuw, Belgium
Tel.: (32) 11 78 22 66
Fax: (32) 11 78 46 66
Web Site: www.huizephilemonbaucis.be
Nursing Home Operators
S.I.C.: 8082
N.A.I.C.S.: 621610

Mabeco NV (1)
Begijnenvest 113
2000 Antwerp, Belgium
Tel.: (32) 3 231 87 70
Fax: (32) 3 225 25 33
E-Mail: info@avh.be
Emp.: 35
Financial Management Services
S.I.C.: 6211
N.A.I.C.S.: 523999
Luc Bertrand *(CEO)*

Nationale Maatschappij der Pijpleidingen NV (1)
Bischoffsheimlaan 11
1000 Brussels, Belgium
Tel.: (32) 22370696
Fax: (32) 22302326
E-Mail: nmp-sntc@nmp-sntc.be
Emp.: 5
Real Estate Management Services
S.I.C.: 6531
N.A.I.C.S.: 531390
Gue De Schrijver *(Mgr)*

Rusthuis Kruyenberg Nv (1)
Turfputstraat 100
9290 Berlare, Belgium
Tel.: (32) 52423057
Fax: (32) 52426474
E-Mail: info@rusthuiskruyenberg.be
Web Site: www.rusthuiskruyenberg.be
Emp.: 66
Senior Citizen Homes Management Services
S.I.C.: 6531
N.A.I.C.S.: 531390
Kathleen de Cock *(Gen Mgr)*

Sofinim N.V. (1)
Begignvest 113
B-2000 Antwerp, Belgium (74%)
Tel.: (32) 38979230
Fax: (32) 32252533
E-Mail: info@sofinim.be
Web Site: www.sofinim.be
Emp.: 7
Private Equity Investment Firm
S.I.C.: 6211
N.A.I.C.S.: 523999
Marc De Pauw *(Mng Dir)*
Andre-Xavier Cooreman *(COO)*

Holding:

Dynea N.V. (2)
Moervaartkaai 7
B 9042 Gent, Belgium (100%)
Tel.: (32) 93423434
Fax: (32) 93423450
Emp.: 35
Resin Mfr
S.I.C.: 2821
N.A.I.C.S.: 325211
Guido Duytschaeve *(Mgr-Sharepoint)*

Non-U.S. Joint Venture:

Euro Media Groupe SA (2)
2 Avenue de l Europe
Paris, 94360, France
Tel.: (33) 1 49 83 40 00
Fax: (33) 1 49 83 43 06
Audiovisual Technical Services
S.I.C.: 7389
N.A.I.C.S.: 541990

Van Breda Car Finance Nv (1)
Ledeganckkaai 7
Antwerp, 2000, Belgium
Tel.: (32) 32175333
Fax: (32) 32354934
Financial Management Services
S.I.C.: 6211
N.A.I.C.S.: 523999

Vandendorpe NV (1)
Rue Aurimont 10
1457 Walhain-Saint-Paul, Belgium
Tel.: (32) 10237960
Fax: (32) 10237969
E-Mail: vandendorpe@vandendorpe.be
Web Site: www.vandendorpe.be
Building Materials Mfr
S.I.C.: 3448
N.A.I.C.S.: 332311

Wefima N.V (1)
Antwerpsesteenweg 320
2070 Zwijndrecht, Belgium
Tel.: (32) 3 252 20 20
Fax: (32) 3 252 20 40
Construction Engineering Services
S.I.C.: 8711
N.A.I.C.S.: 541330

Joint Venture:

TRASYS S.A (1)
Tarhulpsestaanveg No C 1660
B 1200 Hoeilaart, Belgium BE
Tel.: (32) 27737111
Fax: (32) 27737900
E-Mail: info@trasys.be
Web Site: www.trasys.be
Emp.: 600
IT & Software Business Support Services
S.I.C.: 7371
N.A.I.C.S.: 541511
Chris de Hous *(CEO)*
Philippe Mestdag *(CFO)*

Non-U.S. Subsidiaries:

TRASYS Greece (2)
3 Arkadias St
11526 Athens, Attica, Greece
Tel.: (30) 2107769800
Fax: (30) 2107769801
E-Mail: info@trasys.gr
Web Site: www.trasys.gr
Emp.: 30
IT & Software Business Support Services
S.I.C.: 7371
N.A.I.C.S.: 541511
Phillip Mestbag *(CFO)*

TRASYS Luxembourg (2)
Route d'Arlon 283
8011 Strassen, Luxembourg
Tel.: (352) 261110
Fax: (352) 26111033
E-Mail: info@trasys.be
Web Site: www.trasys.lu
Emp.: 29
IT & Software Business Support Services
S.I.C.: 7371
N.A.I.C.S.: 541511
Pascal Desart *(Country Mgr)*

Subsidiary:

TRASYS Charleroi (2)
Terhulp Sesteenwg 6C
1560 Hoeilaart, Belgium BE
Tel.: (32) 71378211
Fax: (32) 78931400
E-Mail: info@trasys.be
Web Site: www.trasys.be
Emp.: 130
IT & Software Business Support Services
S.I.C.: 7371
N.A.I.C.S.: 541511
Chris De Hous *(CEO, Pres & Gen Mgr)*

Non-U.S. Subsidiary:

EXTENSA ROMANIA S.R.L (1)
Ady Endre Street 7
01373 Bucharest, Romania
Tel.: (40) 31 425 40 62
Fax: (40) 31 425 40 63
E-Mail: info@extensa.be
Web Site: www.extensa.be/nl/contact
Emp.: 4
Real Estate Management Services
S.I.C.: 6531
N.A.I.C.S.: 531390
Razvan Oprescu *(Gen Mgr)*

ACKG LTD.

Sumitomo Fudosan Nishi Shinjuku
6th Building 3 12 1 Honmachi
Shibuya ku, Tokyo, 151 0071, Japan
Tel.: (81) 3 6311 6641
Fax: (81) 3 6311 6642
Web Site: www.ack-g.com
Year Founded: 2006
2498—(JAS)
Sls.: $406,405,700
Assets: $225,914,140
Liabilities: $155,135,180
Net Worth: $70,778,960
Earnings: $2,957,810
Fiscal Year-end: 09/30/12

Business Description:
Engineering Services
S.I.C.: 8711
N.A.I.C.S.: 541330

Personnel:
Akihiko Hirotani *(Pres)*

Board of Directors:
Mitsunobu Hirayama
Akihiko Hirotani
Hidenori Nozaki

Subsidiaries:

A-TEC Co., Ltd. (1)
Sumitomo Fudosan Izumi-Nishi Shinjuku Bldg 6F 4-12-7
Honnmachi Shibuya-ku, Tokyo, 151-0071, Japan
Tel.: (81) 3 6311 8151
E-Mail: info-mov@kk-atec.jp
Web Site: www.kk-atec.jp
Engineering Consulting Services
S.I.C.: 8711
N.A.I.C.S.: 541330
Katsumune Suzuki, *(Pres & CEO)*

Asano Taiseikiso Engineering Co., Ltd. (1)
Kitaueno 2-8-7
Taito-ku, Tokyo, 110-0014, Japan
Tel.: (81) 3 5246 4150
E-Mail: atk-info@atk-eng.jp
Web Site: www.atk-eng.jp
Environmental Engineering Services
S.I.C.: 8711
N.A.I.C.S.: 541330
Shinya Shigematsu, *(Pres)*

Chuou Sekkei Engineering Company Limited (1)
2-13-37 Hirooka St Kanazawa Bldg 5F
Kanazawa, 920-0031, Japan
Tel.: (81) 76 263 1220
Fax: (81) 76 262 9442
E-Mail: niwa@cser.co.jp
Web Site: www.cser.co.jp
Emp.: 130
Environmental Engineering Services
S.I.C.: 8711
N.A.I.C.S.: 541330
Nakatsuji Eiji, *(Gen Mgr)*

ACKNIT INDUSTRIES LTD.

224 AJC Bose Road
Kolkata, 700017, India
Tel.: (91) 33 22878293
Fax: (91) 33 22878269
Web Site: www.acknitindia.com
530043—(BOM)

Business Description:
Hand Glove & Safety Products Mfr
S.I.C.: 2389
N.A.I.C.S.: 315990

Personnel:
S. K. Saraf *(Chm & Mng Dir)*
Deepa Singh *(Sec)*

Board of Directors:
S. K. Saraf
S. K. Ghosh
M. K. Nath
D. K. Saraf

ACKROO INC.

(Formerly Rare Earth Industries Ltd.)
436 Hazeldean Road Suite 202
Ottawa, ON, K2L 1T9, Canada
Tel.: (613) 599-2396
Fax: (613) 280-1551
E-Mail: jchapman@ackroo.com
Web Site: ackroo.com
AKR—(TSXV)

Business Description:
Customer Loyalty Programs
S.I.C.: 7389
N.A.I.C.S.: 561499

Personnel:
Jeff Durno *(Chm)*
Eamonn Garry *(CEO)*
John Chapman *(CFO)*

Board of Directors:
Jeff Durno
John Chapman
Greg Feller
Eamonn Garry
Jay Malowney

Transfer Agent:
Computershare Trust Company of Canada
100 University Avenue 9th Floor
Toronto, ON, M5J 2Y1, Canada
Tel.: (416) 663-9097
Fax: (416) 263-9694

ACL AIRSHOP HOLDING B.V.

Kantoorweg 7
NL-1525 RJ West-Knollendam, Netherlands
Tel.: (31) 756226050
Fax: (31) 756225988
E-Mail: info@aclairshop.com
Web Site: www.aclairshop.com

Business Description:
Holding Company; Air Cargo Container Sales, Repair & Leasing Services
S.I.C.: 6719
N.A.I.C.S.: 551112

Personnel:
Anthony P. Morgan *(Pres/CEO-ACL-USA)*

Subsidiary:

Air Shop B.V. (1)
Kantoorweg 7
West Knollendam, NL-1525 RJ
Wormerveer, Netherlands NL
Tel.: (31) 756226050
Fax: (31) 756225988
E-Mail: info@culair-shop.nl
Web Site: www.air-shop.nl
Air Cargo Container Sales, Repair & Leasing Services
S.I.C.: 7359
N.A.I.C.S.: 532411
Maurice Van Terheijden *(Mgr-Logistics & Sls)*

U.S. Subsidiary:

Airline Container Leasing, LLC (1)
436 Saco Lowell Rd
Easley, SC 29640 SC
Tel.: (864) 306-1350
Fax: (864) 306-1331
E-Mail: sales@aclairshop.com
Web Site: www.aclairshop.com
Emp.: 85
Air Cargo Container Sales, Repair & Leasing Services
S.I.C.: 7359
N.A.I.C.S.: 532411
Anthony P. Morgan *(Pres & CEO)*
Thomas M. Tucker *(COO)*
Anthony B. Quartararo *(VP & Chief Legal Counsel)*

Units:

Airline Container Leasing, LLC - New York (2)
3800 Hampton Rd
Oceanside, NY 11572
Tel.: (516) 678-4334
Fax: (516) 678-4337
E-Mail: sales@aclairshop.com
Web Site: www.aclairshop.com
Sls.: $10,300,000
Emp.: 30
Air Cargo Container Sales, Repair & Leasing Services
S.I.C.: 7359
N.A.I.C.S.: 532411
Thomas Tucker *(COO)*

ACL CABLES PLC

60 Rodney Street
Colombo, 08, Sri Lanka
Tel.: (94) 112697652
Fax: (94) 112699503
E-Mail: info@acl.lk
Web Site: www.acl.lk
ACL—(COL)
Rev.: $88,913,188
Assets: $85,636,949
Liabilities: $35,378,730
Net Worth: $50,258,218
Earnings: $4,635,298
Emp.: 1,238
Fiscal Year-end: 03/31/13

Business Description:
Power Cables & Conductors Mfr
S.I.C.: 3357
N.A.I.C.S.: 335929

Personnel:
U. G. Madanayake *(Chm)*
Suren Madanayake *(Mng Dir)*

Board of Directors:
U. G. Madanayake
Hemaka Amarasuriya
P. S. Rajiv Casie Chitty
Ajit M. S. De S. Jayaratne
N. C. Madanayake
Suren Madanayake
Daya D. Wahalatantiri

Plant:

ACL Cables PLC - Factory (1)
Madapatha Piliyandala
Colombo, Sri Lanka
Tel.: (94) 112707361
Fax: (94) 112706805
E-Mail: info@acl.lk
Web Site: www.acl.lk/conus_acl.html
Emp.: 600
Cables Mfr
S.I.C.: 3357
N.A.I.C.S.: 335921
Rohitha Amarasekera *(Gen Mgr-Ops)*

ACL SEMICONDUCTORS INC.

(Name Changed to USmart Mobile Device Inc.)

ACL SERVICES LTD.

1550 Alberni Street
Vancouver, BC, Canada V6G 1A5
Tel.: (604) 669-4225
Fax: (604) 669-3557
Toll Free: (888) 669-4225
E-Mail: sales@acl.com
Web Site: www.acl.com
Year Founded: 1987
Rev.: $10,346,449
Emp.: 130

Business Description:
Software Services
S.I.C.: 7372
N.A.I.C.S.: 511210

Personnel:
Harald Will *(Chm)*
Laurie Schultz *(CEO)*
Terry Ingram *(CFO)*

ACM SHIPPING GROUP PLC

Grand Buildings 1 3 Strand
London, WC2N 5HR, United Kingdom
Tel.: (44) 20 7484 6311
Fax: (44) 20 7930 8243
Web Site: www.acmshippinggroup.co.uk
ACMG—(LSE)
Rev.: $37,983,504
Assets: $26,682,105
Liabilities: $13,645,066
Net Worth: $13,037,039
Earnings: ($2,588,456)
Emp.: 143
Fiscal Year-end: 03/31/13

Business Description:
Shipping Services
S.I.C.: 4731
N.A.I.C.S.: 488510

Personnel:
John Plumbe *(Chm)*
James Gundy *(CEO)*
Michael Amyas Charles Rudd *(COO)*
Ian Hartley *(Sec & Dir-Fin)*

Board of Directors:
John Plumbe
Jurgen-Heinz Breuer
David Cobb
James Gundy
Ian Hartley
Timothy Jaques
Michael Amyas Charles Rudd
Mark Jason Tracey

Legal Counsel:
Dechert LLP
160 Queen Victoria Street
London, United Kingdom

Subsidiary:

ACM Shipping Limited (1)
Grand buildings 1-3 Strand
London, WC2N 5HR, United Kingdom
Tel.: (44) 2079307555
Fax: (44) 2079300115
E-Mail: brokers@acmshipping.co.uk
Web Site: www.acmshipping.co.uk
Emp.: 16
Shipping Services
S.I.C.: 4731
N.A.I.C.S.: 488510
John Plumbe *(CEO)*
James Gundy *(COO)*

Non-U.S. Subsidiaries:

ACM Shipping Asia Pte. Limited (2)
16 Collyer Quay 30-02 Hitachi Tower
Singapore, 049318, Singapore
Tel.: (65) 62360822
Fax: (65) 65352145
E-Mail: brokers@acmshipping.com.sg
Web Site: www.acmshipping.com.sg
Emp.: 23
Ship Broking Services
S.I.C.: 4412
N.A.I.C.S.: 483111

ACM Shipping India Limited (2)
Maker Chambers 5
1118 Nariman Pt, Mumbai, Maharastra, 400 021, India
Tel.: (91) 2240949300
Fax: (91) 2240949301
E-Mail: brokers@acmshipping.co.uk
Web Site: www.acmshipping.com
Emp.: 7
Ship Broking Services
S.I.C.: 4731
N.A.I.C.S.: 488510
Sanjeev Juneja *(Mng Dir)*

ACME CAPITAL CORPORATION

500 1414 8th Street S.W
Calgary, AB, T2R 1J6, Canada
Tel.: (403) 539-4447
Fax: (403) 444-5042
E-Mail: al@kasten.ca
Year Founded: 2011
AMN.P—(TSXV)

Business Description:
Investment Services
S.I.C.: 6211
N.A.I.C.S.: 523999

Personnel:
Al J. Kroontje *(Pres, CEO, CFO & Sec)*

Board of Directors:
Wayne H. Henuset
Al J. Kroontje
Michael D. Resendes

Transfer Agent:
Olympia Trust Company
125 9th Avenue SE Suite 2300
Calgary, AB, T2G 0P6, Canada
Tel.: (403) 261-0900

ACME RESOURCES INC.

910 - 1050 West Pender Street
Vancouver, BC, V6E 3S7, Canada
Tel.: (604) 689-0299
Fax: (604) 689-0288
E-Mail: info@krl.net
Web Site: www.acmeresources.ca
ARI—(TSXV)
Assets: $422,284
Liabilities: $10,816
Net Worth: $411,468
Earnings: ($1,440,358)
Emp.: 2
Fiscal Year-end: 06/30/13

Business Description:
Gold, Silver & Other Precious Metals Mining Services
S.I.C.: 1041
N.A.I.C.S.: 212221

Personnel:
Seamus Young *(Pres & CEO)*
Abdul Allibhai *(CFO)*

Board of Directors:
Tim Barry
Shauna Lynn Hartman
Shaun Maskerine
Seamus Young

Legal Counsel:
Miller Thomson LLP
1000 840 Howe St
Vancouver, BC, Canada

Transfer Agent:
Computershare Investor Services Inc
4th Floor 510 Burrard Street
Vancouver, BC, Canada

ACMOS INC.

Nomura Kanda Ogawamachi Bldg
3-26-8 Kanda Ogawamachi
Chiyoda-Ku, Tokyo, Japan 101-0052
Tel.: (81) 3 5217 3121
Fax: (81) 3 5217 3122
Web Site: www.acmos.co.jp
Year Founded: 1991
6888—(JAS)
Sls.: $29,227,000
Assets: $25,465,000
Liabilities: $9,064,000
Net Worth: $16,401,000
Earnings: ($132,000)
Fiscal Year-end: 06/30/13

Business Description:
Information Technology Services
S.I.C.: 7389
N.A.I.C.S.: 519190

Personnel:
Hideyuki Iijima *(CEO)*

Board of Directors:
Hideyuki Iijima
Minoru Ishikawa
Osamu Miyamoto
Keiichi Ogiwara
Shuuichi Sato
Yohichi Shibata

Subsidiary:

ACMOS Sourcing Service Inc. (1)
3-26-8 Kandaogawamachi
Chiyoda-Ku, Tokyo, 101-0052, Japan
Tel.: (81) 352173332
Web Site: www.acmos-ss.jp
Information Technology Consulting Services
S.I.C.: 7373
N.A.I.C.S.: 541512

ACNE STUDIO

Lilla Nygatan 23
111 28 Stockholm, Sweden
Tel.: (46) 855 579 900
Fax: (46) 855 579 999
E-Mail: csr@acnestudios.com
Web Site: www.acnestudios.com
Year Founded: 1996
Sales Range: $10-24.9 Million
Emp.: 100

Business Description:
Unisex Jeans Mfr & Clothing Retailer
S.I.C.: 5699
N.A.I.C.S.: 315220

Personnel:
Jonny Johansson *(Creative Dir)*

ACNOVER, S.L.

(d/b/a ANV Central Bureau of Services)
Avenida Diagonal 123 planta 9
08005 Barcelona, Spain
Tel.: (34) 93 545 9000
E-Mail: getstarted@anv.eu.com
Web Site: www.anv.eu.com
Emp.: 150

Business Description:
Insurance Underwriting & Agency Development Services
S.I.C.: 6411
N.A.I.C.S.: 524298

Personnel:
R. Matthew Fairfield *(Founder & CEO)*
Jochi Jimenez *(Gen Counsel)*

Non-U.S. Subsidiary:

ANV Syndicate Management Limited (1)
1 Minister Court Mincing Lane 4th Floor
London, EC3R 7AA, United Kingdom UK
Tel.: (44) 20 7456 1800
Fax: (44) 2074561810
E-Mail: getstarted@anv.eu.com
Emp.: 7
Reinsurance Underwriting Services
S.I.C.: 6411
N.A.I.C.S.: 524298
Vincent Dupuis *(Mng Dir)*
Ian Mallery *(COO & Dir-Ops)*

ACOM CO., LTD.

Meiji Yasuda Seimei Building 1-1
Marunouchi 2 Chome Chiyoda Ku
Tokyo, 100-8307, Japan
Tel.: (81) 355330811
Fax: (81) 332153190
E-Mail: ir@acom.co.jp
Web Site: www.acom.co.jp
Year Founded: 1936
8572—(TKS)
Rev.: $2,123,308,000
Assets: $12,821,336,000
Liabilities: $9,667,526,000
Net Worth: $3,153,810,000
Earnings: $229,229,000
Emp.: 5,766
Fiscal Year-end: 03/31/13

Business Description:
Loan & Financial Services
S.I.C.: 6726
N.A.I.C.S.: 525990

Personnel:
Shigeyoshi Kinoshita *(Chm, Pres & CEO)*
Toshiaki Kajiura *(Deputy Chm)*
Michio Atsuda *(Exec Mng Officer-Overseas, Guarantee Bus Dept)*
Makoto Kondo *(Exec Officer-Guarantee Bus Dept)*
Teruyuki Sagehashi *(Exec Mng Officer-HR, Sys Dev & Admin Dept)*
Etsuro Tabuchi *(Exec Mng Officer-Special Mission)*
Kiyoshi Tachiki *(Sr Exec Mng Officer-Plng, Fin, Treasury & Gen Affairs Dept)*

Board of Directors:
Shigeyoshi Kinoshita
Kazuo Fukumoto
Toshiaki Kajiura
Tadachiyo Osada
Kiyoshi Tachiki
Tatsuo Taki
Satoru Tomimatsu

Transfer Agent:
Mitsubishi UFJ Trust & Banking Corporation
4-5 Marunouchi 1-Chome Chiyoda-ku
Tokyo, 100-8212, Japan
Tel.: (81) 3 3212 1211

Subsidiaries:

IR Loan Servicing, Inc. **(1)**
4 Koji-Machi 3-Chome Chiyoda-Ku
Tokyo, 1020083, Japan
Tel.: (81) 87866253
Emp.: 295
Loan Servicing
S.I.C.: 6726
N.A.I.C.S.: 525990

ACORN GLOBAL INVESTMENTS INC.

1267 Cornwall Road Ste 201
Oakville, ON, L6J 7T5, Canada
Tel.: (905) 257-0773
Fax: (888) 582-7863
E-Mail: service@acorn.ca
Web Site: www.acorn.ca
Emp.: 6

Business Description:
Financial Investments
S.I.C.: 6211
N.A.I.C.S.: 523999

Personnel:
Jason Russell *(Pres & Chief Investment Officer)*
Nicholas Markos *(Mng Partner-Res)*
Jean Marchand *(Mng Dir)*
Jeff Crich *(COO)*

Non-U.S. Subsidiary:

Dhir India Investments plc **(1)**
Top Floor 14 Athol Street
Douglas, IM1 1JA, Isle of Man IM
Tel.: (44) 2079203150
E-Mail: contactus@dhirindia.com
Web Site: www.dhirindia.com
Investment Management Services
S.I.C.: 6211
N.A.I.C.S.: 523999
Sarah Marshall *(Sec)*

ACORN INCOME CORP.

Unit 1606 Meredith Road NE
Calgary, AB, T2E 5A8, Canada
Tel.: (403) 265-6540
Fax: (403) 206-7185
Year Founded: 1997
ACI—(CNSX)
Rev.: $66,991
Assets: $642,602
Liabilities: $16,401
Net Worth: $626,201
Earnings: ($263,405)
Fiscal Year-end: 10/31/12

Business Description:
Investment Services
S.I.C.: 6211
N.A.I.C.S.: 523999

Personnel:
Elias A. Foscolos *(Chm, Pres, CEO & CFO)*
Leigh D. Stewart *(Sec)*

Board of Directors:
Elias A. Foscolos
Michael Charlton
Sean McPherson
Leigh D. Stewart

Legal Counsel:
Davis LLP
1000 250 2nd St SW
Calgary, AB, Canada

Transfer Agent:
Olympia Trust Company
2300 125 9 Avenue SW
Calgary, AB, Canada

ACORN INTERNATIONAL, INC.

18/F 20th Building 487 Tianlin Road
Shanghai, 200233, China
Tel.: (86) 21 5151 8888
Fax: (86) 21 64320096
E-Mail: elizadai@chinadrtv.com
Web Site: www.chinadrtv.com
Year Founded: 1998
ATV—(CHI NYSE)
Rev.: $242,573,674
Assets: $207,396,564
Liabilities: $27,595,386
Net Worth: $179,801,178
Earnings: ($17,918,395)
Emp.: 1,781
Fiscal Year-end: 12/31/12

Business Description:
Direct Sales Services
S.I.C.: 5963
N.A.I.C.S.: 454390

Personnel:
Robert W. Roche *(Co-Founder & Chm)*
Don Dongjie Yang *(Co-Founder & CEO)*

Board of Directors:
Robert W. Roche
William Liang
Jing Wang
Mingdong Wu
Ying Wu
Andrew Y. Yan
Don Dongjie Yang
Jun Ye

Legal Counsel:
O'Melveny & Myers LLP
Plaza 66 37th Floor 1266 Nanjing Road West
Shanghai, China
Tel.: (86) 21 2307 7000
Fax: (86) 21 2307 7300

ACOT GROUP OF COMPANIES

17 Jurong Port Road
Singapore, 619092, Singapore
Tel.: (65) 62687740
Fax: (65) 62680559
E-Mail: marketing@acotgroup.com
Web Site: www.acotgroup.com
Emp.: 10,000

Business Description:
Holding Company; Moulded Plastic Products Mfr
S.I.C.: 6719
N.A.I.C.S.: 551112

Personnel:
Graham Wright *(Mng Dir-Europe)*

ACOTEL GROUP S.P.A.

Via della Valle dei Fontanili 29/37
00168 Rome, Italy
Tel.: (39) 0661141000
Fax: (39) 066149936
E-Mail: segreteria@acotel.com
Web Site: www.acotel.com
ACO—(ITA)
Rev.: $136,517,792
Assets: $130,241,948
Liabilities: $48,203,655
Net Worth: $82,038,292
Earnings: ($8,148,367)
Emp.: 481
Fiscal Year-end: 12/31/12

Business Description:
Wireless Applications, Security Equipment & Network Infrastructure Services
S.I.C.: 7373
N.A.I.C.S.: 541512

Personnel:
Claudio Carnevale *(Chm, Pres & CEO)*
Luca De Rita *(CFO)*

Board of Directors:
Claudio Carnevale
Francesco Ago
Margherita Argenziano
Raffaele Cappiello
Cristian Carnevale
Giovanni Galoppi
Giorgio Angelo Girelli
Giuseppe Guizzi
Giovanni La Croce

U.S. Subsidiary:

Flycell, Inc. **(1)**
120 Broadway 15th Fl
New York, NY 10271 (100%)
Tel.: (212) 400-1212
Web Site: www.flycell.com
Sales Range: $25-49.9 Million
Mobile & Online Media & Entertainment Services
S.I.C.: 4812
N.A.I.C.S.: 517210
Cristian Carnevale *(CEO)*

Non-U.S. Subsidiaries:

Emirates for Information Technology Co. **(1)**
Urwa Bin Uthayna Street Tla Al-Ali Area
11194 Amman, Jordan
Tel.: (962) 65531140
Fax: (962) 65531141
Application Service Provider
S.I.C.: 7374
N.A.I.C.S.: 518210

Info2cell.com FZ-LLC **(1)**
Dubai Internet City Concord Tower Office 2301
PO Box 500067
Dubai, United Arab Emirates
Tel.: (971) 43912800
Fax: (971) 4 391 2822
E-Mail: sales@info2cell.com
Web Site: www.info2cell.com
Wireless Mobile Application Service Provider
S.I.C.: 4899
N.A.I.C.S.: 517919
Bashar Dahabra *(Founder & CEO)*

Jinny Software Ltd. **(1)**
29 North Anne Street
Dublin, Ireland
Tel.: (353) 18872626
Fax: (353) 18872692
E-Mail: info@jinnysoftware.com
Web Site: www.jinnysoftware.com
Emp.: 250
Telecommunication Software Development Services
S.I.C.: 7371
N.A.I.C.S.: 541511
Antoine Ghaoui *(Co-Founder & CTO)*
George Yazbek *(Co-Founder & Dir-Strategic Mktg)*
Max Wilkie *(CEO)*
Patrick Dillon *(COO)*
Richard Choi *(Chief Comml Officer)*

Non-U.S. Subsidiary:

Millennium Software SAL **(2)**
1st Floor Antoine Samra Center Main Road
Fanar, Lebanon
Tel.: (961) 1900818
Fax: (961) 1 900819
Business Planning Software Development Services
S.I.C.: 7371
N.A.I.C.S.: 541511

ACOUSTECH BERHAD

No 2 Jalan 1 Bandar Sultan Suleiman
Taiwanese Industrial Park, 42000
Port Klang, Selangor, Malaysia
Tel.: (60) 33176 2700
Fax: (60) 33176 2710
E-Mail: enquiry@fp-group.com
Web Site: www.acoustech.com.my
ACOSTEC—(KLS)
Rev.: $103,897,322
Assets: $70,413,163
Liabilities: $17,848,321
Net Worth: $52,564,842
Earnings: $3,518,695
Fiscal Year-end: 12/31/12

Business Description:
Audio, Chemical & Electrical Equipment Mfr
S.I.C.: 3651
N.A.I.C.S.: 334310

Personnel:
Cheng Tao Su *(Mng Dir)*
Hooi Mooi Lim *(Co-Sec)*
Wai Foong Wong *(Co-Sec)*

Board of Directors:
Song Hai Chang
Po Hsiung Chen
Ngai Seng Leong
Abdul Aziz Mohamed Kamil
Chao Yuan Shih
Kwai Choy Soon
Cheng Tao Su

Subsidiaries:

Formosa Prosonic Chemicals Sdn. Bhd. **(1)**
2 Jalan 1 Bandar Sultan Sulaiman
Taiwanese Industrial Park, 42000 Port Klang, Selangor, Malaysia
Tel.: (60) 331763376
Fax: (60) 331763370
E-Mail: fclim@fp-group.com
Web Site: www.acoustech.com
Emp.: 40
Chemical Paints Mfr
S.I.C.: 2851
N.A.I.C.S.: 325510
Chen Po Hsiung *(Exec Dir)*

Formosa Prosonic Equipment Sdn. Bhd. **(1)**
Lot 11 Jalan Sultan Mohd 5 Bandar Sultan Sulaiman
Taiwanese Industrial Park, 42000 Port Klang, Selangor, Malaysia
Tel.: (60) 331764584
Fax: (60) 331764600
E-Mail: swchan@fp-group.com
Web Site: www.fp-group.com
Emp.: 100
Electrical Equipment Mfr
S.I.C.: 3699
N.A.I.C.S.: 335999
Andrew Lee Szehow *(Mng Dir)*

Formosa Prosonic Technics Sdn. Bhd. (1)
1 Jalan 1 Bandar Sultan Sulaiman
Taiwanese Industrial Park, Port Klang,
Selangor, Malaysia
Tel.: (60) 331762700
Fax: (60) 331762710
Speakers & Mold Plastics Mfr
S.I.C.: 3651
N.A.I.C.S.: 334310
James Chao Yuan Shih *(Mng Dir)*

ACP MARKETING, INC.
8375 Bougainville Ste 100
Montreal, QC, H4P 2G5, Canada
Tel.: (514) 733-5247
Fax: (514) 733-5541
E-Mail: info@acpmarketing.net
Web Site: www.acpmarketing.net
Year Founded: 1994
Emp.: 35
Business Description:
Rail Ticket & Rail Pass Marketer, Retailer & Distr
S.I.C.: 4789
N.A.I.C.S.: 488999
Personnel:
Alex Popescu *(Founder & Pres)*

U.S. Subsidiary:

ACP Marketing US Inc. (1)
2 Hudson Pl Ste 100
Hoboken, NJ 07030
Tel.: (201) 798-4553
Fax: (201) 798-4605
E-Mail: info@britrail.net
Web Site: www.britrail.com
Emp.: 15
Rail Ticket & Rail Pass Marketer, Retailer & Distr
S.I.C.: 4729
N.A.I.C.S.: 561599

Non-U.S. Subsidiary:

ACP Marketing UK Ltd. (1)
Sutton House
158 Victoria St 2nd Fl, London, SW1E 5LB, United Kingdom
Tel.: (44) 2078344712
Fax: (44) 2078216667
Web Site: www.acp.com
Emp.: 7
Rail Ticket & Rail Pass Marketer, Retailer & Distr
S.I.C.: 4789
N.A.I.C.S.: 488999
Anthony Gay *(VP)*

ACQUISIO INC.
6300 Auteuil ste 300
Brossard, QC, J4Z 3P2, Canada
Tel.: (450) 465-2631
Fax: (450) 465-2841
Toll Free: (866) 493-9070
E-Mail: sales@acquisio.com
Web Site: www.acquisio.com
Year Founded: 2003
Sales Range: $1-9.9 Million
Emp.: 120
Business Description:
Search Engine Marketing Software
S.I.C.: 7372
N.A.I.C.S.: 511210
Personnel:
Marc Poirier *(Co-Founder & Exec VP-Bus Dev)*
Richard Couture *(Co-Founder & VP-Product Mgmt)*
Martin LeSauteur *(Pres & CEO)*
Martin Mailloux *(CFO & VP-Tech)*
Tracy Smith *(CMO)*
Board of Directors:
Andre Gauthier
Luc Filiatreault
Jean-Philippe Gauthier
Martin LeSauteur
Marc Poirier

ACQUITY GROUP LTD.
(Acquired by Accenture plc)

ACREX VENTURES LTD.
Suite 2300-1066 West Hastings Street
Vancouver, BC, V6E 3X2, Canada
Tel.: (604) 618-1758
Fax: (604) 277-0815
E-Mail: info@acrexventures.com
Web Site: www.acrexventures.com
Year Founded: 1969
AKV—(TSXV)
Int. Income: $5,566
Assets: $1,481,691
Liabilities: $50,506
Net Worth: $1,431,185
Earnings: ($525,278)
Fiscal Year-end: 12/31/12
Business Description:
Mineral Exploration Services
S.I.C.: 1081
N.A.I.C.S.: 213114
Personnel:
T. J. Malcolm Powell *(Pres & CEO)*
Carl Roland Jonsson *(CFO & Sec)*
Board of Directors:
Carl Roland Jonsson
Robin Merrifield
Jason Powell
T. J. Malcolm Powell
Arthur G. Troup
Legal Counsel:
Tupper Jonsson & Yeadon
17th Floor 1177 West Hastings Street
Vancouver, BC, Canada
Transfer Agent:
Computershare Trust Company
510 Burrard Street 3rd Floor
Vancouver, BC, Canada

ACRO INC.
1 Ben Gurion Street
Bnei Brak, Israel 5120149
Tel.: (972) 4 636 0297
Web Site: www.acrosec.com
ACRI—(OTC)
Assets: $4,890
Liabilities: $169,609
Net Worth: ($164,719)
Earnings: ($137,036)
Fiscal Year-end: 12/31/12
Business Description:
Military & Commercial Explosives Detection Products Mfr
S.I.C.: 3812
N.A.I.C.S.: 334511
Personnel:
Asaf Porat *(Chm, Pres, CEO & CFO)*
Board of Directors:
Asaf Porat
Baruch Mitzengendler

ACRODEA, INC.
5F Yanase Shibuya Bldg 2-16-10 Higashi
Shibuya-ku, Tokyo, 150-0011, Japan
Tel.: (81) 357784600
Fax: (81) 357784602
E-Mail: info@acrodea.co.jp
Web Site: www.acrodea.co.jp
3823—(TKS)
Sls.: $42,085,120
Assets: $16,250,400
Liabilities: $12,356,160
Net Worth: $3,894,240
Earnings: ($810,080)
Emp.: 137
Fiscal Year-end: 08/31/13
Business Description:
Consultation Services for Software Planning & Design
S.I.C.: 7373
N.A.I.C.S.: 541512
Personnel:
Junya Tsutsumi *(Pres)*
Yoshio Kuniyoshi *(Exec VP)*
Board of Directors:
Takehiko Hatta
Tatsuya Kato
Joon Hyung Kim
Tsuguhiro Kimura
Yoshio Kuniyoshi
Takashi Kuwahara
Junya Tsutsumi

Subsidiary:

AMS, Inc. (1)
4F Yanase Shibuya Building 2-16-10 Higashi
Shibuya-ku, Tokyo, 150-0011, Japan
Tel.: (81) 3 6427 2507
Fax: (81) 3 6427 2405
E-Mail: products@amsinc.co.jp
Emp.: 50
Mobile Product Development Services
S.I.C.: 8742
N.A.I.C.S.: 541613
Shinichi Murai *(Pres)*

U.S. Subsidiary:

Acrodea America Inc. (1)
3020 Old Ranch Pkwy Ste 300
Seal Beach, CA 90740
Tel.: (562) 799-5576
Fax: (562) 799-5501
Web Site: www.acrodea.com
Mobile Communication Services
S.I.C.: 3669
N.A.I.C.S.: 334290

Non-U.S. Subsidiary:

Acrodea Korea, Inc. (1)
18F Korea Sanhak Foundation Building 1337-31
Seocho-dong Seocho-gu, Seoul, Korea (South)
Tel.: (82) 56176016
Fax: (82) 25534979
E-Mail: joohopark@acrodea.co.kr
Web Site: www.acrodea.co.kr
Mobile Communication Services
S.I.C.: 4899
N.A.I.C.S.: 517919

ACRODEX INC.
11420 170 Street
Edmonton, AB, T5S 1L7, Canada
Tel.: (780) 426-4444
Fax: (780) 426-2233
Toll Free: (800) 456-2667
Web Site: www.acrodex.com
Year Founded: 1984
Rev.: $80,685,040
Emp.: 410
Business Description:
IT Services
S.I.C.: 7376
N.A.I.C.S.: 541513
Personnel:
Yasmin Jivraj *(Pres)*
Karim Amarshi *(CEO)*
Jaferali Surmawala *(CFO)*
Salma Rajwani *(CIO)*

ACRON GROUP
World Trade Centre 12
Krasnopresnenskaya Naberezhnaya
Moscow, 123610, Russia
Tel.: (7) 4954115594
Fax: (7) 4992462359
E-Mail: info@acron.ru
Web Site: www.acron.ru
AKRN—(LSE)
Rev.: $2,351,673,840
Assets: $5,179,390,330
Liabilities: $2,562,891,930
Net Worth: $2,616,498,400
Earnings: $491,453,270
Emp.: 15,644
Fiscal Year-end: 12/31/12
Business Description:
Mineral Fertilizer Mfr
S.I.C.: 1479
N.A.I.C.S.: 212393
Personnel:
Vladimir Gavrikov *(Chm)*
Vladimir Kunitsky *(Chm-Mgmt Bd & CEO)*
Alexander Popov *(Deputy Chm, Deputy Chm-Mgmt Bd & Sr VP)*
Oscar Valters *(Deputy Chm-Mgmt Bd & Sr VP)*
Ivan Antonov *(Member-Mgmt Bd & VP-Production & Dev)*
Alexei Milenkov *(Member-Mgmt Bd & Dir-Fin)*
Board of Directors:
Vladimir Gavrikov
Igor Belikov
Alexander Dynkin
Egor Gissin
Viktor Kochubey
Alexander Popov
Valery Shvalyuk

Baker Tilly Russaudit Ltd
Zubarev pereulok 15-1
Moscow, Russia

ACROPETAL TECHNOLOGIES LTD.
#74/75 3rd Cross 1st Main
NS Palya Bannerghatta Road,
Bengaluru, 560 076, India
Tel.: (91) 80 4908 4000
Fax: (91) 80 4908 4100
E-Mail: corp@acropetal.com
Web Site: www.acropetal.com
Year Founded: 2001
ACROPETAL—(BOM NSE)
Sales Range: $50-74.9 Million
Emp.: 321
Business Description:
Information Technology Services
S.I.C.: 7373
N.A.I.C.S.: 541512
Personnel:
D. Ravi Kumar *(Chm & Mng Dir)*
R. Vijayendra *(Sec)*
Board of Directors:
D. Ravi Kumar
Ramdas Janardhana Kamath
Mathew J. Manimala
Mohan Hosahally Ramakrishna
M. Madhu Sudhana Reddy
D. K. Subramanyam

U.S. Subsidiaries:

Acropetal, Inc. (1)
2 Embarcadero Ctr Ste 460
San Francisco, CA 94111 CA
Tel.: (415) 291-8818
Fax: (415) 291-8815
Web Site: www.acropetal.com
Emp.: 20
IT Services
S.I.C.: 7373
N.A.I.C.S.: 541512
Joel Vasa *(Mgr-Bus Dev)*

Optech Consulting, Inc. (1)
5005 LBJ Freeway
Dallas, TX 75244 TX
Tel.: (215) 272-2240 (100%)
Emp.: 42
IT Services
S.I.C.: 7373
N.A.I.C.S.: 541512
Krishna Reddy *(Pres)*

ACROPOLIS TELECOM S.A.
163 avenue Gallienili Porte de Bagnolet
93170 Paris, France
Tel.: (33) 170725000
Fax: (33) 143620918
E-Mail: contact-invest@acropolistelecom.net

Acropolis Telecom S.A.—(Continued)

Web Site: www.acropolistelecom.net
MLACR—(EUR)
Sales Range: $1-9.9 Million
Emp.: 30
Business Description:
IP, VoIP Telephony, Voice, Video & Data Convergence Services
S.I.C.: 3661
N.A.I.C.S.: 334210
Personnel:
Samir Kolietat *(Chm)*

ACROW INDIA LTD.

Plot No 2 & 3
PO Ravalgaon
Taluka Malegaon, Nasik, Maharashtra, 423108, India
Tel.: (91) 2554645913
Fax: (91) 2554270386
Web Site: www.acrowindia.com
513149—(BOM)
Rev.: $380,478
Assets: $2,335,187
Liabilities: $637,739
Net Worth: $1,697,448
Earnings: $7,750
Fiscal Year-end: 03/31/13
Business Description:
Sugar Elevator Mfr & Distr
S.I.C.: 3534
N.A.I.C.S.: 333921
Personnel:
Harshavardhan B. Doshi *(Chm)*
Snehal J. Shah *(CFO)*
Board of Directors:
Harshavardhan B. Doshi
Ashok S. Ashtekar
Vikram Bhat
Nihal H. Doshi
Narayan K. Varma
Transfer Agent:
Freedom Registry Ltd
Plot No. 101/102 19th Street MIDC Industrial Area Satpur
Nasik, India

ACRUX LIMITED

103-113 Stanley Street
Melbourne, VIC, 3003, Australia
Tel.: (61) 383790100
Fax: (61) 383790101
Web Site: www.acrux.com.au
ACR—(ASX)
Rev.: $17,361,386
Assets: $55,121,880
Liabilities: $6,400,578
Net Worth: $48,721,301
Earnings: $7,217,585
Emp.: 18
Fiscal Year-end: 06/30/13
Business Description:
Health Care Products Development
S.I.C.: 8082
N.A.I.C.S.: 621610
Personnel:
Ross Dobinson *(Chm)*
Tony Di Pietro *(CFO & Sec)*
Clive Blower *(COO)*
Board of Directors:
Ross Dobinson
Ross Barrow
Tim Oldham
Bruce Parncutt

Subsidiaries:

Acrux DDS Pty Ltd **(1)**
103 113 Stanley St
Melbourne, VIC, 3003, Australia
Tel.: (61) 393268300
Fax: (61) 383790101
Web Site: www.acrux.com.au
Medicine Mfr
S.I.C.: 2834
N.A.I.C.S.: 325412

Acrux Pharma Pty Ltd **(1)**
103 113 Stanley St
Melbourne, VIC, 3003, Australia
Tel.: (61) 383790100
E-Mail: info@acrux.com.au
Web Site: www.acrux.com.au
Pharmaceutical Products Mfr
S.I.C.: 2834
N.A.I.C.S.: 325412

Fempharm Pty Ltd **(1)**
103 113 Stanley St
Melbourne, VIC, 3003, Australia
Tel.: (61) 383790100
Fax: (61) 383790101
Web Site: www.acrux.com.au
Pharmaceutical Products Mfr
S.I.C.: 2834
N.A.I.C.S.: 325412

ACRYLON PLASTICS INC.

122 Paquin Road
Winnipeg, MB, R2J 3V4, Canada
Tel.: (204) 669-2224
Toll Free: (866) 418-2345
E-Mail: info@acrylon.com
Web Site: www.acrylon.com
Year Founded: 1978
Rev.: $13,654,933
Emp.: 100
Business Description:
Plastic Products Mfr
S.I.C.: 3089
N.A.I.C.S.: 326199
Personnel:
Craig McIntosh *(Pres & CEO)*

ACRYSIL LTD.

704 Centre Point J B Nagar Andheri-Kurla Road
Andheri East, Mumbai, 400 059, India
Tel.: (91) 2266711101
Fax: (91) 2266711109
E-Mail: info@carysil.com
Web Site: www.acrysil.com
524091—(BOM)
Rev.: $14,856,679
Assets: $14,561,191
Liabilities: $9,354,010
Net Worth: $5,207,181
Earnings: $879,389
Emp.: 186
Fiscal Year-end: 03/31/13
Business Description:
Kitchen Accessories Mfr & Distr
S.I.C.: 3999
N.A.I.C.S.: 332215
Personnel:
Ashwin Mohanlal Parekh *(Chm)*
Chirag A. Parekh *(Vice Chm & Mng Dir)*
Damodar Sejpal *(Compliance Officer & Sec)*
Board of Directors:
Ashwin Mohanlal Parekh
Minoo D. Daver
Pradeep H. Gohil
Shyam Mariwala
Rustam Mulla
Jagdish R. Naik
Chirag A. Parekh
M. Nageswara Rao
Ajit R. Sanghvi
Transfer Agent:
Bigshare Services Pvt. Ltd.
E-2/3 Ansa Industrial Estate Sakivihar Road
Saki Naka Andheri E
Mumbai, India

ACS, ACTIVIDADES DE CONSTRUCCION Y SERVICIOS, S.A.

(d/b/a Grupo ACS / ACS Group)
Avda Pio XII 102
28036 Madrid, Spain
Tel.: (34) 913439200
Fax: (34) 91 343 94 56
E-Mail: rsc@grupoacs.com
Web Site: www.grupoacs.com
ACS—(MAD)
Rev.: $51,687,782,938
Assets: $55,951,369,870
Liabilities: $48,262,709,146
Net Worth: $7,688,660,724
Earnings: ($1,891,032,308)
Emp.: 162,471
Fiscal Year-end: 12/31/12
Business Description:
Construction & Engineering Services
S.I.C.: 1629
N.A.I.C.S.: 237990
Personnel:
Florentino Perez Rodriguez *(Chm & CEO)*
Antonio Garcia Ferrer *(Vice Chm)*
Pablo Vallbona Vadell *(Vice Chm)*
Board of Directors:
Florentino Perez Rodriguez
Agustin Batuecas Torrego
Alvaro Cuervo Garcia
Juan March de la Lastra
Manuel Delgado Solis
Sabina Fluxa Thienemann
Antonio Garcia Ferrer
Joan-David Grima i Terre
Santos Martinez-Conde Gutierrez-Barquin
Pedro Lopez Jimenez
Javier Echenique Landiribar
Jose Maria Loizaga Viguri
Javier Monzon de Caceres
Miquel Roca i Junyent
Julio Sacristan Fidalgo
Pablo Vallbona Vadell

Subsidiaries:

ACS Servicios Comunicaciones y Energia, S.L. **(1)**
Cardenal Marcelo Spinola 10
Madrid, 28016, Spain
Tel.: (34) 91 456 95 00
Fax: (34) 91 456 94 50
Industrial Cleaning Services
S.I.C.: 4959
N.A.I.C.S.: 562998

ACS Servicios y Concesiones, S.L. **(1)**
Avenida Camino De Santiago 50-Edif 1 Planta 4a
Madrid, 28050, Spain
Tel.: (34) 917036000
Fax: (34) 917016013
Emp.: 2
Environment Consulting Services
S.I.C.: 8999
N.A.I.C.S.: 541620
Reinoso Torres Francisco *(Gen Mgr)*

ACS Telefonia Movil, S.L. **(1)**
Avda Pio XII 102
28036 Madrid, Spain
Tel.: (34) 91 343 92 00
Web Site: www.grupoacs.com
Telecommunication Services
S.I.C.: 4899
N.A.I.C.S.: 517919

Albatros Logistic, S.A. **(1)**
C/ Franklin 16 a 22
28096 Getafe, Madrid, Spain
Tel.: (34) 91 665 46 40
Fax: (34) 91 683 00 82
E-Mail: clientes@albatroslogistic.es
Web Site: www.albatroslogistic.es
Logistic Consulting Services
S.I.C.: 4731
N.A.I.C.S.: 541614

Antennea Technologies, S.L. **(1)**
Calle De Sepulveda p I Alcobendas 6
Alcobendas, 28108, Spain
Tel.: (34) 916232200
Civil Engineering Construction Services
S.I.C.: 1629
N.A.I.C.S.: 237990

API Fabricacion, S.A. **(1)**
Calle Del Raso De La Estrella S/N
Aranjuez, Madrid, 28300, Spain
Tel.: (34) 918090990
Fax: (34) 918090993
Emp.: 80
Industrial Machinery Mfr
S.I.C.: 3559
N.A.I.C.S.: 333249
Juan Cruz Martinez Madrid *(Gen Mgr)*

API Movilidad, S.A. **(1)**
Avenida Manoteras 26
Madrid, 28050, Spain
Tel.: (34) 917443900
Fax: (34) 917443901
Highway Construction Services
S.I.C.: 1611
N.A.I.C.S.: 237310

Asistencia Offshore, S.A. **(1)**
Benitez Perez Galdos
Cadiz, 11003, Spain
Tel.: (34) 956290940
Fax: (34) 956210393
Emp.: 3
Oil & Gas Offshore Engineering Services
S.I.C.: 8711
N.A.I.C.S.: 541330
Juan Carlos Vichera *(Gen Mgr)*

Atil-Cobra, S.A. **(1)**
Calle Orense 4
Madrid, 28020, Spain
Tel.: (34) 915551315
Fax: (34) 915556936
Construction Engineering Services
S.I.C.: 8711
N.A.I.C.S.: 541330
Felix Pereira Lopez *(Gen Mgr)*

Audeli, S.A. **(1)**
Calle De Ana Isabel Segura 11 A Second Floor C
Alcobendas, Madrid, 28108, Spain
Tel.: (34) 916259900
Fax: (34) 913123000
Logistics Consulting Services
S.I.C.: 4731
N.A.I.C.S.: 541614

Autovia de La Mancha, S.A **(1)**
21 500 de la CM-42 en el
54430 Mascaraque, Toledo, Spain
Tel.: (34) 925 30 15 40
Fax: (34) 925 30 14 56
Web Site: www.aumancha.com
Highway Construction Services
S.I.C.: 1622
N.A.I.C.S.: 237310

Autovia del Camp del Turia, S.A. **(1)**
Calle Alvaro De Bazan 10-Ent
Valencia, 46010, Spain
Tel.: (34) 960454500
Fax: (34) 960454501
Emp.: 7
Highways Construction Services
S.I.C.: 1611
N.A.I.C.S.: 237310
Miguel Escriva *(Gen Mgr)*

Autovia del Pirineo, S.A. **(1)**
Calle Emilio Arrieta 8-Plt 6
Pamplona, Navarra, 31002, Spain
Tel.: (34) 948223754
Fax: (34) 948225194
Highways Construction Services
S.I.C.: 1622
N.A.I.C.S.: 237310

Autovia Medinaceli-Calatayud Soc.Conces.Estado, S.A. **(1)**
Avenida Camino De Santiago 50
Madrid, 28050, Spain
Tel.: (34) 976897000
Business Support Services
S.I.C.: 7389
N.A.I.C.S.: 561499

Can Brians 2, S.A. **(1)**
Avenida Josep Tarradellas 34-36 9 E D
Barcelona, 8029, Spain
Tel.: (34) 934443236
Fax: (34) 934191770
Real Estate Agency Services
S.I.C.: 6531
N.A.I.C.S.: 531210

Cariatide, S.A. **(1)**
Avenida Pio XII 102
Madrid, Spain
Tel.: (34) 913439337

Construction Engineering Services
S.I.C.: 8711
N.A.I.C.S.: 541330

CAT Desenvolupament de Concessions Catalanes, S.L (1)
Avenida Josep Tarradellas 8-10 Second Floor
Barcelona, 08029, Spain
Tel.: (34) 934443236
Fax: (34) 934191770
Web Site: www.acs.com
Investment Management Services
S.I.C.: 6211
N.A.I.C.S.: 523999

Catalana de Treballs Publics, S.A. (1)
Carretera Mig 37
Cornella de Llobregat, Barcelona, 08940, Spain
Tel.: (34) 938499736
Fax: (34) 938459762
Civil Construction Engineering Services
S.I.C.: 1629
N.A.I.C.S.: 237990

Centro de Transferencias, S.A (1)
Poligono Los Barriales S/N
Santovenia de Pisuerga, Valladolid, 47155, Spain
Tel.: (34) 983310520
Fax: (34) 983259493
Industrial Waste Treatment & Disposal Services
S.I.C.: 4953
N.A.I.C.S.: 562219

Cesionaria Valles Occidental, S.A. (1)
Avenida Josep Tarradellas 34-36 Plt Novena D
Barcelona, 08029, Spain
Tel.: (34) 934443236
Fax: (34) 934443236
Construction Engineering Services
S.I.C.: 1629
N.A.I.C.S.: 237990

Claerh, S.A. (1)
Poligono Industrial Oeste Avda Del Descubrimiento Parc 5 5
Alcantarilla, Murcia, 30820, Spain
Tel.: (34) 968897005
Fax: (34) 968897133
Sanitary Waste Collection & Treatment Services
S.I.C.: 4953
N.A.I.C.S.: 562219

Clece, S.A. (1)
Avda Tenerife 4 y 6
28700 San Sebastian de los Reyes, Madrid, Spain (76.5%)
Tel.: (34) 91 745 91 00
Fax: (34) 91 745 91 30
Web Site: www.clece.es
Emp.: 50,000
Public Organizations Cleaning Services
S.I.C.: 7349
N.A.I.C.S.: 561720

Cobra Concesiones Brasil, S.L. (1)
Calle Cardenal Marcelo Spinola 10
Madrid, 28016, Spain
Tel.: (04) 014560500
Financial Management Services
S.I.C.: 6211
N.A.I.C.S.: 523999

Cobra Concesiones, S.L. (1)
Calle Cardenal Marcelo Spinola 10
Madrid, 28016, Spain
Tel.: (34) 914569500
Fax: (34) 914569455
Civil Engineering Construction Services
S.I.C.: 1629
N.A.I.C.S.: 237990

Cobra Gestion de Infraestructuras, S.L.U (1)
Calle Cardenal Marcelo Spinola 10
Madrid, 28016, Spain
Tel.: (34) 914569500
Fax: (34) 914569450
Civil Engineering Construction Services
S.I.C.: 1629
N.A.I.C.S.: 237990

Cobra Infraestructuras Hidraulicas, S.A. (1)
Calle Cardenal Marcelo Spinola 10
Madrid, 28016, Spain
Tel.: (34) 914569500
Fax: (34) 914569477
Construction Engineering Services
S.I.C.: 1629
N.A.I.C.S.: 237990
Eugenio Llorente Gomez *(Gen Mgr)*

Cobra Instalaciones y Servicios Internacional, S.L. (1)
Calle Cardenal Marcelo Spinola 10
Madrid, 28016, Spain
Tel.: (34) 914569500
Fax: (34) 913801847
Water Treatment Plant Construction Services
S.I.C.: 1623
N.A.I.C.S.: 237110

Cobra Servicios Auxiliares, S.A. (1)
Calle Cardenal Marcelo Spinola 10
Madrid, 28016, Spain
Tel.: (34) 914569500
Fax: (34) 914569451
Electrical Installation Services
S.I.C.: 1731
N.A.I.C.S.: 238210

Cobra Sistemas de Seguridad, S.A. (1)
Calle Cardenal Marcelo Spinola 10
Madrid, 28016, Spain
Tel.: (34) 914569500
Fax: (34) 914569462
E-Mail: central@grupocobra.com
Web Site: www.groupocobra.com
Emp.: 20,000
Security System Installation Services
S.I.C.: 1731
N.A.I.C.S.: 238210

Cobra Sistemas y Redes, S.A. (1)
Calle Cardenal Marcelo Spinola 10
Madrid, 28016, Spain
Tel.: (34) 914569500
Fax: (34) 914568902
Emp.: 200
Electrical Contracting Services
S.I.C.: 1731
N.A.I.C.S.: 238210
Antonio Gomez Zamora *(Gen Mgr)*

Cobra Termosolar USA, S.L. (1)
Calle Cardenal Marcelo Spinola 10
Madrid, 28016, Spain
Tel.: (34) 914569500
Fax: (34) 914569470
Web Site: www.grupocobra.com
Electric Power Generation Services
S.I.C.: 4911
N.A.I.C.S.: 221118

Cobra-Udisport Conde de Guadalhorce, S.L (1)
Paseo Cerrado De Calderon 18-Ed Mercurio
Malaga, 29018, Spain
Tel.: (34) 952041098
Sports Facilities Operation & Maintenance Services
S.I.C.: 7991
N.A.I.C.S.: 713940

Concesionaria San Rafael, S.A. (1)
Calle Del Diputat Josep Ribas S/N
San Antonio Abad, Baleares, 07820, Spain
Tel.: (34) 915969715
Fax: (34) 971198613
Web Site: www.concesionariasanrafael.com
Highway Construction Services
S.I.C.: 1622
N.A.I.C.S.: 237310

Concesionaria Santiago Brion, S.A. (1)
Lugar Costoia Ctro Control Autovia Ag 5 S/N
Ames, La Coruna, 15864, Spain
Tel.: (34) 981884933
Fax: (34) 981891578
E-Mail: sanbrion@sanbrion.com
Web Site: www.sanbrion.com
Highway Construction Services
S.I.C.: 1611
N.A.I.C.S.: 237310

Consenur, S.A. (1)
C/Rio Ebro s/n Poligono Industrial Finanzauto
Arganda del Rey, 28500, Spain
Tel.: (34) 918 76 06 70
Fax: (34) 918 76 06 71
Web Site: www.consenur.es
Clinical Waste Management Services
S.I.C.: 4959
N.A.I.C.S.: 562998

Construrail, S.A. (1)
Orense 11-2
28020 Madrid, Spain
Tel.: (34) 915 980 770
Fax: (34) 915 980 774
E-Mail: constru-rail@constru-rail.es
Web Site: www.constru-rail.es
Rail Cargo Operating Services & Coal Distr
S.I.C.: 4789
N.A.I.C.S.: 488210
Francisco Bonache Cordoba *(Pres)*

Continental Rail, S.A. (1)
Orense 11-2
28020 Madrid, Spain
Tel.: (34) 915 980 773
Fax: (34) 915 980 774
E-Mail: continentalrail@continentalrail.es
Web Site: www.continentalrail.es
Rail Freight Transportation Services
S.I.C.: 4731
N.A.I.C.S.: 488510

Control y Montajes Industriales CYMI, S.A. (1)
Calle Teide n 4-Edif F7
28703 San Sebastian de los Reyes, Madrid, Spain
Tel.: (34) 91 659 33 60
Fax: (34) 91 659 33 80
E-Mail: cymimasa@cymimasa.com
Web Site: www.cymi.es
Electrical Installation & Assembly Services
S.I.C.: 1731
N.A.I.C.S.: 238210

U.S. Subsidiaries:

ACT Industrial Process Services LLC (2)
5315 Greenwood Rd
Shreveport, LA 71109
Tel.: (318) 675-1772
Fax: (318) 675-1776
Web Site: www.appcontech.com
Electrical Engineering Services
S.I.C.: 8711
N.A.I.C.S.: 541330
Ritchie Thompson *(Pres)*

Applied Control Technology, LLC. (2)
5005 Stateline Ave
Texarkana, TX 75503
Tel.: (903) 791-3000
Fax: (903) 791-3001
E-Mail: info@appcontech.com
Web Site: www.appcontech.com
Electrical Engineering Services
S.I.C.: 8711
N.A.I.C.S.: 541330
Jason Leeper *(Pres)*
Chris Lewis *(Partner)*

COSERSA CONTRATAS Y SERVICIOS, S.A. (1)
C/ Bronce 23
28500 Arganda del Rey, Madrid, Spain
Tel.: (34) 902 877 744
Fax: (34) 91 872 90 86
E-Mail: contratasyservicios@coser-sa.com
Web Site: www.cosersa.com.es
Industrial Cleaning Services
S.I.C.: 4959
N.A.I.C.S.: 562998

Cymi Seguridad, S.A. (1)
Calle Teide 5
San Sebastian de los Reyes, Madrid, 28703, Spain
Tel.: (34) 916593360
Civil Engineering Construction Services
S.I.C.: 1629
N.A.I.C.S.: 237990

Desarrollo de Concesionarias Viarias Dos, S.L. (1)
Avenida Camino De Santiago 50
Madrid, 28050, Spain
Tel.: (34) 917038482
Fax: (34) 917038489
Construction Engineering Services
S.I.C.: 8711
N.A.I.C.S.: 541330
David Cid *(Dir-Admin)*

Desarrollo de Concesionarias Viarias Uno, S.L. (1)
Avenida De Tenerife 4
San Sebastian de los Reyes, Madrid, 28700, Spain
Tel.: (34) 917038482
Civil Engineering Construction Services
S.I.C.: 1629
N.A.I.C.S.: 237990

Desarrollo de Concesiones Ferroviarias, S.L. (1)
Avenida Camino De Santiago 50
Madrid, 28050, Spain
Tel.: (34) 917038708
Fax: (34) 917038726
Railway Construction Services
S.I.C.: 1629
N.A.I.C.S.: 237990

Desarrollo Informatico, S.A. (1)
C/ Pradillo 46
28002 Madrid, Spain
Tel.: (34) 918066300
Fax: (34) 918036868
Web Site: www.dinsa.es
Emp.: 25
Information Technology Consulting Services
S.I.C.: 7373
N.A.I.C.S.: 541512
Pedro Gonzalez *(Mgr)*

Drace Medio Ambiente, S.A. (1)
Avenida Camino de Santiago 50 Edif 4
28050 Madrid, Spain
Tel.: (34) 91 703 56 00
Fax: (34) 91 703 56 40
E-Mail: info@dracemedioambiente.com
Web Site: www.dracemedioambiente.com
Environmental Consulting Services
S.I.C.: 8999
N.A.I.C.S.: 541620

Dragados Inversiones USA, S.L. (1)
Avenida Camino De Santiago 50 Edif 3 Pl 6
Madrid, 28050, Spain
Tel.: (34) 913439300
Fax: (34) 917038302
Construction Engineering Services
S.I.C.: 1629
N.A.I.C.S.: 237990

Dragados Offshore, S.A. (1)
Bajo de la Cabezuela s/n
11510 Puerto Real, Cadiz, Spain
Tel.: (34) 956 47 07 00
Fax: (34) 956 47 07 29
E-Mail: info-dossa@dragadosoffshore.es
Web Site: www.dragadosoffshore.com
Emp.: 5,000
Oil & Gas Offshore Services
S.I.C.: 1389
N.A.I.C.S.: 213112
Pedro Ascorbe *(Chm & CEO)*
Ricardo Rodriguez *(VP & CFO)*

Dragados S.A. (1)
Avda Camino de Santiago 50
28050 Madrid, Spain
Tel.: (34) 913439300
Fax: (34) 913439400
Emp.: 17,533
Building Construction, Maintenance, Civil Works & Infrastructure Maintenance Services
S.I.C.: 1541
N.A.I.C.S.: 236210
Pedro Lopez Jimenez *(Vice Chm)*

Non-U.S. Subsidiary:

Przedsiebiorstwo Robot Inzynieryjnych POL-AQUA S.A. (2)
ul Dworska 1
05-500 Warsaw, Poland (66%)
Tel.: (48) 222017300
Fax: (48) 222017310
E-Mail: recepcja@pol-aqua.com.pl
Web Site: www.pol-aqua.com.pl
PQA—(WAR)
Rev.: $262,855,738
Assets: $252,554,721
Liabilities: $223,199,900
Net Worth: $29,354,821
Earnings: ($55,568,153)
Fiscal Year-end: 12/31/12
Engineering & Construction Services

ACS, Actividades de Construccion y Servicios, S.A.—(Continued)

S.I.C.: 8711
N.A.I.C.S.: 541330
Gustavo Tunell Ayuso *(Chm-Supervisory Bd)*
Servando Sierra Marti *(Chm-Mgmt Bd)*
Eduardo Martinez Martinez *(Vice Chm-Supervisory Bd)*
Marek Sobiecki *(Vice Chm-Mgmt Bd & CFO)*
Mario Serrano Villate *(Member-Mgmt Bd & Dir-Production)*

Subsidiaries:

Dragados USA Inc. (2)
500 5th Ave Fl 38
New York, NY 10110
Tel.: (212) 779-0900
Fax: (212) 764-6020
Emp.: 30
Construction Services
S.I.C.: 1629
N.A.I.C.S.: 237990
Ricardo Franco *(Pres-North America)*
Antonio Nievas *(Exec VP)*

Subsidiaries:

John P. Picone Inc. (3)
31 Garden Ln
Lawrence, NY 11559 NY
Tel.: (516) 239-1600
Fax: (516) 239-1757
E-Mail: info@johnpicone.com
Web Site: www.johnpicone.com
Sales Range: $50-74.9 Million
Emp.: 60
Sewer Line Construction Services
S.I.C.: 1623
N.A.I.C.S.: 237110
John P. Picone, Jr. *(Chm)*
John Taikina *(Pres)*
Gerald E. Rossettie *(CEO)*

Schiavone Construction Co. (3)
150 Meadowlands Pkwy Fl 3
Secaucus, NJ 07094-2304 NJ
Tel.: (201) 867-5070
Fax: (201) 867-0911
E-Mail: info@schiavoneconstruction.com
Web Site: www.schiavoneconstruction.com
Emp.: 250
Provider of Heavy Construction Services
S.I.C.: 1629
N.A.I.C.S.: 236210
Carlos Santiago *(Office Mgr)*

Flota Proyectos Singulares, S.A (2)
Avenida del Camino de Santiago no 50
28050 Madrid, Spain
Tel.: (34) 91 545 4777
Fax: (34) 91 427 6921
E-Mail: info@flotaps.com
Web Site: www.flotaps.com
Emp.: 7
Construction Engineering Services
S.I.C.: 8711
N.A.I.C.S.: 541330
Juan Mata *(Gen Mgr)*

DRAMAR ANDALUCIA TRATAMIENTO DE MARPOLES, S.L.U. (1)
Muelle Isla Verde s/n
11207 Algeciras, Cadiz, Spain
Tel.: (34) 956 57 37 33
Fax: (34) 956 60 09 34
E-Mail: marpoldramar@urbaser.com
Web Site: www.dramarmarpol.com
Emp.: 40
Waste Treatment Services
S.I.C.: 4953
N.A.I.C.S.: 562211
Pablo Horcajada *(Mgr-Svc)*

Ecocivil Electromur G.E., S.L. (1)
Poligono Industrial Oeste Pg Industrial Oeste 13-3
Murcia, 30169, Spain
Tel.: (34) 968826153
Fax: (34) 968826140
Civil Engineering Construction Services
S.I.C.: 1629
N.A.I.C.S.: 237990

Ecologia y Tecnicas Sanitarias, S.L. (1)
Calle Josefina Mayor Ur Ind El Goro 9-Nv 3
Telde, Palmas Las, 35219, Spain
Tel.: (34) 928700980
Fax: (34) 928700751
Sanitary Waste Collection Services
S.I.C.: 4212
N.A.I.C.S.: 562119

Ecoparc de Barcelona S.A. (1)
Calle Lletra A De La Zona Franca 26
Barcelona, 8040, Spain
Tel.: (34) 932623010
Fax: (34) 932623065
Waste Treatment Services
S.I.C.: 4953
N.A.I.C.S.: 562211

Edafologia y Restauracion del Entorno Gallego, S.L. (1)
Rua Enrique Marinas 36-4
15009 La Coruna, Spain
Tel.: (34) 981175100
Fax: (34) 981160145
Waste Treatment Services
S.I.C.: 4953
N.A.I.C.S.: 562211
Fernando Rodriguez *(Gen Mgr)*

Eix Diagonal Concessionaria de la Generalitat de Catalunya, S.A. (1)
Avenida Josep Tarradellas 34-Piso 9 Dr
Barcelona, 08029, Spain
Tel.: (34) 938992079
Road Construction Services
S.I.C.: 1611
N.A.I.C.S.: 237310

Electren, S.A. (1)
Av de Brasil 6 2a
Madrid, 28020, Spain
Tel.: (34) 915548207
Fax: (34) 915354339
E-Mail: electren@electren.es
Web Site: www.electren.es
Electrical Engineering Services
S.I.C.: 8711
N.A.I.C.S.: 541330

Electromur, S.A. (1)
Avda de El Palmar 530
El Palmar, 30120 Murcia, Spain
Tel.: (34) 968 88 08 62
Fax: (34) 968 88 08 66
Web Site: www.electromur.net
Electrical Lightning Installation Services
S.I.C.: 1731
N.A.I.C.S.: 238210

Emurtel, S.A. (1)
Poligono Industrial Oestec Carlos Egea Parc 13/18
30820 Alcantarilla, Murcia, Spain
Tel.: (34) 968 90 11 00
Fax: (34) 968 93 88 90
E-Mail: comercial@emurtel.es
Web Site: www.emurtel.com
Telecommunication Installation Services
S.I.C.: 4813
N.A.I.C.S.: 517110

Energias Ambientales de Novo, S.A. (1)
Calle Jose Luis Bugallal Marchesi 20
La Coruna, 15008, Spain
Tel.: (34) 981169470
Fax: (34) 981150452
Electrical Installation Services
S.I.C.: 1731
N.A.I.C.S.: 238210

Energias Ambientales de Outes, S.A. (1)
Calle Jose Luis Bugallal Marchesi 20
La Coruna, 15008, Spain
Tel.: (34) 981169470
Fax: (34) 981150452
Electric Power Generation Services
S.I.C.: 4931
N.A.I.C.S.: 221118

Energias Ambientales, S.A. (1)
Calle Jose Luis Bugallal Marchesi 20
La Coruna, 15008, Spain
Tel.: (34) 981169470
Fax: (34) 981150452
Electric Power Generation Services
S.I.C.: 4939
N.A.I.C.S.: 221118

Equipos de Senalizacion y Control, S.A. (1)
C/Severino Cobas 100 P I La Bagunda
36214 Vigo, Pontevedra, Spain
Tel.: (34) 98 625 24 33
Fax: (34) 98 625 35 10
E-Mail: esycsa@grupoetra.com
Web Site: www.grupoetra.com
Electrical Installation Services
S.I.C.: 1731
N.A.I.C.S.: 238210

ETRA Catalunya, S.A. (1)
C/Mercuri 30-32 Poligono Industrial Almeda
08940 Cornella de Llobregat, Barcelona, Spain
Tel.: (34) 93 377 81 50
Fax: (34) 93 377 18 46
E-Mail: etracatalunya@grupoetra.com
Electrical Equipment Installation Services
S.I.C.: 1731
N.A.I.C.S.: 238210

Etra Investigacion y Desarrollo, S.A. (1)
Tres Forques 147
46014 Valencia, Spain
Tel.: (34) 963134082
Fax: (34) 963503234
E-Mail: etra-id@grupoetra.com
Electrical Equipment Research & Development Services
S.I.C.: 8731
N.A.I.C.S.: 541712

Etralux, S.A. (1)
Avda Manoteras 28
28050 Madrid, Spain
Tel.: (34) 913 834 120
Fax: (34) 913 026 899
Electrical Equipment Installation Services
S.I.C.: 1731
N.A.I.C.S.: 238210

Etranorte, S.A. (1)
Pi Zabalondo-C/ Erreruena Pabellon G
48100 Munguia, Bizkaia, Spain
Tel.: (34) 946 742 060
Fax: (34) 946 740 994
E-Mail: etra.norte@grupoetra.com
Web Site: www.grupoetra.com
Electrical Equipment Installation Services
S.I.C.: 1731
N.A.I.C.S.: 238210

Explotacion Comercial de Intercambiadores, S.A. (1)
Avenida America Intercambiador De Transportes 9-A
Madrid, 28002, Spain
Tel.: (34) 917130626
Fax: (34) 911900298
Business Support Services
S.I.C.: 7389
N.A.I.C.S.: 561499

Gasoductos y Redes Gisca, S.A. (1)
Orense 11
Madrid, 28020, Spain
Tel.: (34) 915554593
Fax: (34) 915569559
Petroleum Pipeline Construction Services
S.I.C.: 1629
N.A.I.C.S.: 237120

Geotecnia y Cimientos, S.A. (1)
C/ Los Llanos de Jerez 10-12
28823 Coslada, Madrid, Spain
Tel.: (34) 91 660 30 00
Fax: (34) 91 671 64 60
E-Mail: administracion@geocisa.com
Web Site: www.geocisa.com
Highway Construction Services
S.I.C.: 1611
N.A.I.C.S.: 237310

Gestion y Proteccion Ambiental, S.L. (1)
Calle Condado De Trevino 19
Burgos, 09001, Spain
Tel.: (34) 947298687
Fax: (34) 947298676
Web Site: www.gpasl.es
Industrial Waste Collection & Treatment Services
S.I.C.: 4953
N.A.I.C.S.: 562219

Golden State Environmental Tedagua Corporation, S.A. (1)
Calle Cardenal Marcelo Spinola 10
Madrid, 28016, Spain
Tel.: (34) 914569500
Fax: (34) 913223130
Electronic Component Mfr
S.I.C.: 3679
N.A.I.C.S.: 334419

GPL Limpiezas, S.L. (1)
Calle Diputacio 180-10
Barcelona, 08011, Spain
Tel.: (34) 932094300
Fax: (34) 934516393
Interior Cleaning Services
S.I.C.: 1799
N.A.I.C.S.: 238990

Hidrogestion, S.A. (1)
C/ Valdemorillo 87 1a Planta Poligono Industrial Ventorro del Cano
28925 Alcorcon, Madrid, Spain
Tel.: (34) 91 633 24 54
Fax: (34) 91 632 30 25
E-Mail: hidrogestion@hidrogestion.es
Web Site: www.hidrogestion.es
Water Treatment Plant Construction Services
S.I.C.: 1623
N.A.I.C.S.: 237110

Humiclima Centro, S.A. (1)
Calle Orense 4-Primero
Madrid, 28020, Spain
Tel.: (34) 915551315
Fax: (34) 914110139
Air Conditioning System Installation Services
S.I.C.: 1711
N.A.I.C.S.: 238220
Felix Pereira *(Gen Mgr)*

Humiclima Est Catalunya, S.L. (1)
Carretera Mig 37
08041 Cornella de Llobregat, Barcelona, Spain
Tel.: (34) 934464200
Fax: (34) 934504626
Climate Control System Installation Services
S.I.C.: 1711
N.A.I.C.S.: 238220

Humiclima Est, S.A. (1)
Cami Vell de Bunyola 37 Poligono Ind Son Castello
07009 Palma de Mallorca, Spain
Tel.: (34) 971 43 12 16
Fax: (34) 971 20 02 28
E-Mail: Contacthumiclima@humiclima.com
Web Site: www.humiclima.com
Emp.: 60
Air Conditioning System Installation Services & Mfr
S.I.C.: 3585
N.A.I.C.S.: 333415
Antonio Bonet *(Mgr)*

Humiclima Sac, S.A. (1)
Camino Vell De Bunyola 37-Local 9
Palma de Mallorca, Baleares, 07009, Spain
Tel.: (34) 971431090
Fax: (34) 971436599
Air Conditioning System Installation Services
S.I.C.: 1711
N.A.I.C.S.: 238220
Anthony Bonet *(Mgr)*

Humiclima Sur, S.L. (1)
Calle Marruecos Pol Ind El Portal 12
Jerez de la Frontera, Cadiz, 11408, Spain
Tel.: (34) 952105401
Fax: (34) 952173460
Oil & Gas Exploration Services
S.I.C.: 1389
N.A.I.C.S.: 213112

Humiclima Valladolid, S.L. (1)
Calle Puente Colgante 46
Valladolid, 47006, Spain
Tel.: (34) 915551315
Fax: (34) 983457889
Construction Engineering Services
S.I.C.: 8711
N.A.I.C.S.: 541330

ImesAPI, S.A. (1)
Avda Manoteras 26
28050 Madrid, Spain
Tel.: (34) 91 744 39 00
Fax: (34) 91 744 39 01
E-Mail: info@imesapi.es
Web Site: www.imesapi.es
Emp.: 50

Electrical System Installation Services
S.I.C.: 1731
N.A.I.C.S.: 238210
Jose Mario Castello *(Mgr)*

Infraestructuras Energeticas Castellanas, S.L (1)
Calle Aluminio 17
Valladolid, 47012, Spain
Tel.: (34) 983390443
Fax: (34) 983295165
Electric Power Generation Services
S.I.C.: 4911
N.A.I.C.S.: 221118

Initec Energia, S.A. (1)
C/ Via de los poblados 9-11 Edificio Trianon C
28033 Madrid, Spain
Tel.: (34) 911 330 100
E-Mail: info@initec-energia.com
Web Site: www.initec-energia.com
Rev.: $256,259,800
Emp.: 300
Electric Power Plant Construction Services
S.I.C.: 1629
N.A.I.C.S.: 237130
Angel Medina *(Gen Mgr)*

Injar, S.A. (1)
Cl Leon y Castillo N 421 Pi 4 Pta A
Las Palmas, 35007, Spain
Tel.: (34) 928 268 650
Fax: (34) 928 472 280
Air Conditioning Sales & Installation Services
S.I.C.: 5075
N.A.I.C.S.: 423730

Instalaciones y Montajes de Aire Climatizado, S.L. (1)
Camino Bunyola 37
Palma de Mallorca, Baleares, 07009, Spain
Tel.: (34) 971431216
Fax: (34) 971200228
Climate Control System Installation Services
S.I.C.: 1731
N.A.I.C.S.: 238210

Intebe, S.A. (1)
Cl Orense 18
Madrid, 28020, Spain
Tel.: (34) 915 564 750
Telecommunication Plant Construction Engineering Services
S.I.C.: 1623
N.A.I.C.S.: 237130

Intecsa Ingenieria Industrial, S.A. (1)
Via de los Poblados 11
28033 Madrid, Spain
Tel.: (34) 91 749 7000
Fax: (34) 91 749 7001
E-Mail: info@intecsaindustrial.com
Web Site: www.intecsaindustrial.com
Construction Engineering Services
S.I.C.: 8711
N.A.I.C.S.: 541330
Raul Llamazares de la Puente *(CEO)*
Teresa Celestino de la Iglesia *(Sec)*

Integra Manteniment, Gestio i Serveis Integrats, Centre Especial de Treball, Catalunya, S.L (1)
Calle Pamplona 54
Barcelona, 08005, Spain
Tel.: (34) 933568578
Interior Cleaning Services
S.I.C.: 1799
N.A.I.C.S.: 238990

Integra Mantenimiento, Gestion y Servicios Integrados Centro Especial de Empleo Galicia S.L. (1)
Avda Hispanidad 75
36203 Vigo, Pontevedra, Spain
Tel.: (34) 913588033
Interior Cleaning Services
S.I.C.: 1799
N.A.I.C.S.: 238990

Integra Mantenimiento, Gestion y Servicios Integrados Centro Especial de Empleo, S.L. (1)
Avenida Manoteras 46-Bj Modulo C
Madrid, 28050, Spain
Tel.: (34) 913588033
Fax: (34) 913589591
Interior Cleaning Services
S.I.C.: 1799
N.A.I.C.S.: 238990

Intercambiador de Transportes de Principe Pio, S.A. (1)
Avenida America 2-Plt 17 B
28028 Madrid, Spain
Tel.: (34) 917130626
Ground Passenger Transportation Services
S.I.C.: 4111
N.A.I.C.S.: 485999

Interenvases, S.A. (1)
Calle Bariceta Pg Industrial Asparrena-San Millan 8
Araya, Alava, 01250, Spain
Tel.: (34) 945314760
Fax: (34) 945314761
Container Storage Services
S.I.C.: 4226
N.A.I.C.S.: 493190

Iridium Aparcamientos, S.L. (1)
Avenida Camino De Santiago 50
Madrid, 28050, Spain
Tel.: (34) 917038768
Fax: (34) 917038745
Web Site: www.iridiumconcesiones.com
Emp.: 3
Parking Management Consulting Services
S.I.C.: 7521
N.A.I.C.S.: 812930
Salvador Myro *(Gen Mgr)*

Iridium Concesiones de Infraestructuras, S.A. (1)
Avenida del Camino de Santiago 50 Edificio I P1
28050 Madrid, Spain
Tel.: (34) 91 343 9300
Fax: (34) 91 703 8728
E-Mail: info@iridium-acs.com
Web Site: www.iridiumconcesiones.com
Engineering Services
S.I.C.: 8711
N.A.I.C.S.: 541330
Manuel Garcia Buey *(Chm & CEO)*
Francisco Fernandez Lafuente *(Deputy CEO)*
Carlos Reyero Sanchez *(CFO)*
David Cid Grueso *(Chief Acctg Officer)*
Adolfo Valderas Martinez *(Exec VP)*
Eusebio Corregel Barrio *(Sr VP-Ops-Railroad Concessions)*
Salvador Myro Cuenco *(Sr VP-Bus Dev)*
Javier Reviriego Navarro *(Sr VP-Ops-Public Infrastructure Concessions)*

Limpiezas Deyse, S.L. (1)
Calle Lleida 1
Manresa, Barcelona, 08242, Spain
Tel.: (34) 938722777
Fax: (34) 938720103
Interior Cleaning Services
S.I.C.: 1799
N.A.I.C.S.: 238990

Limpiezas Lafuente, S.L. (1)
Calle Puerto de Santa Maria 8
46026 Valencia, Spain
Tel.: (34) 96 334 08 05
Fax: (34) 96 334 65 40
E-Mail: info@limpiezaslafuente.es
Web Site: www.limpiezaslafuente.es
Emp.: 1,500
Industrial Cleaning Services
S.I.C.: 4959
N.A.I.C.S.: 562998

Lireba Serveis Integrats, S.L. (1)
Camino De Jesus S/N-Edf Son Valenti 8 Plt 1
Palma de Mallorca, Baleares, 07011, Spain
Tel.: (34) 971758410
Fax: (34) 971213659
Interior Cleaning Services
S.I.C.: 1799
N.A.I.C.S.: 238990

Lumican, S.A. (1)
Calle Arco 40
Las Palmas, 35004, Spain
Tel.: (34) 928482120
Fax: (34) 928480335
E-Mail: carmengonzalez.lumicam@grupoetra.com
Web Site: www.groupoetra.com
Emp.: 40
Electrical Installation Services
S.I.C.: 1731
N.A.I.C.S.: 238210

Maessa Telecomunicaciones, S.A. (1)
Parque Empresarial Plaza C Bari 33 Edificio 3
50197 Zaragoza, Spain
Tel.: (34) 976 066 666
Fax: (34) 976 066 667
E-Mail: maetel@maetel.com
Web Site: www.maetel.com
Emp.: 300
Electric Power Generation & Distribution Services
S.I.C.: 4931
N.A.I.C.S.: 221118
Jose Luis Celorrio Garcia *(Gen Mgr)*

Makiber, S.A. (1)
Paseo de la Castellana 182
28046 Madrid, Spain
Tel.: (34) 91 4843000
Fax: (34) 91 4843094
E-Mail: makiber@makiber.com
Web Site: www.makiber.es
Emp.: 30
Logistics Consulting Services
S.I.C.: 4731
N.A.I.C.S.: 541614
Jose Manuel Gomez-Aleixandre *(Pres)*

Manchasol 1 Central Termosolar Uno, S.L. (1)
Calle Cardenal Marcelo Spinola 10
Madrid, 28016, Spain
Tel.: (34) 914569500
Fax: (34) 914569462
E-Mail: central@gruppocobra.com
Web Site: www.gruppocobra.com
Emp.: 2,000
Electric Power Generation Services
S.I.C.: 4931
N.A.I.C.S.: 221118

Manchasol 2 Central Termosolar Dos, S.L. (1)
Calle Cardenal Marcelo Spinola 10
Madrid, 28016, Spain
Tel.: (34) 914569486
Renewable Energy Generation Services
S.I.C.: 9631
N.A.I.C.S.: 926130

Mant. Ayuda a la Explot. y Servicios, S.A (1)
Cardenal Marcelo Spinola St 42- Fl 11
28016 Madrid, Spain
Tel.: (34) 914 360 480
Fax: (34) 915 767 566
E-Mail: info@grupomaessa.com
Web Site: www.maessa.com
Rev.: $359,613,200
Emp.: 2,564
Industrial Assembly & Maintenance Services
S.I.C.: 7699
N.A.I.C.S.: 811310

Manteniment i Conservacio del Valles, S.A. (1)
Avenida Josep Tarradellas 34-36 9 D
Barcelona, 8029, Spain
Tel.: (34) 934443236
Fax: (34) 934191770
Real Estate Development Services
S.I.C.: 6531
N.A.I.C.S.: 531390

Mantenimiento y Montajes Industriales, S.A (1)
Calle Teide 5-Plt 1 Ed Milenium
San Sebastian de los Reyes, Madrid, 28703, Spain
Tel.: (34) 914843030
Fax: (34) 914843173
Industrial Machinery Maintenance Services
S.I.C.: 7699
N.A.I.C.S.: 811310

Mapide, S.A. (1)
C/ Sta Juliana 16
28039 Madrid, Spain
Tel.: (34) 91 311 60 02
Fax: (34) 91 459 92 09
E-Mail: recepcionmapide@mapide.com
Web Site: www.mapide.es
Interior Cleaning Services
S.I.C.: 1799
N.A.I.C.S.: 238990

Masa Algeciras, S.A. (1)
Avenida Blas Infante Ed Centro Blas Infante Loc 8
Algeciras, Cadiz, 11201, Spain
Tel.: (34) 956635636
Fax: (34) 956631769
Industrial Machinery Maintenance Services
S.I.C.: 7699
N.A.I.C.S.: 811310

Masa Galicia, S.A. (1)
Poligono Industrial De La Grela Bens Cl Guttenberg 2
La Coruna, Galicia, 15008, Spain
Tel.: (34) 981262011
Fax: (34) 981279363
Industrial Machinery Maintenance Services
S.I.C.: 7699
N.A.I.C.S.: 811310

Masa Huelva, S.A. (1)
Calle Alonso De Ojeda 1
Huelva, 21002, Spain
Tel.: (34) 959253308
Fax: (34) 959253640
Industrial Machinery Maintenance Services
S.I.C.: 7699
N.A.I.C.S.: 811310

Masa Norte, S.A. (1)
Calle Ribera De Axpe Etorbidea 50-30 Plt
Erandio, Vizcaya, 48950, Spain
Tel.: (34) 944316277
Fax: (34) 944316260
Industrial Machinery Maintenance Services
S.I.C.: 7699
N.A.I.C.S.: 811310

Masa Puertollano, S.A. (1)
Carretera Cr-503 Calzada De Calatrava Km 3 400
Puertollano, Ciudad Real, 13500, Spain
Tel.: (34) 926425654
Fax: (34) 926432200
Industrial Equipment Maintenance Services
S.I.C.: 7699
N.A.I.C.S.: 811310

Masa Servicios, S.A. (1)
Calle Lletra B De La Zona Franca Sector B 4 Numero
Barcelona, 08040, Spain
Tel.: (34) 932630120
Fax: (34) 933356952
Industrial Machinery Maintenance Services
S.I.C.: 7699
N.A.I.C.S.: 811310
Jose Maria Bello *(Mng Dir)*

Masa Tenerife, S.A. (1)
Calle La Marina 7-50 Oficina 66
Santa Cruz de Tenerife, Tenerife, 38002, Spain
Tel.: (34) 922278593
Fax: (34) 922246691
Industrial Machinery Maintenance Services
S.I.C.: 7699
N.A.I.C.S.: 811310

Moncobra, S.A. (1)
Calle Cardenal Marcelo Spinola 10
Madrid, 28016, Spain
Tel.: (34) 914569500
Fax: (34) 914569462
Industrial Machinery Maintenance Services
S.I.C.: 7699
N.A.I.C.S.: 811310

Monegros Depura, S.A. (1)
Cm De Albalatillo-Estacion Depuradora S/N
Sarinena, Huesca, 22200, Spain
Tel.: (34) 876242600
Fax: (34) 876242604
Water Treatment Services
S.I.C.: 4941
N.A.I.C.S.: 221310

Monelec, S.L. (1)
Ceramista 14
Malaga, 29006, Spain
Tel.: (34) 952311649
Fax: (34) 952 314 048
E-Mail: monelec@monelec.com
Web Site: www.monelec.com
Electrical Installation Services
S.I.C.: 1731
N.A.I.C.S.: 238210

Murciana de Trafico, S.A. (1)
Carril Molino Nerva 21
30007 Murcia, Spain

ACS, Actividades de Construccion y Servicios, S.A.—(Continued)

Tel.: (34) 968 242 347
Fax: (34) 968 242 451
E-Mail: murtrafic@grupoetra.com
Electrical Installation Services
S.I.C.: 1731
N.A.I.C.S.: 238210

Net Brill, S.L. (1)
Lugar Caminet De Les Vinyes 15
Mataro, Barcelona, 8302, Spain
Tel.: (34) 937 996 514
Fax: (34) 937 983 648
E-Mail: comercial.netbrill@netbrill.cat
Web Site: www.netbrill.cat
Interior Cleaning Services
S.I.C.: 1799
N.A.I.C.S.: 238990

Oficina Tecnica de Estudios y Control de Obras, S.A (1)
C/ Guzman el Bueno 133 Edificio Britannia-10 Planta
28003 Madrid, Spain
Tel.: (34) 91 535 22 10
Fax: (34) 91 535 37 42
E-Mail: ofiteco@ofiteco.es
Web Site: www.ofiteco.es
Emp.: 150
Engineering Consulting Services
S.I.C.: 8711
N.A.I.C.S.: 541330
Jurgen Fleitz *(CEO)*

Opade Organizac. y Promoc de Actividades Deportivas, S.A. (1)
C/ Arte 21 3 A
28033 Madrid, Spain
Tel.: (34) 91 725 10 20
Fax: (34) 91 725 10 43
E-Mail: opade@opade.net
Web Site: www.opade.net
Sports Activities Promoting Services
S.I.C.: 7999
N.A.I.C.S.: 711310

Orto Parques y Jardines, S.L. (1)
San Roman No 18-Orto
15318 Abegondo, A Coruna, Spain
Tel.: (34) 981 676 812
Fax: (34) 981 676 924
E-Mail: ortosl@arrakis.es
Web Site: www.orto.es
Emp.: 75
Garden Maintenance Services
S.I.C.: 0783
N.A.I.C.S.: 561730
Jose Antonio *(Gen Mgr)*

Publimedia Sistemas Publicitarios, S.L. (1)
Avenida de Tenerife 4-6
San Sebastian de los Reyes, Madrid, 28050, Spain
Tel.: (34) 914842290
Fax: (34) 916626292
E-Mail: info@publimedia-sp.com
Web Site: www.publimedia-sp.com
Outdoor Advertising Services
S.I.C.: 7312
N.A.I.C.S.: 541850

Puerto Seco Santander-Ebro, S.A. (1)
C/ Ramon y Cajal 17
50640 Luceni, Zaragoza, Spain
Tel.: (34) 976 65 12 20
Fax: (34) 976 65 12 21
E-Mail: gerencia@puertoseco-se.com
Web Site: www.puertoseco-se.com
Automobile Maintenance Services
S.I.C.: 7549
N.A.I.C.S.: 811198

Recuperacion de Rodas e Madeira, S.L. (1)
Calle F Parc 5 Pol Industrial Lalin 2000
Lalin, Pontevedra, 36500, Spain
Tel.: (34) 986787517
Fax: (34) 986787536
Water Treatment Services
S.I.C.: 4941
N.A.I.C.S.: 221310

Remodelacion Ribera Norte, S.A (1)
Avenida Josep Tarradellas 34 36 9 D
Barcelona, 8029, Spain
Tel.: (34) 934443236
Fax: (34) 934191770
Civil Engineering Construction Services
S.I.C.: 1629
N.A.I.C.S.: 237990

Residencial Monte Carmelo, S.A (1)
c/ Bolonia 4 2 Izquierda
50008 Zaragoza, Spain
Tel.: (34) 976 237 338
Fax: (34) 976 302 475
Web Site: www.residencialmontecarmelo.com
Residential Property Management Services
S.I.C.: 6531
N.A.I.C.S.: 531311

Residuos Industriales de Zaragoza, S.A (1)
Carretera Castellon Cartuja Baja Km 8 3
Zaragoza, 50720, Spain
Tel.: (34) 976469725
Industrial Waste Treatment Services
S.I.C.: 4953
N.A.I.C.S.: 562211

RetraOil, S.L. (1)
Poligono Industrial Tambarria Par 20
Alfaro, La Rioja, 26540, Spain
Tel.: (34) 941184203
Fax: (34) 941184277
E-Mail: comercialretraoil@urbaser.com
Web Site: www.retraoil.es
Emp.: 30
Oil Waste Treatment & Recycling Services
S.I.C.: 4953
N.A.I.C.S.: 562219
Carmelo Areche *(Gen Mgr)*

Ribagrande Energia, S.L. (1)
Calle Cardenal Marcelo Spinola 10
Madrid, 28016, Spain
Tel.: (34) 914569500
Fax: (34) 914569472
Emp.: 60
Renewable Energy Generation Services
S.I.C.: 9631
N.A.I.C.S.: 926130
Antonio Gomez Zamora *(Gen Mgr)*

Roura Cevasa, S.A (1)
C/ Caracas 5
08030 Barcelona, Spain
Tel.: (34) 93 3600080
Fax: (34) 93 3600165
E-Mail: info@roura-cevasa.com
Web Site: www.roura-cevasa.com
Emp.: 342
Signage Mfr
S.I.C.: 3993
N.A.I.C.S.: 339950

Salins Residuos Automocion, S.L. (1)
Calle Numero 31 Chaflan Cl 27 Pg Ind Catarroja
Catarroja, Valencia, 46470, Spain
Tel.: (34) 961220445
Petroleum Refinery Services
S.I.C.: 1311
N.A.I.C.S.: 211111

Salmantina de Seguridad Vial, S.A. (1)
Calle Cascajales Pg Ind Los Villares 65-69
Villares de la Reina, Salamanca, 37184, Spain
Tel.: (34) 923220107
Fax: (34) 923221366
Civil Engineering Construction Services
S.I.C.: 1629
N.A.I.C.S.: 237990

Sanypick Plastic, S.A. (1)
C/ Carlos Jimenez Diaz 23
28806 Alcala de Henares, Madrid, Spain
Tel.: (34) 91 884 11 86
Fax: (34) 91 884 11 61
E-Mail: trading@sanypick.com
Web Site: www.sanypick.com
Emp.: 15
Hospital Waste Container Mfr
S.I.C.: 3089
N.A.I.C.S.: 326199
David Gonzalez *(Gen Mgr)*

Seguridad Integral Metropolitana, S.A. (1)
Calle De La Granja Pg Ind 29
Alcobendas, Madrid, 28108, Spain
Tel.: (34) 916232200
Fax: (34) 916629572
Security System Maintenance Services
S.I.C.: 7382
N.A.I.C.S.: 561621

Sermicro, S.A. (1)
C/ Pradillo 48-50
28002 Madrid, Spain
Tel.: (34) 91 744 86 00
Fax: (34) 963460475
E-Mail: sermicro@sermicro.com
Web Site: www.sermicro.com
Software Consulting Services
S.I.C.: 7373
N.A.I.C.S.: 541512

Serveis Catalans, Serveica, S.A. (1)
Calle Dels Enamorats 117
Barcelona, 08026, Spain
Tel.: (34) 933070708
Fax: (34) 933085315
Electrical System Installation Services
S.I.C.: 1731
N.A.I.C.S.: 238210

Sice Energia, S.L. (1)
C/ Sepulveda 6
28108 Alcobendas, Madrid, Spain
Tel.: (34) 91 623 22 00
Fax: (34) 91 623 22 01
E-Mail: energia@sice.com
Web Site: www.sice.es/contenidos/referencias/energia/energia_011.html?sector=14
Photovoltaic Generating System Installation Services
S.I.C.: 1731
N.A.I.C.S.: 238210

Sice Tecnologia y Sistemas, S.A. (1)
Calle De Sepulveda Pol Industrial Alcobendas 6
Alcobendas, Madrid, 28108, Spain
Tel.: (34) 916616927
Fax: (34) 916614926
Electrical System Installation Services
S.I.C.: 1731
N.A.I.C.S.: 238210

Sidetel, S.A (1)
Avenida Manoteras 28
Madrid, 28050, Spain
Tel.: (34) 913834120
Fax: (34) 913026899
Electrical Installation Services
S.I.C.: 1731
N.A.I.C.S.: 238210

Sintax Logistica, S.A. (1)
c/Diputacion no 279 Atico 60
Barcelona, 08007, Spain
Tel.: (34) 93 496 25 00
Fax: (34) 93 496 25 26
E-Mail: sintax@sintax.com
Web Site: www.sintax.com
Logistics Consulting Services
S.I.C.: 4731
N.A.I.C.S.: 541614

Sistemas Integrales de Mantenimiento, S.A. (1)
C/ Teide 5-1
28709 San Sebastian de los Reyes, Madrid, Spain
Tel.: (34) 926421658
Industrial System Maintenance Services
S.I.C.: 7699
N.A.I.C.S.: 811310

Sistemas Radiantes F. Moyano, S.A. (1)
C/ Canada No 53
28850 Torrejon de Ardoz, Madrid, Spain
Tel.: (34) 91 6610750
Fax: (34) 91 6615447
Web Site: www.moyano.com
Emp.: 37
Radiant System Installation Services & Mfr
S.I.C.: 3699
N.A.I.C.S.: 335999
Gonzalo Lasa *(Gen Mgr)*

Soc. Espanola de Montajes Industriales, S.A. (1)
C/ Manzanares No 4
28005 Madrid, Spain
Tel.: (34) 917 017 700
Fax: (34) 915 218 597
E-Mail: seml@semi.es
Web Site: www.semi.es
Transmission Line Construction & Installation Services
S.I.C.: 1629
N.A.I.C.S.: 237130

Soc Iberica de Construcciones Electricas de Seguridad, S.L. (1)
Calle De La Granja P I Alcobendas 29
Alcobendas, 28108, Spain
Tel.: (34) 916616927
Security System Installation Services
S.I.C.: 1731
N.A.I.C.S.: 238210

Socamex, S.A. (1)
Calle Cobalto Pol Ind San Cristobal 12-Parc 213 Nave A
Valladolid, 47012, Spain
Tel.: (34) 983208011
Fax: (34) 983392910
Water Treatment Plant Construction Services
S.I.C.: 1623
N.A.I.C.S.: 237110

Sociedad de Generacion Eolica Manchega, S.L. (1)
Calle Cardenal Marcelo Spinola 10
Madrid, 28016, Spain
Tel.: (34) 914569500
Fax: (34) 914569472
Emp.: 200
Electric Power Generation Services
S.I.C.: 4931
N.A.I.C.S.: 221118
Antonio Gomez *(Gen Mgr)*

Sumipar, S.A. (1)
Pol Ind Zona Franca Calle B n 4
08040 Barcelona, Spain
Tel.: (34) 93 335 31 00
Fax: (34) 93 335 37 71
E-Mail: sumipar@sice.com
Web Site: www.sumipar.com
Emp.: 30
Parking Equipment Installation Services
S.I.C.: 1799
N.A.I.C.S.: 238990

Talher, S.A. (1)
Avda Tenerife 4-6
28700 San Sebastian de los Reyes, Madrid, Spain
Tel.: (34) 91 417 12 70
Fax: (34) 91 417 12 80
E-Mail: talher@talher.com
Web Site: www.talher.com
Gardening Services
S.I.C.: 5261
N.A.I.C.S.: 444220

Tecnicas de Desalinizacion de Aguas, S.A. (1)
Cardenal Marcelo Spinola 10
28016 Madrid, Spain
Tel.: (34) 91 456 95 00
Fax: (34) 91 456 89 29
E-Mail: central@tedagua.com
Web Site: www.tedagua.com
Emp.: 32
Water Treatment Plant Construction Services
S.I.C.: 1629
N.A.I.C.S.: 237110
Miguel Angel Fernandez *(Gen Mgr)*

Tecnicas e Imagen Corporativa, S.L. (1)
Avenida De Paris 1-Esq Av De La Industria
Azuqueca de Henares, Guadalajara, 19200, Spain
Tel.: (34) 949277859
Fax: (34) 949277874
Signage Mfr
S.I.C.: 3993
N.A.I.C.S.: 339950

Tecnotel Clima, S.L. (1)
Poligono Industrial Valle De Guimar Cl Manzana 6 12
Arafo, Tenerife, 38550, Spain
Tel.: (34) 922583166
Fax: (34) 922583175
Climate Control System Installation Services
S.I.C.: 1711
N.A.I.C.S.: 238220

Tecsa Empresa Constructora, S.A. (1)
Avda Madariaga 1-4a Planta
48014 Bilbao, Spain

Tel.: (34) 94 448 86 00
Fax: (34) 94 476 22 84
Web Site: www.tecsa-constructora.com
Railway Construction Engineering Services
S.I.C.: 1629
N.A.I.C.S.: 237990

Tedagua Internacional, S.L. (1)
Calle Cardenal Marcelo Spinola 10
Madrid, 28016, Spain
Tel.: (34) 914569500
Fax: (34) 914568929
E-Mail: tedagua@tedagua.com
Web Site: www.tedagua.com
Emp.: 30
Civil Engineering Construction Services
S.I.C.: 1629
N.A.I.C.S.: 237990
Miguel Fernandez *(Gen Mgr)*

Telsa Instalaciones de Telecomunicaciones y Electricidad, S.A. (1)
C/ La Granja 29 P I Alcobendas
28108 Alcobendas, Madrid, Spain
Tel.: (34) 91 657 40 04
Fax: (34) 91 662 45 97
E-Mail: info@telsa.com
Web Site: www.telsa.com
Telecommunication & Electrical Installation Services
S.I.C.: 1731
N.A.I.C.S.: 238210
Francisco Gallo *(Dir Gen)*

Tirmadrid, S.A. (1)
Calle Canada Real De Merinas-Valdemingomez S/N
Madrid, 28052, Spain
Tel.: (34) 913324131
Fax: (34) 913322780
E-Mail: tirmadrid@tirmadrid.es
Web Site: www.tirmadrid.es
Emp.: 118
Solid Waste Treatment Services
S.I.C.: 4953
N.A.I.C.S.: 562211
Maria-Jesus Ramirez *(Mng Dir)*

Tratamiento Integral de Residuos de Cantabria S.L.U. (1)
Barrio Vierna San Bartolome S/N
San Miguel de Meruelo, Cantabria, 39192, Spain
Tel.: (34) 942674898
Fax: (34) 942637073
Waste Treatment Services
S.I.C.: 4959
N.A.I.C.S.: 562998

Trenmedia, S.A. (1)
Avenida Manoteras 46-Bis Planta 2
Madrid, 28050, Spain
Tel.: (34) 914842290
Fax: (34) 915120473
Advertising Agency Services
S.I.C.: 7311
N.A.I.C.S.: 541810

Tresima Limpiezas Industriales, S.A (1)
Calle Copernico Pol Ind A Grela 1-Plt 1
La Coruna, Galicia, 15008, Spain
Tel.: (34) 981175100
Fax: (34) 981160145
Industrial Cleaning Services
S.I.C.: 1799
N.A.I.C.S.: 238990

Urbacet, S.L. (1)
Calle Fra Juniper Serra 59-75
Barcelona, 08030, Spain
Tel.: (34) 933984646
Garden Maintenance Services
S.I.C.: 0783
N.A.I.C.S.: 561730

Urbaenergia, S.L. (1)
Calle Cardenal Marcelo Spinola 10
Madrid, 28016, Spain
Tel.: (34) 914569500
Fax: (34) 914569472
Electric Power Generation Services
S.I.C.: 4931
N.A.I.C.S.: 221118

Urbamar Levante Residuos Industriales, S.L. (1)
Olg Ind Catarroja N 31 Chaflan
Catarroja, Valencia, 46470, Spain
Tel.: (34) 961 220 445
Industrial Waste Treatment Services
S.I.C.: 4953
N.A.I.C.S.: 562211

Urbana de Servicios Ambientales, S.L. (1)
Avenida Jose Ortega Y Gasset 194
Malaga, 29006, Spain
Tel.: (34) 952109895
Solid Waste Collection & Street Cleaning Services
S.I.C.: 4212
N.A.I.C.S.: 562111

Urbaoil, S.A. (1)
Avenida De Tenerife 4-6
San Sebastian de los Reyes, 28703, Spain
Tel.: (34) 911218000
Fax: (34) 915351284
Oil Refinery Services
S.I.C.: 1389
N.A.I.C.S.: 213112

Urbaser, S.A. (1)
Avda de Tenerife 4-6
San Sebastian de los Reyes, 28703
Madrid, Spain
Tel.: (34) 911218000
Fax: (34) 913041522
Web Site: www.urbaser.es
Solid Waster Treatment & Management Services
S.I.C.: 4212
N.A.I.C.S.: 562111

Non-U.S. Subsidiary:

Urbaser, Ltd. (2)
Unit F 2nd Floor Pate Court
St Margarets Road, Cheltenham, GL50 4DY, United Kingdom UK
Tel.: (44) 124224880 (100%)
Fax: (44) 1242261535
Solid Waste Management Services
S.I.C.: 9511
N.A.I.C.S.: 924110

Joint Ventures:

Mercia Waste Management Ltd. (3)
The Marina Kings Road
Evesham, Worcestershire, WR11 3XZ, United Kingdom UK
Tel.: (44) 1386 861 434
Fax: (44) 1386 861 556
E-Mail: enquiries@severnwaste.co.uk
Web Site: www.severnwaste.com
Emp.: 100
Waste Management Services
S.I.C.: 9511
N.A.I.C.S.: 924110

Severn Waste Services Limited (3)
The Marina Kings Road
Evesham, Worcs, WR11 3XZ, United Kingdom UK
Tel.: (44) 1386 443 376
Fax: (44) 1386 446 757
E-Mail: enquiries@severnwaste.co.uk
Web Site: www.severnwaste.com
Emp.: 12
Solid Waster Management Services
S.I.C.: 9511
N.A.I.C.S.: 924110
Jim Haywood *(Dir-Fin)*

Urbaser Transportes, S.L. (1)
Calle Fra Juniper Serra 59-75
Barcelona, 08030, Spain
Tel.: (34) 933137300
Fax: (34) 932788146
Automotive Parts Distr
S.I.C.: 5013
N.A.I.C.S.: 423120

Viabal Manteniment i Conservacio, S.A. (1)
Calle Gerrers Pol Industrial De Marratxi Naves 26 Y 27
Marratxi, Baleares, 07141, Spain
Tel.: (34) 971431163
Fax: (34) 971431972
Painting & Signalling Equipment Installation Services
S.I.C.: 1721
N.A.I.C.S.: 238320

Viass y Construcciones S.A. (1)
C/ Orense n 11
28020 Madrid, Spain
Tel.: (34) 914 179 800
Fax: (34) 914 179 830
E-Mail: vias@vias.es
Web Site: www.vias.es
Construction Engineering Services
S.I.C.: 1629
N.A.I.C.S.: 237990
Manuel Pertz Beato De Cos *(Chm)*
Gonzalo Gomez-Zamalloa Baraibar *(CEO)*

Villa Aurea, S.L. (1)
Avenida Pio Xii 102
Madrid, 28036, Spain
Tel.: (34) 913439200
Construction Engineering Services
S.I.C.: 8711
N.A.I.C.S.: 541330

Villanova, S.A. (1)
Avenida Pio Xii 102
Madrid, 28036, Spain
Tel.: (34) 913439200
Construction Engineering Services
S.I.C.: 8711
N.A.I.C.S.: 541330

Zenit Servicios Integrales, S.A. (1)
Calle Cardenal Marcelo Spinola 42
Madrid, 28016, Spain
Tel.: (34) 913836800
Airport Integral Services
S.I.C.: 4581
N.A.I.C.S.: 488119

U.S. Subsidiaries:

ACS Infrastructure Development, Inc. (1)
1 Alhambra Plz Ste 710
Coral Gables, FL 33134-5216
Tel.: (305) 423-7606
Fax: (305) 424-5401
Construction Engineering Services
S.I.C.: 1629
N.A.I.C.S.: 237990
Jose Luque *(Project Mgr)*

California Sun Power, LLC. (1)
15500 Erwin St Ste No 1121
Van Nuys, CA 91411-1027
Tel.: (818) 782-2000
Electric Power Generation Services
S.I.C.: 4911
N.A.I.C.S.: 221118

I 595 Express, LLC (1)
10368 State Rd 84 Ste 202
Davie, FL 33324
Tel.: (954) 671-5500
Fax: (954) 513-3201
E-Mail: info@i595express.com
Web Site: www.i595express.com
Highway Road Construction Services
S.I.C.: 1622
N.A.I.C.S.: 237310
Pamala Decor *(Gen Mgr)*

Pulice Construction, Inc. (1)
2033 W Mtn View Rd
Phoenix, AZ 85021
Tel.: (602) 944-2241
Fax: (602) 906-3783
E-Mail: puliceinfo@pulice.com
Web Site: www.pulice.com
Highway Construction Engineering Services
S.I.C.: 1611
N.A.I.C.S.: 237310
Roger J. Eischen *(Pres)*
Tom A. Lawless *(CFO & VP)*
Mark B. Soyster *(Sr VP)*

Red Top Wind Power, LLC. (1)
2800 Post Oak Blvd Ste 5858
Houston, TX 77056-5399
Tel.: (713) 599-1188
Fax: (713) 400-3597
Electric Power Generation Services
S.I.C.: 4911
N.A.I.C.S.: 221118

SICE, Inc. (1)
2 Alhambra Plz Ste 1106
Coral Gables, FL 33134
Tel.: (305) 222-7040
Fax: (305) 443-5453
E-Mail: sicecorp@sicecorp.com
Web Site: www.sice.com
Construction Engineering Services
S.I.C.: 8711
N.A.I.C.S.: 541330

Non-U.S. Subsidiaries:

ACS Infrastructure Canada, Inc. (1)
155 University Ave Ste 1800
Toronto, ON, M5H 3B7, Canada
Tel.: (416) 642-2161
Fax: (416) 642-2162
E-Mail: rcanada@acsinfra.com
Emp.: 10
Building Construction Services
S.I.C.: 1542
N.A.I.C.S.: 236220
Lissette Alizaga *(Office Mgr)*

Actividades de Servicios e Instalaciones Cobra, S.A. (1)
29 Av 13-35 Zona 17 Complejo De Ofibodegas Las Almendras Bodega 3
Guatemala, Guatemala
Tel.: (502) 23896600
Fax: (502) 22798510
Industrial Building Construction Services
S.I.C.: 1541
N.A.I.C.S.: 236210

Albatros Logistic, Maroc, S.A. (1)
Hangars 10 11 et 12 Lotissement At-Tawfik rue Ibnou el Koutia
Ain Sebaa, Casablanca, Morocco
Tel.: (212) 522 66 62 33
Fax: (212) 522 66 62 36
E-Mail: commercial@albatroslogistic.ma
Web Site: www.albatroslogistic.ma
Logistics Consulting Services
S.I.C.: 4731
N.A.I.C.S.: 541614

Argencobra, S.A. (1)
Nicaragua 5935 Piso 2
Buenos Aires, 1414, Argentina
Tel.: (54) 1147746200
Fax: (54) 1147748511
Emp.: 5
Auxiliary Electric Power Distribution Services
S.I.C.: 4931
N.A.I.C.S.: 221122
Dracut Xavier *(Gen Mgr)*

Artemis Transmissora de Energia, Ltda. (1)
Rua Deputado Antonio Edu Vieira 999 Terreo
Bairro Pantanal, Florianopolis, 88040-901, Brazil
Tel.: (55) 48 3231 7282
Fax: (55) 48 3234 2776
Web Site: www.artemisenergia.com.br
Electricity Transmission Line Construction Services
S.I.C.: 1623
N.A.I.C.S.: 237130

Barra do Peixe Montagens e Servicos, Ltda. (1)
Mal Camara 160
Rio de Janeiro, 20020-080, Brazil
Tel.: (55) 2122157317
Construction Engineering Services
S.I.C.: 8711
N.A.I.C.S.: 541330

Benisaf Water Company, Spa (1)
Villa N14 Cooperative Iris Garidi
Kouba, Algiers, Algeria
Tel.: (213) 21 56 12 88
Fax: (213) 21 56 13 04
E-Mail: contact@benisafwater.com
Web Site: www.benisafwater.com
Water Treatment & Recycling Services
S.I.C.: 4971
N.A.I.C.S.: 221310

Catxere Transmissora de Energia, S.A. (1)
Av Marechal Camara 160 - sala 1036
Rio de Janeiro, 20020-080, Brazil
Tel.: (55) 21 2101 9970
Fax: (55) 21 2101 9937
Emp.: 9
Electric Power Transmission Services
S.I.C.: 4931
N.A.I.C.S.: 221121
Marcelo Lede *(Mgr)*

CCR Platforming Cangrejera S.A. de C.V. (1)
Carretera Coatzacoalcos-Villahermosa Km 11 Complejo Petroquimico
Cangrejera, Coatzacoalcos, Veracruz, 96400, Mexico

ACS, Actividades de Construccion y Servicios, S.A.—(Continued)

Tel.: (52) 9212112170
Fax: (52) 9212112170
Construction Engineering Services
S.I.C.: 1629
N.A.I.C.S.: 237990

Central Termica de Mejillones, S.A. (1)
Av Chacaya S/N
Mejillones, Chile
Tel.: (56) 55566900
Construction Engineering Services
S.I.C.: 1629
N.A.I.C.S.: 237990

CME Chile, SPA (1)
Puerto Madero 970 35 Y 36-A Pudahuel
Santiago, Chile
Tel.: (56) 25858161
Emp.: 150
Logistic Consulting Services
S.I.C.: 4731
N.A.I.C.S.: 541614
Rui Casaleiro *(Gen Mgr)*

Cobra Chile, S.A. (1)
Av Jose Pedro Alessandri 2323 Macul
Santiago, Chile
Tel.: (56) 22379700
Fax: (56) 22372100
Electrical Equipment Installation Services
S.I.C.: 1731
N.A.I.C.S.: 238210

Cobra La Rioja Sur SA (1)
Concepcion Arenal 2630
Buenos Aires, C1426 DGB, Argentina
Tel.: (54) 11 4774 6200
Fax: (54) 11 4774 8511
E-Mail: info@cobralariojasur.com.ar
Web Site: www.cobralariojasur.com.ar
Electric Power Generation & Distribution Services
S.I.C.: 4931
N.A.I.C.S.: 221118

Cobra Peru, S.A. (1)
Av Victor A Belaunde Na 887 Urb Carmen De La Legua Reynoso
Carmen De La Legua, Callao, Peru
Tel.: (51) 15623003
Fax: (51) 14641754
Construction Engineering Services
S.I.C.: 8711
N.A.I.C.S.: 541330

Consorcio Tecdra, S.A. (1)
Almirante Pastene 244 Oficina 702
Providencia
Santiago, Chile
Tel.: (56) 2 6162500
E-Mail: personal@tecdracentro.cl
Web Site: www.tecdracentro.cl
Railway Construction Engineering Services
S.I.C.: 1629
N.A.I.C.S.: 237990

Constructora Dycven, S.A. (1)
Urbanizacion Las Mercedes Calle Veracruz Edificio Torreon
3er Piso Oficina 3B, Caracas, 1060, Venezuela
Tel.: (58) 212 992 31 11
Fax: (58) 212 992 77 24
E-Mail: dycvensa@dycvensa.com.ve
Web Site: www.dycvensa.com.ve
Emp.: 40
Civil Engineering Construction Services
S.I.C.: 1629
N.A.I.C.S.: 237990
Fernando Jose Bolinaga Hernandez *(Gen Mgr)*

Cymi do Brasil, Ltda. (1)
Av Presidente Wilson 231/1701
Centro, Rio de Janeiro, Brazil
Tel.: (55) 21 2101 9900
Fax: (55) 21 2101 9900
Web Site: www.cymi.com.br
Power Plant Construction Services
S.I.C.: 1629
N.A.I.C.S.: 237130

Cymi Holding, S.A. (1)
Presidente Wilson 231 Sala 1701
Rio de Janeiro, 20030-021, Brazil
Tel.: (55) 2121019900
Fax: (55) 2121019999
Financial Investment Services
S.I.C.: 6211
N.A.I.C.S.: 523999

Dragados Gulf Construction, Ltda. (1)
Al Saeed Building Dammam-Khobar Highway Al- Khobar
PO Box 39477
Dhahran, 31942, Saudi Arabia
Tel.: (966) 3 814 7525
Fax: (966) 3 814 7524
E-Mail: info@dragadosgulf.com
Web Site: www.dragadosgulf.com
Construction Engineering Services
S.I.C.: 1629
N.A.I.C.S.: 237990
Jose Luis Ayala *(Gen Mgr)*

Dragados Offshore de Mejico KU-A2, S.A de C.V. (1)
Juan Racine n 112 Piso 8
Col Los Morales, Mexico, 11510, Mexico
Tel.: (52) 938 131 0697
Metal Mining Services
S.I.C.: 1099
N.A.I.C.S.: 212299

Etra Interandina, S.A. (1)
Calle 100 No 8A-49 Torre B Ofic 610 World Trade Center
Bogota, Colombia
Tel.: (57) 1 611 29 25
Fax: (57) 1 611 28 90
E-Mail: etra.interandina@grupoetra.com
Electrical Equipment Installation Services
S.I.C.: 1731
N.A.I.C.S.: 238210

France Semi, S.A. (1)
20-22 Rue Louis Armand
75015 Paris, France
Tel.: (33) 140604040
Fax: (33) 140609006
Emp.: 24
Electrical Installation Services
S.I.C.: 1731
N.A.I.C.S.: 238210
Illy Laurent *(Gen Dir)*

Hidraulica del Chiriqui, S.A. (1)
Dr Ernesto Perez Balladares
Panama, Panama
Tel.: (507) 7759944
Construction Engineering Services
S.I.C.: 8711
N.A.I.C.S.: 541330

HOCHTIEF AG (1)
Opernplatz 2
D-45128 Essen, Germany De
Tel.: (49) 2018240 (50.35%)
Fax: (49) 2018242777
E-Mail: info@hochtief.de
Web Site: www.hochtief.de
HOT—(DEU OTC)
Sls.: $34,364,653,525
Assets: $22,834,193,238
Liabilities: $17,121,307,569
Net Worth: $5,712,885,669
Earnings: $519,049,498
Emp.: 79,987
Fiscal Year-end: 12/31/12
Planning, Design, Financing & Construction of Building & Civil Engineering Work; Airport Management; Project Development; Facility Management
S.I.C.: 1629
N.A.I.C.S.: 237990
Thomas Eichelmann *(Chm-Supervisory Bd)*
Ulrich Best *(Deputy Chm-Supervisory Bd)*
Peter Wilhelm Sassenfeld *(CFO & Member-Exec Bd)*
Jennifer Siebert *(Press Officer)*
Patricia Wischerhoff *(Press Officer)*
Peter J. Davoren *(Pres/CEO-Turner Construction Company)*
John A. DiCiurcio *(CEO-Flatiron Construction Corp)*
Lars Petzold *(Sr VP-Corp Controlling & IR)*
Bernd Putter *(Sr VP-Corp Comm)*

Groups:

HOCHTIEF Americas GmbH (2)
Opernplatz 2
Essen, 45128, Germany De
Tel.: (49) 2018240
Fax: (49) 2018242777
Web Site: www.hochtief.com
Holding Company
S.I.C.: 6719
N.A.I.C.S.: 551112

U.S. Subsidiaries:

EE Cruz & Company Inc. (3)
165 Ryan St
South Plainfield, NJ 07080 (100%)
Tel.: (732) 946-9700
Fax: (732) 946-7592
E-Mail: info@eecruz.com
Web Site: www.eecruz.com
Sales Range: $125-149.9 Million
Emp.: 150
Heavy Civil Construction Services
S.I.C.: 1622
N.A.I.C.S.: 237310
Edward Cruz *(CEO)*
David Casey *(CFO)*
Jeffrey R. Cruz *(Gen Counsel)*
Bennett Klausner *(Sec & VP-Fin)*

Flatiron Construction Corp. (3)
10188 E. I-25 Frontage Rd
Firestone, CO 80504 (100%)
Mailing Address:
PO Box 2239
Longmont, CO 80502
Tel.: (303) 485-4050
Fax: (303) 485-3922
Web Site: www.flatironcorp.com
Sales Range: $1-4.9 Billion
Emp.: 50
Heavy Civil Construction Services
S.I.C.: 1629
N.A.I.C.S.: 237990
John A. DiCiurcio *(CEO)*
Blair Brandon *(Pres-Canadian Div)*
Terry Poole *(Pres-Heavy Civil Div)*
Curt Weltz *(Pres-Western Div)*
Matt Girard *(Exec VP-Bus Dev)*
Jerry Hartbarger *(Sr VP-HR)*

Divisions:

Ellsworth Paulsen Construction Co. (4)
195 E 600 S
American Fork, UT 84003
Tel.: (801) 756-0404
Fax: (801) 756-0411
E-Mail: epco@e-p.com
Web Site: www.e-p.com
Sales Range: $25-49.9 Million
Emp.: 17
Industrial Building Construction
S.I.C.: 1541
N.A.I.C.S.: 236210
Richard Ellsworth *(Pres)*
Brent Openshaw *(CFO)*

Flatiron Construction Corp. - Heavy Civil Division (4)
1380 Forest Park Cir Ste 202
Lafayette, CO 80026
Tel.: (303) 485-4050
Fax: (303) 776-0072
Web Site: www.flatironcorp.com
Heavy Civil Engineering & Construction
S.I.C.: 1622
N.A.I.C.S.: 237310
Tom Rademacher *(Chm & CEO)*
Terry Poole *(Pres)*
Robert W. French *(COO)*

The Turner Corporation (3)
2001 N Lamar Ste 100
Dallas, TX 75202 DE
Tel.: (214) 721-8400 (100%)
Fax: (214) 721-8493
E-Mail: turner@tcco.com
Web Site: www.turnerconstruction.com
Sales Range: $1-4.9 Billion
Emp.: 4,700
Construction Company
S.I.C.: 1542
N.A.I.C.S.: 236220
Peter J. Davoren *(Pres & CEO)*
Debi A. Herman *(Treas & VP)*
Nicholas E. Billotti *(Exec VP)*
William M. Brennan *(Exec VP)*
Pat A. Di Filippo *(Exec VP)*
Kenneth J. Leach *(Exec VP)*
Rodney J. Michalka *(Exec VP)*
Stuart B. Robinson *(Exec VP)*
Richard C. Bach *(Sr VP)*
Mark A. Boyle *(Sr VP)*
Charles T. Buuck *(Sr VP)*
Rory C. DeJohn *(Sr VP)*
Thomas B. Gerlach, Jr. *(Sr VP)*
Saro J. LaScala *(Sr VP)*
Nicholas T. Makes *(Sr VP)*
Edward V. McNeill *(Sr VP)*
Charles F. Murphy *(Sr VP)*
Michael E. O'Brien *(Sr VP)*
Matthew A. Papenfus *(Sr VP)*
Hilton O. Smith *(Sr VP)*
Roderick F. Wille *(Sr VP-Market Segments)*

Subsidiaries:

The Lathrop Company, Inc. (4)
460 W Dussel Dr
Maumee, OH 43537-4205 OH
Mailing Address: (100%)
PO Box 772
Toledo, OH 43697-0772
Tel.: (419) 893-7000
Fax: (419) 893-1741
Web Site: www.turnerconstruction.com
Emp.: 106
Contracting & Construction Services
S.I.C.: 1542
N.A.I.C.S.: 236220
Stephen J. Klepper *(VP & Gen Mgr)*

Subsidiaries:

Service Products Buildings, Inc. (5)
460 W Dussel Dr
Maumee, OH 43537-4205 (100%)
Tel.: (419) 897-0708
Fax: (419) 897-0938
Web Site: www.turnerconstruction.com
Emp.: 4
Pre-Engineered Metal Buildings Mfr
S.I.C.: 1629
N.A.I.C.S.: 236210

Tomkins Builders, Inc. (4)
1110 Vermont Ave NW Ste 200
Washington, DC 20005-3563 DC
Tel.: (202) 789-0770
Fax: (202) 898-2531
E-Mail: info@tbius.com
Web Site: www.tompkinsbuilders.com
Emp.: 200
Construction Services
S.I.C.: 1542
N.A.I.C.S.: 236220
Ed Small *(Pres)*

Turner Construction Company (4)
375 Hudson St
New York, NY 10014-3658 NY
Tel.: (212) 229-6000 (100%)
Fax: (212) 229-6390
E-Mail: cmurphy@tcco.com
Web Site: www.turnerconstruction.com
Emp.: 506
Non-Residential & Industrial Construction
S.I.C.: 1542
N.A.I.C.S.: 236220
Mark Boyle *(Chief Procurement Officer)*
Pasquale A. DiFilippo *(Exec VP)*
Charles F. Murphy *(Sr VP & Gen Mgr)*
Tom Manahan *(Sr VP)*
Matt Papenfus *(Sr VP-Texas Reg)*
Karen Sweeney *(Sr VP)*

Turner Construction International LLC (4)
375 Hudson St
New York, NY 10014-3658 DE
Tel.: (212) 229-6388 (100%)
Fax: (212) 229-6418
E-Mail: turner@tcco.com
Web Site: www.turnerconstruction.com
Emp.: 500
Provider of Program & Project Management Services; Construction Consulting
S.I.C.: 1542
N.A.I.C.S.: 236220
Abrar Sheriff *(Pres & CEO)*
Uwe Krueger *(Sr VP-Mktg)*

Non-U.S. Subsidiary:

Clark Builders Limited (4)
4703 52 Avenue
Edmonton, AB, T6B 3R6, Canada
Tel.: (780) 395-3300
Fax: (780) 395-3545
E-Mail: edmonton@clarkbuilders.com
Web Site: www.clarkbuilders.com
Sales Range: $450-499.9 Million
Emp.: 700
Construction Services

S.I.C.: 1542
N.A.I.C.S.: 236220
Andrew Clark *(Founder & CEO)*
Paul Verhesen *(Pres)*
Bill Giebelhaus *(COO)*

Non-U.S. Subsidiaries:

HOCHTIEF Construcciones S.A. **(3)**
Av Corrientes 222 Piso 11
C 1043 AAP Buenos Aires, Argentina
Tel.: (54) 11 4510 0410
Fax: (54) 11 4311 4219
E-Mail: htc@hochtief.com.ar
Web Site: www.hochtief.com.ar
Construction of Buildings & Civil Engineering Projects
S.I.C.: 1611
N.A.I.C.S.: 237310

HOCHTIEF do Brasil S.A. **(3)**
Av Alfredo Egidio De Souza
Aranha 145, CEP 04726 170 Sao Paulo, Brazil (100%)
Tel.: (55) 1156430100
Fax: (55) 1156410436
E-Mail: hochtief@hochtief.com.br
Web Site: www.hochtief.com.br
Emp.: 100
Construction of Building & Civil Engineering Work
S.I.C.: 1611
N.A.I.C.S.: 237310
Andre Alexandre Glogowsky *(Chm)*

HOCHTIEF Asia Pacific GmbH **(2)**
Opernplatz 2
45128 Essen, Germany De
Tel.: (49) 2018240
Fax: (49) 2018242777
Web Site: www.hochtief.com
Emp.: 5,000
Holding Company
S.I.C.: 6719
N.A.I.C.S.: 551112
Dieter Teloh *(Mng Dir)*

Non-U.S. Affiliate:

Leighton Holdings Limited **(3)**
472 Pacific Highway
Saint Leonards, NSW, 2065, Australia AU
Tel.: (61) 299256666 (58.8%)
Fax: (61) 299256000
E-Mail: leighton@leighton.com.au
Web Site: www.leighton.com.au
LEI—(ASX)
Rev.: $19,749,566,570
Assets: $11,677,981,020
Liabilities: $8,638,279,530
Net Worth: $3,039,701,490
Earnings: $460,712,410
Emp.: 56,323
Fiscal Year-end: 12/31/12
Holding Company
S.I.C.: 6719
N.A.I.C.S.: 551112
Robert Douglas Humphris *(Chm)*
Marcelino Fernandez Verdes *(CEO)*
Jamila Gordon *(CIO)*
Dharma Chandran *(Chief HR Officer & Chief Corp Svcs Officer)*
Mike Rollo *(Chief Risk Officer)*
Vanessa Hobyn Hees *(Sec)*

Subsidiaries:

John Holland Group Pty. Ltd. **(4)**
70 Trenerry Crescent
Abbotsford, VIC, 3067, Australia (70%)
Tel.: (61) 399345209
Telex: 30774
Fax: (61) 399345275
E-Mail: reception.me@jhj.com.au
Web Site: www.johnholland.com.au
Emp.: 260
Engineering, Commercial & Industrial Construction
S.I.C.: 1542
N.A.I.C.S.: 236220
Janet L. Holmes A Court *(Chm)*
Wal M. King *(Deputy Chm)*

Subsidiary:

John Holland Constructions Pty Ltd. **(5)**
70 Trenerry Crescent
Abbotsford, VIC, 3067, Australia
Tel.: (61) 399345209
Fax: (61) 399345275
E-Mail: info@johnholland.com.au
Web Site: www.johnholland.com.au
Emp.: 7
Construction
S.I.C.: 1542
N.A.I.C.S.: 236220
Tlann Pilan *(Mng Dir)*

Leighton Contractors Pty Limited **(4)**
Level 8 Tower 1
495 Victoria Avenue, Chatswood, NSW, 2067, Australia
Tel.: (61) 286686000
Fax: (61) 286686666
Web Site: www.broad.com.au
Emp.: 500
Contractor Services
S.I.C.: 1542
N.A.I.C.S.: 236220
Peter McMorrow *(Mng Dir)*

Subsidiaries:

Leighton Contractors Pty Limited **(5)**
Level 1 13 Greenhill Rd
Wayville, SA, 5034, Australia
Tel.: (61) 882385000
Telex: AA 881111
Fax: (61) 882385001
Web Site: www.leightoncontractors.com.au
Emp.: 250
Engineering Services
S.I.C.: 8711
N.A.I.C.S.: 541330
Alan Steele *(Gen Mgr)*

Thiess Pty Limited **(4)**
Level 7 189 Grey St
Southbank, QLD, 4101, Australia
Tel.: (61) 731218500
Fax: (61) 731218710
E-Mail: thiesspr@thiess.com.au
Web Site: www.thiess.com.au
Emp.: 350
Construction Engineering & Mining
S.I.C.: 1611
N.A.I.C.S.: 237310
Bruce Munro *(Mng Dir)*

Subsidiaries:

Quantum Explosives **(5)**
Level 7 371 Queen St
Brisbane, QLD, 4001, Australia
Tel.: (61) 7 3221 4066
Fax: (61) 7 3229 2847
Mining Contractor
S.I.C.: 1081
N.A.I.C.S.: 213114

Tarong Coal Ltd **(5)**
280 Nibby Smith Way
PO Box 36
Nanango, QLD, 4615, Australia (100%)
Tel.: (61) 741607211
Fax: (61) 741607200
Web Site: www.thiess.com
Emp.: 230
Coal Mining
S.I.C.: 1221
N.A.I.C.S.: 212111

HOCHTIEF Concessions AG **(2)**
Opernplatz 2
45128 Essen, Germany
Tel.: (49) 2018240
Fax: (49) 2018242777
Web Site: www.hochtief.com
Industrial Infrastructure Service, Including Airports, Roads & Social Infrastructure Segments
S.I.C.: 8711
N.A.I.C.S.: 541330

HOCHTIEF Solutions AG **(2)**
Opernplatz 2
45126 Essen, Germany De
Tel.: (49) 2018244261 (100%)
Fax: (49) 2018244263
E-Mail: info-solutions@hochtief.de
Web Site: www.hochtief-solutions.com
Emp.: 8,500
Building Construction & Civil & Structural Engineering
S.I.C.: 8711
N.A.I.C.S.: 541330
Marcelino Fernandez Verdes *(Chm-Exec Bd & CEO)*
Essimari Kairisto *(Member-Exec Bd & CFO)*
Nikolaus Graf von Matuschka *(Member-Exec Bd)*

Subsidiaries:

car.e Facility Management GmbH **(3)**
Oststrasse 2 C
38122 Braunschweig, Germany
Tel.: (49) 1 505 8791
Fax: (49) 1 505 8701
Facility Management Services
S.I.C.: 8744
N.A.I.C.S.: 561210

HOCHTIEF Energy Management GmbH **(3)**
Speditionstrasse 15
40221 Dusseldorf, Germany
Tel.: (49) 211 60 170 550
Fax: (49) 211 60170 599
E-Mail: info-em@hochtief.de
Web Site: www.hochtief-energymanagement.com
Emp.: 300
Energy Consulting Services
S.I.C.: 8999
N.A.I.C.S.: 541690
Jobst Klien *(Chm-Mgmt Bd)*
Peter Antic *(Member-Mgmt Bd)*
Holger Treckmann *(Member-Mgmt Bd)*

HOCHTIEF PPP Solutions GmbH **(3)**
Alfredstrasse 236
45133 Essen, Germany
Tel.: (49) 2018241284
Fax: (49) 2018242030
E-Mail: info-ppp@hochtief.de
Web Site: www.ppp.hochtief.com
Emp.: 150
Infrastructure Construction Services
S.I.C.: 1629
N.A.I.C.S.: 237990
Bernward Kulle *(CEO)*

Non-U.S. Subsidiary:

HOCHTIEF PPP Solutions (UK) Ltd. **(4)**
Epsilon Windmill Hill Business Park
Whitehill Way, Swindon, Wilts, SN5 6NX, United Kingdom
Tel.: (44) 1793 735 594
Fax: (44) 1793 755557
Web Site: www.ppp.hochtief.com
Infrastructure Construction Services
S.I.C.: 1629
N.A.I.C.S.: 237990
Roger Potts *(Dir)*

HOCHTIEF Projektentwicklung GmbH **(3)**
Alfredstrasse 236
45133 Essen, Germany
Tel.: (49) 2018241217
Fax: (49) 2018241728
E-Mail: info.htp@hochtief.de
Web Site: www.hochtief-projektentwicklung.de
Emp.: 260
Project Development of Office, Hotel, Mixed-Use & Special-Purpose Properties
S.I.C.: 6531
N.A.I.C.S.: 531390
Rainer Eichholz *(Chm-Mgmt Bd & Mng Dir)*
Robert Bambach *(Mng Dir)*
Christoph Husmann *(Mng Dir)*

Subsidiary:

HOCHTIEF Projektentwicklung Helfmann Park GmbH & Co. KG **(4)**
Opernplatz 2
Essen, North Rhine, 45128, Germany
Tel.: (49) 201824
Real Estate Management Services
S.I.C.: 6531
N.A.I.C.S.: 531390

HOCHTIEF Property Management GmbH **(3)**
Alfredstrasse 236
45133 Essen, Germany
Tel.: (49) 201 824 7978
Fax: (49) 201 824 8031
E-Mail: info@hochtief.de
Web Site: www.hochtief-propertymanagement.de
Emp.: 500
Real Estate Management Services
S.I.C.: 6531
N.A.I.C.S.: 531390
Michael Beer *(Mng Dir)*

Streif Baulogistik GmbH **(3)**
Alfredstrasse 236
45133 Essen, Germany (100%)
Tel.: (49) 2011064700
Fax: (49) 2011064709
E-Mail: info@streif-baulogistik.de
Web Site: www.streif-baulogistik.de
Emp.: 3,000
Construction Site Logistics, Including Services Related to Construction Site Equipment, Execution of Construction Work & Operations; Building Machinery & Equipment Leasing, Scaffolding & Shuttering & Logistics Engineering Services
S.I.C.: 7353
N.A.I.C.S.: 532412
Joerg Meckbach *(Mng Dir)*
Thorsten Wiesendorfer *(Mng Dir)*
Verena Blaschke *(PR Officer)*

Subsidiary:

Prum-Turenwerk GmbH **(4)**
Andreas Stihl Strasse
54595 Weinheim, Germany (100%)
Tel.: (49) 065511201
Fax: (49) 0655112550
E-Mail: kontact@tuer.de
Web Site: www.tuer.de
Sales Range: $50-74.9 Million
Emp.: 450
Production & Marketing of Prefabricated Homes
S.I.C.: 2452
N.A.I.C.S.: 321992

Turner HOCHTIEF Construction Management GmbH **(3)**
Opernplatz 2
Essen, 45128, Germany
Tel.: (49) 2018244261
Construction Engineering Services
S.I.C.: 8711
N.A.I.C.S.: 541330

Non-U.S. Subsidiaries:

HOCHTIEF Construction Austria GmbH & Co KG **(3)**
Amalienstrasse 65
1130 Vienna, Austria (100%)
Tel.: (43) 190769070
Fax: (43) 1 9076907 50
E-Mail: info-construction@hochtief.at
Web Site: www.hochtief-construction.at
Civil Engineering & Construction Services
S.I.C.: 1629
N.A.I.C.S.: 237990
Thomas Pracher *(Head-Pur)*

HOCHTIEF Facility Management Ireland Ltd. **(3)**
Landscape House Landscape Road
Churchtown
Dublin, 14, Ireland (100%)
Tel.: (353) 12157000
Fax: (353) 12157070
E-Mail: helpdesk@ie.hsgzander.com
Web Site: www.hsgzander.com
Emp.: 200
Facility Management Services
S.I.C.: 7349
N.A.I.C.S.: 561790
Jeff Smith *(CEO)*

HOCHTIEF (UK) Construction Ltd. **(3)**
Epsilon Windmill Hill Business Park
Whitehill Way, Swindon, Wilts, SN5 6NX, United Kingdom (100%)
Tel.: (44) 1793755555
Fax: (44) 1793755556
E-Mail: enquiries@hochtief.co.uk
Web Site: www.hochtief-construction.co.uk
Sales Range: $50-74.9 Million
Emp.: 150
Construction of Building & Civil Engineering Work
S.I.C.: 1622
N.A.I.C.S.: 237310
Tim P. Lloyd *(Sec & Dir-Fin)*

ACS, Actividades de Construccion y Servicios, S.A.—(Continued)

Subsidiaries:

Dieter Hafemeister Erdbau GmbH & Co. (2)
Baureutherstrasse 36
18789 Berlin, Germany (100%)
Tel.: (49) 30332060
Fax: (49) 303316841
Web Site: www.hafemeister.de
Civil Works Construction & Engineering
S.I.C.: 1629
N.A.I.C.S.: 237990

Eurafrica Baugesellschaft mbH (2)
Steinstrasse 1
45128 Essen, Germany
Tel.: (49) 201 8240
Fax: (49) 201 8242227
E-Mail: info@hochtief.de
Construction Engineering Services
S.I.C.: 8711
N.A.I.C.S.: 541330
Frank Stieler *(Gen Mgr)*

HOCHTIEF Global One GmbH (2)
Opernplatz 2
Essen, 45128, Germany
Tel.: (49) 2018241925
Construction Engineering Services
S.I.C.: 8711
N.A.I.C.S.: 541330

HOCHTIEF Global Trade GmbH (2)
Alfredstrasse 236
45133 Essen, Germany
Tel.: (49) 201 824 1939
Fax: (49) 201 824 2002
E-Mail: global-trade@hochtief.de
Web Site: www.hochtief-globaltrade.com
Construction Materials Whslr
S.I.C.: 5039
N.A.I.C.S.: 423390
Ralf Behn *(Mng Dir)*
Klaus Blachnik *(Mng Dir)*
Dirk Schenke *(Mng Dir)*

HOCHTIEF Insurance Broking & Risk Management Solutions GmbH (2)
Opernplatz 2
45128 Essen, Germany
Tel.: (49) 2018240
Fax: (49) 2018242271
E-Mail: info@hochtief.de
Web Site: www.hochtief.com
Emp.: 12
Insurance & Risk Management Services
S.I.C.: 6411
N.A.I.C.S.: 524298
Lutz Kalkofen *(Mng Dir)*

HOCHTIEF Verkehrswegebau GmbH (2)
Opernplatz 2
D-45128 Essen, Germany (100%)
Tel.: (49) 2018240
Fax: (49) 2018242777
E-Mail: info@hochtief.de
Web Site: www.hochtief.com
Emp.: 50
Road Construction
S.I.C.: 1611
N.A.I.C.S.: 237310
Mr Kuepers *(Gen Mgr)*

Suddeutsche Wohnungsbau GmbH (2)
Klosestrasse 42
76137 Karlsruhe, Germany (100%)
Tel.: (49) 721 31140
Manages Flats & Industrial Units
S.I.C.: 3564
N.A.I.C.S.: 333413

ZOB an der Hackerbrucke GmbH & Co. KG (2)
Alfredstr 236
45133 Essen, Germany
Tel.: (49) 201 8241223
Fax: (49) 201 8241290
Real Estate Management Services
S.I.C.: 6531
N.A.I.C.S.: 531390

Affiliates:

Rheinische Baustoffwerke GmbH & Co. KG (2)
Auenheimer Strasse
50129 Bergheim, Germany (33%)
Tel.: (49) 227175125468
Fax: (49) 227175125717
E-Mail: info@rheinischebaustoffwerke.de
Web Site: www.rheinischebaustoffwerke.de
Emp.: 200
Sale of Sand & Gravel
S.I.C.: 1442
N.A.I.C.S.: 212321
Michael Groezinger *(Pres)*

Sudwestdeutsche Rohrleitungsbau GmbH (2)
Intze St 14-16
60314 Frankfurt am Main, Germany (45%)
Tel.: (49) 699443250
Fax: (49) 69435425
E-Mail: info@swr-gmbh.de
Web Site: www.swr-gmbh.de
Emp.: 150
Construction & Operation of Pipe Networks
S.I.C.: 1629
N.A.I.C.S.: 237120
Walter Herlitschke *(Gen Mgr)*

Non-U.S. Subsidiaries:

DURST-BAU GmbH (2)
Analienstrasse 65
1130 Vienna, Austria
Tel.: (43) 1877944110
Fax: (43) 1877944119
E-Mail: hubert.niedermayer@hochtief.de
Web Site: www.hochtief-construction.de
Emp.: 50
Construction Services
S.I.C.: 1629
N.A.I.C.S.: 237990
Stephan Schmiedehausen *(Chm-Mgmt Bd)*

HOCHTIEF Aktiengesellschaft Vorm. Gebr. Helfman Ges. M.b.H. (2)
Rossaugasse 3
6020 Innsbruck, Austria (100%)
Tel.: (43) 512334230
Fax: (43) 5123342333
E-Mail: simone.stimmelmayr@hochtief.de
Web Site: www.hochtief.de
Heavy Construction
S.I.C.: 1629
N.A.I.C.S.: 237990

HOCHTIEF CZ a.s. (2)
Plzenska 16/3217
150 00 Prague, Czech Republic
Tel.: (420) 257 406 000
Fax: (420) 257 406 001
E-Mail: info@hochtief.cz
Web Site: www.hochtief.cz
Emp.: 1,250
Construction Engineering Services
S.I.C.: 8711
N.A.I.C.S.: 541330
Eimert Los *(Chm-Supervisory Bd)*
Tomas Bilek *(Chm-Exec Bd & CEO)*
Peter Maronna *(Member-Exec Bd & CFO)*

HOCHTIEF-Luxembourg S.A. (2)
4 Rue De Neurburg S
2215 Luxembourg, Luxembourg (100%)
Tel.: (352) 4266301
Fax: (352) 426670
E-Mail: info@hochtief.lu
Web Site: www.hochtief.lu
Emp.: 130
Construction of Building & Civil Engineering Work
S.I.C.: 1622
N.A.I.C.S.: 237310
Daniel Debras *(Mng Dir)*

HOCHTIEF Polska Sp. z.o.o. (2)
Ul Elblaska 14
01 737 Warsaw, Poland (100%)
Tel.: (48) 225600800
Fax: (48) 226339786
E-Mail: Info@hochtief.pl
Web Site: www.hochtief.pl
Emp.: 240
Construction of Building & Civil Engineering Work
S.I.C.: 1622
N.A.I.C.S.: 237310
Hemryk J. Liszka *(CEO)*

HOCHTIEF VSB A/S (2)
Primatorska 361323
18000 Prague, 8, Czech Republic (100%)
Tel.: (420) 283843272
Fax: (420) 283840642
E-Mail: info@hochtief-vsb.cz
Web Site: www.hochtief-vsb.cz
Sales Range: $125-149.9 Million
Emp.: 1,800
Construction of Building & Civil Engineering Work
S.I.C.: 8712
N.A.I.C.S.: 541310

Non-U.S. Joint Venture:

Athens International Airport S.A. (2)
Eleftherios Venizelos Administration Bldg 17
Spata, 190 19 Athens, Greece (36.13%)
Tel.: (30) 210 3530000
Fax: (30) 210 3532284
E-Mail: airport_info@aia.gr
Web Site: www.aia.gr
Airline Services
S.I.C.: 4581
N.A.I.C.S.: 488119

Iberoamericana de Hidrocarburos, S.A. de C.V. (1)
Batallon De San Patricio No 111 Int 109
Valle Oriente
Garza Garcia, Nuevo Leon, 66260, Mexico
Tel.: (52) 8183638290
Industrial Plant Construction Services
S.I.C.: 1629
N.A.I.C.S.: 236210

Instalaciones y Servicios Codeven, C.A. (1)
Avda Sfco Miranda Torre Parque Cristal
Torre Este Planta 8 Oficiana
Chacao, Caracas, Venezuela
Tel.: (58) 212 793 1415
Fax: (58) 212 793 3106
Construction Engineering Services
S.I.C.: 1629
N.A.I.C.S.: 237990

Jingtang International Container Terminal Co. Ltd. (1)
Jingtang Port
Tangshan, Hebei, China
Tel.: (86) 315 2915963
Fax: (86) 315 2915963
Commercial Storage Services
S.I.C.: 4226
N.A.I.C.S.: 493190

Octeva, S.A.S. (1)
Za Marcel Doret 293 Rue Jacques Monod
BP 100
62100 Calais, Pas De Calais, France
Tel.: (33) 321977420
Fax: (33) 321972650
Emp.: 1
Waste Treatment Services
S.I.C.: 4959
N.A.I.C.S.: 562998
Stephane Bisensang *(Gen Mgr)*

Semi Maroc, S.A. (1)
5 Rue Fakir Mohamed
Casablanca, Morocco
Tel.: (212) 522 47 68 74
Fax: (212) 522 47 66 02
Electrical Assembly Services
S.I.C.: 1731
N.A.I.C.S.: 238210

Servicios Corporativos TWC, S.A. de C.V. (1)
Lazaro Cardenas Km 6 Las Minitas
Hermosillo, Sonora, 83310, Mexico
Tel.: (52) 6622178330
Fax: (52) 6622178330
Business Support Services
S.I.C.: 7389
N.A.I.C.S.: 561499
Francisco Estrella Gonzalez *(Gen Mgr)*

Servicios Cymimex, S.A. de C.V. (1)
Juan Racine 112 60 Piso Colonia Los Morales
11510 Mexico, Mexico
Tel.: (52) 55 5010 4600
Fax: (52) 55 5010 4602
Electrical Equipment Installation Services
S.I.C.: 1731
N.A.I.C.S.: 238210

Sice Hellas Sistemas Tecnologicos Sociedad Unipersonal de Responsabilidad Limitada (1)
Omirou 2 2nd Floor
Kifissia, Athens, 14562, Greece
Tel.: (30) 210 62 34 032
Construction Engineering Services
S.I.C.: 8711
N.A.I.C.S.: 541330
Jose Luis *(Mgr-Project)*

SICE PTY, Ltd. (1)
Level 3 44 Caroline St South Yarra
Melbourne, VIC, 3141, Australia
Tel.: (61) 382566900
Fax: (61) 398209554
E-Mail: pbeltran@sice.com.au
Web Site: www.sice.com
Civil Engineering Construction Services
S.I.C.: 1629
N.A.I.C.S.: 237990

Sintax Logistica Transportes, S.A. (1)
Estrada Algeruz Setubal
Setubal, 2910-279, Portugal
Tel.: (351) 265739600
Fax: (351) 265739606
Logistics Consulting Services
S.I.C.: 4731
N.A.I.C.S.: 541614

Sintax Navigomes, Ltda. (1)
Av Luisa Todi Nr 73
Setubal, 2904-505, Portugal
Tel.: (351) 265546300
Fax: (351) 265546370
Logistics Services
S.I.C.: 4731
N.A.I.C.S.: 541614
Pedro Rodrigues *(Gen Mgr)*

Sistemas Sec, S.A. (1)
Miraflores 383 Oficina 1004
Santiago, Chile
Tel.: (56) 2 345 46 00
Fax: (56) 2 345 46 02
E-Mail: contacto@sistemas-sec.cl
Web Site: www.sistemas-sec.cl
Communication Line Construction Services
S.I.C.: 1623
N.A.I.C.S.: 237130

Small Medium Enterprises Consulting, B.V. (1)
De Lairessestraat 154
Amsterdam, Noord-Holland, 1075 HL, Netherlands
Tel.: (31) 885609950
Management Consulting Services
S.I.C.: 8748
N.A.I.C.S.: 541618

Sociedad Concesionaria Ruta del Canal, S.A. (1)
Antonio Varas No 216 Oficina 701
Puerto Montt, Chile
Tel.: (56) 65 263 6
Fax: (56) 65 263 664
E-Mail: info@rutadelcanal.cl
Web Site: www.rutadelcanal.cl
Emp.: 11
Road Construction Services
S.I.C.: 1611
N.A.I.C.S.: 237310
Ricardo Trencado *(Gen Mgr)*

Tecmed Maroc, S.A.R.L. (1)
Quartier Souissi 292 Rue Mohamed
Belyazid Cite OLM
Rabat, 10000, Morocco
Tel.: (212) 537650011
Fax: (212) 537639943
Solid Waste Treatment Services
S.I.C.: 4953
N.A.I.C.S.: 562219
Luis Masiello *(Gen Mgr)*

Tecneira, S.A. (1)
Rua Rui Teles Palhinha 4 Leiao
2740 278 Porto Salvo, Portugal
Tel.: (351) 214233770
Fax: (351) 214233789
E-Mail: geral@tecneira.pt
Web Site: www.tecneira.pt
Electric Power Generation Services
S.I.C.: 4939
N.A.I.C.S.: 221118

Tesca Ingenieria del Ecuador, S.A. (1)
Av 6 De Diciembre 3445 Y Checoslovaquia
Quito, Pichincha, Ecuador
Tel.: (593) 22454960
Fax: (593) 22459264
Civil Engineering Construction Services

S.I.C.: 1629
N.A.I.C.S.: 237990

Trafiurbe, S.A. (1)
Est Octavio Pato 175-177 Ed A no 4
2785-601 Sao Domingos de Rana, Portugal
Tel.: (351) 214 239 410
Fax: (351) 214 239 419
E-Mail: geral@trafiurbe.pt
Web Site: www.trafiurbe.pt
Emp.: 33
Construction Engineering Services
S.I.C.: 8711
N.A.I.C.S.: 541330

Trans Inter Europe, S.A.S (1)
Rue De Phaffans
90380 Roppe, France
Tel.: (33) 384299125
Logistics Services
S.I.C.: 4731
N.A.I.C.S.: 541614

Uirapuru Transmissora de Energia, Ltda (1)
Av Deputado Antonio Edu Vieira 999 Terreo
Bairro Pantanal
Florianopolis, Santa Catarina, 88040-901, Brazil
Tel.: (55) 48 3231 7282
Fax: (55) 48 3234 2776
Web Site: www.uirapuruenergia.com.br
Power Transmission Line Construction Services
S.I.C.: 1623
N.A.I.C.S.: 237130

Urbaser Environnement, S.A.S. (1)
1140 Avenue Albert Einstein Immeuble
Symphonie Sud
BP 51
34935 Montpellier, France
Tel.: (33) 4 67 99 41 00
Fax: (33) 4 67 99 41 01
E-Mail: contact@urbaserenvironnement.fr
Web Site: www.urbaserenvironnement.fr
Waste Treatment Services
S.I.C.: 4959
N.A.I.C.S.: 562998

Urbaser San Diego, C.A. (1)
Cent Com Fin de Siglo Pta Baja Av D Julio
Centeno Sector
La Esmeralda Local 11, San Diego, Venezuela
Tel.: (58) 241 8726377
Fax: (58) 241 5113046
E-Mail: infor@urbasersandiego.com
Web Site: www.urbasersandiego.com
Solid Waste Collection Services
S.I.C.: 4212
N.A.I.C.S.: 562111

Urbaser Valencia, C.A. (1)
Av Paseo Cabriales Sector Kerdell Torre
Movilnet Piso 11 Oficina 2
Valencia, Venezuela
Tel.: (58) 241 8234210
Fax: (58) 241 8237245
E-Mail: infor@urbaservalencia.com
Web Site: www.urbaservalencia.com
Solid Waste Collection & Street Cleaning Services
S.I.C.: 4212
N.A.I.C.S.: 562111
Juan Lozano *(Gen Mgr)*

Urbasys, S.A.S. (1)
Route Du Tremblay
91480 Varennes-Jarcy, Essonne, France
Tel.: (33) 169005741
Waste Treatment Services
S.I.C.: 4959
N.A.I.C.S.: 562998

Valorga International, S.A.S. (1)
1140 Avenue Albert Einstein
BP 51
34935 Montpellier, France
Tel.: (33) 4 67 99 41 00
Fax: (33) 4 67 99 41 01
E-Mail: contact@valorgainternational.fr
Web Site: www.valorgainternational.fr
Waste Treatment Plant Construction Services
S.I.C.: 1623
N.A.I.C.S.: 237110
Jose Daniel Fernandez Moreno *(Pres)*
Claude Saint-Joly *(Pres)*

Venezolana de Limpiezas Industriales, C.A. (1)
Piso 6 Plaza Venezuela
Caracas, 1050, Venezuela
Tel.: (58) 212 782 9075
Fax: (58) 212 781 1135
E-Mail: venelin@cantv.net
Web Site: www.venelin.com.ve
Industrial Cleaning & Maintenance Services
S.I.C.: 4959
N.A.I.C.S.: 562998

ACS BUSINESS SUPPLIES LIMITED

5-6 Aire Valley Business Park Wagon Lane
Bingley, BD16 1WA, United Kingdom
Tel.: (44) 8444 123 170
Fax: (44) 8444 123 171
E-Mail: info@acsacs.co.uk
Web Site: www.acsacs.co.uk
Year Founded: 2008
Sales Range: $10-24.9 Million
Emp.: 75
Business Description:
Office Product Whslr
S.I.C.: 5112
N.A.I.C.S.: 424120
Personnel:
Mike Hussain *(Mng Dir)*

ACS LIMITED

(See Under Active Exhaust Corp.)

ACS - MOTION CONTROL LTD.

Ramat Gabriel Industrial Park
PO Box 5668
Migdal Ha'Emeq, 10500, Israel
Tel.: (972) 46546440
Fax: (972) 46546443
E-Mail: info@acsmotioncontrol.com
Web Site: www.acsmotioncontrol.com
Year Founded: 1985
ACSEF—(OTC)
Sales Range: $1-9.9 Million
Emp.: 65
Business Description:
Mfr. of Motion Control Devices & Equipment
S.I.C.: 3823
N.A.I.C.S.: 334513
Personnel:
Ze'ev Kirshenboim *(Chm, Pres & CFO)*
Dror Marom *(CEO)*
Ilana Kirshenboim *(Sec & VP-HR)*
Board of Directors:
Ze'ev Kirshenboim
Eli Dayan
Jacob Engel
Shmuel Olek
Alexandra Pluber
Ze'ev Ritman
Abraham Yoskovitz

ACSUD

ZI Courtine Chaternay BP 1016
84096 Avignon, Vaucluse, France
Tel.: (33) 432743000
Web Site: www.acsud.com
Sales Range: $25-49.9 Million
Emp.: 48
Business Description:
Automobile Parts Mfr
S.I.C.: 3711
N.A.I.C.S.: 336111

ACT CO., LTD.

1-202 Woram-dong Dalseo-gu
Dalseo, Daegu, Korea (South)
Tel.: (82) 53 593 8560
Fax: (82) 53 602 4399
Web Site: www.actfpc.com
131400—(KRS)
Emp.: 320
Business Description:
Printed Circuit Boards Mfr & Distr
S.I.C.: 3672
N.A.I.C.S.: 334412
Personnel:
Jong-Chan An *(Co-CEO)*
Seung-Pyeong Koo *(Co-CEO)*

ACT360 SOLUTIONS LTD.

Suite 1116 207 West Hastings Street
Vancouver, BC, V6B 1H7, Canada
Tel.: (604) 638-1553
E-Mail: info@act360.com
Web Site: www.act360.com
Year Founded: 1997
AKM—(TSXV)
Sls.: $1,037,718
Assets: $361,468
Liabilities: $97,519
Net Worth: $263,948
Earnings: $70,559
Fiscal Year-end: 09/30/13
Business Description:
Educational Support Services
S.I.C.: 8299
N.A.I.C.S.: 611710
Personnel:
Dickson Hall *(Chm)*
Vincent Wong *(CEO)*
Ronald Erdman *(Acting CFO & Sec)*
Board of Directors:
Dickson Hall
Ronald Erdman
Howard Louie
Vincent Wong
Transfer Agent:
Computershare Trust Company of Canada
510 Burrard St 3rd Fl
Vancouver, BC, V6C 3B9, Canada

ACTA S.P.A.

Via di Lavoria 56/g - Loc Lavoria
56040 Crespina, Pisa, Italy
Tel.: (39) 050 644281
Fax: (39) 050 642251
Web Site: www.actagroup.it
Year Founded: 2004
A6E—(AIM DEU)
Sales Range: $1-9.9 Million
Business Description:
Clean Technology Product Mfr
S.I.C.: 3699
N.A.I.C.S.: 335999
Personnel:
Robert Drummond *(Chm)*
Paolo Bert *(CEO)*
Paul Barritt *(CFO)*
Board of Directors:
Robert Drummond
Paul Barritt
Paolo Bert
Aldo Filippini
Rodney Westhead

ACTAVIS PLC

1 Grand Canal Square Docklands
Dublin, 2, Ireland
Tel.: (353) 1 897 2000
Web Site: www.actavis.com
Year Founded: 2013
ACT—(NYSE)
Rev.: $8,677,600,000
Assets: $22,725,900,000
Liabilities: $13,188,800,000
Net Worth: $9,537,100,000
Earnings: $751,100,000
Emp.: 19,200
Fiscal Year-end: 12/31/13
Business Description:
Holding Company; Pharmaceutical Developer, Mfr & Distr
S.I.C.: 6719
N.A.I.C.S.: 551112
Personnel:
Paul M. Bisaro *(Chm, Pres & CEO)*
Sigurdur Oli Olafsson *(Pres-Actavis Pharma)*
George Frederick Wilkinson *(Pres-Global R&D)*
Board of Directors:
Paul M. Bisaro
James H. Bloem
Christopher W. Bodine
Tamar D. Howson
John A. King
Catherine M. Klema
Jiri Michal
Jack Michelson
Patrick J. O'Sullivan
Sigurdur Oli Olafsson
Ronald R. Taylor
Andrew L. Turner
Fred G. Weiss

Co-Headquarters:

Actavis, Inc. (1)
(Formerly Watson Pharmaceuticals, Inc.)
Morris Corp Ctr III 400 Interpace Pkwy
Parsippany, NJ 07054 NV
Tel.: (862) 261-7000
Toll Free: (800) 249-5499
E-Mail:
Web Site: www.actavis.com
Rev.: $5,914,900,000
Assets: $14,103,500,000
Liabilities: $10,247,100,000
Net Worth: $3,856,400,000
Earnings: $98,300,000
Emp.: 17,700
Fiscal Year-end: 12/31/12
Holding Company; Pharmaceutical Developer & Mfr
Import
S.I.C.: 6719
N.A.I.C.S.: 551112
David A. Buchen *(Chief Legal Officer-Global)*
Charles M. Mayr *(Chief Comm Officer-Global)*
James D'Arecca *(Chief Acctg Officer)*
Patrick J. Eagan *(Chief HR Officer-Global)*
Sigurdur Oli Olafsson *(Pres-Pharma)*
Robert A. Stewart *(Pres-Global Ops)*
George Frederick Wilkinson *(Pres-Global R&D)*

Subsidiaries:

ANDA PHARMACEUTICALS, INC (2)
6500 Adelaide Ct
Groveport, OH 43125
Tel.: (614) 497-5840
Fax: (614) 497-5873
Pharmaceutical Product Distr
S.I.C.: 5122
N.A.I.C.S.: 424210

Andrx Corporation (2)
4955 Orange Dr
Davie, FL 33314 DE
Tel.: (954) 585-1400
Fax: (954) 217-4327
Toll Free: (800) 621-7143
E-Mail: andrxinfo@watsonandandrx.com
Web Site: www.watson.com
Emp.: 1,600
Generic Pharmaceuticals Mfr
S.I.C.: 2834
N.A.I.C.S.: 325412
Thomas R. Giordano *(CIO & Sr VP)*

Subsidiaries:

Anda, Inc. (3)
2915 Weston Rd
Weston, FL 33331 FL
Tel.: (954) 217-4774
Fax: (954) 217-4199
Toll Free: (877) ANDANET
E-Mail: anda@andanet.com
Web Site: www.andanet.com
Sales Range: $100-124.9 Million
Emp.: 200
Onliner Generic Pharmaceuticals Distr
S.I.C.: 5122
N.A.I.C.S.: 424210

Actavis plc—(Continued)

Albert Paonessa *(COO & Exec VP)*

ValMed Pharmaceutical, Inc. (3)
3000 Alt Blvd
Grand Island, NY 14072 NY
Tel.: (716) 773-4600
Fax: (716) 773-5617
E-Mail: infovip@vippharm.com
Web Site: www.vippharm.com
Sales Range: $75-99.9 Million
Emp.: 70
Distr Generic Pharmaceuticals
S.I.C.: 5122
N.A.I.C.S.: 424210

Warner Chilcott Corporation (2)
100 Enterprise Dr
Rockaway, NJ 07866 DE
Tel.: (973) 442-3200
Fax: (973) 442-3283
E-Mail: ir@wcrx.com
Web Site: www.wcrx.com
Emp.: 582
Women's Healthcare & Dermatology Pharmaceuticals Mfr
Import Export
S.I.C.: 2834
N.A.I.C.S.: 325412
Roger M. Boissonneault *(CEO)*
Paul S. Herendeen *(CFO & Exec VP)*
W. Carlton Reichel *(Pres-Pharmaceuticals)*
Izumi Hara *(Gen Counsel, Sec & Sr VP)*
Anthony D. Bruno *(Exec VP-Corp Dev)*
Leland H. Cross *(Sr VP-Technical Ops)*
Herman Ellman *(Sr VP-Clinical Dev)*
Alvin D. Howard *(Sr VP-Regulatory Affairs)*

Subsidiaries:

Warner Chilcott Company, Inc. (3)
Union St Km 1.1
Fajardo, PR 00738 PR
Tel.: (787) 863-1850
Fax: (787) 863-5355
Web Site: www.warnerchilcott.com
Emp.: 340
Mfr of Pharmaceuticals
S.I.C.: 2834
N.A.I.C.S.: 325412
Claire Gilligan *(VP-Quality)*

Warner Chilcott Holdings Company III, Limited (3)
100 Enterprise Dr
Rockaway, NJ 07866
Tel.: (973) 442-3200
Investment Management Services
S.I.C.: 6211
N.A.I.C.S.: 523999

Non-U.S. Subsidiaries:

Warner Chilcott (Ireland) Limited (4)
Building B Xerox Technology Park
Dundalk, Louth, Ireland
Tel.: (353) 429395900
Web Site: www.wcrx.com
Pharmaceutical Products Mfr
S.I.C.: 2834
N.A.I.C.S.: 325412

Warner Chilcott Nederland B.V (4)
Lichtenauerlaan 102 120
3062 ME Rotterdam, Netherlands
Tel.: (31) 10 2045557
Fax: (31) 10 2863169
Pharmaceutical Products Mfr
S.I.C.: 2834
N.A.I.C.S.: 325412

Non-U.S. Subsidiaries:

Warner Chilcott Italy S.r.l. (5)
Viale Giorgio Ribotta 11
00144 Rome, Italy
Tel.: (39) 06 87504060
Fax: (39) 06 87504061
Pharmaceutical Products Mfr
S.I.C.: 2834
N.A.I.C.S.: 325412

Warner Chilcott Pharmaceuticals B.V.B.A. (5)
Pegasuslaan 5
1831 Diegem, Belgium
Tel.: (32) 2 709 20 69
Fax: (32) 2 709 23 70
Pharmaceutical Products Mfr
S.I.C.: 2834
N.A.I.C.S.: 325412

Warner Chilcott Pharmaceuticals S.a.r.l. (5)
Avenue des Morgines 12
1213 Petit-Lancy, Switzerland
Tel.: (41) 22 879 19 00
Fax: (41) 42 9395 901
Pharmaceutical Products Mfr
S.I.C.: 2834
N.A.I.C.S.: 325412

WC Pharmaceuticals I Limited (4)
Icom House Suite 3 Second Floor 1/5
Irish Town, Gibraltar, Gibraltar
Tel.: (350) 200 50418
Pharmaceutical Products Mfr
S.I.C.: 2834
N.A.I.C.S.: 325412

U.S. Subsidiary:

Warner Chilcott Company, LLC (5)
Union St Rd 195 Km 1 1
Fajardo, PR 00738
Tel.: (787) 863-1850
Fax: (787) 863-5355
Pharmaceutical Products Mfr
S.I.C.: 2834
N.A.I.C.S.: 325412

Warner Chilcott Puerto Rico LLC (3)
RR 2
Manati, PR 00674-9801 DE
Mailing Address:
PO Box 1055
Manati, PR 00674-8502
Tel.: (787) 854-1520
Sales Range: $25-49.9 Million
Emp.: 126
Pharmaceutical Mfr
S.I.C.: 2834
N.A.I.C.S.: 325412
Dave Cabarrery *(Plant Mgr)*

Warner Chilcott (US), LLC (3)
100 Enterprise Dr
Rockaway, NJ 07866-2198
Tel.: (973) 442-3200
Toll Free: (800) 521-8813
Pharmaceutical Preparation Mfr
S.I.C.: 2834
N.A.I.C.S.: 325412
Roger M. Boissonneault *(CEO)*

Non-U.S. Subsidiary:

Warner Chilcott UK Ltd. (3)
Old Belfast Rd
Milbrook, Larne, Co Antrim, BT40 2SH, United Kingdom
Tel.: (44) 2828267222
Fax: (44) 2828279448
E-Mail: info@warnerchilcott.com
Web Site: www.wcx.com
Developer & Mfr of Pharmaceuticals for Dermatology & Women's Health
S.I.C.: 2834
N.A.I.C.S.: 325412
Clarie Gilligan *(VP-Ops)*

Subsidiary:

Warner Chilcott Pharmaceuticals UK Limited (4)
Rusham Park Whitehall Ln
Egham, TW20 9NW, United Kingdom
Tel.: (44) 1784 474900
Fax: (44) 1784 431 080
Pharmaceutical Products Mfr & Distr
S.I.C.: 2834
N.A.I.C.S.: 325412

Non-U.S. Subsidiary:

Warner Chilcott Deutschland GmbH (4)
Dr -Otto-Rohm-Str 2-4
64331 Weiterstadt, Germany
Tel.: (49) 6151 877 0
Fax: (49) 6151 89 55 94
Web Site: www.wcrx.com
Pharmaceutical Product Mfr
S.I.C.: 2834
N.A.I.C.S.: 325412

Watson Laboratories, Inc. (2)
311 Bonnie Cir
Corona, CA 91720 NV
Tel.: (951) 493-5300 (100%)
Fax: (951) 493-5816
Web Site: www.watson.com
Emp.: 5,000
Pharmaceuticals
S.I.C.: 2834
N.A.I.C.S.: 325412

Watson Laboratories, Inc. (2)
33 Ralph Ave
Copiague, NY 11726 NY
Tel.: (631) 693-8000 (100%)
Fax: (631) 693-8001
Web Site: www.watson.com
Sales Range: $25-49.9 Million
Emp.: 100
Mfr. of Pharmaceutical Products
S.I.C.: 2834
N.A.I.C.S.: 325412

Watson Pharmaceuticals, Inc. - Puerto Rico (2)
Texaco Plz Ste 412
Guaynabo, PR 00968
Tel.: (787) 782-3411
Fax: (787) 782-3411
Web Site: www.watson.com
Sales Range: $150-199.9 Million
Emp.: 1
Mfr. of Pharmaceuticals
S.I.C.: 2834
N.A.I.C.S.: 325412

Non-U.S. Subsidiaries:

Actavis Group ehf. (2)
Dalshrauni 1
220 Hafnarfjordur, Iceland IS
Tel.: (354) 5352300 (100%)
Fax: (354) 5352301
E-Mail: actavis@actavis.com
Web Site: www.actavis.com
Sales Range: $1-4.9 Billion
Emp.: 750
Holding Company; Pharmaceutical Products Developer & Mfr
S.I.C.: 6719
N.A.I.C.S.: 551112
Claudio Albrecht *(CEO)*
Gudbjorg Edda Eggertsdottir *(Deputy CEO)*
Gunnar Beinteinsson *(Exec VP-HR)*
Aidan Kavanagh *(Exec VP-Ops-Central Eastern Europe & Asia)*
Mark Burgess Keatley *(Exec VP-Fin & IT)*
Fearghal Murphy *(Exec VP-Supply Chain Ops)*
Valur Ragnarsson *(Exec VP-Thirp Party Sls)*
Scott Richards *(Exec VP-Global Hospital Bus)*
Stefan J. Sveinsson *(Exec VP-R&D)*
Hordur Thorhallsson *(Exec VP-Emerging Markets)*
Jonas Tryggvason *(Exec VP-Sls)*

Subsidiaries:

Actavis Equity ehf. (3)
Reykjavikurvegi 76-78
220 Hafnarfirdi, Iceland
Tel.: (354) 5503300
Fax: (354) 5503301
E-Mail: actavis@actavis.is
Web Site: www.actavis.is
Emp.: 800
Other Holding Companies Offices
S.I.C.: 6719
N.A.I.C.S.: 551112
Gudbjorg Edda Eggersdottir *(Pres)*

Actavis hf. (Delta hf.) (3)
Reykjavikurvegi 76-78
220 Hafnarfirdi, Iceland
Tel.: (354) 5503300
Fax: (354) 5503301
E-Mail: actavis@actavis.com
Web Site: www.actavis.is
Emp.: 750
Pharmaceutical Preparation Mfr
S.I.C.: 2834
N.A.I.C.S.: 325412
Jon Gunnar Jonsson *(Mng Dir)*

Actavis SD ehf (3)
Reykjavikurvegi 76-78
220 Hafnarfirdi, Iceland
Tel.: (354) 5503300
Fax: (354) 5503301
E-Mail: actavis@actavis.is
Web Site: www.actavis.is
Emp.: 800
Drug and Medicine Development
S.I.C.: 8071
N.A.I.C.S.: 621511
Jon Gunnar Jonsson *(Mng Dir)*

Medis ehf (3)
Reykjavikurvegi 76-78
220 Hafnarfirdi, Iceland
Tel.: (354) 5503200
Fax: (354) 5503201
E-Mail: info@medis.is
Web Site: www.medis.is
All Other Basic Inorganic Chemical Mfr
S.I.C.: 2819
N.A.I.C.S.: 325180
Jon Gunnar Jonsson *(Mng Dir)*

U.S. Subsidiary:

Actavis U.S. (3)
200 Elmora Ave
Elizabeth, NJ 07207
Tel.: (908) 527-9100
Fax: (908) 527-9891
E-Mail: infous@actavis.com
Web Site: www.actavis.us
Emp.: 1,400
Generic Pharmaceutical Products Mfr
S.I.C.: 2834
N.A.I.C.S.: 325412
David Myers *(Sr Mgr-Products & Comm)*

Non-U.S. Subsidiaries:

Actavis A/B (3)
Strandbergsgatan 61
11289 Stockholm, Sweden
Tel.: (46) 8136370
Fax: (46) 86569690
E-Mail: info@actavis.com
Web Site: www.actavis.se
Emp.: 15
Pharmaceutical Products
S.I.C.: 5912
N.A.I.C.S.: 446110
Anders Jungpeck *(Mng Dir)*

Actavis A/S (3)
Ornegardsvej 16
2820 Gentofte, Denmark
Tel.: (45) 72223000
Fax: (45) 45740040
E-Mail: kundeservice.dk@actavis.dk
Web Site: www.actavis.dk
Drugs & Druggists Sundries Whslr
S.I.C.: 5122
N.A.I.C.S.: 424210
Puk Thomas *(Mng Dir)*

Actavis BV (3)
Baarn Australian Dijk 1
NL-3740 Baarn, Netherlands NL
Mailing Address:
Postbus 313
3740 AH Baarn, Netherlands
Tel.: (31) 355429933
Fax: (31) 355429932
E-Mail: info@actacis.nl
Web Site: www.actavis.nl
Sales Range: $10-24.9 Million
Emp.: 60
Pharmaceutical Mfr & Whslr
S.I.C.: 2834
N.A.I.C.S.: 325412

Actavis (China) Holding Ltd (3)
SATRA Building Unit 702
275 B Pham Ngu Lao St District, Ho Chi Minh City, Vietnam
Tel.: (84) 8 8386498
Fax: (84) 8 8386499
E-Mail: ctantis@actavis.sg
Web Site: www.actavis.com
Holding Company; Representative Office
S.I.C.: 6719
N.A.I.C.S.: 551112

Actavis Deutschland GmbH & Co. KG (3)
Elisabeth Selbert Strasse 1
40764 Langenfeld, Germany De
Tel.: (49) 217316740
Fax: (49) 21731674240
E-Mail: info.de@actavis.de
Web Site: www.actavis.de
Emp.: 150
Pharmaceutical Mfr & Whslr
S.I.C.: 2834
N.A.I.C.S.: 325412
Thomas Heinemann *(Mng Dir)*

Actavis GmbH (3)
Munchner Bundesstrasse 142
5020 Salzburg, Austria
Tel.: (43) 66243523500
Fax: (43) 66243523501
Emp.: 20
Pharmaceutical Preparation Mfr
S.I.C.: 2834
N.A.I.C.S.: 325412
Siegfried Leitner *(CEO)*

Actavis Italy S.p.A (3)
Viale Pasteur 10
20014 Nerviano, MI, Italy
Tel.: (39) 0331583111
Fax: (39) 0331583450
E-Mail: infoactavisitaly@actavis.com
Web Site: www.actavis.com
Emp.: 13
Pharmaceutical Preparation Mfr
S.I.C.: 2834
N.A.I.C.S.: 325412
Sergio Vella *(Mng Dir)*

Actavis Ltd (3)
B16 Bulebel Industrial Estate
ZTN08 Zejtun, Malta
Tel.: (356) 21693533
Fax: (356) 21693604
E-Mail: info@actavis.com.mt
Web Site: www.actavis.com.mt
Emp.: 600
Pharmaceutical Preparation Mfr
S.I.C.: 2834
N.A.I.C.S.: 325412
Sergio Vella *(Gen Mgr)*

Actavis Nordic A/S (3)
Ornegardsvej 16
2820 Gentofte, Denmark
Tel.: (45) 72223000
Fax: (45) 45740040
E-Mail: actavis@actavis.dk
Web Site: www.actavis.dk
Emp.: 120
Drugs & Druggists Sundries Whslr
S.I.C.: 5122
N.A.I.C.S.: 424210
Svent Antersen *(Mng Dir)*

Actavis Norway A/S (3)
Hoffsveien 1 D 409
0213 Oslo, Norway
Tel.: (47) 32225000
Fax: (47) 21549790
Web Site: www.actavis.com
Emp.: 1,000
Pharmaceutical Preparation Mfr
S.I.C.: 2834
N.A.I.C.S.: 325412
Vidar Oyehaug *(Mng Dir)*

Actavis Pharma Development Centre Pvt.Ltd (3)
No 15 80 Feet Road Koramangala
560095 Bengaluru, India
Tel.: (91) 8025633097
Fax: (91) 8025633101
Web Site: www.actavis.com
Emp.: 75
Pharmaceutical Preparation Mfr
S.I.C.: 2834
N.A.I.C.S.: 325412
G. Shankar *(Mng Dir)*

Actavis Polska Sp.zoo (3)
Ul Odrowaza 15
03-310 Warsaw, Poland
Tel.: (48) 228141239
Fax: (48) 5122997
E-Mail: biuro@actavis.com
Web Site: www.actavispolska.pl
Emp.: 175
Psychiatric & Substance Abuse Hospitals
S.I.C.: 8063
N.A.I.C.S.: 622210
Roderg Czernit *(Mng Dir)*

Actavis Portugal AS (3)
Rua Virgilio Correia 11
1600-219 Lisbon, Portugal
Tel.: (351) 217220650
Fax: (351) 217272744
E-Mail: webmaster@actavis.pt
Web Site: www.actavis.pt
Emp.: 53
Pharmaceutical Preparation Mfr
S.I.C.: 2834
N.A.I.C.S.: 325412
Duarte Sinoes *(Mng Dir)*

Actavis s.r.o. (3)
Popradska 34
82160 Bratislava, Slovakia
Tel.: (421) 232553800
Fax: (421) 245526006
E-Mail: actavis@actavis.sk
Web Site: www.actavis.sk
Emp.: 35
Pharmacies and Drug Stores
S.I.C.: 5912
N.A.I.C.S.: 446110
Sarotna Eva *(Mng Dir)*

Actavis Switzerland AG (3)
Wehntalerstrasse 190
8105 Regensdorf, Switzerland
Tel.: (41) 448709700
Fax: (41) 448709701
E-Mail: info@actavis.ch
Web Site: www.actavis.ch
Emp.: 20
Marketing Consulting Services
S.I.C.: 8742
N.A.I.C.S.: 541613

BIOVENA Pharma Sp.z o.o. (3)
ul Odrowaza 13
03-310 Warsaw, Poland
Tel.: (48) 228141239
Fax: (48) 228141241
E-Mail: biuro@actavis.com
Web Site: www.actavispolska.pl/pl/contacts
Emp.: 160
Pharmaceutical Preparation Mfr
S.I.C.: 2834
N.A.I.C.S.: 325412
Roderg Czernit *(Mng Dir)*

Higia EAD (3)
YPI 3392 Star Lozenskipat
Sofia, Bulgaria
Tel.: (359) 29421700
Fax: (359) 29421717
Web Site: www.higia.bg
Drugs & Druggists Sundries Whslr
S.I.C.: 5122
N.A.I.C.S.: 424210

Hurtownia BIOVENA Pharma (3)
Ul Lopuszanska 38 B
02-232 Warsaw, Poland
Tel.: (48) 228680117
Fax: (48) 228680797
E-Mail: biuro@actavis.com
Web Site: www.actavispolska.pl/pl/contacts/
Psychiatric & Substance Abuse Hospitals
S.I.C.: 8063
N.A.I.C.S.: 622210
Izabela Zimmermann *(Gen Mgr)*

Medis Ltd. (3)
2nd Floor Atlantic House
Circular Road, Douglas, IM1 1AG, Isle of Man
Tel.: (44) 1624692962
Fax: (44) 1624666541
E-Mail: medis@medis.is
Web Site: www.medis.is/About/uk.htm
Emp.: 12
Pharmaceutical Preparation Mfr
S.I.C.: 2834
N.A.I.C.S.: 325412

Medis Pharma GmbH (3)
Rheinstrasse 63
55218 Ingelheim, Germany
Tel.: (49) 6132990380
Fax: (49) 613299040
E-Mail: tmoller@medis.is
Web Site: www.medis.is
Emp.: 5
Pharmacies and Drug Stores
S.I.C.: 5912
N.A.I.C.S.: 446110
Thomas Moller *(Mng Dir)*

Oncopharma AG (3)
Obmoos 4
6300 Zug, Switzerland
Tel.: (41) 417202000
Fax: (41) 417202001
Emp.: 5
Drugs & Druggists Sundries Whslr
S.I.C.: 5122
N.A.I.C.S.: 424210
Stephan Koch *(Mng Dir)*

Ophtha A/S (3)
Ornegardsvej 16
2820 Gentofte, Denmark
Tel.: (45) 72223000
E-Mail: info@actavis.dk
Web Site: www.actavis.dk
Emp.: 104
Pharmaceutical Preparation Mfr
S.I.C.: 2834
N.A.I.C.S.: 325412
Svent Andersen *(Mng Dir)*

Pharma Avalanche s.r.o. (3)
Na Zvahove 25
15200 Prague, Czech Republic
Tel.: (420) 251001680
Fax: (420) 251554667
Emp.: 30
Marketing Consulting Services
S.I.C.: 8742
N.A.I.C.S.: 541613
Euart Siroty *(Mng Dir)*

PT Actavis (Indonesia) (3)
Jalan Ayavogor km 28
PO Box 144
Jakarta, 13710, Indonesia Id
Tel.: (62) 218710311
Fax: (62) 218710044
Web Site: www.actavis.com
Emp.: 120
Generic Pharmaceutical Products Mfr
S.I.C.: 2834
N.A.I.C.S.: 325412
Hemy Prasetya *(Dir-Supply Chain)*

Zdravlje AD (3)
Vlajkova 199
16000 Leskovac, Serbia
Tel.: (381) 16242414
Fax: (381) 3811650511
E-Mail: info@zdravlje.co.yu
Web Site: www.zdravlje.co.yu
Emp.: 917
Pharmaceutical Preparation Mfr
S.I.C.: 2834
N.A.I.C.S.: 325412
Goran Stojilkovic *(Mng Dir)*

Non-U.S. Holding:

Actavis UK Limited (3)
Whiddon Valley
Barnstaple, Devon, EX32 8NS, United Kingdom UK
Tel.: (44) 1271311200
Fax: (44) 1271346106
E-Mail: actavis@actavis.co.uk
Web Site: www.actavis.co.uk
Emp.: 480
Pharmaceutical Mfr, Marketer & Whslr
S.I.C.: 2834
N.A.I.C.S.: 325412
Sara Vincent *(CEO & Mng Dir)*

ARROW FARMACEUTICA LTDA (2)
Rua Barao de Petrepolis 311
Rio Comprido, Rio de Janeiro, 20251-061, Brazil
Tel.: (55) 2132939500
E-Mail: arrow@erowlabs.com.br
Web Site: www.erowlabs.com.br
Pharmaceutical Product Mfr
S.I.C.: 2834
N.A.I.C.S.: 325412

Arrow Generics Ltd. (2)
2 Eastman Way
Stevenage, Herts, SG1 4SZ, United Kingdom
Tel.: (44) 1438737630
Fax: (44) 1438745900
E-Mail: mail@arrowgenerics.com
Web Site: www.arrowgenerics.com
Sales Range: $650-699.9 Million
Emp.: 30
Generic Pharmaceutical Mfr
S.I.C.: 2834
N.A.I.C.S.: 325412
Anthony Selwyn Tabatznik *(CEO)*

ARROW GENERIQUES SAS (2)
26 Avenue Tony Garnier
69007 Lyon, France
Tel.: (33) 472726072
Fax: (33) 472726093
E-Mail: contactweb@arrow-generiques.com
Web Site: www.arrow-generiques.com
Generic Drug Product Mfr
S.I.C.: 2834
N.A.I.C.S.: 325412
Tony Tabatznik *(Founder & CEO)*

ARROW GROUP APS (2)
Hovedgaden 41 2 Sal
Horsholm, 2970, Denmark
Tel.: (45) 45170300
Generic Drug Product Mfr
S.I.C.: 2834
N.A.I.C.S.: 325412

ARROW NO 7 LTD (2)
7 Cavendish Square
London, W1G 0PE, United Kingdom
Tel.: (44) 2076127612
Fax: (44) 2076127620
E-Mail: mail@arrowno7.com
Emp.: 50
Pharmaceutical Product Mfr
S.I.C.: 2834
N.A.I.C.S.: 325412
Anish Mehta *(Gen Mgr)*

ARROW PHARMA APS (2)
St Peter's Strait 2
4000 Roskilde, Denmark
Tel.: (45) 45170300
E-Mail: infodk@arrow.nu
Web Site: www.arrowpharma.dk
Pharmaceutical Product Mfr
S.I.C.: 2834
N.A.I.C.S.: 325412
Jette Lambert *(Country Mgr)*

ARROW PHARMA HOLDINGS BV (2)
Kabelweg 21
1014 BA Amsterdam, Netherlands
Tel.: (31) 206828700
Pharmaceutical Product Mfr
S.I.C.: 2834
N.A.I.C.S.: 325412

ARROW PHARMACEUTICALS (NZ) LTD (2)
33A Normanby Road Mt Eden
PO Box 128 244
Remuera, Auckland, 2022, New Zealand
Tel.: (64) 96304488
Fax: (64) 800800662
E-Mail: enquiries@arrowpharma.co.nz
Web Site: www.arrowpharma.co.nz
Generic Drug & Beauty Product Mfr
S.I.C.: 2834
N.A.I.C.S.: 325412

ASCENT PHARMACEUTICALS LTD (2)
151-153 Clarendon Street
Melbourne, VIC, 3205, Australia
Tel.: (61) 386776600
Fax: (61) 386776666
E-Mail: info@ascentpharma.com.au
Web Site: www.ascentpharma.com.au
Pharmaceutical Product Mfr
S.I.C.: 2834
N.A.I.C.S.: 325412
Dennis Bastas *(Mng Dir & CEO)*
Karen McTavish *(Mng Dir)*
Andrew Burgess *(CFO)*

Ascent Pharmahealth Limited (2)
151-153 Clarendon St
Melbourne, VIC, 3205, Australia (50.1%)
Tel.: (61) 386776600
Fax: (61) 386776666
E-Mail: info@ascentpharma.com.au
Web Site: www.ascentpharmahealth.com
Sales Range: $100-124.9 Million
Emp.: 65
Pharmaceutical Mfr & Distr
S.I.C.: 2834
N.A.I.C.S.: 325412
Dennis Bastas *(Founder, CEO & Mng Dir)*
Andrew Burgess *(CFO & Co-Sec)*
Michael Story *(Sr VP-Ops Dev)*

Subsidiary:

Pharmasave Australia Pty Ltd. (3)
280 City Road
Southbank, VIC, 3006, Australia
Tel.: (61) 3 9981 1200
Fax: (61) 3 9981 1222
E-Mail: info@pharmasave.com.au
Web Site: www.pharmasave.com.au
Emp.: 8
Pharmaceutical Products Distr
S.I.C.: 5122
N.A.I.C.S.: 424210
Michele Buttazzoni *(CEO)*

Actavis plc—(Continued)

Non-U.S. Subsidiaries:

Ascent Pharmahealth Asia (Malaysia) SDN. BHD. (3)
304 Uptown 2 2 Jalan SS21/37 Damansara Uptown
47400 Petaling Jaya, Malaysia
Tel.: (60) 3 7710 9552
Fax: (60) 3 7710 9554
Pharmaceutical Products Mfr
S.I.C.: 2834
N.A.I.C.S.: 325412

Ascent Pharmahealth (Asia) Pte Ltd. (3)
2 Chia Ping Road 09-01
Singapore, 619968, Singapore
Tel.: (65) 6265 2777
Fax: (65) 6261 5887
E-Mail: enquiries@ascentpharma.asia
Web Site: www.ascentpharma.asia
Pharmaceutical Products Mfr & Distr
S.I.C.: 5122
N.A.I.C.S.: 424210

Drug Houses of Australia (Asia) Pte. Ltd. (3)
09 01/02 Haw Par Tiger Balm Bldg
2 Chia Ping Rd, Singapore, 619968, Singapore
Tel.: (65) 62652777
Telex: rs 25997
Fax: (65) 62615887
E-Mail: mktg.dha@dha.asia
Web Site: www.dha.com.sg
Emp.: 150
Pharmaceutical Distr
S.I.C.: 2834
N.A.I.C.S.: 325412
Mohan Kumar *(CEO)*

Eden Biodesign Ltd. (2)
National Biomanufacturing Centre Estuary Banks
Estuary Commerce Park
Speke Road, Liverpool, L24 8RB, United Kingdom
Tel.: (44) 1517281750
Fax: (44) 1517281751
Web Site: www.edenbiodesign.com
Emp.: 80
Biopharmaceutical Research & Development Services
S.I.C.: 8731
N.A.I.C.S.: 541712
Crawford Brown *(CEO)*
Derek Ellison *(COO)*
Anita Bate *(Chief Scientific Officer)*

U.S. Subsidiary:

Eden Biodesign, Inc. (3)
2530 Meridian Pkwy Ste 300
Durham, NC 27713
Tel.: (919) 806-4949
Fax: (919) 349-2770
Web Site: www.edenbiodesign.com
Biopharmaceutical Research & Development Services
S.I.C.: 8731
N.A.I.C.S.: 541712
Roger Lias *(Pres)*

ERIS PHARMACEUTICALS AUSTRALIA PTY LTD (2)
6 Eastern Road
Melbourne, VIC, 3205, Australia
Tel.: (61) 396908473
Fax: (61) 396908479
E-Mail: info@eris-pharma.com
Web Site: www.eris-pharma.com
Pharmaceutical Product Mfr
S.I.C.: 2834
N.A.I.C.S.: 325412

JUTA PHARMA GMBH (2)
Gutenbergstrasse 13
24941 Flensburg, Germany
Tel.: (49) 4619957990
Fax: (49) 46199579940
E-Mail: juta@jutapharma.de
Web Site: www.jutapharma.de
Generic Drug Product Mfr
S.I.C.: 2834
N.A.I.C.S.: 325412

NICOBRAND LTD (2)
189 Castleroe Road
Coleraine, Londonderry, BT51 3RP, United Kingdom
Tel.: (44) 2870868733
Fax: (44) 2870868735
Web Site: www.nicobrand.com
Nicotine Pharmaceutical Product Mfr
S.I.C.: 2834
N.A.I.C.S.: 325412
Jane Robinson *(Head-Quality)*

Spirit Pharmaceuticals Pty. Ltd. (2)
117 Harrington Street
Sydney, NSW, 2000, Australia AU
Tel.: (61) 292511088
Fax: (61) 292511099
E-Mail: info@spiritpharma.com.au
Web Site: www.spiritpharma.com.au
Prescription Pharmaceuticals Distr
S.I.C.: 5122
N.A.I.C.S.: 424210
Gary Waters *(Mng Dir)*

WATSON PHARMA COMPANY (2)
2295 Bristol Circle Unit 104
Oakville, ON, L6H 6P8, Canada
Tel.: (905) 829-2979
Fax: (905) 855-4433
Toll Free: (855) 892-8766
E-Mail: canadainfo@watson.com
Web Site: www.watsonpharmacompany.ca
Pharmaceutical Product Mfr & Distr
S.I.C.: 2834
N.A.I.C.S.: 325412
Rob Tessarolo *(Gen Mgr)*

WATSON PHARMA (PTY)LTD (2)
5th Str (Norwich Close) Sandown
Sandton, Gauteng, 2196, South Africa
Tel.: (27) 105910100
Pharmaceutical Product Mfr
S.I.C.: 2834
N.A.I.C.S.: 325412

WILLOW PHARMACEUTICALS PTY LTD (2)
Level 4 5 Essex Street
Sydney, NSW, 2000, Australia
Tel.: (61) 292412235
Fax: (61) 292412217
E-Mail: info@willowpharma.com
Web Site: www.willowpharma.com.au
Pharmaceutical Product Distr
S.I.C.: 5122
N.A.I.C.S.: 424210
Paul Ottaviano *(Mng Dir)*

ACTCALL INC.

2-12-5 Yotsuya
Shinjuku-ku, Tokyo, 160-0004, Japan
Tel.: (81) 3 53122300
Web Site: www.actcall.jp
Year Founded: 2005
6064—(TKS)
Sales Range: $10-24.9 Million
Emp.: 50

Business Description:
Computer Related Services
S.I.C.: 7379
N.A.I.C.S.: 541519

Personnel:
Toshihiro Hirai *(Pres)*

ACTELION LTD.

Gewerbestrasse 16
CH-4123 Allschwil, Switzerland
Tel.: (41) 615656565
Fax: (41) 615656500
E-Mail: info@actelion.com
Web Site: www.actelion.com
Year Founded: 1997
ATLN—(SWX)
Rev.: $1,865,492,371
Assets: $2,907,996,766
Liabilities: $1,268,893,923
Net Worth: $1,639,102,842
Earnings: $327,277,886
Emp.: 2,433
Fiscal Year-end: 12/31/12

Business Description:
Biopharmaceutical Research, Development & Manufacturing Services
S.I.C.: 8731
N.A.I.C.S.: 541711

Personnel:
Jean-Paul Clozel *(Co-Founder, CEO & Mng Dir)*
Andre J. Mueller *(Co-Founder & CFO)*
Martine Clozel *(Co-Founder, Chief Scientific Officer & Sr VP)*
Thomas Widmann *(Co-Founder)*
Jean-Pierre Garnier *(Chm)*
Otto Schwarz *(COO & Exec VP)*
Nicholas Franco *(Chief Bus Dev Officer & Exec VP)*
Marian Borovsky *(Gen Counsel, Sec & Sr VP)*
Guy Braunstein *(Exec VP & Head-Clinical Dev)*
Christian Albrich *(Sr VP & Head-Global HR)*

Board of Directors:
Jean-Pierre Garnier
Juhani Antilla
Robert J. Bertolini
Jean-Paul Clozel
Carl B. Feldbaum
John J. Greisch
Peter Gruss
Werner Henrich
Michael Jacobi
Armin M. Kessler
Jean Malo

Subsidiaries:

Actelion Participation GmbH (1)
Gewerbestrasse 16
Allschwil, Switzerland
Tel.: (41) 615656565
Fax: (41) 615656500
E-Mail: info@actelion.com
Pharmaceutical Products Mfr
S.I.C.: 2834
N.A.I.C.S.: 325412

Actelion Pharma Schweiz AG (1)
Stadtturmstrasse 5
CH-5400 Baden, Switzerland
Tel.: (41) 562002940
Fax: (41) 562002941
Web Site: www.actelion.ch
Emp.: 12
Biopharmaceutical Research, Development & Manufacturing Services
S.I.C.: 8731
N.A.I.C.S.: 541711
Etienne Bucher *(Gen Mgr)*

Actelion Pharmaceuticals Ltd. (1)
Gewerbestrasse 16
4123 Allschwil, Switzerland (100%)
Tel.: (41) 615656565
Fax: (41) 615656500
E-Mail: info@actellion.com
Web Site: www.actelion.com
Emp.: 1,000
Biopharmaceutical Research, Development & Manufacturing Services
S.I.C.: 8731
N.A.I.C.S.: 541711
Jean Paul Clozel *(Pres)*

U.S. Subsidiaries:

Actelion Clinical Research, Inc. (1)
1820 Chapel Ave W Ste 300
Cherry Hill, NJ 08002
Tel.: (856) 773-4300
Fax: (856) 773-4246
Emp.: 120
Biopharmaceutical Research & Development Services
S.I.C.: 8731
N.A.I.C.S.: 541712

Actelion Pharmaceuticals US, Inc. (1)
5000 Shoreline Ct Ste 200
South San Francisco, CA 94080 DE
Tel.: (650) 624-6900
Fax: (650) 589-1501
Web Site: www.actelionus.com
Emp.: 85
Biopharmaceutical Research, Development & Manufacturing Services
S.I.C.: 8731
N.A.I.C.S.: 541711
Shalom Jacobovitz *(Pres)*
Rob Etherington *(Sr VP-Sls & Mktg)*

Actelion US Holding Co. (1)
5000 Shoreline Ct Ste 200
South San Francisco, CA 94080-1956
Tel.: (650) 624-6900
Fax: (650) 589-1501
Toll Free: (866) 228-3546
Emp.: 200
Investment Management Services
S.I.C.: 6211
N.A.I.C.S.: 523999

Subsidiary:

Ceptaris Therapeutics, Inc. (2)
(Formerly Yaupon Therapeutics, Inc.)
101 Lindenwood Dr Ste 400
Malvern, PA 19355
Tel.: (610) 975-9290
Fax: (610) 975-9012
Web Site: www.ceptaris.com
Emp.: 25
Pharmaceutical Research & Development
S.I.C.: 8731
N.A.I.C.S.: 541711
Stephen Tullman *(Chm & CEO)*
Doug Gessl *(CFO & COO)*
Kamil Ali-Jackson *(Chief Legal Officer)*
H. Jeffrey Wilkins *(Chief Medical Officer)*
Tim Henkel *(Exec VP & Head-R & D)*
Evan Dick *(Sr VP-Bus Dev)*

Non-U.S. Subsidiaries:

Actelion Ilac Ticaret Limited Sirketi (1)
Kurucesme Cad No 17.4
Kurucesme, 34345 Istanbul, Turkey
Tel.: (90) 2123621000
Fax: (90) 2122570267
E-Mail: info@actelion.com
Web Site: www.actelion.com
Emp.: 25
Biopharmaceutical Research, Development & Manufacturing Services
S.I.C.: 8731
N.A.I.C.S.: 541711
Murat Uslu *(Gen Mgr)*

Actelion Paris Organization SAS (1)
21 Boulevard de La Madeleine
75001 Paris, France (100%)
Tel.: (33) 158623232
Fax: (33) 158623222
E-Mail: accueil.france@actelion.com
Emp.: 100
Biopharmaceutical Research, Development & Manufacturing Services
S.I.C.: 8731
N.A.I.C.S.: 541711
Annick Schwebig *(Mng Dir)*

Actelion Pharma Polska Sp. z.o.o. (1)
ul Nowogrodzka 21
00-511 Warsaw, Poland
Tel.: (48) 22 262 31 00
Fax: (48) 22 262 31 01
Web Site: www1.actelion.com
Pharmaceutical Products Distr
S.I.C.: 5122
N.A.I.C.S.: 424210
Ewa Solarska *(Gen Mgr)*

Actelion Pharmaceuticals Australia Pty Ltd (1)
Suite 6 13B Narabang Way
Belrose, NSW, 2085, Australia (100%)
Tel.: (61) 294864600
Fax: (61) 299861344
E-Mail: australia@actelion.com
Emp.: 50
Biopharmaceutical Research, Development & Manufacturing Services
S.I.C.: 8731
N.A.I.C.S.: 541712
Bill Fairey *(Mng Dir)*

Actelion Pharmaceuticals Austria GmbH (1)
Saturn Tower Leonard-Bernstein-Strasse 10
1220 Vienna, Austria
Tel.: (43) 1 505 45 27
Fax: (43) 1 505 45 62
Web Site: www.actelion.com
Pharmaceutical Products Distr
S.I.C.: 5122

N.A.I.C.S.: 424210
Martina Schmidt *(Gen Mgr)*

Actelion Pharmaceuticals Belgium NV (1)
Bedrijvenlaan 1
2800 Mechelen, Belgium
Tel.: (32) 15284777
Fax: (32) 15284779
Web Site: www.actelion.com
Emp.: 9
Biopharmaceutical Research, Development & Manufacturing Services
S.I.C.: 8731
N.A.I.C.S.: 541712
Peter Dezaeger *(Country Mgr)*

Actelion Pharmaceuticals Canada, Inc. (1)
2550 Daniel-Johnson Blvd Ste 701
Suite 701, Laval, QC, H7T2L1, Canada
Tel.: (450) 681-1664
Fax: (450) 681-9545
Web Site: www.actelion.com
Emp.: 20
Biopharmaceutical Research, Development & Manufacturing Services
S.I.C.: 8731
N.A.I.C.S.: 541711
Jacques Archambault *(Gen Mgr)*

Actelion Pharmaceuticals CZ, s.r.o. (1)
Londynska 506/41
1200 00 Prague, Czech Republic
Tel.: (420) 221968011
Fax: (420) 221968012
Web Site: www.actelion.com
Emp.: 8
Biopharmaceutical Research, Development & Manufacturing Services
S.I.C.: 8731
N.A.I.C.S.: 541711
Vaclava Zimova *(Gen Mgr)*

Actelion Pharmaceuticals Deutschland GmbH (1)
Basler Strasse 63 65
79100 Freiburg, Germany
Tel.: (49) 76145640
Fax: (49) 761456445
E-Mail: michaeldanzl@actelion.de
Web Site: www.actelion.de
Emp.: 30
Biopharmaceutical Research, Development & Manufacturing Services
S.I.C.: 8731
N.A.I.C.S.: 541712
Michael Danzl *(Gen Mgr)*

Actelion Pharmaceuticals do Brasil Ltda. (1)
Praia de Botafogo 501
1 Andar Bloco Corcovado, 22250-040 Rio de Janeiro, Brazil
Tel.: (55) 2132666200
Fax: (55) 2132666213
E-Mail: info.brazil@actelion.com
Web Site: www.actelion.com.br
Emp.: 36
Biopharmaceutical Research, Development & Manufacturing Services
S.I.C.: 8731
N.A.I.C.S.: 541711
Roberto Dodel *(Mng Dir)*

Actelion Pharmaceuticals Espana, S.L.U. (1)
Via Augusta 281 3 B
08017 Barcelona, Spain
Tel.: (34) 932531064
Fax: (34) 934186097
Web Site: www.actelion.com
Emp.: 30
Biopharmaceutical Research, Development & Manufacturing Services
S.I.C.: 8731
N.A.I.C.S.: 541711

Actelion Pharmaceuticals France SAS (1)
21 blvd de la Madeleine
75001 Paris, France
Tel.: (33) 158623232
Fax: (33) 0158623265
E-Mail: accueil.france@actelion.com
Web Site: www.actelion.com
Emp.: 25
Biopharmaceutical Research, Development & Manufacturing Services
S.I.C.: 8731
N.A.I.C.S.: 541711
Annick Schwebig *(Mng Dir)*

Actelion Pharmaceuticals Hellas SA (1)
6-8 Agisilaou Str Blue Land Center Agios Thomas
Marousi, 15123 Athens, Greece
Tel.: (30) 210 675 25 00
Fax: (30) 210 675 25 32
Pharmaceutical Products Distr
S.I.C.: 5122
N.A.I.C.S.: 424210
Eleni Tentou *(Gen Mgr)*

Actelion Pharmaceuticals Hungaria LLC (1)
Rakoczi Ut 42
1072 Budapest, Hungary
Tel.: (36) 1 327 42 15
Emp.: 4
Pharmaceutical Products Distr
S.I.C.: 5122
N.A.I.C.S.: 424210

Actelion Pharmaceuticals Israel Ltd (1)
Hayetzira St Aviv
52521 Ramat Gan, Israel (100%)
Tel.: (972) 36125500
Fax: (972) 36126600
Web Site: www.actelion.nl
Emp.: 13
Biopharmaceutical Research, Development & Manufacturing Services
S.I.C.: 8731
N.A.I.C.S.: 541711
Itzik Mizraji *(Mng Dir)*

Actelion Pharmaceuticals Italia Srl (1)
via Lasie 10/L
40026 Imola, Bologna, Italy
Tel.: (39) 0542648711
Fax: (39) 0542648734
E-Mail: actelion.italy@actelion.com
Emp.: 13
Biopharmaceutical Research, Development & Manufacturing Services
S.I.C.: 8731
N.A.I.C.S.: 541711
Roberto Montanari *(Gen Mgr)*

Actelion Pharmaceuticals Japan Ltd (1)
Ebisu Prime Square Tower
1-1-39 Hiroo Shibuya-Ku, 150-0012 Tokyo, Japan (100%)
Tel.: (81) 357744151
Fax: (81) 357744890
Web Site: www.actelion.com
Emp.: 150
Biopharmaceutical Research, Development & Manufacturing Services
S.I.C.: 8731
N.A.I.C.S.: 541712
Satoshi Panaka *(CEO)*

Actelion Pharmaceuticals Korea Ltd (1)
6F Gangnam Finance Center 737 Yeoksam-dong
Seoul, 135-984, Korea (South)
Tel.: (82) 2 2112 2833
Fax: (82) 2 2112 2835
Pharmaceutical Products Distr
S.I.C.: 5122
N.A.I.C.S.: 424210
Sang Kyun Lee *(Gen Mgr)*

Actelion Pharmaceuticals Mexico S.A. De C.V. (1)
Insurgentes Sur No 670 Piso 3
Colonia del Valle, Mexico, 03100, Mexico
Tel.: (52) 55 42 12 50 60
Emp.: 15
Pharmaceutical Products Distr
S.I.C.: 5122
N.A.I.C.S.: 424210
Gina Grethel Garcia *(Gen Mgr)*

Actelion Pharmaceuticals Nederland BV (1)
Beneluxlaan 2B
3446 GR Woerden, Netherlands
Tel.: (31) 348 435 950
Fax: (31) 348 420 904
Emp.: 30
Pharmaceutical Products Distr
S.I.C.: 5122
N.A.I.C.S.: 424210
Han Brouwer *(Gen Mgr)*

Actelion Pharmaceuticals Portugal Lda. (1)
Praca Marques de Pombal 15 8
Lisboa, 1250 163 Lisbon, Portugal
Tel.: (351) 121 358 6120
Fax: (351) 121 358 6129
Web Site: www.actelion.com
Emp.: 11
Biopharmaceutical Research, Development & Manufacturing Services
S.I.C.: 8731
N.A.I.C.S.: 541711
Antonio Neves *(Gen Mgr)*

Actelion Pharmaceuticals Sverige AB (1)
Svardvagen 3
18233 Danderyd, Sweden
Tel.: (46) 854498250
Fax: (46) 854498269
E-Mail: info@actelion.com
Web Site: www.actelion.com
Emp.: 17
Biopharmaceutical Research, Development & Manufacturing Services
S.I.C.: 8731
N.A.I.C.S.: 541711
Jorgten Lydrup *(Mng Dir)*

Actelion Pharmaceuticals Taiwan Ltd (1)
7F-2 No 28 Qingcheng St
Taipei, 105, Taiwan
Tel.: (886) 2 21750500
Fax: (886) 21750510
Pharmaceutical Products Distr
S.I.C.: 5122
N.A.I.C.S.: 424210

Actelion Pharmaceuticals UK Ltd. (1)
BSI Building 13th Floor
389 Chiswick High Road, London, W4 4AL, United Kingdom
Tel.: (44) 2089873333
Fax: (44) 2089873322
E-Mail: info@actelion.com
Emp.: 40
Biopharmaceutical Research, Development & Manufacturing Services
S.I.C.: 8731
N.A.I.C.S.: 541711

ACTEOS S.A.

2-4 rue Duflot
F-59100 Roubaix, France
Tel.: (33) 320114464
Fax: (33) 320114465
Web Site: www.acteos.com
Year Founded: 1986
EOS—(EUR)
Sls.: $15,311,338
Earnings: $37,693
Emp.: 120
Fiscal Year-end: 12/31/12

Business Description:
Supply Chain Management Services
S.I.C.: 7389
N.A.I.C.S.: 561499

Personnel:
Josephi Felfel *(Chm & CEO)*
Christophe Sion *(CFO)*

ACTERA GROUP

Stratejik Yonetim Hizmetleri AS
Kizilserce Sokak No 30
34810 Anadolu Hisari, Istanbul, Turkey
Tel.: (90) 216 516 0100
Fax: (90) 216 516 0101
E-Mail: info@acteragroup.com
Web Site: www.acteragroup.com

Business Description:
Private Equity Firm
S.I.C.: 6211
N.A.I.C.S.: 523999

Personnel:
Isak Antika *(Co-Founder & Mng Partner)*
Murat Cavusoglu *(Co-Founder & Mng Partner)*

ACTIA GROUP SA

5 rue Jorge Semprun
31432 Toulouse, France
Tel.: (33) 561176198
Fax: (33) 561554231
E-Mail: contact@actiagroup.com
Web Site: www.actiagroup.com
ATI—(EUR)
Rev.: $389,191,209
Assets: $347,678,018
Liabilities: $250,539,737
Net Worth: $97,138,281
Earnings: $5,554,297
Emp.: 2,768
Fiscal Year-end: 12/31/12

Business Description:
Electronic & Automotive Equipment Mfr
S.I.C.: 3679
N.A.I.C.S.: 334419

Personnel:
Louis Pech *(Chm-Supervisory Bd)*
Christian Desmoulins *(Chm-Exec Bd)*
Pierre Calmels *(Vice Chm-Supervisory Bd)*
Marine Candelon-Bonnemaison *(Member-Exec Bd)*
Catherine Mallet *(Member-Exec Bd)*

Supervisory Board of Directors:
Louis Pech
Henri Paul Brochet
Pierre Calmels
Alain Costes
Gunther Thrum
Veronique Vedrine
Eric Seyvos

11 rue Laborde
Paris, France

Divisions:

Actia Group SA - ACTIA MULLER (France) Division (1)
5 rue de la Taye
28110 Luce, Eure-et-Loir, France
Tel.: (33) 2 3733 3400
Fax: (33) 2 3733 3435
Web Site: www.actiamuller.com
Automotive Repair & Maintanence Services
S.I.C.: 7538
N.A.I.C.S.: 811111
Olivier Duranell *(Dir-Worldwide Diagnostic & Mgr-Export)*

Actia Group SA - Colomiers Division (1)
10 Avenue Edouard Serres
31772 Colomier, Haute-Garonne, France
Tel.: (33) 5 6274 3400
Fax: (33) 5 6274 3434
Emp.: 250
Automotive Electrical Components Mfr
S.I.C.: 3714
N.A.I.C.S.: 336320
Cristian Desmoulins *(Gen Mgr)*

Subsidiaries:

Actia-Aixia (1)
Savoie Technolac
PO Box 282
73375 Le Bourget du Lac, Cedex, France
Tel.: (33) 479252390
Fax: (33) 479252923
E-Mail: info@actia-aixia.com
Web Site: www.aixia-actia.com
Emp.: 11
Industrial & On-Board Electronic Devices Mfr
S.I.C.: 3825
N.A.I.C.S.: 334515
Davide Loy *(Gen Mgr)*

Actia S.A. (1)
25 Chemin de Pouvourville
BP 4215
31432 Toulouse, Cedex 04, France

Actia Group SA—(Continued)

Tel.: (33) 561176161
Fax: (33) 561554231
E-Mail: info@actia.com
Web Site: www.actia.com
Emp.: 500
Automotive Electronics
S.I.C.: 3699
N.A.I.C.S.: 335999
Louis Pech *(Chm)*

Aton Systemes S.A. **(1)**
14 rue Charles Martigny
94700 Maisons-Alfort, France
Tel.: (33) 142071800
Fax: (33) 142078555
E-Mail: info@aton-sys.fr
Web Site: www.aton-sys.fr
Emp.: 15
Develops, Manufactures & Sells PC Compatible Boards for Industrial Applications
S.I.C.: 3571
N.A.I.C.S.: 334111
Marc Menviel *(Gen Mgr)*

U.S. Subsidiary:

ACTIA Corporation **(1)**
52765 Bridger Ct
Elkhart, IN 46514
Tel.: (574) 264-2373
Fax: (574) 266-2702
E-Mail: info@actaus.com
Web Site: www.actiaus.com
Automotive Electrical Components Distr
S.I.C.: 5013
N.A.I.C.S.: 423120
Satish Kirtikar *(Pres)*

Non-U.S. Divisions:

Actia Group SA - ACTIA Tunisie Division **(1)**
Impasse des Entrepreneurs ZI La Charguia 2
Ariana Aeroport, Tunis, 2080, Tunisia
Tel.: (216) 71 941 922
Fax: (216) 71 942 245
E-Mail: info@actia.com
Emp.: 200
Automotive Diagnostic Equipment Mfr
S.I.C.: 3714
N.A.I.C.S.: 336390
Safouane Fatnassi *(Mng Dir)*

Actia Group SA - CIPI ACTIA Division **(1)**
Rue des Entrepreneurs ZI Charguia 2 Tunis Ariana Aeroport
2080 Tunis, Tunisia
Tel.: (216) 70838115
Fax: (216) 70838136
E-Mail: cipi@cipi.com.tn
Web Site: www.actia.com
Emp.: 680
Automotive Electrical Diagnostic Equipment Mfr
S.I.C.: 3714
N.A.I.C.S.: 336390
R. Rouvrais *(Gen Mgr)*

Non-U.S. Subsidiaries:

Actia China Automotive Electronics Co., Ltd **(1)**
4/F #5 Building 128 Jiu Jing Road
Songjiang High-Tech Park
Jiuting Songjiang, Shanghai, 201615, China
Tel.: (86) 2137639808
Fax: (86) 2137633360
Web Site: www.actia.com.cn
Emp.: 130
Automotive Electronics Mfr
S.I.C.: 3714
N.A.I.C.S.: 336320
Xiaoping Zhang *(Gen Mgr)*

ACTIA de Mexico S.A. de C.V. **(1)**
Av Central No 176 Nueva Industrial Vallejo
Mexico, 07700, Mexico
Tel.: (52) 55 5119 2350
Fax: (52) 55 5752 7643
E-Mail: ventas@actia.com.mx
Web Site: www.actia.com.mx
Emp.: 100
Automotive Diagnostic Equipment Mfr
S.I.C.: 3714
N.A.I.C.S.: 336320
Jose Oriol Admirable *(Gen Mgr)*

Actia do Brasil Ind. e Com. Ltda. **(1)**
555 Sao Paulo Street
Porto Alegre, Rio Grande do Sul, 90230-161, Brazil
Tel.: (55) 51 3358 0200
Fax: (55) 51 3337 6081
E-Mail: actia@actia.com.br
Web Site: www.actia.com.br
Automotive Electronic Devices Mfr
S.I.C.: 3651
N.A.I.C.S.: 334310

ACTIA INDIA Pvt Ltd **(1)**
C-15 Sector-58
Noida, Uttar Pradesh, 201 301, India
Tel.: (91) 1202582290
Fax: (91) 1202582293
E-Mail: info@actia.com
Web Site: www.actia.com
Emp.: 50
Automotive Diagnostic Equipment Mfr
S.I.C.: 3714
N.A.I.C.S.: 336390
Vijayakumar Gupta *(COO)*

ACTIA Italia Srl **(1)**
Corso Unione Sovietica 612 / 15 B
10135 Turin, Italy
Tel.: (39) 0113402711
Fax: (39) 0113470468
E-Mail: info@actiaitalia.com
Web Site: www.actiaitalia.com
Emp.: 50
Automotive Diagnostic Equipment Mfr
S.I.C.: 3714
N.A.I.C.S.: 336390
Christian Desmoulins *(Co-Pres & Owner)*
Pierre Calmels *(Co-Pres)*
Davide Loy *(Mng Dir)*

ACTIA Nederland BV **(1)**
Steenovenweg 1
5708 HN Helmond, North Brabant, Netherlands
Tel.: (31) 492562111
Fax: (31) 492562102
Web Site: www.actia.nl
Automotive Diagnostic Equipment Whslr
S.I.C.: 5013
N.A.I.C.S.: 423120
P. F. Calmels *(Principal)*

ACTIA Nordic AB **(1)**
Hammarbacken 4a
191 49 Sollentuna, Sweden
Tel.: (46) 84747200
Fax: (46) 84747290
E-Mail: info@actia.se
Web Site: www.actia.se
Emp.: 75
Automotive Electronic Equipment Mfr
S.I.C.: 3714
N.A.I.C.S.: 336390

ACTIA-POLSKA Sp. z o.o. **(1)**
Ul Pulawska 38
05-500 Piaseczno, Poland
Tel.: (48) 227263590
Fax: (48) 227263591
E-Mail: actiapolska@actiapolska.pl
Web Site: www.actiapolska.pl
Emp.: 12
Automotive Diagnostic Equipment Whslr
S.I.C.: 5013
N.A.I.C.S.: 423120
Riguet Gilles *(Chm)*

Actia (UK) Limited **(1)**
Unit 81 Mochdre Enterprise Park
Newtown, Powys, SY16 4LE, United Kingdom
Tel.: (44) 16 8661 1150
Fax: (44) 16 8662 1686
E-Mail: mail@actia.co.uk
Web Site: www.actia.co.uk
Emp.: 25
Automotive Diagnostic Equipment Mfr
S.I.C.: 3714
N.A.I.C.S.: 336390
Michael Neave *(Dir-Fin)*

Subsidiary:

Actia Muller (UK) Ltd. **(2)**
Unit 81 Mochdre Industrial Estate
Newtown, Powys, SY16 4LE, United Kingdom
Tel.: (44) 16 8661 1177
Fax: (44) 16 8662 1068
E-Mail: mail@actiamuller.co.uk
Web Site: www.actiamuller.co.uk
Garage Equipments & Diagnostic Tools Distr
S.I.C.: 5013
N.A.I.C.S.: 423120
Simon Stone *(Mgr)*

ACTIA VIDEO BUS, S.A. **(1)**
Pol Ind Los Olivos C Calidad 66
28906 Getafe, Madrid, Spain
Tel.: (34) 91 665 2626
Fax: (34) 91 665 2324
E-Mail: sales@vbactia.com
Web Site: www.vbactia.com
Emp.: 50
Automotive Audio & Video Equipments Mfr
S.I.C.: 3651
N.A.I.C.S.: 334310
Christian Desmoulin *(Pres)*
Jesus Corrales Bolanos *(Gen Dir)*

ATAL spol s.r.o. **(1)**
Lesni 47
Horky, 390 01 Tabor, Czech Republic
Tel.: (420) 381 251 791
Fax: (420) 381 253 043
E-Mail: atal@atal.cz
Web Site: www.atal.cz
Emp.: 45
Electronic Equipments Distr
S.I.C.: 5065
N.A.I.C.S.: 423690
Horejsi Joses *(Mgr)*

I+ME ACTIA GmbH **(1)**
Dresdenstr 17/18
38124 Braunschweig, Germany
Tel.: (49) 531387010
Fax: (49) 5313870188
E-Mail: info@ime-actia.de
Web Site: www.ime-actia.de
Emp.: 100
Automotive Diagnostic Equipment Mfr
S.I.C.: 3714
N.A.I.C.S.: 336390
Jens Uphoff *(Mng Dir)*

ACTINOGEN LIMITED

Level 2 1 Walker Avenue
West Perth, WA, 6005, Australia
Tel.: (61) 8 9481 3860
Fax: (61) 8 9321 1204
E-Mail: info@actinogen.com.au
Web Site: www.actinogen.com.au
ACW—(ASX)
Rev.: $2,749
Assets: $287,278
Liabilities: $84,743
Net Worth: $202,535
Earnings: ($171,595)
Emp.: 1
Fiscal Year-end: 06/30/13

Business Description:
Biotechnology Research
S.I.C.: 8731
N.A.I.C.S.: 541711

Personnel:
Peter Webse *(Sec)*

Board of Directors:
Brendan de Kauwe
Daniel Parasiliti
Anton Uvarov

Legal Counsel:
Lawton Gillon
Level 11 16 St Georges Terrace
Perth, Australia

ACTINVER S.A. DE C.V.

Guillermo Gonzalez Camarena 1200
Centro de Cd
Piso 9 10 y 11 Del Alvaro Obregon
Santa Fe, 01210 Mexico, DF, Mexico
Tel.: (52) 1103 6600
Fax: (52) 1103 6755
Web Site: www.actinver.com
ACTINVRB—(MEX)
Sales Range: $150-199.9 Million
Emp.: 1,200

Business Description:
Brokerage & Investment Services
S.I.C.: 6211
N.A.I.C.S.: 523110

Personnel:
Hector Madero Rivero *(Chm)*

ACTION ASIA LIMITED

3 Anson Road 27-01 Springleaf Tower
Singapore, 079909, Singapore
Tel.: (65) 65323488
Fax: (65) 65354188
E-Mail: enquiry@actionind.com.my
Web Site: www.actionind.com.my
Year Founded: 1987
A59—(SES)
Sls.: $152,731,558
Assets: $151,542,948
Liabilities: $66,693,342
Net Worth: $84,849,606
Earnings: $4,008,726
Emp.: 400
Fiscal Year-end: 12/31/12

Business Description:
Mobile Audio & Video Entertainment Products Mfr
S.I.C.: 3651
N.A.I.C.S.: 334310

Personnel:
Chiun-Ping Peng *(Chm)*
Wen-Chih Peng *(Mng Dir)*
Yih Min Sun *(CFO)*
Juliana Joo Hui Loh *(Sec)*

Board of Directors:
Chiun-Ping Peng
Pin Yong Lai
Jack Yuan-Chen Li
Wen-Chih Peng
Wen-Chih Shung
Edmund Koon Kay Tang

ACTION CHEVROLET BUICK GMC

7955 Chemin Chambly
Saint-Hubert, QC, J3Y 5K2, Canada
Tel.: (450) 445-7333
Fax: (450) 445-9751
Toll Free: (888) 319-6046
Web Site: www.actionchevrolet.com
Rev.: $11,600,000
Emp.: 35

Business Description:
New & Used Car Dealers
S.I.C.: 5511
N.A.I.C.S.: 441110

Personnel:
Stephane Guilbault *(Pres)*

ACTION CONSTRUCTION EQUIPMENT LTD.

5th Floor TDI Center Jasola
New Delhi, 76, India
Tel.: (91) 11 40549900
Fax: (91) 11 40549922
E-Mail: marketing@ace-cranes.com
Web Site: www.ace-cranes.com
532762—(BOM)
Rev.: $124,771,030
Assets: $112,614,945
Liabilities: $59,616,260
Net Worth: $52,998,685
Earnings: $1,372,720
Fiscal Year-end: 03/31/13

Business Description:
Construction Equipment Mfr
S.I.C.: 3531
N.A.I.C.S.: 333120

Personnel:
Vijay Agarwal *(Chm & Mng Dir)*
Rajan Luthra *(CFO & Sec)*

Board of Directors:
Vijay Agarwal
Keshav Chandra Agarwal
Mona Agarwal
Sorab Agarwal
Surbhi Garg

Girish Narain Mehra
Amar Singhal
Subhash Chander Verma
Transfer Agent:
Karvy Computershare Private Limited
Karvy House 46 Avenue 4 Street No.1 Banjara Hills
Hyderabad, India

ACTION FINANCIAL SERVICES (INDIA) LTD.

31 Rajgir Chambers 4th Floor 12/14 S B Road
Fort, Mumbai, 400 001, India
Tel.: (91) 22 40624444
Fax: (91) 22 43654446
E-Mail: info@actionfin.com
Web Site: www.actionfin.com
511706—(BOM)
Rev.: $897,132
Assets: $5,999,544
Liabilities: $1,271,844
Net Worth: $4,727,700
Earnings: $20,413
Fiscal Year-end: 03/31/13
Business Description:
Financial Services
S.I.C.: 6211
N.A.I.C.S.: 523999
Personnel:
Milan R. Parekh *(Chm & Co-Mng Dir)*
Bakul R. Parekh *(Co-Mng Dir)*
Prem Choudhary *(Compliance Officer)*
Board of Directors:
Milan R. Parekh
Harbhajan Singh Dhillon
Ketan H. Mehta
Bakul R. Parekh
Atul Anopchand Zatakia
Transfer Agent:
Link Intime India Pvt. Ltd
C-13 Pannalal Silk Mills Compound LBS Marg
Bhandup (West)
Mumbai, India

ACTION FLOORING

810 Development Drive
Kingston, ON, K7M 5V7, Canada
Tel.: (613) 634-3657
Fax: (613) 634-3641
E-Mail: 1action@kos.net
Web Site: www.actionflooringkingston.com
Year Founded: 1992
Rev.: $18,532,799
Emp.: 40
Business Description:
Flooring Contractors
S.I.C.: 1752
N.A.I.C.S.: 238330
Personnel:
Alan Thomson *(Pres)*

ACTION HOTELS PLC

The Gate Village 2 Level 4
PO Box 66345
Dubai, United Arab Emirates
Tel.: (971) 4 328 92 11
Fax: (971) 4 328 94 42
E-Mail: hotels@actionhotels.com
Web Site: www.actionhotels.com
Year Founded: 2009
AHCG—(AIM)
Business Description:
Hotel Developer & Owner
S.I.C.: 7011
N.A.I.C.S.: 721110
Personnel:
Mubarak A.M. Al-Sabah *(Chm)*
Stefan Allesch-Taylor *(Deputy Chm)*
Alain Debare *(CEO)*
Board of Directors:
Mubarak A.M. Al-Sabah
Stefan Allesch-Taylor
Raymond Chigot
Alain Debare
John Johnston
Alaister Murray

ACTIONS SEMICONDUCTOR CO., LTD.

No 1 Ke Ji Si Road Technology Innovation Coast of Hi-Tech Zone
Zhuhai, Guangdong, 519085, China
Tel.: (86) 756 339 2353
Fax: (86) 756 339 2251
E-Mail: investor-relations@actions-semi.com
Web Site: www.actions-semi.com
Year Founded: 2001
ACTS—(NASDAQ)
Rev.: $54,329,000
Assets: $322,188,000
Liabilities: $43,428,000
Net Worth: $278,760,000
Earnings: ($2,210,000)
Emp.: 614
Fiscal Year-end: 12/31/12
Business Description:
Integrated Circuit Designer & Mfr
S.I.C.: 3674
N.A.I.C.S.: 334413
Personnel:
Hsiang-Wei Lee *(Chm)*
Zhenyu Zhou *(CEO)*
Nigel Liu *(CFO)*
Shao Chuan Li *(CTO)*
Board of Directors:
Hsiang-Wei Lee
Chin-Hsin Chen
Shao Chuan Li
Yu-Hsin Casper Lin
Hui-Dong Tien
Nan-Horng Yeh

Non-U.S. Subsidiary:

Actions Technology (HK) Company Limited (1)
Room F 6th Floor West Gate Tower
Lai Chi Kok, Kowloon, China (Hong Kong) (100%)
Tel.: (852) 27436925
Fax: (852) 27425889
Other Electronic Parts & Equipment Whslr
S.I.C.: 5065
N.A.I.C.S.: 423690

ACTIONWEAR SASKATOON INC.

114 Melville Street
Saskatoon, SK, S7J 0R1, Canada
Tel.: (306) 933-3088
Fax: (306) 934-2922
Toll Free: (866) 933-3088
E-Mail: actionwest@actionwearinc.com
Web Site: www.actionwearinc.com
Year Founded: 1974
Rev.: $13,479,361
Emp.: 110
Business Description:
Apparel Mfr
S.I.C.: 2389
N.A.I.C.S.: 315990
Personnel:
Kathy Reaser *(Founder)*

ACTIS LLP

2 More London Riverside
London, SE1 2JT, United Kingdom
Tel.: (44) 20 7234 5000
Fax: (44) 20 7234 5010
E-Mail: info@act.is
Web Site: www.act.is
Year Founded: 2004
Managed Assets: $5,000,000,000
Emp.: 264
Business Description:
Private Equity Firm
S.I.C.: 6211
N.A.I.C.S.: 523999
Personnel:
Paul Fletcher *(Sr Partner)*
Alistair Mackintosh *(Partner & Chief Investment Officer)*
Paul Owers *(Partner & Gen Counsel)*
Jonathon Bond *(Partner & Head-Investor Dev)*
Torbjorn Caesar *(Partner & Co-Head-Energy)*
Simon Harford *(Partner & Co-Head-Africa)*
Patrick Ledoux *(Partner & Co-Head-Latin America)*
Meng Ann Lim *(Partner & Head-China & Southeast Asia)*
David Morley *(Partner & Head-Real Estate)*
Mark Richards *(Partner & Head-Fin Svcs)*
Joe Sinyor *(Partner & Head-Value Creation Grp)*
Michael Till *(Partner & Co-Head-Energy)*
J.M. Trivedi *(Partner & Head-South Asia)*
Chris Coles *(Partner-Fin Svcs)*
Murray Grant *(Partner-Africa)*
David Grylls *(Partner-Energy)*
Mikael Karlsson *(Partner-Energy)*
Nick Luckock *(Partner-Fin Svcs)*
Ron Bell *(COO & Dir)*
Lou Baran *(Chief HR Officer & Dir)*

Non-U.S. Branches:

Actis LLP - Beijing Office (1)
713 China World Tower 2 No 1 Jianguomenwai Avenue
Chaoyang District, Beijing, 100004, China
Tel.: (86) 10 6535 4800
Fax: (86) 10 6505 8111
E-Mail: info@act.is
Web Site: www.act.is
Private Equity Firm
S.I.C.: 6211
N.A.I.C.S.: 523999
Meng Ann Lim *(Partner & Head-China & Southeast Asia)*
Dong Zhong *(Partner-Consumer)*

Actis LLP - Mumbai Office (1)
4th Floor Avantha House Dr Annie Besant Road
Worli, Mumbai, 400 030, India
Tel.: (91) 22 6146 7900
Fax: (91) 22 2423 1549
Web Site: www.act.is
Emp.: 26
Private Equity Firm
S.I.C.: 6211
N.A.I.C.S.: 523999
J.M. Trivedi *(Partner & Head-South Asia)*
Sanjiv Aggarwal *(Partner-Energy)*
Mahesh Chhabria *(Partner-Indus)*
Shomik Mukherjee *(Partner-Consumer)*

Actis LLP - Sao Paulo Office (1)
Rua Sao Tome 86 8th Floor Vila Olimpia
04551-080 Sao Paulo, SP, Brazil
Tel.: (55) 11 3844 6300
Fax: (55) 11 3844 6301
E-Mail: actislatam@act.is
Web Site: www.act.is
Emp.: 10
Private Equity Firm
S.I.C.: 6211
N.A.I.C.S.: 523999
Chu Kong *(Partner & Co-Head-Latin America)*
Patrick Ledoux *(Partner & Co-Head-Latin America)*
Michael Till *(Partner & Co-Head-Energy-Global)*

Non-U.S. Holdings:

Globeleq Generation Limited (1)
11 New Street
Saint Peter Port, GY1 2PF, Guernsey
Tel.: (44) 1481 726 034
Fax: (44) 1481 726 029
Holding Company; Electric Power Generation
S.I.C.: 4911
N.A.I.C.S.: 221118
Mikael Karlsson, *(CEO)*
Susan Wilkins *(CFO & Head-Legal)*

U.S. Holding:

Globeleq Inc. (2)
9801 Westheimer Ste 302
Houston, TX 77042
Tel.: (713) 355-3450
Fax: (713) 355-3847
Toll Free: (888) 581-6923
E-Mail: info@globeleq.com
Web Site: www.globeleq.com
Emp.: 55
Administrative Management & General Management Consulting Services; Energy & Power Solutions
S.I.C.: 8742
N.A.I.C.S.: 541611
Mikael Karlsson *(CEO)*
Susan Wilkins *(CFO)*

Non-U.S. Holdings:

Globeleq Advisors Limited (2)
2 More London Riverside
London, SE1 2JT, United Kingdom
Tel.: (44) 20 7 234 5400
Fax: (44) 20 7 237 5486
E-Mail: info@globeleq.com
Web Site: www.globeleq.com
Advisory & Support Services
S.I.C.: 7389
N.A.I.C.S.: 561499
Mikael Karlsson *(CEO)*
Susan Wilkens *(CFO & Head-Legal)*

Globeleq Mesoamerica Energy (2)
Centro Corporative El Cedral
Edificio 1 Local 111, Escazu, Costa Rica
Tel.: (506) 2228 9300
Fax: (506) 2228 9930
E-Mail: info@mesoamericaenergy.com
Web Site: www.globeleqmesoamericaenergy.com
Development, Construction & Operation of Renewable Energy Projects
S.I.C.: 4911
N.A.I.C.S.: 221118
Jay Gallegos, *(Mng Dir)*
Rodolfo Echeverria *(CFO)*

Songas Limited (2)
Corner Nelson Mandela & Morogoro Road
Dar es Salaam, Tanzania
Mailing Address:
PO Box 6342
Dar es Salaam, Tanzania
Tel.: (255) 222452160
Fax: (255) 22 245 2161
Web Site: www.globeleq.com
Natural Gas Operations
S.I.C.: 4922
N.A.I.C.S.: 486210
Sebastian Kastuli *(Mgr-Comml)*

Vlisco Netherlands B.V. (1)
Binnen Parallelweg 27
5701 PH Helmond, Netherlands NI
Mailing Address:
PO Box 21
5700 MA Helmond, Netherlands
Tel.: (31) 492570563
Fax: (31) 492570230
E-Mail: info@vlisco.com
Web Site: www.vlisco.com
Sales Range: $200-249.9 Million
Emp.: 2,100
Wax Prints & Java Prints Sales Marketing & Mfr
S.I.C.: 2393
N.A.I.C.S.: 314910
Hans Ouwendijk *(CEO)*

Subsidiaries:

Vlisco Helmond B.V. (2)
Binnen Barallelweg 27
Postbus 21
5701 PH Helmond, Netherlands NL
Tel.: (31) 492570922
Fax: (31) 492 57 02 30
E-Mail: vlisco@vlisco.com
Web Site: www.vlisco.com
Emp.: 450

Actis LLP—(Continued)

Fabrics Mfr
S.I.C.: 2299
N.A.I.C.S.: 313210

Non-U.S. Subsidiaries:

John Walkden et Compagnie S.A. (2)
Rue du Governeur General Roume
PO Box 24
Cotonou, Benin BJ
Tel.: (229) 21313037
Web Site: www.vlisco.com
Wax Prints & Java Prints Sales, Marketing & Mfr
S.I.C.: 2297
N.A.I.C.S.: 313230

Niger-Afrique S.A. (2)
Ave Du President Luebke
PO Box 11 050
Niamey, 00227, Niger Ne
Tel.: (227) 20 73 33 19
Fax: (227) 20 73 37 68
E-Mail: na@intnet.ne
Web Site: www.vlisco.com
Emp.: 11
Wax Prints & Java Prints Sales, Marketing & Mfr
S.I.C.: 2297
N.A.I.C.S.: 313230

VAC Ghana (2)
PO Box 606
Tema, Ghana GH
Tel.: (233) 22304234
Fax: (233) 22302995
Web Site: www.vlisco.com
Wax Prints & Java Prints Sales, Marketing & Mfr
S.I.C.: 2297
N.A.I.C.S.: 313230
Baaba Owusu-Ansah *(Mgr)*

Subsidiaries:

Ghana Textile Printing Company Ltd. (3)
PO Box 606
Tema, Ghana GH
Tel.: (233) 303 30 42 34
Fax: (233) 22302995
E-Mail: info@vilscogh.com
Web Site: www.vlisco.nl
Emp.: 500
Wax Prints & Java Prints Sales, Marketing & Mfr
S.I.C.: 2297
N.A.I.C.S.: 313230

VAC-Togo S.A. (2)
16 Rue du Commerce
PO Box 345
Lome, Togo TO
Tel.: (228) 2212800
Fax: (228) 2215999
E-Mail: vactogo@yahoo.fr
Web Site: www.vlisco.nl
Wax Prints & Java Prints Sales, Marketing & Mfr
S.I.C.: 2297
N.A.I.C.S.: 313230

Vlisco France S.A. (2)
5 Bis Rue Du Cirque
750008 Paris, France FR
Tel.: (33) 142259425
Fax: (33) 142257671
E-Mail: n.niskanen@vlisco.com
Web Site: www.vlisco.nl
Emp.: 5
Wax Prints & Java Prints Sales, Marketing & Mfr
S.I.C.: 2297
N.A.I.C.S.: 313230
Nana Niskanen *(Country Mgr)*

Wintex-Department Vlisco (2)
Avenue du General de Gaulle
Immeuble Woodin, BP 5855 Abidjan, 01, Cote d'Ivoire CI
Tel.: (225) 08 30 9274
Web Site: www.vlisco.com
Wax Prints & Java Prints Sales, Marketing & Mfr
S.I.C.: 3999
N.A.I.C.S.: 339999

ACTIV C.S.A.

56-60, bd Amiral Mouchez
BP 643
76059 Le Havre, France
Tel.: (33) 35247474
Fax: (33) 35247475
E-Mail: contact@activfrance.com
Web Site: www.activfrance.com
Sales Range: $10-24.9 Million
Emp.: 112

Business Description:
Office Equipment
S.I.C.: 5044
N.A.I.C.S.: 423420

Personnel:
Henri Roth *(Pres)*

ACTIV8 DISTRIBUTION LTD.

Greenhill House 26 Greenhill Crescent
Watford, WD18 8JA, United Kingdom
Tel.: (44) 845 45 85 008
Fax: (44) 845 458 1526
E-Mail: sales@a8uk.com
Web Site: www.a8uk.com
Year Founded: 2000
Sales Range: $10-24.9 Million
Emp.: 30

Business Description:
Mobile Accessory Whslr
S.I.C.: 5065
N.A.I.C.S.: 423690

Personnel:
Stuart Conroy *(Mng Dir)*

ACTIVA CAPITAL S.A.S.

Rue du Faubourg Saint-Honore
75008 Paris, France
Tel.: (33) 143125012
Fax: (33) 143125013
E-Mail: reception@activacapital.com
Web Site: www.activacapital.com
Emp.: 17

Business Description:
Investment Services
S.I.C.: 6211
N.A.I.C.S.: 523999

Personnel:
Jean-Louis de Bernardy *(Partner)*
Charles Diehl *(Partner)*
Michael Diehl *(Partner)*
Philippe Latorre *(Partner)*
Christophe Parier *(Partner)*

Holding:

Selpro S.A. (1)
Le Chateau Rouge 276 Ave De La Marne
F 59700 Marcq-en-Baroeul, France FR
Tel.: (33) 320661766
Fax: (33) 32066170078
E-Mail: direction.generale@selpro.fr
Web Site: www.selpro.fr
Sales Range: $75-99.9 Million
Emp.: 120
Employment Agency Services
S.I.C.: 7361
N.A.I.C.S.: 561311
Jack Caroen *(CEO)*

Joint Venture:

Nexeya SA (1)
Centrale Parc 2 avenue Sully prud hommes
92290 Chatenay-Malabry, France
Tel.: (33) 1 41 87 30 00
Fax: (33) 1 41 87 30 08
Web Site: www.nexeya.com
ALNEX—(EUR)
Emp.: 1,200
Industrial Engineering Services
S.I.C.: 8711
N.A.I.C.S.: 541330
Philippe Gautier *(Co-Chm & Mng Dir)*
Jean-Yves Riviere *(Co-Chm & Mgr-HR)*
Benoit de La Motte *(CFO)*

ACTIVA RESOURCES AG

Hessenring 107
61348 Bad Homburg, Germany
Tel.: (49) 6172 4 83 23 52
Fax: (49) 6172 4 83 23 53
Web Site: www.activaresources.com
NXI—(DEU)
Rev.: $6,725,341
Assets: $18,387,977
Liabilities: $13,594,548
Net Worth: $4,793,429
Earnings: ($1,074,015)
Emp.: 9
Fiscal Year-end: 12/31/12

Business Description:
Oil & Gas Exploration Services
S.I.C.: 1389
N.A.I.C.S.: 213112

Personnel:
Walter Bluementhal *(Chm-Supervisory Bd)*
Axel Vedder *(Deputy Chm-Supervisory Bd)*
Leigh A. Hooper *(CEO & Member-Mgmt Bd)*
John W. Hayes *(Pres-Activa Resources LLC)*

Supervisory Board of Directors:
Walter Bluementhal
Gerd Escher
Axel Vedder

Mittreu GmbH
Frankfurt am Main, Germany

Legal Counsel:
Hogan Lovells
Frankfurt, Germany

U.S. Subsidiary:

Activa Resources, LLC (1)
403 E Commerce Str
San Antonio, TX 78205
Tel.: (210) 271-9875
Fax: (210) 224-0280
Oil & Gas Exploration Services
S.I.C.: 1389
N.A.I.C.S.: 213112
John W. Hayes *(Pres & Member-Mgmt Bd)*
Douglas Coyle *(Member-Mgmt Bd & Mgr-Exploration)*

ACTIVE ALLIANCE, INCORPORATED

Bldg 1428 POL Pier Compound
Argonaut Highway, Subic, 2200, Philippines
Tel.: (63) 28443906
Fax: (63) 472526325
Web Site: www.activealliance inc.com
AAI—(PHI)
Sales Range: Less than $1 Million

Business Description:
Holding Company; Printed Circuit Boards & Other Electronic Components Mfr & Distr Import Export
S.I.C.: 6719
N.A.I.C.S.: 551112

Personnel:
Bienvenido A. Tan *(Chm & Pres)*
Crisanto Roy B. Alcid *(Treas)*
Christine P. Base *(Sec)*

Board of Directors:
Bienvenido A. Tan
Gabriel H. Alcantara
Crisanto Roy B. Alcid
Manolo E. Aquino
Albert C. Eufemio
Edgardo R. Veron Cruz
Michael B. Zalamea

ACTIVE BIOTECH AB

Scheelevagen 22
PO Box 724
220 07 Lund, Sweden
Tel.: (46) 46 19 20 00
E-Mail: info@activebiotech.com
Web Site: www.activebiotech.com
Year Founded: 1983
BTPC—(DEU)
Sls.: $35,280,158
Assets: $107,854,888
Liabilities: $55,235,581
Net Worth: $52,619,306
Earnings: ($27,092,322)
Emp.: 76
Fiscal Year-end: 12/31/12

Business Description:
Biotechnology Product Research & Development Services
S.I.C.: 8731
N.A.I.C.S.: 541711

Personnel:
Mats Arnhog *(Chm)*
Tomas Leanderson *(Pres & CEO)*
Hans Kolam *(CFO)*
Goran Forsberg *(Chief Bus Officer)*
Helen Tuvesson *(Chief Scientific Officer)*

Board of Directors:
Mats Arnhog
Karin Hallbeck
Peter Hofvenstam
Klas Karre
Mef Nilbert
Magnhild Sandberg-Wollheim
Peter Sjostrand
Anette Sundstedt
Peter Thelin

ACTIVE CONTROL TECHNOLOGY INC.

3200 Ridgeway Drive Unit 17
Mississauga, ON, L5L 5Y6, Canada
Tel.: (905) 670-5500
Fax: (905) 364-0057
Toll Free: (888) 887-0738
E-Mail: info@activecontrol.com
Web Site: www.activecontrol.com
ACT—(TSXV)
Sls.: $4,079,969
Assets: $1,905,376
Liabilities: $1,041,371
Net Worth: $864,005
Earnings: ($572,327)
Fiscal Year-end: 07/31/13

Business Description:
Wireless Communications Equipment Mfr
S.I.C.: 3663
N.A.I.C.S.: 334220

Personnel:
Jonathan Emanuel *(CEO)*
Graham C. Warren *(CFO)*
William R. Johnstone *(Sec)*

Board of Directors:
Doug Barre
Steve Barrett
Jonathan Emanuel
William R. Johnstone
Esther Schwartz
Graham C. Warren
Michael Wolfe

Legal Counsel:
Gardiner Roberts LLP
Scotia Plaza 40 King Street West Suite 3100
Toronto, ON, Canada

Transfer Agent:
Equity Transfer & Trust Company
200 University Avenue Ste 400
Toronto, ON, M5H 4H1, Canada
Tel.: (416) 361-0152
Fax: (416) 361-0470

Subsidiary:

PowerCart Systems Inc. (1)
3200 Ridgeway Drive Unit 17
Mississauga, ON, L5L 5Y6, Canada
Tel.: (905) 364-0050
Fax: (905) 364-0057
Toll Free: (866) 387-6937
E-Mail: sales@powercart.com
Web Site: www.powercart.com
Industrial Printing Cart Mfr
S.I.C.: 3999
N.A.I.C.S.: 339999

ACTIVE ENERGY GROUP PLC
3rd Floor Greener House 66-68 Haymarket
London, SW1Y 4RF, United Kingdom
Tel.: (44) 2071480960
Fax: (44) 2074953108
E-Mail: info@active-energy.com
Web Site: www.active-energy-group.com
AEG—(AIM)
Rev.: $364,358
Assets: $3,291,329
Liabilities: $759,386
Net Worth: $2,531,943
Earnings: ($2,181,685)
Emp.: 5
Fiscal Year-end: 12/31/12
Business Description:
Engineering Services
S.I.C.: 8711
N.A.I.C.S.: 541330
Personnel:
Richard Spinks *(CEO)*
Board of Directors:
Colin Hill
Richard Spinks
Giuseppe Valoroso
Legal Counsel:
Pritchard Englefield
14 New Street
London, EC2M 4HE, United Kingdom
DWF LLP
Capital House 85 King William Street
London, EC4N 7BL, United Kingdom
Tel.: (44) 3333 20 22 20
Subsidiaries:

Active Energy Limited (1)
75 Brook Street
Mayfair, London, W1K 4AD, United Kingdom (100%)
Tel.: (44) 20 7491 9533
Fax: (44) 20 7629 8940
E-Mail: info@active-energy.com
Web Site: www.active-energy.com
Emp.: 50
Voltage Optimising Transformers Mfr & Distr
S.I.C.: 3612
N.A.I.C.S.: 335311
Gavin Little *(Chm)*
Kevin Baker *(Mng Dir)*

Redline Engineering Services Ltd (1)
75 Brook Street
London, W1K 4AD, United Kingdom (100%)
Tel.: (44) 2074919533
Fax: (44) 207 495 3108
E-Mail: info@active-energy-group.com
Web Site: www.redlineengservices.com
Engineering Services
S.I.C.: 8711
N.A.I.C.S.: 541330
Roy Booth *(Dir-Technical)*

Non-U.S. Subsidiary:

Derlite Co Ltd. (1)
324 Moo 4 Soi 6B Bangpoo Indus Estate Sukhumvit Rd
Tambon Pragsa, Samut Prakan, 10280, Thailand
Tel.: (66) 27094892
Fax: (66) 27094894
E-Mail: sales@derlite.com
Web Site: www.derlite.com
Emp.: 136
Gas Ignition Components Mfr & Distr
S.I.C.: 3822
N.A.I.C.S.: 334512
Kevin Baker *(Mng Dir)*

ACTIVE EXHAUST CORP.
1865 Birchmount Road
Toronto, ON, M1P 2J5, Canada
Tel.: (416) 445-9610
Fax: (416) 445-9765
E-Mail: inquiries@activeexhaust.com
Web Site: www.activeexhaust.com
Year Founded: 1973
Emp.: 200
Business Description:
Exhaust Systems & Tubular Metals
S.I.C.: 3714
N.A.I.C.S.: 336390
Personnel:
Peter Hampton *(Pres)*

ACTIVE GROUP HOLDINGS LIMITED
Shoes Industrial Park Baogai Town
Shishi, Fujian, China
Tel.: (86) 59583099030
Fax: (86) 59583952000
Web Site: www.activegroup-int.com
1096—(HKG)
Sls.: $107,938,257
Assets: $183,467,302
Liabilities: $88,049,284
Net Worth: $95,418,018
Earnings: $11,566,186
Emp.: 1,779
Fiscal Year-end: 12/31/12
Business Description:
Men's Footwear Mfr
S.I.C.: 2389
N.A.I.C.S.: 316210
Personnel:
Xiuman Cai *(Chm)*
Wenbin Zhang *(CEO)*
Yuanjian Chen *(CFO)*
Jianren Huang *(COO)*
Suk Yan Yau *(Sec & Controller-Fin)*
Board of Directors:
Xiuman Cai
Yuanjian Chen
Jianren Huang
Thomas Ho Yiu Lee
Xiaoqiu Wu
Lin Ye
Wenbin Zhang
Codan Trust Company (Cayman) Limited
Cricket Square Hutchins Drive
PO Box 2681
Georgetown, Grand Cayman, Cayman Islands
Transfer Agent:
Codan Trust Company (Cayman) Limited
Cricket Square Hutchins Drive
PO Box 2681
Georgetown, Grand Cayman, Cayman Islands

ACTIVE GROWTH CAPITAL INC.
866 3e Avenue
Val d'Or, QC, J9P 1T1, Canada
Tel.: (819) 825-0001
Year Founded: 2012
ACK—(TSXV)
Assets: $579,207
Liabilities: $28,161
Net Worth: $551,046
Earnings: ($1,292,993)
Fiscal Year-end: 12/31/12
Business Description:
Mineral Exploration Services
S.I.C.: 1099
N.A.I.C.S.: 212299
Personnel:
Marc Labrecque *(Acting Pres, CEO & CFO)*
Maxime Lemieux *(Sec)*
Board of Directors:
Marc Labrecque
Jean-Francois Lemay
Maxime Lemieux

ACTIVE PRIVATE EQUITY ADVISORY LLP
5th Floor 6 Chesterfield Gardens
London, W1J 5BQ, United Kingdom
Tel.: (44) 207 016 6480
Fax: (44) 207 016 6490
Web Site: www.apeq.co.uk
Business Description:
Private Equity Firm
S.I.C.: 6211
N.A.I.C.S.: 523999
Personnel:
Gavyn Davies *(Founding Partner)*
Spencer Skinner *(Founding Partner)*
Nick Evans *(Partner)*
Holding:

Evans Holdings Ltd. (1)
Camino Park James Watt Way
Crawley, West Sussex, RH10 9TZ, United Kingdom
Tel.: (44) 1293 574900
Fax: (44) 1293614672
Web Site: www.evanscycles.com
Sales Range: $125-149.9 Million
Emp.: 1,500
Bicycle Retailer
S.I.C.: 5941
N.A.I.C.S.: 451110
Nick Evans *(Chm)*
Nick Wilkinson *(CEO)*
Mike Rice *(Mng Dir)*

ACTIVE RISK GROUP PLC
(Acquired by Sword Group SE)

ACTIVE WITH ME INC.
2005 Lakeshore Road
Sarnia, ON, N7X 1G4, Canada
Tel.: (519) 337-9048
Year Founded: 2012
Business Description:
Online Travel Resources
S.I.C.: 2741
N.A.I.C.S.: 519130
Personnel:
Sheri Strangway *(Pres, CEO, CFO & Sec)*
Board of Directors:
Sheri Strangway

ACTIVEIN, INC.
1 Leshem Street
82000 Kiryat Gat, Israel
Tel.: (972) 505265078
Fax: (972) 39067225
Web Site: www.activein.co.il
Year Founded: 2007
Premiums: $1,000,000
Emp.: 10
Fiscal Year-end: 12/31/12
Business Description:
Intravenous Catheter Developer & Mfr
S.I.C.: 3841
N.A.I.C.S.: 339112
Personnel:
Adi Plaschkes *(CEO & CFO)*
Yoav Paz *(Chief Medical Officer)*
Board of Directors:
Boaz Dor
Eitan Kyiet
Anat Segal
Ilan Shalev

ACTIVEX LIMITED
117 Quay Street
Brisbane, QLD, 4000, Australia
Mailing Address:
PO Box 1533
Milton, QLD, 4064, Australia
Tel.: (61) 7 3236 4188
Fax: (61) 7 3236 4288
E-Mail: admin@activex.com.au
Web Site: www.activex.com.au
AIV—(ASX)
Rev.: $25,158
Assets: $6,506,054
Liabilities: $289,091
Net Worth: $6,216,963
Earnings: ($3,323,251)
Fiscal Year-end: 06/30/13
Business Description:
Mineral Exploration Services
S.I.C.: 1481
N.A.I.C.S.: 213115
Personnel:
Douglas I. Young *(Mng Dir)*
Paul Anthony Crawford *(Sec)*
Board of Directors:
Min Yang
Geoff Baker
Paul Anthony Crawford
Grant Thomas
Douglas I. Young
Legal Counsel:
Carter Newell
Level 13 215 Adelaide St
Brisbane, Australia

ACTIVIDADES DE CONSTRUCCION Y SERVICIOS, S.A.
(See Under ACS, Actividades de Construccion y Servicios, S.A.)

ACTIVINSTINCT LTD.
60 The Broadway Mill Hill
London, NW7 3TE, United Kingdom
Tel.: (44) 208 959 5539
Web Site: www.activinstinct.com
Year Founded: 1987
Sales Range: $10-24.9 Million
Emp.: 75
Business Description:
Electronic Shopping Services
S.I.C.: 5961
N.A.I.C.S.: 454111
Personnel:
Mike Thornhill *(CEO)*

ACTIVNER S.A. DE C.V.
Guillermo Gonzalez Camarena 1200
Centro de Cd
Santa Fe, 01210 Mexico, Mexico
Tel.: (52) 5511036600
Fax: (52) 11036755
E-Mail: activner@activner.com.mx
Web Site: www.activner.com
Sales Range: $200-249.9 Million
Emp.: 1,500
Business Description:
Investment Banking Services
S.I.C.: 6211
N.A.I.C.S.: 523110
Personnel:
Alonso Madero Rivero *(Dir-Investments)*

ACTIX LIMITED
200 Hammersmith Road
London, W6 7DL, United Kingdom
Tel.: (44) 2087356300
Fax: (44) 2087356301
E-Mail: info@actix.com
Web Site: www.actix.com
Year Founded: 1992
Rev.: $24,848,834
Emp.: 76
Business Description:
Software Development Services
S.I.C.: 7371
N.A.I.C.S.: 541511
Personnel:
Bill McHale *(CEO)*
Richard Thompson *(CFO)*
Richard Kateley *(CTO)*
Chris Beukers *(Sr VP)*

ACTOM (PTY) LTD.
(Formerly Luwa South Africa (Pty) Ltd.)
27-29 Circuit Rd Westmead
Pinetown, 3600, South Africa

ACTOM (Pty) Ltd.—(Continued)

Mailing Address:
PO Box 413
Pinetown, 3610, South Africa
Tel.: (27) 317003286
Fax: (27) 317004101
E-Mail: frank.van-dongen@actom.co.za
Web Site: www.actom-hvac.co.za
Year Founded: 1938
Emp.: 35
Business Description:
Air-Conditioning Services
S.I.C.: 3589
N.A.I.C.S.: 333318
Personnel:
Frank Van Dongen *(Gen Mgr)*
Subsidiaries:

LH Marthinusen (Pty.) Ltd. **(1)**
338 Main Reef Road
Denver, 2011 Johannesburg, South Africa
Tel.: (27) 116156722
Fax: (27) 11616 6808
Web Site: www.lhm.co.za
Emp.: 500
Electro-Mechanical Repair & Manufacturing Services
S.I.C.: 7699
N.A.I.C.S.: 811219
Altino Da Silva *(Mng Dir)*

Marthinusen & Coutts (Pty.) Ltd. **(1)**
53 Hospital St
PO Box 40018
Cleveland, 2022, South Africa
Tel.: (27) 116071700
Fax: (27) 0865240757
E-Mail: commercial@mandc.co.za
Web Site: www.mandc.co.za
Emp.: 320
Electric Motor Repair Services
S.I.C.: 7699
N.A.I.C.S.: 811219
Richard Botton *(Mng Dir)*

Reid & Mitchell (Pty.) Ltd. **(1)**
24 Van Dyk Road
Benoni, 1502, South Africa
Tel.: (27) 119149600
Fax: (27) 119142013
E-Mail: enquiries@reidmitchell.co.za
Web Site: www.reidmitchell.co.za
Emp.: 132
Repair of Electrical Motors
S.I.C.: 7699
N.A.I.C.S.: 811219
Terry Lawrenson *(Mng Dir)*

Transwire (Pty.) Ltd. **(1)**
28 Main Rd
PO Box 92
Olifantsfontein, 1665, South Africa
Tel.: (27) 113162480
Fax: (27) 113164085
E-Mail: sales@transwire.co.za
Web Site: www.transwire.co.za
Emp.: 150
Magnet Wire Mfr
S.I.C.: 3496
N.A.I.C.S.: 332618
Howard Eldridge *(CEO)*

Wire Electric (Pty.) Ltd. **(1)**
6 Old Mutual Mini Park Cnr Outspan & Heidelburg Rds
City Deep Ext 7, Johannesburg, 2049, South Africa
Mailing Address:
PO Box 86330
City Deep, Johannesburg, 2049, South Africa
Tel.: (27) 116299300
Fax: (27) 116137107
E-Mail: info@wilec.co.za
Web Site: www.wilec.co.za
Emp.: 150
Electrical & Industrial Product Distr
S.I.C.: 5063
N.A.I.C.S.: 423610
Steve Jordaan *(Mng Dir)*

ACTON LEATHER CO. INC.
(d/b/a Olde Hide House, The)
49 Eastern Avenue
Acton, ON, L7J 2E6, Canada
Tel.: (519) 853-1031
Fax: (519) 858-4514
Toll Free: (877) 453-2843
Web Site: www.hidehouse.ca
Year Founded: 1980
Rev.: $10,715,710
Emp.: 60
Business Description:
Leather Goods Mfr
S.I.C.: 3199
N.A.I.C.S.: 316998
Personnel:
John Brison *(Pres)*

ACTUAL EXPERIENCE LTD.
The Tramshed Beehive Yard Walcot Street
Bath, BA1 5BB, United Kingdom
Tel.: (44) 1225 731 340
E-Mail: enquiries@actual-experience.com
Web Site: www.actual-experience.com
ACT—(AIM)
Business Description:
IT Apllication Solutions
S.I.C.: 7372
N.A.I.C.S.: 511210
Personnel:
David John Page *(Chm & CEO)*

ACTURIS LTD.
Courtyard Suite 100 Hatton Garden
London, EC1N 8NX, United Kingdom
Tel.: (44) 2070794000
Fax: (44) 2070794100
E-Mail: info@acturis.com
Web Site: www.acturis.com
Year Founded: 2000
Sales Range: $10-24.9 Million
Emp.: 200
Business Description:
Insurance Software Developer
S.I.C.: 7372
N.A.I.C.S.: 511210
Personnel:
Theo Duchen *(Co-CEO)*
David McDonald *(Co-CEO)*
Board of Directors:
Shay Bhatia
Theo Duchen
Tony Goddard
David McDonald
Simon Ronaldson

ACTUS MINERALS CORP.
511 - 475 Howe Street
Vancouver, BC, V6C 2B3, Canada
Tel.: (604) 678-9639
Fax: (604) 602-9640
E-Mail: info@actusminerals.com
Web Site: actusminerals.com
Year Founded: 2006
AAC—(TSXV)
Assets: $384,767
Liabilities: $22,496
Net Worth: $362,272
Earnings: ($299,393)
Fiscal Year-end: 04/30/13
Business Description:
Metal Mining Services
S.I.C.: 1099
N.A.I.C.S.: 212299
Personnel:
Carl Alexander Von Eisiedel *(Pres & CEO)*
James Gilbert Henderson *(CFO)*
Kathryn Ellen Witter *(Sec)*
Board of Directors:
Daniel Coch
John DeHart
James Gilbert Henderson
Carl Alexander Von Eisiedel
Transfer Agent:
Pacific Corporate Trust Company
2nd Floor 510 Burrard Street
Vancouver, BC, V6V 3B9, Canada

ACUCAP PROPERTIES LIMITED
Suite A11 Westlake Square Westlake Drive Westlake
Cape Town, South Africa
Mailing Address:
PO Box 31079
Tokai, 7966, South Africa
Tel.: (27) 217022745
Fax: (27) 217022738
E-Mail: info@acucap.co.za
Web Site: www.acucap.co.za
ACP—(JSE)
Rev.: $72,693,243
Assets: $1,155,945,657
Liabilities: $613,448,804
Net Worth: $542,496,853
Earnings: $81,842,478
Fiscal Year-end: 03/31/13
Business Description:
Property Holding Services
S.I.C.: 6331
N.A.I.C.S.: 524126
Personnel:
Paul Theodosiou *(Mng Dir)*
Baden Marlow *(CFO)*
Henry H. O. Steyn *(Sec)*
Board of Directors:
Brian Kantor
Frank Berkely
Rolf Frolich
Nyami Mandindi
Baden Marlow
Sello Moloko
Jonathan Rens
Bryan Stevens
Paul Theodosiou
Norman Whale
Transfer Agent:
Computershare Investor Services (Pty) Ltd.
70 Marshall Street
Johannesburg, 2001, South Africa
Tel.: (27) 11 370 5000
Fax: (27) 11 370 5487
Subsidiaries:

Acucap Investments 2 (Proprietary) Limited **(1)**
Ste A11-Westlake Sq
Westlake, Cape Town, Western Cape, 7495, South Africa
Tel.: (27) 217022745
Fax: (27) 217022738
E-Mail: info@acucap.co.za
Emp.: 19
Shopping Mall Management Services
S.I.C.: 6512
N.A.I.C.S.: 531120
Paul Theodosiou *(Gen Mgr)*

Acucap Management Services (Proprietary) Limited **(1)**
121 Roodebloem Rd
Cape Town, Western Cape, 7925, South Africa
Tel.: (27) 214472010
Fax: (27) 214471559
E-Mail: lisa@accucap.co.za
Emp.: 22
Shopping Mall Management Services
S.I.C.: 6512
N.A.I.C.S.: 531120
Lisa De Boer *(Gen Mgr)*

ACURITY HEALTH GROUP LIMITED
Florence Street Newtown
Wellington, 6021, New Zealand
Mailing Address:
Private Bag 7909
Wellington, 6242, New Zealand
Tel.: (64) 4 920 0131
Fax: (64) 4 381 8102
E-Mail: admin@acurity.co.nz
Web Site: www.acurity.co.nz
ACY—(NZE)
Rev.: $66,114,630
Assets: $141,842,205
Liabilities: $46,292,796
Net Worth: $95,549,409
Earnings: $4,914,864
Emp.: 600
Fiscal Year-end: 03/31/13
Business Description:
Surgical & Medical Health Care Services
S.I.C.: 6324
N.A.I.C.S.: 524114
Personnel:
Alan Isaac *(Chm)*
Ian England *(CEO)*
Matthew Kenny *(CFO & Sec)*
Board of Directors:
Alan Isaac
Rick Christie
Jacqueline Gray
Geoffrey Horne
Brian Martin
Mark Stewart
Jay Tyler
Warwick Webb

ACUVAX LIMITED
Suite 2 16 Ord Street
Po Box 1779
West Perth, WA, 6005, Australia
Tel.: (61) 8 9429 2900
Fax: (61) 8 9486 1011
E-Mail: contactus@acuvax.com.au
Web Site: www.acuvax.com.au
Year Founded: 2001
ACU—(ASX)
Rev.: $19,920
Assets: $377,694
Liabilities: $264,079
Net Worth: $113,615
Earnings: ($1,006,367)
Emp.: 3
Fiscal Year-end: 06/30/13
Business Description:
Oncology Related Medical Products Including Vaccines & Viruses Researcher & Mfr
S.I.C.: 8731
N.A.I.C.S.: 541711
Personnel:
Roland Berzins *(Sec)*
Board of Directors:
Ian Murie
Roland Berzins
Legal Counsel:
Steinepreis Paganin
Level 4 The Read Building 16 Milligan Street
Perth, WA, 6000, Australia
Tel.: (61) 8 9321 4000
Fax: (61) 8 9321 4333

AD DULAYL INDUSTRIAL PARK & REAL ESTATE CO.
Absan Street Near Al Khaldi Hospital
Villa No 6
PO Box 470
Amman, 11118, Jordan
Tel.: (962) 64624290
Fax: (962) 64625701
E-Mail: info@dleil.com
Web Site: www.dleil.com
IDMC—(AMM)
Sales Range: Less than $1 Million
Emp.: 10
Business Description:
Real Estate Development Services
S.I.C.: 6531
N.A.I.C.S.: 531390
Personnel:
Jack George Khayat *(Gen Mgr)*

AD INSURANCE POLICY
Kliment Ohridski BB
1000 Skopje, Macedonia
Tel.: (389) 2 3290 760
Fax: (389) 2 3290 789
Web Site: www.insurancepolicy.co m.mk
OSPO—(MAC)
Business Description:
Insurance Services
S.I.C.: 6411
N.A.I.C.S.: 524298
Personnel:
Vasil Vlashki *(Chm)*
Vladimir Toshevski *(Gen Dir)*

AD JAVNA SKLADISTA SUBOTICA
BB Tuk Ugarnice
24000 Subotica, Serbia
Tel.: (381) 24 546 281
Web Site: www.javnaskladista.rs
JASKS—(BEL)
Business Description:
Goods Storage Services
S.I.C.: 4226
N.A.I.C.S.: 493190
Personnel:
Lazic Gordan *(Gen Mgr)*

AD-MANUM FINANCE LTD.
Agarwal House 5 yeshwant Colony
Ground Floor
Indore, 452003, India
Tel.: (91) 731 2548851
Fax: (91) 731 4030009
E-Mail: ho@admanumfinance.com
Web Site: www.admanumfinance.co m
511359—(BOM)
Rev.: $6,146,524
Assets: $22,875,624
Liabilities: $15,430,691
Net Worth: $7,444,933
Earnings: $1,532,407
Fiscal Year-end: 03/31/13
Business Description:
Vehicle Finance Services
S.I.C.: 6726
N.A.I.C.S.: 525990
Personnel:
Vinod Kumar Agarwal *(Mng Dir)*
Mohd. Raees Sheikh *(Compliance Officer & Sec)*
Board of Directors:
Vinod Kumar Agarwal
Jayanta Nath Choudhury
Vishnu Gupta
Devi Prasad Kori
Aseem Trivedi
Transfer Agent:
Ankit Consultancy Pvt. Ltd
Plot No 60 Electronic Complex Pardeshipura
Indore, India

AD MISSIONS
120 Avenue Charles De Gaulle
92200 Neuilly-sur-Seine, Hauts De Seine, France
Tel.: (33) 141929860
Fax: (33) 141929861
E-Mail: contact@admissions.fr
Web Site: www.admissions.fr/
Rev.: $20,900,000
Emp.: 23
Business Description:
Management Consulting Services
S.I.C.: 8748
N.A.I.C.S.: 541618
Personnel:
Gilles Guilhaume *(Mgr)*
Board of Directors:
Richard Puybasset

AD PEPPER MEDIA INTERNATIONAL NV
Hogehilweg 15
1101 CB Amsterdam, Netherlands
Tel.: (31) 203113850
Fax: (31) 203630916
E-Mail: info@adpepper.com
Web Site: www.adpepper.com
Year Founded: 1999
APM—(DEU)
Rev.: $74,068,966
Assets: $43,234,942
Liabilities: $18,404,836
Net Worth: $24,830,106
Earnings: ($6,884,313)
Emp.: 259
Fiscal Year-end: 12/31/12
Business Description:
Advertising, Affiliate Marketing, Public Relations
S.I.C.: 7311
N.A.I.C.S.: 541810
Personnel:
Michael Oschmann *(Chm-Supervisory Bd)*
Ulrike Handel *(CEO)*
Jens Korner *(CFO)*
Supervisory Board of Directors:
Michael Oschmann
Thomas Bauer
Eun-Kyung Park
Stephan Roppel

Non-U.S. Subsidiary:

Webgains Ltd. (1)
3rd Floor Buchanan House 30 Holborn
London, EC1N 2HS, United Kingdom
Tel.: (44) 207 269 1230
Fax: (44) 207 269 1249
E-Mail: info@webgains.com
Web Site: www.webgains.com
Affiliate Advertising
S.I.C.: 7311
N.A.I.C.S.: 541810
Robert Glasgow *(Mng Dir)*

AD PLASTIK D.D.
Matoseva 8
21 210 Solin, Croatia
Tel.: (385) 21 206 444
Fax: (385) 21 206 599
E-Mail: informacije@adplastik.hr
Web Site: www.adplastik.hr
Year Founded: 1992
ADPL—(ZAG)
Sales Range: $100-124.9 Million
Business Description:
Plastic Product Mfr
S.I.C.: 3089
N.A.I.C.S.: 326199
Personnel:
Nikola Zovko *(Chm-Supervisory Bd)*
Josip Boban *(Chm-Mgmt Bd)*
Marijo Grgurinovic *(Deputy Chm-Supervisory Bd)*
Katija Klepo *(Member-Mgmt Bd)*
Mladen Peros *(Member-Mgmt Bd)*
Ivica Tolic *(Member-Mgmt Bd)*
Supervisory Board of Directors:
Nikola Zovko
Ivka Bogdan
Dmitrij Leonidovic Drandin
Tomislav Dulic
Marijo Grgurinovic
Nadezhda Anatolyevna Nikitina
Igor Antoljevic Solomatin

AD PUTEVI UZICE
38 Nikole Pasica St
31000 Uzice, Serbia
Tel.: (381) 31 512 655
E-Mail: office@puteviuzice.com
Web Site: www.puteviuzice.com
Year Founded: 1962
PUUE—(BEL)
Emp.: 795
Business Description:
Road Construction Services
S.I.C.: 1622
N.A.I.C.S.: 237310
Personnel:
Vasilije Micic *(Pres)*

AD SERVO MIHALJ INZENJERING
Petra Drapsina 15
23 000 Zrenjanin, Serbia
Tel.: (381) 23 544 725
Fax: (381) 23 544 725
Web Site: www.sming.co.rs
Year Founded: 1947
SMIN—(BEL)
Emp.: 25
Business Description:
Engineering & Consulting Services
S.I.C.: 8711
N.A.I.C.S.: 541330
Personnel:
Cedomir Ivkovic *(Chm-Mgmt Bd)*
Jelica Ivkovic *(Member-Mgmt Bd)*
Slavica Mikic *(Member-Mgmt Bd)*
Vesna Stankovic *(Member-Mgmt Bd)*
Borislav Umicevic *(Member-Mgmt Bd)*

AD-SOL NISSIN CORPORATION
Rivarge Shinagawa 4-1-8 Konan
Minato Ward
Tokyo, 108-0075, Japan
Tel.: (81) 3 5796 3131
Fax: (81) 3 5796 3265
Web Site: www.adniss.jp
Year Founded: 1976
3837—(JAS)
Sls.: $88,924,000
Assets: $41,327,000
Liabilities: $21,175,000
Net Worth: $20,152,000
Earnings: $1,265,000
Fiscal Year-end: 03/31/13
Business Description:
Information Systems Solutions
S.I.C.: 7389
N.A.I.C.S.: 519190
Personnel:
Tomizo Ueda *(Pres)*

A.D. USLUGA
Edvarda Kardelja 12
24300 Backa Topola, Vojvodina, Serbia
Tel.: (381) 24 715 329
Fax: (381) 24 715 432
E-Mail: usluga@stcable.rs
Web Site: www.usluga.co.rs
Year Founded: 1959
USBT—(BEL)
Business Description:
Funeral Outfit Mfr
S.I.C.: 3999
N.A.I.C.S.: 339999
Personnel:
Juhas Sandor *(Mgr-Pur)*

A.D. WORKS CORPORATION
Kyoto Shimbun Ginza Building 6th Floor
2-8 Ginza 8-chome
Chuo-ku, Tokyo, 104-0061, Japan
Tel.: (81) 3 3572 7561
Fax: (81) 3 3572 7563
E-Mail: info@adw-net.co.jp
Web Site: www.adw-net.co.jp
Year Founded: 1936
3250—(JAS)
Sales Range: $50-74.9 Million
Emp.: 44
Business Description:
Real Estate Services
S.I.C.: 6531
N.A.I.C.S.: 531390
Personnel:
Hideo Tanaka *(Pres & CEO)*

ADACEL TECHNOLOGIES LIMITED
Suite 1 342 South Road
Melbourne, VIC, 3188, Australia
Tel.: (61) 385307777
Fax: (61) 395550068
E-Mail: info@adacel.com
Web Site: www.adacel.com
Year Founded: 1987
ADA—(ASX)
Rev.: $32,612,520
Assets: $24,293,435
Liabilities: $12,276,980
Net Worth: $12,016,455
Earnings: $844,101
Emp.: 202
Fiscal Year-end: 06/30/13
Business Description:
Software Design Services for Aviation
S.I.C.: 7373
N.A.I.C.S.: 541512
Personnel:
Seth P. Brown *(CEO & CFO)*
Gary Pearson *(COO)*
Sophie Karzis *(Sec)*
Board of Directors:
Peter Darren John Landos
Julian Beale
Kevin Courtney
Silvio Salom
David W. Smith
Legal Counsel:
Ogletree Deakins Nash Smoak & Stewart P.C.
One Ninety One Peachtree Tower 191
Peachtree St NE Suite 4800
Atlanta, GA 30303

Ashurst Australia
Level 26 181 William Street
Melbourne, Australia

U.S. Subsidiary:

Adacel Systems, Inc. (1)
5945 Hazeltine Nation
Orlando, FL 32822 TX
Tel.: (407) 581-1560
Fax: (407) 581-1581
E-Mail: info@adacel.com
Web Site: www.adacel.com
Sales Range: $1-9.9 Million
Emp.: 43
Search & Navigation Equipments Mfr
S.I.C.: 3812
N.A.I.C.S.: 334511
Seth Brown *(CEO)*

Non-U.S. Subsidiary:

Adacel Inc. (1)
4005 Matte Blvd
Brossard, QC, J4Y 2P4, Canada
Tel.: (450) 444-2687
Fax: (450) 444-4249
E-Mail: info@adacel.com
Emp.: 120
Software Solutions
S.I.C.: 7371
N.A.I.C.S.: 541511
Seth Brown *(CEO & Sr VP)*

ADAM SUGAR MILLS LIMITED
Haji Adam Chambers Altaf Hussain Road New Challi
74700 Karachi, Sindh, Pakistan
Tel.: (92) 2132401139
Fax: (92) 212417907
E-Mail: info@adam.com.pk
Web Site: www.adam.com.pk/ada msugar.htm
ADAMS—(LAH)
Sls.: $16,889,524
Assets: $28,753,282
Liabilities: $21,994,093
Net Worth: $6,759,189
Earnings: $469,816

Adam Sugar Mills Limited—(Continued)

Fiscal Year-end: 09/30/12
Business Description:
Sugar Mfr
S.I.C.: 2062
N.A.I.C.S.: 311314
Personnel:
Ghulam Ahmed Adam *(CEO)*
Qamar Rafi Khan *(Sec & Dir-Fin)*
Board of Directors:
Ghulam Ahmed Adam
Junaid G. Adam
Mustafa G. Adam
Omar G. Adam
Jawaid Ahmed
Muhammad Mujtaba
Rafique Mohammad Shah

ADAMA TECHNOLOGIES CORP.

76/7 Zalman Shazar Street
Hod Hasharon, Israel 45350
Tel.: (972) 72 2121324
Year Founded: 2007
ADAC—(OTC)
Assets: $601
Liabilities: $601,154
Net Worth: ($600,553)
Earnings: ($2,613,019)
Fiscal Year-end: 12/31/12
Business Description:
Wireless Data Technology Developer
S.I.C.: 3663
N.A.I.C.S.: 334220
Personnel:
Michael J. Gelmon *(Chm & CEO)*
Uri Mingelgrin *(Chief Scientific Officer)*
Board of Directors:
Michael J. Gelmon
Oren Gayer

ADAMAS FINANCE ASIA LIMITED

(Formerly China Private Equity Investment Holdings Limited)
1810 18/F Tai Yau Building 181 Johnston Road
Wanchai, China (Hong Kong)
Tel.: (852) 3793 6200
Fax: (852) 2117 1410
E-Mail: info@adamasfinance.com
Web Site: www.adamasfinance.com
ADAM—(AIM)
Rev.: $275,000
Assets: $23,652,000
Liabilities: $478,000
Net Worth: $23,174,000
Earnings: ($10,373,000)
Emp.: 6
Fiscal Year-end: 12/31/12
Business Description:
Investment Services
S.I.C.: 6211
N.A.I.C.S.: 523999
Personnel:
John M. Croft *(Chm)*
Alan Lau *(CFO & COO)*
Barry Lau *(Chief Investment Officer)*
Board of Directors:
John M. Croft
Conor MacNamara
Ernest Yiu Kit Wong
Legal Counsel:
Pinsent Masons LLP
30 Crown Place Earl Street
London, EC2A 4ES, United Kingdom
Pinsent Masons
50th Floor Central Plaza 18 Harbour Road
Hong Kong, China (Hong Kong)
Conyers Dill & Pearman
Commerce House, Wickhams Cay 1
PO Box 3140
Road Town, Tortola, Virgin Islands (British)

ADAMAS VENTURES, INC.

Room 1403 No 408 Jie Fang Zhong Road
Guangzhou, Guangdong, 510030, China
Tel.: (86) 2028 8808
Fax: (86) 8333 2588
E-Mail: adamasventuresinc@gmail.com
Year Founded: 2014
Business Description:
Baby Products Distr
S.I.C.: 5092
N.A.I.C.S.: 423920
Personnel:
Jinshan Dai *(Pres, CEO, CFO, Principal Acctg Officer, Treas & Sec)*
Board of Directors:
Jinshan Dai

ADAMERA MINERALS CORP.

1100 - 1111 Melville Street
Vancouver, BC, V6E 3V6, Canada
Tel.: (604) 689-2010
Fax: (604) 484-7143
E-Mail: info@adamera.com
Web Site: www.adamera.com
Year Founded: 2006
ADZ—(TSXV)
Business Description:
Gold & Silver Exploration Services
S.I.C.: 1081
N.A.I.C.S.: 213114
Personnel:
Mark Kolebaba *(Pres & CEO)*
Pat Tanaka *(CFO)*
Janice Davies *(Sec)*
Board of Directors:
Maynard E. Brown
Bernard H. Kahlert
Mark Kolebaba
Geir Liland
Yale R. Simpson
Legal Counsel:
Salley Bowes Harwardt
1750 - 1185 West Georgia Street
Vancouver, BC, Canada
Transfer Agent:
Canadian Stock Transfer
320 Bay Street
P.O. Box 1
Toronto, ON, Canada

ADAMJEE INSURANCE COMPANY LIMITED

6th Floor Adamjee House I I
Chundrigar Road
Karachi, 74000, Pakistan
Tel.: (92) 21 2412623
Fax: (92) 21 2412627
E-Mail: info@adamjeeinsurance.com
Web Site: www.adamjeeinsurance.com
Year Founded: 1960
AICL—(KAR)
Rev.: $79,646,294
Assets: $269,232,658
Liabilities: $134,468,507
Net Worth: $134,764,151
Earnings: $4,472,881
Emp.: 786
Fiscal Year-end: 12/31/12
Business Description:
Marine, Fire, Motor & Medical Insurance Services
S.I.C.: 6399
N.A.I.C.S.: 524128
Personnel:
Akbar D. Vazir *(Deputy CEO)*
Manzar Mushtaq *(CEO & Mng Dir)*
Rehan Ahmed *(CFO)*
Tameez-ul Haque *(Sec)*
Board of Directors:
Umer Mansha
Fredrik Coenrard de Beer
Ahmed Ebrahim Hasham
S. M. Jawed
Shahid Malik
Imran Maqbool
Ali Munir
Manzar Mushtaq
Kamran Rasool
Ibrahim Shamsi
Muhammad Umar Virk

Subsidiary:

Adamjee Life Assurance Company Limited (1)
The Forum Suite No 301 3rd Floor Plot G 20 Block 9 Clifton
Karachi, Sindh74200, Pakistan
Tel.: (92) 21 5362620
Fax: (92) 21 5362621
E-Mail: info@adamjeelife.com
Web Site: www.online.adamjeelife.com
Life Insurance Services
S.I.C.: 6311
N.A.I.C.S.: 524113

Non-U.S. Subsidiary:

Adamjee Insurance Company Limited (1)
The City Business Centre Suite 18
2 London Wall Building
London Wall, London, EC2M 5UU, United Kingdom
Tel.: (44) 20 75885506
Fax: (44) 20 75885509
Insurance Services
S.I.C.: 6411
N.A.I.C.S.: 524298

ADAMS ENTERPRISES (1993) LTD

PO Box 973
Whitecourt, AB, T7S 1N9, Canada
Tel.: (780) 778-8440
Fax: (780) 778-8468
Year Founded: 1991
Rev.: $14,503,435
Emp.: 40
Business Description:
General Freight Trucking Services
S.I.C.: 4212
N.A.I.C.S.: 484110
Personnel:
Sharon Adams *(Owner)*

ADAMS PLC

IOMA House Hope Street
Douglas, Isle of Man IM1 1AP
Tel.: (44) 1624 681250
Web Site: www.adamsplc.co.uk
ADA—(AIM)
Rev.: $32,028,001
Assets: $418,512
Liabilities: $30,007
Net Worth: $388,505
Earnings: ($12,924,909)
Emp.: 4
Fiscal Year-end: 03/31/13
Business Description:
Real Estate Investment Services
S.I.C.: 6531
N.A.I.C.S.: 531390
Personnel:
Philip Peter Scales *(Sec)*
Board of Directors:
Nicholas Christian Paul Nelson
Nicholas James Woolard
Legal Counsel:
Olswang
90 High Holborn
London, WC1V 6XX, United Kingdom

ADAMSON ASSOCIATES ARCHITECTS

401 Wellington St W 3rd Floor
Toronto, ON, M5V 1E7, Canada
Tel.: (416) 967-1500
Fax: (416) 967-7150
E-Mail: info@adamson-associates.com
Web Site: www.adamson-associates.com
Year Founded: 1934
Rev.: $10,000,000
Emp.: 200
Business Description:
Architectural Services
S.I.C.: 8712
N.A.I.C.S.: 541310
Personnel:
Bill Bradley *(Partner)*
Greg Dunn *(Partner)*
David Jansen *(Partner)*

ADANAC MOLYBDENUM CORPORATION

204-16055 Fraser Highway
Surrey, BC, V4N 0G2, Canada
Tel.: (604) 535-6834
Fax: (604) 536-8411
E-Mail: info@adanacmoly.com
Web Site: www.adanacmoly.com
Year Founded: 1992
AUAYD—(DEU OTC)
Rev.: $41,647
Assets: $6,055,919
Liabilities: $1,796
Net Worth: $6,054,123
Earnings: ($38,348,544)
Emp.: 15
Fiscal Year-end: 02/28/13
Business Description:
Molybdenum Mining Services
S.I.C.: 1099
N.A.I.C.S.: 212299
Personnel:
Leonard J. Sojka *(Pres & CEO)*
Alicia D. Marshall *(CFO)*
Board of Directors:
John W. Cutler
Robert H. Pinsent
Leonard J. Sojka
Legal Counsel:
Macdonald Tuskey
Suite 400 570 Granville Street
Vancouver, BC, Canada
Transfer Agent:
Computershare
3rd Floor 510 Burrard Street
Vancouver, BC, Canada

U.S. Subsidiary:

Nev-Adanac Corp (1)
2533 N Carson St Ste 3911
Carson City, NV 89701
Tel.: (775) 841-7461
Molybdenum Mining Services
S.I.C.: 1099
N.A.I.C.S.: 212299

ADANI ENTERPRISES LIMITED

(d/b/a Adani Group)
Adani House Nr Mithakhali Circle
Navrangpura, Ahmedabad, 380009, India
Tel.: (91) 7926565555
Fax: (91) 7926565500
E-Mail: info@adani.com
Web Site: www.adani.com
Year Founded: 1988
512599—(BOM NSE)
Rev.: $8,778,992,202
Assets: $20,812,725,900
Liabilities: $16,234,719,714
Net Worth: $4,578,006,186
Earnings: $225,737,478
Emp.: 703
Fiscal Year-end: 03/31/13
Business Description:
Agro Products, Coal & Coke Products, Textiles, Fertilizers & Steel

Scrap, Marine Products, Petrochemicals, Petroleum & Lubricants Trading Services
S.I.C.: 7389
N.A.I.C.S.: 425120
Personnel:
Gautam S. Adani *(Chm)*
Rajesh S. Adani *(Mng Dir)*
Devang S. Desai *(CFO)*
Parthiv Parikh *(Compliance Officer & Sec)*
Board of Directors:
Gautam S. Adani
Rajesh S. Adani
Vasant S. Adani
Anil Ahuja
Berjis Desai
Devang S. Desai
Ravindra Harshadrai Dholakia
Surendra Kumar Tuteja
Transfer Agent:
Sharepro Services (India) Private Limited
416-420 4th Fl Devnandan Mall
Ahmedabad, India
Subsidiaries:

Adani Agri Fresh Ltd (1)
Plot No 83 Institutional Area Sector 32
Gurgaon, Haryana, 122001, India
Tel.: (91) 9873588521
E-Mail: customercare.aafl@adani.com
Web Site: www.farmpik.com
Fruits Whslr
S.I.C.: 5148
N.A.I.C.S.: 424480
Srinivasan Ramanujam *(Head-Bus)*

Adani Agri Logistics Ltd (1)
Adani House Plot No 83 Sector 32 Institutional Area
Gurgaon, Haryana, 122001, India
Tel.: (91) 1242555000
Fax: (91) 1242555210
E-Mail: customercare@adanilogistics.com
Web Site: www.adanilogistics.com
Emp.: 250
Logistics Consulting Services
S.I.C.: 4731
N.A.I.C.S.: 541614
Amit Das *(Gen Mgr-HR)*

Adani Gas Ltd (1)
8th Floor Heritage Building Nr Gujarat Vidhyapith Bh Visnaga
Nagrik Bank Usmanpura, Ahmedabad, Gujarat, India
Tel.: (91) 79 27623264
Web Site: www.adanigas.com
Natural Gas Distribution Services
S.I.C.: 4924
N.A.I.C.S.: 221210

Adani Ports and Special Economic Zone Limited (1)
Adani House Shrimali Society Near Mithakhali Circle
Navrangpura, Ahmedabad, 380 009, India
Tel.: (91) 7925555101
Fax: (91) 7925555500
E-Mail: info@mundraport.com
Web Site: www.mundraport.com
532921—(BOM NSE)
Rev.: $712,134,378
Assets: $3,904,449,840
Liabilities: $2,692,197,108
Net Worth: $1,212,252,732
Earnings: $300,944,988
Emp.: 1,181
Fiscal Year-end: 03/31/13
Port Operations
S.I.C.: 4491
N.A.I.C.S.: 488310
Gautam S. Adani *(Founder, Chm & Mng Dir)*
B. Ravi *(CFO)*
Dipti Shah *(Compliance Officer & Sec)*

Adani Power Limited (1)
Sambav House Judges Bunglow Road
Bodakdev, Ahmedabad, 380 015, India (81.53%)
Tel.: (91) 7925556900
Fax: (91) 7925557155
E-Mail: info@adani.com
Web Site: www.adanipower.com
533096—(BOM NSE)
Rev.: $1,292,239,854
Assets: $10,190,410,884
Liabilities: $9,394,412,670
Net Worth: $795,998,214
Earnings: ($425,494,854)
Emp.: 1,383
Fiscal Year-end: 03/31/13
Power Generator & Distr
S.I.C.: 4939
N.A.I.C.S.: 221122
Gautam S. Adani *(Chm)*
Vneet S. Jaain *(CEO)*
Rajesh S. Adani *(Mng Dir)*
Prabal Banerji *(CFO)*
Rahul C. Shah *(Sec)*

U.S. Subsidiary:

Adani Virginia Inc. (1)
4300 Buell St
Chesapeake, VA 23324-1008
Tel.: (757) 543-7464
Fax: (757) 543-2424
Ship Dismantling Services
S.I.C.: 3731
N.A.I.C.S.: 336611

Non-U.S. Subsidiaries:

Adani Global FZE (1)
Jebel Ali Free Zone
PO Box 17186
Dubai, Dubai, United Arab Emirates
Tel.: (971) 48818048
Fax: (971) 48818207
Ferrous & Non Ferrous Metals Import & Distr
S.I.C.: 1623
N.A.I.C.S.: 237120

Adani Global Ltd. (1)
Suite 501 Saint James Court Saint Denis Street
Port Louis, Mauritius
Tel.: (230) 2109961
Fax: (230) 2115703
Oil & Gas Exploration Services
S.I.C.: 1389
N.A.I.C.S.: 213112

Rahi Shipping Pte. Ltd (1)
10 Anson Road 34 16 International Plaza
Singapore, 079903, Singapore
Tel.: (65) 65764621
Fax: (65) 62252537
Web Site: www.adanipower.com
Emp.: 4
Ship Management Services
S.I.C.: 4412
N.A.I.C.S.: 483111
Pranav Vora *(Mng Dir)*

Vanshi Shipping Pte. Ltd (1)
80 Raffels Place UOB Plaza 2 Level 33
Singapore, 48624, Singapore
Tel.: (65) 65764621
Fax: (65) 62252537
Web Site: www.adani.com
Emp.: 3
Coal Mining & Distr
S.I.C.: 1241
N.A.I.C.S.: 213113

ADAPTIT HOLDINGS LIMITED

5 Rydall Vale Office Park Rydall Vale Crescent La Lucia Ridge
PO Box 5207
Durban, KwaZulu-Natal, 4019, South Africa
Tel.: (27) 315147300
Fax: (27) 866028961
E-Mail: enquiries@adaptit.co.za
Web Site: www.adaptit.co.za
ADI—(JSE)
Rev.: $34,184,115
Assets: $19,963,309
Liabilities: $9,660,807
Net Worth: $10,302,502
Earnings: $2,690,926
Emp.: 313
Fiscal Year-end: 06/30/13
Business Description:
Software Solution Services
S.I.C.: 7372
N.A.I.C.S.: 511210
Personnel:
Sibusiso Shabalala *(CEO)*
Board of Directors:
Craig Chambers
Thembisa Dingaan
Tiffany Dunsdon
Oliver Fortuin
Bongiwe Ntuli
Sibusiso Shabalala
Transfer Agent:
Computershare Investor Services (Proprietary) Limited
70 Marshall Street
Johannesburg, South Africa

ADAPTRONIC PRUFTECHNIK GMBH

Dorlesberg Ernsthof
97877 Wertheim, Germany
Tel.: (49) 93459300
Fax: (49) 4993459301
E-Mail: info@adaptronic.de
Web Site: www.adaptronic.de
Rev.: $11,178,451
Emp.: 69
Business Description:
Test Systems Mfr
S.I.C.: 3999
N.A.I.C.S.: 339999
Personnel:
Peter Muller *(Pres)*

ADARSH PLANT PROTECT LTD.

604 G I D C Vitthal Udyognagar
Anand, Gujarat, 388121, India
Tel.: (91) 2692 236705
Fax: (91) 2692 236704
E-Mail: info@adarshplant.com
Web Site: www.adarshplant.com
Year Founded: 1992
526711—(BOM)
Rev.: $682,979
Assets: $1,643,567
Liabilities: $933,696
Net Worth: $709,871
Earnings: ($27,298)
Fiscal Year-end: 03/31/13
Business Description:
Plant Protection Equipment Mfr
S.I.C.: 3523
N.A.I.C.S.: 333111
Personnel:
Naishadbhai N. Patel *(Chm & Mng Dir)*
Board of Directors:
Naishadbhai N. Patel
Atish Patel
Jagdishbhai Patel
Jyotiben Patel
Kiranbhai Patel
Arvindbhai Shah
Transfer Agent:
Link Intime India Private Limited
Unit No 303 3rd Floor Shoppers Plaza V Opp Municipal Market
Behind Shoppers Plaza II Off C G Road, Ahmedabad, 380009, India

ADASTRA CORPORATION

Le Parc Office Tower 8500 Leslie Street Suite 600
Markham, ON, Canada L3T 7M8
Tel.: (905) 881-7946
Fax: (905) 881-4782
E-Mail: info@adastracorp.com
Web Site: www.adastracorp.com
Year Founded: 2000
Rev.: $28,564,314
Emp.: 240
Business Description:
IT Services
S.I.C.: 7376
N.A.I.C.S.: 541513
Personnel:
Jan Cervinka *(Co-Founder)*
Petr Jech *(Co-Founder)*
Jan Mrazek *(Co-Founder)*
Darren Edery *(CEO)*
Oliver Fuchs *(Sr VP-Ops)*
Nelio Lucas *(Sr VP-Tech)*

ADAVALE RESOURCES LIMITED

Level 5 151 Castlereagh Street
Sydney, NSW, 2000, Australia
Tel.: (61) 2 8263 0515
Fax: (61) 2 9227 8901
Web Site: www.adavaleresources.com.au
ADD—(ASX)
Rev.: $53,116
Assets: $1,458,614
Liabilities: $417,068
Net Worth: $1,041,546
Earnings: ($4,569,229)
Fiscal Year-end: 06/30/13
Business Description:
Mining Exploration
S.I.C.: 1241
N.A.I.C.S.: 213113
Personnel:
Haryono Eddyarto *(Chm)*
Eka Antasari Nugraha *(Deputy CEO)*
Leanne Ralph *(Sec)*
Board of Directors:
Haryono Eddyarto
Albert Cheok
Peter Murphy
Saharto Sahardjo

ADC AFRICAN DEVELOPMENT CORPORATION GMBH & CO. KGAA

Gruneburgweg 18
60322 Frankfurt am Main, Germany
Tel.: (49) 697191280119
Fax: (49) 697191280011
E-Mail: info@african-development.com
Web Site: www.african-development.com
Year Founded: 2007
AZC—(DEU)
Sales Range: $10-24.9 Million
Emp.: 24
Business Description:
Financial Investment Services
S.I.C.: 6211
N.A.I.C.S.: 523999
Personnel:
Alastair Newton *(Chm-Supervisory Bd)*
Dirk Harbecke *(CEO)*
Olaf Meier *(Mng Dir & CFO)*
Sascha Beliuli *(COO)*
Mark M. Schneiders *(Chief Dev Officer)*
Supervisory Board of Directors:
Alastair Newton
Jyrki Koskelo
Pierre Lorinet
Non-U.S. Subsidiary:

SIMTEL S.A. (1)
Plot 1200 Kacyiru-Opposite Minagri
PO Box 615
Kigali, Rwanda
Tel.: (250) 252 591600
Fax: (250) 252 585615
E-Mail: info@simtel.co.rw
Web Site: www.simtel.co.rw
Information Technology Consulting Services
S.I.C.: 7373
N.A.I.C.S.: 541512
Konde Bugingo *(Gen Mgr)*

ADC CABLE PLC

Kurfurstendamm 30
10719 Berlin, Germany

ADC Cable PLC—(Continued)

Tel.: (49) 30 6483 5918
Web Site: www.adccableplc.com
7AP—(DEU)
Business Description:
Electric Cable Distr
S.I.C.: 5063
N.A.I.C.S.: 423610
Personnel:
Michael J. Freestone *(Chm-Supervisory Bd & CEO)*
Supervisory Board of Directors:
Michael J. Freestone
Trevor Reddy
Pieter H. Steyn

Non-U.S. Subsidiary:

ADC Cable Pty. Ltd. **(1)**
Unit G9 Palisades Park 39 Kelly Road
Jet Park, Boksburg, 1469, South Africa ZA
Tel.: (27) 83 475 4192
Fax: (27) 11 397 8232
Copper Cable Mfr
S.I.C.: 3357
N.A.I.C.S.: 335929
Michael Freestone *(CEO)*

ADCHINA LTD.

20/F Media Zone Jing An 211 Shi Men Yi Road
Shanghai, 200041, China
Tel.: (86) 21 6267 5588
Fax: (86) 21 6267 9378
E-Mail: sales@adchina.com
Web Site: www.adchina.com
Year Founded: 2007
Sales Range: $50-74.9 Million
Emp.: 491
Business Description:
Internet Advertising Services
S.I.C.: 7319
N.A.I.C.S.: 541890
Personnel:
Alan Fangjun Yan *(Chm & CEO)*
Huayi Cheng *(Pres & CTO)*
Bonnie Yi Zhang *(CFO)*
Peter Cheng *(COO)*
Min Tang *(CMO)*
Board of Directors:
Alan Fangjun Yan
Peter Cheng
Jeffrey M. Crowe
Peter Kellner
Richard Lim

ADCOCK INGRAM HOLDINGS LTD.

(Acquired by The Bidvest Group Limited)

ADCONION MEDIA GROUP LTD.

180 Great Portland Street
London, W1W 5QZ, United Kingdom
Tel.: (44) 20 3 073 2900
Fax: (44) 20 3 073 2935
E-Mail: info-uk@adconion.com
Web Site: www.adconion.com
Sales Range: $200-249.9 Million
Emp.: 700
Business Description:
Advertising Content Distribution Software Publisher
S.I.C.: 7372
N.A.I.C.S.: 511210
Personnel:
T. Tyler Moebius *(Founder & CEO)*
Neil V. Sunderland *(Chm)*
Fred Krueger *(Vice Chm)*
Kim Reed Perell *(Pres & CEO-Adconion Direct)*
Steve Brown *(Mng Dir)*
Patrick Meininger *(CFO)*
Scott Sullivan *(CTO)*
Board of Directors:
Neil V. Sunderland
Frank Boehnke
Robert Dighero
Thomas Falk
Fred Krueger
T. Tyler Moebius
Kim Reed Perell
Dominique Vidal
Giuseppe Zocco

U.S. Subsidiary:

Adconion Media Inc. **(1)**
3301 X Precision
Santa Monica, CA 90404
Tel.: (310) 382-5500
Fax: (310) 382-5501
E-Mail: info-us@adconion.com
Web Site: www.adconion.com
Media Buying Services
S.I.C.: 7319
N.A.I.C.S.: 541830
T. Tyler Moebius *(Pres, CEO & Exec Dir)*
Jeremy Daw *(CTO)*

Branch:

Adconion Media Inc. **(2)**
230 Park Ave
New York, NY 10017
Tel.: (212) 808-6587
Fax: (212) 808-3020
Media Buying
S.I.C.: 7319
N.A.I.C.S.: 541830
Cliff Paulson *(VP-Video-North America)*

Non-U.S. Subsidiaries:

Adconion GmbH **(1)**
Lindwurmstrasse 114
80337 Munich, Germany
Tel.: (49) 89780178
Fax: (49) 89 780 178 3
E-Mail: info-de@adconion.com
Media Buying
S.I.C.: 7319
N.A.I.C.S.: 541830
Oliver Hulse *(Mng Dir)*

Branches:

Adconion GmbH **(2)**
Heuberg 1
20354 Hamburg, Germany
Tel.: (49) 403099780
Fax: (49) 4030997850
E-Mail: info-de@adconion.com
Media Buying
S.I.C.: 7319
N.A.I.C.S.: 541830
Oliver Hulse *(Mng Dir)*

Adconion GmbH **(2)**
Neusser Strasse 72
40219 Dusseldorf, Germany
Tel.: (49) 2119943070
Fax: (49) 21199430730
E-Mail: info-de@adconion.com
Media Buying
S.I.C.: 7319
N.A.I.C.S.: 541830
Oliver Hulse *(Mng Dir)*

Adconion Media Inc. **(1)**
20 Maud St Suite 305
Toronto, ON, MV5 2M5, Canada
Tel.: (416) 637-4658
Fax: (416) 981-3951
Media Buying
S.I.C.: 7319
N.A.I.C.S.: 541830
T. Tyler Moebius *(Pres, CEO & Exec Dir)*

Adconion Pty. Ltd. **(1)**
Level 9 28 Freshwater Pl
Southbank, VIC, 3006, Australia
Tel.: (61) 386212300
Fax: (61) 294754324
E-Mail: info-au@adconion.com
Media Buying
S.I.C.: 7319
N.A.I.C.S.: 541830
Alexander Littlejohn *(Pres)*

Adconion S.L. **(1)**
Guzman el Bueno, 133
Parque de las Naciones,
Edificio Germania, Principal C, 28003
Madrid, Spain
Tel.: (34) 915987836
Fax: (34) 911817685
E-Mail: info-es@adconion.com
Media Buying
S.I.C.: 7319
N.A.I.C.S.: 541830
Rick Bilberry *(VP-Global Sls)*

ADCORP AUSTRALIA LIMITED

Level 1 7 Kelly Street
Ultimo, NSW, 2007, Australia
Tel.: (61) 2 8524 8500
Fax: (61) 2 8524 8700
E-Mail: sydney@adcorp.com.au
Web Site: www.adcorp.com.au
Year Founded: 1981
AAU—(ASX)
Rev.: $21,767,385
Assets: $22,361,382
Liabilities: $20,753,422
Net Worth: $1,607,960
Earnings: ($7,176,943)
Emp.: 235
Fiscal Year-end: 06/30/13
Business Description:
Advertising Services
S.I.C.: 7311
N.A.I.C.S.: 541810
Personnel:
David Morrison *(CEO & Mng Dir)*
Craig McMenamin *(CFO & Sec)*
Nadia Barry *(Exec-Acct-Sydney)*
Rachel Sultana *(Sr Exec-Acct-Sydney)*
Board of Directors:
Ian Rodwell
Dean Capobianco
Garry Lemair
David Morrison

Subsidiaries:

Adcorp Australia (QLD) Pty Ltd **(1)**
Level 16 484 Adelaide St
Brisbane, QLD, 4000, Australia
Tel.: (61) 7 3302 8500
Fax: (61) 7 3302 8599
Emp.: 20
Advertising Agency
S.I.C.: 7311
N.A.I.C.S.: 541810
Michelle Muirhead, *(Gen Mgr)*

Adcorp Australia (VIC) Pty Ltd **(1)**
Level 2 1 Collins St
Melbourne, VIC, 3000, Australia
Tel.: (61) 3 9223 0999
Fax: (61) 3 9653 5050
Advertising Agency
S.I.C.: 7311
N.A.I.C.S.: 541810

Quadrant Creative Pty Ltd **(1)**
66 Township Drive
PO Box 388
Burleigh Heads, QLD, 4219, Australia
Tel.: (61) 7 5508 2900
E-Mail: info@quadrant.com.au
Web Site: www.quadrant.com.au
Advertising Agency
S.I.C.: 7311
N.A.I.C.S.: 541810
Tony Scott *(CEO)*

Non-U.S. Subsidiaries:

Adcorp New Zealand Limited **(1)**
Level 2 20 Beaumont Street
Auckland, 1010, New Zealand
Tel.: (64) 9 968 4800
Fax: (64) 9 968 4810
E-Mail: auckland@adcorp.co.nz
Web Site: www.adcorp.co.nz
Advertising Agency
S.I.C.: 7311
N.A.I.C.S.: 541810
Craig McMenamin *(CFO)*

ADCORP HOLDINGS LIMITED

Nicolway Bryanston Cnr William Nicol & Wedgewood Link
PO Box 70635
Bryanston, 2021, South Africa
Tel.: (27) 112445300
Telex: 424739
Fax: (27) 112445309
E-Mail: info@adcorp.co.za
Web Site: www.adcorp.co.za
Year Founded: 1972
ADRJ—(JSE)
Rev.: $962,501,251
Assets: $461,085,983
Liabilities: $249,340,650
Net Worth: $211,745,334
Earnings: $20,034,624
Emp.: 3,000
Fiscal Year-end: 02/28/13
Business Description:
Staffing & Recruitment Consulting
S.I.C.: 8999
N.A.I.C.S.: 541612
Personnel:
Mfundiso Johnson Ntabankulu Njeke *(Chm)*
Richard Linden Pike *(CEO)*
Anthony Mark Sher *(CFO & Acting Sec)*
Petrus Cornelius Swart *(COO)*
Board of Directors:
Mfundiso Johnson Ntabankulu Njeke
Campbell Bomela
Gugu Patricia Dingaan
Sindi Mabaso Konyana
Louisa Madiako Mojela
Mncane Esau Mthunzi
Nontobeko Ndhlazi
Richard Linden Pike
Muthanyi Robinson Ramaite
Timothy Dacre Aird Ross
Anthony Mark Sher
Michael Spicer
Petrus Cornelius Swart
Legal Counsel:
Webber Wentzel
18 Fricker Road Illovo Boulevard Illovo
Johannesburg, 2196, South Africa

Rudolph Burnstein & Associates
Block A Eton Road Office Park 7 Eton Road
Sandhurst
Sandton, 2196, South Africa

Baker & McKenzie
4 Sandown Valley Crescent
Sandton, 2196, South Africa
Transfer Agent:
Link Market Services SA (Pty) Limited
11 Diagonal Street
Johannesburg, 2001, South Africa

Non-U.S. Subsidiary:

Paxus Australia Pty. Limited **(1)**
Level 1 380 Docklands Drive Waterfront City Docklands
Melbourne, VIC, 3008, Australia
Tel.: (61) 386804200
Fax: (61) 386804299
E-Mail: hof@paxus.com.au
Web Site: www.paxus.com.au
Information Technology Staffing Services
S.I.C.: 8999
N.A.I.C.S.: 541612

Subsidiaries:

Adcorp Fulfilment Services (Pty) Limited **(1)**
112 Burnett Street
Pretoria, Gauteng, 0083, South Africa
Tel.: (27) 124236600
Fax: (27) 866000558
Management Services
S.I.C.: 8741
N.A.I.C.S.: 551114

Adcorp Management Services (Pty) Limited **(1)**
3 Angus Crescent Long Medor Business Park Estate
Edenvale, Gauteng, 1609, South Africa
Tel.: (27) 114578007
Fax: (27) 114578104
Emp.: 120
Investment Management Services
S.I.C.: 6799

N.A.I.C.S.: 523920
Raeesa Tayob *(Gen Mgr)*

Capital Outsourcing Group (Pty) Limited (1)
21a Hampden Court Hampden Road
Morningside, Durban, KwaZulu-Natal, 4001, South Africa
Tel.: (27) 313628000
Fax: (27) 313628321
E-Mail: capdbn@cog.co.za
Web Site: www.cog.co.za
Rev.: $135,270,000
Recruitment & Training Services
S.I.C.: 7363
N.A.I.C.S.: 561320
Paul Gerricke *(Sr Mgr-IR)*

DAV Professional Placement Group (Pty) Limited (1)
3rd Floor West Towers Nelson Mandela Square at Sandton City
Fifth Street off Rivonia Road, 2146
Sandton, South Africa
Tel.: (27) 112170000
Fax: (27) 112170001
E-Mail: dav@dppg.co.za
Web Site: www.dav.co.za
Emp.: 150
Employment Placement Agencies
S.I.C.: 7361
N.A.I.C.S.: 561311
Jacqie Bosch *(Head-Fin Markets)*

Gold Fields External Training Services (Pty) Limited (1)
Pamodzi FS 1 Shaft
Welkom, Free State, 9459, South Africa
Tel.: (27) 573919300
Fax: (27) 573919329
Artisan & Mining Commercial Training Services
S.I.C.: 8331
N.A.I.C.S.: 624310

Paracon Holdings Limited (1)
Adcorp Office Park Nicolway
Bryanston, South Africa
Tel.: (27) 114606000
Fax: (27) 117064366
E-Mail: info@paracon.co.za
Web Site: www.paracon.co.za
Sales Range: $125-149.9 Million
Emp.: 260
ICT Resource & Talent Management Services
S.I.C.: 1731
N.A.I.C.S.: 238210
Mark Jurgens *(CEO)*
Ronald J. Wasley *(Sec & Dir-Mktg)*

Subsidiaries:

allaboutXpert (Pty) Limited (2)
Adcorp Office Park Nicolway
Bryanston, South Africa (70%)
Tel.: (27) 115498600
Fax: (27) 115498635
E-Mail: bookings@xpert.co.za
Web Site: www.allaboutxpert.com
Emp.: 165
Project Management Services
S.I.C.: 8741
N.A.I.C.S.: 561110
Matthew Pitman *(CEO)*

Paracon SA (Pty) Limited (2)
Adcorp Office Park Nicolway
Bryanston, South Africa
Tel.: (27) 114606000
Fax: (27) 117604366
E-Mail: info@paracon.co.za
Emp.: 70
Information & Communication Technology Services
S.I.C.: 7373
N.A.I.C.S.: 541512
Chantel Bertram *(Sr Acct Mgr)*

Production Management Institute of South Africa (Pty) Limited (1)
1st Floor Quest House 3 Margaret Avenue
Kempton Park, Gauteng, 1619, South Africa
Tel.: (27) 219496652
Fax: (27) 117864136
Web Site: www.pmi-sa.co.za
Emp.: 30
Educational Support Services
S.I.C.: 8299
N.A.I.C.S.: 611710

Quest Flexible Staffing Solutions (Pty) Limited (1)
No 33 Hoofd Street Forum 5 Braampark
2017 Johannesburg, South Africa
Tel.: (27) 116280300
Fax: (27) 116280416
Web Site: www.quest.co.za
Emp.: 200
Employment Placement Agencies
S.I.C.: 7361
N.A.I.C.S.: 561311
Kay Vittee *(CEO)*

ADCURAM GROUP AG

Theatinerstrasse 7 Arco Palais
80333 Munich, Germany
Tel.: (49) 8920209590
Fax: (49) 8920209599
E-Mail: kontakt@adcuram.de
Web Site: www.adcuram.de
Emp.: 4,000

Business Description:
Holding Company
S.I.C.: 6719
N.A.I.C.S.: 551112

Personnel:
Matthias Meise *(Co-Founder & Member-Exec Bd)*
Florian Meise *(Co-Founder & Member-Exec Bd)*
Yorck von Schmeling-Diringshofen *(Chm-Supervisory Bd)*
Friedrich-Wilhelm Hoche *(Vice Chm-Supervisory Bd)*

Supervisory Board of Directors:
Yorck von Schmeling-Diringshofen
Friedrich-Wilhelm Hoche
Rainer Hocherl

Holdings:

CaseTech GmbH & Co. KG (1)
August-Wolff-Strasse 13
Bomlitz, Walsrode, 29699, Germany De
Tel.: (49) 5161443902
Fax: (49) 516144143902
E-Mail: info@walsroder.com
Web Site: www.walsroder.com
Sales Range: $50-74.9 Million
Emp.: 240
Cellulose & Plastic Sausage Casing Mfr
S.I.C.: 2823
N.A.I.C.S.: 325220
Robert Kaska *(Mng Dir)*
Jens Roesler *(Mng Dir)*

DURAN Group GmbH (1)
Hattenbergstrasse 10
55122 Mainz, Germany
Tel.: (49) 6131664131
Fax: (49) 6131664038
E-Mail: info.duran@duran-group.com
Web Site: www.duran-group.com
Emp.: 600
Laboratory Glass Equipment Mfr
S.I.C.: 3221
N.A.I.C.S.: 327213
Michael Merz *(Mng Dir)*
Armin Reiche *(Mng Dir)*

Hennecke GmbH (1)
Birlinghovener Strasse 30
Saint Augustin, 53757, Germany
Tel.: (49) 22413390
Fax: (49) 2241339204
E-Mail: hennecke@hennecke.com
Web Site: www.hennecke.com
Sales Range: $100-124.9 Million
Emp.: 500
Polyurethane Materials & Products Mfr
S.I.C.: 3086
N.A.I.C.S.: 326150
Alouis Schmid *(Mng Dir)*

U.S. Subsidiary:

Hennecke Inc. (2)
55 Park Dr PO Box 617
Lawrence, PA 15055
Tel.: (412) 777-3633
Fax: (724) 271-3680
E-Mail: service@us.hennecke.com
Web Site: www.henneckeinc.com
Emp.: 50
Polyurethane Products Developer & Mfr
S.I.C.: 3086
N.A.I.C.S.: 326150
George See *(Project Mgr-Engrg & Mechanical)*

IMA Klessmann GmbH (1)
Industriestrasse 3
32312 Lubbecke, Germany
Tel.: (49) 57413310
Fax: (49) 57414201
E-Mail: contact@ima.de
Web Site: www.ima.de
Emp.: 700
Industrial Machinery Mfr
S.I.C.: 3559
N.A.I.C.S.: 333249
Andreas Bollmann *(Mng Dir)*
Rudiger Schliekmann *(Mng Dir)*

Nuvisan Pharma Services GmbH & Co KG (1)
Wegenerstrasse 13
89231 Neu-Ulm, Germany De
Tel.: (49) 7319840000
Fax: (49) 7319840280
E-Mail: studinfo@nuvisan.de
Web Site: www.nuvisan.de
Emp.: 300
Pharmaceutical Testing Services
S.I.C.: 8734
N.A.I.C.S.: 541380
Dietrich Bruchmann *(Gen Mgr)*

ADDCHANCE HOLDINGS LIMITED

Sungs Tower 15-19 Lam Tin Street
Kwai Chung, NT, China (Hong Kong)
Tel.: (852) 36577888
Fax: (852) 24800663
E-Mail: info@addchance.com.hk
Web Site: www.addchance.com.hk
3344—(HKG)
Rev.: $187,004,451
Assets: $324,225,561
Liabilities: $185,303,084
Net Worth: $138,922,477
Earnings: $3,940,841
Fiscal Year-end: 12/31/12

Business Description:
Dyed Yarn & Knitted Sweaters Mfr
S.I.C.: 2259
N.A.I.C.S.: 315190

Personnel:
Chung Kwun Sung *(Chm)*
Chiu Hong Wong *(Mng Dir)*
Ka Lai Fung *(Sec & Controller-Fin)*

Board of Directors:
Chung Kwun Sung
Xiu Ling Cai
Jacky Tsz Fu Chan
Siu Lam Ip
Gary Q. Lau
Man Kin Ng
Kim Ping Sung
Chiu Hong Wong

Computershare Hong Kong Investor Services Limited
Shops 1712-1716 17th Floor Hopewell Centre
183 Queens Road East
Wanchai, China (Hong Kong)

Transfer Agents:
Royal Bank of Canada Trust Company (Cayman) Limited
4th Floor Royal Bank House 24 Shedden Road
Georgetown, Cayman Islands

Computershare Hong Kong Investor Services Limited
Shops 1712-1716 17th Floor Hopewell Centre
183 Queens Road East
Wanchai, China (Hong Kong)

ADDEX THERAPEUTICS LTD.

12 Chemin des Aulx 1228 Plan-les-Ouates
Geneva, Switzerland
Tel.: (41) 228841555
Fax: (41) 228841556
E-Mail: info@addextherapeutics.com
Web Site: www.addextherapeutics.com
ADXN—(SWX)
Rev.: $130,694
Assets: $23,459,765
Liabilities: $5,876,682
Net Worth: $17,583,083
Earnings: ($29,161,960)
Emp.: 56
Fiscal Year-end: 12/31/12

Business Description:
Pharmaceutical Research & Development Services
S.I.C.: 8731
N.A.I.C.S.: 541712

Personnel:
Tim Dyer *(Founder & CFO)*
Andre J. Mueller *(Chm)*
Vincent Lawton *(Vice Chm)*
Graham Dixon *(Chief Scientific Officer)*
Charlotte Keywood *(Chief Medical Officer)*

Board of Directors:
Andre J. Mueller
Hoyoung Huh
Vincent Lawton
Oleg Nodelman

Subsidiary:

Addex Pharma S.A. (1)
Chemin Des Aulx 12
1228 Plan-les-Ouates, Switzerland
Tel.: (41) 228841555
Fax: (41) 228841556
Web Site: www.addexpharma.com
Emp.: 100
Physical Science Research & Development Services
S.I.C.: 8731
N.A.I.C.S.: 541712

ADDICTION WORLDWIDE LTD.

(Acquired by The Mission Marketing Group plc)

ADDISON SAWS LIMITED

Attwood Street Lye
Stourbridge, West Midlands, DY9 8RU, United Kingdom
Tel.: (44) 1384456333
Telex: 338630
Fax: (44) 1384264955
E-Mail: info@addisonsaws.co.uk
Web Site: www.addisonsaws.co.uk
Year Founded: 1956
Sales Range: $10-24.9 Million
Emp.: 29

Business Description:
Metal Sawing Machines
S.I.C.: 3542
N.A.I.C.S.: 333517

Personnel:
Gary Knight *(Pres)*

Subsidiaries:

SAW MART LTD (1)
Attwood Street Lye
Stourbridge, West Midlands, DY9 8RU, United Kingdom
Tel.: (44) 1384 264950
Fax: (44) 1384 264955
E-Mail: sales@addisonsaws.co.uk
Web Site: www.sawmart.co.uk
Emp.: 30
Workshop Sawing Machine Mfr
S.I.C.: 3542
N.A.I.C.S.: 333517
Gary Walter Knight, *(Mng Dir)*

Tube Fabrication Machinery Limited (1)
Attwood Street Lye
Stourbridge, West Midlands, DY9 8RU, United Kingdom
Tel.: (44) 1384 264950
Fax: (44) 1384 264955

Addison Saws Limited—(Continued)

E-Mail: sales@tubefab.co.uk
Web Site: www.tubefab.co.uk
Tube Bending Machine Mfr
S.I.C.: 3559
N.A.I.C.S.: 333249
Alan Price, *(Mng Dir)*

ADDNODE AB
(See Under Addnode Group AB)

ADDNODE GROUP AB
(Formerly Addnode AB)
Hudiksvallsgatan 4B
SE-113 30 Stockholm, Sweden
Tel.: (46) 850666210
Fax: (46) 850666225
E-Mail: info@addnode.com
Web Site: www.addnodegroup.com
ANOD B—(OMX)
Sls.: $211,255,560
Assets: $206,905,680
Liabilities: $84,025,440
Net Worth: $122,880,240
Earnings: $13,436,640
Emp.: 849
Fiscal Year-end: 12/31/12

Business Description:
Information Technology Services
S.I.C.: 7379
N.A.I.C.S.: 541519

Personnel:
Sigrun Hjelmquist *(Chm)*
Staffan Hanstorp *(CEO)*
Johan Andersson *(CFO)*

Board of Directors:
Sigrun Hjelmquist
Jan Andersson
Kristofer Arwin
Dick Hasselstrom
Eva Listi
Thord Wilkne

Subsidiaries:

Arkiva AB (1)
Brandthovdagatan 9
721 35 Vasteras, Sweden
Tel.: (46) 21 18 70 10
E-Mail: info@arkiva.se
Web Site: www.arkiva.se
Software Development Services
S.I.C.: 7371
N.A.I.C.S.: 541511
Carin Andersson *(Mng Dir)*

Cad-Quality Sverige AB (1)
Forskargatan 3
781 27 Borlange, Sweden
Tel.: (46) 243 736 60
Fax: (46) 243 736 66
E-Mail: info@cad-q.se
Web Site: www.cad-q.com
Computer Aided Design Services
S.I.C.: 7373
N.A.I.C.S.: 541512
Rolf Kjaernsli *(Mng Dir)*

Cartesia GIS AB (1)
Hudiksvallsgatan 4
11330 Stockholm, Sweden (100%)
Tel.: (46) 95012005
Fax: (46) 850666200
E-Mail: info@cartesia.se
Web Site: www.cartesia.se
Emp.: 100
Computer Related Services
S.I.C.: 7379
N.A.I.C.S.: 541519
Lennrat Nielsen *(Chm)*

Decerno AB (1)
Electrum 234
164 40 Kista, Sweden
Tel.: (46) 8 630 75 00
Fax: (46) 8 630 75 01
E-Mail: info@decerno.se
Web Site: www.decerno.se
Computer Peripheral Equipment Whslr
S.I.C.: 5045
N.A.I.C.S.: 423430

Ida Infront AB (1)
St Larsgatan 18
Linkoping, 58224, Sweden (100%)
Tel.: (46) 13373700
Fax: (46) 13373790
E-Mail: info@idainfront.se
Web Site: www.a-novo.it
Emp.: 60
Computer Related Services
S.I.C.: 7379
N.A.I.C.S.: 541519
Stefan Jonegard *(Pres)*

Kartena AB (1)
Otterhallegatan 1
411 18 Gothenburg, Sweden
Tel.: (46) 31 777 77 90
Fax: (46) 31 77 44 396
E-Mail: info@kartena.se
Web Site: www.kartena.se
Geographic Information Technology Consulting Services
S.I.C.: 7373
N.A.I.C.S.: 541512

Linewise AB (1)
Hudiksvallsgatan 4
11330 Stockholm, Sweden (100%)
Tel.: (46) 856240000
Fax: (46) 850666200
E-Mail: info@linewise.se
Web Site: www.linewise.se
Emp.: 15
Computer Related Services
S.I.C.: 7379
N.A.I.C.S.: 541519
Johannes Blome *(Mng Dir)*

Linewise Services AB (1)
Hudiksvallsgatan 4
113 30 Stockholm, Sweden
Tel.: (46) 8 562 400 00
Fax: (46) 8 562 400 51
E-Mail: info@linewise.se
Web Site: www.linewise.se
Emp.: 30
Business Process Outsourcing Services
S.I.C.: 7389
N.A.I.C.S.: 561499
Johannes Blome *(Mng Dir)*

Mittbygge AB (1)
Kungsgatan 5
352 30 Vaxjo, Sweden
Tel.: (46) 70 60 46 120
E-Mail: info@mittbygge.se
Web Site: www.mittbygge.se
Residential Construction Management Services
S.I.C.: 6531
N.A.I.C.S.: 531311
Hans-Peter Aineskog *(Mng Dir)*

Mogul AB (1)
Hudiksvallsgatan 4
11330 Stockholm, Sweden (100%)
Tel.: (46) 850666100
Fax: (46) 850666200
E-Mail: info@mogul.com
Web Site: www.mogul.com
Emp.: 120
Computer Related Services
S.I.C.: 7379
N.A.I.C.S.: 541519
Urban Nasman *(CEO)*

Prosilia Software AB (1)
Sveavagen 39
11330 Stockholm, Sweden
Tel.: (46) 8202950
Fax: (46) 8204790
E-Mail: info@prosilia.se
Web Site: www.prosilia.se
Computer Related Services
S.I.C.: 7379
N.A.I.C.S.: 541519

Technia AB (1)
Isafjordsgatan 15
16440 Kista, Sweden
Tel.: (46) 859920400
Fax: (46) 859921424
E-Mail: jg@technia.com
Web Site: www.technia.com
Computer Related Services
S.I.C.: 7379
N.A.I.C.S.: 541519

Non-U.S. Subsidiaries:

Technia AS (2)
Gullhaug Torg 4 A
0401 Oslo, Norway
Tel.: (47) 93205521
Fax: (47) 22020708
Web Site: www.technia.com
Emp.: 10
Computer Related Services
S.I.C.: 7379
N.A.I.C.S.: 541519

Technia Oy (2)
Vaisalantie 4
Falcon Business Park Hali, 2130 Espoo, Finland
Tel.: (358) 4247221
Fax: (358) 424722222
E-Mail: Cetri.Hautakangas@technia.com
Web Site: www.technia.com
Emp.: 100
Computer Related Services
S.I.C.: 7379
N.A.I.C.S.: 541519
Cetri Hautakangas *(Acct Mgr)*

Tekis AB (1)
Box 315
731 27 Koping, Sweden
Tel.: (46) 221 168 70
Fax: (46) 560 388 53
E-Mail: info@tekis.se
Web Site: www.tekis.se
Emp.: 45
Information Technology Consulting Services
S.I.C.: 7373
N.A.I.C.S.: 541512
Carin Andersson *(Mng Dir)*

Teknik I Media Datacenter Stockholm AB (1)
Gjorwellsgatan 30
10026 Stockholm, Sweden
Tel.: (46) 850638000
Fax: (46) 850638001
E-Mail: info@dcsto.se
Web Site: www.dcsto.se
Emp.: 20
Computer Related Services
S.I.C.: 7379
N.A.I.C.S.: 541519

U.S. Subsidiary:

Technia Inc. (1)
200 E 5th Ave Ste 124
Naperville, IL 60563-3173
Tel.: (978) 973-9349
Fax: (866) 981-7664
Software Development Services
S.I.C.: 7371
N.A.I.C.S.: 541511

Non-U.S. Subsidiaries:

Cad Quality A/S (1)
Mars Alle 38
8700 Horsens, Denmark
Tel.: (45) 76281415
Fax: (45) 7628 1414
E-Mail: info@cad-q.dk
Web Site: www.cad-q.dk
Emp.: 4
Computer Aided Design Services
S.I.C.: 7373
N.A.I.C.S.: 541512
Jorn Robdrup *(Gen Mgr)*

Cad-Quality Finland Oy (1)
Ayritie 8 B
1510 Vantaa, Finland
Tel.: (358) 9 5422 6500
Fax: (358) 9 5422 6600
E-Mail: info@cad-q.fi
Web Site: www.cad-q.fi
Emp.: 20
Data Management Services
S.I.C.: 7379
N.A.I.C.S.: 541519

ADDTECH AB
Sturegatan 38
SE-102 43 Stockholm, Sweden
Tel.: (46) 84704900
Fax: (46) 84704901
E-Mail: info@addtech.com
Web Site: www.addtech.com
ADDTB—(OMX)
Sls.: $836,384,400
Assets: $473,997,600
Liabilities: $297,835,200
Net Worth: $176,162,400
Earnings: $50,000,400
Emp.: 1,815
Fiscal Year-end: 03/31/13

Business Description:
Industrial Products & Components Developer & Seller
S.I.C.: 3699
N.A.I.C.S.: 335999

Personnel:
Anders Borjesson *(Chm)*
Tom Hedelius *(Vice Chm)*
Johan Sjo *(Pres & CEO)*
Kristina Willgard *(CFO)*
Anders Claeson *(Exec VP)*

Board of Directors:
Anders Borjesson
Eva Elmstedt
Tom Hedelius
Ulf Mattsson
Johan Sjo
Lars Spongberg

Subsidiaries:

Abatel AB (1)
Domherrev 11 B
Sollentuna, Stockholm, Sweden
Tel.: (46) 8 444 59 60
Fax: (46) 8 96 67 00
E-Mail: order@abatel.com
Web Site: www.abatel.com
Battery Mfr
S.I.C.: 3692
N.A.I.C.S.: 335912
Jesper Bjoerken *(Mng Dir)*
Mats Melin *(CTO)*

Addtech A/S (1)
Fturegatan 38
5112
10243 Stockholm, Sweden (100%)
Tel.: (46) 84704900
Fax: (46) 86801111
Web Site: www.addtech.com
Emp.: 10
All Other Business Support Services
S.I.C.: 7389
N.A.I.C.S.: 561499
Johan Fjoo *(Mng Dir)*

Addtech Business Support AB (1)
sturegatan 8
PO Box 6068
14106 Stockholm, Sweden (100%)
Tel.: (46) 84704900
Fax: (46) 86807761
E-Mail: jefper@addtech.biz
Emp.: 15
Data Processing Services
S.I.C.: 7379
N.A.I.C.S.: 518210
John Sjo *(Mng Dir)*

Addtech Components AB (1)
23045
10435 Stockholm, Sweden (100%)
Tel.: (46) 854541400
Fax: (46) 854541401
E-Mail: info@addtech.com
Emp.: 15
Electrical Apparatus & Equipment Wiring Supplies & Related Equipment Merchant Whslr
S.I.C.: 5063
N.A.I.C.S.: 423610
Anders Dafnas *(Mgr-Bus Area)*

Addtech Energy & Equipment AB (1)
Fakturavagen 6
17562 Jarfalla, Sweden (100%)
Tel.: (46) 84458440
Fax: (46) 84458449
E-Mail: info@kmc.se
Web Site: www.kmc.se
Emp.: 16
Industrial Machinery & Equipment Merchant Whslr
S.I.C.: 5084
N.A.I.C.S.: 423830
Lars Jansson *(Mng Dir)*

Subsidiary:

KMC AB (2)
Fakturavagen 6
17562 Jarfalla, Sweden (100%)

Tel.: (46) 84458440
Fax: (46) 84458449
E-Mail: info@kmc.se
Web Site: www.kmc.se
Emp.: 20
Industrial Machinery & Equipment Merchant Whslr
S.I.C.: 5084
N.A.I.C.S.: 423830
Mikael Keranen *(Mng Dir)*

Non-U.S. Subsidiary:

Hansabattery Oy (2)
Hoylaamontie 11A
00380 Helsinki, Finland
Tel.: (358) 2079996
Telex: 122874 nife sf
Fax: (358) 207631889
Web Site: www.hansabattery.fi
Emp.: 5
Battery Mfr
S.I.C.: 3691
N.A.I.C.S.: 335911
Jon Sandstrom *(Mng Dir)*

Addtech Life Science AB (1)
St Eriksgatan 117
PO Box 23045
10435 Stockholm, Sweden (100%)
Tel.: (46) 859411350
Fax: (46) 854541401
E-Mail: goran.brandt@addtech.com
Web Site: www.addtech.com
Emp.: 3
Professional Equipment & Supplies Whslr
S.I.C.: 5049
N.A.I.C.S.: 423490
Johan Brendt *(Mng Dir)*

Addtech Transmission AB (1)
Eriksgatan 117
23087
10435 Stockholm, Sweden (100%)
Tel.: (46) 854546925
Fax: (46) 854541401
Web Site: www.addtech.com
Emp.: 4
Electrical Apparatus & Equipment Wiring Supplies & Related Equipment Merchant Whslr
S.I.C.: 5063
N.A.I.C.S.: 423610
Hikan Franzen *(Mng Dir)*

Adiator AB (1)
Halsingeg 40 14 Floor
113 43 Stockholm, Sweden
Tel.: (46) 8 729 17 00
Fax: (46) 8 729 17 17
E-Mail: info@adiator.se
Web Site: www.adiator.se
Electrical Switch Products Distr
S.I.C.: 5063
N.A.I.C.S.: 423610

Adigo Drives AB (1)
Neongatan 10
PO Box 8
431 21 Molndal, Sweden
Tel.: (46) 31 672 340
Fax: (46) 31 672 350
E-Mail: order@adigodrives.se
Web Site: www.adigodrives.se
Emp.: 12
Electrical Equipment Mfr
S.I.C.: 3699
N.A.I.C.S.: 335999
Peter Mayer *(Gen Mgr)*

Allan Rehnstrom AB (1)
Raelsgatan 6A
Box 644
801 27 Gavle, Sweden
Tel.: (46) 26 100 100
Fax: (46) 26 109 987
E-Mail: info@rehnstrom.se
Web Site: www.rehnstrom.se
Vacuum Pumps Distr
S.I.C.: 5064
N.A.I.C.S.: 423620

Alvetec Kontest AB (1)
Fakturavagen 6
175 62 Jarfalla, Sweden
Tel.: (46) 8 626 40 50
Fax: (46) 8 754 88 67
Web Site: www.kontest.com
Electronic Equipment Mfr
S.I.C.: 3679
N.A.I.C.S.: 334419

Aratron AB (1)
Smidesvagen 4-8
171 41 Solna, Sweden
Tel.: (46) 8 40 41 600
E-Mail: info@aratron.se
Web Site: www.aratron.se
Mechanical Component Distr
S.I.C.: 5085
N.A.I.C.S.: 423840

Batteriunion AB (1)
Aggelundavagen 2
175 62 Jarfalla, Sweden
Tel.: (46) 8 795 28 50
Fax: (46) 8 795 28 69
E-Mail: mailbox@batteriunion.se
Web Site: www.batteriunion.se
Battery Mfr
S.I.C.: 3691
N.A.I.C.S.: 335911

BergmanLabora AB (1)
Box 705
182 17 Danderyd, Sweden
Tel.: (46) 8 625 18 50
Fax: (46) 8 625 18 70
E-Mail: info@bergmanlabora.se
Web Site: www.bergmanlabora.se
Emp.: 30
Laboratory Instrument Distr
S.I.C.: 5047
N.A.I.C.S.: 423450

Bevi Nord AB (1)
Kontaktvagen 8
901 33 Umea, Sweden
Tel.: (46) 90 70 44 30
Fax: (46) 90 13 96 60
E-Mail: bevinord@bevi.se
Electric Motor & Generator Mfr
S.I.C.: 3621
N.A.I.C.S.: 335312

BEVI Teknik & Service AB (1)
Bevivagen 1
384 30 Blomstermala, Sweden
Tel.: (46) 499 271 00
Fax: (46) 499 208 60
E-Mail: production@bevi.se
Electric Motor Mfr
S.I.C.: 3621
N.A.I.C.S.: 335312

Beving Elektronik AB (1)
Box 93
127 22 Skarholmen, Sweden
Tel.: (46) 8 680 11 99
Fax: (46) 8 680 11 88
E-Mail: info@beving.se
Web Site: www.bevingelektronik.se
Electric Meters Mfr
S.I.C.: 3699
N.A.I.C.S.: 335999
Lars G. Pahlsson *(Gen Mgr)*

Blasterprodukter i Koping AB (1)
Glasgatan 21
731 22 Koping, Sweden
Tel.: (46) 221 760 880
Fax: (46) 221 760 881
Web Site: www.blasterprodukter.se
Abrasive & Diamond Tools Whslr
S.I.C.: 5085
N.A.I.C.S.: 423840

BTC Industribatterier AB (1)
Grustagsvagen 1
572 36 Oskarshamn, Sweden
Tel.: (46) 491 844 55
Fax: (46) 491 766 410
E-Mail: info@btc.nu
Web Site: www.btc.nu
Rev.: $3,752,400
Emp.: 5
Battery Distr
S.I.C.: 5065
N.A.I.C.S.: 423690

CALDARO AB (1)
Warfvinges vag 39
112 51 Stockholm, Sweden
Tel.: (46) 8 736 12 70
Fax: (46) 8 736 12 90
E-Mail: info@caldaro.com
Web Site: www.caldaro.com
Emp.: 15
Electronic Component Distr
S.I.C.: 5065
N.A.I.C.S.: 423690
Stefan Aase *(Mng Dir)*

Carbex AB (1)
PO Box 115
592 22 Vadstena, Sweden
Tel.: (46) 143 294 40
Fax: (46) 143 135 80
E-Mail: info@carbex.se
Web Site: www.carbex.se
Emp.: 28
Carbon Brush Mfr
S.I.C.: 3624
N.A.I.C.S.: 335991
Stefan Stroeberg *(Mng Dir)*

Cellite AB (1)
Tredenborgsvagen 16
294 25 Solvesborg, Sweden
Tel.: (46) 456 234 56
Fax: (46) 456 153 77
Web Site: www.cellite.se
Emp.: 3
Battery Distr
S.I.C.: 5065
N.A.I.C.S.: 423690
Peter Fischer *(Pres)*

Celltech Energy Systems AB (1)
Tredenborgsvagen 16
294 35 Solvesborg, Sweden
Tel.: (46) 456 234 56
Fax: (46) 456 153 77
E-Mail: info@celltech.se
Web Site: www.celltech.se
Battery Mfr
S.I.C.: 3691
N.A.I.C.S.: 335911

COLUMBIA ELEKTRONIK AB (1)
Sjoviksvagen 53
618 30 Kolmarden, Sweden
Tel.: (46) 11 398005
Fax: (46) 11 397641
Web Site: www.columbia.se
Electronic Component Mfr
S.I.C.: 3679
N.A.I.C.S.: 334419
Mats Klarholm *(Mng Dir)*

Compotech AB (1)
Halsingegatan 43
Box 21029
100 31 Stockholm, Sweden
Tel.: (46) 8 441 58 00
Fax: (46) 8 441 58 29
E-Mail: info@compotech.se
Web Site: www.compotech.se
Emp.: 20
Electronic Component Mfr
S.I.C.: 3679
N.A.I.C.S.: 334419
Jan Eriksson *(Gen Mgr)*

Cumatix AB (1)
Halsingegatan 43 6tr
113 31 Stockholm, Sweden
Tel.: (46) 8 768 65 91
Fax: (46) 8 768 65 91
E-Mail: info@cumatix.se
Web Site: www.cumatix.se
Electromechanical Component Distr
S.I.C.: 5065
N.A.I.C.S.: 423690

Electra-Box Diagnostica AB (1)
Solkraftsvagen 18B
135 70 Stockholm, Sweden
Tel.: (46) 8 448 73 70
Fax: (46) 8 712 65 09
Laboratory Products Distr
S.I.C.: 5047
N.A.I.C.S.: 423450

Electra-Box Pharma AB (1)
Solkraftsvagen 18B
135 70 Stockholm, Sweden
Tel.: (46) 8 448 73 70
Fax: (46) 8 712 65 09
Web Site: www.electrabox.com
Emp.: 13
Diagnostic Products & Equipment Distr
S.I.C.: 5047
N.A.I.C.S.: 423450
Kjell Blomberg *(Gen Mgr)*

Emcomp International AB (1)
Box 7
710 41 Fellingsbro, Sweden
Tel.: (46) 581 62 15 50
Fax: (46) 581 62 15 60
E-Mail: info@emcomp-international.com
Web Site: www.emcomp.se/english/Contact/tabid/121/language/en-US/Default.aspx
Electronic Component Whslr
S.I.C.: 5065
N.A.I.C.S.: 423690

Emcomp Scandinavia AB (1)
Smidesvagen 4-8
171 41 Solna, Sweden
Tel.: (46) 8 564 899 00
Fax: (46) 8 564 899 19
E-Mail: info@emcomp.se
Web Site: www.emcomp.se
Emp.: 4
Electronic Component Whslr
S.I.C.: 5065
N.A.I.C.S.: 423690
Anders Dafnas *(Gen Mgr)*

ESD-Center AB. (1)
Ringugnsgatan 8
21616 Malmo, Sweden
Tel.: (46) 40 363 240
Fax: (46) 40 151 683
E-Mail: info@esd-center.se
Web Site: www.esd-center.se
Sls.: $7,035,750
Emp.: 12
Electronic Products Packaging Materials Distr
S.I.C.: 5085
N.A.I.C.S.: 423840
Stefan Sjoekvist *(Mng Dir)*

FB Kedjor AB (1)
Sattargatan 4
Eskilstuna, Sodermanland, 631 04, Sweden
Tel.: (46) 16 15 33 00
Fax: (46) 16 14 27 57
E-Mail: info@fbkedjor.se
Web Site: www.fbkedjor.se
Emp.: 16
Roller Chain Mfr
S.I.C.: 3568
N.A.I.C.S.: 333613
Roger Holm *(CEO)*

Gevea AB (1)
Vagngatan 9
603 63 Norrkoping, Sweden
Tel.: (46) 11 18 48 00
Fax: (46) 11 18 23 50
E-Mail: info@gevea.se
Web Site: www.gevea.com
Electrical Power Products Mfr & Distr
S.I.C.: 3825
N.A.I.C.S.: 334515

Hjulex AB (1)
Jitegatan 10
265 38 Astorp, Sweden
Tel.: (46) 42 567 00
Fax: (46) 42 567 10
E-Mail: info@hjulex.se
Web Site: www.hjulex.com
Emp.: 11
Roller Conveyor Products Distr
S.I.C.: 5085
N.A.I.C.S.: 423840

Immunkemi F&D AB (1)
Veddestra Centrum
175 72 Jarfalla, Sweden
Tel.: (46) 8 583 615 00
Fax: (46) 8 583 615 01
E-Mail: sales@immunkemi.se
Web Site: www.immunkemi.se
Diagnostics & Biochemical Research Services
S.I.C.: 8731
N.A.I.C.S.: 541711

LabRobot Products AB (1)
Munkerodsvagen 5
444 32 Stenungsund, Sweden
Tel.: (46) 303 846 73
Fax: (46) 303 652 55
E-Mail: kontakt@labrobot.com
Web Site: www.labrobot.com
Laboratory Instruments Mfr & Distr
S.I.C.: 3826
N.A.I.C.S.: 334516
Herve Laisis *(CEO)*

Metric Industrial AB (1)
Sjoangsvagen 5
SE 192 72 Sollentuna, Sweden

Addtech AB—(Continued)

Tel.: (46) 86264840
Fax: (46) 86265710
E-Mail: sls@metric.se
Web Site: www.metric.se
Sales Range: $10-24.9 Million
Emp.: 10
Automation & Test & Measurement Equipment
S.I.C.: 3825
N.A.I.C.S.: 334515
Richard Norden *(VP & Mng Dir)*

Nordic Battery AB (1)
Fakturavagen 6
175 62 Jarfalla, Sweden
Tel.: (46) 8 760 42 93
Fax: (46) 8 760 85 27
E-Mail: info@nordicbattery.com
Web Site: www.nordicbattery.se
Battery Mfr & Whslr
S.I.C.: 3691
N.A.I.C.S.: 335911

OmniProcess AB (1)
Vretenvagen 12
171 54 Solna, Sweden
Tel.: (46) 8 56480840
Fax: (46) 8 56480850
E-Mail: info@omniprocess.se
Web Site: www.omniprocess.se
Emp.: 25
Analytical Laboratory Equipment Distr
S.I.C.: 5049
N.A.I.C.S.: 423490

R&K TECH AB (1)
Smidesvagen 4-8
171 41 Solna, Sweden
Tel.: (46) 8 544 40 560
Fax: (46) 8 732 7440
E-Mail: info@rk.se
Web Site: www.rk.se
Electronic Equipment Whslr
S.I.C.: 5065
N.A.I.C.S.: 423690
Patrick Hahne *(Gen Mgr)*

SABP Elteknik AB (1)
Hybovagen 8
827 35 Ljusdal, Sweden
Tel.: (46) 651 711801
Fax: (46) 651 15679
E-Mail: info@sabp.se
Web Site: www.sabp.se
Emp.: 9
Power Industrial Machinery Mfr
S.I.C.: 3559
N.A.I.C.S.: 333249
Bengt Pettersson *(Gen Mgr)*

Stig Wahlstrom Automatik AB (1)
Box 64
123 43 Farsta, Sweden
Tel.: (46) 8 683 33 00
Fax: (46) 8 605 81 74
E-Mail: mailbox@wahlstrom.se
Web Site: www.wahlstrom.se/index.asp
Emp.: 60
Electronic Equipment Whslr
S.I.C.: 5065
N.A.I.C.S.: 423690
Robert Svantesson *(Gen Mgr)*

Stig Wahlstrom Hydraulik AB (1)
Box 64
123 43 Farsta, Sweden
Tel.: (46) 8 683 33 00
Fax: (46) 8 605 81 74
E-Mail: mailbox@wahlstrom.se
Web Site: www.addtech.com
Pump Mfr
S.I.C.: 3561
N.A.I.C.S.: 333911

Switchgear AB (1)
Nedre Akargatan 71
802 51 Gavle, Sweden
Tel.: (46) 26 541550
Fax: (46) 26 541559
Web Site: www.switchgear.se
Emp.: 20
Switchgear Mfr & Distr
S.I.C.: 3613
N.A.I.C.S.: 335313

Teknikprodukter Nordic AB (1)
Box 173
Bankeryd, 564 24 Jonkoping, Sweden
Tel.: (46) 36 37 62 00
Fax: (46) 36 37 22 93
E-Mail: border@teknikprodukter.se
Web Site: www.teknikprodukter.se
Industrial Component Distr
S.I.C.: 5084
N.A.I.C.S.: 423830
Tommy Marklund *(CEO)*

Trinergi AB (1)
Halltorpsvagen 1
702 29 Orebro, Sweden
Tel.: (46) 19 18 86 60
Fax: (46) 19 24 00 60
E-Mail: info@trinergi.se
Web Site: www.trinergi.se
Electrical Power Measurement Products Distr
S.I.C.: 5063
N.A.I.C.S.: 423610

Tube Control AB (1)
Box 292
127 25 Skarholmen, Sweden
Tel.: (46) 8 555 92100
Fax: (46) 8 555 92150
E-Mail: info@tubecontrol.se
Web Site: www.tubecontrol.se
Rev.: $15,635,000
Emp.: 20
Hydraulic Components Whslr
S.I.C.: 5085
N.A.I.C.S.: 423840
Peter Johansson *(Gen Mgr)*

Tufvassons Transformator AB (1)
Marstavagen 20
193 40 Sigtuna, Sweden
Tel.: (46) 8 594 809 00
Fax: (46) 8 592 527 68
E-Mail: reception@tufvassons.se
Web Site: www.tufvassons.se
Transformer Mfr
S.I.C.: 3676
N.A.I.C.S.: 334416

Wendler AB (1)
Stockstigen 11
132 46 Stockholm, Sweden
Tel.: (46) 8 19 08 68
Fax: (46) 8 744 31 25
E-Mail: info@wendler.se
Web Site: www.wendler.se
Fuses & Exterior Lightning Distr
S.I.C.: 5063
N.A.I.C.S.: 423610
Michelle James *(Gen Mgr)*

Non-U.S. Subsidiaries:

Acc Systems OY (1)
Malminkaari 9
Helsinki, Finland 00700
Tel.: (358) 9 340 4900
Fax: (358) 9 340 4901
E-Mail: sales@accsystems.fi
Web Site: www.accsystems.fi
Emp.: 4
Telecommunication Accessories & Component Mfr
S.I.C.: 3669
N.A.I.C.S.: 334290
Ilari Huikuri *(Mng Dir)*

Akkuvoima Oy (1)
PL 22
00371 Helsinki, Finland
Tel.: (358) 207 999 640
Fax: (358) 207 999 641
E-Mail: info@akkuvoima.fi
Web Site: www.akkuvoima.fi
Emp.: 16
Battery Mfr & Sales
S.I.C.: 3691
N.A.I.C.S.: 335911
Peter Andersson *(Gen Mgr)*

Amitronic Oy (1)
Aniankatu 1
15 210 Lahti, Finland
Tel.: (358) 3 876 100
Fax: (358) 3 751 0253
E-Mail: sales@amitronic.fi
Web Site: www.amitronic.fi
Electronic Component Mfr
S.I.C.: 3679
N.A.I.C.S.: 334419

Aratron Kurt Wiig AS (1)
Skvadronveien 25
4050 Sola, Norway
Tel.: (47) 51 71 99 00
Fax: (47) 51 71 99 01
E-Mail: post@aratronkurtwiig.no
Web Site: www.aratronkurtwiig.no
Hydraulic Component Distr
S.I.C.: 5085
N.A.I.C.S.: 423840

Bergman AS (1)
Postboks 364
2001 Lillestrom, Norway
Tel.: (47) 63 83 56 00
Fax: (47) 63 83 56 10
E-Mail: info@bergman.no
Web Site: www.bergman.no
Laboratory Instrumentation Mfr
S.I.C.: 3826
N.A.I.C.S.: 334516

Bergman Diagnostika AS (1)
Jogstadveien 21
2007 Kjeller, Norway
Tel.: (47) 63835750
Fax: (47) 63835740
E-Mail: info@bergmandiag.no
Web Site: www.bergmandiag.no
Emp.: 19
Diagnostic Equipment Mfr
S.I.C.: 3845
N.A.I.C.S.: 334510
Tove Nyhus *(Gen Mgr)*

Betech Seals A/S (1)
Vesterlundvej 4
2730 Herlev, Denmark
Tel.: (45) 4485 8100
Fax: (45) 4492 7800
E-Mail: info@betechseals.dk
Web Site: www.betechseals.dk
Emp.: 7
Polymer Product Mfr & Sales
S.I.C.: 3053
N.A.I.C.S.: 339991
Per Hyldstrup *(Sr Product Mgr)*

Bevi China (1)
Room 801 Shanghai 201 Xin Jinqiao Road
Pudong New District, Shanghai, 201206, China
Tel.: (86) 21 50325200
Fax: (86) 2150325202
E-Mail: bevi@bevi.cn
Web Site: www.bevi.com
Emp.: 5
Electric Motor & Generator Mfr
S.I.C.: 3621
N.A.I.C.S.: 335312
Diane Chen *(Mgr)*

Bevi Danmark A/S (1)
Baldersbuen 14
2640 Hedehusene, Denmark
Tel.: (45) 39 673605
Fax: (45) 39 675660
E-Mail: bevi@bevi.dk
Web Site: www.bevi.dk
Emp.: 6
Electric Motor Distr
S.I.C.: 5063
N.A.I.C.S.: 423610
Michael Hallengren *(Gen Mgr)*

Bevi Est Ou (1)
Parnu mnt 238
116 24 Tallinn, Estonia
Tel.: (372) 6828 755
Fax: (372) 6828 754
E-Mail: bevi@bevi.ee
Web Site: www.bevi.ee
Electric Motor & Generator Mfr
S.I.C.: 3621
N.A.I.C.S.: 335312

BEVI Finland Oy (1)
Hannuksenpelto 6
02270 Espoo, Finland
Tel.: (358) 9 27091210
Fax: (358) 9 27091219
E-Mail: info@bevi.fi
Web Site: www.bevi.fi
Electric Motor & Generator Mfr
S.I.C.: 3621
N.A.I.C.S.: 335312

Bevi Norge AS (1)
Ulvenveien 90B
Oslo, 0581, Norway
Tel.: (47) 22076650
Fax: (47) 22721669
Electric Motor & Generator Mfr
S.I.C.: 3621
N.A.I.C.S.: 335312

Bevi UAB (1)
Savanoriu pr 219
2300 Vilnius, Lithuania
Tel.: (370) 5 2611112
Fax: (370) 5 2032177
E-Mail: info@bevi.lt
Web Site: www.bevi.lt
Electric Motor & Generator Mfr
S.I.C.: 3621
N.A.I.C.S.: 335312

Bondy LMT A/S (1)
Hassellunden 14
2765 Smorum, Denmark
Tel.: (45) 7015 1414
Fax: (45) 4464 1416
E-Mail: info@bondylmt.dk
Web Site: www.bondylmt.dk
Emp.: 11
Motors & Gear Mfr
S.I.C.: 3566
N.A.I.C.S.: 333612
Leif Johansson *(Gen Mgr)*

CellTech-Harring A/S (1)
Rugmarken 9
3520 Farum, Denmark
Tel.: (45) 7025 2201
Fax: (45) 7025 2202
E-Mail: info@celltech.dk
Web Site: www.celltech.dk
Emp.: 2
Battery Mfr
S.I.C.: 3691
N.A.I.C.S.: 335911
Michael Ankjaer *(Mng Dir)*

Chemo Electric A/S (1)
Hassellunden 14
2765 Smorum, Denmark
Tel.: (45) 3677 3044
Fax: (45) 3677 3088
E-Mail: Info@chemolec.dk
Web Site: www.chemoelectric.dk
Emp.: 1
Electronic Equipment Distr
S.I.C.: 5065
N.A.I.C.S.: 423690
Allan Jensen *(Mng Dir)*

Codan Tech Qingdao Rubber & Plastic Parts Co., Ltd. (1)
Jinling Industrial Zone Jihongtan Town
Chengyang District, Qingdao, Shandong, China
Tel.: (86) 532 87909363
Fax: (86) 532 87909092
E-Mail: info@codantech.com
Web Site: www.codantech.com
Rubber & Molded Plastic Parts Mfr
S.I.C.: 3069
N.A.I.C.S.: 326299

Egil Eng & Co. AS (1)
Jernkroken 7
0976 Oslo, Norway
Tel.: (47) 22 90 05 60
Fax: (47) 22 16 15 55
E-Mail: firma@egileng.no
Web Site: www.egileng.no
Construction Equipment Distr
S.I.C.: 5082
N.A.I.C.S.: 423810

Electra-Box Diagnostica A/S (1)
Strandveien 6
3050 Mjondalen, Norway
Tel.: (47) 32237950
Fax: (47) 32237949
E-Mail: salg.norge@electrabox.com
Laboratory Products Distr
S.I.C.: 5049
N.A.I.C.S.: 423490

Electra-Box Diagnostica APS (1)
Hvidsvaermervej 147
2610 Rodovre, Denmark
Tel.: (45) 44 53 62 11
Fax: (45) 44 53 62 12
Emp.: 5
Diagnostic Products Distr
S.I.C.: 5122
N.A.I.C.S.: 424210
Stefan Korpe *(Gen Mgr)*

Electra-Box Diagnostica Oy (1)
Lyhytie 8
00700 Helsinki, Finland

Tel.: (358) 9 72 44 330
Fax: (358) 9 72 44 331
Emp.: 2
Medical Equipment Distr
S.I.C.: 5047
N.A.I.C.S.: 423450
Stuart West *(Gen Mgr)*

Elgood Oy (1)
Malminkaari 10
00700 Helsinki, Finland
Tel.: (358) 207 981 140
Fax: (358) 207 981 141
E-Mail: info@elgood.fi
Web Site: www.elgood.fi
Emp.: 10
Electronic Component Retailer
S.I.C.: 5734
N.A.I.C.S.: 443142
Jukka Anttila *(Gen Mgr-Sls)*

Eltech Automation A/S (1)
Hassellunden 14
2765 Smorum, Denmark
Tel.: (45) 7010 1410
Fax: (45) 4320 0777
E-Mail: mail@eltech.dk
Web Site: www.eltech.dk
Emp.: 1
Electronic Product Distr
S.I.C.: 5065
N.A.I.C.S.: 423690
Kent Koehler *(Gen Mgr)*

Eltech Components A/S (1)
Hassellunden 14
2765 Smorum, Denmark
Tel.: (45) 7625 1818
Fax: (45) 4320 0777
E-Mail: mail@eltechcomp.dk
Web Site: www.eltechcomp.dk
Emp.: 6
Electronic Component Mfr
S.I.C.: 3679
N.A.I.C.S.: 334419
Christine Lee *(Mgr)*

Elteco AS (1)
Floodmyrveien 24
3946 Porsgrunn, Norway
Tel.: (47) 35 56 20 70
Fax: (47) 35 56 20 99
E-Mail: firmapost@elteco.no
Web Site: www.elteco.no
Emp.: 19
Industrial Automation Component Distr
S.I.C.: 5085
N.A.I.C.S.: 423840
Svein Holla *(Gen Mgr)*

Eurolaite Oy (1)
Hoeylaeaemoetie 11 A
00380 Helsinki, Finland
Tel.: (358) 20 155 7444
Fax: (358) 20 155 7445
E-Mail: eurolaite@eurolaite.fi
Web Site: www.eurolaite.fi
Emp.: 5
Electrical Products Whslr
S.I.C.: 5063
N.A.I.C.S.: 423610
Tuomo Luukkainen *(Gen Mgr)*

FB Chain Limited (1)
Jubilee Rd
Letchworth, SG6 1NE, United Kingdom
Tel.: (44) 1462670844
Fax: (44) 1462480745
E-Mail: sales@fbchain.com
Web Site: www.fbchain.com
Emp.: 15
Conveyor Chain Mfr
S.I.C.: 3568
N.A.I.C.S.: 333613
Peter Church *(Gen Mgr)*

FB Ketjutekniikka Oy (1)
Kokemaentie 451
27710 Koylio, Finland
Tel.: (358) 2 540 111
Fax: (358) 2 540 1100
E-Mail: fb@fbketjutekniikka.fi
Web Site: www.fbketjutekniikka.fi
Conveyor Chain Mfr
S.I.C.: 3535
N.A.I.C.S.: 333922

FB Ketten GmbH (1)
Stakelbrauk 11
59889 Eslohe, Arnsberg, Germany
Tel.: (49) 2973 97914 0
Fax: (49) 2973 97914 20
E-Mail: fbkettenbrd@fbketten.com
Web Site: www.fb-ketten.de
Conveyor Chain Mfr
S.I.C.: 3535
N.A.I.C.S.: 333922
Matthias Berls *(Gen Mgr)*

FB Ketten Handels Gmbh (1)
Gewerbepark Sud 5
6330 Kufstein, Austria
Tel.: (43) 5372 61466
Fax: (43) 5372 6146620
E-Mail: fbketten@fb-ketten.com
Web Site: www.fb-ketten.at
Wood Product Mfr
S.I.C.: 2499
N.A.I.C.S.: 321999

FB Kjeder AS (1)
Bjornerudveien 17
1266 Oslo, Norway
Tel.: (47) 23 19 16 50
Fax: (47) 23 19 16 51
E-Mail: fbkjeder@fbkjeder.no
Web Site: www.fbkjeder.no
Precision Machine Tools Mfr
S.I.C.: 3451
N.A.I.C.S.: 332721

Fox Electronics AS (1)
Postboks 67
Kjelsas, 0411 Oslo, Norway
Tel.: (47) 23896900
Fax: (47) 22181701
E-Mail: post@foxelectronics.no
Web Site: www.foxelectronics.no
Emp.: 7
Fibre Optic Component Mfr
S.I.C.: 3679
N.A.I.C.S.: 334419

Holm & Halby A/S (1)
Vallensbaekvej 35
2605 Brondby, Denmark
Tel.: (45) 4326 9400
Fax: (45) 43269410
E-Mail: info@holm-halby.dk
Web Site: www.holm-halby.dk
Emp.: 42
Laboratory Equipment Distr
S.I.C.: 5049
N.A.I.C.S.: 423490
Morten Dyrner *(Gen Mgr)*

Hydro Service A/S (1)
Glarmerstervej 18
6710 Esbjerg, Denmark
Tel.: (45) 7515 5855
Fax: (45) 7515 5093
Web Site: www.hydroservice.dk
Emp.: 7
Hydraulic Components & Pump Mfr
S.I.C.: 3561
N.A.I.C.S.: 333911

Immuno Diagnostic Oy (1)
Kaivokatu 16
13100 Hameenlinna, Finland
Tel.: (358) 3 615 370
Fax: (358) 3 682 2039
E-Mail: info@immunodiagnostic.fi
Web Site: www.immunodiagnostic.fi
Emp.: 10
Diagnostic & Research Services
S.I.C.: 8731
N.A.I.C.S.: 541711
Jarmo Laakkonen *(CEO & Mng Dir)*

Insatech A/S (1)
Algade 133
4760 Vordingborg, Denmark
Tel.: (45) 5537 2095
Fax: (45) 5537 7018
E-Mail: mail@insatech.com
Web Site: www.insatech.com
Emp.: 55
Industrial Component Distr
S.I.C.: 5084
N.A.I.C.S.: 423830
Alan Christoffersen *(Mng Dir)*

Kouvo Automation Oy (1)
Puhjontie 17
45720 Kuusankoski, Finland
Tel.: (358) 5 363 1655
Fax: (358) 5 363 1663
E-Mail: kouvo@kouvo.fi
Web Site: www.kouvo.fi
Emp.: 6
Measuring Equipment Distr
S.I.C.: 5084
N.A.I.C.S.: 423830
Kimmo Haemaelaeinen *(Mng Dir)*

Maxeta AS (1)
Amtmand Aallsgate 89
Postboks 177
3701 Skien, Norway
Tel.: (47) 35 91 40 00
Fax: (47) 35 91 40 10
E-Mail: maxeta@maxeta.no
Web Site: www.maxeta.no
Emp.: 55
Electrical Equipment Distr
S.I.C.: 5063
N.A.I.C.S.: 423610
Eivind Walstad *(Gen Mgr)*

Metric Industrial A/S (1)
Hassellunden 16
2765 Smorum, Denmark
Tel.: (45) 70 300 310
Fax: (45) 43 200 769
E-Mail: metric@metric.dk
Web Site: www.metric.dk
Emp.: 5
Testing & Measurement Services
S.I.C.: 8734
N.A.I.C.S.: 541380
Jens Bundgrrat *(Gen Mgr)*

Metric Industrial AS (1)
Bjornerudveien 17
1266 Oslo, Norway
Tel.: (47) 4000 4054
Fax: (47) 4000 4053
E-Mail: epost@metricindustrial.no
Web Site: www.metricindustrial.no
Industrial Automation Equipment Mfr
S.I.C.: 3559
N.A.I.C.S.: 333249
Per Myhrvold *(Gen Mgr)*

Metric Industrial Oy (1)
Piispantilankuja 4
PL 14
02241 Espoo, Finland
Tel.: (358) 9 4761 600
Fax: (358) 9 4761 6700
E-Mail: sales@metric.fi
Web Site: www.metric.fi
Emp.: 19
Testing & Measuring Equipment Distr
S.I.C.: 5084
N.A.I.C.S.: 423830
Pekka Jolanki *(Mng Dir)*

Movetec Oy (1)
Hannuksentie 1
02270 Espoo, Finland
Tel.: (358) 9 525 9230
Fax: (358) 9 5259 2333
E-Mail: info@movetec.fi
Web Site: www.movetec.fi
Emp.: 35
Industrial Equipment Whslr
S.I.C.: 5084
N.A.I.C.S.: 423830
Pekka Jokinen *(Product Mgr)*

Nordic Battery AS (1)
Bjornerud Veien 17
1266 Oslo, Norway
Tel.: (47) 22 76 38 80
Fax: (47) 22 61 91 95
E-Mail: post@nordicbattery.com
Web Site: www.nordicbattery.no
Battery Mfr
S.I.C.: 3691
N.A.I.C.S.: 335911

PLD Finland Oy (1)
Hannuksentie 1
Espoo, Finland
Tel.: (358) 207 410 270
Fax: (358) 207 410 277
E-Mail: sales@pld.fi
Web Site: www.pld.fi
Emp.: 7
Analytical Laboratory Instrument Mfr
S.I.C.: 3826
N.A.I.C.S.: 334516

Triolab A/S (1)
Vallensbaekvej 35
2605 Brondby, Denmark
Tel.: (45) 43 96 00 12
Fax: (45) 43 96 43 12
E-Mail: triolab@triolab.dk
Web Site: www.triolab.dk
Emp.: 18
Diagnostic Equipment Mfr
S.I.C.: 3845
N.A.I.C.S.: 334510
Finn Ulbaek Andersen *(Gen Mgr)*

Vactek A/S (1)
Tinvej 20A
3060 Espergaerde, Denmark
Tel.: (45) 4824 4433
Fax: (45) 4824 4437
E-Mail: info@vactek.dk
Web Site: www.vactek.dk
Emp.: 4
Electronic Component Distr
S.I.C.: 5065
N.A.I.C.S.: 423690
Rainer Joachim Wagner *(Gen Mgr)*

ADDVALUE TECHNOLOGIES LTD.

28 Tai Seng Street 06-02
Singapore, 534106, Singapore
Tel.: (65) 65095700
Fax: (65) 65095701
E-Mail: sales@addvalue.com.sg
Web Site: www.addvaluetech.com
Year Founded: 1994
A31—(SES)
Rev.: $10,170,852
Assets: $25,332,697
Liabilities: $6,547,706
Net Worth: $18,784,991
Earnings: ($87,362)
Fiscal Year-end: 03/31/13

Business Description:
Wireless & Broadband Communication Solutions
S.I.C.: 4812
N.A.I.C.S.: 517210

Personnel:
Colin Kum Lok Chan *(Co-Founder, Chm & CEO)*
Khai Pang Tan *(Co-Founder, COO & CTO)*
Juay Hwa Tan *(Co-Founder)*
Soon Soo Foo *(Sec)*

Board of Directors:
Colin Kum Lok Chan
Eng Lim Ang
Michael Butler
Han Boon Lim
Juay Hwa Tan
Khai Pang Tan

Subsidiaries:

Addvalue Innovation Pte Ltd (1)
28 Tai Seng Street 06-02
Singapore, 534106, Singapore
Tel.: (65) 95700
Fax: (65) 95701
Telecommunications Services
S.I.C.: 4899
N.A.I.C.S.: 517919

ADECCO S.A.

Sagereistrasse 10
CH-8152 Glattbrugg, Switzerland
Tel.: (41) 448788888
Fax: (41) 44 829 8888
E-Mail: investor.relations@adecco.com
Web Site: www.adecco.com
Year Founded: 1957
ADEN—(SWX)
Rev.: $27,644,947,120
Assets: $12,942,078,380
Liabilities: $7,962,595,550
Net Worth: $4,979,482,830
Earnings: $508,852,260
Emp.: 32,000
Fiscal Year-end: 12/31/12

Business Description:
Holding Company; Human Resource & Business Consulting Services
S.I.C.: 6719

Adecco S.A.—(Continued)

N.A.I.C.S.: 551112

Personnel:

Rolf Dorig *(Chm)*
Andreas Jacobs *(Vice Chm)*
Patrick G. De Maeseneire *(CEO)*
Dominik de Daniel *(CFO)*
Sergio Picarelli *(Chief Sls Officer)*
Christian Vasino *(Chief HR Officer)*
Hans R. Brutsch *(Sec)*

Board of Directors:

Rolf Dorig
Dominique-Jean Chertier
Alexander Gut
Andreas Jacobs
Didier Lamouche
Thomas Charles O'Neill
David Prince
Wanda Rapaczynski

Subsidiaries:

Adecco Management & Consulting S.A. **(1)**
Sagereistrasse 10
CH-8152 Glattbrugg, Switzerland CH
Tel.: (41) 44 878 8888
Fax: (41) 44 829 8888
Web Site: www.adecco.ch
Workforce Management & Human Resource Consulting Services
S.I.C.: 8999
N.A.I.C.S.: 541612
Stephan Howeg *(Head-Grp Comm)*

Adecco Ressources Humaines S.A. **(1)**
Rue des Fontenailles 16
1002 Lausanne, Switzerland CH
Tel.: (41) 213419292 (100%)
Fax: (41) 213419212
E-Mail: info@adecco.ch
Web Site: www.adecco.ch
Emp.: 140
Staffing & Recruiting Services
S.I.C.: 7363
N.A.I.C.S.: 561330
Stephan Howeg *(Mgr-Mktg)*

U.S. Subsidiary:

Adecco USA, Inc. **(1)**
175 Broadhollow Rd
Melville, NY 11747-4902 DE
Tel.: (631) 844-7800
Fax: (631) 844-7577
Toll Free: (800) 836-7723
E-Mail: usadecco.mail@adecci.com
Web Site: www.adeccousa.com
Emp.: 600
Temporary Personnel & Healthcare Services
S.I.C.: 7363
N.A.I.C.S.: 561320
Joyce Russell *(Pres & Exec VP)*
Brane Acamann *(CIO)*
Ed Blust *(CMO-Mktg, Comm & PR)*
Rebecca Rogers Tijerino *(Chief Sls Officer)*
Joe Sabia *(Sr VP)*
Andrea Sugden *(Sr VP-Southern Div)*
Kristy Willis *(Sr VP-Southwest Div)*

Branches:

Adecco Puerto Rico **(2)**
A6 Calle Marginal Urb San Salvador
Manati, PR 00674
Tel.: (787) 854-4264
Fax: (787) 854-3410
Web Site: www.adeccopr.com
Emp.: 120
Employment Services
S.I.C.: 7361
N.A.I.C.S.: 561311

Subsidiaries:

Ajilon North America, LLC **(2)**
175 Broad Hollow Rd
Melville, NY 11747 DE
Tel.: (631) 844-7800 (100%)
Fax: (410) 321-7918
Toll Free: (800) 320-2342
E-Mail: info@ajilon.com
Web Site: www.ajilonconsulting.com
Sales Range: $400-449.9 Million
Emp.: 4,000
Business Information Technology Services
S.I.C.: 7373
N.A.I.C.S.: 541512
Carl Deal *(Sr VP)*
Robert Knight *(Sr VP-Natl Sls)*
Thomas McKenty *(Sr VP-North East)*
Walt Strausbaugh *(Sr VP-Field Ops)*
Marty Sylvester *(Sr VP)*

Subsidiaries:

Ajilon Professional Staffing LLC **(3)**
Pk 80 W Plz 2 Fl 9
Saddle Brook, NJ 07663 (100%)
Tel.: (201) 843-0006
Fax: (201) 712-1033
Web Site: www.ajilon.com
Emp.: 300
Accounting Firm
S.I.C.: 7361
N.A.I.C.S.: 561311
Joe Fink *(Mng Dir)*
Kathy Gans *(Sr VP-Sls-Ops-South Central Reg)*

Non-U.S. Subsidiaries:

Jonathan Wren Australia Pty. Ltd. **(3)**
Level 2
68 Pitt St, Sydney, NSW, 2000, Australia AU
Tel.: (61) 28031 6202 (100%)
Fax: (61) 29232 1963
E-Mail: sydney@jwren.com.au
Web Site: www.jwren.com.au
Emp.: 30
Temporary Employee Recruitment Services
S.I.C.: 7363
N.A.I.C.S.: 561330

TAD **(3)**
Level 12 37 St Georges Terr
Perth, WA, 6000, Australia AU
Tel.: (61) 894614610 (100%)
Fax: (61) 894614633
E-Mail: perth@tad.com.au
Web Site: www.tad.com.au
Emp.: 20
Engineering & Technical Employment Services
S.I.C.: 7363
N.A.I.C.S.: 561330
Eatric Kelly *(Mng Dir)*

Corelink Staffing Services Inc. **(2)**
36 Discovery
Irvine, CA 92618
Tel.: (949) 250-6565
Fax: (949) 450-0711
Web Site: www.corelinkstaffing.com
Sls.: $13,000,000
Emp.: 5
Temporary Staffing Services
S.I.C.: 7363
N.A.I.C.S.: 561320
Sy Hasan *(Branch Mgr)*

Lee Hecht Harrison, Inc. **(2)**
50 Tice Blvd
Woodcliff Lake, NJ 07677-7654 NY
Tel.: (201) 930-9333 (100%)
Fax: (201) 307-0878
Toll Free: (800) 611-4544
Web Site: www.lhh.com
Emp.: 85
Management Consulting & Outplacement Services
S.I.C.: 8742
N.A.I.C.S.: 541611
Peter Alcide *(Pres & COO)*
Keith Emerson *(Mng Dir)*
Nick Goldberg *(Mng Dir)*
Andrea Huff *(Exec VP & Chief Learning Officer)*
Diane Kozlak *(Sr VP & Gen Mgr-Bloomington)*

Branches:

Lee Hecht Harrison **(3)**
500 W Monroe St Ste 3200
Chicago, IL 60661
Tel.: (312) 377-2300
Fax: (312) 930-9035
E-Mail:
Emp.: 40
Employment Agencies
S.I.C.: 5947
N.A.I.C.S.: 453220
Linda Guza *(Office Mgr)*

Lee Hecht Harrison **(3)**
1122 Kenilworth Dr Ste 310
Baltimore, MD 21204-2139
Tel.: (410) 494-0960
Fax: (410) 828-1929
E-Mail:
Emp.: 3
Human Resource Consulting Services
S.I.C.: 8999
N.A.I.C.S.: 541612

Lee Hecht Harrison **(3)**
7676 Woodway Dr Ste 325
Houston, TX 77063
Tel.: (713) 952-2000
Fax: (713) 861-5680
Emp.: 300
Human Resources Consulting Services
S.I.C.: 8748
N.A.I.C.S.: 541618

Subsidiaries:

Lee Hecht Harrison, LLC **(3)**
200 Park Ave 26th Fl
New York, NY 10166
Tel.: (212) 557-0009
Fax: (212) 557-9807
E-Mail:
Web Site: www.lhh.com
Sales Range: $100-124.9 Million
Human Resource Services
S.I.C.: 8999
N.A.I.C.S.: 541612
Karen O'Boyle *(Exec VP-Sls-Global)*
Charlotte A. Lee *(Sr VP)*

Affiliate:

Messenger Associates, Inc. **(4)**
4719 Limberlost Ln
Manlius, NY 13104 NY
Tel.: (607) 772-8607
Fax: (607) 797-9424
Web Site: www.amgr.com
Emp.: 15
Management Consulting Services
S.I.C.: 8742
N.A.I.C.S.: 541611
Anne L. Messenger *(Pres)*
Francis J. O'Connor *(Exec VP)*

Unit:

The Center for Executive Options **(4)**
200 Park Ave
New York, NY 10166
Tel.: (212) 299-3333
Fax: (212) 299-3334
Web Site: www.ceo-home.com
Emp.: 6
Executive Placement
S.I.C.: 8999
N.A.I.C.S.: 541612

MasteryWorks, Inc. **(3)**
The Renaissance 2230 George C Marshall Dr Ste 122
Falls Church, VA 22043
Tel.: (703) 256-5712
Fax: (703) 256-9564
Toll Free: (800) 229-5712
Web Site: www.masteryworks.com
Emp.: 10
Staffing & Career Management Services
S.I.C.: 7361
N.A.I.C.S.: 561311
Caela Farren *(CEO)*
Tom Karl *(Exec VP)*

Non-U.S. Branches:

Lee Hecht Harrison **(3)**
888 3rd St SW
Calgary, AB, T2P 5C5, Canada AB
Tel.: (403) 269-7828
Fax: (403) 265-2412
Web Site: www.lhh-canada.ca/default.aspx
Emp.: 8
Management Consulting Services & Outplacement Agency
S.I.C.: 8999
N.A.I.C.S.: 541611
Terry Lende *(Office Mgr)*

Lee Hecht Harrison **(3)**
77 City Centre Dr Ste 401 East Tower
Mississauga, ON, L5B 1M5, Canada ON
Tel.: (905) 277-4700 (100%)
Fax: (905) 277-4747
Web Site: www.lhh-canada.ca/default.aspx
Emp.: 15
Management Consulting Services
S.I.C.: 8742
N.A.I.C.S.: 541611

Non-U.S. Subsidiaries:

Lee Hecht Harrison AG **(3)**
Stampfenbachstrasse 138
CH 8006 Zurich, Switzerland (100%)
Tel.: (41) 443859955
Fax: (41) 0582336019
E-Mail: zurich@lhh.ch
Web Site: www.lhh.ch
Emp.: 20
Management Consulting & Outplacement Services
S.I.C.: 7363
N.A.I.C.S.: 561330
Pascal Scheiwiller *(Mng Dir)*

MPS Group, Inc. **(2)**
10151 Deerwood Park Blvd Bldg 200 Ste 400
Jacksonville, FL 32256 FL
Tel.: (904) 360-2000 (100%)
Fax: (904) 360-2972
Sales Range: $1-4.9 Billion
Emp.: 3,500
Professional Staffing Services
S.I.C.: 7363
N.A.I.C.S.: 561330
Theron I. Gilliam, Jr. *(CEO)*
Stephen Nolan *(CFO)*
Gregory D. Holland *(Chief Legal Officer, Sec & Sr VP)*

Divisions:

Accounting Principals Inc. **(3)**
10201 Centurion Pkwy N Ste 400
Jacksonville, FL 32256 FL
Tel.: (904) 360-2400 (100%)
Fax: (904) 360-2000
Toll Free: (800) 981-3849
E-Mail: jacksonville@accountingprincipals.com
Web Site: www.accountingprincipals.com
Financial Staffing Service
S.I.C.: 7361
N.A.I.C.S.: 561311
John Marshall *(Pres)*

Branch:

Accounting Principals Inc.-Atlanta **(4)**
3455 Peachtree Rd NE Ste 110
Atlanta, GA 30326 GA
Tel.: (770) 671-9647
Fax: (770) 671-1341
E-Mail: atlanta@accountingprincipals.com
Web Site: www.accountingprincipals.com
Sales Range: $1-9.9 Million
Emp.: 10
Labor Resource Services Supplier
S.I.C.: 7363
N.A.I.C.S.: 561320
John P. Marshall, III *(Pres)*

Unit:

Parker & Lynch **(4)**
700 N Pearl St Ste 950
Dallas, TX 75201-2838
Tel.: (972) 385-1002
Fax: (972) 385-1564
Toll Free: (800) 981-3849
E-Mail: downtowndallas@parkerlynch.com
Web Site: www.parkerlynch.com
Sales Range: $10-24.9 Million
Emp.: 15
Accounting & Financial Executive Recruitment & Staffing
S.I.C.: 7361
N.A.I.C.S.: 561311
Bob Crouch *(Pres)*

Beeline **(3)**
14911 Quorum Dr Ste 120
Dallas, TX 75254 TX
Tel.: (972) 813-0465
E-Mail: Support@Beeline.com
Web Site: www.beeline.com

Sales Range: $10-24.9 Million
Emp.: 6
Training Tech Writing Courseware Development
S.I.C.: 7371
N.A.I.C.S.: 541511

Subsidiaries:

Beeline.com, Inc. (3)
12724 Gran Bay Pkwy W Ste 200
Jacksonville, FL 32258 FL
Tel.: (904) 527-5700 (100%)
Fax: (904) 527-5827
Toll Free: (866) BEELINE
E-Mail: Support@Beeline.com
Web Site: www.beeline.com
Sales Range: $25-49.9 Million
Emp.: 170
Recruitment & Management of Permanent, Contract, & Service Labor
S.I.C.: 7361
N.A.I.C.S.: 561311

Subsidiary:

Employer Services Corporation (4)
20 Pineview Dr
Amherst, NY 14228 NY
Tel.: (716) 691-4455 (100%)
Fax: (716) 691-4234
E-Mail: info@myesc.com
Web Site: www.myesc.com
Sales Range: $25-49.9 Million
Emp.: 40
Recruitment Process Outsourcing Services
S.I.C.: 7363
N.A.I.C.S.: 561330
John D. Hawkins *(Pres)*
Joseph Kreuz *(CEO & Mng Partner)*

Entegee Inc. (3)
70 Blanchard Rd
Burlington, MA 01803 MA
Tel.: (781) 221-5800
Fax: (781) 221-4541
Toll Free: (800) 368-3433
Web Site: www.entegee.com
Sales Range: $10-24.9 Million
Emp.: 50
Engineering & Technical Employee Recruitment
S.I.C.: 7361
N.A.I.C.S.: 561311
Robert L. Cecchini *(Pres)*

Modis, Inc. (3)
10151 Deerwood Park Blvd Bldg 200 Ste 400
Jacksonville, FL 32256 FL
Tel.: (904) 360-2000
Fax: (904) 360-2110
Toll Free: (877) Modis-IT
E-Mail: info@modis.com
Web Site: www.modis.com
Information Technology Staffing Services & Project Managment
S.I.C.: 7361
N.A.I.C.S.: 561311
John P. Cullen *(Pres)*

Branch:

Modis, Inc.-National Enterprise Practice (4)
400 Southpointe Blvd
Canonsburg, PA 15317-8549 FL
Tel.: (724) 745-4900
Fax: (724) 745-5960
Web Site: www.modisit.com
Sales Range: $10-24.9 Million
Emp.: 17
Computer Related Consulting Services
S.I.C.: 7373
N.A.I.C.S.: 541512

Non-U.S. Subsidiaries:

Modis Canada Inc. (4)
10 Bay Street 7th Floor
Toronto, ON, M5J 2R8, Canada
Tel.: (416) 367-2020
Fax: (416) 366-2001
Toll Free: (800) 842-5907
E-Mail: toronto@modis.com
Web Site: www.modiscanada.com
Emp.: 150
Information Technology Staffing Services
S.I.C.: 7361
N.A.I.C.S.: 561311
Jack Cullen *(Pres)*

Modis International Co. (4)
10 Bay St 7 Fl
Toronto, ON, M5J 2M2, Canada
Tel.: (416) 492-5656
Fax: (416) 366-2001
E-Mail: toronto@modis.com
Web Site: www.modis.com
Sales Range: $10-24.9 Million
Emp.: 20
Management Consulting Services
S.I.C.: 8742
N.A.I.C.S.: 541611
David Colella *(Mng Dir)*

Modis International Limited (4)
33 Queen Street
London, EC4R 1BR, United Kingdom UK
Tel.: (44) 2070386400
Fax: (44) 2070386401
E-Mail: info@modisintl.com
Web Site: www.modisintl.com
Sales Range: $75-99.9 Million
Payroll Contracting Solutions
S.I.C.: 8721
N.A.I.C.S.: 541214
Roy Dunjworth *(Gen Mgr)*

Subsidiary:

Modis London (5)
33 Queen St
London, EC4R 1BR, United Kingdom UK
Tel.: (44) 2070386400
Fax: (44) 2070386401
E-Mail: london@modisintl.com
Web Site: www.modisintl.com
Sales Range: $10-24.9 Million
Emp.: 25
Information Technology Staffing Solutions
S.I.C.: 7361
N.A.I.C.S.: 561311

Non-U.S. Subsidiaries:

Modis Europe Nederland B.V. (5)
Beukenlaan 125
PO Box 155
5611 ZB Eindhoven, Netherlands NL
Tel.: (31) 407999010
Fax: (31) 407999011
E-Mail: mid.office@ajilon.nl
Web Site: www.ajilon.nl
Sales Range: $10-24.9 Million
Emp.: 20
Information Technology Staffing Services & Project Managment
S.I.C.: 7361
N.A.I.C.S.: 561311
Chris Wright *(Acct Mgr)*

Branch:

Modis Amsterdam (6)
Kabelweg 37
Amsterdam, 1014 BA, Netherlands NL
Tel.: (31) 205914175
Fax: (31) 205914176
E-Mail: amsterdam@modisintl.com
Web Site: www.modisnederland.nl
Sales Range: $100-124.9 Million
Emp.: 13
Information Technology Staffing Solutions
S.I.C.: 7361
N.A.I.C.S.: 561311
Steven Beekhuis *(Gen Mgr)*

Modis International-Brussels (5)
9-13 Rue D'Idalie
Brussels, B 1050, Belgium BE
Tel.: (32) 27916550
Fax: (32) 27916551
E-Mail: brussels@modisintl.com
Web Site: www.modisintl.com
Sales Range: $100-124.9 Million
Information Technology Staffing
S.I.C.: 7361
N.A.I.C.S.: 561311

Modis Polska Sp.z.o.o (5)
Buma Business Center ul Wadowicka 6
Krakow, 30-415, Poland PL
Tel.: (48) 122923905
Fax: (48) 122923901
E-Mail: krakow@modisintl.com
Web Site: www.modisintl.com
Sales Range: $100-124.9 Million
Emp.: 15
Staffing Solutions
S.I.C.: 7361
N.A.I.C.S.: 561311
Bartosz Toporkiewicz *(Gen Mgr)*

Personality IT People Power GmbH (5)
Theodor-Heuss Strasse 14
Stuttgart, 70174, Germany De
Tel.: (49) 7113516630
E-Mail: info@personality-it.de
Web Site: www.personality-it.de
Sales Range: $100-124.9 Million
Information Technology Staffing Solutions
S.I.C.: 7361
N.A.I.C.S.: 561311

Paladin Companies Inc. (3)
10 S LaSalle Dr
Chicago, IL 60603 FL
Tel.: (312) 654-2600 (100%)
Fax: (312) 654-2608
Toll Free: (888) PALADIN
E-Mail: central@paladinstaff.com
Web Site: www.paladinstaff.com
Sales Range: $25-49.9 Million
Emp.: 15
Marketing, Creative & Communications Staff Recruitment
S.I.C.: 7361
N.A.I.C.S.: 561311
Jadey Ryndak *(Reg Mgr)*

Special Counsel Inc. (3)
1 Independent Dr
Jacksonville, FL 32202 MD
Tel.: (904) 360-2340 (100%)
Toll Free: (800) 737-3436
E-Mail: info@specialcounsel.com
Web Site: www.specialcounsel.com
Sales Range: $75-99.9 Million
Emp.: 100
Legal Staffing Placement & Recruiting Service
S.I.C.: 7361
N.A.I.C.S.: 561311
David Maldonado *(Gen Counsel & Sr VP)*

Branches:

Special Counsel Inc.-Brentwood (4)
10 Cadillac Dr Ste 340
Brentwood, TN 37027 FL
Tel.: (615) 320-7700
Fax: (615) 373-1851
E-Mail: nashville@specialcounsel.com
Web Site: www.specialcounsel.com
Sales Range: $1-9.9 Million
Emp.: 8
Employment Agencies
S.I.C.: 7361
N.A.I.C.S.: 561311
Tara Boosey *(Exec Dir)*

Special Counsel Inc. (4)
20 S Charles St Ste 406
Baltimore, MD 21201-3797
Tel.: (410) 385-5350
Fax: (410) 385-5352
E-Mail: baltimore@specialcounsel.com
Web Site: www.specialcounsel.com
Sales Range: $1-9.9 Million
Emp.: 5
Temporary Help Service
S.I.C.: 7363
N.A.I.C.S.: 561330
Christopher Poverman *(Exec Dir)*

Special Counsel Inc. (4)
60 E 42nd St Ste 1730
New York, NY 10165-6223
Tel.: (212) 218-7155
Fax: (212) 218-7170
Web Site: www.specialcounsel.com
Sales Range: $1-9.9 Million
Emp.: 10
Temporary Help Service
S.I.C.: 7363
N.A.I.C.S.: 561330

Non-U.S. Holding:

Adecco Employment Services Limited (2)
10 Bay St 7th Fl
Toronto, ON, M5J 2R8, Canada (100%)
Tel.: (416) 364-2020
Fax: (416) 366-8035
Toll Free: (866) 646-3322
E-Mail: sandra.hokansson@adecco.ca
Web Site: www.adecco.ca
Emp.: 35
Employment Agency
S.I.C.: 7361
N.A.I.C.S.: 561311
Sandra Hokansson *(Pres & Country Mgr)*

Non-U.S. Subsidiaries:

Adecco spol. s r.o. (1)
Avenir Business Park
Radlicka 113a 714, 15800 Prague, Czech Republic (100%)
Tel.: (420) 251001404
Fax: (420) 251001400
E-Mail: adecco@adecco.cz
Web Site: www.adecco.cz
Emp.: 24
Temporary & Permanent Personnel, Accountancy Services, Employment Agencies, Executive Search, Personnel Management & Outplacement Services
S.I.C.: 7363
N.A.I.C.S.: 561330
Francisco Ugliano *(Dir-Fin)*

Adecco Argentina S.A. (1)
Carlos Pellegrini 855
C1009ABQ Buenos Aires, Argentina
Tel.: (54) 11 4131 9900
Web Site: www.adecco.com.ar
Human Resource Consulting Services
S.I.C.: 8999
N.A.I.C.S.: 541612
Patricio Dewel *(Dir-Comml)*

Adecco Australia Pty Ltd. (1)
Level 16 28 Freshwater Place
Southbank, Melbourne, 3006, Australia AU
Tel.: (61) 399542100 (100%)
Fax: (61) 1300780700
Web Site: www.adecco.com.au
Emp.: 150
Employee Recruiting Services
S.I.C.: 7363
N.A.I.C.S.: 561330

Subsidiary:

Icon Recruitment Pty. Ltd. (2)
165 Green Sall
Adelaide, VIC, 5000, Australia AU
Tel.: (61) 883068282 (100%)
Fax: (61) 882328466
E-Mail: iconrecic@iconrec.com.au
Web Site: www.iconrec.com.au
Emp.: 30
Temporary Employee Recruitment Services
S.I.C.: 7363
N.A.I.C.S.: 561330
S. Leesy Gardener *(Mgr)*

Non-U.S. Subsidiaries:

Icon Recruitment Limited (3)
Qantas House Level 8 191 Queen St
Auckland, New Zealand (100%)
Tel.: (64) 93773848
Fax: (64) 93094197
Emp.: 8
Temporary Employment Services
S.I.C.: 7363
N.A.I.C.S.: 561330
Amanda Allen *(Branch Mgr)*

Icon Recruitment Ltd. (3)
Mezzanine 330 Lambton Quay
6011 Wellington, New Zealand (100%)
Tel.: (64) 44721566
Fax: (64) 44990350
Emp.: 12
Employee Recruiter Services
S.I.C.: 7363
N.A.I.C.S.: 561330
Amanda Allan *(Gen Mgr)*

Non-U.S. Subsidiary:

Adecco Personnel Limited (2)
Level 8 Quantas House
191 Queen St, Auckland, 1007, New Zealand NZ
Tel.: (64) 3097572 (100%)
Fax: (64) 3094197
E-Mail: enquiries@adecco.co.nz
Web Site: www.adecco.co.nz
Emp.: 25
Temporary & Permanent Personnel, Accountancy Services, Employment Agencies, Executive Search, Personnel Management & Outplacement Services

Adecco S.A.—(Continued)

S.I.C.: 7363
N.A.I.C.S.: 561330
Emilie Charlotte Grillo *(Dir-New Zealand)*

Adecco Beteiligungs GmbH (1)
Niederkasseler Lohweg 18
40547 Dusseldorf, Germany
Tel.: (49) 211301400
Fax: (49) 21130140100
Employment Consulting Services
S.I.C.: 8999
N.A.I.C.S.: 541612

Adecco Caledonie SARL (1)
19 Quai St Gules Serry BT 807
98845 Noumea, Cedex, New Caledonia (100%)
Tel.: (687) 249294
Fax: (687) 249295
E-Mail: adecco@adecco.nc
Web Site: www.adecco.nc
Emp.: 30
Temporary Employment Recruitment Services
S.I.C.: 7363
N.A.I.C.S.: 561330
Danielle Brault *(Country Mgr & Dir-Subsidiaries)*

Adecco-Colombia (1)
Calle 70A No 9-46
Bogota, Colombia Co (70%)
Tel.: (57) 1 347 5766
Fax: (57) 1 544 7599
Web Site: www.adecco.com.co/htm/oficinas.htm
Temporary & Permanent Personnel, Accountancy Services, Employment Agencies, Executive Search, Personnel Management & Outplacement Services
S.I.C.: 7363
N.A.I.C.S.: 561320

Adecco Coordination Center NV (1)
Noordkustlaan 16B
1702 Groot-Bijgaarden, Belgium
Tel.: (32) 2 5839111
Fax: (32) 2 5839112
E-Mail: info@adecco.be
Web Site: www.adecco.be
Business Management Consulting Services
S.I.C.: 8742
N.A.I.C.S.: 541611
Geert van Droogenbroeck *(Mgr-Mktg)*

Adecco Denmark A/S (1)
Falkoner Alle 1
2000 Frederiksberg, Denmark DK (100%)
Tel.: (45) 38889400
Fax: (45) 38889401
E-Mail: adecco@adecco.dk
Web Site: www.adecco.dk
Emp.: 70
Temporary & Permanent Personnel, Accountancy Services, Employment Agencies, Executive Search, Personnel Management & Outplacement Services
S.I.C.: 7363
N.A.I.C.S.: 561330
Torben Sneve *(Gen Mgr)*

Adecco Detachering BV (1)
Hogeweg 123
5301 LL Zaltbommel, Netherlands
Tel.: (31) 418 784 000
Fax: (31) 418 784 111
E-Mail: info@adecco.nl
Emp.: 150
Human Resource Consulting Services
S.I.C.: 8999
N.A.I.C.S.: 541612
Patrick Bekker *(Gen Mgr)*

Adecco do Brasil Ltda. (1)
Alameda Joaquim Eugenio de Lima 696 12 andar
01403-000 Sao Paulo, SP, Brazil
Tel.: (55) 31780400
Web Site: www.adecco.com.br
Temporary & Permanent Personnel, Accountancy Services, Employment Agencies, Executive Search, Personnel Management & Outplacement Services
S.I.C.: 7363
N.A.I.C.S.: 561330

Adecco Finland Oy (1)
Opastinsilta 8 B 4th Fl
00520 Helsinki, Finland FI (100%)
Tel.: (358) 467102500
Fax: (358) 467102535
E-Mail: adecco@adecco.fi
Web Site: www.adecco.fi
Emp.: 125
Temporary Staffing, Recruitment Services, Outsourcing, Data Entry Services
S.I.C.: 7363
N.A.I.C.S.: 561330
Aki Miikkulainen *(Acting Country Mgr)*

Adecco France SASU (1)
4 rue Louis Guerin
69100 Villeurbanne, France
Tel.: (33) 4 72 82 58 58
Fax: (33) 4 72 82 58 60
Web Site: www.adecco.fr
Recruitment Services
S.I.C.: 7361
N.A.I.C.S.: 561311
FrancoisFrancois Davy *(Pres)*

Adecco GmbH (1)
Mariahilferstrasse 123/6 Stock
1060 Vienna, Austria AT (100%)
Tel.: (43) 5 9911 20000
Fax: (43) 5 9911 5 20000
E-Mail: office@adecco.at
Web Site: www.adecco.at
Emp.: 40
Temporary Staffing, Recruitment Services, Outsourcing, Data Entry Services
S.I.C.: 7363
N.A.I.C.S.: 561330
Mario Trusgnach *(Mng Dir)*

Adecco Groupe France (1)
4 Rue Louis Guerin
69626 Villeurbanne, Cedex, France FR (100%)
Tel.: (33) 472825858
Fax: (33) 472825860
Web Site: www.adecco.fr
Emp.: 4,000
Temporary Staffing, Recruitment Services, Outsourcing, Data Entry Services
S.I.C.: 7363
N.A.I.C.S.: 561330
Francois Davy *(Pres)*

Subsidiary:

Adia France (2)
7 Rue Louis Guerin
PO Box 2133
69626 Villeurbanne, Cedex, France (100%)
Tel.: (33) 472822828
Fax: (33) 472822829
E-Mail: info@adia.fr
Web Site: www.adia.fr
Emp.: 140
Temporary & Permanent Personnel, Accountancy Services, Employment Agencies, Executive Search, Personnel Management & Outplacement Services
S.I.C.: 7363
N.A.I.C.S.: 561330

Subsidiary:

Movadis SA (3)
57-59 Boulevard Malesherbes
BP 40213
75364 Paris, France
Tel.: (33) 177691310
Fax: (33) 181973071
Web Site: www.movadis.fr
Temporary & Permanent Personnel, Accountancy Services, Employment Agencies, Executive Search, Personnel Management & Outplacement Services
S.I.C.: 7363
N.A.I.C.S.: 561330

Adecco Hizmet Ve Danisnanlik A/S (1)
Selvili Sk No 7 14 Levent
80620 Istanbul, Turkey TR (100%)
Tel.: (90) 2122837750
Fax: (90) 2122837869
E-Mail: info@adecco.com.tr
Web Site: www.adecco.com.tr
Temporary Staffing, Recruitment Services, Outsourcing, Data Entry Services
S.I.C.: 7363
N.A.I.C.S.: 561330
Asiye Ozhelik *(Mng Dir-Sls)*

Adecco Holding France SASU (1)
69 Boulevard Bataille De Stalingrad, Villeurbanne, 69100, France
Tel.: (33) 1 77 69 13 25
Investment Management Services
S.I.C.: 6211
N.A.I.C.S.: 523999

Adecco Iberia SA (1)
C Orense 4 3a planta
28020 Madrid, Spain ES (100%)
Tel.: (34) 914325628
Fax: (34) 914364403
E-Mail: info@adecco.es
Web Site: www.adecco.es
Emp.: 200
Temporary Staffing, Recruitment Services, Outsourcing, Data Entry Services
S.I.C.: 7363
N.A.I.C.S.: 561330

Adecco India Private Limited (1)
No 2 Nal Wind Tunnel Road Murugeshpalya
Bengaluru, Karnataka, 560 017, India
Tel.: (91) 80 3989 7070
Fax: (91) 80 41119020
E-Mail: hrsolutions@adecco.co.in
Web Site: www.adecco.co.in
Emp.: 500
Human Resource Consulting Services
S.I.C.: 8999
N.A.I.C.S.: 541612
Sudhakar Balakrishnan *(CEO & Mng Dir)*

Adecco Industrial Pty Ltd (1)
L 16 28 Freshwater Pl
Southbank, VIC, 3006, Australia
Tel.: (61) 399542400
Emp.: 180
Human Resource Consulting Services
S.I.C.: 8999
N.A.I.C.S.: 541612

Adecco Israel Staffing Services Ltd. (1)
Nitsba Building 17 Yitzhak Sade
Tel Aviv, 67775, Israel IL (100%)
Tel.: (972) 35652007
Fax: (972) 35652008
E-Mail:
Web Site: www.adecco.co.il
Emp.: 80
Temporary & Permanent Personnel, Accountancy Services, Employment Agencies, Executive Search, Personnel Management & Outplacement Services
S.I.C.: 7363
N.A.I.C.S.: 561330
Einav Dalah *(Dir-Sls & Ops)*

Adecco Italy Spa (1)
Piazza Diaz 2
I 20123 Milan, Italy IT (100%)
Tel.: (39) 0288141
Fax: (39) 0288142800
Web Site: www.adecco.it
Temporary & Permanent Personnel, Accountancy Services, Employment Agencies, Executive Search, Personnel Management & Outplacement Services
S.I.C.: 7363
N.A.I.C.S.: 561330

Adecco Kft (1)
Vaci ut 45 Atrium Park Building G 7Emelet
1134 Budapest, Hungary HU (100%)
Tel.: (36) 1 323 3500
Fax: (36) 1 323 3529
E-Mail: adehuadeccodl@adecco.com
Web Site: www.adecco.hu
Emp.: 90
Temporary Staffing, Recruitment Services, Outsourcing, Data Entry Services
S.I.C.: 7363
N.A.I.C.S.: 561330

Adecco-Kuala Lumpur (1)
Suite 32 03 Level 32 Menara Citibank 165 Jalan Ampang
50450 Kuala Lumpur, Malaysia (100%)
Tel.: (60) 321625724
Fax: (60) 3 2162 5734
E-Mail: ampang@adecco-asia.com
Emp.: 100
Temporary & Permanent Personnel, Accountancy Services, Employment Agencies, Executive Search, Personnel Management & Outplacement Services
S.I.C.: 7363
N.A.I.C.S.: 561330
Alma Othman *(Gen Mgr)*

Adecco Ltd. (1)
Kowa Bldg No 45 1-15-9 Minami Aoyama
Tokyo, 107 0062, Japan JP (100%)
Tel.: (81) 334709300
Fax: (81) 64397594
E-Mail: info@adecco.co.jp
Web Site: www.adecco.co.jp
Emp.: 2,600
Temporary & Permanent Personnel, Accountancy Services, Employment Agencies, Executive Search, Personnel Management & Outplacement Services
S.I.C.: 7363
N.A.I.C.S.: 561330
Shinsuke Okumura *(Pres)*

Adecco Luxembourg S.A. (1)
26 Pl De La Gare
Luxembourg, 8070, Luxembourg LU (100%)
Tel.: (352) 4825511
Fax: (352) 406536
E-Mail: contact@adecco.lu
Web Site: www.adecco.lu
Emp.: 10
Temporary & Permanent Personnel, Accountancy Services, Employment Agencies, Executive Search, Personnel Management & Outplacement Services
S.I.C.: 7363
N.A.I.C.S.: 561330
Noel Dubois *(Mng Dir)*

Adecco Medical SASU (1)
26 Rue Bellecordiere
69002 Lyon, France
Tel.: (33) 4 72 56 08 88
Web Site: www.adeccomedical.fr
Emp.: 300
Medical Staffing Services
S.I.C.: 7363
N.A.I.C.S.: 561320
Jerick Develle *(Gen Mgr)*

Adecco Monaco SAM (1)
4 Rue Baron De Sainte Suzanne
Monaco, 98000, Monaco MC (100%)
Tel.: (377) 97975300
Fax: (377) 97975301
E-Mail: aurelie.martim@adecco.mc
Web Site: www.adecco.mc
Emp.: 10
Temporary & Permanent Personnel, Accountancy Services, Employment Agencies, Executive Search, Personnel Management & Outplacement Services
S.I.C.: 7363
N.A.I.C.S.: 561330
Cherry Manon *(Mgr-Fin)*

Adecco Morocco (1)
125 Blvd Zerktouni
20190 Casablanca, Morocco Ma (100%)
Tel.: (212) 522991023
Fax: (212) 522991026
E-Mail: adecco.emploi@adecco.co.ma
Web Site: www.adecco-maroc.com
Sales Range: $1-9.9 Million
Emp.: 50
Temporary & Permanent Personnel, Accountancy Services, Employment Agencies, Executive Search, Personnel Management & Outplacement Services
S.I.C.: 7361
N.A.I.C.S.: 561311
Jerick Develle *(CEO)*

Adecco Netherlands Beheer B.V. (1)
Hogeweg 123
NL 5301 LL Zaltbommel, Netherlands (100%)
Mailing Address:
PO Box 5
5300 AA Zaltbommel, Netherlands
Tel.: (31) 418784000
Fax: (31) 418784111
E-Mail: info@addeco.nl
Web Site: www.adecco.nl
Emp.: 150
Temporary & Permanent Personnel, Accountancy Services, Employment Agencies, Executive Search, Personnel Management & Outplacement Services
S.I.C.: 7363
N.A.I.C.S.: 561330
Patrick Bakkar *(Gen Mgr)*

Adecco Norge AS (1)
Rosenkrantzgate 16
0164 Oslo, Norway (100%)
Tel.: (47) 23290000
Fax: (47) 23290001
E-Mail: info@adecco.no
Web Site: www.adecco.no

Emp.: 200
Temporary & Permanent Personnel, Accountancy Services, Employment Agencies, Executive Search, Personnel Management & Outplacement Services
S.I.C.: 7363
N.A.I.C.S.: 561330
Anders Owre-Johnsen *(CEO)*

Adecco Personaldienstleistungen GmbH (1)
Niederkasseler Lohweg 18
40547 Dusseldorf, Germany
Tel.: (49) 211 30140 0
Fax: (49) 211 30140 100
E-Mail: info@adecco.de
Web Site: www.adecco.de
Professional Employment Services
S.I.C.: 7361
N.A.I.C.S.: 561311
Thomas Rinne *(CFO)*

Adecco Personeelsdiensten BV (1)
Venne 129
9671 ER Winschoten, Netherlands
Tel.: (31) 597 421522
Fax: (31) 597 415592
Emp.: 4
Recruitment Services
S.I.C.: 7361
N.A.I.C.S.: 561311

Adecco Personnel Consultants Co., Ltd. Taiwan (1)
Song Xinyi District
High Road 18th Floor No 11, Taipei, 110, Taiwan TW
Tel.: (886) 255526168 (100%)
Fax: (886) 255526161
E-Mail: adeccotw.taipei@adecco.com
Web Site: www.adecco.com.tw
Emp.: 10
Temporary & Permanent Personnel, Accountancy Services, Employment Agencies, Executive Search, Personnel Management & Outplacement Services
S.I.C.: 7363
N.A.I.C.S.: 561330

Adecco Personnel Pte. Ltd. (1)
3 Bishan Place
05-02 CPF Bishan Building, Singapore, 579838, Singapore SG
Tel.: (65) 67566686 (100%)
Fax: (65) 67564063
E-Mail: singapore@adecco-asia.com
Web Site: www.adecco-asia.com
Sales Range: $1-9.9 Million
Emp.: 200
Temporary & Permanent Personnel, Accountancy Services, Employment Agencies, Executive Search, Personnel Management & Outplacement Services
S.I.C.: 7363
N.A.I.C.S.: 561330

Adecco Personnel Services S.A. (1)
Noordkustlaan 16B
B 1702 Groot-Bijgaarden, Belgium (100%)
Tel.: (32) 25839111
Fax: (32) 25839112
E-Mail: info@adecco.be
Web Site: www.adecco.be
Emp.: 120
Temporary & Permanent Personnel, Accountancy Services, Employment Agencies, Executive Search, Personnel Management & Outplacement Services
S.I.C.: 7363
N.A.I.C.S.: 561330
Erwin Zan Iersel *(Mng Dir)*

Adecco Peru S.A. (1)
Amador Merino Reyna N 285 Piso 3
San Isidro, Lima, Peru PE
Tel.: (51) 6114444 (100%)
Fax: (51) 2227426
E-Mail: joseluis.revilla@adecco.com.pe
Web Site: www.adecco.com.pe
Emp.: 50
Temporary & Permanent Personnel, Accountancy Services, Employment Agencies, Executive Search, Personnel Management & Outplacement Services
S.I.C.: 7363
N.A.I.C.S.: 561330

Adecco Phaholyothin (1)
979/25 SM Tower 25th Floor Phaholyothin Road
Samsennai Phayathai, Bangkok, Thailand (100%)
Tel.: (66) 2298017080
Fax: (66) 26170911
E-Mail: phaholyothin@adecco-asia.com
Web Site: www.adecco.co.th/
Temporary & Permanent Personnel, Accountancy Services, Employment Agencies, Executive Search, Personnel Management & Outplacement Services
S.I.C.: 7363
N.A.I.C.S.: 561330
Suchata Chinnatha *(Gen Mgr)*

Adecco Poland Sp. z o.o. (1)
Al Jana Pawla II 19
20854 Warsaw, Poland PL
Tel.: (48) 223760900 (100%)
Fax: (48) 223760901
E-Mail: biuro.hq@adecco.com
Web Site: www.adecco.pl
Emp.: 55
S.I.C.: 7363
N.A.I.C.S.: 561330
Anna Wicha *(Gen Mgr)*

Adecco Rama IV Recruitment Ltd. (1)
990 Abdulrahim Place 10th Floor
Unit 1003 Rama IV Rd Silom, Bangkok, Bangrak, 10500, Thailand (100%)
Tel.: (66) 26361950
Fax: (66) 26361949
E-Mail: rama4@adecco-asia.com
Web Site: www.adecco.co.th/en/contact-adecco-office-location-map.html
Emp.: 19
Temporary & Recruitment Services
S.I.C.: 8999
N.A.I.C.S.: 541612
Mark Du Ree *(Regional Head-Asia & Japan)*

Adecco Recruitment Services (1)
Derby Downs Office Park Building 5 Level 3 Unit 5 & 6
Westville, 3629, South Africa (100%)
Tel.: (27) 312671433
Fax: (27) 312671451
Web Site: www.adecco.co.za
Emp.: 50
Temporary & Permanent Personnel, Accountancy Services, Employment Agencies, Executive Search, Personnel Management & Outplacement Services
S.I.C.: 7363
N.A.I.C.S.: 561330
Mark Smith *(Gen Mgr)*

Adecco Recursos Humanos S.A. (1)
Coronel Pereira 72 Fl 6 La Condes
Santiago, Chile CL
Tel.: (56) 25607200 (100%)
Fax: (56) 25607273
E-Mail: adeccochile@adecco.cl
Web Site: www.adecco.cl
Emp.: 3,000
Temporary & Permanent Personnel, Accountancy Services, Employment Agencies, Executive Search, Personnel Management & Outplacement Services
S.I.C.: 7363
N.A.I.C.S.: 561330

Adecco Recursos Humanos (1)
Avddjoao Lote 1 06 2 5 th Fl
1150-045 Lisbon, Portugal PT
Tel.: (351) 213168300 (100%)
Fax: (351) 211156849
Web Site: www.adecco.pt
Emp.: 100
Temporary & Permanent Personnel, Accountancy Services, Employment Agencies, Executive Search, Personnel Management & Outplacement Services
S.I.C.: 7363
N.A.I.C.S.: 561330

Adecco-Shanghai (1)
Room 1801 Hong Kong New World Tower
No 300 Middle Huai Hai Road, Shanghai, 200021, China CN
Tel.: (86) 2133119518 (100%)
Fax: (86) 2133119519
E-Mail: shanghai.cn@adecco.com
Web Site: china.adecco.com
Temporary & Permanent Personnel, Accountancy Services, Employment Agencies, Executive Search, Personnel Management & Outplacement Services
S.I.C.: 7363
N.A.I.C.S.: 561330

Adecco-Stockholm (1)
Kungsgatan 60
PO Box 1240
SE 111 82 Stockholm, Sweden SE
Tel.: (46) 859898400 (100%)
Fax: (46) 859898299
E-Mail:
Web Site: www.adecco.se
Emp.: 12
Temporary & Permanent Personnel, Accountancy Services, Employment Agencies, Executive Search, Personnel Management & Outplacement Services
S.I.C.: 7363
N.A.I.C.S.: 561330
Per-Aine Gulbrandsen *(Mng Dir)*

Adecco Sweden AB (1)
Kungsgatan 60
111 22 Stockholm, Sweden
Tel.: (46) 8 598 980 10
Fax: (46) 8 598 982 99
Web Site: www.adecco.se
Emp.: 150
Professional Employment Services
S.I.C.: 7361
N.A.I.C.S.: 561311
Perarne Guldbrandsen *(Branch Mgr)*

Adecco TT SA (1)
Goya 29
28001 Madrid, Spain
Tel.: (34) 914 32 56 70
Fax: (34) 914 32 57 02
Employment Consulting Services
S.I.C.: 8999
N.A.I.C.S.: 541612

Adecco UK Ltd. (1)
Hazlitt House 4 Bouverie Street
London, EC4Y 8AX, United Kingdom UK
Tel.: (44) 2073009000 (100%)
Fax: (44) 2083076700
E-Mail: info@adecco.co.uk
Web Site: www.adecco.co.uk
Emp.: 250
Job Recruitment & Training
S.I.C.: 7363
N.A.I.C.S.: 561330
Peter Searle *(CEO)*
Neil Martin *(CFO)*

Subsidiaries:

Roevin Limited (2)
4th Floor Clydesdale Bank House
33 Lower Regent Street, London, SW1Y 4NB, United Kingdom UK
Tel.: (44) 8456430486
Fax: (44) 8707598443
E-Mail: info@adecco.co.uk
Web Site: www.adecco.co.uk
Emp.: 400
Temporary & Permanent Personnel, Accountancy Services, Employment Agencies, Executive Search, Personnel Management & Outplacement Services
S.I.C.: 7363
N.A.I.C.S.: 561330

Subsidiary:

Roevin Management Services Ltd. (3)
57 Spring Gardens
Manchester, M2 2BY, United Kingdom UK
Tel.: (44) 8456430518 (100%)
Fax: (44) 8703305750
E-Mail: engineering@roevin.co.uk
Web Site: www.roevin.co.uk
Emp.: 60
Temporary & Permanent Personnel, Accountancy Services, Employment Agencies, Executive Search, Personnel Management & Outplacement Services
S.I.C.: 7363
N.A.I.C.S.: 561330
Mike Parker *(Gen Mgr)*

Non-U.S. Subsidiary:

Roevin Technical People Limited (3)
5770 Hurontario St Ste 300
Mississauga, ON, L5R 3G5, Canada (100%)
Tel.: (905) 826-4155
Fax: (905) 366-3913
E-Mail: resumes@roevin.ca
Web Site: www.roevin.ca
Emp.: 7
Temporary & Permanent Personnel, Accountancy Services, Employment Agencies, Executive Search, Personnel Management & Outplacement Services
S.I.C.: 7361
N.A.I.C.S.: 561311
Mark Matters *(VP)*

Spring Group Limited (2)
Hazlitt House 4 Bouverie Street
London, EC4Y 8AX, United Kingdom UK
Tel.: (44) 2073009000 (100%)
Fax: (44) 2073009090
E-Mail: corp@spring.com
Web Site: www.spring.com
Sales Range: $700-749.9 Million
Emp.: 150
Employment Placement Agency
S.I.C.: 7361
N.A.I.C.S.: 561311
Peter W. Searle *(CEO)*

Subsidiaries:

Hy-Phen.com Limited (3)
Hazlitt House
4 Bouverie Street, London, EC4Y 8AX, United Kingdom (100%)
Tel.: (44) 2073009000
Fax: (44) 2073009090
E-Mail: info@hyphen.com
Web Site: www.hyphen.com
Emp.: 100
Employment Placement Agencies
S.I.C.: 7361
N.A.I.C.S.: 561311
Neil Jones *(Mng Dir)*

Office Angels Limited (3)
2nd Floor 30-38 Hammersmith Broadway
London, W6 7AB, United Kingdom UK
Tel.: (44) 2087418080
Fax: (44) 2087419212
E-Mail: info@office-angels.com
Web Site: www.office-angels.com
Emp.: 6
Help Supply Services
S.I.C.: 7363
N.A.I.C.S.: 561320
Sarah Day *(Branch Mgr)*

Spring Personnel Limited (3)
Hazlitt House 4 Bouverie Street
London, EC4Y 8AX, United Kingdom UK
Tel.: (44) 2073009000 (100%)
Fax: (44) 2073009090
E-Mail: personnel_london@spring.com
Web Site: www.springpersonnel.com
Emp.: 300
Employment Placement Agencies
S.I.C.: 7361
N.A.I.C.S.: 561311
Steven Kirkpatrick *(CEO)*

Spring Technology Staffing Services Limited (3)
Hazlitt House 4 Bouverie Street
London, EC4Y 8AX, United Kingdom UK
Tel.: (44) 2073009000 (100%)
Web Site: www.spring-technology.co.uk
Emp.: 300
Employment Placement Agencies
S.I.C.: 7361
N.A.I.C.S.: 561311
Stephen Kirkpatrick *(Mng Dir)*

Non-U.S. Subsidiaries:

Adecco Ireland Ltd. (3)
45 Grafton Street
Dublin, 2, Ireland IE
Tel.: (353) 16717933 (100%)
Fax: (353) 16717934
E-Mail: alex.smolinski@adecco.co.uk
Temporary & Permanent Personnel, Accountancy Services, Employment Agencies, Executive Search, Personnel Management & Outplacement Services
S.I.C.: 7363
N.A.I.C.S.: 561330
Kate Macdermott *(Branch Mgr)*

Spring Group Australia Pty Limited (3)
Level 6 80 Mount Street
Sydney, NSW, 2060, Australia
Tel.: (61) 289050555

Adecco S.A.—(Continued)

Fax: (61) 289050900
Web Site: www.springfg.com
Temporary & Permanent Personnel, Accountancy Services, Employment Agencies, Executive Search, Personnel Management & Outplacement Services
S.I.C.: 7363
N.A.I.C.S.: 561330
Peter Mortimore *(Sr Mgr-Consultanting)*

Spring Professional Staffing (ASIA) Pte Ltd (3)
55 Market St
60 Robinson Rd, 068892 Singapore, Singapore
Tel.: (65) 65937950
Fax: (65) 65937951
E-Mail: enqiries@springasia.com
Web Site: www.springasia.com
Emp.: 50
Temporary & Permanent Personnel, Accountancy Services, Employment Agencies, Executive Search, Personnel Management & Outplacement Services
S.I.C.: 7361
N.A.I.C.S.: 561311
Serge Shine *(Mng Dir)*

Adecco Uruguay S.A. (1)
18 de Julio 2319
11200 Montevideo, Uruguay UY
Tel.: (598) 2 402 11 18 (100%)
E-Mail: comercial@adecco.com.uy
Web Site: www.adecco.com.uy
Sales Range: $1-9.9 Million
Temporary & Permanent Personnel, Accountancy Services, Employment Agencies, Executive Search, Personnel Management & Outplacement Services
S.I.C.: 7363
N.A.I.C.S.: 561330
Marcelo Frechero *(Mgmt Coord-HR)*

Adecco-Venezuela (1)
Avenida Francisco de Miranda Edif Cavendes
Floor 3 ofics 301-302
Los Palos Grandes, Caracas, Venezuela
Tel.: (58) 2122867016
Fax: (58) 212 286 91 55
Web Site: www.adecco.com.ve
Temporary & Permanent Personnel, Accountancy Services, Employment Agencies, Executive Search, Personnel Management & Outplacement Services
S.I.C.: 7363
N.A.I.C.S.: 561330

Adecco-Wanchai (1)
12/F Fortis Tower 77-79 Gloucester Road
Wanchai, China (Hong Kong) HK
Tel.: (852) 28952616 (100%)
Fax: (852) 28953571
E-Mail: hongkong@adecco.com
Web Site: www.adecco.com.hk
Emp.: 30
Temporary & Permanent Personnel, Accountancy Services, Employment Agencies, Executive Search, Personnel Management & Outplacement Services
S.I.C.: 7363
N.A.I.C.S.: 561330
Jennifer Eustace *(Branch Mgr)*

Subsidiary:

Templar International Consultants Limited (2)
12 Floor Fortis Tower
77-79 Gloucester Road, Wanchai, China (Hong Kong)
Tel.: (852) 29702722
Fax: (852) 28953571
E-Mail: hongkong@templarsearch.com
Web Site: www.templarsearch.com
Emp.: 100
Temporary & Permanent Personnel, Accountancy Services, Employment Agencies, Executive Search, Personnel Management & Outplacement Services
S.I.C.: 7363
N.A.I.C.S.: 561330
Audrey Low *(Branch Mgr)*

Non-U.S. Subsidiaries:

Templar Human Search Inc (3)
6th Floor Dong Sung Building 158-24
Samsung-dong, 135-880 Seoul, Korea (South)
Tel.: (82) 260003800
Fax: (82) 234521911
Temporary & Permanent Personnel, Accountancy Services, Employment Agencies, Executive Search, Personnel Management & Outplacement Services
S.I.C.: 7361
N.A.I.C.S.: 561330

Templar International Consultants Limited-Guangzhou (3)
Room 605, 6th Floor Yi An Plaza
33 Jin She Liu Ma Road, 510060
Guangzhou, China
Tel.: (86) 2083633227
Fax: (86) 2083634027
Temporary & Permanent Personnel, Accountancy Services, Employment Agencies, Executive Search, Personnel Management & Outplacement Services
S.I.C.: 7361
N.A.I.C.S.: 561311
Rosemary Leung *(Mng Dir)*

Altedia SAS (1)
5 Rue de Milan
Paris, 75319, France
Tel.: (33) 1 44 91 50 00
Fax: (33) 1 44 91 50 01
E-Mail: communication@altedia.fr
Web Site: www.altedia.fr
Human Resource Consulting Services
S.I.C.: 8999
N.A.I.C.S.: 541612
Xavier Lacoste *(Mng Dir)*

Ecco Servicios de Personal SA de CV (1)
Montecito No 38 Piso 10 Int 28
Mexico, 03810, Mexico
Tel.: (52) 55 5062 5000
Employment Consulting Services
S.I.C.: 8999
N.A.I.C.S.: 541612

euro engineering AG (1)
Lise-Meitner-Str 15
89081 Ulm, Germany
Tel.: (49) 211 530653 941
Fax: (49) 7319 356 525
E-Mail: ulm@ee-ag.com
Web Site: www.ee-ag.com
Engineering Services
S.I.C.: 8711
N.A.I.C.S.: 541330

TUJA Zeitarbeit GmbH (1)
Friedrich-Ebert-Strasse 110
48153 Munster, Germany
Tel.: (49) 251 7184 0
Fax: (49) 251 7184 101
E-Mail: info@tuja.de
Web Site: www.tuja.de
Emp.: 40
Employment Consulting Services
S.I.C.: 8999
N.A.I.C.S.: 541612
Thomas Baumer *(CEO)*
Thomas Rinne *(CFO)*

ADECOAGRO S.A.

13-15 Avenue de la Liberte
L-1931 Luxembourg, Luxembourg
Tel.: (352) 2689 8213
Web Site: www.adecoagro.com
AGRO—(NYSE)
Rev.: $379,526,000
Assets: $1,777,955,000
Liabilities: $751,912,000
Net Worth: $1,026,043,000
Earnings: $9,279,000
Emp.: 7,051
Fiscal Year-end: 12/31/12

Business Description:
Farming Crops, Agricultural Products, Cattle & Dairy Operations, Sugar, Ethanol & Energy Production, Land Transformation
S.I.C.: 0191
N.A.I.C.S.: 111998

Personnel:
Abbas Farouq Zuaiter *(Chm)*
Mariano Bosch *(CEO)*
Carlos A. Boero Hughes *(CFO)*
Emilio Federico Gnecco *(Chief Legal Officer)*
Walter Marcelo Sanchez *(Chief Comml Officer)*

Board of Directors:
Abbas Farouq Zuaiter
Mariano Bosch
Alan Leland Boyce
Julio Moura Neto
Plinio Villares Musetti
Mark Schachter
Guillaume van der Linden
Andres Velasco Branes
Paulo Albert Weyland Vieira

Transfer Agent:
The Bank of New York Mellon
New York, NY 17310

ADEFFECTIVE LTD.

Level 1 61 Spring Street
Melbourne, VIC, 3000, Australia
Tel.: (61) 392867500
Fax: (61) 396505571
Web Site: www.adeffective.com
ABN—(ASX)
Rev.: $2,907,665
Assets: $1,153,678
Liabilities: $487,814
Net Worth: $665,863
Earnings: $47,385
Fiscal Year-end: 06/30/13

Business Description:
Advertising Services
S.I.C.: 2741
N.A.I.C.S.: 511199

Personnel:
Simon Crean *(CEO)*
Sophie Karzis *(Sec)*

Board of Directors:
Andrew Plympton
Domenic Carosa
Mark Goulopoulos
Sophie Karzis
Damian London

Legal Counsel:
HWL Ebsworth
Level 26 530 Collins Street
Melbourne, VIC, 3000, Australia

ADEKA CORPORATION

7-2-35 Higashi-ogu Arakawa-ku
Tokyo, 116-8554, Japan
Tel.: (81) 344552811
Web Site: www.adk.co.jp
Year Founded: 1917
4401—(TKS)
Sls.: $20,328,000
Assets: $2,448,644,000
Liabilities: $939,147,000
Net Worth: $1,509,497,000
Earnings: $836,000
Emp.: 3,027
Fiscal Year-end: 03/31/13

Business Description:
Resins, Surfactants, Organic Chemicals, Inorganic Chemicals & Edible Oils
S.I.C.: 2869
N.A.I.C.S.: 325199

Personnel:
Kunihiko Sakurai *(Chm)*
Akio Kohri *(Pres)*
Shuji Hojo *(Operating Officer)*
Takumi Iio *(Mng Operating Officer)*
Akira Momose *(Mng Operating Officer)*
Kazuhiko Morio *(Mng Operating Officer)*
Hiroshi Serata *(Mng Operating Officer)*
Haruhiko Tomiyasu *(Operating Officer)*
Hikaru Tsujimoto *(Operating Officer)*

Board of Directors:
Kunihiko Sakurai
Shuji Hojo
Takumi Iio
Akio Kohri
Akira Momose
Kazuhiko Morio
Kazuyuki Nagai
Hiroshi Serata
Haruhiko Tomiyasu
Hikaru Tsujimoto

Transfer Agent:
Sumitomo Mitsui Trust Bank Limited
2 8 4 Izumi Suginami ku
Tokyo, 168-0063, Japan

Subsidiaries:

Adeka Chemical Supply Corporation (1)
Yoko Bldg Bunkyo-Ku
Tokyo, Japan
Tel.: (81) 338117191
Fax: (81) 338815465
Chemical & Allied Products Merchant Whslr
S.I.C.: 5169
N.A.I.C.S.: 424690

Adeka Clean Aid Corporation (1)
1-4-5 Hongo Bunkyo-ku
113-8422 Tokyo, Japan
Tel.: (81) 338161271
Fax: (81) 338122912
Web Site: www.adekacleanair.com
Emp.: 145
Chemical & Allied Products Whslr
S.I.C.: 5169
N.A.I.C.S.: 424690
Nobuo Sato *(Mgr)*

Adeka Fine Foods Corporation (1)
207 Takenouchidanchi
Sakaiminato, Tottori, Japan
Tel.: (81) 859454771
Fax: (81) 859454080
Mayonnaise Dressing & Sauce Mfr
S.I.C.: 2035
N.A.I.C.S.: 311941

Adeka Foods Sales Corporation (1)
1-4-5 Hongo Bunkyo-ku
Tokyo, Japan
Tel.: (81) 338119719
Fax: (81) 38113535
Web Site: www.adeka-fs.co.jp
Emp.: 25
Confectionery Whslr
S.I.C.: 5145
N.A.I.C.S.: 424450
Akira Hashimoto *(Gen Mgr)*

Oxirane Chemical Corporation (1)
4-1-13 Nihonbashi Honcho Chiyoda-ku
Tokyo, 103-0023, Japan
Tel.: (81) 332311761
Fax: (81) 332311765
Organic Chemical Mfr
S.I.C.: 2899
N.A.I.C.S.: 325199

Tokyo Environmental Measurement Center Co., Ltd (1)
6-43-9 Higashi-Ogu Arakawa-ku
Tokyo, Japan
Tel.: (81) 338951141
Fax: (81) 338954396
E-Mail: kmk-koyama@toukansoku.co.jp
Web Site: www.toukansoku.co.jp
Emp.: 50
Environmental Consulting Services
S.I.C.: 8999
N.A.I.C.S.: 541620
Yajima Akimasa *(Pres)*

Uehara Foods Industry Co., Ltd (1)
5-48-5 Higashi-Nippori Arakawa-ku
Tokyo, Japan
Tel.: (81) 338078161
Web Site: www.adk.co.jp/en/company/group_j.html
Durable Goods Whslr
S.I.C.: 5099
N.A.I.C.S.: 423990

Yongo Co., Ltd (1)
2-1102 Kamisuge Meito-ku
Nagoya, Aichi, Japan
Tel.: (81) 527744511
Fax: (81) 52774518
Web Site: www.yongo.co.jp

Confectionery Whslr
S.I.C.: 5145
N.A.I.C.S.: 424450

Non-U.S. Subsidiary:

Adeka Korea Corporation (1)
839 Bongdong-Up
Wanju-Gun, Yeongam, Jeollabuk-do, 565-904, Korea (South) Ks
Tel.: (82) 63 260 0400
Fax: (82) 63 262 7338
Web Site: www.adekakorea.co.kr
Emp.: 98
Plastic Additives Mfr
S.I.C.: 3089
N.A.I.C.S.: 326199
Kenji Nakazawa *(Pres & CEO)*

Non-U.S. Joint Venture:

Chang Chiang Chemical Co., Ltd. (1)
301 Songkiang Rd 8th Fl
Taipei, 104, Taiwan
Tel.: (886) 225097431
Fax: (886) 225097433
E-Mail: tjlin@ccp.com.tw
Emp.: 10
Antioxidants & PVC Products
S.I.C.: 2821
N.A.I.C.S.: 325211
Toru Yamada *(VP)*

ADELAIDE BRIGHTON LTD.

Level 1 157 Grenfell Street
GPO Box 2155
Adelaide, SA, 5000, Australia
Tel.: (61) 882238000
Fax: (61) 882150030
E-Mail: adelaidebrighton@adbri.com.au
Web Site: www.adbri.com.au
Year Founded: 1882
ABC—(ASX)
Rev.: $1,225,718,020
Assets: $1,684,763,070
Liabilities: $634,222,060
Net Worth: $1,050,541,010
Earnings: $160,587,610
Emp.: 1,600
Fiscal Year-end: 12/31/12

Business Description:
Construction Materials, Cement & Lime Mfr & Marketer
Export
S.I.C.: 3241
N.A.I.C.S.: 327310

Personnel:
Mark P. Chellew *(Mng Dir)*
Michael Kelly *(CFO)*
Marcus R. D. Clayton *(Gen Counsel & Sec)*

Board of Directors:
Raymond D. Barro
Mark P. Chellew
Les V. Hosking
Graeme F. Pettigrew
Ken B. Scott-Mackenzie
Arlene M. Tansey

Divisions:

Cockburn Cement (1)
242 Russell Rd E
Munster, Perth, WA, 6166, Australia (100%)
Tel.: (61) 894111000
Fax: (61) 894111150
E-Mail: info@cockburn.com.au
Web Site: www.cockburncement.com.au
Emp.: 100
Mfr. of Cement
S.I.C.: 3241
N.A.I.C.S.: 327310
Martin Brydon *(Gen Mgr)*

Subsidiaries:

Adbri Masonry Group Pty. Ltd. (1)
264 Keilor Road
North Essendon, Melbourne, VIC, 3041, Australia
Tel.: (61) 93050900
Fax: (61) 93744736
E-Mail: info@cmbrick.com.au
Web Site: www.cmbrick.com.au
Masonry Products
S.I.C.: 3271
N.A.I.C.S.: 327331
John Kenneth Dyson *(CEO)*

Subsidiary:

Adbri Masonry Pty. Ltd. (2)
6 Tennant Street
Fyshwick, ACT, 2609, Australia
Tel.: (61) 262391255
Fax: (61) 262807284
E-Mail: contracting@adbri.com.au
Web Site: www.adbrimasonry.com.au
Emp.: 2
Masonry Products Supplier
S.I.C.: 5211
N.A.I.C.S.: 444190
Marcus Roland Dean Clayton *(Sec)*

Adelaide Brighton Cement Ltd. (1)
62 Elder Rd
Birkenhead, SA, 5015, Australia
Tel.: (61) 883000300
Fax: (61) 883000430
E-Mail: adelaidebrighton@adbri.com.au
Web Site: www.adelaidebrighton.com.au
Emp.: 100
Cement Mfr
S.I.C.: 3241
N.A.I.C.S.: 327310
Shane Boswell *(Officer-Sls & Logistics)*

Hurd Haulage Pty. Ltd. (1)
Lot 132 Diamond Head Road
Dunbogan, NSW, 2443, Australia
Tel.: (61) 265599834
Fax: (61) 265598261
Web Site: www.adelaidebrighton.com.au
Emp.: 10
Sand & Soil & Gravel Hauling Services
S.I.C.: 4212
N.A.I.C.S.: 484220
Marcus Roland Dean Clayton *(Sec)*

Hy-Tec Industries (Queensland) Pty. Ltd. (1)
42-48 Fishermans Rd
Maroochydore, QLD, 4558, Australia
Tel.: (61) 754795100
Fax: (61) 754436618
Concrete Mfr
S.I.C.: 3273
N.A.I.C.S.: 327320

U.S. Subsidiary:

Adelaide Brighton Cement (Florida) Inc. (1)
12567 NE 7th Ave
Miami, FL 33161-4811
Tel.: (305) 893-2008
Cement Mfr
S.I.C.: 3241
N.A.I.C.S.: 327310

ADELAIDE RESOURCES LIMITED

69 King William Road
PO Box 1210
Unley, SA, 5061, Australia
Tel.: (61) 8 8271 0600
Fax: (61) 8 8271 0033
E-Mail: adres@adelaideresources.com.au
Web Site: www.adelaideresources.com.au
ADN—(ASX)
Rev.: $149,563
Assets: $17,876,815
Liabilities: $537,192
Net Worth: $17,339,623
Earnings: ($6,759,629)
Emp.: 10
Fiscal Year-end: 06/30/13

Business Description:
Mineral Exploration Services
S.I.C.: 1481
N.A.I.C.S.: 213115

Personnel:
Christopher G. Drown *(Mng Dir)*
Nicholas J. Harding *(CFO & Sec)*

Board of Directors:
Michael I. Hatcher
John J. den Dryver
Christopher G. Drown
John P. Horan

Legal Counsel:
Kelly & Co. Lawyer
Level 17 Westpac House 91 King William Street
Adelaide, Australia

ADELINE SA

116 Rue D Alsace
88100 Saint-Die-des-Vosges, Vosges, France
Tel.: (33) 329565456
Fax: (33) 329560514
E-Mail: adeline@orange.fr
Sls.: $12,300,000
Emp.: 43
S.I.C.: 5411
N.A.I.C.S.: 445110

Personnel:
Fabien Artuso *(Mgr)*

ADENT CAPITAL CORP.

Suite 1010 609 Granville Street
Vancouver, BC, V7Y 1G5, Canada
Tel.: (604) 689-0037
Fax: (604) 926-5806
E-Mail: paulcox@pilotagecc.com
Year Founded: 2012
ANT.P—(TSXV)

Business Description:
Investment Services
S.I.C.: 6211
N.A.I.C.S.: 523999

Personnel:
Paul Cox *(Pres, CEO, CFO & Sec)*

Board of Directors:
Colin K. Benner
Paul Cox
Richard Godfrey
Karen Richardson

Transfer Agent:
Equity Financial Trust Company
1185 West Georgia Street Suite 1620
Vancouver, BC, Canada

ADEPT SOLUTIONS LIMITED

(See Under Emerchants Limited)

ADEPT TELECOM PLC

77 Mount Ephraim
Tunbridge Wells, Kent, TN4 8BS, United Kingdom
Tel.: (44) 8445577200
Fax: (44) 18928550201
E-Mail: business.services@adept-telecom.co.uk
Web Site: www.adept-telecom.co.uk
ADT—(AIM LSE)
Sales Range: $25-49.9 Million
Emp.: 65

Business Description:
Telecommunications & Internet Services
S.I.C.: 4813
N.A.I.C.S.: 517110

Personnel:
Ian Fishwick *(Founder & Mng Dir)*
Roger Wilson *(Chm)*
Chris Fishwick *(Deputy Chm)*

Board of Directors:
Roger Wilson
Chris Fishwick
Ian Fishwick
Dusko Lukic
Edward Williams
Amanda Woodruffe

ADERA ENERGY PLC

33 Throgmorton Street
London, EC2N 2BR, United Kingdom
Tel.: (44) 207 156 5253
Fax: (44) 207 156 5001
E-Mail: info@aderaenergy.com
Web Site: www.aderaenergy.com
1AD—(DEU)

Business Description:
Wind Energy Generation
S.I.C.: 4931
N.A.I.C.S.: 221118

Personnel:
Gary Lo *(Pres)*
Marco Chan *(CFO)*

Board of Directors:
Marco Chan
Christopher Hatch
Gary Humphreys
Gary Lo

ADERANS CO., LTD.

Sumitomo Fudosan Yotsuya Building
6F 7F 13-4 Arakі-cho Shinkjuku-ku
Tokyo, 160-0007, Japan
Tel.: (81) 333503268
Fax: (81) 333529628
Web Site: www.aderans.com
Year Founded: 1969
8170—(TKS)
Sls.: $561,979,000
Assets: $449,944,000
Liabilities: $117,535,000
Net Worth: $332,409,000
Earnings: $36,311,000
Emp.: 4,286
Fiscal Year-end: 02/28/13

Business Description:
Holding Company; Wigs & Accessories Mfr & Whslr
Export
S.I.C.: 3999
N.A.I.C.S.: 339999

Personnel:
Nobuo Nemoto *(Chm & Pres)*
Masaaki Furukawa *(Exec Officer-Medical Bus, Trng & Education & Sls-Western Japan)*
Yuji Hirahara *(Exec Officer-Overseas Bus)*
Norihiko Ishiodori *(Exec Officer-Supply Chain Mgmt & Production Mgmt)*
Misaki Shimada *(Gen Counsel)*
Shigeru Ishiko *(Exec VP)*

Board of Directors:
Nobuo Nemoto
Shigeru Ishiko
Hisatake Kanazawa
Joshua Schechter
Katsuyoshi Tanaka
Yoshihiro Tsumura

Transfer Agent:
The Chuo Mitsui Trust & Banking Co., Ltd
8-4 Izumi 2-chome Suginami-ku
Tokyo, Japan

U.S. Subsidiaries:

Aderans Hairgoods, Inc. (1)
15551 Cabrito Rd
Van Nuys, CA 91406-1410
Tel.: (818) 908-3103
Wig Retailer
S.I.C.: 5699
N.A.I.C.S.: 448150

Aderans Research Institute, Inc. (1)
2211 New Market Pkwy Ste S
Marietta, GA 30067-9399
Tel.: (678) 213-1919
Web Site: www.aderansresearch.com
Wigs Mfr
S.I.C.: 3999
N.A.I.C.S.: 339999
Ken Washenik *(CEO)*
Vern L. Liebmann *(COO)*

Bosley Medical (1)
9100 Wilshire Blvd E Tower
Beverly Hills, CA 90212
Tel.: (310) 288-9999

Aderans Co., Ltd.—(Continued)

Fax: (310) 887-0947
Toll Free: (800) 474-1254
Web Site: www.bosley.com
Hair Restoration
S.I.C.: 5047
N.A.I.C.S.: 423450
Armen Markarian *(Pres & CEO)*
Roger Aull *(Gen Counsel)*

Hair Club for Men, Ltd., Inc. (1)
1515 S Federal Hwy Ste 401
Boca Raton, FL 33432-7450 FL
Tel.: (561) 361-7600
Fax: (561) 361-7680
Toll Free: (888) 888-8986
Web Site: www.hairclub.com
Sales Range: $125-149.9 Million
Emp.: 500
Hair Restoration Services
S.I.C.: 7299
N.A.I.C.S.: 812199
Darryll Porter *(Pres & CEO)*

Subsidiaries:

Hair Club for Men, Ltd., Inc. (2)
115 E 57th St 4th Fl 450
New York, NY 10022-2049
Tel.: (212) 758-9232
Fax: (646) 871-0931
Web Site: www.hairclub.com
Sales Range: $50-74.9 Million
Emp.: 50
Hair Restoration Centers Operator
S.I.C.: 7299
N.A.I.C.S.: 812199
Darryll Porter *(Pres & CEO)*

Hair Club for Men, LLC (2)
9201 Sunset Blvd Ste 510
Los Angeles, CA 90069
Tel.: (310) 601-4660
Toll Free: (888) 888-8986
Beauty Salon Operator
S.I.C.: 7231
N.A.I.C.S.: 812112

International Hairgoods Inc. (1)
18684 Lake Dr E
Chanhassen, MN 55317 (100%)
Tel.: (952) 906-9900
Fax: (952) 906-3400
E-Mail: info@inthair.com
Web Site: www.internationalhairgoods.com
Emp.: 23
Mfr. & Sales of Wigs
S.I.C.: 3999
N.A.I.C.S.: 339999
Peter Gensler *(Pres)*

Rene' of Paris (1)
9100 Wilshire Blvd E Tower 9th Fl
Beverly Hills, CA 90212
Tel.: (818) 908-3100
Fax: (424) 239-1424
E-Mail: info@reneofparis.com
Web Site: www.reneofparis.com
Sales Range: $1-9.9 Million
Emp.: 25
Wig Importing & Designing
S.I.C.: 5199
N.A.I.C.S.: 424990

TressAllure/General Wig (1)
1480 Sw 3rd St Ste 3
Pompano Beach, FL 33069-3225
Tel.: (305) 823-0600
Fax: (305) 823-0626
Toll Free: (800) 777-9447
Web Site: www.tressallure.com
Emp.: 100
Mfr. of Wigs & Hairpieces
S.I.C.: 5199
N.A.I.C.S.: 424990
Michelle Pitter *(Creative Svcs Mgr)*

Non-U.S. Subsidiaries:

Aderans France SAS (1)
6 Allee des Saules
Europarc, 94042 Creteil, France
Tel.: (33) 1 48 90 30 60
Fax: (33) 1 43 99 55 26
Web Site: www.universal-hair.com
Investment Management Services
S.I.C.: 6211
N.A.I.C.S.: 523999

Aderans Inc (1)
3 F 39 Chung Hsiao West Road Section 1
Taipei, 10041, Taiwan
Tel.: (886) 223888905
Fax: (886) 223111629
Cosmetic Products Mfr & Whslr
S.I.C.: 2844
N.A.I.C.S.: 325620

Aderans Philippines, Inc. (1)
Lot A 5 Clark Premiere Industrial Park M A
Roxas Highway
Clark Freeport Zone 2009, Pampanga,
2009, Philippines
Tel.: (63) 455996477
Fax: (63) 455996474
E-Mail: jenny@aderans.co.ph
Web Site: www.aderans.com
Emp.: 1,400
Wigs Mfr
S.I.C.: 3999
N.A.I.C.S.: 339999
Hiroko Oshima *(Gen Mgr)*

Aderans (Shanghai) Co., Ltd (1)
15th Floor 1 Grand Gateway No 1
Hongqiao Rd
Shanghai, 200030, China
Tel.: (86) 2164486300
Fax: (86) 2164486304
Web Site: www.universal-hair.com
Wigs Whslr
S.I.C.: 5199
N.A.I.C.S.: 424990

Aderans (Shanghai) Trading Co., Ltd (1)
15th Floor 1 Grand Gateway No 1
Hongqiao Road
Shanghai, 200030, China
Tel.: (86) 21 6448 6300
Fax: (86) 21 6448 6304
Web Site: www.universal-hair.com
Hair Care Services
S.I.C.: 7299
N.A.I.C.S.: 812199

Aderans Thai., Ltd. (Buriram Factory) (1)
122 Moo 9 Sai Buriram Prakonchai Road
Tambol I-San Amphur Muang
Bangkok, Buriram, 3100, Thailand
Tel.: (66) 44 613 000
Fax: (66) 44 613 372
Web Site: www.aderans.com
Hair & Wig Production for Men & Women, also Inspection & Hair Repairs
S.I.C.: 5199
N.A.I.C.S.: 424990

Aderans Thai. Ltd. (1)
109 Moo1 Export Processing Zone Banwah
Hi-tech Industrial Estate,
Amphur Bangpa-in, 13160 Ayutthaya,
Thailand
Tel.: (66) 35 350 540 1
Fax: (66) 35 350 542
E-Mail: AderansThai@thailand.com
Web Site: www.universal-hair.com
Wigs Whslr
S.I.C.: 5199
N.A.I.C.S.: 424990

Camaflex S.A. (1)
107 Blvd Richard Lenoir
F-75011 Paris, France
Tel.: (33) 153561717
Fax: (33) 1 4338 1077
Web Site: www.camaflex.com
Sales of Wigs & Hair Products
S.I.C.: 5199
N.A.I.C.S.: 424990

Carl M Lundh AB (1)
Kalendegatan 12
PO Box 30136
200 61 Malmo, Sweden
Tel.: (46) 40 36 87 20
Fax: (46) 40 16 38 40
E-Mail: info@carlmlundh.se
Web Site: www.carlmlundh.se
Hair Care Product Mfr & Sales
S.I.C.: 3999
N.A.I.C.S.: 339999
Ulf Rittmar *(CEO)*

Creations de Paris Camaflex Vertriebs GmbH (1)
Ettore Bugatti St 7
51149 Cologne, 51149, Germany (100%)
Tel.: (49) 2203977020
Fax: (49) 2203301544
E-Mail: info@camaflex.de
Web Site: www.camaflex.de
Emp.: 30
Sale of Wigs
S.I.C.: 5199
N.A.I.C.S.: 424990
Shigru Ishito *(Mng Dir)*

D. van Nooijen B.V. (1)
Rue Van Hammee 17
1030 Brussels, Belgium (100%)
Tel.: (32) 2 215 5800
Fax: (32) 2 215 4829
E-Mail: info@camaflex.be
Web Site: www.camaflex.be
Sales Range: $1-9.9 Million
Emp.: 25
Retail & Wholesale of Wigs & Hair Extensions
S.I.C.: 5199
N.A.I.C.S.: 424990
Joachim Mels *(Gen Mgr)*

D. van Nooijen B.V. (1)
Eglantierbaan 49
Capelle aan den IJssel, 2908 LV,
Netherlands (100%)
Tel.: (31) 22155800
Fax: (31) 22154829
E-Mail: info@camaflex.be
Web Site: www.vannooijen.nl
Emp.: 5
Sale of Women's & Men's Wigs
S.I.C.: 5199
N.A.I.C.S.: 424990

Monfair Moden Vertriebs GmbH (1)
Ettore Bugatti Strasse 7
51149 Cologne, Germany De
Tel.: (49) 22033697413 (100%)
Fax: (49) 22033697421
E-Mail: info@camaflex.de
Web Site: www.camaflex.de
Sales Range: $10-24.9 Million
Emp.: 100
Sales of Wigs, Hairpieces & Wig-Related Products
S.I.C.: 5199
N.A.I.C.S.: 424990
Harald Heinz *(Dir-Sls)*

Trendco Hair Supplies Co., Ltd (1)
Sheridan House 114/116 Western Road
Hove, BN3 1DD, United Kingdom
Tel.: (44) 1273 774977
Fax: (44) 1273 720116
E-Mail: info@trendco.co.uk
Web Site: www.trendco.co.uk
Hair Care Product Distr
S.I.C.: 8099
N.A.I.C.S.: 621999
Lynne Harris *(Mng Dir-Brighton)*

ADESSO AG

Stockholmer Allee 24
44269 Dortmund, Germany
Tel.: (49) 2319309330
Fax: (49) 2319309331
E-Mail: info@adesso.de
Web Site: www.adesso.de
ADN1—(DEU)
Rev.: $166,478,152
Assets: $103,120,661
Liabilities: $57,163,763
Net Worth: $45,956,898
Earnings: ($123,848)
Emp.: 1,084
Fiscal Year-end: 12/31/12

Business Description:
Information Technology Services
S.I.C.: 7389
N.A.I.C.S.: 519190

Personnel:
Volker Gruhn *(Chm-Supervisory Bd)*
Michael Kenfenheuer *(Co-CEO)*
Rudiger Striemer *(Co-CEO)*
Christoph Junge *(Member-Exec Bd)*

Supervisory Board of Directors:
Volker Gruhn
Willibald Folz
Friedrich Wobking

Subsidiaries:

adesso mobile solutions GmbH (1)
Stockholmer Allee 24
44269 Dortmund, Germany
Tel.: (49) 231 930 9310
Fax: (49) 231 930 9317
E-Mail: info@adesso-mobile.de
Web Site: www.adesso-mobile.de
Mobile Solution Development & Consulting Services
S.I.C.: 8748
N.A.I.C.S.: 541618

ARITHNEA GmbH (1)
Prof-Messerschmitt-Strabe 1
85579 Neubiberg, Germany
Tel.: (49) 89 244 105 400
Fax: (49) 89 189 325 95
E-Mail: info@arithnea.de
Web Site: www.arithnea.de
Content Management Services
S.I.C.: 7376
N.A.I.C.S.: 541513

e-Spirit AG (1)
Barcelonaweg 14
44269 Dortmund, Germany
Tel.: (49) 231 477 77 0
Fax: (49) 231 477 77 499
E-Mail: info@e-spirit.com
Web Site: www.e-Spirit.com
Content Management Services
S.I.C.: 7376
N.A.I.C.S.: 541513
Joern Bodemann *(Chm & CEO)*
Johannes Haeusele *(Member-Exec Bd)*
Christoph Junge *(Member-Exec Bd)*

evu.it GmbH (1)
Freie-Vogel-Str 391
44269 Dortmund, Germany
Tel.: (49) 231 930 1155
Fax: (49) 231 930 1108
E-Mail: info@evu-it.de
Web Site: www.evu-it.de
Environmental Consulting Services
S.I.C.: 8999
N.A.I.C.S.: 541620

gadiv GmbH (1)
Bovingen 148
53804 Much, Germany
Tel.: (49) 2245 9160 0
Fax: (49) 2245 9160 21
E-Mail: info@gadiv.de
Web Site: www.gadiv.de
Software Development Services
S.I.C.: 7371
N.A.I.C.S.: 541511

percision GmbH (1)
Agrippinawerft 28
50678 Cologne, Germany
Tel.: (49) 221 34667 40
Fax: (49) 221 34667 11
E-Mail: info@percision.eu
Web Site: www.percision.eu/en/
Recruitment Services
S.I.C.: 7361
N.A.I.C.S.: 561311

Non-U.S. Subsidiaries:

adesso Austria GmbH (1)
Floridsdorfer Hauptstr 1
1210 Vienna, Austria
Tel.: (43) 1 2198790 0
Fax: (43) 1 2198790 13
E-Mail: info@adesso.at
Web Site: www.adesso.at
Emp.: 40
Software Development Services
S.I.C.: 7371
N.A.I.C.S.: 541511
Rudolf Gotsmy *(Sr Acct Mgr)*

adesso Schweiz AG (1)
Gewerbestrasse 4
8162 Steinmaur, Switzerland
Tel.: (41) 44 85486 00
Fax: (41) 44 85486 05
E-Mail: info@adesso.ch
Web Site: www.adesso.ch
Software Development Services
S.I.C.: 7371
N.A.I.C.S.: 541511

ADEX MINING INC.

67 Yonge Street Suite 900
Toronto, ON, M5E 1J8, Canada
Tel.: (416) 941-9663
Fax: (416) 941-9080
E-Mail: info@adexmining.com

Web Site: www.adexmining.com
ADE—(TSXV)
Rev.: $62,729
Assets: $15,595,741
Liabilities: $393,712
Net Worth: $15,202,029
Earnings: ($1,733,923)
Emp.: 5
Fiscal Year-end: 12/31/12
Business Description:
Metal Ore Mining Services
S.I.C.: 1099
N.A.I.C.S.: 212299
Personnel:
Kim Po Yan *(Chm, Interim Pres & CEO)*
Douglas Bolton *(Interim CFO)*
Board of Directors:
Kim Po Yan
Norman M. Betts
William B. Burton
Linda Lam Kwan
Joseph Kit Ying Lau
Joe Foon Kin Tai
Transfer Agent:
Equity Financial Trust Company
200 University Avenue Suite 400
Toronto, ON, Canada
Subsidiary:

Adex Minerals Corp. (1)
Mount Pleasant
PO Box 1106
Saint George, NB, E5C3S9, Canada
Mailing Address:
PO Box 1106
Saint George, NB, Canada
Tel.: (506) 755-3393
Web Site: www.adexmining.com
Emp.: 3
Mining Services
S.I.C.: 1479
N.A.I.C.S.: 212393

ADEX SECURITIES, INC.

1095 W Pender St Ste 900
Vancouver, BC, V6E 2M6, Canada
Tel.: (604) 681-8882
Fax: (604) 683-2668
Emp.: 2
Business Description:
Securities Brokering
S.I.C.: 6211
N.A.I.C.S.: 523120
Personnel:
Terence Hui *(Pres & CEO)*
Subsidiary:

Concord Pacific Group (1)
1095 W Pender St 9th Fl
Vancouver, BC, V6E 2M6, Canada
Tel.: (604) 681-8882
Fax: (604) 895-8296
E-Mail: info@concordpacific.com
Web Site: www.concordpacific.com
Emp.: 40
Urban Residential Real Estate Developer
S.I.C.: 6531
N.A.I.C.S.: 531210
Terence Hui *(Pres & CEO)*
Dennis Au-Yeung *(CFO & VP)*

ADF FOODS LTD.

Unit No 2/B 2nd Floor 570 PB Marg Worli
Mumbai, 400 018, India
Tel.: (91) 2261415555
Fax: (91) 22 6662 7373
E-Mail: info@adf-foods.com
Web Site: www.adf-foods.com
Year Founded: 1932
519183—(BOM)
Rev.: $33,809,804
Assets: $39,932,639
Liabilities: $12,392,507
Net Worth: $27,540,132
Earnings: $2,554,701
Emp.: 320
Fiscal Year-end: 03/31/13
Business Description:
Indian Foods Production & Marketing Services
S.I.C.: 2099
N.A.I.C.S.: 311999
Personnel:
Ramesh H. Thakkar *(Chm)*
Ashok H. Thakkar *(Vice Chm)*
Bimal R. Thakkar *(Mng Dir)*
Shalaka Ovalekar *(Sec)*
Board of Directors:
Ramesh H. Thakkar
Ravinder Kumar Jain
Jay M. Mehta
Viren A. Merchant
Nipun C. Shah
Ashok H. Thakkar
Bhavesh R. Thakkar
Bimal R. Thakkar
Yasir J. Varawala

BSR & Co.
Mumbai, India
Transfer Agent:
Link Intime India Pvt. Ltd.
C-13 Pannalal Silk Mills Compound
LBS Marg
Bhandup, Mumbai, 400 078, India
Tel.: (91) 22 2596 3838
Fax: (91) 22 2594 6969

U.S. Subsidiary:

Elena's Food Specialties, Inc. (1)
405 Allerton Ave
South San Francisco, CA 94080-4818 CA
Tel.: (650) 871-8700
Fax: (650) 871-0502
Rev.: $9,000,000
Emp.: 60
Food Mfr
S.I.C.: 2038
N.A.I.C.S.: 311412
Mark Cooley *(CFO)*

ADF GROUP INC.

300 Henry Bessemer Street
Terrebonne, QC, J6Y 1T3, Canada
Tel.: (450) 965-1911
Fax: (450) 965-8558
Toll Free: (800) 263-7560
E-Mail: info@adfgroup.com
Web Site: www.adfgroup.com
Year Founded: 1956
DRX—(TSX)
Rev.: $41,164,356
Assets: $105,892,951
Liabilities: $15,013,678
Net Worth: $90,879,273
Earnings: ($1,544,707)
Emp.: 248
Fiscal Year-end: 01/31/13
Business Description:
Steel Superstructures & Architectural & Various Other Metals Designer, Engineering, Mfr & Installer
S.I.C.: 1791
N.A.I.C.S.: 238120
Personnel:
Jean Paschini *(Chm & CEO)*
Pierre Paschini *(Pres & COO)*
Jean-Francois Boursier *(CFO)*
Marise Paschini *(Treas, Sec & Exec VP)*
Board of Directors:
Jean Paschini
Marc L. Belcourt
Marc A. Benoit
Marc A. Filion
Antonio P. Meti
Robert Pare
Marise Paschini
Pierre Paschini
Legal Counsel:
Fasken Martineau DuMoulin LLP
Tour de la bourse 800 Place Victoria Suite 3400
Montreal, QC, Canada
Transfer Agent:
Computershare Investor Services Inc
1500 University Ste 700
Montreal, QC, Canada

ADFAST CORP.

2670 rue Paulus
Saint Laurent, QC, H4S 1G1, Canada
Tel.: (514) 337-7307
Fax: (514) 745-2969
Web Site: www.adfastcorp.com
Year Founded: 1989
Rev.: $20,033,742
Emp.: 150
Business Description:
Construction, Packaging & Engineering Industries
S.I.C.: 8711
N.A.I.C.S.: 541330
Personnel:
Claude Dandurand *(Co-Owner)*
David Van Wely *(Co-Owner)*
Yves Dandurand *(Pres)*

ADFONIC LTD.

Level 10 Orion House 5 Upper St Martins Lane
London, WC2H 9EA, United Kingdom
Tel.: (44) 203 021 1250
E-Mail: support@adfonic.com
Web Site: www.adfonic.com
Emp.: 80
Business Description:
Mobile Advertising Services
S.I.C.: 7319
N.A.I.C.S.: 541890
Personnel:
Victor Malachard *(CEO)*
Arthur Crocker *(CFO)*
Paul Childs *(CMO)*
Wesley Biggs *(CTO)*
U.S. Subsidiary:

Adfonic Inc. (1)
37 W 26th St Ste 317
New York, NY 10010
Tel.: (212) 686-5925
Mobile Advertising Services
S.I.C.: 7319
N.A.I.C.S.: 541890
James Macdonald *(Gen Mgr)*

Non-U.S. Subsidiaries:

Adfonic Asia-Pacific (1)
16 Raffles Quay
Singapore, 048581, Singapore
Tel.: (65) 816 724 85
Mobile Advertising Services
S.I.C.: 7319
N.A.I.C.S.: 541890
Kartik Ram *(Gen Mgr)*

Adfonic France (1)
8 Rue de la Terrasse
75017 Paris, France
Tel.: (33) 685 83 82 01
Fax: (33) 957 34 84 70
Mobile Advertising Services
S.I.C.: 7319
N.A.I.C.S.: 541890

Adfonic GmbH (1)
Ludwigstrasse 8
80539 Munich, Germany
Tel.: (49) 89 20 60 21 170
Mobile Advertising Services
S.I.C.: 7319
N.A.I.C.S.: 541890
Albert Pescheck *(Gen Mgr)*

Adfonic Spain (1)
c/ Josefa Valcarcel 8-2 plta
28027 Madrid, Spain
Tel.: (34) 913 202 884
Mobile Advertising Services
S.I.C.: 7319
N.A.I.C.S.: 541890

ADG GLOBAL SUPPLY LIMITED

19 Walters Drive
Osborne Park, WA, 6017, Australia
Mailing Address:
PO Box 709
Osborne Park, WA, 6916, Australia
Tel.: (61) 893295900
Fax: (61) 893295999
E-Mail: info@adgglobalsupply.com
Web Site: www.adgglobalsupply.com
ADQ—(ASX)
Rev.: $82,715,645
Assets: $38,912,014
Liabilities: $17,604,195
Net Worth: $21,307,819
Earnings: ($1,074,405)
Emp.: 55
Fiscal Year-end: 06/30/13
Business Description:
Industrial Products Distr & Global Procurement & Supply Chain Management Services
S.I.C.: 4731
N.A.I.C.S.: 541614
Personnel:
John Mancini *(Mng Dir)*
Paul Roberts *(CFO & Sec)*
Board of Directors:
David J. Schwartz
John Mancini
Charles Morgan
Legal Counsel:
Steinepreis Paganin
Level 4 Next Building 16 Milligan St
Perth, Australia
Subsidiaries:

ADG Global Supply Pty Ltd (1)
Unit 1 6 Oxleigh Drive
Malaga, WA, 6090, Australia
Tel.: (61) 892497599
Fax: (61) 892497699
E-Mail: info@adgglobalsupply.com
Web Site: www.adgglobalsupply.com
Emp.: 27
Industrial Equipment Suppliers
S.I.C.: 5084
N.A.I.C.S.: 423830
Mike Arnold *(Gen Mgr)*

ADG Technology (Qld) Pty Ltd (1)
Unit 2 1288 Boundary Rd
Wacol, 4076, Australia
Tel.: (61) 732715900
Fax: (61) 7 32715907
Web Site: www.adgglobalsupply.com
Boring & Drilling Equipments Mfr & Whslr
S.I.C.: 5084
N.A.I.C.S.: 423830
Andy Greathead *(Mng Dir)*

ADG Technology (Vic) Pty Ltd (1)
Unit 6 8 Garden Rd
Clayton, Victoria, 3168, Australia
Tel.: (61) 3 95451277
Fax: (61) 393385041
Web Site: www.adgglobalsupply.com
Drilling Contract Services
S.I.C.: 1381
N.A.I.C.S.: 213111

ADGAR INVESTMENTS AND DEVELOPMENT LIMITED

35 Efal St
49511 Petah Tiqwa, Israel
Tel.: (972) 39166691
Fax: (972) 39191911
E-Mail: leasing@adgar.com
Web Site: www.adgar.com
ADGR—(TAE)
Sales Range: $50-74.9 Million
Business Description:
Real Estate Construction, Property Development & Leasing Services
S.I.C.: 6519
N.A.I.C.S.: 531190
Personnel:
Doron Schneidman *(Chm)*
Roy Gadish *(CEO)*
Ronen Nakar *(Deputy CFO)*
Benjamin Adar *(Sec)*
Board of Directors:

ADGAR INVESTMENTS AND DEVELOPMENT LIMITED—(Continued)

Doron Schneidman
Zeev Abeles
Orit Merom Albeck
Dani Ben-Shahar
Roy Gadish
Avinoam Schneidman
Muki Schneidman
Shalom Schneidman

ADGS ADVISORY, INC.

(Formerly LIFE NUTRITION PRODUCTS, INC.)
Units 2611-13A 26th Floor
113 Argyle Street Mongkok, Kowloon, China (Hong Kong)
Tel.: (852) 2374 0002
Web Site:
Year Founded: 2005
ADGS—(OTC OTCB)
Rev.: $3,898,160
Assets: $4,765,877
Liabilities: $4,844,725
Net Worth: ($78,848)
Earnings: $624,797
Emp.: 25
Fiscal Year-end: 08/31/13
Business Description:
Investment Services
S.I.C.: 6211
N.A.I.C.S.: 523999
Personnel:
Lai Ying Li *(Chm, CEO & Sec)*
Michelle Tong Wing Shan *(CFO)*
Yin Yee Tso *(COO)*
Board of Directors:
Lai Ying Li
Kei Man Derek Fu
Yiu Kwong Pang
Yin Yee Tso

ADHUNIK METALIKS LIMITED

Lansdowne Towers 2/1A Sarat Bose Road
Kolkata, West Bengal, 700020, India
Tel.: (91) 33 30517100
Fax: (91) 33 22890285
E-Mail: info@adhunikgroup.com
Web Site: www.adhunikgroup.com
ADHUNIK—(NSE)
Rev.: $572,740,090
Assets: $1,669,248,474
Liabilities: $1,291,714,634
Net Worth: $377,533,839
Earnings: $16,166,509
Emp.: 1,798
Fiscal Year-end: 06/30/13
Business Description:
Metals Industry
S.I.C.: 3399
N.A.I.C.S.: 331110
Personnel:
Sanjay Sharma *(CEO & Head-Bus)*
Manoj Kumar Agarwal *(Mng Dir)*
Harpreet Singh *(COO & Pres-AAPL)*
Sanjeev Kumar *(Pres/CIO-Bus Excellence)*
Anil Shende *(Pres/Head-HR)*
Naresh Goyal *(Pres-Power-APNRL)*
S. S. H. Naqvi *(Pres-IOBP & Pellet Project & Ops)*
Amritanshu Prasad *(Sr Exec Pres-Corp Affairs, IR & HR Strategy)*
Mahesh Raheja *(Pres-Mines)*
Anand Sharma *(Sec & VP-Legal)*
Board of Directors:
Ghanshyam Das Agarwal
Jugal Kishore Agarwal
Mahesh Kumar Agarwal
Manoj Kumar Agarwal
Mohan Lal Agarwal
Nirmal Kumar Agarwal
Ramgopal Agarwala
Gopal Dikshit
Nihar Ranjan Hota
Surendra Mohan Lakhotia
Nandanandan Mishra
Raghaw Sharan Pandey
Transfer Agent:
Karvy Computershare Private Limited
Karvy House 46 Avenue 4 Street No.1 Banjara Hills
Hyderabad, India
Subsidiaries:

Adhunik Power & Natural Resources Ltd. **(1)**
2 Inner Cir Rd Shanti Hari Tower
Bistupur, Jamshedpur, Jharkhand, 832001, India
Tel.: (91) 6572224678
Fax: (91) 6572227980
Web Site: www.adhunikgroup.com.in
Emp.: 500
Power Generation Services
S.I.C.: 4911
N.A.I.C.S.: 221112
Naresh Goel *(Gen Mgr)*

Unistar Galvanisers & Fabricators Pvt. Ltd. **(1)**
2 1A Sarat Bose Rd Lansdowne Towers
Kolkata, West Bengal, 700020, India
Tel.: (91) 3330517100
Fax: (91) 3322890285
E-Mail: info@adhunikgroup.com
Emp.: 250
Fabricated Metal Structures Mfr
S.I.C.: 3441
N.A.I.C.S.: 332312
Manoj Kumar Agarwal *(Mng Dir)*

ADI CORPORATION

4F No 2 Lane 235 Bauchiau Road
Shindian City, Taipei, 231, Taiwan
Tel.: (886) 289115123
Fax: (886) 289118177
E-Mail: marketing@mail.adi.com.tw
Web Site: www.adi.com.tw
Year Founded: 1979
Sales Range: $50-74.9 Million
Emp.: 32
Business Description:
Mfr, Designer & Marketer of Computer Monitors & Telecommunications Products
S.I.C.: 3679
N.A.I.C.S.: 334419
Personnel:
James C. Liao *(Chm & Pres)*

ADI FINECHEM LIMITED

253/P Chekhala Sanand-Kadi Highway
Taluka Sanand, Ahmedabad, Gujarat, 382 115, India
Tel.: (91) 2717 222618
Fax: (91) 2717 222616
E-Mail: adi@adifinechem.com
Web Site: www.adifinechem.com
530117—(BOM)
Rev.: $24,845,401
Assets: $11,055,505
Liabilities: $5,342,724
Net Worth: $5,712,781
Earnings: $1,554,785
Emp.: 151
Fiscal Year-end: 03/31/13
Business Description:
Specialty Chemical Mfr
S.I.C.: 2899
N.A.I.C.S.: 325998
Personnel:
Nahoosh J. Jariwala *(Mng Dir)*
Rajen N. Jhaveri *(Sec & VP)*
Board of Directors:
Utkarsh B. Shah
Ganpatraj L. Chowdhary
Nahoosh J. Jariwala
Bimal D. Parikh
Kalpesh A. Patel
Nitin R. Patel
Bhavin A. Shah
Hemant N. Shah
Jayesh K. Shah
Transfer Agent:
Sharepro Services (India) Pvt. Ltd.
13AB Samhita Warehousing Complex 2nd Floor
Sakinaka Tele Exchange Lane
Andheri East, Mumbai, 400 072, India

ADI GROUP INC.

370 Wilsey Rd
Fredericton, NB, E3B 6E9, Canada
Tel.: (506) 452-9000
Fax: (506) 451-7451
Web Site: www.adi.ca
Year Founded: 1945
Rev.: $30,096,000
Emp.: 200
Business Description:
Construction & Water Treatment Services
S.I.C.: 9511
N.A.I.C.S.: 924110
Personnel:
Hazen Hawker *(CEO)*

ADIDAS AG

Adi Dassler Strasse 1
91074 Herzogenaurach, Germany
Tel.: (49) 9132840
Fax: (49) 9132842241
E-Mail: corporate.press@adidas-group.com
Web Site: www.adidas-group.com
Year Founded: 1949
ADS—(DEU)
Sls.: $20,035,048,110
Assets: $15,684,226,670
Liabilities: $8,561,641,200
Net Worth: $7,122,585,470
Earnings: $705,393,080
Emp.: 46,306
Fiscal Year-end: 12/31/12
Business Description:
Sporting & Athletic Goods Mfr
S.I.C.: 3949
N.A.I.C.S.: 339920
Personnel:
Igor Landau *(Chm-Supervisory Bd)*
Sabine Bauer *(Deputy Chm-Supervisory Bd)*
Willi Schwerdtle *(Deputy Chm-Supervisory Bd)*
Herbert Hainer *(CEO)*
Hermann Deininger *(CMO-Adidas Brand)*
Jan Runau *(Chief Corp Comm Officer)*
Glenn Bennett *(Member-Exec Bd-Global Ops)*
Robin J. Stalker *(Member-Exec Bd-Fin)*
Natalie Knight *(Sr VP-Comml Brand Fin)*
Supervisory Board of Directors:
Igor Landau
Sabine Bauer
Dieter Hauenstein
Wolfgang Jager
Stefan Jentzsch
Herbert Kauffmann
Roland Nosko
Alexander Popov
Hans Ruprecht
Willi Schwerdtle
Heidi Thaler-Veh
Christian Tourres
Subsidiaries:

adidas Beteiligungsgesellschaft mbH **(1)**
Adi-Dassler-Str 1
91074 Herzogenaurach, Germany
Tel.: (49) 9132 840
Fax: (49) 9132 842241
Web Site: www.adidas-group.com
Financial Management Services
S.I.C.: 6211
N.A.I.C.S.: 523999
Herbert Hainer *(CIO)*

Non-U.S. Subsidiary:

adidas Sports (China) Co. Ltd. **(2)**
F29 Building 1 1 Hongqiao Rd
Shanghai, 200030, China
Tel.: (86) 29 2401 0600
Fax: (86) 21 6448 3796
Athletic & Sports Product Mfr & Distr
S.I.C.: 3949
N.A.I.C.S.: 339920

adidas CDC Immobilieninvest GmbH **(1)**
Adi-Dassler-Str 1
91074 Herzogenaurach, Bavaria, Germany
Tel.: (49) 9132 84 0
Fax: (49) 9132 84 2241
E-Mail: customerservice@adidas.com
Web Site: www.adidas.com
Financial Investment Services
S.I.C.: 6211
N.A.I.C.S.: 523999

adidas Insurance & Risk Consultants GmbH **(1)**
Adi-Dassler-Str 1
91074 Herzogenaurach, Germany
Tel.: (49) 9132 84 0
Fax: (49) 9132 842215
General Insurance Services
S.I.C.: 6411
N.A.I.C.S.: 524210

GEV Grundstucksgesellschaft Herzogenaurach mbH & Co. KG **(1)**
Adi-Dassler-Str 1
91074 Herzogenaurach, Bavaria, Germany
Tel.: (49) 9132 84 4766
Fax: (49) 9132 84 9247 66
Financial Investment Services
S.I.C.: 6211
N.A.I.C.S.: 523999

Immobilieninvest und Betriebsgesellschaft Herzo-Base GmbH & Co. KG **(1)**
Adi-Dassler-Str 1
91074 Herzogenaurach, Bavaria, Germany
Tel.: (49) 9132 844089
Fax: (49) 9132 845511
Real Estate Management Services
S.I.C.: 6531
N.A.I.C.S.: 531390

Immobilieninvest und Betriebsgesellschaft Herzo-Base Verwaltungs GmbH **(1)**
Adi-Dassler-Str 1
Herzogenaurach, Bayern, 91074, Germany
Tel.: (49) 9132844089
Fax: (49) 9132845511
Real Estate Investment Services
S.I.C.: 6531
N.A.I.C.S.: 531390

U.S. Subsidiaries:

adidas America, Inc. **(1)**
5055 N Greeley Ave
Portland, OR 97217 OR
Tel.: (971) 234-2300 (100%)
Fax: (971) 234-2450
Toll Free: (800) 423-4327
E-Mail: customerservice@shopadidas.com
Web Site: www.adidas.com
Sales Range: $1-4.9 Billion
Emp.: 1,200
Holding Company; Regional Managing Office
S.I.C.: 6719
N.A.I.C.S.: 551112
Hermann Deininger *(CMO)*

Subsidiaries:

adidas Team, Inc. **(2)**
951 32nd Ave SW
Cedar Rapids, IA 52404-3905
Tel.: (319) 368-0338
Fax: (319) 368-0314
Web Site: www.adidas-team.com
Sporting Goods Distr

S.I.C.: 5091
N.A.I.C.S.: 423910

Mitchell & Ness Nostalgia Company (2)
121 S Broad St 4th Fl
Philadelphia, PA 19107
Tel.: (215) 399-0315
Fax: (215) 731-0131
E-Mail: info@mitchellandness.com
Web Site: www.mitchellandness.com
Sales Range: $10-24.9 Million
Emp.: 55
Vintage Sports Jerseys & Memorabilia
S.I.C.: 5941
N.A.I.C.S.: 451110
Peter Capolino *(Founder)*
Sean McKinney *(Pres)*

Reebok International Ltd. (2)
1895 JW Foster Blvd
Canton, MA 02021-1099 MA
Tel.: (781) 401-5000
Fax: (781) 401-7402
E-Mail: corporate@reebok.com
Web Site: www.reebok.com
Sales Range: $1-4.9 Billion
Emp.: 9,102
Mfr, Distr & Marketer of Footwear & Athletic Apparel
Import Export
S.I.C.: 2389
N.A.I.C.S.: 316210
Herbert Hainer *(CEO)*
Sharon Bryan *(COO)*
Matt O'Toole *(CMO)*

Subsidiaries:

OnField Apparel Group LLC (3)
8677 Logo Athletic Ct
Indianapolis, IN 46219-1430 VA
Tel.: (317) 895-7000
Fax: (317) 895-7250
Web Site: www.reebok.com
Emp.: 1,000
Mfr & Distr of Licensed Sports Apparel
S.I.C.: 3949
N.A.I.C.S.: 339920
Blake Lundberg *(COO)*

Branch:

OnField Apparel Group LLC (4)
5 Industrial Dr
Mattapoisett, MA 02739-1300 MA
Tel.: (508) 758-6101
Fax: (508) 758-4786
Web Site: www.reebok.com
Emp.: 45
Mfr & Distr of Licensed Sports Apparel
S.I.C.: 3949
N.A.I.C.S.: 339920
Steve Cabucio *(VP-Sports Sls)*

RBK Thailand, Inc. (3)
1895 J W Foster Blvd
Canton, MA 02021-1099
Tel.: (781) 401-5000
Footwear Whslr
S.I.C.: 5139
N.A.I.C.S.: 424340

RFC, Inc. (3)
1105 N Market St
Wilmington, DE 19801-1216
Tel.: (302) 427-2512
Sporting Goods Distr
S.I.C.: 5091
N.A.I.C.S.: 423910

The Rockport Company, LLC (3)
1895 J W Foster Blvd
Canton, MA 02021 (100%)
Tel.: (781) 401-5000
Fax: (781) 401-5230
Toll Free: (800) ROCKPORT
E-Mail: rockport@custhelp.com
Web Site: www.rockport.com
Sales Range: $350-399.9 Million
Emp.: 400
Mfr, Distr & Marketer of Comfort Footwear
Import Export
S.I.C.: 2389
N.A.I.C.S.: 316210
Sharon Bryan *(COO)*

Non-U.S. Subsidiaries:

adidas France S.a.r.l. (3)
4 Route De Saessolsheim
PO Box 80067
67700 Landersheim, France
Tel.: (33) 3 88 87 88 00
Fax: (33) 3 88 87 89 80
Web Site: www.adidas.fr
Sporting Goods Distr
S.I.C.: 5091
N.A.I.C.S.: 423910

Reebok-CCM Hockey GmbH (3)
Klausnerring 26
Heimstetten, 85551, Germany
Tel.: (49) 89 990 2250
Fax: (49) 89 990 22555
E-Mail: info@reebok-ccm.com
Emp.: 15
Sports Equipment & Apparel Mfr & Distr
S.I.C.: 3949
N.A.I.C.S.: 339920

Reebok-CCM Hockey, Inc. (3)
3400 Raymond Lasnier
Ville Saint Laurent, QC, H4R 3L3, Canada
Tel.: (514) 461-8000
Fax: (514) 461-8020
Toll Free: (800) 636-5895
E-Mail: reception@reebokccm.com
Web Site: www.ccmhockey.com
Sales Range: $200-249.9 Million
Emp.: 1,376
Sporting Goods & Equipment Mfr
Import Export
S.I.C.: 3949
N.A.I.C.S.: 339920
Philippe Dube *(Pres)*
Matt O'Toole *(CEO)*
Tony Pichirallo *(CFO & VP-Fin-Admin)*
Len Rhodes *(Sr VP & Gen Mgr)*

Reebok de Mexico, S.A. de C.V. (3)
Blvd Adolfo Ruiz Cortinez No 3642 Piso 11
Jardines Del Pedregal
Alvaro Obregon, Mexico, 1900, Mexico
Tel.: (52) 5554818100
Fax: (52) 5554818110
Sporting & Athletic Goods Distr
S.I.C.: 5091
N.A.I.C.S.: 423910

Reebok India Company (3)
7th Floor Unitech Commercial Tower-II
Block B Greenwood City Sector 45
Gurgaon, Haryana, 122001, India
Tel.: (91) 1244124100
Fax: (91) 1242805036
Sporting & Athletic Goods Distr
S.I.C.: 5091
N.A.I.C.S.: 423910

Reebok Jofa AB (3)
Box 66
782 22 Malung, Sweden
Tel.: (46) 280 444 00
Fax: (46) 280 444 01
E-Mail: sport@jofa.se
Web Site: www.jofa.se
Sporting Equipment Distr
S.I.C.: 5091
N.A.I.C.S.: 423910
Janne Heino *(Gen Mgr)*

Reebok Jofa AS (3)
Pancoveien 26
1624 Gressvik, Norway
Tel.: (47) 69 36 45 55
Fax: (47) 69 36 45 65
Web Site: www.reebokhockey.com
Sporting & Athletic Goods Whslr
S.I.C.: 5091
N.A.I.C.S.: 423910
Tryve Skoen *(Mgr)*

Sports Licensed Division of the adidas Group, LLC (2)
1895 J W Foster Blvd
Canton, MA 02021-1099
Tel.: (781) 401-5000
Web Site: www.reeebok.com
Emp.: 1,200
Sporting & Athletic Goods Distr
S.I.C.: 5091
N.A.I.C.S.: 423910
John Warren *(Gen Mgr)*

Stone Age Equipment, Inc. (2)
1419 W State St
Redlands, CA 92373-8164
Tel.: (909) 798-4222
Fax: (909) 798-5272
Emp.: 37
Footwear Retailer
S.I.C.: 5139
N.A.I.C.S.: 424340
Charles David Cole *(Pres)*

Non-U.S. Subsidiary:

Five Ten Europe NV/SA (3)
Avenue Lavoisier 13
1300 Wavre, Belgium
Tel.: (32) 10 23 23 50
Web Site: www.fiveteneurope.be
Sporting Goods Distr
S.I.C.: 5091
N.A.I.C.S.: 423910

TaylorMade-adidas Golf (2)
5545 Fermi Ct
Carlsbad, CA 92008-7324
Tel.: (760) 918-6000
Fax: (760) 918-6014
E-Mail: info@taylormadegolf.com
Web Site: www.taylormadegolf.com
Sales Range: $1-4.9 Billion
Emp.: 1,195
Golf Equipment Mfr
S.I.C.: 3949
N.A.I.C.S.: 339920
Mark King *(Pres & CEO)*
Klauf Flock *(CFO)*
Bob Maggiore *(CMO)*
Ben Sharpe *(Exec VP-Golf & Ashworth)*
Pete Sanchez *(Sr VP-HR-Global)*

Subsidiaries:

Adams Golf, Inc. (3)
2801 E Plano Pkwy
Plano, TX 75074-7418 DE
Tel.: (972) 673-9000
Fax: (972) 398-8818
Toll Free: (800) 709-6142
E-Mail: info@adamsgolf.com
Web Site: www.adamsgolf.com
Emp.: 131
Holding Company; Golf Clubs & Accessories Designer, Mfr & Distr
Import Export
S.I.C.: 6719
N.A.I.C.S.: 551112
John Ward *(Pres)*
Pamela J. High *(CFO)*

Subsidiaries:

Adams Golf Holding Corp. (4)
2801 E Plano Pkwy
Plano, TX 75074-7418 DE
Tel.: (972) 673-9000 (100%)
Fax: (972) 398-8880
E-Mail: info@adamsgolf.com
Web Site: www.adamsgolf.com
Sales Range: $10-24.9 Million
Emp.: 20
Holding Company
S.I.C.: 6719
N.A.I.C.S.: 551112
Pamela J. High *(CFO)*

Adams Golf IP, L.P. (4)
2801 E Plano Pkwy
Plano, TX 75074-7418 DE
Tel.: (972) 673-9000
Fax: (972) 398-8818
E-Mail: info@adamsgolf.com
Web Site: www.adamsgolf.com
Intellectual Property Holding Company
S.I.C.: 6719
N.A.I.C.S.: 551112

Adams Golf, Ltd. (4)
2801 E Plano Pkwy
Plano, TX 75074-7418 TX
Tel.: (972) 673-9000 (100%)
Fax: (972) 398-8818
E-Mail: info@adamsgolf.com
Web Site: www.adamsgolf.com
Emp.: 150
Golf Club Design, Assembly & Retail Sales
S.I.C.: 3949
N.A.I.C.S.: 339920
John Ward *(Pres)*
Pamela J. High *(CFO & Sr VP)*

Adams Golf Management Corp. (4)
2801 E Plano Pkwy
Plano, TX 75074-7418 DE
Tel.: (972) 673-9000 (100%)
Fax: (972) 673-9200
E-Mail: info@adamsgolf.com
Web Site: www.adamsgolf.com
Sales Range: $10-24.9 Million
Emp.: 150
Intra-Company Management & Consulting Services
S.I.C.: 8742
N.A.I.C.S.: 541611
Pamela J. High *(CFO)*

Taylor Made Golf Co. Inc. (3)
5545 Fermi Ct
Carlsbad, CA 92008
Tel.: (760) 918-6000
Fax: (760) 918-6014
Web Site: www.taylormadegolf.com
Emp.: 710
Golf Equipment Mfr
S.I.C.: 3949
N.A.I.C.S.: 339920
Mark King *(Pres & CEO)*
Benoit Vincent *(CTO)*
Sean Toulon *(Exec VP-TaylorMade Product Creation)*
Chuck Presto *(Sr VP-Global Sports Mktg)*

Non-U.S. Subsidiary:

Ashworth UK Limited (3)
21 St Thomas Street
Bristol, BS1 6JS, United Kingdom
Tel.: (44) 8701666555
Fax: (44) 8701666767
Web Site: www.ashwortheurope.com
Sports Apparel, Headwear & Shoes Mfr, Designer, Marketer & Distr
S.I.C.: 2329
N.A.I.C.S.: 315220
Jon Camp *(Mng Dir)*

Tee Off, LLC (2)
16 Downing Dr
Phenix City, AL 36869-3341
Tel.: (334) 291-5151
Sporting Goods Distr
S.I.C.: 5091
N.A.I.C.S.: 423910

Non-U.S. Division:

adidas (Canada) Ltd. (2)
3210 Langstaff Rd
Concord, ON, L4K 5B2, Canada
Tel.: (905) 761-9900
Telex: 65-27277
Fax: (905) 761-9911
Web Site: www.adidas.com
Emp.: 100
Marketer & Retailer of Sporting & Athletic Goods
S.I.C.: 5091
N.A.I.C.S.: 423910
Jim Gabel *(Pres)*
Jackie Tumber *(Coord-Mktg)*

Subsidiaries:

CCM Holdings (1983) Inc. (3)
3400 Rue Raymond-Lasnier
Montreal, QC, H4R 3L3, Canada
Tel.: (514) 461-8000
Investment Management Services
S.I.C.: 6211
N.A.I.C.S.: 523999

R.C. Investments Ltd. (3)
6655 178 St NW Ste 462
Edmonton, AB, T5T 4J5, Canada
Tel.: (780) 444-6698
Financial Management Services
S.I.C.: 6211
N.A.I.C.S.: 523999

Sport Maska Inc. (3)
15855 Ave Hubert Ste 800
Saint-Hyacinthe, QC, J2T4C9, Canada
Tel.: (450) 773-5258
Fax: (450) 773-7924
Sporting & Athletic Goods Mfr & Distr
S.I.C.: 3949
N.A.I.C.S.: 339920

adidas North America, Inc. (1)
5055 N Greeley Ave
Portland, OR 97217-3524
Tel.: (971) 234-2300
Fax: (971) 234-2450
Sporting Goods Distr
S.I.C.: 5091
N.A.I.C.S.: 423910
Patrick Nilsson *(Pres)*
Klaus Flock *(CFO)*

adidas AG—(Continued)

Textronics, Inc. (1)
4 Hillman Dr Ste 130
Chadds Ford, PA 19317
Tel.: (302) 351-5152
Fax: (302) 998-7870
Web Site: www.textronicsinc.com
Wearable Sports Electronics Mfr
S.I.C.: 3949
N.A.I.C.S.: 339920

Non-U.S. Subsidiaries:

adidas Argentina S.A. (1)
Von Wernicke 3023
San Isidro, Buenos Aires, Argentina
Tel.: (54) 1148147200
Fax: (54) 1148147257
Web Site: www.adidas.com
Emp.: 120
Sporting Equipment & Accessories Distr
S.I.C.: 5091
N.A.I.C.S.: 423910
Walter Koll *(Gen Mgr)*

adidas Australia Pty. Limited (1)
767 Springvale Rd
3170 Mulgrave, VIC, Australia
Tel.: (61) 61392635299
Fax: (61) 395453070
Web Site: www.adidas.com
Emp.: 200
Sporting & Athletic Goods Distr
S.I.C.: 5091
N.A.I.C.S.: 423910
David Gaythorpe *(Sec)*

adidas Austria GmbH (1)
Adi Dasse St 1
9073 Viktring, Klagenfurt, Austria (100%)
Tel.: (43) 463284855
Fax: (43) 46328428279
Web Site: www.adidas.com
Emp.: 50
Marketer & Retailer of Sporting & Athletic Goods
S.I.C.: 5091
N.A.I.C.S.: 423910
Erntarb Szuvak *(Mng Dir)*

Non-U.S. Subsidiary:

LLC adidas, Ltd. (2)
Proektiruemy Proezd 5231 Bldg 4/1
119361 Moscow, Russia
Tel.: (7) 495 981 65 55
Fax: (7) 495 981 65 57
E-Mail: info@adidas.ru
Web Site: www.adidas.ru
Emp.: 600
Sporting Goods Distr
S.I.C.: 5091
N.A.I.C.S.: 423910
Martin Shenkland *(Mng Dir)*

adidas Baltics SIA (1)
6 Maskavas Street
Riga, 1050, Latvia
Tel.: (371) 67359400
Fax: (371) 67359409
Emp.: 8
Sporting & Athletic Goods Distr
S.I.C.: 5091
N.A.I.C.S.: 423910

adidas Belgium N.V. (1)
Atomiumsquare 1
BP 320
1020 Brussels, Belgium
Tel.: (32) 24 77 19 89
Fax: (32) 24 77 19 89
Web Site: www.adidas.com
Sports Goods Mfr & Distr
S.I.C.: 3949
N.A.I.C.S.: 339920

adidas Benelux B.V. (1)
Plesmanstraat 1
Leusden, 3833 LA, Netherlands
Tel.: (31) 334963301
Fax: (31) 334963307
Web Site: www.adidas.com
Emp.: 70
Sporting Goods Distr
S.I.C.: 5091
N.A.I.C.S.: 423910
Paul Boerboom *(Gen Mgr)*

adidas Budapest Kft. (1)
Ratrium 45 G Bldg
PO Box 79
1334 Budapest, Hungary (100%)
Tel.: (36) 14511400
Fax: (36) 14511401
E-Mail: info@adidas.com
Web Site: www.adidas.com
Emp.: 95
Marketer & Retailer of Sporting & Athletic Goods
S.I.C.: 5091
N.A.I.C.S.: 423910
Peter Szado *(Mng Dir)*

adidas Bulgaria EAD (1)
Sredets Distr 5 Vitosha
Sofia, 1000, Bulgaria
Tel.: (359) 28114200
Fax: (359) 29802165
Web Site: www.adidas
Emp.: 23
Sporting & Athletic Goods Distr
S.I.C.: 5091
N.A.I.C.S.: 423910
Galina Prangova *(Gen Mgr)*

adidas Chile Ltda. (1)
Av Las Condes 13033
Las Condes, Santiago, Chile
Tel.: (56) 2 431 3800
Fax: (56) 2 715 6801
Web Site: www.adidas.com
Emp.: 650
Sporting Goods Distr
S.I.C.: 5091
N.A.I.C.S.: 423910
Manuel Ovalle *(Gen Mgr)*

adidas (China) Ltd. (1)
29-32/F Tower 1 Grand Gateway 1 Hong Qiao Road
Shanghai, 200030, China
Tel.: (86) 21 2401 0600
Fax: (86) 21 6407 8689
Web Site: www.adidas.com
Sporting & Athletic Products Mfr & Distr
S.I.C.: 3949
N.A.I.C.S.: 339920

adidas Colombia Ltda. (1)
Av Calle 100 No 19-54
Cundinamarca, Bogota, Colombia
Tel.: (57) 16339000
Fax: (57) 16339045
Sporting Equipment & Accessories Distr
S.I.C.: 5091
N.A.I.C.S.: 423910

adidas CR s.r.o. (1)
Zirovnicka 5
10617 Prague, Czech Republic (100%)
Tel.: (420) 267287444
Fax: (420) 272762545
Web Site: www.adidas.com
Emp.: 35
Marketer & Retailer of Sporting & Athletic Goods
S.I.C.: 5091
N.A.I.C.S.: 423910

adidas Croatia d.o.o. (1)
Oreskoviceva 6H
Zagreb, 10000, Croatia
Tel.: (385) 1 5630 700
Fax: (385) 1 5630 709
E-Mail: info.croatia@adidas.com
Web Site: www.adidas.com
Sporting & Athletic Goods Distr
S.I.C.: 5091
N.A.I.C.S.: 423910

adidas (Cyprus) Limited (1)
140 Athalassis Ave
Nicosia, 2024 Strovolos, Cyprus
Tel.: (357) 22519701
Fax: (357) 22519808
Web Site: www.adidas.com
Emp.: 1
Sporting & Athletic Goods Distr
S.I.C.: 5091
N.A.I.C.S.: 423910
Panayiota Ioannou *(Mgr-Fin)*

adidas Danmark A/S (1)
Pilestrade 10
1112 Copenhagen, Denmark
Tel.: (45) 77 55 15 00
Fax: (45) 77 55 1509
Web Site: www.adidas.com
Sporting And Recreation Goods
S.I.C.: 5091
N.A.I.C.S.: 423910

adidas de Mexico S.A. de C.V. (1)
Av Ermita Iztapalapa 1777
Col 8A Ampliacin De San Miguel, 09837
Mexico, Mexico
Tel.: (52) 5556853228
Fax: (52) 5554818150
Web Site: www.adidas.com
Emp.: 200
Sales & Marketing of Sporting & Athletic Goods
S.I.C.: 5091
N.A.I.C.S.: 423910

adidas do Brasil Ltda. (1)
Av Dr Cardoso De Mello 1995 9th Fl
Vila Olimpia, Sao Paulo, 04548 005, Brazil (100%)
Tel.: (55) 1130462900
Fax: (55) 1130463677
Web Site: www.adidas.com.br
Emp.: 140
Sales & Marketing of Sporting & Athletic Goods
S.I.C.: 5091
N.A.I.C.S.: 423910

adidas Emerging Market L.L.C. (1)
9th Floor Easa Saleh Al Gurg Tower
Baniyas Road
PO Box 32512
Dubai, United Arab Emirates
Tel.: (971) 4 2273033
Fax: (971) 4 2226675
Emp.: 115
Sporting & Athletic Goods Distr
S.I.C.: 5091
N.A.I.C.S.: 423910
Osman Ayaz *(Gen Mgr)*

adidas Emerging Markets FZE (1)
Jebel Ali Free Zone
Box 32512
Dubai, United Arab Emirates
Tel.: (971) 4 2068000
Fax: (971) 4 2226675
Emp.: 30
Sports Equipment Distr
S.I.C.: 5091
N.A.I.C.S.: 423910
Osman Ayaz *(Mng Dir)*

Non-U.S. Subsidiary:

adidas Levant Limited (2)
Arar Mustafa Wahbi Al Tal St
Amman, Jordan
Tel.: (962) 6 5602383
Sporting Goods Distr
S.I.C.: 5091
N.A.I.C.S.: 423910

adidas Espana S.A. (1)
Avenida Maria Zambrano 31 Edificio WTC - Torre Este 4a Planta
Zaragoza, 50018, Spain
Tel.: (34) 976 710 100
Fax: (34) 976 710 103
Web Site: www.adidas.com
Sporting Athletic Goods Mfr & Distr
S.I.C.: 3949
N.A.I.C.S.: 339920

adidas Finance Spain S.A. (1)
Calle Maria Zambrano Ed Wtc Torre Este 31
Zaragoza, 50018, Spain
Tel.: (34) 902311000
Fax: (34) 976710103
Financial Management Services
S.I.C.: 6211
N.A.I.C.S.: 523999

adidas Hellas A.E. (1)
38-40 26th Oktovriou
Thessaloniki, 54627, Greece
Tel.: (30) 2310505399
Fax: (30) 2310526397
Web Site: www.adidas.com
Sporting & Athletic Goods Distr
S.I.C.: 5091
N.A.I.C.S.: 423910

adidas Hong Kong Ltd. (1)
18Fl Aia Kowloon Tower Landmark East Ste100
Howming St Kundong, Kowloon, China (Hong Kong) (100%)
Tel.: (852) 21493888
Fax: (852) 21493898
E-Mail: contact@adidas.com
Web Site: www.adidas.com.hk
Emp.: 100
Sales & Marketing of Sporting & Athletic Goods
S.I.C.: 5091
N.A.I.C.S.: 423910
Colin Currie *(Mng Dir-Hong Kong & Taiwan)*

adidas (ILKLEY) Limited (1)
Pepper Road Hazel Grova Stockport
Ilkley, SK7 5SA, United Kingdom
Tel.: (44) 161 419 2500
Emp.: 5
Sporting & Athletic Goods Whslr
S.I.C.: 5091
N.A.I.C.S.: 423910

adidas India Private Ltd. (1)
Unitech Commercial Tower-II 5th Floor
Sector-45 Block-B
Greenwood City, Gurgaon, Gurgaon, 122001, India
Tel.: (91) 124 4569100
Fax: (91) 124 4569160
Web Site: www.adidas.co.in
Sportswear & Equipment Distr
S.I.C.: 5091
N.A.I.C.S.: 423910
Erick Haskell *(Mng Dir)*

adidas Industrial, S.A. de C.V. (1)
Blvd Adolfo Ruiz Cortinez No 3642 Piso 11
Jardines Del Pedregal
Alvaro Obregon, Mexico, 1900, Mexico
Tel.: (52) 5554818100
Fax: (52) 5554818110
Web Site: www.adidas.mx
Sporting Goods Mfr & Distr
S.I.C.: 3949
N.A.I.C.S.: 339920

adidas International Finance B.V. (1)
Hoogoorddreef 9a
Amsterdam, Zuidoost, 1101 BA, Netherlands
Tel.: (31) 205734573
Fax: (31) 205734586
Financial Management Services
S.I.C.: 6211
N.A.I.C.S.: 523999
Dougall Macarthur *(Mgr-Fin)*

adidas International Marketing B.V. (1)
Atlas Complex Africa Building
Hoogoorddreef 9a
1101 BA Amsterdam, Netherlands
Tel.: (31) 20 573 4573
Fax: (31) 20 573 4586
Web Site: www.adidasgroup.com
Sporting & Athletic Goods Whslr
S.I.C.: 5091
N.A.I.C.S.: 423910

adidas International Trading B.V. (1)
Hoogoorddreef 9a
Amsterdam, Zuidoost, 1101, Netherlands
Tel.: (31) 205734573
Fax: (31) 205734586
Web Site: www.adidas.com
Emp.: 50
Sport Goods Whslr
S.I.C.: 5091
N.A.I.C.S.: 423910
Katrin Ley *(Mgr-E-Commerce)*

adidas (Ireland) Ltd. (1)
Leopardstown Office Pk
Sandyford, Dublin, 18, Ireland (100%)
Tel.: (353) 12940850
Fax: (353) 12940826
E-Mail: info@adidas.com
Web Site: www.adidas.com
Emp.: 9
Sporting Goods Distributor
S.I.C.: 5941
N.A.I.C.S.: 451110
Sarah Gower *(Head-PR-UK & Ireland)*

Subsidiary:

Reebok Ireland Limited (2)
Unit 10 Leopardstown Office Park
Foxrock, Dublin, 18, Ireland
Tel.: (353) 1294 35 50
Fax: (353) 1294 35 54
E-Mail: consumer.servicesuk@reebok.com
Web Site: www.reebok.com
Emp.: 4
Sporting Goods Distr

S.I.C.: 5091
N.A.I.C.S.: 423910
Jonathan Kidd *(Gen Mgr)*

adidas Israel Ltd. (1)
6 Hamachtesh
Holon, 58810, Israel
Tel.: (972) 36505300
Fax: (972) 35598807
Sporting & Athletic Goods Distr
S.I.C.: 5091
N.A.I.C.S.: 423910

adidas Italy S.p.A (1)
Via Monte San Primo
Monza, Italy
Tel.: (39) 039 27 15 1
Fax: (39) 039 79 1465
E-Mail: customer.service@adidas.com
Web Site: www.adidas.com
Sporting Athletic Goods Mfr & Distr
S.I.C.: 3949
N.A.I.C.S.: 339920

adidas Japan K.K. (1)
77 Yaraicho Shinjuku-ku
Tokyo, 162-0805, Japan
Tel.: (81) 3 5228 8400
Fax: (81) 3 5228 8405
Web Site: www.adidas.com
Sporting & Athletic Goods Distr
S.I.C.: 5091
N.A.I.C.S.: 423910

adidas Korea Ltd. (1)
Samsunglife Seocho Tower 9F 1321-15
Seocho2-dong
Seocho-gu, Seoul, 137-857, Korea (South)
Tel.: (82) 2 2186 0402
Fax: (82) 2 2564 2912
Web Site: www.adidas.com
Sporting & Athletic Goods Mfr & Distr
S.I.C.: 3949
N.A.I.C.S.: 339920
Zion Armstrong *(Gen Mgr)*

adidas Latin America, S.A. (1)
Business Park Costa Del Este Piso 3 Y 4
Panama, Panama
Tel.: (507) 2083700
Fax: (507) 3035801
Sporting Goods & Accessories Distr
S.I.C.: 5091
N.A.I.C.S.: 423910
Andre Maestrini *(Gen Mgr)*

adidas (Malaysia) Sdn. Bhd. (1)
D-15-03 15th Floor Menara Taiko PJ Trade
Centre No 8 Jalan PJU 8/8A
Bandar Damansara Perdana, 47820
Petaling Jaya, Malaysia
Tel.: (60) 3 7494 9500
Fax: (60) 3 7494 1109
Web Site: www.adidas.com
Sporting & Athletic Goods Distr
S.I.C.: 5091
N.A.I.C.S.: 423910

adidas New Zealand Limited (1)
14 A George Bourke Drive Mt Wellington
Auckland, New Zealand
Tel.: (64) 92597700
Fax: (64) 92597705
Web Site: www.adidas.co.nz
Emp.: 150
Sporting & Athletic Goods Mfr
S.I.C.: 3949
N.A.I.C.S.: 339920
David Huggett *(Dir-Ecommerce)*

adidas Norge A/S (1)
Sommerrovn 5
2816 Gjovik, Norway (100%)
Tel.: (47) 61136500
Fax: (47) 61136585
Web Site: www.adidas.com
Emp.: 40
Marketer & Retailer of Sporting & Athletic Goods
S.I.C.: 5091
N.A.I.C.S.: 423910

Subsidiary:

Reebok-CCM Hockey AS (2)
Pancoveien 26
Gressvik, 1624, Norway
Tel.: (47) 69364555
Fax: (47) 69364565
Sporting Equipment Whslr
S.I.C.: 5091
N.A.I.C.S.: 423910

adidas Poland Sp. z. o. o. (1)
Olbrachta 94
01 102 Warsaw, Poland (100%)
Tel.: (48) 225331800
Fax: (48) 225331801
Web Site: www.adidas.com
Emp.: 60
Marketer & Retailer of Sporting & Athletic Goods
S.I.C.: 5091
N.A.I.C.S.: 423910

adidas Romania S.R.L. (1)
42-44 Sos 2nd Floor Building A
Bucharest, Romania
Tel.: (40) 213067900
Fax: (40) 213067929
Web Site: www.adidas.com
Emp.: 20
Sporting & Athletic Goods Distr
S.I.C.: 5091
N.A.I.C.S.: 423910
Dimitris Karakassis *(Gen Mgr)*

adidas-Salomon Espana S.A. (1)
Maria Sambrano no 31
50018 Zaragoza, Spain
Tel.: (34) 976710100
Fax: (34) 976710103
E-Mail: communication@adidas.com
Web Site: www.adidas.com
Sales Range: $25-49.9 Million
Emp.: 1,100
Sporting & Athletic Goods Marketer & Retailer
Export
S.I.C.: 5091
N.A.I.C.S.: 423910
Carlos Campos *(VP-Mktg)*

adidas Sarragan France S.A.R.L. (1)
Rte De Saessolsheim
PO Box 67
67702 Landersheim, Saverne Cedex, France (100%)
Tel.: (33) 388878800
Fax: (33) 388699725
Web Site: www.adidas.com
Emp.: 1,000
Sales & Marketing of Sporting & Athletic Goods
S.I.C.: 5091
N.A.I.C.S.: 423910

adidas Serbia d.o.o. (1)
Milutina Milankovica 11a
Belgrade, 11070, Serbia
Tel.: (381) 11 285 49 00
Fax: (381) 11 2607699
E-Mail: info.serbia@adidas.com
Emp.: 25
Sporting & Athletic Goods Distr
S.I.C.: 5091
N.A.I.C.S.: 423910
Steven Baker *(Gen Mgr)*

adidas Services Limited (1)
10/F City Plaza Ph 4 12 Taikoo Wan Rd
Taikoo Shing, China (Hong Kong)
Tel.: (852) 23028888
Fax: (852) 23028866
Business Support Services
S.I.C.: 7389
N.A.I.C.S.: 561499

adidas Singapore Pte. Ltd. (1)
77 Robinson Road 05-00
Singapore, 068896, Singapore
Tel.: (65) 65386200
Fax: (65) 65386400
Web Site: www.adidas.com
Sporting & Athletic Goods Distr
S.I.C.: 5091
N.A.I.C.S.: 423910

adidas Slovakia s.r.o. (1)
Galvaniho 15/A
Bratislava, 82104, Slovakia
Tel.: (421) 244451982
Fax: (421) 244451983
Web Site: www.adidas.com
Emp.: 90
Sporting & Athletic Goods Distr
S.I.C.: 5091
N.A.I.C.S.: 423910
Peter Virsik *(Gen Mgr)*

adidas Sourcing Limited (1)
10/F 21-22/F Suites 1407-1470 City Plaza
Four 12 Taikoo Wan Road
Island East, Taikoo Shing, China (Hong Kong)
Tel.: (852) 2149 3888
Fax: (852) 2149 3898
Web Site: www.adidasgroup.com
Sporting & Athletic Goods Distr
S.I.C.: 5091
N.A.I.C.S.: 423910

Non-U.S. Subsidiary:

adidas Korea Technical Services Ltd. (2)
609-809 83 - 8 Geumsa-dong
Geumjeong-gu
Pusan, 609-809, Korea (South)
Tel.: (82) 515201100
Fax: (82) 515258464
Footwear Mfr
S.I.C.: 2389
N.A.I.C.S.: 316210

adidas (South Africa) (Pty) Ltd. (1)
3rd Flr Block 2c Black River Prk North Fir Rd
Cape Town, 7925, South Africa
Tel.: (27) 214426200
Fax: (27) 214480580
Web Site: www.adidas.com
Emp.: 15
Sporting & Athletic Goods Distr
S.I.C.: 5091
N.A.I.C.S.: 423910
Roddy van Breda *(Mng Dir)*

adidas Spor Malzemeleri Satis ve Pazarlama A.S. (1)
Sakir Kesbir Cad Gazi Umur Pasa Sk 25-27
Balmumcu Besiktas, Istanbul, Turkey
Tel.: (90) 212 355 36 00
Fax: (90) 212 267 37 93
Sporting & Athletic Goods Distr
S.I.C.: 5082
N.A.I.C.S.: 423810

adidas Sport GmbH (1)
Brunnmatt 20
6330 Cham, Switzerland
Tel.: (41) 417841414
Fax: (41) 417841415
E-Mail: adidas.swiss@adidas.com
Web Site: www.adidas.com
Emp.: 50
Marketer & Retailer of Sporting & Athletic Goods
S.I.C.: 5091
N.A.I.C.S.: 423910

adidas Suomi Oy (1)
Porkkalankatu 13 J
00180 Helsinki, Finland
Tel.: (358) 30 647 7030
Fax: (358) 30 647 7039
E-Mail: weborder.fi@adidas.com
Web Site: www.adidas.fi
Emp.: 20
Sporting Goods Distr
S.I.C.: 5091
N.A.I.C.S.: 423910
Tuomas Tarvo *(Country Mgr)*

adidas (Suzhou) Co. Ltd. (1)
3/f C No 5 Xinghan Street Industrial Park
Suzhou, Jiangsu, 215021, China
Tel.: (86) 512 67611502
Sporting & Athletic Goods Distr
S.I.C.: 5091
N.A.I.C.S.: 423910

adidas Sverige AB (1)
Gardsvagen 13
169 27 Solna, Sweden (100%)
Tel.: (46) 859929100
Fax: (46) 859929199
E-Mail: kundservice@adidas.se
Web Site: www.adidas.com
Emp.: 150
Marketer & Retailer of Sporting & Athletic Goods
S.I.C.: 5091
N.A.I.C.S.: 423910
Ian Brown *(Dir-Sls)*

Subsidiary:

Reebok-CCM Hockey AB (2)
Vastra Industrigatan 10
Malung, Dalarna, 782 33, Sweden
Tel.: (46) 28044400
Fax: (46) 28014340
Sports Goods Mfr
S.I.C.: 3949
N.A.I.C.S.: 339920

adidas Taiwan Limited (1)
13f 2 Min Chuan E Rd Sec 3
Taipei, 10477, Taiwan
Tel.: (886) 225095900
Fax: (886) 225095905
Web Site: www.adidas.com
Sporting & Athletic Goods Mfr & Distr
S.I.C.: 3949
N.A.I.C.S.: 339920

adidas (Thailand) Co., Ltd. (1)
22nd Floor CRC Tower All Seasons Place
87/2 Wireless Road Lumpini
Patumwan, Bangkok, 10330, Thailand
Tel.: (66) 2 660 3900
Fax: (66) 2 660 3999
Sporting & Athletic Goods Distr
S.I.C.: 5091
N.A.I.C.S.: 423910

adidas Trefoil Trading (U.K.) Limited (1)
The Adidas Centre Pepper Road
Stockport, SK7 5SA, United Kingdom
Tel.: (44) 1614 192500
Web Site: www.adidas.com
Emp.: 50
Clothing & Footwear Whslr
S.I.C.: 5139
N.A.I.C.S.: 424340

adidas Trgovina d.o.o. (1)
Zelezna Cesta 8A
1000 Ljubljana, Slovenia
Tel.: (386) 51 368891
Fax: (386) 42 517701
Emp.: 7
Sporting & Athletic Goods Distr
S.I.C.: 5091
N.A.I.C.S.: 423910

adidas (UK) Ltd. (1)
The Adidas Ctr Pepper Rd
Hazel Grove, Stockport, SK7 5SD, United Kingdom
Tel.: (44) 8702404204
Fax: (44) 1619302384
E-Mail: customercareuk@adidas.com
Web Site: www.adidas.co.uk
Emp.: 450
Sporting & Athletic Goods Distr
S.I.C.: 5091
N.A.I.C.S.: 423910
Nick Craggs *(Head-Mktg)*

Life Sport Ltd. (1)
6 Hamachtesh
Holon, 58810, Israel
Tel.: (972) 36505300
Fax: (972) 36505301
Sportswear Distr
S.I.C.: 5136
N.A.I.C.S.: 424320

P.T. adidas Indonesia Ltd. (1)
Plaza DM 11th Floor Jl Jenderal Sudirman Kav 25
Jakarta, 12920, Indonesia Id
Tel.: (62) 2 1520 5566
Fax: (62) 2 1520 5577
Sporting & Athletic Goods Distr
S.I.C.: 5091
N.A.I.C.S.: 423910

Reebok-CCM Hockey Oy (1)
Kaukjarventie 284
Forssa, 30101, Finland
Tel.: (358) 3 41421
Sporting Goods Distr
S.I.C.: 5091
N.A.I.C.S.: 423910

Reebok Produtos Esportivos Brasil Ltda. (1)
Rua do Retiro 1371 / Bl 2 Ap 73 - Jardim Paris
Jundiai, Sao Paulo, Brazil
Tel.: (55) 11 4522 4087
Sporting Good Mfr
S.I.C.: 3949
N.A.I.C.S.: 339920

Rockport (Europe) B.V. (1)
Hoogoorddreef 9A
1101 BA Amsterdam, Zuidoost, Netherlands

adidas AG—(Continued)

Tel.: (31) 20 573 45 73
E-Mail: reception.nl@addidas.com
Footwear & Athletic Goods Mfr
S.I.C.: 3949
N.A.I.C.S.: 339920
Katrin Ley *(Mgr-E-Commerce)*

SC adidas Ukraine (1)
Bud 15/15 Vul Vikentiya Khvoiky
Kiev, 01021, Ukraine
Tel.: (380) 444902830
Fax: (380) 444902835
Sporting & Athletic Goods Distr
S.I.C.: 5091
N.A.I.C.S.: 423910

Taylor Made Golf Limited (1)
TaylorMade Court Viables Business Park
Jays Close
Basingstoke, RG22 4BS, United Kingdom
Tel.: (44) 1256 479797
Emp.: 200
Sports Equipment Distr
S.I.C.: 5091
N.A.I.C.S.: 423910
Ben Sharpe *(Mng Dir)*

Taylor Made Korea Ltd. (1)
Seocho 2-dong 1321-15 Samsung Life
Seocho Tower 8th Floor
Seoul, Korea (South)
Tel.: (82) 2 2186 0800
Fax: (82) 2 2186 0801
Web Site: korea.taylormadegolf.com
Sporting Goods Distr
S.I.C.: 5091
N.A.I.C.S.: 423910

ADIL BEY HOLDING A.S.

Oymaci Sok No 1 51 Altunizade
34662 Istanbul, Uskudar, Turkey
Tel.: (90) 2165569000
Fax: (90) 216 556 93 98
Business Description:
Holding Company
S.I.C.: 6719
N.A.I.C.S.: 551112

Subsidiary:

Dogan Sirketler Grubu Holding A.S. (1)
Burhaniye Mahallesi Kisikli Caddesi No 65
Uskudar, 34676 Istanbul, Turkey
Tel.: (90) 2165569000
Fax: (90) 2165569284
Web Site: www.doganholding.com.tr
DOHOL—(IST)
Sls.: $1,783,846,408
Assets: $4,898,921,521
Liabilities: $2,587,301,336
Net Worth: $2,311,620,185
Earnings: $145,571,272
Emp.: 13,750
Fiscal Year-end: 12/31/12
Energy Distribution, Insurance, Media, Industry, Trade & Tourism
S.I.C.: 4939
N.A.I.C.S.: 221122
Yasar Begumhan Dogan Faralyali *(Chm)*
Hanzade V. Dogan Boyner *(Vice Chm)*
Yahya Uzdiyen *(CEO)*
Ahmet Toksoy *(CFO)*
Erem Turgut Yucel *(Chief Legal Officer)*

ADIMMUNE CORPORATION

3 Sec 1 Tanxing Rd
Tanzi District, Taichung, 42723, Taiwan
Tel.: (886) 4 25381220
Fax: (886) 4 25395133
E-Mail: biz@adimmune.com.tw
Web Site: www.adimmune.com.tw
Year Founded: 1965
4142—(TAI)
Sales Range: $1-9.9 Million
Emp.: 260
Business Description:
Human Vaccine Mfr & Distr
S.I.C.: 2834
N.A.I.C.S.: 325412
Personnel:
Chi-Shean Chan *(Chm & Gen Mgr)*

ADINATH BIO-LABS LTD.

4 N S Road 1st Floor
Kolkata, 700 001, India
Tel.: (91) 33 22315718
E-Mail: info@adinathbio.com
Web Site: www.adinathbio.com
590088—(BOM)
Rev.: $7,969,056
Assets: $5,414,421
Liabilities: $30,315
Net Worth: $5,384,107
Earnings: $129,264
Emp.: 25
Fiscal Year-end: 03/31/13
Business Description:
Pharmaceutical Research & Development Services
S.I.C.: 2834
N.A.I.C.S.: 325412
Personnel:
Sujata Dange *(Compliance Officer & Sec)*
Board of Directors:
M. K. Bothra
A. K. Jain
Jyotiraaditya Singha
Alam Ali Sisodia
Transfer Agent:
Adroit Corporate Services Pvt. Ltd.
19, Jaferbhoy Industrial Estate 1st Floor
Makwana Road
Marol Naka Andheri E, 400 059 Mumbai, India

ADINATH EXIM RESOURCES LTD.

6th Floor Astron Tower Opp Fun Republic Cinema
Nr Iscon Temple Satellite S G Highway, Ahmedabad, 380015, India
Tel.: (91) 79 26862076
Fax: (91) 79 26862078
Web Site: www.adinatheximresources.com
Year Founded: 1995
532056—(BOM)
Rev.: $52,884
Assets: $1,290,573
Liabilities: $9,910
Net Worth: $1,280,663
Earnings: $24,422
Fiscal Year-end: 03/31/13
Business Description:
Financial Management Services
S.I.C.: 6211
N.A.I.C.S.: 523999
Personnel:
Bharat Suthar *(Compliance Officer)*
Board of Directors:
Manish B. Joshi
Manoj S. Savla
Paras S. Savla
Shetal A. Shah
Transfer Agent:
Bigshare Services Pvt Ltd
E-2 Ansa Industrial Estate Sakivihar Rd
Sakinaka Andheri E
Mumbai, India

ADING SKOPJE

Ul Novoselski pat bb
1000 Skopje, Macedonia
Tel.: (389) 2 2034 800
Fax: (389) 2 2034 810
E-Mail: ading@ading.com.mk
Web Site: www.ading.com.mk
Year Founded: 1969
ADIN—(MAC)
Business Description:
Construction Materials Distr
S.I.C.: 5039
N.A.I.C.S.: 423390
Personnel:
Doncev Blagoja *(Chm & Gen Mgr)*
Mojsovski Blagoja *(Pres)*
Filiposki Petre *(Deputy Pres & Gen Mgr)*
Board of Directors:
Belev Aleksandar
Doncev Blagoja
Mojsovski Blagoja
Stojanovski Boro
Karatukov Donco
Ivanovska Vukelik Milica
Filiposki Petre
Aleksandar Velickovic
Petrovski Zoran

ADINOTEC AG

Bunsenstrasse 5
D-64347 Griesheim, Germany
Tel.: (49) 6155824400
Fax: (49) 6155824495
E-Mail: info@adinotec.com
Web Site: www.adinotec.com
Year Founded: 2004
N1N—(DEU)
Sls.: $1,857,715
Assets: $10,500,126
Liabilities: $8,077,020
Net Worth: $2,423,106
Earnings: ($1,076,936)
Emp.: 13
Fiscal Year-end: 12/31/12
Business Description:
Medical Products Mfr
S.I.C.: 2834
N.A.I.C.S.: 325412
Personnel:
Thomas Milde *(Chm-Supervisory Bd)*
Christian Eigen *(Deputy Chm-Supervisory Bd)*
Edmund Krix *(CEO & Member-Exec Bd)*
Bruno Wuethrich *(COO & Member-Exec Bd)*
Supervisory Board of Directors:
Thomas Milde
Christian Eigen
Marian von Korff

ADIPOSET LTD.

Cardinal House 46 St Nicholas Street
Ipswich, Suffolk, IP1 1TT, United Kingdom
Mailing Address:
IP City
1 Bath Street, Ipswich, Suffolk, IP2 8SD, United Kingdom
E-Mail: enquiries@adiposet.com
Web Site: www.adiposet.com
Year Founded: 2011
Emp.: 4
Business Description:
Operates as Tissue Bank for Storage of Adipose Tissue
S.I.C.: 3841
N.A.I.C.S.: 339112
Personnel:
Timothy Charles Bullock *(CEO)*
Mark Paul Smyth *(Sec)*

Subsidiary:

Altrika Limited (1)
The Innovation Centre 217 Portobello
Sheffield, South Yorkshire, S1 4DP, United Kingdom
Tel.: (44) 1142220985
Fax: (44) 1142224165
E-Mail: info@regenerys.com
Web Site: www.regenerys.com
Emp.: 7
Pharmaceutical Products Mfr
S.I.C.: 2834
N.A.I.C.S.: 325412
David Haddow *(Dir-Ops)*

ADIRA ENERGY LTD.

120 Adelaide Street West Suite 1204
Toronto, ON, M5H 1T1, Canada
Tel.: (416) 250-6500
Fax: (416) 250-6330
Web Site: www.adiraenergy.com
Year Founded: 1997
ADL—(OTC TSXV)
Rev.: $1,889,000
Assets: $15,340,000
Liabilities: $10,330,000
Net Worth: $5,010,000
Earnings: ($10,557,000)
Emp.: 16
Fiscal Year-end: 12/31/12
Business Description:
Oil & Gas Exploration Services
S.I.C.: 1311
N.A.I.C.S.: 211111
Personnel:
Dennis Bennie *(Co-Chm)*
Amos Lasker *(Co-Chm)*
Colin B. Kinley *(Pres & COO)*
Jeffrey E. Walter *(CEO)*
Alan Friedman *(Exec VP-Corp Dev)*
Board of Directors:
Dennis Bennie
Amos Lasker
Richard P. Crist
Alan Friedman
Colin B. Kinley
Jeffrey E. Walter
Legal Counsel:
Aird & Berlis LLP
Brookfield Place 181 Bay Street Suite 1800 Box 754
Toronto, ON, Canada
Transfer Agent:
Computershare Trust Company of Canada
510 Burrard St 3rd Fl
Vancouver, BC, V6C 3B9, Canada

Subsidiary:

Adira Energy Corp (1)
Unit 1204 120 Adelaide St W
Toronto, ON, M4V 3A1, Canada
Tel.: (416) 250-1955
Fax: (416) 250-6330
E-Mail: contact@adiraenergy.com
Web Site: www.adiraenergy.com
Emp.: 3
Oil & Gas Exploration Services
S.I.C.: 1311
N.A.I.C.S.: 211111
Colin B. Kinley *(Pres)*

Non-U.S. Subsidiary:

Adira Energy Israel Ltd. (1)
12 Abba Hillel Silver 12th Floor
Ramat Gan, 52506, Israel
Tel.: (972) 3 373 0166
Fax: (972) 3 373 0167
Oil & Gas Exploration Services
S.I.C.: 1389
N.A.I.C.S.: 213112
Hezi Kugler *(CEO)*

THE ADITYA BIRLA GROUP

Aditya Birla Centre 1st Floor C Wing
SK Ahire Marg
Mumbai, Worli, 400 030, India
Tel.: (91) 22 6652 5000
Fax: (91) 22 6652 5741
Web Site: www.adityabirla.com
Year Founded: 1857
Sales Range: $25-49.9 Billion
Emp.: 133,000
Business Description:
Holding Company: Synthetic Fiber Operations
S.I.C.: 6719
N.A.I.C.S.: 551112
Personnel:
Kumar Mangalam Birla *(Chm)*
Pragnya Ram *(Grp Exec Pres-Corp Comm)*
Santrupt B. Misra *(CEO-Carbon Black Bus & Grp Dir-HR)*
Ajay Srinivasan *(CEO-Fin Svcs)*

Subsidiaries:

Aditya Birla Management Corporation Limited (1)
Aditya Birla Centre 3rd Floor SK Ahire Marg
Worli, Mumbai, 400 025, India (100%)
Tel.: (91) 225 652 5000
Fax: (91) 225 652 5750
E-Mail: chmo@adityabirla.com
Web Site: www.adityabirla.com
Emp.: 50
Management Services & Various Manufacturing Operations
S.I.C.: 8748
N.A.I.C.S.: 541618
Kumar Mangalam Birla *(Chm)*
Santrupt B. Misra *(CEO-Carbon Black & Dir-Grp HR)*

Aditya Birla Nuvo Limited (1)
Indian Rayon Compound Veraval
Ahmedabad, Gujarat, 362 266, India In
Tel.: (91) 2876 245711 (51.05%)
Fax: (91) 2876 243220
E-Mail: abnlsecretarial@adityabirla.com
Web Site: www.adityabirlanuvo.com
500303—(BOM)
Rev.: $4,821,080,418
Assets: $10,586,938,842
Liabilities: $8,672,735,754
Net Worth: $1,914,203,088
Earnings: $196,318,206
Emp.: 19,000
Fiscal Year-end: 03/31/13
Rayon Yarn Mfr
S.I.C.: 2299
N.A.I.C.S.: 313110
Rakesh Jain *(Mng Dir, Head-Agri & Insulators & Dir-IT-ITeS)*
Sushil Agarwal *(CFO)*
Hutokshi Wadia *(Compliance Officer, Sec & VP)*
Ashish Dikshit *(CEO-Madura Fashion & Lifestyle)*
Lalit Naik *(Deputy Mng Dir & Head-Agri, Insulators & Viscose Filament Yarn)*

Subsidiaries:

Aditya Birla Minacs Worldwide Limited (2)
Campus 4A Ecospace Business Park Outer Ring Road
Bellandur, Bengaluru, Maharashtra, 560103, India In
Tel.: (91) 80 4144 6000
E-Mail: info@minacs.adityabirla.com
Web Site: www.minacs.adityabirla.com
Sales Range: $25-49.9 Million
Business Process Outsourcing Services
S.I.C.: 7389
N.A.I.C.S.: 561499
Anil Bhalla *(Pres & COO)*
Deepak Patel *(Mng Dir & CEO)*
Ramesh Kamath *(CFO)*
Michael Iseyemi *(Chief Security Officer)*
Guy Brosseau *(Pres-Info Sys)*

Subsidiary:

Aditya Birla Minacs IT Services Limited (3)
Campus 4A Ecospace Business Park Outer Ring Road Bellandur
Bengaluru, 560 103, India (70%)
Tel.: (91) 80 4144 6000
Fax: (91) 80 5661 8499
E-Mail: info@minacs.adityabirla.com
Web Site: www.minacs.adityabirla.com
Sales Range: $300-349.9 Million
Emp.: 500
Information Technology Services
S.I.C.: 7374
N.A.I.C.S.: 518210
Paneesh Rao *(Pres)*
Deepak Patel *(CEO)*

Non-U.S. Subsidiary:

Minacs Worldwide Inc. (3)
1189 colonel Sam Dr
Toronto, ON, L1H 8W8, Canada ON
Tel.: (416) 380-3800
Fax: (416) 380-3665
Toll Free: (888) 646-2271
E-Mail: investors@minacs.com
Web Site: www.minacs.com
Sales Range: $200-249.9 Million
Emp.: 7,030
Business Process Outsourcing Services
S.I.C.: 7389
N.A.I.C.S.: 561499
Edpek Patel *(CEO)*
Gerry McDonald *(COO-North America & Europe)*
G. Sivaramakrishnan *(Chief Sls/Mktg Officer)*
Paneesh Rao *(Chief People Officer-IT/ ITES)*
Anil Bhalla *(Pres-Ops-North America & Europe)*
Sax Krishna *(Pres-Hitech)*
Tanvir Khan *(Exec VP-Sls)*
Sandra Smith *(Exec VP-Sls-Automotive)*

U.S. Subsidiary:

Minacs Group (U.S.A.) Inc. (4)
34115 W 12 Mile Rd
Farmington Hills, MI 48331
Tel.: (248) 553-8355
Fax: (248) 488-3696
Toll Free: (800) 832-1935
Web Site: www.minacs.com
Sales Range: $100-124.9 Million
Emp.: 100
Business Process Outsourcing Services
S.I.C.: 7389
N.A.I.C.S.: 561499
Deepak Patel *(CEO)*
Ramesh Kamath *(CFO)*
Gerry McDonald *(COO)*

Aditya Birla Money Limited (2)
Ali Centre 53 Greams Road
Chennai, 600006, India
Tel.: (91) 4428294702
Fax: (91) 4428290835
E-Mail: abm.investorgrievance@adityabirla.com
Web Site: www.adityabirlamoney.com
BIRLAMONEY—(NSE)
Rev.: $17,397,448
Assets: $37,070,264
Liabilities: $30,420,729
Net Worth: $6,649,535
Earnings: ($2,838,930)
Emp.: 897
Fiscal Year-end: 03/31/13
Asset Management Services
S.I.C.: 6799
N.A.I.C.S.: 523920
Sudhakar Ramasubramanian *(Mng Dir)*
Manoj Kumar Gandhi *(CFO)*
Ravishankar Gopalan *(COO)*
Saurabh Shukla *(Chief Sls Officer)*
S. Balaji *(Compliance Officer & Sec)*

Subsidiary:

Aditya Birla Money Mart Limited (3)
1 Indiabulls Centre Tower 1 14th Floor 841 SB Marg
Elphinstone Road, Mumbai, 400 013, India
Tel.: (91) 22 43568300
Fax: (91) 22 43568310
E-Mail: connect@birlasunlife.com
Web Site: www.adityabirlamoney.com
Financial Services
S.I.C.: 6211
N.A.I.C.S.: 523999
Sudhakar Ramasubramanian *(CEO)*

Indo Gulf Fertilisers Limited (2)
Jagdishpur Industrial Area
Jagdishpur, Sultanpur, Uttar Pradesh, 227 817, India
Tel.: (91) 5361270032
Fax: (91) 5361270595
E-Mail: igfl@adityabirla.com
Web Site: www.indo-gulf.com
Nitrogenous Fertilizer
S.I.C.: 2873
N.A.I.C.S.: 325311
Jayant Dua *(CEO)*

Affiliates:

Grasim Industries Limited (1)
Birlagram
Nagda, Madhya Pradesh, 456 331, India
Tel.: (91) 7366246760
Fax: (91) 7366246024
E-Mail: shares@adityabirla.com
Web Site: www.grasim.com
500300—(BOM)
Rev.: $5,762,678,814
Assets: $8,171,245,440
Liabilities: $3,373,553,232
Net Worth: $4,797,692,208
Earnings: $501,393,906
Emp.: 7,301
Fiscal Year-end: 03/31/13
Cement, Fibers & Chemicals Mfr
S.I.C.: 3241
N.A.I.C.S.: 327310
Pavan K. Jain *(Pres-Corp Fin Div)*
K. K. Maheshwari *(Mng Dir & Head-Fibre & Pulp Bus)*
Adesh Gupta *(CFO)*
S. N. Jajoo *(CMO-Cement Bus)*
Ashok Malu *(Compliance Officer & Sec)*

Subsidiary:

UltraTech Cement Ltd. (2)
B Wing 2nd Floor Ahura Centre Mahakali Caves Road Andheri East
Mumbai, 400 093, India
Tel.: (91) 2266917800
Fax: (91) 2266928109
E-Mail: sharesutcl@adityabirla.com
Web Site: www.ultratechcement.com
532538—(BOM NSE)
Sls.: $4,422,186,756
Assets: $5,485,952,628
Liabilities: $2,647,903,194
Net Worth: $2,838,049,434
Earnings: $496,451,142
Emp.: 12,660
Fiscal Year-end: 03/31/13
Cement Mfr
S.I.C.: 3241
N.A.I.C.S.: 327310
Rahul Mohnot *(Sr Pres-Birla White)*
K. C. Birla *(CFO)*
S. N. Jajoo *(CMO)*
C. B. Tiwari *(Chief People Officer)*
S. K. Chatterjee *(Compliance Officer & Sec)*
R. K. Shah *(Chief Mfg Officer)*
Pragnya Ram *(Pres-Corp Comm & CSR)*
Prabir Ray *(Pres-RMC, BPD & Key Accts)*
Vivek Agrawal *(CEO-Star Cement Co LLC)*

Non-U.S. Holding:

AV Cell Inc. (2)
175 Mill Rd
Atholville, Saint John, NB, E3N 4S7, Canada (45%)
Tel.: (506) 789-4343
Fax: (506) 789-4103
E-Mail: sv.sharda@avg.adityabirla.com
Web Site: www.adityabirla.com
Emp.: 300
Specialty Cellulose Mills
S.I.C.: 2899
N.A.I.C.S.: 325199
S. V. Sharda *(CFO & VP)*

Hindalco Industries Ltd. (1)
Century Bhavan 3rd Floor Dr Annie Besant Road
Worli, Mumbai, 400 030, India (32.08%)
Tel.: (91) 2266626666
Fax: (91) 2224362516
E-Mail: info@hindalco.com
Web Site: www.hindalco.com
500440—(BOM)
Rev.: $15,247,850,346
Assets: $22,357,313,694
Liabilities: $15,480,918,540
Net Worth: $6,876,395,154
Earnings: $561,185,406
Emp.: 20,238
Fiscal Year-end: 03/31/13
Aluminum & Copper Products Mfr
S.I.C.: 3365
N.A.I.C.S.: 331524
Debu Bhattacharya *(Mng Dir)*
Praveen Maheshwari *(CFO)*
Sachin Satpute *(CMO-Aluminium)*
Vineet Kaul *(Chief People Officer)*
Anil Malik *(Compliance Officer & Sec)*
Satish M. Bhatia *(Pres-Foil & Pkg)*
R. S. Dhulkhed *(Sr Pres-Ops)*
Dilip Singh Gaur *(Pres-Copper)*
Sanjay Sehgal *(Pres-Chemicals)*
Satish Pai *(Deputy Mng Dir)*

Subsidiaries:

Aditya Birla Chemicals (India) Ltd. (2)
Ghanshyam Kunj Garhwa Road
PO Rehla
822 124 Palamau, Jharkhand, India
Tel.: (91) 6584262211
Fax: (91) 6584262205
E-Mail: abcil@adityabirla.com
Web Site: www.adityabirlachemicals.com
500057—(BOM)
Rev.: $164,735,576
Assets: $269,955,044
Liabilities: $200,032,083
Net Worth: $69,922,961
Earnings: $3,642,888
Emp.: 929
Fiscal Year-end: 03/31/13
Chemicals Business
S.I.C.: 2833
N.A.I.C.S.: 325411
V. R. Agrawal *(Mng Dir & Head-Renukoot Unit)*
Akash Mishra *(Compliance Officer & Sec)*

U.S. Subsidiary:

Novelis Inc. (2)
3560 Lenox Rd Ste 2000
Atlanta, GA 30326 Ca
Tel.: (404) 760-4000
Fax: (404) 814-4219
E-Mail: media.relations@novelis.com
Web Site: www.novelis.com
Sls.: $9,812,000,000
Assets: $8,522,000,000
Liabilities: $8,283,000,000
Net Worth: $239,000,000
Earnings: $203,000,000
Emp.: 10,970
Fiscal Year-end: 03/31/13
Aluminum Rolled Semi-Finished Products Mfr
Import Export
S.I.C.: 3355
N.A.I.C.S.: 331318
Kumar Mangalam Birla *(Chm)*
Debnarayan Bhattacharya *(Vice Chm)*
Philip R. Martens *(Pres & CEO)*
Steven R. Fisher *(CFO & Sr VP)*
Karen K. Renner *(CIO & VP)*
Leslie J. Parrette, Jr. *(Chief Compliance Officer, Gen Counsel, Sec & Sr VP)*
Jack Clark *(CTO)*
Robert Nelson *(Chief Acctg Officer, VP-Fin & Controller)*
John Gardner *(Chief Sustainability Officer & VP)*
Manfred Stanek *(Chief Comml Officer & VP-Strategy)*
Leslie W. Joyce *(Chief People Officer)*
Shashi K. Maudgal *(Pres-Asia & Sr VP)*
Antonio Tadeu Coelho Nardocci *(Pres-South America & Sr VP)*
Marco Antonio Palmieri *(Pres-North America & Sr VP)*
Randal Miller *(VP & Treas)*

Subsidiary:

Novelis Corporation (3)
3560 Lenox Rd Ne Ste 2000
Atlanta, GA 30326-4271 TX
Tel.: (440) 423-6600
Fax: (440) 423-6610
Web Site: www.novelis.com
Emp.: 200
Aluminum Products Mfr
S.I.C.: 3353
N.A.I.C.S.: 331315
Gary Yogan *(VP-Sls)*

Units:

Novelis Industrial Products Group (4)
6060 Parkland Blvd
Mayfield Heights, OH 44124-4185
Tel.: (440) 423-6600
Fax: (440) 423-6654
Web Site: www.ipg.novelis.com
Goods & Services to Users of Aluminum Products
S.I.C.: 3355
N.A.I.C.S.: 331318
George Pursey *(Market Dir)*

Novelis Light Gauge Products (4)
6060 Parkland Blvd
Mayfield Heights, OH 44124
Tel.: (440) 423-6600
Fax: (440) 423-6655
Web Site: www.lightgauge.novelis.com
Light Gauge Aluminum Products Mfr
S.I.C.: 3355
N.A.I.C.S.: 331318

The Aditya Birla Group—(Continued)

Non-U.S. Unit:

Novelis Foil Products (4)
191 Evans Ave
Toronto, ON, M8Z 1J5, Canada
Tel.: (416) 503-6700
Fax: (416) 503-6720
Emp.: 200
Household Foil Product & Packaging Mfr & Whslr
S.I.C.: 3353
N.A.I.C.S.: 331315

U.S. Branch:

Novelis Foil Products USA (5)
1706 Shorewood Dr
Barnesville, GA 30240
Tel.: (706) 812-2000
Fax: (706) 812-2039
Toll Free: (800) 776-8701
Web Site: www.foil.novelis.com
Emp.: 50
Household Foil Product & Packaging Whslr
S.I.C.: 5099
N.A.I.C.S.: 423990
Charlie Ahern *(Gen Mgr)*

Non-U.S. Subsidiaries:

Aluminum Company of Malaysia Berhad (3)
3 Persiaran Waji Kawasan Perindustrian Bukit
Kelang, Selangor Darul Eshan, 41050, Malaysia
Tel.: (60) 333466262
Telex: MA 39403 ALCOM
Fax: (60) 33412793
Web Site: www.novalis.com
Sls.: $71,048,072
Emp.: 360
Aluminum Rolling & Processing
Import Export
S.I.C.: 3353
N.A.I.C.S.: 331315

Novelis do Brasil Ltda. (3)
Av Nacoes Unidas 12551 15th Fl
Sao Paulo, 04578 000, Brazil
Tel.: (55) 1155030722
Telex: 1136391
Fax: (55) 1155030791
Web Site: www.novelis.com.br
Emp.: 60
Bauxite Mining, Alumina, Primary Aluminum, Plate, Sheet, Plain & Converted Foil & Foil Containers
S.I.C.: 1099
N.A.I.C.S.: 212299
Alexandre Moreira Martins de Almeida *(Pres)*

Novelis Italia SpA (3)
Via Vittorio Veneto 106
I 20091 Milan, Italy
Tel.: (39) 02614541
Telex: 312319
Fax: (39) 0261454208
Web Site: www.novelis-painted.com
Emp.: 500
Aluminum Coil & Sheet Mfr
Import Export
S.I.C.: 3354
N.A.I.C.S.: 331318
Steve Clark *(Mng Dir)*
Erwin Mayr *(Pres-Europe)*

Novelis Korea Limited (3)
Yonseijaedan Severance Building 23rd Floor
84-11 5-ga Namdaemun-ro, Seoul, Jung-gu, 100-753, Korea (South)
Tel.: (82) 222591600
Fax: (82) 22591414
E-Mail: webmaster_korea@novelis.com
Web Site: www.novelis.co.kr
Emp.: 1,200
Rolled Aluminum
S.I.C.: 3354
N.A.I.C.S.: 331318
Michael Hong *(CFO)*

Novelis PAE S.A.S. (3)
Centr Alp 725 rue Aristide Berges
F-38340 Voreppe, France
Tel.: (33) 476578500
Fax: (33) 476566539
E-Mail: pae.marketing@novelis.com
Web Site: www.novelis.com
Emp.: 100
Aluminum Casting & Molten Metal Treatments
S.I.C.: 3364
N.A.I.C.S.: 331523
Philippe Charlier *(VP)*

Non-U.S. Subsidiary:

Aditya Birla Minerals Limited (2)
Level 3 Septimus Roe Square
256 Adelaide Terrace, Perth, WA, 6000, Australia
Tel.: (61) 893668800
Fax: (61) 93668805
E-Mail: investorrelations@adityabirla.com.au
Web Site: www.adityabirlaminerals.com.au
ABY—(ASX)
Rev.: $523,481,219
Assets: $698,482,114
Liabilities: $167,222,661
Net Worth: $531,259,454
Earnings: ($8,656,725)
Emp.: 597
Fiscal Year-end: 03/31/13
Copper Exploration, Mining, Processing & Marketing
S.I.C.: 1021
N.A.I.C.S.: 212234
Sunil Kulwal *(CEO & Mng Dir)*
Shanti Lal Dugar *(CFO)*
Peter Patrick Torre *(Sec)*

Joint Ventures:

Century Enka Ltd. (1)
Century Arcade 2nd Floor Narangi Baug Road
Pune, 411 001, India In
Tel.: (91) 202616 6511
Fax: (91) 202616 6511
E-Mail: regdoffice@centuryenka.com
Web Site: www.centuryenka.com
500280—(BOM KOL NSE)
Rev.: $290,024,928
Assets: $205,705,008
Liabilities: $84,484,926
Net Worth: $121,220,082
Earnings: $4,058,406
Emp.: 1,496
Fiscal Year-end: 03/31/13
Synthetic Fibers Mfr
S.I.C.: 2299
N.A.I.C.S.: 314999
C. B. Gagrani *(Sec)*

Tanfac Industries Limited (1)
14 Sipcot Inustrial Complex
SAV District, Cuddalore, 607 005, India
Tel.: (91) 4142239001
Fax: (91) 4142239008
E-Mail: sendhil.naathan@adityabirla.com
Web Site: www.tanfac.com
Emp.: 50
Fluorine Chemicals Mfr
S.I.C.: 2899
N.A.I.C.S.: 325998
S. Prasath *(Sec)*

U.S. Subsidiary:

Columbian Chemicals Company (1)
1800 W Oak Commons Ct
Marietta, GA 30062-2253
Tel.: (770) 792-9400
Fax: (770) 792-9328
Toll Free: (800) 235-4003
Web Site: www.columbianchemicals.com
Sales Range: $800-899.9 Million
Emp.: 1,300
Carbon Black & Synthetic Iron Oxide Mfr
S.I.C.: 2819
N.A.I.C.S.: 325180
Kevin Boyle *(Pres & CEO)*
Mark Breen *(CFO & Sr VP-Fin)*
Ronaldo Silva Duarte *(Pres-South America)*

Subsidiary:

Columbian International Chemicals Corporation (2)
1800 W Oak Commons Ct
Marietta, GA 30062
Tel.: (770) 792-9400
Fax: (770) 792-9623
Toll Free: (800) 235-4003
Web Site: www.columbianchemicals.com
Holding Company for International Operations
S.I.C.: 6719
N.A.I.C.S.: 551112

Non-U.S. Subsidiaries:

Columbian Chemicals Brasil, Ltda. (3)
Rua Dr Candido Espinheira 560
7 andar cjs 71 e 72
Perdizes, Sao Paulo, SP, 05004 000, Brazil
Tel.: (55) 11 3598 3800
Carbon Black Sales & Mfr
S.I.C.: 2819
N.A.I.C.S.: 325180

Columbian Chemicals Europa GmbH (3)
Podbielski Strasse 160
30177 Hannover, Germany
Tel.: (49) 511 63089 0
Fax: (49) 511 63089 12
Carbon Black Sales
S.I.C.: 5169
N.A.I.C.S.: 424690

Columbian Chemicals Korea Co., Ltd. (3)
7th Floor Tae-woo Building 1357-10 Seocho-Dong
Seocho-Gu, Seoul, 137 070, Korea (South) Ks
Tel.: (82) 2 775 1674
Carbon Black Sales
S.I.C.: 5169
N.A.I.C.S.: 424690

Non-U.S. Subsidiaries:

Aditya Birla Chemicals (Thailand) Ltd., Epoxy Division (1)
888 167 Mahatun Plaza Bldg 16th Floor Ploenchit Rd
Bangkok, 10330, Thailand
Tel.: (66) 2 253 5031 (-3)
Fax: (66) 2 253 5030
E-Mail: epotec@thaiepoxy.com
Web Site: www.epotec.info
Emp.: 200
Adhesive Chemical Products Mfr
S.I.C.: 2891
N.A.I.C.S.: 325520
H. Agarwal *(Pres)*

PT Elegant Textile Industry (1)
Desa Ubrug Jatiluhur
Purwakarta, Jawa Bharat, 41152, Indonesia
Tel.: (62) 264202151
Fax: (62) 264201047
E-Mail: factory.pte@adityabirla.com
Web Site: www.adityabirla-yarn.com
Emp.: 1,800
Spun Rayon Mfr
S.I.C.: 2399
N.A.I.C.S.: 313110
Kishan Singhania *(Mgr-Mktg-Domestic)*

Non-U.S. Affiliates:

Thai Rayon Public Company Limited (1)
888/160-1 Mahatun Plaza Building 16th Floor Ploenchit Road Lumpini
Pathumwan, Bangkok, 10330, Thailand
Tel.: (66) 22536745
Fax: (66) 22543181
E-Mail: rayon@thairayon.com
Web Site: www.thairayon.com
TR—(THA)
Rev.: $400,313,674
Assets: $798,140,654
Liabilities: $128,639,310
Net Worth: $669,501,345
Earnings: ($11,871,769)
Emp.: 987
Fiscal Year-end: 03/31/13
Viscose Rayon Staple Fibre Mfr
S.I.C.: 2823
N.A.I.C.S.: 325220
Kumar Mangalam Birla *(Chm)*
Hari Krishna Agarwal *(Pres)*
Prasan Kumar Sipani *(Pres-Works)*
Suwanna Chalermwat *(Sec)*

Affiliates:

Thai Acrylic Fibre Company Limited (2)
Mahatun Plaza Bldg 16th Floor
888 168-169 Ploenchit Road, Bangkok, Thailand TH
Tel.: (66) 22536740 (30%)
Fax: (66) 22534679
E-Mail: marketing@thaiacrylic.com
Web Site: www.thaiacrylic.com
Emp.: 400
Acrylic Fiber Mfr
S.I.C.: 2399
N.A.I.C.S.: 314999
Biswajit Chaudhuri *(CMO)*

Thai Carbon Black Public Co., Ltd. (2)
888/122 888/128 Mahatun Plaza 12th Floor
Ploenchit Road Lumpini
Pratumwan, Bangkok, 10330, Thailand TH
Tel.: (66) 2 2536745 (24.98%)
E-Mail: tcb.marketing@adityabirla.com
Web Site: www.birlacarbon.com
TCB—(THA)
Rev.: $79,856,883
Assets: $525,462,341
Liabilities: $183,455,056
Net Worth: $342,007,285
Earnings: $7,742,481
Emp.: 301
Fiscal Year-end: 03/31/13
Carbon Black Mfr
S.I.C.: 2819
N.A.I.C.S.: 325180
Kumar Mangalam Birla *(Chm)*
Sanjeev Sood *(Pres)*
Prabhat Gupta *(CFO & VP-Fin & Comml)*
John Loudermilk *(CTO & Pres-North America)*
Eric Gregoire *(Pres-Europe & Africa-Birla Carbon)*
Ajay Rastogi *(Pres-Mfg)*
S. S. Rathi *(Pres-South Asia & Middle East)*
Santrupt B. Misra *(CEO-Birla Carbon)*
Rajesh Jha *(Sec)*
Rajiv Gupta *(Sr VP-Mktg)*
Surendra Pandey *(Sr VP-Mfg)*

Thai Polyphosphate & Chemicals Co., Ltd. (2)
77 Moo 6 Soi Sukhaphiban 1
Poochaosaming Prai Road
Sam Rong Phra Pradaeng, Samut Prakan, 10130, Thailand TH
Tel.: (66) 23961715 (49%)
Telex: 81187
Fax: (66) 23980774
E-Mail: tpc@thaipoly.com
Web Site: www.thaipoly.com
Emp.: 15
Chemicals Mfr
S.I.C.: 2899
N.A.I.C.S.: 325998
E. R. Narayanan *(Pres)*

ADITYA ISPAT LTD.

Plot No 20 Phase V IDA Jeedimetla
Hyderabad, AP, 500 055, India
Tel.: (91) 40 2309 7396
E-Mail: info@adityaispat.com
Web Site: www.adityaispat.com
513513—(BOM)
Rev.: $4,050,163
Assets: $2,679,098
Liabilities: $1,346,182
Net Worth: $1,332,916
Earnings: $43,039
Fiscal Year-end: 03/31/13

Business Description:
Steel Bars Mfr
S.I.C.: 3399
N.A.I.C.S.: 331110

Personnel:
Satya Bhagwan Chachan *(Chm & Mng Dir)*

Board of Directors:
Satya Bhagwan Chachan
Swami S. B. Das
H. M. Duggar
Sanjay Solanki

Transfer Agent:
XL Softech Systems Private Limited
Road No 2 Banjara Hills Sagar Society
Hyderabad, India

ADIUVA CAPITAL GMBH

Messberg 1
20095 Hamburg, Germany

Tel.: (49) 40 3019 1670
Fax: (49) 40 3019 1675
E-Mail: info@adiuvacapital.com
Web Site: www.adiuvacapital.com
Year Founded: 2011
Business Description:
Private Equity Firm
S.I.C.: 6211
N.A.I.C.S.: 523999
Personnel:
Tobias Osing *(Co-Founder & Partner)*
Tobias Wollenhaupt *(Co-Founder & Partner)*

ADJUVANT COSME JAPAN CO., LTD.
5-5-5 Shimoyamate-dori Chuo-ku
Kobe-shi, Hyogo, 650-0011, Japan
Tel.: (81) 78 351 3100
Fax: (81) 78 351 3108
Web Site: www.adjuvant.co.jp
4929—(TKS)
Sls.: $49,148,000
Assets: $61,897,000
Liabilities: $19,338,000
Net Worth: $42,559,000
Earnings: $5,863,000
Emp.: 100
Fiscal Year-end: 03/31/13
Business Description:
Cosmetics Mfr & Sales
S.I.C.: 2844
N.A.I.C.S.: 325620
Personnel:
Yutaka Nakamura *(Pres)*

ADL PLC
Corbie Steps 89 Harehills Ln
LS7 4HA Leeds, United Kingdom
Tel.: (44) 1132392957
Fax: (44) 1133070121
Web Site: www.adlcare.com
Sales Range: $1-9.9 Million
Emp.: 30
Business Description:
Nursing Facilities
S.I.C.: 8051
N.A.I.C.S.: 623110
Personnel:
William Wells *(Chm)*
Jeremy Davies *(Mng Dir & Sec)*
Board of Directors:
William Wells
Jeremy Davies
Pearl Jackson

ADLER MODEMARKTE AG
(Acquired by Steilmann Holding AG)

ADLER REAL ESTATE AG
Neuer Wall 77
20354 Hamburg, Germany
Tel.: (49) 402981300
Fax: (49) 4029813099
E-Mail: info@adler-ag.de
Web Site: www.adler-ag.de
ADL—(DEU)
Rev.: $7,673,169
Assets: $58,962,246
Liabilities: $23,423,358
Net Worth: $35,538,888
Earnings: $673,085
Emp.: 10
Fiscal Year-end: 12/31/12
Business Description:
Real Estate Services
S.I.C.: 6531
N.A.I.C.S.: 531390
Personnel:
Dirk Hoffmann *(Chm-Supervisory Bd)*
Ralf Preyer *(Vice Chm-Supervisory Bd)*
Peter Stommel *(CTO & Mng Dir-Munchener Baugesellschaft mbH)*
Axel Harloff *(Member-Mgmt Bd)*
Ulrich Muller *(Gen Counsel)*
Supervisory Board of Directors:
Dirk Hoffmann
Ralf Preyer
Thomas Katzuba von Urbisch

Subsidiaries:

Achte ADLER Real Estate GmbH & Co. KG (1)
Holzdamm 28-32
20099 Hamburg, Germany
Tel.: (49) 404293230
Fax: (49) 4042932318
E-Mail: info@alder-real-estate.de
Real Estate Management Services
S.I.C.: 6531
N.A.I.C.S.: 531312

Adler Real Estate Hotel GmbH (1)
Neuer Wall 77
20354 Hamburg, Germany
Tel.: (49) 402981300
Fax: (49) 4029815099
E-Mail: info@adler-ag.de
Real Estate Management Services
S.I.C.: 6531
N.A.I.C.S.: 531312

Adler Real Estate Properties GmbH & Co. KG (1)
Neuer Wall 77
20354 Hamburg, Germany
Tel.: (49) 4029813030
Fax: (49) 4029813099
E-Mail: info@alder-ag.de
Web Site: www.alder-ag.de
Real Estate Management Services
S.I.C.: 6531
N.A.I.C.S.: 531312

Dritte ADLER Real Estate GmbH & Co. KG (1)
Neuer Wall 77
20354 Hamburg, Germany
Tel.: (49) 402981300
Fax: (49) 4029813099
E-Mail: info@adler-ag.de
Real Estate Management Services
S.I.C.: 6531
N.A.I.C.S.: 531312

MBG Dallgow GmbH & Co. KG (1)
Neuer Wall 77
20354 Hamburg, Germany
Tel.: (49) 69 97 20 80 0
Fax: (49) 69 97 20 80 18
E-Mail: info@Dallgow-Berlin.de
Web Site: www.dallgow-berlin.de
Real Estate Management Services
S.I.C.: 6531
N.A.I.C.S.: 531312

Munchener Baugesellschaft mbH (1)
Herriotstrasse 5
60528 Frankfurt am Main, Hesse, Germany
Tel.: (49) 699720800
Fax: (49) 6997208018
E-Mail: info@muenchener-bau.de
Web Site: www.muenchener-bau.de
Emp.: 3
Real Estate Management Services
S.I.C.: 6531
N.A.I.C.S.: 531312
Axel Harloff *(CEO)*
Peter Stommel *(Mng Dir)*

ADLINK TECHNOLOGY, INC.
9th Floor No 166 Jian Yi Road
Zonghe District, New Taipei City, 235, Taiwan
Tel.: (886) 2 8226 5877
Fax: (886) 2 8226 5717
E-Mail: service@adlinktech.com
Web Site: www.adlinktech.com
6166—(TAI)
Sales Range: $75-99.9 Million
Business Description:
Measurement & Automation Products Mfr
S.I.C.: 3674
N.A.I.C.S.: 334413
Personnel:
Jim Liu *(Pres & CEO)*
Jeff Munch *(CTO)*
Transfer Agent:
Taiwan Securities Co., Ltd.
B1 No 96 Sector 1
Chien-Kuo North Road, Taipei, Taiwan
Tel.: (886) 2 2504 8125
Fax: (886) 2 2515 4900

U.S. Subsidiary:

Ampro ADLINK Technology, Inc. (1)
5215 Hellyer Ave #110
San Jose, CA 95138
Tel.: (408) 360-0200
Fax: (408) 360-0222
Toll Free: (800) 966-5200
E-Mail: info@adlinktech.com
Web Site: www.adlinktech.com
Electronic Automation Software Development Services
S.I.C.: 7371
N.A.I.C.S.: 541511
Matthias Huber *(VP-Mktg-Americas)*

Non-U.S. Subsidiaries:

ADLINK Technology (China) Co., Ltd. (1)
300 Fang Chun Road Zhangjiang Hi-Tech Park
Pudong New Area, Shanghai, 201203, China
Tel.: (86) 21 5132 8988
Fax: (86) 21 5132 3588
E-Mail: market@adlinktech.com
Industrial Measuring Equipment Distr
S.I.C.: 5084
N.A.I.C.S.: 423830

ADLINK Technology Japan Corporation (1)
Kanda 374 Building 4F 3-7-4 Kanda Kajicho
Chiyoda-ku, Tokyo, 101-0045, Japan
Tel.: (81) 3 4455 3722
Fax: (81) 3 5209 6013
E-Mail: japan@adlinktech.com
Industrial Measuring Equipment Distr
S.I.C.: 5084
N.A.I.C.S.: 423830

ADLINK Technology Singapore Pte. Ltd. (1)
84 Genting Lane 07-02A
Cityneon Design Centre, Singapore, 349584, Singapore
Tel.: (65) 6844 2261
Fax: (65) 6844 2263
E-Mail: singapore@adlinktech.com
Web Site: www.adlinktech.com
Emp.: 15
Electronic Testing Instrument Mfr
S.I.C.: 3825
N.A.I.C.S.: 334515
Jason Ng *(Gen Mgr)*

LIPPERT ADLINK Technology GmbH (1)
Hans-Thoma-Strasse 11
D-68163 Mannheim, Germany
Tel.: (49) 621 432140
Fax: (49) 621 4321430
E-Mail: emea@adlinktech.com
Measurement & Automation Products Mfr
S.I.C.: 3823
N.A.I.C.S.: 334513

ADLON DATENVERARBEITUNG SYSTEMS GMBH
Albersfelder Str 30
88213 Ravensburg, Germany
Tel.: (49) 75176070
Fax: (49) 751760788
E-Mail: zentrale@adlon.de
Web Site: www.adlon.com
Rev.: $48,000,000
Emp.: 87
Business Description:
IT Service
S.I.C.: 7371
N.A.I.C.S.: 541511
Personnel:
Andreas Richstatter *(CEO & Mng Dir)*

ADLPARTNER SA
3 rue Henri Rol Tanguy
93100 Montreuil, France
Tel.: (33) 141587000
Fax: (33) 141587053
Web Site: www.adlpartner.com
Year Founded: 1993
ALP—(EUR)
Sls.: $153,257,416
Assets: $92,376,878
Liabilities: $71,908,363
Net Worth: $20,468,515
Earnings: $7,564,129
Emp.: 245
Fiscal Year-end: 12/31/12
Business Description:
Periodical Loyalty Marketing & Management Services
S.I.C.: 8742
N.A.I.C.S.: 541613
Personnel:
Philippe Vigneron *(Chm-Supervisory Bd)*
Jean-Marie Vigneron *(Chm-Mgmt Bd)*
Robin Bill Smith *(Vice Chm-Supervisory Bd)*
Olivier Ries *(Mng Dir & Member-Mgmt Bd)*
Eric Bayle *(CFO & Member-Exec Bd)*
Isabelle Monset *(Deputy Mng Dir-Mktg Div & Member-Exec Bd)*
Olivier Porte *(Deputy Mng Dir-Sls Div & Dev & Member-Exec Bd)*
Claude Charpin *(Member-Exec Bd & Dir-Bus Dev)*
Michel Fagot *(Member-Exec Bd & Dir-HR)*
Thierry Vasseur *(Member-Exec Bd & Dir-Info Sys)*
Emmanuel Gougeon *(Member-Exec Bd & Mgr-Intl Dev)*
Supervisory Board of Directors:
Philippe Vigneron
Xavier Bouton
Claire Brunel
Michel Gauthier
Dinesh Katiyar
Isabelle Laurioz
Thierry Lovenbach
Roland Massenet
Robin Bill Smith

Subsidiaries:

OFUP (1)
3 Avenue de Chartres
BP 90132
60501 Chantilly, Oise, France
Tel.: (33) 978 971 450
Fax: (33) 344 584 622
E-Mail: relations-clients@ofup.fr
Web Site: www.ofup.com
Magazine Publishing Services
S.I.C.: 2731
N.A.I.C.S.: 511130
Jean-Christophe Chopin *(Mgr)*

SIDD Sarl (1)
88 Rue Saint Denis
93130, Noisy-le-Sec, Seine-Saint-Denis, France
Tel.: (33) 148304286
Financial Management Services
S.I.C.: 8742
N.A.I.C.S.: 541611

Non-U.S. Subsidiaries:

Suscripciones Espana (1)
Calle Velazquez No 126 Seventh Floor AB
28006 Madrid, Spain
Tel.: (34) 915611400
Fax: (34) 915647334
Magazine Marketing Services
S.I.C.: 8742
N.A.I.C.S.: 541613
Michel Gauthier *(Mgr)*

ADMEDUS LIMITED
(Formerly Allied Healthcare Group)

Admedus Limited—(Continued)

Level 1 197 Adelaide Terrace
Perth, WA, 6000, Australia
Mailing Address:
PO Box 6879
East Perth, WA, 6892, Australia
Tel.: (61) 8 9266 0100
Fax: (61) 8 9266 0199
E-Mail: info.au@admedus.com
Web Site: www.admedus.com
AHZ—(ASX OTC)
Sales Range: $1-9.9 Million
Business Description:
Medical & Surgical Product Development Services
S.I.C.: 2834
N.A.I.C.S.: 325412
Personnel:
Chris Catlow *(Chm)*
Lee Rodne *(Mng Dir)*
Stephen Mann *(CFO & Sec)*
Julian Chick *(COO)*
Board of Directors:
Chris Catlow
Michael C. Bennett
Lee Rodne
Graeme Rowley
Peter Turvey
Legal Counsel:
Hardy Bowen
Level 1 28 Ord Street
West West Perth, WA, 6005, Australia

ADMIRAL GROUP PLC

Capital Tower Greyfriars Road
Cardiff, CF10 3AZ, United Kingdom
Tel.: (44) 871 882 8282
Web Site: www.admiralgroup.co.uk
Year Founded: 1993
ADM—(LSE)
Rev.: $1,826,448,885
Assets: $5,060,361,018
Liabilities: $4,332,782,115
Net Worth: $727,578,903
Earnings: $408,088,536
Emp.: 6,500
Fiscal Year-end: 12/31/12
Business Description:
Automobile Insurance Services
S.I.C.: 6399
N.A.I.C.S.: 524128
Personnel:
Alastair Lyons *(Chm)*
Henry Engelhardt *(CEO)*
Kevin Chidwick *(CFO)*
David Stevens *(COO)*
Mark Waters *(Sec)*
Board of Directors:
Alastair Lyons
Roger Abravanel
Manfred Aldag
Kevin Chidwick
Annette Elizabeth Court
Henry Engelhardt
Colin Holmes
Martin Jackson
Margaret Johnson
Lucy Kellaway
David Stevens
John G. Sussens
Legal Counsel:
Norton Rose
3 More London Riverside
London, United Kingdom SE1 2AQ

Non-U.S. Subsidiary:

Admiral Insurance (Gibraltar) Limited (1)
Eurolife Bldg Ste 3G
1 Corral Rd, Gibraltar, Gibraltar
Tel.: (350) 20042575
Fax: (350) 20042439
E-Mail: admiral@sapphirenet.gi
Emp.: 2
Insurance Services
S.I.C.: 6411
N.A.I.C.S.: 524210

Subsidiary:

Able Insurance Services Limited (1)
No 1 Langdon Rd Admiral Grp House
Swansea Waterfront, Swansea, SA1 8AG, United Kingdom
Tel.: (44) 8718828283
Insurance Services
S.I.C.: 6411
N.A.I.C.S.: 524210

ADMIRAL MARINE SUPPLIES LIMITED

Unit 4b Severnside Trading Estate St Andrew's Road
Avonmouth, Bristol, BS11 9YQ, United Kingdom
Tel.: (44) 117 982 1229
Fax: (44) 117 982 2214
E-Mail: enquiries@admiral-marine.com
Web Site: www.admiral-marine.com
Sales Range: $10-24.9 Million
Emp.: 44
Business Description:
Marine Products Distr
S.I.C.: 5088
N.A.I.C.S.: 423860
Personnel:
R. T. Blake *(Mng Dir)*

ADMIRALTY RESOURCES NL

Level 16 379 Collins St
Melbourne, VIC, 3000, Australia
Tel.: (61) 396212322
Fax: (61) 396701898
E-Mail: pthomas@ady.com.au
Web Site: www.ady.com.au
ADY—(ASX OTC)
Sales Range: $1-9.9 Million
Business Description:
Mineral Mining
S.I.C.: 1499
N.A.I.C.S.: 212399
Personnel:
Alan Preston Beasley *(Chm)*
Hanrui Zhong *(CEO & Mng Dir)*
Robert Kineavy *(Sec)*
Board of Directors:
Alan Preston Beasley
Michael Stephen Perry
Hanjing Xu
Hanrui Zhong
Qing Zhong
Legal Counsel:
Hall & Wilcox
Level 30 600 Bourke Street
Melbourne, Australia
Transfer Agent:
Computershare Investor Services Pty. Ltd.
GPO Box 523
Brisbane, QLD, 4001, Australia
Tel.: (61) 7 3237 2173
Fax: (61) 7 3237 2152

ADOCIA

115 avenue Lacassagne
69003 Lyon, France
Tel.: (33) 4 72 610 610
Fax: (33) 4 72 36 39 67
Web Site: www.adocia.com
Year Founded: 2005
ADOC—(EUR)
Rev.: $5,384,680
Assets: $49,269,822
Liabilities: $18,307,912
Net Worth: $30,961,910
Earnings: ($8,077,020)
Emp.: 70
Fiscal Year-end: 12/31/12
Business Description:
Biotechnology Products Mfr
S.I.C.: 8731
N.A.I.C.S.: 541711
Personnel:
Gerard Soula *(Chm & CEO)*
Valerie Danaguezian *(CFO & Dir-Admin & Fin)*
Board of Directors:
Gerard Soula
Laurent Arthaud
Jerome Feraud
Thierry Laugel
Olivier Martinez
Olivier Soula
Dominique Takizawa

ADOLF SCHUCH GMBH

Mainzer Str 172
DE 67547 Worms, Germany
Tel.: (49) 624140910
Fax: (49) 6241409129
E-Mail: info@schuch.de
Web Site: www.schuch.de
Rev.: $50,419,134
Emp.: 327
Business Description:
Light Fitting Mfr
S.I.C.: 3646
N.A.I.C.S.: 335122
Personnel:
Norbert Kern *(Dir-Sls)*

ADOLFO DOMINGUEZ, S.A.

Poligono San Ciprian de Vinas Calle 4 Parcela 8
San Ciprian de Vinas, 32901 Orense, Spain
Tel.: (34) 988398705
Fax: (34) 988246761
E-Mail: info@adolfodominguez.es
Web Site: www.adolfodominguez.com
Sales Range: $125-149.9 Million
Emp.: 1,195
Fiscal Year-end: 12/31/12
Business Description:
Mfr., Designer, Retailer & Distributor of Clothing & Accessories
S.I.C.: 2389
N.A.I.C.S.: 315990
Personnel:
Adolfo Dominguez Fernandez *(Chm)*
Berta Rodriguez *(Sec)*

ADOMOS SA

75 Avenue Des Champs Elysees
75008 Paris, France
Tel.: (33) 158364500
Fax: (33) 388192869
E-Mail: presse@adomos.com
Web Site: www.adomos.com
ALADO—(EUR)
Sales Range: $10-24.9 Million
Emp.: 40
Business Description:
Real Estate Brokerage Services
S.I.C.: 6531
N.A.I.C.S.: 531210
Personnel:
Fabrice Rosset *(Pres)*

ADONIS CONSTRUCTION LTD

Ham Lane
Kingswinford, West Midlands, DY6 7JU, United Kingdom
Tel.: (44) 1384298989
Fax: (44) 1384282814
E-Mail: info@adonis-group.co.uk
Web Site: www.adonis-group.co.uk
Year Founded: 1978
Rev.: $74,612,938
Emp.: 20
Business Description:
Construction Services
S.I.C.: 1542
N.A.I.C.S.: 236220
Personnel:
Neville Clements *(Chm)*

ADOR WELDING LTD

Ador House 6 K Dubash Marg Fort
Mumbai, 400001, India
Tel.: (91) 22 2284 2525
Fax: (91) 22 2287 3083
E-Mail: cmo@adorians.com
Web Site: www.adorwelding.com
517041—(BOM)
Rev.: $74,677,822
Assets: $49,310,745
Liabilities: $15,515,032
Net Worth: $33,795,713
Earnings: $3,129,552
Emp.: 776
Fiscal Year-end: 03/31/13
Business Description:
Welding Equipments & Accessories
S.I.C.: 3548
N.A.I.C.S.: 333992
Personnel:
A. B. Advani *(Chm)*
Satish M. Bhat *(Mng Dir)*
J. Mani *(CFO)*
L. Sundar *(CTO)*
V. M. Bhide *(Compliance Officer, Sec & Head-Corp Admin)*
G. Banerjee *(Sr VP-Sls & Mktg)*
Board of Directors:
A. B. Advani
Satish M. Bhat
P. K. Gupta
Anil Harish
D. A. Lalvani
M. K. Maheshwari
A. T. Malkani
R. A. Mirchandani
N. Malkani Nagpal
R. N. Sapru
Vippen Sareen
Legal Counsel:
Nanu Hormasjee & Co.
Mumbai, India
Transfer Agent:
Sharex Dynamic (India) Pvt. Ltd.
Unit No 1 Luthra Industrial Premises Andheri-Kurla Road
Safed Pool Andheri E, 400 072 Mumbai, India

Subsidiaries:

Ador Fontech Ltd. (1)
Belview 7 Haudin Road
Bengaluru, 560 042, India
Tel.: (91) 8025596045
Fax: (91) 8025597085
E-Mail: customerservice@adorfon.com
Web Site: www.adorfon.com
530431—(BOM)
Rev.: $30,398,184
Assets: $21,651,012
Liabilities: $7,236,162
Net Worth: $14,414,850
Earnings: $3,837,780
Emp.: 246
Fiscal Year-end: 03/31/13
Mineral Resources Distr
S.I.C.: 5051
N.A.I.C.S.: 423510
N. Malkani Nagpal *(Chm)*
H. P. Ledwani *(Mng Dir)*
D. Geetha *(Compliance Officer & Sec)*

Ador Multiproducts Ltd. (1)
A-13&14 III Stage Peenya Industrial Estate
Bengaluru, 560058, India
Tel.: (91) 80 2836 0271
Fax: (91) 80 2836 1631
E-Mail: contactus@adormultiproducts.com
Web Site: www.adormultiproducts.com
523120—(BOM)
Personal Care Products Mfr & Distr
S.I.C.: 2844
N.A.I.C.S.: 325620

Ador Powertron Ltd. (1)
Plot 51 Ramnagar Complex D II Block
MIDC Chinchwad
Pune, Maharashtra, 411 019, India

Tel.: (91) 2027472532
Fax: (91) 2027475817
E-Mail: cmo@adorpower.com
Web Site: www.adorpowertronltd.com
Battery Testing Equipment Mfr
S.I.C.: 3825
N.A.I.C.S.: 334515
Prakash Inamdar *(Mgr)*

ADORABLE LINGERIE INC.

710 rue Deslauriers
Montreal, QC, H4N 1W5, Canada
Tel.: (514) 593-1717
Fax: (514) 593-6100
Toll Free: (866) 593-1717
Web Site: www.adorableintimates.com
Rev.: $20,871,772
Emp.: 47
Business Description:
Apparel Stores
S.I.C.: 5621
N.A.I.C.S.: 448120
Personnel:
Mikael Abergel *(Pres)*

ADORES INC.

2-1-3 Nihonbashi Bakurocho Chuo ward
Tokyo, 103-0002, Japan
Tel.: (81) 3 5623 1100
Fax: (81) 3 5623 1112
Web Site: www.adores.co.jp
Year Founded: 1964
4712—(JAS)
Sales Range: $300-349.9 Million
Emp.: 356
Business Description:
Amusement Arcades
S.I.C.: 7993
N.A.I.C.S.: 713120
Personnel:
Nobuyoshi Fujisawa *(Chm)*
Takeo Nakagawa *(Pres)*
Board of Directors:
Nobuyoshi Fujisawa
Kiyotaka Ishida
Masamitsu Ishida
Takeo Nakagawa
Satoru Oki
Satoshi Onda
Hiroaki Onodera
Hiroshi Tsuchiya

ADOS PAKISTAN LIMITED

House 88 Khayaban-e-Iqbal F-8/2
Islamabad, Pakistan
Tel.: (92) 51 2264308
Fax: (92) 51 2281678
E-Mail: ados@akbarassociates.com
Web Site: www.akbarassociates.com
ADOS—(ISL)
Business Description:
Oilfield Equipment Mfr
S.I.C.: 3999
N.A.I.C.S.: 339999
Personnel:
Zia Akbar Ansari *(CEO)*

ADR CAPITAL CORP.

(Name Changed to Delta Gold Corp.)

ADRIA AIRWAYS D.D.

Zgornji Brnik 13h
SI 4210 Brnik, Slovenia
Tel.: (386) 42594506
Fax: (386) 42594572
E-Mail: pr@adria.si
Web Site: www.adria.si
Year Founded: 1961
Sales Range: $150-199.9 Million
Emp.: 552
Business Description:
Air Transportation Services
S.I.C.: 4512
N.A.I.C.S.: 481111
Supervisory Board of Directors:
Anton Grabeljsek
Deana Potza
Ales Vehar

ADRIACHEM D.D.

Ulica dr F Tudmana 344
21212 Kastel Sucurac, Croatia
Tel.: (385) 21224944
Fax: (385) 21225113
E-Mail: adriachem@st.t-com.hr
Web Site: www.adriachem.com
Emp.: 400
Business Description:
Plastic & Chemical Products
S.I.C.: 2899
N.A.I.C.S.: 325998

ADRIANA RESOURCES INC.

15 Toronto Street Suite 1000
Toronto, ON, M5C 2E3, Canada
Tel.: (416) 363-2200, ext. 224
Fax: (416) 363-2202
E-Mail: info@adrianaresources.com
Web Site: www.adrianaresources.com
A7R—(DEU TSXV)
Business Description:
Iron Ore Mining Services
S.I.C.: 1011
N.A.I.C.S.: 212210
Personnel:
Donald K. Charter *(Chm)*
Allen J. Palmiere *(Pres & CEO)*
Daniel Im *(CFO)*
Board of Directors:
Donald K. Charter
Brian L. Acton
Ronald P. Gagel
Allen J. Palmiere
Weike Peng
Ronald S. Simkus
David S. Warner
Paul Yeou

ADRIS GRUPA D.D.

Obala Vladimira Nazora 1
HR-52210 Rovinj, Croatia
Tel.: (385) 52801122
Fax: (385) 52813587
E-Mail: adris@adris.hr
Web Site: www.adris.hr
ADRS-R-A—(ZAG)
Rev.: $515,077,152
Assets: $1,595,633,211
Liabilities: $232,720,486
Net Worth: $1,362,912,725
Earnings: $89,895,492
Emp.: 3,926
Fiscal Year-end: 12/31/12
Business Description:
Tourism Services & Tobacco Products Mfr
S.I.C.: 2131
N.A.I.C.S.: 312230
Personnel:
Rino Bubicic *(Chm-Supervisory Bd)*
Ante Vlahovic *(Chm-Mgmt Bd)*
Tomislav Budin *(Deputy Chm-Supervisory Bd)*
Marica Sorak-Pokrajac *(Deputy Chm-Supervisory Bd)*
Plinio Cuccurin *(Member-Mgmt Bd)*
Zelimir Vukina *(Member-Mgmt Bd)*
Branko Zec *(Member-Mgmt Bd)*
Supervisory Board of Directors:
Rino Bubicic
Tomislav Budin
Andrea Cerin
Teodora Hodak
Hrvoje Patajac
Roberto Skopac
Marica Sorak-Pokrajac
Subsidiaries:

Abilia d.o.o. (1)
Obala V Nazora 1
52210 Rovinj, Croatia
Tel.: (385) 52801207
Fax: (385) 52813587
E-Mail: prodaja@abilia.hr
Web Site: www.abilia.hr
Emp.: 14
Commercial Building Construction Services
S.I.C.: 1542
N.A.I.C.S.: 236220
Daimer Gandjalac *(Mng Dir)*

Adria Resorts d.o.o. (1)
Obala Vladimira Nazora 6
52210 Rovinj, Croatia
Tel.: (385) 52800300
Fax: (385) 52815111
E-Mail: adriaresorts@adriaresorts.hr
Web Site: www.adris.hr/eng/dodatno/kontakt.asp
Tourism Management Services
S.I.C.: 7389
N.A.I.C.S.: 561591
Daniela Moressa *(Fin Dir)*

Cromaris d.d. (1)
Trg tri bunara 5
23000 Zadar, Croatia
Tel.: (385) 23254960
Fax: (385) 23350883
E-Mail: info@cromaris.hr
Web Site: www.cromaris.hr
Emp.: 200
Finfish Production Services
S.I.C.: 0912
N.A.I.C.S.: 114111
Goran Markulin *(Gen Mgr)*

Istragrafika d.d. (1)
Obala Vladimira Nazora 1
52210 Rovinj, Croatia
Tel.: (385) 52844800
Fax: (385) 52844971
E-Mail: istragrafika@istragrafika.hr
Web Site: www.istragrafika.hr
Emp.: 150
General Packaging Products Mfr
S.I.C.: 2671
N.A.I.C.S.: 326112

Rovinjturist d.d. (1)
Monsena Bb
52210 Rovinj, Croatia
Tel.: (385) 52805504
Fax: (385) 52811541
Tourist Accommodation Services
S.I.C.: 7999
N.A.I.C.S.: 713990

TDR d.o.o., Rovinj (1)
Obala Vladimira Nazora 1
52210 Rovinj, Croatia
Tel.: (385) 52801122
Fax: (385) 52844870
E-Mail: tdr@tdr.hr
Web Site: www.tdr.hr
Emp.: 700
Cigarettes Mfr
S.I.C.: 2131
N.A.I.C.S.: 312230
Davor Tomaskovic *(Pres & Mng Dir)*
Josip Lozancic *(CFO)*

Non-U.S. Subsidiaries:

Opresa d.d. (1)
Trg Ivana Krndelja 11 C
88000 Sarajevo, Bosnia & Herzegovina
Tel.: (387) 36551125
Fax: (387) 36550124
Fish Farming Services
S.I.C.: 0921
N.A.I.C.S.: 112511
Arben Gagani *(CIO)*

TDR d.o.o., Beograd (1)
Milentija Popovica 5a
11070 Belgrade, Serbia
Tel.: (381) 116149113
Fax: (381) 00381116149117
E-Mail: nicolina.sljevar@tdr.hr
Web Site: www.tdr.hr
Cigarettes Mfr
S.I.C.: 2131
N.A.I.C.S.: 312230

TDR d.o.o., Blazuj (1)
Blazuj 78
Blazuj, Ilidza, Bosnia & Herzegovina
Tel.: (387) 33770350, ext. 564300
Fax: (387) 33770351
E-Mail: tdr.bih@tdr.hr
Web Site: www.tdr.hr/bosna-i-hercegovina/index.htm
Cigarettes Mfr
S.I.C.: 2131
N.A.I.C.S.: 312230
Zoarn Vesmait *(Gen Mgr)*

TDR Germany GmbH (1)
Brennerstrasse 90
2009 Hamburg, Germany
Tel.: (49) 4028669855
Fax: (49) 4055502742
E-Mail: info@tdrgermany.de
Emp.: 3
Tobacco Products Distr
S.I.C.: 5194
N.A.I.C.S.: 424940
Marko Duritic *(Mgr-Sls)*

TDR Rovita d.o.o. (1)
Dunajska Cesta 22
1000 Ljubljana, Slovenia
Tel.: (386) 14305761
Fax: (386) 14305762
E-Mail: info@rovita.si
Web Site: www.tdr.hr
Emp.: 6
Tobacco Cigarette Mfr
S.I.C.: 2131
N.A.I.C.S.: 312230
Stipic Dare *(Pres)*

TDR Sh.p.k. (1)
Lagjia Fakultteti Ekonomik
Lamela 1 Objekti A, 10000 Pristina, Kosovo, Serbia
Tel.: (381) 38248808
Fax: (381) 38248310
Emp.: 6
Tobacco Mfr
S.I.C.: 2131
N.A.I.C.S.: 312230
Milorad Krstevski *(Gen Mgr)*

TDR Skopje d.o.o.e.l. (1)
St 8 September 16
1000 Skopje, Macedonia
Tel.: (389) 23093737
Fax: (389) 2 3093737
E-Mail: office@tdr.mk
Web Site: www.tdr.hr
Emp.: 11
Cigarettes Mfr
S.I.C.: 2131
N.A.I.C.S.: 312230

ADRITEC GROUP INTERNATIONAL, E.C.

PO Box 5474
Amman, 11183, Jordan
Tel.: (962) 65603779
Fax: (962) 65603780
E-Mail: sales@adritec.com
Web Site: www.adritec.com
Year Founded: 1999
Business Description:
Holding Company: Offshore Investments
S.I.C.: 6719
N.A.I.C.S.: 551112
Personnel:
Hatim Sharif Zu'bi *(Chm)*
Tarek Hatem Zu'bi *(Co-Vice Chm & Grp CEO)*
Fawaz Hatim Zu'bi *(Co-Vice Chm)*
Assem S. Suleiman *(Mng Dir)*
Husni Abdel Majid *(CFO)*
Board of Directors:
Hatim Sharif Zu'bi
Olga Aburdene
Fawaz Hatim Zu'bi
Namek T. Zu'bi
Tarek Hatem Zu'bi
Subsidiaries:

Adritec Jordan (1)
PO Box 5474
Amman, 11183, Jordan (100%)

Adritec Group International, E.C.—(Continued)

Tel.: (962) 65603779
Fax: (962) 65603780
E-Mail: sales@adritec.com
Web Site: www.adritec.com
Emp.: 150
Micro-Irrigation & Filtration Systems Mfr
S.I.C.: 4941
N.A.I.C.S.: 221310
Garek Gudi *(Mng Dir)*

Adritec Trading & Services Company (1)
Abdul Hameed Sharaf Street
PO Box 5474
Amman, 11183, Jordan
Tel.: (962) 65603779
Fax: (962) 65603780
E-Mail: sales@adritec.com
Emp.: 125
Irrigation Services
S.I.C.: 4971
N.A.I.C.S.: 221310
Luay Qaisi *(Gen Mgr)*

Non-U.S. Subsidiaries:

Adritec De Las Americas S. de R.L. de C.V. (1)
Kanalto 481 Col Loma Bonita Ejidal
Zapopan, Guadalajara, CP, 45080, Mexico
Tel.: (52) 3335638842
Fax: (52) 3335638843
E-Mail: awasfi@adritec.com
Web Site: www.adritec.com
Emp.: 10
Irrigation, Drip & Sprinkler Products Distr
S.I.C.: 4971
N.A.I.C.S.: 221310
Ali Wasfi *(Mgr)*

Adritec Europe (1)
16th Km Larissa AGIA
Platykampos, Larissa, Greece
Tel.: (30) 2410975170
Fax: (30) 2410975265
E-Mail: info@adritec.com
Web Site: www.adritec.com
Emp.: 50
Drip Irrigation Products Mfr
S.I.C.: 4941
N.A.I.C.S.: 221310
Yannis Bozikis *(Mng Partner)*

Adritec Maroc (1)
Zone Industrielle
El Jadida, Morocco (100%)
Tel.: (212) 523372043
Fax: (212) 523351795
E-Mail: adritecmaroc@yahoo.fr
Irrigation Components & Accessories Distr
S.I.C.: 4971
N.A.I.C.S.: 221310
Aiman Shabaro *(Mng Dir)*

Adritec Turkey (1)
Cilek Mahallesi 133 Cadde No 76
Ankara, 33020, Turkey (100%)
Tel.: (90) 324 221 2042
Fax: (90) 324 221 2026
E-Mail: adtr@adritec.com
Web Site: www.adritec.com
Emp.: 5
Irrigation Distribution Systems
S.I.C.: 4971
N.A.I.C.S.: 221310
Mohamad Darawwad *(Gen Mgr)*

Non-U.S. Joint Ventures:

Adritec Tunis (1)
ZI Ksar Said 2086
Douar Hicher, Tunis, Tunisia
Tel.: (216) 71546404
Fax: (216) 71545558
Web Site: www.adritec.com
Irrigation Components & Accessories Mfr & Distr; 50% Owned by Adritec Group International, E.C. & 50% Owned by Societe Commerciale et Industrielle des Produits en Plastique
S.I.C.: 4941
N.A.I.C.S.: 221310

Arab Drip Irrigation Technology Company Ltd. (1)
PO Box 270
Lattakia, Syria
Tel.: (963) 41461861
Fax: (963) 41468239
E-Mail: info@fleinan-agri.com
Web Site: www.sleiman-agri.com
Emp.: 70
Irrigation Systems; 50% Owned by Adritec Group International, E.C. & 50% Owned by Sleiman Agricultural Establishment
S.I.C.: 4971
N.A.I.C.S.: 221310

ADROIT RESOURCES INC.

510 -1190 Melville Street
Vancouver, BC, V6E 3W1, Canada
Tel.: (604) 688-3304
Fax: (604) 682-6038
E-Mail: info@adroitresources.ca
Web Site: www.adroitresources.ca
ADT—(TSXV)
Assets: $4,495,512
Liabilities: $1,699,418
Net Worth: $2,796,094
Earnings: ($3,432,219)
Fiscal Year-end: 05/31/13
Business Description:
Mineral Exploration Services
S.I.C.: 1081
N.A.I.C.S.: 213114
Personnel:
Graeme Rowland *(Chm, Pres & CEO)*
Scott Davis *(CFO)*
Frances Murphy *(Sec)*
Board of Directors:
Graeme Rowland
Mark Fedikow
Dave Hutchinson
Johan Juntop
Legal Counsel:
Holmes & King Barristers & Solicitors
1300 - 1111 West Georgia Street
Vancouver, BC, Canada
Transfer Agent:
Computershare Investor Services
200 510 Burrard Street
Vancouver, BC, Canada

ADS INC.

485 rue des Erables
Quebec, QC, G0S 2J0, Canada
Tel.: (418) 387-5910
Fax: (418) 387-4326
E-Mail: ads@adsinc.ca
Web Site: www.adsinc.ca
Sales Range: $75-99.9 Million
Emp.: 250
Business Description:
Nonwoven Materials Designer, Developer & Mfr
S.I.C.: 2297
N.A.I.C.S.: 313230
Personnel:
Paul Drouin *(Chm)*
Guy Drouin *(Pres, CEO, Treas & Sec)*
Guy Berube *(CFO & VP-Ops)*
Rene Drouin *(Exec VP)*
Board of Directors:
Paul Drouin
Christian Bernard
Guy Berube
Guy Drouin
Rene Drouin

ADSERVE LTD.

Unit 301, 3/F, Hung To Centre, 94-96 How Ming Street, Kwun Tong
Kowloon, China (Hong Kong)
Tel.: (852) 30592559
Fax: (852) 30201572
Web Site: www.adserve.com
Sales Range: $1-9.9 Million
Business Description:
Media Buying Solutions
S.I.C.: 7319
N.A.I.C.S.: 541830

ADSLOT LTD.

(Formerly Webfirm Group Limited)
Level 2 85 Coventry Street
South Melbourne, VIC, 3205, Australia
Tel.: (61) 3 8695 9199
Fax: (61) 3 9696 0700
Web Site: www.adslot.com
ADJ—(ASX)
Rev.: $4,226,467
Assets: $17,760,737
Liabilities: $1,795,503
Net Worth: $15,965,235
Earnings: ($6,732,953)
Emp.: 60
Fiscal Year-end: 06/30/13
Business Description:
Advertising Services
S.I.C.: 7319
N.A.I.C.S.: 541890
Personnel:
Ian Lowe *(CEO)*
Brendan Maher *(CFO & Sec)*
Julian Sonego *(CMO)*
Michael Hart *(CTO)*
Raj Chauhan *(Pres-North America)*
Board of Directors:
Adrian Giles
Andrew Barlow
Tiffany Fuller
Ian Lowe
Chris Morris
Legal Counsel:
Hall & Wilcox Lawyers
Level 30 Bourke Place 600 Bourke Street
Melbourne, Vic, 3000, Australia
Subsidiaries:

Ansearch.com.au Pty Ltd (1)
85 Coventry Street
South Melbourne, VIC, 3205, Australia
Tel.: (61) 3 8695 9199
Fax: (61) 392212640
E-Mail: mail@ansearch.com.au
Web Site: www.ansearch.com.au
Emp.: 40
Internet Search Portal Operation Services
S.I.C.: 2741
N.A.I.C.S.: 519130

Facilitate Digital Holdings Limited (1)
Level 6 241 Commonwealth St
Surry Hills, NSW, 2010, Australia
Mailing Address:
PO Box 1721
Darlinghurst, NSW, 1300, Australia
Tel.: (61) 296903900
Fax: (61) 296903901
E-Mail: infoAU@facilitatedigital.com
Web Site: www.facilitatedigital.com
Rev.: $5,479,031
Assets: $8,999,991
Liabilities: $2,225,372
Net Worth: $6,774,619
Earnings: ($862,671)
Emp.: 50
Fiscal Year-end: 06/30/13
Integrated Digital Marketing Solutions for Media Agencies, Advertisers & Publishers
S.I.C.: 8742
N.A.I.C.S.: 541613
Ben Dixon *(Acting CEO)*
Tom Peacock *(COO)*
Robyn Parker *(CIO)*
Brendan Maher *(Sec)*
Julian Baring *(Sr VP-North America)*

Non-U.S. Subsidiary:

Facilitate Digital Europe Marketing Technology Limited (2)
Stuurmankade 276
1019 WD Amsterdam, Netherlands
Tel.: (31) 20 77 32 842
Fax: (31) 20 89 07 935
E-Mail: infoNL@facilitatedigital.com
Web Site: www.facilitatedigital.com
Commercial Digital Printing Services
S.I.C.: 2759
N.A.I.C.S.: 323111

Webfirm Pty Ltd (1)
85 Coventry Street Level 2
Melbourne, VIC, 3006, Australia
Tel.: (61) 1300 932 347
Fax: (61) 3 9696 0700
E-Mail: info@webfirm.com
Web Site: www.webfirm.com
Emp.: 30
Website Design Development & Online Marketing Services
S.I.C.: 7389
N.A.I.C.S.: 541490
Matt Chamle *(Gen Mgr)*

Webfirm Search Pty Ltd (1)
Ste 4 Boston Gardens 16 Broadie Hall Dr
Tech Park
Bentley, WA, 6102, Australia
Tel.: (61) 862525252
Fax: (61) 8 9361 1597
E-Mail: info@searchworld.com.au
Web Site: www.searchworld.com.au
Search Engine Portals Development & Optimization Services
S.I.C.: 2741
N.A.I.C.S.: 519130

ADTEC ENGINEERING CO., LTD.

Toranomon 37 Mori Bldg 11F 3-5-1
Toranomon Minato-ku
Tokyo, 105-0001, Japan
Tel.: (81) 3 3433 4600
Fax: (81) 3 3433 4330
Web Site: www.adtec.com
Year Founded: 1983
6260—(JAS)
Emp.: 232
Business Description:
Industrial Machinery Manufacturing
S.I.C.: 3559
N.A.I.C.S.: 333249
Personnel:
Keizo Tokuhiro *(Chm)*
Osamu Mizuno *(Pres)*
Hiroyuki Kubo *(Sr Corp Officer)*
Takeshi Kusano *(Corp Officer)*
Yukio Nakano *(Corp Officer)*
Hideaki Onishi *(Corp Officer)*
Chikao Takano *(Corp Officer)*
Koichiro Takeda *(Corp Officer)*
Tsuneo Yamazaki *(Corp Officer)*
Board of Directors:
Keizo Tokuhiro
Shigeru Goto
Toyoharu Inoue
Takuo Kinoshita
Shunichi Kojima
Osamu Mizuno

ADTEC PLASMA TECHNOLOGY CO., LTD.

6-10 5-chome Hikino-cho
Fukuyama, Hiroshima, 721-0942, Japan
Tel.: (81) 84 945 1359
Fax: (81) 84 945 1440
Web Site: www.adtec-rf.com
Year Founded: 1985
6668—(TKS)
Business Description:
Electrical Component Mfr
S.I.C.: 3699
N.A.I.C.S.: 335999
Personnel:
Shuitsu Fujii *(Pres)*

ADTHINK MEDIA SA

79 rue Francois Mermet
BP 30
Tassin, 69160 Lyon, France
Tel.: (33) 478429099
Fax: (33) 478422554
E-Mail: contact@adthink-media.com
Web Site: www.adthink-media.com
ALADM—(EUR)
Sales Range: $25-49.9 Million
Emp.: 91
Business Description:
Internet Services
S.I.C.: 2741

N.A.I.C.S.: 519130
Personnel:
Sylvain Morel *(Co-Founder & Pres)*
Bertrand Gros *(Founder & Mng Dir)*

ADUNO HOLDING AG
(d/b/a Aduno Group)
Hagenholzstrasse 56
Oerlikon, 8050 Zurich, Switzerland
Tel.: (41) 589586000
Fax: (41) 589586001
E-Mail: info@aduno-gruppe.ch
Web Site: www.aduno-gruppe.ch
Year Founded: 2006
Emp.: 800
Business Description:
Credit Card Issuing; Credit & Leasing Services; Payment Services
S.I.C.: 6141
N.A.I.C.S.: 522210
Personnel:
Martin Huldi *(CEO)*
Conrad Auerbach *(CFO)*
Daniel Anders *(COO)*
Roland Zwyssig *(CMO)*
Daniel Bodmer *(Chief Sls Officer)*
Subsidiaries:

Aduno SA (1)
Via Argine 5
CH 6930 Bedano, Switzerland
Tel.: (41) 582345678
Fax: (41) 582345108
E-Mail: info@aduno.ch
Web Site: www.aduno.ch
Emp.: 110
Payment Services
S.I.C.: 6159
N.A.I.C.S.: 522298
Martin Huldi *(CEO)*

cashgate AG (1)
Bionstrasse 4
CH 9001 Saint Gallen, Switzerland
Tel.: (41) 800554433
Fax: (41) 800554434
Web Site: www.cashgate.ch
Credit & Leasing Services
S.I.C.: 6726
N.A.I.C.S.: 525990
Beat Stocker *(CEO)*

Viseca Card Services SA (1)
Europa-Strasse 18
8152 Glattbrugg, Switzerland
Tel.: (41) 589588200
Fax: (41) 589588201
Web Site: www.viseca.ch
Credit Intermediation
S.I.C.: 6159
N.A.I.C.S.: 522298
Fabio Rutschi *(Controller-Fin)*

ADVA AG
(See Under ADVA Optical Networking SE)

ADVA OPTICAL NETWORKING SE
Fraunhoferstrasse 9a
82152 Munich, Germany
Tel.: (49) 898906650
Fax: (49) 89890665699
E-Mail: info@advaoptical.com
Web Site: www.advaoptical.com
ADV—(DEU)
Rev.: $444,328,986
Assets: $382,440,166
Liabilities: $175,252,488
Net Worth: $207,187,679
Earnings: $22,510,655
Emp.: 1,378
Fiscal Year-end: 12/31/12
Business Description:
Optical Ethernet Solutions
S.I.C.: 3357
N.A.I.C.S.: 335921
Personnel:
Anthony T. Maher *(Chm-Supervisory Bd)*
Johanna Hey *(Vice Chm-Supervisory Bd)*
Brian L. Protiva *(CEO)*
Jaswir Singh *(CFO & COO)*
Christian Unterberger *(CMO & Chief Sls Officer)*
Christoph Glingener *(CTO)*
Supervisory Board of Directors:
Anthony T. Maher
Johanna Hey
Eric Protiva
Legal Counsel:
Linklaters
Munich, Germany
Non-U.S. Subsidiaries:

ADVA Optical Networking AS (1)
Fyrstikkalleen 3 A
P O Box 6379
Etterstad, 0604 Oslo, Norway
Tel.: (47) 21609950
Fax: (47) 21609951
E-Mail: naaland@advaoptical.com
Web Site: www.advaoptical.com
Emp.: 29
Communication Devices Mfr
S.I.C.: 3661
N.A.I.C.S.: 334210

ADVA Optical Networking Corp. (1)
Ibasen Bldg 7F Nihonbashi-kobunacho 4-1
Chuoku, Tokyo, 103 0024, Japan
Tel.: (81) 366675830
Fax: (81) 366675839
E-Mail: info-asiapacific@advaoptical.com
Web Site: www.advaoptical.com
Emp.: 6
Optical Networking Equipments Mfr
S.I.C.: 3661
N.A.I.C.S.: 334210

ADVA Optical Networking Hong Kong, Ltd. (1)
Unit 1511 Prosperity Millennia Plz
663 King Rd, Hong Kong, China (Hong Kong)
Tel.: (852) 28569090
Fax: (852) 28569191
E-Mail: ryu@advaoptical.com
Emp.: 5
Optical Networking Equipments Mfr
S.I.C.: 3661
N.A.I.C.S.: 334210
Rudi Yu *(Mng Dir)*

ADVA Optical Networking (Shenzhen) Ltd (1)
Rm 901-917 Xi Hai Ming Zhu Bldg F
Taoyuan Rd
Nanshan District, Shenzhen, 518059, China
Tel.: (86) 75586217400
Fax: (86) 75586217401
Web Site: www.advaoptical.com
Communication Systems Mfr
S.I.C.: 3661
N.A.I.C.S.: 334210

ADVA Optical Networking Sp. z.o.o. (1)
Ul Slaska 35/37
81-310 Gdynia, Poland
Tel.: (48) 587716100
Fax: (48) 587716999
Web Site: www.advaoptical.com
Emp.: 182
Optical Networking Equipments Mfr
S.I.C.: 3661
N.A.I.C.S.: 334210
Kazimierz Miotk *(Mng Dir)*

ADVAL TECH HOLDING AG
Freiburgstrasse 556
3172 Niederwangen, Switzerland
Tel.: (41) 319808444
Fax: (41) 319808260
E-Mail: info@advaltech.com
Web Site: www.advaltech.com
ADVN—(SWX)
Rev.: $301,815,648
Assets: $257,550,576
Liabilities: $199,439,988
Net Worth: $58,110,589
Earnings: ($16,595,624)
Emp.: 2,239
Fiscal Year-end: 12/31/12
Business Description:
Tools, Subassemblies Systems & Volume Components Supplier & Mfr
S.I.C.: 3545
N.A.I.C.S.: 333515
Personnel:
Willy Michel *(Chm)*
Michael Pieper *(Vice Chm)*
Rene Rothen *(CEO)*
Markus Reber *(CFO)*
Board of Directors:
Willy Michel
Leonardo Attanasio
Hans Dreier
Michael Pieper
Roland Waibel
Subsidiaries:

Adval Tech Management Ltd (1)
Freiburgstrasse 556
Niederwangen, CH 3172, Switzerland
Tel.: (41) 319808444
Fax: (41) 319808260
E-Mail: info@advaltech.com
Metal Stamping Mfr
S.I.C.: 3469
N.A.I.C.S.: 332119

Awm Mold Tech Ltd. (1)
Pilatusrint 2
CH 5630 Muri, Switzerland
Tel.: (41) 566754444
Fax: (41) 566754443
E-Mail: moldtech@advaltech.com
Web Site: www.advaltech.com
Emp.: 70
Plastic Molding Mfr
S.I.C.: 3559
N.A.I.C.S.: 333249
Matthias Behr *(Mgr-Production)*

Awm Plast Tech Ltd. (1)
Industrie Nord 1
Merenschwand, Muri, 5630, Switzerland
Tel.: (41) 566754600
Fax: (41) 566754610
E-Mail: plasttech@awm.ch
Web Site: www.awm.ch
Emp.: 15
Injection Molding Machinery Mfr
S.I.C.: 3559
N.A.I.C.S.: 333249
Hansard Kaiser *(Mgr-Production)*

Awm Plastpack Ltd. (1)
Pilatusstr 19
CH 5630 Muri, Switzerland
Tel.: (41) 566754455
Fax: (41) 566754442
E-Mail: erna.burkart@advaltech.com
Web Site: teuscher-ag.ch/advaltech/locations/awm.html
Emp.: 80
Injection Molding Machinery Mfr
S.I.C.: 3559
N.A.I.C.S.: 333249
Harald Folk *(Gen Mgr)*

Styner+Bienz Formtech Ltd. (1)
Freiburgstrasse 556
Niederwangen, Switzerland
Tel.: (41) 319808111
Fax: (41) 319808155
E-Mail: info@advaltech.com
Web Site: www.advaltech.ch
Injection Molding Machicnery Mfr
S.I.C.: 3559
N.A.I.C.S.: 333249
Rene Rothen *(Mng Dir)*

Teuscher Kunststoff-Technik Ltd (1)
Niklaus-Wengi-St 38
CH 2540 Grenchen, Switzerland
Tel.: (41) 326531935
Fax: (41) 326531550
E-Mail: info@teuscher-ag.ch
Web Site: www.awm.ch
Emp.: 35
Injection Molding Machinery Mfr
S.I.C.: 3544
N.A.I.C.S.: 333511
Steven Myers *(Gen Mgr)*
U.S. Subsidiaries:

Awm Mold Service Us Inc. (1)
900 Cummings Ctr Ste 219u
Beverly, MA 01915-6182
Tel.: (978) 720-4080
Fax: (978) 720-4084
E-Mail: mosterode@awm-us.com
Emp.: 1
Injection Molding Machinery Mfr
S.I.C.: 3559
N.A.I.C.S.: 333249
John Ransdell *(Pres)*

FOBOHA US Inc. (1)
900 Cummings Ctr Ste 219u
Beverly, MA 01915-6182
Tel.: (978) 720-4080
Fax: (978) 720-4084
E-Mail: foboha-usa@foboha.com
Web Site: www.foboha.com
Emp.: 1
Injection Molding Machinery Mfr
S.I.C.: 3544
N.A.I.C.S.: 333511
Non-U.S. Subsidiaries:

Awm Mold Tech International Trading (Shanghai) Co. Ltd. (1)
Room 1807 He Yi Bldg
420 Jiang Ning Road
Shanghai, China
Tel.: (86) 2162678603
Fax: (86) 2162678513
E-Mail: awm@awm.sh.cn
Emp.: 2
Injection Molding Machinery Mfr
S.I.C.: 3559
N.A.I.C.S.: 333249
Roy Clements *(Gen Mgr)*

Awm Swiss Technology Ltd. (1)
Room 1701 Billion Trade Ctr
31 Hung To Rd Kwun Tong, Kowloon, China (Hong Kong)
Tel.: (852) 26706000
Fax: (852) 26701918
E-Mail: awm@awm.hk
Emp.: 6
Injection Molding Technology
S.I.C.: 3544
N.A.I.C.S.: 333511

Foboha Gmbh (1)
Im Muhlegrun 8
77716 Haslach im Kinzigtal, Germany
Tel.: (49) 78327980
Fax: (49) 7832798988
E-Mail: foboha@advaltech.com
Web Site: www.advaltech.com
Emp.: 180
Injection Molding Machinery Mfr
S.I.C.: 3559
N.A.I.C.S.: 333249
Arm Bruster *(Gen Mgr)*

Omni Engineering Shanghai Co. Ltd (1)
Part No 49 Plant No 199
Shanghai, 200131, China
Tel.: (86) 2150460808
Industrial Mold Mfr
S.I.C.: 3544
N.A.I.C.S.: 333511

Omni Investors Pte. Ltd (1)
331 North Bridge Road 13-04/06 Odeon Towers
Singapore, 188720, Singapore
Tel.: (65) 65577900
Fax: (65) 63374131
Investment Management Services
S.I.C.: 6211
N.A.I.C.S.: 523999
Paul Sharp *(Gen Mgr)*

Omni Manufacturing Services S.A. de C.V. (1)
Av La Noria Lote 13 Manzana 3 No 125
Parque Industrial Queretaro
Santa Rosa Jauregui, Queretaro, 76220, Mexico
Tel.: (52) 4422389200
Fax: (52) 4422389226
Industrial Plastic Products Mfr
S.I.C.: 3089
N.A.I.C.S.: 326199

Adval Tech Holding AG—(Continued)

Omni Plastics (Thailand) Co. Ltd **(1)**
64/65 Eastern Seaboard Industrial Estate
Moo 4 Highway 331
T Pluakdaeng A Pluakdaeng, Rayong, 21140, Thailand
Tel.: (66) 38 656 051
Web Site: www.advaltech.com
Plastic Products Mfr & Distr
S.I.C.: 3089
N.A.I.C.S.: 326199

Omni Plastics (Xiamen) Co. Ltd **(1)**
No 33 Xiangxing Rd 1st Xiangyu Free Trade Zone
Xiamen, 361006, China
Tel.: (86) 592 574 7060
Fax: (86) 592 574 7860
Injection Molding Plastic Products Mfr
S.I.C.: 3089
N.A.I.C.S.: 326199

Omni Precision Sdn. Bhd. **(1)**
No 9 Jalan Tampoi 7/4
81200 Johor Bahru, Malaysia
Tel.: (60) 7 340 2100
Fax: (60) 7 334 3353
Injection Molding Machinery Mfr
S.I.C.: 3559
N.A.I.C.S.: 333249

QSCH Termelo es Kereskedelmi Kft **(1)**
Matyas kiraly u 67
H 7100 Szekszard, Hungary
Tel.: (36) 36 74 512580
Fax: (36) 36 74 512587
Emp.: 180
Metal Stamping Mfr
S.I.C.: 3466
N.A.I.C.S.: 332119
Bernd Kunze *(Mng Dir)*

ADVANCE DOOR SYSTEMS LTD

34 Great Plains Road Emerald Park
Regina, SK, S4L 1B6, Canada
Tel.: (306) 781-0207
Fax: (306) 781-0231
Web Site: www.advancedoor.com
Rev.: $10,868,119
Emp.: 30
Business Description:
Doors Mfr
S.I.C.: 2431
N.A.I.C.S.: 321911
Personnel:
Len Bedal *(Owner)*

ADVANCE ENERGY LIMITED

Suite 2 16 Ord Street
Perth, WA, 6005, Australia
Mailing Address:
PO Box 1779
West Perth, WA, 6872, Australia
Tel.: (61) 8 9429 2900
Fax: (61) 8 9486 1011
E-Mail: info@advanceenergyltd.co m.au
Web Site: www.advanceenergyltd.co m.au
AVD—(ASX)
Rev.: $211,583
Assets: $4,182,991
Liabilities: $8,773,857
Net Worth: ($4,590,866)
Earnings: ($1,518,288)
Fiscal Year-end: 12/31/12
Business Description:
Oil & Gas Exploration Services
S.I.C.: 1389
N.A.I.C.S.: 213112
Personnel:
Anthony Short *(Chm & Mng Dir)*
Alistair Jobling *(Sec)*
Board of Directors:
Anthony Short
Alistair Jobling
Kip Plankinton
Legal Counsel:
Hardy Bowen
28 Ord Street
West Perth, WA, 6005, Australia

ADVANCE GOLD CORP.

432 Royal Avenue
Kamloops, BC, V2B 3P7, Canada
Tel.: (250) 314-0186
Fax: (250) 828-2269
E-Mail: info@advancegold.ca
Web Site: www.advancegold.ca/s/Ho me.asp
Year Founded: 2007
AAX—(TSXV)
Assets: $415,234
Liabilities: $29,131
Net Worth: $386,103
Earnings: ($422,307)
Fiscal Year-end: 05/31/13
Business Description:
Gold Mining Services
S.I.C.: 1041
N.A.I.C.S.: 212221
Personnel:
James T. Gillis *(Pres & CEO)*
Marie Cupello *(CFO & Sec)*
Board of Directors:
Jeffrey Scott Ackert
Ali Afif Fawaz
James T. Gillis
Osvaldo Iadarola
Guido Edward M. Pas
Christopher J. Wild

ADVANCE LIFESTYLES LIMITED

254-B 4th Floor Nirlon House Dr
Annie Beasant Road
Worli, Mumbai, 400001, India
Tel.: (91) 22 42 31 99 00
Fax: (91) 22 42 31 99 50
E-Mail: info@advance.net.in
Web Site: www.advance.net.in
521048—(BOM)
Business Description:
Real Estate Management Services
S.I.C.: 6531
N.A.I.C.S.: 531390
Personnel:
Phulchand Agarwal *(Chm & Mng Dir)*
Sundeep Agarwal *(CFO)*
Binal Gandhi *(Compliance Officer & Sec)*
Board of Directors:
Phulchand Agarwal
M. S. Bhardwaj
S. Srinivasan
S. D. Vyas
Transfer Agent:
Sharepro Services (India) Pvt. Ltd.
416-420 4th Floor Devnandan Mall Opp.
Sanyash Ashram Ellisbridge
Ahmedabad, India

ADVANCE PETROCHEMICALS LIMITED

36 Kothari Market Opp Hirabhai
Market Kankaria
Ahmedabad, Gujarat, 380 022, India
Tel.: (91) 79 25454795
Fax: (91) 79 25454586
E-Mail: Info@advancepetro.com
Web Site: www.advancepetro.com
Year Founded: 1985
506947—(BOM)
Business Description:
Petrochemical Mfr Distr
S.I.C.: 2869
N.A.I.C.S.: 325110
Personnel:
Ashok Goenka *(Chm & Mng Dir)*
Board of Directors:
Ashok Goenka
Arvind Goenka
Omprakash Jalan
Nirish J. Parikh
Shailesh Singh Rajput
J. K. Trivedi

ADVANCE RESIDENCE INVESTMENT CORPORATION

326 Kanda Nishiki-cho
Chiyoda-ku, Tokyo, 101-0054, Japan
Tel.: (81) 3 3518 0480
Web Site: www.adr-reit.com
3269—(TKS)
Business Description:
Real Estate Investment Trust
S.I.C.: 6726
N.A.I.C.S.: 525990
Personnel:
Kenji Kosaka *(Exec Dir)*

ADVANCE SCT LIMITED

65 Tech Park Crescent
Singapore, 637787, Singapore
Tel.: (65) 63685788
Fax: (65) 63685766
E-Mail: singapore@advancesct.com
Web Site: www.advancesct.com
5FH—(SES)
Rev.: $30,222,116
Assets: $19,470,375
Liabilities: $41,688,804
Net Worth: ($22,218,429)
Earnings: ($22,326,926)
Fiscal Year-end: 12/31/12
Business Description:
Recycling & Waste Management Services
S.I.C.: 9511
N.A.I.C.S.: 924110
Personnel:
Simon Eng *(Chm & CEO)*
Attlee Kuan Yew Hue *(Vice Chm)*
Daming Wang *(Pres-Ops-China & Gen Mgr-B&F Envirotech Shenyang Co Ltd)*
Shirley Guat Hua Lim *(Sec)*
Darren Poon Guan Tan *(Sr VP-Ops)*
Jeffrey Tian Hong Tan *(Sr VP-Bus Dev)*
Board of Directors:
Simon Eng
Yiowmin Chay
Peter Chee Kong Choo
Attlee Kuan Yew Hue
Transfer Agent:
Boardroom Corporate & Advisory Services Pte. Ltd.
50 Raffles Place 32-01 Singapore Land Tower
Singapore, Singapore

Subsidiaries:

Ever Glory Logistics Pte Ltd **(1)**
No 10 Kranji Crescent
Singapore, Singapore
Tel.: (65) 6269 8417
Fax: (65) 6368 6850
Freight Trucking & Logistics Management Services
S.I.C.: 4214
N.A.I.C.S.: 484110

New Tsingyi Pte Ltd **(1)**
No 10 Kranji Crescent
Singapore, Singapore
Tel.: (65) 63685788
Fax: (65) 63685766
E-Mail: enquiry@newtsingyi.com
Web Site: www.newtsingyi.com
Scrap Materials Collection Services
S.I.C.: 4212
N.A.I.C.S.: 562119
Janice Mandelini *(Sec)*

Tsing Yi Enterprises Pte Ltd **(1)**
10 Kranji Crescent
728660 Singapore, Singapore
Tel.: (65) 63685788
Fax: (65) 63685766
E-Mail: tsingyi@advancesct.com
Web Site: www.advancesct.com
Emp.: 80
Metal Scrap Recycling Services
S.I.C.: 7389
N.A.I.C.S.: 561990

Tsingtech Recycling Pte Ltd **(1)**
12 Defu Lane 7
Singapore, Singapore
Tel.: (65) 62835188
Fax: (65) 6283 5155
E-Mail: tsingtech@advancesct.com
Emp.: 22
Metal Scrap Recycling Services
S.I.C.: 7389
N.A.I.C.S.: 561990
Lim Hock Chye *(Gen Mgr)*

Non-U.S. Subsidiaries:

SCT Copper Industry (Shenyang) Co., Ltd. **(1)**
106 Dong Da Ying Road North Xinmin City
Economic Development Zone
Shenyang, Liaoning, 110000, China
Tel.: (86) 2487526039
Fax: (86) 2487526023
Copper Smelting Services
S.I.C.: 3339
N.A.I.C.S.: 331410

SCT Technologies (Kunshan) Ltd. **(1)**
No 115 Zhonghuan Road
Kunshan, Jiangsu, 215300, China
Tel.: (86) 51257172233
Fax: (86) 51257175727
E-Mail: info@sct-tech.cn
Web Site: www.sct-tech.cn
Electrical Products Inspection Services
S.I.C.: 8734
N.A.I.C.S.: 541380

SCT Technologies (Thailand) Co., Ltd. **(1)**
14/48-49 M 10 Phaholyothin Road
T Klongnueng, Khlong Luang, Pathum Thani, 12120, Thailand
Tel.: (66) 2 529 4646
Fax: (66) 2 529 2029
E-Mail: scttech14@hotmail.com
Web Site: www.sctthailand.com
Emp.: 22
Printed Circuit Board Drilling Services
S.I.C.: 7389
N.A.I.C.S.: 561990
Thirapan Piangkantha *(Mgr)*

ADVANCE SYNERGY BERHAD

Level 3 West Wing Wisma Synergy
No 72 Pesiaran Jubli Perak
Seksyen 22, 40000 Shah Alam, Selangor Darul Ehsan, Malaysia
Tel.: (60) 351928822
Fax: (60) 351928811
E-Mail: investor_relations@asb.co m.my
Web Site: www.asb.com.my
Year Founded: 1920
ASB—(KLS)
Rev.: $75,358,967
Assets: $207,934,072
Liabilities: $44,810,596
Net Worth: $163,123,476
Earnings: $1,932,433
Fiscal Year-end: 12/31/12
Business Description:
Property Development Services
S.I.C.: 1531
N.A.I.C.S.: 236117
Personnel:
Ahmad Sebi Bakar *(Chm)*
Su Nie Lee *(Mng Dir)*
Tze Leng Wong *(Chm-Unified Comm Holdings Ltd)*
Joon Hian Wong *(COO-Fin Svcs & CEO/Mng Dir-Synergy Cards Sdn Bhd)*
Anton Syazi Ahmad Sebi *(CEO-Unified Communications Holdings Limited & Gen Mgr-Corp Dev)*
Fabio Delisi *(CEO-Synergy Tours Sdn Bhd)*

Chee Kong Yap *(CEO-Dama TCM Sdn Bhd)*
Tsae Feng Ho *(Sec & Mgr-Secretarial)*
Board of Directors:
Ahmad Sebi Bakar
Masri Khaw Abdullah
Aryati Sasya Ahmad Sebi
Al'Azmy Ahmad
Su Nie Lee
Ahmad Ghiti Mohd Daud
Teck Ming Yong
Subsidiaries:

Advance Synergy Capital Berhad (1)
Level 3 Wisma ASCAP-QBC No 72
Pesiaran Jubli Perak
Seksyen 22, 40000 Shah Alam, Selangor
Darul Ehsan, Malaysia
Tel.: (60) 351921886
Fax: (60) 351921886
Management Services
S.I.C.: 8741
N.A.I.C.S.: 551114
Wong Joon Hian *(Mng Dir)*

Subsidiary:

Quality Bus & Coach (M) Sdn. Bhd. (2)
2 Persiaran Jubli Perak Lion Industrial Pk
Section 22, Shah Alam, Selangor, 40000, Malaysia
Tel.: (60) 351922522
Fax: (60) 351922514
Web Site: www.quality-bus.com
Automobile & Automotive Components Mfr
S.I.C.: 3711
N.A.I.C.S.: 336111
Deanne Turrisi *(Gen Mgr)*

Advance Synergy Realty Sdn. Bhd. (1)
Lot 6807 6808 Synergy Square Jalan Matang
93050 Kuching, Sarawak, Malaysia
Tel.: (60) 82646617
Fax: (60) 82646208
Web Site: www.asrsynergy.com.my
Property Development Services
S.I.C.: 6531
N.A.I.C.S.: 531311
Sng Ngiap Koon *(COO & Exec Dir)*

Alangka-Suka Hotels & Resorts Sdn. Bhd. (1)
B 16 8 Megan Avenue II
12 Jalan Yap Kwan Seng, 50744 Kuala Lumpur, Malaysia
Tel.: (60) 321622922
Fax: (60) 321622937
E-Mail: centralresv@holidayvilla.com.my
Web Site: www.holidayvilla.com.my
Hotel Management Services
S.I.C.: 7011
N.A.I.C.S.: 721110
Adibah Ishak *(Mgr)*

Subsidiaries:

Alor Setar Holiday Villa Sdn. Bhd. (2)
Lot 162/163 Jalan Tunku Ibrahim Bandar
Alor Setar Mukim Kota Setar
PO Box 319
Pejabat Pos Besar, 05000 Alor Setar, Kedah Darul Aman, Malaysia
Tel.: (60) 47349999
Fax: (60) 47341954
E-Mail: reservation@holidayvillaalorstar.com.my
Web Site: www.holidayvillaalorstar.com
Hotel Management Services
S.I.C.: 8741
N.A.I.C.S.: 561110
Mavis Masri Azman *(Mng Dir)*

Cherating Holiday Villa Berhad (2)
Lot 1303 Mukim Sungai Karang Cherating
26080 Pahang, Kuantan, Malaysia
Tel.: (60) 95819500
Fax: (60) 95819178
E-Mail: fomchv@holidayvilla.com.my
Web Site: www.holidayvillahotels.com
Emp.: 65
Hotel & Resort Management Services
S.I.C.: 7011
N.A.I.C.S.: 721110
Adibah Ishak *(Mgr)*

Langkawi Holiday Villa Sdn. Bhd. (2)
Lot 1698 Pantai Tengah
Mukim Kedawang, 07100 Kuah, Kedah, Malaysia
Tel.: (60) 49529999
Fax: (60) 49552211
Resort & Spa Operation Services
S.I.C.: 7011
N.A.I.C.S.: 721110
Hossam Suwailem *(Gen Mgr)*

Non-U.S. Subsidiary:

P.T. Diwangkara Holiday Villa Bal (2)
Jl Hang Tuah 54
Denpasar, Bali, 80030, Indonesia
Tel.: (62) 361288577
Fax: (62) 361288894
E-Mail: dhvbali@indosat.net.id
Web Site: www.indosat.net.id
Emp.: 45
Hotel Management Services
S.I.C.: 7011
N.A.I.C.S.: 721110
Ang Cheng *(Gen Mgr)*

Orient Escape Travel (Sabah) Sdn. Bhd. (1)
Shop No 17 1st Floor Block K Sadong Jaya
Jalan Ikan Juara 1 Karamunsing, 88100
Kota Kinabalu, Sabah, Malaysia
Tel.: (60) 88 246 406
Fax: (60) 88 246 409
Travel & Tour Operating Agencies
S.I.C.: 4724
N.A.I.C.S.: 561510
Ahmad Sebi Bakar *(Mgr)*

Sadong Development Sdn. Bhd. (1)
1st Floor Blok K Sadong Jaya Jln Ikan Juara
1 Karamunsing, 88100 Kota Kinabalu, Sabah, Malaysia
Tel.: (60) 88238995
Fax: (60) 88238962
Emp.: 3
Property Managing Services
S.I.C.: 6531
N.A.I.C.S.: 531311
Liew Chaw Thai *(Mgr)*

Synergy Cards Sdn. Bhd. (1)
Level 2 Wisma Triton 72 Persiaran Jubli Perak
Seksyen 22, 40000 Shah Alam, Selangor, Malaysia
Tel.: (60) 351912229
Fax: (60) 351910088
Emp.: 25
Credit Card Issuing Services
S.I.C.: 6153
N.A.I.C.S.: 522210
Yap Chee Kong *(CEO)*

Synergy Tours Sdn. Bhd. (1)
Level 23 Menara Etiqa 23 Jalan Melaka
50100 Kuala Lumpur, Malaysia
Tel.: (60) 326971133
Fax: (60) 326971122
E-Mail: malaysia@synergy-tours.com
Web Site: www.synergy-tours.com
Emp.: 15
Travel & Tour Operating Agencies
S.I.C.: 4724
N.A.I.C.S.: 561510
Fabio Delisi *(CEO)*

Non-U.S. Subsidiary:

Advansa Pty. Ltd. (1)
258 Halifax Street
Wingfield, Adelaide, SA, 5000, Australia
Tel.: (61) 882439100
Fax: (61) 882439185
E-Mail: siles@advansa.com.au
Web Site: www.advansa.com.au
Emp.: 12
Hardware Whslr
S.I.C.: 5072
N.A.I.C.S.: 423710

ADVANCE UK TRUST PLC

c/o Progressive Asset Management
145-157 Saint John Street
London, EC1V 4RU, United Kingdom
Tel.: (44) 2075665580
Fax: (44) 2073360865
E-Mail: info@pro-asset.com
Web Site: www.pro-asset.com
ADU—(LSE)
Sales Range: $1-9.9 Million
Emp.: 20
Business Description:
Investment Trust Services
S.I.C.: 6733
N.A.I.C.S.: 523991
Personnel:
Philip J. Rowen *(Chm)*
Legal Counsel:
Freshfields Bruckhaus Deringer
Dusseldorf, Germany

ADVANCED BRAKING TECHNOLOGY LTD.

Unit 1 3 McDonald Street
Osborne Park, WA, 6017, Australia
Mailing Address:
PO Box 1177
Osborne Park, WA, 6916, Australia
Tel.: (61) 892734800
Fax: (61) 892019986
E-Mail: info.perth@advancedbraking.com
Web Site: www.advancedbraking.com
ABV—(ASX)
Rev.: $8,496,241
Assets: $11,521,458
Liabilities: $2,035,221
Net Worth: $9,486,236
Earnings: ($958,732)
Emp.: 56
Fiscal Year-end: 06/30/13
Business Description:
Vehicle Braking Systems Mfr & Distr
S.I.C.: 3714
N.A.I.C.S.: 336340
Personnel:
Graeme Sumner *(Mng Dir)*
Clare Madelin *(CFO & Sec)*
Kevin Clapham *(Trng & Field Support Officer)*
Dave Skinner *(Technical Support & Trng Officer)*
Board of Directors:
Bruce Grey
Adam Levine
David Slack
Legal Counsel:
HopgoodGanim
Level 4 105 St Georges Terrace
Perth, WA, 6000, Australia
Subsidiary:

Advanced Braking Pty Ltd (1)
Unit 1 3 McDonald Street
Osborne Park, Perth, WA, 6016, Australia
Tel.: (61) 8 9273 4800
Fax: (61) 8 92019986
E-Mail: info.perth@advancedbraking.com
Web Site: www.advancedbraking.com
Emp.: 3
Automotive Braking System Mfr
S.I.C.: 3714
N.A.I.C.S.: 336340

Non-U.S. Subsidiary:

Safe Effect (Thailand) Co Ltd (1)
242 Moo 3
Si Racha, 20230 Chon Buri, Thailand
Tel.: (66) 38401413
Fax: (66) 38401495
E-Mail: info@advancedbraking.com
Web Site: www.advancedbraking.com
Emp.: 2
Automotive Brake System Mfr
S.I.C.: 3714
N.A.I.C.S.: 336340
Nicolas Jolif *(Gen Mgr)*

ADVANCED BUSINESS ANALYTICS (M) SDN. BHD.

C-12-08 Block C Plaza Mont' Kiara
2 Jilan Kiara Mont' Kiara, 50480
Kuala Lumpur, Malaysia
Tel.: (60) 3 6203 2300
Fax: (60) 3 6201 9560
E-Mail: enquiry@spss.com.my
Web Site: www.spss.com.my
Sales Range: $1-9.9 Million
Emp.: 9
Business Description:
Predictive Analytics & Data Mining Software Distr
S.I.C.: 5045
N.A.I.C.S.: 423430
Personnel:
Carol Kha *(Bus Mgr)*

ADVANCED CELLULAR INC.

(Name Changed to MAKISM 3D CORP.)

ADVANCED CHEMICAL INDUSTRIES LIMITED

ACI Centre 245 Tejgaon Industrial Area
Dhaka, 1208, Bangladesh
Tel.: (880) 28878603
Fax: (880) 28878626
E-Mail: info@aci-bd.com
Web Site: www.aci-bd.com
ACI—(DHA)
Rev.: $119,839,162
Assets: $163,496,062
Liabilities: $100,589,739
Net Worth: $62,906,323
Earnings: $6,748,535
Emp.: 4,560
Fiscal Year-end: 12/31/12
Business Description:
Pharmaceutical Mfr
S.I.C.: 2834
N.A.I.C.S.: 325412
Personnel:
M. Anis Ud Dowla *(Chm)*
Arif Dowla *(Mng Dir)*
Muallem A. Choudhury *(CFO & Exec Dir-Fin & Plng)*
Sheema Abed Rahman *(Sec & Dir-Corp Affairs)*
Board of Directors:
M. Anis Ud Dowla
Waliur Rahman Bhuiyan
Juned Ahmed Choudhury
Abdul-Muyeed Chowdhury
Arif Dowla
Najma Dowla
Md. Fayekuzzaman
Golam Mainuddin
Sheema Abed Rahman
Subsidiaries:

ACI Formulations Limited (1)
ACI Centre 245 Tejgaon Industrial Area
Dhaka, 1208, Bangladesh
Tel.: (880) 28878603
Fax: (880) 28878626
E-Mail: info@aci-bd.com
Web Site: www.aci-bd.com
ACIFORMULA—(DHA)
Rev.: $31,953,318
Assets: $35,274,151
Liabilities: $14,058,032
Net Worth: $21,216,119
Earnings: $1,856,552
Emp.: 921
Fiscal Year-end: 12/31/12
Herbicides Mfr
S.I.C.: 2879
N.A.I.C.S.: 325320
M. Anis Ud Dowla *(Chm)*
Shusmita Anis *(Mng Dir)*
Sheema Abed Rahman *(Sec)*

ACI Logistics Limited (1)
Level 8 Novo Tower 270 Tejgaon Industrial Area
Dhaka, 1208, Bangladesh
Tel.: (880) 28825940
Fax: (880) 28829680
Agricultural Products Import & Distr

Advanced Chemical Industries Limited—(Continued)

S.I.C.: 5191
N.A.I.C.S.: 424910

ACI Motors Limited (1)
245 Tejgaon Industrial Area
Dhaka, 1208, Bangladesh
Tel.: (880) 29885694
Fax: (880) 2 9884784
Farm Machinery Distr
S.I.C.: 5083
N.A.I.C.S.: 423820

ACI Pure Flour Limited (1)
ACI Center 245 Tejgoan Industrial Area
Dhaka, 1208, Bangladesh
Tel.: (880) 29885694
Fax: (880) 29886029
E-Mail: info@aci-bd.com
Web Site: www.aciflour.com
Wheat Flour Mfr
S.I.C.: 2098
N.A.I.C.S.: 311824
Anis ud Dowla *(Chm)*
Arif ud Dowla *(Mng Dir)*

ADVANCED COMPUTER SOFTWARE PLC

Munro House Portsmouth Road
Cobham, Surrey, KT11 1TF, United Kingdom
Tel.: (44) 8451 606 162
Fax: (44) 1932 584 001
E-Mail: investor-relations@advancedcomputersoftware.com
Web Site: www.advcomputersoftware.com
ASW—(AIM)
Rev.: $190,958,271
Assets: $344,717,945
Liabilities: $125,015,017
Net Worth: $219,702,928
Earnings: $14,422,076
Emp.: 951
Fiscal Year-end: 02/28/13

Business Description:
Software & Information Technology Services
S.I.C.: 7372
N.A.I.C.S.: 511210

Personnel:
Michael Jackson *(Chm)*
Vinodka Murria *(CEO)*
Guy Millward *(CFO)*
Paul Gibson *(COO)*
Barbara Firth *(COO-Acq & Integration & Sec)*

Board of Directors:
Michael Jackson
Barbara Firth
Paul Gibson
Christopher Hand
Mike McGoun
Guy Millward
Vinodka Murria

Legal Counsel:
Morrison & Foerster (UK) LLP
CityPoint One Ropemaker Street
London, United Kingdom

Subsidiaries:

Adastra Software Ltd. (1)
Unit 4 Eurogate Bus Park
Ashford, Kent, TN24 8SB, United Kingdom
Tel.: (44) 1233722700
Fax: (44) 1233722701
E-Mail: support@adastra.com
Web Site: www.advancedcomputersoftware.com
Emp.: 130
Application Software Development Services
S.I.C.: 7372
N.A.I.C.S.: 511210
Vin Murria *(CEO)*
James Berry *(CTO)*

Advanced Business Solutions (1)
Munro House
Portsmouth Road, Cobham, Surrey, KT11 1TF, United Kingdom UK
Tel.: (44) 1932584000 (100%)
Fax: (44) 1932584001
E-Mail: liz.ebbrell@coasolutions.com
Web Site: www.coasolutions.com
Emp.: 60
Business Software & Consultancy
S.I.C.: 5946
N.A.I.C.S.: 443142
Dean Dickinson *(Mng Dir-Pub Sector & Enterprise)*

Business Systems Holdings Group Plc (1)
BSG House 226-236 City Road
London, EC1V 2TT, United Kingdom
Tel.: (44) 2078808888
Fax: (44) 2073908500
E-Mail: bsg.reception@advanced365.com
Web Site: www.advanced365.com
Emp.: 100
Information Technology Outsourcing Services
S.I.C.: 7373
N.A.I.C.S.: 541512
Neil Cross *(Mng Dir)*

Healthy Software Ltd. (1)
Pacific House The Wyvern Business Park
Stanier Way, Derby, DE21 6BF, United Kingdom
Tel.: (44) 1332680022
Fax: (44) 1332680033
E-Mail: info@healthysoftware.co.uk
Web Site: www.healthysoftware.co.uk
Medical Application Software Development Services
S.I.C.: 7371
N.A.I.C.S.: 541511
Rob England *(Mng Dir)*

StaffPlan Ltd. (1)
BSG House, 226-236 City Rd
London, EC1V 2QY, United Kingdom
Tel.: (44) 2087728773
Fax: (44) 2086759833
E-Mail: gary.drew@advancedcomputersoftware.com
Web Site: www.advancedcomputersoftware.com
Monitoring System Software Publishers
S.I.C.: 7372
N.A.I.C.S.: 511210
Jim Chase *(Mng Dir)*
Gary Drew *(Mng Dir)*

ADVANCED DIGITAL BROADCAST HOLDINGS SA

Ave de Tournay 7
1292 Chambesy, Switzerland
Tel.: (41) 225928400
Fax: (41) 225928402
E-Mail: IR@adbglobal.com
Web Site: www.adbholdings.com
ADBN—(SWX)
Rev.: $451,582,167
Assets: $228,053,628
Liabilities: $171,020,103
Net Worth: $57,033,525
Earnings: $8,462,525
Emp.: 894
Fiscal Year-end: 12/31/12

Business Description:
Digital Television Broadcast
S.I.C.: 4833
N.A.I.C.S.: 515120

Personnel:
Andrew N. Rybicki *(Chm, Pres & CEO)*
Francois Pogodalla *(Deputy CEO)*
Alessandro Brenna *(CFO & Exec VP)*
John Justo *(COO & Gen Mgr-Svcs Div)*
Krzysztof Kolbuszewski *(CTO & Exec VP)*
William G. Luehrs *(Chief Admin Officer & Exec VP-Cable Div-US)*
Janusz C. Szajna *(Pres-ABD Polska & Exec VP)*
Krzysztof Bilinski *(Exec VP-Brdcst Div)*
Jas Saini *(Exec VP-Strategy & Tech)*
Francesco Schiavinato *(Exec VP-BrdBand Div)*
Belinda Wong *(Exec VP-Fin)*
Tina Nyfors *(Sr VP-IR & Comm)*

Board of Directors:
Andrew N. Rybicki
Philippe Geyres
Jean-Christophe Hocke
Thomas Steinmann

Subsidiaries:

ADB Services S.A. (1)
Ave De Tournay 7
1292 Pregny, Geneva, Switzerland
Tel.: (41) 227990799
Fax: (41) 227990790
Digital Television Equipments Retailer
S.I.C.: 5064
N.A.I.C.S.: 423620
Andrew N. Rybicki *(CEO)*

Advanced Digital Broadcast S.A. (1)
Advanced Digital Broadcast S.A.
1292 Pregny, Geneva, Switzerland
Tel.: (41) 227990799
Fax: (41) 227990790
E-Mail: info@adbglobal.com
Web Site: www.adbglobal.com
Digital Television Equipment Sales & Support Services
S.I.C.: 5064
N.A.I.C.S.: 423620

U.S. Subsidiary:

Advanced Digital Broadcast Inc. (1)
10901 W 120th Ave Ste 230
Broomfield, CO 80021-3426
Tel.: (303) 474-8600
Fax: (303) 474-8687
Web Site: www.adbhoding.com
Emp.: 13
Set Top Box Distr
S.I.C.: 5064
N.A.I.C.S.: 423620
Francois Pogodalla *(CEO)*
Tomasz Koslowski *(CTO)*

Non-U.S. Subsidiaries:

Advanced Digital Broadcast Hong Kong Ltd. (1)
Unit No 2704 W Tower Shun Tak Ctr 168-200 Connaught Rd
Central, China (Hong Kong)
Tel.: (852) 23245222
Digital Television Equipments Retailer
S.I.C.: 5064
N.A.I.C.S.: 423620

Advanced Digital Broadcast Italia S.r.l (1)
Via Cassanese 224
20090 Segrate, Milano, Italy
Tel.: (39) 02 8907 8154
Fax: (39) 02 8907 8156
Web Site: www.adbglobal.com
Digital Television Equipments Retailer
S.I.C.: 5064
N.A.I.C.S.: 423620

Advanced Digital Broadcast Ltd. (1)
15F 205 Sec 3 Pei-Hsin Road
Hsin Tien, 231, Taiwan
Tel.: (886) 289131500
Fax: (886) 2891315106
E-Mail: sales-asia@adbglobal.com
Emp.: 100
Digital Television Equipment Sales & Support Services
S.I.C.: 5064
N.A.I.C.S.: 423620
Christina Chang *(Mgr-HR)*

Advanced Digital Broadcast Polska Sp. z.o.o. (1)
Trasa Polnocna 16
65 119 Zielona Gora, Lubusz, Poland
Tel.: (48) 684515151
Fax: (48) 684515154
Web Site: www.adbglobal.com
Digital Television Equipment Sales & Technical Support Services
S.I.C.: 5064
N.A.I.C.S.: 423620
Jamusz C. Szajna *(Mng Dir)*

Advanced Digital Broadcast Spain S.L.U. (1)
Edificio America II Calle de Procion 7
Bloque 2 1 E
28023 Madrid, Spain
Tel.: (34) 917080690
Fax: (34) 917080754
E-Mail: c.quetelas@centromedeco.com
Web Site: www.centromedeco.com
Emp.: 22
Digital Television Equipment Sales & Support Services
S.I.C.: 4899
N.A.I.C.S.: 517919

ADB Broadband S.p.A. (1)
Viale Sarca 336
20126 Milan, Italy
Tel.: (39) 0264429253
Fax: (39) 0264429250
Web Site: broadband.adbglobal.com
Broadband Solutions, Products & Platforms
S.I.C.: 4899
N.A.I.C.S.: 517919

ADVANCED DYNAMICS CORPORATION LTD.

1700 Marie Victorin
Saint-Bruno, QC, J3V 6B9, Canada
Tel.: (450) 653-7220
Fax: (450) 653-8460
E-Mail: sales@advanceddynamics.com
Web Site: www.advanceddynamics.com
Year Founded: 1965
Rev.: $13,041,743
Emp.: 150

Business Description:
Engineering Services
S.I.C.: 8711
N.A.I.C.S.: 541330

Personnel:
Peter Hanna *(Pres)*

ADVANCED ELECTRONICS COMPANY

King Khaled Air Port Industrial
PO Box 90916
Riyadh, 11623, Saudi Arabia
Tel.: (966) 12201350
Fax: (966) 12201355
E-Mail: info@aecl.com
Web Site: www.aecl.com
Year Founded: 1988
Sales Range: $100-124.9 Million
Emp.: 800

Business Description:
Military & Commercial Electronic Components Mfr
S.I.C.: 3679
N.A.I.C.S.: 334419

Personnel:
Ghassan A. Al Shibl *(Pres, CEO & Mng Dir)*

ADVANCED ENERGY MANAGEMENT LTD.

222 Edinburgh Drive
Moncton, NB, E1E 4C7, Canada
Tel.: (506) 857-0818
Fax: (506) 857-0867
E-Mail: inquiries@aemltd.com
Web Site: www.aemltd.com
Year Founded: 1985
Rev.: $11,737,568
Emp.: 40

Business Description:
Heating & Air Conditioning Equipment Distr
S.I.C.: 5075
N.A.I.C.S.: 423730

Personnel:
Rino Levesque *(Founder)*

ADVANCED ENERGY SYSTEMS LIMITED

285 Goodwood Road
Kings Park, SA, 5034, Australia
Tel.: (61) 882714001
Fax: (61) 882716378

AES—(ASX)
Rev.: $61,585
Assets: $24,580,191
Liabilities: $20,741,893
Net Worth: $3,838,298
Earnings: ($89,734)
Fiscal Year-end: 06/30/13

Business Description:
Real Estate Development Services
S.I.C.: 6531
N.A.I.C.S.: 531390

Personnel:
Chenghui Xu *(Chm, CEO & Mng Dir)*
Elias Farah *(Sec)*

Board of Directors:
Chenghui Xu
Chunying Leng
Chuanlong Mu

ADVANCED ENGINE COMPONENTS LIMITED

14 Energy Street
PO Box 3126
Malaga, WA, 6090, Australia
Tel.: (61) 892096900
Fax: (61) 892096999
E-Mail: enquire@advancedengine.com
Web Site: www.advancedengine.com
ACE—(ASX)
Sales Range: $1-9.9 Million
Emp.: 40

Business Description:
Research & Development of Electronic Fuel Injection & Engine Management Technologies
S.I.C.: 3714
N.A.I.C.S.: 336390

Personnel:
Antony Middleton *(Mng Dir)*
Alicia Mitton *(Sec)*

Board of Directors:
Manharlal Bhaichand Gathani Jain
Graham Keys
Antony Middleton
Vivekananthan M. V. Nathan
Albert Pun

Legal Counsel:
Griffith Hack
256 Adelaide Terrace
6000 Perth, WA, Australia

Non-U.S. Subsidiary:

AEC China Limited (1)
Heqiao Dasha A407 8A Guanghua Rd
Beijing, Chaoyang, 100026, China
Tel.: (86) 1065814430
Fax: (86) 10 65814439
Emp.: 9
Engines Mfr
S.I.C.: 3519
N.A.I.C.S.: 333618
David Wang *(Gen Mgr)*

ADVANCED EXPLORATIONS INC.

Simpson Tower 401 Bay Street Suite 2828
Toronto, ON, M5H 2Y4, Canada
Tel.: (416) 203-0059
Fax: (416) 203-9900
E-Mail: info@advanced-exploration.com
Web Site: www.advanced-exploration.com
AXI—(DEU OTC TSXV)
Assets: $68,777,461
Liabilities: $13,309,627
Net Worth: $55,467,835
Earnings: ($5,540,348)
Fiscal Year-end: 12/31/12

Business Description:
Mining Company
S.I.C.: 1499
N.A.I.C.S.: 212399

Personnel:
James D. Excell *(Acting Chm)*
M. Louis Nagy *(CFO)*
Joseph Chiummiento *(Sec)*

Board of Directors:
James D. Excell
Robert Collette
John C. Gingerich
Lei Guo
Robert Telewiak
Yaogan Zeng
Raziel Zisman

Legal Counsel:
Wildeboer Dellelce LLP
Wildeboer Dellelce Place 365 Bay Street Suite 800
Toronto, ON, Canada

Transfer Agent:
Equity Transfer & Trust Company
200 University Avenue Ste 400
Toronto, ON, M5H 4H1, Canada
Tel.: (416) 361-0152
Fax: (416) 361-0470

ADVANCED HOLDINGS LTD.

29 Senoko South Road
Singapore, 758083, Singapore
Tel.: (65) 68549000
Fax: (65) 67795400
E-Mail: sales@advancedholdings.com
Web Site: www.advancedholdings.com
Year Founded: 1993
51A—(SES)
Rev.: $88,361,998
Assets: $86,888,380
Liabilities: $32,107,860
Net Worth: $54,780,520
Earnings: $3,664,612
Emp.: 60
Fiscal Year-end: 12/31/12

Business Description:
Chemical & Petrochemical, Oil & Gas, Power Generation & Micro-Electronics Process Equipment Designer & Supplier
S.I.C.: 3823
N.A.I.C.S.: 334513

Personnel:
Kar King Wong *(Mng Dir)*
Axron Gwee Koon Lim *(COO)*
Susan Janette Foulk *(Pres-Guided Wave Inc)*
Beng Hong Ong *(Sec)*

Board of Directors:
Emily Boy Lee Choo
Alastair Lindsay Crawford
Choon Hou Ho
Axron Gwee Koon Lim
Boon Cheng Lim
Kai Bing Siau
Gim Teik Soh
Kar King Wong

Subsidiaries:

Advanced Controls Pte Ltd (1)
29 Senoko S Rd
Singapore, 758083, Singapore
Tel.: (65) 67795100
Fax: (65) 67795400
Web Site: www.advanceholding.com
Chemical & Petrochemical, Oil & Gas, Power Generation & Micro-Electronics Process Equipment Designer & Supplier
S.I.C.: 3823
N.A.I.C.S.: 334513
Kar King Wong *(Mng Dir)*

Non-U.S. Subsidiaries:

Advanced Controls (China) Ltd. (2)
Unit 903 Hua Xia Bank Tower 256 Pudong South Rd
New Pudong District, Shanghai, 200120, China CN
Tel.: (86) 2151150988
Fax: (86) 2151150989
E-Mail: tony.xie@advancedholdings.com
Web Site: www.advancedholdings.com
Emp.: 10
Chemical & Petrochemical, Oil & Gas, Power Generation & Micro-Electronics Process Equipment Designer & Supplier
S.I.C.: 3823
N.A.I.C.S.: 334513
Xiao Feng Yang *(Gen Mgr)*

Branch:

Advanced Controls (China) Ltd. (3)
Ste C1018 Jun Feng Hua Ting Bldg No 69 BeiChen West Road
Chao Yang District, Beijing, PR, 100029, China
Tel.: (86) 1058772833
Fax: (86) 1058772852
E-Mail: beijing@advancedholdings.com
Web Site: www.advancedholdings.com
Emp.: 8
Chemical & Petrochemical, Oil & Gas, Power Generation & Micro-Electronics Process Equipment Designer & Supplier
S.I.C.: 3823
N.A.I.C.S.: 334513
Xiao Feng Yang *(Gen Mgr)*

Advanced Controls Co., Ltd. (2)
Room 405 Daejong Building 51-11 Bangi-Dong Songpa-Gu, Seoul, 138-050, Korea (South)
Tel.: (82) 2 423 4235
Fax: (82) 2 423 4207
Web Site: www.advancedholdings.com
Chemical & Petrochemical, Oil & Gas, Power Generation & Micro-Electronics Process Equipment Designer & Supplier
S.I.C.: 3823
N.A.I.C.S.: 334513

Advanced Controls (M) Sdn. Bhd (2)
1019 10th Floor Block A Damamsara Intan Jalan SS 20 27, Petaling Jaya, Selangor, 47400, Malaysia
Tel.: (60) 377285400
Fax: (60) 377286400
E-Mail: sales@advancedholdings.com
Emp.: 10
Industrial Machinery Mfr & Distr
S.I.C.: 3824
N.A.I.C.S.: 334514
Irane Wong *(Mgr)*

Advanced Engineering Holdings Pte. Ltd (1)
29 Senoko S Rd
Singapore, 758083, Singapore
Tel.: (65) 67795100
Fax: (65) 67795400
E-Mail: sales@advancedholdings.com
Emp.: 70
Industrial Equipments Mfr
S.I.C.: 3559
N.A.I.C.S.: 333249
King Wong Kar *(Mng Dir)*

Subsidiary:

Applied Engineering Pte Ltd (2)
46 Tuas Road
Singapore, 638499, Singapore
Tel.: (65) 6862 1726
Fax: (65) 6862 3486
E-Mail: enquiry@aepl.com.sg
Web Site: www.appliedengineering.com.sg
Design & Fabrication of Processing Equipment
S.I.C.: 3499
N.A.I.C.S.: 332999
Mong Teck Tan *(Gen Mgr)*

Advanced Environmental Technologies Pte. Ltd. (1)
29 Senoko S Rd
Singapore, 758083, Singapore
Tel.: (65) 67795100
Fax: (65) 67795400
E-Mail: sales@advancedholdings.com
Web Site: www.advancedholdings.com
Emp.: 80
Oilfield Equipments Mfr & Distr
S.I.C.: 3533
N.A.I.C.S.: 333132
Pauline Ng *(Mgr-Sls)*

Advanced Green Energy Pte Ltd (1)
30 Woodlands Loop
Singapore, 738319, Singapore
Tel.: (65) 68549000
Fax: (65) 67795400
E-Mail: sales@advancedholdings.com
Web Site: www.advancedholdings.com
Emp.: 100
Oil Field Equipments Mfr
S.I.C.: 3533
N.A.I.C.S.: 333132
Kar Wong *(Mng Dir)*

Advanced Resources Holdings Pte. Ltd. (1)
29 Senoko South Road
Singapore, 758083, Singapore
Tel.: (65) 68549000
Fax: (65) 67795400
E-Mail: sales@advancedholdings.com
Web Site: www.advancedholdings.com
Emp.: 50
Petrochemical Products Mfr
S.I.C.: 2869
N.A.I.C.S.: 325110
Kar Wong *(Mng Dir)*

Control & Applications Asia Pte Ltd (1)
29 Senoko South Road
Singapore, 758083, Singapore
Tel.: (65) 68549001
Fax: (65) 6758 7389
E-Mail: marketing@caeasia.com.sg
Web Site: www.caeasia.com.sg
Analyzers Mfr & Installation Services
S.I.C.: 3823
N.A.I.C.S.: 334513
K. T. Quah *(Gen Mgr)*

U.S. Subsidiary:

Guided Wave Inc. (1)
3033 Gold Canal Dr
Rancho Cordova, CA 95670-6129 CA
Tel.: (916) 638-4944 (91.5%)
Fax: (916) 635-8458
E-Mail: gwsales@guided-wave.com
Web Site: www.guided-wave.com
Emp.: 20
Optical Measurement Instrument Mfr & Installation Services
S.I.C.: 3823
N.A.I.C.S.: 334513
Susan Foulk *(Pres)*

Non-U.S. Subsidiary:

Guided Wave Asia Pte Ltd (2)
29 Senoko South Road
Singapore, 758083, Singapore
Tel.: (65) 68549000
Fax: (65) 6779 5400
E-Mail: gwsales@guided-wave.com
Optical Measurement Instruments Whslr
S.I.C.: 5049
N.A.I.C.S.: 423490

Non-U.S. Subsidiaries:

Advanced Water Reclamation (Chengdu) Co., Ltd (1)
Block 2 No 12 03 Greenwich Village No 1 Wangjiang Road
Chengdu, Sichuan, 610041, China
Tel.: (86) 2885292768
Fax: (86) 28 8529 2769
Wastewater Treatment Plant Development & Operation Services
S.I.C.: 1629
N.A.I.C.S.: 237110

Guided Wave Europe BVBA (1)
Leo de Bethunelaan 105
9300 Aalst, Belgium
Tel.: (32) 53 631165
Fax: (32) 53 631696
E-Mail: andre.cdbroeck@guided-wave-europe.com
Web Site: www.guided-wave-europerbu.com
Emp.: 1
Electronic Devices Sales
S.I.C.: 5049
N.A.I.C.S.: 423490
Paul Warburton *(Mgr-Section)*

ADVANCED INFO SERVICE PLC

414 Phaholyothin Rd Samsen Nai Phayathai
Bangkok, 10400, Thailand
Tel.: (66) 22996000

Advanced Info Service Plc—(Continued)

Fax: (66) 22995165
E-Mail: investor@ais.co.th
Web Site: www.ais.co.th
ADVA—(THA)
Rev.: $4,690,157,743
Assets: $3,345,066,434
Liabilities: $1,902,524,900
Net Worth: $1,442,541,534
Earnings: $1,156,206,467
Emp.: 8,000
Fiscal Year-end: 12/31/12
Business Description:
Mobile Network System Services
S.I.C.: 4812
N.A.I.C.S.: 517210
Personnel:
Paiboon Limpaphayom *(Chm)*
Somprasong Boonyachai *(Vice Chm)*
Wichian Mektrakarn *(CEO)*
Pong-Amorn Nimpoonsawat *(CFO)*
Weng Cheong Hui *(COO)*
Somchai Lertsutiwong *(CMO)*
Suwimol Kaewkoon *(Chief Org Dev Officer)*
Vilasinee Puddhikarant *(Chief Customer Officer)*
Chavin Chaivatcharaporn *(Sec)*
Board of Directors:
Paiboon Limpaphayom
Somprasong Boonyachai
Vithit Leenutaphong
Allen Yoong Keong Lew
Jeann Ngiap Jong Low
Tasanee Manorot
Wichian Mektrakarn
Hubert Ching-Wah Ng
Surasak Vajasit
Aviruth Wongbuddhapitak

Subsidiaries:

Advanced Contact Center Co., Ltd. **(1)**
414 Phaholyothin Road Samsen Nai
Phaya Thai, Bangkok, 10400, Thailand
Tel.: (66) 2271 9300
Fax: (66) 2071 9353
E-Mail: bs@ais.co.th
Web Site: www.acc-contactcenter.com
Contact Center Solutions
S.I.C.: 7334
N.A.I.C.S.: 561439

Advanced Datanetwork Communications Co. Ltd. **(1)**
Shinnawatra1 Phaholyothin Road
Samsennai Phayathai, 10400 Bangkok, Thailand (51%)
Tel.: (66) 22995014
Fax: (66) 22569922
Web Site: www.ais.co.th
Cellular & Wireless Telecommunications
S.I.C.: 4812
N.A.I.C.S.: 517210
Aphiwan Rattanin Saipradit *(Mng Dir)*

Advanced Magic Card Co., Ltd. **(1)**
414 Phaholyothin Road Samsen Nai
Phaya Thai, Bangkok, 10400, Thailand
Tel.: (66) 2 299 5000
Fax: (66) 2 615 3330
Cash Cards Distr
S.I.C.: 6141
N.A.I.C.S.: 522210

Advanced MPAY Co., Ltd. **(1)**
9th Floor Phaholyothin Place
Phaya Thai, Bangkok, 10400, Thailand
Tel.: (66) 2 271 9181
Fax: (66) 2 271 9090
E-Mail: mpay@ais.co.th
Web Site: www.mpay.co.th
Mobile Payment Services
S.I.C.: 6099
N.A.I.C.S.: 522320
Konsam Bupppanimite *(Mng Dir-Mktg)*

AIN GlobalComm Co., Ltd. **(1)**
408/127 Phaholyothin Place 29th Floor
Phaholyothin Road
Phaya Thai, Bangkok, 10400, Thailand
Tel.: (66) 2 271 9005
Fax: (66) 2 278 7027
E-Mail: info@ain.co.th
Web Site: www.ain.co.th
Telecommunication Services
S.I.C.: 4899
N.A.I.C.S.: 517919

Wireless Device Supply Co., Ltd. **(1)**
404 Phahonyothin Road
Phaya Thai, Bangkok, 10400, Thailand
Tel.: (66) 22995983
Fax: (66) 22995032
Mobile Phones & Calling Cards Distr
S.I.C.: 5065
N.A.I.C.S.: 423690
Somprasong Boonyachai *(Chm)*
Wichian Mektrakarn *(CEO)*

Non-U.S. Subsidiary:

SingTel Strategic Investments Pte Ltd. **(1)**
53 Ang Mo Kio Ave 3
B1-55-56-57 Ang Mo Kio Hub, 569933
Singapore, Singapore
Tel.: (65) 68383388
Fax: (65) 67328428
Web Site: www.singtel.com
Cellular & Wireless Telecommunications
S.I.C.: 4812
N.A.I.C.S.: 517210
Chua Sock Koong *(CEO)*
Jeann Ngiap Jong Low *(CFO)*
Yoke Weng Ng *(CIO)*

ADVANCED INFORMATION TECHNOLOGY PCL

37/2 Suthisarnvinijchai Rd
Samseannok Huaykwang
10320 Bangkok, Thailand
Tel.: (66) 22759400
Fax: (66) 22759100
E-Mail: ralf@ait.co.th
Web Site: www.ait-international.com
Year Founded: 1992
AIT—(BAK)
Rev.: $138,750,480
Assets: $121,713,827
Liabilities: $47,922,932
Net Worth: $73,790,895
Earnings: $12,169,269
Emp.: 286
Fiscal Year-end: 12/31/12
Business Description:
Systems Integration & Services
S.I.C.: 2741
N.A.I.C.S.: 519130
Personnel:
Thana Chaiprasit *(Chm)*
Pongthep Polanun *(Vice Chm)*
Siripong Oontornpan *(Pres)*
Voravit Wattanakuljarus *(Sec & Sr VP)*
Sureerat Prachayanukul *(Sr VP-Fin Controller)*
Metta Charuchinda *(Sr VP-Office)*
Narachet Chattratitiphan *(Sr VP-Govt Sls)*
Putti Dhanrongsirivadh *(Sr VP-Customer Svcs)*
Supat Dulyakupt *(Sr VP-Technical Support)*
Chodiwat Duntanasarn *(Sr VP-Sls)*
Kittipan Gannigatananon *(Sr VP-Project Mgmt)*
Ong-ard Harntaweesompone *(Sr VP-Telecom Sls)*
Ralf Hundertmark *(Sr VP-Bus Dev)*
Asawin Kangvolkij *(Exec Sr VP-Fin & Corp Strategy)*
Kijja Laoboonchai *(Exec Sr VP-Sls & Mktg)*
Chumkiat Leoseriwatanakul *(Sr VP-Mktg)*
Kriengkrai Nissyan *(Sr VP-Bus Dev)*
Netnapit Oontompan *(Exec Sr VP-Corp Affairs)*
Suraporn Raktaprachit *(Exec Sr VP-Fin)*
Somchai Vibhubhinyo *(Sr VP-AT&AS)*
Board of Directors:
Thana Chaiprasit
Pisak Charudilaka
Chodiwat Duntanasarn
Kijja Laoboonchai
Siripong Oontornpan
Thanarak Phongphatar
Pongthep Polanun
Suraporn Raktaprachit
Sripop Sarasas
Kittisak Sopchokchai
Chokechai Tanpoonsinthana

ADVANCED INTEGRATED MANUFACTURING CORP. LTD.

23 Ubi Crescent
Singapore, 408579, Singapore
Tel.: (65) 62388882
Fax: (65) 62388828
E-Mail: corporate@aimcorp.com.sg
Web Site: www.aimcorp.com.sg
A54—(SES)
Rev.: $58,848,495
Assets: $55,046,079
Liabilities: $25,156,079
Net Worth: $29,890,000
Earnings: $1,699,418
Fiscal Year-end: 12/31/12
Business Description:
Electronics Manufacturing Services
S.I.C.: 3679
N.A.I.C.S.: 334418
Personnel:
Kim Yong Tan *(Chm & CEO)*
Beng Hong Ong *(Co-Sec)*
Swee Gek Tan *(Co-Sec)*
Board of Directors:
Kim Yong Tan
Yeow Hua Lim
Robert Henry Keith Sloan
Gim Seng Tan

Subsidiary:

Advanced Manufacturing Corporation Pte. Ltd. **(1)**
23 Ubi Crescent
Singapore, Singapore
Tel.: (65) 62388882
Fax: (65) 62388828
E-Mail: enquiry@aimcorp.com.sg
Electronic Components Mfr
S.I.C.: 3679
N.A.I.C.S.: 334419
Joseph Ong *(Mgr-Bus Dev)*

Non-U.S. Subsidiary:

Advanced Manufacturing Corp Sdn. Bhd. **(1)**
PT1866 Tingkat Perusahaan 6 Prai Free Industrial Zone
13600 Perai, Penang, Malaysia
Tel.: (60) 43902882
Fax: (60) 43900082
Web Site: www.aimcorp.com.sg
Emp.: 46
Electronic Components Mfr
S.I.C.: 3679
N.A.I.C.S.: 334418
Jupri Suep *(Gen Mgr)*

ADVANCED LEISURE TECHNOLOGIES PLC

Suite 38 Pinewood Studios
Pinewood Road, Iver Heath, Bucks, SL0 0NH, United Kingdom
Tel.: (44) 8702430908
Fax: (44) 870 242 6998
Web Site: www.venuesolutionsplc.com
Sales Range: $1-9.9 Million
Emp.: 28
Business Description:
Venue Management Software & Services
S.I.C.: 7372
N.A.I.C.S.: 511210
Personnel:
Stephen Thomson *(Chm)*
Oliver Iny *(CEO)*
Board of Directors:
Stephen Thomson
Kenneth Harris
Oliver Iny

ADVANCED MANUFACTURING CONTROL SYSTEMS LTD.

Fanningstown
Limerick, Crecora, Ireland
Tel.: (353) 61 390 600
Fax: (353) 61 390 886
E-Mail: info@amcsgroup.com
Web Site: www.amcsgroup.com
Business Description:
Waste & Recycling Software Mfr
S.I.C.: 5045
N.A.I.C.S.: 423430
Personnel:
Jimmy Martin *(Co-Founder & CEO)*
Austin Ryan *(Co-Founder & Dir-Bus Dev)*
Eamon Hynes *(CTO)*

U.S. Subsidiary:

PC Scale, Inc. **(1)**
119 S 5th St
Oxford, PA 19363
Tel.: (610) 932-4006
Toll Free: (800) 962-9264
E-Mail: info@pcscale.com
Web Site: www.pcscaletower.com
Emp.: 25
Solid Waste & Recycling Software Mfr
S.I.C.: 7371
N.A.I.C.S.: 541511
Donald P. Tefft *(Pres & CEO)*
Joe Callan *(CFO)*
Ken Good *(COO)*

ADVANCED MEDIA, INC.

6F Sunshinecity Bunkakaikan
3-1-4 Higashi Ikebukuro
Toshima-ku, Tokyo, 170-8630, Japan
Tel.: (81) 359581031
Fax: (81) 359581032
E-Mail: info@advanced-media.co.jp
Web Site: www.advanced-media.co.jp
Year Founded: 1997
3773—(TKS)
Sales Range: $10-24.9 Million
Emp.: 100
Business Description:
Voice Recognition & Voice Verification Systems Mfr
S.I.C.: 3679
N.A.I.C.S.: 334419
Personnel:
Kiyoyuki Suzuki *(Pres & CEO)*
Board of Directors:
Yasuhiko Fujita
Nobusuke Mori
Kiyoyuki Suzuki
Katsumi Tatematu
Transfer Agent:
The Chuo Mitsui Trust & Banking Company Limited
33-1 Shiba 3 chome Minato-ku
Tokyo, Japan

ADVANCED MEDICAL INSTITUTE INC.

Level 4 80 William Street
Sydney, NSW, 2011, Australia
Tel.: (61) 2 9640 5253
Web Site: www.amiaustralia.com.au
Emp.: 184
Business Description:
Erectile Dysfunction & Premature Ejaculation Treatment Programs
S.I.C.: 8011
N.A.I.C.S.: 621111

Personnel:
Jacov Vaisman *(Pres & CEO)*
Forhad Khan *(Sec & Exec VP)*

ADVANCED MEDICAL SOLUTIONS GROUP PLC

Premier Park 33 Road 1 Winsford Industrial Estate
Winsford, Cheshire, CW7 3RT, United Kingdom
Tel.: (44) 1606863500
Fax: (44) 1606863600
E-Mail: info@admedsol.com
Web Site: www.admedsol.com
Year Founded: 1993
AMS—(LSE)
Rev.: $83,053,282
Assets: $154,072,374
Liabilities: $37,681,860
Net Worth: $116,390,514
Earnings: $15,306,479
Emp.: 453
Fiscal Year-end: 12/31/12
Business Description:
Designer, Developer & Producer of High Performance Polymers for the Healthcare & Specialized Non-Medical Markets
S.I.C.: 2821
N.A.I.C.S.: 325211
Personnel:
Andrew Christopher Meredith *(CEO)*
Mary Geraldine Tavener *(Sec & Dir-Fin)*
Board of Directors:
Donald William Evans
Stephen Gerard Bellamy
Penelope Anne Freer
Andrew Christopher Meredith
Peter M. Steinmann
Mary Geraldine Tavener
Legal Counsel:
Wragge & Co.
55 Colmore Row
Birmingham, B3 2AS, United Kingdom
Marks & Clerks
Sussex House 83 85 Mosley Street
Manchester, United Kingdom
Foley & Lardner, LLC
Building 3 Palo Alto Square 3000 El Camino Real
Palo Alto, CA 94306
Transfer Agent:
Capita Registrars
The Registry 34 Beckenham Road
Beckenham, United Kingdom
Subsidiaries:

Advanced Medical Solutions Ltd. **(1)**
Premier Park 33 Road One Winsford Industrial Estate
Winsford, Cheshire, CW7 3RT, United Kingdom (100%)
Tel.: (44) 1606863500
Fax: (44) 1606863600
E-Mail: info@admedsol.com
Web Site: www.admedsol.com
Emp.: 250
Developer & Manufacturer of Woundcare Dressings
S.I.C.: 3842
N.A.I.C.S.: 339113
Mary Geraldine Tavener *(Dir-Fin)*

Advanced Medical Solutions (Plymouth) Ltd. **(1)**
Western Wood Way Langage Science Park
Plympton, Devon, PL7 5BG, United Kingdom (100%)
Tel.: (44) 1752 209955
Fax: (44) 1752209956
E-Mail: sales@mlgl.co.uk
Web Site: www.medlogic.com
Emp.: 39
Developer & Mfr of Medical Cyanoacrylate Technologies
S.I.C.: 3999
N.A.I.C.S.: 339999
Richard Stenton *(VP-Grp Ops)*

Subsidiary:

MedLogic Global Holdings Limited **(2)**
2 Western Wood Way
Plympton, Devon, PL7 5BG, United Kingdom
Tel.: (44) 1752209955
Fax: (44) 1752343041
E-Mail: sales@admedsol.com
Emp.: 30
Medical Adhesives Mfr & Distr
S.I.C.: 3841
N.A.I.C.S.: 339113
Richard Stenton *(Mng Dir)*

Advanced Medical Solutions (UK) Ltd. **(1)**
Premier Park 33 Road One
Winsford, Cheshire, CW7 3RT, United Kingdom (100%)
Tel.: (44) 1606863500
Fax: (44) 1606863600
E-Mail: info@admedsol.com
Web Site: www.admedsol.com
Emp.: 170
Holding Company
S.I.C.: 6719
N.A.I.C.S.: 551112
Chris Meredith *(CEO)*

U.S. Subsidiary:

Advanced Medical Solutions (US) Inc **(1)**
26 Manning Rd
Dedham, MA 02026-6008
Tel.: (781) 467-9764
Medical Equipment Whslr
S.I.C.: 5047
N.A.I.C.S.: 423450
Ronald Kolakowski *(Pres & CEO)*

Non-U.S. Subsidiary:

Advanced Medical Solutions B.V. **(1)**
Munnikenheiweg 35
4879 NE Etten-Leur, Netherlands NL
Tel.: (31) 76 503 94 20 (100%)
Fax: (31) 76 503 08 04
Web Site: www.admesol.com
Emp.: 250
Medical Plastics Material & Resin Mfr
S.I.C.: 2821
N.A.I.C.S.: 325211
Pieter van Hoof *(Gen Mgr)*

ADVANCED NANO PRODUCTS CO., LTD.

244 Buyong Industrial Complex Kumho-Ri
Buyong-Myeon
Chungwon-Kun, Cheongwon, Chungcheongeuk-Do, 363-942, Korea (South)
Tel.: (82) 43 2156962
Fax: (82) 43 2156960
E-Mail: webadmin@anapro.com
Web Site: www.anapro.com
121600—(KRS)
Sales Range: $10-24.9 Million
Emp.: 110
Business Description:
Chemical Coatings & Powders Mfr
S.I.C.: 2899
N.A.I.C.S.: 325998
Personnel:
Jang Wu Park *(CEO)*

ADVANCED PACKAGING TECHNOLOGY (M) BHD

Level 8 Symphony House Block D13 Pusat Dagangan Dana 1 Jalan PJU 1A 46
47301 Petaling Jaya, Selangor Darul Ehsan, Malaysia
Tel.: (60) 378418000
Fax: (60) 378418199
E-Mail: apt@advancedpack.com.my
Web Site: www.advancedpack.com.my
ADVPKG—(KLS)
Rev.: $7,679,909
Assets: $11,754,358
Liabilities: $1,928,381
Net Worth: $9,825,977
Earnings: $866,663
Emp.: 89
Fiscal Year-end: 12/31/12
Business Description:
Packaging Materials Mfr
S.I.C.: 3221
N.A.I.C.S.: 327213
Personnel:
Sam Fatt Chee *(Chm)*
Cheng Keat Tan *(Mng Dir)*
Shiak Wan Leong *(Co-Sec)*
Siew Cheng See *(Co-Sec)*
Board of Directors:
Sam Fatt Chee
Ismail Ahmad
Hock Seng Eu
Sah Lim Law
Siew Seng Mah
Ghazali Mat Ariff
Choo Tim Ng
Cheng Keat Tan
Tek Ling Yeo
Transfer Agent:
Symphony Share Registrars Sdn Bhd
Level 6 Symphony House Block D13 Pusat Dagangan Dana 1 Jalan PJU 1A/46
Petaling Jaya, Malaysia

ADVANCED POWER COMPONENTS PLC

47 Riverside Medway City Estate
Rochester, Kent, ME2 4DP, United Kingdom
Tel.: (44) 1634290588
Fax: (44) 1634719672
Web Site: www.apc-plc.co.uk
APC—(LSE)
Emp.: 60
Business Description:
Electronic Component Manufacturing
S.I.C.: 3679
N.A.I.C.S.: 334419
Personnel:
Mark Roger Robinson *(CEO)*
Rob Smith *(Sec & Dir-Fin)*
Board of Directors:
William Nigel David
Ian Davidson
Phillip James Lancaster
Mark Roger Robinson
Rob Smith
Legal Counsel:
Ashurst LLP
Broadwalk House 5 Appold Street
London, EC2A 2HA, United Kingdom

ADVANCED POWER ELECTRONICS CORP.

2F-1 120 Sec 2 Gongdaowu Rd
Hsin-chu, Taiwan
Tel.: (886) 35750576
Fax: (886) 35737701
E-Mail: sales@a-power.com.tw
Web Site: www.a-power.com.tw
Year Founded: 1998
8261—(TAI)
Sales Range: $75-99.9 Million
Emp.: 90
Business Description:
Transistors & Related Products Mfr & Distr
S.I.C.: 3669
N.A.I.C.S.: 334290
Personnel:
Luke Teng *(Chm)*
Eric Kwat *(Pres)*

ADVANCED PRIMARY MINERALS CORPORATION

Metropolitan Place Suite 1480 99 Wyse Road
Halifax, NS, Canada B3A 4S5
Tel.: (902) 466-7255
Fax: (902) 423-6432
Toll Free: (877) 539-7255
E-Mail: info@advminerals.com
Web Site: www.advminerals.com
Year Founded: 2002
APD—(TSXV)
Sales Range: Less than $1 Million
Business Description:
Kaolin Exploration & Development Services
S.I.C.: 1455
N.A.I.C.S.: 212324
Personnel:
Philip S. Martin *(Chm)*
Michael A. O'Keefe *(CFO)*
Suzan Frazer *(Sec)*
Board of Directors:
Philip S. Martin
J. Chris Cowan
Charles Pitcher
Philip L. Webster
Legal Counsel:
McInnes Cooper
Halifax, NS, Canada
Transfer Agent:
Computershare Trust Company of Canada
Purdy's Wharf Tower II 2008-1969 Upper Water Street
Halifax, NS, Canada

ADVANCED SEMICONDUCTOR ENGINEERING, INC.

26 Chin Third Road Nantze Export Processing Zone
Nantze, Kaohsiung, Taiwan
Tel.: (886) 73617131
Fax: (886) 73614546
E-Mail: ase_webmaster@aseglobal.com
Web Site: www.aseglobal.com
ASX—(NYSE TAI)
Rev.: $6,569,844,917
Assets: $8,349,094,375
Liabilities: $4,540,105,742
Net Worth: $3,808,988,633
Earnings: $458,901,514
Emp.: 57,259
Fiscal Year-end: 12/31/12
Business Description:
Semiconductor Packaging Services
S.I.C.: 3674
N.A.I.C.S.: 334413
Personnel:
Jason C.S. Chang *(Chm & CEO)*
Richard H.P. Chang *(Vice Chm & Pres)*
Joseph Tung *(CFO)*
Tien Wu *(COO)*
Jeffrey Chen *(Exec VP)*
Board of Directors:
Jason C.S. Chang
Richard H.P. Chang
Rutherford H.P. Chang
Jeffrey Chen
Ta-lin Hsu
Raymond Lo
Joseph Tung
Tien Wu
Shen-Fu Yu

Subsidiaries:

ASE (Chung Li), Inc. **(1)**
550 Chung Hwa Rd Section 1
Chung-li, 320, Taiwan (100%)
Tel.: (886) 34527121
Fax: (886) 34515975
E-Mail: info@aseglobal.com
Web Site: www.ase.com
Emp.: 5,000
Semiconductor Mfr
S.I.C.: 3674
N.A.I.C.S.: 334413

Advanced Semiconductor Engineering, Inc.—(Continued)

ASE Kaohsiung (1)
No 26 Chin 3rd Road Nantze Export Processing Zone
Kaohsiung, Taiwan
Tel.: (886) 7 361 7131
Web Site: www.asetwn.com.tw
Semiconductor Device Mfr
S.I.C.: 3674
N.A.I.C.S.: 334413

ASE Test, Inc. (1)
No 10 W 5th St Nantze Export Processing Zone
Kaohsiung, Taiwan
Tel.: (886) 7 363 6641
Fax: (886) 7 361 6663
Integrated Circuit Testing Services
S.I.C.: 8734
N.A.I.C.S.: 541380
Raymond Lo *(Pres)*

ASE Test Limited (1)
26 Chin 3rd Road NEPZ
Nantze District, Kaohsiung, Taiwan (50.5%)
Tel.: (886) 73617131
Fax: (886) 7 361 3094
Sales Range: $500-549.9 Million
Emp.: 5,302
Semiconductor Chip Testing Services
S.I.C.: 3674
N.A.I.C.S.: 334413
Jason C.S. Chang *(Chm)*
Raymond Lo *(Pres)*
Kenneth Hsiang *(CFO)*

J&R Industrial Inc. (1)
107 Neihuan North Road Nanzih Export Processing Zone
Kaohsiung, 811, Taiwan
Tel.: (886) 7 3617131
Fax: (886) 7 3613094
Semiconductor Device Distr
S.I.C.: 5065
N.A.I.C.S.: 423690

StarChips Technology Inc. (1)
4F No 5 Technology Rd Science-Based Industrial Park
Hsin-chu, Taiwan
Tel.: (886) 3 577 5767
Fax: (886) 3 577 6575
E-Mail: service@starchips.com.tw
Web Site: www.starchips.com.tw
Semiconductor Device Mfr
S.I.C.: 3674
N.A.I.C.S.: 334413

Universal Scientific Industrial Co., Ltd. (1)
No 141 Lane 351 Taiping Road Section 1
Tsao Tuen
Nant'ou, Taiwan
Tel.: (886) 492350876
Fax: (886) 492329561
E-Mail: usi@ms.usi.com.tw
Web Site: www.usi.com.tw
Emp.: 10,787
Electronics Mfr for Computing, Communications, Consumer Electronics & Car Electronics Industries
S.I.C.: 3674
N.A.I.C.S.: 334419
Richard Hung-Pen Chang *(Chm)*
Xiao-Ming Liu *(CEO)*
Brian Shih *(CFO)*

U.S. Subsidiaries:

USI @Work, Inc. (2)
2020 Garner Station Blvd
Raleigh, NC 27603
Tel.: (919) 771-2788
Fax: (919) 771-2786
E-Mail: us-east@usiglobal.com
Emp.: 13
Electronic Circuit Board Assembly & Repair Services
S.I.C.: 3679
N.A.I.C.S.: 334418
Lihwa Christensen *(Principal)*

Non-U.S. Subsidiaries:

USI Japan Co., Ltd. (2)
East Tower 12F Yokohama Business Park 134
Godo Cho Hodogaya Ku, Yokohama, Kanagawa, 240 0005, Japan
Tel.: (81) 453483885
Fax: (81) 453361683
Circuit Board Assembly Services
S.I.C.: 3679
N.A.I.C.S.: 334418

USI Scientific Industrial (Shanghai) Co., Ltd. (2)
200 JinQiu Road PuDong New Area
Shanghai, 2012 03, China
Tel.: (86) 2158966996
Fax: (86) 2158967931
Circuit Board Assembly Services
S.I.C.: 3679
N.A.I.C.S.: 334418

Yang Ting Tech Co., Ltd. (1)
No 5-2 S 2nd Rd
Tanzi Shiang, Taichung, 42760, Taiwan
Tel.: (886) 4 25343141
Fax: (886) 4 25330041
Web Site: www.yangting.com.tw
Semiconductor Device Mfr
S.I.C.: 3674
N.A.I.C.S.: 334413

U.S. Subsidiaries:

Advanced Semiconductor Engineering Test (USA), Inc. (1)
3590 Peterson Way
Santa Clara, CA 95054
Tel.: (408) 986-6500
Fax: (408) 565-0289
E-Mail: marketing@aseus.com
Web Site: www.aseglobal.com
Emp.: 80
Tester of Semiconductor Chips
S.I.C.: 5065
N.A.I.C.S.: 423690
Patricia MaCLeod *(Mktg Mgr)*

ISE Labs, Inc. (1)
46800 Bayside Pkwy
Fremont, CA 94538
Tel.: (510) 687-2500
Fax: (510) 687-2413
Web Site: www.iselabs.com
Semiconductor Engineering & Testing Services
S.I.C.: 3674
N.A.I.C.S.: 334413
Tien Wu *(CEO)*

Non-U.S. Subsidiaries:

ASE Assembly & Test (Shanghai) Limited (1)
No 669 Guoshoujing Road Zhangjiang Hi-Tech Park
Pudong New Area, Shanghai, 201203, China
Tel.: (86) 21 50801060
Web Site: www.asesh.com.cn
Semiconductor Device Packaging & Testing Services
S.I.C.: 7389
N.A.I.C.S.: 561910

ASE Electronics Inc (1)
40 Phase IV Free Industrial Zone Bayan Lepas
Bayan Lepas, 11900, Malaysia
Tel.: (60) 103 631578
Semiconductor Device Mfr
S.I.C.: 3674
N.A.I.C.S.: 334413

ASE Electronics (M) Sdn. Bhd. (1)
Phase 4 Bayan Lepas Free Industrial Zone
11900 Penang, 11900, Malaysia (100%)
Tel.: (60) 46328888
Fax: (60) 46448411
Web Site: www.asemal.com.my
Sales Range: $75-99.9 Million
Emp.: 4,000
S.I.C.: 3674
N.A.I.C.S.: 334413
Lee Kwai Mun *(Pres)*

ASE Japan Co., Ltd. (1)
992-0324 1863 Iryuda Takahata-machi
Higashiokitama-gun, Yamagata, Japan
Tel.: (81) 238 57 2211
E-Mail: asej_market@asejp.aseglobal.com
Web Site: www.asejp.aseglobal.com
Emp.: 648
Electronic Component Mfr & Distr
S.I.C.: 3679
N.A.I.C.S.: 334419

ASE Korea Inc. (1)
494 Moonbal Ri Gyoha Eup Paju Si
Kyung Gi Do, Seoul, 413 830, Korea (South) (100%)
Tel.: (82) 319400114
Fax: (82) 319400539
Web Site: www.asekr.com
Emp.: 1,300
Semiconductor Assemblies & Test Solution Services
S.I.C.: 3674
N.A.I.C.S.: 334413
U. Bae *(Pres)*

Non-U.S. Subsidiary:

ASE (Weihai), Inc. (2)
16-1 Hainan Road Economic Techinal Development
Weihai, Shangdong, 264205, China
Tel.: (86) 631 5915000
Fax: (86) 631 5915000
E-Mail: wh_customer@aseglobal.com
Web Site: www.asewh.com
Emp.: 2,000
Semiconductor Device Packaging & Testing Services
S.I.C.: 7389
N.A.I.C.S.: 561910
J. H. Lee *(Sr VP & Plant Mgr)*

Non-U.S. Plant:

ASE (Weihai), Inc. - Paju, Korea Plant (3)
494 Moonbal-ri gyoha-eup
P'aju, Gyeonggi-do, Korea (South)
Tel.: (82) 31 9400114
Fax: (82) 31 9400539
Semiconductor Device Mfr
S.I.C.: 3674
N.A.I.C.S.: 334413

ADVANCED SEMICONDUCTOR MANUFACTURING CORPORATION LIMITED

385 Hong Cao Road
Shanghai, 200233, China
Tel.: (86) 2164851900
Fax: (86) 2164853925
E-Mail: ir@asmc.com.cn
Web Site: www.asmcs.com
3355—(HKG)
Rev.: $135,586,576
Assets: $160,526,026
Liabilities: $25,504,638
Net Worth: $135,021,388
Earnings: $7,073,591
Emp.: 1,384
Fiscal Year-end: 12/31/12

Business Description:
Semiconductor Device Mfr
S.I.C.: 3674
N.A.I.C.S.: 334413

Personnel:
Chunlei Xu *(Chm-Supervisory Bd)*
Qingyu Wang *(Pres)*
Wei Jing *(Co-Sec)*
Gloria Sau Kuen Ma *(Co-Sec)*

Board of Directors:
Jianming Chen
Enhua Chen
Qingtang Jiang
Winfried Lodewijk Peeters
Hanhu Pu
Qing Shen
Qingyu Wang
James Arthur Watkins
Yi Wu
Ding Xu
Jian Zhu

Supervisory Board of Directors:
Chunlei Xu
Yan Chen
Guojin Pan
Biyuan Sun
Yanhul Yang
Chengjie Zhou

Transfer Agent:
Computershare Hong Kong Investor Services Limited
Shops 1712-1716 17th Floor Hopewell Centre
183 Queens Road East
Wanchai, China (Hong Kong)

ADVANCED SHARE REGISTRY SERVICES PTY LTD.

Unit 2 150 Stirling Highway
PO Box 1156
Nedlands, WA, 6009, Australia
Tel.: (61) 893898033
Fax: (61) 893897871
E-Mail: admin@advancedshare.com.au
Web Site: www.advancedshare.com.au
Year Founded: 1996
ASW—(ASX)
Rev.: $5,329,708
Assets: $9,030,354
Liabilities: $753,960
Net Worth: $8,276,394
Earnings: $1,635,672
Emp.: 19
Fiscal Year-end: 06/30/13

Business Description:
Stock Share Registry Services
S.I.C.: 7389
N.A.I.C.S.: 561499

Personnel:
Kim Phin Chong *(CEO & Mng Dir)*
Alan Charles Winduss *(Sec)*

Board of Directors:
Simon Kenneth Cato
Kim Phin Chong
Alvin Tan
Alan Charles Winduss

Legal Counsel:
Kott Gunning
Level 8 AMP Building 140 St Georges Terrace
Perth, WA, 6000, Australia

ADVANCED SURGICAL DESIGN & MANUFACTURE LTD.

Unit 2 12 Frederick Street St Leonards
Sydney, NSW, 2065, Australia
Tel.: (61) 2 9439 4448
Fax: (61) 2 9439 4441
E-Mail: reception@asdm.com.au
Web Site: www.asdm.com.au
AMT—(ASX)
Rev.: $8,173,190
Assets: $11,209,870
Liabilities: $6,829,923
Net Worth: $4,379,946
Earnings: ($595,039)
Emp.: 40
Fiscal Year-end: 06/30/13

Business Description:
Medical Devices & Surgical Tools Mfr
S.I.C.: 3845
N.A.I.C.S.: 334510

Personnel:
Tom Milicevic *(CEO & CFO)*
Peter Welsh *(Mng Dir)*
Jari Hyvarinen *(COO & Head-Design Engrg)*
Richard Ulrick *(Sec)*

Board of Directors:
Peter Kazacos
John O'Meara
Peter Welsh

Legal Counsel:
Watson Mangioni
Level 13 50 Carrington Street
Sydney, Australia

ADVANCED SYSTEMS AUTOMATION LIMITED

Blk 25 Kallang Avenue 02-01 Kallang Basin Industrial Estate
Singapore, 339416, Singapore

Tel.: (65) 6309 5500
Fax: (65) 6292 5636
E-Mail: sales@asa.com.sg
Web Site: www.asa.com.sg
Year Founded: 1986
5TY—(CAT)
Rev.: $16,465,652
Assets: $19,218,564
Liabilities: $5,969,771
Net Worth: $13,248,794
Earnings: ($2,093,832)
Fiscal Year-end: 12/31/12

Business Description:
Semiconductor Equipment Mfr
S.I.C.: 3674
N.A.I.C.S.: 334413

Personnel:
Michael Soon Gnee Loh *(Chm & CEO)*
Kwek Kiong Woo *(CFO)*
Timothy Boon Liat Lim *(Admin Officer)*
Nancy Sok Cher Quek *(Co-Sec)*
Searn Por Theng *(Co-Sec)*

Board of Directors:
Michael Soon Gnee Loh
Gark Kim Khor
Mohd Sopiyan Mohd Rashdi
Kenneth Keung Yum Yu

ADVANCED TECHNOLOGY & SYSTEMS CO., LTD.

JR Shinagawa E Bldg 8F
2-18-1 Kounan
Minato-ku, Tokyo, 108-0075, Japan
Tel.: (81) 367175700
Fax: (81) 367175701
Web Site: www.adtx.com
Year Founded: 1993
Sales Range: $100-124.9 Million
Emp.: 50

Business Description:
Multimedia Products Including Disk Array Products (RAID), Mirror Drive Products & SCSI-IDE Converter Cards Mfr & Marketer
S.I.C.: 7373
N.A.I.C.S.: 541512

Personnel:
Daisaku Maeda *(CEO)*

Board of Directors:
Daisaku Maeda

ADVANCED TECHNOLOGY COMPANY K.S.C.C.

ATC Tower Salmiya Salem Al Mubarak St Block 4
PO Box 44558
Street 1 opposite Layla Tower
Hawalli, Kuwait, 32060, Kuwait
Tel.: (965) 22247444
Fax: (965) 25711761
E-Mail: mhelo@atc.com.kw
Web Site: www.atc.com.kw
ATC—(KUW)
Rev.: $233,008,760
Assets: $348,366,789
Liabilities: $216,966,929
Net Worth: $131,399,861
Earnings: $14,532,263
Emp.: 600
Fiscal Year-end: 12/31/12

Business Description:
Medical, Dental, Laboratory, Diagnostic, Pharmaceutical, Sterilization, Disinfection, Agriculture, Veterinary, Health, Fitness & Commercial Kitchen Equipment Importer & Supplier & Maintenance Services
S.I.C.: 5047
N.A.I.C.S.: 423450

Personnel:
Fouad Mohammed Thunyan Al Ghanim *(Chm & Mng Dir)*
Faisal Mansour Sarkhou *(Deputy Chm)*
Ghassan M. Mamlouk *(CEO)*
Singhvi Nitin *(CFO)*

Board of Directors:
Fouad Mohammed Thunyan Al Ghanim
Abdulwahab Sulaiman Al Fouzan
Sadoun Abdulla Ali
Ahmad Yousef Behbahani
Faisal Mansour Sarkhou

ADVANCED VENTURES CORP.

No 6 Houjiayu Wangzuoxiang
Beijing, China 100000
Tel.: (86) 85253872543
Year Founded: 2010
ANCV—(OTC OTCB)
Rev.: $703
Assets: $342
Liabilities: $121,909
Net Worth: ($121,567)
Earnings: ($86,944)
Fiscal Year-end: 12/31/12

Business Description:
Development Stage Company of Urethral Catheters
S.I.C.: 3841
N.A.I.C.S.: 339112

Personnel:
Sae-Chua Supachai *(CEO & CFO)*

Board of Directors:
Vincent Kim
Sae-Chua Supachai

Transfer Agent:
Nevada Agency & Transfer Company
50 W Liberty St
Reno, NV 89501
Tel.: (775) 322-0626
Fax: (775) 322-5623

ADVANCED VISION TECHNOLOGY LTD.

6 Hanagar St
Hod Hasharon, 45241, Israel
Tel.: (972) 9 7614444
Fax: (972) 9 7614555
E-Mail: info@avt-inc.com
Web Site: www.avt-inc.com
Year Founded: 1992
VSJ—(DEU)
Rev.: $48,014,000
Assets: $41,329,000
Liabilities: $14,024,000
Net Worth: $27,305,000
Earnings: $4,905,000
Emp.: 194
Fiscal Year-end: 12/31/12

Business Description:
Commercial Printing Services
S.I.C.: 2759
N.A.I.C.S.: 323111

Personnel:
Yehoshua Agassi *(Chm)*
Jaron Lotan *(CEO)*
Nadav Yassour *(CFO)*
Koby Shtaierman *(Pres-Europe & Exec VP-Sls)*
Amir Dekel *(Pres-AVT Inc.)*

Board of Directors:
Yehoshua Agassi
Ytzhak Edelman
Nurit Nahum
Ofer Neeman
Arie Weisberg

ADVANEX INC.

Asuka Tower Bldg 6-1-1 Tabata
Kita-ku, Tokyo, 114-8581, Japan
Tel.: (81) 338225860
Fax: (81) 338225871
E-Mail: info@advanex.co.jp
Web Site: www.advanex.co.jp
Year Founded: 1946
5998—(TKS)
Sls.: $259,061,000
Assets: $203,159,000
Liabilities: $158,367,000
Net Worth: $44,792,000
Earnings: $5,258,000
Emp.: 2,365
Fiscal Year-end: 03/31/13

Business Description:
Precision Springs & Precision Component Parts & Motors Mfr & Sales
S.I.C.: 3451
N.A.I.C.S.: 332721

Personnel:
Yuichi Kato *(Chm & CEO)*
Tsuneo Shibano *(Pres & COO)*
Toshiya Ohno *(CFO)*
Mitsuo Kotani *(Exec Officer)*

Board of Directors:
Yuichi Kato
Masaho Hirota
Seiya Kato
Foo Yoke Khan
Masami Obara
Toshiya Ohno
Tsuneo Shibano
Eiichi Takeda

Subsidiaries:

Accurate Inc. (1)
Minami Koshigaya 4 16 13
Koshigaya, Saitama, 343-0845, Japan
Tel.: (81) 489869621
Fax: (81) 489869630
E-Mail: info@accurate.jp
Web Site: www.accurate.jp
Sls.: $6,915,755
Emp.: 35
Mechanical Components Sales
S.I.C.: 3568
N.A.I.C.S.: 333613
Kazunobu Tsuchiya *(Pres & CEO)*

Daiichi Kasei Co., Ltd. (1)
154 Shimokoyama
Shimotsuke, Tochigi, 329-0502, Japan
Tel.: (81) 285537211
Fax: (81) 285521745
Web Site: www.ikka.co.jp
Emp.: 320
Precision Injection Moldings & Assemblies Mfr
S.I.C.: 3999
N.A.I.C.S.: 339999
Masami Obara *(Pres)*

Non-U.S. Subsidiaries:

IKKA (HONG KONG) CO., LIMITED (2)
Room 802 Empire Centre 68 Mody Road
Tsimshatsui East
Kowloon, China (Hong Kong)
Tel.: (852) 26340633
Fax: (852) 26341300
Emp.: 3
Precision Tools Distr
S.I.C.: 5084
N.A.I.C.S.: 423830
Taka Yuki Saito *(Mng Dir)*

Non-U.S. Subsidiary:

IKKA Technology DongGuan Co., Ltd. (3)
15 Building The Shilong Hi Tech Infomation Industrial Park
Shilong Town, Dongguan, Guangdong, 523000, China
Tel.: (86) 76986186060
Fax: (86) 769 86186066
Precision Moldings & Assemblies Mfr
S.I.C.: 3544
N.A.I.C.S.: 333511

IKKA TECHNOLOGY (VIETNAM) CO., LTD. (2)
Lot 6 4 Tan Truong Industrial Zone
Cam Giang, Hai Duong, Vietnam
Tel.: (84) 3203570188
Fax: (84) 3203570198
Emp.: 100
Precision Moldings & Assemblies Mfr
S.I.C.: 3442
N.A.I.C.S.: 332321

M.A.C. Technology (M) Sdn. Bhd. (2)
Lot 16 Jalan Bunga Tanjung 2
Senawang Industrial Park, 70400
Seremban, Negeri Sembilan, Malaysia
Tel.: (60) 66781311
Fax: (60) 66781322
Emp.: 200
Automotive Moldings Mfr
S.I.C.: 3999
N.A.I.C.S.: 339999
Hitoshi Idei *(Mng Dir)*

FUJI MICRO CO., LTD. (1)
Matsuura Building 2F Uchi-kanda 3-16-9
Chiyoda-ku, Tokyo, 101-0047, Japan
Tel.: (81) 335266121
Fax: (81) 335266217
E-Mail: info@fuji-micro.co.jp
Web Site: www.fuji-micro.co.jp
Rev.: $42,415,490
Emp.: 40
Motors Mfr & Distr
S.I.C.: 3621
N.A.I.C.S.: 335312
Katou Kiyoshi *(Chm)*
Maruyama Cyusaku *(Pres)*

Non-U.S. Subsidiary:

Fuji Micro Electronics Co., Ltd. (2)
118 Shitanxi Road Shijing
Guangzhou, Guangdong, 510430, China
Tel.: (86) 2086421716
Fax: (86) 2086420405
E-Mail: info@fmgz.com
Emp.: 1,000
Motor Assemblies Mfr
S.I.C.: 3052
N.A.I.C.S.: 326220
LieHong Li *(Dir-Prosecution-Layout)*

U.S. Subsidiary:

Kato Spring of California, Inc. (1)
5780 Cerritos Ave
Cypress, CA 90630
Tel.: (714) 995-4519
Fax: (714) 995-7294
Toll Free: (800) 966-3302
E-Mail: sales@katospring.com
Web Site: www.katospring.com
Emp.: 70
Precision Springs & Wire Forms Mfr
S.I.C.: 3315
N.A.I.C.S.: 331222
James Grueser *(Exec VP)*

Non-U.S. Subsidiaries:

Advanex Europe Ltd. (1)
Mill Park Way off Station Road
Southwell, Notts, NG25 0ET, United Kingdom
Tel.: (44) 1636815555
Fax: (44) 1636817725
E-Mail: general@advanexeurope.co.uk
Web Site: www.advanexeurope.co.uk
Emp.: 175
Precision Springs Mfr & Distr
S.I.C.: 3495
N.A.I.C.S.: 332613
Paul Clifford *(Mng Dir)*

Subsidiary:

MOTOFIT LIMITED (2)
Lath Lane Spon Lane South
Smethwick, West Midlands, B66 1EA, United Kingdom
Tel.: (44) 1215537222
Fax: (44) 1215533577
E-Mail: sales@porticoproducts.com
Web Site: www.porticoproducts.com
Emp.: 5
Electrical Parts & Shutter Components Distr
S.I.C.: 5051
N.A.I.C.S.: 423510
Karl Williams *(Gen Mgr)*

ADVANEX (HK) LTD. (1)
Room No 802B 8/F Empire Centre 68 Mody Road Tsimshatsui East
Kowloon, China (Hong Kong)
Tel.: (852) 27088806
Fax: (852) 27088773
Web Site: www.advanex.co.jp/company_e/group_companies.php

Advanex Inc.—(Continued)

Precision Tools Distr
S.I.C.: 5084
N.A.I.C.S.: 423830

ADVANEX PRECISION COMPONENTS (DALIAN) CO., LTD. **(1)**
Dong Bei Street 3-29 Dalian Development Zone
Dalian, Liaoning, 116600, China
Tel.: (86) 411 87505525
Fax: (86) 411 87505529
Web Site: www.advanex.co.jp/company_e/group_companies.php
Precision Springs Mfr & Distr
S.I.C.: 3495
N.A.I.C.S.: 332613
Yecheng Lu *(Gen Mgr)*

ADVANEX PRECISION COMPONENTS (DONGGUAN) CO., LTD. **(1)**
No 9 Xi-Hu Hi-Tech Information Industrial Park
Shilong Town, Dongguan, Guangdong, 523325, China
Tel.: (86) 76986186600
Fax: (86) 76986186660
Web Site: www.advanex.co.jp/company_e/group_companies.php
Precision Components Mfr
S.I.C.: 3451
N.A.I.C.S.: 332721
Tsuneo Shibano *(Gen Mgr)*

Advanex (Thailand) Ltd. **(1)**
Hi-Tech Insudtrial Estate 151 Moo 1 Tambol Bann-Len
Amphur Bang Pa-In, Ayutthaya, 13160, Thailand
Tel.: (66) 35314200
Fax: (66) 35 314208
Web Site: www.advanex.co.th
Precision Springs Mfr
S.I.C.: 3495
N.A.I.C.S.: 332613

Kato-Entex Limited **(1)**
Glaisdale Dr
Bilborough, Nottingham, NG8 4JY, United Kingdom
Tel.: (44) 1159293931
Fax: (44) 1159295773
E-Mail: springs@advanexeurope.co.uk
Web Site: www.advanex.co.uk
Emp.: 70
Compression Springs, Tension Springs, Torsion Springs, Flat Springs, Power Springs, Spiral Springs, Wire Forms, Pressings, Assemblies & Associated Components Mfr
S.I.C.: 3315
N.A.I.C.S.: 331222
Caroline Moss *(Mgr-HR)*

KATO SPRING (SHANGHAI) CO., LTD. **(1)**
Standard Building 54 No 199 North Ri Ying Road
Waigaoqiao Free Trade Zone, Shanghai, 200131, China
Tel.: (86) 2150461717
Fax: (86) 2150460707
Web Site: www.kato.com.sg/shanghai.htm
Emp.: 200
Precision Spring Mfr
S.I.C.: 3493
N.A.I.C.S.: 332613
Yoke Khan Foo *(Chm)*

ADVANI HOTELS & RESORTS (INDIA) LIMITED

18 A B Jolly Makers II Nariman Point
Mumbai, 400 021, India
Tel.: (91) 2222850101
Fax: (91) 2222040744
E-Mail: sales.ho@advanihotels.com
Web Site: caravelabeachresort.com
ADVANIHOTR—(NSE)
Rev.: $7,377,553
Assets: $11,327,318
Liabilities: $5,349,473
Net Worth: $5,977,845
Earnings: $486,957
Emp.: 173
Fiscal Year-end: 03/31/13

Business Description:
Hotel & Resort Management Services
S.I.C.: 7011
N.A.I.C.S.: 721110

Personnel:
Sunder G. Advani *(Chm & Mng Dir)*
Shankar Kulkarni *(CFO & Gen Mgr-Fin)*
Kumar Iyer *(Compliance Officer & Sec)*

Board of Directors:
Sunder G. Advani
Haresh G. Advani
Menaka S. Advani
Anil Harish
K. Kannan
Prakash V. Mehta

Transfer Agent:
Datamatics Financial Services Ltd
Plot No B 5 Part B Crosslane MIDC Marol
Andheri East
Mumbai, India

ADVANTA INDIA LIMITED

Krishnama House 8-2-418 4th Floor
Road No 7 Banjara Hills
Hyderabad, AP, 500034, India
Tel.: (91) 40 6628 4000
Fax: (91) 40 6628 4040
E-Mail: email@advantaindia.com
Web Site: www.advantaindia.com
ADVANTA—(NSE)
Rev.: $198,933,199
Assets: $294,932,892
Liabilities: $189,891,927
Net Worth: $105,040,966
Earnings: $11,005,845
Emp.: 630
Fiscal Year-end: 12/31/12

Business Description:
Holding Company; Agricultural Field Crop & Plant Seeds Developer & Distr
S.I.C.: 6719
N.A.I.C.S.: 551112

Personnel:
Manoj Gupta *(CFO)*
Pushpalatha Katkuri *(Compliance Officer & Sec)*

Board of Directors:
Jaidev R. Shroff
Vasant P. Gandhi
Kaundinya V. R.
Vinod Sethi
Vikram R. Shroff
Hardeep Singh

Transfer Agent:
Sharepro Services (India) Private Limited
Samhita Complex Gala No 52 to 56 Building No 13A-B
Near Sakinaka Tele, Mumbai, India

Subsidiary:

Unicorn Seeds Limited **(1)**
Plot No 3 Unicorn House Balaji Enclave Transport Road
Diamond Point, Hyderabad, Andhra Pradesh, 500009, India
Tel.: (91) 4027899728
Fax: (91) 4027842399
E-Mail: info@goldenadvanta.com
Web Site: www.choiceseed.com
Vegetable Farming Services
S.I.C.: 0182
N.A.I.C.S.: 111419
Amul Sanghani *(Mng Dir)*

Corporate Headquarters:

Advanta India Limited **(1)**
8-2-418 3rd Fl Krishnamma House
Rd No 7 Banjara Hills, Hyderabad, 500 034, India (100%)
Tel.: (91) 4066284000
Fax: (91) 4023350856
E-Mail: email@advantaindia.com
Web Site: www.advantaseeds.com
Emp.: 300
Agricultural Field Crop & Plant Seeds Developer & Distr
S.I.C.: 0721
N.A.I.C.S.: 115112
V. R. Kaundinya *(CEO & Mng Dir)*
Manoj Gupta *(CFO)*

Non-U.S. Subsidiaries:

Advanta Semillas S.A.I.C. **(2)**
Ruta 7 Km 261
Casilla de Correo 91, CP 6000 Junin, Buenos Aires, Argentina Ar
Tel.: (54) 2362433406 (100%)
Fax: (54) 2362447029
E-Mail: advanta.semillas@advantasemillas.com.ar
Web Site: www.advantasemillas.com.ar
Sales Range: $1-9.9 Million
Emp.: 100
Agricultural Crop & Plant Seeds Developer & Distr
S.I.C.: 0721
N.A.I.C.S.: 115112
Eduardo Liguori *(Chm)*

Pacific Seeds Pty. Ltd. **(2)**
268 Anzac Ave
PO Box 337
Toowoomba, QLD, 4350, Australia AU
Tel.: (61) 746902666 (100%)
Fax: (61) 746301063
E-Mail: info@pacseeds.com.au
Web Site: www.pacseeds.com.au
Sales Range: $25-49.9 Million
Emp.: 70
Agricultural Crop & Plant Seeds Developer & Distr
S.I.C.: 0711
N.A.I.C.S.: 115112
Barry Croker *(Mng Dir)*

Pacific Seeds (Thai) Ltd. **(2)**
Moo 13 Phraholyothin Road
Phraputtabat, Saraburi, Thailand TH
Tel.: (66) 36266316 (100%)
Fax: (66) 36266508
E-Mail: sk@pacthai.co.th
Web Site: www.pacthai.co.th
Sales Range: $10-24.9 Million
Emp.: 200
Agricultural Crop & Plant Seeds Developer & Distr
S.I.C.: 0711
N.A.I.C.S.: 115112
Pacholk Pongpanich *(Mng Dir)*

U.S. Subsidiary:

Advanta US Inc. **(1)**
PO Drawer 2420
Hereford, TX 79045
Tel.: (806) 364-0560
Fax: (806) 364-3103
Toll Free: (800) 333-9048
E-Mail: info@advantaus.com
Web Site: www.advantaus.com
Agricultural Research & Development Services
S.I.C.: 8731
N.A.I.C.S.: 541711
Steve Ligon *(Gen Mgr)*

Non-U.S. Subsidiaries:

Advanta Finance B.V. **(1)**
Strawinskylaan 1143
Amsterdam, North-Holland, 1077 XX, Netherlands
Tel.: (31) 205788388
Fax: (31) 205788389
E-Mail: reception.amsterdam@emicorp.com
Emp.: 30
Financial Support Services
S.I.C.: 6211
N.A.I.C.S.: 523999

Advanta International B.V. **(1)**
Strawinskylaan 1143
Amsterdam, North-Holland, 1077 XX, Netherlands
Tel.: (31) 205788388
Fax: (31) 205788389
E-Mail: reception.amsterdam@amicorp.com
Web Site: www.amicorp.com
Emp.: 200
Agricultural Supplies Distr
S.I.C.: 5191
N.A.I.C.S.: 424910
Ugo DiLeva *(Mng Dir)*

ADVANTAGE OIL & GAS LTD.

Suite 700 400 3 Avenue SW
Calgary, AB, T2P 4H2, Canada
Tel.: (403) 718-8000
Fax: (403) 718-8300
Toll Free: (866) 393-0393
E-Mail: ir@advantageog.com
Web Site: www.advantageog.com
Year Founded: 1997
AAV—(NYSE TSX)
Sls.: $267,296,948
Assets: $1,902,351,500
Liabilities: $700,869,586
Net Worth: $1,201,481,914
Earnings: ($88,592,032)
Emp.: 121
Fiscal Year-end: 12/31/12

Business Description:
Oil & Gas Exploration Services
S.I.C.: 1311
N.A.I.C.S.: 211111

Personnel:
Steven Sharpe *(Chm)*
Andy J. Mah *(Pres & CEO)*
Craig Blackwood *(Interim CFO)*
Jay P. Reid *(Sec)*
Patrick J. Cairns *(Sr VP)*

Board of Directors:
Steven Sharpe
Stephen E. Balog
Paul G. Haggis
Andy J. Mah
Ronald A. McIntosh
Sheila O'Brien
Carol D. Pennycook
Jay P. Reid

Legal Counsel:
Burnett Duckworth & Palmer
350 7th Ave SW Ste 1400
Calgary, AB, T2P 3N9, Canada

Transfer Agent:
Computershare Trust Company of Canada
530 8th Ave SW 6th Floor
Calgary, AB, T2P 3S8, Canada
Tel.: (403) 267-6800
Fax: (403) 267-6529

ADVANTAGE PARTNERS LLP

17F Toranomon Towers 4-1-28
Toranomon
Minato-ku, Tokyo, 105 0001, Japan
Tel.: (81) 351570170
E-Mail: master@advantagegroup.co.jp
Web Site: www.advantagepartners.com
Year Founded: 1992

Business Description:
Private Equity Firm
S.I.C.: 6211
N.A.I.C.S.: 523999

Personnel:
Richard L. Folsom *(Partner)*
Taisuke Sasanuma *(Partner)*

Subsidiary:

United Cinemas Co., Ltd. **(1)**
Izumiakasaka Bldg 2-22-24 Akasaka
Minato-Ku, Tokyo, 107-0052, Japan (100%)
Tel.: (81) 332243200
Fax: (81) 332243212
Web Site: www.unitedcinemas.jp
Motion Picture Theater Operating Services
S.I.C.: 7832
N.A.I.C.S.: 512131
Yoshihiko Muto *(Pres & CEO)*

Holdings:

INTERAC Co., Ltd. **(1)**
Fujimi West 3F Fujimi 2-14-36
Chiyoda-ku, Tokyo, 102-0071, Japan
Tel.: (81) 3 3234 7840

Web Site: www.interac.co.jp
Foreign Teachers for Schools & Commercial & Government Organizations
S.I.C.: 9411
N.A.I.C.S.: 923110
Darrin McNeal *(Dir-Bus Dev & Global Solutions)*

Xacti Corporation (1)
1-1 Sanyocho
Daito, Osaka, 574-8534, Japan JP
Tel.: (81) 72 870 6204 (100%)
Web Site: www.xacti-co.com
Emp.: 507
Digital Cameras Mfr & Distr
S.I.C.: 3579
N.A.I.C.S.: 333316
Takeo Isaji *(Chm & CEO)*
Takao Nishiyama *(Pres & COO)*

U.S. Holdings:

GST AutoLeather, Inc. (1)
20 Oak Hollow Dr Ste 300
Southfield, MI 48033 DE
Tel.: (248) 436-2300 (100%)
Fax: (248) 436-2390
Web Site: www.gstautoleather.com
Leather Motor Vehicle Interiors Mfr
S.I.C.: 2396
N.A.I.C.S.: 336360
Dennis E. Hiller *(Pres & CEO)*
Eric Evans *(CFO & Sr VP)*
Stephen Jeske *(Sr VP-Product Dev, Mktg & Sls)*

TeleGuam Holdings, LLC (1)
624 North Marine Corps Drive
Tamuning, GU 96913
Tel.: (671) 644-4482
Web Site: www.gta.net
Telecommunications Services
S.I.C.: 4899
N.A.I.C.S.: 517919

ADVANTAGE RISK MANAGEMENT CO.,LTD.

Nakameguro GT Tower 17F 2-1-1
Kamimeguro Meguro-ku
Tokyo, 153-0051, Japan
Tel.: (81) 3 5794 3807
Fax: (81) 3 5794 3909
E-Mail: info-en@armg.jp
Web Site: www.armg.jp
Year Founded: 1999
8769—(JAS)
Rev.: $29,216,000
Assets: $29,447,000
Liabilities: $14,531,000
Net Worth: $14,916,000
Earnings: $1,892,000
Emp.: 164
Fiscal Year-end: 03/31/13

Business Description:
Psychological Health Care Services
S.I.C.: 8082
N.A.I.C.S.: 621610

Personnel:
Shinji Torigoe *(Pres & CEO)*

ADVANTAGED PREFERRED SHARE TRUST

4th Floor South Tower Royal Bank Plaza 200 Bay Street
PO Box 50
Toronto, ON, M5J 2W7, Canada
Tel.: (416) 842-7705
Fax: (416) 842-7555
Year Founded: 2006
PFR.UN—(TSX)
Rev.: $741
Assets: $53,221,188
Liabilities: $750,334
Net Worth: $52,470,854
Earnings: ($172,838)
Fiscal Year-end: 12/31/12

Business Description:
Financial Investment Services
S.I.C.: 6211
N.A.I.C.S.: 523999

Personnel:
Edward Jackson *(Pres & CEO)*
Nick Tomovski *(CFO & Sec)*

Transfer Agent:
Computershare Trust Company of Canada
100 University Avenue 11th Floor
Toronto, ON, M5J 2Y1, Canada
Tel.: (416) 891-9633
Toll Free: (800) 663-9097

ADVANTECH ADVANCED MICROWAVE TECHNOLOGIES INC.

657 Orly Avenue
Dorval, QC, H9P 1G1, Canada
Tel.: (514) 420-0045
Fax: (514) 420-0073
Web Site: www.advantechwireless.com
Year Founded: 1985
Rev.: $20,314,800
Emp.: 171

Business Description:
Wireless Communication Equipment Mfr
S.I.C.: 3669
N.A.I.C.S.: 334290

Personnel:
David Gelerman *(Founder)*
Vagan Shakhgildian *(Pres)*
Igor Perlitch *(Chief Dev Officer & VP-IP & Telecom Products)*

ADVANTECH CO., LTD.

No 1 Alley 20 Lane 26 Rueiguang Road
Neihu District, Taipei, 11491, Taiwan
Tel.: (886) 2 2792 7818
Fax: (886) 2 2794 7301
E-Mail: info@advantech.com.tw
Web Site: www.advantech.com
Year Founded: 1983
2395—(TAI)
Rev.: $933,181,871
Assets: $813,708,020
Liabilities: $210,475,191
Net Worth: $603,232,829
Earnings: $118,064,385
Emp.: 5,905
Fiscal Year-end: 12/31/12

Business Description:
Holding Company; Integrated Computer Systems & Components Designer, Mfr & Distr
S.I.C.: 6719
N.A.I.C.S.: 551112

Personnel:
K. Chen Liu *(Chm & CEO)*
Chaney Ho *(Pres)*
Eric Chen *(CIO & Assoc VP)*
Jeff Chen *(CTO)*
Ming-Chin Wu *(Pres-Indus Automation Grp)*

Board of Directors:
K. Chen Liu
Allen Fan
Ted Hsu
Gary Tseng
Joseph Chwo-Ming Yu

Supervisory Board of Directors:
Thomas Chen
Sharon Su
James K.F. Wu

Group:

Advantech Embedded ePlatform Group (1)
No 33 Lane 365 Yang Guang Street
Neihu District, Taipei, 11491, Taiwan
Tel.: (886) 2 2792 7818
Web Site: www.advantech.com
Computer Circuit Board Designer & Mfr
S.I.C.: 3679
N.A.I.C.S.: 334418
Miller Chang, *(VP-Embedded Design-In Svcs)*

Subsidiary:

Advantech Automation Corp. (1)
4F No 108-3 Ming-Chuan Road
Shing-Tien District, Taipei, 231, Taiwan VG
Tel.: (886) 2 2218 4567 (100%)
Web Site: www.advantech.com
Industrial Automation Computer, Computer Component & Software Mfr & Distr
S.I.C.: 3575
N.A.I.C.S.: 334118
Ming-Chin Wu, *(Pres)*

U.S. Subsidiary:

Advantech Corporation (1)
380 Fairview Way
Milpitas, CA 95035-3062 CA
Tel.: (408) 519-3898
Toll Free: (888) 576-9668
Web Site: www.adventech.com
Computer & Computer Components Whslr
S.I.C.: 5045
N.A.I.C.S.: 423430
Christine Huang *(Ops Mgr)*

Non-U.S. Subsidiaries:

Advantech Australia Pty. Limited (1)
Unit 1 3 Southpark Close
Keysborough, VIC, 3173, Australia AU
Tel.: (61) 3 9797 0100 (100%)
E-Mail: info@advantech.net.au
Web Site: www.advantech.net.au
Emp.: 4
Computer Related Products & Services
S.I.C.: 7379
N.A.I.C.S.: 541519
Jasmine Harrison *(Reg Mgr)*

Advantech Brazil Ltda. (1)
Rua Caramuru 374
04138-001 Sao Paulo, Brazil BR
Tel.: (55) 1155925355 (43.28%)
Fax: (55) 1155925353
E-Mail: info@advantech.com.br
Web Site: www.advantechsg.com.br
Emp.: 30
Computer & Computer Peripheral Equipment & Software Whslr
S.I.C.: 5045
N.A.I.C.S.: 423430
Mario Franco *(Mng Dir)*

Advantech Co. Malaysia Sdn. Bhd. (1)
Ste 12 1st Fl Jalan Todak 3
Bandar Sunway, 13700 Penang, Seberang Jaya, Malaysia MY
Tel.: (60) 43973788 (100%)
E-Mail: callcenter@advantech.com.my
Web Site: www.advantech.com.my
Emp.: 20
Computer Systems Design Services
S.I.C.: 7373
N.A.I.C.S.: 541512
Elvin Ng *(Gen Mgr)*

Advantech Co. Singapore Pte. Ltd. (1)
6 Serangoon Ave 5 Unit 03 A
554910 Singapore, Singapore SG
Tel.: (65) 64421000 (100%)
Fax: (65) 64421001
E-Mail: sg@advantech.com
Web Site: www.advantech.com
Emp.: 32
Other Electronic Parts & Equipment Whslr
S.I.C.: 5065
N.A.I.C.S.: 423690
David Soon *(Mng Dir)*

Advantech Europe Holding B.V (1)
Ekkersrijt 5708
Science Park Eindhoven, 5692 ER Son, Netherlands NL
Tel.: (31) 402677000
Fax: (31) 402677085
E-Mail:
Web Site: www.advantech.nl
Holding Company; Regional Managing Office
S.I.C.: 6719
N.A.I.C.S.: 551112
Peter Young *(Mng Dir)*

Subsidiary:

Advantech Europe B.V. (2)
Ekkersrijt 5708
Science Park Eindhoven, 5692 ER Son, Netherlands NL
Tel.: (31) 40 267 7000 (100%)
Fax: (31) 40 267 7001
E-Mail: info@advantech.com
Web Site: www.advantech.nl
Computer & Computer Components Whslr & Technical Support Services
S.I.C.: 5045
N.A.I.C.S.: 423430
Peter Young *(Mng Dir)*

Non-U.S. Subsidiaries:

DLoG Gesellschaft fur elektronische Datentechnik mbH (2)
Industriestrasse 15
82110 Germering, Germany De
Tel.: (49) 89 411 1910
Fax: (49) 89 411 191900
E-Mail: info@dlog.com
Web Site: www.dlog.com
Emp.: 80
Industrial Computer Terminal Designer, Mfr & Distr
S.I.C.: 3577
N.A.I.C.S.: 334118
Ke-Cheng Liu *(Mng Dir)*

Advantech Japan Co., Ltd. (1)
Toyoto Taitoku Asakusa 66-16-3 2-5-5 Hitotsubasi
Chiyoda-Ku, Tokyo, Japan (100%)
Tel.: (81) 368021021
Fax: (81) 368021020
E-Mail: ajp_sales@advantech.com
Web Site: www.advantech.co.jp
Electrical Apparatus & Equipment Wiring Supplies & Construction Material Whslr
S.I.C.: 5063
N.A.I.C.S.: 423610

Advantech Technology (China) Company Ltd. (1)
No 600 Hanpu Rd
Kunshan Development Zone, Kunshan, China (100%)
Tel.: (86) 51257775666
Fax: (86) 51257785388
Web Site: www.advantech.com.tw
Relay & Industrial Control Mfr
S.I.C.: 3625
N.A.I.C.S.: 335314

ADVANTECH TECHNOLOGIES LTD.

2 BSR Building 1 Ben Gurion St
Bnei Brak, 51201, Israel
Tel.: (972) 3 5775050
Fax: (972) 3 5775060
E-Mail: mail@advantech.co.il
Web Site: www.advantech.co.il
ADVT—(TAE)

Business Description:
IT Services
S.I.C.: 7373
N.A.I.C.S.: 541512

Personnel:
Zeev Yanai *(Chm & CEO)*

Non-U.S. Subsidiaries:

NessPRO Italy S.p.A. - Rome (1)
Via V Lamaro 21
00173 Rome, Italy (100%)
Tel.: (39) 06724331
Fax: (39) 0672901841
E-Mail: info.nesspro.italy@nesspro.it
Web Site: www.nesspro.it
Emp.: 98
Information Technology Services
S.I.C.: 7373
N.A.I.C.S.: 541512
Pasquale Favale *(CEO)*

NessPRO Italy S.p.A. - Milan (1)
Via A Volta 16
20093 Cologno Monzese, Italy (100%)
Tel.: (39) 022515181
Fax: (39) 0227301170
E-Mail: info.nesspro.italy@nesspro.it
Web Site: www.nesspro.it
Emp.: 26
Information Technology Services
S.I.C.: 7373
N.A.I.C.S.: 541512
Pasquale Favale *(CEO)*

Advantech Technologies Ltd.—(Continued)

NessPRO Portugal (1)
Av de Liberdade 110
1269-046 Lisbon, Portugal (100%)
Tel.: (351) 213404500
Fax: (351) 213404575
E-Mail:
Emp.: 14
Information Technology Solutions
S.I.C.: 7373
N.A.I.C.S.: 541512

NessPRO Spain S.A. (1)
C/Mesena 22-3 x Planta
28033 Madrid, Spain (100%)
Tel.: (34) 916303737
Fax: (34) 916303799
E-Mail: esmad.info@nesspro.es
Web Site: www.nesspro.es
Emp.: 50
IT Services
S.I.C.: 7373
N.A.I.C.S.: 541512
Mario Lapid *(CEO)*

ADVANTEST CORPORATION

Shin Marunouchi Center Building 1-6-2 Marunouchi
Chiyoda-ku, Tokyo, 100-0005, Japan
Tel.: (81) 3 3214 7500
Fax: (81) 3 3214 7711
E-Mail: info@advantest.co.jp
Web Site: www.advantest.co.jp
Year Founded: 1954
ATE—(NYSE TKS)
Sls.: $1,461,933,000
Assets: $2,480,665,000
Liabilities: $927,014,000
Net Worth: $1,553,651,000
Earnings: ($42,031,000)
Emp.: 4,575
Fiscal Year-end: 03/31/13

Business Description:
Electronic Measuring Instruments, Automatic Test Equipment & Electron Beam Lithography Systems Mfr & Whslr
Import Export
S.I.C.: 3829
N.A.I.C.S.: 334519

Personnel:
Toshio Maruyama *(Chm)*
Haruo Matsuno *(Pres & CEO)*
Hideaki Imada *(Mng Exec Officer)*
Yasuhiro Kawata *(Exec Officer)*
R. Keith Lee *(Exec Officer)*
Sae Bum Myung *(Mng Exec Officer)*
Makoto Nakahara *(Exec Officer)*
Hiroshi Nakamura *(Mng Exec Officer)*
Toshiyuki Okayasu *(Exec Officer)*
Kenji Sato *(Exec Officer)*
Josef Schraetzenstaller *(Exec Officer)*
Takashi Sekino *(Exec Officer)*
Masao Shimizu *(Mng Exec Officer)*
Takashi Sugiura *(Exec Officer)*
Soichi Tsukakoshi *(Exec Officer)*
Hans-Juergen Wagner *(Mng Exec Officer)*
Ch Wu *(Exec Officer)*
Kazuhiro Yamashita *(Exec Officer)*
Yoshiaki Yoshida *(Mng Exec Officer)*

Board of Directors:
Toshio Maruyama
Naoyuki Akikusa
Yasushige Hagio
Osamu Karatsu
Yuichi Kurita
Shinichiro Kuroe
Haruo Matsuno
Sae Bum Myung
Hiroshi Nakamura
Yoshiaki Yoshida

Transfer Agent:
Mitsubishi UFJ Trust & Banking Corporation
4-5 Marunouchi 1-Chome Chiyoda-ku
Tokyo, 100-8212, Japan
Tel.: (81) 3 3212 1211

Subsidiaries:

Advanfacilities Co., Ltd. (1)
1-5 Shin-tone
Kazo, Saitama, 349-1158, Japan
Tel.: (81) 480 72 7002
Fax: (81) 480 72 7634
E-Mail: afc-info@ml.advantest.com
Web Site: www.advantest.co.jp/about/advantest-group/subsidiaries/en-index.shtml
Facility Management Services
S.I.C.: 8744
N.A.I.C.S.: 561210

Advansoft Development Corporation (1)
336-1 Owa Meiwamachi
Oura, Gunma, 370-0718, Japan
Tel.: (81) 276 84 5831
Fax: (81) 276 84 1032
Software Development Services
S.I.C.: 7371
N.A.I.C.S.: 541511

Advantest Academy, KK. (1)
336-1 Ohwa Meiwa-machi
Ora-gun, Gunma, 370-0718, Japan
Tel.: (81) 276 70 3425
Fax: (81) 276 70 3426
Semiconductor Device Mfr
S.I.C.: 3674
N.A.I.C.S.: 334413

Advantest Component, Inc. (1)
48-2 Matsubara Kami-Ayashi
Aoba-ku, Sendai, Miyagi, 989-3124, Japan
Tel.: (81) 22 392 9711
Fax: (81) 22 392 9712
E-Mail: info@aci-advantest.co.jp
Semiconductor Device Mfr
S.I.C.: 3674
N.A.I.C.S.: 334413

Plant:

Advantest Component, Inc. - Sendai Factory (2)
48-2 Matsubara Kami-Ayashi
Aoba-ku, Sendai, Miyagi, 989-3124, Japan
Tel.: (81) 22 392 9711
Fax: (81) 22 392 9712
Web Site: www.advantest.co.jp/about/advantest-group/head-office/en-index.shtml
Semiconductor Device Mfr
S.I.C.: 3674
N.A.I.C.S.: 334413

Advantest Finance Inc (1)
Shin Marunouchi Center Building 1-6-2 Marunouchi
Chiyoda-ku, Tokyo, Japan 100-0005
Tel.: (81) 3 3214 7620
Fax: (81) 3 3214 7720
Web Site: www.afi-advantest.co.jp
Semiconductor Test System Rental Services
S.I.C.: 7359
N.A.I.C.S.: 532490
Yoshio Endo *(Pres)*

Advantest Green Corporation (1)
1-5 Shin-tone
Kazo, Saitama, 349-1158, Japan
Tel.: (81) 480 72 6821
Fax: (81) 480 72 6828
E-Mail: agc-info@ml.advantest.com
Web Site: www.advantest.co.jp/about/advantest-group/subsidiaries/en-index.shtml
Environmental Consulting Services
S.I.C.: 8999
N.A.I.C.S.: 541620

Advantest Kyushu Systems Co., Ltd (1)
1-5-1 Higashida
Yahatahigashi-ku, Kitakyushu, Fukuoka, 805-0071, Japan
Tel.: (81) 93 681 0200
Fax: (81) 93 681 0276
Web Site: www.advantest.co.jp/about/advantest-group/subsidiaries/en-index.shtml
Laboratory Research Instrument Distr
S.I.C.: 5047
N.A.I.C.S.: 423450

Advantest Laboratories Ltd (1)
48-2 Matsubara Kami-Ayasi
Aobe-Ku, Sendai, Miyagi, 989-3124, Japan
Tel.: (81) 22 392 8731
Fax: (81) 22 392 8737
Emp.: 10
Laboratory Research Equipment Mfr
S.I.C.: 3826
N.A.I.C.S.: 334516

Advantest Media Service Corporation (1)
1-5 Shin-tone
Kazo, Saitama, 349-1158, Japan
Tel.: (81) 480 72 7021
Fax: (81) 480 72 7150
E-Mail: ams-info@ml.advantest.com
Emp.: 22
Commercial Printing Services
S.I.C.: 2759
N.A.I.C.S.: 323111
Takayuki Yamada *(Gen Mgr)*

Advantest Systems Corporation (1)
336-1 Ohwa Meiwa-machi
Ora-gun, Gunma, 370-0718, Japan
Tel.: (81) 276 84 5831
Fax: (81) 276 84 1032
E-Mail: ats-saiyo@ml.advantest.com
Web Site: www.advantest.co.jp/about/advantest-group/subsidiaries/en-index.shtml
Semiconductor Device Mfr
S.I.C.: 3674
N.A.I.C.S.: 334413

Japan Engineering Co., Ltd. (1)
2-9-2 Ikuta
Tama-ku, Kawasaki, Kanagawa, 214-0038, Japan (100%)
Tel.: (81) 449311311
Fax: (81) 449311320
E-Mail: jec-webmaster@ml.advantest.com
Web Site: www.jec.co.jp
Emp.: 53
Semiconductor Testing Equipment Developer & Mfr
S.I.C.: 3674
N.A.I.C.S.: 334413
Hitoshi Sugae *(Pres)*

Plants:

Advantest Corporation - Gunma Factory 2 (1)
3685-1 Akahori Ora-machi
Ora-gun, Gunma, 370-0614, Japan
Tel.: (81) 276 80 9700
Fax: (81) 276 88 9072
Web Site: www.advantest.co.jp/about/advantest-group/head-office/en-index.shtml
Electronic Measuring Instrument Mfr
S.I.C.: 3823
N.A.I.C.S.: 334513

Advantest Corporation - Gunma Factory (1)
54-1 Shinozuka Ora-machi
Ora-gun, Gunma, 370-0615, Japan
Tel.: (81) 276 88 7500
Fax: (81) 276 89 1030
Web Site: www.advantest.co.jp/about/advantest-group/head-office/en-index.shtml
Electronic Measuring Instrument Mfr
S.I.C.: 3823
N.A.I.C.S.: 334513

U.S. Subsidiaries:

Advantest America Inc. (1)
3201 Scott Blvd
Santa Clara, CA 95054-3008 (100%)
Tel.: (408) 988-7700
Fax: (408) 987-0680
E-Mail: info@advantest.com
Web Site: www.advantest.com
Emp.: 93
Semiconductor Testing Equipment Developer & Mfr
S.I.C.: 3674
N.A.I.C.S.: 334413
R. Keith Lee *(Pres & CEO)*

Subsidiary:

Advantest America R&D Center, Inc. (2)
3201 Scott Blvd
Santa Clara, CA 95054-3008 (100%)
Tel.: (408) 727-2222
Fax: (408) 727-5764
Web Site: www.advantest-ard.com
Sls.: $21,000,000
Emp.: 23
Development & Testing of IC Equipment Software
S.I.C.: 8731
N.A.I.C.S.: 541712

Non-U.S. Subsidiaries:

Advantest (China) Co., Ltd. (1)
C Block Bldg 3 168 Hua Tuo Road
Zhangjiang Hi-Tech Park, Shanghai, 201203, China
Tel.: (86) 21 6163 2600
Fax: (86) 21 2028 7600
E-Mail:
Emp.: 150
Semiconductor Test Systems Mfr
S.I.C.: 3674
N.A.I.C.S.: 334413

Subsidiary:

Advantest (Suzhou) Co., Ltd. (2)
Airport Rd 328 Industry Pk
Suzhou, 215021, China (100%)
Tel.: (86) 51262568318
Fax: (86) 51262568328
Web Site: www.advantest.com.cn
Emp.: 20
Provider of Electricity Measurement Instruments
S.I.C.: 3824
N.A.I.C.S.: 334514

Advantest (Europe) GmbH (1)
Stefan George Ring 2
81929 Munich, Germany (100%)
Tel.: (49) 89993120
Fax: (49) 8999312101
E-Mail: info@eu.advantest.com
Web Site: www.advantest.com
Emp.: 100
Semiconductor Testing Equipment Developer & Mfr
S.I.C.: 3674
N.A.I.C.S.: 334413
Josef Schraetzenstaller *(Mng Dir)*
Peter Wewerka *(CFO & VP)*
Michael Stichlmair *(CMO & VP)*

Branch:

Advantest - Boblingen (2)
Herrenberger Strasse 130
71034 Boblingen, Germany
Tel.: (49) 7031 4357 000
Fax: (49) 7031 4357 497
Emp.: 400
Semiconductor Test Systems Mfr
S.I.C.: 3674
N.A.I.C.S.: 334413
Hans-Juergen Wagner *(VP)*

Subsidiaries:

Advantest Europe Systems GmbH (2)
Wasserburger Strasse 44
83123 Amerang, Germany De
Tel.: (49) 8075 17 0
Fax: (49) 8075 17 1000
E-Mail: info@eu.advantest.com
Web Site: www.advantest.de
Semiconductor Testing Equipment Developer & Mfr
S.I.C.: 3674
N.A.I.C.S.: 334413
Josef Schraetzenstaller *(Mng Dir)*

Non-U.S. Subsidiary:

Advantest Europe R&D S.A.R.L. (2)
5 Ave De Quebec ZA
BP 203
91941 Courtaboeuf, Cedex, France (100%)
Tel.: (33) 169182500
Fax: (33) 169829224
E-Mail: i.granger@fr.advantest.com
Web Site: www.advantest.com
Emp.: 17
Provider of Electricity Measurement Instruments
S.I.C.: 3823
N.A.I.C.S.: 334513
Kakizaki Koji *(Mng Dir)*

Advantest Korea Co., Ltd. (1)
421 Chaam-dong
Seobuk-gu, Cheonan, 135 280, Korea (South) (100%)
Tel.: (82) 41 901 3900
Web Site: www.advantest.com
Emp.: 90

Electricity Measurement Instruments
S.I.C.: 3824
N.A.I.C.S.: 334514

Advantest (Singapore) Pte. Ltd. (1)
438A Alexandra Rd Fl 8 Unit 3 6
Singapore, 119967, Singapore (100%)
Tel.: (65) 6755 2033
Fax: (65) 6754 3946
E-Mail: recruit@sg.advantest.com
Web Site: www.advantest.co.sg
Emp.: 82
Provider of Electricity Measurement Instruments
S.I.C.: 3823
N.A.I.C.S.: 334513
Lee Koon Seet *(CFO)*

Non-U.S. Subsidiaries:

Advantest-Engineering (Malaysia) Sdn. Bhd. (2)
Plot 5 Technoplex Medan Bayan Lepas Pk bhafd IV
11900 Penang, Malaysia (100%)
Tel.: (60) 46413980
Fax: (60) 6046413978
E-Mail: atemcomm@my.advantest.com
Web Site: www.advantest.com
Sales Range: $1-9.9 Million
Emp.: 23
Joint Venture of Advantest (65%) & Eng. Technologi Holdings Bhd. (35%)
S.I.C.: 6719
N.A.I.C.S.: 551112
Makoto Sagawa *(Mng Dir)*

Advantest (Malaysia) Sdn. Bhd. (2)
Ste 2 3 Fl 2 N Tatt Bldg No 2 SIME UEP Indus Pk
47600 Subang Jaya, Selangor Darul Ehsan, Malaysia (100%)
Tel.: (60) 380234088
Fax: (60) 380234788
E-Mail: info@advantest.com
Web Site: www.advantest.com
Emp.: 22
Provider of Electricity Measurement Instruments
S.I.C.: 3823
N.A.I.C.S.: 334513
Cheng Sui Yoong *(Mng Dir)*

Advantest Philippines, Inc. (2)
Unit 2203 04 Richville Tower 1107 Alabang Zapote Rd
Madrigal Business Park Ayala A, Muntinlupa, Philippines (100%)
Tel.: (63) 28427297
E-Mail: apiinfo@api.advantest.co.jp
Web Site: www.atasp.advantest.co.jp
Emp.: 14
Provider of Electricity Measurement Instruments
S.I.C.: 3825
N.A.I.C.S.: 334515

Advantest (Thailand) Ltd. (2)
Rasa Tower 12th Floor Unit 1202 555 Phaholyothin Road
Chatuchak, Bangkok, 10900, Thailand
Tel.: (66) 2 937 0285
Fax: (66) 2 937 0286
Semiconductor Device Mfr
S.I.C.: 3674
N.A.I.C.S.: 334413
Cheng Sui Yoong *(Mng Dir)*

Advantest Taiwan, Inc. (1)
No 1 Alley 17 Ln 62 Chung Ho St
Chu Pei, Hsin-chu, Hsein, 302, Taiwan (100%)
Tel.: (886) 35532111
Fax: (886) 35541031
Web Site: www.advantest.com.tw
Emp.: 100
Provider of Electricity Measurement Instruments
S.I.C.: 3823
N.A.I.C.S.: 334513
Chio Chu *(Pres)*

ADVANTEX MARKETING INTERNATIONAL INC.

600 Alden Road Suite 606
Markham, ON, L3R OE7, Canada
Tel.: (905) 470-9558
Fax: (905) 946-2984
Toll Free: (800) 663-1114
E-Mail: info@advantex.com
Web Site: www.advantex.com
Year Founded: 1994
ADX—(CNSX)
Rev.: $16,808,687
Assets: $17,155,038
Liabilities: $18,201,634
Net Worth: ($1,046,597)
Earnings: $36,036
Emp.: 45
Fiscal Year-end: 06/30/13

Business Description:
Online & Offline Customer Relationship Marketing Programs
S.I.C.: 7319
N.A.I.C.S.: 541870

Personnel:
Kelly E. Ambrose *(Pres & CEO)*
Mukesh Sabharwal *(CFO & VP)*

Board of Directors:
Kelly E. Ambrose
Stephen E. Burns
William H. Polley
Barry M. Wainstein

Legal Counsel:
Goodman & Carr
2300 200 King St W
Toronto, ON, M5H 3W5, Canada

Transfer Agent:
CIBC Mellon Trust Company
320 Bay Street B1 Level
Toronto, ON, Canada

Subsidiaries:

Advantex Dining Corporation (1)
493-6400 Roberts St
Burnaby, BC, V5G 4C9, Canada
Tel.: (604) 205-5022
Emp.: 5
Marketing Management Services
S.I.C.: 8742
N.A.I.C.S.: 541613
Suzanne Wensley *(Mgr)*

Advantex Marketing Corporation (1)
600 Alden Rd Ste 606
Markham, ON, L3R 0E7, Canada
Tel.: (905) 470-9558
Fax: (905) 946-2984
Marketing Management Services
S.I.C.: 8742
N.A.I.C.S.: 541613
Kelly Ambrose *(CEO)*

ADVENT COMPUTER SERVICES LTD.

New No 121 Old No 347 Pantheon Road
Egmore, Chennai, 600008, India
Tel.: (91) 44 45580095
Fax: (91) 44 28193688
E-Mail: compliance.officer@adventcomputer.in
Web Site: www.adventcomputer.in
531429—(BOM)
Sales Range: Less than $1 Million

Business Description:
Information Technology Software Services
S.I.C.: 7373
N.A.I.C.S.: 541512

Personnel:
Michael Arul *(Chm & Mng Dir)*

Board of Directors:
Michael Arul
Shaji John Abraham
Suvash Biswas
R. Mohanlal
Madhavaraj Suresh

ADVENT WIRELESS INC.

1103 - 3779 Sexsmith Road
Richmond, BC, V6X 3Z9, Canada
Tel.: (604) 279-8868
Fax: (604) 279-0880
Year Founded: 1984
AWI—(TSXV)
Rev.: $24,838,976
Assets: $19,755,111
Liabilities: $6,001,176
Net Worth: $13,753,935
Earnings: ($1,754,582)
Fiscal Year-end: 12/31/12

Business Description:
Cellular & Wireless Product Whslr
S.I.C.: 5065
N.A.I.C.S.: 423690

Personnel:
Gen Wong *(Pres & CEO)*
Edgar Pang *(CFO & Sec)*

Board of Directors:
Anthony Chan
Alice Chiu
Bill Hui
Edgar Pang
Ken Vong
Gen Wong
Sin-Kuen Yau

ADVENTO, INC.

(Name Changed to Joymain International Development Group Inc.)

ADVENTURE GOLD INC.

1812 - 1 Place Ville-Marie
Montreal, QC, H3B 4A9, Canada
Tel.: (514) 525-5575
Fax: (819) 797-9740
E-Mail: info@adventure-gold.com
Web Site: www.adventure-gold.com
Year Founded: 2007
AGE—(TSXV)
Rev.: $24,120
Assets: $9,692,681
Liabilities: $963,458
Net Worth: $8,729,223
Earnings: ($877,604)
Fiscal Year-end: 07/31/13

Business Description:
Gold Mining Services
S.I.C.: 1041
N.A.I.C.S.: 212221

Personnel:
Stephane Le Bouyonnec *(Chm)*
Marco Gagnon *(Pres & CEO)*
Robert Boisjoli *(CFO & Sec)*

Board of Directors:
Stephane Le Bouyonnec
Marco Gagnon
Marc L'Heureux
Michael J. Williams

Legal Counsel:
Fasken Martineau
800 Victoria Square Suite 3700
Montreal, QC, H4Z 1E9, Canada

Transfer Agent:
Computershare Trust Company of Canada
1500 University St 7th Floor
Montreal, QC, Canada

ADVENTUS HOLDINGS LIMITED

20 Maxwell Road 05-09 Maxwell House
Singapore, 069113, Singapore
Tel.: (65) 63822110
Fax: (65) 63822420
E-Mail: info@adventusholdings.com
Web Site: www.adventusholdings.com
5EF—(SES)
Rev.: $3,174,333
Assets: $8,752,668
Liabilities: $2,920,033
Net Worth: $5,832,634
Earnings: ($5,592,854)
Fiscal Year-end: 12/31/12

Business Description:
Telecommunication Services
S.I.C.: 4813
N.A.I.C.S.: 517110

Personnel:
Jonathan Keng Hock Lim *(Chm)*
Bee Fong Lee *(Sec)*

Board of Directors:
Jonathan Keng Hock Lim
Ping Wei Kum
Soon Teik Ong
Allan Poh Chye Tan
Gersom G. Vetuz

ADVEO GROUP INTERNATIONAL, S.A.

Avenida de los Artesanos 28
Tres Cantos, 28760 Madrid, Spain
Tel.: (34) 918069610
Fax: (34) 91 902 215 316
E-Mail: comercial@unipapel.com
Web Site: www.adveo.com
Year Founded: 1976
ADV—(MAD)
Rev.: $1,539,614,629
Assets: $853,397,741
Liabilities: $625,479,044
Net Worth: $227,918,697
Earnings: $19,053,690
Emp.: 1,339
Fiscal Year-end: 12/31/12

Business Description:
Stationery Products Mfr & Retailer
S.I.C.: 2678
N.A.I.C.S.: 322230

Personnel:
Juan Antonio Hernandez-Rubio Munoyerro *(Chm)*
Eladio Bezares Munilla *(Vice Chm)*
Millan Alvarez Miranda *(CEO)*
Daniel Lozano Lozano *(CFO)*
Jean-Yves Sebaoun *(COO)*
Juan Venegas Valladares *(Gen Counsel)*

Board of Directors:
Juan Antonio Hernandez-Rubio Munoyerro
Juan Nunez Gallego
Julian Cepeda Herreros
Xabier Arratibel Imaz
Francisco Javier Diaz Marroquin
Millan Alvarez Miranda
Pablo Iqartua Moreno
Eladio Bezares Munilla
Alvaro Videgain Muro
Ricardo Muquerza Uralde

Subsidiary:

Spicers Administracion y Servicios, S.L. (1)
Edificio Madison Ctra Nacional 340 122-A 2 Planta
08960 Barcelona, Spain ES
Tel.: (34) 93 503 80 00
Fax: (34) 93 503 80 01
E-Mail: direccion@spicers.es
Web Site: www.spicers.es
Stationery & Office Products Distr
S.I.C.: 5112
N.A.I.C.S.: 424120
Eric Schmidt *(Mng Dir)*

Non-U.S. Branch:

Spicers Italia (2)
Viale dell'Industria 31
29015 Castel San Giovanni, Piacenza, Italy
Tel.: (39) 523866411
Fax: (39) 0523 866412
E-Mail: info@spicers.it
Web Site: www.spicers.it
Stationery & Office Products Whslr
S.I.C.: 5112
N.A.I.C.S.: 424120

Non-U.S. Subsidiaries:

Spicers Belgium NV (2)
Europalaan 69
9800 Deinze, Belgium

ADVEO Group International, S.A.—(Continued)

Tel.: (32) 93810505
Fax: (32) 93810535
E-Mail: info@spicers.be
Web Site: www.spicers.be
Stationery & Office Products Distr
S.I.C.: 5112
N.A.I.C.S.: 424120

Spicers Deutschland GmbH (2)
Gretlade 1
31319 Sehnde, Germany
Tel.: (49) 5132 929 0
Fax: (49) 5132 929 444
Web Site: www.spicers.de
Stationery & Office Product Whslr
S.I.C.: 5112
N.A.I.C.S.: 424120
Thomas Apelrath *(Mng Dir)*

Spicers France SAS (2)
Zone Industrielle de Paris Nord II 47 allee des Impressionnistes
BP 55402
95943 Roissy-en-France, France
Tel.: (33) 1 49 38 83 00
Fax: (33) 1 49 38 83 01
Web Site: www.spicers.fr
Consumer Goods Distr
S.I.C.: 5199
N.A.I.C.S.: 424990

ADVEQ MANAGEMENT AG

Affolternstrasse 56
CH-8050 Zurich, Switzerland
Tel.: (41) 432883200
Fax: (41) 584455556
E-Mail: info@adveq.com
Web Site: www.adveq.com
Year Founded: 1997
Emp.: 60

Business Description:
Private Equity Fund of Funds Investment Management Services
S.I.C.: 6282
N.A.I.C.S.: 523920

Personnel:
Bruno E. Raschle *(Founder & Mng Dir)*
Philippe Bucher *(Mng Dir)*
Rainer Ender *(Mng Dir)*
Nils Rode *(Mng Dir)*

Board of Directors:
Allan S. Bufferd
Tim Creed
Patrick Kuentscher
Sasha Kugler
Viswanathan Parameswar
Bruno E. Raschle

ADVFN PLC

26 Throgmorton Street
London, EC2N 2AN, United Kingdom
Tel.: (44) 207 0700 961
Fax: (44) 207 070 0959
E-Mail: ir@advfn.com
Web Site: www.advfn.com
AFN—(AIM OTC)
Rev.: $12,755,925
Assets: $8,782,432
Liabilities: $3,488,652
Net Worth: $5,293,780
Earnings: ($851,237)
Emp.: 37
Fiscal Year-end: 06/30/13

Business Description:
Online Financial News
S.I.C.: 2741
N.A.I.C.S.: 519130

Personnel:
Michael J. Hodges *(Chm & Sec)*
Clement Hadrian Chambers *(CEO & Mng Dir)*
Jonathan B. Mullins *(CFO & Dir-Technical)*

Board of Directors:
Michael J. Hodges
Clement Hadrian Chambers
Robert Anthony Bernard Emmet
Jonathan B. Mullins
Raymond J. Negus
Yair Tauman

Legal Counsel:
Field Fisher Waterhouse
35 Vine Street
London, United Kingdom

Subsidiaries:

ALL IPO plc (1)
26 Throgmorton Street
London, EC2N 2AN, United Kingdom
Tel.: (44) 2070700991
E-Mail: support@allipo.com
Web Site: www.allipo.com
Sales Range: Less than $1 Million
Emp.: 10
Online Business Information Services
S.I.C.: 7389
N.A.I.C.S.: 561499
Clem Chambers *(Mng Dir)*
Chris Newland *(COO)*

Throgmorton Street Capital Ltd. (1)
26 Throgmorton St
London, EC2N 2AN, United Kingdom UK (100%)
Tel.: (44) 2070700973
Fax: (44) 2076287220
E-Mail: info@throgmortonstreetcapital.com
Web Site: www.throgmortonstreetcapital.com
Emp.: 30
Boutique Investment Bank
S.I.C.: 6211
N.A.I.C.S.: 523110
Clem Chambers *(CEO)*

ADVIK LABORATORIES LTD.

203 106-07 Allied House 1 LSC
Madangir, New Delhi, 110 062, India
Tel.: (91) 11 41649171
Fax: (91) 11 41649171
E-Mail: mail@advikindia.com
Web Site: www.advikindia.com
531686—(BOM)
Sales Range: $1-9.9 Million

Business Description:
Laboratory Services
S.I.C.: 8734
N.A.I.C.S.: 541380

Personnel:
V. K. Jain *(Mng Dir)*
Kanupriya Tulsyan *(Sec)*

Board of Directors:
V. K. Jain
Kishan Kumar
Sushil Kr. Singh

Transfer Agent:
Beetal Financial & Computer Services Pvt. Ltd
Beetal House 3rd Floor 99 Madangir Behind L S C Near Dada Harsukh Dass
New Delhi, India

ADVINI S.A.

BP 1
34725 Saint-Felix-de-Lodez, France
Tel.: (33) 4 67 88 80 00
Fax: (33) 4 67 96 65 67
E-Mail: contact@advini.com
Web Site: www.advini.com
ADVI—(EUR)
Sales Range: $200-249.9 Million
Emp.: 544

Business Description:
Wine Producer
S.I.C.: 2084
N.A.I.C.S.: 312130

Personnel:
Bernard Jeanjean *(Chm-Supervisory Bd)*
Philippe Jeanjean *(Vice Chm)*
Antoine Leccia *(CEO)*

Supervisory Board of Directors:
Bernard Jeanjean
Jean-Francois Jamet
Hugues Jeanjean
Philippe Jeanjean
Philippe Lauthier
Vincent Rieu

Subsidiaries:

Antoine Moueix SAS (1)
Route du Milieu
BP 40100
Saint-Emilion, France
Tel.: (33) 5 57 55 58 00
Fax: (33) 5 57 74 18 47
Web Site: www.advini.com
Wine Mfr
S.I.C.: 2084
N.A.I.C.S.: 312130

Gassier SAS (1)
Chemin De La Colle Jas Du Luc
13114 Puyloubier, France
Tel.: (33) 4 42 66 38 74
Fax: (33) 4 42 66 38 77
E-Mail: gassier@chateau-gassier.fr
Web Site: www.chateau-gassier.com
Emp.: 8
Wine Mfr
S.I.C.: 2084
N.A.I.C.S.: 312130
Olivier Souvelain *(Mng Dir)*

Ogier SAS (1)
10 Avenue Louis Pasteur
BP 75
84232 Chateauneuf-du-Pape, France
Tel.: (33) 4 9039 3232
Fax: (33) 4 9083 7251
Web Site: www.advini.com
Grape Vineyard & Winery
S.I.C.: 2084
N.A.I.C.S.: 312130

Rigal SAS (1)
Chateau Saint Didier
46140 Parnac, France
Tel.: (33) 565 307 010
Fax: (33) 565 307 813
E-Mail: marketing@rigal.fr
Web Site: www.rigal.fr
Emp.: 15
Wine Mfr
S.I.C.: 2084
N.A.I.C.S.: 312130
Marc Lecomte *(Pres)*
Olivier Pieron *(Mng Dir)*

Non-U.S. Subsidiaries:

AdVini Polska, Sp. z.o.o. (1)
Chalubinskiego 8
Warsaw, 00-613, Poland
Tel.: (48) 226250950
Fax: (48) 226213284
E-Mail: office@jeanjean.pl
Emp.: 8
Wine Mfr & Distr
S.I.C.: 2084
N.A.I.C.S.: 312130
Krzysztof Boguszewski *(Gen Mgr)*

L'Avenir (1)
L'Avenir Wine Estate - Klapmuts Road R44
Stellenbosch, Western Cape, 7599, South Africa
Tel.: (27) 21 889 5001
Fax: (27) 21 889 525
E-Mail: info@larochewines.com
Wine Mfr & Distr
S.I.C.: 2084
N.A.I.C.S.: 312130

ADVTECH LIMITED

ADvTECH House Inanda Greens 54 Wierda Road West Wierda Valley
Sandton, 2196, South Africa
Tel.: (27) 116768000
Fax: (27) 117832640
E-Mail: info@advtech.co.za
Web Site: www.advtech.co.za
ADH—(JSE)
Rev.: $188,460,240
Assets: $149,197,690
Liabilities: $60,608,420
Net Worth: $88,589,270
Earnings: $15,459,280
Emp.: 4,037
Fiscal Year-end: 12/31/12

Business Description:
Education Training & Staff Placement Services
S.I.C.: 8299
N.A.I.C.S.: 611710

Personnel:
Frank R. Thompson *(CEO)*
Siza Dlamini *(Exec-Corp Affairs)*

Board of Directors:
Leslie Massdorp
Christopher Boulle
Brenda Gourley
Jonathan Jansen
Hymie Levin
Jeffrey Livingstone
Didier Oesch
Frank R. Thompson
Shirley Zinn

Transfer Agent:
Link Market Services South Africa (Proprietary) Limited
13 Floor Rennie House 19 Ameshoff Street
Braamfontein, South Africa

Subsidiaries:

ADvTECH Resourcing (Pty) Ltd (1)
No 3 Edlin Rd
Sunninghill Park, Sandton, Gauteng, 2199, South Africa
Tel.: (27) 112342404
Fax: (27) 112345192
Web Site: www.advtech.co.za
Emp.: 1,500
Recruitment Consulting Services
S.I.C.: 8999
N.A.I.C.S.: 541612

Divisions:

ADvTECH Resourcing (Pty) Ltd - Communicate Personnel Division (2)
The Crescent 1st Fl W Bldg 3 Eglin Rd
Sunninghill, Johannesburg, Gauteng, 2157, South Africa
Tel.: (27) 112342404
Fax: (27) 112345192
E-Mail: info@communicate.co.za
Web Site: www.communicate.co.za
Emp.: 50
Staffing & Recruitment Solutions
S.I.C.: 7361
N.A.I.C.S.: 561311
Shelley Ball *(Mng Dir)*

ADvTECH Resourcing (Pty) Ltd - Insource.ICT Division (2)
First Fl Engen House Waterfall Ofc Park Bekker Rd
Midrand, Gauteng, 1685, South Africa
Tel.: (27) 113159451
Fax: (27) 113159455
E-Mail: midrand@insource.co.za
Web Site: www.insource.co.za
Emp.: 45
Information Technology Staffing Solutions
S.I.C.: 7361
N.A.I.C.S.: 561311
Shelley Ball *(Mng Dir)*

ADvTECH Resourcing (Pty) Ltd - IT Edge Division (2)
Eva Park Block C Unit C112 C/O Beyers Naude & Judges Ave
Blackheath, Johannesburg, Gauteng, 2195, South Africa
Tel.: (27) 116783131
Fax: (27) 116783800
E-Mail: kvain@itedge.co.za
Web Site: www.itedge.co.za
Emp.: 5
Information Technology Professionals Recruitment Services
S.I.C.: 7361
N.A.I.C.S.: 561311
Kate Vain *(Mgr)*

ADvTECH Resourcing (Pty) Ltd - Network Recruitment Division (2)
Menlyn Ofc Park
Newlands, Pretoria, Gauteng, 0181, South Africa
Tel.: (27) 123480279
Fax: (27) 0114445192
E-Mail: customercare@networkrecruitment.co.za

Web Site: www.networkrecruitment.co.za
Emp.: 14
Recruitment Services
S.I.C.: 7361
N.A.I.C.S.: 561311
Niteske Marshall *(Mng Dir)*

ADvTECH Resourcing (Pty) Ltd - Pro Rec Recruitment Division (2)
The Crescent S Block Entrance 2 3 Eglin Rd
Sunninghill, Johannesburg, Gauteng, 2125, South Africa
Tel.: (27) 11 803 5708
Fax: (27) 11 803 6224
E-Mail: response@prorec.co.za
Web Site: www.prorec.co.za
Emp.: 4
Recruitment Services
S.I.C.: 7361
N.A.I.C.S.: 561311
Candice McCumskey *(Mng Dir)*

ADvTECH Resourcing (Pty) Ltd - Tech-Pro Personnel Division (2)
Block C Ground Fl St Andrews Ofc Park Meadowbrook Ave
Epsom Downs, Johannesburg, Gauteng, 2194, South Africa
Tel.: (27) 115140463
Fax: (27) 115140505
E-Mail: info@tech-pro.co.za
Web Site: www.tech-pro.co.za
Emp.: 15
Supply Chain Management Recruitment Services
S.I.C.: 8999
N.A.I.C.S.: 541612
Inez Van Aswegen *(Gen Mgr)*

Subsidiaries:

Cassel & Company (2)
The Crescent Ofc Park N Bldg First Fl 3 Eglin Rd
Sunninghill, Johannesburg, Gauteng, 2157, South Africa
Tel.: (27) 112341432
Fax: (27) 112341542
E-Mail: cassel@cassel.co.za
Web Site: www.cassel.co.za
Emp.: 24
Staffing & Recruitment Solutions
S.I.C.: 7361
N.A.I.C.S.: 561311
Natasha Bell *(Mgr-Gen Fin)*

Kapele Appointments (Pty) Ltd (2)
Inanda Greens Business Park 54 Wierda Road West Wierda Valley
Sandton, 2196, South Africa
Tel.: (27) 11 676 8000
Web Site: www.advtech.co.za
Staffing & Recruitment Services
S.I.C.: 8999
N.A.I.C.S.: 541612
Frank Thompson *(CEO)*

Divisions:

Kapele Appointments (Pty) Limited - The Working Earth Division (3)
The Working Earth Bldg
Weltevreden Park, Roodepoort, Gauteng, 1715, South Africa
Tel.: (27) 114759668
Fax: (27) 114756748
E-Mail: info@theworkingearth.com
Web Site: www.theworkingearth.co.za
Emp.: 30
Online Recruitment Services
S.I.C.: 2741
N.A.I.C.S.: 519130

Kapele Appointments (Pty) Ltd - Vertex-Kapele Division (3)
Unit 3 Ground Fl Northdowns Ofc Park 17 Georgian Crescent W
Bryanston, Gauteng, 2152, South Africa
Tel.: (27) 11 514 0899
Fax: (27) 11 514 0901
E-Mail: vertex@vertexsa.com
Web Site: www.vertexsa.com
Emp.: 14
Human Resource Consulting Services
S.I.C.: 8999
N.A.I.C.S.: 541612

The Independent Institute of Education (Pty) Ltd (1)
ADvTECH House Inanda Greens 54 Wierda Rd W
Wierda Valley, Gauteng, 2196, South Africa
Tel.: (27) 116768021
Fax: (27) 117832574
E-Mail: contact@iie.edu.co.za
Web Site: www.advtech.co.za
Emp.: 5,000
Educational Institute Management Services
S.I.C.: 9411
N.A.I.C.S.: 923110
Frank Thompson *(CEO)*

ADWAYS INC.

4F Sumitomo Fudousan Shinjuku OakTower 6-8-1 Nishi-Shinjuku
Shinjuku, Tokyo, 163-6004, Japan
Tel.: (81) 3 5339 7150
Fax: (81) 3 5339 7151
Web Site: www.adways.net
Year Founded: 2001
2489—(TKS)
Emp.: 1,100

Business Description:
Mobile Advertising Services
S.I.C.: 7311
N.A.I.C.S.: 541810

Personnel:
Haruhisa Okamura *(Founder & CEO)*
Takanori Kamioka *(Exec VP)*
Shingo Kano *(Exec VP)*
Yoshiharu Matsushima *(Exec VP)*
Michio Seita *(Exec VP)*
Yoichi Shimizu *(Exec VP)*
Junko Yoshino *(Exec VP)*

Board of Directors:
Takenobu Miki
Akihiko Nishioka
Nobuyoshi Noda
Haruhisa Okamura
Koki Sato
Die Su

ADX ENERGY LIMITED

Suite 1 45 Ord Street
PO Box 913
West Perth, WA, 6872, Australia
Tel.: (61) 8 9226 2822
Fax: (61) 8 9226 5333
E-Mail: admin@adxenergy.com.au
Web Site: www.adxenergy.com.au
ADX—(ASX)
Sales Range: Less than $1 Million

Business Description:
Oil & Gas Exploration Services
S.I.C.: 1311
N.A.I.C.S.: 211111

Personnel:
Wolfgang Zimmer *(Mng Dir)*
Peter Ironside *(Sec)*

Board of Directors:
Ian Tchacos
Andrew Childs
Paul Fink
Wolfgang Zimmer

Legal Counsel:
Herbert Smith Freehills
250 St Georges Terrace
Perth, WA, 6000, Australia

Non-U.S. Subsidiary:

AuDAX Energy GmbH (1)
Kundratstr 6 2 1
Vienna, 1100, Austria
Tel.: (43) 16410189
Fax: (43) 1641018920
E-Mail: audaxvienna@audax-resources.com
Web Site: www.audax.com.au
Emp.: 3
Oil & Gas Field Exploration Services
S.I.C.: 1389
N.A.I.C.S.: 213112

AE MULTI HOLDINGS BERHAD

Lot 87 Persiaran 11 Kawasan Perusahaan Bakar Arang
08000 Sungai Petani, Kedah Darulaman, Malaysia
Tel.: (60) 44213715
Fax: (60) 44225200
Web Site: www.amallionpcb.com
AEM—(KLS)
Rev.: $16,309,534
Assets: $18,830,159
Liabilities: $10,624,465
Net Worth: $8,205,694
Earnings: ($251,228)
Fiscal Year-end: 12/31/12

Business Description:
Printed Circuit Boards Mfr
S.I.C.: 3672
N.A.I.C.S.: 334412

Personnel:
Wu-Hsiung Yang *(Chm)*
Chao-Tung Yang *(Mng Dir)*
Wai Hong Chee *(Co-Sec)*
Li Ling Foo *(Co-Sec)*

Board of Directors:
Wu-Hsiung Yang
Saffie Bakar
Hock Hai Goh
Hock Chye Oon
Tee Beng Tan
Chao-Tung Yang
Chueh-Kuang Yang

Legal Counsel:
Wong Beh & Toh
Suite 4, 1st Floor No 173 & 174 Jalan Kelab Cinta Sayang, Taman
Sungai Petani, Malaysia

Subsidiary:

AE Corporation (M) Sdn. Bhd. (1)
No 87 Kaw Perindustrian No 11 Bakar Arang
08000 Sungai Petani, Kedah Darul Aman, Malaysia
Tel.: (60) 44213715
Fax: (60) 44225200
E-Mail: aemulti@aemulti.com.my
Emp.: 226
Printed Circuit Board Mfr
S.I.C.: 3672
N.A.I.C.S.: 334412
C K Yang *(Gen Mgr)*

Non-U.S. Subsidiary:

Amallion Enterprise (Thailand) Corporation Ltd. (2)
707 Moo 4 Bangpoo Industrial Estate
Praksa Muang, Samut Prakan, 10280, Thailand
Tel.: (66) 27092601
Fax: (66) 2 324 0307
E-Mail: amallionmkt@amallion.co.th
Web Site: www.amallionpcb.com
Emp.: 260
Printed Circuit Board Mfr
S.I.C.: 3672
N.A.I.C.S.: 334412

A.E. SMITH & SON PTY LTD

21 29 Miles St
Mulgrave, VIC, 3170, Australia
Tel.: (61) 392711999
Fax: (61) 392711992
E-Mail: corporate@aesmith.com.au
Web Site: www.aesmith.com.au
Year Founded: 1898
Emp.: 600

Business Description:
Heating, Ventilation, Air Conditioning & Building Management Services
S.I.C.: 1711
N.A.I.C.S.: 238220

Personnel:
Andrew Permezel *(CEO)*
Roff Cochrane *(CFO)*

AEC EDUCATION PLC

167 Jalan Bukit Merah Connection 1 Tower 4 02-13
Singapore, 150167, Singapore
Tel.: (65) 64120700
Fax: (65) 64120747
E-Mail: info@aeceducationplc.co.uk
Web Site: www.aeceducationplc.co.uk
AEC—(LSE)
Rev.: $23,836,530
Assets: $19,924,684
Liabilities: $12,498,419
Net Worth: $7,426,265
Earnings: ($5,607,715)
Emp.: 255
Fiscal Year-end: 12/31/12

Business Description:
Educational Support Services
S.I.C.: 8299
N.A.I.C.S.: 611710

Personnel:
William Joseph Swords *(Chm)*
David Peng Cheong Ho *(CEO)*

Board of Directors:
William Joseph Swords
David Peng Cheong Ho
Ramasamy Jayapal
Sabin Joshi
Gopinath Pillai
Munish Rao
Haider M. Sithawalla

Legal Counsel:
Shoosmiths
Witan Gate House 500 600 Witan Gate West
Milton Keynes, United Kingdom

Non-U.S. Subsidiaries:

AEC Bilingual Pte Ltd. (1)
167 Jalan Bukit Merah Tower 5 No 03-11
150167 Singapore, Singapore
Tel.: (65) 63366905
Fax: (65) 63362825
Web Site: www.aec.edu.sg
Emp.: 80
Business School Operation Services
S.I.C.: 8221
N.A.I.C.S.: 611310

AEC Edu Group Pte Ltd. (1)
167 Jalan Bukit Merah Connection 1 Tower 4 No 02-13
Singapore, 150167, Singapore
Tel.: (65) 64120700
Fax: (65) 64120750
E-Mail: knowledge@aec.edu.sg
Web Site: www.aec-college.edu.sg
Emp.: 60
Training & Educational Services
S.I.C.: 8299
N.A.I.C.S.: 611710
David Ho *(Mng Dir)*
Nabs Naidu *(COO)*

Subsidiaries:

AEC College Pte. Ltd. (2)
167 Jln Bukit Merah Connection 1 Tower 4 02-13
Singapore, 150167, Singapore
Tel.: (65) 64120700
Fax: (65) 64120750
E-Mail: knowledge@aec.edu.sg
Web Site: www.aec-college.edu.sg/
Emp.: 100
Business Schools Management Services
S.I.C.: 8221
N.A.I.C.S.: 611310
David Ho *(CEO)*

AEC Resource Development Pte Ltd. (2)
167 Jalan Bukit Merah Connection 1 Tower 4 No 02-13
Singapore, Singapore
Tel.: (65) 64120700
Fax: (65) 64120750
E-Mail: knowledge@aec.edu.sg
Web Site: www.aec.edu.sg
Emp.: 40
Educational Services
S.I.C.: 8299
N.A.I.C.S.: 611710
David Ho *(CEO)*

Brighton Commercial Training Centre Pte Ltd. (2)
43 Mid Rd Boon Sing Bldg No 01-00
Singapore, Singapore

AEC Education plc—(Continued)

Tel.: (65) 62258030
Fax: (65) 62207438
E-Mail: info@bristol.edu.sg
Web Site: www.bristol.edu.sg
Emp.: 30
Educational Support Services
S.I.C.: 8299
N.A.I.C.S.: 611710
Betty Chua *(Mgr)*

Smartworks Learning Centre Pte Ltd. **(2)**
167 Jln Bukit Merah Connection 1 Tower 4 No 02-13
Singapore, Singapore 150167
Tel.: (65) 6412 0706
Fax: (65) 6412 0700
E-Mail: knowledge@aec.edu.sg
Educational Training Services
S.I.C.: 8299
N.A.I.C.S.: 611430
Wan Fook Kong *(Mng Dir)*

AECI LIMITED

1st Floor AECI Place 24 The Woodlands Woodlands Drive Woodmead
Sandton, 2052, South Africa
Mailing Address:
Private Bag X21
Gallo Manor, 2052, South Africa
Tel.: (27) 118068700
Fax: (27) 118068701
E-Mail: groupcommunication@aeci.co.za
Web Site: www.aeci.co.za
Year Founded: 1930
AFE—(JSE)
Rev.: $1,666,117,200
Assets: $1,459,472,200
Liabilities: $815,074,900
Net Worth: $644,397,300
Earnings: $71,264,600
Emp.: 6,895
Fiscal Year-end: 12/31/12
Business Description:
Specialty Chemical Mfr
S.I.C.: 2819
N.A.I.C.S.: 325130
Personnel:
Mark Dytor *(CEO)*
Mark Kathan *(CFO & Dir-Fin)*
Khosi Matshitse *(Exec-Human Capital)*
Trevor Starke *(Treas)*
Nomini Rapoo *(Sec)*
Board of Directors:
Schalk Engelbrecht
Richard Matthew Wingfield Dunne
Mark Dytor
Zellah Fuphe
Mark Kathan
Michael Leeming
Liziwe Mda
Allen Morgan
Litha Nyhonyha
Rams Ramashia
Transfer Agents:
Computershare Investor Services PLC
PO Box 82 The Pavilions
Bridgwater Road, Bristol, B599 7NH, United Kingdom
Tel.: (44) 870 702 0001

Computershare Investor Services (Pty) Ltd
70 Marshall Street
Johannesburg, South Africa

Subsidiaries:

AEL Holdco Limited **(1)**
No 1 Platinum Drive Long Meadow Buss Estate
Edenvale, 1644, South Africa
Tel.: (27) 116060000
Fax: (27) 116050000
Mining Engineering Services
S.I.C.: 8711
N.A.I.C.S.: 541330

African Explosives Holdings (Pty) Limited **(1)**
1 Platinum Drive Longmeadow Business Estate
Modderfontein, 1645, South Africa
Tel.: (27) 116060000
Fax: (27) 116050000
Emp.: 200
Specialty Chemicals Mining Services
S.I.C.: 1479
N.A.I.C.S.: 212393
Schalk Venter *(Gen Mgr)*

African Explosives Limited **(1)**
Platform House 1 Platinum Dr
Modderfont, Gauteng, 1645, South Africa ZA
Tel.: (27) 116060000 (100%)
Fax: (27) 116050000
Web Site: www.explosives.co.za
Emp.: 3,000
Explosives Mfr
S.I.C.: 2892
N.A.I.C.S.: 325920
Tobie Louw *(Mng Dir & Member-Exec Committee)*

Atlas Consolidated Industries (Pty) Limited **(1)**
114 Terrace Rd
Edenvale, 1609, South Africa
Tel.: (27) 119221900
Fax: (27) 119760872
Industrial Chemicals Mfr
S.I.C.: 2899
N.A.I.C.S.: 325998

Chemical Services Ltd. **(1)**
Chemserve Place Turnberry Office Park
Private Bag X137
48 Grosvenor Road, Bryanston, 2021, South Africa
Tel.: (27) 115484500
Fax: (27) 115484700
E-Mail: chemserve@chemserve.co.za
Web Site: www.chemserve.co.za
Sales Range: $100-124.9 Million
Emp.: 1,700
Specialty Industrial Chemicals Mfr
S.I.C.: 2899
N.A.I.C.S.: 325998
Graham Edwards *(Chm)*
Alan Roth *(Mng Dir)*

Subsidiaries:

Akulu Marchon (Pty) Limited **(2)**
AECI Place Woodlands Office Park Woodlands Drive Bldg 23/24
Woodmead, 2196, South Africa ZA
Tel.: (27) 11 806 8700
Fax: (27) 11 806 8701
E-Mail: info@akulu.co.za
Web Site: www.akulu.co.za
Emp.: 40
Chemical Mfr & Whslr
S.I.C.: 2899
N.A.I.C.S.: 325998
Glen Sullivan *(Mng Dir)*

Chemfit (Pty) Limited **(2)**
10 Top Road
Boksburg North
Gauteng, South Africa ZA
Tel.: (27) 119181900
Fax: (27) 11 918 2628
E-Mail: charles@chemfit.co.za
Web Site: www.chemfit.co.za
Chemicals Whslr & Distr
S.I.C.: 5169
N.A.I.C.S.: 424690
Charles Biddulph *(Mng Dir)*

Chemical Initiatives (Pty) Limited **(2)**
Woodlands Drive Woodmead Building 24
Bryanston, 2196, South Africa ZA
Tel.: (27) 115484600
Fax: (27) 118068979
Web Site: www.cheminit.co.za
Emp.: 27
Sulphur Based Chemicals Mfr & Whslr
S.I.C.: 2869
N.A.I.C.S.: 325199
Graham Sanders *(Mng Dir)*

Chemiphos SA (Pty) Limited **(2)**
P.O. Box 4104
Halfway House, Gauteng, 1685, South Africa ZA
Tel.: (27) 119221600
Fax: (27) 113934587
E-Mail: chemiphos@chemiphos.co.za
Web Site: www.chemiphos.com
Emp.: 20
Phosphoric Acid Mfr & Whslr
S.I.C.: 2819
N.A.I.C.S.: 325180
Mike Peach *(Mng Dir)*

Chemserve Perlite (Pty) Limited **(2)**
Cnr Cullinan & Turk Street
Olifantsfontein, Johannesburg, South Africa
Tel.: (27) 879402999
Fax: (27) 879402807
Perlite Mineral Products Mfr
S.I.C.: 3299
N.A.I.C.S.: 327999
Jaco Engelbrecht *(Mng Dir)*

Subsidiary:

Senmin International (Pty) Limited **(3)**
Block 5 Level 2 Falconview House
Constantia Office Park Cnr 14th Ave
Hendrik Potgieter Street, Gauteng, 1725, South Africa
Tel.: (27) 11 246 6300
Fax: (27) 11 246 6373
E-Mail: enquiries@senmin.co.za
Web Site: www.senmin.co.za
Emp.: 19
Ore Beneficiation Chemicals Mfr & Distr
S.I.C.: 2899
N.A.I.C.S.: 325998
Theunis Botha *(Mng Dir)*

Chemserve Systems (Pty) Limited **(2)**
200 Bergrivier Drive
Chloorkop Kempton Park, Gauteng, 1624, South Africa ZA
Tel.: (27) 119221600 (100%)
Fax: (27) 119761706
E-Mail: chemsystems@chemsystems.co.za
Web Site: www.chemsystems.co.za
Emp.: 150
Chemical Products Mfr
S.I.C.: 5169
N.A.I.C.S.: 424690
Edwin Ludick *(Mng Dir)*

ImproChem (Pty) Limited **(2)**
138 Plane Rd
Spartan, Kempton Park, 1619, South Africa ZA
Tel.: (27) 119710400
Fax: (27) 113943436
E-Mail: improchem@improchem.co.za
Web Site: www.improserv.co.za
Emp.: 85
Water Treatment & Management Services
S.I.C.: 9511
N.A.I.C.S.: 924110
L. du Toit *(Mng Dir)*

Lake International Technologies (Pty) Limited **(2)**
8 Kariga Street
Stickland Belville, Cape Town, 7530, South Africa
Tel.: (27) 21 948 1383
Fax: (27) 21 948 1381
E-Mail: communication@lake.co.za
Web Site: www.lake.co.za
S.I.C.: 2099
N.A.I.C.S.: 311999
Hanzubeth Labuschagne *(Reg Mgr)*

Joint Venture:

Crest Chemicals (Pty) Limited **(2)**
247 15th Rd Randjespark
PO Box 4280
Midrand, Gauteng, 1685, South Africa ZA
Tel.: (27) 112543300 (50%)
Fax: (27) 113142222
E-Mail: info@crestchem.co.za
Emp.: 200
Chemicals Distr
S.I.C.: 5169
N.A.I.C.S.: 424690
Michiel Vijverberg *(CEO)*

Cobito (Pty) Limited **(1)**
Dekama Road
Germiston, 1422, South Africa
Tel.: (27) 118748960
Fax: (27) 118748963
E-Mail: info@cobito.co.za
Emp.: 6
Mining Engineering Services
S.I.C.: 8711
N.A.I.C.S.: 541330
Mark Cox *(Mng Dir)*

Duco Speciality Coatings (Pty) Limited **(1)**
249 Flamming Street
Edenvale, 1614, South Africa
Tel.: (27) 116630300
Fax: (27) 114533237
E-Mail: info@duco.co.za
Web Site: www.duco.co.za
Emp.: 24
Automotive Paint Finishes Distr
S.I.C.: 5198
N.A.I.C.S.: 424950
Mulder Llewelyn *(Mng Dir)*

Heartland Properties (Pty) Limited **(1)**
Heartland House 1 Casino Road
PO Box 500
Modderfontein, Gauteng, 1645, South Africa
Tel.: (27) 11 579 1000
Fax: (27) 11 579 1001
E-Mail: gautengsales@heartland.co.za
Web Site: www.heartland.co.za
Emp.: 40
Property Management Services
S.I.C.: 6531
N.A.I.C.S.: 531311
Anthony Diepenbroek *(CEO)*

Industrial Oleochemical Products (Pty) Limited **(1)**
323 Chamberlain Road
Jacobs, 4052, South Africa
Tel.: (27) 31 461 8680
Fax: (27) 31 461 3743
E-Mail: oleo@oleo.co.za
Web Site: www.oleo.co.za
Emp.: 120
Fatty Acids Mfr
S.I.C.: 2869
N.A.I.C.S.: 325199
Martin Godbold *(Mng Dir)*

Plaaskem (Pty) Limited **(1)**
14 Field Road Cnr Bird Street
Lilianton, Boksburg, 1459, South Africa
Tel.: (27) 11 823 8000
Fax: (27) 11 826 7241
E-Mail: info@plaaskem.co.za
Web Site: www.plaaskem.co.za
Emp.: 143
Chemical Products Mfr & Distr
S.I.C.: 2899
N.A.I.C.S.: 325998
Hugo Minnaar *(Mng Dir)*
Vanessa Kirkby *(Officer-Procurement)*

SA Paper Chemicals (Pty) Limited **(1)**
100 On Armstrong Ave Block 4B
La Lucia, Durban, 4051, South Africa
Tel.: (27) 119221600
Fax: (27) 119762338
Web Site: www.chemisphere.co.za
Emp.: 2
Chemical Products Mfr
S.I.C.: 2899
N.A.I.C.S.: 325998
Sean Perry *(Mng Dir)*

Simitri Specialty Chemicals (Pty) Limited **(1)**
200 Bergrivier Dr
PO Box 12055
Chloorkop, Kempton Park, 1624, South Africa
Tel.: (27) 119221674
Fax: (27) 119765511
E-Mail: simitri@simitri.co.za
Web Site: www.simitri.co.za
Specialty Chemicals Distr
S.I.C.: 5169
N.A.I.C.S.: 424690
Jaco Engelbrecht *(Mng Dir)*

U.S. Subsidiaries:

SANS Fibers Incorporated **(1)**
2575 Pembroke Rd
Gastonia, NC 28054-4712
Tel.: (704) 869-8311
Fax: (704) 869-9697

E-Mail: sansfibers@sansfibers.com
Web Site: www.sansfibers.com
Emp.: 6
Nylon Yarn Distr
S.I.C.: 5199
N.A.I.C.S.: 424990
Stephen Myers *(Gen Mgr)*

SANS Technical Fibers LLC (1)
2575 Pembroke Rd
Gastonia, NC 28054
Tel.: (704) 869-8311
Fax: (704) 869-9697
E-Mail: sansfibers@sansfibers.com
Web Site: www.sansfibers.com
Emp.: 6
Textured Yarn Mfr
S.I.C.: 2299
N.A.I.C.S.: 313110
Steve Meyers *(Office Mgr)*

Non-U.S. Subsidiaries:

African Explosives (Botswana) Limited (1)
Unit 2 Plot 117 Millenium Park
Gaborone, Botswana
Tel.: (267) 3938133
Fax: (267) 3938134
Commercial Explosive Mfr
S.I.C.: 2892
N.A.I.C.S.: 325920

African Explosives (Tanzania) Limited (1)
Plot No 159 Capri Point Industrial Area
Mwanza, Tanzania
Tel.: (255) 282502927
Fax: (255) 282500593
Mining Explosives Mfr
S.I.C.: 2892
N.A.I.C.S.: 325920
Julian Julian *(Gen Mgr)*

AECON GROUP INC.

20 Carlson Court Suite 800
Toronto, ON, M9W 7K6, Canada
Tel.: (416) 293-7004
Fax: (416) 293-0271
Toll Free: (877) 232-2677
E-Mail: aecon@aecon.com
Web Site: www.aecon.com
ARE—(TSX)
Rev.: $2,929,174,160
Assets: $2,116,548,894
Liabilities: $1,570,267,310
Net Worth: $546,281,583
Earnings: $80,456,973
Emp.: 8,373
Fiscal Year-end: 12/31/12

Business Description:
Holding Company; Construction, Engineering, Procurement, Project Management, Development & Financing & Facilities Management Services
S.I.C.: 1542
N.A.I.C.S.: 236220

Personnel:
John M. Beck *(Chm & CEO)*
Brian V. Tobin *(Vice Chm)*
Terrance L. McKibbon *(Pres & COO)*
David Smales *(CFO & Exec VP)*
Paula Palma *(CIO)*
Paul P. Koenderman *(Chm-Aecon Industrial Group & Exec VP)*
Maurice D'Aoust *(Pres-Canonbie Contracting Limited)*
Bob Dautovich *(Pres-Innovative Steam Technologies)*
George Kramer *(Pres-Aecon Buildings-Seattle)*
Steven Nackan *(Pres-Aecon Concessions)*
Frank Ross *(Pres-Buildings Grp)*
Stan Shewchuck *(Pres-Western Ops)*
Stan Shewchuk *(Pres-Aecon Industrial Western)*
Doug Steels *(Pres-Aecon Constructors Intl)*
Ian Turnbull *(Pres-Indus-Central)*
John Scott *(CEO-Scott Construction-Vancouver)*
L. Brian Swartz *(Sec, Sr VP-Legal & Comml Svcs)*
Paul Pastirik *(Exec VP-Fin-Infrastructure)*
Mark Rivett *(Exec VP-Infrastructure)*
Phil Ward *(Exec VP-Mining)*
Vincent Borg *(Sr VP-Corp Affairs)*
Don Brophy *(Sr VP-Constructors)*
Bob Darton *(Sr VP-Aecon Atlantic)*
Roger Howarth *(Sr VP-Project Controls)*
Mathew Kattapuram *(Sr VP-Strategic Bus Dev)*
Gerard A. Kelly *(Sr VP-Fin)*
Guy E. Rene *(Sr VP-Aecon Quebec Ltee)*
Greg Rooney *(Sr VP-HR)*
Mark Scherer *(Sr VP-Utilities)*
John Singleton *(Sr VP-Mining)*

Board of Directors:
John M. Beck
Austin C. Beutel
Michael A. Butt
Joseph A. Carrabba
Anthony P. Franceschini
J. D. Hole
Rolf Kindbom
Monica Sloan
Brian V. Tobin

Transfer Agent:
Computershare Investor Services Inc.
100 University Avenue 8th Floor
Toronto, ON, M5J 2Y1, Canada
Tel.: (514) 982-7555

Divisions:

Aecon Buildings (1)
20 Carlson Court
Toronto, ON, M9W 7K6, Canada
Tel.: (416) 754-8870
Fax: (416) 754-8871
E-Mail: aecon@aecon.com
Web Site: www.aecon.com
Emp.: 60
General Contracting, Construction Management & Design-Build Services
S.I.C.: 1542
N.A.I.C.S.: 236220
George Kramer *(Pres-Seattle)*
Frank Ross *(Pres-Building)*

U.S. Division:

Aecon Buildings (2)
19020 33rd Ave W Ste 500
Lynnwood, WA 98036
Tel.: (425) 774-2945
Fax: (425) 771-8094
Web Site: www.usa.aecon.com
Sales Range: $150-199.9 Million
Emp.: 30
General Contracting, Construction Management & Design-Build Services
S.I.C.: 1542
N.A.I.C.S.: 236220
George Kramer *(Pres)*

Aecon Constructors (1)
20 Carlson Court Suite 800
Toronto, ON, M9W 7K6, Canada
Tel.: (416) 293-7004
Web Site: www.aecon.com
Sales Range: $350-399.9 Million
Emp.: 500
Construction & Project Management of Large Scale Energy Developments, Subways, Bridges, Dams, Tunnels, Highways & Airports
S.I.C.: 1611
N.A.I.C.S.: 237310
Doug Steels *(Pres)*

Aecon Group Inc. - Aecon Concessions Division (1)
20 Carlson Court Suite 800
Toronto, ON, Canada M9W 7K6
Tel.: (416) 293-7004
Web Site: www.aecon.com
Infrastructure Development Services
S.I.C.: 0781
N.A.I.C.S.: 541320

Aecon Group Inc. - Aecon Utility Engineering Division (1)
20 Carlson Crt Suite 800
Toronto, ON, M9W 7K6, Canada
Tel.: (416) 297-2600, ext. 3705
Fax: (519) 621-8430
Toll Free: (877) 232-2677
Emp.: 50
Industrial Engineering & Designing Services
S.I.C.: 8711
N.A.I.C.S.: 541330
John M. Beck *(Pres)*

Aecon Group Inc. - Bremar Division (1)
6827 - Calgary Trail 104 Street
Edmonton, AB, T6H 2L5, Canada
Tel.: (403) 589-7861
Web Site: www.aecon.com
Utility Line Construction Services
S.I.C.: 1623
N.A.I.C.S.: 237130

Aecon Group Ltd. (1)
1387 Eastern Passage Hwy
Eastern Passage, Halifax, NS, B3G 1M5, Canada
Tel.: (902) 429-9341
Fax: (902) 465-4986
Web Site: www.aecon.com
Emp.: 15
Construction & Project Management of Large Scale Energy Developments, Subways, Bridges, Dams, Tunnels, Highways & Airports
S.I.C.: 1629
N.A.I.C.S.: 237990
Frank Ross *(Pres)*

Aecon Industrial (1)
150 Sheldon Dr
Cambridge, ON, N1R 7K9, Canada
Tel.: (519) 653-3200
Fax: (519) 621-8430
E-Mail: info@aecon.com
Web Site: www.aecon.com
Emp.: 100
Industrial Construction & Fabrication for Mechanical & Electrical Installations
S.I.C.: 1541
N.A.I.C.S.: 236210
Paul P. Koenderman *(CEO & Exec VP)*
Ian Turnbull *(Pres-Central Canada Div)*

Division:

Aecon Industrial (2)
Ste 301 1003 Ellwood Rd
Edmonton, AB, T6X 0B3, Canada
Tel.: (416) 754-8735
Fax: (780) 430-4775
Web Site: www.aecon.com
Industrial Construction Services
S.I.C.: 1629
N.A.I.C.S.: 236210

Aecon Utilities (1)
20 Carlson Ct Ste 800
Toronto, ON, M9W 7K6, Canada
Tel.: (416) 293-7004
Fax: (416) 940-2285
Emp.: 400
Infrastructure Building Services
S.I.C.: 1623
N.A.I.C.S.: 237120
Terrance L. McKibbon *(CEO-Infrastructure)*

AGI Traffic Technology, Inc. (1)
2960 Markham Rd
Scarborough, ON, M1X 1E6, Canada
Tel.: (416) 742-8900
Fax: (416) 746-1920
Web Site: www.aecon.com
Emp.: 150
Construction of Building & Civil Engineering Work
S.I.C.: 1622
N.A.I.C.S.: 237310

Subsidiaries:

Aecon Atlantic Industrial Inc. (1)
61 Estates Road
Dartmouth, NS, B2Y 4K3, Canada
Tel.: (902) 482-6500
Fax: (902) 482-6501
Web Site: www.aeconatlantic.com
Industrial Construction & Power Generation Services
S.I.C.: 4931
N.A.I.C.S.: 221118
Ken McCormick *(VP & Gen Mgr)*

Aecon Construction & Materials Ltd. (1)
20 Carlson Ct Ste 800
Toronto, ON, M9W 7K6, Canada
Tel.: (416) 293-7004
Fax: (416) 754-8736
E-Mail: hr@aecon.com
Web Site: www.aecon.com
Emp.: 150
Provider of Construction Services
S.I.C.: 8711
N.A.I.C.S.: 541330
John Beck *(CEO)*

Aecon Construction Group Inc. (1)
6284 104 Street NW
Edmonton, AB, T6H 2L5, Canada
Tel.: (780) 430-4070
Fax: (780) 430-4775
Construction Engineering Services
S.I.C.: 8711
N.A.I.C.S.: 541330

Aecon Construction Management Inc. (1)
1003 Ellwood Rd SW Suite 301
Edmonton, AB, T6X 0B3, Canada
Tel.: (780) 791-5477, ext. 3302
Civil Engineering Construction Services
S.I.C.: 1629
N.A.I.C.S.: 237990

Aecon Industrial Western Inc. (1)
261 2055 Premier Way
Sherwood Park, AB, T8H 0G2, Canada
Tel.: (780) 410-7957
Fax: (780) 410-7952
Web Site: www.aecon.com
Construction Management Services
S.I.C.: 1629
N.A.I.C.S.: 237990
Stan Shewchuk *(Pres)*

Aecon Materials Engineering Corp. (1)
117 Ringwood Drive Unit 6
Stouffville, ON, L4A 8C1, Canada
Tel.: (905) 640-7772
Fax: (905) 640-8512
E-Mail: ame.east@amecrop.ca
Web Site: www.aecon.com
Emp.: 12
Construction Engineering Services
S.I.C.: 8711
N.A.I.C.S.: 541330

Aecon Mining Inc. (1)
316 MacKay Crescent
Fort McMurray, AB, T9H 4E4, Canada
Tel.: (780) 791-5477
Fax: (780) 743-3073
Web Site: www.aecon.com
Industrial Sand Mining Services
S.I.C.: 1446
N.A.I.C.S.: 212322

Canadian Highways Infrastructure Corporation (1)
20 Carlson Ct Ste 800
Toronto, ON, M9W 7K6, Canada
Tel.: (416) 293-8020
Fax: (416) 940-2288
Emp.: 75
Development, Management, Finance, Design, Construction & Operation of Toll Highways
S.I.C.: 1629
N.A.I.C.S.: 237990

Canonbie Contracting Limited (1)
161 2055 Premier Way
Sherwood Park, AB, T8H 0G2, Canada
Tel.: (780) 410-6900
Fax: (780) 410-6944
Toll Free: (877) 477-5020
E-Mail: inquiry@canonbie.ca
Web Site: www.canonbie.ca
Emp.: 5
Building Electrical & Mechanical Equipment Installation Services
S.I.C.: 1731
N.A.I.C.S.: 238210
Maurice D'Aoust *(Pres)*

Construction Armbro BFC Inc. (1)
2540 Daniel Johnson Blvd Ste 1106
Laval, QC, H7T 2S3, Canada QC

Aecon Group Inc.—(Continued)

Tel.: (450) 687-4221
Fax: (450) 687-1069
Emp.: 8
Construction & Project Management of Large Scale Energy Developments, Subways, Bridges, Dams, Tunnels, Highways & Airports
S.I.C.: 1611
N.A.I.C.S.: 237310

Groupe Aecon Quebec Ltee (1)
255 Cremazie E Boul Suite 300
Montreal, QC, H2M 1M2, Canada
Tel.: (514) 352-0100
Fax: (514) 352-0524
E-Mail: info@aecon.com
Web Site: www.aeconquebec.com
Construction Engineering Services
S.I.C.: 8711
N.A.I.C.S.: 541330

Innovative Steam Technologies (1)
549 Conestoga Blvd
Cambridge, ON, N1R 7P4, Canada ON
Tel.: (519) 740-0036
Fax: (519) 740-2051
E-Mail: service@otsg.com
Web Site: www.otsg.com
Sales Range: $10-24.9 Million
Emp.: 50
Mfg. & Installation of Steam Generators
S.I.C.: 3511
N.A.I.C.S.: 333611
Bob Dautovich *(Pres)*

Karson Asphalt Paving Inc. (1)
3725 Carp Road
Carp, ON, K0A 1L0, Canada
Tel.: (613) 839-2816
Fax: (613) 839-0528
Web Site: www.karson.ca
Asphalt Paving Mixture Mfr
S.I.C.: 2951
N.A.I.C.S.: 324121
Peter Pellietier *(Mgr)*

Karson Konstruction Limited (1)
3725 Carp Road
Box 264
Carp, ON, K0A 1L0, Canada
Tel.: (613) 839-2816
Fax: (613) 839-0528
Web Site: www.karson.ca/contact-us/
Road Construction Engineering Services
S.I.C.: 1611
N.A.I.C.S.: 237310
Glenn Falls *(VP)*

Lockerbie & Hole Contracting Limited (2)
401 Salter St New Westminster
Vancouver, BC, V3M 5Y1, Canada
Tel.: (250) 370-2999
Fax: (604) 777-5945
Web Site: www.Lockerbiehole.com
Emp.: 30
Construction Contractor
S.I.C.: 1622
N.A.I.C.S.: 237310
Don Nishimura *(Branch Mgr)*

Lockerbie & Hole Contracting Limited (2)
401 Salter Street
New Westminster, BC, V3M 5Y1, Canada
Tel.: (604) 777-5950
Fax: (604) 777-5945
Web Site: www.lockerbiehole.com
Emp.: 40
Construction Contractor
S.I.C.: 1622
N.A.I.C.S.: 237310
Don Nishimura *(VP & Reg Mgr)*

Lockerbie & Hole Eastern Inc. (2)
451 Elgin Street
Brantford, ON, N3S 7P5, Canada
Mailing Address:
PO Box 875
Brantford, ON, N3T 5R7, Canada
Tel.: (519) 751-8000
Fax: (519) 751-8018
Toll Free: (800) 669-2083
E-Mail: info@lockerbiehole.com
Web Site: www.lockerbiehole.com
Rev.: $28,158,736
Emp.: 95
Construction Contractor
S.I.C.: 1611
N.A.I.C.S.: 237310
Phil Ward *(Pres & COO)*

Lockerbie & Hole Inc. (1)
14940 121 A Ave
Edmonton, AB, T5V 1A3, Canada AB
Tel.: (780) 452-1250
Fax: (780) 452-1284
Toll Free: (800) 417-2329
E-Mail:
Web Site: www.lockerbiehole.com
Sales Range: $300-349.9 Million
Emp.: 315
Mechanical, Electrical, Instrumentation, Pipe Fabrication, Module Assembly, Boiler Erection, Insulation & Civil Construction Contractor
S.I.C.: 1542
N.A.I.C.S.: 236220
James D. Hole *(Chm)*
Gordon L. Panas *(Pres & CEO)*

Subsidiaries:

Lockerbie & Hole Contracting Limited (2)
7335 Flint Road Southeast
Calgary, AB, T2H 1G3, Canada
Tel.: (403) 571-2121
Fax: (403) 253-5725
Web Site: www.LockerbieHole.com
Emp.: 16
Construction Contractor
S.I.C.: 1611
N.A.I.C.S.: 237310
Bill Clark *(VP & Reg Mgr)*

Lockerbie & Hole Industrial Inc. (2)
53367 Range Road 232
Sherwood Park, AB, T8A 4V2, Canada
Tel.: (780) 416-5700
Fax: (780) 416-5840
Toll Free: (800) 378-2496
Web Site: www.lockerbieandhole.com
Emp.: 50
Construction Contractor
S.I.C.: 1611
N.A.I.C.S.: 237310

Miwel Construction Limited (1)
1631 Bethesda Sideroad
Richmond Hill, ON, L4E 0G8, Canada
Tel.: (905) 888-5270, ext. 302
Fax: (905) 888-4968
Web Site: www.aecon.com
Emp.: 200
Industrial Building Construction Services
S.I.C.: 1629
N.A.I.C.S.: 236210
Wayne Bruce *(Gen Mgr)*

QX Ltd. (1)
4-4140A Sladeview Crescent
Mississauga, ON, L5L 6A1, Canada
Tel.: (905) 828-9055
Fax: (905) 828-9056
Toll Free: (888) 565-9615
E-Mail: info@qxtechnology.com
Web Site: www.qxtechnology.com
Emp.: 80
Wireless & Fibre Communication Equipment Distr
S.I.C.: 5063
N.A.I.C.S.: 423610
Brad Bowes *(Gen Mgr)*

South Rock Ltd. (1)
590 Highway Ave NE
PO Box 460
Redcliff, AB, T0J 2P0, Canada
Tel.: (403) 548-3961
Fax: (403) 548-7740
E-Mail: reception@southrock.ca
Web Site: www.southrock.ca
Emp.: 20
Road Construction Engineering Services
S.I.C.: 1622
N.A.I.C.S.: 237310
Larry McGregor *(VP)*

Tristar Electric Inc. (1)
6068 Netherhart Rd Unit 1
Mississauga, ON, Canada L5T 1N3
Tel.: (905) 670-1642
Fax: (905) 670-1932
E-Mail: info@tristarelectric.ca
Web Site: www.tristarelectric.ca
Airport Lighting Installation Services
S.I.C.: 4581
N.A.I.C.S.: 488119

AED OIL LIMITED

c/ Grant Thornton Level 30 525 Collins Street
Melbourne, VIC, 3000, Australia
Tel.: (61) 396567800
Fax: (61) 396547006
Web Site: www.aedoil.com
AED—(ASX)
Assets: $465,509
Liabilities: $87,796,214
Net Worth: ($87,330,704)
Earnings: ($9,727,745)
Emp.: 29
Fiscal Year-end: 06/30/13

Business Description:
Oil Exploration & Development
S.I.C.: 1389
N.A.I.C.S.: 213112

Personnel:
David Dix *(Chm)*
John Imle *(CEO)*
Richard Little *(CFO)*
Trevor Slater *(Sec)*

Board of Directors:
David Dix
Tim Baldwin
John Branson
John Imle
George Edward McGuiness

Legal Counsel:
Corrs Chambers Westgarth
Bourke Place 600 Bourke Street
Melbourne, Victoria, 3000, Australia
Tel.: (61) 3 9672 3000

AEDES S.P.A.

Bastioni di Porta Nuova 21
20121 Milan, Italy
Tel.: (39) 0262431
Fax: (39) 0229002719
E-Mail: info@aedesgroup.com
Web Site: www.aedesgroup.com
Year Founded: 1905
AE—(ITA)
Sales Range: $100-124.9 Million
Emp.: 91

Business Description:
Residential, Commercial & Industrial Property Investment Services
S.I.C.: 6531
N.A.I.C.S.: 531390

Personnel:
Giuseppe Grassano *(Chm)*
Paolo Ingrassia *(Exec Vice Chm)*
Annapaola Negri-Clementi *(Co-Vice Chm)*
Pio Giovanni Scarsi *(Co-Vice Chm)*
Francesco Montescani *(CFO)*

Board of Directors:
Giuseppe Grassano
Antonella Amenduni Gresele
Domenico Bellomi
Alberto Carletti
Antonio De Silvestri
Paolo Ingrassia
Francesco Montescani
Annapaola Negri-Clementi
Luca Savino
Pio Giovanni Scarsi

Subsidiary:

Agora S.r.l. (1)
Bastioni di Porta Nuova 21
20121 Milan, Italy (85%)
Tel.: (39) 0262439700
Fax: (39) 0229001228
Web Site: www.agora-we-know-how.it
Emp.: 60
Other Management Consulting Services
S.I.C.: 8748
N.A.I.C.S.: 541618
Francesco Della Cioppa *(Mng Dir)*

Non-U.S. Subsidiaries:

Aedes Luxembourg S.A. (1)
33 rue Notre-Dame
L-2240 Luxembourg, Luxembourg (100%)
Tel.: (352) 267360
Web Site: www.aedes.com
Emp.: 150
Real Estate Services
S.I.C.: 6531
N.A.I.C.S.: 531210
Agrata Eugeneo *(Mng Dir)*

AEDIAN SA

2/4 rue Helene
75017 Paris, France
Tel.: (33) 1 5635 3000
Fax: (33) 1 5635 3079
E-Mail: accuil@aedian.com
Web Site: www.aedian.com
Year Founded: 1984
AEDI—(EUR)
Emp.: 385

Business Description:
Information Technology Consulting Services
S.I.C.: 8999
N.A.I.C.S.: 541690

Personnel:
Jean-Francois Gautier *(Chm)*
Stephane Morvillez *(CEO & Mng Dir)*

Subsidiary:

Aedian Consulting (1)
2-4 Rue Helene
75015 Paris, France
Tel.: (33) 156353000
Fax: (33) 156353079
E-Mail: aiccueil@aedian.com
Web Site: www.aedian.com
Rev.: $18,600,000
Emp.: 114
S.I.C.: 8742
N.A.I.C.S.: 541611
Guillaume Garo *(Dir-Fin)*

AEDIFICA SA

Avenue Louise 331
1050 Brussels, Belgium
Tel.: (32) 26260770
Fax: (32) 26260771
E-Mail: info@aedifica.be
Web Site: www.aedifica.be
AED—(EUR)
Sales Range: $25-49.9 Million
Emp.: 28

Business Description:
Real Estate Investment Services
S.I.C.: 6531
N.A.I.C.S.: 531390

Personnel:
Jean-Louis Duplat *(Chm)*
Stefaan Gielens *(CEO & Mng Dir)*
Jean Kotarakos *(CFO)*
Sarah Everaert *(Legal Counsel)*

Board of Directors:
Jean-Louis Duplat
Galila Barzilai Hollander
Jacques Blanpain
Stefaan Gielens
Brigitte Gouder de Beauregard
Pierre Iserbyt
Jean Kotarakos
Sophie Maes
Adeline Simont

Subsidiary:

Aedifica Invest SA (1)
Avenue Louise 33-1333
Brussels, 1050, Belgium
Tel.: (32) 26260770
Fax: (32) 26260771
Web Site: www.aedifica.be
Emp.: 35
Real Estate Management Services
S.I.C.: 6531
N.A.I.C.S.: 531390
Stefaan Gielens *(Gen Mgr)*

AEFFE SPA

(d/b/a Aeffe Fashion Group)
Via Delle Querce 51
47842 Castel San Giovanni, Marignano, Italy
Tel.: (39) 0541965211
Fax: (39) 0541955461
E-Mail: info@aeffe.com
Web Site: www.aeffe.com
Sales Range: $300-349.9 Million
Emp.: 1,300

Business Description:
Men's Wear, Women's Wear, Shoes, Lingerie, Swimwear, Leather Goods, Eyewear, Perfume & Other Accessories
S.I.C.: 5137
N.A.I.C.S.: 424330

Personnel:
Alberta Ferretti *(Deputy Chm)*
Massimo Ferretti *(Pres)*

Board of Directors:
Massimo Ferretti
Simone Badioli
Alberta Ferretti
Roberto Lugano
Umberto Paolucci
Marcello Tassinari
Gianfranco Vanzini

Subsidiaries:

Moschino S.P.A (1)
28 Via San Gregorio
Milano, Milan, Italy (100%)
Tel.: (39) 26787731
Fax: (39) 0267877301
E-Mail: info@moschino.it
Web Site: www.moschino.it
Emp.: 100
Family Clothing Stores
S.I.C.: 5651
N.A.I.C.S.: 448140
Alessandro Varisco *(Mng Dir)*

Nuova Stireria Tavoleto Srl (1)
Via Dell Artigianato 4
Urbino, Italy (100%)
Tel.: (39) 0722629185
Textile Mill
S.I.C.: 2389
N.A.I.C.S.: 314999

Pollini S.P.A (1)
Via Bezzecca 5
20135 Milan, Italy (100%)
Tel.: (39) 0541816311
E-Mail: info@pollini.com
Web Site: www.pollini.com
Emp.: 20
Design Services
S.I.C.: 7389
N.A.I.C.S.: 541490

Velmar S.P.A (1)
Via delle Robinie 43
I-47842 Rimini, Italy (75%)
Tel.: (39) 0541825717
Fax: (39) 0541829677
E-Mail: velmar@velmar.it
Web Site: www.velmar.it
Womens & Girls Cut & Sew Lingerie Loungewear & Nightwear Mfr
S.I.C.: 2389
N.A.I.C.S.: 315240

U.S. Subsidiary:

Aeffe USA Inc (1)
30 W 56th St
New York, NY 10019-3801 (100%)
Tel.: (212) 632-9300
Fax: (212) 307-4405
Web Site: www.aeffeusa.com
Emp.: 200
Womens Childrens & Infants Clothing & Accessories Whslr
S.I.C.: 5137
N.A.I.C.S.: 424330
Michelle Stein *(Pres)*

Non-U.S. Subsidiaries:

Aeffe France S.a.r.l (1)
6 rue Caffarelli
Paris, 75003, France (100%)
Tel.: (33) 144543935
Fax: (33) 1530188439
E-Mail: press.fr@moscheno.com
Web Site: www.aeffe.com
Emp.: 15
Design, Production & Distr of Fashion & Luxury Products
S.I.C.: 5137
N.A.I.C.S.: 424330
Stephan Medollmonet *(Gen Mgr)*

Fashoff UK Ltd (1)
28-29 Conduit St
W1S2YB London, United Kingdom (100%)
Tel.: (44) 2073180500
Fax: (44) 2076298090
Web Site: www.moschino.it
Emp.: 20
Other Specialized Design Services
S.I.C.: 7389
N.A.I.C.S.: 541490

Moschino France S.a.r.l (1)
15 Place De La Republique
Paris, France (100%)
Tel.: (33) 153018410
Fax: (33) 1530188439
Emp.: 12
Family Clothing Stores
S.I.C.: 5651
N.A.I.C.S.: 448140
Maximo Caltagiroe *(Head-Comml)*

Moschino Retail GMBH (1)
Friedrichstr 71
Berlin, Germany (100%)
Tel.: (49) 3020946155
Fax: (49) 3020946157
E-Mail: berlin@moschino.it
Web Site: www.moschino.it
Emp.: 5
Family Clothing Stores
S.I.C.: 5651
N.A.I.C.S.: 448140
Beate Herzog *(CEO)*

Pollini France S.a.r.l. (1)
352 Rue Saint Honore
Paris, 75001, France (100%)
Tel.: (33) 142601494
Fax: (33) 142601489
E-Mail: info@pollini.com
Web Site: www.pollini.com
Family Clothing Stores
S.I.C.: 5651
N.A.I.C.S.: 448140

AEGEAN AIRLINES S.A.

31 Viltanioti St
14564 Kifissia, Athens, Greece
Tel.: (30) 2106261700
Fax: (30) 2106261900
E-Mail: wwwcontact@aegeanair.com
Web Site: www.aegeanair.com
AEGN—(ATH)
Rev.: $879,571,876
Assets: $534,642,198
Liabilities: $328,389,475
Net Worth: $206,252,723
Earnings: ($14,129,481)
Emp.: 1,347
Fiscal Year-end: 12/31/12

Business Description:
Airline Services
S.I.C.: 4512
N.A.I.C.S.: 481111

Personnel:
Theodore Vassilakis *(Chm)*
Eftichios Vassilakis *(Vice Chm)*
Dimitrios Gerogiannis *(CEO & Mng Dir)*
Michael Kouveliotis *(CFO)*

Board of Directors:
Theodore Vassilakis
Achilleas Constantakopoulos
Anastasios David
Iakovos Georganas
Dimitrios Gerogiannis
Christos Ioannou
Panagiotis Laskaridis
Alexandros Makridis
Victor Pizante
Markos Tsaktanis
Eftichios Vassilakis
George Vassilakis

Subsidiary:

Olympic Air S.A. (1)
Athens International Airport El Venizelos Building 56 - Hangar
Spata, 190 19 Athens, Greece
Tel.: (30) 210 3576617
Fax: (30) 210 6628745
E-Mail: amssales@olympicair.com
Web Site: www.olympicair.com
Freight & Passenger Air Transportation Services
S.I.C.: 4512
N.A.I.C.S.: 481112
John Karakadas *(Pres)*
George Efstratiadis *(Deputy CEO)*

AEGEAN MARINE PETROLEUM NETWORK INC.

10 Akti Kondili
Piraeus, Athens, 185 45, Greece
Tel.: (30) 210 458 6200
Fax: (30) 210 4586271
E-Mail: investor@ampni.com
Web Site: www.ampni.com
ANW—(NYSE)
Rev.: $7,258,960,000
Assets: $1,431,843,000
Liabilities: $927,325,000
Net Worth: $504,518,000
Earnings: $22,449,000
Emp.: 1,213
Fiscal Year-end: 12/31/12

Business Description:
Marine Fuel Distr
Export
S.I.C.: 5989
N.A.I.C.S.: 454310

Personnel:
Peter C. Georgiopoulos *(Chm)*
E. Nikolas Tavlarios *(Pres)*
Apostolos Rizakos *(Mng Dir)*
Spyros Gianniotis *(CFO)*

Board of Directors:
Peter C. Georgiopoulos
Spyridon Fokas
George J. Konomos
Konstantinos Koutsomitopoulos
Yannis N. Papanicolaou
John P. Tavlarios

Legal Counsel:
Seward & Kissel LLP
One Battery Park Plz
New York, NY 10004
Tel.: (212) 574-1200
Fax: (212) 480-8421

Transfer Agent:
Computershare Trust Company, N.A.
350 Indiana St Ste 800
Golden, CO 80228
Tel.: (303) 986-5400

Subsidiaries:

Aegean Ace Maritime Company (1)
42 Hatzikyriakou Avenue
Piraeus, Athens, 18538, Greece
Tel.: (30) 210 458 6200
Refined Marine Fuel Distr
S.I.C.: 5172
N.A.I.C.S.: 424720

Aegean Ostria Maritime Company (1)
10 Akti Kondyli
10845 Piraeus, Greece
Tel.: (30) 2104586000
Fax: (30) 2104586270
Petroleum Products Distr
S.I.C.: 5172
N.A.I.C.S.: 424720

Aegean Rose Maritime Company (1)
44 Hatzikiriakou Street
Piraeus, Greece
Tel.: (30) 210 458 6200
Petroleum Product Distr
S.I.C.: 5172
N.A.I.C.S.: 424720

Aegean Ship III Maritime Company (1)
42 Hatzikyriakou Avenue
Piraeus, Athens, 18538, Greece
Tel.: (30) 210 458 6200
Petroleum Product Distr
S.I.C.: 5172
N.A.I.C.S.: 424720

Aegean Ship VIII Maritime Company (1)
42 Hatzikyriakou Avenue
Piraeus, Athens, 18538, Greece
Tel.: (30) 210 458 6200
Petroleum Products Distr
S.I.C.: 5172
N.A.I.C.S.: 424720

Aegean Ship XII Maritime Company (1)
42 Hatzikyriakou Avenue
Piraeus, Athens, 18538, Greece
Tel.: (30) 210 458 6200
Petroleum Product Distr
S.I.C.: 5172
N.A.I.C.S.: 424720

Aegean Tiffany Maritime Company (1)
42 Hatzikyriakou Avenue
Piraeus, Athens, 18538, Greece
Tel.: (30) 210 458 6200
Petroleum Products Mfr
S.I.C.: 5172
N.A.I.C.S.: 424720

U.S. Subsidiaries:

Aegean Maritime Petroleum Inc. (1)
18001 Old Cutler Rd Ste 315 Palmetto Bay
Miami, FL 33157 (100%)
Tel.: (210) 458-6000
Fax: (210) 458-6245
E-Mail: marinefuels@ampni.com
Web Site: www.ampni.com
Marine Petroleum Traders
S.I.C.: 5171
N.A.I.C.S.: 424710

Aegean Maritime Petroleum Network Inc. (1)
20 Signal Rd
Stamford, CT 06902 (100%)
Tel.: (212) 763-5670
Fax: (212) 763-5664
E-Mail: aegeanusa@ampni.com
Web Site: www.ampni.com
Emp.: 25
Maritime Petroleum Traders
S.I.C.: 5171
N.A.I.C.S.: 424710
Georgia Kounalakis *(Reg Mgr-Mktg)*

Aegean Oil (USA) LLC (1)
299 Park Ave 2nd Fl
New York, NY 10171
Tel.: (212) 763-5670
Fax: (212) 763-5664
Lubricant Oil Distr
S.I.C.: 5172
N.A.I.C.S.: 424720

AMPN USA LLC (1)
299 Park Ave 2nd Fl
New York, NY 10171-0000
Tel.: (646) 369-6164
Petroleum Product Distr
S.I.C.: 5172
N.A.I.C.S.: 424720

Non-U.S. Subsidiaries:

Aegean Agency (Gibraltar) Limited (1)
Suite 2 1st Floor Watergardens 4
Gibraltar, Gibraltar
Tel.: (350) 200 50246
Fax: (350) 200 45421
E-Mail: agency@aegeangib.gi
Web Site: www.ampni.com
Petroleum Products Distr
S.I.C.: 5172
N.A.I.C.S.: 424720
John Ghio *(Mgr-Ops)*

Aegean Bunkering (C Verde) LDA (1)
Edificio Enacol Largo John Miller
Sao Vicente, 1359 Mindelo, Cape Verde

Aegean Marine Petroleum Network Inc.—(Continued)

Tel.: (238) 231 93 20
Fax: (238) 231 93 21
Petroleum Product Distr
S.I.C.: 5172
N.A.I.C.S.: 424720

Aegean Bunkering (Ghana) Ltd (1)
Community One
PO Box 1087
Tema, Ghana GH
Tel.: (233) 22214666
Fax: (233) 22214682
E-Mail: ghana@ampni.com
Web Site: www.ampni.com
Emp.: 6
Suppliers of Refined Maritime Petroleum Products
S.I.C.: 5171
N.A.I.C.S.: 424710
Theofilos Pizanias *(Station Mgr)*

Aegean Bunkering (Gibraltar) Limited (1)
Suite 2 Block 4 Water Gardens
Gibraltar, Gibraltar
Tel.: (350) 200 502 45
Fax: (350) 200 454 21
E-Mail: mail@aegeangib.gi
Web Site: www.ampni.com
Petroleum Products Distr
S.I.C.: 5172
N.A.I.C.S.: 424720

Aegean Bunkering (Hong Kong) Limited (1)
Unit 9/25th Floor Tower 2 Lipo Centre No 89 Queensway Str
Admiralty, Hong Kong, China (Hong Kong)
Tel.: (852) 2 801 7291
Fax: (852) 2 530 9929
E-Mail: bshongkong@ampni.com
Web Site: www.ampni.com
Emp.: 1
Petroleum Products Distr
S.I.C.: 5172
N.A.I.C.S.: 424720
Galonis Dimitrios *(Gen Mgr)*

Aegean Bunkering (Jam) Ltd (1)
Harbour Head Pen Rock Fort
Kingston, 2, Jamaica JM
Tel.: (876) 9387752
Fax: (876) 9388638
E-Mail: operations@aegeanjam.com
Web Site: www.ampni.com
Emp.: 8
Suppliers of Refined Maritime Petroleum Products
S.I.C.: 5171
N.A.I.C.S.: 424710
Georgios Kontogeorgis *(Gen Mgr)*

Aegean Bunkering (Singapore) Pte Ltd. (1)
22 Jalan Kilang No 06-0 Mova Bldg
159419 Singapore, Singapore SG
Tel.: (65) 65010100
Fax: (65) 62700705
E-Mail: singapore@ampni.com
Web Site: www.ampni.com
Emp.: 20
Suppliers of Refined Maritime Petroleum Products
S.I.C.: 5171
N.A.I.C.S.: 424710
Dennis Ho *(Gen Mgr)*

Aegean Bunkering (Trinidad) Ltd. (1)
3 French Street Woodbrook
Port of Spain, Trinidad & Tobago
Tel.: (868) 627 3005
Fax: (868) 627 3007
E-Mail: operations@aegean.tt
Web Site: www.ampni.com
Petroleum Products Distr
S.I.C.: 5172
N.A.I.C.S.: 424720

Aegean Bunkers at Sea NV (1)
Nijzerheidstraat No 7
2960 Antwerp, Belgium BE
Tel.: (32) 32023060
Fax: (32) 35414021
E-Mail: aegeanbas@ampni.com
Web Site: www.ampni.com
Emp.: 8
Refined Maritime Petroleum Products
S.I.C.: 5171
N.A.I.C.S.: 424710
Jack Doornbos *(Mgr-Comml)*

Non-U.S. Subsidiary:

ICS Petroleum Ltd. (2)
Suite 1450 - Oceanic Plaza 1066 West Hastings Street
Vancouver, BC, V6E 3X1, Canada
Tel.: (604) 685-6221
Fax: (604) 685-7329
E-Mail: bunkers@ics-vcr.com
Marine Fuel Distr
S.I.C.: 5172
N.A.I.C.S.: 424720

Aegean (Fujairah) Bunkering SA (1)
PO Box 2688
Fujairah, Dubai, United Arab Emirates AE
Tel.: (971) 92281600
Fax: (971) 92281588
E-Mail: aegeangr@emirates.net.ae
Web Site: www.ampni.com
Emp.: 10
Suppliers of Refined Maritime Petroleum Products
S.I.C.: 5171
N.A.I.C.S.: 424710
Nick Kachrilas *(Mng Dir & Station Mgr)*

Aegean Marine Petroleum LLC (1)
PO Box 2688
Fujairah, United Arab Emirates
Tel.: (971) 9 2281600
Fax: (971) 9 2281588
E-Mail: agngr@emirates.net.ae
Emp.: 12
Petroleum Products Distr
S.I.C.: 5172
N.A.I.C.S.: 424720
Danilo Lamadrid *(Safety Officer)*

Blatoma N.V. (1)
Nijverheidsstraat 7
Brecht, Antwerp, 2960, Belgium
Tel.: (32) 36520608
Petroleum Products Distr
S.I.C.: 5172
N.A.I.C.S.: 424720

ICS Bunkering Services Ltd. (1)
1066 West Hastings Street Suite 1450
Oceanic Plaza, Vancouver, BC, V6E 3X1, Canada
Tel.: (604) 685-6221
Petroleum Products Distr
S.I.C.: 5172
N.A.I.C.S.: 424720

ICS Petroleum (Montreal) Ltd. (1)
Suite 302 430 Ste-Helen Street
Montreal, QC, H2Y 2K7, Canada
Tel.: (514) 849-1223
Fax: (514) 849-0517
E-Mail: bunkers@ics-mtl.com
Web Site: www.ampni.com
Petroleum Products Distr
S.I.C.: 5172
N.A.I.C.S.: 424720
Gayle Lewis *(Gen Mgr)*

Jadaco BV (1)
Oost Kanaalweg 22
Postbus 15
4424 NC Wemeldinge, Netherlands
Tel.: (31) 113 621261
Fax: (31) 113 622354
Petroleum Products Distr
S.I.C.: 5172
N.A.I.C.S.: 424720

Lefkas Shipping (Pte.) Ltd. (1)
06-01 22 Jalan Kilang
159419 Singapore, Singapore
Tel.: (65) 6501 0100
Fax: (65) 6270 0705
E-Mail: singapore@ampni.com
Emp.: 20
Petroleum Products Mfr
S.I.C.: 2999
N.A.I.C.S.: 324199
Dennis Ho *(Gen Mgr)*

Maritime Dedicated Control N.V. (1)
Nijverheidsstraat 7
2960 Brecht, Belgium
Tel.: (32) 36520608
Fax: (32) 32721863
Petroleum Products Distr
S.I.C.: 5172
N.A.I.C.S.: 424720

Naxos Shipping (Pte.) Ltd. (1)
06-01 22 Jalan Kilang
Singapore, 159419, Singapore
Tel.: (65) 6501 0100
Fax: (65) 6270 0705
Marine Transportation Services
S.I.C.: 4412
N.A.I.C.S.: 483111

Paros Shipping (Pte.) Ltd. (1)
06-01 22 Jalan Kilang
159419 Singapore, Singapore
Tel.: (65) 6501 0100
Fax: (65) 6270 0705
Petroleum Products Distr
S.I.C.: 5172
N.A.I.C.S.: 424720

Portland Bunkers International Ltd. (1)
The Old Guardhouse Incline Rd
Portland Port, Dorset, DT5 1PH, United Kingdom UK
Tel.: (44) 1305824620
Fax: (44) 1305824621
E-Mail: ukoperations@ampni.com
Web Site: www.ampni.com
Emp.: 15
Suppliers of Refined Maritime Petroleum Products
S.I.C.: 5171
N.A.I.C.S.: 424710
Roger Lawn *(Mgr-Ops)*

AEGEAN METALS GROUP INC.

410-325 How Street
Vancouver, BC, V6C 1Z7, Canada
Tel.: (416) 845-8495
E-Mail: echow@aegeanmg.com
Web Site: www.aegeanmg.com
Year Founded: 2008
AGN—(TSXV)

Business Description:
Gold & Copper Mining
S.I.C.: 1041
N.A.I.C.S.: 212221

Personnel:
Cesar Lopez *(Chm)*
Eric Roth *(Pres & CEO)*
Stephanie Ashton *(CFO)*
Winnie Wong *(Sec)*

Board of Directors:
Cesar Lopez
Hikmet Akin
George Elliott
Eric Roth

AEGEK GROUP

18-20 Amaroussiou Halandriou Str
151 25 Maroussi, Greece
Tel.: (30) 2106306000
Fax: (30) 2106306136
E-Mail: central@aegekconstruction.gr
Web Site: www.aegek.gr
Sales Range: $25-49.9 Million
Emp.: 1,400

Business Description:
General Construction Services
S.I.C.: 1623
N.A.I.C.S.: 237110

Personnel:
Sotirios Gavriel *(Pres)*
Ioannis Maroulis *(Mng Dir & CEO)*

Board of Directors:
Sotirios Gavriel
Dimitrios Bourlos
Athanasios Evmorfopoulos
Evangelos Garbis
Michail Korallis
Ioannis Maroulis
Thalia Pouskoulou-Latsenere
Michael Simmas
Georgios Skoulas

Subsidiary:

Astakos Terminal S.A. (1)
18-20 Amarousiou Halandriou Str
151 25 Maroussi, Greece (50%)
Tel.: (30) 2106194003
Fax: (30) 2106194006
Emp.: 4
Real Estate Lessor Services
S.I.C.: 6513
N.A.I.C.S.: 531110

AEGIS ENGINEERING LIMITED

5 Chesford Grange
Woolston, Warrington, Cheshire, WA1 4RQ, United Kingdom
Tel.: (44) 1925840048
Fax: (44) 1925840033
E-Mail: info@aegis-eng.com
Web Site: www.aegis-eng.com
Sales Range: $10-24.9 Million
Emp.: 40

Business Description:
Body Armour Systems & Other Homeland Security Products Mfr & Distr
S.I.C.: 5999
N.A.I.C.S.: 453998

Personnel:
Steve Jenkins *(CEO)*

AEGIS GROUP PLC

(Acquired by Dentsu Inc. & Name Changed to Dentsu Aegis Network Ltd.)

AEGIS LOGISTICS LTD.

403 Peninsula Chambers Peninsula Corporate Park G K Marg Lower Parel W
Mumbai, 400 013, India
Tel.: (91) 2266663666
Fax: (91) 2266663777
E-Mail: aegis@aegisindia.com
Web Site: www.aegisindia.com
500003—(BOM)
Rev.: $781,190,186
Assets: $186,387,107
Liabilities: $128,057,393
Net Worth: $58,329,714
Earnings: $6,229,143
Fiscal Year-end: 03/31/13

Business Description:
Logistics & Physical Distribution Services
S.I.C.: 4731
N.A.I.C.S.: 541614

Personnel:
Kapoor M. Chandaria *(Chm)*
Raj K. Chandaria *(Vice Chm & Mng Dir)*
Sudhir O. Malhotra *(Pres & COO)*
Anish K. Chandaria *(CEO & Mng Dir)*
Bharat I. Gosalia *(CFO)*
Monica T. Gandhi *(Compliance Officer, Sec & Mgr-Legal)*
Rajiv Chohan *(Pres-Bus Dev)*
Kamlakar S. Sawant *(Pres-Ops & Projects)*

Board of Directors:
Kapoor M. Chandaria
Anil M. Chandaria
Anish K. Chandaria
Raj K. Chandaria
Rajnikant J. Karavadia
Dinesh J. Khimasia
Kanwaljit S. Nagapal
Vasantrai H. Pandya

Legal Counsel:
AZB & Partners
Mumbai, India

Transfer Agent:
Sharepro Services (India) Pvt. Ltd.
13 AB Samhita Warehousing Complex 2nd Floor Andheri Kurla Road
Mumbai, India

AEGON N.V.

Aegonplein 50
2501 CB Hague, Netherlands

Mailing Address:
PO Box 85
2501 CB Hague, Netherlands
Tel.: (31) 70 344 32 10
Telex: 31657 aegon nl
Fax: (31) 70 347 5238
E-Mail: e-mailir@aegonusa.com
Web Site: www.aegon.com
Year Founded: 1983
AEK—(EUR LSE NYSE)
Rev.: $63,555,378,040
Assets: $492,787,067,220
Liabilities: $452,858,318,850
Net Worth: $39,928,748,370
Earnings: $2,062,332,440
Emp.: 24,407
Fiscal Year-end: 12/31/12

Business Description:
Holding Company; Insurance Services
S.I.C.: 6719
N.A.I.C.S.: 551112

Personnel:
Robert J. Routs, III *(Chm-Supervisory Bd)*
Irving W. Bailey, II *(Vice Chm-Supervisory Bd)*
Jan J. Nooitgedagt *(CFO)*
Brenda K. Clancy *(Global CTO)*
Tom Grondin *(Chief Risk Officer)*
Alexander R. Wynaendts *(Chm/CEO-Exec & Mgmt Bd)*
Marco B. A. Keim *(CEO-Netherlands)*
Gabor Kepecs *(CEO-Central & Eastern Europe)*
Willem Beltman *(Sec)*

Supervisory Board of Directors:
Robert J. Routs, III
Irving W. Bailey, II
Shemaya Levy
Jan J. Nooitgedagt
Karla M. H. Peijs
Kornelis J. Storm
Ben van der Veer
Leo M. van Wijk
Dirk P. M. Verbeek

Subsidiaries:

AEGON Nederland N.V. (1)
AEGONplein 50
PO Box 202
2591 TV Hague, Netherlands (100%)
Tel.: (31) 703443210
Fax: (31) 703475238
Web Site: www.aegon.nl
Emp.: 2,000
Provider of Interest-Sharing Life Insurance & Other Insurance Products
S.I.C.: 6399
N.A.I.C.S.: 524128
Alexander R. Wyaendts *(Chm)*
Kees Smaling *(CIO)*

Subsidiaries:

AEGON Levensverzekering N.V. (2)
AEGONplein 50
PO Box 202
2501 CE Hague, Netherlands
Tel.: (31) 703443210
Fax: (31) 703475238
E-Mail: info@aegon.nl
Web Site: www.aegon.nl
Emp.: 200
Provider of Life Insurance Products
S.I.C.: 6311
N.A.I.C.S.: 524113
Alex Wynaents *(Chm)*
Marco Kim *(Mng Dir)*

AEGON (2)
Aegonplein 50
PO Box 202
2591 TV 8 Hague, 2501 CE, Netherlands (100%)
Mailing Address:
P.O. Box 202
2501 AC Hague, Netherlands
Tel.: (31) 0703443210
Telex: 31657
Fax: (31) 0703475462
E-Mail: info@aegon.nl
Web Site: www.aegon.nl
Emp.: 3,000
Provider of Accident Insurance Products
S.I.C.: 6311
N.A.I.C.S.: 524113
Alexander R. Wyaendts *(CEO)*
J. Hendriks *(Sr VP)*

Non-U.S. Subsidiary:

AEGON Belgium (2)
Avenue du Port 86c b113
1000 Brussels, Belgium
Tel.: (32) 80099123
Fax: (32) 22256991
E-Mail: info@moneymaxx.be
Web Site: www.moneymaxx.be
Emp.: 10
Life Insurance Savings Products
S.I.C.: 6399
N.A.I.C.S.: 524128

AXENT/AEGON N.V. (1)
Euclideslaan 251
3584 BV Utrecht, Netherlands
Mailing Address:
Postbus 104
3500AC Utrecht, Netherlands
Tel.: (31) 302563760
Fax: (31) 302514691
E-Mail: info@axent.aegon.nl
Web Site: www.axentaegon.nl
Personal Life & Non-Life Insurance & Savings Products
S.I.C.: 6399
N.A.I.C.S.: 524128

Spaarbeleg Kas N.V. (1)
Nevelgaarde 60
3436 ZZ Nieuwegein, Netherlands
Tel.: (31) 306074411
Fax: (31) 306043737
Web Site: www.aegon.nl
Emp.: 100
Provider of Insurance-Linked Savings Products
S.I.C.: 6036
N.A.I.C.S.: 522120

U.S. Subsidiaries:

AEGON USA, Inc. (1)
4333 Edgewood Rd NE
Cedar Rapids, IA 52499-0010
Tel.: (319) 398-8511
Fax: (319) 369-2147
E-Mail: ir@aegonusa.com
Web Site: www.aegonins.com
Sales Range: $5-14.9 Billion
Emp.: 12,000
Insurance Services
S.I.C.: 6311
N.A.I.C.S.: 524113
Mark Mullin *(Pres & CEO)*
Darryl D. Button *(CFO)*

Branch:

AEGON USA, Inc. (2)
2 E Chase St
Baltimore, MD 21202 (100%)
Tel.: (410) 685-2900
Telex: 464414
Web Site: www.aegonins.com
Insurance Holding Company
S.I.C.: 6311
N.A.I.C.S.: 524113
Eric Goodman *(Chief Investment Officer)*
James A. Beardsworth *(Treas-Corp Dev)*

Divisions:

Advisor Resources (2)
400 W Market St Fl 12
Louisville, KY 40202-3300
Tel.: (502) 587-7371
Fax: (502) 560-3610
Toll Free: (800) 797-9177
Web Site: www.advisorresources.com
Emp.: 450
Advisors for Investment Managers
S.I.C.: 7389
N.A.I.C.S.: 561499

Aegon Companies of Florida (2)
570 Carillon Pkwy
Saint Petersburg, FL 33716 FL
Tel.: (727) 299-1800 (100%)
Web Site: www.aegon.com
Emp.: 1,200
Investor Services
S.I.C.: 6211
N.A.I.C.S.: 523120

AEGON Financial Services Group, Inc. Structured Settlements and Income Annuities (2)
AEGON Ctr 400 W Mkt St
Louisville, KY 40202
Tel.: (502) 560-2000
Fax: (502) 560-2099
Toll Free: (800) 879-4431
E-Mail: info@aegonusa.com
Web Site: www.aegonusa.com
Emp.: 70
Provider of Structured Settlement & Income Annuities
S.I.C.: 8742
N.A.I.C.S.: 541611
Sharon Long *(Mgr-Facilities)*

AEGON Institutional Markets, Inc. (2)
400 W Market St
Louisville, KY 40202-3346 PA
Tel.: (502) 560-2825 (100%)
Fax: (502) 560-3975
E-Mail: info@aegon.com
Web Site: www.advisorresources.com
Emp.: 700
Financial Services
S.I.C.: 8742
N.A.I.C.S.: 541611
Jackie Griffin *(Pres)*

Subsidiary:

Veterans Life Insurance Co. (3)
Liberty Park
Valley Forge, PA 19493-0001 IL
Toll Free: (800) 872-8387 (100%)
Provider of Life Insurance Services
S.I.C.: 6411
N.A.I.C.S.: 524210

AEGON USA-Financial Markets Division (2)
4333 Edgewood Rd NE
Cedar Rapids, IA 52499-0001
Tel.: (319) 355-8511
Fax: (319) 298-4385
Web Site: www.aegonins.com
Insurance Services
S.I.C.: 6282
N.A.I.C.S.: 523930

AEGON USA, Inc. (2)
292 Madison Ave 5th Fl
New York, NY 10017-6321 NY
Tel.: (212) 251-0101 (100%)
Fax: (212) 251-0149
Web Site: www.aegonusa.com
Emp.: 13
Leasing & Financial Consulting
S.I.C.: 6311
N.A.I.C.S.: 524113

AEGON USA-Individual Division (2)
4333 Edgewood Rd NE
Cedar Rapids, IA 52499-0001
Tel.: (319) 398-8511
Web Site: www.aegonins.com
Emp.: 2,000
Provider of Insurance Services
S.I.C.: 6282
N.A.I.C.S.: 523930
Mark Mullin *(Pres)*

AEGON USA-Long Term Care Division (2)
1900 L Don Dodson Dr
Bedford, TX 76021 (100%)
Tel.: (817) 285-3300
Fax: (817) 285-3450
Web Site: www.aegonins.com
Emp.: 250
Provider of Insurance Services
S.I.C.: 6411
N.A.I.C.S.: 524210
Lynn Hartung *(Mgr-Adv)*

AEGON USA-Monumental Division (2)
Two E Chase St
Baltimore, MD 21202-2505 KY
Tel.: (410) 685-2900 (100%)
Web Site: www.aegonins.com
Emp.: 469
Life & Health Insurance
S.I.C.: 6311
N.A.I.C.S.: 524113

Subsidiaries:

Monumental Life Insurance Company (3)
2 E Chase St
Baltimore, MD 21202-2505 MD
Tel.: (410) 685-2900 (100%)
Fax: (410) 223-4475
Web Site: www.monlife.com
Emp.: 1,325
Life Insurance Services
S.I.C.: 6311
N.A.I.C.S.: 524113
Pete Atkins *(CEO)*
Susan Reier *(Chief Admin Officer & VP)*
Steven J. Cammarata *(Chief Actuary & VP)*

Monumental Life Insurance Co. (3)
1207 Stafford Dr
Princeton, WV 24740 WV
Tel.: (304) 431-3555
Fax: (304) 431-3563
E-Mail: webmaster@monlife.com
Web Site: www.monlife.com
Rev.: $2,400,000
Emp.: 23
Insurance Agents Brokers & Service
S.I.C.: 6411
N.A.I.C.S.: 524210
Susan Reier *(Chief Admin Officer & VP)*
H. Stacey Boyer *(Gen Counsel, Sec & VP)*

Monumental Life (3)
300 W Morgan St
Durham, NC 27701-2162
Mailing Address:
PO Box 61
Durham, NC 27702-0061
Tel.: (919) 687-8200
Fax: (919) 687-8486
Web Site: www.monlife.com
Life Insurance Services
S.I.C.: 6311
N.A.I.C.S.: 524113

AEGON USA-Special Markets Group-Consumer Direct (2)
300 Eagle View Blvd
Exton, PA 19341
Tel.: (610) 648-5000
Fax: (610) 648-5364
Toll Free: (800) 678-5901
E-Mail: info@aegonusa.com
Web Site: www.aegonusa.com
Emp.: 500
Provider of Insurance Marketing Services
S.I.C.: 6411
N.A.I.C.S.: 524210
Brian A. Smith *(Pres)*

AEGON (2)
300 Eagleview Blvd
Exton, PA 19341 PA
Tel.: (610) 648-5000 (100%)
Fax: (877) 355-5573
Web Site: www.aegonusa.com
Emp.: 400
Life & Health Insurance
S.I.C.: 6411
N.A.I.C.S.: 524210

AUSA Life Insurance Co. (2)
1111 N Charles St
Baltimore, MD 21201-5505 MD
Tel.: (410) 576-4571 (100%)
Fax: (410) 347-8685
Sls.: $188,546,097
Holding Company; Property Development
S.I.C.: 6311
N.A.I.C.S.: 524113

Subsidiaries:

International Life Investors Insurance Company (3)
4333 Edgewood Rd NE
Cedar Rapids, IA 52499 NY
Tel.: (319) 398-8511 (100%)
Web Site: www.aegonins.com
Life Insurance
S.I.C.: 6311
N.A.I.C.S.: 524113

AEGON N.V.—(Continued)

Divisions:

AEGON USA Realty Advisors, LLC (4)
330 Madison Ave 22nd Fl
New York, NY 10001 NY
Tel.: (212) 251-0101 (100%)
Fax: (866) 352-6681
Web Site: www.aegonrealty.com
Emp.: 10
Real Estate Leasing & Financial Consulting
S.I.C.: 6531
N.A.I.C.S.: 531210
Scott Cote *(Sr VP & Head-Mortgage Loan Production)*

Money Services Inc. (3)
4333 Edgewood Rd NE
Cedar Rapids, IA 52499-0001 IA
Tel.: (319) 398-8511
Web Site: www.aegonins.com
Emp.: 1
Investment Advice
S.I.C.: 6282
N.A.I.C.S.: 523930

Western Reserve Life Assurance Co. of Ohio (3)
570 Carillon Pkwy
Saint Petersburg, FL 33716 OH
Tel.: (727) 299-1800 (100%)
Fax: (727) 299-1620
Toll Free: (800) 851-9777
Web Site: www.westernreserve.com
Emp.: 50
Insurance
S.I.C.: 6311
N.A.I.C.S.: 524113
Jay E. Washington *(Dir-Internal Sls)*

Creditor Resources, Inc. (2)
2839 Paces Ferry Rd Se Ste 750
Atlanta, GA 30339-5763 MI
Tel.: (678) 402-2100 (100%)
Fax: (404) 257-2937
Web Site: www.creditorresources.com
Emp.: 160
Credit Insurance Services
S.I.C.: 6411
N.A.I.C.S.: 524210

Non-U.S. Subsidiary:

CRI Canada Inc. (3)
A350 -4185 Still Creek Dr
Burnaby, BC, V5C 6G9, Canada
Tel.: (604) 438-7785
Fax: (604) 438-7795
Web Site: www.cricanada.net
Emp.: 30
Credit Union Services
S.I.C.: 6061
N.A.I.C.S.: 522130
Nicole Benson *(Pres)*

Diversified Investment Advisors, Inc. (2)
440 Mamaroneck Ave
Harrison, NY 10528
Tel.: (914) 627-3000
Fax: (914) 697-8000
Web Site: www.divinvest.com
Emp.: 1,000
Insurance Services
S.I.C.: 6282
N.A.I.C.S.: 523930
Mark Mullin *(CEO)*
Gerry Katz *(Sr VP-Strategy)*

Transamerica Employee Benefits (2)
1400 Centerview Dr
Little Rock, AR 72211
Tel.: (501) 213-6590
Fax: (866) 945-8710
Toll Free: (866) 224-3100
Web Site: www.transamericaemployeebenefits.com
Employee Benefits & Insurance Services
S.I.C.: 6311
N.A.I.C.S.: 524113
Mark Mullin *(Pres & CEO)*
Gregory Tucker *(Sr VP & Head-Corp Comm-Americas)*

Subsidiaries:

AEGON Direct Marketing Services, Inc. (2)
520 Pk Ave
Baltimore, MD 21201 (100%)
Tel.: (410) 685-5500
Fax: (410) 209-5902
Web Site: www.aegondms.com
Emp.: 405
Life Insurance, Supplemental Health Insurance Products & Fee-Based Programs Direct Marketer
S.I.C.: 6411
N.A.I.C.S.: 524298
Marilyn Carp *(CEO)*

AEGON USA Investment Management LLC (2)
4333 Edgewood Rd NE
Cedar Rapids, IA 52499-0001
Tel.: (319) 398-8511
Web Site: www.aegonins.com
Emp.: 3,500
Investment Services
S.I.C.: 6211
N.A.I.C.S.: 523999
Eric Goodman *(Pres & Chief Investment Officer)*
Brad Beman *(Chief Investment Officer)*

Life Investors Insurance Company of America (2)
4333 Edgewood Rd NE
Cedar Rapids, IA 52499-0001 IA
Tel.: (319) 398-8511
Web Site: www.aegonins.com
Emp.: 2,400
Life Insurance Services
S.I.C.: 6311
N.A.I.C.S.: 524113

Peoples Benefit Life Insurance Company (2)
4333 Edgewood Rd NE
Cedar Rapids, IA 52499
Tel.: (319) 398-8511
Fax: (319) 369-2206
Toll Free: (800) 523-5626
Web Site: www.aegonins.com
Sls.: $981,000,000
Emp.: 3,000
Life Insurance & Investment Services
S.I.C.: 6311
N.A.I.C.S.: 524113

Transamerica Life Insurance Company (2)
4333 Edgewood Rd NE
Cedar Rapids, IA 52499-0001 IA
Tel.: (319) 398-8511
Web Site: www.aegonins.com
Sales Range: $1-4.9 Billion
Emp.: 3,000
Life Insurance
S.I.C.: 6311
N.A.I.C.S.: 524113
Brenda Clancy *(COO)*

Clark Consulting (1)
2100 Ross Ave Ste 2200
Dallas, TX 75201 DE
Fax: (214) 720-6050
Toll Free: (800) 510-2050
E-Mail: kurt.laning@clarkconsulting.com
Web Site: www.clarkconsulting.com
Sales Range: $250-299.9 Million
Emp.: 70
Corporate Financial Investment & Consulting Services
S.I.C.: 6411
N.A.I.C.S.: 524210
Kurt Laning *(Pres)*

Prime Times Newspaper (1)
394 W Ironwood Rd
Salt Lake City, UT 84115 UT
Mailing Address:
PO Box 651663
Salt Lake City, UT 84165-1663
Tel.: (801) 485-5511
Rev.: $130,000
Emp.: 4
Newspaper Publishing
S.I.C.: 2711
N.A.I.C.S.: 511110
Fred Henkel *(Gen Mgr)*

Stonebridge Casualty Insurance Company (1)
51 JFK Pkwy
Short Hills, NJ 07078 NY
Tel.: (973) 564-5110 (100%)
Fax: (973) 564-5131
Emp.: 6
Reinsurance Services
S.I.C.: 6361
N.A.I.C.S.: 524127

Transamerica Capital, Inc. (1)
4600 S Syracuse St Ste 1100
Denver, CO 80237-2743
Tel.: (720) 482-1500
Fax: (720) 482-1518
Web Site: www.transamericacapital.com
Emp.: 150
Insurance Services
S.I.C.: 6722
N.A.I.C.S.: 525910
Lon Olejniczak *(Mng Dir)*
Michael Petko *(Exec VP & Mgr-Natl-Sls)*

Transamerica Consumer Finance Holding Company (1)
1150 S Olive St
Los Angeles, CA 90015-2211 CA
Tel.: (213) 742-2111
Fax: (213) 741-7331
Web Site: www.aegonins.com
Investment Holding Companies
S.I.C.: 6719
N.A.I.C.S.: 551112
Robert A. Watson *(Pres)*

Transamerica Insurance & Investment Group (1)
1150 S Olive St
Los Angeles, CA 90015-2211 CA
Tel.: (213) 742-2111 (100%)
Fax: (213) 746-7025
E-Mail: tii.customerservice@transamerica.com
Web Site: www.transamerica.com
Emp.: 1,500
All Forms of Life, Accident & Group Insurance; Design, Underwriting, Sales & Service of Life Insurance, Pension Products, Reinsurance, Structured Settlements, Annuities & Investment Products, Long Term Care
S.I.C.: 6411
N.A.I.C.S.: 524210
James T. Harvey *(Chm)*
Bill Tate *(CMO & Exec VP)*

Division:

Transamerica Life Insurance of New York (2)
4 Manhattanville Rd
Purchase, NY 10577-2134 NY
Mailing Address:
PO Box 2101
Los Angeles, CA 90051
Tel.: (914) 697-8000
Fax: (914) 697-8324
Toll Free: (888) 617-6781
E-Mail: tii.customerservice@transamerica.com
Web Site: www.transamerica.com
Rev.: $364,607,974
Emp.: 7
Life Insurance Carriers
S.I.C.: 7359
N.A.I.C.S.: 532490

Subsidiaries:

Transamerica Brokerage Group (2)
1150 S Olive St
Los Angeles, CA 90015-2211 CA
Tel.: (213) 742-2111 (100%)
Web Site: www.transamerica.com
Rev.: $102,222,647
Emp.: 26
Brokerage Services
S.I.C.: 6411
N.A.I.C.S.: 524210

Transamerica Financial Advisors, Inc. (2)
1150 S Olive St
Los Angeles, CA 90015-2211 CA
Mailing Address:
PO Box 9053
Clearwater, FL 33758-9053
Tel.: (800) 322-7161
Fax: (213) 742-2610
Web Site: www.tfa.transamerica.com
Emp.: 62
Investment Firm
S.I.C.: 6211
N.A.I.C.S.: 523120
Dan Trivers *(Sr VP-Admin)*

TransAmerica Financial Advisors, Inc. (2)
570 Carillon Pkwy
Saint Petersburg, FL 33716-1294 DE
Tel.: (727) 299-1800 (100%)
Fax: (800) 322-7358
Web Site: www.transamerica.com
Emp.: 100
Security Brokers
S.I.C.: 6282
N.A.I.C.S.: 523920
Seth Miller *(Pres)*
Mike Scherrman *(COO)*
Shawn Mihal *(VP & Chief Compliance Officer)*

Non-U.S. Holding:

Transamerica Life Canada (2)
5000 Young Street
Toronto, ON, M2N 7J8, Canada (100%)
Tel.: (416) 883-5000
Fax: (416) 883-5520
Web Site: www.aegoncanada.ca
Emp.: 700
Life Insurance
S.I.C.: 6311
N.A.I.C.S.: 524113
Doug Brooks *(Pres & CEO)*

Transamerica Investment Management (1)
Ste 820 11111 Santa Monica Blvd
Los Angeles, CA 90025-3342 DE
Mailing Address: (100%)
PO Box 2101
Los Angeles, CA 90015
Tel.: (310) 996-3200
Fax: (310) 477-9767
Web Site: www.transamerica.com
Emp.: 50
Investment Management & Life Insurance Services
S.I.C.: 6282
N.A.I.C.S.: 523930
Gary Rolle *(CEO)*

Non-U.S. Subsidiaries:

AEGON Espana S.A. (1)
Principe De Vergara 154 165
28002 Madrid, Spain (99.98%)
Tel.: (34) 915636222
Fax: (34) 915632764
Web Site: www.aegon.es
Emp.: 758
Provider of Life, Health & General Insurance Products
S.I.C.: 6331
N.A.I.C.S.: 524126
Jaime Kirkpatrick *(Mng Dir)*

AEGON Magyarorszag Altalanos Biztosito Zrt. (1)
Ulloi Ut 1
PO Box 1813
H-1091 Budapest, Hungary (100%)
Tel.: (36) 14765765
Fax: (36) 14765838
Web Site: www.aegon.hu
Sales Range: $100-124.9 Million
Emp.: 865
Personal & Group Life & Non-Life Insurance, Savings & Pension Products
S.I.C.: 6399
N.A.I.C.S.: 524128
Peter Zatyko *(CEO)*

AEGON UK plc (1)
3 Lochside Ave Edinburgh Park
Edinburgh, EH12 9SE, United Kingdom (100%)
Tel.: (44) 8706000337
Fax: (44) 1315494225
E-Mail: info@aegon.co.uk
Web Site: www.aegon.co.uk
Emp.: 3,000
Insured Pension, Personal Investment, Employee Benefits & Protection Products
S.I.C.: 6371
N.A.I.C.S.: 524292
Otto Thoresen *(CEO)*
Charles Garthwaite *(Chief Risk Officer)*

Subsidiaries:

AEGON Scottish Equitable plc (2)
Scottish Equitable House
Edinburgh, EH12 9SE, United Kingdom

Tel.: (44) 1313399191
Fax: (44) 1313399567
E-Mail: inquiries@aegon.co.uk
Web Site: www.aegon.co.uk
Sales Range: $1-4.9 Billion
Emp.: 3,000
Life Insurance & Investment Services
S.I.C.: 6311
N.A.I.C.S.: 524113
Adrian Grace *(CEO)*

Kames Capital (2)
Kames House 3 Lochside Crescent
Edinburgh, EH12 9SA, United Kingdom UK
Tel.: (44) 8706090101 (100%)
Fax: (44) 8706090102
E-Mail: help@kamescapital.info
Web Site: www.kamescapital.com
Emp.: 2,000
Provider of Asset Management Services & Institutional & Retail Asset Management Products
S.I.C.: 6531
N.A.I.C.S.: 531390
Sarah Russell *(Interim CEO)*
Greg Cooper *(Chief Administration Officer)*
Stephen Jones *(Chief Investment Officer)*

AEI CORPORATION LTD

12 Penjuru Lane
Singapore, 609192, Singapore
Tel.: (65) 62612244
Fax: (65) 62640080
E-Mail: aei@aei.com.sg
Web Site: www.aei.com.sg
A18—(SES)
Rev.: $33,365,293
Assets: $59,496,906
Liabilities: $13,912,732
Net Worth: $45,584,174
Earnings: $3,786,873
Fiscal Year-end: 12/31/12

Business Description:
Precision Aluminium Extrusion Products
S.I.C.: 3354
N.A.I.C.S.: 331318

Personnel:
Ian Chu En Tan *(CEO)*
Soh Ping Lum *(CFO)*
Soon Soo Foo *(Co-Sec)*
Zee Moey Ngiam *(Co-Sec)*

Board of Directors:
Alias David Koon Sang Yeung
Sinta Muchtar
Vasoo Sushilan
Ian Chu En Tan
Cheong Kwee Teng

Transfer Agent:
Boardroom Corporate & Advisory Services Pte. Ltd.
50 Raffles Place 32-01 Singapore Land Tower
Singapore, Singapore

Subsidiary:

AEI Engineering Pte Ltd (1)
12 Penjuru Ln
Block C, Singapore, 609192, Singapore
Tel.: (65) 62652646
Fax: (65) 62658702
E-Mail: aei@aei.com.sg
Web Site: www.aei.com.sg
Emp.: 30
Engineering Services
S.I.C.: 8711
N.A.I.C.S.: 541330

AEKYUNG PETROCHEMICAL CO., LTD.

106 3 Guro Dong
Guro Ku
150055 Seoul, Korea (South)
Tel.: (82) 28502000
Fax: (82) 28388435
Web Site: www.akp.co.kr
Year Founded: 1970
006840—(KRS)
Sales Range: $450-499.9 Million

Business Description:
Petrochemical, Resins & Dye Mfr
S.I.C.: 2869
N.A.I.C.S.: 325110

Personnel:
Young-Sin Jang *(Chm)*
Kyu-Whan Boo *(CEO)*

Joint Venture:

Aekyung Chemical Co., Ltd. (1)
5th Fl 2nd Misung Bldg 106-5 Guro 5 Dong
Guro Ku, Seoul, 152842, Korea (South) KS
Tel.: (82) 28607503
Fax: (82) 28607599
Web Site: www.akc.co.kr
Emp.: 192
Mfr. & Sales of Synthetic Resins
S.I.C.: 2821
N.A.I.C.S.: 325211

Plant:

Aekyung Petrochemical Co Ltd - Ulsan Plant (1)
724 Sangke-Dong
Nam-Ku, Ulsan, Korea (South)
Tel.: (82) 5 2296363
Fax: (82) 522731216
Petrochemical Products Mfr
S.I.C.: 2911
N.A.I.C.S.: 324110

Non-U.S. Subsidiary:

Aekyung HongKong Co., Ltd (1)
Rm 2802-2803 28 F Bank of America 12 Harcourt Rd
Central, China (Hong Kong)
Tel.: (852) 25378382
Fax: (852) 25378891
Emp.: 4
Petrochemicals Mfr
S.I.C.: 2911
N.A.I.C.S.: 324110
M. H. Cho *(Mgr)*

AEM HOLDINGS LTD

52 Serangoon North Avenue 4
Singapore, 555853, Singapore
Tel.: (65) 64831811
Fax: (65) 64831822
Web Site: www.aem.com.sg
A10—(SES)
Rev.: $60,344,641
Assets: $71,906,061
Liabilities: $14,423,640
Net Worth: $57,482,422
Earnings: ($2,117,313)
Fiscal Year-end: 12/31/12

Business Description:
Electroplating Mfr
S.I.C.: 3559
N.A.I.C.S.: 333249

Personnel:
Albert Aik Khoon Ng *(CEO)*
Wai Kong Soh *(Sec)*

Board of Directors:
Wai San Loke
Adrian Pengee Chan
Basil Chan
Albert Aik Khoon Ng

Non-U.S. Subsidiaries:

AEM (HongKong) Pte Ltd (1)
Suite 2301 23 Floor World-Wide House 19 Des Voeux Road
Central, China (Hong Kong)
Tel.: (852) 28620093
Fax: (852) 28620000
Packaging Machinery Mfr
S.I.C.: 3565
N.A.I.C.S.: 333993

AEM Microtronics (M) Sdn. Bhd. (1)
Plot 155 Jalan Sungai Bayan Lepas FIZ Phase I
11900 Bayan Lepas, Penang, Malaysia
Tel.: (60) 46407200
Fax: (60) 46407210
E-Mail: amm@aem.com.sg
Emp.: 60
Packaging Machinery Import & Distr
S.I.C.: 5084
N.A.I.C.S.: 423830
Goh Hoon Har *(Mgr-Fin)*

AEM (Suzhou) Co., Ltd. (1)
83 QunXin Yi Road Tong Yuan Road
Suzhou Industrial Park, Suzhou, Jiangsu, 215006, China
Tel.: (86) 51267603000
Fax: (86) 51267605000
Semiconductor Making Machinery Mfr
S.I.C.: 3559
N.A.I.C.S.: 333242

LaserOp Ltd. (1)
6 Hamagshimim St
PO Box 7760
49170 Petah Tiqwa, Israel
Tel.: (972) 39220353
Fax: (972) 3 922 0443
E-Mail: laserop@laserop.com
Web Site: www.laserop.com
Emp.: 20
Laser Systems Mfr & Distr
S.I.C.: 3845
N.A.I.C.S.: 334510

AEMOS SDN BHD

Level 36 Menara Maxis
Kuala Lumpur City Centre, 50088
Kuala Lumpur, Malaysia
Tel.: (60) 326157250
Fax: (60) 326150088
Web Site: www.aemos-international.com
Sales Range: $10-24.9 Million
Emp.: 100

Business Description:
IT & Business Consultancy Services
S.I.C.: 7371
N.A.I.C.S.: 541511

Personnel:
Sufineh Mahmood *(Mng Dir)*

AENIX INFORMATIQUE S.A.

Domaine Technologique 4 Rue Rene Razel
91400 Paris, France
Tel.: (33) 169187650
Fax: (33) 164464284
Web Site: www.aenix.fr
Year Founded: 1990
Rev.: $12,000,000
Emp.: 34

Business Description:
Industrial Logistics Consultation & Implementation
S.I.C.: 4731
N.A.I.C.S.: 541614

Personnel:
Patrick Cadet *(Chm)*

Board of Directors:
Patrick Cadet

AEON CO., LTD.

1-5-1 Nakase Mihama-ku Chiba-shi
Chiba, 261-8515, Japan
Tel.: (81) 432126042
Telex: 2225528
Fax: (81) 432126849
Web Site: www.aeon.info
8267—(TKS)
Rev.: $62,538,333,000
Assets: $62,984,482,000
Liabilities: $47,059,749,000
Net Worth: $15,924,733,000
Earnings: $821,667,000
Fiscal Year-end: 02/28/13

Business Description:
Holding Company; Multi-Platform Retailer
S.I.C.: 6719
N.A.I.C.S.: 551112

Personnel:
Naoki Hayashi *(Chm)*
Motoya Okada *(Pres & CEO)*
Kazuhide Kamitani *(Co-CEO-Fin Svc Bus, EMoney Bus Officer & VP)*
Seiichi Chiba *(CFO & VP)*
Yoshiki Mori *(COO, CEO-Fin Svcs Bus & Sr Exec VP)*
Jerry T. Black *(Chief Strategy, Digital & IT Officer & Exec VP)*
Hiroharu Kinoshita *(Chief Admin Officer & VP-Risk Mgmt)*
Hiroshi Yokoo *(Chief Mdse Officer, CEO-Strategic Small-Size Store Bus & Exec VP)*
Hidehiro Hirabayashi *(Chief Environmental Officer, CEO-Drugstore & Pharmacy Bus & VP)*
Atsunobu Agata *(IT Officer & VP)*
Kunihiko Hisaki *(Mdsg Officer & VP)*
Masato Nishimatsu *(Corp Control & Acctg Officer & VP)*
Kazumi Uchiyama *(Supermarket Bus Officer & VP)*
Cenk Gurol *(Chief Logistics Officer)*
Keiji Ono *(Customer Svcs Officer)*
Yukimi Sanda *(Discount Store Bus Officer)*
Kunio Sakano *(CEO-Supermarket Bus & Discount Store Bus & Sr Exec VP)*
Shouhei Murai *(CEO-Gen Mdse Store Bus & Exec VP)*
Masaaki Toyoshima *(CEO-Bus Dev & Exec VP)*
Tsunekazu Haraguchi *(CEO-Fin Svcs Bus & VP)*
Soichi Okazaki *(CEO-Shopping Center Dev Bus & VP)*
Manabu Oshima *(CEO-Bus Svcs & VP)*
Nagahisa Oyama *(CEO-Asean Bus & VP)*
Haruyoshi Tsuji *(CEO-China Bus & VP)*
Kazunori Umemoto *(CEO-Svc Bus, Specialty Store Bus & EMoney Bus & VP)*
Takeshi Kodama *(CEO-ECommerce Bus)*
Noriyuki Murakami *(Exec VP)*

Board of Directors:
Naoki Hayashi
Masaharu Ikuta
Yoshiki Mori
Motoya Okada
Ken Sato
Takejiro Sueyoshi
Keiichi Tadaki
Masaaki Toyoshima
Yukako Uchinaga

Transfer Agent:
Sumitomo Mitsui Trust Bank Limited
1-4-1 Marunouchi Chiyoda-ku
Tokyo, Japan

Subsidiaries:

AEON AGRI CREATE Co., Ltd (1)
1-5-1 Nakase
Mihama-ku, Chiba, Japan
Tel.: (81) 43 212 6462
Fax: (81) 43 212 6034
Web Site: www.aeonagricreate.co.jp
Emp.: 20
Cabbage Cultivation Services
S.I.C.: 0721
N.A.I.C.S.: 115112
Shigeo Fuji *(Pres)*

AEON BODY Co., Ltd (1)
Koshigaya
Saitama, 343-0826, Japan
Tel.: (81) 489724336
Fax: (81) 489724346
Web Site: www.aeonbody.com
Emp.: 40
Cosmetic Products Retailer
S.I.C.: 5122
N.A.I.C.S.: 446120
Takashi Muramatsu *(Gen Mgr)*

AEON Co., Ltd.—(Continued)

AEON CINEMAS CO., LTD (1)
Yamatochoniiji 2965 Saga Yamato
Saga, 840-0201, Japan
Tel.: (81) 952648788
Web Site: www.aeoncinema.co.jp
Motion Picture Exhibition Services
S.I.C.: 7833
N.A.I.C.S.: 512132

AEON Eaheart Co., LTD (1)
1-3 Nakase Makuhari Techno Garden B 10 Fl
Mihama-Ku, Chiba, 261-0023, Japan
Tel.: (81) 432962350
Fax: (81) 432962360
Web Site: www.aeoneaheart.co.jp
Emp.: 20
Restaurant Operation Services
S.I.C.: 5812
N.A.I.C.S.: 722511
Koji Namara *(Gen Mgr)*

Aeon Fantasy Co., Ltd. (1)
1-5-1 Nakase
Mihama-ku, Chiba, 261-8504, Japan
Tel.: (81) 43 212 6203
Fax: (81) 43 212 6840
Web Site: www.fantasy.co.jp
4343—(TKS)
Sales Range: $450-499.9 Million
Indoor Theme Park Operator
S.I.C.: 7993
N.A.I.C.S.: 713120
Nao Kataoka, *(Pres)*

AEON Financial Service Co., Ltd (1)
(Formerly AEON Credit Service Co., Ltd.)
Kanda Mitoshiro-cho 1 Chiyoda-ku
Tokyo, 101-8445, Japan JP
Tel.: (81) 352812056 (50%)
Fax: (81) 352812043
Web Site: www.aeoncredit.co.jp/aeon/eng/index.html
8570—(TKS)
Sales Range: $1-4.9 Billion
Emp.: 5,655
Consumer Credit Card Services, Vehicle Purchase & Personal Loan Financing
S.I.C.: 6141
N.A.I.C.S.: 522291
Tsunekazu Haraguchi *(Chm)*
Kazuhide Kamitani *(Pres & CEO)*
Takashi Kiyonaga *(Sr Mng Exec Officer)*
Masao Mizuno *(Sr Mng Exec Officer)*
Hideki Wakabayashi *(Sr Mng Exec Officer)*

Non-U.S. Subsidiaries:

AEON Credit Service (Asia) Company Limited (2)
37th Fl The World Trade Ctr
280 Gloucester Rd, Causeway Bay, China (Hong Kong) (100%)
Tel.: (852) 22399888
Fax: (852) 25776186
E-Mail: info@aeon.com.hk
Web Site: www.aeon.com.hk
Sls.: $1,287,770
Emp.: 300
Consumer Credit Card Services, Vehicle Purchase & Personal Loan Financing
S.I.C.: 6141
N.A.I.C.S.: 522291

AEON Credit Service (M) Berhad (2)
Level 29 Menara Olympia No 8 Jalan Raja Chulan
50200 Kuala Lumpur, Malaysia MY
Tel.: (60) 327729000
Fax: (60) 327714110
E-Mail: corporate@aeonmalaysia.com.my
Web Site: www.aeonmalaysia.com.my
AEONCR—(KLS)
Rev.: $153,180,286
Assets: $798,624,566
Liabilities: $657,879,007
Net Worth: $140,745,559
Earnings: $43,982,598
Emp.: 1,900
Fiscal Year-end: 02/20/13
Consumer Credit Card Services, Vehicle Purchase & Personal Loan Financing
S.I.C.: 6141
N.A.I.C.S.: 522291
Yasuhiro Kasai *(Mng Dir)*
Lee Wah Choong *(Co-Sec)*
Yit Chan Tai *(Co-Sec)*

AEON FOOD SUPPLY Co., Ltd (1)
24-12 Takasecho
Funabashi, 273-0014, Japan
Tel.: (81) 474318396
Fax: (81) 474323748
Web Site: www.aeon-fs.com
Food Products Retailer
S.I.C.: 5499
N.A.I.C.S.: 445299

AEON FOREST CO., LTD (1)
3-6 Kioicho Kioicho Park Bldg 6 Fl
Chiyoda-ku, Tokyo, 102-0094, Japan
Tel.: (81) 352156120
Fax: (81) 352156130
Web Site: www.the-body-shop.co.jp
Emp.: 1,000
Cosmetic Products Retailer
S.I.C.: 5122
N.A.I.C.S.: 446120
Yoshio Shishikura *(Pres)*

AEON GLOBAL MERCHANDISING CO., LTD (1)
1-5-1 Nakase
Mihama-Ku, Chiba, 261-0023, Japan
Tel.: (81) 432126705
Fax: (81) 432126760
General Merchandise Retailer
S.I.C.: 5399
N.A.I.C.S.: 452990

AEON GLOBAL SCM CO., LTD (1)
1-5-1 Nakase
Mihama-Ku, Chiba, 261-0023, Japan
Tel.: (81) 432126115
General Merchandise Retailer
S.I.C.: 5399
N.A.I.C.S.: 452990

AEON INSURANCE SERVICE CO., LTD (1)
Mihamaku Nakase 1-3 Makuhari Techno Garden 10F
Chiba, 261-8501, Japan
Tel.: (81) 43 274 9478
Fax: (81) 43 274 2462
General Insurance Services
S.I.C.: 6411
N.A.I.C.S.: 524298

AEON Integrated Business Service Co., Ltd (1)
1-5-1 Nakase
Mihama-ku, Chiba, 261-0023, Japan
Tel.: (81) 432126290
Web Site: www.ecohana.jp
Cosmetic Product Retailer
S.I.C.: 5122
N.A.I.C.S.: 424210

Aeon Mall Co., Ltd. (1)
1-5-1 Nakase
Mihama-ku, Chiba, 261-8539, Japan
Tel.: (81) 43 212 6450
Fax: (81) 43 212 6737
Web Site: www.aeonmall.com
8905—(TKS)
Emp.: 1,043
Shopping Mall Operator
S.I.C.: 6512
N.A.I.C.S.: 531120
Noriyuki Murakami *(Chm)*
Soichi Okazaki *(Pres & CEO)*

AEON Pet Co., Ltd. (1)
3-21-1 Takasu Aeon Marine Pia Semmonkan 3 F
Mihama-ku, Chiba, 261-0004, Japan JP
Tel.: (81) 43 270 5170
Fax: (81) 43 270 5811
Web Site: www.petcity.co.jp
Pet Foods Retailers
S.I.C.: 5149
N.A.I.C.S.: 424490

AEON Retail Co., Ltd (1)
1-31-1 Nakase
Mihama-Ku, Chiba, 261-0023, Japan
Tel.: (81) 43 212 6036
Fax: (81) 43 212 6810
Web Site: www.aeonretail.jp
General Merchandise Retailer
S.I.C.: 5399
N.A.I.C.S.: 452990

Subsidiaries:

AEON DELIGHT CO., LTD. (2)
Minamisemba Heart Building 5-7F
2-3-2 Minamisemba Chuo-ku, Osaka, 542-0081, Japan JP
Tel.: (81) 662605621
Web Site: www.aeondelight.co.jp
9787—(TKS)
Sls.: $2,737,636,000
Assets: $1,107,689,000
Liabilities: $397,672,000
Net Worth: $710,017,000
Earnings: $82,599,000
Emp.: 6,441
Fiscal Year-end: 02/28/13
Building Management Services
S.I.C.: 7349
N.A.I.C.S.: 561790
Ippei Nakayama *(Pres & CEO)*

AEON RYUKYU CO., LTD (1)
5141 Kanegusuku Haebearu-cho
Naha, Okinawa, 901-1111, Japan
Tel.: (81) 98 889 5464
Fax: (81) 98 888 2205
Web Site: www.aeon-ryukyu.jp
Emp.: 2,664
Supermarket Management Services
S.I.C.: 5411
N.A.I.C.S.: 445110

AEON SUPERCENTER Co., Ltd. (1)
1-11-5 Saien
Morioka, Iwate, 020-0024, Japan
Tel.: (81) 196058800
Fax: (81) 196058818
Web Site: www.aeonsupercenter.co.jp
Supermarket Management Services
S.I.C.: 5411
N.A.I.C.S.: 445110

AEON Topvalu Co., Ltd. (1)
(Formerly AIC Inc.)
Shinkawa East Building 23-5 1 Chome Shinakawa
Chuo-Ku, Tokyo, 104-8284, Japan JP
Tel.: (81) 3 5541 2060 (88.7%)
Fax: (81) 3 5541 2140
Web Site: www.aicincjp.com
Emp.: 330
General Merchandise Stores Operator
S.I.C.: 5399
N.A.I.C.S.: 452990
Takashi Hamabe *(Pres)*
Masato Sekino *(Co-Mng Dir)*
Masayuki Yamamoto *(Co-Mng Dir)*

AT Japan Co., Ltd (1)
1-5-1 Nakase
Mihama-Ku, Chiba, 261-0023, Japan
Tel.: (81) 432126473
Fax: (81) 433795238
Supermarket Management Services
S.I.C.: 5411
N.A.I.C.S.: 445110

Cordon Vert CO., LTD (1)
3-7-35 Tsutsujigaoka Miyagino-ku Sompo Japan Sendai Bldg 10 F
Sendai, Miyagi, 983-0852, Japan
Tel.: (81) 227423120
Fax: (81) 227423139
Web Site: www.cordonvert.jp
Emp.: 20
Liquor Import & Distr
S.I.C.: 2064
N.A.I.C.S.: 311352
Hiroshi Asada *(Chm)*
Hiroaki Yamauchi *(Pres)*
Takashi Fukui *(Sr VP)*

JUSVEL CO., LTD (1)
2-6 Nakase World Business Garden Maribu East 19f
Mihama-Ku, Chiba, 261-0023, Japan
Tel.: (81) 432974300
Fax: (81) 432978188
Web Site: www.jusvel.co.jp
Emp.: 280
Supermarket Management Services
S.I.C.: 5411
N.A.I.C.S.: 445110
Kayaji Shigeo *(Gen Mgr)*

Kohyo Co., Ltd. (1)
5-4-19 Shinsho
Yokkaichi, Mie, 510-0064, Japan JP
Tel.: (81) 593545411
Fax: (81) 593543447
E-Mail: Kohyo@kohyoj.co.jp
Web Site: www.kohyoj.co.jp
Processed Seafoods Mfr
S.I.C.: 2038
N.A.I.C.S.: 311412
Shintaro Hayashi *(Pres)*

U.S. Subsidiary:

Kohyo America, Inc. (2)
12826 SE 40th Ln Ste 200
Bellevue, WA 98006
Tel.: (425) 373-0545
Fax: (425) 373-0288
E-Mail: export@kohyoamerica.com
Web Site: www.kohyoj.co.jp/group_e/group.htm
Farm Products Distr
S.I.C.: 5191
N.A.I.C.S.: 424910

Non-U.S. Subsidiary:

Kohyo Holland B.V. (2)
Planetenweg 15
2132 HN Hoofddorp, North Holland, Netherlands (100%)
Tel.: (31) 235624160
Fax: (31) 235624228
E-Mail: kohyo@xs4all.nl
Web Site: www.kohyoj.co.jp/en/index.html
Emp.: 2
Processed Seafoods Whslr
S.I.C.: 5146
N.A.I.C.S.: 424460
Yutaka Miwa *(Gen Mgr)*

LOC DEVELOPMENT CO., LTD (1)
67 Kandasakumagashi Mbr 99 Building 5F
Chiyoda-Ku, Tokyo, 101-0026, Japan
Tel.: (81) 338640609
Fax: (81) 338640610
Sales Range: $200-249.9 Million
Commercial Property Development Services
S.I.C.: 1541
N.A.I.C.S.: 236210

MaxValu Kyushu Co., Ltd. (1)
3-13-21 Hakataeki Higashi
Hakata-ku, Fukuoka, 812-0013, Japan
Tel.: (81) 92 433- 1228
Web Site: www.mv-kyushu.co.jp
3171—(JAS)
Sales Range: $1-4.9 Billion
Emp.: 985
Supermarket Owner & Operator
S.I.C.: 5411
N.A.I.C.S.: 445110
Eiji Shibata *(Pres)*

MEGA PETRO Co., Ltd (1)
3-13-2 Takasu Mihama-ku Ion Inage Kaigan Jimusho 6 F
Chiba, 261-0004, Japan
Tel.: (81) 432988531
Fax: (81) 432988532
Pharmaceutical Products Retailer
S.I.C.: 5122
N.A.I.C.S.: 424210

Mega Sports Co., Ltd (1)
Nihombashikakigaracho 1-36-5
Chuo-Ku, Tokyo, 103-0014, Japan
Tel.: (81) 356443666
Fax: (81) 356443668
Web Site: www.sportsauthority.co.jp
Emp.: 2,500
Sporting Goods Retailer
S.I.C.: 5941
N.A.I.C.S.: 451110
Manuabu Minamiyama *(Pres)*

Ministop Co., Ltd. (1)
AEON Tower 1-5-1 Nakase
Mihama-ku, Chiba, 261-8515, Japan
Tel.: (81) 43 212 6471
E-Mail: info@ministop.co.jp
Web Site: www.ministop.co.jp
9946—(TKS)
Emp.: 893
Convenience Store Operator
S.I.C.: 5411
N.A.I.C.S.: 445120
Naoyuki Miyashita *(Pres)*

ORIGIN TOSHU CO., LTD (1)
3-2-4 Senkawa-cho
Chofu, Tokyo, 182-0002, Japan
Tel.: (81) 333050180
Web Site: www.toshu.co.jp
Emp.: 570
Frozen Food Products Sales
S.I.C.: 5142
N.A.I.C.S.: 424420

Reform Studio Co., Ltd. (1)
2-62-6 Nihombashihama-cho
Chuo-ku, Tokyo, 103-0007, Japan

Tel.: (81) 336615575
Fax: (81) 336615576
Web Site: www.reform-s.com
Sales Range: $25-49.9 Million
Emp.: 70
Fashion Apparel & Shoe Retailer & Repair
S.I.C.: 5699
N.A.I.C.S.: 448150
Yoshihito Watanabe *(Pres)*

Research Institute For Quality Living Co., Ltd. (1)
1-5-1 Nakase Ion Tower Nai
Mihama-Ku, Chiba, 261-0023, Japan
Tel.: (81) 432126189
Fax: (81) 432134166
E-Mail: ni_inaba@aeon.biz
Web Site: www.riql.jp
Food Safety Regulation & Inspection Services
S.I.C.: 7389
N.A.I.C.S.: 561990

TAKIYA Co., Ltd (1)
1-5-1 Nakase
Mihama-ku, Chiba, 261-8515, Japan
Tel.: (81) 432126042
Fax: (81) 432126849
Supermarket Management Services
S.I.C.: 5411
N.A.I.C.S.: 445110

Welpark Co., Ltd. (1)
6-1-1 Sakaecho Inageya Bldg 6 F
Tachikawa, Tokyo, 190-0003, Japan
Tel.: (81) 425375274
Fax: (81) 425345596
E-Mail: soumu@welpark.jp
Web Site: www.welpark.jp
Sls.: $4,247,280
Supermarket Management Services
S.I.C.: 5411
N.A.I.C.S.: 445110

U.S. Subsidiary:

AEON (U.S.A.) Inc. (1)
450 7th Ave
New York, NY 10123 (100%)
Tel.: (212) 946-8780
Fax: (212) 695-7139
Web Site: www.aeon.info
Emp.: 6
Grocery, Retail & Clothing Stores Owner & Operator
S.I.C.: 5149
N.A.I.C.S.: 424490
Milagros Simon *(Sr Mgr-Acctg)*

Non-U.S. Subsidiaries:

AEON BIG (M) Sdn. Bhd. (1)
No 3 Jalan SS 16/1
Subang Jaya, Kuala Lumpur, 47500, Malaysia MY
Tel.: (60) 380223600
Fax: (60) 356337735
Hypermarkets Operator
S.I.C.: 5411
N.A.I.C.S.: 445110
Nagahisa Oyama *(CEO)*

AEON Co. (M) Bhd. (1)
3rd Floor AEON Taman Maluri Shopping Centre Jalan Jejaka Taman Maluri
Cheras, 55100 Kuala Lumpur, Malaysia
Tel.: (60) 392072005
Fax: (60) 392072006
E-Mail: feedback@aeonretail.com.my
Web Site: www.aeonretail.com.my
AEON—(KLS)
Rev.: $1,067,598,978
Assets: $879,537,842
Liabilities: $397,805,327
Net Worth: $481,732,516
Earnings: $69,789,574
Fiscal Year-end: 12/31/12
Retailing & Property Management Services
S.I.C.: 5722
N.A.I.C.S.: 443141
Nagahisa Oyama *(Vice Chm)*
Qamarina Chew Abdullah *(Mng Dir)*
Irene Liew *(Co-Sec)*
Yit Chan Tai *(Co-Sec)*

AEON Stores (Hong Kong) Co., Limited (1)
3rd Floor Stanhope House 738 King's Road
Quarry Bay, China (Hong Kong) (100%)
Tel.: (852) 25653600
Fax: (852) 25638654
Web Site: www.jusco.com.hk
0984—(HKG)
Rev.: $951,293,551
Assets: $651,888,156
Liabilities: $411,640,122
Net Worth: $240,248,035
Earnings: $32,346,463
Emp.: 9,300
Fiscal Year-end: 12/31/12
Operator of General Merchandise Stores
S.I.C.: 5399
N.A.I.C.S.: 452990
Christine Pui Man Chan *(Mng Dir)*
Junichi Suzuki *(Deputy Mng Dir)*
Eric Kwong Leung Chan *(Sec)*

AEON (Thailand) CO., LTD (1)
78 Chaengwattana Road
Bang Khen, Bangkok, 10220, Thailand
Tel.: (66) 2970182530
Fax: (66) 297018234
Consumer Lending Services
S.I.C.: 6141
N.A.I.C.S.: 522291

Qingdao AEON Dongtai Co., Ltd. (1)
No 72 Xianggang Middle Road
Shinan District, Qingdao, Shandong, 266071, China
Tel.: (86) 53285719659
Fax: (86) 53285719522
Web Site: www.qdaeon.com
Supermarkets Stores
S.I.C.: 5411
N.A.I.C.S.: 445110

Tasmania Feedlot Pty. Ltd. (1)
14532 Midlands Highway
PO Box 58
7300 Powranna, TAS, 7300, Australia
Tel.: (61) 363986244
Fax: (61) 363986297
Emp.: 40
General Merchandise Stores
S.I.C.: 5399
N.A.I.C.S.: 452990
Andrew Thompson *(Mng Dir)*

AEON CO. (M) BHD.

(See Under AEON Co., Ltd.)

AEON DELIGHT CO., LTD.

(See Under AEON Co., Ltd.)

AEON METALS LIMITED

Level 3 Suite 11 88 Pitt Street
Sydney, NSW, 2000, Australia
Mailing Address:
PO Box 8155
Gold Coast, QLD, 9726, Australia
Tel.: (61) 7 5574 3830
Fax: (61) 7 5574 3568
E-Mail: info@aeonmetals.com.au
Web Site: www.aeonmetals.com.au
AQR—(ASX)
Rev.: $32,305
Assets: $24,369,509
Liabilities: $341,809
Net Worth: $24,027,700
Earnings: ($77,115)
Emp.: 3
Fiscal Year-end: 06/30/13
Business Description:
Copper Ore Mining Services
S.I.C.: 1021
N.A.I.C.S.: 212234
Personnel:
Hamish E. Collins *(Mng Dir)*
Stephen J. Lonergan *(Sec)*
Board of Directors:
Thomas Joseph Mann
Hamish E. Collins
John Leslie Goody
Edgar George Newman

AEONIAN INVESTMENTS COMPANY LTD.

NKM International House 178
Backbay Reclamation
BC Road Churchgate, Mumbai, 400020, India
Tel.: (91) 22 2283 8293
Fax: (91) 22 2283 8291
E-Mail: info@aeonianinvestment.com
Web Site: www.aeonianinvestment.com
503655—(BOM)
Sales Range: Less than $1 Million
Business Description:
Investment Management Services
S.I.C.: 6282
N.A.I.C.S.: 523920
Personnel:
Dhiren P. Mehta *(Compliance Officer)*
Board of Directors:
Amit C. Choksey
Priti A. Choksey
Bipin V. Jhaveri
Dhiren P. Mehta
Manubhai G. Patel
Bhanushankar R. Trivedi
Transfer Agent:
Link Intime India Private Limited
C-13 Pannalal Silk Mills Compound L.B.S. Marg
Bhandup
Mumbai, India

AER ARANN EXPRESS LTD.

1 N Wood Ave Santry
9 Dublin, Ireland
Tel.: (353) 18447700
Fax: (353) 8447701
E-Mail: info@aerarann.com
Web Site: www.aerarann.com
Sls.: $113,487,140
Emp.: 400
Business Description:
Air Transportation Services
S.I.C.: 4512
N.A.I.C.S.: 481111
Personnel:
Sean Brogan *(CEO)*

AER LINGUS GROUP PLC

Head Office Building Dublin Airport
Dublin, Ireland
Tel.: (353) 18868202
Fax: (353) 18863832
E-Mail: investor.relations@aerlingus.com
Web Site: www.aerlingus.com
Year Founded: 1936
EIL1—(ISE LSE)
Rev.: $1,875,597,122
Assets: $2,398,512,820
Liabilities: $1,274,849,913
Net Worth: $1,123,662,907
Earnings: $45,806,127
Emp.: 3,566
Fiscal Year-end: 12/31/12
Business Description:
Passenger Air Transportation Services
S.I.C.: 4512
N.A.I.C.S.: 481111
Personnel:
Colm Barrington *(Chm)*
Christoph Mueller *(CEO)*
Andrew Macfarlane *(CFO)*
Fergus Wilson *(COO)*
Ravindra Simhambhatla *(CTO)*
Stephen Kavanagh *(Chief Comml Officer)*
Andrew Cornish *(Chief Customer & Brand Officer)*
Michael Grealy *(Chief People & Change Officer)*
Donal Moriarty *(Exec Counsel)*
Meabh Gallagher *(Sec)*
Board of Directors:
Colm Barrington
David Begg
Montie R. Brewer
Laurence Crowley
John Hartnett
Andrew Macfarlane
Christoph Mueller
Nigel Northridge
Nicola Shaw
William Slattery
Nicholas Villen
Legal Counsel:
Arthur Cox
Earlsfort Terrace
Dublin, 2, Ireland
Subsidiary:

AER Turas Teo (1)
Head Office Bldg
Dublin Airport, Dublin, Ireland (100%)
Tel.: (353) 1 886 6724
Telex: 33393
Fax: (353) 1 886 3876
International Air Cargo Carrier
S.I.C.: 4522
N.A.I.C.S.: 481212

U.S. Subsidiary:

Aer Lingus (1)
300 Jericho Quadrangle Suite 130
Jericho, NY 11753
Tel.: (516) 622-4022
Fax: (516) 622-4281
E-Mail: goldcircleusa@aerlingus.com
Web Site: www.aerlingus.com
Sls.: $90,000,000
Emp.: 300
Air Transportation Services
S.I.C.: 4512
N.A.I.C.S.: 481111
Colm Barrington *(Chm)*
Christoph Mueller *(CEO & Acting COO)*
Andrew MacFarlane *(CFO)*
Stephen Kavanagh *(Chief Comml Officer)*

Non-U.S. Branch:

Aer Lingus France (1)
11 Rue Auber
75009 Paris, France
Tel.: (33) 170200072
Fax: (33) 153437919
Web Site: www.aerlingus.com
Airline Transportation Services
S.I.C.: 4512
N.A.I.C.S.: 481111

AERCAP HOLDINGS N.V.

AerCap House Stationsplein 965
1117 CE Schiphol, Netherlands
Tel.: (31) 20 655 9655
Fax: (31) 20 655 9100
E-Mail: khelming@aercap.com
Web Site: www.aercap.com
AER—(NYSE)
Rev.: $1,050,066,000
Assets: $9,451,141,000
Liabilities: $7,021,909,000
Net Worth: $2,429,232,000
Earnings: $295,402,000
Emp.: 163
Fiscal Year-end: 12/31/13
Business Description:
Aviation Services; Aircraft & Engine Leasing, Trading & Parts Sales; Aircraft Management & Maintenance Services
S.I.C.: 5088
N.A.I.C.S.: 423860
Personnel:
Pieter Korteweg *(Chm)*
Gerald Porter Strong *(Vice Chm)*
Aengus Kelly *(CEO)*
Keith A. Helming *(CFO)*
Wouter M. den Dikken *(COO)*
Kenneth Wigmore *(CMO)*
Joe Venuto *(CTO)*
Paul E. Rofe *(Grp Treas)*
Board of Directors:
Pieter Korteweg
James N. Chapman
Paul T. Dacier
Richard Gradon
W. Brett Ingersoll
Marius Jacques Leonard Jonkhart
Aengus Kelly

AerCap Holdings N.V.—(Continued)

Gerald Porter Strong
Robert G. Warden

Subsidiaries:

AerCap B.V. (1)
Station Stlein 965
1117 CE Schiphol, Netherlands (100%)
Tel.: (31) 206559655
Fax: (31) 206559100
E-Mail: reception@aercap.com
Emp.: 85
Aircraft Manufacturing
S.I.C.: 3721
N.A.I.C.S.: 336411
Klaus Heinamen *(CEO)*

AerCap Dutch Aircraft Leasing B.V. (1)
Stationspleim 965
1117 CE Schiphol, Netherlands (100%)
Tel.: (31) 206559655
Fax: (31) 206559100
E-Mail: reception@aercap.com
Web Site: www.bulgaria.bnpparibas.com
Emp.: 85
Aircraft Manufacturing
S.I.C.: 3721
N.A.I.C.S.: 336411
Klaus Heinamen *(CEO)*

AerCap Group Services B.V. (1)
Aercap House Stationsplein 965
1117 CE Schiphol, Netherlands
Tel.: (31) 206559655
Fax: (31) 206559100
E-Mail: contact@aercap.com
Emp.: 85
Aircraft Leasing Services
S.I.C.: 7359
N.A.I.C.S.: 532411
Aengus Kelly *(CEO)*

AerCap Netherlands B.V. (1)
Stetion Tlibn 965
1117 CE Schiphol, Netherlands (100%)
Tel.: (31) 206559655
Fax: (31) 206559100
E-Mail: info@aercap.com
Web Site: www.aercap.com
Emp.: 95
Aircraft Manufacturing
S.I.C.: 3721
N.A.I.C.S.: 336411
Aengus Kelly *(CEO)*

AMS AerCap B.V. (1)
AerCap house Stationssplein plane 965
1117 CE Schiphol, Netherlands (100%)
Tel.: (31) 206559655
Fax: (31) 206559100
E-Mail: reception@aercap.com
Web Site: www.aercap.com
Emp.: 100
Aircraft Manufacturing
S.I.C.: 3721
N.A.I.C.S.: 336411
Klaus Heinamen *(CEO)*

U.S. Subsidiary:

AerCap USA, Inc (1)
100 NE 3rd Ave Ste 800
Fort Lauderdale, FL 33301-1156 (100%)
Tel.: (954) 760-7777
Fax: (954) 760-7716
Emp.: 18
Aircraft Manufacturing
S.I.C.: 3721
N.A.I.C.S.: 336411
Joe Venuto *(Head-Tech-Americas)*

Non-U.S. Subsidiaries:

Aercap Financial Services (Ireland) Ltd (1)
4450 W Pk
Shannon, Co Clare, Ireland (100%)
Tel.: (353) 61360000
Fax: (353) 35361360113
Emp.: 65
Aircraft Manufacturing
S.I.C.: 3721
N.A.I.C.S.: 336411
Klaus Heinamen *(CEO)*

AerFi Group Limited (1)
G P A House
Kilrush, Ireland (100%)
Tel.: (353) 61723800
Aircraft Manufacturing
S.I.C.: 3721
N.A.I.C.S.: 336411
Klaus Heinamen *(CEO)*

Genesis Lease Limited (1)
4450 Atlantic Avenue
Westpark, Shannon, Ireland BM
Tel.: (353) 61 233 300 (100%)
Fax: (353) 61 364 642
Sales Range: $200-249.9 Million
Emp.: 18
Commercial Jet Aircraft & Other Aviation Assets Acquisition & Leasing
S.I.C.: 7359
N.A.I.C.S.: 532411

Irish Aerospace Leasing Limited (1)
4450 Atlantic Ave West Park
Shannon, Co Claire, Ireland (100%)
Tel.: (353) 61360000
Fax: (353) 61723850
Emp.: 100
Aircraft Manufacturing
S.I.C.: 3721
N.A.I.C.S.: 336411
Klaus Heinamen *(CEO)*

Marco Aircraft Leasing Limited (1)
AerCap House
Kilrush, Ireland (100%)
Tel.: (353) 61706500
Fax: (353) 61723850
Web Site: www.gecas.com
Emp.: 55
Aircraft Manufacturing
S.I.C.: 3721
N.A.I.C.S.: 336411

Toulouse Location S.A.R.L. (1)
104 Avenue De Lombez
31300 Toulouse, France (100%)
Tel.: (33) 561427511
Fax: (33) 561422108
Aircraft Manufacturing
S.I.C.: 3721
N.A.I.C.S.: 336411

AERGO CAPITAL LTD.

38 Wellington Road
Mount Street Crecent, Dublin, 4, Ireland
Tel.: (353) 16761077
Fax: (353) 16615383
E-Mail: info@aergogroup.com
Web Site: www.aergocapital.com
Year Founded: 1999

Business Description:
Commercial Jet Aircraft Leasing Services
S.I.C.: 7359
N.A.I.C.S.: 532411

Personnel:
Fred Browne *(CEO)*
Eugene O'Reilly *(Exec VP)*

Subsidiary:

Safair (Pty) Limited (1)
Bonaero Dr Bonaero Park
Kempton Park, Johnannesburg, 1619, South Africa
Tel.: (27) 119280000
Fax: (27) 113951314
E-Mail: marketing@safair.co.za
Web Site: www.safair.co.za
Emp.: 470
Aircraft Leasing Services
S.I.C.: 7359
N.A.I.C.S.: 532411
Elmar Conradie *(Exec VP-Fin & IT)*

AERIS ENVIRONMENTAL LTD

5/26-34 Dunning Avenue
Rosebery, NSW, 2018, Australia
Tel.: (61) 2 8344 1315
Fax: (61) 2 9697 0944
E-Mail: info@aeris.com.au
Web Site: www.aerisenvironmental.com
AEI—(ASX)
Rev.: $572,181
Assets: $357,799
Liabilities: $1,442,144
Net Worth: ($1,084,346)
Earnings: ($1,179,823)
Fiscal Year-end: 06/30/13

Business Description:
Environmental Services Including Removal of Bacteria & Mold in Air-Conditioning, Cold Storage & Bulk Water Systems
S.I.C.: 8999
N.A.I.C.S.: 541620

Personnel:
Peter Bush *(Mng Dir, CEO & CFO)*
Robert Waring *(Sec)*

Board of Directors:
Maurie Stang
David Fisher
Steven Kritzler
Bernard Stang

Subsidiaries:

Aeris Biological Systems Pty Ltd. (1)
5 26-34 Dunning Ave
Rosebery, NSW, 2018, Australia
Tel.: (61) 283441315
Fax: (61) 2 96970944
E-Mail: info@aeris.com.au
Web Site: www.aeris.com.au
Emp.: 3
Cold Storage Systems
S.I.C.: 4222
N.A.I.C.S.: 493120
Andrew Yong *(Gen Mgr)*

Aeris Hygiene Services Pty Ltd. (1)
5 26-34 Dunning Ave
Rosebery, NSW, 2018, Australia
Tel.: (61) 283441315
Fax: (61) 296970944
E-Mail: info@aeris.com.au
Web Site: www.aeriscoldstorage.com
Emp.: 3
Cold Storage Maintenance Services
S.I.C.: 4226
N.A.I.C.S.: 493190
Andrew Young *(Gen Mgr)*

AERO AVIATION LTD.

13 2139 Pegasus Way NE
Calgary, AB, T2E 8T2, Canada
Tel.: (403) 250-7553
Fax: (403) 250-7578
E-Mail: aeroav@aeroav.com
Web Site: www.aeroav.com
Year Founded: 1979
Rev.: $13,857,093
Emp.: 120

Business Description:
Aviation Services
S.I.C.: 4581
N.A.I.C.S.: 488190

Personnel:
Adrian Cruse *(Pres)*

AERO D.D.

Ipavceva ulica 32 pp 430
3000 Celje, Slovenia
Tel.: (386) 34235100
Fax: (386) 34235245
E-Mail: info@aero.si
Web Site: www.aero.si
Year Founded: 1921
Sales Range: $25-49.9 Million
Emp.: 350

Business Description:
Photographic Equipment & Supplies Mfr
S.I.C.: 3579
N.A.I.C.S.: 333316

Personnel:
Ludvik Stepancic *(Asst Mng Dir)*
Milena Brezigar *(Mng Dir)*

Subsidiaries:

Aero Copy d.o.o. (1)
Ipavceva Ulica 32 pp 430
3000 Celje, Slovenia
Tel.: (386) 34235100
Fax: (386) 34235245
E-Mail: info@aero.si
Web Site: www.aero.si/ps/about_us.htm
Emp.: 200
Paper Mfr
S.I.C.: 2679
N.A.I.C.S.: 322299
Zvone Gecic *(Gen Mgr)*

Aero Papirotti d.o.o. (1)
Ipavceva ulica 32 pp 430
3000 Celje, Slovenia
Tel.: (386) 34235100
Fax: (386) 34235245
Web Site: www.aero.si/ps/about_us_PAP.htm
Emp.: 97
Paper Mfr
S.I.C.: 2679
N.A.I.C.S.: 322299

AERO INVENTORY PLC

30 Lancaster Rd
New Barnet, EN4 8AP, United Kingdom
Tel.: (44) 2084499263
Fax: (44) 2084493555
E-Mail: info@aero-inventory.com
Web Site: www.aero-inventory.com
Sales Range: $400-449.9 Million
Emp.: 115

Business Description:
Procurement & Inventory Management Solution Services for Aerospace Industry
S.I.C.: 4731
N.A.I.C.S.: 541614

Personnel:
Nigel Mccorkell *(Chm)*
Collin Trupp *(CEO)*

Board of Directors:
Nigel Mccorkell
Roger Davis
Laurence Heyworth
Collin Trupp
Frank Turner
Martin Jeffrey Webster

Subsidiary:

Aero Inventory (UK) Limited (1)
30 Lancaster Road
New Barnet, Herts, EN4 8AP, United Kingdom
Tel.: (44) 2084499263
Fax: (44) 2084493555
E-Mail: info@aero-inventory.com
Web Site: www.aeroinv.com
Emp.: 60
Procurement & Inventory Management Services
S.I.C.: 8741
N.A.I.C.S.: 561110
Andrew Pye *(Program Dir)*

U.S. Subsidiary:

Aero Inventory (USA) Inc (1)
12257 Florence Ave
Santa Fe Springs, CA 90670
Tel.: (562) 236-5500
Fax: (562) 236-5565
E-Mail: enquiries.usa@aero-inventory.com
Emp.: 6
Aerospace Industry Services
S.I.C.: 3812
N.A.I.C.S.: 334511
Jenni Finsen *(Sr Mgr-HR)*

Non-U.S. Subsidiaries:

Aero Inventory (Canada) Inc (1)
394 Isabey Ste 250
Saint Laurent, QC, H4T 1V3, Canada
Tel.: (514) 764-9520
Fax: (514) 764-9527
E-Mail: enquiries.canada@aero-inventory.com
Emp.: 60
Aerospace Industry Services
S.I.C.: 3624
N.A.I.C.S.: 335991

Aero Inventory (Hong Kong) Limited (1)
Units 01-06 6th Fl Airport Freight Forwarding Ctr
2 Chun Wan Rd Chek Lap Kok, Hong Kong, China (Hong Kong)

Tel.: (852) 3657 2600
Fax: (852) 3657 2601
E-Mail: enquiries.hk@aero-inventory.com
Procurement & Inventory Management Services
S.I.C.: 8741
N.A.I.C.S.: 561110
Martin Dodge *(Mng Dir)*

Aero Inventory (Japan) KK (1)
Utility Ctr Bldg 4th Fl
3-5-10 Haneda Airport Otaku, Tokyo, 144 0041, Japan
Tel.: (81) 357567700
Fax: (81) 357560303
E-Mail: enquiries.japan@aero-inventory.com
Aerospace Industry Services
S.I.C.: 3812
N.A.I.C.S.: 334511

AEROC INTERNATIONAL AS

Vaike-Manniku Tn 3
Tallinn, Estonia
Tel.: (372) 679 9080
E-Mail: aeroc@aeroc.eu
Web Site: www.aeroc.eu
Sales Range: $10-24.9 Million

Business Description:
Aerated Concrete Products Mfr
S.I.C.: 3272
N.A.I.C.S.: 327390

Personnel:
Ivar Papalavskis *(CEO)*
Ivar Sikk *(CFO)*
Toomas Nilson *(CTO)*

Non-U.S. Subsidiary:

Jamera-kivitalot Oy (1)
Fallaker 1
02740 Espoo, Finland
Tel.: (358) 207 524 270
Fax: (358) 207 524 277
Web Site: www.jamera.fi
Stone House Mfr
S.I.C.: 3271
N.A.I.C.S.: 327331

AEROCOM GMBH & CO.

Adam-Riese-Strasse 16
D-73529 Schwabisch Gmund, Germany
Tel.: (49) 717110450
Fax: (49) 71711045299
E-Mail: info@aerocom.de
Web Site: www.aerocom.de
Year Founded: 1956
Rev.: $25,794,780
Emp.: 170

Business Description:
Pneumatic Tube Systems Mfr
S.I.C.: 3589
N.A.I.C.S.: 333318

Personnel:
Wolfram Pfitzer *(Owner)*

AEROCRINE AB

Rasundavagen 18 8th floor
SE-169 67 Solna, Sweden

Mailing Address:
PO Box 1024
SE-171 21 Solna, Sweden
Tel.: (46) 86290780
Fax: (46) 86290781
E-Mail: info@aerocrine.com
Web Site: www.aerocrine.com
AERO B—(OMX)
Sls.: $22,756,993
Assets: $47,103,008
Liabilities: $11,256,592
Net Worth: $35,846,417
Earnings: ($31,200,095)
Emp.: 124
Fiscal Year-end: 12/31/12

Business Description:
Medical Monitoring Systems
S.I.C.: 3841
N.A.I.C.S.: 339112

Personnel:
Rolf A. Classon *(Chm)*
Anders Williamsson *(Chm)*
Scott Myers *(Pres & CEO)*
Michael Colerus *(CFO)*
Mats Carlson *(CTO)*
Kathleen Rickard *(Chief Medical Officer)*
Ken Marshall *(Pres-Aerocrine Inc)*

Board of Directors:
Rolf A. Classon
Anders Williamsson
Scott A. Beardsley
Thomas Eklund
Lars Gustafsson
Dennie Kane
Staffan Lindstrand

Subsidiary:

Aerocrine ESOP AB (1)
Sundbybergsvagen 9
PO Box 1024
171 73 Solna, Stockholm, Sweden
Tel.: (46) 8 629 07 80
Fax: (46) 8 629 07 81
E-Mail: info@aerocrine.com
Web Site: www.aerocrine.com
Emp.: 100
Medical Diagnostic Services
S.I.C.: 7629
N.A.I.C.S.: 811219
Scott Myers *(Gen Mgr)*

U.S. Subsidiary:

Aerocrine, Inc. USA (1)
562 Central Ave
New Providence, NJ 07974
Tel.: (908) 464-1116
Fax: (908) 464-1185
Toll Free: (866) 275-6469
E-Mail: info.us@aerocrine.com
Web Site: www.aerocrine.com
Medical Diagnostic Equipment Mfr & Sales
S.I.C.: 3841
N.A.I.C.S.: 339112
Ken Marshall *(Pres)*

Non-U.S. Subsidiaries:

Aerocrine AG (1)
Hessenring 119-121
61348 Bad Homburg, Hesse, Germany
Tel.: (49) 6172 925 824
Fax: (49) 6172 925 886
E-Mail: info@aerocrine.de
Web Site: www.aerocrine.com
Medical Diagnostic Services
S.I.C.: 8071
N.A.I.C.S.: 621512

Aerocrine Ltd (1)
960 Capability Green
Luton, Bedfordshire, LU1 3PE, United Kingdom
Tel.: (44) 1582635723
Fax: (44) 1582635001
E-Mail: sales.uk@aerocrine.com
Web Site: www.aerocrine.com
Emp.: 4
General Medical Services
S.I.C.: 8062
N.A.I.C.S.: 622110
David Plotts *(Mng Dir)*

AERODROM LJUBLJANA, D.D.

Zg Brnik 130a
Brnik-aerodrom, 4210 Ljubljana, Slovenia
Tel.: (386) 42061000
Fax: (386) 42021220
E-Mail: info@lju-airport.si
Web Site: www.lju-airport.si
Year Founded: 1963
AELG—(LJU)
Rev.: $41,524,041
Assets: $175,384,004
Liabilities: $7,875,930
Net Worth: $167,508,074
Earnings: $6,990,727
Emp.: 400
Fiscal Year-end: 12/31/12

Business Description:
Airport Operator
S.I.C.: 4512
N.A.I.C.S.: 481111

Personnel:
Milan Perovic *(Chm-Supervisory Bd)*
Zmago Skobir *(Chm-Mgmt Board)*
Bernarda Trebusak *(Member-Mgmt Bd)*

Supervisory Board of Directors:
Milan Perovic
Drago Cotar
Peter Grasek
Peter Marn
Nina Mauhler
Tadeja Strupi

AEROMECHANICAL SERVICES LTD.

(See Under FLYHT Aerospace Solutions Ltd.)

AEROPLEX OF CENTRAL EUROPE LTD.

Ferenc Liszt International Airport
1185 Budapest, Hungary
Tel.: (36) 1 296 8597
Fax: (36) 1 296 7593
E-Mail: marketing@aeroplex.com
Web Site: www.aeroplex.com
Year Founded: 1992
Emp.: 350

Business Description:
Aircraft Maintenance & Overhaul
S.I.C.: 4581
N.A.I.C.S.: 488119

Personnel:
Zoltan Erdodi *(Mng Dir)*
Peter Juhasz *(Deputy Mng Dir-Ops)*
Janos Theobald *(Deputy Mng Dir-Admin)*

AEROPORTO DI FIRENZE S.P.A.

Via del Termine 11
Florence, 50127, Italy
Tel.: (39) 5530615
Fax: (39) 553061355
E-Mail: advertising@aeroporto.firenze.it
Web Site: www.aeroporto.firenze.it
Year Founded: 1984
AFI—(ITA)

Business Description:
Freight Services
S.I.C.: 4731
N.A.I.C.S.: 488510

Personnel:
Marco Carrai *(Chm)*
Umberto Preziosa *(Dir Gen-Airport & Mgr-Accountable)*

Board of Directors:
Marco Carrai
Alberto Cammilli
Stefano Cao
Aldighiero Fini
Marco Giustiniani
Carlo Longo
Mario Mauro
Jacopo Mazzei
Maurizio Montagnese
Aldo Napoli
Fausto Palombelli
Saverio Panerai

AEROPORTS DE MONTREAL

975 Romeo Vachon Blvd N
Dorval, QC, H4Y 1H1, Canada
Tel.: (514) 394-7377
Fax: (514) 394-7356
Toll Free: (800) 465-1213
Web Site: www.admtl.com
Year Founded: 1992
Sales Range: $250-299.9 Million
Emp.: 600

Business Description:
Airport Management Services
S.I.C.: 4581
N.A.I.C.S.: 488119

Personnel:
Real Raymond *(Chm)*
James C. Cherry *(Pres & CEO)*
Philippe Rainville *(CFO & VP-Fin-Admin)*

Board of Directors:
Real Raymond
Laurent N Benarrous
Robert Bouchard
Jean Jacques Bourgeault
Michele Gouin
Robert Guay
Isabelle Hudon
Charles Lapointe
Madeleine Paquin
Pierre Pilote
Raymond Reid
Louis A Tanguay

AEROPORTS DE PARIS S.A.

291 boulevard Raspail
75675 Paris, Cedex 14, France
Tel.: (33) 143357000
Fax: (33) 143357200
E-Mail: adpweb@adp.fr
Web Site: www.aeroportsdeparis.fr
ADP—(EUR)
Rev.: $3,554,494,577
Assets: $12,630,773,875
Liabilities: $7,606,030,117
Net Worth: $5,024,743,758
Earnings: $459,282,242
Emp.: 9,035
Fiscal Year-end: 12/31/12

Business Description:
Commercial Airport Operator
S.I.C.: 4581
N.A.I.C.S.: 488119

Personnel:
Augustin de Romanet *(Chm & CEO)*
Francois Rubichon *(COO)*
Corinne Bokobza-Servadio *(Press Officer-Audiovisuals)*
Aurelie Cohen *(IR Officer)*
Jerome Landras *(Press Officer)*
Jerome Marmet *(Press Officer-Fin, Real Estate & Subsidiaries)*
Didier Hamon *(Gen Sec)*

Board of Directors:
Augustin de Romanet
Regine Brehier
Dominique Bureau
Els A. de Groot
Marie-Anne Donsimoni
Jerome Fournel
Arnaud Framery
Serge Gentili
Nicolas Golias
Jacques Gounon
Catherine Guillouard
Jean-Paul Jouvent
Solenne Lepage
Francoise Malrieu
Frederic Mougin
Jos Nijhuis
Frederic Perrin
Jean-Claude Ruysschaert

Ernst & Young et Autres
1-2 Place des Saisons Paris La Defense 1
92400 Courbevoie, France

Subsidiaries:

ADP Ingenierie (1)
Airport Orly Cent Pk Bldg 641
91200 Athis-Mons, Essonne, France
Tel.: (33) 149751100
Fax: (33) 149751391
Emp.: 25
Airport Fields & Terminal Services
S.I.C.: 4581
N.A.I.C.S.: 488119

Aeroports de Paris S.A.—(Continued)

Pierre Graff *(CEO)*
Francois Rubichon *(Mng Dir)*

Non-U.S. Subsidiary:

ADPI Libya **(2)**
El Nasser St
Tripoli, Libya
Tel.: (218) 21 333 8430
Web Site: www.adp-i.com
Airport Fields & Terminal Services
S.I.C.: 4581
N.A.I.C.S.: 488119

Alyzia **(1)**
Roissypole Le Dome 4 rue de la Haye
BP 11911
93731 Charles de Gaulle, France
Tel.: (33) 174371109
Fax: (33) 148162468
Web Site: www.alyzia.com
Rev.: $203,875,200
Emp.: 2,000
Airport Ground Handling Services
S.I.C.: 4581
N.A.I.C.S.: 488119
Jacques Salina *(Chm & CEO)*
Francois Guth *(Deputy CEO)*

Subsidiary:

ALYZIA SURETE **(2)**
4 rue de la Haye
Le Vesinet, Yvelines, 95731, France
Tel.: (33) 148168330
Fax: (33) 148 625767
Air Freight Transportation Services
S.I.C.: 4581
N.A.I.C.S.: 488190
Francis Gisselman *(Mgr)*

Hub Telecom **(1)**
Roissypole Le Dome
4 rue de la Haye, Roissy-en-France, Val-d Oise, France
Tel.: (33) 170038500
Fax: (33) 170039635
E-Mail: business@hubtelecom.com
Web Site: www.hubtelecom.com
Sales Range: $150-199.9 Million
Emp.: 700
Telecommunication Services
S.I.C.: 4899
N.A.I.C.S.: 517919
Soukeyna Gueye *(Gen Mgr)*

AEROSTAR S.A.

9 Condorilor Street
Bacau, 600302, Romania
Tel.: (40) 234575070
Fax: (40) 234572023
E-Mail: aerostar@aerostar.ro
Web Site: www.aerostar.ro
ARS—(BUC)
Rev.: $63,836,523
Assets: $73,985,040
Liabilities: $34,583,232
Net Worth: $39,401,808
Earnings: $4,636,122
Emp.: 1,376
Fiscal Year-end: 12/31/12

Business Description:
Aviation & Defense Systems Maintenance Services
S.I.C.: 4581
N.A.I.C.S.: 488190

Personnel:
Grigore Filip *(Chm & Gen Dir)*
Doru Damaschin *(Vice Chm & Dir-Acctg)*

Board of Directors:
Grigore Filip
Doru Damaschin
Marin-Ilie Nijnic
Mihail-Nicolae Toncea
Daniel Virna

AEROSVIT AIRLINES

58A T Chevchenko Blvd
01032 Kiev, Ukraine
Tel.: (380) 444903490
Fax: (380) 44 496 2881
E-Mail: info@aerosvit.com
Web Site: www.aerosvit.com
Year Founded: 1994
Sales Range: $150-199.9 Million
Emp.: 1,600

Business Description:
International Air Transportation Services
Import Export
S.I.C.: 4512
N.A.I.C.S.: 481111

Personnel:
Aron Mayberg *(Chm-Supervisory Bd)*

Supervisory Board of Directors:
Aron Mayberg

AERTE GROUP PLC

Masters House 107 Hammersmith Road
London, W14 0QH, United Kingdom
Tel.: (44) 2076031515
Fax: (44) 2076038448
E-Mail: aertegroup@aerte.com
Web Site: www.aertegroup.com
Sales Range: Less than $1 Million
Emp.: 23

Business Description:
Air Cleaning & Disinfection Device Mfr
S.I.C.: 3564
N.A.I.C.S.: 333413

Personnel:
Andrew Tonks *(CEO)*
John Morton *(COO)*
Tony Hunter *(Sec)*

Board of Directors:
Glenn Cooper
Esteban Monegal
Andrew Tonks

Legal Counsel:
Hogan Lovells International LLP
Atlantic House Holborn Viaduct
London, EC1A 2FG, United Kingdom

Subsidiaries:

AD Science Limited **(1)**
Mill Court Feathstone Road
Milton Keynes, Buckinghamshire, MK12 5EU, United Kingdom
Tel.: (44) 1908 682522
Emp.: 20
Air Disinfectants Distr
S.I.C.: 5169
N.A.I.C.S.: 424690
Stephen Howard *(Mgr-Logistic)*

AERTICKET AG

Boppstrasse 10
10967 Berlin, Germany
Tel.: (49) 30 6980 2180
Fax: (49) 30 6980 2178
E-Mail: info@aer.de
Web Site: www.aerticket.de
Year Founded: 2002
Rev.: $54,011,033
Assets: $57,058,762
Liabilities: $41,071,647
Net Worth: $15,987,115
Earnings: $4,980,829
Emp.: 450
Fiscal Year-end: 12/31/12

Business Description:
Airline Ticket Commercial Whslr
S.I.C.: 7389
N.A.I.C.S.: 425120

Personnel:
Wolfgang Altmuller *(Chm-Supervisory Bd)*
Rainer Klee *(Chm-Mgmt Bd)*
Roland Kreling-Behmenburg *(CFO & Member-Mgmt Bd)*
Jttka Zimmermann *(Member-Mgmt Bd-HR, Ops & Sls)*
Uwe Zobel *(Member-Mgmt Bd-IT)*

Supervisory Board of Directors:
Wolfgang Altmuller
Kay Fischer
Rainer Hageloch
Gerd Massheimer
Christoph Rische

Non-U.S. Subsidiary:

Airtrade Holland B.V. **(1)**
Nobelstraat 19
2011 TX Haarlem, Netherlands NL
Tel.: (31) 23 5160 260
Fax: (31) 23 5329 992
E-Mail: info@airtrade.nl
Web Site: www.airtrade.com
Sales Range: $300-349.9 Million
Airline Ticket Commercial Whslr
S.I.C.: 7389
N.A.I.C.S.: 425120
Wim Butte *(Co-Founder & CEO)*
Andre Hesselink *(Co-Founder)*
Frank Wester *(CFO & Head-Ops & IT)*

AESICA PHARMACEUTICALS LIMITED

Q5 Quorum Business Park Benton Lane
Newcastle, Tyne & Wear, NE12 8BS, United Kingdom
Tel.: (44) 191 218 1960
Fax: (44) 191 218 1960
E-Mail: info@aesica-pharma.com
Web Site: www.aesica-pharma.com
Year Founded: 2004
Sales Range: $250-299.9 Million
Emp.: 1,200

Business Description:
Pharmaceutical Product Mfr
S.I.C.: 2834
N.A.I.C.S.: 325412

Personnel:
Robert Hardy *(CEO)*
Nick Jones *(CFO)*
Chris Gowland *(COO)*

AESSEAL PLC

Mill Close
Rotherham, S60 1BZ, United Kingdom
Tel.: (44) 1709 369966
Fax: (44) 1709 720788
E-Mail: seals@aesseal.com
Web Site: www.aesseal.co.uk
Year Founded: 1979
Sales Range: $25-49.9 Million
Emp.: 1,268

Business Description:
Metal Product Mfr
S.I.C.: 3499
N.A.I.C.S.: 332999

Personnel:
Chris Rea *(Mng Dir)*

AETERNA ZENTARIS, INC.

1405 du Parc Technologique Blvd
Quebec, QC, G1P 4P5, Canada
Tel.: (418) 652-8525
Fax: (418) 652-0881
E-Mail: cgravel@aezsinc.com
Web Site: www.aezsinc.com
Year Founded: 1990
AEZS—(NASDAQ TSX)
Rev.: $33,665,000
Assets: $67,665,000
Liabilities: $74,360,000
Net Worth: ($6,695,000)
Earnings: ($20,412,000)
Emp.: 81
Fiscal Year-end: 12/31/12

Business Description:
Pharmaceutical Developer
S.I.C.: 2834
N.A.I.C.S.: 325412

Personnel:
Juergen Ernst *(Chm)*
David Alan Dodd *(Pres & CEO)*
Dennis Turpin *(CFO & Sr VP)*
Paul Blake *(Chief Medical Officer & Sr VP)*
Jude Dinges *(Chief Comml Officer & Sr VP)*
Richard Sachse *(Chief Scientific Officer & Sr VP)*
Nicholas J. Pelliccione *(Sr VP-Regulatory Affairs & Quality Assurance)*
Matthias Seeber *(Sr VP-Admin & Legal Affairs)*

Board of Directors:
Juergen Ernst
Marcel Aubut
David Alan Dodd
Jose P. Dorais
Pierre Lapalme
Gerard A. Limoges
Michael Evan Meyers

Legal Counsel:
Ogilvy Renault
500 Grande Allee East, Suite 520
Quebec, QC, Canada G1R 2J7

Haynes and Boone, LLP
901 Main St Ste 3100
Dallas, TX 75202

Arnold & Porter
399 Park Ave.
New York, NY 10022-4690

Transfer Agent:
National Bank Trust
1100 University Fl 12
Montreal, QC, H3B 2J7, Canada
Tel.: (514) 871-7240
Fax: (514) 871-7587

U.S. Subsidiary:

AEterna Zentaris, Inc. **(1)**
20 Independence Blvd 4th Fl
Warren, NJ 07059 (100%)
Tel.: (908) 625-5428
Fax: (908) 326-5426
Web Site: www.aezsinc.com
Pharmaceutical Development Services
S.I.C.: 2834
N.A.I.C.S.: 325412

Non-U.S. Subsidiary:

AEterna Zentaris GmbH **(1)**
Weismullerstrasse 50
60314 Frankfurt am Main, Germany (100%)
Tel.: (49) 69426023228
Fax: (49) 69426023444
Web Site: www.aezsinc.com
Emp.: 100
Pharmaceutical Product Developer
S.I.C.: 2834
N.A.I.C.S.: 325412
Juegen Engel *(Mng Dir)*

AEVIS HOLDING SA

Rue Hans-Geiler 6
1700 Fribourg, Switzerland
Tel.: (41) 26 350 02 02
Fax: (41) 26 350 02 03
E-Mail: info@aevis.com
Web Site: www.aevis.com
Year Founded: 2002
G5L—(DEU SWX)
Rev.: $371,724,284
Assets: $792,704,415
Liabilities: $618,351,062
Net Worth: $174,353,353
Earnings: $3,588,739
Emp.: 1,435
Fiscal Year-end: 12/31/12

Business Description:
Investment Management Services
S.I.C.: 6211
N.A.I.C.S.: 523999

Personnel:
Christian Wenger *(Chm)*
Raymond Loretan *(Vice Chm)*
Beat Rothlisberger *(CEO)*
Pierre-Olivier Haenni *(Mng Dir)*
Antoine Hubert *(Mng Dir)*
Gilles Frachon *(CFO)*
Severine Van der Schueren *(Chief Admin Officer)*

Board of Directors:
Christian Wenger
Cedric A. George
Antoine Hubert
Antoine Kohler
Raymond Loretan
Michel Reybier

Subsidiary:

Genolier Swiss Medical Network SA (1)
Route du Muids 3
Case Postale
CH-1272 Genolier, Switzerland
Tel.: (41) 22 366 9990
Fax: (41) 22 366 9998
E-Mail: info@gsmn.ch
Web Site: www.gsmn.ch
Medical Clinic Operator
S.I.C.: 8062
N.A.I.C.S.: 622110

AEVITAS, INC.

(Formerly Contech PCB Containment Technology Inc)
75 Wanless Court
Ayr, ON, N0B 1E0, Canada
Tel.: (519) 740-1333
Fax: (519) 740-2320
Web Site: www.aevitas.ca
Business Description:
Waste Treatment & Disposal
S.I.C.: 4953
N.A.I.C.S.: 562211
Personnel:
Byron Day *(CEO)*

U.S. Subsidiary:

Aevitas Specialty Services Corp. (1)
663 Lycaste St
Detroit, MI 48214 MI
Tel.: (313) 924-5175
Fax: (313) 499-8998
Toll Free: (800) 323-9905
Web Site: www.aevitas.us.com
Emp.: 25
Oil Recycling
S.I.C.: 5093
N.A.I.C.S.: 423930
Adam Westerdale *(CEO)*

AEXIS N.V.

392B Leuvensesteenweg
1932 Brussels, Belgium
Tel.: (32) 27251644
Fax: (32) 27253032
E-Mail: info@aexis.com
Web Site: www.aexis.com
Emp.: 200
Business Description:
IT & Customer Service Management Solutions Distr, Supplier & Integrator
S.I.C.: 7373
N.A.I.C.S.: 541512
Personnel:
Frank Peeters *(Mng Dir)*

Non-U.S. Subsidiary:

Aexis Nederland (1)
Plesmanstraat 2
3833 LA Leusden, Netherlands (100%)
Tel.: (31) 334321540
Fax: (31) 334321521
E-Mail: info@nl.aexis.com
Web Site: www.aexis.nl
Emp.: 35
Business Intelligence Solutions
S.I.C.: 3652
N.A.I.C.S.: 334614

AF AB

(d/b/a AF Group)
Frosundaleden 2
Solna, Sweden
Tel.: (46) 10 505 00 00
E-Mail: info@afconsult.com
Web Site: www.afconsult.com
AF B—(OMX)
Rev.: $897,654,240
Assets: $1,163,461,320
Liabilities: $633,813,120
Net Worth: $529,648,200
Earnings: $54,690,840
Emp.: 6,867
Fiscal Year-end: 12/31/12
Business Description:
Holding Company; Technical Consulting & Engineering Services
S.I.C.: 6719
N.A.I.C.S.: 551112
Personnel:
Ulf Dinkelspiel *(Chm)*
Jonas Wistrom *(Pres & CEO)*
Stefan Johansson *(CFO)*
Jacob Landen *(Chief Legal Officer)*
Eero Auranne *(Pres-Intl-North Div)*
Roberto Gerosa *(Pres-Intl Div)*
Viktor Svensson *(Exec VP-Corp Info)*
Board of Directors:
Ulf Dinkelspiel
Anders Forslund
Marika Fredriksson
Bengt Lerken
Anders Narvinger
Bjorn O. Nilsson
Maud Olofsson
Joakim Rubin
Kristina Schauman
Anders Snell
Fredrik Sundin
Anders Toll
Lena Treschow Torell

Divisions:

AF-Consult AB (1)
Frosundaleden 2
SE-169 99 Stockholm, Sweden SE (100%)
Tel.: (46) 105050000
Fax: (46) 105050010
E-Mail: info@afconsult.com
Web Site: www.afconsult.com
Sales Range: $150-199.9 Million
Emp.: 950
Energy Industry Consulting & Engineering Services
S.I.C.: 8999
N.A.I.C.S.: 541690
Jonas Wistrom *(CEO)*

Non-U.S. Subsidiaries:

AF-Automatikka OU (2)
Lesta 14
13516 Tallinn, Harju, Estonia
Tel.: (372) 6718130
Fax: (372) 6718140
E-Mail: post@automaatika.ee
Web Site: www.automaatika.ee
Emp.: 17
Industrial Automation Services
S.I.C.: 7389
N.A.I.C.S.: 561990
Karl Kurm *(Mng Dir)*

AF-Consult OY (2)
Bertel Jungin aukio 9
02600 Espoo, Finland, Finland
Tel.: (358) 403485511
Fax: (358) 934870810
E-Mail: info@afconsult.com
Web Site: www.afconsult.com
Sales Range: $150-199.9 Million
Emp.: 270
Design, Engineering, Consulting & Project Management Services
S.I.C.: 8999
N.A.I.C.S.: 541690
Peter Kling *(VP-Waste)*

Affiliate:

Elron Oy (3)
Yliopistonkatu 5
00100 Helsinki, Finland
Tel.: (358) 503719052
Web Site: www.elron.fi
Emp.: 20
Financial & Project Development Advisory Services
S.I.C.: 6282
N.A.I.C.S.: 523930
Martti Lehtinen *(Mng Dir)*

Non-U.S. Subsidiaries:

AF-Consult, LLC (3)
Office 11 Malaya Pirogovskaya Str 16
119435 Moscow, Russia
Tel.: (7) 495 647 1051
Fax: (7) 495 647 1052
Web Site: www.afconsult.com
Emp.: 300
Technical Consulting Services
S.I.C.: 8999
N.A.I.C.S.: 541690
Timur Panfiorov *(CFO)*

AF-Consult UAB (3)
(Formerly UAB AF-Enprima)
Lvovo Str 25
09320 Vilnius, Lithuania
Tel.: (370) 5 210 72 10
Fax: (370) 5 210 72 11
E-Mail: info.lt@afconsult.com
Web Site: www.afconsult.com
Emp.: 25
Engineering Consulting Services
S.I.C.: 8711
N.A.I.C.S.: 541330
Darius Cicinskas *(Mng Dir)*

AF-Estivo AS (3)
Vaike Ameerica 8 3rd Fl
10129 Tallinn, Estonia
Tel.: (372) 6053150
Fax: (372) 6053155
E-Mail: estivo@afconsults.com
Web Site: www.estivo.ee
Sls.: $79,301
Emp.: 17
Design, Engineering, Consulting & Project Management Services
S.I.C.: 8999
N.A.I.C.S.: 541620
Juri Alasi *(Mng Dir)*

AF-Consult Switzerland Ltd. (2)
Tafernstrasse 26
CH-5405 Baden, Switzerland CH
Tel.: (41) 56 483 1212
Fax: (41) 56 483 1255
E-Mail: swiss-info@afconsult.com
Web Site: www.afconsult.com
Emp.: 230
Energy & Environmental Technology Engineering & Consulting Services
S.I.C.: 8711
N.A.I.C.S.: 541330
Eero Kalevi Auranne *(Chm)*
Roberto Gerosa *(CEO)*
Hubert Hosp *(Mng Dir & Sr VP-Energy & Environmental)*
Dominik Heitzmann *(CFO)*

Non-U.S. Subsidiaries:

AF-Colenco Thailand Ltd. (3)
UBC II Building 24th Floor 591 Sukhumvit Road 33 North Klongton
Watthana, Bangkok, 10110, Thailand
Tel.: (66) 22610294
Fax: (66) 22610297
E-Mail: colenco-thailand@afconsult.com
Web Site: www.colenco.ch
Emp.: 5
Environmental Engineering Services
S.I.C.: 8711
N.A.I.C.S.: 541330

AF-Consult India Pvt. Ltd. (3)
A-152 Sector 63
Noida, Uttar Pradesh, 201301, India
Tel.: (91) 120 30961 31
Fax: (91) 120 30961 50
E-Mail: afconsultindia@afconsult.com
Web Site: www.colenco.ch/eng/address/int_offices.html
Emp.: 40
Environmental Engineering Services
S.I.C.: 8711
N.A.I.C.S.: 541330
Jothi Ekanthapa *(Mgr)*

AF-Engineering Oy (2)
Vuolteenkatu 20
33100 Tampere, Pirkanmaa, Finland
Tel.: (358) 10 425 1600
Fax: (358) 357 57 657
Web Site: www.afconsult.com
Civil Engineering Services
S.I.C.: 8711
N.A.I.C.S.: 541330

AF-Engineering s.r.o (2)
Krizikova 68
612 00 Brno, Czech Republic
Tel.: (420) 532043051
Fax: (420) 532043052
E-Mail: info@afconsult.com
Web Site: www.afconsult.com
Emp.: 8
Engineering Services
S.I.C.: 8711
N.A.I.C.S.: 541330
Mrichal Kovirik *(Gen Mgr)*

AF-Industry AB (1)
Frosundaleden 2
SE-169 99 Stockholm, Sweden SE (100%)
Tel.: (46) 105059597
Fax: (46) 10 505 0010
E-Mail: info@afconsult.com
Emp.: 1,350
Industrial Automation, IT & Mechanical Engineering Consulting Services
S.I.C.: 8999
N.A.I.C.S.: 541690
Per Magnusson *(Pres)*

Subsidiary:

OrbiTec AB (2)
Glansgatan 2
Jonkoping, Smaland, 554 54, Sweden
Tel.: (46) 36162870
Fax: (46) 36167660
Emp.: 35
Technical Consulting Services
S.I.C.: 8999
N.A.I.C.S.: 541690
Jan-Erik Andersson *(Mgr-Sls)*

Non-U.S. Subsidiaries:

AF A/S (2)
Engelsholmvej 26
8940 Randers, Denmark
Tel.: (45) 70104043
Fax: (45) 70 10 49 45
Web Site: www.af.se/sv/Kontakt/Adresser2/Danmark/
Emp.: 100
Industrial Automation, IT & Mechanical Engineering Consulting Services
S.I.C.: 8999
N.A.I.C.S.: 541690
Anders Bennermark *(Gen Mgr)*

AF Industrier AS (2)
Haslevangen 15
NO-0579 Oslo, Norway NO (100%)
Tel.: (47) 24101010
Fax: (47) 24101011
E-Mail: firmapost@afconsult.com
Emp.: 100
Industrial Automation, IT & Mechanical Engineering Consulting Services
S.I.C.: 8999
N.A.I.C.S.: 541690
Ove Guttormsen *(Mgr-Ops)*

Subsidiaries:

AF-Ingemansson AB (1)
Frosundaleden 2
SE-169 99 Stockholm, Sweden SE (100%)
Tel.: (46) 10 505 1014
Web Site: www.ingemansson.com
Sound & Vibration Technical Consulting Services
S.I.C.: 8999
N.A.I.C.S.: 541690
Maira Slokenbergs *(Gen Mgr)*

Nordblads VVS-Konstruktioner AB (1)
Halleblrg Gata 1
Malmo, Scania, 21119, Sweden
Tel.: (46) 105055250
Fax: (46) 105053801
Web Site: www.afconsult.com
Emp.: 50
Technical Consulting Services
S.I.C.: 8999
N.A.I.C.S.: 541690
Mats Tahlssln *(Mgr-Div)*

Non-U.S. Subsidiaries:

AF Brasil Consultoria Em Processos Industrias Ltda. (1)
Rua Humberto Zanato 10 Pinheirinho
81870-250 Curitiba, Parana, Brazil

AF AB—(Continued)

Tel.: (55) 4136163616
E-Mail: comercial@a1.img.br
Web Site: www.afconsult.com
Technical Consulting Services
S.I.C.: 8742
N.A.I.C.S.: 541611

AF-Hansen & Henneberg A/S (1)
Lyskar 3 Sal Ef
2400 Herlev, Hovedstaden, Denmark
Tel.: (45) 38165000
E-Mail: mail@afhh.dk
Emp.: 90
Civil Engineering Services
S.I.C.: 8711
N.A.I.C.S.: 541330

AF Norge AS (1)
Haslevangen 15
NO-0579 Oslo, Norway NO
Tel.: (47) 24101010 (100%)
Fax: (47) 24101011
E-Mail: info.no@afconsult.com
Web Site: www.afconsult.no
Emp.: 100
Infrastructure Consulting Services
S.I.C.: 8999
N.A.I.C.S.: 541690
Reinert E. Vigtel *(CFO)*
Ove Guttormsen *(CEO-Norway)*

AFA FOREST PRODUCTS INC.

244 Ellwood Drive West
PO Box 892
Bolton, ON, L7E 5T5, Canada
Tel.: (905) 857-6423
Fax: (905) 857-5626
Web Site: www.afaforest.com
Year Founded: 1974
Rev.: $34,633,250
Emp.: 170

Business Description:
Plywood & Lumber Products Distr
S.I.C.: 5031
N.A.I.C.S.: 423310

Personnel:
Frank Ingoldsby *(Co-Founder)*
Alan Jack *(Co-Founder)*
Gord Pace *(Co-Founder)*
Al Young *(Co-Founder)*
Grant Yegavian *(CFO)*

AFAQ FOR ENERGY CO. PLC

PO Box 925988
Amman, 11110, Jordan
Tel.: (962) 6 5734030
Fax: (962) 6 5734070
Year Founded: 2008
MANE—(AMM)
Rev.: $604,059,289
Assets: $305,639,355
Liabilities: $135,243,332
Net Worth: $170,396,023
Earnings: $10,248,428
Emp.: 647
Fiscal Year-end: 12/31/12

Business Description:
Investment Management Services
S.I.C.: 6211
N.A.I.C.S.: 523999

Personnel:
Ziad Khalaf Mohamed Manasir *(Chm)*

AFARAK GROUP PLC

(Formerly Ruukki Group Oyj)
Kasarmikatu 36
00130 Helsinki, Finland
Tel.: (358) 104407000
Fax: (358) 104407001
E-Mail: feedback@ruukkigroup.fi
Web Site: www.ruukkigroup.fi
AFAGR—(HEL LSE)
Rev.: $175,529,799
Assets: $420,655,240
Liabilities: $130,932,533
Net Worth: $289,722,707
Earnings: ($22,602,194)
Emp.: 782
Fiscal Year-end: 12/31/12

Business Description:
Mining & Mineral Production Services
S.I.C.: 1099
N.A.I.C.S.: 212299

Personnel:
Jelena Manojlovic *(Chm)*
Bernice Marguerite Smart *(Deputy Chm)*
Danko Koncar *(CEO)*
Stefano Bonati *(Chief Comml Officer)*
Alistair Ruiters *(Chm-South Africa)*

Board of Directors:
Jelena Manojlovic
Markku Kankaala
Danko Koncar
Michael Lillja
Alfredo Parodi
Bernice Marguerite Smart

Capita Registrars
The Registry 34 Beckenham Road
Beckenham, United Kingdom

Subsidiary:

Pohjolan Design-Talo Oy (1)
Karhuojantie 2
90460 Oulunsalo, Pohjois Pohjanmaa, Finland
Tel.: (358) 207 463 940
Fax: (358) 207 463 941
E-Mail: myynti@designtalo.fi
Web Site: www.designtalo.fi
Residential Design & Building Services
S.I.C.: 1531
N.A.I.C.S.: 236117

Non-U.S. Subsidiaries:

Elektrowerk Weisweiler GmbH (1)
Duerener Strasse 487
52249 Eschweiler, Germany
Tel.: (49) 2403646380
Telex: 832193
Fax: (49) 2403646376
E-Mail: info@elektrowerk.de
Web Site: www.elektrowerk.com
Sales Range: $25-49.9 Million
Emp.: 110
Electrometallurgical Products Mfr
S.I.C.: 3399
N.A.I.C.S.: 331110
Christoph Schneider *(Mng Dir)*

Mogale Alloys (Pty) Ltd (1)
Deep Shaft Road West Rand Consolidated Mine
Krugersdorp, Gauteng, 1739, South Africa
Tel.: (27) 116683800
Fax: (27) 116683899
Silico Manganese Mining Services
S.I.C.: 1099
N.A.I.C.S.: 212299
Callie Pienaar *(Gen Mgr)*

RCS Ltd (1)
2nd Floor Europa Centre John Lopez Street
Floriana, 1400, Malta
Tel.: (356) 27 030 462
Fax: (356) 21241120
Chemical Products Mfr
S.I.C.: 2899
N.A.I.C.S.: 325998
Stefano Bonati *(Gen Mgr)*

Turk Maadin Sirketi A.S. (1)
Cemil Totuzlucad Suappasa Sok Dalyan Konuk
Site Si A Blok B 12 Senerbahce, 34726
Istanbul, Turkey
Tel.: (90) 2163024265
Telex: 25180
Fax: (90) 2163024269
Web Site: www.ruukkigroup.fi/In_English/Businesses/Minerals/Ferrochrome_and_alloys/Operations.iw3
Emp.: 300
Mining of Chrome Ore
S.I.C.: 1011
N.A.I.C.S.: 212210
Ahmet Hacikeramojnu *(Mgr-Fin)*

AFAS ERP SOFTWARE B.V.

Philipsstraat 9
3833 LC Leusden, Netherlands
Tel.: (31) 33 4341800
E-Mail: info@afas.nl
Web Site: www.afas.nl
Sales Range: $50-74.9 Million
Emp.: 350
Fiscal Year-end: 12/31/12

Business Description:
Enterprise Resource Planning Software Publisher
S.I.C.: 7372
N.A.I.C.S.: 511210

Personnel:
Bas van der Veldt *(CEO)*

AFC AJAX NV

Arena Boulevard 29
1101 AX Amsterdam, Netherlands
Tel.: (31) 20 3111 444
Fax: (31) 20 3111 480
E-Mail: info@ajax.nl
Web Site: www.ajax.nl
AJAX—(EUR)
Sales Range: $75-99.9 Million
Emp.: 284

Business Description:
Soccer Team Owner & Operator
S.I.C.: 7999
N.A.I.C.S.: 711219

Personnel:
Uri Coronel *(Chm-Supervisory Bd)*
Rik van den Boog *(CEO)*
Jeroen Slop *(Mng Dir)*
Henri van der Aat *(Chief Comml Officer)*

Supervisory Board of Directors:
Uri Coronel
Frank Eijken
Joop Krant
Cor van Eijden

AFC ENERGY PLC

Unit 71 4 Dunsfold Park Stovolds Hill
Cranleigh, Surrey, GU6 8TB, United Kingdom
Tel.: (44) 1483276726
Fax: (44) 1483266839
E-Mail: info@afcenergy.com
Web Site: www.afcenergy.com
Year Founded: 2006
AFC—(AIM OTC)
Rev.: $564,386
Assets: $20,167,964
Liabilities: $691,269
Net Worth: $19,476,695
Earnings: ($5,992,340)
Emp.: 29
Fiscal Year-end: 10/31/12

Business Description:
Fuel Cell Producer & Marketer
S.I.C.: 5989
N.A.I.C.S.: 454310

Personnel:
Ian Williamson *(CEO)*
David Marson *(Sec & Dir-Fin)*

Board of Directors:
Timothy Stephen Kenneth Yeo
Adam Steven Bond
Mitchell Field
Gene Lewis
David Marson
Eugene Shvidler
John Michael Sunderland
Eugene Alexander Tenenbaum
Ian Williamson

Legal Counsel:
Eversheds LLP
One Wood Street
EC2V 7WS London, United Kingdom

AFFCO HOLDINGS LIMITED

Great South Road
Private Bag 3301
Hamilton, Horotiu, New Zealand
Tel.: (64) 78292888
Fax: (64) 78292889
E-Mail: operations@affco.co.nz
Web Site: www.affco.co.nz
Year Founded: 1904
AFF—(NZE)
Sales Range: $500-549.9 Million
Emp.: 24

Business Description:
Meat & Associated Products Processor & Marketer
S.I.C.: 5421
N.A.I.C.S.: 445210

Personnel:
Sam Lewis *(Chm)*
Hamish Simson *(CEO)*
Nigel Stevens *(CFO & Sec)*

Board of Directors:
Sam Lewis
Bob W. Carter
Mike J. McCredie
Hamish Simson
Christopher A. Spencer
Andrew Talley
Michael Talley
Arthur W. Young

Subsidiaries:

AFFCO New Zealand Limited (1)
Imlay Place Gonville
PO box 425
Wanganui, New Zealand (100%)
Tel.: (64) 63445179
Fax: (64) 63493442
Web Site: www.AFFCO.com
Emp.: 600
Meat Markets
S.I.C.: 5421
N.A.I.C.S.: 445210
Shiun O'neill *(Mgr-Plant)*

Land Meat New Zealand Limited (1)
Great S Rd Horotiu
Private Bag 3301
Hamilton, 3240, New Zealand (100%)
Tel.: (64) 78292888
Fax: (64) 78292889
E-Mail: reception@affco.co.nz
Web Site: www.affco.co.nz
Emp.: 75
Meat & Meat Product Whslr
S.I.C.: 5147
N.A.I.C.S.: 424470
Hamish Sinsin *(CEO)*

South Pacific Meats Limited (1)
86 Kekeno Pl Awarua
1774 Invercargill, New Zealand (70%)
Tel.: (64) 32183617
Fax: (64) 32149165
Web Site: www.affco.com
Emp.: 1,000
Livestock Whslr
S.I.C.: 5154
N.A.I.C.S.: 424520
Kevin Hamilton *(Mgr-Plant)*

Non-U.S. Subsidiary:

AFFCO Europe Limited (1)
1st Fl Intl House Dover Pl
Ashford, Kent, TN23 1HU, United Kingdom (100%)
Tel.: (44) 1233640728
Fax: (44) 1233661339
E-Mail: info@affcoeurope.co.uk
Web Site: www.affco.co.nz/index1ab3.html?option=com_content&view=article&id=76&Itemid=59
Emp.: 3
Meat Markets
S.I.C.: 5421
N.A.I.C.S.: 445210
Stephen Clapham *(Mgr)*

AFFECTO PLC

Atomitie 2
FI-00370 Helsinki, Finland
Tel.: (358) 20577711
Fax: (358) 205777199
E-Mail: info.fi@affecto.com
Web Site: www.affecto.com
Year Founded: 2004
AFE1V—(OMX)

Sls.: $179,579,078
Assets: $199,117,389
Liabilities: $108,551,110
Net Worth: $90,566,279
Earnings: $10,197,238
Emp.: 1,096
Fiscal Year-end: 12/31/12
Business Description:
Business Intelligence; Document & Knowledge Management; Digital Location-Based Information Systems; Payroll & Material Management Solutions; Cartographic Services & Products
S.I.C.: 7379
N.A.I.C.S.: 541519
Personnel:
Aaro Cantell *(Chm)*
Jukka Ruuska *(Vice Chm)*
Pekka Eloholma *(CEO)*
Satu Kankare *(CFO)*
Rene Lykkeskov *(Chief Strategy Officer)*
Juko Nortio *(Sr VP-Mktg & Comm)*
Hannu Nyman *(Sr VP-IR & M&A)*
Board of Directors:
Aaro Cantell
Magdalena Persson
Jukka Ruuska
Olof Sand
Tuija Soanjarvi
Lars Wahlstrom
Subsidiary:

Affecto Finland Oy (1)
Atomitie 2
00370 Helsinki, Finland FI
Tel.: (358) 205 777 1911
Fax: (358) 205 777 199
Business Intelligence & IT Services
S.I.C.: 7389
N.A.I.C.S.: 561499

Non-U.S. Subsidiaries:

Affecto Denmark A/S (1)
Lyngbyvej 22nd Fl
2100 Copenhagen, Denmark
Tel.: (45) 39 25 00 00
Fax: (45) 39 25 00 01
E-Mail: info.dk@affecto.com
Web Site: www.affecto.dk
Emp.: 70
Information Technology Consulting Services
S.I.C.: 7389
N.A.I.C.S.: 519190
Claus Karuse *(Mng Dir)*

Affecto Estonia OU (1)
Toompuiestee 35
10133 Tallinn, Estonia
Tel.: (372) 6505050
Fax: (372) 650 5010
E-Mail: info.ee@affecto.com
Information Technology Consulting Services
S.I.C.: 7389
N.A.I.C.S.: 519190

Affecto Latvia, SIA (1)
Zigfrida Annas Meierovica bulvaris 16
1050 Riga, Latvia
Tel.: (371) 67201780
Emp.: 180
Business Management Software Development Services
S.I.C.: 7371
N.A.I.C.S.: 541511
Kestutis Naujokaitis *(Gen Mgr)*

Affecto Lietuva UAB (1)
Perkunkiemio Strasse 4A
LT-12128 Vilnius, Lithuania
Tel.: (370) 52123712
Fax: (370) 52123713
E-Mail: info@affecto.lt
Web Site: www.affecto.lt
IT Services
S.I.C.: 7379
N.A.I.C.S.: 541519
Kestutis Naujokaitis *(Head-IT)*

Non-U.S. Subsidiaries:

Mebius IT OU (2)
Tulika 19
10613 Tallinn, Estonia
Tel.: (372) 6505050
Fax: (372) 6505010
E-Mail: andrus.altrov@mebius.ee
Web Site: www.mebius.ee
Emp.: 15
IT Services
S.I.C.: 7379
N.A.I.C.S.: 541519
Andrus Altrov *(Mng Dir)*

Mebius IT, SIA (2)
37 Dzirnavu Str
LV-1010 Riga, Latvia
Tel.: (371) 7201780
Fax: (371) 7201784
IT Services
S.I.C.: 7379
N.A.I.C.S.: 541519

Affecto Norway AS (1)
Grev Wedels plass 5
0103 Oslo, Norway
Tel.: (47) 22 40 20 00
E-Mail: info.no@affecto.com
Web Site: www.affecto.no
Business Management Software Development Services
S.I.C.: 7371
N.A.I.C.S.: 541511

Affecto Poland Sp.z..o.o. (1)
Stawki 2
00-139 Warsaw, Poland
Tel.: (48) 224651440
E-Mail: info.pl@affecto.com
Web Site: www.affecto.pl
Emp.: 20
Business Management Consulting Services
S.I.C.: 8742
N.A.I.C.S.: 541611
Wojoch Popioek *(Gen Mgr)*

Affecto Sweden AB (1)
Hollandar Gatan 17
111 60 Stockholm, Sweden
Tel.: (46) 8 444 98 00
Fax: (46) 8 444 9820
E-Mail: info@affecto.se
Web Site: www.affecto.se
Emp.: 80
Business Administrative Software Development Services
S.I.C.: 7371
N.A.I.C.S.: 541511
Helen Wohlin Lidgard *(Mng Dir)*

AFFERRO MINING INC.
(Acquired & Absorbed by International Mining & Infrastructure Corporation plc)

AFFICHAGE HOLDING SA
(See Under APG/SGA SA)

AFFILIATED CUSTOMS BROKERS LTD
411 Rue Des Recollets
Montreal, QC, H2Y 1W3, Canada
Tel.: (514) 288-1211
Fax: (514) 288-9161
Toll Free: (888) 683-9883
E-Mail: affiliated@affiliated.ca
Web Site: www.affiliated.ca
Emp.: 540
Business Description:
Customs Brokers
S.I.C.: 6221
N.A.I.C.S.: 523140
Personnel:
Gilles M. Remillard *(Pres)*

AFFIN HOLDINGS BERHAD
7th Floor Chulan Tower 3 Jalan Conlay
50450 Kuala Lumpur, Malaysia
Tel.: (60) 321429569
Fax: (60) 321431057
Web Site: www.affin.com.my
AFFIN—(KLS)
Rev.: $974,487,406
Assets: $18,309,180,705
Liabilities: $16,327,066,953
Net Worth: $1,982,113,752
Earnings: $206,242,661
Emp.: 3,853
Fiscal Year-end: 12/31/12
Business Description:
Commercial Banking Services
S.I.C.: 6211
N.A.I.C.S.: 523110
Personnel:
Kasinathan T. Kasipillai *(Chief Risk Officer)*
Nimma Safira Khalid *(Sec)*
Board of Directors:
Mohd Zahidi Zainuddin
Abd Malik A Rahman
Aman Ahmad
Arthur Kwok Cheung Li
David Kwok-po Li
Mustafa Mohamad Ali
Alaudin Mohd Sheriff
Lodin Wok Kamaruddin
Subsidiary:

AFFIN Moneybrokers Sdn. Bhd. (1)
25th Floor Menara Boustead Jalan Raja Chulan
50200 Kuala Lumpur, Federal Territory, Malaysia
Tel.: (60) 321489222
Fax: (60) 327115652
E-Mail: affinmoney@affinmoneybrokers.com.my
Web Site: www.affinmoneybrokers.com.my
Emp.: 46
Money Broking Services
S.I.C.: 6221
N.A.I.C.S.: 523140
Chandra Nair *(CEO)*
Norzaitolshima Ahmad Tajuddin *(Sec)*

AFFINAGE CHAMPAGNE ARDENNES
19 Route De Bazancourt
51110 Isles-sur-Suippe, Marne, France
Tel.: (33) 326038060
Fax: (33) 326038650
Web Site: www.afica.fr
Rev.: $32,500,000
Emp.: 53
Business Description:
Copper Alloy Producer from Recycling Metals
S.I.C.: 1021
N.A.I.C.S.: 212234
Personnel:
Jeanine Rousseaux *(Chm)*
Eric Rousseaux *(Mng Dir)*

AFFINE S.A.
5 Rue Saint Georges
75009 Paris, France
Tel.: (33) 1 44 90 43 00
Fax: (33) 1 44 90 01 48
E-Mail: info@affine.fr
Web Site: www.affine-group.com
IML—(EUR)
Rev.: $62,498,635
Assets: $1,025,992,889
Liabilities: $552,937,981
Net Worth: $473,054,907
Earnings: $6,235,459
Emp.: 42
Fiscal Year-end: 12/31/12
Business Description:
Commercial Property Investment & Management Services
S.I.C.: 6512
N.A.I.C.S.: 531120
Personnel:
Maryse Aulagnon *(Chm & CEO)*
Alain Chaussard *(Vice Chm & Deputy CEO)*
Board of Directors:
Maryse Aulagnon
Stephane Bureau
Jean-Louis Charon
Alain Chaussard
Joelle Chauvin
Arnaud de Bresson
Bertrand de Feydeau
Michel Garbolino
Andrew Walker

Cailliau Dedouit & Associes
19 Rue Clement Marot
75008 Paris, France

Subsidiaries:

Concerto Development SAS (1)
5 rue Saint-Georges
75009 Paris, France
Tel.: (33) 155047901
Fax: (33) 1449001448
E-Mail: info@affine.fr
Web Site: www.warehouse-france.com
Emp.: 5
Commercial Property Development Services
S.I.C.: 1542
N.A.I.C.S.: 236220
Ariel Lahmi *(CEO)*

Non-U.S. Subsidiary:

Banimmo S.A. (1)
Lenneke Marelaan 8
1932 Zaventem, Belgium (50%)
Tel.: (32) 27105311
Fax: (32) 27105313
E-Mail: info@banimmo.be
Web Site: www.banimmo.be
BANI—(EUR)
Rev.: $21,729,876
Assets: $540,227,444
Liabilities: $361,252,797
Net Worth: $178,974,648
Earnings: $3,599,659
Emp.: 30
Fiscal Year-end: 12/31/12
Real Estate Services
S.I.C.: 6531
N.A.I.C.S.: 531390
Maryse Aulagnon *(Chm)*
Didrik van Caloen *(CEO)*
Christian Terlinden *(CFO)*
Filip De Poorter *(COO & Chief Comml Officer)*

Subsidiaries:

Eeklo Invest S.A. (2)
Hippokrateslaan 16
1932 Zaventem, Belgium
Tel.: (32) 2 710 53 11
Fax: (32) 2 710 53 13
Property Repositioning Services
S.I.C.: 1522
N.A.I.C.S.: 236118
Terre Keslanske *(Mng Dir)*

IMMO KONINGSLO S.A. (2)
Hippokrateslaan 16
1932 Zaventem, Belgium
Tel.: (32) 27105311
Fax: (32) 27105313
E-Mail: info@banimmo.be
Web Site: www.banimmo.be
Property Repositioning Services
S.I.C.: 1522
N.A.I.C.S.: 236118
Amaury De Crombrugghe *(Gen Mgr)*

Non-U.S. Subsidiary:

Banimmo France SAS (2)
27 29 Rue des Poissonniers
92522 Neuilly-sur-Seine, France
Tel.: (33) 146417980
Fax: (33) 146419071
E-Mail: banimmo@banimmo.fr
Web Site: www.banimmo.be/Banimmo/EN/Other+Pages/Contact/page.aspx/292
Emp.: 5
Property Repositioning Services
S.I.C.: 1522
N.A.I.C.S.: 236118
Oliver Durand *(Gen Mgr)*

AFFINITY EDUCATION GROUP LIMITED
170 Scarborough Street
Southport, QLD, 4215, Australia

Affinity Education Group Limited—(Continued)

Mailing Address:
PO Box 642
Biggera Waters, Southport, QLD, 4216, Australia
Tel.: (61) 7 5528 0633
Web Site: www.affinityeducation.com.au
AFJ—(ASX)
Business Description:
Child Care Centers
S.I.C.: 8351
N.A.I.C.S.: 624410
Personnel:
Stuart James *(Chm)*
Justin Laboo *(CEO)*
John Bairstow *(CFO & Sec)*
Gabriel Giufre *(COO)*
Board of Directors:
Stuart James
Stephanie Daveson
Jeff Forbes
Gabriel Giufre
Justin Laboo

AFFINITY EQUITY PARTNERS (HK) LTD.

Suite 4002 40th Floor One Exchange Sq
8 Connaught Place, Central, China (Hong Kong)
Tel.: (852) 31028329
Fax: (852) 31028321
E-Mail: phyllischik@affinityequity.com
Web Site: www.affinityequity.com
Sales Range: $10-24.9 Million
Business Description:
Private Equity Firm
S.I.C.: 6211
N.A.I.C.S.: 523999
Personnel:
Kok-Yew Tang *(Chm & Mng Partner)*
Lee Chul-Joo *(Partner)*
Park Young-Taeg *(Partner)*
Queenie Ho *(Mng Dir)*

Non-U.S. Subsidiary:

Affinity Equity Partners (Australia) Pty. Ltd. **(1)**
Level 7 61 York
Sydney, NSW, 2000, Australia
Tel.: (61) 292990889
Fax: (61) 292990809
E-Mail: nicoledann@affinityequity.com
Web Site: www.affinityequity.com
Private Equity Firm
S.I.C.: 6211
N.A.I.C.S.: 523999
Brett Sutton *(Pres & Partner)*

Holding:

P&M Smallgoods Pty Ltd. **(2)**
18 Hume Highway
Chullora, NSW, 2190, Australia
Tel.: (61) 2 9742 0000
Fax: (61) 2 9742 0011
Web Site: www.primosmallgoods.com.au
Emp.: 500
Poultry Slaughtering & Processing; Packaged Frozen Food
N.A.I.C.S.: 311615
Paul Lederer, *(CEO)*

Non-U.S. Holding:

Tegel Foods Limited **(2)**
4th Floor Tower B 100 Carlton Gore Road
Private Bag 99-927
Newmarket, Auckland, 1023, New Zealand (100%)
Tel.: (64) 99779000
Fax: (64) 99779216
Web Site: www.tegel.co.nz
Sales Range: $300-349.9 Million
Emp.: 1,550
Breeding, Hatching, Processing, Marketing & Distribution of Poultry Products; Animal Feed & Animal Health Products
S.I.C.: 0251
N.A.I.C.S.: 112320
Janice Brunton *(Mgr-Corp Svc)*

AFFINOR RESOURCES INC.

410 St-Nicolas Street Suite 236
Montreal, QC, H2Y 2P5, Canada
Tel.: (514) 360-3676
Fax: (514) 907-9017
AFI—(CNSX)
Assets: $141,975
Liabilities: $287,393
Net Worth: ($145,418)
Earnings: ($232,478)
Fiscal Year-end: 05/31/13
Business Description:
Mining Services
S.I.C.: 1099
N.A.I.C.S.: 212299
Personnel:
Claude Veillette *(Chm)*
Sebastien Plouffe *(Pres & CEO)*
Martin Nicoletti *(CFO)*
Board of Directors:
Claude Veillette
Eddy Escalante
Sebastien Plouffe

AFFIRMATIVE FINANCE LIMITED

7-9 St James Square
Manchester, M2 6XX, United Kingdom
Tel.: (44) 8701 123 111
Fax: (44) 8701 125 931
E-Mail: enquiries@afff.co.uk
Web Site: www.affirmativefinance.co.uk
Sales Range: $10-24.9 Million
Emp.: 20
Business Description:
Business Credit & Lending Services
S.I.C.: 6099
N.A.I.C.S.: 522390
Personnel:
Eugene Esterkin *(Mng Dir)*

AFFITECH A/S

c/o COBIS Ole Maaloes Vej 3
2200 Copenhagen, Denmark
Tel.: (45) 39178259
E-Mail: ir@affitech.com
Web Site: www.affitech.com
Year Founded: 1997
Rev.: $1,104,344
Assets: $17,631,092
Liabilities: $5,576,370
Net Worth: $12,054,721
Earnings: ($3,421,970)
Emp.: 39
Fiscal Year-end: 12/31/12
Business Description:
Pharmaceutical Products Mfr
S.I.C.: 2834
N.A.I.C.S.: 325412
Personnel:
Aleksandr Shuster *(Chm-Supervisory Bd)*
Stig Jarle Pettersen *(CFO)*
Alexander Duncan *(Chief Scientific Officer & Sr VP-R&D)*
Supervisory Board of Directors:
Aleksandr Shuster
Igor Fisch
Steven Morrell
Andrei Petrov
Yegor S. Vassetzky

AFG ARBONIA-FORSTER-HOLDING AG

Amraswalerstrasse 50
9320 Arbon, Switzerland
Tel.: (41) 714474141
Fax: (41) 714474588
E-Mail: info.holding@afg.ch
Web Site: www.afg.ch
AFGN—(SWX)
Rev.: $1,311,870,287
Assets: $1,234,297,400
Liabilities: $763,903,840
Net Worth: $470,393,560
Earnings: ($80,400,705)
Emp.: 5,736
Fiscal Year-end: 12/31/12
Business Description:
Holding Company
S.I.C.: 6719
N.A.I.C.S.: 551112
Personnel:
Rudolf Graf *(Chm)*
Daniel Frutig *(CEO)*
Felix Bodmer *(CFO)*
Board of Directors:
Rudolf Graf
Peter E. Bodmer
Andreas Guhring
Markus Oppliger
Christian Stambach

Subsidiaries:

AFG International AG **(1)**
Amriswilerstrasse 50
Postfach 134
9320 Arbon, Thurgau, Switzerland
Tel.: (41) 714474141
Fax: (41) 714474589
E-Mail: info.holding@afg.ch
Modular Kitchen Design & Installation Services
S.I.C.: 7389
N.A.I.C.S.: 541490
Felix Bodmer *(CFO)*

AFG Kuchenvertrieb (Schweiz) AG **(1)**
Egnacherstrasse 37
9320 Arbon, Thurgau, Switzerland
Tel.: (41) 714474141
Fax: (41) 714474650
Kitchen Cabinets Retailer
S.I.C.: 5046
N.A.I.C.S.: 423440
Daniel Frutig *(CEO)*

AFG Management AG **(1)**
Amriswilerstrasse 50
Postfach 134
9320 Arbon, Thurgau, Switzerland
Tel.: (41) 714474141
Fax: (41) 714474588
E-Mail: afgmanagement@afg.ch
Business Support Services
S.I.C.: 7389
N.A.I.C.S.: 561499
Felix Bodmer *(CFO)*

AFG Schweiz AG **(1)**
Amriswilerstrasse 50
9320 Arbon, Thurgau, Switzerland
Tel.: (41) 714474141
Fax: (41) 714474588
Web Site: www.afg.ch/pages/folgeseite.php?IDurub=168&IDuurub=204&IDrub=10&sprache=1
Kitchen Cabinets Mfr
S.I.C.: 2434
N.A.I.C.S.: 337110
Felix Bodmer *(Dir-Fin)*

AFG Services AG **(1)**
Amriswilerstrasse 50
Postfach 550
9320 Arbon, Thurgau, Switzerland
Tel.: (41) 714474545
Fax: (41) 714475130
E-Mail: info@afg.ch
Kitchen & Sanitary Equipments Distr
S.I.C.: 5023
N.A.I.C.S.: 423220
Felix Bodmer *(Mgr-Fin)*

Arbonia AG **(1)**
Amriswilerstrasse 50
9320 Arbon, Thurgau, Switzerland
Tel.: (41) 714474747
Fax: (41) 714474847
E-Mail: verkauf@arbonia.ch
Web Site: www.arbonia.ch
Household Radiators Mfr
S.I.C.: 3433
N.A.I.C.S.: 333414

Arbonia-Forster-Beteiligungs AG **(1)**
Amriswilerstrasse 50
Postfach 134
9320 Arbon, Thurgau, Switzerland
Tel.: (41) 714474141
Fax: (41) 714474588
Emp.: 500
Kitchen Furnitures Mfr
S.I.C.: 2512
N.A.I.C.S.: 337121
Christoph Schoenenberger *(Mng Dir)*

Asta AG **(1)**
Industriestrasse 12
PO Box 650
9320 Arbon, Thurgau, Switzerland
Tel.: (41) 714474949
Fax: (41) 714474950
E-Mail: asta@afg.ch
Web Site: www.asta.ch
General Freight Trucking Services
S.I.C.: 4214
N.A.I.C.S.: 484110
Roger Z'Brun *(Mgr)*

Bruno Piatti AG **(1)**
Riedmuhlestrasse 16
8305 Dietlikon, Zurich, Switzerland
Tel.: (41) 448355111
Fax: (41) 448330741
E-Mail: info@piatti.ch
Web Site: www.piatti.ch
Emp.: 300
Modular Kitchen Design & Installation Services
S.I.C.: 7389
N.A.I.C.S.: 541490
Edgar Oehler *(Pres)*
Felix Bodmer *(CFO)*

EgoKiefer AG **(1)**
Schontalstrasse 2
9450 Altstatten, Sankt Gallen, Switzerland
Tel.: (41) 717573333
Fax: (41) 717573550
E-Mail: zentrale@egokiefer.ch
Web Site: www.egokiefer.ch
Rev.: $253,702,800
Emp.: 950
Windows, Doors Mfr & Distr
S.I.C.: 2431
N.A.I.C.S.: 321911
Thomas Gerosa *(CEO)*

Forster Kuchen- & Kuhltechnik AG **(1)**
Forster Kitchens Egnacherstrasse 37
PO Box 600
9320 Arbon, Thurgau, Switzerland
Tel.: (41) 714474141
Fax: (41) 714474650
E-Mail: forster.kuechen@afg.ch
Web Site: www.forster-kuechen.ch
Prefabricated Kitchen Installation Services
S.I.C.: 1751
N.A.I.C.S.: 238350
Felix Bodmer *(CFO)*

Forster Rohr- & Profiltechnik AG **(1)**
Industriestrasse 24
Postfach 450
9320 Arbon, Thurgau, Switzerland
Tel.: (41) 714474444
Fax: (41) 714474374
E-Mail: forster.rohre@afg.ch
Web Site: www.forster-rohre.ch
Emp.: 300
Steel Tubes Mfr
S.I.C.: 3317
N.A.I.C.S.: 331210
Philippe Heiniger *(Mgr)*

Heizkorper Prolux AG **(1)**
Amriswilerstrasse 50
9320 Arbon, Thurgau, Switzerland
Tel.: (41) 714474848
Fax: (41) 714474849
E-Mail: verkauf@prolux-ag.ch
Web Site: www.prolux-ag.ch
Emp.: 20
Household Radiators Mfr & Distr
S.I.C.: 3433
N.A.I.C.S.: 333414
Edgar Edgar *(Chm)*

RWD Schlatter AG **(1)**
St Gallerstrasse 21
9325 Roggwil, Thurgau, Switzerland

Tel.: (41) 714546300
Fax: (41) 714546363
E-Mail: info@rwdschlatter.ch
Web Site: www.rwdschlatter.ch
Emp.: 116
Doors & Frames Mfr
S.I.C.: 3442
N.A.I.C.S.: 332321
Christian Girsberger *(Mgr-Fin)*

STI Hartchrom AG (1)
Schulstrasse 70
9323 Steinach, Sankt Gallen, Switzerland
Tel.: (41) 714479797
Fax: (41) 71 447 97 92
E-Mail: hartchrom@hartchrom.com
Web Site: www.hartchrom.com
Rev.: $47,733,712
Emp.: 517
Surface Treatment & Coating Services
S.I.C.: 3479
N.A.I.C.S.: 332812
Thomas Reifler *(CEO)*

STI Surface Technologies International Holding AG. (1)
Schulstrasse 70
9320 Steinach, Sankt Gallen, Switzerland
Tel.: (41) 714479797
Fax: (41) 714479792
E-Mail: sti@hartchrom.com
Emp.: 300
Surface Treatment & Coating Services
S.I.C.: 3479
N.A.I.C.S.: 332812
Hannes Schmueser *(Mng Dir)*

Usines Ego SA (1)
Zone Industrielle A11
1844 Villeneuve, Vaud, Switzerland
Tel.: (41) 219670800
Fax: (41) 21 967 08 10
E-Mail: villeneuve@egokiefer.ch
Windows & Doors Mfr
S.I.C.: 2431
N.A.I.C.S.: 321911

U.S. Subsidiary:

STI Hartchrom Inc. (1)
25 Gibson St
Watervliet, NY 12189-3342
Tel.: (518) 880-0411
Fax: (518) 880-0450
E-Mail: hwv@hartchrom.com
Web Site: www.hartchrom.com
Emp.: 20
Metal Surface Coating Services
S.I.C.: 3479
N.A.I.C.S.: 332812
Michael Flaherty *(Mng Dir)*

Non-U.S. Subsidiaries:

AFG Arbonia-Forster-Riesa GmbH (1)
Heinrich-Schonberg-Str 3
01591 Riesa, Saxony, Germany
Tel.: (49) 35257460
Fax: (49) 3525 746 122
E-Mail: info@arbonia.de
Web Site: www.arbonia.de
Emp.: 50
Household Radiators Mfr
S.I.C.: 3433
N.A.I.C.S.: 333414

AFG Warendorfer Immobilien GmbH. (1)
Mielestrasse 1
48231 Warendorf, Nordrhein-Westfalen, Germany
Tel.: (49) 2581590
Fax: (49) 2581592090
E-Mail: info@warendorf.eu
Web Site: www.warendorf.eu
Emp.: 180
Kitchenware Mfr
S.I.C.: 3269
N.A.I.C.S.: 327110
Thorsten Pree *(Pres)*

Arbonia France S.a.r.l. (1)
ZA Grand Rue
68130 Walheim, Haut-Rhin, France
Tel.: (33) 389400253
Fax: (33) 389400425
E-Mail: info@arbonia.fr
Web Site: www.arbonia.fr
Emp.: 11
Interior Designing Services
S.I.C.: 7389
N.A.I.C.S.: 541410
Serge Probst *(Mgr)*

Chromage Pyreneen SA. (1)
Route de Pau ZA du Gabarn
Escout, 64870 Oloron Sainte Marie, Pyrenees-Atlantiques, France
Tel.: (33) 559397101
Fax: (33) 559392333
E-Mail: chromage-pyreneen@hartchrom.com
Web Site: www.hartchrom.com
Emp.: 72
Industrial Engineering Services
S.I.C.: 8711
N.A.I.C.S.: 541330
Paerre Aubert *(Gen Mgr)*

Hartchrom Schoch GmbH. (1)
Muhlackerstr 10
Diefenbach, 75447 Sternenfels, Baden-Wurttemberg, Germany
Tel.: (49) 704395320
Fax: (49) 70439532299
E-Mail: schoch@hartchrom.com
Web Site: www.schoch-hartchrom.com
Emp.: 100
Surface Treatment & Coating Services
S.I.C.: 1221
N.A.I.C.S.: 212111
Wolfgang Stuckert *(Head-Production)*

Hartchrom Teikuro Automotive GmbH. (1)
Muhlackerstrasse 10
Diefenbach, 75447 Sternenfels, Baden-Wurttemberg, Germany
Tel.: (49) 70439532500
Fax: (49) 70439532599
E-Mail: hartchrom.teikuro@hartchrom.com
Web Site: www.hartchrom.com
Emp.: 117
Surface Treatment & Industrial Engineering Services
S.I.C.: 8711
N.A.I.C.S.: 541330
Wolfgang Stuckert *(Head-Production)*

Hydrometal SA (1)
ZI Le Touya
BP 17
64260 Arudy, Pyrenees-Atlantiques, France
Tel.: (33) 559056034
Fax: (33) 559056496
E-Mail: hydrometal.sa@wanajoo.fr
Web Site: www.hartchrom.com
Emp.: 36
Aircraft Components Mfr
S.I.C.: 3728
N.A.I.C.S.: 336413

Kermi GmbH (1)
Pankofen Bahnhof 1
D-94447 Plattling, Germany
Tel.: (49) 99315010
Fax: (49) 99313075
E-Mail: info@kermi.de
Web Site: www.kermi.de
Sales Range: $200-249.9 Million
Emp.: 1,500
Plumbing Products
S.I.C.: 3432
N.A.I.C.S.: 332913
Edgar Oehler *(Chm)*
Theo Bubendorff *(CEO)*
Knut Bartsch *(Mng Dir)*
Peter Krayer *(Mng Dir)*
Roger Schoenborn *(Mng Dir)*

Non-U.S. Subsidiaries:

Kermi Sp.z.o.o. (2)
Ul Graniczna 8b
54-610 Wroclaw, Lower Silesian, Poland
Tel.: (48) 713540374
Fax: (48) 713540463
E-Mail: info@kermi.pl
Web Site: www.kermi.pl
Household Radiators & Shower Enclosures Mfr
S.I.C.: 3433
N.A.I.C.S.: 333414
Bartsch Knut *(Mng Dir)*

Kermi s.r.o. (2)
Dukelska 1427
349 01 Stribro, Plzen, Czech Republic
Tel.: (420) 374611111
Fax: (420) 374611100
E-Mail: info@kermi.cz
Web Site: www.kermi.cz
Household Radiators & Shower Enclosures Mfr
S.I.C.: 3585
N.A.I.C.S.: 333415

Kermi (UK) Ltd. (2)
7 Brunel Road Earlstrees Industrial Estate
Corby, Northants, NN17 4JW, United Kingdom
Tel.: (44) 1536400004
Fax: (44) 1536 446614
E-Mail: info@kermi.co.uk
Web Site: www.kermi.co.uk
Household Radiators & Shower Enclosures Distr
S.I.C.: 5075
N.A.I.C.S.: 423730
Edgar Oehler *(Chm)*
Peter Krayer *(Co-Mng Dir)*
Roger Schonborn *(Co-Mng Dir)*

Slovaktual s.r.o. (1)
Pravenec 272
97216 Pravenec, Trencin, Slovakia
Tel.: (421) 46 544 79 16
Fax: (421) 46 544 74 30
E-Mail: slovaktual@slovaktual.sk
Web Site: www.slovaktual.sk
Emp.: 277
Windows & Doors Mfr
S.I.C.: 2431
N.A.I.C.S.: 321911
Marian Krc *(Mgr)*

STI Immobilien (Deutschland) GmbH (1)
Muhlackerstrasse 10
Diefenbach, 75447 Sternenfels, Baden-Wurttemberg, Germany
Tel.: (49) 704395320
Fax: (49) 70439532299
E-Mail: schoch@hartchrom.com
Web Site: www.hartchrom.com
Emp.: 110
Real Estate Property Development Services
S.I.C.: 6531
N.A.I.C.S.: 531210
Matthias Tannenbaum *(Mgr)*

STI Precision Machining (Changshu) Co. Ltd. (1)
No 1 Dongnan Road Changshu Southeast Economic Development Zone, Changshu, Jiangsu, 215500, China
Tel.: (86) 51252358958
Fax: (86) 52906299
E-Mail: hartchrom@hartchrom.com
Web Site: www.hartchrom.com
Emp.: 83
Surface Treatment & Coating Services
S.I.C.: 3479
N.A.I.C.S.: 332812
Edgar Oehler *(Gen Mgr)*

AFG FLAMEGUARD LTD.

1150-750 West Pender Street
Vancouver, BC, V6C 2T8, Canada
Tel.: (604) 657-7701
E-Mail: useit@afgflameguardltd.com
Web Site: www.afg5.com
Year Founded: 1997
Sls.: $107,713
Assets: $776,732
Liabilities: $860,831
Net Worth: ($84,099)
Earnings: ($492,409)
Fiscal Year-end: 12/31/12

Business Description:
Environmentally Friendly Fire & Life Safety Products Distr
S.I.C.: 9224
N.A.I.C.S.: 922160

Personnel:
Donald Gordon *(Acting CFO)*

Board of Directors:
Donald Gordon
John Russell
Frans Volgelzangs

Legal Counsel:
Forth & Company Barristers & Solicitors
Suite 1600 777 Dunsmuir Street
Vancouver, BC, V7Y 1K4, Canada
Tel.: (604) 689-4899
Fax: (604) 688-0094

Transfer Agent:
Computershare Services
4th Floor 510 Burrard Street
Vancouver, BC, V6C 3B9, Canada
Tel.: (604) 661-9400
Fax: (604) 661-9401

AFG GROUP NIJMEGEN B.V.

Hulzenseweg 10 20
6534 AN Nijmegen, Netherlands
Mailing Address:
PO Box 6572
6503 GB Nijmegen, Netherlands
Tel.: (31) 24 352 25 70
E-Mail: info@afggroup.nl
Web Site: www.afggroup.nl
Emp.: 100

Business Description:
Fire Prevention Equipment Mfr
S.I.C.: 3999
N.A.I.C.S.: 339999

Personnel:
Frans Vogelzangs *(CEO)*

Subsidiary:

Flame Guard B.V. (1)
Hulzenseweg 10 20
6534 AN Nijmegen, Netherlands
Mailing Address:
PO Box 6572
6503 GB Nijmegen, Netherlands
Tel.: (31) 24 3789581
Fax: (31) 24 3787583
E-Mail: info@flameguard.nl
Web Site: www.flameguard.nl
Fire Resistant Materials Mfr
S.I.C.: 2899
N.A.I.C.S.: 325998

AFGRI LIMITED

12 Byls Bridge Boulevard Highveld Ext 73
Centurion, 0157, South Africa
Mailing Address:
PO Box 11054
Centurion, 0046, South Africa
Tel.: (27) 11 063 2347
Fax: (27) 879427463
E-Mail: afgri@afgri.co.za
Web Site: www.afgri.co.za
AFR—(JSE)
Rev.: $957,604,100
Assets: $826,133,200
Liabilities: $555,819,200
Net Worth: $270,314,000
Earnings: $11,058,300
Emp.: 4,148
Fiscal Year-end: 06/30/13

Business Description:
Agricultural Services
S.I.C.: 0119
N.A.I.C.S.: 111191

Personnel:
C. P. Venter *(CEO)*
Marion D. Shikwinya *(Sec)*

Board of Directors:
Jethro P. R. Mbau
David D. Barber
Linda de Beer
G. J. Geel
Lwazi M. Koyana
B. A. Mabuza
L. Stephens
C. P. Venter
L. L. von Zeuner
C. T. Vorster
N. C. Wentzel

Transfer Agent:
Computershare Investor Services 2004 (Proprietary) Limited
70 Marshall Street
Johannesburg, South Africa

AFGRI Limited—(Continued)

Subsidiaries:

AFGRI Animal Feeds Eastern Cape (Pty) Ltd. **(1)**
22 Buchner Street
Paterson, Eastern Cape, 6130, South Africa
Tel.: (27) 422351114
Fax: (27) 422351208
E-Mail: afgri@afgri.co.za
Emp.: 100
Animal Feeds Mfr
S.I.C.: 2048
N.A.I.C.S.: 311119
Pikkie van Rensburg *(Mng Dir)*

AFGRI Animal Feeds **(1)**
23 Frank Rd Bldg 3 HP&D Office Pk
Private Bag X2001
Isando, 1600, South Africa
Tel.: (27) 113064300
Fax: (27) 113064301
Web Site: www.afgri-ir.co.za
Emp.: 40
Animal Feeds Production & Distribution
S.I.C.: 2048
N.A.I.C.S.: 311119
Henry Cottle *(Mgr)*

AFGRI Financial and Logistics Services **(1)**
267 West Avenue 3rd Floor
PO Box 11054
Centurion, 0046, South Africa
Tel.: (27) 0126438000
Fax: (27) 126430029
Web Site: www.afgri.com
Financial & Logistics Services for Agriculture Industry
S.I.C.: 6211
N.A.I.C.S.: 523999
Chrs Genter *(CEO)*

AFGRI Premium Snacks **(1)**
12 Byls Bridge Blvd
PO Box 11054
Highveld Ex 73, Centurion, 0046, South Africa
Tel.: (27) 1106323474
E-Mail: afgri@afgri.co.za
Web Site: www.afgri-ir.co.za
Emp.: 500
Maize Based Snack Products
S.I.C.: 2052
N.A.I.C.S.: 311919
G.J. Geel *(COO)*

Clark Cotton **(1)**
The Atrium 9th Floor 41 Stanley Road
PO Box 7787
Auckland Park, Johannesburg, 2000, South Africa
Tel.: (27) 11 726 7210
Fax: (27) 11 726 2715
Cotton Producer & Processor
S.I.C.: 0131
N.A.I.C.S.: 111920

Daybreak Farms (Pty) Ltd **(1)**
Main Road
PO Box 186
Sundra, Delmas, Mpumalanga, 2200, South Africa
Tel.: (27) 136611063
Fax: (27) 1429867
E-Mail: info@daybreakfarms.co.za
Web Site: www.daybreakfarms.co.za
Frozen Chicken Products Distr
S.I.C.: 5144
N.A.I.C.S.: 424440
Steve Steenkamp *(Mng Dir)*

Daybreak Superior Marketing (Pty) Ltd. **(1)**
31 Collet Street
Alberton, Gauteng, 1449, South Africa
Tel.: (27) 136611247
Fax: (27) 136611307
Emp.: 10
Broiler Chicken Whslr
S.I.C.: 5144
N.A.I.C.S.: 424440

Dormanko Dertig (Pty) Ltd. **(1)**
3 Louw Street
Bethlehem, Free State, 9701, South Africa
Tel.: (27) 583031906
Fax: (27) 583033356
Emp.: 18
Farm & Garden Machinery Whslr
S.I.C.: 5083
N.A.I.C.S.: 423820

Labworld (Pty) Ltd. **(1)**
123 Witch Hazel Ave Technopark
Highveld, Centurion, Gauteng, 0157, South Africa
Tel.: (27) 126859600
Fax: (27) 126651869
E-Mail: sales@labworld.co.za
Web Site: www.labworld.co.za
Emp.: 32
Laboratory & Scientific Analytical Equipment Distr
S.I.C.: 5049
N.A.I.C.S.: 423490
Sharon Soh *(Mgr)*

Nedin Pty. Ltd. **(1)**
6 Charolais Street
Potgietersrus, Limpopo, 0601, South Africa
Tel.: (27) 154914338
Fax: (27) 154916284
Emp.: 145
Cottonseed Oil Mfr
S.I.C.: 2079
N.A.I.C.S.: 311224
Steve Botha *(Mgr-Ops)*

Partmaster (Pty) Ltd. **(1)**
42 Naude Street
Bethlehem, Free State, 9700, South Africa
Tel.: (27) 583076500
Fax: (27) 583037594
E-Mail: sales@partrite.co.za
Web Site: www.partrite.co.za
Emp.: 60
Agricultural Machinery Parts Distr
S.I.C.: 5083
N.A.I.C.S.: 423820
Jan van der Walt *(Mng Dir)*

AFH FINANCIAL GROUP PLC

St Johns House 16 Church Street
Bromsgrove, Worcs, B61 8DN, United Kingdom
Tel.: (44) 1527577775
Fax: (44) 1527577624
E-Mail: mail@afhgroup.com
Web Site: www.afhifs.co.uk
Business Description:
Financial Holding Company
S.I.C.: 6719
N.A.I.C.S.: 551112
Personnel:
Alan Hudson *(Mng Dir)*
Board of Directors:
Alan Hudson
Toby Denne
John Wheatley

AFICOM

7 Rue Edmond Roger
75015 Paris, France
Tel.: (33) 145753594
Fax: (33) 145757608
E-Mail: aficom@aficom.com.fr
Web Site: www.aficom.fr
Sls.: $23,200,000
Emp.: 15
Business Description:
Drugs, Proprietaries & Sundries
S.I.C.: 5122
N.A.I.C.S.: 424210
Personnel:
Francois Marchand *(Pres)*

AFONE S.A.

11 place Francois Mitterrand
49100 Angers, France
Tel.: (33) 2 41860504
Fax: (33) 2 41861211
E-Mail: ir@afone.com
Web Site: www.afone.com
AFO—(EUR)
Sls.: $96,618,659
Earnings: $7,067,393
Emp.: 306
Fiscal Year-end: 12/31/12
Business Description:
Telecommunications Services
S.I.C.: 4899
N.A.I.C.S.: 517919
Personnel:
Philip Fournier *(Chm & CEO)*
Eric Durand-Gasselin *(Deputy CEO)*
Bernard Puchois *(CFO)*
Board of Directors:
Philip Fournier
Eric Durand-Gasselin
Vincent Kemmoun

AFONWEN LAUNDRY LIMITED

Afonwen
Pwllheli, Gwynedd, LL53 6NQ, United Kingdom
Tel.: (44) 1766 810264
Fax: (44) 1766 810040
E-Mail: info@afonwenlaundry.com
Web Site: www.afonwenlaundry.com
Year Founded: 1935
Sales Range: $10-24.9 Million
Emp.: 400
Business Description:
Laundry & Dry Cleaning Services
S.I.C.: 7219
N.A.I.C.S.: 812320
Personnel:
Mark Woolfenden *(Mng Dir)*

Subsidiary:

Whiteriver Laundry Ltd **(1)**
Unit 8 Millshaw Park Industrial Estate
Leeds, LS11 0LR, United Kingdom
Tel.: (44) 113 272 0700
Fax: (44) 113 272 0077
E-Mail: lukegledhill@whiteriverlaundry.com
Web Site: www.whiteriverlaundry.com
Laundry Services
S.I.C.: 7219
N.A.I.C.S.: 812320
Luke Gledhill *(Mng Dir)*

AFRE CORPORATION

ReNaissance Park Borrowdale Rd
PO Box BW178
Harare, Zimbabwe
Tel.: (263) 4886000
Fax: (263) 4886041
E-Mail: info@afrecorporation.com
Web Site: www.afrecorporation.com
AFRE—(ZIM)
Rev.: $92,660,357
Assets: $176,303,072
Liabilities: $113,091,292
Net Worth: $63,211,780
Earnings: $13,451,040
Fiscal Year-end: 12/31/12
Business Description:
Financial & Investment Services
S.I.C.: 6282
N.A.I.C.S.: 523930
Personnel:
Douglas Hoto *(CEO)*
Pfungwa Dhliwayo *(Exec-HR)*
Farayi Mangwende *(Exec-Corp Affairs)*
Joseph Mhlabi *(Exec-Internal Audit)*
Max Ncube *(Exec-Bus Dev)*
Bianca Mwaemudza Pasipanodya *(Exec-Info Comm & Tech)*
Sheila Frances Lorimer *(Sec)*
Board of Directors:
Innocent Chagonda
John Chikura
Christopher Urombo Hokonya
Douglas Hoto
Thembelihle Khumalo-Sachikonye
Misheck Manyumwa
William Marere
James Mwaiyapo Matiza
Elisha Moyo
Oliver Mtasa
Israel Ndhlovu

AFREN PLC

Kinnaird House 1 Pall Mall East
London, SW1Y 5AU, United Kingdom
Tel.: (44) 20 7864 3700
Fax: (44) 20 7864 3701
E-Mail: info@afren.com
Web Site: www.afren.com
Year Founded: 2004
AFR—(LSE)
Rev.: $1,498,800,000
Assets: $3,584,400,000
Liabilities: $2,157,000,000
Net Worth: $1,427,400,000
Earnings: $203,400,000
Emp.: 316
Fiscal Year-end: 12/31/12
Business Description:
Oil & Gas Exploration & Production
S.I.C.: 1311
N.A.I.C.S.: 211111
Personnel:
Osman Shahenshah *(CEO)*
Shahid Ullah *(COO)*
Shirin Johri *(Gen Counsel & Co-Sec)*
Daniel Sasegbon *(Gen Counsel-Nigeria)*
Elekwachi Ukwu *(Co-Sec)*
Board of Directors:
Egbert Imomoh
Peter Bingham
Sheree Bryant
Darra Comyn
Toby Hayward
Patrick Obath
Ennio Sganzerla
Osman Shahenshah
John St. John
Shahid Ullah
Legal Counsel:
White & Case LLP
5 Old Broad Street
London, United Kingdom

Mildwaters Consulting LLP
Walton House 25 Bilton Road
Rugby, United Kingdom

U.S. Subsidiary:

Afren USA Inc. **(1)**
10001 Woodloch Forest Dr
The Woodlands, TX 77380
Tel.: (281) 363-8600
Fax: (281) 292-0019
E-Mail: hustonreception@afren.com
Emp.: 50
Oil & Gas Field Services
S.I.C.: 1389
N.A.I.C.S.: 213112
Michael Cochran *(Mgr-HR)*

Non-U.S. Subsidiaries:

Afren Energy Resources Limited **(1)**
1st Fl The Octagon 13A A J Marinho Dr
Victoria Is Annexe, Lagos, Nigeria
Tel.: (234) 146101307
Fax: (234) 14610139
Web Site: www.afrennigeria.com
Oil & Gas Production Services
S.I.C.: 1389
N.A.I.C.S.: 213112
Egbert U. Imomoh *(Mng Dir)*

Black Marlin Energy Holdings Limited **(1)**
Office 1008 10th Floor Fortune Tower
Jumeirah Lake Towers
PO Box 450307, Dubai, United Arab Emirates AB
Tel.: (971) 4 437 6700
Fax: (971) 4 423 3730
Oil & Gas Exploration Services
S.I.C.: 1311
N.A.I.C.S.: 211111
Richard Schmitt *(CEO)*
William Evaroa *(CFO)*
Barrington P. Rogers *(COO)*
J. Christopher McLean *(Sec)*

AFRI-CAN MARINE MINERALS CORPORATION
1801 McGill College Avenue Suite 950
Montreal, QC, H3A 2N4, Canada
Tel.: (514) 846-2133
Fax: (514) 372-0066
Toll Free: (866) 206-7475
E-Mail: info@afri-can.com
Web Site: www.afri-can.com
AFA—(TSXV)
Int. Income: $2,922
Assets: $4,727,128
Liabilities: $1,132,710
Net Worth: $3,594,418
Earnings: ($10,660,992)
Fiscal Year-end: 08/31/13
Business Description:
Mineral Exploration Services
S.I.C.: 1081
N.A.I.C.S.: 213114
Personnel:
Michael J. Brown *(Chm)*
Pierre Leveille *(Pres & CEO)*
Bernard J. Tourillon *(CFO & Exec VP)*
Board of Directors:
Michael J. Brown
Pierre Leveille
Richard M. Tait
Andre Thibault
Bernard J. Tourillon
Raymond Chabot Grant Thornton LLP
Ste 2000 National Bank Tower 600 De La Gauchetiere Street West
Montreal, QC, Canada
Legal Counsel:
Lavery de Billy
Montreal, QC, Canada
Transfer Agent:
Computershare
100 University Avenue 9 Floor
Toronto, ON, Canada

AFRICA HYDROCARBONS INC.
Suite 200 521-3rd Ave SW
Calgary, AB, T2P 3T3, Canada
Tel.: (403) 265-8011
E-Mail: info@africahydrocarbons.com
Web Site: www.africahydrocarbons.com
Year Founded: 1983
NFK—(TSXV)
Assets: $14,544,312
Liabilities: $251,344
Net Worth: $14,292,968
Earnings: ($2,103,674)
Fiscal Year-end: 09/30/12
Business Description:
Oil & Gas Extraction Services
S.I.C.: 1311
N.A.I.C.S.: 211111
Personnel:
John Nelson *(CEO)*
Charidy Lazorko *(CFO)*
Trevor Wong-Chor *(Sec)*
Board of Directors:
David M. Antony
Gordon McKay
John Nelson
Binh Vu
Transfer Agent:
Computershare Trust Company of Canada
100 University Avenue 9th Floor
Toronto, ON, M5J 2Y1, Canada
Tel.: (416) 663-9097
Fax: (416) 263-9694

AFRICA ISRAEL INVESTMENTS LTD.
4 Derech Hachoresh Street
Yehud, Israel
Tel.: (972) 35393535
Fax: (972) 36321730
E-Mail: info@africa-israel.com
Web Site: www.afigroup-global.com
AFIL—(TAE)
Rev.: $1,822,924,481
Assets: $6,611,346,158
Liabilities: $4,593,056,120
Net Worth: $2,018,290,038
Earnings: ($374,951,538)
Emp.: 1,184
Fiscal Year-end: 12/31/12
Business Description:
Investment Services
S.I.C.: 6282
N.A.I.C.S.: 523930
Personnel:
Lev Leviev *(Chm)*
Nadav Grinshpon *(Vice Chm)*
Avraham Novogrocki *(CEO)*
Menashe Sagiv *(CFO)*
Avi Barzilai *(CEO/VP-Europe)*
Chagit Sofiev-Leviev *(CEO-US)*
Larisa Cohen *(Sec)*
Board of Directors:
Lev Leviev
Nadav Grinshpon
Subsidiaries:

AFI Europe N.V (1)
4 Derech Hachoresh St
56470 Yehud, Israel
Tel.: (972) 35393625
Fax: (972) 35393514
Web Site: www.afi-europe.eu/contact_us.aspx
Emp.: 250
Other Miscellaneous Durable Goods Merchant Whslr
S.I.C.: 5099
N.A.I.C.S.: 423990
Avi Barzilay *(CEO)*

Africa Israel (Finance) 1985 Ltd. (1)
4 Hachoresh Rd
Yehud, 56470, Israel
Tel.: (972) 35393535
Fax: (972) 36321730
Investment Management Services
S.I.C.: 6799
N.A.I.C.S.: 523920

Africa Israel Hotels Ltd. (1)
Moshe Dayan St
56450 Yehud, Israel
Tel.: (972) 35394477
Fax: (972) 35394494
E-Mail: prsec@hiil.co.il
Web Site: www.hiil.co.il
Emp.: 100
Hotel Operator
S.I.C.: 7011
N.A.I.C.S.: 721110
Ron Yarin *(Gen Mgr)*

Africa Israel International Holdings Ltd. (1)
4 Derech Hachoresh Street
Yehud, 56470, Israel
Tel.: (972) 35393586
Fax: (972) 35393523
Web Site: www.africa-israel.co.il
Emp.: 250
Miscellaneous Financial Investment Activities
S.I.C.: 6211
N.A.I.C.S.: 523999
Izzy Chohen *(CEO)*

Africa Israel Properties Ltd. (1)
4 Derech Hachoresh St
Yehud, Israel
Tel.: (972) 35393535
Fax: (972) 36321740
Web Site: www.africa-israel.co.il
Emp.: 250
Other Holding Companies Offices
S.I.C.: 6719
N.A.I.C.S.: 551112
Lev Leviev *(Chm)*

Subsidiary:

Africa Israel International Properties (2002) Ltd. (2)
4 Hahoresh Rd
Yehud, Israel
Tel.: (972) 3 5393586
Real Estate Leasing & Rental Services
S.I.C.: 6531
N.A.I.C.S.: 531390

Non-U.S. Subsidiaries:

AFI Europe B.V. (2)
Keizersgracht 604
1017 EP Amsterdam, Netherlands
Tel.: (31) 20 421 8928
Fax: (31) 20 428 3189
Web Site: www.afi-europe.eu
Emp.: 4
Real Estate Investment Services
S.I.C.: 6531
N.A.I.C.S.: 531390
Abraham Novogrocki *(Chm)*
Avi Barzilay *(CEO)*
Ariel Goldstein *(CFO & VP-Fin)*
Nir Geva *(Gen Counsel & Sec)*

Flamingo Ltd. (2)
32 Gen Gurko Str Flr 4
Burgas, Bulgaria
Tel.: (359) 56 843819
Fax: (359) 56 840652
Emp.: 3
Property Management Services
S.I.C.: 6531
N.A.I.C.S.: 531311

Africa Israel Residences Ltd. (1)
4 Derech Hachoresh St
Yehud, Israel
Tel.: (972) 35393535
Fax: (972) 36321730
E-Mail: africa@africa-israel.com
Emp.: 53
Real Estate Management Services
S.I.C.: 7349
N.A.I.C.S.: 561790
Gili Dekel *(CEO)*

Africa Israel Trade & Agencies Ltd. (1)
4 Derech Hachoresh St
Yehud, Israel
Tel.: (972) 35393535
Web Site: www.africa-israel.co.il
Emp.: 250
Holding Company
S.I.C.: 6719
N.A.I.C.S.: 551112

Crown Plaza Ltd (1)
111 Yese Nof
34454 Haifa, Israel (100%)
Tel.: (972) 48350835
Fax: (972) 48350836
E-Mail: hi_gmsec@crownplaza-il.com
Web Site: www.h-i.co.il
Hotel Operator
S.I.C.: 7011
N.A.I.C.S.: 721110
Herzel Levi *(Gen Mgr)*

Givat Savyon Ltd. (1)
4 Derech Hachoresh St
Yehud, Israel
Tel.: (972) 35393535
Fax: (972) 5393503
E-Mail: yuliaz@africa-israel.com
Emp.: 250
Real Estate Services
S.I.C.: 6531
N.A.I.C.S.: 531210
Yulia Zgut *(Mgr)*

Gottex Models Ltd. (1)
Yoni Netanyahu St
New Industrial Zone, Yehud, Israel
Tel.: (972) 35387777
Fax: (972) 35333423
E-Mail: marketing2@gottexmodels.com
Web Site: www.gottex.co.il
Emp.: 24
Swimsuit Designer, Mfr & Exporter
S.I.C.: 2399
N.A.I.C.S.: 315990
Joey Schwebel *(Mng Dir)*

Affiliate:

Mapal Communications Ltd. (1)
2 Raoul Wallenberg St
Tel Aviv, Israel (20%)
Tel.: (972) 37684000
Fax: (972) 37684001
E-Mail: nadav@mapal.co.il
Web Site: www.mapal.co.il
Investment Banking & Securities Dealing
S.I.C.: 6211
N.A.I.C.S.: 523110
Nadav Palti *(Co-Founder & Chm)*

U.S. Subsidiaries:

20 Pine Street LLC (1)
20 Pine St
New York, NY 10005
Tel.: (212) 344-4000
Fax: (212) 344-4011
Web Site: www.20pine.com
Emp.: 20
Real Estate Management Services
S.I.C.: 6531
N.A.I.C.S.: 531390

A.I. Holdings (USA) Corp. (1)
40 Wall St Fl 56
New York, NY 10005
Tel.: (212) 471-3300
Investment Management Services
S.I.C.: 6282
N.A.I.C.S.: 523920

Internet Garage, L.L.C (1)
218 Bedford Ave
Brooklyn, NY 11211-3234
Tel.: (718) 486-0059
Internet Service Providers
S.I.C.: 4899
N.A.I.C.S.: 517919

Irene Garage LLC (1)
900 Biscayne Blvd
Miami, FL 33132
Tel.: (305) 416-9779
Automotive Repairing Services
S.I.C.: 7539
N.A.I.C.S.: 811198

Non-U.S. Subsidiaries:

ADUT s.r.o (1)
Vinohradska 151
13000 Prague, Czech Republic
Tel.: (420) 235351377
E-Mail: info@afi-europe.cz
Web Site: www.adut.cz
Emp.: 25
Business Support Services
S.I.C.: 7389
N.A.I.C.S.: 561499
David Halfi *(Mng Dir)*

AFI Development PLC (1)
Berezhkovskaya nab16 A build 5
Moscow, 121059, Russia
Tel.: (7) 495 796 9988
Fax: (7) 495 796 9989
E-Mail: info@afid.ru
Web Site: www.afi-development.ru/en/
AFID—(LSE)
Sales Range: $25-49.9 Million
Emp.: 170
Commercial & Residential Real Estate Development & Other Real Estate Related Services
S.I.C.: 1542
N.A.I.C.S.: 236220
Lev Leviev *(Chm)*
Mark Groysman *(CEO-AFI RUS LLC)*

AFI Europe Czech Republic, s.r.o. (1)
Classic 7 Business Park
1037 49 Prague, Czech Republic
Tel.: (420) 255743111
Fax: (420) 255743170
E-Mail: info@afi-europe.cz
Web Site: www.afi-europe.cz
Emp.: 20
Property Management Services
S.I.C.: 6531
N.A.I.C.S.: 531312
Doron Klein *(CEO)*

AFI Europe Financing B.V. (1)
Keizersgracht 604
Amsterdam, 1017 EP, Netherlands
Tel.: (31) 204218928
Financial Management Services
S.I.C.: 6211
N.A.I.C.S.: 523999

AFI Europe Infrastructure B.V. (1)
Keizersgracht 604
1017 EP Amsterdam, Netherlands

Africa Israel Investments Ltd.—(Continued)

Tel.: (31) 20 4218928
Real Estate Management Services
S.I.C.: 6531
N.A.I.C.S.: 531390

AFI Europe Management SRL (1)
4 Vasile Milea Blvd 6th District
Bucharest, 61344, Romania
Tel.: (40) 2141202220
Fax: (40) 213118136
Web Site: www.eu.afi-g.com
Emp.: 5
Real Estate Development Services
S.I.C.: 6531
N.A.I.C.S.: 531390
David Hay *(CEO)*

AFI Germany GmbH (1)
Kronenstr 3
Berlin, 10117, Germany
Tel.: (49) 3028045095
Fax: (49) 3028045097
Web Site: www.afi-europe.eu
Emp.: 3
Real Estate Management Services
S.I.C.: 6531
N.A.I.C.S.: 531390
Doron Klein *(Gen Mgr)*

AFI Germany Investment GmbH (1)
Kronen Str 3
Berlin, 10117, Germany
Tel.: (49) 3028045095
Fax: (49) 3028045097
Web Site: www.asi-europe.de
Emp.: 5
Investment Management Services
S.I.C.: 6211
N.A.I.C.S.: 523999
Karin Shalev *(COO)*

AFI Management SIA (1)
Gertrudes 10/12-6
Riga, 1010, Latvia
Tel.: (371) 67846525
Fax: (371) 167846526
E-Mail: arielg@afi-europe.eu
Web Site: eu.afi-g.com
Emp.: 1
Real Estate Management Services
S.I.C.: 6531
N.A.I.C.S.: 531390
Joris Hoppener *(COO)*

AFI Properties Development B.V. (1)
Keizersgracht 604
Amsterdam, 1017 EP, Netherlands
Tel.: (31) 204223227
Property Development Services
S.I.C.: 6531
N.A.I.C.S.: 531390

AFI RUS LLC (1)
Gruzinsky Val 29
Moscow, 123056, Russia
Tel.: (7) 495 796 9988
Fax: (7) 495 796 9989
Real Estate Development Services
S.I.C.: 6531
N.A.I.C.S.: 531390

AFI Rus Parking Management (1)
31 Ul Gruzinski Val
Moscow, 123056, Russia
Tel.: (7) 4957969988
Fax: (7) 4957969989
Web Site: www.afi-development.com
Investment Management Services
S.I.C.: 6211
N.A.I.C.S.: 523999

Africa Israel (East Europe) Investments B.V. (1)
Noordendijk 189
Dordrecht, Netherlands
Tel.: (31) 786481555
Real Estate Investment Trusts
S.I.C.: 6726
N.A.I.C.S.: 525990

Airport City Belgrade d.o.o. (1)
88 Omladinskih Brigada Street
Belgrade, 11070, Serbia
Tel.: (381) 11 2090 525
Fax: (381) 113189519
E-Mail: office@airportcitybelgrade.com
Web Site: www.airportcitybelgrade.com
Emp.: 25
Commercial Building Construction Services
S.I.C.: 1542
N.A.I.C.S.: 236220
Gili Dekel *(Pres)*
Adir El-Al *(CEO)*

Subsidiary:

Airport City Property Management d.o.o. (2)
Omladinskih Brigada 88-90
Belgrade, 11070, Serbia
Tel.: (381) 11 2090 525
Fax: (381) 11 3189 519
Emp.: 25
Property Management Services
S.I.C.: 6531
N.A.I.C.S.: 531312
Adir El-al *(CEO)*

Anninmuizas IPASUMS SIA (1)
Gertrudes St 1012
Riga, 1010, Latvia
Tel.: (371) 67277776
Fax: (371) 67846526
Emp.: 9
Real Estate Leasing Services
S.I.C.: 6519
N.A.I.C.S.: 531190
Ilona Striga *(CEO)*

Aristeya LLC (1)
8 Str 6 Nab Paveletskaya
Moscow, 115114, Russia
Tel.: (7) 4957969988
Fax: (7) 4957969989
Investment Management Services
S.I.C.: 6211
N.A.I.C.S.: 523999

Bellgate Construction Ltd. (1)
Omiros & Araouzos Tower 25 Olympion Street
Limassol, Cyprus
Tel.: (357) 25839777
Fax: (357) 25839999
Residential Building Construction Services
S.I.C.: 1531
N.A.I.C.S.: 236117

Borenco Enterprises Ltd. (1)
Omiros And Araouzos Tower
25 Olympion Street, Limassol, Cyprus
Tel.: (357) 25839777
Fax: (357) 25839999
E-Mail: s.kalenikov@emerald-grp.com
Web Site: www.emerald-grp.com
Emp.: 10
Management Consulting Services
S.I.C.: 8748
N.A.I.C.S.: 541618

Non-U.S. Subsidiary:

AFI Rus Management LLC (2)
31 Ul Gruzinski Val
Moscow, 123056, Russia
Tel.: (7) 4957969988
Fax: (7) 4957969989
Emp.: 200
Investment Management Services
S.I.C.: 6211
N.A.I.C.S.: 523999
Mark Groysman *(Mgr)*

B.R. Holdings SIA (1)
Gertrudes Iela 10/12
Riga, 1010, Latvia
Tel.: (371) 67846523
Fax: (371) 67846526
Emp.: 10
Investment Management Services
S.I.C.: 6211
N.A.I.C.S.: 523999
Ilona Striga *(Gen Mgr)*

Business Park Varna AD (1)
Business Park Varna Building 8 Floor 4
Varna, 9009, Bulgaria
Tel.: (359) 52 912 601
Fax: (359) 52 912 602
E-Mail: office@bpv.bg
Web Site: www.bpv.bg
Emp.: 5
Real Estate Development Services
S.I.C.: 6531
N.A.I.C.S.: 531390
Tsahi Tabakman *(CEO)*

Christina America Inc (1)
5555 Cypihot
Montreal, QC, H4S 1R3, Canada
Tel.: (514) 381-2365
Fax: (514) 850-5532
E-Mail: info@christina.ca
Web Site: www.christina.ca
Emp.: 200
Womens Clothing Stores
S.I.C.: 5621
N.A.I.C.S.: 448120
Kathy Vanness *(Pres)*

Controceni Park S.A. (1)
B-dul Vasile Milea 4
Bucharest, 61346, Romania
Tel.: (40) 31 425 75 10
Fax: (40) 31 425 75 13
Web Site: www.aficotroceni.ro
Commercial Building Construction Services
S.I.C.: 1542
N.A.I.C.S.: 236220

Czerwone Maki Project SP. Z.O.O. (1)
Bobrzynskiego 37
Krakow, 30-348, Poland
Tel.: (48) 122627641
Fax: (48) 122627558
Emp.: 2
Investment Management Services
S.I.C.: 6211
N.A.I.C.S.: 523999
Sebastian Kiec *(Pres)*

Danya Dutch BV (1)
Watermanweg 100
3067 Rotterdam, GG, Netherlands
Tel.: (31) 102861922
Fax: (31) 102861922
Emp.: 6
Holding Company
S.I.C.: 6719
N.A.I.C.S.: 551112
Redmond Schley *(Mng Dir)*

Investments Africa Israel s.r.o (1)
Jankovcova 2
17000 Prague, Czech Republic
Tel.: (420) 255743111
Fax: (420) 266314469
E-Mail: info@afi-europe.cz
Web Site: www.afi-europe.cz
Emp.: 20
All Other Business Support Services
S.I.C.: 7389
N.A.I.C.S.: 561499
Doron Klein *(CEO)*
David Hay *(CEO-Czech Republic, Germany, Poland & Latvia & VP)*

M.D.C. LTD (1)
Berkshire House
252-256 Kings Rd, Reading, United Kingdom
Tel.: (44) 1189448811
Fax: (44) 1189888882
E-Mail: info@mdc-ltd.com
Web Site: www.mdc-ltd.com
Emp.: 6
Collection Agencies
S.I.C.: 7322
N.A.I.C.S.: 561440
Stefanie Spaude *(Dir-Sls)*

NOVE Modrany S.R.O (1)
Jankovcova 37
Prague 7, 17000 Prague, Czech Republic
Tel.: (420) 255743111
Fax: (420) 255743177
E-Mail: info@afi-europe.cz
Web Site: www.afi-europe.cz
Emp.: 25
Business Support Services
S.I.C.: 7389
N.A.I.C.S.: 561499
David Hay *(CEO-Czech Republic, Germany, Poland & Latvia & VP)*

Novo Maar SP. Z.O.O. (1)
Bobrzynskiego 37
Krakow, 30-348, Poland
Tel.: (48) 122627406
Fax: (48) 122627558
Web Site: www.afi-europe.eu/
Real Estate Development Services
S.I.C.: 6531
N.A.I.C.S.: 531390

Rapo LLC (1)
9 Korp 21 Ul Kosinskaya
Moscow, 111538, Russia
Tel.: (7) 4957969988
Fax: (7) 4957969989
Web Site: www.rpdevelopment.com
Investment Management Services
S.I.C.: 6211
N.A.I.C.S.: 523999

Star Estate SRL (1)
4 B-Dul Vasile Milea
61344 Bucharest, Romania
Tel.: (40) 214120220
Fax: (40) 213118136
Investment Management Services
S.I.C.: 6211
N.A.I.C.S.: 523999
David Hay *(CEO)*

Tulip Management SRL (1)
4 B-Dul Vasile Milea Blvd
Bucharest, 61344, Romania
Tel.: (40) 214120220
Fax: (40) 213118136
Emp.: 15
Real Estate Property Renting Services
S.I.C.: 6519
N.A.I.C.S.: 531190

Tulipa Rokytka s.r.o. (1)
Classic 7 Business Park Building C 4th Floor Jankovcova 1037/49
170 00 Prague, Czech Republic
Tel.: (420) 800 123 200
E-Mail: info@afi-europe.cz
Web Site: www.tuliparokytka.cz
Residential Building Construction Services
S.I.C.: 1522
N.A.I.C.S.: 236116

Tulipa Vokovice s.r.o. (1)
Jankovtova 1037/49
17 000 Prague, Czech Republic
Tel.: (420) 255743111
E-Mail: info@afi-europe.cz
Emp.: 20
Residential Building Construction Services
S.I.C.: 1522
N.A.I.C.S.: 236116
Doron Klein *(CEO)*

AFRICA OIL CORPORATION

Suite 2000 - 885 West Georgia Street
Vancouver, BC, V6C 3E8, Canada
Tel.: (604) 689-7842
Fax: (604) 689-4250
E-Mail: africaoilcorp@namdo.com
Web Site: www.africaoilcorp.com
AOI—(OMX OTC TSXV)
Rev.: $1,727,000
Assets: $559,457,000
Liabilities: $39,304,000
Net Worth: $520,153,000
Earnings: ($20,117,000)
Fiscal Year-end: 12/31/12

Business Description:
Oil & Gas Exploration Services
S.I.C.: 1311
N.A.I.C.S.: 211111

Personnel:
Keith C. Hill *(Pres & CEO)*
Ian Gibbs *(CFO)*
Nicholas Walker *(COO)*

Board of Directors:
James Cameron Bailey
Bryan M. Benitz
John Hunter Craig
Gary Stephen Guidry
Keith C. Hill

Transfer Agent:
Computershare Trust Company of Canada
510 Burrard St
Vancouver, BC, Canada

Non-U.S. Subsidiaries:

Africa Oil Ethiopia B.V. (1)
Teleportboulevard 140-5
1043 EJ Amsterdam, Netherlands
Tel.: (31) 205405800
Oil & Gas Exploration Services
S.I.C.: 1389
N.A.I.C.S.: 213112
Mark Dingley *(Pres)*

Africa Oil Kenya B.V. (1)
Westlands Office Park
Nairobi, 63298, Kenya

Tel.: (254) 20 4456173
Oil & Gas Exploration Services
S.I.C.: 1389
N.A.I.C.S.: 213112

Africa Oil Turkana B.V. (1)
Amaliastraat 5
2514 JC Hague, South Holland, Netherlands
Tel.: (31) 703717811
Fax: (31) 703819354
Oil & Gas Exploration Services
S.I.C.: 1311
N.A.I.C.S.: 211111
Bosje Tjerk *(Gen Mgr)*

AFRICA OILFIELD LOGISTICS LIMITED

Richmond House Julian's Avenue
Saint Peter Port, GY1 1GZ, Guernsey
Tel.: (44) 20 7408 9200
E-Mail: info@africaoilfieldlogistics.com
Web Site: www.africaoilfieldlogistics.com
AOL—(AIM)

Business Description:
Oil & Gas Exploration
S.I.C.: 1311
N.A.I.C.S.: 211111

Personnel:
Phil Edmonds *(Chm)*
Carl Esprey *(CEO)*
Andrew Burns *(CFO)*

Board of Directors:
Phil Edmonds
Ian Mann
Jonathan Wright

AFRICAN BANK INVESTMENTS LIMITED

(d/b/a ABIL)
59 16th Road
Private Bag x170
Midrand, 1685, South Africa
Tel.: (27) 112569000
Fax: (27) 112569217
E-Mail: info@africanbank.co.za
Web Site: www.africanbank.co.za
Year Founded: 1994
ABL—(JSE)
Rev.: $2,455,741,480
Assets: $8,157,027,380
Liabilities: $6,180,214,410
Net Worth: $1,976,812,970
Earnings: $359,036,270
Emp.: 14,430
Fiscal Year-end: 09/30/12

Business Description:
Bank Holding Company
S.I.C.: 6712
N.A.I.C.S.: 551111

Personnel:
Leonidas Kirkinis *(CEO)*
Nithiananthan Nalliah *(CFO)*
Tami Sokutu *(Chief Risk Officer)*
Charles Chemel *(Exec-Sls, Distr, Mktg & Product)*
Steven Kahanovitz *(Exec-Corp Fin)*
Lindiwe Miyambu *(Exec-Human Capital)*
George Roussos *(Exec-Central Support Svcs)*
Antonio Fourie *(CEO-Ellerine Holdings Limited)*
Leeanne M. Goliath *(Sec)*

Board of Directors:
Mutle Constantine Mogase
Nicholas Adams
Antonio Fourie
Mojankunyane Florence Gumbi
Leonidas Kirkinis
Jack Koolen
Ntombi Langa-Royds
Nithiananthan Nalliah
Samuel Sithole
Thamsanqa Mthunzi Sokutu
Robert John Symmonds

Transfer Agent:
Link Market Services
Rennie House 13th Fl 19 Ameshoff Street
4844
Johannesburg, South Africa

Subsidiaries:

African Bank Limited (1)
59 16th Rd
Halfway House, Johannesburg, South Africa
Tel.: (27) 112569128
Fax: (27) 112569217
E-Mail: leon@africanbank.co.za
Web Site: www.africanbank.co.za
Commercial Banking
S.I.C.: 6029
N.A.I.C.S.: 522110
Antonio Fourie *(Exec Dir)*

Credit Indemnity Property (Pty) Limited (1)
59 16th Avenue
Halfway House, Johannesburg, South Africa
Tel.: (27) 112569000
Fax: (27) 112569216017
E-Mail: info@africanbank.co.za
Emp.: 1,000
Credit Unions
S.I.C.: 6062
N.A.I.C.S.: 522130
Leonidas Kirkinis *(CEO)*

The SPAR Group Limited (1)
22 Chancery Lane
3600 Pinetown, South Africa
Tel.: (27) 317191900
Fax: (27) 317191990
Web Site: www.spar.co.za
Emp.: 150
Financial Investment Activities
S.I.C.: 6211
N.A.I.C.S.: 523999
Wayne Hook *(CEO)*

The Standard General Insurance Company Limited (1)
5916 Halfway House
Private Bank X170, Midrand, 1685, South Africa ZA
Tel.: (27) 112569000 (100%)
Fax: (27) 11207
E-Mail: wharris@africanbank.co.za
Emp.: 1,000
Credit Life Insurance
S.I.C.: 6311
N.A.I.C.S.: 524113
William Harris *(Mgr-Insurance)*

AFRICAN CONSOLIDATED RESOURCES PLC

Nettlestead Place Maidstone Road
Nettlestead, Maidstone, Kent, ME18 5HA, United Kingdom
Tel.: (44) 1622816918
Fax: (44) 1622814510
Web Site: www.afcrplc.com
AFCR—(AIM)
Rev.: $3,686
Assets: $44,739,382
Liabilities: $837,200
Net Worth: $43,902,182
Earnings: ($11,015,681)
Emp.: 115
Fiscal Year-end: 03/31/13

Business Description:
Mineral Mining Services
S.I.C.: 1499
N.A.I.C.S.: 212399

Personnel:
Roy Clifford Tucker *(Chm)*
Eve Mkondo *(CFO)*
Andrew Prelea *(CEO-Romania & VP-Corp Strategy & Mktg)*

Board of Directors:
Roy Clifford Tucker
Herbert Stuart Bottomley
Michael Wallis Kellow
Lloyd Munyaradzi Manokore
Neville Francis Nicolau

AFRICAN DAWN CAPITAL LIMITED

1st Floor Quadrum 4 Quadrum Office Park 50 Constantia Boulevard
Constantia Kloof Ext 28, Constantia, South Africa

Mailing Address:
PO Box 5455
Roodepoort, 1715, South Africa
Tel.: (27) 11 475 7465
Fax: (27) 11 475 7413
E-Mail: info@afdawn.co.za
Web Site: www.afdawn.co.za
Year Founded: 1998
ADW—(JSE)
Rev.: $3,745,636
Assets: $13,576,241
Liabilities: $6,511,104
Net Worth: $7,065,137
Earnings: ($235,687)
Emp.: 102
Fiscal Year-end: 02/28/13

Business Description:
Financial Services
S.I.C.: 6159
N.A.I.C.S.: 522298

Personnel:
Jacques Groenewald *(Acting CEO)*
W. Somerville *(Sec)*

Board of Directors:
J. S. van der Merwe
H. H. Hickey
V. Lessing
W. N. Luhabe
G. Eddie Stoop
J. K. van Zyl

Transfer Agent:
Computershare Investor Services (Pty) Ltd
70 Marshall Street
Johannesburg, South Africa

AFRICAN EAGLE RESOURCES PLC

1st Floor 6 7 Queen Street
London, EC4N 1SP, United Kingdom
Tel.: (44) 2072486059
Fax: (44) 2076917745
E-Mail: info@africaneagle.co.uk
Web Site: www.africaneagle.co.uk
AFE—(LSE)
Rev.: $171,296
Assets: $6,245,604
Liabilities: $3,566,241
Net Worth: $2,679,363
Earnings: ($45,697,915)
Emp.: 56
Fiscal Year-end: 12/31/12

Business Description:
Gold & Copper Exploration Services
S.I.C.: 1041
N.A.I.C.S.: 212221

Personnel:
Robert Jonathan McLearon *(Interim Mng Dir)*
David Ronald Newbold *(CFO)*

Board of Directors:
Paul Colucci
Julian Alexander McIntyre
Venkat Siva
Mark Thompson

Legal Counsel:
Werksmans Inc.
155 5th Street
Sandton, 2196, South Africa

Mayer Brown International LLP
201 Bishopsgate
London, United Kingdom

Transfer Agent:
Computershare Investor Services 2004 (Proprietary) Limited
70 Marshall Street
Johannesburg, South Africa

Subsidiary:

Twigg Resources Limited (1)
1st Floor 6-7 Queen Street
London, EC4N 1SP, United Kingdom
Tel.: (44) 2072486059
E-Mail: info@africaneagle.co.uk
Emp.: 3
Mineral Exploration Services
S.I.C.: 1481
N.A.I.C.S.: 213115
Mark Parker *(Mng Dir)*

Non-U.S. Subsidiary:

Twigg Gold Limited (2)
PO Box 1866
Mwanza, Tanzania
Tel.: (255) 282 500 727
Fax: (255) 282 500 727
E-Mail: admin@twigg.co.tz
Mineral Exploration Services
S.I.C.: 1481
N.A.I.C.S.: 213115
John McDonald *(Country Mgr)*

AFRICAN ENERGY RESOURCES LIMITED

Level 1 8 Colin Street
West Perth, WA, 6005, Australia

Mailing Address:
PO Box 886
West Perth, WA, 6872, Australia
Tel.: (61) 8 6465 5500
Fax: (61) 8 6465 5599
E-Mail: info@africanenergyresources.com
Web Site: www.africanenergyresources.com
AFR—(ASX)
Rev.: $50,282
Assets: $25,189,029
Liabilities: $5,821,560
Net Worth: $19,367,469
Earnings: ($12,547,719)
Emp.: 21
Fiscal Year-end: 06/30/13

Business Description:
Energy Resources Development
S.I.C.: 8322
N.A.I.C.S.: 624229

Personnel:
Alasdair Cooke *(Chm)*
David Walton *(CEO)*
Charles Frazer Tabeart *(Mng Dir)*
Daniel Davis *(Sec)*

Board of Directors:
Alasdair Cooke
Valentine Chitalu
Philip Clark
Michael Paul Curnow
Gregory William Fry
Vincent Masterton-Hume
Charles Frazer Tabeart

Legal Counsel:
Fairweather Corporate Lawyers
595 Stirling Highway
Cottesloe, Australia

AFRICAN EXPORT IMPORT BANK LIMITED

(d/b/a Afreximbank)
72 B El Maahad El Eshteraky Street
Cairo, 11341, Egypt
Tel.: (20) 24564100
Telex: 20003 AFRXM UN
Fax: (20) 24564110
E-Mail: info@afreximbank.com
Web Site: www.afreximbank.com
Year Founded: 1993
Emp.: 41

Business Description:
Banking Institution
S.I.C.: 6035
N.A.I.C.S.: 522120

Personnel:
Jean-Louis Ekra *(Chm & Pres)*
Getachew Telahun *(Sec)*
B. O. Oramah *(Exec VP)*

African Export Import Bank Limited—(Continued)

Board of Directors:
Jean-Louis Ekra
T. Baccar
Charles Boamah
M. Farag
Caleb Fundanga
Gideon Gono
Franklin Kennedy
Laurent-Jules Mabert
Victor Nembelessini-Silue
O. Saeed
S. Usman

Deloitte & Touche
1 Town Planning Way Ilupeju
PO Box 965, Lagos, Nigeria
Tel.: (234) 4930720 4930724
Fax: (234) 4970023

AFRICAN GOLD GROUP, INC.

Sun Life Financial Tower Suite 2518
150 King Street West
Toronto, ON, M5H 1J9, Canada
Tel.: (416) 644-8892
Fax: (416) 644-8893
E-Mail: info@africangoldgroup.com
Web Site: www.africangoldgroup.com
Year Founded: 2002
3A6—(DEU TSXV)
Sales Range: Less than $1 Million
Business Description:
Gold Exploration Services
S.I.C.: 1041
N.A.I.C.S.: 212221
Personnel:
Michael A. J. Nikiforuk *(Co-Founder & Pres)*
Marco J. Durante *(Co-Founder, Sec & VP)*
Jaimie Macpherson *(CFO)*
Board of Directors:
David S. Brown
Marco J. Durante
Pierre Lalande
Jean-Jacques Lefebvre
Michael A. J. Nikiforuk

THE AFRICAN LAKES CORPORATION PLC

Chenil House 181-183 Kings Road
Chelsea, London, SW3 5EB, United Kingdom
Tel.: (44) 2073514815
Fax: (44) 2073513408
E-Mail: office@africanlakes.com
Year Founded: 1877
Sales Range: $10-24.9 Million
Emp.: 300
Business Description:
Information Technology & Internet Services Specializing in Trade, Transportation & Motor Vehicles
S.I.C.: 7373
N.A.I.C.S.: 541512
Personnel:
David Montgomery *(Chm)*
Richard Wilkinson *(Deputy Chm)*
J. Leslie Davey *(COO & Dir-Fin)*
Donald R. MacKenzie *(Chm-Automotive Div)*
Board of Directors:
David Montgomery
Benjamin Cleminson
Colin D.T. Fitch
Donald R. MacKenzie
Miles Q. Morland
Richard Wilkinson

Non-U.S. Subsidiaries:

Africa Online Egypt Ltd. (1)
67 El Sewesry B
Nasr City, Cairo, Egypt
Tel.: (20) 24125651
E-Mail: info@africaonline.com
Internet Service
S.I.C.: 4899
N.A.I.C.S.: 517919

Africa Online Ghana Limited (1)
Kwame Nkrumah Cir 5th Fl GCB Twr
PO Box STC 84
Kaneshie, Accra, Ghana GH
Tel.: (233) 212460659 (96%)
Fax: (233) 21246182
E-Mail: info@africaonline.co.gh
Internet Service
S.I.C.: 7373
N.A.I.C.S.: 541512

Africa Online Kenya Limited (1)
15th Floor Rahimtulla Tower
Upper Hill Road
Upper Hill, Nairobi, Kenya KE
Mailing Address:
P.O. Box 63017-00200
Nairobi, Kenya
Tel.: (254) 202792000
Fax: (254) 202710010
E-Mail: info@africaonline.co.ke
Web Site: www.africaonline.co.ke/index.php?option=com_contact&view=contact&id=2&Itemid=49
Emp.: 200
Internet Service
S.I.C.: 7373
N.A.I.C.S.: 541512

Africa Online Namibia (Pty) Limited (1)
NUA Building Robert Mugabe Avenue
Windhoek, Namibia NA
Tel.: (264) 612058111 (100%)
Fax: (264) 612058244
E-Mail: info@africaonline.com.na
Web Site: www.africaonline.com.na
Internet Service
S.I.C.: 7373
N.A.I.C.S.: 541512

Africa Online Swaziland (Pty) Limited (1)
Embassy House Msakato Street
PO Box 5833
Mbabane, H100, Swaziland
Tel.: (268) 4044705
Fax: (268) 4044783
E-Mail: info@africaonline.co.sz
Web Site: www.africaonline.com
Emp.: 10
Internet Service
S.I.C.: 3291
N.A.I.C.S.: 327910

Africa Online Tanzania Limited (1)
3rd Floor ANC Building
PO Box 2721
50 Mirambo Street, Dar es Salaam, Tanzania TZ
Tel.: (255) 222116090 (95%)
Fax: (255) 222116089
E-Mail: info@africaonline.co.tz
Web Site: www.africaonline.co.tz
Emp.: 50
Internet Service
S.I.C.: 7373
N.A.I.C.S.: 541512
Ken Munyi *(Gen Mgr)*

Africa Online Uganda Limited (1)
5th Floor Commercial Plaza 7 Kampala Road
PO Box 29331
Kampala, Uganda UG
Tel.: (256) 41258143 (100%)
Fax: (256) 41258144
E-Mail: info@africaonline.co.ug
Web Site: www.africaonline.co.ug
Emp.: 50
Internet Service
S.I.C.: 7373
N.A.I.C.S.: 541512

Africa Online Zimbabwe (Pvt) Limited (1)
2h Floor Goldbridge South Eastgate Centre 2nd St
P O Box A1571, Harare, Zimbabwe ZW
Tel.: (263) 4702202 (70%)
Fax: (263) 4702203
E-Mail: info@africaonline.co.zw
Web Site: www.africaonline.co.zw
Emp.: 40
Internet Service
S.I.C.: 7373
N.A.I.C.S.: 541512
Nyagura Nhena *(Gen Mgr)*

AFRICAN MEDIA ENTERTAINMENT LIMITED

AME House Oxford Office Park No 5
8th Street Houghton Estate
Johannesburg, South Africa
Tel.: (27) 861237234
Fax: (27) 114420658
Web Site: www.ame.co.za
AME—(JSE)
Rev.: $24,204,050
Assets: $27,016,432
Liabilities: $9,031,950
Net Worth: $17,984,482
Earnings: $4,647,167
Emp.: 132
Fiscal Year-end: 03/31/13
Business Description:
Radio Broadcasting Services
S.I.C.: 4832
N.A.I.C.S.: 515112
Personnel:
Valerie-Joan Slabbert *(Sec)*
Board of Directors:
A. C. G. Molusi
Angela J. Davies
Lawrence K. Dube
Michelle Mynhardt
Martinus J. Prinsloo
Navin Sooka
Wilfred Tshuma
Legal Counsel:
Martini-Patlansky Attorneys
32 St John Road Houghton
Johannesburg, South Africa

Fluxmans Attorneys
11 Biermann Avenue Rosebank
2196 Johannesburg, South Africa
Transfer Agent:
Computershare Investor Services (Proprietary) Limited
Ground Floor 70 Marshall St
Johannesburg, South Africa

Subsidiaries:

Seyalemoya Communications (Pty) Ltd (1)
6 Lombard St
Potchefstroom, 2531, South Africa
Tel.: (27) 515050900
Fax: (27) 515050929
Radio Broadcasting Services
S.I.C.: 4832
N.A.I.C.S.: 515111

Umoya Communications (Pty) Ltd (1)
Marine Drive
Port Elizabeth, Eastern Cape, 6001, South Africa
Tel.: (27) 415059497
Fax: (27) 415835555
Radio Broadcasting Services
S.I.C.: 4832
N.A.I.C.S.: 515112
David Tiltmann *(Mng Dir)*

AFRICAN MEDICAL INVESTMENT PLC

3rd Floor Exchange House 54 62 Athol Street
Douglas, IM1 1JD, Isle of Man
Tel.: (44) 20 7236 1177
Web Site: www.amiplc.com
AMEI—(AIM)
Sales Range: $10-24.9 Million
Emp.: 286
Business Description:
Hospital Management, Emergency & Evacuation Services
S.I.C.: 8062
N.A.I.C.S.: 622110
Personnel:
Peter Botha *(Chm & CEO)*
Board of Directors:
Peter Botha
Joseph Cleverdon
Altaf Mackeen
Legal Counsel:
Salans LLP
Millennium Bridge House 2 Lambeth Hill
London, United Kingdom

Cains
Fort Anne
Douglas, Isle of Man

AFRICAN METALS CORPORATION

Suite 205 - 16055 Fraser Highway
Surrey, BC, V4N 0G2, Canada
Tel.: (604) 507-2181
Fax: (604) 507-2187
E-Mail: info@africanmetals.com
Web Site: www.africanmetals.com
Year Founded: 1980
AFR—(TSXV)
Int. Income: $65
Assets: $14,368,907
Liabilities: $5,827,408
Net Worth: $8,541,499
Earnings: ($1,117,796)
Fiscal Year-end: 05/31/13
Business Description:
Mineral Exploration Services
S.I.C.: 1081
N.A.I.C.S.: 213114
Personnel:
Nigel Ferguson *(Pres & CEO)*
Sheryl Jones *(CFO)*
Peter Rook-Green *(Treas & Sec)*
Board of Directors:
Nigel Ferguson
Simeon Tshisangma
Michael J. Velletta
Legal Counsel:
James L. Harris Law Corp
Suite 300 - 576 Seymour Street
Vancouver, BC, Canada
Transfer Agent:
Computershare Trust Company of Canada
510 Burrard St
Vancouver, BC, Canada

AFRICAN MINERALS LIMITED

Stratton House 5 Stratton Street
London, W1J8 LA, United Kingdom
Tel.: (44) 20 3435 7600
Web Site: www.african-minerals.com
OUV—(DEU)
Sales Range: $1-9.9 Million
Business Description:
Mineral Exploration Services
S.I.C.: 1481
N.A.I.C.S.: 213115
Personnel:
Vasile Timis *(Chm)*
Ian David Cockerill *(Vice Chm)*
Bernard Pryor *(CEO)*
Matthew Hird *(CFO)*
Board of Directors:
Vasile Timis
Gibril Bangura
Ian David Cockerill
Dermot Coughlan
Jurong Cui
William Murray John
Zhimin Li
Roger Liddell
Bernard Pryor
Nina Shapiro

AFRICAN MINING & EXPLORATION PLC

Third Floor 55 Gower Street
London, WC1E 6HQ, United Kingdom
Tel.: (44) 2074995881
Fax: (44) 2074994050
E-Mail: info@ameplc.co.uk
Web Site: www.ameplc.co.uk

AME—(LSE)
Rev.: $20,156
Assets: $6,481,967
Liabilities: $313,789
Net Worth: $6,168,178
Earnings: ($1,486,777)
Emp.: 32
Fiscal Year-end: 12/31/12

Business Description:
Gold Exploration Services
S.I.C.: 1041
N.A.I.C.S.: 212221

Personnel:
Michael McGarty *(CFO)*
Stephen F. Ronaldson *(Sec)*

Board of Directors:
Mike Johnson
David Archer
Charles Cannon-Brookes

Legal Counsel:
Ronaldsons LLP
55 Gower Street
London, EC1E 6HQ, United Kingdom

AFRICAN POTASH LIMITED
Richmond House St Julian's Avenue
Saint Peter Port, GY1 1GZ, Guernsey
Tel.: (44) 20 7408 9200
E-Mail: info@africanpotash.com
Web Site: www.africanpotash.com
Year Founded: 2011
AFPO—(AIM)

Business Description:
Potash Mining
S.I.C.: 1474
N.A.I.C.S.: 212391

Personnel:
Jean-Pierre Conrad *(Chm)*
Edward Marlow *(CEO)*

Board of Directors:
Jean-Pierre Conrad
Simon Dorling
Philippe Edmonds
Andrew Groves
Edward Marlow

AFRICAN QUEEN MINES LTD.
Suite 1450 650 West Georgia Street
PO Box 11553
Vancouver, BC, V6B 4N8, Canada
Tel.: (604) 899-0100
Fax: (604) 899-0200
E-Mail: info@africanqueenmines.com
Web Site: www.africanqueenmines.com
Year Founded: 2008
AQ—(TSXV)
Assets: $3,588,974
Liabilities: $142,801
Net Worth: $3,446,172
Earnings: ($703,352)
Fiscal Year-end: 09/30/13

Business Description:
Mineral Exploration Services
S.I.C.: 1081
N.A.I.C.S.: 213114

Personnel:
Irwin A. Olian, Jr. *(Chm, Pres & CEO)*
Jennifer Todhunter *(CFO & Sec)*

Board of Directors:
Irwin A. Olian, Jr.
W. Benjamin Catalano
Ardito Martohardjono
Edward A. Schiller
Gregory Sparks
Jennifer Todhunter

Transfer Agent:
TMX Equity Transfer Services
200 University Ave Suite 300
Toronto, ON, Canada

AFRICAN RAINBOW MINERALS LIMITED
ARM House 29 Impala Road
Chislehurston, Sandton, 2196, South Africa

Mailing Address:
PO Box 786136
Sandton, 2146, South Africa
Tel.: (27) 117791300
Fax: (27) 117791312
E-Mail: ir.admin@arm.co.za
Web Site: www.arm.co.za
ARI—(JSE OTC)
Rev.: $2,290,743,600
Assets: $4,258,115,700
Liabilities: $1,413,898,600
Net Worth: $2,844,217,100
Earnings: $199,049,400
Emp.: 13,731
Fiscal Year-end: 06/30/13

Business Description:
Metal & Coal Mining Services
S.I.C.: 1099
N.A.I.C.S.: 212299

Personnel:
Patrice Motsepe *(Chm)*
Michael P. Schmidt *(CEO)*
Johan Pistorius *(CIO)*
Rilette Avenant-Buys *(Exec-Logistics)*
Bennie Boshielo *(Exec-Corp Affairs-Platinum)*
Nerine Botes-Schoeman *(Exec-Sustainable Dev)*
J. Mark Brasler *(Exec-Ops Support)*
Graham Butler *(Exec-Exploration & Project Investment)*
Pierre Joubert *(Exec-Ops-Copper)*
Sandile Langa *(Exec-Legal-Coal)*
Peter J. Manda *(Exec-Legal)*
Kolobe Stephen Mashalane *(Sr Exec-Corp Affairs)*
Busi Mashiane *(Exec-HR)*
Imrhan Paruk *(Exec-Corp Dev)*
Claus Schlegel *(Exec-Exploration)*
Stompie Shiels *(Exec-Bus Dev & IR)*
Mandla Tobela *(Exec-Legal-Ferrous)*
Andre Joubert *(CEO-Ferrous)*
Thando Mkatshana *(CEO-Coal)*
Daniel Simelane *(CEO-Copper)*
Jan C. Steenkamp *(CEO-Exploration & Technical Svcs)*
Francois Uys *(CEO-Platinum)*
Alyson D'Oyley *(Sec)*

Board of Directors:
Patrice Motsepe
Frank Abbott
Michael Arnold
Mmapusetso Manana Maria Bakane-Tuoane
Thomas Andrew Boardman
Anton Dirk Botha
Joaquim Alberto Chissano
Wilson Mangisi Gule
Alexander Komape Maditsi
Michael P. Schmidt
Daniel Simelane
Rejoice Vakashile Simelane
Bernard Swanepoel
Andre Jacobus Wilkens

Transfer Agent:
Computershare Investor Services (Pty) Limited
Ground Floor 70 Marshall Street
Johannesburg, South Africa

Subsidiary:

Two Rivers Platinum (Proprietary) Limited **(1)**
2 Rivers Platinum Mine Dwarsriver Farm KT 372
Steelpoort, Mpumalanga, 1133, South Africa
Tel.: (27) 132302600
Fax: (27) 865947739
Platinum Mining Services
S.I.C.: 1099
N.A.I.C.S.: 212299
Adriaan Debeer *(Gen Mgr)*

AFRICAN SUN HOTELS
54 Park Lane Crowne Plaza Monomotapa
Harare, Zimbabwe
Tel.: (263) 4736645
Fax: (263) 4736646
E-Mail: info@zimsun.co.zw
Web Site: www.africansunhotels.com
Year Founded: 1968
Sales Range: $25-49.9 Million
Emp.: 1,600

Business Description:
Hotels, Resorts, Casinos & Time Shares Owner & Manager
S.I.C.: 7011
N.A.I.C.S.: 721120

Personnel:
Shingi A. Munyeza *(Grp CEO)*
N. Mangwiro *(Grp CFO)*
E. T. Shangwa *(Sec & Dir-Fin Ops)*

AFRICAN SUN LIMITED
17th Floor Office No 1708 Crowne Plaza Monomotapa 54 Park Lane
PO Box CY 1211
Causeway, Harare, Zimbabwe
Tel.: (263) 4 700521 7
E-Mail: edwin.shangwa@africansunhotels.com
Web Site: www.africansuninvestor.com
ASUN—(ZIM)
Rev.: $54,426,751
Assets: $53,210,551
Liabilities: $35,078,805
Net Worth: $18,131,746
Earnings: $3,348,102
Emp.: 1,744
Fiscal Year-end: 09/30/12

Business Description:
Hotel Management Services
S.I.C.: 7011
N.A.I.C.S.: 721110

Personnel:
Bekithemba Lloyd Nkomo *(Chm)*
Shingirai Albert Munyeza *(Grp CEO)*
Nigel Mangwiro *(Grp Dir-Fin & IR Officer)*
Edwin T. Shangwa *(Sec)*

Board of Directors:
Bekithemba Lloyd Nkomo
David William Birch
E. A. Fundira
Vernon Wright Lapham
A. Makamura
Nigel Mangwiro
N. G. Maphosa
Shingirai Albert Munyeza
Nonhlanhla Rene Ramikosi

Legal Counsel:
Dube, Manikai & Hwacha
6th Floor Gold Bridge Eastgate Complex Robert Mugabe Road
Harare, Zimbabwe

Transfer Agent:
Corpserve (Private) Limited
2nd Floor ZB Bank Centre cnr Kwame Nkrumah Avenue First Street
PO Box 2208
Harare, Zimbabwe

Subsidiary:

African Sun Zimbabwe (Private) Limited **(1)**
Crowne Plaza Monomotapa 54 Park Lane
Harare, Zimbabwe
Tel.: (263) 4700521
Fax: (263) 4734739
E-Mail: tatendata@africansun.co.zw
Web Site: www.africansun.com
Hotel Management Services
S.I.C.: 7011
N.A.I.C.S.: 721110
Helijah Nyakurerwa *(Mgr-HR)*

AFRICO RESOURCES LTD.
520 800 West Pender St
Vancouver, BC, V6C 2V6, Canada
Tel.: (604) 646-3225
Fax: (604) 646-3226
Toll Free: (877) 648-3225
E-Mail: info@africoresources.com
Web Site: www.africoresources.com
Year Founded: 2006
ARL—(TSX)
Rev.: $701,283
Assets: $85,591,316
Liabilities: $1,359,499
Net Worth: $84,231,817
Earnings: ($7,640,172)
Emp.: 6
Fiscal Year-end: 12/31/12

Business Description:
Mineral Exploration & Development Services
S.I.C.: 3299
N.A.I.C.S.: 327999

Personnel:
Chris Theodoropoulos *(Chm & Acting CEO)*
Godefroy Ilunga *(Logistics Officer-Lubumbashi)*
Lukas Marthinus Maree *(Sec)*

Board of Directors:
Chris Theodoropoulos
James Cook
Beat Ehrensberger
Charles Forster

Computershare Investor Services Inc.
510 Burrard St
Vancouver, BC, V6C 3B9, Canada

Transfer Agents:
Computershare Investor Services Inc.
100 University Ave 9th Floor
Toronto, ON, Canada

Computershare Investor Services Inc.
510 Burrard St
Vancouver, BC, V6C 3B9, Canada

Subsidiary:

Africo Resources (B.C.) Ltd. **(1)**
Suite 1108 1030 Georgia St W
Vancouver, BC, V6E 3B9, Canada
Tel.: (604) 646-3225
Mineral Exploration Services
S.I.C.: 1481
N.A.I.C.S.: 213115

AFRILAND FIRST BANK
1063 Place de l'Independance
BP 11834
Yaounde, Cameroon
Tel.: (237) 22220888
Fax: (237) 22221785
E-Mail: firstbank@afrilandfirstbank.com
Web Site: www.afrilandfirstbank.com
Sales Range: $10-24.9 Million
Emp.: 240

Business Description:
Banking Services
S.I.C.: 6029
N.A.I.C.S.: 522110

Personnel:
Paul K. Fokam *(Chm)*

Board of Directors:
Paul K. Fokam
Julienne Kammogne Fokam
Albert Nigri
Richard Noukelack
Warren Weinstein

AFRIMAT LIMITED
Tyger Valley Office Park No 2 Cnr Willie van Schoor & Old Oak Rd
Bellville, South Africa

Mailing Address:
PO Box 5278
Tyger Valley, Bellville, 7536, South Africa
Tel.: (27) 219178840
Fax: (27) 219141174
E-Mail: info@afrimat.co.za
Web Site: www.afrimat.co.za
AFT—(JSE)
Rev.: $149,408,196
Assets: $134,181,127
Liabilities: $49,082,232

Afrimat Limited—(Continued)

Net Worth: $85,098,894
Earnings: $11,591,917
Emp.: 2,085
Fiscal Year-end: 02/28/13

Business Description:
Construction Material Supplier
S.I.C.: 1541
N.A.I.C.S.: 236210

Personnel:
Andries J. van Heerden *(CEO)*
Pieter G. S. de Wit *(Sec)*

Board of Directors:
Marthinus W. von Wielligh
Gert Coffee
Loyiso Dotwana
Francois du Toit
Laurie Korsten
Phuti Tsukudu
Andries J. van Heerden
Hendrik J. E. van Wyk
Hendrik P. Verreynne

Legal Counsel:
Webber Wentzel
10 Fricker Road
Illovo, South Africa

Transfer Agent:
Computershare Investor Services (Pty) Limited
Ground Floor 70 Marshall Street
Johannesburg, South Africa

Subsidiaries:

Afrimat Readymix (Cape) (Pty) Limited **(1)**
189 Blouberg Rd
Cape Town, Western Cape, 7441, South Africa
Tel.: (27) 215563255
Fax: (27) 215563258
E-Mail: info@afrimat.co.za
Emp.: 98
Ready Mix Concrete Mfr
S.I.C.: 3273
N.A.I.C.S.: 327320
Billy Paton *(Mng Dir)*

Boublok (Pty) Limited **(1)**
38 Samuel Walter St
Worcester, Western Cape, 6850, South Africa
Tel.: (27) 233423639
Fax: (27) 233471505
E-Mail: boublok@afrimat.co.za
Web Site: www.afrimat.co.za
Emp.: 47
Ready Mix Concrete Mfr
S.I.C.: 3273
N.A.I.C.S.: 327320
F J Walters *(Gen Mgr)*

Denver Quarries (Pty) Limited **(1)**
Mission Rd
Port Elizabeth, Eastern Cape, 6390, South Africa
Tel.: (27) 413721122
Fax: (27) 413722236
Stone Quarrying Services
S.I.C.: 1411
N.A.I.C.S.: 212311

Infrasors Holdings Limited **(1)**
Lyttelton Dolomite Mine
PO Box 14014
Botha Avenue Lyttelton, 14014 Pretoria, South Africa ZA
Tel.: (27) 12 664 5649 (50.7%)
E-Mail: contact@infrasors.co.za
Web Site: www.infrasors.co.za
IRA—(JSE)
Rev.: $32,393,335
Assets: $41,994,620
Liabilities: $24,857,830
Net Worth: $17,136,791
Earnings: $33,813,712
Emp.: 259
Fiscal Year-end: 02/28/13
Dolomite & Silica Mining Services
S.I.C.: 1429
N.A.I.C.S.: 212319
Mochele Noge *(Chm)*
Louis Loubser *(Mng Dir)*
Pieter de Wit *(Sec)*

Subsidiaries:

Delf Sand (Pty) Limited **(2)**
Portion 10 Farm Pienaarspoort
Pretoria, Gauteng, 0002, South Africa
Tel.: (27) 127362240
Fax: (27) 127362241
Plaster Sand Distr
S.I.C.: 5032
N.A.I.C.S.: 423320

Plant:

Delf Silica Coastal **(2)**
Tongaat Industrial Park 9 Walter Reid Road
Tongaat, 102, South Africa
Tel.: (27) 32 944 5870
Fax: (27) 32 944 4976
Metal Mining Services
S.I.C.: 1099
N.A.I.C.S.: 212299
Andrew Michael Wray *(Project Mgr)*

Lancaster Pre-Cast (Pty) Limited **(1)**
15 Bloekom St
Vryheid, Kwazulu-Natal, 3100, South Africa
Tel.: (27) 349809411
Fax: (27) 349822245
Ready Mix Concrete Mfr
S.I.C.: 3273
N.A.I.C.S.: 327320

Lancaster Quarries (Pty) Limited **(1)**
15 High St
Vryheid, KwaZulu Natal, 3100, South Africa
Tel.: (27) 349809411
Fax: (27) 349822245
E-Mail: shantel.cloete@afrimat.co.za
Stone Quarrying Services
S.I.C.: 1411
N.A.I.C.S.: 212311

Maritzburg Quarries (Pty) Limited **(1)**
Cliffdale Rd
Hammarsdale, Kwazulu-Natal, 3700, South Africa
Tel.: (27) 317362036
Fax: (27) 317361350
Emp.: 50
Stone Quarrying Services
S.I.C.: 1411
N.A.I.C.S.: 212311
Piete Strauss *(Mng Dir)*

Rodag Properties (Pty) Limited **(1)**
15 Bloekom St
Vryheid, 3100, South Africa
Tel.: (27) 349809411
Fax: (27) 349822245
Property Management Services
S.I.C.: 6531
N.A.I.C.S.: 531312

AFRIPACK (PTY) LTD
75 Richard Carte Rd
4092 Durban, Mobeni, South Africa
Tel.: (27) 314521300
Fax: (27) 314629240
Web Site: www.afripack.co.za
Year Founded: 1933
Sales Range: $10-24.9 Million
Emp.: 300

Business Description:
Paper Sack Mfr
S.I.C.: 2672
N.A.I.C.S.: 322220

Personnel:
Arnold Vermaak *(CEO)*

Subsidiaries:

Astra Repro (Pty) Ltd **(1)**
29 Gillitts Road
3610 Pinetown, South Africa (100%)
Tel.: (27) 317010898
Fax: (27) 317010910
Emp.: 32
Plastics Material & Resin Mfr
S.I.C.: 2821
N.A.I.C.S.: 325211
Craig Oliver *(Mng Dir)*

Tamperpak (Pty) Ltd **(1)**
22 Witkoppen Road
Paulshoff, 2157 Sandton, South Africa (100%)
Tel.: (27) 112346844
Fax: (27) 112348547
E-Mail: gilest@tamper-pak.co.za
Emp.: 8
Packaging & Labeling Services
S.I.C.: 7389
N.A.I.C.S.: 561910
James Hynd *(Mng Dir)*

AFRISAM (SOUTH AFRICA) (PTY) LTD.
Constantia Park AfriSam House
Cnr 14th Avenue, 1715 Roodepoort, South Africa
Tel.: (27) 116705500
Fax: (27) 116705793
Web Site: www.afrisam.co.za
Year Founded: 2007
Sales Range: $900-999.9 Million
Emp.: 1,800

Business Description:
Cement & Concrete Mfr
S.I.C.: 3241
N.A.I.C.S.: 327310

Personnel:
Stephen Olivier *(CEO)*
Duncan Matshoba *(CFO)*
Grant Neser *(COO-Aggregate & Readymix)*
Louis Vinderbank *(CIO)*

AFROCENTRIC INVESTMENT CORPORATION LIMITED
37 Conrad Road Florida North
Roodepoort, 1709, South Africa
Mailing Address:
Private Bag X34
Benmore, 2010, South Africa
Tel.: (27) 11 6712000
Fax: (27) 11 7587911
E-Mail: info@afrocentric.za.com
Web Site: www.afrocentric.za.com
Year Founded: 2006
ACT—(JSE)
Rev.: $197,745,861
Assets: $170,751,434
Liabilities: $53,122,510
Net Worth: $117,628,924
Earnings: $20,777,205
Fiscal Year-end: 06/30/13

Business Description:
Investment Management Services
S.I.C.: 6799
N.A.I.C.S.: 523920

Personnel:
J. Meyer Kahn *(Co-Founder)*
Michael I. Sacks *(Co-Founder)*
Anna T. Mokgokong *(Chm)*
Ronelle Kleyn *(Sec)*

Board of Directors:
Anna T. Mokgokong
N. Brigalia Bam
Wallace Holmes
Brian Joffe
J. Meyer Kahn
M. Joe Madungandaba
Yasmin Masithela
Garth Napier
Michael I. Sacks

Transfer Agent:
Computershare Investor Services (Pty) Ltd
70 Marshall Street
Johannesburg, South Africa

AFT CORPORATION LIMITED
Unit 7 6-8 Herbert Street St Leonards
PO Box 285
Sydney, NSW, 2065, Australia
Tel.: (61) 1300 794 907
Fax: (61) 9437 9104
E-Mail: info@aftcorp.net
Web Site: www.aftcorp.net
AFT—(ASX)
Rev.: $6,699,842
Assets: $4,395,984
Liabilities: $1,195,401
Net Worth: $3,200,583
Earnings: ($1,176,048)
Fiscal Year-end: 12/31/12

Business Description:
Logistics Services
S.I.C.: 4731
N.A.I.C.S.: 541614

Personnel:
Stone H. Wang *(Chm, CEO & Mng Dir)*
Maurice Watson *(Sec)*

Board of Directors:
Stone H. Wang
Neil Bourne
John Zhang

Legal Counsel:
Juris Bridge
Suite 1104 Level 11 265 Castlereagh Street
2000 Sydney, NSW, Australia

AFTEK LIMITED
703-706 7th Floor Makhija Chambers
196 Turner Road
Opp H P Petrol Pump Bandra West, Mumbai, 400 050, India
Tel.: (91) 2226413665
Fax: (91) 2226413668
E-Mail: information@aftek.com
Web Site: www.aftek.com
530707—(BOM)
Sls.: $20,565,273
Assets: $112,363,153
Liabilities: $29,048,250
Net Worth: $83,314,904
Earnings: ($4,670,430)
Emp.: 400
Fiscal Year-end: 03/31/13

Business Description:
Software Publisher
S.I.C.: 7372
N.A.I.C.S.: 511210

Personnel:
Ranjit M. Dhuru *(Chm, CEO & Mng Dir)*
Nitin K. Shukla *(CFO)*
C. G. Deshmukh *(Compliance Officer & Sec)*
Ravindranath Malekar *(Sr VP-Software Driven Products-Support)*
Amit Raje *(Sr VP-Engrg)*

Board of Directors:
Ranjit M. Dhuru
Mukul S. Dalal
Mahesh Naik
Sandip C. Save
Nitin K. Shukla

Legal Counsel:
Kanga & Co.
Readymoney Mansion 43 Veer Nariman Rd
Mumbai, India

Transfer Agent:
Bigshare Services Pvt. Ltd.
E-2/3 Ansa Industrial Estate Sakivihar Road
Saki Naka Andheri E
Mumbai, India

Subsidiary:

Digihome Solutions Private Limited **(1)**
Survey No 120 Saikar Complex Baner Road Baner
Pune, Maharashtra, 411045, India
Tel.: (91) 2064006912
E-Mail: info@digihome.co.in
Web Site: www.digihome.co.in
Resource Planning Software Development Services
S.I.C.: 7371
N.A.I.C.S.: 541511

Plant:

Aftek Limited - Solapur Factory **(1)**
A 19/2 M I D C
Chincholi, Sholapur, Maharashtra, 413255, India
Tel.: (91) 217 2357637
Fax: (91) 217 2357692

Web Site: www.aftek.com
Software Development Services
S.I.C.: 7371
N.A.I.C.S.: 541511

U.S. Subsidiary:

Opdex Inc. (1)
2940 Freedom Cir
Santa Clara, CA 95054
Tel.: (408) 238-5667
Web Site: www.opdex.com
Software Development Services
S.I.C.: 7372
N.A.I.C.S.: 511210

Non-U.S. Subsidiary:

Arexera Information Technologies GmbH (1)
Fraunhoferstr 17
82152 Martinsried, Germany (100%)
Tel.: (49) 8985651660
Fax: (49) 8985651661
E-Mail: info@arexera.de
Emp.: 20
Software Reproducing
S.I.C.: 3652
N.A.I.C.S.: 334614
Mahesh Valdya *(Mng Dir)*

AG AJIKAWA CORPORATION

4 11 88 Takeshima Nishi
Yodogawaku
Osaka, 555 0011, Japan
Tel.: (81) 664742050
Telex: 5242164
Fax: (81) 664747866
Web Site: www.ag-ajikawa.co.jp/ag-intl/en/index.php
Year Founded: 1930
Emp.: 200
Business Description:
Mfr. of Steel Transmission Towers; Galvanization, Plastic Powder Coating of Steel Structures; Hobby Products
Import Export
S.I.C.: 3325
N.A.I.C.S.: 331513
Personnel:
Hideki Yoshida *(Pres)*

U.S. Subsidiary:

AG Industries, Inc. (1)
18404 Cascade Ave S Ste 140
Seattle, WA 98188
Mailing Address:
PO Box 455
Preston, WA 98050-0455
Tel.: (425) 282-5460
Fax: (425) 282-5464
Web Site: www.whitewings.com
Emp.: 3
Mfr. of Toys, Hobby Items, Gifts, Optical Goods; Distributor of Transmission Line Steel Towers & Galvanized Steel Structures
S.I.C.: 5092
N.A.I.C.S.: 423920

A.G. BARR PLC

Westfield House 4 Mollins Road
Westfield
Cumbernauld, G68 9HD, United Kingdom
Tel.: (44) 1236852400
Fax: (44) 1236852477
E-Mail: info@agbarr.co.uk
Web Site: www.agbarr.co.uk
Year Founded: 1951
BAG—(LSE)
Rev.: $375,231,408
Assets: $339,291,505
Liabilities: $132,960,425
Net Worth: $206,331,080
Earnings: $40,372,970
Emp.: 976
Fiscal Year-end: 01/26/13
Business Description:
Holding Company; Soft Drink Mfr
Export
S.I.C.: 6719
N.A.I.C.S.: 551112
Personnel:
Ronald G. Hanna *(Chm)*
Roger A. White *(CEO)*
Julie A. Barr *(Sec)*
Board of Directors:
Ronald G. Hanna
W. Robin G. Barr
Martin A. Griffiths
Jonathan D. Kemp
Andrew L. Memmott
John R. Nicolson
Pam Powell
Alex B. C. Short
Roger A. White

AG CAPITAL

47 A Tsarigradsko Shosse Blvd
Sofia, 1124, Bulgaria
Tel.: (359) 2 810 31 06
Fax: (359) 2 810 33 73
E-Mail: office@agcapital.bg
Web Site: www.agcapital.bg
Business Description:
Real Estate Investment Services
S.I.C.: 6211
N.A.I.C.S.: 523999
Personnel:
Christo T. Iliev *(Exec Chm)*

Subsidiary:

BLD Asset Management EAD (1)
47A Tsarigradsko shosse Blvd 3rd Floor
1124 Sofia, Bulgaria BG
Tel.: (359) 2 805 1910
Fax: (359) 2 805 1914
E-Mail: office@bld.bg
Web Site: www.bld-am.com
Real Estate Asst Management Services
S.I.C.: 6282
N.A.I.C.S.: 523920
Christo Iliev *(Chm)*
Dimitar Savov *(CEO)*

Joint Venture:

Bulgarian Land Development EAD (1)
47A Tsarigradsko Shose Blvd
1124 Sofia, Bulgaria BG
Tel.: (359) 2 805 1910
Fax: (359) 2 805 1914
E-Mail: office@bld.bg
Web Site: www.bld.bg
Emp.: 15
Commercial & Residential Real Estate Development & Construction Management Services
S.I.C.: 6552
N.A.I.C.S.: 237210
Dimitar Safov *(Gen Mgr)*

AG DER DILLINGER HUTTENWERKE

(d/b/a Dillinger Hutte GTS)
Werkstrasse 1
66763 Dillingen, Saar, Germany
Tel.: (49) 6831972555
Fax: (49) 6831972557
E-Mail: info@dillinger.diz
Web Site: www.dillinger.de
Sales Range: $1-4.9 Billion
Emp.: 8,200
Business Description:
Steel Plate Mfr
S.I.C.: 3399
N.A.I.C.S.: 331221
Personnel:
Karlheinz Blessing *(CEO)*
Fred Metzken *(CFO)*
Norbert Bannenberg *(CTO)*
Peter Schweda *(Chief HR Officer & Dir-Labour)*
Board of Directors:
Norbert Bannenberg
Karlheinz Blessing
Fred Metzken
Peter Schweda

Subsidiaries:

Ancofer Stahlhandel GmbH (1)
Rheinstrabe 163
45478 Mulheim an der Ruhr, Germany
Tel.: (49) 208 58 02 0
Fax: (49) 208 58 02 259
E-Mail: info@as.dillinger.biz
Web Site: www.ancofer.de
Emp.: 119
Steel Product Distr
S.I.C.: 5085
N.A.I.C.S.: 423840
Andre Gehrke, *(Mng Dir)*

DH Nordenham Projekt GmbH (1)
Werkstr 1
66763 Dillingen, Germany
Tel.: (49) 4731 36332 0
E-Mail: info@swn.Dillingen.biz
Emp.: 20
Steel Product Distr
S.I.C.: 5085
N.A.I.C.S.: 423840
Dieter Sichau *(Mng Dir)*

Dillinger Hutte Vertrieb GmbH (1)
Werkstr 1
Dillingen, Saarland, 66763, Germany
Tel.: (49) 6831972555
Steel Plate Distr
S.I.C.: 5085
N.A.I.C.S.: 423840

Jebens GmbH (1)
Daimlerstrabe 35-37
70825 Korntal-Munchingen, Germany
Tel.: (49) 711 80 02 0
Fax: (49) 711 80 02 100
E-Mail: info@jebens.dillinger.biz
Web Site: www.jebens.de
Steel Plate Mfr & Distr
S.I.C.: 3312
N.A.I.C.S.: 331110

Saarlux Stahl GmbH & Co. KG (1)
Herzogstr 6a
Stuttgart, Baden-Wurttemberg, 70176, Germany
Tel.: (49) 71161460
Steel Plate Distr
S.I.C.: 5085
N.A.I.C.S.: 423840

Non-U.S. Subsidiaries:

AncoferWaldram Steelplates B.V. (1)
Damweg 12
4905 BS Oosterhout, Netherlands
Mailing Address:
PO Box 190
4900 AD Oosterhout, Netherlands
Tel.: (31) 162 491500
Fax: (31) 162 429806
E-Mail: sales@aws.dillinger.biz
Web Site: www.ancoferwaldram.nl
Emp.: 90
Steel Plate Mfr
S.I.C.: 3399
N.A.I.C.S.: 331110
Joost Van Dijk *(Mng Dir)*

Dillinger Espana S.L.U. (1)
Calle Cronos 24 Bloque 1 Escalera 1 2 B-1
28037 Madrid, Spain
Tel.: (34) 917 43 0942
Fax: (34) 917 43 1475
Steel Plate Distr
S.I.C.: 5085
N.A.I.C.S.: 423840

Dillinger Hutte GTS Nederland B.V. (1)
Spuiboulevard 340
3311 GR Dordrecht, Netherlands
Tel.: (31) 78 6127208
Fax: (31) 78 6127434
Steel Plate Distr
S.I.C.: 5085
N.A.I.C.S.: 423840
Zoltan Szabo *(Mgr-Sls)*

Dillinger Hutte Services B.V. (1)
Scheepmakerij 148
3331 MA Zwijndrecht, Netherlands
Tel.: (31) 6 53331666
Steel Plate Distr
S.I.C.: 5085
N.A.I.C.S.: 423840

Dillinger Middle East FZE (1)
Road 1241 Between Junction 12 & 13
Jebel Ali Free Zone
PO Box 17592
Dubai, United Arab Emirates
Tel.: (971) 4 883 3894
Fax: (971) 4 883 3895
E-Mail: sales@dme.dillinger.biz
Web Site: www.dillingermiddleeast.com
Steel Plate & Fabricated Metal Product Distr
S.I.C.: 5051
N.A.I.C.S.: 423510
P. J. Narayanan *(Gen Mgr-Sls)*

Non-U.S. Subsidiary:

Dillinger India Steel Service Center Private Ltd. (2)
604 Maithili Signet Sector 30 A Opp Inorbit Mall
Vashi, Mumbai, 400705, India
Tel.: (91) 22 41230270
Fax: (91) 22 41230271
E-Mail: sales-dissc@dme.dillinger.biz
Web Site: www.dillinger-india-ssc.com
Emp.: 6
Steel Plate Distr
S.I.C.: 5085
N.A.I.C.S.: 423840
Ranjit Menon *(Mgr-Sls)*

Dillinger Norge AS (1)
Akersgata 41
0158 Oslo, Norway
Tel.: (47) 23 31 83 30
Steel Plate Mfr
S.I.C.: 3312
N.A.I.C.S.: 331110

Eurodecoupe S.A.S. (1)
17 Avenue de la Vertonne
44124 Vertou, France
Tel.: (33) 2 40 80 29 29
Fax: (33) 2 40 34 56 24
E-Mail: commercial.adv@edox.dillinger.biz
Web Site: www.eurodecoupe.fr
Steel Plate Mfr
S.I.C.: 3399
N.A.I.C.S.: 331110

Trans-Overseas B.V. (1)
Scheepmakerij 148
Zwijndrecht, South Holland, 3331 MA, Netherlands
Tel.: (31) 786201212
Fax: (31) 786201219
Emp.: 5
Steel Plate Mfr
S.I.C.: 3312
N.A.I.C.S.: 331110
Hans-Joachim Welsch *(Mng Dir)*

AG FINANCE, INCORPORATED

Unit 2205A East Tower Philippine Stock Exchange Centre
Exchange Road
Ortigas Center, Pasig, 1605, Philippines
Tel.: (63) 2 6352835
Fax: (63) 2 6872319
E-Mail: info@agfinance.ph
Web Site: www.agfinance.ph
Year Founded: 2001
AGF—(PHI)
Int. Income: $2,019,297
Assets: $8,594,768
Liabilities: $2,790,515
Net Worth: $5,804,253
Earnings: $1,057,651
Emp.: 26
Fiscal Year-end: 12/31/12
Business Description:
Loan Financing
S.I.C.: 6163
N.A.I.C.S.: 522310
Personnel:
Tony O. King *(Chm)*
Leila E. Jorge *(Pres)*
Desiree I. Ong *(IR Officer & Compliance Officer)*

AG Finance, Incorporated—(Continued)

Sharone O. King *(Treas & Head-Fin)*
Christine P. Base *(Sec)*
Board of Directors:
Tony O. King
Christine P. Base
Leila E. Jorge
Peter O. Kho
Charmainne O. King
Sharone O. King
Joselyn C. Tiu
Daleson G. Uy

AG GROWTH INTERNATIONAL INC.

1301 Kenaston Blvd
Winnipeg, MB, R3P 2P2, Canada
Tel.: (204) 489-1855
Fax: (204) 488-6929
Web Site: www.aggrowth.com
AFN—(OTC TSX)
Rev.: $312,462,235
Assets: $368,266,518
Liabilities: $179,704,900
Net Worth: $188,561,618
Earnings: $17,085,216
Emp.: 1,232
Fiscal Year-end: 12/31/12
Business Description:
Grain Equipment Mfr
S.I.C.: 3523
N.A.I.C.S.: 333111
Personnel:
William A. Lambert *(Chm)*
Gary Anderson *(Pres & CEO)*
Steve Sommerfeld *(CFO & Exec VP)*
Eric Lister *(Gen Counsel)*
Paul Franzman *(Sr VP-Ops)*
Dan Donner *(Sr VP-Sls & Mktg)*
Board of Directors:
William A. Lambert
Gary Anderson
Janet P. Giesselman
William S. Maslechko
Malcolm F. Moore
David A. White
Transfer Agent:
Computershare Investor Services Inc.
Montreal, QC, Canada

U.S. Subsidiary:

U.S. Division:

Hansen Manufacturing Corp. (1)
5100 W 12th St
Sioux Falls, SD 57107-0154
Tel.: (605) 332-3200
Fax: (605) 332-1107
Toll Free: (800) 328-1785
E-Mail: sales@hiroller.com
Web Site: www.hiroller.com
Emp.: 87
Conveyors Mfr & Sales
S.I.C.: 3535
N.A.I.C.S.: 333922
Sally Dieltz *(Controller)*

U.S. Subsidiaries:

Applegate Livestock Equipment, Inc. (1)
902 S State Rd 32
Union City, IN 47390
Tel.: (765) 964-4631
Fax: (765) 964-3529
Toll Free: (800) 354-9502
E-Mail: sales@applegatelivestockequipment.com
Web Site: www.applegatelivestockequipment.com
Emp.: 100
Livestock Handling & Containment Equipments Mfr
S.I.C.: 3523
N.A.I.C.S.: 333111
Aaron Applegate *(Mgr-Sls)*

Tramco Inc. (1)
1020 E 19th St N
Wichita, KS 67214
Tel.: (316) 264-4604
Fax: (316) 264-7963
E-Mail: client-services@tramco.com
Web Site: www.tramcoinc.com
Sales Range: $25-49.9 Million
Emp.: 90
Mfr. of Conveyors & Conveying Equipment
S.I.C.: 3535
N.A.I.C.S.: 333922
Steve Cloud *(Pres)*

Union Iron Inc. (1)
601 S 27th St
Decatur, IL 62525
Tel.: (217) 429-5148
Fax: (217) 429-5149
Toll Free: (800) 333-5148
E-Mail: sales@unionironworks.com
Web Site: www.unionironworks.com
Elevators & Conveyors Mfr
S.I.C.: 3534
N.A.I.C.S.: 333921
Robert Curry *(Pres)*
Colleen Greenwell *(Sec)*

Westfield Distributing (North Dakota) Inc. (1)
11500 38th St S
Horace, ND 58047-9511
Tel.: (701) 588-9269
Fax: (866) 768-4852
Web Site: www.grainaugers.com
Emp.: 10
Agricultural Machinery & Equipment Distr
S.I.C.: 5083
N.A.I.C.S.: 423820
Todd Kankelfritz *(Branch Mgr)*

Non-U.S. Division:

Mepu Oy. (1)
Mynamaentie 59
21900 Ylane, Western Finland, Finland
Tel.: (358) 22754444
Fax: (358) 22563361
E-Mail: mepu@mepu.com
Web Site: www.mepu.fi
Emp.: 80
Grain Handling & Heating Systems Mfr
S.I.C.: 3523
N.A.I.C.S.: 333111
Ritva Siren *(Sec-Sls)*

Plant:

Mepu Oy. - Pyharanta factory (2)
Vanha Turuntie 210
27320 Pyharanta, Western Finland, Finland
Tel.: (358) 28236368
Fax: (358) 28236369
E-Mail: hannu.virtanen@mepu.com
Web Site: www.mepu.com
Emp.: 7
Grain Handling & Heating Systems Mfr
S.I.C.: 3523
N.A.I.C.S.: 333111
Artoz Sainio *(Mng Dir)*

Divisions:

Ag Growth Industries Limited Partnership (1)
1301 Kenaston Blvd
Winnipeg, MB, R3P 2P2, Canada
Tel.: (204) 489-1855
Fax: (204) 488-6929
Emp.: 45
Farming Equipments Mfr
S.I.C.: 3523
N.A.I.C.S.: 333111
Daniel Donner *(VP-Sls & Mktg)*

Ag Growth International - Edwards Grain Guard Division (1)
215 Barons St
Nobleford, AB, T0L 1S0, Canada
Tel.: (403) 320-5585
Fax: (403) 320-5668
Toll Free: (800) 565-2840
E-Mail: sales@edwardsgroup.ca
Web Site: www.grainguard.com
Grain Handling & Storage Equipments Mfr
S.I.C.: 3523
N.A.I.C.S.: 333111

Ag Growth International - Westfield Division (1)
74 Hwy 205 E
PO Box 39
Rosenort, MB, R0G 1W0, Canada
Tel.: (204) 746-2396
Fax: (204) 746-2679
Toll Free: (866) 467-7207
E-Mail: sales@grainaugers.com
Web Site: www.grainaugers.com
Emp.: 350
Portable Grain Augers Mfr
S.I.C.: 3531
N.A.I.C.S.: 333120
Ron Braun *(Gen Mgr)*

Batco Manufacturing Ltd. (1)
2165 North Service Rd W
Swift Current, SK, S9H 5k9, Canada
Tel.: (306) 773-7779
Fax: (306) 778-2524
Toll Free: (877) 667-7421
E-Mail: info@batcomfg.com
Web Site: www.batcomfg.com
Emp.: 70
Agricultural Machinery & Equipment Mfr
S.I.C.: 3535
N.A.I.C.S.: 333922
Doug Bender *(Gen Mgr)*

AG INDUSTRIES LIMITED

1 Setchell Rd Roodekop
1428 Johannesburg, South Africa
Tel.: (27) 117246000
Fax: (27) 117246041
Web Site: www.ag-industries.com
Emp.: 1,853
Business Description:
Glass & Aluminium Fabrication Distr
S.I.C.: 5039
N.A.I.C.S.: 423390
Personnel:
Roy Douglas *(CEO)*

Subsidiaries:

AGI Aluminium (Pty) Limited (1)
40 Corobrick Rd
Effingham Heights, Durban, Kwazulu-Natal, 4051, South Africa
Tel.: (27) 119081500
Fax: (27) 119556451
Aluminum Windows & Doors Sales
S.I.C.: 5031
N.A.I.C.S.: 423310

AGI Glass (Pty) Limited (1)
77 Park Ave S
Pretoria, Gauteng, 0157, South Africa
Tel.: (27) 126610415
Fax: (27) 126618004
Glass & Wallpaper Whslr
S.I.C.: 5039
N.A.I.C.S.: 423390

AGI Manufacturing (Pty) Limited (1)
1 Setchell Rd
Roodekop, Germiston, Gauteng, 1401, South Africa
Tel.: (27) 117246000
Fax: (27) 1147246041
Aluminum & Glass Windows & Doors Mfr
S.I.C.: 3442
N.A.I.C.S.: 332321

Ralph's Mirror and Glass (Pty) Limited (1)
75 Zeiler Street
Pretoria, Gauteng, 0183, South Africa
Tel.: (27) 123274598
Fax: (27) 123275884
Mirror & Glass Distr
S.I.C.: 5023
N.A.I.C.S.: 423220

West Cape Safety Glass (Pty) Limited (1)
8 Hawkins Ave Epping Industria
Cape Town, Western Cape, 7475, South Africa
Tel.: (27) 215317429
Fax: (27) 215317433
E-Mail: wesafety@iafrica.com
Emp.: 50
Safety Glass Mfr
S.I.C.: 3231
N.A.I.C.S.: 327215
Roy Schreiber *(Mng Dir)*

Non-U.S. Subsidiaries:

AG Industries Vietnam Company Limited (1)
Hoa Rang Bldg 3rd Fl Ste 303 32-34 Ngo Duc Ke St
Ben Nghe Ward Dist 1, Ho Chi Minh City, Vietnam
Tel.: (84) 8 2220 0622
Fax: (84) 8 2220 0633
E-Mail: loantran@ag-industries.com
Emp.: 3
Aluminum Windows & Doors Sales
S.I.C.: 2431
N.A.I.C.S.: 321911
Thibault Danjou *(Gen Dir)*

Aluminium Glass Industries (Mauritius) Limited (1)
1 Concorde Ave La Tour Koenig
Pointe aux Sables, Port Louis, Mauritius
Tel.: (230) 2342525
Fax: (230) 2342336
E-Mail: agimtius@intnet.mu
Emp.: 18
Aluminum & Glass Windows & Doors Distr
S.I.C.: 5031
N.A.I.C.S.: 423310
Vicky Chadee *(Mgr)*

KAB Allglass GmbH (1)
Schmidts Breite 17
21107 Hamburg, Germany
Tel.: (49) 407520190
Fax: (49) 4075201919
E-Mail: info@kab-allglass.de
Web Site: www.kab-allglass.de
Emp.: 20
Glass Warehousing & Distr
S.I.C.: 5039
N.A.I.C.S.: 423390
Darko Grnjak *(Mng Dir)*

A.G. PETZETAKIS S.A.

1-3 Patr Grigoriou Str
166 74 Glyfada, Nottinghamshire, DN22 7AN, Greece
Tel.: (30) 2108937300
Fax: (30) 2108937309
E-Mail: hr@petzetakis.gr
Web Site: www.petzetakis.gr
PETZK—(ATH)
Sales Range: $150-199.9 Million
Emp.: 1,194
Business Description:
Plastic Pipe Mfr
S.I.C.: 3089
N.A.I.C.S.: 326122
Personnel:
George Arist Petzetakis *(Chm & Pres)*
Spyridon Dontas *(Vice Chm)*
Board of Directors:
George Arist Petzetakis
Spyridon Dontas
Vasilios Kousidis
Georgios Lagouranis
Jamil Mawji
Georgios Papageorgantas
Petros T. Tzannetakis

Subsidiary:

Petzetakis North Greece S A (1)
Industrial Zone Of Sindos
Thessaloniki, Greece (100%)
Tel.: (30) 2310576600
Fax: (30) 2310576649
Web Site: www.petzetakis.com
Emp.: 150
Unsupported Plastics Film & Sheet (except Packaging) Mfr
S.I.C.: 3081
N.A.I.C.S.: 326113
Petrelis Manolis *(Mng Dir)*

Non-U.S. Subsidiaries:

Behkaplast GMBH (1)
Dulkenerstrasse 179
41366 Schwalmtal, Germany (100%)
Tel.: (49) 216394520
Fax: (49) 2163945252
All Other Rubber Product Mfr

S.I.C.: 3069
N.A.I.C.S.: 326299

Eurohose Ltd (1)
Unit 5 Ravenself Park Cheney Manor Industrial Estate
Swindon, Wiltshire, SN2 2QJ, United Kingdom (100%)
Tel.: (44) 1793480300
Fax: (44) 1793480451
E-Mail: info@eurohose.co.uk
Web Site: www.eurohose.co.uk
Emp.: 30
Rubber & Plastics Hoses & Belting Mfr
S.I.C.: 3052
N.A.I.C.S.: 326220
Petz Etakis *(Mng Dir)*

FLEXIPLAS S.A (1)
Pol Ind Seat Vial Centro Technico S/N Apdo Correos 29
08760 Martorell, Barcelona, Spain
Tel.: (34) 937 75 52 11
Fax: (34) 937 75 12 62
E-Mail: comercial@flexiplas.es
Web Site: www.flexiplas.es
Emp.: 30
Pipe Mfr & Whslr
S.I.C.: 3084
N.A.I.C.S.: 326122

Induplas SPA (1)
Via CaBassa 15
21100 Varese, Italy (100%)
Tel.: (39) 0332339311
Fax: (39) 0332339336
E-Mail: gianfranco.petuzzo@induplas.it
Web Site: www.induplas.it
Emp.: 50
Rubber & Plastics Hoses & Belting Mfr
S.I.C.: 3052
N.A.I.C.S.: 326220

Petzetakis Africa (Pty) Ltd (1)
No1 Piet Pretorius Str
Pretoria, South Africa (100%)
Tel.: (27) 125411080
Fax: (27) 125413044
E-Mail: e.hewitt@petzetakis.co.za
Web Site: www.petzetakis.co.za
Emp.: 350
Plastics Pipe & Pipe Fitting Mfr
S.I.C.: 3089
N.A.I.C.S.: 326122
Edwin Hewitt *(Mng Dir)*

Petzetakis GMBH (1)
Dulkenerstrasse 179
41366 Schwalmtal, Germany (100%)
Tel.: (49) 2163949960
Fax: (49) 21639499629
Web Site: www.heliflex.de
Emp.: 45
Plastics Materials & Basic Forms & Shapes Wholesalers
S.I.C.: 5162
N.A.I.C.S.: 424610

Subsidiary:

PETZETAKIS DEUTSHLAND (.BEHKA - PLAST GMBH) (2)
Dulkener Str 179
41366 Schwalmtal, Germany
Tel.: (49) 2163 94996 0
Fax: (49) 2163 94996 29
E-Mail: info@petzetakis.de
Web Site: www.petzetakis.de
Emp.: 50
Plastic Pipes Mfr
S.I.C.: 3089
N.A.I.C.S.: 326122
A. Bies *(Mng Dir)*

Petzetakis Romania SRL (1)
Bd Preciziei nr 11
camera C7p Sector 6, Bucharest, Romania (100%)
Tel.: (40) 374200765
Fax: (40) 374200769
E-Mail: office@petzetakis.ro
Web Site: www.petzetakis.ro
Emp.: 5
Construction Material Whslr
S.I.C.: 5039
N.A.I.C.S.: 423390
Alena Obreja *(Mng Dir)*

AGA FINANCIAL GROUP INC.

4150 rue Ste-Catherine Ouest Suite 490
Westmount, QC, H3Z 2W8, Canada
Tel.: (514) 935-5444
Fax: (514) 935-1147
Toll Free: (800) 363-6217
E-Mail: info@gfaga.com
Web Site: www.gfaga.com
Year Founded: 1978
Emp.: 90

Business Description:
Insurance & Annuity Plan Brokerage Services
S.I.C.: 6411
N.A.I.C.S.: 524210

Personnel:
Martin Papillon *(Pres & CEO)*
Chantal Dufresne *(Sr VP-Fin & Admin)*
Gabriel Gagnon *(Sr VP-Bus Strategy)*

AGA KHAN DEVELOPMENT NETWORK

1-3 Avenue de la Paix
PO Box 2049
1211 Geneva, Switzerland
Tel.: (41) 229097200
Fax: (41) 229097336
E-Mail: akdn@akdn.org
Web Site: www.akdn.org
Emp.: 100

Business Description:
Health, Education, Culture & Economic Development Services
S.I.C.: 9611
N.A.I.C.S.: 926110

Personnel:
Aga Khan *(Founder & Chm)*

Subsidiary:

Aga Khan Fund for Economic Development S.A. (1)
1-3 Avennue de la Paix
PO Box 2049
1211 Geneva, Switzerland
Tel.: (41) 229097200
Fax: (41) 229097292
E-Mail: aks@akdn.org
Web Site: www.akdn.org
Economic Development
S.I.C.: 9611
N.A.I.C.S.: 926110
Aga Khan *(Chm)*

Non-U.S. Subsidiary:

Air Burkina SA (1)
29 Av de la Nation
BP 1459
Ouagadougou, 01, Burkina Faso
Tel.: (226) 50 49 23 40
Fax: (226) 50 31 45 17
Web Site: www.air-burkina.com
Emp.: 130
Air Transportation Services
S.I.C.: 4512
N.A.I.C.S.: 481111

AGA RANGEMASTER GROUP PLC

Juno Drive
Leamington Spa, Warwickshire, CV31 3RG, United Kingdom
Tel.: (44) 1926455755
Fax: (44) 1926455749
E-Mail: info@agarangemaster.com
Web Site: www.agarangemaster.com
Year Founded: 1939
AGA—(LSE)
Rev.: $386,294,334
Assets: $375,713,091
Liabilities: $152,717,343
Net Worth: $222,995,748
Earnings: $10,739,172
Emp.: 2,497
Fiscal Year-end: 12/31/12

Business Description:
Holding Company; Household Cooking, Heating & Refrigeration Appliance Mfr & Distr; Wood Cabinetry Mfr; Cookware, Wall & Floor Coverings Retailer
Import Export
S.I.C.: 6719
N.A.I.C.S.: 551112

Personnel:
William McGrath *(CEO)*
Pam Sissons *(Sec)*

Board of Directors:
John Coleman
Jonathan Carling
Paul Dermody
Paul Jackson
William McGrath
Shaun Smith
Rebecca Worthington

Legal Counsel:
DLA Piper LLP
Victoria Square House Victoria Square
Birmingham, B3 3SF, United Kingdom

Allen & Overy LLP
One Bishops Square
London, United Kingdom

Subsidiaries:

AGA Consumer Products Ltd. (1)
Juno Dr
Leamington Spa, Warks, CV31 3RG, United Kingdom (100%)
Tel.: (44) 1926455755
Fax: (44) 1926455749
E-Mail: mbufton@rangemaster.co.uk
Web Site: www.agarangemaster.com
Emp.: 2,600
Household Cooking, Heating & Refrigeration Appliance Mfr & Distr; Cookware, Wall & Floor Coverings Retailer
S.I.C.: 3631
N.A.I.C.S.: 335221
Jeff Killer *(Dir-Fin)*

Subsidiary:

Fired Earth Ltd. (2)
3 Twyford Mill Oxford Road
Adderbury, Oxon, OX17 3SX, United Kingdom UK (100%)
Tel.: (44) 1295812088
Fax: (44) 1295810832
E-Mail: enquiries@firedearth.com
Web Site: www.firedearth.com
Emp.: 250
Wall & Floor Tiles, Paint & Other Coverings Retailer
S.I.C.: 5713
N.A.I.C.S.: 442210

U.S. Subsidiary:

AGA Marvel (2)
1260 E Van Deinse St
Greenville, MI 48838-1400 MI (100%)
Tel.: (616) 754-5601
Fax: (616) 754-0970
Toll Free: (800) 223-3900
Emp.: 400
Refrigeration & Wine Storage Equipment Mfr
S.I.C.: 3632
N.A.I.C.S.: 335222
Gerry Reda *(Sr VP-Sls)*
Brad Stauffer *(Sr VP-Ops)*

Non-U.S. Subsidiaries:

La Cornue S.A. (2)
14 Rue Du Bois Du Pont
Zone Industrielle Les Bethunes, F-95310 Saint-Ouen, France FR
Mailing Address:
BP 9006
95070 Cergy, Cedex, France
Tel.: (33) 134483636
Fax: (33) 134643265
E-Mail: a.table@la-cornue.com
Web Site: www.lacornue.com
Emp.: 50
Household Cooking Appliance Mfr
S.I.C.: 3631
N.A.I.C.S.: 335221
Xavier Dupuy *(Pres)*

Waterford Stanley Ltd. (2)
Unit 210 Waterford Industrial Estate
Cork Road, Waterford, Ireland IE (100%)
Tel.: (353) 51302300
Fax: (353) 51302315
E-Mail: sales@waterfordstanley.com
Web Site: www.waterfordstanley.com
Emp.: 100
Household Cooking Appliance & Wood Stove Mfr & Distr
S.I.C.: 3631
N.A.I.C.S.: 335221
Owen Power *(Dir-Comml)*

Mercury Appliances Limited (1)
Whisby Rd
Lincoln, LN6 3QZ, United Kingdom UK (100%)
Tel.: (44) 1522881717
Fax: (44) 1522 880220
E-Mail: sales@mercury-appliances.co.uk
Web Site: www.mercury-appliances.co.uk
Emp.: 50
Household Appliance Retailer
S.I.C.: 5722
N.A.I.C.S.: 443141
Jenny Hyatt *(Mng Dir)*

U.S. Subsidiaries:

AGA Marvel (USA) (1)
1260 E Van Deinse St
Greenville, MS 48838
Tel.: (800) 223-3900
Fax: (616) 754-9690
E-Mail: customerservice@agamarvel.com
Web Site: www.agamarvel.com
Cooking Appliances Mfr
S.I.C.: 3631
N.A.I.C.S.: 335221
Brad Stauffer *(VP-Sls)*

Non-U.S. Subsidiary:

Grange S.A. (1)
Zone Industrielle Le Plomb
F-69590 Saint-Symphorien-sur-Coise, France FR (75%)
Tel.: (33) 478443939
Fax: (33) 478443900
Web Site: www.grange.fr
Wood Kitchen & Bathroom Cabinetry & Specialty Furniture Mfr
S.I.C.: 2434
N.A.I.C.S.: 337110
Drazen Babic *(Mng Dir)*

AGALAWATTE PLANTATIONS PLC

10 Gnanartha Pradeepa Mawatha
Colombo, 8, Sri Lanka
Tel.: (94) 112697965
Fax: (94) 112699454
E-Mail: apl@mackwoods.com
Web Site: www.mackwoods.com
AGAL—(COL)
Rev.: $19,897,521
Assets: $32,954,614
Liabilities: $23,455,156
Net Worth: $9,499,458
Earnings: $1,084,336
Emp.: 7,741
Fiscal Year-end: 12/31/12

Business Description:
Tea Mfr & Sales
S.I.C.: 0191
N.A.I.C.S.: 111998

Personnel:
S. C. J. Devendra *(CEO)*

Board of Directors:
Chris N. A. Nonis
R. T. de Sylva
S. C. J. Devendra
F. Lalith Fonseka
S. N. Guneratne
R. K. M. Ng
S. M. A. Nonis Ranaweera
L. L. Samarasinghe
N. S. M. Samaratunga

Legal Counsel:
F.J. & G. De Saram
No. 216 De Saram Place
Colombo, Sri Lanka

AGARWAL INDUSTRIAL CORPORATION LTD.

4-B SITA Estate Mahul Road Aziz Baug
Chembur, Mumbai, Maharashtra, 400 074, India
Tel.: (91) 2225549202
Fax: (91) 2225549288
E-Mail: contact@aicltd.in
Web Site: www.aicltd.in
531921—(BOM)
Rev.: $22,386,512
Assets: $12,334,384
Liabilities: $6,009,370
Net Worth: $6,325,014
Earnings: $632,121
Fiscal Year-end: 03/31/13

Business Description:
Liquid Petroleum Gas Transportation Services
S.I.C.: 4789
N.A.I.C.S.: 488999

Personnel:
Jaiprakash Agarwal *(Mng Dir)*

Board of Directors:
Jaiprakash Agarwal
Lalit Agarwal
Mahendra Agarwal
Ramchandra Agarwal
Alok Bharara
Rajkumar Mehta
Jawahar D. Patil
Harikrishna Patni
Ramdas Trimbak Rajguroo
Jaswant D. Sharma

Transfer Agent:
Ankit Consultancy Pvt Ltd
60 Electronics Complex Pardehsipura
Indore, India

Subsidiary:

Bituminex Cochin Pvt Ltd **(1)**
HOC Road Ambalamugal
Cochin, Kerala, 682 302, India
Tel.: (91) 484 2720259
Fax: (91) 484 2720635
E-Mail: sales@bituminexcochin.com
Web Site: www.bituminexcochin.com
Bituminous Product Mfr
S.I.C.: 2899
N.A.I.C.S.: 325998

AGASTI HOLDING ASA

Bolette brygge 1
PO Box 1753
0252 Oslo, Norway
Mailing Address:
PO Box 1753
Vika, 0122 Oslo, Norway
Tel.: (47) 21 00 33 00
Fax: (47) 21 00 33 65
E-Mail: siw.hauge@acta.no
Web Site: www.agasti.no
ACTA—(OSL)
Rev.: $66,218,811
Assets: $61,267,106
Liabilities: $27,904,857
Net Worth: $33,362,249
Earnings: ($9,750,655)
Emp.: 213
Fiscal Year-end: 12/31/12

Business Description:
Investment Management Services
S.I.C.: 6799
N.A.I.C.S.: 523920

Personnel:
Merete Haugli *(Chm)*
Stein Aukner *(Vice Chm)*
Jorgen Pleym Ulvness *(Deputy CEO & CEO-Agasti Wunderlich Capital Markets AS)*
Christian Tunge *(CFO)*
Tor Arne Olsen *(Chief Comm Officer)*
Stein Morten Bjelland *(CEO-Acta Asset Management AS)*
Bjarne Eggesbo *(CEO-Obligo Investment Management AS)*
Kjersti Aksnes Gjesdahl *(Acting CEO-Navigea Securities AS)*
Ole Jorgen Jacobsen *(CEO-Navigea Securities AS)*

Board of Directors:
Merete Haugli
Stein Aukner
Pia Gideon
Sissel Knutsen Hegdal
Erling Meinich-Bache

Subsidiaries:

Acta Asset Management ASA **(1)**
Bolette Brygge 1
Post Box 2654
0203 Oslo, Norway (100%)
Tel.: (47) 21001000
Fax: (47) 21003001
Emp.: 150
Management Consulting Services
S.I.C.: 8748
N.A.I.C.S.: 541618
Jostein Viken *(Mng Dir)*
Stein Morten Bjelland *(Deputy Mng Dir)*

Acta Corporate Services AS **(1)**
Borehaugen 1
Stavanger, NO 4006, Norway (100%)
Tel.: (47) 21003000
Web Site: www.acta.no
Securities Brokerage
S.I.C.: 6211
N.A.I.C.S.: 523120
Morten Florenaess *(Mng Dir)*

Acta Kapitalforvaltning AS **(1)**
Borehaugen 1
Stavanger, Rogaland, 4006, Norway
Tel.: (47) 21003100
Fax: (47) 21003001
E-Mail: info@actakapitalforvaltning.dk
Emp.: 250
Investment Management Services
S.I.C.: 6211
N.A.I.C.S.: 523999
Sveinung Byberg *(Mng Dir)*

Acta Markets AS **(1)**
Henrik Ibsens Gate 90
0255 Oslo, Norway
Tel.: (47) 21001000
Fax: (47) 21001201
E-Mail: oslo@acta.no
Investment Advisory Services
S.I.C.: 6282
N.A.I.C.S.: 523930
Ole Jacobsen *(Gen Mgr)*

Non-U.S. Subsidiary:

Acta Forsakringsplanering AB **(1)**
Kungsgatan 8
Stockholm, Sweden (100%)
Tel.: (46) 857944000
Fax: (46) 857944001
E-Mail: info@acta.se
Web Site: www.acta.se
Emp.: 75
Insurance Agencies & Brokerages
S.I.C.: 6411
N.A.I.C.S.: 524210
Christian Kvist *(Mng Dir)*

AGEAS SA/NV

(d/b/a Ageas Holding Belgium)
Rue du Marquis 1
BE-1000 Brussels, Belgium
Tel.: (32) 25575711
Fax: (32) 25575750
Web Site: www.ageas.com
Year Founded: 1993
AGS—(EUR OTC)
Rev.: $21,053,964,183
Assets: $130,730,472,593
Liabilities: $116,210,548,356
Net Worth: $14,519,924,237
Earnings: $1,250,322,696
Emp.: 13,335
Fiscal Year-end: 12/31/12

Business Description:
Holding Company; Insurance Products & Services
S.I.C.: 6719
N.A.I.C.S.: 551112

Personnel:
Chevalier Guy de Selliers de Moranville *(Vice Chm)*
Bart Karel August De Smet *(CEO)*
Christophe Boizard *(CFO)*
Barry Smith *(COO)*
Kurt De Schepper *(Chief Risk Officer-Risk, Legal, Compliance & Support Functions)*
Emmanuel Van Grimbergen *(Grp Risk Officer)*
Steven Braekeveldt *(CEO-Continental Europe)*
Antonio Cano *(CEO-AG Insurance)*
Gary Lee Crist *(CEO-Asia)*
Andy Watson *(CEO-UK)*
Valerie van Zeveren *(Sec)*

Board of Directors:
Jozef De Mey
Stephen William Broughton
Chevalier Guy de Selliers de Moranville
Bart Karel August De Smet
Jan H. J. Zegering Hadders
Jane Murphy
Roel Nieuwdorp
Lionel Perl

Co-Headquarters:

Ageas N.V. **(1)**
Archimedeslaan 6
NL-3584 BA Utrecht, Netherlands NL
Mailing Address:
PO Box 2551
NL-3500 GN Utrecht, Netherlands
Tel.: (31) 302525304
Fax: (31) 302525310
E-Mail: info@ageas.com
Web Site: www.ageas.com
Emp.: 50
Holding Company; Insurance Products & Services
S.I.C.: 6719
N.A.I.C.S.: 551112
Chevalier Guy de Selliers de Moranville *(Vice Chm)*
Bart Karel August De Smet *(CEO)*
Bruno Colmant *(Deputy CEO)*
Kurt De Schepper *(Chief Risk Officer)*
Steven Braekeveldt *(CEO-Continental Europe)*
Antonio Cano *(CEO-AG Insurance)*
Dennis J. Ziengs *(CEO-Asia)*

Non-U.S. Subsidiaries:

AG Insurance N.V. **(2)**
Boulevard Emile Jacqmain 53
1000 Brussels, Belgium BE
Tel.: (32) 26648111 (75%)
Fax: (32) 26648150
E-Mail: fo-ra@aginsurance.be
Web Site: www.aginsurance.be
Sales Range: $5-14.9 Billion
Emp.: 4,135
Life Insurance Products & Services
S.I.C.: 6311
N.A.I.C.S.: 524113
Antonio Cano *(CEO)*
Philippe Latour *(CFO)*

Subsidiaries:

AG Real Estate **(3)**
4-10 Boulevard Saint Lazare
1210 Brussels, Belgium
Tel.: (32) 2609 6800
Fax: (32) 2609 6810
E-Mail: info@agrealestate.eu
Web Site: www.agrealestate.eu
Real Estate Investment, Development & Management Services
S.I.C.: 6531
N.A.I.C.S.: 531390
Serge Fautre *(CEO)*

Ageas Asia Holdings Limited **(2)**
27/F Wing On Centre 111 Connaught Road
Central, China (Hong Kong) HK
Tel.: (852) 28668898 (100%)
Fax: (852) 2264 3222
E-Mail: aica.mkt@ageas.com.hk
Web Site: www.ageas.com.hk
Sales Range: $100-124.9 Million
Holding Company; Insurance Products & Services
S.I.C.: 6719
N.A.I.C.S.: 551112
Dennis J. Ziengs *(CEO)*
Charles Stuart Fraser *(CEO-Insurance Asia)*

Subsidiary:

Ageas Insurance Company (Asia) Limited **(3)**
27/F Wing On Centre
111 Connaught Road, Central, China (Hong Kong) BM
Tel.: (852) 28668898
Fax: (852) 22643222
Web Site: www.ageas.com.hk
Emp.: 2,200
Life, Property & Casualty Insurance Products & Services
S.I.C.: 6311
N.A.I.C.S.: 524113
Charles Stuart Fraser *(CEO)*

Ageas France S.A. **(2)**
1 rue Blanche
F-75440 Paris, Cedex 09, France FR
Tel.: (33) 149701717
Fax: (33) 148782497
E-Mail: cil@ageas.fr
Web Site: www.ageas.fr
Emp.: 300
Life Insurance, Pension Products & Wealth Management Services
S.I.C.: 6311
N.A.I.C.S.: 524113
Alain Regnault *(Dir Gen)*

Ageas Insurance Limited **(2)**
Ageas House
Tollgate, Eastleigh, Hants, SO53 3YA, United Kingdom UK
Tel.: (44) 2380644455
Fax: (44) 2380641146
E-Mail: info@ageas.co.uk
Web Site: www.ageas.co.uk
Emp.: 1,000
Personal & Commercial Insurance Products & Services
S.I.C.: 6411
N.A.I.C.S.: 524298
Andy Watson *(CEO)*
Mark Cliff *(Mng Dir)*

Subsidiary:

Groupama Insurance Company Limited **(3)**
6th Floor One America Square 17 Crosswall
London, EC3N 2LB, United Kingdom UK
Tel.: (44) 8708508510 (100%)
Telex: 883823
Fax: (44) 2072642862
Web Site: www.groupama.co.uk
Sales Range: $700-749.9 Million
Emp.: 600
Property & Casualty Insurance Products & Services
S.I.C.: 6351
N.A.I.C.S.: 524126
Francois-Xavier Boisseau *(CEO)*
Laurent Matras *(Mng Dir)*

Muang Thai Life Assurance Co., Ltd. **(2)**
250 Rachadaphisek Rd
Huanykwang, Bangkok, 10310, Thailand
Tel.: (66) 227610257
Fax: (66) 2276 1997 8
E-Mail: mtlfacebook@muangthai.co.th
Web Site: www.muangthai.co.th
General Insurance Services
S.I.C.: 6411
N.A.I.C.S.: 524210
Photipong Lamsam *(Chm)*
Jozef De Mey *(Vice Chm)*
Krisada Lamsam *(Vice Chm)*
Sara Lamsam *(Pres & CEO)*
Pakineenard Tiyachate *(Sec & Sr Exec VP)*

AGELLAN COMMERCIAL REAL ESTATE INVESTMENT TRUST

156 Front Street West Suite 303
Toronto, ON, M5J 2L6, Canada
Tel.: (416) 593-6800

Fax: (416) 593-6700
E-Mail: ddermott@agellancapital.com
Year Founded: 2012
ACR.UN—(TSX)
Business Description:
Real Estate Investment Services
S.I.C.: 6211
N.A.I.C.S.: 523999
Personnel:
Derek Dermott *(Pres)*
Frank Camenzuli *(CEO)*
Daniel Millett *(CFO)*
Terra Attard *(Sec)*
Transfer Agent:
Computershare Trust Company of Canada
Toronto, ON, Canada

AGENCE EURO SERVICES

22 Rue Michelet
92100 Boulogne-Billancourt, Hauts De Seine, France
Tel.: (33) 148251188
Web Site: v2.euro-services.fr/agences.html
Sales Range: $10-24.9 Million
Emp.: 45
Business Description:
Advertising
S.I.C.: 7311
N.A.I.C.S.: 541810
Personnel:
Edmond Fellous *(Mng Partner)*

AGENCE FRANCE-PRESSE

11-15 Place de la Bourse
75002 Paris, France
Tel.: (33) 140414646
Fax: (33) 140414904
E-Mail: info@afp.com
Web Site: www.afp.com
Year Founded: 1835
Sales Range: $300-349.9 Million
Emp.: 2,000
Business Description:
International News Services
S.I.C.: 7383
N.A.I.C.S.: 519110
Personnel:
Emmanuel Hoog *(CEO)*
Remi Tomaszewski *(Mng Dir)*
Emmanuel Marcovitch *(Deputy Mng Dir)*

Non-U.S. Subsidiary:

Sport-Informations-Dienst GmbH und Co. KG (1)
Hammfelddamm 10
41460 Neuss, Germany
Tel.: (49) 213113100
Fax: (49) 2131131112
E-Mail: redaktion@sid.de
Web Site: www.sid.de
German Language Internet Sports Service
S.I.C.: 2741
N.A.I.C.S.: 519130
Michael Cremer *(Mng Dir)*

Subsidiary:

Inedit (1)
33 avenue Philippe Auguste
75011 Paris, France
Tel.: (33) 142610264
Fax: (33) 142610264
Editorial Engineering: Integration of Information Technology for Media Companies
S.I.C.: 2741
N.A.I.C.S.: 519130

AGENCE MEESTERS

3 rue Jacques Coeur
75004 Paris, France
Tel.: (33) 144786030
Fax: (33) 144786044
E-Mail: franck.meesters@meesters.com
Web Site: www.meesters.com
Year Founded: 1981
Sales Range: $10-24.9 Million
Emp.: 3
Business Description:
Advertising Services
S.I.C.: 7311
N.A.I.C.S.: 541810
Personnel:
Claude Meesters *(Chm)*
Franck Meesters *(Exec VP)*

AGENCE SCHILLING COMMUNICATION

2 place Cap Quest
BP 20169
17005 La Rochelle, Cedex1, France
Tel.: (33) 5 46 50 15 15
Fax: (33) 5 46 50 15 19
E-Mail: agence.schilling@n-schilling.com
Web Site: www.n-schilling.com
Year Founded: 1974
Sales Range: $10-24.9 Million
Emp.: 9
Business Description:
Public Relations
S.I.C.: 8743
N.A.I.C.S.: 541820
Personnel:
Karl Wheeler *(Head-Graphic Design)*

AGENCIA EFE, S.A.

Espronceda 32
E-28003 Madrid, Spain
Tel.: (34) 913467100
Fax: (34) 913467689
E-Mail: efe@efe.es
Web Site: www.efe.com
Emp.: 1,000
Business Description:
News Services
S.I.C.: 7383
N.A.I.C.S.: 519110
Personnel:
Jose Antonio Vera *(Pres)*

U.S. Subsidiaries:

EFE News Services (US) Inc. (1)
5959 Blue Lagoon Dr Ste 308
Miami, FL 33126
Tel.: (305) 262-7575
Fax: (305) 262-7557
E-Mail: ecsanchez@efeamerica.com
Web Site: www.efe.com
News Services
S.I.C.: 7383
N.A.I.C.S.: 519110
Jose Manuel Sanz *(VP)*

EFE News Services (US) Inc. (1)
529 14th St NW Ste 1220
Washington, DC 20045
Tel.: (202) 745-7692
Fax: (202) 393-4118
E-Mail: jm.sanz@efeamerica.com
Web Site: www.efe.com
Emp.: 45
News Services
S.I.C.: 7383
N.A.I.C.S.: 519110
Azpiazu Maria *(Exec VP)*

Non-U.S. Subsidiaries:

Agencia EFE, S.A. (1)
Rua Castilho 13 D-5 A
1250 066 Lisbon, Portugal
Tel.: (351) 213513931
News Services
S.I.C.: 7383
N.A.I.C.S.: 519110

Agencia EFE, S.A. (1)
Coronel Santiago Bueras 188
Santiago, Chile
Tel.: (56) 26324946
Fax: (56) 26321330
News Services
S.I.C.: 7383
N.A.I.C.S.: 519110

Agencia EFE, S.A. (1)
Alicia Moreau de Justo 1720 1st Fl
Apartment F, Buenos Aires, C1107AFJ, Argentina
Tel.: (54) 1143125521
Fax: (54) 1143125527
E-Mail: reeadccion@efe.com.er
Web Site: www.efe.com
Emp.: 20
News Services
S.I.C.: 7383
N.A.I.C.S.: 519110
Mar Mirim *(Gen Mgr)*

Agencia EFE, S.A. (1)
Quintas Altas Cumbres centre Calles Coro Y San Cristobal Las Palmas, 1050 Caracas, Venezuela
Tel.: (58) 2127935752
Fax: (58) 212 7934920
News Services
S.I.C.: 7383
N.A.I.C.S.: 519110

Agencia EFE, S.A. (1)
Lafayette 69
Anzures Miguel Hidalgo, Mexico, DF, 11590, Mexico
Tel.: (52) 5552554085
Fax: (52) 5552541412
E-Mail: redaccion@efe.com.mx
Web Site: www.efe.com.mx
Emp.: 20
News Services
S.I.C.: 7383
N.A.I.C.S.: 519110
Agustin de Gracia *(Gen Mgr)*

Agencia EFE, S.A. (1)
Gonzalez Olaechea 207
San Isidro, Lima, Peru
Tel.: (51) 14412094
Fax: (51) 14412422
Web Site: www.efe.com
Emp.: 11
News Services
S.I.C.: 7383
N.A.I.C.S.: 519110
Xavier Otazu *(Mgr)*

Agencia EFE, S.A. (1)
Praia de Botafogo 228
Sala 605-B, Rio de Janeiro, RJ, 22359-900, Brazil
Tel.: (55) 2125536355
Fax: (55) 2125538823
E-Mail: real@efebrasil.com.br
Web Site: www.efe.com
Emp.: 30
News Services
S.I.C.: 7383
N.A.I.C.S.: 519110
Jaine Ortega *(Gen Mgr)*

Agencia EFE, S.A. (1)
Carrera 16 39A-69
Bogota, Colombia
Tel.: (57) 12323528
Web Site: www.efe.com
News Services
S.I.C.: 7383
N.A.I.C.S.: 519110

Agencie EFE (1)
Residence Pl Rue de la Loi 155
1040 Brussels, Belgium
Tel.: (32) 22854830
Fax: (32) 22309319
E-Mail: bruselas@efe.com
Web Site: www.efe.com
Emp.: 10
News Services
S.I.C.: 7383
N.A.I.C.S.: 519110
Mario Billar *(Coord)*

AGENDIA NV

Science Park 406
1098 XH Amsterdam, Netherlands
Tel.: (31) 204621500
Fax: (31) 3120462150
E-Mail: customerservice@agendia.com
Web Site: www.agendia.com
Year Founded: 2003
Business Description:
Molecular Diagnostic Services
S.I.C.: 2835
N.A.I.C.S.: 325413
Personnel:
Hessel Lindenbergh *(Chm-Supervisory Bd)*
David Macdonald *(CEO)*
Kurt Schmidt *(CFO & VP)*
Neil M. Barth *(Chief Medical Officer)*
Rene Bernards *(Chief Scientific Officer)*
Laura van 't Veer *(Chief Res Officer)*
Supervisory Board of Directors:
Hessel Lindenbergh
Albert Luderer
Gertjan van der Baan
Pieter Van Der Meer
Wim H. van Harten

AGENIX LIMITED

Ground Floor 156 Collins Street
Melbourne, VIC, 3000, Australia
Tel.: (61) 3 8616 0379
Fax: (61) 3 8616 0382
E-Mail: info@agenix.com
Web Site: www.agenix.com
Year Founded: 1987
AGX—(ASX)
Rev.: $14,042
Assets: $755,917
Liabilities: $536,104
Net Worth: $219,813
Earnings: ($3,395,651)
Fiscal Year-end: 06/30/13
Business Description:
Pharmaceutical Product Mfr
S.I.C.: 2834
N.A.I.C.S.: 325412
Personnel:
Nicholas Weston *(Chm & CEO)*
Gary Taylor *(CFO & Sec)*
Mike Gerometta *(Chief Science Officer-ThromboView)*
Board of Directors:
Nicholas Weston
Craig Chapman
Anthony Vui Han Lee
Chris McNamara

AGENNIX AG

Fraunhoferstrasse 20
82152 Martinsried, Germany
Tel.: (49) 8985652600
Fax: (49) 8985652610
E-Mail: info@agennix.com
Web Site: www.agennix.com
Year Founded: 2009
AGX—(DEU)
Sales Range: $1-9.9 Million
Emp.: 65
Business Description:
Holding Company; Biopharmaceutical Products Developer & Mfr
S.I.C.: 6719
N.A.I.C.S.: 551112
Personnel:
Christof Hettich *(Chm-Supervisory Bd)*
Frank Young *(Vice Chm-Supervisory Bd)*
Torsten Hombeck *(CFO & Sr VP)*
Colin Freund *(Chief Bus Officer & Sr VP)*
Rajesh Malik *(Chief Medical Officer & Sr VP)*
Brent Hatzis-Schoch *(Gen Counsel & Sr VP)*
Christine Boisclair *(Sr VP-Global Regulatory Affairs)*
Gregory H. Hamm *(Sr VP-HR & Corp Integration)*

Agennix AG—(Continued)

Jill Porter *(Sr VP-Pharmaceutical Dev)*
John Schaumberg *(Sr VP-Clinical Ops)*
Supervisory Board of Directors:
Christof Hettich
Alan Feinsilver
Bernd R. Seizinger
Friedrich von Bohlen und Halbach
James D. Weaver, III
Frank Young

U.S. Subsidiary:

Agennix Incorporated (1)
8 E Greenway Plz Ste 910
Houston, TX 77046 DE
Tel.: (713) 552-1091 (100%)
Fax: (713) 552-0795
E-Mail: dduke@agennix.com
Web Site: www.agennix.com
Biopharmaceutical Products Developer & Mfr
S.I.C.: 2836
N.A.I.C.S.: 325414
Rajesh Malik *(Grp Chief Medical Officer)*
John Schaumberg *(Sr VP-Clinical Ops)*

Branch:

Agennix Inc. - Princeton (2)
101 College Rd E
Princeton, NJ 08540
Tel.: (609) 524-1000
Fax: (609) 524-1050
E-Mail: hr.princeton@agennix.com
Web Site: www.agennix.com
Emp.: 40
Biopharmaceutical Products Developer & Mfr
S.I.C.: 8731
N.A.I.C.S.: 541711
Laurie Doyle *(Dir-IR & Corp Comm)*

AGENZIA NAZIONALE PER L'ATTRAZIONE DEGLI INVESTIMENTI E LO SVILLUPO D'IMPRESA SPA

(d/b/a INVITALIA)
Via Calabria 46
00187 Rome, Italy
Tel.: (39) 06421601
Fax: (39) 0642160937
Web Site: www.invitalia.it
Sales Range: $1-4.9 Billion
Emp.: 106,000
Business Description:
Holding Company; Agency for Enterprise & Inward Investment Development
S.I.C.: 6719
N.A.I.C.S.: 551112
Personnel:
Nicolo Piazza *(Pres)*

Subsidiaries:

Innovazione Italia S.p.A. (1)
Via Boncompagni 16
Roma, Latina, Italy
Tel.: (39) 06420329
Management Consulting Services
S.I.C.: 8748
N.A.I.C.S.: 541618

Italia Navigando S.p.A. (1)
Via Calabria
Latina, 00187, Italy
Tel.: (39) 064203291
Fax: (39) 0685375455
E-Mail: info@italianavigando.it
Web Site: www.italianavigando.it/
Land Subdivision
S.I.C.: 6552
N.A.I.C.S.: 237210

Strategia Italia Sgr SpA (1)
Corso Vittorio Emanuele II 88
Milan, Italy
Tel.: (39) 0115575201
Fax: (39) 0115573
Open-End Investment Funds
S.I.C.: 6722
N.A.I.C.S.: 525910

Sviluppo Italia Abruzzo S.p.A. (1)
Mazzarino 108
L'Aquila, 67100 Rome, Italy
Tel.: (39) 086248581
Fax: (39) 08624858222
Web Site: www.sviluppoitaliaabruzzo.it
Holding Company
S.I.C.: 6719
N.A.I.C.S.: 551112

Sviluppo Italia Bic Umbria SpA (1)
Strada Delle Campore 11/13
Terni, 5100, Italy
Tel.: (39) 074480601
Fax: (39) 0744800760
E-Mail: sargenti@sviluppoitaliaumbria.it
Web Site: www.inbitalia.it
Emp.: 5
Management Consulting Services
S.I.C.: 8748
N.A.I.C.S.: 541618
Corrodo Diotelli *(Gen Mgr)*

Sviluppo Italia Campania SpA (1)
Via A Olivetti 1
Pozzuoli, Italy
Tel.: (39) 0815255111
Web Site: www.sviluppoitaliacampania.it
Management Consulting Services
S.I.C.: 8748
N.A.I.C.S.: 541618

Sviluppo Italia Engineering SpA (1)
Via P Boccanelli 30
Roma, 00138 Latina, Italy
Tel.: (39) 064540081
Fax: (39) 06454008342
Web Site: www.sviluppoitalia.it/societa.jsp?ID_LINK=1391&area=126
Engineering Services
S.I.C.: 8711
N.A.I.C.S.: 541330

Sviluppo Italia Marche SpA (1)
Via Ludovico Menicucci 6
60121i Ancona, Italy
Tel.: (39) 0715021444
E-Mail: info@sviluppoitaliamarche.it
Management Consulting Services
S.I.C.: 8748
N.A.I.C.S.: 541618
Roberto Tontini *(Gen Mgr)*

Sviluppo Italia Molise SpA (1)
Via Don Giuseppe Mucciardi 5
86020 Naples, Italy
Tel.: (39) 0874774210
Fax: (39) 0874774221
Management Consulting Services
S.I.C.: 8748
N.A.I.C.S.: 541618
Gianfranco Battistutti *(Mgr)*

Sviluppo Italia Puglia SpA (1)
Via Giovanni Amendola 168 5
Bari, Italy
Tel.: (39) 0805461637
Web Site: por.regione.puglia.it/index_it.php?id=0
Management Consulting Services
S.I.C.: 8748
N.A.I.C.S.: 541618

U.S. Subsidiary:

SI Factor LLC (1)
13816 Lexington Pl
Broomfield, CO 80020-9377
Tel.: (303) 255-1242
Engineering Services
S.I.C.: 8711
N.A.I.C.S.: 541330

AGF MANAGEMENT LIMITED

Toronto Dominion Bank Tower 31st Floor 66 Wellington Street West
PO Box 50
Toronto, ON, M5K 1E9, Canada
Tel.: (416) 367-1900
Fax: (416) 865-4197
Toll Free: (888) 243-4668
E-Mail: tiger@agf.com
Web Site: www.agf.com
Year Founded: 1957
AGF.B—(TSX)
Rev.: $507,164,908
Assets: $1,675,352,123
Liabilities: $626,340,949
Net Worth: $1,049,011,174
Earnings: $52,110,504
Emp.: 510
Fiscal Year-end: 11/30/12
Business Description:
Investment Services
S.I.C.: 6211
N.A.I.C.S.: 523999
Personnel:
Blake C. Goldring *(Chm & CEO)*
W. Robert Farquharson *(Vice Chm)*
Robert J. Bogart *(CFO & Exec VP)*
Judy G. Goldring *(COO & Exec VP)*
Martin Hubbes *(Chief Investment Officer & Exec VP-Investments)*
Mario Causarano *(Pres/COO-AGF Trust)*
Gordon Forrester *(Exec VP-Product & Mktg & Head-Retail)*
Rose Cammareri *(Exec VP-Retail Distr)*
A. Patrica Perez-Coutts *(Sr VP & Portfolio Mgr)*
Stephen W. Way *(Sr VP & Portfolio Mgr)*
Board of Directors:
Blake C. Goldring
Sarah Davis
Douglas L. Derry
W. Robert Farquharson
Judy G. Goldring
Donald G. Lang
William Morneau
Winthrop H. Smith, Jr.
G. Wayne Squibb
Transfer Agent:
Computershare Trust Company of Canada
100 University Avenue 11th Floor
Toronto, ON, M5J 2Y1, Canada
Tel.: (416) 891-9633
Toll Free: (800) 663-9097

Subsidiaries:

AGF Funds Inc. (1)
2920 Matheson Blvd E
Mississauga, ON, L4W 5J4, Canada (100%)
Tel.: (905) 214-8203
Fax: (905) 214-8243
Web Site: www.agf.com
Open-End Investment Funds
S.I.C.: 6722
N.A.I.C.S.: 525910
Robert Lyon *(Sr VP & Portfolio Mgr)*

AGF Investments Inc. (1)
Ste 3100 66 Wellington St W Toronto Dominion Bank Tower
Toronto, ON, M5K 1E9, Canada
Tel.: (416) 367-1900
Web Site: www.agf.com
Investment Management Services
S.I.C.: 6211
N.A.I.C.S.: 523999
Chris Boyle *(Sr VP-Institutional)*
Peter Frost *(Sr VP)*

Subsidiaries:

Acuity Funds Ltd (2)
40 King St W
Toronto, ON, M5H 3Y2, Canada
Tel.: (416) 366-9933
Fax: (416) 366-2568
Toll Free: (800) 461-4570
E-Mail: mail@acuityfunds.com
Investment Management Services
S.I.C.: 6211
N.A.I.C.S.: 523999

Acuity Investment Management Inc (2)
40 King St W Scotia Plaza Bldg
Toronto, ON, M1L 3Y2, Canada
Tel.: (416) 366-9933
Fax: (888) 957-4125
Web Site: www.agf.com
Investment Management Services
S.I.C.: 6211
N.A.I.C.S.: 523999
Hugh McCauley *(Mng Dir & Mgr-Lead Portfolio)*

Doherty & Associates Ltd. (2)
56 Sparks St Ste 700
Ottawa, ON, K1P 5A9, Canada
Tel.: (613) 238-6727
Fax: (613) 238-3957
E-Mail: info@doherty.ca
Web Site: www.doherty.ca
Emp.: 1
Investment Management Services
S.I.C.: 6211
N.A.I.C.S.: 523999
Ian S. Sterling *(Pres)*
Bill Wolfenden *(Chief Investment Officer & Sr VP)*
Goldstein Goldstein *(Sr VP)*

AGF Securities (Canada) Ltd. (1)
Toronto Dominion Bank Twr Ste 3100 31st Fl 66 Welling
Toronto, ON, M5K 1E9, Canada (100%)
Tel.: (416) 865-4176
Fax: (416) 814-9043
Investment Banking & Securities Dealing
S.I.C.: 6211
N.A.I.C.S.: 523110

Cypress Capital Management Ltd. (1)
1055 Georgia St W Ste 1700
Vancouver, BC, V6E 3P3, Canada (100%)
Tel.: (604) 659-1850
Fax: (604) 659-1899
E-Mail: reception@cypresscap.com
Web Site: cypresscap.com
Emp.: 20
Investment Banking & Securities Dealing
S.I.C.: 6211
N.A.I.C.S.: 523110
Gregory Bay *(Pres & CEO)*

Highstreet Asset Management Inc. (1)
244 Pall Mall St Ste350
N6A 5P6 London, ON, Canada
Tel.: (519) 850-9500
Fax: (519) 850-1214
E-Mail: info@highstreet.ca
Web Site: www.highstreet.ca
Emp.: 38
Investment Services
S.I.C.: 6211
N.A.I.C.S.: 523999
Paul Brisson *(Pres)*
Dawn Butler *(CFO & COO)*
Doug Crocker *(Chief Risk Officer)*
Shaun Arnold *(Chief Investment Officer)*
Jim McGill *(Exec VP)*
Grant McIntosh *(Sr VP-Investments)*

P.J. Doherty & Associates Co. Ltd. (1)
56 Sparks St
Ottawa, ON, K1P 5A9, Canada (100%)
Tel.: (613) 238-6727
Fax: (613) 238-3957
E-Mail: info@doherty.ca
Web Site: www.doherty.ca
Emp.: 10
Open-End Investment Funds
S.I.C.: 6722
N.A.I.C.S.: 525910
Ian Sterling *(Pres)*
William Wolfenden *(CFO)*

Non-U.S. Subsidiaries:

AGF Asset Management Asia Ltd. (1)
80 Raffles Place
Singapore, Singapore
Tel.: (65) 64381633
Fax: (65) 64380043
E-Mail: info@agf.com
Emp.: 5
Open-End Investment Funds
S.I.C.: 6722
N.A.I.C.S.: 525910
Dlake Golbering *(Chm)*
Eng Hock Ong *(Mng Dir)*

AGF International Advisors Company Ltd. (1)
34 Molesworth St
Dublin, Ireland (100%)

Tel.: (353) 16613466
Fax: (353) 16613520
Emp.: 18
Investment Advice
S.I.C.: 6282
N.A.I.C.S.: 523930
W. Robert Farquharson *(Chm)*
John Arnold *(Mng Dir)*

Subsidiary:

AGFIA Limited (2)
34 Molesworth St
Dublin, Ireland
Tel.: (353) 1 661 3466
Fax: (353) 1 661 3520
Web Site: www.agf.com
Emp.: 12
Investment Management Services
S.I.C.: 6211
N.A.I.C.S.: 523999
Rory Flynn *(CIO)*

AGF International Company Ltd. (1)
34 Molesworth St
Dublin, 2, Ireland (100%)
Tel.: (353) 16613466
Fax: (353) 16613520
E-Mail: johna@agf.ie
Emp.: 18
Investment Advice
S.I.C.: 6282
N.A.I.C.S.: 523930
John Arnold *(Mng Dir)*

AGFA-GEVAERT N.V.

Septestraat 27
B-2640 Mortsel, Belgium
Tel.: (32) 34442111
Fax: (32) 34447094
Web Site: www.agfa.com
Year Founded: 1894
AGFB—(EUR FRA)
Rev.: $4,161,011,470
Assets: $3,809,661,100
Liabilities: $2,524,068,750
Net Worth: $1,285,592,350
Earnings: ($41,731,270)
Emp.: 11,408
Fiscal Year-end: 12/31/12

Business Description:
Imaging Systems Mfr & Distr for Printing, Graphic Arts, Motion Picture & Medical Imaging Processes
Export
S.I.C.: 3579
N.A.I.C.S.: 333316

Personnel:
Julien De Wilde *(Chm)*
Christian Reinaudo *(Pres & CEO)*
Kris Hoornaert *(CFO)*
Luc Delagaye *(Pres-Agfa Materials)*
Luc Thijs *(Pres-Agfa HealthCare)*
Stefaan Vanhooren *(Pres-Agfa Graphics)*
Wilfried Van Lishout *(Sec)*

Board of Directors:
Julien De Wilde
Michel Akkermans
Jo Cornu
Willy Duron
Roland Junck
Christian Leysen
Christian Reinaudo

Subsidiaries:

AGFA FINANCE NV (1)
Septestraat 27
Mortsel, 2640, Belgium
Tel.: (32) 34447190
Financial Management Services
S.I.C.: 6211
N.A.I.C.S.: 523999

AGFA-GEVAERT INTERNATIONAL NV (1)
Septestraat 27
Mortsel, 2640, Belgium
Tel.: (32) 34445065
Photographic Equipment Distr
S.I.C.: 5043
N.A.I.C.S.: 423410
Kris Hoornaert *(Mng Dir)*

Agfa-Gevaert Investment Fund NV (1)
Septestraat 27
2640 Mortsel, Belgium
Tel.: (32) 34442111
Fax: (32) 34445632
Web Site: www.agfa.com
Emp.: 3,800
Financial Management Services
S.I.C.: 6211
N.A.I.C.S.: 523999
Christian Reinaudo *(CEO)*

Agfa Graphics NV (1)
Septestraat 27
2640 Mortsel, Belgium
Tel.: (32) 34442111
Fax: (32) 34447094
E-Mail: info@agfa.link.be
Emp.: 3,500
Prepress Solutions for Printing & Publishing Industries
S.I.C.: 2759
N.A.I.C.S.: 323120
Stefaan Vanhooren *(Pres)*

Agfa HealthCare NV (1)
Septestraat 27
2640 Mortsel, Belgium
Tel.: (32) 34442111
Fax: (32) 34447094
E-Mail: info@agfa.com
Diagnostic Imaging & Healthcare IT Solutions
S.I.C.: 7379
N.A.I.C.S.: 541519
Geertrui De Smet *(Mgr-Global Mktg Comm)*

Non-U.S. Subsidiary:

Agfa HealthCare UK (2)
Vantage West
Great West Road, Brentford, Middlesex, TW8 9AX, United Kingdom
Tel.: (44) 2082315984
Fax: (44) 2082315590
E-Mail: healthcare@agfa.com
Web Site: www.agfa.com
Emp.: 50
Diagnostic Imaging & Healthcare IT Solutions
S.I.C.: 5045
N.A.I.C.S.: 423430
Grant Witheridge *(Mng Dir)*

LUITHAGEN NV (1)
Septestraat 27
Mortsel, 2640, Belgium
Tel.: (32) 3 450 97 11
Fax: (32) 3 450 98 88
Printing Equipment Distr
S.I.C.: 5084
N.A.I.C.S.: 423830

U.S. Subsidiaries:

Agfa Corporation (1)
100 Challenger Rd
Ridgefield Park, NJ 07660 DE
Tel.: (201) 440-2500 (100%)
Fax: (201) 342-4742
Web Site: www.agfa.com
Emp.: 100
Mfr & Marketer Electronic Imaging Systems for Medical Pre-Press & Photography Processes; Mfr of Films, Laser Imaging Systems & Digital Radiography Systems
Import Export
S.I.C.: 3579
N.A.I.C.S.: 333316
Peter Wilkens *(Pres)*
Gunther Mertens *(CFO & VP)*

Subsidiaries:

Agfa Materials Corporation (2)
1658 Bushy Park
Goose Creek, SC 29445
Tel.: (843) 574-2600
Fax: (843) 820-6708
Web Site: www.agfa.com
Imagesetters, Computer to Plate Recorders, Workflow Systems & Laser Images Mfr
S.I.C.: 3575
N.A.I.C.S.: 334118

Harold M. Pitman Company, Inc. (2)
721 Union Blvd
Totowa, NJ 07512-2207 IL
Tel.: (973) 812-0400
Fax: (973) 812-1630
Toll Free: (800) 274-8626
E-Mail: totowa_cs@pitman.com
Web Site: www.pitman.com
Sales Range: $500-549.9 Million
Emp.: 500
Digital Imaging Services
S.I.C.: 7336
N.A.I.C.S.: 541430
Paul F. Schmidt *(Chm & CEO)*
Peter J. Moore *(Pres)*
John Eichner *(CFO & Exec VP)*
William A. Ceperich *(Exec VP)*
Steve Raboin *(Exec VP-Mktg & New Bus Dev)*

NEW PROIMAGE AMERICA INC. (1)
103 Carnegie Ctr Ste 300
Princeton, NJ 08540-6235
Tel.: (609) 844-7576
Fax: (609) 895-2666
E-Mail: pia@newsway.com
Web Site: www.newsway.com
Emp.: 20
Software Development Services
S.I.C.: 7371
N.A.I.C.S.: 541511
Andy Scott *(Dir-Bus Dev)*

Non-U.S. Subsidiaries:

AGFA DE MEXICO S.A. DE C.V. (1)
Insurgentes Sur 1196 Col Tlacoquemecatl Del Valle
Del Benito Juarez, 03200 Mexico, Mexico
Tel.: (52) 55 5488 8500
Fax: (52) 55 5575 7813
E-Mail: servicio.equipos.mx@agfa.com
Web Site: www.agfa.com
Medical Equipment Repair & Maintenance Services
S.I.C.: 7629
N.A.I.C.S.: 811219

AGFA FINANCE INC. (1)
77 Belfield Rd
Etobicoke, Toronto, ON, M9W 1G6, Canada
Tel.: (416) 241-5409
Fax: (416) 241-5409
Financial Management Services
S.I.C.: 6211
N.A.I.C.S.: 523999

Agfa-Gevaert AB (1)
Torshamnsgatan 32 C
PO Box 6
S 16493 Kista, Stockholm, Sweden (100%)
Tel.: (46) 87930100
Fax: (46) 87930171
E-Mail: info@agfa.se
Web Site: www.agfa.se
Emp.: 100
Photographic Equipment & Supplies
S.I.C.: 3579
N.A.I.C.S.: 333316
Erik Ygansen *(Gen Mgr)*

AGFA-GEVAERT A.E.B.E. (1)
Stylianou Gonata 16
PO Box 42017
Peristeri, Greece
Tel.: (30) 1 576 3200
Emp.: 47
Photographic Film Mfr
S.I.C.: 3861
N.A.I.C.S.: 325992
Konstantinos Panis *(Gen Mgr)*

Agfa-Gevaert AG/SA (1)
Stettbachstrasse 7
PO Box 738
CH 8600 Dubendorf, Switzerland
Tel.: (41) 18237422
Fax: (41) 18237214
Emp.: 90
Photographic Equipment & Supplies
S.I.C.: 3579
N.A.I.C.S.: 333316
Moritz Rogger *(Reg Pres)*

Agfa-Gevaert Argentina S.A. (1)
Venezuela 4269
C 1211 ABE Buenos Aires, Argentina (100%)
Tel.: (54) 1149589300
Fax: (54) 1149835875
E-Mail: info@agfa.com
Web Site: www.agfa.com
Emp.: 100
Mfr of Photographic Supplies
S.I.C.: 3579
N.A.I.C.S.: 333316

Agfa Gevaert B.V. (1)
Polakweg 10-11
NL-2288 GG Rijswijk, Netherlands (100%)
Tel.: (31) 704131211
Fax: (31) 704131390
E-Mail: healthcare.nl@agfa.com
Web Site: www.agfa.com
Sls.: $137,000,000
Emp.: 60
Photographic Equipment & Supplies
S.I.C.: 3579
N.A.I.C.S.: 333316
Can Zonneveld *(Gen Mgr)*

AGFA-GEVAERT DO BRASIL LTDA. (1)
Rua Alexandre Dumas 1711 3 Andar
Edificio Birmann 12
04717-004 Sao Paulo, Brazil
Tel.: (55) 11 5188 6444
Fax: (55) 11 5188 6469
E-Mail: sacgs.br@agfa.com
Web Site: www.agfa.com
Emp.: 150
Photographic Equipment Distr
S.I.C.: 5043
N.A.I.C.S.: 423410
Fabrizio Valentini *(Pres)*

Agfa-Gevaert do Brasil Ltd. (1)
Rua Alexandre Dumas 1711 3 4 Andar Conj 301
Ed Birmann 12, 04717 004 Rio de Janeiro, Brazil
Tel.: (55) 151886444
Fax: (55) 151886449
Web Site: www.agfa.com.br
Mfr of Imagesetters, Computer to Plate Recorders, Workflow Systems & Laser Imagers
S.I.C.: 3577
N.A.I.C.S.: 334118

AGFA-GEVAERT GRAPHIC SYSTEMS GMBH (1)
Im Mediapark 5b
Cologne, 50670, Germany
Tel.: (49) 611 962 09
Photographic Film Mfr
S.I.C.: 3861
N.A.I.C.S.: 325992

AGFA-GEVAERT HEALTHCARE GMBH (1)
Tegernseer Landstrasse 161
81539 Munich, Germany
Tel.: (49) 89 6207 0
Fax: (49) 89 6207 7716
Web Site: www.agfahealthcare.com
Emp.: 800
Digital Imaging System Mfr & Distr
S.I.C.: 3845
N.A.I.C.S.: 334510

Agfa-Gevaert Japan, Ltd. (1)
8 1 Higashiyama 3 Chome
Meguro Ku, 153-0043 Tokyo, Japan (94%)
Tel.: (81) 357043071
Fax: (81) 357043084
Web Site: www.agfa.co.jp
Emp.: 100
Wholesale Distribution of Cameras & Supplies
S.I.C.: 5734
N.A.I.C.S.: 443142
Hiroyuki Matsuishi *(Pres-Japan)*

AGFA-GEVAERT LTDA. (1)
Avda Presidente Riesco 5435 - Piso 13
Las Condes, Santiago, Chile
Tel.: (56) 2 595 76 00
Emp.: 25
Photographic Imaging System Distr
S.I.C.: 5043
N.A.I.C.S.: 423410
Hector Rojas Sanchez *(Gen Mgr)*

Agfa-Gevaert Ltd. (1)
Bantage W Great W Rd
Brentford, Mddx, TW8 9AX, United Kingdom (100%)
Tel.: (44) 2082314983
Fax: (44) 2082314277
E-Mail: info@agfa.com
Web Site: www.agfa.co.uk

Agfa-Gevaert N.V.—(Continued)

Emp.: 200
Mfr of Photographic Equipment
S.I.C.: 3579
N.A.I.C.S.: 333316
Kris Hoornaert *(CFO)*

AGFA-GEVAERT LIMITED (1)
15 Dalmore Drive
PO Box 9149
Scoresby, Melbourne, VIC, 3179, Australia
Tel.: (61) 3 9756 4100
Fax: (61) 3 9756 4400
Photographic Equipment Distr
S.I.C.: 5043
N.A.I.C.S.: 423410

Agfa-Gevaert S.A. (1)
212 avenue Paul Doumer
F 92508 Rueil-Malmaison, Cedex, France FR
Tel.: (33) 147771000 (99.9%)
Telex: 631 050
Fax: (33) 147771050
Web Site: www.agfa.com
Emp.: 1,328
Scanner & Medical Equipment Mfr & Sales
S.I.C.: 3841
N.A.I.C.S.: 339112

AGFA-GEVAERT S.A.U. (1)
Napoles 249 4th Fl
08013 Barcelona, Spain
Tel.: (34) 93 476 78 00
Fax: (34) 93 458 25 03
E-Mail: pedidos.gs@agfa.com
Web Site: www.agfa.com
Emp.: 80
Software Development Services
S.I.C.: 7371
N.A.I.C.S.: 541511
Angel Ardola *(Gen Mgr)*

Agfa-Gevaert S.p.A. (1)
Viamrssemo Gorci 69
I 20092 Milan, Italy (100%)
Tel.: (39) 02 3088 220
Fax: (39) 02 30088 807
E-Mail: info@agfa.com
Web Site: www.agfa.com
Emp.: 464
Photographic Equipment & Supplies
S.I.C.: 3579
N.A.I.C.S.: 333316
Zelakk Robrtr *(Gen Mgr)*

AGFA GRAPHICS ARGENTINA S.A. (1)
Venezuela 4269
C1211ABE Buenos Aires, Argentina
Tel.: (54) 11 4958 9300
Fax: (54) 11 4983 5052
Emp.: 35
Printing Machinery Distr
S.I.C.: 5084
N.A.I.C.S.: 423830

AGFA GRAPHICS AUSTRIA GMBH (1)
Lehrbachgasse 2
1121 Vienna, Austria
Tel.: (43) 1 891 12 0
Fax: (43) 1 891 12 3380
E-Mail: info-graphics.de@agfa.com
Printing Machinery Distr
S.I.C.: 5084
N.A.I.C.S.: 423830

AGFA GRAPHICS GERMANY GMBH & CO. KG (1)
Zweigniederlassung Dusseldorf Paul-Thomas-Strasse 58
40599 Dusseldorf, Germany
Tel.: (49) 211 22 986 0
Fax: (49) 211 22 986 130
Printing Machinery Distr
S.I.C.: 5084
N.A.I.C.S.: 423830

AGFA GRAPHICS LTD. (1)
Coal Road
Seacroft, Leeds, LS14 2AL, United Kingdom
Tel.: (44) 113 251 4000
Fax: (44) 113 2 51 4060
Emp.: 95
Printing Equipment Mfr & Distr
S.I.C.: 5084
N.A.I.C.S.: 423830

AGFA GRAPHICS MIDDLE EAST FZCO (1)
P110 East Wing 1 Dubai Airport Free Zone
PO Box 36159
Dubai, United Arab Emirates
Tel.: (971) 42996969
Fax: (971) 42994119
E-Mail: infome@agfa.com
Emp.: 25
Printing Machinery Distr
S.I.C.: 5084
N.A.I.C.S.: 423830
Panos Bartziokas *(Gen Mgr)*

AGFA GRAPHICS SP. Z.O.O. (1)
Aleje Jerozolimskie 195 A
02-222 Warsaw, Poland
Tel.: (48) 22 3 111 900
Fax: (48) 22 3 111 966
Printing Equipment Mfr & Distr
S.I.C.: 3555
N.A.I.C.S.: 333244

AGFA GRAPHICS S.R.L. (1)
Via Gorki 69
Cinisello Balsamo, Milan, 20092, Italy
Tel.: (39) 02 30088 1
Fax: (39) 02 30088 807
Web Site: www.agfagraphics.com
Emp.: 64
Printing Machinery Mfr & Distr
S.I.C.: 3555
N.A.I.C.S.: 333244
Roberto Ziletti *(Gen Mgr)*

AGFA GRAPHICS SWITZERLAND AG (1)
Stettbachstrasse 7
8600 Dubendorf, Switzerland
Tel.: (41) 44 823 71 11
Fax: (41) 44 823 72 14
E-Mail: ccc-vertrieb.ch@agfa.com
Printing Machinery Distr
S.I.C.: 5084
N.A.I.C.S.: 423830

AGFA HEALTHCARE AG (1)
Stettbachstrasse 7
8600 Dubendorf, Switzerland
Tel.: (41) 44 823 7111
Fax: (41) 44 823 7203
Web Site: www.agfa.com
Emp.: 50
Medical Equipment Mfr
S.I.C.: 3845
N.A.I.C.S.: 334510
Moretz Roger *(CEO)*

AGFA HEALTHCARE ARGENTINA S.A. (1)
Venezuela 4269
C1211ABE Buenos Aires, Argentina
Tel.: (54) 11 4958 9300
Fax: (54) 11 4958 5707
Medical Software Development Services
S.I.C.: 7371
N.A.I.C.S.: 541511

AGFA HEALTHCARE AUSTRALIA LIMITED (1)
15 Dalmore Drive
Scoresby, Melbourne, VIC, 3179, Australia
Tel.: (61) 397564100
Fax: (61) 3 9756 4402
Web Site: www.agfa.com
Emp.: 25
Medical Device Distr
S.I.C.: 5047
N.A.I.C.S.: 423450
Dean Adams *(Mng Dir)*
Brenda Battin Cianciosi *(Mng Dir)*

AGFA HEALTHCARE BRAZIL IMPORTACAO E SERVICOS LTDA. (1)
Rua Alexandre Dumas 1711 - 3 Andar - Edificio Birmann 12
04717-004 Sao Paulo, Brazil
Tel.: (55) 11 5188 6444
Fax: (55) 11 5188 6429
Emp.: 70
Medical Device Distr
S.I.C.: 5047
N.A.I.C.S.: 423450
Jose Laska *(Country Mgr)*

AGFA HEALTHCARE COLOMBIA LTDA. (1)
Edificio Torre Central Carrera 68D No 25-B-86 906
Bogota, Colombia
Tel.: (57) 1 4578888
Fax: (57) 1 4272773
E-Mail: agfacol@agfa.com
Web Site: www.agfahealthcare.com
Healthcare Software Development Services
S.I.C.: 7371
N.A.I.C.S.: 541511

AGFA HEALTHCARE DENMARK A/S (1)
Arne Jacobsens Alle 7 5th Floor
2300 Copenhagen, Denmark
Tel.: (45) 36 94 48 20
Fax: (45) 36 94 45 10
Healthcare Software Development Services
S.I.C.: 7371
N.A.I.C.S.: 541511

AGFA HEALTHCARE FINLAND OY AB (1)
Keilasatama 3
02150 Espoo, Finland
Tel.: (358) 9 2510 7222
Web Site: www.agfahealthcare.com
Healthcare Software Development Services
S.I.C.: 7371
N.A.I.C.S.: 541511

AGFA HEALTHCARE GERMANY GMBH (1)
Konrad-Zuse-Platz 1-3
53227 Bonn, Germany
Tel.: (49) 228 26 68 000
Fax: (49) 228 26 68 001
Web Site: www.agfa.com
Healthcare Information Technology Consulting Services
S.I.C.: 7373
N.A.I.C.S.: 541512

AGFA HEALTHCARE GMBH (1)
Konrad-Zuse-Platz 1-3
53227 Bonn, Germany
Tel.: (49) 228 26 68 000
Fax: (49) 228 26 68 001
E-Mail: marketing.dach@agfa.com
Web Site: www.agfahealthcare.com
Healthcare Software Development Services
S.I.C.: 7371
N.A.I.C.S.: 541511

AGFA HEALTHCARE HONG KONG LTD. (1)
Unit 504 Stanhope House 734 King's Road
Quarry Bay, Hong Kong, China (Hong Kong)
Tel.: (852) 28739321
Fax: (852) 25183050
Web Site: www.agfahealthcare.com
Emp.: 12
Medical Equipment Distr
S.I.C.: 5047
N.A.I.C.S.: 423450
Pip Wong *(Gen Mgr)*

AGFA HEALTHCARE HUNGARY KFT. (1)
Kapas U 6-12
1027 Budapest, Hungary
Tel.: (36) 1 393 5000
Fax: (36) 1 393 5009
E-Mail: service.hu@agfa.com
Web Site: www.agfa.com
Medical Equipment Repair & Maintenance Services
S.I.C.: 7699
N.A.I.C.S.: 811219

AGFA HEALTHCARE IMAGING AGENTS GMBH (1)
Am Coloneum 4
Cologne, 50829, Germany
Tel.: (49) 221 5717712
Fax: (49) 221 5717710
Medical Instrument Distr
S.I.C.: 5047
N.A.I.C.S.: 423450

AGFA HEALTHCARE INC. (1)
77 Belfield Rd
Etobicoke, Toronto, ON, M9W 1G6, Canada
Tel.: (519) 746-2900
Fax: (519) 746-3745
Healthcare Software Development Services
S.I.C.: 7371
N.A.I.C.S.: 541511

AGFA HEALTHCARE - KNIGHTSBRIDGE GMBH (1)
Diefenbachgasse 35
1150 Vienna, Austria
Tel.: (43) 1 899 66
Fax: (43) 1 899 66 110
Healthcare Software Development Services
S.I.C.: 7371
N.A.I.C.S.: 541511

AGFA HEALTHCARE LUXEMBOURG S.A. (1)
Route De Longwy 74
Helfenterbruck, 8080 Luxembourg, Bertrange, Luxembourg
Tel.: (352) 4420441
Fax: (352) 44204437
Web Site: www.agfahealthcare.com
Emp.: 2
Software Development Services
S.I.C.: 7371
N.A.I.C.S.: 541511
Frank Michiels *(Country Mgr)*

AGFA HEALTHCARE MEXICO S.A. DE C.V. (1)
Insurgentes Sur No 1196 Piso 16
Tlacoquemecatl Benito Juarez
Mexico, 3200, Mexico
Tel.: (52) 5554885450
Photo Sensitive Printing Plate Mfr
S.I.C.: 3861
N.A.I.C.S.: 325992

AGFA HEALTHCARE NORWAY AS (1)
Nydalsveien 33
484 Oslo, Norway
Tel.: (47) 6705 7670
Fax: (47) 6705 7671
Digital Imaging Equipment Distr
S.I.C.: 5047
N.A.I.C.S.: 423450

AGFA HEALTHCARE SHANGHAI LTD. (1)
15F No 388 West Nanjing Road CIRO's Plaza
200003 Shanghai, China
Tel.: (86) 21 24122000
Fax: (86) 21 24122062
Healthcare Software Development Services
S.I.C.: 7371
N.A.I.C.S.: 541511

AGFA HEALTHCARE SINGAPORE PTE. LTD. (1)
10 Changi South Street 2 Level 3
486596 Singapore, Singapore
Tel.: (65) 6214 06 22
Fax: (65) 6214 00 62
Web Site: www.agfa.com
Healthcare Imaging Equipment Distr
S.I.C.: 5047
N.A.I.C.S.: 423450
Paul de Kruyff *(Gen Mgr)*

AGFA HEALTHCARE SOUTH AFRICA PTY. LTD. (1)
Unit 2 B Isando Business Park Cnr Hulley/Andre Greyvenstein Roads
Isando Ext 3, 1600 Isando, South Africa
Tel.: (27) 11 921 4686
Fax: (27) 11 921 4689
Web Site: www.agfahealthcare.com
Emp.: 3
Digital Imaging System Whslr
S.I.C.: 5047
N.A.I.C.S.: 423450
Bets Swart *(Country Mgr)*

Agfa HealthCare Spain, S.A.U. (1)
Provenca 392
08025 Barcelona, Spain (100%)
Tel.: (34) 934767600
Fax: (34) 934767681
Web Site: www.agfa.com
Emp.: 200
Photographic Equipment & Supplies
S.I.C.: 3579
N.A.I.C.S.: 333316
Dolores Clavera *(Mgr-Mktg & Comm)*

AGFA HEALTHCARE SWEDEN AB (1)
Arne Beurlings Torg 9A
164 40 Kista, Sweden
Tel.: (46) 8 79 30 100
Fax: (46) 8 79 30 171
E-Mail: info@agfa.com
Web Site: www.agfa.com
Emp.: 5
Medical Device Mfr & Distr

S.I.C.: 3845
N.A.I.C.S.: 334510
Franz Tiani *(Mng Dir)*

Agfa Imaging Products (Shenzhen) Co., Ltd. (1)
7/F South Union Hotel 2002 Shennan East Road
Luohu, Shenzhen, 518001, China
Tel.: (86) 755 82135000
Fax: (86) 755 82135020
Emp.: 10
Photographic Equipment Mfr
S.I.C.: 3579
N.A.I.C.S.: 333316

Agfa Inc. (1)
77 Belfield Road
M9W 1G6 Toronto, ON, Canada
Tel.: (416) 241-1110
Fax: (416) 240-7359
Web Site: www.agfahealthcare.com
Emp.: 130
Photo Equipment & Supplies
S.I.C.: 5043
N.A.I.C.S.: 423410
Michael Green *(Pres & CEO)*

AGFA INDIA PRIVATE LTD. (1)
2nd Floor Plot No B-14 Road No-1 Wagle Estate Near Mulund Check Naka
Thane West, Mumbai, Maharashtra, 400601, India
Tel.: (91) 22 40642900
Fax: (91) 22 40642929
Digital Imaging System Distr
S.I.C.: 5043
N.A.I.C.S.: 423410

AGFA INDUSTRIES KOREA LTD. (1)
631-4 Sunggok-dong
Danwon-gu, 425-833 Ansan, Gyeonggi, Korea (South)
Tel.: (82) 31 490 9101
Fax: (82) 31 495 2054
Web Site: www.agfa.com
Emp.: 39
Printing Machinery Mfr
S.I.C.: 3555
N.A.I.C.S.: 333244
Pyung Hwa Oh *(Plant Mgr)*

AGFA LIMITED (1)
John F Kennedy Drive Naas Road
PO Box 368
Dublin, Ireland
Tel.: (353) 1 4506733
Fax: (353) 1 4565267
Emp.: 2
Photographic Equipment Mfr & Distr
S.I.C.: 3861
N.A.I.C.S.: 325992
John O'Hara *(Mng Dir)*

Agfa Materials Japan Ltd. (1)
8-1 Higashiyama3-chome
153-0043 Tokyo, Megoru-ku, Japan
Tel.: (81) 357043071
Fax: (81) 357043083
Web Site: www.agfa.com
Imagesetters, Computer to Plate Recorders, Workflow Systems & Laser Images Mfr
S.I.C.: 3577
N.A.I.C.S.: 334118

Agfa Materials Taiwan Co., Ltd. (1)
3F 237 Sung Chiang Road
10483 Taipei, Taiwan
Tel.: (886) 225168899
Fax: (886) 225055018
E-Mail: albert.lo@agfa.com
Emp.: 11
Imagesetters, Computer to Plate Recorders, Workflow Systems & Laser Images Mfr
S.I.C.: 3575
N.A.I.C.S.: 334118
Benjamin Cheng *(Gen Mgr)*

Agfa Materials (UK) Ltd. (1)
11th Floor Vantage West
27 Great West Road, Brentford, TW8 9AX, United Kingdom
Tel.: (44) 2082314983
Fax: (44) 208 231 4951
Web Site: www.agfa.com
Imagesetters, Computer to Plate Recorders, Workflow Systems & Laser Images Mfr
S.I.C.: 3575
N.A.I.C.S.: 334118

AGFA SINGAPORE PTE. LTD. (1)
10 Changi South Street 2 03-00 Abx Logistics Centre
Singapore, 486596, Singapore
Tel.: (65) 62140110
Fax: (65) 62140770
Web Site: www.agfa.com
Emp.: 20
Printing Equipment Sales & Maintenance Services
S.I.C.: 5046
N.A.I.C.S.: 423440
Teri Teo *(Gen Mgr)*

INSIGHT AGENTS FRANCE S.R.L. (1)
282 Avenue Marne
59700 Marcq-en-Baroeul, France
Tel.: (33) 8 00 10 60 26
Fax: (33) 320804554
Emp.: 15
Software Development Services
S.I.C.: 7371
N.A.I.C.S.: 541511
John Dudus *(Mng Dir)*

LASTRA ATTREZZATURE S.R.L. (1)
Via Lombardia 45
25025 Manerbio, Brescia, Italy
Tel.: (39) 030 993 7059
Fax: (39) 030 993 8105
Emp.: 5
Printing Equipment Distr
S.I.C.: 5084
N.A.I.C.S.: 423830

Maersk Oil Middle East A/S (1)
Suite 1220
PO Box 45200
Abu Dhabi, United Arab Emirates
Tel.: (971) 2 596 4896
Fax: (971) 2 697 9291
Web Site: www.maerskoil.com
Emp.: 3
Oil & Gas Exploration Services
S.I.C.: 1389
N.A.I.C.S.: 213112
Richard Doidge *(Mng Dir)*

NEW PROIMAGE LTD. (1)
Poleg Industrial Park 4 Hagavish St
PO Box 8764
Netanya, 42507, Israel
Tel.: (972) 732 600 300
Fax: (972) 732 600 333
E-Mail: pii@proimage.co.il
Emp.: 18
Software Development Services
S.I.C.: 7371
N.A.I.C.S.: 541511
Ilan Vinner *(Gen Mgr)*

Smart Packaging Solutions SAS (1)
Avenue Olivier Perroy
Zone Industrielle Rousset, 13790 Rousset, France
Tel.: (33) 4 42 53 84 40
Fax: (33) 4 42 53 84 48
Web Site: www.s-p-s.com
Imagesetters, Computer to Plate Recorders, Workflow Systems & Laser Images Mfr
S.I.C.: 3575
N.A.I.C.S.: 334118

AGFEED INDUSTRIES, INC.

(Filed Ch 11 Bankruptcy #13-11761 on 7/16/13 in U.S. Bankruptcy Ct, Dist of DE, Wilmington)
Rm A1001-1002 Tower 16 Hengmao Intl Center
333 South Guangchang Road,
Nanchang, Jiangxi, 330003, China
Tel.: (86) 791 666 9099
E-Mail: info@agfeedinc.com
Web Site: www.agfeedinc.com
Year Founded: 2005
ALHOG—(EUR OTC)
Sales Range: $200-249.9 Million
Emp.: 532
Business Description:
Hog Raising & Pig Feed Mfr
S.I.C.: 2048
N.A.I.C.S.: 311119
Personnel:
Gerry Daignault *(Interim CFO)*
Edward Pazdro *(Chief Acctg Officer)*
Keith A. Maib *(Chief Restructuring Officer)*
Feng Zhou *(Sec, VP & Controller)*
Board of Directors:
Bruce K. Ginn
H. David Sherman
Todd J. Zelek

Subsidiary:

AgFeed Animal Nutrition Holdings, Inc. (1)
Suite A1001-1002 Tower 16
Hengmao International Center, Nanchang, Jiangxi, 330003, China VG
Tel.: (86) 791 6669090
Emp.: 508
Animal Nutrition Products
S.I.C.: 2048
N.A.I.C.S.: 311119
Junhong Xiong *(Chm & Treas)*
Gerard Daignault *(Pres & CEO)*
Edward Pazdro *(CFO)*
Summer Xie *(Sec)*

AGGIE GREY'S HOTEL & BUNGALOWS

PO Box 67
Apia, Samoa (Western)
Tel.: (685) 22880
Fax: (685) 23626
E-Mail: aggiegreys@aggiegreys.ws
Web Site: www.aggiegreys.com
Emp.: 300
Business Description:
Hotel & Resort Owner & Operator
S.I.C.: 7011
N.A.I.C.S.: 721110
Personnel:
Rosa Stowers *(CFO)*

AGGREKO PLC

120 Bothwell Street
Glasgow, G2 7JS, United Kingdom
Tel.: (44) 1412255900
Fax: (44) 1412255949
E-Mail: investors@aggreko.com
Web Site: www.aggreko.com
Year Founded: 1997
AGK—(LSE OTC)
Rev.: $2,500,331,928
Assets: $3,353,464,386
Liabilities: $1,703,422,194
Net Worth: $1,650,042,192
Earnings: $435,884,040
Emp.: 5,316
Fiscal Year-end: 12/31/12
Business Description:
Power Generators, Temperature Control Equipment & Compressed Air Systems Mfr
S.I.C.: 3621
N.A.I.C.S.: 335312
Personnel:
Angus G. Cockburn *(Interim CEO)*
Carole Cran *(Interim CFO)*
Peter Kennerley *(Sec & Dir-Legal Affairs)*
Board of Directors:
Ken Hanna
Angus G. Cockburn
Debajit Das
David Hamill
Peter Kennerley
Russell King
Diana Layfield
Robert MacLeod
Ian D. Marchant
Rebecca A. McDonald
David Taylor-Smith
Transfer Agent:
Capita Registrars
The Registry 34 Beckenham Road
Beckenham, United Kingdom

Subsidiary:

Aggreko Holdings Ltd. (1)
121 W Regent St
Glasgow, G2 SD, United Kingdom (100%)
Tel.: (44) 412255900
Fax: (44) 412255949
Web Site: www.aggreko.co.uk/about-aggreko/aggreko-worldwide/aggreko-europe.aspx
Emp.: 30
Holding Company
S.I.C.: 6719
N.A.I.C.S.: 551112

Subsidiaries:

Aggreko UK Ltd. (2)
121 W Rigent St
Glasgow, G2 SD, United Kingdom (100%)
Tel.: (44) 412255900
Fax: (44) 412255949
Web Site: www.aggreko.co.uk/about-aggreko/aggreko-worldwide/aggreko-europe.aspx
Supplier of Temporary Power, Temperature Control & Oil Free Compressed Air
S.I.C.: 3823
N.A.I.C.S.: 334513

U.S. Subsidiary:

Aggreko Holdings Inc. (1)
4607 W Admiral Doyle
New Iberia, LA 70560-9134 (100%)
Tel.: (337) 367-7884
Fax: (337) 367-0870
Emp.: 600
Holding Company
S.I.C.: 7359
N.A.I.C.S.: 532490
Asterios Satrazemis *(Pres-Americas)*
George Walker *(Pres-North America)*

Subsidiary:

Aggreko USA LLC (2)
4607 W Admiral Doyle
New Iberia, LA 70560-9134 (100%)
Tel.: (337) 367-7884
Fax: (337) 367-0870
Web Site: www.aggreko.com
Supplier of Temporary Power, Temperature Control & Oil Free Compressed Air
S.I.C.: 7359
N.A.I.C.S.: 532490
George Walker *(Pres)*

AGILE PROPERTY HOLDINGS LIMITED

(d/b/a BeBevCo)
33/F Citibank Tower 3 Garden Road
Central, China (Hong Kong)
Tel.: (852) 2847 3383
Fax: (852) 2780 8822
E-Mail: ir@agile.com.cn
Web Site: www.agile.com.cn
3383—(HKG OTC)
Rev.: $4,777,262,525
Assets: $14,572,430,710
Liabilities: $10,138,640,168
Net Worth: $4,433,790,542
Earnings: $817,545,511
Emp.: 13,439
Fiscal Year-end: 12/31/12
Business Description:
Investment Holding Services
S.I.C.: 6211
N.A.I.C.S.: 523999
Personnel:
Zhuo Lin Chen *(Chm)*
Cheuk Yin Chan *(Vice Chm & Co-Pres)*
Fion Sin Fong Luk *(Vice Chm & Co-Pres)*
Fengchao Huang *(Pres-Hainan & Yunan & VP)*
Zhengjian Liang *(Pres-Southern China & VP)*
Jianping Mao *(Pres-Eastern China & VP)*
Ching Sum Wai *(Sec & Gen Mgr-Hong Kong)*

Agile Property Holdings Limited—(Continued)

Cheuk Hei Chan *(Sr VP)*
Cheuk Hung Chan *(Sr VP)*
Cheuk Nam Chan *(Sr VP)*

Board of Directors:
Zhuo Lin Chen
Cheuk Hei Chan
Cheuk Hung Chan
Cheuk Nam Chan
Cheuk Yin Chan
Hon Kwan Cheng
Edward Wing Yui Cheung
Gordon Che Keung Kwong
Fion Sin Fong Luk

Legal Counsel:
Jingtian & Gongcheng
15/F The Union Plaza 20 Chaoyangmen Wai Dajie
Beijing, 100020, China

Iu, Lai & Li
20th Floor, Gloucestor Tower, 11 Pedder Street
Central, China (Hong Kong)

Conyers Dill & Pearman
Cricket Square, Hutchins Drive P.O. Box 2681
KY1-1111 Georgetown, Cayman Islands

Royal Bank of Canada Trust Company (Cayman) Limited
4th Floor Royal Bank House 24 Shedden Road
Georgetown, Cayman Islands

Transfer Agents:
Tricor Investor Services Limited
26/F Tesbury Centre 28 Queen's Road East
Hong Kong, China (Hong Kong)

Royal Bank of Canada Trust Company (Cayman) Limited
4th Floor Royal Bank House 24 Shedden Road
Georgetown, Cayman Islands

AGILITY
Sulaibiya Beside Land Customs Clearing Area
PO Box 25418
Safat, Kuwait, 13115, Kuwait
Tel.: (965) 1809222
Fax: (965) 24679617
E-Mail: kuwaithq@agilitylogistics.com
Web Site: www.agilitylogistics.com
Year Founded: 1979
AGLTY—(DFM KUW)
Rev.: $5,023,924,723
Assets: $5,077,340,798
Liabilities: $1,853,021,170
Net Worth: $3,224,319,628
Earnings: $144,015,041
Emp.: 22,000
Fiscal Year-end: 12/31/12

Business Description:
Logistics & Warehousing Services
S.I.C.: 4789
N.A.I.C.S.: 488999

Personnel:
Tarek Abdulaziz Sultan Al Essa *(Chm & Mng Dir)*
Adel Mohammed Al-Bader *(Vice Chm)*
John Klompers *(Chief Comml Officer)*
Essa Anwar Al-Saleh *(Pres/CEO-Global Integrated Logistics)*
Grant Wattman *(Pres/CEO-Project Logistics)*
Francesc Casamitjana *(CEO-Americas)*
Elias Monem *(CEO-Middle East & Africa)*
Chris Price *(CEO-Asia Pacific)*
Jean DeSombre *(Gen Counsel)*
Sylvain Kluba *(VP-Strategic Programs)*
Mokhtar Bazaraa *(Sr VP-Supply Chain Solutions)*
Julia Saia *(Sr VP-People & Process Mgmt)*
Steve Sienkiewicz *(Sr VP-Global Sls & Mktg)*

Board of Directors:
Tarek Abdulaziz Sultan Al Essa
Esam Khaleel Mohammad Al Refaei
Henadi Anwar Essa Al Saleh
Adel Mohammed Al-Bader
Ayman Bader Sultan Al-Essa
Jameel Sultan Al-Essa
Naser Mohammed Fahed Al-Rashed

Albazie & Co.
Kuwait Airways Building 7th Floor
Shuhada Street
PO Box 2115 Safat, 13022 Kuwait, Kuwait
Tel.: (965) 241 0010
Fax: (965) 241 2761

Subsidiaries:

Metal & Recycling Company K.S.C.C. **(1)**
PO Box 4520 Safat
Kuwait, 13045, Kuwait
Tel.: (965) 2457 7772
Fax: (965) 2467 2168
E-Mail: mrc@mrc.com.kw
Web Site: www.mrckw.com
MRC—(KUW)
Sales Range: $50-74.9 Million
Emp.: 600
Scrap Metal Buying, Selling & Recycling Services
S.I.C.: 5051
N.A.I.C.S.: 423510
Tarek Ibrahim Al-Mousa *(Chm & Mng Dir)*
Henadi Anwar Issa Al-Saleh *(Vice Chm)*
Eman El-Ansari *(CFO)*
Nawaf H. Al-Mutawa *(Pres-Energy Sector)*
Mohammad T. Al-Nouri *(Pres-Indus Sector)*
Sager Al-Sharhan *(Pres-Waste Mgmt & Recycling Sector)*

PWC Transport Company W.L.L. **(1)**
Sulaibiya Beside Land Customs Clearing Area
PO Box 25418
Safat, 13115 Kuwait, Kuwait
Tel.: (965) 1809222
Fax: (965) 24678072
E-Mail: info@agilitylogistics.com
Emp.: 25
Freight Transportation Services
S.I.C.: 4731
N.A.I.C.S.: 488510
Ronny Abraham *(Sr Mgr-Sls-Freight Svcs)*

U.S. Subsidiaries:

Agility Holdings Inc. **(1)**
240 Commerce
Irvine, CA 92602
Tel.: (714) 617-6300
Fax: (714) 244-6943
E-Mail: info@agilitylogistics.com
Air & Sea Freight Transportation Services
S.I.C.: 4512
N.A.I.C.S.: 481112

Agility Logistics Corp. **(1)**
240 Commerce
Irvine, CA 92602
Tel.: (714) 617-6300
Fax: (714) 242-6943
E-Mail: salesusa@agilitylogistics.com
Web Site: www.agilitylogistics.com
Logistics & Distribution Services
S.I.C.: 4731
N.A.I.C.S.: 541614

Agility Project Logistics Inc. **(1)**
15600 Morales Rd
Houston, TX 77032-2118
Tel.: (713) 452-3500
Fax: (713) 452-3501
E-Mail: projects@agilitylogistics.com
Emp.: 300
Logistics & Distribution Services
S.I.C.: 4731
N.A.I.C.S.: 541614
Grant Wattman *(Pres & CEO)*

Agility Transoceanic Logistics Inc. **(1)**
3850 N Causeway Blvd Ste 1330
Metairie, LA 70002
Tel.: (504) 465-1000
Fax: (504) 465-1023
Web Site: www.agility.com
Sls.: $25,600,000
Emp.: 75
Freight Forwarding Services
S.I.C.: 4731
N.A.I.C.S.: 488510
Peggy Beebe *(Sr VP)*

GeoLogistics Corporation **(1)**
1251 E Dyer Rd
Santa Ana, CA 92705-5639 DE
Tel.: (714) 513-3000
Fax: (714) 513-3120
E-Mail: salesusa@geo-logistics.com
Web Site: www.geo-logistics.com
Sales Range: $1-4.9 Billion
Emp.: 759
Transportation & Business Management Services
S.I.C.: 4731
N.A.I.C.S.: 488510

Non-U.S. Subsidiaries:

Agility Company L.L.C. **(1)**
Eastern Ring Road Southern Istanbul Street Exit 18
PO Box 55073
Sulay, Riyadh, 11534, Saudi Arabia
Tel.: (966) 12911143
Fax: (966) 18742899
E-Mail: ksa@agilitylogistics.com
Web Site: www.directory.agilityportal.com
Emp.: 400
Logistics & Freight Forwarding Services
S.I.C.: 4731
N.A.I.C.S.: 488510
Wael Kabbani *(CEO)*

Agility International Logistics Pte. Ltd. **(1)**
1 Changi North Way
Singapore, 498802, Singapore
Tel.: (65) 62209055
Fax: (65) 62244939
E-Mail: singapore@agilitylogistics.com
Web Site: www.agilitylogistics.com
Emp.: 400
Logistics & Distribution Services
S.I.C.: 4731
N.A.I.C.S.: 541614
Mykell Lee *(CEO)*

Agility Logistics GmbH **(1)**
Heidenkampsweg 82
20097 Hamburg, Germany
Tel.: (49) 40237130
Fax: (49) 4023713109
E-Mail: germany@agilitylogistics.com
Logistics & Distribution Services
S.I.C.: 7389
N.A.I.C.S.: 561990

Agility Logistics Holdings Pte. Ltd. **(1)**
Trans-link Logistics Centre 7 Toh Tuck Link
Singapore, Singapore
Tel.: (65) 64639868
Fax: (65) 64674800
Logistics & Distribution Services
S.I.C.: 4731
N.A.I.C.S.: 541614

Agility Logistics International B.V. **(1)**
Anthony Fokker Business Park Fokkerweg 300 Building 2A
1438 AN Oude Meer, North Holland, Netherlands
Tel.: (31) 884360000
Fax: (31) 884360109
E-Mail: netherlands@agilitylogistics.com
Web Site: www.agilitylogistics.com
Emp.: 60
Logistics & Distribution Services
S.I.C.: 4731
N.A.I.C.S.: 541614
Thomas Blank *(Mng Dir-Central Europe)*

Agility Logistics LLC **(1)**
11 M Raskovoy Street Ofc 611
02002 Kiev, Ukraine
Tel.: (380) 443907020
Fax: (380) 443907021
Web Site: www.directory.agilityportal.com
Emp.: 7
Logistics & Freight Forwarding Services
S.I.C.: 4731
N.A.I.C.S.: 488510

Agility Logistics Limited **(1)**
Unit 6 North Radius Park Faggs Road
Feltham, Middlesex, TW14 0NG, United Kingdom
Tel.: (44) 2089173000
Fax: (44) 2089173001
E-Mail: uk@agilitylogistics.com
Web Site: www.agilitylogistics.com
Emp.: 100
Logistics Management Services
S.I.C.: 4731
N.A.I.C.S.: 541614
Chris Price *(CEO)*

Agility Logistics Limited **(1)**
19/F Broadway Centre 93 Kwai Fuk Road
Kwai Chung, New Territories, China (Hong Kong)
Tel.: (852) 22118888
Fax: (852) 27642455
Logistics & Distribution Services
S.I.C.: 4731
N.A.I.C.S.: 541614

Tristar Transport LLC **(1)**
Plot B158 Al Aweer Ras Al Khor
PO Box 51328
Dubai, United Arab Emirates
Tel.: (971) 43331310
Fax: (971) 4 3331638
E-Mail: startran@emirates.net.ae
Web Site: www.tristar-transport.com
Emp.: 400
Bulk Liquid Transportation Services
S.I.C.: 4213
N.A.I.C.S.: 484230
Eugene Mayne *(CEO)*

AGILITY INC.
(d/b/a AgilityCMS)
3rd Floor 490 Adelaide Street West
Toronto, ON, M5V 1T2, Canada
Tel.: (416) 591-2500
Fax: (416) 352-5270
Toll Free: (888) 299-2998
Web Site: www.agilitycms.com
Year Founded: 2002
Sales Range: $1-9.9 Million

Business Description:
Cloud Content Management System
S.I.C.: 7372
N.A.I.C.S.: 511210

Personnel:
Michael Assad *(Co-Founder & CEO)*
Jonathan Voight *(Co-Founder & CTO)*

AGINCOURT AUTOHAUS INC.
3450 Sheppard Avenue East
Toronto, ON, M1T 3K4, Canada
Tel.: (416) 291-6456
E-Mail: sales@agnidirect.ca
Web Site: www.agincourtvw.ca
Rev.: $29,039,613
Emp.: 60

Business Description:
New & Used Car Dealers
S.I.C.: 5511
N.A.I.C.S.: 441110

Personnel:
Ken Laird *(Pres & Gen Mgr)*

AGIO PAPER & INDUSTRIES LIMITED
505 Diamond Prestige 41 A AJC Bose Road
Kolkata, West Bengal, 700 017, India
Tel.: (91) 33 4022 5900
Fax: (91) 33 4022 5999
E-Mail: ho@agiopaper.com
Web Site: www.agiopaper.com
Year Founded: 1984
516020—(BOM)
Rev.: $92,692
Assets: $8,384,361
Liabilities: $8,391,892
Net Worth: ($7,531)
Earnings: ($1,505,842)
Fiscal Year-end: 03/31/13

Business Description:
Paper Mfr
S.I.C.: 2621
N.A.I.C.S.: 322121

Personnel:
Saikat Ghosh *(Sec)*

Board of Directors:

Ankit Jalan
Sheo Shankar Joshi
Kamal Kumar Khetawat
Davinder Kumar
Transfer Agent:
Maheshwari Datamatics Private Limited
6 Mangoe Lane
Kolkata, India

AGIS-AGROINDUSTRIJA

Branimira Cosica 2/III
Novi Sad, Serbia
Tel.: (381) 21 442 377
Fax: (381) 21 442 059
E-Mail: office@agis.co.yu
Web Site: ww.agis.co.rs
Year Founded: 1989
AGIN—(BEL)
Business Description:
Frozen Vegetable Mfr
S.I.C.: 2037
N.A.I.C.S.: 311411
Personnel:
Paja Apic *(Chm)*
Board of Directors:
Paja Apic
Tihomir Dunderski
Vesna Jelinek
Miroslav Kovac

AGL ENERGY LIMITED

Level 22 101 Miller Street
Sydney, NSW, 2060, Australia
Mailing Address:
Locked Bag 1837
Saint Leonards, NSW, 2065, Australia
Tel.: (61) 2 9921 2999
Fax: (61) 2 9921 2465
E-Mail: ir@agl.com.au
Web Site: www.agl.com.au
Year Founded: 1837
AGK—(ASX)
Rev.: $10,124,730,970
Assets: $13,928,500,180
Liabilities: $6,280,528,280
Net Worth: $7,647,971,900
Earnings: $405,064,270
Emp.: 2,750
Fiscal Year-end: 06/30/13
Business Description:
Solar Heating Services
S.I.C.: 4931
N.A.I.C.S.: 221118
Personnel:
Michael Fraser *(CEO & Mng Dir)*
Brett Redman *(CFO)*
Owen Coppage *(CIO)*
Paul McWilliams *(Sec & Head-Corp Support Svcs)*
Board of Directors:
Jeremy Maycock
Michael Fraser
Leslie V. Hosking
Graeme Peter Hunt
Belinda J. Hutchinson
Sandra McPhee
Bruce Phillips
John Stanhope
Subsidiaries:

AGL ACT Retail Investments Pty Limited **(1)**
L 22 101 Miller St
North Sydney, 2060, Australia
Tel.: (61) 299212999
Electric Power Generation Services
S.I.C.: 4931
N.A.I.C.S.: 221118

AGL Corporate Services Pty Limited **(1)**
Level 22 101 Miller St
North Sydney, NSW, 2060, Australia
Tel.: (61) 299212999
Electric Power Generation Services
S.I.C.: 4931
N.A.I.C.S.: 221118

AGL Electricity (VIC) Pty Limited **(1)**
L 22 101 Miller St
Sydney, NSW, 2060, Australia
Tel.: (61) 299212999
Fax: (61) 299212552
Electric Power Distr
S.I.C.: 4939
N.A.I.C.S.: 221122

AGL Energy Services Pty Limited **(1)**
L 22 101 Miller St
Sydney, NSW, 2060, Australia
Tel.: (61) 299212999
Fax: (61) 299212552
Energy Consulting Services
S.I.C.: 8999
N.A.I.C.S.: 541690

AGL Hydro Partnership **(1)**
L 22 600 Bourke St
Melbourne, 3000, Australia
Tel.: (61) 357543222
Fax: (61) 392017602
Electric Power Distribution Services
S.I.C.: 4911
N.A.I.C.S.: 221122

AGL Pipelines Investments (QLD) Pty Limited **(1)**
L 22 101 Miller St
North Sydney, 2060, Australia
Tel.: (61) 299212999
Fax: (61) 299212552
E-Mail: northsydneyreception@agl.com.au
Electric Power Distribution Services
S.I.C.: 4911
N.A.I.C.S.: 221122
Michael Fraser *(Mng Dir)*

AGL Power Generation Pty Limited **(1)**
L 22 101 Miller St
North Sydney, 2060, Australia
Tel.: (61) 299212999
Fax: (61) 299212998
Web Site: www.agl.com
Electric Power Generation Services
S.I.C.: 4911
N.A.I.C.S.: 221118

AGL SA Generation Pty Limited **(1)**
Level 22 101 Miller Street
North Sydney, 2060, Australia
Tel.: (61) 299212999
Fax: (61) 299212552
Electric Power Generation Services
S.I.C.: 4911
N.A.I.C.S.: 221118

AGL Sales Pty Limited **(1)**
L 22 120 Spencer St
Melbourne, 3000, Australia
Tel.: (61) 386336000
Fax: (61) 386336002
Renewable Energy Project Development Services
S.I.C.: 1629
N.A.I.C.S.: 237990
Michael Fraser *(Gen Mgr)*

AGL Sales (Queensland Electricity) Pty Limited **(1)**
Complex 1/303 Burwood Highway
Burwood East, Melbourne, VIC, 3151, Australia
Tel.: (61) 388056633
Fax: (61) 388056699
E-Mail: info@powerdirect.com.au
Web Site: www.powerdirect.com.au
Electric Power Distributors
S.I.C.: 4931
N.A.I.C.S.: 221122

AGL Southern Hydro (NSW) Pty Limited **(1)**
L 22 120 Spencer St
Melbourne, 3000, Australia
Tel.: (61) 386336000
Fax: (61) 386336888
Electric Power Generation Services
S.I.C.: 4911
N.A.I.C.S.: 221118

AGL Southern Hydro Pty Limited **(1)**
L 22 101 Miller St
Sydney, 2060, Australia
Tel.: (61) 299212999
Fax: (61) 396291878
Electric Power Generation Services
S.I.C.: 4939
N.A.I.C.S.: 221118

AGL Torrens Island Holdings Pty Limited **(1)**
L 22 101 Miller St
North Sydney, NSW, 2060, Australia
Tel.: (61) 299212999
Web Site: www.agl.com.au
Emp.: 2,000
Electric Power Generation Services
S.I.C.: 4911
N.A.I.C.S.: 221118
Michael Anthony Fraser *(Mng Dir & CEO)*

AGL Torrens Island Pty Limited **(1)**
L 22 101 Miller St
North Sydney, NSW, 2060, Australia
Tel.: (61) 299212999
Fax: (61) 299212552
Web Site: www.agl.com
Electric Power Generation Services
S.I.C.: 4939
N.A.I.C.S.: 221118
Michael Fraser *(CEO & Mng Dir)*

Antiga Pty Ltd **(1)**
16 Georgina Crescent
Darwin, NT, 0830, Australia (100%)
Tel.: (61) 889248100
Fax: (61) 889321663
E-Mail: contactus@antiga.com.au
Web Site: www.apa.com.au
Emp.: 25
Natural Gas Distribution Pipeline System
S.I.C.: 4924
N.A.I.C.S.: 221210
Windy Olden *(Gen Mgr)*

Australian Energy Ltd **(1)**
L 22 120 Spencer St
Melbourne, 3000, Australia
Tel.: (61) 388056600
Fax: (61) 388056699
Electric Power Generation Services
S.I.C.: 4911
N.A.I.C.S.: 221118

The Australian Gas Light Company **(1)**
189 Gladstone St
Fyshwick, ACT, 2609, Australia (100%)
Tel.: (61) 262955444
Fax: (61) 262392388
Web Site: www.agl.com.au
Emp.: 50
Natural Gas Distribution Pipeline System
S.I.C.: 4924
N.A.I.C.S.: 221210

The Australian Gas Light Company **(1)**
Level 3 333 Collins St
Melbourne, VIC, 3000, Australia (100%)
Tel.: (61) 392017000
Fax: (61) 386336002
Web Site: www.agl.com.au
Emp.: 1,000
Electricity Distribution Network
S.I.C.: 4939
N.A.I.C.S.: 221122
Greg Martin *(Mng Dir)*
Michael Fraser *(Mng Dir)*

The Australian Gas Light Company **(1)**
Level 22
101 Miller St, Mount Gravatt, QLD, 2060, Australia (100%)
Tel.: (61) 299212999
Web Site: www.agl.com.au
Emp.: 80
Natural Gas Distribution Pipeline System
S.I.C.: 4924
N.A.I.C.S.: 221210

The Australian Gas Light Company **(1)**
72 Christie St
Saint Leonards, NSW, 2065, Australia (100%)
Tel.: (61) 99212999
Fax: (61) 99212018
Web Site: www.agl.com.au
Emp.: 300
Natural Gas Distr
S.I.C.: 4924
N.A.I.C.S.: 221210

Australian Power & Gas Company Limited **(1)**
Level 9 341 George Street
Sydney, NSW, 2000, Australia AU
Mailing Address:
Locked Bag 5004
Royal Exchange, Sydney, NSW, 1225, Australia
Tel.: (61) 289082700
Fax: (61) 289082701
E-Mail: enquiries@australianpowerandgas.com.au
Web Site: www.australianpowerandgas.com.au
Rev.: $504,646,304
Assets: $234,950,824
Liabilities: $193,183,456
Net Worth: $41,767,368
Earnings: ($8,902,660)
Emp.: 140
Fiscal Year-end: 06/30/13
Energy Supplier
S.I.C.: 4911
N.A.I.C.S.: 221122
Warren Kember *(Interim CEO)*
Phillip Ridley *(CIO & Gen Mgr)*
Joanne Tseng *(Co-Sec & Gen Mgr-Legal, Regulatory & Risk)*
David Franks *(Co-Sec)*

Subsidiary:

Australian Power & Gas Pty. Limited **(2)**
L 9 Ste 41 George St
Sydney, NSW, 2000, Australia AU
Tel.: (61) 289082700
Fax: (61) 289082701
Electricity & Gas Sales
S.I.C.: 4924
N.A.I.C.S.: 221210
David Goaday *(Gen Mgr)*

Subsidiary:

APG Operations Pty Limited **(3)**
L2 6a Glen St
Milsons Point, NSW, 2061, Australia
Tel.: (61) 289082724
Fax: (61) 2 89082701
Electricity & Gas Distribution Services
S.I.C.: 4924
N.A.I.C.S.: 221210

AGL Loy Yang Pty Ltd **(1)**
Bartons Lane
Traralgon, VIC, 3844, Australia
Tel.: (61) 3 5173 2000
Fax: (61) 351733533
E-Mail: loyyang@agl.com.au
Web Site: www.loyyangpower.com.au
Sales Range: $25-49.9 Million
Emp.: 500
Power Distr
S.I.C.: 4911
N.A.I.C.S.: 221122
Mark Ryan *(Gen Mgr-HR & Sec)*

Powerdirect **(1)**
Complex 1 303 Burwood Highway
Burwood East, Glen Waverley, VIC, 3151, Australia
Mailing Address:
PO Box 1028
Glen Waverley, VIC, 3150, Australia
Tel.: (61) 1300307966
Fax: (61) 388056699
E-Mail: info@powerdirect.com.au
Web Site: www.powerdirect.com.au
Emp.: 80
Electric Power Distr
S.I.C.: 4931
N.A.I.C.S.: 221122
Mark Enzinger *(CFO)*

AGLAND CORP.

Highway 16W Range Road 14
Lloydminster, AB, T9V2B7, Canada
Tel.: (780) 875-4471
Fax: (780) 875-6606
E-Mail: solutions@aglandcorp.com
Web Site: www.aglandcorp.com
Year Founded: 1958
Rev.: $36,258,586
Emp.: 78

Agland Corp.—(Continued)

Business Description:
Agricultural Equipment Services
S.I.C.: 5083
N.A.I.C.S.: 423820
Personnel:
Kenneth Garne Kay *(Pres)*

AGLUKON SPEZIALDUNGER GMBH & CO. KG

Heerdter Landstrasse 199
PO Box 19
40549 Dusseldorf, Germany
Tel.: (49) 2115064237
Fax: (49) 2115064249
E-Mail: info@aglukon.com
Web Site: www.aglukon.com
Year Founded: 1928
Sales Range: $10-24.9 Million
Emp.: 75
Business Description:
Fertilizer Mfr
S.I.C.: 2873
N.A.I.C.S.: 325311
Personnel:
Hans Ulrich Born *(Mng Dir)*

AGN AGROINDUSTRIAL, PROJETOS E PARTICIPACOES LTDA.

Avenida Juscelino Kubistchek 1830
Tower 1 12 andar
04543-900 Sao Paulo, SP, Brazil
Tel.: (55) 11 3897 7349
Business Description:
Investment Holding Company
S.I.C.: 6719
N.A.I.C.S.: 551112
Personnel:
Roger Agnelli *(Founder & CEO)*

Joint Venture:

B&A Mineracao S.A. (1)
Avenida do Contorno 5919 5 andar
Savassi, 30110-035 Belo Horizonte, Brazil BR
Tel.: (55) 31 2552 1588
Web Site: www.bamineracao.com
Holding Company; Fertilizer Minerals, Iron Ore & Copper Mining
S.I.C.: 6719
N.A.I.C.S.: 551112
Roger Agnelli *(Chm)*
Eduardo Ledsham *(CEO)*

Subsidiary:

B&A Fertilizers Limited (2)
Avenida do Contorno 5919 5 andar
Savassi, 30110-035 Belo Horizonte, Brazil VG
Tel.: (55) 31 2552 1588
Fertilizer Mineral Mining
S.I.C.: 1479
N.A.I.C.S.: 212393
Roger Agnelli *(Chm)*
Eduardo Ledsham *(CEO)*

AGNI SYSTEMS LIMITED

Navana Tower 11th Floor Suite A 45
Gulshan Avenue Gulshan 1
Dhaka, 1212, Bangladesh
Tel.: (880) 2 8812379
Fax: (880) 2 8811902
E-Mail: info@agni.com
Web Site: www.agni.com
AGNISYSL—(DHA)
Business Description:
Internet Services Provider
S.I.C.: 4899
N.A.I.C.S.: 517919
Personnel:
Muhammed Shariful Islam *(Sec)*

AGNICO-EAGLE MINES LIMITED

145 King Street East Suite 400
Toronto, ON, M5C 2Y7, Canada
Tel.: (416) 947-1212
Fax: (416) 367-4681
Toll Free: (888) 822-6714
E-Mail: info@agnico-eagle.com
Web Site: www.agnico-eagle.com
Year Founded: 1972
AEM—(NYSE TSX)
Rev.: $1,917,714,000
Assets: $5,255,842,000
Liabilities: $1,845,630,000
Net Worth: $3,410,212,000
Earnings: $310,916,000
Emp.: 4,045
Fiscal Year-end: 12/31/12
Business Description:
Gold Exploration & Mining Services
S.I.C.: 1041
N.A.I.C.S.: 212221
Personnel:
James D. Nasso *(Chm)*
Sean Boyd *(Vice Chm, Pres & CEO)*
David L. Smith *(CFO & Sr VP-Fin)*
R. Gregory Laing *(Gen Counsel, Sec & Sr VP-Legal)*
Donald G. Allan *(Sr VP-Corp Dev)*
Alain Blackburn *(Sr VP-Exploration)*
Picklu Datta *(Sr VP-Treasury & Fin)*
Louise Grondin *(Sr VP-Environment & Sustainable Dev)*
Timothy Haldane *(Sr VP-Latin America)*
Marc Legault *(Sr VP-Project Evaluations)*
Jeanluk Pellerin *(Sr VP-HR)*
Jean Robitaille *(Sr VP-Tech Svcs & Project Dev)*
Yvon Sylvestre *(Sr VP-Ops)*
Board of Directors:
James D. Nasso
Leanne M. Baker
Douglas R. Beaumont
Sean Boyd
Martine A. Celej
Clifford J. Davis
Robert J. Gemmell
Bernard L. Kraft
Mel Leiderman
Sean Riley
J. Merfyn Roberts
Howard Roger Stockford
Pertti Voutilainen
Legal Counsel:
Troutman Sanders Mays & Valentine
1660 International Dr., Ste. 600
McLean, VA 22102
Davies, Ward & Beck
1 First Canadian Place, 44th Floor
P.O. Box 63
Toronto, ON, M5X 1B1, Canada
Tel.: (416) 863-0900
Transfer Agent:
Computershare Trust Company of Canada
8th Fl 100 University Ave
Toronto, ON, Canada

Divisions:

Agnico-Eagle Mines Limited-Exploration Division (1)
1953 3 rd Ave W
87
Val d'Or, QC, G9P 4M9, Canada (100%)
Tel.: (819) 874-5980
Fax: (819) 874-0060
E-Mail: mathieu.gremier@agnico-eagle.com
Web Site: www.agnico-eagle.com
Emp.: 200
Gold Exploration
S.I.C.: 1041
N.A.I.C.S.: 212221
Evon Sylzestre *(Mgr)*

Agnico-Eagle Mines Limited-LaRonde Division (1)
10 200, Route De Preissac
Rouyn-Noranda, QC, J0Y 1C0, Canada (100%)
Tel.: (819) 759-3644
Fax: (819) 759-3641
E-Mail: info@agnico-eagle.com
Web Site: www.agnicoeagle.com
Emp.: 900
Gold Mining
S.I.C.: 1041
N.A.I.C.S.: 212221
Paul Henri Girard *(Project Mgr)*

Agnico-Eagle Mines Limited-Meadowbank (1)
Two Bentall Centre 555 Burrard St Ste 375
Vancouver, BC, V7X 1M8, Canada BC
Tel.: (604) 608-2557
Fax: (604) 608-2559
E-Mail: info@agnico-eagle.com
Web Site: www.agnico-eagle.com
Sales Range: $25-49.9 Million
Emp.: 25
Mineral Exploration Services
S.I.C.: 3299
N.A.I.C.S.: 327999
Kerry M. Curtis *(Pres & CEO)*

U.S. Subsidiary:

Agnico-Eagle (USA) Limited (1)
5470 Louie Ln Ste 102
Reno, NV 89511 (100%)
Tel.: (775) 828-6070
Fax: (775) 828-6089
E-Mail: info@agnico-eagle.com
Web Site: www.agnico-eagle.com
Emp.: 4
Gold Mining
S.I.C.: 1041
N.A.I.C.S.: 212221

Non-U.S. Subsidiaries:

Agnico Eagle Mexico S.A. de C.V. (1)
Hacienda del Carrizal 3400-8
Fraccionamiento las Haciendas, Chihuahua, Chihuahua, CP 31238, Mexico
Tel.: (52) 6144301483
Fax: (52) 614 430 1479
Web Site: www.agnico-eagle.com
Gold Mining
S.I.C.: 1041
N.A.I.C.S.: 212221
Luis Felipe Medina *(Mng Dir)*

Agnico-Eagle Mines Mexico Cooperatie U.A. (1)
Amsteldijk 166 Suite 1 17
Amsterdam, 1079 LH, Netherlands
Tel.: (31) 206441805
Mineral Mining Services
S.I.C.: 1481
N.A.I.C.S.: 213115

Non-U.S. Subsidiary:

Tenedora Agnico Eagle Mexico S.A. de C.V. (2)
Mirador 7724 Colinas Delvalle
31217 Chihuahua, Mexico
Tel.: (52) 6354576000
Emp.: 1,200
Mineral Mining Services
S.I.C.: 1481
N.A.I.C.S.: 213115
Marco Perea *(Gen Mgr)*

Agnico-Eagle Mines Sweden Cooperatie U.A. (1)
Amsteldijk 166 Suite 1 17
Amsterdam, 1079 LH, Netherlands
Tel.: (31) 206441805
Fax: (31) 206448837
Mineral Mining Services
S.I.C.: 1481
N.A.I.C.S.: 213115

Non-U.S. Subsidiary:

Agnico-Eagle Finland Oy (2)
Pokantie 541
99250 Kittila, Finland
Tel.: (358) 16 338 0700
Fax: (358) 16 3380 7701
Gold Mining Services
S.I.C.: 1041
N.A.I.C.S.: 212221

Riddarhyttan Resources AB (1)
Aurorum 30
977 75 Lulea, Sweden (75%)
Tel.: (46) 92075897
Fax: (46) 92075892
E-Mail: info@riddarhyttan.se
Web Site: www.riddarhyttan.se
Sales Range: Less than $1 Million
Emp.: 973
Metal Exploration Services
S.I.C.: 1041
N.A.I.C.S.: 212221

AGNITE EDUCATION LIMITED

Teledata Tower 1st Fl No 37/1
Velachery Tambaram Main Rd
Velachery, Chennai, 600 042, India
Tel.: (91) 4442207000
Fax: (91) 4422432727
E-Mail: corpcomm@teledatain.com
Web Site: www.teledatain.com
532358—(BOM NSE)
Emp.: 300
Business Description:
Software Products & Services
S.I.C.: 3652
N.A.I.C.S.: 334614
Personnel:
K. Balasubramanian *(Chm)*
K. Padmanabhan *(Mng Dir)*
N. Ramanathan *(Sec)*
Board of Directors:
K. Balasubramanian
K. Padmanabhan
R. Ravichandran
N. Sakthivel
M. Seetharaman

U.S. Subsidiaries:

AlphaSoft Services Corporation (1)
2121 N California Blvd Ste 345
Walnut Creek, CA 94596
Tel.: (925) 952-6300
Fax: (925) 932-3743
E-Mail: enterprise@alphasoftservices.com
Web Site: www.alphasoftservices.com
Emp.: 120
Outsourced Software Development & Systems Integration Services
S.I.C.: 7371
N.A.I.C.S.: 541511

Teledata Informatics Ltd. (1)
235 Main St Ste 520
White Plains, NY 10601-2421
Tel.: (914) 686-2100
Fax: (914) 686-7900
E-Mail: info@teledata-usa.com
Web Site: www.teledata-usa.com
Software Products & Services
S.I.C.: 3652
N.A.I.C.S.: 334614
Anush Ramachandran *(Owner)*

Subsidiary:

Transworld Information Systems (2)
485A Route 1 S Ste 200
Iselin, NJ 08830-2719 NJ
Tel.: (732) 634-0550
Fax: (732) 634-5520
Web Site: www.transwld.com
Emp.: 95
Computer Related Consulting Services
S.I.C.: 5012
N.A.I.C.S.: 423110
Venk Gopal *(CTO)*

Non-U.S. Subsidiary:

eSys Technologies Pte. Ltd. (1)
1 Changi North Street 1
Singapore, 498789, Singapore (51%)
Tel.: (65) 64910250
Fax: (65) 64910260
E-Mail:
Sales Range: $1-4.9 Billion
Emp.: 500
IT Products Distr
S.I.C.: 5045
N.A.I.C.S.: 423430
Vikas Goel *(Chm & Mng Dir)*

AGORA HOSPITALITY GROUP CO., LTD.

7F Toranomon Dai2 Waiko Bldg 5-2-6 Toranomon
Minato-ku, Tokyo, 105-0001, Japan

Tel.: (81) 3 3436 1860
Fax: (81) 3 3436 1861
E-Mail: info@agorahospitalities.com
Web Site: www.agorahospitalities.com
Year Founded: 2007
9704—(TKS)
Emp.: 8
Business Description:
Hotel Management Services
S.I.C.: 7011
N.A.I.C.S.: 721110
Personnel:
Chris Cheong Thard Hoong *(Pres)*
Aya Aso *(CEO)*
Board of Directors:
Aya Aso
Chris Cheong Thard Hoong

AGORA S.A.

Czerska 8/10
Warsaw, 00-732, Poland
Tel.: (48) 225556000
Fax: (48) 225554850
E-Mail: press@agora.pl
Web Site: www.agora.pl
AGO—(WAR)
Sls.: $361,080,412
Assets: $540,014,989
Liabilities: $157,540,353
Net Worth: $382,474,637
Earnings: ($2,570,339)
Emp.: 3,085
Fiscal Year-end: 12/31/12
Business Description:
Newspaper & Magazine Publisher; Radio Broadcasting Station Owner & Operator
S.I.C.: 2711
N.A.I.C.S.: 511110
Personnel:
Andrzej Szlezak *(Chm-Supervisory Bd)*
Wanda Rapaczynski *(Chm-Mgmt Bd)*
Bartosz Hojka *(Member-Mgmt Bd)*
Tomasz Jagiello *(Member-Mgmt Bd)*
Grzegorz Kossakowski *(Member-Mgmt Bd)*
Robert Musial *(Member-Mgmt Bd)*
Supervisory Board of Directors:
Andrzej Szlezak
Dariusz Formela
Helena Luczywo
Tomasz Sielicki
Slawomir S. Sikora

Subsidiaries:

AdTaily Sp. z o.o (1)
ul Starowislna 55/7
31-038 Krakow, Poland
Tel.: (48) 668347783
E-Mail: kontakt@adtaily.com
Web Site: www.adtaily.pl
Emp.: 12
Online Advertising Services
S.I.C.: 8742
N.A.I.C.S.: 541613
Jakub Krzych *(Gen Mgr)*

Agora Poligrafia Sp. z o.o (1)
Towarowa 4
43-100 Tychy, Poland
Tel.: (48) 32 325 22 01
Fax: (48) 32 325 22 02
E-Mail: drukarnia@katowice.agora.pl
Web Site: www.agora.pl/agora_eng/1,67058,2821459.html
Emp.: 130
Newspaper Printing Services
S.I.C.: 2621
N.A.I.C.S.: 322122
Wojciech Swierczynski *(Head-Printing Plant)*

Agora TC Sp. z o. o. (1)
Czerska 8/10
Warsaw, 00-732, Poland (100%)
Tel.: (48) 60005556001
Fax: (48) 5554780
E-Mail: sprzedaz-korporacyjna@agora.pl
Web Site: www.agora.pl/
Machinery Mfr
S.I.C.: 3589
N.A.I.C.S.: 333318

Art Marketing Syndicate SA (1)
Jana Pawla Ii 14
61139 Poznan, Poland (100%)
Tel.: (48) 225556400
Emp.: 300
Advertising Agencies
S.I.C.: 7311
N.A.I.C.S.: 541810
Piotr Parnowski *(Chm)*

Subsidiaries:

Akcent Media Sp. z o. o. (2)
Ul Jana Pawla II 14
61-139 Poznan, Poland (100%)
Tel.: (48) 618751024
Fax: (48) 618791211
Advertising Agencies
S.I.C.: 7311
N.A.I.C.S.: 541810

Polskie Badania Outdooru Sp. z o. o. (2)
Czerska 8/ 10
00-728 Warsaw, Poland
Tel.: (48) 225556031
Fax: (48) 225559031
E-Mail: pbo@pbo.org.pl
Web Site: www.pbo.org.pl
Emp.: 2
Radio & Television Broadcasting & Wireless Communications Equipment Mfr
S.I.C.: 3663
N.A.I.C.S.: 334220
Waldemar Kruk *(Mng Dir)*

GRA Sp. z o. o. (1)
Jakuba 13
87100 Torun, Poland (100%)
Tel.: (48) 523253820
Fax: (48) 523253828
E-Mail: info@gra.pl
Web Site: www.gra.fm
Emp.: 80
Advertising Agencies
S.I.C.: 7311
N.A.I.C.S.: 541810

Subsidiary:

IM 40 Sp. z o.o (2)
ul Czerska 14
Warsaw, 00-732, Poland
Tel.: (48) 22 555 51 00
Fax: (48) 22 555 51 02
E-Mail: program@radiopogoda.pl
Radio & Television Broadcasting Services
S.I.C.: 3291
N.A.I.C.S.: 327910

Helios S.A (1)
Kosciuszki 17
Lodz, 90-418, Poland
Tel.: (48) 326030101
Fax: (48) 426321339
E-Mail: lodz@heliosnet.pl
Web Site: www.heliosnet.pl
Multi Cinema Complex Management Services
S.I.C.: 7832
N.A.I.C.S.: 512131

Subsidiary:

Kinoplex Sp. z o.o (2)
Kosciuszki 17
Lodz, 90-418, Poland
Tel.: (48) 426303601
Fax: (48) 426321339
Web Site: www.kinoplex.gazeta.pl
Emp.: 14
Video Production Services
S.I.C.: 7812
N.A.I.C.S.: 512110
Thomas Jagiello *(Gen Mgr)*

Inforadio Sp. z o. o. (1)
Ul Czerska 14
Warsaw, Poland (66.1%)
Tel.: (48) 225555100
Radio Stations
S.I.C.: 4832
N.A.I.C.S.: 515112
Bartosz Hojka *(Gen Mgr)*

Polskie Badania Internetu Sp. z o. o. (1)
Al Jerozolimskie 65-79
00-697 Warsaw, Poland
Tel.: (48) 226307268
Fax: (48) 226307267
E-Mail: biuro@pbi.org.pl
Web Site: www.pbi.org.pl
Emp.: 5
Radio & Television Broadcasting & Wireless Communications Equipment Mfr
S.I.C.: 3663
N.A.I.C.S.: 334220
Andrzej Garapieh *(CEO)*

Radiowe Doradztwo Reklamowe Sp. z.o.o. (1)
ul sw Marcin 80/82
61-809 Poznan, Poland (100%)
Tel.: (48) 8528623
Fax: (48) 8536059
E-Mail: biuro@radiopoznan.pl
Web Site: www.bor.com.pl
Radio Station Operator
S.I.C.: 4832
N.A.I.C.S.: 515112
Maria Pawlow *(Mng Dir)*
Hanna Stachowiak *(Sec)*

Trader.com (Polska) Sp. z o.o (1)
ul Czerska 8/10
00-732 Warsaw, Poland
Tel.: (48) 22 455 33 00
Fax: (48) 22 455 33 01
E-Mail: info@trader.pl
Web Site: www.trader.pl
Newspaper Classifieds Publishing Services
S.I.C.: 2711
N.A.I.C.S.: 511110
Anna Podkowinska *(Pres)*

Non-U.S. Subsidiary:

LLC Agora Ukraine (1)
vul Vel Vasylkivska 77
Kiev, 03150, Ukraine
Tel.: (380) 44 586 6100
E-Mail: office@agora.ua
Web Site: www.agora.ua
Internet Publishing & Advertising Services
S.I.C.: 2741
N.A.I.C.S.: 519130
Anastasiya Fomenko *(Mng Dir)*

AGOSTINI'S LIMITED

18 Victoria Avenue
PO Box 191
Port of Spain, Trinidad & Tobago
Tel.: (868) 623 4871
Fax: (868) 623 1966
E-Mail: marketing@agostini-mktg.com
Web Site: www.agostinislimited.com
Year Founded: 1925
AGL—(TRI)
Sls.: $200,034,930
Assets: $129,778,661
Liabilities: $60,547,389
Net Worth: $69,231,271
Earnings: $10,082,548
Emp.: 1,027
Fiscal Year-end: 09/30/12
Business Description:
Fast Moving Consumer Goods Distr
S.I.C.: 5099
N.A.I.C.S.: 423990
Personnel:
Joseph P. Esau *(Chm)*
Anthony J. Agostini *(Mng Dir)*
Lisa M. Mackenzie *(Sec & Dir-Fin)*
Board of Directors:
Joseph P. Esau
Anthony J. Agostini
Reyaz W. Ahamad
Barry A. Davis
Roger A. Farah
E. Gillian Warner Hudson
Lisa M. Mackenzie
Amalia L. Maharaj
Christian E. Mouttet
Gregor Nassief
P. Terrence Rajnauth
Legal Counsel:
Pollonais Blanc De la Bastide & Jacelon
17 Pembroke Street
Port of Spain, Trinidad & Tobago

Subsidiaries:

Agostini Marketing (1)
4 Nelson St
Port of Spain, Trinidad & Tobago
Tel.: (868) 623 2236
Fax: (868) 624 6751
E-Mail: scrouch@agostini-mktg.com
Emp.: 100
Construction Material Distr
S.I.C.: 5032
N.A.I.C.S.: 423320
Andrew Pashley *(CEO)*

Subsidiary:

Fastening & Building Systems Limited (2)
3 Duncan Street
Port of Spain, Trinidad & Tobago
Tel.: (868) 623 9004
Fax: (868) 624 6751
Construction Material Distr
S.I.C.: 5039
N.A.I.C.S.: 423390

Hand Arnold Trinidad Limited (1)
Hand Arnold Commercial Complex Chootoo Road
El Socorro, San Juan, Trinidad & Tobago
Tel.: (868) 674 8001
Fax: (868) 674 8966
E-Mail: info@handarnold.com
Web Site: www.handarnold.com
Grocery Product Distr
S.I.C.: 5149
N.A.I.C.S.: 424490
Anthony J. Agostini *(Chm)*
Sharon A. Gunness-Balkissoon *(CEO)*

Rosco Petroavance Limited (1)
2-4 Rodriguez Avenue Cross Crossing
San Fernando, Trinidad & Tobago
Tel.: (868) 657 1541
Fax: (868) 652 7964
E-Mail: rosco@roscopetro.com
Web Site: www.roscopetro.com
Emp.: 40
Industrial Valve Whslr
S.I.C.: 5084
N.A.I.C.S.: 423830
Wayne Bernard, *(CEO)*
Vanita Balroop *(CFO & Sec)*

SuperPharm Limited (1)
Lot Nos 19 20 & 21 Union Park West
Marabella, San Fernando, Trinidad & Tobago
Tel.: (868) 675 5666
Fax: (868) 658 6007
E-Mail: info@superpharmtt.com
Web Site: www.superpharm.co.tt
Pharmacy Operator
S.I.C.: 5912
N.A.I.C.S.: 446110

AGRA LIMITED

8 Bessemer Street
Private Bag 12011
Windhoek, Namibia
Tel.: (264) 61 290 9111
Fax: (264) 61 290 9250
E-Mail: info@agra.com.na
Web Site: www.agra.com.na
AGR—(JSE)
Rev.: $122,719,057
Assets: $48,049,513
Liabilities: $25,228,602
Net Worth: $22,820,911
Earnings: $3,428,664
Emp.: 850
Fiscal Year-end: 07/31/13
Business Description:
Agricultural Product Distr
S.I.C.: 5191
N.A.I.C.S.: 424910
Personnel:
R. van der Merwe *(Chm)*
B. H. Mouton *(Vice Chm)*

Agra Limited—(Continued)

Peter M. Kazmaier *(CEO)*
Antionette Mans *(Recruitment & Trng Officer)*
Albe Snyman *(Comm Officer)*
Board of Directors:
R. van der Merwe
B. H. Mouton
P. Schonecke
L. C. van Wyk
J. W. Visagie
S. Wilckens

AGRA STAHLHANDELS-GMBH

Vilstalstrasse 84
92245 Amberg, Germany
Tel.: (49) 9621917080
Fax: (49) 9621705829
E-Mail: info@agra-stahlhandel.de
Web Site: www.agra-stahlhandel.com
Rev.: $18,227,254
Emp.: 5
Business Description:
Stainless Steel Plates & Aluminium Sheets Mfr
S.I.C.: 3353
N.A.I.C.S.: 331315
Personnel:
Peter Gradl *(Mng Dir)*

AGRALYS SERVICES

Rue De Courtalain
La Chapelle Du Noyer, 28200
Orleans, Eure Et Loir, France
Tel.: (33) 237975900
Fax: (33) 237458561
Web Site: www.agralys.com
Rev.: $24,700,000
Emp.: 230
Business Description:
Management Consulting Services
S.I.C.: 8748
N.A.I.C.S.: 541618
Personnel:
Francois Lagrange *(Dir-Admin)*
Board of Directors:
Guy Crapez

AGRANA BETEILIGUNGS-AG

Friedrich-Wilhelm-Raiffeisen-Platz 1
1020 Vienna, Austria
Tel.: (43) 1211370
Fax: (43) 12113712998
E-Mail: info.ab@agrana.at
Web Site: www.agrana.com
Year Founded: 1988
AGR—(BER DEU VIE)
Rev.: $4,127,230,680
Assets: $3,470,760,110
Liabilities: $1,839,072,838
Net Worth: $1,631,687,272
Earnings: $210,651,374
Emp.: 8,449
Fiscal Year-end: 02/28/13
Business Description:
Sugar & Starch Mfr
S.I.C.: 2062
N.A.I.C.S.: 311314
Personnel:
Christian Konrad *(Chm-Supervisory Bd)*
Erwin Hameseder *(Vice Chm-Supervisory Bd)*
Wolfgang Heer *(Vice Chm-Supervisory Bd)*
Johann Marihart *(CEO & Member-Mgmt Bd-Bus Strategy, Production, HR, Comm & R&D)*
Fritz Gattermayer *(Member-Mgmt Bd-Pur, Sls & Raw matls)*
Walter Grausam *(Member-Mgmt Bd-Fin, Controlling, IT, Org & Subsidiaries)*
Thomas Kolbl *(Member-Mgmt Bd-Internal Auditing)*
Supervisory Board of Directors:
Christian Konrad
Thomas Buder
Jochen Fenner
Hans Joerg Gebhard
Gerhard Glatz
Erwin Hameseder
Wolfgang Heer
Ernst Karpfinger
Thomas Kirchberg
Josef Proll
Stephan Savic
Peter Vymyslicky

Subsidiaries:

AGRANA Frucht GmbH & Co KG (1)
Donau-City-Strasse 9
A-1220 Vienna, Austria (100%)
Tel.: (43) 1211370
Fax: (43) 12113712998
Emp.: 150
Fruit Preparation & Concentrate Mfr & Distr
S.I.C.: 2037
N.A.I.C.S.: 311411
Johann Marihart *(CEO)*

AGRANA Fruit Austria GmbH (1)
Kroellendorf 51
A-3365 Allhartsberg, Austria
Tel.: (43) 744838480
Fax: (43) 7448384839
Fruit & Vegetable Preparations
S.I.C.: 2037
N.A.I.C.S.: 311411
Heinz Scharl *(Mng Dir)*

AGRANA Starke GmbH (1)
Donau-City-Strasse 9
A-1120 Vienna, Austria (100%)
Tel.: (43) 1211370
Fax: (43) 12113712929
E-Mail: info.ab@agrana.at
Web Site: www.agrana.at
Starch Mills & Mfr
S.I.C.: 2099
N.A.I.C.S.: 311999

AGRANA Zucker GmbH (1)
Josef-Reither-Strasse 21-23
3430 Tulln, Austria (100%)
Tel.: (43) 22726020
Fax: (43) 227260211225
E-Mail: info.ab@agrana.at
Emp.: 400
Sugar Factory
S.I.C.: 2061
N.A.I.C.S.: 311314
Martin Doppler *(CEO)*

Joint Venture:

AUSTRIA JUICE GmbH (1)
(Formerly YBBSTALER AGRANA JUICE GmbH)
Kroellendorf 45
A- 3365 Allhartsberg, Austria
Tel.: (43) 7448 2304 0
Fax: (43) 7448 2304 312
E-Mail: sales@austriajuice.com
Web Site: www.austriajuice.com
Emp.: 900
Juice Concentrate Mfr
S.I.C.: 2033
N.A.I.C.S.: 311421
Stephan Buttner *(CEO)*

Subsidiary:

Ybbstaler Fruit Austria GmbH (2)
Kroellendorf 45
3365 Allhartsberg, Austria
Tel.: (43) 744823040
Fax: (43) 74482304900
E-Mail: info@ybbstaler.at
Web Site: www.ybbstaler.at
Emp.: 60
Beverage Compounds Mfr & Whslr
S.I.C.: 2086
N.A.I.C.S.: 312111
Stephan Buttner *(Mng Dir)*

Non-U.S. Subsidiaries:

Lukta Polska Sp. z o.o (2)
ul Plantowa 231
96-230 Biala Rawska, Poland
Tel.: (48) 814 60 25
Fruit Juices Mfr & Whslr
S.I.C.: 2037
N.A.I.C.S.: 311411

Ybbstaler Fruit Polska Sp. z o.o (2)
Ul Plantowa 231
Biala Rawska, Poland
Tel.: (48) 825622150
Fax: (48) 825622112
Web Site: www.ybbstaler.pl
Fruit Juices Whslr
S.I.C.: 5149
N.A.I.C.S.: 424490
Helmut Stoger *(Gen Mgr)*

U.S. Subsidiary:

AGRANA Fruit US, Inc. (1)
6850 Southpointe Pkwy
Brecksville, OH 44141
Tel.: (440) 546-1199
Fax: (440) 546-0038
Toll Free: (800) 477-3788
Web Site: www.agrana.us
Fruit & Vegetable Preparations
S.I.C.: 2037
N.A.I.C.S.: 311411
Lori Rajewski *(Mgr-HR)*

Non-U.S. Subsidiaries:

AGRANA Fruit Argentina S.A (1)
Juramento 2089 piso 8 oficina 803
Buenos Aires, C1428, Argentina
Tel.: (54) 1147880505
Fax: (54) 1147886426
Web Site: www.agrana.com.ar
Fruit & Vegetable Preparations
S.I.C.: 2037
N.A.I.C.S.: 311411

AGRANA Fruit Australia Pty. Ltd. (1)
200 George Downes Drive
Central Mangrove, NSW, 2250, Australia
Tel.: (61) 243731245
Fax: (61) 2 4373 1046
E-Mail: information@agrana.com.au
Web Site: www.agrana.com.au
Emp.: 50
Fruit & Vegetable Preparations
S.I.C.: 2037
N.A.I.C.S.: 311411
Francois Cassagne *(Mgr-Ops)*

AGRANA Fruit Dachang Co. Ltd. (1)
29 Xia-An Road Dachang Hui
Langfang, Hebei, China
Tel.: (86) 3168829374
Fax: (86) 3618829354
Web Site: www.agrana.com.cn
Emp.: 25
Fruit & Vegetable Preparations
S.I.C.: 2037
N.A.I.C.S.: 311411

AGRANA Fruit Fiji Pty. Ltd. (1)
Nayama Road
PO Box 80
Sigatoka, Fiji
Tel.: (679) 6500162
Fax: (679) 6520009
Emp.: 30
Fruit & Vegetable Preparations
S.I.C.: 2037
N.A.I.C.S.: 311411
Dean Tams *(CEO & Mng Dir)*

AGRANA Fruit France S.A. (1)
17 avenue du 8 mai 1945
BP 504
77295 Mitry-Mory, Cedex, France
Tel.: (33) 164675600
Fax: (33) 164277228
Web Site: www.agrana.fr
Fruit & Vegetable Preparations
S.I.C.: 2037
N.A.I.C.S.: 311411

AGRANA Fruit Istanbul Gida San Ve Tic A.S. (1)
Kore Sehitleri Cad Deniz Is Hani No 34 5
Zincirlikuyu, 34394 Istanbul, Turkey
Tel.: (90) 2123476000
Fax: (90) 2123476001
Web Site: www.agrana.com.tr
Emp.: 22
Fruit & Vegetable Preparations
S.I.C.: 2037
N.A.I.C.S.: 311411
Heinz Scharl *(Mng Dir)*

AGRANA Fruit Korea Co. Ltd. (1)
3rd Floor Hyowon Bldg 99-5 Karak-Dong
Songpa-Ku, Seoul, 138-720, Korea (South)
Tel.: (82) 24489100
Fax: (82) 24484985
E-Mail: agranakorea@agrana.co.kr
Web Site: www.agrana.co.kr
Emp.: 10
Fruit & Vegetable Preparations
S.I.C.: 2037
N.A.I.C.S.: 311411
Jin Chul Choi *(Pres)*

AGRANA Fruit Mexico SA de CV (1)
Martinez de Navarrete 83 B
Col Gral Francisco Villa
Jacona, 59845 Michoacan, Mexico
Tel.: (52) 3515309600
Fax: (52) 3515162660
Web Site: www.agrana.com.mx
Fruit & Vegetable Preparations
S.I.C.: 2037
N.A.I.C.S.: 311411
Juan C. Sarracino *(Mng Dir)*

AGRANA Fruit Polska Sp z.o.o. (1)
ul Lawska 2
07-410 Ostroleka, Poland
Tel.: (48) 297670602
Fax: (48) 297605046
Web Site: www.agrana.pl
Fruit & Vegetable Preparations
S.I.C.: 2037
N.A.I.C.S.: 311411

AGRANA Fruit South Africa Pty. Ltd.. (1)
10 Brigid Road
Diep River, 7945 Cape Town, South Africa
Tel.: (27) 217050210
Fax: (27) 217051451
E-Mail: info@agrana.co.za
Web Site: www.agrana.co.za
Emp.: 100
Fruit & Vegetable Preparations
S.I.C.: 2037
N.A.I.C.S.: 311411
Philippe Gomez *(Mng Dir)*

Dirafrost Frozen Fruit Industry N.V. (1)
Industriezone Daelemveld 1025
B 3540 Herk-de-Stad, Belgium
Tel.: (32) 13552701
Fax: (32) 13553211
E-Mail: info@dirafrost.be
Web Site: www.dirafrost.be
Emp.: 50
Fruit & Vegetable Preparations
S.I.C.: 2037
N.A.I.C.S.: 311411
Carlos Franssen *(Mng Dir)*

SC AGRANA Romania SA (1)
Soseaua Straulesti nr 178-180 sector 1
013339 Bucharest, Romania
Tel.: (40) 372 381 000
Fax: (40) 21 269 33 98
E-Mail: sales.romania@agrana.com
Web Site: www.agrana.ro
BETA—(BUC)
Sugar Mfr
S.I.C.: 2063
N.A.I.C.S.: 311313
Martin Doppler *(Pres)*

AGRANI INSURANCE COMPANY LIMITED

Saiham Sky View Tower 45 Bijoy Nagar 14th Floor
Dhaka, 1000, Bangladesh
Tel.: (880) 2 8391571
Fax: (880) 2 8391575
E-Mail: agraniin@citech.net
Web Site: www.agraniins.com
Year Founded: 2000
AGRANINS—(DHA)
Sales Range: $1-9.9 Million
Business Description:
Insurance Services
S.I.C.: 6411
N.A.I.C.S.: 524298
Personnel:
Rezaul Huq Khan *(Chm)*

Hussain Ahmed *(Mng Dir)*
Mohammed Anwar Hossain *(Mng Dir)*
Mohammed Azharul Islam *(Mng Dir)*
Farad Uddin Bhuiyan *(Asst Mng Dir)*
Mohammed Imamul Hossain *(Asst Mng Dir)*
Santosh Kumar Nandi *(Deputy Mng Dir)*
Mohasin Siddiquee *(Asst Mng Dir)*
Sharif Mahmud *(Sec & Sr VP)*
Enamul Haque *(Sr Exec VP)*
Anwar Hossain Munshl *(Sr Exec VP)*
S.M. Kamal Uddin *(Sr Exec VP)*
Nurul Amin *(Sr VP)*
Ayesha Mahmud *(Sr VP)*
Abdul Malek Miah *(Sr VP)*
Mohammad Golam Rabbani *(Sr VP)*
Mohammad Harunar Rashid *(Sr VP)*
Ashim Kumar Roy *(Sr VP)*
Board of Directors:
Rezaul Huq Khan
Mohammed Anwar Hossain
Sharif Mahmud

AGRAR INVEST ROMANIA AG

Martin-Niemoller-Strasse 1
D-83301 Traunreut, Germany
Tel.: (49) 8669 35 900 52
E-Mail: info@agrarinvestments.com
Web Site: www.agrarinvestments.com
RAR—(DEU)
Business Description:
Agricultural Investment
S.I.C.: 6211
N.A.I.C.S.: 523999
Personnel:
Theo Haeni *(Chm)*

AGRARIUS AG

Louisenstrasse 125
61348 Bad Homburg, Germany
Tel.: (49) 61726816990
Fax: (49) 6172 6 81 69 93
E-Mail: info@agrarius.de
Web Site: www.agrarius.de
A0SLN9—(DEU)
Business Description:
Agricultural Services
S.I.C.: 0139
N.A.I.C.S.: 111998
Personnel:
Bruno Otto Kling *(Chm-Supervisory Bd)*
Erwin Loeber *(Deputy Chairman-Supervisory Bd)*
Supervisory Board of Directors:
Bruno Otto Kling
Erwin Loeber
Joachim Von Harbou

AGRENCO LTD.

Av Pres Juscelino Kubitscheck 1400 - 7 Andar
4543000 Sao Paulo, Brazil
Tel.: (55) 11 3572 0100
Fax: (55) 11 3572 0100
E-Mail: ri@agrenco.com.br
Web Site: www.agrenco.com.br
Year Founded: 2007
AGEN33 —(BRAZ)
Emp.: 200
Business Description:
Oilseed Mfr
S.I.C.: 0119
N.A.I.C.S.: 111120
Personnel:
Nils Bjellum *(Dir-IR)*
Board of Directors:
Nils Bjellum
Hendrik Laverge

AGREX, INC.

Shinjuku Sumitomo Building 2-6-1
Nishi Shinjuku
Shinjuku-ku, Tokyo, 163-0216, Japan
Tel.: (81) 353219561
Fax: (81) 353219563
Web Site: www.agrex.co.jp
Year Founded: 1965
4799—(TKS)
Sls.: $315,386,676
Assets: $148,621,770
Liabilities: $58,966,248
Net Worth: $89,655,522
Earnings: $4,304,971
Emp.: 2,236
Fiscal Year-end: 03/31/13
Business Description:
Data Processing, Entry & Collecting, Printing, Mailing & Other Office Services
S.I.C.: 7374
N.A.I.C.S.: 518210
Personnel:
Masao Ueno *(Chm)*
Katsunori Yamaguchi *(Pres)*
Mikio Andou *(Mng Exec Officer)*
Akira Murata *(Exec Officer)*
Toshimasa Nakai *(Exec Officer)*
Fumiyo Nakamura *(Mng Exec Officer)*
Hajime Nakayama *(Mng Exec Officer)*
Hiroaki Nishimoto *(Mng Exec Officer)*
Takerou Ogawa *(Exec Officer)*
Takemi Sanada *(Mng Exec Officer)*
Masato Takeda *(Exec Officer)*
Hiroshi Yoshino *(Exec Officer)*
Board of Directors:
Masao Ueno
Youichi Arama
Norio Maenishi
Hajime Nakayama
Hiroaki Nishimoto
Takerou Ogawa
Katsunori Yamaguchi

AGRIA CORPORATION

Room 1206 Huantai Building 12
Zhongguancun South Street
Haidian District, Beijing, 100081, China
Tel.: (86) 10 8438 1060
Web Site: www.agriacorp.com
GRO—(NYSE)
Rev.: $936,573,564
Assets: $581,590,516
Liabilities: $383,580,178
Net Worth: $198,010,337
Earnings: ($196,828,970)
Emp.: 1,832
Fiscal Year-end: 06/30/13
Business Description:
Agricultural Products Mfr, Researcher & Developer
S.I.C.: 0119
N.A.I.C.S.: 111191
Personnel:
Alan Guanglin Lai *(Chm)*
Patrick Wai Yip Tsang *(CFO)*
Mark Dewdney *(CEO-PGW)*
Board of Directors:
Alan Guanglin Lai
Joo Hai Lee
Sean S. Shao
Wah Kwong Tsang

U.S. Subsidiary:

Agria Corporation (1)
2 Park Pl Ste 2
Bronxville, NY 10708 DE
Tel.: (914) 337-1117 (100%)
Web Site: www.agriacorp.com
Agri-Solutions & Sheep Breeding Products
S.I.C.: 0119
N.A.I.C.S.: 111199
David Pasquale *(Sr VP-US)*

Non-U.S. Subsidiary:

PGG Wrightson Limited (1)
57 Waterloo Road
PO Box 292
Christchurch, 8042, New Zealand (50.01%)
Tel.: (64) 3 372 0800
Fax: (64) 3 372 0801
E-Mail: enquiries@pggwrightson.co.nz
Web Site: www.pggwrightson.co.nz
PGW—(NZE)
Rev.: $947,355,939
Assets: $518,528,196
Liabilities: $304,167,474
Net Worth: $214,360,722
Earnings: ($256,544,685)
Emp.: 450
Fiscal Year-end: 06/30/13
Rural Services; Irrigation & Pumping Services, Livestock Marketing & Supply, Seed & Grain, Farm Consultancy, Farm Finance & Insurance & Real Estate Services
S.I.C.: 5154
N.A.I.C.S.: 424520
Alan Guanglin Lai *(Chm)*
Mark Dewdney *(CEO)*
Rob Woodgate *(CFO)*
Julian Daly *(Gen Counsel & Sec)*

Subsidiaries:

Agri-Feeds Limited (2)
61A Hull Rd
PO Box 4180
Mount Maunganui S, Mount Maunganui, 3149, New Zealand
Tel.: (64) 75474540
Fax: (64) 75474541
E-Mail: info@agrifeeds.co.nz
Web Site: www.agrifeeds.co.nz
Emp.: 20
Animal Feeds Mfr
S.I.C.: 2048
N.A.I.C.S.: 311119
Rob Dorey *(Gen Mgr)*

PGG Wrightson Seeds Limited (2)
57 Waterloo Rd
Hornby, Christchurch, 8042, New Zealand
Tel.: (64) 33720834
Fax: (64) 33720801
E-Mail: info@pggwrightsonseeds.co.nz
Web Site: www.pggwrightsonseeds.com
Emp.: 200
Agro Products Mfr & Distr
S.I.C.: 0119
N.A.I.C.S.: 111199
Paul Maguire *(Sls Mgr-Southern North Island Area)*

Subsidiary:

Agricom Limited (3)
PO Box 3761
Christchurch, New Zealand
Tel.: (64) 33414580
Fax: (64) 33414581
E-Mail: info@agricom.co.nz
Web Site: www.agricom.co.nz
Emp.: 12
Forage Seeds Distr
S.I.C.: 5191
N.A.I.C.S.: 424910
Mark Brown *(Mgr-Sls & Mktg)*

Non-U.S. Subsidiaries:

PGG Wrightson Seeds (Australia) Pty Limited (2)
7-9 Distribution Dr
Truganina, Melbourne, VIC, 3029, Australia
Tel.: (61) 393943400
Fax: (61) 393943432
E-Mail: ngauci@pggwsa.com.au
Web Site: www.pggwrightsonseeds.com.au
Forage Seeds Production & Distr
S.I.C.: 0119
N.A.I.C.S.: 111120
Rob Salmon *(Mgr-Product Dev)*

Subsidiary:

AusWest Seeds Pty Limited (3)
2-8 Tobias Street
Forbes, NSW, 2871, Australia
Tel.: (61) 268521500
Fax: (61) 268521393
E-Mail: auswest@auswestseeds.com.au
Web Site: www.auswestseeds.com.au
Emp.: 21
Forage Seeds Whslr
S.I.C.: 5191
N.A.I.C.S.: 424910
Catherine Baker *(Officer-Customer Svc)*

Subsidiary:

Stephen Pasture Seeds Pty Limited (4)
27 Wiltshire Ln
Ballarat, VIC, 3356, Australia
Tel.: (61) 353358055
Fax: (61) 353358088
E-Mail: info@stephenpastureseeds.com.au
Web Site: www.stephenpastureseeds.com.au
Emp.: 16
Pasture Seeds Whslr
S.I.C.: 5191
N.A.I.C.S.: 424910
Steve Blayney *(Mgr-Warehouse)*

Wrightson Pas S.A. Limited (2)
Maximo Santos 4900
12400 Montevideo, Uruguay
Tel.: (598) 23557753
Fax: (598) 23557754
E-Mail: wpas@wpas.com.uy
Web Site: www.wrightsonpas.com.uy
Emp.: 25
Forage Seeds Production & Distr
S.I.C.: 0119
N.A.I.C.S.: 111199
David Meluish *(Gen Mgr)*

AGRIA GROUP HOLDING JSC

Business Center Dimyat 9 Floor 111
Kniaz Boris I Str
Varna, 9002, Bulgaria
Tel.: (359) 52 55 40 00
Fax: (359) 52 511 602
E-Mail: office@agriabg.com
Web Site: www.agriabg.com
A72—(BUL)
Sls.: $57,155,637
Assets: $90,356,650
Liabilities: $55,064,127
Net Worth: $35,292,523
Earnings: $4,213,778
Fiscal Year-end: 12/31/12
Business Description:
Professional, Scientific & Technical Activities
S.I.C.: 7389
N.A.I.C.S.: 541990
Personnel:
Emil Veselinov Raykov *(Chm & CEO)*
Board of Directors:
Emil Veselinov Raykov
Anna Dimitrova Belchinska
Kristina Zheleva Bozhkova
Deyan Rosenov Ovcharov
Daniela Dimitrova Taneva

Subsidiaries:

Kristera AD (1)
Industrial Area
7800 Popovo, Bulgaria
Tel.: (359) 608 4 78 58
Fax: (359) 608 4 78 47
E-Mail: kristera_popovo@mail.bg
Wheat Farming Services
S.I.C.: 0111
N.A.I.C.S.: 111140

Kristera-Agro EOOD (1)
Business Center Dimyat 9 Floor 111 Kniaz Boris I Str
9002 Varna, Bulgaria
Tel.: (359) 52 55 40 00
Fax: (359) 52 511 602
E-Mail: office_korn@mbox.contact.bg
Wheat Farming Services
S.I.C.: 0111
N.A.I.C.S.: 111140
Emil Raykov, *(Exec Dir)*

AGRICO CANADA LIMITED

2896 Slough St Unit 6
Mississauga, ON, L4T 1G3, Canada
Tel.: (905) 672-5610
Fax: (905) 672-5544
E-Mail: mail@agricocanada.com
Web Site: www.agricocanada.com
Sales Range: $100-124.9 Million
Emp.: 55

Agrico Canada Limited—(Continued)

Business Description:
Fertilizer Whslr
S.I.C.: 2875
N.A.I.C.S.: 325314
Personnel:
Robert L Whitelaw *(Pres)*
Murray Martin *(Sr VP-Ops & Gen Mgr)*

AGRICOLA GROUP LTD

3-5 Alton Business Centre
Valley Lane, Ipswich, Wherstead, IP9 2AX, United Kingdom
Tel.: (44) 147323 22 22
E-Mail: info@agricola.co.uk
Web Site: www.agricola.co.uk
Year Founded: 1998
Sales Range: $900-999.9 Million
Emp.: 961
Business Description:
Nutrition for Farm Animals
S.I.C.: 2048
N.A.I.C.S.: 311119
Personnel:
Nicholas Ian Coleman *(Sec)*
Subsidiary:

BOCM PAULS Ltd. (1)
3-5 Alton Business Centre
Valley Lane Wherstead, Ipswich, Suffolk, IP9 2AX, United Kingdom
Mailing Address:
PO Box 39
Ipswich, Suffolk, IP4 1BX, United Kingdom
Tel.: (44) 1473556500
Fax: (44) 1473 230 509
E-Mail: info@bocmpauls.co.uk
Web Site: www.bocmpauls.co.uk
Sales Range: $900-999.9 Million
Emp.: 900
Animal Feed Mfr
S.I.C.: 2011
N.A.I.C.S.: 311611

Division:

Feedex Nutrition (2)
The Airfield Rougham
Bury St Edmunds, IP309NH Thetford, Suffolk, United Kingdom (100%)
Tel.: (44) 1359272936
Fax: (44) 1359272927
E-Mail: info@feedex.co.uk
Web Site: www.feedex.co.uk
Emp.: 50
Animal Food Mfr
S.I.C.: 2048
N.A.I.C.S.: 311119
Bruce Colman *(Mgr-Sls)*

AGRICULTURAL BANK OF CHINA LIMITED

No 69 Jianguomennei Avenue
Doncheng District, Beijing, 100005, China
Tel.: (86) 1085109619
Fax: (86) 1085108557
Web Site: www.abchina.com
1288—(HKG OTC SHG)
Int. Income: $89,919,107,550
Net Worth: $119,352,582,900
Earnings: $23,054,059,350
Emp.: 461,100
Fiscal Year-end: 12/31/12
Business Description:
Banking Services
S.I.C.: 6029
N.A.I.C.S.: 522110
Personnel:
Chaoliang Jiang *(Chm)*
Yingxin Che *(Chm-Supervisory Bd)*
Yun Zhang *(Vice Chm & Pres)*
Zhenjiang Li *(Sec)*
Huaxiang Cai *(Exec VP)*
Chao Gong *(Exec VP)*
Haoda Guo *(Exec VP)*
Wenlong Lou *(Exec VP)*
Board of Directors:
Chaoliang Jiang
Fengchao Cheng
Haoda Guo
Yelin Li
Damao Lin
Wenlong Lou
Frederick Si-Hang Ma
Dong Qiu
Bingxi Shen
Tiejun Wen
Anthony Ting Yuk Wu
Shusheng Xiao
Francis Tin Fan Yuen
Yun Zhang
Chao Zhao
Supervisory Board of Directors:
Yingxin Che
Genyou Dai
Xiangsen Jia
Hong Liu
Yurui Wang
Chongwen Yan
Xin Zheng

Deloitte Touche Tohmatsu
35F 1 Pacific Place 88 Queensway
Hong Kong, China (Hong Kong)

Legal Counsel:
King & Wood Mallesons Lawyers
40 F Office Tower A Beijing Fortune Plaza
7 East 3rd Ring Middle Road, Beijing, Chaoyang, China

Freshfields Bruckhaus Deringer
11 F Two Exchange Square
Central, China (Hong Kong)

China Securities Depository & Clearing Corporation Limited
36/F China Insurance Building No 166 Lujiazui Dong Road
Pudong New Area, Shanghai, China

Subsidiaries:

ABC Ansai Rural Bank Limited Liability Company (1)
Majiagou Village Zhenwudong County
Ansai Town, Majiagou, Shaanxi, 717400, China
Tel.: (86) 9116229906
Fax: (86) 911 6229906
Commercial Banking Services
S.I.C.: 6029
N.A.I.C.S.: 522110

ABC-CA Fund Management Co., Ltd. (1)
7/F Puxiang Business Plaza 1600 Century Road
Shanghai, 200122, China
Tel.: (86) 21 61095588
Fax: (86) 21 61095556
E-Mail: service@abc-ca.com.cn
Web Site: www.abchina.com
Emp.: 80
Fund Management Services
S.I.C.: 6282
N.A.I.C.S.: 523920
Xuhong Po *(Gen Mgr)*

ABC Financial Leasing Co., Ltd. (1)
5-6 F East Yanan Road
Huangpu District, Shanghai, 200120, China
Tel.: (86) 2168776699
Fax: (86) 21 68777599
Web Site: www.abcleasing.com
Commercial Banking Services
S.I.C.: 6029
N.A.I.C.S.: 522110

ABC Hubei Hanchuan Rural Bank Limited Liability Company (1)
Jianshece Road Xinhe Power Plant
Hanchuan, Hubei, 431600, China
Tel.: (86) 7128412338
Fax: (86) 7128412338
Commercial Banking Services
S.I.C.: 6029
N.A.I.C.S.: 522110

Non-U.S. Divisions:

Agricultural Bank of China - Hong Kong (1)
Tower 1 Admiralty Center
18 Harcourt Road, Hong Kong, China (Hong Kong)
Tel.: (852) 28618000
Fax: (852) 28660133
Web Site: www.abchina.com.hk
Emp.: 1
Commercial Banking Services
S.I.C.: 6029
N.A.I.C.S.: 522110

Agricultural Bank of China - Singapore (1)
7 Tomashi Blvd
Contact Twr 1 30-01, Singapore, 03897, Singapore
Tel.: (65) 65355255
Fax: (65) 65387960
Web Site: www.abchina.com.sg
Emp.: 45
Commercial Banking Services
S.I.C.: 6029
N.A.I.C.S.: 522110

Agricultural Bank of China - Tokyo (1)
503 Kishimoto Building 2-1 2-Chome
Marunouchi, Chiyoda-Ku Tokyo, Japan
Tel.: (81) 332114628
Fax: (81) 332125047
Commercial Banking Services
S.I.C.: 6029
N.A.I.C.S.: 522110

Agricultural Bank of China - UK (1)
1 Bartholomew Ln
London, EC2nN 2AX, United Kingdom
Tel.: (44) 2073748900
Fax: (44) 2073746425
Web Site: www.abchina.com
Emp.: 30
Commercial Banking Services
S.I.C.: 6029
N.A.I.C.S.: 522110

China Agricultural Finance Co., Ltd. (1)
Tower 1 Admiralty Center
18 Harcourt Road, Hong Kong, China (Hong Kong)
Tel.: (852) 28618000
Fax: (852) 2861013
Web Site: www.abchina.com.hk/main/perso nal-privacy-eng.html
Financial Investment & Management Services
S.I.C.: 6211
N.A.I.C.S.: 523999

Non-U.S. Subsidiary:

ABC International Holdings Limited (1)
701 7 F1 One Pacific Place No 88
Queensway, Central, China (Hong Kong)
Tel.: (852) 36660000
Fax: (852) 36660009
E-Mail: enquiry@abchina.com
Commercial Banking Services
S.I.C.: 6029
N.A.I.C.S.: 522110

AGRICULTURAL DEVELOPMENT BANK LIMITED

Ramshah Path
Kathmandu, Nepal
Tel.: (977) 1 4262885
Fax: (977) 1 4262616
E-Mail: info.remit@adbl.gov.np
Web Site: www.adbl.gov.np
Year Founded: 1968
ADBL—(NEP)
Business Description:
Banking Services
S.I.C.: 6029
N.A.I.C.S.: 522110
Personnel:
Pramod Kumar Karki *(Chm)*
Tej Bahadur Budhathoki *(CEO)*
Dashrath Joshi *(Sec)*
Board of Directors:
Pramod Kumar Karki
Tej Bahadur Budhathoki
Mira Dhonju
Shisir Kumar Dhungana
Ramesh Kumar Mahat
Laxmi Devi Manandhar
Ram Prasad Pulami
Chhetra Bahadur Sejuwal
Janak Raj Shah

AGRICULTURE PRINTING & PACKAGING JOINT STOCK COMPANY

72 Truong Chinh St
Dong Da, Phuong Mai, Vietnam
Tel.: (84) 4 3869 5605
E-Mail: info@appprinto.vn
Web Site: www.appprintco.com
INN—(HNX)
Business Description:
Printed Packaging Product Mfr
S.I.C.: 2759
N.A.I.C.S.: 323111
Personnel:
Thanh Nam Nguyen *(Chm & Gen Mgr)*

AGRIFOODS INTERNATIONAL COOPERATIVE LTD

11671 160th St
Edmonton, AB, T5M 3Z3, Canada
Tel.: (780) 486-4115
Fax: (780) 486-0821
Web Site: www.agrifoods.ca
Sls.: $14,000,000
Emp.: 100
Business Description:
Dairy Cooperative
S.I.C.: 2026
N.A.I.C.S.: 311511
Personnel:
Ben Brandsema *(Chm)*
Board of Directors:
Ben Brandsema
Albert DeBoer
Jack Ford
Elvin Haupstein
Bill Van Rootselaar

Joint Venture:

Ultima Foods Inc. (1)
2177 Blvd Fernand Lafontaine
Longueuil, QC, J4G 2V2, Canada
Tel.: (450) 651-3737
Fax: (450) 651-6868
Web Site: www.ultimayog.ca
Emp.: 650
Dairy Products Mfr
S.I.C.: 2026
N.A.I.C.S.: 311511
Gerry J. Doutre *(Pres & CEO)*

AGRIMARINE HOLDINGS INC.

Suite 1218 - 1030 West Georgia St
Vancouver, BC, V6E 2Y3, Canada
Tel.: (604) 568-4672
Fax: (604) 568-4673
Web Site: www.agrimarine.com
FSH—(OTC TSXV)
Sls.: $424,447
Assets: $6,852,774
Liabilities: $8,850,754
Net Worth: ($1,997,980)
Earnings: ($5,883,604)
Fiscal Year-end: 03/31/13
Business Description:
Aquaculture Services
S.I.C.: 0273
N.A.I.C.S.: 112519
Personnel:
Horst Eckhard Hueniken *(Chm)*
Sean Wilton *(Pres, CEO & Sec)*
Orest Zajcew *(CFO)*
Lily Gao *(COO)*
Board of Directors:
Horst Eckhard Hueniken
Robert P. Leckie
Sean Wilton
Orest Zajcew

Legal Counsel:
McMillan LLP
1500 1055 West Georgia Street
V6E4N7 Vancouver, BC, Canada
Transfer Agent:
Computershare Investor Services
2nd Floor 510 Burrard Street
Vancouver, BC, Canada
Subsidiary:

AgriMarine Industries Inc **(1)**
PO Box 317 Station A
Campbell River, BC, V9W 5B1, Canada
Tel.: (250) 286-3656
Fax: (250) 286-3651
Emp.: 10
Aquaculture Services
S.I.C.: 0273
N.A.I.C.S.: 112519

AGRIMONY COMMODITIES LTD

701 7th Floor Kingston Tejpal Road
Vile Parle East, Mumbai, 400057, India
Tel.: (91) 22 26124294
Web Site: www.agrimonycommodities.com
537492—(BOM)
Emp.: 9
Business Description:
Natural Resources, Precious Metals, Textiles & Agricultural Products Trading
S.I.C.: 7389
N.A.I.C.S.: 425120
Personnel:
Anandrao Gole *(Mng Dir)*
Shailesh Vallabhbhai Rakhasiya *(Compliance Officer & Sec)*
Board of Directors:
Mani an Ananthanarayan
Jairaj Bafna
Anandrao Gole
Suresh Kulkarni

AGRINURTURE, INC.

54 National Road Dampol II A Pulilan
Bulacan, 3005, Philippines
Tel.: (63) 25510773
Fax: (63) 28793135
Web Site: www.ani.com.ph
Year Founded: 1997
ANI—(PHI)
Rev.: $57,060,402
Assets: $119,831,076
Liabilities: $34,399,138
Net Worth: $85,431,939
Earnings: ($3,551,308)
Emp.: 639
Fiscal Year-end: 12/31/12
Business Description:
Fresh & Processed Fruits & Vegetables Supplier
S.I.C.: 5148
N.A.I.C.S.: 424480
Personnel:
Antonio L. Tiu *(Chm, Pres & CEO)*
Kenneth S. Tan *(CFO & Treas)*
Karen V. de Asis *(CMO)*
Jennifer Ong *(Asst Info Officer & Asst Sec)*
Lenie Basilio *(Compliance Officer)*
Martin C. Subido *(Sec)*
Board of Directors:
Antonio L. Tiu
Senen C. Bacani
John Aloysius Bernas
Leonor Magtolis Briones
Mark Kenneth O. Duca
Alfonso Y. Go
Tai-Chuan Lin
James Sayre
Dennis S. Sia
George Y. Uy
Chung Ming Yang

AGRITRADE RESOURCES LIMITED

Room 1705 17th Floor Harcourt House 39 Gloucester Road
Wanchai, China (Hong Kong)
Tel.: (852) 3106 0668
Fax: (852) 3106 0227
E-Mail: info@agritraderesources.com
Web Site: www.agritraderesources.com
1131—(HKG)
Rev.: $90,379,894
Assets: $415,908,754
Liabilities: $168,040,290
Net Worth: $247,868,464
Earnings: $11,454,113
Emp.: 262
Fiscal Year-end: 03/31/13
Business Description:
Holding Company; Coal Mining
S.I.C.: 6719
N.A.I.C.S.: 551112
Personnel:
Rashid Maidin *(CEO)*
Ashok Kumar Sahoo *(CFO)*
Xinwei Ng *(COO)*
Peter Gunn *(CTO)*
Diyah Sasanti *(Legal Counsel)*
David Chan *(Sec & Controller-Fin)*
Board of Directors:
Ng Say-pek
Cheong Yee Chan
Chou Mei Mei Chen
Lee Chang Chong
Lulu Beng Kim Lim
Rashid Maidin
Xinwei Ng
Ashok Kumar Sahoo
Kin Wai Siu
Ambrish L. Thakker
Terence Chang Xiangwen
Legal Counsel:
Michael Li & Co
19/F Prosperity Tower 39 Queen's Road Central
Central, China (Hong Kong)
Butterfield Fulcrum Group (Bermuda) Limited
Rosebank Centre 11 Bermudiana Rd
Pembroke, Bermuda
Transfer Agents:
Tricor Secretaries Limited
26th Floor Tesbury Centre 28 Queen's Road East
Wanchai, China (Hong Kong)
Butterfield Fulcrum Group (Bermuda) Limited
Rosebank Centre 11 Bermudiana Rd
Pembroke, Bermuda
Subsidiaries:

Kwong Hing Knitting Fabric Trading Co. Limited **(1)**
Block D 8 F Mai Shun Indus Bldg 18-24 Kwai Cheong Rd
Kwai Chung, New Territories, China (Hong Kong)
Tel.: (852) 24222208
Fax: (852) 24892325
E-Mail: info@kwonghing.com
Emp.: 10
Dyed Yarns & Knitted Fabrics Sales
S.I.C.: 5131
N.A.I.C.S.: 424310
Fok Lewis *(Mgr)*

Unite Might Investment Limited **(1)**
8 F Mai Shun Indus Bldg 18-24 Kwai Cheong Rd
Kwai Chung, New Territories, China (Hong Kong)
Tel.: (852) 29459656
Fax: (852) 24892325
Web Site: www.kwonghing.com
Administration Services
S.I.C.: 8741
N.A.I.C.S.: 561110

AGRIUM INC.

13131 Lake Fraser Drive Southeast
Calgary, AB, T2J 7E8, Canada
Tel.: (403) 225-7000
Fax: (403) 225-7609
Toll Free: (877) 247-4861
E-Mail: naretail@agrium.com
Web Site: www.agrium.com
Year Founded: 1993
AGU—(NYSE TSX)
Sls.: $15,727,000,000
Assets: $15,977,000,000
Liabilities: $9,181,000,000
Net Worth: $6,796,000,000
Earnings: $1,063,000,000
Emp.: 15,800
Fiscal Year-end: 12/31/13
Business Description:
Fertilizer, Seed Treatment, Plant Nutrition & Farm Management Products Mfr & Distr
S.I.C.: 2873
N.A.I.C.S.: 325311
Personnel:
Victor J. Zaleschuk *(Chm)*
Charles Victor Magro *(Pres & CEO)*
Eric Miller *(Chief Legal Officer & Sr VP)*
Leslie A. O'Donoghue *(Chief Risk Officer & Exec VP-Corp Dev & Strategy)*
Stephen G. Dyer *(Pres-Retail & Exec VP)*
Ron A. Wilkinson *(Pres-Wholesale Bus Unit & Sr VP)*
Gary J. Daniel *(Sec)*
James M. Grossett *(Sr VP-HR)*
Andrew K. Mittag *(Sr VP)*
Board of Directors:
Victor J. Zaleschuk
David C. Everitt
Russell K. Girling
Susan A. Henry
Russell J. Horner
David J. Lesar
John E. Lowe
Charles Victor Magro
A. Anne McLellan
Derek G. Pannell
Frank William Proto
Mayo M. Schmidt
Michael M. Wilson
Transfer Agent:
CST Trust Company
PO Box 700
Postal Station B, Montreal, QC, Canada
Subsidiary:

Agrium Advanced Technologies Inc. **(1)**
10 Craig St
Brantford, ON, N3R 7J1, Canada
Tel.: (519) 757-0077
Fax: (519) 757-0080
Web Site: www.agriumat.com
Emp.: 40
Fertilizer Mfr & Distr
S.I.C.: 2875
N.A.I.C.S.: 325314
Andrew K. Mittag *(Pres)*

U.S. Subsidiary:

Agrium Advanced Technologies (U.S.) Inc. **(2)**
1309 Edward St
Sylacauga, AL 35151
Tel.: (256) 249-6888
Fax: (256) 249-7428
Web Site: www.polyon.com
Sls.: $28,400,000
Emp.: 100
Nitrogenous Fertilizers
S.I.C.: 2873
N.A.I.C.S.: 325311
Steve Patterson *(Chm)*

U.S. Subsidiaries:

Agrium U.S. Inc. **(1)**
4582 S Ulster St Ste 1700
Denver, CO 80237-2636 CO
Tel.: (303) 804-4400 (100%)
Fax: (303) 804-4478
Web Site: www.agrium.com
Emp.: 60
Fertilizer, Seed Treatment, Plant Nutrition & Crop Protection Product Retailer
S.I.C.: 5191
N.A.I.C.S.: 424910
Tom Warner *(Interim Pres-Retail-North America)*

Unit:

Agrium Inc. - Kenai Nitrogen Operations **(2)**
Mile 21 Spur Hwy
Kenai, AK 99611-0575 (100%)
Mailing Address:
PO Box 575
Kenai, AK 99611-0575
Tel.: (907) 776-8121
Fax: (907) 776-5579
E-Mail: donation@agrium.com
Web Site: www.agrium.com
Emp.: 3
Nitrogen Fertilizers Mfr
Export
S.I.C.: 2873
N.A.I.C.S.: 325311
Steve Wendt *(Gen Mgr)*

Crop Production Services, Inc. **(1)**
3005 Rocky Mountain Ave
Loveland, CO 80538 DE
Tel.: (970) 685-3300
Fax: (303) 222-2708
E-Mail: info@cpsagu.com
Web Site: www.cpsagu.com
Emp.: 400
Agronomic Consulting Services & Supplies Distr
S.I.C.: 5191
N.A.I.C.S.: 424910
Richard Gearheard Loveland *(Pres-Retail)*

Subsidiaries:

Loveland Products, Inc. **(2)**
3005 Rocky Mountain Ave
Loveland, CO 80538-9001
Tel.: (970) 356-8920
Web Site: www.lovelandproducts.com
Fertilizer, Plant Nutrition, Seed Treatment & Crop Protection Products Distr
S.I.C.: 5191
N.A.I.C.S.: 424910
Michael Totora *(Pres/CEO-Agricen)*

Non-U.S. Subsidiary:

United Agri Products Canada Inc. **(2)**
789 Donnybrook Dr
Dorchester, ON, N0L 1G5, Canada Ca
Tel.: (519) 268-8001
Fax: (519) 268-8013
Toll Free: (800) 265-4624
E-Mail: customerservice@uap.ca
Web Site: www.uap.ca
Sales Range: $75-99.9 Million
Emp.: 111
Agricultural Chemical, Fertilizer & Seed Distr
S.I.C.: 5191
N.A.I.C.S.: 424910
Murray Pickel *(Gen Mgr)*

Non-U.S. Subsidiaries:

Agrium Europe S.A. **(1)**
Avenue Louise 326/36
1050 Brussels, Belgium
Tel.: (32) 2 646 70 00
Fax: (32) 2 646 68 60
E-Mail: agrium@agrium.eu
Emp.: 25
Fertilizer Distr
S.I.C.: 5169
N.A.I.C.S.: 424690
Nancy Vanveroost *(Mgr-HR)*

Non-U.S. Subsidiaries:

AGRIUM- AGROPORT ROMANIA S.A. **(2)**
Regiment 11 Siret St 2D
800322 Galati, Romania
Tel.: (40) 236416204
Fax: (40) 236460194
E-Mail: office@agrium-agroport.ro
Web Site: www.agrium.eu/offices.jsp

Agrium Inc.—(Continued)

Emp.: 15
Fertilizer Distr
S.I.C.: 5191
N.A.I.C.S.: 424910
Florin Radu *(Gen Mgr)*

Agrium Deutschland GmbH (2)
Kirchenstrasse 5
21244 Buchholz, Germany
Tel.: (49) 4181 30060
Fax: (49) 4181 300699
E-Mail: info@agrium.eu
Emp.: 6
Fertilizer Materials Whslr
S.I.C.: 5191
N.A.I.C.S.: 424910
Joachim Rellmann *(Gen Mgr)*

Agrium France SAS (2)
Rue Sait Just 6-8
BP 2026
51070 Reims, France
Tel.: (33) 3 26 47 45 10
Fax: (33) 3 26 40 49 98
E-Mail: fertilisants@agrium.eu
Web Site: www.agrium.eu/offices.jsp
Fertilizer Distr
S.I.C.: 5169
N.A.I.C.S.: 424690

Agrium Italia S.p.A. (2)
Via Delle Cateratte 68
57122 Livorno, Italy
Tel.: (39) 0 586 249999
Fax: (39) 0 586 828007
E-Mail: italy@agrium.eu
Fertilizer Distr
S.I.C.: 5169
N.A.I.C.S.: 424690

Agrium UK & Ireland Ltd. (2)
2 Otterwood Bank
Wetherby, Yorkshire, LS22 7XT, United Kingdom
Tel.: (44) 1 937 520 332
Fax: (44) 87 00 51 30 22
E-Mail: fertilizers@agrium.eu
Fertilizer Distr
S.I.C.: 5191
N.A.I.C.S.: 424910

Agro Baltic GmbH (2)
Rungestrasse 17
Rostock Rostock, Germany
Tel.: (49) 381 497870
Fax: (49) 381 4978730
E-Mail: info@agro-baltic.de
Web Site: www.agrium.eu/offices.jsp
Emp.: 10
Fertilizer Materials Whslr
S.I.C.: 5191
N.A.I.C.S.: 424910
Ruediger Gen Mgr *(Gen Mgr)*

Landmark Rural Holdings Limited (1)
153 Chester Pass Rd
Albany, WA, 6330, Australia
Tel.: (61) 898427888
Fax: (61) 898415607
Web Site: www.landmark.com.au
Emp.: 1,000
Farm Supplies Distr; Agricultural Support Services
S.I.C.: 5191
N.A.I.C.S.: 424910

Subsidiaries:

Landmark Operations Limited (2)
32 Farrall Road
Midvale, Perth, WA, 6056, Australia
Tel.: (61) 893743470
Fax: (61) 892741331
E-Mail: asklandmark@landmark.com.au
Web Site: www.landmark.com.au
Emp.: 20
Agriculture Merchandise & Fertilizer Distr
S.I.C.: 5191
N.A.I.C.S.: 424910
Richard Norton *(Mng Dir)*

Subsidiary:

Landmark Global Exports Pty. Ltd. (3)
380 La Trobe Street
Melbourne, VIC, 3000, Australia
Tel.: (61) 392092681
Fax: (61) 392092526
Web Site: www.landmarkglobalexports.com.au
Livestock Export & Breeding Services
S.I.C.: 0752
N.A.I.C.S.: 115210
Sophie Wang *(Mng Dir)*

Landmark Wool Pty. Ltd. (2)
201 Sussex Street
Sydney, NSW, 2000, Australia
Tel.: (61) 407780722
E-Mail: risk.management@landmark.com.au
Web Site: wool.landmark.com.au
Wool Distr
S.I.C.: 5159
N.A.I.C.S.: 424590
Richard Norton *(Dir-Landmark Global Exports & Gen Mgr-Agency Ops)*

Non-U.S. Joint Ventures:

Canpotex International Pte. Limited (1)
30 Hill Street 04 01
Singapore, 179360, Singapore
Tel.: (65) 67330221
Fax: (65) 67330178
E-Mail: marketing@canpotex.com
Web Site: www.canpotex.com
Sales Range: $10-24.9 Million
Emp.: 15
Potash Product Exporter, Marketer & Distr; Owned by Agrium Inc., by Potash Corporation of Saskatchewan Inc. & by The Mosaic Canada ULC
S.I.C.: 5159
N.A.I.C.S.: 424590
Steven Dechka *(Pres & CEO)*

Non-U.S. Subsidiaries:

Canpotex (Hong Kong) Limited (2)
Unit 1610 Devon House
979 King's Road, Quarry Bay, China (Hong Kong)
Tel.: (852) 25909056
Fax: (852) 25165805
Web Site: www.canpotex.com
Potash Products Exporter, Marketer & Distr
S.I.C.: 1474
N.A.I.C.S.: 212391
Andrew Law *(Gen Mgr)*

Canpotex International (Canada) Limited (2)
100 Park Royal South Suite 1111
Vancouver, BC, V7T 1A2, Canada
Tel.: (604) 903-7140
Fax: (604) 926-8863
Web Site: www.canpotex.com
Potash Exporter, Marketer & Distr
S.I.C.: 5159
N.A.I.C.S.: 424590
Matt Albrecht *(VP-Mktg-Latin America)*

Canpotex (Japan) Limited (2)
Suite 1908 East Tower Shin Aoyama Building
1 1 1 Minami Aoyama Minato ku, Tokyo, 107 0062, Japan
Tel.: (81) 334788260
Fax: (81) 354143308
Web Site: canpqlx.sasktelwebhosting.com
Emp.: 2
Potash Products Exporter, Marketer & Distr
S.I.C.: 5159
N.A.I.C.S.: 424590
Hiro Ishii *(Mng Dir)*

Canpotex Limited (2)
111 2nd Avenue South Suite 400
Saskatoon, SK, S7K 1K6, Canada
Tel.: (306) 931-2200
Fax: (306) 653-5505
Web Site: www.canpotex.com
Emp.: 50
Potash Export, Marketer & Distr
S.I.C.: 5159
N.A.I.C.S.: 424590
Dwayne Dahl *(CFO & VP-Fin)*
Ted J. Nieman *(Gen Counsel, Sec & Sr VP)*
Scott Rudderham *(Sr VP-Ops)*

Profertil S.A. (1)
Av Alicia Moreau de Justo 140 Piso 1
Buenos Aires, 1107, Argentina
Tel.: (54) 1141212000
Fax: (54) 11 4316 8012
Web Site: www.profertil.com.ar
Fertilizer Production & Whslr
S.I.C.: 2873
N.A.I.C.S.: 325311
Antonio Allegretta *(Gen Mgr)*

AGRO-100 LTEE

1090 rang Sud St Thomas
Joliette, QC, J0K 3L0, Canada
Tel.: (450) 759-8887
Fax: (450) 759-0223
E-Mail: info@agro-100.com
Web Site: www.agro-100.com
Year Founded: 1990
Rev.: $10,636,745
Emp.: 15

Business Description:
Fertilizer Mfr
S.I.C.: 2875
N.A.I.C.S.: 325314

Personnel:
Stephane Beaucage *(Pres)*
Jean-Marc Harnois *(Pres)*

AGRO DUTCH INDUSTRIES LTD.

Village Tofapur Near Lalru Teh
Rajpura, Patiala, Punjab, India
Tel.: (91) 1762 505201
Fax: (91) 1726 505231
E-Mail: enquiry@agro-dutch.com
Web Site: www.agro-dutch.com
519281—(BOM)
Sales Range: $10-24.9 Million

Business Description:
Mushroom Mfr & Distr
S.I.C.: 0182
N.A.I.C.S.: 111411

Personnel:
Malvinder Singh *(Chm & Mng Dir)*
Vivek Atri *(Sec)*

Board of Directors:
Malvinder Singh
S. R. K. Agnihotri
H. S. Garcha
Jalesh Grover
Arvind Kalra
Rajesh Malhotra
Harpreet Singh Nagra

Transfer Agent:
Karvy Computershare Private Limited
Plot No 17-24 Vittal Rao Nagar Madhapur
Hyderabad, 500 081, India
Tel.: (91) 40 2342 0818

AGROFERT HOLDING, A.S.

Rohacova 83 1099
Psaelska Prague 4, 130 00 Prague, 3, Czech Republic
Tel.: (420) 272192111
Fax: (420) 272192272
E-Mail: agrofert@agrofert.cz
Web Site: www.agrofert.cz
Year Founded: 1993
Sales Range: $800-899.9 Million
Emp.: 120

Business Description:
Holding Company; Agriculture, Food & Chemicals
S.I.C.: 6719
N.A.I.C.S.: 551112

Personnel:
Andrej Babis *(Chm)*
Zbynek Prusa *(Vice Chm)*
Josef Mraz *(Mng Dir)*

Board of Directors:
Andrej Babis
Jaroslav Faltynek
Jiri Haspeklo
Jaroslav Kurcik
Zbynek Prusa

Subsidiary:

Precheza, a.s. (1)
Nabrezi Dr E Benese 24
751 62 Prerov, Czech Republic (98.4%)
Tel.: (420) 581252111
Fax: (420) 581 217 048
E-Mail: precheza@precheza.cz
Web Site: www.precheza.cz
Chemicals & Fertilizers Mfr
S.I.C.: 2873
N.A.I.C.S.: 325311
Petr Cingr *(Chm)*

Subsidiary:

DEZA, a.s. (2)
Masarykova 753
757 28 Valasske Mezirici, Czech Republic
Tel.: (420) 571691111
Fax: (420) 571611546
E-Mail: posta@deza.cz
Web Site: www.deza.cz
Emp.: 1,000
Crude Benzol & Tar Processor
S.I.C.: 2819
N.A.I.C.S.: 325180
Karel Jiricek *(Vice Chm & Dir-Fin)*
Abynek Prusa *(CEO)*

Non-U.S. Subsidiaries:

Agrofert China Co Ltd (1)
905 Huixin Apartment Yayuncun
100101 Beijing, China
Tel.: (86) 1064993943
Fax: (86) 1064993807
E-Mail: agrofert@agrofert.com.cn
Web Site: www.agrofert.com.cn
Chemical & Allied Products Merchant Whslr
S.I.C.: 5169
N.A.I.C.S.: 424690
Yubin Li *(Mng Dir)*

Agrofert Hungaria Kft. (1)
Somloi Ut 31 II 5
1118 Budapest, Hungary
Tel.: (36) 12791795
Fax: (36) 14669833
E-Mail: info@agrofert.hu
Web Site: www.agrofert.hu
Emp.: 3
Plastics Materials & Basic Forms & Shapes Whslr
S.I.C.: 5162
N.A.I.C.S.: 424610
Andrej Babis *(CEO)*

Agrofert Italy SA (1)
Viale Repubblica 74
Muggio, 20053 Muggia, Italy
Tel.: (39) 039792651
Fax: (39) 039794415
E-Mail: mailbox@agrofert.it
Web Site: www.agrofert.it
Emp.: 10
Pesticide & Agricultural Chemical Mfr
S.I.C.: 2879
N.A.I.C.S.: 325320
Clavio Fabino *(Mng Dir)*

Agrofert Norden A/S (1)
Teglporten 2 2 Sal
PO Box 343
3460 Birkerod, Denmark
Tel.: (45) 45825008
Fax: (45) 45812340
E-Mail: agrofertnorden@agrofertnorden.com
Web Site: www.agrofertnorden.com
Emp.: 20
Chemical & Allied Products Merchant Whslr
S.I.C.: 5169
N.A.I.C.S.: 424690
Andrej Babis *(CEO)*

Fertagra Deutschland GmbH (1)
Schillerstrasse 12
60313 Frankfurt, Germany
Tel.: (49) 69921889011
Fax: (49) 699218999
E-Mail: fertagra@t-online.de
Plastics Materials & Basic Forms & Shapes Whslr
S.I.C.: 5162
N.A.I.C.S.: 424610
Alexej Brencic *(Mng Dir)*

Hydina ZK as (1)
Napajadla 1
Kosice, 042 47, Slovakia
Tel.: (421) 55 6709101
Fax: (421) 55 6709103
E-Mail: hydinazk@hydinazk.sk
Web Site: www.hydinazk.sk
Poultry Processing

S.I.C.: 0251
N.A.I.C.S.: 112320

AGROGENERATION SA

33 rue d'Artois
75008 Paris, France
Tel.: (33) 156436860
Fax: (33) 156437550
E-Mail: contact@agrogeneration.com
Web Site: www.agrogeneration.com
Year Founded: 2007
ALAGR—(EUR)
Rev.: $63,843,458
Assets: $96,679,237
Liabilities: $52,357,936
Net Worth: $44,321,301
Earnings: ($7,605,861)
Emp.: 721
Fiscal Year-end: 12/31/12
Business Description:
Grain & Oilseed Farming
S.I.C.: 0119
N.A.I.C.S.: 111191
Personnel:
Charles Beigbeder *(Chm-Supervisory Bd)*
Charles Vilgrain *(Chm-Exec Bd)*
Constant Pellissier *(Vice Chm-Supervisory Bd)*
Alain de Woillemont *(CFO & Member-Exec Bd)*
Supervisory Board of Directors:
Charles Beigbeder
Claude Chambard
Niels Court-Payen
Nicolas Denjoy
Jerome Knaepen
Alain Mallart
Constant Pellissier
Pascal Prot
Vivek Tandon
Olivier Tonneau
Jean-Pascal Tranie

Ernst & Young et Autres
1-2 Place des Saisons Paris La Defense 1
92400 Courbevoie, France

AGROINDUSTRIAL DEL NOROESTE S. DE R.L. DE C.V.

Calle 4a 3207 Col Santa Rosa
Chihuahua, Chih, 31050, Mexico
Tel.: (52) 614 415 9322
Web Site: www.chihuahuacountry.com
Sales Range: $100-124.9 Million
Emp.: 1,450
Business Description:
Beef Processor
S.I.C.: 5147
N.A.I.C.S.: 311612

Joint Venture:

Norson Alimentos S de RL de CV (1)
Calle de la Plata s/n
PO Box 1223
Parque Industrial Hermosillo, 83299
Sonora, Mexico
Tel.: (52) 6622595800
Fax: (52) 66 22 51 01 82
E-Mail: customerservice@norson.net
Web Site: www.norson.net
Sales Range: $100-124.9 Million
Emp.: 700
Pork Processing Services
S.I.C.: 2034
N.A.I.C.S.: 311423
Jesus Huerta *(Pres)*

AGROKULTURA AB

(Formerly Alpcot Agro AB)
Birger Jarlsgatan 32B
114 29 Stockholm, Sweden
Tel.: (46) 8 46 33940
E-Mail: info@agrokultura.com
Web Site: www.agrokultura.com
Year Founded: 2006
AGRA—(OMX)
Rev.: $116,553,409
Assets: $240,682,885
Liabilities: $46,075,291
Net Worth: $194,607,594
Earnings: ($15,815,606)
Emp.: 1,401
Fiscal Year-end: 12/31/12
Business Description:
Agricultural Investment Holding Company
S.I.C.: 6719
N.A.I.C.S.: 551112
Personnel:
Mikael Nachemson *(Chm)*
Stephen Pickup *(Grp Mng Dir)*
Kristian Shaw *(CFO)*
Board of Directors:
Mikael Nachemson
Niclas Eriksson
Sture Gustavsson
Simon Hallqvist
Michael Rosenlew
Katre Saard

Non-U.S. Subsidiaries:

LLC Management Company Agrokultura (1)
4th Dobryninsky Lane 8 Office Nr E02-303
119049 Moscow, Russia RU
Tel.: (7) 4957253970
E-Mail: moscow@agrokultura.com
Web Site: www.alpcotagro.com
Emp.: 1,300
Farm Management Services
S.I.C.: 8741
N.A.I.C.S.: 551114
Vladimir Primak *(Mng Dir)*

AGROKUMANOVO

Industrijska Str
1300 Skopje, Macedonia
Tel.: (389) 31 412 777
Fax: (389) 31 429 337
Web Site: www.agrokumanovo.com.mk
Year Founded: 1979
AGKU—(MAC)
Business Description:
Ferrous Metallurgy Services
S.I.C.: 3356
N.A.I.C.S.: 331491
Personnel:
Mihajil Saltirovski *(CEO & Gen Mgr)*

AGROLI GROUP

Aleea Combinatului nr 486
Crevedia, Romania
Tel.: (40) 21 352 67 77
Fax: (40) 21 352 67 75
Web Site: www.agroli.ro
Business Description:
Holding Company; Poultry Production
S.I.C.: 6719
N.A.I.C.S.: 551112
Personnel:
Rami Ghaziri *(CEO)*

Subsidiary:

Avicola Crevedia (1)
Aleea Combinatului nr 486 Crevedia-judetul Dambovita
Targoviste, 894520, Romania
Tel.: (40) 21 352 67 77
Fax: (40) 21 352 67 75
Web Site: www.agroli.ro
AVRE—(BUC)
Poultry Processing
S.I.C.: 2015
N.A.I.C.S.: 311615
Rami Ghaziri *(Gen Mgr)*

AGROPECUARIA DE GUISSONA, S. COOP. LTDA.

Avenida Verge Del Claustre 32
25210 Guisona, Baleares, Spain
Tel.: (34) 973550100
Telex: 52.150
Fax: (34) 973550788
Web Site: www.cag.es
Year Founded: 1959
Sales Range: $200-249.9 Million
Emp.: 138
Business Description:
Animal Feed & Agricultural Services
S.I.C.: 2011
N.A.I.C.S.: 311611
Personnel:
Rosendo Camats Ribera *(Dir-Fin)*

AGROPUR COOPERATIVE

510 Principale Street
Granby, QC, J2G 7G2, Canada
Tel.: (450) 375-1991
Telex: 5832510
Fax: (450) 375-2099
E-Mail: info@agropur.com
Web Site: www.agropur.com
Year Founded: 1938
Sls.: $3,633,361,784
Assets: $1,346,779,806
Liabilities: $436,580,542
Net Worth: $910,199,264
Earnings: $39,054,052
Emp.: 5,568
Fiscal Year-end: 11/03/12
Business Description:
Agricultural Cooperative; Dairy Production & Research
Import Export
S.I.C.: 2026
N.A.I.C.S.: 311511
Personnel:
Serge Riendeau *(Chm)*
Rene Moreau *(Vice Chm)*
Robert Coallier *(CEO)*
Jocelyn Lauziere *(CFO & Sr VP)*
Louis Lefebvre *(Pres-Cheese & Ingredients Div)*
Serge Paquette *(Pres-Div Natrel)*
Lorraine Bedard *(Sec & Sr VP-Legal Affairs & Member Rels)*
Benoit Gagnon *(Exec VP-Global Dev)*
Dominique Benoit *(Sr VP-Institutional Affairs & Comm)*
Serge Fortier *(Sr VP-IT)*
Robert Gour *(Sr VP-Change Mgmt)*
Scott McDonald *(Sr VP-HR)*
Board of Directors:
Serge Riendeau
Real Brunet
Luc Chasse
Michel Couture
Celine Delhaes
Jean Filiatrault
Darie Gagne
Daniel Gagnon
Gaetan Jodoin
Jean-Pierre Lacombe
Daniel Lamy
Valere Lieutenant
Roger Massicotte
Rene Moreau
Lorna Jean Neveu
Vital Vouligny

Divisions:

Cheese & Functional Products Division (1)
510 Principale St
Granby, QC, J2G 7G2, Canada (100%)
Tel.: (450) 375-1991
Fax: (450) 375-2099
Web Site: www.agropur.com
Emp.: 150
Cheese Mfr
S.I.C.: 2022
N.A.I.C.S.: 311513
Louis Lefebvre *(Pres)*

Division Natrel (1)
101 Roland Therrien Blvd Ste 600
Longueuil, QC, J4H 4B9, Canada (100%)
Tel.: (450) 646-1010
Fax: (450) 646-8169
E-Mail:
Web Site: www.agropur.com
Emp.: 250
Dairy Products Mfr & Distr
S.I.C.: 2026
N.A.I.C.S.: 311511
Serge Paquette *(Pres)*

Farmers Co-operative Dairy Limited (1)
745 Hammonds Plains Road
Bedford, NS, B3K 5Y6, Canada
Tel.: (902) 835-4005
Web Site: www.farmersdairy.ca
Sales Range: $150-199.9 Million
Dairy Cooperative
S.I.C.: 0241
N.A.I.C.S.: 112120
Andrea Hickey *(Sr Brand Mgr)*

Fine Cheese Division (1)
4700 Armand-Frappier Street
Saint-Hubert, QC, J3Z 1G5, Canada (100%)
Tel.: (450) 443-4838
Fax: (450) 443-6196
Web Site: www.agropur.com
Sales Range: $125-149.9 Million
Emp.: 160
Fine Cheese Mfr
S.I.C.: 2022
N.A.I.C.S.: 311513
Robert Gour *(Pres)*

U.S. Subsidiaries:

Schroeder Company (1)
2080 Rice St
Maplewood, MN 55113
Tel.: (651) 487-1471
Fax: (651) 487-1476
Web Site: www.schroedermilk.com
Emp.: 230
Milk Production
S.I.C.: 2026
N.A.I.C.S.: 311511
Bob Kirchoff *(Pres)*

Plant:

Schroeder Company-Grand Rapids (2)
5252 Clay Ave SW
Grand Rapids, MI 49548-5658
Tel.: (616) 538-3822
Fax: (616) 538-3844
Emp.: 100
Milk Processing
S.I.C.: 2026
N.A.I.C.S.: 311511

Trega Foods, Inc. (1)
2701 Freedom Rd
Appleton, WI 54913-9315
Tel.: (920) 788-2115
Fax: (920) 788-1424
Web Site: www.tregafoods.com
Sls.: $74,700,000
Emp.: 260
Cheese Mfr
S.I.C.: 2022
N.A.I.C.S.: 311513
Doug Simon *(Pres)*
Bill Diedrich *(CFO)*

Joint Venture:

Ultima Foods Inc. (1)
2177 Blvd Fernand Lafontaine
Longueuil, QC, J4G 2V2, Canada
Tel.: (450) 651-3737
Fax: (450) 651-6868
Web Site: www.ultimayog.ca
Emp.: 650
Dairy Products Mfr
S.I.C.: 2026
N.A.I.C.S.: 311511
Gerry J. Doutre *(Pres & CEO)*

AGROSALGA, S.L.

C Zurbano no 43 1 izqda
E-28010 Madrid, Spain
Tel.: (34) 913103715
Fax: (34) 913193959
E-Mail: correo@agrosintesis.es
Sales Range: Less than $1 Million

Agrosalga, S.L.—(Continued)

Emp.: 50
Business Description:
Grains
S.I.C.: 5153
N.A.I.C.S.: 424510
Personnel:
Manuel Bermejo *(Gen Mgr)*

Subsidiary:

Agroexpansion, S.A. **(1)**
Centro de Transportes Benavente
PO Box 152
Nave E, Oficina 2, E-49600 Benavente, Zamora, Spain ES
Tel.: (34) 980638365
Fax: (34) 980634577
Leaf Tobacco Products
S.I.C.: 5993
N.A.I.C.S.: 453991

AGROTON PUBLIC LTD

9 50 let oborony Luganska St
91045 Luhans'k, Ukraine
Tel.: (380) 642 345379
E-Mail: info@agroton.lg.ua
Web Site: www.agroton.com.ua
A2TA—(DEU WAR)
Rev.: $88,001,000
Assets: $187,106,000
Liabilities: $60,503,000
Net Worth: $126,603,000
Earnings: $6,787,000
Emp.: 2,651
Fiscal Year-end: 12/31/12
Business Description:
Grain Growing, Livestock Farming & Food Processing Operations
S.I.C.: 0119
N.A.I.C.S.: 111191
Personnel:
Iurii Zhuravlov *(CEO)*
Tamara Lapta *(Deputy CEO)*
Larysa Orlova *(CFO)*
Board of Directors:
Volodymyr Kudryavtsev
Tamara Lapta
Larysa Orlova
Borys Supikhanov
Iurii Zhuravlov
Legal Counsel:
K. Chrysostomides & Co LLC
1 Lampousas Street
Nicosia, Cyprus

Subsidiaries:

ALLC Shiykivske **(1)**
Vul Kalinina 4 Harkivska Obl
63809 Shvaykovka, Ukraine
Tel.: (380) 575962216
Fax: (380) 575 96 22 16
Crop Farming Services
S.I.C.: 0191
N.A.I.C.S.: 111998

CJSC Agroton **(1)**
50 let Oborony Luhanska 9
Luhans'k, 91045, Ukraine
Tel.: (380) 642 34 53 79
Fax: (380) 642 42 05 78
E-Mail: info@agrotonlg.ua
Web Site: www.agrotonlg.ua
Crop Farming & Land Cultivation Services
S.I.C.: 0139
N.A.I.C.S.: 111998

AGROWILL GROUP AB

Smolensk g 10
LT-03201 Vilnius, Lithuania
Tel.: (370) 5 233 5340
Fax: (370) 5 233 5345
E-Mail: info@agrowill.lt
Web Site: www.agrowill.lt
Year Founded: 2003
AVG1L—(VSE WAR)
Rev.: $33,312,465
Assets: $113,450,600
Liabilities: $66,172,632
Net Worth: $47,277,968
Earnings: $2,266,099
Emp.: 540
Fiscal Year-end: 12/31/12
Business Description:
Agricultural Products
S.I.C.: 0241
N.A.I.C.S.: 112120
Personnel:
Ramunas Audzevicius *(Chm-Supervisory Bd)*
Vladas Bagavicius *(Chm-Mgmt Bd)*
Marius Zutautas *(CEO, Gen Dir & Member-Mgmt Bd)*
Domantas Savicius *(Member-Mgmt Bd & Dir-Production & Fin)*
Vytautas Buivydas *(Member-Mgmt Bd)*
Linas Strelis *(Member-Mgmt Bd)*
Supervisory Board of Directors:
Ramunas Audzevicius
Dziuginta Balciune
Ceslav Okincic
Aurimas Sanikovas
Gediminas Ziemelis

Subsidiaries:

Gruduva UAB **(1)**
Gotlybiskiai village
Sakiai, 71372, Lithuania
Tel.: (370) 345 51139
Fax: (370) 834551139
E-Mail: gruduva@agrowill.it
Emp.: 10
Mixed Crop & Livestock Farming Services
S.I.C.: 0139
N.A.I.C.S.: 111998
Remigijus Kromelis *(Chm)*

UAB "Agro Management Team" **(1)**
Smolensko str 10 A
3201 Vilnius, Lithuania
Tel.: (370) 5259 5657
Fax: (370) 5233 7347
E-Mail: info@agroMT.lt
Web Site: www.agromt.lt
Agricultural Property Management Services
S.I.C.: 6519
N.A.I.C.S.: 531190

UAB "Agrowill Trade" **(1)**
Smolensko g 10
3201 Vilnius, Lithuania
Tel.: (370) 52335340
Fax: (370) 52335345
E-Mail: info@agrowill.it
Emp.: 1
Agricultural Supplies Distr
S.I.C.: 5191
N.A.I.C.S.: 424910
Romas Kukta *(Gen Mgr)*

UAB "AVG Investment 2" **(1)**
Smolensko st 10
Vilnius, Lithuania
Tel.: (370) 5233 5340
Fax: (370) 5233 5345
E-Mail: info@agrowill.it
Farmland Leasing Services
S.I.C.: 6519
N.A.I.C.S.: 531190

UAB "AWG Trade" **(1)**
Smolensko st 10
Vilnius, Lithuania
Tel.: (370) 5233 5340
Fax: (370) 5233 5345
E-Mail: info@agrowill.it
Farm Supplies Whslr
S.I.C.: 5191
N.A.I.C.S.: 424910

UAB "Zemes vystymo fondas 1" **(1)**
Smolensko G 10
03201 Vilnius, Lithuania
Tel.: (370) 52335369
Fax: (370) 52138594
E-Mail: info@zvf.it
Emp.: 2
Real Estate Development Services
S.I.C.: 6531
N.A.I.C.S.: 531390
Arturas Klangauskas *(Office Mgr)*

UAB "Zemes vystymo fondas 11" **(1)**
Smolensko G 10
3201 Vilnius, Lithuania
Tel.: (370) 52335369
Fax: (370) 52138594
Agricultural Funding Services
S.I.C.: 6722
N.A.I.C.S.: 525910

UAB "Zemes vystymo fondas 12" **(1)**
Smolensko g 10
03201 Vilnius, Lithuania
Tel.: (370) 52335369
Fax: (370) 52138594
E-Mail: info@zvf.it
Emp.: 2
Real Estate Development Services
S.I.C.: 6531
N.A.I.C.S.: 531390
Marius Iutautas *(Gen Mgr)*

UAB "Zemes vystymo fondas 15" **(1)**
Smolensko G 10
3201 Vilnius, Lithuania
Tel.: (370) 52335369
Fax: (370) 52138594
E-Mail: info@zvf.it
Emp.: 2
Real Estate Development Services
S.I.C.: 6531
N.A.I.C.S.: 531390

UAB "Zemes vystymo fondas 22" **(1)**
Smolensko g 10
3201 Vilnius, Lithuania
Tel.: (370) 52335369
Fax: (370) 52138594
E-Mail: info@zvf.lt
Emp.: 1
Agricultural Funding Services
S.I.C.: 6722
N.A.I.C.S.: 525910
Arturas Klangauskas *(Mgr)*

UAB "Zemes vystymo fondas 3" **(1)**
Smolensko g 10
03201 Vilnius, Lithuania
Tel.: (370) 52335369
Fax: (370) 52335345
E-Mail: info@zvf.it
Emp.: 45
Farmland Leasing Services
S.I.C.: 6519
N.A.I.C.S.: 531190
Vladas Bagavicius *(Mgr)*

UAB "Zemes vystymo fondas 8" **(1)**
Smolensko G 10
3201 Vilnius, Lithuania
Tel.: (370) 52335369
Fax: (370) 52138594
E-Mail: info@zvf.it
Emp.: 2
Real Estate Development Services
S.I.C.: 6531
N.A.I.C.S.: 531390
Arturas Klagauskas *(Gen Mgr)*

ZUB "Agrowill Jurbarkai" **(1)**
Klisiai village
74205 Jubarkas, Lithuania
Tel.: (370) 447 72290
E-Mail: jurbarkai@agrowill.lt
Emp.: 3
Mixed Crop & Livestock Farming Services
S.I.C.: 0191
N.A.I.C.S.: 111998
Saulius Drulia *(Chm)*
Kenth Koehler *(Chm)*

ZUB "Agrowill Lankesa" **(1)**
Ukmerges str 44
Bukoniai village, Jonava, Lithuania 55075
Tel.: (370) 349 49794
Fax: (370) 349 49784
E-Mail: lankesa@agrowill.lt
Mixed Crop & Livestock Farming Services
S.I.C.: 0191
N.A.I.C.S.: 111998
Arturas Narkevicius *(Chm)*

ZUB "Agrowill Mantviliskis" **(1)**
Mantviliskis village
Dotnuva parish, Kedainiai, Lithuania 58332
Tel.: (370) 347 59623
Fax: (370) 347 37949
E-Mail: mantviliskis@agrowill.lt
Mixed Crop Farming Services
S.I.C.: 0191
N.A.I.C.S.: 111998
Aloyzas Vazgys *(Chm)*

ZUB "Agrowill Nausode" **(1)**
Kirmeliai village
Troskunai parish, Anyksciai, Lithuania 29178
Tel.: (370) 381 47592
Fax: (370) 381 47518
E-Mail: nausode@agrowill.lt
Mixed Corp & Livestock Farming Services
S.I.C.: 0139
N.A.I.C.S.: 111998
Ceslovas Valiuskevicius *(Chm)*

ZUB "Agrowill Skemiai" **(1)**
Skemiai village
Radviliskis, Lithuania 82350
Tel.: (370) 422 45123
E-Mail: skemiai@agrowill.lt
Mixed Crop & Livestock Farming Services
S.I.C.: 0191
N.A.I.C.S.: 111998
Aloyzas Vazgys *(Chm)*

ZUB "Agrowill Smilgiai" **(1)**
Panevezio str 23
Smilgiai village, Panevezys, Lithuania
Tel.: (370) 455 53526
E-Mail: smilgiai@agrowill.lt
Web Site: www.agrowill.lt/en/about-us/managed-company/smilgiai
Mixed Crop & Livestock Farming Services
S.I.C.: 0191
N.A.I.C.S.: 111998
Mindaugas Petrauskas *(Chm)*

ZUB "Agrowill Spindulys" **(1)**
Vaitiekunai village
Grinkiskis parish, Radviliskis, Lithuania 82380
Tel.: (370) 422 47274
Fax: (370) 422 47266
E-Mail: spindulys@agrowill.lt
Mixed Crop Farming Services
S.I.C.: 0191
N.A.I.C.S.: 111998
Adolfas Sniauka *(Chm)*

ZUB "Agrowill Zelsvele" **(1)**
Zelsva village
Zelsva village, Marijampole, Lithuania 69193
Tel.: (370) 343 22047
Fax: (370) 343 22287
E-Mail: zelsvele@agrowill.lt
Mixed Crop & Livestock Farming Services
S.I.C.: 0139
N.A.I.C.S.: 111998
Mamertas Krasauskas *(Chm)*

AGS AUTOMOTIVE SYSTEMS

675 Progress Avenue
Toronto, ON, M1H 2W9, Canada
Tel.: (416) 438-6650
Fax: (416) 431-8775
E-Mail: inquiries@agsautomotive.com
Web Site: www.agsautomotive.com
Year Founded: 1947
Sales Range: $250-299.9 Million
Emp.: 1,200
Business Description:
Automotive Metal Stampings, Plating, Painting, Plastics, Sequencing & Assembly Services
S.I.C.: 3465
N.A.I.C.S.: 336370
Personnel:
Joseph Leon *(Co-Pres)*
Joe Loparco *(Co-Pres)*

AGS CORPORATION

4-2-11 Harigaya Urawa-ku Saitama-shi
Saitama, 330-0075, Japan
Tel.: (81) 488256000
Fax: (81) 488227337
Web Site: www.ags.co.jp
Year Founded: 1971

3648—(TKS)
Sales Range: $150-199.9 Million
Emp.: 923

Business Description:
Computer Related Services
S.I.C.: 7379
N.A.I.C.S.: 541519

Personnel:
Hazime Ogawa *(Pres & CEO)*

Subsidiaries:

AGS Business Computer Co., Ltd. (1)
1-4-10 Nakacho Urawa Shoko Building 5F
Urawa-ku, Saitama, 330-0062, Japan
Tel.: (81) 488245080
Fax: (81) 488245419
Web Site: www.ags-bc.co.jp
Computer Software Consulting Services
S.I.C.: 7373
N.A.I.C.S.: 541512

AGS Pro Service Co., Ltd. (1)
4-2-11 Harigaya Sakuraurawa Building
Urawa-Ku, Saitama, 330-0075, Japan
Tel.: (81) 48 825 5462
Fax: (81) 48 825 6008
Web Site: www.ags-ps.co.jp
Business Process Outsourcing Services
S.I.C.: 7389
N.A.I.C.S.: 561499

AGS System Advisory Co., Ltd. (1)
4-2-11 Harigaya
Urawa-ku, Saitama, 330-0075, Japan
Tel.: (81) 488256000
Fax: (81) 488227337
Information Technology Consulting Services
S.I.C.: 7373
N.A.I.C.S.: 541512

AGS TRANSACT TECHNOLOGIES LTD.

601-602 B-Wing Trade World Kamala City Senapati Bapat Marg
Lower Parel, Mumbai, 400 013, India
Tel.: (91) 22 6781 2000
Fax: (91) 22 2493 5384
Web Site: www.agsttl.com
Year Founded: 1992

Business Description:
ATM & Point-of-Sale Equipment & Solutions
S.I.C.: 7389
N.A.I.C.S.: 561439

Personnel:
Ravi B. Goyal *(Chm & Mng Dir)*
Amitabh Jaipuria *(CEO-Banking Bus)*

Board of Directors:
Ravi B. Goyal
Sudip Bandyopadhyay
S. P. Chaudhry
Badrinarain Goyal
Varun Kapur
Vish Narain

AGTA RECORD AG

Allmendstrasse 24
CH-8320 Fehraltorf, Switzerland
Tel.: (41) 44 954 91 91
Fax: (41) 44 954 92 00
E-Mail: info@agta-record.com
Web Site: www.agtarecord.com
AGTA—(SWX)
Rev.: $341,423,712
Assets: $331,226,475
Liabilities: $108,073,220
Net Worth: $223,153,255
Earnings: $26,009,351
Emp.: 1,804
Fiscal Year-end: 12/31/12

Business Description:
Automatic Door System Mfr
S.I.C.: 3442
N.A.I.C.S.: 332321

Personnel:
Hubert Jouffroy *(Chm)*
Werner Sprenger *(Vice Chm)*
Stefan Riva *(CEO)*
Raymund Scheffrahn *(CFO)*
Michael Hirt *(CMO)*
Franz Eigl *(CTO)*

Board of Directors:
Hubert Jouffroy
Peter Altorfer
Bertrand Ghez
Michele Rota
Werner Sprenger
Rolf Thurnherr

Subsidiaries:

agtatec ag (1)
Allmendstrasse 24
8320 Fehraltorf, Switzerland
Tel.: (41) 449549316
Fax: (41) 449549200
Automatic Door Mfr
S.I.C.: 3442
N.A.I.C.S.: 332321
Franz Eigl *(Mgr)*

record international ltd (1)
Allmendstrasse 24
8320 Fehraltorf, Switzerland
Tel.: (41) 449549191
Fax: (41) 449549200
E-Mail: international@agta-record.com
Web Site: www.agta-record.com
Automatic Door Mfr
S.I.C.: 3442
N.A.I.C.S.: 332321
Olivier Biard-Knobel *(Mgr)*

record Turautomation AG (1)
Allmendstrasse 24
8320 Fehraltorf, Switzerland
Tel.: (41) 449549191
Fax: (41) 449549200
E-Mail: gch@record.ch
Web Site: www.record.ch
Automatic Door Mfr
S.I.C.: 3442
N.A.I.C.S.: 332321

U.S. Subsidiaries:

record Indiana (1)
756 International Dr
Franklin, IN 46131
Tel.: (317) 738-0076
Fax: (317) 738-0082
E-Mail: doors@record-indiana.com
Web Site: www.agta-record.com
Automatic Doors Mfr
S.I.C.: 3442
N.A.I.C.S.: 332321
Marty Licciardello *(Mgr)*

Record - USA Inc (1)
4324 Phil Hargett Ct
Monroe, NC 28110
Tel.: (704) 289-9212
Fax: (704) 289-2024
E-Mail: info@record-usa.com
Web Site: www.record-usa.com
Emp.: 60
Automatic Door Mfr
S.I.C.: 3442
N.A.I.C.S.: 332321
Marty Licciardello *(Pres)*

Non-U.S. Subsidiaries:

Automatismes Batiment SA (1)
6 rue de l Orme
Saint-Germain, 91165, France
Tel.: (33) 1 69 79 31 20
Fax: (33) 1 69 79 31 26
E-Mail: automatismes.batiment@wanadoo.fr
Web Site: www.automatismes-batiment.fr
Automatic Doors & Gates Distr
S.I.C.: 5031
N.A.I.C.S.: 423310

BLASI GmbH (1)
Carl-Benz-Str 5-15
77972 Mahlberg, Germany
Tel.: (49) 7822 893 0
Fax: (49) 7822893169
E-Mail: info@blasi.info
Web Site: www.blasi.info
Emp.: 100
Automatic Door Mfr
S.I.C.: 3442
N.A.I.C.S.: 332321
Remy Deschenaux *(Mng Dir)*

CORDVER S.A (1)
37 Portes du Grand Lyon ZAC du Champ Perier
01700 Neyron, France
Tel.: (33) 437497520
Fax: (33) 4 37 49 75 29
E-Mail: cordver@cordver.fr
Emp.: 10
Flexible Doors Mfr
S.I.C.: 3442
N.A.I.C.S.: 332321
Stefan Riva *(Gen Mgr)*

PACA ASCENSEURS SERVICES SARL (1)
ZAC de L Agavon 4 Ave Lamartine
13170 Les Pennes-Mirabeau, France
Tel.: (33) 442341370
Fax: (33) 442341373
Web Site: www.paca-ascenseursservices.fr
Elevator Repair & Maintenance Services
S.I.C.: 7629
N.A.I.C.S.: 811219

Record Ajto kft (1)
Leshegy ut 8
2310 Szigetszentmiklos, Hungary
Tel.: (36) 24 51 53 90
Fax: (36) 24 51 53 92
E-Mail: info@record.hu
Web Site: www.recordajto.hu
Emp.: 14
Automatic Doors Mfr
S.I.C.: 3442
N.A.I.C.S.: 332321
Arpap Jambor *(Gen Mgr)*

record Austria GmbH (1)
Zwingenstrasse 17
2380 Perchtoldsdorf, Austria
Tel.: (43) 18658875
Fax: (43) 1865887514
E-Mail: office@record.co.at
Web Site: www.record.co.at
Automatic Door Mfr
S.I.C.: 3442
N.A.I.C.S.: 332321

record avtomatska vrata d.o.o. (1)
Poslovna cona A 26
4208 Sencur, Slovenia
Tel.: (386) 59074100
Fax: (386) 59074101
E-Mail: info@record.si
Web Site: www.record.si
Emp.: 10
Automatic Door Mfr
S.I.C.: 3442
N.A.I.C.S.: 332321
Bojan Resman *(Mgr-Sls)*

Record BMT as (1)
Hovedstensvej 33
2650 Hvidovre, Denmark
Tel.: (45) 36782300
Fax: (45) 3677 1628
E-Mail: salg@recordbmt.dk
Web Site: www.recordbmt.dk
Emp.: 25
Automatic Doors Mfr
S.I.C.: 3442
N.A.I.C.S.: 332321

record dorrautomatik sweden AB (1)
Fagelviksvagen 9
Stockholm, 145 84, Sweden
Tel.: (46) 855064630
Fax: (46) 855069920
E-Mail: info@rdarecord.se
Web Site: www.rdarecord.se
Automatic Door Mfr
S.I.C.: 3442
N.A.I.C.S.: 332321
Anders Busson *(Pres)*

record drzwi automatyczne Sp.zo.o (1)
Stara Iwiczna ul Nowa 23
05-500 Piaseczno, Poland
Tel.: (48) 227377100
Fax: (48) 227377008
E-Mail: biuro@record.pl
Web Site: www.record.pl
Emp.: 20
Automatic Door Mfr
S.I.C.: 3442
N.A.I.C.S.: 332321
Darek Gawin *(Mng Dir)*

record Elemat, S.A. (1)
C Francesc Vila 20 Pol Ind Can Magi-Apdo 185
08173 Sant Cugat del Valles, Barcelona, Spain
Tel.: (34) 936742650
Fax: (34) 936754921
E-Mail: info.es@agta-record.com
Web Site: www.record.elemat.es
Automatic Door Mfr
S.I.C.: 3442
N.A.I.C.S.: 332321
Maria Alvarez *(Mng Dir)*

record Holding Nederland B.V. (1)
Cardanuslaan 30
6865 HK Doorwerth, Netherlands
Tel.: (31) 263399777
Fax: (31) 26 33 99 770
E-Mail: directie@record-automatischedeuren.nl
Emp.: 90
Automatic Door Mfr
S.I.C.: 3442
N.A.I.C.S.: 332321
Hans Wijnstekers *(Mgr)*

Subsidiary:

record automatische deuren B.V. (2)
Cardanuslaan 30
6865 HK Doorwerth, Netherlands
Tel.: (31) 26 33 99 777
Fax: (31) 26 33 99 770
E-Mail: info@record-automatischedeuren.nl
Web Site: www.record-automatischedeuren.nl
Emp.: 100
Automatic Door Mfr
S.I.C.: 3442
N.A.I.C.S.: 332321

Record Industry (1)
les Tribouilleres
38460 Cremieu, France
Tel.: (33) 474905290
Fax: (33) 474905291
E-Mail: record.industry@cordver.fr
Emp.: 25
Automatic Doors Mfr
S.I.C.: 3442
N.A.I.C.S.: 332321

Record Portes Automatiques S.A (1)
6 rue de l Orme
91165 Saint-Germain, France
Tel.: (33) 169793110
Fax: (33) 169793129
E-Mail: record@cordver.fr
Web Site: www.record-portes-automatiques.fr
Flexible Doors Mfr
S.I.C.: 3442
N.A.I.C.S.: 332321

Record Turautomation GmbH (1)
Otto Wels Str 9
42111 Wuppertal, Germany
Tel.: (49) 202 60 90 10
Fax: (49) 202 60 90 111
E-Mail: info@record.de
Web Site: www.record.de
Automatic Doors Mfr
S.I.C.: 3442
N.A.I.C.S.: 332321

record UK ltd (1)
Garrion Business Park Smith Avenue
Wishaw, ML2 0RY, United Kingdom
Tel.: (44) 1698376411
Fax: (44) 1698376422
E-Mail: info@recorduk.co.uk
Web Site: www.recorduk.co.uk
Emp.: 180
Automatic Door Mfr
S.I.C.: 3442
N.A.I.C.S.: 332321
Stefan Riva *(Mng Dir)*

Svaton SA (1)
60 rue Marcel Dassault
93147 Bondy, France
Tel.: (33) 148473112
Fax: (33) 1 48 47 31 08
E-Mail: svaton.sas@svaton.fr
Automatic Door Mfr
S.I.C.: 3442
N.A.I.C.S.: 332321

Van Nelfen Deurtechniek B.V. (1)
Houtduifstraat 6
4901 BP Oosterhout, Netherlands

Agta Record AG—(Continued)

Tel.: (31) 162447720
Fax: (31) 162447730
E-Mail: directie@record-automatischedeuren.nl
Web Site: www.vannelfen.com
Automatic Door Mfr
S.I.C.: 3442
N.A.I.C.S.: 332321

VERCOR S.A (1)
ZA de la Prairie
Voglans, France
Tel.: (33) 479520950
Fax: (33) 479520955
E-Mail: pmoudot@cordver.fr
Web Site: www.vercor.fr
Emp.: 530
Automatic Doors Distr
S.I.C.: 5031
N.A.I.C.S.: 423310
Jean Srancois Baylot *(Mng Dir)*

AGTECH HOLDINGS LIMITED

Unit 3912 39/F Tower Two Times Square
Causeway Bay, China (Hong Kong)
Tel.: (852) 2506 1668
Fax: (852) 2506 1228
E-Mail: info@agtech.com
Web Site: www.agtech.com
8279—(DEU HKG OTC)
Rev.: $29,571,910
Assets: $148,573,276
Liabilities: $11,196,269
Net Worth: $137,377,006
Earnings: ($4,237,573)
Emp.: 198
Fiscal Year-end: 12/31/12

Business Description:
Sports Consultancy Services
S.I.C.: 7999
N.A.I.C.S.: 711310

Personnel:
Ho Sun *(Chm & CEO)*
Ming Hui Chen *(Officer & Dir-China Lottery Mgmt Co Ltd)*
Wai Sing Wong *(Sec & Sr Controller-Fin)*

Board of Directors:
Ho Sun
Jinmin Bai
Eric King Fung Ho
Fengmao Hua
Wing Leung Andy Kwok
Yu Liang
Monica Maria Nunes
Robert Geoffrey Ryan
Ronghua Wang
Yang Yang

HSBC Bank Bermuda Limited
6 Front Street
Hamilton, Bermuda

AGTHIA GROUP PJSC

Sky Tower 17th Floor Al Reem Island
PO Box 37725
Abu Dhabi, United Arab Emirates
Tel.: (971) 2 596 0600
Fax: (971) 2 672 6070
E-Mail: info@agthia.com
Web Site: www.agthia.com
Year Founded: 2004
AGTHIA—(EMI)
Rev.: $361,075,349
Assets: $466,325,994
Liabilities: $159,053,554
Net Worth: $307,272,440
Earnings: $33,951,189
Emp.: 1,900
Fiscal Year-end: 12/31/12

Business Description:
Food & Beverages Mfr
S.I.C.: 2099
N.A.I.C.S.: 311999

Personnel:
Ilias Assimakopoulos *(CEO)*
Iqbal Hamzah *(CFO)*

Board of Directors:
Rashed Mubarak Al Hajeri
Suhail M. Al Ameri
Juma K. Al Khaili
Tareq Al Masaood
Majed Salem Al Romaithi
Mohammed Thani Murshed Al Rumaithi
Abu Bakr Siddiq Khouri

AGUA Y SANEAMIENTOS ARGENTINOS, S.A.

Calle Tucuman 752
Buenos Aires, 1049, Argentina
Tel.: (54) 1163190000
Fax: (54) 1163190000
E-Mail: prensa@aysa.com.ar
Web Site: www.aysa.com.ar
Emp.: 3,800

Business Description:
Water Supply & Treatment Services
S.I.C.: 4941
N.A.I.C.S.: 221310

Personnel:
Carlos Humberto Ben *(Pres)*

AGUAS DO AMAZONAS S.A.

(Name Changed To Manaus Ambiental S.A.)

AGUIA RESOURCES LIMITED

Suite 1002 Level 10 131 Macquarie Street
Sydney, NSW, 2000, Australia
Tel.: (61) 2 9247 3203
Fax: (61) 2 9251 7707
E-Mail: info@aguiaresources.com.au
Web Site: www.aguiaresources.com.au
Year Founded: 2007
AGR—(ASX)
Rev.: $187,191
Assets: $39,643,908
Liabilities: $534,844
Net Worth: $39,109,064
Earnings: ($2,481,923)
Emp.: 1
Fiscal Year-end: 06/30/13

Business Description:
Minerals Mining Services
S.I.C.: 1099
N.A.I.C.S.: 212299

Personnel:
David Gower *(Interim Chm)*
Simon J. R. Taylor *(CEO & Mng Dir)*
Prakash Hariharan *(Mng Dir)*
Andrew William Bursill *(Sec)*

Board of Directors:
David Gower
Prakash Hariharan
Brian Moller
Allan Pickett
Fernando Tallarico
Simon J. R. Taylor

Legal Counsel:
Addisons Lawyers
Level 12 60 Carrington Street
Sydney, Australia

AGUILA AMERICAN GOLD LIMITED

1090 West Georgia Street
Vancouver, BC, V6E 3V7, Canada
Tel.: (604) 685-9316
Fax: (604) 683-1585
Web Site: www.aguilaamerican.ca
Year Founded: 1997
AGL—(TSXV)

Business Description:
Mineral Exploration Services
S.I.C.: 1081
N.A.I.C.S.: 213114

Personnel:
John F. Huguet *(Chm)*
D. Blair Way *(Pres & CEO)*
Nick DeMare *(CFO & Corp Sec)*
Christopher R. Verrico *(COO)*

Board of Directors:
John F. Huguet
Dusan Berka
John Bortnak
Nick DeMare
James McCrea
Christopher R. Verrico
D. Blair Way

Transfer Agent:
Computershare Investor Services Inc
Vancouver, BC, Canada

AGVA CORPORATION

63 Kaki Bukit Pl
Singapore, 416234, Singapore
Tel.: (65) 67431232
Fax: (65) 67436642
E-Mail: agva.sg@agva.com
Web Site: www.agvagroup.com
Sales Range: $25-49.9 Million
Emp.: 1,453

Business Description:
Media Storage Products, Lifestyle Accessories & Plastic Products Mfr
S.I.C.: 2821
N.A.I.C.S.: 325211

Personnel:
Albert Beng Guan Lim *(Pres & CEO)*

Board of Directors:
Albert Beng Guan Lim

Subsidiary:

AGVA Singapore Pte Ltd (1)
63 Kaki Bukit Place
416234 Singapore, Singapore
Tel.: (65) 67431232
Fax: (65) 67436642
E-Mail: agva.sg@agvagroup.com
Web Site: www.agvagroup.com
Emp.: 6
Electronic Products & Components Mfr
S.I.C.: 3699
N.A.I.C.S.: 335999
Benjamin Neo *(Mgr-Sls & Ops)*

A.H. AL-ZAMIL GROUP OF COMPANIES

PO Box 9
Al Khobar, 31952, Saudi Arabia
Tel.: (966) 38824888
Fax: (966) 38822509
E-Mail: info@zamil.com
Web Site: www.zamil.com
Emp.: 10,000

Business Description:
Holding Company; Industrial & Commercial Products & Services
S.I.C.: 6719
N.A.I.C.S.: 551112

Personnel:
Khalid Abdullah Al-Zamil *(Pres)*

Board of Directors:
Abdul Rahman Al-Zamil
Adib Al-Zamil
Ahmed Abdullah Al-Zamil
Fahd Al-Zamil
Hamad Al-Zamil
Khalid Abdullah Al-Zamil
Sulaiman Abdullah Al-Zamil
Taufik Al-Zamil
Waleed Abdullah Al-Zamil

Subsidiaries:

Al Tawfiq Plastic Co. for Plastic & Woven Sacks Industries Ltd. (1)
PO Box 32368
Jeddah, 21428, Saudi Arabia
Tel.: (966) 2 6081033
Fax: (966) 2 6380549
E-Mail: info@apws.com.sa
Web Site: www.apws.com.sa
Bag Mfr
N.A.I.C.S.: 322220

Technical Seal Company Ltd. (1)
PO Box 7480
Dammam, 31462, Saudi Arabia
Tel.: (966) 13 8472703
Fax: (966) 13 8471485
E-Mail: info@technicalseal.com.sa
Building Material Distr
N.A.I.C.S.: 423390

Zamil Food Industries Ltd. (1)
PO Box 240
Al Jubayl, 31951, Saudi Arabia
Tel.: (966) 3 341 5235
Fax: (966) 3 341 8235
Web Site: www.zamilfood.com
Food Product Distr
N.A.I.C.S.: 424490
Abdalla Ali Al-Yami, *(Mgr-Ops)*

Zamil Group Commercial Division (1)
PO Box 13793
Dammam, 31414, Saudi Arabia
Tel.: (966) 3 847 3232
Fax: (966) 3 847 3131
E-Mail: sales@zamilcd.com.sa
Web Site: www.zamilcd.com.sa
Commerical Equipment Distr
N.A.I.C.S.: 423440
Nurul Islam *(Supvr-Sls-Chemical Div)*

Zamil Industrial Coating (1)
PO Box 4672
Al Khobar, 31952, Saudi Arabia
Tel.: (966) 13 8473833
Fax: (966) 13 8472822
Coating Material Mfr
N.A.I.C.S.: 325510
Ghassan H. Al-Zamil *(Mgr-Mktg & Sls)*

Zamil Ladder Factory (1)
PO Box 3408
Dammam, 31471, Saudi Arabia
Tel.: (966) 3 847 3544
Fax: (966) 3 847 1459
E-Mail: info@zamilladders.com
Web Site: www.zamilladders.com
Ladder Mfr
N.A.I.C.S.: 332999
Binu Cherian *(Mgr-Production)*

Zamil Operations & Maintenance Co. Ltd (1)
Al-Zamil Building
PO Box 1922
Al Khobar, 31952, Saudi Arabia
Tel.: (966) 3 8822494
Fax: (966) 3 8822032
E-Mail: zomco@zamil-om.com
Web Site: www.zamil-om.com
Ship Building & Maintenance Services
N.A.I.C.S.: 336611
Mohammed A. Al Zamil *(Chm)*
Hamed A. Al-Zamil *(Vice Chm)*
Zamil A. Al Zamil *(Pres)*

Zamil Partition Industries Company (1)
PO Box 1633
Dammam, 31441, Saudi Arabia
Tel.: (966) 3 847 3810
Fax: (966) 3 847 2180
E-Mail: info@zamilptn.com
Web Site: www.zamilptn.com
Partition Wall Installation Services
N.A.I.C.S.: 238390

Zamil Plastic Industries (1)
Dammam Second Industrial City Street 23 Cross 68
PO Box 1748
Al Khobar, 31952, Saudi Arabia
Tel.: (966) 38121114
Fax: (966) 38121477
E-Mail: info@zamilplastic.com
Web Site: www.zamilplastic.com
Plastic Product Mfr
N.A.I.C.S.: 326199
Adel Alghassab *(Mng Dir)*

Zamil Travel (1)
Zamil Building Prince Talal St
Al Khobar, Saudi Arabia
Tel.: (966) 3 898 3350
Fax: (966) 3 898 3354
E-Mail: zatravelk@zamiltravel.com
Web Site: www.zamiltravel.com

Travel Agency Operator
N.A.I.C.S.: 561510
Mirza Baig *(Mgr-Sls)*

Joint Venture:

Gulf Stabilizers Industries Ltd. (1)
Box 240
Al Jubayl, 31951, Saudi Arabia SA
Tel.: (966) 33413155
Fax: (966) 33419319
Web Site: www.gsi.com.sa/contactus.htm
Mfr. of Chemical Products; Joint Venture of Great Lakes Chemical Products & A.H. Al-Zamil Group of Companies
S.I.C.: 2899
N.A.I.C.S.: 325998

Non-U.S. Subsidiaries:

S.A. Al Zamil Trading Est. (1)
PO Box 51327
Dubai, United Arab Emirates
Tel.: (971) 4 294 0424
Fax: (971) 4 294 0434
Architectural Services
N.A.I.C.S.: 541310
Vinod Ravindran *(Engr-Sls)*

Zamil Architectural Co. Ltd (1)
PO Box 36450
Kuwait, 24755, Kuwait
Tel.: (965) 22449540
Fax: (965) 22405154
Architectural Services
N.A.I.C.S.: 541310

A.H. ALGOSAIBI & BROS.

PO Box 106
Al Khobar, 31952, Saudi Arabia
Tel.: (966) 38822666
Fax: (966) 38822470
E-Mail: mailbox@ahalgosaibi.com
Web Site: www.ahalgosaibi.com
Emp.: 1,000

Business Description:
Private Investment Company
S.I.C.: 6282
N.A.I.C.S.: 523930

Personnel:
Yousef Ahmad Algosaibi *(Pres)*
Saud Abdulaziz Algosaibi *(Mng Dir)*
Dawood Sulaiman Algosaibi *(Sr VP-Hotel & Govt Affairs)*
Mohammed S. Hindi *(Sr VP)*

Board of Directors:
Abdul Mohsen Ahmad Algosaibi
Dawood Sulaiman Algosaibi
Khaled Ahmad Algosaibi
Saud Abdulaziz Algosaibi
Yousef Ahmad Algosaibi
Mohammed S. Hindi

Joint Venture:

Jeddah Beverage Can Making Co. Ltd. (1)
Industrial city phase 3 Rd 153 Street 31
PO Box 16626
Jeddah, B21474, Saudi Arabia
Tel.: (966) 26361750
Fax: (966) 26362341
E-Mail: jbcmc@jbcmc.com
Web Site: www.jbcmc.com
Emp.: 256
Mfr. of Packaging Products for Consumer Goods; Joint Venture of Crown Cork & Seal Co., Inc. & A.H. Algosaibi & Bros.
S.I.C.: 3089
N.A.I.C.S.: 326199
Riyadh Hindi *(Gen Mgr)*

AH-VEST LIMITED

103 Booysens Reserve Road Crown Mines
Johannesburg, 2092, South Africa

Mailing Address:
PO Box 2152
Southdale, 2135, South Africa
Tel.: (27) 11 496 1800
Fax: (27) 11 496 1594
Web Site: www.alljoy.co.za
Year Founded: 1988
AHL—(JSE)
Sales Range: $10-24.9 Million

Business Description:
Sauce Mfr
S.I.C.: 2035
N.A.I.C.S.: 311941

Personnel:
Marci Pather *(CEO)*

AHB HOLDINGS BERHAD

Unit B-11-10 Block B Megan Avenue
2 Jalan Yap Kwan Seng
50450 Kuala Lumpur, Malaysia
Tel.: (60) 321669718
Fax: (60) 321669728
E-Mail: mailbox@ahb.com.my
Web Site: www.ahb.com.my
AHB—(KLS)
Rev.: $4,089,938
Assets: $8,081,185
Liabilities: $6,752,344
Net Worth: $1,328,842
Earnings: ($3,016,912)
Fiscal Year-end: 06/30/13

Business Description:
Office Interior Products Sales
S.I.C.: 7389
N.A.I.C.S.: 541410

Personnel:
Yoke Keong Yong *(CEO & Mng Dir)*
Wei Fong Wong *(Sec)*

Board of Directors:
Mirzan Mahathir
Chow Hun Chan
Jee Yoong Folk
Teck Ming Hee
Yoke Keong Yong

Subsidiaries:

AHB Distribution Sdn. Bhd. (1)
No 17 Jalan Industri PBP 11 Pusat Bandar
47100 Puchong, Selangor, Malaysia
Tel.: (60) 3 8061 7171
Fax: (60) 3 5882 2222
Emp.: 30
Office Furniture Whslr
S.I.C.: 5021
N.A.I.C.S.: 423210
Yong Yoke Keong *(CEO)*

AHB Technology Sdn. Bhd. (1)
17 Jalan Industri Pbp 11 Pusat Bandar Puchong
Puchong, Selangor, 47100, Malaysia
Tel.: (60) 358822882
Fax: (60) 358822222
E-Mail: mailbox@artwright.com
Web Site: www.artwright.com
Emp.: 75
Office Equipments Whslr
S.I.C.: 5044
N.A.I.C.S.: 423420
Yee Ping Chua *(Gen Mgr & Sr Mgr)*

AHC LIMITED

112 Siganto Drive
PO Box 34
Oxenford, QLD, 4212, Australia
Tel.: (61) 755732666
Fax: (61) 755733324
E-Mail: ahc1@ahc.com.au
Web Site: www.ahc.com.au
Rev.: $10,245,193
Assets: $71,086,683
Liabilities: $43,010,121
Net Worth: $28,076,561
Earnings: $63,090
Emp.: 10
Fiscal Year-end: 06/30/13

Business Description:
Building Development
S.I.C.: 1522
N.A.I.C.S.: 236116

Personnel:
Ian Roderick Macleod *(Chm)*
Rod Lindsay Macleod *(CEO & Mng Dir)*
Sheryl Anne Macleod *(CFO & Sec)*

Board of Directors:
Ian Roderick Macleod
Wayne Benson Lester
Rod Lindsay Macleod
Sheryl Anne Macleod
Rodney Joseph Walsh

AHEARN & SOPER INC.

100 Woodbine Downs Blvd
Rexdale, ON, M9W 5S6, Canada
Tel.: (416) 675-3999
Fax: (416) 675-3457
Toll Free: (800) 263-4258
Web Site: www.ahearn.com
Year Founded: 1881
Sales Range: $25-49.9 Million
Emp.: 150

Business Description:
Industrial Barcode Equipment Including Barcode Computers, Scanners, Printers & Label Applicators Mfr, Sales & Services
Import Export
S.I.C.: 3575
N.A.I.C.S.: 334118

Personnel:
John Paul *(Pres)*
Kamal Rashid *(CFO)*

Divisions:

Ahearn & Soper Inc. (1)
3375 Griffith
Saint Laurent, QC, H4T 1W5, Canada
Tel.: (514) 341-7671
Fax: (514) 341-2978
Toll Free: (800) 361-9584
E-Mail: real@ahearn.com
Emp.: 10
Industrial Barcode Equipment Including Barcode Computers, Scanners, Printers & Label Applicators Sales & Services
S.I.C.: 7629
N.A.I.C.S.: 811212
Real Lebel *(Mgr-Svc)*

Ahearn & Soper Inc. (1)
380 Jamieson Pkwy Ste 4
Cambridge, ON, N3C 4N4, Canada
Tel.: (519) 885-2260
Fax: (416) 675-6589
E-Mail: info@ahearn.com
Web Site: www.ahearn.com
Emp.: 5
Industrial Barcode Equipment Including Barcode Computers, Scanners, Printers & Label Applicators Sales & Services
S.I.C.: 7378
N.A.I.C.S.: 811212
John Paul *(Pres)*

Ahearn & Soper Inc. (1)
2915 19th Street Northeast Bay 1
Calgary, AB, T2E 7A2, Canada
Tel.: (403) 291-0300
Fax: (403) 291-0312
Toll Free: (800) 468-7025
E-Mail: info@ahearn.com
Web Site: www.ahearn.com
Emp.: 5
Industrial Barcode Equipment Including Barcode Computers, Scanners, Printers & Label Applicators Sales & Services
S.I.C.: 7629
N.A.I.C.S.: 811212
Julie Hazelwander *(Mgr-Svc)*

Ahearn & Soper Inc. (1)
38 Antares Drive Suite 110
Ottawa, ON, K2E 7V2, Canada
Tel.: (613) 226-4520
Fax: (613) 226-1183
Web Site: www.ahearn.com
Industrial Barcode Equipment Including Barcode Computers, Scanners, Printers & Label Applicators Sales
S.I.C.: 5045
N.A.I.C.S.: 423430
Gerry Ferris *(Mgr-Sls)*

U.S. Subsidiary:

Ahearn & Soper Inc. (1)
6695 E Clyde Rd
Howell, MI 48855-8070
Tel.: (248) 489-1950
Fax: (248) 489-1953
Web Site: www.ahern.com
Emp.: 60
Industrial Barcode Equipment Including Barcode Computers, Scanners, Printers & Label Applicators Mfr, Sales & Services
S.I.C.: 3575
N.A.I.C.S.: 334118
Scott Hunt *(Pres)*

AHEIM CAPITAL GMBH

Schlossbergstrasse 1
82319 Starnberg, Germany
Tel.: (49) 81 51 655 98 0
Fax: (49) 81 51 655 98 98
E-Mail: info@aheim.com
Web Site: www.aheim.com

Business Description:
Private Equity Firm
S.I.C.: 6211
N.A.I.C.S.: 523999

Personnel:
Peter Blumenwitz *(Mng Dir)*
Frank Henkelmann *(Mng Dir)*
Herbert Seggewiss *(Mng Dir)*

Holdings:

Metzgerei Zeiss GmbH (1)
Moselstrasse 70
63452 Hanau, Germany
Tel.: (49) 6181 9150 0
Fax: (49) 6181 9150 15
E-Mail: zentrale@erich-zeiss.de
Web Site: www.erich-zeiss.de
Sales Range: $50-74.9 Million
Emp.: 7
Catering Services
S.I.C.: 5812
N.A.I.C.S.: 722310

Remy & Geiser GmbH (1)
Remy & Geiser Strasse 1
56584 Anhausen, Germany
Tel.: (49) 2639 9311 0
Fax: (49) 2639 1230
E-Mail: info@remy-geiser.de
Web Site: www.remy-geiser.org
Emp.: 22
Pharmaceutical Packaging Mfr
S.I.C.: 2671
N.A.I.C.S.: 322220
Christoph Hanschke *(CEO)*

AHLCON PARENTERALS (INDIA) LTD.

(Acquired by B. Braun Melsungen AG)

AHLEIA INSURANCE GROUP

Al-Jalaa Tower
PO Box 1214
Rimal, Gaza, Palestine
Tel.: (970) 2824035
E-Mail: info@aig.ps
Web Site: www.aig.ps
Year Founded: 1994
AIG—(PAL)

Business Description:
Insurance & Risk Management Services
S.I.C.: 6411
N.A.I.C.S.: 524298

Personnel:
Mohamed Al Sabawi *(Chm & CEO)*
Omar Al Sarraj *(Vice Chm)*

Board of Directors:
Mohamed Al Sabawi
Majed Al Helow
Nahed Al Qishawi
Khaled Al Sabawi
Ahmad Al Salahat
Omar Al Sarraj

AHLI BANK Q.S.C.

Suhim Bin Hamad St
Doha, Qatar

Ahli Bank Q.S.C.—(Continued)

Mailing Address:
PO Box 2309
Doha, Qatar
Tel.: (974) 44232222
Fax: (974) 44444652
E-Mail: info@ahlibank.com.qa
Web Site: www.ahlibank.com.qa
ABQK—(QE)
Int. Income: $206,785,348
Assets: $5,503,899,994
Liabilities: $4,584,645,429
Net Worth: $919,254,565
Earnings: $124,243,969
Emp.: 420
Fiscal Year-end: 12/31/12

Business Description:
Commercial Banking
S.I.C.: 6029
N.A.I.C.S.: 522110

Personnel:
Faisal AbdulAziz Jasem Al-Thani *(Chm)*
Salah Jassim Murad *(CEO)*
Yehia Gamaleldin El Batrawi *(Deputy CEO-Retail)*
Mahmoud Yahya Malkawi *(Sr Deputy CEO-Corp Banking)*
Andrew McKechnie *(Deputy CEO)*
Mahalingam Shankar *(Deputy CEO-Fin, Ops, Svcs & Tech)*

Board of Directors:
Faisal AbdulAziz Jasem Al-Thani
Victor Nazeem Reddha Agha
Ahmed Abdulrahman Nasser Fakhro
Mohamed Falah Jassim Al Thani
Ahmed H. Yousif Obidan
Nasser Ali Saud Al-Thani

AHLI BANK S.A.O.G.

Mina Al Fahal
PO Box 545
116 Muscat, Oman
Tel.: (968) 24577000
Fax: (968) 24568001
E-Mail: info@ahlibank-oman.com
Web Site: ahlibank.com
Year Founded: 1997
ABOB—(MUS)
Int. Income: $130,439,202
Assets: $2,844,499,456
Liabilities: $2,411,020,128
Net Worth: $433,479,328
Earnings: $56,264,796
Emp.: 340
Fiscal Year-end: 12/31/12

Business Description:
Banking Services
S.I.C.: 6029
N.A.I.C.S.: 522110

Personnel:
Hamdan Ali Nasser Al Hinai *(Chm)*
Hamad Abdulmohsen H. D. Al Marzouq *(First Deputy Chm)*
Munir Abdulnabi Yousef Makki *(Secound Deputy Chm)*
Abdul Aziz Al Balushi *(CEO)*
Chandrashekhar Chetty *(Deputy CEO-Support Svcs)*
C. B. Ganesh *(Deputy CEO-Comml Banking, Investment & Treasury)*
Ashish Sood *(Deputy CEO-Retail & Private Banking)*

Board of Directors:
Hamdan Ali Nasser Al Hinai
Safana Mohamed Al Barwani
Usama Mohammed Al Barwani
Rashad Khamis Hamed Al Battashi
Sayyid Khalid Hamad Hamood Al Busaidi
Hamad Abdulmohsen H. D. Al Marzouq
Mustafa Shafqat Anwar
Sanjeev Baijal
Adel Mohamed Abdelshafe El-Labban
Keith Henry Gale
Munir Abdulnabi Yousef Makki

AHLI UNITED BANK BSC

Building 2495 Road 2832 Al Seef
District 428
PO Box 2424
Manama, Bahrain
Tel.: (973) 17585858
Fax: (973) 17580569
E-Mail: info@ahliunited.com
Web Site: www.ahliunited.com
AUB—(BAH)
Rev.: $1,070,638,000
Assets: $29,896,422,000
Liabilities: $26,699,593,000
Net Worth: $3,196,829,000
Earnings: $377,735,000
Fiscal Year-end: 12/31/12

Business Description:
Bank Holding Company
S.I.C.: 6712
N.A.I.C.S.: 551111

Personnel:
Hamad A. Al Marzouq *(Deputy Chm)*
Adel A. El-Labban *(CEO & Mng Dir)*
Sawsan Abulhassan *(Deputy CEO-Private Banking & Wealth Mgmt)*
Abdulla Al-Raeesi *(Deputy CEO-Retail Banking)*
Shafqat Anwar *(Deputy CEO-Ops & Tech Grp)*
Sanjeev Baijal *(Deputy CEO-Fin & Strategic Dev)*
Keith Gale *(Deputy CEO-Risk, Legal & Compliance)*
Lloyd Maddock *(Deputy CEO-Corp Banking)*

Board of Directors:
Fahad Al-Rajaan
Hamad A. Al Marzouq
Mohammed Al-Ghanim
Mohammed Jassim Al-Marzouk
Rashid Ismail Al-Meer
Abdulla M. H. Al-Sumait
Mohammed Saleh Behbehani
Adel A. El-Labban
Michael Essex
Turki Mohammed Al-Khater
Herschel Post

Non-U.S. Subsidiaries:

Ahli United Bank (U.K.) PLC **(1)**
35 Portman Square
London, W1H 6LR, United Kingdom (100%)
Tel.: (44) 2074876500
Fax: (44) 2074876808
E-Mail: info@ahliunited.com
Web Site: www.ahliunited.com
Emp.: 100
Commercial Banking
S.I.C.: 6029
N.A.I.C.S.: 522110
Fahad Al Rajaan *(Chm)*
Rashid Ismail Al-Meer *(Gen Dir)*

Al Ahli Bank of Kuwait KSC **(1)**
Ahmad Al Jaber Street Safat Square
PO Box 1387
Kuwait, Safat, 13014, Kuwait KW
Tel.: (965) 22400900
Fax: (965) 22417284
Web Site: www.eahli.com
ABK—(KUW)
Int. Income: $416,750,989
Assets: $10,535,160,398
Liabilities: $8,704,063,420
Net Worth: $1,831,096,979
Earnings: $106,403,377
Fiscal Year-end: 12/31/12
Banking Services
S.I.C.: 6029
N.A.I.C.S.: 522110
Ahmed Yousuf Behbehani *(Chm)*
Ali Hilal Al-Mutairi *(Deputy Chm)*
Colin Plowman *(CEO & Gen Mgr)*
Mohammed Sallam *(Gen Counsel & Head-Legal Div)*

Subsidiary:

Kuwait & Middle East Financial Investment Company K.S.C.C. **(2)**
Al-Merqab Block 1 Al-Soor Street Jassim Tower Floors 10 12 14 & 15
Safat, Kuwait, 13009, Kuwait (48%)
Tel.: (965) 22 25 55 55
Fax: (965) 22 25 25 63
E-Mail: info@kmefic.com.kw
Web Site: www.kmefic.com.kw
KMEFIC—(KUW)
Rev.: $14,193,042
Assets: $183,746,378
Liabilities: $99,997,612
Net Worth: $83,748,767
Earnings: ($3,856,007)
Emp.: 220
Fiscal Year-end: 12/31/12
Investment Management Services
S.I.C.: 6211
N.A.I.C.S.: 523999
Jihad Al-Humaidhi *(Chm)*
Hamed Al Sanee *(Vice Chm & CEO)*
Christian Shomber *(Chief Investment Officer)*

AHLIA INSURANCE COMPANY (S.A.)

904 St 80 H 10 1 Al Tahreeat Sq T
Baghdad, Iraq
Tel.: (964) 7904565829
Fax: (964) 7705855715
E-Mail: info@aic-iraq.com
Web Site: www.aic-iraq.com
Year Founded: 2001
NAHF—(IRAQ)

Business Description:
Insurance Management Services
S.I.C.: 6411
N.A.I.C.S.: 524298

Personnel:
Hamed Abd Ali *(Chm)*
Moaayd Salh Mohamed *(Vice Chm)*

Board of Directors:
Hamed Abd Ali
Abd Alkarem Hadi Al-Atrakche
Sadoon M. Khamis Al-Rubaiay
Mohammed Esam Hosam Al-Deen
Moaayd Salh Mohamed

AHLSTROM CORPORATION

Alvar Aallon katu 3 C
PO Box 329
00101 Helsinki, Finland
Tel.: (358) 108880
Fax: (358) 108884709
E-Mail: corporate.marketing@ahlstrom.com
Web Site: www.ahlstrom.com
Year Founded: 1851
AHL1V —(OMX)
Sls.: $1,360,708,636
Assets: $1,868,214,726
Liabilities: $1,136,032,863
Net Worth: $732,181,863
Earnings: ($942,319)
Emp.: 5,145
Fiscal Year-end: 12/31/12

Business Description:
Fiber Composites & Specialty Paper Mfr
Import Export
S.I.C.: 2676
N.A.I.C.S.: 322291

Personnel:
Pertti Korhonen *(Chm)*
Peter Seligson *(Vice Chm)*
Jan Lang *(Pres & CEO)*
Sakari Ahdekivi *(CFO)*
Paula Aarnio *(Exec VP-HR & Sustainability)*
Roberto Boggio *(Exec VP-Medical Bus)*
Fulvio Capussotti *(Exec VP-Advanced Filtration)*
Omar Hoek *(Exec VP-Food Bus)*
Arnaud Marquis *(Exec VP-Building & Energy)*
Rami Raulas *(Exec VP-Sls-Europe, Middle East & India)*
Luc Rousselet *(Exec VP-Supply Chain)*
Aki Saarinen *(Exec VP-Strategic Bus Dev)*
Paul H. Stenson *(Exec VP-Product & Tech Dev)*
Timo Vuorio *(Sr VP-HR)*

Board of Directors:
Pertti Korhonen
Robin Ahlstrom
Lori J. Cross
Esa Ikaheimonen
Daniel Meyer
Anders Moberg
Peter Seligson

Subsidiaries:

Ahlstrom Capital Oy **(1)**
Etelaesplanadi 14
PO Box 2169
FIN-00101 Helsinki, Finland
Tel.: (358) 1088818
Telex: 124518 altim sf
Fax: (358) 108884769
E-Mail: info@ahlstromcapital.com
Web Site: www.ahlstromcapital.com
Emp.: 10
Investment Services
S.I.C.: 6211
N.A.I.C.S.: 523999
Stig Gustavson *(Chm)*
Panu Routila *(Pres & CEO)*
Johan Borgstrom *(Gen Counsel)*

Subsidiary:

Sonoco Alcore Ltd. **(2)**
Karhulante 160
48601 Karhula, Finland (65%)
Tel.: (358) 102342300
Telex: 53179 alcor sf
Fax: (358) 5266887
Web Site: www.sonoco.com
Sales Range: $1-9.9 Million
Emp.: 12,000
Mfr of Core Boards & Core
S.I.C.: 3499
N.A.I.C.S.: 332999

Non-U.S. Subsidiaries:

Ahlstrom Cores AB **(2)**
PO Box 61
S 864 00 Matfors, Sweden (100%)
Tel.: (46) 6021680
Telex: 71166 almat s
Fax: (46) 6024473
Emp.: 21
Mfr. of Core Boards for Packaging Products
S.I.C.: 2653
N.A.I.C.S.: 322211

Non-U.S. Holding:

AR Packaging Group AB **(2)**
Adelgatan 6
SE 211 22 Malmo, Sweden
Tel.: (46) 46 287 33 00
Fax: (46) 46 287 33 04
Web Site: www.ar-carton.com
Sales Range: $600-649.9 Million
Emp.: 2,000
Packaging Mfr
S.I.C.: 2657
N.A.I.C.S.: 322212
Stig Gustavson *(Chm)*

Subsidiaries:

A&R Carton AB **(3)**
Adelgatan 6
SE 211 22 Malmo, Sweden
Tel.: (46) 406615660
Fax: (46) 406116605
Web Site: www.ar-carton.com
Sls.: $362,192,992
Emp.: 17
Folding Cartons & Packaging Machinery Mfr
S.I.C.: 2653
N.A.I.C.S.: 322211
Morten Ahlstrom *(Chm)*

Subsidiary:

A&R Carton Lund AB (4)
Maskinvagen 1
221 00 Lund, Sweden
Tel.: (46) 46183020
Fax: (46) 4646183295
E-Mail: lund@ar-carton.com
Web Site: www.ar-carton.com
Emp.: 80
Folding Cartons & Packaging Machinery Mfr
S.I.C.: 2653
N.A.I.C.S.: 322211
Claf Goran Wigstrand *(VP-Specialty Pkg)*

U.S. Subsidiary:

A&R Carton North America Inc. (4)
1400 N Brook Pkwy Ste 350
Suwanee, GA 30052
Tel.: (770) 623-8235
Fax: (770) 623-8236
E-Mail: atlanta@ar-carton.com
Web Site: www.ar-carton.com
Emp.: 2
Folding Cartons & Packaging Machinery Solutions
S.I.C.: 2653
N.A.I.C.S.: 322211

Non-U.S. Subsidiaries:

A&R Carton A/S (4)
Bredmyra 4 N
Box 33
Borgenhaugen, NO-1739 Sarpsborg, Norway
Tel.: (47) 69973803
Telex: 77532 ahlas n
Fax: (47) 69973801
E-Mail: skjeberg@ar-carton.com
Web Site: www.ar-carton.com
Emp.: 100
Folding Cartons & Packaging Machinery Mfr
S.I.C.: 2653
N.A.I.C.S.: 322211
Pal Wikstrom *(Gen Mgr)*

A&R Carton BV (4)
Steenhouwersstraat 4
NL-8601 WD Sneek, Netherlands
Tel.: (31) 515422922
Fax: (31) 515423215
E-Mail: sneek@ar-carton.com
Web Site: www.ar-carton.com
Emp.: 110
Folding Cartons & Packaging Machinery Mfr
S.I.C.: 2653
N.A.I.C.S.: 322211
Gerard De Vries *(Mng Dir)*

A&R Carton cdf SA (4)
Boulevard du Cormier
FR-49302 Cholet, Cedex, France
Tel.: (33) 241462940
Fax: (33) 241628046
E-Mail: cholet@ar-carton.com
Web Site: www.ar-carton.com
Folding Cartons & Packaging Machinery Mfr
S.I.C.: 2653
N.A.I.C.S.: 322211

A&R Carton Oy (4)
Luvalahdentie 1
PO Box 120
FI-27501 Kauttua, Finland
Tel.: (358) 10 430 500
Telex: 124518 altim sf
Fax: (358) 10 430 55 34
E-Mail: kauttua@ar-carton.com
Web Site: www.ar-carton.com
Folding Cartons & Packaging Machinery Mfr
S.I.C.: 2657
N.A.I.C.S.: 322212
Harald Schulz *(Pres & CEO)*

A&R Carton St Petersburg ZAO (4)
Volkhonskoye Shosse 4
Lomonosov District
Poselok Gorelovo, 198323 Saint Petersburg, Russia
Tel.: (7) 8123466167
Fax: (7) 812 3466165
E-Mail: st.petersburg@ar-carton.com
Web Site: www.ar-carton.com
Emp.: 25
Folding Cartons & Packaging Machinery Mfr
S.I.C.: 2653
N.A.I.C.S.: 322211

A&R Carton (4)
Romuvos str 32 C
47197 Kaunas, 21, Lithuania
Tel.: (370) 37460626
Fax: (370) 37432001
Web Site: www.ar-carton.com
Folding Cartons & Packaging Machinery Mfr
S.I.C.: 2653
N.A.I.C.S.: 322211

Flextrus AB (3)
Lund Business Park Maskinvagen 1
PO Box 22
SE-221 00 Lund, Sweden
Tel.: (46) 46 18 30 00
Fax: (46) 46 211 36 00
E-Mail: info@flextrus.com
Web Site: www.flextrus.com
Flexible Packaging Mfr
S.I.C.: 2672
N.A.I.C.S.: 322220
Per Nystrom *(CEO)*

Ahlstrom Glassfibre Oy (1)
Ahlstromintie 19
PO Box 140
48601 Kotka, Finland
Tel.: (358) 10 888 11
Fax: (358) 10 888 2510
Fiber Glass Products Mfr
S.I.C.: 3231
N.A.I.C.S.: 327215
Pekka Helynranta *(CEO)*

Subsidiary:

Karhulan Teollisuuskerays Oy (2)
Itaranta 1270
48700 Kotka, Finland
Tel.: (358) 10 8880
Fax: (358) 10 8884910
Waste Management Services
S.I.C.: 4959
N.A.I.C.S.: 562998
Pekka Helynranta *(Gen Mgr)*

Plants:

Ahlstrom Glassfibre Oy - Mikkeli Plant (2)
Insinoorinkatu 2
50 100 Mikkeli, Finland
Tel.: (358) 1088812
Telex: 55150 fiber sf
Fax: (358) 108882900
E-Mail: matti.valkonen@ahlstrom.com
Web Site: www.ahlstrom.com
Emp.: 6,700
Mfr. of Glassfiber & Products
S.I.C.: 3221
N.A.I.C.S.: 327213
Matti Valkonen *(Mng Dir)*

Ahlstrom Russia Oy (1)
Ahlstromintie 19
48600 Kotka, Finland
Tel.: (358) 108 880
Fax: (358) 10 888 4709
Web Site: www.ahlstrom.com
Paper Products Mfr
S.I.C.: 2679
N.A.I.C.S.: 322299
Yan Lang *(CEO)*

Non-U.S. Subsidiaries:

Ahlstrom Sales LLC (2)
ul Zemlianoy Val 54 Build 2
109004 Moscow, Russia
Tel.: (7) 495 626 4661
Fax: (7) 495 626 4663
Paper Products Distr
S.I.C.: 5113
N.A.I.C.S.: 424130

Ahlstrom Tver LLC (2)
Promyshlennaya Str 11
Redkino, 171261 Tver, Russia
Tel.: (7) 495 644 13 50
Fax: (7) 495 644 13 51
Web Site: www.ahlstrom.com
Emp.: 75
Glass Products Mfr
S.I.C.: 3231
N.A.I.C.S.: 327215
Harri Rantonen *(Gen Dir)*

Ahlstrom Sales Helsinki Oy (1)
Salmisaarenaukio 1
00180 Helsinki, Finland
Tel.: (358) 10 8880
Fax: (358) 10 8884190
Emp.: 100
Specialty Papers & Packaging Materials Distr
S.I.C.: 5113
N.A.I.C.S.: 424130
Jan Lang *(Gen Mgr)*

Ahlstrom Tampere Oy (1)
Paperitehtaantie 15
PO Box 55
27501 Kauttua, Finland
Tel.: (358) 10 303 200
Fax: (358) 10 303 2491
Web Site: www.ahlstrom.com
Paper Products Mfr
S.I.C.: 2679
N.A.I.C.S.: 322299

Ahlstrom (1)
Ahostromimtig 19
PO Box 18
Karhula, FIN 48601, Finland (100%)
Tel.: (358) 52241111
Telex: 53169 ahlph sf
Fax: (358) 52242223
Web Site: www.ahlstrom.com
Mfr. & Supplier of Industrial Pumps
S.I.C.: 3561
N.A.I.C.S.: 333911

Fiberflow Oy (1)
PO Box 329
Helsinki, 101, Finland
Tel.: (358) 108880
Fax: (358) 108884709
Printing Machinery & Equipment Mfr
S.I.C.: 3555
N.A.I.C.S.: 333244
Jan Lang *(Gen Mgr)*

U.S. Subsidiary:

Ahlstrom North America LLC (1)
300 Knightsbridge Pkwy
Lincolnshire, IL 60069
Tel.: (847) 478-8840
Emp.: 50
Paper Products Mfr
S.I.C.: 2679
N.A.I.C.S.: 322299
William Casey *(Exec VP-Sls-Americas)*

Subsidiary:

Ahlstrom USA Inc. (2)
2 Elm St
Windsor Locks, CT 06096-2335
Tel.: (860) 654-8300
Fax: (860) 654-8301
Emp.: 400
Specialty Paper Products Mfr
S.I.C.: 2679
N.A.I.C.S.: 322299
Steven Budnick *(Controller)*

Subsidiaries:

Ahlstrom Filtration LLC (3)
1200 E Elm St PO Box 680
Taylorville, IL 62568
Tel.: (217) 824-9611
Fax: (217) 824-9514
Web Site: www.ahlstrom.com
Emp.: 90
Filtration Solutions
S.I.C.: 2621
N.A.I.C.S.: 322121

Ahlstrom Filtration, LLC (3)
215 Nebo Rd
Madisonville, KY 42431
Mailing Address:
PO Box 1708
Madisonville, KY 42431
Tel.: (270) 821-0140
Fax: (270) 326-3290
Web Site: www.ahlstrom.com
Emp.: 100
Mfr of Automotive Filters
S.I.C.: 3711
N.A.I.C.S.: 336111
Dennis Molle *(Plant Mgr)*

Ahlstrom Glass Nonwovens LLC (3)
227 Browntown Rd
Bishopville, SC 29010
Tel.: (803) 423-6120
Fax: (803) 423-6116
Web Site: www.ahlstrom.com
Non Woven Fabric Material Mfr
S.I.C.: 2269
N.A.I.C.S.: 313310

Ahlstrom Mount Holly Springs (3)
122 W Butler St
Mount Holly Springs, PA 17065 (100%)
Tel.: (717) 486-3438
Telex: 650-3549
Fax: (717) 486-4863
Web Site: www.ahlstrom.com
Emp.: 50
Filtration Papers Mfr
S.I.C.: 2621
N.A.I.C.S.: 322121

Ahlstrom Nonwovens LLC (3)
2 Elm St
Windsor Locks, CT 06096-2335 DE
Tel.: (860) 654-8300 (100%)
Fax: (860) 654-8301
Toll Free: (800) 733-9837
Web Site: www.ahlstrom.com
Sales Range: $150-199.9 Million
Emp.: 500
Mfr of Nonwoven Fabrics & Specialty Papers
Export
S.I.C.: 2676
N.A.I.C.S.: 322291
J. Michael Joyce *(Health & Safety)*

Ahlstrom Windsor Locks LLC (3)
2 Elm St
Windsor Locks, CT 06096
Tel.: (860) 654-8300
Fax: (860) 654-8301
Web Site: www.ahlstrom.com
Sls.: $63,100,000
Emp.: 510
Sanitary Paper Products
S.I.C.: 2676
N.A.I.C.S.: 322291
William Casey *(VP)*

Non-U.S. Subsidiaries:

Ahlstrom Asia Holdings Pte Ltd (1)
14 Ann Siang Road 02-01
Singapore, 69694, Singapore
Tel.: (65) 6861 2700
Fax: (65) 6861 2400
Web Site: www.ahlstrom.com
Investment Management Services
S.I.C.: 6211
N.A.I.C.S.: 523999
Jari Koikkalainen *(Exec VP-Transportation Filtration & Sls)*

Subsidiary:

Ahlstrom Machinery (Asia-Pacific) Pte Ltd. (2)
10-01/03 Pacific Plaza 9 Scotts Road
Singapore, 0922, Singapore
Tel.: (65) 67332522
Telex: 37694 ahlsi rs
Fax: (65) 67328211
S.I.C.: 2653
N.A.I.C.S.: 322211

Non-U.S. Subsidiary:

Ahlstrom Korea Co., Ltd. (2)
7 KeumLi YugaMyoun Dalsung County
Daegu, 711-882, Korea (South) (100%)
Tel.: (82) 536600491
Fax: (82) 536110493
Web Site: www.ahlstrom.co.kr
Sls.: $30,000,000
Emp.: 120
Automotive Filter Papers Mfr & Sales
S.I.C.: 2653
N.A.I.C.S.: 322211
Roberto Poccio *(Gen Mgr)*

Plant:

Ahlstrom Korea Co., Ltd.-Hyun Poon Mill (3)
7 Keumdong Li Yuga Myon Dalsung Kun
Kyongsangbuk Do, Seoul, 711882, Korea (South) (100%)
Tel.: (82) 536110491
Fax: (82) 536110493
Web Site: www.ahlstrom.co.kr
Emp.: 130
Mfr. of Automotive Filter Papers
S.I.C.: 2679

Ahlstrom Corporation—(Continued)

N.A.I.C.S.: 322299
Roberto Poggio *(CEO)*

Non-U.S. Plant:

Ahlstrom Asia Holdings Pte Ltd - Binzhou Plant **(2)**
Ahlstrom Binzhou No 209 Huanghe 5 Road
Binzhou, Shangdong, 256600, China
Tel.: (86) 543 340 9777
Fax: (86) 543 340 2215
Web Site: www.ahlstrom.com
Emp.: 170
Paper Products Mfr
S.I.C.: 2679
N.A.I.C.S.: 322299
Tommy Biome *(Gen Mgr)*

Ahlstrom Australia Pty Ltd **(1)**
Office 2 6 Gurrigal Street
Mosman, NSW, 2088, Australia
Tel.: (61) 2 9960 4519
Fax: (61) 2 9968 1917
Web Site: www.ahlstrom.com
Paper Products Mfr & Distr
S.I.C.: 2679
N.A.I.C.S.: 322299

Ahlstrom Brignoud SA **(1)**
Rue Alfred Fredet
38196 Brignoud, France
Tel.: (33) 4 7645 3515
Fax: (33) 4 7671 2720
Emp.: 11
Paper Products Mfr
S.I.C.: 2679
N.A.I.C.S.: 322299
Remy Baars *(Gen Mgr)*

Ahlstrom Chirnside Ltd **(1)**
Chirnside
Duns, GB-Berwickshire, TD11 3JW, United Kingdom (100%)
Tel.: (44) 1890818303
Fax: (44) 1890818256
Web Site: www.ahlstrom.com
Emp.: 250
S.I.C.: 2653
N.A.I.C.S.: 322211
Stuart Nixon *(Gen Mgr)*

Ahlstrom Fabriano S.r.l. **(1)**
Localita Campoginepro 2 Frazione Gaville
60041 Sassoferrato, Ancona, Italy
Tel.: (39) 073 29127
Fax: (39) 073 2970464
Web Site: www.ahlstrom.com
Paper Products Mfr
S.I.C.: 2679
N.A.I.C.S.: 322299

Ahlstrom Fiber Composites India Private Ltd **(1)**
108-109 Prakashdeep Bldg 7 Tolstoy Marg
New Delhi, 110 001, India
Tel.: (91) 11 23753680
Fax: (91) 11 23753681
Fiber Composite Materials Mfr
S.I.C.: 2652
N.A.I.C.S.: 322219
Rahul Dharmadhikary *(Mng Dir)*

Ahlstrom Holding GmbH **(1)**
Romereschstrasse 33
PO Box 3407 09
49090 Osnabruck, Germany De
Tel.: (49) 5416040 (100%)
Telex: 94848 kaeosn d
Fax: (49) 541604210
Emp.: 350
Holding Company; Paper Products Mfr & Distr
S.I.C.: 6719
N.A.I.C.S.: 551112

Subsidiaries:

Ahlstrom Munich GmbH **(2)**
Brahmsstrasse 32
81677 Munich, Germany De
Tel.: (49) 89 419 4380
Telex: 524681 imex d
Fax: (49) 89 470 1380
Paper Products Whslr
S.I.C.: 5113
N.A.I.C.S.: 424130

Ahlstrom Numbrecht Verwaltung GmbH **(2)**
PO Box 1240
51582 Numbrecht, Germany De
Tel.: (49) 22934010
Fax: (49) 2293401151
Emp.: 35
Paper Products Whslr
S.I.C.: 5113
N.A.I.C.S.: 424130

Ahlstrom Japan Inc. **(1)**
13-6 Ebisu 1-Chrome
Shibuya-Ku, Tokyo, 150-0013, Japan
Tel.: (81) 3 3442 1611
Fax: (81) 3 3442 1626
Web Site: www.ahlstrom.com
Paper Products Distr
S.I.C.: 5113
N.A.I.C.S.: 424130

Ahlstrom Labelpack SAS **(1)**
Chemin Cartallier
38780 Pont-l'Eveque, France
Tel.: (33) 4 7416 1010
Fax: (33) 4 7416 1011
Web Site: www.ahlstrom.com
Packaging Paper Products Mfr
S.I.C.: 2671
N.A.I.C.S.: 322220

Ahlstrom Malmedy SA **(1)**
Avenue de Pont de Warche 1
4960 Malmedy, Belgium BE
Tel.: (32) 8079 5411
Fax: (32) 8079 5416
Web Site: www.ahlstrom.com
Paper Products Mfr
S.I.C.: 2679
N.A.I.C.S.: 322299
Anthony Lemonnier *(Gen Mgr)*

Ahlstrom Monterrey, S. de R.L. de C.V. **(1)**
Trujillo No 633 Col Lindavista Delegacion Gustavo A Madero
07300 Mexico, Mexico
Tel.: (52) 55 5586 5388
Fax: (52) 55 5586 5380
Web Site: www.ahlstrom.com
Emp.: 1
Paper & Cardboard Products Distr
S.I.C.: 5113
N.A.I.C.S.: 424130
Salvador Perea *(Gen Mgr)*

Ahlstrom Norrkoping AB **(1)**
Lindovagen 77
Box 6074
S-600 06 Norrkoping, Sweden
Tel.: (46) 11282200
Telex: 64328 alswed s
Fax: (46) 11282284
Web Site: www.sonoco.com
Emp.: 24
Mfr. of Equipment for the Pulp & Paper Industry
S.I.C.: 3554
N.A.I.C.S.: 333243
Michael Fajer *(Mng Dir)*

Ahlstrom Research and Services SA **(1)**
Immeuble Perigares B 201 Rue Carnot
94127 Fontenay-sous-Bois, France
Tel.: (33) 1 4974 4900
Fax: (33) 4 7416 3241
Web Site: www.ahlstrom.com
Paper Products Mfr
S.I.C.: 2679
N.A.I.C.S.: 322299

Ahlstrom Seoul Co. Ltd **(1)**
Room 601 Kanglim Building 448-7 Seongnae-dong
Gangdong-gu, 134-030 Seoul, Korea (South)
Tel.: (82) 2 3452 7314
Fax: (82) 2 3452 8316
Web Site: www.ahlstrom.com
Pulp Paper Products Mfr & Distr
S.I.C.: 2621
N.A.I.C.S.: 322121

Ahlstrom Specialties SA **(1)**
15 Rue des Papetiers
27500 Pont Audemer, France
Tel.: (33) 2 3241 6100
Fax: (33) 2 3241 4431
Paper Products Mfr
S.I.C.: 2679
N.A.I.C.S.: 322299

Ahlstrom Stalldalen AB **(1)**
Stalldergvagen
Stalldalen, 71481, Sweden (100%)
Tel.: (46) 58029100
Fax: (46) 58020521
Emp.: 120
S.I.C.: 2653
N.A.I.C.S.: 322211
Lars Olos Nibert *(Mgr-Fin)*

Ahlstrom Turin S.p.A. **(1)**
Via Stura 98
10075 Mathi, Torino, Italy (100%)
Tel.: (39) 119260111
Telex: 21043 bosso i
Fax: (39) 0119269617
Emp.: 600
Paper Impregnation Processes for Making Masking Tape
S.I.C.: 2653
N.A.I.C.S.: 322211
Francesca Camerano *(Dir-Mktg & Comm)*

Ahlstrom (UK) Limited **(1)**
20 Tollgate Chandlers Ford
Eastleigh, Hampshire, SO53 3TG, United Kingdom
Tel.: (44) 2380 65 2265
Fax: (44) 2380 65 3276
Emp.: 1
Paper Products Mfr & Distr
S.I.C.: 2679
N.A.I.C.S.: 322299

Ahlstrom Warsaw Sp. Z.o.o **(1)**
Al Niepodleglosci 124 Lok 5
02-577 Warsaw, Poland
Tel.: (48) 22 201 1504
Fax: (48) 22 201 1501
Emp.: 5
Industrial Paper Products Distr
S.I.C.: 5113
N.A.I.C.S.: 424130
Magdalena Elzbieta Zydowicz *(Gen Mgr)*

Nordica S.r.l. **(1)**
Via Della Geiustizia 9
I 20125 Milan, Italy
Tel.: (39) 0266981335
Telex: 314308 nordi i
Fax: (39) 0266980480
Emp.: 10
Paper, Paperboard & Cardboard
S.I.C.: 2653
N.A.I.C.S.: 322211

AHLUWALIA CONTRACTS (INDIA) LIMITED

Ahluwalia House 4 Community Centre
New Delhi, 110017, India
Tel.: (91) 1140504557
Fax: (91) 1140504558
E-Mail: mail@acilnet.com
Web Site: www.acilnet.com
AHLUCONT—(NSE)
Rev.: $268,429,541
Assets: $199,027,021
Liabilities: $161,135,849
Net Worth: $37,891,172
Earnings: ($13,221,475)
Emp.: 18,076
Fiscal Year-end: 03/31/13

Business Description:
Construction Engineering Services
S.I.C.: 8711
N.A.I.C.S.: 541330

Personnel:
Bikramjit Ahluwalia *(Chm & Mng Dir)*
Vipin Kumar Tiwari *(Compliance Officer, Sec & Gen Mgr-Corp)*
Shobhit Uppal *(Deputy Mng Dir)*

Board of Directors:
Bikramjit Ahluwalia
Vikaas Ahluwalia
Sushil Chandra
S. K. Chawla
Arun Kumar Gupta
Vinay Pal
Shobhit Uppal

Transfer Agent:
Link Intime India Pvt Ltd
Narang Tower 44 Community Ceneter Nariana Industrial Area Phase-I
New Delhi, 110028, India
Tel.: (91) 1141410592
Fax: (91) 1141410591

Subsidiary:

Ahlcon Ready Mix Concrete Pvt. Ltd. **(1)**
Safdarjang Enclave
New Delhi, 110029, India
Tel.: (91) 11 46003600
Fax: (91) 11 26714755
E-Mail: mail@ahlconrmc.com
Web Site: www.ahlconrmc.com
Ready Mix Concrete Mfr
S.I.C.: 3273
N.A.I.C.S.: 327320

Plant:

Ahlcon Ready Mix Concrete Pvt. Ltd. - Bommenhalli Plant **(2)**
Bommenhalli Village Bidarahalli Hobli
Bangalore East Taluk
Urban District, Bengaluru, Karnataka, 560049, India
Tel.: (91) 80 28470444
Fax: (91) 80 28470333
E-Mail: bangalore@ahlconrmc.com
Web Site: www.ahlconrmc.com
Ready Mix Concrete Mfr
S.I.C.: 3273
N.A.I.C.S.: 327320
Ranjeet Kumar *(Gen Mgr)*

AHMAD HASSAN TEXTILE MILLS LIMITED

46-Hassan Parwana Colony
60000 Multan, Pakistan
Tel.: (92) 614512933
Fax: (92) 614512361
E-Mail: export@ahtml.com.pk
Web Site: www.ahtml.com.pk
AHTM—(KAR)
Sales Range: $25-49.9 Million

Business Description:
Spinning & Weaving Mill
S.I.C.: 2397
N.A.I.C.S.: 313220

Personnel:
Muhammad Javed Anwar *(Chm)*
Mian Muhammad Parvez *(CEO)*

Board of Directors:
Muhammad Javed Anwar
Muhammad Aurangzeb
Muhammad Harris
Syed Raza Abbas Jaffari
Salma Javed
Mian Muhammad Parvez
Waheeda Parvez

AHMAD ZAKI RESOURCES BERHAD

No 71 Persiaran Gurney
54000 Kuala Lumpur, Malaysia
Tel.: (60) 3 2698 7171
Fax: (60) 3 2694 8181
E-Mail: azrb@azrb.com
Web Site: www.azrb.com
AZRB—(KLS)
Rev.: $221,231,092
Assets: $237,591,876
Liabilities: $167,728,609
Net Worth: $69,863,267
Earnings: $6,095,075
Fiscal Year-end: 12/31/12

Business Description:
Civil & Structural Construction Services
S.I.C.: 1521
N.A.I.C.S.: 236115

Personnel:
Zaki Muda *(Vice Chm)*
Zakariah Muda *(Mng Dir)*
Bahari Johari *(Sec)*
Seuhailey Shamsudin *(Sec)*
Maw Chuan Wong *(Sec)*

Board of Directors:
Aman Ahmad
Omar Abdullah
Yin Pin Lau

Mustaffa Mohamad
Zakariah Muda
Zaki Muda
Zulkifli Muda
Mansor Said

AHMED H. FITAIHI COMPANY

(d/b/a Fitaihi Holding Group)
Madina Rd
PO Box 2606
Jeddah, 21461, Saudi Arabia
Tel.: (966) 26517505
Fax: (966) 26514860
E-Mail: info@fitaihi.com.sa
Web Site: www.fitaihigroup.com
Year Founded: 1907
4180—(SAU)
Sales Range: $50-74.9 Million
Emp.: 420

Business Description:
Jewelry Mfr & Whslr
S.I.C.: 3914
N.A.I.C.S.: 339910

Personnel:
Ahmed Hassan Fitaihi *(Chm)*

Board of Directors:
Ahmed Hassan Fitaihi
Ibrahim Al-Madhoun
Osama A. Elkhereij
Mohammad Fitaihi
Walid A. Fitaihi
Majed Diaa-Ul-Din Kareem
Ihab Samannoudi

AHMED MANSOOR AL-A'ALI CO.

PO Box 778
Manama, Bahrain
Tel.: (973) 17250521
Fax: (973) 1 7258899
E-Mail: mail@alaali.com
Web Site: www.alaali.com
Emp.: 4,350

Business Description:
Non-Residential Construction Services
S.I.C.: 1542
N.A.I.C.S.: 236220

Personnel:
Ahmed Mansoor Al A'ali *(Chm)*
Hassan Abdul Aziz Al A'ali *(CEO)*

Joint Venture:

Comsip Al A'ali W.L.L. **(1)**
PO Box 26949
Adliya, Bahrain
Tel.: (973) 17773006
Fax: (973) 17770045
E-Mail: comsip@batelco.com.bh
Web Site: www.comsip.com.bh
Emp.: 400
Electrical Work & Instrumentation Mfr
S.I.C.: 1731
N.A.I.C.S.: 238210
Francois Husson *(Mng Dir)*

Non-U.S. Subsidiaries:

Comsip Al A'ali W.L.L. **(2)**
PO Box 23342
Doha, Qatar
Tel.: (974) 444 0232
Fax: (974) 444 0292
Web Site: www.comsip.com.bh/contactus.htm
Electrical Work
S.I.C.: 1731
N.A.I.C.S.: 238210
Syed Ali *(Gen Mgr)*

AHMEDABAD STEELCRAFT LTD.

401 4th Floor 637 Complex Panchvati 2nd Lane
Gulbai Tekra, Ahmedabad, 380 006, India
Tel.: (91) 7926401996
Fax: (91) 7926404656
E-Mail: ascsteelad1@gmail.com
Web Site: www.steelcraft.co.in
522273—(BOM)
Rev.: $1,598,472
Assets: $4,910,765
Liabilities: $145,981
Net Worth: $4,764,784
Earnings: $145,175
Fiscal Year-end: 03/31/13

Business Description:
Steel Fabricated Products Mfr
S.I.C.: 3317
N.A.I.C.S.: 331210

Personnel:
Ashok C. Gandhi *(Chm)*
Darshan A. Jhaveri *(Mng Dir)*
Anand V. Shah *(Mng Dir)*

Board of Directors:
Ashok C. Gandhi
Anand N. Jhaveri
Darshan A. Jhaveri
Viral A. Jhaveri
Kanishka H. Kaji
Malay Mahadevia
Anand V. Shah
Girish D. Shah
Shashank I. Shah

Transfer Agent:
Link Intime India Private Limited
303 3rd Floor Shopper's Plaza 5 Near 5 Government Society
Opp Municipal Market C G Road, Ahmedabad, 380009, India

AHMEDNAGAR FORGINGS LIMITED

(See Under Amtek Auto Limited)

AHNLAB, INC.

6 Fl CCMM Bldg 12
Yoido Dong Yongdungpo Gu
150869 Seoul, Korea (South)
Tel.: (82) 221866000
Fax: (82) 221866100
E-Mail: customer@ahnlab.com
Web Site: www.ahnlab.com
53800—(KRS)
Sales Range: $50-74.9 Million
Emp.: 500

Business Description:
Security Solutions
S.I.C.: 8999
N.A.I.C.S.: 541690

Personnel:
Charles Ahn *(Chm)*
Philip Kim *(Pres & CEO)*

Board of Directors:
Charles Ahn
Seokgyun Kwon
Namseob Seo
Yeonsoo Yoon

AHOKU ELECTRONIC COMPANY

5F No 88 Sec 1 Nei-Hu Rd
Taipei, Taiwan
Tel.: (886) 227991199
Fax: (886) 227999099
Web Site: www.ahoku.com
3002—(TAI)
Sales Range: $10-24.9 Million
Emp.: 1,200

Business Description:
Power Devices Mfr
S.I.C.: 3643
N.A.I.C.S.: 335931

Personnel:
Anthony Lee *(Chm & Gen Mgr)*

Subsidiary:

ACPA Technology Co., Ltd. **(1)**
No 4 Sansai Lane 311 Chieh Shou Road Section 4
Taipei, Taiwan
Tel.: (886) 286716551
Fax: (886) 2 8671 6552
Web Site: www.acpa.com.tw
Electronic Components Mfr
S.I.C.: 3679
N.A.I.C.S.: 334419

Non-U.S. Subsidiary:

Ahoku Techland Electronics Ltd. **(1)**
5 DaBanDi 1st Road ShaBen ChangAn
Dongguan, Guangdong, 523876, China
Tel.: (86) 76987088788
Fax: (86) 76987088799
Power Devices & Electronic Components Mfr
S.I.C.: 3679
N.A.I.C.S.: 334419

AHRESTY CORPORATION

Sumitomo Nakanosakaue Bldg 11F
1-38-1 Chu
Nakako-ku, Tokyo, 164-0011, Japan
Tel.: (81) 353326001
E-Mail: ahresty_ga0@ahresty.co.jp
Web Site: www.ahresty.co.jp
Year Founded: 1943
5852—(TKS)
Sales Range: $1-4.9 Billion
Emp.: 3,628

Business Description:
Die Cast Aluminum Products Mfr
S.I.C.: 3364
N.A.I.C.S.: 331523

Personnel:
Arata Takahashi *(Pres & CEO)*
Shigeru Furuya *(Exec Officer)*
Teiichi Hayashi *(Exec Officer)*
Akira Ogi *(Sr Mng Exec Officer)*

Board of Directors:
Shigeru Furuya
Teiichi Hayashi
Tadakazu Miyauchi
Akira Ogi
Arata Takahashi

Subsidiaries:

Ahresty Die Mold Hamamatsu Corporation **(1)**
5-3-10 Sakuradai
Nishi-ku, Hamamatsu, Shizuoka, 431-1104, Japan
Tel.: (81) 534361711
Fax: (81) 53436133
Aluminium Die Casting Products Mfr
S.I.C.: 3364
N.A.I.C.S.: 331523
Masahiro Fukushima *(Pres)*

Ahresty Kumamoto Corporation **(1)**
36 Urakawachi Matsubase-machi
Uki, Kumamoto, 869-0521, Japan
Tel.: (81) 964333111
Fax: (81) 964333214
E-Mail: ahresty_ga0@ahresty.co.jp
Die Casting Products Mfr
S.I.C.: 3541
N.A.I.C.S.: 333517
Arata Takahashi *(Pres)*

Ahresty Pretech Corporation **(1)**
3-8-38 Takaoka-higashi
Naka-Ku, Hamamatsu, Shizuoka, 433-8117, Japan
Tel.: (81) 534362121
Fax: (81) 534374581
Web Site: www.tokaiseiko.co.jp
Emp.: 300
Automotive & Motorcycle Components Mfr
S.I.C.: 3751
N.A.I.C.S.: 336991

Ahresty Techno Service Corporation **(1)**
938 Nagashima
Hamakita-ku, Hamamatsu, Shizuoka, 434-0013, Japan
Tel.: (81) 535841488
Fax: (81) 535858611
E-Mail: info@ahresty-tec.jp
Web Site: www.ahresty-tec.jp
Emp.: 100
Die Casting Peripheral Equipment Mfr & Distr
S.I.C.: 3542
N.A.I.C.S.: 333517
Kunio Yoshida *(Pres)*

Ahresty Tochigi Corporation **(1)**
4060 Oaza Mibu Otsu
Shimotsuga-gun, Mibu, Tochigi, 321-0215, Japan
Tel.: (81) 282825111
Fax: (81) 282826330
Die Casting Products Mfr
S.I.C.: 3541
N.A.I.C.S.: 333517

Ahresty Yamagata Corporation **(1)**
65 Oaza Arato
Nishiokitama-gun, Shirataka, Yamagata, 992-0832, Japan
Tel.: (81) 238855233
Aluminium Die Casting Products Mfr
S.I.C.: 3364
N.A.I.C.S.: 331523

Plants:

AHRESTY CORPORATION - Higashimatsuyama Plant **(1)**
25-27 Oaza Miyako
Hiki-gun, Namegawa, Saitama, 355-0812, Japan
Tel.: (81) 493564421
Fax: (81) 493564427
Web Site: www.ahresty.com
Emp.: 100
Aluminium Die Casting Products Mfr
S.I.C.: 3364
N.A.I.C.S.: 331523
Arata Takahashi *(Pres)*

AHRESTY CORPORATION - Kumagaya Plant **(1)**
284-11 Miizugahara
Kumagaya, Saitama, 360-8543, Japan
Tel.: (81) 485335161
Fax: (81) 485335160
Web Site: www.ahresty.co.jp
Emp.: 60
Aluminium Secondary Ingot Products Mfr
S.I.C.: 3399
N.A.I.C.S.: 331314
Sakai Kazuyuki *(Gen Mgr)*

U.S. Subsidiary:

Ahresty Wilmington Corporation **(1)**
2627 S S St
Wilmington, OH 45177
Tel.: (937) 382-6112
Fax: (937) 382-5871
Web Site: www.ahresty.com
Aluminum Die Casting Mfr
S.I.C.: 3364
N.A.I.C.S.: 331523
Justin Rummer *(Pres)*

AI CHAMPDANY INDUSTRIES LIMITED

25 Princep Street
Kolkata, 700 072, India
Tel.: (91) 33 2237 7880
Fax: (91) 33 2236 3754
E-Mail: cil@ho.champdany.co.in
Web Site: www.jute-world.com
Year Founded: 1873
532806—(BOM)
Rev.: $66,550,813
Assets: $53,948,804
Liabilities: $34,206,615
Net Worth: $19,742,189
Earnings: $170,160
Fiscal Year-end: 03/31/13

Business Description:
Jute Product Mfr & Whslr
S.I.C.: 2299
N.A.I.C.S.: 313110

Personnel:
Wajid Ali *(CFO)*
Surajit Sen *(Compliance Officer, Sec & Controller-Fin & Accts)*

Board of Directors:
G. J. Wadhwa
N. Das
G. Goswami
S. M. Palia
N. Pujara

Ai Champdany Industries Limited—(Continued)

B. Sen
Harbhajan Singh
B. Wadhwa
D. J. Wadhwa

Transfer Agent:
MCS Limited
77/2A Hazra Road Ground Floor
Kolkata, 700 029, India

AI CLAIMS SOLUTIONS PLC

Indemnity House Sir Frank Whittle Way
Blackpool, Lancs, FY4 2FB, United Kingdom
Tel.: (44) 844 571 3333
Fax: (44) 1253 441 504
E-Mail: info@aiclaimssolutions.com
Web Site: www.aiclaimssolutions.com
Sales Range: $150-199.9 Million
Emp.: 471

Business Description:
Holding Company; Automotive Insurance Claims Management Services
S.I.C.: 6719
N.A.I.C.S.: 551112

Personnel:
Simon Nicholas Pook *(COO)*

Board of Directors:
Stephen William Broughton
Christopher J. Baker
Peter J. Harrison
Simon Nicholas Pook

Legal Counsel:
Cobbetts LLP
58 Mosley Street
Manchester, United Kingdom

Subsidiary:

Ai Claims Solutions (UK) Limited **(1)**
Indemnity House Sir Frank Whittle Way
Blackpool, Lancs, FY4 2FB, United Kingdom
Tel.: (44) 844 571 3333
Fax: (44) 1253 441 504
E-Mail: info@aiclaimssolutions.com
Web Site: www.aiclaimssolutions.com
Automotive Insurance Claims Management Services
S.I.C.: 6411
N.A.I.C.S.: 524291
Peter J. Harrison *(Fin Dir)*

AI ENERGY PUBLIC COMPANY LIMITED

55/2 Moo 8 Sethakit 1 Road
Klongmadua
Krathum Baen, Samut Sakhon, 74110, Thailand
Tel.: (66) 34 877 485
Fax: (66) 34 877 491
E-Mail: aienergy@aienergy.co.th
Web Site: www.aienergy.co.th
AIE—(THA)
Rev.: $114,694,072
Assets: $76,684,023
Liabilities: $71,655,883
Net Worth: $5,028,140
Earnings: ($1,717,459)
Fiscal Year-end: 12/31/12

Business Description:
Biodiesel Producer & Distr
S.I.C.: 2999
N.A.I.C.S.: 324199

Personnel:
Narong Thareratanavibool *(Chm)*
Thanit Thareratanavibool *(Vice Chm)*
Anurak Thareratanavibool *(CEO)*

Board of Directors:
Narong Thareratanavibool
Kaweephong Hirankasi
Sampan Hunpayon
Damrong Jungwong
Choti Sontiwattananont
Anurak Thareratanavibool
Noppol Thareratanavibool
Thanit Thareratanavibool

AIA ENGINEERING LTD.

115 GVMM Estate Odhav Road
Ahmedabad, 382410, India
Tel.: (91) 79 22901078
Fax: (91) 79 22901077
E-Mail: info@aiaengineering.com
Web Site: www.aiaengineering.com
532683—(BOM)
Rev.: $340,579,374
Assets: $341,999,445
Liabilities: $77,640,162
Net Worth: $264,359,283
Earnings: $39,234,960
Emp.: 616
Fiscal Year-end: 03/31/13

Business Description:
Engineering Services
S.I.C.: 8711
N.A.I.C.S.: 541330

Personnel:
Bhadresh K. Shah *(Mng Dir)*
S. N. Jetheliya *(Compliance Officer & Sec)*

Board of Directors:
Rajendra Shantilal Shah
Dileep C. Choksi
Sanjay Shailesh Majmudar
Vinod Narain
Yashwant M. Patel
Bhadresh K. Shah
S. Srikumar

Transfer Agent:
Link Intime India Pvt Ltd
C-13 Kantilal Maganlal Estate Pannalal Silk Mills Compound L B S Marg
Bhandup West, Mumbai, India

AIB-VINCOTTE BELGIUM VZW

Business Class Kantoren Park
Jan Olieslagerslaan 35, 1800
Vilvoorde, Belgium
Tel.: (32) 26745711
Fax: (32) 26745959
E-Mail: info@aib-vincotte.be
Web Site: www.aib-vincotte.com
Sales Range: $250-299.9 Million
Emp.: 2,500

Business Description:
Business Management & Consulting Services
S.I.C.: 8742
N.A.I.C.S.: 541611

Personnel:
Michel Vandegard *(CMO)*

AICA KOGYO COMPANY, LIMITED

2288 Nishi-horie
Kiyosu, Aichi, 452-0917, Japan
Tel.: (81) 52 409 8291
Fax: (81) 52 409 8187
Web Site: www.aica.co.jp
Year Founded: 1936
4206—(TKS)
Sales Range: $1-4.9 Billion
Emp.: 3,434

Business Description:
Wood Product & Adhesive Mfr
S.I.C.: 2499
N.A.I.C.S.: 321999

Personnel:
Yuji Ono *(Pres)*

THE AICHI BANK, LTD.

14-12 Sakae 3-chome
Naka-ku, Nagoya, 460-8678, Japan
Tel.: (81) 522513211
Fax: (81) 522625793
Web Site: www.aichibank.co.jp
Year Founded: 1910
8527—(TKS)
Rev.: $546,711,000
Assets: $31,032,166,000
Liabilities: $28,914,754,000
Net Worth: $2,117,412,000
Earnings: $29,931,000
Emp.: 1,808
Fiscal Year-end: 03/31/13

Business Description:
Banking Services
S.I.C.: 6029
N.A.I.C.S.: 522110

Personnel:
Shinichi Koide *(Chm)*
Kenzo Haba *(Pres)*
Katsuyuki Yazawa *(Sr Mng Dir)*
Haruhiko Ando *(Co-Mng Dir)*
Jun Hayakaya *(Co-Mng Dir)*
Eiji Miyachi *(Co-Mng Dir)*
Toshiyuki Suzuki *(Co-Mng Dir)*

Board of Directors:
Shinichi Koide
Haruhiko Ando
Kenzo Haba
Jun Hayakaya
Akio Hayashi
Noboru Hayashi
Yoshihiro Ito
Yukinori Ito
Masato Kobayashi
Takashi Kouzaki
Eiji Miyachi
Minoru Ogura
Toshiyuki Suzuki
Katsuyuki Yazawa

Subsidiaries:

Aigin Business Service Co., Ltd. **(1)**
3-14-12 Sakae
Naka-ku, Nagoya, 460-0008, Japan
Tel.: (81) 522629580
Fax: (81) 522513404
Web Site: www.aichibank.co.jp/ar/ar2004/contents/directory.html
Emp.: 80
Business Support Services
S.I.C.: 7389
N.A.I.C.S.: 561499
Toshio Takabatake *(Pres)*

Aigin Computer Service Co., Ltd. **(1)**
2-17-21 Nishiki
Naka-ku, Nagoya, 460-0003, Japan
Tel.: (81) 522181184
Fax: (81) 522048180
Emp.: 9
Computer Services
S.I.C.: 7379
N.A.I.C.S.: 541519

Aigin DC Card Co., Ltd. **(1)**
14-12 Sakae 3-chome
Naka-ku, Nagoya, 460-8678, Japan
Tel.: (81) 5225 13211
Fax: (81) 5 2261 1260
Emp.: 22
Credit Card Services
S.I.C.: 6153
N.A.I.C.S.: 522210

Aigin Lease Co., Ltd. **(1)**
14-12 Sakae 3-chome
Naka-ku, Nagoya, 460-8678, Japan
Tel.: (81) 522513211
Fax: (81) 529618410
Emp.: 23
Equipment Rental & Leasing Services
S.I.C.: 7359
N.A.I.C.S.: 532490

AICHI CORPORATION

1152 Ryoke Ageo-shi
Saitama, 362-8550, Japan
Tel.: (81) 48 781 1111
Web Site: www.aichi-corp.co.jp
Year Founded: 1962
6345—(TKS)
Sales Range: $400-449.9 Million
Emp.: 1,033

Business Description:
Industrial Truck Mfr & Whslr
S.I.C.: 3537
N.A.I.C.S.: 333924

Personnel:
Norio Sato *(Chm)*
Kimpei Mithuya *(Pres)*
Osamu Miura *(Sr Mng Dir)*
Takuo Suzuki *(Mng Dir)*
Tomomasa Ebara *(Exec Officer)*
Yukihiro Mizuno *(Exec Officer)*
Akihiko Ohira *(Exec Officer)*
Hironao Ookabe *(Exec Officer)*
Toru Sakamoto *(Exec Officer)*
Kenichi Shimada *(Exec Officer)*
Kazuhiro Shindo *(Exec Officer)*
Yoshio Tagami *(Exec Officer)*
Keiichi Tsuchiya *(Exec Officer)*
Fumihiro Tsuzuki *(Exec Officer)*
Hiromi Yabata *(Exec Officer)*

Board of Directors:
Norio Sato
Akio Kawai
Kimpei Mithuya
Osamu Miura
Masami Ogino
Hisao Suzuki
Takeshi Suzuki
Takuo Suzuki
Nobuyuki Yamaguchi

AICHI ELECTRIC CO., LTD.

1 Aichi cho
Kasugai, Aichi, 486-8666, Japan
Tel.: (81) 568351211
Telex: 781-448-5022
Fax: (81) 568351255
E-Mail: aichidenki@adkk.co.jp
Web Site: www.aichidenki.jp
Year Founded: 1942
Sales Range: $400-449.9 Million
Emp.: 727

Business Description:
Electric Power Transformer Mfr
S.I.C.: 3612
N.A.I.C.S.: 335311

Personnel:
Isao Yamada *(Pres)*

Divisions:

Aichi Electric & Electronic Products Division **(1)**
1 Aichi-cho
Kasugai, Aichi, 486-8666, Japan
Tel.: (81) 568351211
Fax: (81) 568351255
E-Mail: info@mtsui.hongkong.icesdkk.co.jp
Web Site: www.aichidenki.jp/english/contact/index.html
Emp.: 800
Small Motor & Motor Applied Apparatus Mfr
S.I.C.: 3621
N.A.I.C.S.: 335312
Maghui Hideo *(Mgr)*

Aichi Electric Development & Environment Division **(1)**
2 Aichi-cho
Kasugai, Aichi, 486-8666, Japan
Tel.: (81) 568351211
Fax: (81) 568351243
E-Mail: info@aichidenki.jp
Web Site: www.aichidenki.jp/english/contact/index.html
Emp.: 800
Research & Product Development Services
S.I.C.: 8731
N.A.I.C.S.: 541712
Yamaga Isao *(Pres)*

Aichi Electric Power Products Division **(1)**
2 Aichi-cho
Kasugai, Aichi, 486-8666, Japan
Tel.: (81) 568351211
Fax: (81) 568351243
Web Site: www.aichidenki.jp/english/contact/index.html
Emp.: 8,000
Transformer & Switchgear Mfr
S.I.C.: 3612
N.A.I.C.S.: 335311

AICHI STEEL CORPORATION

1 Wanowari Arao-cho Tokai-shi
Aichi, 476-8666, Japan
Tel.: (81) 52 604 1111
Fax: (81) 52 603 1835
E-Mail: admin@he.aichi-steel.co.jp
Web Site: www.aichi-steel.co.jp
Year Founded: 1940
5482—(TKS)
Sales Range: $1-4.9 Billion
Emp.: 2,360

Business Description:
Speciality Steel, Forged Products, Electronic & Magnetic Parts Mfr & Whslr
Import Export
S.I.C.: 3325
N.A.I.C.S.: 331513

Personnel:
Takahiro Fujioka *(Pres)*

Transfer Agent:
Mitsubishi UFJ Trust & Banking Corporation
7-10-11 Higashisuna Koto-ku
Tokyo, Japan

U.S. Subsidiary:

Aichi USA Inc. **(1)**
596 Triport Rd
Georgetown, KY 40324-9529 (100%)
Tel.: (502) 863-2233
Fax: (502) 863-2234
Web Site: www.aichi-steel.com
Emp.: 8
Sales of Hot Forged Products & Rolled Steel Bars
S.I.C.: 5093
N.A.I.C.S.: 423930

Subsidiary:

Aichi Forge & Gear Works, LLC **(2)**
596 Triport Rd
Georgetown, KY 40324-9529 KY
Tel.: (502) 863-7575
Fax: (502) 863-4928
Web Site: www.aichiforge.com
Emp.: 375
Mfr. & Sales of Hot Forged Products
Import Export
S.I.C.: 3462
N.A.I.C.S.: 332111

Non-U.S. Subsidiary:

Aichi Forging Company of Asia, Inc. **(1)**
Barrio Pulong Santa Cruz
Santa Rosa, 1043 AP Laguna, Philippines (62%)
Tel.: (63) 28922260
Fax: (63) 28922281
E-Mail: agscphil@laduna.net
Sales Range: $10-24.9 Million
Emp.: 270
Specialty Steel, Forged Products, Electronic & Magnetic Parts Mfr & Sales
S.I.C.: 3312
N.A.I.C.S.: 331110
Edwin Tirona *(VP-HR)*

AICO AFRICA LIMITED

First Floor SAZ Building Northridge Park Highlands
PO Box BW 537
Harare, Zimbabwe
Tel.: (263) 4 852 795
Fax: (263) 4 850 705
E-Mail: info@aicoafrica.com
Web Site: www.aicoafrica.com
Year Founded: 2008
AICO—(ZIM)
Rev.: $263,922,000
Assets: $288,284,000
Liabilities: $175,032,000
Net Worth: $113,252,000
Earnings: ($2,091,000)
Fiscal Year-end: 03/31/13

Business Description:
Holding Company; Agro-Industrial Business
S.I.C.: 6719
N.A.I.C.S.: 551112

Personnel:
Patrick Devenish *(CEO)*
Pious Manamike *(Sec)*

Board of Directors:
Bekithemba Nkomo
Innocent Chagonda
Catherine Chitiyo
Patrick Devenish
Pious Manamike
Bernard Mudzimuirema
Albert Nhau
Lawrence F. Preston
John P. Rooney

Legal Counsel:
Kantor & Immerman
19 Selous Avenue
Harare, Zimbabwe

Gil Godlonton & Gerrans
Beverly Court 100 Nelson Mandela Avenue
Harare, Zimbabwe

Atherstone & Cook
7th Floor Mercury House George Silundika Avenue
Harare, Zimbabwe

Transfer Agent:
First Transfer Secretaries
1 Armagh Avenue (Off Enterprise Road) Eastlea
P O Box 11
Harare, Zimbabwe

Subsidiaries:

The Cotton Company of Zimbabwe Limited **(1)**
1 Lytton Road Workington
PO Box 2697
Harare, Zimbabwe (100%)
Tel.: (263) 4749458
Fax: (263) 4753854
E-Mail: cottco@cottco.co.zw
Web Site: www.thecottoncompany.com
Sales Range: $350-399.9 Million
Emp.: 620
Purchaser & Processor of Cotton
S.I.C.: 0723
N.A.I.C.S.: 115114
Patison Sithole *(Chm)*
David Machingaidze *(Mng Dir)*
Pious Manamike *(Sec)*

Seed Co. Limited **(1)**
1st Floor Standards Association of Zimbabwe Building Northend Close
Northridge Park Borrowdale, Harare, Zimbabwe ZW
Tel.: (263) 4882485 (51.21%)
Fax: (263) 4304841
E-Mail: seedco@seedco.co.zw
Web Site: www.seedcogroup.com
SEED—(ZIM)
Rev.: $110,641,877
Assets: $160,913,552
Liabilities: $76,879,855
Net Worth: $84,033,697
Earnings: $12,621,755
Emp.: 420
Fiscal Year-end: 03/31/13
Seed Farming, Marketing & Production Services
S.I.C.: 0191
N.A.I.C.S.: 111998
Morgan Nzvere *(CEO)*
Samson Ruwisi *(Treas)*
John Matorofa *(Sec & Dir-Fin)*

Non-U.S. Subsidiary:

Seed Co International Limited **(2)**
43173 Unit 12b
Phakalane, 47143 Gaborone, Botswana
Tel.: (267) 3911907
Fax: (267) 3911830
E-Mail: olefilera@seedco.co.bw
Web Site: www.seedcogroup.com
Emp.: 3
Farming Seed Production
S.I.C.: 5159
N.A.I.C.S.: 424590
Olesile Ramaabya *(Country Mgr)*

Non-U.S. Subsidiary:

Seed Co Limited **(3)**
Area 29 Plot 24 Pvt Bag 421
Kanengo, Lilongwe, Malawi
Tel.: (265) 1712074
Fax: (265) 1712312
E-Mail: seedco@seedcomalawi.net
Web Site: www.seedcogroup.com
Emp.: 36
Farming Seed Production
S.I.C.: 5159
N.A.I.C.S.: 424590
D.W Phiri *(Mng Dir)*

Joint Venture:

Olivine Industries (Private) Limited **(1)**
36 Birmingham Road Southerton
PO Box 797
Harare, Zimbabwe (49%)
Tel.: (263) 4754568
Fax: (263) 4754569
E-Mail: admin@olivine.co.zw
Emp.: 1,200
Manufactures Cooking Oils, Fats & Soaps
S.I.C.: 2841
N.A.I.C.S.: 325611
Patrick Pevenish *(Vice Chm)*
J. Mushangari *(Mng Dir)*

AICON S.P.A.

Via Larga 15
20122 Milan, ME, Italy
Tel.: (39) 0909610211
Fax: (39) 0909384462
E-Mail: info@aiconyachts.com
Web Site: www.aiconyachts.com
AIC—(ITA)
Sales Range: $75-99.9 Million
Emp.: 471

Business Description:
Yacht Mfr
S.I.C.: 3732
N.A.I.C.S.: 336612

Personnel:
Pasquale Siclari *(Chm & CEO)*

Board of Directors:
Pasquale Siclari
Giovanni Grasso
Angelo Sidoti
Antonio Sorrentino

Subsidiary:

Europlastic Sud S.R.L. **(1)**
2 Via Corbino Orso Mario
72100 Brindisi, Italy
Tel.: (39) 0831573931
Fax: (39) 0831574274
Boats & Yachts Mfr
S.I.C.: 3291
N.A.I.C.S.: 327910

AIDA ENGINEERING LTD.

2-10 Ohyama-cho
Midori Ward, Sagamihara, 252-5181, Japan
Tel.: (81) 427725231
Fax: (81) 427725263
Web Site: www.aida.co.jp
6118—(OTC TKS)
Sls.: $635,932,000
Assets: $903,298,000
Liabilities: $320,540,000
Net Worth: $582,758,000
Earnings: $41,833,000
Emp.: 1,647
Fiscal Year-end: 03/31/13

Business Description:
Press Machines Mfr
S.I.C.: 3555
N.A.I.C.S.: 333244

Personnel:
Kimikazu Aida *(Pres & CEO)*
Naoyoshi Nakanishi *(COO & Exec VP)*
Sadayuki Kanemura *(Mng Exec Officer)*
Hiromichi Kataoka *(Mng Exec Officer)*
Ken Masuda *(Exec Officer)*
Yap Teck Meng *(Exec Officer)*
Takashi Yagi *(Mng Exec Officer)*

Board of Directors:
Kimikazu Aida
Sadayuki Kanemura
Hiromichi Kataoka
Ken Masuda
Yap Teck Meng
Naoyoshi Nakanishi
Kimio Oiso
Takashi Yagi
Takeru Yamazaki

Transfer Agent:
Mizuho Trust & Banking Co., Ltd.
2-1 Yaesu 1-Chome Chuo-ku
Tokyo, 103 8670, Japan
Tel.: (81) 332788111
Fax: (81) 332816947

Subsidiaries:

Access Ltd. **(1)**
1080 Kozumachi
Hakusan, Ishikawa, 924-0821, Japan
Tel.: (81) 762748200
Fax: (81) 762748210
Web Site: www.kkaccess.co.jp
Emp.: 104
Metal Processing Machines Mfr & Sales
S.I.C.: 3559
N.A.I.C.S.: 333249
Maoyoshi Nakanishi *(Pres)*

AIDA BUSINESS CORP. **(1)**
2-10 Ohyama-cho
Sagamihara, Kanagawa, 229-1181, Japan
Tel.: (81) 427794810
Fax: (81) 427725263
Web Site: www.aida.co.jp
Emp.: 700
Insurance & Personnel Dispatch Services
S.I.C.: 6411
N.A.I.C.S.: 524298
Kimikazu Aida *(Pres)*
Eiji Takei *(Pres)*

Non-U.S. Subsidiaries:

Aida Canada Inc. **(1)**
131 Saunders Rd Unit 9
Barrie, ON, L4N 9A7, Canada
Tel.: (705) 734-9692
Fax: (705) 734-9695
E-Mail: info@aida-america.com
Web Site: www.aida-global.com
Emp.: 4
Metal Stamping Presses Mfr
S.I.C.: 3469
N.A.I.C.S.: 332119
Steve Mirrles *(Mgr-Svc)*

AIDA Engineering China Co., LTD. **(1)**
Hua Jing Rd 9 Waigaoqiao Free Trade Zone
Pudong New Area, Shanghai, 200131, China
Tel.: (86) 2150462066
Fax: (86) 2150463872
Emp.: 100
Metal Stamping Presses Mfr
S.I.C.: 3559
N.A.I.C.S.: 333249
Tommy Shu *(CEO)*

AIDA Hong Kong, LTD. **(1)**
Unit 901-902 9 F 29 Austin Rd
Tsimshatsui, Kowloon, China (Hong Kong)
Tel.: (852) 27360118
Fax: (852) 23756581
Web Site: www.aida.com.hk
Metal Stamping Presses Mfr
S.I.C.: 3541
N.A.I.C.S.: 333517

AIDA PRESSEN GmbH **(1)**
Steuerungsbau Sdfeld 9d
59174 Kamen, Kamen, Germany
Tel.: (49) 23074386420
Fax: (49) 23074386440
E-Mail: info-de@aida-europe.com
Web Site: www.aida-global.com
Emp.: 10
Metal Stamping Presses Mfr
S.I.C.: 3541
N.A.I.C.S.: 333517
Troy S. Robert *(Mng Dir)*

AIDA Stamping Technology Pte Ltd **(1)**
Blk 16 Boon Lay Way No 01-55 TradeHub 21
Singapore, 609966, Singapore

AIDA ENGINEERING LTD.—(Continued)

Tel.: (65) 67952688
Fax: (65) 67952676
E-Mail: enquiry@aida.com.sg
Web Site: www.aida.com.sg
Emp.: 20
Metal Stamping Presses Mfr
S.I.C.: 3541
N.A.I.C.S.: 333517

Non-U.S. Subsidiaries:

AIDA Stamping Technology (India) Pvt Ltd. (2)
Bldg No 10C Upper Ground Fl
DLF Cybercity Phase II, Gurgaon, Haryana, 122002, India
Tel.: (91) 1244716888
Fax: (91) 1244716889
Web Site: www.aida.com.sg
Emp.: 13
Metal Stamping Presses Mfr
S.I.C.: 3541
N.A.I.C.S.: 333517
C. L. Goh *(Mgr)*

AIDA Stamping Technology (Thailand) Co., Ltd. (2)
41 23 Moo 6 Bangna-Trad Km 16 5 Tambol Bangchalong
Bang Phli, Samut Prakan, 10540, Thailand
Tel.: (66) 23370197
Fax: (66) 23370198
E-Mail: service@aida.co.th
Web Site: www.aida.com.sg
Emp.: 22
Metal Stamping Presses Mfr
S.I.C.: 3542
N.A.I.C.S.: 333517
Haruo Takano *(Mng Dir)*

PT AIDA Stamping Technology Indonesia (2)
Ruko Mall Bekasi Fajar Blok B No 22
Kawasan Industri MM2100
Cikarang Barat, Bekasi, West Java, 17520, Indonesia
Tel.: (62) 2189982432
Fax: (62) 2189982433
E-Mail: enquiry@aida.com.sg
Web Site: www.aida.com.sg
Emp.: 20
Metal Stamping Presses Mfr
S.I.C.: 3541
N.A.I.C.S.: 333517

AIFUL CORPORATION

381-1 Takasago-cho Gojo-Agaru
Karasuma-Dori
Shimogyo-ku, Kyoto, 600-8420, Japan
Tel.: (81) 752012000
Fax: (81) 752012019
E-Mail: info@aiful.co.jp
Web Site: www.ir-aiful.com
Year Founded: 1967
8515—(TKS)
Rev.: $1,195,513,000
Assets: $6,678,991,000
Liabilities: $5,523,903,000
Net Worth: $1,155,088,000
Earnings: $249,766,000
Emp.: 1,437
Fiscal Year-end: 03/31/13

Business Description:
Consumer Finance, Mortgage Loan, Guaranteed Loan & Real Estate Services
S.I.C.: 6163
N.A.I.C.S.: 522310

Personnel:
Yoshitaka Fukuda *(Pres & CEO)*
Mitsuhide Fukuda *(Exec Officer)*
Taichi Kawakita *(Sr Mng Exec Officer)*
Toshikazu Moriwaki *(Mng Exec Officer)*
Tsuguo Nakagawa *(Mng Exec Officer)*
Kazumitsu Oishi *(Mng Exec Officer)*
Masayuki Sato *(Sr Mng Exec Officer)*
Nobuyuki Wakuta *(Mng Exec Officer)*

Board of Directors:
Mitsuhide Fukuda
Yoshitaka Fukuda
Taichi Kawakita
Toshikazu Moriwaki
Tsuguo Nakagawa
Kazumitsu Oishi
Masayuki Sato
Nobuyuki Wakuta

Transfer Agent:
Sumitomo Mitsui Trust Bank Limited
1-4-1 Marunouchi Chiyoda-ku
Tokyo, Japan

Subsidiaries:

AsTry Loan Services Corporation (1)
Nihombashi MS Bldg Fl 2 2-9-8
Horidomecho Nihombashi Chuo-ku, Tokyo, Japan
Tel.: (81) 3 6361 6800
Web Site: www.astry-s.co.jp
Loan Services
S.I.C.: 7349
N.A.I.C.S.: 561790

New Frontier Partners Co Ltd (1)
5F 1-2-2 Yuurakuchou Chuo-ku
Tokyo, 100 0006, Japan
Tel.: (81) 345036400
Fax: (81) 345036491
Web Site: www.nf-partners.co.jp
Venture Capital Funding Services
S.I.C.: 6211
N.A.I.C.S.: 523999
Toshihito Hayano *(Pres)*

Tryto Corporation (1)
Aiful Honsha Bldg 9f 381-1
Karasumadori Gojo Shimogyo K, Kyoto, Japan
Tel.: (81) 753535035
Web Site: www.365157.jp
Financial Services
S.I.C.: 6211
N.A.I.C.S.: 523999

Non-U.S. Subsidiaries:

Passkey Co Ltd (1)
1st F 11 Hairong Xincun Gangyi Rd
Xiawan Zhuhai, 519020 Qingyuan, Guangdong, China
Tel.: (86) 7568532105
Fax: (86) 7568532106
Web Site: www.passkey.co.jp
Emp.: 13
Home Loan Services
S.I.C.: 7349
N.A.I.C.S.: 561790
John Ma *(Gen Mgr)*

WIDE Corporation (1)
Leaders Tower Bldg 7FL
456 Gomae dong Giheung gu, Yongin, Gyeonggi do, 446 901, Korea (South)
Tel.: (82) 312181600
Fax: (82) 312747400
E-Mail: info@widecorp.com
Web Site: www.widecorp.com
Emp.: 81
Image Quality Assurance Systems Mfr
S.I.C.: 3825
N.A.I.C.S.: 334515
Woongkyeom Kim *(Pres & CEO)*

AII DATA PROCESSING LTD.

64 Kiril i Metodii Street
1202 Sofia, Bulgaria
Tel.: (359) 28012600
Fax: (359) 28012801
E-Mail: info@aiidatapro.com
Web Site: www.aiidatapro.com
Year Founded: 1999
Emp.: 250

Business Description:
Information Services, Data Processing & Business Services
S.I.C.: 7374
N.A.I.C.S.: 518210

Personnel:
Ilia Krustev *(CEO)*

AIKANG REMETECH CO. LTD

Ildong Bldg 3F 60 Yangjae-dong
Socho-Ku, Seoul, 137-733, Korea (South)
Tel.: (82) 2 578 8131
Fax: (82) 2 577 0617
Web Site: www.akrmt.co.kr
Year Founded: 1990
022220—(KRS)

Business Description:
Plumbing Services
S.I.C.: 1711
N.A.I.C.S.: 238220

Personnel:
Chan Mo Yang *(CEO)*

AIKBEE RESOURCES BERHAD

B-8-7 Megan Ave 1 189 Jalan Tun Razak
50400 Kuala Lumpur, Malaysia
Tel.: (60) 321616322
Fax: (60) 321610501
E-Mail: aikbeegroup@yahoo.com
Web Site: www.aikbee.com.my
Sales Range: $10-24.9 Million

Business Description:
Molding Timbers Mfr
S.I.C.: 2439
N.A.I.C.S.: 321213

Personnel:
Yen Siew Lim *(Deputy Chm)*
Aik Hong Tan *(Mng Dir)*
Yean Yean Wong *(Sec)*

Board of Directors:
Mohd Nor Abdul Wahid
Kamal Abu
Chan Loong Bong
Mohd Zaki Hamzah
Yen Siew Lim
Chee Hock Low
Meng Meng Ng
Aik Hong Tan
Keat Choon Yap

Subsidiary:

Aikbee Timbers (Sabah) Sdn. Bhd. (1)
Batu 6 1/2 Jalan Kepong
52000 Kuala Lumpur, Malaysia
Tel.: (60) 362511122
Fax: (60) 362511613
E-Mail: aikbee@hotmail.com
Emp.: 120
Timber Logging Services
S.I.C.: 0811
N.A.I.C.S.: 113110
Low Chee Hock *(Mgr)*

AIKCHOL HOSPITAL PUBLIC COMPANY LIMITED

68/3 Moo 2 Prayasatja Rd
Chon Buri, 20000, Thailand
Tel.: (66) 38 939 999
Fax: (66) 38 273 848
E-Mail: marketing@aikchol.com
Web Site: www.aikchol.com
Year Founded: 1978
AHC—(THA)
Rev.: $42,653,823
Assets: $39,177,147
Liabilities: $5,476,805
Net Worth: $33,700,342
Earnings: $5,710,368
Emp.: 1,159
Fiscal Year-end: 12/31/12

Business Description:
Health Care Services
S.I.C.: 8099
N.A.I.C.S.: 621999

Personnel:
Apirag Vanich *(Chm)*
Vichai Dhepchalerm *(Vice Chm)*
Phortchana Manoch *(Vice Chm)*

Board of Directors:
Apirag Vanich
Krisada Banchuin
Kanchana Chitrudiamphai
Vichai Dhepchalerm
Phortchana Manoch
Sirichai Manoch
Sucha Nimmannit
Kitti Toranin
Oranuj Vanich
Sawaek Weerakiet

Legal Counsel:
Dherakupt Law Office Co. Ltd
546 Univest Complex Building 15th Fl
Ratchadaphisek Rd Ladyao Jatujak
Bangkok, Thailand

AILSEN LIMITED.

Finch Close Lenton Lane
Nottingham, NG7 2NN, United Kingdom
Tel.: (44) 1159869686
Fax: (44) 1159861430
E-Mail: mail@ailsen.co.uk
Web Site: www.ailsen.ltd.uk
Year Founded: 1975
Rev.: $12,208,631
Emp.: 35

Business Description:
Building Services
S.I.C.: 7349
N.A.I.C.S.: 561790

Personnel:
Jeremy Hall *(Mng Dir)*

AIM EXPLORATION INC.

Suite 514 VGP Center 6772 Ayala Avenue
Makati City, Manila, Philippines
Tel.: (63) 2 7549929
Year Founded: 2010
AEXE—(OTC OTCB)
Assets: $8,146
Liabilities: $62,460
Net Worth: ($54,314)
Earnings: ($45,866)
Emp.: 1
Fiscal Year-end: 08/31/13

Business Description:
Metal Mineral Exploration
S.I.C.: 1099
N.A.I.C.S.: 212299

Personnel:
Gregorio Formoso *(Pres, CEO, CFO, Treas & Sec)*

Board of Directors:
Gregorio Formoso
Guil Rivera

AIM EXPLORATIONS LTD.

311 409 Granville Street
Vancouver, BC, Canada
Tel.: (604) 602-0001
E-Mail: gbalderson@telus.net
Year Founded: 2011
AXN.P—(TSXV)

Business Description:
Investment Services
S.I.C.: 6211
N.A.I.C.S.: 523999

Personnel:
Geoff Balderson *(Pres, CEO, CFO & Sec)*

Board of Directors:
Geoff Balderson
Bruno Maruzzo
Robert E. Shea
David Toyoda

Transfer Agent:
Computershare Investor Services Inc.
3rd Floor 510 Burrard Street
Vancouver, BC, Canada

AIMCO PESTICIDES LIMITED

Akhand Jyoti 8th Road Santacruz East
Mumbai, 400 055, India
Tel.: (91) 22 6760 4000
Fax: (91) 22 6760 4060

E-Mail: aimco@aimcopesticides.com
Web Site: www.aimcopesticides.com
Year Founded: 1987
Emp.: 300
Business Description:
Agrochemical Manufacturing, Formulation & Marketing of Insecticides, Fungicides & Herbicides
S.I.C.: 2879
N.A.I.C.S.: 325320
Personnel:
Pradeep P. Dave *(Chm)*
Board of Directors:
Pradeep P. Dave
Ashit Dave

AIMIA INC.

5100 De Maisonneuve Boulevard West
Montreal, QC, H4A 3T2, Canada
Tel.: (514) 205-7856
E-Mail: info@aimia.com
Web Site: www.aimia.com
Year Founded: 2008
AIM—(TSX)
Rev.: $2,235,469,470
Assets: $5,215,206,446
Liabilities: $3,895,742,310
Net Worth: $1,319,464,136
Earnings: $165,662,379
Emp.: 4,009
Fiscal Year-end: 12/31/12
Business Description:
Consumer Loyalty Management & Promotion Services
S.I.C.: 7389
N.A.I.C.S.: 561499
Personnel:
Robert Ellis Brown *(Chm)*
Rupert Duchesne *(Pres & CEO)*
David L. Adams *(CFO & Exec VP)*
David Johnston *(COO)*
Susan Doniz *(CIO)*
Mark Hounsell *(Chief Legal Officer & Sec)*
Jay Lee *(Chief Strategy Officer-US)*
Kevin O'Brien *(Chief Comml Officer-Aeroplan Canada)*
Sandy Walker *(Chief Talent Officer)*
Vince Timpano *(Pres/CEO-Canada & Exec VP)*
Michael Zea *(Pres/CEO-US)*
Jan-Pieter Lips *(Pres-Europe, Middle East & Africa & Exec VP)*
Fay Beauchine *(Pres-Bus Loyalty-US)*
Peter Gleason *(Pres-Intelligent Shopper Solutions)*
Michael O'Sullivan *(Pres-Proprietary Loyalty Svcs-Canada)*
Karl Schuster *(Pres-Proprietary Loyalty-Asia Pacific)*
Brian Sinclair *(Pres-Coalition-US)*
Eric Monteiro *(Exec VP-Global Strategy)*
Melissa Sonberg *(Sr VP-Global Brands, Comm & External Affairs)*
Board of Directors:
Robert Ellis Brown
Roman Doroniuk
Rupert Duchesne
Joanne S. Ferstman,
Michael M. Fortier
John M. Forzani
Beth S. Horowitz
David H. Laidley
Douglas D. Port
Alan P. Rossy
Transfer Agent:
CIBC Mellon Trust Company
320 Bay Street B1 Level
Toronto, ON, Canada

Subsidiary:

Aeroplan Canada Inc (1)
Pointe Claire Dorval Station
PO Box 21000
Dorval, QC, Canada
Tel.: (902) 367-8445
Web Site: www.aeroplan.com
Loyalty Management Services
S.I.C.: 8742
N.A.I.C.S.: 541611
Kevin O'Brien *(Chief Comml Officer)*

U.S. Subsidiaries:

Carlson Marketing (1)
1405 Xenium Ln N
Plymouth, MN 55441 NJ
Tel.: (763) 445-3000
Web Site: www.carlsonmarketing.com
Emp.: 3,000
Advertising Agency
S.I.C.: 8742
N.A.I.C.S.: 541613
Dave Zitur *(CIO & VP)*
Mike Kust *(CMO)*
Jon Von Rentzell *(Chief Client Officer)*
Faye Beauchine *(Pres-Global Engagement & Events-US)*

Excellence In Motivation, Inc. (1)
6 N Main St Ste 370
Dayton, OH 45402 OH
Tel.: (937) 222-2900
Fax: (937) 824-8393
Toll Free: (800) 963-9235
E-Mail: solutions@eim-inc.com
Web Site: www.eim-inc.com
Sales Range: $10-24.9 Million
Emp.: 175
Administrative Management & General Management Consulting Service
S.I.C.: 8742
N.A.I.C.S.: 541611
Richelle Taylor *(Sr Mgr-Product Mktg)*

Smart Button Associates, Inc. (1)
1501 Casho Mill Rd Ste 14
Newark, DE 19711
Tel.: (302) 283-0200
Toll Free: (800) 611-2265
E-Mail: sales@smartbutton.com
Web Site: www.smartbutton.com
Emp.: 15
Customer Relationship Marketing Software Mfr
S.I.C.: 7371
N.A.I.C.S.: 541511
James Altrichter *(VP)*

Non-U.S. Subsidiaries:

Aimia Acquisition UK Limited (1)
80 Strand
London, WC2R ONN, United Kingdom UK
Tel.: (44) 2071524700
Fax: (44) 2071524300
E-Mail: enquiries@loyalty.co.uk
Emp.: 400
Marketing Consulting Services
S.I.C.: 8742
N.A.I.C.S.: 541613

Subsidiaries:

LMG Insight & Communication (2)
80 Strand
London, WC2R 0NN, United Kingdom
Tel.: (44) 2071524700
Fax: (44) 2071524300
Web Site: www.loyalty.co.uk
Emp.: 300
Business Management Services
S.I.C.: 8741
N.A.I.C.S.: 561110
Peter Gleason *(Pres)*
Mike Blyth *(Pres-United States)*

Loyalty Management UK Limited (2)
80 Strand 3rd Floor
London, WC2R 0NN, United Kingdom UK
Tel.: (44) 2071524700
Fax: (44) 20 7152 4300
Consumer Loyalty Program Operating Services
S.I.C.: 8742
N.A.I.C.S.: 541613

Air Miles Middle East (1)
PO Box 43004
Dubai, United Arab Emirates
Tel.: (971) 43913400
E-Mail: contact@airmilesme.com
Web Site: www.uae.airmilesme.com
Loyalty Management Services
S.I.C.: 8742
N.A.I.C.S.: 541611

AIMS FINANCIAL GROUP

Level 16 Central Square 323 Castlereagh Street
Sydney, NSW, 2000, Australia
Tel.: (61) 292172727
Fax: (61) 292817611
Web Site: www.aims.com.au
Emp.: 50
Business Description:
Financial & Investment Services
S.I.C.: 6211
N.A.I.C.S.: 523110
Personnel:
George Wang *(Chm & CEO)*
Greg Bundy *(Deputy Chm)*

Subsidiary:

MacarthurCook Limited (1)
Level 16 Central Square 323 Castlere
Sydney, NSW, 2000, Australia
Tel.: (61) 292172727
Fax: (61) 292817611
E-Mail: mail@macarthurcook.com.au
Web Site: www.macarthurcook.com.au
Emp.: 35
Real Estate Property & Investment Manager
S.I.C.: 6531
N.A.I.C.S.: 531390
George Wang *(Chm)*
John Snowden *(Mng Dir & Head-Property Securities)*

Subsidiary:

MacarthurCook Fund Management Limited (2)
Level 9 350 Collins Street
Melbourne, VIC, 3000, Australia
Tel.: (61) 396604555
Fax: (61) 396391440
E-Mail: mail@macarthurcook.com.au
Web Site: www.macarthurcook.com.au
Investment Fund Manager
S.I.C.: 6722
N.A.I.C.S.: 525910
George Wang *(CEO)*

AIMSHELL ACQUISITIONS PLC

Stanhope Road
Swadlincote, Derbyshire, United Kingdom
Tel.: (44) 1283 550033
Fax: (44) 1283 550298
E-Mail: sales@autoclenz.co.uk
Web Site: www.autoclenz.co.uk/autoclenz/site.nsf/autoclenz/contact
ASAP—(LSE)
Assets: $3,870,000
Liabilities: $20,000
Net Worth: $3,850,000
Earnings: ($6,630,000)
Emp.: 25
Fiscal Year-end: 12/31/12
Business Description:
Investment Services
S.I.C.: 6726
N.A.I.C.S.: 525990
Personnel:
James Leek *(Chm)*
Michael Stone *(Sec)*
Board of Directors:
James Leek
Michael Stone

Subsidiary:

Autoclenz Services Limited (1)
Stanhope Road
Swadlincote, Derbyshire, DE11 9BE, United Kingdom
Tel.: (44) 1283 552272
Automotive Cleaning Services
S.I.C.: 7542
N.A.I.C.S.: 811192

AIN PHARMACIEZ INC.

5-2-4-30 Higashisapporo Shiroishi-ku
Sapporo, Hokkaido, 003-0005, Japan
Tel.: (81) 117830189
Web Site: www.ainj.co.jp
9627—(TKS)
Sls.: $1,700,171,000
Assets: $1,054,240,000
Liabilities: $632,313,000
Net Worth: $421,927,000
Earnings: $55,825,000
Emp.: 3,551
Fiscal Year-end: 04/30/13
Business Description:
Pharmacy & Drug Store Management & Franchising Services
S.I.C.: 5912
N.A.I.C.S.: 446110
Personnel:
Kiichi Otani *(Pres)*
Junichi Kawai *(Sr Mng Dir)*
Toshihide Mizushima *(Sr Mng Dir)*
Masato Sakurai *(Sr Mng Dir)*
Shoichi Shudo *(Sr Mng Dir)*
Hiromi Kato *(Exec VP)*
Tadashi Nagumo *(Exec VP)*
Board of Directors:
Hiromi Kato
Junichi Kawai
Masao Kiuchi
Tsuyoshi Kobayashi
Hikaru Minami
Toshihide Mizushima
Ko Mori
Tadashi Nagumo
Miya Oishi
Kiichi Otani
Masato Sakurai
Shoichi Shudo

Subsidiaries:

AIN TOKAI Inc. (1)
Soa Bldg 2
1 2 3 Izumi Higashi, Nagoya, Aichi, 461 0001, Japan
Tel.: (81) 529553111
Fax: (81) 529553100
E-Mail: info@aint.jp
Web Site: www.aint.jp
Emp.: 300
Drug Stores Management Services
S.I.C.: 5912
N.A.I.C.S.: 446110
Tatsuyuki Satake *(Gen Mgr)*

Daitiku Co., Ltd. (1)
Hunan 24 2 Chuo ku
950 1151 Niigata, Japan
Tel.: (81) 252880228
Fax: (81) 252880220
E-Mail: info@daichiku.com
Web Site: www.daichiku.com
Emp.: 240
Drug Stores Management Services
S.I.C.: 5912
N.A.I.C.S.: 446110

Heartland Medical Corporation (1)
No 16 Second Fl
Jonan cho 1 chome, Yamagata, Yamagata, Japan
Tel.: (81) 236463222
Fax: (81) 236462022
E-Mail: info@m-heartland-aing.jp
Web Site: www.m-heartland-aing.jp
Emp.: 93
Medical Drugs & Health Care Related Products Sales
S.I.C.: 5047
N.A.I.C.S.: 423450
Hide Hiroshi Awazi *(Pres)*

Rejoice Pharmacy Inc (1)
Akino Nakagyo Karasuma-ku Kyoto Dai-ichi Life Izumiya 7F, Kyoto, 604 0847, Japan
Tel.: (81) 752310172
Fax: (81) 752316890
E-Mail: kyoto-mail@rejoice-pharmacy.co.jp
Web Site: www.rejoice-pharmacy.co.jp
Emp.: 170

AIN PHARMACIEZ INC.—(Continued)

Medical Services
S.I.C.: 6324
N.A.I.C.S.: 524114
Niiyama Noriyoshi *(Pres)*

AINSWORTH GAME TECHNOLOGY LIMITED

10 Holker Street
Newington, NSW, 2127, Australia
Tel.: (61) 297398000
Fax: (61) 297379483
Web Site: www.ainsworth.com.au
AGI—(ASX)
Rev.: $206,488,989
Assets: $256,435,800
Liabilities: $43,411,802
Net Worth: $213,023,998
Earnings: $54,399,704
Emp.: 200
Fiscal Year-end: 06/30/13
Business Description:
Gaming Machines Mfr
S.I.C.: 7999
N.A.I.C.S.: 713290
Personnel:
Leonard Hastings Ainsworth *(Chm)*
Danny Eric Gladstone *(CEO)*
Mark L. Ludski *(CFO & Sec)*
Doug Beavers *(Exec-Acct-Southern NV & Oregon)*
Chris O'Toole *(Exec-Sls-Northern Territory)*
Toni Odgers *(Exec-South Australian Sls)*
Kate Pang *(Exec-Key Acct Sls-Asia)*
Jonathan Siah *(Exec-Key Acct Sls-Asia)*
Mike Dreitzer *(Pres-North America)*
Board of Directors:
Leonard Hastings Ainsworth
Graeme John Campbell
Danny Eric Gladstone
Colin John Henson
David Hugh Macintosh
Michael Bruce Yates

Subsidiaries:

AGT Pty Ltd **(1)**
10 Holker St
Newington, NSW, 2127, Australia
Tel.: (61) 297398000
Fax: (61) 97379514
E-Mail: reception@ainsworth.com.au
Web Site: www.ainsworth.com.au
Gaming Machine Mfr & Sales
S.I.C.: 3944
N.A.I.C.S.: 339930
Jenny Goadstone *(CEO)*

AGT Service (NSW) Pty Ltd **(1)**
10 Holker St
Newington, NSW, 2127, Australia
Tel.: (61) 297398000
Fax: (61) 97379514
Transportation Services
S.I.C.: 4789
N.A.I.C.S.: 488999

U.S. Subsidiary:

Ainsworth Game Technology Inc **(1)**
6600 NW 12th Ave Ste 201
Fort Lauderdale, FL 33309
Tel.: (954) 317-5500
Fax: (954) 317-5555
Web Site: www.ainsworth.com.au/contact.htm
Emp.: 30
Gaming Machine Mfr & Sales
S.I.C.: 3944
N.A.I.C.S.: 339930
Danny Gladstone *(CEO & Exec Dir)*

AINSWORTH LUMBER CO. LTD.

(See Under Brookfield Asset Management Inc.)

AINTREE RESOURCES INC.

Suite 125A 1030 Denman Street
Vancouver, BC, V6G 2M6, Canada
Tel.: (604) 818-2617
Fax: (604) 648-9013
E-Mail: walterbrenner@hotmail.com
Year Founded: 2009
AIN.P—(TSXV)
Business Description:
Investment Services
S.I.C.: 6211
N.A.I.C.S.: 523999
Personnel:
Walter Brenner *(Pres, CEO & CFO)*
Board of Directors:
Walter Brenner
Michael B. England
Barry Underhill

AIOLOS INC

2150 Islington Avenue
Etobicoke, ON, M9P 3V4, Canada
Tel.: (416) 674-3017
Fax: (416) 674-7055
E-Mail: sales@aiolos.com
Web Site: www.aiolos.com
Rev.: $51,123,631
Emp.: 50
Business Description:
Wind Tunnels Mfr
S.I.C.: 8711
N.A.I.C.S.: 541330
Personnel:
Gary Elfstrom *(VP)*

AION RENEWABLES S.P.A.

Via Cappuccini 4
20122 Milan, Italy
Tel.: (39) 02 321 65 71
Fax: (39) 02 321 657 59
E-Mail: info@aionrenewables.com
Web Site: www.aionrenewables.com
AIN—(ITA)
Emp.: 500
Business Description:
Photovoltaic Device Mfr
S.I.C.: 3674
N.A.I.C.S.: 334413
Personnel:
Marco Giorgi *(Vice Chm & CEO)*

AIPHONE CO., LTD.

218 Jinno-cho Atsuta-ku
Nagoya, ACH 456-8666, Japan
Tel.: (81) 526826191
Web Site: www.aiphone.co.jp
Year Founded: 2005
6718—(TKS)
Emp.: 1,437
Business Description:
Electronic Communications Equipment Mfr & Whslr
S.I.C.: 3679
N.A.I.C.S.: 334419
Personnel:
Shusaku Ichikawa *(Pres)*
Toru Hotta *(Mng Dir & CTO)*
Masamichi Ando *(Chief Dir-Admin & Acctg)*
Hironori Terao *(Chief Dir-Sls & Dir-Set Renewel Promo)*
Yoshio Kamitani *(Exec Officer & Dir-Sls-Tech)*
Takesji Wada *(Dir-IT, Exec Officer & Dir-Gen Affairs)*
Osamu Okada *(Exec Officer & Mgr-Product Plng)*
Board of Directors:
Atsuo Hirako
Shusaku Ichikawa
Hironori Terao

AIPTEK INTERNATIONAL INC.

No 19 Industry E Rd 4 Science Park
300 Hsin-chu, Taiwan
Tel.: (886) 35678138
Fax: (886) 35678569
E-Mail: contact1@aiptek.com.tw
Web Site: www.aiptek.com.tw
6225—(TAI)
Sales Range: $25-49.9 Million
Business Description:
Camera & Camcorder Mfr
S.I.C.: 3663
N.A.I.C.S.: 334220
Personnel:
Peter Chen *(Chm)*
Frank Sheu *(CEO & Gen Mgr)*

U.S. Subsidiary:

AIPTEK Inc. **(1)**
51 Discovery Ste 100
Irvine, CA 92618 CA
Tel.: (949) 585-9600
Fax: (949) 585-9345
Web Site: www.aiptek.com
Emp.: 15
Digital Imaging Equipments Distr
S.I.C.: 5043
N.A.I.C.S.: 423410
Peter Chen *(Pres)*

Non-U.S. Subsidiaries:

AIPTEK International GmbH **(1)**
Halskestr 13
47877 Willich, Nordrhein-Westfalen, Germany
Tel.: (49) 2154923550
Fax: (49) 21549235680
E-Mail: info@aiptek.de
Web Site: www.aiptek.de
Electronic Gadgets Distr
S.I.C.: 5064
N.A.I.C.S.: 423620
David Tong *(Mng Dir)*

AIPTEK International Trading Co., Ltd. **(1)**
Room C-D 14th Chaoyangmen No 567 Zhonghua Rd
Shanghai, China
Tel.: (86) 21 33674488
E-Mail: aiptek@aiptek.com.cn
Web Site: www.aiptek.com.cn
Video Cameras & Electronics Distr
S.I.C.: 5043
N.A.I.C.S.: 423410

AIR ARABIA PJSC

Sharjah International Airport
PO Box 132
Sharjah, United Arab Emirates
Tel.: (971) 65088888
Fax: (971) 65580011
E-Mail: investorrelations@airarabia.com
Web Site: www.airarabia.com
Year Founded: 2003
AIRARABIA—(DFM)
Rev.: $800,870,053
Assets: $2,189,673,130
Liabilities: $708,838,918
Net Worth: $1,480,834,212
Earnings: $115,624,786
Emp.: 2,000
Fiscal Year-end: 12/31/12
Business Description:
Scheduled Air Passenger Transportation Services
S.I.C.: 4512
N.A.I.C.S.: 481111
Personnel:
Abdulla Mohamed Al Thani *(Chm)*
Adel Abdulla Ali *(CEO)*
Board of Directors:
Abdulla Mohamed Al Thani
Ghanem Mohamed Al Hajri
Abdul Wahab Mohammad Al Roomi
Mohammed Abdullah Al Thani
Adel Abdulla Ali
Arif Naqvi
Taryam Matar Taryam

AIR BALTIC CORPORATION AS

Riga International Airport Marupes
1053 Riga, Latvia
Tel.: (371) 6 7207069
Fax: (371) 6 7207369
E-Mail: info@airbaltic.lv
Web Site: www.airbaltic.lv
Rev.: $61,957,911
Emp.: 290
Business Description:
Air Transportation Services
S.I.C.: 4512
N.A.I.C.S.: 481111
Personnel:
Martin Gauss *(CEO)*
Vitolds Jakovlevs *(CFO)*
Martin Sedlacky *(COO)*
Board of Directors:
Martin Gauss
Vitolds Jakovlevs
Martin Sedlacky

Subsidiary:

airBaltic Training **(1)**
Pilotu Iela 6 Riga International Airport
Riga, Latvia 1044
Tel.: (371) 676 68 512
Fax: (371) 676 68 511
E-Mail: training@airbaltic.com
Web Site: www.airbaltictraining.com
Flight Training Services
S.I.C.: 8249
N.A.I.C.S.: 611512

AIR BERLIN PLC & CO. LUFTVERKEHRS KG

Saatwinkler Damm 42 43
D-13627 Berlin, Germany
Tel.: (49) 30 34 34 34 34
Fax: (49) 30 41 02 10 03
E-Mail: service-center@airberlin.com
Web Site: www.airberlingroup.com
Year Founded: 1978
AB1—(DEU)
Sales Range: $5-14.9 Billion
Emp.: 9,113
Business Description:
Air Transportation Services
S.I.C.: 4512
N.A.I.C.S.: 481111
Personnel:
Hans-Joachim Korber *(Chm)*
Hartmut Mehdorn *(CEO)*
Ulf Huttmeyer *(CFO)*
Helmut Himmelreich *(COO)*
Paul Gregorowitsch *(Chief Comml Officer)*
Board of Directors:
Hans-Joachim Korber
Paul Gregorowitsch
Saad Hammad
Helmut Himmelreich
James Hogan
Joachim Hunold
Ulf Huttmeyer
Niki Lauda
Hartmut Mehdorn
Peter R. Oberegger
James Rigney
Ali Ismail Sabanci
Heinz-Peter Schluter
Nicholas Teller
Johannes Zurnieden

Subsidiaries:

Ab Dritte Flugzeugvermietungs GmbH **(1)**
Saatwinkler Damm 42-43
13627 Berlin, Germany
Tel.: (49) 3041013473
Fax: (49) 3034345509
Management Consulting Services
S.I.C.: 8748
N.A.I.C.S.: 541618
Karl Friedrich Lotz *(COO)*

Ab Erste Flugzeugvermietungs GmbH (1)
Saatwinkler Damm 42-43
13627 Berlin, Germany
Tel.: (49) 3034345500
Fax: (49) 3034345509
Management Consulting Services
S.I.C.: 8748
N.A.I.C.S.: 541618
Karl Friedrich Lotz *(COO)*

AB Vierte Flugzeugvermietungs GmbH (1)
Saatwinkler Damm 42-43
13627 Berlin, Germany
Tel.: (49) 3034345500
Fax: (49) 34345529
Management Consulting Services
S.I.C.: 8748
N.A.I.C.S.: 541618
Karl Friedrich Lotz *(COO)*

AB Zweite Flugzeugvermietungs GmbH (1)
Saatwinkler Damm 42-43
13627 Berlin, Germany
Tel.: (49) 3034345500
Fax: (49) 3034345509
Management Consulting Services
S.I.C.: 8748
N.A.I.C.S.: 541618
Karl Friedrich Lotz *(COO)*

Air Berlin Gmbh & Co. Funfte Flugzeugvermietungs Ohg (1)
Zeppelinstr 3
12529 Brandenburg, Germany
Tel.: (49) 1801737800
Fax: (49) 304132003
Management Consulting Services
S.I.C.: 8748
N.A.I.C.S.: 541618

Air Berlin Luftfahrttechnischer Betrieb GmbH (1)
Saatwinkler Damm 42-43
13627 Berlin, Germany
Tel.: (49) 1805737800
Fax: (49) 3041021003
Web Site: www.airberlin.com
Management Consulting Services
S.I.C.: 8748
N.A.I.C.S.: 541618
Karl Friedrich Lotz *(COO)*

CHS Cabin and Handling Service Bayern GmbH (1)
Postfach 24 14 44
85356 Munich, Germany
Tel.: (49) 2119649228
Fax: (49) 2119649245
Full-Service Restaurants
S.I.C.: 5812
N.A.I.C.S.: 722511
Karl Friedrich Lotz *(COO)*

CHS Cabin And Handling Service GmbH (1)
Heinrichstr 169 A
40239 Dusseldorf, Germany
Tel.: (49) 211964920
Fax: (49) 2119649246
Management Consulting Services
S.I.C.: 8748
N.A.I.C.S.: 541618
Karl Friedrich Lotz *(COO)*

CHS Cabin and Handling Service Mitte GmbH (1)
Peter Muller St 20
40468 Dusseldorf, Germany
Tel.: (49) 211964920
Fax: (49) 021196492299
Emp.: 150
Business Support Services
S.I.C.: 7389
N.A.I.C.S.: 561499
Markus Weigel *(Mng Dir)*

CHS Cabin and Handling Service Sud-West GmbH (1)
Terminal 2 Postfach 64
60549 Frankfurt, Germany
Tel.: (49) 2119649220
Fax: (49) 2119649245
Personal Services
S.I.C.: 7299
N.A.I.C.S.: 812990
Karl Friedrich Lotz *(COO)*

Euconus Flugzeugleasinggesellschaft mbH (1)
Zeppelinstr 3
13657 Brandenburg, Germany
Tel.: (49) 3034345524
Management Consulting Services
S.I.C.: 8748
N.A.I.C.S.: 541618
Karl Friedrich Lotz *(COO)*

AIR CHANGE INTERNATIONAL LIMITED

2 Ashford Avenue
Milperra, NSW, 2214, Australia
Mailing Address:
PO Box 252
Milperra, NSW, 1891, Australia
Tel.: (61) 2 8774 1400
Fax: (61) 2 8774 1490
E-Mail: admin@airchange.com.au
Web Site: www.airchange.com.au
Year Founded: 2000
AHJ—(ASX)
Rev.: $20,629,987
Assets: $14,890,926
Liabilities: $4,474,003
Net Worth: $10,416,923
Earnings: $1,275,398
Fiscal Year-end: 06/30/13

Business Description:
Air Conditioning Mfr & Sales
S.I.C.: 3585
N.A.I.C.S.: 333415

Personnel:
Steve Atherton *(CEO)*
Neil Raymond Fimeri *(Mng Dir)*
Robert Edward Lees *(Sec)*

Board of Directors:
Alan S. Jones
Neil Raymond Fimeri
John M. Langley

Legal Counsel:
Addisons Lawyers
60 Carrington Street
Sydney, NSW, 2000, Australia

Subsidiary:

Air Change Pty Ltd (1)
12 Parraweena Rd
Caringbah, NSW, 2229, Australia
Tel.: (61) 295314699
Fax: (61) 295315294
Web Site: www.air-change.com
Emp.: 50
Heating, Ventilation & Air Conditioning Systems Mfr
S.I.C.: 3585
N.A.I.C.S.: 333415
Stephen Atherton *(Mgr)*

AIR CREEBEC INC.

101 7th Street
PO Box 430
Val d'Or, QC, J9P 4P4, Canada
Tel.: (819) 825-8375
Fax: (819) 825-0885
Toll Free: (800) 567-6567
E-Mail: lefebvrep@aircreebec.ca
Web Site: www.aircreebec.ca
Year Founded: 1979
Rev.: $29,500,000
Emp.: 180

Business Description:
Air Transportation Services
S.I.C.: 4512
N.A.I.C.S.: 481112

Personnel:
Albert Diamond *(Pres)*

AIR FRANCE-KLM GROUP

45 rue de Paris
95747 Roissy-en-France, Cedex, France
Tel.: (33) 141567800
Telex: PAREPAF
Fax: (33) 141567029
E-Mail: mail.saphir@airfrance.fr
Web Site: www.airfrance.com
Year Founded: 1933
AF—(EUR OTC)
Sls.: $34,506,375,610
Assets: $36,984,674,580
Liabilities: $30,280,747,980
Net Worth: $6,703,926,600
Earnings: ($1,597,903,790)
Emp.: 100,744
Fiscal Year-end: 12/31/12

Business Description:
Passenger Airline & Cargo Transportation Services
S.I.C.: 4512
N.A.I.C.S.: 481111

Personnel:
Jean-Cyril Spinetta *(Chm & CEO)*
Alexandre Begougne de Juniac *(Chm/CEO-Air France)*
Peter Frans Hartman *(Pres/CEO-KLM)*
Lionel Guerin *(CEO-HOP)*
Frederic Gagey *(CFO-Air France & Exec VP-Fleet Mgmt & Pur)*
Bertrand Lebel *(Sec)*
Camiel Eurlings *(Mng Dir-KLM & Exec VP-Cargo)*
Patrick Alexandre *(Exec VP-Intl Sls & Netherlands)*
Christian Guy Marie Boireau *(Exec VP-French Sls)*
Pieter Bootsma *(Exec VP-Comml Mktg-Passenger Bus)*
Philippe Calavia *(Exec VP-Fin)*
Wim Kooijman *(Exec VP-Mgmt Dev)*
Jean-Christophe Lalanne *(Exec VP-IT)*
Franck Terner *(Exec VP-Strategy, Comml Engrg & Maintenance)*
Dominique Barbarin *(Sr VP-IR)*

Board of Directors:
Jean-Cyril Spinetta
Maryse Aulagnon
Patricia Marie Marguerite Barbizet
Isabelle Bouillot
Regine Brehier
Jean-Dominique Comolli
Jaap de Hoop Scheffer
Alexandre Begougne de Juniac
Jean-Francois Dehecq
Peter Frans Hartman
Solenne Lepage
Christian Magne
Bernard Pedamon
Cornelis Josephus Antonius van Lede
Leo M. van Wijk

Deloitte & Associes
185 avenue Charles-de-Gaulle
Neuilly-sur-Seine, France

Subsidiaries:

Air France C.S. Participation (1)
45 Rue De Paris
95747 Roissy-en-France, France (100%)
Tel.: (33) 141567800
Fax: (33) 141568409
Rev.: $31,560,757
Emp.: 10,000
S.I.C.: 4512
N.A.I.C.S.: 481111

Brit Air (1)
Aeroport Cf 27925 29679
29600 Morlaix, France FR
Tel.: (33) 298621022 (100%)
Fax: (33) 298627798
E-Mail: info@britair.com
Web Site: www.britair.com
Emp.: 1,300
Regional Airline Operator
S.I.C.: 4729
N.A.I.C.S.: 561599
Marc Lamidey *(Chm & Mng Dir)*

Subsidiary:

Centre de Formation Aeronautique ICARE (2)
Aeroport CS 27925
PO Box 83
29679 Morlaix, France FR
Tel.: (33) 298881010 (99.96%)
Fax: (33) 298885555
E-Mail: information@icare.fr
Web Site: www.icare.fr
Emp.: 45
Airline Training Services
S.I.C.: 4581
N.A.I.C.S.: 488119
Marc Lamidey *(Chm)*
Jean-Pierre Garsaball *(Mng Dir)*

CARI S.A.S (1)
Europarc Batiment 10 7 Avenue Leonard De Vinci
33600 Pessac, France
Tel.: (33) 556363049
Fax: (33) 556363005
Air Transportation Services
S.I.C.: 4581
N.A.I.C.S.: 488190

Compagnie d'Exploitaition des Services Auxiliaires Aeriens (1)
10-14 rue de Rome
BP 19701
Tremblay, 95726 Roissy-en-France, Cedex, France FR
Tel.: (33) 1 48 64 8585 (97.58%)
Telex: 204 530
Fax: (33) 1 48 64 8500
Web Site: www.servair.fr
Sales Range: $550-599.9 Million
Emp.: 10,000
Airport & Airline Catering & Cabin Cleaning Services
S.I.C.: 4581
N.A.I.C.S.: 488119
Boris Eloy *(Dir-Comm)*

Subsidiaries:

ACNA (2)
22 Ave Des Nations
93420 Villepinte, France FR
Mailing Address: (100%)
BP 50379
Villepinte, 95943, France
Tel.: (33) 149388282
Fax: (33) 149388283
Web Site: www.acna.fr
Rev.: $970,500,000
S.I.C.: 4512
N.A.I.C.S.: 481111

Branches:

ACNA (3)
Orly Sud 182
94542 Orly, France FR
Tel.: (33) 141752223 (100%)
Fax: (33) 148648585
Web Site: www.servair.fr
Emp.: 300
Airport & Airline Services
S.I.C.: 4581
N.A.I.C.S.: 488119

Subsidiaries:

Aeroform (3)
22 Ave Des Nations Le Rousseau
PO Box 2
BP 85931 Villepinte, France FR
Tel.: (33) 148177380 (100%)
Fax: (33) 148177381
E-Mail: stephene.perreau@servair.fr
Web Site: www.servair.fr
Sls.: $3,000,000
Emp.: 18
Airport & Airline Services
S.I.C.: 4581
N.A.I.C.S.: 488119
Stephen Perreau *(Mng Dir)*

AeroSur (3)
10 rue des Iris
95723 Roissy-en-France, France FR
Tel.: (33) 148625787
Fax: (33) 148625594
Web Site: www.aerosur.com
Emp.: 150
Airline Services
S.I.C.: 4581
N.A.I.C.S.: 488119
Franz Ennesser *(Dir-Admin)*

LogAir (3)
ZAC du Parc
12 rue Saint Exupery, 77290 Compans, France FR

Air France-KLM Group—(Continued)

Tel.: (33) 160217219
Fax: (33) 160217220
Airport & Airline Services
S.I.C.: 4581
N.A.I.C.S.: 488119

Passerelle (3)
Zone Boutiquaires Terminal 2 Hall AC
95724 Roissy-en-France, Cedex, France FR
Tel.: (33) 148165437 (100%)
Fax: (33) 148161353
Emp.: 140
Airport & Airline Services
S.I.C.: 4581
N.A.I.C.S.: 488119

Servantage (3)
8 Chemin des Glirettes
95000 Le Thillay, France FR
Tel.: (33) 130180341 (100%)
Fax: (33) 139885669
Emp.: 50
Airport & Airline Services
S.I.C.: 4581
N.A.I.C.S.: 488119

Cremonini (2)
83 Rue Du Chalolais
75010 Paris, France FR
Tel.: (33) 59754611 (100%)
Fax: (33) 59754699
E-Mail: info@cremonini.com
Web Site: www.cremonini.com
Emp.: 360
S.I.C.: 4512
N.A.I.C.S.: 481111

Culin'Air Paris (2)
8 Rue Des Acacias
77230 Villeneuve sous Dammartin, France FR
Tel.: (33) 160546770 (56%)
Fax: (33) 148166211
E-Mail: regulation@servair.fr
Web Site: www.servair.fr
Emp.: 60
Airline Catering
S.I.C.: 4581
N.A.I.C.S.: 488119
Michel Pierlovisi *(Dir Gen)*

Jet Chef (2)
Zone d'Aviation d'Affaires
Aeroport du Bourget, 93350 Le Bourget, France FR
Tel.: (33) 1 48646326 (100%)
Fax: (33) 1 48646318
Web Site: www.jetchef.fr
Emp.: 157
Air Transportation Catering Services
S.I.C.: 5812
N.A.I.C.S.: 722320

Orly Air Traiteur (2)
1 Rue Du Pont Des Pierres
91422 Wissous, France FR
Tel.: (33) 149758200 (66%)
Telex: ORYQ SAF
Fax: (33) 149758204
Web Site: www.servair.fr
Sales Range: $10-24.9 Million
Emp.: 800
S.I.C.: 4512
N.A.I.C.S.: 481111
Alain Muders *(Gen Mgr)*

U.S. Subsidiary:

European Catering Services Inc. (2)
1209 N Orange St
Wilmington, DE 19801 DE
S.I.C.: 4512 (100%)
N.A.I.C.S.: 481111

Non-U.S. Subsidiaries:

Abidjan Catering S.A. (2)
Aeroport International FHB
BP 8
Abidjan, 07, Cote d'Ivoire
Tel.: (225) 2021278046
Fax: (225) 21278772
ABJC—(BRVM)
Sales Range: $25-49.9 Million
Airplane Catering Services
S.I.C.: 5812
N.A.I.C.S.: 722320
M. Fousseni Konate *(Chm & Pres)*

Societe de Restauration Industrielle (2)
Zone de Fret Nord Aeroport Pole Caraibes
97139 Abymes, Guadeloupe GP
Tel.: (590) 211714 (50%)
Telex: PTPQSAF
Fax: (590) 211731
S.I.C.: 4512
N.A.I.C.S.: 481111

CRMA (1)
ZA De La Clef De Saint Pierre 14 Avenue Gay Lussac
78 990 Elancourt, France
Tel.: (33) 1 30 68 00 68
Fax: (33) 1 30 68 00 62
Web Site: www.crma.fr
Rev.: $68,712,280
Emp.: 32
Aircraft Component Repair & Maintenance Services
S.I.C.: 7549
N.A.I.C.S.: 811198
Mathieu Bobinet *(Mgr-Customer Support)*

LYON MAINTENANCE (1)
Lyon Saint Eiupery Airport
Box 386
69145 Lyon, France
Tel.: (33) 4 72 22 80 65
Fax: (33) 472228060
E-Mail: pa.brocard@britair.fr
Emp.: 50
Aircraft Equipment Maintenance Services
S.I.C.: 7539
N.A.I.C.S.: 811198
Patrice Brocard *(Gen Mgr)*

PRESTAIR (1)
1 Rue Du Pont De Pierre
91320 Wissous, France
Tel.: (33) 149758972
Airline Catering Services
S.I.C.: 5812
N.A.I.C.S.: 722320

Regional Compagnie Aerienne Europeenne (1)
Aeroport De Nantes Atlantique
44345 Bouguenais, France FR
Tel.: (33) 240135300 (100%)
Fax: (33) 20135308
E-Mail: contact@regional.com
Web Site: www.regional.com
Sales Range: $350-399.9 Million
Emp.: 1,700
Regional Airline Operator
S.I.C.: 4729
N.A.I.C.S.: 561599
Jean Grosse *(Mng Dir)*

Societe de Construction et de Reparation de Materiel Aeronautique (1)
14 Ave Gay Lussac
78996 Elancourt, France (100%)
Mailing Address:
ZA de la Clef de Saint-Pierre
BP 10F
78996 Elancourt, France
Tel.: (33) 0130680068
Fax: (33) 130680068
E-Mail: standard@crma.sr
Web Site: www.crma.com
Emp.: 300
Maintenance of Aircraft Parts
S.I.C.: 4581
N.A.I.C.S.: 488119

SoDExl (1)
Rue des Voyelles
BP 16041
Tremblay-en-France, 95723 Roissy-en-France, CDG Cedex, France (100%)
Tel.: (33) 141845500
Telex: 231283
Fax: (33) 141569890
E-Mail: sodexi@sodexi.fr
Web Site: www.sodexi.fr
Sls.: $17,234,603
Emp.: 400
International Express Parcel Service; Joint Venture of Groupe Air France (60%), TAT S.A. (20%) & La Poste (20%)
S.I.C.: 4513
N.A.I.C.S.: 492110
Jean-Charles Foucault *(Pres)*

TEAMTRACKERS SA (1)
57 Rue Ledru Rollin
94200 Ivry-sur-Seine, France
Tel.: (33) 1 46 71 05 63
Fax: (33) 1 46 71 52 19
E-Mail: sales@team-trackers.com
Web Site: www.team-trackers.com
Emp.: 300
Airline Customer Service Management Services
S.I.C.: 4581
N.A.I.C.S.: 488119

TRANSAVIA FRANCE S.A.S. (1)
18 Av Louis Bleriot
91550 Paray-Vielle-Poste, France
Tel.: (33) 156307000
Fax: (33) 156307098
E-Mail: awtueil@fr.transavia.com
Web Site: www.transavia.com
Emp.: 40
Air Transportation Services
S.I.C.: 4581
N.A.I.C.S.: 488190
Antoine Pussiau *(CEO)*

U.S. Branch:

Air France, USA (1)
125 W 55th St 2nd Fl
New York, NY 10019
Tel.: (212) 830-4000
Fax: (212) 830-4244
Web Site: www.airfrance.com
Emp.: 400
International Air Transportation (Passenger & Cargo)
Import Export
S.I.C.: 4512
N.A.I.C.S.: 481111
Jean-Cyril Spinetta *(Chm & CEO)*

U.S. Subsidiaries:

AEROMAINTENANCE GROUP LLC (1)
2200 NW 84th Ave
Miami, FL 33122
Tel.: (305) 436-5464
Fax: (305) 436-6064
E-Mail: amg@aerotechnologies.net
Web Site: www.aeromaintenancegroup.com
Aircraft Component Repair & Maintenance Services
S.I.C.: 7549
N.A.I.C.S.: 811198
Christian Tallec *(CEO)*
Jerome Colombel *(CFO)*
Michael Olesik *(COO)*

INTERNATIONAL AIRLINE SERVICES AMERICAS L.P. (1)
4635 S W Freeway Ste 500
Houston, TX 77027
Tel.: (713) 355-1799
Fax: (713) 355-5289
Toll Free: (800) 906-7211
Web Site: www.ias-global.com
Airline Transportation Services
S.I.C.: 4581
N.A.I.C.S.: 488190
Rafael Alcala *(Gen Mgr)*

Non-U.S. Subsidiaries:

AIRPORT MEDICAL SERVICES C.V. (1)
Stationsplein-No 236
Schiphol, 1117 CJ, Netherlands
Tel.: (31) 206494364
Fax: (31) 206488577
Emp.: 10
Air Transportation Health Care Services
S.I.C.: 4581
N.A.I.C.S.: 488119
Paula Knape *(Gen Mgr)*

AMSTERDAM SCHIPHOL PIJPLEIDING C.V. (1)
Oude Vijfhuizerweg 6
Schiphol, 1118 LV, Netherlands
Tel.: (31) 206493063
Fax: (31) 206488080
Air Transportation Services
S.I.C.: 4581
N.A.I.C.S.: 488190

BLUE CROWN B.V. (1)
Amsterdamseweg 55
Amstelveen, 1182 GP, Netherlands
Tel.: (31) 206499959
Airline Transportation Services
S.I.C.: 4581
N.A.I.C.S.: 488190

BlueLink International CZ s. r. o. (1)
Olivova 4
Prague, 110 00, Czech Republic
Tel.: (420) 296 341 311
Fax: (420) 296 341 503
Web Site: www.bluelinkservices.com
Airport Luggage Claim Management Services
S.I.C.: 4581
N.A.I.C.S.: 488119
Vincent Leonardi *(Head-Ops & Customer Relationship Mgmt)*

CITYJET LTD (1)
Swords Business Campus Balheary Road
Swords County
Swords County, Dublin, Ireland
Tel.: (353) 1 8700 100
Fax: (353) 1 8700 115
E-Mail: info@cityjet.com
Web Site: www.cityjet.com
Emp.: 20
Air Transportation Services
S.I.C.: 4581
N.A.I.C.S.: 488190
Christine Ourmieres *(CEO)*

Cobalt Ground Solutions Ltd (1)
Room 2535 Terminal 4 Heathrow Airport
London
Hounslow, Middlesex, United Kingdom
Tel.: (44) 20 8750 9881
Fax: (44) 20 8750 9890
E-Mail: info@cobaltgs.com
Web Site: www.cobaltgs.com
Emp.: 800
Airport Ground Handling Services
S.I.C.: 4581
N.A.I.C.S.: 488119
Jan de Vegt *(Mng Dir)*

CYGNIFIC B.V. (1)
Stationsplein 11c
7511 JD Enschede, Netherlands
Tel.: (31) 20 201 3000
Fax: (31) 20 201 3152
Web Site: www.cygnific.com
Emp.: 700
Airline Travel Agency Services
S.I.C.: 4729
N.A.I.C.S.: 561599
Ton Ridder *(Gen Mgr)*

INTERNATIONAL AIRLINE SERVICES EUROPE LIMITED (1)
Bridge House 4 Borough High Street
London, SE1 9QQ, United Kingdom
Tel.: (44) 20 7378 9133
Fax: (44) 20 7378 9131
Web Site: www.ias-global.com
Airline Transportation Services
S.I.C.: 4581
N.A.I.C.S.: 488190
Bernard Rafferty *(Mng Dir)*

INTERNATIONAL AIRLINE SERVICES LIMITED (1)
Bridge Ho 4 Borough High St
London, SE1 9QQ, United Kingdom
Tel.: (44) 20 7378 9133
Fax: (44) 20 7378 9131
Airline Transportation Services
S.I.C.: 4581
N.A.I.C.S.: 488190

INTERNATIONAL MARINE AIRLINE SERVICES LIMITED (1)
Bridge House 4 Borough High Street
London, SE1 9QQ, United Kingdom
Tel.: (44) 20 7403 8112
Fax: (44) 20 7357 0585
Air Transportation Services
S.I.C.: 4581
N.A.I.C.S.: 488190

KES AIRPORT EQUIPMENT FUELLING B.V. (1)
Pakhuisstraat 1
Postbus 7700
1117 ZL Schiphol, Netherlands
Tel.: (31) 20 6492236
Fax: (31) 20 6493199
Emp.: 146
Aircraft Fueling Distr

S.I.C.: 5172
N.A.I.C.S.: 424720
Peter Bos *(Gen Mgr)*

KLM CATERING SERVICES SCHIPHOL B.V. (1)
Havenmeesterweg 1 Gebouw 540
1118 CB Schiphol, Netherlands
Tel.: (31) 20 6494707
Web Site: www.kcs.nl
Airline Catering Services
S.I.C.: 5812
N.A.I.C.S.: 722320
Jacques Blaauw *(Gen Mgr)*

KLM FINANCIAL SERVICES B.V. (1)
Amsterdamseweg 55
Amstelveen, 1182 GP, Netherlands
Tel.: (31) 206491359
Fax: (31) 206475211
Financial Management Services
S.I.C.: 6211
N.A.I.C.S.: 523999
Bas Brouns *(VP-Aircraft Financing)*

KLM HEALTH SERVICES B.V. (1)
Postbus 7700
Schiphol, 1117 ZL Amsterdam, Netherlands
Tel.: (31) 20 64 95 187
E-Mail: info.health@klm.com
Web Site: www.klmhealthservices.nl
Health Care Services
S.I.C.: 8099
N.A.I.C.S.: 621999

KLM LUCHTVAARTSCHOOL B.V. (1)
Burg J G Legroweg 43
Eelde, 9761 TA, Netherlands
Tel.: (31) 503098200
Fax: (31) 503094675
Flight Training Services
S.I.C.: 8249
N.A.I.C.S.: 611512

KLM OLIEMAATSCHAPPIJ B.V. (1)
Amsterdamseweg 55
Amstelveen, Amsterdam, Netherlands
Tel.: (31) 20 6499123
Petroleum Products Distr
S.I.C.: 5172
N.A.I.C.S.: 424720

KLM Royal Dutch Airlines (1)
55 Amsterdamseweg
NL 1182 GP Amstelveen, Netherlands NL
Mailing Address: (100%)
PO Box 7700
Schiphol Airport, 1117ZL Amsterdam, Netherlands
Tel.: (31) 206499123
Telex: 11252
Fax: (31) 203042009
E-Mail: publicrelations@klm.com
Web Site: www.klm.nl
Sales Range: $5-14.9 Billion
Emp.: 30,000
Scheduled Air Transport; Freight Arrangements
Import Export
S.I.C.: 4512
N.A.I.C.S.: 481111
Kornelis J. Storm *(Chm-Supervisory Board)*
Camiel Eurlings *(Pres & CEO)*
Vincent Knoops *(Sr VP-Corp Comm)*

Subsidiaries:

KLM Cityhopper (2)
Schiphol Airport
PO Box 7700
1117 ZL Amsterdam, Netherlands (100%)
Tel.: (31) 206492227
Fax: (31) 206482625
E-Mail: charters@klm.com
Web Site: www.klm.com
Rev.: $256,000,000
Emp.: 1,000
Domestic & Regional Airline
S.I.C.: 4512
N.A.I.C.S.: 481111
E. G. Kreiken *(Mng Dir)*

Transavia Airlines C.V. (2)
Westelijke Randweg 3
PO Box 7777
1118 ZM Schiphol, Centrum, Netherlands
Tel.: (31) 206406566
Fax: (31) 206015093
E-Mail: info@transavia.com
Web Site: www.transavia.com
Sales Range: $600-649.9 Million
Emp.: 1,482
Air Transportation Services
S.I.C.: 4581
N.A.I.C.S.: 488190
Onno P. M. van den Brink *(Pres & CEO)*
Tjero R. Zomer *(CFO & Exec VP)*

Joint Venture:

Martinair Holland N.V. (2)
Martinair Bldg
PO Box 7507
Schiphol Airport, 1118 ZG Amsterdam, Netherlands (100%)
Tel.: (31) 206011100
Fax: (31) 206011303
Web Site: www.martinair.nl
Rev.: $1,157,590,528
Emp.: 3,647
International Charter Airline; Passenger & Freight; Joint Venture of KLM Royal Dutch Airlines (50%) & Royal Nedlloyd N.V. (50%)
S.I.C.: 4512
N.A.I.C.S.: 481112
Arie Verberk *(Pres)*

U.S. Division:

KLM Royal Dutch Airlines (2)
565 Taxter Rd 3rd Fl
Elmsford, NY 10523
Tel.: (914) 784-2000
Web Site: www.klm.com
Emp.: 60
International Airline Services
S.I.C.: 4512
N.A.I.C.S.: 481111
Jan Willem Smeulers *(VP-North America)*

Non-U.S. Subsidiaries:

KLM UK ENGINEERING LIMITED (2)
Liberator Road Norwich International Airport
Norwich, NR6 6ER, United Kingdom
Tel.: (44) 1603 254400
Fax: (44) 1603 254410
E-Mail: sales@klmuk.com
Web Site: www.klmukengineering.co.uk
Emp.: 400
Aircraft Repair & Maintenance Services
S.I.C.: 7539
N.A.I.C.S.: 811198
Arjan Meijer *(Mng Dir)*

KLM UK Ltd. (2)
Leeds Bradford International Airport
Leeds, LS19 7TU, United Kingdom UK
Tel.: (44) 871 231 0000
Telex: 817312
Web Site: www.klmuk.com
Sls.: $589,000,000
Emp.: 1,400
Scheduled International & Charter Airline
Export
S.I.C.: 4512
N.A.I.C.S.: 481111

SKYCHEF LTD (1)
Seychelles International Airport
PO Box 450
Victoria, Seychelles
Tel.: (248) 438 17 63
Fax: (248) 437 34 56
E-Mail: skychef@seychelles.net
Airport Restaurant Operating Services
S.I.C.: 5812
N.A.I.C.S.: 722511

TRANSAVIA AIRLINES B.V. (1)
Piet Guilonardweg 15 Transport Building
Schiphol Centrum
Amsterdam, 1117 EE, Netherlands
Tel.: (31) 20 604 6555
Fax: (31) 20 601 5093
Airline Transportation Services
S.I.C.: 4581
N.A.I.C.S.: 488190

VLM Airlines NV (1)
Luchthavengebouw B50
B 2100 Antwerp, Belgium
Tel.: (32) 32878080
Fax: (32) 32856829
E-Mail: info@flyvlm.com
Web Site: www.flyvlm.com
Emp.: 450
Air Transportation Services
S.I.C.: 4512
N.A.I.C.S.: 481111
Rony Timmermans *(CFO, Exec Dir-Fin & Commerce)*

Non-U.S. Holdings:

Air France (1)
7 Megalou Alexandrou & Karaiskaki Str
164 52 Athens, Argyroupoli, Greece (100%)
Tel.: (30) 2109980222
Fax: (30) 210 9980 090
Web Site: www.airfrance.gr
Emp.: 42
Airline Transportation Services
S.I.C.: 4512
N.A.I.C.S.: 481111
Jean-Cyril Spinetta *(Chm)*
Pierre-Henri Gourgeon *(CEO)*
Philippe Calavia *(CFO)*
Alain Bassil *(COO)*
Jacques Pichot *(Sec)*
Patrick Alexandre *(Exec VP-Intl Comml Affairs)*
Edouard Odier *(Exec VP-IT)*
Francois Brousse *(Sr VP-Corp Comm)*

City Jet Ltd (1)
Swords Business Campus
Balheary Rd, Dublin, Swords, Ireland IE
Tel.: (353) 18700170 (100%)
E-Mail: info@cityjet.com
Web Site: www.cityjet.com
Emp.: 400
Regional Airline Operator
S.I.C.: 4729
N.A.I.C.S.: 561599
Christine Ourmieres *(Mng Dir)*

Societe Nouvelle Air Ivoire S.A. (1)
Pl de la Republique
Abidjan, Cote d'Ivoire CI
Tel.: (225) 20251561 (76%)
Fax: (225) 20320490
E-Mail: rh@airivoire.com
Web Site: www.airivoire.com
Emp.: 50
Airline Operator
S.I.C.: 4581
N.A.I.C.S.: 488119
Hanns Mariensen *(Gen Mgr)*

Non-U.S. Joint Venture:

Global Logistics System Europe Company for Cargo Information Services GmbH (1)
Lyoner St 36
60528 Frankfurt am Main, Germany
Tel.: (49) 69669060
Fax: (49) 6966906231
E-Mail: info@traxon.com
Web Site: www.traxon.com
Emp.: 30
Support Activities for Air Transportation; Owned by Air France-KLM Group & by Deutsche Lufthansa AG
S.I.C.: 4581
N.A.I.C.S.: 488190
Felix Keck *(Mng Dir)*

AIR GREENLAND A/S

PO Box 1012
DK 3900 Nuuk, Greenland
Tel.: (299) 343434
Fax: (299) 327288
E-Mail: info@airgreenland.gl
Web Site: www.airgreenland.com
Year Founded: 1960
Sales Range: $125-149.9 Million
Emp.: 600

Business Description:
Scheduled, Charter & Freight Airline Services
S.I.C.: 4512
N.A.I.C.S.: 481112

Personnel:
Julia Pars *(Chm)*
Micheal Tinzer *(Pres)*
Mogens E. Jensen *(CFO)*
Ove Nielsen *(CFO)*
Morten Nielsen *(COO)*

Subsidiary:

Hotel Arctic A/S (1)
PO Box 1501
DK 3952 Ilulissat, Greenland
Tel.: (299) 0299 94 41
Fax: (299) 0299 94 40
E-Mail: booking@hotel-arctic.gl
Web Site: www.hotelarctic.com
Hotel & Conference Center Operator
S.I.C.: 7011
N.A.I.C.S.: 721110
Erik Bjerregaard *(Gen Mgr)*

Non-U.S. Subsidiary:

Greenlands Rejsebureau A/S (1)
Wilders Plads 13A 1 sal
1403 Copenhagen, Denmark
Tel.: (45) 33 13 10 11
E-Mail: info@greenland-travel.dk
Web Site: www.greenland-travel.dk
Travel Agency Operator
N.A.I.C.S.: 561510

AIR INDIA LIMITED

Air India Bldg 218 Backbay Reclamation
Nariman Pt, Mumbai, 400 021, India
Tel.: (91) 2222796666
Telex: 112427
Fax: (91) 2222048521
Web Site: www.airindia.in
Year Founded: 1932
Sales Range: $1-4.9 Billion
Emp.: 16,274

Business Description:
International Airline
S.I.C.: 4512
N.A.I.C.S.: 481111

Personnel:
Rohit Nandan *(Chm & Mng Dir)*
S. Venkat *(Sec & Dir-Fin)*

Board of Directors:
Rohit Nandan
G. D. Brara
N. K. Jain
S. Machendranathan
Fali H. Major
Harsh Vardhan Neotia
Vipin Kumar Sharma
K. M. Unni
S. Venkat

U.S. Branch:

Air India (1)
570 Lexington Ave 15th Fl
New York, NY 10022 NY
Tel.: (212) 407-1300
Telex: 12352
Fax: (212) 838-9533
Toll Free: (800) 223-7776
Web Site: www.airindia.com
Emp.: 100
International Airline Svcs
S.I.C.: 4729
N.A.I.C.S.: 561599
Arvind Jadhav *(Chm & Mng Dir)*
Urmila Subbarao *(Chief Vigilence Officer)*

AIR JAMAICA

4 Saint Lucia Ave
72-76 Harbour Street, Kingston, Jamaica
Tel.: (876) 9223460
Fax: (876) 9295643
E-Mail: info@airjamaica.com
Web Site: www.airjamaica.com
Year Founded: 1969
Emp.: 800

Business Description:
Commercial Airline Services
S.I.C.: 4512
N.A.I.C.S.: 481111

Personnel:
Owen K. Melhado *(Chm)*
Bruce Nobles *(Pres & CEO)*
Thomas Hill *(Chief Revenue Officer)*
Paul Pennicook *(Sr VP-Sls & Mktg)*
William B. Rodgers *(Sr VP-Indus Affairs)*
Sue Rosen *(Sr VP-Customer Svc)*
Lloyd Tai *(Sr VP-Flight Ops)*

Board of Directors:

Air Jamaica—(Continued)

Owen K. Melhado
Millicent Hughs
Noel A. Hylton
Derick Latibeaudiere
Sophia Lowe
Jeffrey William Meeks
Rex Nettleford
Horace Reid
Senator Noel Sloley

U.S. Branch:

Air Jamaica Ltd. (1)
8300 NW 33rd St Ste 440
Miami, FL 33122-1940
Tel.: (305) 670-3222
Fax: (305) 669-6632
Web Site: www.airjamaica.com
Emp.: 1,500
Provider of Commercial Air Line Services
S.I.C.: 4512
N.A.I.C.S.: 481112

AIR LIQUIDE S.A.

75 Quai d'Orsay
75007 Paris, France
Tel.: (33) 140625555
E-Mail: shareholders@airliquide.com
Web Site: www.airliquide.com
Year Founded: 1902
AI—(EUR)
Rev.: $20,631,805,271
Assets: $33,659,634,680
Liabilities: $19,599,831,349
Net Worth: $14,059,803,331
Earnings: $2,255,507,835
Emp.: 49,500
Fiscal Year-end: 12/31/12

Business Description:
Industrial & Medical Gas Mfr
S.I.C.: 2813
N.A.I.C.S.: 325120

Personnel:
Benoit Potier *(Chm & CEO)*
Pierre Michel Dufour *(Sr Exec VP)*
Jean-Pierre Duprieu *(Exec VP)*
Francois Darchis *(Sr VP-R&D, New Bus Innovation, Tech, Engrg & Construction)*
Jean-Marc de Royere *(Sr VP-Asia Pacific)*
Michael J. Graff *(Sr VP-Americas)*

Board of Directors:
Benoit Potier
Jean-Paul Agon
Beatrice Majnoni d'Intignano
Gerard de la Martiniere
Thierry Desmarest
Pierre Michel Dufour
Sian Herbert-Jones
Alain Joly
Karen L. Katen
Thierry Peugeot
Paul Skinner
Cornelis Josephus Antonius van Lede

Ernst & Young et Autres
Tour First 1 Place des Saisons
TSA 14444
92037 Paris, Cedex, France

Divisions:

Air Liquide Electronics Europe (1)
75 Quai d'Orsay
75321 Paris, Cedex, 07, France
Tel.: (33) 1 40 62 55 55
Web Site: www.airliquide.com
Mfr & Distr of Specialized Gases for the Electronics Industry
S.I.C.: 2813
N.A.I.C.S.: 325120

Subsidiary:

Ales - Air Liquide Electronics Systems (2)
8 Rue Des Meridiens
38130 Echirolles, France (100%)
Tel.: (33) 438498800
Fax: (33) 476294037
E-Mail: echrrolles@airliquide.com
Emp.: 103
Mfr & Distribution of Specialised Gases & Chemicals for the Electronics Industry
S.I.C.: 2813
N.A.I.C.S.: 325120

Air Liquide Sante (1)
28 Rue Arcueil
75341 Gentilly, Cedex, France (100%)
Tel.: (33) 144110000
E-Mail: info@airliquidesante.com
Web Site: www.airliquidesante.com
Emp.: 100
Mfr & Supplier of Medical Gases & Infection Control Solutions
S.I.C.: 3841
N.A.I.C.S.: 339112

Subsidiaries:

Air Liquide Sante France S.A. (2)
Tour Ariane Paris la Defense 9
92800 Puteaux, France
Tel.: (33) 1 44 11 00 00
Fax: (33) 1 44 11 00 90
Web Site: www.airliquidesante.fr
Industrial Gas Mfr
S.I.C.: 5047
N.A.I.C.S.: 423450

Subsidiaries:

ADEP Assistance (3)
2 Rue Benoit Malon
Suresnes, 92150, France
Tel.: (33) 1 46 97 12 87
Fax: (33) 1 46 97 16 94
E-Mail: adepassistance@adepassistance.fr
Web Site: www.adepassistance.fr
Home Respiratory Healthcare Services
S.I.C.: 8099
N.A.I.C.S.: 621999

Air Liquide Sante Domicile (3)
28 Rue D Arcueil
94250 Gentilly, France (100%)
Tel.: (33) 149694600
Fax: (33) 149694601
E-Mail: alsd.accueil@airliquide.com
Web Site: www.airliquide.com
Emp.: 100
Supplier of Home-based Medical Care Svcs
S.I.C.: 8082
N.A.I.C.S.: 621610
Pissarg Jeanflancois *(Gen Mgr)*

Orkyn (3)
28 Rue d'Arcueil
94250 Gentilly, France (100%)
Tel.: (33) 149698200
Fax: (33) 15549694624
E-Mail: info@orkyn.fr
Web Site: www.orkyn.fr
Emp.: 800
Provider of Home-based Health Care Svcs
S.I.C.: 8082
N.A.I.C.S.: 621610
Vie Jean Francois *(Gen Mgr)*

Air Liquide Sante (International) (2)
Tour Ariane Paris la Defense 9
92800 Puteaux, France
Tel.: (33) 1 44 11 00 00
Fax: (33) 1 44 11 00 90
Industrial Gas Mfr & Distr
S.I.C.: 2813
N.A.I.C.S.: 325120

Air Liquide Sante Services S.A. (2)
6 Rue Cognacq Jay
75007 Paris, France
Tel.: (33) 1 40 62 55 55
Medical Equipment Mfr
S.I.C.: 3841
N.A.I.C.S.: 339112

Seppic S.A. (2)
Tour Kupka C
92039 Paris, La Defense Cedex, France (100%)
Tel.: (33) 155915700
Fax: (33) 155915050
E-Mail: info.seppic@airliquide.com
Web Site: www.seppic.com
Emp.: 170
Mfr of Chemical & Biological Products
S.I.C.: 2899
N.A.I.C.S.: 325998

Subsidiaries:

Givaudan-Lavirotte (3)
56 rue Paul Cazeneuve
PO Box 8344
Lyon, 08, France
Tel.: (33) 478615500
Fax: (33) 478615594
Web Site: www.seppic.com
Emp.: 70
Mfr of Chemical & Biological Products
S.I.C.: 2899
N.A.I.C.S.: 325998

SEPIPROD Castres (3)
127 Chemin De La Poudrerie
81108 Castres, France (100%)
Tel.: (33) 563726969
Fax: (33) 563726970
Web Site: www.seppic.com
Emp.: 300
Mfr of Chemical & Biological Products
S.I.C.: 2899
N.A.I.C.S.: 325998

Seppic Belgium (3)
Nieuwe Weg 1 Part-1
2070 Antwerp, Belgium
Tel.: (32) 32503911
Fax: (32) 32503912
Web Site: www.seppic.com
Emp.: 42
Mfr of Chemical & Biological Products
S.I.C.: 2899
N.A.I.C.S.: 325998
Frank Breugelmans *(Mng Dir)*

Seppic China (3)
Room 510 Jin Ta 58 S Mao Ming Rd
Shanghai, 200020, China (100%)
Tel.: (86) 2164660149
Fax: (86) 2164661109
E-Mail: info.seppic@airliquide.com
Web Site: www.seppic.com
Emp.: 40
Mfr of Chemical & Biological Products
S.I.C.: 2899
N.A.I.C.S.: 325998
Nadia Lezebot *(Gen Mgr)*

Seppic GmbH (3)
Ettore Bugatti Strasse 6-14
51149 Cologne, Germany (100%)
Tel.: (49) 22038903100
Fax: (49) 22038903199
E-Mail: info.seppic@airliquide.com
Web Site: www.seppic.com
Sales Range: $10-24.9 Million
Emp.: 12
Mfr of Chemical & Biological Products
S.I.C.: 2899
N.A.I.C.S.: 325998

Seppic Inc. (3)
30 Two Bridges Rd Ste 210
Fairfield, NJ 07004-1530
Tel.: (973) 882-5597
Fax: (973) 882-5178
E-Mail: info.seppic@airliquide.com
Web Site: www.seppic.com
Emp.: 25
Mfr of Chemical & Biological Products
S.I.C.: 5169
N.A.I.C.S.: 424690
Donna Olear *(Office Mgr)*

Seppic Italia Srl (3)
Via Quarenghi 27
20151 Milan, Italy (100%)
Tel.: (39) 0238009110
Fax: (39) 0238009140
E-Mail: info.seppic@airliquide.com
Web Site: www.seppic.com
Emp.: 12
Mfr of Chemical & Biological Products
S.I.C.: 2899
N.A.I.C.S.: 325998
Antonio Maino *(Mng Dir)*

Seppic UK Ltd (3)
50 Salisbury Rd
PO Box 338
Hounslow, Greater London, TW4 6SH, United Kingdom (100%)
Tel.: (44) 2085778800
Fax: (44) 2085702106
Web Site: www.seppic.com
Emp.: 6
Mfr of Chemical & Biological Products
S.I.C.: 2899
N.A.I.C.S.: 325998

Taema (3)
6 Rue Georges Besse CE 80
92182 Antony, Cedex, France (100%)
Tel.: (33) 140966600
Fax: (33) 140966700
E-Mail: info@taema.com
Web Site: www.taema.com
Emp.: 200
Mfr & Supplier of Respirators & Medical Gases
S.I.C.: 3841
N.A.I.C.S.: 339112
Lorbert Reigh *(Mng Dir)*

VitalAire S.A. (3)
10 rue Cognacq-Jay
75341 Paris, Cedex 07, France (100%)
Tel.: (33) 144110550
Fax: (33) 144110299
Supplier of Medical Gas Systems to the Healthcare Industry
S.I.C.: 3841
N.A.I.C.S.: 339112

Subsidiaries:

DinnoSante (4)
1 Rue Raoul Follereau - Bussy St Georges
77608 Marne-la-Vallee, France
Tel.: (33) 1 64 77 30 00
Fax: (33) 1 64 77 48 10
E-Mail: info@dinnosante.fr
Web Site: www.dinnosante.fr
Medical Equipment Mfr & Distr
S.I.C.: 3841
N.A.I.C.S.: 339112

VitalAire Canada, Inc. (4)
6990 Credit View Rd Unit #6
Mississauga, ON, L5N 8R9, Canada (100%)
Tel.: (905) 890-7100
Fax: (905) 890-7491
E-Mail: info@vitalaire.com
Web Site: www.vitalaire.com
Emp.: 200
Supplier of Medical Gas Systems to the Healthcare Industry
S.I.C.: 3841
N.A.I.C.S.: 339112

VitalAire GmbH (4)
Bei der Pulvermuehle 7
22453 Hamburg, Germany (100%)
Tel.: (49) 40320910
Fax: (49) 4032091100
E-Mail: info@vitalaire.de
Web Site: www.vitalaire.de
Emp.: 250
Supplier of Medical Gas Systems to the Healthcare Industry
S.I.C.: 3841
N.A.I.C.S.: 339112
Diana Shilliag *(Mng Dir)*

Subsidiaries:

Fabig-Peters Medizintechnik GmbH & Co. KG (5)
Prof - Hugo - Jung - Str 3
99310 Arnstadt, Thuringen, Germany
Tel.: (49) 3628 58 25 0
Fax: (49) 3628 58 25 31
E-Mail: info@fp-med.de
Web Site: www.fp-med.de
Surgical & Medical Equipment Mfr & Distr
S.I.C.: 3841
N.A.I.C.S.: 339112

Jonas Medizintechnik Handels GmbH (5)
Oderstrasse 73
14513 Teltow, Germany
Tel.: (49) 3328 3375 0
Fax: (49) 3328 3375 10
E-Mail: info@jonasmed.de
Web Site: www.jonasmed.de
Medical Equipment Mfr & Distr
S.I.C.: 3841
N.A.I.C.S.: 339112

Licher MT GmbH (5)
Langer Acker 18
30900 Wedemark, Germany
Tel.: (49) 5130 5833 0
Fax: (49) 5130 5833 400
E-Mail: mailbox@lichermt.de
Web Site: www.lichermt.de

Emp.: 62
Medical Equipment Distr
S.I.C.: 5047
N.A.I.C.S.: 423450
Dominic Benning *(Gen Mgr)*

Nord Service Projects GmbH (5)
Krogerskoppel 1
24558 Henstedt-Ulzburg, Germany
Tel.: (49) 4193 75 76 77
Fax: (49) 4193 75 76 88
E-Mail: info@nordserviceprojects.de
Web Site: www.nordserviceprojects.com
Industrial Gas Mfr & Whslr
S.I.C.: 2813
N.A.I.C.S.: 325120

Werner & Muller Medizintechnik Service GmbH (5)
Mannheimer Strasse 105 A
Edingen-Neckarhausen, 68535, Germany
Tel.: (49) 621 400 410 0
Fax: (49) 621 400 410 40
Web Site: www.wernerundmueller.de
Home Respiratory Healthcare Services
S.I.C.: 8099
N.A.I.C.S.: 621999

Zuther & Hautmann GmbH & Co. KG (5)
Siegfried-Marcus-Str 31
Muritz, 17192 Waren, Germany
Tel.: (49) 3991 6428 0
Fax: (49) 3991 6428 19
E-Mail: info@z-h.de
Web Site: www.z-h.de
Medical & Surgical Equipment Distr
S.I.C.: 5047
N.A.I.C.S.: 423450
Olaf Zuther *(Gen Mgr)*

Non-U.S. Subsidiary:

VitalAire Italia S.p.A (5)
Via Del Bosco Rinnovato 6
20090 Assago, Italy
Tel.: (39) 0240211
Fax: (39) 024021806
Web Site: www.airliquide.com
Supplier of Medical Gas Systems to the Healthcare Industry
S.I.C.: 3841
N.A.I.C.S.: 339112
Margaria Franco *(Pres)*

Air Liquide Welding SA (1)
13 rue d'Epluches
BP 70024
95315 Saint-Ouen-l'Aumone, Cedex, France FR
Tel.: (33) 134213333 (100%)
Fax: (33) 134213130
Web Site: www.airliquidewelding.com
Emp.: 3,000
Welding Equipment & Accessories Designer, Mfr & Distr
S.I.C.: 3548
N.A.I.C.S.: 333992
Organi Pont *(Mng Dir)*

Subsidiary:

Air Liquide Welding France S.A. (2)
13 rue d'Epluches
BP 70024
95315 Saint-Ouen-l'Aumone, Cedex, France FR
Tel.: (33) 1 3421 3333
Fax: (33) 1 3421 3158
Web Site: www.airliquidewelding.com
Emp.: 130
Welding Equipment & Accessories Mfr
S.I.C.: 3548
N.A.I.C.S.: 333992
Luc Doyon *(Gen Mgr)*

Subsidiaries:

Fluigetec SA (3)
46 Route De Pierrelatte
26130 Saint-Paul-Trois-Chateaux, France
Tel.: (33) 4 75 96 76 99
Fax: (33) 4 75 96 08 45
Industrial Gas Distr
S.I.C.: 5169
N.A.I.C.S.: 424690

Non-U.S. Subsidiaries:

Air Liquide Soldadura Lda (2)
Rua Dr Antonio Loureiro Borges 4
1495 131 Alges, Portugal (100%)
Tel.: (351) 214164900
Fax: (351) 214164904
E-Mail: linha.directa@airliquide.com
Web Site: www.alsoldadura.pt
Emp.: 17
Design & Mfr of Welding Equipment
S.I.C.: 3548
N.A.I.C.S.: 333992
Paulo Adreano *(Dir-Comml)*

Air Liquide Welding S.A. (2)
ZI West Grijpen
Grijpenlaan 5, B 3300 Tienen, Brabanc, Belgium (100%)
Tel.: (32) 016804820
Fax: (32) 16792922
E-Mail: safoerlikon.tienen@tiscali.be
Web Site: www.saf-airliquide.com
Design & Mfr of Welding Equipment
S.I.C.: 3548
N.A.I.C.S.: 333992

Air Liquide Welding UK Limited (2)
Low March London Road
Daventry, Northants, NN11 4SD, United Kingdom
Tel.: (44) 1 327 70 55 11
Fax: (44) 1 327 70 13 10
Emp.: 30
Welding Equipment Mfr
S.I.C.: 3548
N.A.I.C.S.: 333992
Andrew Biscoe *(Reg Mgr-Dev)*

Air Liquide Welding (2)
Grijpenlaan 5 Industriezone
West-Grijpen, L 3300 Tienen, Belgium
Tel.: (32) 16804820
Fax: (32) 16782922
E-Mail: alwlux@pt.lu
Web Site: www.airliquide.lu/
Design & Mfr of Welding Equipment
S.I.C.: 3548
N.A.I.C.S.: 333992
Franz Teughels *(Dir Gen)*

Air Liquide Weldings Netherlands B.V. (2)
Rudonk 6 B
NL 4824 AJ Breda, Netherlands (100%)
Tel.: (31) 765410080
Fax: (31) 765415896
E-Mail: info@alwn.nl
Web Site: www.saf-oerlikon.nl
Emp.: 30
Design & Mfr of Welding Equipment
S.I.C.: 3548
N.A.I.C.S.: 333992
W. Yensen *(Mng Dir)*

FRO S.r.l (2)
Via Torricelli 15/A
37135 Verona, Italy
Tel.: (39) 0458291511
Fax: (39) 0458291500
E-Mail: info@fro.it
Web Site: www.fro.it
Emp.: 100
Design & Mfr of Welding Equipment
S.I.C.: 3548
N.A.I.C.S.: 333992

Isaf S.p.A. (2)
Zona Industriale Via I Maggio 4
38089 Storo, Trentino, Italy
Tel.: (39) 0465 681411
Fax: (39) 0465 681431
E-Mail: isaf@isaf.it
Web Site: www.isaf.it
Mild Steel & Welding Wire Mfr
S.I.C.: 3548
N.A.I.C.S.: 333992

Non-U.S. Subsidiary:

DZW Drahtzieherei Wiesenburg GmbH (3)
Gorzkerstrasse 7
Wiesenburg, Germany
Tel.: (49) 33849 50395
Fax: (49) 33849 50398
E-Mail: office@drahtzieherei-wiesenburg.de
Web Site: www.isaf.it/ing/pagine/company..html
Mild Steel & Welding Wire Mfr
S.I.C.: 3496
N.A.I.C.S.: 332618

Oerlikon Scandinavia AB (2)
Kross Verks Gatan 7F
21616 Limhamn, Sweden (100%)
Tel.: (46) 406701500
Fax: (46) 406701501
E-Mail: info@oerlikon.se
Web Site: www.oerlikon.se
Emp.: 11
Design & Mfr of Welding Equipment
S.I.C.: 3548
N.A.I.C.S.: 333992
Tommy Ercisson *(Mng Dir)*

Oerlikon Schweissautomatik (2)
Konstantinstrasse1
PO Box 350162
D 41238 Monchengladbach, Germany (100%)
Tel.: (49) 216698720
Fax: (49) 216698722
Web Site: www.saf-schweissautonatik.de
Emp.: 30
Design & Mfr of Welding Equipment
S.I.C.: 3548
N.A.I.C.S.: 333992
Fritz Derchmann *(Dir-Sls)*

Oerlikon Schweisstechnik AG (2)
Mandachstrasse 54
CH 8155 Zurich, Niederhasli, Switzerland (100%)
Tel.: (41) 44 307 6111
Fax: (41) 44 307 6112
E-Mail: oerlikon.schweisstechnik@airliquide.com
Web Site: www.oerlikon-schweisstechnik.ch
Emp.: 100
Design & Mfr of Welding Equipment
S.I.C.: 3548
N.A.I.C.S.: 333992
Sandra Antenori *(Mgr-Sls)*

Oerlikon Schweisstechnik GmbH (2)
Industriestrasse 12
D-67304 Eisenberg, Germany
Tel.: (49) 6351476331
Fax: (49) 6351476375
Web Site: www.oerlikon.de
Design & Mfr of Welding Equipment
S.I.C.: 3548
N.A.I.C.S.: 333992

Subsidiary:

Oerlikon Schweisstechnik Nordrhein Westfalen GmbH (3)
Zum Ludwigstal 41
45527 Hattingen, Germany (50.5%)
Tel.: (49) 23243970
Fax: (49) 232439748
E-Mail: info@oerlikon-nrw.de
Web Site: www.oerlikon-nrw.de
Emp.: 30
Design & Mfr of Welding Equipment
S.I.C.: 3548
N.A.I.C.S.: 333992

Oerlikon Soldadura SA (2)
Poligono Industrial La Noria Castellon Km 15 5
El Burgo de Ebro, 50730 Zaragoza, Spain (100%)
Tel.: (34) 976104701
Fax: (34) 976104267
E-Mail: oerlikon.es@airliquide.com
Web Site: www.oerlikon.es
Emp.: 95
Design & Mfr of Welding Equipment
S.I.C.: 3548
N.A.I.C.S.: 333992

SAF Oerlikon UK Ltd (2)
Low March London Road
Daventry, Northants, NN11 4SD, United Kingdom (100%)
Tel.: (44) 1327705511
Fax: (44) 1327701310
E-Mail: info@saf-wp.co.uk
Web Site: www.saf-wp.co.uk
Emp.: 50
Design & Mfr of Welding Equipment
S.I.C.: 3548
N.A.I.C.S.: 333992
John Garland *(Mng Dir)*

SAF Welding Products Ltd (2)
5 South Elgin Pl
Glasgow Rd, Clydebank, G81 1X, United Kingdom (100%)
Tel.: (44) 1419518883
Fax: (44) 1419518830
Design & Mfr of Welding Equipment
S.I.C.: 3548
N.A.I.C.S.: 333992

SAF Welding Products Ltd (2)
Tyler St
Sheffield, S91 DH, United Kingdom (100%)
Tel.: (44) 114232234
Fax: (44) 1142440007
Design & Mfr of Welding Equipment
S.I.C.: 3548
N.A.I.C.S.: 333992

Aqualung International (1)
1ere Ave 14 St DP 148
06513 Carros, Cedex, France (100%)
Tel.: (33) 492082888
Fax: (33) 492082899
E-Mail: support@aqualung.com
Web Site: www.aqualung.com
Emp.: 120
Mfr of Diving Equipment
S.I.C.: 3949
N.A.I.C.S.: 339920
Jean-Luc Luc Diainville *(Mng Dir)*

Subsidiaries:

Aqua Lung America, Inc. (2)
2340 Cousteau Ct
Vista, CA 92081 CA
Tel.: (760) 597-5000
Fax: (760) 597-4900
E-Mail: support@aqualung.com
Web Site: www.aqualung.com
Emp.: 400
Sport & Commercial Diving Life Support Products & Protective Breathing Systems Mfr
S.I.C.: 3949
N.A.I.C.S.: 339920
Robbert Bruins *(Product Mgr-Dev)*

Aqua Lung Canada (2)
6820 Kirkpatrick Cres
Central Saanich, Vancouver, BC, V8M 2A6, Canada
Tel.: (250) 652-5881
Fax: (250) 652-5891
Web Site: www.aqualung.com
Emp.: 40
Diving Equipment Mfr
S.I.C.: 3949
N.A.I.C.S.: 339920
Debbie Ashford *(Gen Mgr)*

Aqua Lung Japan, Ltd (2)
2229 4 Nurumizu
Atsugi, 243 0033, Japan (100%)
Tel.: (81) 462473222
Fax: (81) 462473225
E-Mail: aqualung@aqualung.co.jp
Web Site: www.aqualung.com
Emp.: 15
Mfr of Diving Equipment
S.I.C.: 3949
N.A.I.C.S.: 339920
Koichi Takeda *(Pres)*

Aqualung Espana (2)
Vilay Vila 82
8004 Barcelona, Spain (100%)
Tel.: (34) 965127170
Fax: (34) 34419083
Web Site: www.aqualung.com
Mfr of Diving Equipment
S.I.C.: 3949
N.A.I.C.S.: 339920

Aqualung Tauchsportartikel GmbH (2)
Josef-Schuttler-Str 12
D-78224 Singen, Germany
Tel.: (49) 773193450
Fax: (49) 7731934540
E-Mail: werner.thomaier@aqualung.de
Web Site: www.aqualung.de
Emp.: 25
Mfr of Diving Equipment
S.I.C.: 3949
N.A.I.C.S.: 339920
Werner Thomaier *(Mng Dir)*

Technisub S.p.A (2)
Via Gualco 42
16165 Genoa, Italy (100%)
Tel.: (39) 01054451
Fax: (39) 01054452445
E-Mail: info@technisub.com
Web Site: www.technisub.com
Mfr of Diving Equipment
S.I.C.: 3949

Air Liquide S.A.—(Continued)

N.A.I.C.S.: 339920
Maello Mauro *(Mgr-Ops)*

US Divers Japan (2)
816-1 Sanda Atsugi
Kanagawa, Atsugi, Japan
Tel.: (81) 462 42 6537
Web Site: www.aqualung.com
Mfr of Diving Equipment
S.I.C.: 3949
N.A.I.C.S.: 339920

US Divers (2)
2340 Cousteau Ct
Vista, CA 92081
Tel.: (760) 597-5000
Fax: (760) 597-4900
Web Site: www.usdivers.com
Emp.: 200
Mfr of Diving Equipment
S.I.C.: 3949
N.A.I.C.S.: 339920
Stephan Murnane *(VP)*

GIE Cryospace (1)
75 Quai d'Orsay
75321 Paris, Cedex, 07, France (100%)
Tel.: (33) 1 40 62 5555
Web Site: www.france.airliquide.com
Supplier of Industrial Gases & Equipment to the European Space Programme
S.I.C.: 5085
N.A.I.C.S.: 423840

Subsidiaries:

Air Liquide Spatial Guyane (2)
Route de l'Espace
BP 826
Ensemble de Lancement, 97388 Kourou, Cedex, French Guiana
Tel.: (594) 5 94 33 75 69
Fax: (594) 5 94 33 75 77
Web Site: www.airliquide.com
Supplier of Industrial Gases to the European Space Programme
S.I.C.: 5085
N.A.I.C.S.: 423840

DTA (2)
2 Rue Clemenciere
PO Box 15
38360 Sassenage, France (100%)
Tel.: (33) 476436030
Fax: (33) 476436171
E-Mail: dta.gcom@airliquide.com
Web Site: www.dta.airliquide.com
Emp.: 350
Mfr of Industrial Gases
S.I.C.: 2813
N.A.I.C.S.: 325120

Subsidiaries:

Air Liquide Electronics Materials S.A. (1)
6 Rue Cognacq Jay
Paris, 75007, France
Tel.: (33) 1 40 62 55 55
Fax: (33) 1 40 62 55 26
Industrial Gas Mfr
S.I.C.: 2813
N.A.I.C.S.: 325120
Werner Schleser *(Dir-Technical)*

Air Liquide Engineering S.A. (1)
7 Rue Cognacq Jay
75007 Paris, France
Tel.: (33) 1 40 62 55 55
Fax: (33) 1 40 62 50 22
Industrial & Medical Gas Mfr
S.I.C.: 2813
N.A.I.C.S.: 325120

Air Liquide Finance SA (1)
6 Rue Cognacq-Jay
Paris, 75007, France
Tel.: (33) 1 40 62 55 55
Financial Management Services
S.I.C.: 6211
N.A.I.C.S.: 523999

Air Liquide Hydrogen Energy SA. (1)
1 Chemin de la Porte des Loges
BP 126
78350 Les Loges-en-Josas, France
Tel.: (33) 1 39 07 64 96
Fax: (33) 1 39 07 62 64
E-Mail: h2energy@airliquide.com
Web Site: www.airliquide-hydrogen-energy.com
Emp.: 35
Hydrogen Filling Station Operator
S.I.C.: 4931
N.A.I.C.S.: 221111
Eric Prades *(CEO)*

Air Liquide Innovation SA (1)
6 Rue Cognacq Jay
75007 Paris, France
Tel.: (33) 1 40 62 55 55
Fax: (33) 1 40 62 54 65
Industrial Gas Mfr
S.I.C.: 2813
N.A.I.C.S.: 325120

Air Liquide International S.A. (1)
75 Quai d Orsay
Paris, 75007, France FR
Tel.: (33) 1 40 62 55 55
Fax: (33) 1 40 62 55 26
Holding Company
S.I.C.: 6719
N.A.I.C.S.: 551112

Air Liquide Medical Systems S.A. (1)
Parc de Haute Technologie 6 Rue Georges Besse
92182 Antony, France
Tel.: (33) 1 40 96 66 00
Fax: (33) 1 40 96 67 00
Web Site: www.airliquidemedicalsystems.com
Respiratory Assistance Equipment Mfr & Distr
S.I.C.: 3842
N.A.I.C.S.: 339113
Giner Jean Marc *(Mng Dir)*

Belle Etoile Utilite (1)
Avenue Ramboz
69190 Saint-Fons, France
Tel.: (33) 4 72 89 37 03
Fax: (33) 4 72 89 37 01
Industrial Gas Mfr
S.I.C.: 2813
N.A.I.C.S.: 325120

Btl S.A. (1)
Pave Des Moulins
59260 Hellemmes-Lille, France
Tel.: (33) 3 20 67 67 67
Fax: (33) 3 20 67 67 68
Emp.: 400
Industrial Gas Mfr
S.I.C.: 2813
N.A.I.C.S.: 325120

Subsidiary:

Laboratoires Anios S.A. (2)
Pave du moulin
59260 Hellemmes-Lille, France FR
Tel.: (33) 3 20 67 67 67
Fax: (33) 3 20 67 67 68
Web Site: www.anios.com
Sales Range: $200-249.9 Million
Emp.: 450
Hygiene & Disinfectant Products Mfr
S.I.C.: 2842
N.A.I.C.S.: 325612
Bertrand Letartre *(Mng Dir)*

Non-U.S. Subsidiaries;

Farmec Nuova S.r.l. (2)
Via W Flemming 7 Zone Industriale
37026 Pescantina, Verona, Italy
Tel.: (39) 045 6767672
Fax: (39) 045 6767668
E-Mail: farmec@farmec.it
Web Site: www.farmec.it
Emp.: 70
Pharmaceutical Products Mfr
S.I.C.: 2834
N.A.I.C.S.: 325412
Vincent Bellette *(Mng Dir)*

Unident S.A. (2)
Rue Francois Perreard 4
Case Postale 142
Chene-Bourg, 1225 Geneva, Switzerland
Tel.: (41) 22 839 79 00
Fax: (41) 22 839 79 10
E-Mail: info@unident.ch
Web Site: www.unident.ch
Emp.: 15
Dental Hygiene Products Mfr & Whslr
S.I.C.: 2842
N.A.I.C.S.: 325612
Keith Bruton *(Mgr-Mktg)*

Chemoxal SA (1)
75 Quai D Orsay
75007 Paris, France
Tel.: (33) 1 40 62 55 55
Fax: (33) 1 45 55 03 89
Pharmaceutical Product Mfr
S.I.C.: 2834
N.A.I.C.S.: 325412

Cogenal SRL (1)
6 Rue Cognacq Jay
75007 Paris, France
Tel.: (33) 1 40 62 55 55
Fax: (33) 1 40 62 55 26
Air Conditioning Equipment Mfr
S.I.C.: 3585
N.A.I.C.S.: 333415

Cryolor SA (1)
Argancy Z I des Jonquieres
BP 7
Ennery, 57365, France
Tel.: (33) 3877 08520
Fax: (33) 3877 08544
E-Mail: info@cryolor.com
Web Site: www.cryolor.com
Emp.: 200
Cryogenic & Hydrocarbon Gas Storage Services
S.I.C.: 4923
N.A.I.C.S.: 486210
Hadi Moussavi *(Mng Dir)*

Cryopal (1)
Parc Gustave Eiffel Bussy Saint Georges 8 av Gutenberg
77607 Marne-la-Vallee, France
Tel.: (33) 1 64 76 15 00
Fax: (33) 1 64 76 16 98
E-Mail: sales.cryopal@airliquide.com
Web Site: www.cryopal.com
Emp.: 200
Cryogenic Vessel Mfr & Distr
S.I.C.: 3443
N.A.I.C.S.: 332420
Vincent Michelet *(Mgr-Procurement)*

Helium Services S.A. (1)
6 Rue Cognacq Jay
75007 Paris, France
Tel.: (33) 140625555
Fax: (33) 140625526
Industrial Gas Mfr
S.I.C.: 2813
N.A.I.C.S.: 325120

Omasa France (1)
2 Rue des Orangers
94385 Bonneuil-sur-Marne, France
Tel.: (33) 1 56 71 18 50
Fax: (33) 1 43 77 32 37
Web Site: www.omasa.fr
Emp.: 45
Medical & Surgical Equipment Mfr
S.I.C.: 3841
N.A.I.C.S.: 339112
Timothee Graber *(Gen Mgr)*

SOBEGI (1)
Pole 4 Avenue du lac
64150 Mourenx, France
Tel.: (33) 5 59 92 22 82
E-Mail: service.commercial@sobegi.com
Web Site: www.sobegi.com
Oil & Gas Exploration Services
S.I.C.: 1389
N.A.I.C.S.: 213112
Francois Virely *(Pres)*

Societe d'Exploitation de Produits pour les Industries Chimiques (1)
22 Terrasse Bellini - Paris
La Defense, 92800 Puteaux, France FR
Tel.: (33) 1 42 91 40 00
Fax: (33) 1 42 91 41 11
E-Mail: info.seppic@airliquide.com
Web Site: www.seppic.com
Emp.: 167
Specialty Chemicals Mfr & Distr
S.I.C.: 2899
N.A.I.C.S.: 325998
Charles-Henri des Villettes *(Chm-Mgmt Bd)*

Societe d'Oxygene et d Acetylene d Extreme-Orient SA (1)
75 Quai d'Orsay
Paris, 75007, France
Tel.: (33) 1 40 62 55 41
Fax: (33) 1 40 62 54 65
Industrial Gas Mfr & Distr
S.I.C.: 2813
N.A.I.C.S.: 325120

Sudac Air Services (1)
1 avenue des Lys - ZAC des petits carreaux
94380 Bonneuil-sur-Marne, France
Tel.: (33) 1 41 94 50 50
Fax: (33) 1 41 94 50 82
Web Site: www.sudac.fr
Compressor Repair & Maintenance Services
S.I.C.: 7699
N.A.I.C.S.: 811310

U.S. Subsidiary:

Air Liquide America Corporation (1)
2700 Post Oak Blvd Ste 1800
Houston, TX 77056-5797 (100%)
Mailing Address:
PO Box 460229
Houston, TX 77056-8229
Tel.: (713) 624-8000
Fax: (713) 624-8030
Toll Free: (800) 820-2522
Web Site: www.airliquide.com
Emp.: 600
Supplier of Industrial Gases
Import Export
S.I.C.: 2813
N.A.I.C.S.: 325120

Subsidiary:

American Air Liquide Holdings, Inc. (2)
2700 Post Oak Blvd Ste 1800
Houston, TX 77056
Tel.: (877) 855-9533
Fax: (877) 715-4799
E-Mail: Info.Electronics-US@airliquide.com
Industrial Gas Mfr
S.I.C.: 2813
N.A.I.C.S.: 325120
Michael J. Graff *(Pres & CEO)*

Subsidiary:

Air Liquide USA LLC (3)
2700 Post Oak Blvd 1800
Houston, TX 77056-5784
Tel.: (713) 624-8000
Fax: (713) 624-8085
Industrial Gas Mfr
S.I.C.: 2813
N.A.I.C.S.: 325120
Michael J. Graff *(Pres & CEO)*

Subsidiaries:

Air Liquide Advanced Technologies U.S. LLC (4)
200 GBC Dr
Newark, DE 19702-2462
Tel.: (302) 286-5524
Fax: (302) 286-5583
E-Mail: gcom.dta@airliquide.com
Web Site: www.airliquideadvancedtechnologies.com
Cryogenic Equipment Mfr
S.I.C.: 3443
N.A.I.C.S.: 332420

Air Liquide America L.P. (4)
821 Chesapeake Dr
Cambridge, MD 21613
Tel.: (410) 228-6400
Fax: (410) 228-4251
Toll Free: (800) 638-1197
E-Mail: info@calgaz.com
Web Site: www.calgaz.com
Emp.: 60
Mfr of Gas Calibration & Regulation Equipment
S.I.C.: 2813
N.A.I.C.S.: 325120

Air Liquide America Specialty Gases LLC (4)
6141 Easton Rd PO Box 310
Plumsteadville, PA 18949-0310 PA
Mailing Address:
PO Box 310
Plumsteadville, PA 18949
Tel.: (215) 766-8861
Fax: (215) 766-0320

Toll Free: (800) 21SCOTT
Web Site: www.scottgas.com
Sales Range: $75-99.9 Million
Emp.: 450
Pure Gases, Gas Mixtures, Pure & Mixed Gases In Disposable Containers, Gas Handling Equipment & Services
Import Export
S.I.C.: 2813
N.A.I.C.S.: 325120

Air Liquide Electronics, LP (4)
9101 LBJ Freeway Ste 800
Dallas, TX 75243
Tel.: (972) 301-5200
Fax: (972) 301-5275
Web Site: www.airliquide.com
Mfr & Distribution of Specialised Gases for the Electronics Industry
S.I.C.: 5084
N.A.I.C.S.: 423830
Michael Rosen *(Comm Mgr)*

Air Liquide Healthcare America Corporation (4)
2700 Post Oak Blvd Ste 1800
Houston, TX 77056
Tel.: (713) 896-2816
Fax: (713) 896-2258
Web Site: www.us.airliquidehealthcare.com
Medical Gas Distr
S.I.C.: 5047
N.A.I.C.S.: 423450

Air Liquide Helium America, Inc. (4)
2700 Post Oak Blvd
Houston, TX 77056-5784
Tel.: (713) 624-8000
Industrial Gas Mfr
S.I.C.: 2813
N.A.I.C.S.: 325120

Air Liquide Industrial U.S. LP (4)
12800 W Little York Rd
Houston, TX 77041
Tel.: (713) 896-2315
Fax: (713) 896-2332
Industrial Gas Distr
S.I.C.: 4924
N.A.I.C.S.: 221210
Tim Bruce *(VP-Primary Production & Field Svc)*

Subsidiary:

Voltaix LLC (5)
197 Meister Ave
Branchburg, NJ 08876 NJ
Tel.: (908) 231-9060
Fax: (908) 895-0857
Web Site: www.voltaix.com
Sales Range: $25-49.9 Million
Emp.: 185
Specialty Chemicals Mfr
S.I.C.: 2899
N.A.I.C.S.: 325998
John P. de Neufville *(Chm & Chief Scientist)*
Matthew D. Stephens *(CTO & Exec VP-Sls & Mktg)*
Mark A. Wilkinson *(Exec VP-Ops & Tech)*
Michael Pikulin *(Sr VP)*

Air Liquide Large Industries U.S. LP (4)
8000 N Cir 225 E
Pittsboro, IN 46167
Tel.: (317) 892-5221
Fax: (317) 892-4375
Industrial Gas Mfr
S.I.C.: 2813
N.A.I.C.S.: 325120
Cari Carter *(Office Mgr)*

Air Liquide Process & Construction, Inc. (4)
2700 Post Oak Blvd
Houston, TX 77056-5784
Tel.: (713) 624-8800
Fax: (713) 624-8794
Engineering Services
S.I.C.: 8711
N.A.I.C.S.: 541330
Kim Gomez *(Office Mgr)*

Non-U.S. Subsidiaries:

Air Liquide Argentina S.A. (3)
Monsenor Magliano 3079
B1642GLA San Isidro, Buenos Aires, Argentina
Tel.: (54) 11 4708 2200
Fax: (54) 11 4735 2341
Web Site: www.ar.airliquide.com
Emp.: 415
Industrial & Medical Gas Mfr
S.I.C.: 2813
N.A.I.C.S.: 325120

Air Liquide Brasil S.A. (3)
Edificio Bolsa De Imoveis
11541 19 Brooklin Novo, 04578 000 Sao Paulo, Brazil BR (100%)
Tel.: (55) 55098300
Fax: (55) 55098330
Web Site: www.airliquide.com.br
Emp.: 500
Mfr. & Sale of Industrial Gases
S.I.C.: 2813
N.A.I.C.S.: 325120

Air Liquide Canada Inc. (3)
1250 Boulevard Rene Levesque West Suite 1800
Montreal, QC, H3B 5E6, Canada (100%)
Tel.: (514) 933-0303
Fax: (514) 846-7700
E-Mail:
Web Site: www.airliquide.com
Emp.: 200
Mfr of Industrial Gases
S.I.C.: 2813
N.A.I.C.S.: 325120
Adam Peters *(Pres & CEO)*
Michael J. Graff *(CEO-Canada)*

Subsidiary:

Keops (4)
1155 University St Ste 1100
Montreal, QC, H3B 3A7, Canada (100%)
Tel.: (514) 876-2855
Fax: (514) 876-3664
E-Mail: info@keops.com
Web Site: www.keops.com
Emp.: 70
Information Technology Solutions
S.I.C.: 7373
N.A.I.C.S.: 541512
Christian Morin *(Pres)*

Air Liquide Chile S.A. (3)
Av Kennedy 5454
Santiago, Chile
Tel.: (56) 2 4657600
Fax: (56) 2 4657640
E-Mail: alchile@airliquide.cl
Web Site: www.airliquide.cl
Industrial Gas Mfr
S.I.C.: 2813
N.A.I.C.S.: 325120

Air Liquide Mexico (3)
Ave Jose Clemente Orozco No 329 Pisco 20
Nuevo Leon, Mexico
Tel.: (52) 81 8851 0600
Web Site: www.airliquide.com
Emp.: 55
Industrial Gas Mfr
S.I.C.: 2813
N.A.I.C.S.: 325120
Albert Correa *(Gen Mgr)*

Air Liquide Uruguay SA (3)
Sede Central Ave Burgues 3230
Montevideo, Uruguay
Tel.: (598) 2203 4203
Fax: (598) 2203 4203
Industrial Gas Mfr
S.I.C.: 2813
N.A.I.C.S.: 325120

Non-U.S. Subsidiaries:

Air Liquide Algerie - SIDAL Spa (1)
02 Boulevard Aissatidir Place 1er Mai
Algiers, Algeria
Tel.: (213) 21 65 06 58
Fax: (213) 21 65 06 92
Oil & Gas Exploration Services
S.I.C.: 1389
N.A.I.C.S.: 213112

Subsidiary:

Societe d'Installations et de Diffusion de Materiel Technique S.P.A. (2)
2 Boulevard Aissat Idir Alger Premier Mai
Algiers, Algeria
Tel.: (213) 21 65 06 96
Fax: (213) 21 65 06 75
Industrial Gas Mfr
S.I.C.: 2813
N.A.I.C.S.: 325120

Air Liquide Angola Ltda (1)
Estrada do Cacuaco 288
Luanda, Angola
Tel.: (244) 222 01 57 31
Web Site: www.airliquide.com
Industrial Gas Mfr
S.I.C.: 2813
N.A.I.C.S.: 325120

Air Liquide Asia - Pacific Co., Ltd (1)
1-9-1 Shinonome
Koto-Ku, Tokyo, 135-0062, Japan
Tel.: (81) 355738556
Industrial Gas Mfr
S.I.C.: 2813
N.A.I.C.S.: 325120
Jean-Marc de Royere *(Chm & CEO)*

Air Liquide Australia Ltd. (1)
Level 9 380 St Kilda Road
Melbourne, WA, 6150, Australia AU
Tel.: (61) 3 9697 9888
Fax: (61) 3 9690 7107
E-Mail: ALAVicSales@airliquide.com
Web Site: www.airliquide.com.au
Industrial Gas Mfr & Distr
S.I.C.: 2813
N.A.I.C.S.: 325120
Mac Redfern *(Mng Dir)*

Subsidiary:

Air Liquide Healthcare P/L (2)
Unit 5/476 Gardeners Road
Alexandria, NSW, 2015, Australia
Tel.: (61) 2 9364 7474
Fax: (61) 2 8338 9797
E-Mail: alhenquiries@airliquide.com
Web Site: www.airliquidehealthcare.com.au
Emp.: 50
Medical Gas Distribution Services
S.I.C.: 8099
N.A.I.C.S.: 621999
Yvoine McCort *(Mng Dir)*

Air Liquide Austria GmbH (1)
Sendnergasse 30
2320 Schwechat, Austria
Tel.: (43) 1 70109 0
Fax: (43) 1 70109 318
E-Mail: healthcare@airliquide.at
Web Site: www.airliquide.at
Industrial Gas Mfr
S.I.C.: 2813
N.A.I.C.S.: 325120

Air Liquide Belge S.A. (1)
Siege Social Parc d'affaires Zenobe Gramme Quai des Vennes 8
4020 Liege, Belgium
Tel.: (32) 43 49 89 89
Fax: (32) 43 41 20 70
Web Site: www.airliquide.be
Emp.: 40
Industrial Gas Mfr
S.I.C.: 2813
N.A.I.C.S.: 325120

Subsidiaries:

Air Liquide Belgium S.A. (2)
Parc d'affaires Zenobe Gramme Quai des Vennes 8
Liege, 4020, Belgium
Tel.: (32) 4 349 8989
Fax: (32) 43 42 85 14
Web Site: www.airliquide.be
Industrial Gas Mfr
S.I.C.: 2813
N.A.I.C.S.: 325120

Air Liquide Benelux S.A. (2)
Siege Social Parc d'affaires Zenobe Gramme Quai des Vennes 8
4020 Liege, Belgium
Tel.: (32) 43 49 89 89
Fax: (32) 43 41 20 70
Industrial Gas Mfr
S.I.C.: 2813
N.A.I.C.S.: 325120

Air Liquide Medical S.A. (2)
Parc d'affaires Zenobe Gramme Quai des Vennes 8
4020 Liege, Belgium
Tel.: (32) 43 49 89 89
Fax: (32) 43 41 20 70
Web Site: www.airliquide.be/fr/contacte z-nous.html
Industrial Gas Mfr
S.I.C.: 2813
N.A.I.C.S.: 325120

Air Liquide Bulgaria EOOD (1)
1 Business Park Sofia Street Building 7-B Floor 5
1766 Sofia, Bulgaria
Tel.: (359) 2 4899782
Fax: (359) 2 4899285
E-Mail: info.bg@airliquide.com
Web Site: www.airliquide.bg
Emp.: 31
Industrial Gas Mfr & Distr
S.I.C.: 2813
N.A.I.C.S.: 325120
Francis Bucquet *(Gen Mgr)*

Air Liquide B.V. (1)
De Witbogt 1
5652 AG Eindhoven, Netherlands (100%)
Tel.: (31) 402503503
Fax: (31) 402503533
E-Mail: info@airliquide.com
Web Site: www.airliquide.nl
Sls.: $24,293,572
Emp.: 150
Mfr of Industrial Gases
S.I.C.: 2813
N.A.I.C.S.: 325120
Yan Niging *(Gen Mgr)*

Subsidiaries:

Air Liquide Acetylene B.V. (2)
Kerenshofweg 101
Geleen, 6167 AE, Netherlands
Tel.: (31) 40 250 3920
Web Site: www.chemelot.nl/default.aspx?id=3&template=bedrijf.htm&bid=143&taal=en
Emp.: 75
Acetylene Distr
S.I.C.: 5169
N.A.I.C.S.: 424690
Eric Heetkamp *(Gen Mgr)*

Scott Speciality Gases Netherlands B.V. (2)
Takkebijsters 46-48
4817 BL Breda, Netherlands
Tel.: (31) 76 5711828
Fax: (31) 76 5713267
E-Mail: info.scott@airliquide.com
Web Site: www.scottecatalog.com
Emp.: 40
Industrial Gas Mfr
S.I.C.: 2813
N.A.I.C.S.: 325120
Pim Aardse *(Coord-Transport & Stock)*

VitalAire B.V. (2)
De Witbogt 1
5652 AG Eindhoven, Netherlands
Tel.: (31) 40 250 3502
Fax: (31) 40 250 3533
E-Mail: info@vitalaire.com
Web Site: www.airliquide.nl/nl/wie-zijn-wij/air-liquide-in-the-netherlands.html
Medical Gas Mfr
S.I.C.: 2813
N.A.I.C.S.: 325120

Subsidiary:

Comcare Medical B.V. (3)
Langendijk 27 A
5652 AX Eindhoven, Netherlands
Tel.: (31) 40 250 35 02
Fax: (31) 40 255 59 31
E-Mail: info@comcaremedical.com
Web Site: www.comcaremedical.com
Health Care Services
S.I.C.: 8099
N.A.I.C.S.: 621999
Patrick Hondsmerk *(Gen Mgr)*

Air Liquide CZ, s.r.o. (1)
Jinonicka 80
158 00 Prague, Czech Republic
Tel.: (420) 257 290 384
Fax: (420) 257 290 428
E-Mail: airliquide@airliquide.cz
Web Site: www.airliquide.cz
Emp.: 35
Industrial Gas Mfr
S.I.C.: 2813

Air Liquide S.A.—(Continued)

N.A.I.C.S.: 325120

Subsidiary:

AIR LIQUIDE WELDING CZ, s.r.o. (2)
Areal Svum Podnikatelska 565
Bechovice, 190 11 Prague, Czech Republic
Tel.: (420) 274 023 163
Fax: (420) 274 023 233
E-Mail: welding.cz@airliquide.com
Web Site: www.airliquidewelding.cz
Emp.: 5
Welding & Cutting Equipment Mfr
S.I.C.: 3548
N.A.I.C.S.: 333992
Michael Schlixbier *(Gen Mgr)*

Air Liquide Danmark A.S. (1)
Hoje Taastrup Vej 42
2630 Tastrup, Denmark
Tel.: (45) 43 55 50 50
Fax: (45) 43 55 50 65
E-Mail: info.denmark@airliquide.com
Web Site: www.airliquide.dk
Industrial Gas Mfr
S.I.C.: 2813
N.A.I.C.S.: 325120

Air Liquide Deutschland GmbH (1)
Hans Gunther Sohl Strasse 5
40235 Dusseldorf, Germany (100%)
Tel.: (49) 21166990
Fax: (49) 2116699222
E-Mail: info@airliquide.com
Web Site: www.airliquide.de
Emp.: 350
Mfr of Industrial Gases
S.I.C.: 2813
N.A.I.C.S.: 325120

Subsidiaries:

Air Liquide Electronics GmbH (2)
Hans-Gunther-Sohl-Str 5
40235 Dusseldorf, Germany
Tel.: (49) 211 6699 0
Fax: (49) 211 6699 222
E-Mail: info@airliquide.com
Web Site: www.airliquide.de/ueberuns/wer-wir-sind/ald/beteiligungen.html
Electronic Device & System Mfr
S.I.C.: 3679
N.A.I.C.S.: 334419

Air Liquide Industriegase GmbH & Co. KG (2)
Hans-Gunther-Sohl-Str 5
40235 Dusseldorf, Germany
Tel.: (49) 211 66990
Fax: (49) 211 6699222
Industrial Gas Mfr
S.I.C.: 2813
N.A.I.C.S.: 325120

Air Liquide Medical GmbH (2)
Hans-Gunther-Sohl-Str 5
40235 Dusseldorf, Germany
Tel.: (49) 211 6699 0
Fax: (49) 211 6699 222
E-Mail: medizin@airliquide.de
Web Site: www.airliquide.de/ueberuns/wer-wir-sind/ald/beteiligungen.html
Medical Gas Mfr
S.I.C.: 2813
N.A.I.C.S.: 325120

AST Service GmbH (2)
Alter Flughafen 14a
30179 Hannover, Germany
Tel.: (49) 511 350 66 26
Fax: (49) 511 350 66 31
E-Mail: info@ast-service.com
Web Site: www.ast-service.org
Emp.: 45
Industrial Gas Mfr
S.I.C.: 2813
N.A.I.C.S.: 325120
Jan Kocna *(Mng Dir)*

Cryotherm GmbH & Co. KG (2)
Euteneuen 4
Sieg, 57548 Kirchen, Germany
Tel.: (49) 2741 9585 0
Fax: (49) 27 41 69 00
E-Mail: info@cryotherm.de
Web Site: www.cryotherm.de
Insulated Container & Transfer Pipe Mfr
S.I.C.: 1389
N.A.I.C.S.: 213112
Peter Siara *(Gen Mgr)*

EVC Dresden-Wilschdorf GmbH & Co. KG (2)
Rosenstr 32-34
Dresden, Saxony, 01067, Germany
Tel.: (49) 3518399330
Energy Consulting Services
S.I.C.: 8748
N.A.I.C.S.: 541618
Kai Princkmann *(Gen Mgr)*

INTEGA GmbH (2)
Raiffeisenallee 6a
Oberhaching, Germany
Tel.: (49) 89 61 38 72 0
Fax: (49) 89 61 33 00 2
E-Mail: info@intega.de
Web Site: www.intega.de
Engineering Services
S.I.C.: 8711
N.A.I.C.S.: 541330

Schulke & Mayr GmbH (2)
Robert Koch Strasse 2
22851 Norderstedt, Germany (100%)
Tel.: (49) 40521000
Fax: (49) 4052100134
E-Mail: mail@schuelke-mayr.com
Web Site: www.schuelke-mayr.com
Emp.: 300
Mfr of Infection Control Products
S.I.C.: 3841
N.A.I.C.S.: 339112
Sylvia Rahde *(Asst Mgr-Mktg)*

U.S. Subsidiary:

schulke inc. (3)
30 Two Bridges Rd Ste 225
Fairfield, NJ 07004
Tel.: (973) 770-7300
Fax: (973) 770-7302
E-Mail: SAIUS@schuelke.com
Web Site: www.schuelke.com
Pension Fund Management Services
S.I.C.: 6371
N.A.I.C.S.: 524292
Linda Sedlewicz *(Gen Mgr)*

Non-U.S. Subsidiaries:

Schulke & Mayr AG (3)
Sihlfeldstr 58
8003 Zurich, Switzerland
Tel.: (41) 44 466 55 44
Fax: (41) 44 466 55 33
E-Mail: mail.ch@schuelke.com
Web Site: www.schuelke.com
Hygiene & Preservation Products Mfr
S.I.C.: 2834
N.A.I.C.S.: 325412
Marco Waiz *(Mgr-Sls)*

Schulke & Mayr (Asia) Pte. Ltd. (3)
61 Yishun Industrial Park A 04-03 Five Star Building
Singapore, 768767, Singapore
Tel.: (65) 6257 2388
Fax: (65) 6257 9388
E-Mail: mail.sg@schuelke.com
Web Site: www.schuelke.com
Emp.: 10
Pharmaceutical Products Mfr & Distr
S.I.C.: 2834
N.A.I.C.S.: 325412
Alessandra Muller *(Gen Mgr)*

Schulke & Mayr (Asia) Sdn.Bhd. (3)
Block A Plaza Glomac Lot A-06-01 & A-06-02 No 6 Jalan SS7/19
Kelana Jaya, 47301 Petaling Jaya, Selangor, Malaysia
Tel.: (60) 3 78 85 80 20
Fax: (60) 3 78 85 80 21
Web Site: www.schuelke.com
Hygiene & Infection Control Products Mfr
S.I.C.: 2843
N.A.I.C.S.: 325613

Schulke & Mayr Belgium NV (3)
Bourgetlaan 44
1130 Brussels, Belgium (100%)
Tel.: (32) 24797335
Fax: (32) 24799966
E-Mail: sales.benelux@schuelke-mayr.com
Web Site: www.schulke-mayr.com
Emp.: 11
Mfr of Infection Control Products
S.I.C.: 3842
N.A.I.C.S.: 339113
Gerard Vanmaurs *(Gen Mgr)*

Schulke & Mayr Benelux BV (3)
Prens Brenard Lan 2 C
PO Box 9546
2003 LM Haarlem, Netherlands (100%)
Tel.: (31) 235352634
Fax: (31) 235367970
E-Mail: salesbenelux@schulke.com
Web Site: www.schulke.com
Emp.: 10
Mfr of Infection Control Products
S.I.C.: 3842
N.A.I.C.S.: 339113
Gerod Meers *(Gen Mgr)*

Schulke & Mayr Ges.m.b.H (3)
Seidengasse 9
1070 Vienna, Austria (100%)
Tel.: (43) 15232501
Fax: (43) 1523903579
E-Mail: officeaustria@schulke.com
Web Site: www.schulke.com
Emp.: 27
Mfr of Infection Control Products
S.I.C.: 3841
N.A.I.C.S.: 339113
Alfred Green *(Mng Dir)*

Schulke & Mayr Italia S.r.l. (3)
Via Capecelatro 69
20148 Milan, Italy
Tel.: (39) 02 4026590
Fax: (39) 02 4026609
E-Mail: info-italia@schuelke.com
Web Site: www.schulke.com
Emp.: 4
Mfr of Infection Control Products
S.I.C.: 3842
N.A.I.C.S.: 339113
Auiarue Granata *(Gen Mgr)*

Schulke & Mayr UK Ltd (3)
Cygnet House 1 Jenkin Rd
Sheffield, S Yorkshire, S9 1AT, United Kingdom (100%)
Tel.: (44) 01142543500
Fax: (44) 1142543501
E-Mail: mail.uk@schulke-mayr.com
Web Site: www.uk.schulke-mayr.com
Emp.: 30
Mfr of Infection Control Products
S.I.C.: 3841
N.A.I.C.S.: 339112

Schulke France sarl (3)
28 rue d'Arcueil
94250 Gentilly, France
Tel.: (33) 1 49 69 83 78
Fax: (33) 1 49 69 83 85
E-Mail: schuelkefrance.info@schuelke.com
Web Site: www.schuelke.com
Pharmaceutical Products Distr
S.I.C.: 5122
N.A.I.C.S.: 424210

Schulke Polska Sp.z o.o. (3)
ul Rydygiera 8
01-793 Warsaw, Poland
Tel.: (48) 22 568 22 02
Fax: (48) 22 568 22 03
E-Mail: schulke.polska@schuelke.com
Web Site: www.schulke.pl
Emp.: 11
Pharmaceutical Products Distr
S.I.C.: 5122
N.A.I.C.S.: 424210
Peter Starzenska *(Mng Dir)*

Air Liquide Dominicana S.A. (1)
Av Jose F Pena Gomez Casi Esquina Carretera Sanchez Vieja
Haina, San Cristobal, Dominican Republic
Tel.: (809) 594 8306
Web Site: www.airliquide.com
Oil & Gas Exploration Services
S.I.C.: 1389
N.A.I.C.S.: 213112

Air Liquide Egypte S.a.e. (1)
25 Misr Helwan Agricultural Road El Zeini Tower
El Maadi, Cairo, Egypt
Tel.: (20) 2 27687600
Fax: (20) 2 23589291
E-Mail: Egypt.CCS@airliquide.com
Web Site: www.airliquide.com.eg
Industrial & Medical Gas Mfr & Distr
S.I.C.: 2813
N.A.I.C.S.: 325120

Air Liquide Engineering Middle East (1)
Salam Tower 8th Floor Al Corniche
PO Box 24472
Doha, Qatar
Tel.: (974) 44020460
Fax: (974) 44838189
E-Mail: info@airliquide.com
Web Site: www.www.airliquide.com
Industrial Gas Mfr & Distr
S.I.C.: 5169
N.A.I.C.S.: 424690
Danilo Nucup *(Project Mgr)*

Air Liquide Espana SA (1)
Paseo De La Castellana 35
28046 Madrid, Spain (100%)
Tel.: (34) 915029300
Fax: (34) 815028318
Emp.: 200
Mfr of Industrial Gases
S.I.C.: 2813
N.A.I.C.S.: 325120

AIR LIQUIDE FINLAND OY (1)
Typpitie 1
90650 Oulu, Finland
Tel.: (358) 20 779 0580
Fax: (358) 20 779 0581
E-Mail: info.finland@airliquide.fi
Web Site: www.airliquide.fi
Emp.: 50
Industrial Gas Mfr
S.I.C.: 2813
N.A.I.C.S.: 325120
Pasi Pirnes *(Mgr-Supply Chain)*

AIR LIQUIDE GABOA (1)
Z I d'Owendo
BP 545
Libreville, Gabon
Tel.: (241) 70 06 10
Fax: (241) 70 27 15
Web Site: www.ga.airliquide.com
Emp.: 57
Industrial Gas Storage Equipment Mfr
S.I.C.: 3533
N.A.I.C.S.: 333132

Air Liquide Gas A.B. (1)
Lundavagen 151
PO Box 2911
212 09 Malmo, Sweden
Tel.: (46) 40 38 10 00
Fax: (46) 40 43 69 43
E-Mail: Kundservice.sweden@airliquide.com
Web Site: www.airliquide.se
Emp.: 95
Industrial Gas Mfr
S.I.C.: 2813
N.A.I.C.S.: 325120
Thomas Nyman *(Mgr-Maintenance & Dev)*

Subsidiaries:

Aiolos Medical A.B. (2)
Fjarrviksvagen 4
Karlstad, 653 50, Sweden
Tel.: (46) 54 534805
Fax: (46) 54 534787
E-Mail: air@aiolos.se
Web Site: www.aiolos.se
Emp.: 13
Medical Device & Equipment Mfr
S.I.C.: 3841
N.A.I.C.S.: 339112
Asa Leijon *(Gen Mgr)*

Air Liquide Medicinal SL (2)
Paseo de La Castellana 35
28046 Madrid, Spain (100%)
Tel.: (34) 915029300
Fax: (34) 915029300
Web Site: www.airliquidemedicinal.es
Mfr & Supply of Medicinal Gases & Equipment
S.I.C.: 3841
N.A.I.C.S.: 339112

Air Liquide Hellas S.A. (1)
Thesi Stefani
Aspropyrgos, Athens, Greece
Tel.: (30) 210 5582700
Fax: (30) 210 5579630
E-Mail: Orders.alhsouth@airliquide.com

Web Site: www.airliquide.gr
Emp.: 80
Industrial Gas Mfr & Distr
S.I.C.: 2813
N.A.I.C.S.: 325120
Christi Tsaka *(Mgr-Procurement)*

AIR LIQUIDE Holding Co., Ltd. (1)
4F Building 18 No 1515 Gu Mei Road
200233 Shanghai, China
Tel.: (86) 21 6090 3688
Investment Management Services
S.I.C.: 6211
N.A.I.C.S.: 523999

Subsidiary:

Air Liquide China Holding Co., Ltd (2)
Building 18 No 1515 Gu Mei Road
Shanghai, 200233, China
Tel.: (86) 21 60903688
Fax: (86) 21 60903200
E-Mail: alhz@airliquide.com
Web Site: www.cn.airliquide.com
Emp.: 4,000
Industrial Gas Mfr
S.I.C.: 2813
N.A.I.C.S.: 325120
Remi Charachon *(Pres & CEO)*

Subsidiaries:

Air Liquide (Beijing) Co., Ltd (3)
Rm 1101-1103 Central Office Tower China Overseas Plaza No 8
Chaoyang District, Beijing, 100022, China
Tel.: (86) 10 65681255
Fax: (86) 10 65682205
Industrial Gas Mfr
S.I.C.: 2813
N.A.I.C.S.: 325120

Air Liquide Changshu Co., Ltd (3)
No 8 Yehui Road Economic Development Zone
Changshu, Sichuan, 215500, China
Tel.: (86) 51252656623
Industrial Gas Mfr
S.I.C.: 2813
N.A.I.C.S.: 325120

Air Liquide (Chengdu) Co., Ltd (3)
Rm 603 Building B Gaoxin International Plaza North Tianfu Ave
Chengdu, 610041, China
Tel.: (86) 28 85339190
Fax: (86) 28 85320065
Web Site: www.cn.airliquide.com
Industrial Gas Mfr
S.I.C.: 2813
N.A.I.C.S.: 325120

Air Liquide Dalian Co., Ltd (3)
Rm 1505 Yoma International Financial Center No 128 Jinma Road
Dalian, 116600, China
Tel.: (86) 411 87921970
Fax: (86) 411 87921974
Web Site: www.cn.airliquide.com
Emp.: 50
Industrial Gas Mfr
S.I.C.: 2813
N.A.I.C.S.: 325120
Chun Wang Quan *(Gen Mgr)*

Air Liquide Engineering Services Asia (Shanghai) Company Ltd (3)
6th Floor A3 Building Cao He Jing Modern Service High-tech Park
No 1528 Gumei Road, Shanghai, 200233, China
Tel.: (86) 21 60919000
Fax: (86) 21 60919198
Web Site: www.cn.airliquide.com
Engineering Services
S.I.C.: 8711
N.A.I.C.S.: 541330

Air Liquide (Guangdong) Industrial Gas Co., Ltd. (3)
Rm 2501 Dong Bao Plaza No 767 Dongfeng Dong Road
Yue Xiu District, Guangzhou, 510080, China
Tel.: (86) 20 87679600
Fax: (86) 20 87679601
Web Site: www.cn.airliquide.com
Industrial Gas Mfr
S.I.C.: 2813
N.A.I.C.S.: 325120

Air Liquide Hangzhou Co., Ltd (3)
No 1-1 Miaochangqiao Road Gouzhuang Industrial Park
Yuhang District, Hangzhou, 311112, China
Tel.: (86) 571 89019118
Fax: (86) 571 89019555
E-Mail: alhz@airliquide.com
Web Site: www.cn.airliquide.com
Emp.: 800
Construction Engineering Services
S.I.C.: 8711
N.A.I.C.S.: 541330

Air Liquide Healthcare (3)
Building 18 No 1515 Gumei Road
Shanghai, 200233, China
Tel.: (86) 21 60903688
Fax: (86) 21 60903200
Web Site: www.cn.airliquide.com
Health Care Services
S.I.C.: 8099
N.A.I.C.S.: 621999

Air Liquide (Qingdao) Co., Ltd (3)
No 8 Huaihe Dong Road Qingdao Economic & Technical Development Zone
Qingdao, 266500, China
Tel.: (86) 532 86911188
Fax: (86) 532 86911189
Web Site: www.cn.airliquide.com
Industrial Gas Mfr
S.I.C.: 2813
N.A.I.C.S.: 325120

Air Liquide Shanghai Co., Ltd (3)
Building 18 No 1515 Gumei Road
Shanghai, 200233, China
Tel.: (86) 21 60903688
Fax: (86) 21 60903200
Industrial Gas Mfr
S.I.C.: 2813
N.A.I.C.S.: 325120

Air Liquide Shanghai International Trading Co., Ltd (3)
No 18 Bldg No 1515 Gumei Rd
Shanghai, China
Tel.: (86) 2160903688
Chemical Products Whslr
S.I.C.: 5169
N.A.I.C.S.: 424690

Air Liquide Shenyang Teisan Co., Ltd. (3)
No 26 Xihe Ninth North StreetShenyang Economic and Technical Developme
Shenyang, 110142, China
Tel.: (86) 24 25175856
Fax: (86) 24 25175855
Web Site: www.cn.airliquide.com
Industrial & Medical Gas Mfr
S.I.C.: 2813
N.A.I.C.S.: 325120

Air Liquide Tianjin Co., Ltd (3)
21F Tianxin Building No 125 Weidi Road
Hexi District, Tianjin, 300074, China
Tel.: (86) 22 28408422
Fax: (86) 22 28408433
Web Site: www.cn.airliquide.com
Industrial Gas Mfr
S.I.C.: 2813
N.A.I.C.S.: 325120

Air Liquide (Wuhan) Co., Ltd. (3)
No 61 Liufang Road East Lake Hi-tech Development Zone
Wuhan, Hubei, 430205, China
Tel.: (86) 27 81309600
Fax: (86) 27 87227379
Industrial Gas Mfr
S.I.C.: 2813
N.A.I.C.S.: 325120

Air Liquide India Holding Pvt. Ltd. (1)
A-24/9 Mohan Co-Operative Industrial Estate Mathura Road
Behind American Express, New Delhi, 110044, India
Tel.: (91) 11 40550200
Fax: (91) 11 40550201
Emp.: 300
Industrial Gas Mfr
S.I.C.: 2813
N.A.I.C.S.: 325120

Subsidiary:

Pure Helium India Pvt. Ltd. (2)
406 Balarama Bandra-Kurla Complex
Bandra East, Mumbai, 400 051, India
Tel.: (91) 22 2659 1911
Fax: (91) 22 2659 1919
Emp.: 14
Liquid Helium & Diving Gases Distr
S.I.C.: 4924
N.A.I.C.S.: 221210
Guruprasad Rao *(Mgr-Sls)*

Air Liquide Industrie B.V. (1)
Corkstraat 46
3047 AC Rotterdam, Netherlands
Tel.: (31) 10 238 22 20
Fax: (31) 10 437 44 80
Natural Gas Distribution Services
S.I.C.: 4924
N.A.I.C.S.: 221210

Subsidiaries:

Loofbeen B.V. (2)
Corkstraat 46
3047 AC Rotterdam, Netherlands
Tel.: (31) 102622077
Financial Management Services
S.I.C.: 6211
N.A.I.C.S.: 523999

Maasvlakte Energie B.V. (2)
Corkstraat 46
3047 AC Rotterdam, Netherlands
Tel.: (31) 10 2622077
Fax: (31) 10 4374480
Electric Power Generation Services
S.I.C.: 4911
N.A.I.C.S.: 221118

AIR LIQUIDE ITALIA SIEGE (1)
Via Capecelatro 69
20148 Milan, Italy
Tel.: (39) 02 40 261
Web Site: www.airliquide.com
Industrial Gas Mfr
S.I.C.: 2813
N.A.I.C.S.: 325120

Air Liquide Italia Srl (1)
Via Capecelatro 69
20148 Milan, Italy IT
Tel.: (39) 0240261 (100%)
Fax: (39) 0248705895
E-Mail: fatture.fornitori@airliquide.com
Web Site: www.airliquide.it
Emp.: 300
Mfr of Industrial Gases
S.I.C.: 2813
N.A.I.C.S.: 325120
Olivier Imbault *(Dir Gen)*

Subsidiaries:

Air Liquide Italia Service S.r.l. (2)
Via Alfonso Capecelatro 69
Milan, 20148, Italy
Tel.: (39) 024 0261
Industrial Gas Mfr & Distr
S.I.C.: 2813
N.A.I.C.S.: 325120

Air Liquide Sanita S.p.A (2)
Via Ciardi 9
20148 Milan, Italy
Tel.: (39) 0000240211
Fax: (39) 0248704291
Web Site: www.airliquide.com
Mfr & Supplier of Medical Gases & Infection Control Solutions
S.I.C.: 3841
N.A.I.C.S.: 339112

Markos-Mefar S.p.A (2)
Via del Prati, 62
Bovezzo, 25073 Brescia, Italy
Tel.: (39) 030-20159
Fax: (39) 030-2000551
Web Site: www.markosmefar.it
Mfr of Aerosol Therapy & Respiratory Equipment
S.I.C.: 3845
N.A.I.C.S.: 334510

Tecno Gas S.r.l. (2)
Viale L Da Zara 10
35020 Albignasego, Padua, Italy
Tel.: (39) 049 8625910
Fax: (39) 049 8625911
E-Mail: amministrazione@tecnogas.eu
Web Site: www.tecnogas.org
Plumbing & Heating Equipment Mfr
S.I.C.: 3088
N.A.I.C.S.: 326191

Air Liquide Japan Ltd. (1)
9-1 Shinonome 1-chome
Koto-ku, Tokyo, 135-0062, Japan JP
Tel.: (81) 0335362330 (100%)
Telex: 2425612
Fax: (81) 3 3536 2392
Web Site: www.jp.airliquide.com
Sales Range: $1-4.9 Billion
Emp.: 2,700
Industrial & Medical Gas Mfr & Plant Engineering
S.I.C.: 2813
N.A.I.C.S.: 325120
Toyofumi Shimohata *(Chm)*
Francois Jackow *(Pres & CEO)*
Eiji Hayashitani *(Exec Officer)*
Jean-Francois LeCouffe *(Exec Officer)*

Subsidiaries:

Air Liquide Engineering Japan, Co. (2)
16 Hijima Harima-cho
Hyogo, 675-0181, Japan
Tel.: (81) 794372714
Fax: (81) 794377314
Web Site: www.jp.airliquide.com
Emp.: 100
Gas Plant Engineering & Construction Services
S.I.C.: 1629
N.A.I.C.S.: 236210
Takao Yamamoto *(VP-Products & Strategic Plng)*

Japan Air Gases, Co. (2)
9 1 Shinonome 1 chome
Koto ku, Tokyo, 135 0062, Japan JP
Tel.: (81) 335362330 (100%)
Fax: (81) 335362392
Web Site: www.japanairgases.co.jp
Industrial & Medical Gas Mfr
S.I.C.: 2813
N.A.I.C.S.: 325120
Francois Jackow *(Pres)*

Toshiba Nano Analysis K.K. (2)
8 Shinsugita-cho
Isogo-ku, Yokohama, Japan
Tel.: (81) 45 770 3471
Fax: (81) 45 770 3479
E-Mail: support@nanoanalysis.co.jp
Web Site: www.nanoanalysis.co.jp
Medical Research & Development Services
S.I.C.: 8731
N.A.I.C.S.: 541712

Subsidiary:

Toshiba Nanoanalysis Corporation (3)
1 Komukai Toshibacho
Saiwai-ku, Kawasaki, Kanagawa, 212 8583, Japan (51%)
Tel.: (81) 445492981
Fax: (81) 445492881
Web Site: www.nanoanalysis.co.jp
Emp.: 253
Semiconductor Devices Evaluation & Analysis Services
S.I.C.: 3674
N.A.I.C.S.: 334413
Keisuke Matsumura *(Pres)*

Air Liquide Korea Co., Ltd. (1)
6th Fl A-dong J Tower 538 Sinsa-dong
Gangnam-gu, Seoul, Korea (South)
Tel.: (82) 2 3019 2500
Fax: (82) 2 511 2977
E-Mail: corp.kr@airliquide.com
Web Site: www.kr.airliquide.com
Industrial Gas Mfr
S.I.C.: 2813
N.A.I.C.S.: 325120

Air Liquide Luxembourg S.A. (1)
Zone PE D Grand Duche du Luxembourg
BP 20
Rodange, Luxembourg
Tel.: (352) 50 62 63 1
Fax: (352) 50 62 63 218
Web Site: www.airliquide.com
Industrial Gas Mfr & Distr
S.I.C.: 2813
N.A.I.C.S.: 325120

Air Liquide S.A.—(Continued)

Air Liquide Malaysia Sdn Bhd (1)
C-31-6 Jaya One No 72A Jalan University
46200 Petaling Jaya, Selangor, Malaysia
Tel.: (60) 3 79475688
Fax: (60) 3 79601601
Web Site: www.airliquide.com
Industrial Gas Mfr
S.I.C.: 2813
N.A.I.C.S.: 325120

Air Liquide Maroc S.A. (1)
Casa-Rabat MA - Ain Sebaa
Casablanca, 20400, Morocco
Tel.: (212) 5 22 76 20 00
Fax: (212) 5 22 75 49 12
Emp.: 350
Industrial Gas Mfr
S.I.C.: 2813
N.A.I.C.S.: 325120
Virginie Reynaud *(Gen Mgr)*

Air Liquide Middle East & North Africa FZCO (1)
Suite 829 West Wing Block B Dubai Airport Free Zone
PO Box 54638
Dubai, United Arab Emirates
Tel.: (971) 4 299 3444
Fax: (971) 4 299 3668
Emp.: 60
Industrial Gas Mfr
S.I.C.: 2813
N.A.I.C.S.: 325120
Jean-Luc Labat *(Gen Mgr)*

Subsidiary:

Pure Helium Gulf FZE (2)
Near Round About 5 Jebel Ali Free Zone
PO Box 16848
Jebel Ali, United Arab Emirates
Tel.: (971) 4 8816001
Fax: (971) 4 8816323
E-Mail: uae.sales@airliquide.com
Emp.: 100
Industrial Gas Mfr & Distr
S.I.C.: 5169
N.A.I.C.S.: 424690
Roderick Percha *(Chief Accountant)*

Air Liquide Nigeria plc (1)
104/106 Lapido Street Matori Mushin
21551 Ikeja, Lagos, Nigeria
Tel.: (234) 17742352
Fax: (234) 14521251
E-Mail: kayode.odukoya@airliquide.com
Web Site: www.ng.airliquide.com
Industrial Gas Mfr & Distr
S.I.C.: 4924
N.A.I.C.S.: 221210
Henry Ekwonye *(Engr-Sls-Gas & Welding)*

Air Liquide Norway AS (1)
Ryghgata 2B
Postboks 243
3050 Mjondalen, Norway
Tel.: (47) 32 27 41 40
Fax: (47) 32 27 41 59
E-Mail: info.norway@airliquide.com
Web Site: www.no.airliquide.com
Emp.: 33
Industrial Gas Mfr
S.I.C.: 2813
N.A.I.C.S.: 325120
Mark Appleby *(Gen Mgr)*

Subsidiary:

Air Liquide Offshore AS (2)
Bleivassveien 73
5363 Agotnes, Norway
Tel.: (47) 56 33 44 33
Fax: (47) 56 33 44 34
E-Mail: sales@aloffshore.com
Web Site: www.airliquide.no/no/offshore.html
Emp.: 5
Oil & Gas Exploration Services
S.I.C.: 1389
N.A.I.C.S.: 213112

Air Liquide Panama S.A. (1)
Av Jose Agustin Arango
Juan Diaz, Panama, Panama
Tel.: (507) 2530483
Fax: (507) 2330470
Medical & Industrial Gas Distr
S.I.C.: 4924
N.A.I.C.S.: 221210

Air Liquide Philippines Inc. (1)
Lot 37 DBP Avenue FTI Complex
Taguig, Manila, Philippines
Tel.: (63) 2 838 1780
Fax: (63) 2 838 1753
Web Site: www.ph.airliquide.com
Emp.: 240
Industrial Gas Mfr & Distr
S.I.C.: 2813
N.A.I.C.S.: 325120

Plant:

Air Liquide Philippines Inc. - Main Plant (2)
Sandoval Avenue Barrio Pinagbuhatan
Pasig, Metro Manila, Philippines
Tel.: (63) 2 642 1274
Fax: (63) 2 642 939
Industrial Gas Mfr
S.I.C.: 2813
N.A.I.C.S.: 325120

Air Liquide Polska Sp. z o.o (1)
ul Josepha Conrada 63
31-357 Krakow, Poland
Tel.: (48) 12 62 79 300
Fax: (48) 12 62 79 333
E-Mail: airliquide.polska@airliquide.com
Web Site: www.poland.airliquide.com
Industrial Gas Mfr & Distr
S.I.C.: 1389
N.A.I.C.S.: 213112
Malgorzata Walkowicz-Furmanek *(Mgr-Compensation & Remuneration)*

Air Liquide Progetti Italia S.p.A. (1)
Via Guglielmo Ciardi 9
20148 Milan, Italy
Tel.: (39) 02 4021203
Fax: (39) 02 4021850
Industrial Gas Mfr
S.I.C.: 2813
N.A.I.C.S.: 325120

Air Liquide Proprietary Limited (1)
Cor Andre Marais Street & Vereeniging Road
Gauteng, 1450 Alberton, South Africa
Tel.: (27) 11 389 7000
Fax: (27) 11 617 7500
Web Site: www.airliquide.com
Industrial Medical Gas Mfr
S.I.C.: 2813
N.A.I.C.S.: 325120
Alain Larousse *(CEO)*

Non-U.S. Subsidiary:

Air Liquide Botswana Properietary Limited (2)
Nakedi Road
PO Box 40431
Broadhurst, Gaborone, Botswana
Tel.: (267) 3912988
Fax: (267) 3956463
Web Site: www.airliquide.com
Industrial Gas Mfr
S.I.C.: 2813
N.A.I.C.S.: 325120
Yvonne Mmanoko Modisaotsile *(Acct Mgr)*

Air Liquide Romania S.r.l (1)
Bvd Mircea Eliade Nr 18 1st Floor
1st District, Bucharest, Romania
Tel.: (40) 21 311 96 80
Fax: (40) 21 311 96 85
E-Mail: office.romania@airliquide.com
Web Site: www.airliquide.ro
Industrial Gas Mfr
S.I.C.: 2813
N.A.I.C.S.: 325120
Florin Ciobanu *(Mgr-Bus Dev)*

Air Liquide Russie S.A. (1)
17 Vorontsovskaya Str
Moscow, 109147, Russia
Tel.: (7) 495 641 2898
Fax: (7) 495 641 2891
E-Mail: info.moscow@airliquide.com
Web Site: www.airliquide.ru
Industrial Gas Mfr
S.I.C.: 2813
N.A.I.C.S.: 325120

Subsidiary:

Air Liquide OOO (2)
17 Ulitsa Vorontsovskaya
109147 Moscow, Russia
Tel.: (7) 495 641 28 98
Fax: (7) 495 641 28 91
E-Mail: info.moscow@airliquide.com
Web Site: www.airliquide.com
Emp.: 200
Industrial Gas Mfr & Distr
S.I.C.: 2813
N.A.I.C.S.: 325120
Dmitry Ermolov *(Gen Mgr)*

Air Liquide Shuaiba Oxygen (1)
Mina Abdullah Area 4 Bl 72 Street MA7
PO Box 23192
13092 Kuwait, Kuwait
Tel.: (965) 668 68 254
Industrial Gas Mfr
S.I.C.: 2813
N.A.I.C.S.: 325120

Air Liquide Sivoa (1)
131 Bd de Marseille 01
BP 1753
Abidjan, Cote d'Ivoire
Tel.: (225) 21 21 04 57
Fax: (225) 21 25 87 44
Industrial Gas Mfr & Distr
S.I.C.: 2813
N.A.I.C.S.: 325120

Air Liquide Slovakia, s.r.o. (1)
Prievozska 4/A
821 09 Bratislava, Slovakia
Tel.: (421) 2 5810 1051
Fax: (421) 2 5810 1052
E-Mail: info@airliquide.sk
Web Site: www.airliquide.sk
Emp.: 15
Industrial Gas Mfr
S.I.C.: 2813
N.A.I.C.S.: 325120

Air Liquide Sohar Industrial Gases LLC (1)
No 731 Al Amal Bldg Road No 7 124
PO Box No 66
327 Sohar, Oman
Tel.: (968) 26 85 02 00
Fax: (968) 26 85 02 03
Web Site: www.omzest.com
Emp.: 10
Industrial Gas Mfr & Distr
S.I.C.: 4924
N.A.I.C.S.: 221210
Mehdi Benzaari *(Gen Mgr)*

Air Liquide Thailand Ltd (1)
14/F Vorawat Building Unit 1401-1402 849 Silom Road
Bangrak, Bangkok, 10500, Thailand
Tel.: (66) 2 6351600
Fax: (66) 2 6351601
E-Mail: sales.bangkok@airliquide.com
Web Site: www.th.airliquide.com
Industrial Gas Mfr & Distr
S.I.C.: 4924
N.A.I.C.S.: 221210

Air Liquide Trinidad and Tobago Ltd (1)
Unit D2 02-04 Atlantic Plaza Atlantic Avenue
Point Lisas, Couva, Trinidad & Tobago
Tel.: (868) 679 1117
Fax: (868) 679 7710
Oil & Gas Exploration Services
S.I.C.: 1389
N.A.I.C.S.: 213112

Air Liquide Ukraine S.A. (1)
8A Rizhska Street
04112 Kiev, Ukraine
Tel.: (380) 445 830 089
Fax: (380) 445 830 088
Web Site: www.airliquide.com
Industrial Gas Mfr
S.I.C.: 2813
N.A.I.C.S.: 325120
Francois Court *(Gen Mgr)*

Air Liquide UK Ltd. (1)
Station Rd
Coleshill, Birmingham, B46 1JY, United Kingdom (100%)
Tel.: (44) 1675462424
Fax: (44) 1675467022
E-Mail: info@uk.airliquide.com
Web Site: www.uk.airliquide.com
Emp.: 100
Industrial & Medical Gases Mfr
S.I.C.: 2813
N.A.I.C.S.: 325120

Subsidiaries:

Air Liquide Ltd. (2)
Station Road
Coleshill, Birmingham, B46 1JY, United Kingdom
Tel.: (44) 800 637 747
Fax: (44) 1675 467022
Web Site: www.uk.airliquide.com
Sales Range: $75-99.9 Million
Emp.: 280
Industrial Gases Mfr
S.I.C.: 2813
N.A.I.C.S.: 325120
Jean Baptiste Dellon *(Mng Dir)*

Subsidiary:

Air Liquide South East Ltd (3)
Enterprise Drive Four Ashes
Wolverhampton, West Midlands, WV10 7DF, United Kingdom
Tel.: (44) 1902 798000
Industrial & Medical Gas Distr
S.I.C.: 4924
N.A.I.C.S.: 221210

Calgaz International LLC (2)
Unit 5 Crown Royal Industrial Park
Shawcross St, Stockport, Cheshire, SK1 3EY, United Kingdom (100%)
Tel.: (44) 161 968 5060
Fax: (44) 161 477 0590
E-Mail: info@airliquide.co.uk
Web Site: www.calgaz.com
Emp.: 25
Mfr of Industrial Gases
S.I.C.: 2813
N.A.I.C.S.: 325120

Air Liquide Vietnam Co., Ltd (1)
Unit 2-3 7th Floor 17 Ngo Quyen
Hoan Kiem, Hanoi, Vietnam
Tel.: (84) 4 39361940
Fax: (84) 4 39361945
E-Mail: info.vietnam@airliquide.com
Web Site: www.airliquide.vn
Industrial Gas Mfr & Distr
S.I.C.: 2813
N.A.I.C.S.: 325120

AL Air Liquide Espana S.A. (1)
P de la Castellana 35
28046 Madrid, Spain
Tel.: (34) 91 5029300
Fax: (34) 91 5029330
E-Mail: pedidobotellas.es@airliquide.com
Web Site: www.es.airliquide.com
Industrial Gas Mfr
S.I.C.: 2813
N.A.I.C.S.: 325120

Carbagas S.A. (1)
Hofgut Hintere Dorfgasse 9
3073 Gumligen, Switzerland
Tel.: (41) 31 950 50 50
Fax: (41) 31 950 50 51
E-Mail: info@carbagas.ch
Web Site: www.carbagas.ch
Emp.: 350
Industrial Gas Mfr
S.I.C.: 2813
N.A.I.C.S.: 325120
Helen Hasselman *(Gen Mgr)*

Celki International Ltd (1)
21/F Tins Enterprises Centre 777 Lai Chi Kok Road
Cheung Sha Wan, Kowloon, China (Hong Kong)
Tel.: (852) 2332 3366
Fax: (852) 2744 2313
E-Mail: celkimed@celki.com
Web Site: www.celki.com
Respiratory Care Products Mfr
S.I.C.: 3841
N.A.I.C.S.: 339112
Vincent Rouvier *(CEO)*

La Oxigena Paraguaya S.A. (1)
Avenida Eusebio Ayala 3650 Km 4
Asuncion, 1910, Paraguay
Tel.: (595) 21550607
Fax: (595) 21550534
Industrial Gas Mfr
S.I.C.: 2813
N.A.I.C.S.: 325120

Lurgi AG (1)
Lurgiallee 5
60295 Frankfurt am Main, Germany
Tel.: (49) 6958080
Telex: 41 236-0 lg d
Fax: (49) 6958083888
E-Mail: kommunikation@lurgi.com
Web Site: www.lurgi.com
Sales Range: $1-4.9 Billion
Emp.: 1,300
Design, Construction & Consulting of Industrial Chemical & Metallurgical Plants; Contract Processing of Minerals & Ores; Production of Sponge Iron; Project Management Services
S.I.C.: 8711
N.A.I.C.S.: 541330

Subsidiaries:

Air Liquide Forschung und Entwicklung GmbH (2)
Gwinnerstrasse 27-33
60388 Frankfurt am Main, Germany
Tel.: (49) 69 4011 201
Fax: (49) 69 4011 479
E-Mail: info@aqualung.de
Web Site: www.airliquide.de/ueberuns/wer-wir-sind/ald/beteiligungen.html
Emp.: 55
Industrial Gas Mfr
S.I.C.: 2813
N.A.I.C.S.: 325120
Frank Castillo-Welter *(Dir-Program)*

Plauen Stahl Technologie GmbH (2)
Hammerstrasse 88
8529 Plauen, Sachsen, Germany
Tel.: (49) 37412830
Fax: (49) 3741283717
E-Mail: pst@plauen-stahl.de
Web Site: www.plauen-stahl.de
Emp.: 200
Steelwork Contractor
S.I.C.: 1791
N.A.I.C.S.: 238120
Hermann Haeuser *(Mng Dir-Comml)*

U.S. Subsidiary:

Lurgi, Inc. (2)
6750 Poplar Ave Ste 720
Germantown, TN 38138-7421 TN
Tel.: (901) 756-8250
Fax: (901) 756-8253
E-Mail: info@lurgi.com
Web Site: www.lurgi.com
Emp.: 100
Plant Contracting & Process Engineering
S.I.C.: 1542
N.A.I.C.S.: 236220
Mike Flippin *(VP-Fin)*

Non-U.S. Subsidiaries:

Air Liquide Engineering Services Asia Co., Ltd. (2)
5F Building 18 No 1515 Gu Mei Road
Shanghai, 200233, China
Tel.: (86) 21 60 91 90 00
Fax: (86) 21 60 90 35 80
Engineering Services
S.I.C.: 8711
N.A.I.C.S.: 541330

APSA (2)
C/o Aljomaih Holding Co Al-Jomaih Bldg 5th Floor King Abdulaziz
PO Box 132
Old Airport Road, Riyadh, 11411, Saudi Arabia
Tel.: (966) 1478 21 00
Fax: (966) 1478 74 82
Industrial Plant Construction Services
S.I.C.: 1629
N.A.I.C.S.: 236210
Juergen Villmer *(Mgr)*

Beijing Lurgi Engineering Consulting Co. Ltd. (2)
Unit 0408 Landmark Tower 2 8 North Dongsanhuan Road
Chaoyang District, Beijing, 100004, China
Tel.: (86) 10 65 90 67 97
Fax: (86) 10 65 90 67 81
E-Mail: lurgible@public3.bta.net.cn
Web Site: www.lurgi.com
Emp.: 20
Engineering Services
S.I.C.: 8711
N.A.I.C.S.: 541330
Xian-ji Guo *(VP)*

EUROTECNICA S.A. (2)
Martin Lezica 3043 - 2 Piso B
B1642GJA San Isidro, Buenos Aires, Argentina
Tel.: (54) 11 47 63 38 38
Fax: (54) 11 52 92 60 89
E-Mail: eurotec@fibertel.com.ar
Web Site: www.lurgi.com
Engineering Services
S.I.C.: 8711
N.A.I.C.S.: 541330

Lurgi Caribbean Ltd. (2)
202 Brook Road Goodwood Park
Trincity, Trinidad & Tobago
Tel.: (868) 6 33 67 18
Fax: (868) 6 33 67 19
Web Site: www.lurgi.com
Emp.: 5
Construction Engineering Services
S.I.C.: 1623
N.A.I.C.S.: 237120
Friedhelm Deetjen *(Pres)*

Lurgi do Brasil Instalacoes Industriais Ltda. (2)
Av Brig Faria Lima 2369-19 Andar
01462-900 Sao Paulo, Brazil
Tel.: (55) 11 30 38 06 00
Fax: (55) 11 30 38 06 06
E-Mail: lurgidobrasil@lurgi.com.br
Web Site: www.lurgi.com
Emp.: 5
Industrial Plant Construction Services
S.I.C.: 1629
N.A.I.C.S.: 236210

Lurgi (Pty) Ltd. (2)
PO Box 98527
Sloane Park, 2152, South Africa
Tel.: (27) 11 2 44 46 00
Fax: (27) 11 2 44 48 00
E-Mail: info.zajb@lurgi.com
Web Site: www.lurgi.com
Emp.: 54
Industrial Plant Construction Services
S.I.C.: 1629
N.A.I.C.S.: 236210
Sherrylynn Smith *(Project Mgr-Procurement)*

Lurgi, S.A. (2)
Avda General Peron 29-9
28046 Madrid, Spain
Tel.: (34) 915981519
Telex: 22 402 lurg e
Fax: (34) 915564277
E-Mail: info@lurgi.com
Web Site: www.lurgi.com
Emp.: 20
Plant Construction & Engineering Services
S.I.C.: 8711
N.A.I.C.S.: 541330

Lurgi Sdn. Bhd. (2)
Suite A-9-1 Wisma HB Megan Avenue II 12
Jalan Yap Kwan Seng
50450 Kuala Lumpur, Malaysia
Tel.: (60) 3 21 64 64 46
Fax: (60) 3 21 64 54 48
Web Site: www.lurgiinc.com
Emp.: 5
Business Management Consulting Services
S.I.C.: 8748
N.A.I.C.S.: 541618
Deepak Wadhwa *(Mng Dir)*

Lurgi Turkiye (2)
Meclis - I Mebusan Cd 139A Atlanktik Han Kat 4
Findikli, 80040 Istanbul, Turkey
Tel.: (90) 2 12 2 52 25 00
Fax: (90) 2 12 2 43 20 54
Industrial Gas Mfr
S.I.C.: 2813
N.A.I.C.S.: 325120

P.T. Air Liquide Indonesia (1)
Blok I No 1-2 MM2100 Industrial Town
Cibitung, Bekasi, Indonesia Id
Tel.: (62) 21 898 0071
Fax: (62) 21 8980072
Web Site: www.id.airliquide.com
Industrial Gas Mfr
S.I.C.: 2813
N.A.I.C.S.: 325120

Plant:

P.T. Air Liquide Indonesia - Cilegon Factory (2)
Jl Australia II Kav M1
Cilegon, Banten, Indonesia
Tel.: (62) 254 393358
Fax: (62) 254 393359
Web Site: www.id.airliquide.com
Emp.: 100
Industrial Gas Mfr
S.I.C.: 2813
N.A.I.C.S.: 325120
Xu Yan *(Pres)*

SIEGE AIR LIQUIDO SA (1)
Rua Doctor Antonio Loureiro Borges 4
Arquiparque Miraflores, Alges, 1495-131, Portugal
Tel.: (351) 2141 64900
Web Site: www.airliquide.com
Industrial Gas Mfr
S.I.C.: 2813
N.A.I.C.S.: 325120

Singapore Oxygen Air Liquide Pte. Ltd. (1)
16 Jalan Buroh
Jurong, 619475, Singapore SG
Tel.: (65) 62653788
Telex: RS 21150 SOXAL
Fax: (65) 62651441
E-Mail: info@soxal.com.sg
Web Site: www.soxal.com
Emp.: 500
Industrial, Medical & Scientific Gases Mfr
S.I.C.: 2813
N.A.I.C.S.: 325120
Woo Siew Wah *(Mng Dir)*
Claire Wong *(CFO)*

SOAL-Industrial Gases (1)
El-Midane
BP 175523/4
Dekwaneh, Beirut, Lebanon
Tel.: (961) 1 692 380
Fax: (961) 1 692 386
Web Site: www.lb.airliquide.com
Industrial Gas Mfr & Distr
S.I.C.: 2813
N.A.I.C.S.: 325120
Fouad Haddad *(CEO)*

Societe Beninoise des Gaz Industriels S.A. (1)
2 7 Zone Industrielle Route De Porto-Novo
BP 674
Cotonou, Benin
Tel.: (229) 21 33 10 75
Fax: (229) 21 33 10 54
Industrial Gas Mfr
S.I.C.: 2813
N.A.I.C.S.: 325120

Societe Burkinabe des Gaz Industriels S.A. (1)
Zone Industrielle de Gounghin 01
BP 623
Ouagadougou, Burkina Faso
Tel.: (226) 50 34 42 43
Fax: (226) 50 34 42 63
Industrial Gas Mfr
S.I.C.: 2813
N.A.I.C.S.: 325120

Societe des Gaz Industriels de la Guadeloupe (1)
Lauricisque Zone des Petites Industrie
Pointe-a-Pitre, 97110, Guadeloupe
Tel.: (590) 590894740
Industrial Gas Mfr
S.I.C.: 2813
N.A.I.C.S.: 325120

Societe Guyanaise de L'Air Liquide (1)
Zi Pariacabo
BP 804
97388 Kourou, French Guiana
Tel.: (594) 594 32 10 09
Fax: (594) 594 32 23 06
Industrial Gas Mfr
S.I.C.: 2813
N.A.I.C.S.: 325120

Societe Ivoirienne d Oxygene et d Acetylene (1)
131 Blvd de Marseille
BP 1753
Abidjan, Cote d'Ivoire
Tel.: (225) 21 21 04 57
Fax: (225) 21 25 87 44
Industrial Gas Mfr
S.I.C.: 2813
N.A.I.C.S.: 325120
Ano Adou *(Gen Mgr)*

Societe Martiniquaise de L Air Liquide (1)
Quartier Californie
Lamentin, 97232, Martinique
Tel.: (596) 596500596
Fax: (596) 596774920
Emp.: 40
Industrial Gas Mfr
S.I.C.: 2813
N.A.I.C.S.: 325120
Lucie Prost *(Gen Mgr)*

Societe Senegalaise d Oxygene et d Acetylene (1)
Km 3 5 Bd Du Centenaire De
BP 45
Dakar, Senegal
Tel.: (221) 338493030
Fax: (221) 338328565
Health Care Services
S.I.C.: 8099
N.A.I.C.S.: 621999

Swazi Gases (Pty.) Limited (1)
PO 2444
Mbabane, Swaziland
Tel.: (268) 505 2062
Industrial Gas Mfr
S.I.C.: 2813
N.A.I.C.S.: 325120

AIR MALAWI LIMITED

PO Box 84
Blantyre, Malawi
Tel.: (265) 1820811
Fax: (265) 1821396
E-Mail: cd@airmalawi.net
Web Site: www.airmalawi.com
Year Founded: 1967
Emp.: 441

Business Description:
Government Operated Airline Services
S.I.C.: 4512
N.A.I.C.S.: 481111

Personnel:
Patrick Chilambe *(CEO)*

AIR MALTA PLC

Level 2 Sky Park Business Center
Malta International Airport
Luqa, LQA 4000, Malta
Tel.: (356) 22999000
Telex: MW1389, MW1589
Web Site: www.airmalta.com
Year Founded: 1973
Emp.: 1,400

Business Description:
Airline Operator
S.I.C.: 4512
N.A.I.C.S.: 481111

Personnel:
Louis Giordimaina *(CEO)*
Nicholas Xuereb *(CFO)*
Philip Saunders *(Chief Comml Officer)*
Ray Hart *(Chief Restructuring Officer)*
Joshua Zammit *(Chief Org Dev Officer)*

Board of Directors:
Louis A. Farrugia
Alison Attard
Andrew Calascione
Alan Caruana
Roderick Chalmers
Adrian Coppini
Helga Ellul
Mark Micallef Eynaud
Louis Giordimaina

Subsidiary:

Osprey Insurance Brokers Co. Ltd. (1)
Aviation Pk Aviation Ave
LQA 9023 Luqa, Malta

Air Malta plc—(Continued)

Tel.: (356) 22999250
Fax: (356) 22999433
E-Mail: martin-j.azzopardi@ospreyins.com
Web Site: www.malta.com
Emp.: 9
Insurance
S.I.C.: 6351
N.A.I.C.S.: 524126
Martin Azzopardi *(Mng Dir)*

AIR MARSHALL ISLANDS, INC.

PO Box 1319
Majuro, Marshall Islands
Tel.: (692) 6253731
Fax: (692) 6253730
Web Site: www.airmarshallislands.com
Emp.: 100

Business Description:
Air Transportation Services
S.I.C.: 4512
N.A.I.C.S.: 481111

Personnel:
Mike Cornelius *(Chm)*

AIR MAURITIUS LIMITED

Air Mauritius Centre President John Kennedy Street
Port Louis, Mauritius
Tel.: (230) 2077070
Fax: (230) 2088331
E-Mail: contact@airmauritius.com
Web Site: www.airmauritius.com
Year Founded: 1967
AIRM—(MAU)
Rev.: $608,642,496
Assets: $469,335,440
Liabilities: $369,830,592
Net Worth: $99,504,848
Earnings: ($3,369,464)
Emp.: 2,340
Fiscal Year-end: 03/31/13

Business Description:
Airline Services
S.I.C.: 4512
N.A.I.C.S.: 481111

Personnel:
Appalsamy Thomas *(Chm)*
Andries Nathaniel Viljoen *(CFO)*
Fooad Nooraully *(Sec & Exec VP-Legal & Corp Comm)*
Pramil Banymandhub *(Exec VP-Flight Ops)*
Indradev Rajah Buton *(Exec VP-Info Sys, Procurement & Facilities)*
Donald Payen *(Exec VP-Customer Experiences, Ground & In-flight Svcs)*
Shashi Puddoo *(Exec VP-HR & Org Dev)*
Sudh Ramjutun *(Exec VP-Strategic Plng, Network, Fleet, Alliances & Cargo)*
Vijay Seetul *(Exec VP-Fin)*
Derek Shanks *(Exec VP-Comml)*

Board of Directors:
Appalsamy Thomas
Kremchand Beegoo
Dheerendra Kumar Dabee
Gerard Espitalier-Noel
Philippe Espitalier-Noel
Ramapatee Gujadhur
Ali Mansoor
Rohit Nandan
Dominique Patry
Raj Ringadoo
Jean Michel Louis Rivalland
Suresh Seeballuck
Aisha Timol
Andries Nathaniel Viljoen
Francois Shing Hai Woo

Subsidiary:

Airmate Ltd (1)
10th Floor Wing A Cyber Tower
Ebene, Reduit, Mauritius (100%)
Tel.: (230) 4030165
Fax: (230) 4669014
E-Mail: contact@airmate.mu
Web Site: www.airmate.mu
Emp.: 65
Other Airport Operations
S.I.C.: 4581
N.A.I.C.S.: 488119
Ashwveen Goorah *(Gen Mgr)*

Non-U.S. Subsidiaries:

Air Mauritius South Africa (Pty) Limited (1)
Grayston Ridge Office Park
Ground Floor Block A, Sandton, South Africa
Tel.: (27) 114444600
E-Mail: jnbmk@airmauritius.com
Web Site: www.airmauritius.com
Emp.: 13
Other Support Activities for Air Transportation
S.I.C.: 4581
N.A.I.C.S.: 488190

AIR NAMIBIA (PTY) LTD.

Reg Nr 97 086 Trans Namib Building
Bahnhof Street
PO Box 731
Windhoek, Namibia
Tel.: (264) 612996000
Fax: (264) 612996168
E-Mail: ben.kakonda@airnamibia.aero
Web Site: www.airnamibia.com.na
Year Founded: 1946
Emp.: 500

Business Description:
Air Transportation Services
S.I.C.: 4512
N.A.I.C.S.: 481111

Personnel:
Theo Namases *(Mng Dir)*

AIR NEW ZEALAND LIMITED

185 Fanshawe Street
Auckland, 1010, New Zealand

Mailing Address:
Private Bag 92007
Auckland, 1142, New Zealand
Tel.: (64) 93362400
Fax: (64) 93362401
E-Mail: investor@airnz.co.nz
Web Site: www.airnewzealand.co.nz
Year Founded: 1939
AIR—(NZE)
Rev.: $3,865,266,000
Assets: $4,697,244,000
Liabilities: $3,177,252,000
Net Worth: $1,519,992,000
Earnings: $152,334,000
Emp.: 10,336
Fiscal Year-end: 06/30/13

Business Description:
Domestic & International Air Passenger & Cargo Services; Aviation Overhaul & Maintenance Services
S.I.C.: 4512
N.A.I.C.S.: 481111

Personnel:
Antony John Carter *(Chm)*
Janice Dawson *(Deputy Chm)*
Christopher Luxon *(CEO)*
Norm Thompson *(Deputy CEO & Acting Chief Sls Officer)*
Robert McDonald *(CFO)*
Bruce Parton *(COO)*
Mike Tod *(CMO & Chief Customer Officer)*
Stephen Jones *(Chief Strategy Officer & Chief Networks & Alliances Officer)*
Lorraine Murphy *(Chief People Officer)*
David Morgan *(Chief Flight Ops & Safety Officer)*
John Blair *(Gen Counsel & Sec)*

Board of Directors:
Antony John Carter
Paul Bingham
Janice Dawson
James Charles Fox
Roger France
Robert Jager
Jonathan Mason
John Leonard Palmer

Legal Counsel:
Russell McVeagh McKenzie Bartleet & Co.
P.O. Box 8
Auckland, 1, New Zealand

Bell Gully Buddle Weir
34 Shortland St.
Auckland, New Zealand

Link Market Services Limited
Level 7 Zurich House 21 Queen Street
Auckland, 1010, New Zealand

Subsidiaries:

Air Nelson Limited (1)
Private Bag 32
Nelson, 7011, New Zealand
Tel.: (64) 35478700
E-Mail: airnelsonadmin@airnz.co.nz
Web Site: www.airnelson.co.nz
Air Transportation Services
S.I.C.: 4581
N.A.I.C.S.: 488190
Darin Stringer *(Acting Gen Mgr)*

Air New Zealand Aircraft Holdings Limited (1)
Air New Zealand House 185 Fanshawe Street
Auckland, 1010, New Zealand
Tel.: (64) 93362400
Fax: (64) 93362401
Air Transportation Services
S.I.C.: 4522
N.A.I.C.S.: 481212

Air New Zealand Holidays Limited (1)
Air New Zealand House 185 Fanshaw Street
Auckland, 1010, New Zealand
Tel.: (64) 93573000
Fax: (64) 93362895
Air Transportation Services
S.I.C.: 4522
N.A.I.C.S.: 481212

Air New Zealand International Limited (1)
185 Fanshawe St
Private Bag 92007
1142 Auckland, 1020, New Zealand NZ
Tel.: (64) 93362400 (100%)
Fax: (64) 93362401
E-Mail: hrsolutions@airnz.co.nz
Emp.: 1,000
International Air Passenger Transportation
S.I.C.: 4512
N.A.I.C.S.: 481111
Rob Syfe *(CEO)*

Altitude Aerospace Interiors Limited (1)
Ground Floor Isitt House 1 Leonard Isitt Drive
Mangere, Auckland, New Zealand
Tel.: (64) 92563242
Fax: (64) 9 255 8328
Web Site: www.altitude-ai.com
Aerospace Engineering Services
S.I.C.: 8711
N.A.I.C.S.: 541330

Eagle Air Maintenance Limited (1)
Boyd Road Hamilton Airport
Hamilton, New Zealand
Tel.: (64) 78571000
Fax: (64) 8571081
Web Site: www.eagleair.co.nz
Emp.: 80
Air Transportation Services
S.I.C.: 4522
N.A.I.C.S.: 481212
Martin Vincent *(Mgr-Fin)*

Eagle Airways Limited (1)
Boyd Road Hamilton Airport R D 2
Hamilton, 3282, New Zealand
Tel.: (64) 78571000
Fax: (64) 78571081
Web Site: www.eagleair.co.nz
Emp.: 75
Air Transportation Services
S.I.C.: 4522
N.A.I.C.S.: 481212
Carrie Hurihanganui *(Gen Mgr)*

Eagle Aviation Ltd. (1)
Private Bag 3048
3240 Hamilton, New Zealand (100%)
Tel.: (64) 78571000
Fax: (64) 78571081
Sales Range: $300-349.9 Million
Emp.: 190
Commuter Airline
S.I.C.: 4512
N.A.I.C.S.: 481111
Carrie Hurihanganui *(Gen Mgr)*

Mount Cook Airline Limited (1)
Unit 3 Aviation House 12 Orchard Road
8544 Christchurch, New Zealand
Tel.: (64) 33581200
Fax: (64) 33581201
Air Transportation Services
S.I.C.: 4522
N.A.I.C.S.: 481211
Sirah Williamson *(Gen Mgr)*

Safe Air Limited (1)
PO Box 244
Blenheim, 7240, New Zealand
Tel.: (64) 35728416
Fax: (64) 5729015
E-Mail: info@safeair.co.nz
Web Site: www.safeair.co.nz
Emp.: 260
Aviation Engineering Services
S.I.C.: 8711
N.A.I.C.S.: 541330
Heather Deacon *(Gen Mgr)*

Units:

Air New Zealand Cargo Services (1)
185 sainshiwe Street
1010 Auckland, New Zealand (100%)
Tel.: (64) 93362400
Fax: (64) 93362922
E-Mail: info@airnz.co.nz
Web Site: www.airnewzealand.co.nz
Emp.: 3,000
Cargo & Transport Services
S.I.C.: 4512
N.A.I.C.S.: 481111
Mark Street *(Mgr-Grp External Comm)*

Air New Zealand Engineering Services (1)
5 Geoffrey Roberts Road Mangere
Private Bag 92007
2022 Auckland, New Zealand (100%)
Tel.: (64) 93362400
Fax: (64) 93362922
E-Mail: info@airnz.co.nz
Web Site: www.airnewzealand.co.nz
Emp.: 200
Aviation Overhaul & Maintenance
S.I.C.: 4581
N.A.I.C.S.: 488119
Mark Street *(Head-Customer Loyalty)*

U.S. Branch:

Air New Zealand Ltd. (U.S.A.) (1)
1960 E Grand Ave
El Segundo, CA 90245-5000
Tel.: (310) 648-7000
Fax: (310) 648-7017
Toll Free: (800) 262-1234
Web Site: www.airnz.com
Emp.: 80
Operator of Commercial & Cargo Air Lines
S.I.C.: 4724
N.A.I.C.S.: 561510
Roger Poulton *(VP)*

Non-U.S. Subsidiaries:

Air New Zealand (Australia) Pty Limited (1)
L 11 151 Clarence St
Sydney, NSW, 2000, Australia
Tel.: (61) 282359999
Web Site: www.airnz.com.au
Air Transportation Services
S.I.C.: 4581
N.A.I.C.S.: 488190

Leanne Geraghty *(Gen Mgr)*

Subsidiaries:

Masling Industries Pty Limited (2)
Hangar 3 Jack Masling Dr
Cootamundra, NSW, 2590, Australia
Tel.: (61) 269423155
Fax: (61) 269423250
Emp.: 12
Transportation Services
S.I.C.: 4581
N.A.I.C.S.: 488190

Safe Air Australia Pty Limited (2)
7 Planetree Avenue
Dingley, Melbourne, VIC, 3172, Australia
Tel.: (61) 395518766
Fax: (61) 3 9551 8677
E-Mail: info@safeairau.com
Web Site: www.safeairau.com
Emp.: 15
Repair & Maintenance Services
S.I.C.: 7539
N.A.I.C.S.: 811118
Doug Keesing *(Mgr-Propulsion Bus)*

TAE Pty Limited (2)
L1 Tae House 52 Mcdougall St
Milton, QLD, 4064, Australia
Tel.: (61) 733674811
Fax: (61) 733674855
E-Mail: info@tae.com.au
Web Site: www.tae.com.au
Aerospace Engineering Services
S.I.C.: 8711
N.A.I.C.S.: 541330

Subsidiaries:

TAE Aviation Pty Limited (3)
Hangar 1C James Schofield Dr
Adelaide, SA, 5850, Australia
Tel.: (61) 881500200
Fax: (61) 8 8150 0270
E-Mail: sales@taeaviation.com.au
Web Site: www.tae.com.au
Emp.: 60
Aerospace Engineering Services
S.I.C.: 8711
N.A.I.C.S.: 541330
Andrew Sanderson *(Gen Mgr)*

TAE Gas Turbines Pty Limited (3)
L 1 Tae House 52 Mcdougall St
Milton, QLD, 4064, Australia
Tel.: (61) 733674811
Fax: (61) 733674855
Aerospace Engineering Service
S.I.C.: 8711
N.A.I.C.S.: 541330

Blue Pacific Tours (1)
Room 404 Shin Kokusai Building
3 4 1 Marunouchi Chiyoda Ku, Tokyo, 100 0005, Japan (100%)
Tel.: (81) 332118071
Fax: (81) 332118090
Web Site: www.bpt.co.jp
Emp.: 20
S.I.C.: 4512
N.A.I.C.S.: 481111

AIR NIGERIA DEVELOPMENT LIMITED

9th Floor Etiebets Place 21 Mobolaji Bank Anthony Way
Ikeja, Lagos, Nigeria
Tel.: (234) 1 2711144
E-Mail: corpcomm@myairnigeria.com
Web Site: www.myairnigeria.com
Year Founded: 2004
Emp.: 1,000

Business Description:
Commercial Air Transportation
S.I.C.: 4512
N.A.I.C.S.: 481111

Personnel:
Jimoh Ibrahim *(Owner & Chm)*
Kinfe Fekadu Kahssaye *(CEO & Mng Dir)*

AIR PACIFIC LIMITED

Nasoso Rd Nadi Airport
Nadi, Fiji
Tel.: (679) 6737357
Fax: (679) 6720704
E-Mail: corporate@airpacific.com.fj
Web Site: www.airpacific.com
Sales Range: $250-299.9 Million
Emp.: 800

Business Description:
Air Transportation Services
S.I.C.: 4512
N.A.I.C.S.: 481111

Personnel:
Nalin Patel *(Chm)*
Aubrey Swift *(Acting CEO)*

Board of Directors:
Peter Collins
Geoff Dixon
Paul Edwards
Daniel Elisha
Damend Gounder
Charles Harvey
Simon Hickey
Sekonaia Tui Mailekai
Nalin Patel
Radike Qereqeretabua
Sitiveni Weleilakeba

AIR PARTNER PLC

2 City Place Beehive Ring Road
Gatwick, West Sussex, RH6 0PA, United Kingdom
Tel.: (44) 1293844800
Fax: (44) 1293539263
E-Mail: info@airpartner.com
Web Site: www.airpartner.com
AIP—(LSE)
Emp.: 215

Business Description:
Aircraft Charter Services
S.I.C.: 4522
N.A.I.C.S.: 481211

Personnel:
Mark A. Briffa *(CEO)*
Gavin Charles *(CFO)*
Philip Mathews *(Pres-Air PartnerInc-US)*
Graeme Manning *(Sec)*

Board of Directors:
Richard L. Everitt
Mark A. Briffa
Gavin Charles
Grahame Chilton
Anthony G. Mack
Charles W. Pollard
Andrew Wood

Legal Counsel:
ASB Law LLP
Innovis House 108 High Street
Crawley, United Kingdom

Subsidiary:

Air Partner Travel Consultants Ltd (1)
253 Beehive Ring Rd
RH6 0PA Gatwick, United Kingdom (100%)
Tel.: (44) 1293844855
Fax: (44) 1293844859
Web Site: www.airpartner.com
Emp.: 80
Travel Agencies
S.I.C.: 4724
N.A.I.C.S.: 561510
Mark Briffa *(Mng Dir)*

U.S. Subsidiary:

Air Partner Inc (1)
1100 Lee Wagener Blvd
Fort Lauderdale, FL 33315-3570 (100%)
Tel.: (954) 359-4300
Fax: (954) 359-3930
Web Site: www.airpartner.com
Emp.: 10
Travel Agencies
S.I.C.: 4724
N.A.I.C.S.: 561510
Mark Briffa *(Pres)*

Non-U.S. Subsidiaries:

Air Partner Havacilik ve Tasimacilik Ltd. (1)
Istanbul Caddesi Cimen Apt No 81/6
Yesilkoy
Istanbul, 34149, Turkey
Tel.: (90) 212 6631020
Fax: (90) 212 6631015
E-Mail: turkey@airpartner.com
Web Site: www.airpartner.com
Emp.: 4
Air Transportation Services
S.I.C.: 4512
N.A.I.C.S.: 481111
Anil Dede *(Mgr-Fin)*

Air Partner International GmbH (1)
TechnologiePark Haus 56
Friedrich-Ebert-Strape, 51429 Bergisch Gladbach, Germany (100%)
Tel.: (49) 220495050
Fax: (49) 220495051
E-Mail: info@airpartner.com
Web Site: www.airpartner.com
Emp.: 250
Travel Agencies
S.I.C.: 4724
N.A.I.C.S.: 561510
Pueschal Kipke *(Mng Dir)*

Air Partner International SAS (1)
89 R Du Faubourg Saint Honore
Paris, 75008, France (100%)
Tel.: (33) 142441100
Fax: (33) 142441101
E-Mail: france@airpartner.com
Web Site: www.airpartner.com
Emp.: 25
Travel Agencies
S.I.C.: 4724
N.A.I.C.S.: 561510
Lomin Taty *(Mng Dir)*

Air Partner Srl (1)
Via Valtellina 67
Milan, 20159, Italy
Tel.: (39) 0266825117
Fax: (39) 0260737939
E-Mail: italy@airpartner.com
Emp.: 8
Aircraft Charter Brokering Services
S.I.C.: 4522
N.A.I.C.S.: 481219
Alessio Altamura *(Mgr)*

Air Partner Sweden AB (1)
Norra Vallgatan 70
Malmo, Scania, 211 22, Sweden
Tel.: (46) 4010 776 0
Fax: (46) 4012 603 3
E-Mail: sweden@airpartner.com
Emp.: 3
Air Transportation Services
S.I.C.: 4512
N.A.I.C.S.: 481111
Roland Senften *(Pres)*

Air Partner Switzerland AG (1)
8058 Zurich Airport
2118
8060 Zurich, Switzerland (100%)
Tel.: (41) 223672948
Fax: (41) 448133444
Web Site: www.airpartner.com
Emp.: 3
Travel Agencies
S.I.C.: 4724
N.A.I.C.S.: 561510
Tom Engelhard *(Mgr)*

AIR SEYCHELLES LTD.

Pointe Lorue
PO Box 386
Victoria, Mahe, Seychelles
Tel.: (248) 391002
Fax: (248) 391005
E-Mail: info@airseychelles.com
Web Site: www.airseychelles.com
Year Founded: 1971
Rev.: $121,943,139
Emp.: 800

Business Description:
Air Transportation Services
S.I.C.: 4512
N.A.I.C.S.: 481111

Personnel:
Manoj Papa *(CEO)*
Gary Albert *(Deputy CEO)*
Shelley Cole *(CFO)*

Board of Directors:
Eddie Belle
Francis Chang Leng
Maurice Loustau-Lalanne
Sylvestre Radegonde
Francis Chang Sam

AIR TAHITI

PO Box 314
Papeete, French Polynesia
Tel.: (689) 482847
Fax: (689) 864099
Web Site: www.airtahiti.aero
Emp.: 970

Business Description:
Air Transportation Services
S.I.C.: 4512
N.A.I.C.S.: 481111

Personnel:
Christian Vernaudon *(Mng Dir)*

AIR VANUATU LTD

Air Vanuatu House
Rue de Paris, Port-Vila, Vanuatu
Tel.: (678) 23838
Fax: (678) 23250
E-Mail: sales@airvanuatu.com.vu
Web Site: www.airvanuatu.com
Emp.: 200

Business Description:
Air Transportation Services
S.I.C.: 4512
N.A.I.C.S.: 481111

Personnel:
Joseph Laloyer *(CEO & Mng Dir)*

AIR WATER INC.

12-8 Minami Semba 2-chome
Chuo-ku, Osaka, 542-0081, Japan
Tel.: (81) 6 6252 5411
Fax: (81) 6 6252 3965
E-Mail: info-h@awi.co.jp
Web Site: www.awi.co.jp
Year Founded: 1929
4088—(OTC TKS)
Sls.: $5,940,176,000
Assets: $5,327,619,000
Liabilities: $3,136,287,000
Net Worth: $2,191,332,000
Earnings: $202,026,000
Emp.: 8,937
Fiscal Year-end: 03/31/13

Business Description:
Gases for Industrial, Medical & Food Processing Operations
S.I.C.: 2813
N.A.I.C.S.: 325120

Personnel:
Hiroshi Aoki *(Chm & CEO)*
Masahiro Toyoda *(Vice Chm & Gen Mgr)*
Yasuo Imai *(Pres & COO)*
Takashi Izumida *(Sr Mng Dir & Chief Agriculture & Food Bus Officer)*
Junichi Nakagawa *(Sr Mng Dir & Exec VP)*
Toshihiko Akatsu *(Sr Mng Dir)*
Yuu Karato *(Co-Mng Dir)*
Yukio Matsubara *(Co-Mng Dir)*
Akira Yoshino *(CTO & Exec VP)*
Noriyasu Saeki *(Pres-Compliance Center & Chief CSR Officer)*
Masato Machida *(Chief Corp Plng Officer)*
Akira Fujita *(Pres-Ops-Hokkaido & Exec VP)*
Kikuo Toyoda *(Exec VP & Sr Exec Mgr-Hospital Support Div)*

Board of Directors:
Hiroshi Aoki

Air Water Inc.—(Continued)

Toshihiko Akatsu
Akira Fujita
Yasuo Imai
Takashi Izumida
Yuu Karato
Masato Machida
Yukio Matsubara
Yukio Murakami
Minoru Nagata
Junichi Nakagawa
Noriyasu Saeki
Seiji Shirai
Yasushi Sogabe
Kikuo Toyoda
Masahiro Toyoda
Akira Yoshino

Subsidiaries:

Air Water, Inc.-Hokkaido (1)
1 2 Kita 3 Jo Nishi
Chuo Ku, Sapporo, 060 0003, Japan (100%)
Tel.: (81) 112122821
Fax: (81) 112223217
Web Site: www.awi.co.jp
S.I.C.: 2813
N.A.I.C.S.: 325120

Air Water, Inc.-Tokyo (1)
18 19 Toranomon 3 Chome
Minato Ku, Tokyo, 105 0001, Japan (100%)
Tel.: (81) 335787801
Fax: (81) 335787819
Web Site: www.awi.co.jp
Emp.: 100
S.I.C.: 2813
N.A.I.C.S.: 325120

Healthcare-Tech Corporation (1)
7F 2-12-3 Nishi-Gotanda
Shinagawa-ku, Tokyo, 141 0031, Japan (60%)
Tel.: (81) 3 5437 3535
Fax: (81) 3 5437 3545
Web Site: www.healthcare-tech.co.jp
Emp.: 303
Nutritional Supplements Import & Distr
S.I.C.: 5122
N.A.I.C.S.: 424210
Kenichi Watanabe *(Pres)*

Printec Co., Ltd. (1)
5-32-1 Tomuro Atsugi
Atsugi, 243-0031, Japan (100%)
Tel.: (81) 462245731
Fax: (81) 462245905
E-Mail: info-kanri@printec.co.jp
Web Site: www.printec.co.jp
Emp.: 100
Printed Wiring Boards & Electronic Apliances Mfr & Sales
S.I.C.: 3672
N.A.I.C.S.: 334412
Katsuki Sino *(Pres)*

Tateho Chemical Industries Co., Ltd. (1)
974 Kariya
Ako, Hyogo, 678-0239, Japan
Tel.: (81) 791425041
Fax: (81) 791452040
E-Mail: info@tateho.co.jp
Web Site: www.tateho.co.jp
Emp.: 270
Industrial Chemicals Mfr
S.I.C.: 2899
N.A.I.C.S.: 325998
Tetsunori Minato *(Pres)*

Joint Venture:

C-Chem Co., Ltd. (1)
Akihabara UDX 13F 4-14-1 Sotokanda
Chiyoda-ku, Tokyo, Japan
Tel.: (81) 352077635
Fax: (81) 352077660
Web Site: www.c-chem.co.jp
Sales Range: $400-449.9 Million
Emp.: 120
Manufacture & Sale of Coal Chemicals
S.I.C.: 2899
N.A.I.C.S.: 325998
Toshihiro Nada *(Pres)*
Osamu Yamakawa *(Mng Dir)*

Plants:

AIR WATER BELLPEARL INC. (1)
20-16 Higashi Shinsaibashi 1-chome
Chuo-ku, Osaka, 542-0083, Japan
Tel.: (81) 662521802
Fax: (81) 662521750
E-Mail: ibaraki-sin@awi.co.jp
Emp.: 50
Phenolic Resins Mfr
S.I.C.: 2821
N.A.I.C.S.: 325211
Shingo Ibaraki *(Pres)*

AIR WATER INC. - Kashima Plant (1)
No 3 Hikari
Kashima, Ibaraki, 314-0014, Japan
Tel.: (81) 299843511
Fax: (81) 299843600
E-Mail: yamata-kun@awi.co.jp
Emp.: 200
Organic Chemicals Mfr
S.I.C.: 2833
N.A.I.C.S.: 325411

AIR WATER INC. - Wakayama Plant (1)
No 1850 Minato
Wakayama, 640-8555, Japan
Tel.: (81) 734512121
Fax: (81) 734535712
Web Site: www.aw-chem.jp
Organic Chemicals Mfr
S.I.C.: 2833
N.A.I.C.S.: 325411

AIRA CAPITAL PUBLIC COMPANY LIMITED

2/4 Nai Lert Tower 2nd & 8th Floor
Wireless Road
Lumpini Pathumwan, Bangkok, 10330, Thailand
Tel.: (66) 26848888
Fax: (66) 26505477
E-Mail: info@aira.co.th
Web Site: www.aira.co.th
Business Description:
Holding Company; Securities Dealing
S.I.C.: 6719
N.A.I.C.S.: 551112
Personnel:
Suphachai Phisitvanich *(Chm)*
Pairoj Laungthaleongpong *(CEO)*
Nakorn Kolsrichai *(Mng Dir)*
Board of Directors:
Suphachai Phisitvanich
Chiraporn Chemnasiri
Wisoot Karnchanapunyapong
Nakorn Kolsrichai
Pairoj Laungthaleongpong
Nalinee Ngamsettamas
Nopporn Picha
Anchalee Pipatanasern
Visit Vongruamlarp

AIRA FACTORING PUBLIC COMPANY LIMITED

319 Chamchuri Square 20th Floor
Phayathai Road Pathumwan Sub-District
Pathumwan Disrict, Bangkok, 10330, Thailand
Tel.: (66) 26576222
Fax: (66) 26576244
E-Mail: mailadmin@airafactoring.co.th
Web Site: www.airafactoring.co.th
Year Founded: 1997
AF—(THA)
Rev.: $5,789,836
Assets: $86,266,953
Liabilities: $75,125,204
Net Worth: $11,141,749
Earnings: $1,458,921
Emp.: 32
Fiscal Year-end: 12/31/12
Business Description:
Financial Investment Services
S.I.C.: 6211
N.A.I.C.S.: 523999
Personnel:
Chatchaval Bhanalarp *(Chm)*
Wiwat Kongkasai *(Mng Dir)*
Jirasak Arkawat *(Asst Mng Dir-Ops)*
Kanokkit Navasiri *(Asst Mng Dir-Credit & Mktg)*
Kittikarn Pacome *(Sec)*
Board of Directors:
Chatchaval Bhanalarp
Wutthiphum Jurangkool
Wiwat Kongkasai
Suwat Lauparadorachai
Kunakorn Makchaidee
Nalinee Ngamsetthamas
Chantima Sirisaengtaksin
Ladavan Tanatanit
Poonsak Thiapairat
Visit Vongruamlarp

AIRASIA BERHAD

LCC Terminal Jalan KLIA S3
Southern Support Zone KLIA
64000 Sepang, Selangor Darul Ehsan, Malaysia
Tel.: (60) 386604333
Fax: (60) 387751100
E-Mail: investorrelations@airasia.com
Web Site: www.airasia.com
AIRASIA—(KLS)
Rev.: $1,621,922,161
Assets: $5,491,044,338
Liabilities: $3,555,628,034
Net Worth: $1,935,416,304
Earnings: $600,532,357
Emp.: 5,644
Fiscal Year-end: 12/31/12
Business Description:
Air Transportation Services
S.I.C.: 4512
N.A.I.C.S.: 481111
Personnel:
Anthony Fernandes *(Grp CEO)*
Aireen Omar *(CEO)*
Kamarudin Meranun *(Deputy CEO)*
Andrew Littledale *(CFO)*
Amisha Sethi *(Chief Comml Officer-India)*
S. Ramadorai *(Chm-India)*
Tassapon Bijleveld *(CEO-Thailand)*
Mittu Chandilya *(CEO-India)*
Captain Dharmadi *(CEO-Indonesia)*
Marianne Hontiveros *(CEO-Philippines)*
Yoshinori Odagiri *(CEO-Japan)*
Logan Velaitham *(CEO-Singapore)*
Jasmindar Kaur *(Sec)*
Board of Directors:
Abdul Aziz Abu Bakar
Lee Ee Fam
Anthony Fernandes
Khee Seong Leong
Conor McCarthy
Kamarudin Meranun
Mohamed Khadar Merican
Mohd Omar Mustapha
Aireen Omar

AIRBATH GROUP PLC

Rotterdam Road Sutton Fields Industrial Estate
Kingston upon Hull, HU7 0XD, United Kingdom
Tel.: (44) 1482327704
Fax: (44) 1482585273
E-Mail: sales@reva-industries.com
Web Site: www.airbath.co.uk
Year Founded: 2001
Sales Range: $25-49.9 Million
Emp.: 192
Business Description:
Baths & Bathing Accessories Mfr
S.I.C.: 3088
N.A.I.C.S.: 326191
Personnel:
Gary Stevens *(Mng Dir)*

AIRBORNE ENERGY SOLUTIONS LTD.

Hangar 1 Whitecourt Municipal Airport
PO Box 1229
Whitecourt, AB, T7S 1P1, Canada
Tel.: (780) 778-3080
Fax: (780) 778-6652
Toll Free: (888) 496-3222
Web Site: www.airbornesolutions.com
Year Founded: 1985
Rev.: $35,147,798
Emp.: 200
Business Description:
Heliportable Coiled Tubing & Wireline Providers
S.I.C.: 3482
N.A.I.C.S.: 332992
Personnel:
Tony Hunley *(Pres)*

AIRBOSS OF AMERICA CORP.

16441 Yonge Street
Newmarket, ON, L3X 2G8, Canada
Tel.: (905) 751-1188
Fax: (905) 751-1101
E-Mail: info@airbossofamerica.com
Web Site: www.airbossofamerica.com
BOS—(TSX)
Rev.: $248,698,000
Assets: $118,821,000
Liabilities: $39,834,000
Net Worth: $78,987,000
Earnings: $7,170,000
Emp.: 607
Fiscal Year-end: 12/31/12
Business Description:
Rubber Based Products Developer & Mfr
S.I.C.: 3052
N.A.I.C.S.: 326220
Personnel:
P. Grenville Schoch *(Chm)*
Timothy Toppen *(Pres & COO)*
Robert L. Hagerman *(CEO)*
Wendy Ford *(Interim CFO)*
Earl Laurie *(Pres-Defense-AirBoss Engineered Products Inc)*
Robert Dodd *(Exec VP)*
Board of Directors:
P. Grenville Schoch
Richard F. Crowe
Robert L. Hagerman
Mary Matthews
Robert L. McLeish
Brian A. Robbins
Alan J. Watson
Legal Counsel:
Davies, Ward, Phillips & Vineberg LLP
Toronto, ON, Canada
Transfer Agent:
Computershare Investor Services Inc.
Montreal, QC, Canada

Division:

AirBoss Rubber Compounding (1)
101 Glasgow St
Kitchener, ON, N2G 4X8, Canada (100%)
Tel.: (519) 576-5565
Fax: (519) 576-1315
Web Site: www.airbossrubbercompounding.com
Sales Range: $50-74.9 Million
Emp.: 300
S.I.C.: 3052
N.A.I.C.S.: 326220
John Tomins *(VP-Sls & Mktg)*

Subsidiary:

AirBoss Engineering Products, Inc. (1)
881 Landry St
Acton Vale, QC, J0H 1A0, Canada Ca
Tel.: (450) 546-2776 (100%)
Fax: (450) 546-3735
Web Site: www.airboss-acton.com
Emp.: 230
Rubber Products
S.I.C.: 3052
N.A.I.C.S.: 326220
Earl Laurie *(Pres-Defense Products)*

U.S. Subsidiaries:

Flexible Products Co., Inc. (1)
2600 Auburn Ct
Auburn Hills, MI 48326
Tel.: (248) 852-5500
Fax: (248) 852-8620
Molded Rubber Mfr
S.I.C.: 3069
N.A.I.C.S.: 326299

AIRBUS GROUP N.V.

(Formerly European Aeronautic Defence & Space Company EADS N.V.)
Mendelweg 30
2333 CS Leiden, Netherlands
Mailing Address:
PO Box 32008
2303 DA Leiden, Netherlands
Tel.: (31) 715245600
Telex: AISPA X 620 059F
Fax: (31) 71 52 328 07
E-Mail: ir@eads.com
Web Site: www.airbus-group.com
Year Founded: 2000
AIR—(EUR MAD)
Rev.: $76,031,681,600
Assets: $123,984,949,340
Liabilities: $109,939,011,560
Net Worth: $14,045,937,780
Earnings: $1,654,442,930
Emp.: 140,405
Fiscal Year-end: 12/31/12

Business Description:
Airplanes, Helicopters, Tactical Missiles & Space/Strategic Systems Mfr
S.I.C.: 3721
N.A.I.C.S.: 336411

Personnel:
Denis Ranque *(Chm)*
Thomas Enders *(CEO)*
Harald Wilhelm *(CFO)*
Marwan Lahoud *(CMO & Chief Strategy Officer)*
Jean Botti *(CTO)*
Thierry Baril *(Chief HR Officer)*
Allan McArtor *(Chm/CEO-North America)*
Charles Champion *(Chm-Airbus India)*
Rafael Alonso *(Pres-Latin America & Caribbean)*
Fabrice Bregier *(CEO-Airbus)*
Srinivasan Dwarakanath *(CEO-Airbus India)*
Guillaume Faury *(CEO-Airbus Helicopters)*
Bernhard Gerwert *(CEO-Defence & Space)*
Francois Auque *(Exec VP-Space Sys-Airbus Defence & Space)*
Domingo Urena-Raso *(Exec VP-Military Aircraft-Airbus Defence & Space)*

Board of Directors:
Denis Ranque
Manfred Bischoff
Ralph D. Crosby, Jr.
Thomas Enders
Hans-Peter Keitel
Hermann-Josef Lamberti
Anne Lauvergeon
Lakshmi Niwas Mittal
John L. Parker
Michel Pebereau
Josep Pique i Camps
Jean-Claude Trichet

Ernst & Young Accountants LLP
Rotterdam, Netherlands

U.S. Subsidiary:

Airbus Group, Inc. (1)
(Formerly EADS North America, Inc.)
2550 Wasser Ter Ste 9000
Herndon, VA 20171 DE
Tel.: (703) 466-5600
Fax: (703) 466-5601
Web Site: northamerica.airbus-group.com
Emp.: 130
Holding Company; Regional Managing Office
S.I.C.: 6719
N.A.I.C.S.: 551112
Sean O'Keefe *(Chm & CEO)*
Harald Wilhelm *(CFO)*
Paul Pastorek *(Chief Admin Officer, Gen Counsel & Sec)*
Dave Tarbell *(Chief Compliance Officer & VP-Trade & Security)*
Christine Tovee *(CTO)*
David M. Fink *(Chief HR Officer)*
Rafael Alonso *(Pres-Latin America & Caribbean)*
Michael Cosentino *(Sr VP, Head-Strategy & Dev & Acting Head-Sls-Americas)*
Guy Hicks *(Sr VP-Corp Comm & Governmental Rels)*

Subsidiaries:

EADS Sodern North America, Inc. (2)
10455 Pacific Ctr Ct
San Diego, CA 92121 DE
Tel.: (858) 457-2000
Fax: (858) 457-2002
E-Mail: space@sodern.fr
Optical & Space Instrument Mfr
S.I.C.: 3827
N.A.I.C.S.: 333314

EADS Supply & Services, Inc. (2)
7646 Standish Pl
Rockville, MD 20855 DE
Tel.: (301) 424-8096
Fax: (301) 424-7341
E-Mail: eads.nasupplier@airbus.com
Web Site: northamerica.airbus-group.com
Avionics Hardware & Systems Acquisition
S.I.C.: 7389
N.A.I.C.S.: 561499

Fairchild Controls Corporation (2)
540 Highland St
Frederick, MD 21701 DE
Tel.: (301) 228-3400
Fax: (301) 682-6885
Toll Free: (800) 695-5378
E-Mail:
Web Site: northamerica.airbus-group.com
Emp.: 200
Aircraft Air Turbine Drive & Environmental Control Systems Mfr
S.I.C.: 3728
N.A.I.C.S.: 336413
Peter Borgel *(CEO)*

i-cubed, LLC (2)
1600 Prospect Pkwy
Fort Collins, CO 80525
Tel.: (970) 482-4400
Fax: (970) 482-4499
Toll Free: (800) 472-8328
E-Mail: info@i3.com
Web Site: www.i3.com
Geospatial Mapping Services
S.I.C.: 8713
N.A.I.C.S.: 541370
David Steveley *(VP-Sls)*

Spot Image Corporation, Inc. (2)
14595 Avion Pkwy Ste 500
Chantilly, VA 20151
Tel.: (703) 715-3100
Fax: (703) 715-3120
Rev.: $3,404,000
Emp.: 15
Aerospace Engineering Services
S.I.C.: 8711
N.A.I.C.S.: 541330
Neal Carney *(CEO)*

Non-U.S. Subsidiary:

EADS Canada, Inc. (2)
Constitution Square I 360 Albert Street Suite 530
Ottawa, ON, K1R 7X7, Canada
Tel.: (613) 230-3902
Fax: (613) 230-1442
Web Site: www.eads.com
Emp.: 10
Aircraft Security System Mfr
S.I.C.: 3728
N.A.I.C.S.: 336413
Pierre Delestrade *(Pres & CEO)*

Subsidiaries:

Composites Atlantic Limited (3)
71 Hall St
PO Box 1150
Lunenburg, NS, B0J 2C0, Canada NS
Tel.: (902) 634-8448
Fax: (902) 634-8398
E-Mail: cbaril@compositesatlantic.com
Web Site: www.compositesatlantic.com
Sales Range: $10-24.9 Million
Emp.: 200
Aircraft Parts & Equipment
S.I.C.: 3728
N.A.I.C.S.: 336413
Claude Baril *(Pres)*

EADS Composites Atlantic Limited (3)
71 Hall Street
PO Box 1150
Lunenburg, NS, B0J 2C0, Canada
Tel.: (902) 634-8448
Fax: (902) 634-8398
Web Site: www.compositesatlantic.com
Emp.: 350
Aircraft Composite Mfr
S.I.C.: 3728
N.A.I.C.S.: 336413
Claude Baril *(Pres & CEO)*
David Aulenback *(CFO & VP)*
Mark Olivella *(COO & VP)*

Non-U.S. Groups:

Airbus Helicopters Holding S.A.S. (1)
(Formerly Eurocopter Holding S.A.)
Aeroport International Marseille Provence
13752 Marignane, Cedex, France FR
Tel.: (33) 4 4285 2892
Fax: (33) 4 4285 8595
Web Site: www.airbushelicopters.com
Holding Company; Helicopter Mfr & Support Services
S.I.C.: 6719
N.A.I.C.S.: 551112
Herve Berriet *(CEO)*

Subsidiary:

Airbus Helicopters S.A.S. (2)
(Formerly Eurocopter S.A.)
Aeroport International Marseille Provence
13725 Marignane, Cedex, France FR
Tel.: (33) 4 4285 2892 (100%)
Telex: AISPA X 410 975 F
Fax: (33) 4 4285 8595
Web Site: www.airbushelicopters.com
Sales Range: $5-14.9 Billion
Emp.: 1,100
Helicopter Mfr
S.I.C.: 3721
N.A.I.C.S.: 336411
Berdertlang Lutz *(Chm)*
Guillaume Faury *(CEO)*

Subsidiaries:

Eurocopter Training Services S.A.S (3)
Aeroport Marseille Provence
Marignane, 13725, France
Tel.: (33) 4 42 85 68 75
Fax: (33) 4 42 85 91 32
E-Mail: marketing.ets@eurocopter.com
Web Site: www.eurocoptertrainingservices.com
Training & Educational Support Services
S.I.C.: 8299
N.A.I.C.S.: 611430
Herve Berriet *(CEO)*

HELISIM (3)
Helisim Aeroport International Marseille
13725 Marignane, France
Tel.: (33) 4 42 77 39 00
Fax: (33) 4 42 77 39 51
E-Mail: helisim.marketing@eurocopter.com
Web Site: www.helisim.fr
Emp.: 48
Aerospace Training Center Operator
S.I.C.: 8249
N.A.I.C.S.: 611512
Alain Salendre *(CEO)*

U.S. Subsidiary:

Airbus Helicopters, Inc. (3)
2701 Forum Dr
Grand Prairie, TX 75052-7027 DE
Tel.: (972) 641-0000
Fax: (972) 641-3550
E-Mail:
Web Site: www.airbushelicoptersinc.com
Sales Range: $300-349.9 Million
Emp.: 560
Helicopters Mfr & Marketing Import Export
S.I.C.: 3721
N.A.I.C.S.: 336411
Marc Paganini *(Pres & CEO)*
Fernando Lombo *(CFO & VP)*
Eric Walden *(Sr VP-Bus Dev)*

Non-U.S. Subsidiaries:

Australian Aerospace Limited (3)
65-75 Pandanus Avenue
Brisbane Airport, Brisbane, QLD, 4007, Australia AU
Tel.: (61) 7 3637 3000
Fax: (61) 7 3637 3955
Web Site: www.ausaero.com.au
Emp.: 1,200
Helicopter Mfr & Distr
S.I.C.: 3721
N.A.I.C.S.: 336411
Jens Goennemann *(CEO)*

Subsidiary:

Australian Aerospace Composites Pty Ltd. (4)
65-75 Pandanus Ave Brisbane Airport
Brisbane, QLD, 4007, Australia
Tel.: (61) 736373000
Aerospace Operating Services
S.I.C.: 4581
N.A.I.C.S.: 488190

Eurocopter Canada Ltd. (3)
1100 Gilmore Rd
PO Box 250
Fort Erie, ON, L2A 5M9, Canada
Tel.: (905) 871-7772
Fax: (905) 871-3320
Web Site: www.eurocopter.ca
Sales Range: $25-49.9 Million
Emp.: 140
Mfr. & Distribution of Helicopters & Parts
S.I.C.: 3721
N.A.I.C.S.: 336411
Romain Trapp *(Pres & CEO)*

Subsidiary:

Vector Aerospace Corporation (4)
2 Bloor Street East 1920 Suite 2100
Toronto, ON, M4W 1A8, Canada
Tel.: (416) 925-1143
Fax: (416) 925-7214
E-Mail: info@vectoraerospace.com
Web Site: www.vectoraerospace.com
Sales Range: $550-599.9 Million
Emp.: 2,400
Aerospace Engines & Equipment Mfr
S.I.C.: 3724
N.A.I.C.S.: 336412
Donald K. Jackson *(Chm)*
Declan O'Shea *(Pres & CEO)*
Randal L. Levine *(CFO, Sec & Sr VP)*
Paul Cockell *(Pres-Helicopter Svcs-North America)*
Jeff Poirier *(Pres-Engine Svcs-Atlantic)*
John MacDougall *(Sr VP-Sls & Mktg)*
Brian Thompson *(Sr VP-Global Engine Svcs)*

Division:

Pathix ASP (5)
9 Austin Street
Saint John's, NL, A1B 4B7, Canada (100%)

Airbus Group N.V.—(Continued)

Tel.: (709) 724-8500
Fax: (709) 724-8545
Toll Free: (866) 724-8500
E-Mail: inquiries@pathix.com
Web Site: www.pathix.com
Emp.: 30
Management Consulting Services
S.I.C.: 8748
N.A.I.C.S.: 541618
Trevor Lewis *(Pres)*

Subsidiaries:

Vector Aerospace Engine Services-Atlantic, Inc. (5)
800 Aerospace Blvd Hangar 8
Summerside, PE, C1N 4P6, Canada
Tel.: (902) 436-1333
Fax: (902) 436-0777
Aircraft Engine Repair & Maintenance Services
S.I.C.: 4581
N.A.I.C.S.: 488190
Jeff Poirier *(Pres)*

Vector Aerospace-Helicopter Services Inc. (5)
4551 Agar Dr
Richmond, BC, V7B 1A4, Canada
Tel.: (604) 276-7600
Fax: (604) 276-7667
Toll Free: (888) 729-2276
Web Site: www.vectoraerospace.com
Emp.: 350
Airport Operations
S.I.C.: 4581
N.A.I.C.S.: 488119
Paul Cockell *(Pres)*

Vector Aerospace Holdings Ltd. (5)
2 Bloor St W Suite 2100
Toronto, ON, M4W 3E2, Canada
Tel.: (416) 925-1143
Fax: (416) 925-7214
E-Mail: investorinfo@vectoraerospace.com
Emp.: 20
Aircraft Repair & Maintenance Services
S.I.C.: 4581
N.A.I.C.S.: 488190

U.S. Subsidiaries:

Vector Aerospace Corporation-Atlantic Engine Services (5)
1680 Roberts Blvd Ste 404
Kennesaw, GA 30144
Tel.: (770) 427-2428
Fax: (770) 427-2269
E-Mail: sales.esa@vectoraerospace.com
Web Site: www.vectoraerospace.com
Emp.: 2
Aircraft Repair & Maintenance Services
S.I.C.: 4581
N.A.I.C.S.: 488190
John Martin *(Mgr-Svc)*

Vector Aerospace Helicopter Services California, Inc. (5)
318 Paseo Tesoro
Walnut, CA 91789-2725
Tel.: (909) 594-8835
Aircraft Parts Repair & Maintenance Services
S.I.C.: 4581
N.A.I.C.S.: 488190

Vector Aerospace USA Holdings, Inc. (5)
22378 Billie Blackmon Rd
Andalusia, AL 36421
Tel.: (334) 222-1277
Investment Management Services
S.I.C.: 6211
N.A.I.C.S.: 523999

Vector Aerospace USA, Inc. (5)
22378 Billie Blackmon Rd
Andalusia, AL 36421
Tel.: (334) 222-1277
Fax: (334) 222-1954
Aircraft Parts Repair & Maintenance Services
S.I.C.: 4581
N.A.I.C.S.: 488190

Non-U.S. Division:

Vector Aerospace Engine Services UK (5)
12 Imperial Way
Croydon, Surrey, CR9 4LE, United Kingdom (100%)
Tel.: (44) 2086887777
Fax: (44) 2086886603
E-Mail: sales.esuk@vectoraerospace.com
Web Site: www.vectoraerospace.com
Emp.: 220
Gas Turbine Engines for Fixed Wing Aircraft & Civil & Military Operations
S.I.C.: 3724
N.A.I.C.S.: 336412
Tim Rice *(Mng Dir)*

Non-U.S. Subsidiaries:

Vector Aerospace Africa (Proprietary) Limited (5)
Hangar 25 Lanseria International Airport
Lanseria, 1748 Johannesburg, South Africa
Tel.: (27) 117013035
Fax: (27) 117013464
E-Mail: sales.esa@vectoraerospace.com
Web Site: www.vectoraerospace.com
Aircraft Repair & Maintenance Services
S.I.C.: 4581
N.A.I.C.S.: 488190
Mark Puth *(Gen Mgr)*

Vector Aerospace International Ltd. (5)
Fleetlands
Gosport, Hampshire, PO13 0AN, United Kingdom
Tel.: (44) 2392 946100
Fax: (44) 2392 946103
Aircraft Parts Mfr
S.I.C.: 3728
N.A.I.C.S.: 336413

Eurocopter Chile SA (3)
Av Jose Arrieta La Reina
Santiago, Chile
Tel.: (56) 24134300
Fax: (56) 24134338
E-Mail: alexandre.ceccacci@eurocopter.cl
Web Site: www.eurocopter.cl
Sales Range: $1-9.9 Million
Emp.: 100
Distributor of Eurocopter Products & Services
S.I.C.: 3721
N.A.I.C.S.: 336411
Alexandre Ceccacci *(Mng Dir)*

EUROCOPTER CHINA CO LTD (3)
22D Jin An Bldg N 908 Dongdaming Road
200082 Shanghai, China
Tel.: (86) 21 6595 6101
Fax: (86) 21 6595 6100
E-Mail: contact@eurocopter-china.com
Web Site: www.eurocopter-china.com
Emp.: 55
Aircraft Machinery Distr
S.I.C.: 5084
N.A.I.C.S.: 423830
Bruno Boulnois *(Pres)*

Subsidiary:

General Aviation Maintenance & Engineering Co., Ltd (4)
Shenzhen Heliport N 21 Qilin Road
Nan Shan District, Shenzhen, 518051, China
Tel.: (86) 755 267 26 492
Fax: (86) 755 269 749 28
Aircraft Equipment Maintenance Services
S.I.C.: 4581
N.A.I.C.S.: 488190
Jiang Nan Li *(Mng Dir)*

Eurocopter de Mexico S.A. (3)
Hangar N 1 Zona G de Hangares
Aeropuerto International, Mexico, 15620, Mexico
Tel.: (52) 5557167555
Fax: (52) 5557167526
Web Site: www.eurocopter.com.mx/
Sales Range: $25-49.9 Million
Emp.: 400
Helicopters & Parts
S.I.C.: 3721
N.A.I.C.S.: 336411
Serge Durand *(Gen Mgr)*

Eurocopter Deutschland GmbH (3)
Industriestr 4
Donauworth, Bayern, 86609, Germany
Tel.: (49) 906710
Fax: (49) 906714011
Aerospace Training Center Operator
S.I.C.: 8249
N.A.I.C.S.: 611512

Subsidiaries:

Eurocopter Deutschland Real Estate GmbH & Co. KG (4)
Emil-Riedl-Weg 6 I Isartal
Pullach, 82049, Germany
Tel.: (49) 906710
Fax: (49) 906714011
Real Estate Management Services
S.I.C.: 6531
N.A.I.C.S.: 531390

MOTORFLUG BADEN-BADEN GmbH (4)
Flugstrassee 12
76532 Baden-Baden, Germany
Tel.: (49) 7229 30 14 0
Fax: (49) 7229 30 14 25
E-Mail: info@motorflug.com
Web Site: www.motorflug.com
Emp.: 150
Aircraft Parts Sales & Maintenance Services
S.I.C.: 5088
N.A.I.C.S.: 423860
Bernhard Meier *(CEO)*

Subsidiary:

SPAERO TRADE GmbH (5)
Baden-Airpark Summersite Ave C-312
77836 Rheinmunster, Germany
Tel.: (49) 7229 301416
Fax: (49) 7229 301425
E-Mail: spaero@spaero.de
Web Site: www.spaero.de
Aircraft Parts Distr
S.I.C.: 5088
N.A.I.C.S.: 423860
Michaela Eisberg *(Mng Dir)*

Eurocopter Espana SA (3)
Carretera Del Barrio De La Fortuna 10
Cuatro Vientos, 28044 Madrid, Spain
Tel.: (34) 913797200
Fax: (34) 915083958
Web Site: www.eurocopter.com
Sales Range: $1-9.9 Million
Emp.: 15
Marketer & Retailer of Eurocopter Products & Services
S.I.C.: 3721
N.A.I.C.S.: 336411

Eurocopter India Pvt Ltd (3)
Teri University Campus Plot No 10 Vasant Kunj Institutional Area
Vasant Kunj, New Delhi, 110 070, India
Tel.: (91) 11 4580 1100
Web Site: www.eurocopter.com
Rev.: $4,360,587
Emp.: 21
Aircraft Parts Distr
S.I.C.: 5088
N.A.I.C.S.: 423860
Xavier Hay *(CEO)*

Eurocopter Japan Co. (3)
Roppongi Hills Mori Tower 19F 6-10-1
Roppongi Minato-ku
Tokyo, 107 0062, Japan
Tel.: (81) 357756262
Fax: (81) 354143328
E-Mail: info@eurocopter.co.jp
Web Site: www.eurocopter.co.jp
Sales Range: Less than $1 Million
Emp.: 80
Eurocopter Support Network Services
S.I.C.: 3721
N.A.I.C.S.: 336411
Stephane Ginoux *(Pres & CEO)*

Subsidiaries:

Eurocopter Japan RG Co. Ltd. (4)
Roppongi Hills Mori Tower 19F 6-10-1 Roppongi
Minato-Ku, Tokyo, 106 6119, Japan
Tel.: (81) 3 5414 3346
Fax: (81) 3 5414 3328
Aircraft Parts Distr
S.I.C.: 5088
N.A.I.C.S.: 423860
Stephane Ginoux *(Pres & CEO)*

EUROCOPTER KHDS Limited (3)
539-14 Yesu-Ri Jeongdong-Myeon
Sacheon, Gyeongsangnam-do, 664-932, Korea (South)
Tel.: (82) 55 855 2323
Fax: (82) 55 855 2324
Web Site: www.eurocopter.com
Rev.: $53,648,434
Emp.: 22
Aerospace Technical Consulting Services
S.I.C.: 8999
N.A.I.C.S.: 541690
Gilles Armstrong *(CEO)*

Eurocopter Philippines Inc. (3)
2 Manila Domestic Airport
PO Box 2
Pasay, 1300, Philippines
Tel.: (63) 28538857
Fax: (63) 28540757
E-Mail: eurothils@eurocopter.com.ph
Web Site: www.eurocopter.com
Sales Range: $1-9.9 Million
Emp.: 50
Distribution of Eurocopter Products & Services
S.I.C.: 3721
N.A.I.C.S.: 336411
Yves Rossy *(Pres)*

Eurocopter Romania SA (3)
Aeroportului Street 1A
Ghimbav, Brasov, 507075, Romania
Tel.: (40) 268303000
Fax: (40) 268303099
E-Mail: office@eurocopterromania.ro
Web Site: www.eurocopterromania.ro
Emp.: 190
Repairer & Overhauler of Old Range Products
S.I.C.: 4581
N.A.I.C.S.: 488190
Jean-Louis Mascle *(Mng Dir)*

Eurocopter South East Asia Pte. Ltd. (3)
48 Loyang Way
Singapore, 508740, Singapore
Tel.: (65) 65434101
Fax: (65) 65428797
E-Mail: bruno.boulnois@eurocoptersea.com.sg
Web Site: www.eurocoptersea.com.sg
Sales Range: $25-49.9 Million
Emp.: 180
Distributor of Eurocopter Products & Services
S.I.C.: 3721
N.A.I.C.S.: 336411
Brenner Bernhard *(Pres & CEO)*

Eurocopter Southern Africa Pty. Ltd. (3)
Hangar 27 Lanseria Airport
PO Box 135
Lanseria, 1748, South Africa
Tel.: (27) 117998300
Fax: (27) 117013043
E-Mail: marketing@eurocopter.co.za
Web Site: www.eurocopter.co.za
Sales Range: $1-9.9 Million
Emp.: 82
Distribution & Customization of Eurocopter Products & Services
S.I.C.: 3721
N.A.I.C.S.: 336411
Fabrice Cagnat *(Mng Dir)*

Eurocopter UK Ltd. (3)
Langford Lane
Kidlington, Oxfordshire, OX5 1QZ, United Kingdom
Tel.: (44) 1865 852400
Fax: (44) 1865 842827
E-Mail: sales@eurocopter.co.uk
Web Site: www.eurocopter.co.uk
Emp.: 250
Helicopter Charter Services
S.I.C.: 4522
N.A.I.C.S.: 481211
David Lewis *(Dir-Sls-Natl Resilience)*

EUROCOPTER VOSTOK (3)
Yakimanskaya Emb 4 Bld 1
119180 Moscow, Russia

Tel.: (7) 495 663 1556
Fax: (7) 495 663 1559
E-Mail: info@eurocopter.ru
Web Site: www.eurocopter.ru
Emp.: 29
Helicopter Mfr
S.I.C.: 3721
N.A.I.C.S.: 336411
Laurence Rigolini *(Mng Dir)*

Helibras (3)
Rua Santos Dumont 200 Distrito Industrial
CEP 37504 900 Itajuba, Minas Gerais, Brazil
Tel.: (55) 3536293000
Fax: (55) 3536293004
E-Mail: helibras@helibras.com.br
Web Site: www.helibras.com.br
Sales Range: $25-49.9 Million
Emp.: 359
Helicopters & Parts
S.I.C.: 3721
N.A.I.C.S.: 336411
Eduardo Marson *(Pres & CEO)*

Non-U.S. Joint Venture:

Eurocopter Malaysia Sdn Bhd (3)
Terminal 2 Sultan Abdul Aziz Shah Airport
47200 Subang Jaya, Selangor, Malaysia
Tel.: (60) 378483408
Fax: (60) 378483409
Web Site: www.eurocopter.com.my
Sls.: $15,695,030
Emp.: 40
Fleet Services
S.I.C.: 4581
N.A.I.C.S.: 488190

Airbus S.A.S. (1)
1 Rond Point Maurice Bellonte
31707 Blagnac, Cedex, France (100%)
Tel.: (33) 561933333
Fax: (33) 561935948
E-Mail: media@airbus.com
Web Site: www.airbus.com
Sales Range: $25-49.9 Billion
Emp.: 57,000
Military & Commercial Aircraft Mfr
Import Export
S.I.C.: 3721
N.A.I.C.S.: 336411
Fabrice Bregier *(Pres & CEO)*
Harald Wilhelm *(CFO)*
Guenter Butschek *(COO)*
Alain Flourens *(Exec VP)*
Didier Lux *(Exec VP-Customer Svcs)*
Manuel Hita-Romero *(Sr VP-Airbus Spain & Gen Mgr-Airbus Spain)*
Claude Lelaie *(Sr VP-Flight Div)*
Pilar Albiac Murillo *(Sr VP-Lean)*

Subsidiaries:

Airbus Corporate Jet Centre S.A.S. (2)
316 Route De Bayonne
Toulouse, 31000, France
Tel.: (33) 5 61 18 39 35
Fax: (33) 5 67 19 51 99
Airbus Cabin Outfitting Services
S.I.C.: 4581
N.A.I.C.S.: 488190
Benoit Defforge *(Mng Dir & Head-Cabin Completions)*
Tom Williams *(Exec VP-Programmes)*

Airbus Invest II S.A.S. (2)
1 Rond Point Maurice Bellonte
Blagnac, 31707, France
Tel.: (33) 5 61 93 33 33
Fax: (33) 5 61 93 44 51
Aircraft Parts Mfr
S.I.C.: 3728
N.A.I.C.S.: 336413

Airbus Prosky S.A.S. (2)
1 Rond-Point Maurice Bellonte
31707 Blagnac, France
Tel.: (33) 5 61 93 33 33
Fax: (33) 5 82 05 00 00
Web Site: www.airbusprosky.com
Aircraft Development & Research Services
S.I.C.: 8731
N.A.I.C.S.: 541712
Eric Stefanello *(CEO)*
Daniel Janouschek *(CFO)*
Marc Hamy *(COO)*

Airbus Transport International S.N.C. (2)
12 Rue Gabriel Clerc Cedex
Blagnac, 31700, France
Tel.: (33) 5 62 11 81 96
Fax: (33) 5 61 93 46 11
Aircraft Fleet Management Services
S.I.C.: 4581
N.A.I.C.S.: 488190
Thierry Larroque *(Mng Dir)*

U.S. Subsidiaries:

Airbus Americas, Inc. (2)
2550 Wasser Terr Ste 9100
Herndon, VA 20171 VA
Tel.: (703) 834-3400
Fax: (703) 834-3593
Web Site: www.airbus.com
Emp.: 1,200
Jet Aircraft & Airplanes Mfr & Distr
Import Export
S.I.C.: 3721
N.A.I.C.S.: 336411
Barry Eccleston *(Pres & CEO)*
Robert Geckle *(Gen Counsel, Chief Compliance Officer & VP)*

Subsidiaries:

Airbus Military North America (3)
2550 Wasser Ter Ste 9000
Herndon, VA 20171
Tel.: (703) 466-5600
Fax: (703) 466-5601
Web Site: www.eadsnorthamerica.com
Aircraft Parts Sales & Maintenance Services
S.I.C.: 5088
N.A.I.C.S.: 423860
Jose M. Morales *(CEO)*

Metron Aviation, Inc. (3)
45300 Catalina Ct Ste 101
Dulles, VA 20166
Tel.: (703) 456-0123
Fax: (703) 456-0133
E-Mail: info@metronaviation.com
Web Site: www.metronaviation.com
Air Traffic Management Services
S.I.C.: 9621
N.A.I.C.S.: 488111
Michael Gundling *(CMO & Sr VP)*
Rick Ducharme *(Exec VP-Indus Rels)*
Alan Bloodgood *(Sr VP & Gen Mgr-Advanced Res & Engrg)*

Non-U.S. Subsidiaries:

Airbus China (2)
Beijing Tianzhu Airport Industrial Zone
Tianwei Erjie, Beijing, Shunyi, 101312, China
Tel.: (86) 1080486161
Fax: (86) 1080486194
Web Site: www.airbus.com
Airplane Distr
S.I.C.: 7359
N.A.I.C.S.: 532411
Eric Chen *(Pres)*
Rafa Gonzalez *(COO)*

Airbus Deutschland GmbH (2)
Kreetslag 10
PO Box 950109
D 21129 Hamburg, Germany
Tel.: (49) 4074370
Fax: (49) 407434422
Web Site: www.airbus.com
Rev.: $672,947,968
Emp.: 18,000
Aircraft Mfr
S.I.C.: 3721
N.A.I.C.S.: 336411
Guenter Butschek *(Mgr)*

Subsidiaries:

Airbus Operations GmbH (3)
Kreetslag 10
Hamburg, 21129, Germany
Tel.: (49) 40 743 70
Fax: (49) 40 74 34 422
Aircraft Mfr
S.I.C.: 3721
N.A.I.C.S.: 336411

Airspares (3)
Weg Beim Jaeger 150
PO Box 630107
22335 Hamburg, Germany
Tel.: (49) 4050760
Telex: 212742
Fax: (49) 40592398
E-Mail: airspares@airspares.com
Web Site: www.airspares.com
Emp.: 600
Aircraft Parts Distr
S.I.C.: 5088
N.A.I.C.S.: 423860
Heino Ostermeier *(Mng Dir)*

KID-Systeme GmbH (3)
Lueneburger Schanze 30
21614 Buxtehude, Germany
Tel.: (49) 40 743 7 16 33
Fax: (49) 40 743 8 38 29
E-Mail: info@kid-systeme.com
Web Site: www.kid-systeme.de
Aircraft Cabin Electronic Component Mfr
S.I.C.: 3728
N.A.I.C.S.: 336413
Patrick Schrot *(Exec Dir)*

Airbus Japan KK (2)
ERK Mori Building
1 12 32 Akasaka Minato Ku, Tokyo, 107 6035, Japan
Tel.: (81) 355738400
Fax: (81) 355738401
E-Mail: info@airbusjapan.com
Web Site: www.airbusjapan.com
Airplane Distr
S.I.C.: 7359
N.A.I.C.S.: 532411

Airbus Operations Ltd. (2)
Chester Road Broughton
Chester, CH4 0DR, United Kingdom
Tel.: (44) 1244 520444
Fax: (44) 1244 523000
Aircraft Mfr
S.I.C.: 3721
N.A.I.C.S.: 336411

Airbus Real Estate Premium AEROTEC Nord GmbH & Co. KG (2)
Emil-Riedl-Weg 6 I Isartal Bayern
Pullach, 82049, Germany
Tel.: (49) 407 4370
Real Estate Development Services
S.I.C.: 6531
N.A.I.C.S.: 531390

Airbus UK (2)
Gulf Cruz Lane Filton House Filton
PO Box 77
Bristol, BS99 7AR, United Kingdom
Tel.: (44) 79693831
Telex: 44163 BAEFIL G
Fax: (44) 79693831
E-Mail: info@airbus.com
Web Site: www.airbus.com
Emp.: 7,000
Airplane Component Mfr
S.I.C.: 3728
N.A.I.C.S.: 336413

Satair A/S (2)
Amager Landevej 147A
DK 2770 Kastrup, Denmark
Tel.: (45) 32470100
Fax: (45) 32513434
E-Mail: info@satair.com
Web Site: www.satair.com
Sales Range: $400-449.9 Million
Emp.: 488
Supplier of Aircraft Parts & Service Solutions
S.I.C.: 3728
N.A.I.C.S.: 336413
Niels Erik Nielsen *(Chm)*
John Staer *(CEO)*
Michael Hojgaard *(CFO)*
Morten Olsen *(COO & Head-Global Sls)*

U.S. Subsidiary:

Satair USA Inc. (3)
3993 Tradeport Blvd
Atlanta, GA 30354
Tel.: (404) 675-6333
Fax: (404) 675-6311
E-Mail: satairinq@satair.com
Web Site: www.satair.com
Emp.: 50
Aircraft Equipments & Parts Distr
S.I.C.: 5088
N.A.I.C.S.: 423860
Rick Tonney *(Mng Dir)*

Branch:

Satair USA Inc. - Miami (4)
4301 NW 36th St
Miami Springs, FL 33166
Tel.: (305) 883-8424
Fax: (305) 883-6179
Toll Free: (800) 709-3882
Web Site: www.satair.com
Sales Range: $10-24.9 Million
Emp.: 200
Distr & Retailer of Hydraulic Equipment & Supplies
S.I.C.: 5084
N.A.I.C.S.: 423830
Luis Abellon *(Pres)*
Jim Inglis *(CEO)*

Non-U.S. Subsidiaries:

Satair China (3)
CASC Airbus No 5 Tianzhu Donglu Tianzhu Airport Industrial Zone
PO Box 3412
101312 Beijing, China
Tel.: (86) 10 8048 6340
Fax: (86) 10 8048 6599
E-Mail: info@satair.com
Aircraft Parts Distr
S.I.C.: 5088
N.A.I.C.S.: 423860

Satair Pte. Ltd. (3)
27 Loyang Way
Singapore, 508728, Singapore
Tel.: (65) 65430977
Fax: (65) 65430737
Web Site: www.satair.com
Aircraft Parts Distr
S.I.C.: 5088
N.A.I.C.S.: 423860
Rene Frandsen *(Gen Mgr)*

Satair UK (3)
Purdeys Way Purdeys Industrial Estate
Rochford, Essex, SS4 1NE, United Kingdom
Tel.: (44) 1702560700
Fax: (44) 1702 560750
Aircraft Parts Distr
S.I.C.: 5088
N.A.I.C.S.: 423860

Astrium Holding S.A.S. (1)
6 Rue Laurent Pichat
75116 Paris, France FR
Tel.: (33) 1 39 06 25 60
Fax: (33) 1 39 06 12 54
Holding Company
S.I.C.: 6719
N.A.I.C.S.: 551112

Subsidiary:

Astrium S.A.S. (2)
31 rue des Cosmonautes
31402 Toulouse, Cedex 4, France FR
Tel.: (33) 562196219
Fax: (33) 0561545710
Web Site: www.astrium.eads.net
Sales Range: $5-14.9 Billion
Emp.: 4,000
Engineering Services
S.I.C.: 8711
N.A.I.C.S.: 541330
Francois Auque *(CEO)*

Subsidiaries:

Astrium Space Transportation (3)
66 Route De Verneuil
78 133 Les Mureaux, France
Tel.: (33) 1 39 06 12 34
Fax: (33) 1 39 06 12 54
Air Transportation Services
S.I.C.: 4581
N.A.I.C.S.: 488190

Vizada SAS (3)
137 rue du Faubourg St Denis
75010 Paris, France
Tel.: (33) 1 53 35 95 00
Fax: (33) 1 53 35 82 20
E-Mail: sales.europe@vizada.com
Web Site: www.vizada.com
Sales Range: $650-699.9 Million
Emp.: 700
Satellite-Based Mobility Communication Services
S.I.C.: 4899

Airbus Group N.V.—(Continued)

N.A.I.C.S.: 517410
Bertrand Pivin *(Chm)*

U.S. Subsidiary:

Vizada Americas (4)
2600 Tower Oaks Blvd
Rockville, MD 20852 (100%)
Tel.: (301) 838-7800
Fax: (301) 838-7801
E-Mail: sales.usa@vizada.com
Emp.: 170
Satellite-Based Mobility Communication Services
S.I.C.: 4899
N.A.I.C.S.: 517410
Robert Baker *(CEO)*

Non-U.S. Subsidiaries:

Vizada AS (4)
Lysaker Torg 45
1327 Lysaker, Norway
Tel.: (47) 22 58 20 50
Fax: (47) 22 58 20 01
E-Mail: contactus@vizada.com
Satellite-Based Mobility Communication Services
S.I.C.: 4899
N.A.I.C.S.: 517410

Vizada B.V. (4)
Binckhorstlaan 151-A
2516 BA Hague, Netherlands
Tel.: (31) 70 3001818
Fax: (31) 70 3001870
E-Mail: sales.europe@vizada.com
Telecommunication Services
S.I.C.: 4899
N.A.I.C.S.: 517919

Vizada GmbH (4)
Konrad-Adenauer-Ufer 41-45
50668 Cologne, Germany
Tel.: (49) 221 995 91 0
Fax: (49) 221 995 91 999
E-Mail: sales.europe@vizada.com
Telecommunication Services
S.I.C.: 4899
N.A.I.C.S.: 517919

Vizada Networks Ltd. (4)
Alpha House New Bagamoyo Rd
PO Box 105905
Dar es Salaam, Tanzania
Tel.: (255) 22 276 1341
Fax: (255) 22 276 1345
E-Mail: sales@vizadanetworks.com
Telecommunication Services
S.I.C.: 4899
N.A.I.C.S.: 517919

Vizada RO Hong Kong (4)
35F Central Plaza 18 Harbour Rd
Wanchai, China (Hong Kong)
Tel.: (852) 6386 5490
Fax: (852) 8147 0037
E-Mail: sales.asia@vizada.com
Satellite-Based Mobility Communication Services
S.I.C.: 4899
N.A.I.C.S.: 517410

Vizada RO Singapore (4)
131 Neil Road
088860 Singapore, Singapore
Tel.: (65) 64027003
E-Mail: sales.seasia@vizada.com
Emp.: 30
Satellite Communications
S.I.C.: 4899
N.A.I.C.S.: 517410

U.S. Subsidiary:

Astrium North America, Inc. (3)
16055 Space Center Blvd Ste 480
Houston, TX 77062 DE
Tel.: (281) 461-8409
Fax: (281) 461-9158
Web Site: www.astrium-na.com
Emp.: 21
Engineering Services
S.I.C.: 7373
N.A.I.C.S.: 541512
Ronald Dunklee *(Pres & CEO)*
Michael Kostelnik *(Pres-Americas)*

Subsidiary:

Marlink, Inc. (4)
11777 S Sam Houston Pkwy W Ste C
Houston, TX 77031
Tel.: (713) 910-3352
Fax: (713) 946-0403
E-Mail: houston@marlink.com
Satellite Telecommunication Services
S.I.C.: 4899
N.A.I.C.S.: 517410

Non-U.S. Subsidiaries:

Astrium GmbH (3)
Airbus-Allee 1
28199 Bremen, Germany De
Tel.: (49) 42159300
Fax: (49) 4215394534
Web Site: www.astrium.eads.net
Engineering Services
S.I.C.: 8711
N.A.I.C.S.: 541330

Astrium Ltd. (3)
Anchorage Road
Portsmouth, Hampshire, PO3 5PU, United Kingdom
Tel.: (44) 23 9270 5705
Fax: (44) 1338 773637
Aeronautical Engineering Services
S.I.C.: 8711
N.A.I.C.S.: 541330

Astrium Services GmbH (3)
Willy-Messerschmitt-Str 1
Bayern, Ottobrunn, 85521, Germany
Tel.: (49) 896070
Fax: (49) 8960726481
Satellite Communication Services
S.I.C.: 4899
N.A.I.C.S.: 517410

ASTRIUM Space Transportation GmbH (3)
Airbus-Allee 1
28 199 Bremen, Germany
Tel.: (49) 421 539 0
Fax: (49) 421 539 4534
Web Site: www.eads.com
Engineering Services
S.I.C.: 8711
N.A.I.C.S.: 541330
Bart Reijnen *(Head-Orbital Sys & Space Exploration)*

Computadoras, Redes e Ingenieria SA (3)
C/ Torres Quevedo 9 PTM
Tres Cantos, 28760 Madrid, Spain
Tel.: (34) 918068600
Fax: (34) 918060235
E-Mail: infocrescantos@astrium.eads.net
Web Site: www.crisa.es
Emp.: 400
Aviation Electronic Equipment Mfr
S.I.C.: 3728
N.A.I.C.S.: 336413
Fernando del Ray Garcia *(Mng Dir)*

Dutch Space B.V. (3)
Mendelweg 30
2333 CS Leiden, Zuid-Holland, Netherlands
Tel.: (31) 715245000
Fax: (31) 715245999
E-Mail: info@dutchspace.nl
Web Site: www.dutchspace.nl
Emp.: 250
Aircraft Parts Mfr
S.I.C.: 3728
N.A.I.C.S.: 336413
Rob van Hassel *(Mgr-Sls)*

Infoterra Limited (3)
Europa House Southwood Crescent
Farnborough, GU14 0NL, United Kingdom UK
Tel.: (44) 252362000
Fax: (44) 252375016
Web Site: www.infoterra-global.com
Emp.: 60
Supplying & Processing Remotely Sensed Data & Imagery Acquired from Earth Observation Satellites
S.I.C.: 4899
N.A.I.C.S.: 517410
David Fox *(CEO)*

Subsidiary:

Imass Holding Limited Group (4)
41 Wembley Road
Leicester, LE3 1UT, United Kingdom
Tel.: (44) 191 213 5555
Investment Management Services
S.I.C.: 6282
N.A.I.C.S.: 523920

Non-U.S. Subsidiaries:

Infoterra GmbH (4)
Claude-Dornier-Str Immenstaad Am Bodensee
Immenstaad, Baden-Wurttemberg, 88090, Germany
Tel.: (49) 754589969
Fax: (49) 754581337
Emp.: 80
Information Technology Consulting Services
S.I.C.: 7373
N.A.I.C.S.: 541512
Corinna Prietzsch *(Mgr-Trng)*

Infoterra Magyarorszag Kft. (4)
Malom Udvar Soroksari Ut 48
1095 Budapest, Hungary
Tel.: (36) 1 323 3750
Fax: (36) 1 323 3777
E-Mail: info@infoterra.hu
Web Site: www.eads.com
Emp.: 70
Aircraft Engineering Services
S.I.C.: 8711
N.A.I.C.S.: 541330
Olga Kadar *(Gen Mgr)*

Infoterra Servicios de Geoinformacion SA (4)
Paseo De La Catellana 149 1a
28046 Madrid, Spain
Tel.: (34) 91 449 0149
Fax: (34) 91 571 8414
Geospatial Mapping Services
S.I.C.: 8713
N.A.I.C.S.: 541370

Jena-Optronik GmbH (3)
Prussingstrasse 41
7745 Jena, Germany (100%)
Tel.: (49) 3641200110
Fax: (49) 3641200222
E-Mail: info@jena-optronik.de
Web Site: www.jena-optronik.de
Emp.: 130
Opto-Electronic Instruments & Sensory Equipment Mfr
S.I.C.: 3812
N.A.I.C.S.: 334511
Michael Mertin *(Chm-Exec Bd)*

ND Satcom GmbH (3)
Graf-von-Soden-Strasse
88090 Immenstaad, Baden-Wurttemberg, Germany
Tel.: (49) 75459390
Fax: (49) 75459398780
Web Site: www.ndsatcom.com
Telecommunication Services
S.I.C.: 4899
N.A.I.C.S.: 517410
Julian Bott *(Pres & CEO)*

Subsidiaries:

ND SatCom Defence GmbH (4)
Graf-Von-Soden-Str Immenstaad Am Bodensee
Immenstaad, Baden-Wurttemberg, 88090, Germany
Tel.: (49) 75459390
Fax: (49) 75459398780
Communication Equipment Distr
S.I.C.: 5065
N.A.I.C.S.: 423690
Christopher Morris *(CEO)*
Julian Bott *(Mng Dir)*

ND SatCom Products GmbH (4)
Graf-Von-Soden-Str Immenstaad Am Bodensee
Immenstaad, Baden-Wurttemberg, 88090, Germany
Tel.: (49) 75459390
Fax: (49) 75459398780
Telecommunication Services
S.I.C.: 4899
N.A.I.C.S.: 517919

U.S. Subsidiary:

ND Satcom, Inc. (4)
3801 E Plano Pkwy Ste 200
Plano, TX 75074
Tel.: (214) 231-3400
Fax: (214) 231-3399
Web Site: www.ndsatcom.com
Satellite Communication Equipment Distr
S.I.C.: 5065
N.A.I.C.S.: 423690
David Bowne *(VP)*

Non-U.S. Subsidiary:

ND SatCom Satellite Communication Systems (Beijing) Co. Ltd. (4)
Rm 3110 Tengda Bldg No 168 Xizhimenwai St
Chaoyang District, Beijing, 100004, China
Tel.: (86) 10 6590 6869
Engineering & Telecommunication Services
S.I.C.: 8711
N.A.I.C.S.: 541330

Paradigm Services Ltd. (3)
Portsmouth Site Anchorage Road
Portsmouth, Hampshire, P03 5PU, United Kingdom
Tel.: (44) 1438282828
Fax: (44) 2392705706
Satellite Communication Services
S.I.C.: 4899
N.A.I.C.S.: 517410

Surrey Satellite Technology Ltd. (3)
Tycho House 20 Stephenson Road Surrey Research Park
Guildford, Surrey, GU2 7YE, United Kingdom
Tel.: (44) 1483 803803
Fax: (44) 1483 803804
E-Mail: info@sstl.co.uk
Web Site: www.sstl.co.uk
Satellite Telecommunication Services
S.I.C.: 4899
N.A.I.C.S.: 517410
Martin Sweeting *(Chm)*
John Forrest *(Deputy Chm)*
John Paffett *(CEO)*

Subsidiary:

Surrey Satellite Services Ltd. (4)
20 Stephenson Road
Guildford, GU2 7YE, United Kingdom
Tel.: (44) 1483803803
Fax: (44) 1483803804
Emp.: 500
Satellite Communication Services
S.I.C.: 4899
N.A.I.C.S.: 517919

U.S. Subsidiary:

Surrey Satellite Technology US LLC (4)
8310 S Valley Hwy Fl 3
Englewood, CO 80112
Tel.: (303) 790-0653
Fax: (303) 792-2386
Web Site: www.sst-us.com
Emp.: 50
Satellite Imaging Equipment Sales & Maintenance Services
S.I.C.: 5065
N.A.I.C.S.: 423690
John Paffett *(CEO)*
Doug Gerull *(COO)*

Non-U.S. Subsidiaries:

Construcciones Aeronauticas, S.A. (1)
Avenida Aragon 404
28022 Madrid, Spain
Tel.: (34) 915857000
Telex: 27418 CAS-E
Fax: (34) 5857457
Web Site: www.eavs.es
Emp.: 7,400
Military & Commercial Aircraft Mfr
S.I.C.: 3721
N.A.I.C.S.: 336411
Domingo Urena *(Mng Dir)*

U.S. Subsidiary:

EADS Casa (2)
8100 Airbus Military Dr
Mobile, AL 36608
Tel.: (251) 338-0700
Telex: 090 11 09
Fax: (251) 338-0800
Web Site: www.casa.eads.net
Emp.: 29
Mfr. & Sales of Aircraft

S.I.C.: 5088
N.A.I.C.S.: 423860

EADS Australia Pacific Pty Ltd (1)
Suite 1002 Level 10 1 Macquarie Place
Sydney, NSW, 2000, Australia
Tel.: (61) 2 8864 0500
Fax: (61) 2 8864 0501
Web Site: www.eads.com
Aircraft Parts Mfr
S.I.C.: 3728
N.A.I.C.S.: 336413

EADS Chile (1)
Av Isidora Goyenechea 3356 60
3356 Las Condes, Santiago, Chile
Tel.: (56) 2 333 4333
Fax: (56) 2 333 4777
Web Site: www.eads.com
Engineering Services
S.I.C.: 8711
N.A.I.C.S.: 541330

EADS China (1)
11th Fl Tower B Ping An International Financial Center N 1-3 Xinyuan South Road Chaoyang District, Beijing, 100027, China
Tel.: (86) 10 6461 1266
Fax: (86) 10 6461 0409
Web Site: www.eads.com
Aerospace Engineering Services
S.I.C.: 8711
N.A.I.C.S.: 541330

EADS Deutschland GmbH (1)
Willy Messerschmitt Strasse
85521 Ottobrunn, Germany
Tel.: (49) 896070
Fax: (49) 8960726481
Web Site: www.eads.com
Rev.: $9,859,999,744
Emp.: 50,784
Researcher & Developer of Aerospace Defense Technology & Propulsion Systems
S.I.C.: 3721
N.A.I.C.S.: 336411

Division:

EADS Deutschland GmbH - Cassidian Division (2)
Landshuter Strasse 26
85716 Unterschleissheim, Germany
Tel.: (49) 89 3179 0
E-Mail:
Web Site: www.cassidian.com
Military Aircraft & Space Vehicles, Electronic Components & Support Equipment Designer & Mfr
S.I.C.: 3728
N.A.I.C.S.: 336413

Subsidiaries:

Cassidian Air Systems GmbH. (3)
Rechliner Strasse
85077 Manching, Germany
Tel.: (49) 84 59 81 0
Defense & Security Services
S.I.C.: 8999
N.A.I.C.S.: 541690

Cassidian Communications GmbH (3)
Worthstrasse 85
89077 Ulm, Germany De
Tel.: (49) 7313920
Fax: (49) 7313923393
Web Site: www.cassidian.com
Emp.: 2,000
Researcher & Developer of Aerospace Defense Technology & Propulsion Systems
S.I.C.: 3812
N.A.I.C.S.: 334511

Cassidian Real Estate Manching GmbH & Co. KG (3)
Emil-Riedl-Weg 6
Pullach, 82049, Germany
Tel.: (49) 896070
E-Mail: poststelle-manching@cassidian.com
Emp.: 4,500
Real Estate Development Services
S.I.C.: 6531
N.A.I.C.S.: 531390

Cassidian Real Estate Ulm/ Unterschleissheim GmbH & Co. KG (3)
Landshuter Strasse 26
85716 Unterschleissheim, Germany De
Tel.: (49) 896070
Fax: (49) 8931792219
E-Mail: internet@cassidian.com
Web Site: www.cassidian.com
Industrial Real Estate Investment & Development Services
S.I.C.: 6531
N.A.I.C.S.: 531390
Bernhard Gerwert *(CEO)*

U.S. Subsidiaries:

Cassidian Communications, Inc. (3)
42505 Rio Nedo
Temecula, CA 92590
Tel.: (951) 719-2100
Fax: (951) 296-2727
Toll Free: (800) 491-1734
Web Site: www.cassidiancommunications.com
Sales Range: $10-24.9 Million
Emp.: 240
Critical Call-Center Network Services
S.I.C.: 7389
N.A.I.C.S.: 561421
Robert Freinberg *(Pres & CEO)*
Stephane Legout *(CFO)*
Jeroen de Witte *(CTO & VP-R&D)*
Jeff Wittek *(Chief Strategic Officer)*
Paula Graham *(Gen Counsel)*

Cassidian Optronics USA, Inc. (3)
152 Capcom Ave Ste 104
Wake Forest, NC 27587
Tel.: (919) 556-9340
Fax: (919) 556-1271
E-Mail: usa@cassidian-optronics.com
Web Site: www.cassidian.com
Communication Equipment Mfr
S.I.C.: 3669
N.A.I.C.S.: 334290

Non-U.S. Subsidiaries:

Cassidian Belgium N.V. (3)
Siemenslaan 16
8020 Oostkamp, Belgium
Tel.: (32) 50831811
Fax: (32) 50831803
Aircraft Engineering Services
S.I.C.: 8711
N.A.I.C.S.: 541330

Cassidian Defesa e Seguranca do Brasil Ltda. (3)
Rua Joaquim Floriano 960 - 12 Andar Itaim Bibi
04534 004 Sao Paulo, Brazil
Tel.: (55) 11 3093 9799
Defense & Security Services
S.I.C.: 8999
N.A.I.C.S.: 541690

Subsidiary:

ODEBRECHT-CASSIDIAN DEFESA S.A (4)
Rua Hungria 1240 - 5 Andar Edificio Riverside
Jardim Europa, 01455 000 Sao Paulo, Brazil
Tel.: (55) 11 2144 9501
Aircraft Engineering Services
S.I.C.: 8711
N.A.I.C.S.: 541330

Cassidian Finland Oy (3)
Mattilanniemi 6
40100 Jyvaskyla, Finland
Tel.: (358) 104080000
Fax: (358) 104080004
Web Site: www.cassidian.com
Engineering Services
S.I.C.: 8711
N.A.I.C.S.: 541330

Cassidian Hong Kong Limited (3)
Unit 905-909 Level 9 Tower 1 Millennium City 1 388 Kwun Tong Road
Kwun Tong, Kowloon, China (Hong Kong)
Tel.: (852) 2285 9511
Fax: (852) 2285 9987
Web Site: www.eads.com
Emp.: 18
Engineering Services
S.I.C.: 8711
N.A.I.C.S.: 541330
Angela Chan *(Gen Mgr)*

Cassidian Ltd. (3)
Cassidian Quadrant House Celtic Springs Coedkernew
Newport, Gwent, NP10 8FZ, United Kingdom
Tel.: (44) 1633 713000
Fax: (44) 1633 713333
Web Site: www.cassidian.com
Emp.: 600
Information Technology Consulting Services
S.I.C.: 7373
N.A.I.C.S.: 541512
Michael Stevens *(CEO)*

Cassidian Mexico S.A de C.V. (3)
Insurgentes Sur 1106 Piso 8 Colonia Noche Buena
03720 Mexico, Mexico
Tel.: (52) 55 54 88 83 40
Fax: (52) 55 75 42 07
Web Site: www.cassidian.com
Aerospace Engineering Services
S.I.C.: 8711
N.A.I.C.S.: 541330

Cassidian Optronics (Pty) Ltd. (3)
Nellmapius Drive
Irene, 0046, South Africa
Tel.: (27) 12 674 0215
Fax: (27) 12 674 0198
E-Mail: southafrica@cassidian-optronics.com
Engineering Services
S.I.C.: 8711
N.A.I.C.S.: 541330

Cassidian S.A.S. (3)
Metapole 1 Boulevard Jean Moulin
78990 Elancourt, France
Tel.: (33) 1 61 38 50 00
Fax: (33) 1 61 38 58 10
Web Site: www.cassidian.com
Emp.: 50
Network Security System Mfr
S.I.C.: 3669
N.A.I.C.S.: 334290

Subsidiaries:

Cassidian CyberSecurity SAS (4)
1 boulevard Jean Moulin
78990 Elancourt, France
Tel.: (33) 1 61 38 50 00
Fax: (33) 1 61 38 58 10
Computer Security Services & Solutions
S.I.C.: 7372
N.A.I.C.S.: 511210
Francois Lavaste, *(CEO)*

Subsidiary:

Arkoon Network Security SA (5)
1 Place Verrazzano
69009 Lyon, Cedex 09, France
Tel.: (33) 472530101
Fax: (33) 472531260
E-Mail: contactfi@arkoon.net
Web Site: www.arkoon.net
Sls.: $15,415,073
Assets: $24,486,773
Liabilities: $13,228,852
Net Worth: $11,257,921
Earnings: $2,151,503
Emp.: 90
Fiscal Year-end: 12/31/12
Computer Network Security Services
S.I.C.: 7373
N.A.I.C.S.: 541512
Francois Lavaste *(CEO)*
Pierre-Yves Hentzen *(CFO)*
Pierre Calais *(COO)*
Thierry Rouquet *(Pres-SkyRecon)*

Cassidian Test & Services S.A.S. (4)
5 avenue Guynemer
BP 86
31772 Colomiers, France
Tel.: (33) 5 34 55 40 00
Fax: (33) 5 34 55 40 56
E-Mail: sales.ts@cassidian.com
Web Site: www.eads-ts.com
Emp.: 300
Electronic Equipment Repair & Maintenance Services
S.I.C.: 7699
N.A.I.C.S.: 811219
Patrick Freneuil *(CEO)*

Cassidian Solutions S.A.U. (3)
Barajas Park Edificio A1
28042 Madrid, Spain
Tel.: (34) 917461440
Fax: (34) 917461445
E-Mail: info@cassidian.com
Web Site: www.eadscassidian.com
Emp.: 80
Electronic Components Mfr
S.I.C.: 3679
N.A.I.C.S.: 334418
Jaime Perez-Guerra *(Head-Comm)*

Cassidian SPA (3)
Via Francesco Cangiullo N 24
00142 Rome, Italy
Tel.: (39) 06 59 47 57 00
Fax: (39) 06 59 47 57 16
Defense & Security Services
S.I.C.: 8999
N.A.I.C.S.: 541690

Cassidian Test & Services Ltd. (3)
23-25 Cobham Road Ferndown Industrial Estate
Wimborne Minster, Dorset, BH21 7PE, United Kingdom
Tel.: (44) 1202 872800
Fax: (44) 1202 870 810
E-Mail: infouk@eads-ts.com
Web Site: www.eads-ts.com
Emp.: 35
Test Engineering Services
S.I.C.: 8711
N.A.I.C.S.: 541330
Dave Aspin *(Acct Mgr)*

Subsidiaries:

CTC GmbH (2)
Airbus-Strasse 1
21684 Stade, Germany
Tel.: (49) 4141 938 500
Fax: (49) 4141 938 530
Web Site: www.ctc-gmbh.com
Carbon Fiber Reinforced Polymer Mfr
S.I.C.: 3624
N.A.I.C.S.: 335991
Axel Herrmann *(Co-CEO)*
Jens Walla *(Co-CEO)*
Martin Roehrig *(COO)*
Bianca Bracht *(Member-Mgmt Bd)*
Juergen Kotzelski *(Member-Mgmt Bd)*
Yvonne Luehrs *(Member-Mgmt Bd)*

DADC Luft- und Raumfahrt Beteiligungs AG (2)
Willy-Messerschmitt-Str
85521 Ottobrunn, Germany
Tel.: (49) 89 6070
Defense & Security Services
S.I.C.: 8999
N.A.I.C.S.: 541690

Dornier GmbH (2)
Prinzregentenplatz 11
Munich, Bavaria, 81675, Germany
Tel.: (49) 894194030
Fax: (49) 89419410050
Emp.: 16
Industrial Machinery Mfr
S.I.C.: 3559
N.A.I.C.S.: 333249
Dirk Ruettgers *(CEO)*

Subsidiaries:

Dornier Consulting GmbH (3)
Burogebaude 10
Graf von Soden Strasse, 88090 Immenstaad, Germany De
Tel.: (49) 754585440
Fax: (49) 754585442
E-Mail: info@dornier-consulting.com
Web Site: www.dornier-consulting.com
Emp.: 25
Transportation, Infrastructure & Environmental Engineering Consulting
S.I.C.: 8711
N.A.I.C.S.: 541330
Jurgen R. Koffler *(Pres & CEO)*
Gerd Hubner *(CFO)*
Martin Both *(COO & Head-Transportation & Infrastructure)*

Dornier MedTech Europe GmbH (3)
Argelsrieder Feld 7
D 82234 Wesseling, Germany
Tel.: (49) 81538880
Fax: (49) 8153888800
E-Mail: info@dornier.com
Web Site: www.dornier.com
Medical Instruments

Airbus Group N.V.—(Continued)

S.I.C.: 3841
N.A.I.C.S.: 339112

U.S. Subsidiaries:

American Dornier Machinery Corporation (4)
4101 Performance Rd
Charlotte, NC 28214-8091 NC
Mailing Address:
PO Box 668865
Charlotte, NC 28266-8865
Tel.: (704) 394-6192
Fax: (704) 399-2018
E-Mail: admin@american-dornier.com
Web Site: www.american-dornier.com
Emp.: 30
Weaving Goods & Supplies
S.I.C.: 5949
N.A.I.C.S.: 451130
Peter Dornier *(Pres)*

Dornier Medtech America (4)
1155 Roberts Blvd NW
Kennesaw, GA 30144-3617
Tel.: (770) 426-1315
Fax: (770) 426-6115
E-Mail: info@dornier.com
Web Site: www.dornier.com
Emp.: 68
Distribution of Medical Equipment
S.I.C.: 5047
N.A.I.C.S.: 423450
Brian Walsh *(Gen Mgr)*

wpm Projektmanagement GmbH (3)
Industriestrasse 5
D 70565 Stuttgart, Badin Wirttamberg, Germany
Tel.: (49) 7878260
Fax: (49) 78782626
E-Mail: info.wpm@dornierconsulting.com
Web Site: www.wpmgmbh.com
Emp.: 20
Engineering Services
S.I.C.: 8711
N.A.I.C.S.: 541330
Martin Knoblauch *(Gen Mgr)*

EADS Management Service GmbH (2)
Willy-Messerschmitt-Str 1 Bayern
Ottobrunn, 85521, Germany
Tel.: (49) 894 4490
Business Management Consulting Services
S.I.C.: 8742
N.A.I.C.S.: 541611

EADS Real Estate Premium AEROTEC Augsburg GmbH & Co. KG (2)
Emil-Riedl-Weg 6 I Isartal
Pullach, Bayern, 82049, Germany
Tel.: (49) 82180162893
Real Estate Development Services
S.I.C.: 6531
N.A.I.C.S.: 531390

EADS Real Estate Taufkirchen GmbH & Co. KG (2)
Emil-Riedl-Weg 6 I Isartal
Pullach, Bavaria, 82049, Germany
Tel.: (49) 896070
Real Estate Development Services
S.I.C.: 6531
N.A.I.C.S.: 531390

Elbe-Flugzeugwerke GmbH (2)
PO Box 800137
01101 Dresden, Germany
Tel.: (49) 35188390
Fax: (49) 35188392178
Web Site: www.efw.eads.net
Rev.: $186,586,400
Emp.: 868
Mfr. of Aircraft Parts
S.I.C.: 3728
N.A.I.C.S.: 336413

FLUGZEUG-UNION SUD GMBH (2)
Rudolf-Diesel-Str 26
85521 Ottobrunn, Germany
Tel.: (49) 89 607 25931
Fax: (49) 89 607 25925
E-Mail: fus@eads.com
Web Site: www.fus.de
Emp.: 50
Defense & Aircraft Machinery Mfr
S.I.C.: 3728
N.A.I.C.S.: 336413
Heinz-Jurgen Rommel *(Mng Dir)*

Gesellschaft fur Flugzieldarstellung mbH (2)
Flugplatz Hohn
24806 Hohn, Germany
Tel.: (49) 4335 92 020
Fax: (49) 4335 92 02 15
E-Mail: mail@gfd-hohn.de
Web Site: www.gfd-hohn.de
Air Charter Services
S.I.C.: 4522
N.A.I.C.S.: 481219

Matra Holding GmbH (2)
Berliner Str 56
Kehl, 77694, Germany
Tel.: (49) 7851 74810
Investment Management Services
S.I.C.: 6799
N.A.I.C.S.: 523920

MCG Marlink Comm Gmbh (2)
Johann-Mohr-Weg 2
22763 Hamburg, Germany
Tel.: (49) 40 41 00 48 0
Fax: (49) 40 41 00 48 40
E-Mail: hamburg@marlink.com
Web Site: www.marlink.com
Emp.: 3
Communication Services
S.I.C.: 4899
N.A.I.C.S.: 517919
Frank Reichenbach *(Country Mgr)*

MilSat Services GmbH (2)
Airbus-Allee 1
Bremen, 28199, Germany
Tel.: (49) 8960733668
Fax: (49) 8960722630
E-Mail: info@mss.de
Web Site: www.milsatservices.de
Data Information Management Services
S.I.C.: 8748
N.A.I.C.S.: 541618

Premium AEROTEC GmbH (2)
Haunstetter Str 225
86179 Augsburg, Germany
Tel.: (49) 821 801 0
Fax: (49) 821 801 62090
Web Site: www.premium-aerotec.com
Rev.: $1,717,807,000
Emp.: 8,000
Aircraft Parts Mfr & Distr
S.I.C.: 3728
N.A.I.C.S.: 336413
Kai Horten *(Pres & CEO)*
Helmut Kretschmer *(CFO)*
Michael Colberg *(COO)*
Joachim Naegele *(Head-Programmes & Sls)*
Wolfram Sauer *(Head-HR)*
Ralf Schoenzler *(Head-Procurement & Supply Chain Mgmt)*

Plants:

Premium AEROTEC GmbH - Augsburg Plant (3)
Haunstetter Str 225
86179 Augsburg, Germany
Tel.: (49) 821 801 0
Fax: (49) 821 801 62090
Web Site: www.premium-aerotec.com
Emp.: 4,000
Aircraft Parts Mfr
S.I.C.: 3728
N.A.I.C.S.: 336413

Premium AEROTEC GmbH - Bremen Plant (3)
Airbus-Allee 1
28199 Bremen, Germany
Tel.: (49) 421 538 0
Fax: (49) 421 538 3320
Emp.: 410
Aircraft Parts Mfr
S.I.C.: 3728
N.A.I.C.S.: 336413

Premium AEROTEC GmbH - Nordenham Plant (3)
Bergstr 4
26954 Nordenham, Germany
Tel.: (49) 4731 3620
Fax: (49) 4731 36211
Web Site: www.premium-aerotec.com
Emp.: 3,000
Fuselage Shell Mfr
S.I.C.: 3728
N.A.I.C.S.: 336413
Helmut Farber *(Plant Mgr)*

Premium AEROTEC GmbH - Varel Plant (3)
Riesweg 151-155
26316 Varel, Germany
Tel.: (49) 4451 121 0
Fax: (49) 4451 121 444
Web Site: www.premium-aerotec.com
Emp.: 2,200
Aircraft Parts Mfr
S.I.C.: 3728
N.A.I.C.S.: 336413

Non-U.S. Subsidiary:

Premium AEROTEC SRL (3)
Str Aeroportului Nr 9 Ghimbav
Ghimbav, 507075 Brasov, Romania
Tel.: (40) 368 081 002
Fax: (40) 368 081 010
Web Site: www.premium-aerotec.com
Aircraft Parts Mfr
S.I.C.: 3728
N.A.I.C.S.: 336413

Plant:

Premium AEROTEC SRL - Brasov Plant (4)
Str Aeroportului Nr 9
507075 Ghimbav, Brasov, Romania
Tel.: (40) 368 081 002
Fax: (40) 368 081 010
E-Mail: personal@premium-aerotec.com
Web Site: www.premium-aerotec.com
Emp.: 500
Aircraft Mfr
S.I.C.: 3721
N.A.I.C.S.: 336411
Hans-Joachim von Wurmb *(Mgr)*

RST Rostock System-Technik GmbH (2)
Friedrich-Barnewitz-Strasse 9
18119 Rostock, Germany
Tel.: (49) 381 56 0
Fax: (49) 381 56 202
E-Mail: info@rst-rostock.com
Web Site: www.rst-rostock.com
Emp.: 150
Project Management Consulting Services
S.I.C.: 8748
N.A.I.C.S.: 541618
Ulrich Scheib *(Mng Dir)*

TESAT-Spacecom GmbH & Co. KG (2)
Gerberstrasse 49
71522 Backnang, Germany
Tel.: (49) 71919300
Fax: (49) 9301835
E-Mail: info@tesat.de
Web Site: www.tesat.de
Satellite Communication Services
S.I.C.: 4899
N.A.I.C.S.: 517919
Peter Schlote *(CEO)*
Jochen Huppert *(CFO)*
Guenther Adam *(COO)*
E. Auer *(CTO)*

Subsidiary:

TESAT-Spacecom Geschaftsfuhrung GmbH (3)
Gerberstrasse 49
71522 Backnang, Germany
Tel.: (49) 71919300
Satellite Communication Equipment Mfr
S.I.C.: 3669
N.A.I.C.S.: 334290

EADS France S.A.S. (1)
37 bd de Montmorency
75016 Paris, France
Tel.: (33) 1 42 24 24 24
Fax: (33) 1 42 24 26 19
Web Site: www.eads.com
Aircraft Component Mfr
S.I.C.: 3728
N.A.I.C.S.: 336413
Klaus Richter *(Chief Procurement Officer)*

Subsidiaries:

Aerolia S.A.S. (2)
13 rue Marie`Louise Cedex 3
BP 73216
31027 Toulouse, France
Tel.: (33) 5 81 91 40 00
E-Mail: contact@aerolia.com
Web Site: www.aerolia.com
Aircraft Parts Mfr
S.I.C.: 3728
N.A.I.C.S.: 336413

Plants:

Aerolia S.A.S. - Meaulte Facility (3)
BP 70210
80302 Albert, France
Tel.: (33) 3 22 64 30 00
Web Site: www.aerolia.com
Emp.: 1,350
Aircraft Parts Mfr
S.I.C.: 3728
N.A.I.C.S.: 336413

Aerolia S.A.S. - Saint-Nazaire Facility (3)
Boulevard des Apprentis
BP 50301
44605 Saint Nazaire, France
Tel.: (33) 2 53 48 50 00
E-Mail: presse@aerolia.com
Web Site: www.aerolia.com
Emp.: 650
Aircraft Parts Mfr
S.I.C.: 3728
N.A.I.C.S.: 336413

Aerolia S.A.S. - Toulouse Facility (3)
13 Rue Marie Louise Dissard
BP 73216
31027 Toulouse, France
Tel.: (33) 5 81 91 40 00
Fax: (33) 5 81 91 43 35
E-Mail: aerolia.accueil@airbus.com
Web Site: www.aerolia.com
Emp.: 400
Aircraft Machinery Mfr
S.I.C.: 3728
N.A.I.C.S.: 336413
Sven Kaesser *(Head-Info Sys)*

Aerospatiale Matra ATR (2)
37 Blvd De Montmorency
75781 Paris, France
Tel.: (33) 42242424
Fax: (33) 142242619
Web Site: www.eads.net
Sales Range: $1-9.9 Million
Emp.: 110
Engineering Services
S.I.C.: 8711
N.A.I.C.S.: 541330

Aerospatiale Matra Missiles (2)
37 Blvd De Montmorency
75016 Paris, France
Tel.: (33) 142242424
Fax: (33) 142242619
Web Site: www.eads.net
Sales Range: $1-9.9 Million
Emp.: 350
Engineering Services
S.I.C.: 8711
N.A.I.C.S.: 541330
Louis Gallois *(CEO)*

APSYS (2)
22 Gallieni
92150 Suresnes, France
Tel.: (33) 142045000
Fax: (33) 147729920
E-Mail: ais@apsys.eads.net
Web Site: www.apsys.eads.net
Emp.: 350
Sensor Systems & Instruments for Aircraft
S.I.C.: 3812
N.A.I.C.S.: 334511
Christian Forestier *(CEO)*

Non-U.S. Subsidiaries:

APSYS Risk Engineering UK Limited (3)
Unit 3 Dyce Avenue Kirkhill Estate
Aberdeen, AB21 0LQ, United Kingdom
Tel.: (44) 1224 452 880
E-Mail: info@apsysoilandgas.com
Web Site: www.apsysoilandgas.com
Software Development Services

S.I.C.: 7371
N.A.I.C.S.: 541511
Pierre Secher *(Bus Mgr & Product Mgr)*

APSYS UK (3)
Building 07V New Filton House
Filton, Bristol, BS997AR, United Kingdom
Tel.: (44) 117 936 0201
Aircraft Management Services
S.I.C.: 4581
N.A.I.C.S.: 488190

CILAS SA (2)
8 Avenue Buffon Z I La Source
BP 6319
45063 Orleans, France
Tel.: (33) 2 38 64 15 55
Fax: (33) 2 38 64 40 11
Web Site: www.cilas.com
Emp.: 170
Communication Services
S.I.C.: 4899
N.A.I.C.S.: 517919
Philippe Lucherini *(CEO)*

CIMPA S.A.S. (2)
4 Avenue Didier Daurat
31700 Blagnac, France
Tel.: (33) 5 61 18 60 95
Fax: (33) 5 61 18 64 17
Software Development Services
S.I.C.: 7371
N.A.I.C.S.: 541511

Non-U.S. Subsidiaries:

CIMPA GmbH (3)
Notkestrasse 11
Hamburg, 22607, Germany
Tel.: (49) 40881300
Fax: (49) 4088130599
Software Development Services
S.I.C.: 7371
N.A.I.C.S.: 541511

CIMPA Ltd. (3)
New Filton House 20B Golf Course Lane
Filton, Bristol, BS34 7QW, United Kingdom
Tel.: (44) 117 936 4789
Fax: (44) 117 936 4786
Product Lifecycle Management Services
S.I.C.: 8748
N.A.I.C.S.: 541618

EADS ATR S.A. (2)
5 Avenue Georges Guynemer
Colomiers, Haute-Garonne, 31770, France
Tel.: (33) 562216221
Air Transportation Services
S.I.C.: 4581
N.A.I.C.S.: 488190

EADS Composites Aquitaine (2)
19 Rue De Lacanau
33160 Salaunes, France
Tel.: (33) 556685500
Fax: (33) 556585193
E-Mail: stephanie.garcia@caq.eigs.com
Web Site: www.composites-aquitaine.com
Emp.: 400
Engineering Services
S.I.C.: 8711
N.A.I.C.S.: 541330
Stephanie Gorcia *(Dir-Fin)*

EADS Defense & Security Networks (2)
Rue Jean Pierre Timbaud
BP 26
78063 Bois-d'Arcy, France
Tel.: (33) 134608020
Fax: (33) 134608152
Web Site: www.eads-telecom.com
Telephony & Contact Center Solutions
S.I.C.: 4813
N.A.I.C.S.: 517110

EADS Multicoms (2)
6 Allee Latecoere
P O Box 280
F 78147 Velizy-Villacoublay, France
Tel.: (33) 134584900
Fax: (33) 134584949
Satellite Communications Carrier
S.I.C.: 4899
N.A.I.C.S.: 517410

EADS Seca S.A.S. (2)
1 Boulevard du 19 Mars 1962
BP 50064
95503 Gonesse, France
Tel.: (33) 1 30 18 54 44
Fax: (33) 1 49 34 54 35
Web Site: www.seca.eads.net
Aircraft Parts Mfr
S.I.C.: 3728
N.A.I.C.S.: 336413
Nicolas Thillier *(CFO)*

EADS Sogerma S.A. (2)
Zone Industrielle De Lancien Arsenal
Rochefort, 17300, France
Tel.: (33) 5 46 82 82 82
Fax: (33) 5 46 82 83 76
Web Site: www.sogerma.eads.net
Rev.: $622,374,690
Emp.: 1,200
Aircraft Parts Mfr
S.I.C.: 3728
N.A.I.C.S.: 336413
Jean Michel Leonard *(Pres & CEO)*
Isabelle Esparbes *(CFO)*

Subsidiary:

Composites Aquitaine S.A. (3)
19 route de Lacanau
33160 Salaunes, France
Tel.: (33) 5 56 68 55 00
Fax: (33) 5 56 58 51 93
E-Mail: info@caq.eads.net
Web Site: www.composites-aquitaine.com
Rev.: $64,748,110
Emp.: 530
Aircraft & Defense Machinery Mfr
S.I.C.: 3728
N.A.I.C.S.: 336413
J. M. Leonard *(Pres)*
Christian Valade *(CEO)*

EADS Systems & Defense Electronics (2)
1 Blvd Jean Moulin ZAC de la Clef Saint Pierre
78990 Elancourt, France
Tel.: (33) 161385000
Fax: (33) 161387070
E-Mail: info@eads.com
Web Site: www.eads.com
Emp.: 2,500
Engineering Services
S.I.C.: 8711
N.A.I.C.S.: 541330
Herve Juillou *(Mng Dir)*

EADS Transportation (2)
66 Rte De Verneuel
PO Box 3002
78130 Les Mureaux, Cedex, France
Tel.: (33) 139061234
Fax: (33) 139063915
E-Mail: dir-com@space.eads.net
Web Site: www.space.eads.net
Emp.: 100
S.I.C.: 8711
N.A.I.C.S.: 541330
A. Charmeau *(CEO)*

Fondation d'entreprise EADS (2)
37 Boulevard de Montmorency
75781 Paris, France
Tel.: (33) 1 42 24 24 93
E-Mail: fondation@eads.net
Web Site: www.fondation.eads.com
Emp.: 3
Scientific Research & Development Services
S.I.C.: 8999
N.A.I.C.S.: 541690
Marie-Claire Certiat *(Mng Dir)*

Get Electronique S.A.S. (2)
14 Rue Henri Regnault - Zac De La Chartreuse
81100 Castres, France
Tel.: (33) 563728200
Fax: (33) 563728201
Voltage Regulator Mfr & Distr
S.I.C.: 3679
N.A.I.C.S.: 334419

IFR France S.A.S. (2)
8 Av G Guynemer CS 30324
31773 Colomiers, France
Tel.: (33) 5 62 74 75 00
Fax: (33) 5 62 74 75 01
E-Mail: commercial@ifrskeyes.com
Web Site: www.ifrskeyes.com
Emp.: 80
Aircraft Maintenance Services
S.I.C.: 4581
N.A.I.C.S.: 488119
Patrick Mathieu *(Gen Mgr)*

Matra Espace Participations (2)
121 avenue de Malakoff
75216 Paris, Cedex, France
Tel.: (33) 140691600
Fax: (33) 140698414
E-Mail: ybuyer@lagerdere.fr
Web Site: www.eadf.net
Emp.: 50
Engineering Services
S.I.C.: 8711
N.A.I.C.S.: 541330

Matra Nortel Communications Toulouse (2)
51 avenue Cornobraaeos
F 31700 Toulouse, France
Tel.: (33) 561192021
Fax: (33) 561192067
E-Mail: helene.pregeame@amecspie.com
Web Site: www.amecspie.com
Emp.: 180
Telecommunications Mfr
S.I.C.: 4812
N.A.I.C.S.: 517210
Wannick Razaudet *(Gen Mgr)*

Nucletudes (2)
Avenue du Hoggar
91944 Les Ulis, Cedex, France
Tel.: (33) 160926100
Fax: (33) 160926169
E-Mail: info@nucletudes.com
Web Site: www.nucletudes.com
Emp.: 50
Engineering Services
S.I.C.: 8711
N.A.I.C.S.: 541330
Philippe Lugherini *(Pres)*
Laurent Bouaziz *(CEO)*

SECA (Societe d'Exploitation et de Construction Aeronautiques) (2)
1 Boulevard du 19 Mars 1962
BP 50064
95503 Gonesse, France
Tel.: (33) 130185336
Fax: (33) 130185275
E-Mail: theirry.poulard@seca.eads.net
Web Site: www.seca.eads.net
Sales Range: $125-149.9 Million
Emp.: 300
Aircraft Engines
S.I.C.: 3721
N.A.I.C.S.: 336411
Massimo S. Lattmann *(Chm)*

SMPE Group (2)
12 Qui Henri IV
75004 Paris, France
Tel.: (33) 148046666
Fax: (33) 142778082
E-Mail: marketing@smpe.com
Web Site: www.smpe.com
Emp.: 200
Engineering Services
S.I.C.: 8711
N.A.I.C.S.: 541330

Sodern S.A. (2)
20 Avenue Descartes
BP 23
94451 Limiel Brevannes, France
Tel.: (33) 1 45 95 70 00
Fax: (33) 1 45 95 71 64
E-Mail: optic@sodern.fr
Web Site: www.sodern.fr
Rev.: $77,962,010
Emp.: 330
Attitude Sensor Mfr & Distr
S.I.C.: 3812
N.A.I.C.S.: 334511

Spot Image S.A.S. (2)
5 Rue des Satellites
Toulouse, 31400, France
Tel.: (33) 5 62 19 40 40
Fax: (33) 5 62 19 40 11
Data Information Management Services
S.I.C.: 7389
N.A.I.C.S.: 519190

Technologies Montmorency (2)
37 Blvd De Montmorency
75781 Paris, Cedex, France
Tel.: (33) 142242424
Telex: AISPA X 620 059 F
Fax: (33) 142242619
Web Site: www.dacs.net
Emp.: 90
Mfr. of Airplanes
S.I.C.: 3721
N.A.I.C.S.: 336411
Louis Gallois *(Gen Mgr)*

Unit:

EADS France S.A.S. - Innovation Works (2)
5 Quai Marcel Dassualt
92150 Suresnes, France
Tel.: (33) 1 46 97 30 00
Fax: (33) 1 46 97 35 35
Web Site: www.eads.com
Aerospace Engineering Services
S.I.C.: 8711
N.A.I.C.S.: 541330

EADS Hellas S.A. (1)
124 Kifissias Avenue 15th Floor
11526 Athens, Greece
Tel.: (30) 210 69 83 871
Fax: (30) 210 69 83 870
Web Site: www.eads.com
Emp.: 4
Aerospace Engineering Services
S.I.C.: 8711
N.A.I.C.S.: 541330
Catherine Dalleggio *(Office Mgr)*

EADS India Pvt Ltd (1)
Teri University Campus Plot N 10 Vasant Kunj Institutional Area
New Delhi, 110070, India
Tel.: (91) 114 580 1100
Fax: (91) 114 580 1124
Aerospace Engineering Services
S.I.C.: 8711
N.A.I.C.S.: 541330
Yves Guillaume *(CEO)*

EADS Indonesia (1)
One Pacific Place Building 12th Floor Suite 1207 Sudirman Central
Business District Lot 3-5 Jl, Jakarta, 12190, Indonesia
Tel.: (62) 21 57 97 36 15
Fax: (62) 21 57 97 36 16
Web Site: www.eads.com
Aerospace Engineering Services
S.I.C.: 8711
N.A.I.C.S.: 541330

EADS KOREA CO., LTD. (1)
3rd Fl Volvo Building 130 Hannam-Dong
Yongsan-Gu, Seoul, 140-210, Korea (South)
Tel.: (82) 2 798 49 25
Fax: (82) 2 798 49 27
Web Site: www.eads.com
Aerospace Engineering Services
S.I.C.: 8711
N.A.I.C.S.: 541330

Eads Mexico, S.A. de C.V. (1)
Campos Eliseos No 345 Piso 8 Edificio Omega
Polanco, 11560, Mexico
Tel.: (52) 55 4777 5100
Fax: (52) 55 4777 3274
Web Site: www.eads.com
Aerospace Engineering Services
S.I.C.: 8711
N.A.I.C.S.: 541330

EADS Norway NUF (1)
Aker Brygge Stranden 1A 6th Floor
0250 Oslo, Norway
Tel.: (47) 22 00 95 50
Fax: (47) 22 00 95 51
Web Site: www.eads.com
Aircraft Parts Distr
S.I.C.: 5088
N.A.I.C.S.: 423860

EADS Secure Networks (1)
Centro Direzionale Lombardo
Via Roma 108
20060 Milan, Cassina De' Pecchi, Italy
Tel.: (39) 02 952551
Fax: (39) 02 95255 5802
Web Site: www.eads.com
Telecommunication Installer & Services
S.I.C.: 4812
N.A.I.C.S.: 517210

Eads Singapore Pte Ltd (1)
16 Collyer Quay 08-00
Singapore, 049318, Singapore

Airbus Group N.V.—(Continued)

Tel.: (65) 6325 0380
Fax: (65) 6325 0320
Web Site: www.eads.com
Aerospace Engineering Services
S.I.C.: 8711
N.A.I.C.S.: 541330

EADS South Africa Pty. Ltd. (1)
Ground Fl Block D Cambridge Park 5
Bauhinia Road Entrance Oak Ave
Highveld Techno Park, Centurion, South Africa
Tel.: (27) 12 686 8900
Fax: (27) 12 686 8911
Web Site: www.eads.com
Aerospace Engineering Services
S.I.C.: 8711
N.A.I.C.S.: 541330

EADS TAIWAN CO., LTD (1)
14th Fl Bank Tower Suite 1403 205 Tun Hua North Road
Taipei, 105, Taiwan
Tel.: (886) 2 2712 1594
Fax: (886) 2 2712 1089
Defense & Security Services
S.I.C.: 8999
N.A.I.C.S.: 541690

EADS Thailand (1)
999/9 The Offices At Central World Unit 3607 - 3609 36th Floor
Rama I Road Pathumwan, Bangkok, 10330, Thailand
Tel.: (66) 2 610 4300
Fax: (66) 2 610 4301
Web Site: www.eads.com
Emp.: 20
Aerospace Engineering Services
S.I.C.: 8711
N.A.I.C.S.: 541330

EADS Turkey (1)
Sedat Simavi Sokak No 56/5
Cankaya, 06550 Ankara, Turkey
Tel.: (90) 312 439 89 64
Fax: (90) 312 439 70 07
Web Site: www.eads.com
Aerospace Engineering Services
S.I.C.: 8711
N.A.I.C.S.: 541330

EADS UK Ltd. (1)
111 Strand
London, WC2R 0AG, United Kingdom
Tel.: (44) 20 7845 8400
Fax: (44) 20 7845 8401
E-Mail: reception@eads-uk.com
Web Site: www.eads.com
Emp.: 15,000
Aerospace Engineering Services
S.I.C.: 8711
N.A.I.C.S.: 541330
Geoff Telford *(VP-Corp Bus Dev)*

Subsidiaries:

DMC International Imaging Ltd. (2)
Tycho House 20 Stephenson Road Surrey Research Park
Guildford, GU2 7YE, United Kingdom
Tel.: (44) 1483 804299
Fax: (44) 1483 803804
E-Mail: info@dmcii.com
Web Site: www.dmcii.com
Emp.: 50
Satellite Imaging Equipment Sales & Maintenance Services
S.I.C.: 5065
N.A.I.C.S.: 423690

The Sigma Aerospace Pension Trustee Ltd. (2)
12 Imperial Way
Croydon, Surrey, CR9 4LE, United Kingdom
Tel.: (44) 20 8688 7777
Fax: (44) 20 8688 6603
Pension Trust Management Services
S.I.C.: 6733
N.A.I.C.S.: 525920

Turbo-Union Ltd. (2)
Gyps Patch Ln
PO Box 3
Filton, BS12 7QE, United Kingdom
Tel.: (44) 179791234
Fax: (44) 179797575
Aircraft Parts Mfr
S.I.C.: 3728
N.A.I.C.S.: 336413

European Aeronautic Defense And Space Co. (1)
Chelm Ul 19
00-021 Warsaw, Poland
Tel.: (48) 226270528
Fax: (48) 226270535
E-Mail: eadsbzl@zl.eads.net
Sales Range: $1-9.9 Million
Emp.: 3
Engineering & Construction Services
S.I.C.: 8711
N.A.I.C.S.: 541330
Laurence Barron *(Chm & CEO)*
David R. Oliver, Jr. *(COO & Exec VP)*
Marwan Lahoud *(CMO & Chief Strategy Officer)*

Korean Helicopter Development Support Ltd. (1)
539-14 Yesu-Ri Jeongdong-Myeon
Sacheon, Gyeongsangnam-do, 664 932, Korea (South)
Tel.: (82) 55 855 2323
Fax: (82) 55 855 2324
Web Site: www.eurocopter.com
Rev.: $53,648,434
Emp.: 22
Helicopter Technical Assistance & Support Services
S.I.C.: 4581
N.A.I.C.S.: 488190
Gilles Armstrong *(CEO)*

Mobsat Holding Norway AS (1)
Lysaker Torg 45
Akershus, Lysaker, 1366, Norway
Tel.: (47) 67890000
Investment Management Services
S.I.C.: 6282
N.A.I.C.S.: 523920

OOO EADS (1)
40/2 Ul Bolshaya Ordynka
119017 Moscow, Russia
Tel.: (7) 4957975368
Fax: (7) 4957975366
Emp.: 20
Air Charter Services
S.I.C.: 4522
N.A.I.C.S.: 481219

Space Engineering S.p.A. (1)
Via dei Berio 91
Rome, 00155, Italy IT
Tel.: (39) 06 22595 1
Fax: (39) 06 2280739
Web Site: www.space.it
Emp.: 150
Telecommunications & Radar System Mfr
S.I.C.: 3669
N.A.I.C.S.: 334290
Raimondo Lo Forti *(Pres)*

Non-U.S. Joint Ventures:

ATLAS ELEKTRONIK GmbH (1)
Sebaldsbruecker Heerstr 235
28309 Bremen, Germany De
Tel.: (49) 421 457 02
Fax: (49) 421 457 3699
E-Mail: info@atlas-elektronik.com
Web Site: www.atlas-elektronik.com
Sales Range: $450-499.9 Million
Emp.: 1,800
Maritime Combat System Developer & Mfr
S.I.C.: 3812
N.A.I.C.S.: 334511
Alexander Kocherscheidt *(Mng Dir)*

Subsidiaries:

ATLAS HYDROGRAPHIC GmbH (2)
Kurfuerstenallee 130
28211 Bremen, Germany
Tel.: (49) 4214573205
Fax: (49) 4214573449
Web Site: www.atlashydro.atlas-elektronik.com
Emp.: 25
Hydrographic System Designer & Mfr
S.I.C.: 3812
N.A.I.C.S.: 334511
Emil Klann *(Mng Dir)*

Hagenuk Marinekommunikation GmbH (2)
Hamburger Chaussee 25
24220 Flintbeck, Germany
Tel.: (49) 4347714142
Fax: (49) 4347714110
E-Mail: info@hmk.atlas-elektronik.com
Web Site: www.hmk.atlas-elektronik.com
Marine Integrated Communication System Mfr
S.I.C.: 3663
N.A.I.C.S.: 334220
Georg Marschall *(Gen Mgr)*

U.S. Subsidiary:

ATLAS North America, LLC (2)
208 Golden Oak Ct Ste 415
Virginia Beach, VA 23452
Tel.: (757) 463-0670
Fax: (757) 463-0673
E-Mail: stan.degeus@na-atlas.com
Web Site: www.na.atlas-elektronik.com
Defense Products & Vehicles Distr
S.I.C.: 3812
N.A.I.C.S.: 334511
Adrian J. Culbreath *(VP-Bus Ops)*

Non-U.S. Subsidiaries:

ATLAS ELEKTRONIK CANADA Ltd (2)
Suite 2202D-4464 Markham Street
Victoria, BC, V8Z 7X8, Canada
Tel.: (778) 224-1010
E-Mail: sales@canada.atlas-elektronik.com
Web Site: www.canada.atlas-elektronik.com
Command & Control, Sonar & Unmanned Vehicles Mfr, Sales & Support Services
S.I.C.: 3769
N.A.I.C.S.: 336419
Kristy Seiler, *(Office Mgr)*

ATLAS ELEKTRONIK Finland Oy (2)
Hiomotie 32
00380 Helsinki, Finland
Tel.: (358) 20 7790 180
E-Mail: jaakko.savisaari@atlas-elektronik.com
Web Site: www.finland.atlas-elektronik.com
Combat & Mission Management Systems for Ships
S.I.C.: 7373
N.A.I.C.S.: 541512
Jaakko Savisaari *(CEO)*

ATLAS ELEKTRONIK UK Ltd. (2)
Meadows Road
Queensway Meadows Ind Est, Newport, South Wales, NP19 4SS, United Kingdom
Tel.: (44) 1633292025
Fax: (44) 1633713333
E-Mail: enquiries@uk.atlas-elektronik.com
Web Site: www.uk.atlas-elektronik.com
Emp.: 200
Maritime Defense Electronic System Designer & Mfr
S.I.C.: 3812
N.A.I.C.S.: 334511
Bob Waters *(Mng Dir)*

ATLAS MARIDAN Aps (2)
Agern Alle 3
2970 Horsholm, Denmark
Tel.: (45) 45764050
Fax: (45) 45764051
E-Mail: info@atlasmaridan.com
Web Site: www.atlasmaridan.com
Emp.: 7
Autonomous Underwater Vehicle Designer & Mfr
S.I.C.: 3812
N.A.I.C.S.: 334511
Allan Bertelsen *(Mng Dir)*

ATLAS NAVAL SYSTEMS MALAYSIA SDN BHD (2)
18 Lumut Waterfront Villa
Jalan Titi Panjang, 32200 Perak, Malaysia
Tel.: (60) 56804330
Fax: (60) 56804332
E-Mail: atlasmal@streamyx.com
Web Site: www.atlashydro.atlas-elektronik.com
Maritime Combat System Developer & Mfr
S.I.C.: 3812
N.A.I.C.S.: 334511
Albin Fleckenstein *(Mng Dir)*

SONARTECH ATLAS Pty. Ltd. (2)
Level 2 6-10 Talavera Rd
Macquarie, NSW, 2113, Australia
Tel.: (61) 294373499
Fax: (61) 298886144
E-Mail: enquiries@sonartech.com.au
Web Site: www.sonartech.atlas-elektronik.com
Emp.: 40
Sonar System Designer & Mfr
S.I.C.: 3812
N.A.I.C.S.: 334511
Mark Baker *(Mng Dir)*

Avions de Transport Regional (1)
1 Allee Pierre Nadot
31712 Blagnac, Cedex, France
Tel.: (33) 562216221
Fax: (33) 562216636
E-Mail: accueil@atr.fr
Web Site: www.atraircraft.com
Sales Range: $1-4.9 Billion
Emp.: 1,000
Turboprop Commuter Aircraft Mfr Import Export
S.I.C.: 3721
N.A.I.C.S.: 336411
Meyer Stephene *(CEO)*
Eric Baravian *(CFO & Sr VP)*
Sylvie Kande de Beaupuy *(Gen Counsel)*
Aldo Mucciardi *(Sec & Sr VP)*
Lilian Brayle *(Sr VP-Product Support & Svcs)*
Thierry Casale *(Sr VP-Ops)*
Jean-Pierre Cousserans *(Sr VP-Customer Svcs)*
Jacques Desbarats *(Sr VP-Comml)*
John Moore *(Sr VP-Comml)*
Carmine Orsi *(Sr VP-Technical)*

Eurockot Launch Services GmbH (1)
Flughafenallee 26
28199 Bremen, Germany De
Mailing Address:
PO Box 28 61 46
28361 Bremen, Germany
Tel.: (49) 4215396501
Fax: (49) 4215396500
E-Mail: eurockot@astrium.eads.net
Web Site: www.eurockot.com
Emp.: 10
Commercial Rocket Launch Services
S.I.C.: 9661
N.A.I.C.S.: 927110
Matthias Oehm *(CEO)*
Kathrin Kappes *(Sec)*

MBDA Holdings S.A.S. (1)
37 Boulevard de Montmorency
75016 Paris, France FR
Tel.: (33) 142242424
Fax: (33) 145245414
Web Site: www.mbda-systems.com
Holding Company; Guided Missiles & Missle Systems Mfr
S.I.C.: 6719
N.A.I.C.S.: 551112
Antoine Bouvier *(CEO)*
Peter Bols *(CFO)*
Antonio Perfetti *(COO)*

Subsidiary:

MBDA France SAS (2)
1 Ave Reaumer
92358 Le Plessis-Robinson, Cedex, France FR
Tel.: (33) 171541000
Telex: AISPA X 250 881 F
Fax: (33) 171540190
Web Site: www.mbda.fr
Emp.: 100
Missiles & Missile Systems
S.I.C.: 3724
N.A.I.C.S.: 336412

Joint Ventures:

EUROSAM (3)
Centre d'affaires de la Boursidiere Batiment Kerguelen
92357 Le Plessis-Robinson, France FR
Tel.: (33) 1 4187 1416
Fax: (33) 1 4187 1442
Web Site: www.eurosam.com
Emp.: 100
Missile Defense Systems Mfr Import
S.I.C.: 3761
N.A.I.C.S.: 336414

ROXEL S.A.S. (3)
La Boursidi Immeuble Jura
92357 Le Plessis-Robinson, France

Tel.: (33) 141 07 82 95
Fax: (33) 146 30 22 37
Web Site: www.roxelgroup.com
Propulsion System Mfr
S.I.C.: 3764
N.A.I.C.S.: 336415
David Quancard *(CEO)*

Subsidiary:

ROXEL France (4)
Route D Ardon
45240 La Ferte-Saint-Aubin, France FR
Tel.: (33) 238516666
Fax: (33) 238516633
Emp.: 300
Rocket Propulsion Systems Mfr
S.I.C.: 3621
N.A.I.C.S.: 335312

Non-U.S. Subsidiaries:

MBDA Deutschland GmbH (2)
Hagenauer Forst 27
Schrobenhausen, Germany
Tel.: (49) 8252 99 0
Fax: (49) 8252 99 6120
Aircraft Machinery Mfr
S.I.C.: 3728
N.A.I.C.S.: 336413
Thomas Homberg *(Mng Dir)*

Subsidiaries:

Bayern-Chemie Gesellschaft fur Flugchemische Antriebe mbH (3)
Liebigstr 17
PO Box 11
D 84544 Aschau, Germany
Tel.: (49) 86386010
Fax: (49) 8638601399
E-Mail: info-de@mbda-systems.de
Web Site: www.bayernchemie.de
Rev.: $71,900,000
Emp.: 160
Rocket Propulsion Systems Mfr
S.I.C.: 3764
N.A.I.C.S.: 336415
Stoerchlee Ulrich *(CEO)*

TDW-Gesellschaft fur verteidigungstechnische Wirksysteme GmbH (3)
Hagenauer Forst 27
86529 Schrobenhausen, Germany
Tel.: (49) 8252 99 0
Fax: (49) 8252 99 6120
E-Mail: empfang-sob@mbda-systems.com
Web Site: www.eads.com
Emp.: 1,000
Aircraft Parts Mfr
S.I.C.: 3728
N.A.I.C.S.: 336413
Thomas Homberg *(Gen Mgr)*

MBDA Italia SpA (2)
Via Carciano 4-50/60-70
00131 Rome, Italy
Tel.: (39) 06 87711
Web Site: www.mbda-systems.com
Missile Systems Developer & Mfr
S.I.C.: 3761
N.A.I.C.S.: 336414

MBDA UK Ltd. (2)
Six Hills Way
Stevenage, SG1 2DA, United Kingdom UK
Tel.: (44) 1438312422
Fax: (44) 1438753377
Web Site: www.mbda.co.uk
Emp.: 2,000
Missile Mfr
S.I.C.: 3761
N.A.I.C.S.: 336414
Steve Wadey *(Mng Dir)*

Branch:

MBDA UK (3)
11 Strand
London, WC2N 5HR, United Kingdom
Tel.: (44) 1714516000
Fax: (44) 1714516001
Web Site: www.mbda.co.uk
Missile Mfr
S.I.C.: 3761
N.A.I.C.S.: 336414

Nahuelsat S.A. (1)
Bouchard 1680 12th Fl
Capital Federal, 1106 Buenos Aires, Argentina
Tel.: (54) 158112600
Fax: (54) 1158112688
E-Mail: info@nahuelsat.com.ar
Web Site: www.nahuelsat.com.ar
Emp.: 50
Communications Equipment Mfr
S.I.C.: 3669
N.A.I.C.S.: 334290
Ruben Carrillo *(Mng Dir)*
Diego Santos *(Mng Dir)*

Panavia Aircraft GmbH (1)
Am Soeldnermoos 17
85399 Hallbergmoos, Germany De
Tel.: (49) 811800
Telex: 529 825
Fax: (49) 801427
E-Mail: info@panavia.de
Web Site: www.panavia.de
Emp.: 100
Military Aircraft Designer & Mfr
S.I.C.: 3721
N.A.I.C.S.: 336411

Starsem (1)
2 Rue Francois Truffaut
91042 Evry, France
Tel.: (33) 169870110
Fax: (33) 160783199
E-Mail: communication@starsem.com
Web Site: www.starsem.com
Emp.: 12
Commercial Rocket Launch Services
S.I.C.: 9661
N.A.I.C.S.: 927110
Stephane Israel *(Chm & CEO)*
Victor Nikolaev *(COO)*

AIRCRAFT APPLIANCES & EQUIPMENT LIMITED

150 East Drive
Brampton, ON, L6T 1C1, Canada
Tel.: (905) 791-1666
Fax: (905) 791-1863
E-Mail: info@aaeltd.com
Web Site: www.aaeltd.com
Year Founded: 1949
Rev.: $17,097,570
Emp.: 70
Business Description:
Aircraft Equipment Mfr
S.I.C.: 3728
N.A.I.C.S.: 336413
Personnel:
Bryan Dawson *(Pres)*

AIRDRIE CHRYSLER DODGE JEEP

139 East Lake Crescent
Airdrie, AB, T4A 2H7, Canada
Tel.: (403) 948-2600
Fax: (403) 948-6201
Toll Free: (888) 313-9548
E-Mail: service@airdriechrysler.com
Web Site: www.airdriechrysler.com
Year Founded: 1984
Rev.: $62,484,437
Emp.: 120
Business Description:
New & Used Car Dealers
S.I.C.: 5511
N.A.I.C.S.: 441110
Personnel:
Larry McCook *(Owner)*
Brad Styner *(Principal)*
Zia Khan *(Treas & Sec)*

AIREA PLC

Victoria Mills The Green
Ossett, W Yorkshire, WF5 0AN, United Kingdom
Tel.: (44) 1924262525
Fax: (44) 1924280033
E-Mail: info@aireaplc.co.uk
Web Site: www.aireaplc.co.uk
AIEA—(LSE)
Rev.: $39,559,635
Assets: $37,675,542
Liabilities: $17,607,504
Net Worth: $20,068,038
Earnings: $699,625
Emp.: 221
Fiscal Year-end: 06/30/13
Business Description:
Carpet & Rug Mills
S.I.C.: 2299
N.A.I.C.S.: 313110
Personnel:
Neil Rylance *(CEO & Mng Dir)*
Roger Salt *(Sec & Dir-Fin)*
Board of Directors:
Martin Toogood
Neil Rylance
Roger Salt
Legal Counsel:
Hammonds
2 Park Lane
Leeds, United Kingdom

Eversheds
Cloth Hall Court Infirmary Street
Leeds, LS1 2JB, United Kingdom

Subsidiaries:

Burmatex Limited (1)
Victoria Mills The Green
Ossett, West Yorkshire, WF5 0AN, United Kingdom
Tel.: (44) 1924262525
Fax: (44) 1924280033
E-Mail: projects@burmatex.co.uk
Web Site: www.burmatex.co.uk
Emp.: 200
Carpet Designing & Manufacturing Services
S.I.C.: 2499
N.A.I.C.S.: 321999
Neil Rylance *(Mng Dir)*

Non-U.S. Subsidiary:

Burmatex Sp. z.o.o. (2)
Ul Diamentowa 7
62 500 Konin, Greater Poland, Poland
Tel.: (48) 609611211
Fax: (48) 632444691
E-Mail: tsb@burmatex-europe.com
Web Site: www.burmatex.pl
Carpet Mfr
S.I.C.: 2499
N.A.I.C.S.: 321999

Ryalux Carpets Limited (1)
Mossfield Mill Chesham Fold Rd
Bury, Lancashire, BL9 6JZ, United Kingdom
Tel.: (44) 1617623030
Fax: (44) 161 762 3031
E-Mail: info@ryalux.co.uk
Web Site: www.ryalux.com
Carpet Mfr & Distr
S.I.C.: 2273
N.A.I.C.S.: 314110
Carl Quail *(Mgr-Sls)*

AIRESIS S.A.

Chemin du Pierrier 1
CH 1815 Clarens, Montreux, Switzerland
Tel.: (41) 219898250
Fax: (41) 219898259
E-Mail: info@airesis.com
Web Site: www.airesis.com
Year Founded: 1814
AIRE—(SWX)
Sls.: $205,445,324
Assets: $162,134,371
Liabilities: $95,639,625
Net Worth: $66,494,747
Earnings: $6,880,665
Fiscal Year-end: 12/31/12
Business Description:
Holding Company; Sporting Equipment Retailer
S.I.C.: 5941
N.A.I.C.S.: 451110
Personnel:
Philippe Erard *(Chm)*
Philippe Crottaz *(Vice Chm)*
Marc-Henri Beausire *(CEO)*
Yves Corthesy *(CFO)*
Board of Directors:
Philippe Erard
Marc-Henri Beausire
Philippe Crottaz
Urs Linsi
Gilles Robert-Nicoud

Subsidiary:

A2I SA (1)
Chemin du Pierrier 1
CH-1815 Clarens, Montreux, Switzerland (100%)
Tel.: (41) 219898250
Fax: (41) 219898259
Web Site: www.airesis.com
Sports Mfr & Distr
S.I.C.: 3949
N.A.I.C.S.: 339920
Marc-Henri Beausire *(CEO)*

AIREX INC.

5 Sandhill Court Unit C
Brampton, ON, L6T 5J5, Canada
Tel.: (905) 790-8667
Fax: (905) 790-1133
Toll Free: (888) 824-7398
E-Mail: info@airex.ca
Web Site: www.airex.ca
Year Founded: 1982
Rev.: $17,000,000
Emp.: 150
Business Description:
Air Conditioning Products Mfr
S.I.C.: 3585
N.A.I.C.S.: 333415
Personnel:
Enzo Iantorno *(Pres)*

AIRIQ, INC.

1815 Ironstone Manor Unit 10
Pickering, ON, L1W 3W9, Canada
Tel.: (905) 831-6444
Fax: (905) 831-0567
Toll Free: (888) 606-6444
E-Mail: info@airiq.com
Web Site: www.airiq.com
IQ.H—(TSXV)
Rev.: $2,310,102
Assets: $1,082,488
Liabilities: $1,417,473
Net Worth: ($334,985)
Earnings: ($434,387)
Emp.: 32
Fiscal Year-end: 03/31/13
Business Description:
Wireless Location-Based Fleet Management Services
S.I.C.: 7389
N.A.I.C.S.: 561990
Personnel:
Vernon F. Lobo *(Chm)*
Michael J. Robb *(CFO)*
Board of Directors:
Vernon F. Lobo
George Christopoulos
Emmanuel Mounouchos
Legal Counsel:
Owens, Wright LLP
20 Holly Street Suite 300
Toronto, ON, Canada
Transfer Agent:
Computershare Investor Services
100 University Ave 8th Fl
Toronto, ON, Canada

AIRKENYA AVIATION LTD.

Wilson Airport
PO Box 30357
100 Nairobi, Kenya
Tel.: (254) 203916000
Fax: (254) 206002951
E-Mail: resvns@airkenya.com
Web Site: www.airkenya.com
Year Founded: 1985
Emp.: 160

AirKenya Aviation Ltd.—(Continued)

Business Description:
Scheduled Air Transportation Services
S.I.C.: 4512
N.A.I.C.S.: 481111
Personnel:
Dino M. Bisleti *(Gen Mgr-Flight Ops & Mktg)*

AIRKIT S.A.
Avenue Loopold III 25
7134 Binche, Belgium
Tel.: (32) 64 27 32 21
Fax: (32) 64 27 32 29
E-Mail: fmattioli@airkit.be
Web Site: www.airkit.be
MLAIR—(EUR)
Sales Range: $1-9.9 Million
Business Description:
Industrial Automation, Home Automation Systems & Heating Pumps Mfr & Sales
S.I.C.: 3823
N.A.I.C.S.: 334513
Personnel:
Adriano Costantini *(Chm & CEO)*

AIRMATE (CAYMAN) INTERNATIONAL CO. LIMITED
19 Shin Chung Road
An Ping Industrial District, T'ainan, Taiwan
Tel.: (886) 755 27655988
Fax: (886) 755 27643640
Web Site: www.airmate-china.com
1626—(TAI)
Sls.: $392,140,459
Fiscal Year-end: 12/31/12
Business Description:
Electrical Fans, Heaters, Cookers & Other Home Appliances Mfr
S.I.C.: 3639
N.A.I.C.S.: 335228
Personnel:
Li Ping Cheng *(Chm)*

AIRMEDIA GROUP INC.
17/F Sky Plaza No 46
Dongzhimenwai Street
Dongcheng District, Beijing, 100027, China
Tel.: (86) 10 8438 6868
Fax: (86) 10 8460 8658
Web Site: www.airmedia.net.cn
AMCN—(NASDAQ)
Rev.: $292,965,000
Assets: $343,867,000
Liabilities: $104,432,000
Net Worth: $239,435,000
Earnings: ($32,241,000)
Emp.: 795
Fiscal Year-end: 12/31/12
Business Description:
China Air Travel Media Network
S.I.C.: 4729
N.A.I.C.S.: 561599
Personnel:
Herman Man Guo *(Chm & CEO)*
James Zhonghua Feng *(Pres)*
Henry Hin-hung Ho *(CFO)*
Board of Directors:
Herman Man Guo
Junjie Ding
James Zhonghua Feng
Shichong Shan
Songzuo Xiang
Conor Chia-hung Yang

AIROIL FLAREGAS PVT. LTD.
204 Sumer Kendra Pandurang
Budhkar Marg Worli
Mumbai, 400 018, India
Tel.: (91) 2224965031
Fax: (91) 2224961073
E-Mail: corphq@hs.co.in
Web Site: www.airoilflaregas.com
Year Founded: 1984
Sales Range: $75-99.9 Million
Emp.: 50
Business Description:
Industrial Combustion Equipment Developer & Mfr
S.I.C.: 3567
N.A.I.C.S.: 333994
Personnel:
Hasu Sheth *(Mng Dir)*

AIRPARK LTD.
2nd floor Venture Castle 82-18
Nonhyun-dong
Gangnam-gu, Seoul, 135-818, Korea (South)
Tel.: (82) 2 6917 5300
Fax: (82) 2 6917 5301
E-Mail: lrmaster@lgairpark.com
Web Site: www.lgairpark.com
060900—(KRS)
Sales Range: $25-49.9 Million
Business Description:
Air Conditioning System Installation Services
S.I.C.: 1711
N.A.I.C.S.: 238220
Personnel:
Yeong Jun Hong *(CEO)*

AIRPORTS OF THAILAND PUBLIC COMPANY LIMITED
333 Cherdwutugard Road Srikan Don Mueang
Bangkok, 10210, Thailand
Tel.: (66) 2535 1111
Fax: (66) 2535 4061
E-Mail: aotpr@airportthai.co.th
Web Site: www.airportthai.co.th
AOT—(OTC THA)
Rev.: $1,029,787,652
Assets: $4,756,867,435
Liabilities: $2,289,993,791
Net Worth: $2,466,873,645
Earnings: $206,305,825
Emp.: 4,940
Fiscal Year-end: 09/30/12
Business Description:
International Airport Services
S.I.C.: 4581
N.A.I.C.S.: 488119
Personnel:
Sita Divari *(Chm)*
Thanapich Mulapruk *(Vice Chm)*
Araya Ngampramuan *(Vice Chm)*
Pongsak Semson *(Acting Pres)*
Shanalai Chayakul *(Sec)*
Supaporn Burapakusolsri *(Sr Exec VP-Plng & Fin)*
Duangchai Condee *(Sr Exec VP-Bus & Mktg Dev)*
Vilaiwan Nadvilai *(Acting Sr Exec VP-Bus Dev & Mktg)*
Chaowalit Paka-Ariya *(Sr Exec VP-Reg Airports)*
Somchai Sawasdeepon *(Sr Exec VP-Engrg & Construction)*
Sasisubha Sukontasap *(Sr Exec VP-Admin)*
Rawewan Netrakavesna *(Exec VP & Gen Mgr-Chiang Mai International Airport)*
Noranit Pholkanond *(Exec VP & Gen Mgr-Hat Yai International Airport)*
Prathuang Sornkhom *(Exec VP & Gen Mgr-Phuket International Airport)*
Paranee Vatanotai *(Exec VP & Gen Mgr-Don Mueang International Airport)*
Ittipol Boonaree *(Exec VP & Deputy Gen Mgr-Ops-Suvarnabhumi Airport)*
Suwanna Natpracha *(Exec VP & Deputy Gen Mgr-Admin-Suvarnabhumi Airport)*
Suk Puangthum *(Exec VP & Deputy Gen Mgr-Maintenance & IT-Suvarnabhumi Airport)*
Angkana Thantavivattananont *(Exec VP & Deputy Gen Mgr-Comml-Suvarnabhumi Airport)*
Lukchai Chaleoyprach *(Exec VP-Aerodrome Standards & Occupational Health Line)*
Sirote Duangratana *(Exec VP-Bus & Mktg Dev)*
Montri Mongkoldaow *(Exec VP-Admin)*
Noppadon Mongkonsin *(Exec VP-Plng & Fin)*
Sayan Sonchareon *(Exec VP-IT & Comm Tech)*
Amarit Thongsiriprapa *(Exec VP-Engrg & Construction)*
Naris Yoadchan *(Exec VP-Reg Airports)*
Board of Directors:
Sita Divari
Thanin Angsuwarangsi
Wutisak Lapcharoensap
Thanapich Mulapruk
Araya Ngampramuan
Pornthip Paksanont
Norahuch Ployyai
Krisna Polananta
Somchai Poolsavasdi
Montien Prateepavanich
Sutthirat Rattanachot
Pongsak Semson
Chantima Sirisaengtaksin
Arkhom Termpittayapaisith
Wattana Tiengkul

AIRPORTS VANUATU LTD
Bauerfield Airport
PO Box 131
Port-Vila, Vanuatu
Tel.: (678) 25111
Fax: (678) 25532
E-Mail: info@vli.aero
Web Site: www.airports.vu
Year Founded: 2000
Emp.: 200
Business Description:
Airport Management & Operation
S.I.C.: 4581
N.A.I.C.S.: 488119
Personnel:
Peter Bong *(CEO)*

AIRSHIP & BALLOON COMPANY LTD.
82 Henbury Road
Bristol, BS10 7AA, United Kingdom
Tel.: (44) 845 643 6016
Fax: (44) 845 643 1316
E-Mail: info@airshipandballoon.com
Web Site: www.airshipandballoon.com
Emp.: 30
Business Description:
Hot Air Balloon Operator
S.I.C.: 7319
N.A.I.C.S.: 541890
Personnel:
Nick Langley *(Mng Dir)*

AIRSPRUNG GROUP PLC
Canal Road
Trowbridge, Wiltshire, BA14 8RQ, United Kingdom
Tel.: (44) 1225 754411
Fax: (44) 1225 777423
E-Mail: group@airsprung-group.co.uk
Web Site: www.airsprung-group.co.uk
APG—(AIM LSE)
Sales Range: $50-74.9 Million
Emp.: 578
Business Description:
Mfr of Mattresses, Beds & Upholstered Furniture
S.I.C.: 2515
N.A.I.C.S.: 337910
Personnel:
Stuart Randolph Lyons *(Chm)*
Tony Lisanti *(CEO)*
Tean Elizabeth Dallaway *(Sec & Dir-Fin)*
Board of Directors:
Stuart Randolph Lyons
Tean Elizabeth Dallaway
Tony Lisanti
John David Newman
Stephen E. Yates
Subsidiaries:

Airsprung Furniture Limited (1)
Canal Road
Trowbridge, Wiltshire, BA14 8RQ, United Kingdom
Tel.: (44) 1225754411
Fax: (44) 1225777423
E-Mail: sales@airsprung.com
Web Site: www.airsprung.com
Emp.: 500
Bed & Upholstered Furniture Mfr
S.I.C.: 2514
N.A.I.C.S.: 337124

Collins & Hayes Furniture Ltd. (1)
Menzies Road
Ponswood, Saint Leonards, E Sussex, TN38 9XF, United Kingdom
Tel.: (44) 1424720027
Fax: (44) 1424720270
E-Mail: sales@collinsandhayes.com
Web Site: www.collinsandhayes.com
Sales Range: $10-24.9 Million
Emp.: 160
Upholstered Furniture Mfr
S.I.C.: 2512
N.A.I.C.S.: 337121
Martin Huggins *(Mng Dir)*

AIRSYS COMMUNICATIONS TECHNOLOGY LIMITED
35 City Industrial Park Southern Road
Southampton, SO15 1HG, United Kingdom
Tel.: (44) 2380718700
Fax: (44) 2380718770
E-Mail: sales@airsys.co.uk
Web Site: www.airsys.co.uk
Year Founded: 1992
Rev.: $17,734,558
Emp.: 20
Business Description:
Communication Devices Distr
S.I.C.: 4812
N.A.I.C.S.: 517210
Personnel:
Russell Daniels *(Controller-Fin)*

AIRTEC PNEUMATIC GMBH
Westerbachstr 7
61476 Kronberg, Germany
Tel.: (49) 6173956200
Fax: (49) 6173956249
E-Mail: info@airtec.de
Web Site: www.airtec.de
Year Founded: 1975
Rev.: $25,998,559
Emp.: 178
Business Description:
Machinery Products Mfr
S.I.C.: 3589
N.A.I.C.S.: 333318
Personnel:
Dirk C. Dammann *(Owner & CEO)*

AIRTECH JAPAN, LTD.
14-9 1chome Iriya
Taito-ku, Tokyo, 110-8686, Japan

Tel.: (81) 3 3872 6611
Fax: (81) 3 3872 6615
E-Mail: info@airtech.co.jp
Web Site: www.airtech.co.jp
Year Founded: 1973
6291—(TKS)

Business Description:
Air Purification Equipment Mfr
S.I.C.: 3564
N.A.I.C.S.: 333413

Personnel:
Shinya Hirasawa *(Pres)*

Board of Directors:
Toru Kawamata
Kazuyoshi Ooshige
Hirokazu Watanabe
Tsutomu Yamanishi

AIRTEX MANUFACTURING PARTNERSHIP

1401 Hastings Cr SE
Calgary, AB, T2G 4C8, Canada
Tel.: (403) 287-2590
Fax: (403) 243-5059
E-Mail: admin@engineeredair.com
Web Site: www.engineeredair.com
Year Founded: 1964
Sales Range: $100-124.9 Million
Emp.: 1,000

Business Description:
Heating Equipment Mfr
S.I.C.: 3433
N.A.I.C.S.: 333414

Personnel:
Don Taylor *(CEO)*

AIRWAIR INTERNATIONAL LTD./R. GRIGGS GROUP LTD.

(See Under R. Griggs Group Limited)

A.I.S. AG

Havelpassage 2
Hennigsdorf, 16761 Berlin, Germany
Tel.: (49) 6201 393895
Fax: (49) 6201 393896
E-Mail: info@ais-ag.eu
Web Site: www.ais-ag.info
LUM—(DEU)
Sales Range: $1-9.9 Million

Business Description:
Waste Management & Electric Power Generation Services
S.I.C.: 9511
N.A.I.C.S.: 924110

Personnel:
Klaus Willmann *(Chm-Supervisory Bd)*
Johan Charles Bendien *(Member-Mgmt Bd)*

Supervisory Board of Directors:
Klaus Willmann
Markus Neth
Juergen Tiedtke

AISAN INDUSTRY CO., LTD.

1-1-1 Kyowa-cho
Obu, Aichi, 474-8588, Japan
Tel.: (81) 562471131
Fax: (81) 562486333
E-Mail: post@aisan-ind.co.jp
Web Site: www.aisan-ind.co.jp
Year Founded: 1938
7283—(TKS)
Sls.: $1,873,278,000
Assets: $1,636,833,000
Liabilities: $966,383,000
Net Worth: $670,450,000
Earnings: ($8,613,000)
Emp.: 7,373
Fiscal Year-end: 03/31/13

Business Description:
Automotive Parts Mfr & Sales
S.I.C.: 3714
N.A.I.C.S.: 336390

Personnel:
Nobuo Kobayashi *(Pres)*
Masataka Nakano *(Sr Mng Officer)*
Tomoya Ishida *(Mng Officer)*
Kunio Nakashima *(Mng Officer)*
Takaaki Takagi *(Mng Officer)*
Hisanao Torii *(Mng Officer)*
Hiroyuki Inoue *(Officer)*
Yoshifumi Kosaka *(Officer)*
Kazuaki Koyanagi *(Officer)*
Takehiro Nakajima *(Officer)*
Toru Nakane *(Officer)*
Kazuhiko Nishimura *(Officer)*
Masanori Senda *(Officer)*
Genjiro Tada *(Officer)*
Haruki Tokimura *(Officer)*
Yojiro Ueki *(Officer)*
Hideo Yamada *(Officer)*
Masahiro Yamaguchi *(Officer)*

Board of Directors:
Tomoya Ishida
Toru Nakane
Masataka Nakano
Kunio Nakashima
Genjiro Tada
Takaaki Takagi
Hisanao Torii
Hideo Yamada

Transfer Agent:
Mitsubishi UFJ Trust & Banking Corporation
1 4 5 Marunouchi Chiyoda ku
Tokyo, 1008212, Japan

Plants:

Aisan Industry Co., Ltd - ANJO Plant **(1)**
100 Kitayama Higashibata-cho
Anjo, Aichi, Japan
Tel.: (81) 566 92 0611
Emp.: 965
Engine Valve Mfr
S.I.C.: 3714
N.A.I.C.S.: 336310

Aisan Industry Co., Ltd. - TOYOTA Plant **(1)**
635-30 Komugio Nishihirose-cho
Toyota, Japan
Tel.: (81) 565 46 0021
Web Site: www.aisan-ind.co.jp/company/e_domestic.htm
Emp.: 539
Automotive Parts Mfr
S.I.C.: 3714
N.A.I.C.S.: 336390

U.S. Subsidiaries:

Aisan Corporation of America, Inc. **(1)**
888 W Big Beaver Rd Ste 870
Troy, MI 48084 (100%)
Tel.: (248) 434-5011
Fax: (248) 434-5011
Web Site: www.aisan-ind.co.jp/company/e_overseas.htm
Industrial Machinery & Equipment Whslr
S.I.C.: 5084
N.A.I.C.S.: 423830
Y. Pan *(Pres)*

Franklin Precision Industry, Inc. **(1)**
3220 Bowling Green Rd
Franklin, KY 42134
Tel.: (270) 586-4450
Fax: (270) 598-4446
E-Mail: esh@fpik.com
Web Site: www.fpik.com
Emp.: 370
Throttle Bodies, Carbon Canisters & Fuel Pump Modules Mfr
S.I.C.: 3711
N.A.I.C.S.: 336211
Kaneo Immamura *(Pres)*

Non-U.S. Subsidiaries:

Aisan Bitron Czech s.r.o. **(1)**
Prumyslova 2727
440 01 Louny, Czech Republic
Tel.: (420) 415930530
Fax: (420) 415930580
E-Mail: info@aisan.cz
Web Site: www.aisan.cz
Emp.: 500
Fuel Pumps Mfr
S.I.C.: 3594
N.A.I.C.S.: 333996
Teijaro Takamura *(Pres)*

Aisan Bitron Louny S.r.o. **(1)**
Osvoboditelu 896
44001 Louny, Czech Republic (95%)
Tel.: (420) 415930530
Fax: (420) 415930529
E-Mail: personalni@ablouny.cz
Emp.: 257
Fluid Power Pump & Motor Mfr
S.I.C.: 3594
N.A.I.C.S.: 333996

Aisan Corporation Europe S.A. **(1)**
Belgicastraat 13
1930 Zaventem, Belgium (100%)
Tel.: (32) 25414756
Fax: (32) 25414762
E-Mail: k_banno@aisan.be
Web Site: www.aisan-ind.co.jp/company/e_overseas.htm
Emp.: 4
Automotive Parts & Accessories Stores
S.I.C.: 5013
N.A.I.C.S.: 441310
Koji Banno *(Mng Dir)*

Aisan Corporation Gauangzhou Co., Ltd **(1)**
Room 1809 Grand Tower Site 1 of 228
Tianhe Rd Tianhe Qu, 510620 Guangzhou, China (100%)
Tel.: (86) 2038330920
Fax: (86) 2038331764
Automotive Parts & Accessories Stores
S.I.C.: 5531
N.A.I.C.S.: 441310

Aisan (Fhoshan) Auto Parts Co., Ltd **(1)**
5 Xinhui Road Wusha Daliang Town Shunde
528333 Foshan, Guangdong, China (95%)
Tel.: (86) 75722808200
Fax: (86) 75722800581
Web Site: www.aisan-ind.co.jp/company/e_overseas.htm
Emp.: 278
Motor Vehicle Parts Mfr
S.I.C.: 3714
N.A.I.C.S.: 336390
Toyohiko Inoue *(Mng Dir)*

Aisan Industry Czech s.r.o. **(1)**
Prumyslova 2727
440 01 Louny, Czech Republic
Tel.: (420) 415 930 530
Fax: (420) 415 930 580
E-Mail: info@aisan.cz
Web Site: www.aisan.cz
Electric Fuel Pump Mfr
S.I.C.: 3714
N.A.I.C.S.: 336320
Kunio Kadowaki *(Pres)*

Aisan Industry France SA **(1)**
1 Rue des Grands Champs
58000 Nevers, France (100%)
Tel.: (33) 386718210
Fax: (33) 386613245
E-Mail: aisan.industry.france@aisan-ind.fr
Web Site: www.aisan-ind.co.jp/company/e_overseas.htm
Emp.: 200
Pump & Pumping Equipment Mfr
S.I.C.: 3561
N.A.I.C.S.: 333911
Franco Orsi *(Mng Dir)*

Aisan Industry Louny s.r.o. **(1)**
Prumyslova 2725
440 01 Louny, Czech Republic
Tel.: (420) 415 930 530
Fax: (420) 415 930 529
E-Mail: info@aisan.cz
Web Site: www.aisan.cz/abl/En/
Emp.: 300
Automotive Parts Mfr
S.I.C.: 3714
N.A.I.C.S.: 336390
Kunio Kadowaki *(Pres)*

Aisan (Tianjin) Auto Parts Co., Ltd **(1)**
No 169 Xijiu Road Tianjin Airport Industrial Park
300308 Tianjin, China (96.3%)
Tel.: (86) 2224893048
Fax: (86) 2224891145
Web Site: www.aisan-ind.co.jp/company/e_overseas.htm
Emp.: 112
Motor Vehicle Parts
S.I.C.: 3714
N.A.I.C.S.: 336390

D&H Co., Ltd. **(1)**
5/F Daeho Bldg 207-30 Geoje 1 Il-Dong
Yeonje-Gu, Pusan, 611071, Korea (South)
Tel.: (82) 515037089
Fax: (82) 515027089
Automotive Parts Mfr & Distr
S.I.C.: 3714
N.A.I.C.S.: 336390

Hyundam Industrial Co., Ltd. **(1)**
343-21 Yeok-ri Youngin-myun Asan-si
Chung Cheong Nam-do, Yesan, Korea (South) (91%)
Tel.: (82) 415397200
Fax: (82) 415397380
Emp.: 583
Fluid Power Pump & Motor Mfr
S.I.C.: 3594
N.A.I.C.S.: 333996

Hyundam Slovakia s.r.o. **(1)**
M R Stefanika 71
Zilina, 01001, Slovakia
Tel.: (421) 415166155
Emp.: 60
Automotive Parts Mfr & Distr
S.I.C.: 3714
N.A.I.C.S.: 336390
Kilo Wong *(Mng Dir)*

IHD Industries Pvt. Ltd. **(1)**
B-25 And 26 Sipcot Industrial Park
Irrungattukottai Kancheepuram, 602105
Chennai, Tamilnadu, India (100%)
Tel.: (91) 4427156863
Fax: (91) 4427156865
E-Mail: ihd@ihdindustries.com
Web Site: www.ihdindustries.com
Fluid Power Pump & Motor Mfr
S.I.C.: 3594
N.A.I.C.S.: 333996
Kim Jung Ki *(Mng Dir)*

P.T. Aisan Nasmoco Industri **(1)**
East Jakarta Industrial Park Plot 9L
Cikarang Selatan
Bekasi, West Java, 17550, Indonesia Id
Tel.: (62) 21 897 1577
Fax: (62) 21 897 1578
Automotive Parts Mfr
S.I.C.: 3714
N.A.I.C.S.: 336390

Shenyang Xuantan Automobile Parts Co., Ltd. **(1)**
Shaling Village Shaling Town YuHong District
Shenyang, Liaoning, China (100%)
Tel.: (86) 2425377151
Fax: (86) 2425368276
Web Site: www.hyundam.com.cn/contactus.asp
Engineering Services
S.I.C.: 8711
N.A.I.C.S.: 541330

AISEI PHARMACY CO., LTD.

Marunouchi Mitsui Building 2-2-2 Marunouchi
Chiyoda-ku, Tokyo, 100-0005, Japan
Tel.: (81) 3 32400222
Fax: (81) 3 62124193
Web Site: www.aisei.co.jp
Year Founded: 1984
3170—(JAS)
Sls.: $464,750,000
Assets: $237,710,000
Liabilities: $193,644,000
Net Worth: $44,066,000
Earnings: $4,598,000
Emp.: 2,144
Fiscal Year-end: 03/31/13

Aisei Pharmacy Co., Ltd.—(Continued)

Business Description:
Pharmacies Owner & Operator
S.I.C.: 5912
N.A.I.C.S.: 446110
Personnel:
Yukihiko Okamura *(Pres & CEO)*
Board of Directors:
Emi Fujii
Koji Horita
Takehiko Ikeda
Kuniaki Imagawa
Bun'ichi Murayama
Kazuo Ohsako
Yukihiko Okamura
Takashi Yamaguchi

AISHWARYA TECHNOLOGIES AND TELECOM LIMITED

(Formerly Aishwarya Telecom Limited)
1-3-1026 & 1027 Singadikunta Kawadiguda
Near Hotel Marriott Courtyard, Hyderabad, Andra Pradesh, 500 080, India
Tel.: (91) 40 2753 1324
Fax: (91) 40 2753 5423
E-Mail: sales@aishwaryatechteleco m.com
Web Site: www.aishwaryatechtele. com
532975—(BOM)
Rev.: $4,689,362
Assets: $9,500,941
Liabilities: $7,492,833
Net Worth: $2,008,108
Earnings: $226,632
Emp.: 60
Fiscal Year-end: 03/31/13
Business Description:
Fiber Optic Test Equipment & Cable Fault Locators Mfr
S.I.C.: 3699
N.A.I.C.S.: 335999
Personnel:
G. Rama Manohar Reddy *(Mng Dir)*
S. Sarweswar Reddy *(Sec)*
Board of Directors:
G. Rama Krishna Reddy
Harish K. Jain
G. Amulya Reddy
G. Rama Manohar Reddy
Maligi Madhusudhana Reddy
D. Venkata Subbiah
Transfer Agent:
Bigshare Services Private Limited
E 2/3 Ansa Industrial Estate Sakivihar Road
Sakinaka Andheri(E)
Mumbai, India

AISHWARYA TELECOM LIMITED

(Name Changed to Aishwarya Technologies and Telecom Limited)

AISIN SEIKI CO., LTD.

2-1 Asahi-machi
Kariya, Aichi, 448-8650, Japan
Tel.: (81) 566248441
Telex: ASCO J J59590
Fax: (81) 566248003
Web Site: www.aisin.com
Year Founded: 1949
7259—(NGO OTC TKS)
Sls.: $27,829,604,000
Assets: $24,729,100,000
Liabilities: $12,229,327,000
Net Worth: $12,499,773,000
Earnings: $852,698,000
Emp.: 83,378
Fiscal Year-end: 03/31/13
Business Description:
Automotive Parts & Housing-Related Equipment Mfr
S.I.C.: 3714
N.A.I.C.S.: 336390
Personnel:
Kanshiro Toyoda *(Chm)*
Fumio Fujimori *(Pres)*
Koji Aoki *(Mng Officer)*
Katsuhiko Eguchi *(Mng Officer)*
Takashi Enomoto *(Sr Mng Officer)*
Shigeki Fuji *(Mng Officer)*
Naofumi Fujie *(Sr Mng Officer)*
Takahisa Hirose *(Sr Mng Officer)*
Masanobu Ishikawa *(Mng Officer)*
Hirotoshi Ito *(Mng Officer)*
Shintaro Ito *(Mng Officer)*
Yoshiaki Kato *(Sr Mng Officer)*
Naoki Katsurayama *(Mng Officer)*
Toshiyuki Mizushima *(Sr Mng Officer)*
Akira Nakamura *(Mng Officer)*
Ryuji Nakamura *(Mng Officer)*
Takafumi Nakano *(Mng Officer)*
Masahiro Nishikawa *(Mng Officer)*
Hitoshi Okabe *(Sr Mng Officer)*
Masayasu Saito *(Sr Mng Officer)*
Shingo Sanjo *(Mng Officer)*
Masato Shimei *(Mng Officer)*
Masayasu Sugiura *(Mng Officer)*
Seiichi Takahashi *(Sr Mng Officer)*
Motohiro Takemura *(Mng Officer)*
Hiroaki Tatematsu *(Mng Officer)*
Hitoshi Tauchi *(Mng Officer)*
Shinsuke Yagi *(Sr Mng Officer)*
Makoto Yoshida *(Mng Officer)*
Shinzo Kobuki *(Exec VP)*
Makoto Mitsuya *(Exec VP)*
Takashi Morita *(Exec VP)*
Toshikazu Nagura *(Exec VP)*
Board of Directors:
Kanshiro Toyoda
Naofumi Fujie
Fumio Fujimori
Toshiyuki Ishikawa
Mutsumi Kawamoto
Takeshi Kawata
Shinzo Kobuki
Makoto Mitsuya
Takashi Morita
Toshikazu Nagura
Kazumi Usami
Transfer Agent:
Mitsubishi UFJ Trust & Banking Corporation
7-10-11 Higashisuna Koto-ku
Tokyo, Japan
Subsidiaries:

AD Green Co., Ltd. (1)
129 Akiba Takaokahonmachi
Toyota, Aichi, 473-0922, Japan
Tel.: (81) 565528771
Greening & Exterior Refurbishing Services
S.I.C.: 7349
N.A.I.C.S.: 561790

AD Nobi Co., Ltd. (1)
4-23-2 Chiyoda
Naka-Ku, Nagoya, Aichi, 460-0012, Japan
Tel.: (81) 523229811
Web Site: www.nobi.co.jp
Condominiums Building Services
S.I.C.: 1531
N.A.I.C.S.: 236117

AD Sunutopia Co., Ltd. (1)
3-3 Aioi-Cho
Kariya, 448-8525, Japan
Tel.: (81) 566 63 6282
E-Mail: mail.sunutopia@aisin-ad.co.jp
Web Site: www.sunutopia.co.jp
Emp.: 16
Real Estate Management Services
S.I.C.: 6531
N.A.I.C.S.: 531390

ADVICS Co., Ltd. (1)
2 1 Showa-cho
Kariya, Aichi, 448-8688, Japan (50%)
Tel.: (81) 566638000
Fax: (81) 566248274
Web Site: www.advics.co.jp
Emp.: 730
Research, Development & Sales of Brake Systems & Components
S.I.C.: 3714
N.A.I.C.S.: 336340

U.S. Subsidiaries:

ADVICS MANUFACTURING INDIANA, LLC. (2)
10550 James Adams St
Terre Haute, IN 47802
Tel.: (812) 298-1617
Fax: (812) 298-1756
Web Site: www.advics.co.jp/eng/compa ny/map/company10.html
Sls.: $127,000,000
Emp.: 384
Automotive Brake Component Mfr
S.I.C.: 3714
N.A.I.C.S.: 336340

ADVICS North America, Inc. (2)
45300 Polaris Ct
Plymouth, MI 48170 MI
Tel.: (734) 414-5100 (100%)
Fax: (734) 414-5110
Web Site: www.aisinworld.com
Emp.: 70
Brake Systems Mfr & Seller
S.I.C.: 3714
N.A.I.C.S.: 336340
Kenji Yasuda *(Pres)*

Divisions:

ADVICS Manufacturing Ohio, Inc. (3)
1650 Kingsview Dr
Lebanon, OH 45036-0149 MI
Tel.: (513) 932-7878 (100%)
Fax: (513) 932-9073
Web Site: www.advics-ohio.com
Emp.: 500
Braking System Mfr
S.I.C.: 3714
N.A.I.C.S.: 336340
Geoffrey Hearsum *(Pres)*

SAFA, LLC (3)
1621 Lukken Industrial Dr W
Lagrange, GA 30240-5703 GA
Tel.: (706) 812-0007 (100%)
Fax: (706) 812-0665
Web Site: www.aisin.com
Emp.: 2,000
Wire Harness Mfr
S.I.C.: 3496
N.A.I.C.S.: 332618
Minoru Hirai *(Pres)*

Non-U.S. Subsidiaries:

ADVICS ASIA PACIFIC CO., LTD. (2)
235 Moo 7 Simahaphot
Tha Tum District, Prachin Buri, Thailand
Tel.: (66) 37 414 093
Fax: (66) 37 414 094
Sls.: $358,650,720
Emp.: 26
Automotive Component Distr
S.I.C.: 5013
N.A.I.C.S.: 423120

PT. ADVICS INDONESIA (2)
East Jakarta Industrial Park EJIP Plot 5J
Cikarang Selatan
Jawa Barat, Bekasi, Indonesia
Tel.: (62) 218970973
Fax: (62) 218970429
Web Site: www.advics.co.jp/eng/compa ny/map/company5.html
Sls.: $21,672,200
Emp.: 6
Automotive Component Distr
S.I.C.: 5013
N.A.I.C.S.: 423120

AI Dream Life Support Co., Ltd. (1)
4-188 Hantsukicho
Obu, Aichi, 474-0037, Japan
Tel.: (81) 562 47 7190
Fax: (81) 562 47 7197
Web Site: www.aisin-ad.co.jp/sawayaka/co mpany/index.html
Senior Citizen Home Services
S.I.C.: 8361
N.A.I.C.S.: 623312

AI Machine Tech Co., Ltd. (1)
4-2-1 Izumicho Kitaogi
Anjo, Aichi, 444-1223, Japan
Tel.: (81) 566 92 5122
Web Site: www.ai-machinetech.com
Machine Tool Mfr
S.I.C.: 3545
N.A.I.C.S.: 333515

Aichi Giken Co., Ltd. (1)
50-1 Kojiritsuki Hitotsugi-cho
Kariya, Aichi, 448-0003, Japan
Tel.: (81) 566 23 2731
Fax: (81) 566 21 8457
E-Mail: aichigiken@aichigiken.co.jp
Web Site: www.aichigiken.co.jp
Automotive Parts Mfr
S.I.C.: 3714
N.A.I.C.S.: 336390

Aisin AI Co., Ltd. (1)
Kojiritsuki 17 1 Hitotsugi Cho
Kariya, Aichi, 448 0003, Japan (100%)
Tel.: (81) 566293120
Fax: (81) 566610567
E-Mail: info@imra.co.jp
Web Site: www.imra.co.jp
Sales Range: $1-9.9 Million
Emp.: 20,000
Mfr. & Sale of Manual Transmissions, Transfers & Attachments
S.I.C.: 3714
N.A.I.C.S.: 336350

Aisin AW Co., Ltd. (1)
10 Takane Fujii Cho
Anjo, Aichi, 444 1192, Japan (50%)
Tel.: (81) 566731138
Fax: (81) 566731656
Web Site: www.aisin-aw.co.jp/en/index.html
Sales Range: $5-14.9 Billion
Emp.: 12,329
Mfr & Sale of Automatic Transmissions & Car Navigation Systems
S.I.C.: 3714
N.A.I.C.S.: 336350
Tsutomu Ishikawa *(Pres)*

U.S. Subsidiary:

AW TECHNICAL CENTER U.S.A., INC (2)
1203 Woodridge Ave
Ann Arbor, MI 48105
Tel.: (734) 741-9900
Fax: (734) 741-9700
Web Site: www.aisinworld.com
Emp.: 52
Automatic Transmission Component Research & Development Services
S.I.C.: 8731
N.A.I.C.S.: 541712
Takao Mizutani *(Pres)*

Aisin AW Industries Co., Ltd. (1)
38 Ikenokami Cho
Takefu, Fukui, 915 8520, Japan (59%)
Tel.: (81) 778256611
Fax: (81) 778256665
Web Site: www.awi.co.jp
Emp.: 1,000
Mfr. & Sale of Automatic Transmission Parts
S.I.C.: 3714
N.A.I.C.S.: 336350

Aisin Chemical Co., Ltd. (1)
1141 1 Okawagahara
Fujioka Eiino Cho, Toyota, Aichi, 470 0492, Japan
Tel.: (81) 565766689
Fax: (81) 565761101
E-Mail: ac-somu@aisin-chem.co.jp
Web Site: www.aisin-chem.co.jp
Emp.: 1,000
Mfr. & Sale of Molded Plastic Automotive Parts, Automotive Friction Materials, Paints, Adhesives & Molding Sand Adhesives
S.I.C.: 5013
N.A.I.C.S.: 441310
Yasuhide Shibata *(Pres)*

U.S. Subsidiary:

AISIN CHEMICAL INDIANA, LLC (2)
1001 Industrial Way
Crothersville, IN 47229
Tel.: (812) 793-2888
Fax: (812) 793-3684
Web Site: www.aisinworld.com
Emp.: 40
Wet Friction Material Mfr
S.I.C.: 3714

N.A.I.C.S.: 336390
Tim Carter *(Gen Mgr)*

Aisin Collabo Co., Ltd. (1)
2-3 Showacho Aishin Seiki Jimu Honkannai
Kariya, Aichi, 448-8650, Japan
Tel.: (81) 566 24 9833
E-Mail: job-info@ai-collabo.co.jp
Web Site: www.ai-collabo.co.jp
Human Resource Consulting Services
S.I.C.: 8999
N.A.I.C.S.: 541612

Aisin Comcruise Co., Ltd. (1)
Daini Toyota Bldg Higashikan 8F 4-11-27 Meieki
Nakamura-ku, Nagoya, Aichi, 450-0002, Japan
Tel.: (81) 52 533 7051
Fax: (81) 52 533 7052
Web Site: www.aisin-comcruise.com
Software Development Services
S.I.C.: 7371
N.A.I.C.S.: 541511

Aisin Cosmos R&D Co., Ltd. (1)
2-36 Hachikencho
Kariya, Aichi, 448-8650, Japan
Tel.: (81) 566 20 6700
Web Site: www.ai-cosmos.com
Biotechnology Research & Development Services
S.I.C.: 8731
N.A.I.C.S.: 541711

Aisin Development Co., Ltd. (1)
3 3 Aioi Cho
Kariya, Aichi, 448 8525, Japan
Tel.: (81) 566278700
Fax: (81) 243159
Web Site: www.aisin.com
Design & Contracting of Civil Engineering; Construction, Gardening & Horticulture; Indemnity & Life Insurance Agency; Real Estate Agency
S.I.C.: 1629
N.A.I.C.S.: 237990

Aisin Engineering Co., Ltd. (1)
RF Kariya Ekimae Building 1-1-1 Aioi-Cho
Kariya, Aichi, 448-8605, Japan
Tel.: (81) 566 62 8170
Web Site: www.ai-e.co.jp
Sls.: $188,373,600
Emp.: 1,594
Computer Peripheral Equipment Mfr
S.I.C.: 3577
N.A.I.C.S.: 334118
Suzuki Mitsuyuki *(Pres)*

Aisin Hokkaido Co., Ltd. (1)
32-5 Kashiwabara
Tomakomai, Hokkaido, 059-1362, Japan
Tel.: (81) 144 53 7111
Fax: (81) 144 53 7511
Web Site: www.ai-h.co.jp
Aluminum Casting Products Mfr & Distr
S.I.C.: 3364
N.A.I.C.S.: 331523

Aisin Infotex Co., Ltd. (1)
3-11-34 Mita
Minato-Ku, Tokyo, Aichi, 108-0073, Japan
Tel.: (81) 3 5730 9300
Fax: (81) 3 5730 9302
Web Site: www.aisinix.com
Software Consulting Services
S.I.C.: 7373
N.A.I.C.S.: 541512

Aisin Keikinzoku Co., Ltd. (1)
12-3 Nagonoe Imizu
Toyama, 934-8588, Japan
Tel.: (81) 766828800
Fax: (81) 7 66848572
Web Site: www.aisin-ak.co.jp/
Sales Range: $550-599.9 Million
Emp.: 1,399
Mfr & Sale of Die-Cast Aluminum Products, Aluminum Mold Cast Products & Aluminum Products
S.I.C.: 3364
N.A.I.C.S.: 331523
Masaki Horiba *(Pres)*

Aisin Kiko Co., Ltd. (1)
70 6 Aza Ikegami Oaza Tomokuni Kira Cho Hazu Gu
Kariya, Aichi, 444 0504, Japan
Tel.: (81) 563353850
Fax: (81) 563353896
Web Site: www.aisinkiko.co.jp
Emp.: 1,200
Mfr. & Sale of Automotive Parts & Industrial Vehicle Parts
S.I.C.: 5013
N.A.I.C.S.: 441310

Aisin Kyushu Casting Co., Ltd (1)
1227-1 Jonammachimainohara
Shimomashiki-gun, Kumamoto, 861-4214, Japan
Tel.: (81) 964281611
Aluminum Die Casting Mfr
S.I.C.: 3364
N.A.I.C.S.: 331523

Aisin Kyushu Co., Ltd. (1)
500-1 Nishi Amainohara Jonan Machi
Shimomashiki-gun, Kumamoto, Japan
Tel.: (81) 964 28 8181
Fax: (81) 964 28 8155
E-Mail: saiyo@aisin-kyushu.co.jp
Web Site: www.aisin-kyushu.co.jp
Automotive Parts Mfr
S.I.C.: 3714
N.A.I.C.S.: 336390

Aisin Maintenance Co., Ltd. (1)
3-3 Aioicho
Kariya, Aichi, 448-0027, Japan
Tel.: (81) 566626771
Automotive Parts Repair & Maintenance Services
S.I.C.: 7539
N.A.I.C.S.: 811198

Aisin Metaltech Co., Ltd. (1)
615 Fukujima Nyuzenmachi
Shimoniikawa-Gun, Toyama, 939-0645, Japan
Tel.: (81) 765 72 5511
Web Site: www.aisin-metaltech.jp
Automotive Parts Mfr
S.I.C.: 3714
N.A.I.C.S.: 336390

AISIN SIN'EI CO., LTD. (1)
2-8-12 Konan-machi
Hekinan, Aichi, 447-8508, Japan
Tel.: (81) 566 48 7000
Web Site: www.aisin-sinei.co.jp
Sls.: $325,584,000
Emp.: 632
Automotive Parts Mfr
S.I.C.: 3714
N.A.I.C.S.: 336390

Aisin Sinwa Co., Ltd. (1)
2458 Nyuzen Nyuzen-Cho
Shimoshinkawa-Gun, Toyama, 939 0626, Japan
Tel.: (81) 765725811
Fax: (81) 765725861
Emp.: 760
Mfr. & Sale of Cast Components for Automobiles, Industrial Machinery, Home Electric Appliances, Agricultural Equipment & Forged Automotive Components
S.I.C.: 5531
N.A.I.C.S.: 441310

Aisin Takaoka Co., Ltd. (1)
1 Tennoh Takaokashin Machi
Toyota, Aichi, 473 8501, Japan (45%)
Tel.: (81) 565541123
Fax: (81) 565541200
Web Site: www.at-takaoka.co.jp
Emp.: 3,000
Mfr. & Sale of Cast Components For Automobiles, Industrial Machinery & Home Appliances
S.I.C.: 5013
N.A.I.C.S.: 441310

U.S. Subsidiaries:

ATTC MANUFACTURING, INC. (2)
10455 State Rd 37
Tell City, IN 47586
Tel.: (812) 547-5060
Fax: (812) 547-8390
E-Mail: tellcityattc@attcmfg.com
Web Site: www.attcmanufacturing.com
Emp.: 380
Automotive Parts Mfr
S.I.C.: 3714
N.A.I.C.S.: 336390
Frank Yuda *(Asst Mgr-Trng)*

Intat Precision, Inc. (2)
2148 N State Rd 3
Rushville, IN 46173 (98%)
Tel.: (765) 932-5323
Fax: (765) 932-3032
Web Site: www.intat.com
Gray & Ductile Iron Castings for Automotive Industry
S.I.C.: 3322
N.A.I.C.S.: 331511
David Reid *(Controller & Treas)*

Non-U.S. Subsidiary:

Takaoka Lioho (Tianjin) Industries Co., Ltd (2)
Tianjin BeiChen Economic Development Area ShuanChenZhongLu
Tianjin, China
Tel.: (86) 22 8699 5950
Fax: (86) 2 8699 5951
Web Site: www.atl.com.cn
Automotive Parts Mfr
S.I.C.: 3714
N.A.I.C.S.: 336390

Aisin Tohoku Co., Ltd. (1)
6 Moriyama Nishine Kanegasaki-Cho
Iwate, 029-4503, Japan
Tel.: (81) 197 44 2663
Fax: (81) 197 44 3540
Web Site: www.aisin-tohoku.co.jp
Exhaust System Parts Mfr
S.I.C.: 3714
N.A.I.C.S.: 336390

AKKM Co., Ltd. (1)
165 Nodacho
Kariya, Aichi, 448-0803, Japan
Tel.: (81) 566 62 6870
Fax: (81) 566 23 6323
Web Site: www.akk-m.co.jp
Emp.: 70
Greening & Landscaping Design Services
S.I.C.: 0782
N.A.I.C.S.: 561730

AS Brake Systems, Inc. (1)
1-1-1 Koyakita
Itami, Hyogo, 664-0016, Japan
Tel.: (81) 727712400
Brake System Mfr
S.I.C.: 3714
N.A.I.C.S.: 336340

AW-I S Co., Ltd. (1)
38 Ikenokami-cho
Echizen, Fukui, 915-8520, Japan
Tel.: (81) 778 25 7860
Fax: (81) 778 25 7861
Web Site: www.aw-is.co.jp
Human Resource Consulting Services
S.I.C.: 8999
N.A.I.C.S.: 541612

AW Maintenance Co., Ltd. (1)
80-1 Nishiotsubo Higashibata-cho
Anjo, Aichi, 444-1213, Japan
Tel.: (81) 566 92 6702
Fax: (81) 566 92 6418
Web Site: www.aw-m.co.jp
Equipment Mfr & Maintenance Services
S.I.C.: 3699
N.A.I.C.S.: 335999

AW Service Co., Ltd. (1)
68 Ogakiecho
Kariya, Aichi, 448-0813, Japan
Tel.: (81) 566 92 5877
Fax: (81) 566 92 5827
Web Site: www.aw-s.co.jp
Environmental Consulting Services
S.I.C.: 8999
N.A.I.C.S.: 541620

AW Software Co., Ltd. (1)
2-1-6 Techno-park Shimonopporo
Atsubetsu-ku, Sapporo, Hokkaido, 004-0015, Japan
Tel.: (81) 11 898 2953
Web Site: www.aw-sw.co.jp
Emp.: 168
Car Navigation Systems Software Development Services
S.I.C.: 7371
N.A.I.C.S.: 541511

Awquis Japan Co., Ltd... (1)
3-2-7 Shimizucho
Takahama, Aichi, 444-1312, Japan
Tel.: (81) 566527751
Air Terrain Vehicles Repair & Rebuilding Services
S.I.C.: 7539
N.A.I.C.S.: 811198

CVTEC Co., Ltd. (1)
2-2-65 Midorigahama
Tahara, Aichi, 444-3401, Japan
Tel.: (81) 531 24 1329
Fax: (81) 531 24 1310
Web Site: www.cvtec.co.jp
Industrial Belts Mfr
S.I.C.: 3535
N.A.I.C.S.: 333922

Equos Research Co., Ltd. (1)
Gotoh-Bldg 2-19-12 Sotokanda
Chiyoda-ku, Tokyo, 101-0021, Japan
Tel.: (81) 3 3255 9766
Fax: (81) 3 3255 9760
E-Mail: info@equos.co.jp
Web Site: www.equos.co.jp
Emp.: 80
Automotive Parts Mfr
S.I.C.: 3714
N.A.I.C.S.: 336390
Masao Ando *(Pres)*

FT Techno Inc. (1)
918-11 Sakashita Mitsukuricho
Toyota, Aichi, 470-0424, Japan
Tel.: (81) 565 75 1441
Fax: (81) 565 75 1503
E-Mail: cop@fttechno.aisin.co.jp
Web Site: www.fttechno.co.jp
Automotive Parts Repair & Maintenance Services
S.I.C.: 7549
N.A.I.C.S.: 811198

Hekinan Unso Co., Ltd. (1)
3 Tenno Takaokashinmachi
Toyota, Aichi, 473-0921, Japan
Tel.: (81) 565527728
E-Mail: saiyo@hekiun.co.jp
Web Site: www.hekiun.co.jp
Truck Transportation Services
S.I.C.: 4789
N.A.I.C.S.: 488999

HOSEI BRAKE INDUSTRY CO., LTD. (1)
10 Michigami Kazue-cho
Toyota, Aichi, 470-1293, Japan
Tel.: (81) 565 21 1213
Fax: (81) 565 21 1052
Web Site: www.hosei.co.jp
Brake System Mfr
S.I.C.: 3714
N.A.I.C.S.: 336340
Genshiroh Mizuno *(Pres)*

Plants:

HOSEI BRAKE INDUSTRY CO., LTD. - Okazaki Factory (2)
183 Ogoya-nishi Hashime-cho
Okazaki, Aichi, 444-0909, Japan
Tel.: (81) 564 32 3425
Fax: (81) 564 33 1148
Web Site: www.hosei.co.jp/english/menu 03/01.html
Brake System Mfr
S.I.C.: 3714
N.A.I.C.S.: 336340

HOSEI BRAKE INDUSTRY CO., LTD. - Takahama Factory (2)
1-2 Shinden-cho
Takahama, Aichi, 444-1301, Japan
Tel.: (81) 566 53 0101
Fax: (81) 566 52 6110
Web Site: www.hosei.co.jp/english/menu 03/01.html
Brake System Mfr
S.I.C.: 3714
N.A.I.C.S.: 336340

IMRA Material R&D Co., Ltd. (1)
2-1 Asahimachi
Kariya, Aichi, 448-0032, Japan
Tel.: (81) 566249380
Automotive Parts Mfr
S.I.C.: 3714
N.A.I.C.S.: 336390

Konan Kogyo Co., Ltd. (1)
2-5 Showacho
Kariya, Aichi, 448-0029, Japan
Tel.: (81) 566211450
Web Site: www.konankogyo.co.jp
Automotive Products Distr

Aisin Seiki Co., Ltd.—(Continued)

S.I.C.: 5013
N.A.I.C.S.: 423120

Kotobuki Industry Co., Ltd. (1)
148 Yokoyama Ikomacho
Toyota, Aichi, 473-0928, Japan
Tel.: (81) 565 57 2011
Fax: (81) 565 57 1977
Web Site: www.kotobukigiken.co.jp
Door Hinge & Window Regulator Mfr
S.I.C.: 3714
N.A.I.C.S.: 336390

Sanetsu Transport Co., Ltd. (1)
1230-1 Nyuzen-machi
Shimoniikawa-gun, Toyama, 939-0653, Japan
Tel.: (81) 765 72 2121
Fax: (81) 765 74 1950
Web Site: www.sanetsu-u.com
Truck Transportation Services
S.I.C.: 4789
N.A.I.C.S.: 488999

Shinko Seiki Co., Ltd. (1)
708-8 Ishimaru
Takaoka, Toyama, 934-0095, Japan
Tel.: (81) 766 84 8196
Fax: (81) 766 84 9007
Web Site: www.shinko-seiki.co.jp
Industrial Molds Mfr
S.I.C.: 3321
N.A.I.C.S.: 331511

Techno Metal Co., Ltd. (1)
3-169 Kamiinoshinmachi
Toyama, 930-0825, Japan
Tel.: (81) 764510099
Aluminum Alloy Refining Services
S.I.C.: 3399
N.A.I.C.S.: 331314

Tonamino Kogyo Co., Ltd. (1)
320-1 Shogawamachi Goka
Tonami, Toyama, 932-0313, Japan
Tel.: (81) 763 82 5225
Fax: (81) 763 82 5459
Web Site: www.tonamino.co.jp
Automotive Parts Mfr
S.I.C.: 3714
N.A.I.C.S.: 336390

Yamagata Clutch Co., Ltd. (1)
43 Azashonan Shimoyamazoe
Tsuruoka, Yamagata, 997-0341, Japan
Tel.: (81) 235572880
Automotive Parts Mfr
S.I.C.: 3714
N.A.I.C.S.: 336390

Affiliate:

Technova, Inc. (1)
Imperial Hotel Tower 13F 1 1 Uchisaiwaicho
1 Chome Chiyoda Ku
Tokyo, 100 0011, Japan (100%)
Tel.: (81) 335082280
Fax: (81) 335087578
E-Mail: technova@technova.co.jp
Web Site: www.technova.co.jp
Emp.: 20
S.I.C.: 3714
N.A.I.C.S.: 336340

Plants:

Aisin Seiki Co., Ltd. - Anjo Plant (1)
1-11-2 Mikawaanjo-cho
Anjo, Aichi, 446-8524, Japan
Tel.: (81) 566 76 9111
Fax: (81) 566 76 9134
Web Site: www.aisin.com
Emp.: 325
Air Conditioner Mfr
S.I.C.: 3714
N.A.I.C.S.: 336390

Aisin Seiki Co., Ltd. - Handa Electronics Plant (1)
4-29 Nitto-cho
Handa, Aichi, 475-0033, Japan
Tel.: (81) 569 24 6810
Fax: (81) 569 24 6799
Web Site: www.aisin.com
Emp.: 944
Electronic Component Mfr
S.I.C.: 3679
N.A.I.C.S.: 334419

Aisin Seiki Co., Ltd. - Handa Plant (1)
4-29 Nitto-cho
Handa, Aichi, 475-0033, Japan
Tel.: (81) 569 24 6710
Fax: (81) 569 24 6799
Web Site: www.aisin.com
Emp.: 828
Automotive Brake System Mfr
S.I.C.: 3714
N.A.I.C.S.: 336340

Aisin Seiki Co., Ltd. - Kinuura Plant (1)
2-8-12 Kohnan-machi
Hekinan, Aichi, 447-0824, Japan
Tel.: (81) 566 46 3800
Fax: (81) 566 46 6105
Web Site: www.aisin.com
Emp.: 560
Door Handles & Sunroofs Mfr
S.I.C.: 3714
N.A.I.C.S.: 336390

Aisin Seiki Co., Ltd. - Machinery & Equipment Plant (1)
80 Kowari Minaminakane-cho
Nishio, Aichi, 445-0801, Japan
Tel.: (81) 563 57 6660
Fax: (81) 563 57 6666
Emp.: 328
Automotive Assembling Component Mfr
S.I.C.: 3714
N.A.I.C.S.: 336330

Aisin Seiki Co., Ltd. - Nishio Die-casting Plant (1)
80 Kowari Minaminakane-cho
Nishio, Aichi, 445-0801, Japan
Tel.: (81) 563 57 6200
Fax: (81) 563 57 6205
Emp.: 993
Transmission & Transaxle Case Mfr
S.I.C.: 3499
N.A.I.C.S.: 332999

Aisin Seiki Co., Ltd. - Nishio Engine Components Plant (1)
80 Kowari Minaminakane-cho
Nishio, Aichi, 445-0801, Japan
Tel.: (81) 563 57 6300
Fax: (81) 563 57 6000
Web Site: www.aisin.com
Emp.: 1,065
Oil & Water Pump Mfr
S.I.C.: 3561
N.A.I.C.S.: 333911

Aisin Seiki Co., Ltd. - Ogawa Plant (1)
1 Kukui Ogawa-cho
Anjo, Aichi, 444-1162, Japan
Tel.: (81) 563 57 6701
Fax: (81) 563 57 6708
Emp.: 724
Automatic Transmission Mfr
S.I.C.: 3714
N.A.I.C.S.: 336350

Aisin Seiki Co., Ltd. - Shinkawa Plant (1)
4-75 Rokuken-cho
Hekinan, Aichi, 447-0861, Japan
Tel.: (81) 566 41 3321
Fax: (81) 566 41 5424
Emp.: 423
Automotive Parts Mfr
S.I.C.: 3714
N.A.I.C.S.: 336390

Aisin Seiki Co., Ltd. - Shintoyo Plant (1)
1 Tennoh Takaokashin-machi
Toyota, Aichi, 473-0921, Japan
Tel.: (81) 565 54 8611
Fax: (81) 565 54 8730
Web Site: www.aisin.com
Emp.: 1,356
Automotive Parts Mfr
S.I.C.: 3714
N.A.I.C.S.: 336390

U.S. Subsidiaries:

AISIN AUTOMOTIVE CASTING TENNESSEE, INC. (1)
221 Frank L Diggs Dr
Clinton, TN 37716
Tel.: (865) 457-4581
Fax: (865) 457-4583
Web Site: www.aisinworld.com
Emp.: 480
Aluminum Casting Mfr
S.I.C.: 3353
N.A.I.C.S.: 331315
Robin Watson *(Mgr-HR)*

Aisin Holdings of America, Inc. (1)
46501 Commerce Center Dr
Plymouth, MI 48170
Tel.: (734) 453-5551
Fax: (734) 453-4670
E-Mail: humanresources@aisinworld.com
Web Site: www.aisinworld.com
Emp.: 200
Holding Company
S.I.C.: 6719
N.A.I.C.S.: 551112

Subsidiaries:

AISIN ELECTRONICS ILLINOIS, LLC (2)
11200 Redco Dr
Marion, IL 62959
Tel.: (618) 997-9800
Fax: (618) 997-9888
E-Mail: info@aisineil.com
Web Site: www.aisinillinois.com
Electronic Equipment Mfr
S.I.C.: 3679
N.A.I.C.S.: 334419
Akito Yamauchi *(Pres)*

Aisin World Corp. of America (2)
46501 Commerce Ctr Dr
Plymouth, MI 48170
Tel.: (734) 453-5551
Fax: (734) 453-4670
Web Site: www.aisinworld.com
Emp.: 10,000
Automotive Components Supplier
S.I.C.: 5013
N.A.I.C.S.: 423120
Don Whitsitt *(Pres)*

Subsidiaries:

Aisin Automotive Casting, LLC (3)
4870 E Hwy 552
London, KY 40744-9430
Tel.: (606) 878-6523
Fax: (606) 878-6522
E-Mail: info@aisinauto.com
Web Site: www.aisinauto.com
Emp.: 500
Mfr. of Auto Parts
S.I.C.: 3364
N.A.I.C.S.: 331523
Dale Gentry *(CFO)*
Hisashi Hatta *(Treas & Sec)*
Brian Walter *(Exec VP)*

Aisin Brake & Chassis, Inc. (3)
10550 James Adams St
Terre Haute, IN 47802
Tel.: (812) 298-1617
Fax: (812) 298-1756
Web Site: www.aisinbrake.com
Emp.: 500
Brake System Components Mfr
S.I.C.: 3714
N.A.I.C.S.: 336340

Aisin Drivetrain, Inc. (3)
1001 Industrial Way
Crothersville, IN 47229-9415
Tel.: (812) 793-2427
Fax: (812) 793-3684
Web Site: www.aisindrive.com
Emp.: 375
Mfr. Torque Converters & Transmissions for Heavy Industrial Trucks & Brake Assembly Components
S.I.C.: 3714
N.A.I.C.S.: 336350
Scott Turpin *(VP)*

Aisin Electronics, Inc. (3)
199 Frank W Cir
Stockton, CA 95206-4002 (100%)
Tel.: (209) 983-4988
Fax: (209) 983-4989
Web Site: www.aisin.com
Emp.: 110
Mfr. of Automotive Parts for Electronic Components
S.I.C.: 3625
N.A.I.C.S.: 335314
Shawn Maguire *(Mgr-Production Control & Pur Dept)*

Aisin USA Manufacturing Inc. (3)
1700 E 4th St
Seymour, IN 47274-4309 (100%)
Tel.: (812) 523-1969
Fax: (812) 523-1984
Web Site: www.aisinusa.com
Emp.: 1,750
Mfr. of Automotive Parts
S.I.C.: 3714
N.A.I.C.S.: 336390

AW North Carolina, Inc. (3)
4112 Old Oxford Hwy
Durham, NC 27712
Tel.: (919) 479-6550
Fax: (919) 479-6580
Web Site: www.aw-nc.com
Emp.: 950
Automotive Transmissions Components Mfr
S.I.C.: 3714
N.A.I.C.S.: 336350
Susumu Kasai *(Pres)*

AW Transmission Engineering U.S.A., Inc. (3)
14920 Keel St
Plymouth, MI 48170
Tel.: (734) 454-1710
Fax: (734) 454-1091
Web Site: www.awtec.com
Emp.: 180
Transmission Remanufacturing
S.I.C.: 3714
N.A.I.C.S.: 336350

IMRA America, Inc. (3)
1044 Woodridge Ave
Ann Arbor, MI 48105-9748 (100%)
Tel.: (734) 930-2560
Fax: (734) 930-9957
Web Site: www.imra.com
Emp.: 70
Fibre Optics Research
S.I.C.: 8732
N.A.I.C.S.: 541910
Takashi Omitsu *(Pres)*

AISIN LIGHT METALS, LLC (1)
10900 Redco Dr
Marion, IL 62959
Tel.: (618) 997-7900
Fax: (618) 997-1550
Web Site: www.aisinillinois.com
Aluminum Automotive Parts Mfr
S.I.C.: 3353
N.A.I.C.S.: 331315
Katsunori Maeda *(Pres)*

AISIN TECHNICAL CENTER OF AMERICA, INC. (1)
46501 Commerce Ctr Dr
Plymouth, MI 48170
Tel.: (734) 453-5551
E-Mail: info@aisintca.com
Web Site: www.aisintca.com
Automotive Product Development Services
S.I.C.: 4789
N.A.I.C.S.: 488999
Takashi Aoyama *(Pres)*

FT TECHNO OF AMERICA, LLC (1)
1750 Smith Rd
Fowlerville, MI 48836
Tel.: (517) 223-6777
Fax: (517) 223-6788
E-Mail: fpg@ftt-a.com
Web Site: www.ftt-a.com
Emp.: 11
Vehicle Performance Testing Services
S.I.C.: 4789
N.A.I.C.S.: 488999
Tetsuya Takano *(VP)*

Non-U.S. Subsidiaries:

AISIN AI (THAILAND) CO., LTD. (1)
Wellgrow Industrial Estate Phase2 80 Moo5
Km36 Bangna Trad Tambol Bang
Amphur Bangpakong, Chachoengsao, 24180, Thailand
Tel.: (66) 38 570 062
Automotive Parts Mfr & Distr
S.I.C.: 3714
N.A.I.C.S.: 336390

AISIN ASIA PACIFIC CO., LTD (1)
1 Soi Bangna Trad 25 Bang Na Trad Road
Bangna, Bangkok, 10260, Thailand

Tel.: (66) 23986308
Fax: (66) 23986309
Automotive Parts Mfr
S.I.C.: 3714
N.A.I.C.S.: 336390

Aisin Asia Pte. Ltd. (1)
10 Anson Rd Unit 31-11- 12 International Plz
Singapore, 079903, Singapore
Tel.: (65) 62220592
Telex: 23134
Fax: (65) 62250911
E-Mail: info@aisin.com
Web Site: www.aisin.com.sg
Emp.: 30
S.I.C.: 3714
N.A.I.C.S.: 336340

Aisin (Australia) Pty. Ltd. (1)
593 599 Somarville Road Sunshine
Melbourne, VIC, 3020, Australia (100%)
Tel.: (61) 383119100
Telex: 24413
Fax: (61) 383119101
E-Mail: reception@aisin.com.au
Web Site: www.aisin.com
Emp.: 100
S.I.C.: 3714
N.A.I.C.S.: 336340
Kazuhiko Asai *(Mng Dir)*

AISIN CANADA, INC (1)
969 Juliana Drive
Stratford, ON, N4Z 1H3, Canada
Tel.: (519) 271-1575
Fax: (519) 271-1376
Web Site: www.aisinworld.com
Automotive Parts Mfr & Distr
S.I.C.: 3714
N.A.I.C.S.: 336390

AISIN CHEMICAL (THAILAND) CO., LTD. (1)
5/6 Moo 11 Rojana Industrial Park
Ban Khai, Rayong, 21120, Thailand
Tel.: (66) 389619516
Fax: (66) 38961958
Automobile Brake Pads Mfr
S.I.C.: 3714
N.A.I.C.S.: 336390

Aisin do Brasil Com. e. Ind. Ltda. (1)
Alameda Tocantins 679 Alphaville
Barueri, 06455 923 Sao Paulo, Brazil (100%)
Tel.: (55) 1132015800
Telex: 1122106
Fax: (55) 1132015824
Web Site: www.aisin.com
Emp.: 150
Auto Parts Mfr
S.I.C.: 3714
N.A.I.C.S.: 336340

AISIN EUROPE MANUFACTURING CZECH s. r. o. (1)
Cizovska 456
397 01 Pisek, Czech Republic
Tel.: (420) 382 909 111
Fax: (420) 382 909 110
E-Mail: info@aisin.co.cz
Web Site: www.aisin.co.cz
Emp.: 440
Automotive Parts Mfr & Distr
S.I.C.: 3714
N.A.I.C.S.: 336390
Milos Hnizdil *(Pres)*

Aisin Europe Manufacturing (UK) Ltd. (1)
Unit 1 Bell Heath Way Woodgate Business Park
Birmingham, B32 3BZ, United Kingdom (100%)
Tel.: (44) 1214215688
Fax: (44) 1214215633
Web Site: www.aisin.com
Emp.: 150
S.I.C.: 3714
N.A.I.C.S.: 336340
Hideki Aichi *(Mng Dir)*

Aisin Europe S.A. (1)
Ave De I Indus 21
Parc Indus, 1420 Braine-l'Alleud, Belgium
Tel.: (32) 23870707
Telex: 25449
Fax: (32) 23871766
Web Site: www.aisin-europe.com
Emp.: 70
Marketing of Automotive Parts
S.I.C.: 5013
N.A.I.C.S.: 441310

Aisin Mexicana S.A. De. C.V. (1)
Calle Texas 100 Oriente Parque Industrial Nacional
Cienega De Flores, NL Mexico, CP 65550, Mexico
Tel.: (52) 8183197733
Fax: (52) 8183197735
E-Mail: gonzalez@aisinmx.com
Web Site: www.aisin.com
Emp.: 500
Mfr. and Sale of Automotive Parts
S.I.C.: 3714
N.A.I.C.S.: 336340

AISIN MFG. AGUASCALIENTES, S. A. DE C.V. (1)
Av Mexico 208 Parque Industrial San Fransisco
20300 Mexico, Aguascalientes, Mexico
Tel.: (52) 4659673236
All Other Motor Vehicle Parts Manufacturing
S.I.C.: 3714
N.A.I.C.S.: 336390

AISIN OTOMOTIV PARCALARI SANAYI VE TICARET A. S. (1)
10 Mermerciler Organize Sanayi Bolgesi 1 Sanayi Caddesi
Istanbul, Turkey
Tel.: (90) 2165932130
Fax: (90) 2165932141
Automotive Parts Mfr
S.I.C.: 3714
N.A.I.C.S.: 336390

Aisin Seiki (Foshan) Body Parts Co., Ltd. (1)
High-Tech Industrial Park Zone A 5th Ring Road
Nanhai, Foshan, Guangdong, 523888, China
Tel.: (86) 75728620890
Fax: (86) 75728620910
Web Site: www.asfb.cn
Emp.: 300
Automotive Parts Mfr & Sales
S.I.C.: 3714
N.A.I.C.S.: 336390

AW EUROPE S.A. (1)
Avenue de l'Industrie 19
1420 Braine-l'Alleud, Belgium
Tel.: (32) 2 389 12 00
Fax: (32) 2 389 1210
E-Mail: info@aweurope.be
Web Site: www.aw-europe.be
Car Navigation Systems Mfr & Distr
S.I.C.: 3714
N.A.I.C.S.: 336390

Aw Technical Center Europe S.A. (1)
Avenue de l'Industrie 19
1420 Braine-l'Alleud, Belgium
Tel.: (32) 23891200
Fax: (32) 2 389 12 10
Web Site: www.awtce.be
Car Navigation Systems Mfr & Distr
S.I.C.: 3714
N.A.I.C.S.: 336390

Elite Sewing Machine Mfg. Co., Ltd. (1)
3 3rd Road Taichung Industrial Park
Taichung, Taiwan
Tel.: (886) 423591111
Telex: 51170
Fax: (886) 423500713
Web Site: www.twelite.com.tw
Sls.: $102,256,853
Emp.: 658
Household Sewing Machines & Automotive Parts Mfr & Sales
S.I.C.: 3639
N.A.I.C.S.: 335228

FT TECHNO EUROPE GmbH (1)
Odenwaldstr 3
Neu-Isenburg, Hesse, 63263, Germany
Tel.: (49) 61023678951
Fax: (49) 6102799064
Web Site: www.fttechno.co.jp
Emp.: 1
Automotive Parts Repair Services
S.I.C.: 7549
N.A.I.C.S.: 811198
Masao Kawauchi *(Gen Mgr)*

IMRA Europe S.A. (1)
220 Rue Albert Caquot Sophia Antipolis
PO Box 213
6904 Valbonne, France (100%)
Mailing Address:
PO Box: BP 213
06904 Sophia-Antipolis, Cedex, France
Tel.: (33) 493957373
Fax: (33) 493957383
Web Site: www.imra-europe.com
Emp.: 25
S.I.C.: 3714
N.A.I.C.S.: 336340
Takashi Mitsumoto *(Pres)*

Liberty Mexicana S.A. de C.V. (1)
Km 15 100 Carretera Mexico Laredo
Santa Clara, Estado De Mexico, 554000, Mexico (100%)
Tel.: (52) 5555692333
Telex: 1771964
Fax: (52) 5557550069
Web Site: www.libertymexicana.com
Emp.: 94
Mfr. of Sewing Machines for Home & Industrial Use
S.I.C.: 3639
N.A.I.C.S.: 335228

P.T. Aisin Indonesia (1)
E Jakarta Industrial Park Plot 5J
Lemahabang, Bekasi, West Java, Indonesia Id (100%)
Tel.: (62) 218970909
Fax: (62) 218970910
Emp.: 1,000
S.I.C.: 3714
N.A.I.C.S.: 336340

Siam Aisin Co., Ltd. (1)
235 Moo 7 Tha Tum District
Simahaphot, Prachin Buri, 25140, Thailand
Tel.: (66) 37208612
Fax: (66) 37208581
E-Mail: hanakuma@siamaisin.co.ch
Web Site: www.siamaisin.co.ch
Emp.: 2,000
S.I.C.: 3714
N.A.I.C.S.: 336340
Hanakuma Makoto *(CEO)*

Tangshan Aisin Automotive Parts Co., Ltd (1)
No 297 Weiguo North Road High Tech Development Zone
Tangshan, Hebei, 063020, China
Tel.: (86) 3153852168
Fax: (86) 3153177982
Automotive Parts Mfr
S.I.C.: 3714
N.A.I.C.S.: 336390

Tangshan Aisin Gear Co., Ltd. (1)
Feng Run Qu
Hebei, Tangshan, Hebei, China
Tel.: (86) 3153086114
Fax: (86) 3153242352
Web Site: www.tagc.com.cn
Auto Parts Development, Design, Manufacturing & Sales
S.I.C.: 3714
N.A.I.C.S.: 336340

Tianjin Aisin Automobile Parts Co., Ltd. (1)
8 BeiCang Road
Tianjin, BeiChan District, China
Tel.: (86) 22 2681 1524
Fax: (86) 22 2639 0977
Web Site: www.aisinworld.com
Emp.: 620
Manufacture & Sale of Automotive Parts
S.I.C.: 3714
N.A.I.C.S.: 336340
Masahiko Komuro *(Pres)*

YCK (THAILAND) CO., LTD. (1)
74/4 Moo 7 Bangbuathong Suphanburi Road Laharn
Amphur Bangbuathong, Nonthaburi, 11110, Thailand
Tel.: (66) 2925 5164
Fax: (66) 2925 5166
Automotive Parts Mfr
S.I.C.: 3714
N.A.I.C.S.: 336390

AISINO CO., LTD

No 18A Xingshikou street
Haidian District, Beijing, China 100195
Tel.: (86) 10 88896666
Fax: (86) 10 88896888
E-Mail: stock@aisino.com
Web Site: www.aisino.com
Year Founded: 2000
600271—(SHG)

Business Description:
Information Technology Services
S.I.C.: 7373
N.A.I.C.S.: 541512

Personnel:
Zhennan Liu *(Gen Mgr)*

AIT CORPORATION

Nissei Fushimimachi-Bldg 2F 4-4-1 Fushimimachi
Chuo-ku Osaka-shi, Osaka, 541-0044, Japan
Tel.: (81) 662052612
Fax: (81) 662052613
Web Site: www.ait-jp.com
Year Founded: 1988
9381—(TKS)
Sales Range: $100-124.9 Million
Emp.: 200

Business Description:
Freight Forwarding & Ship Brokerage Services
S.I.C.: 4731
N.A.I.C.S.: 488510

Personnel:
Hidekazu Yagura *(Pres & CEO)*

AITKEN CHEVROLET BUICK GMC

51 Queensway E
Simcoe, ON, N3Y 4M5, Canada
Tel.: (519) 426-1680
Fax: (519) 426-5584
Toll Free: (866) 920-5328
Web Site: www.aitkenchev.ca
Year Founded: 1922
Rev.: $12,751,926
Emp.: 70

Business Description:
New & Used Car Dealers
S.I.C.: 5511
N.A.I.C.S.: 441110

Personnel:
Paul Cripps *(Owner)*

AITKEN SPENCE & CO., LTD.

305 Vauxhall Street
Colombo, 2, Sri Lanka
Tel.: (94) 1 308308
E-Mail: info@aitkenspence.lk
Web Site: www.aitkenspence.lk
SPEN—(COL)
Sales Range: $200-249.9 Million
Emp.: 5,328

Business Description:
Tourism, Cargo Handling, Printing & Packaging, Plantations, Property Development & Management Services; Manufacture of Clothing
S.I.C.: 4725
N.A.I.C.S.: 561520

Personnel:
D. H. S. Jayawardena *(Chm)*
J. M. S. Brito *(Deputy Chm & Mng Dir)*
Nilanthi Sivapragasam *(CFO)*
Nimmi W. de A. Guneratne *(Member-Mgmt Bd)*
Vipula M. Gunatilleka *(Member-Mgmt Bd)*
C. M. Susith Jayawickrama *(Member-Mgmt Bd)*
Ranjan E. V. Casie Chetty *(Sec)*

Board of Directors:

Aitken Spence & Co., Ltd.—(Continued)

D. H. S. Jayawardena
R. N. Asirwatham
J. M. S. Brito
Niranjan J. de Silva Deva Aditya
Parakrama Dissanayake
Rohan M. Fernando
V. Manilal Fernando
Charles H. Gomez
Gehan M. Perera
G. C. Wickremasinghe

Subsidiary:

Aitken Spence Hotel Holdings PLC (1)
No 315 Vauxhall Street
Colombo, 2, Sri Lanka
Tel.: (94) 112308308
Fax: (94) 112446838
Web Site: www.aitkenspencehotels.com
AHUN—(COL)
Rev.: $94,481,579
Assets: $175,524,422
Liabilities: $51,263,318
Net Worth: $124,261,104
Earnings: $21,480,300
Emp.: 2,274
Fiscal Year-end: 03/31/13
Hotel Management Services
S.I.C.: 7011
N.A.I.C.S.: 721110
Deshamanya D. Harry S. Jayawardena *(Chm)*
Joseph Suresh Michael Brito *(Deputy Chm & Mng Dir)*
Lakshman Ekanayake *(CEO-Indian Sector)*
Ranjan Emmanuel Victor Casie Chetty *(Sec)*

AIV GMBH + CO. KG

Tatschenweg 1
74078 Heilbronn, Germany
Tel.: (49) 71315930
Fax: (49) 71315953639
E-Mail: info@aiv.de
Web Site: www.aiv.de
Year Founded: 1976
Rev.: $19,181,725
Emp.: 90

Business Description:
Cabling & Accessory Distr
S.I.C.: 4813
N.A.I.C.S.: 517110

Personnel:
Marc Seigerschmidt *(Co-Mng Dir)*
Armin Strassburger *(Co-Mng Dir)*

AIVTECH INTERNATIONAL GROUP CO.

1305 East Hightech Plaza Phase 2
Tian'An Cyber Park
Futian District, Shenzhen, Guangdong, China
Tel.: (86) 139 2349 3889
Web Site: www.aivtechgroup.com
Year Founded: 2007
AIVI—(OTC)
Sales Range: $50-74.9 Million
Emp.: 693

Business Description:
Consumer Electronic Products Mfr
S.I.C.: 3679
N.A.I.C.S.: 334419

Personnel:
JinLin Guo *(Chm, Pres & CEO)*
YiLin Shi *(CFO)*
Yiheng Chen *(COO)*
Hu Fan *(Sec)*

Board of Directors:
JinLin Guo
James C. Hansel
YiLin Shi
Jian Wang
Wenbing Wu

Transfer Agent:
Island Stock Transfer Inc
100 Second Avenue South Suite 705S
Saint Petersburg, FL 33701

AIXTRON SE

Kaiserstr 98
52134 Herzogenrath, Germany
Tel.: (49) 241 8909 0
Fax: (49) 241 8909 40
E-Mail: info@aixtron.com
Web Site: www.aixtron.com
Year Founded: 1983
AIXG—(DEU NASDAQ)
Rev.: $251,153,187
Assets: $773,517,426
Liabilities: $134,309,676
Net Worth: $639,207,750
Earnings: ($138,740,425)
Emp.: 776
Fiscal Year-end: 12/31/13

Business Description:
Semiconductor Devices Mfr
S.I.C.: 3674
N.A.I.C.S.: 334413

Personnel:
Kim Schindelhauer *(Chm-Supervisory Bd)*
Holger Jurgensen *(Deputy Chm-Supervisory Bd)*
Martin Goetzeler *(Pres & CEO)*
Wolfgang Breme *(CFO)*
Bernd Schulte *(COO)*

Supervisory Board of Directors:
Kim Schindelhauer
Wolfgang Blattchen
Petra Denk
Holger Jurgensen
Karl-Hermann Kuklies
Rudiger von Rosen

U.S. Subsidiary:

AIXTRON Inc. (1)
1139 Karlstad Dr
Sunnyvale, CA 94089-2117 CA
Tel.: (408) 747-7120
Fax: (408) 747-7199
E-Mail: usinfo@aixtron.com
Web Site: www.aixtron.com
Emp.: 100
Capital Equipment & Processes Designer, Mfr & Marketer For Advanced Semiconductor Manufacturing Export
S.I.C.: 3443
N.A.I.C.S.: 332410
Sasangan Ramanathan *(CTO)*

AIZAWA SECURITIES CO., LTD.

1-20-3 Nihonbashi Chuo-ku
Tokyo, 103-0027, Japan
Tel.: (81) 3 3272 3127
Fax: (81) 3 3272 4818
Web Site: www.aizawa.co.jp
Year Founded: 1918
8708—(JAS)
Rev.: $125,147,000
Assets: $804,661,000
Liabilities: $321,453,000
Net Worth: $483,208,000
Earnings: $20,119,000
Fiscal Year-end: 03/31/13

Business Description:
Security Services
S.I.C.: 7382
N.A.I.C.S.: 561621

Personnel:
Motoya Aizawa *(Chm, Pres & CEO)*
Kouzou Saitou *(Sr Mng Dir)*
Akira Hasunuma *(Exec Officer)*
Fumitoshi Ishikawa *(Exec Officer)*
Atsushi Ohishi *(Exec Officer)*
Takaaki Okada *(Exec Officer)*

Board of Directors:
Motoya Aizawa
Yuuji Kakubou
Kouzou Saitou
Hideo Sakurna
Sumio Yui

AJ BELL HOLDINGS LIMITED

Trafford House Chester Road
Manchester, M32 0RS, United Kingdom
Tel.: (44) 845 40 89 100
Fax: (44) 845 40 89 200
E-Mail: enquiry@ajbell.co.uk
Web Site: www.ajbell.co.uk
Rev.: $94,773,522
Assets: $159,117,770
Liabilities: $81,565,074
Net Worth: $77,552,696
Earnings: $94,773,522
Emp.: 495
Fiscal Year-end: 09/30/13

Business Description:
Pension Services
S.I.C.: 6371
N.A.I.C.S.: 524292

Personnel:
Andy Bell *(CEO & Member-Mgmt Bd)*
Michael Summersgill *(CFO & Member-Mgmt Bd)*
Richard Taylor *(COO & Member-Mgmt Bd)*
Roger Stott *(Chief Risk Officer & Member-Mgmt Bd)*
Bruce Robinson *(Member-Mgmt Bd, Sec & Dir-Legal Svcs)*
Charles Galbraith *(Member-Mgmt Bd & Mng Dir-Youinvest)*
Fergus Lyons *(Member-Mgmt Bd & Mng Dir-Sippcentre)*

Board of Directors:
Les Platts
Andy Bell
Bruce Robinson
Michael Summersgill

Subsidiary:

AJ Bell Securities Limited (1)
Calverley House 55 Calverley Road
Tunbridge Wells, Kent, TN1 2TU, United Kingdom UK
Tel.: (44) 1892 523 346
Fax: (44) 1892 525 003
E-Mail: ajbellsecurities@ajbell.co.uk
Web Site: www.ajbellsecurities.co.uk
Securities Dealing
S.I.C.: 6211
N.A.I.C.S.: 523110
Martyn Ault *(Dir-Ops)*

A.J. LUCAS GROUP LIMITED

Level 3 394 Lane Cove Road
Macquarie Park, NSW, 2113, Australia
Mailing Address:
Locked Bag 2113
North Ryde, NSW, 1670, Australia
Tel.: (61) 294904000
Fax: (61) 294904200
E-Mail: mail@lucas.com.au
Web Site: www.lucas.com.au
AJL—(ASX)
Rev.: $307,201,701
Assets: $347,411,130
Liabilities: $210,229,086
Net Worth: $137,182,044
Earnings: ($132,342,532)
Emp.: 500
Fiscal Year-end: 06/30/13

Business Description:
Pipeline & Drilling Services
S.I.C.: 3533
N.A.I.C.S.: 333132

Personnel:
Phillip Arnall *(Interim CEO)*
Mark Summergreene *(CFO)*
Brett Tredinnick *(COO)*
Simon Soon *(CIO)*
Nicholas Swan *(Sec)*

Board of Directors:
Julian Ball
Genelle Coghlan
Martin Green
Mike McDermott

Subsidiaries:

AJ Lucas Coal Technologies Pty Limited (1)
616 Danjrry RD
Brisbane, QLD, 4077, Australia
Tel.: (61) 733637333
Fax: (61) 733637399
Emp.: 80
Drilling Services
S.I.C.: 1381
N.A.I.C.S.: 213111
Brett Tredinnick *(Gen Mgr)*

AJ Lucas Drilling Pty Limited (1)
Locked Bag 2113
North Ryde, NSW, 1670, Australia
Tel.: (61) 294904000
Fax: (61) 294904200
E-Mail: mail@lucas.com.au
Emp.: 1,400
Drilling Services
S.I.C.: 1629
N.A.I.C.S.: 237110

AJ Lucas Operations Pty Limited (1)
157 Church St
Ryde, NSW, 2113, Australia
Tel.: (61) 2 9809 6866
Fax: (61) 2 9490 4200
Emp.: 90
Building Construction & Drilling Services
S.I.C.: 1629
N.A.I.C.S.: 236210

AJ Lucas Plant & Equipment Pty Limited (1)
394 Lane Cove Rd
Macquarie Park, NSW, 2113, Australia
Tel.: (61) 294904000
Fax: (61) 294904200
E-Mail: mail@lucas.com.au
Drilling Well & Pipiline Services
S.I.C.: 1629
N.A.I.C.S.: 237110

AJ Lucas Testing Pty Limited (1)
Locked Bag 2113
North Ryde, NSW, 1670, Australia
Tel.: (61) 294904000
Fax: (61) 294904200
Emp.: 200
Inspecting & Testing Services
S.I.C.: 7389
N.A.I.C.S.: 541350
Ian Ridsein *(Gen Mgr)*

Geosearch Drilling Service Pty Ltd (1)
51-57 Johnson St
Rockhampton, QLD, 4701, Australia
Tel.: (61) 7 4936 4700
Fax: (61) 7 4936 4707
Coal Mining Services
S.I.C.: 1241
N.A.I.C.S.: 213113
Doug Newtrn *(Mgr)*

Lucas Energy Pty Limited (1)
Level 8 160 Queen St
Melbourne, VIC, 3000, Australia
Tel.: (61) 386157800
Fax: (61) 386157888
E-Mail: mail@lucas.com.au
Web Site: www.lucas.com.au/contactus/OurOffices.htm
Emp.: 5
Drilling Services
S.I.C.: 1381
N.A.I.C.S.: 213111
Michael Arbon *(Gen Mgr)*

McDermott Drilling Pty Ltd (1)
24-16 Airds Rd
Minto, Sydney, NSW, 2259, Australia
Tel.: (61) 2 8796 0900
Fax: (61) 2 8795 0633
Emp.: 60
Coal Drilling & Exploration Service
S.I.C.: 1241
N.A.I.C.S.: 213113
Michael McDermott *(Mng Dir)*

Non-U.S. Subsidiary:

Lucas SARL (1)
8 Rue Du Gen Barbot
Saint-Laurent-Blangy, Pas-de-Calais, 62223, France
Tel.: (33) 975524660

Fax: (33) 321242462
Machine Tools Mfr
S.I.C.: 3541
N.A.I.C.S.: 333517

A.J. PLAST PUBLIC COMPANY LIMITED

95 Thakarm Rd Samaedam
Bangkhuntien, Bangkok, 10150, Thailand
Tel.: (66) 2 415 0035
Fax: (66) 2 415 3795
E-Mail: export@ajplast.co.th
Web Site: www.ajplast.co.th
Year Founded: 1987
AJ—(THA)
Rev.: $175,144,833
Assets: $202,351,329
Liabilities: $84,466,579
Net Worth: $117,884,750
Earnings: $6,294,922
Fiscal Year-end: 12/31/12

Business Description:
Biaxially Oriented Film Mfr
S.I.C.: 3999
N.A.I.C.S.: 339999

Personnel:
Narong Suthisamphat *(Chm)*
Napaporn Suthipongchai *(Exec VP)*
Kittiphat Suthisamphat *(Exec VP)*

Board of Directors:
Narong Suthisamphat
Surasak Kosiyachinda
Ninnat Olanvoravuth
Thien Ratitamkul
Chavida Srisangnam
Napaporn Suthipongchai
Kittiphat Suthisamphat
Supote Tonurat

AJ POWER LIMITED

1 Charlestown Drive Carn Industrial Area
Craigavon, BT63 5GA, United Kingdom
Tel.: (44) 28 3836 1000
Fax: (44) 28 3836 1010
E-Mail: info@ajpower.net
Web Site: www.ajpower.net
Year Founded: 2003
Sales Range: $50-74.9 Million
Emp.: 74

Business Description:
Diesel Generator Mfr
S.I.C.: 3621
N.A.I.C.S.: 335312

Personnel:
Ashley Pigott *(Founder & Mng Dir)*

AJACCIO AUTOMOBILES

Vignetta Campo Dell Oro
20090 Ajaccio, Corse, France
Tel.: (33) 495239090
Fax: (33) 495239083
Sls.: $21,300,000
Emp.: 66

Business Description:
New & Used Car Dealers
S.I.C.: 5511
N.A.I.C.S.: 441110

Personnel:
Marc Baldi *(Dir-Mktg)*

Board of Directors:
Jean-Baptiste Paoli

AJANTA PHARMA LIMITED

98 Ajanta House Charkop Kandivili West
Mumbai, 400 067, India
Tel.: (91) 2266061000
Fax: (91) 2266061200
E-Mail: info@ajantapharma.com
Web Site: www.ajantapharma.com
AJANTPHARM—(NSE)
Rev.: $174,155,490
Assets: $133,157,988
Liabilities: $60,216,066
Net Worth: $72,941,922
Earnings: $20,785,194
Emp.: 4,000
Fiscal Year-end: 03/31/13

Business Description:
Pharmaceutical Products Mfr
S.I.C.: 2834
N.A.I.C.S.: 325412

Personnel:
Madhusudan B. Agrawal *(Vice Chm)*
Rajesh M. Agrawal *(Mng Dir)*
Yogesh M. Agrawal *(Mng Dir)*
Arvind K. Agrawal *(CFO)*
Deodatta Pandit *(Compliance Officer, Sec & Gen Mgr-Legal)*

Board of Directors:
Mannalal B. Agrawal
Madhusudan B. Agrawal
Rajesh M. Agrawal
Yogesh M. Agrawal
Chandrakant M. Khetan
Anil Kumar
Subal Chandra Saha
K. H. Vishwanathan

Transfer Agent:
Link Intime India Private Limited
C-13 Pannalal Silk Mills Compound L.B.S. Marg Bhandup
Mumbai, India

Non-U.S. Subsidiaries:

Ajanta Pharma (Mauritius) Limited **(1)**
BPML Building
Goodlands, Mauritius
Tel.: (230) 2836591
Fax: (230) 2831172
E-Mail: apml.info@ajantapharma.com
Pharmaceutical Products Mfr
S.I.C.: 2834
N.A.I.C.S.: 325412

Ajanta Pharma Philippines Inc. **(1)**
710 AXA Life Center Sen Gil Puyat Ave c/r Tindalo Street
San Antonio Village, Makati, Metro Manila, 12000, Philippines
Tel.: (63) 2 844 7350
Fax: (63) 2 844 3580
E-Mail: inquiry@ajantapharma.com.ph
Pharmaceutical Products Mfr
S.I.C.: 2834
N.A.I.C.S.: 325412

AJANTA SOYA LIMITED

12th Floor Bigjos Tower A-8 Netaji Subhash Place
Wazirpur District Centre, Delhi, 110 034, India
Tel.: (91) 11 42515151
Fax: (91) 11 42515100
E-Mail: info@ajantasoya.com
Web Site: www.ajantasoya.com
Year Founded: 1992
519216—(BOM)
Rev.: $77,795,277
Assets: $13,583,400
Liabilities: $8,705,163
Net Worth: $4,878,237
Earnings: $97,012
Fiscal Year-end: 03/31/13

Business Description:
Edible Oil Mfr
S.I.C.: 2075
N.A.I.C.S.: 311224

Personnel:
Sushil Goyal *(Chm & Mng Dir)*
Tajinder Singh Bhatia *(Compliance Officer)*
Shalini Agrawal *(Sec)*

Board of Directors:
Sushil Goyal
Hement Kumar Bansal
Abhey Goyal
Bishan Goyal
Babu Lal Jain
Harsh Chander Kansal

Transfer Agent:
Skyline Financial Services Pvt Ltd.
D 153A 1st Floor Okhla Industrial Area Phase 1
New Delhi, India

AJAX JEEP EAGLE LTD

(d/b/a Menzies Chrysler Inc)
1602 Champlain Ave
Whitby, ON, L1N 6A7, Canada
Tel.: (905) 683-4100
Fax: (905) 428-3463
Toll Free: (866) 981-4314
Web Site: www.menzieschrysler.autotrader.ca
Rev.: $109,202,857
Emp.: 165

Business Description:
New & Used Car Dealers
S.I.C.: 5511
N.A.I.C.S.: 441110

Personnel:
Todd Menzies *(Owner)*

AJCON GLOBAL SERVICES LTD.

408 Express Zone A - Wing Cello-Sonal Realty Near Patels
Western Express Highway Goregaon East, Mumbai, 400063, India
Tel.: (91) 22 67160400
Fax: (91) 22 28722061
E-Mail: ajcon@ajcon.net
Web Site: www.ajcononline.com
511692—(BOM)
Rev.: $1,697,251
Assets: $8,709,042
Liabilities: $5,292,101
Net Worth: $3,416,942
Earnings: $130,961
Fiscal Year-end: 03/31/13

Business Description:
Financial Advisory Services
S.I.C.: 6282
N.A.I.C.S.: 523930

Personnel:
Ashok Kumar Ajmera *(Chm, CEO, Mng Dir & CFO)*
Shailendra Pathak *(Compliance Officer & Sec)*
Abhishek Mishra *(Sr Exec-Corp Advisory & Merchant Banking Div)*
Pallavi Ajmera *(Sr VP-Investment Banking)*

Board of Directors:
Ashok Kumar Ajmera
Ankit Ajmera
Anuj Ajmera
Narayan Atal
Rajendra Bakiwala
Sameer Biswas

Transfer Agent:
Bigshare Services Pvt. Ltd.
E-2/3 Ansa Industrial Estate Sakivihar Road Saki Naka Andheri E
Mumbai, India

AJEL LTD.

106 Mhada Shopping Complex New Link Road Oshilwara
Jogeshwari West, Mumbai, Maharashtra, India
Tel.: (91) 22 2630 3342
Fax: (91) 22 2634 9264
E-Mail: info@ajel.com
Web Site: www.ajel.in
530713—(BOM)
Sales Range: $10-24.9 Million

Business Description:
Information Technology Consulting Services
S.I.C.: 7373
N.A.I.C.S.: 541512

Personnel:
Bharat C. Sutaria *(Chm)*
Srinivasa Reddy Arikatla *(Vice Chm & Mng Dir)*

Board of Directors:
Bharat C. Sutaria
Srinivasa Reddy Arikatla
Venkateswarlu Arikatla
Vijay S. Chokshi
Darshan Majmudar
Mahender R Musuku
Jadda Amara Reddy

U.S. Subsidiary:

Ajel Technologies Inc **(1)**
45 Brunswick Ave Ste 222
Edison, NJ 08817
Tel.: (732) 476-6000
Fax: (732) 476-6001
Toll Free: (800) 514-2535
E-Mail: info@ajel.com
Web Site: www.ajel.com
Information Technology Services
S.I.C.: 7371
N.A.I.C.S.: 541511
Sam Joseph *(VP)*

AJIAL REAL ESTATE ENTERTAINMENT COMPANY K.S.C.C.

PO Box 22448
Safat, Kuwait, 13058, Kuwait
Tel.: (965) 1829000
Fax: (965) 22233062
E-Mail: info@ajial-realestate.com
Web Site: www.ajial-realestate.com
AREEC—(KUW)
Rev.: $13,600,298
Assets: $454,422,894
Liabilities: $47,512,455
Net Worth: $406,910,440
Earnings: $772,503
Fiscal Year-end: 12/31/12

Business Description:
Real Estate & Entertainment Services
S.I.C.: 6531
N.A.I.C.S.: 531390

Personnel:
Khalid Othman Al Othman *(Chm & Mng Dir)*
Bader Jasmin Al Sumait *(Vice Chm)*

Board of Directors:
Khalid Othman Al Othman
Waleed Abdullatif Al Nusif
Ali Al Abdulla Al Khalifa Al Sabah
Bader Yousif Al Salman
Bader Jasmin Al Sumait

AJINEXTEK CO., LTD.

9-3 Holim-dong Dalseo-gu
Daegu, Korea (South)
Tel.: (82) 53 593 3700
Fax: (82) 53 593 3703
Web Site: www.ajinextek.com
Year Founded: 1995
059120—(KRS)

Business Description:
Semiconductor Devices Mfr
S.I.C.: 3674
N.A.I.C.S.: 334413

Personnel:
Chang-Ho Kim *(Pres)*

AJINOMOTO COMPANY, INC.

15-1 Kyobashi 1-chome Chuo-ku
Tokyo, 104 8315, Japan
Tel.: (81) 352508111
Fax: (81) 3 5250 8378
E-Mail: pr_info@ajinomoto.com
Web Site: www.ajinomoto.com
Year Founded: 1909
2802—(TKS)
Sls.: $12,896,862,000
Assets: $12,009,151,000
Liabilities: $4,400,341,000
Net Worth: $7,608,810,000

Ajinomoto Company, Inc.—(Continued)

Earnings: $532,103,000
Emp.: 27,518
Fiscal Year-end: 03/31/13

Business Description:
Seasoning, Vegetable Oils, Processed Foods, Beverages & Dairy Products, Amino Acids & Specialty Chemicals Mfr
S.I.C.: 2099
N.A.I.C.S.: 311999

Personnel:
Norio Yamaguchi *(Chm)*
Masatoshi Ito *(Pres & CEO)*
Yutaka Kunimoto *(Deputy Pres)*
Hideki Takeuchi *(Corp Exec Officer)*
Alain Vrillon *(Corp Exec Officer)*
Hiroshi Motoyama *(Pres-Osaka Office)*
Koji Igarashi *(Sr VP-Bus Strategy & Dev Dept)*
Tamotsu Iwamoto *(Sr VP-Internal Auditing Dept, Gen Affairs & Risk Mgmt Dept)*

Board of Directors:
Norio Yamaguchi
Hiroshi Fukushi
Sakie Tachibana Fukushima
Koji Igarashi
Masatoshi Ito
Tamotsu Iwamoto
Yutaka Kunimoto
Takashi Nagamachi
Takaaki Nishii
Hiromichi Ono
Yasuo Saito
Hideaki Shinada
Etsuhiro Takato
Masaya Tochio

Subsidiaries:

AJINOMOTO LOGISTICS CORPORATION **(1)**
1-17-24 Shinkawa
Chuo-Ku, Tokyo, 104-0033, Japan
Tel.: (81) 355423636
Fax: (81) 35553162
Web Site: www.ab-kk.co.jp
Logistics Consulting Services
S.I.C.: 4731
N.A.I.C.S.: 541614

Ajinomoto Pharmaceuticals Co., Ltd. **(1)**
1-1 Irifune 2-chome
Chuo-ku, Tokyo, 104-0042, Japan
Tel.: (81) 3 6280 9500
Fax: (81) 3 6280 9912
Web Site: www.ajinomoto-seiyaku.co.jp
Emp.: 200
Pharmaceuticals Products Mfr & Distr
S.I.C.: 2834
N.A.I.C.S.: 325412
Tomoyasu Toyoda *(Pres & CEO)*

Ajinomoto Treasury Management, Inc. **(1)**
1-15-1 Kyobashi
Chuo-Ku, Tokyo, 104-0031, Japan
Tel.: (81) 352508676
Treasury Management Services
S.I.C.: 8748
N.A.I.C.S.: 541618

Knorr Foods Co., Ltd. **(1)**
12-1 Shimonoge 2-chome
Takatsu-ku, Kawasaki, Kanagawa, 213-8505, Japan
Tel.: (81) 448113111
Fax: (81) 448449154
Web Site: www.ajinomoto.co.jp/ktc/e/company/index.html
Processed Food Distr
S.I.C.: 5142
N.A.I.C.S.: 424420

U.S. Subsidiaries:

Ajinomoto U.S.A., Inc. **(1)**
One Parker Plz 400 Kelby St
Fort Lee, NJ 07024 NY
Tel.: (201) 292-3200
Web Site: www.ajinomoto-usa.com
Emp.: 50
Provider of Food Enhancement Products Import Export
S.I.C.: 5142
N.A.I.C.S.: 424420
Shinichi Suzuki *(Pres & CEO)*

Subsidiaries:

Ajinomoto AminoScience LLC **(2)**
4020 Ajinomoto Dr
Raleigh, NC 27610-2911
Tel.: (919) 231-0100
Fax: (919) 231-6275
Toll Free: (800) 682-0982
Web Site: www.ajinomoto-usa.com
Emp.: 130
Mfr. of Amino Acids
S.I.C.: 2869
N.A.I.C.S.: 325199
Jack Heaton *(Pres)*

Ajinomoto Frozen Foods U.S.A., Inc. **(2)**
7124 N Marine Dr
Portland, OR 97203-6480
Tel.: (503) 286-6548
Fax: (503) 286-7089
Web Site: www.ajinomotofoods.com
Emp.: 100
Frozen Foods Mfr
S.I.C.: 2037
N.A.I.C.S.: 311411
Haruo Kurata *(Pres)*

Ajinomoto Heartland LLC **(2)**
8430 W Bryn Mawr Ave Ste 650
Chicago, IL 60631-3421 (100%)
Tel.: (773) 380-7000
Telex: 350 467
Fax: (773) 380-7006
Web Site: www.lysine.com
Emp.: 20
Mfr. of Amino Acids for Feed Use
S.I.C.: 2048
N.A.I.C.S.: 311119
Dennis Mullane *(Treas & VP)*

Ajinomoto Althea, Inc **(1)**
(Formerly Althea Technologies, Inc.)
11040 Roselle St
San Diego, CA 92121
Tel.: (858) 882-0123
Fax: (858) 882-0133
Toll Free: (888) 425-8432
Web Site: www.altheatech.com
Sales Range: $75-99.9 Million
Emp.: 220
Biological Product Contract Research & Manufacturing Services
S.I.C.: 2834
N.A.I.C.S.: 325412
Francois Ferre *(Co-Founder & Co-Chm)*
Magda Marquet *(Co-Founder & Co-Chm)*
Hiroshi Shiragami *(Co-Chm)*
J. David Enloe, Jr. *(Pres & CEO)*
Martha J. Demski *(CFO & Sr VP)*
E. J. Brandreth *(Sr VP-Quality & Regulatory)*
Christopher Duffy *(Sr VP-Ops)*

Non-U.S. Subsidiaries:

A.I.F. Investments Pte. Ltd. **(1)**
Ocean Bldg 10 Collyer Quay No 19 08
Singapore, 049315, Singapore
Tel.: (65) 65365355
Fax: (65) 65361360
Investment Services
S.I.C.: 6211
N.A.I.C.S.: 523999

Ajinomoto Bioitalia S.p.A. **(1)**
Via Gramsci 1
45013 Bottrighe, Italy (100%)
Tel.: (39) 0426995311
Fax: (39) 0426995303
Web Site: www.ajinomoto-europe.com
Emp.: 90
S.I.C.: 2033
N.A.I.C.S.: 311421

Ajinomoto Biolatina Industria e Comercio Ltda. **(1)**
Rua Joaquim Tavora 541
04015 001 Sao Paulo, SP, Brazil (90%)
Tel.: (55) 1155796971
Fax: (55) 1155757146
Web Site: www.lisina.com.br
Emp.: 15
S.I.C.: 2033
N.A.I.C.S.: 311421

Ajinomoto (China) Co., Ltd. **(1)**
Room 2201 A Tower A Full Link Plz 18
Chaoyangmerwai Ave
Chaoyang District, Beijing, 100020, China
Tel.: (86) 10 6588 0220
Fax: (86) 10 6588 0330
Web Site: www.ajinomoto.com.cn
Food Mfr & Marketer
S.I.C.: 2033
N.A.I.C.S.: 311421

Ajinomoto Co., (Hong Kong) Ltd. **(1)**
21 F Bangkok Bank Bldg 14 20 Bonham Strand W
Hong Kong, China (Hong Kong) (100%)
Tel.: (852) 25342888
Fax: (852) 25342899
E-Mail: sales@ajinomoto.com.hk
Web Site: www.ajinomoto.com.hk
Emp.: 6
S.I.C.: 2033
N.A.I.C.S.: 311421
Masachi Shimbo *(Mng Dir)*

Ajinomoto Co., (Thailand) Ltd. **(1)**
487/1 Si Ayutthaya Road Khwaeng Thanon Phaya Thai
Khet Ratchathewi, Bangkok, 10400, Thailand (100%)
Tel.: (66) 22477000
Web Site: www.ajinomoto.co.th
Emp.: 40
S.I.C.: 2033
N.A.I.C.S.: 311421

Subsidiaries:

Fuji Ace Co., Ltd. **(2)**
487 1 Si Ayutahaya Rd Khwaeng Thanon Phayathai Khet Rachathewi
Bangkok, 10400, Thailand (100%)
Tel.: (66) 22460828
Fax: (66) 22460829
Web Site: www.fujiseal.co.jp
Emp.: 1,000
S.I.C.: 2033
N.A.I.C.S.: 311421
Yusuke Konishi *(VP)*

Wan Thai Foods Industry Co., Ltd. **(2)**
Bangchan Industrial Estate Plot Khor 1 Moo 14
Serithai Rd Minburi, Bangkok, 10510, Thailand
Tel.: (66) 25170944
Fax: (66) 25179564
E-Mail: sales@yumyumfoods.com
Web Site: www.yumyumfoods.com
Emp.: 500
S.I.C.: 2033
N.A.I.C.S.: 311421
Sathoru Nakamura *(Pres)*

Joint Ventures:

Ajinomoto Betagro Frozen Foods (Thailand) Co., Ltd. **(2)**
Betagro Twr N Pk 323 Vibhavadi Rangsit Rd
Bangkok, 10210, Thailand
Tel.: (66) 29550555
Fax: (66) 29550390
E-Mail: info@betagro.com
Web Site: www.betagro.com
Emp.: 60
Frozen Process Chicken Production
S.I.C.: 2038
N.A.I.C.S.: 311412
Vanus Taetaisitthon *(Chm)*

Ajinomoto Betagro Specialty Foods (Thailand) Co., Ltd. **(2)**
323 Moo 6
Lak si, Bangkok, 10210, Thailand
Tel.: (66) 28338000
Frozen Food Products Mfr & Distr
S.I.C.: 2038
N.A.I.C.S.: 311412

Ajinomoto del Peru S.A. **(1)**
Ave Republica De Panama 2455 La Victoria
Lima, 13, Peru (100%)
Mailing Address:
PO Box 14-0431
Lima, Peru
Tel.: (51) 14706050
Fax: (51) 14720274
E-Mail: postmaster@lima.ajinomoto.com
Web Site: www.ajinomoto.com.pe
Emp.: 300
S.I.C.: 2033
N.A.I.C.S.: 311421
Kunio Egashira *(Pres)*

Ajinomoto do Brasil Ind. e Com. de Alimentos Ltda. **(1)**
Oriento S/N Laranja Paulista
Sao Paulo, 18500-000, Brazil
Tel.: (55) 1532839000
Fax: (55) 1532839010
Web Site: www.ajinomoto.com.br
Food Products Mfr & Distr
S.I.C.: 2099
N.A.I.C.S.: 311999

Ajinomoto Euro-Aspartame S.A. **(1)**
ZIP Des Huttes Rte De La Grande Hernesse
59820 Gravelines, France (100%)
Tel.: (33) 328227400
Fax: (33) 328227501
Web Site: www.Aji-Aspartame.eu
Emp.: 100
Artificial Sweetener Mfr
S.I.C.: 2033
N.A.I.C.S.: 311421
Satoshi Inamori *(Pres)*

Ajinomoto Eurolysine S.A.S. **(1)**
153 Rue De Courcelles
75817 Paris, Cedex, 17, France (50%)
Tel.: (33) 1 44 40 1212
Fax: (33) 1 44 40 1213
E-Mail: ael@eli.ajinomoto.com
Web Site: www.ajinomoto-eurolysine.com
Emp.: 25
Mfr of Amino Acids for Animal & Human Nutritional Products
S.I.C.: 2819
N.A.I.C.S.: 325180
Jean Falgoux *(Pres)*

Ajinomoto Europe S.A.S **(1)**
153 Rue De Courcelles
75817 Paris, Cedex, France (100%)
Tel.: (33) 0147669863
Fax: (33) 147669856
E-Mail: info@ehq.ajinomoto.com
Web Site: www.ajinomoto-europe.com
Emp.: 11
S.I.C.: 2033
N.A.I.C.S.: 311421
Hiroakai Momura *(Pres)*

Ajinomoto Foods Deutschland GmbH **(1)**
Stubbenhuk 3
D 20459 Hamburg, Germany (100%)
Tel.: (49) 403749360
Fax: (49) 403720878
Web Site: www.ajinomoto-foods-deutschland.de
Emp.: 20
S.I.C.: 2033
N.A.I.C.S.: 311421

AJINOMOTO FOODS EUROPE S.A.S **(1)**
153 rue de Courcelles
75817 Paris, France
Tel.: (33) 143180586
Fax: (33) 1 43 80 90 10
Emp.: 8
Food Products Mfr
S.I.C.: 2099
N.A.I.C.S.: 311999
Masaru Kano *(VP)*

Ajinomoto-Genetika Research Institute **(1)**
1st Dorozny pr-d 1-1
117545 Moscow, Russia (100%)
Tel.: (7) 4956623200
Fax: (7) 4953150640
Web Site: www.ajinomoto.ru
Emp.: 100
Food Production & Research
S.I.C.: 2099
N.A.I.C.S.: 311999

Ajinomoto Interamericana Industria e Comercio Ltda. **(1)**
Rua Joaquim Tavora 541
Villa Mariana, 04015 901 Sao Paulo, SP, Brazil (100%)

Tel.: (55) 1155796971
Fax: (55) 1155757146
Web Site: www.ajinomoto.com.br
Emp.: 300
S.I.C.: 2033
N.A.I.C.S.: 311421

AJINOMOTO KOREA, INC. (1)
5F Samheung Bldg 748-16 Banpo-dong
Seocho-gu, Seoul, 137-810, Korea (South)
Tel.: (82) 2 3443 0010
Fax: (82) 2 3443 1070
E-Mail: ajikor@ajinomoto.co.kr
Web Site: www.ajinomoto.co.kr
Emp.: 16
Food Products Mfr & Distr
S.I.C.: 2099
N.A.I.C.S.: 311999
Carsten Hermann *(Gen Mgr)*

Ajinomoto (Malaysia) Berhad (1)
Lot 5710 Jalan Kuchai Lama
58200 Kuala Lumpur, Malaysia (100%)
Mailing Address:
PO Box 12507
50780 Kuala Lumpur, Malaysia
Tel.: (60) 379806958
Fax: (60) 379811731
E-Mail: info@ajinomoto-malaysia.com
Web Site: www.ajinomoto-malaysia.com
Emp.: 400
S.I.C.: 2033
N.A.I.C.S.: 311421
Ryoichi Ebata *(Mng Dir)*
Katsuhide Shirai *(CFO)*

Ajinomoto Pharmaceuticals Europe Ltd. (1)
Aubrey House 10 15
Queen St, London, EC4N 1TX, United Kingdom
Tel.: (44) 2072360160
Fax: (44) 1737378430
Web Site: www.ajinomoto-europe.com
S.I.C.: 2033
N.A.I.C.S.: 311421

Ajinomoto Philippines Corporation (1)
Union Ajinomoto Bldg 331 Sen Gil J Puyat Ave
Makati, Metro Manila, 1200, Philippines
Tel.: (63) 28956081
Fax: (63) 8906328
E-Mail: info@ajinomoto.com.ph
Web Site: www.ajinomoto.com.ph
Emp.: 200
S.I.C.: 2033
N.A.I.C.S.: 311421
Rodel Castro *(Mgr-IT)*

Ajinomoto Poland Sp. z o.o. (1)
ul Sobieskiego
00 764 Warsaw, Poland
Tel.: (48) 228404258
Fax: (48) 228511990
Web Site: www.ajinomoto.com.pl
Emp.: 18
Vegetables & Fruits
S.I.C.: 2033
N.A.I.C.S.: 311421
Nikulfki Robert *(Gen Mgr)*

Ajinomoto (Singapore) Pte. Ltd. (1)
460 Elexendra Road 11 04 05 PSA Building
119963 Singapore, 758299, Singapore (100%)
Tel.: (65) 62572022
Fax: (65) 62576866
E-Mail: enquiry@ajinomoto.com.sg
Web Site: www.ajinomoto.com.sg
Emp.: 50
S.I.C.: 2033
N.A.I.C.S.: 311421
Zhu Enlien *(Gen Mgr)*

Ajinomoto Sweeteners Europe S.A.S. (1)
Zip des Huttes Route de la Grande Hernesse
59820 Gravelines, France
Tel.: (33) 32822 7474
Fax: (33) 32822 7575
Web Site: www.aminosweet.eu
Emp.: 100
Aspartame Sweetener Mfr & Distr
S.I.C.: 2099
N.A.I.C.S.: 311999
Satoshi Inamori *(Pres)*

Ajinomoto Switzerland A.G. (1)
Innere Guterstrasse 2 4
PO Box 4559
CH-6304 Zug, Switzerland
Tel.: (41) 4017286666
Fax: (41) 7286565
Web Site: www.ajinomoto.com.hk/contact_world.asp
S.I.C.: 2033
N.A.I.C.S.: 311421

AJINOMOTO TAIWAN INC. (1)
15F-2 No 178 Fu-Hsing N Rd
Taipei, Taiwan
Tel.: (886) 2 8712 2069
Fax: (886) 2 7701 2168
Web Site: www.ajinomoto.com.tw
Food Products Mfr
S.I.C.: 2099
N.A.I.C.S.: 311999

Ajinomoto Vietnam Co., Ltd. (1)
Bien Hoa Industrial Zone
An Bien, Dong Nai, Vietnam (100%)
Tel.: (84) 61831289
Fax: (84) 61831288
Web Site: www.ajinomoto.com
Emp.: 900
S.I.C.: 2033
N.A.I.C.S.: 311421

Amoy Food Ltd. (1)
11-15 Dai Fu Street
Tai Po Industrial Estate, Tai Po, NT, China (Hong Kong)
Tel.: (852) 26656633
Fax: (852) 26656838
E-Mail: sales.amoy@amoy.ajinomoto.com
Web Site: www.amoy.com
Emp.: 20
Asian Sauces & Frozen Dim Sum Mfr
S.I.C.: 2035
N.A.I.C.S.: 311941
Henry Yim *(Gen Mgr)*

California Manufacturing Co., Inc. (1)
Km 18 East Service Road
South Superhighway, Paranaque, Metro Manila, 1702, Philippines
Mailing Address:
P.O. Box 1955
Makati Central Post Office, 1299 Makati, Philippines
Tel.: (63) 28238021
S.I.C.: 2033
N.A.I.C.S.: 311421

Chuanhua Ajinomoto Co., Ltd. (1)
Qingbaijiang
Chengdu, Sichuan, 610301, China
Tel.: (86) 28 8360 4305
Fax: (86) 28 8360 4053
Web Site: www.ajinomoto.com
S.I.C.: 2033
N.A.I.C.S.: 311421

Henan Ajinomoto Amino Acid Co., Ltd. (1)
Erhuan Road
Xiangcheng, Henan, 466200, China (100%)
Tel.: (86) 394 421 6331
Fax: (86) 3944315574
Web Site: www.ajinomoto.com
S.I.C.: 2033
N.A.I.C.S.: 311421

Lianhua Ajinomoto Co., Ltd. (1)
Rm 2201 Lianwei Rd
Xiangcheng, Henan, 10020, China
Tel.: (86) 1065880110
Fax: (86) 1065880330
E-Mail: info@ajinomoto.com.cn
Web Site: www.ajinomoto.com.cn
Emp.: 20
Fruit & Vegetable Canning
S.I.C.: 2033
N.A.I.C.S.: 311421
Matsunada Shuji *(Pres)*

P.T. Ajinomoto Indonesia (1)
Jl Laksda Yos Sudarso 77 78 Sunter
Jakarta, 14350, Indonesia Id (100%)
Tel.: (62) 2165304455
Fax: (62) 2165304443
Web Site: www.ajinomoto.co.id
Emp.: 150
S.I.C.: 2033
N.A.I.C.S.: 311421

S.A. Ajinomoto Omnichem N.V. (1)
Industrial Research Park Fleming
B 1348 Louvain-la-Neuve, Belgium (100%)
Tel.: (32) 010483111
Fax: (32) 10450693
E-Mail: jobs@omnichem.be
Web Site: www.omnichem.be
Emp.: 160
S.I.C.: 2033
N.A.I.C.S.: 311421
Gwin Bompas *(Mng Dir)*

Shanghai Ajinomoto Amino Acid Co., Ltd. (1)
518 Rongle Road East Songjiang
Shanghai, 201613, China (100%)
Tel.: (86) 2157740370
Fax: (86) 21 5774 0433
Web Site: www.ajinomoto.com
Emp.: 100
Pharmaceutical & Amino Acid Research
S.I.C.: 2819
N.A.I.C.S.: 325180
Patricio Massera *(Gen Mgr)*

Shanghai Ajinomoto Seasoning Co., Ltd. (1)
3000 Shen Gang Rd
Songjiang, Shanghai, 201611, China
Tel.: (86) 2167600909
Fax: (86) 21 6760 0808
Processed Food Products Mfr
S.I.C.: 2099
N.A.I.C.S.: 311999

Taiso Commerce, Inc. (1)
10 Fl No 68 Changshan N Rd
Taipei, 104, Taiwan (70%)
Tel.: (886) 225210150
Fax: (886) 225215704
Web Site: www.taiso.com.tw
Sales Range: $1-9.9 Million
Emp.: 20
S.I.C.: 2033
N.A.I.C.S.: 311421
Kasai Takehiko *(Mng Dir)*

West African Seasoning Co., Ltd. (1)
37 Creek Road
Apapa, Lagos, Nigeria
Tel.: (234) 5804920
Fax: (234) 5804927
Web Site: www.ajinomoto.com
S.I.C.: 2033
N.A.I.C.S.: 311421

Non-U.S. Joint Ventures:

Lianyungang Ajinomoto Ruyi Foods Co., Ltd. (1)
Dingzi Road East
Xinpu, Lianyungang, Jiangsu, 222002, China CN
Tel.: (86) 51885150741
Fax: (86) 51885150740
Web Site: www.ajinomoto.com
Frozen Food Mfr & Distr
S.I.C.: 5142
N.A.I.C.S.: 424420

Shanghai Amoy Foods Co. Ltd. (1)
633 Guoguan Rd N
200 434 Shanghai, China
Tel.: (86) 2155033275
Fax: (86) 2155032144
Web Site: www.amoy.com
Emp.: 100
Sauces & Frozen Products Mfr
S.I.C.: 2035
N.A.I.C.S.: 311941
Hanlong Chen *(Gen Mgr)*

AJIYA BERHAD

Suite 6 1A Level 6 Menara Pelangi
Jalan Kuning Taman Pelangi
80400 Johor Bahru, Johor, Malaysia
Tel.: (60) 73323536
Fax: (60) 73324536
E-Mail: enquiry@ajiya.com
Web Site: www.ajiya.com
AJIYA—(KLS)
Rev.: $124,349,468
Assets: $117,621,771
Liabilities: $25,922,521
Net Worth: $91,699,250
Earnings: $7,277,105
Fiscal Year-end: 11/30/12

Business Description:
Metal Doors & Window Frames Mfr
S.I.C.: 3442
N.A.I.C.S.: 332321

Personnel:
Wah Kiang Chan *(Mng Dir)*
Ngeok Mui Chin *(Sec)*
Wui Koon Chong *(Sec)*
Siew Foong Leong *(Sec)*

Board of Directors:
Mohd Aminuddin Mohd Rouse
Wah Kiang Chan
Peak Yih Low
Seng Kee Tan
Book Theng
Ann Seck Yeo

Subsidiaries:

Ajiya Safety Glass Sdn. Bhd. (1)
Lot 575 1 KM Lebuh Raya Segamat-Kuantan
85000 Segamat, Johor, Malaysia
Tel.: (60) 79313133
Fax: (60) 79313142
E-Mail: enquiry@ajiya.com
Glass Materials Mfr
S.I.C.: 3229
N.A.I.C.S.: 327212
Sow Kim Chong *(Gen Mgr)*

Subsidiary:

ASG Marketing Sdn. Bhd. (2)
No 6 Jalan Tpu 3 Tamen Perindustrian Puchong Utama
Puchong, Selangor, 47100, Malaysia
Tel.: (60) 380623939
Fax: (60) 380621113
E-Mail: enquiry@ajiya.com
Emp.: 100
Safety Glass Distr
S.I.C.: 5199
N.A.I.C.S.: 424990
Chan Wah Kiang *(Mng Dir)*

Ajiya STI Sdn. Bhd. (1)
No 4 Jalan Sungai Pelubung 32/149
Seksyen 32
40460 Shah Alam, Selangor, Malaysia
Tel.: (60) 351210011
Fax: (60) 351210111
E-Mail: asti@ajiya.com
Construction Materials Mfr
S.I.C.: 3271
N.A.I.C.S.: 327331
Michael Lee *(Mng Dir)*

ARI Utara Sdn. Bhd. (1)
Lot 28 Taman Perindustrian Bukit Makmur
08000 Sungai Petani, Kedah Darul Aman, Malaysia
Tel.: (60) 44422899
Fax: (60) 44422799
E-Mail: enquiry@ajiya.com
Emp.: 50
Construction Materials Mfr
S.I.C.: 3999
N.A.I.C.S.: 339999
Sing Huat Tee *(Mng Dir)*

AJMAN BANK PJSC

Ajman Free Zone Block C 13th Floor
Al Mina Road
PO Box 7770
Ajman, United Arab Emirates
Tel.: (971) 67479999
Fax: (971) 67479990
E-Mail: info@ajmanbank.ae
Web Site: www.ajmanbank.ae
Year Founded: 2008
AJMANBAN—(DFM)
Rev.: $79,221,527
Assets: $1,494,197,161
Liabilities: $1,207,006,434
Net Worth: $287,190,727
Earnings: $9,123,746
Fiscal Year-end: 12/31/12

Business Description:
Commercial Banking Services
S.I.C.: 6029
N.A.I.C.S.: 522110

Ajman Bank PJSC—(Continued)

Personnel:
Ammar Humaid Al Nuaimi *(Chm)*
Ahmed Humaid Al Nuaimi *(Deputy Chm)*
Seifeldin Abdelkareem *(Acting CEO)*
Ashraf Shokry *(CIO)*
Talal Soubra *(Chief Risk Officer)*
Ahmad Fadl *(Gen Counsel)*
Akram Khan *(Exec VP & Head-Corp Banking)*
Ahmad Fuad Elayyan *(Sr VP & Head-Central Ops)*
Rafeek K. P. *(Sr VP & Head-Treasury & Fin Institutions)*
Board of Directors:
Ammar Humaid Al Nuaimi
Ali Abdullah Al Hamrani
Salem Rashid Al Khudur
Ali Rashid Abdullah Al Nuaimi
Mohammed Hussain Mohammed Al Shaali
Yousef Ali Fadil Fadil
Ahmed Humaid Al Nuaimi
Rashid Humaid Al Nuaimi

AJMERA REALTY & INFRA INDIA LIMITED
2nd Floor Citi Mall Link Road Andheri West
Mumbai, 400 053, India
Tel.: (91) 2266984000
Fax: (91) 2226325902
E-Mail: ajmera@vsnl.com
Web Site: www.ajmera.com
AJMERA—(NSE)
Rev.: $16,460,850
Assets: $163,146,475
Liabilities: $85,905,071
Net Worth: $77,241,404
Earnings: $2,871,883
Fiscal Year-end: 03/31/13
Business Description:
Real Estate Management Services
S.I.C.: 6531
N.A.I.C.S.: 531390
Personnel:
Rajnikant Shamalji Ajmera *(Chm & Co-Mng Dir)*
Manoj Ishwarlal Ajmera *(Co-Mng Dir)*
Harshini D. Ajmera *(Compliance Officer & Sec)*
Board of Directors:
Rajnikant Shamalji Ajmera
Ashwin Bhogilal Ajmera
Atul C. Ajmera
Bandish Bhogilal Ajmera
Bhogilal Shamalji Ajmera
Dhaval Rajnikant Ajmera
Ishwarlal Shamalji Ajmera
Manoj Ishwarlal Ajmera
Natwarlal Shamalji Ajmera
Nimish Shashikant Ajmera
Sanjay C. Ajmera
Shashikant Shamalji Ajmera
Transfer Agent:
Sharex Dynamic (India) Pvt. Ltd.
Unit No 1 Luthra Industrial Premises Andheri-Kurla Road
Safed Pool Andheri E, 400 072 Mumbai, India

AJU-CAPITAL CORPORATION
1329-3 Cheongnam Building 11th Floor Socho-Dong
Socho-Gu, Seoul, 100-714, Korea (South)
Tel.: (82) 220175122
Web Site: www.ajucapital.co.kr
Year Founded: 1994
033660—(KRS)
Business Description:
Financial Products & Services
S.I.C.: 6211
N.A.I.C.S.: 523999
Personnel:
Yoon Jong Lee *(Pres & CEO)*
Hak-Ju Kim *(Deputy Pres)*
Hwa-Kuyng Oh *(Gen Dir-Sls & Mktg)*

AJWA FUN WORLD & RESORT LIMITED
A Tower 1st floor Kunj Plaza Palace Road
Vadodara, Gujarat, 390 001, India
Tel.: (91) 265 2434864
Fax: (91) 265 2415579
E-Mail: info@ajwaworld.com
Web Site: www.ajwaworld.com
Year Founded: 1992
526628—(BOM)
Sales Range: Less than $1 Million
Business Description:
Amusement Park Operator
S.I.C.: 7999
N.A.I.C.S.: 713990
Personnel:
Rajesh C. Jain *(Chm, Mng Dir & Compliance Officer)*
Board of Directors:
Rajesh C. Jain
Rahil R. Jain
Surbhi N. Kothari
Babubhai D. Makwana
Pradhuman I. Pandya
Kalindi V. Patel
Paresh K. Patel

AJWA GROUP FOR FOOD INDUSTRIES HOLDING LTD. CO.
Al Balad Al Mahamal Tower King Abdulaziz St
PO Box 16645
Jeddah, 21474, Saudi Arabia
Tel.: (966) 26420552
Fax: (966) 26440047
E-Mail: info@ajwa.com
Web Site: www.ajwagroup.com
Year Founded: 1992
Sales Range: $450-499.9 Million
Emp.: 5,000
Business Description:
Food Products Processor & Distr
S.I.C.: 5149
N.A.I.C.S.: 424490
Personnel:
Ahmad Al Towaijri *(Grp-Gen Mgr)*

Subsidiary:

Gulf Vegetable Oil Company (Nabati) (1)
King Abdul Aziz
Al Khobar, 31482, Saudi Arabia
Mailing Address:
PO Box 8421
Dammam, 31482, Saudi Arabia
Tel.: (966) 38590061
Fax: (966) 38591577
Web Site: www.ajwa.com
Emp.: 225
Edible Oils Processor & Distr
S.I.C.: 2079
N.A.I.C.S.: 311224

Non-U.S. Subsidiaries:

Misr Gulf Oil Processing Co. (1)
95C El Merghany Street
Heliopolis Horreya
PO Box 2788, Cairo, Egypt
Tel.: (20) 2 417 8182
Fax: (20) 2 418 6302
Web Site: www.migop.com.eg/contactus.htm
Emp.: 720
Edible Oils Processor, Packer, Sales & Distr
S.I.C.: 2079
N.A.I.C.S.: 311224

Saudi Tunisian Company (1)
Zone Industrielle Bir El Kassaa
En Face Mache du Gros
Ben Arous, 2013 Tunis, Tunisia
Tel.: (216) 7138 8888
Fax: (216) 7138 7777
Web Site: www.battariat.com
Emp.: 55
Edible Oils Processor & Distr
S.I.C.: 2079
N.A.I.C.S.: 311224

A.K. AL-MUHAIDIB & SONS GROUP OF COMPANIES
PO Box 30
Dammam, 31411, Saudi Arabia
Tel.: (966) 38322033
Fax: (966) 38336082
E-Mail: mail@muhaidib.com
Web Site: www.muhaidib.com
Year Founded: 1946
Sales Range: $200-249.9 Million
Emp.: 3,500
Business Description:
Holding Company; Building Materials & Food Stuffs Whslr
S.I.C.: 6719
N.A.I.C.S.: 551112
Personnel:
Suleiman Abdulkader Al Muhaidib *(Chm)*
Emad Abdul Kadi Al Muhaidib *(Vice Chm)*
Essam Abdulkader Al Muhaidib *(Mng Dir)*

Subsidiaries:

Al-Muhaidib Hardware (1)
Amir Salman Street
PO Box 42300
Riyadh, 11541, Saudi Arabia
Tel.: (966) 14488404
Fax: (966) 14461160
E-Mail: info@mhw.com.sa
Web Site: www.mhw.com.sa/contacts.htm#5
Emp.: 250
Hardware Importer, Distr & Whslr
S.I.C.: 5072
N.A.I.C.S.: 423710

Riyadh Cables Group of Companies (1)
PO Box 26862
Riyadh, 11496, Saudi Arabia
Tel.: (966) 12651415
Fax: (966) 12651423
E-Mail: rcgc@riyadh-cables.com
Web Site: www.riyadh-cables.com
Sales Range: $550-599.9 Million
Emp.: 1,800
Electrical Cables, Copper Rods, Telecommunications & Fiber Optics Cables Mfr & Distr
S.I.C.: 3357
N.A.I.C.S.: 335921
Hikmat Saaduddin Al Zaim *(Chm)*

Subsidiaries:

Saudi Modern Company for Cables Industry Ltd. (2)
PO Box 26862
Riyadh, 11496, Saudi Arabia
Tel.: (966) 12651415
Web Site: www.riyadh-cables.com
Cable Mfr
S.I.C.: 3357
N.A.I.C.S.: 335921

Saudi Modern Company for Metals, Cables and Plastic Industry Ltd. (2)
PO Box 26862
Riyadh, 11496, Saudi Arabia
Tel.: (966) 012651415
Cable & Wire Mfr
S.I.C.: 3357
N.A.I.C.S.: 335921

Saudi Modern Company for Special Electric Wire & Cables Industry Ltd. (2)
Al Kharj Road Street No 4
PO Box 26862
2nd Industrial City Zone D, Riyadh, 11496, Saudi Arabia
Tel.: (966) 12651415
Fax: (966) 2651423
Wire & Cable Mfr
S.I.C.: 3357
N.A.I.C.S.: 335929
Hikmat Saaduddin Al Zaim *(Chm)*

Saudi Modern Company for Telephone Cable Industry Ltd. (2)
PO Box 26862
Riyadh, 11496, Saudi Arabia
Tel.: (966) 12651415
Telephone Cable Mfr
S.I.C.: 3357
N.A.I.C.S.: 335929

Saudi Industrial Paint Company (1)
PO Box 5795
Dammam, 31432, Saudi Arabia
Tel.: (966) 38472299
Fax: (966) 38473780
E-Mail: sipco@sipcopaints.com
Web Site: www.sipcopaints.com
Emp.: 200
Sealants & Industrial Coating Mfr
S.I.C.: 2851
N.A.I.C.S.: 325510
Ahmed I. Jomha *(Gen Mgr)*

United Sugar Company (1)
PO Box 23023
Jeddah, Saudi Arabia
Tel.: (966) 26492222
Fax: (966) 26490088
E-Mail: tosman@savola.com
Web Site: www.unitedsugar.com
Sugar Processor & Distr
S.I.C.: 0133
N.A.I.C.S.: 111930

Non-U.S. Subsidiaries:

Reem Rice Mills (Private) Limited (1)
13/123 E-1 Hall Road Gulberg III
Lahore, Pakistan
Tel.: (92) 425760101
Fax: (92) 425760104
E-Mail: reem@brain.net.pk
Web Site: www.reemriz.com
Rice Producer
S.I.C.: 2044
N.A.I.C.S.: 311212
Essa Abdulla Ahmed Al Ghurair *(Pres)*

Veetee Rice Limited (1)
Veetee House Neptune Close
Medway City Estate, Rochester, Kent, ME2 4LT, United Kingdom
Tel.: (44) 1634290092
Fax: (44) 1634297792
E-Mail: info@veetee.com
Web Site: www.veetee.com
Emp.: 60
Rice Distr
S.I.C.: 2044
N.A.I.C.S.: 311212
Moni Varma *(CEO)*

Non-U.S. Subsidiaries:

Kawther Grain (Private) Limited (2)
219-E Sarwar Road
Lahore, Pakistan
Tel.: (92) 42 6664 465
Fax: (92) 42 6664 431
E-Mail: kawther@lhr.comsats.net.pk
Web Site: www.kawthergrain.com
Rice Processor
S.I.C.: 2044
N.A.I.C.S.: 311212

PICRIC Limited (2)
5th Fl 'B' Tower Aggarwal Cyber Plaza
Netaji Subash Place, Delhi, Pitampura, 110034, India
Tel.: (91) 1127352506
Fax: (91) 1127355578
Web Site: www.picricltd.com
Rice Producer & Exporter
S.I.C.: 2044
N.A.I.C.S.: 311212

A.K. CAPITAL SERVICES LTD.
609 6th Floor Antriksh Bhawan 22 Kasturba Gandhi Marg Connaught Place
New Delhi, 110 001, India
Tel.: (91) 1123739628
Fax: (91) 1123739627
E-Mail: akdelhi@akgroup.co.in

Web Site: www.akcapindia.com
530499—(BOM)
Rev.: $36,588,993
Assets: $143,137,130
Liabilities: $83,531,942
Net Worth: $59,605,188
Earnings: $8,521,915
Emp.: 100
Fiscal Year-end: 03/31/13
Business Description:
Commercial Banking Services
S.I.C.: 6029
N.A.I.C.S.: 522110
Personnel:
A. K. Mittal *(CEO & Mng Dir)*
Vikas S. Agarwal *(CFO & Compliance Officer)*
Kanchan Singh *(Sec)*
Vikas Jain *(Sr VP)*
Neetan Singh *(Sr VP)*
Board of Directors:
Subhash Chandra Bhargava
Subhash Chandra Madan
A. K. Mittal
Anshu Mittal
Deepak Mittal
Raghubinder Kishori Lal Rai
Transfer Agent:
Abhipra Capital Ltd
Abhipra Complex A-387 Dilkhush Industrial Area
G.T Karnal Road Azadpur
Delhi, India

AKA GROUP LIMITED
115 Shaftesbury Avenue
London, WC2H 8AF, United Kingdom
Tel.: (44) 20 7836 4747
Fax: (44) 20 7836 8787
Web Site: www.akauk.com
Year Founded: 1995
Sales Range: $75-99.9 Million
Emp.: 194
Business Description:
Internet Publishing Services
S.I.C.: 2741
N.A.I.C.S.: 519130
Personnel:
Carla Moran *(Head-Partnerships)*

AKAR TOOLS LTD.
304 Abhay Steel House Baroda
Street Carnac Bunder
Mumbai, 400 009, India
Tel.: (91) 22 23714886
Fax: (91) 22 2373 5654
E-Mail: mumbaioffice@akartoolsltd.com
Web Site: www.akartoolsltd.com
530621—(BOM)
Rev.: $28,818,175
Assets: $20,189,535
Liabilities: $15,641,956
Net Worth: $4,547,579
Earnings: $172,156
Emp.: 345
Fiscal Year-end: 03/31/13
Business Description:
Precision Engineering Products Mfr
S.I.C.: 3423
N.A.I.C.S.: 332216
Personnel:
R. L. Gupta *(Chm)*
Sunil Todi *(Mng Dir)*
Rajashree V. Dubey *(Compliance Officer & Sec)*
Board of Directors:
R. L. Gupta
N. K. Gupta
Ravi Machhar
C. K. R. Murugan
Bhagwan Das Narang
Pradeep M. Nijampurkar
Sunil Todi
Transfer Agent:
Bigshare Services Pvt. Ltd.
E-2 Ansa Industrial Estate Saki Vihar Road
Andheri East
Mumbai, India

AKARY FOR INDUSTRIES & REAL ESTATE INVESTMENTS PLC
Wasfi Attal St - Building 105
PO Box 1728
Gardens, Amman, 11118, Jordan
Tel.: (962) 6 5563887
Fax: (962) 6 5563887
Year Founded: 1961
WOOL—(AMM)
Rev.: $1,185,394
Assets: $2,002,304
Liabilities: $808,528
Net Worth: $1,193,776
Earnings: $514,216
Emp.: 29
Fiscal Year-end: 12/31/12
Business Description:
Woolen Yarn Mfr
S.I.C.: 2299
N.A.I.C.S.: 313110
Personnel:
Malik Arabiat *(Gen Mgr)*

AKASAKA DIESELS LIMITED
14th fl South Tower Yurakucho Denki Bldg 1-7-1 Yurakucho
Chiyoda-ku, Tokyo, 100-0006, Japan
Tel.: (81) 3 6860 9081
E-Mail: info@akasaka.co.jp
Web Site: www.akasaka-diesel.jp
Year Founded: 1910
6022—(TKS)
Emp.: 330
Business Description:
Diesel Engine Mfr & Whslr
S.I.C.: 3519
N.A.I.C.S.: 333618
Personnel:
Zenshichi Akasaka *(Pres & CEO)*

AKBANK T.A.S.
Sabanci Center 4 Levent
34330 Istanbul, Turkey
Tel.: (90) 2123855555
Fax: (90) 2122697787
E-Mail: investor.relations@akbank.com
Web Site: www.akbank.com
Year Founded: 1948
AKBNK—(IST)
Int. Income: $6,380,023,267
Assets: $88,077,509,930
Liabilities: $75,693,998,212
Net Worth: $12,383,511,718
Earnings: $1,667,055,512
Emp.: 16,315
Fiscal Year-end: 12/31/12
Business Description:
Commercial Banking Services
S.I.C.: 6029
N.A.I.C.S.: 522110
Personnel:
Suzan Sabanci Dincer *(Chm)*
Hayri Culhaci *(Vice Chm)*
Hakan Binbasgil *(CEO)*
K. Atil Ozus *(CFO & Exec VP)*
Tunc Akyurt *(Exec VP-Strategy, CRM & Product & Channel Dev)*
Ahmet Fuat Ayla *(Exec VP-Credits)*
Osman Saltik Galatali *(Exec VP-Private Banking)*
Turgut Guney *(Exec VP-IT)*
Cenk Kaan Gur *(Exec VP-Comml & SME Banking)*
Bade Sipahioglu Isik *(Exec VP-HR)*
Hulya Kefeli *(Exec VP-Intl Banking)*
Orkun Oguz *(Exec VP-Direct Banking)*
Sevilay Ozsoz *(Exec VP-Ops)*
Kerim Rota *(Exec VP-Treasury)*
Osman Mehmet Sindel *(Exec VP-Payment Sys)*
A. Galip Tozge *(Exec VP-Consumer Banking)*
Zeki Tuncay *(Exec VP-Credit Follow-Up & Support Svcs)*
Alper Hakan Yuksel *(Exec VP-Corp Banking)*
Board of Directors:
Suzan Sabanci Dincer
Hikmet Bayar
Hakan Binbasgil
James C. Cowles
Hayri Culhaci
Aykut Demiray
Ozen Goksel
Erol Sabanci
Kaan Terzioglu
Yaman Toruner
Subsidiaries:

Ak Asset Management (1)
Ak Porfoy Yonetimi A S Sabanci Center
Hazine Binasi Kat 1 4 Levent
Besiktas, 34330 Istanbul, Turkey
Tel.: (90) 2123852700
Fax: (90) 2123192469
E-Mail: info@akportfoy.com.tr
Web Site: www.akportfoy.com.tr
Emp.: 30
Portfolio Management & Financial Advisory Services
S.I.C.: 6799
N.A.I.C.S.: 523920
Alp Keler *(CEO)*

Ak Finansal Kiralama A.S. (1)
Inonu Cad No 42 K 6 Gumussuyu Taksim
Istanbul, 34437, Turkey
Tel.: (90) 2123348000
Fax: (90) 2123348041
E-Mail: info@aklease.com
Web Site: www.aklease.com
Emp.: 62
Financial Leasing Services
S.I.C.: 7359
N.A.I.C.S.: 532411
Salih Tuncer Mutlucan *(Gen Mgr)*

Ak Securities (1)
Inonu Cad No 42
Gumussu yu Taksim, 34437 Istanbul, Turkey TR
Tel.: (90) 2123349500
Fax: (90) 2122928401
E-Mail: sales@akyatirim.com.tr
Web Site: www.akyatirim.com.tr
Emp.: 60
International Banking & Securities Trading
S.I.C.: 6211
N.A.I.C.S.: 523110
Attila Penbeci *(CEO)*

Ak Yatirim Menkul Degerler A.S. (1)
Inonu Cag No 42 Gumussuyu Taksim
Istanbul, 34437, Turkey
Tel.: (90) 2123349500
Fax: (90) 2122928401
E-Mail: sales@akyatirim.com.tr
Web Site: www.akyatirim.com.tr
Emp.: 50
Investment Management Services
S.I.C.: 6282
N.A.I.C.S.: 523930
Pinar Aras *(Head-Sls)*

Ak Yatirim Ortakligi A.S. (1)
Ak B Tipi Yatirim Ortakligi AS Inonu Cad No 42
Gumussuyu, Istanbul, 34437, Turkey
Tel.: (90) 2123349585
Fax: (90) 2122510242
E-Mail: akyo@akyatirimortakligi.com.tr
Web Site: www.akyatirimortakligi.com.tr
Emp.: 3
Investment Management Services
S.I.C.: 6282
N.A.I.C.S.: 523930
Yasar Akkoyunlu *(Gen Mgr)*

Non-U.S. Subsidiaries:

Akbank (Dubai) Limited (1)
Gate Bldg Level 15 Ofc No 5
PO Box 506828
Dubai, United Arab Emirates
Tel.: (971) 44486466
Fax: (971) 44019578
E-Mail: info@akbank.ae
Web Site: www.akbank.ae
Emp.: 5
Commercial Banking Services
S.I.C.: 6029
N.A.I.C.S.: 522110
Cem Atac *(CEO)*

Akbank International N.V. (1)
Amstelplein 1
1096 HA Amsterdam, Netherlands NL (100%)
Tel.: (31) 880063950
Fax: (31) 88 0063 901
E-Mail: info@akbank.nl
Web Site: www.akbank.nl
Sales Range: $1-9.9 Million
Emp.: 30
Banking
S.I.C.: 6211
N.A.I.C.S.: 523110
K. Banu Ozcan *(Sr Mng Dir)*

Akbank N.V. (1)
Amstelplein 1
1096 HA Amsterdam, North Holland, Netherlands
Tel.: (31) 880063950
Fax: (31) 880063901
E-Mail: info@akbanknv.com
Web Site: www.akbanknv.com
Emp.: 45
Commercial Banking Services
S.I.C.: 6029
N.A.I.C.S.: 522110
K. Banu Ozcan *(Sr Mng Dir)*

Non-U.S. Subsidiary:

Akbank AG (2)
Taunsgor 2
60311 Frankfurt am Main, Germany
Tel.: (49) 6929717131
Fax: (49) 6929717240
E-Mail: corbanking@akbank.de
Web Site: www.akbank.de
Emp.: 30
Commercial Banking Services
S.I.C.: 6029
N.A.I.C.S.: 522110
Karl-Friedrich Rieger *(Sr Mng Dir)*

AKBAR GROUP
No 1 First Floor Services Club Ext Bldg
Mereweather Road, Karachi, 75520, Pakistan
Tel.: (92) 21 568 0307
Fax: (92) 21 568 4522
E-Mail: info@akbargroup.com
Web Site: www.akbargroup.com.pk
Business Description:
Investment Holding Company
S.I.C.: 6719
N.A.I.C.S.: 551112
Personnel:
M. I. Akbar *(Founder & Chm)*
Ghouse Akbar *(Mng Dir)*
H. Zafar Ahmed *(Exec VP)*
Kersi R. Daroga *(Exec VP)*
Joint Venture:

Fauji Akbar Portia Marine Terminals Limited (1)
10 2nd Floor Services Club Extension Bldg
Mereweather Road, Karachi, 75520, Pakistan PK
Tel.: (92) 21 3567 8985
Fax: (92) 21 3567 4233
Web Site: www.fapterminals.com
Grain, Oilseeds & Fertilizer Port Terminal Operator
S.I.C.: 4491
N.A.I.C.S.: 488310
Muhammad Mustafa Khan *(Chm)*
Ghouse Akbar *(Vice Chm)*
Ahmed Rana *(CEO)*
Hassan Sobuctageen *(COO)*
Aurangzeb Ahmed Khan *(Sec & Head-IR)*

AKD CAPITAL LIMITED
416-418 Continental Trade Ctr
Main Clifton Rd
74000 Karachi, Pakistan

AKD Capital Limited—(Continued)

Tel.: (92) 215302902
Fax: (92) 215302913
Web Site: www.akdsecurities.net
AKDCL—(KAR)
Sales Range: Less than $1 Million
Business Description:
Investment Management Services
S.I.C.: 6282
N.A.I.C.S.: 523920
Personnel:
Aqeel A. Karim Dhedhi *(Chm)*
Nessar Ahmed *(CEO)*
Board of Directors:
Aqeel A. Karim Dhedhi
Nessar Ahmed
Ayesha Aqeel
Yaseem Aqeel
Mehrunnisa Siddique
Mohammad Sohail

AKD SA

56 rue Pasteur
94120 Fontenay-sous-Bois, France
Tel.: (33) 1 48 73 14 78
Fax: (33) 1 48 75 20 35
Web Site: www.akd.fr
Year Founded: 2005
MLAKD—(EUR)
Sales Range: $1-9.9 Million
Emp.: 14
Business Description:
Cosmetics
S.I.C.: 2844
N.A.I.C.S.: 325620
Personnel:
Alain Legout *(Chm & CEO)*

AKEBONO BRAKE INDUSTRY CO., LTD.

19-5 Nihonbashi Koami-cho
Chuo-ku, Tokyo, 103-8534, Japan
Tel.: (81) 3 3668 5171
Fax: (81) 3 5695 7391
E-Mail: ir_pr@akebono-brake.co.jp
Web Site: www.akebono-brake.com
Year Founded: 1929
7238—(TKS)
Sls.: $2,266,550,000
Assets: $2,052,292,000
Liabilities: $1,460,525,000
Net Worth: $591,767,000
Earnings: $5,698,000
Emp.: 8,279
Fiscal Year-end: 03/31/13
Business Description:
Automotive Brakes & Accessories Mfr
S.I.C.: 3714
N.A.I.C.S.: 336340
Personnel:
Hisataka Nobumoto *(Chm, Pres & CEO)*
Takeshi Okumura *(CFO)*
Masaaki Ando *(Exec Officer)*
Yuji Ando *(Mng Exec Officer)*
Jean de Montlaur *(Exec Officer)*
Katsuji Hidaka *(Mng Exec Officer)*
Akira Hosoya *(Exec Officer)*
Takashi Kudo *(Sr Mng Exec Officer)*
Kazuo Matsumoto *(Sr Mng Exec Officer)*
Kanji Miyajima *(Sr Mng Exec Officer)*
Masahiro Miyamoto *(Mng Exec Officer)*
Toshiyuki Negishi *(Exec Officer)*
Toshimitsu Nishigaki *(Sr Mng Exec Officer)*
Seiji Nishimura *(Exec Officer)*
Seiji Onoda *(Mng Exec Officer)*
Hadrian Rori *(Exec Officer)*
Takeshi Saito *(Sr Mng Exec Officer)*
Peter Schmitz *(Exec Officer)*
Yoichi Shinagawa *(Exec Officer)*
Seiki Takahashi *(Mng Exec Officer)*
Yoshimasa Ogino *(Exec VP)*
Board of Directors:
Hisataka Nobumoto
Kunio Ito
Takashi Kudo
Kazuo Matsumoto
Kanji Miyajima
Toshimitsu Nishigaki
Yoshimasa Ogino
Takeshi Saito
Takuo Tsurushima
Transfer Agent:
Mitsubishi UFJ Trust & Banking Corporation
10-11 Higashisuna 7-chome Koto-ku
Tokyo, 137 8081, Japan
Subsidiary:

Akebono Brake Fukushima Manufacturing Co., Ltd. **(1)**
10 Shinjuku Narita Aza
Koori-machi O-aza Date-gun, Fukushima, Japan JP
Automotive Brake Components Mfr
S.I.C.: 3714
N.A.I.C.S.: 336340

U.S. Subsidiary:

Akebono Brake Corporation **(1)**
310 Ring Rd
Elizabethtown, KY 42701
Tel.: (270) 234-5500
Fax: (270) 234-5504
E-Mail: amsales@akebono-usa.com
Web Site: www.akebonobrakes.com
Sales Range: $1-4.9 Billion
Emp.: 3,300
Brake Components Mfr
S.I.C.: 3714
N.A.I.C.S.: 336340
Kanji Miyajima *(Pres & CEO)*
Kyoichi Miki *(CFO & Sr VP)*
Brandon Kessinger *(Gen Counsel & VP)*
Yoshiharu Aizawa *(Exec VP-Mfg Support)*
Masaaki Ando *(Exec VP-Sls)*
Seiya Odaka *(Exec VP-Quality Assurance & Pur)*
Hadrian Rori *(Exec VP-Engrg & R&D)*
David K. Wheeler *(Sr VP-Mfg)*

Division:

Akebono R&D Engineering Center **(2)**
34385 W Twelve Mile Rd
Farmington Hills, MI 48331
Tel.: (248) 489-7400
Fax: (248) 489-7401
Brake Systems Engineering & Research
S.I.C.: 8731
N.A.I.C.S.: 541712
Hadrian Rori *(Exec VP)*
Bill Hillbrandt *(Sr VP-Engrg & Program Mgmt)*

Plants:

Akebono Brake - Clarksville Plant **(2)**
780 International Blvd
Clarksville, TN 37040-5327
Tel.: (931) 553-6500
Fax: (931) 553-6577
Web Site: www.akebonobrakes.com
Emp.: 250
Brake Components Mfr
S.I.C.: 3714
N.A.I.C.S.: 336340
Tom Lewandowski *(Gen Mgr)*

Akebono Brake - Elizabethtown Plant **(2)**
300 Ring Rd
Elizabethtown, KY 42701 (100%)
Tel.: (270) 737-4906
Fax: (270) 737-3044
Emp.: 1,100
Disc & Drum Brake Assemblies & Components
S.I.C.: 3714
N.A.I.C.S.: 336340
Doug Morgan *(Plant Mgr)*

Non-U.S. Subsidiaries:

Akebono Advanced Engineering (UK) Ltd. **(1)**
415 Wharfedale Road Winnersh Triangle
Wokingham, Berkshire, RG41 5RA, United Kingdom
Tel.: (44) 1189445100
Fax: (44) 1189445101
Brake Parts Mfr
S.I.C.: 3714
N.A.I.C.S.: 336340
Hideki Takayama *(Mgr)*

Akebono Brake Europe N.V. **(1)**
Pegasuslaan 5
1831 Diegem, Flemish Brabant, Belgium
Tel.: (32) 27092034
Fax: (32) 27092222
Web Site: www.akebono-brake.com
Automotive Parts Distr
S.I.C.: 5013
N.A.I.C.S.: 423120
Kenkichi Komiyama *(Mng Dir)*
Miki Kyoichi *(Mng Dir)*

Akebono Brake (Thailand) Co., Ltd. **(1)**
700/880 Moo 1 Tambol Panthong
Amphur Panthong, Chon Buri, 20160, Thailand
Tel.: (66) 38185082
Fax: (66) 38185089
Brake Parts Distr
S.I.C.: 5013
N.A.I.C.S.: 423120
Fuyuki Sekine *(Pres)*

Akebono Corporation (Guangzhou) **(1)**
No 8 Hefeng 1st Street Yonghe Economic Zone
Guangzhou Development District, Guangzhou, Guangdong, China
Tel.: (86) 2082986818
Fax: (86) 2082986820
Emp.: 100
Drum & Disc Brakes Mfr
S.I.C.: 3714
N.A.I.C.S.: 336340

Akebono Corporation (Suzhou) **(1)**
TingLan Road No 168 Chang Yang Street
Industrial Park, Suzhou, Jiangsu, 215021, China
Tel.: (86) 512 6283 1577
Fax: (86) 512 6283 1580
Emp.: 180
Disc Brake Pads Mfr & Whslr
S.I.C.: 3714
N.A.I.C.S.: 336340
Watanabe Masayuki *(Gen Mgr)*

Akebono Europe S.A.S (Arras) **(1)**
Site Artoipole 244 Allee d'Espagne
62118 Monchy-le-Preux, Pas-de-Calais, France
Tel.: (33) 321244800
Fax: (33) 3 2124 4801
Emp.: 90
Brake Components Mfr
S.I.C.: 3714
N.A.I.C.S.: 336340
Marc Landou *(Mgr-HR)*

Akebono Europe S.A.S (Gonesse) **(1)**
6 Avenue Pierre Salvi
BP 90111
95505 Gonesse, Val-d'Oise, France
Tel.: (33) 134451770
Fax: (33) 134451771
Emp.: 50
Brake Components Import & Distr
S.I.C.: 5013
N.A.I.C.S.: 423120
Jean De Montlaur *(CEO)*

P.T. Tri Dharma Wisesa **(1)**
J Pegangsaan Dua Block A1
Km 1 6 Kelapa Gading, Jakarta, Indonesia (50%)
Tel.: (62) 214602755
Fax: (62) 2146826659
Motor Vehicle Brake Component Marketing
S.I.C.: 5013
N.A.I.C.S.: 423120

AKEMI CHEMISCH TECHNISCHE SPEZIALFABRIK GMBH

Lechstrasse 28
D-90451 Nuremberg, Germany
Tel.: (49) 911642960
Fax: (49) 911644456
E-Mail: info@akemi.de
Web Site: www.akemi.de
Year Founded: 1933
Rev.: $19,818,967
Emp.: 100
Business Description:
Adhesive Mfr
S.I.C.: 2891
N.A.I.C.S.: 325520
Personnel:
Dirk C. Hamann *(Co-Mng Dir)*
Torsten Hamann *(Co-Mng Dir)*

AKENERJI ELEKTRIK URETIM A.S.

Miralay Sefik Bey Sokak 15-17 Akhan
Gumussuyu
34437 Istanbul, Turkey
Tel.: (90) 2122498282
Fax: (90) 2122497355
E-Mail: info@akenerji.com.tr
Web Site: www.akenerji.com.tr
AKENR—(IST)
Rev.: $453,223,721
Assets: $1,595,648,858
Liabilities: $1,061,920,787
Net Worth: $533,728,071
Earnings: $45,840,956
Emp.: 314
Fiscal Year-end: 12/31/12
Business Description:
Electricity Power Generation & Distribution Services
S.I.C.: 4911
N.A.I.C.S.: 221111
Personnel:
Mehmet Ali Berkman *(Chm)*
Tomas Pleskac *(Vice Chm)*
Board of Directors:
Mehmet Ali Berkman
Hamdi Yaman Akar
Hakan Akbas
Peter Bodnar
Ahmet Umit Danisman
Raif Ali Dinckok
Vratislav Domalip
Ahmet Cemal Dorduncu
Martin Pacovsky
Tomas Pleskac
Jiri Schwarz
Petr Stulc

AKER ASA

Fjordalleen 16
0250 Oslo, Norway
Mailing Address:
PO Box 1423
Vika, 0115 Oslo, Norway
Tel.: (47) 24130000
Fax: (47) 24130101
E-Mail: info@akerasa.com
Web Site: www.akerasa.com
Year Founded: 1841
AKER—(OSL)
Rev.: $1,077,252,480
Assets: $6,988,204,890
Liabilities: $3,566,769,930
Net Worth: $3,421,434,960
Earnings: ($33,302,160)
Emp.: 27,000
Fiscal Year-end: 12/31/12
Business Description:
Energy Resource, Energy Technology, Maritime Technology & Seafood & Marine Biotechnology Investment Services
S.I.C.: 6211
N.A.I.C.S.: 523999
Personnel:
Kjell Inge Rokke *(Chm)*
Oyvind Eriksen *(Pres & CEO)*
Trond Brandsrud *(CFO)*
Board of Directors:
Kjell Inge Rokke

Tommy Angeltveit
Harald Magne Bjornsen
Christine Bosse
Kristin Krohn Devold
Nina Hansen
Leif O. Hoegh
Finn Berg Jacobsen
Karen Simon
Arnfinn Stenso
Atle Tranoy

Subsidiaries:

Aker BioMarine ASA (1)
Fjordalleen 16 Vika
PO Box 1423
0115 Oslo, Norway NO
Tel.: (47) 24130000
Fax: (47) 24130110
E-Mail: post@akerbiomarine.com
Web Site: www.akerbiomarine.com
Rev.: $84,884,310
Assets: $377,545,140
Liabilities: $142,982,100
Net Worth: $234,563,040
Earnings: ($11,945,340)
Emp.: 58
Fiscal Year-end: 12/31/12
Biotechnology Products Research & Development Services
S.I.C.: 8731
N.A.I.C.S.: 541711
Trond Brandsrud *(Chm)*
Bjorn Flatgard *(Deputy Chm)*
Hallvard Muri *(CEO)*
Fredrik Dokk Nygaard *(CFO & Exec VP)*
Matts Johansen *(COO)*
Aaron Kramer *(Pres-Pharmaceutical)*
Webjorn Eikrem *(Exec VP-Upstream Ops)*

Aker Floating Production ASA (1)
Fjordalleen 16
250 Oslo, Norway
Tel.: (47) 24 13 00 00
Fax: (47) 85 40 18 80
E-Mail: post@aker-fp.com
Web Site: www.akerfloatingproduction.com
Emp.: 455
Oil & Gas Drilling Services
S.I.C.: 1381
N.A.I.C.S.: 213111
James H. Miller *(Chm)*
Kristian Rokke *(Pres & CEO)*
Havard Garseth *(Mng Dir)*
Jeffrey Theisen *(CFO)*
Brian Watkinson *(CTO & Sr VP)*
Dean Grabelle *(Gen Counsel)*
Mikkel Martens *(Exec VP-Project Dev)*
Scott Clapham *(Sr VP-Projects & Bus Improvements)*

Aker Solutions ASA (1)
Snaroyveien 20 Fornebu
PO Box 169
1325 Lysaker, Norway NO
Tel.: (47) 67513000
Fax: (47) 67513010
Web Site: www.akersolutions.com
AKSO—(OSL OTC)
Rev.: $8,038,308,870
Assets: $7,278,512,850
Liabilities: $5,110,252,650
Net Worth: $2,168,260,200
Earnings: $409,037,400
Emp.: 27,554
Fiscal Year-end: 12/31/12
Engineering, Project Management, Technical & Administrative Services
S.I.C.: 8711
N.A.I.C.S.: 541330
Oyvind Eriksen *(Chm)*
Leif Borge *(Pres & CFO)*
Bunny Nooryani *(Chief Comm Officer & Head-Comm Grp)*
Asmund Boe *(CTO)*
Sissel Lindland *(Chief HR Officer)*
David Currie *(Pres-UK)*
Niels Didrich Buch *(Exec VP)*
Lasse Torkildsen *(Sr VP-IR)*

Subsidiaries:

Aker Egersund AS (2)
Hovlandsveien 160
NO 4370 Egersund, Norway NO
Tel.: (47) 51469000
Telex: 33283 kbe n
Fax: (47) 51469400
Web Site: www.akersolutions.com
Emp.: 470
Modules, Steel Jackets & Flare Booms Mfr for Offshore Installations
S.I.C.: 3829
N.A.I.C.S.: 334519
Svein Oskar Nuland *(Mng Dir)*
Bente Ransland *(Sec)*

Aker Engineering & Technology AS (2)
Snaroyveien 36
N 1364 Fornebu, Norway
Mailing Address:
PO Box 222
1326 Lysaker, Norway
Tel.: (47) 67595050
Fax: (47) 67513590
Web Site: www.akersolutions.com
Emp.: 800
Technology, Development, Studies & Engineering, Project Management, Procurement & Construction Support Services for Offshore Oil & Gas Projects
S.I.C.: 8711
N.A.I.C.S.: 541330
Valborg Lundegard *(Mng Dir)*

Aker MH AS (2)
Dvergsnes
N 4604 Kristiansand, Norway
Tel.: (47) 38057000
Fax: (47) 38057501
E-Mail: mh@akersolutions.com
Web Site: www.akersolutions.com
Emp.: 550
Drilling Equipment & Facilities Supplier
S.I.C.: 3533
N.A.I.C.S.: 333132
Bjorg Hansen *(VP-HR)*

Division:

Aker MH AS-Stavanger Supply Division (3)
Nedrevei 8
3183 Horten, Norway
Tel.: (47) 38057000
Fax: (47) 33039032
E-Mail: info@akerkvaerner.com
Web Site: www.akerkvaerner.com
Emp.: 6
Drilling Equipment & Facilities Supplier
S.I.C.: 3533
N.A.I.C.S.: 333132

U.S. Subsidiary:

Aker Solutions Drilling Technologies, Inc. (3)
28377 FM 529
Katy, TX 77493
Mailing Address:
PO Box 578
Katy, TX 77492
Tel.: (281) 371-2424
Fax: (713) 371-2426
Web Site: www.akersolutions.com
Emp.: 150
Drilling Equipment Mfr
S.I.C.: 3533
N.A.I.C.S.: 333132
Glen Ellis *(Pres)*

Non-U.S. Subsidiaries:

Aker MH Azerbaijan (3)
Ipekyol Business Center Khojali pr 37
AZ 1025 Baku, Azerbaijan
Tel.: (994) 412 4906901
Fax: (994) 412 4906906
E-Mail: mh@akersolutions.com
Web Site: www.akersolutions.com
Drilling Equipment & Facilities Supplier
S.I.C.: 3533
N.A.I.C.S.: 333132

Aker MH Singapore Pte. Ltd. (3)
Loyang Offshore Supply Base
Loyang Crescent, Singapore, 508988, Singapore
Tel.: (65) 65421512
Fax: (65) 65430882
E-Mail: mhsing@kvaerner.com.sg
Web Site: www.akerkvaerner.com
Emp.: 15
Drilling Equipment & Facilities Supplier
S.I.C.: 3533
N.A.I.C.S.: 333132

Aker MH UK Ltd. (3)
Fyvie Bldg Howe Moss Ave
Dyce, Aberdeen, AB21 0NA, United Kingdom
Tel.: (44) 1224424800
Fax: (44) 1224424808
E-Mail: general.enquiries@akersolutions.com
Web Site: www.akersolutions.com
Sales Range: $1-9.9 Million
Emp.: 25
Drilling Equipment & Facilities Supplier
S.I.C.: 3533
N.A.I.C.S.: 333132
Knut Mjaland *(Sr VP)*

Aker Offshore Partner AS (2)
Badehusgt 39
PO Box 589
Stromsteinen, N 4003 Stavanger, Norway
Tel.: (47) 51898000
Fax: (47) 51893533
Web Site: www.akersolutions.com
Emp.: 1,600
Maintenance & Modifications (Engineering, Fabrication & Installation); Wellhead Platforms Engineering; Field Development Studies; Field Abandonment Services
S.I.C.: 8711
N.A.I.C.S.: 541330

Subsidiary:

Aker Inspection & Consulting AS (3)
Sandslimarka 251
Sandsli, N 5861 Bergen, Norway
Mailing Address:
PO Box 71
Sandsli, N-5861 Bergen, Norway
Tel.: (47) 55224800
Fax: (47) 55224802
E-Mail: aic@akerkvaerner.com
Web Site: www.akersolution.no
Emp.: 120
Inspection, Testing & Technical Services
S.I.C.: 7389
N.A.I.C.S.: 541990
Atle Vagstol *(Pres)*
Lasse Ozoea *(Mng Dir)*
Erik Sordosbeen *(Mng Dir)*

Aker Subsea AS (2)
Snaroyveien 36
1364 Fornebu, Norway NO
Mailing Address:
PO Box 94
1325 Lysaker, Norway
Tel.: (47) 6751 3000
Fax: (47) 6782 6950
Emp.: 250
Petroleum Sub-Surface Consultancy Specializing in Geological & Geophysical Interpretation, Petrophysics, Reservoir Modelling & Technology & Operation & Wellside Geology
S.I.C.: 1311
N.A.I.C.S.: 211111
Matts Anderson *(Gen Mgr)*

Branch:

Aker Subsea AS (Moss) (3)
Verftsgt 15
PO Box 1002
Moss, 1510, Norway
Tel.: (47) 69912900
Fax: (47) 6991 2901
Emp.: 180
Ship Gears, Pressure Vessel & Industrial Service Steel Projects Mfr
S.I.C.: 3491
N.A.I.C.S.: 332911
Egil Martinussen *(Pres-Asia Pacific)*
Mads Andersen *(Sr VP-Subsea Sys)*

Non-U.S. Subsidiary:

Aker Subsea Ltd (Aberdeen) (3)
Craigievar Building Howe Moss Ave
Kirkhill Industrial Estate, Dyce, Aberdeen, AB21 0GP, United Kingdom
Tel.: (44) 1224255000
Fax: (44) 1224255242
Web Site: www.akersolutions.com
Emp.: 900
Wellhead Equipment, Subsea Trees, Production Control Systems Mfr & Designer
S.I.C.: 3829
N.A.I.C.S.: 334519
Remi Birkeland *(Mng Dir & Sr VP-Grp Control Bus)*

Midsund Bruk AS (2)
Kolbeingjerdet
N-6475 Midsund, Norway
Tel.: (47) 71270100
Fax: (47) 71270101
E-Mail: post@mibas.no
Web Site: www.midsundbruk.no
Emp.: 50
Pressure Vessels, Storage Tanks & Steel Constructions Mfr
S.I.C.: 3443
N.A.I.C.S.: 332420
Peter Andreas Tennfjord *(Mng Dir)*

U.S. Subsidiaries:

Aker Solutions Inc. (2)
3010 Briarpark Dr Ste 500
Houston, TX 77042-3755
Tel.: (713) 988-2002
Fax: (713) 772-4673
Web Site: www.akersolutions.com
Emp.: 1,200
Wellhead Equipment, Subsea Trees, Production Control Systems Mfr & Designer
S.I.C.: 3533
N.A.I.C.S.: 333132
Erik Wiik *(Pres & Country Mgr)*
Gary Mandel *(Exec VP-Process & Construction Bus Area)*

Branch:

Aker Solutions Inc. (3)
1320 E Los Angeles Ave
Shafter, CA 93263-9631 CA
Mailing Address:
PO Box 21535
Bakersfield, CA 93390
Tel.: (661) 746-2206
Fax: (661) 746-2209
Toll Free: (888) 323-8581
Web Site: www.separationspecialists.com
Sales Range: $1-9.9 Million
Emp.: 20
Oil & Water Separation Products & Services
S.I.C.: 3533
N.A.I.C.S.: 333132
Dale McBride *(VP)*

Non-U.S. Subsidiaries:

Aker Engineering Malaysia Sdn Bhd (2)
Level 16 Integra Tower The Intermark
348 Jalan Tun Razak, 50400 Kuala Lumpur, Malaysia
Tel.: (60) 3 2381 8388
Fax: (60) 3 2381 3560
Web Site: www.akersolutions.com
Emp.: 80
Engineering & Design Services for the Oil, Gas, Hydrocarbon & Process Industries
S.I.C.: 8711
N.A.I.C.S.: 541330

Aker Process Systems (2)
Quarry Pk Rd SE
Calgary, AB, T2C 5G9, Canada
Tel.: (403) 640-4230
Fax: (403) 252-1186
Web Site: www.akerkvaerner.com
Emp.: 160
Oil & Gas Processing Systems Mfr
S.I.C.: 3533
N.A.I.C.S.: 333132
Mindy Peryk *(Gen Mgr)*

Aker Solutions do Brasil Ltda (Subsea-Curitiba) (2)
Rua Francisco Sobania
1300 CIC, 81460 130 Curitiba, Parana, Brazil
Mailing Address:
CP 14046
Curitiba, Parana, 81460 130, Brazil
Tel.: (55) 4132278400
Fax: (55) 4121024357
E-Mail: rh@akersolutions.com
Web Site: www.akersolutions.com
Emp.: 1,000
Engineering & Construction Services
S.I.C.: 1629
N.A.I.C.S.: 237990
Egil Boyum *(Pres)*

Chantiers de l'Atlantique (2)
Avenue Antoine Bourdelle
PO Box 61775
44617 Saint Nazaire, Cedex, France

Aker ASA—(Continued)

Tel.: (33) 240227681
Fax: (33) 251109797
Emp.: 500
Shipbuilder
S.I.C.: 3731
N.A.I.C.S.: 336611

Havisk ASA (1)
(Formerly Aker Seafoods ASA)
Lovenvoldg 11
6002 Alesund, Norway (73.2%)
Mailing Address:
PO Box 876
6001 Alesund, Norway
Tel.: (47) 70 11 86 00
Fax: (47) 70 11 86 80
E-Mail: post@havfisk.no
Web Site: www.havfisk.no
HFISK—(OSL)
Rev.: $138,457,350
Assets: $395,644,140
Liabilities: $238,001,850
Net Worth: $157,642,290
Earnings: $11,221,380
Emp.: 370
Fiscal Year-end: 12/31/12
Finfish Fishing; Seafood Products Export Services
S.I.C.: 0912
N.A.I.C.S.: 114111
Frank O. Reite *(Chm)*
Olav Holst-Dyrnes *(CEO)*
Eldar Kare Farstad *(CFO)*
Ari Theodor Josefsson *(COO)*

Ocean Yield ASA (1)
Fjordalleen 16
Oslo, Norway (100%)
Tel.: (47) 24 13 00 00
Fax: (47) 24 13 01 01
Web Site: www.oceanyield.no
OCY—(OSL)
Rev.: $188,000,000
Assets: $1,498,400,000
Liabilities: $965,400,000
Net Worth: $533,000,000
Earnings: $37,100,000
Emp.: 19
Fiscal Year-end: 12/31/12
Marine Transportation Services
S.I.C.: 4499
N.A.I.C.S.: 488390
Trond Brandsrud *(Chm)*
Lars Solbakken *(CEO)*
Eirik Eide *(CFO)*

AKFEN HOLDING A.S.

Koza Sok 22 Gaziosmanpasa
06700 Ankara, Turkey
Tel.: (90) 3124081000
Fax: (90) 312 4410782
E-Mail: akfen@akfen.com.tr
Web Site: www.akfen.com.tr
Year Founded: 1976
AKFEN.E—(IST)
Rev.: $635,604,537
Assets: $2,721,020,136
Liabilities: $1,752,044,283
Net Worth: $968,975,854
Earnings: $379,128,198
Emp.: 27,994
Fiscal Year-end: 12/31/12
Business Description:
Holding Company
S.I.C.: 6719
N.A.I.C.S.: 551112
Personnel:
Hamdi Akin *(Chm)*
Selim Akin *(Vice Chm)*
Suha Gucsav *(CEO)*
Kadri Samsunlu *(CFO)*
Sila Ciliz Inanc *(Chief Legal Officer)*
Board of Directors:
Hamdi Akin
Pelin Akin
Selim Akin
Nusret Comert
Irfan Erciyas
Saban Erdikler

Subsidiary:

Akfen Insaat Turizm Ve Ticaret A.S. (1)
Koza Sokak 22
Gaziosmanpasa, 6700 Ankara, Turkey
Tel.: (90) 312 408 10 00
Fax: (90) 312 441 07 82
E-Mail: akfen@akfen.com.tr
Web Site: www.akfen.com.tr
Construction Engineering Services
S.I.C.: 8711
N.A.I.C.S.: 541330
Hamdi Akin *(Gen Mgr)*

AKHURST MACHINERY LIMITED

1669 Fosters Way
Delta, BC, V3M 6S7, Canada
Tel.: (604) 540-1430
Fax: (604) 540-1780
Toll Free: (888) 265-4826
E-Mail: van@akhurst.com
Web Site: www.akhurst.com
Year Founded: 1938
Rev.: $22,953,467
Emp.: 85
Business Description:
Industrial Equipment Distr
S.I.C.: 5084
N.A.I.C.S.: 423830
Personnel:
Eric M. Stebner *(Pres)*

THE AKITA BANK, LTD.

2-1 Sanno 3-chome
Akita, 010-8655, Japan
Tel.: (81) 188631212
Fax: (81) 188641027
E-Mail: info@akita-bank.co.jp
Web Site: www.akita-bank.co.jp
Year Founded: 1879
8343—(TKS)
Sales Range: $500-549.9 Million
Emp.: 1,687
Business Description:
Banking Services
S.I.C.: 6029
N.A.I.C.S.: 522110
Personnel:
Seietsu Fujiwara *(Pres)*

AKITA DRILLING LTD

900 311 - 6th Ave SW
Calgary, AB, T2P 3H2, Canada
Tel.: (403) 292-7979
Fax: (403) 292-7990
E-Mail: akitainfo@akita-drilling.com
Web Site: www.akita-drilling.com
AKT.A—(TSX)
Rev.: $238,220,869
Assets: $291,241,896
Liabilities: $68,583,404
Net Worth: $222,658,492
Earnings: $28,531,356
Emp.: 818
Fiscal Year-end: 12/31/12
Business Description:
Contract Oil & Gas Drilling
S.I.C.: 1381
N.A.I.C.S.: 213111
Personnel:
Linda A. Southern-Heathcott *(Chm)*
Ronald D. Southern *(Deputy Chm)*
Karl A. Ruud *(Pres & CEO)*
Murray J. Roth *(CFO & VP-Fin)*
Colin A. Dease *(Sec)*
Board of Directors:
Linda A. Southern-Heathcott
Loraine M. Charlton
Arthur C. Eastly
Harish K. Mohan
Dale R. Richardson
Karl A. Ruud
Nancy C. Southern
Ronald D. Southern
C. Perry Spitznagel
Charles W. Wilson
Legal Counsel:
Bennett Jones L.L.P.
855 2nd St SW Ste 4500
Calgary, AB, T2P 4K7, Canada
Tel.: (403) 298-3100
Fax: (403) 233-0353
Transfer Agent:
Canadian Stock Transfer Company
Toronto, ON, Canada

AKIYAMA INTERNATIONAL COMPANY LTD.

2 34 11 Takara Machi
Tokyo, 124-0005, Japan
Tel.: (81) 336935191
Fax: (81) 336935194
E-Mail: k.kondo@akiyama-international.com
Web Site: www.akiyama-international.com
Year Founded: 1948
Sales Range: $5-14.9 Billion
Emp.: 200
Business Description:
Printing Press Mfr
S.I.C.: 3555
N.A.I.C.S.: 333244
Personnel:
Kazuhiko Hamada *(Gen Mgr-Intl Sls)*

U.S. Subsidiary:

Akiyama International Corp (USA) (1)
13311 E 166th St
Cerritos, CA 90703
Tel.: (562) 404-4767
Fax: (562) 404-0690
E-Mail: info@akiyama.com
Web Site: www.akiyama.com
Emp.: 20
Printing Press Mfr
S.I.C.: 3555
N.A.I.C.S.: 333244
Tony Takami *(VP)*

Subsidiary:

Akiyama Corporation America (2)
13311 East 166th St
Cerritos, CA 90703
Tel.: (562) 404-4767
Fax: (562) 404-0690
E-Mail: info@akiyama.com
Web Site: www.akiyama.com
Emp.: 20
Printing Trades Machinery, Equipment, & Supplies
S.I.C.: 5084
N.A.I.C.S.: 423830
Keith Huang *(VP)*

AKKA TECHNOLOGIES SA

9/11 rue Montalivet
75008 Paris, France
Tel.: (33) 156692659
Fax: (33) 1 56 69 26 50
E-Mail: n.valtille@akka.fr
Web Site: www.akka.fr
AKA—(EUR)
Rev.: $1,113,667,595
Assets: $823,792,770
Liabilities: $585,557,027
Net Worth: $238,235,743
Earnings: $55,662,783
Emp.: 10,645
Fiscal Year-end: 12/31/12
Business Description:
Technology Consulting & Engineering Services
S.I.C.: 8999
N.A.I.C.S.: 541690
Personnel:
Maurice Ricci *(Chm)*
Stephane Descos *(Co-CEO)*
Jean-Franck Ricci *(Co-CEO)*
Nicolas Valtille *(Co-CEO)*
Board of Directors:
Maurice Ricci
Stephane Descos
Guy Lacroix
Cecile Ricci
Charlotte Ricci
Jean-Franck Ricci
Alain Tisserand
Nicolas Valtille
Deloitte & Associes
81 boulevard de Stalingard
69100 Villeurbanne, France

Non-U.S. Subsidiaries:

AKKA Benelux NV/SA (1)
Av Louise 149 bte 24
B 1050 Brussels, Belgium
Tel.: (32) 2 712 60 00
Fax: (32) 2 712 60 01
E-Mail: mail-benelux@akka.eu
Web Site: www.akka-benelux.eu
Technology Consulting & Engineering Services
S.I.C.: 8999
N.A.I.C.S.: 541690

MBtech Group GmbH & Co. KGaA (1)
Kolumbusstrasse 19+21
D 71063 Sindelfingen, Germany De
Tel.: (49) 7031 686 3000 (65%)
Fax: (49) 7031 686 4500
E-Mail: info@mbtech-group.com
Web Site: www.mbtech-group.com
Sales Range: $450-499.9 Million
Emp.: 3,000
Motor Vehicle Components & Systems Development, Engineering & Testing Services
S.I.C.: 8711
N.A.I.C.S.: 541330
Hartmut Tresp *(Chm)*
Christoph Schmidt-Arnold *(CEO & CFO)*

Subsidiaries:

ATP Automotive Testing Papenburg GmbH (2)
Johann-Bunte-Strasse 176
26871 Papenburg, Germany De
Tel.: (49) 61 975 0
Fax: (49) 61 975 453
E-Mail: info@atp-papenburg.de
Web Site: www.atp-papenburg.de
Emp.: 70
Motor Vehicle Testing Services
S.I.C.: 8734
N.A.I.C.S.: 541380
Rainer Staron *(Mng Dir)*

MBtech Consulting GmbH (2)
Posener Strasse 1
71065 Sindelfingen, Germany De
Tel.: (49) 7031 686 4780
Fax: (49) 7031 686 4644
Web Site: www.mbtech-group.com
Motor Vehicle Design Technical Consulting Services
S.I.C.: 8999
N.A.I.C.S.: 541690
Ralf Bechmann *(Mng Dir)*

U.S. Subsidiary:

MB-technology NA LLC (2)
400 E Big Beaver Rd
Troy, MI 48083 DE
Tel.: (248) 312-0277 (100%)
Fax: (248) 312-0279
E-Mail: info@mbtech-group-na.com
Web Site: www.mbtech-group.com
Sales Range: $10-24.9 Million
Motor Vehicle Components & Systems Development, Engineering & Testing Services
S.I.C.: 8711
N.A.I.C.S.: 541330
Jurgen Kiehne *(Pres)*

Subsidiary:

MBtech Auto Testing Properties LLC (3)
1220 Uniroyal Dr
Laredo, TX 78045 TX
Tel.: (956) 728-8500
Fax: (956) 726-9057
E-Mail: info@mbtech-group-na.com

Web Site: www.mbtech-group.com
Motor Vehicle Testing Services
S.I.C.: 8734
N.A.I.C.S.: 541380
Douglas W. Otto *(VP & Gen Mgr)*

Non-U.S. Subsidiaries:

MBtech Bohemia s.r.o. **(2)**
Daimlerova 1161/6
CZ-301 00 Plzen, Czech Republic CZ
Tel.: (420) 377487300 (100%)
Fax: (420) 377487400
Motor Vehicle Components & Systems Development, Engineering & Testing Services
S.I.C.: 8711
N.A.I.C.S.: 541330

MBtech Polska Sp. z o.o. **(2)**
ul Kamienskiego 51/05
PL-30 644 Krakow, Poland PL
Tel.: (48) 123505525 (100%)
Fax: (48) 123505526
Web Site: www.mbtech-group.com
Motor Vehicle Components & Systems Development, Engineering & Testing Services
S.I.C.: 8711
N.A.I.C.S.: 541330

AKKAYA TRADING GMBH

Wiesenstr 5
45739 Oer-Erkenschwick, Germany
Tel.: (49) 2368 96150 0
Fax: (49) 2368 96150 29
E-Mail: info@akkaya-gmbh.de
Web Site: www.akkaya-gmbh.de
Sales Range: $1-9.9 Million
Business Description:
General Merchandise Whslr
S.I.C.: 7389
N.A.I.C.S.: 425120
Personnel:
Sezai Aksu *(CEO)*

AKKHIE PRAKARN PUBLIC COMPANY LIMITED

792 Moo 2 Soi 1C/1 Bangpoo
Industrail Estate Sukhumwit Rd
Bangpoo Mai
Mueang Samut Prakarn, Samut Prakan, 10280, Thailand
Tel.: (66) 23230714
Web Site: www.akkhie.com
AKP—(THA)
Sales Range: $1-9.9 Million
Business Description:
Hazardous Waste Services
S.I.C.: 4953
N.A.I.C.S.: 562211
Personnel:
U-thai Chantima *(Chm)*

AKN TECHNOLOGY BHD.

Unit 810 Block A Phileo Damansara 2 15
Jalan 16/11, 46350 Petaling Jaya, Selangor Darul Ehsan, Malaysia
Tel.: (60) 3 7665 2282
Fax: (60) 3 7660 2520
E-Mail: aderiana@akn.com.my
Web Site: www.akn.com.my
AKN—(KLS)
Sales Range: $10-24.9 Million
Business Description:
Semiconductor Products Mfr
S.I.C.: 3674
N.A.I.C.S.: 334413
Personnel:
Ahmad Kabeer Mohamed Nagoor *(Chm)*
Hean Kooi Ong *(Vice Chm)*
Zakaria Merican Osman Merican *(Grp CEO)*
Sook Fun Thum *(Sec)*
Board of Directors:
Ahmad Kabeer Mohamed Nagoor
Ibrahim Abdul Ghaffar
Mohamad Najeb bin Ali
As'ari Ibrahim
Kooi Siang Lim
Hean Kooi Ong
Zakaria Merican Osman Merican
Izham Yusoff

Subsidiaries:

AKN Industries Sdn. Bhd. **(1)**
Plot 155 & 156 Phase 1 Bayan Lepas
Free Industrial Zone, 11900 Bayan Lepas, Penang, Malaysia
Tel.: (60) 46412222
Fax: (60) 46411882
Semiconductor Component Mfr
S.I.C.: 3674
N.A.I.C.S.: 334413

ZD Tech Corporation Sdn. Bhd. **(1)**
Plot 131 Lorong Perusahaan 6A Kawasan Perusahaan Perai II
13700 Perai, Pulau Pinang, Malaysia
Tel.: (60) 43982272
Fax: (60) 43982280
E-Mail: market@zdtechcorp.com
Web Site: www.zdtechcorp.com
Metal Plating Services
S.I.C.: 3471
N.A.I.C.S.: 332813

Non-U.S. Subsidiary:

PSC Technology (Ayutthaya) Co.Ltd. **(1)**
593 Moo 2 Tambol Klong Jig
Amphur Bangpa, 13160 Ayutthaya, Thailand
Tel.: (66) 352581525
Fax: (66) 35258156
Recycling Services
S.I.C.: 4959
N.A.I.C.S.: 562998

AKO STONEWOOD INC.

(d/b/a 2264618 Ontario Ltd)
2183 Shawanaga Trail
Mississauga, ON, L5H 3X6, Canada
Tel.: (905) 990-1670
Fax: (905) 990-1875
Rev.: $12,400,000
Emp.: 28
Business Description:
Flooring Contractors
S.I.C.: 1752
N.A.I.C.S.: 238330
Personnel:
Mary Grace Ferrari *(Owner)*

AKRITAS S.A.

3 Sokratis Economou St
68100 Alexandroupoli, Greece
Tel.: (30) 2551089810
Fax: (30) 2551032038
E-Mail: info@akritas.gr
Web Site: www.akritas.gr
Year Founded: 1977
AKRIT—(ATH)
Sls.: $57,107,808
Assets: $128,432,486
Liabilities: $77,142,759
Net Worth: $51,289,727
Earnings: ($13,464,267)
Emp.: 290
Fiscal Year-end: 12/31/12
Business Description:
Reconstituted Wood Mfr
S.I.C.: 2493
N.A.I.C.S.: 321219
Personnel:
Loukia A. Saranti *(Chm)*
Georgios A. Sarantis *(Mng Dir)*
Ioannis Ch. Tzitzikas *(CFO & Deputy Mng Dir)*
Board of Directors:
Loukia A. Saranti
Anastasios G. Chrysochoidis
Saradis P. Gagas
Dimitrios K. Kairdis
Vasilios A. Papadopoulos
Georgios A. Sarantis
Ioannis Ch. Tzitzikas

Non-U.S. Subsidiary:

EMOS LTD **(1)**
Uzundjovska St 7-9
Sofia, Bulgaria
Tel.: (359) 2 981 38 46
Emp.: 7
Timber Mfr & Distr
S.I.C.: 2439
N.A.I.C.S.: 321213

AKSA AKRILIK KIMYA SANAYII A.S.

Miralay Sefik Bey Sk Ak-Han No 15
34437 Gumussuyu, Istanbul, Turkey
Tel.: (90) 212 251 45 00
Fax: (90) 212 25145 07
E-Mail: aksa@aksa.com
Web Site: www.aksa.com
Year Founded: 1968
FQR—(DEU)
Sls.: $918,597,905
Assets: $879,882,544
Liabilities: $331,186,525
Net Worth: $548,696,020
Earnings: $95,304,088
Emp.: 766
Fiscal Year-end: 12/31/12
Business Description:
Textile Product Mfr
S.I.C.: 2299
N.A.I.C.S.: 314999
Personnel:
Mehmet Ali Berkman *(Chm)*
Raif Ali Dinckok *(Deputy Chm)*
Board of Directors:
Mehmet Ali Berkman
Ant Bozkaya
Ali Raif Dinckok
Nilufer Ciftci Dinckok
Raif Ali Dinckok
Ahmet Cemal Dorduncu
Timur Erk
Erol Lodrik
Cengiz Tas
Mustafa Yilmaz

AKSA ENERJI URETIM A.S.

Gulbahar Cad 1
34212 Istanbul, Turkey
Tel.: (90) 212 478 66 66
Fax: (90) 212 657 55 16
E-Mail: enerji@aksaenerji.com.tr
Web Site: www.aksa.com.tr
Year Founded: 1997
AKSEN.E—(IST)
Sls.: $1,040,199,618
Assets: $1,600,470,128
Liabilities: $920,477,834
Net Worth: $679,992,294
Earnings: $124,176,952
Emp.: 611
Fiscal Year-end: 12/31/12
Business Description:
Electric Power Generation
S.I.C.: 4911
N.A.I.C.S.: 221112
Personnel:
Saban Cemil Kazanci *(Chm)*
Cuneyt Uygun *(CFO)*
Board of Directors:
Saban Cemil Kazanci
Yavuz Isbakan
Tulay Kazanci
Serdar Nisli
Yagmur Satana
Yaver Ugur Timurkan
Cetin Yalcin

AKSH OPTIFIBRE LIMITED

J-1/1 B-1 Extension Mohan Co-operative Industrial Estate
Mathura Road, New Delhi, 110044, India
Tel.: (91) 11 2699 1508
Fax: (91) 11 2699 1510
E-Mail: aksh@akshoptifibre.com
Web Site: www.akshoptifibre.com
Year Founded: 1986
—(BOM LUX NSE)
Sales Range: $25-49.9 Million
Business Description:
Fiber Optic Cable Mfr
S.I.C.: 3357
N.A.I.C.S.: 335921
Personnel:
Kailash S. Choudhari *(Chm)*
Satyendra Gupta *(CFO)*
Guarav Mehta *(Sec)*
Board of Directors:
Kailash S. Choudhari
Chetan Choudhari
Narendra Kumbhat
D. K. Mathur
Amrit Nath
B. R. Rakhecha

AKSHARCHEM (INDIA) LIMITED

Asahi House Chhatral-Kadi Road
Mehsana, Gujarat, 382 721, India
Tel.: (91) 2764 233007
Fax: (91) 2764 233550
E-Mail: admin@aksharchemindia.com
Web Site: www.aksharchemindia.com
Year Founded: 1989
524598—(BOM)
Rev.: $17,779,715
Assets: $8,126,702
Liabilities: $4,983,789
Net Worth: $3,142,913
Earnings: $703,273
Fiscal Year-end: 03/31/13
Business Description:
Specialty Chemical Mfr & Distr
S.I.C.: 2899
N.A.I.C.S.: 325998
Personnel:
Paru M. Jaykrishna *(Founder, Chm & Co-Mng Dir)*
Gokul M. Jaykrishna *(Co-Mng Dir)*
Munjal M. Jaykrishna *(Co-Mng Dir)*
Board of Directors:
Paru M. Jaykrishna
Gokul M. Jaykrishna
Munjal M. Jaykrishna
Pradeep Jha
Kiran J. Mehta
Param J. Shah
Transfer Agent:
Link Intime India Pvt Ltd
C-133 Pannalal Silk Mills Compound L B S Marg Bhandup West
Mumbai, 400 078, India

AKTANT BUSINESS GROUP A/S

Struergade 16
Taastrup, 2630 Copenhagen, Denmark
Tel.: (45) 82 100 300
Fax: (45) 82 100 201
E-Mail: aktant@aktant.com
Web Site: www.aktant.com
Emp.: 6
Business Description:
Business Services
S.I.C.: 7389
N.A.I.C.S.: 561499
Personnel:
Per Bo Krogmann *(Chm)*
Anders Millgaard *(Mng Dir)*
Board of Directors:
Per Bo Krogmann
Anders Millgaard

AKTANT Business Group A/S—(Continued)

Non-U.S. Subsidiary:

Aktant GmbH (1)
Geibelstrasse 54
22303 Hamburg, Germany (100%)
Tel.: (49) 403551920
Fax: (49) 4035519222
E-Mail: info@aktant.com
Web Site: www.aktant.com
Sales Range: $1-9.9 Million
Emp.: 4
Business Services
S.I.C.: 6221
N.A.I.C.S.: 523130
Necolas Karck *(Mgr)*

AKTIESELSKABET SCHOUW & CO.

Chr Filtenborgs Plads 1
DK-8000 Arhus, Denmark
Tel.: (45) 86112222
Fax: (45) 86113322
E-Mail: schouw@schouw.dk
Web Site: www.schouw.dk
SCHO—(OMX)
Rev.: $2,250,496,008
Assets: $1,872,371,268
Liabilities: $1,037,791,440
Net Worth: $834,579,828
Earnings: $89,765,172
Emp.: 2,873
Fiscal Year-end: 12/31/12

Business Description:
Holding Company
S.I.C.: 6719
N.A.I.C.S.: 551112

Personnel:
Jorn Ankaer Thomsen *(Chm)*
Erling Eskildsen *(Deputy Chm)*
Jens Bjerg Sorensen *(Pres & Member-Mgmt Bd)*
Erik Weimar Rasmussen *(CFO)*
Peter Kjaer *(Member-Mgmt Bd & VP)*

Board of Directors:
Jorn Ankaer Thomsen
Niels Kristian Agner
Erling Eskildsen
Kjeld Johannesen
Erling Lindahl
Agnete Raaschou-Nielsen
Jorgen Wisborg

Subsidiaries:

BioMar Group A/S (1)
Vaerkmestergade 25 6th Floor
8000 Arhus, Denmark (100%)
Tel.: (45) 86204970
E-Mail: info@biomar.com
Web Site: www.biomar.com
Sales Range: $900-999.9 Million
Emp.: 900
Fish Feed Producer
S.I.C.: 0919
N.A.I.C.S.: 114119
Jens Bjerg Sorensen *(Chm)*
Per Moller *(Vice Chm)*
Torben Svejgard *(CEO)*
Mognes Stemtebjerg *(CFO)*
Niels Alsted *(Exec VP & VP-Continental Europe)*

Subsidiaries:

BioMar A/S (2)
Mylius Erichsensvej 35
7330 Brande, Denmark (68%)
Tel.: (45) 97180722
Fax: (45) 97183012
E-Mail: info@biomar.dk
Web Site: www.biomar.dk
Fish Feed Mfr & Whslr
S.I.C.: 2048
N.A.I.C.S.: 311119
Lars Rahbaek *(Mng Dir)*

Non-U.S. Subsidiaries:

BioMar OOO (3)
4 Shosse Strelninskoe
Ropsha, 188514, Russia
Tel.: (7) 812 741 27 54
Fax: (7) 812 749 89 38
E-Mail: dsa@biomar.com
Web Site: www.biomar.com
Fish Feeding Food Distr
S.I.C.: 5191
N.A.I.C.S.: 424910

BioMar Sp. z.o.o. (3)
Wspolna 23
Pabianice, 95-200, Poland
Tel.: (48) 42 227 02 14
Fax: (48) 42 213 00 99
E-Mail: info@biomar.pl
Medical Dressing Materials Distr
S.I.C.: 5047
N.A.I.C.S.: 423450

Oy BioMar Ab (3)
Ratorpsvagen 41C
01640 Vantaa, Finland
Tel.: (358) 400 157 662
Fax: (358) 10 296 1625
Web Site: www.biomar.com
Fish Feeding Services
S.I.C.: 0921
N.A.I.C.S.: 112511
Henrik Arvonen *(Mgr-Sls)*

Non-U.S. Subsidiaries:

BioMar AS (2)
Bolstadvei 24
8430 Myre, Norway
Tel.: (47) 76119200
Fax: (47) 76185819
E-Mail: info@biomar.com
Web Site: www.biomar.com
Emp.: 14
Fish Food Production
S.I.C.: 2092
N.A.I.C.S.: 311710
Jan Sverre Rosstad *(VP)*

BioMar Chile SA (2)
Bernardino 1994
Parque Indus San Andres, Puerto Montt, Chile
Tel.: (56) 65320600
Fax: (56) 65320640
E-Mail: info@biomar.com
Web Site: www.biomar.com
Emp.: 4,000
Fish Feed Mfr
S.I.C.: 0919
N.A.I.C.S.: 114119
Francisco Arellano *(Mgr-IT)*

BioMar Hellenic SA (2)
2nd Ind Area of Volos
Velestino, 37500 Volos, Greece
Tel.: (30) 2425061500
Fax: (30) 2425024031
E-Mail: info@biomar.gr
Web Site: www.biomar.gr
Emp.: 34
Fish & Seafood Whslr
S.I.C.: 5146
N.A.I.C.S.: 424460
Panos Lagos *(Mng Dir)*

BioMar Ltd. (2)
North Shore Road
Grangemouth Docks, Grangemouth, FK3 8UL, United Kingdom
Tel.: (44) 1324665585
Fax: (44) 1324666815
E-Mail: info@biomar.co.uk
Web Site: www.biomar.co.uk
Emp.: 50
Fish & Seafood Whslr
S.I.C.: 5146
N.A.I.C.S.: 424460
Guy Mace *(Mng Dir)*

BioMar S.A.S. (2)
60, Rue Pierre-Georges Debouchaud
Zone Industrielle, Nersac, 16440 Limoges, France
Tel.: (33) 545903500
Fax: (33) 545909903
E-Mail: biomar@biomar.fr
Web Site: www.biomar.fr
Emp.: 50
Fresh & Frozen Seafood Processing
S.I.C.: 2092
N.A.I.C.S.: 311710

Non-U.S. Subsidiaries:

BioMar Iberia S.A. (3)
A-62 Km 99 Apdo 16
34210 Duenas, Spain
Tel.: (34) 979 76 14 04
Fax: (34) 979 78 03 37
E-Mail: biomariberia@biomar.com
Emp.: 15
Fish Feed Distr
S.I.C.: 5191
N.A.I.C.S.: 424910
Fernando Alonso *(Dir-Fin)*

BioMar Srl (3)
Via Lombardia n 3/C
31050 Monastier di Treviso, Treviso, Italy
Tel.: (39) 0422 898933
Fax: (39) 0422 898931
E-Mail: info@biomar.it
Fish Feeding Food Distr
S.I.C.: 5191
N.A.I.C.S.: 424910

Fibertex A/S (1)
Svendborgvej 2
Aalborg, 9220, Denmark (100%)
Tel.: (45) 96353535
Fax: (45) 98158555
E-Mail: fibertex@fibertex.com
Web Site: www.fibertex.com
Sales Range: $75-99.9 Million
Emp.: 765
Nonwoven Materials Mfr
S.I.C.: 2297
N.A.I.C.S.: 313230
Jorn Ankaer Thomsen *(Chm)*
Jens Bjerg Sorensen *(Deputy Chm)*
Michael Stallaxeln *(Mng Dir)*
Ole Houmann *(CFO)*
Mikael Staal Axelsen *(CEO-Personal Care)*
Jorgen Bech Madsen *(CEO-Indus Nonwovens)*

Subsidiaries:

Fibertex Nonwovens A/S (2)
Svendborgvej 16
9220 Aalborg, Denmark
Tel.: (45) 96 35 35 35
Fax: (45) 98 15 85 55
E-Mail: fibertex@fibertex.com
Web Site: www.fibertex.com
Emp.: 130
Industrial Nonwoven Fabric Mfr
S.I.C.: 2297
N.A.I.C.S.: 313230
Jorgen Bech Madsen *(CEO)*
Henrik Eigenbrod *(CFO)*
Lars Bertelsen *(COO)*
Henrik Kjeldsen *(Chief Comm Officer)*
Marianne Brink *(Mgr-HR & Mktg)*
Nikolaj Klit *(Mgr-Bus Dev)*
Tina Norholm *(Mgr-Pur)*
Tina C. Larsen *(Grp Mgr-Quality & Environmental)*
Keld Lauridsen *(Grp Mgr-R&D)*

Non-U.S. Subsidiaries:

Elephant Nonwovens - Nao Tecidos U.P., Lda. (3)
Rua Conde Moser 86 - 2
Estoril, 2765-428 Cascais, Portugal
Tel.: (351) 21 464 62 10
Fax: (351) 21 464 62 16
E-Mail: elephant@fibertex.com
Fiber Non Woven Products Whslr
S.I.C.: 2297
N.A.I.C.S.: 313230

Fibertex France S.A.R.L. (3)
218 Chaussee Jules Cesar
Beauchamp, 95250 Taverny, France
Tel.: (33) 139 959 520
Fax: (33) 139 959 521
E-Mail: fibertex@fibertex.com
Industrial & Technical Nonwoven Fabric Mfr
S.I.C.: 2297
N.A.I.C.S.: 313230
Christian Langlois *(Mng Dir)*

Fibertex Nonwovens S.A. (3)
3-5 rue de la Croix Renaudeau ZI de la Pierre Blanche
BP 49
49120 Chemille, France (100%)
Tel.: (33) 241715555
Fax: (33) 241715578
E-Mail: saleschemille@fibertex.com
Sales Range: $50-74.9 Million
Nonwoven Fabrics Mfr
S.I.C.: 2297
N.A.I.C.S.: 313230
Jorgen Bech Madsen *(Chm-Exec Bd)*
Ali El Yousofy *(Member-Exec Bd)*
Michel Vincent-Dospital *(Member-Exec Bd)*

Fibertex Personal Care A/S (2)
Svendborgvej 2
9220 Aalborg, Denmark
Tel.: (45) 722 99 722
E-Mail: info@fibertexpersonalcare.com
Web Site: www.fibertexpersonalcare.com
Emp.: 175
Personal Care Nonwoven Fabric Mfr
S.I.C.: 2297
N.A.I.C.S.: 313230
Mikael Staal Axelsen *(Grp CEO)*
Claus Svanberg *(CFO)*
Anders Sogaard *(COO)*
Kenneth Mynster Dolmer *(Chief Comm Officer)*
Mette Due Sogaard *(CTO)*

Non-U.S. Subsidiaries:

Fibertex, a.s. (2)
Prumyslova 2179/20
568 23 Svitavy, Czech Republic
Tel.: (420) 461 573 211
Fax: (420) 461 541 437
E-Mail: Info@fibertex.cz
Emp.: 20
Textile Woven & Yarn Mfr
S.I.C.: 2297
N.A.I.C.S.: 313230
Bjarne Knudsen *(Mng Dir)*

Fibertex Personal Care Sdn Bhd (2)
Jalan Mekanikal 1 - Nilai 3 Industrial Park
71800 Nilai, Negeri Sembilan, Malaysia
Tel.: (60) 6 7982 400
Fax: (60) 6 7982 455
E-Mail: info@fibertexpersonalcare.com
Emp.: 20
Non Woven Fabric Material Mfr
S.I.C.: 2297
N.A.I.C.S.: 313230
Peter Andersen *(CEO)*
Soo Fen Ong *(CFO)*
Peter Bach Sigvardt *(COO)*

Hydra-Grene A/S (1)
Bakgardsvej 36
6900 Skjern, Denmark
Tel.: (45) 97 35 05 99
Fax: (45) 97 35 37 37
E-Mail: hg-oest@hydra.dk
Web Site: www.hydra.dk
Emp.: 15
Hydraulic Component Distr
S.I.C.: 5084
N.A.I.C.S.: 423830
Soren Nielsen *(Country Mgr)*

Non-U.S. Subsidiaries:

Hydra Grene Hydraulics Equipment Accessory (Tianjin) Co. Ltd (2)
Room 1704 DiYang Tower No H2 Dong San Huan Bei Lu
Chaoyang District, Beijing, 100027, China
Tel.: (86) 10 8453 7125
Fax: (86) 10 8453 6210
Emp.: 12
Hydraulic Equipment Distr
S.I.C.: 5084
N.A.I.C.S.: 423830
Lichun Xun *(Vice Gen Mgr)*

Hydra Grene India Private Limited (2)
Shed No 208 Sidco Industrial Es
Ambattur, 600098 Chennai, India
Tel.: (91) 44 4202 2556
E-Mail: veku@hydragrene.com
Emp.: 8
Hydraulic Machinery Distr
S.I.C.: 5084
N.A.I.C.S.: 423830
Venkatesh Kumar *(Country Mgr)*

P. Grene A/S (1)
Kobbervej 6
6900 Skjern, Denmark (100%)
Tel.: (45) 96808500
Fax: (45) 96808511
E-Mail: grene@grene.dk
Web Site: www.grene.com
Sales Range: $300-349.9 Million
Emp.: 200
Supplier of Technical Parts & Hydraulic Components

S.I.C.: 3523
N.A.I.C.S.: 333111
Carsten Thygesen *(CEO)*
Soren Jakobsen *(CFO)*

Subsidiaries:

Grene Danmark A/S (2)
Kobbervej 6
6900 Skjern, Denmark
Tel.: (45) 96808500
Fax: (45) 96808511
E-Mail: grene@grene.dk
Industrial Machinery Distr
S.I.C.: 5084
N.A.I.C.S.: 423830

Grene Industri-service A/S (2)
Edwin Rahrs Vej 52
Brabrand, 8220, Denmark
Tel.: (45) 86 24 42 25
Fax: (45) 86 24 42 35
E-Mail: gis-middelfart@grene.dk
Agricultural Machinery Distr
S.I.C.: 5083
N.A.I.C.S.: 423820

Non-U.S. Subsidiaries:

Grene Ab OY (2)
Mestarintie 2
Kimitoon, 25700, Finland
Tel.: (358) 242064600
Fax: (358) 2423834
E-Mail: grene@grene.fi
Emp.: 15
Agricultural Machinery Equipment Whslr
S.I.C.: 5083
N.A.I.C.S.: 423820
Carsten Thygesen *(Mng Dir)*

Grene AS (2)
Vestvollveien 34 E
518 Skedsmokorset, Norway
Tel.: (47) 22 80 38 30
Fax: (47) 22803888
E-Mail: Grene@Grene.no
Web Site: www.Grene.no
Emp.: 2
Industrial Machinery Distr
S.I.C.: 5084
N.A.I.C.S.: 423830
Tony Isler *(Mng Dir)*

Grene Sp. z o.o. (2)
Modla Krolewska ul Skandynawska 1
62-571 Stare Miasto, Poland
Tel.: (48) 63 240 91 00
Fax: (48) 63 240 91 01
E-Mail: grene@grene.pl
Web Site: www.grene.pl
Emp.: 20
Agriculture & Forestry Equipment Distr
S.I.C.: 5084
N.A.I.C.S.: 423830

Subsidiary:

Grene Dustrybucja Sp. z o.o. (3)
Modla Krolewska Skandynawska 1
Stare Miasto, 62-571, Poland
Tel.: (48) 632409211
Fax: (48) 632409101
E-Mail: personel@grene.pl
Agricultural Machinery Distr
S.I.C.: 5083
N.A.I.C.S.: 423820
Marian Fedko *(Mng Dir)*

Schouw & Co. Finans A/S (1)
Chr Filtenborgs Plads 1
8000 Arhus, Denmark
Tel.: (45) 87345800
Fax: (45) 86113322
E-Mail: schouw@schouw.dk
Web Site: www.schouw.dk
Financial Management Services
S.I.C.: 6211
N.A.I.C.S.: 523999
Jens Sorensen *(Gen Mgr)*

Non-U.S. Subsidiary:

NATRIUM Sp. zo.o. (1)
ul Grodziska 15
05-870 Blonie, Poland
Tel.: (48) 22 731 13 52
Fax: (48) 22 731 13 50
Emp.: 60
Lamp Mfr & Whslr
S.I.C.: 3641
N.A.I.C.S.: 335110
Georg Ludwig *(Pres)*

AKTIV KAPITAL ASA

Christian Kroghs Gate 16
0186 Oslo, Norway
Tel.: (47) 2410 3100
Fax: (47) 2410 3101
E-Mail: info@aktivkapital.com
Web Site: www.aktivkapital.com
Year Founded: 1991
Sales Range: $150-199.9 Million
Emp.: 300
Business Description:
Credit Administrative & Financial Services
S.I.C.: 6099
N.A.I.C.S.: 522390
Personnel:
Fredrik Halvorsen *(Chm)*
Geir Langfeldt Olsen *(CEO & Acting CFO)*
Tiku Patel *(COO)*
Jan Husby *(CIO)*
Board of Directors:
Fredrik Halvorsen
Per Erik Asmyr
Cecilie Astrup Fredriksen

Subsidiary:

Aktiv Kapital Financial Services AS (1)
Christian Krohgs Gate 16
NO-0186 Oslo, Norway NO
Tel.: (47) 2410 3150 (100%)
Fax: (47) 2410 3101
Web Site: www.aktivkapital.no
Financial Management Services
S.I.C.: 6211
N.A.I.C.S.: 523999

Non-U.S. Subsidiaries:

Aktiv Kapital Canada Ltd (2)
700-200 Queens Avenue
London, ON, N6A 1J3, Canada Ca
Tel.: (519) 964-3106 (100%)
Toll Free: (866) 266-8881
E-Mail: scoffin@portfoliomci.com
Web Site: www.aktivkapital.ca
Credit Administrative & Financial Services
S.I.C.: 6211
N.A.I.C.S.: 523999
Ramesh Kashyap *(Head-Investments)*

Aktiv Kapital Inkasso GmbH (2)
Marktstrasse 3
Eisenstadt, Burgenland, 7000, Austria De
Tel.: (43) 2682704340 (100%)
Fax: (43) 2682704348
E-Mail: office@aktivkapital.at
Web Site: www.aktivkapital.at
Emp.: 35
Financial Management Services
S.I.C.: 6211
N.A.I.C.S.: 523999
Titu Paten *(Country Mgr)*

Aktiv Kapital (UK) Limited (2)
Wells House 15 17 Elmfield Road
Bromley, Kent, BR1 1LT, United Kingdom UK
Tel.: (44) 2083130033 (100%)
Fax: (44) 2083131022
E-Mail: enquiries@activkapital.com
Web Site: www.activkapital.com
Emp.: 100
Debt Collection Services
S.I.C.: 7322
N.A.I.C.S.: 561440

AKYUREK TUKETIM URUNLERI PAZARLAMA DAGITIM VE TICARET AS

Tekstilkent Koza Plaza B Blok 24
Esenler, Istanbul, Turkey
Tel.: (90) 212 438 47 67
Fax: (90) 212 438 63 70
Web Site: www.akyurekpazarlama.com.tr
AKPAZ—(IST)
Business Description:
Food Products Distr
S.I.C.: 5149
N.A.I.C.S.: 424490
Personnel:
Serdal Akyurek *(Chm)*
Sekip Akyurek *(Deputy Chm)*
Board of Directors:
Serdal Akyurek
Sekip Akyurek
Kerem Alkin
Ferda Besli

AKZO NOBEL N.V.

Strawinskylaan 2555
1077 ZZ Amsterdam, Netherlands
Tel.: (31) 205027555
Telex: 454 38
Fax: (31) 205027666
E-Mail: info@akzonobel.com
Web Site: www.akzonobel.com
Year Founded: 1968
AKZA—(EUR OTC)
Rev.: $20,717,556,300
Assets: $24,181,251,710
Liabilities: $14,277,479,020
Net Worth: $9,903,772,690
Earnings: ($2,835,034,020)
Emp.: 50,600
Fiscal Year-end: 12/31/12
Business Description:
Holding Company; Healthcare Products, Coatings & Chemicals Mfr Import Export
S.I.C.: 2851
N.A.I.C.S.: 325510
Personnel:
Karel Vuursteen *(Chm-Supervisory Bd)*
Uwe-Ernst Bufe *(Deputy Chm-Supervisory Bd)*
Ton Buchner *(CEO)*
Keith Nichols *(CFO & Member-Mgmt Bd)*
Pieter Schoehuijs *(CIO)*
Oskar Bosson *(Media officer-Specialty Chemicals & Performance Coatings)*
Tineke Dikken *(Media Officer)*
Ton Geurts *(Chief Procurement Officer)*
Jeroen Pul *(Media Officer-Decorative Paints)*
Dieuwertje Ten Feld *(Media Officer-Sustainability)*
Sven Dumoulin *(Member-Mgmt Bd & Gen Counsel)*
Marjan M. J. Oudeman *(Member-Mgmt Bd & HR & Organisational Dev)*
Graeme Armstrong *(Member-Mgmt Bd-Res, Dev & Innovation)*
Werner Fuhrmann *(Member-Mgmt Bd-Supply Chain & Specialty Chemicals)*
Tex Gunning *(Member-Mgmt Bd-Decorative Paints)*
Conrad Keijzer *(Member-Mgmt Bd)*
Els van der Hulst *(Sec-IR)*
Supervisory Board of Directors:
Karel Vuursteen
Sari Maritta Baldauf
Peggy B. Bruzelius
Uwe-Ernst Bufe
Antony Burgmans
Peter Ellwood
Louis R. Hughes
Dolf van den Brink
Bernardus Johannes Maria Verwaayen

Groups:

Akzo Nobel Chemicals bv (1)
Boortorenweg 27
7554 RS Hengelo, Netherlands NL
Mailing Address: (100%)
Postbus 25
7550 GC Hengelo, Netherlands
Tel.: (31) 742449111
Telex: 44312
Fax: (31) 742443010
E-Mail: e.schasfoort@akzonobel.com
Web Site: www.akzonobel-hengelo.com
Emp.: 400
Mfr. of Salt & Basic Chemicals
S.I.C.: 2869
N.A.I.C.S.: 325199
E. Schasfoort *(Mgr)*

Joint Venture:

Delamine B.V. (2)
Svionselein 4
PO Box 473, 3800 AL Amersfoort, Netherlands NL
Mailing Address:
PO Box 247
3800AE Amersfoort, Netherlands
Tel.: (31) 334676897
Telex: 43532 DELAM NL
Fax: (31) 334676891
E-Mail: info@delamine.com
Web Site: www.delamine.com
Emp.: 60
Ethylene Amines Mfr; Owned by Akzo Nobel N.V. & by TOSOH Corporation
S.I.C.: 2899
N.A.I.C.S.: 325199
Jacko Moerdijk *(Mgr-Export)*

U.S. Subsidiaries:

Akzo Nobel Inc. (2)
525 W Van Buren St
Chicago, IL 60607 DE
Tel.: (312) 544-7000
Telex: 9102401634
Fax: (312) 544-6901
Web Site: www.akzelnobel.com
Emp.: 250
Mfr. Specialty Chemicals & Industrial Products
S.I.C.: 2899
N.A.I.C.S.: 325199
Hans Wijers *(CEO)*

Subsidiaries:

Akzo Nobel Chemicals Inc. (3)
2153 Lockport Olcott Rd
Burt, NY 14028-9788
Tel.: (716) 778-8554
Fax: (716) 778-0054
Web Site: www.akzonobelusa.com
Organic Peroxides, Free Radical Initiators, Anit-Static & Plastic Additives, Resins
S.I.C.: 2869
N.A.I.C.S.: 325199

Akzo Nobel Chemicals Inc. (3)
13000 Bay Park Rd
Pasadena, TX 77507-1104
Tel.: (281) 474-2864
Telex: 4940900
Fax: (281) 474-0351
Emp.: 300
Mfr., Marketing & Sales of Spent Catalysts
S.I.C.: 2819
N.A.I.C.S.: 325180

Akzo Nobel N.V. (3)
Ste 1C-511 3100 S Sheridan Blvd
Denver, CO 80227-5541 CO
Mailing Address:
PO Box 40350
Denver, CO 80204-0350
Tel.: (303) 937-7482
Fax: (303) 936-3989
Web Site: www.akzonobelusa.com
Emp.: 1
Chemicals & Allied Products Mfr
S.I.C.: 2899
N.A.I.C.S.: 325998

Expancel Inc. (3)
2240 Northmont Pkwy
Duluth, GA 30096-5895 GA
Tel.: (770) 813-9126
Fax: (770) 813-8639
E-Mail: info@expancel.com

Akzo Nobel N.V.—(Continued)

Web Site: www.expancel.com
Emp.: 30
Manufacture of Chemical & Allied Products
S.I.C.: 5169
N.A.I.C.S.: 424690

International Paint Inc. (3)
6001 Antoine Dr
Houston, TX 77091-3503 TX
Mailing Address:
PO Box 4806
Houston, TX 77210-4806
Tel.: (713) 682-1711
Fax: (713) 682-0065
Web Site: www.internationalpaint.com
Rev.: $114,300,000
Emp.: 200
Mfr. of Paints
S.I.C.: 2851
N.A.I.C.S.: 325510
Ian Walton *(CEO)*

AkzoNobel Surface Chemistry (2)
909 Mueller Dr
Chattanooga, TN 37406-0401
Tel.: (423) 629-1405
Telex: 755002
Fax: (423) 698-8723
Toll Free: (800) 251-1080
Web Site: www.akzonobel.com
Emp.: 150
Specialty Chemicals Mfr
Export
S.I.C.: 2819
N.A.I.C.S.: 325180

Eka Chemicals Inc. (2)
1775 W Oak Commons Ct
Marietta, GA 30062-2254 GA
Tel.: (770) 578-0858
Fax: (770) 578-1359
Web Site: www.eka.com
Emp.: 90
Mfr. of Sodium Chloride Refined
S.I.C.: 2899
N.A.I.C.S.: 325998
Michel Gregoire *(VP)*

Non-U.S. Subsidiaries:

Akzo Nobel Chemical Ltd. (2)
1 City Ctr Dr Ste 318
Mississauga, ON, L5B 1M2, Canada ON
Tel.: (905) 273-5959 (100%)
Fax: (905) 273-7339
Toll Free: (800) 489-9124
E-Mail: nancy.law@akzonnobel.com
Web Site: www.akzonnobel.com
Emp.: 4
Industrial Inorganic Chemicals
S.I.C.: 2899
N.A.I.C.S.: 325998
Bridge Cueva *(Controller & Gen Mgr)*

Akzo Nobel Chemicals GmbH (2)
Geestemunderstrasse 26
50735 Cologne, Germany (100%)
Mailing Address:
PO Box 600129
50681 Cologne, Germany
Tel.: (49) 22174960
Telex: 8885377
Fax: (49) 2217496190
E-Mail: info@akzonobel.de
Web Site: www.akzonobel.de
Emp.: 150
Production of Thiocyanites, Amonium Sulfide, Sodium, Hydrosulfide
S.I.C.: 2899
N.A.I.C.S.: 325998

Akzo Nobel Chemicals GmbH (2)
Industriestrasse 10
46446 Emmerich am Rhein, Germany De
Mailing Address:
PO Box 100 963
46429 Emmerich am Rhein, Germany
Tel.: (49) 2822976900
Fax: (49) 28229769070
Web Site: www.akzonobel.com
Polymer Chemicals Marketing, Sales & Mfr
S.I.C.: 2899
N.A.I.C.S.: 325998
Cor Koppert *(Mng Dir)*
David Loose *(Mng Dir)*

Akzo Nobel Chemicals Sa de CV (2)
Av Morelos 49 Col Tecamachalco
56500 Los Reyes, La Paz, Mexico MX
Tel.: (52) 5558580700 (100%)
Fax: (52) 5558580704
E-Mail: polymerchemicals.mx@akzonobel.com
Web Site: www.akzonobel.com
Emp.: 200
Organic Peroxides & Other Specialty Chemicals
S.I.C.: 2899
N.A.I.C.S.: 325199
Ricardo Casdanedo *(Gen Mgr)*

Akzo Nobel Chemicals S.p.A. (2)
Via E Vismara 80
20020 Milan, Italy IT
Tel.: (39) 0321699211
Telex: 332526/332536
Fax: (39) 0293589002
Web Site: www.akzonobel.it
Emp.: 120
Chemical Products Mfr
Export
S.I.C.: 2899
N.A.I.C.S.: 325998
Tino Lomazze *(Gen Mgr)*

Akzo Nobel Chemicals S.p.A. (2)
Via L Gherzi 25
28100 Novara, Italy IT
Tel.: (39) 32169801 (100%)
E-Mail: vendite@akzonobel.com
Web Site: www.akzonobel.com
Emp.: 41
Chemical Products
S.I.C.: 2899
N.A.I.C.S.: 325998

Akzo Nobel Industrial Chemicals GmbH (2)
Hauptstrasse 479
49479 Ibbenburen, Germany (100%)
Mailing Address:
Postfach 1260
49462 Ibbenburen, Germany
Tel.: (49) 5459500
Fax: (49) 545950200
E-Mail: info-irn@bc.akzonobel.com
Web Site: www.akzonobel.com
Sls.: $43,617,600
Emp.: 140
Chloro-Alkaline Mfr
S.I.C.: 2819
N.A.I.C.S.: 325180
Knut Schwalenberg *(Mng Dir)*

Akzo Nobel Packaging Coatings Ltd. (2)
Holden Works
Bordesley Greed Road, Birmingham, B9 4TQ, United Kingdom UK
Tel.: (44) 121 766 6601
Web Site: www.akzonobel.com
Specialized Coatings Sales & Mfr
S.I.C.: 2851
N.A.I.C.S.: 325510

U.S. Subsidiary:

Akzo Nobel Decorative Paints, USA (3)
15885 Sprague Rd
Strongsville, OH 44136 OH
Mailing Address:
PO Box 2535
Hudson, OH 44236-0035
Tel.: (330) 650-4070
Fax: (330) 650-1453
Toll Free: (800) 356-6346
Web Site: www.flood.com
Sales Range: $50-74.9 Million
Emp.: 500
Interior & Exterior Wood Care Products Mfr
Export
S.I.C.: 2851
N.A.I.C.S.: 325510

Non-U.S. Subsidiaries:

AkzoNobel (3)
182 Rue Ludovic Becquet
76320 Saint Pierre-les-Elbeuf, France
Tel.: (33) 232964300
Fax: (33) 235783942
E-Mail: info@akzonobel.com
Web Site: www.akzonobel.com
Emp.: 70
Packaging Coatings Research, Marketing & Mfr
S.I.C.: 2672
N.A.I.C.S.: 322220
Ismael Aguado *(Controller)*

Betonel Ltee (3)
8600 Av de l Epee
H3N2G6 Montreal, QC, Canada (100%)
Tel.: (514) 273-8855
Fax: (514) 273-2615
E-Mail: info@betonel.com
Web Site: www.betonel.com
Emp.: 50
Paint Varnish & Supplies Whslr
S.I.C.: 5198
N.A.I.C.S.: 424950

Non-U.S. Joint Venture:

Pinturas Industriales Sicorel, S.A. de C.V. (3)
Ave Ruiz Cortines 5932
64350 Monterrey, NL, Mexico MX
Tel.: (52) 8181062921
Fax: (52) 8181062992
E-Mail: jonna.metellin@akzonobel.com
Web Site: www.sicoindustrial.com
Emp.: 7
Architectural Paint & Metal Coating Supplier
S.I.C.: 2851
N.A.I.C.S.: 325510

Akzo Nobel Salt A/S (2)
Hadsundvej 17
9550 Mariager, Denmark (50%)
Tel.: (45) 96687888
Telex: 60719
Fax: (45) 96687890
E-Mail: mariager@akzonobel.com
Web Site: www.dansksalt.dk
Emp.: 150
Specialty Chemicals Mfr
S.I.C.: 1479
N.A.I.C.S.: 212393
Tim Andersen *(Mng Dir)*

Akzo Nobel Salt (2)
PO Box 357
40125 Gothenburg, Sweden (100%)
Tel.: (46) 31653000
Telex: 20952
Fax: (46) 31653090
E-Mail: info@jozosalt.se
Web Site: www.jozosalt.se
Emp.: 21
Marketing & Sales of Salt & Basic Chemicals
S.I.C.: 5169
N.A.I.C.S.: 424690
Bosse Kallberg *(Gen Mgr)*

Akzo Nobel UK Limited (2)
The Heath, Runcorn, Cheshire, WA7 4QX, United Kingdom UK
Tel.: (44) 1928 511521
Fax: (44) 1928 515690
Web Site: www.akzonobel.com
Emp.: 100
Research & Development Technologies
S.I.C.: 2899
N.A.I.C.S.: 325998
John Edgar *(CIO)*

AkzoNobel Argentina SAIC (2)
Ruta 11 Km25
2200 San Lorenzo, Santa Fe, Argentina
Tel.: (54) 3476422005
Fax: (54) 3476 425332
Emp.: 180
Sulfuric Acid, Sulphur Derivatives, Polyethylene & Phthalic Anhydride Mfr
S.I.C.: 2819
N.A.I.C.S.: 325180

AkzoNobel Argentina SAIC (2)
Avenida Paseo Colon 221 5 Piso
C1063ACC Buenos Aires, Argentina
Tel.: (54) 1143432011
Fax: (54) 1143404000
Web Site: www.ici.com.ar
Emp.: 90
Mfr. of Wine Chemicals, Tartaric Acid, Vinic Alcohol & Grape Seed Oil
S.I.C.: 2869
N.A.I.C.S.: 325199

AkzoNobel GmbH (2)
Vitalisstrasse 198-226
50827 Cologne, Germany
Tel.: (49) 22158810
Fax: (49) 2215881335
E-Mail: koaln.centrale@akzonobel.com
Web Site: www.akzonobel.com
Emp.: 300
Paint & Coating Mfr
S.I.C.: 2851
N.A.I.C.S.: 325510
Pfurtzan Leuter *(Gen Mgr)*

AkzoNobel (2)
Sutton Fields Industrial Estate
Rotterdam Rd, Hull, HU7 OXX, United Kingdom
Tel.: (44) 1482825101
Fax: (44) 1482838231
Web Site: www.ici.co.uk
Emp.: 60
Coatings Marketing, Production & Research
S.I.C.: 2893
N.A.I.C.S.: 325910

Carbosulf Chemische Werke GmbH (2)
Geestemunderstasse 26
50735 Cologne, Germany DE
Mailing Address: (67%)
Postfach 600129
50681 Cologne, Germany
Tel.: (49) 22174960
Telex: 8885377
Fax: (49) 2217496190
Web Site: www.akzonobel.de
Sales Range: $1-9.9 Million
Emp.: 130
Specialty Chemicals Mfr
S.I.C.: 2899
N.A.I.C.S.: 325998

Eka Chemicals AB (2)
EKA Chemicals
44580 Bohus, Sweden SE
Tel.: (46) 31587000 (100%)
Telex: 2435 ekagbg s
Fax: (46) 31587400
E-Mail: info@eka.com
Web Site: www.eka.com
Sls.: $1,176,165,632
Emp.: 500
Chemical Manufacturer; Ferric Chloride, Hydrochloric Acid, Pure-Grade Sodium Hydroxide & Potassium Hydroxide, Sodium Metasillicate, Sodiumdisillicate, Sodiumperborate, Silicate Binders, Papermaking Chemicals, Sodium Chlorate, Potasssium Perchlorate & Fine Chemicals
S.I.C.: 2899
N.A.I.C.S.: 325998
Jan Svard *(Pres)*

Eka Chemicals Canada, Inc. (2)
1900 Rue St Patrice E
Magog, QC, J1X4X6, Canada QC
Mailing Address: (100%)
PO Box 2000
Magog, QC, J1X 4X6, Canada
Tel.: (819) 843-8942
Fax: (819) 843-3269
E-Mail: info@akzonobel.com
Web Site: www.ekachem.com
Sales Range: $150-199.9 Million
Emp.: 75
Bleaching Chemical Preparations
S.I.C.: 2899
N.A.I.C.S.: 325998
Alain Letourneau *(Controller)*

Non-U.S. Joint Ventures:

Lion Akzo Co., Ltd. (2)
3 17 3-chome Obata
Yokkaichi, Mie, 130 0026, Japan
Tel.: (81) 593468201
Telex: 2623175
Fax: (81) 593470769
E-Mail: k-kino@lion.co.jp
Web Site: www.lion.co.jp
Emp.: 105
Nitriles, Amines, Quarternary Ammonium Salts, Amine Oxides, Monoamides & Alkoxylated Amines Mfr; Joint Venture of Lion Corporation (50%) & Akzo Nobel N.V. (50%)
S.I.C.: 2899
N.A.I.C.S.: 325998

Perla Greek Salt Ltd. (2)
22 Fleming Street
182 33 Agios Ioannis Rentis, Greece GR
Mailing Address:
PO Box 80145
18510 Piraeus, Greece
Tel.: (30) 2104832466

Telex: 212121
Fax: (30) 2104829242
E-Mail: perlagsalt@tee.gr
Web Site: www.perlasalt.gr
Emp.: 30
Salt Producer
S.I.C.: 2899
N.A.I.C.S.: 325998
Theodoros Bertzeletos *(Mng Dir)*

Non-U.S. Plant:

Akzo Nobel Chemicals Ltd. (2)
1-5 Queens Rd
Walton-on-Thames, Hersham, KT12 5NL, United Kingdom UK
Tel.: (44) 1932247891
Telex: 635110
Fax: (44) 1932 231204
Web Site: www.akzonobel.com
Emp.: 130
Production of Specialty Chemicals
S.I.C.: 2899
N.A.I.C.S.: 325998

Subsidiaries:

Akzo Nobel Chemicals bv (2)
Stationstraat 77
PO Box 247
3811 MH Amersfoort, Netherlands NL
Tel.: (31) 334676767 (100%)
Telex: 79 276
Fax: (31) 334676100
E-Mail: info@akzonobel.com
Web Site: www.akzonobel.com
Emp.: 500
Mfr. of Specialty Chemicals
S.I.C.: 2899
N.A.I.C.S.: 325998

Elotex AG (2)
Industriestrasse 17A
Sempach Station, CH 6203 Lucerne, Sursee, CH 6203, Switzerland
Tel.: (41) 414696969
Fax: (41) 414696900
E-Mail: contact.elotex@elotex.com
Web Site: www.elotex.com
Emp.: 150
Researcher & Developer of Specialty Synthetic Polymers
S.I.C.: 8731
N.A.I.C.S.: 541712
Martin Resweck *(CEO)*

Subsidiary:

Claviag AG (3)
Neumattstrasse 196
CH 5054 Moosleerau, Aargau, Switzerland
Tel.: (41) 627388888
Fax: (41) 627388800
E-Mail: contact.elotex@elotex.com
Web Site: www.elotex.ch
Emp.: 55
Synthetic Polymers Mfr
S.I.C.: 2899
N.A.I.C.S.: 325998
Martin Riswick *(Dir-Functional Chemicals)*

Akzo Nobel Coatings B.V. (1)
Rijksstraatweg 31
2171 AJ Sassenheim, Netherlands NL
Mailing Address: (100%)
Postbus 3
2170 BA Sassenheim, Netherlands
Tel.: (31) 713086944
Telex: 42130
Fax: (31) 713082002
E-Mail: diana.kok@akzonobel.com
Web Site: www.akzonobel.com
Sls.: $2,415,886,080
Emp.: 1,200
Holding Company for Coatings & Resins
S.I.C.: 2851
N.A.I.C.S.: 325510
Renus Rooseboom *(Gen Mgr-Decorative Coatings)*

Subsidiary:

Akzo Nobel Coatings International B.V. (2)
Rijksstraatweg 31
PO Box 3
2170 BA Sassenheim, 2171 AJ, Netherlands NL
Mailing Address: (100%)
PO Box 3
2170 BA Sassenheim, Netherlands
Tel.: (31) 713086944
Telex: 39136
Fax: (31) 713082002
E-Mail: peter.knaapvander@akzonobel.com
Web Site: www.akzonobel.com
Emp.: 1,200
Mfr. of Paints, Stains, Synthetic Resins
S.I.C.: 2851
N.A.I.C.S.: 325510
Peter Van Der Knaap *(Plant Mgr)*

Subsidiaries:

Akzo Nobel Decorative Coatings B.V. (3)
Markkade 50
4815 HJ Breda, Netherlands (100%)
Mailing Address:
Postbus 2171
4800 CD Breda, Netherlands
Tel.: (31) 765251000
Telex: 37503
Fax: (31) 765225259
Web Site: www.akzonobel.com
Emp.: 40
Mfr. of Paints
S.I.C.: 2851
N.A.I.C.S.: 325510
Henry Strikker *(Gen Mgr)*

Akzo Nobel Decorative Coatings B.V. (3)
Zevenakkersweg 4
8191 AA Wapenveld, Netherlands (100%)
Mailing Address:
Postbus 7
8190 AA Wapenveld, Netherlands
Tel.: (31) 384471911
Telex: 37503
Fax: (31) 384470042
E-Mail: wapenveld@akzonobel.com
Web Site: www.deco.akzonobel.com
Emp.: 130
Mfr. of Coatings
S.I.C.: 2851
N.A.I.C.S.: 325510
Steve Bartels *(Mgr-Site)*

Akzo Nobel Decorative Coatings B.V. (3)
Ambachtsweg 1
2964 LG Groot-Ammers, Netherlands
Mailing Address:
Postbus 4
2964 ZG Groot-Ammers, Netherlands
Tel.: (31) 0184606464
Telex: 27114
Fax: (31) 0184606299
Web Site: www.akzonobel.com
Emp.: 100
Mfr. of Decorative Coatings
S.I.C.: 2851
N.A.I.C.S.: 325510
Karen Wilms *(Mgr-Mktg)*

Non-U.S. Subsidiaries:

Akzo Nobel Wilton Applied Research Group (2)
Wilton Centre
Wilton, Redcar, TS10 4RF, United Kingdom
Tel.: (44) 642435880
Fax: (44) 642435811
Web Site: www.ici.com
Emp.: 60
Provider of Technological Services.
S.I.C.: 7373
N.A.I.C.S.: 541512

AkzoNobel Coatings Vietnam Ltd. (2)
92 Nguyen Trong Tuyen Street
Ward 15, Ho Chi Minh City, Nhuan District, Vietnam
Tel.: (84) 8 844 5743
E-Mail: akzovnltd@hcm.vnn.vn
Web Site: www.akzonobel.com
Decorative Paints Marketing & Whslr
S.I.C.: 2851
N.A.I.C.S.: 325510

AkzoNobel Deco GmbH (2)
Vitalisstrabe 198-226
Duesseldorfer Strasse 96 100, 40721 Cologne, Germany De
Tel.: (49) 210377800
E-Mail:
Web Site: www.akzonobel.com
Emp.: 200
Decorative Paints Research, Development, Sales & Marketing
S.I.C.: 2851
N.A.I.C.S.: 325510
Marco Sicconi *(Mng Dir)*

AkzoNobel Inc. (2)
8200 Keele St
Concord, ON, L4K 2A5, Canada
Tel.: (905) 669-1020
Fax: (905) 669-3433
E-Mail: info@akzonobel.ca
Web Site: www.akzonobel.ca
Emp.: 100
Decorative Paints Mfr
S.I.C.: 2851
N.A.I.C.S.: 325510
Vince Rea *(Sr VP)*

AkzoNobel India Ltd. (2)
DLF Cyber Terraces Building No 5 Tower A 20th Fl
DLF Cyber City Phase III, Gurgaon, Haryana, 122 002, India
Tel.: (91) 124 2540400
Fax: (91) 124 254 0841
E-Mail: saugata.banerjee@akzonobel.com
Web Site: www.akzonobel.com
Sales Range: $150-199.9 Million
Emp.: 1,200
Supplier of Paints & Chemical Products
S.I.C.: 2899
N.A.I.C.S.: 325998
Nihal Kaviratne *(Chm)*
Jayakumar Krishnaswamy *(Mng Dir)*
Partha Sarathi Basu *(CFO)*

Subsidiaries:

AkzoNobel India Ltd. (3)
Plot No 1 1
Thane Belapur Road
TTC Industrial Area, 400 709 Thane, 400 709, India
Tel.: (91) 22 65161099
Web Site: www.akzonobel.com
Emp.: 82
Decorative Paints Marketer, Researcher & Mfr
S.I.C.: 2851
N.A.I.C.S.: 325510

ICI India Ltd.-Paints Division (3)
DLF Plaza Tower 10th Floor
DLF Qutab Enclave Phase 1, 122 002 Gurgaon, Haryana, India
Tel.: (91) 1242540400
Web Site: www.akzonobel.com
Decorative Paints Mfr
S.I.C.: 2851
N.A.I.C.S.: 325510

AkzoNobel Paints (Asia Pacific) Pte Ltd (2)
1 Maritime Sq Harbourfront Centre
Ste 09-80, Singapore, 099253, Singapore SG
Tel.: (65) 62959361
Web Site: www.akzonobel.com
Emp.: 100
Decorative Paints Mfr & Whslr
S.I.C.: 2851
N.A.I.C.S.: 325510

AkzoNobel Paints (Singapore) Pte Ltd. (2)
22 Soon Lee Rd
Jurong, 628082, Singapore SG
Tel.: (65) 62676100
Web Site: www.dulux.com.sg
Emp.: 80
Decorative Paints Whslr
S.I.C.: 2851
N.A.I.C.S.: 325510

AkzoNobel Paints (Thailand) Ltd. (2)
34 5 Chaeng Watana Road
11120 Nonthaburi, Thailand
Tel.: (66) 25728600
Fax: (66) 29809380
E-Mail: preedawan.chiewchaan@akzonobelpaints.com
Web Site: www.akzonobelpaints.co.th
Emp.: 200
Decorative Paints Mfr
S.I.C.: 2851
N.A.I.C.S.: 325510
Chroond Kanabhapoomi *(Gen Mgr)*

AkzoNobel Polska Sp. Zo.o. (2)
3 ul Przemyslowa
08 440 Pilawa, Poland
Tel.: (48) 257866100
Fax: (48) 48257866214
Web Site: www.akzonobel.com
Emp.: 300
Decorative Paints Mfr
S.I.C.: 2851
N.A.I.C.S.: 325510

AkzoNobel Sdn Bhd (2)
Unit 3-1 Lvl 3 Bldg A Peremba Sq
Saujana Resort Section U 2, 40150 Shah Alam, Selangor, Malaysia
Tel.: (60) 85655650
Fax: (60) 0378455293
Web Site: www.akzonobel.com
Emp.: 300
Decorative Paints Mfr
S.I.C.: 2851
N.A.I.C.S.: 325510
Steven Lim *(Mng Dir)*

Casco Products AB (2)
6 Sickla Industrivag Nacka
PO Box 11538
S 10061 Stockholm, Sweden SE
Tel.: (46) 87434323 (100%)
Telex: 10154 casco s
Fax: (46) 86431607
E-Mail: stefan.groot@akzonobel.com
Web Site: www.akzonobel.se
Emp.: 150
Mfr. of Adhesives, Sealants, Leveling Compounds, Paints & Wood-Processing Resins
S.I.C.: 2891
N.A.I.C.S.: 325520
Stefan Groot *(Gen Mgr)*

CIC Paints (Private) Ltd. (2)
CIC House 199 Kew Rd
Colombo, 2, Sri Lanka
Tel.: (94) 112359210
Fax: (94) 2331788
Decorative Paints Supplier
S.I.C.: 5198
N.A.I.C.S.: 424950

Commenda Adria D.O.O. (2)
23 Franje Lucica
Zagreb, 10090, Croatia
Tel.: (385) 13475688
Fax: (385) 13475682
E-Mail: info@akzonobel.hr
Web Site: www.akzonobel.hr
Emp.: 17
Decorative Paints Distr
S.I.C.: 5198
N.A.I.C.S.: 424950
Adam Klimczak *(Gen Mgr)*

Cuprinol Limited (2)
Wexham Road
Slough, Berkshire, SL2 5DS, United Kingdom
Tel.: (44) 1753550000
Fax: (44) 1753877442
Web Site: www.cuprinol.co.uk
Emp.: 700
Woodcare Products & Damp Proofers Mfr
S.I.C.: 2851
N.A.I.C.S.: 325510

ICI Packaging Coatings Ltda. (2)
Avenida Dos Estados 4826
Utinga, 09220 900 Santo Andre, SP, Brazil
Tel.: (55) 44639000
Fax: (55) 1144639053
Web Site: www.ici.com
Emp.: 140
Mfr. of Packaging Coatings
S.I.C.: 2671
N.A.I.C.S.: 322220

ICI Paints CZ spol.s.r.o. (2)
3 Matechova
142 00 Prague, Czech Republic
Tel.: (420) 241 440 385
Decorative Paints Distr
S.I.C.: 2851
N.A.I.C.S.: 325510

ICI Swire Paints Ltd. (2)
Ste 2806 Island Place
510 King's Road, North Point, China (Hong Kong) HK
Tel.: (852) 28231369
Fax: (852) 28663232
E-Mail: answirepaints.hk@akzonobel.com
Web Site: www.dulux.com.hk
Emp.: 32

Akzo Nobel N.V.—(Continued)

Decorative Paints Mfr & Whslr
S.I.C.: 2851
N.A.I.C.S.: 325510
Steven Yun *(Gen Mgr)*

Non-U.S. Subsidiaries:

ICI Swire Paints (China) Ltd. **(3)**
Beiwei Industrial District Economic & Technical
Development Zone, Guangzhou, 510730, China
Tel.: (86) 2082217755
Web Site: www.swirepacific.com
Decorative Paints Mfr
S.I.C.: 2851
N.A.I.C.S.: 325510

ICI Swire Paints (Shanghai) Ltd. **(3)**
3 F K Wah Centre
1010 Huai Hai road
200031 Shanghai, China
Tel.: (86) 2154050909
Fax: (86) 54050958
Emp.: 200
Decorative Paints Whslr
S.I.C.: 5198
N.A.I.C.S.: 424950

Imperial Chemical Industries PLC **(2)**
Portland House 26th Fl
Bressenden Pl, London, SW1E 5BG, United Kingdom UK
Tel.: (44) 2079329900
Telex: 21324
Fax: (44) 2079329932
Web Site: www.akzonobel.com
Emp.: 31,070
Paints, Foods, Fragrances & Personal Care Products Mfr
Import Export
S.I.C.: 2869
N.A.I.C.S.: 325199

Non-U.S. Joint Ventures:

Akzo Nobel Industrial Finishes AB **(2)**
Odensvivagen 32
SE 594 32 Gamleby, Sweden SE
Tel.: (46) 49314100
Fax: (46) 49314129
E-Mail: annp@coil-akzonobel.com
Web Site: www.akzonobel.com
Sls.: $54,109,200
Emp.: 120
Mfr of Coatings; Joint Venture of Akzo Nobel N.V. (75%) & Nippon Paint Company (25%)
S.I.C.: 2851
N.A.I.C.S.: 325510
Ulf Davidsson *(Mng Dir)*

Akzo Nobel Nippon Paint Espania SA **(2)**
14-20 Feixa Llarga
Zona Franca, 08040 Barcelona, Spain ES
Tel.: (34) 93 484 2541 (75%)
Telex: 52604
Fax: (34) 93 484 2519
Web Site: www.nipponpaint.co.jp/group_e/europe.html
Emp.: 6
Mfr. of Coatings; Joint Venture of Akzo Nobel N.V. (75%) & Nippon Paint Company (25%)
S.I.C.: 2851
N.A.I.C.S.: 325510

Akzo Nobel Nippon Paint GmbH **(2)**
Lochnerstrasse 12
D 90238 Nuremberg, Germany De
Mailing Address:
Postfach 710110
Nuremberg, D 90441, Germany
Tel.: (49) 91166880
Fax: (49) 9116688164
Web Site: www.akzonobel.com
Emp.: 150
Mfr of Coatings; Joint Venture of Akzo Nobel N.V. (75%) & Nippon Paint Company (25%)
S.I.C.: 2851
N.A.I.C.S.: 325510

Akzo Nobel Nippon Paint Limited **(2)**
Hollins Rd
PO Box 37
Darwen, Lancashire, BB3 0BG, United Kingdom UK
Tel.: (44) 254760760
Fax: (44) 254701092
E-Mail: more.info@drw.ic-akzonobel.co.uk
Web Site: www.akzonobel-ic.co.uk
Emp.: 20
Mfr. & Sales of Coatings; Joint Venture of Akzo Nobel N.V. (75%) & Nippon Paint Company (25%)
S.I.C.: 2851
N.A.I.C.S.: 325510

Akzo Nobel Nippon Paint Srl **(2)**
Via Emilia 2
26861 Fombio, Lo, Italy IT
Tel.: (39) 0377410390
Fax: (39) 0377410219
Web Site: www.akzonobel.it
Emp.: 11
Mfr. of Coatings; Joint Venture of Akzo Nobel N.V. (75%) & Nippon Paint Company (25%)
S.I.C.: 2851
N.A.I.C.S.: 325510

Divisions:

Akzo Nobel Decorative Paints **(1)**
Rijkstraatweg 31
PO Box 3
2170 BA Sassenheim, Netherlands
Tel.: (31) 205027555
Fax: (31) 713082002
Web Site: www.akzanobel.com
Rev.: $6,519,820,200
Emp.: 1,200
Decorative Coatings Mfr
S.I.C.: 2851
N.A.I.C.S.: 325510
Tex Gunning *(Mng Dir)*

Subsidiaries:

Akzo Nobel Decorative Coatings bv **(2)**
Rijkstraatweg 31
2171 AJ Sassenheim, Netherlands
Tel.: (31) 713086944
Fax: (31) 713082002
Web Site: www.akzonobel.com
Rev.: $3,552,907,100
Decorative Coatings Mfr
S.I.C.: 2851
N.A.I.C.S.: 325510
Ruud Joosten *(Mng Dir-Northern & Eastern Europe)*

Subsidiaries:

Akzo Coatings Ltda -Tintas **(3)**
Rua Assumpta Sabatini Rossi 1650
San Bernardo Do Campo, 09842 000 Sao Paulo, Brazil BR
Tel.: (55) 1143461818 (100%)
Telex: 34966
Fax: (55) 1121651754
E-Mail: sbc@akzonobel.com
Web Site: www.akzonobel.com
Emp.: 200
Performance Coatings, Marine & Protective Coatings Sales & Marketing
S.I.C.: 2851
N.A.I.C.S.: 325510
Sabiola Spila *(Mgr-Comm)*

Akzo Nobel Aerospace Coatings **(3)**
Cironvallazione Nomemtona 180 B
00162 Rome, Italy IT
Tel.: (39) 697749411
Web Site: www.akzonobel.com
Emp.: 38
Mfr. of Adhesive & Coating Systems
S.I.C.: 2891
N.A.I.C.S.: 325520

Akzo Nobel Coatings Ltd. **(3)**
110 Woodbine Downs Blvd Ste 4
Etobicoke, ON, M9W 5S6, Canada (100%)
Tel.: (416) 674-6633
Telex: 6989403
Fax: (416) 674-6640
Web Site: www.akzonobel.com
Emp.: 30
Mfg., Marketing & Sales of Coatings
S.I.C.: 2851
N.A.I.C.S.: 325510
David Smeth *(Mng Dir)*

Akzo Nobel Coatings SA **(3)**
64 Blvd Moulay Slimaine
PO Box 10610
Casablanca, 20300, Morocco Ma
Tel.: (212) 22678787
E-Mail: hamid.elhalfi@akzonobel.ma
Web Site: www.akzonobel.ma
Emp.: 450
Coatings Mfr
S.I.C.: 2851
N.A.I.C.S.: 325510

Akzo Nobel Coatings SA **(3)**
Juan Zufriategui 4501
Villa Martelli, 1603 Buenos Aires, Argentina AR
Tel.: (54) 1147093109 (100%)
Fax: (54) 1147093788
Web Site: www.akzonobel.com
Emp.: 50
Performance Coatings Mfr
S.I.C.: 2851
N.A.I.C.S.: 325510

Akzo Nobel Coatings S.p.A. **(3)**
Dascoli 11
28040 Dormelletto, Italy IT
Tel.: (39) 2486051 (100%)
Fax: (39) 0322401606
Web Site: www.plastics-akzonobel.com
Mfr. of Protective Coatings
S.I.C.: 2851
N.A.I.C.S.: 325510

Akzo Nobel UK Ltd **(3)**
Bressenden Place
Portland House, London, SW1E 5BG, United Kingdom UK
Tel.: (44) 2079329900 (100%)
Fax: (44) 2079329932
Web Site: www.internationalpaint.com
Emp.: 40
Mfr. of Protective Coatings
S.I.C.: 2851
N.A.I.C.S.: 325510

Subsidiary:

AkzoNobel Decorative Paints **(4)**
Wexham Road
Slough, Berkshire, SL2 5DS, United Kingdom
Tel.: (44) 1753550000
Web Site: www.AkzoNobel.com
Emp.: 1,000
Lubricants Mfr
S.I.C.: 2851
N.A.I.C.S.: 325510

Subsidiary:

AkzoNobel **(5)**
Needham Rd
Stowmarket, Suffolk, IP14 2QP, United Kingdom
Tel.: (44) 1449778000
Fax: (44) 1449778034
Emp.: 100
Decorative Paints Mfr
S.I.C.: 2851
N.A.I.C.S.: 325510
John Kennedy *(Mgr-Safety & Quality)*

Non-U.S. Subsidiaries:

AkzoNobel Ltd. **(5)**
Parque Ind Pl 24
3942 Santa Cruz, Bolivia
Tel.: (591) 33467069
Fax: (591) 33467069
E-Mail: pinturascoral@entelnet.bo
Web Site: www.pinturascoral.com.bo
Emp.: 19
Decorative Paints Mfr
S.I.C.: 2851
N.A.I.C.S.: 325510
Angelino Mancini *(Gen Mgr)*

AkzoNobel Paints Espana **(5)**
Pol Ind Domensys II
Agricultura 7 10, 08720 Vilafranca del Penedes, 08495, Spain ES
Tel.: (34) 938191000
Fax: (34) 938191010
E-Mail: miguel.coza@akzo.com
Web Site: www.akzo.com
Emp.: 60
Decorative Paints Mfr
S.I.C.: 2851
N.A.I.C.S.: 325510
Gabriel Gimenez *(Gen Mgr)*

AkzoNobel Paints Sp. z o.o. **(5)**
6 D Ul Wybrzeze Gdynskie
01-531 Warsaw, Poland
Tel.: (48) 223212020
Fax: (48) 223212021
E-Mail: lidia_brzezinska@ici.com
Emp.: 72
Decorative Paints & Packaging Coatings Sales
S.I.C.: 5198
N.A.I.C.S.: 424950
Miroslaw Stachowicd *(Mng Dir)*

AkzoNobel SA **(5)**
Centre d' Affaires Objectif
2 rue Louis Armand, Asnieres, 92607, France
Tel.: (33) 146883000
Fax: (33) 0344649190
E-Mail: maryse.bonnet@akzonobel.com
Emp.: 900
Decorative Paints Supplier
S.I.C.: 5198
N.A.I.C.S.: 424950
Maryse Bonnet *(Asst Mgr)*

AkzoNobel **(5)**
Lambroek Straat 5 D
1831 Diegem, Belgium BE
Tel.: (32) 27159595
Telex: 24548
Fax: (32) 27209063
Web Site: www.akzonobel.com
Emp.: 35
Deco Paints Marketing & Sales
S.I.C.: 2851
N.A.I.C.S.: 325510
Theo Chantillon *(Mng Dir)*

AkzoNobel **(5)**
Matechova 3
142 00 Prague, Czech Republic CZ
Tel.: (420) 241440385
Fax: (420) 241441098
Web Site: www.akzonobel.com
Paints Distr
S.I.C.: 2851
N.A.I.C.S.: 325510

Alabastine Holland BV **(5)**
Hogesteeg 27 E
5324 AA Ammerzoden, Netherlands NL
Tel.: (31) 735999333
Fax: (31) 735999399
E-Mail: alabastine@exsonobel.com
Web Site: www.alabastine.nl
Emp.: 140
Deco Paints Mfr
S.I.C.: 2851
N.A.I.C.S.: 325510
Nelleke Ceoogd *(Office Mgr)*

Dulux Paints Ireland Ltd. **(5)**
Unit J South Park Business Park
Killinarden Tallaght, Dublin, 24, Ireland
Tel.: (353) 14556099
Fax: (353) 1800455455
E-Mail: info@dulux.ie
Web Site: www.dulux.ie
Emp.: 65
Decorative Paints Supplier
S.I.C.: 5198
N.A.I.C.S.: 424950
Diarmuid Conifrey *(Gen Mgr)*

Unitecta Italiana S.p.A. **(5)**
Via Martelli 8
Zibido San Giacomo, 20080 Milan, Italy IT
Tel.: (39) 029 00 23913
E-Mail: unitectaItaliana@ici.com
Emp.: 27
Decorative Paints Mfr
S.I.C.: 2851
N.A.I.C.S.: 325510
Guido Cella *(Mng Dir)*

U.S. Subsidiary:

International Paint LLC **(4)**
2270 Morris Ave
Union, NJ 07083
Mailing Address:
PO Box 386
Union, NJ 07083
Tel.: (908) 686-1300
Fax: (908) 964-2219
Web Site: www.yachtpaint.com
Emp.: 85
International Marine Coatings, Protective Coatings, Interlux Yacht Finishes, Intergard Epoxy Coatings, Inter-Zinc Zinc Silicates, Interthane Polyurethanes, Intl. Antifouling Coatings, Powder Coatings

S.I.C.: 5231
N.A.I.C.S.: 444120
Micheal Del Mauro *(VP-Ops)*

Akzo Nobel (2)
2505 De La Metropole St
Longueuil, QC, J4G 1E5, Canada QC
Tel.: (514) 527-5111
Telex: 5268858
Fax: (450) 646-7699
Web Site: www.akzonobel.com
Emp.: 1,000
Architectural Paint & Metal Coating Mfr
Export
S.I.C.: 2851
N.A.I.C.S.: 325510
Pierre Dufresne *(Mng Dir)*
Martine Bazinet *(Sec & VP-Legal Affairs)*

AkzoNobel (Asia Pacific) Pte. Ltd. (2)
1 Maritime Square Harbourfront Centre
09-80, Singapore, 099253, Singapore
Tel.: (65) 62959361
Fax: (65) 62787181
Web Site: www.akzonobel.com
Rev.: $912,112,400
Decorative Coatings Mfr
S.I.C.: 2851
N.A.I.C.S.: 325510
Tony Britt *(Mng Dir)*

SA Alba (Deco Paints Latin America) (2)
Ruta Panamericana KM 37 5
B 1619 IEA Buenos Aires, Garin, Argentina
Tel.: (54) 3327447777
Fax: (54) 3327447777
Web Site: www.akzonobel.com
Decorative Coatings Mfr
S.I.C.: 2851
N.A.I.C.S.: 325510
Rodolfo Sero *(Mng Dir)*

Subsidiaries:

Pinturas Inca S.A. (3)
7897 Camino Carlos A Lopez
Montevideo, 16900, Uruguay
Tel.: (598) 2 320 891
Fax: (598) 2 320 223
Decorative Paints Mfr
S.I.C.: 2851
N.A.I.C.S.: 325510
Rodolpho Mercadio *(Gen Mgr)*

Tintas Coral Ltda (3)
Av Papa Jopo XXIII 2100
Sertaozinho, Maua, SP, 09370-800, Brazil
Tel.: (55) 1145435511
Fax: (55) 11 7555 800
E-Mail: sueli_freitas@ici.com
Web Site: www.tintascoral.com.br/coralBrasil/empresaCidada/doacao_de_tintas.shtml
Decorative Paints Mfr
S.I.C.: 2851
N.A.I.C.S.: 325510

Akzo Nobel Performance Coatings (1)
Strawinskylaan 2555
PO Box 75730
1070 AS Amsterdam, Netherlands
Tel.: (31) 205027555
Fax: (31) 205027666
Web Site: www.akzonobel.com
Sales Range: $5-14.9 Billion
Emp.: 21,000
Performance Coatings Mfr
S.I.C.: 2869
N.A.I.C.S.: 325998

U.S. Subsidiary:

Akzo Nobel Coatings Inc. (2)
2031 Nelson Miller Pkwy
Louisville, KY 40223 KY
Tel.: (502) 254-0470 (100%)
Fax: (502) 254-0600
Web Site: www.akzonobel.com
Emp.: 25
Industrial Finishes Mfr
S.I.C.: 2851
N.A.I.C.S.: 325510
Robert Taylor *(Mng Dir)*

Branches:

Akzo Nobel Coatings Inc. (KY) (3)
4730 Critten Dr
Louisville, KY 40209 KY
Tel.: (502) 367-6111 (100%)
Fax: (502) 375-5566
Web Site: www.akzonobel-if.com
Emp.: 50
Mfr of Plastic & Wood Adhesive & Coating Products
S.I.C.: 2891
N.A.I.C.S.: 325520

Akzo Nobel Coatings Inc. (MI) (3)
1845 Maxwell Dr
Troy, MI 48084-4510 DE
Tel.: (248) 637-0400 (100%)
Telex: 211847WPMI UR
Web Site: www.akzonobel-ccna.com
Resins & Coatings
Import Export
S.I.C.: 2851
N.A.I.C.S.: 325510

Akzo Nobel Coatings Inc. (3)
1629 Vanderbilt Rd
Birmingham, AL 35234-1413
Tel.: (205) 323-5201
Fax: (205) 324-4124
Web Site: www.akzonobel-ccna.com
Emp.: 46
Mfr. of Coil Coatings
S.I.C.: 2851
N.A.I.C.S.: 325510
David Jackson *(Gen Mgr)*

Akzo Nobel Coatings Inc. (3)
1 E Water St
Waukegan, IL 60085-5635
Tel.: (847) 623-4200
Fax: (847) 872-1470
Emp.: 50
Paint and Coatings
S.I.C.: 2851
N.A.I.C.S.: 325510

Akzo Nobel Coatings Inc. (3)
1000 Industrial Park Dr
Clinton, MS 39056-3210
Tel.: (601) 924-7222
Fax: (601) 925-1190
Web Site: www.akzonobel.com
Paints and Coatings
S.I.C.: 2851
N.A.I.C.S.: 325510
Misti Moore *(Mgr-HR)*

Akzo Nobel Coatings Inc. (3)
1313 Windsor Ave
Columbus, OH 43211-2851
Mailing Address:
PO Box 489
Columbus, OH 43216-0489
Tel.: (614) 294-3361
Fax: (614) 294-0436
Web Site: www.akzonobel.com
Sls.: $25,000,000
Emp.: 180
Chemical Coatings Mfr
S.I.C.: 2851
N.A.I.C.S.: 325510
Scott Hanna *(Mgr-IF Coil-Americas)*

Akzo Nobel Coatings Inc. (3)
1550 Progress Dr
Springfield, OH 45505-4456
Tel.: (937) 322-2671
Fax: (937) 322-7685
Web Site: www.akzonobel.com
Emp.: 12
S.I.C.: 2851
N.A.I.C.S.: 325510
Tom Stubbs *(Plant Mgr)*

Subsidiary:

Casco Adhesives AB (3)
Smedjegatan 32
Nacka, SE-100 61 Stockholm, Sweden SE
Mailing Address: (100%)
PO Box 11538
100 61 Stockholm, Sweden
Tel.: (46) 87434000
Fax: (46) 86431607
E-Mail: woodad.info@akzonobel.com
Web Site: www.cascoadhesives.com
Emp.: 160
Industrial Wood Adhesives & Resins Mfr
S.I.C.: 2891
N.A.I.C.S.: 325520
Stephen Groot *(Gen Mgr)*

Non-U.S. Subsidiary:

PT Casco Persada (4)
Jalan Industri Utara 1 Blok SS No 18-19
Kawasan Industri Cikarang, Bekasi, 17550, Indonesia
Tel.: (62) 218935858
Fax: (62) 218935915
Web Site: www.cascoadhesives.com
Emp.: 100
Industrial Finishes Mfr
S.I.C.: 2851
N.A.I.C.S.: 325510
Yapp Shih Chen *(Mgr)*

Subsidiaries:

Akzo Nobel Car Refinishes bv (2)
Rijksstraatweg 31
2171 AJ Sassenheim, Netherlands NL
Tel.: (31) 713086944 (100%)
Fax: (31) 713082002
E-Mail: cr.communications@akzonobel.com
Web Site: www.akzonobel.com
Emp.: 1,200
Car Refinish Production & Research & Development
S.I.C.: 2851
N.A.I.C.S.: 325510
Jim Rees *(Gen Mgr)*

Akzo Nobel Package Coatings GmbH (2)
Dusseldorfer Strasse 96-100
40721 Hilden, Germany
Tel.: (49) 2103771
Web Site: www.akzonobel.com
Emp.: 180
Package Coatings Marketing, Sales, Research & Mfr
S.I.C.: 2851
N.A.I.C.S.: 325510
Sjirk Altena *(Mng Dir)*

Akzo Nobel Powder Coatings Ltd. (2)
Stoneygate Lane
Felling, Gateshead, Tyne and Wear, NE10 0JY, United Kingdom
Tel.: (44) 1914696111
Fax: (44) 1914691560
E-Mail: rob.molenaar@akzonobel.com
Web Site: www.akzonobel.com
Sales Range: $1-4.9 Billion
Emp.: 1,000
Chemical Coatings
S.I.C.: 2851
N.A.I.C.S.: 325510
Rob Molenaar *(Mng Dir)*

Subsidiary:

Lucoat Powder Coatings tld (3)
203-5 Ba Shihwa Industrial Complex
676-12 Seonggok-dong Danwon-gu, Ansan, 425836, Korea (South)
Tel.: (82) 314321100
Fax: (82) 314327416
E-Mail:
Web Site: www.interpon.com
Emp.: 50
Powder Coatings Whslr
S.I.C.: 2843
N.A.I.C.S.: 325613
Cheol Bong Kim *(Gen Mgr)*

International Paint Ltd (2)
Portland House Bressenden Place
London, SW1E 5BG, United Kingdom UK
Tel.: (44) 2079329900
Fax: (44) 2079329932
Web Site: www.internationalpaint.com
Sales Range: $1-4.9 Billion
Emp.: 60
Marine & Protective Coatings
Import Export
S.I.C.: 2851
N.A.I.C.S.: 325510

Akzo Nobel Specialty Chemicals (1)
Strawinskylaan 2555
PO Box 75730
1070 AS Arnhem, Netherlands
Tel.: (31) 334676767
Fax: (31) 205027666
Web Site: www.akzonobel.com
Sales Range: $5-14.9 Billion
Emp.: 13,300
Chemicals Mfr
S.I.C.: 2819
N.A.I.C.S.: 325180
Rob Frohn *(Member-Mgmt Bd & Sr Dir-Specialty Chemicals)*

Subsidiaries:

Akzo Nobel Functional Chemicals bv (2)
Stationsstraat 77
3811 MH Amersfoort, Netherlands
Tel.: (31) 334676767
Fax: (31) 334676100
Web Site: www.akzonobel.com
Sales Range: $1-4.9 Billion
Chemical Intermediates & Performance Chemicals Mfr
S.I.C.: 2819
N.A.I.C.S.: 325998
Bob Margevich *(Mng Dir)*

Akzo Nobel Industrial Chemicals bv (2)
Stationsstraat 77
3811 MH Amersfoort, Netherlands
Tel.: (31) 334676767
Fax: (31) 334676100
E-Mail: info@akzonobel.com
Web Site: www.akzonobel.com
Sales Range: $1-4.9 Billion
Emp.: 500
Industrial Chemicals Mfr
S.I.C.: 2899
N.A.I.C.S.: 325998
Wernder Fuhrmann *(Mng Dir)*

Akzo Nobel Polymer Chemicals LLC (2)
525 W Van Buren St
Chicago, IL 60607
Tel.: (312) 544-7000
Fax: (312) 544-7167
Web Site: www.akzonobel.com
Sales Range: $650-699.9 Million
Polymer Chemicals Mfr
S.I.C.: 2899
N.A.I.C.S.: 325998
Hans Wijers *(CEO)*

Akzo Nobel Pulp and Performance Chemicals AB (2)
(Formerly Eka Chemicals AB)
Industrivag 6
131 54 Nacka, Sweden
Tel.: (46) 8 7434000
E-Mail:
Sales Range: $1-4.9 Billion
Emp.: 400
Pulp & Paper Chemicals Mfr
S.I.C.: 2899
N.A.I.C.S.: 325998
Jan Svard *(Mng Dir)*

Akzo Nobel Surface Chemistry LLC (2)
525 W Van Buren St
Chicago, IL 60607
Tel.: (312) 544-7000
Fax: (312) 544-6901
Web Site: www.surface.akzonobel.com
Sales Range: $1-4.9 Billion
Emp.: 50
Surface Active Agents Mfr
S.I.C.: 2843
N.A.I.C.S.: 325613
Frank Sherman *(Mng Dir)*

Subsidiaries:

Akzo Nobel Assurantie N.V. (1)
Oude Velperweg 76
6824 BM Arnhem, Netherlands
Tel.: (31) 26 3664433
Paint & Coating Mfr
S.I.C.: 2851
N.A.I.C.S.: 325510

Akzo Nobel (C) Holdings B.V. (1)
Velperweg 76
Arnhem, 6824 BM, Netherlands
Tel.: (31) 26366 44 33
Fax: (31) 26366 32 50
Investment Management Services
S.I.C.: 6282
N.A.I.C.S.: 523920

Akzo Nobel Center Energie B.V. (1)
Oude Velperweg 76
6824 BM Arnhem, Netherlands
Tel.: (31) 26 3664433
Fax: (31) 26 3663250
Paint & Coating Mfr
S.I.C.: 2851
N.A.I.C.S.: 325510

Akzo Nobel N.V.—(Continued)

Akzo Nobel Chemicals International B.V. (1)
Stationsplein 4
Amersfoort, 3813 LE, Netherlands
Tel.: (31) 33 467 6767
Fax: (31) 33 467 6100
Investment Management Services
S.I.C.: 6282
N.A.I.C.S.: 523920

Akzo Nobel China Beheer B.V. (1)
Velperweg 76
6824 BM Arnhem, Netherlands
Tel.: (31) 263663627
Paint & Coating Mfr
S.I.C.: 2851
N.A.I.C.S.: 325510

Akzo Nobel China B.V. (1)
Velperweg 76
6824 BM Arnhem, Netherlands
Tel.: (31) 26 3662488
Paint & Coating Mfr
S.I.C.: 2851
N.A.I.C.S.: 325510

Akzo Nobel Decorative Coatings Turkey B.V. (1)
Oude Velperweg 76
6824 BM Arnhem, Netherlands
Tel.: (31) 26 3664433
Paint & Coating Mfr
S.I.C.: 2851
N.A.I.C.S.: 325510

Akzo Nobel Energie Hengelo B.V. (1)
Boortorenweg 20
7554 RS Hengelo, Netherlands
Tel.: (31) 742 44 91 11
Fax: (31) 742 44 35 51
Paint & Coating Mfr
S.I.C.: 2851
N.A.I.C.S.: 325510

Akzo Nobel Energy B.V. (1)
Welplaatweg 12 Havennr 4150
Rotterdam, 3197 KS, Netherlands
Tel.: (31) 10 438 9240
Fax: (31) 10 438 9295
Electric Power Generation & Distribution Services
S.I.C.: 4939
N.A.I.C.S.: 221118

Akzo Nobel Engineering & Operational Solutions B.V. (1)
Oude Velperweg 76
6824 BM Arnhem, Netherlands
Tel.: (31) 26 3664433
Paint & Coating Mfr
S.I.C.: 2851
N.A.I.C.S.: 325510

Akzo Nobel Holding Duitsland B.V. (1)
Velperweg 76
Arnhem, 6824 BM, Netherlands
Tel.: (31) 26 366 4433
Fax: (31) 26 366 3250
Investment Management Services
S.I.C.: 6799
N.A.I.C.S.: 523920

Akzo Nobel Insurance Management B.V. (1)
Oude Velperweg 76
6824 BM Arnhem, Netherlands
Tel.: (31) 26 3664433
Fax: (31) 26 3663250
Emp.: 1,100
General Insurance Services
S.I.C.: 6411
N.A.I.C.S.: 524298

Akzo Nobel Management B.V. (1)
Velperweg 76
Arnhem, 6824 BM, Netherlands
Tel.: (31) 263664433
Investment Management Services
S.I.C.: 6799
N.A.I.C.S.: 523920

Akzo Nobel Nederland BV (1)
Velperweg 76
6824 BM Arnhem, Netherlands
Tel.: (31) 26 366 4433
E-Mail: info@akzonobel.com
Web Site: www.akzonobel.com
Emp.: 1,100
Specialty Chemical Mfr
S.I.C.: 2899
N.A.I.C.S.: 325998
Frans Grasso *(Mgr-Common Solution)*

Akzo Nobel Polymer Chemicals B.V. (1)
Zutphenseweg 10
7418 AJ Deventer, Netherlands
Tel.: (31) 570 679222
Fax: (31) 570 636646
Web Site: www.akzonobel.com
Emp.: 500
Polymer Additive Mfr
S.I.C.: 2899
N.A.I.C.S.: 325998
Ted Kampen *(Mgr-Technical Sls)*

Akzo Nobel Powder Coatings B.V. (1)
Rijksstraatweg 31
Sassenheim, 2171 AJ, Netherlands
Tel.: (31) 713086944
Fax: (31) 713082002
Powder Coating Mfr
S.I.C.: 2851
N.A.I.C.S.: 325510

Akzo Nobel Pulp and Paper Chemicals B.V. (1)
Oude Velperweg 76
6824 BM Arnhem, Netherlands
Tel.: (31) 26 3664433
Chemical Product Mfr
S.I.C.: 2899
N.A.I.C.S.: 325998

Akzo Nobel Representative Offices B.V. (1)
Oude Velperweg 76
6824 BM Arnhem, Netherlands
Tel.: (31) 26 3664433
Paint & Coating Mfr
S.I.C.: 2851
N.A.I.C.S.: 325510

Akzo Nobel Salt B.V. (1)
Stationsplein 77
3811 MH Amersfoort, Netherlands
Tel.: (31) 33 4676767
Fax: (31) 33 4676141
Web Site: www.akzonobelsalt.com
Salt Mfr & Distr
S.I.C.: 2899
N.A.I.C.S.: 325998

Akzo Nobel Sino Coatings B.V. (1)
Rijksstraatweg 31
2171 AJ Sassenheim, Netherlands
Tel.: (31) 71 3086944
Paint & Coating Mfr
S.I.C.: 2851
N.A.I.C.S.: 325510

Akzo Nobel Sourcing B.V. (1)
Oude Velperweg 76
6824 BM Arnhem, Netherlands
Tel.: (31) 26 3664433
Chemical Product Mfr
S.I.C.: 2899
N.A.I.C.S.: 325998

Brunob VII B.V. (1)
Velperweg 76
6824 BM Arnhem, Netherlands
Tel.: (31) 26 3662488
Fax: (31) 263665646
Paint & Coating Mfr
S.I.C.: 2851
N.A.I.C.S.: 325510

Carelaa B.V. (1)
Velperweg 76
6824 BM Arnhem, Netherlands
Tel.: (31) 26 3662488
Paint & Coating Mfr
S.I.C.: 2851
N.A.I.C.S.: 325510

De Sikkens Grossier B.V. (1)
Handelsweg 26
1525 RG West-Knollendam, Netherlands
Tel.: (31) 756 47 62 00
Fax: (31) 756 47 62 11
Paint & Coating Mfr
S.I.C.: 2851
N.A.I.C.S.: 325510

ICI Omicron B.V. (1)
Velperweg 76
Arnhem, 6824 BM, Netherlands
Tel.: (31) 263664514
Fax: (31) 263664096
Paint & Coating Mfr
S.I.C.: 2851
N.A.I.C.S.: 325510

ICI Paints Mercosur B.V. (1)
Velperweg 76
Arnhem, 6824 BM, Netherlands
Tel.: (31) 26 366 4514
Fax: (31) 35 699 5040
Paint & Coating Mfr
S.I.C.: 2851
N.A.I.C.S.: 325510

ICI Paints Uruguay Holdings B.V. (1)
Huizerstraatweg 28
1411 GP Naarden, Netherlands
Tel.: (31) 356999111
Investment Management Services
S.I.C.: 6282
N.A.I.C.S.: 523920

ICI Theta B.V. (1)
Blaak 40
3011 TA Rotterdam, Netherlands
Tel.: (31) 735999333
Paint & Coating Mfr
S.I.C.: 2851
N.A.I.C.S.: 325510

International Paint (Nederland) B.V. (1)
Kleidijk 88
Rhoon, 3161 HJ, Netherlands
Tel.: (31) 10 503 3500
Fax: (31) 10 501 4459
E-Mail: pc.communication@akzonobel.com
Web Site: www.international-pc.com
Paint & Coating Distr
S.I.C.: 5198
N.A.I.C.S.: 424950
Rob Remans *(Mgr-Sls-Marine Coatings)*

IJsselmij Warmtekracht Hengelo B.V. (1)
Stationsstraat 77
3811 MH Amersfoort, Netherlands
Tel.: (31) 33 4676767
Fax: (31) 73 8531210
Paint & Coating Mfr
S.I.C.: 2851
N.A.I.C.S.: 325510

Nobel Industries Holding B.V. (1)
Velperweg 76
6824 BM Arnhem, Netherlands
Tel.: (31) 263664433
Fax: (31) 263663250
Investment Management Services
S.I.C.: 6282
N.A.I.C.S.: 523920

Panter B.V. (1)
Frt St Michielstr 23
5922 XC Venlo, Netherlands
Tel.: (31) 77 3821609
Fax: (31) 77 0773873535
Paint & Coating Mfr
S.I.C.: 2851
N.A.I.C.S.: 325510

Remmert Holland B.V. (1)
Velperweg 76
6824 BM Arnhem, Netherlands
Tel.: (31) 26 3665337
Paint & Coating Mfr
S.I.C.: 2851
N.A.I.C.S.: 325510

Salinco V.O.F. (1)
Boortorenweg 27
7554 RS Hengelo, Netherlands
Tel.: (31) 74244 30 96
Fax: (31) 74244 39 00
Emp.: 40
Electric Power Generation Services
S.I.C.: 4939
N.A.I.C.S.: 221118
Egbert Schasfoort *(Gen Mgr)*

Sikkens Verkoop B.V. (1)
Korte Huifakkerstraat 12
4815 PS Breda, Netherlands
Tel.: (31) 765222112
Fax: (31) 765217544
E-Mail: sikkens.breda@akzonobel.com
Emp.: 2
Paint Supplies Distr
S.I.C.: 5198
N.A.I.C.S.: 424950

Van Noordenne Verf B.V. (1)
Transportweg 29
3371 MA Hardinxveld-Giessendam, Netherlands
Tel.: (31) 184 675895
Fax: (31) 184 611806
Paint & Coating Mfr
S.I.C.: 2851
N.A.I.C.S.: 325510

U.S. Subsidiaries:

Akzo Nobel Cellulosic Specialties Inc. (1)
281 Fields Ln
Brewster, NY 10509 CT
Tel.: (845) 276-8230 (100%)
Fax: (845) 277-1404
Web Site: www.cs.akzonobel.com
Rev.: $2,400,000
Emp.: 12
Chemicals & Adhesives Mfr
S.I.C.: 5169
N.A.I.C.S.: 424690
Jim Reid *(Gen Mgr)*

Akzo Nobel Inc. (1)
525 W Van Buren St 14, 15, 16 Fl
Chicago, IL 60607 DE
Tel.: (312) 544-7000
Fax: (312) 544-6901
Web Site: www.akzonobel.com
Emp.: 100
Mfr. of Healthcare Products, Coatings & Chemicals
Import Export
S.I.C.: 2899
N.A.I.C.S.: 325199

Akzo Nobel Paints LLC (1)
16651 W Sprague Rd
Strongsville, OH 44136
Tel.: (440) 826-5100
Fax: (440) 826-5233
Adhesive Mfr & Distr
S.I.C.: 2891
N.A.I.C.S.: 325520

Akzo Nobel Paints (Puerto Rico) Inc. (1)
630 Calle Feria Av 65 Infanteria Km 13 4
Carolina, PR 00988
Tel.: (787) 641-8900
Fax: (787) 641-8920
Paint & Coating Mfr
S.I.C.: 2851
N.A.I.C.S.: 325510

Akzo Noble Finance United States Inc (1)
1105 N Market St
Wilmington, DE 19801
Tel.: (302) 478-1820
Financial Management Services
S.I.C.: 6211
N.A.I.C.S.: 523999

National Starch Personal Care (1)
10 Finderne Ave
Bridgewater, NJ 08807-3355 DE
Tel.: (908) 685-5000
Fax: (908) 685-5005
E-Mail: personalcare.usa@akzonobel.com
Web Site: www.personalcarepolymers.com
Emp.: 1,200
Sales of Industrial Chemicals, Paints, Specialty Chemicals & Surfactants Mfr.
Import Export
S.I.C.: 2821
N.A.I.C.S.: 325211
John D.G. McAdam *(CEO)*

Nobel Industries USA Inc. (1)
525 W Van Buren St
Chicago, IL 60607 IL
Tel.: (312) 544-7000
Fax: (312) 544-6901
Rev.: $99,500,000
Emp.: 100
Mfr. of Healthcare Products, Coatings & Chemicals
S.I.C.: 2899
N.A.I.C.S.: 325199
Hans Wijers *(Pres)*

Soliant, LLC (1)
1872 Hwy 9 Bypass W
Lancaster, SC 29720-4702
Tel.: (803) 285-9401
Fax: (803) 313-8331
Web Site: www.paintfilm.com
Emp.: 80
Mfr. of Coating, Laminating & Film Products
S.I.C.: 2671
N.A.I.C.S.: 322220
Hans Nelissen *(Gen Mgr)*

Non-U.S. Subsidiaries:

Akzo Nobel AB (1)
Sickla industrivag 6
Nacka, Sweden
Tel.: (46) 8 743 40 00
Paint & Coating Mfr
S.I.C.: 2851
N.A.I.C.S.: 325510

Akzo Nobel Aerospace Coatings GmbH (1)
In de Tarpen 41
22848 Norderstedt, Germany
Tel.: (49) 40 5268380
Fax: (49) 40 52683838
Web Site: www.anac.com
Aerospace Coating Mfr
S.I.C.: 2851
N.A.I.C.S.: 325510

Akzo Nobel Aerospace Coatings Ltd (1)
Unit 1 Meridian West Meridian Business Park
Leicester, LE19 1WX, United Kingdom
Tel.: (44) 116 223 4123
Fax: (44) 116 223 4139
E-Mail: info@akzonobel.com
Web Site: www.anac.com
Aerospace Coating Mfr
S.I.C.: 2851
N.A.I.C.S.: 325510
Martin Carter *(Mgr-Sls-OEM)*

Akzo Nobel Argentina S.A. (1)
Buenos Aires Av Paseo Colon 221
C1063ACC Buenos Aires, Argentina
Tel.: (54) 11 4343 2011
Fax: (54) 11 4709 3788
Paint & Coating Mfr
S.I.C.: 2851
N.A.I.C.S.: 325510

Akzo Nobel Asia Co., Ltd. (1)
22F Eco City 1788 West Nan Jing Road
Shanghai, 200040, China
Tel.: (86) 21 2220 5000
Fax: (86) 21 2220 5558
E-Mail: polymerchemicals.ap@akzonobel.com
Web Site: www.akzonobel.com
Organic Chemical Distr
S.I.C.: 5169
N.A.I.C.S.: 424690

Akzo Nobel (Australia) Pty Ltd (1)
2 Capelli Road
Wingfield, Adelaide, SA, Australia
Tel.: (61) 8 8359 4333
Web Site: www.akzonobel.com
Paint & Coating Mfr
S.I.C.: 2851
N.A.I.C.S.: 325510

Akzo Nobel Automotive and Aerospace Coatings Mexico S.A. de C.V. (1)
Roberto Fulton No 2
Tlalnepantla, 54030, Mexico
Tel.: (52) 5558640715
Aerospace Coating Mfr
S.I.C.: 2851
N.A.I.C.S.: 325510

Akzo Nobel Baltics AS (1)
Tobiase Str 8
Tallinn, 10147, Estonia
Tel.: (372) 630 52 99
Fax: (372) 630 51 11
Web Site: www.akzonobel.com
Paint & Coating Distr
S.I.C.: 5198
N.A.I.C.S.: 424950

Akzo Nobel Baltics SIA (1)
Ciekurkalna 1 gara linija 11
Riga, 1026, Latvia
Tel.: (371) 6736 84 91
Fax: (371) 751 70 16
Emp.: 10
Paint & Coating Distr
S.I.C.: 5198
N.A.I.C.S.: 424950
Vitalis Nikandros *(Mng Dir)*

Akzo Nobel Baltics, UAB (1)
Savanoriu prospekt 178
Vilnius, 03154, Lithuania
Tel.: (370) 523 11 132
Fax: (370) 526 53 484
Web Site: www.akzonobel.com
Paint & Coating Mfr
S.I.C.: 2851
N.A.I.C.S.: 325510
Darius Burneika *(Gen Mgr)*

Akzo Nobel Boya Sanayi Ve Ticaret AS (1)
Akcay Caddesi Ege Serbest Bolgesi
Gaziemir 144
35410 Izmir, Turkey
Tel.: (90) 232 2522700
Fax: (90) 232 2521 517
E-Mail: info.turkey@akzonobel.com
Web Site: www.interpon.com.tr
Emp.: 210
Powder Coating Mfr
S.I.C.: 2851
N.A.I.C.S.: 325510
Sanal Limoncuoglu *(Gen Mgr)*

Akzo Nobel Bygglim AB (1)
Sickla Industrivag 1 C
Box 11550
100 61 Stockholm, Sweden
Tel.: (46) 8 743 40 00
Fax: (46) 8 643 63 70
E-Mail: schonox@akzonobel.com
Web Site: www.schonox.se
Paint & Coating Mfr
S.I.C.: 2851
N.A.I.C.S.: 325510

Akzo Nobel Canada Inc. (1)
2505 De la Metropole
Longueuil, QC, J4G 1E5, Canada
Tel.: (450) 670-7426
Fax: (450) 651-1257
Web Site: www.akzonobel.com
Paint & Coating Mfr
S.I.C.: 2851
N.A.I.C.S.: 325510

Akzo Nobel Car Refinishes A/S (1)
Baldersbuen 31
2640 Hedehusene, Denmark
Tel.: (45) 46 565666
E-Mail: sikkensdk@akzonobel.com
Web Site: www.akzonobel.com
Automotive Coating Mfr
S.I.C.: 2851
N.A.I.C.S.: 325510

Akzo Nobel Car Refinishes AB (1)
Mediavagen 1
135 27 Tyreso, Sweden
Tel.: (46) 8 503 04 100
Fax: (46) 8 503 04 137
Web Site: www.akzonobel.com
Emp.: 20
Automotive Coating Distr
S.I.C.: 5198
N.A.I.C.S.: 424950
Andres Dingvall Rauchwerger *(Reg Mgr-Sls)*

Akzo Nobel Car Refinishes AG (1)
Adetswilerstrasse 4
Postfach 8623
8344 Baretswil, Switzerland
Tel.: (41) 449 31 44 44
Fax: (41) 449 31 44 55
Paint & Coating Distr
S.I.C.: 5198
N.A.I.C.S.: 424950
Markus Ineichen *(Mgr-Supply Chain & IT)*

Akzo Nobel Car Refinishes Australia Pty Ltd (1)
269 Williamstown Road Port
Melbourne, 3207, Australia
Tel.: (61) 3 96441711
Fax: (61) 3 9644 1777
Web Site: www.akzonobel.com
Automotive Coating Mfr
S.I.C.: 2851
N.A.I.C.S.: 325510

Akzo Nobel Car Refinishes (Hong Kong) Limited (1)
Wing Chai Ind Bldg San Po Kong
Wong Tai Sin, Hong Kong, China (Hong Kong)
Tel.: (852) 2775 5300
Fax: (852) 2347 0715
Automotive Coating Mfr
S.I.C.: 2851
N.A.I.C.S.: 325510

Akzo Nobel Car Refinishes India Pvt Ltd (1)
62P Hoskote Industrial Area
562 114 Bengaluru, India
Tel.: (91) 80 2204 7000
Fax: (91) 80 797 1407
E-Mail: cradmin@akzonobel.com
Web Site: www.akzonobel.com
Emp.: 39
Automotive Coating Mfr & Distr
S.I.C.: 2851
N.A.I.C.S.: 325510
Hitesh Mehta *(Gen Mgr-Mktg)*

Akzo Nobel Car Refinishes (Ireland) Ltd (1)
Unit 1d Avonbeg Industrial Estate Longmile Road
Dublin, Ireland
Tel.: (353) 1 4501344
Fax: (353) 1 4501397
Emp.: 8
Automotive Coating Mfr
S.I.C.: 2851
N.A.I.C.S.: 325510
Jon Amor *(Mgr-Sls)*

Akzo Nobel Car Refinishes Korea Co. Ltd (1)
Yang Jae-Dong 423-4
SeoCho-Ku, 137-897 Seoul, Korea (South)
Tel.: (82) 2577 7233
Web Site: www.akzonobel.com
Automotive Coating Mfr
S.I.C.: 2851
N.A.I.C.S.: 325510

Akzo Nobel Car Refinishes SAS (1)
Rue Jean Casse - ZI les Bas Pres
60160 Montataire, France
Tel.: (33) 3 44 28 53 00
Fax: (33) 3 44 28 53 90
Automotive Coating Mfr
S.I.C.: 2851
N.A.I.C.S.: 325510

Akzo Nobel Car Refinishes (Singapore) Pte. Ltd. (1)
510 Thomson Road 16-03 SLF Building
Singapore, 298135, Singapore
Tel.: (65) 6254 8477
Fax: (65) 6354 6871
Web Site: www.wandarefinish.asia
Car Refinish Paint Mfr
S.I.C.: 2851
N.A.I.C.S.: 325510

Akzo Nobel Car Refinishes SL (1)
Feixa Llarga 14-20 P I Zona Franca
08040 Barcelona, Spain
Tel.: (34) 932670800
Fax: (34) 932670801
Automotive Coating Mfr
S.I.C.: 2851
N.A.I.C.S.: 325510
Sergio Olivas *(Mgr)*

Akzo Nobel Car Refinishes (Suzhou) Co. Ltd (1)
Xiang Yang Road 125
215009 Suzhou, China
Tel.: (86) 512 68257828
Automotive Coating Mfr
S.I.C.: 2851
N.A.I.C.S.: 325510

Akzo Nobel Chang Cheng Coatings (Guangdong) Co Ltd (1)
Luo Tian da Dao Road Yan Chuan Chun Village
Songgang Town, 518105 Shenzhen, China
Tel.: (86) 755 2714 8450
Fax: (86) 755 2993 6451
Powder Coating Mfr
S.I.C.: 2851
N.A.I.C.S.: 325510

Akzo Nobel Chang Cheng Coatings (Suzhou) Co Ltd (1)
Xiang Yang Road 125
215011 Suzhou, China
Tel.: (86) 512 68257828
Web Site: www.akzonobel.com
Powder Coating Mfr
S.I.C.: 2851
N.A.I.C.S.: 325510

Akzo Nobel Chang Cheng Limited (1)
88 Quach Dinh Bao Street Phu Thanh Ward
Tan Phu District, 70000 Ho Chi Minh City, Vietnam
Tel.: (84) 8 3 8221612
Web Site: www.akzonobel.com
Powder Coating Mfr
S.I.C.: 2851
N.A.I.C.S.: 325510

Akzo Nobel Chang Cheng (Taiwan) Ltd (1)
Kon 6th Road Lin Kou 21
244 Taipei, Taiwan
Tel.: (886) 2 26035700
Fax: (886) 2 2601 8520
Paint & Coating Mfr
S.I.C.: 2851
N.A.I.C.S.: 325510

Akzo Nobel ChangCheng Coating (Langfang) Co., Ltd. (1)
Quanxing Road 32
065001 Langfang, China
Tel.: (86) 316 5919519
Powder Coating Mfr
S.I.C.: 2851
N.A.I.C.S.: 325510

Akzo Nobel Chemicals Holding GmbH (1)
Kreuzauer Str 46
52355 Duren, Germany
Tel.: (49) 2421 595 488
Fax: (49) 2421 595 450
Investment Management Services
S.I.C.: 6282
N.A.I.C.S.: 523920

Akzo Nobel Chemicals Holdings Limited (1)
Unit 1 Caroline Street
Wigan, Lancashire, WN3 4EL, United Kingdom
Tel.: (44) 1942 242 745
Investment Management Services
S.I.C.: 6282
N.A.I.C.S.: 523920

Akzo Nobel Chemicals MCA (Taixing) Co. Ltd. (1)
No 9 Bin Jiang Bei Road Taixing Economic Development Area
Taixing, Jiangsu, 225404, China
Tel.: (86) 523 87676001
Polymer Chemical Product Mfr
S.I.C.: 2899
N.A.I.C.S.: 325998

Akzo Nobel Chemicals NV/SA (1)
Parc Industriel de Ghlin Zone A
7011 Ghlin, Belgium
Tel.: (32) 65 76 07 11
Fax: (32) 65 64 23 85
Web Site: www.akzonobel.com
Emp.: 250
Polymer Chemical Mfr
S.I.C.: 2899
N.A.I.C.S.: 325199
Cees van Dongen *(Gen Mgr)*

Akzo Nobel Chemicals Pty Ltd (1)
8 Kellaway Pl
Wetherill Park, NSW, 2164, Australia
Tel.: (61) 2 9616 6900
Fax: (61) 2 9609 6316
Emp.: 3
Chemical Product Mfr
S.I.C.: 2869
N.A.I.C.S.: 325199
Brian Patten *(Country Mgr)*

Akzo Nobel Chemicals Representation Services Sp. Z o.o. (1)
Ul Domaniewska 41 Budynek Neptun Parter
02-672 Warsaw, Poland
Tel.: (48) 95 960 2890
Fax: (48) 95 960 2885
Web Site: www.akzonobel.com
Chemical Product Mfr

Akzo Nobel N.V.—(Continued)

S.I.C.: 2899
N.A.I.C.S.: 325998

Akzo Nobel Chemicals S.A. (1)
Autovia de Castelldefels Km 4 65
08820 El Prat de Llobregat, Barcelona, Spain
Tel.: (34) 93 4784411
Fax: (34) 93 4780734
E-Mail: polymerchemicals@akzonobel.com
Web Site: www.akzonobel.com
Chemical Product Mfr
S.I.C.: 2899
N.A.I.C.S.: 325998
Merce Estivill Costa *(Mgr-Customer Svc)*

Akzo Nobel Chemicals (1)
12-1 Goban-cho
Chiyoda-ku, Tokyo, 102-0076, Japan
Tel.: (81) 352756300
Fax: (81) 332630713
Web Site: www.akzonobel.com
Emp.: 15
Chemical Product Mfr
S.I.C.: 2899
N.A.I.C.S.: 325998
Hiro Okitsu *(Controller-Fin)*

Akzo Nobel Coatings A.E. (1)
Parodos Kolokotronis 10
Kryoneri, 14568 Markopoulon, Greece
Tel.: (30) 2106220621
Fax: (30) 2108161835
E-Mail: sikkins.greece@akzonobel.com
Web Site: www.sikkenscr.gr
Emp.: 20
Paint & Coating Mfr
S.I.C.: 2851
N.A.I.C.S.: 325510
Yannis Ioannidis *(Gen Mgr)*

Akzo Nobel Coatings AG (1)
Taschmattstrasse 16
6015 Lucerne, Switzerland
Tel.: (41) 41 268 14 14
Fax: (41) 41 455 45 90
E-Mail: info.ch@akzonobel.com
Web Site: www.akzonobel.com
Paint & Coating Mfr
S.I.C.: 2851
N.A.I.C.S.: 325510

Akzo Nobel Coatings AS (1)
Floisbonnveien Sofiemyr 6
1412 Kolbotn, Norway
Tel.: (47) 66819400
Fax: (47) 66819550
E-Mail: norway@akzonobel.com
Web Site: www.akzonobel.com
Emp.: 70
Paint & Coating Distr
S.I.C.: 5198
N.A.I.C.S.: 424950
Christian Brevik *(Mgr-Sls)*

Akzo Nobel Coatings (Dongguan) Co. Ltd. (1)
Dalingshan Science & Industrial Park
523816 Dongguan, China
Tel.: (86) 769 85620333
Fax: (86) 769 85603100
Web Site: www.akzonobel.com
Emp.: 300
Coil & Extrusion Coating Mfr
S.I.C.: 2851
N.A.I.C.S.: 325510
James Chen *(Gen Mgr)*

Akzo Nobel Coatings GmbH (1)
Zetschegasse 9
1230 Vienna, Austria
Tel.: (43) 1 767 4488 322
E-Mail: info.at@akzonobel.com
Web Site: www.akzonobel.com
Paint & Coating Distr
S.I.C.: 5198
N.A.I.C.S.: 424950
Andreas Eberle *(Country Mgr)*

Akzo Nobel Coatings GmbH (1)
Kruppstrasse 30
70469 Stuttgart, Germany
Tel.: (49) 711 8951 0
Web Site: www.akzonobel.com
Paint & Coating Mfr
S.I.C.: 2851
N.A.I.C.S.: 325510

Akzo Nobel Coatings India Private Ltd (1)
2B - 2nd Floor Shyams Garden No 10 Khader
Nawaz Khan Road, 600 034 Chennai, India
Tel.: (91) 44 42903737
Fax: (91) 44 42903720
Web Site: www.akzonobel.com
Paint & Coating Mfr
S.I.C.: 2851
N.A.I.C.S.: 325510

Akzo Nobel Coatings (Jiaxing) Co. Ltd (1)
No 1 Dongsheng Road
Jiashan, Jiaxing, Zhejiang, 314100, China
Tel.: (86) 573 8425 3015
Fax: (86) 573 8425 3002
Web Site: www.akzonobel.com
Coil & Extrusion Coating Mfr
S.I.C.: 2851
N.A.I.C.S.: 325510

Akzo Nobel Coatings K.K. (1)
3-20 Yoshino-cho
Suita, Osaka, 564-0054, Japan
Tel.: (81) 6 6330 1151
Fax: (81) 6 6330 0053
Web Site: www.akzonobel.com
Paint & Coating Mfr
S.I.C.: 2851
N.A.I.C.S.: 325510
Sosuke Shinozaki *(Gen Mgr)*

Akzo Nobel Coatings Oy (1)
Malmarintie 20
01380 Vantaa, Finland
Tel.: (358) 108 419 500
Fax: (358) 207 501 517
Web Site: www.akzonobel.com
Paint & Coating Mfr
S.I.C.: 2851
N.A.I.C.S.: 325510

Akzo Nobel Coatings, S.L. (1)
Felix Llarga 14
08040 Barcelona, Spain
Tel.: (34) 934842730
Fax: (34) 935708899
Paint & Coating Mfr
S.I.C.: 2851
N.A.I.C.S.: 325510

Akzo Nobel Coatings sp. z o.o. (1)
Ul Cybernetyki 7B
02-677 Warsaw, Poland
Tel.: (48) 22 321 0621
Web Site: www.akzonobel.com
Automotive Paint Distr
S.I.C.: 5198
N.A.I.C.S.: 424950

Akzo Nobel Coatings SrL (1)
Bd Regiei nr 6D bl 4 parter sector 6
Bucharest, 060204, Romania
Tel.: (40) 721240584
Paint & Coating Distr
S.I.C.: 5198
N.A.I.C.S.: 424950

Akzo Nobel Coatings (Tianjin) Co., Ltd. (1)
110 Tai Hua Road Teda
Tianjin, China 300457
Tel.: (86) 22 2529 3001
Fax: (86) 22 66230953
Paint & Coating Mfr
S.I.C.: 2851
N.A.I.C.S.: 325510

Akzo Nobel Coatings Trading Ltd (1)
98/21 Moo 11 Phuddamonthon 5 Rd Raikhing
Sam Phran, 73210, Thailand
Tel.: (66) 2811 8421
Fax: (66) 2811 8114
Paint & Coaitng Mfr
S.I.C.: 2851
N.A.I.C.S.: 325510

Akzo Nobel Coatings Vietnam Limited (1)
Lot 107 Amata Industrial Park
Bien Hoa, Dong Nai, Vietnam
Tel.: (84) 61 3936 389
Fax: (84) 61 3936 386
Emp.: 80
Paint & Coating Mfr
S.I.C.: 2851
N.A.I.C.S.: 325510

Akzo Nobel Coatings Zrt (1)
Montevideo u 3/B
1037 Budapest, Hungary
Tel.: (36) 1 430 3950
Fax: (36) 1 430 3969
Web Site: www.akzonobel.com
Paint & Coating Mfr
S.I.C.: 2851
N.A.I.C.S.: 325510

Akzo Nobel Coil Coatings SA (1)
Zi Les Bas Pres
Montataire, 60761, France
Tel.: (33) 3 44 31 38 89
Fax: (33) 3 44 28 50 70
Coil Coating Mfr
S.I.C.: 2851
N.A.I.C.S.: 325510

Akzo Nobel Cross Linking Peroxides (Ningbo) Co. Ltd (1)
No 501 Hongyuan Road Houhaitang Industrial Estate
Zhenhai, Ningbo, 315200, China
Tel.: (86) 574 8625 2484
Fax: (86) 574 8625 5297
Chemical Product Mfr
S.I.C.: 2899
N.A.I.C.S.: 325998

Akzo Nobel Deco A/S (1)
Holmbladsgade 70
2300 Copenhagen, Denmark
Tel.: (45) 32 698000
Fax: (45) 32 698484
Web Site: www.akzonobel.com
Emp.: 40
Paint & Coating Mfr
S.I.C.: 2851
N.A.I.C.S.: 325510
Johnny Anderson *(Controller-Fin)*

Akzo Nobel Deco GmbH (1)
Vetales Strasse 198-226
50827 Cologne, Germany
Tel.: (49) 2103 77800
Fax: (49) 2215 881335
E-Mail: koeln.zentrale@akzonobel.com
Web Site: www.akzonobel.com
Emp.: 500
Decorative Paint Mfr
S.I.C.: 2851
N.A.I.C.S.: 325510
Thomas Biemann *(Mgr)*

Akzo Nobel Decorative Coatings A/S (1)
Torshovgt 3
0476 Oslo, Norway
Tel.: (47) 22806150
Web Site: www.akzonobel.com
Decorative Coating Mfr
S.I.C.: 2851
N.A.I.C.S.: 325510

Akzo Nobel Decorative Coatings Sverige AB (1)
Staffanstorpsvagen 50
205 17 Malmo, Sweden
Tel.: (46) 40 355000
Fax: (46) 40 355223
E-Mail: info@mma.akzonobel.com
Web Site: www.akzonobel.com
Emp.: 500
Paint & Coating Mfr
S.I.C.: 2851
N.A.I.C.S.: 325510
Annika Karlsson *(Mgr-Mktg)*

Akzo Nobel Decorative International (1)
Bonsiepen 5
45136 Essen, Germany
Tel.: (49) 201 565 860
Fax: (49) 201 565 678
E-Mail: Cascoadhesives@schoenox.de
Web Site: www.akzonobel.com
Emp.: 3
Decorative Paint Distr
S.I.C.: 5198
N.A.I.C.S.: 424950
Klaus Rosskothen *(Mgr-Sls)*

Akzo Nobel Decorative Paints Belgium nv (1)
Gustaaf Levisstraat 2
1800 Vilvoorde, Belgium
Tel.: (32) 2 254 2211
Fax: (32) 2 254 2335
E-Mail: velvoorde@akzonobel.com
Web Site: www.akzonobel.com
Emp.: 400
Paint & Coating Mfr
S.I.C.: 2851
N.A.I.C.S.: 325510
Katrien Clou *(Mgr-Tech & Laboratory)*

Akzo Nobel Decorative Paints Sp. Z o.o (1)
Ul Wybrzeze Gdynskie 6 d
01-531 Warsaw, Mazowieckie, Poland
Tel.: (48) 22 321 20 45
Fax: (48) 22 321 20 82
Decorative Paint Mfr
S.I.C.: 2851
N.A.I.C.S.: 325510

Akzo Nobel Distribution Ile de France S.A.S. (1)
2-4 Avenue De L'Industrie Ville
69969 Corbas, France
Tel.: (33) 4 72 21 90 56
Fax: (33) 4 72 51 46 46
Paint & Coating Mfr
S.I.C.: 2851
N.A.I.C.S.: 325510

Akzo Nobel Distribution Ouest S.A.S. (1)
Service Client 2 Boulevard des Bretonnieres
49182 Saint Barthelemy-d'Anjou, France
Tel.: (33) 2 41 37 50 00
Fax: (33) 2 41 37 45 05
E-Mail: contactgo@akzonobel.com
Paint Supplies Distr
S.I.C.: 5198
N.A.I.C.S.: 424950

Akzo Nobel Distribution SAS (1)
23 Rue Georges Bonnet Ville
26000 Valence, France
Tel.: (33) 4 75 82 05 10
Fax: (33) 4 75 55 00 70
Emp.: 6
Paint & Coating Mfr
S.I.C.: 2851
N.A.I.C.S.: 325510

Akzo Nobel Farben Beteiligungs-GmbH (1)
Magirusstr 14 Feuerbach
70469 Stuttgart, Baden-Wurttemberg, Germany
Tel.: (49) 71189510
Fax: (49) 7118951389
Paint & Coating Mfr
S.I.C.: 2851
N.A.I.C.S.: 325510

Akzo Nobel Faser Pensionsverwaltungs-GmbH (1)
Kasinostr 19-21
100149 Wuppertal, Germany
Tel.: (49) 202322539
Paint & Coating Mfr
S.I.C.: 2851
N.A.I.C.S.: 325510

Akzo Nobel Functional Chemicals AB (1)
Horneborgsvagen 11
891 26 Ornskoldsvik, Sweden
Tel.: (46) 660 75500
Fax: (46) 660 75303
Web Site: www.akzonobel.com
Cellulose Derivative Mfr
S.I.C.: 2899
N.A.I.C.S.: 325998
Eike Kantzer *(Mgr-R&D & Innovation)*

Akzo Nobel Functional Chemicals GmbH & Co. KG (1)
Liebigstrasse 7
07973 Greiz, Germany
Tel.: (49) 3661 780
Fax: (49) 3661 78219
Web Site: www.akzonobel.com
Chemical Product Mfr
S.I.C.: 2899
N.A.I.C.S.: 325998
Dirk Stoeppler *(Dir-Site)*

Akzo Nobel Functional Chemicals S.A. (1)
Ruta 11 Km 25
S2200MEC San Lorenzo, Santa Fe, Argentina

Tel.: (54) 3476 422005
Web Site: www.akzonobel.com
Sulfuric Acid Mfr
S.I.C.: 2819
N.A.I.C.S.: 325180

Akzo Nobel Functional Chemicals Verwaltungs-GmbH (1)
Liebigstrasse 7
07973 Greiz, Germany
Tel.: (49) 3661 780
Fax: (49) 3661 78219
Chemical Product Mfr
S.I.C.: 2899
N.A.I.C.S.: 325998

Akzo Nobel GmbH (1)
Kasinostrasse 19-21
42103 Wuppertal, Germany
Tel.: (49) 202 322571
Fax: (49) 202 322576
E-Mail: info@akzonobel.com
Web Site: www.akzonobel.com
Emp.: 6
Paint & Coating Mfr
S.I.C.: 2851
N.A.I.C.S.: 325510

Akzo Nobel Holding Osterreich GmbH (1)
Aubergstr 7
5161 Elixhausen, Salzburg, Austria
Tel.: (43) 662 48989 0
Fax: (43) 662 4898911
Investment Management Services
S.I.C.: 6282
N.A.I.C.S.: 523920

Akzo Nobel Inda, S.A. de C.V. (1)
2da de San Francisco 1775 Ote Colonia Reforma
Monterrey, Nuevo Leon, 64550, Mexico
Tel.: (52) 81 8374 3244
Fax: (52) 81 8372 8642
Web Site: www.interpon.com.mx
Powder Coating Mfr
S.I.C.: 2851
N.A.I.C.S.: 325510

Akzo Nobel India Limited (1)
Geetanjali Apartment 1st Floor 8 B
Middleton Street
Kolkata, 700071, India
Tel.: (91) 3322267462
Fax: (91) 3322277925
Web Site: www.akzonobel.co.in
AKZOINDIA—(NSE)
Sls.: $448,834,860
Assets: $427,384,080
Liabilities: $222,461,460
Net Worth: $204,922,620
Earnings: $40,565,520
Emp.: 1,795
Fiscal Year-end: 03/31/13
Paints, Chemicals & Starch Mfr
S.I.C.: 2851
N.A.I.C.S.: 325510
Jayakumar Krishnaswamy *(Mng Dir)*
R. Guha *(Compliance Officer & Sec)*

Akzo Nobel Industrial Chemicals AB (1)
Drakegatan 6
41 250 Gothenburg, Sweden
Tel.: (46) 31 733 1880
Fax: (46) 31 733 1899
E-Mail: Industrialchemicals.csdse@akzonobel.com
Web Site: www.akzonobel.com
Emp.: 5
Industrial Chemical Mfr & Distr
S.I.C.: 2899
N.A.I.C.S.: 325998
Ulf Sandberg *(Mgr-Sls)*

Akzo Nobel Industrial Chemicals (1)
Bin Jiang Bei Rd 2-8
225404 Taixing, China
Tel.: (86) 523 8767 6001
Web Site: www.akzonobel.com
Chemical Product Mfr & Distr
S.I.C.: 2899
N.A.I.C.S.: 325998

Akzo Nobel Industrial Coatings AB (1)
Odensvivagen 32
594 32 Gamleby, Sweden
Tel.: (46) 493 14100
Fax: (46) 493 14129
E-Mail: anif.se@akzonobel.com
Web Site: www.akzonobel.com
Emp.: 170
Industrial Coating Mfr
S.I.C.: 2851
N.A.I.C.S.: 325510

Akzo Nobel industrial Coatings Korea Ltd. (1)
5ba-203 Sihwa Industrial Complex 676-12
Seonggok-Dong Danwon-gu, Ansan, 425-836, Korea (South)
Tel.: (82) 31 432 1100
Fax: (82) 31 432 1108
Powder Coating Mfr
S.I.C.: 2851
N.A.I.C.S.: 325510

Akzo Nobel Industrial Coatings Ltd (1)
Unit 04A Mercer Way Shadsworth Business Park
Blackburn, Lancashire, BB1 2QZ, United Kingdom
Tel.: (44) 1254 687 950
Fax: (44) 1254 687 960
E-Mail: Sales.Shadsworth@akzonobel.com
Web Site: www.akzonobel.com
Emp.: 25
Industrial Coating Distr
S.I.C.: 5198
N.A.I.C.S.: 424950

Akzo Nobel Industrial Coatings Mexico SA de CV (1)
Anillo Periferico 205 km 16 64
Villa de Garcia, Nuevo Leon, Mexico 66000
Tel.: (52) 81 1365 3000
Fax: (52) 81 1365 3098
Web Site: www.akzonobel.com
Emp.: 5
Coil & Extrusion Coating Mfr
S.I.C.: 2851
N.A.I.C.S.: 325510
Miguel Rocha *(Gen Mgr)*

Akzo Nobel Industrial Coatings SA (1)
Poligono Industrial Can Prunera 9
08759 Vallirana, Spain
Tel.: (34) 93 680 69 00
Industrial Coating Mfr
S.I.C.: 2851
N.A.I.C.S.: 325510

Akzo Nobel Industrial Coatings Sdn Bhd (1)
Lot 1&2 Jalan Gangsa
81700 Pasir Gudang, Johor, Malaysia
Tel.: (60) 7 254 1122
Fax: (60) 7 252 4559
Industrial Coating Mfr
S.I.C.: 2851
N.A.I.C.S.: 325510

Akzo Nobel Industrial Coatings Sp. z o.o. (1)
ul Polna 1A
62-025 Kostrzyn, Poland
Tel.: (48) 61 897 05 00
Fax: (48) 61 897 05 19
Web Site: www.akzonobel.poznan.pl
Emp.: 20
Industrial Coating Mfr
S.I.C.: 2851
N.A.I.C.S.: 325510

Akzo Nobel Industrial Finishes GmbH (1)
Lochnerstrasse 12
90441 Nuremberg, Germany
Tel.: (49) 911 66880
Fax: (49) 911 6688164
E-Mail: nbc_info@akzonobel.com
Web Site: www.akzonobel.com
Industrial Coating Mfr
S.I.C.: 2851
N.A.I.C.S.: 325510

Akzo Nobel Industrial Finishes S.A.S. (1)
34 Avenue Leon Jouhaux
92160 Antony, Hauts-de-Seine, France
Tel.: (33) 1 46 11 51 73
Fax: (33) 1 46 11 51 00
Emp.: 7
Paint & Coating Mfr
S.I.C.: 2851
N.A.I.C.S.: 325510
Jean-Philippe Robin *(Mgr-Sls)*

Akzo Nobel Industrial Paints, S.L. (1)
Poligono Industrial Can Prunera s/n
Apartado de Correos 9
08759 Vallirana, Barcelona, Spain
Tel.: (34) 9 3 680 6900
Fax: (34) 9 3 680 6921
E-Mail: akzonobel.Vallirana@akzonobel.com
Web Site: www.interpon.com
Emp.: 150
Industrial Paint Mfr
S.I.C.: 2851
N.A.I.C.S.: 325510
Pere Camps Sabate *(Mgr-Production)*

Akzo Nobel Industries Limited (1)
8 Callaway Pl
Wetherill Park, NSW, 2164, Australia
Tel.: (61) 2 9616 6900
Paint & Coating Mfr
S.I.C.: 2851
N.A.I.C.S.: 325510

Akzo Nobel Kemipol A.S. (1)
Ankara Karayolu 25 Km
35177 Kemalpasa, Izmir, Turkey
Tel.: (90) 232 870 1470
Fax: (90) 232 877 0834
E-Mail: info@akzonobelkemipol.com.tr
Web Site: www.akzonobel.com
Emp.: 181
Paint & Coating Mfr
S.I.C.: 2851
N.A.I.C.S.: 325510

Akzo Nobel Lakokraska Ltd (1)
Sovkhoznaya Street 38
142603 Orekhovo-Zuyevo, Russia
Tel.: (7) 495 411 7350
Fax: (7) 495 411 8420
E-Mail: Info.Lako@interpon.com
Web Site: www.interpon.ru
Emp.: 140
Powder Paint Mfr
S.I.C.: 2851
N.A.I.C.S.: 325510
Schennikov Nikita *(Mgr-Credit Control)*

Akzo Nobel Ltda. (1)
Rodovia Akzo Nobel 707 Itupeva
Sao Paulo, 13295-000, Brazil BR
Tel.: (55) 11 4591 8939
Fax: (55) 11 4591 1744
Chemical Product Mfr
S.I.C.: 2899
N.A.I.C.S.: 325998

Akzo Nobel Limited (1)
Portland House
London, SW1E 5BG, United Kingdom
Tel.: (44) 1254 704951
Fax: (44) 1254 774414
Paint & Coating Mfr
S.I.C.: 2851
N.A.I.C.S.: 325510

Akzo Nobel (Malaysia) Sdn Bhd (1)
Plo 285 Jln Pekeliling Timur
Pasir Gudang, 81707, Malaysia
Tel.: (60) 7 251 8000
Fax: (60) 7 251 1066
Chemical Product Mfr
S.I.C.: 2899
N.A.I.C.S.: 325998

Akzo Nobel Packaging Coatings S.A. (1)
Poligono Domenys II c/Agricultura 7-10
08720 Vilafranca del Penedes, Spain
Tel.: (34) 93 819 1000
Fax: (34) 93 819 1010
Web Site: www.akzonobel.com
Emp.: 60
Paint & Coating Mfr
S.I.C.: 2851
N.A.I.C.S.: 325510
Rafael Lopez *(Mgr-IT)*

Akzo Nobel Packaging Coatings S.A.S. (1)
182 Rue Ludovic Becquet
76320 Saint Pierre-les-Elbeuf, France
Tel.: (33) 2 32 96 43 00
Fax: (33) 2 35 78 39 42
Web Site: www.akzonobel.com
Marine & Automotive Coating Mfr & Distr
S.I.C.: 2851
N.A.I.C.S.: 325510

Akzo Nobel Paints Belgium NV/SA (1)
Gustave Levisstraat 2
Vilvoorde, 1800, Belgium
Tel.: (32) 2 254 22 11
Fax: (32) 2 252 18 46
E-Mail: info@akzonobel.com
Emp.: 500
Paint & Coating Mfr
S.I.C.: 2851
N.A.I.C.S.: 325510
Dirk van Ussel *(Mgr-Natl Sls)*

Akzo Nobel Paints (Singapore) Pte Limited (1)
22 Soon Lee Road
Singapore, 628082, Singapore
Tel.: (65) 62650677
Fax: (65) 62654775
E-Mail: customer.care.sg@akzonobel.com
Paint Mfr
S.I.C.: 2851
N.A.I.C.S.: 325510

Akzo Nobel Paints Taiwan Limited (1)
52 Tung Yuan Rd Jhongli Ind Park
Chung-li, 32063, Taiwan
Tel.: (886) 34523116
Paint Mfr
S.I.C.: 2851
N.A.I.C.S.: 325510

Akzo Nobel Paints Vietnam Ltd (1)
Level 5 Kumho Asiana Plz 39 Le Duan Boulevard
District 1, Ho Chi Minh City, Vietnam
Tel.: (84) 8 3822 1612
Fax: (84) 8 3824 1894
Paint Distr
S.I.C.: 5198
N.A.I.C.S.: 424950

Akzo Nobel Pakistan Limited (1)
346 Ferozepur Road
PO Box 273
Lahore, 54600, Pakistan
Tel.: (92) 42 111 551 111
Fax: (92) 42 3583 5011
E-Mail: communications.pakistan@akzonobel.com
Web Site: www.akzonobel.com
AKZO—(LAH)
Paintings & Coatings Mfr
S.I.C.: 2851
N.A.I.C.S.: 325510
Mueen Afzal *(Chm)*
Jehanzeb Khan *(CEO)*
Zia U. Syed *(CFO)*

Akzo Nobel Pensions GmbH (1)
Kasinostr 19-21
42103 Wuppertal, Germany
Tel.: (49) 202 322539
Fax: (49) 202 324278
Pension Fund Services
S.I.C.: 6371
N.A.I.C.S.: 525110

Akzo Nobel Peru S.A.C. (1)
Cal Campo Primavera Cap Laredo 0
Tableros Peruanos
Trujillo, Peru
Tel.: (51) 44435453
Paint & Coating Mfr
S.I.C.: 2851
N.A.I.C.S.: 325510

Akzo Nobel Polymer Chemicals (Ningbo) Co., Ltd. (1)
No 1801 Mid-Haitian Rd Xiepu Town
Zhenhai District, Ningbo, 315204, China
Tel.: (86) 574 86621239
Chemical Product Mfr
S.I.C.: 2899
N.A.I.C.S.: 325998

Akzo Nobel Powder Coatings A.E. (1)
10 Kolokotroni str
Krioneri Attikis, 14568 Athens, Greece
Tel.: (30) 210 8160 160
Fax: (30) 210 8161 843
Emp.: 14
Powder Coating Mfr
S.I.C.: 2851
N.A.I.C.S.: 325510

Akzo Nobel N.V.—(Continued)

Vaggelis Manolopoulos *(Mgr-Technical Support)*

Akzo Nobel Powder Coatings (Chengdu) Co., Ltd. (1)
Building 9C Dragon fly industrial park
610100 Chengdu, China
Tel.: (86) 28 8484 7422
Powder Coating Mfr
S.I.C.: 2851
N.A.I.C.S.: 325510

Akzo Nobel Powder Coatings Fze (1)
Plot n FZS2AC 9 10
PO Box 262203
Jebel Ali Free Zone, Dubai, United Arab Emirates
Tel.: (971) 4 8862181
Fax: (971) 4 8862180
Powder Paint Mfr
S.I.C.: 2851
N.A.I.C.S.: 325510

Akzo Nobel Powder Coatings GmbH (1)
Markwiesen Strasse 50
72770 Reutlingen, Germany
Tel.: (49) 7121 5190
Fax: (49) 7121 519212
E-Mail: resicoat@akzonobel.com
Web Site: www.akzonobel.com
Powder Coating Mfr
S.I.C.: 2851
N.A.I.C.S.: 325510

Akzo Nobel Powder Coatings Korea Co., Limited (1)
203-5Ba Shihwa Industrial Complex 676-12
Seonggok-Dong Danwon-gu, Ansan, Korea (South)
Tel.: (82) 31 434 1100
Fax: (82) 31 434 1108
Powder Coating Mfr
S.I.C.: 2851
N.A.I.C.S.: 325510

Akzo Nobel Powder Coatings (Langfang) Co. Ltd. (1)
No 32 Quanxing Street Langfang Economic & Technical Development Zone
Langfang, Hebei, 065001, China
Tel.: (86) 316 5919519
Fax: (86) 316 5919512
Web Site: www.interpon.com
Powder Coating Mfr
S.I.C.: 2851
N.A.I.C.S.: 325510

Akzo Nobel Powder Coatings (Ningbo) Co., Ltd. (1)
Ningchuan Road
Wuxiang Town, Ningbo, Zhejiang, 315111, China
Tel.: (86) 574 5680 1404
Fax: (86) 574 5680 9882
Emp.: 300
Powder Coating Mfr
S.I.C.: 2851
N.A.I.C.S.: 325510
Eddie Wang *(Gen Mgr)*

Akzo Nobel Powder Coatings SNC (1)
Rue de la Gaudree - ZI La Gaudree
91410 Dourdan, France
Tel.: (33) 1 60 81 81 81
Fax: (33) 1 60 81 81 96
Powder Coating Mfr
S.I.C.: 2851
N.A.I.C.S.: 325510

Akzo Nobel Powder Coatings South Africa (Proprietary) Limited (1)
14 Union Street
Alberton, 1449, South Africa
Tel.: (27) 11 907 8195
Fax: (27) 11 907 2316
Powder Coating Mfr
S.I.C.: 2851
N.A.I.C.S.: 325510

Akzo Nobel Powder Coatings (Suzhou) Co., Ltd. (1)
125 Xiang Yang Road Suzhou New District
Suzhou, 215011, China
Tel.: (86) 512 6825 7828
Fax: (86) 5126 825 9139
Powder Coating Mfr
S.I.C.: 2851
N.A.I.C.S.: 325510

Akzo Nobel Powder Coatings (Vietnam) Co., Ltd. (1)
Road No 2 Nhon Trach Industrial Zone
Nhon Trach, Dong Nai, Vietnam
Tel.: (84) 613560730
Powder Coating Mfr
S.I.C.: 2851
N.A.I.C.S.: 325510

Akzo Nobel Protective Coatings (Suzhou) Co. Ltd (1)
No 129 Hongxi Road
Suzhou, 215151, China
Tel.: (86) 51 2825 1299
Fax: (86) 51 2825 3900
Protective Coating Mfr & Distr
S.I.C.: 2851
N.A.I.C.S.: 325510

Akzo Nobel S.A.S. (1)
34 Avenue Leon Jouhaux
Antony, 92164, France
Tel.: (33) 1 46 11 51 15
Fax: (33) 1 46 66 49 22
Chemical Product Mfr & Distr
S.I.C.: 2899
N.A.I.C.S.: 325998

Akzo Nobel (Shanghai) Co. Ltd. (1)
No 137 Jiang Tian East Road Song Jiang Industrial Zone
Shanghai, 201600, China
Tel.: (86) 21 57745700
Fax: (86) 21 67742936
Web Site: www.sc.akzonobel.com
Emp.: 400
Paint & Coating Mfr
S.I.C.: 2851
N.A.I.C.S.: 325510

Akzo Nobel Specialty Chemicals (Shanghai) Co., Ltd (1)
Part Southwest No 3 Building No 450 Hua Tie Road
Songjiang, Shanghai, 201600, China
Tel.: (86) 57745700
Chemical Product Mfr
S.I.C.: 2899
N.A.I.C.S.: 325998

Akzo Nobel Surface Chemistry AB (1)
Stenunge Alle 3
444 85 Stenungsund, Sweden
Tel.: (46) 303 850 00
Fax: (46) 303 88 910
E-Mail: surfactants.europe@akzonobel.com
Web Site: www.akzonobel.com
Chemical Product Distr
S.I.C.: 5169
N.A.I.C.S.: 424690

Akzo Nobel Swire Paints (Guangzhou) Limited (1)
Guangzhou Economic & Technological Development Zone
Beiwei Industrial District, Guangzhou, China 510730
Tel.: (86) 20 8221 7755
Fax: (86) 20 8221 7745
Paint & Coating Mfr
S.I.C.: 2851
N.A.I.C.S.: 325510

Akzo Nobel Swire Paints Limited (1)
Suite 2806 Island Place Tower 510 King's Road
North Point, China (Hong Kong)
Tel.: (852) 2823 1388
Fax: (852) 2866 3232
Web Site: www.ici.com.hk
Paint Mfr
S.I.C.: 2851
N.A.I.C.S.: 325510

Akzo Nobel Thioplast Chemicals (Taixing) Co., Ltd. (1)
No 9 Bin Jiang Bei Road Taixing Economic Development Area
Taixing, Jiangsu, 225404, China
Tel.: (86) 523 87676001
Chemical Product Mfr & Distr
S.I.C.: 2899
N.A.I.C.S.: 325998

Akzo Nobel Tintas para Automoveis Lda (1)
Carregado Park - Q Carregado
Carregado, Lisbon, 2580-512, Portugal
Tel.: (351) 263856060
Fax: (351) 263856068
Emp.: 9
Paint & Coating Mfr
S.I.C.: 2851
N.A.I.C.S.: 325510
Damiao Monho *(Mgr-Natl Sls)*

Akzo Nobel Wood Coatings Ltd (1)
155 Rose Glen Rd N
Port Hope, ON, L1A 3V6, Canada
Tel.: (905) 885-6388
Fax: (905) 885-7587
E-Mail: Chemcraft.CA@akzonobel.com
Web Site: www.chemcraft.com
Wood Coating Distr
S.I.C.: 5198
N.A.I.C.S.: 424950

Balakom Slovakia s.r.o. (1)
Bytcicka 89
010 08 Zilina, Slovakia
Tel.: (421) 415 640 612
Fax: (421) 415 620 526
Web Site: www.interpon.com
Emp.: 100
Powder Coating Mfr
S.I.C.: 2851
N.A.I.C.S.: 325510

Carbide Sweden AB (1)
Stockviksvagen 2 Stockviksverken
Sundsvall, 850 13, Sweden
Tel.: (46) 60 13 40 00
Fax: (46) 60 13 40 65
Chemical Product Mfr & Distr
S.I.C.: 2899
N.A.I.C.S.: 325998

Casco Adhesives (Asia) Pte Ltd (1)
14 Sungei Kadut Way
Singapore, 728788, Singapore
Tel.: (65) 6762 2088
Fax: (65) 6365 5852
Web Site: www.akzonobel.com
Emp.: 45
Adhesive Distr
S.I.C.: 5169
N.A.I.C.S.: 424690
Rebecca Chew *(Mgr-Mktg)*

Casco Adhezivi d.o.o. (1)
Spruha 19
1236 Trzin, Slovenia
Tel.: (386) 1 721 99 85
Fax: (386) 1 721 99 86
Adhesive Distr
S.I.C.: 5169
N.A.I.C.S.: 424690

Casco Byglim A/S (1)
Tempovej 16
2750 Ballerup, Denmark
Tel.: (45) 702 77 703
Fax: (45) 702 77 704
E-Mail: byglim@casco.dk
Web Site: www.casco.dk
Emp.: 6
Adhesive Distr
S.I.C.: 5169
N.A.I.C.S.: 424690
Ann-Cathrine Anki Andersson *(Controller-Sls & Bus)*

Cegecol SNC (1)
34 Av Leon Jouhaux
92160 Antony, France
Tel.: (33) 1 46 11 51 15
Fax: (33) 1 46 66 49 22
Paint & Coating Mfr
S.I.C.: 2851
N.A.I.C.S.: 325510

Compania Mexicana de Pinturas international SA De CV (1)
Ernesto Monroy S/N
Toluca, 50223, Mexico
Tel.: (52) 7225222300
Paint & Coating Mfr
S.I.C.: 2851
N.A.I.C.S.: 325510

Decorative Ouest S.A.S. (1)
2 Boulevard Des Bretonnieres
BP 40115
49124 Saint Barthelemy-d'Anjou, France
Tel.: (33) 2 41 37 50 00
Fax: (33) 2 41 37 50 10
Paint & Coating Mfr
S.I.C.: 2851
N.A.I.C.S.: 325510

Dulux Botswana (Pty) Limited (1)
Plot 1240 Haile Selassie Rd
Gaborone, Botswana
Tel.: (267) 395 1011
Fax: (267) 390 3387
Paint & Coating Mfr
S.I.C.: 2851
N.A.I.C.S.: 325510
Kopano Phetlhu *(Mgr-Production)*

Dulux Limited (1)
PO Box 30013
Blantyre, Malawi
Tel.: (265) 1 871 767
Fax: (265) 1 871 108
Paint & Coating Distr
S.I.C.: 5198
N.A.I.C.S.: 424950

Dulux Namibia (Pty) Limited (1)
7 Industrial Gachari Park
Windhoek, Namibia
Tel.: (264) 61 22 1242
Fax: (264) 61 22 1975
E-Mail: rec@duluxnamibia.com
Emp.: 14
Paint & Coating Mfr
S.I.C.: 2851
N.A.I.C.S.: 325510
Bjoern Eichhoff *(Office Mgr)*

Dulux Paints ZA (1)
8 Juyn Street
PO Box 123704
Alrode, Alberton, 1451, South Africa
Tel.: (27) 11 861 1000
Fax: (27) 11 864 6701
E-Mail: info@dulux.co.za
Web Site: www.dulux.co.za
Paint & Coating Mfr
S.I.C.: 2851
N.A.I.C.S.: 325510
Delaine Naidoo *(Mgr-HR)*

Dulux Swaziland (Pty) Limited (1)
10th St Matsapha Industrial Site
Box 1020
Matsapha, Swaziland
Tel.: (268) 2518 4091
Fax: (268) 2518 6236
Paint Mfr
S.I.C.: 2851
N.A.I.C.S.: 325510

E.Beffa S.A. (1)
Rue des Draizes 2-4
2000 Neuchatel, Switzerland
Tel.: (41) 32 737 70 50
Fax: (41) 32 737 70 55
E-Mail: e-beffa-sa@swisslack.ch
Web Site: www.beffasa.ch
Paint Supplies Distr
S.I.C.: 5198
N.A.I.C.S.: 424950

Eka Bahia S.A. (1)
Fazenda Brasilandia Rod BA 275 Km 24
Lote 10 Zona Rural, Eunapolis, Bahia, 45820-970, Brazil
Tel.: (55) 73 31661100
Fax: (55) 73 3166 1100
Chemical Product Mfr & Distr
S.I.C.: 2899
N.A.I.C.S.: 325998

Eka Chemicals AS (1)
Svaddeveien 119
3660 Rjukan, Norway
Tel.: (47) 35 08 08 80
Fax: (47) 35 08 08 88
Web Site: www.akzonobel.com
Chemical Product Mfr
S.I.C.: 2899
N.A.I.C.S.: 325998

Eka Chemicals (Australia) Pty Ltd (1)
15 Conquest Way
Hallam, VIC, Australia
Tel.: (61) 3 9702 3422
Fax: (61) 3 9703 1859
Chemical Product Mfr & Distr
S.I.C.: 2899
N.A.I.C.S.: 325998

Eka Chemicals (Chile) S.A. (1)
Av Rocoto No 2911 Zona Industrias
15th Floor
Talcahuano, Chile
Tel.: (56) 2412503200
Fax: (56) 2412542825
Chemical Product Mfr
S.I.C.: 2899
N.A.I.C.S.: 325998

Eka Chemicals de Colombia Limitada (1)
Nueva Autopista Cali-Yumbo Carrera 23 12-81
Cali, Colombia
Tel.: (57) 2 666 5035
Fax: (57) 2 666 5033
Chemical Product Mfr
S.I.C.: 2899
N.A.I.C.S.: 325998

Eka Chemicals do Brasil S.A. (1)
Rod Dom Gabriel Paulino Bueno Couto Km 65 2
PO Box 151
13200-970 Jundiai, Sao Paulo, Brazil
Tel.: (55) 11 45 89 48 00
Fax: (55) 11 45 82 63 78
Web Site: www.ekachemicals.com.br
Chemical Product Mfr
S.I.C.: 2899
N.A.I.C.S.: 325998

Eka Chemicals (Guangzhou) Co., Ltd. (1)
61 Hong Jing Rd East Section
Guangzhou Economic & Technolog,
Guangzhou, 510760, China
Tel.: (86) 20 839 696 88
Fax: (86) 20 822 647 78
E-Mail: info.expancel@akzonobel.com
Chemical Product Mfr & Distr
S.I.C.: 2899
N.A.I.C.S.: 325998

Eka Chemicals K.K. (1)
KSK Build 2F 1-2-34 IchigayaSadohara-cho
Shinjuku-ku, Tokyo, 162-0842, Japan
Tel.: (81) 3 3235 91 21
Fax: (81) 3 3235 91 27
Web Site: www.akzonobel.com
Emp.: 15
Chemical Product Mfr & Distr
S.I.C.: 2899
N.A.I.C.S.: 325998
Mikiya Nomura *(Mgr-Sls)*

Eka Chemicals Korea Co. Ltd (1)
1631-1 Soryong-Dong
Gunsan, Jeonbuk, 573-400, Korea (South)
Tel.: (82) 63 468 63 63
Fax: (82) 63 468 63 64
Web Site: www.akzonobel.com
Emp.: 35
Industrial Chemical Mfr
S.I.C.: 2899
N.A.I.C.S.: 325998
Jae-hoon Lee *(Gen Mgr)*

Eka Chemicals Oy (1)
Mannerheimintie 15a B
00260 Helsinki, Finland
Tel.: (358) 20 7515 500
Fax: (358) 20 7515 630
Web Site: www.akzonobel.com
Emp.: 65
Specialty Chemical Distr
S.I.C.: 5169
N.A.I.C.S.: 424690
Timo Korva *(Mgr-Site)*

Eka Chemicals (Taiwan) Co., Ltd (1)
6th Fl No 51 Sec 2 Gongyi Road
Nantun District, Taichung, Taiwan
Tel.: (886) 4 2327 0520
Fax: (886) 4 2327 0580
Chemical Product Mfr & Distr
S.I.C.: 2899
N.A.I.C.S.: 325998

Eka Chimie S.A.S. (1)
Z I du Bec
33810 Ambes, France
Tel.: (33) 5 56 33 45 45
Fax: (33) 5 56 77 04 05
Web Site: www.akzonobel.com
Emp.: 60
Chemical Product Mfr & Distr
S.I.C.: 2899
N.A.I.C.S.: 325998

Eric Padovani *(Gen Dir & Dir-Mktg)*

ES Sadolin AS (1)
Kastani Street 7
Rapla, 79514, Estonia
Tel.: (372) 48 92 321
Fax: (372) 48 92 399
E-Mail: info.ee@akzonobel.com
Web Site: www.sadolin.ee
Paint & Coating Mfr & Distr
S.I.C.: 2851
N.A.I.C.S.: 325510
Tiit Romulus *(Mgr-Logistic)*

Hammerite Products Limited (1)
ICI Paints Wexham Road
Slough, Berkshire, SL2 5DS, United Kingdom
Tel.: (44) 1753 550555
E-Mail: info_hammerite@ici.com
Web Site: www.hammerite.com
Metal Paint Mfr
S.I.C.: 2851
N.A.I.C.S.: 325510

Ichem Insurance Company Limited (1)
1 Adam Street
London, WC2N 6AB, United Kingdom
Tel.: (44) 20 79309766
Fax: (44) 20 78397479
Insurance Management Services
S.I.C.: 6411
N.A.I.C.S.: 524298

ICI Holdings (Australia) Pty Ltd (1)
8 Kellaway Pl
Wetherill Park, NSW, 2164, Australia
Tel.: (61) 2 9616 6980
Investment Management Services
S.I.C.: 6282
N.A.I.C.S.: 523920

ICI Paints Deco France SA (1)
ZI Les Bas Pres
BP 70113
Montataire, 60761, France
Tel.: (33) 3 44 64 91 00
Fax: (33) 3 44 64 91 90
Paint & Coating Mfr
S.I.C.: 2851
N.A.I.C.S.: 325510

ICI South Pacific Holdings Pty Ltd (1)
L 39 101 Collins St
Melbourne, VIC, 3000, Australia
Tel.: (61) 3 9679 3111
Investment Management Services
S.I.C.: 6282
N.A.I.C.S.: 523920

International Coatings Ltd (1)
Stoneygate Lane Felling
Gateshead, Tyne & Wear, NE10 0JY, United Kingdom
Tel.: (44) 191 469 6111
Fax: (44) 191 438 3711
Web Site: www.akzonobel.com
Emp.: 1,000
Marine Paint & Coating Mfr
S.I.C.: 2851
N.A.I.C.S.: 325510

International Coatings Pte Ltd (1)
23 Tingira
Cairns, QLD, 4870, Australia
Tel.: (61) 7 4035 1160
Paint & Coating Mfr
S.I.C.: 2851
N.A.I.C.S.: 325510

International Farbenwerke GmbH (1)
Lauenburger Landstrasse 11
21039 Bornsen, Germany
Tel.: (49) 407 200 30
Fax: (49) 407 208 953
E-Mail: pc.communication@akzonobel.com
Web Site: www.international-pc.com
Marine Coating Mfr
S.I.C.: 2851
N.A.I.C.S.: 325510

International Farg AB (1)
Holmedalen 3
Box 44
424 22 Angered, Sweden
Tel.: (46) 31 928500
Fax: (46) 31 928530
E-Mail: pc.communication@akzonobel.com
Web Site: www.international-pc.com
Marine Paint & Coating Mfr
S.I.C.: 2851
N.A.I.C.S.: 325510

International Maling A/S (1)
Floisbonnvegen 6
1411 Kolbotn, Norway
Tel.: (47) 66 81 94 81
Fax: (47) 66 81 94 79
E-Mail: pc.communication@akzonobel.com
Marine Paint & Coating Mfr
S.I.C.: 2851
N.A.I.C.S.: 325510

International Paint (Akzo Nobel Chile) Ltda (1)
R U T 76 048 140-8 Puerto Madero 9710
Oficina 47-Pudahuel, Santiago, Chile
Tel.: (56) 2 544 8452
Fax: (56) 2 544 8457
Emp.: 10
Paint & Coating Distr
S.I.C.: 5198
N.A.I.C.S.: 424950
Marcelo Ferrari *(Gen Mgr)*

International Paint (Belgium) NV (1)
G Levisstraat 2
Vilvoorde, Vlaams-Brabant, 1800, Belgium
Tel.: (32) 3 644 0066
Fax: (32) 644 0006
E-Mail: pc.communication@akzonobel.com
Web Site: www.international-pc.com
Emp.: 50
Marine Paint & Coating Mfr
S.I.C.: 2851
N.A.I.C.S.: 325510
Geelkerken Nicolaas *(Gen Mgr)*

International Paint (East Russia) Ltd (1)
302 Office Kirova Street 23
690068 Vladivostok, Russia
Tel.: (7) 4232 346647
Paint & Coating Mfr
S.I.C.: 2851
N.A.I.C.S.: 325510

International Paint France S.A. (1)
Route Frontonas
38290 La Verpilliere, France
Tel.: (33) 4 74 94 56 28
Fax: (33) 4 74 94 47 65
Paint & Coating Mfr
S.I.C.: 2851
N.A.I.C.S.: 325510

International Paint (Hellas) S.A. (1)
599 Vouliagmenis Ave
16452 Argyroupolis, Greece
Tel.: (30) 210 4295 140
Fax: (30) 210 4295 149
Emp.: 20
Marine Paint & Surface Coating Mfr
S.I.C.: 2851
N.A.I.C.S.: 325510
Ron Harris *(Mgr-Sls)*

International Paint (Hong Kong) Limited (1)
Unit 2005 20/F 148 Electric Rd
North Point, China (Hong Kong)
Tel.: (852) 25 08 7700
Fax: (852) 28 27 9488
Paint & Coating Mfr
S.I.C.: 2851
N.A.I.C.S.: 325510

International Paint Italia SPA (1)
Via de Marini 61/14
Genoa, Italy
Tel.: (39) 0 10 6595 71
Fax: (39) 0 10 6595 759
E-Mail: pc.communication@akzonobel.com
Web Site: www.international-pc.com
Marine Coating Mfr
S.I.C.: 2851
N.A.I.C.S.: 325510

International Paint Japan K.K. (1)
10F Kobe Ito-machi Building 121 Ito-machi
Chuo-ku, Kobe, Hyogo, 650-0032, Japan
Tel.: (81) 78 321 6871
Fax: (81) 78 321 6870
E-Mail: pc.communication@akzonobel.com
Web Site: www.international-pc.com
Emp.: 10
Marine Paint & Coating Mfr
S.I.C.: 2851
N.A.I.C.S.: 325510
Keigo Nakagawa *(Mgr-Sls)*

International Paint (Korea) Ltd (1)
17th Floor National Pension Bldg 1422-8
YeonSan-dong YeonJe-gu, Busan, 611-705, Korea (South)
Tel.: (82) 51 580 6111
Fax: (82) 51 668 7880
E-Mail: pc.communication@akzonobel.com
Web Site: www.international-pc.com
Emp.: 100
Paint & Coating Mfr
S.I.C.: 2851
N.A.I.C.S.: 325510
J. K. Kim *(Dir-Sls)*

Plant:

International Paint (Korea) Ltd - Chilseo Factory (2)
626-6 ChilSeo-myeon
HamAn-gun, Gyenae, Gyeongsangnam-do, Korea (South)
Tel.: (82) 55 586 2310
Fax: (82) 55 587 6276
E-Mail: pc.communication@akzonobel.com
Web Site: www.international-pc.com
Marine Paint & Coating Mfr
S.I.C.: 2851
N.A.I.C.S.: 325510

International Paint Iberia, Lda (1)
Aptdo 37 Estrada Nacional 10 Quinta da Bassaqueira
Azeitao, 2925-511, Portugal
Tel.: (351) 21 219 91 00
Fax: (351) 21 219 91 29
E-Mail: pc.communication@akzonobel.com
Web Site: www.international-pc.com
Emp.: 20
Marine Paint & Coating Mfr
S.I.C.: 2851
N.A.I.C.S.: 325510
Cristina Ferreira *(Gen Mgr)*

International Paint of Shanghai Co Ltd (1)
No 58 New Jinqiao Road
201206 Shanghai, China
Tel.: (86) 21 6163 1515
Fax: (86) 21 6163 1558
Web Site: www.akzonobel.com
Marine Paint & Coating Mfr
S.I.C.: 2851
N.A.I.C.S.: 325510

International Paint Pazarlama Limited Sirketi (1)
Kozyatagi Mah Saniye Ermutlu Sokak
Sasmaz Plaza
No 8 K 4 Kozyatagi, Istanbul, 34742, Turkey
Tel.: (90) 216 445 44 40
Fax: (90) 216 445 45 02
E-Mail: pc.communication@akzonobel.com
Web Site: www.international-pc.com
Emp.: 40
Paint & Coating Mfr
S.I.C.: 2851
N.A.I.C.S.: 325510
Steven Saywell *(Gen Mgr)*

International Paint (Research) Ltd (1)
639-1 Hannae-ri Yeoncho-myeon
Geoje, Gyeongsangnam-do, Korea (South)
Tel.: (82) 55 632 6284
Fax: (82) 55 632 6285
Marine Paint & Coating Mfr
S.I.C.: 2851
N.A.I.C.S.: 325510

International Paint Sdn Bhd (1)
Jalan Tembaga Satu Plo 335
81700 Pasir Gudang, Johor, Malaysia
Tel.: (60) 7 2541112
Web Site: www.akzonobel.com
Marine Paint & Coating Mfr
S.I.C.: 2851
N.A.I.C.S.: 325510

International Paint Singapore Pte Ltd (1)
3 Neythal Road
Jurong Town, Singapore, 628570, Singapore
Tel.: (65) 62615033
Fax: (65) 62644612

Akzo Nobel N.V.—(Continued)

E-Mail: pc.singapore@akzonobel.com
Web Site: www.international-pc.com
Emp.: 200
Paint & Coating Mfr
S.I.C.: 2851
N.A.I.C.S.: 325510

International Paint (Taiwan) Ltd (1)
20 Yu Ming St Ta Fa Industrial District
Kaohsiung, Taiwan 831
Tel.: (886) 7 787 3959
Fax: (886) 7 787 3952
E-Mail: pc.communication@akzonobel.com
Web Site: www.international-pc.com
Paint & Coating Mfr
S.I.C.: 2851
N.A.I.C.S.: 325510

International Paints (Canada) Ltd (1)
2435 Beta Avenue
Burnaby, BC, V5C 5N1, Canada
Tel.: (604) 291-8242
Fax: (604) 291-2769
Web Site: www.akzonobel.com
Paint & Coating Distr
S.I.C.: 5198
N.A.I.C.S.: 424950

International Peinture S.A. (1)
12 rue Theodore Maillard
Le Havre, 76068, France
Tel.: (33) 2 35 22 13 50
Fax: (33) 2 35 22 13 52
E-Mail: pc.communication@akzonobel.com
Web Site: www.international-pc.com
Emp.: 47
Yacht Paint & Coating Mfr
S.I.C.: 2851
N.A.I.C.S.: 325510

J.P. Mcdougall & Co. Limited (1)
Manchester Road West
Timperley, Altrincham, WA14 5PG, United Kingdom
Tel.: (44) 1619 683 160
Fax: (44) 8456 002 500
Web Site: www.duluxdecoratorcentre.co.uk
Paint & Coating Retailer
S.I.C.: 5231
N.A.I.C.S.: 444120

Kayaku Akzo Corporation (1)
2-14 2-Chome Kojimachi
Chiyoda-Ku, Tokyo, 102-0083, Japan
Tel.: (81) 3 3234 0801
Fax: (81) 3 3221 1065
Web Site: www.kayakuakzo.co.jp
Emp.: 100
Chemical Product Mfr & Distr
S.I.C.: 2899
N.A.I.C.S.: 325199

Keum Jung Akzo Nobel Peroxides Ltd (1)
24 5 km Wai Huan Xian West Side
Beichen District, Tianjin, 300400, China
Tel.: (86) 22 2681 3188
Fax: (86) 22 2681 4643
Chemical Products Mfr & Distr
S.I.C.: 2899
N.A.I.C.S.: 325998

Interquim S.A. (1)
Cl 10 S 50 Ff-28 Of 402
Medellin, Colombia
Tel.: (57) 4 3618888
Fax: (57) 4 3619999
E-Mail: interquim@akzonobel.com
Emp.: 114
Paint & Coating Mfr
S.I.C.: 2851
N.A.I.C.S.: 325510
Andres Orozco *(Gen Mgr)*

Maricogen A/S (1)
Hadsundvej 17
9550 Mariager, Denmark
Tel.: (45) 96 68 78 88
Fax: (45) 96 68 78 90
E-Mail: mariager@akzonobel.com
Emp.: 160
Paint & Coating Mfr
S.I.C.: 2851
N.A.I.C.S.: 325510

Nordsjo Butiker AB (1)
Staffanstorpsvagen 50
Malmo, 205 17, Sweden
Tel.: (46) 40 35 50 00
Fax: (46) 4 06 01 52 23
Web Site: www.nordsjoidedesign.se
Paint Retailer
S.I.C.: 5231
N.A.I.C.S.: 444120

OOO Akzo Nobel Trading and Distribution Company (1)
24D Smolnaya
Moscow, 125445, Russia
Tel.: (7) 495 960 29 37
Fax: (7) 495 960 29 38
Emp.: 20
Chemical Product Distr
S.I.C.: 5169
N.A.I.C.S.: 424690
Lashuk Vladimir Viktorovich *(Gen Mgr)*

OOO Akzo Nobel Wood Coatings (1)
4 Litera G Pos Pargolovo Gorskoye Shosse
Saint Petersburg, Russia 194362
Tel.: (7) 812 325 69 56
Fax: (7) 812 325 69 58
Web Site: www.akzonobel.com
Emp.: 13
Wood Coating Mfr
S.I.C.: 2851
N.A.I.C.S.: 325510
Masenko Anton *(Gen Mgr)*

OOO Akzo Nobel (1)
Meridian Commercial Tower Smolnaya Str 24D
125445 Moscow, Russia
Tel.: (7) 495 9602890
Fax: (7) 495 9602882
E-Mail: info.moscow@akzonobel.com
Web Site: www.akzonobel.com
Emp.: 200
Chemical Product Mfr & Distr
S.I.C.: 2899
N.A.I.C.S.: 325998

OOO Petrokom-Lipetsk (1)
1 Trubniy proezd
Lipetsk, 398036, Russia
Tel.: (7) 4742 38 49 54
Fax: (7) 4742 38 49 51
Coil Coating Mfr
S.I.C.: 2851
N.A.I.C.S.: 325510

Peintures Couleurs Decoration S.A.S. (1)
87 Route de Cormeilles
78500 Sartrouville, France
Tel.: (33) 1 30 86 83 83
Fax: (33) 1 30 86 92 75
Web Site: www.peinture-couleurs-decoration.fr
Emp.: 6
Paint & Coating Retailer
S.I.C.: 5231
N.A.I.C.S.: 444120
Olivier Henry *(Mgr-Store)*

Permascand AB (1)
Folkets Husvagen 50
PO Box 42
840 10 Ljungaverk, Sweden
Tel.: (46) 691 355 00
Fax: (46) 691 330 40
E-Mail: permascand@akzonobel.com
Web Site: www.permascand.com
Emp.: 100
Electrode & Electrochemical Equipment Mfr
S.I.C.: 3823
N.A.I.C.S.: 334513
Fredrik Herlitz *(Gen Mgr)*

Pinturas Coral De Bolivia Ltda (1)
Parque Industrial P I 24
Santa Cruz, Bolivia
Tel.: (591) 33467069
Fax: (591) 33467079
Emp.: 18
Paint & Coating Distr
S.I.C.: 5198
N.A.I.C.S.: 424950
Angelino Mancini *(Gen Mgr)*

Proquimio Produtos Quimicos Opoterapicos Ltda. (1)
Avenida Marginal Esquerda Do Rio Tiete 5101
Caixa Postal 11225
Aldeia Velha, 06410-240 Barueri, SP, Brazil BR
Tel.: (55) 1141967979 (100%)
Fax: (55) 1141950952
E-Mail: hmayer@proquimio.com.br
Emp.: 150
Mfr. of Raw Materials for the Pharmaceutical Industry
S.I.C.: 2834
N.A.I.C.S.: 325412

PT Akzo Nobel Car Refinishes Indonesia (1)
Jalan Pulogadung 37
13015 Jakarta, Indonesia
Tel.: (62) 21 4610191
Fax: (62) 21 4610190
Web Site: www.akzonobel.com
Emp.: 200
Automotive Coating Mfr
S.I.C.: 2851
N.A.I.C.S.: 325510
Metria Rozanov *(Mgr-Pur)*

PT Eka Chemicals Indonesia (1)
Jalan Rembang Industri III/32
67152 Pasuruan, Indonesia
Tel.: (62) 343 740127
Fax: (62) 343 740 128
Web Site: www.akzonobel.com
Chemical Product Mfr
S.I.C.: 2899
N.A.I.C.S.: 325998

Rhone Sud Est Decoration S.A. (1)
19 Cours De La Liberte N 19-21
69003 Lyon, France
Tel.: (33) 4 78 60 16 37
Fax: (33) 4 78 60 49 70
Paint & Coating Mfr
S.I.C.: 2851
N.A.I.C.S.: 325510

Sadolin Farveland A/S (1)
Holmbladsgade 70
2300 Copenhagen, Denmark
Tel.: (45) 32 69 80 00
Fax: (45) 32 69 84 85
Web Site: www.sadolinfarveland.dk
Paint & Varnish Distr
S.I.C.: 5198
N.A.I.C.S.: 424950

Sadvel SA (1)
64 Blvd Moulay Slimane
Casablanca, Morocco
Tel.: (212) 5 22 67 87 67
Fax: (212) 22 35 45 24
Paint & Coating Distr
S.I.C.: 5198
N.A.I.C.S.: 424950
Lahcen Chatir *(Gen Mgr)*

Sales Support Group Limited (1)
Manchester Rd West
Altrincham, WA14 5PG, United Kingdom
Tel.: (44) 1753 550000
Sales Management Consulting Services
S.I.C.: 8742
N.A.I.C.S.: 541613

Schonox GmbH (1)
Alfred-Nobel-Str 6
48720 Rosendahl, Germany
Tel.: (49) 2547 910 0
Fax: (49) 2547 910 101
E-Mail: info@schoenox.de
Web Site: www.schoenox.de
Flooring Adhesive Mfr
S.I.C.: 2891
N.A.I.C.S.: 325520
Helmut Twilfer *(Mng Dir)*

Schonox s.r.o. (1)
Skrobarenska 482
617 00 Brno, Czech Republic
Tel.: (420) 511 180 143
Fax: (420) 511 180 131
E-Mail: info@schonox.cz
Web Site: www.schonox.cz
Construction Chemical Distr
S.I.C.: 5169
N.A.I.C.S.: 424690

Schramm Coatings GmbH (1)
Kettelerstrasse 100
63075 Offenbach, Germany
Tel.: (49) 69 8603 0
Fax: (49) 69 8603 229
E-Mail: info@schramm-coatings.de
Web Site: www.schramm-coatings.de
Emp.: 250
Plastic & Metal Coating Product Distr
S.I.C.: 5169
N.A.I.C.S.: 424690
Thomas Mangold *(Mng Dir)*
Hans-Peter Rohricht *(Mng Dir)*

Schramm Coatings Iberica SA (1)
Pl Can Comelles Suc c Fornal 10
08292 Esparraguera, Spain
Tel.: (34) 937 776 241
Fax: (34) 937 709 641
E-Mail: admon@schrammcoatings.com
Web Site: www.schrammcoatings.com
Paint & Coating Distr
S.I.C.: 5198
N.A.I.C.S.: 424950

Schramm Holding AG (1)
Kettelerstrasse 100
63075 Offenbach, Germany De
Tel.: (49) 6986030 (100%)
Fax: (49) 698603229
E-Mail: info@schramm-coatings.de
Web Site: www.schramm-holding.com
Sales Range: $150-199.9 Million
Emp.: 791
Coating Mfr
S.I.C.: 2851
N.A.I.C.S.: 325510
Jung Hyun Oh *(Chm-Supervisory Bd)*
Jeong Ghi Koo *(Vice Chm-Supervisory Bd)*
Peter Brenner *(CEO)*
Sung Su Han *(COO)*
Kyung Seok Chae *(Chief Strategy Officer)*
Kenny Yuen Fai Chan *(Sec)*

Schramm SSCP (Hanoi) Co Ltd. (1)
Lot I2-1 Que Vo
Bac Ninh, Vietnam
Tel.: (84) 1262366025
Chemical Product Distr
S.I.C.: 5169
N.A.I.C.S.: 424690

Schramm SSCP (Thailand) Co., Ltd. (1)
7/206 M 6 Mabyangporn
Pluakdang, Rayong, 21140, Thailand
Tel.: (66) 38 650 430 1
Fax: (66) 38 650 429
Chemical Product Distr
S.I.C.: 5169
N.A.I.C.S.: 424690

Scottish Agricultural Industries Limited (1)
West Mains of Ingleston
Newbridge, Midlothian, EH28 8ND, United Kingdom
Tel.: (44) 131 335 3100
Paint & Coating Mfr
S.I.C.: 2851
N.A.I.C.S.: 325510

Server Boya Matbaa Murekkepleri ve Vernik Sanayi ve Ticaret A.S. (1)
Istanbul Kimyacilar Organize Sanayi Bolgesi
Kristal Sok No 4
Tuzla, 34956 Istanbul, Turkey
Tel.: (90) 216 593 10 30
Fax: (90) 216 593 22 35
E-Mail: Info@serverboya.com
Web Site: www.serverboya.com
Emp.: 50
Paint & Coating Mfr
S.I.C.: 2851
N.A.I.C.S.: 325510
Ugur Yenier *(Mgr-Sls)*

Societe Tunisienne de Peintures Astral S.A. (1)
GP1 Route de Sousse Km 5 5
Megrine, 2033, Tunisia
Tel.: (216) 71 434 700
Fax: (216) 71 434 040
E-Mail: astral.tn@akzonobel.com
Web Site: www.astral-tn.com
Emp.: 150
Paint & Coating Mfr
S.I.C.: 2851
N.A.I.C.S.: 325510
Elboq Mehde *(Gen Mgr)*

Suzhou Eka Trade Co. Ltd (1)
Suzhou Industrial Park No 302
Suzhou, 215122, China
Tel.: (86) 512 62582276
Fax: (86) 512 62586772

Paint & Coating Mfr
S.I.C.: 2851
N.A.I.C.S.: 325510

Techni-Coat Germany GmbH (1)
Imkerstrass 3
Kirchhorst, 30916 Isernhagen, Germany
Tel.: (49) 5136 977 36 0
Fax: (49) 5136 977 36 93
E-Mail: info@techni-coat.de
Web Site: www.techni-coat.de
Paint Mfr
S.I.C.: 2851
N.A.I.C.S.: 325510
Ralf Rollfing *(Mgr-Technical)*

Techni-Coat International N.V. (1)
Franseweg 31
Kalmthout, 2920, Belgium
Tel.: (32) 3 620 21 20
Fax: (32) 3 620 21 30
E-Mail: info.tci@akzonobel.com
Web Site: www.akzonobel.com
Emp.: 6
Plastic Coating Product Distr
S.I.C.: 5162
N.A.I.C.S.: 424610

Tekyar Teknik Yardim A. S. (1)
Tavsanli Koyu Eynarca Mevkii Dilovasi
Gebze, Turkey
Tel.: (90) 262 7547470
Paint & Coating Mfr
S.I.C.: 2851
N.A.I.C.S.: 325510

Tetra Galon SAS (1)
13 Avenue Stalingrad
93170 Bagnolet, France
Tel.: (33) 1 48 59 87 56
Fax: (33) 1 48 59 02 27
Paint & Coating Mfr
S.I.C.: 2851
N.A.I.C.S.: 325510

Tianjin Akzo Nobel Peroxides Co. Ltd (1)
24 5 km Wai Huan Xin west Side
Beichen District, Tianjin, 300400, China
Tel.: (86) 22 2681 3188
Fax: (86) 22 2681 3834
Chemical Product Mfr
S.I.C.: 2899
N.A.I.C.S.: 325998

Vivechrom Dr. Stefanos D. Pateras S.A. (1)
PO Box 4
192 00 Elefsina, Greece
Tel.: (30) 210 5538700
Fax: (30) 210 5550464
E-Mail: vivechrom@vivechrom.gr
Web Site: www.vivechrom.gr
Emp.: 265
Paint & Varnish Mfr
S.I.C.: 2851
N.A.I.C.S.: 325510
Petros Katsampouris *(Mng Dir)*

ZAO Akzo Nobel Dekor (1)
Prokrovskiy Proezd 9 Northern Industrial Zone
Balashikha, 143900, Russia
Tel.: (7) 495 795 01 60
Fax: (7) 495 795 01 63
Paint & Coating Mfr
S.I.C.: 2851
N.A.I.C.S.: 325510

AL-ABBAS CEMENT INDUSTRIES LIMITED
(Name Changed to Power Cement Limited)

AL-ABBAS SUGAR MILLS LIMITED
Pardesi House Survey No 2 1 R Y 16
Old Queens Road
Karachi, 74000, Pakistan
Tel.: (92) 21111111224
Fax: (92) 212470090
E-Mail: info@aasml.com
Web Site: www.aasml.com
AABS—(KAR)
Sls.: $65,605,991
Assets: $52,279,579
Liabilities: $33,274,725
Net Worth: $19,004,854
Earnings: $5,396,006
Emp.: 42
Fiscal Year-end: 09/30/12
Business Description:
Sugarcane Cultivation & Production Services
S.I.C.: 0133
N.A.I.C.S.: 111930
Personnel:
Mohammad Iqbal Usman *(Chm)*
Shunaid Qureshi *(CEO)*
Muhammad Suleman Kanjiani *(CFO & Sec)*
Board of Directors:
Mohammad Iqbal Usman
Muhammad Salman Husain Chawala
Abdul Hamid Ahmed Dagia
Asim Ghani
Shunaid Qureshi
Jahangir Siddiqui

AL-ABRAJ HOLDING COMPANY KSCC
PO Box 3066
Hawally, Kuwait, 32031, Kuwait
Tel.: (965) 22254241
Fax: (965) 24344825
E-Mail: info@alabrajholding.com
Web Site: www.alabrajholding.com
Year Founded: 1999
Sales Range: $50-74.9 Million
Business Description:
Holding Company; Investment Services
S.I.C.: 6211
N.A.I.C.S.: 523999
Personnel:
Jamal Ahmad Al-Kandari *(Chm)*
Samir Nasser Ali Hussein *(Deputy Chm)*
Board of Directors:
Jamal Ahmad Al-Kandari
Yousuf Saqr Abdullah Al-Fahad
Abdul Wahab A. Al-Mutawa
Sami Abdullah Al Abdul Hadi
Samir Nasser Ali Hussein

AL-AHLEIA SWITCHGEAR COMPANY K.S.C.C.
PO Box 25876
Safat, Kuwait, 13119, Kuwait
Tel.: (965) 1822600
E-Mail: ahleia@ahleiasg.com
Web Site: www.ahleiasg.com
Year Founded: 1982
Sales Range: $100-124.9 Million
Emp.: 2,000
Business Description:
High & Low Voltage Switchgear Mfr
S.I.C.: 3613
N.A.I.C.S.: 335313
Personnel:
Nasrallah S.H. Behbehani *(Chm & Mng Dir)*
Abdul Jaleel Boland *(Deputy Chm)*
Board of Directors:
Nasrallah S.H. Behbehani
Fouad S.H. Behbehani
Abdul Jaleel Boland

AL AHLI TAKAFUL COMPANY
Khaldiyah Business Center
PO Box 48510
Jeddah, 21582, Saudi Arabia
Tel.: (966) 26901199
Fax: (966) 26901377
E-Mail: info@alahlitakaful.com
Web Site: www.alahlitakaful.com
8130—(SAU)
Rev.: $40,876,517
Assets: $171,651,388
Liabilities: $135,870,255
Net Worth: $35,781,133
Earnings: $274,555
Fiscal Year-end: 12/31/12
Business Description:
Insurance & Financial Services
S.I.C.: 6282
N.A.I.C.S.: 523920
Personnel:
Bleihid Nasr Al Bleihid *(Chm)*
Saleh Hefni *(Deputy Chm)*
Board of Directors:
Bleihid Nasr Al Bleihid
Adel Al Howar
Abdullah A. Al-Farraj
Manfred Dirrheimer
Markus E. Fischer
Saleh Hefni
Amr Khashoggi
Jamal J. Malaikah
Uwe Reuter

Ernst & Young
P O Box 1994
Jeddah, 21441, Saudi Arabia

AL AHLIA ENTERPRISES PLC
11 August St - Khorma Building
PO Box 830554
Al-Shmisani, Amman, 11183, Jordan
Tel.: (962) 6 5688471
Fax: (962) 6 5688581
E-Mail: admin@alahlia.com.jo
Year Founded: 1993
ABLA—(AMM)
Sales Range: $10-24.9 Million
Emp.: 189
Business Description:
Superstore Management Services
S.I.C.: 5399
N.A.I.C.S.: 452910
Personnel:
Ibraheem Dirkeejan *(Gen Mgr)*

AL-AHSA DEVELOPMENT COMPANY
Office No 103 First Floor Al-Mulhim Tower Al-Thuryat Road
PO Box 2726
Al-Ahsa, 31982, Saudi Arabia
Tel.: (966) 135620799
Fax: (966) 135620774
E-Mail: share@ahsa-dev.com.sa
Web Site: www.ahsa-dev.com.sa
2140—(SAU)
Rev.: $4,361,182
Assets: $149,973,833
Liabilities: $21,174,747
Net Worth: $128,799,086
Earnings: $710,232
Fiscal Year-end: 12/31/12
Business Description:
Industrial Project Development Services
S.I.C.: 8711
N.A.I.C.S.: 541330
Personnel:
Waleed Hassan Al-Afaleq *(Chm)*
Abdulmohsen Mohamed Al-Othman *(Vice Chm)*
Adel Ahmed Yousef Al Saleh *(CEO)*
Board of Directors:
Waleed Hassan Al-Afaleq
Abdullatif Mohammed Al-Barrak
Ali Abdullah Al-Hassoun
Abdullah Ali Al-Majdouie
Saleh Abdullah Al-Naim
Abdulmohsen Mohamed Al-Othman
Tamy Hedaf Albakmy

AL-AMAL FINANCIAL INVESTMENT COMPANY
Housing Bank Complex
PO Box 961598
Amman, 11196, Jordan
Tel.: (962) 6 5671485
Fax: (962) 6 5667993
E-Mail: alamal.investments@gmail.com
Year Founded: 1980
AMAL—(AMM)
Rev.: $1,578,841
Assets: $22,082,568
Liabilities: $2,053,646
Net Worth: $20,028,922
Earnings: $317,331
Emp.: 14
Fiscal Year-end: 12/31/12
Business Description:
Securities Brokerage Services
S.I.C.: 6211
N.A.I.C.S.: 523120
Personnel:
Jawad Al-Kharof *(Gen Mgr)*

AL-AMAN INVESTMENT COMPANY K.S.C.C.
Al Dhou Tower 11 12 13 Floor Sharq Khalid Bin Al Waleed St
PO Box 12466
Shamiya, Kuwait, 71655, Kuwait
Tel.: (965) 1822626
Fax: (965) 22497962
E-Mail: info@alaman.com.kw
Web Site: www.alaman.com.kw
ALAMAN—(KUW)
Rev.: $595,323
Assets: $151,796,765
Liabilities: $88,380,678
Net Worth: $63,416,087
Earnings: ($9,110,570)
Emp.: 25
Fiscal Year-end: 12/31/12
Business Description:
Investment Services; Owned 45% by Securities House K.S.C.C.
S.I.C.: 6211
N.A.I.C.S.: 523999
Personnel:
Khalaf Soulaiman Al-Jasem *(Chm, CEO & Mng Dir)*
Yousef Abdullah Boodai *(Vice Chm)*
Moamen Zahran *(CFO)*
Wafaa M. W. Badawy *(Sr VP-Res & Consulting)*
Board of Directors:
Khalaf Soulaiman Al-Jasem
Madi Talal Al-Khamis
Abdullateif Mohamed Al-Shayea
Abdulrahman Jasem Al-Yaseen
Yossef Ibrahim Alghanem
Meshari Ayman Boodai
Yousef Abdullah Boodai

AL AMIN FOR INVESTMENT P.L.C.
Jordan Islamic Bank Building 8th Floor August Street Shmeisani Area 11
PO Box 940216
Amman, 11118, Jordan
Tel.: (962) 6 5677377
Fax: (962) 6 5698355
Year Founded: 1989
AAFI—(AMM)
Rev.: $1,196,528
Assets: $20,252,821
Liabilities: $2,093,922
Net Worth: $18,158,899
Earnings: $535,659
Emp.: 3
Fiscal Year-end: 12/31/12
Business Description:
Investment Management Services
S.I.C.: 6211
N.A.I.C.S.: 523999
Personnel:
Asa'd Addese *(Gen Mgr)*

AL ANWAR CERAMIC TILES CO. SAOG
(d/b/a Al-Shams)

Al Anwar Ceramic Tiles Co. SAOG—(Continued)

Al Harthy Complex
PO Box 143
Muscat, 118, Oman
Tel.: (968) 24571359
Fax: (968) 24571680
E-Mail: ghoshroy@alshams.org
Web Site: www.alshams.org
Year Founded: 1998
AACT—(MUS)
Sales Range: $25-49.9 Million
Emp.: 272
Business Description:
Ceramic Tile Mfr
S.I.C.: 3259
N.A.I.C.S.: 327120
Personnel:
Adil Mohammed Hassan Taqi *(Deputy Chm)*
Hussain Ali Habib Sajwani *(Chm)*
A. Shamsuddin *(Mng Dir)*
A. Suresh *(Sec)*
Board of Directors:
Hussain Ali Habib Sajwani
A.V. Babu
Sofyan Khatib
Akshay Kothari
A. Shamsuddin
Adil Mohammed Hassan Taqi

AL AQEEQ REAL ESTATE DEVELOPMENT COMPANY

PO Box 4646
Medina, Saudi Arabia
Tel.: (966) 48378888
Fax: (966) 48368888
E-Mail: info@alaqeeq.com.sa
Web Site: www.alaqeeq.com.sa
Business Description:
Real Estate & Construction Services
S.I.C.: 6531
N.A.I.C.S.: 531390
Personnel:
Sulieman Bin Salih Al-Medehaim *(Chm)*
Abdulaziz Bin Abdullah Al-Shabbana *(CEO)*
Board of Directors:
Sulieman Bin Salih Al-Medehaim
B. Bin Abdullah Al-Essa
Mohamed Bin Ibrahin Al-Essa
Ahmed Bin Mohamed Al-Gamdi
Mohamed Bin Abdulrahman Al-Samhan
Abdulaziz Bin Abdullah Al-Shabbana
Khalid Bin Ali Al-Sultan

AL-ARAFAH ISLAMI BANK LIMITED

36 Dilkusha 6-9 Floor C/A
Dhaka, 1000, Bangladesh
Tel.: (880) 27123255
Fax: (880) 29569351
E-Mail: aibl@al-arafahbank.com
Web Site: www.al-arafahbank.com
ALARABANK—(DHA)
Rev.: $185,682,693
Assets: $1,848,586,108
Liabilities: $1,674,638,578
Net Worth: $173,947,530
Earnings: $24,084,017
Emp.: 2,110
Fiscal Year-end: 12/31/12
Business Description:
Banking & Investment Services
S.I.C.: 6211
N.A.I.C.S.: 523110
Personnel:
Badiur Rahman *(Chm)*
Sarker Mohammad Shameem Iqbal *(Vice Chm)*
Ekramul Hoque *(Mng Dir)*
Md. Mofazzal Hossain *(Deputy Mng Dir & Sec)*
Kazi Towhidul Alam *(Deputy Mng Dir)*
Khondoker Nayeemul Kabir *(Deputy Mng Dir)*
Md.Golam Rabbani *(Deputy Mng Dir)*
Masodul Bari *(Exec VP)*
Md. Mominul Haque Bhuiyan *(Exec VP)*
Md. Mahmoodul Haque *(Exec VP)*
Md. Fazlul Karim *(Exec VP)*
Muhammed Nadim *(Exec VP)*
Board of Directors:
Badiur Rahman
Kh. Mesbahuddin Ahmed
Momtaz Uddin Ahmed
Niaz Ahmed
Ahamedul Haque
Ekramul Hoque
Anwar Hossain
Md. Ashik Hossain
Sarker Mohammad Shameem Iqbal
Nazmul Ahsan Khaled
Md. Harun-ar-Rashid Khan
M. A. Malek
Hafez Md. Enayetullah
Abdul Moktadir
Abdul Malek Mollah
Mohammded Emadur Rahman
Abdus Salam
Abdus Samad
Abu Naser Mohammad Yeahea

Masih Muhith Haque & Co
UTC Building 13th Floor 8 Panthapath
Dhaka, 1215, Bangladesh

AL-BABTAIN GROUP

PO Box 766
Safat, Kuwait, 13008, Kuwait
Tel.: (965) 826000
Fax: (965) 4720064
E-Mail: corporate@babtain.com.kw
Web Site: www.babtain.com
Year Founded: 1948
Sales Range: $250-299.9 Million
Emp.: 1,038
Business Description:
Consumer Goods Importer & Distr; Investment Services
S.I.C.: 5012
N.A.I.C.S.: 423110
Personnel:
Saleh A. Al-Babtain *(Chm)*

Subsidiaries:

Al-Babtain Body Manufacturing Co. (1)
Street 94 Block 8
South Subhan
Safat, Kuwait, Kuwait
Tel.: (965) 474 2279
Fax: (965) 475 0731
Truck Body Mfr
S.I.C.: 3537
N.A.I.C.S.: 333924

Kuwait Paint Co. (1)
Shuwaikh Industrial Area
PO Box 42255
Safat, 70653 Kuwait, Kuwait
Tel.: (965) 4832644
Fax: (965) 4834971
Emp.: 80
Paint Mfr
S.I.C.: 2851
N.A.I.C.S.: 325510
Mohmmed Al Assqal *(Dir-Tech)*

National Computer Services (1)
PO Box 766
Safat, Kuwait, Kuwait
Tel.: (965) 4755127
Fax: (965) 24341024
Web Site: www.nts-me.com
Emp.: 32
Computer Installation & Maintenance Services
S.I.C.: 7379
N.A.I.C.S.: 541519
Mohammed El-Sayed Shalaby *(Mng Dir)*

AL-BAGHLI SPONGE MANUFACTURING COMPANY

Div No 415 Block No 1 Main Street
Sabhan Industrial Area S
Al Rai Area, Kuwait, Safat, 13160, Kuwait
Tel.: (965) 24761444
Fax: (965) 24762999
E-Mail: sponge@albaghli.com
Web Site: www.albaghli-united.com
Year Founded: 1972
Emp.: 300
Business Description:
Foam Products Importer & Mfr
S.I.C.: 3086
N.A.I.C.S.: 326140

AL BARAKA BANKING GROUP BSC

Al-Baraka Tower Building No 238
Road No 1704 Block No 317
PO Box 1882
Diplomatic Area, Manama, Bahrain
Tel.: (973) 17541122
Fax: (973) 17536533
Web Site: www.albaraka.com
BARKA—(BAH)
Rev.: $1,018,482,000
Assets: $19,055,131,000
Liabilities: $17,087,451,000
Net Worth: $1,967,680,000
Earnings: $235,242,000
Emp.: 9,398
Fiscal Year-end: 12/31/12
Business Description:
Banking Services
S.I.C.: 6029
N.A.I.C.S.: 522110
Personnel:
Saleh Abdullah Kamel *(Chm)*
Abdullah Saleh Kamel *(Vice Chm)*
Abdulla A. Saudi *(Vice Chm)*
Adnan Ahmed Yousif *(Pres & CEO)*
Majeed H. Alawi *(Exec VP & Head-Internal Audit)*
K. Krishnamoorthy *(Exec VP & Head-Strategic Plng)*
Abdulrahman Shehab *(Exec VP & Head-Ops & Admin)*
Salah Othman Abuzaid *(Sr VP & Head-Legal Affairs & Compliance)*
Hamad Abdulla Ali Eqab *(Sr VP & Head-Fin Control)*
Jozsef Peter Szalay *(Sr VP & Head-Credit & Risk Mgmt)*
Board of Directors:
Saleh Abdullah Kamel
Fahad Abdullah Al Rajhi
Ibrahim Fayez Al Shamsi
Saleh Al Yousef
Bassem Ibrahim Awadallah
Yousef Ali Fadil Fadil
Jamal Ghalaita
Anwar Ibrahim
Abdullah Saleh Kamel
Mohyedin Saleh Kamel
Abdul Elah Sabbahi
Abdulla A. Saudi
Adnan Ahmed Yousif

Subsidiary:

Al Baraka Islamic Bank E.C. (1)
PO Box 1882
Manama, Bahrain
Tel.: (973) 17535300
Fax: (973) 17530695
Web Site: www.Barakaonline.com
Banking Services
S.I.C.: 6029
N.A.I.C.S.: 522110
Mohamed Al-Mutaweh *(CEO)*

Non-U.S. Subsidiaries:

Al Baraka Bank Lebanon SAL (1)
2nd Floor Verdun 2000 Centre
PO Box 113/5683
Rachid Karame Street, Beirut, Lebanon (98.71%)
Tel.: (961) 180643
Fax: (961) 1806499
Web Site: www.al-baraka.com
Emp.: 112
Banking Services
S.I.C.: 6029
N.A.I.C.S.: 522110

Al Baraka Bank Ltd. (1)
134 Drive AB zuma street
PO Box 4395
Durban, 4001, South Africa (62.15%)
Tel.: (27) 313662950
Fax: (27) 313052631
E-Mail: info@albaraka.co.za
Web Site: www.albaraka.co.za
Emp.: 70
Banking Services
S.I.C.: 6029
N.A.I.C.S.: 522110

Al Baraka Bank Sudan (1)
Baraka Tower Zubeir Pasha Street
PO Box 3583
Khartoum, Sudan (82.08%)
Tel.: (249) 183780688
Fax: (249) 183788585
Web Site: www.albarakasudan.com
Emp.: 640
Banking Services
S.I.C.: 6029
N.A.I.C.S.: 522110
Osman Ahmed Sulieman *(Chm)*

Al Baraka Bank Syria (1)
9 Tulaytulah Street Al Malki Square
Damascus, Syria
Mailing Address:
PO Box 100
Hijaz Post Center, Damascus, Syria
Tel.: (963) 113321980
Fax: (963) 113321981
E-Mail: albaraka@albarakasyria.com
Web Site: www.barakaonline.com
Banking Services
S.I.C.: 6029
N.A.I.C.S.: 522110
Mamoun Darkazally *(Gen Mgr)*

Albaraka Turkish Finance House (1)
Buyukdere Caddesi No 78
Mediciyekoy, 34387 Istanbul, Turkey
Tel.: (90) 2122749900
Fax: (90) 2166661600
Web Site: www.albarakaturt.com.tr
Banking Services
S.I.C.: 6029
N.A.I.C.S.: 522110
Adnan Ahmad Yousuf *(CEO)*

Banque Al Baraka d'Algerie (1)
32 rue des Freres Djillali Birkhadem
Algiers, Algeria
Tel.: (213) 21 916 450
Fax: (213) 21 916 457
Web Site: www.albaraka-bank.com
Emp.: 381
Banking Services
S.I.C.: 6029
N.A.I.C.S.: 522110

Egyptian Saudi Finance Bank (1)
60 Mohie Elddin Abu El Ezz Street
PO Box 455
Dokki, Cairo, Egypt
Tel.: (20) 27481222
Fax: (20) 27611436
E-Mail: mohandessin@esf-bank.com
Web Site: www.esf-bank.com
Emp.: 200
Banking Services
S.I.C.: 6029
N.A.I.C.S.: 522110

Jordan Islamic Bank (1)
PO Box 926225
Amman, 11190, Jordan (66.01%)
Tel.: (962) 65666325
Fax: (962) 65666326
E-Mail: jib@islamicbank.com.jo
Web Site: www.jordanislamicbank.com
JOIB—(AMM)
Rev.: $205,839,207
Assets: $4,243,459,099
Liabilities: $1,284,396,282
Net Worth: $2,959,062,816
Earnings: $51,202,485
Emp.: 2,000

Fiscal Year-end: 12/31/12
Banking Services
S.I.C.: 6029
N.A.I.C.S.: 522110
Adnan Ahmad Yousif *(Chm)*
Musa Abdul-Aziz Shihadeh *(Vice Chm, CEO & Gen Mgr)*

AL BATINAH DEVELOPMENT & INVESTMENT HOLDING CO. SAOG

Al Wadi Al Kabir
PO Box 68
117 Muscat, Oman
Tel.: (968) 24478667
Fax: (968) 24478448
Web Site: www.albatinah.com
Year Founded: 1997
DBIH—(MUS)
Rev.: $4,225,747
Assets: $10,330,178
Liabilities: $1,917,501
Net Worth: $8,412,678
Earnings: ($750,439)
Fiscal Year-end: 12/31/12
Business Description:
Real Estate Development Services
S.I.C.: 6531
N.A.I.C.S.: 531390
Personnel:
Ali Abdullah Al Badi *(Chm)*
Nasser Ahmed Al Huqani *(Deputy Chm)*
Saleh Ahmed Al Badi *(CEO)*
Board of Directors:
Waseem Salah Abd Qaraeen
Nasser Ahmed Al Huqani
Ali Abdullah Al Badi
Nasser Said Al Harthi
Khalfan Salim Al Kaabi
Salah Helal Al Mawali
Mshari Yasin Al Onaizy
Galal Hassan Ismail

Subsidiary:

National Cans & Packing Industry LLC (1)
Road No 18 Rusayl Industrial Estate
PO Box 102
124 Muscat, Oman
Tel.: (968) 24446650
Fax: (968) 24446893
E-Mail: info@ncpioman.com
Web Site: www.ncpioman.com
Emp.: 460
Can Mfr
S.I.C.: 3411
N.A.I.C.S.: 332431
Salah Hilal Al Ma'awali *(Chm)*

AL-BILAD MEDICAL SERVICES CO.

Istiklal St - Istiklal Hospital
PO Box 1493
Amman, 11821, Jordan
Tel.: (962) 6 5652600
Fax: (962) 6 5652710
Year Founded: 1997
ABMS—(AMM)
Rev.: $17,962,329
Assets: $52,829,349
Liabilities: $21,966,068
Net Worth: $30,863,281
Earnings: $3,046,206
Emp.: 436
Fiscal Year-end: 12/31/12
Business Description:
General Hospital Services
S.I.C.: 8062
N.A.I.C.S.: 622110
Personnel:
Ismail Dkeidek *(Gen Mgr)*

AL BILAD SECURITIES & INVESTMENT CO.

Wadi Saqra Street
PO Box 3275
Amman, 11181, Jordan
Tel.: (962) 65531900
Fax: (962) 65518100
E-Mail: info@biladcapital.com
Web Site: www.biladcapital.com
Year Founded: 2006
BLAD—(AMM)
Sales Range: $1-9.9 Million
Emp.: 21
Business Description:
Portfolio Management & Brokerage Services
S.I.C.: 6282
N.A.I.C.S.: 523920
Personnel:
Sharif Al-Rawashdeh *(Chm)*
Ishmael Dkaidek *(Vice Chm)*
Hala Al-shanqeeti *(Mng Dir & Sec)*
Board of Directors:
Sharif Al-Rawashdeh
Musaed Al-Mineefi
Faisal Al-Omran
Adnan Al-Sheikh
Ishmael Dkaidek
Farid Hanna
Essam Hashem

AL BUHAIRA NATIONAL INSURANCE COMPANY P.S.C.

Al Buhaira Tower Khalid Lagoon
PO Box 6000
Sharjah, United Arab Emirates
Tel.: (971) 6 5174444
Fax: (971) 6 5748855
E-Mail: abnicho@albuhaira.com
Web Site: www.albuhaira.com
Year Founded: 1978
ABNIC—(EMI)
Rev.: $152,208,467
Assets: $499,391,224
Liabilities: $333,670,444
Net Worth: $165,720,780
Earnings: $4,657,734
Emp.: 300
Fiscal Year-end: 12/31/12
Business Description:
Insurance Services
S.I.C.: 6411
N.A.I.C.S.: 524298
Personnel:
Faisal Khalid Sultan Al Qassemi *(Chm)*
Abdulla Mohd Ali Al Thani *(Vice Chm)*
Khaled Abdulla Sultan Al Qassimi *(Mng Dir)*
Board of Directors:
Faisal Khalid Sultan Al Qassemi
Khaled Abdulla Sultan Al Qassimi
Abdalla Juma Al Sari
Rashid Ali Rashid Dimas Al Suwaidi
Abdulla Mohd Ali Al Thani
Nader T. Qaddumi
Humaid Mohamed Humaid Mohamed Shattaf

AL DANUBE BUILDING MATERIALS TRADING CO., LLC

(d/b/a Danube)
PO Box 18022
Jebel Ali, United Arab Emirates
Tel.: (971) 48871234
Fax: (971) 48871235
E-Mail: info@aldanube.com
Web Site: www.aldanube.com
Year Founded: 1993
Sales Range: $100-124.9 Million
Emp.: 900
Business Description:
Building Materials Distr
S.I.C.: 5211
N.A.I.C.S.: 444190
Personnel:
Rizwan Sajan *(Chm)*
Anis Sajan *(Mng Dir)*

AL-DAR NATIONAL REAL ESTATE COMPANY K.S.C.C.

Sharq Ahmet Al Jaber Street Dar Al Awadi Building
PO Box 22242
Safat, Kuwait, 13083, Kuwait
Tel.: (965) 22324445
Fax: (965) 22324421
E-Mail: info@adnrec.com
Web Site: www.adnrec.com
Year Founded: 2000
ADNC—(KUW)
Sales Range: $1-9.9 Million
Emp.: 8
Business Description:
Real Estate Services
S.I.C.: 6531
N.A.I.C.S.: 531390
Personnel:
Yousuf M. Al-Summait *(Chm)*
Abdul-Muttalab Marafi *(Vice Chm)*
Board of Directors:
Yousuf M. Al-Summait
Eyyad Al-Humood
Abdul Mohsen Al-Kandari
Ahmed Al-Roomi
Abdul-Muttalab Marafi

AL DAWLIYAH FOR HOTELS & MALLS PLC

Alal Al-Fasi st
PO Box 942175
Shmeisany, Amman, 11194, Jordan
Tel.: (962) 6 5604731
Fax: (962) 6 5680105
Year Founded: 1994
MALL—(AMM)
Rev.: $23,567,859
Assets: $89,031,392
Liabilities: $8,666,306
Net Worth: $80,365,086
Earnings: $4,345,533
Emp.: 8
Fiscal Year-end: 12/31/12
Business Description:
Construction Engineering Services
S.I.C.: 8711
N.A.I.C.S.: 541330
Personnel:
Osama Madanat *(Gen Mgr)*

AL-DEERA HOLDING CO. K.S.C.C.

Salhia Commercial Complex
Entrance No 8 5th Floor
PO Box 4839
Safat, Kuwait, 13049, Kuwait
Tel.: (965) 22493955
Fax: (965) 22493963
E-Mail: info@aldeeraholding.com
Web Site: www.aldeeraholding.com
Year Founded: 1998
ALDEERA—(KUW)
Int. Income: $556,344
Assets: $379,390,920
Liabilities: $226,545,252
Net Worth: $152,845,667
Earnings: ($59,138,974)
Fiscal Year-end: 12/31/12
Business Description:
Investment & Financial Services
S.I.C.: 6211
N.A.I.C.S.: 523999
Personnel:
Abdulwahab Ahmad Al-Nakib *(Chm & Mng Dir)*
Nouf Jassim Al-Bahar *(Vice Chm)*
Mohammed Farid Mostafa *(CFO)*
Khaled Magdy El-Marsafy *(Pres-Al-Deera Holding USA Inc & Gen Mgr)*
Rami Habli *(Exec VP-Investments)*
Board of Directors:
Abdulwahab Ahmad Al-Nakib
Nouf Jassim Al-Bahar
Yousef Shamlan Al-Essa
Turki Nasser Al-Mutawa Al-Otaibi
Rasem Zouq

AL-DORRA PETROLEUM SERVICES KSCC

Al Mirqab Abdullah Al Mubarak St
Al-Nafisi Tower 6th Fl
PO Box 26583
Safat, Kuwait, 13126, Kuwait
Tel.: (965) 22954560
Fax: (965) 22460733
E-Mail: al-dorra@al-dorra.com
Web Site: www.al-dorra.com
Emp.: 15
Business Description:
Oil & Gas Services
S.I.C.: 1389
N.A.I.C.S.: 213112
Personnel:
Sager Al Sharhan *(Chm)*
Khaled Abdullah Al Saqer *(Deputy Chm)*
Board of Directors:
Sager Al Sharhan
Abdul Razzaq Al Awadhi
Adnan Shehab Al Din
Waleed Al Houti
Fahad Al Rashed
Riadh Al Saleh
Khaled Abdullah Al Saqer
Bader Al Sayer
Fahad Al Youaan
Maher R. Hammoud
Abdul Hussain Shehab

AL DUCA D'AOSTA SPA

Via Volturno 7
30173 Maestre, VE, Italy
Tel.: (39) 0412620111
Telex: 431450
Fax: (39) 0412620100
E-Mail: info@alducadaosta.com
Web Site: www.alducadaosta.com
Year Founded: 1902
Sales Range: $10-24.9 Million
Emp.: 125
Business Description:
Clothing Retailer
Import
S.I.C.: 5651
N.A.I.C.S.: 448140
Personnel:
Alvise Ceccato *(Co-Owner)*
Cristiano Ceccato *(Co-Owner)*
Matteo Ceccato *(Pres)*
Nicolo Ceccato *(Mng Dir)*

AL ENTKAEYA FOR INVESTMENT & REAL ESTATE DEVELOPMENT CO. PLC

6th circle - Emmar Towers - building C 4th floor
PO Box 14412
Amman, 11814, Jordan
Tel.: (962) 65777416
Fax: (962) 65777417
E-Mail: Entkaiah@hotmail.com
Year Founded: 2007
ENTK—(AMM)
Rev.: $107,461
Assets: $5,891,135
Liabilities: $662,289
Net Worth: $5,228,846
Earnings: ($398,219)
Emp.: 6
Fiscal Year-end: 12/31/12
Business Description:
Real Estate Development Services
S.I.C.: 6531
N.A.I.C.S.: 531390
Personnel:
Saad Allah Abdul Razak Saad Allah *(Chm)*

AL-EQBAL INVESTMENT CO. (PLC)
PO Box 911145
Amman, 11191, Jordan
Tel.: (962) 64656662
Fax: (962) 64656669
E-Mail: info@eqbal-invest.com
Web Site: www.eqbal-invest.com
EICO—(AMM)
Sales Range: $100-124.9 Million
Emp.: 8
Business Description:
Cigarette & Tobacco Mfr
S.I.C.: 2131
N.A.I.C.S.: 312230
Personnel:
Samer Tawfiq Fakhouri *(Chm)*
Walid Tawfiq Fakhouri *(Deputy Chm)*
Board of Directors:
Samer Tawfiq Fakhouri
Abdel Rahim Ali Al-Zu'bi
Mohammad Naser Barakat
Sakher Marwan Doudeen
Walid Tawfiq Fakhouri
Hassan Jaser
Yousef Omar
Haitham Mohammad Qteshat
Raed Fathi Samara

THE AL FADL GROUP OF COMPANIES
Al Hamra Street
PO Box 15
21411 Jeddah, Saudi Arabia
Tel.: (966) 26603996
Fax: (966) 26603682
E-Mail: alfadlgroup@nesma.net.sa
Web Site: www.alfadlgroup.com
Year Founded: 1947
Emp.: 350
Business Description:
Holding Company
S.I.C.: 6719
N.A.I.C.S.: 551112
Personnel:
Abdul Kader Al Fadl *(Chm)*
Abdul Aziz Al Fadl *(Pres)*

Holdings:

Al Fadl BRC (Saudia) Ltd. **(1)**
Industrial Area Phase 1
PO Box 5489
Jeddah, Saudi Arabia
Tel.: (966) 26364724
Fax: (966) 26375474
Web Site: www.brc.com.sa
Emp.: 200
Welded Wire Mesh Mfr
S.I.C.: 3496
N.A.I.C.S.: 332618

Aldewan Fastfood Company Ltd. **(1)**
PO Box 15
Jeddah, Saudi Arabia
Tel.: (966) 26672653
Fax: (966) 2 660 3682
Emp.: 220
Fast Food Restaurant Operator
S.I.C.: 5812
N.A.I.C.S.: 722513

Alpha Trading & Shipping Agencies Ltd. **(1)**
Al Mahmal Tower 14th Fl Ste 1401
King Abdul Aziz St, Jeddah, 21411, Saudi Arabia
Tel.: (966) 26440808
Fax: (966) 26421188
E-Mail: central@alpha-trading.com
Web Site: www.alpha-trading.com
Sls.: $250,000,000
Emp.: 20
Foodstuffs & Related Commodities Marketing Services
S.I.C.: 5148
N.A.I.C.S.: 424480
Abdul Kader Al Fadl *(Chm)*
Loucas P. Ellinas *(Mng Dir)*

Rabya Trading and Agriculture Company Ltd. **(1)**
Palestine Street
PO Box 5536
21432 Jeddah, Saudi Arabia
Tel.: (966) 26602856
Fax: (966) 26601603
E-Mail: rabyah@rabya.com
Web Site: www.rabya.com
Emp.: 3,000
Landscaping & Garden Services
S.I.C.: 5261
N.A.I.C.S.: 444220
Mohammed Al Fadl *(Pres)*

Sahara Building Contractors Ltd. **(1)**
Childerns Hospital Street Al Hamrah Dist
PO Box 11852
Jeddah, 21463, Saudi Arabia
Tel.: (966) 26615050
Fax: (966) 26650710
E-Mail: saharajed@saharabuilding.com
Web Site: www.saharabuilding.com
Emp.: 700
Industrial Contracting Services
S.I.C.: 1791
N.A.I.C.S.: 238120
Abdul Aziz Al Fadl *(Chm)*

AL FAHIM GROUP
Mussafah Industrial Area Street 10
Area 5
PO Box 279
Abu Dhabi, United Arab Emirates
Tel.: (971) 24449666
Fax: (971) 26567999
E-Mail: afg@alfahim.ae
Web Site: www.alfahim.com
Year Founded: 1954
Emp.: 1,300
Business Description:
Holding Company
S.I.C.: 6719
N.A.I.C.S.: 551112
Personnel:
Saeed Abdul Jalil Al Fahim *(Chm)*
Rashed Abdul Jalil Al Fahim *(Mng Dir)*
Board of Directors:
Saeed Abdul Jalil Al Fahim
Aamer Abdul Jalil Mohammed Al Fahim
Abdullah Abdul Jalil Al Fahim
Ahmed Abdul Jalil Al Fahim
Eissa Abdul Jalil Al Fahim
Taha Abdul Jalil Al Fahim

Subsidiaries:

Central Motors Co. **(1)**
Hamdan St
PO Box 46193
Abu Dhabi, United Arab Emirates
Tel.: (971) 25546333
Fax: (971) 5547973
E-Mail: cm@alfahimgroup.ae
Web Site: www.alfahim.ae
Emp.: 180
Automobile Distr, Motor Vehicle Supplies & Parts Whslr
S.I.C.: 5012
N.A.I.C.S.: 423110
Moahammed Almomnai *(Gen Mgr)*

Emirates Motor Co. **(1)**
PO Box 279
Abu Dhabi, United Arab Emirates
Tel.: (971) 2 444 000
Fax: (971) 2 448 126
E-Mail: emc@alfahimgroup.ae
Web Site: www.emc.mercedes-benz.com
New & Used Car Sales
S.I.C.: 5511
N.A.I.C.S.: 441110

Emirates Property Investment Co. **(1)**
PO Box 101
Abu Dhabi, United Arab Emirates
Tel.: (971) 800 37426
Fax: (971) 2 656 7360
E-Mail: epico@alfahim.ae
Web Site: www.epico.ae
Property Development & Real Estate
S.I.C.: 6531
N.A.I.C.S.: 531210

Marjan Industrial Development Co. **(1)**
Liwa Street
PO Box 6644
Abu Dhabi, United Arab Emirates
Tel.: (971) 26222114
Fax: (971) 26222115
E-Mail: ajidmos@emirates.net.ae
Web Site: www.alfahim.com
Mechanical, Electrical & Oil Equipment Contractors
S.I.C.: 1731
N.A.I.C.S.: 238210

Safar Travel Services **(1)**
Liwa Street
PO Box 507
Abu Dhabi, United Arab Emirates
Tel.: (971) 26225225
Fax: (971) 26227395
E-Mail: info@safar.ae
Web Site: www.safar.ae
Emp.: 30
Travel & Cargo Services
S.I.C.: 4724
N.A.I.C.S.: 561510
Mohammed Alfahim *(Gen Mgr)*

AL FAISALIAH GROUP
PO Box 16460
Riyadh, 11464, Saudi Arabia
Tel.: (966) 14610077
Fax: (966) 14640498
E-Mail: netadmin@alfaisaliah.com
Web Site: www.alfaisaliah.com
Year Founded: 1970
Sales Range: $650-699.9 Million
Emp.: 5,270
Business Description:
Electrical & Electronic Equipment, Computers, Communications & Broadcast Products, Petrochemicals, Dairy & Agricultural Products Trading Services
S.I.C.: 7389
N.A.I.C.S.: 425120

Subsidiaries:

Al Faisaliah Electronics Services **(1)**
PO Box 16460
Riyadh, 11464, Saudi Arabia
Tel.: (966) 14407799
Fax: (966) 1 450 8652
E-Mail: info@alfaisaliah.com
Web Site: www.alfaisaliah.com
Emp.: 133
Computer Maintenance, Network Services & Cabling
S.I.C.: 7379
N.A.I.C.S.: 541519

Al Faisaliah Medical Systems **(1)**
Olaya Road Al Nemer Center
PO Box 62961
Riyadh, 11595, Saudi Arabia
Tel.: (966) 1 2119999
Fax: (966) 1 4629720
Web Site: www.alfaisaliah.com
Emp.: 100
Medical Equipment Distr
S.I.C.: 5047
N.A.I.C.S.: 423450

Modern Electronics Establishment (MEE) **(1)**
King Fahd Highway near Riyadh Bank
PO Box 2769
Al Khobar, 31952, Saudi Arabia
Tel.: (966) 38949078
Fax: (966) 38941755
E-Mail: sonysa-kingfahd@alfaisaliah.com
Web Site: www.mee.com.sa
Computer & Electronic Product Mfr
S.I.C.: 3575
N.A.I.C.S.: 334118
Mohammed Al Ariefy *(Pres)*

Joint Venture:

Al Safi Danone Co. **(1)**
PO Box 15025
Riyadh, 11443, Saudi Arabia
Tel.: (966) 1 211 9999
Fax: (966) 1 462 5112
E-Mail: info@alsafidanone.com
Web Site: www.alsafidanone.com.sa
Dairy Products; Owned by Group Danone SA & Al Faisaliah Group
S.I.C.: 0241
N.A.I.C.S.: 112120

AL-FARIS NATIONAL COMPANY FOR INVESTMENT & EXPORT PLC
Queen Rania street Abu Elhaj complex 6th floor
PO Box 414
Amman, 11953, Jordan
Tel.: (962) 6 5629999
Fax: (962) 6 5629988
E-Mail: info@optimizasolutions.com
Web Site: www.optimizasolutions.com
Year Founded: 2005
CEBC—(AMM)
Rev.: $18,316,352
Assets: $46,017,183
Liabilities: $39,142,584
Net Worth: $6,874,599
Earnings: ($2,434,365)
Emp.: 492
Fiscal Year-end: 12/31/12
Business Description:
Information Technology Consulting Services
S.I.C.: 7373
N.A.I.C.S.: 541512
Personnel:
Rudain Kawar *(Chm)*
Ambassador Karim Kawar *(Vice Chm)*
Majed Sifri *(CEO)*
Saif Khouri *(COO)*
Board of Directors:
Rudain Kawar
Saad Al Khushman
Usamah Fayyad
Ambassador Karim Kawar
Abdul Majid Khadir
Samir Murad
Ramzi Zabaneh

AL FATIHOUN AL ARAB PLC
Wasfi Al Tal St Islamic Bank Complex
Building No 23
PO 927588
11190 Amman, Jordan
Tel.: (962) 65540255
Fax: (962) 65540253
E-Mail: info@fatihounarab.com
Web Site: www.fatihounarab.com
Year Founded: 2007
FATI—(AMM)
Sales Range: Less than $1 Million
Emp.: 7
Business Description:
Automotive Mfr
S.I.C.: 3711
N.A.I.C.S.: 336111
Personnel:
Mazin Khayri Ayass *(Chm)*
Dawood Salman AL-Obaidi *(Vice Chm)*
Board of Directors:
Mazin Khayri Ayass
Rabei Al Azzawi
Dawood Salman AL-Obaidi
Mohammed Ayass
Tariq Hammouri
Shihab Hanayneh
Odeh Shawabkeh

AL FUJAIRAH NATIONAL INSURANCE COMPANY (P.S.C.)
8th Floor Insurance Bldg Hamad Bin Abdullah St

PO Box 277
Fujairah, United Arab Emirates
Tel.: (971) 9 2233355
Fax: (971) 9 2224344
Web Site: www.afnic.ae
Year Founded: 1976
AFNIC—(EMI)
Sales Range: $25-49.9 Million

Business Description:
Insurance Services
S.I.C.: 6411
N.A.I.C.S.: 524298

Personnel:
Abdul Ghaffour Behroozian *(Chm)*
Mohammed Abdulla S Alsalami *(Vice Chm)*

Board of Directors:
Abdul Ghaffour Behroozian
Shareif Al Awadhi
Sulaiman Moosa Al Jassim
Saeed Mubarak Al Zahmy
Mohammed Abdulla S Alsalami
Humaid Mohamed Humaid Alyamahi
Salem Abdo Khalil
Saif Salami

AL-FUTTAIM PRIVATE COMPANY LLC

(d/b/a Al-Futtaim Group)
PO Box 152
Dubai, United Arab Emirates
Tel.: (971) 47062222
Fax: (971) 42212933
E-Mail: corporatecommunications@alfuttaim.ae
Web Site: www.al-futtaim.ae
Emp.: 10,000

Business Description:
Diverse Trading Company; Automotive; Electronics; Insurance; Real Estate; Retail
S.I.C.: 7389
N.A.I.C.S.: 561499

Personnel:
Omar Al Futtaim *(Vice Chm)*

Subsidiaries:

AFTRON Electronics (1)
PO Box 28657
Dubai, United Arab Emirates
Tel.: (971) 4 2103784
Fax: (971) 4 2713862
E-Mail: aftron@alfuttaim.ae
Web Site: www.aftron.com
Household Appliance Whslr
S.I.C.: 5064
N.A.I.C.S.: 423620
Anil Kumar Neelakandhan *(Mgr-Natl Sls)*

Al-Futtaim ACE Company L.L.C (1)
PO Box 7880
Dubai, United Arab Emirates
Tel.: (971) 4 206 6700
Fax: (971) 4 206 6701
E-Mail: ace@alfuttaim.ae
Web Site: www.aceuae.com
Household Product Distr
S.I.C.: 5064
N.A.I.C.S.: 423620
Kathryn Brown *(Mgr-Internal Comm & Design)*

Al-Futtaim Automall (1)
Sheikh Zayed Road
Dubai, United Arab Emirates
Tel.: (971) 4 3472212
E-Mail: automall@alfuttaim.ae
Web Site: www.automalluae.com
Used Car Dealer
S.I.C.: 5521
N.A.I.C.S.: 441120
Atul Naran *(Branch Mgr-Sls)*

Al-Futtaim Electronics (1)
PO Box 5559
Dubai, United Arab Emirates
Tel.: (971) 4 3599979
Fax: (971) 4 3512066
E-Mail: electronics@alfuttaim.ae
Household Appliance Whslr
S.I.C.: 5064
N.A.I.C.S.: 423620
Ankit Agrawal *(Asst Product Mgr)*

Al-Futtaim Engineering Company LLC (1)
Airport Road
PO Box 159
Dubai, United Arab Emirates
Tel.: (971) 4 2119111
Fax: (971) 4 2829748
E-Mail: afengineering@alfuttaim.ae
Web Site: www.engineeringuae.com
Air Conditioning Installation Services
S.I.C.: 1711
N.A.I.C.S.: 238220
Srinivasa Chakravarthy *(Asst Mgr)*

Al-Futtaim Motors Company LLC (1)
PO Box 11052
Dubai, United Arab Emirates
Tel.: (971) 4 2066000
Fax: (971) 4 2066105
E-Mail: afmotors@alfuttaim.ae
Web Site: www.alfuttaimmotors.ae
Automotive Parts Whslr
S.I.C.: 5013
N.A.I.C.S.: 423120
Alan Carpenter *(Gen Mgr-Sls & Mktg)*

Al-Futtaim Panatech Company LLC (1)
PO Box 531
Dubai, United Arab Emirates
Tel.: (971) 4 2103333
Fax: (971) 4 2710284
E-Mail: afpanatech@alfuttaim.ae
Web Site: www.panasonicuae.com
Household Appliance Whslr
S.I.C.: 5064
N.A.I.C.S.: 423620
Shaun Sullivan *(Gen Mgr)*

Al-Futtaim Technologies LLC (1)
Suite 401 Business Centre
PO Box 5866
Dubai, United Arab Emirates
Tel.: (971) 43977800
Fax: (971) 43972244
E-Mail: aftech@alfuttaim.ae
Web Site: www.alfuttaimtechnologies.com
Information Technology Consulting Services
S.I.C.: 7373
N.A.I.C.S.: 541512
Jafar Naqvi *(Head-Ops)*

Al-Futtaim Trading Enterprises Company L.L.C (1)
PO Box 5628
Dubai, United Arab Emirates
Tel.: (971) 4 2954246
Fax: (971) 4 2954461
E-Mail: tradingent@alfuttaim.ae
Web Site: www.tradingenterprises.ae
Emp.: 1,200
New Car Dealer
S.I.C.: 5511
N.A.I.C.S.: 441110
Shishir Jain *(Mgr-Sls Accessories)*

Al-Futtaim Travel (1)
101 Business Point Behind Nissan Showroom
Deira, Dubai, United Arab Emirates
Tel.: (971) 4 231 9200
Fax: (971) 4 294 2746
E-Mail: aftravel@alfuttaim.ae
Web Site: www.alfuttaimtravel.ae
Travel Agency Operator
S.I.C.: 4729
N.A.I.C.S.: 561599
William Horsley, *(Gen Mgr)*

Al-Futtaim Watches and Jewellery (1)
PO Box 7916
Dubai, United Arab Emirates
Tel.: (971) 4 2224142
Fax: (971) 4 2224599
E-Mail: watches@alfuttaim.ae
Web Site: www.watches.ae
Jewlery Store Operator
S.I.C.: 5944
N.A.I.C.S.: 448310
Mohammed Ikram Hussain Siddiqui *(Mgr-Ops)*

Arab Orient Insurance Company (1)
Orient Building Al Badia Business Park
PO Box 27966
Dubai, United Arab Emirates
Tel.: (971) 4 253 1300
Fax: (971) 4 2531500
Web Site: www.insuranceuae.com
General Insurance Services
S.I.C.: 6411
N.A.I.C.S.: 524210
Abdulla Hamad *(Chm)*
Omar Abdulla *(Vice Chm)*
Fadi Awni Al Ahmadi *(Sr VP-Sls & Mktg)*
Wissam Khalifeh *(Sr VP-Medical)*
Selvan Raman *(Sr VP-Life)*
Mohammed Husain Suleman *(Sr VP-Fin)*
K. V. Suresh *(Sr VP-Broker Rels)*

Emirates Investment Bank P.J.S.C. (1)
Level 15 Festival Tower Dubai Festival City
PO Box 5503
Dubai, United Arab Emirates (50.26%)
Mailing Address:
PO Box 5503
Dubai, United Arab Emirates
Tel.: (971) 42317777
Fax: (971) 42317788
E-Mail: info@eibank.com
Web Site: www.eibank.com
EIBANK—(DFM)
Rev.: $23,469,537
Assets: $497,670,243
Liabilities: $418,350,186
Net Worth: $79,320,057
Earnings: $7,165,411
Fiscal Year-end: 12/31/12
Banking Services
S.I.C.: 6029
N.A.I.C.S.: 522110
Omar Abdulla Al Futtaim *(Chm)*
Khaled Sifri *(CEO)*
Jean-Paul Petoud *(Chief Investment Officer)*
Vivek Daphtary *(Treas)*

IKEA UAE (1)
Al Rebat Road
PO Box 50618
Dubai, United Arab Emirates
Tel.: (971) 4 203 7555
Fax: (971) 4 203 7620
E-Mail: ikea_dubai@alfuttaim.ae
Web Site: www.ikea.com
Home Furnishing Product Retailer
S.I.C.: 5719
N.A.I.C.S.: 442299
Renato Mrgeski, *(Mgr-Store)*

Marks & Spencer (1)
PO Box 7976
Dubai, United Arab Emirates
Tel.: (971) 4 2222000
Cloth Store Operator
S.I.C.: 5651
N.A.I.C.S.: 448140
Muhiba Gaayte *(Mgr-Comml Dept)*

Plug-Ins Electronix (1)
PO Box 2798
Dubai, United Arab Emirates
Tel.: (971) 4 2825995
Fax: (971) 4 2831271
E-Mail: plugins.dcc@alfuttaim.ae
Web Site: www.pluginsuae.com
Household Appliance Whslr
S.I.C.: 5064
N.A.I.C.S.: 423620
Sadiq Pasha *(Supvr-IT Sls)*

Toys "R" Us (1)
1st Floor Festival Centre
PO Box 12602
Dubai, United Arab Emirates
Tel.: (971) 4 206 6568
Fax: (971) 4 375 0540
E-Mail: customercare@alfuttaim.ae
Web Site: www.toysrusuae.com
Toy Store Operator
S.I.C.: 5945
N.A.I.C.S.: 451120
Neetu Mandal *(Mgr-Mktg)*

Non-U.S. Subsidiaries:

KOLBER S A, GENEVE (1)
17-21 Rue Marziano
PO Box 1525
1211 Geneva, Switzerland
Tel.: (41) 22 3002210
Fax: (41) 22 3000181
Watch Whslr
S.I.C.: 5094
N.A.I.C.S.: 423940

Trade Alliance(S) PTE. LTD (1)
80 Anson Road 27-02 IBM Towers
Singapore, Singapore
Tel.: (65) 2217524
Fax: (65) 2255894
Trading Services
N.A.I.C.S.: 522293

AL-GHAZI TRACTORS LIMITED

11th Floor NICL Building Abbasi Shaheed Road
Karachi, 74400, Pakistan
Tel.: (92) 2135660881
Fax: (92) 2135689387
E-Mail: agtl@alghazitractors.com
Web Site: www.alghazitractors.com
AGTL—(KAR)
Sls.: $149,716,983
Assets: $95,853,616
Liabilities: $15,617,310
Net Worth: $80,236,306
Earnings: $19,414,327
Emp.: 369
Fiscal Year-end: 12/31/12

Business Description:
Tractor Mfr
S.I.C.: 3537
N.A.I.C.S.: 333924

Personnel:
Parvez Ali *(CEO & Mng Dir)*
Kashif Lawai *(CFO)*
Sobika Muzammil *(Sec)*

Board of Directors:
Charles Leonard Hunt
Parvez Ali
Giovanna Barbieri
Damiano Cretarola
Kunwar Idris
Kashif Lawai
Nasir Mahmood
Stefano Pampalone

Legal Counsel:
Saiduddin & Co
Karachi, Pakistan

AL GHURAIR GROUP

Salahuddin Road
Dubai, United Arab Emirates
Tel.: (971) 4 2623377
Fax: (971) 4 2623388
E-Mail: hr@alghurair.com
Web Site: www.alghurair.com
Sales Range: $5-14.9 Billion
Emp.: 25,000

Business Description:
Holding Company
S.I.C.: 6719
N.A.I.C.S.: 551112

Personnel:
Abdulrahman Saif Al Ghurair *(Chm)*
Rashid Saif Al Ghurair *(Chm/Mng Dir-Taghleef Industries)*

Subsidiary:

Taghleef Industries L.L.C. (1)
Jebel Ali Industrial Zone
Dubai, United Arab Emirates AE
Tel.: (971) 4 880 1100
Fax: (971) 880 1122
E-Mail: info@ti-films.com
Web Site: www.ti-films.com
Sales Range: $75-99.9 Million
Emp.: 30
Polypropylene & Biodegradable Packaging & Label Films Mfr & Whslr
S.I.C.: 2671
N.A.I.C.S.: 326112
Rashid Saif Al Ghurair *(Chm)*
Detlef Schuhmann *(CEO)*
Chandan Ghatak *(CFO)*
Van Zyl Wiese *(COO)*
Patrick Desies *(CMO & Chief Sls Officer)*
Andreas Mueller *(Chief Supply Chain Officer)*

U.S. Subsidiary:

Taghleef Industries Inc. (2)
(Formerly Applied Extrusion Technologies, Inc.)

Al Ghurair Group—(Continued)

2751 Centerville Rd Ste 400
Wilmington, DE 19808 DE
Tel.: (302) 326-5500
Fax: (302) 326-5501
Toll Free: (800) 688-2044
E-Mail: staff.usa@ti-films.com
Web Site: www.ti-films.com
Polypropylene Packaging Films Mfr & Whslr
S.I.C.: 2671
N.A.I.C.S.: 326112
Thomas M. Mohr *(Pres & CEO)*

Non-U.S. Subsidiary:

Taghleef Industries Canada Inc. (3)
(Formerly Applied Extrusion Technologies (Canada), Inc.)
3362 Chemin de la Baronnie
Varennes, QC, J3X 1T2, Canada DE
Tel.: (450) 652-9851 (100%)
Fax: (450) 652-9855
Web Site: www.ti-films.com
Emp.: 100
Polypropylene Packaging Films Mfr & Whslr
S.I.C.: 2671
N.A.I.C.S.: 326112
Richard Bisson *(Mng Dir)*

Non-U.S. Subsidiaries:

Taghleef Industries GmbH (2)
Reutig 2
56357 Holzhausen an der Haide, Germany De
Tel.: (49) 6772 9676 011 (100%)
Fax: (49) 6772 9676 099
Web Site: www.ti-films.com
Polypropylene Packaging Films Distr
S.I.C.: 5162
N.A.I.C.S.: 424610
Andreas Mueller *(Mng Dir)*

Taghleef Industries Pty. Ltd. (2)
11 Moloney Drive
Wodonga, VIC, 3690, Australia AU
Tel.: (61) 2 6022 0220 (100%)
Fax: (61) 2 6022 0292
E-Mail: staffaus@ti-films.com
Web Site: www.ti-films.com
Polypropylene & Biodegradable Packaging Film Mfr & Whslr
S.I.C.: 2671
N.A.I.C.S.: 326112
Elie Jarrous, *(CEO)*

Taghleef Industries S.A.O.C. (2)
PO Box 38
Sohar Industrial Estate, 327 Sohar, Oman OM
Tel.: (968) 2675 1823 (-1825)
Fax: (968) 2675 1822
E-Mail: staff.mena@ti-films.com
Web Site: www.ti-films.com
Emp.: 190
Polypropylene Packaging & Label Films Mfr & Whslr
S.I.C.: 2671
N.A.I.C.S.: 326112
Sundeep Mudgal *(Reg Mgr)*

Taghleef Industries S.p.A. (2)
Via E Fermi 46
33058 San Giorgio di Nogaro, UD, Italy IT
Tel.: (39) 0431 627 111
Fax: (39) 0431 627 590
E-Mail: staff@ti-films.com
Web Site: www.ti-films.com
Polypropylene & Biodegradable Packaging Film Mfr & Whslr
S.I.C.: 2671
N.A.I.C.S.: 326112
Valerio Garzitto, *(CEO-Europe)*

Non-U.S. Subsidiary:

Taghleef Industries Kft (3)
PO Box 259
3581 Tiszaujvaros, Hungary HU
Tel.: (36) 49 521 954
Fax: (36) 49 521 286
E-Mail: staff.hu@ti-films.com
Web Site: www.ti-films.com
Polypropylene & Biodegradable Packaging Film Mfr & Whslr
S.I.C.: 2671
N.A.I.C.S.: 326112

AL GHURAIR INVESTMENT LLC

PO Box 6999
Dubai, United Arab Emirates
Tel.: (971) 4 20 29777
Fax: (971) 4 29 42664
E-Mail: connect@al-ghurair.com
Web Site: www.al-ghurair.com
Business Description:
Investment Holding Company
S.I.C.: 6719
N.A.I.C.S.: 551112
Personnel:
Abdul Aziz Al Ghurair *(Chm)*
Constantin Salameh *(CEO)*

AL HABTOOR GROUP LLC

PO Box 25444
Dubai, United Arab Emirates
Tel.: (971) 43941444
Fax: (971) 43949990
Web Site: www.habtoor.com
Emp.: 40,000
Business Description:
Construction Services
S.I.C.: 1542
N.A.I.C.S.: 236220
Personnel:
Khalaf Al Habtoor *(Chm)*
Mohammed Khalaf Al Habtoor *(Vice Chm & CEO)*
Board of Directors:
Khalaf Al Habtoor
Mohammed Khalaf Al Habtoor
Maan Halabi

Subsidiary:

Al Habtoor Leighton Group (1)
PO Box 320
Dubai, United Arab Emirates
Tel.: (971) 42857551
Fax: (971) 42857479
E-Mail: info@hlgroup.com
Web Site: www.hlgroup.com
Emp.: 15,000
Construction & Engineering Services
S.I.C.: 1542
N.A.I.C.S.: 236220
Khalif Al Habtoot *(Chm)*

AL HAMAD CONTRACTING COMPANY LLC

PO Box 6275
Sharjah, United Arab Emirates
Tel.: (971) 65349666
Fax: (971) 65349966
E-Mail: info@al-hamad.com
Web Site: www.al-hamad.com
Year Founded: 1985
Sales Range: $50-74.9 Million
Emp.: 3,250
Business Description:
Building Contractor
S.I.C.: 1542
N.A.I.C.S.: 236220
Personnel:
Thamin Sulaiman Fakhoury *(Mng Dir)*

Subsidiaries:

Al Hamad Industrial Company LLC (1)
PO Box 4713
Ajman, United Arab Emirates
Tel.: (971) 67438212
Fax: (971) 67434298
Nonresidential Construction
S.I.C.: 1541
N.A.I.C.S.: 236210

Dubai Civil Engineering Est (1)
PO Box 21706
Dubai, United Arab Emirates
Tel.: (971) 042574441
Fax: (971) 2574568
Special Trade Contracting
S.I.C.: 1799
N.A.I.C.S.: 238990

AL-HASAWI INDUSTRIAL GROUP

PO Box 1175
13012 Kuwait, Kuwait
Tel.: (965) 4769100
Fax: (965) 4720091
E-Mail: sales@alhasawi.com
Web Site: www.alhasawi.com
Year Founded: 1960
Emp.: 830
Business Description:
Refrigerators, Water Coolers, Split A/C Units, Cold Stores, Transport Refrigeration Boxes & Water Heaters Mfr & Distr
S.I.C.: 3632
N.A.I.C.S.: 335222
Personnel:
Abdul Karim Al Hasawi *(Chm)*
Hasan Al Hasawi *(Pres)*

Subsidiary:

Alhasawi Factories for Water Heaters W.L.L. (1)
PO Box 1175
Kuwait, 13012, Kuwait
Tel.: (965) 24769100
Fax: (965) 24720091
E-Mail: info@alhasawi.com
Water Heater Mfr
S.I.C.: 3639
N.A.I.C.S.: 335228
Hasan Alhasawi, *(CEO & Pres)*

AL HASSAN ENGINEERING COMPANY S.A.O.G.

Sultanate of Oman
PO Box 1948
Ruwi, 112, Oman
Tel.: (968) 24810575
Fax: (968) 24817082
E-Mail: seccorp@al-hassan.com
Web Site: www.al-hassan.com
Year Founded: 1998
HECI—(MUS)
Rev.: $128,540,726
Assets: $144,270,503
Liabilities: $114,401,181
Net Worth: $29,869,322
Earnings: ($9,727,224)
Emp.: 3,200
Fiscal Year-end: 12/31/12
Business Description:
Construction & Contracting Services
S.I.C.: 1629
N.A.I.C.S.: 237990
Personnel:
Hassan Ali Salman *(Chm)*
Maqbool Ali Salman *(Deputy Chm & Mng Dir)*
Peter Hall *(CEO)*
Ria Mukherjee *(Exec-Corp Comm)*
Abbas Jamal *(CEO-Mfg & Trading)*
Murtadha Mohsin Ali Al-Lawati *(Sec)*
Board of Directors:
Hassan Ali Salman
Ali Abdul Khaliq Ibrahim
Saud Ahmed Al Nahari
Salim S. E. Al-Ghatami
Maqbool Ali Salman
Ali Mohammed Juma

Subsidiaries:

Al Hassan Electricals LLC (1)
PO Box 1948
Ruwi, 112, Oman
Tel.: (968) 24810575
Fax: (968) 24810287
E-Mail: trading@al-hassan.com
Web Site: www.al-hassan.com
Engineering Services
S.I.C.: 8711
N.A.I.C.S.: 541330
Abbas Jamal *(Gen Mgr-Electrical Trading)*

Al Hassan Engineering Co. SAOG (1)
PO Box 1948
Ruwi, 112, Oman
Tel.: (968) 24810575
Fax: (968) 24815953
E-Mail: contracting@al-hassan.com
Web Site: www.al-hassan.com
Engineering Services
S.I.C.: 8711
N.A.I.C.S.: 541330
Jasbir Singh *(Gen Mgr)*

Al Hassan Lighting & Fans Industries (1)
Madilat sultan quaboos
PO Box 130
Madinat Qaboos, 115 Muscat, Oman
Tel.: (968) 24591283
Fax: (968) 24596899
E-Mail: secahsg@al-hassan.com
Web Site: www.al-hassan.com
Emp.: 200
Engineering Services
S.I.C.: 8711
N.A.I.C.S.: 541330
Akos Naar *(Gen Mgr)*

Al Hassan Power Industries (1)
PO Box 130
Madinat Qaboos, 115 Muscat, Oman
Tel.: (968) 24591283
Fax: (968) 24596899
E-Mail: secahsg@al-hassan.com
Web Site: www.al-hassan.com
Emp.: 200
Engineering Services
S.I.C.: 8711
N.A.I.C.S.: 541330
Joseph Chandru *(Gen Mgr)*

Al Hassan Switchgear Manufacturing (1)
PO Box 130
Madinat Qaboos, 115 Muscat, Oman
Tel.: (968) 24591283
Fax: (968) 24596899
E-Mail: secahsg@al-hassan.com
Web Site: www.al-hassan.com
Emp.: 200
Engineering Services
S.I.C.: 8711
N.A.I.C.S.: 541330
Joseph Chandru *(Gen Mgr)*

Hi-Tech Services & Supplies LLC (1)
PO Box 2992
Ruwi, 112, Oman
Tel.: (968) 24810575
Fax: (968) 24810287
E-Mail: hitech@al-hassan.com
Web Site: www.al-hassan.com
Engineering Services
S.I.C.: 8711
N.A.I.C.S.: 541330
Hassan Ali Salamn *(Pres)*

Non-U.S. Subsidiaries:

Al Hamas Trading Company LLC (1)
P O Box 19546
Dubai, United Arab Emirates
Tel.: (971) 14 3350020
Fax: (971) 14 3356648
E-Mail: alhamas@alhamas.ae
Web Site: www.al-hassan.com
Engineering Services
S.I.C.: 8711
N.A.I.C.S.: 541330
Krishna Moorthy *(Gen Mgr)*

Al Hassan Engineering Co. Abu Dhabi LLC (1)
PO Box 47943
Abu Dhabi, United Arab Emirates
Tel.: (971) 25513858
Fax: (971) 25513859
E-Mail: sufyan@alhassan.ae
Engineering Services
S.I.C.: 8711
N.A.I.C.S.: 541330
Craig Marshall *(Gen Mgr)*

Al Hassan Engineering Co. Dubai LLC (1)
PO Box 47943
Dubai, United Arab Emirates
Tel.: (971) 43350020, ext. 25513858
Fax: (971) 43356648, ext. 25513859
E-Mail: sufyan@alhassan.ae
Emp.: 40
Engineering Services
S.I.C.: 8711

N.A.I.C.S.: 541330
Craig Marshall *(Gen Mgr)*

Al Sahwa Trading Co. LLC (1)
Khaleefa St
PO Box 45491
Abu Dhabi, United Arab Emirates
Tel.: (971) 26273270
Fax: (971) 26270960
E-Mail: alsahwa@alhassan.ae
Web Site: www.al-hassan.com
Emp.: 8
Engineering Services
S.I.C.: 8711
N.A.I.C.S.: 541330
Chandru Joseph *(Gen Mgr)*

Noor Al Khaleej LLC (1)
P O Box 45261
Abu Dhabi, United Arab Emirates
Tel.: (971) 12 6273270
Fax: (971) 12 6270960
E-Mail: nooralkhaleej@alhassan.ae
Web Site: www.al-hassan.com
Engineering Services
S.I.C.: 8711
N.A.I.C.S.: 541330

AL-HASSAN G.I. SHAKER COMPANY

(d/b/a Shaker Group)
PO Box 5124
11411 Riyadh, Saudi Arabia
Tel.: (966) 14011450
Web Site: www.shaker.com.sa
Year Founded: 1950
Emp.: 728

Business Description:
Air Conditioning Products & Home Appliances Importer & Distr
S.I.C.: 5075
N.A.I.C.S.: 423730

Personnel:
Hussein G.I. Shaker *(Chm & CEO)*

AL ISRAA FOR ISLAMIC FINANCE & INVESTMENT PLC

Madina Munawara St Building No 197
PO Box 4544
Tilaa Ali, Amman, 11953, Jordan
Tel.: (962) 6 5527584
Fax: (962) 6 5521694
E-Mail: Info@israa.com.jo
Web Site: www.israa.com.jo
ISRA—(AMM)
Rev.: $1,130,127
Assets: $25,987,711
Liabilities: $707,324
Net Worth: $25,280,387
Earnings: $154,565
Emp.: 14
Fiscal Year-end: 12/31/12

Business Description:
Financial Management Services
S.I.C.: 6211
N.A.I.C.S.: 523999

Personnel:
Fuad Mohammed Ahmed Muhasen *(Gen Mgr)*

AL JABER GROUP

PO Box 2175
Abu Dhabi, United Arab Emirates
Tel.: (971) 25554300
Fax: (971) 25553370
E-Mail: aje@emirates.net.ae
Web Site: www.aljaber.com
Emp.: 15,000

Business Description:
Holding Company
S.I.C.: 6719
N.A.I.C.S.: 551112

Personnel:
Obaid Khalifa Al Murri *(CEO)*

Subsidiaries:

Al Jaber Aluminum Extrusion L.L.C. (1)
PO Box 41073
Abu Dhabi, United Arab Emirates
Tel.: (971) 25553707
Fax: (971) 25553977
E-Mail: ajesigns@emirates.net.ae
Aluminum Mfr for Architectural & Industrial Applications
S.I.C.: 3354
N.A.I.C.S.: 331318
Nabil Salman *(Gen Mgr)*

Al Jaber Building L.L.C. (1)
Sector 6 & 7 St
PO Box 2175
Abu Dhabi, United Arab Emirates
Tel.: (971) 25554376
Fax: (971) 25552881
E-Mail: building.div@aje.ae
Web Site: www.aljaber.com
Housing Construction
S.I.C.: 1522
N.A.I.C.S.: 236116
Jihad Khaled *(Mng Dir)*

Al Jaber Carpentry & Decor L.L.C (1)
PO Box 41073
Abu Dhabi, United Arab Emirates
Tel.: (971) 25547075
Fax: (971) 25553977
Web Site: www.aljaber.com
Emp.: 300
Carpentry Services
S.I.C.: 1751
N.A.I.C.S.: 238350

Al Jaber Delta Energy Services & General Construction (1)
PO Box 2175
Abu Dhabi, United Arab Emirates
Tel.: (971) 22040350
Fax: (971) 25553370
Building Construction
S.I.C.: 1531
N.A.I.C.S.: 236117

Al Jaber Energy Services (1)
Al Jaber Yard
PO Box 47467
Mussafah Industrial Area, Abu Dhabi, United Arab Emirates
Tel.: (971) 25546550
Fax: (971) 25546106
E-Mail: info@ajes.ae
Web Site: www.ajes.ae
Emp.: 10,000
Mechanical, Electrical & Contracting Services
S.I.C.: 1731
N.A.I.C.S.: 238210
Ronald Metcalf *(Mng Dir)*

Al Jaber Fusion-Bonded Epoxy Coating Plant (1)
PO Box 41073
Abu Dhabi, United Arab Emirates
Tel.: (971) 25541050
Fax: (971) 025553977
E-Mail: ajesigns@emirates.net.ae
Emp.: 200
Concrete Reinforcement Bars
S.I.C.: 3272
N.A.I.C.S.: 327390
Obaid Khalifa Al Jaber *(Chm)*

Al Jaber L.E.G.T. Engineering & Contracting L.L.C. (1)
PO Box 27639
Dubai, United Arab Emirates
Tel.: (971) 44290599
Fax: (971) 44290216
E-Mail: dubaioffice@alec.ae
Web Site: www.alec.ae
Commercial Building Construction
S.I.C.: 1542
N.A.I.C.S.: 236220
Kez Taylor *(Mng Dir)*

Al Jaber Precision Engineering Establishment (1)
PO Box 2175
Abu Dhabi, United Arab Emirates
Tel.: (971) 25020602
Fax: (971) 25020600
E-Mail: info@ajeprecision.com
Web Site: www.ajeprecision.com
Emp.: 600
Mfr of High Precision Engineering Components & Units, Specializing in Matching, Gearing, Heat Treatment, Plasma Coating, CNC, Steel Fabrication & Inspection Services
S.I.C.: 3499
N.A.I.C.S.: 332999
Obaid Khalifa Al Jaber *(Mng Dir)*

Al Jaber Protective Coating L.L.C. (1)
PO Box 41073
Abu Dhabi, United Arab Emirates
Tel.: (971) 25541050
Fax: (971) 25553977
Web Site: www.aljaber.com
Emp.: 250
Epoxy Coatings for Reinforcement Steel Bars
S.I.C.: 2851
N.A.I.C.S.: 325510
Ragesh Vr *(Plant Mgr & Gen Mgr)*

Al Jaber Shipping Agency & Marine Works (1)
PO Box 2175
Abu Dhabi, United Arab Emirates
Tel.: (971) 25554300
Fax: (971) 25553370
E-Mail: hanza.altanger@aje.ae
Web Site: www.ajshipping.com
Emp.: 350
Shipping Logistics
S.I.C.: 4731
N.A.I.C.S.: 541614
Obaid Khalifa Al Jaber *(Chm)*
Rafid Azzawi *(CFO)*

Al Jaber Signs L.L.C. (1)
PO Box 2175
Abu Dhabi, United Arab Emirates (100%)
Tel.: (971) 25553707
Fax: (971) 25553977
E-Mail: ajesigns@emirates.net.ae
Web Site: www.aljaber.com
Emp.: 2,300
Supply, Erection & Maintenance of Various Road & Street Fixtures
S.I.C.: 3499
N.A.I.C.S.: 332999
David Abdo *(Mng Dir)*

Al Jaber Steel Products L.L.C. (1)
PO Box 2175
Abu Dhabi, United Arab Emirates
Tel.: (971) 25020705
Fax: (971) 25546316
E-Mail: sarkisaj@hotmail.com
Emp.: 220
Steel Structures Mfr
S.I.C.: 3462
N.A.I.C.S.: 332111
Sarkis Karkamazian *(Gen Mgr)*

Al Jaber Trailers, Steel and Metal Works Establishment (1)
PO Box 2175
Abu Dhabi, United Arab Emirates
Tel.: (971) 25554300
Fax: (971) 25553370
Designer & Fabricator of Custom Made Equipment & Components for the Construction & Transportation Industry
S.I.C.: 3531
N.A.I.C.S.: 333120

Al Jaber Transport & General Contracting Co. (1)
PO Box 2175
Abu Dhabi, United Arab Emirates
Tel.: (971) 25554300
Fax: (971) 25553370
E-Mail: aje@emirates.net.ae
Road Construction & Infrastructure Development
S.I.C.: 1611
N.A.I.C.S.: 237310
Mohammed Khalifa Al Jaber *(Pres)*

Non-U.S. Subsidiary:

Al Jaber & Partners L.L.C. (2)
PO Box 23007
Doha, Qatar
Tel.: (974) 4411880
Fax: (974) 4411885
E-Mail: aje@qatar.net.qa
Web Site: www.aljaber.com
Emp.: 2,800
Construction Services
S.I.C.: 1611
N.A.I.C.S.: 237310

Al Jaber Tunneling & Mechanical Works Est (1)
PO Box 9755
Abu Dhabi, United Arab Emirates
Tel.: (971) 25553335
Fax: (971) 25553336
Web Site: www.aljaber.com
Tunneling, Sewage Pipes & Water Pipes Networks
S.I.C.: 1623
N.A.I.C.S.: 237110

Middle East Equipment & Trading (1)
PO Box 29151
Abu Dhabi, United Arab Emirates
Tel.: (971) 25559559
Fax: (971) 25543249
E-Mail: meet@emirates.net.ae
Web Site: www.aljaber.com
Emp.: 100
Sells Used Equipment & Refurbished Construction Plants, Machines & Equipment
S.I.C.: 5932
N.A.I.C.S.: 453310
Obaid Khalifa Al Jaber *(CEO)*

AL JAMIL FOR INVESTMENT COMPANY

Um Uthainah
PO Box 2036
Amman, Jordan
Tel.: (962) 6 5522508
Fax: (962) 6 5522512
E-Mail: aljamil.inv@gmail.com
Year Founded: 2006
JMIL—(AMM)
Sales Range: $1-9.9 Million
Emp.: 15

Business Description:
Financial Investment Services
S.I.C.: 6211
N.A.I.C.S.: 523999

Personnel:
Hani Jamil Barakat *(Gen Mgr)*

AL-JAZEERA SATELLITE NETWORK

(d/b/a Al Jazeera Network)
PO Box 23123
Doha, Qatar
Tel.: (974) 489 6000
Fax: (974) 488 5333
Web Site: english.aljazeera.net
Year Founded: 1996
Emp.: 3,000

Business Description:
Media Holding Company; Satellite Television & Online News, Documentary & Sports Network Owner & Operator
S.I.C.: 6719
N.A.I.C.S.: 551112

Personnel:
Hamad bin Khalifa al-Thani *(Owner & Chm)*
Ahmed Jassim Al Thani *(Dir Gen)*

Subsidiary:

Al Jazeera English (1)
PO Box 23127
Doha, Qatar
Tel.: (974) 4890777
Web Site: english.aljazeera.net
Emp.: 1,000
English-Language Satellite Television & Internet Broadcasting News Network Operator
S.I.C.: 4841
N.A.I.C.S.: 515210
Hamad bin Thame Al Thani *(Chm)*

U.S. Subsidiary:

Al Jazeera America, LLC (1)
435 Hudson St
New York, NY 10014 DE
Tel.: (212) 207-4742
E-Mail: america@aljazeera.net
Web Site: america.aljazeera.com
Emp.: 170
Cable Television & Online News Network Operator
S.I.C.: 4841
N.A.I.C.S.: 515210

Al-Jazeera Satellite Network—(Continued)

Kate O'Brian *(Pres)*
Ehab Al Shihabi *(Interim CEO)*
Terry Baker *(Exec VP-Brdcst Production)*
Dawn Bridges *(Exec VP-Corp Comm)*
David Harleston *(Exec VP-Bus & Legal Affairs)*
Shelley Lewis *(Exec VP-Programming)*
Ken Ripley *(Exec VP-Adv Sls)*
Mark Coatney *(Sr VP-Digital Media)*
David Doss *(Sr VP)*
Shannon High-Bassalik *(Sr VP)*
Marcy McGinness *(Sr VP)*

AL JAZEERA STEEL PRODUCTS COMPANY S.A.O.G.

Sohar Industrial Estate
PO Box 40
Sohar, 327, Oman
Tel.: (968) 26751763
Fax: (968) 26751766
E-Mail: marketing@jazeerasteel.com
Web Site: www.jazeerasteel.com
ATMI—(MUS)
Rev.: $254,410,703
Assets: $209,498,310
Liabilities: $119,508,287
Net Worth: $89,990,023
Earnings: $8,845,181
Emp.: 609
Fiscal Year-end: 12/31/12
Business Description:
Steel Pipes & Tubes Mfr
S.I.C.: 3317
N.A.I.C.S.: 331210
Personnel:
Sulaiman Mohammed Shaheen Al-Rubaie *(Chm)*
Rajeev Kulkarni *(Vice Chm)*
Bhaskar Dutta *(CEO)*
Board of Directors:
Sulaiman Mohammed Shaheen Al-Rubaie
Ghanem Sulaiman Al-Ghenaiman
Sharad Deoraj Jain
Ahmad Khamis
Rajeev Kulkarni
Rajiv Nakani
Taki Ali Sultan

AL JAZIRA TAKAFUL TA'AWUNI COMPANY

Al Madinah Road 3
PO Box 6277
21442 Jeddah, Saudi Arabia
Tel.: (966) 2 6688877
Fax: (966) 2 6677284
E-Mail: info@ajt.com.sa
Web Site: www.ajt.com.sa
8012—(SAU)
Business Description:
Insurance Services
S.I.C.: 6411
N.A.I.C.S.: 524298
Personnel:
Abdulmajeed Al Sultan *(Chm)*
Sager Abdullatif Nadershah *(CEO & Mng Dir)*
Ayed Al Githami *(Sec & VP-Internal Audit)*
Board of Directors:
Abdulmajeed Al Sultan
Ziad Tariq Aba Al Khail
Saad Ibrahim Al Mushwah
Abdullatif Mohammed Ghaiths
Sager Abdullatif Nadershah

AL KAMIL POWER COMPANY SAOG

PO Box 1360
Ruwi, 112, Oman
Tel.: (968) 24607466
Fax: (968) 24607441
E-Mail: akpc@alkamilpower.com
Web Site: www.alkamilpower.com
KPCS—(MUS)
Rev.: $53,904,795
Assets: $110,371,433
Liabilities: $60,671,683
Net Worth: $49,699,750
Earnings: $7,462,984
Emp.: 4
Fiscal Year-end: 12/31/12
Business Description:
Power Generation
S.I.C.: 4911
N.A.I.C.S.: 221118
Personnel:
Matti Castren *(Chm)*
Johan Van Kerrebroeck *(Deputy Chm)*
Carol Rees *(Vice Chm)*
Navneet Kasbekar *(CEO)*
Board of Directors:
Matti Castren
Khalil Ahmed Abdulla Al-Harthy
Micah Jahnke
Johan Van Kerrebroeck
Ajeet Walavalkar

AL-KHAIR GADOON LIMITED

92/3 Phase-III Industrial Estate
Gadoon Amazai
Swabi, Pakistan
Tel.: (92) 938 270260
Fax: (92) 938 270270
E-Mail: alkhairgroup@hotmail.com
Web Site: www.alkhairgroup.com
Year Founded: 1980
AGKL—(ISL)
Business Description:
Foam Products Mfr
S.I.C.: 3086
N.A.I.C.S.: 326150
Personnel:
Mohammed Saeed Sheikh *(CEO)*

AL KHALEEJ TAKAFUL GROUP Q.S.C.

PO Box 4555
Doha, Qatar
Tel.: (974) 4441 4151
Fax: (974) 4443 0530
E-Mail: ktg@alkhaleej.com
Web Site: www.alkhaleej.com
Year Founded: 1978
AKHI—(QE)
Business Description:
Insurance Services
S.I.C.: 6411
N.A.I.C.S.: 524298
Personnel:
Abdulla Mohamed Jabor Al-Thani *(Chm)*
Abdulla Ahmed Al Ahmed Al-Thani *(Vice Chm)*
Saud Abdulla Mohamed Jabor Al Thani *(Mng Dir)*
Board of Directors:
Abdulla Mohamed Jabor Al-Thani
Abdulla Ahmed Al Ahmed Al-Thani
Hassan Bin Hassan Al Mulla
Abdulla Ali Mohamed Al-Ansari
Ali Ridha Al-Banai
Fahad Ebrahim Al-Hamad Al-Manaa
Khaled Abdul Aziz Al-Baker
Saud Abdulla Mohamed Jabor Al Thani
Fahad Mohamed Jabor Al-Thani
Jassim Abdullah Mohamed Jabor Al-Thani

Subsidiary:

Qatar Takaful Company S.O.C. **(1)**
Nr Lulu Hypermarket D Ring Rd
PO Box 23553
Doha, Qatar
Tel.: (974) 44299000
Fax: (974) 44299001
General Insurance Services
S.I.C.: 6411
N.A.I.C.S.: 524210

AL KHALIJ COMMERCIAL BANK

Asia Street 60 West Bay
PO Box 28000
Doha, Qatar
Tel.: (974) 44940000
Fax: (974) 4490808
E-Mail: info@alkhaliji.com
Web Site: www.alkhaliji.com
Year Founded: 2007
KCBK—(LSE QE)
Int. Income: $221,369,809
Assets: $8,993,826,457
Liabilities: $7,479,092,207
Net Worth: $1,514,734,250
Earnings: $136,813,695
Emp.: 372
Fiscal Year-end: 12/31/12
Business Description:
Banking Services
S.I.C.: 6029
N.A.I.C.S.: 522110
Personnel:
Hamad Faisal Thani Al-Thani *(Chm & Mng Dir)*
Abdullah Nasser Al-Misnad *(Vice Chm)*
Robin McCall *(CEO)*
Christiaan De Beer *(CFO)*
Hesham EzzEldin *(COO)*
Mohamad Abdelkhalek *(Chief Bus Officer)*
Oliver Schwarzhaupt *(Chief Risk Officer)*
Pauline Bejjani *(Sr IR Officer)*
Rima Boutros *(Sec)*
Board of Directors:
Hamad Faisal Thani Al-Thani
Mohammed Khalid Al Mana
Saif Al-Madfaa
Abdullah Nasser Al-Misnad
Rashid Al-Naimi
Hisham S. Al-Saie
Abdul Salam Mohammed Al-Murshidi

AL-KHALIJ HOLDING COMPANY Q.S.C.

(Name Changed to Qatari Investors Group Q.S.C.)

AL KHALILI UNITED ENTERPRISES LLC

(d/b/a Al Khalili Group)
CR 2435
Muscat, 112, Oman
Mailing Address:
PO Box 1869
Al-Ghubra, 112, Oman
Tel.: (968) 2481630
Fax: (968) 24818582
E-Mail: buildingmaterial@alkhalili.com
Web Site: www.alkhalili.com
Emp.: 3,000
Business Description:
Wholesale Trading Services; Construction, Electrical, Hardware & IT Products
S.I.C.: 7389
N.A.I.C.S.: 425120
Personnel:
Ayub Khan *(CEO)*

AL KHAZNA INSURANCE COMPANY P.S.C.

Villa No 51 East of Al Nahyan Camp
Delma Street No 13
PO Box 73343, Abu Dhabi, United Arab Emirates
Tel.: (971) 2 696 9700
Fax: (971) 2641 7998
E-Mail: khazana@emirates.net.ae
Web Site: www.alkhazna.com
Year Founded: 1996
AKIC—(ABU)
Sales Range: $25-49.9 Million
Emp.: 150
Business Description:
Insurance Services
S.I.C.: 6411
N.A.I.C.S.: 524298
Personnel:
Khalifa Mohamed Rubaya Al-Muhairi *(Chm)*
Salah Salem Omeir Al-Shamsi *(Vice Chm)*
Sameer Alwazzan *(Interim CEO)*
Ahmed Mohammed Al-Romaithi *(Mng Dir)*
Rubaya M. Al-Rubaya *(Sec)*
Board of Directors:
Khalifa Mohamed Rubaya Al-Muhairi
Hamad Jassim Al-Darwish
Sultan Suroor Sultan Al-Dhahiri
Fatima Obaid Al-Jaber
Dheya Ebrahim Al-Khalifa
Abdul Ghaffar Abdul Khaleq Al-Khouri
Daham Al Fandi Rashed Al-Mazrouei
Ahmed Mohammed Al-Romaithi
Rubaya M. Al-Rubaya
Buti Saif Saeed Al-Sabousi
Salah Salem Omeir Al-Shamsi

Divisions:

Al Khazna Insurance Company - Abu Dhabi Traffic **(1)**
Najda Street
PO Box 73343
Abu Dhabi, United Arab Emirates (100%)
Tel.: (971) 24493497
Fax: (971) 24493506
E-Mail: khazna@alkhazna.ae
Web Site: www.alkhazna.com
Insurance Services
S.I.C.: 6411
N.A.I.C.S.: 524298
Ibrahim Al Wazan *(CEO)*

Al Khazna Insurance Company - Al Ain Branch **(1)**
Oud Al Tuba St.
PO Box 20755
Al Ain, United Arab Emirates (100%)
Tel.: (971) 37661700
Fax: (971) 37666404
E-Mail: alkhazna@emirates.net.ae
Emp.: 600
Insurance Services
S.I.C.: 6411
N.A.I.C.S.: 524298
Abdula Al Shamisi *(Mng Dir)*

Al Khazna Insurance Company - Al Ain Traffic **(1)**
Al Khazna Tower Oud Al Tuba St
PO Box 20755
Al Ain, United Arab Emirates
Tel.: (971) 3 766 1700
Fax: (971) 3 766 6404
Web Site: www.alkhazna.com
Insurance Services
S.I.C.: 6411
N.A.I.C.S.: 524298

Al Khazna Insurance Company - Al Mussafah **(1)**
Villa No 51 Opp Al Nahyan camp
PO Box 73343
Delma Street No 13, Abu Dhabi, United Arab Emirates
Tel.: (971) 26969700
Fax: (971) 26417998
E-Mail: emailkhazna@emirates.net.ae
Web Site: www.alkhazna.com
Emp.: 88
Insurance Services
S.I.C.: 6411
N.A.I.C.S.: 524298
Samir Alwazan *(CEO)*

Al Khazna Insurance Company - Al Mussafah Light Vehicle **(1)**
PO Box 73343
Abu Dhabi, United Arab Emirates

Tel.: (971) 25544561
Insurance Services
S.I.C.: 6411
N.A.I.C.S.: 524298

Al Khazna Insurance Company - Al Wagan (1)
The Mair Road
PO Box 20755
Al Ain, United Arab Emirates (100%)
Tel.: (971) 37352065
Fax: (971) 37352065
Web Site: www.alkhazna.com
Sales Range: $1-9.9 Million
Emp.: 200
Insurance Services
S.I.C.: 6411
N.A.I.C.S.: 524298
Fatih Yaswen *(Gen Mgr)*

Al Khazna Insurance Company - Beda Zayed (1)
PO Box 73343
Abu Dhabi, United Arab Emirates
Tel.: (971) 28844290
Fax: (971) 28841761
Web Site: www.alkhazna.com
Insurance Services
S.I.C.: 6411
N.A.I.C.S.: 524298

Al Khazna Insurance Company - Dubai (1)
Al Ittihad Road
PO Box 8953
Dubai, United Arab Emirates (100%)
Tel.: (971) 4 2173333
Fax: (971) 4 2560840
E-Mail: alkhazna@emirates.uae
Web Site: www.alkhazna.com
Emp.: 15
Insurance Services
S.I.C.: 6411
N.A.I.C.S.: 524298
Sameer Alwazzan *(Gen Mgr)*

AL-KO KOBER AG

Ichenhauser Strasse 14
D 89359 Kotz, Germany
Tel.: (49) 8221970
Fax: (49) 8221978449
E-Mail: info@al-ko.de
Web Site: www.al-ko.de
Year Founded: 1931
Emp.: 4,000

Business Description:
Chassis & Trailers, Automotive Conversions for Motor Homes, Industrial Trailers, Caravan Accessories & Garden Care Accessories
S.I.C.: 5084
N.A.I.C.S.: 423830

Personnel:
Wilhelm Kober *(Mng Dir)*
Roland Kober *(CFO & Dir-IT)*

U.S. Subsidiary:

AL-KO Kober Corp. (1)
21611 Protecta Dr
Elkhart, IN 46516-9543
Tel.: (574) 294-6651
Fax: (574) 294-7267
Web Site: www.al-kousa.com
Emp.: 100
Axles & Brakes Mfr
S.I.C.: 3714
N.A.I.C.S.: 336350

AL-KOUT INDUSTRIAL PROJECTS COMPANY K.S.C.C.

2nd Floor Al Abrar Complex Behind Al Mutanna Complex Fahed Al Salem St
Kuwait, Kuwait
Tel.: (965) 22404697
Fax: (965) 22404695
E-Mail: info@alkoutprojects.com.kw
Web Site: www.alkoutprojects.com
ALKOUT—(KUW)
Rev.: $54,365,138
Assets: $121,058,680
Liabilities: $36,048,105
Net Worth: $85,010,575
Earnings: $15,542,083
Emp.: 180
Fiscal Year-end: 12/31/12

Business Description:
Salt & Chlorine Products Mfr & Sales
S.I.C.: 2819
N.A.I.C.S.: 325180

Personnel:
Fahad Yacoub Al Jouan *(Chm)*
Bader Musaed Abdullah Al Sayer *(Deputy Chm)*

Board of Directors:
Fahad Yacoub Al Jouan
Fahad Abdulrahman Al Sane
Salah Nasser Al Saqabi
Hamad Abdulaziz Al Saqer
Bader Musaed Abdullah Al Sayer
Bader Musaed Bader Al Sayer
Othman Zahim Al Zahim

AL KUHAIMI METAL INDUSTRIES LTD.

PO Box 545
Dammam, 31421, Saudi Arabia
Tel.: (966) 38472777
Fax: (966) 38472591
E-Mail: info@alkuhaimi.com
Web Site: www.alkuhaimi.com
Year Founded: 1975
Emp.: 700

Business Description:
Metal Doors Mfr
S.I.C.: 3442
N.A.I.C.S.: 332321

Personnel:
Mohammed Ahmed Al Kuhaimi *(Chm)*

AL-MADAR FINANCE & INVESTMENT CO. K.S.C.C.

14th Floor Al Salam Tower Fahed Al Salem Street
PO Box 1376
Safat, Kuwait, 13014, Kuwait
Tel.: (965) 22324200
Fax: (965) 22324201
E-Mail: info@almadar-fi.com
Web Site: www.almadar-fi.com
MADAR—(KUW)
Sales Range: $25-49.9 Million

Business Description:
Investment Management & Advisory Services
S.I.C.: 6211
N.A.I.C.S.: 523110

Personnel:
Nabil Ahmed Mohamed Ameen *(Chm & Mng Dir)*
Khaled Bader Al-Roomi *(Vice Chm)*

Board of Directors:
Nabil Ahmed Mohamed Ameen
Khalid Abdullah Al-Fadalah
Mubarak Naser Al-Majroob
Mona Khalifa Al-Musallam
Derar Khaled Al-Robah
Khaled Bader Al-Roomi
Nadar Hamd Sultan Alissa

Al Nisf & Partners
PO Box 25578
Safat, Kuwait

AL-MADINA FOR FINANCE & INVESTMENT COMPANY KSCC

Mirgab-Al-Sour Street Jasem Al-Asfor Tower
PO Box 2799
Safat, 13028 Kuwait, Kuwait
Tel.: (965) 22960777
Fax: (965) 22476857
E-Mail: info@almadinainvest.com
Web Site: www.almadinainvest.com
Year Founded: 1980
ALMADINA—(DFM KUW)
Rev.: $27,975,832
Assets: $509,535,535
Liabilities: $246,169,257
Net Worth: $263,366,278
Earnings: ($9,799,089)
Fiscal Year-end: 12/31/12

Business Description:
Investment & Financial Services
S.I.C.: 6211
N.A.I.C.S.: 523999

Personnel:
Faisal Abdulrahman Al-hattam *(Chm)*
Mohammed Darweesh Al-Shamali *(Vice Chm)*

Board of Directors:
Faisal Abdulrahman Al-hattam
Rasid Shibib Al-Ajmi
Meshael Malek Al-Sabah
Mohammed Darweesh Al-Shamali
Emad Hussain Neama

Al Ateeqi Certified Accountant
Ali Al-Salem Str Thuwaini Bldg 3rd Flr 636
Kuwait, Kuwait

AL MAHA PETROLEUM PRODUCTS MARKETING COMPANY S.A.O.G.

PO Box 57
Muscat, 116, Oman
Tel.: (968) 24610200
Fax: (968) 24610201
E-Mail: cs@almaha.com.om
Web Site: www.almaha.com.om
MHAS—(MUS)
Rev.: $788,635,581
Assets: $186,983,019
Liabilities: $81,937,742
Net Worth: $105,045,277
Earnings: $25,953,232
Emp.: 127
Fiscal Year-end: 12/31/12

Business Description:
Petroleum Products Marketer & Distr
S.I.C.: 5172
N.A.I.C.S.: 424720

Personnel:
Noor Mohamed Abdulrahman Al-Zadjali *(Chm)*
Al Sayyid Munther Saif Hamed Al-Busaidi *(Deputy Chm)*
Ibrahim Salem Abdulla Al Dhaheri *(Mng Dir)*

Board of Directors:
Noor Mohamed Abdulrahman Al-Zadjali
Ibrahim Salem Abdulla Al Dhaheri
Al Sayyid Munther Saif Hamed Al-Busaidi
Mohammed Ali Said Al-Qassabi
Rashed Saif Mohamed Al-Saadi
Sultan Khalifa Saleh Al-Tai
Hamdi Mohamed Ahmed Elsayed

AL-MAL INVESTMENT COMPANY KSCC

Al-Sharq Gulf Street Ahmed Tower 23rd Floor
PO Box 26308
Safat, Kuwait, 13124, Kuwait
Tel.: (965) 22428132
Fax: (965) 22428088
E-Mail: info@almal.com.kw
Web Site: www.almal.org
ALMAL—(KUW)
Rev.: $22,058,848
Assets: $487,293,235
Liabilities: $293,324,206
Net Worth: $193,969,029
Earnings: ($21,867,494)
Fiscal Year-end: 12/31/12

Business Description:
Investment Services
S.I.C.: 6211
N.A.I.C.S.: 523999

Personnel:
Loay Jassim Al-Kharafi *(Chm & Mng Dir)*
Abdul Kareem A. Al Mutawa *(Deputy Chm)*
Fawzi Abdul Rahman Al Jouder *(CEO)*
Adel Nasr *(CFO)*

Board of Directors:
Loay Jassim Al-Kharafi
Abdul Kareem A. Al Mutawa
Sullaimant T. Al-Abduljader
Dherar M. Al-Nisf
Khalid A. H. Al-Nughaimish
Salah Abdullah Ali Dashti

Grant Thornton Al Qatami Al-Aiban & Partners
Souq Al Kabeer Building Block A 9th Floor
Kuwait, Kuwait

AL-MAMOURA COMPANY FOR REAL ESTATE INVESTMENT

Arsat Al-handia 929/35/26 Al-Elwiah
PO Box 4377
Baghdad, Iraq
Tel.: (964) 1 7186293
E-Mail: info@mamorairaq.com
Web Site: www.mamorairaq.com
Year Founded: 1993
SMRI—(IRAQ)

Business Description:
Real Estate Investment Services
S.I.C.: 6531
N.A.I.C.S.: 531390

Personnel:
Abdul Kareem Abbas Al-Saadi *(Pres)*

AL-MANARA INSURANCE PLC CO.

Shemesani Shaker Bin Zaid St
Amman, Jordan
Tel.: (962) 65656012
Fax: (962) 65658482
E-Mail: info@almanarainsurance.com
Web Site: www.almanarainsurance.com
Year Founded: 1974
ARSI—(AMM)
Sales Range: $1-9.9 Million
Emp.: 59

Business Description:
Insurance Services
S.I.C.: 6411
N.A.I.C.S.: 524298

Personnel:
Naief Abd allatife AL-Ahmad *(Chm)*
Akef Tanbouz *(Vice Chm)*

Board of Directors:
Naief Abd allatife AL-Ahmad
Ali AL-Shanti
Naser Alomar
Issa Bosheh
Mahmoud Hamdan
Fadi Hashem
Akef Tanbouz

AL MASAOOD OIL INDUSTRY SUPPLIES & SERVICES CO.

PO Box 4352
Abu Dhabi, United Arab Emirates
Tel.: (971) 26267666
Fax: (971) 26273422
E-Mail: masoil@eim.ae
Web Site: www.almasaoodoiss.com
Year Founded: 1971
Sales Range: $25-49.9 Million
Emp.: 500

Business Description:
Oil, Construction & Engineering Services

Al Masaood Oil Industry Supplies & Services Co.—(Continued)

S.I.C.: 1389
N.A.I.C.S.: 213112
Personnel:
Rahma Al Masaood *(Chm)*

AL-MASSALEH REAL ESTATE COMPANY K.S.C.C.

PO Box 719
Safat, Kuwait, 13008, Kuwait
Tel.: (965) 1887000
Fax: (965) 22458930
E-Mail: info@almassaleh.com
Web Site: www.almassaleh.com
MASSALEH—(KUW)
Rev.: $35,152,477
Assets: $545,362,920
Liabilities: $334,889,946
Net Worth: $210,472,974
Earnings: $1,704,027
Emp.: 59
Fiscal Year-end: 12/31/12
Business Description:
Real Estate Services
S.I.C.: 6531
N.A.I.C.S.: 531390
Personnel:
Hamad Fawzi Hamad Al Eisa *(Chm)*
Mehdi Rajab Malaki *(Vice Chm)*
Board of Directors:
Hamad Fawzi Hamad Al Eisa
Najeeb Hamad Musaad Al Saleh
Faisal Youssif Alawadi
Tareq Abdulrazzaq Alkandari
Hassan Bassam El Houry
Tarik Kaoukji
Mehdi Rajab Malaki

Abdul Rahman Al-Qaoud & Partners
PO Box 26111
Kuwait, Kuwait

Subsidiary:

Taameer Real Estate Investment Co. KSCC (1)
Universal Tower Ahmad Al Jaber Street
PO Box 29295
13153 Kuwait, Kuwait
Tel.: (965) 22496321
Fax: (965) 22496324
E-Mail: admin@altaameer.com.kw
Web Site: www.altaameer.com.kw
TAAMEER—(KUW)
Sales Range: $10-24.9 Million
Emp.: 12
Real Estate Investment Services
S.I.C.: 6531
N.A.I.C.S.: 531390
Jamal Al Hazeem *(Chm)*
Najeeb Hamad Musaad Alsaleh *(Vice Chm)*
Fawaz Al Bader *(CEO)*

Non-U.S. Subsidiaries:

Taameer Hospitality for Hotel Management S.A. (2)
50 Mohamed Mazhar Street Office # 3
El Zamalek, Cairo, Egypt
Tel.: (20) 2 2736 4873
Fax: (20) 2 2736 4874
Hotel Management Services
S.I.C.: 6531
N.A.I.C.S.: 531390

Taameer Hotel Management Company & Consultancy S.A. (2)
85 avenue des FAR
Fes, 30000, Morocco
Tel.: (212) 5 3594 8000
Fax: (212) 5 3594 2504
Hotel Management Services
S.I.C.: 6531
N.A.I.C.S.: 531390

Taameer Lebanon Holding Company-S.A.L. (2)
Ramada Downtown Hotel Chateaubriand St
Minet El Hosn Sector
Beirut, 00961, Lebanon
Tel.: (961) 1990299
Fax: (961) 1990399
E-Mail: info@ramadalebanon.com
Web Site: www.ramadalebanon.com
Emp.: 50
Real Estate & Design Consulting Services
S.I.C.: 6531
N.A.I.C.S.: 531390
Yasmine Maalouf *(Gen Mgr)*

Subsidiaries:

Star Tower S.A.L. (3)
Minet El Hosn Chateaubriand Street
PO Box 11215
Beirut, Lebanon
Tel.: (961) 1 990299
Fax: (961) 1 990399
Hotel Operator
S.I.C.: 7011
N.A.I.C.S.: 721110

Taameer Hospitality-S.A.L. (3)
1st Fl Block O2B Azarieh Bldg
PO Box 11-215
Downtown, Beirut, 1107, Lebanon
Tel.: (961) 1995990
Fax: (961) 1990399
Emp.: 77
Hotel Management Services
S.I.C.: 7011
N.A.I.C.S.: 721110
Yasmine Maalouf *(Gen Mgr)*

AL-MAZAYA HOLDING COMPANY KSCC

Salhiya Complex Gate 7 3rd Floor
Fahad Salem Street
PO Box 3546
Kuwait, 13036, Kuwait
Tel.: (965) 22243333
Fax: (965) 22411901
E-Mail: info@mazayarealestate.com
Web Site: www.mazayarealestate.com
MAZAYA—(KUW NASDAQDBAI)
Rev.: $115,141,870
Assets: $783,321,200
Liabilities: $472,052,254
Net Worth: $311,268,946
Earnings: $1,031,185
Emp.: 65
Fiscal Year-end: 12/31/12
Business Description:
Holding Company; Real Estate Services
S.I.C.: 6531
N.A.I.C.S.: 531390
Personnel:
Rashid Yaqoub Yousef Al-Nafisi *(Chm)*
Abdulaziz Basem Essa Al Loughani *(Vice Chm)*
Shlash Al Hajraf *(Acting CEO-Ops-Dubai Office)*
Ibrahim Al Saqabi *(Acting CEO)*
Abdulaziz A. Jarkas *(Exec VP-Projects)*
Salwa N. Malhas *(Exec VP-Bus Dev, Real Estate & Mktg Mgmt)*
Ayman A. Sheet *(Exec VP-Investment & Fin)*
Board of Directors:
Rashid Yaqoub Yousef Al-Nafisi
Abdulaziz Basem Essa Al Loughani
Mohammed Khaled Othman Al Othman
Abdulrahman Mohamed Rashed Alshared Alfalasi
Abdul Hamid Mihrez

Subsidiary:

First Dubai for Real Estate Development Company K.S.C.C. (1)
Salhiya Complex Gate 8 3rd Floor
PO Box 26858
Safat, Kuwait, 13129, Kuwait
Tel.: (965) 22419999
Fax: (965) 22454134
E-Mail: info@1stdubai.com
Web Site: www.1stdubai.com
FIRSTDUBAI—(KUW)
Rev.: $9,794,483
Assets: $235,354,617
Liabilities: $53,936,983
Net Worth: $181,417,634
Earnings: $2,778,175
Fiscal Year-end: 12/31/12
Real Estate Services
S.I.C.: 6531
N.A.I.C.S.: 531390
Seraj S. Al-Baker *(Chm)*
Khaled S. Esbaitah *(Vice Chm)*
Nedal Yaiesh *(Sr VP-Bus Dev & Projects)*

AL MEERA CONSUMER GOODS COMPANY Q.S.C.

Asim Bin Amrr Street
Doha, Qatar
Tel.: (974) 44320222
Fax: (974) 44365554
E-Mail: m_hatami@almeera.com.qa
Web Site: www.almeera.com
Year Founded: 2004
MERS—(QE)
Sls.: $401,589,383
Assets: $279,433,385
Liabilities: $197,905,425
Net Worth: $81,527,959
Earnings: $28,086,206
Fiscal Year-end: 12/31/12
Business Description:
Foodstuff & Consumer Goods Commodities Whlsr
S.I.C.: 5499
N.A.I.C.S.: 445299
Personnel:
Abdulla Khalid Al Qahtani *(Chm)*
Saif Said Al Sowaidi *(Vice Chm)*
Guy Sauvage *(CEO)*
Mohammed Nasser Al-Qahtani *(Deputy CEO)*
Board of Directors:
Abdulla Khalid Al Qahtani
Mohammad Abdulla Al Mustafawi Al Hashemi
Ahmed Abdullah Mohammed Ali Al Khulaifi
Jassim Mohammed Al Kubaisi
Saleh Mohammed Salem Al Nabit
Saif Said Al Sowaidi
Mohammed Ibrahim Mohammed Al Sulaiti

AL MOUWASAT MEDICAL SERVICES COMPANY

Block 71 King Fahad Road
PO Box 282
Uhod District, Dammam, 31411, Saudi Arabia
Tel.: (966) 38200000
Fax: (966) 38203436
E-Mail: nassersultan@mouwasat.com
Web Site: www.mouwasat.com
Year Founded: 1974
4002—(SAU)
Sales Range: $125-149.9 Million
Business Description:
Hospitals, Medical Centers, Medicine Warehouses & Pharmacies Owner, Manager & Operator
S.I.C.: 8062
N.A.I.C.S.: 622110
Personnel:
Mohammed Sultan Al-Subaie *(Chm)*
Nasser Sultan Al-Subaie *(Vice Chm)*
Mohammed Suliman Al-Saleem *(Mng Dir)*
Mahmoud Suliman Shurrab *(CFO, Chief Admin Officer & Sec)*
Issam Younis Assaf *(CMO & Chief Promo Officer)*
Omar Fadlalla El-Sharif *(Chief Medical Officer)*
Marwan Toufiq Khatib *(Chief Central Procurement Officer)*
Mustafa Husny Mustafa *(Shareholder Rels Officer)*
Khalid Suliman Al-Saleem *(Deputy Mng Dir)*
Board of Directors:
Mohammed Sultan Al-Subaie
Ibrahim Hammad Al-Babtain
Abdulaziz Saad Al-Mangoor
Khalid Suliman Al-Saleem
Mohammed Suliman Al-Saleem
Khalid Mohammed Al-Subaie
Nasser Sultan Al-Subaie
David Anthony Price

AL-MOWASAT HOLDING COMPANY K.S.C.C.

Salmiya Plot 2 Block 3 G 79
PO Box 982
Salmiya, Kuwait, 22010, Kuwait
Tel.: (965) 24613434
Fax: (965) 24613687
E-Mail: info@newmowasat.com
Web Site: www.newmowasat.com
MHC—(KUW)
Emp.: 20
Business Description:
Hospital & Other Healthcare Facilities Owner & Operator
S.I.C.: 8062
N.A.I.C.S.: 622110
Personnel:
Salah Mohamed Abdoulaziz Al-Wazan *(Chm & Mng Dir)*
Adnan Mohamed Aboudlaziz Al-Wazan *(Vice Chm)*
Board of Directors:
Salah Mohamed Abdoulaziz Al-Wazan
Tareq Fahed Al-Oun
Adnan Mohamed Aboudlaziz Al-Wazan
Qutaiba Adnan Mohamed Al-Wazan
Ahmed Mohamed Ben Thani

AL-MUNTASER TRADING & CONTRACTING CO. W.L.L.

Saleh Al-Mutawa Building Mezzanine Floor
(PAMA) Area 30, Al Sharq Kuwait, Kuwait
Mailing Address:
PO Box 28250
Safat, Kuwait, Kuwait
Tel.: (965) 2410861
Fax: (965) 2410853
E-Mail: mtc@muntaser.com
Web Site: www.muntaser.com
Year Founded: 1977
Sales Range: $250-299.9 Million
Emp.: 300
Business Description:
Oil & Gas, Refining & Petrochemicals, Power Generation, Water Desalination & Wastewater Treatment Services
S.I.C.: 1389
N.A.I.C.S.: 213112

Division:

Al-Muntaser Trading & Contracting Co. W.L.L. - Contracting Division (1)
KFH Building 206 Behind Fisheries Building
1st Floor Office No 04
Suhada Street Sharq, Kuwait, 13120, Kuwait
Tel.: (965) 2241 3249
Fax: (965) 2241 3248
E-Mail: enquiries@muntaser.com
Emp.: 400
Oil & Gas Pipeline Engineering Services
S.I.C.: 8711
N.A.I.C.S.: 541330

AL OMANIYA FINANCIAL SERVICES (SAOG)

PO Box 1087
Jibroo, 114, Oman

Tel.: (968) 24811164
Fax: (968) 24813258
E-Mail: aofsoman@omantel.net.om
Web Site: www.aofsoman.com
AOFS—(MUS)
Rev.: $42,592,865
Assets: $544,063,516
Liabilities: $422,643,848
Net Worth: $121,419,668
Earnings: $14,637,296
Emp.: 152
Fiscal Year-end: 12/31/12

Business Description:
Financial Services
S.I.C.: 6211
N.A.I.C.S.: 523999

Personnel:
Khalid Said Al Wahaibi *(Chm)*
Khalid Mustahil Ahmed Al Mashani *(Deputy Chm)*
Aftab Patel *(CEO)*
Salim Abdullah Al Awadi *(Deputy CEO)*

Board of Directors:
Khalid Said Al Wahaibi
Saif Ali Shaikhan Al Amri
Hamood Mustahil Ahmed Al Mashani
Khalid Mustahil Ahmed Al Mashani
Zaki Hassan Al Naseeb
Ibrahim Said Salim Al Wahaibi
Shikar Bipin Dharamsey Nensey
K. K. Abdul Razak
Ketan Dinkarrai Vasa

AL-OSAIS INTERNATIONAL HOLDING COMPANY

PO Box 1083
Dammam, 31431, Saudi Arabia
Tel.: (966) 38113333
Fax: (966) 38113334
E-Mail: info@alosais.com
Web Site: www.alosais.com
Year Founded: 1972
Emp.: 3,000

Business Description:
Holding Company
S.I.C.: 6719
N.A.I.C.S.: 551112

Personnel:
Amer A. Moraisel *(Chm)*
Ghurm A. Moraisel *(Pres)*

Subsidiaries:

Al Arabi Steel Structure Manufacturing Co. (1)
Dammam Second Industrial City
PO Box 14044
Dammam, 31424, Saudi Arabia
Tel.: (966) 38123070
Fax: (966) 38123339
E-Mail: info@asfsteel.com
Web Site: www.asfsteel.com
Emp.: 160
Structural Steel Frames, Girders, Structural Beams & Miscellaneous Steel Structures Mfr
S.I.C.: 3441
N.A.I.C.S.: 332312
Saeed Abdullah Al Musbeh *(Mng Dir)*

Al-Berri United Food Co. Ltd. (1)
PO Box 29
Al Jubayl, 31951, Saudi Arabia
Tel.: (966) 33612827
Fax: (966) 33621593
E-Mail: info@alberri.com
Web Site: www.alberri.com
Emp.: 80
Importer & Supplier of Frozen Food Products
S.I.C.: 5142
N.A.I.C.S.: 424420
Hashim G. Moraisel *(Gen Mgr)*

Al-Osais Contracting Co. (1)
PO Box 1083
Dammam, 31431, Saudi Arabia
Tel.: (966) 3 811 3333
Fax: (966) 3 811 3334
Web Site: www.alosais.com
Residential & Commercial Construction
S.I.C.: 1542
N.A.I.C.S.: 236220
Ahmed M. Alabdulaali *(Mng Dir)*

Al-Osais Hiring Co. (1)
PO Box 1083
Dammam, 31431, Saudi Arabia
Tel.: (966) 38110196
Fax: (966) 38113004
E-Mail: eqptdivn@alosais.com
Web Site: www.alosais.com
Emp.: 600
Employment Services
S.I.C.: 7361
N.A.I.C.S.: 561311
Adullah G. Moraisel *(Gen Mgr)*

Al-Osais Industrial & Structural Supply Co. (1)
PO Box 13376
Dammam, Saudi Arabia
Tel.: (966) 38112225
Fax: (966) 3 811 5969
Web Site: www.alosais.com
Industrial & Construction Consumables & Materials Supplier
S.I.C.: 5039
N.A.I.C.S.: 423390
Sayed Zahir Shah *(Mgr-Bus Dev)*

Al-Osais MCM Co. Ltd. (1)
PO Box 9724
Dammam, 31431, Saudi Arabia
Tel.: (966) 38116372
Fax: (966) 38116374
E-Mail: jamil@osais.com
Web Site: www.al-osais.com
Emp.: 50
Construction & Civil Engineering Services
S.I.C.: 8711
N.A.I.C.S.: 541330
Habib Younes *(CFO)*

Al-Osais Petroleum Services Co. (1)
PO Box 14044
Dammam, 31424, Saudi Arabia
Tel.: (966) 38203390
Fax: (966) 3 820 5750
Web Site: www.alosais.com
Motor Fuel Retail
S.I.C.: 5541
N.A.I.C.S.: 447190
Abdullah Musbeh *(Gen Mgr)*

Al-Osais Real Estate Co. (1)
PO Box 1083
Dammam, 31431, Saudi Arabia
Tel.: (966) 38113333
Fax: (966) 38113334
Web Site: www.al-osais.com
Emp.: 100
Ownership of Land, Buildings & Rentals; Property Management Services
S.I.C.: 6519
N.A.I.C.S.: 531210
Abdul Rahman Moraisel *(VP)*

Al-Osais Transportation & Road Construction Co. (1)
PO Box 14044
Dammam, 31424, Saudi Arabia
Mailing Address:
PO Box 28
Al Jubayl, 31951, Saudi Arabia
Tel.: (966) 38203390
Fax: (966) 38205750
E-Mail: transport@al-osais.com
Web Site: www.al-osais.com
Road Construction & Maintenance; Quarries; Asphalt Production
S.I.C.: 1622
N.A.I.C.S.: 237310
Abdullah Musbeh *(VP)*

Arabian Pipeline & Services Co. Ltd. (1)
PO Box 234
Al Jubayl, 31951, Saudi Arabia
Tel.: (966) 33620556
Fax: (966) 33614990
E-Mail: info@anabeeb.com
Web Site: www.anabeeb.com
Emp.: 2,000
Pipeline Construction
S.I.C.: 1623
N.A.I.C.S.: 237120
Hashim Moraisel *(Gen Mgr)*

Baseelah Mechanical Works (1)
PO Box 8275
Dammam, 31482, Saudi Arabia
Tel.: (966) 38111555
Fax: (966) 38111444
E-Mail: baseelah@alosais.com
Web Site: www.alosais.com
Emp.: 500
Heating, Ventilation & Air Conditioning Design & Installation
S.I.C.: 1711
N.A.I.C.S.: 238220
Leo G. Lumanang *(Gen Mgr)*

MGA Trading Est. (1)
PO Box 9377
Dammam, 31413, Saudi Arabia
Tel.: (966) 38584783
Fax: (966) 38584782
E-Mail: mga@mgat.com
Web Site: www.mgat.com
Emp.: 20
Electrical, Construction & Industrial Material & Equipment Supplier
S.I.C.: 5039
N.A.I.C.S.: 423390
Mohammad G. Moraisel *(Gen Mgr)*

Middle East Resources Co. (1)
PO Box 13376
Dammam, 31493, Saudi Arabia
Tel.: (966) 38120999
Fax: (966) 38121199
E-Mail: mercowax@osais.com
Web Site: www.mercowax.com
Emp.: 22
Development & Manufacturing of Petroleum & Industrial Chemical Products
S.I.C.: 2999
N.A.I.C.S.: 324199
Abdul Rahman Moraisel *(Gen Mgr)*

AL-OTHAIM HOLDING COMPANY

Eastern Roundabout Street Exit 14
PO Box 28090
Al Rabwah Area, Riyadh, 11437, Saudi Arabia
Tel.: (966) 12540000
Fax: (966) 1254 6666
E-Mail: info@othaim.com
Web Site: www.othaimholding.com
Year Founded: 1956

Business Description:
Investment Holding Company
S.I.C.: 6719
N.A.I.C.S.: 551112

Personnel:
Abdullah bin Saleh Al-Othaim *(Chm & CEO)*

Subsidiary:

Abdullah Al-Othaim Investment & Real Estate Development Company (1)
Eastern Roundabout Street Exit 14
PO Box 28090
Al Rabwah Area, Riyadh, 11437, Saudi Arabia SA
Tel.: (966) 12415503 (81.3%)
Fax: (966) 12415719
E-Mail: malls@othaim.com
Web Site: www.othaimmalls.com
Real Estate Investment Trust; Shopping Centers Developer, Owner & Lessor
S.I.C.: 6726
N.A.I.C.S.: 525990
Fahad bin Abdullah Saleh Al-Othaim *(CEO)*

AL QUDS READYMIX

PO Box 710078
Amman, 11171, Jordan
Tel.: (962) 64202575
Fax: (962) 64203732
E-Mail: info@qrm.jo
Web Site: www.qrm.jo
Year Founded: 1996
AQRM—(AMM)
Sales Range: $10-24.9 Million
Emp.: 200

Business Description:
Ready Mix Concrete Mfr
S.I.C.: 3273
N.A.I.C.S.: 327320

Personnel:
Ayman Haza'a AL-Majali *(Chm)*
Jawdat AL-Alami *(Vice Chm)*

Board of Directors:
Ayman Haza'a AL-Majali
Jawdat AL-Alami
Alaa Al-Masry
Ala'a Barkat
Moh'd Reyad Khawam
Hani Rabe'e
Sameer Theodory
Faisal Zawati
Khalil Zuayter

AL-QURAIN HOLDING CO. K.S.C.C

Al-Qeblah Ahmed Al-Jaber Street Al-Zumorrodah Tower 18th Floor
PO Box 28341
Safat, Kuwait, 13144, Kuwait
Tel.: (965) 22916888
Fax: (965) 22916898
E-Mail: info@qurainholding.com
Web Site: www.qurainholding.com
Year Founded: 2003
QURAINHLD—(KUW)
Sales Range: $1-9.9 Million

Business Description:
Investment Services
S.I.C.: 6211
N.A.I.C.S.: 523999

Personnel:
Duaij Khaleefah M. Al-Sabah *(Chm)*
Ahmed M. H. Al-Ajlan *(Vice Chm)*
Shahnaz H. Qabazard *(CEO)*

Board of Directors:
Duaij Khaleefah M. Al-Sabah
Ahmed M. H. Al-Ajlan

AL RAJHI BANK

PO Box 28
Riyadh, 11411, Saudi Arabia
Tel.: (966) 1 279 58 57
Fax: (966) 1 279 58 60
E-Mail: aljarbouka@alrajhibank.com.sa
Web Site: www.alrajhibank.com.sa
Year Founded: 1976
1120—(SAU)
Sales Range: $1-4.9 Billion
Emp.: 9,282

Business Description:
Banking Services
S.I.C.: 6029
N.A.I.C.S.: 522110

Personnel:
Sulaiman Abdul Aziz Al Rajhi *(Chm)*
Sulaiman Abdul Aziz Al-Zubn *(CEO)*
Iain Blacklaw *(COO)*

Board of Directors:
Sulaiman Abdul Aziz Al Rajhi
Mohammed Othman Al Bishr
Saeed Omar Al Esayi
Abdul Aziz Khalid Al Ghefaily
Salah Ali Aba Al Khail
Abdullah Abdul Aziz Al Rajhi
Bader Mohammed Al Rajhi
Mohamed Abdullah Al Rajhi
Sulaiman Saleh Al Rajhi
Abdullah Sulaiman Al Rajihi
Ali Ahmed Al Shiddi

Ernst & Young
PO Box 2732
Riyadh, Saudi Arabia

Subsidiary:

Al Rajhi Development Company Ltd. (1)
PO Box 4301
Riyadh, Saudi Arabia (99%)
Tel.: (966) 14761581
Fax: (966) 14769775
E-Mail: admin@alrajhidevelopmentcompany.com
Web Site: www.alrajhidevelopmentcompany.com

Al Rajhi Bank—(Continued)

Emp.: 100
Support Activities for Transportation
S.I.C.: 4789
N.A.I.C.S.: 488999
Osama Al-Dahshan *(Sec)*

Non-U.S. Subsidiary:

Al Rajhi Banking & Investment Corporation Bhd (1)
16 Fl Menara Chan Jalan Ampang
Kuala Lumpur, 50450, Malaysia (100%)
Tel.: (60) 323017000
Fax: (60) 323326053
E-Mail: customersupport@alrajhibank.com.my
Web Site: www.alrajhibank.com.my
Emp.: 150
Miscellaneous Financial Investment Activities
S.I.C.: 6211
N.A.I.C.S.: 523999
Syed Maqbul Quader *(Chm)*
Azrulnizam Abdul Aziz *(CEO)*

AL-RAKAEZ PLC

PO Box 928482
Amman, 11190, Jordan
Tel.: (962) 65548961
Fax: (962) 65548960
E-Mail: info@alrakaez.com
Web Site: www.alrakaez.com
Year Founded: 2006
RICS—(AMM)
Sales Range: Less than $1 Million
Emp.: 11
Business Description:
Real Estate Development Services
S.I.C.: 6531
N.A.I.C.S.: 531390
Personnel:
Mazin Khairy Ayass *(Chm & Gen Mgr)*

Subsidiary:

Al-Jazeera Trading FZCo. (1)
Islamic Bank Complex Wasfi Al-Tal St
972 34 Amman, Jordan
Tel.: (962) 6 5517311
Fax: (962) 6 5517310
E-Mail: info@aljazeera-trading.com
Web Site: www.aljazeera-trading.com
Emp.: 300
Tire Import & Distr
S.I.C.: 5014
N.A.I.C.S.: 423130
Mazin Ayass *(Gen Mgr)*

AL RAWABI DAIRY COMPANY L.L.C.

PO Box 50368
Dubai, United Arab Emirates
Tel.: (971) 42892123
Fax: (971) 4 2892494
E-Mail: sales@alrawabi.ae
Web Site: www.alrawabidairy.com
Sales Range: $550-599.9 Million
Emp.: 900
Business Description:
Dairy Products Mfr
S.I.C.: 2026
N.A.I.C.S.: 311511
Personnel:
Ahmed El Tigani *(Mng Dir)*

AL-RUBAIYAT COMPANY

El-Khayyat Centre
PO Box 5967
Tahlia Street, Jeddah, 21432, Saudi Arabia
Tel.: (966) 26606699
Fax: (966) 22830961
E-Mail: enquiries@rubaiyat.com
Web Site: www.rubaiyat.com
Emp.: 300
Business Description:
Clothing Retailer
S.I.C.: 5651
N.A.I.C.S.: 448140
Personnel:
Abdullah S. Binzagr *(Chm)*

AL-SAFAT ENERGY HOLDING K.S.C.C.

Hawally - Beirut Street Al-Safat Tower 7th Floor
PO Box 5288
Kuwait, 32083, Kuwait
Tel.: (965) 22675000
Fax: (965) 22675346
E-Mail: info@safatenergy.com
Web Site: www.safatenergy.com
SENERGY—(KUW)
Rev.: $66,073,779
Assets: $230,010,883
Liabilities: $26,871,043
Net Worth: $203,139,840
Earnings: $4,971,657
Emp.: 80
Fiscal Year-end: 12/31/12
Business Description:
Oil & Gas Investment Services
S.I.C.: 6211
N.A.I.C.S.: 523999
Personnel:
Nasser Bader Al-Sharhan *(Chm)*
Abdulaziz Saud Al-Gharabally *(Vice Chm & Mng Dir)*
Musaad S. Al-Saeed *(CEO)*
Adel M. Al-Khayat *(Exec VP-Ops)*
Mohammed H. Al-Salem *(Exec VP-Upstream)*
Adnan Saleh Ashkanani *(Exec VP-Fin & Admin)*
Board of Directors:
Nasser Bader Al-Sharhan
Hamed Rasheed Al-Bassam
Abdulaziz Saud Al-Gharabally
Talal Z. Al-Hathal
Hamad Mohammed Al-Matar
Ibrahim Adel Al-Mawad
Khaldoun Abdul Latif Al-Sane

Subsidiary:

Eastern National Oilfield Services Co. (1)
PO Box 9377
Ahmadi, 61004, Kuwait
Tel.: (965) 23970000
Fax: (965) 23970001
E-Mail: info@eastern-national.com
Web Site: www.eastern-national.com
Emp.: 40
Wireline & Perforation Services
S.I.C.: 1389
N.A.I.C.S.: 213112
Adel Alkhayap *(Chm & Mng Dir)*

Non-U.S. Subsidiaries:

Eastern Industrial & Oilfield Services Company (1)
Mushtan Bldg Ofc 54 Bldg 2415
Rd 2831 Block 428 Al-Seef, Manama, Bahrain
Tel.: (973) 17565522
Fax: (973) 17587244
E-Mail: info@eiosholding.com
Web Site: www.eiosholding.com
Emp.: 30
Engineering Solutions & Services
S.I.C.: 8711
N.A.I.C.S.: 541330
Majdi Khalaf *(Mng Dir)*

Emirates Western Petroleum Services (1)
PO Box 8107
Abu Dhabi, United Arab Emirates
Tel.: (971) 26725637
Fax: (971) 26781578
E-Mail: ewpsco@ewpsco.ae
Web Site: www.ewpsco.ae
Emp.: 110
Offshore Drilling Fluid Services
S.I.C.: 1381
N.A.I.C.S.: 213111
Rasheed Al Shaibani *(Mng Dir & Gen Mgr)*

AL-SAFAT INVESTMENT COMPANY K.S.C.C.

Hawalli Beirut Street Facing Al-Qadessya Club
PO Box 20133
Safat, Kuwait, 13062, Kuwait
Tel.: (965) 22675130
Fax: (965) 22675232
E-Mail: info@alsafatinvest.com
Web Site: www.alsafatinvest.com
ALSAFAT—(KUW)
Sales Range: $1-9.9 Million
Business Description:
Investment Services
S.I.C.: 6211
N.A.I.C.S.: 523110
Personnel:
Abdullah Ahmad Al Sharhan *(Chm & Mng Dir)*
Adel Yousef Al Saqabi *(Vice Chm)*
Talal Zebin Al Hathal *(Exec VP-Investment Banking)*
Adel Jasem Al-Sane *(Exec VP-Fin, Admin & Asset Mgmt Div)*
Board of Directors:
Abdullah Ahmad Al Sharhan
Tawfik Salah Al Din Ahmed Deyab
Azam Abdulaziz Al Fuliaj
Abdullah Hammad Al Hudaib
Abdulwahab Al Mefleh
Khaldoun Abdullatif Al Sane
Adel Yousef Al Saqabi

Al Ateeqi Certified Accountant
Ali Al-Salem Str Thuwaini Bldg 3rd Flr 636
Kuwait, Kuwait

AL-SAFAT TEC HOLDING COMPANY K.S.C.C.

Safat Jaber Al Mubarak Street Sharq
ACICO Building 16th Floor
PO Box 29022
Safat Kuwait, 13151, Kuwait
Tel.: (965) 2 224 5555
Fax: (965) 2 224 5559
Web Site: www.safattec.com
SAFTEC—(KUW)
Sales Range: $100-124.9 Million
Business Description:
Technology Investment Services
S.I.C.: 6211
N.A.I.C.S.: 523999
Personnel:
Khaldoun Abdullatif Al-Sanea *(Chm)*
Abdullah Ahmad Al-Shaheen *(Vice Chm)*
Khaled Ahmed Al-Bader *(CEO)*
Board of Directors:
Khaldoun Abdullatif Al-Sanea
Hamed Rashed Al-Bassam
Abdulaziz Saud Al-Gharabally
Abdullah Ahmad Al-Shaheen
Fahed Mohammed Al-Sharekh
Abdullah Ahmed Al-Sharhan
Ziad Ahmed Al-Sharhan

AL-SAFWA GROUP HOLDING CO. K.S.C.C.

Beirut Street 11th Floor
PO Box 26552
Hawally, Kuwait, 13126, Kuwait
Tel.: (965) 22675110
Fax: (965) 22675215
E-Mail: info@alsafwagroup.net
Web Site: www.alsafwagroup.net
ALSAFWA—(KUW)
Sales Range: $125-149.9 Million
Business Description:
Holding Company
S.I.C.: 6719
N.A.I.C.S.: 551112
Personnel:
Waleed Abdul Rahim Al-Asfoor *(Chm)*
Abdullah Ahmad Al-Sharhan *(Vice Chm)*
Adel Yousef Saleh Al-Saqabi *(CEO)*
Board of Directors:
Waleed Abdul Rahim Al-Asfoor
Khalid Abdul Ghani Mohammad Al-Abdul Ghani
Bassem Mohammad Al-Modhafar
Abdulwahab Ahmad Abdulwahab Al-Mofleh
Adel Yousef Saleh Al-Saqabi
Shaheen Ahmad Al-Shaheen
Abdullah Ahmad Al-Sharhan

Al Ateeqi Certified Accountant
Ali Al-Salem Str Thuwaini Bldg 3rd Flr 636
Kuwait, Kuwait

Subsidiaries:

Al Safat United Food Company K.S.C. (1)
PO Box 27660
Kuwait, 13137, Kuwait
Tel.: (965) 22659629
Fax: (965) 22659668
Fine Dining Restaurant Operation Services
S.I.C.: 5812
N.A.I.C.S.: 722511

Danah Al Safat Foodstuff Company K.S.C. (1)
PO Box 22044
Safat, Kuwait, 13081, Kuwait
Tel.: (965) 1828486
Fax: (965) 24345004
E-Mail: info@danahalsafat.com
Web Site: www.danahalsafat.com
DANAH—(KUW)
Rev.: $98,448,017
Assets: $176,835,772
Liabilities: $40,109,895
Net Worth: $136,725,877
Earnings: ($27,367,146)
Emp.: 430
Fiscal Year-end: 12/31/12
Shrimp Fishing, Processing & Marketing Services
S.I.C.: 0913
N.A.I.C.S.: 114112
Adel Youssef Al-Saqobi *(Chm)*
Abdullatif AbdulWahab Al Thammar *(Vice Chm)*

Shuaiba Industrial Company K.S.C.C. (1)
PO Box 10088 Shuaiba
Kuwait, 65451, Kuwait
Tel.: (965) 24711020
Fax: (965) 24738667
E-Mail: info@sic-kwt.com
Web Site: www.sic-kwt.com
PAPER—(KUW)
Rev.: $35,017,756
Assets: $65,797,379
Liabilities: $10,588,247
Net Worth: $55,209,132
Earnings: ($3,589,657)
Emp.: 200
Fiscal Year-end: 12/31/12
Paper Packaging Mfr, Importer & Exporter
S.I.C.: 2621
N.A.I.C.S.: 322121
Adel Al Sane *(Chm)*
Suleiman Al Nawawreh *(Vice Chm)*
S. Farid Ahmed *(Pres)*
Adel Al Saqabi *(CEO)*

AL-SAFWEH FOR FINANCIAL INVESTMENTS CO. PLC

Al Husseini Complex 58 Ground Floor Prince Shaker Bin Zaid Street
PO Box 2729
Al Shmeisani Area, Amman, 11953, Jordan
Tel.: (962) 6 520 1233
Fax: (962) 6 520 1244
E-Mail: safweh_inv@yahoo.com
Year Founded: 2005
SFWA—(AMM)
Rev.: $225,342
Assets: $2,721,643
Liabilities: $266,997

Net Worth: $2,454,646
Earnings: ($244,893)
Emp.: 6
Fiscal Year-end: 12/31/12
Business Description:
Investment Banking & Brokerage Services
S.I.C.: 6211
N.A.I.C.S.: 523110
Personnel:
Zuhair Hashim Shakir Khalil *(Chm)*

AL-SAGR NATIONAL INSURANCE COMPANY

Al Hilal Building 3rd Floor Flat No 301/302 Al Garhoud Road
PO Box 14614 & 10276
Dubai, United Arab Emirates
Tel.: (971) 47028500
Fax: (971) 42821873
E-Mail: asnic@eim.ae
Web Site: www.alsagrins.ae
Year Founded: 1979
ASNIC—(DFM)
Premiums: $101,778,136
Assets: $316,905,335
Liabilities: $155,963,001
Net Worth: $160,942,334
Earnings: $7,984,978
Fiscal Year-end: 12/31/12
Business Description:
Insurance Services
S.I.C.: 6411
N.A.I.C.S.: 524298
Personnel:
Abdulla Juma Al Sari *(Chm)*
Khalid Abdulla Omran *(Vice Chm)*
Khalil Saeed *(Asst CEO)*
Sami Shakhshir *(CEO)*
Board of Directors:
Abdulla Juma Al Sari
Amjad Mohd Yusri Al Dweik
Majid Abdulla Al Sari
Mohamed Abdulla Al Sari
Khalid Abdulla Omran
Sami Shakhshir

AL SALAM BANK-BAHRAIN B.S.C.

MS Centre Building 22 Avenue 58
PO Box 18282
Al Seef District, 436 Manama, Bahrain
Tel.: (973) 17560000
Fax: (973) 17560003
E-Mail: info@sg.alsalambahrain.com
Web Site: www.alsalambahrain.com
Year Founded: 2006
SALAM—(DFM)
Rev.: $114,173,379
Assets: $2,441,861,591
Liabilities: $1,855,273,992
Net Worth: $586,587,599
Earnings: $26,714,316
Emp.: 201
Fiscal Year-end: 12/31/12
Business Description:
Commercial Banking Services
S.I.C.: 6029
N.A.I.C.S.: 522110
Personnel:
Ahmed Swaleh Abdisheikh *(Acting CEO-Bahraini Saudi Bank)*
Yousif Abdulla Taqi *(CEO)*
Anwar Al Sadah *(Deputy CEO)*
Mukundan Raghavachari *(Deputy CEO)*
Janaka Mendis *(COO)*
Nabeel Ebrahim Al Tattan *(Exec VP & Head-MENA Reg)*
Mohammed Burhan Arbouna *(Exec VP & Head-Shari'a Compliance)*
Board of Directors:
Shaikha Hessa Khalifa Hamad Al Khalifa
Essam Abdulkadir Al Muhaideb
Adnan Abdulla Al Bassam
Fahad Sami Al Ebrahim
Salman Saleh Al Mahmeed
Hussein Mohammed Al Meeza
Hamad Tarek Alhomaizi
Habib Ahmed Kassem
Yousif Abdulla Taqi
Mohammed Omeir Yussef
Subsidiary:

BankMuscat International (BMI) **(1)**
Bahrain World Trade Center
PO Box 350
Manama, Bahrain
Tel.: (973) 175 08080
Fax: (973) 17 226641
E-Mail: inquiry@bmi.com.bh
Web Site: www.bmibank.com.bh
Emp.: 180
Commercial Banking
S.I.C.: 6029
N.A.I.C.S.: 522110
Sulaiman Mohammed Al Yahyai *(Vice Chm)*
Jamal Ali Al-Hazeem *(CEO)*

Non-U.S. Subsidiary:

Al Salam Asia-Pacific Pte Ltd. **(1)**
80 Raffles Place UOB Plaza 2 17-23
Singapore, 48624, Singapore
Tel.: (65) 6236 9602
Fax: (65) 6226 2129
E-Mail: info@sg.alsalambahrain.com
Private Equity Investment Services
S.I.C.: 6211
N.A.I.C.S.: 523999

AL SALAM BANK - SUDAN

Al Jame'a Street Ma'amoun Al Burair Group Building
Khartoum, Sudan
Tel.: (249) 183747000
Fax: (249) 183747006 (Local); (249) 183747007 ((Intl))
E-Mail: info@alsalambank.net
Web Site: www.alsalam-bank.net
Year Founded: 2004
ALSALAMSUDAN—(DFM)
Sales Range: $25-49.9 Million
Emp.: 148
Business Description:
Commercial Banking Services
S.I.C.: 6029
N.A.I.C.S.: 522110
Personnel:
Mohammed Omeir Yousef *(Chm)*
Mohammed Ibrahim *(Compliance Officer)*
Board of Directors:
Mohammed Omeir Yousef
Saud Mamoun Al Burair
Kamal Hamza Al Hasan
Abdelbasit Hamza Al Hassan
Mohammed Shareef Alrafi

AL SALAM GROUP HOLDING COMPANY KSCC

Murgab-Alsoor St Jasim Alasfoor Tower
PO Box 435
Safat, Kuwait, 13002, Kuwait
Tel.: (965) 229 60777
Fax: (965) 229 60955
E-Mail: info@alsalamholding.com
Web Site: www.alsalamholding.com
ALSALAM—(KUW)
Sales Range: $10-24.9 Million
Emp.: 15
Business Description:
Investment Services
S.I.C.: 6211
N.A.I.C.S.: 523999
Personnel:
Meshare Ahmed Al-Maged *(Chm)*
Tariq Mohammed Al-Suwaidan *(Vice Chm)*
Board of Directors:
Meshare Ahmed Al-Maged
Hassan Darweesh Al-shimaly
Subah Salman Al-Subah
Tariq Mohammed Al-Suwaidan
Mamdouh Abdulghani Alsherbiny

AL-SANABEL INTERNATIONAL FOR ISLAMIC INVESTMENT (HOLDING) PLC

PO Box 142791
Amman, 11814, Jordan
Tel.: (962) 65800500
Fax: (962) 65821489
E-Mail: info@sanabelintl.com
Web Site: www.sanabelintl.com
Year Founded: 2006
SANA—(AMM)
Sales Range: Less than $1 Million
Emp.: 16
Business Description:
Investment Banking Services
S.I.C.: 6211
N.A.I.C.S.: 523110
Personnel:
Khaldoun Malkawi *(Chm & CEO)*
Ahmad Malkawi *(Deputy Chm)*
Hisham Thiabat *(CFO)*
Hala Hijazi *(Chief Investment Officer)*
Board of Directors:
Khaldoun Malkawi
Obaid Al Mutaiwie
Zohar Al Omar
Ahmad Malkawi
Sleman Manasrah

AL-SAWANI GROUP

PO Box 1223344
Jeddah, 2145, Saudi Arabia
Tel.: (966) 26912612
Fax: (966) 26911320
E-Mail: info@al-sawani.com
Web Site: www.al-sawani.com
Emp.: 650
Business Description:
Department Store
S.I.C.: 5311
N.A.I.C.S.: 452111

AL SHAFAR GROUP

PO Box 2185
Dubai, United Arab Emirates
Tel.: (971) 4 3969999
Fax: (971) 4 3969910
E-Mail: personal@alshafar.ae
Web Site: www.alshafar.ae/
Year Founded: 1960
Sales Range: $500-549.9 Million
Emp.: 3,000
Business Description:
Holding Company for Special Trade Contractors
S.I.C.: 6719
N.A.I.C.S.: 551112
Personnel:
Ahmed Abdullah Shafar *(Co-Chm)*
Ali Abdullah Shafar *(Co-Chm)*

AL-SHAMEKHA FOR REAL ESTATE & FINANCIAL INVESTMENTS CO., LTD.

Jabal Al-Hussein - Firas Circle
PO Box 921196
Amman, 11192, Jordan
Tel.: (962) 6 5662103
Fax: (962) 6 5662105
E-Mail: tfc.vfed@yahoo.com
Year Founded: 1974
VFED—(AMM)
Rev.: $219,493
Assets: $2,698,197
Liabilities: $513,205
Net Worth: $2,184,992
Earnings: $7,863
Emp.: 4
Fiscal Year-end: 12/31/12
Business Description:
Real Estate Investment Services
S.I.C.: 6531
N.A.I.C.S.: 531390
Personnel:
Mohammad Amin Abu Assaf *(Gen Mgr)*

AL SHARQ INVESTMENTS PROJECTS(HOLDING) P.L.C.

Al-Jbeha-facing Royal Scientific Society
PO Box 941166
Amman, 11194, Jordan
Tel.: (962) 6 5333645
Fax: (962) 6 5333645
Year Founded: 1994
AIPC—(AMM)
Rev.: $10,334,347
Assets: $29,814,351
Liabilities: $1,555,192
Net Worth: $28,259,159
Earnings: $2,386,584
Emp.: 3
Fiscal Year-end: 12/31/12
Business Description:
Tour Management Services
S.I.C.: 4725
N.A.I.C.S.: 561520
Personnel:
Ahmad Al-Horani *(Gen Mgr)*

AL SLATTERY FORD SALES

607 Niagara St
Welland, ON, L3C 1L9, Canada
Tel.: (905) 734-7443
Year Founded: 1979
Rev.: $18,447,786
Emp.: 40
Business Description:
New Car Dealers
S.I.C.: 5511
N.A.I.C.S.: 441110
Personnel:
Al Slattery *(Pres)*

AL SORAYAI GROUP

(d/b/a Al Sorayai Trading & Industrial Group)
PO Box 1563
Jeddah, 21441, Saudi Arabia
Tel.: (966) 26918222
Fax: (966) 26974771
E-Mail: info@al-sorayai.com
Web Site: www.al-sorayai.com
Emp.: 2,200
Business Description:
Carpets, Rugs, Fabrics, Blinds, Curtains, Blankets, Mattresses & Furniture Mfr, Distr, Importer & Sales
S.I.C.: 2273
N.A.I.C.S.: 314110
Personnel:
Mohammed Abdullah Al Sorayai *(Chm)*
Saleh Nasseer Al Sorayai *(Mng Dir)*
Board of Directors:
Mohammed Abdullah Al Sorayai
Yaseen A. Rahman Hussan Al Ghafri
Sulman Abdullah H. Al Hamdan
Ahmen Saleh Ali Al Nashar
Mansour Abdullah Al Sorayai
Saleh Nasseer Al Sorayai
Abdul Aziz Nasser Sorayai

AL TAHDITH FOR REAL ESTATE INVESTMENTS COMPANY

Madinah Monawarah St Madinah Monawarah Complex
PO Box 334
Amman, 11831, Jordan

Al Tahdith for Real Estate Investments Company—(Continued)

Tel.: (962) 6 5548211
Year Founded: 2006
THDI—(AMM)
Rev.: $1,633,147
Assets: $4,015,249
Liabilities: $222,643
Net Worth: $3,792,606
Earnings: $157,005
Emp.: 40
Fiscal Year-end: 12/31/12
Business Description:
Real Estate Investment Services
S.I.C.: 6531
N.A.I.C.S.: 531390
Personnel:
Mamdoh Al-Zboon *(Gen Mgr)*

AL TAJAMOUAT FOR CATERING & HOUSING COMPANY, PLC.

PO Box 5376
Amman, 11183, Jordan
Tel.: (962) 65670090
Fax: (962) 65670616
E-Mail: info@altajamouat.com
Web Site: www.altajamouat.com
Year Founded: 2003
JNTH—(AMM)
Sales Range: $1-9.9 Million
Emp.: 66
Business Description:
Catering & Housekeeping Services
S.I.C.: 7349
N.A.I.C.S.: 561720
Personnel:
Halim Usama Salfiti *(Chm)*
Dawoud Hajjar *(CEO)*
Board of Directors:
Halim Usama Salfiti
Ramiz R. Manneh

AL TAJAMOUAT FOR TOURISTIC PROJECTS CO PLC

Taj Mall - Abdoun
PO Box 5376, Amman, 11183, Jordan
Tel.: (962) 6 5921122
Fax: (962) 6 5921120
E-Mail: touristic@altajamouat.com
Year Founded: 1983
TAJM—(AMM)
Rev.: $14,740,450
Assets: $222,734,042
Liabilities: $99,445,261
Net Worth: $123,288,781
Earnings: ($5,894,500)
Emp.: 10
Fiscal Year-end: 12/31/12
Business Description:
Investment Management Services
S.I.C.: 6211
N.A.I.C.S.: 523999
Personnel:
Mohammed Nabil Kamel Mohammed *(Gen Mgr)*

AL TAYYAR TRAVEL GROUP

PO Box 52660
Riyadh, 11573, Saudi Arabia
Tel.: (966) 1 4633667
Fax: (966) 1 4644572
Web Site: www.altayyargroup.com
1810—(SAU)
Emp.: 2,100
Business Description:
Travel, Tourism, Hospitality & Cargo Services
S.I.C.: 4729
N.A.I.C.S.: 561599
Personnel:
Sultan bin Mohamed bin Saud Al Kabeer *(Chm)*
Nasser bin Aqeel Al Tayyar *(Pres)*
Fahad bin Ibrahim Al Jarboa *(CEO)*
Yousef Mousa Yousef *(CFO)*
Board of Directors:
Sultan bin Mohamed bin Saud Al Kabeer
Ammar bin Abdulwahed Faleh Al Khudairi
Nasser Mohamed Al-Mutawa Al Otaibi
Nasser bin Aqeel Al Tayyar
Ahmed Samer Hamdi Saadadine Al Zaim
Omar Ali Obeid Balsharaf

Non-U.S. Subsidiaries:

Al Tayyar Holiday Travel Group (1)
5 Al Obour Building Salah Salem Avenue
Cairo, Egypt
Tel.: (20) 224042118
Fax: (20) 224042119
E-Mail: tours@altayyareg.com
Web Site: www.altayyareg.com
Tour Operator
S.I.C.: 4725
N.A.I.C.S.: 561520
Yousry Abdel Wahab, *(Gen Mgr)*

Al-Tayyar Travel & Tourism (1)
PO Box 28060
Dubai, United Arab Emirates
Tel.: (971) 4 2249240
Fax: (971) 4 2219648
E-Mail: sales@altayyardubai.ae
Web Site: www.altayyardubai.com
Emp.: 30
Tour Operator
S.I.C.: 4725
N.A.I.C.S.: 561520
Shahid Bouramen, *(Gen Mgr)*

Belantara Holidays Sdn Bhd (1)
Unit B-15-2 Block B Megan Avenue II No12
Jalan Yap Kwan Seng
50450 Kuala Lumpur, Malaysia
Tel.: (60) 3 2166 2299
Fax: (60) 3 2166 0303
E-Mail: inbound@belantaraholidays.com.my
Web Site: www.belantaraholidays.com.my
Emp.: 25
Tour Operator
S.I.C.: 4725
N.A.I.C.S.: 561520
T. S. Chuah *(Exec Dir)*

Lena Tours and Travel (1)
37 Main Office St Georges Center Ground Floor
Sin El Fil, Beirut, Lebanon
Tel.: (961) 1 496696
Fax: (961) 1 496796
E-Mail: lenacar@cyberia-net.ib
Web Site: www.lenatours.com
Tour Operator
S.I.C.: 4725
N.A.I.C.S.: 561520

AL-TUWAIRQI GROUP

Dammam Ksobar Rd Bar Al Rakkah
PO Box 7600
31472 Dammam, Saudi Arabia
Tel.: (966) 38579922
Fax: (966) 038579014
E-Mail: atg@altuwairqi.com.sa
Web Site: www.altuwairqi.com.sa
Year Founded: 1977
Sales Range: $400-449.9 Million
Emp.: 3,000
Business Description:
Diversified Holding & Trading Company; Steel Products Mfr & Building Materials Distr
S.I.C.: 6719
N.A.I.C.S.: 551112
Personnel:
Hilal Hussain Al Tuwairqi *(Chm)*
Anthony Phillips *(COO)*

Subsidiaries:

Al-Faisal Steel Products Company (1)
PO Box 2705
31461 Dammam, Saudi Arabia
Tel.: (966) 38122212
Fax: (966) 38122128
E-Mail: fspc@altuwairqi.com.sa
Web Site: www.altuwairqi.com
Steel Investment Foundries
S.I.C.: 3324
N.A.I.C.S.: 331512
K. A. Levin *(Gen Mgr-Project)*

Al Ittefaq Steel Products Company (1)
PO Box 7600
Dammam, 31472, Saudi Arabia
Tel.: (966) 38121143
Fax: (966) 38121059
E-Mail: ispc@altuwairqu.com.sa
Web Site: www.altuwairqu.com.sa
Emp.: 750
Steel Producer
S.I.C.: 3312
N.A.I.C.S.: 331110

Al Tuwairqi Trading & Contracting (1)
PO Box 2705
Dammam, 31461, Saudi Arabia
Tel.: (966) 38579922
Fax: (966) 38579014
E-Mail: atg@altuwairqi.com.sa
Web Site: altuwairqi.tripod.com
Emp.: 600
Contracting & Manufacturing Services
S.I.C.: 1542
N.A.I.C.S.: 236220
Mohammed Tariq Barlas *(Vice Chm)*

Direct Reduction Iron Company (1)
PO Box 7600
31472 Dammam, Saudi Arabia
Tel.: (966) 38122966
Fax: (966) 38122991
E-Mail: dric@altuwairqi.com.sa
Web Site: www.altuwairqi.com
Iron & Steel Forging
S.I.C.: 3462
N.A.I.C.S.: 332111

The International Electrical Products Company (TIEPCO) (1)
PO Box 2705
31461 Dammam, Saudi Arabia SA
Tel.: (966) 3 857 9922
Fax: (966) 3 859 4695
E-Mail: tiepco@altuwairqi.com.sa
Web Site: www.altuwairqi.com.sa
Switchgear & Switchboard Apparatus Mfr
S.I.C.: 3613
N.A.I.C.S.: 335313
Zaigham Adil Rizvi *(Gen Mgr)*

National Steel Company Limited (1)
PO Box 7600
31472 Dammam, Saudi Arabia
Tel.: (966) 38122966
Fax: (966) 38122991
E-Mail: nasco@altuwairqi.com.sa
Electronic & Precision Equipment Repair & Maintenance
S.I.C.: 7699
N.A.I.C.S.: 811219
K. A. Levin *(Gen Mgr-Project)*

AL WASEET INTERNATIONAL

Dubai Media City
PO Box 42747
Dubai, United Arab Emirates
Tel.: (971) 4 3600911
Fax: (971) 4 3688184
E-Mail: info@alwaseetintl.com
Web Site: www.alwaseetintl.com
Emp.: 5,000
Business Description:
Holding Company; Periodical Publisher & TV Broadcaster
S.I.C.: 6719
N.A.I.C.S.: 551112
Personnel:
Mohammed Abdulaziz Mohammed Al-Otaibi *(Chm)*
Sabah Jaber Mubarak Al-Sabah *(Vice Chm)*
Bashar Kiwan *(CEO)*
John Fawaz *(Mng Dir)*
Majd Sleiman *(COO)*
Board of Directors:
Mohammed Abdulaziz Mohammed Al-Otaibi
Sabah Jaber Mubarak Al-Sabah
John Fawaz
Bashar Kiwan
Majd Sleiman

AL-WATANIA INSURANCE COMPANY YSC

Palace Road Nasser Ali Zayid Building
PO Box 15497
Sana'a, Yemen
Tel.: (967) 1272713
Fax: (967) 1272924
E-Mail: alwatania-ins@y.net.ye
Web Site: www.alwataniains.com
Year Founded: 1993
Sales Range: $150-199.9 Million
Emp.: 20
Business Description:
Insurance Services
S.I.C.: 6411
N.A.I.C.S.: 524298
Personnel:
Al-Haj Yousef Abdulwadood Saeed *(Chm)*
Abdulkarim Yehya Hurab *(Deputy Chm)*
Board of Directors:
Al-Haj Yousef Abdulwadood Saeed
Abdulkarim Yehya Hurab

AL WATHBA NATIONAL INSURANCE COMPANY P.S.C.

Po Box 45154
Abu Dhabi, United Arab Emirates
Tel.: (971) 24185300
Fax: (971) 26776628
E-Mail: alwathba@awnic.com
Web Site: www.awnic.com
Year Founded: 1997
AWNIC—(EMI)
Premiums: $104,585,982
Assets: $255,646,154
Liabilities: $133,041,040
Net Worth: $122,605,114
Earnings: $8,223,919
Fiscal Year-end: 12/31/12
Business Description:
Insurance Services
S.I.C.: 6411
N.A.I.C.S.: 524298
Personnel:
Saif Mohammed Butti Al Hamed *(Chm)*
Rashed Darweesh Al Ketbi *(Vice Chm)*
Board of Directors:
Saif Mohammed Butti Al Hamed
Ahmed Ali Khalfan Al Dhaheri
Aamer Abdul Jalil Al Fahim
Khalifa Saif Darwish Ahmed Al Ketbi
Rashed Darweesh Al Ketbi
Saeed Omeir Al Mheiri
Shukri Salem Al Muhairi
Rasheed Ali Rasheed Naser Al Omaira
Mohammed Saeed Al Qubaisi

AL-WAZZAN HOLDING GROUP

PO Box 1251
Safat, Kuwait, 13013, Kuwait
Tel.: (965) 1881000
Fax: (965) 24847397
E-Mail: info@wazzangroup.com
Web Site: www.wazzangroup.com
Sales Range: $350-399.9 Million
Emp.: 3,000
Business Description:
Holding Company
S.I.C.: 6719
N.A.I.C.S.: 551112

Personnel:
Salah Mohammad Al-Wazzan *(CEO)*

Holding:

Mushrif Trading & Contracting Company S.A.K.C. **(1)**
Area 1 Street 7 Plot 1666 Al Rai
Kuwait, Kuwait
Tel.: (965) 24766172
Fax: (965) 24741423
E-Mail: info@mushrif.com
Web Site: www.mushrif.com
MTCC—(KUW)
Rev.: $132,394,121
Assets: $272,692,610
Liabilities: $169,988,362
Net Worth: $102,704,248
Earnings: $5,689,659
Emp.: 3,500
Fiscal Year-end: 12/31/12
Heavy Civil Building & Infrastructure Contractor
S.I.C.: 1629
N.A.I.C.S.: 237990
Faisal Belhoul *(Chm)*
Khaldoun Hasan *(Vice Chm)*
Mohsen Dehghani *(CEO)*
Manish Dangi *(CFO)*

AL YOUSEF GROUP

PO Box 200
Muscat, 113, Oman
Tel.: (968) 24564322
Fax: (968) 24565322
Web Site: www.alyousefgroup.com
Business Description:
Investment Holding Company
S.I.C.: 6719
N.A.I.C.S.: 551112
Personnel:
Mohamed Musa Al-Yousef *(Chm)*
Qais Mohamed Al-Yousef *(CEO)*
Faisal Mohamed Al-Yousef *(COO)*
Board of Directors:
Mohamed Musa Al-Yousef
Faisal Mohamed Al-Yousef
Qais Mohamed Al-Yousef

Holding:

Al Anwar Holdings S.A.O.G **(1)**
Villa No 897 Way No 3013 Shatti Al Qurum
PO Box 468
Near Al Sarooj Filling Station, Muscat, 131, Oman
Tel.: (968) 24692503
Fax: (968) 24692507
E-Mail: info@alanwarholdings.com
Web Site: www.alanwarholdings.com
AAIT—(MUS)
Premiums: $27,569,569
Assets: $109,320,819
Liabilities: $49,653,171
Net Worth: $59,667,648
Earnings: $4,707,063
Emp.: 220
Fiscal Year-end: 03/31/13
Investment Holding Company
S.I.C.: 6211
N.A.I.C.S.: 523999
Masoud Humaid Malik Al Harthy *(Chm)*
Qais Mohamed Al Youse *(Deputy Chm)*
Reji Joseph *(CEO)*

AL YUSR INDUSTRIAL CONTRACTING COMPANY WLL

Al Jubayl Industrial City
PO BOX 10270
Al Jubayl, 31961, Saudi Arabia
Tel.: (966) 3 341 5224
E-Mail: info@aytb.com
Web Site: www.aytb.com
Year Founded: 1979
Emp.: 4,000
Business Description:
Support Activities for Oil & Gas Operations
S.I.C.: 1389
N.A.I.C.S.: 213112
Personnel:
Abdulmohsen Ogaili *(CEO)*

AL-ZAMIN INVESTBANK

101-108 Kassam Court
BC-9 Block 5
Clifton, Karachi, 75600, Pakistan
Tel.: (92) 21 5876651
Fax: (92) 21 5870408
E-Mail: contact@alzamin.com.pk
Web Site: www.alzamin.com.pk
ALZM—(ISL KAR LAH)
Sales Range: $1-9.9 Million
Emp.: 144
Business Description:
Financial Service
S.I.C.: 6099
N.A.I.C.S.: 522320
Personnel:
Zafar Iqbal *(Chm)*
Basheer Ahmed Chowdry *(CEO)*
Mohammad Naim Ashraf *(CFO)*
Mohammad Moizul Haque *(COO)*
Hamida Aqeel *(Sec)*
Board of Directors:
Zafar Iqbal
Rashid Ahmed
Najib Amanullah
Sohail Ansar
Namoos Baquar
Basheer Ahmed Chowdry
Sheikh Arshad Farooq
Manzoor Hussain Shah Kazmi
Mohammad Aslam Khan
Muhammad Kamal Abdul Nasir
Afzal Rashid
Mohammad Imran ul Haque
Muhammad Zahid
Anis Wahab Zuberi

AL-ZARQA EDUCATIONAL & INVESTMENT CO P.L.C

Commercial Area
PO Box 3331
Amman, 13111, Jordan
Tel.: (962) 6 5 3986946
Fax: (962) 6 5 3998835
E-Mail: zarka_eic@zpu.edu.jo
Year Founded: 1992
ZEIC—(AMM)
Rev.: $23,749,185
Assets: $51,346,170
Liabilities: $20,297,252
Net Worth: $31,048,918
Earnings: $5,104,508
Emp.: 14
Fiscal Year-end: 12/31/12
Business Description:
Educational Support Services
S.I.C.: 8299
N.A.I.C.S.: 611710
Personnel:
Mahmoud Abu-Shaireh *(Gen Mgr)*

AL ZAYANI INVESTMENTS WLL

Zayani House
PO Box 5553
Manama, Bahrain
Tel.: (973) 17531177
Fax: (973) 17532912
E-Mail: zayanis@alzayani.com
Web Site: www.alzayani.com
Emp.: 50
Business Description:
Equity Investment Firm
S.I.C.: 6211
N.A.I.C.S.: 523999
Personnel:
Hamid Rashid Al Zayani *(Chm)*
Zayed Rashid Alzayani *(Mng Dir)*
Nawaf Khalid Alzayani *(Deputy Mng Dir)*
Board of Directors:
Hamid Rashid Al Zayani
Abdul Rahmad Hamid Al Zayani
Nawaf Khalid Alzayani
Zayed Rashid Alzayani

Joint Venture:

Gulf Closures W.L.L. **(1)**
PO Box 2715
Manama, Bahrain BH
Tel.: (973) 17735565
Fax: (973) 17735318
E-Mail: closures@batelco.com.ph
Sales Range: $10-24.9 Million
Emp.: 91
Aluminum & Plastic Closure Mfr; Owned by Closure Systems International, Inc. & by Al Zayani Investments WLL
S.I.C.: 3354
N.A.I.C.S.: 331318

ALACER GOLD CORP.

Level 3 18 Parliament Place
West Perth, WA, 6005, Australia
Tel.: (61) 8 9226 0625
Fax: (61) 8 9226 0629
Web Site: www.alacergold.com
AQG—(ASX OTC TSX)
Rev.: $718,890,000
Assets: $1,460,381,000
Liabilities: $293,344,000
Net Worth: $1,167,037,000
Earnings: ($342,359,000)
Fiscal Year-end: 12/31/12
Business Description:
Gold & Mineral Exploration & Mining
S.I.C.: 1041
N.A.I.C.S.: 212221
Personnel:
Richard P. Graff *(Interim Chm)*
Mark Murchison *(Interim CFO)*
Geoffrey T. Williams, Jr. *(Chief Legal Officer & Sec)*
Chris Newman *(Chief Exploration Officer & Chief Geology Officer)*
Louw Smith *(Chief Technical Svcs Officer)*
Howard H. J. Stevenson *(Pres/COO-Englewood)*
Anthony James *(Pres-Ops-Australia)*
Rodney P. Antal *(CEO-Englewood)*
Board of Directors:
Richard P. Graff
Rodney P. Antal
Jan Castro
Edward C. Dowling, Jr.
Transfer Agents:
Link Market Services Limited
Ground Floor 178 St Georges Terrace
Perth, Australia
CIBC Mellon Trust Company
PO Box 700 Station B
Montreal, QC, Canada

Corporate Headquarters:

Alacer Management Corp. **(1)**
9635 Maroon Cir Ste 300
Englewood, CO 80112 CO
Tel.: (303) 292-1299 (100%)
Fax: (303) 297-0538
Web Site: www.alacergold.com
Corporate Office; Gold Exploration & Mining
S.I.C.: 8741
N.A.I.C.S.: 551114
Howard H. J. Stevenson *(Pres & COO)*

ALACRITY SECURITIES LIMITED

101 Hari Darshan B-Wing Bhogilal Fadia Road
Kandivali West, Mumbai, 400 067, India
Tel.: (91) 22 2807 3882
Fax: (91) 22 2807 3967
E-Mail: sales@alacritysec.com
Web Site: www.alacritysec.com
Year Founded: 1995
535916—(BOM)
Rev.: $4,752,043
Fiscal Year-end: 03/31/13
Business Description:
Securities & Financial Services
S.I.C.: 6211
N.A.I.C.S.: 523120
Personnel:
Kinjal Amit Shah *(Compliance Officer & Mgr-Accts & Fin)*
Kishore Vithaldas Shah *(Personnel Rels Officer)*
Nimita Jain *(Sec)*
Board of Directors:
Ramanand Gulabchand Gupta
Jaiprakash Jaswantrai Jindal
Hitten Ramniklal Mehta
Pooja Heemanshu Mehta
Kishore Vithaldas Shah

ALAIN AHLIA INSURANCE COMPANY (PSC)

Al Ain Insurance Company Building
Airport Road
PO Box 3077
Abu Dhabi, United Arab Emirates
Tel.: (971) 2 6119999
Fax: (971) 2 4456685
E-Mail: info@alaininsurance.com
Web Site: www.alaininsurance.com
AAAIC—(EMI)
Premiums: $125,802,140
Assets: $422,409,207
Liabilities: $154,039,182
Net Worth: $268,370,024
Earnings: $13,676,773
Fiscal Year-end: 12/31/12
Business Description:
Insurance Services
S.I.C.: 6411
N.A.I.C.S.: 524298
Personnel:
Mohammed Juan Al Badie *(Chm)*
Khalid Mohammed Juan Al Badie *(Deputy Chm)*
Board of Directors:
Mohammed Juan Al Badie
Mohammed Saad Al Ahbabi
Ahmed Ghanoum Al Hameli
Saeed Ali Saleh Ahmed Al Kuwaiti
Mohammed Al Fandi Al Mazroui
Gaith Hamil Al Gaith Al Qubaisi
Khalid Mohammed Juan Al Badie

ALAM GROUP OF COMPANIES

Casements Complex 5th Street Plot 86 90
PO Box 4641
Kampala, 4641, Uganda
Tel.: (256) 414234001
Fax: (256) 41234301
E-Mail: alam@alam-group.com
Web Site: www.alam-group.com
Year Founded: 1965
Sales Range: $25-49.9 Million
Emp.: 1,200
Business Description:
Holding Company; Construction, Real Estate & Related Services; Manufacturing Services
S.I.C.: 6719
N.A.I.C.S.: 551112
Personnel:
Manzur Alam *(Chm)*
Abid Alam *(Mng Dir)*
Board of Directors:
Manzur Alam
Abid Alam
Khalid Alam
Shahid Alam
Zahid Alam

Subsidiaries:

Alam Constructions Ltd. **(1)**
Plot 86/90 Casements Complex 5th St
Industrial Area, Kampala, Uganda

Alam Group of Companies—(Continued)

Tel.: (256) 41234000
Fax: (256) 41234301
E-Mail: alam@alam-group.com
Web Site: www.alam-group.com
Emp.: 150
Construction Services
S.I.C.: 1629
N.A.I.C.S.: 237110
Abid Alam *(Gen Mgr)*

Ama Ply Ltd. (1)
PO Box 4641
Kampala, Uganda
Tel.: (256) 41340199
Fax: (256) 41234301
Web Site: www.alam-group.com
Wood Flooring Products
S.I.C.: 2599
N.A.I.C.S.: 321912

Crocodile Tool Company (Uganda) Ltd. (1)
Plot 13/19 Eden Road
PO Box 1391
Jinja, Uganda
Tel.: (256) 43123109
Fax: (256) 43234301
Web Site: www.alam-group.com
Emp.: 60
Farm Hand Tools & Hoes Mfr
S.I.C.: 3446
N.A.I.C.S.: 332323

Ekono Homes Ltd. (1)
Plot 86/90 5th Street Ind Area Casement Complex
PO Box 2288
Kampala, Uganda
Tel.: (256) 392884944
Fax: (256) 41234301
E-Mail: info@ekonoprefabs.com
Web Site: www.ekonoprefabs.com
Residential Builder
S.I.C.: 1542
N.A.I.C.S.: 236220

Inns of Uganda (1)
Plot 86/90 Casements Complex 5th St
Industrial Area, Kampala, Uganda
Tel.: (256) 41234000
Fax: (256) 41234301
Hotel Management Services
S.I.C.: 7011
N.A.I.C.S.: 721199

Oxygas Ltd. (1)
Plot 501
Nakawa Industrial Area, Kampala, Uganda
Tel.: (256) 41505865
Fax: (256) 41505866
E-Mail: oxygas@alam-group.com
Web Site: www.alam-group.com
Emp.: 50
Industrial & Medical Oxygen & Dissolved Acetylene
S.I.C.: 2813
N.A.I.C.S.: 325120

Roofclad Ltd. (1)
Plot 86/90 Casements Complex 5th St
Industrial Area, Kampala, Uganda
Tel.: (256) 41234000
Fax: (256) 41234301
E-Mail: info@alam-group.com
Web Site: www.alam-group.com
Emp.: 550
Wire Products & Security Systems Mfr
S.I.C.: 3496
N.A.I.C.S.: 332618
Abid Alam *(Mng Dir)*

SIAMMCO Ltd. (1)
Cementry Road
Soroti, Uganda
Tel.: (256) 4561361
Web Site: www.alam-group.com
Agricultural Implements & Machinery Mfr
S.I.C.: 3446
N.A.I.C.S.: 332323

Steel Rolling Mills Ltd. (1)
PO Box 22431
Masese, Jinja, Uganda
Tel.: (256) 43120987
Fax: (256) 43123183
E-Mail: alam@alam-group.com
Web Site: www.alamgroup.com
Emp.: 400
Steel Products Producer
S.I.C.: 3325
N.A.I.C.S.: 331513
Aidi Alam *(Mng Dir)*

ALAM MARITIM RESOURCES BERHAD

No 38F Level 3 Jalan Radin Anum
Bandar Baru Sri Petaling
57000 Kuala Lumpur, Malaysia
Tel.: (60) 390582244
Fax: (60) 390596845
E-Mail: info@alam-maritim.com.my
Web Site: www.alam-maritim.com.my
ALAM—(KLS)
Rev.: $164,743,609
Assets: $426,170,995
Liabilities: $253,036,056
Net Worth: $173,134,939
Earnings: $18,267,841
Fiscal Year-end: 12/31/12

Business Description:
Offshore Supply Vessels & Services
S.I.C.: 4499
N.A.I.C.S.: 488330

Personnel:
Azmi Ahmad *(CEO & Mng Dir)*
Shaharuddin Warno *(COO)*
Azman Abbas *(CEO-TH Alam Mgmt)*
Haniza Sabaran *(Sec & Head-Corp Secretarial)*

Board of Directors:
Ahmad Sufian
Ahmad Hassanudin Ahmad Kamaluddin
Azmi Ahmad
Fina Norhizah Baharu Zaman
Ab Razak Hashim
Ab Wahab Ibrahim
Mohd Abd Rahman Mohd Hashim
Shaharuddin Warno

Legal Counsel:
Zul Rafique & Partners
D3-3-8 Solaris Dutamas No. 1 Jalan Dutamas 1
Kuala Lumpur, Malaysia

Subsidiary:

Alam Maritim (M) Sdn. Bhd. (1)
No 38F Level 2 Jalan Radin Anum
Bandar Baru Sri Petaling, 57000 Kuala Lumpur, Federal Territory, Malaysia
Tel.: (60) 390582244
Fax: (60) 390596845
Web Site: www.alam-maritim.com.my/career.html
Emp.: 100
Ship Repair & Maintenance Services
S.I.C.: 3731
N.A.I.C.S.: 336611

Subsidiaries:

Alam Food Industries (M) Sdn. Bhd. (2)
PT 6867 Ground Floor Bukit Kuang Business Centre
Jalan Kemunting, 24000 Kemaman, Trengganu, Malaysia
Tel.: (60) 9 859 3543
Fax: (60) 9 859 3543
Web Site: www.alam-maritim.com.my/Contact/corpDir.html
Emp.: 45
Catering Services
S.I.C.: 5812
N.A.I.C.S.: 722320
Azmi Ahmad *(Mng Dir)*

Alam Hidro (M) Sdn. Bhd. (2)
No 38 D & E Level 4 Bandar Baru Sri Petaling
57000 Kuala Lumpur, Federal Territory, Malaysia
Tel.: (60) 390562155
Fax: (60) 390563155
E-Mail: info@alam-maritim.com.my
Web Site: www.alam-maritim.com.my/Contact/corpDir.html
Emp.: 20
Construction Engineering Services
S.I.C.: 8711
N.A.I.C.S.: 541330
Ahmad Hassanudin *(Chm)*

KJ Waja Engineering Sdn. Bhd. (2)
Bt 32 Jalan Linggi Tanjung Agas Kuala Linggi
Daerah Alor Gajah, 78200 Melaka, Malaysia
Tel.: (60) 63841895
Fax: (60) 63843985
E-Mail: kamarul@kjwaja.com.my
Emp.: 23
Ship Repair & Maintenance Services
S.I.C.: 3731
N.A.I.C.S.: 336611
Kamarul Zaman Jantan *(Mng Dir)*

Non-U.S. Subsidiary:

Eastar Offshore Pte. Ltd. (1)
19 Bukit Batok St 22
Singapore, 659588, Singapore
Tel.: (65) 66655322
Fax: (65) 66650889
E-Mail: admin@eastaroffshore.com
Web Site: www.eastaroffshores.com
Emp.: 22
Remotely Operated Underwater Vehicles Mfr & Distr
S.I.C.: 3999
N.A.I.C.S.: 339999
Qiong Wu *(Mng Dir)*

Subsidiary:

Alam Subsea Pte. Ltd. (2)
19 Bukit Batok St 22
Singapore, 659588, Singapore
Tel.: (65) 66655322
Fax: (65) 675750
E-Mail: info@alamsubsea.com
Web Site: www.alamsubsea.com
Emp.: 20
Remotely Operated Vehicle Mfr & Support Services
S.I.C.: 3999
N.A.I.C.S.: 339999
Qiong Wu *(Mng Dir)*

ALAMOS GOLD INC.

2200-130 Adelaide Street West
Toronto, ON, M5H 3P5, Canada
Tel.: (416) 368-9932
Fax: (416) 368-2934
Toll Free: (866) 788-8801
E-Mail: info@alamosgold.com
Web Site: www.alamosgold.com
AGI—(NYSE TSX)
Rev.: $329,372,000
Assets: $753,856,000
Liabilities: $93,384,000
Net Worth: $660,472,000
Earnings: $117,956,000
Emp.: 630
Fiscal Year-end: 12/31/12

Business Description:
Gold Mining & Exploration Services
S.I.C.: 1041
N.A.I.C.S.: 212221

Personnel:
Mark Wayne *(Chm)*
John A. McCluskey *(Pres & CEO)*
James R. Porter *(CFO)*
Manley R. Guarducci *(COO & VP)*
Matthew Howorth *(Sec & VP-Legal)*

Board of Directors:
Mark Wayne
Anthony W. Garson
David Patrick Gower
John A. McCluskey
Paul J. Murphy
Kenneth George Stowe

Computershare Trust Company of Canada
510 Burrard St
Vancouver, BC, Canada

Transfer Agents:
Computershare Trust Company of Canada
510 Burrard St
Vancouver, BC, Canada

Computershare Trust Company of Canada
66 Wellington Street West Suite 5210 PO Box 240 TD Centre
Toronto, ON, M5K 1J3, Canada

Non-U.S. Subsidiary:

Minas de Oro Nacional S.A. de C.V. (1)
De Los Pimas Parque Industrial
83299 Hermosillo, Sonora, Mexico
Tel.: (52) 662 217 3707
Gold Ore Mining Services
S.I.C.: 1041
N.A.I.C.S.: 212221
Brian Peer, *(Gen Mgr)*

ALAN NUTTALL LTD.

Orchard House Dodwells Road
Hinckley, Leicestershire, LE10 3BZ, United Kingdom
Tel.: (44) 1455 638300
Fax: (44) 1455 638302
E-Mail: fsc@nuttalls.co.uk
Web Site: www.nuttalls.co.uk
Year Founded: 1988
Sales Range: $100-124.9 Million
Emp.: 489

Business Description:
Display Cabinet Mfr
S.I.C.: 2521
N.A.I.C.S.: 337211

Personnel:
Alan Nuttall *(Founder)*

ALANDSBANKEN ABP

Nygatan 2
22101 Mariehamn, Finland
Tel.: (358) 20429011
Fax: (358) 204291228
E-Mail: info@alandsbanken.fi
Web Site: www.alandsbanken.fi
ALBBV—(HEL)
Int. Income: $115,948,314
Assets: $4,896,324,524
Liabilities: $4,645,949,020
Net Worth: $250,375,504
Earnings: $16,384,235
Emp.: 569
Fiscal Year-end: 12/31/12

Business Description:
Banking Services
S.I.C.: 6029
N.A.I.C.S.: 522110

Personnel:
Kaj-Gustaf Bergh *(Chm)*
Folke Husell *(Deputy Chm)*
Peter Wiklof *(CEO & Mng Dir)*
Jan-Gunnar Eurell *(CFO & Deputy Mng Dir)*
Tove Erikslund *(Chief Admin Officer)*
Juhana Rauthovi *(Chief Risk Officer)*

Board of Directors:
Kaj-Gustaf Bergh
Folke Husell
Agneta Karlsson
Anders A. Karlsson
Annika Wijkstrom
Anders Wiklof

Subsidiaries:

Alandsbanken Asset Management Ab (1)
Bulevardi 3 3 krs
00120 Helsinki, Finland
Tel.: (358) 204 293 700
Fax: (358) 204 293 710
E-Mail: aam@alandsbanken.fi
Web Site: www.alandsbanken.fi
Commercial Banking Services
S.I.C.: 6029
N.A.I.C.S.: 522110

Alandsbanken Equities Research Ab (1)
Bulevardi 3
00120 Helsinki, Finland
Tel.: (358) 2042 9011
Fax: (358) 2042 93610
E-Mail: bulevardi@alandsbanken.fi
Web Site: www.alandsbanken.fi
Commercial Banking Services
S.I.C.: 6029
N.A.I.C.S.: 522110
Peter Wikstroem *(Gen Mgr)*

Alandsbanken Fondbolag Ab (1)
Nygatan 9
22100 Mariehamn, Finland
Tel.: (358) 204 29 088
Fax: (358) 204 291 439
Commercial Banking Services
S.I.C.: 6029
N.A.I.C.S.: 522110
Tom Pettersson *(Mng Dir)*

Crosskey Banking Solutions Ab Ltd. (1)
Elverksgatan 10
22 100 Mariehamn, Finland
Tel.: (358) 20429022
E-Mail: information@crosskey.fi
Web Site: www.crosskey.fi
Emp.: 200
Commercial Banking Services
S.I.C.: 6029
N.A.I.C.S.: 522110
Carita Weiss *(Mng Dir)*

Non-U.S. Subsidiary:

Alandsbanken Sverige AB (1)
Stureplan 19
107 81 Stockholm, Sweden
Tel.: (46) 87914800
Fax: (46) 86112690
E-Mail: info@alandsbanken.se
Web Site: www.alandsbanken.se
Emp.: 130
Banking Services
S.I.C.: 6029
N.A.I.C.S.: 522110
Peter Wiklof *(Pres)*

ALANG INDUSTRIAL GASES LIMITED

108 Kesri Nandan Complex Near Galaxy Cinema Bhid Bhanjan
Bhavnagar, Gujarat, 364 001, India
Tel.: (91) 22 28067285
E-Mail: info@alangindustrialgases.com
Web Site: www.alangindustrialgases.com
531517—(BOM)
Business Description:
Industrial Gas Whslr
S.I.C.: 5169
N.A.I.C.S.: 424690
Personnel:
Dilip B. Sheth *(Compliance Officer)*
Board of Directors:
Mayur M. Shah
Rajeshkumar S. Shah
Dilip B. Sheth
Nayan B. Sheth
Transfer Agent:
Sharex Dynamic (India) Private Limited
Unit No1 Luthra Indus Premises Andheri Kurla Rd Safed Pool Andheri(E)
Mumbai, India

ALAPIS S.A.

2 Aftokratoros Nikolaou Str
176 71 Athens, Greece
Tel.: (30) 213 0175000
Fax: (30) 2109238460
E-Mail: info@alapis.inu
Web Site: www.alapis.gr
ALAPIS—(ATH)
Sales Range: $1-4.9 Billion
Emp.: 1,208
Business Description:
Pharmaceuticals, Cosmetics, Detergents & Organic Products Mfr
S.I.C.: 2834
N.A.I.C.S.: 325412
Personnel:
Aristotelis Charalampakis *(Chm)*
Periklis Livas *(Mng Dir & VP)*
Leda Basta *(IR Officer)*
Board of Directors:
Aristotelis Charalampakis
Evridiki Georgagaki
Nikolaos Karantanis
Nikolaos Korbis
Periklis Livas
Subsidiaries:

Alapis Cropscience S.A. (1)
Thesi Vargo
Aspropirgos, 19300 Athens, Greece
Tel.: (30) 2105508709
Fax: (30) 2109221502
Veterinary Pharmaceuticals Mfr
S.I.C.: 2834
N.A.I.C.S.: 325412
John Minagias *(Dir)*

Alapis Pharma S.A. (1)
6 Kartsivani
Palaio Faliro, 17564 Athens, Greece
Tel.: (30) 2130175000
Fax: (30) 2109460400
E-Mail: hr@alapis.eu
Web Site: www.alapis.eu
Pharmaceutical Products Mfr
S.I.C.: 2834
N.A.I.C.S.: 325412
Stelios Kimbaridis *(VP & CEO)*

Biochem Diagnostics S.A. (1)
9 Zaloggou St
Alimos, 174 55 Athens, Greece
Tel.: (30) 2109801000
Fax: (30) 210 980 1001
E-Mail: info@biochem.gr
Web Site: www.biochem.gr/
Diagnostic Instruments Mfr
S.I.C.: 3845
N.A.I.C.S.: 334510

Biodomus S.A. (1)
1st KM Markopoulou Kalivion
19010 Athens, Kalivia Attica, Greece
Tel.: (30) 22990 61061
Fax: (30) 22990 61064
Web Site: www.biodomus.gr
Detergents & Cosmetics Mfr
S.I.C.: 5122
N.A.I.C.S.: 446120

Marinopoulos SA (1)
Agiou Dimitriou 63
Alimos, 17456 Athens, Greece
Tel.: (30) 210 9893400
Fax: (30) 210 9893825
E-Mail: Carrefour_Greece@carrefour.com
Web Site: www.marinopoulos.gr/carrefour.html
Owner & Operator of Hypermarkets, Supermarkets, Grocery & Convenience Stores
S.I.C.: 5411
N.A.I.C.S.: 445110
Jerome Loubre *(Mng Dir)*

Farmakemporiki S.A. (1)
226 Peiraios
17778 Tavros, Greece
Tel.: (30) 210 3413 1216
Fax: (30) 210 341 3120
E-Mail: farmakemporikiath@forthnet.gr
Emp.: 40
Pharmaceuticals Whslr
S.I.C.: 5122
N.A.I.C.S.: 424210
Kalampounias Spyros *(Gen Mgr)*

K. P. Marinopoulos S.A. (1)
150 Tatoiou St
Metamorfosi, 14452 Athens, Greece
Tel.: (30) 210 2853000
Fax: (30) 2102853030
E-Mail: info@kpmarinopoulos.gr
Web Site: www.kpmarinopoulos.gr
Emp.: 300
Pharmaceutical Products Distr
S.I.C.: 5122
N.A.I.C.S.: 424210
Gerasimos Partidas *(Gen Mgr)*

Lamda Applied S.A. (1)
Laviro Technological Cultural Park
Athens Lavrio Ave, Lavrio, 19500, Greece
Tel.: (30) 2292069485
Fax: (30) 2292069141
Web Site: www.lapplied.gr/
Pharmaceutical Products Mfr
S.I.C.: 2834
N.A.I.C.S.: 325412

Pharmagora S.A. (1)
1st Km Triaviou Thermi
PO Box 60252
57001 Thessaloniki, Greece
Tel.: (30) 2310463400
Fax: (30) 2310489748
E-Mail: e.votika@pharmagora.gr
Web Site: www.pharmagora.gr
Emp.: 65
Pharmaceuticals Whslr
S.I.C.: 5122
N.A.I.C.S.: 424210
Stellios Kymparidin *(CEO)*

Provet S.A. (1)
6 Kartsivani
Palaio Faliro, 17564 Athens, Greece
Tel.: (30) 2105573803
Fax: (30) 21 05573806
E-Mail: info@provet.gr
Veterinary Pharmaceuticals Mfr
S.I.C.: 2834
N.A.I.C.S.: 325412

SANTE Hellas S.A. (1)
Industrial Area
Thermi, 570 01 Thessaloniki, Greece
Tel.: (30) 2310464727
Fax: (30) 2310467059
E-Mail: info@santehellas.gr
Web Site: www.santehellas.gr/en_contact.asp
Emp.: 9
Bandages & Sterilized Dressings Mfr
S.I.C.: 3842
N.A.I.C.S.: 339113
John Karastergio *(Mng Dir)*

Non-U.S. Subsidiaries:

Alapis Romania S.R.L. (1)
Str Jean-Louis Calderon Nr 59 Ap 5
Bucharest, Bucuresti, Romania
Tel.: (40) 21 3145935
Fax: (40) 21 3145824
E-Mail: dianai@veterin.roveterin.ro
Emp.: 35
Veterinary Pharmaceuticals Mfr
S.I.C.: 2834
N.A.I.C.S.: 325412
Patrice Noble *(Gen Mgr)*

Pharmacare Ltd (Cyprus) (1)
35 Machaira
Nicosia, Cyprus
Tel.: (357) 22323460
Fax: (357) 22322749
Emp.: 7
Veterinary Pharmaceuticals Mfr
S.I.C.: 2834
N.A.I.C.S.: 325412
Kyriakidis Kritos *(Gen Mgr)*

Sumadijalek S.A. (1)
Kralja Petra I 5
32000 Cacak, Serbia
Tel.: (381) 32224241
Fax: (381) 32224271
Emp.: 80
Pharmaceutical Products Mfr
S.I.C.: 2834
N.A.I.C.S.: 325412
Dimitrios Thomopoulos *(Mng Dir)*

ALARA RESOURCES LIMITED

Level 3 35 Havelock Street
West Perth, WA, 6005, Australia
Tel.: (61) 8 6323 5900
Fax: (61) 8 6323 5999
E-Mail: info@alararesources.com
Web Site: www.alararesources.com
AUQ—(ASX)
Rev.: $294,991
Assets: $42,774,128
Liabilities: $3,745,990
Net Worth: $39,028,138
Earnings: ($7,193,875)
Emp.: 475
Fiscal Year-end: 06/30/13
Business Description:
Exploration of Resource
S.I.C.: 1081
N.A.I.C.S.: 213114
Personnel:
Philip H. Hopkins *(CEO & Mng Dir)*
Julian Tambyrajah *(Acting CFO)*
Justin Richard *(Gen Counsel & Mgr-Saudi Arabia & Oman)*
Victor Poh Hong Ho *(Sec)*
Board of Directors:
Ian J. Williams
Abdullah Mosaad Abdulaziz Al Saud
John D. Hopkins
Philip H. Hopkins

ALARGAN INTERNATIONAL REAL ESTATE CO. K.S.C.C.

PO Box 8904 Salmiya
22060 Kuwait, Kuwait
Tel.: (965) 24820440
Fax: (965) 24823298
E-Mail: alargan@alargan.com
Web Site: www.alargan.com
ARGAN—(KUW)
Rev.: $67,175,836
Assets: $451,828,987
Liabilities: $204,341,117
Net Worth: $247,487,869
Earnings: $15,513,837
Fiscal Year-end: 12/31/12
Business Description:
Real Estate Services
S.I.C.: 6531
N.A.I.C.S.: 531390
Personnel:
Khaled Khudair Al-Mashaan *(Chm & Mng Dir)*
Hamad Al-Mudhaf *(Vice Chm)*
Sherif Fawzy Omara *(CFO)*
Falah Jamal Al-Salman *(COO-Projects Ops)*
Tony Safarian *(CMO)*
Ramy Echo *(Chief Investment Officer)*
Marwan Asa'd *(Chief Plng Officer-Project Plng & Dev)*
Pierre Abou Khalil *(Chief Support Officer)*
Jamila Abdul Razzaq Al-Adwani *(Sr VP-Asset Mgmt & Advisory Svcs)*
Renimah Ali Al-Mattar *(Sr VP-IR & Res)*
Saad Nasser Al-Muneefi *(Sr VP-Bus Dev & Advisory Svcs)*
Board of Directors:
Khaled Khudair Al-Mashaan
Abdulaziz Khaled Al-Abdulrazaq
Haitham Al-Khaled
Faisal Khudair Al-Mashaan
Hamad Al-Mudhaf

ALARIS ROYALTY CORP.

Suite 232 2031 33rd Avenue SW
Calgary, AB, T2T 1Z5, Canada
Tel.: (403) 221-7304
Fax: (403) 228-0906
Web Site: www.alarisroyalty.com
Year Founded: 2006
AD—(TSX)
Rev.: $31,913,921
Assets: $330,949,725
Liabilities: $53,867,428
Net Worth: $277,082,297
Earnings: $17,927,750
Emp.: 665
Fiscal Year-end: 12/31/12
Business Description:
Investment Fund Services
S.I.C.: 6722
N.A.I.C.S.: 525910
Personnel:
Jack C. Lee *(Chm)*
Stephen W. King *(Pres & CEO)*

Alaris Royalty Corp.—(Continued)

Darren Driscoll *(CFO)*
Rachel Colabella *(Gen Counsel & Sec)*

Board of Directors:
Jack C. Lee
John P. A. Budreski
Stephen W. King
Gary Patterson
Mary C. Ritchie
E. Mitchell Shier

Transfer Agent:
Computershare Trust Company of Canada
600 530 8th Avenue SW
Calgary, AB, T2P 3S8, Canada
Tel.: (403) 267-6555
Toll Free: (800) 558-0046

ALARKO HOLDING A.S.

Muallim Naci Cad 69 Ortakoy
34347 Istanbul, Turkey
Tel.: (90) 212 310 33 00
Fax: (90) 212 227 04 27
E-Mail: info@alarko.com.tr
Web Site: www.alarko.com.tr
ALARK—(IST)
Rev.: $914,746,275
Assets: $1,220,658,584
Liabilities: $594,361,979
Net Worth: $626,296,605
Earnings: $43,869,825
Emp.: 4,104
Fiscal Year-end: 12/31/12

Business Description:
Portfolio Management Services
S.I.C.: 6282
N.A.I.C.S.: 523920

Personnel:
Ishak Alaton *(Chm & Pres)*
Vedat Aksel Alaton *(Vice Chm & Co-Mng Dir)*
Izzet Garih *(Vice Chm & Co-Mng Dir)*
Ayhan Yavrucu *(CEO)*
Alper Kaptanoglu *(Deputy CEO-Contracting)*
Aykut Baycan *(Exec VP-Contracting & Acctg)*
Onat Bitik *(Exec VP-Contracting & Construction)*
Bekir Bora *(Exec VP-Contracting, Project Fin & Local Bus Dev)*
Edip Ilkbahar *(Exec VP-Tourism)*
A. Onder Kazazoglu *(Exec VP-Energy Distr)*
Harun H. Moreno *(Exec VP-Land Dev & Bus Dev)*
H. Onder Sahin *(Exec VP-Indus & Trade)*
Adnan Yagmur *(Exec VP-Energy Production)*
Mehmet Ahkemoglu *(Sr VP-Auditing)*
Omer Celik *(Sr VP-Fin)*
Mustafa Filiz *(Sr VP-Acctg)*
Umit Nuri Yildiz *(Sr VP-Fin Analysis, Sys & Plng)*

Board of Directors:
Ishak Alaton
Leyla Alaton
Vedat Aksel Alaton
Dalia Garih
Izzet Garih
Ahmet Zeyyat Hatipoglu
Izzet Cemal Kismir
Ayhan Yavrucu

Subsidiary:

Alarko Carrier Sanayi ve Ticaret A.S. **(1)**
Muallim Naci Cad No 69 Ortakoy
34347 Istanbul, Turkey
Tel.: (90) 2123103300
Fax: (90) 2122270427
E-Mail: info@alarko-carrier.com.tr
Web Site: www.alarko-carrier.com.tr
ALCAR—(IST)
Rev.: $199,897,636
Assets: $192,948,252
Liabilities: $33,220,607
Net Worth: $159,727,645
Earnings: $15,212,889
Emp.: 621
Fiscal Year-end: 12/31/12
Circulation Pumps, Pressure Tanks & Boilers Mfr
S.I.C.: 3433
N.A.I.C.S.: 333414
Ishak Alaton *(Chm)*
Philippe Didier Delpech *(Vice Chm)*
Alper Kaptanoglu *(Deputy CEO)*
Aykut Baycan *(Exec VP-Acctg)*
Onat Bitik *(Exec VP-Construction)*
Bekir Bora *(Exec VP-Project Fin & Local Bus Dev)*
A. Onder Kazazoglu *(Exec VP-Energy Distr)*
Adnan Yagmur *(Exec VP-Energy Production)*
Mehmet Ahkemoglu *(Sr VP-Auditing)*
Mustafa Filiz *(Sr VP-Acctg)*

ALARMFORCE INDUSTRIES INC.

675 Garyray Drive
Toronto, ON, M9L 1R2, Canada
Tel.: (416) 445-2001
Fax: (416) 445-8358
Toll Free: (800) 267-2001
E-Mail: customerservice@alarmforce.com
Web Site: www.alarmforce.com
Year Founded: 1988
AF—(TSX)
Rev.: $44,568,398
Assets: $42,822,595
Liabilities: $10,460,772
Net Worth: $32,361,823
Earnings: $1,156,467
Emp.: 157
Fiscal Year-end: 10/31/12

Business Description:
Two-Way Voice Home Security Systems Mfr
S.I.C.: 7382
N.A.I.C.S.: 561621

Personnel:
Anthony Pizzonia *(Interim Pres & Inteirm CEO)*

Board of Directors:
Pavel Begun
Charles S. Mayer
Anthony Pizzonia
N. Peter Silverberg

Legal Counsel:
Macleod Dixon LLP
Toronto, ON, Canada

Transfer Agent:
Equity Financial Trust Company
Toronto, ON, Canada

ALAS HOLDING A.D.

Danila Kisa
21000 Novi Sad, Serbia
Tel.: (381) 21 457 949
Fax: (381) 21 557 236
Web Site: ww.alas-holding.rs
ZONE—(BEL)

Business Description:
Brick & Clay Mfr
S.I.C.: 3255
N.A.I.C.S.: 327120

Personnel:
Roman Kratochvil *(Gen Mgr)*

Board of Directors:
Markus Bogdanovic
Roman Kratochvil
Dusanka Matic

ALASKA HYDRO CORPORATION

11906 - 194B Street
Pitt Meadows, BC, V3Y 1K2, Canada
Tel.: (604) 916-9185
Toll Free: (866) 571-1068
E-Mail: info@alaskahydro.com
Web Site: www.alaskahydro.com
Year Founded: 2006
AKH—(TSXV)
Int. Income: $5
Assets: $28,194
Liabilities: $866,228
Net Worth: ($838,034)
Earnings: ($13,428)
Fiscal Year-end: 12/31/12

Business Description:
Renewable Energy Acquisition & Development Services
S.I.C.: 4911
N.A.I.C.S.: 221111

Personnel:
Matthew Bell *(Co-Chm)*
Cliff Grandison *(Co-Chm)*
Doug Bishop *(Pres & CEO)*
Len Schmidt *(CFO)*
Michael Hoole *(Sec)*

Board of Directors:
Matthew Bell
Cliff Grandison
Doug Bishop
Michael Hoole
Steve Marmon
Chris Spens

Legal Counsel:
Miller Thomson LLP
Robson Court 100 840 Howe Street
Vancouver, BC, Canada

Transfer Agent:
Computershare
510 Burrard St 2nd Floor
Vancouver, BC, Canada

U.S. Subsidiary:

Cascade Creek LLC **(1)**
3633 Alderwood Ave
Bellingham, WA 98225
Tel.: (360) 738-9999
Fax: (360) 733-3056
Web Site: www.thomasbayhydro.com
Hydroelectric Power Generation Services
S.I.C.: 4911
N.A.I.C.S.: 221111
Chris Spens *(Project Mgr)*

ALBA GRUPO MARCH

Castello 77 5th Fl
28006 Madrid, Spain
Tel.: (34) 914363710
Fax: (34) 915756737
E-Mail: alba@corporacionalba.es
Web Site: www.cf-alba.com
Emp.: 25

Business Description:
Financial Services
S.I.C.: 7389
N.A.I.C.S.: 561499

Personnel:
Juan March Delgado *(Co-Chm & Pres)*
Carlos March Delgado *(Co-Chm)*
Santos Marinez-Conde Gutierrez-Barquin *(CEO)*
Santos Martinez-Conde *(Mng Dir)*

Board of Directors:
Carlos March Delgado
Juan March Delgado
Alfonso Tolcheff Alvarez
Nicholas Brookes
Santos Marinez-Conde Gutierrez-Barquin
Alfredo Lafita Pardo
Francisco Verdu Pons
Manuel Soto Serrano
Pablo Vallbona Vadell

Subsidiaries:

Banca March S.A. **(1)**
Avenida Alejandro Rossello 8
E-07002 Palma de Mallorca, Balearic Islands, Spain ES
Tel.: (34) 971779363
Telex: 68661 bmpex e
Fax: (34) 971779187
E-Mail: international@bancamarch.es
Web Site: www.bancamarch.es
Emp.: 1,171
Full Banking Services
S.I.C.: 6029
N.A.I.C.S.: 522110
Alberto del Cid Picado *(Mgr-Treasury & Foreign Exchange)*

Subsidiaries:

March Correduria de Seguros S.A. **(2)**
Avenida A Rossello 8
07002 Palma de Mallorca, Spain ES
Tel.: (34) 971779368 (80.37%)
Fax: (34) 971779401
E-Mail: correduriabaleares@marchunidsa.es
Web Site: www.marchunidsa.es
Emp.: 40
Insurance Broker
S.I.C.: 6411
N.A.I.C.S.: 524298
Pedro Ballesteros *(Mng Dir)*

March Inversiones S.A. **(2)**
Avda A Rossello 8
Palma de Mallorca, Spain ES
Tel.: (34) 971779256 (100%)
Fax: (34) 971779294
S.I.C.: 6282
N.A.I.C.S.: 523930

March Patrimonios S.A. **(2)**
Avda. A. Rossello, 8
Palma de Mallorca, Spain ES
Tel.: (34) 971779256 (100%)
Fax: (34) 971771294
S.I.C.: 6141
N.A.I.C.S.: 522210

March - Unipsa Correduria de Seguros, S.A.U **(2)**
C/ Lagasca 88 2 Planta
Madrid, 28001, Spain
Tel.: (34) 91 781 1515
Fax: (34) 915766530
Full Banking Services
S.I.C.: 6029
N.A.I.C.S.: 522110

Subsidiaries:

March-JLT Correduria de Seguros, SA **(3)**
Calle de Lagasca 88
28001 Madrid, Spain (75%)
Tel.: (34) 917 81 15 15
Web Site: www.march-jlt.es
Insurance Consulting & Risk Management Services
S.I.C.: 6411
N.A.I.C.S.: 524298
Carlos Navarro, *(Mng Dir)*

Non-U.S. Branch:

Banca March-London **(2)**
30 Eastcheap
London, EC3M 1HD, United Kingdom
Tel.: (44) 2072207488
Fax: (44) 2079292446
E-Mail: enquires@bancamarch.co.uk
Web Site: www.bancamarch.co.uk
Full Banking Services
S.I.C.: 6029
N.A.I.C.S.: 522110

Non-U.S. Affiliate:

Balboa Finance S.A. **(2)**
6 Rue Ceard
CH-1204 Geneva, Switzerland (30%)
Tel.: (41) 223108922
Fax: (41) 22 310 6480
Personal Financing Services
S.I.C.: 6141
N.A.I.C.S.: 522210

Corporacion Financiera Alba S.A. **(1)**
Castello 77 5th Fl
28006 Madrid, Spain ES
Tel.: (34) 914363710 (53.18%)
Fax: (34) 915756737
E Mail: alba@corporacionalba.es
Web Site: www.cf-alba.com
17160—(MAD)

Emp.: 35
Investment Holding Company
S.I.C.: 6719
N.A.I.C.S.: 551112
Carlos March Delgado *(Co-Chm)*
Juan March Delgado *(Co-Chm)*
Isidro Fernandez Barreiro *(Vice Chm)*
Pablo Vallbona Vadell *(Vice Chm)*
Santos Martinez-Conde Gutierrez-Barquin *(CEO)*
Jose Ramon del Cano Palop *(Sec)*

ALBA MINERAL RESOURCES PLC

Third Floor 16 Dover Street
London, W1S 4LR, United Kingdom
Tel.: (44) 2074955326
Fax: (44) 2076295834
E-Mail: info@albamineralresources.com
Web Site: www.albamineralresources.com
ALBA—(LSE)
Business Description:
Mineral Exploration Services
S.I.C.: 1481
N.A.I.C.S.: 213115
Personnel:
Michael Nott *(Chm & Grp Mng Dir)*
Nigel John Duxbury *(Sec & Dir-Fin)*
Board of Directors:
Michael Nott
Sandy Archibald
Nigel John Duxbury
Legal Counsel:
Memery Crystal
44 Southampton Buildings
WC2A 1AP London, United Kingdom

ALBA SE

Stollwerckstrasse 9A
51149 Cologne, Germany
Tel.: (49) 220391470
Fax: (49) 220391471394
E-Mail: alba-se@albagroup.de
Web Site: www.albagroup.de
ABA—(DEU)
Rev.: $2,593,950,085
Assets: $769,900,278
Liabilities: $513,489,299
Net Worth: $256,410,980
Earnings: $44,884,751
Emp.: 1,910
Fiscal Year-end: 12/31/12
Business Description:
Metal Recycling & Waste Treatment Services
S.I.C.: 5051
N.A.I.C.S.: 423510
Personnel:
Eric Schweitzer *(Chm-Supervisory Bd)*
Axel Schweitzer *(Chm-Mgmt Bd)*
Friedrich Carl Janssen *(Vice Chm-Supervisory Bd)*
Peter Zuhlsdorff *(Vice Chm-Supervisory Bd)*
Rob Nansink *(Member-Mgmt Bd-Trading Dept)*
Joachim Wagner *(Member-Mgmt Bd-Steel & Metals Recycling)*
Supervisory Board of Directors:
Eric Schweitzer
Werner Holzmayer
Joachim Edmund Hunold
Friedrich Carl Janssen
Roland Junck
Peter Zuhlsdorff

ALBALACT S.A.

DN 1 Km 392 + 600 comuna Galda De Jos Oiejdea, 517293 Alba Iulia, Romania
Tel.: (40) 258846980
Fax: (40) 258815418
E-Mail: office@albalact.ro
Web Site: www.albalact.ro
Year Founded: 1971
ALBZ—(BUC)
Rev.: $107,803,497
Assets: $62,469,938
Liabilities: $31,107,910
Net Worth: $31,362,028
Earnings: $2,252,432
Emp.: 631
Fiscal Year-end: 12/31/12
Business Description:
Dairy Products Mfr
S.I.C.: 0241
N.A.I.C.S.: 112120
Personnel:
Raul Ciurtin *(Pres & CEO)*
Adrian Radovici *(CFO)*

ALBARAKA TURK KATILIM BANKASI A.S.

Saray Mahallesi Dr Adnan Buyukdeniz Caddesi No 6
Umraniye, 34768 Istanbul, Turkey
Tel.: (90) 216 666 01 01
Fax: (90) 216 666 16 00
E-Mail: albarakaturk@albarakaturk.com.tr
Web Site: en.albarakaturk.com.tr
Year Founded: 1984
ALBRK—(IST)
Rev.: $563,337,408
Assets: $6,966,727,105
Liabilities: $6,278,210,577
Net Worth: $688,516,528
Earnings: $108,411,714
Emp.: 2,601
Fiscal Year-end: 12/31/12
Business Description:
Banking Services
S.I.C.: 6029
N.A.I.C.S.: 522110
Personnel:
Adnan Ahmed Yusuf Abdulmalek *(Chm)*
Yalcin Oner *(Vice Chm)*
Board of Directors:
Adnan Ahmed Yusuf Abdulmalek
Mitat Aktas
Osman Akyuz
Fahad Abdullah A. Alrajhi
Ibrahim Fayez Humaid Alshamsi
Hamad Abdulla A. Eqab
Khalifa Taha Hamood
Hood Hashem Ahmed Hashem
Yalcin Oner
Ekrem Pakdemirli
Fahrettin Yahsi

ALBEDO LIMITED

8 Boon Lay Way 09-11
Singapore, 609964, Singapore
Tel.: (65) 68624272
Fax: (65) 68623378
Web Site: www.albedo.com
5IB—(SES)
Rev.: $12,323,330
Assets: $8,878,951
Liabilities: $7,853,896
Net Worth: $1,025,055
Earnings: ($1,109,262)
Fiscal Year-end: 12/31/12
Business Description:
Iron Rolls Mfr
S.I.C.: 2816
N.A.I.C.S.: 325130
Personnel:
Kok Chuan Tai *(Founder & CEO)*
Donahue Yew Hing Chong *(Deputy Mng Dir-TTS2003)*
Beng Hong Ong *(Co-Sec)*
Swee Gek Tan *(Co-Sec)*
Board of Directors:
Kok Pun Chan
Kok Chuan Tai
Sunny Fook Choy Wong
Subsidiary:

Albedo Corporation Pte. Ltd. (1)
8 Boon Lay Way Ste 09-11 TradeHub 21
Singapore, 609964, Singapore
Tel.: (65) 68624272
Fax: (65) 68623378
E-Mail: sales@albedo.com
Web Site: www.albedo.com
Emp.: 10
Industrial Supplies Distr
S.I.C.: 5051
N.A.I.C.S.: 423510
Tai Kok Chuan *(Mng Dir)*

Non-U.S. Subsidiary:

Albedo Sdn. Bhd. (1)
27-2 Jalan Pu 7/3 Taman Puchong Utama
47140 Puchong, Selangor, Malaysia
Tel.: (60) 380652558
Fax: (60) 380652550
E-Mail: sales@albedo.com
Customer Care Services
S.I.C.: 7389
N.A.I.C.S.: 561422
Ferris Chan *(Gen Mgr)*

ALBEMARLE & BOND HOLDINGS PLC

2nd Floor 2 Burgage Square
Merchant Gate
Wakefield, WF1 2TS, United Kingdom
Tel.: (44) 1189558100
Fax: (44) 1189569223
E-Mail: info@albemarlebond.com
Web Site: www.albemarlebond.com
Year Founded: 1986
ABM—(LSE)
Rev.: $169,093,001
Assets: $222,093,973
Liabilities: $100,554,974
Net Worth: $121,539,000
Earnings: $5,584,369
Emp.: 1,099
Fiscal Year-end: 06/30/13
Business Description:
Loans & Related Services; Used Merchandise Retailer
S.I.C.: 6163
N.A.I.C.S.: 522310
Personnel:
Chris Gillespie *(CEO)*
Liam Moran *(CFO)*
Colin Whipp *(Chief Restructuring Officer)*
Paula M. Watts *(Sec)*
Board of Directors:
Greville V. Nicholls
Chris Gillespie
Liam Moran
Colin Whipp
Legal Counsel:
Burges Salmon
Narrow Quay House Narrow Quay
Bristol, United Kingdom
Subsidiaries:

Albemarle & Bond Cheque Cashers Limited (1)
2nd Fl County House 17 Friar St
Reading, Berkshire, RG1 1DB, United Kingdom
Tel.: (44) 1189569055
Fax: (44) 1189521499
Mental Health Services
S.I.C.: 8049
N.A.I.C.S.: 621330

Albemarle & Bond Jewellers & Pawnbrokers Limited (1)
17 Friar Street Reading
County House, Reading, Berkshire, RG1 1DB, United Kingdom
Tel.: (44) 1189558100
Fax: (44) 1934841940
E-Mail: info@albemarlebond.com
Web Site: www.albemarlebondplc.com
Emp.: 12
Pawnbroking Services
S.I.C.: 6726
N.A.I.C.S.: 525990
Greville V. Nicholls *(Chm)*
Barry Stevenson *(CEO)*

Albemarle & Bond Trustee Limited (1)
County House 17
Friar St, Reading, Berkshire, RG1 1DB, United Kingdom
Tel.: (44) 1189558100
Fax: (44) 1189521499
E-Mail: info@albemarlebond.com
Emp.: 16
Pawnbroking Services
S.I.C.: 6726
N.A.I.C.S.: 525990
Greville V. Nicholls *(Chm)*

Early Payday Loan Limited (1)
Suite 4 Maple Court Grove Business Park
Waltham Road, Maidenhead, Berks, SL6 3LW, United Kingdom
Tel.: (44) 845 653 1365
E-Mail: info@cashwindow.co.uk
Web Site: www.cashwindow.co.uk
Short Term Lending
N.A.I.C.S.: 522291

Herbert Brown & Son Limited (1)
2nd Floor 2 Burgage Square
Merchant Gate, Wakefield, West Yorkshire, WF1 2TS, United Kingdom
Tel.: (44) 1189558100
Fax: (44) 1189569223
E-Mail:
Web Site: www.herbertbrown.co.uk
Emp.: 60
Jewellers & Pawnbrokers
S.I.C.: 5944
N.A.I.C.S.: 448310
Gerry Daly *(Head-Fin)*

ALBENA TOUR LTD

33-35 St Ivan Rilski str
1000 Sofia, Bulgaria
Tel.: (359) 2 9532599
Fax: (359) 2 9532926
E-Mail: sofia@albena.bg
Web Site: www.albena.bg
6AB—(BUL)
Business Description:
Hotel Management Services
S.I.C.: 7011
N.A.I.C.S.: 721110
Personnel:
Petko Gerdzhikov *(Dir-IR)*

ALBERCO CONSTRUCTION LTD.

14 Rayborn Crs Riel Business Park
Saint Albert, AB, Canada T8N 5C2
Tel.: (780) 459-7110
Fax: (780) 459-7185
E-Mail: info@alberco.com
Web Site: www.alberco.com
Year Founded: 1962
Rev.: $28,521,500
Emp.: 30
Business Description:
Bridge Construction Services
S.I.C.: 1611
N.A.I.C.S.: 237310
Personnel:
Ron Simonsmeier *(Pres & Gen Mgr)*

ALBERCO HOLDING B.V.

PO Box 351
8912 AX Leeuwarden, Netherlands
Tel.: (31) 582330660
Fax: (31) 582120237
E-Mail: info@sceensma.com
Web Site: www.sceensma.com
Emp.: 120
Business Description:
Holding Company
S.I.C.: 6719
N.A.I.C.S.: 551112

Alberco Holding B.V.—(Continued)

Personnel:
Alfred Bruin *(CEO)*

Subsidiary:

Steensma B.V. (1)
Galvanistraat 1
8912 AX Leeuwarden, Netherlands
Mailing Address:
PO Box 351
8901 BD Leeuwarden, Netherlands
Tel.: (31) 582330660
Fax: (31) 582120237
E-Mail: info@steensma.com
Web Site: www.steensma.com
Sales Range: $10-24.9 Million
Emp.: 60
Food Ingredients & Raw Materials Producer & Exporter
S.I.C.: 2099
N.A.I.C.S.: 311999
R. de Jong *(Mng Dir)*

ALBERT BALLIN KG

Ballindamm 25
20095 Hamburg, Germany
Tel.: (49) 4030010
Fax: (49) 40330053
Web Site: www.hlag.com
Year Founded: 2009

Business Description:
Holding Company; Owned by Kuhne Holding AG, Signal Iduna Gruppe, HSH Nordbank, M.M. Warburg Bank & HanseMerkur
S.I.C.: 6719
N.A.I.C.S.: 551112

Personnel:
Klaus-Michael Kuehne *(Chm)*

U.S. Subsidiaries:

Hapag-Lloyd (America) Inc. (1)
399 Hoes Ln
Piscataway, NJ 08854
Tel.: (732) 562-1800
Fax: (732) 885-6210
Container Shipping Services
S.I.C.: 4412
N.A.I.C.S.: 483111
Hercules Angelatos *(Sr VP-Bus Admin & Fin-America)*

Luis A. Ayala Colon Sucrs Inc. (1)
3091 Santiago De Los Cabelleros Ave
Ponce, PR 00716
Tel.: (787) 848-9000
Fax: (787) 848-0070
Container Shipping Services
S.I.C.: 4412
N.A.I.C.S.: 483111

Subsidiary:

Hapag-Lloyd AG (1)
Ballindamm 25
D 20095 Hamburg, Germany
Tel.: (49) 4030010
Fax: (49) 40330053
E-Mail: info@hapag-lloyd.com
Web Site: www.hapag-lloyd.com
Sales Range: $5-14.9 Billion
Emp.: 3,937
Maritime Freight Shipping Services
S.I.C.: 4412
N.A.I.C.S.: 483111
Michael Frenzel *(Chm-Supervisory Bd)*
Michael Behrendt *(Chm-Exec Bd)*
Karl Gernandt *(Vice Chm)*
Barbara Ruthmann *(Deputy Chm-Supervisory Bd)*
Peter Ganz *(Member-Exec Bd)*
Ulrich Kranich *(Member-Exec Bd)*

Non-U.S. Subsidiaries:

Adriatikagent Internationla Shipping Agency d.o.o. (2)
Cesta Dveh Cesarjev 403
1000 Ljubljana, Slovenia
Tel.: (386) 01 4769821
Fax: (386) 01 4769916
Container Shipping ervices
S.I.C.: 4412
N.A.I.C.S.: 483111

Agencia Maritima Remar S.R.L. (2)
Estrella 692 Floor 8 Ste 81
Asuncion, Paraguay
Tel.: (595) 21 497715
Fax: (595) 21 495597
Container Shipping Services
S.I.C.: 4412
N.A.I.C.S.: 483111

Agencia Naviera Europa S.A. (2)
Edif Plaza Maritima 4 Calle Entre
1 Y 2 Ave Barrio Guamilito, San Pedro Sula, Honduras
Tel.: (504) 2544 0450
Fax: (504) 2552 2192
Container Shipping Services
S.I.C.: 4412
N.A.I.C.S.: 483111

Agencias Continental S.A. (2)
Edif Eurocentro Ave Abel Bravo
Obarrio, Panama, Panama
Tel.: (507) 300 1400
Fax: (507) 300 1414
Container Shipping Services
S.I.C.: 4412
N.A.I.C.S.: 483111

Alson's Shipping Ltd. (2)
3 Abercromby Street
Port of Spain, Trinidad & Tobago
Tel.: (868) 6252201 5
Fax: (868) 6253691
Container Shipping Services
S.I.C.: 4412
N.A.I.C.S.: 483111

Aquamarine Shipping Co. Ltd. (2)
Room 8D Penthouse Building No 24-26
Race Course Condo
South Race Course Street, 11201 Yangon, Myanmar
Tel.: (95) 1 542725
Fax: (95) 1 542725
Container Shipping Services
S.I.C.: 4412
N.A.I.C.S.: 483111

Arkas Algerie S.p.A. (2)
7 rue de Sidi Yahi Lot B
16 016 Hydra, 16040 Algiers, Algeria
Tel.: (213) 21 43 58 82
Fax: (213) 21 43 58 96
Container Shipping Services
S.I.C.: 4412
N.A.I.C.S.: 483111

Arkas Shipping & Transport S.A. (2)
Liman Cadessi Arkas Binasi N 38
Alsancak, Tripoli, Libya
Tel.: (218) 21 340 25 28
Fax: (218) 21 340 34 96
Container Shipping Services
S.I.C.: 4412
N.A.I.C.S.: 483111

B ianchi & Co. (1916) Ltd. (2)
Palazza Marina
143 Saint Christopher Street, Valletta, Malta
Tel.: (356) 21232241
Fax: (356) 21237717
Container Shipping Services
S.I.C.: 4412
N.A.I.C.S.: 483111

Blue Funnell Angola (2)
AV 4 de Fevererio
1214 Luanda, Angola
Tel.: (244) 2 310007
Fax: (244) 2 310879
Contianer Shipping Services
S.I.C.: 4412
N.A.I.C.S.: 483111

Cargo Marine Ltd. (2)
Rear Port Area
AMA Building, Ashdod, Israel
Tel.: (972) 8 8527543
Fax: (972) 8 8527435
Container Shipping Services
S.I.C.: 4412
N.A.I.C.S.: 483111

Catoni 7 Co. (2)
3 8 Lessia Ukranka Street Apartment 8
0108 Tbilisi, Georgia
Tel.: (995) 32 989230
Fax: (995) 32 922264
Container Shipping Services
S.I.C.: 4412
N.A.I.C.S.: 483111

Coconut Products Ltd. (2)
Level 1 Carpenter House
Waigani Drive Sec 136 Allotment 4 Hohola, Port Moresby, Papua New Guinea
Tel.: (675) 3255166
Fax: (675) 3024290
Container Shipping Services
S.I.C.: 4412
N.A.I.C.S.: 483111

Delta Transport (Pvt.) Ltd. (2)
P 61 Ground Floor Chenab Market
Madina Town Susan Road, Faisalabad, Pakistan
Tel.: (92) 41 8728378
Fax: (92) 41 8710523
Container Shipping Services
S.I.C.: 4412
N.A.I.C.S.: 483111

GAC Shipping Nigeria Limited (2)
2 4 Edde Street
Kazuma Plaza Apapa, PMB 1285 Lagos, Nigeria
Tel.: (234) 1 764 1303
Fax: (234) 44 207 067 8857
Container Shipping Services
S.I.C.: 4412
N.A.I.C.S.: 483111

GBX Logistics Ltd. (2)
Ayub Trade Center 3rd Floor
1269 B SK Mujin Road Agrabad
Commercial Area, Chittagong, Bangladesh
Tel.: (880) 31 2516868
Fax: (880) 31 2516917
Container Shipping Services
S.I.C.: 4412
N.A.I.C.S.: 483111

Global Maritime Services Ltd. (2)
9 Pozitano St Entrance A
6th Floor office 20, 1303 Sofia, Bulgaria
Tel.: (359) 2 950 3530
Fax: (359) 2 981 9838
Container Shipping Services
S.I.C.: 4412
N.A.I.C.S.: 483111

Grindrod Ships Agencies Lda (2)
51 Praca Dos Trabalhadores 4th Floor
Maputo, Mozambique
Tel.: (258) 21 325891
Fax: (258) 21 322262
Container Shipping Services
S.I.C.: 4412
N.A.I.C.S.: 483111

Haji Abdullah Alireza & Co. Ltd. (2)
Shipping Department
Dammam, 31411, Saudi Arabia
Tel.: (966) 3 8324133
Fax: (966) 3 8337575
Container Shipping Services
S.I.C.: 4412
N.A.I.C.S.: 483111

Hapac-Lloyd (Schweiz) AG (2)
Suedquaistrasse 14
CH-4057 Basel, Switzerland
Tel.: (41) 61 63822 33
Fax: (41) 61 63822 70
Container Shipping Services
S.I.C.: 4412
N.A.I.C.S.: 483111

Hapag-Llotd (Japan) K.K. (2)
4 87 Ichibancho Chiyoda-Ku
Hapag-Lloyd House, Tokyo, 102-0082, Japan
Tel.: (81) 3 52126155
Fax: (81) 3 52126150
Container Shipping Services
S.I.C.: 4412
N.A.I.C.S.: 483111

Hapag-Lloyd (Africa) Pty. Ltd. (2)
13 Waterford News
Waterford Place Century City Blvd, 7441
Cape Town, South Africa
Tel.: (27) 21 527 5800
Fax: (27) 21 551 7792
Container Shipping Services
S.I.C.: 4412
N.A.I.C.S.: 483111

Hapag-Lloyd Agency LLC (2)
Office Court Building POB 124474
Suite 107-108 Oud Metha Road, Dubai, United Arab Emirates
Tel.: (971) 4 3871300
Fax: (971) 4 3708101
Container Shipping Services
S.I.C.: 4412
N.A.I.C.S.: 483111

Hapag-Lloyd Antwerpen (2)
Kattendukdok
B-2000 Antwerp, Belgium
Tel.: (32) 3 5450 611
Container Shipping Services
S.I.C.: 4412
N.A.I.C.S.: 483111

Hapag-Lloyd Argentina S.R.L. (2)
Bouchard 557 23rd Fl
C1106ABG Buenos Aires, Argentina
Tel.: (54) 11 4323 1000
Fax: (54) 11 4323 1045
Container Shipping Services
S.I.C.: 4412
N.A.I.C.S.: 483111

Hapag-Lloyd (Australia) Pty. Ltd. (2)
Unit 3 463 Nudgee Road
Hendra, Brisbane, QLD, 4011, Australia
Tel.: (61) 7 38682137
Fax: (61) 7 36301847
Container Shipping Services
S.I.C.: 4412
N.A.I.C.S.: 483111

Hapag-Lloyd Austria GmbH (2)
Gonzagogasse 1 1 11
A-1010 Vienna, Austria
Tel.: (43) 1 53448 0
Fax: (43) 1 53448 295
Container Shipping Services
S.I.C.: 4412
N.A.I.C.S.: 483111

Hapag-Lloyd Brazil (2)
Avenida Luis Carlos Berrini 1645
Brooklyn Novo, 04571-011 Sao Paulo, Brazil
Tel.: (55) 11 5504 9555
Fax: (55) 11 5506 1180
Container Shipping Services
S.I.C.: 4412
N.A.I.C.S.: 483111

Hapag-Lloyd (Canada) Inc. (2)
6708 Bayne St 2nd Fl
Fairview Cover Container Terminal, Halifax, NS, B3K 0A8, Canada
Tel.: (877) 893-4426
Liner Shipping Services
S.I.C.: 4412
N.A.I.C.S.: 483111

Hapag-Lloyd Chile Ag. Mar. Ltda. (2)
Ave El Bosque Norta 500 Piso 14
755-0092 Santiago, Chile
Tel.: (56) 2 24819400
Fax: (56) 2 24819498
Container Shipping Services
S.I.C.: 4412
N.A.I.C.S.: 483111

Hapag-Lloyd (China) Shipping Ltd. (2)
8F Citic Plaza
No 1350 North Sichuan Road, 200080 Shanghai, China
Tel.: (86) 21 26066000
Fax: (86) 21 26066001
Container Shipping Servicesfre
S.I.C.: 4412
N.A.I.C.S.: 483111

Hapag-Lloyd Colombia Ltda. (2)
Carrera 9A 99-02 Oficina 502B
Bogota, Colombia
Tel.: (57) 1 632 6030
Fax: (57) 1 236 4541
Container Shipping Services
S.I.C.: 4412
N.A.I.C.S.: 483111

Hapag-Lloyd Costa Rica S.A. (2)
Oficentro La Sabana
Torre 7 Piso 6, 1000 San Jose, Costa Rica
Tel.: (506) 2519 5900
Fax: (506) 2291 4631
Liner Shipping Services
S.I.C.: 4412
N.A.I.C.S.: 483111

Hapag-Lloyd Denamrk (2)
Roejelskaer15
DK-2840 Holte, Denmark

Tel.: (45) 45465 600
Fax: (45) 45465 601
Continer Shipping Services
S.I.C.: 4412
N.A.I.C.S.: 483111

Hapag-Lloyd (France) SAS (2)
99 Quai Du Docteur Dervaux
F-92600 Paris, France
Tel.: (33) 1 40802250
Fax: (33) 1 40802290
Container Shipping Services
S.I.C.: 4412
N.A.I.C.S.: 483111

Hapag-Lloyd Guatamala S.A. (2)
Avenida Reforma 9-55 Zona 10
Edif Reforma 10 Ofic 601A, Guatemala, 01010, Guatemala
Tel.: (502) 2205 4000
Fax: (502) 2360 2559
Container Shipping Services
S.I.C.: 4412
N.A.I.C.S.: 483111

Hapag-Lloyd (Ireland) Ltd. (2)
3rd Floor Russell House
Stokes Place Saint Stephens Green, 02 Dublin, Ireland
Tel.: (353) 1 4052542
Fax: (353) 1 4750252
Container Shipping Services
S.I.C.: 4412
N.A.I.C.S.: 483111

Hapag-Lloyd (korea) Ltd. (2)
Ste 902 Hanjin New Buildign
51 Sogong Dong Jung-Gu, Seoul, 100-070, Korea (South)
Tel.: (82) 2 37063000
Fax: (82) 2 7711330
Container Shipping Services
S.I.C.: 4412
N.A.I.C.S.: 483111

Hapag-Lloyd Lanka (Pvt.) Ltd. (2)
Level 1 Aitken Spence Tower II
No 315 Vauxhall Street, 02 Colombo, Sri Lanka
Tel.: (94) 11 2499505
Fax: (94) 11 2499517
Container Shipping Services
S.I.C.: 4412
N.A.I.C.S.: 483111

Hapag-Lloyd (Malaysia) Sdn. Bhd. (2)
45th Floor North Wing Menara TM
Jalan Pantai Baharu, 59200 Kuala Lumpur, Malaysia
Tel.: (60) 3 2245 8888
Fax: (60) 3 2240 0900
Container Shipping Services
S.I.C.: 4412
N.A.I.C.S.: 483111

Hapag-Lloyd Mexico S.A. De C.V. (2)
Sierra De Las Palomas 125 Interior
Bosques Del Prado Sur, 20130 Aguascalientes, Mexico
Tel.: (52) 449 9965434
Fax: (52) 449 2516075
Container Shipping Services
S.I.C.: 4412
N.A.I.C.S.: 483111

Hapag-Lloyd Overseas Transport S.A. (2)
Kasap Sokak
Arkas Binasi 2 4, TR-34394 Istanbul, Turkey
Tel.: (90) 212 3180044
Fax: (90) 212 2740280
Container Shipping Services
S.I.C.: 4412
N.A.I.C.S.: 483111

Hapag-Lloyd Peru S.A.C. (2)
Amador Merino Reyna 267 Ste 901
San Isidro, Peru
Tel.: (51) 1 3174100
Fax: (51) 1 3174188
Container Shipping Services
S.I.C.: 4412
N.A.I.C.S.: 483111

Hapag-Lloyd (Philippines) Inc. (2)
Door 4 Esperanza Building
AC Cortes Avenue, Mandaue, Philippines
Tel.: (63) 32 346 7716
Fax: (63) 32 346 9079
Container Shipping services
S.I.C.: 4412
N.A.I.C.S.: 483111

Hapag-Lloyd Polska SP. z.o.o. (2)
Ul Wspolna 35 12
00 519 Warsaw, Poland
Tel.: (48) 22 52278 00
Fax: (48) 22 52278 10
Container Shipping Services
S.I.C.: 4412
N.A.I.C.S.: 483111

Hapag-Lloyd Portugal Lda. (2)
Avenida D. Carlos I 44 5
P-1200-649 Lisbon, Portugal
Tel.: (351) 213943000
Fax: (351) 213964462
Container Shipping Services
S.I.C.: 4412
N.A.I.C.S.: 483111

Hapag-Lloyd Pte. Ltd. (2)
200 Cantonment Road 08-03
Southpoint Building, Singapore, 089763, Singapore
Tel.: (65) 62236119
Fax: (65) 62232182
Container Shipping services
S.I.C.: 4412
N.A.I.C.S.: 483111

Hapag-Lloyd Rotterdam (2)
Waalhaven O.Z. 79
3087 Rotterdam, Netherlands
Tel.: (31) 10 240 4400
Fax: (31) 10 240 4310
Container Shipping Services
S.I.C.: 4412
N.A.I.C.S.: 483111

Hapag-Lloyd Spain S.L. (2)
C Comtal 32-1
E-08002 Barcelona, Spain
Tel.: (34) 933436000
Fax: (34) 934121618
Container Shipping Services
S.I.C.: 4412
N.A.I.C.S.: 483111

Hapag-Lloyd Sweden AB (2)
Marieholsgatan 1
S-415 02 Gothenburg, Sweden
Tel.: (46) 31 3378 200
Fax: (46) 31 196446
Container Shipping Services
S.I.C.: 4412
N.A.I.C.S.: 483111

Hapag-Lloyd Taiwan Ltd. (2)
11F 285 Chung Hsiao Road east Road Sec 4
Taipei, 106, Taiwan
Tel.: (886) 2 21731600
Fax: (886) 2 27310062
Container Shipping Services
S.I.C.: 4412
N.A.I.C.S.: 483111

Hapag-Lloyd (Thailand) Ltd. (2)
127-29 Panjathani Tower 24th Floor
Nonsee Road Chong Nonsee Yannawa, Bangkok, 10120, Thailand
Tel.: (66) 2 6854200
Fax: (66) 2 6854280
Container Shipping Services
S.I.C.: 4412
N.A.I.C.S.: 483111

Hapag-Lloyd Venezuela, C.A. (2)
Av Fransisco De Miranda Edificio
Parque Cristol Piso 6 OFc 6-11, 1060 Caracas, Venezuela
Tel.: (58) 2122 2781000
Fax: (58) 212 2781050
Container Shipping Services
S.I.C.: 4412
N.A.I.C.S.: 483111

Hapag-Lloyd (Vietnam) (2)
4th Floor 1 C Ngo Quyen Street
Hoen Kiem District, Hanoi, Vietnam
Tel.: (84) 4 39366206
Fax: (84) 4 39366205
Container Shipping Services
S.I.C.: 4412
N.A.I.C.S.: 483111

Harbour Link Shipping Sdn. Bhd. (2)
Lot 11620 Unit 4 Ground Floor Block A
Scouts HQ Jln Gadong, BA1779 Bandar Seri Begawan, Brunei Darussalam
Tel.: (673) 2 456618
Fax: (673) 2 456347
Container Shipping Services
S.I.C.: 4412
N.A.I.C.S.: 483111

Hub Dacia S.R.L. (2)
157B Barbu Vacarescu Street Sector 2
R-020276 Bucharest, Romania
Tel.: (40) 21 2088700
Fax: (40) 21 2088711
Container Shipping Services
S.I.C.: 4412
N.A.I.C.S.: 483111

Hub Dunav d.o.o. (2)
22 Boze Jankovica 1st Floor Suite 2
11000 Belgrade, Serbia
Tel.: (381) 11 3988003
Fax: (381) 11 2495318
Container Shipping Services
S.I.C.: 4412
N.A.I.C.S.: 483111

Hub Levant Limited (2)
Baghdad Street
Montana Building 3rd Floor, Lattakia, Syria
Tel.: (963) 41 469194
Fax: (963) 41 470148
Container Shipping Services
S.I.C.: 4412
N.A.I.C.S.: 483111

Humberto Alvarez Sucesores De Nicaragua S.A. (2)
Carretera Norte De Los Semaforos
De La Sebasta 1 Km Al Norte, Managua, Nicaragua
Tel.: (505) 2263 1400
Fax: (505) 2263 1400
Contaier Shipping Services
S.I.C.: 4412
N.A.I.C.S.: 483111

Inchcape Shipping Services (Cambodia) Ltd. (2)
Ground Floor Regency Complex C Street
217 Number 18-20A 168
Vithei Preah Monireth, 12000 Phnom Penh, Cambodia
Tel.: (855) 23 424 731 6
Fax: (855) 23 424737
Container Shipping Services
S.I.C.: 4412
N.A.I.C.S.: 483111

Inchcape Shipping Services LLC (2)
Al Noor Street Way Number 3109
Buildign Number 483 Ground Floor, 112 Muscat, Ruwi, Oman
Tel.: (968) 24701291
Fax: (968) 24701713
Container Shipping Services
S.I.C.: 4412
N.A.I.C.S.: 483111

Inchcape Shipping Services WLL (2)
Buildign 1378 Office 22 2nd Floor
Buashurah, Sitra, Bahrain
Tel.: (973) 17 747445
Fax: (973) 17 720675
Container Shipping Services
S.I.C.: 4412
N.A.I.C.S.: 483111

ISS Shipping India Pvt. Ltd. (2)
4th Floor Office 402
Loha Bhavan NR Old High Court
ICICI Bank Lane Income Tax, Ahmedabad, Gujarat, 380006, India
Tel.: (91) 99989 45698
Container Shipping Services
S.I.C.: 4412
N.A.I.C.S.: 483111

Marine Trading Ltd. (2)
Black Rock Main Road
Saint Michael, Bridgetown, Barbados
Tel.: (246) 4291292
Fax: (246) 4298121
Container Shipping Services
S.I.C.: 4412
N.A.I.C.S.: 483111

Medlevant Shipping S.A.E. (2)
9 Hussein Hassab Street
From El Sultan Hussein, Alexandria, Egypt
Tel.: (20) 3 4885600
Fax: (20) 3 4833661
Container Shipping Services
S.I.C.: 4424
N.A.I.C.S.: 483113

Ocean Container Service (OCS) (2)
Ganibu Gambis
1005 Riga, Latvia
Tel.: (371) 6 77839 49
Fax: (371) 6 77839 47
Container Shipping Services
S.I.C.: 4412
N.A.I.C.S.: 483111

OCS Kaliningrad (2)
Gvardeiskii Prt 15 Of 610
236040 Kaliningrad, Russia
Tel.: (7) 4012 576105
Fax: (7) 112 576105
Container shipping Services
S.I.C.: 4412
N.A.I.C.S.: 483111

OCS Ocean Container Services Ltd. (2)
17 Sadama Street
E 10111 Tallinn, Estonia
Tel.: (372) 6 4018 02
Fax: (372) 6 4018 03
Container Shipping Services
S.I.C.: 4412
N.A.I.C.S.: 483111

OCS Ocean Container Services Ltd. (2)
Okeaninu Konteineriu Servisas
18 6 Birutes Street, 91210 Klaipeda, Lithuania
Tel.: (370) 46 3811 96
Fax: (370) 46 3811 82
Container Shipping Services
S.I.C.: 4412
N.A.I.C.S.: 483111

Oil & Marine Agencies (O.M.A.) SARL (2)
Concession Otam
Zone Portuire Port De Peche, Lome, Togo
Tel.: (228) 2 71 2776
Fax: (228) 2 71 2775
Container Shipping Services
S.I.C.: 4412
N.A.I.C.S.: 483111

Oil and Marine Agencies (Ghana) Ltd. (2)
2nd Floor North Wing
Atlantic Plaza Community 1, Tema, Ghana
Tel.: (233) 303 203 945
Fax: (233) 303 203 763
Container Shipping Services
S.I.C.: 4412
N.A.I.C.S.: 483111

Oil and Marine Agencies SARL (2)
08 BP 799
Cotonou, Benin
Tel.: (229) 21 315288
Fax: (229) 21 315431
Container Transport Services
S.I.C.: 4412
N.A.I.C.S.: 483111

Ot Hapag-Lloyd Finland AB (2)
MannerHeiminitie 14 A
FIN-00100 Helsinki, Finland
Tel.: (358) 9 689131
Container Shipping Services
S.I.C.: 4412
N.A.I.C.S.: 483111

Overseas Transport (Hellas) SA (2)
33 Akti Miaouli Street
GR-18535 Piraeus, Greece
Tel.: (30) 210 4596000
Fax: (30) 210 4293858
Container Shipping Services
S.I.C.: 4412
N.A.I.C.S.: 483111

Overseas Transport Ukraine Ltd. (2)
Office 4 Ul Uspenskaya 39
65125 Odessa, Ukraine
Tel.: (380) 48 7342174 75
Fax: (380) 48 7342182
Container Shipping Services
S.I.C.: 4412
N.A.I.C.S.: 483111

Papeete Seirland Transports (PST) (2)
Immeuble Franco-Oceanienne
Fare-Ute, Papeete, French Polynesia

Albert Ballin KG—(Continued)

Tel.: (689) 549700
Fax: (689) 549701
Container Shipping Services
S.I.C.: 4412
N.A.I.C.S.: 483111

Perez Y Cia Jamaica Ltd. (2)
6-12 Newport Blvd
13 Kingston, Jamaica
Tel.: (876) 757 6996
Fax: (876) 901 6114
Container Shipping Services
S.I.C.: 4412
N.A.I.C.S.: 483111

PT Samudera Indonesia, TBK. (2)
Cyber 2 Tower Level # A E F
JL Hr Rasuna Said Block X5 No 13,
Jakarta, 12950, Indonesia
Tel.: (62) 21 2934 3600
Fax: (62) 21 2934 3692
Container Shipping Services
S.I.C.: 4412
N.A.I.C.S.: 483111

Qatar Maritime & Mercantile Intl. Co. (2)
Suite 202 Al Jaber Towers 2nd Floor
Al Mudhaf Near Musium R B, Doha, Qatar
Tel.: (974) 44329810
Fax: (974) 44315190
Container Shipping Services
S.I.C.: 4412
N.A.I.C.S.: 483111

Quay Cargo Services Ltd. (2)
Victoria House 28 West Bank Road
Belfast, United Kingdom
Tel.: (44) 28 90371195
Fax: (44) 28 90371194
Container Shipping Services
S.I.C.: 4412
N.A.I.C.S.: 483111

Saget Maroc/Worms S.M. Group (2)
Port Agadir Immeuble Le Dauphin
Agadir, Morocco
Tel.: (212) 522 48 47 30
Container Shipping Services
S.I.C.: 4412
N.A.I.C.S.: 483111

SAM Shipping & Clearing Co. Ltd. (2)
Meena Street
Hodeidah, Hodeidah, Yemen
Tel.: (967) 3 203544/46/47
Fax: (967) 3 203551
Container Shipping Services
S.I.C.: 4412
N.A.I.C.S.: 483111

Societe Maritime Genmar SarL (2)
Zone Portuire Rades
2040 Tunis, Tunisia
Tel.: (216) 71 469070
Fax: (216) 71 469924
Container Shipping Services
S.I.C.: 4412
N.A.I.C.S.: 483111

Tourism & Shipping Services SarL (2)
386 Pasteur Street
Gemmayze, Beirut, Lebanon
Tel.: (961) 1 570771
Fax: (961) 1 570773
Container Shipping Services
S.I.C.: 4412
N.A.I.C.S.: 483111

Trans Global S.R.L. (2)
Calle 9 de Obrajes Edif El Zodiaco
Pio 1 of 101, La Paz, Bolivia
Tel.: (591) 2 2786881
Fax: (591) 2 2786701
Container Shipping Services
S.I.C.: 4412
N.A.I.C.S.: 483111

Transmeres S.A. De C.V. (2)
79 Ave Sur Colonia Escalon
EDF Plaza Cristol, San Salvador, El Salvador
Tel.: (503) 22065400
Fax: (503) 22065423
Liner Shipping Services
S.I.C.: 4412
N.A.I.C.S.: 483111

Transoceana Cia. Ltda. (2)
Malecon 1401 E Illingworth 3rd Fl
Guayaquil, Ecuador
Tel.: (593) 4 2598380
Fax: (593) 4 2598381
Container Shipping Services
S.I.C.: 4412
N.A.I.C.S.: 483111

Vassilopoulos Shipping Ltd. (2)
20 Strovolos Ave 2011
Nicosia, 1687, Cyprus
Tel.: (357) 22710000
Fax: (357) 22514000
Container Shipping Services
S.I.C.: 4412
N.A.I.C.S.: 483111

VR Shipping (Aruba) N.V. (2)
Caya GF Betico Croes Unit 12
Cayena Mall, Oranjestad, Aruba
Tel.: (297) 5824124
Fax: (297) 5825988
Container Shipping Services
S.I.C.: 4412
N.A.I.C.S.: 483111

VR Shipping NV (2)
Scarlet Building
Fokkerweg 26, Willemstad, Curacao
Tel.: (599) 9 4614700
Fax: (599) 9 4612576
Container Shipping Services
S.I.C.: 4412
N.A.I.C.S.: 483111

WSS Alarbab Shipping Co. (2)
University Area Buildign Number 1 5
Kabashi Issa Street, Khartoum, Sudan
Tel.: (249) 311 834153
Fax: (249) 311 834151
Container Shipping Services
S.I.C.: 4412
N.A.I.C.S.: 483111

ALBERT DAVID LTD

15 Chittar anjan Avenue 2nd Floor
Kolkata, 700072, India
Tel.: (91) 22129700
Fax: (91) 3322258714
E-Mail: adlho@adlindia.in
Web Site: www.albertdavidindia.com
524075—(BOM)
Rev.: $49,340,632
Assets: $38,858,487
Liabilities: $23,821,193
Net Worth: $15,037,293
Earnings: $1,586,783
Emp.: 1,500
Fiscal Year-end: 03/31/13

Business Description:
Pharmaceuticals Mfr
S.I.C.: 2834
N.A.I.C.S.: 325412

Personnel:
A. K. Kothari *(Chm & Mng Dir)*
S. C. Shah *(CFO & VP-Fin)*
Indrajit Dhar *(Compliance Officer, Sec & Assoc VP-Accts & Tax)*
H. P. Kabra *(Pres-Comml)*

Board of Directors:
A. K. Kothari
P. L. Agarwal
D. D. Binani
A. V. Iyengar
H. Kampani
K. P. Mundhra
R. Singhi

Transfer Agent:
Maheshwari Datamatics Pvt. Ltd.
6 Mangoe Lane 2nd Fl
Kolkata, 700 001, India
Tel.: (91) 33 22435029
Fax: (91) 913322484787

Unit:

Albert David Ltd. - Kolkatta Unit (1)
5/11 D Gupta Ln
Kolkata, West Bengal, 700 050, India
Tel.: (91) 3325571131
Fax: (91) 3325571181
E-Mail: hpkid@cal.vsnl.net.in
Web Site: www.albertdavidindia.com
Emp.: 300
Medicinal Products Mfr
S.I.C.: 2834
N.A.I.C.S.: 325412
T. Neogi *(VP)*

ALBERT GREIFENBERG GMBH & CO. KG

Gottwaldstr 17
D-45525 Hattingen, Germany
Tel.: (49) 232450080
Fax: (49) 232424757
E-Mail: info@albert-greifenberg.de
Web Site: www.albert-greifenberg.de
Year Founded: 1952
Rev.: $65,811,184
Emp.: 161

Business Description:
Pipe Connection Parts Mfr
S.I.C.: 3494
N.A.I.C.S.: 332919

Personnel:
Albert Greifenberg *(Founder & Co-Mng Dir)*
Maria Greifenberg-Bell *(Co-Mng Dir)*

ALBERT PASVAHL (GMBH & CO.)

Oehleckerring 23
22419 Hamburg, Germany
Tel.: (49) 40 53 28 52 0
Fax: (49) 40 53 28 52 52
E-Mail: info@pasvahl.de
Web Site: www.pasvahl.de
Year Founded: 1933
Rev.: $12,414,600
Emp.: 25

Business Description:
Connection Elements & Accessories Mfr
S.I.C.: 3452
N.A.I.C.S.: 332722

Personnel:
Helmut E. Kindler *(Mng Dir)*

ALBERT SCHUCK GMBH & CO. KG

Industriestr 20 - 22
D-63811 Stockstadt, Germany
Tel.: (49) 602720890
Fax: (49) 6027208949
E-Mail: info@albertschuck.de
Web Site: www.albertschuck.de
Year Founded: 1934
Rev.: $28,967,400
Emp.: 195

Business Description:
General Freight Trucking Services
S.I.C.: 4214
N.A.I.C.S.: 484110

Personnel:
Albert Schuck *(Co-Mng Dir)*
Anja Schuck *(Co-Mng Dir)*

ALBERT ZIEGLER GMBH & CO. KG

Memminger Strasse 28
89537 Giengen an der Brenz, Germany
Tel.: (49) 73229510
Fax: (49) 7322951211
E-Mail: ziegler@ziegler.de
Web Site: www.ziegler.de
Year Founded: 1891
Rev.: $284,288,442
Emp.: 636

Business Description:
Fire Service Vehicle Pump & Hose Mfr
S.I.C.: 3799
N.A.I.C.S.: 336999

Personnel:
Albert Jugel *(CEO)*

ALBERTA INVESTMENT MANAGEMENT CORPORATION

(d/b/a AIMCo)
1100-10830 Jasper Ave
Edmonton, AB, T5J 2B3, Canada
Tel.: (780) 392-3600
Fax: (780) 392-3899
E-Mail: inquiries@aimco.alberta.ca
Web Site: www.aimco.alberta.ca
Year Founded: 2008
Managed Assets: $70,000,000,000
Emp.: 250

Business Description:
Investment Management Services
S.I.C.: 6371
N.A.I.C.S.: 524292

Personnel:
A. Charles Baillie *(Chm)*
George F.J. Gosbee *(Vice Chm)*
Leo de Bever *(CEO & Chief Investment Officer)*
Jagdeep Singh Bachher *(COO)*
John Osborne *(Chief Risk Officer)*
Carole Hunt *(Sec)*
Lorne R. Anderson *(Sr VP-HR)*
Michael Dal Bello *(Sr VP-Real Estate)*
George Engman *(Sr VP-Private Equity)*
Brian Gibson *(Sr VP-Pub Equities)*
Dale MacMaster *(Sr VP-Fixed Income Investments)*
Robert Mah *(Sr VP-Infrastructure & Timber Investments)*

Board of Directors:
A. Charles Baillie
Clive Beddoe
J. Richard Bird
John T. Ferguson
George F.J. Gosbee
Ross Grieve
Virginia Holmes
Daryl A. Katz
Andrea Sarah Rosen
Mac H. Van Wielingen
Robert L. Vivian, Jr.
Cathy L. Williams

U.S. Joint Venture:

Puget Energy, Inc. (1)
10885 NE 4th St Ste 1200
Bellevue, WA 98004-5591 WA
Mailing Address:
PO Box 97034
Bellevue, WA 98009-9734
Tel.: (425) 454-6363
Fax: (425) 424-6537
Toll Free: (888) 225-5773
E-Mail: durga.waite@pse.com
Web Site: www.pugetenergy.com
Rev.: $3,187,297,000
Assets: $12,906,575,000
Liabilities: $9,226,896,000
Net Worth: $3,679,679,000
Earnings: $285,728,000
Fiscal Year-end: 12/31/13
Holding Company; Electric Power & Gas Distr
S.I.C.: 4911
N.A.I.C.S.: 221122
William S. Ayer *(Chm)*
Kimberly J. Harris *(Pres & CEO)*
Daniel A. Doyle *(CFO & Sr VP)*
Michael J. Stranik *(Chief Acctg Officer & Controller)*
Don E. Gaines *(Treas & VP-Fin)*

Subsidiary:

Puget Sound Energy, Inc. (2)
10885 NE 4th St Ste 1200
Bellevue, WA 98004-5591 WA
Mailing Address:
PO Box 97034
Bellevue, WA 98009-9734
Tel.: (425) 454-6363

Fax: (425) 424-6537
Web Site: www.pse.com
Rev.: $3,187,335,000
Assets: $10,808,888,000
Liabilities: $7,368,131,000
Net Worth: $3,440,757,000
Earnings: $356,129,000
Emp.: 2,700
Fiscal Year-end: 12/31/13
Electric Power & Natural Gas Distribution & Generation Services
S.I.C.: 4939
N.A.I.C.S.: 221122
William S. Ayer *(Chm)*
Kimberly J. Harris *(Pres & CEO)*
Daniel A. Doyle *(CFO & Sr VP)*
Rudiger H. Wolf *(CIO & VP)*
Jennifer L. O'Connor *(Gen Counsel, Sec, Sr VP, Chief Ethics & Compliance Officer)*
Eric M. Markell *(Chief Strategy Officer & Sr VP)*
Marla D. Mellies *(Sr VP & Chief Admin Officer)*
James W. Eldredge *(Chief Acctg Officer, VP & Controller)*
Steve R. Secrist *(VP, Gen Counsel & Chief Ethics & Compliance Officer)*
Donald E. Gaines *(Treas & VP-Fin)*
Paul M. Wiegand *(Sr VP-Energy Ops)*

Subsidiaries:

Hydro Energy Development Corp. (3)
10885 NE 4th St Ste 1200
Bellevue, WA 98004 WA
Tel.: (425) 456-2570
Fax: (425) 456-3128
Emp.: 3
Small Hydro Development
S.I.C.: 6794
N.A.I.C.S.: 533110
Martin Thompson *(VP)*

Puget Western, Inc. (3)
19515 North Creek Pkwy Ste 310
Bothell, WA 98011-8200 WA
Tel.: (425) 487-6550
Fax: (425) 487-6565
Web Site: www.pugetwestern.com
Emp.: 5
Real Estate Holding & Developing
S.I.C.: 6552
N.A.I.C.S.: 237210
Gus Erikson *(Pres)*

ALBERTA OILSANDS INC.

350 7th Ave SW Ste 2800
Calgary, AB, T2P 3N9, Canada
Tel.: (403) 263-6700
Fax: (403) 263-6702
E-Mail: mlee@aboilsands.ca
Web Site: www.aboilsands.ca
AOS—(TSXV)
Sales Range: $1-9.9 Million
Emp.: 15

Business Description:
Oil & Gas Exploration Services
S.I.C.: 1311
N.A.I.C.S.: 211111

Personnel:
Shabir Premji *(Chm)*
Michael L. Lee *(Pres)*
Michael Galloro *(Interim CFO)*
Binh Vu *(Sec)*
Chad Dust *(Exec VP-Fin & Bus Dev)*

Board of Directors:
Shabir Premji
Curtis Cohen
Jack Crawford
Adrian Goodisman
Michael Langley
Bill Matheson
Leonard Jay Sokolow
Binh Vu

Legal Counsel:
McLeod Dixon LLP
Calgary, AB, Canada

Blake, Cassels & Graydon LLP
Calgary, AB, Canada

ALBERTA PACIFIC FOREST INDUSTRIES INC

1199 W Hastings St Ste 300
Vancouver, BC, V6E 3T5, Canada
Tel.: (780) 525-8000
Fax: (780) 525-8189
Toll Free: (800) 661-5210
E-Mail: info@alpac.ca
Web Site: www.alpac.ca
Sales Range: $100-124.9 Million
Emp.: 450

Business Description:
Lumber Pulp Mill
S.I.C.: 5031
N.A.I.C.S.: 423310

Personnel:
Sam Terao *(Chm & CEO)*
Albert Ward *(Pres & COO)*
Bob Demcoe *(CFO & Exec VP)*

ALBERTA PENSION SERVICES CORPORATION

5103 Windermere Blvd SW
Edmonton, AB, T6W 0S9, Canada
Tel.: (780) 427-2782
Toll Free: (800) 661-8198
E-Mail: memberservices@apsc.ca
Web Site: www.apsc.ca
Year Founded: 1995

Business Description:
Pension Fund Administration Services
S.I.C.: 6371
N.A.I.C.S.: 524292

Personnel:
Karen Adams *(Pres & CEO)*

Affiliate:

Local Authorities Pension Plan (1)
5103 Windermere Blvd SW
Edmonton, AB, T6W 0S9, Canada
Mailing Address:
PO Box 1315
Edmonton, AB, T5J 2M8, Canada
Tel.: (780) 427-5447
Fax: (780) 427-5030
Web Site: www.lapp.ca
Pension Fund
S.I.C.: 6371
N.A.I.C.S.: 525110
Meryl Whittaker *(Pres & CEO)*
Roni DeBock *(Sec)*

ALBERTA STAR DEVELOPMENT CORP.

506-675 West Hastings Street
Vancouver, BC, V6B1N2, Canada
Tel.: (604) 488-0860
Fax: (604) 408-3884
E-Mail: astar@telus.net
Web Site: www.alberta-star.com
ASX—(TSXV)
Rev.: $2,407,781
Assets: $8,587,173
Liabilities: $2,059,536
Net Worth: $6,527,637
Earnings: ($3,454,829)
Emp.: 3
Fiscal Year-end: 11/30/12

Business Description:
Oil & Natural Gas Resource Exploration & Development
S.I.C.: 1381
N.A.I.C.S.: 213111

Personnel:
Stuart Rogers *(Interim CEO)*
Gordon Steblin *(CFO)*

Board of Directors:
Edward Burylo
Guido Cloetens
Robert T. Hall
Brian Morrison
Tom Ogryzlo
Stuart Rogers

ALBERTA TREASURY BRANCHES

(d/b/a ATB Financial)

ATB Financial 9888 Jasper Avenue
Edmonton, AB, T5J 1P1, Canada
Tel.: (780) 408-7000
E-Mail: atbinfo@atb.com
Web Site: www.atb.com
Year Founded: 1938
Rev.: $1,617,458,410
Assets: $32,882,275,038
Liabilities: $30,640,301,695
Net Worth: $2,241,973,343
Earnings: $243,336,096
Emp.: 5,250
Fiscal Year-end: 03/31/13

Business Description:
Financial Services
S.I.C.: 6726
N.A.I.C.S.: 525990

Personnel:
Brian W. Hesje *(Chm)*
David Mowat *(Pres & CEO)*
Jim McKillop *(CFO)*
Curtis Stange *(COO & Chief Strategy Officer)*
Dale Schitka *(CIO)*
Bob Mann *(Chief Risk Officer)*
Lorne Rubis *(Chief People Officer)*
Sheldon Dyck *(Pres-Investor Svcs)*
Vic Israni *(Treas & Sr VP)*
Stuart McKellar *(Sec & VP-Properties & Legal Svcs)*
Rob Bennett *(Exec VP-Retail Fin Svcs)*
Wellington Holbrook *(Exec VP-Bus & Agriculture)*
Ian Wild *(Exec VP-Corp Fin Svcs)*
Peggy Garritty *(Sr VP-Reputation & Brand)*
Brian Kjenner *(Sr VP-Advisory Svcs)*
Dwayne Mann *(Sr VP-Credit)*
Rajesh Ramakrishnan *(Sr VP-Products & Pricing-Retail Fin Svcs)*

Board of Directors:
Brian W. Hesje
Garnet Altwasser
Doug Baker
James E. C. Carter
Bob Carwell
Lloyd Craig
James M. Drinkwater
Arthur Froehlich
Joan Hertz
Bern Kotelko
Colette Miller
Michael Percy

Transfer Agent:
International Financial Data Services
Toronto, ON, Canada

ALBIDON LIMITED

(Acquired by Jinchuan Group Limited)

ALBINI & PITIGLIANI S.P.A.

Viale G Marconi 46
59100 Prato, Italy
Tel.: (39) 05745730
Fax: (39) 0574571791
Web Site: www.albinipitigliani.it
Emp.: 400

Business Description:
Freight Forwarding Services
S.I.C.: 4731
N.A.I.C.S.: 488510

Personnel:
Sandro Pitigliani *(Pres)*

U.S. Subsidiary:

ALPI USA, Inc. (1)
700 Nicholas Blvd Ste 411
Elk Grove Village, IL 60007
Tel.: (847) 364-5342
Fax: (847) 364-4904
Toll Free: (888) 742-2574
E-Mail: sales@alpiusa.com
Web Site: www.alpiusa.com
Emp.: 9
Foreign Freight Forwarding
S.I.C.: 4731
N.A.I.C.S.: 488510
Piero Albini *(Pres)*

ALBIOMA SA

22 place des Vosges Immeuble Le Monge
La Defense 5, 92400 Courbevoie, France
Tel.: (33) 1 41 16 82 00
Web Site: www.albioma.com
Year Founded: 1982
33S—(DEU)
Rev.: $503,213,154
Assets: $1,610,918,562
Liabilities: $1,135,922,477
Net Worth: $474,996,085
Earnings: $52,951,597
Fiscal Year-end: 12/31/12

Business Description:
Power Generation Services
S.I.C.: 4931
N.A.I.C.S.: 221117

Personnel:
Jacques Petry *(Chm & CEO)*
Michel Bleitrach *(Vice Chm)*
Julien Gauthier *(CFO)*
Pascal Langeron *(Co-COO)*
Frederic Moyne *(Co-COO)*
Mickael Renaudeau *(Sec)*

Board of Directors:
Jacques Petry
Jean-Carlos Angulo
Michel Bleitrach
Patrick de Giovanni
Myriam Maestroni
Edgard Misrahi
Michele Remillieux
Maurice Tchenio
Daniel Valot

Mazars
Tour Exaltis 61 rue Henri-Regnault
Courbevoie, France

ALBION VENTURES LLP

1 Kings Arm Yard
London, EC2R 7AF, United Kingdom
Tel.: (44) 2076011850
Fax: (44) 2076011875
E-Mail: info@albion-ventures.co.uk
Web Site: www.albion-ventures.co.uk
Sales Range: $250-299.9 Million
Emp.: 35

Business Description:
Venture Capital Trust Management Services
S.I.C.: 6211
N.A.I.C.S.: 523999

Personnel:
Patrick Reeve *(Mng Dir)*

ALBIS CO., LTD.

3-4 Mitoda Ryutsu Center
Imizu-shi, Toyama, 939-0402, Japan
Tel.: (81) 766567200
Fax: (81) 766567520
Web Site: www.albis.co.jp
7475—(TKS)
Sales Range: $650-699.9 Million
Emp.: 720

Business Description:
Supermarket Owner & Operator
S.I.C.: 5411
N.A.I.C.S.: 445110

Personnel:
Minoru Ohmori *(Pres)*

ALBIS OPTOELECTRONICS AG

(Formerly Enablence Switzerland AG)
Moosstrasse 2a
Ruschlikon, Zurich, 8803, Switzerland
Tel.: (41) 433880610
Fax: (41) 433880611

Albis Optoelectronics AG—(Continued)

Web Site: www.albisopto.com
Emp.: 16
Business Description:
Optical Component Mfr
S.I.C.: 3827
N.A.I.C.S.: 333314
Personnel:
Vincent Grundlehner *(CEO)*
Markus Blaser *(CTO)*

ALBORZ INSURANCE COMPANY

No 1320 Next to Aban St S Hariati Ave
Tehran, Iran
Tel.: (98) 21 88803821
Fax: (98) 21 88908088
E-Mail: Info@alborzins.com
Web Site: en.alborzins.com
Year Founded: 1959
BALB—(THE)
Business Description:
Insurance Services
S.I.C.: 6411
N.A.I.C.S.: 524298
Personnel:
Amin Mohammad Ebrahim *(Chm & Mng Dir)*
Board of Directors:
Amin Mohammad Ebrahim
Tavakoli Hossein
Taghvaei Mohammadreza
Tajdar Rasool

ALBOURNE PARTNERS LIMITED

16 Palace Street
London, SW1E 5JD, United Kingdom
Tel.: (44) 207 346 7000
Fax: (44) 207 346 7001
Web Site: www.albourne.com
Year Founded: 1994
Sales Range: $50-74.9 Million
Emp.: 200
Business Description:
Investment Advisor & Consulting
S.I.C.: 6799
N.A.I.C.S.: 523930
Personnel:
Simon Ruddick *(Mng Dir)*

ALCATEL-LUCENT

3 avenue Octave Greard
75007 Paris, France
Tel.: (33) 1 40 76 10 10
Telex: 651953
Fax: (33) 1 40 76 14 00
E-Mail: execoffice@alcatel-lucent.com
Web Site: www.alcatel-lucent.com
Year Founded: 1898
ALU—(EUR NYSE TKS)
Rev.: $19,446,771,820
Assets: $28,760,922,050
Liabilities: $25,138,378,580
Net Worth: $3,622,543,470
Earnings: ($1,953,292,670)
Emp.: 72,344
Fiscal Year-end: 12/31/12
Business Description:
Wireline & Mobile Telecommunications Infrastructure Design Services
S.I.C.: 4899
N.A.I.C.S.: 517919
Personnel:
Philippe Camus *(Chm)*
Michel Combes *(CEO)*
Jean Raby *(CFO & Chief Legal Officer)*
Paul J. Tufano *(CFO)*
Tim Krause *(CMO)*
Marcus Weldon *(Corp CTO)*
Philippe Keryer *(Chief Strategy & Innovation Officer)*
Georges Nazi *(Pres-Global Customer Delivery, Chief Quality Officer & Exec VP)*
Stephan Vantomme *(Treas)*
Yohann Benard *(Sec)*
Gabrielle Gauthey *(Exec VP & Head-Global Pub Affairs)*
Kenneth Frank *(Exec VP)*
Rod H. E. Powell *(Exec VP-Ops)*
Board of Directors:
Philippe Camus
Daniel Bernard
Carla Cico
Stuart E. Eizenstat
Kim Crawford Goodman
Louis R. Hughes
Sylvia Jay
Jean C. Monty
Olivier Piou
Jean-Cyril Spinetta

Deloitte & Associes
Neuilly-sur-Seine, France

Subsidiaries:

Alcatel CIT (S.A.) (1)
7-9 Avenue Morane Saulnier
78141 Valence, Cedex, France
Tel.: (33) 130773077
Telex: 696 539
Fax: (33) 130779750
Web Site: www.all.alcatel-lucent.com
Emp.: 7,000
Telecommunication Equipment Research & Development Services
Import Export
S.I.C.: 4813
N.A.I.C.S.: 517110
Perre Cossinieres *(CFO)*

Subsidiary:

Alcatel Space (2)
54 Rue La Boetie
75008 Paris, France (100%)
Tel.: (33) 146526200
Fax: (33) 146526250
Web Site: www.alcatel.com
Mfr. & Developer of Space-Based Communication Systems Hardware
S.I.C.: 4812
N.A.I.C.S.: 517210

Alcatel-Lucent International SAS (1)
3 Avenue Octave Greard
75007 Paris, France
Tel.: (33) 130773077
Web Site: www.alcatel-lucent.com
Investment Management Services
S.I.C.: 6211
N.A.I.C.S.: 523999

Alcatel Participations SA (1)
3 Avenue Octave Greard
75007 Paris, France (100%)
Tel.: (33) 140761010
Telex: 202 707
Fax: (33) 140761400
Web Site: www.alcatel.fr
Emp.: 66
Holding Company
S.I.C.: 6719
N.A.I.C.S.: 551112
Pierre Solal *(Pres & Gen Dir)*
Serge Gchuruk *(Mng Dir)*

Subsidiaries:

Alcatel Business Systems (France) (2)
32 Ave Kleber
92707 Colombes, Cedex, France
Tel.: (33) 155667000
Telex: 202707
Fax: (33) 155664338
Web Site: www.alcatellucent.com
Emp.: 500
Telephone Sets, Videotext Terminals, Telefax Equipment, Telex, Data Communication Systems & Mail Processing Systems Mfr & Developer
S.I.C.: 3661
N.A.I.C.S.: 334210

Alcatel Business Systems (2)
1 Rte du Dr Albert Schweitzer
67400 Illkirch-Graffenstaden, France
Tel.: (33) 390676790
Fax: (33) 390677361
E-Mail: celine.westphal@alcatellucent.fr
Web Site: www.alcatellucent.com
Emp.: 600
Telephone Sets, Videotext Terminals, Telefax Equipment, Telex, Data Communication Systems & Mail Processing Systems Mfr & Developer
S.I.C.: 3661
N.A.I.C.S.: 334210

Alcatel Submarine Networks S.A. (1)
Centre de Villarceaux
Route de Villejust, 91620 Nozay, Cedex, France (100%)
Tel.: (33) 130773077
Fax: (33) 130776806
Web Site: www.alcatel.com
Emp.: 1,000
Undersea Communications Networks Provider
S.I.C.: 3669
N.A.I.C.S.: 334290

Non-U.S. Subsidiaries:

Alcatel Submarine Networks Marine A/S (2)
Marine Maintenance Center
Islands Brygge 43, DK 2300 Copenhagen, Denmark (100%)
Tel.: (45) 4480 7544
Fax: (45) 4480 7579
E-Mail: ove.smidt@alcatel-lucent.dk
Web Site: www1.alcatel-lucent.com
Emp.: 160
Telecommunications Equipment & Services
S.I.C.: 3669
N.A.I.C.S.: 334290
Ove Smidt *(Reg Dir)*

Alcatel Submarine Networks (2)
6 Commonwealth Land #01-01
GMTI Building, 149547 Singapore, Singapore
Tel.: (65) 65861377
Fax: (65) 6586 1480
Undersea Communications Networks Provider
S.I.C.: 3669
N.A.I.C.S.: 334290

Alcatel Transport Automation Solutions (1)
7-9 Ave Morane Saulnier
PO Box 57
78141 Velizy-Villacoublay, France (100%)
Tel.: (33) 130773077
Fax: (33) 130779570
Web Site: www.alcatel.com
Train Control & Signalling Equipment Mfr
S.I.C.: 3669
N.A.I.C.S.: 334290

Non-U.S. Operating Divisions:

Alcatel Transport Automation Solutions (Austria) (2)
Scheydgasse 41
A 1210 Vienna, Austria (100%)
Tel.: (43) 1277220
Fax: (43) 1277221115
E-Mail: office@alcatel-lucent.com
Web Site: www.alcatel.at
Emp.: 600
Train Control & Signalling Equipment Mfr
S.I.C.: 3669
N.A.I.C.S.: 334290
Harald Himmer *(Mng Dir)*

Alcatel Transport Automation Solutions (China) (2)
17F Central Tower Junefield Plz 10
Xuanwumenwai St
Xuanwu District, 100052 Beijing, China (100%)
Tel.: (86) 1063108822
Train Control & Signalling Equipment Mfr
S.I.C.: 3669
N.A.I.C.S.: 334290

Alcatel Transport Automation Solutions (2)
170 Burg Elsenlaan
PO Box 3292
NL-2288 BH Rijswijk, Netherlands
Tel.: (31) 703079111
Fax: (31) 703079274
E-Mail: info@alcatel-lucent.com
Web Site: www.alcatel-lucent.nl
Emp.: 500
Train Control & Signalling Equipment Mfr
S.I.C.: 3669
N.A.I.C.S.: 334290
Ben Verwaaijen *(Gen Mgr)*

Alcatel Transport Automation Solutions (2)
Lorenzstrasse 10
70435 Stuttgart, Germany (100%)
Tel.: (49) 71182138700
Fax: (49) 7118211111
E-Mail: info@alcatel-lucent.com
Web Site: www.alcatel-lucent.de
Emp.: 3,000
Train Control & Signalling Equipment Mfr
S.I.C.: 3669
N.A.I.C.S.: 334290
Wilhelm Dresselhaus *(Gen Mgr)*

Coralec (1)
21 Rue Des Ecoles
Aulnay-sous-Bois, Seine Saint Denis, 93600, France
Tel.: (33) 1 48 66 17 92
Fax: (33) 1 48 79 23 04
Communication Software Development Services
S.I.C.: 7371
N.A.I.C.S.: 541511

U.S. Subsidiaries:

Alcatel-Lucent Puerto Rico (1)
654 Plz Bldg Ste 1207 654 Munoz Rivera Ave
San Juan, PR 00918
Tel.: (787) 641-2602
Telecommunication Services
S.I.C.: 4899
N.A.I.C.S.: 517919

Alcatel-Lucent USA Inc. (1)
600-700 Mountain Ave
New Providence, NJ 07974 DE
Tel.: (908) 508-8080
Web Site: www.alcatel-lucent.com
Wireline & Mobile Telecommunications Infrastructure Design Services
S.I.C.: 4899
N.A.I.C.S.: 517919
Sandip Mukerjee *(Pres-IMS Solutions)*
Janet Davidson *(Exec VP)*

Co-Headquarters:

Alcatel-Lucent USA Inc. (2)
3400 W Plano Pkwy
Plano, TX 75019 DE
Tel.: (972) 519-3000
Fax: (972) 477-6878
Toll Free: (800) ALCATEL
Web Site: www.alcatel-lucent.com
Sales Range: $600-649.9 Million
Emp.: 6,753
Mfr., Designer, Developer & Marketer of Digital Switching, Transmission, Access & Private Network System Products
Import Export
S.I.C.: 3661
N.A.I.C.S.: 334210
Kenneth Frank *(Pres-Solutions, Exec VP & Mktg)*

Branches:

Alcatel-Lucent USA Inc. - Calabasas (3)
26801 W Agoura Rd
Calabasas, CA 91301-5122
Tel.: (818) 880-3500
Fax: (818) 880-3505
Toll Free: (800) 995-2612
Web Site: www.alcatellucent.com
Emp.: 300
IP Communications Infrastructure & Solutions Provider
S.I.C.: 3575
N.A.I.C.S.: 334118

Alcatel-Lucent USA Inc. - Raleigh (3)
2301 Sugar Bush Rd
Raleigh, NC 27612
Tel.: (919) 850-6000
Fax: (919) 850-5274

Web Site: www.alcatel-lucent.com
Emp.: 250
Telecommunications Equipment Mfr
S.I.C.: 3661
N.A.I.C.S.: 334210

Subsidiaries:

Alcatel-Lucent Bell Labs (3)
600-700 Mountain Ave
New Providence, NJ 07974-0636
Tel.: (908) 582-8500
Fax: (908) 508-2576
E-Mail: execoffice@lucent.com
Web Site: www.bell-labs.com
Sales Range: $1-4.9 Billion
Emp.: 80,000
Research & Manufacturing
S.I.C.: 7299
N.A.I.C.S.: 812990
Marcus Weldon *(Pres)*

Units:

Bell Labs Nanofabrication Center (4)
600-700 Mountain Ave
New Providence, NJ 07974
Tel.: (908) 582-8200
Fax: (908) 582-2793
Toll Free: (877) NJNC-ORG
E-Mail: info@njnano.org
Web Site: www.njnano.org
Emp.: 10
Nanotechnology Research & Development Services
S.I.C.: 7373
N.A.I.C.S.: 541512
Alice E. White *(Pres)*

Non-U.S. Subsidiary:

Bell Labs Research, India (4)
Salarpuria Ascent 3rd Floor No 77 Jyothi Nivas College Rd
Bengaluru, 560095, India
Tel.: (91) 8039832000
Fax: (91) 8039832499
Computer & Communications Research
S.I.C.: 8731
N.A.I.C.S.: 541712
Rajeev Rastogi *(Exec Dir)*

Non-U.S. Unit:

Alcatel-Lucent Bell Labs Ireland Research Center (4)
Blanchardstown Industrial Park
Blanchardstown, Dublin, 15, Ireland
Tel.: (353) 18864444
Web Site: www.alcatel-lucent.com
Emp.: 50
Computer & Communications Research & Development
S.I.C.: 8731
N.A.I.C.S.: 541712
Julie Byrne *(Mng Dir)*

ALCATEL-LUCENT INTERNATIONAL HOLDINGS Inc. (3)
2711 Centerville Rd Ste 400
Wilmington, DE 19808
Tel.: (302) 636-5400
Investment Management Services
S.I.C.: 6282
N.A.I.C.S.: 523920

Alcatel Lucent Security (3)
2500 W Utopia Rd
Phoenix, AZ 85027-4129
Tel.: (623) 582-7000
Fax: (623) 581-4158
Emp.: 212
Switching Equipment for Telephones Mfr
S.I.C.: 3661
N.A.I.C.S.: 334210
David P. Strand *(Dir)*

Capella Photonics, Inc. (3)
5390 Hellyer Ave
San Jose, CA 95138 DE
Tel.: (408) 360-4240
Fax: (408) 225-6248
E-Mail: info@capellainc.com
Web Site: www.capellainc.com
Sales Range: $1-9.9 Million
Emp.: 19
Wavelength Selective Switch Technology Developer & Mfr
S.I.C.: 3669
N.A.I.C.S.: 334290
George Berberis *(COO)*
Byron Trop *(Exec VP-Sls)*

LGS Innovations LLC (3)
13665 Dulles Technology Dr Ste 301
Herndon, VA 20171
Tel.: (866) 547-4243
Fax: (703) 394-1420
Web Site: www.lgsinnovations.com
Emp.: 650
Network Designing Services
S.I.C.: 7373
N.A.I.C.S.: 541512
Kevin L. Kelly *(CEO)*
Debra Pfaff *(CFO)*
Rich Martin *(CIO)*
Robert Farr *(CMO)*

Motive Product Group (3)
12515 Research Blvd Bldg 5
Austin, TX 78759 DE
Tel.: (512) 339-8335
Fax: (512) 339-9040
E-Mail: pr@motive.com
Web Site: www.motive.com
Sales Range: $75-99.9 Million
Emp.: 205
Digital Life Management Software & Services
S.I.C.: 7372
N.A.I.C.S.: 511210
Markus Remark *(Sr VP-Svcs-Worldwide)*

ReachView Technologies (3)
800 North Point Pkwy
Alpharetta, GA 30005-4124
Tel.: (770) 612-0995
Fax: (770) 612-0882
E-Mail: info@reachview.com
Web Site: www.reachview.com
Sales Range: $1-9.9 Million
Emp.: 85
Software & Consulting Services
S.I.C.: 5045
N.A.I.C.S.: 423430
Frank Wood *(VP-Solution Architecture)*

Non-U.S. Subsidiaries:

Alcatel-Lucent Australia Limited (1)
5 Rider Boulevard Rd
Rhodes, NSW, 2138, Australia
Tel.: (61) 283065222
Fax: (61) 283065111
E-Mail: alcatel@lucent.com.al
Web Site: www.alcatel.com
Emp.: 800
Telecommunications & Internet Products & Services
S.I.C.: 4899
N.A.I.C.S.: 517919
Andrew Butterworth *(VP)*

Branches:

Alcatel-Lucent Australia Limited (2)
5 Rider A Boulevard Rhodes
2138 Sydney, NSW, Australia AU
Mailing Address: (100%)
GPO Box 525
Sydney, NSW, 2001, Australia
Tel.: (61) 283065222
Fax: (61) 283065111
Web Site: www.alcatellucent.com
Rev.: $409,640,000
Emp.: 900
Mfr. of Telephones, Switching & Transmission Equipment, Power Rectrifiers & Computers
S.I.C.: 4813
N.A.I.C.S.: 517110
Henry Betterworth *(Mng Dir)*

Alcatel-Lucent Australia Limited (2)
68-72 Waterloo Road
North Ryde, NSW, 2113, Australia
Tel.: (61) 294916500
Fax: (61) 294916900
Emp.: 500
Business & Consumer Telecommunications Systems
S.I.C.: 4812
N.A.I.C.S.: 517110
George Sideris *(Gen Counsel, Sec & Dir)*

Alcatel-Lucent Austria AG (1)
Scheydgasse 41
1210 Vienna, Austria AT
Tel.: (43) 1277220 (100%)
Telex: 1147573; 114579
Fax: (43) 1277221115
E-Mail: office@alcatel-lucent.com
Web Site: www.alcatel.com
Rev.: $207,480,000
Emp.: 601
Mfr. of Telecommunications Equipment, Railway Signalling Equipment & Electronic Components
S.I.C.: 3679
N.A.I.C.S.: 334418
Harald Himmer *(CEO)*
Erwin Teufner *(Chief Tech Officer)*

Joint Venture:

TETRON Sicherheitsnetz Errichtungs und BetriebsgmbH (2)
Hohenbergstrasse 1/Objekt 3
1120 Vienna, Austria AT
Tel.: (43) 181514130
Fax: (43) 18151413937099
Web Site: www.tetron.at
Secure Radio Network
S.I.C.: 4832
N.A.I.C.S.: 515111
Albert Schauer *(CEO & Chm-Mgmt Bd)*
Stefan Semlegger *(Mng Dir & Member-Mgmt Bd)*

Alcatel-Lucent Baltics SIA (1)
Biroju Centrs Europa Ropazu Iela 10 9th Floor
Riga, 1039, Latvia
Tel.: (371) 67085200
Fax: (371) 67085205
E-Mail: info@alcatel-lucent.lv
Emp.: 2
Networking & Communication Technology Services
S.I.C.: 4899
N.A.I.C.S.: 517919
Armands Dirins *(Mng Dir)*

Alcatel-Lucent Brasil S/A (1)
Av Marginal Direita Da Anchieta 400 Km 11 5 Jardim Santa Cruz
Sao Paulo, 04182-901, Brazil
Tel.: (55) 1129478133
Fax: (55) 1129478289
E-Mail: alcatel_lucent.brasil@alcatel-lucent.com
Web Site: www.alcatel-lucent.com.br
Emp.: 2,000
Communication Equipment Mfr
S.I.C.: 3669
N.A.I.C.S.: 334290
Jonio Kahan Foigel *(Pres)*

Subsidiaries:

Alcatel-Lucent Technologies Brasil Ltda. (2)
700 Avenida das Americas Terceiro Piso Sala 321 Edificio Citta
Americas Barra da Tijuca, CEP 22640-100
Rio de Janeiro, RJ, Brazil
Tel.: (55) 11 2947 8133
Web Site: www3.alcatel-lucent.com
Business & Consumer Telecommunications Systems
S.I.C.: 4813
N.A.I.C.S.: 517110

Alcatel-Lucent Telecomunication (2)
Ave Marginal Direita Anchieta 400 Km 115
Jardim Santa Cruz, Sao Paulo, 04182-901, Brazil (100%)
Tel.: (55) 1129478133
Fax: (55) 1129478674
Web Site: www.alcatel-lucent.com
Emp.: 1,151
Telecommunications Infrastructure Services
S.I.C.: 4813
N.A.I.C.S.: 517110
Jonio Kahan Foigel *(Pres)*

Joint Venture:

Lucent Technologies Network Systems do Brasil S.A. (2)
Rua Thomas Nilsen Jr 150
Parqui Imperador, 13097 660 Campinas, SP, Brazil
Tel.: (55) 937077000
Fax: (55) 551130000000
Web Site: www.lucent.com.br
Emp.: 250
Joint Venture Among Lucent Technologies International Inc. (49%), SID Telecommunication Centrales (49%) & Marcep S.A. (2%)
S.I.C.: 4813
N.A.I.C.S.: 517110

Alcatel-Lucent Brunei (1)
Block B Unit 1 Hassanin Complex Spg 42
Jln Muara Kg Pancha Delima
Bandar Seri Begawan, 4513, Brunei Darussalam
Tel.: (673) 2266 500
Fax: (673) 2266 588
Emp.: 50
Communication Equipment Mfr
S.I.C.: 3669
N.A.I.C.S.: 334290
Euu Nguang Pang *(Dir-Sls & Mktg)*

Alcatel-Lucent Cambodia (1)
23rd Floor Canadia Tower No 315 Ang Duong Street Corner Monivong Blvd
Sangkat Wat Phnom, Phnom Penh, Cambodia
Tel.: (855) 23 43 22 33
Fax: (855) 23 43 11 22
Emp.: 3
Communication Equipment Mfr
S.I.C.: 3669
N.A.I.C.S.: 334290
Malcolm Penn *(CEO)*

Alcatel-Lucent Canada Inc. (1)
600 March Road
Ottawa, ON, K2K 2E6, Canada ON
Tel.: (613) 591-3600 (100%)
Fax: (613) 784-8919
E-Mail: hrc.nar@alcatel-lucent.com
Emp.: 2,500
Telecommunications Networking Company Export
S.I.C.: 4813
N.A.I.C.S.: 517110
Susan Brewer *(Dir-Mktg-Alcatel Canada)*

Branches:

Alcatel-Lucent Canada Inc. - Markham (2)
1380 Rodick Rd
Markham, ON, L3R 4G5, Canada
Tel.: (905) 943-5000
Fax: (905) 752-8780
Emp.: 150
Cable & Telephone Switches
S.I.C.: 3661
N.A.I.C.S.: 334210
Alex Giosa *(Pres)*

Unit:

Alcatel-Lucent Transport Automation (3)
1380 Rodick Rd
Markham, ON, L3R4G5, Canada
Tel.: (905) 943-5000
Fax: (905) 752-8780
E-Mail: infotas.ca@tas.alcatel.ca
Emp.: 55
Train Control & Signalling Equipment Mfr
S.I.C.: 3669
N.A.I.C.S.: 334290
Kevin Fitzgerald *(Dir-Lab Support)*

Alcatel-Lucent Canada Inc. - Montreal (2)
600 de Maisonneuve Boulevard West Suite 750
Montreal, QC, H3A 3J2, Canada
Tel.: (514) 935-7750
Fax: (514) 935-8405
Web Site: www.alcatel.com
Sales Range: $10-24.9 Million
Emp.: 100
Communications Solutions Provider
S.I.C.: 3669
N.A.I.C.S.: 334290
Pascal Allard *(Mng Dir)*

Alcatel-Lucent Canada Inc. - Toronto (2)
2425 Matheson Boulevard East Suite 600
Mississauga, ON, L4W 5K4, Canada
Tel.: (905) 282-8572
Fax: (905) 238-0581
Emp.: 80
Communications Solutions Provider
S.I.C.: 3669
N.A.I.C.S.: 334290
Susan Brewer *(Gen Mgr)*

Subsidiary:

Alcatel Holdings Canada Limited (2)
600 March Rd
Ottawa, ON, K2K 2E6, Canada

Alcatel-Lucent—(Continued)

Tel.: (613) 591-3600
Fax: (613) 784-8919
Investment Management Services
S.I.C.: 6211
N.A.I.C.S.: 523999

Alcatel-Lucent Chili S.A. (1)
Avenida Providencia 1760 Piso 20
750 0498 Santiago, Chile
Tel.: (56) 2 230 3500
Fax: (56) 2 230 3909
Web Site: www.Alcatel.com
Emp.: 20
Wired Telecommunication Services
S.I.C.: 4813
N.A.I.C.S.: 517110
Johnson Chen *(Country Mgr)*

ALCATEL-LUCENT CHINA INVESTMENT CO., LTD (1)
8/F Bldg 3 No 388 Ningqiao Road Jinqiao Exporting Processing
Shanghai, 201206, China
Tel.: (86) 2138561000
Fax: (86) 2138561006
Investment Management Services
S.I.C.: 6799
N.A.I.C.S.: 523920

Alcatel-Lucent Colombia (1)
Carrera 16 No 100 20 Piso 6
Bogota, Colombia
Tel.: (57) 1 6342500, ext. 2950
Fax: (57) 1 6111552
Emp.: 10
Wireless Telecommunication Services
S.I.C.: 4812
N.A.I.C.S.: 517210
Carlos Alberto Pena Perez *(Gen Mgr)*

Alcatel-Lucent Czech s.r.o (1)
U Uranie 18/954
170 00 Prague, Czech Republic (100%)
Tel.: (420) 281080111
Fax: (420) 281080222
Web Site: www.alcatel-lucent.cz
Emp.: 11
Telecommunications Equipment & Solutions Provider
S.I.C.: 3669
N.A.I.C.S.: 334290
David Grundel *(Mng Dir)*

Alcatel-Lucent Danmark A/S (1)
Islands Brygge 43
2300 Copenhagen, Denmark (100%)
Tel.: (45) 44807500
Fax: (45) 44807579
E-Mail:
Web Site: www.alcatel.dk
Emp.: 25
Telecommunications Equipment & Services Provider
S.I.C.: 3669
N.A.I.C.S.: 334290
Peter Sinpk *(Gen Mgr)*

Alcatel-Lucent de Costa Rica S.A. (1)
Officio Centro Ejecutivo La Sabana Torre 7 Piso 8
PO Box 303 1007
Sabana Sur, San Jose, Costa Rica CR
Tel.: (506) 2242 1801
Fax: (506) 2242 1905
Emp.: 38
Business & Consumer Telecommunications Systems
S.I.C.: 4812
N.A.I.C.S.: 517110
Lizbeth Johanna Ulett Alvarez *(Comm Mgr)*

Alcatel-Lucent Dooel Skopje (1)
Vasil Glavinov bb DC Inteks
1000 Skopje, Macedonia
Tel.: (389) 23 297 500
Fax: (389) 297 519
E-Mail: alcatel-lucent@alcatel-lucent.com.mk
Web Site: www.alcatel-lucent.com
Emp.: 5
Communication Equipment Mfr
S.I.C.: 3669
N.A.I.C.S.: 334290
Borislav Nestorovski *(Mgr)*

Alcatel-Lucent Ecuador S.A. (1)
Pinta 236 y Rabida
Quito, Ecuador EC
Tel.: (593) 2 2940700
Fax: (593) 2 2940796
E-Mail: alcatel.ecuador@alcatel_lucent.com
Emp.: 29
Telecommunication Services
S.I.C.: 4899
N.A.I.C.S.: 517919
Rebeca Villota *(Dir-Comm)*

Alcatel-Lucent Egypt S.A.E. (1)
Building 144 Smart Village KM 28 Cairo - Alex Desert Road
PO Box 5
12577 Giza, Egypt
Tel.: (20) 2 3539 55 55
Fax: (20) 2 3539 23 30
Web Site: www.alcatel-lucent.com
Telecommunication Services
S.I.C.: 4813
N.A.I.C.S.: 517110

Alcatel-Lucent Espana S.A. (1)
Maria Tubau 9
28050 Madrid, Spain ES (78.6%)
Tel.: (34) 913304000
Fax: (34) 913305000
Web Site: www.alcatel-lucent.es
Emp.: 750
Telecommunication Equipment Mfr
S.I.C.: 3669
N.A.I.C.S.: 334290
Federico Guillen *(Pres)*

Subsidiaries:

Alcatel-Lucent Automizacion del Transporte S.A (2)
Avenida de Bruselas 8
28108 Madrid, Spain (100%)
Tel.: (34) 91 714 84 00
Emp.: 250
Transport Automation Solutions
S.I.C.: 4789
N.A.I.C.S.: 488210
Alfredo Redondo *(Pres-Ibeira Activities)*

Alcatel-Lucent Espana S.A. - Barcelona (2)
Numancia 46
08029 Barcelona, Spain
Tel.: (34) 934952300
Fax: (34) 934952478
Emp.: 60
Mfr. of Telecommunication & Air Navigation Equipment
S.I.C.: 4813
N.A.I.C.S.: 517110
Jose Marrase *(Dir-Sls)*

Lucent Technologies Espana S.A. (2)
Avenida de Bruselas 8
28100 Madrid, Spain
Tel.: (34) 917148400
Fax: (34) 917148909
Web Site: www.lucent.es
Business & Consumer Telecommunications Systems
S.I.C.: 4813
N.A.I.C.S.: 517110

Alcatel-Lucent Estonia (1)
Ravala Pst 5
10143 Tallinn, Estonia
Tel.: (372) 6 150 010
Communication Equipment Mfr
S.I.C.: 3669
N.A.I.C.S.: 334290

Alcatel-Lucent Hellas S.A (1)
32 Kifissias Avenue Atrina Center - Building A
Marousi, 15125 Athens, Greece
Tel.: (30) 210 8115700
Fax: (30) 210 8115799
Web Site: www.alcatel-lucent.gr
Telecommunication Services
S.I.C.: 4899
N.A.I.C.S.: 517919

Alcatel-Lucent Holding GmbH (1)
Lorenzstr 10
Stuttgart, 70435, Germany De
Tel.: (49) 7118210
Fax: (49) 7118211111
Web Site: www.Alcatel-Lucent.com
Emp.: 200
Holding Company
S.I.C.: 6719
N.A.I.C.S.: 551112
Wilhelm Dresselhaus *(CEO)*

Subsidiary:

Alcatel-Lucent Deutschland AG (2)
Lorenzstrasse 10
70435 Stuttgart, Baden Wurttemberg, Germany De (100%)
Mailing Address:
PO Box 400749
70407 Stuttgart, Germany
Tel.: (49) 7118210
Telex: 725260
Fax: (49) 7118211111
E-Mail: redaktion@alcatel-lucent.de
Web Site: www.alcatel-lucent.de
Emp.: 1,700
Mfr. of Switching & Transmission Equipment, Mobile Telephones, Air Navigation, Radar & Air Traffic Control
S.I.C.: 3568
N.A.I.C.S.: 333613
Hans-Joerg Daub *(Dir-Fin)*

Subsidiary:

Alcatel-Lucent SEL Siftung (3)
Lorenz strasse 10
70435 Stuttgart, Germany (100%)
Tel.: (49) 71182145002
Fax: (49) 7118211111
E-Mail: stiftung@alcatel-lucent.de
Web Site: www.stiftungaktuell.de
Emp.: 7
Scientific Research Foundation
S.I.C.: 8731
N.A.I.C.S.: 541712

Alcatel-Lucent Holding, S.A. de C.V. (1)
Av Ciencia No 13 Fracc Industrial
Cuautitlan Izcalli, 54758, Mexico MX
Tel.: (52) 5558709000
Fax: (52) 5558709000
Holding Company
S.I.C.: 6719
N.A.I.C.S.: 551112

Subsidiaries:

Alcatel-Lucent Indetel Industria de Telecomunicacion S.A. de C.V. (2)
Cuautitlan Izcalli Av Ciencia No 13
Fracc Ind Cuautitlan Izcalli, 54758 Mexico, Mexico MX
Tel.: (52) 5558709000
Telex: 177-2772; 177-5845
E-Mail: comunicacion.mx@alcatel-lucent.com
Web Site: www.alcatel-lucent.com
Sls.: $204,820,000
Emp.: 3,552
Mfr. & Supplier of Telecommunication Equipment
S.I.C.: 4813
N.A.I.C.S.: 517110
Angel Gutierrez *(CEO)*

Alcatel-Lucent Mexico S.A. de C.V. (2)
Av Ciencia N 13 Fracc Ind
Cuautitlan Izcalli, 54758, Mexico
Tel.: (52) 55 5870 9000
E-Mail: comunicacion.mx@alcatel-lucent.com
Telecommunication Services
S.I.C.: 4899
N.A.I.C.S.: 517919

Lucent Technologies de Mexico S.R.D.L. de C.V. (2)
Calle 10
145 Col San Pedro de los Pinos, Mexico, DF, 1180, Mexico
Tel.: (52) 5552787000
Fax: (52) 5552787201
Emp.: 300
Business & Consumer Telecommunications Systems
S.I.C.: 4813
N.A.I.C.S.: 517110

Alcatel-Lucent Honduras (1)
Col Lomas del Mayab Edificio Orion 5 to Piso Oficina 505 506
Tegucigalpa, Honduras
Tel.: (504) 2290 7200
Fax: (504) 2290 7221
Emp.: 13
Telecommunication Services
S.I.C.: 4899
N.A.I.C.S.: 517919
Armando Ernesto Basilio Garcia *(Project Mgr)*

Alcatel-Lucent India (1)
DLF Cyber Greens 14th & 15th Floors Tower C
122002 Gurgaon, India
Tel.: (91) 1244159999
Fax: (91) 1244114307
E-Mail: info@alcatel.co.in
Web Site: www.alcatel.co.in
Emp.: 200
Business & Consumer Telecommunications Systems
S.I.C.: 4812
N.A.I.C.S.: 517110
Sanjay Panday *(CEO)*

Alcatel-Lucent Israel Ltd (1)
94 Em-Hamoshavot Road
PO Box 4079
Petah Tiqwa, 49572, Israel
Tel.: (972) 3 928 3333
Fax: (972) 3 928 3192
Telecommunication Services
S.I.C.: 4899
N.A.I.C.S.: 517919

Alcatel-Lucent Italia S.p.A. (1)
Via Trento 30
20871 Vimercate, Italy
Tel.: (39) 039 6861
Fax: (39) 039 6081483
E-Mail: info.mst@alcatel-lucent.com
Telecommunication Services
S.I.C.: 4899
N.A.I.C.S.: 517919
Gianluca Baini *(Chm & CEO)*

Subsidiaries:

Alcatel-Lucent Technologies Italia S.p.A. (2)
Via Cesare Giulio Viola 65
Parco dei Medici, 00148 Rome, Italy
Tel.: (39) 06651821
Fax: (39) 0665182423
Web Site: www.lucent.it
Telecommunications
S.I.C.: 4813
N.A.I.C.S.: 517110
Stefano Lorenzi *(CEO)*

Alcatel-Lucent Technologies Italia S.p.A. (2)
Vimercate
Via Trento 30, 20134 Milan, Italy IT
Tel.: (39) 02752901
Fax: (39) 0275290616
Web Site: www.lucent.it
Telecommunications
S.I.C.: 4813
N.A.I.C.S.: 517110

Alcatel Lucent Malaysia Sdn Bhd (1)
Level 25 The Gardens South Tower Mid Valley City Lingkaran Syed Putra
59200 Kuala Lumpur, Malaysia
Tel.: (60) 3 2028 0018
Fax: (60) 3 2028 0422
Web Site: www.alcatel-lucent.com.my
Emp.: 30
Telecommunication Services
S.I.C.: 4899
N.A.I.C.S.: 517919
Mohd Fazlin Shah Mohd Salleh *(CFO)*

Alcatel-Lucent Moldova (1)
M Kogalniceanu 87
2009 Chisinau, Moldova
Tel.: (373) 22 233277
Fax: (373) 22 233271
E-Mail:
Emp.: 2
Communication Software Development Services
S.I.C.: 7371
N.A.I.C.S.: 541511
Marios Bugiu *(Gen Mgr)*

Alcatel-Lucent Nicaragua (1)
Managa Edificio Opus 2 Semaforos Villa Fontana 1 Cuad Arriba
1 Cuad Lago, Managua, Nicaragua
Tel.: (505) 2278 7605
Fax: (505) 2278 7554
Emp.: 1
Communication Equipment Mfr

S.I.C.: 3669
N.A.I.C.S.: 334290
Carlos Barrientos *(Dir-Comml)*

Alcatel-Lucent Norway AS (1)
Martin Linges vei 25
1330 Oslo, Norway (100%)
Tel.: (47) 67188400
Fax: (47) 67188450
E-Mail: oslo.reception@alcatel-lucent.no
Web Site: www.alcatel.no
Emp.: 120
Telecommunications Equipment & Services Provider
S.I.C.: 3669
N.A.I.C.S.: 334290
Bjorn Rydland *(Gen Mgr)*

Alcatel-Lucent NV (1)
Burgemeester Elsenlaan 170
P O Box 3292
2280 GG Rijswijk, Netherlands (100%)
Tel.: (31) 703079111
Fax: (31) 703079274
E-Mail: info@alcatel-lucent.nl
Web Site: www.alcatel.nl
Emp.: 700
Holding Company
S.I.C.: 6719
N.A.I.C.S.: 551112
Coert de Boer *(Mng Dir)*

Subsidiary:

Alcatel-Lucent Nederland B.V. (2)
Antareslaan 1
2123 JE Hoofddorp, Netherlands NL
Tel.: (31) 703079111 (100%)
Telex: 15151
Fax: (31) 703079274
Web Site: www.alcatel-lucent.nl
Sales Range: $200-249.9 Million
Emp.: 500
Mfr. of Public & Private Telecom Switching & Transmission Systems, Equipment & Components for Voice, Graphics, & Television
S.I.C.: 3577
N.A.I.C.S.: 334118
Jeanine van der Vlist *(Mng Dir)*

Branch:

Alcatel-Lucent Nederland B.V. (3)
Capitool 5
7521 Enschede, Netherlands
Tel.: (31) 35 687 5700
Fax: (31) 35 687 5777
E-Mail: netherlands@lucent.com
Mfr. of Telecommunication Equipment
S.I.C.: 4813
N.A.I.C.S.: 517110
Dennis Bijwaard *(Gen Mgr)*

Subsidiary:

Alcatel-Lucent Network Systems BV (3)
Larenseweg 50
1221 CN Hilversum, Netherlands
Tel.: (31) 35 687 2323
Fax: (31) 35 687 5820
Mfr. of Telecommunication Equipment
S.I.C.: 4813
N.A.I.C.S.: 517110
W. van Willigenburg *(Gen Mgr)*

Alcatel-Lucent Panama (1)
Calle 50 Edificio Credicorp Bank Oficina 1706 Piso 17
Panama, Panama
Tel.: (507) 297 5700
Communication Equipment Mfr
S.I.C.: 3669
N.A.I.C.S.: 334290

Alcatel-Lucent Peru (1)
Camino Real 348 Torre El Pilar Oficina 801
San Isidro, Lima, 27, Peru
Tel.: (51) 1 5139 500
Fax: (51) 5114226444
Emp.: 15
Telecommunication Services
S.I.C.: 4899
N.A.I.C.S.: 517919

Alcatel-Lucent Polska Sp. z o.o. (1)
Ulica Senatorska 27
00099 Warsaw, Poland
Tel.: (48) 226923600
Fax: (48) 6281290
E-Mail: recepcja@alcatel-lucent.pl
Web Site: www.lucent.com.pl
Business & Consumer Telecommunications Systems
S.I.C.: 4813
N.A.I.C.S.: 517110
Andrzej Dulka *(Gen Mgr)*

Alcatel-Lucent Polska Sp. z o.o. (1)
Ulica Pilicka 6
85776 Warsaw, Poland
Tel.: (48) 523491000
Fax: (48) 225155010
E-Mail: recepcja@alcatel-lucent.pl
Web Site: www.lucent.com.pl
Business & Consumer Telecommunications Systems
S.I.C.: 4813
N.A.I.C.S.: 517110
Andre Dolka *(Mng Dir)*

Alcatel-Lucent Portugal S.A (1)
Estrada da Malveira da Serra 920 Aldeia de Juzo
P 2750 834 Cascais, Portugal (100%)
Tel.: (351) 214859000
Fax: (351) 214866294
E-Mail: ala.portugal@alcatel-lucent.com
Web Site: www.alcatel-lucent.pt
Emp.: 200
Mfr. of Telecommunication Equipment
S.I.C.: 4813
N.A.I.C.S.: 517110
Nakhle Matta *(Mng Dir)*

Alcatel-Lucent SA/NV (1)
Copernicuslaan 50
2018 Antwerp, Belgium BE
Tel.: (32) 32404011 (100%)
Telex: 72128
Fax: (32) 32409999
E-Mail: general.info@alcatel-lucent.com
Web Site: www.alcatel-lucent.be
Emp.: 1,800
Development & Manufacture of Telecommunications & Electronics Equipment
S.I.C.: 4813
N.A.I.C.S.: 517110
Luc Defieuw *(CEO & VP-Benelux)*

Subsidiaries:

Alcatel-Lucent Bell NV (2)
Copernicuslaan 50
2018 Antwerp, Belgium
Tel.: (32) 32404011
Fax: (32) 32409999
E-Mail: corporate.communication@alcatel-lucent.com
Emp.: 150
Communications Technology Research & Development Services
S.I.C.: 8731
N.A.I.C.S.: 541712
Luc Defieuw *(Mgr)*

Alcatel-Lucent SA/NV (2)
Blvd Comte de Smet de Nayer 14
5000 Namur, Belgium
Tel.: (32) 81235211
Fax: (32) 81235299
E-Mail: Denis.Sysette@Alcatel-Lucent.de
Web Site: www.Alcatel-Lucent.de
Emp.: 150
Development & Manufacture of Telecommunications & Electronics Equipment
S.I.C.: 3699
N.A.I.C.S.: 335999
Lefevre Catherine *(Gen Mgr)*

Alcatel-Lucent Schweiz AG (1)
Friesenbergstrasse 75
8055 Zurich, Switzerland (100%)
Tel.: (41) 14652111
Fax: (41) 14652411
Emp.: 100
Mfr. of Switching & Transmission Equipment, Mobile Telephones, Air Navigation, Radar & Air Traffic Control
S.I.C.: 3661
N.A.I.C.S.: 334210
Marcel Morf *(Mng Dir)*

Alcatel-Lucent Serbia (1)
Omladinskih Brigada 88a Airport City Building Orchid
11070 Belgrade, Serbia
Tel.: (381) 11 2286 781
Fax: (381) 11 2288 298
E-Mail: alu.belgrade@alcatel-lucent.com
Web Site: www.alcatel-lucent.com
Telecommunication Services
S.I.C.: 4899
N.A.I.C.S.: 517919
Emil Visloguzov *(Mng Dir)*

Alcatel-Lucent Shanghai Bell Co., Ltd (1)
N 388 Ningqiao Road
Jinqiao Pudong, Shanghai, 201206, China
Tel.: (86) 21 58541240
Fax: (86) 21 58540791
Web Site: www.alcatel-sbell.com.cn
Telecommunication Services
S.I.C.: 4899
N.A.I.C.S.: 517919

Alcatel-Lucent Singapore Pte. Ltd. (1)
Block 750D 06-06 Lobby 2 Chai Chee Road
Technopark Chai Chee
Singapore, 469004, Singapore
Tel.: (65) 6240 8000
Fax: (65) 6240 8882
Web Site: www.alcatel-lucent.sg
Communication Equipment Mfr
S.I.C.: 3669
N.A.I.C.S.: 334290

Alcatel-Lucent Slovakia a.s. (1)
Apollo BC II - B Block Prievozska 4/A
821 09 Bratislava, Slovakia
Tel.: (421) 258 220 661
Fax: (421) 258 220 614
Web Site: www.alcatel-lucent.sk
Emp.: 20
Telecommunication Services
S.I.C.: 4899
N.A.I.C.S.: 517919
Peter Bezecny *(Chm)*

Alcatel-Lucent Suomi Oy (1)
Ansatie 6a
1740 Vantaa, Finland FI
Tel.: (358) 9804060 (100%)
Telex: 124580
Fax: (358) 980406511
E-Mail: finland@alcatel-lucent.com
Web Site: www.alcatel-lucent.fi
Emp.: 10
Mfr. of Telecommunication & Air Navigation Equipment
S.I.C.: 4813
N.A.I.C.S.: 517110
Tertti Tukia *(Gen Mgr)*

Alcatel-Lucent Taiwan (1)
7F No 409 Section 2 Ti-Ding Blvd
Nei Hu District, Taipei, 114, Taiwan
Tel.: (886) 2 2162 1100
Fax: (886) 2 8797 5001
E-Mail: Taiwan@alcatel-lucent.tw
Emp.: 5
Communication Equipment Mfr
S.I.C.: 3669
N.A.I.C.S.: 334290
Ken Wu *(Pres & Mng Dir)*

Alcatel Lucent Technologies Argentina S.A. (1)
Bieytes 1710
1275 Buenos Aires, Argentina
Tel.: (54) 1143408600
Fax: (54) 1143491102
E-Mail: glaris.espina@alcatel-lucent.com
Web Site: www.alcatellucent.com
Emp.: 94
Operator of Business & Consumer Telecommunications Systems
S.I.C.: 4899
N.A.I.C.S.: 517919
Fernando Sofa *(Pres)*

Alcatel-Lucent Technologies (China) Co., Ltd. (1)
17F Central Tower Junefield Plaza No 10 Xuanwumenwai St
Xuanwu District, Beijing, 100052, China
Tel.: (86) 1063108822
E-Mail:
Web Site: www.alcatel-sbell.com.cn
Business & Consumer Telecommunications Systems
S.I.C.: 4812
N.A.I.C.S.: 517110

Alcatel Lucent Technologies Czech Republic s.r.o (1)
Podebradska 57 206
198 00 Prague, Czech Republic
Tel.: (420) 266103111
Fax: (420) 266103403
E-Mail: alcatel-lucent@alcatel-lucent.cz
Web Site: www.alcatel-lucent.cz
Emp.: 80
Business & Consumer Telecommunications Systems
S.I.C.: 4813
N.A.I.C.S.: 517110
Irena Vejmelkova *(CEO & Exec Dir)*

Alcatel-Lucent Technologies Netherland B.V. (1)
Larenseweg 50
1221 CN Hilversum, Netherlands
Mailing Address:
Postbus 1168
1200 BD Hilversum, Netherlands
Tel.: (31) 356872323
Fax: (31) 356875820
Web Site: www.alcatellucent.nl
Emp.: 600
Business & Consumer Telecommunications Systems
S.I.C.: 4813
N.A.I.C.S.: 517110

Non-U.S. Subsidiary:

Lucent Technologies Network Systems GmbH (2)
Thurn und Taxis Strasse 10
90411 Nuremberg, Germany
Tel.: (49) 9115260
Fax: (49) 9115262850
E-Mail: info@de.lucent.com
Web Site: www.lucent.com
Emp.: 600
Business & Consumer Telecommunications Systems
S.I.C.: 4813
N.A.I.C.S.: 517110
Rainer Fechner *(Mng Dir & VP)*

Alcatel-Lucent Thailand (1)
5th Floor 990 Building Rama 4 Road
Silom Bangrak, Bangkok, 10500, Thailand
Tel.: (66) 26385000
Fax: (66) 26385045
Emp.: 44
Business & Consumer Telecommunications Systems
S.I.C.: 4813
N.A.I.C.S.: 517110
Sebastien Laurent *(Pres & Mng Dir)*

Alcatel-Lucent UK Limited (1)
Christchurch Way
Greenwich, London, SE10 0AG, United Kingdom UK
Tel.: (44) 8709 033600
Fax: (44) 2084651933
Emp.: 30
Telecommunication Services
S.I.C.: 4899
N.A.I.C.S.: 517919
Lucy Dimes *(CEO)*

Subsidiaries:

Alcatel-Lucent Telecom Limited (2)
Coldra Wood Chepstow Road Newport
Gwent, SE10 0AG, United Kingdom UK
Tel.: (44) 8709033600 (100%)
E-Mail: asc.atuk@alcatel-lucent.co.uk
Web Site: www.alcatel-lucent.co.uk
Emp.: 100
Communication Equipment Mfr
S.I.C.: 3669
N.A.I.C.S.: 334290

Units:

Alcatel-Lucent Telecom Ltd. - Newport (3)
Coldra Woods Chepstow Road
Newport, S Wales, NP18 2YB, United Kingdom
Tel.: (44) 8709033600
Fax: (44) 1633707232
Web Site: www.alcatel-lucent.co.uk
Emp.: 100
Communications Equipment Mfr
S.I.C.: 3669
N.A.I.C.S.: 334290

Alcatel-Lucent—(Continued)

Alcatel-Lucent Telecom Ltd. - Swindon (3)
Quadrant Building Stonehill Green
Westlea, Swindon, Wilts, SN5 7DJ, United Kingdom
Tel.: (44) 8709033600
Fax: (44) 179377500
Web Site: www.alcatel-lucent.co.uk
Software & Telecommunication Services
S.I.C.: 4813
N.A.I.C.S.: 517110
John Verdon *(Dir-Media Rels)*

Alcatel-Lucent Telecom Ltd. (3)
Shoppenhangers Rd
Maidenhead, SL6 2PJ, United Kingdom
Tel.: (44) 8709033600
Fax: (44) 1628428785
E-Mail: oliver.andre@alcatel-lucent.com
Web Site: www.ria.connect.co.uk
Fraud Management
S.I.C.: 7382
N.A.I.C.S.: 561621
Matthew Bocci *(Gen Mgr)*

VELOCIX Ltd. (2)
3 Ely Road
Milton, Cambridge, CB24 6DD, United Kingdom UK
Tel.: (44) 1223 435 800
Fax: (44) 1223 435 801
E-Mail: info@velocix.com
Web Site: www.velocix.com
Emp.: 10
Digital Software Development Services
S.I.C.: 7371
N.A.I.C.S.: 541511
Paul Larbey *(VP & Gen Mgr)*

Non-U.S. Subsidiaries:

Alcatel-Lucent Ireland (2)
Lake Drive Unit 3013
City West Business Campus, Dublin, 24, Ireland (100%)
Tel.: (353) 1469 0600
Web Site: www.alcatel-lucent.com
Internet Services & Telecommunications Carrier Solutions
S.I.C.: 4899
N.A.I.C.S.: 517919
Mike Devane *(Mng Dir & VP)*

Alcatel Shanghai Bell Co., Ltd. (1)
388 Ningqiao Rd
201206 Shanghai, China (50%)
Tel.: (86) 2158541240
Fax: (86) 2158540791
E-Mail: asb.info@alcatel-sbell.com.cn
Web Site: www.alcatel-sbell.com.cn
Emp.: 1,000
Telecommunications Infrastructure & Equipment Provider
S.I.C.: 3669
N.A.I.C.S.: 334290
Yuan Xin *(Chm)*
Olivia Qiu *(Pres & Head-Bus-East Asia)*

Electro Re S.A. (1)
Rue De Bitbourg 19
Luxembourg, 1273, Luxembourg
Tel.: (352) 292197
Fax: (352) 480077
Emp.: 1
Communication Equipment Mfr
S.I.C.: 3663
N.A.I.C.S.: 334220
Pascal Bertin *(Gen Mgr)*

Lucent Technologies El Salvador S.A. de C.V. (1)
Avenida Olympia 3742
San Salvador, El Salvador
Tel.: (503) 2383300
Fax: (503) 2383363
E-Mail: lmelempe@lucenttechnologies.com
Emp.: 24
Business & Consumer Telecommunications Systems
S.I.C.: 4812
N.A.I.C.S.: 517110

PT Alcatel Lucent Indonesia (1)
Wisma Korindo 8th Floor Jalan MT Haryono Kav 62
Jakarta, 12780, Indonesia
Tel.: (62) 21 2750 9000
Fax: (62) 21 2750 9199
Web Site: www.alcatel-lucent.com
Communication Equipment Mfr
S.I.C.: 3669
N.A.I.C.S.: 334290

ALCEA TECHNOLOGIES INC.

2197 Riverside Drive Suite 204
Ottawa, ON, K1H 7Xe, Canada
Tel.: (613) 563-9595
Fax: (613) 563-9494
Toll Free: (877) 321-4463
E-Mail: info@alceatech.com
Web Site: www.alceatech.com
Year Founded: 1997
Sales Range: $1-9.9 Million
Emp.: 12
Fiscal Year-end: 04/30/13

Business Description:
IT Staffing Services; Software Publisher
S.I.C.: 7363
N.A.I.C.S.: 561320

Personnel:
Robert Lacasse *(Pres)*

Division:

FIT Tracking Solutions (1)
2197 Riverside Drive Suite 204
Ottawa, ON, K1H 7X3, Canada
Tel.: (613) 563-9595
Fax: (613) 563-9494
Toll Free: (877) 321-4463
E-Mail: support@fittrackingsolutions.com
Web Site: www.fittrackingsolutions.com
Software Publisher
S.I.C.: 7372
N.A.I.C.S.: 511210
Robert Lacasse *(Pres)*

ALCEL

40 Rue Victor Hugo
59170 Croix, Nord, France
Tel.: (33) 320899203
Sls.: $20,900,000
Emp.: 49

Business Description:
Grocery Stores
S.I.C.: 5411
N.A.I.C.S.: 445110

Personnel:
Michel Pattou *(Mng Dir)*

Board of Directors:
Michel Pattou
Jean-Luc Le Baron

ALCHEMIA LIMITED

Eight Mile Plains
PO Box 4851
Brisbane, QLD, 4113, Australia
Tel.: (61) 733400200
Fax: (61) 733400222
E-Mail: enquiries@alchemia.com.au
Web Site: www.alchemia.com.au
Year Founded: 1995
ACL—(ASX)
Rev.: $25,319,904
Assets: $43,232,561
Liabilities: $9,490,405
Net Worth: $33,742,156
Earnings: ($4,970,817)
Emp.: 24
Fiscal Year-end: 06/30/13

Business Description:
Biotechnology Research & Development Services
S.I.C.: 8731
N.A.I.C.S.: 541711

Personnel:
Thomas Liquard *(CEO)*
Tracey Brown *(Chief Scientific Officer & VP-Oncology)*
Wim Meutermans *(Chief Scientific Officer-Discovery)*
Stephen Denaro *(Sec)*

Board of Directors:
Santo J. Costa
Nathan Drona
Timothy Hughes
Susan L. Kelley
Tracie Ramsdale

Legal Counsel:
Corrs Chambers Westgarth
Brisbane, QLD, Australia

The Bank of New York
101 Barclay St 22nd Fl
New York, NY 10286

Transfer Agent:
The Bank of New York
101 Barclay St 22nd Fl
New York, NY 10286

U.S. Subsidiary:

Audeo Oncology, Inc. (1)
100 Pine St Ste 2040
San Francisco, CA 94111 DE
Tel.: (415) 984-0300
Web Site: www.audeooncology.com
Emp.: 6
Pharmaceutical Mfr
S.I.C.: 2834
N.A.I.C.S.: 325412
Stephen A. Hill *(Chm)*
Peter Smith *(Pres & CEO)*
Charles Walker *(CFO & Sec)*
Tracey Brown *(Chief Scientific Officer & VP-Oncology)*

Non-U.S. Subsidiary:

Alchemia Oncology Pty Ltd (2)
3 Hi-Tech Court
Eight Mile Plains, NSW, 4113, Australia
Tel.: (61) 733400200
Fax: (61) 733400222
E-Mail: enquiries@alchemia.com.au
Emp.: 7
Pharmaceutical Products Mfr
S.I.C.: 2834
N.A.I.C.S.: 325412
Peter Smith *(CEO)*

ALCHEMIST LTD

SCO 13-19 Sector 9 D Madhya Marg
160009 Chandigarh, Punjab, India
Tel.: (91) 1724680000
Fax: (91) 1724680003
Web Site: www.alchemist.co.in
ALCHEM—(NSE)
Sales Range: $75-99.9 Million
Emp.: 9,800

Business Description:
Holding Company
S.I.C.: 6719
N.A.I.C.S.: 551112

Personnel:
Kanwar Deep Singh *(Chm & Mng Dir)*
Harish Sharma *(Sec)*

Board of Directors:
Kanwar Deep Singh
Asoke K. Chatterjee
R. P. Chhabra
Ravinder Singh
Tarlochan Singh

Subsidiary:

Alchemist Aviation Pvt. Ltd. (1)
Sonari Airport
Jamshedpur, Jharkhand, 831011, India
Tel.: (91) 6572301516
Fax: (91) 6572310229
Web Site: www.alchemistaviation.com
Emp.: 40
Aviation Training Schools
S.I.C.: 8249
N.A.I.C.S.: 611512
S. K. Upadhyay *(Mgr)*

ALCHEMY PARTNERS LLP

25 Palmer Street
London, SW1 0AD, United Kingdom
Tel.: (44) 2072409596
Fax: (44) 2072409594
E-Mail: info@alchemypartners.co.uk
Web Site: www.alchemypartners.com
Year Founded: 2002
Emp.: 30

Business Description:
Private Equity Firm
S.I.C.: 6211
N.A.I.C.S.: 523999

Personnel:
Robert Barnes *(Co-Founder)*
Martin Bolland *(Co-Founder)*
Dominic Slade *(Mng Partner)*
Ian Cash *(Partner)*
Alex Leicester *(Partner)*
Gavin Loughrey *(Partner)*
Simon Oakland *(Partner)*
Frits Prakke *(Partner)*
John Rowland *(CFO & COO)*

Holdings:

Geo Networks Limited (1)
4th Floor Harmsworth House
13 15 Bouverie Street, London, EC4Y 8DP, United Kingdom
Tel.: (44) 2033269500
Fax: (44) 2033269501
E-Mail: enquiries@geo-uk.net
Web Site: www.geo-uk.net
Sales Range: $50-74.9 Million
Emp.: 90
Fibre Optic Network Installation Services
S.I.C.: 1623
N.A.I.C.S.: 237130
Jonathan Watts *(Pres)*
Chris Smedley *(CEO)*
Gary Plumpton *(CFO)*
Mike Ainger *(COO)*
Sheree Jaggard *(Gen Counsel & Sec)*

PD Parks Holdings Ltd. (1)
1 Gosforth Parkway
Gosforth Business Park, Newcastle upon Tyne, NE12 8ET, United Kingdom
Tel.: (44) 20 7240 9596
Private Equity Firm
S.I.C.: 6211
N.A.I.C.S.: 523999
Martin Bolland *(Dir-Monitoring)*

Subsidiary:

Parkdean Holidays Plc (2)
2nd Floor One Gosforth Parkway
Gosforth Business Park, Newcastle upon Tyne, NE12 8ET, United Kingdom
Tel.: (44) 912560700
Fax: (44) 912686004
E-Mail: enquiris@parkdeanholidays.co.uk
Web Site: www.parkdeanholidaysplc.com
Emp.: 1,200
Camping Destinations
S.I.C.: 7032
N.A.I.C.S.: 721214

ALCHEMY RESOURCES LIMITED

Level 2 72 Kings Park Road
West Perth, WA, 6005, Australia
Mailing Address:
GPO Box 2815
Perth, WA, 6001, Australia
Tel.: (61) 8 9481 4400
Fax: (61) 8 9481 4404
E-Mail: alchemy@alchemyresources.com.au
Web Site: www.alchemyresources.com.au
ALY—(ASX)
Rev.: $141,260
Assets: $20,455,798
Liabilities: $289,081
Net Worth: $20,166,717
Earnings: ($2,222,747)
Fiscal Year-end: 06/30/13

Business Description:
Gold & Copper Exploration Services
S.I.C.: 1041
N.A.I.C.S.: 212221

Personnel:
Kevin Cassidy *(CEO)*
Bernard Crawford *(CFO & Sec)*

Board of Directors:
Oscar Aamodt
Sofia Bianchi

Lindsay Dudfield
Anthony Ho

ALCHEMY WORX LIMITED

4th Floor 1 New Oxford Street
London, WC1A 1LW, United Kingdom
Tel.: (44) 870 908 8803
Fax: (44) 870 908 8804
E-Mail: info@alchemyworx.com
Web Site: www.alchemyworx.com
Year Founded: 2001
Sales Range: $1-9.9 Million
Business Description:
Direct Mail Advertising
S.I.C.: 7331
N.A.I.C.S.: 541860
Personnel:
Dela Quist *(Founder & CEO)*
Tim Ferguson *(COO)*
Board of Directors:
Katie Aston
Tim Ferguson
Dela Quist

ALCO HELLAS S.A.

Thesi Kirillo
193 00 Aspropyrgos, Greece
Tel.: (30) 2115595223
Fax: (30) 2105595432
E-Mail: info@alco.gr
Web Site: www.alco.gr
ALCO—(ATH)
Sls.: $346,027,533
Assets: $219,136,922
Liabilities: $151,108,167
Net Worth: $68,028,755
Earnings: ($8,585,310)
Emp.: 1,378
Fiscal Year-end: 12/31/12
Business Description:
Aluminum Mfr
S.I.C.: 3334
N.A.I.C.S.: 331313
Personnel:
Theodoros Tzortzis *(Chm)*
Nikolaos Sofianos *(Vice Chm)*
Georgios Kanakaris *(Mng Dir)*
Board of Directors:
Theodoros Tzortzis
Apostolos Georgiou
Georgios Kanakaris
Patroklos Koudounis
Periklis Melles
Nikolaos Sofianos
Panagiotis Stamogiannos
Non-U.S. Subsidiaries:

ALCO ROM TRADE SRL (1)
Visili Suite No 3-5
Bucharest, Romania
Tel.: (40) 214246042
Fax: (40) 214246041
E-Mail: office@alcoromtrade.ro
Emp.: 9
Aluminum Frames Distr
S.I.C.: 3355
N.A.I.C.S.: 331318

GARTNER EXTRUSION GMBH (1)
Peterswoerther Str 1a
89432 Gundelfingen, Baden-Wurttemberg, Germany
Tel.: (49) 907380000
Fax: (49) 9073 8000 2106
E-Mail: info@gartner-extrusion.de
Web Site: www.gartner-extrusion.de
Emp.: 300
Aluminum Extrusion Products Mfr
S.I.C.: 3334
N.A.I.C.S.: 331313
Harald Westeheide *(Mng Dir)*

GUTMANN AG (1)
Nuernberger Strasse 57
91781 Weissenburg, Germany
Tel.: (49) 91419920
Fax: (49) 9141992212
E-Mail: info@gutmann.de
Web Site: www.gutmann.de
Emp.: 630
Aluminum Products Mfr
S.I.C.: 3334
N.A.I.C.S.: 331313
Charalambos Gotsis *(Chm)*
Theodorus Tzortzis *(CEO)*
Subsidiary:

NORDALU GMBH (2)
Oderstrasse 78-82
24539 Neumunster, Schleswig-Holstein, Germany
Tel.: (49) 43218890
Fax: (49) 432184865
E-Mail:
Emp.: 180
Aluminum Products Mfr
S.I.C.: 3334
N.A.I.C.S.: 331313
Harald Westheide *(CEO)*

GUTMANN ALUMINIUM DRAHT GMBH (1)
Nuernberger Str 57-81
91781 Weissenburg, Bavaria, Germany
Tel.: (49) 91419920
Fax: (49) 9141992327
E-Mail: wire@gutmann-wire.com
Web Site: www.gutmann-wire.de
Emp.: 100
Aluminum Products Distr
S.I.C.: 3479
N.A.I.C.S.: 332812
Paul Habbel *(Mng Dir)*

ALCO HOLDINGS LIMITED

11/F Zung Fu Industrial Bldg 1067 King's Rd
Quarry Bay, China (Hong Kong)
Tel.: (852) 28800698
Fax: (852) 28800858
Web Site: www.alco.com.hk
0328—(HKG)
Rev.: $241,077,312
Assets: $352,657,618
Liabilities: $104,170,194
Net Worth: $248,487,424
Earnings: $7,532,356
Emp.: 3,000
Fiscal Year-end: 03/31/13
Business Description:
Electronic Products Mfr
S.I.C.: 3679
N.A.I.C.S.: 334419
Personnel:
Kimen Kai Ching Leung *(Chm)*
Wilson Wai Sing Leung *(CEO)*
Andrew Kun Man Kuok *(Sec)*
Board of Directors:
Kimen Kai Ching Leung
Andrew Kun Man Kuok
Derrick Wang Yip Lau
Tak Chi Lee
Wilson Wai Sing Leung
Fred Wah Ming Li
HSBC Bank Bermuda Limited
6 Front Street
Hamilton, Bermuda
Subsidiaries:

Advance Packaging Limited (1)
11F Zung Fu Indus Bldg 1067 Kings Rd
Quarry Bay, China (Hong Kong)
Tel.: (852) 25626121
Fax: (852) 28111056
E-Mail: marketing@alco.com.hk
Emp.: 2
Packaging Plastic Products Mfr & Sales
S.I.C.: 3086
N.A.I.C.S.: 326150
Bond Yip *(Mgr-Mktg)*

Alco Digital Devices Limited (1)
11F Zung Fu Indus Bldg 1067 Kings Rd
Quarry Bay, China (Hong Kong)
Tel.: (852) 28800698
Fax: (852) 28800858
Emp.: 100
Software Development & Electronic Products Distr
S.I.C.: 5064
N.A.I.C.S.: 423620

Alco Electronics Limited (1)
11 Fl Zung Fu Indus Bldg 1067 Kings Rd
Quarry Bay, China (Hong Kong)
Tel.: (852) 28800698
Fax: (852) 28809563
E-Mail: ems@alco.com.hk
Web Site: www.alco.com.hk
Emp.: 150
Consumer Electronics Mfr
S.I.C.: 3651
N.A.I.C.S.: 334310
Bond Yip *(Mgr-Sls & Mktg)*

Alco International Limited (1)
11 Fl Zung Fu Indus Bldg 1067 Kings Rd
Quarry Bay, China (Hong Kong)
Tel.: (852) 28800698
Fax: (852) 28800858
E-Mail: marketing@alco.com.hk
Web Site: www.alco.com.hk
Emp.: 50
Consumer Electronics Whslr
S.I.C.: 5064
N.A.I.C.S.: 423620
Bond Yip *(Gen Mgr-Mktg)*

Alco Plastic Products Limited (1)
11/F Zung Fu Indl Bldg
Quarry Bay, New Territories, China (Hong Kong)
Tel.: (852) 24228777
Fax: (852) 24805973
Plastic Products Mfr & Sales
S.I.C.: 2519
N.A.I.C.S.: 337125

Alco Properties Limited (1)
11 F Zung Fu Indus Bldg 1067 Kings Rd
Quarry Bay, China (Hong Kong)
Tel.: (852) 25626121
Fax: (852) 28111056
Emp.: 150
Property Management Services
S.I.C.: 6531
N.A.I.C.S.: 531311
Wilson Leung *(CEO)*

Asia Dragon International Limited (1)
11F Zung Fu Indus Bldg 1067 Kings Rd
Quarry Bay, China (Hong Kong)
Tel.: (852) 25626121
Fax: (852) 28111056
Emp.: 100
Consumer Electronics Whslr
S.I.C.: 5064
N.A.I.C.S.: 423620

Commusonic Industries Limited (1)
11F Zung Fu Indus Bldg 1067 Kings Rd
Quarry Bay, China (Hong Kong)
Tel.: (852) 25626121
Fax: (852) 28111056
E-Mail: marketing@alco.com.hk
Web Site: www.alco.com.hk
Emp.: 150
Consumer Electronics Mfr & Sales
S.I.C.: 3651
N.A.I.C.S.: 334310
Catherine Cheung *(Mgr-HR)*

Multimedia Devices Limited (1)
5 11F Zung Fu Indus Bldg 1067 Kings Rd
Quarry Bay, China (Hong Kong)
Tel.: (852) 28800698
Fax: (852) 28111056
Emp.: 100
Consumer Electronics Whslr
S.I.C.: 5064
N.A.I.C.S.: 423620
Catherine Cheung *(Mgr-HR)*

Non-U.S. Subsidiary:

Alco Electronics (Shenzhen) Limited (1)
23F Huangcheng Plz No 7 Futian S Rd
Futian Dist, Shenzhen, Guangdong, 518045, China
Tel.: (86) 75583694800
Fax: (86) 75583694200
Consumer Electronics Distr
S.I.C.: 5064
N.A.I.C.S.: 423620
Peter Leung *(Gen Mgr)*

ALCO, INC.

25th Floor Fortis Bank Tower No 77-79 Gloucester Road
Wanchai, China (Hong Kong)
Tel.: (852) 2521 0373
Year Founded: 1999
ALCQ—(OTCB)
Rev.: $6,006,543
Assets: $13,443,289
Liabilities: $1,980,258
Net Worth: $11,463,031
Earnings: $538,066
Emp.: 65
Fiscal Year-end: 12/31/12
Business Description:
Marine Insurance Services
S.I.C.: 6411
N.A.I.C.S.: 524210
Personnel:
Andrew Fu Kang Liu *(Chm, Pres & CEO)*
Colman Au Kwok Wai *(CFO & Sec)*
Board of Directors:
Andrew Fu Kang Liu
John Shou Kang Liu

ALCO VENTURES INC.

9747 199A St
Langley, BC, Canada V1M 2X7
Tel.: (604) 888-7655
Fax: (604) 888-1718
Toll Free: (800) 667-2526
E-Mail: info@alcoventures.com
Web Site: www.alcoventures.com
Year Founded: 1970
Rev.: $15,959,663
Emp.: 125
Business Description:
Aluminium Railing Systems Mfr
S.I.C.: 3743
N.A.I.C.S.: 336510
Personnel:
Mark De Beer *(CFO)*

ALCOBRA LTD.

65 Rothschild Blvd
65785 Tel Aviv, Israel
Tel.: (972) 72 220 4661
ADHD—(NASDAQ)
Assets: $201,000
Liabilities: $768,000
Net Worth: ($567,000)
Earnings: ($1,579,000)
Fiscal Year-end: 12/31/12
Business Description:
Pharmaceutical Mfr
S.I.C.: 2834
N.A.I.C.S.: 325412
Personnel:
Aharon Schwartz *(Chm)*
Yaron Daniely *(Pres & CEO)*
Ehud Moshe Gilboa *(CFO & Chief Acctg Officer)*
David C. Baker *(Chief Comml Officer)*
Jonathan Rubin *(Chief Medical Officer)*
Board of Directors:
Aharon Schwartz
Yaron Daniely
Ehud Moshe Gilboa
Dalia Megiddo

ALCOHOL COUNTERMEASURE SYSTEMS CORP.

60 International Boulevard
Toronto, ON, M9W 6J2, Canada
Tel.: (416) 619-3500
Fax: (416) 619-3501
Toll Free: (866) 658-6374
E-Mail: info@acs-corp.com
Web Site: www.acs-corp.com
Year Founded: 1976
Rev.: $10,000,000
Emp.: 300
Business Description:
Alcohol Interlocks & Breath Alcohol Testers Mfr

Alcohol Countermeasure Systems Corp.—(Continued)

S.I.C.: 3829
N.A.I.C.S.: 334519
Personnel:
Bill Burger *(Dir-Technical)*

ALCOMET PLC

Il Industrial Zone
Shumen, 9700, Bulgaria
Tel.: (359) 54 858 601
Fax: (359) 54 858 688
E-Mail: office@alcomet.eu
Web Site: www.alcomet.eu
6AM—(BUL)
Rev.: $172,034,900
Assets: $146,274,468
Liabilities: $80,703,579
Net Worth: $65,570,889
Earnings: $2,657,448
Emp.: 799
Fiscal Year-end: 12/31/12
Business Description:
Modern Production Equipment Services
S.I.C.: 7699
N.A.I.C.S.: 811310
Personnel:
Fikret Ince *(Chm-Supervisory Bd)*
Huseyin Yorucu *(Chm-Mgmt Bd)*
Fikret Kuzucu *(Vice Chm-Supervisory Bd)*
Huseyin Umut Ince *(Vice Chm-Mgmt Bd)*
Esref Alkang *(Member-Mgmt Bd)*
Semih Baturai *(Member-Mgmt Bd)*
Mehmet Dedeoglu *(Member-Mgmt Bd)*
Neli Kancheva Toncheva *(Member-Mgmt Bd)*
Supervisory Board of Directors:
Fikret Ince
Hristo Todorov Dechev
Semih Korai
Fikret Kuzucu
Osman Kerem Kuzucu
Branimir Mladenov Mladenov
Bekir Yudzhel

ALCONIX CORPORATION

Sanno Park Tower 12th Floor 2 11 1
Nagatacho Chiyoda Ku
Tokyo, 100 6112, Japan
Tel.: (81) 3 3596 7400
Fax: (81) 355752727
Web Site: www.alconix.com
Year Founded: 1981
3036—(TKS)
Sls.: $1,812,459,000
Assets: $774,202,000
Liabilities: $600,204,000
Net Worth: $173,998,000
Earnings: $15,730,000
Emp.: 511
Fiscal Year-end: 03/31/13
Business Description:
Aluminum, Copper, Nickel, Titanium, Tungsten, Molybdenum, Rare Metal & Rare Earth Related Products Importer, Exporter & Sales
S.I.C.: 5051
N.A.I.C.S.: 423510
Personnel:
Eiitsu Masaki *(Pres & CEO)*
Michio Komatsu *(Sr Exec Officer)*
Kenichi Kuze *(Exec Officer)*
Muneyoshi Maeda *(Sr Exec Officer)*
Yasushi Miyazaki *(Mng Exec Officer)*
Masato Takei *(Mng Exec Officer)*
Hiroshi Teshirogi *(Mng Exec Officer)*
Board of Directors:
Michio Komatsu
Eiitsu Masaki
Yasushi Miyazaki
Masato Takei
Syunji Tanefusa
Sakutaro Tanino
Hideo Yamashita

Subsidiaries:

Advanced Material Japan Corporation (1)
Sankaido Bldg 4f 1-9-13 Akasaka
Tokyo, Minato-ku, 107 0052, Japan
Tel.: (81) 335605181
Fax: (81) 335605182
E-Mail: web@amjc.co.jp
Web Site: www.amjc.co.jp
Emp.: 30
Rare Metals Mfr
S.I.C.: 3499
N.A.I.C.S.: 332999
Nakamura Shigeo *(Pres)*

Alconix Sanshin Corporation (1)
Sankaido Bldg 4f 1-9-13 Akasaka
Tokyo, Minato-ku, 107 0052, Japan
Tel.: (81) 355752785
Fax: (81) 357752785
Web Site: www.alconix.com
Metals Mfr
S.I.C.: 3499
N.A.I.C.S.: 332999

Hayashi Metal Corp. (1)
4-8-15 Kawaguchi
Osaka, Nishi-ku, 550 0021, Japan
Tel.: (81) 665832575
Fax: (81) 0665832618
Web Site: www.alconix.com
Emp.: 27
Metals Whslr
S.I.C.: 5051
N.A.I.C.S.: 423510
Mitsuo Sugie *(Mng Dir)*

Ohkawa Corp. (1)
2-11-20 Sakura-Shinmachi
Setagaya-Ku, Tokyo, 154 0015, Japan
Tel.: (81) 334293223
Web Site: www.odsinc.co.jp
Emp.: 100
Metals Mfr
S.I.C.: 3499
N.A.I.C.S.: 332999

Non-U.S. Subsidiaries:

Alconix Europe Gmbh (1)
Oststrasse 10
40211 Dusseldorf, Germany
Tel.: (49) 21150080810
Fax: (49) 21150080830
Web Site: www.alconix.com
Emp.: 4
Metals Mfr
S.I.C.: 3499
N.A.I.C.S.: 332999
Kei Takai *(Mng Dir)*

Alconix Hong Kong Corp.,Ltd. (1)
16 Fl Harbour Ctr 25 Harbour Rd
Wanchai, China (Hong Kong)
Tel.: (852) 28441829
Fax: (852) 28454178
Web Site: www.alconix.com
Emp.: 10
Metals Mfr
S.I.C.: 3499
N.A.I.C.S.: 332999
Zhou Zemin *(Gen Mgr)*

Alconix (Malaysia) Sdn. Bhd. (1)
Level 23 Menara Imc No 8 Jalam Sultan Ismail
50250 Kuala Lumpur, Malaysia
Tel.: (60) 320313750
Fax: (60) 320313760
E-Mail: tan.anna@alconix.com.my
Web Site: www.alconix.com
Emp.: 6
Metals Mfr
S.I.C.: 3499
N.A.I.C.S.: 332999
Toshimasa Makasura *(Mng Dir)*

Alconix (Shanghai) Corp. (1)
Rm No 1507 Ruijin Bldg 205 Maoming S Rd
Shanghai, 200020, China
Tel.: (86) 2154662066
Fax: (86) 2154660082
Web Site: www.alconix.com
Emp.: 15
Metals Mfr
S.I.C.: 3499
N.A.I.C.S.: 332999
Bo Fang *(Mgr)*

Alconix (Taiwan) Corporation (1)
7F-6 No 191 Fusing N Rd
Taipei, Songshan, Taiwan
Tel.: (886) 227122926
Web Site: www.alconix.com
Emp.: 3
Metals Mfr
S.I.C.: 3499
N.A.I.C.S.: 332999
K. Jimbo *(Mgr-Factory)*

Alconix (Thailand) Ltd. (1)
Thniya Plz Bldg 11th Fl 52 Silom Rd
Bangkok, Thailand
Tel.: (66) 22312375
Fax: (66) 22312488
Web Site: www.alconix.com
Emp.: 11
Metals Mfr
S.I.C.: 3499
N.A.I.C.S.: 332999
Tanaka Yutaka *(Gen Mgr)*

ALCORN GOLD RESOURCES CORPORATION

(Name Changed to Cosco Capital, Inc.)

ALCUIN CAPITAL PARTNERS LLP

2 Eaton Gate
London, SW1W 9BJ, United Kingdom
Tel.: (44) 203 178 4089
Fax: (44) 203 178 4090
E-Mail: info@alcuincapital.com
Web Site: www.alcuincapital.com
Emp.: 8
Business Description:
Private Investment Firm
S.I.C.: 6211
N.A.I.C.S.: 523999
Personnel:
Ian Henderson-Londono *(Mng Partner)*
Mark Storey *(Mng Partner)*
Adrian Lurie *(Partner)*

Subsidiaries:

AVM Impact Ltd. (1)
Europe House
170 Windmill Road, Sunbury-on-Thames, Middlesex, TW16 7HB, United Kingdom
Tel.: (44) 1932 733700
Fax: (44) 1932 733711
E-Mail: info@avmimpact.com
Web Site: www.avmimpact.com
Sales Range: $50-74.9 Million
Emp.: 200
Video Conferencing & Audio Visual System Design & Installation Services
S.I.C.: 7373
N.A.I.C.S.: 541512
Edward Cook *(CEO)*
Simon Porter *(CFO)*
Jared Lancaster *(CTO)*

Krispy Kreme UK Ltd. (1)
Unit 4 Albany Park
Frimley Road, Camberley, GU16 7PQ, United Kingdom
Tel.: (44) 1276 60 11 70
E-Mail: office@krispykreme.co.uk
Web Site: www.krispykreme.co.uk
Owns & Operates Bakeries
S.I.C.: 5461
N.A.I.C.S.: 311811
Mark Storey *(Chm)*
Richard Cheshire *(Mng Dir)*
Rob Hunt *(Mng Dir)*
Judith Denby *(CMO)*

ALCYONE RESOUCES LTD.

Suite 2 Level 4 85 South Perth Esplanade
South Perth, WA, 6151, Australia
Mailing Address:
PO Box 487
South Perth, WA, 6951, Australia
Tel.: (61) 8 94763000
Fax: (61) 8 9368 1924
E-Mail: info@alcyone.com.au
Web Site: www.aclyone.com.au
AYN—(ASX)
Rev.: $21,562,699
Assets: $33,957,105
Liabilities: $20,006,033
Net Worth: $13,951,072
Earnings: ($10,814,314)
Emp.: 60
Fiscal Year-end: 06/30/13
Business Description:
Silver Mining & Exploration Services
S.I.C.: 1044
N.A.I.C.S.: 212222
Personnel:
Michael Reed *(Mng Dir)*
Trevor Harris *(CFO & Sec)*
Board of Directors:
Paul D'Sylva
Tim Morrison
Michael Reed
Legal Counsel:
Steinepreis Paganin
Level 4 The Read Buildings 16 Milligan Street
Perth, Australia

ALDA PHARMACEUTICALS CORP.

(Name Changed to Nuva Pharmaceuticals Inc.)

ALDACHANIE

6 Rue Des Freres Lumiere
60200 Compiegne, Oise, France
Tel.: (33) 344203621
Fax: (33) 344207410
Sls.: $21,100,000
Emp.: 49
Business Description:
Miscellaneous General Merchandise Stores
S.I.C.: 5211
N.A.I.C.S.: 444190
Personnel:
Patrick De Bosschere *(Pres)*
Board of Directors:
David De Bosschere

ALDAMAN FOR INVESTMENTS PLC

Matalqah Center
PO Box 850194
Shmeisani, Amman, 11185, Jordan
Tel.: (962) 6 5622365
Fax: (962) 6 5622462
Year Founded: 1993
DMAN—(AMM)
Rev.: $756,047
Assets: $14,755,763
Liabilities: $209,057
Net Worth: $14,546,706
Earnings: $260,715
Emp.: 38
Fiscal Year-end: 12/31/12
Business Description:
Investment Management Services
S.I.C.: 6211
N.A.I.C.S.: 523999
Personnel:
Shabeeb Amari *(Gen Mgr)*

ALDAR PROPERTIES PJSC

Al Raha Beach
PO Box 51133
Abu Dhabi, United Arab Emirates
Tel.: (971) 28105555
Fax: (971) 28105550
E-Mail: info@aldar.com
Web Site: www.aldar.com

ALDAR—(ABU)
Rev.: $3,103,919,218
Assets: $8,720,839,631
Liabilities: $6,494,541,416
Net Worth: $2,226,298,215
Earnings: $364,900,294
Emp.: 1,062
Fiscal Year-end: 12/31/12
Business Description:
Real Estate Investment & Development Services
S.I.C.: 6519
N.A.I.C.S.: 531190
Personnel:
Abubaker Seddiq Al Khoori *(Chm)*
Ali Eid Al Mheiri *(Vice Chm)*
Sami Asad *(CEO)*
Mohammed Al Mubarak *(Deputy CEO & Chief Portfolio Mgmt Officer)*
Greg Fewer *(CFO)*
Fahad Al Ketbi *(COO)*
Abdalla Zamzam *(Chief Admin Officer)*
Richard Gray *(Chief Legal Officer)*
Gurjit Singh *(Chief Dev Officer)*
Paul Warren *(Chief Strategy Officer)*
Haider Najim *(Chief Audit Exec)*
Board of Directors:
Abubaker Seddiq Al Khoori
Ali Saeed Abdulla Sulayem Al Falasi
Mubarak Matar Al Humairi
Sultan Ahmed Al Jaber
Mohamed Al Khoori
Ali Majid Al Mansouri
Ahmed Khalifa Mohamed Al Mehairi
Ali Eid Al Mheiri
Mansour Mohamed Al Mulla
Martin Lee Edelman
Legal Counsel:
Norton Rose (Middle East) LLP
15th Floor Al Sila Tower Sowwah Square
P O BOX 105708
Abu Dhabi, United Arab Emirates

Eversheds
PO Box 42182
Abu Dhabi, United Arab Emirates

DLA Piper
PO Box 109950
Abu Dhabi, United Arab Emirates

Berwin Leignton Paisner
Al Bateen Towers Tower C6 Office C504
Abu Dhabi, United Arab Emirates

Allen & Overy
PO Box 7907
Abu Dhabi, United Arab Emirates

Al Tamimi & Co
PO Box 44046
Abu Dhabi, United Arab Emirates

Subsidiaries:

Addar Real Estate Services LLC (1)
P O Box 51133
Abu Dhabi, United Arab Emirates
Tel.: (971) 2 633 6886
Fax: (971) 2 641 7501
Asset & Real Estate Development & Management Services
S.I.C.: 6531
N.A.I.C.S.: 531390

Al Jimi Mall LLC (1)
PO Box 16427
Al Ain, United Arab Emirates
Tel.: (971) 37638883
Fax: (971) 37634747
Web Site: www.aljimimall.com
Emp.: 16
General Stores
S.I.C.: 5399
N.A.I.C.S.: 452990
Wael Barbary *(Mgr)*

Al Raha Gardens Property LLC (1)
PO Box 51133
Abu Dhabi, United Arab Emirates
Tel.: (971) 26964444
Fax: (971) 26417501
Emp.: 300
Property Building & Real Estate Development Services
S.I.C.: 1531
N.A.I.C.S.: 236117
Ahmed Sayegh *(Chm)*

ALDER RESOURCES LTD.

65 Queen St W Suite 800
Toronto, ON, M5H 2M5, Canada
Tel.: (416) 309-2134
Fax: (416) 861-8165
E-Mail: info@alderresources.ca
Web Site: www.alderresources.ca
Year Founded: 2006
ALR—(TSXV)
Int. Income: $1,577
Assets: $3,356,961
Liabilities: $465,851
Net Worth: $2,891,110
Earnings: ($1,434,865)
Fiscal Year-end: 09/30/13
Business Description:
Gold Exploration Services
S.I.C.: 1041
N.A.I.C.S.: 212221
Personnel:
Don Dudek *(Chm, Pres & CEO)*
Ryan Ptolemy *(CFO)*
Josh Van Deurzen *(Sec)*
Board of Directors:
Don Dudek
Rene Bharti
Pierre Pettigrew
Allan Polk
Will Randall
Keith J. Stein
Transfer Agent:
Equity Financial Trust Company
200 University Avenue Suite 400
Toronto, ON, Canada

ALDERON IRON ORE CORP.

Suite 1240 1140 West Pender St
Vancouver, BC, V6E 4G1, Canada
Tel.: (604) 681-8030
Fax: (604) 681-8039
E-Mail: info@alderonironore.com
Web Site: www.alderonironore.com
AXX—(NYSEMKT)
Rev.: $434,888
Assets: $146,460,180
Liabilities: $6,809,381
Net Worth: $139,650,799
Earnings: ($71,053,658)
Emp.: 15
Fiscal Year-end: 12/31/12
Business Description:
Iron Ore Mining
S.I.C.: 1011
N.A.I.C.S.: 212210
Personnel:
Mark Joseph Morabito *(Chm)*
Stan Bharti *(Vice Chm)*
Tayfun Eldem *(Pres & CEO)*
Francois Laurin *(CFO)*
Brian K. Penney *(COO)*
Patrick Gleeson *(Sec)*
Todd Burlingame *(Exec VP-Environ & Aboriginal Affairs)*
Gary Norris *(Exec VP-Govt & Community Affairs)*
Bernard Potvin *(Exec VP-Project Execution)*
Board of Directors:
Mark Joseph Morabito
John Antle Baker
Stan Bharti
Lenard F. Boggio
Bradley J. Boland
Brian Francis Dalton
Tayfun Eldem
R. Bruce Humphrey
David Porter
Mathew Simpson
Diana Walters
Legal Counsel:
Blake, Cassels & Graydon LLP
Suite 2600 Three Bentall Centre 595 Burrard Street
PO Box 49314
Vancouver, BC, Canada
Transfer Agent:
Computershare Investor Services Inc.
3rd Floor 510 Burrard St
V6C 3B9 Vancouver, BC, Canada

ALDERSHOT RESOURCES LTD.

885 West George St Ste 1500
Vancouver, BC, V6C 2B3, Canada
Tel.: (604) 682-6718
Fax: (604) 682-6722
E-Mail: info@aldershotresources.com
Web Site: www.aldershotresources.com
Year Founded: 1987
ALZ—(TSXV)
Rev.: $2,077
Assets: $1,455,524
Liabilities: $465,028
Net Worth: $990,495
Earnings: ($1,404,888)
Fiscal Year-end: 01/31/13
Business Description:
Mineral Exploration Services
S.I.C.: 1081
N.A.I.C.S.: 213114
Personnel:
Michael G. Leidich *(Pres & CEO)*
Frank DeMarte *(CFO & Sec)*
Board of Directors:
Ian Adam
Philip G. Crabb
Marcus F. Flis
Michael G. Leidich

ALDHAFRA INSURANCE COMPANY P.S.C

PO Box 319
Abu Dhabi, United Arab Emirates
Tel.: (971) 2 6721444
Fax: (971) 2 6729833
E-Mail: aldhafra@emirates.net.ae
Web Site: www.aldhafrainsurance.ae
Year Founded: 1979
DHAFRA—(EMI)
Premiums: $77,983,128
Assets: $193,202,162
Liabilities: $108,246,754
Net Worth: $84,955,408
Earnings: $13,439,459
Emp.: 164
Fiscal Year-end: 12/31/12
Business Description:
Insurance Services
S.I.C.: 6411
N.A.I.C.S.: 524298
Personnel:
Mohamed Sultan Al Dhabiry *(Chm)*
Board of Directors:
Mohamed Sultan Al Dhabiry
Hamad Abdullah Rashid Al Shamsi
Saif Saeed Ahmed Ghobash
Obeid Khalifa Al Jaber
Rashid Mohamed Al Mazroi
Yousef Mohammed Ali Al Nowais
Sayah Mohammed Mousa Al Qubeisy
Saif Mubarak Al Riamy
Saleh Rashid Al Dhahiry

ALDI GROUP

Eckenberg Strasse 16
Postfach 13 01 110
45307 Essen, Germany
Tel.: (49) 20185930
Fax: (49) 2018593319
E-Mail: mail@aldinord.de
Web Site: www.aldi.com
Year Founded: 1948
Sales Range: $50-74.9 Billion
Emp.: 133,000
Business Description:
Discount Grocery Retailer
S.I.C.: 5411
N.A.I.C.S.: 445110
Personnel:
Dietmar Stewan *(CFO)*
U.S. Subsidiaries:

Aldi Food Inc. (1)
1200 N Kirk Rd
Batavia, IL 60510-1443 IL
Tel.: (630) 879-8100
Fax: (630) 879-8410
Web Site: www.aldi.com
Emp.: 80
Retailer of Groceries
S.I.C.: 5411
N.A.I.C.S.: 445110

TACT Holding (1)
538 Mission St
South Pasadena, CA 91030-3036 CA
Mailing Address:
PO Box 3270
South Pasadena, CA 91031-6270
Tel.: (626) 441-1177
Fax: (626) 441-9573
Emp.: 4,500
Holding Company
Import
S.I.C.: 5411
N.A.I.C.S.: 445110

Subsidiary:

Trader Joe's Co. (2)
604 W Huntington Dr
Monrovia, CA 91016-6346 CA
Tel.: (626) 358-8884 (100%)
Web Site: www.traderjoes.com
Rev.: $8,000,000,000
Emp.: 3,500
Specialty Market
S.I.C.: 5411
N.A.I.C.S.: 445110
Daniel T. Bane *(Chm & CEO)*
Thomas English *(CIO & VP)*

ALDO GROUP

2300 Emile-Belanger
Saint Laurent, QC, Canada
Tel.: (514) 747-2536
Fax: (514) 747-7993
Toll Free: (888) 298-2536
E-Mail: comments@aldogoup.com
Web Site: www.aldoshoes.com
Emp.: 100
Business Description:
Footwear Mfr & Distr
S.I.C.: 5139
N.A.I.C.S.: 424340
Personnel:
Aldo Bensadoun *(CEO)*

ALDREES PETROLEUM & TRANSPORT SERVICES COMPANY

PO Box 609
Riyadh, 11421, Saudi Arabia
Tel.: (966) 12355555
Fax: (966) 12366666
E-Mail: info@aldrees.com
Web Site: www.aldrees.com
Year Founded: 1920
4200—(SAU)
Rev.: $498,932,765
Assets: $247,048,537
Liabilities: $119,772,214
Net Worth: $127,276,323
Earnings: $25,444,401
Emp.: 1,660
Fiscal Year-end: 12/31/12
Business Description:
Petroleum & Transportation Services
S.I.C.: 4731
N.A.I.C.S.: 488510
Personnel:
Hamad Mohammed Aldrees *(Chm)*
Abdulilah Saad Aldrees *(CEO)*
Rasmy Gerguis Awad *(CFO)*

Aldrees Petroleum & Transport Services Company—(Continued)

Board of Directors:
Abdulilah Saad Aldrees
Hamad Mohammed Aldrees

Subsidiary:

Mohammad Saad Aldrees & Sons Company Limited (1)
PO Box 609
11421 Riyadh, Saudi Arabia (100%)
Tel.: (966) 1 235 5555
Fax: (966) 1 236 6666
E-Mail: info@aldrees.com
Web Site: www.aldrees.com
Emp.: 2,000
Crude Petroleum & Natural Gas Extraction
S.I.C.: 1311
N.A.I.C.S.: 211111
Hamad Aldrees *(Chm)*
Abdulilah Adrasee *(CEO)*

ALDRIDGE MINERALS INC.

10 King Street East Suite 300
Toronto, ON, M5C 1C3, Canada
Tel.: (416) 477-6980
Web Site: www.aldridge.com.tr
Year Founded: 1994
AGM—(TSXV)
Int. Income: $71,705
Assets: $5,227,254
Liabilities: $1,540,139
Net Worth: $3,687,115
Earnings: ($13,592,937)
Fiscal Year-end: 12/31/12
Business Description:
Mineral Exploration Services
S.I.C.: 1081
N.A.I.C.S.: 213114
Personnel:
Barry Hildred *(Chm)*
Jim O'Neill *(CFO)*
Ertan Oner *(IT Officer-Turkey)*
Denise Williams *(Sec)*
Board of Directors:
Barry Hildred
John F. Cook
Daniella Dimitrov
Ed Guimaraes
Martin Oczlon
Meric Oktar
Ahmet Tacyildiz
Hande Tacyildiz
Mike Widmer
Transfer Agent:
Computershare Investor Services Inc.
100 University Avenue 8th Floor
Toronto, ON, M5J 2Y1, Canada
Tel.: (514) 982-7555

ALDRIN RESOURCE CORP.

Suite 2020-401 West Georgia Street
Vancouver, BC, V6B 5A1, Canada
Tel.: (604) 687-7741
Fax: (604) 687-0796
E-Mail: info@aldrinresourcecorp.com
Web Site: www.aldrinresourcecorp.com
Year Founded: 2005
ALN—(TSXV)
Int. Income: $18,284
Assets: $1,063,929
Liabilities: $49,573
Net Worth: $1,014,356
Earnings: ($821,310)
Fiscal Year-end: 11/30/12
Business Description:
Mining Exploration & Development Services
S.I.C.: 1499
N.A.I.C.S.: 212399
Personnel:
Robert Dardi *(Chm)*
Thomas Cavanagh *(Pres)*
Johnathan More *(CEO)*
Cyrus H. Driver *(CFO)*
Board of Directors:
Robert Dardi
Thomas Cavanagh
Cyrus H. Driver
Bert W. Jeffries
Graydon Kowal
Johnathan More
Transfer Agent:
Computershare Investor Services Inc
4th Floor 510 Burrard Street
Vancouver, BC, Canada

ALE PROPERTY GROUP

Level 10 Norwich House 6 O'Connell Street
Sydney, NSW, 2000, Australia
Tel.: (61) 2 8231 8588
Fax: (61) 2 8231 8500
E-Mail: alegroup@alegroup.com.au
Web Site: www.alegroup.com.au
LEP—(ASX)
Rev.: $58,213,790
Assets: $901,477,984
Liabilities: $517,613,154
Net Worth: $383,864,830
Earnings: $15,536,669
Emp.: 11
Fiscal Year-end: 06/30/13
Business Description:
Owner of Pubs
S.I.C.: 6531
N.A.I.C.S.: 531390
Personnel:
Andrew F. O. Wilkinson *(Mng Dir)*
Brendan Howell *(Compliance Officer & Sec)*
Board of Directors:
Peter H. Warne
Pippa Downes
John P. Henderson
James T. McNally
Andrew F. O. Wilkinson
Helen I. Wright
Legal Counsel:
Allens Linklaters
Deutsche Bank Place Corner Hunter & Phillip Streets
Sydney, NSW, 2000, Australia

Subsidiaries:

Australian Leisure & Entertainment Property Management Limited (1)
Level 10 Norwich House 6 O'Connell St
Sydney, NSW, 2000, Australia
Tel.: (61) 282318588
Fax: (61) 282318500
E-Mail: alegroup@alegroup.com.au
Web Site: www.alegroup.com.au
Emp.: 5
Investment Property Management Services
S.I.C.: 8748
N.A.I.C.S.: 541618
Peter Warne *(Chm)*
Andrew Wilkinson *(Mng Dir)*

Australian Leisure & Entertainment Property Trust (1)
Level 10 Norwich House 6 O'Connell St
Sydney, NSW, 2000, Australia
Tel.: (61) 282318588
Fax: (61) 282318500
E-Mail: alegroup@alegroup.com.au
Web Site: www.alegroup.com.au
Emp.: 6
Investment Property Management Services
S.I.C.: 8748
N.A.I.C.S.: 541618
Andrew Wilkinson *(Mng Dir)*

ALEADRI-SCHINNI PARTICIPACOES E REPRESENTACOES S.A.

Av Primo Schincariol 2 300 Itaim
Itu, SP, 13312-900, Brazil
Tel.: (55) 11 2118 9500
Business Description:
Holding Company
S.I.C.: 6719
N.A.I.C.S.: 551112
Personnel:
Alexandre Schincariol *(Co-CEO)*
Andriano Schincariol *(Co-CEO)*

ALEATOR ENERGY LIMITED

18 40 St Quentin Avenue
Claremont, WA, 6010, Australia
Mailing Address:
PO Box 216
Claremont, WA, 6910, Australia
Tel.: (61) 8 9385 0700
Fax: (61) 8 9385 4400
E-Mail: info@aleatorenergy.com.au
Web Site: www.aleatorenergy.com.au
Sales Range: Less than $1 Million
Business Description:
Oil & Gas Exploration Services
S.I.C.: 1311
N.A.I.C.S.: 211111
Personnel:
Lewis Cross *(Chm)*
Wal Muir *(CEO)*
Hamish Carnachan *(CFO)*
Ranko Matic *(Sec)*
Board of Directors:
Lewis Cross
Mark Rowbottam
Gennady Varitsky
Legal Counsel:
Steinepreis Paganin
Level 4 16 Milligan Street
Perth, WA, 6000, Australia

ALECTA PENSIONSFORSAKRING, OMSESIDIGT

Regeringsgatan 107
SE-103 73 Stockholm, Sweden
Tel.: (46) 8 441 60 00
Fax: (46) 8 441 60 90
E-Mail: kundservice@alecta.se
Web Site: www.alecta.se
Year Founded: 1917
Sales Range: $1-4.9 Billion
Emp.: 370
Business Description:
Pension Management
S.I.C.: 6371
N.A.I.C.S.: 524292
Personnel:
Erik Asbrink *(Chm)*
Christer Agren *(Second Vice Chm)*
Cecilia Fahlberg *(First Vice Chm)*
Staffan Grefback *(CEO)*
Katarina Thorslund *(Deputy CEO & Head-Fin & Actuarial)*
Per Frennberg *(Deputy CEO & Head-Investment Mgmt)*
Johan Anderson *(Press Officer)*
Tomas Bergqvist *(Sr VP-HR)*
Board of Directors:
Erik Asbrink
Christer Agren
Britt-Marie Bryngelsson
Gunilla Dahmm
Cecilia Fahlberg
Staffan Grefback
Per Hedelin
Richard Malmborg
Jonas Milton
Mikael Persson
Karl Olof Stenqvist
Kaj Thoren
Magnus von Koch
Lars R. Wedenborn

ALECTO MINERALS PLC

One America Square Crosswall
London, EC3N 2SG, United Kingdom
Tel.: (44) 20 3137 8862
Fax: (44) 20 7182 1744
E-Mail: enquiries@alectominerals.com
Web Site: www.alectominerals.com
ALO—(LSE)
Rev.: $2,683
Assets: $6,755,806
Liabilities: $1,127,659
Net Worth: $5,628,147
Earnings: ($1,739,580)
Fiscal Year-end: 12/31/12
Business Description:
Mineral Resources Exploration
S.I.C.: 1041
N.A.I.C.S.: 212221
Personnel:
Mark C. Jones *(CEO)*
John Bottomley *(Sec)*
Board of Directors:
Michael Johnson
Toby Howell
Legal Counsel:
Kerman & Co. LLP
200 Strand
London, EC1V 9EE, United Kingdom

ALEEDA INC.

7115 Tonken Rd
Mississauga, ON, L5S 1R7, Canada
Tel.: (905) 696-9525
Fax: (905) 696-9526
E-Mail: info@aleedainc.com
Web Site: www.aleedainc.com
Year Founded: 2006
Emp.: 20
Business Description:
Beauty Care Products Mfr
S.I.C.: 5122
N.A.I.C.S.: 446120
Personnel:
Juvenal Alvarez *(Chm)*
Mario Merino *(Pres)*

ALEEYAH CAPITAL CORP.

(Name Changed to Kesselrun Resources Ltd.)

ALEMBIC LIMITED

Alembic Road
Vadodara, Gujarat, 390 003, India
Tel.: (91) 2652280550
Fax: (91) 2652281508
E-Mail: infoal@alembic.co.in
Web Site: www.alembic-india.com
Year Founded: 1907
506235—(BOM)
Rev.: $35,227,205
Assets: $63,774,430
Liabilities: $25,612,528
Net Worth: $38,161,902
Earnings: $2,130,876
Fiscal Year-end: 03/31/13
Business Description:
Pharmaceutical Products Mfr
S.I.C.: 2834
N.A.I.C.S.: 325412
Personnel:
Udit Amin *(CEO & Pres-Real Estate Bus)*
Chirag K. Shukla *(Sec)*
Board of Directors:
Chirayu R. Amin
Udit Amin
C. P. Buch
Saxena R. C.
R. M. Kapadia
Milin Mehta
Ashok Tulankar
Transfer Agent:
Link Intime India Pvt. Ltd.
B-102 & 103 Shangrila Complex First Floor
Near Radhakrishna Char Rasta
Opp.HDFC Bank, Vadodara, India

Subsidiaries:

Alembic Glass Industries Ltd. (1)
Alembic Road
Vadodara, Gujarat, 390 016, India

Tel.: (91) 2652281097
Fax: (91) 2652282515
E-Mail: agi.brd@alembic.co.in
Web Site: www.yera.com
Emp.: 400
Household Glassware Mfr
S.I.C.: 3229
N.A.I.C.S.: 327212
Chirayu R. Amin *(Chm)*

Alembic Pharmaceuticals Limited **(1)**
Alembic Road
Vadodara, Gujarat, 390 003, India
Tel.: (91) 265 228 0550
Fax: (91) 265 228 1508
E-Mail: infoal@alembic.co.in
Web Site: www.alembic-india.com
533573—(BOM)
Rev.: $283,494,565
Assets: $194,266,607
Liabilities: $101,021,030
Net Worth: $93,245,577
Earnings: $30,638,221
Fiscal Year-end: 03/31/13
Pharmaceutical Products Mfr
S.I.C.: 2834
N.A.I.C.S.: 325412
Chirayu R. Amin *(Chm & Mng Dir)*
Rajkumar K. Baheti *(Pres-Fin & Sec)*
Pranav Amin *(Pres-Intl Bus)*
Shaunak Amin *(Pres-Branded Formulations Bus)*

Nirayu Private Limited **(1)**
Alembic Rd
390003 Vadodara, Gujurat, India (100%)
Tel.: (91) 2652280550
Fax: (91) 2653007300
E-Mail: nirayu@alembic.co.in
Basic Organic Chemical Mfr
S.I.C.: 2899
N.A.I.C.S.: 325199

Paushak Limited **(1)**
Alembic Road
Vadodara, Gujarat, 390003, India
Tel.: (91) 2652280550
Fax: (91) 265 228 1508
E-Mail: paushak@alembic.co.in
Web Site: www.paushak.com
Phosgene Gas Producer
S.I.C.: 2899
N.A.I.C.S.: 325998
Chirag K. Shukla *(Sec)*

Shreno Ltd **(1)**
Alembic Road
390003 Vadodara, Gujurat, India (100%)
Tel.: (91) 2653007100
Fax: (91) 2652281380
E-Mail: agibrd@alembic.co.in
Web Site: www.yera.com
Pressed & Blown Glass & Glassware Mfr
S.I.C.: 3229
N.A.I.C.S.: 327212

Plants:

Shreno Ltd - Factory Unit-1 **(2)**
3/23-24 Gorwa Industrial Estate
Vadodara, Gujarat, 390003, India
Tel.: (91) 265 228 2284
Fax: (91) 265 228 0569
E-Mail: shreno1@shreno.com
Emp.: 120
Industrial Machinery Mfr & Distr
S.I.C.: 3556
N.A.I.C.S.: 333241
Yogesh Vyas *(VP)*

Shreno Ltd - Factory Unit-2 **(2)**
4/22-23 Gorwa Industrial Estate
Vadodara, Gujarat, 390003, India
Tel.: (91) 2652280190
Fax: (91) 2652285893
E-Mail: shreno2@shreno.com
Web Site: www.shreno.com
Industrial Machinery Mfr & Sistr
S.I.C.: 3556
N.A.I.C.S.: 333241

ALENT PLC

Forsyth Road Sheerwater
Woking, Surrey, GU21 5RZ, United Kingdom
Tel.: (44) 1483 758400
Fax: (44) 1483 793226
E-Mail: fgibbons@alent.com
Web Site: www.alent.com
ALNT—(LSE)
Rev.: $1,127,455,131
Assets: $1,078,023,354
Liabilities: $642,139,314
Net Worth: $435,884,040
Earnings: $71,068,050
Emp.: 2,580
Fiscal Year-end: 12/31/12

Business Description:
Consumable Engineered Materials for Electronics & Automotive Industries
S.I.C.: 3559
N.A.I.C.S.: 333249

Personnel:
Peter J. Hill *(Chm)*
Steve James Corbett *(CEO)*

Board of Directors:
Peter J. Hill
Steve James Corbett
David John Egan
Emma Theresa FitzGerald
Lars Einar Forberg
Noel Harwerth
Jan Oosterveld
Mark D. Williamson

U.S. Subsidiaries:

Alpha **(1)**
109 Corporate Blvd
South Plainfield, NJ 07080 NJ
Tel.: (908) 791-3000
Fax: (908) 791-3090
E-Mail:
Web Site: www.alpha.alent.com
Sales Range: $650-699.9 Million
Emp.: 1,350
Electronic Assembly Material & Equipment Mfr
Import Export
S.I.C.: 3548
N.A.I.C.S.: 333992
Richard Ertmann *(Pres)*

Subsidiary:

Alpha Metals, Inc. **(2)**
4100 Sixth Ave
Altoona, PA 16602 (100%)
Tel.: (814) 946-1611
Fax: (814) 943-7268
E-Mail:
Emp.: 200
Electronic Assembly Material & Equipment Mfr
S.I.C.: 3548
N.A.I.C.S.: 333992
Bob Davis *(VP-Sls)*

Enthone Inc. **(1)**
350 Frontage Rd
West Haven, CT 06516-4130 NY
Tel.: (203) 934-8611 (100%)
Fax: (203) 799-1513
E-Mail: enthone@enthone.com
Web Site: www.enthone.com
Sales Range: $400-449.9 Million
Emp.: 1,210
High-Performance Specialty Chemicals & Coatings
S.I.C.: 2899
N.A.I.C.S.: 325998
Rick Reagan *(Pres)*
David Crimp *(Exec VP-Europe)*
Robert J. Haskins *(Sr VP & Mng Dir-Asia Reg)*

Non-U.S. Subsidiary:

Alpha Metals Singapore Pte Ltd **(1)**
14 Tuas Avenue 10
Singapore, 639138, Singapore
Tel.: (65) 68611977
Fax: (65) 68611670
Emp.: 5
Electronic Products Mfr
S.I.C.: 3679
N.A.I.C.S.: 334419
Gary Cunning *(Gen Mgr)*

ALERION CLEAN POWER S.P.A.

via Durini 16/18
Milan, Italy 20122
Tel.: (39) 02 7788901
Fax: (39) 02 778890282
E-Mail: info@alerion.it
Web Site: www.alerion.it
Year Founded: 1981
ARN—(ITA)
Sales Range: $100-124.9 Million

Business Description:
Electric Power Generation Services
S.I.C.: 4931
N.A.I.C.S.: 221118

Personnel:
Gastone Colleoni *(Chm)*
Giulio Antonello *(CEO)*

Board of Directors:
Gastone Colleoni
Giulio Antonello
Franco Bonferroni
Michelangelo Canova
Alessandro Crosti
Giuseppina Falappa
Giuseppe Garofano
Pasquale Iannuzzo
Antonio Marino
Ernesto Paolillo
Alessandro Perrone
Marcello Priori
Corrado Santini
Graziano Visentin
Laura Zanetti

ALERT STEEL HOLDINGS LTD.

12 Gompou Street
East Lynne, 0186 Pretoria, South Africa
Tel.: (27) 128000000
Fax: (27) 128000015
E-Mail: info@alertsteel.co.za
Web Site: www.alertsteel.co.za
ALERT—(JSE)
Sales Range: $125-149.9 Million
Emp.: 593

Business Description:
Retailer of Steel, Building Materials, Plumbing & Hardware Products
S.I.C.: 5051
N.A.I.C.S.: 423510

Personnel:
Wynand Frederik Schalekamp *(Chm, CEO & Mng Dir)*
Monika Pretorius *(Sec)*

Board of Directors:
Wynand Frederik Schalekamp
Edwin Hewitt
Rynhardt van Rooyen

Legal Counsel:
Fluxmans Inc
11 Biermann Avenue
Rosebank, 2196, South Africa
Tel.: (27) 11 328 1700
Fax: (27) 11 880 2261

Transfer Agent:
Computershare Investor Services (Proprietary) Limited
Ground Floor 70 Marshall St
Johannesburg, South Africa

Subsidiaries:

Alert Steel Brits (Pty) Ltd **(1)**
21 Van Deventer St
Brits, North West, South Africa
Tel.: (27) 122520773
Fax: (27) 122520775
Emp.: 48
Metal Products Distr
S.I.C.: 5051
N.A.I.C.S.: 423510
Johan du Toit *(CEO)*

Alert Steel (Pty) Ltd **(1)**
162 Main Reef Rd
Johannesburg, Gauteng, 2094, South Africa
Tel.: (27) 128000200
Fax: (27) 128000013
Steel Mfr & Distr
S.I.C.: 3399
N.A.I.C.S.: 331110

Alert Steel Tshwane (Pty) Ltd **(1)**
Shop 11 Lenchen Centre C/O Jakaranda & Lenchen Avenue
Hennopspark, Centurion, Gauteng, South Africa
Tel.: (27) 12 653 5607
Fax: (27) 2 653 0332
Web Site: www.alertsteel.co.za/index.asp?pkCategoryID=38
Emp.: 15
Steel Mfr & Distr
S.I.C.: 3399
N.A.I.C.S.: 331110

ALERTME.COM LTD

30 Station Road
Cambridge, CB1 2RE, United Kingdom
Tel.: (44) 1223 361555
Fax: (44) 1223 361 557
E-Mail: info@alertme.com
Web Site: www.alertme.com
Year Founded: 2006
Sales Range: $10-24.9 Million
Emp.: 92

Business Description:
Internet Application Development Services
S.I.C.: 7371
N.A.I.C.S.: 541511

Personnel:
Mary Turner *(CEO)*

ALES GROUPE SA

99 rue du faubourg Saint Honore
75008 Paris, France
Tel.: (33) 134235000
Fax: (33) 134235001
E-Mail: info@alesgroupe.com
Web Site: www.alesgroupe.com
ALPHY—(EUR)
Sls.: $277,362,174
Earnings: ($9,207,803)
Emp.: 1,020
Fiscal Year-end: 12/31/12

Business Description:
Perfume, Hair & Skin Care Products Mfr & Distr
S.I.C.: 2844
N.A.I.C.S.: 325620

Personnel:
Patrick Ales *(Chm)*
Raphael Yousri *(CEO)*
Stephane Seriset *(Dir Gen-France)*
Olivier Sido *(Dir Gen-Intl)*
Marc Jeremie *(CFO)*
Alexandre de Laborderie *(Sec)*

Subsidiaries:

Ales Groupe Industries **(1)**
99 R Du Faubourg Saint Honore
95870 Paris, France (100%)
Tel.: (33) 153939900
Fax: (33) 135235001
Emp.: 90
Cosmetics Beauty Supplies & Perfume Stores
S.I.C.: 5122
N.A.I.C.S.: 446120
Patrick Ales *(Pres)*

Lab. Lierac SA **(1)**
35 Avenue F Delano Roosevelt
75008 Paris, France (99.95%)
Tel.: (33) 153939905
Fax: (33) 153939901
E-Mail: stand@alesgroupe.com
Web Site: www.lierac.fr/FR/nous_contacter/services/serviceconsommateurs1.html
Emp.: 200
Cosmetics Beauty Supplies & Perfume Stores
S.I.C.: 5122
N.A.I.C.S.: 446120
Patrick Ales *(Gen Mgr)*

Laboratoires PHYTOSOLBA **(1)**
99 rue du Faubourg Saint-Honore
75008 Paris, France (99.96%)
Tel.: (33) 153939906

Ales Groupe SA—(Continued)

E-Mail: presse@phto.com
Web Site: www.alesgroupe.com
Cosmetic Laboratories
S.I.C.: 8734
N.A.I.C.S.: 541380

Parfums Caron (1)
90 R Du Faubourg Saint Honore
75008 Paris, France (99.99%)
Tel.: (33) 142682568
Fax: (33) 142682569
E-Mail: faubourg@alesgruope.com
Web Site: www.parfumscaron.com
Cosmetics Beauty Supplies & Perfume Stores
S.I.C.: 5122
N.A.I.C.S.: 446120
Garance Doin *(Gen Mgr)*

U.S. Subsidiary:

Ales Group Inc (1)
1350 Ave of the Americas
New York, NY 10019 (79.97%)
Tel.: (212) 265-5625
Fax: (866) 588-7950
E-Mail: info@alesgroup.com
Web Site: www.alesgroup.com
Emp.: 45
Cosmetics Beauty Supplies & Perfume Stores
S.I.C.: 5122
N.A.I.C.S.: 446120
Rafrrel Salyousri *(Pres)*

Non-U.S. Subsidiaries:

Ales Group Cosmetic Gmbh (1)
Schwanheimer Strasse 113
60528 Frankfurt, Germany (99.96%)
Tel.: (49) 699688500
Fax: (49) 69681216
E-Mail: info@alesgroupe.com
Web Site: www.alesgroupe.com
All Other Miscellaneous Store Retailers
S.I.C.: 5999
N.A.I.C.S.: 453998

Ales Group Uk Ltd (1)
9 Risborough Street
SE10AX London, United Kingdom (99.96%)
Tel.: (44) 2076201771
Fax: (44) 2076201593
E-Mail: office@alesgroup.co.uk
Web Site: www.phyto.com
Emp.: 13
Cosmetics Beauty Supplies & Perfume Stores
S.I.C.: 5122
N.A.I.C.S.: 446120
Olivier Bianchi *(Mng Dir)*

Ales Groupe Benelux Sprl (1)
Rue Victor Allard 45
1180 Brussels, Belgium (99.7%)
Tel.: (32) 23337272
Fax: (32) 23337273
Web Site: www.alesgroupe.com
Emp.: 10
Cosmetics Beauty Supplies & Perfume Stores
S.I.C.: 5122
N.A.I.C.S.: 446120

Ales Groupe Canada Inc (1)
980 Sainte Catherine W Ste 6
Montreal, QC, H3B 1E5, Canada
Tel.: (514) 932-3636
Fax: (514) 932-2211
Emp.: 8
Cosmetic Products Whslr
S.I.C.: 5122
N.A.I.C.S.: 424210
Benoit Dufour *(Pres)*

ALES GROUPE Cosmetic Deutschland GmbH (1)
Schwanheimer Strasse 113
Frankfurt am Main, Germany
Tel.: (49) 69 96 88 50 0
Fax: (49) 69 68 16 12
Web Site: www.alesgroupe.com
Cosmetics Products Whslr
S.I.C.: 5122
N.A.I.C.S.: 424210

ALES GROUPE ESPANA S.L. (1)
Paseo de la Habana 1 28036
28006 Madrid, Spain
Tel.: (34) 917814750
Fax: (34) 915758001
E-Mail: info@alesgroup.es
Web Site: www.alesgroupe.com
Emp.: 9
Cosmetic Products Whslr
S.I.C.: 5122
N.A.I.C.S.: 424210

ALES GROUPE ITALIA S.p.A (1)
Largo Donegani 2
20121 Milan, Italy
Tel.: (39) 022906671
Web Site: www.alesgroupe.it
Cosmetic Products Whslr
S.I.C.: 5122
N.A.I.C.S.: 424210

Ales Groupe Polska Sp. z o.o. (1)
Ul Zaruby 9-119
02-796 Warsaw, Poland (100%)
Tel.: (48) 226496190
Fax: (48) 226496209
E-Mail: biuro@alesgroupe.com.pl
Web Site: www.lierac.com.pl
Emp.: 10
Cosmetics Beauty Supplies & Perfume Stores
S.I.C.: 5122
N.A.I.C.S.: 446120

Ales Groupe Portugal Lda (1)
Rua do Campo Alegre N 830 8 Andar Sala 37
4150-171 Porto, Portugal
Tel.: (351) 220110030
Fax: (351) 220105408
E-Mail: info.phyto@alesgroupe.pt
Web Site: www.alesgroupe.pt
Emp.: 30
Cosmetics Products Distr
S.I.C.: 5122
N.A.I.C.S.: 446120
Marcos Allen *(Mng Dir)*

ALES GROUPE (SUISSE) SA (1)
Centre Regus Aeroport 18 Ave Louis Casai
1209 Geneva, Switzerland
Tel.: (41) 227477762
Fax: (41) 22 747 76 54
Web Site: www.alesgroupe.com
Cosmetics & Perfumes Mfr & Sls
S.I.C.: 2844
N.A.I.C.S.: 325620

ALESAYI TRADING CORPORATION

Kilo 11 Makkah Road
Jeddah, 21431, Saudi Arabia
Tel.: (966) 26202000
Fax: (966) 26206469
E-Mail: info@alesayi.com.sa
Web Site: www.alesayi-motors.com
Emp.: 1,000
Business Description:
Automobiles Distr
S.I.C.: 5511
N.A.I.C.S.: 441110
Personnel:
Faeed Omar Alesayi *(Chm)*

ALESSANDRO ROSSO GROUP S.P.A.

Via Privata Alessandro Antonelli 3
20139 Milan, MI, Italy
Tel.: (39) 02 87387 201
Fax: (39) 02 87387 219
Web Site: www.alessandrogroup.com
Year Founded: 2002
Sales Range: $100-124.9 Million
Emp.: 250
Business Description:
Holding Company; Incentive Travel, Team Building Events, Convention Organization & Tour Operation Services
S.I.C.: 6719
N.A.I.C.S.: 551112
Personnel:
Alessandro Rosso *(Founder, Chm, Pres & CEO)*

Subsidiaries:

Alessandro Rosso Incentive S.r.l. (1)
Via Privata Alessandro Antonelli 3
20139 Milan, MI, Italy IT
Tel.: (39) 02 87387 201
Fax: (39) 02 87387 219
Web Site: www.arossogroup.com
Incentive Travel & Team Building Services
S.I.C.: 4729
N.A.I.C.S.: 561599

Best Tours S.p.A. (1)
Via Tito Speri 8
20154 Milan, MI, Italy IT
Tel.: (39) 02 33633 1 (100%)
Fax: (39) 02 33103 381
E-Mail: mho@besttours.it
Web Site: www.besttours.it
Tour Operator
S.I.C.: 4725
N.A.I.C.S.: 561520
Alessandro Rosso *(Pres)*
Marco Cisini *(CEO)*
Simone Cavestro *(Mng Dir)*

Subsidiary:

Best Tours Italia S.p.A. (2)
(Formerly Kuoni Italia S.p.A.)
Via Tito Speri 8
20154 Milan, MI, Italy IT
Tel.: (39) 02 33633 1 (100%)
Fax: (39) 02 33103 381
E-Mail: mho@besttours.it
Web Site: www.besttours.it
Tour Operator
S.I.C.: 4725
N.A.I.C.S.: 561520
Alessandro Rosso *(Pres)*
Marco Cisini *(CEO)*
Simone Cavestro *(Mng Dir)*
Stefano Cerrato *(COO)*

ALEX MACINTYRE & ASSOCIATES LTD.

1390 Government Road West
PO Box 517
Kirkland Lake, ON, P2N 3J5, Canada
Tel.: (705) 567-6663
Fax: (705) 567-4925
Web Site: www.macintyremining.com
Year Founded: 1958
Rev.: $32,404,535
Emp.: 150
Business Description:
Mining Services
S.I.C.: 1099
N.A.I.C.S.: 212299
Personnel:
Syd McDougall *(Pres)*

ALEX WILSON COLDSTREAM LTD.

32 Colonization Ave
PO Box 3009
Dryden, ON, P8N 2Y9, Canada
Tel.: (807) 223-2381
Fax: (807) 223-2907
Toll Free: (800) 465-7230
E-Mail: awcl@awcoldstream.com
Web Site: www.awcoldstream.com
Year Founded: 1940
Sls.: $15,000,000
Emp.: 34
Business Description:
Stock Products & Custom Orders Printers
Import Export
S.I.C.: 2759
N.A.I.C.S.: 323111
Personnel:
Roy Wilson *(Pres & CEO)*

ALEXANDER DAVID SECURITIES GROUP PLC

45 Moorfields
London, EC2Y 9AE, United Kingdom
Tel.: (44) 20 7448 9800
Fax: (44) 20 3432 4453
E-Mail: info@ad-securities.com
Web Site: www.ad-securities.com
Year Founded: 1985
ADS—(AIM)
Rev.: $2,231,537
Assets: $1,438,733
Liabilities: $1,204,998
Net Worth: $233,735
Earnings: ($1,026,538)
Emp.: 18
Fiscal Year-end: 12/31/12
Business Description:
Investment Banker & Securities Dealer
S.I.C.: 6211
N.A.I.C.S.: 523110
Personnel:
Alon Bull *(Founder)*
Michael Hicks *(Chm)*
David Scott *(CEO & Head-Corp Fin)*
Angus Rose *(CFO)*
Sandra Scott *(Sec)*
Board of Directors:
Michael Hicks
Alon Bull
Trevor Coote
Angus Rose
David Scott
Legal Counsel:
K&L Gates
110 Cannon Street
London, United Kingdom

Subsidiary:

Alexander David Securities Limited (1)
60 Lombard St
London, EC3V 9EA, United Kingdom
Tel.: (44) 2074489800
Fax: (44) 2034324453
E-Mail: info@ad-securities.com
Web Site: www.ad-securities.com
Emp.: 20
Investment Advisory Services
S.I.C.: 6282
N.A.I.C.S.: 523930
Crevor Coote *(Gen Mgr)*

ALEXANDER DENNIS LIMITED

91 Glasgow Road
Falkirk, Scotland, FK1 4JB, United Kingdom
Tel.: (44) 1324 621 672
Fax: (44) 1324 632 469
Web Site: www.alexander-dennis.com
Sales Range: $550-599.9 Million
Emp.: 2,000
Business Description:
Commercial Bus Mfr, Distr & Whslr
S.I.C.: 3711
N.A.I.C.S.: 336211
Personnel:
Colin Robertson *(CEO)*

U.S. Subsidiary:

Alexander Dennis Incorporated (1)
31566 Railroad Canyon Rd Ste 342
Canyon Lake, CA 92587-9446 DE
Tel.: (951) 244-9429
Fax: (951) 755-0318
Web Site: www.alexander-dennis.com
Commercial Bus & Bus Parts Whslr
S.I.C.: 5012
N.A.I.C.S.: 423110
Judy Lovitt *(Fin Mgr)*

Non-U.S. Subsidiaries:

Alexander Dennis (Asia Pacific) Limited (1)
3rd Floor CAC Tower 165 Hoi Bun Road
Kwun Tong, Kowloon, China (Hong Kong) HK
Tel.: (852) 2757 8057
Fax: (852) 2757 7766
Web Site: www.alexander-dennis.com
Commercial Bus Assembly & Whslr
S.I.C.: 5012

N.A.I.C.S.: 423110

Custom Coaches Pty. Ltd. (1)
44 Biloela Street
Villawood, NSW, 2163, Australia AU
Tel.: (61) 9914 3800
Fax: (61) 297272178
E-Mail: info@custom-coaches.com.au
Web Site: www.custom-coaches.com.au
Sales Range: $25-49.9 Million
Emp.: 350
Bus Designer & Mfr
S.I.C.: 3711
N.A.I.C.S.: 336211
John Goode *(Dir-Ops)*

ALEXANDER ENERGY LTD.

(Formerly Petro-Reef Resources Ltd.)
Suite 1540 Eau Claire Place II 521 3rd Avenue Southwest
Calgary, AB, T2P 3T3, Canada
Tel.: (403) 265-6444
Fax: (403) 264-1348
E-Mail: info@alexanderenergy.ca
Web Site: www.alexanderenergy.ca
ALX—(TSXV)
Rev.: $12,003,786
Assets: $32,587,952
Liabilities: $16,500,732
Net Worth: $16,087,220
Earnings: $815,096
Fiscal Year-end: 12/31/12

Business Description:
Oil & Natural Gas Exploration Services
S.I.C.: 1311
N.A.I.C.S.: 211111

Personnel:
Dan Wilson *(CEO)*

Board of Directors:
Doran Flock
J. Paul Lawrence
William C. Macdonald
James Sanden
Dan Wilson

Legal Counsel:
Fasken Martineau DuMoulin LLP
3400 First Canadian Centre 350 7 Avenue SW
Calgary, AB, Canada

Transfer Agent:
CIBC Mellon Trust Company
Ste 600 333 7th Ave SW
Calgary, AB, T2P 2Z1, Canada
Tel.: (403) 232-2400
Fax: (403) 264-2100
Toll Free: (800) 387-0825

ALEXANDER FORBES EQUITY HOLDINGS (PTY) LIMITED

115 West Street
Sandton, 2196, South Africa

Mailing Address:
PO Box 787240
Sandton, 2146, South Africa
Tel.: (27) 112690000
Fax: (27) 112690149
E-Mail: info@aforbes.co.za
Web Site: www.alexanderforbes.com
Year Founded: 1935
Rev.: $519,293,300
Assets: $31,059,413,700
Liabilities: $30,800,828,200
Net Worth: $258,585,500
Earnings: ($11,170,000)
Emp.: 3,881
Fiscal Year-end: 03/31/13

Business Description:
Financial Management, Insurance & Risk Services
S.I.C.: 6211
N.A.I.C.S.: 523999

Personnel:
Sello Moloko *(Chm)*
Edward Kieswetter *(CEO)*
Deon Marius Viljoen *(CFO)*
Thabo Mashaba *(Chief HR Officer)*
Brad Eliot *(Exec-IT)*
Vishnu Naicker *(Exec-Risk & Compliance)*
Lynn Stevens *(Exec-Brand, Mktg & Comm)*
Peter Edwards *(CEO-Alexander Forbes Financial Services Holdings)*
Grant Stobart *(CEO-Alexander Forbes International Limited)*
Janice E. Salvado *(Sec)*

Board of Directors:
Sello Moloko
Mark Collier
Dave Govender
Lori Hall-Kimm
Edward Kieswetter
Natalie Catherine Kolbe
Len Konar
Hillie Meyer
Barend Petersen
Cyril Ramaphosa
Andre Roux
John Adrian van Wyk
Deon Marius Viljoen

Transfer Agent:
Computershare Investor Services (Proprietary) Limited
Ground Floor 70 Marshall St
Johannesburg, South Africa

Subsidiary:

Alexander Forbes Limited (1)
115 West Street
61 Katherine Street Sandown, Sandton, 2196, South Africa
Tel.: (27) 112690000
Fax: (27) 112631111
E-Mail: afonlinehelp@aforbes.co.za
Web Site: www.alexanderforbesonline.com
Sales Range: $450-499.9 Million
Emp.: 3,500
Financial Management, Insurance & Risk Services
S.I.C.: 6211
N.A.I.C.S.: 523999
Edward Kieswetter *(CEO)*

Subsidiaries:

Alexander Forbes Community Trust (2)
Alexander Forbes Place
90 Rivonia Road, Sandown Sandton, 2196, South Africa
Tel.: (27) 116693000
Fax: (27) 116692924
Web Site: www.alexanderforbes.co.za/ContactCountries/Africa/country_sa.htm
Community Development & Investment Services
S.I.C.: 6211
N.A.I.C.S.: 523999

Alexander Forbes Compensation Technologies (Pty) Ltd (2)
1st Floor Block East Hatfield Gardens
Grosvenor and Arcadia Streets, Pretoria, 0028, South Africa
Tel.: (27) 124319700
Fax: (27) 123420230
Web Site: www.afct.co.za
Emp.: 120
Healthcare Solutions & Accident Insurance Compensation Services
S.I.C.: 6411
N.A.I.C.S.: 524298
Nickey Quinn *(Mng Dir)*

Non-U.S. Branch:

Alexander Forbes International Ltd. - Nottingham Office (2)
6th Fl Market Square House
St Jame's St, Nottingham, NG1 6FG, United Kingdom
Tel.: (44) 1159411031
Fax: (44) 1159241869
Web Site: www.alexanderforbes.co.uk
Emp.: 30
Direct Insurance Broker
S.I.C.: 6411
N.A.I.C.S.: 524210
Lisa Whice *(Office Mgr)*

Non-U.S. Joint Venture:

Alexander Forbes Risk Services Zimbabwe (Pvt) Ltd (2)
Robert Mugabe 12th Ave Amcec Bldg
PO Box 1495
Bulawayo, 1495, Zimbabwe
Tel.: (263) 969195
Telex: 3249 ZW
Fax: (263) 976449
E-Mail: admin@aforbes.co.zw
Emp.: 7
Financial Services
S.I.C.: 6211
N.A.I.C.S.: 523999

ALEXANDER FORBES PREFERENCE SHARE INVESTMENTS LIMITED

Alexander Forbes 115 West Street
PO Box 787240
Sandown, Sandton, 2146, South Africa
Tel.: (27) 112690000
Web Site: www.alexanderforbes.co.za
AFP—(JSE)
Rev.: $45,908,700
Assets: $341,355,200
Liabilities: $258,362,100
Net Worth: $82,993,100
Earnings: ($4,803,100)
Emp.: 6,000
Fiscal Year-end: 03/31/13

Business Description:
Insurance Program Management & Consulting Services
S.I.C.: 6411
N.A.I.C.S.: 524298

Personnel:
John R. P. Doidge *(Chm)*
Deon Marius Viljoen *(CFO)*
A. J. Swart *(Pub Officer)*
J. E. Salvado *(Sec)*

Board of Directors:
John R. P. Doidge
Tim Fearnhead
Brendan Harmse
Deon Marius Viljoen

Transfer Agent:
Computershare Investor Services (Pty) Limited
Ground Floor 70 Marshall Street
Johannesburg, South Africa

ALEXANDER MINING PLC

1st Floor 35 Piccadilly
London, W1J 0DW, United Kingdom
Tel.: (44) 2072921300
Fax: (44) 2072921313
E-Mail: info@alexandermining.com
Web Site: www.alexandermining.com
AXM—(AIM)
Rev.: $45,799
Assets: $1,111,820
Liabilities: $306,382
Net Worth: $805,438
Earnings: ($2,427,369)
Emp.: 5
Fiscal Year-end: 12/31/12

Business Description:
Metal Ore Mining
S.I.C.: 1099
N.A.I.C.S.: 212299

Personnel:
Matthew Sutcliffe *(Chm)*
Martin Rosser *(CEO)*
Terry Cross *(CFO & Sec)*

Board of Directors:
Matthew Sutcliffe
James Bunyan
Alan Clegg
Roger Davey
Emil Morfett
Martin Rosser

Legal Counsel:
Fasken Martineau
17 Hanover Street
London, United Kingdom
Cobbetts LLP
58 Mosley Street
Manchester, United Kingdom

Subsidiary:

MetaLeach Limited (1)
Martin Rosser and Matthew Sutcliffe 1st Fl
35 Piccadilly
London, W1J 0DW, United Kingdom
Tel.: (44) 2072921300
Fax: (44) 20 7292 1313
E-Mail: info@metaleach.com
Web Site: www.metaleach.com
Emp.: 3
Hydrometallurgical Mineral Processing Services
S.I.C.: 8734
N.A.I.C.S.: 541380

Non-U.S. Subsidiary:

Compania Minera Molinetes SAC (1)
Av Paseo De La Republica No 3195 Dpto 906
San Isidro, Lima, Peru
Tel.: (51) 1 4422309
Mineral Mining Services
S.I.C.: 1499
N.A.I.C.S.: 212399

ALEXANDER NUBIA INTERNATIONAL INC.

1 Dundas Street West Suite 2535
Toronto, ON, M5G 1Z3, Canada
Tel.: (647) 504-4747
Fax: (416) 981-7031
Toll Free: (877) 607-4747
E-Mail: info@alexandernubia.com
Web Site: www.alexandernubia.com
Year Founded: 2006
AAN—(TSXV)
Assets: $715,276
Liabilities: $1,311,595
Net Worth: ($596,320)
Earnings: ($2,451,134)
Emp.: 11
Fiscal Year-end: 12/31/12

Business Description:
Metal Exploration Services
S.I.C.: 1081
N.A.I.C.S.: 213114

Personnel:
Alexander Massoud *(CEO)*
Justin Blanchet *(CFO)*

Board of Directors:
Giles Edward Baynham
Mark Campbell
Alexander Massoud

Legal Counsel:
Aird & Berlis LLP
Brookfield Place 181 Bay Street Suite 1800
Toronto, ON, M5J 2T9, Canada

Transfer Agent:
Olympia Transfer Services Inc.
Suite 920 120 Adelaide Street West
Toronto, ON, Canada

ALEXANDER SCHNEIDER LTD.

8a Hazoran St
PO Box 8449
New Industrial Zone, Netanya, 42506, Israel
Tel.: (972) 98924444
Fax: (972) 98924455
E-Mail: info@schneider.co.il
Web Site: www.schneider.co.il
Year Founded: 1963
Sales Range: $10-24.9 Million
Emp.: 100

Business Description:
Electronic Parts & Equipment Distr
S.I.C.: 5065

Alexander Schneider Ltd.—(Continued)

N.A.I.C.S.: 423690
Personnel:
Ronit Meir *(Controller-Fin)*

ALEXANDERWERK AG

Kippdorfstrasse 6-24
42857 Remscheid, Germany
Tel.: (49) 2191 795 0
Fax: (49) 2191 795 202
E-Mail: contact@alexanderwerk.com
Web Site: www.alexanderwerk.com
ALX—(DEU)
Business Description:
Industrial Machinery Mfr
S.I.C.: 5084
N.A.I.C.S.: 423830
Personnel:
Franz-Bernd Daum *(Chm-Supervisory Bd)*
Margarete Skowasch *(Vice Chm-Supervisory Bd)*
Juergen Kullmann *(CEO)*
Manfred Teichelkamp *(CFO)*
Supervisory Board of Directors:
Franz-Bernd Daum
Margarete Skowasch
Uwe Stacklies

ALEXANDRA CAPITAL CORP.

#490 580 Hornby Street
Vancouver, BC, V6C 3B6, Canada
Tel.: (604) 687-6991
Fax: (604) 684-0342
E-Mail: suzannewood@telus.net
Year Founded: 2011
AXC.P—(TSXV)
Business Description:
Investment Services
S.I.C.: 6211
N.A.I.C.S.: 523999
Personnel:
Suzanne L. Wood *(Pres, CEO, CFO & Sec)*
Board of Directors:
Timothy J. Crowhurst
Blake G. Olafson
Suzanne L. Wood
Transfer Agent:
Computershare Investor Services Inc.
510 Burrard Street 2nd Floor
Vancouver, BC, V6C 3B9, Canada

ALEXANDRIA MINERALS CORP.

1 Toronto St Suite 201
PO Box 10
Toronto, ON, M5C 2V6, Canada
Tel.: (416) 363-9372
Fax: (416) 363-6872
E-Mail: info@azx.ca
Web Site: www.azx.ca
Year Founded: 2006
AZX—(OTC TSXV)
Int. Income: $4,328
Assets: $20,747,952
Liabilities: $2,463,991
Net Worth: $18,283,961
Earnings: ($1,292,264)
Fiscal Year-end: 04/30/13
Business Description:
Gold Mining Services
S.I.C.: 1041
N.A.I.C.S.: 212221
Personnel:
Walter C. Henry *(Chm)*
Eric O. Owens *(Pres & CEO)*
Mario A. Miranda *(CFO & Sec)*
Board of Directors:
Walter C. Henry
Robert Geis
Eric O. Owens
Charles Page
Michael S. Pesner
John Alan Thomas
Legal Counsel:
Kevin Sorochan- Miller Thomson LLP
840 Howe St Suite 1000
Vancouver, BC, Canada
Transfer Agent:
Equity Financial Trust Company
200 University Avenue Suite 400
Toronto, ON, M5H 4H1, Canada
Tel.: (416) 361-0152
Fax: (416) 361-0470
Toll Free: (866) 393-4891

ALEXCO RESOURCE CORP.

Suite 1150 200 Granville Street
Vancouver, BC, V6C 1S4, Canada
Tel.: (604) 633-4888
Fax: (604) 633-4887
E-Mail: info@alexcoresource.com
Web Site: www.alexcoresource.com
Year Founded: 2004
AXU—(NYSEMKT TSX)
Rev.: $84,201,446
Assets: $211,030,446
Liabilities: $65,361,785
Net Worth: $145,668,661
Earnings: $3,399,548
Emp.: 243
Fiscal Year-end: 12/31/12
Business Description:
Metal Mining & Processing Services
S.I.C.: 1099
N.A.I.C.S.: 212299
Personnel:
George L. Brack *(Chm)*
Clynton R. Nauman *(Pres & CEO)*
David E. Whittle *(CFO & Sec)*
Bradley A. Thrall *(COO & Exec VP)*
Board of Directors:
George L. Brack
Terry J. Krepiakevich
Clynton R. Nauman
Richard Van Nieuwenhuyse
Michael D. Winn
Legal Counsel:
DuMoulin Black
10th Floor, 595 Howe Street
Vancouver, BC, V6C 2T5, Canada
Transfer Agent:
Computershare Investor Services Inc.
510 Burrard Street 2nd Floor
Vancouver, BC, V6C 3B9, Canada

Subsidiary:

Alexco Keno Hill Mining Corp. **(1)**
PO Box 7
Elsa, YT, Canada
Tel.: (867) 995-3113
Fax: (867) 995-8600
Mineral Exploration Services
S.I.C.: 1481
N.A.I.C.S.: 213115

U.S. Subsidiary:

Alexco Resource US Corp **(1)**
88 Inverness Cir E Ste N102
Englewood, CO 80112-5304
Tel.: (303) 862-3929
Fax: (303) 862-3926
Emp.: 5
Mineral Exploration Services
S.I.C.: 1481
N.A.I.C.S.: 213115
Joe Harrington *(VP-Tech & Strategic Dev)*

ALEXIS MINERALS CORP.

(Name Changed to QMX Gold Corporation)

ALEXIUM INTERNATIONAL GROUP LIMITED

Norfolk House Suite 7 85 Forrest Street
Cottesloe, WA, 6011, Australia
Mailing Address:
PO Box 512
Cottesloe, WA, 6911, Australia
Tel.: (61) 861621358
Fax: (61) 863141623
E-Mail: info@alexiuminternational.com
Web Site: www.alexiuminternational.com
AJX—(ASX DEU OTC)
Rev.: $380,762
Assets: $11,733,336
Liabilities: $4,774,845
Net Worth: $6,958,491
Earnings: ($2,708,901)
Fiscal Year-end: 06/30/13
Business Description:
Business Management Services
S.I.C.: 7389
N.A.I.C.S.: 561499
Personnel:
Gavin John Rezos *(Chm & Pres)*
Nicholas Clark *(CEO)*
Stefan Susta *(COO)*
Cameron Maitland *(Sec)*
Board of Directors:
Gavin John Rezos
Nicholas Clark
Craig Smith-Gander
Legal Counsel:
Steinepreis Paganin
Level 4 The Read Buildings 16 Milligan Street
Perth, Australia

U.S. Subsidiary:

Alexium Inc **(1)**
8 Distribution Ct
Greer, SC 29650
Tel.: (864) 416-1060
Fax: (864) 551-4555
Web Site: www.alexiuminternational.com
Commercial Licensing Services
S.I.C.: 9651
N.A.I.C.S.: 926150
Nicholas Clark *(CEO)*

ALFA ACCIAI SPA

Via San Polo
25134 Brescia, Italy
Tel.: (39) 03023911
Fax: (39) 0302391384
E-Mail: info@alfaacciai.it
Web Site: www.alfaacciai.it
Sales Range: $500-549.9 Million
Emp.: 814
Business Description:
Concrete Reinforcing Steel Mfr
S.I.C.: 3312
N.A.I.C.S.: 331110
Personnel:
Ettore Lonati *(Pres)*
Amato Stabiumi *(Mng Dir)*

Subsidiary:

Acciaierie Di Sicilia S.p.A. **(1)**
1a Stradale Passo Cavaliere
95121 Catania, Italy
Tel.: (39) 0957487811
Fax: (39) 095291110
E-Mail: info@acciaieriedisicilia.it
Web Site: www.acciaieriedisicilia.it
Steel Reinforcements Mfr
S.I.C.: 3462
N.A.I.C.S.: 332111
Alberto Tagliabue *(Mng Dir)*

Non-U.S. Joint Venture:

TSR Recycling GmbH & Co. KG **(1)**
Hafenstr 98
46242 Bottrop, Germany DE
Tel.: (49) 204170600
Fax: (49) 20417060399
E-Mail: info@tsr.eu
Web Site: www.tsr.eu
Emp.: 2,000
Steel Scrap & Non Ferrous Metals Recycling
S.I.C.: 5093
N.A.I.C.S.: 423930

Non-U.S. Subsidiary:

HKS Metals BV **(2)**
Kwadrantweg 2-12
Postbus 8050
1042 AG Amsterdam, Netherlands NL
Mailing Address:
Postbus 5165
NL-3295 ZH 's-Gravendeel, Netherlands
Tel.: (31) 78 673 9200
Fax: (31) 78 673 4060
E-Mail: info@hks.au
Web Site: www.hks.nl
Sales Range: $500-549.9 Million
Emp.: 45
Holding Company; Scrap Metal Recycling
S.I.C.: 6719
N.A.I.C.S.: 551112

Subsidiary:

HKS Scrap Metals BV **(3)**
Havenweg 1
NL 3295 XZ 's-Gravendeel, Netherlands NL
Tel.: (31) 786739200
Fax: (31) 786734060
E-Mail: receptea@hks.nl
Web Site: www.hks.nl
Emp.: 200
Scrap Metal Recycling
S.I.C.: 4953
N.A.I.C.S.: 562920

ALFA FINANCE HOLDING AD

7 Sheinovo str
Sofia, 1504, Bulgaria
Tel.: (359) 2 4893762
Fax: (359) 2 9423120
E-Mail: office@alfafinance.bg
Web Site: www.alfafinance.bg
X26A—(BUL)
Business Description:
Investment Management Services
S.I.C.: 6282
N.A.I.C.S.: 523930
Personnel:
Ivo Prokopiev *(Chm & CEO)*
Yuri Katanov *(Mng Dir)*
Konstantin Nenov *(Mng Dir)*
Board of Directors:
Ivo Prokopiev
Yuri Katanov
Konstantin Nenov

Subsidiaries:

Broker Ins Ltd. **(1)**
3 Karnigradska str
Sofia, 1000, Bulgaria
Tel.: (359) 29 86 79 11
Fax: (359) 29 86 70 62
Web Site: www.brokerins.bg
Insurance Brokerage Services
S.I.C.: 6411
N.A.I.C.S.: 524210
Stefan Enchev, *(Mng Partner)*
Rumen Staykov *(Mng Partner)*

Bulbrokers AD **(1)**
7 Sheynovo Street 1 floor
Sofia, Bulgaria
Tel.: (359) 2 4893 712
Fax: (359) 2 4893 711
E-Mail: office@bulbrokers.com
Web Site: www.bulbrokers.com
Financial Management Services
S.I.C.: 6211
N.A.I.C.S.: 523999
Ivan Nenkov *(Chm)*

Landmark Property Management Jsc **(1)**
30 Ivan Vazov Str
Sofia Sofia, Bulgaria
Tel.: (359) 2 4898 700
Fax: (359) 2 4898 737
Web Site: www.landmark.bg
Real Estate Management Services
S.I.C.: 6531
N.A.I.C.S.: 531390
Jenny Georgieva *(Chief Legal Officer)*

ALFA ICA (INDIA) LTD.
Alfa Palazzo Near Shiv Ranjani
Cross Road Satellite Road
Ahmedabad, 380015, India
Tel.: (91) 79 2675 4030
Fax: (91) 79 2675 4040
E-Mail: info@alfaica.com
Web Site: www.alfaica.com
530973—(BOM)
Sales Range: $1-9.9 Million
Business Description:
Laminated Sheet Mfr
S.I.C.: 3083
N.A.I.C.S.: 326130
Personnel:
Rajendra Tikmani *(Mng Dir)*
Board of Directors:
Inderchand Nahta
Shyam Sunder Tibrewal
Rajendra Tikmani
Rishi Tikmani
Transfer Agent:
MCS Limited
1st Fl Shatdal Complex Opp Bata Show Room
Ashram Rd
Ahmedabad, India

ALFA LAVAL AB
Rudeboksvagen 1
SE 226 55 Lund, Sweden
Mailing Address:
PO Box 73
SE 221 00 Lund, Sweden
Tel.: (46) 46366500
Fax: (46) 46323579
E-Mail: info@alfalaval.com
Web Site: www.alfalaval.com
Year Founded: 1883
ALFA—(OMX)
Sls.: $4,615,052,400
Assets: $5,430,229,200
Liabilities: $3,048,321,600
Net Worth: $2,381,907,600
Earnings: $496,443,600
Emp.: 16,419
Fiscal Year-end: 12/31/12
Business Description:
Foodstuff, Beverage, Pharmaceutical, Chemical, Oil & Water Industrial Heating, Cooling, Separating & Transporting Products Mfr & Environmental Engineering Solutions
S.I.C.: 3559
N.A.I.C.S.: 333249
Personnel:
Anders Narvinger *(Chm)*
Lars Renstrom *(Pres & CEO)*
Thomas Thuresson *(CFO)*
Susanne Pahlen Aklundh *(Pres-Equipment Div)*
Svante Karlsson *(Pres-Process Tech Div)*
Peter Leifland *(Pres-Marine & Diesel Div)*
Goran Mathiasson *(Pres-Ops Div)*
Ray Field *(Exec VP-Asia, India & Oceania)*
Nish Patel *(Exec VP-Western Europe & North America)*
Joakim Vilson *(Exec VP-Central & Eastern Europe, Latin America & Middle East)*
Peter Bailliere *(Sr VP-HR)*
Peter Torstensson *(Sr VP-Corp Comm)*
Board of Directors:
Anders Narvinger
Gunilla Berg
Arne Frank
Bjorn Hagglund
Bror Garcia Lantz
Ulla Litzen
Jan Nilsson
Susanna Norrby
Finn Rausing
Jorn Rausing
Lars Renstrom
Ulf Arne Wiinberg
Subsidiaries:

Ageratec AB (1)
St Herrebro
605 97 Norrkoping, Sweden
Tel.: (46) 853065800
Fax: (46) 111170555
E-Mail: sales.dept@ageratec.com
Web Site: www.ageratec.com
Emp.: 20
Processed Biodiesel Mfr
S.I.C.: 2911
N.A.I.C.S.: 324110
David Frykeras *(Gen Mgr)*

Alfa Laval Corporate AB (1)
Rudeboksvaegen 1
Lund, 221 00, Sweden
Tel.: (46) 46 36 65 00
Fax: (46) 46 30 50 90
E-Mail: info@alfalaval.com
Web Site: www.alfalaval.com
Heat Exchanger Mfr & Distr
S.I.C.: 3443
N.A.I.C.S.: 332410

Non-U.S. Subsidiary:

Definox (Beijing) Stainless Steel Equipment Ltd (2)
No 18 East Road - An Ning Zhuang Quinghe
Beijing Haidian District, Beijing, 100085, China
Tel.: (86) 10 6293 4909
Fax: (86) 10 6293 4835
E-Mail: info@definox.com.cn
Web Site: www.definox.com.cn
Emp.: 15
Industrial Valve Mfr
S.I.C.: 3491
N.A.I.C.S.: 332911
Kai Luk *(Gen Mgr)*

Alfa Laval Holding AB (1)
Rudeboksvagen 1
Lund, 221 00, Sweden
Tel.: (46) 46 36 70 00
Fax: (46) 46 30 50 90
E-Mail: info@alfalaval.com
Investment Management Services
S.I.C.: 6799
N.A.I.C.S.: 523920

Subsidiaries:

Alfa Laval Europe AB (2)
Box 93
221 00 Lund, Sweden
Tel.: (46) 46 36 75 00
Fax: (46) 46 13 76 40
E-Mail: info@alfalaval.com
Heat Exchanger Mfr
S.I.C.: 3443
N.A.I.C.S.: 332410

Alfa Laval Lund AB (2)
PO Box 74
Lund, Skane, 221 00, Sweden
Tel.: (46) 46 366 500
Fax: (46) 46 305 090
E-Mail: info@alfalaval.com
Emp.: 1,000
Heat Exchanger Mfr
S.I.C.: 3443
N.A.I.C.S.: 332410
Fernando Matute *(Controller-Bus)*

Alfa Laval Treasury International AB (2)
Ruben Rausings Gata
223 55 Lund, Sweden
Tel.: (46) 46 36 70 00
Investment Management Services
S.I.C.: 6211
N.A.I.C.S.: 523999

Non-U.S. Subsidiaries:

Alfa Laval Australia Pty Ltd (2)
14 Healey Circuit Blacktown Business Centre
Huntingwood, NSW, 2148, Australia
Tel.: (61) 2 8822 2700
Fax: (61) 2 8822 2799
E-Mail: australia.info@alfalaval.com
Web Site: www.alfalaval.com
Emp.: 50
Fluid Handling Equipment Mfr
S.I.C.: 3492
N.A.I.C.S.: 332912
Gerard Leak *(Gen Mgr)*

Alfa Laval Makine Sanayii ve Ticaret Ltd Sti (2)
Yakacik Caddesi No 23
Samandira-Kartal, Istanbul, 34885, Turkey
Tel.: (90) 216 311 79 00
Fax: (90) 216 561 95 88
E-Mail: turkey@alfalaval.com
Heat Exchanger Mfr
S.I.C.: 3559
N.A.I.C.S.: 332410

Alfa Laval New Zealand Ltd. (2)
307 Sandwich Road
PO Box 20424
Te Rapa, Hamilton, 3200, New Zealand
Tel.: (64) 7 849 60 25
Fax: (64) 7 849 46 19
E-Mail: newzealand.info@alfalaval.com
Web Site: local.alfalaval.com
Fluid Handling Equipment Mfr
S.I.C.: 3492
N.A.I.C.S.: 332912

Alfa Laval SIA (2)
Kr Valdemara Iela 33 - 9
Riga, 1010, Latvia
Tel.: (371) 678 285 08
Fax: (371) 678 285 11
E-Mail: latvia.info@alfalaval.com
Web Site: www.alfalaval.com
Emp.: 8
Heating Equipment Distr
S.I.C.: 5074
N.A.I.C.S.: 423720

Alfa Laval Nordick AB (1)
Hans Stahles Vag
147 80 Tumba, Sweden
Tel.: (46) 853065600
Telex: 102 60 ALSTO S
Fax: (46) 853065660
E-Mail: info@alfalaval.com
Sls.: $652,140,000
Emp.: 5,000
Mfr. of Centrifugal Separators & Decanter Centrifuges, Desalination Plant
S.I.C.: 3585
N.A.I.C.S.: 333415
kerstin Persson *(Mgr-HR)*

Alfa Laval Thermal A/S (1)
Rudeboksvagen 1
PO Box 74
SE-221 00 Lund, 22655, Sweden
Tel.: (46) 46366500
Telex: 333 24 ALTHE S
Fax: (46) 46305090
E-Mail: info@alfalaval.com
Sls.: $305,640,000
Emp.: 1,800
Provider of Heat Exchangers for Heating, Ventilation & Engineering Industry
S.I.C.: 3559
N.A.I.C.S.: 332410
Lars Renstron *(Gen Mgr)*

Alfa Laval Tumba AB (1)
Hansstahlesvag 7
147 80 Tumba, Sweden
Tel.: (46) 853065000
Fax: (46) 853065055
E-Mail:
Web Site: www.alfalaval.com
Emp.: 400
S.I.C.: 2657
N.A.I.C.S.: 322212
Magnus Nordin *(Gen Mgr)*

Alfa Laval Tumba AB (1)
Hanf Stahles Vag 7
SE 147 80 Tumba, Sweden (100%)
Tel.: (46) 853065000
Fax: (46) 853065055
E-Mail: tumba.officesupport@alphalaval.com
Web Site: www.alphalaval.com
Emp.: 450
S.I.C.: 2657
N.A.I.C.S.: 322212
Magnus Nordin *(Mng Dir)*

U.S. Subsidiaries:

Alfa Laval Inc. (1)
5400 International Trade Dr
Richmond, VA 23231 NJ
Tel.: (804) 222-5300
Fax: (804) 236-3276
E-Mail: customerservice.usa@alfalaval.com
Web Site: www.alfalaval.com
Emp.: 100
Milk Plant Separators, Clarifiers, Standardizers, Coolers, Industrial & Marine Centrifugals, Heat Exchangers & Food Processing Equipment, Flow Equipment; Pumps, Valves & Fittings; Computer Based Supervisory & Control Systems
Import Export
S.I.C.: 3556
N.A.I.C.S.: 333241
Anders Narvinger *(Chm)*
Alessandro Terenghi *(Pres & CEO)*
Parvez H. Kader *(Mng Dir)*
Thomas Thuresson *(CFO)*
Svante Karlsson *(Pres-Process Tech Div)*
Ulf Granstrand *(Exec VP-Technology)*
Peter Leifland *(Exec VP)*
Peter Torstensson *(Sr VP-Corp Comm)*

Division:

Alfa Laval, Inc. (2)
955 Mearns Rd
Warminster, PA 18974
Tel.: (215) 443-4000
E-Mail: customerservice.usa@alfalaval.com
Web Site: local.alfalaval.com
Emp.: 90
Mfr. & Distr of Industrial, Environmental & Marine Separators & Decanters
Import Export
S.I.C.: 8742
N.A.I.C.S.: 541613
Susanne Pahlen Aklundh *(Pres-Equipment Div)*

Subsidiaries:

Alfa Laval Flow Inc. (2)
9560 58th Pl Ste 300
Kenosha, WI 53144
Tel.: (262) 605-2600
Fax: (262) 605-2669
E-Mail:
Web Site: www.alfalaval.com
Emp.: 50
Rotary Lube, Peristaltic, Gear, & Diaphragm Pumps
S.I.C.: 5084
N.A.I.C.S.: 423830
Mark Larsen *(Mgr-Sls)*

Alfa Laval Inc. (2)
5400 International Trade Dr
Richmond, VA 23231-2927
Tel.: (804) 222-5300
Fax: (804) 236-3276
Toll Free: (800) 248ALFA
E-Mail: info@alfalaval.com
Web Site: www.alfalaval.com
Rev.: $58,000,000
Emp.: 206
Marketing & Sales of Heat Exchangers
S.I.C.: 3556
N.A.I.C.S.: 333241
Steve Pratt *(VP-Fin)*

Subsidiary:

Alfa Laval Thermal Inc.-Food Center (3)
111 Parker St
Newburyport, MA 01950-4011
Tel.: (978) 465-5777
Fax: (978) 465-6006
Web Site: www.albrew.com
Emp.: 25
Scraped Surface Heat Exchangers
S.I.C.: 3443
N.A.I.C.S.: 332410
Craig Martin *(Ops Mgr)*

Alfa Laval, Inc. (2)
9560 58th Pl Ste 300
Kenosha, WI 53144
Tel.: (262) 605-2600
Toll Free: (866) ALFALAVAL
E-Mail: customerservice.usa@alfalaval.com
Web Site: www.alfalaval.us
Emp.: 100
Flow Equipment Mfr & Retailer
Import Export
S.I.C.: 5084
N.A.I.C.S.: 423830

Alfa Laval Saunders Inc. (2)
16516 Air Center Blvd
Houston, TX 77032-5115

Alfa Laval AB—(Continued)

Tel.: (281) 443-0000
Diaphragm & Butterfly Valves
S.I.C.: 3494
N.A.I.C.S.: 332919

Alfa Laval Sharples (2)
955 Mearns Rd
Warminster, PA 18974-2811
Tel.: (215) 443-4000
Fax: (215) 443-4220
Web Site: www.alfalafa.us.com
Emp.: 80
Mfr. of Centrifuges
S.I.C.: 8742
N.A.I.C.S.: 541613
John Atanasio *(Branch Pres)*

Tetra-Pak Inc. (2)
101 Corporate Woods Pkwy
Vernon Hills, IL 60061-3109
Tel.: (847) 955-6000
Fax: (847) 955-6500
E-Mail: info.us@tetrapak.com
Web Site: www.tetrapak.com
Emp.: 100
Engineering & Distribution of Equipment for Use In Dairy & Liquid Food Processing Equipment
S.I.C.: 2671
N.A.I.C.S.: 322220
Brian Kennell *(CFO & VPFin)*

Autorad, Inc. (1)
2050 N Ruby St
Melrose Park, IL 60160
Tel.: (708) 345-5400
Fax: (708) 345-3513
E-Mail: customerservice@alfalaval.com
Web Site: www.stanref.com
Sales Range: $25-49.9 Million
Emp.: 185
Refrigerants
S.I.C.: 3585
N.A.I.C.S.: 333415

Subsidiary:

Ketema LP (2)
2300 W Marshall Dr
Grand Prairie, TX 75051-3509
Tel.: (972) 647-2626
Fax: (972) 641-1518
E-Mail: mrhodes@ketemalp.com
Web Site: www.ketemalp.com
Emp.: 50
Mfr of Whitlock Hi-Transfer Heat Exchangers for Standard & Custom Heat Transfer Applications; ACME Export
S.I.C.: 3585
N.A.I.C.S.: 333415

Gamajet Cleaning Systems, Inc. (1)
604 Jeffers Cir
Exton, PA 19341
Tel.: (610) 408-9940
Fax: (610) 408-9945
Toll Free: (877) 426-2538
Web Site: www.gamajet.com
Other Commercial & Service Industry Machinery Mfr
S.I.C.: 3589
N.A.I.C.S.: 333318
Robert E. Delaney *(Pres)*

Niagara Blower Company (1)
673 Ontario St
Buffalo, NY 14207 NY
Tel.: (716) 875-2000
Fax: (716) 875-1077
Toll Free: (800) 426-5169
E-Mail: sales@niagarablower.com
Web Site: www.niagarablower.com
Sales Range: $50-74.9 Million
Emp.: 120
Mfr of Process Equipment for Industry & Heat Transfer
S.I.C.: 3585
N.A.I.C.S.: 333415
Peter G. Demakos *(Pres)*

Tranter PHE, Inc. (1)
1900 Old Burk Hwy
Wichita Falls, TX 76307 MI
Mailing Address:
PO Box 2289
Wichita Falls, TX 76307
Tel.: (940) 723-7125
Fax: (940) 723-5131
Web Site: www.tranter.com
Sales Range: $125-149.9 Million
Emp.: 227
Welded & Gasketed Plate Heat Exchangers Mfr
Import Export
S.I.C.: 3443
N.A.I.C.S.: 332410
Feroze Patel *(Exec VP)*

Non-U.S. Subsidiary:

Tranter International AB (2)
Maria Skolgata 79 B
SE 118 53 Stockholm, Sweden (100%)
Tel.: (46) 84424970
Fax: (46) 84424980
E-Mail: info@se.tranter.com
Web Site: www.tranter.com
Emp.: 10
Heat Exchangers Mfr
S.I.C.: 3443
N.A.I.C.S.: 332410
Henrik Johansson *(Gen Mgr)*

Non-U.S. Subsidiary:

Tranter SAS (3)
39 Rue Des Peupliers
Nanterre, 92000, France
Tel.: (33) 1 47 51 75 72
Fax: (33) 1 34 29 60 19
Heat Exchanger Mfr
S.I.C.: 3443
N.A.I.C.S.: 332410

Non-U.S. Subsidiaries:

Aalborg Industries d.o.o. (1)
Zoraniceva 61
21210 Solin, Croatia
Tel.: (385) 21 688 520
Fax: (385) 21 688 522
Web Site: www.alfalaval.com
Emp.: 6
Marine Steam Boiler Mfr
S.I.C.: 3443
N.A.I.C.S.: 332410
Josko Radosevic *(Gen Mgr)*

Alfa Laval A/O (1)
Sovetskaya Str 73
RU 141 070 Kaliningrad, Russia
Tel.: (7) 0952321250
Fax: (7) 4952322273
E-Mail: russia.info@alfalaval.com
Web Site: www.alfalaval.com
Emp.: 50
S.I.C.: 2657
N.A.I.C.S.: 322212
Alexander Terekim *(Gen Mgr)*

Alfa Laval Aalborg A/S (1)
Gasvaerksvej 24
PO Box 844
9100 Aalborg, Denmark
Tel.: (45) 99304000
Fax: (45) 98102865
E-Mail: aal@aalborg-industries.com
Web Site: www.aalborg-industries.com
Sls.: $494,603,600
Emp.: 600
Industrial & Marine Boiler Mfr
S.I.C.: 3559
N.A.I.C.S.: 332410
Sameer Kalra *(Exec VP-Global Sls & Mktg)*

Non-U.S. Subsidiaries:

Aalborg Industries Ltda (2)
Avenida Ver Isaias Prieto 46
Itu, Sao Paulo, 13304-780, Brazil
Tel.: (55) 11 4025 6000
E-Mail: itu@aalborg-industries.com.br
Industrial Machinery Equipment Mfr & Whlsr
S.I.C.: 3559
N.A.I.C.S.: 333249

Alfa Laval Aalborg BV (2)
Ohmweg 8
3208 KE Spijkenisse, Netherlands
Tel.: (31) 181 650 500
Fax: (31) 181 650 501
E-Mail: info.rotterdam@alfalaval.com
Web Site: www.aalborg-industries.com
Heating Equipment Mfr & Distr
S.I.C.: 3433
N.A.I.C.S.: 333414
Dennis Verkaart *(Mng Dir)*

Alfa Laval Aalborg (FPS) Pte Ltd (2)
11 Joo Koon Circle
Jurong, 629043, Singapore
Tel.: (65) 62 61 98 98
Fax: (65) 62 66 11 11
E-Mail: fps@aalborg-industries.com.sg
Boiler & Heat Exchanger Mfr
S.I.C.: 3559
N.A.I.C.S.: 332410
Jeroen van Riel *(Mng Dir)*

Alfa Laval Aalborg Ltd (2)
5th Floor Saesam Bldg 1485-1 Ja-Dong
Haeundae-Ku, Busan, 612-842, Korea (South)
Tel.: (82) 51 703 6162
Fax: (82) 51 704 8184
E-Mail: pusan@aalborg-industries.co.kr
Web Site: www.aalborg-industries.com
Emp.: 50
Boiler & Heat Exchanger Mfr
S.I.C.: 3443
N.A.I.C.S.: 332410
Joon Park Hee *(Mng Dir)*

Alfa Laval Aalborg Nijmegen BV (2)
St Hubertusstraat 10
Nijmegen, 6503 GD, Netherlands
Tel.: (31) 24 352 31 00
Fax: (31) 24 356 49 95
E-Mail: info.nijmegen@alfalaval.com
Web Site: www.alfalaval.com
Emp.: 80
Inert Gas Generator Distr
S.I.C.: 5084
N.A.I.C.S.: 423830
Peter Zoeteman *(Mng Dir)*

Alfa Laval Aalborg Oy (2)
Kaivopuistontie 33
PO Box 9
26101 Rauma, Finland
Tel.: (358) 10 838 3800
Fax: (358) 10 838 3808
E-Mail: rau@alfalaval.fi
Web Site: www.aalborg-industries.com
Industrial Boiler Mfr
S.I.C.: 3559
N.A.I.C.S.: 332410
Harri Lotila *(Mng Dir)*

Alfa Laval Aalborg Pte Ltd (2)
11 Joo Koon Circle Jurong Point
PO Box 259
Singapore, 916409, Singapore
Tel.: (65) 6261 9898
Fax: (65) 6266 1111
E-Mail: infosin@alfalaval.com
Web Site: www.aalborg-industries.com
Emp.: 70
Boiler & Heat Exchanger Mfr
S.I.C.: 3443
N.A.I.C.S.: 332410
Jeroen van Riel *(Mng Dir)*

Alfa Laval HaiPhong Co. Ltd (2)
An Hong Marine Industrial Zone
An Duong District, Haiphong, Vietnam
Tel.: (84) 313 594 116
Fax: (84) 313 594 117
E-Mail: hph@aalborg-industries.com.vn
Web Site: www.alfalaval.com
Emp.: 200
Power Boiler Mfr
S.I.C.: 3559
N.A.I.C.S.: 332410

Alfa Laval (Qingdao) Co. Ltd (2)
No 86 Guangzhou Road North
Jiaozhou, Shandong, 266300, China
Tel.: (86) 532 8229 66 03
Fax: (86) 532 8229 59 08
E-Mail: aalborg@aalborg-industries.cn
Web Site: www.alfalaval.com
Power Boiler & Heat Exchanger Mfr
S.I.C.: 3443
N.A.I.C.S.: 332410

Alfa Laval Aalborg Industria e Comercio Ltda. (1)
Rua Divino Espirito Santo 1 100
Bairro Carangola, 25715-410 Petropolis, Rio de Janeiro, Brazil
Tel.: (55) 24 2233 9963
Fax: (55) 24 2237 6603
E-Mail: rio@aalborg-industries.com.br
Web Site: www.aalborg-industries.com
Emp.: 380
Marine Boiler Installation Services & Mfr
S.I.C.: 1711
N.A.I.C.S.: 238220
Knud B. Bach *(Mng Dir)*

Alfa Laval Aalborg Pty Ltd (1)
10 Lucca Road North
North Wyong, Wyong, NSW, 2259, Australia
Tel.: (61) 2 4399 0000
Fax: (61) 2 4351 1242
E-Mail: info.wyong@alfalaval.com
Web Site: www.aalborg-industries.com
Emp.: 58
Marine Boiler Mfr
S.I.C.: 3443
N.A.I.C.S.: 332410
Graham John Roach *(Mng Dir)*

Alfa Laval AEBE (1)
20 KM Lavrion Avenue
Thesis karella, 19400 Athens, Koropi, Greece
Tel.: (30) 2106683500
Telex: 218729 ALHE GR
Fax: (30) 2106683580
E-Mail: greece.info@alfalaval.com
Web Site: www.alfalaval.gr
Emp.: 22
Industrial Equipment & Machinery Distr
S.I.C.: 5084
N.A.I.C.S.: 423830
Goran Hedbys *(Mng Dir)*

Alfa-Laval Benelux B.V. (1)
Baarschot 2
4817 ZZ Breda, Netherlands
Tel.: (31) 765791200
Fax: (31) 765791211
E-Mail: benelux.info@alfalaval.com
Web Site: www.alfalaval.com
Emp.: 120
Tanks & Cooling Tanks Mfr
S.I.C.: 3443
N.A.I.C.S.: 332420

Alfa-Laval Benelux N.V. (1)
Bazellaan 5 Avenue de Bale
Brussels, B 1140, Belgium (100%)
Tel.: (32) 27283811
Telex: 21089 ALFAB B
Fax: (32) 27283803
E-Mail: belgium.info@alfalaval.com
Web Site: www.alfalaval.com
Emp.: 50
Paper Products
S.I.C.: 2657
N.A.I.C.S.: 322212

Alfa Laval (China) Ltd. (1)
23rd Fl Golden Bell Plz
98 Huai Rd, Shanghai, China
Tel.: (86) 2153858000
Fax: (86) 2153858100
E-Mail: info@alfalaval.com
Web Site: www.alfalaval.com
Emp.: 110
S.I.C.: 2657
N.A.I.C.S.: 322212
Jan Debruyn *(Pres)*

Subsidiaries:

Alfa Laval (Jiangyin) Manufacturing Co Ltd (2)
465 Renmin Road Qiaoqi
Xiake Town, Jiangyin, Jiangsu, 214408, China
Tel.: (86) 510 8656 1280
Fax: (86) 510 8656 1600
E-Mail: china.info@alfalaval.com
Web Site: www.alfalaval.com
Heat Exchanger Mfr
S.I.C.: 3443
N.A.I.C.S.: 332410

Subsidiary:

Alfa Laval Flow Equipment (Kunshan) Co Ltd (3)
Baishu Road Kunshan Economic & Technical Development Zone
Suzhou, 215301, China
Tel.: (86) 512 577 145 04
Fax: (86) 512 577 160 80
E-Mail: china.info@alfalaval.com
Web Site: www.alfalaval.com
Pumping Equipment Mfr
S.I.C.: 3561
N.A.I.C.S.: 333911

Alfa Laval (Shanghai) Technologies Co Ltd (2)
25/F Golden Bell Plaza 98 Huaihai Road M
Shanghai, 200021, China

Tel.: (86) 21 538 580 00
Fax: (86) 21 538 581 00
E-Mail: china.info@alfalaval.com
Web Site: www.alfalaval.com
Air Conditioning & Heating Equipment Mfr
S.I.C.: 3585
N.A.I.C.S.: 333415
Jan Debruyn *(Pres)*

Liyang Sifang Stainless Steel Products Co., Ltd (2)
Industrial Zone Daitou Town
Liyang, Jiangsu, 213300, China
Tel.: (86) 51 9873 60223
Fax: (86) 51 9873 60738
Web Site: www.lysf.com
Sanitary Fluid Pump & Valve Mfr
S.I.C.: 3561
N.A.I.C.S.: 333911

Tranter Heat Exchangers (Beijing) Co Ltd (2)
No 5 Anqing Avenue Area B Tianzhu Airport Development Zone
101318 Beijing, China
Tel.: (86) 10 64379490
Fax: (86) 10 80491413
Emp.: 110
Heat Exchanger Mfr
S.I.C.: 3559
N.A.I.C.S.: 332410
Wen Lou *(Controller-Fin)*

Alfa Laval China Ltd. (1)
Suite # 1206-09 12th fl Two Chinachem Exchange Square,
338 King's Road North Point, Hong Kong, China (Hong Kong) (100%)
Tel.: (852) 28577000
Fax: (852) 28577780
E-Mail: hongkong.info@alfalaval.com
Emp.: 20
S.I.C.: 2657
N.A.I.C.S.: 322212

Alfa Laval Copenhagen A/S (1)
Maskinvej 5
2860 Soborg, Denmark (100%)
Tel.: (45) 39536000
Fax: (45) 39536556
E-Mail: denmark.info@alfalaval.com
Web Site: www.alfalaval.dk
Emp.: 600
Technology Services
S.I.C.: 2079
N.A.I.C.S.: 311224
Peter Hartig *(Mng Dir)*

Alfa Laval Dis Ticaret Ltd Sti (1)
Yakacik Caddesi No 17
Samandira Kartal, 34885 Istanbul, Turkey
Tel.: (90) 2163117900
Fax: (90) 2165619588
E-Mail: turkey@alfalaval.com
Emp.: 40
Paper Products
S.I.C.: 2657
N.A.I.C.S.: 322212
Tayfun Aydemir *(Gen Mgr)*

Alfa Laval EOOD (1)
Brodisce 26
Trzin, 1236, Slovenia
Tel.: (386) 1 563 75 22
Fax: (386) 1 563 75 23
Web Site: www.alfalaval.com
Emp.: 6
Building Material Distr
S.I.C.: 5039
N.A.I.C.S.: 423390

Alfa Laval France SAS (1)
97 Allee Alexandre Borodine
Saint Priest, France
Tel.: (33) 469 16 77 00
Fax: (33) 469 16 77 86
Web Site: local.alfalaval.com
Heating Equipment Mfr & Whlsr
S.I.C.: 3433
N.A.I.C.S.: 333414

Subsidiaries:

Alfa Laval HES SA (2)
Allee des Artisans ZA du Charpenay, Lentilly, Rhone, France
Tel.: (33) 4 74 01 95 00
Fax: (33) 4 74 01 95 48
Web Site: www.alfalaval.com
Water Heater Equipment Mfr
S.I.C.: 3585
N.A.I.C.S.: 333415

Alfa Laval Moatti SAS (2)
La Clef Saint Pierre 10 Rue du Marechal de Lattre de Tassigny
Elancourt, 78997, France
Tel.: (33) 130 81 81 81
Fax: (33) 130 81 81 70
E-Mail: france.info@alfalaval.com
Web Site: www.alfalaval.com
Oil Filter Machinery Mfr
S.I.C.: 3569
N.A.I.C.S.: 333999

Alfa Laval Spiral SAS (2)
10 rue Alfred Masse
Nevers, 58028, France
Tel.: (33) 3 86 59 83 00
Fax: (33) 3 69 55 70 34
E-Mail: france.info@alfalaval.com
Web Site: www.alfalaval.com
Power Boiler & Heat Exchanger Mfr
S.I.C.: 3443
N.A.I.C.S.: 332410

Alfa Laval Vicarb SAS (2)
1 Rue Rif Tronchard
Fontanil-Cornillon, 38522, France
Tel.: (33) 4 76 56 50 50
Fax: (33) 4 76 75 79 09
E-Mail: france.info@alfalaval.com
Web Site: www.alfalaval.com
Emp.: 230
Heat Exchanger Mfr
S.I.C.: 3559
N.A.I.C.S.: 332410
Christian Thompson *(Gen Mgr)*

Definox SAS (2)
3 Rue de la Pepiniere ZI Nord
44190 Getigne, France
Tel.: (33) 2 28 03 98 50
Fax: (33) 2 28 03 88 00
E-Mail: info@definox.com
Web Site: www.definox.com
Stainless Valve Mfr
S.I.C.: 3491
N.A.I.C.S.: 332911
Jean Yves Lemoing *(Mng Dir)*

Alfa Laval Groningen BV (1)
Peizerweg 97
Groningen, 9700 AA, Netherlands
Tel.: (31) 50 5217 555
Fax: (31) 50 5264 878
E-Mail: info.groningen@alfalaval.com
Heat Exchanger Mfr
S.I.C.: 3443
N.A.I.C.S.: 332410

Alfa Laval Holding BV (1)
Baarschot 2
4817 ZZ Breda, Netherlands
Tel.: (31) 765791200
Investment Management Services
S.I.C.: 6282
N.A.I.C.S.: 523920

Alfa Laval Holding GmbH (1)
Wilhelm-Bergner-Strasse 7
Glinde, 21503, Germany
Tel.: (49) 40 72 74 03
Fax: (49) 40 72 74 22 62
E-Mail: alfalaval.germany@alfalaval.com
Web Site: www.alfalaval.com
Heat Exchanger Mfr
S.I.C.: 3443
N.A.I.C.S.: 332410

Subsidiary:

Tranter HES GmbH (2)
Hohe-Flum-Strasse 31
Schopfheim, 79650, Germany
Tel.: (49) 7622 66689 0
Fax: (49) 7622 66689 30
Emp.: 70
Spiral Heat Exchanger Mfr & Whlsr
S.I.C.: 3559
N.A.I.C.S.: 332410
Chuck Monachello *(Pres)*

U.S. Subsidiary:

Alfa Laval USA Inc. (2)
5400 International Trade Dr
Richmond, VA 23231
Tel.: (804) 222-5300
Fax: (804) 236-3276
E-Mail: customerservice.usa@alfalaval.com
Heat Exchanger Mfr
S.I.C.: 3443
N.A.I.C.S.: 332410

Subsidiary:

Alfa Laval US Holding Inc. (3)
5400 International Trade Dr
Richmond, VA 23231
Tel.: (804) 222-5300
Food Processing Machinery Mfr
S.I.C.: 3556
N.A.I.C.S.: 333241

Subsidiaries:

AGC Heat Transfer Inc. (4)
10129 Piper Ln
Bristow, VA 20136
Tel.: (703) 257-1660
Fax: (703) 330-7940
Toll Free: (800) 825-8820
E-Mail: info@agcheattransfer.com
Web Site: www.agcheattransfer.com
Heat Exchanger Mfr & Whslr
S.I.C.: 3443
N.A.I.C.S.: 332410
Wade Chamberlain *(Pres)*

Plant:

AGC Heat Transfer Inc. - Western Factory (5)
9109 SE 64th Ave
Portland, OR 97206
Tel.: (503) 774-7342
Fax: (503) 774-2550
Toll Free: (800) 715-8820
Web Site: www.agcheattransfer.com
Emp.: 54
Heat Exchanger Mfr
S.I.C.: 3559
N.A.I.C.S.: 332410
George Tholl *(Dir-Ops & R&D)*

Alfa Laval Aalborg Inc. (4)
3118 Commerce Pkwy
Miramar, FL 33025
Tel.: (954) 435-5999
Fax: (954) 435-5490
E-Mail: florida@aalborg-industries.com
Web Site: www.aalborg-industries.com
Emp.: 13
Marine Heating Boiler Services & Whlsr
S.I.C.: 5074
N.A.I.C.S.: 423720
Boelo Lussenburg *(Mng Dir)*

Alfa Laval Champ Inc. (4)
2359 Trailmate Dr
Sarasota, FL 34243-4041
Tel.: (941) 727-1900
Fax: (941) 755-7115
E-Mail: champ.info@alfalaval.com
Emp.: 103
Heat Exchanger Mfr
S.I.C.: 3443
N.A.I.C.S.: 332410
John Wurster *(Gen Mgr)*

Definox Inc. (4)
16720 W Victor Rd
New Berlin, WI 53151
Tel.: (262) 797-5730
Fax: (262) 797-5735
Web Site: www.definox.com
Emp.: 5
Stainless Valve Mfr
S.I.C.: 3494
N.A.I.C.S.: 332919
Zielsdorf Matt *(Pres)*

Hutchison Hayes Separation Inc. (4)
3520 E Sam Houston Pkwy N
Houston, TX 77015
Tel.: (713) 455-9600
Fax: (713) 455-7753
E-Mail: sales@hutch-hayes.com
Web Site: www.hutch-hayes.com
Separation Equipment Whslr
S.I.C.: 5084
N.A.I.C.S.: 423830
Mike Dunson *(Pres & CEO)*
Carl Wedemeyer *(CFO)*

Tranter Inc. (4)
1900 Old Burk Hwy
Wichita Falls, TX 76306
Tel.: (940) 723-7125
Fax: (940) 723-5131
Toll Free: (800) 414-6908
E-Mail: sales@tranter.com
Web Site: www.tranter.com
Emp.: 200
Heat Exchanger & Gasket Mfr
S.I.C.: 3559
N.A.I.C.S.: 332410
Snider Blake *(Pres)*

Non-U.S. Subsidiaries:

Alfa Laval Krakow Sp.z.o.o. (2)
Zawila 56
30390 Krakow, Poland
Tel.: (48) 12 252 99 99
Fax: (48) 12 252 99 00
E-Mail: krakow@alfalaval.com
Web Site: www.alfalaval.com
Emp.: 100
Heat Exchanger Mfr
S.I.C.: 3443
N.A.I.C.S.: 332410
Tomasz Krzewski *(Engr-Quality)*

OAO Alfa Laval Potok (2)
Sovetskaya 73
Korolev, Moscow, 141070, Russia
Tel.: (7) 495 232 12 50
Fax: (7) 495 232 25 73
E-Mail: moscow.response@alfalaval.com
Web Site: www.alfalaval.com
Heat Exchanger Mfr
S.I.C.: 3443
N.A.I.C.S.: 332410
Alexander Tereken *(Gen Mgr)*

Alfa Laval Holdings Ltd (1)
7 Doman Road
Camberley, Surrey, United Kingdom
Tel.: (44) 1276633 83
Investment Management Services
S.I.C.: 6282
N.A.I.C.S.: 523920

Alfa Laval Iberia S.A. (1)
C San Rafael 1-1 Edificio Europa III
Alcobendas, 28018 Madrid, Spain
Tel.: (34) 902122532
Telex: 23172 LAVAL E
Fax: (34) 902122533
E-Mail: info.spain@alfalaval.com
Emp.: 200
Mfr of Separators; Pumps; Heat Exchangers; Fresh-Water Distillers; Electrically Heated Boilers; Oil Heaters; Static Separators
S.I.C.: 3556
N.A.I.C.S.: 333241
Christian Thomsen *(Mgr)*

Alfa-Laval Inc. (1)
101 Milner Ave
Scarborough, ON, M1S 4S6, Canada
Tel.: (416) 299-6101
Telex: 65-25495
Fax: (416) 297-8690
E-Mail: alfacan.info@alfalaval.com
Emp.: 60
Sales of Tanks, Cooling Tanks & Cheesemaking Equipment
S.I.C.: 5084
N.A.I.C.S.: 423830
Ashley Davis *(Pres)*

Alfa Laval (India) Ltd (1)
Mumbai Pune Rd Dapodi Pune
Pune, Maharashtra, 411 012, India(88.77%)
Tel.: (91) 2027107100
Telex: 400 001
E-Mail: india.info@alfalaval.com
Web Site: www.alfalaval.com
Sales Range: $150-199.9 Million
Emp.: 1,045
Industrial Equipment Mfr
S.I.C.: 3559
N.A.I.C.S.: 333249
Giuseppe Falciola *(Chm)*
Jose Hernanz *(Mng Dir)*
V. Chandrasekhar *(Sec & Mgr-IR)*

Alfa-Laval Iran Co. (1)
PO Box 95-1626
Tehran, Iran
Tel.: (98) 19935563
Telex: 215 016 ALFA IR
Fax: (98) 218779930
Web Site: www.alfalaval.com
Emp.: 20
S.I.C.: 2657
N.A.I.C.S.: 322212

Alfa Laval AB—(Continued)

Alfa Laval Kft. (1)
Bocskai Ut 134-146
(Dorottya Udvar), HU 1113 Budapest, Hungary (100%)
Tel.: (36) 18899700
Fax: (36) 18899701
E-Mail: info.hu@alfalaval.com
Web Site: www.alfalaval.hu
Sales Range: $1-9.9 Million
Emp.: 20
Heat Transfer & Fluid Handling Mfr
S.I.C.: 3443
N.A.I.C.S.: 332410

Alfa Laval K.K. (1)
Meisan Takahama Bldg Fl 10 2 12 13 Chome
Minato Ku, Tokyo, 108 0075, Japan
Tel.: (81) 354622442
Fax: (81) 354622456
E-Mail: japan.info@alfa.laval.com
Web Site: www.alfalaval.co.jp
Emp.: 200
S.I.C.: 2657
N.A.I.C.S.: 322212

Alfa Laval Kolding A/S (1)
Albuen 31
6000 Kolding, Denmark
Tel.: (45) 7932 2200
Fax: (45) 7932 2581
E-Mail: info.dk@alfalaval.com
Web Site: local.alfalaval.com
Emp.: 560
Industrial Machinery Mfr
S.I.C.: 3559
N.A.I.C.S.: 333249
Jens Soennichsen *(Sr Project Mgr)*

Subsidiaries:

Alfa Laval Nakskov A/S (2)
Stavangervej 10
4900 Nakskov, Denmark
Tel.: (45) 70 20 49 00
Fax: (45) 70 20 49 10
E-Mail: nakskov.nakskov@alfalaval.com
Web Site: local.alfalaval.com
Emp.: 86
Industrial Machinery Mfr
S.I.C.: 3559
N.A.I.C.S.: 333249
John Lazar *(Gen Mgr)*

Alfa Laval Tank Equipment A/S (2)
Baldershoj 19
2635 Ishoj, Denmark
Tel.: (45) 43 55 86 00
Fax: (45) 43 55 86 01
E-Mail: tankequipment.info@alfalaval.com
Emp.: 55
Industrial Tank Mfr
S.I.C.: 3443
N.A.I.C.S.: 332420
Rene Elgaard *(Gen Mgr)*

Alfa Laval Korea Ltd. (1)
Kwanghee Building 216 1ka Kwanghee-dong
Chung-gu, 100-710 Seoul, Korea (South)
Tel.: (82) 234060660
Fax: (82) 234060700
E-Mail: inhwan.jung@alfalaval.com
Web Site: www.alfalaval.com.kr
Emp.: 18
Paper Products
S.I.C.: 2657
N.A.I.C.S.: 322212

Alfa Laval (Kunshan) Manufacturing Co Ltd (1)
Yuyang Road 299 Yushan Zhen
Kunshan, 215300, China
Tel.: (86) 512 368 591 00
Fax: (86) 512 368 591 02
Web Site: www.alfalaval.com
Heat Exchanger Mfr
S.I.C.: 3443
N.A.I.C.S.: 332410

Alfa Laval Ltd (1)
2 Yanko Sakazov Str Kv
Druzhba, Sliven, 8806, Bulgaria
Tel.: (359) 44 674 114
Fax: (359) 44 684 114
E-Mail: bulgaria.info@alfalaval.com
Web Site: www.alfalaval.com
Emp.: 5
Plate Heat Exchanger Mfr
S.I.C.: 3559
N.A.I.C.S.: 332410
Slav Slavov *(Mgr)*

Alfa Laval Limited (1)
7 Doman Road
Camberley, Surrey, GU15 3DN, United Kingdom
Tel.: (44) 27663383
Fax: (44) 27685035
E-Mail: nish.patel@alfalaval.com
Web Site: www.alfalaval.com
Emp.: 100
Mfr. of Vacuum Pumps & Separations for Industrial & Marine Purposes
S.I.C.: 3561
N.A.I.C.S.: 333911

Branches:

Alfa Laval Ltd. (2)
Ste 5 9th Fl Selvesen Tower
Blaikies Quay, Aberdeen, Scotland, AB11 5PW, United Kingdom
Tel.: (44) 1224424300
Fax: (44) 1224424315
E-Mail: energy.uk@alfalaval.com
Web Site: www.alfalaval.co.uk
Emp.: 3
Paper Product Sales
S.I.C.: 2657
N.A.I.C.S.: 322212

Alfa Laval Limited (2)
Birch Rd
Eastbourne, Sussex, BN23 6PQ, United Kingdom
Tel.: (44) 1323412555
Fax: (44) 1323414515
E-Mail: info@alfalaval.com
Web Site: www.alfalaval.com
Emp.: 125
Pumps Mfr
S.I.C.: 3561
N.A.I.C.S.: 333911

Subsidiary:

Alfa Laval Finance Co Ltd (2)
7 Doman Road
Camberley, Surrey, GU15 3DN, United Kingdom
Tel.: (44) 127663383
Financial Management Services
S.I.C.: 6211
N.A.I.C.S.: 523999

Alfa Laval LKM A/S (1)
31 Albuen
PO Box 802
6000 Kolding, Denmark (100%)
Tel.: (45) 79322200
Telex: 51363 LKM DK
Fax: (45) 79322590
Sales Range: $150-199.9 Million
Emp.: 500
Mfr. of Stainless Steel Fittings & Tank Accessories
S.I.C.: 3443
N.A.I.C.S.: 332420

Alfa-Laval (Malaysia) Sdn Bhd (1)
Lot 2 23 Jalan SU7
Perindustrian Subang Utama 400, 40702
Shah Alam, Selangor, Malaysia
Tel.: (60) 351912300
Telex: ALVAL MA 38541
Fax: (60) 351915682
Web Site: www.alfalaval.com.my
Emp.: 60
Paper Products
S.I.C.: 2657
N.A.I.C.S.: 322212
Daniel Ng *(Mng Dir)*

Alfa-Laval Mid Europe AG (1)
Industriestrasse 31
CH 8305 Dietlikon, Switzerland (100%)
Tel.: (41) 448071414
Telex: 868329 ALSU CH
Fax: (41) 448071415
E-Mail: info.mideurope@alfalaval.com
Web Site: www.alfalaval.com
Emp.: 19
Farm Equipment
S.I.C.: 3523
N.A.I.C.S.: 333111

Alfa Laval Mid Europe GmbH (1)
Wilhelm-Bergner-Str 7
21509 Glinde, Germany
Tel.: (49) 40 7274 03
Fax: (49) 40 7274 2515
E-Mail: info.mideurope@alfalaval.com
Web Site: www.alfalaval.de
Emp.: 200
Designer, Mfr & Distr of Process Lines & Components for Heat Transfer, Separation & Fluid Handling
S.I.C.: 3559
N.A.I.C.S.: 333249
Joakim Vilson *(Gen Mgr)*

Alfa Laval Mid Europe GmbH (1)
Industrie Zentrum No Sud Strasse 2 M 7 1
2355 Wiener Neudorf, Austria (100%)
Tel.: (43) 22366820
Telex: 13 21 98 ALW A
Fax: (43) 223665940
E-Mail: info.mideurope@alfalaval.com
Sales Range: $10-24.9 Million
Emp.: 25
Mfr. of Barn Equipment
S.I.C.: 3446
N.A.I.C.S.: 332323
Martin Leodolter *(Mgr-Site)*

Subsidiary:

Tranter Warmetauscher GmbH (2)
Kammeringstrasse 18
2353 Guntramsdorf, Austria
Tel.: (43) 2236 566 23
Fax: (43) 2236 566 21
Plate Heat Exchanger Mfr
S.I.C.: 3559
N.A.I.C.S.: 332410

Alfa Laval Middle East Ltd (1)
Building No 13 Street No 6 Community No 364
Al Quoz Industrial Area, Dubai, United Arab Emirates
Tel.: (971) 4 347 12 00
Fax: (971) 4 347 16 01
E-Mail: alme.marketing@alfalaval.com
Web Site: www.alfalaval.com
Heat Exchanger Mfr
S.I.C.: 3559
N.A.I.C.S.: 332410
Jean Batmanian *(Reg Mgr-HR)*

Alfa Laval Nordic A/S (1)
Billingstadsletta 13
Billingstad, 1300, Norway
Tel.: (47) 66 85 80 00
Fax: (47) 66 85 80 90
E-Mail: info.no@alfalaval.com
Web Site: local.alfalaval.com
Emp.: 69
Heating & Filtering Equipment Distr
S.I.C.: 5074
N.A.I.C.S.: 423720
Casper Andersen *(Gen Mgr)*

Alfa Laval NV (1)
Baarschot 2
4817 ZZ Breda, Netherlands
Tel.: (31) 765791200
Real Estate Management Services
S.I.C.: 6531
N.A.I.C.S.: 531390

Subsidiary:

Alfa Laval Nederland BV (2)
Baarschot 2
4817 ZZ Breda, Netherlands
Tel.: (31) 765 79 12 00
Fax: (31) 302 41 64 62
Financial Management Services
S.I.C.: 6211
N.A.I.C.S.: 523999

Subsidiary:

Helpman Capital BV (3)
Peizerweg 97
9727 AJ Groningen, Netherlands
Tel.: (31) 505 21 75 55
Fax: (31) 505 21 75 04
Financial Management Services
S.I.C.: 6211
N.A.I.C.S.: 523999

Non-U.S. Subsidiary:

Alfa Laval Ltda (2)
Av Mutinga 4 935 Edificio A Vila Jaguara
Sao Paulo, 05110-903, Brazil
Tel.: (55) 11 5188 6000
Fax: (55) 11 5188 6003
E-Mail: alfalaval.br@alfalaval.com
Web Site: www.alfalaval.com.br
Air Conditioner & Refrigerator Mfr & Whlsr
S.I.C.: 3585
N.A.I.C.S.: 333415

Alfa-Laval (N.Z.) Ltd. (1)
307 Sandwich Road
PO Box 20424
Te Rapa, Hamilton, New Zealand
Tel.: (64) 78496025
Telex: 21916 ALFA NZ
Fax: (64) 78494619
E-Mail: newzealand.info@alfalaval.com
Web Site: local.alfalaval.com
Emp.: 25
S.I.C.: 2657
N.A.I.C.S.: 322212

Alfa Laval Olmi SpA (1)
Viale Europa 29
24040 Suisio, Bergamo, Italy
Tel.: (39) 035 999111
Fax: (39) 035 902613
E-Mail: sales@olmi.it
Web Site: www.olmi.it
Heat Exchanger Mfr
S.I.C.: 3443
N.A.I.C.S.: 332410

Alfa Laval Oy (1)
Luoteisrinne 4C
PO Box 51
FI 02271 Espoo, Finland
Tel.: (358) 9804041
Fax: (358) 98042842
E-Mail: info.fi@alfalaval.com
Web Site: www.alfalaval.com
Sales Range: $10-24.9 Million
Emp.: 40
S.I.C.: 2657
N.A.I.C.S.: 322212
Benny Lillqvist *(Mng Dir)*

Subsidiary:

Alfa Laval Vantaa OY (2)
Ansatie 3
01740 Vantaa, Finland
Tel.: (358) 9 894 41
Fax: (358) 9 8944 318
E-Mail: csc@alfalaval.com
Web Site: www.fincoil.fi
Air Conditioning & Heating Equipment Mfr
S.I.C.: 3585
N.A.I.C.S.: 333415
Lindholm Jyrki *(Mng Dir)*

Alfa Laval Packinox (1)
14 rue de Bassano
75116 Paris, La Defense Cedex, France (100%)
Tel.: (33) 1 53 67 41 41
Fax: (33) 1 53 67 41 42
E-Mail:
Web Site: www.alfalaval.fr
Rev.: $2,000,000
Emp.: 9
Mfr of Plate Exchangers
S.I.C.: 3443
N.A.I.C.S.: 332313
Thierrw Sourp *(Pres)*

Non-U.S. Subsidiaries:

Packinox Moscow (2)
15/13 Petrovska Street Apt 19
103031 Moscow, Russia
Tel.: (7) 4952342837
Fax: (7) 4952342830
E-Mail: e.gratcheva@areva.ton.ru
Web Site: www.packinox.com
Distr. of Plate Exchangers
S.I.C.: 5049
N.A.I.C.S.: 423490

Alfa Laval Philippines, Inc. (1)
3rd Fl Molave Bldg
2231 Pasong Tamo, Makati, Metro Manila, Philippines (100%)
Tel.: (63) 28127596
Fax: (63) 28150642
E-Mail: philippines.info@alfalaval.com
Web Site: www.alfalaval.com
Emp.: 15
Paper Products
S.I.C.: 2657
N.A.I.C.S.: 322212

Alfa Laval Polska Sp. zoo (1)
Ul J Dabrowskiego 113
PL 93 208 Lodz, Poland

Tel.: (48) 426426600
Fax: (48) 426417178
E-Mail: poland.info@alfalaval.com
Web Site: www.alfalaval.com
Emp.: 50
S.I.C.: 2657
N.A.I.C.S.: 322212
Mariusz Klofinski *(Gen Mgr)*

Alfa Laval Polska Sp. zoo (1)
Ul Rzymowskiego 53
PL 02 697 Warsaw, Poland (100%)
Tel.: (48) 223366464
Fax: (48) 223366460
E-Mail: poland.info@alfalaval.com
Web Site: www.alfalaval.pl
Emp.: 16
Spare Parts, Separators, Gaskets Mfr
S.I.C.: 3559
N.A.I.C.S.: 333249
Malgorzata Moczynska *(Gen Mgr)*

Alfa Laval (Portugal) Lda (1)
Avenida Forte 12
Edificio Tetra Pak, 2795 503 Carnaxide, Oeiras, Portugal
Tel.: (351) 214166400
Fax: (351) 214166444
E-Mail: portugal.info@alfalaval.com
Web Site: www.alfalaval.pt
Emp.: 14
S.I.C.: 2657
N.A.I.C.S.: 322212
Christian Thompson *(Gen Mgr)*

Alfa Laval (Pty) Ltd (1)
100 Electron Avenue
Isando, 1600, South Africa
Tel.: (27) 11 230 3600
Fax: (27) 11 230 3695
E-Mail: info.sa@alfalaval.com
Web Site: www.alfalaval.com
Emp.: 50
Heat Exchanger Mfr
S.I.C.: 3559
N.A.I.C.S.: 332410
Rolf Ekholm *(Mng Dir)*

Alfa Laval S.A. de C.V. (1)
Via Gustavo Baz 352
Col La Loma, Tlalnepantla, 54060, Mexico
Tel.: (52) 5530032700
Fax: (52) 5530032727
E-Mail: mexico.info@alfalaval.com
Web Site: www.alfalaval.com.mx
Emp.: 75
Industrial Equipment & Machinery Sales, Service & Distr
S.I.C.: 5084
N.A.I.C.S.: 423830

Alfa Laval S.A. (1)
Fermin Tangueis 160 Urb Santa Catalina Alt Cuadra 8 AV Arriola
La Victoria, Lima, Peru
Tel.: (51) 1 619 89 89
Fax: (51) 1 619 89 79
E-Mail: ventas.peru@alfalaval.com
Web Site: www.alfalaval.com
Emp.: 30
Purifier & Separator Whlsr
S.I.C.: 5084
N.A.I.C.S.: 423830
Cibele David *(Gen Mgr)*

Alfa Laval S.A. (1)
Tranversal 93 # 53-48 Int 70
Bogota, Colombia
Tel.: (57) 12916330
Fax: (57) 14303836
E-Mail: info.colombia@alfalaval.com
Web Site: local.alfalaval.com
Emp.: 25
Heat Transfer Mfr & Distr
S.I.C.: 3559
N.A.I.C.S.: 332410
Jorge Delgado *(Gen Mgr)*

Alfa Laval S.A. (1)
Uruguay 2887 San Fernando
Buenos Aires, AR-1646, Argentina
Tel.: (54) 1147257300
Telex: 260 84 LAVAL AR
Fax: (54) 1147460289
E-Mail: argentina.info@alfalaval.com
Web Site: www.alfalaval.com
Emp.: 100
Mfr of Separators, Milking Machines, Plate Heat Exchangers
S.I.C.: 3556
N.A.I.C.S.: 333241

Alfa Laval S.A.C.I. (1)
Correo 35th St Sebastian 2839
PO Box 122
Office 401, Santiago, Chile (100%)
Tel.: (56) 23530300
Telex: 340 727 ALFASA CH
Fax: (56) 22311906
E-Mail: chile.information@alfalaval.com
Web Site: www.alfalaval.cl
Sales Range: $10-24.9 Million
Emp.: 25
S.I.C.: 2657
N.A.I.C.S.: 322212
Civele Gadeg *(Mng Dir)*

Alfa Laval S.A.S (1)
Parc Technologique de Lyon Immeuble Sequoia 3
97 Allee Alexandre Borodine, F 69792 Saint Priest, Cedex, France (100%)
Tel.: (33) 469167700
Telex: 698.748 ALFALAV
Fax: (33) 469167790
E-Mail: france.info@alfalaval.com
Web Site: www.alfalaval.fr
Emp.: 750
Mfr of Processing Equipment; Separators; Heat Exchangers
S.I.C.: 3585
N.A.I.C.S.: 333415
Stephane Ronteix *(COO)*

Alfa Laval Singapore Pte. Ltd. (1)
11 Joo Koon Cir
Jurong, Singapore, 629043, Singapore
Tel.: (65) 65592828
Telex: RS 21079 ALFA LAVAL
Fax: (65) 68623567
Web Site: local.alfalaval.com
Emp.: 50
S.I.C.: 2657
N.A.I.C.S.: 322212

Alfa Laval Slovakia spol, s.r.o. (1)
Racainsta Liceansta 153A
SK 831 54 Bratislava, Slovakia (100%)
Tel.: (421) 244455093
Fax: (421) 244459917
E-Mail: slovakia.info@alfalaval.com
Web Site: www.alfalaval.sk
Emp.: 10
S.I.C.: 2657
N.A.I.C.S.: 322212
Gyula Szkeres *(Gen Mgr)*

Alfa Laval South East Europe Ltd. (1)
Bul Cherni vrah 1 Floor 6
1421 Sofia, Bulgaria
Tel.: (359) 29555666
Fax: (359) 29559194
E-Mail: bulgaria.info@alfalaval.com
Emp.: 14
S.I.C.: 2657
N.A.I.C.S.: 322212

Alfa Laval S.p.A. (1)
Via Delle Albere 5
Alonte, 36040 Vicenza, Italy
Tel.: (39) 0444725411
Telex: 33 33 19 ALFA 1
Fax: (39) 0444725400
E-Mail: alfalavalalonte@alfalalval.com
Emp.: 350
Mfr. Separators
S.I.C.: 3556
N.A.I.C.S.: 333241
Massimo Balestrini *(Office Mgr)*

Subsidiaries:

Alfa Laval Parma Srl (2)
Via Martiri Liberazione 12
43126 Parma, Italy
Tel.: (39) 0521 302811
Fax: (39) 0521 302812
E-Mail: info@astepo.com
Web Site: www.astepo.com
Food Processing Machinery Mfr
S.I.C.: 3556
N.A.I.C.S.: 333241

Tranter Srl (2)
Via Ercolano 24
20052 Monza, Italy
Tel.: (39) 039282821
Fax: (39) 039834315
Heat Exchanger Equipment Mfr
S.I.C.: 3443
N.A.I.C.S.: 332410

Alfa Laval Spol S.R.O. (1)
U Nakladoveho Nadrazi 6
Prague, 130 00, Czech Republic
Tel.: (420) 234 710 700
Fax: (420) 234 710 705
E-Mail: czechrepublic.info@alfalaval.com
Web Site: www.alfalaval.cz
Emp.: 50
Heating Equipment Distr
S.I.C.: 5074
N.A.I.C.S.: 423720
Gyula Szekeres *(Gen Mgr)*

Alfa Laval S.R.L. (1)
35 Baratiei St Sector 3
030197 Bucharest, Romania
Tel.: (40) 213100730
Fax: (40) 21310731
E-Mail: romania.info@alfalaval.com
Web Site: www.alfalaval.ro
Emp.: 15
Heat Transfer & Fluid Handling Distr
S.I.C.: 3594
N.A.I.C.S.: 333996

Alfa Laval, Taiwan (1)
9F 1 No 16 Ln 35 Jihu Rd
Chung Ching N Rd, Taipei, 11492, Taiwan (100%)
Tel.: (886) 266001166
Fax: (886) 266001168
Web Site: www.alfalaval.com
Emp.: 33
Paper Products
S.I.C.: 2657
N.A.I.C.S.: 322212

Alfa Laval (Thailand) Ltd. (1)
222 Krungthep Kreetha Road
Huamark Bangkapi, Bangkok, 10240, Thailand
Tel.: (66) 23794660
Fax: (66) 23794662
E-Mail: thailand.info@alfalaval.com
Web Site: www.alfalaval.com
Emp.: 60
S.I.C.: 2657
N.A.I.C.S.: 322212
Koray Chong *(Mng Dir)*

Alfa Laval UAB (1)
Ovo 25
09320 Vilnius, Lithuania (100%)
Tel.: (370) 52150091
Fax: (370) 52150093
E-Mail: lithuania.info@alfalaval.com
Web Site: www.alfalaval.lt
Emp.: 6
Paper Products
S.I.C.: 2657
N.A.I.C.S.: 322212
Valdas Gylys *(Gen Mgr)*

Alfa Laval Ukraine (1)
82 Mezhigorskaya St
Kiev, 04655, Ukraine
Tel.: (380) 44 462 48 71
Fax: (380) 44 417 50 10
E-Mail: ukraine.info@alfalaval.com
Web Site: www.alfalaval.com
Emp.: 20
Heat Exchanger Mfr & Distr
S.I.C.: 3443
N.A.I.C.S.: 332410
Gennadiy Rudenko *(Gen Mgr)*

Alfa Laval Venezolana S.A. (1)
Apartado Postal 47723
Caracas, 1041, Venezuela (100%)
Tel.: (58) 2127010500
Telex: 24163 ALVSA VE
Fax: (58) 2127518265
Web Site: local.alfalaval.com
Emp.: 12
S.I.C.: 2657
N.A.I.C.S.: 322212

DeLaval S.A. (1)
Antonio De Cabezon 27
E 28034 Madrid, Spain
Tel.: (34) 913790600
Telex: 22497 EAALE
Fax: (34) 913580085
Web Site: www.delaval.com
Emp.: 35
S.I.C.: 3565
N.A.I.C.S.: 333993

DeLaval SIA (1)
Mukusalas Lela 41
LV 1004 Riga, Latvia (100%)
Tel.: (371) 7063175
Fax: (371) 7063179
E-Mail: delaval@delaval.com
Web Site: www.delaval.com
Sales Range: $1-9.9 Million
Emp.: 24
S.I.C.: 2657
N.A.I.C.S.: 322212

Kenus LLP (1)
Tole bi 301
Almaty, 050000, Kazakhstan
Tel.: (7) 727 223 15 78
Heating & Air Conditioning Installation Services
S.I.C.: 1711
N.A.I.C.S.: 238220

MCD Nitrile India Pvt Ltd (1)
324-A 2nd Floor
Jodhpur Park, Kolkata, West Bengal, 700068, India
Tel.: (91) 33 24834928
Fax: (91) 33 24835062
Rubber Gaskets & Plastic Product Mfr
S.I.C.: 3053
N.A.I.C.S.: 339991

Onnuri Industrial Machinery Co. Ltd (1)
Free Trade Zone 2 654-4 Bongam-Dong
Masan Hoewon-Gu, Changwon, Kyeongnam, 630-803, Korea (South)
Tel.: (82) 55 286 5177
Fax: (82) 55 259 5599
E-Mail: info@onnurico.com
Web Site: www.onnurico.com
Emp.: 40
Industrial Machinery Mfr & Distr
S.I.C.: 3559
N.A.I.C.S.: 333249
Wonki Kim *(Mng Dir)*

PT Alfa Laval Indonesia (1)
Graha Inti Fauzi 4th Floor J1 Buncit Raya No 22
Jakarta, 12150, Indonesia
Tel.: (62) 21 7918 2288
Fax: (62) 21 7918 2266
E-Mail: alfalindo@alfalaval.com
Web Site: local.alfalaval.com
Heating Equipment Mfr & Distr
S.I.C.: 3433
N.A.I.C.S.: 333414

SIA Alfa Laval Eesti filiaal (1)
Paernu Mnt 130
Tallinn, 11317, Estonia
Tel.: (372) 6 55 80 23
Fax: (372) 6 55 80 17
E-Mail: estonia.info@alfalaval.com
Web Site: local.alfalaval.com
Heat Exchanger Mfr
S.I.C.: 3443
N.A.I.C.S.: 332410

Tranter Heat Exchangers Canada Inc. (1)
4080 78 Ave NW
Edmonton, AB, T6B 3M8, Canada
Tel.: (780) 465-4582
Fax: (780) 469-5448
Toll Free: (888) 465-1965
E-Mail: servicecanada@tranter.com
Heat Exchanger Mfr
S.I.C.: 3559
N.A.I.C.S.: 332410

Tranter India Pvt Ltd (1)
Gate No 127 & 128 Dhingrajwadi
Tal Shirur District, Pune, Maharashtra, 412 208, India
Tel.: (91) 8447574124
Fax: (91) 2137 392354
Heat Exchanger Mfr
S.I.C.: 3443
N.A.I.C.S.: 332410

Tranter Solarice GmbH (1)
Am Kalkfeld 7
06556 Artern, Germany
Tel.: (49) 3466 339540
Fax: (49) 3466 339541
Web Site: www.solarice.de
Emp.: 4
Air Conditioning Equipment Mfr
S.I.C.: 3585

Alfa Laval AB—(Continued)

N.A.I.C.S.: 333415

ALFA-PLAM A.D.

Radnicka 1
17500 Vranje, Serbia
Tel.: (381) 17 421 121
Fax: (381) 17 424 808
Web Site: www.alfaplam.rs
Year Founded: 1948
ALFA—(BEL)
Emp.: 1,100

Business Description:
Heating Device Mfr
S.I.C.: 3433
N.A.I.C.S.: 333414

Personnel:
Goran Kostic *(Mng Dir)*

Board of Directors:
Zoran Cicak
Miroljub Aleksic
Goran Kostic
Igor Markicevic
Branislav Popovic
Kostadin Popovic
Marija Subotic

ALFA, S.A.B. DE C.V.

Avenida Gomez Morin 1111 Sur Col Carrizalejo San Pedro
Garza Garcia, NL, 66254, Mexico
Tel.: (52) 8187481111
Fax: (52) 8187482552
E-Mail: eflores@alfa.com.mx
Web Site: www.alfa.com.mx
Year Founded: 1974
ALFA—(MEX OTC)
Rev.: $15,749,139,560
Assets: $12,105,547,440
Liabilities: $7,323,613,080
Net Worth: $4,781,934,360
Earnings: $801,277,120
Emp.: 59,847
Fiscal Year-end: 12/31/12

Business Description:
Petrochemicals, Synthetic Fibers, Steel, Refrigerated & Frozen Food, Aluminum Auto Components Producer & Telecommunications Mfr Import Export
S.I.C.: 3399
N.A.I.C.S.: 331221

Personnel:
Armando Garza Sada *(Chm)*
Alvaro Fernandez Garza *(CEO)*
Ramon A. Leal Chapa *(CFO)*
Manuel Rivera Garza *(Sr VP-Dev)*
Jose de Jesus Valdez Simancas *(Pres-Alpek & Newpek)*
Mario H. Paez Gonzalez *(Pres-Sigma)*
Armando Tamez Martinez *(Pres-Nemak)*
Rolando Zubiran Shetler *(Pres-Alestra)*
Carlos Jimenez Barrera *(Sec & Sr VP-Legal & Corp Affairs)*
Alejandro M. Elizondo Barragan *(Sr VP-Dev)*
Paulino Jose Rodriguez Mendivil *(Sr VP-Human Capital)*

Board of Directors:
Armando Garza Sada
Francisco Jose Calderon Rojas
Francisco Javier Fernandez Carbajal
Enrique Luis Castillo Sanchez Mejorada
Federico Toussaint Elosua
Alvaro Fernandez Garza
Claudio X. Gonzalez Laporte
Ricardo Guajardo Touche
David Martinez Guzman
Guillermo Francisco Vogel Hinojosa
Adrian G. Sada Gonzalez

Legal Counsel:
Weil, Gotshal & Manges
767 5th Ave
New York, NY 10153
Tel.: (212) 310-8000
Fax: (212) 310-8007

Subsidiaries:

Alestra, S. de R.L. de C.V. (1)
Av Lazaro Cardenas 2321 9 Fl
Col Residencial San Agustin, Garza Garcia, NL, 66260, Mexico
Tel.: (52) 81 8625 2201
Web Site: www.alestra.com.mx
Rev.: $364,629,163
Assets: $577,943,940
Liabilities: $331,647,137
Net Worth: $246,296,803
Earnings: $50,434,824
Emp.: 1,748
Fiscal Year-end: 12/31/12
Telecommunication Services
S.I.C.: 4899
N.A.I.C.S.: 517919
Bernardo Garcia Reynoso *(CFO & Chief Admin Officer)*

Alfa Corporativo, S.A. de C.V. (1)
Av Gomez Morin No 1111 Sur Carrizalejo
Garza Garcia, Nuevo Leon, 66200, Mexico
Tel.: (52) 8187481111
Fax: (52) 8187482552
Petrochemical Mfr
S.I.C.: 2869
N.A.I.C.S.: 325110

Alpek, S.A. de C.V. (1)
Ave Gomez Morin Sur 1111 Col Carrizalejo
San Pedro, 66250 Garza Garcia, NL, Mexico (100%)
Tel.: (52) 8187481300
Fax: (52) 8187482525
Web Site: www.alpek.com
Sls.: $1,500,000,000
Emp.: 6,550
Petrochemical Group Involved in Raw Material for Polyester, Fibers & Polymers, & Plastics & Chemicals
S.I.C.: 2911
N.A.I.C.S.: 324110
Jose de Jesus Valdez Simancas *(Pres)*

Subsidiaries:

Akra Polyester, S.A. de C.V. (2)
Av Adolfo Ruiz Cortines y Privada El Roble SN
Col Pedro Lozano, Monterrey, Nuevo Leon, 64400, Mexico
Tel.: (52) 81 8389 3100
Web Site: www.akra.com
Polyester Filament & Polyester Polymers Production
S.I.C.: 2869
N.A.I.C.S.: 325110

Indelpro, S.A. de C.V. (2)
Blvd Petrocel Km 05
Altamira, Tamaulipas, 89600, Mexico
Tel.: (52) 8332293900
Fax: (52) 8332240291
E-Mail: ventas@indelpro.com
Web Site: www.indelpro.com
Emp.: 200
Polypropylene Resins Mfr
S.I.C.: 2821
N.A.I.C.S.: 325211

Colombin Bel, S.A. de C.V. (1)
Calle 14 No 2775 Zona Industrial Sector Juarez
Guadalajara, Jalisco, 44940, Mexico
Tel.: (52) 3338128940
Fax: (52) 3338108192
E-Mail: contact@colombinbel.com
Web Site: www.colombinbel.com
Polyurethane Foam Mfr
S.I.C.: 3086
N.A.I.C.S.: 326150

Plants:

Colombin Bel, S.A. de C.V. - SANTA CATARINA PLANT (2)
Galeana 201 Sector Industrial el Lechugal
Santa Catarina, Nuevo Leon, 66350, Mexico
Tel.: (52) 81 87 48 88 00
Fax: (52) 81 87 48 88 48
E-Mail: gcegueda@colombinbel.com
Web Site: www.colombinbel.com
Emp.: 50
Polyurethane Foam Mfr
S.I.C.: 3086
N.A.I.C.S.: 326150
Oscar Cantu *(Office Mgr)*

Colombin Bel, S.A. de C.V. - TLALNEPANTLA PLANT (2)
Fernando Montes de Oca No 20
Fraccionamiento Industrial San Nicolas
Tlalnepantla, 54030, Mexico
Tel.: (52) 55 91 40 02 22
Fax: (52) 5591400288
Web Site: www.colombinbel.com
Polyurethane Foam Mfr
S.I.C.: 3086
N.A.I.C.S.: 326150

Grupo Petrotemex, S.A. de C.V (1)
Corporativo Torre Equus Ricardo Margain 444
Col Valle del Campestre, Piso, Nuevo Leon, 66265, Mexico
Tel.: (52) 8187481500
Fax: (52) 8187481505
E-Mail: info@petrotemex.com
Web Site: www.petrotemex.com
Emp.: 60
Petrochemical Mfr
S.I.C.: 2869
N.A.I.C.S.: 325110
Felipe Garda *(Mng Dir)*

Subsidiaries:

DAK Resinas Americas Mexico, S.A. de C.V. (2)
Vasco de Quiroga 3900 Torre A Piso 2 Oficina 202
Mexico, 05300, Mexico
Tel.: (52) 55 3000 5760
Fax: (52) 55 3000 5778
Web Site: www.dakamericas.com
Resin Products Mfr
S.I.C.: 2821
N.A.I.C.S.: 325211
Alfredo Carrasco *(Gen Mgr)*

Productora de Tereftalatos de Altamira, S.A. de C.V. (2)
Blvd Petrocel Km 1 Puerto Industrial Altamira
Altamira, Zacatecas, 89608, Mexico
Tel.: (52) 8332292200
Fax: (52) 8332292267
Telecommunication Services
S.I.C.: 4899
N.A.I.C.S.: 517919

Petrocel - Temex, S.A. de C.V. (1)
Carretera Tampico Mante km 17.5
Altamira, Tamaulipas, CP89600, Mexico
Tel.: (52) 332292200
Polyester Products Mfr
S.I.C.: 2899
N.A.I.C.S.: 325998

Planetario ALFA (1)
Av Roberto Garza Sada No 1000
Garza Garcia, Nuevo Leon, 66254, Mexico
Tel.: (52) 81 83 03 00 01
Web Site: www.planetarioalfa.org.mx
Science & Technology Museum Services
S.I.C.: 8412
N.A.I.C.S.: 712110

Productora de Tereft de Altamira, S.A. de C.V (1)
Carretera Tampico Mante Km 17 5
Altamira, Tamaulipas, 89600, Mexico
Tel.: (52) 833 229 2200
Textile Products Mfr
S.I.C.: 2399
N.A.I.C.S.: 314999

Sigma Alimentos, S.A. de C.V. (1)
Ave Gomez Morin 1111
Garza Garcia, NL, Mexico (100%)
Tel.: (52) 8187489000
Fax: (52) 8187489075
E-Mail: invesrel@sigma-alimentos.com
Web Site: www.sigma-alimentos.com
Emp.: 200
Refrigerated & Frozen Food Mfr & Distr
S.I.C.: 2038
N.A.I.C.S.: 311991
Mario H. Paez Gonzalez *(Pres)*

Subsidiaries:

Alimentos Finos de Occidente, S.A. de C.V. (2)
Av Fracisco Villa No 68 La Estrella
Lazaro Cardenas, Michoacan, 60990, Mexico
Tel.: (52) 7535327161
Fax: (52) 7535327164
Food Products Mfr
S.I.C.: 2099
N.A.I.C.S.: 311999

Grupo Chen, S. de R.L. de C.V. (2)
Av Gomez Morin No 1111 Carrizalejo
Garza Garcia, Nuevo Leon, 66254, Mexico
Tel.: (52) 8187489000
Fax: (52) 8187489075
Web Site: www.chen.com.mx
Food Products Mfr
S.I.C.: 2099
N.A.I.C.S.: 311999

Sigma Alimentos Noreste, S.A. de C.V (2)
Avenida Gomez Morin 1111 Colonia Carrizalejo
Garza Garcia, Nuevo Leon, 66254, Mexico
Tel.: (52) 8187489000
Fax: (52) 8187489075
Packaged Frozen Food Whslr
S.I.C.: 5142
N.A.I.C.S.: 424420

U.S. Subsidiaries:

Mexican Cheese Producers, Inc. (2)
11718 State Rd 23
Darlington, WI 53530
Tel.: (608) 776-8555
Fax: (608) 776-8555
E-Mail: hr@mexican-cheese.com
Web Site: www.mexican-cheese.com
Sls.: $25,600,000
Emp.: 95
Cheese Mfr
S.I.C.: 2022
N.A.I.C.S.: 311513
David Sandoval *(VP-Ops)*

Sigma Foods Inc. (2)
110 Cypress Station Dr Ste 202
Houston, TX 77090
Tel.: (281) 999-6361
Fax: (281) 999-5957
E-Mail: info@sigmafoodsusa.com
Web Site: www.sigmafoodsusa.com
Emp.: 30
Refrigerated & Frozen Food Mfr & Distr
S.I.C.: 5142
N.A.I.C.S.: 424420
Helio Castano *(VP)*

Subsidiary:

Bar-S Foods Co. (3)
5090 N 40th St
Phoenix, AZ 85018 DE
Tel.: (602) 264-7272
Fax: (602) 285-5252
Web Site: www.bar-s.com
Sales Range: $500-549.9 Million
Emp.: 1,560
Meat & Poultry Products Mfr
S.I.C.: 5147
N.A.I.C.S.: 311612
Timothy T. Day *(Chm)*
Warren Panico *(Pres & CEO)*
James S. Kuykendall *(CFO & VP)*

Versax, S.A. de C.V. (1)
Ave Gomez Morin 1111
Colonel Carrizalejo
San Pedro, Garza Garcia, NL 66254, Mexico (100%)
Tel.: (52) 8187481152
Fax: (52) 8187482519
Emp.: 6,500
Autoparts, Carpets & Home Building Materials
S.I.C.: 2299
N.A.I.C.S.: 313110

Joint Venture:

Terza, S.A. de C.V. (1)
Carretera a Monclova Km 115
El Carmen, Nuevo Leon, 66550, Mexico
Tel.: (52) 8187484900
Fax: (52) 8187484905

E-Mail: info@terza.com
Web Site: www.terza.com
Emp.: 200
Carpet Mfr; Owned by Alfa, S.A.B. de C.V. & Shaw Industries
S.I.C.: 2273
N.A.I.C.S.: 314110
Francisco Orogto *(Mgr)*

U.S. Subsidiary:

DAK Americas LLC (1)
5925 Carnegie Blvd Ste 500
Charlotte, NC 28209
Tel.: (704) 940-7500
Fax: (704) 940-7501
Toll Free: (877) 432-2766
E-Mail: info@dakamericas.com
Web Site: www.dakamericas.com
Sales Range: $300-349.9 Million
Emp.: 697
Terephthalic Acid, Polyester Resin & Polyester Staple Fiber Products Mfr
S.I.C.: 2823
N.A.I.C.S.: 325220
Hector Camberos *(Pres)*
Jorge P. Young *(Exec VP)*
Oscar Montemayor *(Sr VP-Corp Dev)*

Non-U.S. Subsidiaries:

DAK Americas Argentina, S.A. (1)
Av De Libertador 767 Piso 4
Buenos Aires, 1638, Argentina
Tel.: (54) 11 5297 0800
Fax: (54) 11 5297 0810
Web Site: www.dakamericas.com
Resin Product Mfr
S.I.C.: 2821
N.A.I.C.S.: 325211

Nemak Europe GmbH (1)
Giesserweg 10
Wernigerode, 38855, Germany
Tel.: (49) 39436520
Fax: (49) 3943652115
Aluminum Mold Mfr
S.I.C.: 3365
N.A.I.C.S.: 331524

Subsidiaries:

Nemak Dillingen GmbH (2)
Marie Curie Strasse
66763 Dillingen, Saarland, Germany
Tel.: (49) 6831 906 0
Fax: (49) 6831 906 109
E-Mail: info@nemak.com
Emp.: 800
Industrial Mold Mfr
S.I.C.: 3544
N.A.I.C.S.: 333511
Klaus Lellig *(Gen Mgr)*

Nemak Wernigerode GmbH (2)
Giesserweg 10
38855 Wernigerode, Germany
Tel.: (49) 3943 652 0
Fax: (49) 3943 652 1150
Web Site: www.nemak.com
Emp.: 700
Suspension Parts Mfr
S.I.C.: 3714
N.A.I.C.S.: 336330

U.S. Plant:

Nemak Wisconsin-Taylor Facility (2)
3101 S Taylor Dr
Sheboygan, WI 53082
Tel.: (920) 458-7724
Fax: (920) 458-0140
E-Mail:
Web Site: www.nemak.com
Sales Range: $500-549.9 Million
Emp.: 300
Global Designer & Mfr of Die-Cast Aluminum Automotive Components & Assemblies
S.I.C.: 3364
N.A.I.C.S.: 336390
Thomas Musgrave *(Chm, Pres & CEO)*

Non-U.S. Subsidiaries:

Nemak Argentina, S.R.L. (2)
Ruta Nacional N 36 KM 747
San Agustin, Cordoba, 5191, Argentina
Tel.: (54) 3547 491009
Fax: (54) 3547 491009
Web Site: www.nemak.com
Emp.: 200
Industrial Machinery Mfr
S.I.C.: 3559
N.A.I.C.S.: 333249

Nemak Gyor Kft (2)
Ipari Park Nyirfa Sor
9027 Gyor, Gyor-Moson-Sopron, Hungary
Tel.: (36) 96 520 100
Fax: (36) 96 520 112
E-Mail: office.gyoer@nemak.com
Web Site: www.nemakgyorkft-c.cegbongeszo.hu
Aluminium Casting Mfr
S.I.C.: 3364
N.A.I.C.S.: 331523

Nemak Linz GmbH (2)
Zeppelinstrasse 24
4030 Linz, Austria
Tel.: (43) 732 300 103 0
Fax: (43) 7323001035209
Web Site: www.nemak.com
Emp.: 400
Semi Permanent Mold Mfr
S.I.C.: 3544
N.A.I.C.S.: 333511
Andre Troeschel *(Gen Mgr)*

Nemak Poland Sp. z.o.o. (2)
ul Komorowicka 53
43-300 Bielsko-Biala, Poland
Tel.: (48) 33 813 5160
Fax: (48) 33 822 1450
Web Site: www.nemak.com
Emp.: 700
Aluminum Casting Product Mfr
S.I.C.: 3364
N.A.I.C.S.: 331523
Dariusz Kazmierczak *(Gen Mgr)*

Nemak, S.A. (2)
Libramiento Arco Vial Km 308
Villa de Garcia, Nuevo Leon, 66000, Mexico
Tel.: (52) 8187485200
Fax: (52) 8187485230
E-Mail: mx@nemak.com
Web Site: www.nemak.com
Emp.: 2,500
Aluminum Cylinder Head & Block Castings Producer
S.I.C.: 3364
N.A.I.C.S.: 331523
Armando Tamez *(Pres)*

Non-U.S. Subsidiary:

Modellbau Schonheide GmbH (3)
Lindenstrasse 36
08304 Schonheide, Germany
Tel.: (49) 37755 61 0
Fax: (49) 37755 61 123
Web Site: www.mbschoenheide.de
Emp.: 130
Telecommunication Services
S.I.C.: 4899
N.A.I.C.S.: 517919
Frank Mockel *(Gen Mgr)*

Nemak Slovakia, S.r.o. (2)
Ladomerska Vieska 394
965 01 Ziar nad Hronom, Slovakia
Tel.: (421) 456 702 111
Fax: (421) 456 702 302
Web Site: www.nemak.com
Industrial Machinery Mfr
S.I.C.: 3559
N.A.I.C.S.: 333249

Tenedora Nemak, S.A. de C.V. (2)
Libramiento Arco Vial Km 3 08
Villa de Garcia, Nuevo Leon, 66000, Mexico
Tel.: (52) 8187485200
Fax: (52) 615 446 0852
E-Mail: lorem.castellanos@nemak.com
Automotive Aluminum Component Mfr
S.I.C.: 3399
N.A.I.C.S.: 331314

U.S. Subsidiary:

Camen International Trading, Inc. (3)
13713 N Unitec Dr Unitec Industrial Ctr
Laredo, TX 78045
Tel.: (956) 728-8336
Fax: (956) 728-9668
E-Mail: info@cintrading.com
Web Site: www.cintrading.com
Supply Chain Management Services
S.I.C.: 7389
N.A.I.C.S.: 561499

Non-U.S. Subsidiary:

Nemak Czech Republic, S.r.o. (3)
Havran 137
434 40 Most, Czech Republic
Tel.: (420) 605 630 102
Fax: (420) 605 630 110
Web Site: www.nemak.com
Emp.: 200
Industrial Mold Mfr
S.I.C.: 3544
N.A.I.C.S.: 333511
Alejandro Cedillo *(Gen Mgr)*

ALFA TRANSFORMERS LTD.

Plot No 3337 Mancheswar Industrial Estate
Bhubaneswar, Orissa, 751010, India
Tel.: (91) 674 2580484
Fax: (91) 674 2580495
Web Site: www.alfatransformerlimited.com
517546—(BOM)
Rev.: $4,009,460
Assets: $6,876,060
Liabilities: $3,642,480
Net Worth: $3,233,580
Earnings: ($660,821)
Fiscal Year-end: 03/31/13

Business Description:
Transformer Mfr
S.I.C.: 3612
N.A.I.C.S.: 335311

Personnel:
Dillip Kumar Das *(Chm & Mng Dir)*
Susanta Kumar Satpathy *(Compliance Officer & Sec)*

Board of Directors:
Dillip Kumar Das
Debasis Das
Deepak Kumar Das
Niranjan Mohanty
Sambit Mohanty
S. K. Nanda
N. C. Pal
B. N. R. Patnaik
Santosh Kumar Patnaik

Transfer Agent:
MCS Share Transfer Agent Limited
12/1/5 Monoharpukur Road
Kolkata, 700026, India

ALFA-WASSERMANN S.P.A.

Via Ragazzi del 99 N 5
40133 Bologna, Italy
Tel.: (39) 051 6489511
Fax: (39) 051 388593
E-Mail: info@alfawassermann.it
Web Site: www.alfawassermann.it
Emp.: 650

Business Description:
Mfr. of Pharmaceuticals, Medicinal & Botanical Products
S.I.C.: 2834
N.A.I.C.S.: 325412

Personnel:
Marino Golinelli *(Pres)*
Stefano Golinelli *(CEO)*

U.S. Subsidiary:

Alfa-Wassermann Inc. (1)
4 Henderson Dr
West Caldwell, NJ 07006 (100%)
Tel.: (973) 882-8630
Fax: (973) 276-0383
Web Site: www.alfawassermannus.com
Surgical & Medical Instrument Mfr
S.I.C.: 3841
N.A.I.C.S.: 339112
Ira S. Nordlicht *(Pres & CEO)*

U.S. Holding:

Alfa-Wassermann (1)
4 Henderson Dr
West Caldwell, NJ 07006-6608
Tel.: (973) 882-8630
Fax: (973) 276-0383
Web Site: www.alfawassermannus.com
Mfr. of Medical Diagnostic Systems
S.I.C.: 3841
N.A.I.C.S.: 339112
Peter Natoli *(COO)*

Non-U.S. Subsidiaries:

Alfa-Wassermann B.V. (1)
Pompmolenlaan 24
3447 GK Woerden, Netherlands
Tel.: (31) 348487300
Fax: (31) 348433000
E-Mail: info@alfawassermannus.com
Web Site: www.alfawassermannus.com
Emp.: 20
Medical Dental & Hospital Equipment & Supplies Whslr
S.I.C.: 5047
N.A.I.C.S.: 423450
Ira S. Nordlicht *(Pres & CEO)*

Alfa Wassermann Polska Sp.Z o.o. (1)
Wachocka St 1M
03934 Warsaw, Poland
Tel.: (48) 228240364
Fax: (48) 228229771
E-Mail: biuro@alfawassermann.pl
Web Site: www.alfawassermann.pl
Emp.: 16
Pharmaceutical Preparation Mfr
S.I.C.: 2834
N.A.I.C.S.: 325412
Kaparrzna Jasimska Suninska *(Pres)*

Alfa Wassermann Srl (1)
Bd Unirii 20 ap 61 Sector 4
Bucharest, Romania
Tel.: (40) 31805352627
Fax: (40) 318053528
E-Mail: office@alfawassermann.ro
Web Site: www.alfawassermann.it/contenuto.php?view=6
Medicinal & Botanical Mfr
S.I.C.: 2833
N.A.I.C.S.: 325411
Carmela Negulescu *(Mng Dir)*

Alfa Wassermann Tunisie Sarl (1)
Rue Lac Victoria
Res Lac des Cygnes Appt A1 Les, 1053
Tunis, Tunisia
Tel.: (216) 71860224
Fax: (216) 71860249
E-Mail: s.chouchane@alfawassermann.com.tn
Web Site: www.alfawassermann.com.tn
Emp.: 15
Pharmaceutical Preparation Mfr
S.I.C.: 2834
N.A.I.C.S.: 325412
Slem Chouchane *(Mgr)*

Biosaude - Produtos Farmaceuticos, Lda. (1)
Edificio Malhoa Pl No 2 Escritoio 2-2
1070-325 Lisbon, Portugal
Tel.: (351) 217226110
Fax: (351) 217226119
E-Mail: biosaude@biosaude.pt
Web Site: www.biosaude.pt
Emp.: 40
Drugs & Druggists Sundries Whslr
S.I.C.: 5122
N.A.I.C.S.: 424210
Goao Albergaria *(Mng Dir)*

ALFA WOOD BULGARIA S.A.

Industrial area
Dolni Chiflik, 9120, Bulgaria
Tel.: (359) 52 685 806
Fax: (359) 52 685 805
E-Mail: office@alfawood.bg
Web Site: www.alfawood.bg
AL1—(BUL)

Business Description:
Wood Processing
S.I.C.: 2499
N.A.I.C.S.: 321999

Personnel:
Ivan Kiriakov *(Dir-IR)*

ALFAGOMMA S.P.A.

Via Torri Bianche 1
20059 Vimercate, Italy

Alfagomma S.p.A.—(Continued)

Tel.: (39) 03960161
Web Site: www.alfagomma.com
Sales Range: $400-449.9 Million
Emp.: 2,000

Business Description:
Holding Company
S.I.C.: 6719
N.A.I.C.S.: 551112

Personnel:
Enrico Gennasio *(CEO)*
Antonio Maruca *(CIO)*

Non-U.S. Subsidiaries:

Alfagomma Australia Pty Ltd **(1)**
12 Healey Circuit
Huntingwood, NSW, 2148, Australia
Tel.: (61) 2 9853 0950
Fax: (61) 2 9853 0999
Web Site: www.alfagomma.com
Emp.: 200
Rubber Products Mfr
S.I.C.: 3069
N.A.I.C.S.: 326299

Alfagomma Canada, Inc. **(1)**
6540-6550 Abrams
H4S 1Y2 Montreal, QC, Canada
Tel.: (514) 333-5577
Fax: (514) 333-7197
E-Mail: info@alfagomma.com
Emp.: 50
Rubber Products Mfr
S.I.C.: 3069
N.A.I.C.S.: 326299
Ignazeo Blanco *(Gen mgr)*

Alfagomma Fracne Paris IDF **(1)**
Zac Paris Nord II 177
Allee des Erables, 93420 Villepinte, France
Tel.: (33) 1 48 17 21 21
Fax: (33) 1 49 38 05 12
Rubber Products Mfr
S.I.C.: 3069
N.A.I.C.S.: 326299

Alfagomma Germany GmbH **(1)**
Friedrich Der Grosse 10
D 44628 Herne, Germany De
Tel.: (49) 232314730 (100%)
Fax: (49) 23231473235
Rubber Products Mfr
S.I.C.: 3069
N.A.I.C.S.: 326299

Alfagomma Hellas S.A. **(1)**
72 Mikalis St
18540 Piraeus, Greece
Tel.: (30) 4119909
Fax: (30) 42 20 884
Rubber Products Mfr
S.I.C.: 3069
N.A.I.C.S.: 326299

Alfagomma International BV **(1)**
LJ Costerstraat 52
5916 PS Venlo, Netherlands
Tel.: (31) 77 354 59 0
Fax: (31) 77 354 89 89
Rubber Products Mfr
S.I.C.: 3069
N.A.I.C.S.: 326299

Alfagomma Korea Co. Ltd. **(1)**
1018-5 Yongso-Ri
Yangkam-Myun Hwasung-Kun, Songtan, Korea (South)
Tel.: (82) 313528671
Fax: (82) 313528670
Rubber Products Mfr
S.I.C.: 3069
N.A.I.C.S.: 326299
Jonggin Choi *(Gen Mgr)*

Alfagomma (Ningbo) Co Ltd **(1)**
296 Kaiyuan Road
Investment Pioneering Centre, Ningbo, Jiangbei, 315022, China
Tel.: (86) 57488157288
Fax: (86) 574 8815 7299
Rubber Products Mfr
S.I.C.: 3069
N.A.I.C.S.: 326299

Alfagomma Pacific Pte Ltd **(1)**
69 Sungei Kadut Drive Unit 2A
Singapore, 729568, Singapore
Tel.: (65) 63639511
Fax: (65) 63639611
Rubber Products Mfr
S.I.C.: 3069
N.A.I.C.S.: 326299

Alfagomma South Africa Pty Ltd **(1)**
17 Quark Crescent
Linbro Business Park, Sandton, 2065, South Africa
Tel.: (27) 112010900
Fax: (27) 116080593
Emp.: 18
Rubber Products Mfr
S.I.C.: 3069
N.A.I.C.S.: 326299
Lorraine Victor *(Mng Dir)*

Alfagomma UK Ltd. **(1)**
43 Wilcock Road
Old Boston Trading Estate, Haydock, WA11 9SR, United Kingdom
Tel.: (44) 1942407680
Fax: (44) 1942407699
Rubber Products Mfr
S.I.C.: 3069
N.A.I.C.S.: 326299

Hiflex Denmark A/S **(1)**
PO Box 2605
Brondby, DK-2605, Denmark (100%)
Tel.: (45) 43254020
Fax: (45) 43254190
E-Mail: info@dunlophiflex.dk
Web Site: www.dunlophiflex.dk
Emp.: 14
Rubber Hose Whslr
S.I.C.: 3052
N.A.I.C.S.: 326220

ALFANAR TRADING CO.

PO Box 301
Riyadh, 11411, Saudi Arabia
Tel.: (966) 12415566
Fax: (966) 12413341
Web Site: www.alfanartrading.com
Year Founded: 1976
Sales Range: $25-49.9 Million
Emp.: 1,000

Business Description:
Electrical Products Mfr & Contracting Services
S.I.C.: 1731
N.A.I.C.S.: 238210

ALFESCA HF.

Kringlan no 7
103 Reykjavik, Iceland
Tel.: (354) 4777000
Fax: (354) 4777001
E-Mail: alfesca@alfesca.com
Web Site: www.alfesca.com
Year Founded: 1932
Sales Range: $750-799.9 Million

Business Description:
Frozen & Fresh Fish & Saltfish Products Distr & Marketer
S.I.C.: 2092
N.A.I.C.S.: 311710

Personnel:
Olafur J. Olafsson *(Chm)*
Xavier Govare *(CEO)*
Philippe Perrineau *(CFO)*

Board of Directors:
Olafur J. Olafsson
Kristinn Albertsson
Gudmundur Asgeirsson
Bill Ronald
Arni Tomasson

Non-U.S. Subsidiaries:

Blini S.A. **(1)**
77 boulevard Haussmann
75008 Paris, France (100%)
Tel.: (33) 1 5330 7270
Fax: (33) 1 44941599
Web Site: www.blini.fr
Emp.: 150
Seafood & Bakery Products
S.I.C.: 2092
N.A.I.C.S.: 311710

Lyons Seafoods Limited **(1)**
Fairfield House Fairfield Rd
Warminster, Wiltshire, BA12 9DA, United Kingdom UK
Mailing Address:
PO Box 2455
Warminster, Wiltshire, BA12 9XZ, United Kingdom
Tel.: (44) 1985224300
Fax: (44) 1985224330
E-Mail: info@lyons-seafoods.com
Web Site: www.lyons-seafoods.com
Emp.: 280
Mfr. of Frozen Chilled Seafood
S.I.C.: 2092
N.A.I.C.S.: 311710
Ole Norgaard *(CEO)*
Craig Walker *(Mng Dir)*

ALFONSO GALLARDO S.A.

(d/b/a Grupo Alfonso Gallardo)
Ctra de Badajoz 32
06380 Jerez de los Caballeros, Badajoz, Spain
Tel.: (34) 924 759 000
Fax: (34) 924 759 010
E-Mail: info@grupoag.es
Web Site:
Sales Range: $1-4.9 Billion
Emp.: 3,000

Business Description:
Steel Products & Concrete Mfr
S.I.C.: 3462
N.A.I.C.S.: 332111

Personnel:
Santiago Castellano *(Dir)*

Subsidiary:

Siderurgica Balboa, S.A. **(1)**
Ctra de Badajoz 32
06380 Jerez de los Caballeros, Spain ES
Tel.: (34) 924759000
Fax: (34) 924759010
E-Mail: info@grupoag.es
Web Site: www.grupoag.es/siderurgicaba lboa
Emp.: 600
Corrugated Steel Mfr
S.I.C.: 3312
N.A.I.C.S.: 331221
Sebastian Garcia *(Mng Dir)*

ALFRED HERBERT (INDIA) LTD.

13/3 Strand Road
Kolkata, 700 001, India
Tel.: (91) 3322484801
Fax: (91) 3322299124
E-Mail: kolkata@alfredherbert.com
Web Site: www.alfredherbert.co.in
505216—(BOM)
Rev.: $2,512,534
Assets: $7,406,486
Liabilities: $1,528,951
Net Worth: $5,877,535
Earnings: $149,831
Fiscal Year-end: 03/31/13

Business Description:
Industrial Machine Tools Distr
S.I.C.: 5084
N.A.I.C.S.: 423830

Personnel:
A. K. Basu *(CFO & Compliance Officer)*

Board of Directors:
A. V. Lodha
S. Bhandari
S. S. Jain
H. V. Lodha
R. C. Tapuriah

Transfer Agent:
Maheshwari Datamatics Pvt. Ltd
6 Mangoe Lane 1st Floor
Kolkata, India

ALFRED KARCHER GMBH & CO. KG

Alfred Karcher Str 28 40
71364 Winnenden, Germany

Mailing Address:
Postfach 800
D-71364 Winnenden, Germany
Tel.: (49) 7195140
Fax: (49) 7195142212
E-Mail: info@karcher.com
Web Site: www.karcher.com
Year Founded: 1953
Sales Range: $1-4.9 Billion
Emp.: 6,591

Business Description:
Cleaning Equipment Mfr
S.I.C.: 7217
N.A.I.C.S.: 561740

Personnel:
Hartmut Jenner *(Mng Dir)*
Markus Asch *(Member-Mgmt Bd)*
Dieter Grajer *(Member-Mgmt Bd)*

Subsidiaries:

Alfred Karcher Vertriebs-GmbH **(1)**
Friedrich-List-Strasse 4
71364 Winnenden, Germany
Tel.: (49) 71959030
Fax: (49) 7195903032805
E-Mail: info@kaercher.com
Web Site: www.kaercher.de
Emp.: 2,500
Cleaning Equipment Mfr
S.I.C.: 7217
N.A.I.C.S.: 561740
Hartmut Jenner *(Gen Mgr)*

Karcher Anlagenvermietungs GmbH **(1)**
Alfred-Karcher-Strasse 28-40
71364 Winnenden, Germany
Tel.: (49) 7195143030
Fax: (49) 7195142701
Cleaning Equipment Mfr
S.I.C.: 7217
N.A.I.C.S.: 561740

Karcher Leasing GmbH **(1)**
Alfred-Karcher-Strasse 28-40
71364 Winnenden, Germany
Tel.: (49) 7195143030
Fax: (49) 7195142701
Web Site: www.karcher.de
Cleaning Equipment Mfr
S.I.C.: 7217
N.A.I.C.S.: 561740

U.S. Subsidiaries:

C-Tech Industries **(1)**
4275 NW Pacific Rim Blvd
Camas, WA 98607
Tel.: (360) 833-1600
Fax: (360) 833-9200
E-Mail: info@c-techindustries.com
Web Site: www.c-techind.com
Sales Range: $75-99.9 Million
Emp.: 600
High-Pressure Cleaning Equipment Mfr
S.I.C.: 3569
N.A.I.C.S.: 333999
Elliot Younessian *(COO)*

Units:

The Hotsy Corporation **(2)**
4275 NW Pacific Rim Blvd
Camas, WA 98607
Tel.: (360) 834-0983
Fax: (800) 535-9164
Toll Free: (800) 525-1976
E-Mail: info@hotsy.com
Web Site: www.hotsy.com
Emp.: 160
Mfr. of High Pressure Cleaning Equipment & Related Chemicals
Export
S.I.C.: 3589
N.A.I.C.S.: 333318

Landa Water Cleaning Systems **(2)**
4275 NW Pacific Rim Blvd
Camas, WA 98607
Tel.: (360) 833-9100
Fax: (360) 833-9200
Toll Free: (800) 547-8672
E-Mail: info@karcherna.com
Web Site: www.karcherna.com
Sales Range: $50-74.9 Million
Emp.: 300

Industrial Pressure Washers & Water Cleaning Systems Mfr
Import
S.I.C.: 3589
N.A.I.C.S.: 333318
Elliot Younessian *(CEO)*

Karcher Floor Care, Inc. (1)
1351 W Stanford Ave
Englewood, CO 80110
Tel.: (303) 783-5815
Fax: (303) 865-2799
Toll Free: (800) 444-7654
Web Site: www.karcherfloorcare.com
Sls.: $74,400,000
Emp.: 350
Carpet/Floor Care Equipment Mfr
S.I.C.: 3589
N.A.I.C.S.: 333318
Hannes Saeubert *(CEO)*

Subsidiaries:

Graco Manufacturing Co. Inc. (2)
1 T and G Way
Blackwood, NJ 08012
Tel.: (856) 228-1800
Fax: (856) 228-2211
Web Site: www.gracomfg.com
Sales Range: $1-9.9 Million
Emp.: 30
Commercial Cleaning Equipment
S.I.C.: 3589
N.A.I.C.S.: 333318
John C. Grace, Jr. *(Pres & CEO)*

Professional Chemicals Corp. (2)
325 S Price Rd
Chandler, AZ 85224-4934 AZ
Tel.: (480) 899-7000
Fax: (480) 786-9538
Toll Free: (800) 776-2436
E-Mail: information@prochem.com
Web Site: www.prochem.com
Sales Range: $100-124.9 Million
Emp.: 200
Cleaning Equipment, Cleaning & Polishing Preparations & Chemical Products Mfr; Carpet & Upholstery Cleaning Equipment Rental Services
Import Export
S.I.C.: 3589
N.A.I.C.S.: 333318
Glen Wilson *(Gen Mgr)*

Windsor Industries, Inc. (2)
1351 W Stanford Ave
Englewood, CO 80110 CO
Tel.: (303) 762-1800
Fax: (303) 865-2800
Toll Free: (800) 444-7654
E-Mail: info@windsorind.com
Web Site: www.windsorind.com
Sales Range: $1-9.9 Million
Emp.: 350
Mfr of Commercial Floor Cleaning Machines
Import Export
S.I.C.: 3589
N.A.I.C.S.: 333318

Karcher Residential Solutions, Inc. (1)
750 W. Hampden Ave
Englewood, CO 80110
Tel.: (303) 738-2400
Fax: (303) 738-2478
Web Site: www.karcherresidential.com
Cleaning Equipment Mfr
S.I.C.: 7217
N.A.I.C.S.: 561740

Non-U.S. Subsidiaries:

Alfred Karcher Ges.m.b.H. (1)
Lichtblaustrasse 7
1220 Vienna, Austria
Tel.: (43) 1250600
Fax: (43) 125060333
E-Mail: info@karcher.at
Web Site: www.karcher.at
Cleaning Equipment Mfr
S.I.C.: 7217
N.A.I.C.S.: 561740
Michael Trullinger *(Mng Dir)*

C-Tech Industries de Mexico, S. de R.L. de C.F. (1)
Avenida Avante #831
Avenida Avante #831, Apodaca, Mexico
Tel.: (52) 55 5357 0428
Fax: (52) 55 5576 1875
Web Site: www.kaercher.de/int/Service/Addresses_World_wide.htm
Cleaning Equipment Mfr
S.I.C.: 7217
N.A.I.C.S.: 561740

Karcher B.V. (1)
2320 Hoogstraten
Hoogstraten, Belgium
Tel.: (32) 33400711
Fax: (32) 3 3146 443
Web Site: www.karcher.com
Cleaning Equipment Mfr
S.I.C.: 7217
N.A.I.C.S.: 561740

Karcher Canada, Inc. (1)
Millcreek Road Unit 67
Mississauga, ON, L5N 2N2, Canada
Tel.: (905) 672-8233
Fax: (905) 672-3155
E-Mail: info@karcher-centre-mississauga.ca
Emp.: 6
Cleaning Equipment Mfr
S.I.C.: 7217
N.A.I.C.S.: 561740

Karcher Cleaning Systems A.E. (1)
31-33 Nikitara St & Konstantinouloleos St
13671 Athens, Greece
Tel.: (30) 2102316153
Fax: (30) 2102316102
E-Mail: sales@karcher.gr
Web Site: www.karcher.gr/gr/Service/Addresses_World_wide.htm
Emp.: 30
Cleaning Equipment Mfr
S.I.C.: 7217
N.A.I.C.S.: 561740
Fransis Lazaros *(Mng Dir)*

Karcher Co., Ltd. (South Korea) (1)
872-2 Sinjeong-Dong
Seoul, Yangcheon-Gu, 158 856, Korea (South)
Tel.: (82) 23226588
Fax: (82) 2 322 6599
Web Site: www.karcher.gr/gr/Service/Addresses_World_wide.htm
Cleaning Equipment Mfr
S.I.C.: 7217
N.A.I.C.S.: 561740

Karcher Hungaria Kft. (1)
Tormasret ut 2
2051 Biatorbagy, Hungary
Tel.: (36) 23 530 0
Fax: (36) 23 530 341
Web Site: www.karcher.de/int/Service/Addresses_World_wide.htm
Cleaning Equipment Mfr
S.I.C.: 7217
N.A.I.C.S.: 561740

Karcher Industria e Comercio Ltda. (1)
Av Professor Benedicto Montenegro No 419
13140-000 Sao Paulo, Brazil
Tel.: (55) 1938849242
Fax: (55) 1938849120
E-Mail: abilio.cepera@karcher.com.br
Emp.: 260
Cleaning Equipment Mfr
S.I.C.: 7217
N.A.I.C.S.: 561740
Abilio Cepera *(Mng Dir)*

Karcher (Japan) Co., Ltd. (1)
3-2 Matsuzakadaira Taiwa-Cho
Kurokawa-Gun, Miyagi, 981-3408, Japan
Tel.: (81) 223443140
Fax: (81) 223443141
Web Site: www.karcher.co.jp
Emp.: 80
Cleaning Equipment Mfr
S.I.C.: 7217
N.A.I.C.S.: 561740
Hachiro Sato *(Pres)*

Karcher Ltd (1)
12 Willow Bus Pk Nangor Rd
Clondalkin, Dublin, Ireland
Tel.: (353) 14097777
Fax: (353) 14097775
Web Site: www.karcher.de
Cleaning Equipment Mfr
S.I.C.: 7217
N.A.I.C.S.: 561740
Paul Carrol *(Mng Dir)*

Karcher N.V. (1)
Industrieweg 12
2320 Hoogstraten, Belgium
Tel.: (32) 33400711
Fax: (32) 3 3146 443
Web Site: www.karcher.de/int/Service/Addresses_World_wide.htm
Cleaning Equipment Mfr
S.I.C.: 7217
N.A.I.C.S.: 561740

Karcher Oy (1)
Yrittajantie 17
01800 Klaukkala, Finland
Tel.: (358) 9 87919 191
Fax: (358) 9 87919 301
Web Site: www.karcher.de
Cleaning Equipment Mfr
S.I.C.: 7217
N.A.I.C.S.: 561740

Karcher Poland Ltd. Sp. z o.o. (1)
31-346 Krakow
Krakow, Poland
Tel.: (48) 126397222
Fax: (48) 126397123
Web Site: www.karcher.pl/
Cleaning Equipment Mfr
S.I.C.: 7217
N.A.I.C.S.: 561740

Karcher Pty. Ltd. (1)
40 Koornang Road
Scoresby, 3179, Australia
Tel.: (61) 397652300
Fax: (61) 397652398
E-Mail: sales-enquirie@karcher.com.au
Web Site: www.karcher.com.au
Emp.: 50
Cleaning Equipment Mfr
S.I.C.: 7217
N.A.I.C.S.: 561740
Cameron Mole *(Mng Dir)*

Karcher Rengoringssystemer A/S (1)
Slotherrensvej 411 C
2610 Rodovre, Denmark
Tel.: (45) 79321506/
Fax: (45) 40448106
E-Mail: info@karcher.dk
Web Site: www.karcher.dk
Emp.: 15
Cleaning Equipment Mfr
S.I.C.: 7217
N.A.I.C.S.: 561740
Esbern Sjoegaard *(Gen Mgr)*

Karcher, S.A. (1)
Pol Industrial Font del Radium
Calle Doctor Trueta 6-7, 08400 Barcelona, Spain
Tel.: (34) 932651616
Fax: (34) 93 846 5505
Cleaning Equipment Mfr
S.I.C.: 7217
N.A.I.C.S.: 561740

Karcher S.A.S. (1)
5 Avenue des Coquelicots
94865 Bonneuil, France
Tel.: (33) 143996770
Fax: (33) 143394873
Web Site: www.karcher.de/int/Service/Addresses_World_wide.htm
Emp.: 170
Cleaning Equipment Mfr
S.I.C.: 7217
N.A.I.C.S.: 561740

Karcher Servis Ticaret A.S. (1)
Binbasi Resat Mah Akcay Cad No 3B Gaziemir
307 Sokak No 6, Izmir, Turkey
Tel.: (90) 2322520708
Fax: (90) 2322522536
E-Mail: info@karcher.com.tr
Web Site: www.karcher.com.tr
Emp.: 60
Cleaning Equipment Mfr
S.I.C.: 7217
N.A.I.C.S.: 561740
Delikanli Umut *(Mng Dir)*

Karcher (Shanghai) Cleaning Systems Co., Ltd. (1)
Part F 2nd Floor Building 17 No 33 Xi Ya Road
Shanghai, Pudong, 200131, China
Tel.: (86) 2150768018
Fax: (86) 2150768039
Web Site: www.karcher.de/int/Service/Addresses_World_wide.htm
Cleaning Equipment Mfr
S.I.C.: 7217
N.A.I.C.S.: 561740

Karcher South East Asia Pte Ltd. (1)
5 Toh Guan Road East 01-00 Freight Links Express Distripark, Singapore, 608831, Singapore
Tel.: (65) 68971811
Fax: (65) 68971611
E-Mail: info@karcher-asia.com
Web Site: www.karcher.sg/
Emp.: 45
Cleaning Equipment Mfr
S.I.C.: 7217
N.A.I.C.S.: 561740
Kenneth Eng *(Mng Dir)*

Karcher S.p.A. (1)
Via Amerigo Vespucci 19
Gallarate, 21013 Varese, Italy
Tel.: (39) 0332 417 400
Fax: (39) 0332 418 350
Web Site: www.karcher.de/it/Benvenuti.htm
Cleaning Equipment Mfr
S.I.C.: 7217
N.A.I.C.S.: 561740

Karcher Spol. s r.o. (1)
155 00 Praha 5
Prague, Czech Republic
Tel.: (420) 2 3552 1665
Fax: (420) 2 3552 1667
Web Site: www.karcher.de/int/Service/Addresses_World_wide.htm
Cleaning Equipment Mfr
S.I.C.: 7217
N.A.I.C.S.: 561740

ALFRED RAITH GMBH

2 Industriestr 10
68766 Hockenheim, Germany
Tel.: (49) 620530510
Fax: (49) 62053051150
E-Mail: info@alfra.de
Web Site: www.alfra.de
Year Founded: 1973
Rev.: $10,995,197
Emp.: 45
Business Description:
Building Machinery Mfr
S.I.C.: 3531
N.A.I.C.S.: 333120
Personnel:
Markus A Doring *(Mng Partner)*
Ulrich Adam *(Co-Mng Dir)*
Michael Kur *(Co-Mng Dir)*

ALFRED SCHELLENBERG GMBH

An den Weiden 31
D-57078 Siegen, Germany
Tel.: (49) 271890560
Fax: (49) 27189056833
E-Mail: info@schellenberg.de
Web Site: www.schellenberg.de
Year Founded: 1984
Rev.: $27,879,825
Emp.: 75
Business Description:
Shutter Accessories Whslr
S.I.C.: 5031
N.A.I.C.S.: 423310
Personnel:
Sascha Schellenberg *(Mng Dir)*

ALFRED TRONSER GMBH

Quellenweg 14
D-7533 Engelsbrand, Germany
Tel.: (49) 70827980
Fax: (49) 7082798155
E-Mail: info@tronser.com
Web Site: www.tronser.de
Year Founded: 1951
Rev.: $17,932,200
Emp.: 108

Alfred Tronser GmbH—(Continued)

Business Description:
Electronic Components Mfr
S.I.C.: 3675
N.A.I.C.S.: 334416
Personnel:
Alfred Tronser *(Founder)*

ALFRESA CORPORATION
(Name Changed to Alfresa Healthcare Corporation)

ALFRESA HOLDINGS CORPORATION
1-1-3 Otemachi Chiyoda-ku
Tokyo, 100-0004, Japan
Tel.: (81) 352195100
Fax: (81) 352195103
E-Mail: ir@alfresa.com
Web Site: www.alfresa.com
Year Founded: 2003
2784—(TKS)
Sls.: $26,262,621,000
Assets: $13,081,651,000
Liabilities: $9,958,124,000
Net Worth: $3,123,527,000
Earnings: $228,481,000
Emp.: 10,939
Fiscal Year-end: 03/31/13
Business Description:
Holding Company; Drug Products, Diagnostic Reagents & Medical Equipment
S.I.C.: 6719
N.A.I.C.S.: 551112
Personnel:
Denroku Ishiguro *(Pres)*
Shozo Hasebe *(Deputy Pres)*
Hiroyuki Kanome *(Deputy Pres)*
Tsuneo Shinohara *(Deputy Pres)*
Hidetomi Takahashi *(Deputy Pres)*
Yasuo Takita *(Deputy Pres)*
Taizo Kubo *(Sr VP)*
Shunichi Miyake *(Sr VP)*
Board of Directors:
Kunio Fukujin
Shozo Hasebe
Denroku Ishiguro
Hiroyuki Kanome
Kazuko Kimura
Taizo Kubo
Shunichi Miyake
Mitsuru Nishikawa
Haruo Shimada
Tsuneo Shinohara
Hidetomi Takahashi
Yasuo Takita
Transfer Agent:
Mitsubishi UFJ Trust & Banking Corporation
4-5 Marunouchi 1-Chome Chiyoda-ku
Tokyo, 100-8212, Japan
Tel.: (81) 3 3212 1211

Subsidiaries:

Alfresa Healthcare Corporation (1)
(Formerly Alfresa Corporation)
3-11-5 Nihonbashi Honcho Chuo-ku
Tokyo, 103-0023, Japan (100%)
Tel.: (81) 3 3639 6281
Web Site: www.alfresa-hc.com
Emp.: 417
Whslr of OTC Pharmaceuticals, Dairy Products for Infants, Quasi Drugs & Sundries
S.I.C.: 5122
N.A.I.C.S.: 424210
Hisashi Katsuki *(Pres)*

Alfresa Medical Service Corporation (1)
2-23-12 Kikukawa Sumida-Ku
Sumida-Ku, Tokyo, 130-0024, Japan
Tel.: (81) 336357322
Fax: (81) 336357330
Web Site: www.alfresa-ms.co.jp
Emp.: 293
Pharmaceutical Products Whslr
S.I.C.: 5122
N.A.I.C.S.: 424210

Alfresa Nikken Sangyo Corporation (1)
4-20 Imamachi
Gifu, 500-8023, Japan
Tel.: (81) 665325621
Fax: (81) 665320714
Web Site: www.nk-gifu.co.jp/
Emp.: 456
Pharmaceutical Products Whslr
S.I.C.: 5122
N.A.I.C.S.: 424210

Alfresa Pharma Corp. (1)
2-2-9 Kokumachi
Chuo-Ku, Osaka, 540 8575, Japan (100%)
Tel.: (81) 669412806
Fax: (81) 669412831
Web Site: www.alfresa.co.jp
Sales Range: $1-9.9 Million
Emp.: 700
Pharmaceuticals Mfr
S.I.C.: 2834
N.A.I.C.S.: 325412

Alfresa System Corporation (1)
1-1-3 Otemachi
Chiyoda-ku, Tokyo, 100-0004, Japan
Tel.: (81) 3 5219 5630
Web Site: www.alfresa-system.com
Emp.: 51
Software Support Services
S.I.C.: 7373
N.A.I.C.S.: 541512

CS Yakuhin Co., Ltd. (1)
3-2-26 Marunouchi
Naka-Ku, Nagoya, Aichi, 460-0002, Japan
Tel.: (81) 529628201
Fax: (81) 529628205
Web Site: www.cs-yakuhin.com
Emp.: 1,000
Pharmaceutical Products Whslr
S.I.C.: 2834
N.A.I.C.S.: 325412
Ryuji Arakawa *(Pres)*

Kowa Pharmaceuticals Co., Ltd. (1)
1-46-1 Kikutamachi Oroshi
Koriyama, Fukushima, 963-8676, Japan
Tel.: (81) 249596611
Fax: (81) 249596546
Pharmaceutical Products Whslr
S.I.C.: 5122
N.A.I.C.S.: 424210
Yasuo Takita *(Pres)*

Meisho Co., Ltd. (1)
1 Ha Muryoji-machi
Kanazawa, Ishikawa, 920-0332, Japan
Tel.: (81) 762664141
Fax: (81) 762661869
Web Site: www.mshhs.com
Emp.: 500
Pharmaceutical Products Whslr
S.I.C.: 5122
N.A.I.C.S.: 424210
Kenji Orimoto *(Pres)*

Ryuyaku Co., Ltd. (1)
5-6-5 Makiminato
Urasoe, Okinawa, 901-2131, Japan
Tel.: (81) 988781111
Fax: (81) 988781793
Web Site: www.ryuyaku.co.jp
Emp.: 300
Pharmaceutical Products Whslr
S.I.C.: 5122
N.A.I.C.S.: 424210
Asao Kamiya *(Pres)*

Seiwa Sangyo Co., Ltd. (1)
4-57-7 Higashi Komatsugawa
Edogawa-ku, Tokyo, 132-0033, Japan JP
Tel.: (81) 336544151
Fax: (81) 336544155
Web Site: www.seiwa-sangyo.co.jp
Emp.: 20
Commercial Washing, Drying & Sterilization Equipment Mfr, Whslr, Leasing & Maintenance Services
S.I.C.: 3589
N.A.I.C.S.: 333318

Shikoku Alfresa Corporation (1)
4-2 Kameicho
Takamatsu, Kagawa, 760-0050, Japan
Tel.: (81) 878025011
Fax: (81) 878025010
Web Site: www.s-alfresa.com
Pharmaceutical Products Whslr
S.I.C.: 5122
N.A.I.C.S.: 424210

Non-U.S. Subsidiary:

Qingdao Nesco Medical Co., Ltd. (1)
Qingdao Huanhai Economic & Technological Development Zone
Qingdao, Shandong, 266107, China
Tel.: (86) 53266888123
Fax: (86) 53266888124
E-Mail: nescoqd@public.qd.sd.cn
Web Site: www.nescoqd.com.cn
Emp.: 60
Surgical Sutures Mfr
S.I.C.: 3841
N.A.I.C.S.: 339113
Kurihara Hideo *(Pres)*

ALFRESCO SOFTWARE LIMITED
Bridge Ave The Place
Maidenhead, SL6 1AF, United Kingdom
Tel.: (44) 1628 876 600
Web Site: www.alfresco.com
Emp.: 200
Business Description:
Document Management Software
S.I.C.: 7372
N.A.I.C.S.: 511210
Personnel:
John Powell *(Co-Founder)*
John Newton *(Chm & CTO)*
Doug Dennerline *(CEO)*
Carlton Baab *(CFO)*
Paul Warenski *(Chief Legal Officer & Gen Counsel)*
Ray Martinelli *(Chief People Officer)*
Martin Musierowicz *(Chief of Staff)*
Jeff Potts *(Chief Community Officer)*
Board of Directors:
John Newton
Lars Bjork
Kevin Comolli
Doug Dennerline
John Powell
Robin Vasan

U.S. Subsidiary:

Alfresco Software, Inc. (1)
1825 S Grant St Ste 350
San Mateo, CA 94402
Tel.: (888) 317-3395
Web Site: www.alfresco.com
Rev.: $1,500,000
Emp.: 50
Document Management Software
S.I.C.: 7372
N.A.I.C.S.: 511210
Doug Dennerline *(Pres & CEO)*

ALGAE.TEC LIMITED
Ground Floor 516 Hay Street
Subiaco, Perth, WA, 6008, Australia
Tel.: (61) 8 93806790
Fax: (61) 8 93819161
E-Mail: phatfull@algaetec.com.au
Web Site: www.algaetec.com.au
Year Founded: 2008
AEB—(ASX OTC)
Rev.: $3,656,981
Assets: $5,174,377
Liabilities: $4,653,241
Net Worth: $521,135
Earnings: ($4,606,618)
Emp.: 25
Fiscal Year-end: 06/30/13
Business Description:
Alternative Energy Researcher & Developer
S.I.C.: 8731
N.A.I.C.S.: 541712
Personnel:
Roger Sydney Stroud *(Chm)*
Peter Ernest Hatfull *(Mng Dir & Sec)*
Board of Directors:
Roger Sydney Stroud
Peter Ernest Hatfull
Garnet Earl McConchie

ALGERIE TELECOM SPA
Route Nationale 5
Cinq Maisons Mohammadia, 16130
Algiers, Algeria
Tel.: (213) 21823838
Fax: (213) 21823839
E-Mail: contact@algerietelecom.dz
Web Site: www.algerietelecom.dz
Emp.: 23,000
Business Description:
Telecommunications Services
S.I.C.: 4813
N.A.I.C.S.: 517110
Personnel:
Mousa Belgamathy *(Pres)*

ALGETA ASA
(Acquired by Bayer Aktiengesellschaft)

ALGOE
9 Bis Route De Champagne
69134 Ecully, Rhone, France
Tel.: (33) 472181200
Fax: (33) 472181390
E-Mail: sylvie.nietto@algoe.fr
Web Site: www.algoe.fr/page_acces.php
Sales Range: $50-74.9 Million
Emp.: 186
Business Description:
Management Consulting Services
S.I.C.: 8742
N.A.I.C.S.: 541611
Personnel:
Gerard Debrinay *(CEO)*

ALGOL OY
Karapellontie 6
PO Box 13
FIN 02611 Espoo, Finland
Tel.: (358) 950991
Telex: 121430 algolfi
Fax: (358) 9595006
E-Mail: info@algol.fi
Web Site: www.algol.fi
Year Founded: 1894
Sales Range: $10-24.9 Million
Emp.: 450
Business Description:
Industrial & Pharmaceutical Supplier Import
S.I.C.: 2834
N.A.I.C.S.: 325412
Personnel:
Gerhard Wendt *(Chm)*
Magnus Bargum *(Mng Dir)*
Tom Haglund *(CFO)*

Divisions:

Algol Central Storage Depot (1)
Karapellontie 6
02610 Espoo, Finland (100%)
Tel.: (358) 950991
Fax: (358) 9595006
E-Mail: info@algol.fi
Emp.: 200
Storage Services
S.I.C.: 4226
N.A.I.C.S.: 493190
Alexander Bargum *(Gen Mgr)*

Algol Techniques (1)
Karapellontie 6
02610 Espoo, Finland (100%)
Tel.: (358) 950991
Fax: (358) 9595006
E-Mail: infotechniques@algol.fi

Web Site: www.algol.fi
Emp.: 50
Production & Sales of Materials Handling Equipment
S.I.C.: 1799
N.A.I.C.S.: 238290

Subsidiaries:

Algol Technics Oy (1)
Karapellontie 6
PO Box 13
FIN 02611 Espoo, Finland
Tel.: (358) 950991
Fax: (358) 95099259
E-Mail: info.technics.fi@algol.fi
Web Site: www.algol.fi
Emp.: 350
Technical Trade
S.I.C.: 8299
N.A.I.C.S.: 611519
Alexander Bargum *(Mng Dir)*

Suomen Unipol Oy (1)
Karapellontie 8
00210 Espoo, Finland FI
Tel.: (358) 96823260 (60%)
Fax: (358) 968232626
E-Mail: suomen.unipol@unipol.fi
Web Site: www.unipol.fi
Emp.: 4
Wholesale Trade of Industrial Chemicals & Plastic Raw Materials
S.I.C.: 5169
N.A.I.C.S.: 424690
Markku Ekholm *(Mng Dir)*

Non-U.S. Subsidiaries:

Algol Chemicals SIA (1)
Asarisi 3
Marupe District, LV-2167 Riga, Latvia (100%)
Tel.: (371) 67615321
Fax: (371) 67610914
E-Mail: info.chem@algol.lv
Web Site: www.algol.lv
Emp.: 6
Provider of Storage Services
S.I.C.: 4225
N.A.I.C.S.: 493110
Alvils Brants *(Pres)*

Algol-Eesti OU (1)
Vana-Narva mnt 21
Beterb Ori Rd 44
11415 Tallinn, Estonia (50%)
Tel.: (372) 66056010
Fax: (372) 6 6056011
Web Site: www.algol.ee/
Sales Office & Storage Depot
S.I.C.: 4226
N.A.I.C.S.: 493190

UAB Algol Chemicals (1)
Veiveriu St 150
LT-46391 Kaunas, Lithuania
Tel.: (370) 37373220
Fax: (370) 37373429
E-Mail: info.chem.lt@algol.lt
Web Site: www.algol.lt
Emp.: 10
Sales Office & Storage Depot
S.I.C.: 4225
N.A.I.C.S.: 493110
Dariuf Kazlauskas *(Gen Mgr)*

ZAO Algol Chemicals (1)
Sofiskaja Ul 14
192236 Saint Petersburg, Russia (100%)
Tel.: (7) 8123090100
Fax: (7) 8123090300
E-Mail: info.chemicals.ru@algol.ru
Web Site: www.algol.ru
Emp.: 20
Sales Office & Storage Depot
S.I.C.: 4225
N.A.I.C.S.: 493110
Ivanov Uri *(Mng Dir)*

ALGOLD RESOURCES LTD.

(Formerly Kanosak Capital Venture Corporation)
94A avenue Laurier Ouest
Montreal, QC, H2T 2N4, Canada
Tel.: (514) 397-6918
Fax: (514) 397-8515
Web Site: www.kanosakgold.com
Year Founded: 2011
ALG—(TSXV)
Assets: $1,369,050
Liabilities: $109,039
Net Worth: $1,260,011
Earnings: ($193,668)
Fiscal Year-end: 12/31/12
Business Description:
Mineral Exploration Services
S.I.C.: 1081
N.A.I.C.S.: 213114
Personnel:
Benoit La Salle *(Chm)*
Yves Grou *(Vice Chm)*
Francois Auclair *(Pres & CEO)*
Dejan Ristic *(CFO)*
Board of Directors:
Benoit La Salle
Francois Auclair
Yves Grou
Jean-Francois Lalonde
John Sabine
Salma Seelaroo

ALGOMA CENTRAL CORPORATION

63 Church Street Suite 600
Saint Catharines, ON, L2R 3C4, Canada
Tel.: (905) 687-7888
Fax: (905) 687-7840
Web Site: www.algonet.com
Year Founded: 1899
ALC—(TSX)
Rev.: $557,025,946
Assets: $878,429,390
Liabilities: $382,425,339
Net Worth: $496,004,052
Earnings: $43,556,962
Emp.: 2,000
Fiscal Year-end: 12/31/12
Business Description:
Marine Transport Company
S.I.C.: 4499
N.A.I.C.S.: 488390
Personnel:
Duncan N. R. Jackman *(Chm)*
Greg D. Wight *(Pres & CEO)*
Peter D. Winkley *(CFO & VP-Fin)*
William S. Vaughan *(Sec)*
Wayne A. Smith *(Sr VP-Comml)*
Al J. Vanagas *(Sr VP-Technical)*
Board of Directors:
Duncan N. R. Jackman
H. Michael Burns
Richard B. Carty
E. M. Blake Hutcheson
Clive P. Rowe
Harold S. Stephen
William S. Vaughan
Greg D. Wight
Legal Counsel:
Heenan Blaikie LLP
Suite 2600 Royal Bank Plaza 200 Bay Street
South Tower, Toronto, ON, M5J 2J4, Canada
Tel.: (416) 360-6336
Fax: (416) 360-8425
Transfer Agent:
Canadian Stock Transfer Company
320 Bay Street PO Box 1
Toronto, ON, M5H 4A6, Canada

Division:

Algoma Central Corporation - Fraser Marine & Industrial Division (1)
1 Chestnut St
Port Colborne, ON, L3K 1R3, Canada
Tel.: (905) 834-4549
Fax: (905) 834-5644
E-Mail: info@frasermarineandindustrial.com
Web Site: www.frasermarineandindustrial.com
Emp.: 7
Ship Building & Repairing Services
S.I.C.: 3731
N.A.I.C.S.: 336611
Mario Battista *(Controller)*

Subsidiaries:

Algoma Central Properties, Inc. (1)
421 Bay St 608
PO Box 7000
Sault Sainte Marie, ON, P6A 1X3, Canada (100%)
Tel.: (705) 946-7220
Fax: (705) 946-7382
E-Mail: peter.winkley@algonet.com
Transportation Services
S.I.C.: 4581
N.A.I.C.S.: 488190
Greg Wight *(Pres)*

Algoma Tankers (1)
63 Church St Ste 600
Saint Catharines, ON, L2R 3C4, Canada (100%)
Tel.: (905) 687-7888
Fax: (905) 687-7840
Web Site: www.algomanet.com
Emp.: 40
Sea Transportation-Freight
S.I.C.: 4412
N.A.I.C.S.: 483111
Greg Wight *(Pres & CEO)*

Fraser Marine & Industrial (1)
1 Chestnut Street
Port Colborne, ON, L3K1R3, Canada (100%)
Tel.: (905) 834-4549
Fax: (905) 834-1538
E-Mail: frasers@algonet.com
Web Site: www.frasermarineandindustrial.com
Sales Range: $10-24.9 Million
Emp.: 85
S.I.C.: 4789
N.A.I.C.S.: 488210
Mario Battista *(Controller)*

Seaway Marine Transport (1)
20 Corporate Park Dr Ste 300
Saint Catharines, ON, L2S 3W2, Canada
Tel.: (905) 988-2600
Fax: (905) 988-1588
Web Site: www.seawaymarinetransport.com
Emp.: 50
Cargo Ship Management & Marketing Services
S.I.C.: 8742
N.A.I.C.S.: 541611
Dennis McPhee *(VP-Sls & Vessel Traffic)*

U.S. Subsidiaries:

Algoma Shipping Inc. (1)
152 Conant St
Beverly, MA 01915
Tel.: (978) 232-4800
Freight Forwarding Services
S.I.C.: 4731
N.A.I.C.S.: 488510

LAKEN SHIPPING CORPORATION

SMT (USA) INC. (1)
1 Cleveland Ctr 1250 Old River Rd Ste 2 N
Cleveland, OH 44113
Tel.: (216) 771-1999
Ship Repair & Maintenance Services
S.I.C.: 3731
N.A.I.C.S.: 336611

U.S. Joint Venture:

Marbulk Canada Inc. (1)
152 Conant St
Beverly, MA 01915
Tel.: (978) 299-1090
Web Site: www.algonet.com
Holding Company
S.I.C.: 6719
N.A.I.C.S.: 551112

Subsidiary:

Marbulk Shipping Inc. (2)
152 Conant St
Beverly, MA 01915 BB
Tel.: (978) 232-4810
Fax: (978) 232-4805
Emp.: 5
Provider of International Dry Bulk Shipping
S.I.C.: 4432
N.A.I.C.S.: 483113
Dave Geiger *(CFO & Treas)*

ALGONQUIN POWER & UTILITIES CORP.

2845 Bristol Circle
Oakville, ON, L6H 7H7, Canada
Tel.: (905) 465-4500
Fax: (905) 465-4514
Web Site: www.algonquinpower.com
AQN—(TSX)
Rev.: $367,675,076
Assets: $2,761,623,143
Liabilities: $1,367,878,874
Net Worth: $1,393,744,269
Earnings: $21,814,763
Emp.: 830
Fiscal Year-end: 12/31/12
Business Description:
Energy Services
S.I.C.: 4939
N.A.I.C.S.: 221122
Personnel:
Kenneth Moore *(Chm)*
Christopher Jarratt *(Vice Chm)*
Ian E. Robertson *(CEO)*
David Bronicheski *(CFO & Mng Dir-Admin)*
Linda Beairsto *(Gen Counsel & Sec)*
Board of Directors:
Kenneth Moore
Christopher J. Ball
Chris Huskilson
Christopher Jarratt
George L. Steeves
Legal Counsel:
Blake, Cassels & Graydon LLP
Toronto, ON, Canada
Transfer Agent:
CIBC Mellon Trust Company
320 Bay Street
PO Box 1
Toronto, ON, M5H 2A6, Canada
Tel.: (416) 643-5500
Fax: (416) 643-5570
Toll Free: (800) 387-0825

Subsidiaries:

Algonquin Power Fund (Canada) Inc (1)
2845 Bristol Cir
Oakville, ON, L6H 7H7, Canada
Tel.: (905) 465-4500
Fax: (905) 465-4514
Investment Management Services
S.I.C.: 6211
N.A.I.C.S.: 523999

Liberty Utilities (Canada) Corp. (1)
2845 Bristol Circle
Oakville, ON, L6H 7H7, Canada
Tel.: (905) 465-4500
Web Site: www.libertyutilities.com
Water, Electricity & Gas Utility Services
S.I.C.: 4939
N.A.I.C.S.: 221122
David Pasieka *(Pres)*

U.S. Subsidiaries:

Granite State Electric Company (2)
11 Northeastern Blvd
Salem, NH 03079-1953 NH
Tel.: (603) 890-7120 (100%)
Fax: (603) 890-7132
E-Mail:
Emp.: 45
Electric Power & Natural Gas Distr
S.I.C.: 4911
N.A.I.C.S.: 221122
William Sherry *(Exec VP)*

Liberty Utilities (Pine Bluff Water) Inc. (2)
(Formerly United Water Arkansas Inc.)
1100 State St
Pine Bluff, AR 71601 AR
Mailing Address:
PO Box 6070
Pine Bluff, AR 71611-6070
Tel.: (870) 534-2721
Fax: (870) 534-5152
E-Mail:
Web Site: www.libertyutilities.com
Emp.: 37
Water Supply & Treatment
S.I.C.: 4941
N.A.I.C.S.: 221310

Algonquin Power & Utilities Corp.—(Continued)

U.S. Unit:

Liberty Utilities West (2)
7001 National Ave
Tahoe Vista, CA 96148
Tel.: (916) 897-7277
Fax: (916) 405-3671
Toll Free: (800) 782-2506
E-Mail: customerservicewest@libertyutilities.com
Web Site: www.libertyutilities.com
Electric Power Distribution Services
S.I.C.: 4911
N.A.I.C.S.: 221122
Mike Smart *(Pres)*

St. Leon Wind Energy LP (1)
2845 Bristol Circle
Oakville, ON, L6H 7H7, Canada
Tel.: (204) 744-2315
Electric Power Generation Services
S.I.C.: 4911
N.A.I.C.S.: 221111

Joint Venture:

Valley Power Limited Partnership (1)
5302 34th Ave
Drayton Valley, AB, T7A 1S3, Canada
Tel.: (780) 542-7196
Fax: (780) 621-1793
E-Mail: valleypower@telusplanet.net
Emp.: 22
Electrical Contractors
S.I.C.: 1731
N.A.I.C.S.: 238210
Terry McCool *(Mng Dir)*

U.S. Subsidiary:

New England Gas Company (1)
45 N Main St Ste 1
Fall River, MA 02720 RI
Tel.: (508) 324-7811
Fax: (508) 965-4355
Toll Free: (800) 421-6760
Web Site: www.negasco.com
Emp.: 420
Natural Gas Distr
S.I.C.: 4924
N.A.I.C.S.: 221210
James Carey *(Mgr-Mktg)*

ALHAMBRA RESOURCES LTD

Suite 3 4015 1St Street SE
Calgary, AB, T2G 4X7, Canada
Tel.: (403) 228-2855
Fax: (403) 228-2865
Web Site: www.alhambraresources.com
Year Founded: 1993
ALH—(TSXV)
Sls.: $9,518,000
Assets: $108,539,000
Liabilities: $40,255,000
Net Worth: $68,284,000
Earnings: ($4,980,000)
Emp.: 15
Fiscal Year-end: 12/31/12
Business Description:
Gold Exploration & Development
S.I.C.: 1041
N.A.I.C.S.: 212221
Personnel:
John J. Komarnicki *(Chm & CEO)*
Donald D. McKechnie *(CFO & VP-Fin)*
Ihor P. Wasylkiw *(CIO & VP)*
Board of Directors:
John J. Komarnicki
James S. Bunyan
Richard K. Gorton
Patrick Highsmith
John I. Huhs
Graham A. Karklin
Gordon L. Levang
Robin M. Merrifield
Legal Counsel:
Norton Rose Fulbright
Calgary, AB, Canada

Borden Ladner Gervais LLP
1000 Canterra Tower 400 3rd Ave SW
Calgary, AB, T2P 4H2, Canada

Transfer Agent:
Olympia Trust Company
125 9th Avenue SE Suite 2300
Calgary, AB, T2G 0P6, Canada
Tel.: (403) 261-0900

ALHAMRANI GROUP

Aba Alkhail St
Jeddah, 21431, Saudi Arabia
Tel.: (966) 26065555
Fax: (966) 26060265
E-Mail: info@alhamrani.net
Web Site: www.alhamranigroup.com
Sales Range: $800-899.9 Million
Emp.: 3,000
Business Description:
Holding Company
S.I.C.: 6719
N.A.I.C.S.: 551112
Personnel:
Abdullah Ali Alhamrani *(Chm & CEO)*
Mezahem Basrawi *(Pres)*
Zafar Talpur *(Pres)*

Subsidiaries:

Alhamrani Company for Industry (1)
PO Box 5260
21422 Jeddah, Saudi Arabia (100%)
Tel.: (966) 26065555
Fax: (966) 26060265
Web Site: www.aci.alhamrani.net
Emp.: 12,000
Building Material Dealers
S.I.C.: 5211
N.A.I.C.S.: 444190
Ahmed Eissa *(Dir)*

Alhamrani Company For Investment In Trade Limited (1)
PO Box 7656
21452 Jeddah, Saudi Arabia (100%)
Tel.: (966) 26634204
Fax: (966) 26634530
E-Mail: Info@acit.com.sa
Web Site: www.acit.com.sa
Emp.: 600
Automobile & Motor Vehicle Whslr
S.I.C.: 5012
N.A.I.C.S.: 423110
Emad Abdurabo *(Pres)*

Alhamrani Industrial Group Ltd (1)
PO Box 7172
21462 Jeddah, Saudi Arabia (100%)
Tel.: (966) 26360390
Fax: (966) 26375172
Web Site: www.aig.alhamrani.net
Packaging Machinery Mfr
S.I.C.: 3565
N.A.I.C.S.: 333993

Alhamrani Real Estate Development Company (1)
Junction of Sari St Madinah Rd
PO Box 54736
21524 Jeddah, Saudi Arabia (100%)
Tel.: (966) 26978080
Fax: (966) 26978080
E-Mail: info@intertrade.com.sa
Web Site: www.intertrade.com.sa
Emp.: 60
Real Estate Property Lessors
S.I.C.: 6519
N.A.I.C.S.: 531190
Sheikh Khalid *(CEO)*

Alhamrani United Company (1)
PO Box 701
Madinah Rd, 21421 Jeddah, Saudi Arabia (100%)
Tel.: (966) 26696690
Fax: (966) 26674394
E-Mail: info@nissan.co.sa
Web Site: www.nissan.com.sa
Motor Vehicle Supplies & New Parts Whslr
S.I.C.: 5013
N.A.I.C.S.: 423120
Ibrahim Yassin *(CEO)*

Alhamrani Universal Company Ltd (1)
PO Box 1229
21431 Jeddah, Saudi Arabia (100%)
Tel.: (966) 26065555
Fax: (966) 26060265
E-Mail: info@universal.com.sa
Web Site: www.universal.com.sa
Investment Banking & Securities Dealing
S.I.C.: 6211
N.A.I.C.S.: 523110

Mohamed A. Alhamrani & Co Intertrade Co (Ltd) (1)
Jeddah Junction of Sari St
Madinah Rd, 21524 Jeddah, Saudi Arabia (100%)
Tel.: (966) 26978080
E-Mail: aitinfo@alhamrani.net
Web Site: www.alhamrani.net
Motor Vehicle Supplies & New Parts Whslr
S.I.C.: 5013
N.A.I.C.S.: 423120
Ahmed Dakhil *(CEO)*
Kiyad Baban *(COO)*

Joint Venture:

Alhamrani-Fuchs Petroleum Saudi Arabia Ltd. (1)
Tahlia St
PO Box 7103
Jeddah, 21462, Saudi Arabia
Tel.: (966) 26635666
Fax: (966) 26633702
E-Mail: info@fuchs.com.sa
Web Site: www.fuchs.com.sa
Sales Range: $75-99.9 Million
Emp.: 75
Mfr. of Lubricants
S.I.C.: 2992
N.A.I.C.S.: 324191
Zafar Talpur *(Pres)*

ALI ABDULLAH AL TAMIMI COMPANY

PO Box 172
Dammam, 31411, Saudi Arabia
Tel.: (966) 3 807 5700
Fax: (966) 3 847 1592
E-Mail: tamimi-ho@al-tamimi.com
Web Site: www.al-tamimi.com
Emp.: 9,000
Business Description:
Holding Company
S.I.C.: 6719
N.A.I.C.S.: 551112
Personnel:
Tariq A. Tamimi *(Pres)*

Subsidiary:

Tamimi Power and Industrial Group (1)
PO Box 172
Dammam, 31411, Saudi Arabia
Tel.: (966) 3 847 4050
Fax: (966) 3 847 1592
Web Site: www.tamimipowergroup.com
Industrial Support Services
S.I.C.: 1389
N.A.I.C.S.: 213112

Joint Venture:

Aquilex Arabia, Ltd. (2)
Jubail Road Dammam 2nd Industrial City
Al Khobar, 31952, Saudi Arabia
Tel.: (966) 3 8681037
Fax: (966) 3 8682733
Web Site: www.aquilexarabia.com
Machinery Maintenance, Repair & Overhaul Services
S.I.C.: 7699
N.A.I.C.S.: 811310
Amro Felimban *(Mng Dir)*

ALI & ABDUL KARIM GROUP LLC

Way No 5007 Bldg 687
Opp Savoy Hotel Apts Ghala,
Muscat, Oman
Mailing Address:
PO Box 793
112 Ruwi, Oman
Tel.: (968) 2200 4100
Fax: (968) 2200 4101
Web Site: www.aakgc.com
Business Description:
Holding Company
S.I.C.: 6719
N.A.I.C.S.: 551112
Personnel:
Ali Hassan Sulaiman *(Chm)*
Abdul Karim Hassan Sulaiman *(Mng Dir)*
Krishnan Mak *(CFO)*

Subsidiary:

AATCO LLC (1)
Falaj Al Qabail
PO Box 130
Sohar Industrial Estate, 322 Sohar, Oman OM
Tel.: (968) 2675 1591
E-Mail: aatcosmm@aakgc.com
Web Site: www.aakgc.com
Condiment Mfr & Distr
S.I.C.: 2035
N.A.I.C.S.: 311941
Ali Hassan Sulaiman *(Chm)*

ALI ASGHAR TEXTILE MILS LTD.

Room No 306 - 308 Uni Tower II
Chundrigar Road
Karachi, Pakistan
Tel.: (92) 2132416060
Fax: (92) 2132416063
E-Mail: aatml@cyber.net.pk
Web Site: www.aatml.com.pk
AATM—(KAR)
Rev.: $45,366
Assets: $4,736,781
Liabilities: $1,432,688
Net Worth: $3,304,092
Earnings: ($152,178)
Emp.: 23
Fiscal Year-end: 06/30/13
Business Description:
Cotton Yarn Mfr
S.I.C.: 2299
N.A.I.C.S.: 313110
Personnel:
Nadeem Ellahi Shaikh *(CEO)*
Muhammad Suleman *(CFO)*
Abdullah Moosa *(Sec)*
Board of Directors:
Raja Ghanzafar Ali
Marium Humayun
Mohammad Azad Khan
Sultan Mehmood
Abdullah Moosa
Nadeem Ellahi Shaikh
Muhammad Suleman

ALI BIN ALI ESTABLISHMENT

Airport Rd
PO Box 75
Ummguilena, Doha, 00974, Qatar
Tel.: (974) 44469888
Fax: (974) 44433778
Web Site: www.alibinali.com
Year Founded: 1945
Emp.: 1,500
Business Description:
Holding Company
S.I.C.: 6719
N.A.I.C.S.: 551112
Personnel:
Adel Ali Bin Ali *(Chm)*
Nabeel Ali Bin Ali *(Vice Chm & Exec VP)*
Peter D. McElwaine *(CEO)*
Isteeser Ahmed *(CFO)*
Mohamad A. Ebrik *(COO-Info & Comm Tech)*
Nabil Y. Chamas *(Grp Gen Counsel)*

Subsidiary:

Ali Bin Ali & Partners (1)
Opposite Gulf Cinema C Ring Road
PO Box 1993
Doha, Qatar

Tel.: (974) 489 5666 (ext 656)
Fax: (974) 488 6587
Web Site: www.alibinali.com
Emp.: 125
Grocery Distr
S.I.C.: 5141
N.A.I.C.S.: 424410
Wadih Kazan *(Gen Mgr)*

ALI CORPORATION

6/F 246 NeiHu Road Section 1
Taipei, 114, Taiwan
Tel.: (886) 2 8752 2000
Fax: (886) 2 8751 1001
E-Mail: ir@ali.com.tw
Web Site: www.ali.com.tw
Year Founded: 1993
3041—(TAI)
Rev.: $168,481,919
Assets: $227,316,637
Liabilities: $39,486,550
Net Worth: $187,830,087
Earnings: $25,332,898
Emp.: 639
Fiscal Year-end: 12/31/12

Business Description:
Integrated Circuit Chips Research & Development, Design, Testing, Mfr & Distr
S.I.C.: 3674
N.A.I.C.S.: 334413

Personnel:
Ben Lin *(Chm & CEO)*
Cindy Chang *(CFO)*
Daniel Hsueh-Wei Huang *(COO & CTO)*

Board of Directors:
Ben Lin
Tony Chang
Daniel Hsueh-Wei Huang
Frank Lin
Chung-Ping Liu
Shiou-Pyn Shen
Jack Qi Shu

Transfer Agent:
Chinatrust Bank
6F No 83 Sec 1 Chongcing South Rd
Taipei, 100, Taiwan
Tel.: (886) 2 2181 1911

Subsidiary:

ALi (Hsinchu) Corporation (1)
6F No 1 Jinshan 8th St
Hsin-chu, 300, Taiwan
Tel.: (886) 3 578 0589
Fax: (886) 3 577 8395
Web Site: www.ali.com.tw/index.php/contactmethod.html
Integrated Circuit Chips Research & Development, Design, Testing, Mfr & Distr
S.I.C.: 3674
N.A.I.C.S.: 334413

Non-U.S. Subsidiaries:

Abilis Systems Sarl (1)
3 chemin Pre Fleuri
Plan-les-Ouates, 1228 Geneva, Switzerland
Tel.: (41) 22 816 19 00
Fax: (41) 22 816 19 49
E-Mail: geninfo@abilis.com
Web Site: www.abilis.com
Emp.: 48
Electronic Component Mfr
S.I.C.: 3674
N.A.I.C.S.: 334413
Yves Mathys *(CEO)*
Alain Duret *(CTO)*

U.S. Subsidiary:

Abilis Systems LLC (2)
ASU Research Park Transamerica Bldg
7855 S River Pkwy Ste 116
Tempe, AZ 85284
Tel.: (480) 882-8639
Fax: (480) 491-0202
E-Mail: abilisusa@abilis.com
Web Site: www.abilis.com
Electronic Components Sales
S.I.C.: 5065
N.A.I.C.S.: 423690
Kiet Van Kuru *(Gen Mgr)*

ALi (China) Corporation (1)
9F W Plz IER Bldg N Area Shenzhen Hi tech Industrial Park
Shenzhen, Guangdong, 523000, China
Tel.: (86) 75525195788
Fax: (86) 75925195393
Integrated Circuit Chips Research & Development, Design, Testing, Mfr & Distr
S.I.C.: 3674
N.A.I.C.S.: 334413

ALi (Shanghai) Corporation (1)
6F-A Building 3 No 7 Guiqing Road
Shanghai, 200233, China
Tel.: (86) 21 6485 5058
Fax: (86) 21 6495 1498
Web Site: www.ali.com.tw/index.php/contactmethod.html
Integrated Circuit Chips Research & Development, Design, Testing, Mfr & Distr
S.I.C.: 3674
N.A.I.C.S.: 334413

ALi (Zhuhai) Corporation (1)
4F Building 3 No 1 Software Road
Tangjia, Zhuhai, Guangdong, China
Tel.: (86) 756 3392000
Fax: (86) 756 3392008
Web Site: www.ali.com.tw/index.php/contactmethod.html
Integrated Circuit Chips Research & Development, Design, Testing, Mfr & Distr
S.I.C.: 3674
N.A.I.C.S.: 334413

ALI S.P.A.

Via Gobetti 2A
Villa Fiorita, 20063 Cernusco sul Naviglio, Milan, Italy
Tel.: (39) 02921991
Fax: (39) 0292104370
E-Mail: info@aligroup.it
Web Site: www.aligroup.it
Year Founded: 1963
Sales Range: $800-899.9 Million
Emp.: 4,200

Business Description:
Designs, Manufactures, Supplies & Services Equipment for the Foodservice Industry
S.I.C.: 3556
N.A.I.C.S.: 333241

Personnel:
Luciano Berti *(Chm & CEO)*

U.S. Subsidiaries:

Aladdin Temp-Rite, LLC (1)
250 E Main St
Hendersonville, TN 37075 TN
Mailing Address: (100%)
PO Box 2978
Hendersonville, TN 37077-2978
Tel.: (615) 537-3600
Fax: (888) 812-9956
Toll Free: (800) 888-8018
Web Site: www.aladdintemprite.com
Emp.: 200
Mfr. of Insulated Food Service Systems for Hospitals, Correctional Facilities & Institutions
S.I.C.: 5047
N.A.I.C.S.: 423450
Jeff Burns *(CFO)*

Subsidiary:

Aladdin Temp-Rite Puerto Rico (2)
PO Box 19411
San Juan, PR 00910 (100%)
Tel.: (787) 788-5700
Fax: (787) 788-6155
Web Site: www.aladdintemprite.com
Emp.: 5
Providers of Food Service Solutions
S.I.C.: 5963
N.A.I.C.S.: 722330
Bruce Moore *(Gen Mgr)*

Non-U.S. Subsidiary:

Aladdin Temp-Rite Canada (2)
3701Lakeshore Blvd W
PO Box 48559
Toronto, ON, NAW 1P5, Canada (100%)
Tel.: (905) 562-9467
Fax: (905) 562-4618
E-Mail: service@aladdin.com
Web Site: www.aladdintemprite.com
Emp.: 10
Food Service Solutions
S.I.C.: 5963
N.A.I.C.S.: 722330
Heather Walsh Handy *(Dir-Sls)*

Scotsman Industries, Inc. (1)
775 Corporate Woods Pkwy
Vernon Hills, IL 60061 DE
Tel.: (847) 215-4500
Fax: (847) 913-9844
Toll Free: (800) 726-8762
E-Mail: sales@scotsman-ice.com
Web Site: www.scotsmanindustries.com
Emp.: 800
Holding Company; Commercial Ice-Making Equipment Mfr & Distr
S.I.C.: 6719
N.A.I.C.S.: 551112
Filippo Berti *(CEO)*
Christa Miller *(CFO)*

Groups:

Scotsman Group LLC (2)
775 Corporate Woods Pkwy
Vernon Hills, IL 60061-3112 DE
Tel.: (847) 215-4500
Fax: (847) 913-9844
Toll Free: (800) 726-8762
E-Mail: customer.service@scotsman-ice.com
Web Site: www.scotsman-ice.com
Emp.: 100
Commercial Ice-Making Equipment Mfr Import Export
S.I.C.: 3589
N.A.I.C.S.: 333318
Rich Gleitsmann *(Pres)*

Non-U.S. Subsidiaries:

Frimont, S.p.A. (3)
Via Puccini 22
20010 Bettolino di Pogliano, MI, Italy IT
Tel.: (39) 0293960208
Fax: (39) 0293960201
E-Mail: scotsman.europe@frimont.It
Web Site: www.frimont.it
Emp.: 250
Commercial Ice Machines & Refrigeration Systems Mfr
S.I.C.: 3589
N.A.I.C.S.: 333318
Emanuele Lanzani *(Mng Dir)*

Scotsman Ice Systems (Shanghai) Co., Ltd. (3)
Room 405-407 Jing An China Tower 1701 West Beijing Road
Shanghai, 200040, China
Tel.: (86) 21 61313200
Fax: (86) 21 61313330
E-Mail: scotsmansh@online.sh.cn
Web Site: www.scotsman-ice.com
Emp.: 20
Commercial Ice Making Equipment Mfr
S.I.C.: 3589
N.A.I.C.S.: 333318

Subsidiary:

Mile High Equipment LLC (2)
11100 E 45th Ave
Denver, CO 80239-3006 CO
Tel.: (303) 371-3737
Fax: (303) 371-6296
E-Mail: customer.service@iceomatic.com
Web Site: www.iceomatic.com
Emp.: 200
Commercial Ice-Making Equipment Mfr
S.I.C.: 3585
N.A.I.C.S.: 333415

Non-U.S. Subsidiary:

CastelMAC, S.p.A. (2)
Via del Lavoro 9
31033 Castelfranco Veneto, Treviso, Italy
Tel.: (39) 0423 738311
Fax: (39) 0423 722811
E-Mail: info@castelmac.it
Web Site: www.castelmac.it
Emp.: 140
Commercial Ice Machines & Refrigeration Systems Mfr
S.I.C.: 3585
N.A.I.C.S.: 333415
Emanuele Lanzani *(Mng Dir)*
Sabio Dotto *(CFO)*

Non-U.S. Subsidiaries:

The AFE Group Ltd. (1)
Bryggen Road
North Lynn Industrial Estate, King's Lynn, Norfolk, PE30 2HZ, United Kingdom UK
Tel.: (44) 1553817554 (100%)
Fax: (44) 1553817111
E-Mail: info@theafegroup.com
Web Site: www.theafegroup.com
Sales Range: $500-549.9 Million
Emp.: 250
Holding Company; Commercial Cooking Equipment Mfr
S.I.C.: 6719
N.A.I.C.S.: 551112
Tim Smith *(CEO)*

Division:

Williams Refrigeration Ltd. (2)
Bryggen Road
North Lynn Industrial Estate, King's Lynn, PE30 2HZ, United Kingdom UK
Tel.: (44) 1553817000 (100%)
Fax: (44) 1553817111
Web Site: www.williams-refrigeration.com
Emp.: 200
Commercial Refrigeration Equipment Mfr & Distr
S.I.C.: 3585
N.A.I.C.S.: 333415

Non-U.S. Subsidiary:

Williams Refrigeration Australia Pty. Ltd. (3)
38-42 Gaine Road
Dandenong, VIC, 3175, Australia AU
Tel.: (61) 397994900 (100%)
Fax: (61) 387874787
Web Site: www.williamsref.com.au
Emp.: 50
Commercial Refrigeration Equipment Mfr & Distr
S.I.C.: 3585
N.A.I.C.S.: 333415
Brag Dunn *(Mng Dir)*

Subsidiaries:

Falcon Foodservice Equipment (2)
Wallace View Hillfoots Rd
Stirling, FK9 5PY, United Kingdom (100%)
Tel.: (44) 1786455200
Fax: (44) 1786469454
E-Mail: info@falconfoodservice.com
Web Site: www.falconfoodservice.com
Emp.: 300
Commercial Cooking Ranges, Grills, Steamers, Fryers & Kettles Mfr & Distr
S.I.C.: 3589
N.A.I.C.S.: 333318
Lawrence Hughes *(Dir-Sls & Mktg-UK)*

Miller's Vanguard Ltd. (2)
1 Chesham Fold Rd
Bury, Lancs, BL9 6LE, United Kingdom UK
Tel.: (44) 1617647374 (100%)
Fax: (44) 1617615141
E-Mail: info@millersvanguard.co.uk
Web Site: www.millersvanguard.co.uk
Emp.: 250
Commercial Foodservice Equipment Maintenance & Repair Services
S.I.C.: 7699
N.A.I.C.S.: 811412
Andrew Jones *(Mng Dir)*

Mono Equipment Ltd. (2)
Queensway
Swansea West Industrial Pk, Swansea, SA5 4EB, United Kingdom UK
Tel.: (44) 1792561234 (100%)
Fax: (44) 1792561016
Web Site: www.monoequip.com
Emp.: 120
Commercial Modular, Convection, Rack & Deck Ovens & Dough Handling Equipment Mfr & Distr
S.I.C.: 3589
N.A.I.C.S.: 333318
Andrew Jones *(Mng Dir)*

Ali S.p.A.—(Continued)

Serviceline (2)
Maxwell Road
Stevenage, Herts, SG1 2DW, United Kingdom (100%)
Tel.: (44) 1438363000
Fax: (44) 1438363063
E-Mail: servicedesk@service-line.co.uk
Web Site: www.service-line.co.uk
Emp.: 80
Commercial Foodservice Equipment Maintenance Services
S.I.C.: 7699
N.A.I.C.S.: 811412
Steve Elliott *(Mng Dir)*

U.S. Subsidiaries:

ACP Inc. (2)
225 49th Ave Dr SW
Cedar Rapids, IA 52404
Tel.: (319) 368-8120
Fax: (319) 368-8198
Toll Free: (800) 233-2366
Web Site: www.acpsolutions.com
Emp.: 100
Commercial Microwave & Accelerated Cooking Ovens Mfr & Distr
S.I.C.: 3589
N.A.I.C.S.: 333318
Tim K. Garbett *(Pres)*

Belshaw Brothers, Inc. (2)
814 44th St NW Ste 103
Auburn, WA 98001 DE
Tel.: (206) 322-5474 (100%)
Fax: (206) 322-5425
Toll Free: (800) 578-2547
E-Mail: info@belshaw.com
Web Site: www.belshaw.com
Emp.: 100
Commercial & Industrial Bakery & Donut Production Equipment Mfr
Export
S.I.C.: 3556
N.A.I.C.S.: 333241
Roger A. Faw *(Pres)*

Victory Refrigeration Company LLC (2)
110 Woodcrest Rd
Cherry Hill, NJ 08003-3648 DE
Tel.: (856) 428-4200 (100%)
Fax: (856) 428-7299
E-Mail: info@victoryrefrigeration.com
Web Site: www.victoryrefrigeration.com
Sales Range: $25-49.9 Million
Emp.: 150
Commercial Refrigerators, Freezers & Other Foodservice Equipment Mfr
Import Export
S.I.C.: 3585
N.A.I.C.S.: 333415
Jim Kehoe *(Dir-Engrg)*

Non-U.S. Subsidiaries:

Bongard S.A. (2)
32 Route de Wolfisheim
F-67810 Holtzheim, France FR
Tel.: (33) 388780023 (100%)
Telex: 890.321F
Fax: (33) 388761918
E-Mail: bongard@bongard.fr
Web Site: www.bongard.fr
Sales Range: $125-149.9 Million
Emp.: 500
Commercial Bakery Equipment Mfr
S.I.C.: 3556
N.A.I.C.S.: 333241
Didier Peronne *(Mng Dir & Dir-Fin)*

Eloma GmbH (2)
Otto-Hahn-Strasse 10
D-82216 Maisach, Bavaria, Germany De
Tel.: (49) 81413950 (100%)
Fax: (49) 8141395130
E-Mail: info@eloma.com
Web Site: www.eloma.com
Emp.: 350
Commercial Combi-Steamer & Baking Oven Mfr & Distr
S.I.C.: 3589
N.A.I.C.S.: 333318
Stephan Wendler *(CEO)*

Esmach S.p.A. (2)
Via Vittorio Veneto 143
Grisignano di Zocco, Vicenza, Italy IT
Tel.: (39) 0444419777 (100%)
Fax: (39) 0444419708
E-Mail: esmach@esmach.it
Web Site: www.esmach.it
Commercial Cooking Mixers, Dividers & Proofing Cabinets Mfr & Distr
S.I.C.: 3589
N.A.I.C.S.: 333318

Pavailler S.A.S. (2)
Rue Benoit Frachon
BP 54
F-26802 Portes-les-Valence, France FR
Tel.: (33) 475575500
Fax: (33) 475572319
E-Mail: pavailler@pavailler.com
Web Site: www.pavailler.com
Emp.: 100
Commercial Bakery Equipment Mfr
S.I.C.: 3556
N.A.I.C.S.: 333241
Guy Le Blond *(Mng Dir)*

Rosinox SAS (1)
23 Rue Felix Chedin
18020 Bourges, France (100%)
Tel.: (33) 248702828
Fax: (33) 248708426
E-Mail: rosinox@rosinox.com
Web Site: www.rosinox.com
Emp.: 120
S.I.C.: 3639
N.A.I.C.S.: 335228

ALI ZAID AL-QURAISHI & BROTHERS CO.

PO Box 1848
Riyadh, 11441, Saudi Arabia
Tel.: (966) 14771618
Fax: (966) 14786947
E-Mail: azaqriy@alquraishi.com
Web Site: www.alquraishi.com
Year Founded: 1958
Emp.: 970

Business Description:
Marketer & Distr. of Leisure Goods, Cigarettes, Toiletries, Office Furniture & Equipment, Motor Vehicles, Telecommunications & Electronics
S.I.C.: 2131
N.A.I.C.S.: 312230

Personnel:
Abdulaziz Al-Quraishi *(Mng Dir)*

Subsidiaries:

Al Quraishi Electric Services of Saudi Arabia (1)
PO Box 7386
Dammam, 31462, Saudi Arabia
Tel.: (966) 38572537
Fax: (966) 38572541
Web Site: www.aqesa.com
Electrical Apparatus & Materials
S.I.C.: 5063
N.A.I.C.S.: 423610

Al Quraishi Furniture Corp. (1)
PO Box 1848
Riyadh, 11441, Saudi Arabia
Tel.: (966) 1 477-5335
Fax: (966) 1 478-7811
Importation, Selling & Installation of Westinghouse Furniture
S.I.C.: 2521
N.A.I.C.S.: 337211

Al Quraishi Leisure Services (1)
PO Box 1796
Jeddah, Saudi Arabia
Tel.: (966) 26970779
Fax: (966) 26972938
E-Mail: Aqis@alquraishi.com
Emp.: 100
Markets & Distributes Consumer Goods, Recreational Products & Toys
S.I.C.: 5092
N.A.I.C.S.: 423920
Maher Elobeid *(CEO)*

Al Quraishi Marketing Co. Ltd. (1)
PO Box 50995
Jeddah, 21533, Saudi Arabia
Tel.: (966) 26700053
Fax: (966) 26720676
Marketing for Household Products & Cleaners
S.I.C.: 7217
N.A.I.C.S.: 561740

Al Quraishi Services (1)
PO Box 7121
Jeddah, 21462, Saudi Arabia
Tel.: (966) 26700053
Fax: (966) 26171168
E-Mail: aqis@alquraishi.com
Sells & Distributes Tobacco Products
S.I.C.: 2131
N.A.I.C.S.: 312230

Al Sabah Trading & Contracting Inc. (1)
PO Box 11793
Jeddah, 21463, Saudi Arabia
Tel.: (966) 26434175
Fax: (966) 26440593
Trading Company
S.I.C.: 1542
N.A.I.C.S.: 236220

Integrated Systems Co. Ltd. (1)
Al-Hamra District
Jeddah, KSA, Saudi Arabia
Tel.: (966) 26650836
Fax: (966) 2 6650836
Web Site: www.isystems-sa.com
Computer Programming
S.I.C.: 7371
N.A.I.C.S.: 541511

Teamwork Saudi Arabia Ltd. (1)
POBox 10747
Riyadh, Saudi Arabia
Tel.: (966) 14771519
Fax: (966) 14785634
E-Mail: sultan@nascoltd.com
Construction Company
S.I.C.: 1541
N.A.I.C.S.: 236210

Waha Electric Supply Company of Saudi Arabia (1)
First Industrial City of Damman
PO Box 2389
Dammam, 31451, Saudi Arabia
Tel.: (966) 38474242
Fax: (966) 38471684
Web Site: www.wescosa.com
Produces High Voltage Oil-Insulated & Low Voltage Dry-Type Transformers
S.I.C.: 3676
N.A.I.C.S.: 334416

ALIANSCE SHOPPING CENTERS SA

Rua Dias Ferreira, 190 / 3rd Floor
Leblon, Rio de Janeiro, Brazil
Tel.: (55) 2121767272
Fax: (55) 2121767229
E-Mail: ri@aliansce.com.br
Web Site: www.aliansce.com.br
ALSC3—(BRAZ)
Rev.: $165,666,093
Assets: $1,938,373,707
Liabilities: $1,020,781,441
Net Worth: $917,592,265
Earnings: $64,516,784
Emp.: 164
Fiscal Year-end: 12/31/12

Business Description:
Shopping Center Management Services
S.I.C.: 6531
N.A.I.C.S.: 531312

Personnel:
Renato Feitosa Rique *(Chm, Pres, CEO & Member-Exec Bd)*
Renato Ribeiro de Andrade Botelho *(CFO & Member-Exec Bd)*
Delcio Mendes *(COO & Member-Exec Bd)*
Paula Guimaraes Fonseca *(Chief Admin Officer & Member-Exec Bd)*
Henrique C. Cordeiro Guerra Neto *(IR Officer & Member-Exec Bd)*
Ewerton Espinola Visco *(Member-Exec Bd)*

Board of Directors:
Renato Feitosa Rique
Shoaib Z. Khan
Carlos Geraldo Langoni
Sandeep Lakhmi Mathrani
Carlos Alberto Vieira

ALIAXIS S.A./N.V.

Avenue de Tervuren 270
B-1150 Brussels, Brabant, Belgium
Tel.: (32) 27755050
Fax: (32) 27755051
E-Mail: info@aliaxis.com
Web Site: www.aliaxis.com
Rev.: $3,199,827,244
Assets: $3,160,362,924
Liabilities: $1,261,392,252
Net Worth: $1,898,970,672
Earnings: $160,615,581
Emp.: 14,233
Fiscal Year-end: 12/31/12

Business Description:
Plastic Plumbing Products for Construction, Industrial & Public Utilities Applications Mfr
S.I.C.: 3088
N.A.I.C.S.: 326191

Personnel:
Olivier van der Rest *(Chm)*
Yves Mertens *(CEO)*
Colin Leach *(COO)*
Hubert Dubout *(Sec)*

Board of Directors:
Olivier van der Rest
Bruno Emsens
Francis Durman Esquivel
Andrea Hatschek
Frank H. Lakerveld
Jean-Lucien Lamy
Yves Mertens
Kieran Murphy
Yves Noiret
Henri Thijssen
Helene van Zeebroeck
Philippe Voortman

Subsidiary:

Nicoll Belgium S.A. (1)
Parc Indus Des Hauts Sarts
1st Ave 106, Herstal, Belgium (70%)
Tel.: (32) 42488940
Fax: (32) 42480654
E-Mail: info@nicoll.be
Web Site: www.nicoll.be
Emp.: 16
Sanitary; Soil & Waste Removal
S.I.C.: 4959
N.A.I.C.S.: 562998
Gozes Engelen *(Mng Dir)*

Non-U.S. Subsidiaries:

Abu-Plast GmbH (1)
Am Bahnhof 20
96472 Rodental, Germany (100%)
Tel.: (49) 956393210
Fax: (49) 956393231
E-Mail: info@abu.de
Web Site: www.abu.de
Emp.: 150
Sanitary
S.I.C.: 2676
N.A.I.C.S.: 322291
Raimund Au *(Mng Dir)*

Akatherm International B.V. (1)
Undustrieterrein 11
5981 Panningen, Netherlands (100%)
Tel.: (31) 773088650
Fax: (31) 773075232
E-Mail: info@akatherm.nl
Web Site: www.akatherm.nl
Emp.: 75
Sewage & Surface Drainage Provider
S.I.C.: 4952
N.A.I.C.S.: 221320
Mark Amkreutz *(Mng Dir)*

Non-U.S. Subsidiaries:

Akatherm FIP GmbH (2)
Steinzeugstrasse 50
68229 Mannheim, Germany (100%)
Tel.: (49) 6214862901
Fax: (49) 6214862925

E-Mail: info@akatherm-sip.de
Web Site: www.akatherm-fip.de
Emp.: 70
Sewage & Surface Drainage Provider
S.I.C.: 4952
N.A.I.C.S.: 221320
Corrado Mazzacano *(Mng Dir)*

Akatherm N.V. **(2)**
Schoonmansvxld 52
2870 Puurs, Belgium (100%)
Tel.: (32) 38206900
Fax: (32) 38600199
E-Mail: info@akatherm.be
Web Site: www.vigotecakatherm.be
Emp.: 47
Sewage & Surface Drainage Provider
S.I.C.: 4952
N.A.I.C.S.: 221320
Guy Cauwels *(Mgr-Dev)*

Aliaxis Services S.A. **(1)**
1 Rue de l'Amandier
BP 65
78540 Vernouillet, France
Tel.: (33) 139796000
Fax: (33) 139717465
E-Mail: info@aliaxis.com
Web Site: www.aliaxis.com
Injected Plastic Building Materials Mfr
S.I.C.: 3089
N.A.I.C.S.: 326199

Aliaxis **(1)**
Viate Del Lavoro 21-25
Zona Ind Loc Ponte, Vicenza, 36020, Italy (100%)
Tel.: (39) 0444795276
Fax: (39) 0444795289
Emp.: 60
Soil & Waste Removal
S.I.C.: 4212
N.A.I.C.S.: 562119

Arnomij B.V. **(1)**
Delfweg 48
2211 Noordwijkerhout, Netherlands (100%)
Tel.: (31) 252416950
Fax: (31) 252419258
E-Mail: info@arnomij.nl
Web Site: www.arnomij.nl
Emp.: 20
Sewage & Surface Drainage Provider
S.I.C.: 4952
N.A.I.C.S.: 221320
Srad Nijpjas *(Mng Dir)*

Astore Valves & Fittings S.r.l. **(1)**
Via Tangoni 26 Casarzra Ligure
16030 Genoa, Italy
Tel.: (39) 0185470811
Fax: (39) 0185466894
E-Mail: astore@astore.it
Web Site: www.astore.it
Emp.: 43
Plastic Pipes & Plumbing Fixtures
S.I.C.: 3088
N.A.I.C.S.: 326191
Andrea Bisio *(Mng Dir)*

Canplas Industries Ltd. **(1)**
31 Patterson Rd
Barrie, ON, L4N 3V9, Canada (100%)
Mailing Address:
P.O. Box 1800
Barrie, ON, L4M 4V3, Canada
Tel.: (705) 726-3361
Fax: (705) 726-8991
Web Site: www.canplas.com
Emp.: 270
Mfr. of Plastic Fittings
S.I.C.: 3084
N.A.I.C.S.: 326122
Jeff Bayley *(Pres & CEO)*

Dalpex S.p.a. **(1)**
Via della Fiera 13 15
57021 Venturina, Italy
Tel.: (39) 0565 856 611
Fax: (39) 0565 856 666
E-Mail: dalpex.li@dalpex.com
Web Site: www.dalpex.com
Emp.: 120
Water Supply System Solutions
S.I.C.: 4941
N.A.I.C.S.: 221310

Friatec AG **(1)**
Aktiengesellschaft
PO Box 710261
Steinzeugstrasse, D 68229 Mannheim, Germany (100%)
Tel.: (49) 6214860
Fax: (49) 6214861279
E-Mail: info@friatec.de
Web Site: www.friatec.de
Emp.: 1,200
Pipe Systems Products for Water, Gas & Industrial Applications Including Pumps & Valves
S.I.C.: 4619
N.A.I.C.S.: 486990
Hugo K. Fluhr *(Chm-Supervisory Bd)*
Klaus Wolf *(Mng Dir)*
Colin Leach *(COO)*

Divisions:

Friatec Ag-Ceramics Division **(2)**
Steinzeugstrasse
68229 Mannheim, Germany (100%)
Tel.: (49) 6214861339
Fax: (49) 621477999
E-Mail: klaus.wolfe@friatec.de
Web Site: www.friatec.de
Pipe Systems Products for Water, Gas & Industrial Applications Including Pumps & Valves
S.I.C.: 4619
N.A.I.C.S.: 486990
Klaus Wolfe *(Gen Mgr)*

Friatec Ag-Technical Plastics Division **(2)**
Sterinzeugstrasse 50
68229 Mannheim, Germany (100%)
Tel.: (49) 6214861447
Fax: (49) 621479196
E-Mail: info@friatec.de
Web Site: www.friatec.de
Emp.: 800
Pipe Systems Products for Water, Gas & Industrial Applications Including Pumps & Valves
S.I.C.: 4619
N.A.I.C.S.: 486990
Klaus Wolf *(Mng Dir)*

Friatec Building Services **(2)**
Steinzeugstrasse
68229 Mannheim, Germany
Tel.: (49) 6214860
Fax: (49) 621 486 1599
Web Site: www.friatec.de/
Pipe Systems Products for Water, Gas & Industrial Applications Including Pumps & Valves
S.I.C.: 4619
N.A.I.C.S.: 486990

Subsidiary:

Sed Flow Control GmbH **(2)**
Raiffeisenstrasse 10A
74906 Bad Rappenau, Germany
Tel.: (49) 72649210
Fax: (49) 726492121
E-Mail: info@sed-flowcontrol.com
Web Site: www.sed-flowcontrol.com
Emp.: 65
Pipe Systems Products for Water, Gas & Industrial Applications
S.I.C.: 4619
N.A.I.C.S.: 486990
Michael Wittmann *(Mng Dir)*

Non-U.S. Subsidiaries:

Friatec DPL **(2)**
ZA La Grande Borne
Nemours, 77793, France (100%)
Tel.: (33) 164452364
Fax: (33) 164452360
E-Mail: firatecdpl@glennweb.fr
Web Site: www.firatecdpl.com
Emp.: 17
Pipe Systems Products for Water, Gas & Industrial Applications Including Pumps & Valves
S.I.C.: 4619
N.A.I.C.S.: 486990
Seille Jacques *(Mgr)*

Friatec Rheinhutte **(2)**
Pumps & Valves Factory Av Manoel Inacio Peixoto
2150 Sao Paulo, 36771-000, Brazil
Tel.: (55) 32 639 462 07
Fax: (55) 32 369 462 39
Pipe Systems Products for Water, Gas & Industrial Applications Including Pumps & Valves
S.I.C.: 4619
N.A.I.C.S.: 486990

Friatec SARL **(2)**
Route De Montereau
BP 83
Nemours, 77793, France (100%)
Tel.: (33) 164452302
Fax: (33) 164452310
Web Site: www.aliaxis.com
Emp.: 29
Pipe Systems Products for Water, Gas & Industrial Applications Including Pumps & Valves
S.I.C.: 3498
N.A.I.C.S.: 332996

Gie ETEX Plastics Gestion **(1)**
3 Rue De lAmandier
BP 65
78540 Vernouillet, France (100%)
Tel.: (33) 39796060
Telex: 695213 ETEX
Fax: (33) 1 3979 6223
Emp.: 5,800
S.I.C.: 7389
N.A.I.C.S.: 425110

Girpi S.A. **(1)**
Rue Robert Ancel
P O Box 36
76700 Harfleur, France FR
Tel.: (33) 232796000 (100%)
Telex: 699920
Fax: (33) 232796028
E-Mail: contact@girpi.fr
Web Site: www.girpi.fr
Emp.: 200
Injection of Plastic Fittings & Accessories
S.I.C.: 3089
N.A.I.C.S.: 326199
Gilles Heynard *(Gen Mgr)*

Glynwed Pipe Systems Ltd. **(1)**
St Peters Rd
ppe29
PE29 7DA Huntington, United Kingdom UK
Tel.: (44) 148052121 (100%)
Fax: (44) 1480458829
E-Mail: enquiries@glynwed.com
Web Site: www.glynwedpipesystems-uk.com
Emp.: 350
Thermoplastic Pipes, Valves, Fittings, Metal Couplings & Rubber Components for Pipe Lines & Systems Mfr & Distr
S.I.C.: 3494
N.A.I.C.S.: 332919
Dom West *(Dir-Sls)*

U.S. Subsidiary:

Harrington Industrial Plastics Inc. **(2)**
14480 Yorba Ave
Chino, CA 91710 DE
Tel.: (909) 597-8641 (100%)
Fax: (909) 597-9940
Web Site: www.hipco.com
Emp.: 80
Industrial Plastic Pipe Systems, Fittings, Valves, Fiberglass Fans & Air Washers Mfr
S.I.C.: 3498
N.A.I.C.S.: 332996

Non-U.S. Subsidiaries:

Glynwed A/S **(2)**
Sandvadsvej 1
4600 Koge, Denmark DK
Tel.: (45) 46772575 (100%)
Fax: (45) 46755430
E-Mail: info@glynwed.dk
Web Site: www.glynwed.dk
Thermoplastic Pipes, Valves, Fittings, Metal Couplings & Rubber Components for Pipe Lines & Systems Mfr
S.I.C.: 3498
N.A.I.C.S.: 332996
Frederik von Sterneck *(Mng Dir-Scandinavia)*

Glynwed AB **(2)**
Stormbyvagen 6
163 55 Spanga, Sweden SE
Tel.: (46) 84466910 (100%)
Fax: (46) 84466911
Web Site: www.glynwed-se.com
Emp.: 15
Thermoplastic Pipes, Valves, Fittings, Metal Couplings & Rubber Components for Pipe Lines & Systems Mfr
S.I.C.: 3498
N.A.I.C.S.: 332996
Michael Raak *(Area Mgr-Sls)*

Glynwed AG **(2)**
Straubstrasse 13
7323 Neuhausen, Switzerland CH
Tel.: (41) 817254170 (100%)
Fax: (41) 817254101
E-Mail: info@glynwed-ch.ch
Web Site: www.glynwed.ch.ch
Emp.: 60
Thermoplastic Pipes, Valves, Fittings, Metal Couplings & Rubber Components for Pipe Lines & Systems Mfr
S.I.C.: 3498
N.A.I.C.S.: 332996
Marshall Beer *(Mng Dir)*

Glynwed B.V. **(2)**
Steenpad 5
4797 SG Willemstad, Curacao NL
Mailing Address: (100%)
PO Box 53
4797 ZH Willemstad, Curacao
Tel.: (599) 168473651
Fax: (599) 168473200
E-Mail: info@glynwed.nl
Web Site: www.glynwed.nl
Thermoplastic Pipes, Valves, Fittings, Metal Couplings & Rubber Components for Pipe Lines & Systems Mfr
S.I.C.: 3498
N.A.I.C.S.: 332996
Fred Nijpjes *(Mng Dir)*

Glynwed GmbH **(2)**
Birostrasse 13
1230 Vienna, Austria AT
Tel.: (43) 1610570 (100%)
Fax: (43) 161057105
E-Mail: info@glynwed.at
Web Site: www.glynwed.at
Emp.: 25
Thermoplastic Pipes, Valves, Fittings, Metal Couplings & Rubber Components for Pipe Lines & Systems Mfr
S.I.C.: 3498
N.A.I.C.S.: 332996
Reinhold Mayer *(Mng Dir)*

Glynwed N.V. **(2)**
Industriezone Blauwesteen
Heiveldekens 20, 2550 Kontich, Belgium BE
Tel.: (32) 34582400 (100%)
Fax: (32) 34582641
E-Mail: info@glynwed.be
Web Site: www.glynwed.be
Emp.: 17
Thermoplastic Pipes, Valves, Fittings, Metal Couplings & Rubber Components for Pipe Lines & Systems Mfr
S.I.C.: 3498
N.A.I.C.S.: 332996
Helsen Jennis *(Mgr-Svcs)*

Glynwed S.A.S. **(2)**
ZAE Route de Beziers
34140 Meze, France FR
Tel.: (33) 467516330 (100%)
Fax: (33) 467436143
E-Mail: glynwed@glynwed.fr
Web Site: www.glynwed.fr
Thermoplastic Pipes, Valves, Fittings, Metal Couplings & Rubber Components for Pipe Lines & Systems Mfr
S.I.C.: 3498
N.A.I.C.S.: 332996
Raoul Voisinoit *(Mng Dir)*

Glynwed Srl **(2)**
Via Aldo Moro 12 12a
20080 Milan, Carpiano, Italy IT
Tel.: (39) 029850901 (100%)
Fax: (39) 0298859033
E-Mail: info@glynwed.it
Web Site: www.glynwed.it
Emp.: 25
Thermoplastic Pipes, Valves, Fittings, Metal Couplings & Rubber Components for Pipe Lines & Systems Mfr
S.I.C.: 3498
N.A.I.C.S.: 332996

Glynwed s.r.o. **(2)**
Nitrianska 18
SK 917 01 Trnava, Czech Republic CZ
Tel.: (420) 33 5514 626 (100%)

Aliaxis S.A./N.V.—(Continued)

Fax: (420) 33 513 307
E-Mail: glynwed@glynwed.sk
Web Site: www.glynwed.sk
Thermoplastic Pipes, Valves, Fittings, Metal Couplings & Rubber Components for Pipe Lines & Systems Mfr
S.I.C.: 3498
N.A.I.C.S.: 332996
Dusan Prielozny *(Mgr)*

GPS Asia Pte. Ltd. (2)
12 Changi North Way 03-04
Singapore, 498791, Singapore SG
Tel.: (65) 62869555 (100%)
Fax: (65) 62819555
E-Mail: sales@glynwedasia.com.sg
Web Site: www.glynwedasia.com
Emp.: 21
Thermoplastic Pipes, Valves, Fittings, Metal Couplings & Rubber Components for Pipe Lines & Systems Mfr
S.I.C.: 3498
N.A.I.C.S.: 332996
B. J. Shahril *(Mng Dir)*

GPS Iberica S.L. (2)
Ctra N 152 Km-14 9 Pol Ind
Sta Perpetua De Magoda, 08130
Barcelona, Spain ES
Tel.: (34) 935449240 (100%)
Fax: (34) 935449241
E-Mail: glynwed@glynwed.es
Web Site: www.glynwed.es
Emp.: 27
Thermoplastic Pipes, Valves, Fittings, Metal Couplings & Rubber Components for Pipe Lines & Systems Mfr
S.I.C.: 3498
N.A.I.C.S.: 332996

Rhine Ruhr Pumps & Valves (Pty.) Ltd. (2)
354 Angus Cresen Northlands Bussiness Park
New Market Road
Northriding, 2163 Randburg, South Africa ZA
Mailing Address: (90%)
PO Box 2376
Sundowner 2161, Johannesburg, South Africa
Tel.: (27) 117965075
Fax: (27) 866813129
E-Mail: info@rrpumps.co.za
Web Site: www.rrpumps.co.za
Emp.: 15
Thermoplastic Pipes, Valves, Fittings, Metal Couplings & Rubber Components Mfr & Distr for Pipe Lines & Systems
S.I.C.: 3494
N.A.I.C.S.: 332919
Morey Walters *(Mng Dir)*

Hunter Plastics Ltd. (1)
Nathan Way W Thamesmead Bus Pk
London, SE28 OAE, United Kingdom UK
Tel.: (44) 2088559851 (100%)
Telex: 25770
Fax: (44) 2083162319
Web Site: www.hunterplastics.co.uk
Emp.: 30
Drainage Solution Services
S.I.C.: 7389
N.A.I.C.S.: 425110
Steve Dunkley *(Dir-Sls & Mktg)*

Innoage PEI S.a.m. (1)
Immeubie Les Industries
2 Rue Du Gabian, 98007 Monaco, Cedex, 289, Monaco
Tel.: (377) 92055000
Fax: (377) 92055090
Web Site: www.innoage.com
Public Utilities
S.I.C.: 9631
N.A.I.C.S.: 926130
Michel Solliet *(Mng Dir)*

IPEX, Inc. (1)
50 Valleybrook Dr
Toronto, ON, M3B 2S9, Canada (100%)
Tel.: (416) 445-3400
Fax: (416) 445-4461
Web Site: www.ipexinc.com
Emp.: 31
Mfr. of Plastic Pipes & Fittings
S.I.C.: 3084
N.A.I.C.S.: 326122
Curtis Wenzlaff *(Chm)*
Art Wenzlaff *(Pres & CEO)*

U.S. Subsidiary:

IPEX USA Manufacturing/Distribution (2)
10100 Rodney St
Pineville, NC 28134-7538 (100%)
Tel.: (704) 889-2431
Fax: (704) 889-2390
Toll Free: (800) 463-9572
Web Site: www.ipexamerica.com
Emp.: 175
Thermoplastic Piping Systems Mfr
S.I.C.: 3089
N.A.I.C.S.: 326122
Bill Hawke *(Mgr-Mktg)*

Jimten S.A. (1)
Carretera De Ocana 125
03114 Alicante, Spain
Tel.: (34) 965109044
Fax: (34) 965115082
E-Mail: comercial@jimten.com
Web Site: www.jimten.com
Emp.: 18
Mfr of Soil & Waste, Rain Gutter Systems, Utilities, Hot & Cold Water, Industry, Sanitary, Sewage, Ventilation, Irrigation, Floor Drainage Plastic Products
S.I.C.: 0711
N.A.I.C.S.: 115112

Marley Alutec Ltd. (1)
Unit 1 G-H Hudson Road
Elms Farm Industrial Estate, Bedford, MK41 0LZ, United Kingdom (100%)
Tel.: (44) 1234 359438
Fax: (44) 1234 357199
E-Mail: marketing@marleyext.com
Web Site: www.marleyalutec.co.uk
Emp.: 75
Mfr of Roofing Tiles, Blocks, Floor Coverings, Plastic Rainwater Gutters, Underground Drainage Pipe Products, Plastic Moldings & Ventilation Equipment
S.I.C.: 3255
N.A.I.C.S.: 327120

Marley Deutschland GmbH (1)
Postfach 11 40
31513 Wunstorf, Germany (100%)
Tel.: (49) 5031530
Fax: (49) 503153271
E-Mail: info@marley.de
Web Site: www.marley.de
Emp.: 400
Mfr. of Roof Tiles, Blocks, Floor Coverings, Plastic Rainwater Guttering, Pipes Underground Drainage Products, Plastic Moldings & Ventilation Equipment
S.I.C.: 3255
N.A.I.C.S.: 327120
Houdo Heinemann *(Mng Dir)*

Marley Magyarorszag Rt (1)
Palanki Ut 6
7100 Szekszard, Hungary (100%)
Tel.: (36) 74529800
Fax: (36) 74529810
E-Mail: info@marley.hu
Web Site: www.marley.hu
Sales Range: Less than $1 Million
Emp.: 95
Mfr. of Roof Tiles, Blocks, Floor Coverings, Plastic Rainwater Guttering, Pipes Underground Drainage Products, Plastic Moldings & Ventilation Equipment
S.I.C.: 3255
N.A.I.C.S.: 327120
Peter Polgar *(Dir-Fin)*

Marley New Zealand (1)
32 Mahia Rd
Private Bag 802
Manureva, 2243 Auckland, New Zealand (100%)
Tel.: (64) 92792799
Fax: (64) 9272798
E-Mail: donm@marley.co.nz
Web Site: www.marley.co.nz
Sls.: $7,062,850
Emp.: 317
Mfr. of Roof Tiles, Blocks, Floor Coverings, Plastic Rainwater Guttering, Pipes Underground Drainage Products, Plastic Moldings & Ventilation Equipment
S.I.C.: 3259
N.A.I.C.S.: 327120
Don Mckanzie *(Mng Dir)*

Marley Pipe Systems Pty Ltd (1)
1 Bickley Road Pretoriusstad
1491 Nigel, South Africa (100%)
Tel.: (27) 0117398600
Fax: (27) 0117398680
E-Mail: marketing@marleyps.co.za
Web Site: www.marleypipesystems.co.za
Emp.: 500
Mfr. of Roof Tiles, Blocks, Floor Coverings, Plastic Rainwater Guttering, Pipes Underground Drainage Products, Plastic Moldings & Ventilation Equipment
S.I.C.: 3255
N.A.I.C.S.: 327120
Danie Grobbeler *(Gen Mgr)*

Marley Polska Sp. z.o.o. (1)
Ul Postepu 12 Wjazd Od Ulicy Marynarskie 15
02 676 Warsaw, Poland (100%)
Tel.: (48) 228432131
Fax: (48) 228437968
E-Mail: marley@marley.com.pl
Web Site: www.marley.com.pl
Sales Range: $10-24.9 Million
Emp.: 50
Mfr. of Roof Tiles, Blocks, Floor Coverings, Plastic Rainwater Guttering, Pipes Underground Drainage Products, Plastic Moldings & Ventilation Equipment
S.I.C.: 3297
N.A.I.C.S.: 327120

Material de Aireacion S.A. (1)
Pl Zudibiarte sn
01409 Vitoria, Spain
Tel.: (34) 945898200
Fax: (34) 945898126
Polyethylene Pipe Mfr
S.I.C.: 4923
N.A.I.C.S.: 486210

Nicoll e.p.e. (1)
9 Shinon St
Acharnes, 136 77, Greece (100%)
Tel.: (30) 2102465560
Fax: (30) 2102409303
E-Mail: nicoll1@nicoll.com.gr
Web Site: www.nicoll.com.gr
Emp.: 10
Sewage & Surface Drainage
S.I.C.: 4952
N.A.I.C.S.: 221320
Eleni Vassilakou *(Mgr)*

Nicoll Eterplast S.A. (1)
Gr Republica del Ecuador N 308
Lima, Peru
Tel.: (51) 1 4231122
Fax: (51) 1 4313764
Web Site: www.nicoll.com.pe
Sanitary; Soil & Waste Removal
S.I.C.: 4959
N.A.I.C.S.: 562998

Nicoll Eterplast S.A. (1)
Peribebuy 1492
Tablada, B1766AAJ Buenos Aires, Argentina Ar
Tel.: (54) 11 4441 4450 (100%)
Telex: 17075
Fax: (54) 11 4441 1886
E-Mail: info@nicoll.com.ar
Web Site: www.nicoll.com.ar
Construction & Structural Engineering & PVC Pipe Fittings
S.I.C.: 1629
N.A.I.C.S.: 237990
Diego Martin Soto *(Mgr-Irrigation)*

Nicoll S.A. (1)
37 Rue Pierre Et Marie Curie
BP 10966
49309 Cholet, Cedex, France FR
Tel.: (33) 241637383
Telex: 720261
Fax: (33) 2416373457
E-Mail: webmaster@nicoll.fr
Web Site: www.nicoll.fr
Emp.: 180
Mfr of Soil & Waste, Rain Gutter Systems, Sanitary, Sewage, Ventilation & Floor Drainage Products
S.I.C.: 2821
N.A.I.C.S.: 325211
Phillip Mezet *(Mgr-Mktg)*

Nicoll SpA (1)
Via Gorizia 7
S Lucia Di Piave, 31025 Treviso, Italy IT
Tel.: (39) 0438 4697 (100%)
Telex: 410 537 Eplast
Fax: (39) 0438 460766
E-Mail: europlast@europlast.it
Web Site: www.europlast.it
Emp.: 50
Soil & Waste, Ventilation & Floor Drainage Products Mfr
S.I.C.: 4959
N.A.I.C.S.: 562998
Sergio Zunarelli *(Mng Dir)*

Nicoll S.r.l. (1)
Via Gorizia 7
S Lucia di Piave, 31025 Venice, Veneto, Italy
Tel.: (39) 0438700899
Fax: (39) 0438460655
E-Mail: info@nicoll.it
Web Site: www.nicoll-italia.com
Emp.: 30
Sanitary; Soil & Waste Removal
S.I.C.: 4959
N.A.I.C.S.: 562998
Alexandra Bernardi *(Mgr-Export)*

Paling Industries Sdn. Bhd. (1)
Lot 12 Jalan Perusahaan Empat
68100 Batu Caves, Malaysia (60%)
Tel.: (60) 361898333
Fax: (60) 361883810
E-Mail: enquiries@paling.com.my
Web Site: www.paling.com.my
Emp.: 170
Sanitary; Soil & Waste Removal
S.I.C.: 4959
N.A.I.C.S.: 562998
Chew Thong Boon *(Mgr-Sls)*

Philmac Pty. Ltd. (1)
53-59 Deeds Rd
North Plympton South Australia, Melbourne, 5037, Australia
Tel.: (61) 883009200
Fax: (61) 883009390
E-Mail: philmac@philmac.com.au
Web Site: www.philmac.com.au
Emp.: 250
Plastic Pipe Fittings
S.I.C.: 3084
N.A.I.C.S.: 326122
Chris Stathy *(Mng Dir)*

Poliplast sp. z o.o. (1)
Ul Energetyczma 6
56 400 Olesnica, Poland (100%)
Tel.: (48) 713144041
Fax: (48) 713149488
E-Mail: biuro@poliplast.pl
Web Site: www.poliplast.pl
Emp.: 150
Sewage & Drainage
S.I.C.: 4952
N.A.I.C.S.: 221320
Thomas Igmaszak *(Mng Dir)*

Redi S.p.A. (1)
Via Madonna Dei Prati 5 A
Zola Predosa, 40069 Bologna, Italy IT
Tel.: (39) 0516175111 (100%)
Telex: 435 10268
Fax: (39) 051756649
E-Mail: export@redi.it
Web Site: www.redi.it
Emp.: 200
Mfr. of Polypropylene & PVC Soil, Waste & Underground Systems for Civil & Industrial Use
S.I.C.: 2821
N.A.I.C.S.: 325211
Hubert Rousseau *(Mgr-Export)*

Riuvert S.A. (1)
La Llometes 18 A
03109 Alicante, Spain
Tel.: (34) 965617125
Fax: (34) 965617267
E-Mail: comercial@riuvert.es
Web Site: www.riuvert.es
Emp.: 150
Soil & Waste Removal; Sewage & Surface Drainage
S.I.C.: 4952
N.A.I.C.S.: 221320

Sanitaire Accessoires Services S.A.S. (1)
15 Ave Jean Moulin
PO Box 14
69720 Saint Laurent-de-Mure, France (100%)
Tel.: (33) 472483900
Telex: SAS Lyon 900871 F
Fax: (33) 478408578
E-Mail: sas@aliaxis.com
Web Site: www.nicoll.fr/pub/insti/pages/aliaxis/p_sas.htm
Emp.: 180
Mfr. of Sanitary Products
S.I.C.: 2676
N.A.I.C.S.: 322291

Sanitartechnik Eisenberg GmbH (1)
Gewerbegebiet In Der Wiesen 8
07607 Eisenberg, Germany De
Tel.: (49) 366915980 (100%)
Telex: 69588064
Fax: (49) 3669159815
E-Mail: info@sanit.de
Web Site: www.sanit.de
Emp.: 250
Mfr. of Sanitary Plastic Products
S.I.C.: 2676
N.A.I.C.S.: 322291
Raymond Au *(Mng Dir)*

Sicoac (1)
Industrial Area
1009 Jebel Jeloud, Tunisia (40%)
Tel.: (216) 71391075
Fax: (216) 71392271
E-Mail: sicoac.sep@planet.tn
Web Site: www.sicoac.com.tn
Emp.: 100
Extrusion of Pipes in Polyvinyl Chloride (PVC) & in Polyethylene (PE)
S.I.C.: 3354
N.A.I.C.S.: 331318
Ridha Ben Abdelkader *(Mgr-Mktg)*

Universal Hardware & Plastic Factory Limited (1)
Unit A and D 22 Fl Nathan Commercial Bldg
430 436 Nathan Rd, Kowloon, China (Hong Kong) HK
Tel.: (852) 23322878 (100%)
Telex: 39030
Fax: (852) 27822882
E-Mail: universal@hkstar.com
Web Site: www.anchorhk.com
Emp.: 12
S.I.C.: 7389
N.A.I.C.S.: 425110
Monita Ho *(Mgr)*

Non-U.S. Joint Venture:

Vinilit S.A. (1)
Avda Jorge Alessandri Rodriguez N 12900
Casilla 251, San Bernardo, Chile CL
Tel.: (56) 25924000
Fax: (56) 2 59 24 151
E-Mail: info@vinilit.cl
Web Site: www.vinilit.cl
Sales Range: Less than $1 Million
Emp.: 300
Plastic Pipe & Fitting Mfr; Joint Venture of S.A. Etex Group N.V. (60%) & Aliaxis S.A./N.V. (40%)
S.I.C.: 7389
N.A.I.C.S.: 425110

ALIBABA GROUP HOLDING LIMITED

26/F Tower One Times Sq 1
Matheson St
Causeway Bay, China (Hong Kong)
Tel.: (852) 22155100
Fax: (852) 22155200
Web Site: www.alibaba.com
Business Description:
Holding Company; Owned 44% by Yahoo! Inc. & 33.7% by SoftBank Corporation
S.I.C.: 6719
N.A.I.C.S.: 551112
Personnel:
Jack Yun Ma *(Founder & Chm)*
Joseph Chung Tsai *(Founder & Vice Chm)*
Jin Jianhang *(Founder & Sr VP)*
Jonathan Lu *(CEO)*
Maggie Wu *(CFO)*
Zeng Ming *(Chief Strategy Officer)*
Lucy Peng *(CEO-Alipay)*
Polo Shao *(Sr VP)*
Board of Directors:
Jack Yun Ma
Jacqueline D. Reses
Masayoshi Son
Joseph Chung Tsai

Corporate Headquarters:

Alibaba Group Holding Limited - Hangzhou Office (1)
No 699 Wangshang Road
Binjiang District, Hangzhou, 310052, China
Tel.: (86) 57185022088
Fax: (86) 57189815505
Emp.: 1,000
Executive Office
S.I.C.: 9131
N.A.I.C.S.: 921140
Jack Yun Ma *(Chm & CEO)*
Joseph Chung Tsai *(CFO)*
Zeng Ming *(Chief Strategy Officer)*
Lucy Peng *(CEO-Alipay)*
Jin Jianhang *(Sr VP)*

Subsidiaries:

Alibaba.com Limited (2)
699 Wang Shang Road Binjiang District
Hangzhou, 310052, China Ky
Tel.: (86) 57185022088 (100%)
Fax: (86) 571 8981 5505
Web Site: www.alibaba.com
Emp.: 12,878
Online International Business-to-Business Marketplaces & Consumer Websites Operator
S.I.C.: 7389
N.A.I.C.S.: 425110
Maggie Wu *(CFO)*
Andy Ang Li *(CTO)*
Elsa Lai Kin Wong *(Sec)*

Subsidiary:

Alibaba Technology (Shanghai) Co., Ltd. (3)
Rm 3601 3604 Zhaofeng Plz
1027 Chang Ning Rd, Shanghai, 200050, China CN
Tel.: (86) 2152559888 (100%)
Fax: (86) 2151158100
Online Provider of Business Networking Services
S.I.C.: 7389
N.A.I.C.S.: 561499

U.S. Subsidiaries:

Alibaba.com, Inc. (3)
3945 Freedom Cir Ste 600
Santa Clara, CA 95054 DE
Tel.: (408) 748-1200 (100%)
Fax: (408) 748-1218
E-Mail: info@alibaba.com
Web Site: www.alibaba.com
Emp.: 30
Business Networking Services
S.I.C.: 8742
N.A.I.C.S.: 541611

Auctiva Corporation (3)
360 E 6th St
Chico, CA 95928-5631 (100%)
Tel.: (530) 892-9191
Web Site: www.auctiva.com
Emp.: 12
e-Commerce Solutions
S.I.C.: 7372
N.A.I.C.S.: 511210
Jeff Schlicht *(Founder & CEO)*

Vendio Services, Inc. (3)
2800 Campus Dr
San Mateo, CA 94403 (100%)
Tel.: (650) 293-3500
E-Mail: kwray@corp.vendio.com
Web Site: www.vendio.com
Emp.: 50
e-Commerce Solutions
S.I.C.: 7372
N.A.I.C.S.: 511210
Mike Effle *(CEO)*

Non-U.S. Subsidiary:

Alibaba.com Hong Kong Limited (3)
Room 2403 05 Jubilee Centre
18 Fenwick Street, Wanchai, 310013, China (Hong Kong) HK
Tel.: (852) 22155100 (100%)
Fax: (852) 22155200
E-Mail: alibaba@alibaba-inc.com
Web Site: www.alibaba.com
Emp.: 2,000
Operator of International Online Business to Business Marketplaces & Consumer Websites
S.I.C.: 7389
N.A.I.C.S.: 425110
Porter Erisman *(VP-Intl Mktg)*

Taobao (2)
9/F Hua Xing Science & Technology Tower
No 477 Wen San Road, Hangzhou, 310099, China (100%)
Tel.: (86) 57188157858
Fax: (86) 57188157888
Web Site: www.taobao.com.cn
Internet Retail Website Operator
S.I.C.: 5961
N.A.I.C.S.: 454111
Jonathan Lu *(CEO)*

Yahoo! China (2)
9/F Tower A Winterless Center
No 1 West Da Wang Lu
Chaoyang District, Beijing, 100026, China (100%)
Tel.: (86) 10 6598 6666
Fax: (86) 10 6598 6660
Web Site: cn.yahoo.com
Internet Search Portal Operator
S.I.C.: 2741
N.A.I.C.S.: 519130
Qin Zhang *(Dir-Web Search Dept)*

ALICANTO MINERALS LIMITED

181 Roberts Road
Subiaco, WA, 6008, Australia
Tel.: (61) 8 6489 0700
Fax: (61) 8 6489 0710
E-Mail: admin@alicantominerals.com.au
Web Site: www.alicantominerals.com.au
Year Founded: 2011
AQI—(ASX)
Business Description:
Gold & Base Metals Mining
S.I.C.: 1041
N.A.I.C.S.: 212221
Personnel:
Didier Murcia *(Chm)*
Brett Dunnachie *(CFO & Sec)*
Board of Directors:
Didier Murcia
Matthew Bowles
Michael McKevitt
Legal Counsel:
Steinepreis Paganin
Level 4 The Read Building 16 Milligan Street
Perth, WA, 6000, Australia
Tel.: (61) 8 9321 4000
Fax: (61) 8 9321 4333

Non-U.S. Subsidiary:

StrataGold Guyana Inc. (1)
63 Middle St
North Cummingsburg, Georgetown, Guyana
Tel.: (592) 227 2116
Fax: (592) 227 3850
E-Mail: info@stratagoldguyana.com
Web Site: www.stratagoldguyana.com
Gold Mining Services
S.I.C.: 1041
N.A.I.C.S.: 212221

ALICE EVENEMENTS

110 Avenue Victor Hugo
92514 Boulogne-Billancourt, Cedex, France
Tel.: (33) 146251160
Fax: (33) 146251161
Web Site: www.alice-evenements.com
Rev.: $21,100,000
Emp.: 35
Business Description:
Travel Agencies
S.I.C.: 4724
N.A.I.C.S.: 561510
Personnel:
Didier Pachoud *(Dir-Fin)*

ALICROS S.P.A.

Via F Sacchetti 20
20099 Sesto San Giovanni, Italy
Tel.: (39) 0262694051
Fax: (39) 0262694164
E-Mail: info@alicros.it
Web Site: www.alicros.com
Business Description:
Holding Company
S.I.C.: 6719
N.A.I.C.S.: 551112
Personnel:
Luca Garavoglia *(Mng Dir)*

Holding:

Davide Campari-Milano S.p.A. (1)
Via Franco Sacchetti 20
20099 Sesto San Giovanni, Italy (51%)
Tel.: (39) 0262251
Telex: 321171
Fax: (39) 026225312
E-Mail: info@campari.com
Web Site: www.camparigroup.com
CPR—(ISE ITA)
Sls.: $1,804,944,736
Assets: $4,589,766,615
Liabilities: $2,660,570,388
Net Worth: $1,929,196,227
Earnings: $211,617,924
Emp.: 2,450
Fiscal Year-end: 12/31/12
Wines & Liquors Mfr
Import Export
S.I.C.: 2084
N.A.I.C.S.: 312130
Luca Garavoglia *(Chm)*
Robert Kunze-Concewitz *(CEO & Mng Dir)*
Paolo Marchesini *(CFO & Mng Dir)*
Stefano Saccardi *(Mng Dir, Gen Counsel & Officer-Bus Dev)*
Andrea Conzonato *(CMO)*
Franco Peroni *(Officer-Product Supply Chain)*

Subsidiaries:

Campari S.p.A. (2)
Frazione Valpone 79
I 12043 Canale, Italy IT
Tel.: (39) 0173967111
Fax: (39) 0173967153
Emp.: 120
Wine & Spirits Mfr
Import Export
S.I.C.: 2084
N.A.I.C.S.: 312130

U.S. Subsidiaries:

Skyy Spirits LLC (2)
1 Beach St Ste 300
San Francisco, CA 94133
Tel.: (415) 315-8000
Fax: (415) 315-8001
E-Mail: comments@skyyspirits.com
Web Site: www.skyyspirits.com
Emp.: 200
Alcoholic Beverages Mfr
Import Export
S.I.C.: 5182
N.A.I.C.S.: 424820
Gerard Ruvo *(Chm & CEO)*
Roy Danis *(Mng Dir)*
Andrea Conzonato *(COO & CMO)*

Wild Turkey Distillery (2)
1525 Tyrone Rd
Lawrenceburg, KY 40342
Tel.: (502) 839-4544
Fax: (502) 839-3902
Toll Free: (800) 455-5585
Web Site: www.wildturkeybourbon.com

Alicros S.p.A.—(Continued)

Sales Range: $125-149.9 Million
Emp.: 25
Distiller of Bourbon
S.I.C.: 2085
N.A.I.C.S.: 312140
Eddie Russell *(Assoc-Distiller)*

ALIGNA AG

Bernhard-Wicki-Strasse 5
80636 Munich, Germany
Tel.: (49) 89810290
Fax: (49) 8981029201
E-Mail: info@aligna.de
Web Site: www.aligna.de
Year Founded: 1998
Sales Range: $25-49.9 Million
Emp.: 5

Business Description:
Holding Company
S.I.C.: 6719
N.A.I.C.S.: 551112

Personnel:
Wilfried Riggers *(Chm-Supervisory Bd)*
Peter Falk *(CEO)*

Supervisory Board of Directors:
Wilfried Riggers
Bernd Achten

Subsidiaries:

DeltaSelect GmbH (1)
Pettenkofer Ste 22
80336 Munich, Germany
Tel.: (49) 89810290
Fax: (49) 8981029111
E-Mail: mail@plasmaselect.de
Web Site: www.deltaselect.de
Emp.: 25
Pharmaceutical Preparations
S.I.C.: 2834
N.A.I.C.S.: 325412
Bernhard Giessel *(Mng Dir)*
Albrecht Schnell *(Mng Dir)*

ALIMENTA S.A.

154 Rte De Suisse
Versoix, 1290 Geneva, Switzerland
Tel.: (41) 227750200
Fax: (41) 227750292
E-Mail: alimentagva@alimenta.com
Web Site: www.alimenta.com

Business Description:
Producer of Food Products
S.I.C.: 5499
N.A.I.C.S.: 445299

Personnel:
Dikran S. Izmirlian *(Pres)*

ALIMENTATION COUCHE-TARD INC.

4204 Industriel Blvd
Laval, QC, H7L 0E3, Canada
Tel.: (450) 662-6632
Fax: (450) 662-6648
Toll Free: (800) 361-2612
E-Mail: info@couche-tard.com
Web Site: www.couche-tard.com
Year Founded: 1981
ATD—(OTC TSX)
Rev.: $35,543,400,000
Assets: $10,546,200,000
Liabilities: $7,329,500,000
Net Worth: $3,216,700,000
Earnings: $572,800,000
Emp.: 60,000
Fiscal Year-end: 04/28/13

Business Description:
Convenience Store Operator
S.I.C.: 5411
N.A.I.C.S.: 445120

Personnel:
Alain Bouchard *(Founder & Chm)*
Brian P. Hannasch *(Pres & CEO)*
Raymond Pare *(CFO & VP)*
Jean Bernier *(Pres-Fuel-Americas & Ops-North East)*
Jacob Schram *(Pres-Ops-Europe)*
Sylvain Aubry *(Sec & Sr Dir-Legal Affairs)*
Hans-Olav Hoidahl *(Exec VP-Scandinavia)*
Jorn Madsen *(Exec VP-Central & Eastern Europe)*
Darrell Davis *(Sr VP-Ops)*
Geoffrey C. Haxel *(Sr VP-Ops)*
Jonas Palm *(Sr VP-Special Products)*
Dennis Tewell *(Sr VP-Ops)*

Board of Directors:
Alain Bouchard
Nathalie Bourque
Jacques D'Amours
Roger Desrosiers
Jean-Andre Elie
Richard Fortin
Melanie Kau
Daniel Rabinowicz
Jean Turmel

Transfer Agent:
Computershare Trust Company of Canada
9th Floor 100 University Avenue
Toronto, ON, Canada

Subsidiary:

Mac's Convenience Stores, Inc. (1)
305 Milner Avenue 4th Floor
Toronto, ON, M1B 3V4, Canada (100%)
Tel.: (416) 291-4441
Fax: (416) 291-4947
Toll Free: (800) 268-5574
E-Mail: customer.service@macs.ca
Web Site: www.macs.ca
Emp.: 150
Convenience & Specialty Retail Store Owner & Operator
S.I.C.: 5541
N.A.I.C.S.: 447110
Richard Fortin *(CFO)*

Division:

Mac's Convenience Stores, Inc. (2)
85 Patterson Rd
Barrie, ON, L4N 3V9, Canada
Tel.: (705) 737-5112
Fax: (705) 721-9554
Web Site: www.macs.ca/
Sls.: $81,989,000
Emp.: 13
Convenience Stores
S.I.C.: 5411
N.A.I.C.S.: 445120

U.S. Subsidiary:

Circle K Stores Inc. (1)
PO Box 52085
Phoenix, AZ 85072
Tel.: (602) 728-8000
Fax: (602) 728-5284
Web Site: www.circlek.com
Emp.: 600
Convenience Store Operator
S.I.C.: 5411
N.A.I.C.S.: 445120
Geoff Haxel *(VP-Ops)*

Non-U.S. Subsidiary:

Statoil Fuel & Retail ASA (1)
Sorkedalsveien 8
107 Oslo, Norway NO
Mailing Address:
Box 1176
Sentrum, 107 Oslo, Norway
Tel.: (47) 22 96 20 00
Fax: (47) 22 69 32 00
Web Site: www.statoilfuelretail.com
Emp.: 8,400
Road Transportation Fuel Retailer
S.I.C.: 5172
N.A.I.C.S.: 424720
Alain Bouchard *(Chm)*
Klaus-Anders Nysteen *(CFO)*
Sverre Rosen *(Chief Staff Officer)*
Lars Gaustad *(Exec VP-Transport Fuel)*
Hans-Olav Hoidahl *(Exec VP-Scandinavian Bus Area)*
Jonas Palm *(Exec VP-Special Products Bus Area)*
Thomas Stokken *(Exec VP-Sls & Ops)*
Ina Strand *(Exec VP-Market Dev)*
Karen Romer *(Sr VP-Comm)*

Non-U.S. Subsidiary:

Statoil Fuel & Retail Sverige AB (2)
(Formerly Svenska Statoil AB)
Torkel Knutssonsgatan 24
S-11888 Stockholm, Sweden SE
Tel.: (46) 84296000 (100%)
Fax: (46) 84296300
E-Mail: info@statoil.se
Web Site: www.statoil.se
Emp.: 400
Fuel Distr & Gas Service Station Operator
S.I.C.: 5541
N.A.I.C.S.: 447190
Morgan Wiktorsson *(CEO)*

ALIMENTATION DU FLORIVAL

10 Rue Theodore Deck
68500 Guebwiller, Haut Rhin, France
Tel.: (33) 389621462
Fax: (33) 389792930
Sls.: $21,400,000
Emp.: 58

Business Description:
Grocery Stores
S.I.C.: 5411
N.A.I.C.S.: 445110

Personnel:
Rene Kohler *(Pres)*

ALIMENTOS MARAVILLA S.A.

Calzada Roosevelt 43-28 Zone 7
Guatemala, Guatemala
Tel.: (502) 24216300
E-Mail: ventasmaravilla@icasa.com.gt
Web Site: www.alimentosmaravilla.com.gt
Emp.: 350

Business Description:
Fruits, Vegetables & Related Products
S.I.C.: 5148
N.A.I.C.S.: 424480

Personnel:
Jorge Castillo Love *(CEO)*

ALIMENTS KRISPY KERNELS INC

2620 rue Watt
Sainte-Foy, QC, G1P 3T5, Canada
Tel.: (418) 658-1515
Fax: (418) 657-5971
Toll Free: (877) 791-9986
E-Mail: sales@krispykernels.com
Web Site: www.krispykernels.com
Year Founded: 1945
Rev.: $32,589,347
Emp.: 300

Business Description:
Nuts, Peanuts & Snacks Distr
S.I.C.: 2096
N.A.I.C.S.: 311919

Personnel:
Paul Jalbert *(Founder)*
Dennis Jalbert *(Owner)*

ALINMA BANK

Al-Anoud Tower-King Fahad Road
Riyadh, 11586, Saudi Arabia
Tel.: (966) 920028000
Fax: (966) 12185000
Toll Free: 8001208000
E-Mail: info@alinma.com
Web Site: www.alinma.com
1150—(SAU)
Rev.: $435,499,031
Assets: $14,384,048,834
Liabilities: $9,946,373,173
Net Worth: $4,437,675,661
Earnings: $195,240,242
Emp.: 1,552
Fiscal Year-end: 12/31/12

Business Description:
Banking Services
S.I.C.: 6029
N.A.I.C.S.: 522110

Personnel:
Abdulaziz Abdulla Al-Zamil *(Chm)*

Board of Directors:
Abdulaziz Abdulla Al-Zamil
Abdulmohsen Abdulaziz Al-Hussain
Abdulmohsen Abdulaziz Al-Fares
Ibrahim Fahad Al-Ghofaili
Abdulrehman Hamad Al-Harkan
Suliman M. Al-Turki
Saad Ali Al-Kathiry
Saad Attiah Al-Ghamdi
Mohamed Yousuf Naghi

Ernst & Young
PO Box 2732
Riyadh, Saudi Arabia

Joint Venture:

Alinma Tokio Marine Co. (1)
Al Moosa Residential & Commercial Center
Tower C Office 356 5th Fl
PO Box 643
Riyadh, 11421, Saudi Arabia
Tel.: (966) 1 4640256
Fax: (966) 1 4640328
E-Mail: info@atmc.com.sa
Web Site: www.atmc.com.sa
8312—(SAU)
Insurance & Reinsurance Services
S.I.C.: 6311
N.A.I.C.S.: 524113
Abdul Mohsen Al-Fares *(Chm)*
Kiyoshi Izuta *(CEO)*

ALIOR BANK S.A.

ul Domaniewska 52
02-672 Warsaw, Poland
Tel.: (48) 12 19 502
Fax: (48) 22 555 23 23
E-Mail: kontakt@alior.pl
Web Site: www.aliorbank.pl
ALR—(OTC WAR)
Int. Income: $407,061,725
Assets: $6,771,470,121
Liabilities: $6,059,084,511
Net Worth: $712,385,610
Earnings: $55,200,599
Fiscal Year-end: 12/31/12

Business Description:
Banking Services
S.I.C.: 6029
N.A.I.C.S.: 522110

Personnel:
Helene Zaleski *(Chm-Supervisory Bd)*
Wojciech Sobieraj *(CEO & Member-Mgmt Bd)*
Krzysztof Czuba *(Deputy CEO & Member-Mgmt Bd)*
Michal Hucal *(Deputy CEO & Member-Mgmt Bd)*
Niels Lundorff *(Deputy CEO & Member-Mgmt Bd)*
Artur Maliszewski *(Deputy CEO & Member-Mgmt Bd)*
Witold Skrok *(Deputy CEO & Member-Mgmt Bd)*
Katarzyna Sulkowska *(Deputy CEO & Member-Mgmt Bd)*

Supervisory Board of Directors:
Helene Zaleski
Malgorzata Iwanicz-Drozdowska
Marek Michalski
Krzysztof Obloj
Lucyna Stanczak-Wuczynska
Jozef Wancer

ALIRAN IHSAN RESOURCES BERHAD

2-2 Persiaran 65C Pekeliling Bus Ctr
Jalan Pahang Barat
53000 Kuala Lumpur, Malaysia

Tel.: (60) 340241152
Fax: (60) 340241154
E-Mail: corporate@airb.com.my
Web Site: www.airb.com.my
Sales Range: $25-49.9 Million
Emp.: 290
Business Description:
Water Treatment & Water Works Construction Services
S.I.C.: 4971
N.A.I.C.S.: 221310
Personnel:
Azman Avunny *(CEO)*
Board of Directors:
Abdul Jabbar Hassan
Che Khalib Mohamad Noh
Hasmuddin bin Tengku Othman
Legal Counsel:
M Pathmanathan & Co
2A-23A-2 Block 2A Plaza Sentral Jalan Stesen Sentral 5
Kuala Lumpur Sentral, Kuala Lumpur, Malaysia
Hisham Sobri & Kadir
16th Floor Pertama Complex Jalan Tunku Abdul Rahman
Kuala Lumpur, Malaysia

ALISON HAYES

361B-363b Liverpool Rd
London, N1 1NL, United Kingdom
Tel.: (44) 2077008800
Fax: (44) 2077003600
E-Mail: reception@alisonhayes.co.uk
Web Site: www.alisonhayes.co.uk
Sales Range: $50-74.9 Million
Emp.: 90
Business Description:
Ladies Clothing Design & Mfr
S.I.C.: 5699
N.A.I.C.S.: 315240
Personnel:
Robert Chamberlain *(Chm)*

ALISRA FOR EDUCATION & INVESTMENT CO. PLC

PO Box 22 & 33
Amman, Jordan
Tel.: (962) 6 471 1710
Fax: (962) 6 471 1505
Year Founded: 1991
AIFE—(AMM)
Rev.: $23,771,110
Assets: $53,765,181
Liabilities: $7,692,198
Net Worth: $46,072,983
Earnings: $10,034,067
Fiscal Year-end: 12/31/12
Business Description:
Higher Education Services
S.I.C.: 9411
N.A.I.C.S.: 923110
Personnel:
Raed Rais Abdulhalim Suleiman *(Chm)*

ALISTHE INVESTMENTS PTY LTD

Level 1 420 Hay St
Subiaco, WA, 6008, Australia
Tel.: (61) 893882655
Business Description:
Real Estate & Construction Holding Company
S.I.C.: 6719
N.A.I.C.S.: 551112
Personnel:
Harry A. Xydas *(Chm)*
Board of Directors:
Harry A. Xydas
Subsidiary:

Doric Group Holdings Pty Ltd (1)
Level 1 420 Hay Street
Subiaco, WA, 6008, Australia
Tel.: (61) 893882655
Fax: (61) 893881484
E-Mail: marketing@doricgroup.com.au
Web Site: www.doricgroup.com.au
Sales Range: $100-124.9 Million
Emp.: 100
Property Developer
S.I.C.: 6531
N.A.I.C.S.: 531390
Harry A. Xydas *(Chm)*
Peter Iancov *(CEO)*

ALITA RESOURCES LTD.

Suite 1400 570 Granville Street
Vancouver, BC, V6C 3P1, Canada
Tel.: (604) 640-6357
Fax: (604) 681-0139
Web Site: www.alitaresources.com
Year Founded: 2009
AL.P—(TSXV)
Business Description:
Investment Services
S.I.C.: 6211
N.A.I.C.S.: 523999
Personnel:
T.J. Malcolm Powell *(Pres & CEO)*
Carl Roland Jonsson *(CFO & Sec)*
Board of Directors:
Lindsay Richard Bottomer
Carl Roland Jonsson
Jason Powell
T.J. Malcolm Powell
Arthur Troup

ALITALIA-COMPAGNIA AEREA ITALIANA S.P.A.

Pizaaz Almerico da Schio Pal
RPU 00054 Rome, Italy
Tel.: (39) 0665632222
Fax: (39) 066563310012
E-Mail: ufficio.stampa@alitalia.it
Web Site: www.alitalia.com
Business Description:
Holding Company
S.I.C.: 6719
N.A.I.C.S.: 551112
Personnel:
Roberto Colaninno *(Chm)*
Subsidiary:

Alitalia Express S.p.A. (1)
Via Pierpaolo Racchetti
Fiumicino, 00054 Rome, Italy
Tel.: (39) 665631
Regional Airline
S.I.C.: 4512
N.A.I.C.S.: 481111
Massimo Chieli *(Gen Mgr)*

ALIX RESOURCES CORP.

Suite 1220 - 789 West Pender
Vancouver, BC, V6C 1H2, Canada
Tel.: (604) 683-3995
Fax: (604) 683-3988
Toll Free: (888) 945-4770
E-Mail: info@alixresources.com
Web Site: www.alixresources.com
AIX—(TSXV)
Assets: $3,049,633
Liabilities: $964,794
Net Worth: $2,084,840
Earnings: ($2,215,170)
Fiscal Year-end: 01/31/13
Business Description:
Mineral Exploration Services
S.I.C.: 1081
N.A.I.C.S.: 213114
Personnel:
Michael B. England *(Pres & CEO)*
David Cross *(CFO)*
John Masters *(Sec)*
Board of Directors:
Michael B. England
Charles Hawley
David Hedderly-Smith
David Lajack
John Masters
Pierre Vella-Zarb
Legal Counsel:
Richards Buell Sutton LLP
700 401 West Georgia Street
Vancouver, BC, Canada
Transfer Agent:
Equity Transfer & Trust Company
1185 West Georgia Street Suite 1620
Vancouver, BC, V6E 4E6, Canada

ALJANUOB FILTERS MANUFACTURING CO.LTD.

PO Box 963194
Amman, 11196, Jordan
Tel.: (962) 65699245
Fax: (962) 65699246
E-Mail: info@aljanoub-filter.com
Web Site: www.aljanoub-filter.net
Year Founded: 1997
AJFM—(AMM)
Sales Range: $1-9.9 Million
Emp.: 68
Business Description:
Filters Marketing & Mfr
S.I.C.: 3714
N.A.I.C.S.: 336390
Personnel:
Riyadh Al-Dababsah *(Gen Mgr)*

ALKA DIAMOND INDUSTRIES LIMITED

626 Panchratna MP Road Opera House
Mumbai, 400004, India
Tel.: (91) 22 23636534
Web Site: www.alkadiamond.com
Year Founded: 1989
531581—(BOM)
Rev.: $3,604,098
Assets: $2,303,224
Liabilities: $606,136
Net Worth: $1,697,088
Earnings: $35,161
Fiscal Year-end: 03/31/13
Business Description:
Diamond Distr
S.I.C.: 5094
N.A.I.C.S.: 423940
Personnel:
Gopal M. Javda *(Chm & Mng Dir)*
Nilesh Fulchandbhai Parmar *(Compliance Officer)*
Board of Directors:
Gopal M. Javda
Pankaj Kumar Jain
Nilesh Fulchandbhai Parmar
Sanat Upadhyay
Transfer Agent:
Sharex (India) Pvt. Ltd.
No 17/B Dena Bank Building 2nd Floor
Horniman Circle Fort
Mumbai, Maharashtra, 400001, India

ALKALI METALS LIMITED

Plot B-5 Block III IDA Uppal
Hyderabad, 500 039, India
Tel.: (91) 4027201179
Fax: (91) 4027201454
E-Mail: alkalimetals@alkalimetals.com
Web Site: www.alkalimetals.com
Year Founded: 1968
533029—(BOM)
Rev.: $11,627,265
Assets: $18,732,770
Liabilities: $8,963,955
Net Worth: $9,768,814
Earnings: $881,613
Emp.: 537
Fiscal Year-end: 03/31/13
Business Description:
Sodium Derivatives, Pyridine Derivatives & Various Fine Chemicals Mfr
S.I.C.: 2899
N.A.I.C.S.: 325998
Personnel:
Y. S. R. Venkata Rao *(Mng Dir)*
Deepak Tibrewal *(Compliance Officer & Sec)*
Board of Directors:
J. S. Yadav
G. Jayaraman
P. C. Patnaik
Y. Lalithya Poorna
C. H. S. Prasad
Y. S. R. Venkata Rao
Transfer Agent:
Cameo Corporate Services Limited
Subramanian Bldg No 1 Club House Road
Chennai, 600 002, India
Tel.: (91) 44 2846 0390
Fax: (91) 44 2846 0129

ALKALOID A.D.

Blvd Aleksandar Makedonski 12
1000 Skopje, Macedonia
Tel.: (389) 23104000
Fax: (389) 2 3104014
E-Mail: alkaloid@alkaloid.com.mk
Web Site: www.alkaloid.com.mk
Year Founded: 1936
ALK—(MAC)
Sls.: $119,145,783
Assets: $183,000,349
Liabilities: $33,278,111
Net Worth: $149,722,239
Earnings: $12,809,325
Emp.: 1,105
Fiscal Year-end: 12/31/12
Business Description:
Pharmaceuticals, Herbal Materials, Cosmetics, Chemical Products & Coating Agents
S.I.C.: 2834
N.A.I.C.S.: 325412
Personnel:
Miodrag Micajkov *(Chm-Supervisory Bd)*
Zhivko Mukaetov *(Chm-Mgmt Bd & CEO)*
Viktor Stojchevski *(CFO & Member-Mgmt Bd)*
Milkica Gligorova *(Member-Mgmt Bd & Mgr-Production-PC Pharmaceuticals)*
Kire Icev *(Member-Mgmt Bd & Mgr-Gen Affairs)*
Gjorgi Jovanov *(Member-Mgmt Bd & Mgr-Fin)*
Supervisory Board of Directors:
Miodrag Micajkov
Ilija Djonov
Bojancho Kralevski
Subsidiary:

Alkaloid Kons DOOEL (1)
12 Aleksandar Makedonski
1000 Skopje, Macedonia
Tel.: (389) 23204430
Fax: (389) 23204431
Web Site: www.alkaloid.com
Emp.: 23
Pharmaceutical Products Distr
S.I.C.: 5122
N.A.I.C.S.: 424210
Oliver Lazareski *(Gen Mgr)*

U.S. Subsidiary:

Alkaloid USA LLC (1)
6530 West Campus Oval Ste 280
New Albany, OH 43054
Tel.: (614) 855-1800
Fax: (614) 939-9498
Web Site: www.alkaloidusa.com
Pharmaceutical Products Distr
S.I.C.: 5122
N.A.I.C.S.: 424210
Vera Stavroff *(CEO & Pres)*

Non-U.S. Subsidiaries:

ALK&KOS Sh.p.k. (1)
Ganimete Terbeshi nr 19
10000 Pristina, Kosovo, Serbia

Alkaloid A.D.—(Continued)

Tel.: (381) 3 8247 160
Fax: (381) 3 8247 159
E-Mail: alkkos@hotmail.com
Web Site: www.alkaloid.com.mk/subsidaries.nspx
Emp.: 20
Pharmaceutical Products Distr
S.I.C.: 5122
N.A.I.C.S.: 424210
Dritan Ismaili *(Gen Mgr)*

Alkaloid DOO (Podgorica) **(1)**
Blvd Svetog Petra Cetinjskog 1A/ V
20000 Podgorica, Montenegro
Tel.: (382) 20246207
Fax: (382) 20 246 208
E-Mail: alkaloid@t-com.me
Web Site: www.alkaloid.com.mk/alkaloid-in-the-world.nspx
Pharmaceutical Products Distr
S.I.C.: 5122
N.A.I.C.S.: 424210

Alkaloid DOO (Sarajevo) **(1)**
Isevica sokak 4 B
71000 Sarajevo, Bosnia & Herzegovina
Tel.: (387) 33475790
Fax: (387) 33475791
E-Mail: alkaloid@bih.net.ba
Web Site: www.alkaloid.com.mk/subsidaries.nspx
Pharmaceutical Products Distr
S.I.C.: 5122
N.A.I.C.S.: 424210
Boris Jotevski *(Mgr)*

Alkaloid DOO (Zagreb) **(1)**
Grada Vukovara 226
10000 Zagreb, Croatia
Tel.: (385) 16 311 920
Fax: (385) 1 6311 922
E-Mail: alkaloid@alkaloid.hr
Emp.: 30
Pharmaceutical Products Distr
S.I.C.: 5122
N.A.I.C.S.: 424210
Neven Sukarovski *(Reg Dir-Sls)*

Alkaloid d.o.o. **(1)**
Bul Kneza Aleksandra Karadjordjevica
6 Dedinje, 11000 Belgrade, Serbia
Tel.: (381) 112663526
Fax: (381) 113670761
E-Mail: office@alkaloid.co.yu
Web Site: www.alkaloid.co.yu
Pharmaceutical Distr & Sales
S.I.C.: 5122
N.A.I.C.S.: 424210
Ego Peroo *(Gen Mgr)*

Alkaloid-Farm d.o.o. **(1)**
Slanrdova ulica 4
1231 Ljubljana, Slovenia
Tel.: (386) 13004290
Fax: (386) 13004291
E-Mail: alkaloid-farm@alkaloid.si
Web Site: www.alkaloid.com.mk
Emp.: 7
Pharmaceutical Distr & Sales
S.I.C.: 5122
N.A.I.C.S.: 424210
Alma Bunic *(Gen Mgr)*

Alkaloid e.d.o.o **(1)**
Oboriste 20
1504 Sofia, Bulgaria
Tel.: (359) 929434450
Fax: (359) 929434468
Web Site: www.alkaloid.com.mk/html/contact.html
Pharmaceutical Distr & Sales
S.I.C.: 5122
N.A.I.C.S.: 424210

Alkaloid Sh.p.k. (Tirana) **(1)**
Str Brigada 8 3/6 5th Floor Apt 19
1000 Tirana, Albania
Tel.: (355) 42223599
Fax: (355) 42233320
E-Mail: ademiraga@alkaloid.al
Web Site: www.alkaloid.al
Pharmaceutical Products Distr
S.I.C.: 5122
N.A.I.C.S.: 424210
Arben Demiraga *(Mgr)*

Alkaloidpharma SA **(1)**
Rue Georges-Jordil 4
1700 Fribourg, Switzerland
Tel.: (41) 263234190
Fax: (41) 263234172
E-Mail: alkaloidpharm@mcnet.ch
Web Site: www.alkaloid.com.mk/html/contact.html
Emp.: 2,000
Pharmaceutical Distr & Sales
S.I.C.: 5122
N.A.I.C.S.: 424210
Zhivko Mykaelv *(Mng Dir)*

OOO Alkaloid RUS **(1)**
2nd Bld 33 Usacheva Str
119048 Moscow, Russia
Tel.: (7) 4955029297
Fax: (7) 4955029297
Emp.: 55
Pharmaceutical Products Distr
S.I.C.: 5122
N.A.I.C.S.: 424210
Alojzij Pungarsek *(Gen Dir)*

ALKANE ENERGY PLC

Edwinstowe House High Street
Edwinstowe
Nottingham, NG21 9PR, United Kingdom
Tel.: (44) 1623827927
Fax: (44) 1623827930
E-Mail: info@alkane.co.uk
Web Site: www.alkane.co.uk
ALK—(LSE)
Rev.: $23,152,391
Assets: $73,196,933
Liabilities: $34,659,098
Net Worth: $38,537,835
Earnings: $4,553,093
Emp.: 24
Fiscal Year-end: 12/31/12

Business Description:
Power Generation & Oil & Gas Exploration
S.I.C.: 1389
N.A.I.C.S.: 213112

Personnel:
Neil O'Brien *(CEO)*
Stephen Goalby *(Sec & Dir-Fin)*

Board of Directors:
Roger McDowell
Joseph Darby
Cameron Davies
Stephen Goalby
Julia Henderson
Neil O'Brien

Legal Counsel:
Eversheds
1 Royal Standard Place
Nottingham, NG1 6FZ, United Kingdom

Subsidiaries:

Alkane Energy UK Limited **(1)**
Green Energy Park Markham Ln
Bolsover, Chesterfield, Derbyshire, S44 5HS, United Kingdom
Tel.: (44) 1246240578
Waste Treatment Solutions Provider
S.I.C.: 4953
N.A.I.C.S.: 562211

Alkane Services Limited **(1)**
Edwinstowe House High St
Mansfield, Nottinghamshire, NG21 9PR, United Kingdom
Tel.: (44) 1623827927
Fax: (44) 1623827930
E-Mail: info@alkane.co.uk
Waste Treatment Solutions Provider
S.I.C.: 4953
N.A.I.C.S.: 562211
Neil O'Brien *(CEO)*

ALKANE RESOURCES LIMITED

65 Burswood Road
PO Box 4384
Burswood, WA, 6100, Australia
Tel.: (61) 892275677
Fax: (61) 892278178
E-Mail: mail@alkane.com.au
Web Site: www.alkane.com.au
ALK—(ASX OTC)
Rev.: $100,787,744
Assets: $271,790,101
Liabilities: $25,481,429
Net Worth: $246,308,672
Earnings: $69,336,124
Emp.: 10
Fiscal Year-end: 12/31/12

Business Description:
Mineral Mining & Exploration Services
S.I.C.: 1481
N.A.I.C.S.: 213115

Personnel:
David Ian Chalmers *(Mng Dir)*
Michael Ball *(CFO)*
Karen Elizabeth Vere Brown *(Co-Sec)*
Lindsay Arthur Colless *(Co-Sec)*

Board of Directors:
John Stuart Ferguson Dunlop
David Ian Chalmers
Ian Jeffrey Gandel
Anthony Dean Lethlean

ALKERMES PLC

Connaught House 1 Burlington Road
Dublin, Ireland
Tel.: (353) 1 772 8000
E-Mail: financial@alkermes.com
Web Site: www.alkermes.com
ALKS—(NASDAQ)
Rev.: $575,548,000
Assets: $1,470,291,000
Liabilities: $517,917,000
Net Worth: $952,374,000
Earnings: $24,983,000
Emp.: 1,230
Fiscal Year-end: 03/31/13

Business Description:
Pharmaceuticals Mfr
S.I.C.: 2834
N.A.I.C.S.: 325412

Personnel:
Richard F. Pops *(Chm & CEO)*
Shane Cooke *(Pres)*
James M. Frates *(CFO & Sr VP)*
Gordon G. Pugh *(COO, Chief Risk Officer & Sr VP)*
Kathryn L. Biberstein *(Chief Legal Officer, Chief Compliance Officer, Sec & Sr VP)*
Elliot W. Ehrich *(Chief Medical Officer & Sr VP-R&D)*
James L. Botkin *(Sr VP-Ops)*
Michael J. Landine *(Sr VP-Corp Dev)*
Peter Thornton *(Sr VP-Bus Integration)*

Board of Directors:
Richard F. Pops
David W. Anstice
Floyd E. Bloom
Robert A. Breyer
Wendy L. Dixon
Geraldine A. Henwood
Paul J. Mitchell
Nancy J. Wysenski

Plant:

Alkermes plc - Ireland Facility **(1)**
Monksland
Athlone, Westmeath, Ireland
Tel.: (353) 90 649 5000
Fax: (353) 90 649 5141
E-Mail: contracts@alkermes.com
Web Site: www.alkermes.com
Pharmaceutical Products Mfr
S.I.C.: 2834
N.A.I.C.S.: 325412

U.S. Subsidiaries:

Alkermes Gainesville LLC **(1)**
1300 Gould Dr
Gainesville, GA 30504-3947 (100%)
Tel.: (770) 531-8100
Web Site: www.alkermes.com
Emp.: 165
Pharmaceuticals Mfr
S.I.C.: 2834
N.A.I.C.S.: 325412
James L. Botkin *(Sr VP-Ops)*

Alkermes, Inc. **(1)**
852 Winter St
Waltham, MA 02451-1420 PA
Tel.: (718) 609-6000
E-Mail: prodtech@alkermes.com
Web Site: www.alkermes.com
Emp.: 600
Developer of Pharmaceutical Products Based on Specialized Drug Delivery Systems
S.I.C.: 2834
N.A.I.C.S.: 325412
James M. Frates *(CFO & Sr VP)*
Gordon G. Pugh *(COO, Chief Risk Officer & Sr VP)*
Kathryn L. Biberstein *(Chief Compliance Officer, Gen Counsel, Sec & Sr VP-Govt Rels)*
Mark Stejbach *(Chief Comml Officer)*
Jim Botkin *(Sr VP-Ops)*

Subsidiary:

Alkermes Controlled Therapeutics, Inc. **(2)**
852 Winter St
Waltham, MA 02451-1420
Tel.: (781) 609-6000
Pharmaceutical Products Mfr
S.I.C.: 2834
N.A.I.C.S.: 325412

U.S. Plants:

Alkermes plc - Georgia Facility **(1)**
1300 Gould Dr
Gainesville, GA 30504
Tel.: (770) 531-8100
Web Site: www.alkermes.com
Pharmaceutical Products Mfr
S.I.C.: 2834
N.A.I.C.S.: 325412

Alkermes plc - Massachusetts Facility **(1)**
852 Winter St
Waltham, MA 02451
Tel.: (781) 609-6000
Web Site: www.alkermes.com
Pharmaceutical Products Mfr
S.I.C.: 2834
N.A.I.C.S.: 325412

Alkermes plc - Ohio Facility **(1)**
265 Olinger Cir
Wilmington, OH 45177
Tel.: (937) 382-5642
Fax: (937) 382-5949
E-Mail: hrqueryalkermes@alkermes.com
Web Site: www.alkermes.com
Emp.: 320
Pharmaceutical Products Mfr
S.I.C.: 2834
N.A.I.C.S.: 325412
Kristen Parr *(Plant Mgr)*

ALKIM ALKALI KIMYA A.S.

Inonu Caddesi No 13 Taksim
34437 Istanbul, Turkey
Tel.: (90) 2122922266
Fax: (90) 2122527660
E-Mail: alkim@alkim.com
Web Site: www.alkim.com
ALKIM—(IST)
Sls.: $118,783,323
Assets: $150,057,363
Liabilities: $49,138,668
Net Worth: $100,918,694
Earnings: $9,137,545
Emp.: 344
Fiscal Year-end: 12/31/12

Business Description:
Sodium Sulfate Mfr
S.I.C.: 2819
N.A.I.C.S.: 325180

Personnel:
Mehmet Reha Kora *(Chm)*
A. Haluk Kora *(Vice Chm)*
Arkin Kora *(Vice Chm)*
Ferit Kora *(Vice Chm)*

Board of Directors:
Mehmet Reha Kora
Mehmet Halit Guven
A. Haluk Kora
Arkin Kora
Ferit Kora
Ozay Kora
Abdurrahman Yalcin Koyuncu
Tulay Onel
Kerim Oygur

ALKIM KAGIT SANAYI VE TICARET A.S.

Kirovasi Mevkii Kemalpasa
35170 Izmir, Turkey
Tel.: (90) 2328770606
Fax: (90) 2328770605
E-Mail: info@alkimkagit.com.tr
Web Site: www.alkimkagit.com.tr
ALKA—(IST)
Sls.: $69,350,903
Assets: $81,165,451
Liabilities: $22,534,171
Net Worth: $58,631,281
Earnings: $3,825,151
Emp.: 171
Fiscal Year-end: 12/31/12
Business Description:
Photocopy Papers Mfr
S.I.C.: 2621
N.A.I.C.S.: 322121
Personnel:
M. Reha Kora *(Chm)*
Adem Haluk Kora *(Vice Chm)*
Ferit Kora *(Vice Chm)*
Board of Directors:
M. Reha Kora
Hakki Pinar Kilic
Adem Haluk Kora
Arkin Kora
Ferit Kora
Ozay Kora
Namik Kemal Marmara
Tulay Onel
Kerim Oygur

ALKIS H. HADJIKYRIACOS (FROU FROU BISCUITS) PUBLIC LTD.

PO Box 15029
Kokkinotrimithia, Nicosia, Cyprus
Tel.: (357) 22835090
Fax: (357) 22835950
E-Mail: info@froufrou.com.cy
Web Site: www.froufrou.com.cy
Year Founded: 1964
FBI—(CYP)
Sales Range: $25-49.9 Million
Emp.: 208
Business Description:
Biscuits & Snack Foods Mfr
S.I.C.: 2053
N.A.I.C.S.: 311813
Personnel:
Alkis H. Hadjikyriacos *(Chm & Gen Dir)*
Board of Directors:
Alkis H. Hadjikyriacos
Christodoulos Christodoulou
Chryssis Christopoulos
Costas G. Eliades
Charis M. Hadjikyriacos
Kyriacoss Hadjisavvas
Sofia Miltiadous

Subsidiaries:

Frou Frou Cereals Ltd (1)
PO Box 15029
Kokkinotrimithia, 2660 Nicosia, Cyprus
Tel.: (357) 22835090
Fax: (357) 22835950
E-Mail: info@froufrou.com.cy
Web Site: www.froufrou.com.cy
Emp.: 200
Cereals Mfr & Trading Services
S.I.C.: 2043
N.A.I.C.S.: 311230
Micheal Hadjikyriacos *(Gen Mgr)*

Frou Frou Investments Ltd (1)
PO Box 15029
Kokkinotrimithia, 2660 Nicosia, Cyprus
Tel.: (357) 22835090
Fax: (357) 22835950
E-Mail: info@froufrou.com.cy
Web Site: www.froufrou.com.cy
Emp.: 160
Investment Management Services
S.I.C.: 6282
N.A.I.C.S.: 523930
Alkis H. Hadjikyriacos *(Mng Dir)*

ALKYL AMINES CHEMICALS LIMITED

401-407 Nirman Vyapar Kendra Plot
No 10 Sector 17 Vashi
Navi Mumbai, 400 703, India
Tel.: (91) 67946600
Fax: (91) 67946666
E-Mail: legal@alkylamines.com
Web Site: www.alkylamines.com
ALKYLAMINE—(NSE)
Rev.: $73,396,189
Assets: $63,130,851
Liabilities: $41,581,086
Net Worth: $21,549,765
Earnings: $4,473,572
Emp.: 364
Fiscal Year-end: 03/31/13
Business Description:
Specialty Chemicals Distr
S.I.C.: 5169
N.A.I.C.S.: 424690
Personnel:
Yogesh M. Kothari *(Chm & Mng Dir)*
K. P. Rajagopalan *(Compliance Officer, Sec & Gen Mgr-Secretarial & Legal)*
Board of Directors:
Yogesh M. Kothari
Shyam B. Ghia
Premal N. Kapadia
Hemendra M. Kothari
Dilip G. Piramal
K. R. V. Subrahmanian
Shobhan M. Thakore
Tarjani Vakil
Transfer Agent:
Sharex Dynamic (India) Pvt Ltd
Unit No 1 Luthra Indl Premises First floor 44-E
M Vasanji Marg
Andheri-Kurla Road Safed Poo Andheri East, Mumbai, 400 072, India
Tel.: (91) 2228515606

ALL - AMERICA LATINA LOGISTICA S.A.

Rua Emilio Bertolini 100 Vila Oficinas
82920-030 Curitiba, Parana, Brazil
Tel.: (55) 4121417555
Fax: (55) 4121417484
E-Mail: ir@all-logistica.com
Web Site: www.all-logistica.com
Year Founded: 1997
ALL3—(BRAZ)
Emp.: 4,700
Business Description:
Logistics Services
S.I.C.: 4731
N.A.I.C.S.: 541614
Personnel:
Wilson Ferro de Lara *(Chm)*
Rodrigo Barros de Moura Campos *(CFO & IR Officer)*
Board of Directors:
Wilson Ferro de Lara
Paulo Luiz Araujo Basilio
Giancarlo Arduini
Riccardo Arduini
Linneu Carlos da Costa Lima
Henrique Amarante da Costa Pinto
Mario Mendes de Lara Neto
Raimundo Pires Martins da Costa
Wagner Pinheiro de Oliveira
Nelson Rozental
Ricardo Schaefer
Sergio Ricardo Silva Rosa
Carlos Fernando Vieira Gamboa

ALL ASIA ASSET CAPITAL LIMITED

Unit 2302 23/F New World Tower 1
18 Queen's Road, Central, China (Hong Kong)
Tel.: (852) 3756 0124
E-Mail: ir@aaacap.com
Web Site: www.aaacap.com
Year Founded: 2012
AAA—(AIM)
Business Description:
Investment Services
S.I.C.: 6211
N.A.I.C.S.: 523999
Personnel:
Robert Berkeley *(Chm & Dir-Fin)*
Hartati Kurniawan *(CEO)*
Board of Directors:
Robert Berkeley
Yuhi Horiguchi
Hartati Kurniawan
Dominic Boon Chin Seah

ALL IN WEST! CAPITAL CORPORATION

(d/b/a Marwest Management Canada Ltd.)
360 Main Street Suite 300
Winnipeg, MB, R3C 3Z3, Canada
Tel.: (204) 947-1200
Fax: (204) 947-0453
E-Mail: info@marwest.ca
Web Site: www.allinwest.com
ALW—(TSXV)
Rev.: $4,913,369
Assets: $19,788,931
Liabilities: $30,984,692
Net Worth: ($11,195,761)
Earnings: ($1,083,535)
Emp.: 20
Fiscal Year-end: 12/31/12
Business Description:
Real Estate Services
S.I.C.: 6531
N.A.I.C.S.: 531390
Personnel:
Edward Warkentin *(Chm)*
Cornelius Martens *(Pres & CEO)*
Fred Mostowy *(CFO)*
Board of Directors:
Edward Warkentin
Cornelius Martens
Victor Thielmann
Wayne Townsend
Transfer Agent:
CIBC Mellon Trust Company
PO Box 721 Agincourt
Scarborough, ON, Canada

Subsidiary:

Marwest Management Canada Ltd. (1)
300-360 Main St
Winnipeg, MB, R3C 3Z3, Canada
Tel.: (204) 947-1200
Fax: (204) 947-0453
E-Mail: info@marwest.ca
Web Site: www.marwest.ca
Emp.: 10
Real Estate Management Services
S.I.C.: 6531
N.A.I.C.S.: 531390
John Bruce *(Sr Mgr)*

ALL LEISURE GROUP PLC

Lynnem House 1 Victoria Way
Burgess Hill, West Sussex, RH15 9NF, United Kingdom
Tel.: (44) 1444462103
Fax: (44) 1444462161
E-Mail: info@allleisuregroup.com
Web Site: www.allleisuregroup.com
ALLG—(AIM)
Rev.: $201,190,491
Assets: $173,865,615
Liabilities: $123,678,938
Net Worth: $50,186,678
Earnings: $788,066
Emp.: 376
Fiscal Year-end: 10/31/12
Business Description:
Cruise Ship Operator
S.I.C.: 4481
N.A.I.C.S.: 483112
Personnel:
Roger Allard *(Chm)*
Ian Smith *(CEO)*
Andrew Dufty *(CMO)*
Steve Tucker *(Pres-North America)*
Peter E. Buckley *(Sec)*
Board of Directors:
Roger Allard
Rob Bryant
Chris Gadsby
Nigel Jenkins
Philip Ovenden
Ian Smith
Legal Counsel:
Watson, Farley & Williams LLP
15 Appold Street
London, United Kingdom

Thomas Eggar LLP
Belmont House Station Way
Crawley, United Kingdom

Pinsent Masons LLP
3 Colmore Circus
Birmingham, United Kingdom

Divisions:

Swan Hellenic Ltd. (1)
Lynnem House 1 Victoria Way
Burgess Hill, W Sussex, RH15 9NF, United Kingdom UK
Tel.: (44) 8442099000
Fax: (44) 1444 462181
E-Mail: info@swanhellenic.com
Web Site: www.swanhellenic.com
Emp.: 100
Cruise Ship Operator
S.I.C.: 4481
N.A.I.C.S.: 483112
Colin Stone *(Mng Dir)*

Voyages of Discovery (1)
Lynnem House
1 Victoria Way, Burgess Hill, West Sussex, RH15 9NF, United Kingdom
Tel.: (44) 8448220800
Fax: (44) 1444462160
E-Mail: info@voyagesofdiscovery.com
Web Site: www.voyagesofdiscovery.com
Emp.: 100
Cruise Ship Operator
S.I.C.: 4481
N.A.I.C.S.: 483112
David Yellow *(Mng Dir)*

ALL METAL SERVICES LTD.

Unit 6 Horton Road Industrial Park
West Drayton
London, Middlesex, UB7 8JD, United Kingdom
Tel.: (44) 1895 444066
Fax: (44) 1895 420963
Web Site: www.allmetal.co.uk
Year Founded: 1974
Sales Range: $200-249.9 Million
Emp.: 306
Business Description:
Metal Product Mfr
S.I.C.: 3317
N.A.I.C.S.: 331210
Personnel:
Colin Hicks *(Mgr-Sls-Hard Metals)*

ALL NIPPON AIRWAYS CO., LTD.

(Name Changed to ANA Holdings Inc.)

ALL ORE MINERACAO PARTICIPACOES S.A.
Rua Leopoldo Couto de Magalhaes Jr 758 - 2nd floor cj 22 Itaim Bibi
04542-000 Sao Paulo, Brazil
Tel.: (55) 1137774250
Fax: (55) 1137774255
E-Mail: info@steeldobrasil.com.br
Web Site: www.allore.com.br
AORE3—(BRAZ)
Business Description:
Iron Products Mfr & Distr
S.I.C.: 3312
N.A.I.C.S.: 331110
Personnel:
Heinz-Gerd Stein *(Chm)*
Dirk Adamski *(First Vice Chm)*
Marcelo Henrique de C. Silva *(Second Vice Chm)*
Juarez Saliba de Avelar *(CEO & IRO)*
Rita de Cassia Lo Sciuto *(Chief Admin & IR Officer)*
Gerson Luiz Petterle *(Project Officer)*
Board of Directors:
Heinz-Gerd Stein
Dirk Adamski
Marcelo Henrique de C. Silva

ALL POINTS NORTH PLC
Cumbria House Ste 8 Gilwilly Rd
CA11 9FF Penrith, Cumbria, United Kingdom
Tel.: (44) 1768865959
E-Mail: info@allpointsnorthplc.com
Web Site: www.allpointsnorthplc.com
APNO—(LSE)
Sales Range: $1-9.9 Million
Business Description:
Real Estate Agents & Brokers
S.I.C.: 6531
N.A.I.C.S.: 531210
Personnel:
Bernard Keith Chadwick *(Chm)*
John Maxwell Elliott *(Mng Dir)*
Kevin Philbin *(Sec)*
Board of Directors:
Bernard Keith Chadwick
John Maxwell Elliott
John Anthony Lyons
Kevin Philbin

ALL RESPONSE MEDIA
12 St John Sq
London, EC1M 4NL, United Kingdom
Tel.: (44) 2070171450
Fax: (44) 2070171451
E-Mail: enquiries@allresponsemedia.com
Web Site: www.allresponsemedia.com
Year Founded: 1995
Billings: $71,000,000
Emp.: 40
Business Description:
Advertising Agency
S.I.C.: 7311
N.A.I.C.S.: 541810
Personnel:
Andy Sloan *(CEO)*
Michael Court *(Mng Dir)*
Colin Gillespie *(Chief Strategy Officer)*

ALL TREAT FARMS LIMITED
7963 Wellington Rd 109 RR 4
Arthur, ON, N0G 1A0, Canada
Tel.: (519) 848-3145
Fax: (519) 848-2598
E-Mail: alltreat@alltreat.com
Web Site: www.alltreat.com
Rev.: $22,259,925
Emp.: 70
Business Description:
Farm Products Mfr
S.I.C.: 5191
N.A.I.C.S.: 424910
Personnel:
Therese Wright *(Acct Mgr-Natl)*

ALL WEATHER WINDOWS LTD.
18550 118A Avenue NW
Edmonton, AB, T5S 2K7, Canada
Tel.: (780) 451-0670
Fax: (780) 454-7474
Toll Free: (800) 232-9407
E-Mail: info@allweatherwindows.com
Web Site: www.allweatherwindows.com
Year Founded: 1978
Rev.: $125,400,000
Emp.: 2,000
Business Description:
Windows & Doors Mfr
S.I.C.: 2431
N.A.I.C.S.: 321911
Personnel:
Harry Buhler *(Founder)*
Gord Wiebe *(Pres & CEO)*
Richard Scott *(Pres)*
Bill Scott *(Exec VP)*

ALLAHABAD BANK
2 N S Road
Kolkata, 700001, India
Tel.: (91) 332231 9144
Fax: (91) 332210 7425
E-Mail: ibcal@allahabadbank.co.in
Web Site: www.allahabadbank.in
Year Founded: 1865
532480—(BOM)
Rev.: $3,527,477,874
Assets: $37,973,351,754
Liabilities: $35,826,747,912
Net Worth: $2,146,603,842
Earnings: $224,678,844
Emp.: 22,557
Fiscal Year-end: 03/31/13
Business Description:
Banking Services
S.I.C.: 6029
N.A.I.C.S.: 522110
Personnel:
Rakesh Sethi *(Chm & Mng Dir)*
K. S. Venkataraman *(CFO, Compliance Officer & Gen Mgr)*
Atul Kumar Goel *(CFO & Gen Mgr-Fin & Accts)*
Shreya Shah *(Sec)*
Board of Directors:
Rakesh Sethi
Nirmal Kumar Bari
Sudip Chaudhuri
Tilak Raj Chawla
Dinesh Dubey
Shashank Saksena
A. P. V. N. Sarma
Ajay Shukla
Deveshwar Narain Singh
Yogeshwar Prasad Singh
Arun Tiwari
A. Udgata
Ashok Vij

Raghu Nath Rai & Co
9 Mathura Road Jangpura B
New Delhi, 110014, India

N. K. Bhargava & Co
C-31 Ist Floor Acharya Niketan Phase-1 Mayur Vihar
New Delhi, India

M.C.Jain & Co.
3rd Floor 33 Brabourne Road
Kolkata, India

Khandelwal Kakani & Co
8 Johari Palace First Floor M G Road
Indore, MP, 452001, India

Batliboi & Purohit
National Insurance Building 204 Dadabhoy Naoroji Road
400001 Mumbai, India

Transfer Agent:
MCS Limited
77/2A Hazra Road
Kolkata, India

Subsidiary:

AllBank Finance Limited **(1)**
14 India Exchange Place IV Floor
Kolkata, West Bengal, 700001, India
Tel.: (91) 3322487896
Fax: (91) 3322489984
E-Mail: info@allbankfinance.com
Web Site: www.allbankfinance.com
Emp.: 4
Merchant Banking Services
S.I.C.: 6211
N.A.I.C.S.: 523110
Ravinder Singh *(VP)*

ALLAMI AUTOPALYA KEZELO RT.
Vaci St 45 B
PO Box 1170
1134 Budapest, 1380, Hungary
Tel.: (36) 14368200
Fax: (36) 14368210
E-Mail: info@autopalya.hu
Web Site: www.motorway.hu
Year Founded: 2000
Emp.: 1,000
Business Description:
Highway Operations
S.I.C.: 4789
N.A.I.C.S.: 488490
Personnel:
Attila Bako *(CEO)*

ALLAMI NYOMDA NYRT
(Name Changed to ANY Security Printing Company PLC)

ALLAN CRAWFORD ASSOCIATES LIMITED
5805 Kennedy Road
Mississauga, ON, L4Z 2G3, Canada
Tel.: (905) 890-2010
Fax: (905) 890-1959
Web Site: www.aca.ca
Year Founded: 1959
Rev.: $27,967,838
Emp.: 65
Business Description:
Electronic Instruments Distr
S.I.C.: 5065
N.A.I.C.S.: 423690
Personnel:
Allan Crawford *(Chm)*

ALLAN INTERNATIONAL HOLDINGS LIMITED
12th Floor Zung Fu Industrial Building
1067 Kings Road Quarry Bay
Hong Kong, China (Hong Kong)
Tel.: (852) 21037288
Fax: (852) 22149357
E-Mail: info@allan.com.hk
Web Site: www.allan.com.hk
0684—(HKG)
Rev.: $303,852,880
Assets: $226,350,964
Liabilities: $96,559,178
Net Worth: $129,791,786
Earnings: $14,033,113
Emp.: 5,200
Fiscal Year-end: 03/31/13
Business Description:
Electric Appliances Mfr
S.I.C.: 3999
N.A.I.C.S.: 335210
Personnel:
Lun Cheung *(Founder & Chm)*
Albert Shu Wan Cheung *(Mng Dir)*
Lai Yung Wong *(Sec & Mgr-Fin & Acct)*
Board of Directors:
Lun Cheung
How Chun Chan
Albert Shu Wan Cheung
Maggie Lai Chun Cheung
Pui Cheung
Sophie Lai See Cheung
Leon Ah Ming Lai
Chung Mau Lo
Legal Counsel:
Conyers Dill & Pearman
2901 One Exchange Square 8 Connaught Place
Central, China (Hong Kong)

HSBC Securities Services (Bermuda) Limited
6 Front Street
Hamilton, Bermuda

Transfer Agents:
Tricor Standard Limited
26/F Tesbury Centre 28 Queen's Road East
Wanchai, China (Hong Kong)
Tel.: (852) 2980 1333
Fax: (852) 2810 8185

HSBC Securities Services (Bermuda) Limited
6 Front Street
Hamilton, Bermuda

Subsidiaries:

Allan Electric Mfg., Limited **(1)**
12 Fl Zung Fu Indus Bldg 1067 Kings Rd
Quarry Bay, China (Hong Kong)
Tel.: (852) 21037288
Fax: (852) 24149357
E-Mail: info@allan.com.hk
Emp.: 200
Household Electrical Appliances Mfr
S.I.C.: 3999
N.A.I.C.S.: 335210
Michelle Wing Tong Tsang *(Gen Mgr)*

Allan Mould Manufacturing Limited **(1)**
12 F Zung Fu Indus Bldg 1067 Kings Rd
Quarry Bay, China (Hong Kong)
Tel.: (852) 21037288
Fax: (852) 22149357
E-Mail: info@allan.com.hk
Web Site: www.allan.com.hk
Emp.: 100
Plastic Containers Mfr
S.I.C.: 2679
N.A.I.C.S.: 322299
Shu Wan Cheung *(Mng Dir)*

Allan Plastic Mfg., Limited **(1)**
12 F Zung Fu Indus Bldg 1067 Kings Rd
Quarry Bay, China (Hong Kong)
Tel.: (852) 21037288
Fax: (852) 22149357
E-Mail: Info@allan.com.hk
Emp.: 500
Plastic Products Mfr
S.I.C.: 3089
N.A.I.C.S.: 326199

Conan Electric Manufacturing Limited **(1)**
12 F Zung Fu Indus Bldg 1067 Kings Rd
Quarry Bay, China (Hong Kong)
Tel.: (852) 21037288
Fax: (852) 22149357
E-Mail: info@allan.com.hk
Web Site: www.allan.com.hk
Emp.: 100
Household Electrical Appliances Whslr
S.I.C.: 5064
N.A.I.C.S.: 423620
Shu Wan Cheung *(Gen Mgr)*

Global Express (HK) Limited **(1)**
12 F Zung Fu Indus Bldg 1067 Kings Rd
Quarry Bay, China (Hong Kong)
Tel.: (852) 21037288
Fax: (852) 22149357
E-Mail: info@allan.com.hk
Consumer Electronics Whslr
S.I.C.: 5064
N.A.I.C.S.: 423620

Karan Electric Manufacturing Limited **(1)**
12 F Zung Fu Indus Bldg 1067 Kings Rd
Quarry Bay, China (Hong Kong)
Tel.: (852) 21037288

Fax: (852) 22149357
E-Mail: info@allan.com.hk
Emp.: 100
Consumer Electronics Whslr
S.I.C.: 5064
N.A.I.C.S.: 423620
Simon Shu Chun Cheung *(Mgr-Sls)*

Warran Electric Manufacturing Limited (1)
12 F Zung Fu Indus Bldg 1067 Kings Rd
Quarry Bay, China (Hong Kong)
Tel.: (852) 21037288
Fax: (852) 25634307
E-Mail: info@allan.com.hk
Electrical Contracting Services
S.I.C.: 1731
N.A.I.C.S.: 238210

ALLAN WINDOW TECHNOLOGIES LTD.

131 Caldari Road Unit 1
Concord, ON, L4K 3Z9, Canada
Tel.: (905) 738-8600
Fax: (905) 738-1988
Toll Free: (800) 760-5665
Web Site: www.allanwindows.com
Year Founded: 1959
Rev.: $39,299,117
Emp.: 360

Business Description:
Doors & Windows Mfr
S.I.C.: 3442
N.A.I.C.S.: 332321

Personnel:
Stephen J. Miller *(Pres & CEO)*
Brian J. Cohen *(Pres-Eastern Canada)*
Lester Lee Fook *(Pres-Western Canada)*
Jon Snyder *(Pres-Cornwall)*

ALLANA POTASH CORP.

65 Queen Street West Suite 805
PO Box 75
Toronto, ON, M5H 2M5, Canada
Tel.: (416) 861-2267
Fax: (416) 861-8165
E-Mail: info@allanapotash.com
Web Site: www.allanapotash.com
AAA—(OTC TSX)
Int. Income: $415,508
Assets: $127,381,515
Liabilities: $16,996,654
Net Worth: $110,384,861
Earnings: ($8,623,128)
Fiscal Year-end: 07/31/13

Business Description:
Potash Mining Services
S.I.C.: 1474
N.A.I.C.S.: 212391

Personnel:
Mark D. Stauffer *(Chm)*
Farhad Abasov *(Pres & CEO)*
Deborah Lynn Battiston *(CFO)*
Brianna Davies *(Sec)*
Nejib Abba Biya *(Sr VP-Bus Dev-Ethiopia)*
Richard Kelertas *(Sr VP-Corp Dev)*
Peter J. MacLean *(Sr VP-Exploration)*
Jack Scott *(Sr VP-Strategic Projects)*

Board of Directors:
Mark D. Stauffer
Farhad Abasov
Richard J. Lacroix
Lewis Wharton MacKenzie

Transfer Agent:
Equity Financial Trust Company
Toronto, ON, Canada

ALLAND ET ROBERT

125 Rue Grande
27940 Rouen, France
Tel.: (33) 232775177
Fax: (33) 3314272543
Web Site: www.allandetrobert.fr
Sls.: $20,700,000
Emp.: 33

Business Description:
Durable Goods
S.I.C.: 5099
N.A.I.C.S.: 423990

Personnel:
Frederic Alland *(Chm)*

Board of Directors:
Frederic Alland
Xavier Maison

ALLANNIC FRERES SA

ZI de Kerpont 1371 rue Dominique Francois Arago
56850 Caudan, France
Tel.: (33) 297769600
Fax: (33) 297769604
Web Site: allannic.lorient.mercedes.fr
Sls.: $21,200,000
Emp.: 23

Business Description:
Automotive Repair Services
S.I.C.: 7539
N.A.I.C.S.: 811118

Personnel:
Philippe Allannic *(VP)*

ALLANSON INTERNATIONAL INC.

33 Cranfield Road
Toronto, ON, M4B 3H2, Canada
Tel.: (416) 755-1191
Fax: (416) 752-6718
Toll Free: (800) 668-9162
Web Site: www.allanson.com
Rev.: $27,272,343
Emp.: 150

Business Description:
Electrical Products Mfr
S.I.C.: 3699
N.A.I.C.S.: 335999

Personnel:
Rick Woodgate *(Chm & CEO)*

ALLAWASAYA TEXTILE & FINISHING MILLS LTD.

Allawasaya Square Mumtazab industrial Area Vehari Road
Multan, Pakistan
Tel.: (92) 614233624
Fax: (92) 616525202
E-Mail: atm@allawasaya.com
Web Site: www.allawasaya.com
AWTX—(LAH)
Sls.: $20,654,208
Assets: $11,280,725
Liabilities: $3,608,748
Net Worth: $7,671,977
Earnings: $883,279
Emp.: 887
Fiscal Year-end: 06/30/13

Business Description:
Textile Mfr
S.I.C.: 2269
N.A.I.C.S.: 313310

Personnel:
Muhammad Jamil *(Chm)*
Tanvir Ahmad *(CEO & Mng Dir)*
Muhammad Ismail *(CFO & Sec)*

Board of Directors:
Muhammad Jamil
Anis Ahmad
Muhammad Bilal Ahmad
Sarfraz Ahmad
Tanvir Ahmad
Tauqir Ahmad
Nusrat Jamil
Muhammad Alamgir Jamil Khan

ALLCAP ASSET MANAGEMENT LTD

19-20 City Quay
Dublin, 2, Ireland
Tel.: (353) 18974900
Fax: (353) 18974933
E-Mail: info@allcap.com
Web Site: www.allcap.com
Emp.: 25

Business Description:
Asset Management Services
S.I.C.: 6282
N.A.I.C.S.: 523930

Personnel:
Jana Becher *(Mng Dir)*

Board of Directors:
Jana Becher
Brenda King-Geis
Peter Van Dessel

ALLCARGO LOGISTICS LIMITED

5th Floor The Awashya House CST Road
Kalina Santacruz East, Mumbai, 400 098, India
Tel.: (91) 22 6679 8100
Fax: (91) 22 6679 8195
E-Mail: info@allcargoglobal.com
Web Site: www.allcargologistics.com
ALLCARGO—(NSE)
Rev.: $740,194,668
Assets: $554,503,590
Liabilities: $252,492,552
Net Worth: $302,011,038
Earnings: $31,469,796
Fiscal Year-end: 03/31/13

Business Description:
Freight Transportation Arrangement
S.I.C.: 4731
N.A.I.C.S.: 488510

Personnel:
Shashi Kiran Shetty *(Chm & Mng Dir)*
Jatin Chokshi *(CFO & Chief Investment Officer)*
Ajit Jangle *(COO)*
Hrushikesh Joshi *(CIO)*
Shailesh Dholakia *(Compliance Officer & Sec)*
Ajay Rao *(Pres-Strategy & Bus Dev)*
Simon Bajada *(CEO-NVOCC)*
Mike Dye *(CEO-NVOCC)*
Armin Kalyaniwalla *(CEO-Projects Div)*
Shantha Martin *(CEO-ISC-Middle East, South & East Africa)*
Ashok Kumar Shrivastava *(CEO-Shipping Svcs)*
Tim Tudor *(CEO-NVOCC)*
Pramod Kokate *(Sr VP-Container Freight Stations Div)*

Board of Directors:
Shashi Kiran Shetty
Mohinder Pal Bansal
Keki Elavia
Akhilesh Gupta
Adarsh Hegde
Kaiwan Kalyaniwalla
Hari L. Mundra
J. Ramachandran
Arathi Shetty
Umesh Shetty

Appan & Lokhandwala Associates
402 Shiv-Ahish Plot No 10 19th Road
Chembur, Mumbai, 400 071, India

Legal Counsel:
Maneksha & Sethna
8 Ambalal Doshi Marg Hamam Street Fort
Mumbai, India

Transfer Agent:
Link Intime India Pvt. Ltd.
C-13 Pannalal Silk Mills Compound
LBS Marg
Bhandup, Mumbai, 400 078, India
Tel.: (91) 22 2596 3838
Fax: (91) 22 2594 6969

Subsidiary:

Hindustan Cargo Ltd. (1)
B1 & D2 First Fl Dignity Centre No 21
Abdul Razak St
Saidapet, Chennai, Tamil Nadu, 600 015, India
Tel.: (91) 44 459 11500
Fax: (91) 44 2434 4035
E-Mail: sales.hcl@hindustancargoltd.in
Web Site: www.hindustancargoltd.in
Emp.: 40
Freight Forwarding Services
S.I.C.: 4731
N.A.I.C.S.: 488510
Deepal Shah *(CEO)*
Ramesh Mora *(CFO)*

Non-U.S. Subsidiaries:

Deolix S.A. (1)
Zabala 1327
Montevideo, 11000, Uruguay
Tel.: (598) 29170603
Fax: (598) 29170604
E-Mail: birginia@ecumvd.eculine.net
Web Site: www.eculine.net
Emp.: 5
Freight Forwarding Services
S.I.C.: 4731
N.A.I.C.S.: 488510
Ricardo Biernacki *(Gen Mgr)*

ECUHOLD N.V. (1)
Schomhoeveweg No 15
B 2030 Antwerp, Belgium BE
Tel.: (32) 35412466
Fax: (32) 35417961
E-Mail: info@eculines.net
Web Site: www.eculines.be
Emp.: 150
Holding Company
S.I.C.: 6719
N.A.I.C.S.: 551112
Kris De Witte *(Mng Dir)*

Subsidiaries:

ECU Air N.V. (2)
Bldg 734
Brucargo, 1931 Brussels, Belgium
Tel.: (32) 27515051
Fax: (32) 27515413
E-Mail: sue@ecumel.ecuair.net
Web Site: www.ecuair.net
Emp.: 15
Air Freight Forwarding Services
S.I.C.: 4512
N.A.I.C.S.: 481112
Nancy Verbeke *(Branch Mgr)*

ECU International N.V. (2)
Schomhoeveweg 15
2030 Antwerp, Belgium
Tel.: (32) 35443800
Fax: (32) 35417961
E-Mail: info@ecuanr.eculine.net
Web Site: www.eculine.net
Emp.: 150
Freight Forwarding Services
S.I.C.: 4731
N.A.I.C.S.: 488510
Marc Stoffelen *(CEO)*
Ashit Desai *(Mng Dir)*
Shashi Kiran Shetty *(Mng Dir)*
Marc Toffeln *(Mng Dir)*

Ecu-Line N.V. (2)
Schouwkenstraat 1
B 2030 Antwerp, Belgium
Tel.: (32) 35412466
Fax: (32) 35417961
E-Mail: info@ecuims.eculine.net
Web Site: www.eculine.net
Emp.: 300
Provider of Freight Transportation Services
S.I.C.: 4449
N.A.I.C.S.: 483211
Marc Stoffelen *(CEO & Mng Dir)*

U.S. Subsidiaries:

Econocaribe Consolidators Inc. (3)
2401 NW 69th St
Miami, FL 33147-6883 FL
Tel.: (305) 693-5133
Fax: (305) 696-9350
Toll Free: (800) 326-6648
E-Mail: webmaster@econocaribe.com
Web Site: www.econocaribe.com

Allcargo Logistics Limited—(Continued)

Sales Range: $50-74.9 Million
Emp.: 220
Freight Transportation Arrangement
Import Export
S.I.C.: 4731
N.A.I.C.S.: 488510
John Abisch *(Pres)*
Mitch Shapiro *(CFO)*

Ecu International (3)
9130 S Dadeland Blvd Ste
Miami, FL 33156
Tel.: (305) 670-1877
Fax: (305) 670-8511
Web Site: www.eculine.net
Sls.: $16,000,000
Emp.: 150
Freight Consolidation
S.I.C.: 3567
N.A.I.C.S.: 333994

Ecu-Logistics N.V. (2)
Schomhoeveweg 15
2030 Antwerp, Belgium
Tel.: (32) 35412466
Fax: (32) 35417961
E-Mail: antsales@ecuair.eculine.net
Emp.: 150
Logistics Services
S.I.C.: 4731
N.A.I.C.S.: 541614

Ecubro N.V. (2)
Schomhoeveweg 15
2030 Antwerp, Belgium
Tel.: (32) 35412466
Fax: (32) 35423361
Web Site: www.europeancustomsbrokers.be
Emp.: 20
Freight Forwarding Services
S.I.C.: 4731
N.A.I.C.S.: 488510
Jan Hendrickx *(Mng Dir)*

Non-U.S. Subsidiaries:

Conecli International S.A. (2)
De Mc Donald Sabana 200 Este 75 Sur
Frente A Condominios Fasaro
PO Box 1018-1000
Sabana Sur, San Jose, Costa Rica
Tel.: (506) 2 296 6748
Fax: (506) 2 290 3844
E-Mail: cmontoya@ecusjo.eculine.net
Freight Forwarding Services
S.I.C.: 4731
N.A.I.C.S.: 488510
Daniela Andreu *(Mgr-Import)*

ECU Australia Pty Ltd. (2)
Ste 2 35-37 Tullamarine Park Rd
Tullamarine, VIC, 3043, Australia
Tel.: (61) 383368600
Fax: (61) 393300448
E-Mail: sales@ecuaustralia.com
Web Site: www.ecuaustralia.com
Emp.: 20
Freight Forwarding Services
S.I.C.: 4731
N.A.I.C.S.: 488510
Greg Nucifora *(Chm)*
Justin Fitzgerald *(Deputy Chm)*

ECU Line Abu Dhabi LLC (2)
Ahmed Bin Hmouda Bldg Mezzanine Fl Al Naser St
PO Box 7158
Abu Dhabi, United Arab Emirates
Tel.: (971) 26339597
Fax: (971) 26331417
E-Mail: jerna.bardon@auh.eculine.com
Web Site: www.eculine.net
Emp.: 3
Freight Forwarding Services
S.I.C.: 4731
N.A.I.C.S.: 488510
Varuna Wirasinha *(Mng Dir)*

ECU Line Algerie S.A.R.L. (2)
Cooperative Ennahar Villa n 3 2ieme etage
Les Sources
Bir Mourad Rais, Algiers, 16005, Algeria
Tel.: (213) 21563622
Fax: (213) 21563107
E-Mail: info@ecualg.eculine.net
Web Site: www.eculine.net
Emp.: 10
Freight Forwarding Services
S.I.C.: 4731
N.A.I.C.S.: 488510
Abdelmadjid Sellaoui *(Country Mgr-Sls)*

Ecu-Line Canada Inc. (2)
1804 Alstep Dr Unit 2
Toronto, ON, L5S 1W1, Canada
Tel.: (905) 677-8334
Fax: (905) 677-1255
Web Site: www.eculine.ca
Emp.: 10
Freight Forwarding Services
S.I.C.: 4731
N.A.I.C.S.: 488510
Mike McCarthy *(Gen Mgr)*

Ecu Line Chile S.A. (2)
Av Americo Vespucio 80 Piso 8 Of 81 82
Las Condes, Santiago, Chile
Tel.: (56) 24306600
Fax: (56) 23660164
E-Mail: alicia@ecuscl.eculine.net
Web Site: www.eculine.net
Emp.: 36
Freight Forwarding Services
S.I.C.: 4731
N.A.I.C.S.: 488510
Noel Arnauts *(Gen Dir)*
Alicia Perez *(Sec)*

Ecu Line China Ltd. (2)
9F Bldg B Silverbay Tower 469 WuSong Rd
Shanghai, 200 080, China
Tel.: (86) 2163643399
Fax: (86) 2163643391
Freight Forwarding Services
S.I.C.: 4731
N.A.I.C.S.: 488510

Ecu Line Cote d'Ivoire Sarl (2)
10 Rue Pierre Et Marie Curie Zone 4C 18
BP 2528
Abidjan, Cote d'Ivoire
Tel.: (225) 21257179
Fax: (225) 21256079
Freight Forwarding Services
S.I.C.: 4731
N.A.I.C.S.: 488510
Bini Koffi *(Mgr-Export)*

Ecu-Line Czech S.r.o. (2)
Do Certous 2622 14 VG Park - B2
Horni Pocernice, Prague, 19321, Czech Republic
Tel.: (420) 272 701 972
Fax: (420) 272 701 974
E-Mail: info@eculine.cz
Web Site: www.eculine.cz
Freight Forwarding Services
S.I.C.: 4731
N.A.I.C.S.: 488510
Libor Ptacnik *(Mng Dir)*

Ecu-Line De Colombia S.A (2)
Edif Centro Aero Intl Carrera 102A No 25H-45 Of 110
Bogota, Colombia
Tel.: (57) 14139640
Fax: (57) 14135031
E-Mail: customer@ecuvob.eculine.net
Web Site: www.eculine.net
Freight Forwarding Services
S.I.C.: 4731
N.A.I.C.S.: 488510
Patricia Daza *(Mgr-Ops, Export & Import)*

Ecu Line Del Ecuador S.A. (2)
Ciudadela Guayaquil Manzana 3 Solar 5 Av Miguel H Alcivar
Guayaquil, Guayas, Ecuador
Tel.: (593) 42286225
Fax: (593) 42295268
Freight Forwarding Services
S.I.C.: 4731
N.A.I.C.S.: 488510

Ecu Line Doha W.L.L. (2)
22 Abdulla Bin Omar Street Arabian Gulf Petrol Station Bldg 2nd Fl
PO Box 24064
near Mannai Round About, Doha, Qatar
Tel.: (974) 444 38491
Fax: (974) 444 32646
E-Mail: vijayan@ecudoh.eculine.net
Web Site: www.eculine.net
Emp.: 3
Freight Forwarding Services
S.I.C.: 4731
N.A.I.C.S.: 488510
Vijayan Krishnan *(Mgr-Country, Export, Fin, Import & Sls)*

Ecu Line Egypt Ltd. (2)
31 Omar Bakeer St 9th Fl Flat 802
Heliopolis, Cairo, Egypt
Tel.: (20) 226383905
Fax: (20) 226383906
E-Mail: info@ecutai.eculine.net
Web Site: www.eculine.net
Emp.: 14
Freight Forwarding Services
S.I.C.: 4731
N.A.I.C.S.: 488510
Amal Mohammed *(Gen Mgr)*

Ecu-Line (Germany) GmbH (2)
Frankenstrasse 12
20097 Hamburg, Germany
Tel.: (49) 402388900
Fax: (49) 4023889090
E-Mail: ecu-line@eculine.com
Web Site: www.ecu-line.com
Emp.: 50
Freight Forwarding Services
S.I.C.: 4731
N.A.I.C.S.: 488510
Thomas Heydorn *(Mng Dir)*

Ecu-Line Guangzhou Ltd. (2)
Unit 2114-2116 Bai Hui Plz 193 Zhong Shan Wu Rd
Guangzhou, Guangdong, 510030, China
Tel.: (86) 2083649778
Fax: (86) 2083649450
E-Mail: info@ecuccs.eculine.net
Web Site: www.eculine.net
Emp.: 30
Freight Forwarding Services
S.I.C.: 4731
N.A.I.C.S.: 488510
Candy Wong *(Branch Mgr)*

Ecu Line Guatemala S.A. (2)
31 Avenida 0-48 Zona 7
Utatlan 1, 01007 Guatemala, Guatemala
Tel.: (502) 23809300
Fax: (502) 23809301
E-Mail: julio@ecugua.eculine.net
Emp.: 15
Freight Forwarding Services
S.I.C.: 4731
N.A.I.C.S.: 488510
Julio Pineda *(Country Mgr)*

Ecu-Line Hellas Ltd. (2)
Tsokri Sq 1
11742 Athens, Greece
Tel.: (30) 210 924 71 90
Fax: (30) 210 922 99 74
E-Mail: menos@ecupir.eculine.net
Emp.: 10
Freight Forwarding Services
S.I.C.: 4731
N.A.I.C.S.: 488510
Menos Moschoutis *(Mng Dir)*

Ecu-Line Hong Kong Ltd. (2)
Rm 2008 20 Fl Asian House 1 Hennessy Rd
Wanchai, China (Hong Kong)
Tel.: (852) 21809111
Fax: (852) 30098030
Freight Forwarding Services
S.I.C.: 4731
N.A.I.C.S.: 488510

Ecu Line Japan Ltd. (2)
6F General Bldg 1-9-6 Nihonbashi-Horidome-Cho
Chuo-Ku, Tokyo, 103-0012, Japan
Tel.: (81) 356433600
Fax: (81) 356433605
E-Mail: info@ecutyo.eculine.net
Web Site: www.eculine.jp
Emp.: 30
Logistics Services
S.I.C.: 4731
N.A.I.C.S.: 541614
Don Hasegawa *(Pres)*

Ecu-Line (JB) Sdn. Bhd. (2)
40A & 40B Jalan Molek 2 2
Taman Molek, Johor Bahru, Johor, 81100, Malaysia
Tel.: (60) 73521818
Fax: (60) 73526762
E-Mail: ecujb@listm.net.my
Web Site: www.eculine.net
Emp.: 25
Freight Forwarding Services
S.I.C.: 4731
N.A.I.C.S.: 488510

Ecu-Line Malta Ltd. (2)
10 Timberwharf
Marsa, MRS1443, Malta
Tel.: (356) 21340731
Fax: (356) 21338464
E-Mail: sales@ecumla.eculine.net
Web Site: www.eculine.net
Emp.: 20
Freight Forwarding Services
S.I.C.: 4731
N.A.I.C.S.: 488510
Simon Bajada *(Country Mgr)*

Ecu Line Maroc S.A. (2)
353 Angle Blvd Mohammed V Blvd
Resistance 3ieme Etage
Casablanca, Morocco
Tel.: (212) 522402727
Fax: (212) 522401221
E-Mail: info@ecucas.eculine.net
Emp.: 30
Freight Forwarding Services
S.I.C.: 4731
N.A.I.C.S.: 488510
Mouhcine Jamdame *(Head-Export & Import)*

Ecu Line Middleeast LLC (2)
7th R A Jebel Ali Free Zone
PO Box 28430
Jebel Ali, United Arab Emirates
Tel.: (971) 48817696
Fax: (971) 48819545
Web Site: www.eculine.net
Emp.: 30
Freight Forwarding Services
S.I.C.: 4731
N.A.I.C.S.: 488510
Varuna Wirasinha *(Gen Mgr)*

Ecu-Line Panama S.A. (2)
Edificio Aventura Ofic M-10 Ave Ricardo J Alfaro Calle 74
PO Box 0819-02017
Panama, Panama
Tel.: (507) 236 17 75
Fax: (507) 236 57 02
Web Site: www.allcargologistics.com
Emp.: 15
Freight Forwarding Services
S.I.C.: 4731
N.A.I.C.S.: 488510
Celia Martin *(Country Mgr)*

Ecu-Line Peru S.A. (2)
Pezet y Monel 2452
Lima, 14, Peru
Tel.: (51) 14212000
Fax: (51) 14426240
E-Mail: infoperu@eculim.eculine.net
Web Site: www.eculineperu.com
Emp.: 30,000
Freight Forwarding Services
S.I.C.: 4731
N.A.I.C.S.: 488510
Guido Benza *(Country Mgr)*

Ecu Line Philippines Inc. (2)
Unit D5 G F Echelon Tower Bldg 2100 A Mabini St
Malate, 1004 Manila, Philippines
Tel.: (63) 2 4040658
Fax: (63) 2 4040671
E-Mail: service@ecumnl.eculine.net
Emp.: 30
Freight Forwarding Services
S.I.C.: 4731
N.A.I.C.S.: 488510
Manish Gogia *(Country Mgr)*

Ecu Line Romania S.R.L. (2)
Abrud St No 134 Sector 1
Bucharest, 011318, Romania
Tel.: (40) 212243321
Fax: (40) 318176110
E-Mail: eculines@rgsmail.ro
Web Site: ro.eculines.net
Emp.: 8
Freight Forwarding Services
S.I.C.: 4731
N.A.I.C.S.: 488510

Ecu Line Rotterdam B.V. (2)
Nieuwesluisweg 240
3197 KV Rotterdam, Netherlands
Tel.: (31) 104950444
Fax: (31) 10 429 62 99
E-Mail: info@ecurtm.eculine.net
Web Site: www.eculine.nl
Emp.: 25
Freight Forwarding Services

S.I.C.: 4731
N.A.I.C.S.: 488510
Rik Van Riet *(Mng Dir)*

Ecu Line S.A. (Pty) Ltd. (2)
Block B 1st Fl Southern Life Gardens 70 2nd Ave
Newton Park, Port Elizabeth, Eastern Cape, 6055, South Africa
Tel.: (27) 413631749
Fax: (27) 413631754
E-Mail: michelled@ecuplz.eculine.net
Web Site: www.ecuplz.eculine.net
Emp.: 30
Freight Forwarding Services
S.I.C.: 4731
N.A.I.C.S.: 488510
Yvonne Palm *(Country Mgr)*

Ecu Line Singapore Pte. Ltd. (2)
200 Pandan Loop No 05-01 02 Pantech 21
Singapore, Singapore
Tel.: (65) 62203373
Fax: (65) 62201366
E-Mail: general@ecusin.eculine.net
Emp.: 65
Freight Forwarding Services
S.I.C.: 4731
N.A.I.C.S.: 488510
Raymond Yap *(CEO)*

Ecu Line Spain S.L. (2)
Cal Lluquer 15 Zal II
08820 El Prat de Llobregat, Barcelona, Spain
Tel.: (34) 934120061
Fax: (34) 93 412 67 23
E-Mail: info@ecupcn.eculine.net
Freight Forwarding Services
S.I.C.: 4731
N.A.I.C.S.: 488510

Ecu Line (Thailand) Co.Ltd. (2)
295 Rm TR5 2nd Fl Future Mart Rama III Bldg Rama III Rd
Bangkorlaem, Bangkok, 10120, Thailand
Tel.: (66) 2 689 1355
Fax: (66) 2 689 1359
E-Mail: mollyecubkk@eculine.net
Web Site: www.eculine.net
Emp.: 60
Freight Forwarding Services
S.I.C.: 4731
N.A.I.C.S.: 488510
Viraj Nobnomtham *(Country Mgr)*

Ecu-Line UK Ltd. (2)
4b The Courtyard Reddicap Trading Estate
Birmingham, West Midlands, B75 7BU, United Kingdom
Tel.: (44) 121 311 0554
Fax: (44) 121 311 0553
Freight Forwarding Services
S.I.C.: 4731
N.A.I.C.S.: 488510

ECU Logistics S.A. (2)
Av Belgrano 355 Piso 12
Buenos Aires, C1092AAD, Argentina
Tel.: (54) 1153530200
Fax: (54) 11 5273 2323
E-Mail: info@ecuarc.eculine.com
Web Site: www.eculine.net
Freight Forwarding Services
S.I.C.: 4731
N.A.I.C.S.: 488510
Hernan Micieli *(Gen Mgr)*

Ecu Nordic Oy (2)
Lonnrotinkatu 32 D 49
00180 Helsinki, Finland
Tel.: (358) 942412320
Fax: (358) 942412339
E-Mail: anderszilliacus@eculine.com
Web Site: www.eculine.com
Emp.: 10
Freight Forwarding Services
S.I.C.: 4731
N.A.I.C.S.: 488510
Fredrik Aminoff *(Mgr-Sls)*

ELV Multimodal C.A. (2)
Avenida Sucre Torre Centro Parque Boyaca Piso 16-Oficina 164
Los Dos Caminos, Caracas, Miranda, 1070, Venezuela
Tel.: (58) 2122862016
Fax: (58) 2122859320
E-Mail: alcidesl@ecuccs.eculine.net
Web Site: www.eculine.net
Emp.: 10
Freight Forwarding Services
S.I.C.: 4731
N.A.I.C.S.: 488510
Freddy Walter Smidt *(Mgr)*

Flamingo Line El Salvador S.A. De C.V. (2)
6 10 Calle Pomiente 39 Avenida Sur Residential Casa
Magna Apartment 4 A, San Salvador, El Salvador
Tel.: (503) 22754359
Fax: (503) 22754349
E-Mail: pedro@ecusal.eculine.net
Web Site: www.eculine.net
Emp.: 4
Freight Forwarding Services
S.I.C.: 4731
N.A.I.C.S.: 488510
William Martinez *(Mgr)*

Rotterdam Freight Station B.V. (2)
Nieuwesluisweg 240 Haven nummer 5044
Botlek, 3197KV Rotterdam, Zuid-Holland, Netherlands
Tel.: (31) 102961860
Fax: (31) 102961869
E-Mail: info@rotterdamfreightstation.nl
Web Site: www.rotterdamfreightstation.nl
Emp.: 14
Warehousing & Freight Forwarding Services
S.I.C.: 4731
N.A.I.C.S.: 488510
Rik van Riet *(Mng Dir)*

ELWA (GH) Ltd. (1)
Burkina Faso Chamber Of Commerce
Ground Fl Left Graphic Rd 4Th Ln
PO Box 855
Tema Harbour Area, Tema, Ghana
Tel.: (233) 22 20 59 70
Fax: (233) 22 20 59 78
Freight Forwarding Services
S.I.C.: 4731
N.A.I.C.S.: 488510

ALLEGIANCE COAL LIMITED
Level 13 49-51 York Street
Sydney, NSW, 2000, Australia
Tel.: (61) 2 9299 5007
Fax: (61) 2 9299 5006
E-Mail: info@allegiancecoal.com.au
Web Site: www.allegiancecoal.com.au
AHQ—(ASX)
Business Description:
Coal Exploration
S.I.C.: 1222
N.A.I.C.S.: 212112
Personnel:
Anthony W. Howland-Rose *(Chm)*
Colin Randall *(Mng Dir)*
Graham Hurwitz *(Sec)*
Board of Directors:
Anthony W. Howland-Rose
David Deitz
Peter Donkin
Colin Randall

ALLEGIANCE EQUITY CORPORATION
79 Old Forest Hill Road
Toronto, ON, M5P 2R6, Canada
Tel.: (647) 271-7208
Web Site: www.allegianceequity.com
ANQ—(TSXV)
Rev.: $3,167
Assets: $83,698
Liabilities: $360,979
Net Worth: ($277,281)
Earnings: ($422,105)
Fiscal Year-end: 03/31/13
Business Description:
Pharmaceutical Products Mfr
S.I.C.: 2834
N.A.I.C.S.: 325412
Personnel:
Marilyn H. Bloovol *(Pres & CEO)*
Donald Stott *(CFO)*
Barbara J. Kavensky *(Pres-Experchem)*
Board of Directors:
Marilyn H. Bloovol
Philip Bookalam
Melvin Goldberg
Donald Stott
Transfer Agent:
Equity Financial Trust Company
200 University Avenue Suite 400
Toronto, ON, Canada

ALLEGION PLC
(Formerly Ingersoll-Rand Security Technologies)
Block D Iveagh Court Harcourt Road
Dublin, 2, Ireland
Tel.: (353) 1 2546200
Toll Free: 8887589823
Web Site: www.allegion.com
ALLE—(NYSE)
Rev.: $2,093,500,000
Assets: $1,979,900,000
Liabilities: $2,035,600,000
Net Worth: ($55,700,000)
Earnings: $43,500,000
Emp.: 8,000
Fiscal Year-end: 12/31/13
Business Description:
Security Systems Mfr
S.I.C.: 7382
N.A.I.C.S.: 561621
Personnel:
David D. Petratis *(Chm, Pres & CEO)*
John Conover *(Pres)*
Patrick Shannon *(CFO & Sr VP)*
Tracy Kemp *(CIO & VP)*
Timothy P. Eckersley *(Pres-America & Sr VP)*
Lucia Veiga Moretti *(Pres-Europe, Middle East, India & Africa & Sr VP)*
William Yu *(Pres-Asia Pacific & Sr VP)*
Barbara A. Santoro *(Gen Counsel, Sec & Sr VP)*
Ray Lewis *(Sr VP-HR & Comm)*
Chris E. Muhlenkamp *(Sr VP-Global Ops & Integrated Supply Chain)*
Board of Directors:
Michael J. Chesser
Carla Cico
Kirk S. Hachigian
David D. Petratis
Martin E. Welch, III

Branches:

Ingersoll-Rand Security Technologies (1)
735 W SR434 Suite H
Longwood, FL 32750
Tel.: (407) 571-2000
Fax: (407) 571-2006
Web Site: w3.securitytechnologies.com
Sls.: $11,585,091
Emp.: 130
Safety & Security Specialization
S.I.C.: 7382
N.A.I.C.S.: 561621
Erik Wagner *(Mgr-Natl Accts)*

Ingersoll-Rand Security Technologies (1)
7127 Crossroads Blvd Ste 101
Brentwood, TN 37027
Tel.: (615) 376-2664
Fax: (615) 661-9572
Web Site: www.securitytechnologies.ingersollrand.com
Emp.: 10
Security & Safety Products Mfr & Distr
S.I.C.: 3429
N.A.I.C.S.: 332510

Subsidiaries:

LCN Closers (1)
121 W Railroad Ave
Princeton, IL 61356
Mailing Address:
PO Box 100
Princeton, IL 61356-0100
Tel.: (815) 875-3311
Fax: (815) 879-1497
Toll Free: (800) 526-2400
E-Mail: info@lcnclosers.com
Web Site: www.lcnclosers.com
Emp.: 300
Premium Door Closers Mfr
S.I.C.: 3429
N.A.I.C.S.: 332510
Rogers MacCab *(Controller)*

Schlage Lock Company (1)
3899 HANCOCK Expy
Colorado City, CO 80911 CA
Tel.: (317) 810-3700
E-Mail: doris_Stokes@irco.com
Web Site: www.schlage.com
Emp.: 2,712
Locks & Door Hardware Mfr
S.I.C.: 3429
N.A.I.C.S.: 332510
Henry Lardie *(Mgr-Mktg)*

Branch:

Schlage Lock Co. (2)
3899 Hancock Expy
Security, CO 80911-1230
Tel.: (719) 390-5071
Fax: (719) 392-8453
Web Site: www.schlage.com
Emp.: 800
Mfr. of Locks or Lock Sets
S.I.C.: 7699
N.A.I.C.S.: 561622
Bill Strang *(Gen Mgr)*

Unit:

Schlage Electronic Security (2)
11819 N Pennsylvania St
Carmel, IN 46032-4555
Tel.: (860) 584-9158
Fax: (860) 584-2136
Web Site: www.ingersollrand.com
Emp.: 140
Electronic Security Systems
S.I.C.: 7382
N.A.I.C.S.: 561621

Von Duprin LLC (1)
2720 Tobey Dr
Indianapolis, IN 46219 IN
Tel.: (317) 429-2000
Fax: (800) 999-0328
Toll Free: (800) 999-0408
Web Site: www.vonduprin.com
Emp.: 35
Supplier For Builders Hardware
S.I.C.: 3429
N.A.I.C.S.: 332510
Gary Jarvis *(Gen Mgr)*

Unit:

Dor-O-Matic Exit Devices (2)
2720 Tobey Dr
Indianapolis, IN 46219-1418
Tel.: (317) 429-2000
Fax: (317) 810-3991
Toll Free: (877) 243-4830
Web Site: exits.doromatic.com
Sales of Door Hardware
S.I.C.: 3429
N.A.I.C.S.: 332510

Unit:

Ingersoll-Rand Security Technologies Consultants (1)
488 E Santa Clara St Ste101
Arcadia, CA 91006-7230
Tel.: (626) 359-5555
Fax: (626) 359-1511
E-Mail: info@ingersollrand.com
Web Site: securitytechnologies.ingersollrand.com
Emp.: 8
Mfr. of Locks or Lock Sets
S.I.C.: 7382
N.A.I.C.S.: 561621

U.S. Subsidiary:

Allegion Holding Company, Inc. (1)
11819 N. Pennsylvania St.
Carmel, IN 46032
Tel.: (317) 810-3700
Safety Products Mfr
S.I.C.: 7382
N.A.I.C.S.: 561621

Allegion Plc—(Continued)

Non-U.S. Subsidiaries:

Allegion A/S (1)
Mirabellevej 3
8930 Randers, Denmark DK
Tel.: (45) 86 42 75 22
Fax: (45) 86 43 93 14
E-Mail: sales_randi@eu.irco.com
Web Site: www.randi.dk
Emp.: 11
Stainless Steel Product Mfr
S.I.C.: 3399
N.A.I.C.S.: 331110
Carsten Moller *(Mng Dir)*

Allegion B.V. (1)
(Formerly Ingersoll-Rand Security Technologies B.V.)
Witboom 1
4131 PL Vianen, Netherlands NL
Tel.: (31) 347 3258 58
Fax: (31) 347 3258 40
E-Mail: info-interflex-benelux@irco.com
Emp.: 17
Security & Access Control Equipment Mfr
S.I.C.: 3669
N.A.I.C.S.: 334290
Harry Docter *(Acct Mgr)*

Allegion NV (1)
(Formerly Ingersoll-Rand Security Technologies NV)
Pontbeekstraat 2
1702 Groot-Bijgaarden, Belgium BE
Tel.: (32) 2 5830999
Fax: (32) 2 582925
E-Mail: info-interflex-benelux@eu.irco.com
Web Site: www.interflex.ingersollrand.com
Emp.: 20
Security Software Development Services
S.I.C.: 7371
N.A.I.C.S.: 541511
Abhishek Irani *(Mgr-Supply-EMEIA)*

Allegion (UK) Limited (1)
(Formerly Ingersoll-Rand Security Technologies Limited)
Bescot Crescent
Walsall, West Midlands, United Kingdom UK
Tel.: (44) 1922 707400
Fax: (44) 208 6121096
E-Mail: info@ingersollrand.co.uk
Web Site: www.ingersollrand.co.uk
Electronic Safety Equipment Mfr
S.I.C.: 3714
N.A.I.C.S.: 336320

Non-U.S. Subsidiary:

IR SECURITY AND SAFETY (SOUTH EAST) LIMITED (2)
Bescot Crescent
Walsall, West Midlands, WS1 4DL, United Kingdom
Tel.: (44) 1922707400
Security System Devices Mfr
S.I.C.: 7382
N.A.I.C.S.: 561621

IR EMNIYET VE GUVENLIK SISTEMLERI SANAYI A.S. (1)
Kayisdagi Cad Karaman Ciflik Yolu No 45
Kar Plaza Kat 12 Icerenkoy
34752 Istanbul, Turkey
Tel.: (90) 216 5726351
Fax: (90) 216 5726349
E-Mail: gediz@irco.com
Web Site: www.itokilit.com.tr
Emp.: 439
Lock Mfr
S.I.C.: 3429
N.A.I.C.S.: 332510
Volkan Yorutken *(Acct Mgr-Mfg)*

ALLEGRO WIRELESS CANADA INC.

2350 Matheson Blvd E
Mississauga, ON, L4W 5G9, Canada
Tel.: (905) 624-2924
Fax: (905) 624-6917
Toll Free: (888) 626-5262
Web Site: www.allegrowireless.com
Sales Range: $10-24.9 Million

Business Description:
Mobile Information Solutions
S.I.C.: 7373
N.A.I.C.S.: 541512
Personnel:
Wes Rupel *(Co-Founder, Pres & CTO)*
Savino Griesi *(Co-Founder & CEO)*

ALLEN MCGUIRE & PARTNERS LTD.

CA Ph Apex Business Centre
Blackthorn Rd, Dublin, 2, Ireland
Tel.: (353) 12932020
Fax: (353) 12930244
Year Founded: 1989

Business Description:
Private Investment Firm
S.I.C.: 6799
N.A.I.C.S.: 523910
Personnel:
Roisin Hanna *(Mgr-Ops)*

Non-U.S. Subsidiary:

Humbrol Limited (1)
Marfleet
Kingston upon Hull, HU9 5NE, United Kingdom (100%)
Tel.: (44) 1482701191
Fax: (44) 1482712908
Web Site: www.airfix.com
Emp.: 50
Mfr. & Producer of Chemicals
S.I.C.: 2899
N.A.I.C.S.: 325998

ALLENEX AB

FranzEngatan 5
Box 122 83
112 51 Stockholm, Sweden
Tel.: (46) 850893900
Fax: (46) 850893950
E-Mail: info@allenex.se
Web Site: www.allenex.com
Year Founded: 1998
ALNX—(OMX)
Rev.: $18,011,444
Assets: $53,082,158
Liabilities: $19,615,018
Net Worth: $33,467,141
Earnings: $42,570
Emp.: 54
Fiscal Year-end: 12/31/12

Business Description:
Drug Development Services
S.I.C.: 5122
N.A.I.C.S.: 424210
Personnel:
Anders Williamsson *(Chm)*
Anders Karlsson *(CEO)*
Yvonne Axelsson *(CFO)*
Board of Directors:
Anders Williamsson
Oscar Ahlgren
Jan Eriksson
Sven-Olof Johansson
Gunnar Mattsson

ALLER-RETOUR

2550 Daniel Johnson Blvd suite 600
Laval, QC, H7T 2L1, Canada
Tel.: (450) 682-1888
Fax: (450) 682-2209
Toll Free: (800) 663-6361
E-Mail: info@aller-retour.com
Web Site: www.aller-retour.com
Rev.: $20,000,000
Emp.: 25

Business Description:
Travel Agencies
S.I.C.: 4724
N.A.I.C.S.: 561510
Personnel:
Isabelle Feleccia *(Dir-A'la Carte Travel)*

ALLERGY THERAPEUTICS PLC

Dominion Way
Worthing, West Sussex, BN14 8SA, United Kingdom
Tel.: (44) 1903844700
Fax: (44) 1903844726
Web Site: www.allergytherapeutics.com
AGY—(LSE)
Rev.: $62,032,932
Assets: $45,742,556
Liabilities: $22,572,792
Net Worth: $23,169,764
Earnings: $846,499
Emp.: 376
Fiscal Year-end: 06/30/13

Business Description:
Biological Product Mfr
S.I.C.: 2834
N.A.I.C.S.: 325412
Personnel:
Manuel Llobet *(CEO)*
Ian Postlethwaite *(Sec & Dir-Fin)*
Board of Directors:
Peter Jensen
Thomas Lander
Manuel Llobet
Ian Postlethwaite
Stephen Smith
Alejandro Weinstein, Jr.

Legal Counsel:
Reed Smith
The Broadgate Tower 20 Primrose Street
London, United Kingdom

Covington & Burling LLP
265 Strand
London, United Kingdom

Subsidiary:

Allergy Therapeutics (Holdings) Ltd. (1)
Dominion Way
Worthing, West Sussex, BN14 8SA, United Kingdom
Tel.: (44) 1903844700
Fax: (44) 1903 844744
Biological Product Mfr
S.I.C.: 8741
N.A.I.C.S.: 551114

Subsidiary:

Allergy Therapeutics (UK) Ltd. (2)
Dominion Way
Worthing, West Sussex, BN14 8SA, United Kingdom
Tel.: (44) 1903844700
Fax: (44) 1903844744
E-Mail: info@allergytherapeutics.com
Web Site: www.allergytherapeutics.com
Emp.: 240
Pharmaceutical Products Mfr & Sales
S.I.C.: 2834
N.A.I.C.S.: 325412
Manuel Llobet *(CEO)*

Non-U.S. Subsidiaries:

Allergy Therapeutics Iberica S.L. (2)
Joan XXIII 15-19
08950 Esplugues de Llobregat, Barcelona, Spain
Tel.: (34) 934751390
Fax: (34) 934741534
E-Mail: finanzas@allergytherapeutics.com
Web Site: www.allergytherapeutics.com
Emp.: 15
Pharmaceutical Products Distr
S.I.C.: 5122
N.A.I.C.S.: 424210

Allergy Therapeutics Italia s.r.l. (2)
Via IV Novembre 76
20019 Settimo Milanese, Milano, Italy
Tel.: (39) 0245675211
Fax: (39) 0248 920 083
Web Site: www.allergytherapeutics.it
Emp.: 30
Pharmaceutical Products Distr
S.I.C.: 5122
N.A.I.C.S.: 424210
Francesco Pellegrino *(Pres)*

Non-U.S. Subsidiary:

Bencard Allergie GmbH (1)
Messerschmittstrasse 4
80992 Munich, Bavaria, Germany
Tel.: (49) 893681150
Fax: (49) 893681155
E-Mail: info@bencard.de
Web Site: www.bencard.de
Pharmaceutical Product Sales
S.I.C.: 5122
N.A.I.C.S.: 424210
Marion Kreitz *(Chm)*

Non-U.S. Subsidiary:

Bencard Allergie (Austria) GmbH (2)
Lerchenfelder Str. 13/6/42 1070
1100 Vienna, Austria
Tel.: (43) 16061111
Fax: (43) 16061124
E-Mail: office@bencard.com
Web Site: www.bencard.de
Emp.: 6
Pharmaceutical Products Distr
S.I.C.: 5122
N.A.I.C.S.: 424210
Bodo Steinert *(Gen Mgr)*

ALLGEIER HOLDING AG

(See Under Allgeier SE)

ALLGEIER SE

(Formerly Allgeier Holding AG)
Wehrlestrasse 12
D-81679 Munich, Germany
Tel.: (49) 89 9984210
Fax: (49) 89 99842111
E-Mail: info@allgeier.com
Web Site: www.allgeier.com
AEI—(DEU)
Rev.: $569,217,215
Assets: $389,860,255
Liabilities: $264,115,862
Net Worth: $125,744,394
Earnings: $11,851,681
Emp.: 5,730
Fiscal Year-end: 12/31/12

Business Description:
Holding Company; Information Technology Consulting & Support Services
S.I.C.: 6719
N.A.I.C.S.: 551112
Personnel:
Detlef Dinsel *(Chm-Supervisory Bd)*
Carl Georg Durschmidt *(Chm-Exec Bd)*
Thies Eggers *(Deputy Chm-Supervisory Bd)*
Marcus Goedsche *(Member-Exec Bd)*
Eleonor Detels *(Sec)*
Supervisory Board of Directors:
Detlef Dinsel
Christian Eggenberger
Thies Eggers

Non-U.S. Subsidiary:

Terna GmbH (1)
Grabenweg 3a
6020 Innsbruck, Austria AT (100%)
Tel.: (43) 512 362060 0
Fax: (43) 512 362060 600
E-Mail: office@terna.com
Web Site: www.terna.com
Emp.: 150
Business Software Publisher
S.I.C.: 7372
N.A.I.C.S.: 511210
Christian Kranebitter *(Member-Mgmt Bd)*

ALLGEMEINE BAUGESELLSCHAFT - A. PORR AKTIENGESELLSCHAFT

(Name Changed to PORR AG)

ALLGREEN PROPERTIES LTD.

1 Kim Seng Promenade 05 02 Great World City
237994 Singapore, Singapore

Tel.: (65) 67332822
Fax: (65) 67383800
E-Mail: apl@allgreen.com.sg
Web Site: www.allgreen.com.sg
A16—(SES)
Sales Range: $700-749.9 Million
Emp.: 100
Business Description:
Property Development & Investment, Hospitality, Project & Property Management Services
S.I.C.: 6531
N.A.I.C.S.: 531390
Personnel:
Soo Siah Goh *(Chm)*
Isoo Tan *(Legal Counsel & Sec)*
Board of Directors:
Soo Siah Goh
Keng Lam Ang
Michael Teck Chai Chang
Andrew Choo Hoo
Thong Meng Khor
Oon Kwong Kuok

Ernst & Young
One Raffles Quay North Tower Level 18
Singapore, Singapore
Transfer Agent:
Boardroom Corporate & Advisory Services Pte. Ltd.
50 Raffles Place 32-01 Singapore Land Tower
Singapore, Singapore
Subsidiaries:

Allgreen Properties (Shanghai) Pte. Ltd. **(1)**
1 Kim Seng Promenade 05-02 Great World City
Singapore, 237994, Singapore
Tel.: (65) 67332822
Fax: (65) 67383800
Investment Management Services
S.I.C.: 8741
N.A.I.C.S.: 551114
Soo Siah Goh *(CEO)*

Allgreen Properties (Tianjin) Pte. Ltd. **(1)**
1 Kim Seng Promenade 05-02 Great World City
Singapore, 237994, Singapore
Tel.: (65) 67332822
Fax: (65) 67383800
E-Mail: apl@allgreen.com.sg
Real Estate Asset Management Services
S.I.C.: 6531
N.A.I.C.S.: 531390

Allgreen Properties (Vietnam) Pte. Ltd. **(1)**
1 Kim Seng Promenade 05-02
Singapore, 237994, Singapore
Tel.: (65) 67332822
Fax: (65) 67383800
E-Mail: apl@allgreen.com.sg
Web Site: www.allgreen.com.sg
Property Development Services
S.I.C.: 6531
N.A.I.C.S.: 531390

Arcadia Development Pte. Ltd. **(1)**
1 Kim Seng Promenade 05-02 Great World City
Singapore, 237994, Singapore
Tel.: (65) 67332822
Fax: (65) 67387800
Residential Property Development Services
S.I.C.: 1521
N.A.I.C.S.: 236115

Boonridge Pte Ltd **(1)**
921 Bt Timah Road Tan Chwee Boon Building
Singapore, 589624, Singapore
Tel.: (65) 63147555
Fax: (65) 67373822
Real Estate Asset Management Services
S.I.C.: 6531
N.A.I.C.S.: 531390

Cuscaden Properties Pte Ltd **(1)**
163 Tanglin Road
Singapore, Singapore (55.4%)
Tel.: (65) 67364922
Fax: (65) 67344944
E-Mail: apl@allgreen.com.sg
Web Site: www.allgreen.com.sg/allgreenco rp/project_details.cfm?project_uin=32
Hotel & Motels
S.I.C.: 7011
N.A.I.C.S.: 721110
Goh Soo Siah *(CEO)*

Leo Property Management Private Limited **(1)**
Hex 15- 02 1 Kim Seng Promenade
Great World City, 237994 Singapore, Singapore (100%)
Tel.: (65) 67373822
Fax: (65) 67373800
E-Mail: apl@allgreen.com.sg
Web Site: www.allgreen.com.sg
Emp.: 35
Other Real Estate Property Lessors
S.I.C.: 6519
N.A.I.C.S.: 531190
Yong Oon Chen *(Gen Mgr)*

Midpoint Properties Limited **(1)**
Great World City 1 Kim Seng Promenade
No 05-02, 237994 Singapore, Singapore (100%)
Tel.: (65) 68397950
Fax: (65) 68393898
E-Mail: HR@GreatWorld.com.sg
Web Site: www.GreatWorld.com.sg
Other Real Estate Property Lessors
S.I.C.: 6519
N.A.I.C.S.: 531190
Goh Soosiah *(CEO)*

Tanglin Place Development Pte Ltd **(1)**
91 Tanglin Road 01-00 Tanglin Place
Singapore, 247918, Singapore
Tel.: (65) 67346386
Fax: (65) 67364933
Emp.: 22
Residential Property Development Services
S.I.C.: 1521
N.A.I.C.S.: 236115
Evelyn Soh *(Mgr)*

Woodleigh Gardens Pte Ltd **(1)**
14 Woodleigh Close
Singapore, 357909, Singapore
Tel.: (65) 65478768
Fax: (65) 65476766
Apartment & Condominiums Leasing Services
S.I.C.: 6513
N.A.I.C.S.: 531110

Worldwide Apartment Services Pte Ltd **(1)**
1 Kim Seng Promenade
Singapore, Singapore (100%)
Tel.: (65) 67332822
Fax: (65) 67382800
E-Mail: apl@allgreen.com.sg
Web Site: www.allgreen.com.sg
Emp.: 60
Other Real Estate Property Lessors
S.I.C.: 6519
N.A.I.C.S.: 531190
Goh Soosiah *(CEO)*

Wyndham Supplies Pte Ltd **(1)**
1 Kinseng Promenade C-02
Great World City, Singapore, Singapore (100%)
Tel.: (65) 67332822
Fax: (65) 6783800
Lumber Plywood Millwork & Wood Panel Whslr
S.I.C.: 5031
N.A.I.C.S.: 423310
Goh Soo Siah *(CEO)*

ALLGREENTECH INTERNATIONAL PLC

36 Spital Square
London, E1 6DY, United Kingdom
Tel.: (44) 20 7377 6969
Fax: (44) 20 7377 9454
E-Mail: info@allgreentechplc.com
Web Site: www.allgreentechplc.com
V7EA—(DEU)
Sales Range: $25-49.9 Million
Emp.: 227
Business Description:
Investment Holding Company
S.I.C.: 6211
N.A.I.C.S.: 523999
Personnel:
Navin S. Sidhu *(CEO)*
Board of Directors:
Manjit Kaur
Navin S. Sidhu
Non-U.S. Subsidiary:

Malaysian Mega Galvaniser Sdn. Bhd. **(1)**
5th Floor West Wing Quattro West
No 4 Lorong Persiaran Barat, 46200
Petaling Jaya, Selangor, Malaysia (50%)
Tel.: (60) 3 7957 1115
Fax: (60) 3 7957 3115
E-Mail: sales@megagalvanizer.com
Web Site: www.megagalvanizer.com
Metals Galvanizing Services
S.I.C.: 5051
N.A.I.C.S.: 423510
Navin S. Sidhu *(CEO)*

ALLIANCE AGRO ALIMENTAIRE COOPERATIVE SCC

(Acquired by SODIAAL Group)

ALLIANCE AVIATION SERVICES LIMITED

PO Box 1126
Eagle Farm, QLD, 4009, Australia
Tel.: (61) 7 3212 1212
Fax: (61) 7 3212 1522
E-Mail: executive@allianceairlines.com.au
Web Site: www.allianceairlines.com.au
AQZ—(ASX)
Emp.: 400
Business Description:
Air Transportation Services
S.I.C.: 4512
N.A.I.C.S.: 481111
Personnel:
Stephen John Padgett *(Chm)*
Scott Alexander McMillan *(Mng Dir)*
Arthur Jeffrey Childs *(Sec)*
Board of Directors:
Stephen John Padgett
David Charles Crombie
Peter John Housden
Hugh Ross Jones
Scott Alexander McMillan
Subsidiary:

Jet Engine Leasing Pty Ltd **(1)**
Lot 12 Pandanus Avenue
Eagle Farm, QLD, 4009, Australia
Tel.: (61) 732121212
Fax: (61) 732121522
E-Mail: executive@allianceairlines.com.au
Emp.: 200
Passenger Air Transportation Services
S.I.C.: 4512
N.A.I.C.S.: 481111

ALLIANCE BANK JSC

50 Furmanov Street
050004 Almaty, Kazakhstan
Tel.: (7) 727 2584040
Fax: (7) 727 2596787
E-Mail: investorrelations@alb.kz
Web Site: www.alb.kz
Year Founded: 1993
4AB1—(KAZ)
Sales Range: $1-4.9 Billion
Business Description:
Commercial Banking Services
S.I.C.: 6029
N.A.I.C.S.: 522110
Personnel:
Maxat Kabashev *(Chm-Mgmt Bd)*

ALLIANCE ENERGY LTD.

3230 Faithful Avenue
Saskatoon, SK, S7K 8H3, Canada
Tel.: (306) 242-5802
Fax: (306) 242-1694
E-Mail: info@alliance-energy.com
Web Site: www.alliance-energy.com
Year Founded: 1983
Emp.: 200
Business Description:
Electrical Contracting & Maintenance Services
S.I.C.: 1731
N.A.I.C.S.: 238210
Personnel:
Bryan Leverick *(Pres)*
Paul McLellan *(CEO)*
Branch:

Alliance Energy Ltd. - Regina Office **(1)**
(Formerly Sun Electric (1975) Ltd.)
504 Henderson Drive
Regina, SK, S4N 5X2, Canada
Tel.: (306) 721-6484
Fax: (306) 721-9393
E-Mail: reginahr@alliance-energy.com
Web Site: www.alliance-energy.com
Electrical Contracting & Maintenance Services
S.I.C.: 1731
N.A.I.C.S.: 238210

ALLIANCE FINANCE COMPANY PLC

Alliance House 84 Ward Place
Colombo, 07, Sri Lanka
Tel.: (94) 112673673
Fax: (94) 112697205
E-Mail: info@alliancefinance.lk
Web Site: www.alliancefinance.lk
ALLI—(COL)
Rev.: $28,041,272
Assets: $137,757,569
Liabilities: $121,122,804
Net Worth: $16,634,765
Earnings: $4,012,218
Emp.: 812
Fiscal Year-end: 03/31/13
Business Description:
Leasing & Financial Services
S.I.C.: 6719
N.A.I.C.S.: 551112
Personnel:
Romani de Silva *(Deputy Chm & Mng Dir)*
Chamindra De Silva *(CFO)*
Suresh Amerasekera *(COO)*
Board of Directors:
Sunil Karunanayake
Romani de Silva
D. L. S. R. Perera
R. N. Ponnambalam
A. R. Samarasinghe

ALLIANCE FINANCIAL GROUP BERHAD

3rd Floor Menara Multi-Purpose
Capital Square
No 8 Jalan Munshi Abdullah, 50100
Kuala Lumpur, Malaysia
Tel.: (60) 326944888
Fax: (60) 326946200
E-Mail: enquiry@alliancegroup.com.my
Web Site: www.alliancegroup.com.my
AFG—(KLS)
Int. Income: $468,704,254
Assets: $14,327,490,150
Liabilities: $13,004,277,531
Net Worth: $1,323,212,618
Earnings: $170,764,668
Fiscal Year-end: 03/31/13
Business Description:
Commercial Financial Services
S.I.C.: 6029
N.A.I.C.S.: 522110

Alliance Financial Group Berhad—(Continued)

Personnel:
Seow Wah Sng *(CEO)*
Gary Teo *(CFO)*
Raymond Chun-Kow Leung *(COO)*
Mary James *(CIO)*
Andrew Thim Kwong Chow *(Chief Credit Officer)*
Choon Han Pang *(Chief Risk Officer)*
Fozia Amanulla *(CEO-Alliance Islamic Bank Berhad)*
Rafidz Rasiddi *(CEO-Alliance Investment Bank Berhad)*
Wei Yen Lee *(Sec)*
Board of Directors:
Chong Peng Oh
Stephen Sim Whye Geh
Beng Hong Kung
Ah Boon Lee
Dziauddin Mahmud
Thomas Lung Lee Mun
Shian Waei Ou
Seow Wah Sng
Yuen Fah Tan

ALLIANCE GLOBAL GROUP, INC.

7/F 1880 Eastwood Avenue
Eastwood City CyberPark 188E
Rodriguez Jr Ave
Bagumbayan, 1110 Quezon City, Philippines
Tel.: (63) 27092038
Fax: (63) 27091966
E-Mail: jhao@megaworldcorp.com
Web Site: www.allianceglobalinc.com
AGI—(OTC PHI)
Rev.: $2,515,557,208
Assets: $6,674,392,068
Liabilities: $3,147,524,597
Net Worth: $3,526,867,472
Earnings: $501,750,091
Emp.: 28,885
Fiscal Year-end: 12/31/12
Business Description:
Beverages Mfr
S.I.C.: 2082
N.A.I.C.S.: 312120
Personnel:
Andrew L. Tan *(Chm)*
Sergio R. Ortiz-Luis, Jr. *(Vice Chm)*
Kingson U. Sian *(Pres)*
Katherine L. Tan *(Treas)*
Dominic V. Isberto *(Sec)*
Board of Directors:
Andrew L. Tan
Winston S. Co
Sergio R. Ortiz-Luis, Jr.
Kingson U. Sian
Katherine L. Tan
Kevin Andrew L. Tan
Alejo L. Villanueva, Jr.
Transfer Agent:
Banco De Oro
Equitable PCI Bank Towers Makati Avenue cor H V dela Costa St
Makati, Philippines
Subsidiaries:

Emperador Distillers, Inc (1)
7th Floor Bldg 1880 Eastwood Ave Cyber Park
Rodriguez Jr Avenue Bagumbayan, Quezon City, 1110, Philippines
Tel.: (63) 27092222
Fax: (63) 27091998
Emp.: 600
Brandy Mfr
S.I.C.: 2084
N.A.I.C.S.: 312130
Andrew L. Tan *(Chm)*
Winston L. Co *(Pres)*

Subsidiary:

The Bar Beverage, Inc (2)
7th Floor 1880 Building Eastwood Ave
Eastwood City
Libis, Quezon City, Philippines
Tel.: (63) 2 709 2222
Alcoholic Beverages Mfr
S.I.C.: 2085
N.A.I.C.S.: 312140

First Oceanic Property Management, Inc (1)
7/F Paseo Ctr 8757 Paseo De Roxas
Makati, Philippines
Tel.: (63) 28300443
Fax: (63) 28300443
E-Mail: customerservice@firstoceanic.com.ph
Web Site: www.firstoceanic.com.ph
Real Estate Management Services
S.I.C.: 6531
N.A.I.C.S.: 531311
Carmelo J. Canto *(Sec)*

Oceanic Realty Group International, Inc (1)
Penthouse Paseo Center 8757 Paseo de Roxas
Corner Sedeneo & Valero Street, Makati, 1200, Philippines
Tel.: (63) 28678913
Fax: (63) 28678813
Real Estate Management Services
S.I.C.: 6531
N.A.I.C.S.: 531311

Joint Venture:

Travellers International Hotel Group, Inc. (1)
10/F Newport Entertainment & Commercial Centre Newport Boulevard
Newport City, Pasay, Metro Manila, 1309, Philippines
Tel.: (63) 2 908 8833
Fax: (63) 2 836 6333
E-Mail: customerservice@rwmanila.com
Web Site: www.rwmanila.com
RWM—(PHI)
Hotel & Casino Operator
S.I.C.: 7011
N.A.I.C.S.: 721120
Ming Huat Chua *(Chm & CEO)*
Kingson U. Sian *(Pres)*

U.S. Subsidiary:

Great American Foods, Inc (1)
433 Airport Blvd Ste 425
Burlingame, CA 94010-2014
Tel.: (650) 282-4444
Fax: (650) 504-0135
Web Site: www.pik-nik.com
Food Products Mfr
S.I.C.: 2052
N.A.I.C.S.: 311919
Alex Gabaldon *(Pres)*

ALLIANCE GRAIN TRADERS INC.

PO Box 30029
Regina, SK, S4N 7K9, Canada
Tel.: (306) 525-4490
Fax: (306) 525-4463
E-Mail: ir@alliancegrain.com
Web Site: www.alliancegraintraders.com
Year Founded: 2004
AGT—(OTC TSX)
Rev.: $850,209,835
Assets: $708,230,260
Liabilities: $439,996,395
Net Worth: $268,233,865
Earnings: $6,770,852
Emp.: 900
Fiscal Year-end: 12/31/12
Business Description:
Grain Sourcing & Processing
S.I.C.: 0119
N.A.I.C.S.: 111199
Personnel:
Huseyin Arslan *(Chm)*
Murad Al-Katib *(Pres & CEO)*
Lori Ireland *(CFO)*
Gaetan Bourassa *(COO)*
Board of Directors:
Huseyin Arslan
Murad Al-Katib
Drew Franklin
John M. Gardner
Howard N. Rosen
Transfer Agent:
Equity Financial Trust Corporation
Toronto, ON, Canada
Subsidiaries:

Alliance Pulse Processors Inc. (1)
Mailing Address:
PO Box 30029
Regina, SK, S4N 7K9, Canada
Tel.: (306) 525-4490
Fax: (306) 525-4463
Web Site: www.alliancegrain.com
Emp.: 40
Crops Export Services
S.I.C.: 0723
N.A.I.C.S.: 115114
Murad Al-Katib *(Pres & CEO)*

Saskcan Horizon Trading Inc. (1)
PO Box 340
Aberdeen, SK, S0K 0A0, Canada
Tel.: (306) 253-4233
Fax: (306) 253-4624
Web Site: www.saskcan.com
Emp.: 25
Cereal Pulses Whslr
S.I.C.: 5149
N.A.I.C.S.: 424490
Mirad Elquted *(Owner)*

U.S. Subsidiary:

United Pulse Trading Inc. (1)
1611 E Century Ave Ste 102
Bismarck, ND 58503-0780
Tel.: (701) 751-1623
Fax: (701) 751-1626
E-Mail: sales@uspulses.com
Web Site: www.uspulses.com
Emp.: 7
Cereal Pulses Suppliers
S.I.C.: 5149
N.A.I.C.S.: 424490
Eric Bartsch *(Gen Mgr)*

Non-U.S. Subsidiary:

Australia Milling Group Pty Ltd. (1)
47 Golf Course Road
PO Box 838
Horsham, VIC, 3402, Australia
Tel.: (61) 353812555
Fax: (61) 353822612
Web Site: www.aung.com.au
Cereal Pulses Whslr
S.I.C.: 5149
N.A.I.C.S.: 424490
Murid Alkatib *(CEO)*

ALLIANCE GROUP LIMITED

51 Don Street
PO Box 845
Invercargill, 9810, New Zealand
Tel.: (64) 32142700
Fax: (64) 32142708
E-Mail: executive@alliance.co.nz
Web Site: www.alliance.co.nz
Rev.: $1,129,810,755
Assets: $477,701,756
Liabilities: $234,829,975
Net Worth: $242,871,781
Earnings: ($41,861,232)
Emp.: 5,000
Fiscal Year-end: 09/30/12
Business Description:
Processor of Sheep, Lambs, Cattle, Deer & Pigs
S.I.C.: 0214
N.A.I.C.S.: 112410
Personnel:
G. Owen Poole *(Chm)*
Grant Cuff *(CEO)*
J. A. McGrath *(CFO)*
M. J. Horn *(Sec)*
Board of Directors:
G. Owen Poole
Doug A. Brown
Murray W. A. Donald
John A. Lindsay
Jason A. Miller
Dawn Sangster
Murray J. Taggart
John A. Waller
Subsidiary:

Waitaki International Ltd (1)
C 51 Don Street
Invercargill, New Zealand
Tel.: (64) 34331800
Holding Company
S.I.C.: 6712
N.A.I.C.S.: 551111
Michael Ross *(CEO)*

Non-U.S. Subsidiaries:

New Zealand Farmers Ltd. (1)
140-142 Saint John Street
London, EC1V 4UB, United Kingdom
Tel.: (44) 2075665000
Web Site: www.nzfarmers.co.uk
Emp.: 12
Meat & Meat Product Whslr
S.I.C.: 5147
N.A.I.C.S.: 424470

New Zealand Holdings (UK) Ltd (1)
140-142 St John St
London, EC1V 4UB, United Kingdom
Tel.: (44) 2075665000
Fax: (44) 2074902552
Web Site: www.nzfarmers.co.uk
Holding Company
S.I.C.: 6712
N.A.I.C.S.: 551111

ALLIANCE INSURANCE COMPANY LIMITED

Tinkune
PO Box 10811
Kathmandu, Nepal
Tel.: (977) 1 4499220
Fax: (977) 1 4499647
E-Mail: info@allianceinsurance.com.np
Web Site: www.allianceinsurance.com.np
Year Founded: 1996
AIC—(NEP)
Business Description:
Insurance Services
S.I.C.: 6411
N.A.I.C.S.: 524298
Personnel:
Govinda Das Shrestha *(Chm)*
B. K. Shrestha *(Vice Chm)*
Yugesh Bhakta Bade Shrestha *(CEO)*
Board of Directors:
Govinda Das Shrestha
Dharma Bhakta Balla
Rajendra Malla
Radha Krishna Pote
Ranakeshav Pradhan
B. K. Shrestha
Laxman Shrestha
Rajendra Bhakta Shrestha
Rajesh Kaji Shrestha
Sunil Lal Shrestha

ALLIANCE INSURANCE (PSC)

2nd & 3rd Floors Warba Centre
PO Box 5501
Dubai, United Arab Emirates
Tel.: (971) 46051111
Fax: (971) 46051112
E-Mail: alliance@alliance-uae.com
Web Site: www.alliance-uae.com
Year Founded: 1975
ALLIANCE—(DFM)
Sales Range: $10-24.9 Million
Business Description:
Insurance Services
S.I.C.: 6411
N.A.I.C.S.: 524298
Personnel:
Ahmed Saeed Al Maktoum *(Chm)*
Juma Saif Rashid Bakhit *(Vice Chm)*
Wisam Al Haimus *(CEO)*

Board of Directors:
Ahmed Saeed Al Maktoum
Wisam Al Haimus
Khalifa Salim Humaid Al Mashwi
Ahmed Saif Rashid Bakhit
Juma Saif Rashid Bakhit
Steven Ridgeway
Mohammed Hilal Salem Tarraf

ALLIANCE MINING CORP.

888 Dunsmuir St Suite 888
Vancouver, BC, V6C 3K4, Canada
Tel.: (604) 628-6645
Fax: (250) 828-0829
E-Mail: info@alliancemining.com
Web Site: www.alliancemining.com
Year Founded: 2002
ALM—(TSXV)
Assets: $110,384
Liabilities: $153,997
Net Worth: ($43,613)
Earnings: ($867,847)
Emp.: 5
Fiscal Year-end: 12/31/12
Business Description:
Metal Ore Mining Services
S.I.C.: 1099
N.A.I.C.S.: 212299
Personnel:
Christopher R. Anderson *(Pres & CEO)*
Patrick Forseille *(CFO)*
Board of Directors:
Christopher R. Anderson
Antony Claydon
Patrick Forseille
Travis M. Snider

ALLIANCE MINING CORPORATION LIMITED

51 Shannon Road Noordheuwel
Krugersdorp, 1740 Gauteng, South Africa
Tel.: (27) 119546104
Fax: (27) 119546105
E-Mail: info@almc.co.za
Web Site: www.alliancecorp.co.za
ALM—(JSE)
Sales Range: $25-49.9 Million
Emp.: 47
Business Description:
Mining Industry Support Services
S.I.C.: 1081
N.A.I.C.S.: 213114
Personnel:
Carel Neethling *(Acting CEO)*
Mike J. Garbers *(Mng Dir)*
Kevin Coyle *(Interim CFO & Sec)*
Board of Directors:
N. Mathews Phosa
Matilda Gaboo
Mike J. Garbers
P. Maema
Carel Neethling
N. Alfred Nevhutanda
Mitesh Mohanlal Patel
A. J. P. Steenkamp
William R. Wilson

ALLIANCE OIL COMPANY LTD.

Sivtsev Vrazhek 39
Moscow, 119002, Russia
Tel.: (7) 4957771808
E-Mail: info@allianceoilco.com
Web Site: www.allianceoilco.com
AOIL—(OMX)
Rev.: $3,445,239,000
Assets: $5,991,886,000
Liabilities: $2,958,876,000
Net Worth: $3,033,010,000
Earnings: $420,770,000
Emp.: 7,512
Fiscal Year-end: 12/31/12
Business Description:
Oil & Gas Exploration Services
S.I.C.: 1311
N.A.I.C.S.: 211111
Personnel:
Eric Forss *(Chm)*
Arsen E. Idrisov *(Mng Dir)*
Angelika Adieva *(CFO)*
Yevgeny Vorobeichik *(COO)*
Sergey Brezitsky *(CEO-Upstream)*
Alexander Sutyagin *(CEO-Downstream)*
Mugammir Galiullin *(Exec VP-Upstream)*
Board of Directors:
Eric Forss
Isa Bazhaev
Fred Boling
Arsen E. Idrisov
Claes Levin
Raymond Liefooghe
Fernando Martinez-Fresneda

Deloitte AB
Rehnsgatan 11
113 79 Stockholm, Sweden
Tel.: (46) 850 671 000
Fax: (46) 850 672 401

Subsidiary:

LLC Alliance Oil Company MC (1)
39 Sivtsev Vrazhek Lane
119002 Moscow, Russia
Tel.: (7) 495 777 18 08
Fax: (7) 495 777 18 10
Petroleum Products Distr
S.I.C.: 5172
N.A.I.C.S.: 424720

ALLIANCE PETROLEUM CORPORATION

(Name Changed to Malaysia Pro-Guardians Security Management Corporation)

ALLIANCE PHARMA PLC

Avonbridge House Bath Road
Chippenham, Wiltshire, SN15 2BB, United Kingdom
Tel.: (44) 1249466966
Fax: (44) 1249466977
E-Mail: info@alliancepharma.co.uk
Web Site: www.alliancepharma.co.uk
APHA—(AIM LSE)
Rev.: $70,905,383
Assets: $158,917,636
Liabilities: $77,034,608
Net Worth: $81,883,028
Earnings: $13,724,030
Emp.: 63
Fiscal Year-end: 12/31/12
Business Description:
Pharmaceutical Products Sales
S.I.C.: 5122
N.A.I.C.S.: 424210
Personnel:
John Dawson *(CEO)*
Sarah Robinson *(Sec)*
Board of Directors:
Michael R. B. Gatenby
Tony Booley
Peter Butterfield
Thomas Casdagli
John Dawson
Paul Ranson
Andrew Smith
Richard Wright
Legal Counsel:
Taylor Wessing LLP
5 New Street Square
London, United Kingdom

Fasken Martineau LLP
17 Hanover Square
London, United Kingdom

Subsidiary:

Alliance Pharmaceuticals Limited (1)
Avonbridge House Bath Rd
Chippenham, Wiltshire, SN15 2BB, United Kingdom
Tel.: (44) 1249466966
Fax: (44) 1249466977
E-Mail: info@alliancepharma.co.uk
Emp.: 60
Medical Products Mfr
S.I.C.: 2834
N.A.I.C.S.: 325412
John Dawson *(Mng Dir)*

ALLIANCE RESOURCES LIMITED

Ste 3 51-55 City Road
Southbank, VIC, 3006, Australia
Tel.: (61) 3 9697 9090
Fax: (61) 3 9697 9091
E-Mail: info@allianceresources.com.au
Web Site: www.allianceresources.com.au
AGS—(ASX)
Rev.: $1,243,592
Assets: $44,468,990
Liabilities: $1,896,269
Net Worth: $42,572,722
Earnings: ($7,595,201)
Fiscal Year-end: 06/30/13
Business Description:
Mineral Exploration Services
S.I.C.: 1481
N.A.I.C.S.: 213115
Personnel:
Stephen Fredrick Johnston *(Mng Dir)*
Robert Paul Tolliday *(CFO & Sec)*
Board of Directors:
John Stuart Ferguson Dunlop
Ian Jeffrey Gandel
Stephen Fredrick Johnston
Anthony Dean Lethlean

Subsidiary:

Alliance (SA) Pty. Ltd. (1)
Ste 3 51-55 City Rd
Southbank, VIC, 3006, Australia
Tel.: (61) 396979090
Fax: (61) 396979091
E-Mail: info@allianceresources.com.au
Web Site: www.allianceresources.com.au
Emp.: 4
Mineral Exploration Services
S.I.C.: 1481
N.A.I.C.S.: 213115
Steve Johnson *(Mng Dir)*

ALLIANCE SELECT FOODS INTERNATIONAL, INC.

Suites 1206/1405 East Tower
Philippine Stock Exchange Ctr
Exchange Road Ortigas Center,
Pasig, Metro Manilla, 1600, Philippines
Tel.: (63) 26355241
Fax: (63) 26355235
Web Site: www.allianceselectfoods.com
Year Founded: 2003
FOOD—(PHI)
Sales Range: $50-74.9 Million
Emp.: 100
Business Description:
Canned Tuna Proccessor
S.I.C.: 2092
N.A.I.C.S.: 311710
Personnel:
George E. SyCip *(Chm)*
Alvin Y. Dee *(Vice Chm)*
Jonathan Y. Dee *(Pres & CEO)*
Teresita S. Ladanga *(COO & Sr VP)*
Joanna Dee-Laurel *(Treas)*
Erlinda R. Calangi *(Legal Counsel & Sec)*

Non-U.S. Subsidiary:

PT International Alliance Food Indonesia (1)
Jl Raya Madidir Lorong Union Kel Madidir
Unet Lingkungan II Kec
Madidir Kota, Bitung, Indonesia Id
Tel.: (62) 43834573
Tuna Processing Canning Export Services
S.I.C.: 0912
N.A.I.C.S.: 114111

ALLIANCE TRUST PLC

8 West Marketgait
Dundee, DD1 1QN, United Kingdom
Tel.: (44) 1382321000
Fax: (44) 1382321185
E-Mail: investor@alliancetrust.co.uk
Web Site: www.alliancetrust.co.uk
Year Founded: 1888
ATST—(LSE)
Rev.: $514,471,090
Assets: $5,073,439,118
Liabilities: $1,145,898,080
Net Worth: $3,927,541,039
Earnings: $394,261,852
Emp.: 247
Fiscal Year-end: 12/31/12
Business Description:
Investment Services
S.I.C.: 6211
N.A.I.C.S.: 523999
Personnel:
Karin Forseke *(Chm)*
Katherine Garrett-Cox *(CEO)*
Donald McPherson *(Sec)*
Board of Directors:
Karin Forseke
Katherine Garrett-Cox
John Hylands
Alastair Kerr
Susan Noble
Win Robbins
Alan Trotter

Subsidiaries:

Alliance Trust Asset Management Limited (1)
8 W Marketgait
Dundee, DD1 1QN, United Kingdom
Tel.: (44) 1382321000
Fax: (44) 1382321185
E-Mail: assetmanagement@alliancetrust.co.uk
Emp.: 200
Securities Brokerage Services
S.I.C.: 6211
N.A.I.C.S.: 523120
Katherine Garrett-Cox *(CEO)*

Alliance Trust Equity Partners Limited (1)
107 George St
Edinburgh, EH2 3ES, United Kingdom
Tel.: (44) 1312403450
Fax: (44) 1312403469
E-Mail: contact@atep.co.uk
Web Site: www.atep.co.uk
Securities Brokerage Services
S.I.C.: 6211
N.A.I.C.S.: 523120

Alliance Trust Savings Limited (1)
8 W Marketgait
PO Box 164
Dundee, DD1 9YP, United Kingdom
Tel.: (44) 1382201900
Fax: (44) 1382321185
E-Mail: contact@alliancetrust.co.uk
Web Site: www.alliancetrust.co.uk
Emp.: 220
Securities Brokerage Services
S.I.C.: 6211
N.A.I.C.S.: 523120
Katherine Garrett-Cox *(CEO)*
Patrick Mill *(Mng Dir)*

ALLIANDER N.V.

Utrechtseweg 68
6812 AH Arnhem, Netherlands

Alliander N.V.—(Continued)

Mailing Address:
PO Box 50
6920 AB Duiven, Netherlands
Tel.: (31) 268442266
Fax: (31) 268442424
E-Mail: info@alliander.com
Web Site: www.alliander.com
Rev.: $2,385,413,240
Assets: $9,980,504,380
Liabilities: $5,668,721,870
Net Worth: $4,311,782,510
Earnings: $301,542,080
Emp.: 7,140
Fiscal Year-end: 12/31/12

Business Description:
Electric & Gas Grid Network Management Services
S.I.C.: 4939
N.A.I.C.S.: 221121

Personnel:
E. M. d'Hondt *(Chm-Supervisory Bd)*
Peter C. Molengraaf *(Chm-Mgmt Bd & CEO)*
J. C. van Winkelen *(Vice Chm-Supervisory Bd)*
M. R. van Lieshout *(CFO & Member-Mgmt Bd)*
C. M. M. Hofman *(Interim Sec)*

Supervisory Board of Directors:
E. M. d'Hondt
Franswillem C. W. Briet
J. W. E. Spies
J. G. van der Linde
Ada G. M. van der Veer-Vergeer
J. C. van Winkelen

Subsidiaries:

Alliander Finance B.V. (1)
Utrechtseweg 68
NL-6812 AH Arnhem, Netherlands NL
Tel.: (31) 268442266 (100%)
Financial Support Services
S.I.C.: 7389
N.A.I.C.S.: 561499

Liander N.V. (1)
Utrechtseweg 68
NL-6812 AH Arnhem, Netherlands NL
Mailing Address: (100%)
Postbus 50
NL-6920 AB Duiven, Netherlands
Tel.: (31) 26 844 2445
Fax: (31) 26 377 2304
Web Site: www.liander.nl
Sales Range: $1-4.9 Billion
Energy Network Construction & Maintenance Services; Electric Power & Gas Distr
S.I.C.: 1629
N.A.I.C.S.: 237130
Peter C. Molengraaf *(Dir-Ops)*

Liandon B.V. (1)
Dijkgraaf 24
NL-6921 RL Duiven, Gelderland, Netherlands NL
Mailing Address: (100%)
Postbus 50
6920 AB Duiven, Netherlands
Tel.: (31) 268447400
Fax: (31) 268447035
E-Mail: alliander@liandon.com
Web Site: www.liandon.com
Emp.: 700
Private Energy Grid Design, Construction & Management Services
S.I.C.: 7389
N.A.I.C.S.: 541990
P. Molengraas *(Gen Mgr)*

Subsidiary:

Liandon Meetbedrijf N.V. (2)
Coenensparkstraat 25
7202 AN Zutphen, Netherlands NL
Mailing Address: (100%)
Postbus 521
2003 RM Haarlem, Netherlands
Tel.: (31) 57559 7203
Private Energy Grid Monitoring Services
S.I.C.: 7389
N.A.I.C.S.: 541990

Liandyn B.V. (1)
Langegracht 70
NL-2312 NV Leiden, Netherlands NL
Tel.: (31) 71 525 2466 (100%)
Fax: (31) 71 525 2400
E-Mail: info@liandyn.nl
Web Site: www.liandyn.nl
Public Space Lighting, Traffic & Camera Systems Design, Installation & Management Services
S.I.C.: 7389
N.A.I.C.S.: 541990
Wilfred Eleveld *(Mng Dir)*

ALLIANZ SAUDI FRANSI COOPERATIVE INSURANCE COMPANY

PO Box 3540
Riyadh, 11481, Saudi Arabia
Tel.: (966) 18749700
Fax: (966) 18749799
E-Mail: customerservice@allianzsf.com.sa
Web Site: www.allianzsf.com
8040—(SAU)
Premiums: $165,434,086
Assets: $298,453,954
Liabilities: $253,859,610
Net Worth: $44,594,344
Earnings: $1,637,613
Emp.: 462
Fiscal Year-end: 12/31/12

Business Description:
Insurance Services
S.I.C.: 6411
N.A.I.C.S.: 524298

Personnel:
Abdullah Hassan Alabel-gader *(Chm)*
Xavier Denys *(CEO)*
Mohammed Basrawi *(Deputy CEO)*
Abdullah Mansury *(Acting CFO)*
Sulaiman Ben Sulaeym *(Compliance Officer)*

Board of Directors:
Abdullah Hassan Alabel-gader
Alwaleed Al Dryaan
Abdulaziz Al Habdan
Hugues de Roquette Buisson
Heinz Dollberg
Abdulrahman Jawa

Al Bassam Certified Public Accountants & Consultants
PO Box 69658
Riyadh, 11557, Saudi Arabia

ALLIANZ SE

Koniginstrasse 28
80802 Munich, Germany
Tel.: (49) 89 3800 0
Fax: (49) 89 3800 3425
E-Mail: info@allianz.com
Web Site: www.allianz.com
Year Founded: 1890
ALV—(DEU OTC SWX)
Premiums: $4,943,781,055
Assets: $135,198,506,401
Liabilities: $77,501,097,502
Net Worth: $57,697,408,899
Earnings: $3,096,465,619
Emp.: 144,094
Fiscal Year-end: 12/31/12

Business Description:
Holding Company; Industrial, Life, Health & Specialty Insurance & Asset Management Products & Services
S.I.C.: 6719
N.A.I.C.S.: 551112

Personnel:
Helmut Perlet *(Chm-Supervisory Bd)*
Michael Diekmann *(Chm-Mgmt Bd & CEO)*
Wulf H. Bernotat *(Vice Chm-Supervisory Bd)*
Rolf Zimmermann *(Vice Chm-Supervisory Bd)*
Dieter Wemmer *(CFO & Member-Mgmt Bd)*
Christof Mascher *(COO & Member-Mgmt Bd)*
Oliver Bate *(Member-Mgmt Bd-Insurance Western & Southern Europe)*
Manuel Bauer *(Member-Mgmt Bd-Insurance Growth Markets)*
Gary C. Bhojwani *(Member-Mgmt Bd-Insurance USA)*
Clement B. Booth *(Member-Mgmt Bd-Global Insurance Lines & Anglo Markets)*
Helga Jung *(Member-Mgmt Bd-Insurance Iberia, Latin America, M&A & Legal)*
Jay Ralph *(Member-Mgmt Bd-Asset Mgmt-Worldwide)*
Werner Zedelius *(Member-Mgmt Bd-Insurance German Speaking Countries & HR)*
Maximilian Zimmerer *(Member-Mgmt bd-Investments)*

Supervisory Board of Directors:
Helmut Perlet
Dante Barban
Wulf H. Bernotat
Christine Bosse
Gabriele Burkhardt-Berg
Jean-Jacques Cette
Ira Gloe-Semler
Franz Heiss
Renate Kocher
Igor Landau
Peter Denis Sutherland
Rolf Zimmermann

Subsidiaries:

ACP GmbH & Co. Beteiligungen KG (1)
Theresienstr 6-8
80333 Munich, Germany
Tel.: (49) 89 38000
Investment Management Services
S.I.C.: 6211
N.A.I.C.S.: 523999

ACP Vermogensverwaltung GmbH & Co. KG Nr. 4 (1)
Theresienstrasse 6-8
80333 Munich, Germany
Tel.: (49) 89 38000
Asset Management Services
S.I.C.: 6282
N.A.I.C.S.: 523920

ACP Vermogensverwaltung GmbH & Co. KG Nr. 4a (1)
Theresienstr 6-8
80333 Munich, Germany
Tel.: (49) 89 38000
Asset Management Services
S.I.C.: 6799
N.A.I.C.S.: 523920

ACP Vermogensverwaltung GmbH & Co. KG Nr. 4c (1)
Theresienstr 6-8
80333 Munich, Germany
Tel.: (49) 89 38000
Asset Management Services
S.I.C.: 6282
N.A.I.C.S.: 523920

Adeus Aktienregister-Service GmbH (1)
Jurgen-Ponto-Platz 1
D-60301 Frankfurt, Germany
Mailing Address:
Postfach 11 06 53
60041 Frankfurt, Germany
Tel.: (49) 692562703
Fax: (49) 6925627059
E-Mail: info@adeus.de
Web Site: www.adeus.de
Emp.: 19
Financial Services
S.I.C.: 6726
N.A.I.C.S.: 525990
Klaus Schmidt *(CEO)*
Konrad von Nussbaum *(Mng Dir)*

ADIG Fondsvertrieb GmbH (1)
Seidlstrasse 24-24a
80335 Munich, Germany
Tel.: (49) 89 12 20 74 44
Fax: (49) 89 12 20 74 48
E-Mail: vertrieb@adig.de
Web Site: www.adig.de
Emp.: 7
Mutual Fund Management Services
S.I.C.: 6282
N.A.I.C.S.: 523920
Jens Kassow *(Mng Dir)*

Aequitas GmbH Allianz Equity - Alternative Strategies (1)
Seidlstr 24-24a
80333 Munich, Bayern, Germany
Tel.: (49) 89 38000
Financial Management Services
S.I.C.: 6211
N.A.I.C.S.: 523999

AGIS Allianz Dresdner Informationsysteme GmbH (1)
Gutenbergstrasse 8
D-85774 Unterfohring, Germany
Tel.: (49) 89380013800
Fax: (49) 89380013801
E-Mail: info.agis@allianz.com
Web Site: www.asic.de
Computer Related Services
S.I.C.: 7379
N.A.I.C.S.: 541519
Martin Elspermann *(Mng Dir)*

All Net GmbH (1)
Reinsburgstr 19
70178 Stuttgart, Germany
Tel.: (49) 7116631900
Fax: (49) 7116631901
E-Mail: allnet@allianz.com
Web Site: www.allnet.allianz.de
Emp.: 15
Employee Benefits Network
S.I.C.: 6411
N.A.I.C.S.: 524298
Dirk Hellmuth *(Chm)*
Angela Hugman *(Sec)*

Allianz Alternative Assets Holding GmbH (1)
Koniginstr 19
80539 Munich, Germany
Tel.: (49) 893 80 00
Investment Management Services
S.I.C.: 6211
N.A.I.C.S.: 523999

Allianz Automotive Services GmbH (1)
Einsteinring 28
Aschheim, 85609 Munich, Germany
Tel.: (49) 89 2000 48 000
Fax: (49) 89 2000 48 562
E-Mail: garantie@allianz-warranty.com
Web Site: www.allianz-warranty.com
Vehicle Insurance Services
S.I.C.: 6411
N.A.I.C.S.: 524298

Allianz Autowelt GmbH (1)
Kuniginstr 28
80802 Munich, Germany
Tel.: (49) 899233450
Fax: (49) 8992334530
E-Mail: autowelt@allianz.de
Web Site: www.allianz-autowelt.de
Emp.: 8
Insurance Services
S.I.C.: 6411
N.A.I.C.S.: 524298
Ralf Schollenberger *(Mng Dir)*

Allianz AVI 1 Fonds (1)
Mainzer Landstrasse 11-13
Frankfurt am Main, 60329, Germany
Tel.: (49) 18 03 30 33 11
Fax: (49) 92 81 72 24 61 15
Mutual Fund Management Services
S.I.C.: 6282
N.A.I.C.S.: 523920

Allianz AVM B Fonds (1)
Mainzer Landstrasse 11-13
60329 Frankfurt, Germany
Tel.: (49) 18 03 30 33 11
Fax: (49) 92 81 72 24 61 15
Mutual Fund Management Services
S.I.C.: 6799

N.A.I.C.S.: 523920

Allianz AZL Vermogensverwaltung GmbH (1)
Koniginstr 28
80802 Munich, Bayern, Germany
Tel.: (49) 89 38000
Financial Management Services
S.I.C.: 6211
N.A.I.C.S.: 523999

Allianz Beratungs- und Vertriebs-AG (1)
Koniginstrasse 28
80802 Munich, Germany
Tel.: (49) 89 38000
Fax: (49) 89 349941
Insurance Consulting Services
S.I.C.: 6411
N.A.I.C.S.: 524298

Allianz Capital Partners GmbH (1)
Theresienstrasse 6-8
D-80333 Munich, Germany
Tel.: (49) 893800 7010
E-Mail: contact@allianzcapitalpartners.com
Web Site: www.allianzcapitalpartners.com
Emp.: 50
Industrial, Life, Health & Specialty Insurance; Asset Management Services
S.I.C.: 6411
N.A.I.C.S.: 524298
Bettina Schmid *(Mgr-Res)*

Subsidiary:

Allianz Private Equity Partners GmbH (2)
Gheresien St No 6-8
80333 Munich, Germany
Tel.: (49) 89380019900
Fax: (49) 498938007586
E-Mail: kontakt@allianzcapitalpartners.com
Web Site: www.allianzcapitalpartners.com
Emp.: 70
Financial Services
S.I.C.: 6211
N.A.I.C.S.: 523999
Andress Goh *(Mng Dir & Head-Singapore)*
Michael Lindauer *(Mng Dir & Head-Investment Team-Munich)*
Claus Zellner *(CFO)*
Florian Huber *(COO & Gen Counsel)*

Holding:

manroland AG (2)
Muhlheimer Strasse 341
D 63075 Offenbach, Germany DE
Tel.: (49) 6983050 (65%)
Fax: (49) 6983051440
E-Mail: public.relations@manroland.com
Web Site: www.manroland.com
Sales Range: $1-4.9 Billion
Emp.: 8,000
Printing Machinery Mfr
S.I.C.: 3555
N.A.I.C.S.: 333244
Hanno C. Fiedler *(Chm-Supervisory Bd)*
Gerd Finkbeiner *(Chm-Exec Bd)*
Jurgen Kerner *(Deputy Chm-Supervisory Bd)*
Markus Rall *(Member-Exec Bd-Sheetfed)*
Paul Steidle *(Member-Exec Bd-Webfed)*

Subsidiaries:

MAN Plamag Druckmaschinen AG (3)
Pausaer Strasse 284
D 08525 Plauen, Germany (100%)
Mailing Address:
PO Box 47
D-08505 Plauen, Germany
Tel.: (49) 3741500
Fax: (49) 3741505555
Web Site: www.manroland.com
Emp.: 36
Mfr. of Printing Machines
S.I.C.: 3555
N.A.I.C.S.: 333244
Kogeor Reischar *(Sec)*

manroland 1. Verwaltungsgesellschaft mbH (3)
Muhlheimer Str 341
63075 Offenbach, Germany
Tel.: (49) 69 83050
Fax: (49) 69 83051440
Investment Management Services
S.I.C.: 6211
N.A.I.C.S.: 523999

manroland Heusenstamm GmbH (3)
Industriestrasse 25
63150 Heusenstamm, Germany
Tel.: (49) 69 83050
Printing Machinery Mfr
S.I.C.: 3555
N.A.I.C.S.: 333244

manroland Vertrieb und Service GmbH (3)
Borsigstrasse 19
63165 Muhlheim, Germany
Tel.: (49) 69 83 05 00
Fax: (49) 69 83 05 1440
Printing Machinery Mfr
S.I.C.: 3555
N.A.I.C.S.: 333244
Rafael Torres Penuela *(Gen Mgr)*

U.S. Subsidiaries:

manroland Inc. (3)
800 E Oakhill Dr
Westmont, IL 60559 (100%)
Tel.: (630) 920-2000
Fax: (630) 920-2457
Toll Free: (800) 700-2344
E-Mail: marketing@manroland.us
Web Site: www.manroland.us.com
Sls.: $350,000,000
Emp.: 160
Printing Machinery Mfr
Import Export
S.I.C.: 3555
N.A.I.C.S.: 333244
Brian Gott *(CFO)*

Branches:

manroland Inc. - Los Angeles (4)
5750 E Appian Way
Long Beach, CA 90803-3604
Tel.: (714) 849-9614
Fax: (714) 849-9642
Web Site: www.manroland.us.com
Emp.: 40
Printing Machinery Distr
S.I.C.: 3555
N.A.I.C.S.: 333244

Non-U.S. Subsidiary:

manroland Canada Inc. (4)
119 Westcreek Dr
Vaughan, ON, L4L 9N6, Canada ON
Tel.: (905) 265-6300 (100%)
Fax: (905) 265-6304
Toll Free: (800) 268-4673
Web Site: www.manroland.ca
Emp.: 17
Printing Machinery Distr
S.I.C.: 3555
N.A.I.C.S.: 333244
Michael Mugavero *(Mng Dir)*
Brian Gott *(CFO)*

Non-U.S. Subsidiaries:

manroland Benelux N.V. (3)
Koningin Astridlaan 61
1780 Wemmel, Belgium
Tel.: (32) 2 456 85 00
Fax: (32) 2 456 85 85
E-Mail: info@manrolandbenelux.be
Web Site: www.manrolandbenelux.be
Commercial Printing Services
S.I.C.: 2759
N.A.I.C.S.: 323111

manroland (China) Ltd. (3)
Unit 825 845 8 F Hong Kong International Trade & Exhibition Ctr
1 Trademart Dr Kowloon Bay, Kowloon, China (Hong Kong)
Tel.: (852) 28973398
Fax: (852) 25582223
E-Mail: info@manroland.cn
Web Site: www.manroland.cn
Printing Machinery Distr
S.I.C.: 3555
N.A.I.C.S.: 333244
Adam Yuen *(Mng Dir)*

Non-U.S. Subsidiary:

manroland (Taiwan) Ltd. (4)
1 F No 21
Chien Kang Road, Taipei, 235, Taiwan
Tel.: (886) 282282368
Fax: (886) 282287756
Web Site: www.manroland.tw
Emp.: 30
Printing Machinery Distr
S.I.C.: 3555
N.A.I.C.S.: 333244

manroland Danmark A/S (3)
Lautruphoj 1-3
2750 Ballerup, Denmark
Tel.: (45) 44 35 55 55
Fax: (45) 44 35 55 99
E-Mail: info@manroland.dk
Web Site: www.manroland.dk
Commercial Printing Services
S.I.C.: 2759
N.A.I.C.S.: 323113

manroland d.o.o. (3)
Tolstojeva 9A
1000 Ljubljana, Slovenia
Tel.: (386) 1 565 92 30
Fax: (386) 1 568 46 80
Printing Machinery Distr
S.I.C.: 5084
N.A.I.C.S.: 423830

manroland Finland Oy (3)
Muuntotie 3 B
01510 Vantaa, Finland
Tel.: (358) 9 725 66 500
Fax: (358) 9 725 66 555
Web Site: www.manroland.fi
Printing Machinery Distr
S.I.C.: 5084
N.A.I.C.S.: 423830

manroland France SAS (3)
178 rue de la Belle Etoile
Roissy-en-France, 95958, France
Tel.: (33) 1 49 38 40 00
Fax: (33) 1 49 38 40 12
Web Site: www.man-roland.fr
Printing Machinery Distr
S.I.C.: 5084
N.A.I.C.S.: 423830

manroland Iberica Sistemas S.A. (3)
Rua Casal Queimado Edif Man Roland Nr 205-205-A
Cascais, 2750-492, Portugal
Tel.: (351) 214879540
Printing Equipment Mfr
S.I.C.: 3555
N.A.I.C.S.: 333244

manroland Iberica Sistemas S.L. (3)
C/ San Severo 30 Parque Empresarial Barajas Park
Madrid, 28042, Spain
Tel.: (34) 91 329 22 44
Fax: (34) 91 329 36 51
E-Mail: info@man-roland-es.com
Web Site: www.manroland.es
Printing Machinery Distr
S.I.C.: 5084
N.A.I.C.S.: 423830

manroland Ireland Ltd. (3)
Unit N2 Nord Ring Business Park
Santry, Dublin, Ireland
Tel.: (353) 1 832 1355
Fax: (353) 1 832 1357
Printing Machinery Mfr
S.I.C.: 3555
N.A.I.C.S.: 333244

manroland Magyarorszag Kft. (3)
Tablas U 36-38
1097 Budapest, Hungary
Tel.: (36) 1 326 0907
Fax: (36) 1 326 0901
E-Mail: info@manroland.hu
Web Site: www.manroland.hu
Emp.: 6
Printing Equipment Distr
S.I.C.: 5084
N.A.I.C.S.: 423830
Pokornyne Salamon Gyoergyi *(Mgr-Fin)*

manroland Norge AS (3)
Solheimveien 50
1473 Lorenskog, Norway
Tel.: (47) 67 92 11 80
Fax: (47) 67 90 54 50
E-Mail: info.no@manroland.com
Web Site: www.manroland.no
Printing Machinery Mfr
S.I.C.: 3555
N.A.I.C.S.: 333244

manroland Poland Sp. z o.o. (3)
Wolica Katowicka 11
Nadarzyn, Poland
Tel.: (48) 22 738 00 00
Fax: (48) 22 738 00 17
E-Mail: office@manroland.pl
Web Site: www.manroland.pl
Printing Machinery Mfr
S.I.C.: 3555
N.A.I.C.S.: 333244

manroland Printing Equipment (Shanghai) Ltd. (3)
Room 901 Bld A HongKou Plaza No 388 West Jiang Wan Rd
Hong Kou, Shanghai, 200083, China
Tel.: (86) 21 3636 3000
Fax: (86) 21 3636 5040
Printing Machinery Distr
S.I.C.: 5084
N.A.I.C.S.: 423830

manroland Romania S.R.L. (3)
Str Dr Calin Ottoi nr 47 Sector 2
023321 Bucharest, Romania
Tel.: (40) 21 242 0098
Fax: (40) 21 242 0099
E-Mail: office@manroland.ro
Web Site: www.manroland.ro
Printing Machinery Mfr
S.I.C.: 3555
N.A.I.C.S.: 333244
Dan Teoeorestu *(Mng Dir)*

manroland Sverige AB (3)
Nohabgatan 12
Trollhattan, 461 29, Sweden
Tel.: (46) 52 08 93 00
Fax: (46) 52 03 98 88
E-Mail: info.se@manroland.com
Web Site: www.manroland.se
Printing Machinery Mfr
S.I.C.: 3555
N.A.I.C.S.: 333244

manroland Swiss AG (3)
Industrie Neuhof 23
3422 Kirchberg, Switzerland
Tel.: (41) 34 447 71 11
Fax: (41) 34 447 74 22
E-Mail: printservices@manroland.ch
Web Site: www.manroland.ch
Printing Machinery Distr
S.I.C.: 5084
N.A.I.C.S.: 423830

manroland Thailand Ltd. (3)
22/6 Ladprao 21 Jomphol Jatujak
Bangkok, 10900, Thailand
Tel.: (66) 2 513 8629
Fax: (66) 2 513 8628
Web Site: www.manroland-sheetfed.com
Printing Machinery Mfr
S.I.C.: 3555
N.A.I.C.S.: 333244

manroland Western Europe Group B.V. (3)
Kuiperbergweg 50
1101 AG Amsterdam, Netherlands
Tel.: (31) 205872501
Fax: (31) 206118579
Investment Management Services
S.I.C.: 6211
N.A.I.C.S.: 523999

Votra SA (3)
5 Rue la Vigie
CH 1003 Lausanne, Switzerland (100%)
Tel.: (41) 213432300
Fax: (41) 213432333
E-Mail: info@votra.ch
Web Site: www.votra.ch
Emp.: 10
Graphic Systems Services
S.I.C.: 7336
N.A.I.C.S.: 541430
Philippe Orville *(Gen Mgr)*

Non-U.S. Joint Ventures:

Euro Media Groupe SA (2)
2 Avenue de l Europe
Paris, 94360, France
Tel.: (33) 1 49 83 40 00
Fax: (33) 1 49 83 43 06
Audiovisual Technical Services
S.I.C.: 7389

Allianz SE—(Continued)

N.A.I.C.S.: 541990

NET4GAS, s.r.o. (2)
Na Hrebenech II 1718/8
140 21 Prague, Czech Republic
Tel.: (420) 220221111
Fax: (420) 220226918
E-Mail: info@net4gas.cz
Web Site: www.net4gas.cz
Emp.: 245
Natural Gas Transportation Services
S.I.C.: 4922
N.A.I.C.S.: 486210
Andreas Rau *(CEO & Mng Dir)*
Radek Benik *(COO & Mng Dir)*

Allianz Capital Partners Verwaltungs GmbH (1)
Theresienstr 1-7
Munich, 80333, Germany
Tel.: (49) 8938000
Fax: (49) 8938007586
Financial Management Services
S.I.C.: 6211
N.A.I.C.S.: 523999

Allianz DGD Fonds (1)
Mainzer Landstrasse 11-13
Frankfurt am Main, 60329, Germany
Tel.: (49) 18 03 30 33 11
Fax: (49) 92 81 72 24 61 15
Mutual Fund Management Services
S.I.C.: 6799
N.A.I.C.S.: 523920

Allianz Dresdner Bauspar AG (1)
Am Sonnenplatz 1
61116 Bad Vilbel, Germany (100%)
Tel.: (49) 891796167
Fax: (49) 6926356006
E-Mail: service@adbag.de
Web Site: www.adbag.de
Emp.: 300
S.I.C.: 6399
N.A.I.C.S.: 524128
Michael Mehr *(Mng Dir)*

Allianz Dresdner Pension Consult GmbH (1)
Marienstr 50
D-70178 Stuttgart, Germany
Tel.: (49) 71166396096
Fax: (49) 7116635076
E-Mail: adpc.info@allianz.de
Web Site: www.adpc.allianz.de
Emp.: 26
Pension Services
S.I.C.: 6371
N.A.I.C.S.: 525110
Norbert Stenghas *(Mng Dir)*

Allianz Global Corporate & Specialty AG (1)
Fritz Schaeffer St 9
81724 Munich, Germany De
Tel.: (49) 8938000 (100%)
Fax: (49) 01802400104
E-Mail: agcs.communication.germany@allianz.com
Web Site: www.agcs.allianz.com
Emp.: 3,000
Property & Casualty Insurance Products & Services
S.I.C.: 6331
N.A.I.C.S.: 524126
Axel Theis *(CEO & Chm-Mgmt Bd)*
Chris Fischer Hirs *(CFO & Member-Mgmt Bd)*
Robert Tartaglia *(COO & Member-Mgmt Bd)*
Sinead Browne *(Chief Personnel Officer, Chief Risk Svcs Officer & Member-Mgmt Bd)*
Andreas Berger *(Chief Reg & Markets Officer & Member-Mgmt Bd)*
Hermann Jorissen *(Chief Underwriting Officer-Corp Lines & Member-Mgmt Bd)*
Hartmut Mai *(Chief Underwriting Officer-Corp Lines & Member-Mgmt Bd)*
Arthur Moossmann *(Chief Underwriting Officer-Specialty Lines & Member-Mgmt Bd)*
William Scaldaferri *(Chief Underwriting Officer-Risk Transfer & Relns & Member-Mgmt Bd)*

U.S. Subsidiary:

Allianz Global Risks US Insurance Company (2)
225 W Washington St Ste 2000
Chicago, IL 60606 CA
Tel.: (312) 224-3300 (100%)
Telex: 67 243 allienzins isa
E-Mail: agcscommunication@agcs.allianz.com
Web Site: www.agcs.allianz.com
Emp.: 800
Property & Casualty Insurance Products & Services
S.I.C.: 6331
N.A.I.C.S.: 524126
Hugh Burgess *(Pres, CEO & Grp Pres/CEO-Americas)*

Non-U.S. Subsidiary:

AIM Underwriting Limited (3)
1600-130 Adelaide Street
Toronto, ON, M5H 3P5, Canada
Tel.: (416) 849-4542
Fax: (416) 849-4555
Insurance Underwriting Services
S.I.C.: 6361
N.A.I.C.S.: 524127

Non-U.S. Unit:

Allianz Global Corporate & Specialty - Canada (3)
130 Adelaide St W Ste 1600
Toronto, ON, M5H 3P5, Canada
Tel.: (416) 915-4247
Fax: (416) 849-4555
Web Site: www.aic-allianz.ca
Emp.: 100
Property & Casualty Insurance Products & Services
S.I.C.: 6331
N.A.I.C.S.: 524126
Thomas Paap *(Country Mgr-Canada)*

Non-U.S. Subsidiaries:

Allianz Global Corporate & Specialty (France) S.A. (2)
Tour Opus 12 77 Esplanade du General de Gaulle
92076 Paris, La Defense, France FR
Tel.: (33) 1 5885 9550
E-Mail: contact.france@allianz.com
Web Site: www.agcs.allianz.com
Emp.: 3,000
Property & Casualty Insurance Products & Services
S.I.C.: 6331
N.A.I.C.S.: 524126
Thierry van Santen *(CEO)*
Giles Mareuse *(Deputy CEO & Head-Marine Underwriting)*

Allianz Risk Transfer AG (2)
Lavaterstrasse 67
8002 Zurich, Switzerland CH
Tel.: (41) 442851818
Fax: (41) 442851822
E-Mail: reception@art-allianz.com
Web Site: www.art-allianz.com
Sales Range: $900-999.9 Million
Emp.: 20
Financial & Insurance Services
S.I.C.: 6726
N.A.I.C.S.: 525990
Axel Theis *(Chm)*
Bill Scaldaferri *(Pres & CEO)*

U.S. Subsidiary:

Allianz Risk Transfer, Inc. (3)
1330 Ave of the Americas 19th Fl
New York, NY 10019
Tel.: (646) 840-5000
Fax: (212) 754-2330
Web Site: www.art-allianz.com
Emp.: 15
Financial & Insurance Services
S.I.C.: 6726
N.A.I.C.S.: 525990
Bill Scaldaferri *(CEO)*

Non-U.S. Subsidiaries:

AGCS Dubai (3)
Dubai International Financial Center Gate Village 8
Dubai, United Arab Emirates
Tel.: (971) 4 7026666
Web Site: www.allianz.com
Reinsurance Services
S.I.C.: 6399
N.A.I.C.S.: 524130
Sanjeev Badyal *(CEO)*

Allianz Risk Transfer (Bermuda) Limited (3)
Overbay 106 Pitts Bay Rd
HM08 Pembroke, Bermuda
Tel.: (441) 295 4722
Fax: (441) 295 2867
E-Mail: art@art-allianz.com
Web Site: www.art.allianz.com
Emp.: 10
Financial & Insurance Services
S.I.C.: 6726
N.A.I.C.S.: 525990
Richard Morris *(Pres)*

Non-U.S. Units:

Allianz Global Corporate & Specialty - Australia (2)
Level 12 2 Market St
Sydney, NSW, 2000, Australia
Tel.: (61) 293906994
Fax: (61) 293906308
E-Mail: customerservice@allianz.com.au
Web Site: www.agcs.allianz.com
Property & Casualty Insurance Products & Services
S.I.C.: 6351
N.A.I.C.S.: 524126
Holger Schaefer *(Gen Mgr-Pacific)*

Allianz Global Corporate & Specialty - Austria (2)
Hietzinger Kai 101-105
A 1130 Vienna, Austria
Tel.: (43) 1 87807-88700
Telex: 132 355 aewnd e
E-Mail: office@allianz.at
Web Site: www.allianz.at
Emp.: 600
Property & Casualty Insurance Products & Services
S.I.C.: 6331
N.A.I.C.S.: 524126
Thomas Gonser *(Mng Dir)*

Allianz Global Corporate & Specialty - Belgium (2)
Uitbreidingstraat 86
2600 Antwerp, Berchem, Belgium
Tel.: (32) 3 304 1600
E-Mail: petra.heyvaert@allianz.be
Web Site: www.agcs.allianz.com
Emp.: 35
Property & Casualty Insurance Products & Services
S.I.C.: 6351
N.A.I.C.S.: 524126
Ronald Jorssen *(Head-Risk Consulting-Belgium)*

Allianz Global Corporate & Specialty - Ireland (2)
Elmtech Merrion Rd
Dublin, 4, Ireland
Tel.: (353) 16133000
Fax: (353) 16134444
E-Mail: info@allianz.ie
Web Site: www.allianz.ie
Emp.: 500
Property & Casualty Insurance Products & Services
S.I.C.: 6351
N.A.I.C.S.: 524126
Pat Corcoran *(Country Mgr-Ireland)*

Allianz Global Corporate & Specialty - Singapore (2)
3 Temasek Avenue
08-01 Centennial Tower, Singapore, 39190, Singapore
Tel.: (65) 6297 2529
Fax: (65) 6297 1956
E-Mail:
Web Site: www.agcs.allianz.com
Emp.: 70
Property & Casualty Insurance Products & Services
S.I.C.: 6331
N.A.I.C.S.: 524126
Lutz Fullgraf *(Reg CEO-Asia Pacific)*
Kevin Leong *(Reg Mgr-Asia Pacific Market & CEO-Singapore)*

Allianz Global Corporate & Specialty - UK (2)
60 Gracechurch St
London, EC3V 0HR, United Kingdom
Tel.: (44) 20 3451 3000
E-Mail: marketing@allianz.com
Web Site: www.agcs.allianz.com
Emp.: 200
Property & Casualty Insurance Products & Services
S.I.C.: 6331
N.A.I.C.S.: 524126
Carsten Scheffel *(CEO)*

Allianz Global Investors AG (1)
Seidl str 24-24A
80335 Munich, Germany
Tel.: (49) 89122070
Fax: (49) 8912207900
E-Mail: info@allianzgi.com
Web Site: www.allianzglobalinvestors.com
Emp.: 400
Investment & Financial Services
S.I.C.: 6211
N.A.I.C.S.: 523999
Nick Smith *(Mng Dir-Europe)*
Joerg de Vries-Hippen *(Chief Investment Officer-European Equities)*
Neil Dwane *(Chief Investment Officer-Europe & European Equities)*

Subsidiaries:

Allianz Climate Solutions GmbH (2)
Koeniginstrasse 28
80802 Munich, Germany
Tel.: (49) 89 3800 12203
Fax: (49) 89 3800 12210
E-Mail: acs@allianz.com
Web Site: www.acs.allianz.com
General Insurance Services
S.I.C.: 6411
N.A.I.C.S.: 524298
Armin Sandhoevel *(CEO)*
Karsten Loeffler *(CFO & COO)*

Allianz Global Investors Kapitalanlagegesellschaft mbH (2)
Mainzer Landstrasse 11-13
60329 Frankfurt am Main, Germany
Tel.: (49) 1803303311
Fax: (49) 928172246115
E-Mail: info@allianzgi.de
Web Site: www.allianzglobalinvestors.de
Investment Advisory Services
S.I.C.: 6282
N.A.I.C.S.: 523930
Henry J. Durstewitz *(Mng Dir)*

cominvest Asset Management GmbH (2)
Platz Der Einheit 1
60327 Frankfurt am Main, Germany De
Tel.: (49) 6913010
Fax: (49) 6913013578
Web Site: www.cominvest.de
Emp.: 570
Investment Trust
S.I.C.: 6091
N.A.I.C.S.: 523991
Sebastian Klein *(CEO)*

Non-U.S. Subsidiaries:

Cominvest Investment Luxembourg S.A. (3)
25 Rue Edward Steichen
L 2540 Luxembourg, Luxembourg
Tel.: (352) 25111
Fax: (352) 2511288
E-Mail: daneil.es@cominvest-am.lu
Web Site: www.cominvest-am.lu
Investment Advisory Services
S.I.C.: 6282
N.A.I.C.S.: 523930
Daneil Even *(Sec)*

risklab GmbH (2)
Seidlstr 24 - 24a
80335 Munich, Germany
Tel.: (49) 89 1220 7750
Fax: (49) 89 1220 7751
E-Mail: info@risklab.com
Web Site: www.risklab.com
Emp.: 33
Asset Management Services
S.I.C.: 6799
N.A.I.C.S.: 523920

Reinhold Hafner *(CEO)*
Gerhard Scheuenstuhl *(Member-Mgmt Bd)*

U.S. Subsidiaries:

Allianz Global Investors Distributors LLC (2)
1633 Broadway
New York, NY 10019 CA
Tel.: (212) 739-3000
Web Site: www.allianzinvestors.com
Emp.: 115
Mutual Funds
S.I.C.: 6211
N.A.I.C.S.: 523120
Nick Loglisci *(Mng Dir-Consultant Rels)*

Allianz Global Investors (2)
680 Newport Center Dr Ste 250
Newport Beach, CA 92660-6309
Tel.: (949) 219-2200
Fax: (949) 644-6777
Web Site: www.adam-us.com
Emp.: 120
Investment Management
S.I.C.: 6282
N.A.I.C.S.: 523930
Donald Gervais *(Mng Dir & Co-Head-Institutional Sls-North America)*
Jill Lohrfink *(Mng Dir & Head-Institutional-North America)*
Edward Wilkinson *(Mng Dir & Head-Fundamental Equity Client Portfolio Mgmt)*
Mark Porterfield *(Exec VP-Media Rels)*

Fireman's Fund Insurance Co. of Texas (2)
500 N Akard St Lincoln Plz Ste 400
Dallas, TX 75201-2519 TX
Tel.: (214) 220-4000
Fax: (214) 220-4153
Web Site: www.ffic.com
Insurance Services
S.I.C.: 6351
N.A.I.C.S.: 524126

NFJ Investment Group LP (2)
2100 Ross Ave Ste 700
Dallas, TX 75201-2739
Tel.: (214) 754-1780
Fax: (214) 754-1798
E-Mail: marketing@nfjinv.com
Web Site: www.nfjinvestmentgroup.com
Emp.: 45
Investment Advice
Import Export
S.I.C.: 6282
N.A.I.C.S.: 523930
John L. Johnson *(Mng Dir)*
Ben J. Fischer *(Mng Dir)*
Barbara Coaussen *(COO)*

Nicholas-Applegate Capital Management LLC (2)
600 W Broadway Ste 2900
San Diego, CA 92101-3398 CA
Tel.: (619) 687-8000
Fax: (619) 687-8091
E-Mail: rfp@nacm.com
Web Site: www.nicholas-applegate.com
Emp.: 150
Provider of Investment Advice
Import Export
S.I.C.: 6282
N.A.I.C.S.: 523930
Ranjit S. Sufi *(Mng Dir-Global Client Svc-Mktg-Sls)*
Charles Fields *(Gen Counsel)*

Pacific Investment Management Company LLC (2)
840 Newport Ctr Dr Ste 100
Newport Beach, CA 92660-6310
Tel.: (949) 720-6000
Fax: (949) 720-1376
Toll Free: (866) 746-2602
E-Mail: presscenter@pimco.com
Web Site: www.pimco.com
Emp.: 1,000
Investment Advice
Import Export
S.I.C.: 6282
N.A.I.C.S.: 523930
William H. Gross *(Founder, Mng Dir & Chief Investment Officer)*
Douglas M. Hodge *(CEO)*
Tammie Arnold *(Mng Dir & Head-Global Wealth Mgmt)*
Wendy Cupps *(Mng Dir & Head-Product Mgmt Grp)*
Ravi Mattu *(Mng Dir & Head-Analytics)*
Andrew Balls *(Co-Deputy Chief Investment Officer)*
Daniel Ivascyn *(Co-Deputy Chief Investment Officer)*
Mark Kiesel *(Co-Deputy Chief Investment Officer)*
Virginie Maisonneuve *(Co-Deputy Chief Investment Officer)*
Scott Mather *(Co-Deputy Chief Investment Officer)*
Mihir P. Worah *(Co-Deputy Chief Investment Officer)*
Peter Matheos *(Exec VP, Sr Engr-Fin & Head-Portfolio Analytics & Model Valuation)*
David Fisher *(Exec VP & Head-Global & Emerging Markets Product Mgmt)*
Robert Morena *(Exec VP & Head-Bus Dev-New York)*
Christian Stracke *(Exec VP & Co-Head-Credit Res)*
Frank Witt *(Exec VP & Head-Bus Dev-Germany & Austria)*
Ric Okun *(Exec VP & Sr Mgr-Tech)*
Kumaran K. Damodaran *(Exec VP & Portfolio Mgr-Emerging Markets)*
Jonathan L. Horne *(Exec VP & Portfolio Mgr)*
Nicholas J. Johnson *(Exec VP & Portfolio Mgr)*
Elizabeth MacLean *(Exec VP & Portfolio Mgr)*
Mohit Mittal *(Exec VP & Portfolio Mgr)*
John W. Murray *(Exec VP & Portfolio Mgr)*
Marco van Akkeren *(Exec VP & Portfolio Mgr)*
Candice E. Stack *(Exec VP & Acct Mgr)*
Jared B. Gross *(Exec VP & Mgr-Product)*
Yanay Lehavi *(Exec VP & Mgr-IT)*
Rene Martel *(Exec VP & Mgr-Product)*
Neal Reiner *(Exec VP & Mgr-Credit Alternative Strategies Product)*
Greg Sharenow *(Exec VP & Mgr-Real Return Portfolio)*
Ignacio Sosa *(Exec VP & Mgr-Emerging Markets Product)*
John R. Cavalieri *(Exec VP)*
Tony Crescenzi *(Exec VP)*
Jennifer Durham *(Exec VP)*
Joe Fournier *(Exec VP)*
Yuri Garbuzov *(Exec VP)*
Molly Hall *(Exec VP-Newport Beach)*
Gang Hu *(Exec VP)*
Dan Hyman *(Exec VP)*
Richard R. LeBrun *(Exec VP & Atty-Legal/Compliance)*
Julie A. Meggers *(Exec VP)*
Eric Mogelof *(Exec VP)*
Raja Mukherji *(Exec VP)*
Alfred Murata *(Exec VP)*
Robin Nabors *(Exec VP-HR Dept)*
Krishnamoorthy Narasimhan *(Exec VP)*
Arthur Ong *(Exec VP-Legal & Compliance)*
Guillermo Osses *(Exec VP)*
Lupin Rahman *(Exec VP-Emerging Markets Portfolio Mgmt)*
Mark A. Romano *(Exec VP)*
Stacy L. Schaus *(Exec VP)*
Luke Drago Spajic *(Exec VP)*
Scott M. Spalding *(Exec VP)*
Jennifer Strickland *(Exec VP)*
Hozef Arif *(Sr VP & Portfolio Mgr)*
Jason Duko *(Sr VP & Portfolio Mgr)*
Steven L. Jones *(Sr VP & Product Mgr)*
Jeremie Banet *(Sr VP & Mgr-Real Return Portfolio)*
Kofi Bentsi *(Sr VP & Mgr-Emerging Markets Fixed Income Portfolio)*
Kwame Anochie *(Sr VP)*
Kfir Ben-Zvi *(Sr VP)*
Matthew H. Brenner *(Sr VP)*
Jelle Brons *(Sr VP)*
Mike Burdian *(Sr VP)*
Jeff Byer *(Sr VP)*
Michael Chandra *(Sr VP)*
Amit Chopra *(Sr VP)*
Matt Clark *(Sr VP)*
Bill Cumby *(Sr VP)*
Josh Davis *(Sr VP)*
Matthew P. Dorsten *(Sr VP)*
Bob Fields *(Sr VP)*
Brett Gorman *(Sr VP)*
Terrence Ing *(Sr VP)*
Jason Kezelman *(Sr VP)*
Mukund Kumar *(Sr VP)*
Idriss Maoui *(Sr VP)*
Albert Ng *(Sr VP)*
Larry Nguyen *(Sr VP)*
Loren Ollenburger *(Sr VP)*
Steven Pawliczek *(Sr VP)*
Niels Pedersen *(Sr VP)*
Natalie Pickering *(Sr VP-Exchange Traded Funds Offerings)*
Jesse L. Pricer *(Sr VP)*
Ying Qiu *(Sr VP)*
Deepa Salastekar *(Sr VP)*
Matt Shaw *(Sr VP)*
Julie Sheperd *(Sr VP)*
Kimberley G. Stafford *(Sr VP)*
Jason Steiner *(Sr VP)*
Michael A. Terry *(Sr VP)*
Ashish Tiwari *(Sr VP)*
Keith Werber *(Sr VP)*
Timothy C. White *(Sr VP)*
Jing Yang *(Sr VP)*
Vadim Yasnov *(Sr VP)*

Division:

PIMCO Advisory (3)
840 Newport Ctr Dr Ste 100
Newport Beach, CA 92660
Tel.: (949) 720-6426
E-Mail: advisory@pimco.com
Web Site: www.pimco.com
Analyzes, Designs & Manages Asset-Liability Solutions
S.I.C.: 6282
N.A.I.C.S.: 523930
Rod Dubitsky *(Exec VP)*

Subsidiary:

PIMCO Investments LLC (3)
1633 Broadway
New York, NY 10019 DE
Mailing Address:
33 Maiden Ln Fl 6
New York, NY 10038-5104
Tel.: (212) 739-3000
Fax: (212) 739-3926
Web Site: www.pimco.com
Emp.: 400
Partnership Holding Company for Investment Management Services
S.I.C.: 6726
N.A.I.C.S.: 525990
Jay Jacobs *(Mng Dir)*
Emanuele Ravano *(Mng Dir)*
Charles Lahr *(Exec VP & Mgr-Global Equities Portfolio)*
David L. Braun *(Exec VP)*
Tracey Vallarta Jordal *(Exec VP & Atty-Compliance/Legal)*
Kristofer Kraus *(Exec VP-Advisory)*
Cynthia Meyn *(Exec VP)*
Scott Millimet *(Exec VP)*
Scott P. Steele *(Exec VP)*
Libby Cantrill *(Sr VP)*
Richard Colasuonno *(Sr VP)*
Charles de Segundo *(Sr VP)*
Kaela Gibbons *(Sr VP)*
Natalie Karpov *(Sr VP)*
Aaron Kim *(Sr VP)*
Lisa Kim *(Sr VP)*
Trip Lilly *(Sr VP)*
Sean McCarthy *(Sr VP)*
Peter Miller *(Sr VP)*
Jeff Muehlehaler *(Sr VP)*
Chitrang Purani *(Sr VP)*
Alka Singal *(Sr VP)*
Monica Verma *(Sr VP)*

Non-U.S. Subsidiaries:

PIMCO Asia Pte. Ltd. (3)
30 Cecil Street 23-01 Prudential Tower
Singapore, 049712, Singapore
Tel.: (65) 65389600
Fax: (65) 65382700
E-Mail: infoasia@pimco.com
Web Site: www.singapore.pimco.com
Bond Investment Services
S.I.C.: 6211
N.A.I.C.S.: 523999
Brian P. Baker *(CEO, Mng Dir & Head-Firms-Hong Kong)*
Michael Thompson *(Exec VP & Head-Wealth Mgmt Grp)*
Ronie Ganguly *(Sr VP & Corp Portfolio Mgr-Asia Credit & Emerging Market)*
Tim Bruenjes *(Sr VP)*
Roland Mieth *(Sr VP)*

Non-U.S. Subsidiaries:

PIMCO Australia Pty Ltd. (4)
Level 19 363 George Street
Sydney, NSW, 2000, Australia
Tel.: (61) 292791771
Fax: (61) 292792580
E-Mail: australiainfo@au.pimco.com
Web Site: www.pimco.com
Emp.: 30
Bond Investment Services
S.I.C.: 6211
N.A.I.C.S.: 523999
Tracy Chin *(Sr VP)*
Matthew McLenaghan *(Sr VP)*

PIMCO Japan Ltd. (4)
4-1-28 Toranomon Tower Office 18th Fl
Tokyo, 105-0001, Japan
Tel.: (81) 357778150
Fax: (81) 357778151
E-Mail: info@japan.pimco.com
Web Site: www.japan.pimco.com
Emp.: 80
Bond Investment Services
S.I.C.: 6211
N.A.I.C.S.: 523999
Haruki Minaki *(COO & Exec VP)*
Hiroaki Furusho *(Sr VP)*
Koji Ishida *(Sr VP)*
Yayoi Kishimoto *(Sr VP)*
Rafael A. Lopez *(Sr VP)*
Sachiko Nojima *(Sr VP)*
Taro Shiroyama *(Sr VP)*

PIMCO Canada Corp. (3)
120 Adelaide Street West Suite 1901
Toronto, ON, M5H 1T1, Canada
Tel.: (416) 368-3350
Fax: (416) 368-3576
Web Site: www.pimco.com
Emp.: 18
Bond Investment Services
S.I.C.: 6211
N.A.I.C.S.: 523999
Stuart Graham *(Pres)*
Andrew Forsyth *(Sr VP)*

PIMCO Europe Ltd. (3)
11 Baker Street
London, W1U 3AH, United Kingdom UK
Tel.: (44) 2036401000
Fax: (44) 2036401007
Web Site: www.pimco.co.uk
Bond Investment Services
S.I.C.: 6211
N.A.I.C.S.: 523999
Alessandro Gandolfi *(Exec VP & Head-Italy)*
Myles E. Bradshaw *(Exec VP & Portfolio Mgr)*
Gillian O'Connell *(Exec VP & Mgr-Ops)*
Ryan P. Blute *(Exec VP)*
Philippe Bodereau *(Exec VP)*
John Griffiths *(Exec VP)*
Sachin Gupta *(Exec VP)*
Bettina Mazzocchi *(Exec VP)*
Thomas E. Rice *(Exec VP)*
Melissa Tuttle *(Exec VP)*
David Viana *(Exec VP)*
Mangala Ananthanarayanan *(Sr VP)*
Berdibek Ahmedov *(Sr VP)*
Vlad Cara *(Sr VP)*
Ben M. Edwards *(Sr VP)*
Sunil Kothari *(Sr VP)*
Matthieu Loriferne *(Sr VP)*
Alain Mandy *(Sr VP)*
Ewan Markson-Brown *(Sr VP)*
Amit Mehta *(Sr VP)*
Tommy Nguyen *(Sr VP)*
Sheila Pejavar *(Sr VP)*
Rosamond Price *(Sr VP)*
Matthew Putnicki *(Sr VP)*
Pierre-Yves Rahari *(Sr VP)*
Ian Scorah *(Sr VP)*
Alex Struc *(Sr VP)*
Mary Zerner *(Sr VP)*

PIMCO (Switzerland) LLC (3)
Dreikoenigstrasse 31a
8002 Zurich, Switzerland CH
Tel.: (41) 442083867
Web Site: www.pimco.com
Emp.: 4
Risk & Investments Services
S.I.C.: 6211
N.A.I.C.S.: 523999
Christian M. Staub *(Exec VP)*
Juerg Rimle *(Sr VP)*

RCM Capital Management LLC (2)
555 Mission St
San Francisco, CA 94105-5988 DE
Tel.: (415) 954-5400 (100%)
Fax: (415) 954-8200

Allianz SE—(Continued)

Web Site: www.rcm.com
Emp.: 350
Investment Advisory Services
S.I.C.: 6282
N.A.I.C.S.: 523930
Udo Frank *(CEO)*

Non-U.S. Subsidiaries:

Allianz Global Investors Hong Kong Limited (2)
Suite 2003B 21 Fl Cheung Kong Center
Central, China (Hong Kong)
Tel.: (852) 22388688
Fax: (852) 2872533
Web Site: www.allianzglobalinvestors.co m.hk
Emp.: 200
Investment & Financial Services
S.I.C.: 6211
N.A.I.C.S.: 523999
Mark Konyn *(CEO)*
Christina Hui *(CMO & Head-Greater China & Southeast Asia)*

Non-U.S. Subsidiaries:

Allianz Global Investors Korea Ltd. (3)
18th Floor Allianz Tower 45-21 Yoido-dong
Yongdungpo-gu, Seoul, Korea (South)
Tel.: (82) 220719900
Fax: (82) 227821024
E-Mail: hyang-ukrryu@allian.gi-at.com
Web Site: www.allianzglobalinvestors.com
Emp.: 50
Investment & Financial Services
S.I.C.: 6211
N.A.I.C.S.: 523999

Allianz Global Investors Securities Investment Consulting Co. Ltd. (3)
7th Fl 378 Fu-Hsing N Rd
Taipei, 104, Taiwan
Tel.: (886) 225022989
Fax: (886) 225071286
E-Mail: pw.hr@allianzgi-ap.com
Emp.: 200
Investment & Financial Services
S.I.C.: 6211
N.A.I.C.S.: 523999

Allianz Global Investors Singapore Ltd. (3)
3 Temasek Avenue 07-05 Centenniel Tower
039190 Singapore, 049909, Singapore
Tel.: (65) 63118000
Fax: (65) 63118099
E-Mail: marketing@allianzgi-ap.com.sg
Web Site: www.allianzglobalinvestors.co m.sg
Emp.: 30
Investment & Financial Services
S.I.C.: 6211
N.A.I.C.S.: 523999

Allianz Global Investors Taiwan Ltd. (3)
6th Fl 378 Fu-Hsing N Rd
Taipei, 104, Taiwan
Tel.: (886) 225028889
Fax: (886) 225079993
E-Mail: info@allianzglobalinvestors.com.tw
Web Site: www.allianzglobalinvestors.co m.tw
Emp.: 200
Investment & Financial Services
S.I.C.: 6211
N.A.I.C.S.: 523999

RCM Capital Management Pty Ltd (3)
Level 57 MLC Centre 19 29 Martin Pl
Sydney, NSW, 2000, Australia
Tel.: (61) 292382070
Fax: (61) 992382076
E-Mail: info@au.rcm.com
Web Site: www.rcm.com
Investment & Financial Services
S.I.C.: 6211
N.A.I.C.S.: 523999
Mark Konyn *(CEO-Asia Pacific)*

Allianz Global Investors (Luxembourg) S.A. (2)
6A Rte de Treves Senningerbrg
2633 Luxembourg, Luxembourg (100%)
Tel.: (352) 4634631
Fax: (352) 463463620
E-Mail: info@allianzgi.lu
Web Site: www.allianzglobalinvestors.lu
Emp.: 55
International Banking; Asset Management
S.I.C.: 6159
N.A.I.C.S.: 522293
Jean-Christoph Arntz *(Mng Dir)*

Allianz Global Investors (Schweiz) AG (2)
Hohllstriffe 552
8048 Zurich, Switzerland
Tel.: (41) 583580542
Fax: (41) 583580541
Web Site: www.allianzglobalinvestors.com
Investment & Financial Services
S.I.C.: 6211
N.A.I.C.S.: 523999

Allianz Global Investors (UK) Ltd. (2)
1st Floor 155 Bishopsgate
London, EC2M 3AD, United Kingdom
Tel.: (44) 2070651407
Fax: (44) 2076383508
E-Mail: investo.services@allianzgi.co.uk
Web Site: www.allianzglobalinvestors.co.uk
Emp.: 100
Investment & Financial Services
S.I.C.: 6211
N.A.I.C.S.: 523999
Mike Hooper *(Mng Dir)*

Non-U.S. Joint Venture:

Guotai Junan Allianz Fund Management Co., Ltd. (2)
46F Jin Mao Tower 88 Century Boulevard
Shanghai, China
Tel.: (86) 2138784766
Web Site: www.vip-funds.com
Fund Management Services; Owned 33% by Allianz Global Investors AG & 67% by Guotai Junan Securities Co., Ltd.
S.I.C.: 6722
N.A.I.C.S.: 525910

Allianz Global Investors Europe Holding GmbH (1)
Seidlstr 24-24a
80335 Munich, Germany
Tel.: (49) 89122070
Investment Management Services
S.I.C.: 6799
N.A.I.C.S.: 523920
Elizabeth Corley *(Mng Dir)*

Allianz Immobilien GmbH (1)
Charlottenstrasse 3
70182 Stuttgart, Germany (100%)
Tel.: (49) 7116630
Fax: (49) 7116633743
E-Mail: immo.info@allianz.de
Web Site: www.allianz-real-estate-germa ny.de
Emp.: 100
Real Estate Company
S.I.C.: 6531
N.A.I.C.S.: 531210
Stephan Brendgen *(CEO)*

Allianz Investment Management SE (1)
Koniginstr 28
Munich, 80802, Germany
Tel.: (49) 89122070
Insurance Brokerage Services
S.I.C.: 6411
N.A.I.C.S.: 524210

Allianz LAD Fonds (1)
Mainzer Landstrasse 11-13
Frankfurt am Main, 60329, Germany
Tel.: (49) 18 03 30 33 11
Fax: (49) 92 81 72 24 61 15
Mutual Fund Management Services
S.I.C.: 6282
N.A.I.C.S.: 523920

Allianz LEBENCO Fonds (1)
Mainzer Landstrasse 11-13
Frankfurt am Main, 60329, Germany
Tel.: (49) 18 03 30 33 11
Fax: (49) 92 81 72 24 61 15
Mutual Fund Management Services
S.I.C.: 6282
N.A.I.C.S.: 523920

Allianz Lebensversicherungs-AG (1)
Allianz Lebensversicherungs-AG
PO Box 106002
70178 Berlin, Germany (91%)
Tel.: (49) 7116630
Telex: 723571 ales d
Fax: (49) 101802400102
E-Mail: info@allianz.de
Web Site: www.allianz.de
Emp.: 2,000
Life Insurance
S.I.C.: 6311
N.A.I.C.S.: 524113
Michael Beckmann *(CEO)*

Allianz Managed Operations & Services SE (1)
Gutenbergstrasse 8
85774 Unterfohring, Germany
Tel.: (49) 89 3800 0
E-Mail: amos.info@allianz.de
Information Technology Consulting Services
S.I.C.: 7373
N.A.I.C.S.: 541512

Allianz of Asia-Pacific and Africa GmbH (1)
Koniginstr 28
Munich, 80802, Germany
Tel.: (49) 8938000
General Insurance Services
S.I.C.: 6411
N.A.I.C.S.: 524210

Allianz Pension Consult GmbH (1)
Marienstrasse 50
70178 Stuttgart, Germany
Tel.: (49) 711 663 96096
Fax: (49) 711 663 5076
E-Mail: ADPC.info@allianz.de
Web Site: www.apc.allianz.de
Emp.: 35
Pension Fund Management Services
S.I.C.: 6799
N.A.I.C.S.: 523920

Allianz Pensionsfonds Aktiengesellschaft (1)
Reinsburgstrasse 19
70178 Stuttgart, Baden-Wurttemberg, Germany
Tel.: (49) 711 6630
Fax: (49) 711 6632654
Pension Fund Management Services
S.I.C.: 6371
N.A.I.C.S.: 525110

Allianz Private Equity Partners Verwaltungs GmbH (1)
Theresienstr 6-8
Munich, 80333, Germany
Tel.: (49) 8938000
Financial Advisory Services
S.I.C.: 6282
N.A.I.C.S.: 523930

Allianz Private Krankenversicherungs-AG (1)
Fritz-Schaeffer-Strasse 9
D-81727 Munich, Germany
Tel.: (49) 8967850
Fax: (49) 8967853552
E-Mail: service.apkv@allianz.de
Web Site: www.allianz.com
Emp.: 300
Insurance & Financial Services
S.I.C.: 6411
N.A.I.C.S.: 524298
Munika Adam *(Sec)*

Allianz ProzessFinanz GmbH (1)
Koeniginstrasse 28
D-80802 Munich, Germany
Tel.: (49) 89380018370
Fax: (49) 89380018379
E-Mail: allianz.profi@allianz.de
Web Site: www.allianz-profi.de
Emp.: 8
Financial Services
S.I.C.: 6726
N.A.I.C.S.: 525990
Arndt Eversberg *(Mng Dir)*

Allianz Real Estate Germany GmbH (1)
Charlottenstrasse 3
70182 Stuttgart, Germany
Tel.: (49) 711 663 0
Fax: (49) 711 663 3743
Real Estate Management Services
S.I.C.: 6531
N.A.I.C.S.: 531390

Allianz Rechtsschutz-Service GmbH (1)
Koniginstr 28
Munich, 80802, Germany
Tel.: (49) 8938000
Fax: (49) 89 349941
General Insurance Services
S.I.C.: 6411
N.A.I.C.S.: 524210

Allianz Renewable Energy Management GmbH (1)
Feldscheide 2
Sehestedt, Schleswig-Holstein, 24814, Germany
Tel.: (49) 4357 9977 0
Fax: (49) 4357 997710
Electric Power Generation Services
S.I.C.: 4939
N.A.I.C.S.: 221118

Allianz Renewable Energy Subholding GmbH & Co. KG (1)
Str Max Planck St
85609 Aschheim, Germany
Tel.: (49) 89456660
Investment Management Services
S.I.C.: 6282
N.A.I.C.S.: 523920
Joachim Jirdell *(Mgr)*

Allianz Risk Consulting GmbH (1)
Koniginstr 28
Munich, 80802, Germany
Tel.: (49) 89203051000
Fax: (49) 89 38006322
General Insurance Services
S.I.C.: 6411
N.A.I.C.S.: 524210

Allianz Service Center GmbH (1)
Nymphenburger Str 110-112
Munich, 80636, Germany
Tel.: (49) 8918943580
General Insurance Services
S.I.C.: 6411
N.A.I.C.S.: 524210

Allianz SOA Fonds (1)
Mainzer Landstrasse 11-13
Frankfurt am Main, 60329, Germany
Tel.: (49) 18 03 30 33 11
Fax: (49) 92 81 72 24 61 15
Mutual Fund Management Services
S.I.C.: 6282
N.A.I.C.S.: 523920

Allianz Versicherungs AG (1)
Koeninginstrasse 28
80802 Munich, Germany (100%)
Tel.: (49) 8938000
Fax: (49) 8938004581
E-Mail: service@allianz.de
Web Site: www.allianz.de
Emp.: 6,000
Property & Casualty Insurance
S.I.C.: 6331
N.A.I.C.S.: 524126
Henning Schulte Noelle *(Chm)*

Divisions:

Allianz Versicherungs AG (2)
PO Box
10900 Berlin, Germany (100%)
Tel.: (49) 01802100101
Telex: 411376 alf d
Fax: (49) 01802400102
Web Site: www.allianz.de
Emp.: 2,500
Property & Casualty Insurance
S.I.C.: 6331
N.A.I.C.S.: 524126

Allianz Versicherungs-AG (2)
Kaiser Wilhelm Ring 31
D 50672 Cologne, Germany (100%)
Tel.: (49) 22157312437
Fax: (49) 2215731549
Web Site: www.allianz.de
Emp.: 2,000
Insurance Provider
S.I.C.: 6399
N.A.I.C.S.: 524128
F. Caspers *(CEO)*

Allianz Versicherungs-AG (2)
Uhlandstrasse 2
70182 Stuttgart, Germany (100%)
Tel.: (49) 71121730
Fax: (49) 7112173170
E-Mail: ksc.stuggart@allianz.de
Web Site: www.allianz-stuttgart.de
Emp.: 1,500
Insurance Provider
S.I.C.: 6399
N.A.I.C.S.: 524128

Subsidiaries:

Allianz Handwerker Services GmbH (2)
Nocherstreet 224
80541 Munich, Germany
Tel.: (49) 89517190
Fax: (49) 8951719619
E-Mail: info@allianz-services.de
Web Site: www.allianz-services.de
Emp.: 230
Building Restoration & Construction
S.I.C.: 1541
N.A.I.C.S.: 236210
Rudiger Hermann *(Mng Dir)*

esa Euroship Assekuradeurgesellschaft mbH & Co. KG (2)
Friedrichsplatz 2
74177 Bad Friedrichshall, Germany
Tel.: (49) 71369513414
Fax: (49) 71369513455
E-Mail: info@esa-allianz.de
Web Site: www.esa-allianz.de
Emp.: 120
Financial Services
S.I.C.: 6411
N.A.I.C.S.: 524298
Walter Szabados *(Mng Dir)*

Non-U.S. Branch:

Allianz Versicherungs-AG (Dubai Branch) (2)
Alatar Business Tower 29th Fl Office No 2
Sheikh Zayed Rd
PO Box 7659
Dubai, 7659, United Arab Emirates (100%)
Tel.: (971) 43329929
Fax: (971) 43329166
E-Mail: violet.coelho@allianz.ae
Web Site: www.allianz.ae
Emp.: 25
Insurance Provider
S.I.C.: 6399
N.A.I.C.S.: 524128

Allianz Zentrum fuer Technik GmbH (1)
Koenigin Str 28
85737 Ismaning, Germany
Tel.: (49) 8938000
Fax: (49) 8938003425
E-Mail: information@allianz-azt.de
Web Site: www.allianz-azt.de
Emp.: 100
Loss Prevention & Corporate Risk Management Services
S.I.C.: 6411
N.A.I.C.S.: 524298

AllSecur Deutschland AG (1)
Theodor-Stern-Kai 1
60596 Frankfurt am Main, Germany
Tel.: (49) 69 99999 111
Fax: (49) 69 96249 22244
E-Mail: service@allsecur.de
Web Site: www.allsecur.de
Automobile Insurance Services
S.I.C.: 6331
N.A.I.C.S.: 524126

AUG. PRIEN Immobilien PE Verwaltung BrahmsQuartier GmbH (1)
Charlottenstr 3
Stuttgart, 70182, Germany
Tel.: (49) 1724077047
Fax: (49) 40 77125214
Real Estate Management Services
S.I.C.: 6531
N.A.I.C.S.: 531390

AZ-Arges Vermogensverwaltungsgesellschaft mbH (1)
Koniginstr 28
80802 Munich, Germany
Tel.: (49) 8938000
Asset Management Services
S.I.C.: 6799
N.A.I.C.S.: 523920

AZ-Argos 44 Vermogensverwaltungsgesellschaft mbH & Co. KG (1)
Theresienstr 6-8
Munich, Bayern, 80333, Germany
Tel.: (49) 711 6630
Asset Management Services
S.I.C.: 6282
N.A.I.C.S.: 523920

AZ-Argos 50 Vermogensverwaltungsgesellschaft mbH & Co. KG (1)
Koniginstr 28
Munich, Bayern, 80802, Germany
Tel.: (49) 893 8000
Asset Management Services
S.I.C.: 6282
N.A.I.C.S.: 523920

AZ-Argos 51 Vermogensverwaltungsgesellschaft mbH & Co. KG (1)
Koniginstr 28
Munich, Bayern, 80802, Germany
Tel.: (49) 893 8000
Asset Management Services
S.I.C.: 6282
N.A.I.C.S.: 523920

AZ-Argos 56 Vermogensverwaltungsgesellschaft mbH (1)
koniginstrasse 28
80802 Munich, Bayern, Germany
Tel.: (49) 89 3800 0
Asset Management Services
S.I.C.: 6799
N.A.I.C.S.: 523920

AZ-SGD Private Equity Fonds GmbH (1)
Theresienstr 6-8
80333 Munich, Bayern, Germany
Tel.: (49) 89 38000
Investment Management Services
S.I.C.: 6211
N.A.I.C.S.: 523999

Bankhaus W. Fortmann & Sohne KG (1)
Lange Str 12
26122 Oldenburg, Germany
Tel.: (49) 441 21002 0
Fax: (49) 441 21002 38
E-Mail: fortmann@fortmann.de
Web Site: www.fortmann.de
Commercial Banking Services
S.I.C.: 6029
N.A.I.C.S.: 522110

BCA Betriebs Catering GmbH Verpflegungsdienste (1)
Konigsteiner Str 10
65812 Bad Soden am Taunus, Germany
Tel.: (49) 6196 956100
Fax: (49) 6196 956101
Catering Services
S.I.C.: 5812
N.A.I.C.S.: 722320

Blitz 11-471 GmbH (1)
Koniginstr 25
80539 Munich, Bayern, Germany
Tel.: (49) 89 203550050
Fax: (49) 89 203550055
Financial Management Services
S.I.C.: 6211
N.A.I.C.S.: 523999

BrahmsQ Objekt GmbH & Co. KG (1)
Charlottenstr 3
Stuttgart, Baden-Wurttemberg, Germany
Tel.: (49) 40 77125 0
Investment Management Services
S.I.C.: 6211
N.A.I.C.S.: 523999

Burgel Beteiligungs GmbH (1)
Gasstr 18
Hamburg, 22761, Germany
Tel.: (49) 40 8 98 03 0
Fax: (49) 40 8 98 03 777
Investment Management Services
S.I.C.: 6211
N.A.I.C.S.: 523999

Burgel Erfurt Beteiligungsgesellschaft mbH (1)
Schillerstr 62
Erfurt, 99096, Germany
Tel.: (49) 361 340980
Fax: (49) 361 3409815
Investment Management Services
S.I.C.: 6211
N.A.I.C.S.: 523999
Birgit Taubert *(Mng Dir)*

Burgel Erfurt GmbH & Co. KG (1)
Schillerstrasse 62
99096 Erfurt, Germany
Tel.: (49) 361 3 40 98 0
Fax: (49) 361 3 40 98 15
E-Mail: info@buergel.de
Credit Information Services
S.I.C.: 7389
N.A.I.C.S.: 519190

Burgel Internationale Inkassogesellschaft GmbH (1)
Gasstr 18
Hamburg, 22761, Germany
Tel.: (49) 40 89803 0
Fax: (49) 40 89803 777
Debt Collection Services
S.I.C.: 7322
N.A.I.C.S.: 561440

Burgel Wirtschaftsinformationen GmbH & Co. KG (1)
Gasstrasse 18
22761 Hamburg, Germany
Tel.: (49) 40 89 80 3 0
Fax: (49) 40 89 80 3 777
E-Mail: info@buergel.de
Web Site: www.buergel.de
Debt Collection Services
S.I.C.: 7322
N.A.I.C.S.: 561440
Stefan Duncker *(Mng Dir)*
Rolf Pries *(Mng Dir)*
Norbert Sellin *(Mng Dir)*

Subsidiary:

Supercheck GmbH (2)
Sulzburgstrasse 218
50937 Cologne, Germany
Tel.: (49) 221 42060 740
Fax: (49) 221 42060 749
E-Mail: info@supercheck.de
Web Site: www.supercheck.de
Address Investigation Services
S.I.C.: 7299
N.A.I.C.S.: 812990

Burgel Wirtschaftsinformationen Verwaltungs-GmbH (1)
Gasstr 18
Hamburg, 22761, Germany
Tel.: (49) 40 89 80 30
Fax: (49) 40 89 80 31 90
Business Management Consulting Services
S.I.C.: 8748
N.A.I.C.S.: 541618

Deutsche Lebensversicherungs-AG (1)
An Den Treptowers 3
D 12435 Berlin, Germany (100%)
Tel.: (49) 3053831431
Fax: (49) 3053833675
E-Mail: info.dlvag@allianz.de
Web Site: www.dlvag.de
Emp.: 40
Life Insurance Provider
S.I.C.: 6311
N.A.I.C.S.: 524113
Thomas Neugebauer *(Gen Mgr)*

DONATOR Beratungs GmbH (1)
Theresienstr 6-8
80333 Munich, Germany
Tel.: (49) 89 3800 0
Management Consulting Services
S.I.C.: 8742
N.A.I.C.S.: 541611

esa Allianz (1)
Friedrichsplatz 2
74177 Bad Friedrichshall, Germany
Tel.: (49) 7136 95130
Fax: (49) 7136 9513133
E-Mail: info@esa-allianz.de
Web Site: www.esa-allianz.de
Emp.: 40
General Insurance Services
S.I.C.: 6411
N.A.I.C.S.: 524298
Walter Szabados *(Gen Mgr)*

ESA Cargo & Logistics GmbH (1)
Friedrichsplatz 2
74177 Bad Friedrichshall, Germany
Tel.: (49) 7136 9513 0
Fax: (49) 7136 9513 133
E-Mail: info@esa-allianz.de
Web Site: esa.allianz.de/unternehmen/impressum/index.html
Logistics Consulting Services
S.I.C.: 4731
N.A.I.C.S.: 541614

esa EuroShip GmbH (1)
Friedrichsplatz 2
74177 Bad Friedrichshall, Germany
Tel.: (49) 7136 9513 0
Fax: (49) 7136 9513 455
General Insurance Services
S.I.C.: 6411
N.A.I.C.S.: 524210

Euler Hermes Collections GmbH (1)
Zeppelinstr 48
14471 Potsdam, Germany
Tel.: (49) 331 27890 000
Fax: (49) 331 50 57 121
E-Mail: collections.de@eulerhermes.com
Web Site: www.eulerhermes-collections.de
Emp.: 100
Debt Collection Services
S.I.C.: 7322
N.A.I.C.S.: 561440

Euler Hermes Deutschland AG (1)
Friedensallee 254
22763 Hamburg, Germany
Tel.: (49) 40 88340
Fax: (49) 40 88347744
E-Mail: info.de@eulerhermes.com
Web Site: www.eulerhermes.de
Emp.: 300
Credit Information Services
S.I.C.: 6159
N.A.I.C.S.: 522298
Wilfried Verstraete *(Chm-Supervisory Bd)*
Ralf Meurer *(Chm-Mgmt Bd)*
Horst Meyer *(Deputy Chm-Supervisory Bd)*
Silke Grimm *(Member-Mgmt Bd)*
Hans Janus *(Member-Mgmt Bd)*
Thomas Krings *(Member-Mgmt Bd)*
Gert Schlossmacher *(Member-Mgmt Bd)*

Euler Hermes Forderungsmanagement GmbH (1)
Friedensallee 254
22763 Hamburg, Germany
Tel.: (49) 40 88 34 0
Fax: (49) 40 88 34 32 70
E-Mail: customerservice@eulerhermes.com
Web Site: www.eulerhermes-risk.com
Emp.: 1,300
Debt Collection Services
S.I.C.: 7322
N.A.I.C.S.: 561440
Diane Koy *(Mng Dir)*

Euler Hermes Rating Deutschland GmbH (1)
Gasstrasse 18 Haus 2
22761 Hamburg, Germany
Tel.: (49) 40 88 34 64 0
Fax: (49) 40 88 34 64 13
E-Mail: info@eulerhermes-rating.com
Web Site: www.ehrg.de
Marketing Consulting Services
S.I.C.: 8742
N.A.I.C.S.: 541613
Ralf Garrn *(Mng Dir)*

EURO-Pro Gesellschaft fur Data Processing mbH (1)
Lindenhof 1-3
61279 Gravenwiesbach, Germany
Tel.: (49) 6086 3988 0
Fax: (49) 6086 3988 10
E-Mail: info@europro.de
Web Site: www.europro.de
Data Processing Services
S.I.C.: 7374
N.A.I.C.S.: 518210

Allianz SE—(Continued)

EUROGRAFICA Systemplanungs-GmbH (1)
Alois-Senefelder-Allee 1
Augsburg, 86153, Germany
Tel.: (49) 821 21736 0
Fax: (49) 821 21736 22
Business Management Consulting Services
S.I.C.: 8748
N.A.I.C.S.: 541618
Thomas Schonbucher *(Mng Dir)*

Grundstucksgesellschaft der Vereinten Versicherungen mbH (1)
Koniginstrasse 28
80802 Munich, Bayern, Germany
Tel.: (49) 89 38000
Fax: (49) 89 349941
General Insurance Services
S.I.C.: 6411
N.A.I.C.S.: 524298

Jota-Vermogensverwaltungsgesellschaft mbH (1)
Koniginstrasse 28
80802 Munich, Germany
Tel.: (49) 89 38000
Fax: (49) 89 3800 3425
Asset Management Services
S.I.C.: 6282
N.A.I.C.S.: 523920

Munchener und Magdeburger Agrarversicherung Aktiengesellschaft (1)
Albert-Schweitzer-Str 62-64
81735 Munich, Germany
Tel.: (49) 89 678297 0
Fax: (49) 89 6792795
E-Mail: info@mmagrar.de
Web Site: www.mmagrar.de
Agricultural Insurance Services
S.I.C.: 6331
N.A.I.C.S.: 524126

Munsterlandische Bank Thie & Co. KG (1)
Alter Steinweg 1
48143 Munster, Germany
Tel.: (49) 251 48 47 1 0
Fax: (49) 251 48 47 1 27
E-Mail: kontakt@mlb.de
Web Site: www.mlb.de
Credit Information Services
S.I.C.: 6159
N.A.I.C.S.: 522298

Objekt Burchardplatz GmbH & Co. KG (1)
Charlottenstr 3
70182 Stuttgart, Germany
Tel.: (49) 711 6630
Real Estate Management Services
S.I.C.: 6531
N.A.I.C.S.: 531390

OLB-Beteiligungsgesellschaft mbH (1)
Stau 17
26122 Oldenburg, Germany
Tel.: (49) 441 2210
Fax: (49) 441 210 320
Investment Management Services
S.I.C.: 6211
N.A.I.C.S.: 523999

OLB-Immobiliendienst-GmbH (1)
Alexanderstrasse 113
26121 Oldenburg, Germany
Tel.: (49) 441 95072 14
Fax: (49) 441 95072 29
Real Estate Management Services
S.I.C.: 6531
N.A.I.C.S.: 531390

OLB-Service GmbH (1)
Stau 15-17
26122 Oldenburg, Germany
Tel.: (49) 441 2212000
Fax: (49) 441 2212470
Financial Management Services
S.I.C.: 6211
N.A.I.C.S.: 523999
Achim Klassow *(Gen Mgr)*

Oldenburgische Landesbank AG (1)
Stau 15-17
26122 Oldenburg, Germany
Tel.: (49) 4412210
Fax: (49) 4412211457
E-Mail: olb@olb.de
Web Site: www.olb.de
Emp.: 2,000
International Banking
S.I.C.: 6159
N.A.I.C.S.: 522293
Andree Moschner *(Chm)*
Manfred Karsten *(Vice Chm)*
Achim Kassow *(Dir Gen)*

PIMCO Deutschland GmbH (1)
Seidlstr 24-24a
80335 Munich, Germany
Tel.: (49) 89 1220 80
Fax: (49) 89 1220 7315
Web Site: de.pimco.com
Investment Management Services
S.I.C.: 6211
N.A.I.C.S.: 523999

rehacare GmbH (1)
Pilgersheimer Strasse 20
81543 Munich, Germany
Tel.: (49) 89 2000 451 20
Fax: (49) 89 2000 451 75
E-Mail: info@rehacare.net
Web Site: www.rehacare.net
Medical Management Consulting Services
S.I.C.: 8742
N.A.I.C.S.: 541611

Selecta Deutschland GmbH (1)
Konigsteiner Strasse 10
65812 Bad Soden am Taunus, Germany
Tel.: (49) 61 96 956 100
Fax: (49) 61 96 956 101
E-Mail: info@de.selecta.com
Web Site: www.selectavending.de
Vending Machine Mfr
S.I.C.: 3589
N.A.I.C.S.: 333318

Selecta Holding GmbH (1)
Konigsteiner Str 10
65812 Bad Soden am Taunus, Germany
Tel.: (49) 6196 95 61 00
Fax: (49) 6196 95 61 01
Investment Management Services
S.I.C.: 6799
N.A.I.C.S.: 523920
Stefanie Lueck *(CEO)*

Signa 12 Verwaltungs GmbH (1)
Benrather Strasse 18
40213 Dusseldorf, Germany
Tel.: (49) 21116640000
Investment Management Services
S.I.C.: 6211
N.A.I.C.S.: 523999

SITIA Beteiligungs- und Verwaltungs GmbH (1)
Unter Sachsenhausen 4
50667 Cologne, Germany
Tel.: (49) 22114501
Fax: (49) 2211451512
Web Site: www.allianz.com
Investment Advice Services
S.I.C.: 6282
N.A.I.C.S.: 523930

Spherion Objekt GmbH & Co. KG (1)
Charlottenstr 3
70182 Stuttgart, Germany
Tel.: (49) 711 6630
Real Estate Management Services
S.I.C.: 6531
N.A.I.C.S.: 531390

UfS Beteiligungs-GmbH (1)
Koniginstr 28
80802 Munich, Germany
Tel.: (49) 7136 951330
Fax: (49) 7136 951333
Investment Management Services
S.I.C.: 6211
N.A.I.C.S.: 523999

Vereinte Spezial Krankenversicherung Aktiengesellschaft (1)
Fritz-Schaffer-Str 9
81737 Munich, Germany
Tel.: (49) 89 38 00 0
Fax: (49) 89 67 85 6523
General Insurance Services
S.I.C.: 6411
N.A.I.C.S.: 524298

Holdings:

Windpark Emmendorf GmbH & Co.KG (1)
Bevenser Str 7
29579 Emmendorf, Germany
Tel.: (49) 5875 560
Electric Power Generation Services
S.I.C.: 4931
N.A.I.C.S.: 221118

Windpark Kesfeld Heckhuscheid GmbH & Co. KG (1)
Schauenburgerstr 24
25421 Pinneberg, Germany De
Tel.: (49) 4101408890
Fax: (49) 4101204109
Windpark Construction & Operation Services
S.I.C.: 1629
N.A.I.C.S.: 237130

Windpark Kirf GmbH & Co. KG (1)
Schauenburgerstr 24
Pinneberg, Schleswig-Holstein, 25421, Germany De
Tel.: (49) 4101408890
Fax: (49) 4101204109
E-Mail: info@enxco.de
Web Site: www.enxco.de
Emp.: 3
Windpark Management Services
S.I.C.: 1629
N.A.I.C.S.: 237130
Karsten Hansen *(Gen Mgr)*

Windpark Quitzow GmbH & Co. KG (1)
Feldscheide 2
Sehestedt, 24814, Germany
Tel.: (49) 4357 9977 0
Fax: (49) 4357 9977 10
Electric Power Generation Services
S.I.C.: 4931
N.A.I.C.S.: 221118
Torsten Levsen *(Gen Mgr)*

Windpark Redekin GmbH & Co KG (1)
Berliner Chaussee 50Berliner Chaussee 50
39307 Genthin, Germany
Tel.: (49) 3933 93220
Electric Power Generation Servcies
S.I.C.: 4911
N.A.I.C.S.: 221118

Windpark Werder Zinndorf GmbH & Co. KG (1)
Windmuhlenberg
Sehestedt, 24814, Germany
Tel.: (49) 4357 99770
Fax: (49) 4357 997710
Electric Power Generation Services
S.I.C.: 4911
N.A.I.C.S.: 221118

U.S. Subsidiaries:

AGCS Americas (1)
225 W Washington St
Chicago, IL 60606-3484
Tel.: (312) 224-3300
Emp.: 800
General Insurance Services
S.I.C.: 6411
N.A.I.C.S.: 524210
Hugh Burgess *(Pres & CEO)*
Randy Renn *(CFO)*

AGCS Marine Insurance Company (1)
777 San Marin Dr
Novato, CA 94998
Tel.: (415) 899-2000
Fax: (415) 899-3600
Marine Insurance Services
S.I.C.: 6411
N.A.I.C.S.: 524298

Allegiance Marketing Group LLC (1)
5500 Village Blvd Ste 200
West Palm Beach, FL 33407
Tel.: (800) 330-1997
Fax: (561) 845-0366
E-Mail: info@AMGadvisor.com
Web Site: www.amgadvisor.com
Marketing Consulting Services
S.I.C.: 8742
N.A.I.C.S.: 541613
Steve Bates *(Pres)*
Chuck Segal *(Officer-Suitability)*
Kevin Ross *(Sr VP-Sls)*

Allianz Annuity Company of Missouri (1)
120 South Central Ave
Clayton, MO 63105
Tel.: (763) 765-6500
General Insurance Services
S.I.C.: 6411
N.A.I.C.S.: 524210

Allianz Asset Management of America L.P (1)
680 Newport Centre Dr Ste 250
Newport Beach, CA 92660
Tel.: (949) 219-2000
Fax: (949) 219-2245
Asset Management Services
S.I.C.: 6282
N.A.I.C.S.: 523920

Allianz Aviation Managers LLC (1)
317 Madison Ave Ste 1110
New York, NY 10017
Tel.: (646) 472-1400
Fax: (646) 472-1462
General Insurance Services
S.I.C.: 6411
N.A.I.C.S.: 524210

Allianz Global Investors Capital LLC (1)
680 Nwport Ctr Dr Ste 250
Newport Beach, CA 92660
Tel.: (949) 219-2200
Investment Management Services
S.I.C.: 6211
N.A.I.C.S.: 523999

Allianz Global Investors Fund Management LLC (1)
1633 Broadway 41st Fl
New York, NY 10019
Tel.: (212) 739-3000
Fax: (212) 739-3948
Investment Management Services
S.I.C.: 6211
N.A.I.C.S.: 523999

Allianz Global Investors Managed Accounts LLC (1)
1633 Broadway
New York, NY 10019-7585
Tel.: (212) 739-3000
Fax: (212) 739-3948
Web Site: www.allianzinvestors.com
Financial Advisory Services
S.I.C.: 6282
N.A.I.C.S.: 523930

Subsidiaries:

Allianz Life Insurance Company of North America (2)
5701 Golden Hills Dr
Minneapolis, MN 55416-1297 MN
Mailing Address: (100%)
PO Box 1344
Minneapolis, MN 55416-1344
Tel.: (763) 765-6500
Telex: 467 393 NO AMER MPS CI
Toll Free: (800) 950-5872
Web Site: www.allianzlife.com
Sales Range: $5-14.9 Billion
Emp.: 1,647
Life Insurance, Annuity Products, Long Term Care Insurance & Broker-Dealer Services
S.I.C.: 6311
N.A.I.C.S.: 524113
Gary C. Bhojwani *(Chm)*
Walter R. White *(Pres & CEO)*
Giulio Terzariol *(CFO)*
Jeff Palm *(CIO & Sr VP)*
Nancy Jones *(CMO)*
Carsten Quitter *(Chief Investment Officer & Sr VP)*
Catherine Mahone *(Chief Admin Officer)*
Andreas Graser *(Chief Risk Officer & Sr VP-Corp Risk Mgmt)*
Neil McKay *(Chief Actuary & Sr VP)*
Suzanne Dowd Zeller *(Chief HR Officer)*
Dave Stacy *(Chief Info Security Officer & Sr Dir-IT controls & Risk Mgmt)*
Tom Burns *(Chief Distr Officer)*
Gretchen Cepek *(Gen Counsel & Sr VP)*

Bill Gaumond *(Sr VP & Head-Asset Liability Mgmt & Investment Risk Mgmt)*
Bob Densmore *(Sr VP & Dir-District)*
Carl Adamek *(Sr VP-Acct Mgmt)*
Sherri Du Mond *(Sr VP-Distr Trng)*
Jasmine Jirele *(Sr VP-Ops)*

Subsidiaries:

Allianz Life Insurance Company of New York (3)
1 Chase Manhattan Plz 37th Fl
New York, NY 10005-1423
Tel.: (212) 586-7733
Life Insurance Services
S.I.C.: 6311
N.A.I.C.S.: 524113
Walter R. White *(Chm & CEO)*
Thomas P. Burns *(Pres)*
Giulio Terzariol *(CFO & Treas)*
Stewart D. Gregg *(Sr Counsel)*

Allianz of New York (3)
1 Madison 38 Fl
New York, NY 10005-3310 NY
Tel.: (212) 586-7733
Fax: (212) 586-6949
Web Site: www.allianzlife.com
Rev.: $105,780,312
Emp.: 4
Life Insurance Carriers
S.I.C.: 6411
N.A.I.C.S.: 524210
Vincent G. Vitiello *(Pres & CEO)*

Questar Capital Corporation (3)
5701 Golden Hills Dr
Minneapolis, MN 55416
Mailing Address:
PO Box 59177
Minneapolis, MN 55459-0177
Tel.: (763) 765-6500
Fax: (763) 765-5996
Toll Free: (888) 446-5872
E-Mail: info@us.questarcapital.com
Web Site: www.questarcapital.com
Emp.: 70
Securities Brokerage & Financial Services
S.I.C.: 6211
N.A.I.C.S.: 523120
Kevin Bachmann *(Pres)*

Tax Planning Seminars Inc. (3)
Two Echelon Plz 221 Laurel Rd Ste 220
Voorhees, NJ 08043-2315 (100%)
Tel.: (856) 772-6200
Fax: (856) 772-9561
Web Site: www.tpsbrokerage.com
Emp.: 12
Management Consulting Services
Import Export
S.I.C.: 8742
N.A.I.C.S.: 541611

USAllianz Securities Inc. (3)
5701 Golden Hills Dr
Minneapolis, MN 55416-1297
Mailing Address:
PO Box 1344
Minneapolis, MN 55416-1297
Tel.: (763) 765-6500
Fax: (763) 565-7120
Web Site: www.questarcapital.com
Emp.: 2,600
Broker & Dealer Service
Import Export
S.I.C.: 6311
N.A.I.C.S.: 524113
Walter White *(CEO)*

Fireman's Fund Insurance Company (2)
777 San Marin Dr
Novato, CA 94998-0001 (100%)
Tel.: (415) 899-2000
Telex: 176 315 fundam nova
Fax: (415) 899-3600
Toll Free: (800) 227-1700
Web Site: www.firemansfund.com
Emp.: 4,500
Commercial & Personal Property & Liability Insurance Services
S.I.C.: 6351
N.A.I.C.S.: 524126
Andrew Torrance *(Pres & CEO)*
Kevin Walker *(CFO)*
Antonio Derossi *(COO)*
John Elliott *(CIO)*
Juliene Conway *(CMO)*
Gregory Tacchetti *(Chief Admin Officer)*
Christian Kortebein *(Chief Actuary & Sr VP)*
Eric Brandt *(Chief Claims Officer)*
Darryl Page *(Pres-Personal Insurance)*
Sally Narey *(Sec)*
Amy Keyser *(Sr VP-HR)*
Greg Meyer *(Sr VP-Product Mgmt-Personal Insurance Div)*
Eric Shanks *(Sr VP-Personal Insurance Underwriting)*
David Zona *(Sr VP-Product Mgmt)*

Subsidiaries:

Associated Indemnity Corp. (3)
777 San Marin Dr
Novato, CA 94998-0001 CA
Tel.: (415) 899-2000 (100%)
Fax: (415) 899-3600
E-Mail: supportcentral@ffic.com
Web Site: www.ffic.com
Emp.: 1,400
Commercial & Personal Property & Liability Insurance Services
S.I.C.: 6311
N.A.I.C.S.: 524113
Michael Edward Larocco *(Pres & CEO)*

Fireman Fund Speciaties (3)
33 W Monroe St Ste 1200
Chicago, IL 60603 IL
Tel.: (312) 346-6400 (100%)
Fax: (312) 346-5748
Web Site: www.firemanfund.com
Emp.: 450
Surplus Lines Brokerage & Underwriting
S.I.C.: 6331
N.A.I.C.S.: 524126
Michael Larocco *(Pres)*

Fireman's Fund AgriBusiness (3)
11880 College Blvd Ste 130
Overland Park, KS 66210-2768 DE
Tel.: (913) 905-4700
Fax: (913) 905-4718
Toll Free: (800) 870-8849
Web Site: www.firemansfund.com
Rev.: $111,166,167
Emp.: 273
Insurance Services
S.I.C.: 6351
N.A.I.C.S.: 524126

Fireman's Fund Financial Services, LLC (3)
55 Greens Farms Rd
Westport, CT 06880
Tel.: (203) 221-8500
Investment Management Services
S.I.C.: 6211
N.A.I.C.S.: 523999

Fireman's Fund Indemnity Corporation (3)
777 San Marin Dr
Novato, CA 94998
Tel.: (415) 899-2000
Fax: (415) 899-3600
Investment Management Services
S.I.C.: 6211
N.A.I.C.S.: 523999

Fireman's Fund Insurance Co. of Georgia (3)
11475 Great Oaks Way Ste 100
Alpharetta, GA 30022-2440 GA
Tel.: (678) 393-4000 (100%)
Fax: (888) 259-2246
Toll Free: (800) 282-6358
E-Mail: info@firemansfund.com
Web Site: www.firemansfund.com
Emp.: 50
Insurance Services
S.I.C.: 6351
N.A.I.C.S.: 524126

Fireman's Fund Insurance Co. of Hawaii, Inc. (3)
1003 Bishop St Ste 1900
Honolulu, HI 96813 HI
Tel.: (808) 523-6500 (100%)
Fax: (808) 523-6617
Web Site: www.firemansfund.com
Insurance Services
S.I.C.: 6411
N.A.I.C.S.: 524210

Fireman's Fund Insurance Company of Louisiana, Corp. (3)
777 San Marine Dr
Novato, CA 94998
Tel.: (504) 734-2221
Investment Management Services
S.I.C.: 6211
N.A.I.C.S.: 523999

Fireman's Fund Insurance Co. of New Jersey (3)
150 Allen Rd
Liberty Corner, NJ 07938 NJ
Tel.: (908) 542-5600
Fax: (908) 542-5615
E-Mail: objncciae@fsic.com
Web Site: www.firemansfund.com
Emp.: 50
Insurance Services
S.I.C.: 6411
N.A.I.C.S.: 524210

Fireman's Fund Insurance Co. of Ohio (3)
33 W Monroe St Ste 1400
Chicago, IL 60603-5309 OH
Tel.: (513) 762-5700 (100%)
Fax: (513) 762-5840
Web Site: www.ffic.com
Sales Range: $25-49.9 Million
Emp.: 9
Insurance Services
S.I.C.: 6351
N.A.I.C.S.: 524126

Fireman's Fund Insurance Company (3)
33 W Monroe St Ste 1200
Chicago, IL 60603 IL
Tel.: (800) 227-1700 (100%)
Fax: (312) 441-6210
E-Mail: Interstate@ffic.com
Web Site: www.firemansfund.com
Emp.: 435
Insurance Services
S.I.C.: 6331
N.A.I.C.S.: 524126

Fireman's Fund McGee Underwriters (3)
75 Wall St
New York, NY 10005
Tel.: (212) 524-8600
Fax: (212) 524-9446
E-Mail: postmaster@ffic.com
Web Site: www.allianz.com
Insurance Management Services
S.I.C.: 6411
N.A.I.C.S.: 524298

International Film Guarantors LLC (3)
2828 Donald Douglas Loop N 2nd Fl
Santa Monica, CA 90405
Tel.: (310) 309-5660
Fax: (310) 309-5696
E-Mail: usinfo@ifgbonds.com
Web Site: www.ifgbonds.com
Media Insurance Services
S.I.C.: 6411
N.A.I.C.S.: 524298
Steven Mangel *(CEO)*
Michael Harker *(Sr VP-Post Production)*
Frank Issac *(Sr VP-Production)*
Steven Leib *(Sr VP-Bus Affairs)*
Michael Levine *(Sr VP-Production)*

Interstate Fire & Casualty Company (3)
33 W Monroe St Ste 1200
Chicago, IL 60603
Tel.: (415) 899-2482
Fax: (415) 899-3192
Property & Casualty Insurance Services
S.I.C.: 6351
N.A.I.C.S.: 524126

Interstate Insurance Group (3)
33 W Monroe St Ste 1300
Chicago, IL 60603
Tel.: (312) 346-6400
Fax: (312) 441-6210
Emp.: 100
Insurance Services
S.I.C.: 6411
N.A.I.C.S.: 524298

Life Sales LLC (3)
773 San Marin Dr 2160
Novato, CA 94945
Tel.: (800) 486-5400
Fax: (415) 897-0205
E-Mail: info@lifesales.net
Web Site: www.lifesales.net
Life Insurance Services
S.I.C.: 6311
N.A.I.C.S.: 524113
Micheal Goodyear *(Co-Pres)*
Steve Thunen *(Co-Pres)*

Allianz Global Investors Solutions LLC (1)
600 W Broadway Ste 3400
San Diego, CA 92101
Tel.: (619) 687-2799
Fax: (619) 687-2700
Investment Management Services
S.I.C.: 6211
N.A.I.C.S.: 523999

Allianz Investment Company LLC (1)
55 Greens Farms Rd
Westport, CT 06881
Tel.: (203) 221-8500
Fax: (203) 341-5722
Investment Management Services
S.I.C.: 6211
N.A.I.C.S.: 523999

Allianz Investment Management LLC (1)
5701 Golden Hills Dr
Minneapolis, MN 55416
Tel.: (877) 833-7113
Fax: (763) 765-6355
Investment Advisory Services
S.I.C.: 6282
N.A.I.C.S.: 523930
Mike Scriver *(Sr VP-Hedging)*

Allianz of America, Inc. (1)
55 Greens Farms Rd
Westport, CT 06880-6149 DE
Mailing Address: (100%)
PO Box 5160
Westport, CT 06881
Tel.: (203) 221-8500
Fax: (203) 221-4933
Web Site: www.azoa.com
Emp.: 42
Holding Company for Insurance Services
S.I.C.: 6311
N.A.I.C.S.: 524113
Jay Ralph *(Pres & CEO)*
Yvonne Franzese *(Chief HR Officer)*

Allianz Underwriters Insurance Company, Corp. (1)
3400 Riverside Dr Ste 300
Burbank, CA 91505-4669
Tel.: (818) 972-8000
Fax: (818) 972-8466
Insurance Underwriting Services
S.I.C.: 6361
N.A.I.C.S.: 524127

Allianz US Private REIT LP (1)
55 Greens Farms Rd
Westport, CT 68806
Tel.: (203) 221-8500
General Insurance Services
S.I.C.: 6411
N.A.I.C.S.: 524210

American Automobile Insurance Company, Corp. (1)
777 San Marin Dr
Novato, CA 94998
Tel.: (415) 899-2000
Fax: (415) 899-5817
Toll Free: (800) 227-1700
Automotive Insurance Services
S.I.C.: 6331
N.A.I.C.S.: 524126
Lori Dickerson Fouche *(Pres)*

American Financial Marketing Inc. (1)
400 Hwy 169 S Ste 200
Saint Louis Park, MN 55426
Tel.: (763) 593-0905
Toll Free: (800) 880-3072
Web Site: www.afmus.com
General Insurance Services
S.I.C.: 6411
N.A.I.C.S.: 524210
Brian Biwer *(Founder & Partner)*
Rod Prahl *(Founder & Partner)*
Darren Tutt *(Founder & Partner)*
Tom Wade *(Founder & Partner)*
Scott Wheeler *(Founder & Partner)*

Allianz SE—(Continued)

Brad Frene *(Pres)*
Brent Jensen *(Sr VP-Annuity Sls)*
Jeremy Lach *(Sr VP-Annuity Sls)*
Joseph C. Murray *(Sr VP-Mktg)*
Brian Smith *(Sr VP-Annuity Sls)*

The American Insurance Company, Corp. **(1)**
777 San Marin Dr Ste 2160
Novato, CA 94945-1352
Tel.: (415) 899-2000
General Insurance Services
S.I.C.: 6411
N.A.I.C.S.: 524210

American Standard Lloyd's Insurance Company, Corp. **(1)**
777 San Marin Dr
Novato, CA 94998
Tel.: (415) 899-2000
Fax: (415) 899-3600
Toll Free: (800) 227-1700
General Insurance Services
S.I.C.: 6411
N.A.I.C.S.: 524298

Ann Arbor Annuity Exchange Inc. **(1)**
45 Research Dr
Ann Arbor, MI 48103
Tel.: (800) 321-3924
Fax: (734) 786-6101
E-Mail: info@annuity-exchange.com
Web Site: www.annuity-exchange.com
General Insurance Services
S.I.C.: 6411
N.A.I.C.S.: 524210
Robert Burskey *(Co-Pres)*
Van Lumbard *(Co-Pres)*

The Annuity Store Financial & Insurance Services LLC **(1)**
1451 River Park Dr Ste 130
Sacramento, CA 95815
Tel.: (800) 825-6094
Fax: (800) 439-6819
E-Mail: info@theannuitystore.com
Web Site: www.theannuitystore.com
General Insurance Services
S.I.C.: 6411
N.A.I.C.S.: 524210
Richard J. Marasco *(Pres)*

APKV US Private REIT GP LLC **(1)**
1209 Orange St
Wilmington, DE 19801
Tel.: (302) 658-7581
Investment Management Services
S.I.C.: 6211
N.A.I.C.S.: 523999

APKV US Private REIT LP **(1)**
1209 Orange St
Wilmington, DE 19801
Tel.: (302) 658-7581
Investment Management Services
S.I.C.: 6211
N.A.I.C.S.: 523999

AZ Vers US Private REIT GP LLC **(1)**
1209 Orange St
Wilmington, DE 19801
Tel.: (302) 658-7581
Investment Management Services
S.I.C.: 6211
N.A.I.C.S.: 523999

AZ Vers US Private REIT LP **(1)**
55 Greens Farms Rd
Westport, CT 06881
Tel.: (203) 221-8500
Investment Management Services
S.I.C.: 6211
N.A.I.C.S.: 523999

Challenging Financial Careers Insurance Marketing Corp., LLC **(1)**
17011 Beach Blvd Ste 1500
Huntington Beach, CA 92647
Tel.: (714) 960-6122
General Insurance Services
S.I.C.: 6411
N.A.I.C.S.: 524210

Chicago Insurance Company, Corp. **(1)**
33 W Monroe St Fl 3
Chicago, IL 60603
Tel.: (312) 346-6400
General Insurance Services
S.I.C.: 6411
N.A.I.C.S.: 524210

EF Solutions LLC **(1)**
84 Lake Caroline Dr
Ruther Glen, VA 22546-5213
Tel.: (804) 448-5567
Investment Management Services
S.I.C.: 6211
N.A.I.C.S.: 523999

Euler Hermes UMA Inc **(1)**
600 S 7th St
Louisville, KY 40201-1672
Tel.: (502) 583-3600
Fax: (502) 584-0443
E-Mail: collections.information@eulerhermes.com
Debt Collection Services
S.I.C.: 7322
N.A.I.C.S.: 561440
Michael T. Puckett *(Pres)*
James J. Hutchins *(Sec & Mgr-Personnel)*

Melchers Flavors of America **(1)**
5600 W Raymond St
Indianapolis, IN 46241-4343 OH
Tel.: (513) 858-6300
Rev.: $3,000,000
Emp.: 18
Flavoring Extracts & Syrups
S.I.C.: 3498
N.A.I.C.S.: 332996

Mondial Assistance USA **(1)**
2805 N Parham Rd
Richmond, VA 23294
Tel.: (800) 628-4908
E-Mail: info@mondialUSA.com
Web Site: www.mondialusa.com
General Insurance Services
S.I.C.: 6411
N.A.I.C.S.: 524210
Michael Haberland *(Coord-Remittance)*

National Surety Corporation **(1)**
777 San Marin Dr
Novato, CA 94998
Tel.: (415) 899-2000
Toll Free: (800) 227-1700
Property & Casualty Insurance Services
S.I.C.: 6331
N.A.I.C.S.: 524126

Personalized Brokerage Service LLC **(1)**
6001 SW 6th Ave Ste 330
Topeka, KS 66615
Tel.: (800) 225-4896
E-Mail: info@accesspbs.com
Web Site: www.pbsworksforme.com
Insurance Brokerage Services
S.I.C.: 6411
N.A.I.C.S.: 524210
Patrick K. Seelye *(Pres)*

PIMCO Global Advisors LLC **(1)**
840 Newport Centre Dr Ste 100
Newport Beach, CA 92660
Tel.: (949) 219-2200
Investment Advisory Services
S.I.C.: 6282
N.A.I.C.S.: 523930

ppi Media US, Inc. **(1)**
401 N Michigan Ave Ste 1200
Chicago, IL 60611
Tel.: (855) 828-0008
E-Mail: ussales@ppimedia.com
Newspaper Publisher
S.I.C.: 2711
N.A.I.C.S.: 511110
Markus Feldenkirchen *(CEO)*

Questar Agency Inc. **(1)**
5701 Golden Hills Dr
Minneapolis, MN 55416-1297
Tel.: (763) 765-7937
Toll Free: (888) 446-5872
General Insurance Services
S.I.C.: 6411
N.A.I.C.S.: 524210

Roster Financial LLC **(1)**
1000 Voorhees Dr Ste B
Voorhees, NJ 08043
Tel.: (800) 933-6632
Fax: (856) 753-0783
E-Mail: roster@rosterfinancial.com
Web Site: www.rosterfinancial.com
Financial Management Services
S.I.C.: 6211
N.A.I.C.S.: 523999
Tom Yacovino *(Pres)*
Art Troccoli *(CFO)*

San Francisco Reinsurance Company, Corp. **(1)**
777 San Marin Dr
Novato, CA 94998
Tel.: (415) 899-2000
Toll Free: (800) 227-1700
Reinsurance Services
S.I.C.: 6399
N.A.I.C.S.: 524130

Travel Care Inc. **(1)**
6600 W Broad St Ste 100
Richmond, VA 23230-1709
Tel.: (804) 673-1517
Travel Insurance Services
S.I.C.: 6399
N.A.I.C.S.: 524128

Non-U.S. Subsidiaries:

AGA Assistance Australia Pty Ltd. **(1)**
74 High Street
PO Box 162
Toowong, Brisbane, QLD, 4066, Australia
Tel.: (61) 7 3305 7000
E-Mail: assist@allianz-assistance.com.au
Web Site: www.allianz-assistance.com.au
Travel Assistance Services
S.I.C.: 9441
N.A.I.C.S.: 923130

AGA Assistance (India) Private Limited **(1)**
1st Floor DLF Square M-Block Jacaranda Marg Phase-II
Gurgaon, Haryana, 122 002, India
Tel.: (91) 124 4343800
Fax: (91) 124 4343900
E-Mail: contact@allianz-assistance.in
Web Site: www.allianz-assistance.in
Travel Insurance Services
S.I.C.: 6411
N.A.I.C.S.: 524298
Rajesh Sethi *(CEO)*
Puneet Sachdeva *(CFO)*
Harish Wadhwa *(COO)*

AGCS Argentina **(1)**
San Martin 550
Buenos Aires, Argentina
Tel.: (54) 11 43203800
General Insurance Services
S.I.C.: 6411
N.A.I.C.S.: 524210

AGCS Australia **(1)**
2 Market Street
Sydney, NSW, 2000, Australia
Tel.: (61) 2 82585447
Fax: (61) 2 92667517
General Insurance Services
S.I.C.: 6411
N.A.I.C.S.: 524210

AGCS Lebanon **(1)**
Allianz SNA Bldg - Hazmieh
PO Box 16-6528
Beirut, Lebanon
Tel.: (961) 5 956600
Fax: (961) 5 956624
General Insurance Services
S.I.C.: 6411
N.A.I.C.S.: 524210

AGCS North America **(1)**
130 Adelaide Street West Suite 1600
Toronto, ON, M5H 3P5, Canada
Tel.: (416) 915-4247
Fax: (416) 961-5442
Emp.: 125
General Insurance Services
S.I.C.: 6411
N.A.I.C.S.: 524210
Bob Grouchy *(Head-Claims)*

AGCS Singapore **(1)**
3 Temasek Avenue 08-01 Centennial Tower
Singapore, 039190, Singapore
Tel.: (65) 6 2972529
Fax: (65) 6 2971956
Web Site: www.allianz.com
Insurance Management Services
S.I.C.: 6411
N.A.I.C.S.: 524298
Leng-Leng Ng *(Head-Mkt Mgmt)*

AGCS South Africa Limited **(1)**
Firs 2nd Floor 32A Cradock Avenue
Rosebank, 2196, South Africa
Tel.: (27) 11 2147900
E-Mail: info@allianz.co.za
Web Site: www.agcs.allianz.com
General Insurance Services
S.I.C.: 6411
N.A.I.C.S.: 524298
Delphine Maidou *(CEO)*
Kevin Barnes *(Compliance Officer)*

AGF 2X, S.A. **(1)**
87 Rue Richelieu
75113 Paris, France
Tel.: (33) 1 44 86 20 00
General Insurance Services
S.I.C.: 6411
N.A.I.C.S.: 524210

AGF Capital Investissement 2 **(1)**
117 Avenue des Champs-Elysees
Paris, 75008, France
Tel.: (33) 1 58 18 56 56
Fax: (33) 1 58 18 56 89
Investment Management Services
S.I.C.: 6211
N.A.I.C.S.: 523999

AGF Insurance Limited **(1)**
57 Ladymead
Guildford, Surrey, GU1 1DB, United Kingdom
Tel.: (44) 1483 552730
Fax: (44) 1483 532904
General Insurance Services
S.I.C.: 6411
N.A.I.C.S.: 524210

AGF RAS Holding B.V. **(1)**
Keizersgracht 484
1017 EH Amsterdam, Netherlands
Tel.: (31) 20 5569715
Investment Management Services
S.I.C.: 6211
N.A.I.C.S.: 523999

AGF S.A. **(1)**
87 Rue De Richelieu
75113 Paris, Cedex, 02, France (58%)
Tel.: (33) 144862000
Fax: (33) 144864242
E-Mail: agfcomf@agf.fr
Web Site: www.agf.fr
Emp.: 31,855
Life & Health Insurance, Property & Liability Insurance, Reinsurance & Credit Insurance
S.I.C.: 6311
N.A.I.C.S.: 524113
Jean-Philippe Thierry *(Chm & CEO)*

Subsidiaries:

AGF Afrique **(2)**
B 410 87 rue de Richelieu
F-75113 Paris, Cedex, 02, France
Tel.: (33) 144866400
Fax: (33) 144862388
E-Mail: hamonic@allianz.fr
Web Site: www.agf-afrique.com
Sls.: $89,126,096
Emp.: 60
Insurance Services
S.I.C.: 6311
N.A.I.C.S.: 524113
Patrick Rolland *(Mng Dir)*

Non-U.S. Subsidiaries:

AGF Benin Assurances **(3)**
Carre 5 Avenue Delorme 01
BP 5455
01 RP Cotonou, Benin (76%)
Tel.: (229) 21316735
Fax: (229) 21316734
E-Mail: agf.benin@agf-bj.com
Web Site: www.agf-afrique.com
Insurance Services
S.I.C.: 6411
N.A.I.C.S.: 524298

AGF Burkina Assurances Vie **(3)**
Avenue Leo Frobenius
BP 398
Ouagadougou, Burkina Faso (70%)
Tel.: (226) 50306204

Fax: (226) 50310153
E-Mail: agf.burkina@agf-bf.com
Web Site: www.agf-afrique.com
Insurance Services
S.I.C.: 6411
N.A.I.C.S.: 524298

AGF Burkina Assurances (3)
99 Avenue de l'UEMOA
Ouagadougou, Burkina Faso (52%)
Tel.: (226) 50 30 62 04
Fax: (226) 50 31 01 53
E-Mail: allianz.burkina@allianz-bf.com
Web Site: www.allianz-africa.com
Insurance Services
S.I.C.: 6411
N.A.I.C.S.: 524298
Philippe Audouin *(Mng Dir)*

AGF Cameroun Assurances Vie (3)
1124 Rue Manga Bell
BP 105
Douala, Cameroon (76%)
Tel.: (237) 33429203
Fax: (237) 33430224
E-Mail: allianz.cameroun@allianzcm.com
Web Site: www.agf-afrique.com
Emp.: 100
Insurance Services
S.I.C.: 6411
N.A.I.C.S.: 524298
Bernard Girardin *(Mng Dir)*
Christian Marlin *(Mng Dir)*

AGF Cameroun Assurances (3)
1124 Rue Manga Bell
BP 105
Douala, Cameroon (71%)
Tel.: (237) 3429203
Fax: (237) 3430324
E-Mail: agf.cameroun@agf-cm.com
Web Site: www.agf-afrique.com
Insurance Services
S.I.C.: 6411
N.A.I.C.S.: 524298
Adrien Cozza *(Mng Dir)*

Non-U.S. Subsidiary:

AGF Centrafrique Assurances (4)
Boulevard du General de Gaulle
BP 343
Bangui, Central African Republic (83%)
Tel.: (236) 21613666
Fax: (236) 21 613340
E-Mail: agf.centrafrique@agf-cf.com
Web Site: www.agf-afrique.com
Insurance Services
S.I.C.: 6411
N.A.I.C.S.: 524298
Bruno Ribeiron *(Mgr)*

AGF Cote d'Ivoire Assurances Vie (3)
2 Bb Roume 01
BP 1741
Abidjan, Cote d'Ivoire (70%)
Tel.: (225) 20304000
Fax: (225) 20304001
E-Mail: agf.coteivoire@agf-ci.com
Web Site: www.agf-coteivoire.com
Insurance Services
S.I.C.: 6411
N.A.I.C.S.: 524298

AGF Cote d'Ivoire Assurances (3)
2 Bb Roume 01
PO Box 1741
Abidjan, Cote d'Ivoire (73%)
Tel.: (225) 20304000
Fax: (225) 20304001
E-Mail: allianz.coteivoire@allianz-ci.com
Web Site: www.allianz-coteivoire.com
Insurance Services
S.I.C.: 6411
N.A.I.C.S.: 524298
Rene Bucaioni *(Mng Dir)*

AGF Senegal Assurances Vie (3)
Avenue Abdoulaye Fadiga X rue de Thann
BP 2610
Dakar, Senegal (96%)
Tel.: (221) 8494400
Fax: (221) 8231078
E-Mail: agf.senegal@agf-sn.com
Web Site: www.agf-afrique.com
Insurance Services
S.I.C.: 6411
N.A.I.C.S.: 524298

Allianz Mali Assurances (3)
Avenue de la Nation
BP E4447
Bamako, Mali (70%)
Tel.: (223) 20224165
Fax: (223) 20230034
E-Mail: allianz.mali@allianz-ml.com
Web Site: www.allianz-africa.com
Emp.: 24
Insurance Services
S.I.C.: 6411
N.A.I.C.S.: 524298
Olivier Picard *(Gen Mgr)*

Allianz Senegal Assurances (3)
Avenue Abdoulaye Fadiga X rue de Thann
BP 2610
Dakar, Senegal (83%)
Tel.: (221) 338494400
Fax: (221) 338231954
E-Mail: allianz.senegal@allianz-sn.com
Web Site: www.allianz-africa.com
Emp.: 50
Insurance Services
S.I.C.: 6411
N.A.I.C.S.: 524298
Olivier Mallet *(Gen Mgr)*

Allianz Togo Assurances (3)
21 Avenue Duisburg Bd du 13 Janvier
BP 3703
Lome, Togo (94%)
Tel.: (228) 221 9773
Fax: (228) 221 9775
E-Mail: allianz.togo@allianz-tg.com
Web Site: www.allianz-africa.com
Financial Services
S.I.C.: 6411
N.A.I.C.S.: 524298

AGF Asset Management S.A. (2)
20 rue Le Peletier
75444 Paris, France
Tel.: (33) 144862000
Fax: (33) 144864242
Web Site: www.allianz.fr
Emp.: 250
Financial Services
S.I.C.: 6726
N.A.I.C.S.: 525990
Geraud Brac de la Perriere *(Pres)*

Allianz France (2)
87 rue de Richelieu
75002 Paris, France
Tel.: (33) 144862000
Fax: (33) 144864242
E-Mail:
Web Site: www.allianz.fr
Insurance & Financial Services
S.I.C.: 6411
N.A.I.C.S.: 524298

Arcalis (2)
20 Place de Seine
92086 Paris, Cedex, France
Tel.: (33) 144862000
Fax: (33) 144864242
E-Mail: corinne.david@allianz.fr
Web Site: www.allianz.fr
Emp.: 4,000
Financial Services
S.I.C.: 6726
N.A.I.C.S.: 525990
Jacques Richier *(Pres)*

Banque AGF (2)
164 rue Ambroise Croizat
F-93288 Saint Denis, Cedex, France
Tel.: (33) 155877000
E-Mail: webmaster@banqueagf.fr
Web Site: www.banqueagf.fr
Financial Services
S.I.C.: 6726
N.A.I.C.S.: 525990
Laurent Mignon *(Pres & Dir Gen)*

Calypso (2)
410 la Courtine
F-75002 Noisy-le-Grand, France
Tel.: (33) 144862000
Fax: (33) 144864242
E-Mail: wagfcom@agf.fr
Web Site: www.allianz.fr
Insurance & Financial Services
S.I.C.: 6411
N.A.I.C.S.: 524298
Jean-Philippe Thierry *(Chm & CEO)*

Euler Hermes S.A. (2)
1 Place des Saisons
F-92048 Paris, France (68.6%)
Tel.: (33) 1 8411 5000
Fax: (33) 1 8411 5117
E-Mail: webmaster@eulerhermes.com
Web Site: www.eulerhermes.com
ELE—(EUR)
Sls.: $3,227,975,658
Assets: $8,163,386,229
Liabilities: $4,750,845,279
Net Worth: $3,412,540,950
Earnings: $409,918,188
Emp.: 6,277
Fiscal Year-end: 12/31/12
Insurance & Pensions
S.I.C.: 6411
N.A.I.C.S.: 524298
Clement B. Booth *(Chm-Supervisory Bd)*
Wilfried Verstraete *(Chm-Mgmt Bd)*
Brigitte Bovermann *(Vice Chm-Supervisory Bd)*
Frederic Biziere *(CFO & Member-Mgmt Bd-Fin, Compliance, Legal, Tax & Risk)*
Antoine George *(CFO/Chief Admin Officer-Solution Grp)*
Nicolas Delzant *(CEO/Head-France)*
Jochen Dumler *(CEO-United States & Head-America)*
Ralf Meurer *(CEO-Germany & Head-Germany, Austria & Switzerland)*
Michele Pignotti *(CEO-Italy & Head-Mediterranean Countries, Africa & Middle East)*
Milo Bogaerts *(CEO-Netherlands)*
Benoit des Cressonnieres *(CEO-Euler Hermes Reinsurance)*
Rafal Hiszpanski *(CEO-Poland)*
Francis Jespers *(CEO-Belgium)*
Jules Kappeler *(CEO-Nordic Countries)*
Jean Placotaris *(CEO-Euler Hermes Collections)*
Gerard van Kaathoven *(CEO-United Kingdom)*
Gerd-Uwe Baden *(Member-Mgmt Bd-Risk, Info & Litigation Function)*
Dirk Oevermann *(Member-Mgmt Bd-Ops & IT Function)*
Paul Overeem *(Member-Mgmt Bd-Mktg, Sls & Distr)*
Catherine Zeller *(Sec)*
Francis Lallemant *(Exec VP-Internal Audit)*

Subsidiary:

Euler Hermes SFAC (3)
1 rue Euler
75008 Paris, France
Tel.: (33) 140705050
Fax: (33) 140705017
Web Site: www.eulerhermes.com
Emp.: 500
Financial Services
S.I.C.: 6726
N.A.I.C.S.: 525990
Wilfred Werstraiete *(Gen Mgr)*

U.S. Subsidiary:

Euler Hermes ACI (3)
800 Red Brook Blvd
Owings Mills, MD 21117 (55%)
Tel.: (410) 753-0753
Fax: (410) 753-0951
Toll Free: (877) 883-3224
E-Mail: eulerhermes.usa@eulerhermes.com
Web Site: www.eulerhermes.us
Emp.: 110
Holding Company
S.I.C.: 6351
N.A.I.C.S.: 524126

Non-U.S. Subsidiaries:

Euler Hermes Credit Insurance Agency (S) Pte. Ltd. (3)
3 Temasek Avenue 03-02 Centennial Tower
Singapore, 039190, Singapore
Tel.: (65) 6395 8977
Fax: (65) 6297 4529
E-Mail: Enquiries-Asean@eulerhermes.com
Web Site: www.sg.eulerhermes.com
General Insurance Services
S.I.C.: 6411
N.A.I.C.S.: 524298

Euler Hermes Credit Insurance Belgium S.A. (3)
Ave Des Arts 56
1000 Brussels, Belgium
Tel.: (32) 22893111
Fax: (32) 22893299
E-Mail: info.belgium@eulerhermes.com
Web Site: www.eulerhermes.com
Emp.: 200
Credit Insurance Services
S.I.C.: 6399
N.A.I.C.S.: 524128
Bruno Verhostede *(Gen Mgr)*

Euler Hermes Credit Insurance Nordic AB (3)
Klara Veadukten
10134 Stockholm, Sweden
Tel.: (46) 855513600
Fax: (46) 855513601
E-Mail: info.se@eulerhermes.com
Web Site: www.eulerhermes.se
Emp.: 30
Credit Insurance Services
S.I.C.: 6399
N.A.I.C.S.: 524128
Lars Gustafsson *(CEO)*

Euler Hermes Credit Underwriters (HK) Ltd (3)
11/F Great Eagle Ctr
23 Harbour Rd, Wanchai, China (Hong Kong)
Tel.: (852) 28670061
Fax: (852) 28698655
E-Mail: info.hk@eulerhermes.com
Web Site: www.hk.eulerhermes.com
Credit Insurance Services
S.I.C.: 6399
N.A.I.C.S.: 524128

Euler Hermes Kredietverzekering NV (3)
Pettelaarpark 20
5216 's-Hertogenbosch, Netherlands
Tel.: (31) 736889999
Fax: (31) 736889988
E-Mail: info@eulerhermes.nl
Web Site: www.eulerhermes.nl
Emp.: 100
Credit Insurance Services
S.I.C.: 6399
N.A.I.C.S.: 524128
Walter Toemen *(CEO)*

Euler Hermes Kreditversicherungs-AG (3)
Friedensallee 254
22763 Hamburg, Germany
Tel.: (49) 4088340
Fax: (49) 4088347744
E-Mail: info@eulerhermes.com
Web Site: www.eulerhermes.com
Emp.: 1,600
Credit Insurance Services
S.I.C.: 6399
N.A.I.C.S.: 524128
Ralf Meurer *(CEO)*

Euler Hermes SIAC S.p.A. (3)
Via Raffaello Matarazzo 19
00139 Rome, Italy
Tel.: (39) 0687001
Fax: (39) 0687007000
Web Site: www.eulerhermes.it/it/
Financial Services
S.I.C.: 6726
N.A.I.C.S.: 525990

Euler Hermes UK Plc (3)
1 Canada Square
London, E14 5DX, United Kingdom
Tel.: (44) 2075129333
Fax: (44) 2075129186
E-Mail: info@eulerhermes.com
Web Site: www.eulerhermes.com
Sales Range: $200-249.9 Million
Emp.: 600
Credit Insurance Services
S.I.C.: 6399
N.A.I.C.S.: 524128
Siprica Tesnos *(CEO)*

Mondial Assistance Group (2)
54 Rue Ge Lorgemer
F-75394 Paris, France
Tel.: (33) 0153255325
Fax: (33) 153058931
E-Mail: contactus@mondial-assistance.fr
Web Site: www.mondial-assistance.fr
Rev.: $1,543,588,224
Emp.: 8,100
Assistance & Travel Insurance Services; Owned 50% by AGF S.A. & 50% by Riunione Adriatica di Sicurta S.p.A. (Both Companies Owned by Allianz AG)

Allianz SE—(Continued)

S.I.C.: 6411
N.A.I.C.S.: 524298

Subsidiary:

ELVIA Societe d'Assurances de Voyages (3)
36 rue du general de gaulle
F-93173 Bagnolet, Cedex 08, France
Tel.: (33) 0142990299
Fax: (33) 142990300
E-Mail: svc-medical@monderlassistance.fr
Web Site: www.monderlassistance.fr
Emp.: 50,000
Travel & Property Insurance Services
S.I.C.: 6351
N.A.I.C.S.: 524126
Christophe Barbegis *(Mng Dir)*

Non-U.S. Subsidiaries:

Allianz Global Assistance (AGA) International S.A. (4)
Ludmillastrasse 26
D-81543 Munich, Germany
Tel.: (49) 89 6 24 24 460
Fax: (49) 89 6 24 24 244
E-Mail: service@allianz-assistance.de
Web Site: www.allianz-assistance.de/
Rev.: $131,603,216
Emp.: 178
Travel & Property Insurance Services
S.I.C.: 6331
N.A.I.C.S.: 524126
Olaf Nink *(CEO)*

ELVIA Reiseversicherung AG (4)
Pottendorfer Strasse 25 27
A-1120 Vienna, Austria
Tel.: (43) 01525030
Fax: (43) 0152503888
E-Mail: assistance.at@mondeal-assistance.at
Web Site: www.mondeal-assistance-austria.at
Emp.: 120
Travel & Property Insurance Services
S.I.C.: 6351
N.A.I.C.S.: 524126
Christoph Heissenberger *(Mng Dir)*

ELVIA Reiseversicherungs-Gesellschaft AG (4)
Hertistrasse 2
CH-8304 Wallisellen, Switzerland
Tel.: (41) 442833222
Fax: (41) 442833383
E-Mail: info@elvia.ch
Web Site: www.elvia.ch
Emp.: 50
Travel & Property Insurance Services
S.I.C.: 6331
N.A.I.C.S.: 524126
Carlo Pugnetti *(Mng Dir)*

Mondial Assistance-Netherlands (4)
Poeldijkstraat 4
1059 VM Amsterdam, Netherlands
Mailing Address:
Postbus 9444
Amsterdam, 1006 AK, Netherlands
Tel.: (31) 205618711
Fax: (31) 206684091
E-Mail: info@allianz-assistance.com
Web Site: www.allianz-assistance.com
Emp.: 250
Travel Insurance & Personal Services
S.I.C.: 6331
N.A.I.C.S.: 524126
Willem Snijders *(Mng Dir)*

Mondial Assistance Portugal (4)
Rua Quinta da Fonte Edificio Bartolomeu Dias
2774-535 Lisbon, Paco de Arcos, Portugal
Tel.: (351) 217806200
Fax: (351) 217965405
E-Mail: apj@mondial-assistance.pt
Web Site: www.mondial-assistance.com
Emp.: 200
Travel & Property Insurance Services
S.I.C.: 6331
N.A.I.C.S.: 524126
Vincent Bleunven *(Mng Dir)*

U.S. Subsidiary:

World Access Inc. (3)
2805 N Parham Rd
Richmond, VA 23294 VA
Mailing Address:
PO Box 72045
Richmond, VA 23255-2045
Tel.: (804) 285-3300
Fax: (804) 673-1586
Toll Free: (800) 628-4908
E-Mail: info@allianzassistance.com
Web Site: www.allianzassistance.com
Rev.: $57,188,344
Emp.: 800
Travel Insurance Agents & Brokers
S.I.C.: 6411
N.A.I.C.S.: 524210
Johnathan M. Ansell *(Pres & CEO)*

Branch:

World Access Service Corp. (4)
2805 N Parham Rd
Richmond, VA 23230-2942 VA
Mailing Address:
PO Box 72045
Richmond, VA 23255-2045
Tel.: (804) 673-3573
Fax: (804) 673-3570
E-Mail: hr@worldaccess.com
Web Site: www.worldaccess.com
Emp.: 370
Insurance Brokers
S.I.C.: 6411
N.A.I.C.S.: 524210

Non-U.S. Subsidiaries:

AGA Assistance Australia Pty Ltd (3)
74 High Street
Toowong, QLD, 4066, Australia
Mailing Address:
PO Box 162
Toowong, QLD, 4066, Australia
Tel.: (61) 7 3305 7000
Fax: (61) 733057021
E-Mail: assist@allianz-assistance.com.au
Web Site: www.allianz-assistance.com.au
Emp.: 400
Assistance & Travel Insurance Services
S.I.C.: 6411
N.A.I.C.S.: 524298
Ian Norris *(CEO)*

AGA Services (Thailand) Co., Ltd. (3)
7th Floor Citylink Tower 1091/335 Soi Petchburi 35
New Petchburi Rd
Makasan Rajathevi, Bangkok, 10400, Thailand
Tel.: (66) 23058555
Fax: (66) 23058556
E-Mail: contact@allianz-assistance.co.th
Web Site: www.allianz-assistance.co.th
Insurance Services
S.I.C.: 6411
N.A.I.C.S.: 524298

Mondial Assistance Singapore (3)
143 Cecil Street 13-01 GB Building
Singapore, 069542, Singapore
Tel.: (65) 63954800
Fax: (65) 655355052
E-Mail: info@mondial-assistance.com.sg
Web Site: www.mondial-assistance.com.sg
Emp.: 50
Assistance & Travel Insurance Services
S.I.C.: 6411
N.A.I.C.S.: 524298

Subsidiaries:

Club Marine Ltd. (2)
40 The Esplanade
Brighton, VIC, 3186, Australia
Tel.: (61) 385911950
Fax: (61) 385911965
E-Mail: vic@clubmarine.com.au
Web Site: www.clubmarine.com.au
Emp.: 30
Insurance Services
S.I.C.: 6411
N.A.I.C.S.: 524298
Terry Towell *(Mng Dir)*

Hunter Premium Funding Ltd. (2)
Level 7 360 Elizabeth St
Melbourne, 3000, Australia
Tel.: (61) 392243000
Fax: (61) 1300360449
E Mail: inquiry@hpf.com.au
Web Site: www.hpf.com.au
Emp.: 400
Investment Fund Services
S.I.C.: 6722
N.A.I.C.S.: 525910
Terry Towell *(Mng Dir)*

Recovre Pty Ltd. (2)
Level 8 179 Elizabeth Street
Sydney, NSW, 2000, Australia
Mailing Address:
PO Box A2152
Sydney, NSW, 1235, Australia
Tel.: (61) 1300 550276
Fax: (61) 1300 723405
E-Mail: information@recovre.com.au
Web Site: www.recovre.com.au
Emp.: 600
Insurance Services
S.I.C.: 6411
N.A.I.C.S.: 524298

Non-U.S. Subsidiaries:

Adriatica de Seguros C.A. (2)
Avenida Andres Bello Edf Adriatica De Seguros CA
Caracas, Distrito Capital, 1011 A, Venezuela (100%)
Tel.: (58) 2125080477
Telex: 3 121 500 adria ve
Fax: (58) 2125710812
E-Mail: fdesmazes@adriatica.com.ve
Web Site: www.adriatica.com.ve
Emp.: 300
Insurance Provider
S.I.C.: 6311
N.A.I.C.S.: 524113

AGF Allianz Argentina Compania de Seguros Generales S.A. (2)
Corrientes Ave 299
C 1043 AAC Buenos Aires, Argentina (100%)
Tel.: (54) 1143203893
Telex: 2 2 876 arseg ar
Fax: (54) 1143203802
E-Mail: info@allianz.com.ar
Web Site: www.allianz.com.ar
Emp.: 253
Insurance
S.I.C.: 6411
N.A.I.C.S.: 524298
Fabiana Castineira *(CEO)*

AGF Allianz Chile Compania de Seguros Generales S.A. (2)
Hendaya 60 Piso 10
Las Condes, Santiago, Chile
Tel.: (56) 2 330 2000
Fax: (56) 2 330 2619
E-Mail: scliente@agf.cl
Web Site: www.agf.cl
Insurance Provider
S.I.C.: 6399
N.A.I.C.S.: 524128

AGF Assurances Luxembourg S.A. (2)
14 Bd Franklin-Roosevelt
L-2450 Luxembourg, Luxembourg
Tel.: (352) 4723461
Fax: (352) 472346235
E-Mail: agfluasc@pt.lu
Web Site: www.agf.lu
Emp.: 50
Insurance Services
S.I.C.: 6411
N.A.I.C.S.: 524298
Alain Schreggen *(Mng Dir)*

AGF Brasil Seguros SA (2)
Rua Luis Coelho 26 - 8 andar
01309-900 Sao Paulo, SP, Brazil
Tel.: (55) 1131716000
Fax: (55) 11 3171 61 71
E-Mail: aasa-nr@agf.com.br
Web Site: www.agf.com.br
Insurance Provider
S.I.C.: 6399
N.A.I.C.S.: 524128

AGF Life Luxembourg S.A (2)
14 Blvd Franklin-Roosevelt
L-2450 Luxembourg, Luxembourg
Tel.: (352) 4723461
Fax: (352) 472346235
E-Mail: accueil_vie@agf.lu
Web Site: www.agf.lu
Emp.: 60
Life Insurance
S.I.C.: 6311
N.A.I.C.S.: 524113
Alain Schreggen *(Mng Dir)*

Allianz Compania de Seguros y Reaseguros SA (2)
Calle Tarragona 109
E 08014 Barcelona, Spain (100%)
Tel.: (34) 902232629
Fax: (34) 9023333639
E-Mail: fcallcen@allianz.es
Web Site: www.allianz.es
Emp.: 300
Insurance Provider
S.I.C.: 6399
N.A.I.C.S.: 524128

Allianz (2)
35 Rue De Laeken
1000 Brussels, Belgium (100%)
Tel.: (32) 22146111
Telex: 34 116 haine b
Fax: (32) 22146274
E-Mail: info@allianz.be
Web Site: www.allianz.be
Emp.: 800
Insurance Services
S.I.C.: 6399
N.A.I.C.S.: 524128
Robert Franssen *(Gen Dir)*

Subsidiary:

Allianz Belgium S.A. (3)
35 Rue De Laeken
1000 Brussels, Belgium (100%)
Tel.: (32) 22146111
Telex: 3 4116 haine b
Fax: (32) 22146274
E-Mail: info@allianz.be
Web Site: www.allianz.be
Emp.: 1,000
Insurance Provider
S.I.C.: 6399
N.A.I.C.S.: 524128
Robert Franssen *(Chm-Mgmt Bd & CEO)*

Non-U.S. Subsidiary:

Fenix Directo Compania de Seguros y Reaseguros S.A. (3)
35 Ramirez de Arellano Street
28043 Madrid, Spain
Tel.: (34) 902 44 44 44
Fax: (34) 902 272 272
E-Mail: fenixdirecto@fenixdirecto.com
Web Site: www.fenixdirecto.com
Direct Insurance & Reinsurance Services
S.I.C.: 6411
N.A.I.C.S.: 524298

Compania Colombiana de Inversion Colseguros S.A. (2)
Carrera 13 A N 29-24 piso 19
1951 Bogota, Colombia
Tel.: (57) 15616336
Fax: (57) 15616427
Web Site: www.colseguros.com
Insurance Services
S.I.C.: 6411
N.A.I.C.S.: 524298

Hauteville Insurance Company Ltd. (2)
34 Lscanichers
Saint Peter Port, GY1 2LT, Guernsey
Tel.: (44) 1481724212
Fax: (44) 1481720400
E-Mail: service@expat-hic.com
Web Site: www.expat-hic.com
Emp.: 2
Insurance Services
S.I.C.: 6411
N.A.I.C.S.: 524298
Jean-Francois Gelot *(Mng Dir)*

Phenix Compagnie D'Assurances (2)
4 Ave de la Gare
CH-1001 Lausanne, Switzerland
Tel.: (41) 213400404
Fax: (41) 213400405
E-Mail: info@phenix-assurances.com
Web Site: www.phenix-assurances.com
Premiums: $35,249,480
Emp.: 70
Insurance Services
S.I.C.: 6411
N.A.I.C.S.: 524298

Societe Nationale d'Assurances s.a.l. (2)
Immeuble SNA Hazmieh
PO Box 16-6528
Beirut, Lebanon
Tel.: (961) 5956600
Fax: (961) 5956624
E-Mail: info@allianzsna.com
Web Site: www.allianzsna.com
Sales Range: $25-49.9 Million
Financial Services
S.I.C.: 6411
N.A.I.C.S.: 524298
Antoine Bitar *(CFO)*
Ramez Hayek *(COO)*
Bassam Khoueiss *(Chief Mktg & Sls Officer)*

Agricola Underwriting Management Ltd. (1)
Level 6 North Tower 459 Collins Street
Melbourne, VIC, 3000, Australia
Tel.: (61) 3 9603 1050
Fax: (61) 3 9620 1222
Insurance Underwriting Services
S.I.C.: 6361
N.A.I.C.S.: 524127

Allianz Actio France (1)
87 Rue De Richelieu
Paris, 75002, France
Tel.: (33) 1 44 86 20 00
Fax: (33) 1 44 86 27 90
Mutual Fund Management Services
S.I.C.: 6799
N.A.I.C.S.: 523920

Allianz Actions Aequitas (1)
87 Rue De Richelieu
Paris, 75002, France
Tel.: (33) 1 44 86 20 00
Fax: (33) 1 44 86 27 90
Mutual Fund Management Services
S.I.C.: 6282
N.A.I.C.S.: 523920

Allianz Actions Euro Value (1)
87 Rue De Richelieu
Paris, 75002, France
Tel.: (33) 1 44 86 20 00
Fax: (33) 1 44 86 27 90
Mutual Fund Management Services
S.I.C.: 6282
N.A.I.C.S.: 523920

Allianz Actions France MidCap (1)
87 Rue De Richelieu
Paris, 75002, France
Tel.: (33) 1 44 86 20 00
Fax: (33) 1 44 86 27 90
Mutual Fund Management Services
S.I.C.: 6282
N.A.I.C.S.: 523920

Allianz Actions France (1)
87 Rue De Richelieu
Paris, 75002, France
Tel.: (33) 1 44 86 20 00
Fax: (33) 1 44 86 27 90
Mutual Fund Management Services
S.I.C.: 6282
N.A.I.C.S.: 523920

Allianz Actions Japon (1)
87 Rue de Richelieu
Paris, 75002, France
Tel.: (33) 1 44 86 20 00
Fax: (33) 1 44 86 27 90
Mutual Fund Management Services
S.I.C.: 6799
N.A.I.C.S.: 523920

Allianz Africa S.A. (1)
87 Rue De Richelieu
75113 Paris, France
Tel.: (33) 1 44866400
Fax: (33) 1 44862388
General Insurance Services
S.I.C.: 6411
N.A.I.C.S.: 524210

Allianz Argentina Compania de Seguros S.A. (1)
Corrientes 299
C1043AAC Buenos Aires, Argentina
Tel.: (54) 11 4320380001
Fax: (54) 11 4320380002
Web Site: www.allianz.com.ar
General Insurance Services
S.I.C.: 6411
N.A.I.C.S.: 524210

Allianz Australia Advantage Ltd. (1)
GPO Box 4049
Sydney, NSW, 2001, Australia
Tel.: (61) 1300368764
General Insurance Services
S.I.C.: 6411
N.A.I.C.S.: 524210

Allianz Australia Insurance Limited (1)
Level 12 2 Market Street
Sydney, NSW, 2000, Australia
Tel.: (61) 2 9390 6222
Fax: (61) 2 9390 6445
General Insurance Services
S.I.C.: 6411
N.A.I.C.S.: 524210

Allianz Australia Life Insurance Limited (1)
L 12 2 Market St
Sydney, NSW, 2000, Australia
Tel.: (61) 131000
Life Insurance Services
S.I.C.: 6311
N.A.I.C.S.: 524113

Allianz Australia Limited (1)
2 Market Street
Sydney, NSW, 2000, Australia (100%)
Mailing Address:
GPO Box 4049
Sydney, NSW, 2001, Australia
Tel.: (61) 730239322
E-Mail: customerservice@allianz.com.au
Web Site: www.allianz.com.au
Emp.: 2,900
Insurance Services
S.I.C.: 6399
N.A.I.C.S.: 524128
Terry Towell *(Mng Dir)*

Non-U.S. Subsidiaries:

Allianz New Zealand Ltd. (3)
Level 1 152 Fanshawe St
PO Box 794
Auckland, 1010, New Zealand (100%)
Tel.: (64) 93542900
Fax: (64) 093021865
E-Mail: info_nz@allianz.co.nz
Web Site: www.allianz.co.nz
Emp.: 50
Personal, Commercial & Corporate Insurance
S.I.C.: 6399
N.A.I.C.S.: 524128
Bruce Watters *(CEO)*

Axioma Insurance (Cyprus) Ltd (3)
Iris House 2nd Floor Office no 4 John Kennedy St
PO Box 54350
3106 Lemesos, Cy 3723, Cyprus
Tel.: (357) 25588788
Fax: (357) 25591266
E-Mail: axioma@logos.Cy.net
Web Site: www.axioma-insurance.com
Insurance & Financial Services
S.I.C.: 6411
N.A.I.C.S.: 524298

Non-U.S. Affiliates:

Assurances Generales du Laos (2)
2nd Floor Vientiane Commercial Bank Building
33 Lane Xang Avenue, Vientiane, Laos
Tel.: (856) 21217600
Fax: (856) 87875904
E-Mail: guy.atovy@agl-allianz.com
Web Site: www.agl-allianz.com
Emp.: 90
Insurance Services; Owned 51% by AGF S.A. & 49% by the Government of Laos
S.I.C.: 6411
N.A.I.C.S.: 524298
Guy Atovy *(Mng Dir)*

Astree Assurances (2)
45 Avenue Khereddine Pacha
1002 Tunis, Tunisia
Tel.: (216) 71792211
Fax: (216) 71794723
E-Mail: astree@planet.tn
Web Site: www.astree.com.tn
Sales Range: $25-49.9 Million
Emp.: 150
Insurance Services
S.I.C.: 6411
N.A.I.C.S.: 524298
Habib Bensad *(Chm)*

Allianz Australia Services Pty Limited (1)
2 Market St
Sydney, NSW, 2000, Australia
Tel.: (61) 2 93906262
Fax: (61) 2 93906476
Financial Management Services
S.I.C.: 6211
N.A.I.C.S.: 523999

Allianz Australia Workers Compensation (NSW) Limited (1)
Level 12 2 Market Street
Sydney, NSW, 2000, Australia
Tel.: (61) 1300 130 664
Fax: (61) 1300 130 665
E-Mail: Customer_experience_feedback@allianz.com.au
Employee Benefit Services
S.I.C.: 6733
N.A.I.C.S.: 525190

Allianz Australia Workers Compensation (SA) Limited (1)
89 Pirie St
Adelaide, SA, 5000, Australia
Tel.: (61) 8 8394 8111
Employee Benefit Services
S.I.C.: 6733
N.A.I.C.S.: 525190

Allianz Australia Workers Compensation (Victoria) Limited (1)
Level 5 360 Elizabeth Street
Melbourne, VIC, 3001, Australia
Tel.: (61) 3 9234 3800
Fax: (61) 3 9234 3433
Employee Benefit Services
S.I.C.: 6733
N.A.I.C.S.: 525190

Allianz Bank Financial Advisors S.p.A. (1)
Piazzale Lodi 3
20137 Milan, Italy
Tel.: (39) 02 7216 8000
Fax: (39) 02 8901 0884
E-Mail: customer.center@allianzbank.it
Web Site: www.allianzbank.it
Commercial Banking Services
S.I.C.: 6029
N.A.I.C.S.: 522110

Allianz Banque S.A. (1)
14 Rue Halevy
Paris, 75009, France
Tel.: (33) 1 53 24 48 41
E-Mail: serviceclient@allianzbanque.fr
Web Site: www.allianzbanque.fr
Commercial Banking Services
S.I.C.: 6029
N.A.I.C.S.: 522110

Allianz Biznes Sp. z o.o. (1)
Rodziny Hiszpaskich 1
02-685 Warsaw, Poland
Tel.: (48) 22 567 50 00
Financial Management Services
S.I.C.: 6211
N.A.I.C.S.: 523999

Allianz Bulgaria Holding (1)
Bul Dondukov 59
1504 Sofia, Bulgaria
Tel.: (359) 29302120
Fax: (359) 29805201
Web Site: www.allianz.bg
Emp.: 1,400
Insurance Services
S.I.C.: 6411
N.A.I.C.S.: 524298
Dimitar Zhelez *(CEO)*

Allianz Bulgaria Pension Company AD (1)
19B Tzar Boris III Blvd
1612 Sofia, Bulgaria
Tel.: (359) 2 933 48 00
Fax: (359) 2 981 53 02
Pension Fund Management Services
S.I.C.: 6799
N.A.I.C.S.: 523920

Allianz Burkina Assurances Vie (1)
Avenue de l'UEMOA 01
BP 398
Ouagadougou, Burkina Faso
Tel.: (226) 50306204
Fax: (226) 50310153
Life Insurance Services
S.I.C.: 6311
N.A.I.C.S.: 524113

Allianz business services s.r.o. (1)
Karloveska 32
842 02 Bratislava, Slovakia
Tel.: (421) 2 6929 4442
Fax: (421) 2 6929 4656
Web Site: www.allianz-services.sk
Financial Management Services
S.I.C.: 6211
N.A.I.C.S.: 523999

Allianz Centrafrique Assurances (1)
Boulevard Du General De Gaulle
BP 343
Bangui, Central African Republic
Tel.: (236) 21613666
Fax: (236) 21613340
E-Mail: allianz.centrafrique@allianz-cf.com
General Insurance Services
S.I.C.: 6411
N.A.I.C.S.: 524210

Allianz China General Insurance Company Ltd. (1)
Unit 5107 CITIC Plaza 233 Tianhe Beilu
Guangzhou, 510613, China
Tel.: (86) 20 8396 6788
Fax: (86) 20 3891 1890
E-Mail: contact@allianz.cn
Web Site: www.allianz.cn
General Insurance Services
S.I.C.: 6411
N.A.I.C.S.: 524298

Subsidiary:

Commercial Bank Allianz Bulgaria Ad (2)
79 Maria Louisa Boulevard
1202 Sofia, Bulgaria
Tel.: (359) 29215404
Fax: (359) 29819307
E-Mail: support@bank.allianz.bg
Web Site: www.bank.allianz.bg
Sales Range: $100-124.9 Million
Emp.: 918
Banking Services
S.I.C.: 6029
N.A.I.C.S.: 522110
Dimitar Jelev *(Chm)*

Allianz China Life Insurance Co., Ltd. (1)
Unit 5107 CITIC Plaza 233 Tianhe Beilu
Guangzhou, 510613, China
Tel.: (86) 2038911889
Fax: (86) 20 3891 1890
E-Mail: contact@allianz.com.cn
Web Site: www.allianz.com.cn
Life Insurance Services
S.I.C.: 6311
N.A.I.C.S.: 524113

Non-U.S. Subsidiaries:

AGCS Hong Kong (2)
Suites 403-11 4/F Cityplaza Phase Four 12 Tai Koo Wan Road Tai Koo
Shing Island East, Hong Kong, China (Hong Kong) (100%)
Tel.: (852) 2521 6651
Telex: 78075 corno hx
Fax: (852) 2810 6191
E-Mail: contactus@allianz.com.hk
Web Site: www.allianz.com.hk
Sales Range: $150-199.9 Million
Emp.: 100
Insurance Services
S.I.C.: 6411
N.A.I.C.S.: 524298
Kevin Northcott *(CEO)*

Allianz Insurance Management Asia Pacific Pte. Ltd. (2)
3 Temasek Avenue 09 01 Centennial Tower
Singapore, 39190, Singapore (100%)
Tel.: (65) 62978802
Telex: RS25 094 INSURAN
Fax: (65) 62972318
E-Mail: info@allianz.com
Emp.: 100
S.I.C.: 6399
N.A.I.C.S.: 524128

Allianz SE—(Continued)

Allianz Compagnia Italiana Finanziamenti S.p.A. (1)
Corso Italia 23
Milan, 20122, Italy
Tel.: (39) 0272161
Fax: (39) 02721623
Securities Brokerage Services
S.I.C.: 6211
N.A.I.C.S.: 523120

Allianz Direct New Europe Sp. z o.o. (1)
ul Rodziny Hiszpanskich 1
Warsaw, 02-685, Poland
Tel.: (48) 22 567 6767
General Insurance Services
S.I.C.: 6411
N.A.I.C.S.: 524210

Allianz Direct s.r.o. (1)
Ke Stvanici 656/3
Prague, 186 00, Czech Republic
Tel.: (420) 844 855 866
Fax: (420) 2 4245 5910
E-Mail: direct@allianzdirect.cz
Web Site: www.allianzdirect.cz
General Insurance Services
S.I.C.: 6411
N.A.I.C.S.: 524210

Allianz Elementar Versicherungs AG (1)
Hietzinger Kai 101-105
PO Box 2000
A-1130 Vienna, Austria
Tel.: (43) 001878072010
Fax: (43) 18780740202
E-Mail: info@allianz.at
Web Site: www.allianz.at
Emp.: 3,000
Insurance Services
S.I.C.: 6411
N.A.I.C.S.: 524298
Wolfram Littich *(Chm)*

Subsidiary:

Allianz Elementar Lebensversicherungs AG (2)
Hietzinger Kai 101-105
A 1130 Vienna, Austria (100%)
Tel.: (43) 1878070
Telex: 134 222 alwn a
Fax: (43) 18780771000
E-Mail: office@allianz.at
Web Site: www.allianz.at
Emp.: 3,000
Life Insurance
S.I.C.: 6311
N.A.I.C.S.: 524113

Allianz Equity Investments Ltd. (1)
57 Ladymead
Guildford, GU1 1DB, United Kingdom
Tel.: (44) 1483 568 161
Fax: (44) 1483 552 782
Financial Management Services
S.I.C.: 6211
N.A.I.C.S.: 523999

Allianz Europe B.V. (1)
PO Box 9444
1006 AK Amsterdam, Netherlands NL
Tel.: (31) 205618711
Fax: (31) 206684091
E-Mail:
Emp.: 100
Holding Company
S.I.C.: 6719
N.A.I.C.S.: 551112

Non-U.S. Subsidiary:

Allianz Sigorta A.S. (2)
Baglarbasi Kisikli Cad No 13
Altunizade, TR 34662 Istanbul, Turkey TR
Tel.: (90) 2165566666 (84%)
Telex: 29739 ssgo tr
Fax: (90) 2165566777
E-Mail:
Web Site: www.allianzsigorta.com.tr
Sales Range: Less than $1 Million
Emp.: 700
Health, Property & Casualty Insurance Products & Services
S.I.C.: 6411
N.A.I.C.S.: 524298
Rusdu Saracoglu *(Chm)*
Oliver Baete *(Vice Chm)*
Arif Aytekin *(Gen Mgr)*
Aylin Somersan Coqui *(CFO)*
Tolga Gurkan *(COO)*
Arzu Guler *(CIO)*

Subsidiary:

Allianz Hayat ve Emeklilik A.S. (3)
Baglarbasi Kisikli Cad No 13
34662 Altunizade, TR 81180 Istanbul, Turkey TR
Tel.: (90) 2165566666
Fax: (90) 2165566777
E-Mail: info@allianz.com.tr
Web Site: www.allianzemeklilik.com.tr
Sales Range: Less than $1 Million
Emp.: 700
Life Insurance & Pension Products & Services
S.I.C.: 6411
N.A.I.C.S.: 524298
George Sartoral *(CEO)*

Allianz Finance III B.V. (1)
Keizersgracht 484
Amsterdam, 1017 EH, Netherlands
Tel.: (31) 20 5569715
Financial Management Services
S.I.C.: 6211
N.A.I.C.S.: 523999

Allianz Finance Pty Ltd. (1)
Level 9 2 Market Street
Sydney, NSW, 2000, Australia
Tel.: (61) 2 8258 6073
Fax: (61) 2 9390 6308
Financial Management Services
S.I.C.: 6211
N.A.I.C.S.: 523999

Allianz Fire and Marine Insurance Japan Ltd. (1)
Anzen Bldg 1-6-6 Motoakasaka
Minato-ku, Tokyo, 107 0051, Japan (100%)
Tel.: (81) 345887500
Fax: (81) 345887590
Web Site: www.allianz.co.jp
Emp.: 100
Insurance Provider
S.I.C.: 6399
N.A.I.C.S.: 524128
Michael Maicher *(Pres)*

Allianz France Infrastructure 1 (1)
87 Rue De Richelieu
75002 Paris, France
Tel.: (33) 1 44 86 20 00
Fax: (33) 1 44 86 27 90
Financial Management Services
S.I.C.: 6211
N.A.I.C.S.: 523999

Allianz General Insurance Company S.A. (1)
Athinon Ave 110 Bldg C
GR 10442 Athens, Greece (100%)
Tel.: (30) 2106905500
Fax: (30) 2106911150
E-Mail: customercontact@allianz.gr
Web Site: www.allianz.gr
Sales Range: Less than $1 Million
Insurance Provider
S.I.C.: 6399
N.A.I.C.S.: 524128
Petros Papanikolaous *(CEO)*
Peter Papanikolaous *(COO)*

Allianz Global Assistance S.A.S. (1)
37 Rue Taitbout
75009 Paris, France
Tel.: (33) 1 5325 5325
Fax: (33) 1 5325 5404
Web Site: www.allianz-global-assistance.com
Travel Insurance & Medical Assistance Services
S.I.C.: 6411
N.A.I.C.S.: 524298

Allianz Global Corporate & Specialty, National Insurance Company (1)
Unit 12 & 13 Block A Regent Square
Simpang 150
Kampong Kiajong, BE1318, Brunei Darussalam
Tel.: (673) 242 6888
Fax: (673) 242 9888
Web Site: www.allianz.com
Emp.: 38
General Insurance Services
S.I.C.: 6411
N.A.I.C.S.: 524298

Allianz Global Corporate & Specialty (1)
Saridar Building 92 Al Tahrir Street Dokki
Dokki, Giza, Egypt EG
Tel.: (20) 2 37605445 717
Fax: (20) 37605279
General Insurance Services
S.I.C.: 6411
N.A.I.C.S.: 524210

Allianz Global Corporate & Specialty (1)
Corso Italia 23
20122 Milan, Italy IT
Tel.: (39) 02 72162225
Fax: (39) 02 72169227
General Insurance Services
S.I.C.: 6411
N.A.I.C.S.: 524210

Allianz Global Corporate & Specialty (1)
Carrera 13 A N 29-24 Piso 17 Torre Allianz Santa Fe De
Bogota, Colombia Co
Tel.: (57) 1 5600601
Fax: (57) 1 5616698
E-Mail: servicioalcliente@allianz.co
General Insurance Services
S.I.C.: 6411
N.A.I.C.S.: 524210

Allianz Global Corporate & Specialty (1)
ul Rodziny Hiszpanskich 1
02-685 Warsaw, Poland PL
Tel.: (48) 22 567 4000
Fax: (48) 22 567 4040
General Insurance Services
S.I.C.: 6411
N.A.I.C.S.: 524210

Allianz Global Corporate & Specialty (1)
Toedistrasse 61
8002 Zurich, Switzerland CH
Tel.: (41) 44 285 1616
Fax: (41) 44 285 1617
General Insurance Services
S.I.C.: 6411
N.A.I.C.S.: 524210

Allianz Global Corporate & Specialty (1)
Mannerheimintie 12 B
00100 Helsinki, Finland FI
Tel.: (358) 9 25166432
General Insurance Services
S.I.C.: 6411
N.A.I.C.S.: 524210

Allianz Global Corporate & Specialty (1)
Nordic Region Office Pilestraede 58
1112 Copenhagen, Denmark DK
Tel.: (45) 32700001
General Insurance Services
S.I.C.: 6411
N.A.I.C.S.: 524210

Allianz Global Investors Asia Pacific GmbH (1)
27th Floor ICBC Tower 3 Garden Road
Central, China (Hong Kong)
Tel.: (852) 2238 8888
Fax: (852) 2877 2533
Web Site: www.allianzgi.com
Financial Management Services
S.I.C.: 6211
N.A.I.C.S.: 523999

Allianz Global Investors Ireland Ltd. (1)
15/16 Fitzwilliam Place
Dublin, Ireland
Tel.: (353) 1 489 6820
Fax: (353) 1 489 6899
Investment Management Services
S.I.C.: 6211
N.A.I.C.S.: 523999

Allianz Global Investors Italia S.p.A (1)
Piazza Velasca 7/9
20122 Milan, Italy
Tel.: (39) 02 802 003 70
Fax: (39) 02 802 006 01
E-Mail: infoitaly@allianzgi.com
Web Site: www.allianzgi.it
Asset Management Services
S.I.C.: 6282
N.A.I.C.S.: 523920
Elizabeth Corley *(Pres)*

Allianz Global Investors Nominees (UK) Ltd. (1)
155 Bishopsgate
London, EC2M 3AD, United Kingdom
Tel.: (44) 20 7859 9000
Investment Management Services
S.I.C.: 6211
N.A.I.C.S.: 523999
Beatrice Joyce Doran *(Mgr)*

Allianz Global Life Ltd. (1)
Allianz House Elmpark Merrion Road
Dublin, Ireland
Tel.: (353) 1 242 2300
Fax: (353) 1 242 2302
E-Mail: info-agl@allianz.com
Web Site: www.allianzgloballife.com
Life Insurance Services
S.I.C.: 6311
N.A.I.C.S.: 524113
Theo Bouts *(Chm)*

Allianz Group Greece (1)
Athinon Ave 110 Building C
104 42 Athens, Greece
Tel.: (30) 210 6999999
Fax: (30) 210 6905550
E-Mail: customercontact@allianz.gr
Web Site: www.allianz.gr
Emp.: 200
General Insurance Services
S.I.C.: 6411
N.A.I.C.S.: 524210
Petros Papanikolaou *(CEO)*

Allianz Hayat ve Emeklilik AS (1)
Baglarbasi Kisikli Cad No 13
Altunizade, 34662 Istanbul, Turkey
Tel.: (90) 216 5566666
Fax: (90) 216 5566777
E-Mail: info@allianz.com.tr
Web Site: www.allianz.com.tr
General Insurance Services
S.I.C.: 6411
N.A.I.C.S.: 524210
Ruesdue Saracoglu *(Chm)*
Oliver Baete *(Vice Chm)*

Allianz Hellas Insurance Company S.A. (1)
Athinon Avenue 110 Building C
Athens, 10442, Greece
Tel.: (30) 210 69 05 644
Fax: (30) 210 69 05 651
Health Insurance Services
S.I.C.: 6324
N.A.I.C.S.: 524114
Petros Papanikolaou *(CEO)*

Allianz Holding eins GmbH (1)
Hietzinger Kai 101-105
Vienna, 1130, Austria
Tel.: (43) 187807
Investment Management Services
S.I.C.: 6211
N.A.I.C.S.: 523999

Allianz Holding France SAS (1)
87 Rue de Richelieu
75002 Paris, France
Tel.: (33) 9 78 97 80 08
Investment Management Services
S.I.C.: 6211
N.A.I.C.S.: 523999

Allianz Holdings plc (1)
57 Ladymead
Guildford, GU1 1DB, United Kingdom
Tel.: (44) 14 5461 1785
Fax: (44) 14 8352 9717
Investment Management Services
S.I.C.: 6211
N.A.I.C.S.: 523999

Allianz IARD S.A. (1)
87 Rue De Richelieu
Paris, 75113, France
Tel.: (33) 1 44 86 20 00
Fax: (33) 1 49 27 99 57
General Insurance Services
S.I.C.: 6411

N.A.I.C.S.: 524210

Allianz Insurance Company-Egypt S.A.E. (1)
Saridar Building 92 Tahrir Street
Dokki, Cairo, 12311, Egypt
Tel.: (20) 2 3760 5445
Fax: (20) 2 3760 5446
E-Mail: info@allianz.com.eg
Web Site: www.allianz.com.eg
General Insurance Services
S.I.C.: 6411
N.A.I.C.S.: 524210
Udo Krueger *(Chm)*

Allianz Insurance Company Lanka Limited (1)
103/7 Galle Road
Colombo, 00300, Sri Lanka
Tel.: (94) 11 2393393
Fax: (94) 11 2323646
E-Mail: info@allianz.lk
Web Site: www.allianz.com
General Insurance Services
S.I.C.: 6411
N.A.I.C.S.: 524210
Surekha Alles *(CEO)*

Allianz Insurance Company of Singapore Pte Ltd (1)
3 Temasek Ave 09 01 Centennial Twr
Singapore, 39190, Singapore (100%)
Tel.: (65) 62972529
Telex: 25094 insuran rs
Fax: (65) 62971956
E-Mail: info@allianz.com.sg
Web Site: www.allianz.com.sg
Emp.: 100
Insurance
S.I.C.: 6411
N.A.I.C.S.: 524298
Kevin Leong *(Mgr)*

Allianz Insurance Luxembourg (1)
14 Bld F D Roosevelt
2450 Luxembourg, Luxembourg
Tel.: (352) 472 3461
Fax: (352) 472 3446235
Web Site: www.allianz.lu
General Insurance Services
S.I.C.: 6411
N.A.I.C.S.: 524210

Allianz Insurance New Zealand (1)
Level 1 152 Fanshawe St
PO Box 794
Auckland, New Zealand
Tel.: (64) 9 3542900
Fax: (64) 2 3021865
General Insurance Services
S.I.C.: 6411
N.A.I.C.S.: 524210

Allianz Insurance PLC (1)
57 Ladymead
Guildford, Surrey, GU1 1DB, United Kingdom UK
Tel.: (44) 1483568161 (100%)
Telex: 884 786 cornil g
Fax: (44) 1483300952
E-Mail: helpdesk@allianz.co.uk
Web Site: www.allianzcornhill.co.uk
Emp.: 1,000
Insurance Products & Services
S.I.C.: 6311
N.A.I.C.S.: 524298
Mark Churchlow *(CFO)*

Subsidiaries:

Allianz Business Services Limited (2)
Caton Road
Lancaster, LA1 3PE, United Kingdom
Tel.: (44) 1524 597949
E-Mail: partnerships@allianzbusinessservices.co.uk
Web Site: www.allianzbusinessservices.co.uk
General Insurance Services
S.I.C.: 6411
N.A.I.C.S.: 524298

Non-U.S. Subsidiaries:

Allianz Cornhill Information Services Private Ltd. (2)
3rd Floor Chandragiri Technopark
Kariavattom, Trivandrum, Kerala, 695 581, India
Tel.: (91) 471 2335550
Fax: (91) 471 2700967
E-Mail: acis@allianzcornhill.co.in
Web Site: www.acis.co.in
Emp.: 600
Information Technology Consulting Services
S.I.C.: 7373
N.A.I.C.S.: 541512
Rakesh Kumar Gupta *(Mng Dir)*
Krishna Ramachandran *(CFO)*

Allianz Invest Kapitalanlagegesellschaft mbH (1)
Hietzinger Kai 101-105
1130 Vienna, Austria
Tel.: (43) 15055480
Telex: 136990
Fax: (43) 15055481
E-Mail: sales@allianzinvest.at
Web Site: www.allianzinvest.at
Emp.: 60
Banking, Trading & Compensation
S.I.C.: 6159
N.A.I.C.S.: 522298
Martin Bruckner *(Mng Dir)*

Allianz Investment Properties Ltd. (1)
57 Ladymead
Guildford, GU1 1DB, United Kingdom
Tel.: (44) 1483 568161
Fax: (44) 1483300952
Real Estate Management Services
S.I.C.: 6531
N.A.I.C.S.: 531390

Allianz Investmentbank AG (1)
Hietzinger Kai 101-105
1130 Vienna, Austria
Tel.: (43) 150554800
Fax: (43) 15055481
E-Mail: werner.mueller@allianz.at
Web Site: www.allianzinvest.at
Emp.: 60
Financial Services
S.I.C.: 6211
N.A.I.C.S.: 523999
Werner Mueller *(Mng Dir)*

Allianz Life Assurance Company-Egypt S.A.E. (1)
Saridar Building 92 Tahrir Street
Dokki Area, Giza, Egypt
Tel.: (20) 2 3760 5445
Fax: (20) 2 3760 5446
Life Insurance Services
S.I.C.: 6311
N.A.I.C.S.: 524113

Allianz Life Insurance Co., Ltd. (1)
Allianz Tower 45-21 Yeouido-dong
Yeongdeungpo-gu, Seoul, 150-978, Korea (South)
Tel.: (82) 237877000
E-Mail: webadmin@allianz.co.kr
Web Site: www.allianz.co.kr
Life Insurance Services
S.I.C.: 6311
N.A.I.C.S.: 524113

Allianz Life Insurance Company S.A. (1)
Athinon 110 bld C
10442 Athens, Greece (100%)
Tel.: (30) 2106905500
Fax: (30) 2106997574
E-Mail: life@allianz.gr
Web Site: www.allianz.gr
Life Insurance Provider
S.I.C.: 6311
N.A.I.C.S.: 524113
Papa Nicolaou *(Gen Mgr)*

Allianz Life Insurance Company (1)
3rd Samotechny Pereulok 3
127473 Moscow, Russia (100%)
Tel.: (7) 4959376996
Telex: 064 612 154 smail su
Fax: (7) 4959376980
E-Mail: allianz@allianz.ru
Web Site: www.allianz.ru
Emp.: 150
Life Insurance Services
S.I.C.: 6311
N.A.I.C.S.: 524113
Wermer L. Lellinger *(Pres & CEO)*

Subsidiary:

Allianz Risk Audit (2)
3rd Samotechny Pereulok 3
127473 Moscow, Russia
Tel.: (7) 4959376996
Fax: (7) 4959376996
E-Mail: aria@allianz.ru
Web Site: www.allianz.ru
Emp.: 140
Insurance Services
S.I.C.: 6411
N.A.I.C.S.: 524298
Werner L. Lellimger *(Pres & CEO)*

Allianz Life Insurance Japan Ltd. (1)
Anzen Building 6-6 Motoakasaka 1-chome
Minato-ku, Tokyo, 107-0051, Japan
Tel.: (81) 3 45881500
Fax: (81) 3 45881511
E-Mail: contact@allianz.co.jp
Web Site: life.allianz.co.jp
Life Insurance Services
S.I.C.: 6311
N.A.I.C.S.: 524113
Olaf Kliesow *(Chm & Pres)*

Allianz Life Insurance Lanka Ltd. (1)
No 92 Glennie Street
Colombo, Sri Lanka
Tel.: (94) 112300400
Fax: (94) 11 2304404
General Insurance Services
S.I.C.: 6411
N.A.I.C.S.: 524210

Allianz Life Insurance Malaysia Berhad (1)
33 Jalan Gereja
Kuala Lumpur, 50100, Malaysia
Tel.: (60) 3 2050 1188
Fax: (60) 3 2078 9918
E-Mail: partner@allianz.com.my
Web Site: www.allianz.com.my
Emp.: 50
Life Insurance Services
S.I.C.: 6311
N.A.I.C.S.: 524113
Jens Reisch *(CEO)*
Stefan Ritz *(COO)*

Allianz Life Luxembourg S.A. (1)
14 Bld F D Roosevelt
2450 Luxembourg, Luxembourg
Tel.: (352) 472346 1
Fax: (352) 472346 235
Web Site: www.allianz.lu/life-en/
Life Insurance Services
S.I.C.: 6311
N.A.I.C.S.: 524113
Jean-Pascal Vialaron *(Chm)*

Allianz Madagascar (1)
13 Rue Indira Gandhi
BP 8619
Antananarivo, 101, Madagascar
Tel.: (261) 20 2257900
Fax: (261) 20 2257901
Life Insurance Services
S.I.C.: 6311
N.A.I.C.S.: 524113

Allianz Malaysia Berhad (1)
Suite 3A-15 Level 15 Block 3A Plaza Sentral 5
Kuala Lumpur Sentral, 50470 Kuala Lumpur, Malaysia
Tel.: (60) 322641188
Fax: (60) 322641199
E-Mail:
Web Site: www.allianz.com.my
ALLIANZ—(KLS)
Rev.: $1,032,160,664
Assets: $3,013,744,169
Liabilities: $2,410,113,624
Net Worth: $603,630,545
Earnings: $68,077,832
Emp.: 1,706
Fiscal Year-end: 12/31/12
General Insurance Services
S.I.C.: 6351
N.A.I.C.S.: 524126
Jens Reisch *(CEO)*
Charles Eng Chow Ong *(CFO)*
Horst Hermann Habbig *(Chief Sls officer-AGIC)*
Li Meng Lim *(Chief Sls Officer-Partnerhsip Distr-ALIM)*
Pin Hean Ong *(Chief Sls Officer-Agency Distr-ALIM)*
Tze How Chin *(Chief Market Mgmt Officer)*
Zakri Mohd Khir *(CEO-Allianz General Insurance Company)*
Siew Gek Ng *(Sec)*

Allianz Marine (UK) Ltd. (1)
27 Leaden Haoo Street
London, EC3A 1AA, United Kingdom
Tel.: (44) 20 7877 3000
Fax: (44) 20 7702 2133
General Insurance Services
S.I.C.: 6411
N.A.I.C.S.: 524298

Allianz Mexico S.A. (1)
Blvd MA Camacho 164 Col
Lomas De Barrilaco, 11010 Mexico, Mexico (100%)
Tel.: (52) 52013000
Telex: 17 72 617 acsame
Fax: (52) 5540 3204
Web Site: www.allianz.com.mx
Insurance
S.I.C.: 6311
N.A.I.C.S.: 524113

Allianz Nederland Groep NV (1)
Coolsingel 139
3012 AG Rotterdam, Netherlands
Tel.: (31) 104541911
Fax: (31) 104541310
Web Site: www.allianz.nl
Premiums: $1,657,366,144
Emp.: 1,500
Insurance & Financial Services
S.I.C.: 6411
N.A.I.C.S.: 524298

Subsidiaries:

Allianz Global Corporate & Specialty - Netherlands (2)
school single
PO Box 441
3000 AK Rotterdam, Netherlands
Tel.: (31) 10 454 1336
Fax: (31) 104541199
Web Site: www.allianz.nl
Emp.: 40
Property & Casualty Insurance Products & Services
S.I.C.: 6331
N.A.I.C.S.: 524126
Michiel van Houten *(Head-Claims-Netherlands)*

Allianz Nederland Asset Management B.V. (2)
Coolsingel 134
PO Box 40
3430 AA Rotterdam, Netherlands (100%)
Tel.: (31) 30 607 7651
Fax: (31) 30 603 0269
E-Mail: info.am@allianz.nl
Web Site: www.allianz.nl
Emp.: 500
Asset Management & Insurance Services
S.I.C.: 6399
N.A.I.C.S.: 524128
Jay Ralph *(Chm)*
Thomas Naumann *(CFO)*

Allianz Nederland Levensverzekering NV (2)
Coolsingel 139
PO Box 9
3430 AA Rotterdam, Netherlands
Tel.: (31) 302814242
Fax: (31) 302881861
E-Mail: info@allianz.nl
Web Site: www.allianz.nl
Emp.: 1,000
Insurance & Financial Services
S.I.C.: 6411
N.A.I.C.S.: 524298

Allianz Nederland Schadeverzekering NV (2)
Coolsingel 139
3012 AG Rotterdam, Netherlands
Tel.: (31) 104541911
Fax: (31) 104541310
Web Site: www.allianz.nl
Emp.: 500
Insurance & Financial Services
S.I.C.: 6411
N.A.I.C.S.: 524298
Rom Hof *(Mng Dir)*

Allianz Risk Consultants B.V. (2)
Coolsingel 139
3012 AG Rotterdam, Netherlands
Tel.: (31) 104541840
Fax: (31) 104541310

Allianz SE—(Continued)

E-Mail: mail@allianz-arc.com
Web Site: www.arc-allianz.com
Financial Services
S.I.C.: 6726
N.A.I.C.S.: 525990
Rome Hof *(Chm)*

Holland Beleggingsgroep B.V. (2)
Buizerdlaan 12
3435 SB Nieuwegein, Netherlands
Mailing Address:
PO Box 40
3430 AA Nieuwegein, Netherlands
Tel.: (31) 306077651
Fax: (31) 306030269
E-Mail: info@allianz.nl
Web Site: www.allianz.nl
Emp.: 100
Financial Services
S.I.C.: 6091
N.A.I.C.S.: 523991

ITEB B.V. (2)
Coolsingel 139
2800 AA Rotterdam, Netherlands
Tel.: (31) 182569421
Fax: (31) 882569438
E-Mail: secretariaat@iteb.nl
Web Site: www.iteb.nl
Emp.: 90
Financial Services
S.I.C.: 6726
N.A.I.C.S.: 525990
R. Kerzer *(Gen Mgr)*

London Verzekeringen N.V. (2)
PO Box 60
3000 AB Rotterdam, Netherlands
Tel.: (31) 205618618
Fax: (31) 205618680
E-Mail: info@london.nl
Web Site: www.london.nl
Emp.: 150
Insurance Services
S.I.C.: 6411
N.A.I.C.S.: 524298
Egberg Gerritsen *(Mng Dir)*

Universal Leven N.V. (2)
Coolsingel 139
PO Box 9
3435 SB Rotterdam, Netherlands
Tel.: (31) 306986140
Fax: (31) 304541310
E-Mail: midoffice@ul.nl
Web Site: www.allianz.nl
Emp.: 20
Financial Services
S.I.C.: 6726
N.A.I.C.S.: 525990
Barbara Kwant *(Product Mgr)*

Allianz New Europe Holding GmbH (1)
Hietzinger Kai 101-105
Vienna, 1130, Austria
Tel.: (43) 1 87 8070
Fax: (43) 1 87 8077 0700
Investment Management Services
S.I.C.: 6211
N.A.I.C.S.: 523999

Allianz Northern Ireland Ltd (1)
Allianz House 21 Linenhall St
Belfast, Northern Ireland, BT2 8AB, United Kingdom
Tel.: (44) 2890895600
Fax: (44) 2890434222
E-Mail: info@allianz-ni.co.uk
Web Site: www.allianz-ni.co.uk
Emp.: 100
Insurance Services
S.I.C.: 6411
N.A.I.C.S.: 524298
Paul McCrane *(Mgr-Risk Mgmt)*

Allianz Pension Fund Trustees Ltd. (1)
57 Ladymead
Guildford, Surrey, GU1 1DB, United Kingdom
Tel.: (44) 1483 568 161
Fax: (44) 1483 552 782
Pension Fund Management Services
S.I.C.: 6371
N.A.I.C.S.: 525110

Allianz Pensionskasse AG (1)
Hietzinger Kai 1012-105
A-1130 Vienna, Austria
Tel.: (43) 1878074952
Fax: (43) 18780770000
E-Mail: office@allianz.at
Web Site: www.allianzpk.at
Emp.: 20
Pension Management Services
S.I.C.: 6371
N.A.I.C.S.: 525110

Allianz penzijni fond a.s. (1)
Ke Stvanici 656/3
186 00 Prague, Czech Republic
Tel.: (420) 2 24405789
Fax: (420) 2 42455401
E-Mail: penz-fond@allianz.cz
Pension Fund Management Services
S.I.C.: 6371
N.A.I.C.S.: 525110

Allianz Pojistovna A/S (1)
Kestani 656
186 00 Prague, Czech Republic (100%)
Tel.: (420) 224405111
Fax: (420) 242455555
E-Mail: klient@allianz.cz
Web Site: www.allianz.cz
Emp.: 200
Insurance Provider
S.I.C.: 6399
N.A.I.C.S.: 524128
Jacob Strnav *(Mng Dir)*

Allianz Polska Services Sp. z o.o. (1)
ul Rodziny Hiszpanskich 1
02-685 Warsaw, Poland
Tel.: (48) 22 567 40 00
Fax: (48) 22 567 40 40
General Insurance Services
S.I.C.: 6411
N.A.I.C.S.: 524210

Allianz Portugal (1)
Rua Andrade Corvo 32
P 1069014 Lisbon, Codex, Portugal (100%)
Tel.: (351) 213165300
Fax: (351) 213165570
E-Mail: info@allianz.pt
Web Site: www.allianz.pt
Emp.: 100
Insurance Provider
S.I.C.: 6399
N.A.I.C.S.: 524128
Patrick Schwarz *(CEO)*

Allianz Properties Limited (1)
57 Ladymead
Guildford, Surrey, GU1 1DB, United Kingdom
Tel.: (44) 1483 568 161
Fax: (44) 1483 552 782
Real Estate Development Services
S.I.C.: 6531
N.A.I.C.S.: 531390
Stuart John Robertson *(Chief Accountant)*

Allianz plc (1)
Allianz House Elmpark Merrion Road
Dublin, 4, Ireland IE
Tel.: (353) 1 613 3000 (100%)
Fax: (353) 1 613 4444
E-Mail: info@allianz.ie
Web Site: www.allianz.ie
Holding Company; Insurance Products & Services
S.I.C.: 6719
N.A.I.C.S.: 551112
Brendan Murphy *(CEO)*

Subsidiary:

Allianz Re Dublin Ltd. (2)
3 Harbour Master Pla
Dublin, 1, Ireland
Tel.: (353) 15125400
Fax: (353) 15125401
E-Mail: deborah.holton@allianzre.ie
Web Site: www.allianz.ie
Emp.: 16
Reinsurance Services
S.I.C.: 6399
N.A.I.C.S.: 524130
Colin Costello *(Mng Dir)*

Allianz Real Estate Asia Pacific (1)
1 Temasek Avenue 18-04
Singapore, 039192, Singapore
Tel.: (65) 6395 8607
Fax: (65) 6337 3657
Real Estate Management Services
S.I.C.: 6531
N.A.I.C.S.: 531390

Allianz Risk Transfer N.V. (1)
Keizersgracht 482
1017 EG Amsterdam, Netherlands
Tel.: (31) 20 520 3823
Fax: (31) 20 520 3833
General Insurance Services
S.I.C.: 6411
N.A.I.C.S.: 524210

Allianz Risk Transfer (UK) Limited (1)
Allianz House 60 Gracechurch Street
London, EC3V 0HR, United Kingdom
Tel.: (44) 20 3451 3000
Fax: (44) 20 7283 8125
General Insurance Services
S.I.C.: 6411
N.A.I.C.S.: 524210

Allianz Saude S.A. (1)
Rua Luis Coelho 26 3 Andar
01309-900 Sao Paulo, Brazil
Tel.: (55) 11 40015060
Fax: (55) 11 31716171
Health Insurance Services
S.I.C.: 6324
N.A.I.C.S.: 524114

Allianz Seguros S.A. (1)
Rua Luis Coelho 26 8 Andar
01309-900 Sao Paulo, Brazil
Tel.: (55) 11 31564340
Fax: (55) 11 31716171
General Insurance Services
S.I.C.: 6411
N.A.I.C.S.: 524210

Allianz Senegal Assurances Vie (1)
Avenue Abdoulaye Fadiga X Rue de Thann
BP 2610 Dakar, Senegal
Tel.: (221) 33 8494400
Fax: (221) 33 823107
General Insurance Services
S.I.C.: 6411
N.A.I.C.S.: 524210

Allianz Senegal dommages (1)
Avenue Abdoulaye Fadiga X Rue De Thann
Dakar, Senegal
Tel.: (221) 338494400
General Insurance Services
S.I.C.: 6411
N.A.I.C.S.: 524210

Allianz Senegal vie (1)
Avenue Abdoulaye Fadiga X Rue de Thann
BP 2610 Dakar, Senegal
Tel.: (221) 33 849 44 00
Fax: (221) 33 823 10 78
General Insurance Services
S.I.C.: 6411
N.A.I.C.S.: 524210

Allianz Slovenska dochodkova spravcovsa spolocnost, a.s. (1)
Racianska 62
831 02 Bratislava, Slovakia
Tel.: (421) 2 57 10 6811
Fax: (421) 2 57 10 6890
E-Mail: info@asdss.sk
Web Site: www.asdss.sk
Pension Fund Management Services
S.I.C.: 6371
N.A.I.C.S.: 525110
Miroslav Suchy *(Head-Sls & Mktg)*

Allianz Slovenska Poistovna, a.s. (1)
Dostojevskeho Rad 4
SR-815 74 Bratislava, Slovakia Sk
Tel.: (421) 2 5963 1111
Fax: (421) 2 5963 2740
E-Mail: allianzsp@allianzsp.sk
Web Site: www.allianzsp.sk
Rev.: $625,861,356
Assets: $2,992,927,645
Liabilities: $2,261,669,255
Net Worth: $731,258,390
Earnings: $64,962,126
Emp.: 142,000
Fiscal Year-end: 12/31/12
Insurance Products & Services
S.I.C.: 6351
N.A.I.C.S.: 524126
Manuel Bauer *(Chm-Supervisory Bd)*
Marek Jankovic *(Chm-Mgmt Bd)*
Viktor Cingel *(Member-Mgmt Bd)*
Miroslav Pacher *(Member-Mgmt Bd)*
Pavol Pitonak *(Member-Mgmt Bd)*
Todor Todorov *(Member-Mgmt Bd)*

Allianz SNA Sal (1)
Allianz SNA Bldg Hazmieh
PO Box 16-6528
Beirut, Lebanon
Tel.: (961) 5 956600
Fax: (961) 5 956624
E-Mail: info@allianzsna.com
Web Site: www.allianzsna.com
General Insurance Services
S.I.C.: 6411
N.A.I.C.S.: 524210
Adrien Cozza *(CFO)*
Richard Attie *(Chief Sls Officer-Direct Sls Force & Brokers)*
Bassam Khoueiss *(Chief Sls Officer-Direct Bus)*

Allianz South America Holding B.V. (1)
Keizersgracht 484
Amsterdam, 1017 EH, Netherlands
Tel.: (31) 20 556 9715
Fax: (31) 206268149
Investment Management Services
S.I.C.: 6799
N.A.I.C.S.: 523920

Allianz Specialised Investments Limited (1)
27 Knightsbridge
London, SW1X 7LY, United Kingdom
Tel.: (44) 2070713410
Fax: (44) 20 7071 3444
Investment Management Services
S.I.C.: 6211
N.A.I.C.S.: 523999

ALLIANZ SUBALPINA HOLDING S.p.A. (1)
Via Vittorio Alfieri 22
Turin, 10121, Italy
Tel.: (39) 0115161111
Investment Management Services
S.I.C.: 6211
N.A.I.C.S.: 523999

Allianz Suisse Versicherungen (1)
Bleicherweg 19
CH 8022 Zurich, Switzerland (100%)
Tel.: (41) 433119911
Telex: 817656 coall ch
E-Mail: contact@allianz-suisse.ch
Web Site: www.allianz-suisse.ch
Emp.: 3,953
Property, Casualty, Life & Health Insurance & Financial Services
S.I.C.: 6351
N.A.I.C.S.: 524126
Thomas Pleines *(CEO)*

Subsidiaries:

Alba Allgemeine Versicherungs-Gesellschaft (2)
St Alban-Anlage 56
PO Box 101
CH-4020 Basel, Switzerland
Tel.: (41) 612953111
Fax: (41) 612953232
E-Mail: info@alba.ch
Web Site: www.alba.ch
Emp.: 250
Insurance Services
S.I.C.: 6411
N.A.I.C.S.: 524298

Allianz Suisse Immobilien AG (2)
Hauptsitz Brunnenstrasse 7
CH-8604 Volketswil, Switzerland
Tel.: (41) 583580111
Fax: (41) 583580112
E-Mail: contact.immo@allianz-suisse.ch
Web Site: www.allianz-suisse.ch
Emp.: 45
Financial Services
S.I.C.: 6211
N.A.I.C.S.: 523999

Allianz Suisse Insurance Company (2)
Hohlstrasse 552
8048 Zurich, Switzerland
Tel.: (41) 583587111
Fax: (41) 583584101
E-Mail: press@allianz-suisse.ch
Web Site: www.allianz-suisse.ch
Emp.: 500
Insurance Products & Services
S.I.C.: 6411

N.A.I.C.S.: 524298
Hansjoerg Leibundgut *(Mgr-Comm)*

Allianz Suisse Versicherungen - Allianz Suisse Leben (2)
Bleicherweg 19
CH-8022 Zurich, Switzerland
Tel.: (41) 442095111
Fax: (41) 583584042
E-Mail: contact@allianz-suisse.ch
Web Site: www.allianz-suisse.ch
Emp.: 4,000
Financial Services
S.I.C.: 6726
N.A.I.C.S.: 525990
Manfrad Knof *(CEO)*

CAP Rechtsschutz Versicherung (2)
Baslerstrasse 52
PO Box 1840
CH-8048 Zurich, Switzerland
Tel.: (41) 583580900
Fax: (41) 583580901
E-Mail: contact@cap.ch
Web Site: www.cap.ch
Emp.: 100
Insurance & Financial Services
S.I.C.: 6411
N.A.I.C.S.: 524298
Eugster Daniel *(CEO)*

Allianz Taiwan Life Insurance Company Ltd. (1)
110 5F No 100 Sec 5 Xin Yi Road
Taipei, Taiwan
Tel.: (886) 287895858
Fax: (886) 287895008
Web Site: www.allianz.com.tw
Emp.: 1,200
Insurance Services
S.I.C.: 6411
N.A.I.C.S.: 524298
Bruce Bowers *(CEO-Asia Pacific)*

Allianz Takaful B.S.C.(c) (1)
Al Raya Bldg Bldg 1025 Road 3621
Seef District, 436 Manama, Bahrain
Tel.: (973) 17 568 222
Fax: (973) 17 582 114
E-Mail: info@allianz.com.bh
Web Site: www.allianz.com.bh
Life & Health Insurance Services
S.I.C.: 6311
N.A.I.C.S.: 524113
Nidham Yacouby *(Chm-Supervisory Bd)*

Allianz-Tiriac Asigurari S.A. (1)
80-84 Caderea Bastiliei St
010616 Bucharest, Romania
Tel.: (40) 212082105
Fax: (40) 212082211
E-Mail: office@allianztiriac.ro
Web Site: www.allianztiriac.ro
Insurance Services
S.I.C.: 6411
N.A.I.C.S.: 524298
Cristian Marian Ionescu *(Exec Dir-Fin)*

Allianz-Tiriac Pensii Private (1)
Ion Slatineanu 6
010602 Bucharest, Romania
Tel.: (40) 21 207 2100
Fax: (40) 21 207 2170
E-Mail: pensii@allianztiriac.ro
Web Site: pensii.allianztiriac.ro
Emp.: 81
Pension Fund Management Services
S.I.C.: 6371
N.A.I.C.S.: 525110
Rangam Bir *(Pres)*

Allianz (UK) Limited (1)
57 Ladymead
Guildford, GU1 1DB, United Kingdom
Tel.: (44) 14 8356 8161
Fax: (44) 14 8330 2681
General Insurance Services
S.I.C.: 6411
N.A.I.C.S.: 524298

Allianz Worldwide Care Limited (1)
18 B Beckett Way Park West Business Campus Nangor Road
Dublin, 12, Ireland
Tel.: (353) 16301300
Fax: (353) 16301306
E-Mail: client.services@allianzworldwidecare.com
Web Site: www.allianzworldwidecare.com
Emp.: 200
Health Insurance Services
S.I.C.: 6321
N.A.I.C.S.: 524114
Ron Buchan *(CEO)*

Allianz Zagreb d.d. (1)
Selska 17
10000 Zagreb, Croatia
Tel.: (385) 13670367
Fax: (385) 13670414
Web Site: www.allianz.hr
Insurance Services
S.I.C.: 6411
N.A.I.C.S.: 524298
Klaus Junker *(Chm-Supervisory Bd)*

AllSecur B.V. (1)
PO Box 1951
5200 BZ 's-Hertogenbosch, Netherlands
Tel.: (31) 73 5485000
Fax: (31) 73 5485001
E-Mail: info@allsecur.nl
Web Site: www.allsecur.nl
Car Insurance Services
S.I.C.: 6331
N.A.I.C.S.: 524126

AMOS Austria GmbH (1)
Hietzinger Kai 101-105
1130 Vienna, Austria
Tel.: (43) 1 87807 0
Fax: (43) 1 87807 70000
Information Technology Consulting Services
S.I.C.: 7373
N.A.I.C.S.: 541512

Approfrais S.A. (1)
Rue Jean Monnet
BP 1802
27000 Evreux, France
Tel.: (33) 232381409
Fax: (33) 2 32 39 61 41
General Insurance Services
S.I.C.: 6411
N.A.I.C.S.: 524210

AS Selecta s.r.o. (1)
Mileticova 40
821 08 Bratislava, Slovakia
Tel.: (421) 2 555 67 736
E-Mail: info@sk.selecta.com
Web Site: www.selectavending.sk
Vending Machine Distr
S.I.C.: 5046
N.A.I.C.S.: 423440

Assistance Courtage d'Assurance et de Reassurance S.A. (1)
87 Rue De Richelieu
75002 Paris, France
Tel.: (33) 1 45 67 60 68
General Insurance Services
S.I.C.: 6411
N.A.I.C.S.: 524210

Assurance Vie et Prevoyance (AVIP) S.A. (1)
Tour Neptune 20 place de Seine Case Postale 2401
La Defense, Paris, 92086, France
Tel.: (33) 1 58 85 95 00
Fax: (33) 1 58 85 95 67
Web Site: www.avip.fr
General Insurance Services
S.I.C.: 6411
N.A.I.C.S.: 524210

AZ Jupiter 4 B.V. (1)
Keizersgracht 484
1017 EH Amsterdam, North Holland, Netherlands
Tel.: (31) 205569715
Investment Management Services
S.I.C.: 6211
N.A.I.C.S.: 523999

AZ Jupiter 8 B.V. (1)
Keizersgracht 484
1017 EH Amsterdam, North Holland, Netherlands
Tel.: (31) 205569715
Fax: (31) 206268149
Investment Management Services
S.I.C.: 6211
N.A.I.C.S.: 523999

AZ Jupiter 9 B.V. (1)
Keizersgracht 484
1017 EH Amsterdam, North Holland, Netherlands
Tel.: (31) 205569715
Fax: (31) 206268149
Investment Management Services
S.I.C.: 6211
N.A.I.C.S.: 523999

BAWAG Allianz Mitarbeitervorsorgekasse AG (1)
Hietzinger Kai 101-105
1130 Vienna, Austria
Tel.: (43) 1 878075357
Fax: (43) 1 8780740128
E-Mail: abfertigung.neu@allianz.at
Web Site: www.allianz.com
Financial Management Services
S.I.C.: 6211
N.A.I.C.S.: 523999

Bilan Services S.N.C. (1)
25 Boulevard Des Bouvets
92000 Nanterre, France
Tel.: (33) 1 41 97 05 05
Fax: (33) 1 49 00 12 47
General Insurance Services
S.I.C.: 6411
N.A.I.C.S.: 524210

Brasil de Imoveis e Participacoes Ltda. (1)
Luis Coelho 26
Sao Paulo, 01309-000, Brazil
Tel.: (55) 1131716687
Investment Management Services
S.I.C.: 6211
N.A.I.C.S.: 523999

British Reserve Insurance Co. Ltd. (1)
Great West House Great West Road
Brentford, TW8 1AH, United Kingdom
Tel.: (44) 8443 914037
Fax: (44) 870 160 0304
General Insurance Services
S.I.C.: 6411
N.A.I.C.S.: 524210

Bureau d'Expertises Despretz S.A. (1)
Boulevard Du Souverain 360 / 2
1160 Brussels, Belgium
Tel.: (32) 2 649 27 30
Fax: (32) 2 648 61 14
E-Mail: contact@bdexp.be
Web Site: www.bdexp.be
General Insurance Services
S.I.C.: 6411
N.A.I.C.S.: 524210
Jean-Christophe Paquet *(Gen Mgr)*

Cedulas Colon de Capitalizacion Colseguros S.A. (1)
Cr 13 A 29 24 Loc 102
Bogota, Colombia
Tel.: (57) 15600600
Investment Management Services
S.I.C.: 6211
N.A.I.C.S.: 523999

Chateau Larose Trintaudon S.A. (1)
Route de Pauillac
33112 Saint-Laurent-Medoc, France
Tel.: (33) 5 56594192
Fax: (33) 5 56599322
E-Mail: info@trintaudon.com
Web Site: www.chateau-larose-trintaudon.fr
Wine Mfr
S.I.C.: 2084
N.A.I.C.S.: 312130

Companhia de Seguros Allianz Portugal S.A. (1)
Rua Andrade Corvo 32
1069-014 Lisbon, Portugal PT
Tel.: (351) 213165300
Fax: (351) 213165570
E-Mail: info@allianz.pt
Web Site: www.allianz.pt
Emp.: 500
Insurance Products & Services
S.I.C.: 6411
N.A.I.C.S.: 524298
Ivan Galr Sota *(CEO)*

CreditRas Vita S.p.A. (1)
Corso Italia 23
Milan, 20122, Italy
Tel.: (39) 02 7216 1
Fax: (39) 02 7216 2735
E-Mail: info@creditrasvita.it
Web Site: www.creditrasvita.it
Life Insurance Services
S.I.C.: 6311
N.A.I.C.S.: 524113

Darta Saving Life Assurance Ltd. (1)
Allianz House Elmpark Merrion Rd
Dublin, Ireland
Tel.: (353) 1 242 2300
Fax: (353) 1 242 2302
E-Mail: darta.saving@darta.ie
Web Site: www.darta.ie
General Insurance Services
S.I.C.: 6411
N.A.I.C.S.: 524298
Mauro Re *(Chm)*
John Lyons *(CEO)*
John Finnegan *(CFO)*

Euler Gestion (1)
1 Rue Euler
Paris, 75008, France
Tel.: (33) 140 705 050
Investment Management Services
S.I.C.: 6211
N.A.I.C.S.: 523999

Euler Hermes Cescob Service s.r.o. (1)
Molakova 576/11
Prague, 186 00, Czech Republic
Tel.: (420) 266109552
Financial Management Services
S.I.C.: 6211
N.A.I.C.S.: 523999

Euler Hermes Cescob uverova pojistovna a.s. (1)
Molakova 576/11
186 00 Prague, Czech Republic
Tel.: (420) 266109521
Fax: (420) 266109520
General Insurance Services
S.I.C.: 6411
N.A.I.C.S.: 524298

Euler Hermes Collections UK Limited (1)
1 Canada Square
London, E14 5DX, United Kingdom
Tel.: (44) 20 7860 2756
E-Mail: collections.newbusiness@eulerhermes.com
Web Site: www.collections.eulerhermes.co.uk
Debt Collection Services
S.I.C.: 7322
N.A.I.C.S.: 561440

Euler Hermes Colombia (1)
Calle 72 6-44 Piso 3 Edificio APA
Bogota, Colombia
Tel.: (57) 571 3264640
Web Site: www.co.eulerhermes.com
Credit Insurance Services
S.I.C.: 6331
N.A.I.C.S.: 524126
John-Paul Bahamondez, *(Gen Mgr)*

Euler Hermes Credit Management Services Ireland Ltd. (1)
3rd Floor Mespil Court 39a Mespil Road
Dublin, Ireland
Tel.: (353) 1 660 1667
Fax: (353) 1 664 2659
Insurance & Credit Management Services
S.I.C.: 6411
N.A.I.C.S.: 524298

Euler Hermes Credit Services (JP) Ltd. (1)
Kyobashi Nisshoku Bldg 7F 8-7 Kyobashi 1-chome
Chuo-ku, Tokyo, 104-0031, Japan
Tel.: (81) 3 3538 5403
Fax: (81) 3 3538 5395
E-Mail: Info.jp@eulerhermes.com
Emp.: 7
Insurance Management Services
S.I.C.: 6411
N.A.I.C.S.: 524298
Keisuke Moriyama *(Gen Mgr)*

Euler Hermes Danmark (1)
Amerika Plads 19
2100 Copenhagen, Denmark
Tel.: (45) 88 33 33 88
Fax: (45) 88 33 33 89
E-Mail: info.dk@eulerhermes.com
Web Site: www.eulerhermes.dk

Allianz SE—(Continued)

Insurance Management Services
S.I.C.: 6411
N.A.I.C.S.: 524298

EULER HERMES EMPORIKI S.A. (1)
16 Laodikias Str & 1-3 Nymfeou Str
Ilissia, 115 28 Athens, Greece
Tel.: (30) 210 69000 00
Fax: (30) 210 69000 01
Credit Insurance Services
S.I.C.: 6351
N.A.I.C.S.: 524126

Euler Hermes Holdings UK plc (1)
1 Canada Sq
London, E14 5DX, United Kingdom
Tel.: (44) 20 7512 9333
Fax: (44) 20 7512 9186
General Insurance Services
S.I.C.: 6411
N.A.I.C.S.: 524298
Roger Paton *(Mng Dir)*

Euler Hermes Ireland (1)
Arch Blackrock Business Park Carysfort Avenue Blackrock
Dublin, Ireland
Tel.: (353) 1 200 0400
Fax: (353) 1 200 0459
E-Mail: enquiries@eulerhermes.com
Web Site: www.eulerhermes.ie/en
General Insurance Services
S.I.C.: 6411
N.A.I.C.S.: 524298
Dean O'Brien *(Country Mgr)*

Euler Hermes Magyar Koveteleskezelo Kft. (1)
Kiscelii U 104
1037 Budapest, Hungary
Tel.: (36) 14 53 90 00
Fax: (36) 14 53 90 09
Financial Management Services
S.I.C.: 6211
N.A.I.C.S.: 523999

Euler Hermes Management UK Limited (1)
1 Canada Sq
London, E14 5DX, United Kingdom
Tel.: (44) 20 7512 9333
Business Management Consulting Services
S.I.C.: 8748
N.A.I.C.S.: 541618

Euler Hermes Norge (1)
Holbergsgate 21
0166 Oslo, Norway
Tel.: (47) 23 25 60 00
Fax: (47) 23 25 60 10
E-Mail: info.no@eulerhermes.com
Web Site: www.eulerhermes.no
General Insurance Services
S.I.C.: 6411
N.A.I.C.S.: 524298

Euler Hermes Reinsurance AG (1)
Toedistrasse 65
8002 Zurich, Switzerland
Tel.: (41) 44 283 65 65
Fax: (41) 44 283 65 66
Reinsurance Services
S.I.C.: 6399
N.A.I.C.S.: 524130

Euler Hermes Risk Services UK Limited (1)
1 Canada Square
London, E14 5DX, United Kingdom
Tel.: (44) 20 7512 9333
Fax: (44) 20 7512 9186
Financial Management Services
S.I.C.: 6211
N.A.I.C.S.: 523999

Euler Hermes Risk Yonetimi ve Danismanlik Hizmetleri Limited Sirketi (1)
Iz Plaza Giz Ayazaga Yolu No 9 Kat 14
Maslak, 34398 Istanbul, Turkey
Tel.: (90) 212 2907610
Fax: (90) 212 2907610
Web Site: www.allianz.com
Insurance Management Services
S.I.C.: 6411
N.A.I.C.S.: 524298

Euler Hermes Services AG (1)
Todistrasse 65
Zurich, 8002, Switzerland
Tel.: (41) 442836565
Credit Insurance Services
S.I.C.: 6331
N.A.I.C.S.: 524126

Euler Hermes Services Belgium S.A. (1)
15 Rue Montoyer
Brussels, 1000, Belgium
Tel.: (32) 2 289 31 11
Fax: (32) 2 289 37 70
E-Mail: info.belgium@eulerhermes.com
Emp.: 180
Insurance Management Services
S.I.C.: 6411
N.A.I.C.S.: 524298
Paul Becue *(Mgr)*

Euler Hermes Services B.V. (1)
Pettelaarpark 20
Postbus 7051
5201 CZ 's-Hertogenbosch, Netherlands
Tel.: (31) 73 688 99 99
Fax: (31) 73 688 99 88
E-Mail: info@eulerhermes.nl
Web Site: www.eolis.nl
Emp.: 120
General Insurance Services
S.I.C.: 6411
N.A.I.C.S.: 524298
Jean Claus *(Dir-Fin)*

Euler Hermes Services India Private Limited (1)
4th Floor Voltas House 23 J N Heredia Marg Ballard Estate
Mumbai, 400 001, India
Tel.: (91) 22 66232525
Fax: (91) 22 66232555
Web Site: www.allianz.com
Emp.: 18
Financial Management Services
S.I.C.: 6211
N.A.I.C.S.: 523999
Yagya Kalra *(Sec)*

Euler Hermes Servicii Financiare S.R.L. (1)
6 Petru Maior
011264 Bucharest, Romania
Tel.: (40) 21 3020300
Fax: (40) 21 3020302
E-Mail: info.ro@eulerhermes.com
Web Site: www.eulerhermes.ro
Emp.: 30
Insurance Management Services
S.I.C.: 6411
N.A.I.C.S.: 524298

Euler Hermes Servicios S.A. (1)
Blvd Manuel Avila Camacho 164-8
Mexico, Mexico
Tel.: (52) 55 5201 7900
Fax: (52) 55 5201 7901
Credit Insurance Services
S.I.C.: 6331
N.A.I.C.S.: 524126

Euler Hermes SFAC Recouvrement S.A.S. (1)
1 Rue Euler
75008 Paris, France
Tel.: (33) 1 40 70 50 50
Fax: (33) 1 40 70 50 97
Debt Collection Services
S.I.C.: 7322
N.A.I.C.S.: 561440

Euler Hermes Suomi (1)
Mannerheimintie 105
00280 Helsinki, Finland
Tel.: (358) 1 08508500
Fax: (358) 1 08508511
E-Mail: info.fi@eulerhermes.com
Web Site: www.eulerhermes.fi
General Insurance Services
S.I.C.: 6411
N.A.I.C.S.: 524298

Euler Hermes Sverige (1)
Klarabergsviadukten 90
Box 729
101 34 Stockholm, Sweden
Tel.: (46) 8 555 136 00
Fax: (46) 8 555 136 01
E-Mail: info.se@eulerhermes.com
Web Site: www.eulerhermes.se
Financial Management Services
S.I.C.: 6211
N.A.I.C.S.: 523999
Alexis Spanos *(Mgr)*

Euler Hermes Trade Credit Limited (1)
Level 1 152 Fanshawe St
Auckland, 1010, New Zealand
Tel.: (64) 9 3542995
Fax: (64) 9 3542991
Credit Insurance Services
S.I.C.: 6331
N.A.I.C.S.: 524126

Euler Hermes Trade Credit Underwriting Agents Pty Ltd (1)
Level 9 Forecourt Allianz Building 2 Market Street
Sydney, NSW, 2000, Australia
Tel.: (61) 2 8258 5108
Fax: (61) 2 8258 5060
Credit Underwriting Services
S.I.C.: 6331
N.A.I.C.S.: 524126

Euler Hermes World Agency SASU (1)
8 Rue Euler
75008 Paris, France
Tel.: (33) 1 40 70 50 83
Fax: (33) 1 40 70 50 70
Credit Insurance Services
S.I.C.: 6331
N.A.I.C.S.: 524126

Euler SFAC Asset Management (1)
1 Rue Euler
75008 Paris, France
Tel.: (33) 1 40 70 50 50
Asset Management Services
S.I.C.: 6282
N.A.I.C.S.: 523920

Euro Garantie AG (1)
Bannholzstrasse 12
8608 Bubikon, Switzerland
Tel.: (41) 848 488 228
Fax: (41) 848 488 229
E-Mail: info@eurogarantie.ch
General Insurance Services
S.I.C.: 6411
N.A.I.C.S.: 524210

FAI Allianz Ltd. (1)
L 14 2 Market St
Sydney, NSW, 2000, Australia
Tel.: (61) 1300368764
General Insurance Services
S.I.C.: 6411
N.A.I.C.S.: 524210

Global Transport & Automotive Insurance Solutions Pty Limited (1)
Level 6 55 Chandos Street
St Leonards, Sydney, NSW, 2065, Australia
Tel.: (61) 2 9966 8820
Fax: (61) 2 9966 8840
Web Site: www.gtins.com.au
Automobile Insurance Services
S.I.C.: 6331
N.A.I.C.S.: 524126

Havelaar et Van Stolk B.V. (1)
Coolsingel 139
3012 AG Rotterdam, Netherlands
Tel.: (31) 10 281 67 77
Fax: (31) 10 281 67 99
E-Mail: info@havelaar.com
Web Site: www.havelaar.com
General Insurance Services
S.I.C.: 6411
N.A.I.C.S.: 524210

HELVIASS Verzekeringen B.V. (1)
Coolsingel 139
3012 AG Rotterdam, Netherlands
Tel.: (31) 20 5618560
Fax: (31) 20 5618561
E-Mail: info@helviass.nl
Web Site: www.helviass.nl
General Insurance Services
S.I.C.: 6411
N.A.I.C.S.: 524298

Home & Legacy Insurance Services Limited (1)
500 Avebury Boulevard Lower Ground Floor
Milton Keynes, Buckinghamshire, MK9 2LA, United Kingdom
Tel.: (44) 20 3118 7777
Web Site: www.homeandlegacy.co.uk
General Insurance Services
S.I.C.: 6411
N.A.I.C.S.: 524210
Adrian Ewington, *(Product Mgr-Underwriting)*

Immovalor Gestion S.A. (1)
B218 87 Rue De Richelieu
75113 Paris, France
Tel.: (33) 1 55 27 17 00
Fax: (33) 1 55 27 17 10
Web Site: www.immovalor.fr
Asset Management Services
S.I.C.: 6282
N.A.I.C.S.: 523920

International Film Guarantors Ltd. (1)
19 Margaret Street
London, W1W 8RR, United Kingdom
Tel.: (44) 20 7636 8855
Fax: (44) 20 7323 9356
E-Mail: ukinfo@ifgbonds.co.uk
Web Site: www.ifgbonds.com
Media Insurance Services
S.I.C.: 6411
N.A.I.C.S.: 524298
Luke Randolph *(Mng Dir)*

Ken Tame & Associates Pty Ltd (1)
Shop 15 79-83 High St 79 High St
Kew, Melbourne, VIC, 3101, Australia
Tel.: (61) 3 9853 5555
Web Site: www.kentame.com.au
Insurance Brokerage Services
S.I.C.: 6411
N.A.I.C.S.: 524210

Lloyd Adriatico S.p.A. (1)
Largo Ugo Irneri 1
34123 Trieste, Italy (100%)
Tel.: (39) 0407781111
Fax: (39) 0407781311
E-Mail: info@allianzlloydadriatico.it
Web Site: www.allianzlloydadriatico.it
S.I.C.: 6399
N.A.I.C.S.: 524128

Magdeburger Sigorta A.S. (1)
Baglarbasi Kisikli Cad No 13 Altunizade
34662 Istanbul, Turkey
Tel.: (90) 216 556 66 66
Fax: (90) 216 556 67 77
Web Site: www.magdeburger.com.tr
General Insurance Services
S.I.C.: 6411
N.A.I.C.S.: 524210

Managed Insurance Operations B.V. (1)
Coolsingel 139
3012 AG Rotterdam, Netherlands
Tel.: (31) 88 577 32 00
Fax: (31) 88 577 32 01
E-Mail: info@mio-insurance.nl
Web Site: www.mio-insurance.nl
General Insurance Services
S.I.C.: 6411
N.A.I.C.S.: 524210

Medexpress JSIC (1)
Gorokhovaya St 14/26
Saint Petersburg, 191186, Russia
Tel.: (7) 812 4949411
Fax: (7) 812 4949410
Web Site: www.medexpress.ru
Financial Management Services
S.I.C.: 6211
N.A.I.C.S.: 523999

Menzis (1)
Westblaak 67
NL 3600 AB Rotterdam, Netherlands
Tel.: (31) 102706300
Fax: (31) 104138168
Web Site: www.menzis.nl
S.I.C.: 6399
N.A.I.C.S.: 524128

Mondial Assistance Agent de Asigurare SRL (1)
Calea Floreasca Nr 169 Sector 1
Bucharest, 014459, Romania
Tel.: (40) 21 312 22 36
Fax: (40) 21 312 22 38
E-Mail: office.ro@mondial-assistance.at
Web Site: www.mondial-assistance.ro
General Insurance Services

S.I.C.: 6411
N.A.I.C.S.: 524210

Mondial Assistance Asia Pacific Ltd. (1)
143 Cecil Street 13-01 GB Building
Singapore, 069542, Singapore
Tel.: (65) 6535 3585
Fax: (65) 6535 5052
E-Mail: asiapacific@mondial-assistance.com
Web Site: www.mondial-assistance-asiapacific.com
Emp.: 35
Travel Insurance & Assistance Services
S.I.C.: 6411
N.A.I.C.S.: 524298
Mathew Sturgess *(COO)*

Mondial Assistance/Auto Assist Co., Ltd. (1)
29th Floor Grand Amarin Tower 1550 New Petchaburi Road
Makasan Rajathevi, Bangkok, 10400, Thailand
Tel.: (66) 2 305 8555
Fax: (66) 2 305 8556
E-Mail: contact@mondial-assistance-thailand.com
Web Site: www.autoassist.co.th
Travel Insurance & Assistance Services
S.I.C.: 6411
N.A.I.C.S.: 524298

Mondial Assistance Belgium (1)
Rue des Hirondelles 2
1000 Brussels, Belgium
Tel.: (32) 2 2906411
Fax: (32) 2 2906419
E-Mail: tcc@mondial-assistance.be
Web Site: www.mondial-assistance.be
Emp.: 100
Travel Insurance & Medical Assistance Services
S.I.C.: 6411
N.A.I.C.S.: 524298
Frederic Hersleven *(Acct Mgr)*

Mondial Assistance Brazil (1)
Alameda Santos 745 2 Andar - Cj 22
01419-001 Sao Paulo, Brazil
Tel.: (55) 11 30652599
Fax: (55) 11 30652580
Web Site: www.mondial-assistance.com.br
Travel Insurance Services
S.I.C.: 6399
N.A.I.C.S.: 524128

Mondial Assistance France (1)
54 Rue De Londres
75008 Paris, France
Tel.: (33) 1 53 05 86 00
E-Mail: service.conseil.client@mondial-assistance.fr
Travel Insurance Services
S.I.C.: 6399
N.A.I.C.S.: 524128
Michael Rouviere, *(Project Mgr)*

MONDIAL ASSISTANCE GmbH (1)
Pottendorfer Strasse 25-27
1120 Vienna, Austria
Tel.: (43) 1 52503 0
Fax: (43) 1 52503 999
E-Mail: service.at@allianz-assistance.at
Web Site: www.allianz-assistance.at
General Insurance Services
S.I.C.: 6411
N.A.I.C.S.: 524298

Mondial Assistance Greece (1)
10 Premetis St
173 42 Athens, Greece
Tel.: (30) 210 99 88 100
Fax: (30) 210 99 43 053
E-Mail: communication@mondial-assistance.gr
Web Site: www.mondial-assistance.gr
Travel Insurance Services
S.I.C.: 6411
N.A.I.C.S.: 524298

MONDIAL ASSISTANCE IRELAND LIMITED (1)
2 Bracken Court Bracken Road
Sandyford, Dublin, Ireland
Tel.: (353) 1 6373667
Fax: (353) 1 6373649
E-Mail: insurance@mondial-assistance.ie
Web Site: www.mondial-assistance.ie
Emp.: 35
Travel Insurance Services
S.I.C.: 6411
N.A.I.C.S.: 524298
Roland Hesse *(Gen Mgr)*

Mondial Assistance OOO (1)
Timiryazevskaya Str 1
Moscow, 127422, Russia
Tel.: (7) 495 661 47 22
Fax: (7) 495 661 47 21
E-Mail: contactus@mondial-assistance.ru
Web Site: www.mondial-assistance.ru
Travel Insurance Services
S.I.C.: 6411
N.A.I.C.S.: 524298

Mondial Assistance Reunion S.A. (1)
11 rue Roland Garros Residence Les Charmilles
Saint Denis, France
Tel.: (33) 262 90 99 95
Fax: (33) 262 90 99 93
Web Site: www.mondial-assistance.re
General Insurance Services
S.I.C.: 6411
N.A.I.C.S.: 524298

Mondial Assistance SARL (1)
Timiryazevskaya St 1
Moscow, 127422, Russia
Tel.: (7) 495 6614722
Fax: (7) 495 6614721
E-Mail: contactus@mondial-assistance.ru
Web Site: www.mondial-assistance.ru
General Insurance Services
S.I.C.: 6411
N.A.I.C.S.: 524210

Mondial Assistance Sigorta Aracilik Hizmetleri Limited Sirketi, LS (1)
Unsal Carsi K 6/215 1 Halaskargazi Caddesi
Istanbul, Turkey
Tel.: (90) 2164743576
Insurance Management Services
S.I.C.: 6411
N.A.I.C.S.: 524298
Rasim Topuz *(Gen Mgr)*

Mondial Assistance Sp. z o.o. (1)
Ul Domaniewska 50B
02-672 Warsaw, Poland
Tel.: (48) 22 522 25 00
Fax: (48) 22 522 28 01
Web Site: www.mondial-assistance.pl
Travel Insurance Services
S.I.C.: 6411
N.A.I.C.S.: 524298
Piotl Ruszowski *(Mgr-Mktg)*

Mondial Assistance s.r.o (1)
Jankovcova 1596/14b
170 00 Prague, Czech Republic
Tel.: (420) 283 002 711
Fax: (420) 283 002 701
E-Mail: info@mondial-assistance.cz
Web Site: www.mondial-assistance.cz
Travel Insurance & Medical Assistance Services
S.I.C.: 6411
N.A.I.C.S.: 524298
Miroslav Dolezal *(Gen Mgr)*

Mondial Assistance Turkey (1)
Buyukdere C Enka Binasi 108 Kat 10 Esentepe
Istanbul, 34394, Turkey
Tel.: (90) 212 3374337
Fax: (90) 212 3374338
E-Mail: info@mondial-assistance.com.tr
Web Site: www.mondial-assistance.com.tr
Travel & Medical Assistance Services
S.I.C.: 9441
N.A.I.C.S.: 923130

Mondial Service- Belgium S.A. (1)
Rue Des Hirondelles 2
1000 Brussels, Belgium
Tel.: (32) 2 2906411
Fax: (32) 2 2906419
Financial Management Services
S.I.C.: 6211
N.A.I.C.S.: 523999

Mondial Service Italia S.r.l (1)
Via Ampere Andrea Maria 30
20131 Milan, Italy
Tel.: (39) 02 236951
Fax: (39) 02 266 24 822
Insurance Management Services
S.I.C.: 6411
N.A.I.C.S.: 524298

Mondial Services (India) Pvt. Ltd. (1)
1st Floor DLF Square M-Block - Jacaranda Marg Phase-II
Gurgaon, Haryana, 122 002, India
Tel.: (91) 124 4343800
Fax: (91) 124 4343900
E-Mail: contact@mondial-assistance.in
Web Site: www.allianz.com
General Insurance Services
S.I.C.: 6411
N.A.I.C.S.: 524298

Mondial Servicios S.A. de C.V. (1)
Boulevard Adolfo Lopez Mateos 379 Col Atlamaya
01760 Mexico, Mexico
Tel.: (52) 5553773800
Fax: (52) 5537738200
Emp.: 70
Insurance Management Services
S.I.C.: 6411
N.A.I.C.S.: 524298
Hugo Esquivel *(Branch Mgr)*

The Navakij Insurance Co., Ltd. (1)
18th Fl S 26th Fl Sathorn Nakorn Bldg
Sathorn Thani Complex
100 North Sathorn Rd, Bangkok, 10500, Thailand (100%)
Tel.: (66) 26367900
Telex: 82 940 poonpol th
Fax: (66) 22372677
Web Site: www.navakij.co.th
Sales Range: $1-9.9 Million
S.I.C.: 6399
N.A.I.C.S.: 524128
Tanjkeera Wong *(Chm-Exec Bd)*
Suchin Wanglee *(Pres)*

NEM Insurance Ireland Limited (1)
South Leinster Street 7-9
Dublin, Ireland
Tel.: (353) 1 702 30 00
Fax: (353) 1 76 56 25
General Insurance Services
S.I.C.: 6411
N.A.I.C.S.: 524210

Neoasistencia Manoteras S.L. (1)
Av Las Americas 4
28823 Coslada, Spain
Tel.: (34) 916745002
Financial Management Services
S.I.C.: 6211
N.A.I.C.S.: 523999

NEXtCARE Holding WLL (1)
Office 63 Building 485 Euro Tower Road 1010
PO Box 18442
Seef District 410, Manama, Bahrain
Tel.: (973) 17382721
Fax: (973) 17382082
E-Mail: nextcare@nextcare.ae
Web Site: www.nextcarehealth.com
Investment Management Services
S.I.C.: 6282
N.A.I.C.S.: 523920
Ida Luka-Lognone *(Chm & CEO)*

Non-U.S. Subsidiary:

NEXtCARE Egypt LLC (2)
17 Al Ahram Street Building B Floor 7 Roxy Heliopolis
Cairo, Egypt
Tel.: (20) 2 24182564
Fax: (20) 2 22908220
E-Mail: nextcare@nextcare.com.eg
Web Site: www.nextcarehealth.com
Insurance Management Services
S.I.C.: 6411
N.A.I.C.S.: 524298
Luay Jildeh *(Gen Mgr)*

NEXtCARE Lebanon SAL (1)
Saifi Area Pasteur Street Pasteur 40 Building
Beirut, Lebanon
Tel.: (961) 1 577200
Fax: (961) 1 577205
E-Mail: nextcare@nextcare.com.lb
Web Site: www.nextcarehealth.com
Health Insurance Services
S.I.C.: 6324
N.A.I.C.S.: 524114
Marcel Daher *(Gen Mgr)*

NEXtCARE UAE, AGHS LLC (1)
Business Avenue Building 10th Floor
Sheikh Rashid Road
PO Box 80864
Deira, Dubai, United Arab Emirates
Tel.: (971) 4 2095200
Fax: (971) 4 2095302
E-Mail: nextcare@nextcare.ae
Health Insurance Services
S.I.C.: 6324
N.A.I.C.S.: 524114
Christian Gregorowicz *(CEO)*
Bruce Trowbridge *(CFO)*
Jennifer Nuelle-Dimoulas *(COO)*

Nicholas-Applegate Capital Management (1)
Level 29 2 Chifley Square
Sydney, NSW, 2000, Australia
Tel.: (61) 2 93752450
Investment Management Services
S.I.C.: 6211
N.A.I.C.S.: 523999

OJSC ROSNO (1)
Ozerkovskaya Nab 30
115184 Moscow, Russia (97%)
Tel.: (7) 4952323333
Fax: (7) 4952320014
E-Mail: info@allianz.ru
Web Site: www.allianz.com
Sales Range: $650-699.9 Million
Emp.: 6,000
Insurance Services
S.I.C.: 6411
N.A.I.C.S.: 524298
Hannes Shariputra Chopra *(Chm & CEO)*
Dmitry Vladimirovich Popov *(First Deputy CEO & COO)*
Vassily Ivanovich Grishutkin *(Deputy CEO & Head-Central & Far Eastern Directorates)*
Elena Yurievna Belousenko *(Deputy CEO & Head-Intermediary Sls Dept)*
Fahraddin Ragim-ogly Ragimov *(Deputy CEO & Dir-Sls)*
Olga Borisovna Krymova *(Deputy CEO & CFO)*
Denis Igorevich Kuzavlev *(Deputy CEO & Head-Corp Sls Dept)*
Valentina Alexandrovna Rakitina *(Co-Deputy CEO & Head-Directorate-Moscow Reg)*
Elnur Gamidovich Suleymanov *(Deputy CEO & Head-Agency Sls Dept)*

Subsidiaries:

Allianz ROSNO Asset Management (2)
Paveletskaya Square 2 Building 1
115054 Moscow, Russia
Tel.: (7) 4957373773
Fax: (7) 4952313123
E-Mail: info@allianzinvest.ru
Web Site: www.allianzinvest.ru
Sales Range: $150-199.9 Million
Emp.: 50
Asset Management Services
S.I.C.: 6799
N.A.I.C.S.: 523920

Allianz ROSNO Life (2)
Ozerkovskaya Nab 30
Moscow, 115184, Russia
Tel.: (7) 4952323333
Fax: (7) 4952320014
E-Mail: rudinskaya@rosno.ru
Web Site: www.allianzrosnolife.ru
Life Insurance Services
S.I.C.: 6311
N.A.I.C.S.: 524113
Nikolai Timofeev *(Deputy CEO & Head-Partner Sls Channel)*

Non-U.S. Subsidiary:

Allianz Ukraine SLC (2)
Kreschatik str 42
01032 Kiev, Ukraine
Tel.: (380) 444590058
Fax: (380) 444590057
E-Mail: office@allianz.ua
Web Site: www.allianz.ua
Emp.: 200
Insurance Services
S.I.C.: 6411
N.A.I.C.S.: 524298

Allianz SE—(Continued)

Harry Andreasian *(CEO)*

Ontario Limited (1)
834 Yonge St
Toronto, ON, M4W 2H1, Canada
Tel.: (416) 901-6863
Financial Management Services
S.I.C.: 6211
N.A.I.C.S.: 523999

OY Selecta AB (1)
Konalantie 47 B
00390 Helsinki, Finland
Tel.: (358) 20 721 0300
Fax: (358) 20 721 0321
E-Mail: info@fi.selecta.com
Web Site: www.selecta.com
Coffee Machine Mfr
S.I.C.: 3556
N.A.I.C.S.: 333241

Pet Plan Ltd. (1)
Great West House GW2 Great West Road
Brentford, Middlesex, TW8 9DX, United Kingdom
Tel.: (44) 845 077 1934
E-Mail: info@petplan.co.uk
Web Site: www.petplan.co.uk
Pet Insurance Services
S.I.C.: 6399
N.A.I.C.S.: 524128
Carl Stephens *(Mgr-Comm)*

PIMCO Asia Ltd. (1)
24th Floor Units 2402 2403 & 2405 Nine Queen's Road
Central, China (Hong Kong)
Tel.: (852) 3650 7700
Fax: (852) 3650 7900
Web Site: www.pimco.com
Investment Management Services
S.I.C.: 6211
N.A.I.C.S.: 523999

PIMCO Global Advisors (Ireland) Ltd. (1)
Styne House Upper Hatch Street
Dublin, Ireland
Tel.: (353) 1475 2211
Mutual Fund Management Services
S.I.C.: 6282
N.A.I.C.S.: 523920

Popular Gestion SGIIC, S.A. (1)
Labastida 11
28034 Madrid, Spain
Tel.: (34) 915208200
Fax: (34) 915779641
Investment Management Services
S.I.C.: 6211
N.A.I.C.S.: 523999

Progress-Garant Insurance Company OJSC (1)
Seleznevskaya St 32
Moscow, 127473, Russia
Tel.: (7) 495 7816666
Fax: (7) 495 7819399
E-Mail: info@progress.ru
General Insurance Services
S.I.C.: 6411
N.A.I.C.S.: 524210

Progress (1)
61 Str 2 Ul Lesnaya
Moscow, Russia
Tel.: (7) 4959805095
General Insurance Services
S.I.C.: 6411
N.A.I.C.S.: 524210

P.T. Asuransi Allianz Life Indonesia (1)
Summitmas II 19th Fl
Jl Jend Sudirman Kav 61 62, 12190
Jakarta, Indonesia (100%)
Tel.: (62) 2152998888
Fax: (62) 2130003400
E-Mail: life@allianz.co.id
Web Site: www.allianz.co.id
Emp.: 400
Insurance Provider
S.I.C.: 6399
N.A.I.C.S.: 524128

P.T. Asuransi Allianz Utama Indonesia (1)
Summitmas II 9th Fl Jl Jend Sudirman Kav 61 62
Jakarta, 12190, Indonesia (100%)
Tel.: (62) 212522470
Telex: 60 725 azindo ia
Fax: (62) 2 1252 3246
E-Mail: general@allianz.co.id
Web Site: www.allianz.co.id
Emp.: 200
Insurance Provider
S.I.C.: 6399
N.A.I.C.S.: 524128

PT manroland Indonesia (1)
Management Building 2nd Floor Jl Buncit Raya Kav 100
Jakarta, 12510, Indonesia
Tel.: (62) 2179199818
Web Site: www.manroland-sheetfed.com
Printing Machinery Mfr
S.I.C.: 3555
N.A.I.C.S.: 333244

PTE Allianz Polska SA (1)
ul Rodziny Hiszpanskich 1
02-685 Warsaw, Poland
Tel.: (48) 225674000
Fax: (48) 225674028
Web Site: www.allianz.com
Pension Fund Services
S.I.C.: 6371
N.A.I.C.S.: 525110

Quality 1 AG (1)
Bannholzstrasse 12
8608 Bubikon, Switzerland
Tel.: (41) 55 254 30 00
Fax: (41) 55 254 30 05
E-Mail: info@quality1.ch
Web Site: www.quality1.ch
General Insurance Services
S.I.C.: 6411
N.A.I.C.S.: 524210

RB Fiduciaria S.p.A (1)
Piazzale Lodi N 3
20137 Milan, Italy
Tel.: (39) 02 72128236
Fax: (39) 02 72168109
Investment Management Services
S.I.C.: 6211
N.A.I.C.S.: 523999

RCM Asia Pacific Ltd. (1)
27/F ICBC Tower 3 Garden Road
Central, China (Hong Kong)
Tel.: (852) 2238 8888
Fax: (852) 2877 2533
Web Site: www.rcm.com.hk/retirement
Emp.: 300
Investment Management Services
S.I.C.: 6211
N.A.I.C.S.: 523999

RCM (UK) Ltd. (1)
155 Bishopsgate
London, EC2M 3AD, United Kingdom
Tel.: (44) 2078 599 000
Fax: (44) 2076 383 508
Web Site: www.rcm.co.uk
Investment Management Services
S.I.C.: 6211
N.A.I.C.S.: 523999

RHEA, S.A. (1)
Rue Beaumont 11
Luxembourg, 1219, Luxembourg
Tel.: (352) 22 34 22 31
Fax: (352) 47 02 51
Financial Management Services
S.I.C.: 6211
N.A.I.C.S.: 523999

Risikomanagement und Softwareentwicklung GmbH (1)
Hietzinger Kai 101-105
1130 Vienna, Austria
Tel.: (43) 1 878 072 191
Fax: (43) 1 878 072 180
Information Technology Consulting Services
S.I.C.: 7373
N.A.I.C.S.: 541512

Riunione Adriatica di Sicurta S.p.A. (1)
Corso Italia 23
20122 Milan, Italy (100%)
Tel.: (39) 0272161
Telex: 320065 RAS DG I
Fax: (39) 0272165011
E Mail: info@rasnet.it
Web Site: www.ras.it
Emp.: 3,527
Insurance, Property & Financial Services
S.I.C.: 6331
N.A.I.C.S.: 524126

Subsidiaries:

Allianz Subalpina S.p.A. (2)
Via Alfieri 22
I 10122 Turin, Italy (97.9%)
Tel.: (39) 0001151611
Fax: (39) 011 516 1470
Web Site: www.allianzsubalpina.it
Fire, Theft, Hail, Bond & Third-Party Bail Insurance Services
S.I.C.: 6399
N.A.I.C.S.: 524128

Genialloyd SpA (2)
Viale Mansa 2
20127 Milan, Italy (99.9%)
Tel.: (39) 0228351
Fax: (39) 0228352835
E-Mail: webmaster@genialloyd.it
Web Site: www.genialloyd.it
Emp.: 500
Insurance Services
S.I.C.: 6411
N.A.I.C.S.: 524298

Investitori Sgr S.P.A. (2)
Milano Corso Italia 23
20122 Milan, Italy
Tel.: (39) 0272162500
Fax: (39) 0272162750
E-Mail: alessandra.nimour@investitori.it
Web Site: www.investitori.it
Private Banking Services
S.I.C.: 6211
N.A.I.C.S.: 523999

RAS Asset Management SGR S.p.A. (2)
Piazza Velasca 7/9
20122 Milan, Italy
Tel.: (39) 02 802001
Asset Management Services
S.I.C.: 6726
N.A.I.C.S.: 525990

RAS Tutela Giudiziaria S.p.A. (2)
Corso Italia 23
I 20122 Milan, Italy (100%)
Tel.: (39) 02 582801
Fax: (39) 02 58 30 87 45
Web Site: www.allianzras.it
Insurance Provider
S.I.C.: 6399
N.A.I.C.S.: 524128

ROSNO Insurance Company OJSC (1)
Ozerkovskaya Nab 30
Moscow, 115184, Russia
Tel.: (7) 495 2323333
Fax: (7) 495 2320014
E-Mail: info@rosno.ru
General Insurance Services
S.I.C.: 6411
N.A.I.C.S.: 524210

Rosno MS (1)
Ozerkovskaya D 30
115184 Moscow, Russia
Tel.: (7) 495 956 21 05
E-Mail:
Medical Insurance Services
S.I.C.: 6324
N.A.I.C.S.: 524114
Leonid A. Melamed *(Chm)*

SA CARENE ASSURANCE (1)
53 Rue d'Hauteville
Paris, 75010, France
Tel.: (33) 1 42 46 52 52
Fax: (33) 1 42 46 31 19
General Insurance Services
S.I.C.: 6411
N.A.I.C.S.: 524210

Saint-Barth Assurances S.a r.l. (1)
2 Rue Roi Oscar II
97133 Saint Barthelemy-d'Anjou, France
Tel.: (33) 8 99 54 42 84
Fax: (33) 5 90 27 62 05
General Insurance Services
S.I.C.: 6411
N.A.I.C.S.: 524210

Selecta A/S (1)
Krondalvej 9C
2610 Rodovre, Denmark
Tel.: (45) 44 50 34 50
E-Mail: info@dk.selecta.com
Web Site: www.selecta.dk
Vending Machine Distr
S.I.C.: 5046
N.A.I.C.S.: 423440

Selecta Ag (1)
Industrie Neuhof 78
3422 Kirchberg, Switzerland
Tel.: (41) 844 848 844
Fax: (41) 844 808 844
E-Mail: info@ch.selecta.com
Web Site: www.selecta.ch
Vending Machine Distr
S.I.C.: 5046
N.A.I.C.S.: 423440

Selecta AS (1)
Kabelgaten 39
Postboks 67
0508 Oslo, Norway
Tel.: (47) 98 28 50 50
E-Mail: info@no.selecta.com
Web Site: www.selecta.no
Coffee Maker Mfr
S.I.C.: 3556
N.A.I.C.S.: 333241
Claus Magelssen *(Country Mgr)*

Selecta Betriebsverpflegungs GmbH (1)
Iz No-Sud Strasse 16 Objekt 70/3
2355 Wiener Neudorf, Austria
Tel.: (43) 2236 660 500 0
Fax: (43) 2236 660 500 80
E-Mail: info@at.selecta.com
Web Site: www.selecta.at
Vending Machine Distr
S.I.C.: 5046
N.A.I.C.S.: 423440

Selecta Eesti Osauhing (1)
Tookoja 1
11313 Tallinn, Estonia
Tel.: (372) 6363895
E-Mail: info@ee.selecta.com
Web Site: www.selecta.ee
Coffee Machine Mfr
S.I.C.: 3556
N.A.I.C.S.: 333241

Selecta Group B.V. (1)
Keizersgracht 484
1017 EH Amsterdam, Netherlands
Tel.: (31) 205569715
Investment Management Services
S.I.C.: 6211
N.A.I.C.S.: 523999

Selecta Holding AB (1)
Arstaagsvagen 13
Stockholm, 117 60, Sweden
Tel.: (46) 8 57 85 85 85
Investment Management Services
S.I.C.: 6211
N.A.I.C.S.: 523999

Selecta Holding Ltd. (1)
Unit 2 Cartel Business Centre Wade Road
Basingstoke, Hampshire, RG24 8FW, United Kingdom
Tel.: (44) 1256340600
Investment Management Services
S.I.C.: 6211
N.A.I.C.S.: 523999

Selecta Hungary Automatauzemelteto KFT (1)
Fehervari Ut 84/A
Budapest, Hungary
Tel.: (36) 13829091
Vending Machine Distr
S.I.C.: 5046
N.A.I.C.S.: 423440

Selecta Infratechniek B.V. (1)
Pittsburghstraat 57
3047 BL Rotterdam, Netherlands
Tel.: (31) 10 415 40 75
Fax: (31) 10 415 39 95
E-Mail: info@selectaholding.com
Web Site: www.selectaholding.com
Pipeline Construction Engineering Services
S.I.C.: 1629
N.A.I.C.S.: 237120

Selecta Management AG (1)
Hinterbergstrasse 20
6330 Cham, Switzerland

Tel.: (41) 41 727 72 72
Fax: (41) 41 727 72 96
E-Mail: info@selecta.com
Web Site: www.selecta.com
Coffee Maker Mfr
S.I.C.: 3556
N.A.I.C.S.: 333241

Selecta Olland B.V. (1)
Koeweistraat 10
4181 CD Waardenburg, Netherlands
Tel.: (31) 41865 78 00
Emp.: 200
Vending Machine Mfr
S.I.C.: 3589
N.A.I.C.S.: 333318
N. Bron *(Mgr-Mktg)*

Selecta Purchasing AG (1)
Hinterbergstrasse 20
6312 Steinhausen, Switzerland
Tel.: (41) 41 727 72 72
Vending Machine Distr
S.I.C.: 5046
N.A.I.C.S.: 423440

Selecta S.A. (1)
18 Rue Goubet
Paris, 75019, France
Tel.: (33) 144845960
Web Site: www.selecta.fr
Financial Management Services
S.I.C.: 6211
N.A.I.C.S.: 523999

Selecta TMP AG (1)
Hinterbergstrasse 20
Cham, 6330, Switzerland
Tel.: (41) 41 7277272
Fax: (41) 41 7277296
Vending Machine Distr
S.I.C.: 5046
N.A.I.C.S.: 423440

Selecta UK Ltd. (1)
Stanley House Park Lane Castle Vale
Birmingham, B35 6LJ, United Kingdom
Tel.: (44) 844 7360 209
E-Mail: sales@uk.selecta.com
Web Site: www.selecta.co.uk
Vending Machine Operator
S.I.C.: 5962
N.A.I.C.S.: 454210
Andy E. Mee *(Mng Dir)*

Siac Services Srl (1)
Via Friuli 33
Dalmine, 24044, Italy
Tel.: (39) 035565421
Fax: (39) 035563685
General Insurance Services
S.I.C.: 6411
N.A.I.C.S.: 524210

SIFCOM Assurances (1)
BP 8484
Abidjan, Cote d'Ivoire
Tel.: (225) 21757575
General Insurance Services
S.I.C.: 6411
N.A.I.C.S.: 524210

Sistemi Informativi Allianz S.p.c.A. (1)
Corso Italia 23
Milan, Italy
Tel.: (39) 02 7216 1
Information Technology Consulting Services
S.I.C.: 7373
N.A.I.C.S.: 541512

SOCIEDAD MUNDIAL DE ASISTENCIA S.A. (1)
Edificio Delta Norte 3 Avenida de Manoteras 46 Bis
Madrid, 28050, Spain
Tel.: (34) 91 325 54 40
Fax: (34) 91 325 54 43
General Insurance Services
S.I.C.: 6411
N.A.I.C.S.: 524298

Societa Agricola San Felice S.p.A. (1)
Localita San Felice
53019 Castelnuovo Berardenga, Italy
Tel.: (39) 0577 399 203
Fax: (39) 0577 359 223
E-Mail: info@agricolasanfelice.it
Web Site: www.agricolasanfelice.it
Wine Mfr
S.I.C.: 2084
N.A.I.C.S.: 312130
Alessandro Marchionne, *(Gen Mgr)*

Societe Tunisienne d'Assurances et de Reassurances (1)
Square de l Avenue de Paris 1
1002 Tunis, Tunisia
Tel.: (216) 71256800
Telex: 13420 staras tn
Fax: (216) 71340835
E-Mail: star@star.com.tn
Web Site: www.star.com.tn
Emp.: 700
Insurance Provider
S.I.C.: 6399
N.A.I.C.S.: 524128
Lassaad Zarrouk *(Chm)*

TFI Allianz Polska (1)
Ul Rodziny Hiszpanskich 1
02-685 Warsaw, Poland
Tel.: (48) 225674000
Fax: (48) 225674040
E-Mail: info@allianzpolska.pl
Web Site: www.allianzpolska.pl
Insurance & Pension Services
S.I.C.: 6411
N.A.I.C.S.: 524298

Top Versicherungs-Vermittler Service GmbH (1)
Hietzinger Kai 101-105
1130 Vienna, Austria
Tel.: (43) 1 909 44 44
Fax: (43) 1 909 44 44 40286
E-Mail: tvvs.office@tvvs.at
Web Site: www.tvvs.at
Insurance Brokerage Services
S.I.C.: 6411
N.A.I.C.S.: 524210

Top Versicherungsservice GmbH (1)
Hietzinger Kai 101-105
1130 Vienna, Austria
Tel.: (43) 5 9009 0
Fax: (43) 5 9009 71000
E-Mail: service@allianz.at
General Insurance Services
S.I.C.: 6411
N.A.I.C.S.: 524210

Top Vorsorge-Management GmbH (1)
Hietzinger Kai 101-105
Vienna, 1130, Austria
Tel.: (43) 1 54 622 567
Financial Management Services
S.I.C.: 6211
N.A.I.C.S.: 523999

Towarzystwo Ubezpieczen Euler Hermes S.A. (1)
Domaniewska 50B Str
02-672 Warsaw, Poland
Tel.: (48) 22 385 46 55
Fax: (48) 22 385 48 80
E-Mail: info@eulerhermes.pl
General Insurance Services
S.I.C.: 6411
N.A.I.C.S.: 524210

Trafalgar Insurance Public Limited Company (1)
57 Ladymead
Guildford, Surrey, GU1 1DB, United Kingdom
Tel.: (44) 1483 568161
Fax: (44) 1483 300952
General Insurance Services
S.I.C.: 6411
N.A.I.C.S.: 524210

TU Allianz Polska SA (1)
Ul Rodziny Hiszpanskich 1
02-685 Warsaw, Poland
Tel.: (48) 225674000
Fax: (48) 225674040
Web Site: www.allianz.pl/tu_allianz_polska_sa_en,5109.html
Insurance & Financial Services
S.I.C.: 6411
N.A.I.C.S.: 524298

TU Allianz Zycie Polska SA (1)
Ul Rodziny Hiszpanskich 1
02-685 Warsaw, Poland
Tel.: (48) 225674000
Fax: (48) 225674040
Web Site: www.allianz.pl/Allianz/contact/contactus_en.jsp
Insurance & Financial Services
S.I.C.: 6411
N.A.I.C.S.: 524298

TUiR Allianz Polska S.A (1)
ul Rodziny Hiszpanskich 1
02-685 Warsaw, Poland
Tel.: (48) 22 567 4000
Fax: (48) 22 567 4028
Life Insurance Services
S.I.C.: 6311
N.A.I.C.S.: 524113

UAB Selecta (1)
Mindaugo G 42
Vilnius, 03210, Lithuania
Tel.: (370) 5 240 43 43
Fax: (370) 5 240 55 10
E-Mail: info@lt.selecta.com
Web Site: www.selecta.lt
Coffee Machine Mfr
S.I.C.: 3556
N.A.I.C.S.: 333241

Vendcare Services Ltd. (1)
Dudley St
PO Box 6
Bilston, WV14 0JF, United Kingdom
Tel.: (44) 121 313 2442
Vending Machine Repair & Maintance
S.I.C.: 7699
N.A.I.C.S.: 811310

VertBois S.a r.l. (1)
2 Avenue Charles De Gaulle
1653 Luxembourg, Luxembourg
Tel.: (352) 26 43 20 18
Real Estate Management Services
S.I.C.: 6531
N.A.I.C.S.: 531390

Villa La Pagliaia S.r.l. (1)
Loc San Felice
53019 Castelnuovo Berardenga, Italy
Tel.: (39) 0577 3991
Fax: (39) 0577 359223
Wine Mfr
S.I.C.: 2084
N.A.I.C.S.: 312130

Willemsbrug B.V. (1)
Boterdiep 11
3077 AW Rotterdam, Netherlands
Tel.: (31) 10 4790000
Fax: (31) 10 4790128
Financial Management Services
S.I.C.: 6211
N.A.I.C.S.: 523999

World Access Europe Ltd. (1)
Mondial House 102 George Street
Croydon, CR9 6HD, United Kingdom
Tel.: (44) 20 8840 0700
Investment Management Services
S.I.C.: 6211
N.A.I.C.S.: 523999

Yapi Kredi Sigorta A.S. (1)
Yapi Kredi Plaza A Blok
Buyukdere Cad Levent
34330 Istanbul, Turkey (93.9%)
Tel.: (90) 2123360606
Fax: (90) 2123360808
E-Mail: yksigorta@yksigorta.com.tr
Web Site: www.yksigorta.com.tr
Sales Range: $10-24.9 Million
Property & Casualty Insurance Products & Services
S.I.C.: 6351
N.A.I.C.S.: 524126

Subsidiary:

Yapi Kredi Emeklilik A.S. (2)
Yapi Kredi Plaza A Blok Buyukdere Cd Levent
34330 Istanbul, Turkey TR
Tel.: (90) 2123367600
Web Site: www.yapikrediemeklilik.com
Life Insurance & Pension Products & Services
S.I.C.: 6311
N.A.I.C.S.: 524113

Non-U.S. Joint Ventures:

Allianz C.P. General Insurance Co., Ltd. (1)
CP Twr 19 Fl 313 Silom Rd Bangrak
Bangkok, 10500, Thailand
Tel.: (66) 26389000
Fax: (66) 26389020
E-Mail: contact@allianzcp.com
Web Site: www.allianzcp.com
Emp.: 100
Insurance Services; Owned by Allianz AG & by Charoen Pokphang Group
S.I.C.: 6411
N.A.I.C.S.: 524298
Pakit Iamopus *(Pres & CEO)*
Ampai Bumrungsaksilp *(CFO)*

Ayudhya Allianz C.P. Life Pcl. (1)
Ground Floor Ploenchit Tower
898 Ploenchit Road, Bangkok, 10330, Thailand TH
Tel.: (66) 23057000
Fax: (66) 23057999
E-Mail: customercare@aacp.co.th
Web Site: www.aacp.co.th
Life Insurance Products & Services
S.I.C.: 6311
N.A.I.C.S.: 524113
Bryan Smith *(Pres & CEO)*
Ulf Lange *(CFO)*
Robert Paul Gray *(COO)*
Surajak Kotikula *(Chief Investment Officer)*
Patchara Taveechaiwattana *(Chief Market Mgmt Officer & Chief HR Officer)*
Sunchai Larpsumphunchai *(Chief Agency Officer)*
Hadil Tjeng *(Chief IT Officer)*
Sugunya Tongchenchitt *(Chief Regulatory Affairs Officer)*
Kavita Boonpochanasoontorn *(Sr VP-Legal, Compliance & Internal Audit)*

Bajaj Allianz General Insurance Co. Ltd. (1)
1st Floor GE Plaza Airport Road
Yerwada, Pune, Maharashtra, 411006, India
Tel.: (91) 2056026666
Fax: (91) 2056026667
E-Mail: info@bajajallianz.co.in
Web Site: www.bajajallianz.co.in
Sales Range: $250-299.9 Million
Emp.: 1,371
Insurance Services; Owned by Allianz AG & by Bajaj Auto Limited
S.I.C.: 6411
N.A.I.C.S.: 524298

Subsidiary:

Bajaj Allianz Life Insurance Co. Ltd. (2)
Ground Floor GE Plaza Airport Road
Yerwada, Pune, Maharashtra, 411006, India
Tel.: (91) 2066026666
Fax: (91) 2066026667
E-Mail: life@bajajallianz.co.in
Web Site: www.bajajallianz.com
Emp.: 2,000
Life Insurance Services
S.I.C.: 6311
N.A.I.C.S.: 524113
Manoj Agrawal *(Mgr)*

ALLIED ARCHITECTS, INC.

Unosawa Tokyu Building 4F 1-19-15 Ebisu
Shibuya-ku, Tokyo, Japan
Tel.: (81) 3 6408 2791
Fax: (81) 3 6408 2799
Web Site: www.aainc.co.jp
Year Founded: 2005
6081—(TKS)
Rev.: $11,823,581
Emp.: 130
Fiscal Year-end: 12/31/12

Business Description:
Social Media Marketing Consulting Services
S.I.C.: 8742
N.A.I.C.S.: 541613

Personnel:
Masahide Nakamura *(Pres)*

Board of Directors:
Koichiro Matsuo
Hirokazu Nagai
Takaichi Nishida
Kotaro Tsukamoto

ALLIED BLENDERS AND DISTILLERS PVT. LTD.

394/C Ground Fl Lamington Chambers
Lamington Rd, Mumbai, 400 004, India
Tel.: (91) 2267779777
Fax: (91) 2267779725
E-Mail: info@abdindia.com
Web Site: www.abdindia.com
Sls.: $186,703,860
Business Description:
Liquor Producer & Distr
S.I.C.: 2085
N.A.I.C.S.: 312140
Personnel:
Kishore Rajaram Chhabria *(Chm)*
Deepak Roy *(Vice Chm & CEO)*
U.K. Ganguli *(Vice Chm)*
Ramakrishnan Ramaswamy *(CFO)*
Roopak Chaturvedi *(CMO)*
Board of Directors:
Kishore Rajaram Chhabria
U.K. Ganguli
Deepak Roy

ALLIED CEMENT HOLDINGS LIMITED

22nd Floor Allied Kajima Building
138 Gloucester Road, Wanchai, China (Hong Kong)
Tel.: (852) 2533 3233
Fax: (852) 2845 3034
E-Mail: info@alliedcement.com.hk
Web Site: www.alliedcement.com.hk
1312—(HKG)
Business Description:
Cement Mfr
S.I.C.: 3241
N.A.I.C.S.: 327310
Personnel:
Qing Hai Ng *(Mng Dir)*
Ka Hang Wong *(Sec)*
Board of Directors:
Sze Chung Chan
Kin Chung Cheng
Chi Kong Li
Qing Hai Ng
Doris Yan Tung Yang
Zhong Yu
Transfer Agent:
Tricor Secretaries Limited
26th Floor Tesbury Centre 28 Queens Rd E
Hong Kong, China (Hong Kong)

Non-U.S. Subsidiaries:

Shandong Allied Wangchao Cement Limited **(1)**
Dunzhuangcun Jiantouji Town
Taierzhuang District, Zaozhuang, Shandong, 277415, China
Tel.: (86) 632 6818 173
Fax: (86) 632 6818 696
E-Mail: sdsac@sdsac.com
Cement Mfr
S.I.C.: 3241
N.A.I.C.S.: 327310

Shandong Shanghai Allied Cement Co., Ltd. **(1)**
Sunsuzhuang
Jiantouji Town
Taierzhuang District, Zaozhuang, Shandong, 277405, China
Tel.: (86) 632 6811 048
Fax: (86) 632 6812 020
E-Mail: sdsac@sdsac.com
Cement Mfr
S.I.C.: 3241
N.A.I.C.S.: 327310

Shanghai Allied Cement Co., Ltd. **(1)**
02 Buidling 27 1388 Zhangdong Road
Pudong, Shanghai, 200203, China
Tel.: (86) 21 6879 6801
Fax: (86) 21 3872 3527
E-Mail: sac@sac-cement.com
Cement Mfr
S.I.C.: 3241
N.A.I.C.S.: 327310

ALLIED CONSOLIDATED LIMITED

C/- Whittens Lawyers & Consultants
Level 5 137-139 Bathurst Street
Sydney, NSW, 2000, Australia
Tel.: (61) 2 8072 1400
Fax: (61) 2 9238 1970
E-Mail: info@alliedconsolidated.com.au
Web Site: www.alliedconsolidated.com.au
ABQ—(ASX)
Business Description:
Retail Department Store Operator
S.I.C.: 5311
N.A.I.C.S.: 452111
Personnel:
Andrew Whitten *(Sec)*
Board of Directors:
Adir Shiffman
John Kolenda
Calvin Ng
Michael Pollak

ALLIED COOPERATIVE INSURANCE GROUP

Al Jamjoom Center Tower 1 - 12 Floor
PO Box 21462
Jeddah, 7076, Saudi Arabia
Tel.: (966) 26633222
Fax: (966) 26617421
E-Mail: csc@acig.com.sa
Web Site: www.acig.com.sa
8150—(SAU)
Premiums: $49,750,432
Assets: $63,673,928
Liabilities: $39,732,226
Net Worth: $23,941,702
Earnings: ($6,248,729)
Fiscal Year-end: 12/31/12
Business Description:
Cooperative Insurance Services
S.I.C.: 6311
N.A.I.C.S.: 524113
Personnel:
Khaled Hamad A. Al Bassam *(Chm)*
Mohammad Hani Al Bakri *(Deputy Chm)*
Hesham Al Shareef *(CEO)*
Muzaffar M. Shakeel *(COO)*
Mohammed Al Gadhi *(Sr VP-Technical & Ops)*
Board of Directors:
Khaled Hamad A. Al Bassam
Sulaiman Abdullah Alkhoraiji
Abdulatif Mohammed Al Aleshaikh
Mohammad Hani Al Bakri
Khamis Al Kazzah
Hussam Talal El Ghazawi
Thamir Abdullah Mohammad Rayes

Aldar Audit Bureau Abdullah Albasri & Co
PO Box 20142
Jeddah, Saudi Arabia

ALLIED DIGITAL SERVICES LIMITED

81 Harchandrai House 5th Floor
Maharashi Karve Road Marine Lines
Mumbai, Maharashtra, 400 002, India
Tel.: (91) 2266816681
Fax: (91) 2222064170
E-Mail: adsl.contact@allieddigital.net
Web Site: www.allieddigital.net
ADSL—(NSE)
Rev.: $78,324,955
Assets: $160,537,508
Liabilities: $31,514,199
Net Worth: $129,023,308
Earnings: ($940,571)
Fiscal Year-end: 03/31/13
Business Description:
Computer Services
S.I.C.: 7379
N.A.I.C.S.: 541519
Personnel:
Nitin D. Shah *(Chm & Mng Dir)*
Paresh Shah *(CEO)*
Prakash D. Shah *(CFO & Dir-Comml)*
Sanjiv Patki *(COO)*
Manoj R. Shah *(CIO-Ops-US)*
Ravindra Joshi *(Compliance Officer & Sec)*
Arun Kulkarni *(Chief Info Security Officer)*
Jawahar Ali *(CEO-Integrated Solutions Grp)*
Board of Directors:
Nitin D. Shah
Roopkishan Sohanlal Dave
Venugopal R. Iyengar
Shrikant N. Parikh
Paresh Shah
Prakash D. Shah
Transfer Agent:
Link Intime India Pvt. Ltd
C-13 Pannalal Silk Mills Compound LBS Marg
Bhandup (West)
Mumbai, India

U.S. Subsidiary:

En Pointe Global Services, LLC **(1)**
18701 S Figueroa St
Gardena, CA 90248-4506
Tel.: (310) 337-5200
Fax: (310) 258-2304
E-Mail: EPGS@enpointe.com
Web Site: www.enpointe.com
Emp.: 400
Business Management Services
S.I.C.: 8741
N.A.I.C.S.: 561110
Kashif Rasheed *(Gen Mgr)*

ALLIED ELECTRONICS CORPORATION LIMITED

Altron House 4 Sherborne Road
Parktown, Gauteng, 2193, South Africa
Tel.: (27) 116453600
Fax: (27) 117265778
E-Mail: info@altron.co.za
Web Site: www.altron.com
ATN—(JSE)
Rev.: $2,797,973,300
Assets: $1,448,413,900
Liabilities: $865,339,900
Net Worth: $583,074,000
Earnings: ($103,769,300)
Emp.: 12,721
Fiscal Year-end: 02/28/13
Business Description:
Telecommunications & Information Technology Services
S.I.C.: 4813
N.A.I.C.S.: 517110
Personnel:
Robert E. Venter *(CEO)*
Alex M. R. Smith *(CFO & Dir-Fin)*
Seara Macheli-Mkhabela *(Exec-Corp Affairs)*
Robert J. Abraham *(CEO-Bytes)*
Neil Kayton *(CEO-Powertech)*
Craig G. Venter *(CEO-Altech)*
Andrew G. Johnston *(Sec)*
Board of Directors:
Bill P. Venter
Robert J. Abraham
Norman J. Adami
Myron C. Berzac
Grant Glenn Gelink
Mike J. Leeming
Penuell M. Maduna
Jacob R. D. Modise
Dawn N. M. Mokhobo
Alex M. R. Smith
Simon N. Susman
Craig G. Venter
Robert E. Venter
Transfer Agent:
Computershare Investor Services 2004 (Pty) Limited
70 Marshall Street
61051
Johannesburg, South Africa

Subsidiaries:

Altron Finance (Pty) Limited **(1)**
5 Winchester Rd
Parktown, Johannesburg, Gauteng, 2193, South Africa
Tel.: (27) 116453600
Fax: (27) 117261665
Finanicial Advisory Services
S.I.C.: 6282
N.A.I.C.S.: 523930
Bill Venter *(Chm)*
Robert Venter *(CEO)*

Bytes Technology Group (Proprietary) Limited **(1)**
Bytes House Ave N 6 Mellis Rd
Rivonia, Johannesburg, Gauteng, 2128, South Africa
Tel.: (27) 112369500
Fax: (27) 118076909
E-Mail: linda.meyer@bytes.co.za
Web Site: www.btgroup.co.za
Emp.: 18
Information Communications Technology Services
S.I.C.: 4899
N.A.I.C.S.: 517919
Rob Abraham *(CEO)*

Power Technologies (Proprietary) Limited **(1)**
Hampton Park 20 Georgian Crescent
Bryanston, Johannesburg, Gauteng, 0011, South Africa
Tel.: (27) 117067184
Fax: (27) 117061036
E-Mail: info@powertech.co.za
Web Site: www.powertech.co.za
Emp.: 20
Electrical & Electronic Equipments Distr
S.I.C.: 5063
N.A.I.C.S.: 423610
Bill Venter *(Chm)*
Neil Kayton *(CEO)*
Sean Hemphill *(CFO)*
Harry Coetzee *(CEO-Aberdare Cables)*
Glenn Geldenhuis *(CEO-Powertech Batteries)*
Pierre Nothard *(CEO-Powertech Indus)*

ALLIED FARMERS LIMITED

74 Princes Street
PO Box 423
Hawera, 4640, New Zealand
Tel.: (64) 62780800
Fax: (64) 62780380
E-Mail: headoffice@alliedfarmers.co.nz
Web Site: www.alliedfarmers.co.nz
ALF—(NZE)
Rev.: $22,681,863
Assets: $9,643,914
Liabilities: $14,053,230
Net Worth: ($4,409,316)
Earnings: ($2,068,227)
Fiscal Year-end: 06/30/13
Business Description:
Livestock Trading, Finance & Real Estate Services
S.I.C.: 7319
N.A.I.C.S.: 541890
Personnel:
Steve Morrison *(CEO-Allied Farmers Rural)*
Board of Directors:
Garry C. Bluett
Jeffrey W. Keenan
Philip C. Luscombe
G. Andrew McDouall

Legal Counsel:
Quigg Partners
Level 7 The Todd Building 28 Brandon Street
PO Box 3035
Wellington, New Zealand
Morrison Daly
Level 14 45 Johnston Street PO Box 10341
The Terrace
Wellington, New Zealand
Minter Ellison Rudd Watts
Level 20 Lumley Centre 88 Shortland Street
PO Box 3798
Auckland, New Zealand
Tel.: (64) 9 353 9700
Fax: (64) 9 353 9701

ALLIED GLASS CONTAINERS LTD.

South Accommodation Road
Leeds, LS10 1NQ, United Kingdom
Tel.: (44) 113 245 1568
Fax: (44) 113 244 9349
Web Site: www.allied-glass.com
Year Founded: 2002
Sales Range: $10-24.9 Million
Emp.: 620
Business Description:
Glass Container Mfr
S.I.C.: 3221
N.A.I.C.S.: 327213
Personnel:
Alan Henderson *(Mng Dir)*
Board of Directors:
James Hart
Alan Henderson
Philip Morris
John Naughton
Richard Summers

ALLIED GROUP LIMITED

22nd Floor Allied Kajima Building 138 Gloucester Road
Wanchai, China (Hong Kong)
Tel.: (852) 25192288
Fax: (852) 25985518
Web Site: www.alliedgroup.com.hk
0373—(HKG OTC)
Rev.: $579,604,460
Assets: $5,234,738,145
Liabilities: $1,447,670,070
Net Worth: $3,787,068,075
Earnings: $356,469,380
Emp.: 6,267
Fiscal Year-end: 12/31/12
Business Description:
Investment Holding Services
S.I.C.: 6719
N.A.I.C.S.: 551112
Personnel:
Seng Hui Lee *(CEO)*
Wing Han Cho *(Sec)*
Board of Directors:
Arthur George Dew
David Craig Bartlett
Alan Stephen Jones
Seng Hui Lee
Su Hwei Lee
Edwin King Yau Lo
Pak Hung Mak
Po Yan Wong

Subsidiaries:

AG Capital Limited (1)
22 F Allied Kajima Bldg 138 Gloucester Rd
Wanchai, China (Hong Kong)
Tel.: (852) 25192288
Fax: (852) 25985518
Securities Trading & Money Lending Services
S.I.C.: 6141
N.A.I.C.S.: 522291

Yu Ming Investment Management Limited (1)
Rm 1001 10 Fl Aon China Bldg 29 Queens Rd
Central, China (Hong Kong)
Tel.: (852) 28046188
Fax: (852) 28772666
E-Mail: info@ymi.com.hk
Emp.: 12
Investment Advisory Services
S.I.C.: 6282
N.A.I.C.S.: 523930
Warren Lee *(Co-Founder)*

ALLIED HEALTHCARE GROUP

(Name Changed to Admedus Limited)

ALLIED HERBALS LIMITED

13-B 3rd Floor Netaji Subhash Marg
Daryaganj, New Delhi, 110 002, India
Tel.: (91) 11 41513567
Fax: (91) 11 25749113
E-Mail: rajdhanileasing@rediffmail.com
Web Site: www.rajdhanileasing.com
Year Founded: 1985
523030—(BOM)
Assets: $342,756
Liabilities: $42,448
Net Worth: $300,308
Earnings: ($9,223)
Fiscal Year-end: 03/31/13
Business Description:
Personal Care Product Whslr
S.I.C.: 5122
N.A.I.C.S.: 424210
Personnel:
Rohit Chowdhary *(Compliance Officer)*
Raju Singh Tomer *(Sec)*
Board of Directors:
Sanjeev Agarwal
Rohit Chowdhary
Sanjay Jain
Transfer Agent:
Link Intime India Private Limited
44 Community Centre 2nd Floor Naraina
Industrial Area Phase-I
Near PVR Naraina, New Delhi, India

ALLIED HOTEL PROPERTIES INC.

Suite 300 515 West Pender Street
Vancouver, BC, V6B 6H5, Canada
Tel.: (604) 669-5335
Fax: (604) 682-8131
E-Mail: info@alliedhotels.com
Web Site: www.alliedhotels.com
Year Founded: 1982
AHP—(TSXV)
Rev.: $7,748,386
Assets: $21,316,759
Liabilities: $17,084,222
Net Worth: $4,232,537
Earnings: ($6,752,378)
Fiscal Year-end: 12/31/12
Business Description:
Hotel & Real Estate Management Services
S.I.C.: 6531
N.A.I.C.S.: 531390
Personnel:
Peter Y. L. Eng *(Chm & CEO)*
Michael F. Chan *(Pres & CFO)*
Board of Directors:
Peter Y. L. Eng
T. Lloyd Callahan
Michael F. Chan
Patrick K. Kong
Abu Bakar Mohsin Almohdzar
Eng Tee Ng
Francis A. Wong
Transfer Agent:
Valiant Trust Company
Suite 600 750 Cambie Street
Vancouver, BC, Canada

Subsidiary:

Allied Don Valley Hotel Inc. (1)
1250 Eglinton Ave E
North York, ON, M3C 1J3, Canada
Tel.: (416) 449-4111
Fax: (416) 385-6700
Toll Free: (877) 575-8127
Hotel Management Services
S.I.C.: 7011
N.A.I.C.S.: 721110

ALLIED INTERNATIONAL LTD.

10 Rue des Moulins
75001 Paris, France
Tel.: (33) 144550570
Fax: (33) 144550575
E-Mail: maxine.mactherson@allied-international.com
Web Site: www.allied-international.com
Emp.: 10
Business Description:
Destination Management Services
S.I.C.: 4729
N.A.I.C.S.: 561599
Personnel:
Karine Berberian *(Mng Dir)*

U.S. Subsidiary:

PRA Destination Management, Inc. (1)
2456 Broadway
San Diego, CA 92102-2022
Tel.: (760) 496-0540
Fax: (619) 232-5869
E-Mail: info@alliedpra.com
Web Site: www.alliedpra.com
Sales Range: $10-24.9 Million
Emp.: 5
Travel Arrangement & Event Planning Services
S.I.C.: 4729
N.A.I.C.S.: 561599
Laura Rednour *(Pres)*

Non-U.S. Subsidiaries:

Allied Arabia (1)
PO Box 502068
Media city bld 8 off 51, Dubai, United Arab Emirates
Tel.: (971) 44230880
Fax: (971) 44230878
E-Mail: alan.wheatleys@alliedpoa.com
Web Site: www.alliedpoa.com
Emp.: 3
Travel Arrangement Services
S.I.C.: 7011
N.A.I.C.S.: 721199
Alan Wheatley *(Gen Mgr)*

Allied Monte Carlo (1)
57 rue Grimaldi Le Panorama Bloc C D
98000 Monaco, Monaco
Tel.: (377) 97976464
Fax: (377) 97976465
E-Mail: monaco@alliedpra.com
Web Site: www.alliedpra.com
Emp.: 20
Travel Arrangement Services
S.I.C.: 4729
N.A.I.C.S.: 561599
Karine Berberian *(Mng Dir)*

Allied Spain (1)
Gran via de lef corts Catalinis No 649 office 1
08009 Barcelona, Spain
Tel.: (34) 934677780
Fax: (34) 934677781
E-Mail: spain@alliedpra.com
Web Site: www.alliedpra.com
Emp.: 6
Travel Arrangement Services
S.I.C.: 4729
N.A.I.C.S.: 561599
Hannelore Carzon *(Mng Dir)*

Allied UK (1)
Greville House Hatton Road
Bedfont, Heathrow, Mddx, TW14 9PX, United Kingdom
Tel.: (44) 2088444000
Fax: (44) 2088444009
Emp.: 7
Travel Arrangement Services
S.I.C.: 4729
N.A.I.C.S.: 561599

Subsidiary:

Allied France (1)
10 Rue Des
Moulins, 750013, France
Tel.: (33) 144550570
Fax: (33) 144550580
E-Mail: allied@alliedpra.com
Web Site: www.alliedpra.com
Emp.: 8
Travel Arrangement Services
S.I.C.: 4729
N.A.I.C.S.: 561599
Karine Berberian *(Mng Dir)*

ALLIED IRISH BANKS, P.L.C.

(d/b/a AIB Group)
Bankcentre
PO Box 452
Ballsbridge, Dublin, 4, Ireland
Tel.: (353) 1 660 0311
Fax: (353) 1 660 9137
E-Mail: investor.relations@aib.ie
Web Site: www.aibgroup.com
Year Founded: 1966
AIB—(ISE OTC)
Sales Range: $5-14.9 Billion
Emp.: 14,255
Business Description:
Bank Holding Company; Retail, Commercial & Investment Banking Services
S.I.C.: 6712
N.A.I.C.S.: 551111
Personnel:
David H. Hodgkinson *(Chm)*
Michael J. Somers *(Deputy Chm)*
Joseph O'Connor *(Chief Credit Officer)*
David O'Callaghan *(Sec)*
Board of Directors:
David H. Hodgkinson
Declan Collier
Stephen L. Kingon
Anne Maher
James R. O'Hara
David Peter Pritchard
Michael J. Somers
Dick Spring
Catherine Woods
Transfer Agent:
The Bank of New York
PO Box 11002 Church St Sta
New York, NY 10286
Tel.: (800) 225-2719

Subsidiaries:

AIB Capital Markets plc (1)
AIB Bank Centre Ballsbridge
Dublin, 4, Ireland IE
Tel.: (353) 18740222 (100%)
Fax: (353) 16642124
E-Mail: aib@aib.ie
Web Site: www.aib.ie
Emp.: 2,000
International Banking, Treasury, Investment Management & Corporate Banking
S.I.C.: 6159
N.A.I.C.S.: 522298
Cummins Sinead *(Mgr-Mktg)*

AIB Corporate Banking Limited (1)
AIB Bankcentre Ballsbridge
Dublin, Ireland
Tel.: (353) 1 660 0311
Fax: (353) 1 668 2508
E-Mail: investor.relations@aib.ie
Web Site: www.aibcorporate.ie
Emp.: 100
Commercial Banking Services
S.I.C.: 6029
N.A.I.C.S.: 522110
Conor P. Daly *(Head-Food, Drink, Leisure, Media & Education Div)*

AIB Corporate Finance Ltd. (1)
Bankcentre, Ballsbridge
Dublin, 4, Ireland IE
Tel.: (353) 16670233 (100%)
Fax: (353) 16670250
E-Mail: corporate.finance@aib.ie
Web Site: www.aibcf.ie

Allied Irish Banks, p.l.c.—(Continued)

Emp.: 15
Advice on Mergers, Acquisitions, Disposals & Fund Raising
S.I.C.: 6159
N.A.I.C.S.: 522298
Alan Doherty *(Mng Dir)*

AIB Finance & Leasing Ltd. (1)
Bankcentre Ballsbridge
Sandyford, Dublin, 4, Ireland IE
Tel.: (353) 16603011 (100%)
Fax: (353) 12959795
E-Mail: aibfinl@aib.ie
Web Site: www.aib.ie
Emp.: 350
Business & Consumer Asset Financing
S.I.C.: 6799
N.A.I.C.S.: 523910

AIB Insurance Services Limited (1)
AIB Bankcentre Ballsbridge
Dublin, 4, Ireland
Tel.: (353) 16600311
Insurance Brokerage Services
S.I.C.: 6411
N.A.I.C.S.: 524210

AIB International Consultants Ltd. (1)
Bankcentre Ballsbridge
Dublin, 4, Ireland IE
Tel.: (353) 16600311 (100%)
Fax: (353) 16601474
E-Mail: info@aib.ie
Web Site: www.aib.ie
Emp.: 200
Business Consulting Services
S.I.C.: 8742
N.A.I.C.S.: 541611

AIB International Finance (1)
Bankcentre Ballsbridge
Dublin, Ireland
Tel.: (353) 16600311
Financial Management Services
S.I.C.: 6211
N.A.I.C.S.: 523999

AIB Investment Managers Ltd. (1)
Investment House Percy Pl
Dublin, Ireland IE
Tel.: (353) 16617077 (100%)
Fax: (353) 16617038
E-Mail:
Web Site: www.prescient.ie
Emp.: 130
Investment Management
S.I.C.: 6799
N.A.I.C.S.: 523920
Fiona Sweeney *(CIO)*

AIB Securities Services Ltd. (1)
Block L3 Bank Centre ballsbridge
Dublin, 4, Ireland IE
Tel.: (353) 18740222 (100%)
Fax: (353) 16700710
E-Mail: bankcentre.switch@aib.ie
Web Site: www.aibbny.ie
Emp.: 60
Custody Services
S.I.C.: 6733
N.A.I.C.S.: 523991

Allied Irish Banks (Holdings & Investments) Limited (1)
Bankcentre Ballsbridge
Dublin, 4, Ireland
Tel.: (353) 16600311
Fax: (353) 16682508
Web Site: www.aib.ie
Investment Management Services
S.I.C.: 6211
N.A.I.C.S.: 523999

Allied Irish Finance Limited (1)
Bankcentre Ballsbridge
Dublin, Ireland
Tel.: (353) 16600311
Fax: (353) 12959898
Financial Management Services
S.I.C.: 6211
N.A.I.C.S.: 523999

EBS Limited (1)
2 Burlington Road
PO Box 76
Dublin, Ireland
Tel.: (353) 1 665 9000
Fax: (353) 1 874 7416
E-Mail: info@ebs.ie
Web Site: www.ebs.ie
Emp.: 40
Financial Management Services
S.I.C.: 6211
N.A.I.C.S.: 523999
Fergus Murphy *(CEO)*

EBS Mortgage Finance (1)
EBS Building Society 2 Burlington Road
Dublin, Ireland
Tel.: (353) 1 665 9000
Fax: (353) 18747416
Web Site: www.ebs.ie
Mortgage Insurance Services
S.I.C.: 6351
N.A.I.C.S.: 524126
David J. Duffy *(CEO)*

Non-U.S. Subsidiary:

AIB Holdings (NI) Limited (1)
4 Queen s Square
PO Box 4
Belfast, BT1 3DJ, United Kingdom
Tel.: (44) 28 9032 5599
Fax: (44) 28 9032 1754
Investment Management Services
S.I.C.: 6211
N.A.I.C.S.: 523999

ALLIED OVERSEAS LIMITED

9th Floor Allied Kajima Building 138 Gloucester Road
Wanchai, China (Hong Kong)
Tel.: (852) 2598 9133
Fax: (852) 2824 0308
E-Mail: mail@alliedoverseas.com.hk
Web Site: www.alliedoverseas.com.hk
0593—(HKG)
Rev.: $19,850,563
Assets: $203,571,689
Liabilities: $3,299,186
Net Worth: $200,272,503
Earnings: $12,377,911
Emp.: 322
Fiscal Year-end: 12/31/12
Business Description:
Holding Company; Elderly Continuing Care & Assisted Living Facilities Operator
S.I.C.: 6719
N.A.I.C.S.: 551112
Personnel:
Mark Tai Chun Wong *(CEO)*
Sze Wai Lee *(Sec)*
Board of Directors:
Arthur George Dew
Francis J. Chu Fai Chang
Chak Hung Li
Carlisle Caldow Procter
Mark Tai Chun Wong
Legal Counsel:
P. C. Woo & Co
12th Floor Princes Building 10 Chater Road
Central, China (Hong Kong)

Conyers, Dill & Pearman
2901 One Exchange Square
8 Connaught Place, Central, China (Hong Kong)

Butterfield Fulcrum Group (Bermuda) Limited
26 Burnaby Street
Hamilton, HM 11, Bermuda

Subsidiaries:

Senior Care Elderly Limited (1)
6th Floor 303-307 Des Voeux Road
Central District, Sheung Wan, China (Hong Kong) VG
Tel.: (852) 23222033 (100%)
Fax: (852) 25075688
E-Mail: mail@seniorcare.com.hk
Web Site: www.seniorcare.com.hk
Emp.: 30
Elderly Care Services
S.I.C.: 8322
N.A.I.C.S.: 624120
Mark Tai Chun Wong *(CEO)*

Senior Care Nursing Home Limited (1)
6th Floor 303-307 Des Voeux Road Central
Sheung Wan, China (Hong Kong) HK
Tel.: (852) 23222033 (100%)
Fax: (852) 2507 5688
E-Mail: mail@seniorcare.com.hk
Web Site: www.seniorcare.com.hk
Elderly Nursing Homes Operator
S.I.C.: 8361
N.A.I.C.S.: 623312
Mark Tai Chun Wong *(CEO)*

ALLIED PLASTIC SKYLIGHT

707 Arrow Rd
Weston, ON, M9M 2L4, Canada
Tel.: (416) 749-7070
Fax: (416) 749-4440
E-Mail: info@allied2000.com
Web Site: www.allied2000.com
Sales Range: $10-24.9 Million
Emp.: 150
Business Description:
Toys, Word Processing Supplies, Moulds for Plastic Components Mfr & Distr
S.I.C.: 3942
N.A.I.C.S.: 339930
Personnel:
R. Bruhm *(Pres & CEO)*
Boyd Bruhn *(VP-Fin)*

Subsidiaries:

Architectural Plastics Limited (1)
707 Arrow Road
Weston, ON, M9M 2L4, Canada
Tel.: (416) 748-3000
Fax: (416) 749-0889
E-Mail: info@allied2000.com
Web Site: www.architecturalskylights.com
Emp.: 18
Plastics Product Mfr
S.I.C.: 3089
N.A.I.C.S.: 326199
Boyd Bruhm *(Gen Mgr)*

Reliable Toy Corporation (1)
707 Arrow Rd
Weston, ON, M9M 2L4, Canada Ca
Tel.: (416) 762-1111 (100%)
Fax: (416) 762-0889
E-Mail:
Emp.: 15
Toys Mfr
S.I.C.: 3942
N.A.I.C.S.: 339930
Tod Bruhm *(Gen Mgr & Adv Mgr)*

Viceroy Rubber Limited (1)
707 Arrow Rd
Weston, ON, M9M 2L4, Canada
Tel.: (416) 762-1111
Fax: (416) 762-0889
E-Mail: info@viceroyrubber.com
Web Site: www.viceroyrubber.com
Emp.: 15
Mechanical Use Rubber Product Mfr
S.I.C.: 3061
N.A.I.C.S.: 326291
Todd Bruhm *(Gen Mgr)*

ALLIED PROPERTIES (H.K.) LIMITED

22d Fl Allied Kajima Bldg 138 Gloucester Rd
Wanchai, China (Hong Kong)
Tel.: (852) 25192288
Fax: (852) 25985518
Web Site: www.alliedproperties.com.hk
0056—(HKG)
Rev.: $565,897,075
Assets: $5,410,858,055
Liabilities: $1,511,500,320
Net Worth: $3,899,357,735
Earnings: $335,605,270
Emp.: 6,194
Fiscal Year-end: 12/31/12
Business Description:
Property Investment & Development Services
S.I.C.: 6282
N.A.I.C.S.: 523930
Personnel:
Seng Hui Lee *(CEO)*
Tung Ni Lau *(Sec)*
Board of Directors:
Arthur George Dew
David Craig Bartlett
Alan Stephen Jones
Seng Hui Lee
Chi Kong Li
Mark Tai Chun Wong
Steven Samuel Zoellner

ALLIED PROPERTIES REAL ESTATE INVESTMENT TRUST

255 Adelaide St W
Toronto, ON, M5H 1X9, Canada
Tel.: (416) 977-9002
Fax: (416) 977-9053
E-Mail: info@alliedpropertiesreit.com
Web Site: www.alliedpropertiesreit.com
Year Founded: 2003
AP.UN—(TSX)
Sales Range: $150-199.9 Million
Emp.: 30
Business Description:
Investment Trust Services
S.I.C.: 6211
N.A.I.C.S.: 523110
Personnel:
Gordon R. Cunningham *(Chm)*
Michael R. Emory *(Pres & CEO)*
Peter E. Sweeney *(CFO & VP)*
Thomas G. Burns *(COO)*
Wayne L. Jacobs *(Exec VP-Acq)*
Marianne O'Leary *(Sr VP-Real Estate Ops)*
Transfer Agent:
CIBC Mellon Trust Company
PO Box 7010
Adelaide Street Postal Station, Toronto, ON, M5C 2W9, Canada
Tel.: (416) 643-5500
Fax: (416) 643-5501
Toll Free: (800) 387-0825

Subsidiary:

Allied Properties Management Limited Partnership (1)
70 Arthur St
Winnipeg, MB, R3B1G7, Canada
Tel.: (204) 942-8400
Fax: (204) 942-8499
Emp.: 7
Property Managing Services
S.I.C.: 6531
N.A.I.C.S.: 531311

ALLIED RISK MANAGEMENT LIMITED

1317 Dawson St
Dublin, 2, Ireland
Tel.: (353) 17645640
Fax: (353) 16725774
E-Mail: larry.sherin@alliedrisk.ie
Web Site: www.alliedrisk.ie
Year Founded: 1990
Emp.: 300
Business Description:
Insurance Services
S.I.C.: 6411
N.A.I.C.S.: 524298
Personnel:
Larry Sherin *(Mng Dir)*

ALLIED TECHNOLOGIES GROUP, INC.

(Name Changed to Trio Resources, Inc.)

ALLIED TECHNOLOGIES LTD.

25 Bukit Batok Street 22
Singapore, 659591, Singapore

Tel.: (65) 65602011
Fax: (65) 65602055
E-Mail: info@allied-tech.com.sg
Web Site: www.allied-tech.com.sg
A13—(SES)
Rev.: $97,041,814
Assets: $88,883,172
Liabilities: $44,246,708
Net Worth: $44,636,463
Earnings: ($8,173,103)
Fiscal Year-end: 12/31/12
Business Description:
Stamped Metal & Electronics Parts Mfr
S.I.C.: 3679
N.A.I.C.S.: 334419
Personnel:
Ching Yuh Hsu *(CEO & Mng Dir)*
Weng Kheong Soh *(Deputy Mng Dir)*
Foon Yeow Chia *(Sec)*
Board of Directors:
Choon Chiaw Loo
Tat Seng Chua
Ching Yuh Hsu
Yih Pin Sitoh
Weng Kheong Soh
Legal Counsel:
Loo & Partners LLP
16 Gemmill Lane
Singapore, Singapore

Non-U.S. Subsidiaries:

Allied Machineries (Shanghai) Co., Ltd. (1)
No 47 Fenju Rd Waigaoqiao Free Trade Zone Pudong
Shanghai, 200131, China
Tel.: (86) 2150480360
Fax: (86) 2150480612
Emp.: 1,500
Metal Stamp Mfr
S.I.C.: 3466
N.A.I.C.S.: 332119
Lay Thiam Tan *(Deputy Gen Mgr)*

Allied Technologies (Suzhou) Co., Ltd. (1)
No 111 Shihu W Rd
Changqiao Township, Suzhou, Wuzhong, 215128, China
Tel.: (86) 51265651191
Fax: (86) 512 65651195
Metal Stamp Mfr
S.I.C.: 3466
N.A.I.C.S.: 332119

ALLIED TELESIS HOLDINGS K.K.

2 TOC Bldg 7 21 11 Nishi Gotanda
Shinagawa ku
Tokyo, 1410031, Japan
Tel.: (81) 354376000
Fax: (81) 354376008
E-Mail: gonwoka@allied-telesis.co.jp
Web Site: www.allied-telesis.co.jp
6835—(TKS)
Sales Range: $400-449.9 Million
Emp.: 2,222
Business Description:
Telecom Equipment Mfr
S.I.C.: 3663
N.A.I.C.S.: 334220
Personnel:
Takayoshi Oshima *(Chm & CEO)*
Board of Directors:
Takayoshi Oshima
Shinichi Kimura
Jun Kohara
Eu-Jin Lim
Masakazu Murayama
Sachie Oshima
Ashit Padwal
Tomoyuki Sugihara

Subsidiary:

Allied Telesis R&D Center K.K. (1)
Dai2toc Bldg Shinagawa
Tokyo, 141-0031, Japan
Tel.: (81) 354368355
Fax: (81) 354376024
Web Site: www.allied-stelesis.co.jp
Emp.: 100
Business Research & Development Services
S.I.C.: 8732
N.A.I.C.S.: 541720
Taki Oshima *(CEO)*

U.S. Subsidiaries:

Allied Telesis Capital Corp. (1)
3200 N 1 St
San Jose, CA 95134
Tel.: (408) 519-8700
Fax: (408) 519-8701
Toll Free: (800) 424-4284
E-Mail: helpdesk@atccmail.com
Web Site: www.alliedtelesis.com
Emp.: 150
Internet Protocol Technology Services
S.I.C.: 4899
N.A.I.C.S.: 517919
Keith Southard *(CEO)*

Allied Telesis Inc. (1)
3200 N 1 St
San Jose, CA 95134
Tel.: (408) 519-8700
Fax: (408) 519-8701
Toll Free: (800) 424-4284
E-Mail: info@alliedtelesis.com
Web Site: www.alliedtelesis.com
Emp.: 150
Network Management Services
S.I.C.: 8748
N.A.I.C.S.: 541618
Takayoshi Oshima *(Chm & CEO)*
Eu-Jin Lim *(COO & Exec VP)*
Mick Burke *(CIO & Sr VP)*
John Squeo *(CTO & Sr VP-Cloud Svcs-Chicago)*

Non-U.S. Subsidiaries:

Allied Telesis (Hong Kong) Ltd. (1)
Unit 1908 19/F Elite Centre 22 Hung To Road Kwun Tong
Kowloon, China (Hong Kong)
Tel.: (852) 22636566
Fax: (852) 23180720
Web Site: www.alliedtelesis.com.hk
Mobile Communications Services
S.I.C.: 3663
N.A.I.C.S.: 334220

Allied Telesis International Services Ltd. (1)
Unit 24 Westmead Indust Estate
Swindon, Wiltshire, SN5 7YT, United Kingdom
Tel.: (44) 1793501401
Fax: (44) 1793431099
Web Site: www.alliedtelesis.co.uk/
Computer Support Services
S.I.C.: 7371
N.A.I.C.S.: 541511

Allied Telesis International S.L.U (1)
Avda del Mediterraneo 44 5
28007 Madrid, Spain
Tel.: (34) 915591055
Fax: (34) 915592644
E-Mail: marketing_iberia@alliedtelesis.com
Web Site: www.alliedtelesis.es
Network Management Services
S.I.C.: 7371
N.A.I.C.S.: 541511
Remy Millescamps *(Gen Mgr)*

Allied Telesis Labs (Philippines) Inc. (1)
3 F Net One Ctr 3rd Ave Cor 26th St
Bonifacio Global, Taguig, Metro Manila, Philippines
Tel.: (63) 28153130
Fax: (63) 28153170
E-Mail: info@alliedtelesis.com
Web Site: www.alliedtelesis.com
Emp.: 50
Computer Hardware Services
S.I.C.: 7371
N.A.I.C.S.: 541511
Scott Gill *(Mng Dir)*

Allied Telesis Labs S.R.L. (1)
Piazza Tirana N 24 4 B
20147 Milan, Italy
Tel.: (39) 02413041
Fax: (39) 024130200
E-Mail: venturino_intrieri@alliedtelesis.com
Web Site: www.alliedtelesis.com
Emp.: 20
Network Support Services
S.I.C.: 7373
N.A.I.C.S.: 541512

Allied Telesyn (China) Ltd. (1)
No 601 Tower B Tri-Tower 66 Zhong-Guan-Cun
Haidian District, Beijing, 100190, China
Tel.: (86) 1085252299
Fax: (86) 1085252298
Web Site: www.alliedtelesis.com.cn
Emp.: 20
Network Management Services
S.I.C.: 7376
N.A.I.C.S.: 541513

Allied Telesyn International (Asia) Pte. Ltd. (1)
719 A3 Fl Zone D2 KPN Tower Rama 9 Rd
Bangkapi Huaykwang, Bangkok, 10320, Thailand
Tel.: (66) 27170242
Fax: (66) 27170243
Emp.: 10
Network Management Services
S.I.C.: 7373
N.A.I.C.S.: 541512
Peerayut Hontkanakraw *(Country Mgr)*

Allied Telesyn International GmbH (1)
Konrad-Zuse-Platz 11 12
81829 Munich, Germany
Tel.: (49) 894354940
Fax: (49) 89435494422
E-Mail: support_sales@alliedtelesis.com
Web Site: www.alliedtelesis.de
Emp.: 15
Network Management Services
S.I.C.: 7373
N.A.I.C.S.: 541512
Christian Schwaiger *(Mng Dir)*

Allied Telesyn International Ltd. (1)
24 Bridgemead Westmead Indus Estate
Swindon, Wiltshire, SN5 7YT, United Kingdom
Tel.: (44) 1793501436
Fax: (44) 1793 501 417
E-Mail: uk_sales@alliedtelesis.com
Web Site: www.alliedtelesis.com
Emp.: 30
Networking Hardware Devices Mfr
S.I.C.: 3577
N.A.I.C.S.: 334118
Richard Lardner *(Dir-Mktg)*

Allied Telesyn International S.A. (1)
12 Ave de Scandinavie Parc Victoria Immeuble
Le Toronto Courtaboeuf, 91953 Les Ulis, France
Tel.: (33) 160921525
Fax: (33) 169283749
E-Mail: gills_patin@alliedtelesis.com
Web Site: www.alliedtelesis.fr
Emp.: 15
Computer Peripheral Whslr
S.I.C.: 5045
N.A.I.C.S.: 423430
Millescramps Remy *(Mng Dir)*

Allied Telesyn International S.R.L. (1)
Via I Vivanti 151
00144 Rome, Italy
Tel.: (39) 0652244329
Fax: (39) 065297325
E-Mail: allied_mktg@alliedtelesyn.com
Web Site: www.alliedtelesis.it
Emp.: 35
Data Communication Products Whslr
S.I.C.: 3661
N.A.I.C.S.: 334210
Antonella Santoro *(Dir-Ops)*

Allied Telesyn Korea Co., Ltd. (1)
Kyobo Bldg 17F 1 Jongro-1 Ga
Jongro-gu, Seoul, Korea (South)
Tel.: (82) 27347454
Fax: (82) 2 734 7456
Web Site: www.alliedtelesyn.co.kr
Network Management Services
S.I.C.: 8748
N.A.I.C.S.: 541618

Allied Telesyn South Asia Pte. Ltd. (1)
11 Tai Seng Link
534182 Singapore, Singapore
Tel.: (65) 63833832
Fax: (65) 63833830
E-Mail: sales-asia@alliedtelesis.com.sg
Web Site: www.alliedtelesis.sg
Emp.: 20
Network Management Services
S.I.C.: 7371
N.A.I.C.S.: 541511
Takayoshi Oshima *(Pres)*

Allied Telesyn Vertriebsgesellschaft m.b.H. (1)
Business Park Vienna
Wienerbergstr 7 13th Floor, 1100 Vienna, Austria
Tel.: (43) 1 876 2441
Fax: (43) 1 876 2572
E-Mail: austria@alliedtelesis.com
Web Site: www.alliedtelesis.at
Emp.: 6
Communications Equipment Whslr
S.I.C.: 5049
N.A.I.C.S.: 423490
Takayoshi Oshima *(Pres)*

ALLIED WORLD ASSURANCE COMPANY HOLDINGS, AG

Lindenstrasse 8
6340 Baar, Zug, Switzerland
Tel.: (41) 41 768 1080
E-Mail: info@awac.com
Web Site: www.awac.com
Year Founded: 2001
AWH—(NYSE)
Rev.: $2,222,922,000
Assets: $11,945,830,000
Liabilities: $8,426,004,000
Net Worth: $3,519,826,000
Earnings: $417,880,000
Emp.: 940
Fiscal Year-end: 12/31/13
Business Description:
Property-Casualty Insurance & Reinsurance Services
S.I.C.: 6351
N.A.I.C.S.: 524126
Personnel:
Scott A. Carmilani *(Chm, Pres & CEO)*
Bart Friedman *(Vice Chm)*
Thomas A. Bradley *(CFO & Exec VP)*
John J. McElroy *(COO)*
Marshall J. Grossack *(Chief Actuary & Exec VP)*
Kent W. Ziegler *(Chief Acctg Officer & Sr VP-Fin)*
Frank D'Orazio *(Pres-Bermuda & Intl Insurance)*
Julian James *(Pres-Europe)*
Wesley D. Dupont *(Gen Counsel & Exec VP)*
Kevin Marine *(Exec VP-Intl & Global Specialty Bus)*
Joseph Barrett *(Sr VP-Global Marine & Specialty-Allied World Reinsurance Company)*
Michelle Hoppes *(Sr VP-Global Risk Mgmt & Loss Control)*
Iain MacLeod *(Sr VP-Asia Pacific)*
Board of Directors:
Scott A. Carmilani
Barbara T. Alexander
Patrick de Saint-Aignan
James F. Duffy
Bart Friedman
Scott Hunter
Eric Stuart Schwartz
Samuel J. Weinhoff
Legal Counsel:
Conyers, Dill & Pearman
Hamilton, Bermuda

Allied World Assurance Company Holdings, AG—(Continued)

Subsidiary:

Allied World Assurance Company, Ltd **(1)**
27 Richmond Rd
HM 08 Pembroke, Bermuda
Tel.: (441) 2785400
Fax: (441) 2963428
E-Mail: info@awac.com
Web Site: www.awac.com
Holding Company
S.I.C.: 6719
N.A.I.C.S.: 551112
Scott A. Carmilani *(Chm, Pres & CEO)*

U.S. Subsidiaries:

Allied World Assurance Company (U.S.) Inc. **(1)**
199 Water St 24th Fl
New York, NY 10038
Tel.: (646) 794-0500
Web Site: www.awac.com
Emp.: 100
Insurance Services
S.I.C.: 6411
N.A.I.C.S.: 524298
John Gauthier *(Chief Investment Officer)*
Thomas Kelly *(Chief Underwriting Officer-Allied World Reinsurance US)*
Susan Chmieleski *(Pres-Pro Lines)*
Lou Iglesias *(Pres-North America)*
Sarah Doran *(Treas & Sr VP-IR)*
Bobby Bowden *(Exec VP-Mktg & Bus Dev-US)*
Kevin Marine *(Sr VP & Head-Global Marine & Specialty-Allied World Reinsurance)*
Joe Cellura *(Sr VP-Property & Casualty)*
Grace Meek *(Sr VP-Programs)*
John Patin *(Sr VP-Investments)*
Marcel Ricciardelli *(Sr VP-Environmental)*
Robert Staples *(Sr VP-Surety-Philadelphia)*

Divisions:

Allied World Brokerage **(2)**
199 Water St 24th Fl
New York, NY 10038
Tel.: (646) 794-0500
Web Site: www.awac.com
Insurance Brokerage Services
S.I.C.: 6411
N.A.I.C.S.: 524210
John McElroy *(Pres)*
Thomas Kennedy *(Sr VP-Pro Lines)*

Allied World Specialty **(2)**
199 Water St 24th Fl
New York, NY 10038
Tel.: (646) 794-0500
Web Site: www.awac.com
Emp.: 200
Insurance Services
S.I.C.: 6411
N.A.I.C.S.: 524298
Todd Germano *(Pres)*
Michael Waitkus *(Sr VP-Gen Property)*

Darwin National Assurance Company **(2)**
1690 New Britain Ave
Farmington, CT 06032
Tel.: (860) 284-1300
Fax: (860) 284-1301
E-Mail: info@darwinpro.com
Web Site: www.darwinpro.com
Emp.: 100
Insurance Services
S.I.C.: 6411
N.A.I.C.S.: 524298
David Newman *(Chief Underwriting Officer & Sr VP)*

Darwin Professional Underwriters, Inc. **(2)**
9 Farm Springs Rd
Farmington, CT 06032 DE
Tel.: (860) 284-1300
Fax: (860) 284-1301
E-Mail: info@darwinpro.com
Web Site: www.darwinpro.com
Sales Range: $200-249.9 Million
Emp.: 163
Liability Insurance Underwriting Services
S.I.C.: 6411
N.A.I.C.S.: 524298
Robert Asensio *(CIO & Sr VP)*
Paul C. Martin *(Chief Actuary & Sr VP)*
Nicole Haggerty *(Sr VP-Practice Lead)*
Mark Rosen *(Sr VP-Claims & Legal)*

Divisions:

Darwin Professional Insurance Agency **(3)**
9 Farm Springs Rd
Farmington, CT 06032 UT
Tel.: (860) 284-1300
Fax: (860) 284-1301
Web Site: www.alliedworld.com
Professional Liability Insurance
S.I.C.: 6399
N.A.I.C.S.: 524128
Bob Asensio *(Gen Mgr)*

Allied World Assurance Company **(1)**
311 S Wacker Dr Ste 1100
Chicago, IL 60606
Tel.: (312) 646-7700
Fax: (312) 922-1159
Insurance Agencies & Brokerages
S.I.C.: 6411
N.A.I.C.S.: 524210
Richard E. Jodoin *(Pres)*

Allied World Reinsurance Company **(1)**
199 Water St 25th Fl
New York, NY 10038
Tel.: (212) 635-5533
Fax: (212) 635-5532
Property & Casualty Insurance Services Provider
S.I.C.: 6331
N.A.I.C.S.: 524126
Keith Lennox *(CFO & Sr VP)*
Thomas Kelly *(Chief Underwriting Officer & COO)*

Darwin Select Insurance Company **(1)**
9 Farm Springs Rd
Farmington, CT 06032
Tel.: (860) 284-1300
Fax: (860) 284-1301
Web Site: www.awac.com
Workers Compensation Underwriting Services
S.I.C.: 6331
N.A.I.C.S.: 524126
Scott Carmilani *(CEO)*

Non-U.S. Subsidiaries:

Allied World Assurance Company (Europe) Limited **(1)**
3rd Floor West 22 Billiter Street
London, EC3M2RY, United Kingdom
Tel.: (44) 2074804410
Fax: (44) 2074804430
Web Site: www.awac.com
Emp.: 60
Direct Property & Casualty Insurance Carriers
S.I.C.: 6351
N.A.I.C.S.: 524126
Julian James *(Pres)*
Anthony Kashuba *(Sr VP & Mgr-European Gen Casualty)*
Gary Lill *(Sr VP & Mgr-Pro Lines)*
Ed Marchelle *(Sr VP & Mgr-Prof Indemnity)*
Enrico Bertagna *(Sr VP-Bus Dev)*

Allied World Assurance Company (Reinsurance) Limited **(1)**
30 St Mary Axe
London, EC3A 8BF, United Kingdom
Tel.: (44) 2072200600
Fax: (44) 2072200601
E-Mail: info@awac.com
Web Site: www.awac.com
Emp.: 68
Insurance Agencies & Brokerages
S.I.C.: 6411
N.A.I.C.S.: 524210
Frank D'Orazio *(Pres)*

ALLIGATOR ENERGY LIMITED

Suite 1 36 Agnes Street
Fortitude Valley, QLD, 4006, Australia
Mailing Address:
PO Box 338
Spring Hill, QLD, 4004, Australia
Tel.: (61) 7 3852 4712
Fax: (61) 7 3852 5684
E-Mail: info@alligatorenergy.com.au
Web Site: www.alligatorenergy.com.au
AGE—(ASX)
Rev.: $174,289
Assets: $18,234,687
Liabilities: $240,401
Net Worth: $17,994,286
Earnings: ($1,510,437)
Fiscal Year-end: 06/30/13
Business Description:
Uranium Exploration Services
S.I.C.: 1094
N.A.I.C.S.: 212291
Personnel:
Robert Sowerby *(CEO)*
Michael Meintjes *(Sec)*
Board of Directors:
Denis Gately
Paul Dickson
John Main
Peter McIntyre
Robert Sowerby
Andrew J. Vigar

ALLIS ELECTRIC CO., LTD.

12F No 19-11 San-Chung Road
Nangang District, Taipei, 11501, Taiwan
Tel.: (886) 2 2655 3456
Fax: (886) 2 2655 2286
E-Mail: sales@allis.com.tw
Web Site: www.allis.com.tw
1514—(TAI)
Sales Range: $100-124.9 Million
Business Description:
Electrical Equipment Mfr
S.I.C.: 1731
N.A.I.C.S.: 238210
Personnel:
Chen-Hsu Sung *(Chm)*

Subsidiaries:

AIR KING Industrial Co., Ltd. **(1)**
3F No 28 Lane 28 Hsing Chung Rd
Taipei, 115, Taiwan
Tel.: (886) 227893886
Fax: (886) 227893885
Web Site: www.allis.com.tw/en/html/about_subs.asp?did=30&mid=27
Emp.: 500
Environmental & Electrical Engineering Services
S.I.C.: 8711
N.A.I.C.S.: 541330
Erick Huang Wang *(Gen Mgr)*

ALLIS COMMUNICATIONS Co., Ltd. **(1)**
10-3 Floor No 31-1 Lane 169 Kang-Ning Street
Hsi-chieh, Taipei, Taiwan
Tel.: (886) 2 2695 2378
Fax: (886) 2 2695 7078
E-Mail: sales@alliscom.com.tw
Web Site: www.alliscom.com.tw
Sls.: $2,000,000
Emp.: 100
Cellular Antenna Mfr
S.I.C.: 3663
N.A.I.C.S.: 334220
David Sung *(Pres)*

LE MIN Industrial Co., Ltd. **(1)**
20 Lane 268 Hsinshu Rd
Hsinchuang, Taipei, 242, Taiwan
Tel.: (886) 222036203
Fax: (886) 222036211
E-Mail: lmei6748@ms22.hinet.net
Web Site: www.allis.com.tw/en/html/about_subs.asp?did=30&mid=27
Emp.: 35
Metal Forging Materials Mfr
S.I.C.: 3462
N.A.I.C.S.: 332111
Chang Trang Yee *(Pres)*

TAIWAN MARINE Electric Co., Ltd. **(1)**
5F No 5 Lane 223 Chung Hsaio East Road Sec 4
Taipei, 106, Taiwan
Tel.: (886) 227219124
Fax: (886) 227527962
E-Mail: service@lemin.com.tw
Web Site: www.tmc1006.com.tw
Electronic Devices Mfr
S.I.C.: 3679
N.A.I.C.S.: 334419

U.S. Subsidiary:

Impact Power, Inc. **(1)**
18218 E McDurmott Ste E
Irvine, CA 92614
Tel.: (949) 477-9198
Fax: (949) 477-9195
E-Mail: sales@impactpwr.com
Web Site: www.impactpwr.com
Electronic Products Mfr
S.I.C.: 3663
N.A.I.C.S.: 334220
Robert Sung *(Pres)*

ALLIS PARTICIPACOES S.A.

Av Brigadeiro Faria Lima 155 - 15 Andar
1452002 Sao Paulo, SP, Brazil
Tel.: (55) 11 3382 6528
Fax: (55) 11 3382 6521
E-Mail: ri@allis.com.br
Web Site: www.allis.com.br
Year Founded: 2007
SAGP3B—(BRAZ)
Business Description:
Human Resource & Outsourcing Services
S.I.C.: 8999
N.A.I.C.S.: 541612
Personnel:
Alexandre Milani de Oliveira Campos *(Dir-IR)*

ALLO FINANCE SA

17 avenue George V
75008 Paris, France
Tel.: (33) 1 44702080
Fax: (33) 1 44702089
E-Mail: conseiller@allofinance.com
Web Site: www.allofinance.com
MLALO—(EUR)
Sales Range: Less than $1 Million
Business Description:
Financial Investment Consulting Services; 25% Owned by Euroland Finance SA
S.I.C.: 6282
N.A.I.C.S.: 523930
Personnel:
Philippe Demetrius Klocanas *(Chm)*
David Grimbert *(CEO)*

ALLOCATE SOFTWARE PLC

1 Church Road
Richmond, TW9 2QE, United Kingdom
Tel.: (44) 2073555555
Fax: (44) 2073555588
E-Mail: info@allocatesoftware.com
Web Site: www.allocatesoftware.com
Year Founded: 1991
ALL—(LSE)
Rev.: $58,547,439
Assets: $65,835,862
Liabilities: $43,411,524
Net Worth: $22,424,339
Earnings: ($2,263,123)
Emp.: 305
Fiscal Year-end: 05/31/13
Business Description:
Workforce Optimization Software Developer
S.I.C.: 7372
N.A.I.C.S.: 511210

Personnel:
Terry H. Osborne *(Chm)*
Ian James Bowles *(CEO)*
Chris D. Gale *(CFO & Sec)*
Iain Bishop *(CTO)*
Board of Directors:
Terry H. Osborne
Ian James Bowles
Lynn Drummond
Chris D. Gale
Richard W. King
J. Ian Lang
Andrew R. D. Pringle
Allen Arthur Albert Swann
Legal Counsel:
Taylor Wessing
5 New Street Square
London, EC4A 3TW, United Kingdom
Tel.: (44) 20 7300 7000
Fax: (44) 20 7300 7100

Subsidiary:

Dynamic Change Limited (1)
The Innovation Centre 2 Keele University Science Park
Keele, Staffordshire, ST5 5NH, United Kingdom
Tel.: (44) 1782667001
Fax: (44) 1782667009
Web Site: www.allocatesoftware.com
Emp.: 20
Business Management Software Development Services
S.I.C.: 7371
N.A.I.C.S.: 541511
Liz Jones *(Mgr-Mktg)*

U.S. Subsidiary:

Manpower Software Inc. (1)
1111 Lincoln Rd Ste 400
Miami Beach, FL 33139
Tel.: (305) 477-3779
Fax: (786) 364-7126
Web Site: www.allocatesoftware.com
Emp.: 50
Workforce Optimization Software Developer
S.I.C.: 7372
N.A.I.C.S.: 511210

Non-U.S. Subsidiaries:

Allocate Software (Malaysia) Sdn Bhd (1)
Suite A604 6th Floor West Wing Wisma Consplant 2 No 7 Jalan SS 16/1
Subang Jaya, Selangor, 47500, Malaysia
Tel.: (60) 356323568
Web Site: www.allocatesoftware.com
Emp.: 4
Software Development Services
S.I.C.: 7371
N.A.I.C.S.: 541511
Robert George Drake *(Gen Mgr)*

Allocate Software Pty. Ltd. (1)
Level 31 RBS Tower 88 Phillip Street
Sydney, NSW, 2000, Australia
Tel.: (61) 282112792
Fax: (61) 282110555
Web Site: www.allocatesoftware.com
Emp.: 10
Workforce Optimization Software Developer
S.I.C.: 7372
N.A.I.C.S.: 511210
Peter Croft *(Gen Mgr-Australia & New Zealand)*

Time Care AB (1)
Sankt G技ransgatan 143
Stockholm Stockholm, Sweden
Tel.: (46) 850551800
E-Mail: information@timecare.se
Web Site: www.timecare.se
Workforce Management Software Mfr
S.I.C.: 7371
N.A.I.C.S.: 541511
Claes Gordon *(Gen Mgr)*

ALLOT COMMUNICATIONS LTD.

22 Hanagar Street Neve Ne'eman Industrial Zone B
Hod Hasharon, 4501317, Israel
Tel.: (972) 9 761 9200
Fax: (972) 9 744 3626
E-Mail: info@allot.com
Web Site: www.allot.com
Year Founded: 1996
ALLT—(NASDAQ)
Rev.: $104,752,000
Assets: $221,791,000
Liabilities: $52,670,000
Net Worth: $169,121,000
Earnings: ($6,738,000)
Emp.: 442
Fiscal Year-end: 12/31/12
Business Description:
Computer Software & Networking Equipment Mfr
S.I.C.: 7372
N.A.I.C.S.: 511210
Personnel:
Shraga Katz *(Chm)*
Rami Hadar *(Pres & CEO)*
Nachum Falek *(CFO)*
Jay Klein *(CTO & VP)*
Itamar Rosen *(Gen Counsel, Sec & VP-Legal Affairs)*
Board of Directors:
Shraga Katz
Dov Baharav
Nurit Benjamini
Rami Hadar
Yigal Jacoby
Steven D. Levy
Transfer Agent:
American Stock Transfer & Trust Company
59 Maiden Ln
New York, NY 10038

U.S. Subsidiary:

Allot Communications Inc. (1)
300 Trade Ctr Ste 4680
Woburn, MA 01801
Tel.: (781) 939-9300
Fax: (781) 939-9393
Toll Free: (877) 255-6826
E-Mail: sales-usa@allot.com
Web Site: www.allot.com
Emp.: 20
Computer Software Developer
S.I.C.: 7372
N.A.I.C.S.: 511210
Vin Costello *(VP & Gen Mgr)*

Non-U.S. Subsidiaries:

Allot Communications (Asia Pacific) Pte. Ltd. (1)
6 Ubi Road 1
Singapore, 408726, Singapore SG
Tel.: (65) 68413020 (100%)
Fax: (65) 67479173
E-Mail: sales-ap@allot.com
Web Site: www.allot.com
Emp.: 50
Software Development & Sales
S.I.C.: 5045
N.A.I.C.S.: 423430

Allot Communications Europe SARL (1)
NCI Green Side Batiment 1B 400 Avenue Roumanille
PO Box 309
06906 Biot, France (100%)
Tel.: (33) 493001167
Fax: (33) 493001165
E-Mail: sales-emea@allot.com
Web Site: www.allotcommunications.com
Emp.: 5
Software Developer & Sales
S.I.C.: 5045
N.A.I.C.S.: 423430
Cosmat Anne *(Mng Dir)*

Allot Communications Japan K.K. (1)
Puri-zaido Ochanomizu 301 Kanda Surugadai 4-2-3
Tokyo, 101 0062, Japan JP
Tel.: (81) 352977668 (100%)
Fax: (81) 352977669
E-Mail: sales-japan@allot.com
Web Site: www.allot.co.jp
Emp.: 200
Software Developer & Whslr
S.I.C.: 5045
N.A.I.C.S.: 423430
Eli Cohen *(VP-Intl Sls)*

Allot Communications UK Limited (1)
3000 Cathedral Hill
Guildford, GU2 7YB, United Kingdom UK
Tel.: (44) 1483243668 (100%)
Fax: (44) 1483 24 35 01
E-Mail: sales-uk@allot.com
Web Site: www.allot.com
Emp.: 6
Software Developer & Whslr
S.I.C.: 5045
N.A.I.C.S.: 423430

ALLOY COMPUTER PRODUCTS (AUSTRALIA) PTY. LTD.

Unit 4 585 Blackburn Rd
Notting Hill, VIC, 3168, Australia
Tel.: (61) 385629000
Fax: (61) 385629099
E-Mail: accounts@alloy.com.au
Web Site: www.alloy.com.au
Emp.: 20
Business Description:
Networking & Communication Products Mfr, Distr & Whslr
S.I.C.: 3663
N.A.I.C.S.: 334220
Personnel:
John Williams *(Mng Dir)*

U.S. Subsidiary:

Alloy Computer Products LLC (1)
1226 Alderwood Ave
Sunnyvale, CA 94089
Tel.: (408) 740-4016
Toll Free: (888) 895-8256
E-Mail: sales@alloycp.com
Web Site: www.alloycp.com
Communication Equipment Mfr & Distr
S.I.C.: 3663
N.A.I.C.S.: 334220
John Williams, *(CEO)*

ALLOY RESOURCES LIMITED

Suite 6 7 The Esplanade
Mount Pleasant, WA, 6153, Australia
Tel.: (61) 893169100
Fax: (61) 893155475
E-Mail: info@alloyres.com
Web Site: www.alloyres.com
AYR—(ASX)
Rev.: $27,519
Assets: $4,278,161
Liabilities: $91,726
Net Worth: $4,186,436
Earnings: ($1,072,547)
Fiscal Year-end: 06/30/13
Business Description:
Mineral Exploration Services
S.I.C.: 1481
N.A.I.C.S.: 213115
Personnel:
Peter Harold *(Chm)*
Andrew Viner *(Mng Dir)*
Kevin Hart *(Sec)*
Board of Directors:
Peter Harold
Kevin Hart
Andre Marschke
Andrew Viner

ALLREAL HOLDING AG

Grabenstrasse 25
6340 Baar, Switzerland
Tel.: (41) 417113303
Fax: (41) 417113309
E-Mail: info@allreal.ch
Web Site: www.allreal.ch
ALLN—(SWX)
Rev.: $897,778,376
Assets: $4,238,921,368
Liabilities: $2,176,664,644
Net Worth: $2,062,256,724
Earnings: $105,773,360
Emp.: 378
Fiscal Year-end: 12/31/12
Business Description:
Real Estate & Portfolio Services
S.I.C.: 6531
N.A.I.C.S.: 531210
Personnel:
Thomas Lustenberger *(Chm)*
Ralph-Thomas Honegger *(Vice Chm)*
Bruno Bettoni *(CEO)*
Roger Herzog *(CFO)*
Board of Directors:
Thomas Lustenberger
Jakob Baer
Ralph-Thomas Honegger
Albert Leiser
Peter Spuhler
Olivier Steimer

Subsidiaries:

Allreal Finance AG (1)
Grabenstrasse 25
6340 Baar, Switzerland
Tel.: (41) 417113303
Fax: (41) 417113309
E-Mail: info@allreal.ch
Web Site: www.allreal.ch
Emp.: 300
Real Estate Financial Services
S.I.C.: 6531
N.A.I.C.S.: 531390
Bruno Bettoni *(CEO)*

Allreal Generalunternehmung AG (1)
Eggbuhlstrasse 15
8050 Zurich, Switzerland
Tel.: (41) 443191111
Fax: (41) 443191112
E-Mail: info@allreal.ch
Emp.: 250
Real Estate Financial Services
S.I.C.: 6531
N.A.I.C.S.: 531390
Markimo A.G. Hoschgasse *(CEO)*

Allreal Home AG (1)
Eggbuhlstrasse 15
8050 Zurich, Switzerland
Tel.: (41) 443191111
Fax: (41) 443191112
E-Mail: info@allreal.ch
Emp.: 300
Real Estate Financial Services
S.I.C.: 6531
N.A.I.C.S.: 531390
Bruno Bettoni *(CEO)*

Allreal Office AG (1)
Eggbuhlstrasse 15
8050 Zurich, Switzerland
Tel.: (41) 443191111
Fax: (41) 443191112
E-Mail: info@allreal.ch
Emp.: 300
Real Estate Financial Services
S.I.C.: 6531
N.A.I.C.S.: 531390
Bruno Bettoni *(Mng Dir)*

Allreal Toni AG (1)
Eggbuhlstrasse 15
8050 Zurich, Switzerland
Tel.: (41) 443191111
Fax: (41) 443191112
E-Mail: info@allreal.ch
Web Site: www.allreal.ch/weballreal/index/main/anleger/cg-allgemein.htm
Real Estate Financial Services
S.I.C.: 6531
N.A.I.C.S.: 531390

Allreal Vulkan AG (1)
Eggbuhlstrasse 15
8050 Zurich, Switzerland
Tel.: (41) 443191111
Fax: (41) 443191112
E-Mail: info@allreal.ch
Web Site: www.allreal.ch/weballreal/index/kontakte.htm
Emp.: 300
Real Estate Financial Services
S.I.C.: 6531
N.A.I.C.S.: 531390

Allreal Holding AG—(Continued)

Bruno Bettoni *(Gen Mgr)*

Allreal West AG (1)
Eggbuhlstrasse 15
8050 Zurich, Switzerland
Tel.: (41) 443191111
Fax: (41) 443191112
E-Mail: info@allreal.ch
Web Site: www.allreal.ch/weballreal/index/kontakte.htm
Emp.: 250
Real Estate Financial Services
S.I.C.: 6531
N.A.I.C.S.: 531390
Bruno Bettoni *(Mng Dir)*

Apalux AG (1)
Eggbuhlstrasse 15
8050 Zurich, Switzerland
Tel.: (41) 443191111
Fax: (41) 44 319 11 12
E-Mail: info@allreal.ch
Real Estate Financial Services
S.I.C.: 6531
N.A.I.C.S.: 531390

ALLSAFE JUNGFALK GMBH & CO. KG

Gerwigstrasse 31
78234 Engen, Germany
Tel.: (49) 773350020
Fax: (49) 7733500247
E-Mail: info@allsafe-group.com
Web Site: www.allsafe-group.com
Sales Range: $50-74.9 Million
Emp.: 136
Business Description:
Winches, Fasteners & Cargo Nets Mfr
S.I.C.: 3536
N.A.I.C.S.: 333923
Personnel:
Detlef Lohmann *(Mng Dir)*

ALLSEC TECHNOLOGIES LIMITED

46B Velachery Main Road
Velachery, Chennai, 600 042, India
Tel.: (91) 4442997070
Fax: (91) 4422447077
Web Site: www.allsectech.com
Year Founded: 1998
ALLSEC—(NSE)
Rev.: $60,112,242
Assets: $29,899,458
Liabilities: $9,193,986
Net Worth: $20,705,472
Earnings: $361,530
Emp.: 5,513
Fiscal Year-end: 03/31/13
Business Description:
Business Process Outsourcing Services
S.I.C.: 7389
N.A.I.C.S.: 561990
Personnel:
Adi Saravanan *(Co-Founder & Pres)*
Ramamoorthi Jagadish *(Co-Founder & CEO)*
A. Mohan Kumar *(Compliance Officer, Sec & Asst Gen Mgr-Legal)*
R. Vaithiyanathan *(Sr VP-Ops & HR)*
Rafael A. Martinez *(Sr VP-Allsectech Inc)*
Board of Directors:
Bala V. Balachandran
Manish Gaur
Ramamoorthi Jagadish
T. Anantha Narayanan
Mahesh Parasuraman
Adi Saravanan
Aravinthan Wijay
Transfer Agent:
Karvy Computershare Private Limited
Plot No 17 to 24 Vittalrao Nagar Madhapur
Hyderabad, India

ALLSHIPS LTD.

80 Kifissias Avenue
Maroussi, Athens, 15125, Greece
Tel.: (30) 210 809 0570
Fax: (30) 210 809 9585
Year Founded: 1998
Sales Range: Less than $1 Million
Emp.: 2
Business Description:
Ship Repair Services
S.I.C.: 3731
N.A.I.C.S.: 336611
Personnel:
George Economou *(Chm & Pres)*
Niki Fotiou *(CFO & Sec)*
Board of Directors:
George Economou
Niki Fotiou

ALLTEK TECHNOLOGY CORPORATION

9F No 360 Ruei Guang Rd
114 Neihu, Taipei, Taiwan
Tel.: (886) 226275859
Fax: (886) 226275869
E-Mail: business@alltek.com
Web Site: www.alltek.com
3209—(TAI)
Sales Range: $200-249.9 Million
Business Description:
Wireless Communication Equipment Distr
S.I.C.: 4812
N.A.I.C.S.: 517210
Personnel:
Mu-Tsung Wang *(Chm)*
Yuh-Twen Wu *(Pres)*
Hung-Chang Hsieh *(Exec VP)*

Non-U.S. Subsidiary:

Alltek Technology (Singapore) Pte. Ltd. (1)
Block 3 Ang Mo Kio Industrial Park 2A AMK Tech 1 07-14
Singapore, 568050, Singapore
Tel.: (65) 6 483 1126
Fax: (65) 6 483 1128
E-Mail: voip@alltekasia.com
Web Site: www.alltekasia.com
Emp.: 3
Voice & Telecommunication Services
S.I.C.: 4899
N.A.I.C.S.: 517919
Jason Ong *(Mgr-Bus Dev)*

ALLTRONICS HOLDINGS LIMITED

Room 1108 11/F Eastwood Centre
No 5 A Kung Ngam Village Road
Shau Kei Wan, Hong Kong, China (Hong Kong)
Tel.: (852) 29775666
Fax: (852) 29775633
E-Mail: info@alltronics.com.hk
Web Site: www.alltronics.com.hk
0833—(HKG)
Rev.: $101,701,318
Assets: $60,872,653
Liabilities: $31,568,636
Net Worth: $29,304,016
Earnings: $4,808,030
Emp.: 2,610
Fiscal Year-end: 12/31/12
Business Description:
Electronic Products Mfr
S.I.C.: 3679
N.A.I.C.S.: 334419
Personnel:
Yin Kee Lam *(Co-Founder, Chm & CEO)*
Po Wah Yeung *(Co-Founder)*
Fuk Cheung Leung *(Sec)*
Board of Directors:
Yin Kee Lam
William Chung Yue Fan
Eric Chee Tai Lam
Kam Wah Leung
Kin Hung So
Robert Ming Kim Yau
Chi Ying Yeung
Po Wah Yeung

Royal Bank of Canada Trust Company (Cayman) Limited
4th Floor Royal Bank House 24 Shedden Road
Georgetown, Cayman Islands

Transfer Agents:
Tricor Tengis Limited
26/F Tesbury Centre, 28 Queens Road East
Hong Kong, China (Hong Kong)

Royal Bank of Canada Trust Company (Cayman) Limited
4th Floor Royal Bank House 24 Shedden Road
Georgetown, Cayman Islands

ALLTRUE INVESTMENTS PLC

Finsgate 5 7 Cranwood St
London, EC1V 9EE, United Kingdom
Tel.: (44) 2072513762
Web Site: www.alltrueinvestments.co.uk
ATR—(AIM)
Sales Range: $1-9.9 Million
Business Description:
investment Services
S.I.C.: 6211
N.A.I.C.S.: 523999
Personnel:
Leo Ernest Vaughan Knifton *(Chm)*
Stephen Vaughan Oakes *(CEO)*
Board of Directors:
Leo Ernest Vaughan Knifton
Stephen Vaughan Oakes
John Richard Shaw
William Nigel Valentine Weller
Legal Counsel:
Pritchard Englefield
14 New Street
London, EC2M 4HE, United Kingdom

ALM. BRAND A/S

Midtermolen 7
2100 Copenhagen, Denmark
Tel.: (45) 35474747
Fax: (45) 35473547
E-Mail: almbrand@almbrand.dk
Web Site: www.almbrand.dk
ALMB—(CSE)
Rev.: $1,325,104,920
Assets: $7,675,941,240
Liabilities: $6,863,239,080
Net Worth: $812,702,160
Earnings: $57,174,120
Emp.: 1,592
Fiscal Year-end: 12/31/12
Business Description:
Commercial Banking Services
S.I.C.: 6029
N.A.I.C.S.: 522110
Personnel:
Jorgen H. Mikkelsen *(Chm)*
Boris Norgaard Kjeldsen *(Deputy Chm & Mng Dir)*
Soren Boe Mortensen *(CEO & Member-Mgmt Bd)*
Anne Mette Barfoed *(CFO)*
Brian Wahl Olsen *(Sr VP-Claims Processing)*
Board of Directors:
Jorgen H. Mikkelsen
Henrik Christensen
Per Dahlbom
Per Viggo Hasling Frandsen
Helle Lasby Frederiksen
Henning Kaffka
Boris Norgaard Kjeldsen
Susanne Larsen
Arne Nielsen
Jan Skytte Pedersen

ALM EQUITY AB

Jakobsbergsgatan 22
SE-111 44 Stockholm, Sweden
Tel.: (46) 8 562 303 00
Fax: (46) 8 550 029 68
E-Mail: info@almequity.se
Web Site: www.almequity.se
Year Founded: 2006
ALM—(OMX)
Sales Range: $25-49.9 Million
Emp.: 11
Business Description:
Real Estate Development & Investment Services
S.I.C.: 6552
N.A.I.C.S.: 237210
Personnel:
Maria Wideroth *(Chm)*
Joakim Alm *(Pres & CEO)*
Urban Eriksson *(CFO)*
Board of Directors:
Maria Wideroth
Joakim Alm
Ingemar Rindstig
Johan Unger
Gerard Versteegh
Johan Wachtmeister

ALMA MARITIME LIMITED

58 Vouliagmenis Avenue & 37 Asklipiou Street
166 75 Glyfada, Greece
Tel.: (30) 2111024000
Fax: (30) 2109604210
E-Mail: alma@almamaritime.com
Web Site: www.almamaritime.com
Year Founded: 2008
Emp.: 14
Business Description:
Deep Sea Freight Transportation Services
S.I.C.: 4412
N.A.I.C.S.: 483111
Personnel:
Stamatis Molaris *(Chm & CEO)*
Stewart Crawford *(CFO)*
Board of Directors:
Stamatis Molaris
Hans J. Mende

ALMA MARKET S.A.

ul Pilotow 6
30-964 Krakow, Poland
Tel.: (48) 126276320
Fax: (48) 126276165
E-Mail: info@almamarket.pl
Web Site: www.almamarket.pl
ALM—(WAR)
Rev.: $485,059,849
Assets: $239,626,599
Liabilities: $145,586,772
Net Worth: $94,039,827
Earnings: $3,202,696
Fiscal Year-end: 12/31/12
Business Description:
Consumer Goods Selling Services
S.I.C.: 5122
N.A.I.C.S.: 424210
Personnel:
Andrzej Wyrobiec *(Chm-Supervisory Bd)*
Jerzy Mazgaj *(Chm-Mgmt Bd)*
Barbara Mazgaj *(Vice Chm-Supervisory Bd)*
Mariusz Wojdon *(Vice Chm-Mgmt Bd & Mng Dir)*
Malgorzata Moska *(Vice Chm-Mgmt Bd, Deputy Gen Dir & Dir-Sls)*
Supervisory Board of Directors:
Andrzej Wyrobiec
Krystyna Byczkowska
Barbara Mazgaj

Subsidiaries:

Alma Development Sp. z o.o. (1)
Pilotow 6
30-964 Krakow, Lesser Poland, Poland
Tel.: (48) 126276115

Fax: (48) 126276165
E-Mail: bzawillo@almamarket.pl
Real Estate Property Development Services
S.I.C.: 6531
N.A.I.C.S.: 531210
Mazgaj Jerzy *(Chm)*

Krakowski Kredens Sp. z o.o. **(1)**
Grodzka Street Number 7 First Floor
31-006 Krakow, Lesser Poland, Poland
Tel.: (48) 123705801
Fax: (48) 123705800
E-Mail: info@krakowskikredens.pl
Web Site: www.krakowskikredens.pl
Emp.: 2,007
Convenience Food Products Retailer
S.I.C.: 5411
N.A.I.C.S.: 445120
Ewa Lewek *(Mng Dir)*

Paradise Group Sp. z o. o. **(1)**
ul Grodzka 7
31-006 Krakow, Lesser Poland, Poland
Tel.: (48) 124218280
Fax: (48) 124302427
E-Mail: group@paradisegroup.pl
Web Site: www.paradisegroup.pl
Luxury Fashion Apparels Retailer
S.I.C.: 5699
N.A.I.C.S.: 448150
Kaczmarczyk Mariusz Ryszard *(Chm)*

ALMA MEDIA CORPORATION

Alvar Aallon katu 3 C
PO Box 140
FI-00100 Helsinki, Finland
Tel.: (358) 10665000
Fax: (358) 106652270
E-Mail: corporate.comms@almamedia.fi
Web Site: www.almamedia.fi
Year Founded: 1998
ALN1V—(HEL)
Rev.: $430,909,017
Assets: $329,946,267
Liabilities: $216,194,902
Net Worth: $113,751,365
Earnings: $23,423,358
Emp.: 2,851
Fiscal Year-end: 12/31/12

Business Description:
Media Holding Company; Newspaper, Magazine & Internet Publishing & Graphic Services
S.I.C.: 6719
N.A.I.C.S.: 551112

Personnel:
Harri Suutari *(Chm)*
Kai Telanne *(Pres & CEO)*
Juha Nuutinen *(CFO)*
Mikko Korttila *(Gen Counsel-Legal Affairs, M&A & Corp Dev)*
Raimo Makila *(Sr VP & Head-Marketplaces)*
Kari Juutilainen *(Sr VP-Reg Media)*
Kari Kivela *(Sr VP)*
Juha-Petri Loimovuori *(Sr VP-Kauppalehti Grp)*
Minna Nissinen *(Sr VP-Diverso)*

Board of Directors:
Harri Suutari
Timo Aukia
Niklas Herlin
Petri Niemisvirta
Perttu Rinta
Kai Seikku
Erkki Solja
Catharina Stackelberg-Hammaren

Group:

Kauppalehti Oy **(1)**
Etelaesplanadi 20 3rd Fl
FIN-00130 Helsinki, Finland FI
Mailing Address: (100%)
PL 189
FIN-00101 Helsinki, Finland
Tel.: (358) 10665101
Fax: (358) 106652366
E-Mail: hannu.leinonen@kauppalehti.fi
Web Site: www.kauppalehti.fi
Sales Range: $75-99.9 Million
Emp.: 499
Business News & Information Syndicate & Publisher
S.I.C.: 2711
N.A.I.C.S.: 511110
Juha-Petri Loimovuori *(Grp Mng Dir)*

Subsidiaries:

Alma 360 Custom Media **(1)**
Konalantie 6-8 B 3rd Floor
Helsinki, 370, Finland
Tel.: (358) 1066 5102
Fax: (358) 1066 52533
Web Site: www.alma360.fi
Emp.: 5
Newspaper & Magazine Publishing Services
S.I.C.: 2711
N.A.I.C.S.: 511110
Petri Laentinen *(Mng Dir)*

Alma Intermedia Oy **(1)**
Pohjoesranta 11e
Pori, 28100, Finland
Tel.: (358) 25221400
Emp.: 24
Online Directory & Telemarketing Services
S.I.C.: 2741
N.A.I.C.S.: 519130
Pasi Vaelimaa *(Mng Dir)*

Alma Manu Oy **(1)**
Itainenkatu 11
Tampere, 33210, Finland
Tel.: (358) 1066 5112
Fax: (358) 1066 53481
Web Site: www.almamanu.fi
Emp.: 120
Newspaper Printing & Publishing Services
S.I.C.: 2759
N.A.I.C.S.: 323111
Helvi Liukkaala *(Gen Mgr)*

Alma Media Interactive Oy **(1)**
Itainenkatu 11
PO Box 327
FIN 33101 Tampere, Finland (100%)
Tel.: (358) 106338200
Fax: (358) 106653503
Web Site: www.etuovi.com
Emp.: 20
S.I.C.: 4833
N.A.I.C.S.: 515120
Kai Telanne *(Pres)*

Alma Media Ventures Oy **(1)**
Etelaesplanadi 20
00130 Helsinki, Finland
Tel.: (358) 10665000
Newspaper Publishing Services
S.I.C.: 2711
N.A.I.C.S.: 511110

Alma Mediapartners Oy **(1)**
Aleksanterinkatu 9
Helsinki, 100, Finland
Tel.: (358) 1066 5000
Fax: (358) 6653466
E-Mail: info@almamedia.fi
Web Site: www.almamedia.fi
Advertising Agency Services
S.I.C.: 7311
N.A.I.C.S.: 541810

Alpress Oy **(1)**
Etelaesplanadi 14
PO Box 140
FIN 00101 Helsinki, Finland (100%)
Tel.: (358) 950771
Fax: (358) 95078733
E-Mail: info@almamedia.fi
Emp.: 30
Newspaper & Magazine Publishing
S.I.C.: 2711
N.A.I.C.S.: 511110

Subsidiaries:

Alpress Oy **(2)**
Itainenkatu 11
PO Box 327
FIN 33201 Tampere, Finland (100%)
Tel.: (358) 32666111
Fax: (358) 106653471
E-Mail: albilaajaealbelu@aamulehei.fi
Web Site: www.aamulehei.fi
Emp.: 50
S.I.C.: 4833
N.A.I.C.S.: 515120
Juha Ruotsalainen *(CEO)*

Kainuun Sanomain Kirjapaino Oy **(2)**
Kayppakapy
PO Box 150
FIN 87700 Kajaani, Finland (100%)
Tel.: (358) 861661
Fax: (358) 8623013
E-Mail: ks.toiyntys@kainuunsanomat.fi
Web Site: www.kainuunsanomat.fi
Emp.: 100
S.I.C.: 4833
N.A.I.C.S.: 515120
Matti Ilmiualta *(Pres)*

Lapin Kansa Oy **(2)**
Veitikantie 2 8
96100 Rovaniemi, Finland (100%)
Tel.: (358) 10665022
E-Mail: lktoimitus@lapinkansa.fi
Web Site: www.lapinkansa.fi
Emp.: 200
Television Broadcasting
S.I.C.: 4833
N.A.I.C.S.: 515120

Pohjolan Sanomat Oyj **(2)**
Sairaalakatu 2
94100 Kemi, Finland (100%)
Tel.: (358) 10665011
Fax: (358) 106656313
E-Mail: heikki.laakkola@pohjolansanomat.fi
Web Site: www.pohjolansanomat.fi
Sales Range: $10-24.9 Million
Emp.: 80
S.I.C.: 4833
N.A.I.C.S.: 515120
Heikki Laakkola *(Editor-in-Chief)*

Suomen Paikallissanomat Oy **(2)**
Ita inenkatu 11 33210
PO Box 327
33101 Tampere, Finland (100%)
Tel.: (358) 32666111
Fax: (358) 32666305
Web Site: www.stsp.fi
Emp.: 100
S.I.C.: 4833
N.A.I.C.S.: 515120

Kotikokki.net Oy **(1)**
Simonkatu 12 A 4B
Helsinki, 00100, Finland
Tel.: (358) 4059 20671
Web Site: www.kotikokki.net
Online Directory Publishing Services
S.I.C.: 2741
N.A.I.C.S.: 519130
Asmo Halinen *(Gen Mgr)*

Kustannus Oy Aamulehti **(1)**
Itainenkatu 11
PO Box 327
FIN 33101 Tampere, Finland (100%)
Tel.: (358) 32666111
Fax: (358) 32238890
Web Site: www.aamulehti.fi
Sales Range: $100-124.9 Million
Emp.: 200
Television Broadcasting
S.I.C.: 4833
N.A.I.C.S.: 515120
Mervi Juutilainen *(Mng Dir)*

Kustannusosakeyhtio Iltalehti **(1)**
Aleksanterinkatu 9
Helsinki, 100, Finland
Tel.: (358) 1066 5100
Fax: (358) 106652097
Newspaper Publishing & Online Portal Services
S.I.C.: 2711
N.A.I.C.S.: 511110
Kari Kivela *(Mng Dir)*

Monster Oy **(1)**
Alvar Aallon katu 3 C
Helsinki, 100, Finland
Tel.: (358) 106652180
E-Mail: monster.tekniikka@monster.fi
Emp.: 2
Online Recruitment Services
S.I.C.: 2741
N.A.I.C.S.: 519130
Marja Pylkkanen *(Gen Mgr)*

Suomalainen Lehtitaino Oy **(1)**
Ilmalankatu 2C
PO Box 139
240 Helsinki, Finland (100%)
Tel.: (358) 950782
Fax: (358) 95078519
Web Site: www.alprint.fi
Graphic Services
S.I.C.: 7336
N.A.I.C.S.: 541430

Subsidiaries:

Acta Print Tampere **(2)**
Hietalahdenranta 17
00180 Tampere, Finland
Tel.: (358) 106185111
Fax: (358) 106185299
Web Site: www.actaprint.fi
Commercial Printing
S.I.C.: 2759
N.A.I.C.S.: 323111
Seppo Aaltonen *(Mng Dir)*

Alprint Rovaniemi **(2)**
Veitikantie 2 8
FIN 6100 Rovaniemi, Finland
Tel.: (358) 16320011
Fax: (358) 163200345
Web Site: www.lapinkansa.fi
Emp.: 200
Newspaper
S.I.C.: 2711
N.A.I.C.S.: 511110

Non-U.S. Subsidiary:

Ectaprint Oy **(2)**
Armjanskii Per Dom 11 2A Str 1
101983 Moscow, Russia (64%)
Tel.: (7) 4959374144
Fax: (7) 4959374134
Web Site: www.ectaprint.fi
Emp.: 5
Commercial Printing
S.I.C.: 2759
N.A.I.C.S.: 323111

Suomen Business Viestinta SBV Oy **(1)**
Munkkiniemen Puistotie 25
Helsinki, 00330, Finland
Tel.: (358) 10665106
Fax: (358) 9348 15540
Web Site: www.sbv.fi
Emp.: 50
Advertising Agency Services
S.I.C.: 7311
N.A.I.C.S.: 541810
Petri Lantinen *(Gen Mgr)*

Suunnittelutoimisto TTNK Helsinki Oy **(1)**
Palvelukeskus
PL 900
33101 Tampere, Finland
Tel.: (358) 4076 11349
Digital Marketing Communication Services
S.I.C.: 8742
N.A.I.C.S.: 541613

Affiliate:

Forssa Print **(1)**
Teerivuorenkatu 5
FIN 33300 Tampere, Finland (36%)
Tel.: (358) 106185111
Fax: (358) 106185209
Web Site: www.actaprint.fi
Emp.: 300
Commercial Printing
S.I.C.: 2759
N.A.I.C.S.: 323111

Non-U.S. Subsidiaries:

AS Kinnisvaraportaal **(1)**
Parnu mnt 158/1
Tallinn, Harjumaa, 11317, Estonia
Tel.: (372) 6660360
Fax: (372) 6660366
E-Mail: klienditugi@city24.ee
Web Site: www.city24.ee
Emp.: 11
Real Estate Portal Services
S.I.C.: 2741
N.A.I.C.S.: 519130
Karin Noppel *(Gen Mgr)*

Bovision AB **(1)**
Svensknabbevagen 26
393 51 Kalmar, Sweden
Tel.: (46) 480 47 75 50
Fax: (46) 4 80 44 74 71

Alma Media Corporation—(Continued)

E-Mail: info@bovision.se
Online Business Portal Services
S.I.C.: 2741
N.A.I.C.S.: 519130

City24 Polska Sp. z.o.o. (1)
ul E Ciolka 11A Lok 306
01-445 Warsaw, Poland
Tel.: (48) 22 533 62 27
Fax: (48) 22 533 65 22
E-Mail: info@citydom24.pl
Web Site: www.citydom24.pl
Emp.: 4
Online Property Advertising Services
S.I.C.: 2741
N.A.I.C.S.: 519130
Monika Horeczy *(Gen Mgr)*

ETA Uudistetalituse OU (1)
Toompuiestee 35
15043 Tallinn, Estonia
Tel.: (372) 6108865
Fax: (372) 6108802
E-Mail: meedia@monitooring.ee
Web Site: www.monitooring.ee
Emp.: 20
Media Monitoring & Analysis Services
S.I.C.: 7313
N.A.I.C.S.: 541840
Juha-Petri Loimovuori *(Chm)*

Mascus A/S (1)
Agro Food Park 15
8200 Arhus, Denmark
Tel.: (45) 33 39 47 97
Fax: (45) 33 39 37 99
Online Advertising & Online Vehicle Retail Services
S.I.C.: 7319
N.A.I.C.S.: 541890
Charlotte Villum Jensen *(Country Mgr & Mgr-Sls)*

Mediaskopas UAB (1)
Jogailos St 9/1
1116 Vilnius, Lithuania
Tel.: (370) 5 213 59 50
Fax: (370) 2130019
E-Mail: info@mediaskopas.lt
Web Site: www.mediaskopas.lt
Emp.: 47
Media Monitoring Services
S.I.C.: 7313
N.A.I.C.S.: 541840
Vilune Dobravolskaite *(Dir-Media Monitoring & Translations)*

Objektvision AB (1)
Svensknabbevagen 26
393 51 Kalmar, Sweden
Tel.: (46) 480 47 75 60
Fax: (46) 480 47 75 65
E-Mail: info@objektvision.se
Emp.: 12
Online Property Advertising Services
S.I.C.: 2741
N.A.I.C.S.: 519130
Ulf Magnusson *(Gen Mgr)*

SIA City24 (1)
A Caka Street 92/13a
1011 Riga, Latvia
Tel.: (371) 67491017
Fax: (371) 67491046
E-Mail: info@city24.lv
Web Site: www.city24.lv
Real Estate Advertising Services
S.I.C.: 2741
N.A.I.C.S.: 519130
Kristaps Pagils *(Mgr-Sls)*

UAB City24 (1)
J Tumo-Vaizganto Str 8-2
1108 Vilnius, Lithuania
Tel.: (370) 5 2487488
Fax: (370) 5 2487488
E-Mail: info@city24.lt
Web Site: www.city24.lt
Emp.: 3
Real Estate Internet Portal Services
S.I.C.: 2741
N.A.I.C.S.: 519130
Skaiste Kiausaite *(Mgr-Customer Support)*

ALMAC SCIENCES GROUP LTD.

(d/b/a Almac Group)
Almac House 20 Seagoe Industrial Estate
Craigavon, BT63 5QD, United Kingdom
Tel.: (44) 2838332200
Fax: (44) 2838332299
E-Mail: info@almacgroup.com
Web Site: www.almacgroup.com
Year Founded: 1968
Emp.: 3,000

Business Description:
Developer & Marketer of Pharmaceutical Products
S.I.C.: 8731
N.A.I.C.S.: 541712

Personnel:
Alan Armstrong *(Chm & CEO)*
Colin Hayburn *(Gen Counsel, Sec & Exec Dir)*

Divisions:

Almac Clinical Services (1)
9 Charlestown Rd
Seagoe Industrial Estate, Craigavon, BT63 5PW, United Kingdom
Tel.: (44) 2838362436
Fax: (44) 2838363800
E-Mail: info@cts-almac.com
Web Site: www.cts-almac.com
Emp.: 1,100
Management Services for Manufacture, Packaging, Labeling, Release, Distribution, Return & Analysis of Clinical Trial Supplies
S.I.C.: 2834
N.A.I.C.S.: 325412
Robert Dunlop *(Pres & Mng Dir)*

Almac Diagnostics (1)
Marty Murphy Building
19 Seagoe Industrial Estate, Craigavon, BT63 5QD, United Kingdom
Tel.: (44) 2838337575
Fax: (44) 2838398676
E-Mail: diagnostics@almacgroup.com
Emp.: 50
Developer of Genomic Expression Services for the Diagnosis & Treatment of Cancer
S.I.C.: 2835
N.A.I.C.S.: 325413
Patrick G. Johnston *(Co-Founder & Chm)*
Paul Harkin *(Pres & Mng Dir)*

Almac Pharma Services (1)
22 Seagoe Industrial Estate
Craigavon, BT63 5QD, United Kingdom
Tel.: (44) 2838363363
Fax: (44) 2838363300
E-Mail: info@pdms-almac.com
Emp.: 200
Pharmaceutical Development, Analysis, Manufacturing & Packaging Services
S.I.C.: 2834
N.A.I.C.S.: 325412
Graeme McBurney *(Pres & Mng Dir)*

Almac Sciences (1)
Almac House
20 Seagoe Industrial Estate, Craigavon, BT63 5QD, United Kingdom
Tel.: (44) 2838332200
Fax: (44) 2838332299
E-Mail: info@almacgroup.com
Web Site: www.css-almac.com
Emp.: 2,500
Chemical Research & Development Services for Pharmaceutical Industry
S.I.C.: 8731
N.A.I.C.S.: 541712
Stephen Barr *(Pres & Mng Dir)*

Subsidiary:

Galen Limited (1)
Seagoe Industrial Estate
Craigavon, BT63 5UA, United Kingdom
Tel.: (44) 2838334974
Fax: (44) 2838350206
E-Mail: customer.services@galen.co.uk
Web Site: www.galen.co.uk
Sls.: $34,439,510
Emp.: 40
Pharmaceutical Product Marketing Services
S.I.C.: 5122
N.A.I.C.S.: 424210
Alan Armstrong *(CEO)*
Ken Ross *(Sr VP-Sls & Mktg)*

U.S. Division:

Almac Clinical Technologies (1)
25 Fretz Rd
Souderton, PA 18964
Tel.: (215) 660-8500
Fax: (215) 660-8501
E-Mail: clinicaltechnologies@almacgroup.com
Web Site: www.almacgroup.com
Emp.: 800
Interactive Support Services & Online Data Collection for Clinical Trials
S.I.C.: 8999
N.A.I.C.S.: 541690
Jim Murphy *(Pres)*

ALMACENAJES, S.A.

Via Fernandez de Cordoba Vista Hermosa Calle Principal Corregimiento
Apartado Postal 0816-03585
Panama, Panama
Tel.: (507) 224 1111
Fax: (507) 261 1977
E-Mail: contapc@procapi.com
Web Site: www.almacenajes.net
ALMC—(PAN)
Sales Range: $1-9.9 Million
Emp.: 53

Business Description:
Warehousing & Storage Services
S.I.C.: 4225
N.A.I.C.S.: 493110

Personnel:
Carlos Valencia Correa *(Pres)*
Monica Valencia *(Treas)*
Marissa Valencia *(Sec)*

ALMADEN MINERALS LTD.

750 West Pender Street 1103
Vancouver, BC, V6T 2T8, Canada
Tel.: (604) 689-7644
Fax: (604) 689-7645
E-Mail: info@almadenminerals.com
Web Site: www.almadenminerals.com
AAU—(NYSEMKT TSX)
Rev.: $297,378
Assets: $48,838,505
Liabilities: $1,054,485
Net Worth: $47,784,020
Earnings: ($10,177,152)
Emp.: 7
Fiscal Year-end: 12/31/12

Business Description:
Mineral, Gold & Silver Mining Services
S.I.C.: 1099
N.A.I.C.S.: 212299

Personnel:
James Duane Poliquin *(Chm)*
Morgan J. Poliquin *(Pres & CEO)*
Korm Trieu *(CFO)*
Dione Bitzer *(Controller & Sec)*

Board of Directors:
James Duane Poliquin
Mark Thomas Brown
Gerald George Carlson
John D. McCleary
Joseph Hilton Montgomery
Morgan J. Poliquin
Barry W. Smee

Computershare Investor Services Inc.
510 Burrard St 2nd Floor
Vancouver, BC, V6C 3B9, Canada
Tel.: (604) 661-9400

Transfer Agents:
Computershare Investor Services Inc.
510 Burrard St 2nd Floor
Vancouver, BC, V6C 3B9, Canada
Tel.: (604) 661-9400

Computershare Investor Services Inc.
Toronto, ON, Canada

ALMANA NETWORKS SOLUTIONS

Financial Square Building No 1 1st Floor Office No 5 C-Ring Road
PO Box 55229
Doha, Qatar
Tel.: (974) 44073000
Fax: (974) 44622809
E-Mail: info@almananetworks.com
Web Site: WWW.almananetworks.com
Year Founded: 2005

Business Description:
Computer & Communications Systems Design Services
S.I.C.: 7373
N.A.I.C.S.: 541512

Personnel:
Swaraj Bontula *(CEO)*

ALMARAI COMPANY LTD.

Almarai Building Circle Road Exit 7
PO Box 8524
Al Izdihar District, Riyadh, 11492, Saudi Arabia
Tel.: (966) 14700005
Fax: (966) 14701555
E-Mail: info@almarai.com
Web Site: www.almarai.com
Year Founded: 1976
2280—(SAU)
Sls.: $2,631,841,835
Assets: $5,197,815,962
Liabilities: $3,187,399,824
Net Worth: $2,010,416,138
Earnings: $383,639,236
Emp.: 22,224
Fiscal Year-end: 12/31/12

Business Description:
Dairy Foods & Agricultural Services
S.I.C.: 5143
N.A.I.C.S.: 424430

Personnel:
Sultan Mohammed Saud Al Kabir *(Chm)*
Abdullah Abdulkarim *(Asst CEO)*
Abdulrahman Al Fadley *(CEO)*
Abdulrahman Abdulaziz Al Muhanna *(Mng Dir)*
Paul Louis Gay *(CFO)*
Georges Schorderet *(COO)*

Board of Directors:
Sultan Mohammed Saud Al Kabir
Abdulrahman Abdulaziz Al Muhanna
Suliman Abdulgader Al Muhaideb
Ibrahim Hassan Mohammed Al Madhoun
Ibrahim Mohammed Ibrahim Alissa
Abdulraouf Mohammed Abdullah Mana'a
Nasser Mohammed Humoud Al Muttawa
Musa Omran Al Omran
Naif Sultan Mohammed Saud Al Kabeer

Subsidiary:

Hail Agricultural Development Company (1)
PO Box 106
81411 Hail, Saudi Arabia
Tel.: (966) 65200011
Fax: (966) 65200022
E-Mail: info@hadco.com.sa
Web Site: www.hadco.com.sa
Sales Range: $50-74.9 Million
Emp.: 3,000
Wheat, Alfalfa, Yellow Corn, Dates, Grapes, Chicken, Poultry Feed & Animal Feed
S.I.C.: 0191
N.A.I.C.S.: 111998

Non-U.S. Subsidiary:

Continental Farmers Group PLC (1)
33/37 Athol Street
Douglas, IM1 1LB, Isle of Man IM

Tel.: (44) 1624 647 647
E-Mail: info@continentalfarmersgroup.com
Web Site: www.continentalfarmersgroup.com
Emp.: 414
Farming
S.I.C.: 0119
N.A.I.C.S.: 111199
Abdulrahman Al Fadley *(Chm)*
Mark C. Laird *(CEO)*
Alastair Stewart *(CFO)*

ALMATY INTERNATIONAL AIRPORT JSC

Ul Maylina 2
050039 Almaty, Kazakhstan
Tel.: (7) 727 2303333
Web Site: www.alaport.com
Year Founded: 1935
ARAL—(KAZ)
Business Description:
Airport Operations
S.I.C.: 4581
N.A.I.C.S.: 488119
Personnel:
Aibol Anuarovich *(Pres)*

ALMATYENERGOSBYT LLP

7a Dostyk Ave
050002 Almaty, Kazakhstan
Tel.: (7) 7272929292
Fax: (7) 7272928381
Web Site: www.esalmaty.kz
Year Founded: 2006
AESO—(KAZ)
Sales Range: $75-99.9 Million
Emp.: 540
Business Description:
Electric Power Distr
S.I.C.: 4931
N.A.I.C.S.: 221122
Personnel:
Mikhail Gamburger *(Dir Gen)*
Iskakov Myra Erbalaevna *(Deputy Dir Gen-Economy & Fin)*
Beisembaev Arman Kusanovich *(Deputy Dir Gen-New Dev)*

ALMATYTEMIR JSC

2 Auezov Street
050026 Almaty, Kazakhstan
Tel.: (7) 727 3791975
Fax: (7) 727 3691976
E-Mail: zhetysu2003@mail.ru
Web Site: www.almatytemir.kz
ALTM—(KAZ)
Sales Range: $1-9.9 Million
Business Description:
Storehouse Facilities Leasing; Metal Product Sales
S.I.C.: 4225
N.A.I.C.S.: 531130
Personnel:
Kayrolla Kasymkhanov *(Pres)*

ALMEDAHLS OY

Rahkasammaleenkatu 6
20780 Kaarina, Finland
Tel.: (358) 22766366
Fax: (358) 22766365
E-Mail: info@almedahls.fi
Web Site: www.almedahls.fi
Sales Range: $25-49.9 Million
Emp.: 175
Fiscal Year-end: 12/31/12
Business Description:
Textile Mfr
S.I.C.: 2389
N.A.I.C.S.: 314999
Personnel:
Risto Junninen *(Mgr-Pur & Ops)*
Non-U.S. Subsidiary:

Almedahl-Kinna AB **(1)**
Box 265
SE 511 23 Kinna, Sweden
Tel.: (46) 320209500
Fax: (46) 320209530
E-Mail: info@almedahl-kinna.se
Web Site: www.almedahl-kinna.se
Emp.: 100
Textile Mfr
S.I.C.: 2392
N.A.I.C.S.: 314120
Tor Bertil Ahlbom *(Mgr-Mktg)*

Subsidiary:

Ahmedahls AB **(2)**
Lyddevagen 8 Box 265
Box 265
SE 511 23 Kinna, Sweden
Tel.: (46) 33480100
Fax: (46) 33480140
E-Mail: info.contract@almedahls.se
Web Site: www.almedahls.se
Emp.: 20
Household Textiles Mfr
S.I.C.: 2391
N.A.I.C.S.: 314120
Anders Lundstedt *(Mgr-Mktg & Sls)*

ALMEDIO, INC.

32-13 2-chome Sakae-cho
Higashimurayama-shi, Tokyo, 189-0013, Japan
Tel.: (81) 423971780
Fax: (81) 423929256
E-Mail: tm-sales@almedio.co.jp
Web Site: www.almedio.co.jp
Year Founded: 1981
7859—(TKS)
Sales Range: $25-49.9 Million
Emp.: 120
Business Description:
Test Tapes & Discs Mfr, Research, Developer & Sales; CDs & DVDs Mfr & Sales
S.I.C.: 8734
N.A.I.C.S.: 541380
Personnel:
Kazuhiko Numajiri *(Chm)*
Yoshio Iinuma *(Pres)*

ALMEHANYA FOR REAL ESTATE INVESTMENTS & HOUSING

58 Maka street Hijaz Towers 3rd floor
PO Box 5026
Amman, 11953, Jordan
Tel.: (962) 65538140
Fax: (962) 65510690
E-Mail: info@almehanya.com
Web Site: www.almehanya.com
Year Founded: 2007
PROF—(AMM)
Rev.: $2,496,679
Assets: $70,124,753
Liabilities: $9,048,203
Net Worth: $61,076,550
Earnings: $370,977
Emp.: 16
Fiscal Year-end: 12/31/12
Business Description:
Investment Management Services
S.I.C.: 6211
N.A.I.C.S.: 523999
Personnel:
Majed Tabba *(Chm)*
Maein Sehimat *(Deputy Chm)*
Board of Directors:
Majed Tabba
Zuhair Alomari
Nour Emam
Baker Odeh
Maein Sehimat
Fayez Suheimat
Ahmad Tarawneh
Fahd Tawileh
Munther Zmeili

ALMENDRAL S.A.

Avda Isidora Goyenechea 3642
piso 4, Santiago, Chile
Tel.: (56) 2 2334 4815
Fax: (56) 2 2334 4655
E-Mail: gerencia@almendral.cl
Web Site: almendral.cl/
Business Description:
Holding Company
S.I.C.: 6719
N.A.I.C.S.: 551112
Personnel:
Luis Felipe Gazitua Langlois *(Pres)*
Subsidiary:

Empresa Nacional de Telecomunicaciones S.A. **(1)**
Avenida Andres Bello 2687 14th Floor
Santiago, Chile
Mailing Address:
Box 4254
Santiago, Chile
Tel.: (56) 2 2360 0123
Fax: (56) 2 2360 3424
Web Site: www.entel.cl
Mobile Phones & Internet Services
S.I.C.: 4899
N.A.I.C.S.: 517919
Antonio Buchi Buc *(CEO)*

Non-U.S. Subsidiary:

Nextel del Peru S.A. **(2)**
Los Nardos 1018 piso 7
Lima, Peru PE
Tel.: (51) 16111111 (100%)
Fax: (51) 12228616
E-Mail: info@nextel.com.pe
Web Site: www.nextel.com.pe
Sales Range: $10-24.9 Million
Emp.: 50
Digital Wireless Communication Services
S.I.C.: 4812
N.A.I.C.S.: 517210
Miguel Rivera *(Pres)*

ALMIRALL, S.A.

General Mitre 151
08022 Barcelona, Spain
Tel.: (34) 932913000
Fax: (34) 932913180
E-Mail: info.spain@almirall.com
Web Site: www.almirall.com
ALM—(MAD)
Rev.: $1,211,780,503
Assets: $1,825,550,560
Liabilities: $582,137,755
Net Worth: $1,243,412,805
Earnings: $102,700,655
Emp.: 2,800
Fiscal Year-end: 12/31/12
Business Description:
Pharmaceutical Developer
S.I.C.: 2834
N.A.I.C.S.: 325412
Personnel:
Jorge Gallardo Ballart *(Pres)*
Eduardo Javier Sanchiz Yrazu *(CEO & Member-Mgmt Bd)*
Daniel Martinez Carretero *(CFO & Member-Mgmt Bd)*
Luciano Conde Conde *(COO & Member-Mgmt Bd)*
Bertil Lindmark *(Chief Scientific Officer & Member-Mgmt Bd)*
Joan Figueras Carreras *(Member-Mgmt Bd, Gen Counsel & Sr Dir)*
Enrique Dominguez Cruz *(Gen Mgr-Spain & Member-Mgmt Bd)*
Eloi Crespo Cervera *(Member-Mgmt Bd & Sr Dir-Indus Area)*
Javier Arroniz Morera de la Vall *(Member-Mgmt Bd & Dir-HR)*
Board of Directors:
Daniel Bravo Andreu
Luciano Conde Conde
Juan Arena de la Mora
Karin Louise Dorrepaal
Antonio Gallardo Ballart
Jorge Gallardo Ballart
Bertil Lindmark
Gerhard N. Mayr
Tom McKillop
Eduardo Javier Sanchiz Yrazu
Non-U.S. Subsidiary:

Almirall Hermal GmbH **(1)**
Scholtzstrasse 3
D-21465 Reinbek, Germany
Tel.: (49) 40727040
Fax: (49) 407229296
E-Mail: info@almirall.de
Web Site: www.almirall.de
Sales Range: $100-124.9 Million
Emp.: 450
Dermatological Pharmaceuticals Mfr
S.I.C.: 2834
N.A.I.C.S.: 325412
Klaus Treudler *(Mng Dir)*

ALMO CAPITAL CORP.

603 East 30th Avenue
Vancouver, BC, V5V 2V7, Canada
Tel.: (604) 873-8168
Fax: (604) 681-3601
E-Mail: almocapitalcorp@yahoo.ca
Web Site: www.almocapitalcorp.com
Year Founded: 1999
APT—(TSXV)
Int. Income: $6
Assets: $1,641,403
Liabilities: $912,936
Net Worth: $728,468
Earnings: ($56,063)
Fiscal Year-end: 10/31/12
Business Description:
Mineral Exploration Services
S.I.C.: 1081
N.A.I.C.S.: 213114
Personnel:
Ram Vallabh *(Pres & CEO)*
Ena Agarwal *(CFO & Sec)*
Board of Directors:
Amit Agarwal
Bert Gildersleeve
William McKibbin
Ram Vallabh
Wesley H. Wakefield

ALMONDZ CAPITAL & MANAGEMENT SERVICES LTD.

(Name Changed to Avonmore Capital & Management Services Ltd.)

ALMONDZ GLOBAL SECURITIES LIMITED

3 Scindia House 2nd Floor Janpath
New Delhi, 110 001, India
Tel.: (91) 1141514666
Fax: (91) 1141514665
E-Mail: info@almondz.com
Web Site: www.almondzglobal.com
ALMONDZ—(NSE)
Rev.: $19,679,001
Assets: $35,415,041
Liabilities: $12,176,213
Net Worth: $23,238,828
Earnings: $1,054,250
Emp.: 370
Fiscal Year-end: 03/31/13
Business Description:
Securities Brokerage Services
S.I.C.: 6211
N.A.I.C.S.: 523120
Personnel:
Navjeet Singh Sobti *(Vice Chm)*
Vinay Mehta *(CEO & Mng Dir)*
G. P. Agrawal *(CFO)*
Ajay Pratap *(Compliance Officer & Sec)*
Manoj Arora *(Sr VP & Head-Equity & Distr)*
Arindam Biswas *(Sr VP & Head-Distr-East)*
Board of Directors:
Atul Kumar Shukla

Almondz Global Securities Limited—(Continued)

Krishan Lall Khetrapaul
Vinay Mehta
Jagdeep Singh
Navjeet Singh Sobti
Surendar Kumar Sood
Abdulredha Mustafa Sultan
Sanjay Kumar Tiwari

Transfer Agent:
Beetal Financial & Computer Services Pvt. Ltd
Beetal House 3rd Floor 99 Madangir Behind L S C Near Dada Harsukh Dass
New Delhi, India

Subsidiaries:

Almondz Capital Markets Pvt. Ltd. (1)
6th Floor Dinsha Vachha Road Opp K C College
Churchgate, 400 020 Mumbai, India
Tel.: (91) 2267526699
Fax: (91) 2255526999
Securities Brokerage Services
S.I.C.: 6211
N.A.I.C.S.: 523120

Almondz Commodities Pvt. Ltd. (1)
Vaswani Mansion 6th Floor Opp K C College
Churchgate, 400 020 Mumbai, India
Tel.: (91) 22 67526699
Fax: (91) 22 67526502
Commodity Brokerage Services
S.I.C.: 6221
N.A.I.C.S.: 523140

Almondz Insurance Brokers Pvt. Ltd. (1)
2nd Floor 3 Scindia House Janpath
New Delhi, 110 001, India
Tel.: (91) 1149288888
Fax: (91) 1141514665
Web Site: www.almondzin.com
Insurance Brokerage Services
S.I.C.: 6411
N.A.I.C.S.: 524210
Vijay Suri *(CEO)*
Rohit Jain *(Mng Dir)*

Almondz Reinsurance Brokers Private Limited (1)
2nd Floor 3 Scindia House Janpath
New Delhi, 110001, India
Tel.: (91) 1141514666
Fax: (91) 1141514665
Web Site: www.almondz.com
Insurance Brokerage Services
S.I.C.: 6411
N.A.I.C.S.: 524210

ALMONTY INDUSTRIES INC.

The Exchange Tower 130 King Street West Suite 2120
PO Box 221
Toronto, ON, M5X 1C8, Canada
Tel.: (647) 478-5308
Fax: (604) 484-8254
E-Mail: info@almonty.com
Web Site: www.almonty.com
Year Founded: 2009
ALL—(TSXV)

Business Description:
Tungsten Exploration Services
S.I.C.: 1099
N.A.I.C.S.: 212299

Personnel:
Lewis Black *(Pres & CEO)*
Dennis Logan *(CFO & Sec)*

Board of Directors:
Lewis Black
Daniel D'Amato
Dennis Logan
Andrew McIlwain
Mark Trachuk

Transfer Agent:
Computershare Investor Services inc
3rd Fl 510 Burrard Street
Vancouver, BC, Canada

ALNA AB

A Domaseviciaus g 9
LT-01400 Vilnius, Lithuania
Tel.: (370) 52785500
Fax: (370) 52785511
E-Mail: info@alna.lt
Web Site: www.alna.com
Sales Range: $25-49.9 Million
Emp.: 400

Business Description:
IT Services
S.I.C.: 7373
N.A.I.C.S.: 541512

Personnel:
Justina Milaknyte *(Chm)*

Subsidiaries:

Alna Intelligence UAB (1)
A Gostauto 40B
01112 Vilnius, Lithuania
Tel.: (370) 5 210 28 20
Fax: (370) 5 210 28 11
E-Mail: ai@alna.lt
Web Site: www.alna.lt/ai
Emp.: 90
Information Technology Consulting Services
S.I.C.: 7373
N.A.I.C.S.: 541512
Algirdas Sukys *(Mgr-IT Svc)*

Alna Software UAB (1)
A Gostauto 40B
01112 Vilnius, Lithuania
Tel.: (370) 5 239 73 00
Fax: (370) 5 239 73 01
E-Mail: asw@alna.lt
Web Site: www.alna.lt/as/
Emp.: 100
Software Development Services
S.I.C.: 7371
N.A.I.C.S.: 541511
Inga Lukaseviciute *(Mgr-HR)*

BPO House (1)
A Domaseviciaus Str 9
01400 Vilnius, Lithuania
Tel.: (370) 5 278 55 00
Fax: (370) 5 278 55 11
E-Mail: info@bpohouse.lt
Web Site: www.bpohouse.lt
Business Process Outsourcing Services
S.I.C.: 7389
N.A.I.C.S.: 561499
Tomas Milaknis *(CEO)*

DocLogix JSC (1)
J Galvydzio Str 3
08236 Vilnius, Lithuania
Tel.: (370) 5 274 58 53
Fax: (370) 5 274 58 58
E-Mail: info@doclogix.lt
Web Site: www.doclogix.lt
Emp.: 23
Document Management Software Development & Whslr
S.I.C.: 7371
N.A.I.C.S.: 541511

Non-U.S. Subsidiary:

SIA Unitree (1)
Brivibas Gatve 223
Riga, 1039, Latvia
Tel.: (371) 6 7024878
Fax: (371) 6 7024879
E-Mail: info@unitree.lv
Web Site: www.unitree.lv
System Integration & Networking Services
S.I.C.: 7373
N.A.I.C.S.: 541512

ALNO AG

Heiligenberger Strasse 47
88629 Pfullendorf, Germany
Tel.: (49) 7552 21 0
Fax: (49) 755221773316
E-Mail: mail@alno.de
Web Site: www.alno.com
Year Founded: 1927
ANO—(DEU)
Rev.: $614,461,989
Assets: $226,495,795
Liabilities: $236,540,915
Net Worth: ($10,045,121)
Earnings: ($1,911,561)
Emp.: 1,845
Fiscal Year-end: 12/31/12

Business Description:
Kitchen Cabinetry Mfr
Import Export
S.I.C.: 2434
N.A.I.C.S.: 337110

Personnel:
Henning Giesecke *(Chm-Supervisory Bd)*
Max Mueller *(CEO)*
Ipek Demirtas *(CFO)*
Manfred Scholz *(COO)*
Ralph Bestgen *(Chief Sls Officer)*

Supervisory Board of Directors:
Henning Giesecke
Marc Bitzer
Jurgen Diegruber
Jorg Kespohl
Hubertus Krossa
Gerd Meyer
Norbert J. Orth
Werner Rellstab
Anton Walther
Rudolf Wisser

Non-U.S. Subsidiaries:

ABC-HUS Interieur (1)
Haraldsgatan 58
NOR 5500 Haugesund, Norway (100%)
Tel.: (47) 52722355
Fax: (47) 52722572
E-Mail: oerjana@online.no
Wood Kitchen Cabinets Mfr.
S.I.C.: 2434
N.A.I.C.S.: 337110

Abdullah Samad A. Marafie Sons General Trading & Shopping Co. (1)
Shuwaikh Canada Dry Street 22
PO Box 135
Kuwait, Safat, 13002, Kuwait (100%)
Tel.: (965) 4848752
Fax: (965) 4849295
E-Mail: marafie@qualitynet.net
Emp.: 75
Kitchen Cabinet Distributor
S.I.C.: 5712
N.A.I.C.S.: 442110
Abdullah Marafie *(Chm)*

Al Mizan Al Haditha Marketing & Business (1)
PO Box 52132
Jeddah, Al Mousalda, 21563, Saudi Arabia
Tel.: (966) 26689192
Fax: (966) 26689169
Kitchen Furniture
S.I.C.: 2434
N.A.I.C.S.: 337110

ALNO Austria (1)
Strasse 1
2355 Wiener Neudorf, Austria
Tel.: (43) 6645229533
E-Mail: accueil@lgfrance.com
Web Site: www.lgfrance.com
Kitchen Furniture Mfr.
S.I.C.: 2434
N.A.I.C.S.: 337110

ALNO France S.A.R.L. (1)
90 Chemin Du Val Fleuri
F 06800 Cagnes-sur-Mer, France (100%)
Tel.: (33) 492275858
Fax: (33) 493315000
E-Mail: mail@alno.fr
Web Site: www.alno.fr
Emp.: 15
Kitchen Cabinet Mfr.
S.I.C.: 2434
N.A.I.C.S.: 337110

ALNO Hellas (1)
Leof Vouliagmenis 142
Kouki Samouil 2
GR 16674 Glyfada, Athens, Greece
Tel.: (30) 2109927720
Fax: (30) 2109958300
E-Mail: mail@alno.gr
Web Site: www.alno.gr
Emp.: 14
Kitchen Cabinet Mfr.
S.I.C.: 2434
N.A.I.C.S.: 337110
Ioannis Varjiamis *(Mng Dir)*

ALNO Iberica (1)
108 Bia Agusca
08006 Barcelona, Spain (100%)
Tel.: (34) 933689863
Fax: (34) 932177915
E-Mail: correo@alno.es
Web Site: www.alno.es
Emp.: 5
S.I.C.: 2434
N.A.I.C.S.: 337110
Alexis Noguer *(Mgr)*

ALNO Italia S.P.A. (1)
Via F Baracca 15/a
I 50127 Florence, Ferrovia, Italy
Tel.: (39) 055 35 13 11
Fax: (39) 055 35131881
E-Mail: mail@alno.it
Web Site: www.alno.it
Kitchen Cabinets Whslr
S.I.C.: 2434
N.A.I.C.S.: 337110
Marco Antonelli *(Mgr)*

ALNO (Schweiz) AG (1)
Mettenstrasse 24
CH 2560 Nidau, Switzerland (100%)
Tel.: (41) 448008600
Fax: (41) 323299900
E-Mail: mail@alno.ch
Web Site: www.alno.ch
Emp.: 15
Kitchen Furniture Marketing
S.I.C.: 2434
N.A.I.C.S.: 337110
Rolf Habegger *(CEO)*

ALNO Spol s.r.o. (1)
Zborovska 34
PO Box 211
CS150 00 Prague, 5, Czech Republic
Tel.: (420) 257324755
Fax: (420) 257324755
E-Mail: info@alnox.cz
Web Site: www.alnox.cz
Kitchen Cabinet Mfr.
S.I.C.: 2434
N.A.I.C.S.: 337110

ALNO UK Ltd. (1)
Shaw Cross Court
Shaw Cross Business Park, Dewsbury, West Yorkshire, WF12 7RF, United Kingdom (100%)
Tel.: (44) 1924487900
Fax: (44) 1924437305
E-Mail: mail@alno.co.uk
Web Site: www.alno.co.uk
Emp.: 20
Kitchen Cabinets Whslr
S.I.C.: 2434
N.A.I.C.S.: 337110

A.S.M. Distributors C.C. (1)
PO Box 2418
1820 Johannesburg, Lenasia, South Africa (100%)
Tel.: (27) 118542562
Fax: (27) 118526471
E-Mail: asm.aimo@telcomsa.net
Web Site: www.prospec.co.za
Emp.: 5
Kitchen Cabinet Mfr.
S.I.C.: 2434
N.A.I.C.S.: 337110
Ahmed Sayed Mohammed *(Mng Dir)*

Bina Warehouse SDN BHD (1)
No 22 Jalan Kampong Attap
50460 Kuala Lumpur, Malaysia
Tel.: (60) 322746111
Fax: (60) 322721846
E-Mail: binawh@binawarehouse.com
Web Site: www.binawarehouse.com
Emp.: 100
Kitchen Cabinet Mfr.
S.I.C.: 2434
N.A.I.C.S.: 337110
Henry Kok *(Exec Dir)*

Bra Interioer AB (1)
Odengatan 22
S 11351 Stockholm, Sweden (100%)
Tel.: (46) 84429030
Fax: (46) 84429035
E-Mail: richard@bra-interior.se
Web Site: www.bra-interior.se
Kitchen Cabinet Mfr.
S.I.C.: 2434
N.A.I.C.S.: 337110

Ch. Adamy Theis S.A.R.L. (1)
Rudy Adamy Zone Commerciale
Rue De Bettembourg, L 3378 Livange, Luxembourg (100%)

Tel.: (352) 523833
Fax: (352) 523836
E-Mail: info@adamytheis.lu
Web Site: www.adamytheis.lu
Emp.: 50
S.I.C.: 2434
N.A.I.C.S.: 337110
Rudy Adamy *(Pres)*

Cucina Bella S.A. (1)
Av del Libertador 13 570
Martinez, B1640 AOT Buenos Aires, Argentina (100%)
Tel.: (54) 1147985800
Fax: (54) 1147985653
E-Mail: info@cucinabella.com.ar
Web Site: www.cucinabella.com.ar
Emp.: 40
Kitchen Cabinet Mfr.
S.I.C.: 2434
N.A.I.C.S.: 337110

Delta Co. LTD. L.L.C. (1)
PO Box 1537
112 Ruwi, Muscat, Oman
Tel.: (968) 708483
Fax: (968) 708502
E-Mail: deltaco@omantel.net.om
Emp.: 70
Mfr of Kitchen Furniture
S.I.C.: 2434
N.A.I.C.S.: 337110

Dom Interier d.o.o. (1)
Smartinska 152
BTC Hala E, SLO 1000 Ljubljana, Slovenia
Tel.: (386) 615863980
Fax: (386) 615863981
E-Mail: info@dominterier.si
Web Site: www.dominterier.si
Kitchen Cabinet Mfr.
S.I.C.: 2434
N.A.I.C.S.: 337110

Habitat (1)
2 IBN Gavirol St
64077 Tel Aviv, Israel
Tel.: (972) 36951282
Fax: (972) 36969938
E-Mail: habitat@habitat.co.il
Web Site: www.habitat.co.il
Emp.: 15
Kitchen Cabinet Mfr.
S.I.C.: 2434
N.A.I.C.S.: 337110
Rami Meerovitch *(Gen Mgr)*

Home Boutique Co. Ltd. (1)
4 F-3, 109, Sec 6
Min Chuam E. Rd, Taipei, Taiwan
Tel.: (886) 277 52806
Fax: (886) 2 2546 6969
E-Mail: Hobo@ms3.hinet.net
Web Site: www.gaggenau.com
S.I.C.: 2434
N.A.I.C.S.: 337110

Inter Imports C.A. (1)
Chaka Iela 80
1001 Riga, Latvia (100%)
Tel.: (371) 7310567
Fax: (371) 7310568
Web Site: www.alno.lv
Emp.: 20
Kitchen Furniture
S.I.C.: 2434
N.A.I.C.S.: 337110

International Imports (NZ) LTD. (1)
46 Stanley Street
Parnell, Auckland, New Zealand
Tel.: (64) 98372060
Fax: (64) 9 83 72 060
Kitchen Cabinet Mfr
S.I.C.: 2434
N.A.I.C.S.: 337110

Kitchen Design S.A. (1)
P O Box 8061
Panama, 7, Panama
Tel.: (507) 2679597
Fax: (507) 263 6746
Kitchen Furniture
S.I.C.: 2434
N.A.I.C.S.: 337110

K.M. Design AS (1)
Raglamyrveien 5
NOR-5536 Haugesund, Norway
Tel.: (47) 5272090
Fax: (47) 52702095
E-Mail: talfsvaa@sn.no
Kitchen Furniture Mfr.
S.I.C.: 2434
N.A.I.C.S.: 337110

Legion (HK) LTD. (1)
Rm 902 Yue Shing Commercial Bldg
No 15 Queen Victoria St, Central, China (Hong Kong) (50%)
Tel.: (852) 25303099
Fax: (852) 25303173
E-Mail: legionhk@gmail.com
Emp.: 15
Kitchen Furniture
S.I.C.: 2434
N.A.I.C.S.: 337110
Sam Chong *(Gen Mgr)*

Lekka Trading Co. Ltd. (1)
Park Grace 1F 4-32-6 Nishi-Shinjuku
Shinjuku- ku, Tokyo, 160-0023, Japan
Tel.: (81) 5350 4471
Fax: (81) 354 422490
E-Mail: p.martin@lekka-tr.co.jp
Kitchen Furniture Mfr
S.I.C.: 2434
N.A.I.C.S.: 337110

Livart Furniture Co., Ltd. (1)
3rd Floor Nonhyeongong 49 - 4
Gangnam-gu, 135814 Seoul, 137 703, Korea (South) (100%)
Tel.: (82) 234808281
Fax: (82) 263060708
E-Mail: chp@shinbiro.com
Web Site: www.livart.co.kr
Sales Range: $1-9.9 Million
Emp.: 100
Kitchen Cabinet Mfr
S.I.C.: 2434
N.A.I.C.S.: 337110

Medco Trading (1)
22 A Salah Salem Road
Obour Gardens, Heliopolis, Cairo, Egypt
Tel.: (20) 2260 5759
Fax: (20) 2 402 3304
E-Mail: medcotrd@gega.net
Kitchen Furniture
S.I.C.: 2434
N.A.I.C.S.: 337110

Rimal Engineering Products (1)
PO Box 5280
Abu Dhabi, United Arab Emirates (100%)
Tel.: (971) 26332267
Fax: (971) 26339338
E-Mail: rimalad@emirates.net.ae
Web Site: www.rimal.ae
Emp.: 40
Kitchen Furniture
S.I.C.: 2434
N.A.I.C.S.: 337110
Ghassan Elsolh *(Gen Mgr)*

Samico Trading & Contracting EST. (1)
Gulf St 32
PO Box 8258
Doha, Qatar
Tel.: (974) 4428618
Fax: (974) 4328767
E-Mail: samico@qatar.qa
Emp.: 15
Kitchen Furniture Mfr.
S.I.C.: 2434
N.A.I.C.S.: 337110

Sel et Poivre/ Vogue Sofil S.A.L. (1)
Centre Sofi
Beirut, Lebanon (100%)
Tel.: (961) 13325030
Fax: (961) 11326302
E-Mail: selandpoivre@inco.com.lb
Kitchen Furniture
S.I.C.: 2434
N.A.I.C.S.: 337110

Smart Consulting 98 (1)
Vlad Hartia Boulevard Libertatii 8 10 Block 114 115
Parter Sector 5, 040 128 Bucharest, Romania (100%)
Tel.: (40) 213354562
Fax: (40) 213367462
E-Mail: smartconsulting@pcnet.ro
Web Site: www.smartconsulting98.ro
Emp.: 45
Kitchen Furniture
S.I.C.: 2434
N.A.I.C.S.: 337110

TDDF Tuerkdemir Doekuem Fabrikalari (1)
Bahcelievler Mah Bosna Bulvari No 148
34688 Istanbul, Turkey
Tel.: (90) 2165162000
Fax: (90) 2165162004
E-Mail: sezer.yetimaslan@demirdokum.com
Web Site: www.demirdokum.com.tr
Emp.: 30
Kitchen Furniture Mfr
S.I.C.: 2434
N.A.I.C.S.: 337110

Valbra (1)
Vytenio St 13
Vilnius, 03112, Lithuania
Tel.: (370) 52603601
Fax: (370) 52603602
E-Mail: info@valbra.lt
Web Site: www.valbra.lt
Emp.: 5
Kitchen Furniture
S.I.C.: 2434
N.A.I.C.S.: 337110

Vogue Etoile S.A.L. (1)
Starco Center Omar Daouk Street
PO Box 113 5479
Mine El Hosn, Beirut, Lebanon
Tel.: (961) 360720
Fax: (961) 360721
E-Mail: voguetl@cyberia.net.lb
Emp.: 11
Kitchen Furniture
S.I.C.: 2434
N.A.I.C.S.: 337110

ALOIS DALLMAYR KG

Dienerstrasse 14-15
80331 Munich, Germany
Tel.: (49) 8921350
Fax: (49) 892135167
E-Mail: info@dallmayr.de
Web Site: www.dallmayr.de
Emp.: 600

Business Description:
Coffee Mfr; Delicatessen; Vending Machines Network
S.I.C.: 2095
N.A.I.C.S.: 311920

Personnel:
Wolfgang Wille *(Mng Dir)*
Georg Randkofer *(Mng Dir)*

Subsidiaries:

Alois Dallmayr Automaten-Service GmbH Herxheim (1)
Karcherstr 16
66539 Neunkirchen, Germany
Tel.: (49) 727698500
Fax: (49) 6821 33446
Vending Machine Whslr
S.I.C.: 5046
N.A.I.C.S.: 423440

Alois Dallmayr Gastro-Service GmbH & Co KG (1)
Dienerstr 14-15
80331 Munich, Germany
Tel.: (49) 180 332 55 62
E-Mail: gastro-service@dallmayr.de
Coffee Whslr
S.I.C.: 5149
N.A.I.C.S.: 424490

Alois Dallmayr Kaffee OHG (1)
Dienerstr 14-15
80331 Munich, Germany
Tel.: (49) 89 2135 0
Fax: (49) 89 2135 167
E-Mail: info@dallmayr.de
Roast Coffee Mfr & Whslr
S.I.C.: 2095
N.A.I.C.S.: 311920

Dallmayr Automaten-Service GmbH (1)
Stiftswaldstr 4
67657 Kaiserslautern, Germany
Tel.: (49) 631 3407972
Fax: (49) 631 3577792
E-Mail: info@dallmayr-automatenservice-gmbh.de
Vending Machine Whslr
S.I.C.: 5046
N.A.I.C.S.: 423440

Heimbs Kaffee GmbH & Co. KG (1)
Rebenring 30
38106 Braunschweig, Germany
Tel.: (49) 531 3 80 02 0
Fax: (49) 531 3 80 02 31
E-Mail: info@heimbs.de
Web Site: www.heimbs.de
Coffee & Tea Mfr & Whslr
S.I.C.: 2099
N.A.I.C.S.: 311920

ALOK INDUSTRIES LIMITED

Tower B 2nd & 3rd Floor Peninsula Business Park
Ganpatrao Kadam Marg Lower Parel, Mumbai, 400 013, India
Tel.: (91) 22 6178 7000
E-Mail: info@alokind.com
Web Site: www.alokind.com
Year Founded: 1986
521070—(BOM)
Rev.: $4,050,079,686
Assets: $4,857,109,200
Liabilities: $4,210,960,536
Net Worth: $646,148,664
Earnings: $55,011,888
Emp.: 23,000
Fiscal Year-end: 09/30/13

Business Description:
Textile Mfr
S.I.C.: 2399
N.A.I.C.S.: 314999

Personnel:
Ashok B. Jiwrajka *(Chm)*
Dilip B. Jiwrajka *(Mng Dir)*
Surendra B. Jiwrajka *(Mng Dir)*
Sunil O. Khandelwal *(CFO)*
K. H. Gopal *(Sec)*

Board of Directors:
Ashok B. Jiwrajka
Chandra Kumar Bubna
Maya Chakravorty
Timothy Ingram
Dilip B. Jiwrajka
Surendra B. Jiwrajka
Thankom T. Mathew
K. R. Modi
M. V. Muthu
Ashok G. Rajani
David Rasquinha

Transfer Agent:
Link Intime India Pvt. Ltd.
C-13 Pannalal Silk Mills Compound
LBS Marg
Bhandup, Mumbai, 400 078, India
Tel.: (91) 22 2596 3838
Fax: (91) 22 2594 6969

Subsidiaries:

Alok H&A Ltd. (1)
Ashford Center Lower Parel
Mumbai, 400 013, India
Tel.: (91) 22 24997 000
Textile Products Retailer
S.I.C.: 5719
N.A.I.C.S.: 442299

Grabal Alok Impex Limited (1)
Peninsula Towers Peninsula Corporate Park
Ganpatrao Kadam Marg
Lower Parel, 400013 Mumbai, Maharashtra, India (100%)
Tel.: (91) 2224996200
Fax: (91) 2224936078
E-Mail: info@grabalalok.com
Web Site: www.grabalalok.com
Emp.: 1,107
Embroidery Products Mfr
S.I.C.: 3944
N.A.I.C.S.: 339930
Ashok B. Jiwrajka *(Chm)*
Sanjay K. Bhatt *(CEO & Sec)*
Surendra B. Jiwrajka *(Mng Dir)*

Alok Industries Limited—(Continued)

Subsidiary:

Grabal Alok International Limited (2)
Peninsula Corporate Park Ganpatrao Kadam Marg
Lower Parel, Mumbai, Maharashtra, 400013, India
Tel.: (91) 2224996200
Fax: (91) 2224936078
E-Mail: info@alokind.com
Web Site: www.alokind.com
Emp.: 500
Apparel Mfr & Whslr
S.I.C.: 5136
N.A.I.C.S.: 424320
Dilip Jiwrajka *(Mng Dir)*

Non-U.S. Subsidiaries:

Grabal Alok (UK) Ltd. (1)
Unit 1 Plot C1 Central Boulevard
Blythe Valley Business Park, Solihull, B90 8AH, United Kingdom
Tel.: (44) 121 746 7000
E-Mail: customerservices@storetwentyone.co.uk
Web Site: www.storetwentyone.co.uk
Apparel & Accessories Retailer
S.I.C.: 5621
N.A.I.C.S.: 448120

Mileta a.s. (1)
Husova 734
508 01 Horice, Czech Republic
Tel.: (420) 493654400
Fax: (420) 493654415
E-Mail: mileta@mileta.cz
Web Site: www.mileta.cz
Emp.: 300
Shirt Fabrics Mfr
S.I.C.: 2299
N.A.I.C.S.: 313210
Otakar Petracek *(Chm & CEO)*

ALON HOLDINGS BLUE SQUARE-ISRAEL LTD.

2 Amal Street
Rosh Ha'Ayin, 48092, Israel
Tel.: (972) 9 9618 636
Fax: (972) 9 9618 504
E-Mail: yaell@bsi.co.il
Web Site: www.bsi.co.il
Year Founded: 1996
BSI—(NYSE TAE)
Rev.: $15,805,539,000
Assets: $9,493,373,000
Liabilities: $7,887,032,000
Net Worth: $1,606,341,000
Earnings: $41,151,000
Emp.: 8,307
Fiscal Year-end: 12/31/12
Business Description:
Supermarkets & Department Stores Operator
S.I.C.: 5311
N.A.I.C.S.: 452111
Personnel:
Yilzhak Bader *(Chm)*
Limor Ganot *(Co-CEO)*
David Wiessman *(Co-CEO)*
Dror Moran *(CFO & VP)*
Raviv Brookmayer *(CEO-Naaman Grp)*
Motti Keren *(CEO-Megal Retail)*
Zeev Stein *(CEO-Blue Square Real Estate)*
Israel Yaniv *(CEO-Dor Alon)*
Eli Levinson-Sela *(Gen Counsel & Sec)*
Ortal Klein *(Sec)*
Board of Directors:
Yilzhak Bader
David Alphandary
Uzi Baram
Diana Bogoslavsky
Sholmo Even
Avraham Meron
Mordehay Ventura
David Wiessman

Transfer Agent:
The Bank of New York Mellon
1 Wall Street
New York, NY 10286

Subsidiary:

Blue Square Investment Properties Ltd (1)
2 Haamal St Afek Ind Park
Rosh Haayin, Tel Aviv, Israel
Tel.: (972) 39282222
Web Site: www.bsi.co.il/en/index.asp
Grocery & Related Products Merchant Whslr
S.I.C.: 5149
N.A.I.C.S.: 424490
Zeev Vurembrand *(Pres & CEO)*

ALON ISRAEL OIL COMPANY LTD.

France Bldg Europark
PO Box 10
Yakum, 60972, Israel
Tel.: (972) 99618500
Fax: (972) 99514333
E-Mail: alon-oil@alon-oil.co.il
Web Site: www.alon.co.il
Business Description:
Energy, Retail & Infrastructures Holding Company
S.I.C.: 6719
N.A.I.C.S.: 551112
Personnel:
David Wiessman *(Chm, Pres & CEO)*
Ilan Kliger *(CFO)*
Ortal Klein *(Gen Counsel)*

Subsidiary:

ALON USA ENERGY, INC. (1)
12700 Park Central Dr Ste 1600
Dallas, TX 75251 DE
Tel.: (972) 367-3600
Web Site: www.alonusa.com
ALJ—(NYSE)
Sls.: $7,046,381,000
Assets: $2,245,140,000
Liabilities: $1,619,736,000
Net Worth: $625,404,000
Earnings: $48,115,000
Emp.: 2,740
Fiscal Year-end: 12/31/13
Oil & Gas Refining; Marketing Services
S.I.C.: 2911
N.A.I.C.S.: 324110
David Wiessman *(Chm)*
Jeff D. Morris *(Vice Chm)*
W. Paul Eisman *(Pres & CEO)*
Shai Even *(CFO & Sr VP)*
James Ranspot *(Gen Counsel, Sec & Sr VP)*
Claire A. Hart *(Sr VP)*
Alan Moret *(Sr VP-Supply)*
Michael Oster *(Sr VP-Mergers & Acq)*

Subsidiaries:

Alon Assets, Inc. (2)
12700 Park Central Dr Ste 1600
Dallas, TX 75251
Tel.: (972) 367-3600
Asset Management Services
S.I.C.: 8748
N.A.I.C.S.: 541618

Alon Brands, Inc. (2)
7616 LBJ Freeway Ste 300
Dallas, TX 75251 DE
Tel.: (972) 367-3600
E-Mail: info@alonusa.com
Web Site: www.alonusa.com
Oil Refiner & Marketer
S.I.C.: 2911
N.A.I.C.S.: 324110
David Wiessman *(Chm)*
Jeff D. Morris *(Vice Chm)*
Paul Eisman *(Pres & CEO)*
Judge A. Dobrient *(Sr VP-Wholesale Mktg)*
Claire A. Hart *(Sr VP)*
Alan Moret *(Sr VP-Supply)*
Michael Oster *(Sr VP-Mergers & Acq)*

Alon Refining Krotz Springs, Inc. (2)
7616 LBJ Freeway Ste 300
Dallas, TX 75251-7030
Tel.: (972) 367-3600
Fax: (972) 367-3725
Crude Oil Refining Services
S.I.C.: 1311
N.A.I.C.S.: 211111

Alon USA Partners, LP (2)
12700 Park Central Dr Ste 1600
Dallas, TX 75251 DE
Tel.: (972) 367-3600
Web Site: www.alanusa.com
ALDW—(NYSE)
Sls.: $3,430,287,000
Assets: $849,924,000
Liabilities: $704,482,000
Net Worth: $145,442,000
Earnings: $136,222,000
Fiscal Year-end: 12/31/13
Petroleum Products Refining & Marketing
S.I.C.: 2911
N.A.I.C.S.: 324110
David Wiessman *(Chm)*
Paul Eisman *(Pres & CEO)*
Shai Even *(CFO & Sr VP)*
Claire Hart *(Sr VP)*
Alan Moret *(Sr VP-Supply)*
Michael Oster *(Sr VP-Mergers & Acq)*

Paramount Petroleum Corporation of Arizona, Inc. (2)
1935 W McDowell Rd
Phoenix, AZ 85009
Tel.: (602) 252-3061
Fax: (602) 840-3697
E-Mail: asphalt_marketing@ppcla.com
Web Site: www.ppcla.com
Petroleum Product Mfr & Distr
S.I.C.: 5172
N.A.I.C.S.: 424720
Rick Terry *(Reg Mgr-Mktg)*

Paramount Petroleum Corp. (2)
14700 Downey Ave
Paramount, CA 90723-4526 DE
Tel.: (562) 531-2060
Fax: (562) 633-8211
E-Mail: asphalt_marketing@ppcla.com
Web Site: www.ppcla.com
Emp.: 150
Petroleum Refining Services
S.I.C.: 2911
N.A.I.C.S.: 324110
William L. Thorpe *(Sr VP-Asphalt Div)*

Subsidiaries:

Big West of California, LLC (3)
6451 Rosedale Hwy
Bakersfield, CA 93308
Tel.: (661) 326-4201
Oil Refinery
S.I.C.: 2911
N.A.I.C.S.: 324110

Skinny's LLC (2)
3457 Curry Ln
Abilene, TX 79606
Tel.: (325) 692-8200
Fax: (325) 695-0787
Web Site: www.skinnys.com
Sls.: $24,700,000
Emp.: 12
Convenience Stores
S.I.C.: 5411
N.A.I.C.S.: 445120
Pamela Horkulic *(Gen Mgr-Ledger)*

Wright Asphalt Products Company LLC (2)
11931 Wickchester Ste 101
Houston, TX 77043
Tel.: (281) 452-9084
Fax: (281) 452-2562
E-Mail: info@wrightasphalt.com
Web Site: www.wrightasphalt.com
Asphalt Product Research & Development Services
S.I.C.: 8731
N.A.I.C.S.: 541711
Lawrence Peschke *(Controller)*

ALONY HETZ PROPERTIES AND INVESTMENTS LTD.

Aviv Towers 7 Jabotinski St
Ramat Gan, 52520, Israel
Tel.: (972) 37521115
Fax: (972) 37514730
E-Mail: info@alony-hetz.com
Web Site: www.alony-hetz.com
ALHE—(TAE)
Rev.: $268,076,545
Assets: $3,246,394,345
Liabilities: $2,063,615,010
Net Worth: $1,182,779,334
Earnings: $122,035,262
Emp.: 14
Fiscal Year-end: 12/31/12
Business Description:
Real Estate Construction, Property Development & Leasing Services
S.I.C.: 6519
N.A.I.C.S.: 531190
Personnel:
Aviram Wertheim *(Chm)*
Nathan Hetz *(Pres & CEO)*
Oren Frankel *(CFO)*
Hanan Feldmus *(Legal Counsel & Sec)*
Board of Directors:
Aviram Wertheim
Yarom Ariav
Itzhak Forer
Gittit Guberman
Nathan Hetz
Miryam Livne
Aaron Nahumi
Avraham Natan
Adva Sharvit

Subsidiary:

Alony Hetz Global Ltd. (1)
7 Jabotinsky
Ramat Gan, 52520, Israel
Tel.: (972) 37521115
Fax: (972) 37514730
E-Mail: info@alony-hetz.com
Emp.: 12
Real Estate Property Development Services
S.I.C.: 6531
N.A.I.C.S.: 531210
Aviram Wertheim *(Mgr)*

ALOYS F. DORNBRACHT GMBH & CO. KG

Kobbingser Muhle 6
58640 Iserlohn, Germany
Tel.: (49) 2371433470
Fax: (49) 2371433345
E-Mail: mail@dornbracht.de
Web Site: www.dornbracht.com
Year Founded: 1950
Rev.: $165,941,820
Emp.: 800
Business Description:
Bathroom & Kitchen Fittings Mfr
S.I.C.: 3494
N.A.I.C.S.: 332919
Personnel:
Andreas Dornbracht *(Mng Dir)*
Helmut Dornbracht *(Mng Dir)*
Matthias Dornbracht *(Mng Dir)*

A.L.P.A. EQUIPMENT

55 Industrial Avenue
Truro, NS, B2N 6V1, Canada
Tel.: (902) 897-2717
Fax: (902) 897-2759
E-Mail: truro@alpaequipment.com
Web Site: www.alpaequipment.com
Year Founded: 1976
Rev.: $13,665,920
Emp.: 60
Business Description:
Construction & Mining Machinery & Equipment Merchant Whlsr
S.I.C.: 5084
N.A.I.C.S.: 423830
Personnel:
Armand Landry *(Pres)*

ALPA LABORATORIES LTD

33/2 Pigdamber A B Road Rau
Indore, Madhya Pradesh, 453446, India

Tel.: (91) 7314294567
Fax: (91) 7314294444
E-Mail: mail@alpalabs.com
Web Site: www.alpalabs.com
ALPA—(NSE)
Rev.: $10,489,617
Assets: $23,094,351
Liabilities: $5,766,774
Net Worth: $17,327,577
Earnings: ($809,827)
Fiscal Year-end: 03/31/13
Business Description:
Pharmaceutical Products Mfr
S.I.C.: 2834
N.A.I.C.S.: 325412
Personnel:
Purushottam R. Patel *(Chm & Mng Dir)*
Jayesh Patel *(CEO)*
Paresh Chawla *(COO)*
Hemant Jain *(Compliance Officer)*
Shilpesh Dalal *(Sec)*
Board of Directors:
Purushottam R. Patel
Devendra Baheti
Mahendra Singh Chawla
Sharad Chand Lunawat
Krishna Das Malani
Pravin C. Shah
Transfer Agent:
Bigshare Services Pvt. Ltd.
E-2 Ansa Industrial Estate Saki Vihar Road
Andheri East
Mumbai, India

ALPAGEL GAP
83 Avenue d'Embrun
Cedex, 05010 Gap, Hautes Alpes, France
Tel.: (33) 492514868
Fax: (33) 492536927
Web Site: alpes.relaisdor.fr/ou-sommes-nous.php
Sls.: $20,500,000
Emp.: 49
Business Description:
Packaged Frozen Goods
S.I.C.: 5142
N.A.I.C.S.: 424420
Personnel:
Gerard Ubrun *(Chm)*
Board of Directors:
Gerard Ubrun
Bernard Costorier

ALPCOT AGRO AB
(Name Changed to Agrokultura AB)

ALPEN CO., LTD.
Alpen Marunouchi Tower 9-40 2-chome Marunouchi
Naka-ku, Nagoya, Aichi, 460-8637, Japan
Tel.: (81) 525590125
E-Mail: english-info@alpen-group.jp
Web Site: www.alpen-group.jp
Year Founded: 1972
3028—(TKS)
Sls.: $2,240,964,000
Assets: $1,923,845,000
Liabilities: $766,601,000
Net Worth: $1,157,244,000
Earnings: $72,919,000
Fiscal Year-end: 06/30/13
Business Description:
Sports Products Mfr & Sales; Management of Ski Resorts & Golf Courses
S.I.C.: 3949
N.A.I.C.S.: 339920
Personnel:
Taizo Mizuno *(Pres)*
Yoshitaka Ishida *(Co-Mng Dir)*
Kazuo Murase *(Co-Mng Dir)*
Yasuhiko Mizumaki *(Exec VP)*
Takehito Suzuki *(Exec VP)*
Board of Directors:
Yoshitaka Ishida
Yasuhiko Mizumaki
Taizo Mizuno
Kazuo Murase
Takehito Suzuki
Subsidiaries:

Japana Co., Ltd. **(1)**
Alpen Marunouchi Tower 2-9-40 Marunouchi
Naka-ku, Nagoya, Aichi, 460 0002, Japan
Tel.: (81) 525590125
Web Site: www.japana.co.jp
Sporting Goods Mfr
S.I.C.: 5091
N.A.I.C.S.: 423910
Taizo Mizuno *(Pres)*

Non-U.S. Subsidiary:

Wuxi Japana Sports Goods Co., Ltd. **(2)**
1 Lingjiang Rd Development Zone for High & New Tech Wuxi Of China
Wuxi, Jiangsu, 214028, China
Tel.: (86) 510 85216314
Fax: (86) 510 85218164
E-Mail: wxjpn@wxjpn.com
Web Site: www.wxjpn.com
Emp.: 149
Ski & Snowboard Garments & Gloves Mfr
S.I.C.: 3949
N.A.I.C.S.: 339920

Kissmark Japan Co., Ltd. **(1)**
Alpine Marunochi Tower 2 9 40 Marunouchi
Naka-Ku, 460-0002 Nagoya, Aichi, Japan
Tel.: (81) 525591035
Fax: (81) 52 229 8979
E-Mail: kissmark@kissmark.co.jp
Web Site: www.kissmark.co.jp
Emp.: 10
Sporting & Athletic Goods Mfr
S.I.C.: 3949
N.A.I.C.S.: 339920
Taizo Mizuno *(Pres)*

Royal Hills Co., Ltd. **(1)**
Alpine Marunochi Tower 20F 2-9-40 Marunouchi
Naka-Ku, Nagoya, Aichi, 460-0002, Japan
Tel.: (81) 525591040
Fax: (81) 522298841
Emp.: 224
Golf & Skiing Managing Services
S.I.C.: 7999
N.A.I.C.S.: 711310

Sports Logistics Co., Ltd. **(1)**
12 Tsukamotogonishi Hozumitsukamoto Chiakicho, Ichinomiya, Aichi, 491-0803, Japan
Tel.: (81) 586812161
Fax: (81) 586812135
Emp.: 60
Logistics Services
S.I.C.: 4731
N.A.I.C.S.: 541614
Hattori Humitoshi *(CEO)*

ALPES PROVENCE AGNEAUX
10 Allee des Romarins
BP 5
04201 Sisteron, France
Tel.: (33) 492613350
Fax: (33) 492614092
E-Mail: alpagneau@wanadoo.fr
Web Site: www.alpesprovenceagneaux.fr
Sls.: $20,900,000
Emp.: 27
Business Description:
Meat Packing Plants
S.I.C.: 2011
N.A.I.C.S.: 311611
Personnel:
Francois Monge *(Pres)*

ALPETOUR - POTOVALNA AGENCIJA D.D.
Mirka Vadnova 8
4000 Kranj, Slovenia
Tel.: (386) 42013100
Fax: (386) 42013101
E-Mail: info@alpetour.si
Web Site: www.alpetour.si
Year Founded: 1947
APAG—(LJU)
Sales Range: $25-49.9 Million
Emp.: 320
Business Description:
Car Rental & Tourism Services
S.I.C.: 7514
N.A.I.C.S.: 532111
Subsidiaries:

Integral AP Trzic dd **(1)**
Mlaka 4
4290 Trzic, Slovenia
Tel.: (386) 45920940
Fax: (386) 45920943
E-Mail: integral@integral-ap.si
Web Site: www.integral-ap.si
Emp.: 22
Tourism Services
S.I.C.: 7999
N.A.I.C.S.: 713990
Bores Malenfk *(Gen Mgr)*

Integral Avto D.O.O **(1)**
Cesta Marsala Tita 67
Jesenice, 4270, Slovenia
Tel.: (386) 45833350
Fax: (386) 45833360
E-Mail: info@intergral-avto.si
Web Site: www.integral-avto.si
Emp.: 42
Vehicle Sales & Services
S.I.C.: 5599
N.A.I.C.S.: 441228
Izidor Jekovec *(Gen Mgr)*

Kam-Bus dd **(1)**
Perovo 30
1241 Kamnik, Slovenia
Tel.: (386) 18309400
Fax: (386) 18309406
E-Mail: avtobus@kam-bus.si
Web Site: www.kam-bus.si
Emp.: 18
Passenger Transport Services
S.I.C.: 4111
N.A.I.C.S.: 485999
Sonja Zore *(Gen Mgr)*

ALPETRO RESOURCES LTD.
Suite 103 1118 - 12th Ave SW
Calgary, AB, T2R 0P4, Canada
Tel.: (403) 234-9006
Fax: (403) 266-5959
E-Mail: info@alpetroresources.com
Web Site: www.alpetroresources.com
Year Founded: 1994
Sales Range: $1-9.9 Million
Business Description:
Oil & Gas Exploration Services
S.I.C.: 1389
N.A.I.C.S.: 213112
Personnel:
Nazrul Islam *(Pres & CEO)*
Robin Chan *(CFO)*
Board of Directors:
Robin Chan
Nazrul Islam
Vincent Murphy
James Phillips
Transfer Agent:
Computershare Trust Company of Canada
9th Floor 100 University Avenue
Toronto, ON, Canada

ALPHA AND OMEGA SEMICONDUCTOR LIMITED
Clarendon House 2 Church Street
Hamilton, HM 11, Bermuda
Tel.: (441) 295 1422
E-Mail: sales@aosmd.com
Web Site: www.aosmd.com
Year Founded: 2000
AOSL—(NASDAQ)
Rev.: $337,436,000
Assets: $356,321,000
Liabilities: $74,870,000
Net Worth: $281,451,000
Earnings: ($5,575,000)
Emp.: 2,700
Fiscal Year-end: 06/30/13
Business Description:
Holding Company: Semiconductors & Related Devices
S.I.C.: 6719
N.A.I.C.S.: 551112
Personnel:
Mike F. Chang *(Chm & CEO)*
Yifan Liang *(Interim CFO, Chief Acctg Officer & Asst Sec)*
Yueh-Se Ho *(COO)*
Hamza Yilmaz *(CTO)*
Board of Directors:
Mike F. Chang
Chung Te Chang
Robert I. Chen
Yueh-Se Ho
King Owyang
Michael L. Pfeiffer
Michael J. Salameh
Richard W. Sevcik
U.S. Subsidiaries:

Alpha and Omega Semiconductor, Inc. **(1)**
475 Oakmead Parkway
Sunnyvale, CA 94085 (100%)
Tel.: (408) 830-9742
Fax: (408) 830-9749
E-Mail: Inquiries@aosmd.com
Web Site: www.aosmd.com
Software Mfr & Distr
S.I.C.: 7372
N.A.I.C.S.: 511210
Yueh-Se Ho *(COO)*

Jireh Semiconductor Incorporated **(1)**
3131 NE Brookwood Pkwy
Hillsboro, OR 97124
Tel.: (503) 693-4696
Fax: (503) 681-6026
Integrated Semiconductor Chips Mfr
S.I.C.: 3674
N.A.I.C.S.: 334413

Non-U.S. Subsidiaries:

Agape Package Manufacturing (Shanghai) Ltd. **(1)**
Ste B1 Building Dongkai Industrial Park
Songjiang, Shanghai, 201614, China
Tel.: (86) 2157856600
Web Site: www.apmcn.com
Semiconductor Assembly & Testing Services
S.I.C.: 3674
N.A.I.C.S.: 334413

Alpha & Omega Semiconductor (Hong Kong) Limited **(1)**
Room 701 Tesbury Center 28 Queen's Road East
Wanchai, China (Hong Kong)
Tel.: (852) 25292820
Fax: (852) 2529 2823
E-Mail: AOSHK@aosmd.com
Semiconductor Devices Mfr
S.I.C.: 3674
N.A.I.C.S.: 334413

Alpha and Omega Semiconductor (Shanghai) Co., Ltd. **(1)**
Room 1002-1005 Tower 1 Kerry EverBright City 218
Tianmu West Road Bldg A, Shanghai, 200070, China
Tel.: (86) 21 6353 3218
Fax: (86) 21 6353 9339
E-Mail: AOSChina@aosmd.com
Semiconductor Devices Mfr
S.I.C.: 3674
N.A.I.C.S.: 334413

Alpha and Omega Semiconductor (Shenzhen) Co., Ltd. **(1)**
Room F 24/F Shenzhen Special Zone Press Tower
Shenzhen, 518034, China

Alpha and Omega Semiconductor Limited—(Continued)

Tel.: (86) 755 8351 7733
Fax: (86) 755 8351 5883
E-Mail: AOSChina@aosmd.com
Semiconductor Devices Mfr & Whslr
S.I.C.: 3674
N.A.I.C.S.: 334413

Alpha and Omega Semiconductor (Taiwan) Ltd. (1)
9/F No 292 Yangguang Street
Neihu District, Taipei, 11491, Taiwan
Tel.: (886) 287515616
Fax: (886) 2 2627 4762
E-Mail: AOSTaiwan@aosmd.com
Web Site: www.aosmd.com
Semiconductor Devices Mfr & Whslr
S.I.C.: 3674
N.A.I.C.S.: 334413

ALPHA ASSOCIES CONSEIL

49 Avenue Hoche
75008 Paris, France
Tel.: (33) 156602020
Fax: (33) 156601022
E-Mail: alphagroup@groupealpha.fr
Web Site: www.groupealpha.com
Emp.: 25

Business Description:
Private Equity Firm
S.I.C.: 6211
N.A.I.C.S.: 523999

Personnel:
Nicolas ver Hulst *(Chm-Mgmt Bd)*
Nicolas Macquin *(Partner)*
Olaf Kordes *(Mng Dir)*
Herve Hautin *(CFO & Member-Mgmt Bd)*
Christophe Neumann *(Chief Legal Officer)*

Non-U.S. Holding:

Savio Macchine Tessili S.p.A. (1)
via Udine 105
33170 Pordenone, Italy
Tel.: (39) 0434 3971
Fax: (39) 0434 397656
E-Mail: mail@saviospa.it
Web Site: www.saviotechnologies.com
Sales Range: $600-649.9 Million
Emp.: 1,500
Manufacturing Machinery Mfr
S.I.C.: 3569
N.A.I.C.S.: 333999

U.S. Subsidiary:

BMSVision LLC (2)
4420 Taggart Creek Rd Ste 112
Charlotte, NC 28208-5414
Tel.: (704) 392-9371
Fax: (704) 399-5588
Web Site: www.visionbms.com
Emp.: 17
Electronic Inspecting Devices Mfr
S.I.C.: 5046
N.A.I.C.S.: 423440
Dany Claeys *(VP)*

Non-U.S. Subsidiaries:

Sedo Treepoint GmbH (2)
Neuwies 1
35794 Mengerskirchen, Germany (10%)
Tel.: (49) 6476310
Fax: (49) 64763131
E-Mail: sedo@sedo-treepoint.com
Web Site: www.sedo-treepoint.com
Sales Range: $1-9.9 Million
Emp.: 30
Textile Manufacturing Equipment Mfr
S.I.C.: 3569
N.A.I.C.S.: 333999
Maurizio Wermelinger *(Gen Mgr)*

BMS Vision Ltd. (2)
Capricorn Park Blakewater Rd
Blackburn, BB1 5QR, United Kingdom (100%)
Tel.: (44) 1254662244
Fax: (44) 1254582595
Sales Range: $1-9.9 Million
Emp.: 15
Manufacturing Equipment Mfr
S.I.C.: 3569
N.A.I.C.S.: 333999

BMS bvba (2)
Vlamingstraat 16
8560 Wevelgem, Belgium
Tel.: (32) 56 26 26 11
Fax: (32) 56 26 26 90
E-Mail: sales.bv@visionbms.com
Web Site: www.visionbms.com
Manufacturing Equipment Mfr
S.I.C.: 3569
N.A.I.C.S.: 333999
Johan Schepens *(Pres)*

Loepfe Brothers Ltd. (2)
Kastellstrasse 10
PO Box 582
CH 8623 Wetzikon, Switzerland (100%)
Tel.: (41) 434881111
Fax: (41) 434881100
E-Mail: admin@loepfe.com
Web Site: www.loepfe.com
Sales Range: $25-49.9 Million
Emp.: 170
Textile Machinery Mfr
S.I.C.: 3569
N.A.I.C.S.: 333999
Maurizio Wermelinger *(Gen Mgr)*

Non-U.S. Affiliate:

APEF Management Company 5 Limited (1)
22 Grenville Street
PO Box 87
Saint Helier, Channel Islands, JE4 8PX, Jersey JE
Tel.: (44) 1534 609 000
Fax: (44) 1534 609 333
E-Mail: info@alphape.com
Web Site: www.groupealpha.com
Investment Management Services
S.I.C.: 6282
N.A.I.C.S.: 523920

ALPHA ASTIKA AKINITA S.A

43 Panepistimiou Str
10564 Athens, Greece
Tel.: (30) 210 326 6161
Fax: (30) 210 326 6148
E-Mail: astikaakinita@alpha.gr
Web Site: www.astikaakinita.gr
Year Founded: 1942
ASTAK—(ATH)
Emp.: 63

Business Description:
Real Estate Development Services
S.I.C.: 6531
N.A.I.C.S.: 531390

Personnel:
Themistokles I. Corcontzelos *(Chm)*
George N. Contos *(Vice Chm)*
Antonios S. Leoussis *(Mng Dir)*

Board of Directors:
Themistokles I. Corcontzelos
George N. Contos
Aristides A. Despotopoulos
Konstantinos Dorkofikis
Georgios P. Krepis
Antonios S. Leoussis
Theofanis D. Saxonis

ALPHA BANK A.E.

(d/b/a Alpha Bank Group)
40 Stadiou Street
102 52 Athens, Greece
Tel.: (30) 2103260000
Fax: (30) 210 326 5438
E-Mail: secretariat@alpha.gr
Web Site: www.alpha.gr
ALPHA—(ATH)
Rev.: $4,475,863,133
Assets: $78,558,880,195
Liabilities: $77,518,814,445
Net Worth: $1,040,065,750
Earnings: ($1,461,765,618)
Emp.: 13,650
Fiscal Year-end: 12/31/12

Business Description:
Banking Services
S.I.C.: 6029
N.A.I.C.S.: 522110

Personnel:
Yannis S. Costopoulos *(Chm)*
Minas G. Tanes *(Vice Chm)*
Demetrios P. Mantzounis *(CEO & Mng Dir)*
Vassilios E. Psaltis *(CFO & Gen Mgr)*
Spyros N. Filaretos *(COO & Gen Mgr)*
Spiros A. Andronikakis *(Chief Risk Officer)*
Stella Traka *(IR Officer)*
Hector P. Verykios *(Sec)*

Board of Directors:
Yannis S. Costopoulos
George E. Agouridis
Pavlos A. Apostolides
George C. Aronis
Spyros N. Filaretos
Panagiota Iplixian
Evangelos J. Kaloussis
Paul G. Karakostas
Sarantis-Evangelos G. Lolos
Ioannis K. Lyras
Demetrios P. Mantzounis
Ioanna E. Papadopoulou
Minas G. Tanes
Artemis Ch. Theodoridis
Athanassios M. Veremis

Subsidiaries:

IONIAN HOTEL ENTERPRISES S.A. (1)
103 Athinon Ave
104 47 Athens, Greece
Tel.: (30) 2103436288
Fax: (30) 2103436957
E-Mail: ionianhotels@alpha.gr
Web Site: www.ionianhe.gr
IOKA—(ATH)
Emp.: 350
Hotel Management Services
S.I.C.: 7011
N.A.I.C.S.: 721110
Yannis S. Costopoulos *(Chm)*
Pavlos G. Caracostas *(Vice Chm)*
Spyros H. Filaretos *(Mng Dir)*

Non-U.S. Subsidiaries:

Alpha Bank Cyprus Limited (1)
Alpha Bank Building 3 Lemesou Avenue
Aglantzia, 2112 Nicosia, Cyprus CY
Mailing Address: (100%)
PO Box 21661
1596 Nicosia, Cyprus
Tel.: (357) 22 88 8888
Fax: (357) 22 334868
E-Mail: marketing@alphabank.com.cy
Web Site: www.alphabank.com.cy
Int. Income: $329,869,632
Assets: $6,405,827,762
Liabilities: $5,726,314,861
Net Worth: $679,512,901
Earnings: ($41,981,639)
Emp.: 75
Fiscal Year-end: 12/31/12
Commercial Banking Services
S.I.C.: 6029
N.A.I.C.S.: 522110
Spyros N. Filaretos *(Chm)*
George A. Georgiou *(Mng Dir)*

Alpha Finance Romania S.A. (1)
Dorobantilor Way 237B 2nd Fl Sector 1
Bucharest, 010566, Romania
Tel.: (40) 212092233
Fax: (40) 2315332
E-Mail: office@alphafinance.ro
Web Site: www.alphafinance.ro
AFR—(BUC)
Sales Range: $1-9.9 Million
Emp.: 10
Investment & Banking Services
S.I.C.: 6211
N.A.I.C.S.: 523999
Mareus Lupu *(Dir-Brokerage)*

ALPHA CORPORATION

1-6-8 Fukuura
Kanazawa-ku, Yokohama, Kanagawa, 236-0004, Japan
Tel.: (81) 45 7878400
Fax: (81) 45 7878425
E-Mail: alpha-info@kk-alpha.co.jp
Web Site: www.kk-alpha.com
Year Founded: 1923
3434—(TKS)
Sales Range: $500-549.9 Million
Emp.: 3,576

Business Description:
Automobile Parts Mfr
S.I.C.: 3429
N.A.I.C.S.: 332510

Personnel:
Shigeru Kinose *(Pres)*

ALPHA EXPLORATION INC.

Suite 408 1199 West Pender Street
Vancouver, BC, V6E 2R1, Canada
Tel.: (604) 629-0293
Fax: (604) 684-9365
Toll Free: (866) 629-8368
E-Mail: info@alpha-aex.com
Web Site: www.alpha-aex.com
Year Founded: 2013
AEX—(TSXV)

Business Description:
Uranium & Gold Mining
S.I.C.: 1094
N.A.I.C.S.: 212291

Personnel:
Michael Gunning *(Chm)*
Benjamin Ainsworth *(Pres & CEO)*
Kurt Bordian *(CFO & Sec)*

Board of Directors:
Michael Gunning
Benjamin Ainsworth
Charles Roy
Warren Stanyer
James Yates

ALPHA GOLD CORP.

410 Donald Street
Coquitlam, BC, V3K 3Z8, Canada
Tel.: (604) 939-7943
Fax: (604) 939-4981
Web Site: www.alphagoldcorp.com
ALQ—(TSXV)
Int. Income: $2,571
Assets: $11,963,414
Liabilities: $1,168,417
Net Worth: $10,794,998
Earnings: ($182,095)
Fiscal Year-end: 02/28/13

Business Description:
Mineral Exploration Services
S.I.C.: 1081
N.A.I.C.S.: 213114

Personnel:
Carl J. Pines *(CEO)*
Joanne N. Ward *(CFO)*
Jim Ritchie *(Sec)*

Board of Directors:
Neil F. Hummel
Stephen M. Leahy
Carl J. Pines
Joanne N. Ward

ALPHA GRISSIN S.A.

Attica 16km Lavriou Av
190 02 Peania, Greece
Tel.: (30) 2126875400
Fax: (30) 2109353630
E-Mail: alphasa@alphagrissin.gr
Web Site: www.alphagrissin.gr
AGRI—(ATH)
Sales Range: $25-49.9 Million
Emp.: 93

Business Description:
Holding Company; Techonology, Real Estate, Energy
S.I.C.: 6719
N.A.I.C.S.: 551112

Personnel:
Nikolaos Kakousios *(Vice Chm & Mng Dir)*
Dimitrios Parthenis *(Mng Dir)*

Board of Directors:
Vasileios Pappas
Marina Grissin
Nikolaos Kakousios
Marios Kapenekakis
Dimitris Klonis
Michael Michagelidis
Dimitrios Papakonstantinou
Dimitrios Parthenis
Euaggelia Roussou
Stavros Tsoukantas

ALPHA HI-TECH FUEL LTD.

Station Road
Lakhtar, Surendranagar, Gujarat, 382775, India
Tel.: (91) 2759 23284
E-Mail: info@alphahitechfuel.com
Web Site: www.alphahitechfuel.com
531247—(BOM)
Assets: $903,967
Liabilities: $314,411
Net Worth: $589,556
Earnings: ($188,378)
Fiscal Year-end: 03/31/13
Business Description:
Agricultural Waste Recovery Services
S.I.C.: 4953
N.A.I.C.S.: 562920
Personnel:
Haren Shah *(Compliance Officer)*
Board of Directors:
Subhash Nayak
Haren Shah
Uma Kant Shukla
Transfer Agent:
Link Intime India Pvt. Ltd
C-13 Pannalal Silk Mills Compound LBS Marg
Bhandup (West)
Mumbai, India

ALPHA MINERALS INC.

(Acquired & Absorbed by Fission Uranium Corp.)

ALPHA MOS

20 avenue Didier Daurat
31400 Toulouse, France
Tel.: (33) 562475380
Fax: (33) 561545615
E-Mail: communication@alpha-mos.com
Web Site: www.alpha-mos.com
Year Founded: 1993
ALM—(EUR)
Sls.: $11,562,254
Earnings: ($3,314,271)
Fiscal Year-end: 12/31/12
Business Description:
Analytical Laboratory Instrument Mfr
S.I.C.: 3826
N.A.I.C.S.: 334516
Personnel:
Jean-Christophe Mifsud *(Founder & CEO)*
Board of Directors:
Benoit Adelus
Kleber Beauvillain
Pascal Gendrot
Jonathan B. Lapin
Jean-Christophe Mifsud

U.S. Subsidiary:

Alpha MOS America Inc (1)
7502 Connelley Dr Ste 110
Hanover, MD 21076
Tel.: (410) 553-9736
Fax: (410) 553-9871
Web Site: www.alpha-mos.com
Analytical Instrument Distr
S.I.C.: 5049
N.A.I.C.S.: 423490

Non-U.S. Subsidiaries:

Alpha MOS China (1)
Suite 1001-1002 Xin Da Tower 322 Xian Xia Road
Shanghai, China 200336
Tel.: (86) 21 6209 3271
Fax: (86) 21 6295 2259
Web Site: www.alpha-mos.com
Analytical Instrument Mfr
S.I.C.: 3826
N.A.I.C.S.: 334516

Alpha MOS Japan KK (1)
Jowa Takanawa Building 8F 1-5-4 Takanawa
Minato-Ku, Tokyo, 108-0074, Japan
Tel.: (81) 3 5475 3291
Fax: (81) 3 5475 3292
Web Site: www.alpha-mos.com
Emp.: 9
Analytical Instrument Mfr
S.I.C.: 3826
N.A.I.C.S.: 334516

ALPHA NETWORKS INC.

No 8 Li-Shing Rd 7th Science-Based Industrial Park
Hsin-chu, Taiwan
Tel.: (886) 35636666
Fax: (886) 35636789
E-Mail: ir@alphanetworks.com
Web Site: www.alphanetworks.com
3380—(TAI)
Sales Range: $350-399.9 Million
Business Description:
Network & Digital Products Mfr
S.I.C.: 3661
N.A.I.C.S.: 334210
Personnel:
John Lee *(Chm & CEO)*
Board of Directors:
John Lee
Harrison Chang
Harry Huang
Mao-Chao Lin

U.S. Subsidiaries:

Alpha Networks Inc. (1)
2901 Tasman Dr Ste 109
Santa Clara, CA 95054 CA
Tel.: (408) 844-8850
Fax: (408) 844-8841
Web Site: www.alphanetworks.com
Sales Range: $25-49.9 Million
Emp.: 20
Networking Components Distr
S.I.C.: 5065
N.A.I.C.S.: 423690
Hender Hsing *(Pres)*

Alpha Technical and Services Inc. (1)
7 Cushing Spectrum 5
Irvine, CA 92618
Tel.: (714) 540-8800
Fax: (714) 540-8810
Web Site: www.alphanetworks.com
Emp.: 25
Networking Components Distr
S.I.C.: 5065
N.A.I.C.S.: 423690
Alan Chien *(Mgr)*

Non-U.S. Subsidiaries:

Alpha Solutions Co., Ltd. (1)
10F 8-8-15 Nishigotanda
Shinagawa-ku, Tokyo, 141-0031, Japan
Tel.: (81) 354349678
Fax: (81) 354349868
Web Site: www.alphanetworks.com
Emp.: 4
Computer Peripheral Equipments Mfr & Distr
S.I.C.: 3661
N.A.I.C.S.: 334210
Hiroaki Nakajima *(Gen Mgr)*

Dongguan Youxun Electronics Co., Ltd. (1)
Xin'an Area
Chang An, Dongguan, Guangdong, 523000, China
Tel.: (86) 76985318000
Fax: (86) 76985319009
Web Site: www.alphanetworks.com
Networking Components Mfr
S.I.C.: 3661
N.A.I.C.S.: 334210

Mirac Networks (Dongguan) Co., Ltd. (1)
Room 301 No 10 Lane 198 Zhangheng Rd
Zhangjiang Hi-Tech Park
Shanghai, Pudong, 201204, China
Tel.: (86) 21 61609650
Fax: (86) 769 8607 7166
E-Mail: ivan_chou@alphanetworks.com
Web Site: www.alphanetworks.com
Networking Components Mfr
S.I.C.: 3571
N.A.I.C.S.: 334111
Ivan Chou *(Mgr)*

ALPHA PEAK LEISURE INC.

5300 Lancing Road
Richmond, BC, V7C 3A1, Canada
Tel.: (604) 488-5219
E-Mail: thurman@shaw.ca
Year Founded: 2011
AAP.P—(TSXV)
Int. Income: $3,731
Assets: $417,397
Net Worth: $417,397
Earnings: $984
Fiscal Year-end: 09/30/12
Business Description:
Investment Services
S.I.C.: 6211
N.A.I.C.S.: 523999
Personnel:
Dennis Chi-Wai Tam *(Chm & CEO)*
Samuel Yuen-Wai Tsang *(Vice Chm & Pres)*
Thurman Tat Hong So *(CFO & Sec)*
Board of Directors:
Dennis Chi-Wai Tam
Keith Chi Hang Lee
Thurman Tat Hong So
Samuel Yuen-Wai Tsang
Anthony Kan Hee Tyen
Transfer Agent:
Computershare Investor Services Inc.
3rd Floor 510 Burrard Street
Vancouver, BC, Canada

ALPHA PETROVISION HOLDING AG

Rotelistrasse 16
9000 Saint Gallen, Switzerland
Tel.: (41) 71 388 90 00
Fax: (41) 71 388 90 09
E-Mail: info@alpha-petrovision.com
Web Site: www.alpha-petrovision.com
APHN—(SWX)
Rev.: $7,735,554
Assets: $14,135,084
Liabilities: $16,011,713
Net Worth: ($1,876,629)
Earnings: ($23,153,267)
Fiscal Year-end: 12/31/12
Business Description:
Investment Management Services
S.I.C.: 6282
N.A.I.C.S.: 523920
Personnel:
Walter Meier *(Chm & CEO)*
Marc Joye *(CFO)*
Board of Directors:
Walter Meier
Richard Couillard
Peter Kolossa

ALPHA PRO TECH, LTD.

60 Centurian Drive Suite 112
Markham, ON, L3R 9R2, Canada
Tel.: (905) 479-0654
Fax: (905) 479-9732
E-Mail: sales@alphaprotech.com
Web Site: www.alphaprotech.com
Year Founded: 1989
APT—(NYSEMKT)
Sls.: $43,806,000
Assets: $38,563,000
Liabilities: $2,982,000
Net Worth: $35,581,000
Earnings: $2,079,000
Emp.: 121
Fiscal Year-end: 12/31/13
Business Description:
Protective Apparel Mfr for Cleanroom, Industrial, Medical & Dental & Pharmaceutical Industries
S.I.C.: 5047
N.A.I.C.S.: 423450
Personnel:
Alexander W. Millar *(Pres)*
Sheldon Hoffman *(CEO)*
Lloyd Hoffman *(CFO & Sr VP-Fin & Admin)*
Bruce Hayden *(Sr VP-Sls & Mktg-Building Products)*
Chris Louisos *(Sr VP-Sls & Mktg)*
Danny Montgomery *(Sr VP-Mfg)*
Board of Directors:
David B. Anderson
David R. Garcia
Sheldon Hoffman
Russell Manock
Alexander W. Millar
Danny Montgomery
John P. Ritota, Jr.
Legal Counsel:
Foreht Last Landau and Katz LLP
228 E 45th St 17th Fl
New York, NY 10017

U.S. Subsidiary:

Alpha ProTech Engineered Products, Inc. (1)
301 S Blanchard St
Valdosta, GA 31601-2431
Tel.: (229) 242-1931
Fax: (229) 242-1947
Toll Free: (866) 312-1837
E-Mail:
Durable Goods Whslr
S.I.C.: 5099
N.A.I.C.S.: 423990
Al Millar *(Pres)*
Lloyd Hoffman *(CFO)*
Robert Dennis *(Principal)*

U.S. Plants:

Alpha Pro Tech-Nogales (1)
1287 W Fairway Dr
Nogales, AZ 85621
Tel.: (520) 281-0127
Fax: (520) 281-2642
Web Site: www.alphaprotech.com
Sls.: $21,130,000
Emp.: 45
Surgical Appliances & Supplies
S.I.C.: 3842
N.A.I.C.S.: 339113

ALPHA STRATEGIC PLC

(See Under Northill Capital LLP)

ALPHA SYSTEMS INC.

Shionogi Shibuya Bldg 12th Floor
2-17-5 Shibuya
Shibuya-ku, Tokyo, 150-0002, Japan
Tel.: (81) 334865111
Fax: (81) 354667755
Web Site: www.alpha.co.jp
Year Founded: 1972
4719—(TKS)
Sls.: $262,119,000
Assets: $408,980,000
Liabilities: $69,168,000
Net Worth: $339,812,000
Earnings: $12,001,000
Emp.: 2,436
Fiscal Year-end: 03/31/13
Business Description:
Communications Equipment & Systems Mfr
S.I.C.: 3669
N.A.I.C.S.: 334290
Personnel:
Yuko Ishikawa *(Chm)*

Alpha Systems Inc.—(Continued)

Hidetomo Ishikawa *(Vice Chm)*
Ken-ichi Kuroda *(Pres)*
Sakae Asaoka *(Co-Mng Dir)*
Kiyoshi Saito *(Co-Mng Dir)*
Nagomu Ito *(Operating Officer)*
Seiichirou Nishimura *(Operating Officer)*
Board of Directors:
Yuko Ishikawa
Kouji Akazaki
Sakae Asaoka
Hidetomo Ishikawa
Yousaku Kawahara
Takao Kawana
Ken-ichi Kuroda
Satoshi Takada
Toshifumi Takada
Katsumi Tokura
Shin-ichi Yamauchi
Takashi Yanagiya

ALPHA TRUST INVESTMENT SERVICES SA

21 Tatoiou Street
Kifisia, 145 61 Athens, Greece
Tel.: (30) 210 628 9100
E-Mail: info@alphatrust.gr
Web Site: www.alphatrust.gr
Business Description:
Investment Services
S.I.C.: 6211
N.A.I.C.S.: 523999
Personnel:
John Tamvakakis *(Vice Chm)*

Subsidiary:

Kyprou Asset Management Mutual Funds Management Company S.A. **(1)**
26 Feidippidou & Chalkidonos str 6th floor
11527 Athens, Greece
Tel.: (30) 210 77 65 441
Fax: (30) 210 77 65 449
E-Mail: aedak@bankofcyprus.gr
Web Site: www.bankofcyprus.gr
Emp.: 15
Mutual Fund Management Services
S.I.C.: 6799
N.A.I.C.S.: 523920
Christodoulos Patsalides *(Chm)*

Subsidiaries:

Kyprou Asfalistiki **(2)**
Leoforos Mesogeion 170
Cholargos, 15561 Athens, Attica, Greece
Tel.: (30) 2106477382
Fax: (30) 2106477187
Emp.: 60
Insurance Brokerage Services
S.I.C.: 6411
N.A.I.C.S.: 524210
George Makris *(Gen Mgr)*

Kyprou Factors **(2)**
Papada 4
11521 Athens, Greece
Tel.: (30) 210 64 77 571
Fax: (30) 210 64 77 599
E-Mail: kyproufactors@bankofcyprus.gr
Business Management Services
S.I.C.: 7389
N.A.I.C.S.: 561499
John Yeaman *(Gen Mgr)*

ALPHA UNIVERSAL MANAGEMENT PLC

31 Harley Street
London, W1G 9Qs, United Kingdom
Tel.: (44) 207 467 1700
Fax: (44) 207 636 5639
E-Mail: info@aumplc.com
Web Site: www.aumplc.com
Year Founded: 2006
AUNP—(DEU ISDX)
Business Description:
Investment Management Services
S.I.C.: 6211
N.A.I.C.S.: 523999
Personnel:
Gobind Sahney *(Chm & Mng Dir)*
Jonathan Bradley Hoare *(Sec)*
Board of Directors:
Gobind Sahney
Jonathan Bradley Hoare
Legal Counsel:
Burges Salmon LLP
Narrow Quay House Narrow Quay
Bristol, BS1 4AH, United Kingdom

ALPHA WASTEWATER, INC.

Suite 1500 701 West Georgia Street
Vancouver, BC, V7Y 1C6, Canada
Tel.: (604) 601-8503
Fax: (604) 601-8502
E-Mail: info@alphawastewater.com
Web Site: www.alphawastewater.com
Year Founded: 1997
AWWI—(OTC)
Business Description:
Wastewater Treatment
S.I.C.: 4953
N.A.I.C.S.: 562219
Personnel:
Charles James Mayer *(Chm)*
Brian L. Hauff *(Pres & CEO)*
Justin Shengfeng Wang *(CFO, Sec & VP-China Ops)*
Board of Directors:
Charles James Mayer
Karel V. Galland
Brian L. Hauff
Justin Shengfeng Wang
Weibiao Xu

ALPHACHIPS CORP.

(d/b/a Alpha Chips)
Kins Tower 12F 1201 Jeongja-dong
Bundang-gu, Seongnam, Gyeonggi-do, 463-811, Korea (South)
Tel.: (82) 31 2091800
Fax: (82) 31 2091819
E-Mail: alphachip@alphachips.com
Web Site: www.alphachips.com
117670—(KRS)
Sales Range: $25-49.9 Million
Emp.: 60
Business Description:
Semiconductor Chip Mfr
S.I.C.: 3674
N.A.I.C.S.: 334413
Personnel:
K.H. Kim *(CEO)*

ALPHAFORM AG

Kapellenstrasse 10
D-85622 Feldkirchen, Germany
Tel.: (49) 899050020
Fax: (49) 8990500290
E-Mail: info@alphaform.de
Web Site: www.alphaform.de
ATF—(DEU OTC)
Rev.: $36,485,246
Assets: $28,787,845
Liabilities: $11,581,101
Net Worth: $17,206,745
Earnings: $710,778
Emp.: 231
Fiscal Year-end: 12/31/12
Business Description:
Tool Mfr
S.I.C.: 3423
N.A.I.C.S.: 332216
Personnel:
Matti Paasila *(Chm-Supervisory Bd)*
Thomas Vetter *(Chm-Mgmt Bd & CEO)*
Falk F. Strascheg *(Deputy Chm-Supervisory Bd)*
Supervisory Board of Directors:
Matti Paasila
Hans J. Langer
Falk F. Strascheg

Subsidiaries:

Alphaform-Claho GmbH **(1)**
Blauanger 6
82438 Eschenlohe, Bavaria, Germany
Tel.: (49) 899050020
E-Mail: info@alphaform.de
Emp.: 50
Machinery Mfr
S.I.C.: 3559
N.A.I.C.S.: 333249
Oliver Rebele *(Mgr)*

MediMet Precision Casting and Implants Technology GmbH **(1)**
Ohle Ring 23-25
Wiepenkathen, 21684 Stade, Lower Saxony, Germany
Tel.: (49) 414180300
Fax: (49) 4141803020
E-Mail: info@medimet.de
Web Site: www.medimet.de
Emp.: 107
Medical Implants Mfr
S.I.C.: 3841
N.A.I.C.S.: 339113
Reimund Dorschfeld *(CEO)*

Non-U.S. Subsidiaries:

Alphaform Ltd. **(1)**
Swift House Hambridge Lane
Newbury, Berkshire, RG14 5TU, United Kingdom
Tel.: (44) 1635232480
Fax: (44) 1635232489
Web Site: www.alphaform.co.uk
Emp.: 6
Rapid Prototyping & Metal Coating Services
S.I.C.: 3479
N.A.I.C.S.: 332812

Alphaform-RPI Oy **(1)**
Aholantie 17
21290 Rusko, Finland
Tel.: (358) 290091006
Fax: (358) 290091009
E-Mail: sales@alphaform.fi
Web Site: www.alphaform.fi
Emp.: 16
Prototypes & Models Mfr
S.I.C.: 3942
N.A.I.C.S.: 339930
Dan Bjorklof *(Mng Dir)*

ALPHAGEO INDIA LTD

6-3-250/2 Road No 1 Banjara Hills
Hyderabad, Andhra Pradesh, 500034, India
Tel.: (91) 4023320502
Fax: (91) 4023302238
E-Mail: info@alphageoindia.com
Web Site: www.alphageoindia.com
ALPHAGEO—(BOM)
Rev.: $4,413,790
Assets: $13,693,107
Liabilities: $6,078,500
Net Worth: $7,614,608
Earnings: $1,984,361
Fiscal Year-end: 03/31/13
Business Description:
Seismic Survey Services
S.I.C.: 8713
N.A.I.C.S.: 541360
Personnel:
Alla Dinesh *(Mng Dir)*
Pasumarthy Venkatesa Perumallu *(CFO & Compliance Officer)*
Board of Directors:
Z. P. Marshall
Ashwinder Bhel
Alla Dinesh
Alla Rajesh
P. K. Reddy
S. Ravula Reddy
Transfer Agent:
Karvy Computershare Private Limited
Plot No 17 to 24 Vittalrao Nagar Madhapur
Hyderabad, India

ALPHAMIN RESOURCES CORP.

Level 3 Gotthardstrasse 20
CH-6304 Zug, Switzerland
Tel.: (41) 417110281
Fax: (41) 6045072187
E-Mail: info@alphaminresources.com
Web Site: www.alphaminresources.com
Year Founded: 1981
AFM—(TSXV)
Rev.: $27,527
Assets: $40,106,835
Liabilities: $1,467,071
Net Worth: $38,639,764
Earnings: ($2,871,498)
Fiscal Year-end: 12/31/12
Business Description:
Mineral Exploration Services
S.I.C.: 1081
N.A.I.C.S.: 213114
Personnel:
Klaus Eckhof *(Pres & CEO)*
Ross Doyle *(CFO)*
James L. Harris *(Sec)*
Board of Directors:
Tom Borman
Juan Carlos Del Rio
Mark Richard Gasson
Brendon Jones
Rudolf Pretorius
Legal Counsel:
McCullough O'Connor Irwin LLP
Suite 2600 Oceanic Plaza 1066 West Hastings Street
Vancouver, BC, Canada
Transfer Agent:
Montreal Trust Company of Canada
3rd Floor 510 Burrard Street
Vancouver, BC, V6C 3B9, Canada

ALPHANAM JOINT STOCK COMPANY

33A Ba Trieu Street
Hoan Kiem District, Hanoi, Vietnam
Tel.: (84) 439367979
Fax: (84) 439393676
E-Mail: info@alphanam.com
Web Site: www.alphanam.com.vn
ALP—(HOSE)
Sales Range: $50-74.9 Million
Emp.: 1,300
Business Description:
Heavy Electrical & Mechanical Specialized Equipment Mfr
S.I.C.: 3699
N.A.I.C.S.: 335999
Personnel:
Hai Tuan Nguyen *(Gen Dir)*

Subsidiary:

Alphanam Mechanical Electric Joint Stock Company **(1)**
2 Dai Co Viet
Hai Ba Trung, Hanoi, Vietnam
Tel.: (84) 439747979
Fax: (84) 439784885
E-Mail: info@alphanam.com
Web Site: www.alphanam.com.vn
AME—(HNX)
Emp.: 120
Power Transmission Lines & Electrical Systems Mfr
S.I.C.: 1623
N.A.I.C.S.: 237130
Hai Tuan Nguyen *(Gen Dir)*

ALPHAPHARM PTY LTD

Level 1 13 The Bond 30-34 Hickson Road Bistro Nearest Point
Sydney, NSW, 2000, Australia
Tel.: (61) 292983999
Fax: (61) 295664686
E-Mail: information@alphapharm.com.au
Web Site: www.alphapharm.com.au

Sales Range: $400-449.9 Million
Emp.: 700
Business Description:
Medicines Research, Developing & Mfr
S.I.C.: 2834
N.A.I.C.S.: 325412
Personnel:
John Montgomery *(CEO)*
Frank Traugott *(Chief Compliance Officer)*

ALPHARX, INC.
(Name Changed to UMeWorld, Limited)

ALPHAWEST SERVICES PTY LTD
PO Box 888
North Ryde, NSW, 1670, Australia
Tel.: (61) 292635888
Fax: (61) 292635889
Web Site: www.alphawest.com.au
Sales Range: $75-99.9 Million
Emp.: 800
Business Description:
Technology, Software, Business Processes & Services
S.I.C.: 7372
N.A.I.C.S.: 511210
Personnel:
Rob Parcell *(CEO)*

ALPHINAT INC.
2000 Peel Suite 680
Montreal, QC, H3A 2W5, Canada
Tel.: (514) 398-9799
Fax: (514) 398-9353
Toll Free: (877) 773-9799
Web Site: www.alphinat.com
Year Founded: 2004
NPA—(TSXV)
Rev.: $1,615,675
Assets: $613,459
Liabilities: $1,728,222
Net Worth: ($1,114,763)
Earnings: $25,943
Fiscal Year-end: 08/31/13
Business Description:
Software Development Services
S.I.C.: 7371
N.A.I.C.S.: 541511
Personnel:
Michel Lemoine *(Chm)*
Philippe Lecoq *(Pres & CEO)*
Curtis Page *(CFO, COO & Exec VP)*
Board of Directors:
Michel Lemoine
Marcel Cote
Marcel Elefant
Philippe Lecoq
Paul Lowenstein
Curtis Page
Ed Shepherdson
Benoit Ste-Marie

ALPHONSE CHARPIOT ET COMPAGNIE
18 avenue du General de Gaulle
BP 29
90100 Delle, France
Tel.: (33) 384367878
Fax: (33) 384367861
Web Site: www.charpiot.com
Rev.: $21,500,000
Emp.: 181
Business Description:
Freight Transportation Arrangement
S.I.C.: 4731
N.A.I.C.S.: 488510
Personnel:
Yves Locher *(Mgr-Fin)*

ALPIC EVEREST FINANCE LIMITED
The Kathmandu Mall Karmachari Sanchaye Kosh Building 4th floor
PO Box 12034
Sundhara, Kathmandu, Nepal
Tel.: (977) 1 4150301
Fax: (977) 1 4150304
E-Mail: aefl@wlink.com.np
Web Site: www.alpiceverest.com.np
Year Founded: 1994
AEFL—(NEP)
Business Description:
Financial Services
S.I.C.: 6211
N.A.I.C.S.: 523999
Personnel:
Mahendra Raj Tuladhar *(Chm)*
Ram Shant Shrestha *(CEO)*
Rajesh Puri *(Credit Officer)*
Ram Prasad Poudel *(Sec)*
Board of Directors:
Mahendra Raj Tuladhar
Shanker Prasad Dahal
Durga Prasad Pandey
Ram Prasad Poudel
Shyam Bahadur Shahi
Chandra Lok Prasad Shrestha
Ram Shant Shrestha
Hem Bahadur Thakulla

ALPINA, D.D.
2 Strojarska Ulica
4226 Ziri, Slovenia
Tel.: (386) 45158000
Fax: (386) 45158370
E-Mail: alpina@alpina.si
Web Site: www.alpina.si
Year Founded: 1947
Emp.: 500
Business Description:
Footwear Mfr & Sales
S.I.C.: 2389
N.A.I.C.S.: 316210
Supervisory Board of Directors:
Andrej Laznik
Matej Golob Matzele
Tamara Pavlin
Boris Pipan
Milan Sovinc
Peter Trcek
Matjaz Lennasi

U.S. Subsidiary:

ALPINA SPORTS Corp. (1)
93 Etna Rd
Lebanon, NH 03766
Tel.: (603) 448-3101
Fax: (603) 448-1586
E-Mail: info@alpinasports.com
Emp.: 12
Sporting Goods & Supplies Mfr
S.I.C.: 3949
N.A.I.C.S.: 339920
Frank Phibodeau *(Pres)*

Non-U.S. Subsidiaries:

ALPINA BH, d.o.o. (1)
Zmaja od Bosne 7-7A
71000 Sarajevo, Bosnia & Herzegovina
Tel.: (387) 33 590 462
Fax: (387) 33 592 445
E-Mail: alpinabh@bih.net.ba
Emp.: 41
Sporting Goods & Supplies Mfr
S.I.C.: 3949
N.A.I.C.S.: 339920

ALPINA BROMY, d.o.o. (1)
Vukovo bb
74260 Tesanj, Bosnia & Herzegovina
Tel.: (387) 32 667 270
Fax: (387) 32 665 802
Sporting Goods & Supplies Mfr
S.I.C.: 3949
N.A.I.C.S.: 339920

ALPINA CRO, d.o.o. (1)
Radnicka Cesta 80
Zagreb, Croatia
Tel.: (385) 13665761
Sporting Goods & Supplies Mfr
S.I.C.: 3949
N.A.I.C.S.: 339920

ALPINA SIRO, S.R.L. (1)
Str I C Bratianu NR 24
Medias, 551003, Romania
Tel.: (40) 269 844 810
Fax: (40) 269 806 414
Emp.: 140
Sporting Goods & Supplies Mfr
S.I.C.: 3949
N.A.I.C.S.: 339920

ALPINA YUG, d.o.o. (1)
Bulevar umetnosti 4
Belgrade, Serbia
Tel.: (381) 11 21 31 140
Sporting Goods & Supplies Mfr
S.I.C.: 3949
N.A.I.C.S.: 339920

TOV ALPINA UA (1)
Bud 13 Kv 127 Vul Romena Rollana
Kiev, Ukraine
Tel.: (380) 444535583
Sporting Goods & Supplies Mfr
S.I.C.: 3949
N.A.I.C.S.: 339920

ALPINE AEROTECH LTD.
1260 Industrial Rd
Kelowna, BC, V1Z 1G5, Canada
Tel.: (250) 769-6344
Fax: (250) 769-6303
E-Mail: admin@alpineaerotech.com
Web Site: www.alpineaerotech.com
Year Founded: 1990
Rev.: $10,259,504
Emp.: 100
Business Description:
Aircraft Products & Service Provider
S.I.C.: 4581
N.A.I.C.S.: 488190
Personnel:
Jim Campbell *(VP & Gen Mgr)*

ALPINE BAU GMBH
Alte Bundesstrasse 10
5071 Salzburg, Austria
Tel.: (43) 66285820
Fax: (43) 66285829900
E-Mail: office@alpine.at
Web Site: www.alpine.at
Year Founded: 1965
Sales Range: $5-14.9 Billion
Emp.: 15,000
Business Description:
Construction Company
S.I.C.: 1541
N.A.I.C.S.: 237990
Personnel:
Dietmar Aluta Oltyan *(Chm-Supervisory Bd)*
Alejandro Tuya Garcia *(Deputy Chm-Supervisory Bd)*
Supervisory Board of Directors:
Dietmar Aluta Oltyan
Jose Aguinaga
Alejandro Tuya Garcia
Esther Alcocer Koplowitz
Jose Mayor Oreja
Robert Peugeot
Esther Koplowitz Romero de Juseu

Subsidiaries:

Beton- und Monierbau Gesellschaft m.b.H. (1)
Bernhard-Hofel-Strasse 11
6020 Innsbruck, Austria De
Tel.: (43) 51233110
Fax: (43) 512392655
E-Mail: office@alpine-bemo.com
Web Site: www.alpine-bemo.com
Rev.: $131,211,700
Emp.: 200
Tunneling & Underground Structure Construction
S.I.C.: 1611
N.A.I.C.S.: 237310

Grund- Pfahl- und Sonderbau GmbH (1)
Industriestrasse 27a
AT-2325 Himberg, Austria AT
Tel.: (43) 2235877770
Fax: (43) 2235 86 561
E-Mail: office@gps-bau.com
Web Site: www.gps-bau.com
Excavation, Stake-Drilling & Foundation Contracting Services
S.I.C.: 1771
N.A.I.C.S.: 238110
Andreas Forster *(Head-Comml)*

Non-U.S. Subsidiary:

Alpine Bau Deutschland AG (1)
Fuholzener Strasse 12
85386 Eching, Germany
Tel.: (49) 89327110
Fax: (49) 8932711217
E-Mail: info@alpine-bau.de
Web Site: www.alpine-bau.de/en/index.php
Emp.: 315
Construction Company
S.I.C.: 1611
N.A.I.C.S.: 237310
Karsten Hell *(Chm)*
Wolfgang Schwaiger *(Chm-Supervisory Bd)*
Wolfgang Schindler *(Mng Dir)*

ALPINE DEVELOPMENT BANK LIMITED
Main Road Narayani Zone
Makwanpur District, Hetauda, 44104, Nepal
Tel.: (977) 57524674
Fax: (977) 57524673
E-Mail: info@alpinedevbank.com.np
Web Site: www.alpinedevbank.com.np
Year Founded: 2007
ALDBL—(NEP)
Business Description:
Banking Services
S.I.C.: 6029
N.A.I.C.S.: 522110
Personnel:
Navraj Raut *(Chm)*
Sudarshan Prasad Adhikari *(CEO)*
Dev Nath Shrestha *(IT Officer)*
Board of Directors:
Navraj Raut
Sudip Prasad Adhikari
Chiranjibi Basnet
Shuk Dev Joshi
Anant Raj Paudel
Jeevan Kaji Makju Shrestha

ALPINE HOLDING GMBH
Alte-Bundesstrasse 10
Wals, 5071 Salzburg, Austria
Tel.: (43) 66285820
Fax: (43) 662 8582 9900
E-Mail: cms@alpine.at
Web Site: www.alpine.at/en
Year Founded: 1965
Sales Range: $1-4.9 Billion
Emp.: 15,294
Business Description:
Holding Company
S.I.C.: 6719
N.A.I.C.S.: 551112
Personnel:
Dietmar Aluta-Oltyan *(Chm-Supervisory Bd)*
Alejandro Tuya Garcia *(Deputy Chm-Supervisory Bd)*
Johannes Dotter *(Mng Dir)*
Enrique Sanz Herrero *(Mng Dir)*
Werner Watznauer *(Mng Dir)*
Supervisory Board of Directors:
Dietmar Aluta-Oltyan
Willi Bock
Jose Manuel Burgos
Jose Aguinaga Cardenas
Esther Koplowitz Romero de Juseu
Benita Ferrero-Waldner

Alpine Holding GmbH—(Continued)

Alejandro Tuya Garcia
Alicia Alcocer Koplowitz
Esther Alcocer Koplowitz
Jose Mayor Oreja
Robert Peugeot

ALPINE HOUSING DEVELOPMENT CORPORATION LTD.

002 Alpine Arch 10 Langford Road
Bengaluru, Karnataka, 560 027, India
Tel.: (91) 80 40473500
Fax: (91) 80 22128357
E-Mail: contact@alpinehousing.com
Web Site: www.alpinehousing.com
526519—(BOM)
Rev.: $5,996,387
Assets: $23,206,442
Liabilities: $13,460,617
Net Worth: $9,745,825
Earnings: $207,218
Emp.: 160
Fiscal Year-end: 03/31/13

Business Description:
Construction Engineering Services
S.I.C.: 1629
N.A.I.C.S.: 237990

Personnel:
S. A. Kabeer *(Chm & Mng Dir)*
Ashok Kumar Tripathy *(Compliance Officer & Sec)*

Board of Directors:
S. A. Kabeer
K. N. Guha
V. Karthik
Annu Kumari
N. K. Malu
S. M. Mohsin
Mohammed Muneer
S. A. Rasheed

Transfer Agent:
Cameo Corporate Services Limited
Subramanian Building V Floor 1 Club House Road
Chennai, India

Division:

Alpine Housing Development Corporation Ltd. - Alpine Alloys Division **(1)**
263 narasapura bye-pass NH-4
district kolar, Bengaluru, Karnataka, 562122, India
Tel.: (91) 8152 290410
Fax: (91) 8022 128357
E-Mail: contact@alpinealloys.com
Emp.: 20
Iron Casting Mfr
S.I.C.: 3325
N.A.I.C.S.: 331513

ALPINE SELECT AG

Bahnhofstrasse 23
CH-6000 Zug, Switzerland
Tel.: (41) 417204411
Fax: (41) 417204412
E-Mail: info@alpine-select.ch
Web Site: www.alpine-select.ch
ALPN—(SWX)
Rev.: $20,140,111
Assets: $208,179,242
Liabilities: $937,929
Net Worth: $207,241,313
Earnings: $17,736,466
Emp.: 1
Fiscal Year-end: 12/31/12

Business Description:
Investment Management Services
S.I.C.: 6282
N.A.I.C.S.: 523930

Personnel:
Raymond Bar *(Chm)*
Walter Geering *(CEO)*

Board of Directors:
Raymond Bar
Thomas Amstutz
Dieter Dubs
Walter Geering

ALPIQ HOLDING LTD.

Ch de Mornex 10
1003 Lausanne, Switzerland
Tel.: (41) 21 341 2111
Fax: (41) 62 286 7667
E-Mail: info@alpiq.com
Web Site: www.alpiq.com
ALPH—(SWX)
Rev.: $13,718,157,200
Assets: $15,956,666,880
Liabilities: $10,549,273,680
Net Worth: $5,407,393,200
Earnings: ($1,172,141,520)
Emp.: 7,340
Fiscal Year-end: 12/31/12

Business Description:
Holding Company; Energy Generation & Distribution Services
S.I.C.: 6719
N.A.I.C.S.: 551112

Personnel:
Hans E. Schweickardt *(Chm)*
Jasmin Staiblin *(Chm-Exec Bd & CEO)*
Christian Wanner *(Deputy Chm)*
Michael Wider *(Deputy CEO, Member-Exec Bd & Head-Generation)*
Patrick Mariller *(CFO & Member-Exec Bd)*
Reinhold Frank *(Member-Exec Bd & Head-Energy Svcs)*
Benoit Revaz *(Member-Exec Bd & Head-Mgmt Svcs)*
Erik Saether *(Member-Exec Bd & Head-Commerce & Trading)*

Board of Directors:
Hans E. Schweickardt
Conrad Ammann
Michael Baumgartner
Dominique Bompoint
Olivier Fauqueux
Damien Gros
Alex Kummer
Claude Lasser
Rene Longet
Guy Mustaki
Jean-Yves Pidoux
Urs Steiner
Christian Wanner

Subsidiaries:

Advens AG **(1)**
Katharina-Sulzer-Platz 12
8400 Winterthur, Switzerland
Tel.: (41) 52 244 03 30
Fax: (41) 52 244 09 31
E-Mail: info@advens.ch
Web Site: www.advens.ch
Engineering Consulting Services
S.I.C.: 8711
N.A.I.C.S.: 541330

Alpiq AG **(1)**
Bahnhofquai 12
CH 4601 Olten, Switzerland
Tel.: (41) 622867111
Fax: (41) 622867373
E-Mail: info@alpiq.com
Web Site: www.alpiq.ch
Sales Range: $5-14.9 Billion
Emp.: 9,944
Holding Company; Energy Companies & Power Plants
Export
S.I.C.: 3612
N.A.I.C.S.: 335311
Giovanni Leonardi *(CEO)*
Kurt Baumgartner *(CFO)*

Subsidiaries:

Alpiq Central Europe AG **(2)**
Bahnhofqaui 12
4601 Olten, Switzerland CH
Tel.: (41) 622867777 (100%)
Fax: (41) 622867373
E-Mail: info@alpiq.com
Emp.: 100
Electrical Power Trading
S.I.C.: 4931
N.A.I.C.S.: 221122
Reinhold Frank *(Head)*

Alpiq EcoPower Ltd. **(2)**
Bahnhofquai 12
4601 Olten, Switzerland CH
Tel.: (41) 622867111 (100%)
Fax: (41) 622867373
E-Mail: info@alpiq.com
Web Site: www.alpiq.com
Emp.: 600
Hydro Power Plant Operation & Construction
S.I.C.: 4911
N.A.I.C.S.: 221111
Jasmin Staiblin *(Mng Dir)*

Alpiq Hydro Aare AG **(2)**
Aarburgerstrasse 264
4618 Boningen, Switzerland CH
Tel.: (41) 627876911 (100%)
Fax: (41) 627876965
E-Mail: info.hydro.aare@alpiq.com
Emp.: 25
Hydroelectric Power Generator
S.I.C.: 4939
N.A.I.C.S.: 221111
Urs Hofstetter *(Mng Dir)*

Alpiq Hydro Ticino SA **(2)**
Centrale Lucendro
6780 Airolo, Switzerland CH
Tel.: (41) 918733111
Fax: (41) 918733110
E-Mail: info.hydro.ticino@alpiq.com
Emp.: 7
Hydroelectric Power Generator
S.I.C.: 4939
N.A.I.C.S.: 221111
Alfredo Baldi *(Mng Dir)*

Alpiq Intec AG **(2)**
Hohlstrasse 188
8026 Zurich, Switzerland CH
Tel.: (41) 442474000 (100%)
Fax: (41) 442474001
E-Mail: info.ait@alpiq.com
Web Site: www.alpiq-intec.ch
Emp.: 500
Power Generation, Heating & Cooling Technology, Process Automation & Energy Engineering Services
S.I.C.: 4911
N.A.I.C.S.: 221112
Peter Limacher *(Mng Dir)*
Rolf Brunner *(Head-Projects)*
Hans Dapp *(Head-Fin Svcs)*

Subsidiaries:

Alpiq EcoServices Ltd. **(3)**
Hohlstrasse 188
8026 Zurich, Switzerland
Tel.: (41) 44 247 44 44
Fax: (41) 44 247 41 07
E-Mail: info.ecoservices@alpiq.com
Web Site: www.alpiq-ecoservices.ch
Energy Consulting Services
S.I.C.: 8999
N.A.I.C.S.: 541690

Alpiq InTec East Ltd. **(3)**
Hohlstrasse 188
Zurich, 8004, Switzerland
Tel.: (41) 442474444
Electrical Equipment Installation Services
S.I.C.: 1731
N.A.I.C.S.: 238210

Alpiq InTec Ltd. **(3)**
Hohlstrasse 188
8026 Zurich, Switzerland
Tel.: (41) 44 247 44 44
Fax: (41) 44 247 40 01
E-Mail: info.ait.zuerich@alpiq.com
Web Site: www.alpiq-intec.ch
Emp.: 3,700
Facility Management Services
S.I.C.: 8744
N.A.I.C.S.: 561210
Peter Limacher *(Mng Dir)*
Rolf Brunner *(Head-Projects)*
Marius Kramer *(Head-Building Tech)*
Daniel Steiner *(Head-Energy Supply Tech)*
Hans Daepp *(Member-Exec Bd)*
Oliviero Iubatti *(Member-Exec Bd)*

Subsidiaries:

Alpiq InTec Ost AG **(4)**
Hohlstrasse 188
8026 Zurich, Switzerland
Tel.: (41) 44 247 44 44
Fax: (41) 44 247 43 43
E-Mail: info.ait.zuerich@alpiq.com
Web Site: www.alpiq-intec.ch/en/about-alpiq/our-business/energy-services-companies/alpiq-intec-ost.jsp
Emp.: 1,000
Electrical Installation Services
S.I.C.: 1731
N.A.I.C.S.: 238210

Alpiq Prozessautomation AG **(4)**
Webereiweg 10
4802 Strengelbach, Switzerland
Tel.: (41) 62 834 83 40
Fax: (41) 62 834 83 41
E-Mail: info.ait.strengelbach@alpiq.com
Automation Software Development Services
S.I.C.: 7371
N.A.I.C.S.: 541511

Alpiq InTec Management AG **(3)**
Hohlstrasse 188
Zurich, Switzerland CH
Tel.: (41) 442474106 (100%)
Fax: (41) 442474115
E-Mail: info@alpiq.com
Web Site: www.alpiq-intec.ch
Emp.: 100
Electronic Products Mfr
S.I.C.: 3679
N.A.I.C.S.: 334419
Hans Dapp *(Mng Dir)*

Alpiq InTec Romandie SA **(3)**
Route Du Jura 49c
1700 Fribourg, Switzerland
Tel.: (41) 26 460 70 90
Fax: (41) 26 460 70 99
E-Mail: info.ait.fribourg@alpiq.com
Electrical Equipment Installation Services
S.I.C.: 1731
N.A.I.C.S.: 238210
Oliviero Iubatti *(Gen Mgr)*

Alpiq InTec Ticino Ltd. **(3)**
Via Monte Bre 8
6900 Lugano, Switzerland
Tel.: (41) 58 261 00 00
Fax: (41) 58 261 01 97
E-Mail: info.ait.ticino@alpiq.com
Web Site: www.alpiq-intec.ch/ueber-alpiq/unser-unternehmen/konzerngesellschaften/standorte-gebaeudetechnik.jsp
Electrical Engineering Services
S.I.C.: 8711
N.A.I.C.S.: 541330

Alpiq InTec West Ltd. **(3)**
Aarburgerstrasse 39
4601 Olten, Switzerland
Tel.: (41) 62 287 67 67
Fax: (41) 62 287 67 87
E-Mail: info.ait.olten@alpiq.com
Web Site: www.alpiq-intec.ch/en/about-alpiq/our-business/energy-services-companies/standorte-gebaeudetechnik.jsp
Emp.: 60
Electrical Equipment Installation Services
S.I.C.: 1731
N.A.I.C.S.: 238210
Fredy Dubach *(Gen Mgr)*

Kummler + Matter Ltd **(3)**
Hohlstrasse 176
8026 Zurich, Switzerland
Tel.: (41) 44 247 47 47
Fax: (41) 44 247 47 77
E-Mail: kuma@kuma.ch
Web Site: www.kuma.ch
Emp.: 300
Electrical Equipment Installation Services
S.I.C.: 1731
N.A.I.C.S.: 238210
Daniel Steiner *(Gen Mgr)*

Kummler+Matter AG **(3)**
Hohlstrasse 176
CH-8026 Zurich, Switzerland CH
Tel.: (41) 442474747 (100%)
Fax: (41) 442474777
E-Mail: kuma.zuerich@group-ait.com
Web Site: www.kuma.ch
Emp.: 80
Transport Technology Engineering

S.I.C.: 4789
N.A.I.C.S.: 488999
Daniel Steiner *(Mng Dir)*

Mauerhofer et Zuber SA **(3)**
Rue Du Simplon 30
Renens, 1020, Switzerland
Tel.: (41) 216311717
Fax: (41) 216311718
Electrical Equipment Installation Services
S.I.C.: 1731
N.A.I.C.S.: 238210

Non-U.S. Subsidiaries:

Alpiq InTec (FL) AG **(3)**
Austrasse 40
9490 Vaduz, Liechtenstein
Tel.: (423) 237 27 27
Fax: (423) 237 27 28
E-Mail: info.ait.vaduz@alpiq.com
Web Site: www.alpiq-intec.ch/ueber-alpiq/unser-unternehmen/konzerngesellschaften/standorte-gebaeudetechnik.jsp
Facility Management Services
S.I.C.: 8744
N.A.I.C.S.: 561210

Alpiq InTec Management S.r.l. **(3)**
Via Venezia Giulia 5/B
Milan, 20157, Italy
Tel.: (39) 023321101
Fax: (39) 023557574
Emp.: 100
Business Management Consulting Services
S.I.C.: 8742
N.A.I.C.S.: 541611
Fabio Vecchio *(Gen Mgr)*

Alpiq InTec Milano S.p.A. **(3)**
Via Stephenson 73
20157 Milan, Italy
Tel.: (39) 02 33 21 101
Fax: (39) 02 35 57 574
E-Mail: info.ait.milano@alpiq.com
Web Site: www.alpiqintec.com
Emp.: 10
Electrical Engineering Services
S.I.C.: 1731
N.A.I.C.S.: 238210
Fabio Vecchio *(Mng Dir)*

Alpiq InTec Verona S.p.A. **(3)**
Via Germania 11
37136 Verona, Italy
Tel.: (39) 045 86 28011
Fax: (39) 045 95 0092
E-Mail: info.ait.verona@alpiq.com
Electric Power Structure Construction Services
S.I.C.: 1623
N.A.I.C.S.: 237130

Alpiq Netz AG Gosgen **(2)**
Oltnerstrasse 61
5013 Niedergosgen, Switzerland CH
Tel.: (41) 622867777 (100%)
Fax: (41) 628586610
E-Mail: info.netz.goesgen@alpiq.com
Web Site: www.alpiq.ch
Emp.: 100
Electrical Grid Construction, Operation & Maintenance
Export
S.I.C.: 4939
N.A.I.C.S.: 221121
Ch. Brunner *(Mng Dir)*

Alpiq Reseau SA Lausanne **(2)**
Chemin de Mornex 10
1001 Lausanne, Switzerland CH
Tel.: (41) 213412111 (100%)
Fax: (41) 213412049
E-Mail: info.reseau.lausanne@alpiq.com
Web Site: www.alpiq.ch
Electrical Grid Construction, Operation & Maintenance
S.I.C.: 4931
N.A.I.C.S.: 221121
Ch. Brunner *(Mng Dir)*

Non-U.S. Subsidiaries:

Alpiq Anlagentechnik GmbH **(2)**
Im Breitspiel 7
69126 Heidelberg, Germany De
Tel.: (49) 62219410
Fax: (49) 6221942548
E-Mail: info@energie-und-kraftanlagen.de
Web Site: www.energie-und-kraftanlagen.de
Sales Range: $1-4.9 Billion
Emp.: 4,956
Infrastructure Engineering Services
S.I.C.: 1623
N.A.I.C.S.: 237130
Kurt Baumgartner *(Chm-Supervisory Bd)*
Herbert Niklaus *(Chm-Mgmt Bd)*
Alois Bauer *(Deputy Chm-Supervisory Bd)*

Subsidiaries:

Digi Communication Systeme GmbH **(3)**
August-Horch-Strasse 4
D-38518 Gifhorn, Germany De
Tel.: (49) 53715880
Fax: (49) 5371588588
E-Mail: info@digicos.de
Web Site: www.ga-netztechnik.de
Emp.: 650
Telecommunication Services
S.I.C.: 4812
N.A.I.C.S.: 517911
Gregor Killesreiter *(Gen Mgr-Bus Mgmt)*

ECM Ingenieur-Unternehmen fur Energie- und Umwelttechnik GmbH **(3)**
Ridlerstrasse 31a
80339 Munich, Germany
Tel.: (49) 89 62 37 101
Fax: (49) 89 62 37 320
E-Mail: info@ec-muenchen.de
Web Site: www.ec-muenchen.de
Engineering Services
S.I.C.: 8711
N.A.I.C.S.: 541330

ECM Ing.Unternehmen fur Energie- und Umwelttechnik GmbH **(3)**
Ridlerstrasse 31d
D 80339 Munich, Germany De
Tel.: (49) 896237400
Fax: (49) 896237320
E-Mail: info@ec-muenchen.de
Web Site: www.ec-muenchen.de
Emp.: 60
Engineering & Chemical Processor
Export
S.I.C.: 8711
N.A.I.C.S.: 541330
Haenzl Lorson *(Gen Mgr)*

Elektro Stiller GmbH **(3)**
Chemnitzer Strasse 3
30952 Hanover, Germany De
Tel.: (49) 511946960
Fax: (49) 5119469696
E-Mail: info@elektro-stiller.de
Web Site: www.elektro-stiller.de
Sales Range: $1-9.9 Million
Emp.: 77
Power Plant & Electrical Distr
S.I.C.: 4911
N.A.I.C.S.: 221122
Lutz Ebermann *(Gen Mgr)*

FINOW Rohrsysteme GmbH **(3)**
Angermunder Strasse 101
16225 Eberswalde, Germany
Tel.: (49) 3334 57 0
Fax: (49) 3334 57 190
E-Mail: info@finow.de
Web Site: www.finow.de
Steel Pipe Component Mfr
S.I.C.: 3317
N.A.I.C.S.: 331210
Thomas Compart *(Co-Mng Dir & Head-Mfg & Production)*
Ernst-Thomas Krueger *(Co-Mng Dir & Head-Commerce, Intl Sls & Major Projects)*

Franz Lohr GmbH **(3)**
Steinbeisstrasse 10
88214 Ravensburg, Germany De
Tel.: (49) 7518810
Fax: (49) 751881199
E-Mail: info@franz-lohr.de
Web Site: www.franz-lohr.de
Sales Range: $25-49.9 Million
Emp.: 230
Public Utilities
S.I.C.: 4911
N.A.I.C.S.: 221122
Manfred Frick *(Gen Mgr)*

GA-com Telekommunikation und Telematik GmbH **(3)**
Rotestrasse 24
D-74321 Bietigheim-Bissingen, Germany De
Tel.: (49) 7142969122
Fax: (49) 7142969293
E-Mail: info@ga-com.de
Web Site: www.ga-com.de
Sales Range: $50-74.9 Million
Emp.: 225
Telecommunications & Telemarketing Products
S.I.C.: 7389
N.A.I.C.S.: 561422
Simone Wolfram *(Gen Mgr)*

Ingenieurburo Kiefer & Voss GmbH **(3)**
Wetterkreuz 3
91058 Erlangen, Germany
Tel.: (49) 9131 78 77 0
Fax: (49) 9131 78 77 77
E-Mail: info@ibkv.de
Web Site: www.ibkv.de
Emp.: 100
Power Plant Construction Engineering Services & Piping Supplies Distr
S.I.C.: 1623
N.A.I.C.S.: 237130
Stefan Barnert *(Gen Mgr)*

Kraftanlagen Hamburg GmbH **(3)**
Fangdieckstrasse 68
D-22547 Hamburg, Germany
Tel.: (49) 40547160
Fax: (49) 4054716100
E-Mail: info@ka-hamburg.de
Web Site: www.ka-hamburg.de
Emp.: 50
Energy Service
S.I.C.: 4931
N.A.I.C.S.: 221122
Jens Pokoiewski *(Gen Mgr)*

Kraftanlagen Heidelberg GmbH **(3)**
Im Breitspiel 7
69126 Heidelberg, Germany De
Mailing Address:
Postfach 10 32 24
69025 Heidelberg, Germany
Tel.: (49) 62219406
Fax: (49) 6221942539
E-Mail: info@ka-heidelberg.de
Web Site: www.ka-heidelberg.de
Sales Range: $25-49.9 Million
Emp.: 400
Power Distr
S.I.C.: 4939
N.A.I.C.S.: 221122
Peter Dorn *(Mng Dir)*

Kraftanlagen Munchen GmbH **(3)**
Ridlerstrasse 31c
80339 Munich, Germany
Tel.: (49) 89 6237 0
Fax: (49) 89 6237 223
E-Mail: info@ka-muenchen.de
Web Site: www.ka-muenchen.de
Rev.: $524,591,830
Emp.: 2,683
Pipe Line Construction Engineering Services
S.I.C.: 1623
N.A.I.C.S.: 237120
Ludwig Geissinger *(Mng Dir)*
Alexander Gremm *(Mng Dir)*
Mark von Laer *(Mng Dir)*

Non-U.S. Subsidiary:

Kraftanlagen Romania S.R.L. **(4)**
Bulevardul Bucuresti Nr 66
100520 Ploiesti, Judetul Prahova, Romania
Tel.: (40) 344 401995
Fax: (40) 344 401997
E-Mail: info@ka-romania.ro
Web Site: www.ka-romania.ro
Emp.: 200
Power Plant Construction Services
S.I.C.: 1623
N.A.I.C.S.: 237130

te-com Telekommunikations-Technik GmbH **(3)**
Eugen-Adolff-Strasse 122
D-71522 Backnang, Germany De
Tel.: (49) 719132970
Fax: (49) 7191329710
E-Mail: info@te-com.de
Web Site: www.te-com.de
Emp.: 500
Telecommunications & Marketing Services
S.I.C.: 4813
N.A.I.C.S.: 517911
Eugen Ritzer *(Gen Mgr)*

Non-U.S. Subsidiaries:

Caliqua Anlagentechnik GmbH **(3)**
IZ-NO-Sud Strasse 2d Objekt 57
2355 Wiener Neudorf, Austria
Tel.: (43) 2236 65920 0
Fax: (43) 2236 65920 209
E-Mail: info@caliqua.at
Web Site: www.caliqua.at
Emp.: 80
Air Conditioning Equipment Installation Services
S.I.C.: 1711
N.A.I.C.S.: 238220
Wolf Dirnbacher *(Gen Mgr)*

GA Energo technik s.r.o. **(3)**
Na Strilne AB
Orlik-Bolevec, 330 11 Plzen, Czech Republic
Tel.: (420) 373 303 111
Fax: (420) 377 524 137
Web Site: www.gaenergo.cz
Emp.: 33
Electric Power Structure Construction Services
S.I.C.: 1623
N.A.I.C.S.: 237130
Zdenek Zidek *(Gen Mgr)*

Alpiq Csepel Kft. **(2)**
Kalvin Ter 12
1085 Budapest, Hungary HU
Tel.: (36) 14291030
Fax: (36) 12681536
E-Mail: info.csepel@alpiq.com
Web Site: www.csepel.alpiq.hu
Sales Range: $150-199.9 Million
Emp.: 40
Hot Water, Natural Gas & Sewage Utility Services
S.I.C.: 4971
N.A.I.C.S.: 221310
Briglovics Gabor *(Gen Mgr)*

Alpiq Energie France S.A.S. **(2)**
15 19 Rue Louis le Grand
75002 Paris, France
Tel.: (33) 153438420
Fax: (33) 153438429
E-Mail: info.fra@alpiq.com
Web Site: www.alpiq.fr
Energy Services
Export
S.I.C.: 4911
N.A.I.C.S.: 221122

Alpiq Energy Italy S.p.A. **(2)**
Via Montalbino 3/5
20159 Milan, Italy IT
Tel.: (39) 02366981
Fax: (39) 0236698266
E-Mail: info.mercato.ita@alpiq.com
Web Site: www.alpiq.it
Sales Range: $10-24.9 Million
Emp.: 50
Electricity Distr
Export
S.I.C.: 4931
N.A.I.C.S.: 221122

Alpiq Energy SE **(2)**
River Garden Rohanske nabrezi 670/19 8
110 00 Prague, Czech Republic
Tel.: (420) 221720111
Fax: (420) 221720999
E-Mail: info.cee@alpiq.com
Web Site: www.alpiq.cz
Emp.: 80
International Electricity Trading
S.I.C.: 4911
N.A.I.C.S.: 221121
Andy Taylor *(Gen Mgr)*

Alpiq Energy SE **(2)**
al Armii Ludowej 26
00-609 Warsaw, Poland
Tel.: (48) 225796525
Fax: (48) 225796527
E-Mail: info.pol@alpiq.com
Web Site: www.alpiq.pl
Emp.: 12
Electricity Trading
Export
S.I.C.: 4911
N.A.I.C.S.: 221118
Arkadiusz Zielezny *(Mng Dir)*

Alpiq Holding Ltd.—(Continued)

Alpiq Zlin s.r.o. (2)
Trida Tomase Bati 650
760 01 Zlin, Czech Republic CZ
Mailing Address:
Postboks 26
0051 Oslo, Norway
Tel.: (420) 577524855
Fax: (420) 577523538
E-Mail: info.zlin@alpiq.com
Web Site: www.generation.alpiq.cz
Emp.: 160
Heat Generation, Electrical Energy & Compressed Air
Export
S.I.C.: 4939
N.A.I.C.S.: 221122
Milan Prajzler *(CEO)*

Atel Hellas S.A. (2)
iera Odos 150
12242 Athens, Greece
Tel.: (30) 2103467384
Fax: (30) 2103467274
Web Site: www.alpiq.com
Electric Power Distr. Owned 76% by Atel & 24% by Zeritis Group
S.I.C.: 4931
N.A.I.C.S.: 221122

ECK Generating, s.r.o. (2)
Dubska Teplarna
PO Box 201
272 01 Prague, Kladno, Czech Republic CZ
Tel.: (420) 312644853
Fax: (420) 312644850
E-Mail: eckg@eckg.cz
Web Site: www.eckg.cz
Operation & Maintenance of Power Plants
S.I.C.: 4939
N.A.I.C.S.: 221122
Martin Frydl *(Mgr-PR)*

Energipartner AS (2)
Christian Frederiks Plasse 6
0154 Oslo, Norway NO
Tel.: (47) 22814700
Fax: (47) 22814701
E-Mail: firmapost@energipartner.no
Web Site: www.energipartner.no/
Sales Range: $10-24.9 Million
Emp.: 30
Independent Energy Consulting & Portfolio Management Company
Export
S.I.C.: 4911
N.A.I.C.S.: 221122

Kraftszer Kft. (2)
Pap Karoly U 4-6
1139 Budapest, Hungary
Tel.: (36) 14657031
Fax: (36) 13501063
E-Mail: kraftszer@kraftszer.hu
Web Site: www.kraftszer.hu
Sales Range: $10-24.9 Million
Emp.: 200
Designing, Engineering, Environmental Protection, Operation & Maintenance of Power Plants
S.I.C.: 4911
N.A.I.C.S.: 221122
Tibor Valkai *(Mgr-HR)*

Alpiq EcoPower Switzerland Ltd. (1)
Bahnhofquai 12
4601 Olten, Switzerland
Tel.: (41) 62 286 71 11
Fax: (41) 62 286 73 73
Hydroelectric Power Generating Services
S.I.C.: 4939
N.A.I.C.S.: 221111
Gerhard Danioth *(Mng Dir)*

Alpiq Finanzbeteiligungen Ltd. (1)
Bahnhofquai 12
Olten, 4600, Switzerland
Tel.: (41) 622867111
Fax: (41) 622867667
Investment Management Services
S.I.C.: 6211
N.A.I.C.S.: 523999

Alpiq Grid Ltd. (1)
Chemin de Mornex 10
1001 Lausanne, Switzerland
Tel.: (41) 21 341 21 11
Fax: (41) 21 341 20 49
E-Mail: info.reseau.lausanne@alpiq.com
Web Site: www.alpiq.ch/en/projects/power-grid-projects/power-grid-projects.jsp
Electric Power Distribution Services
S.I.C.: 4939
N.A.I.C.S.: 221122

Alpiq Ltd. (1)
Bahnhofquai 12
4601 Olten, Switzerland
Tel.: (41) 62 286 71 11
Fax: (41) 62 286 73 73
E-Mail: info@alpiq.com
Web Site: www.alpiq.ch
Emp.: 700
Electric Power Generation Services
S.I.C.: 4911
N.A.I.C.S.: 221118
Hans E. Schweickardt *(CEO)*
Michael Wider *(Deputy CEO)*
Kurt Baumgartner *(CFO-Fin Svcs)*
Reinhold Frank *(Member-Exec Bd)*
Benoit Revaz *(Member-Exec Bd)*
Erik Saether *(Member-Exec Bd)*

Subsidiary:

Alpiq Swisstrade Ltd. (2)
Bahnhofquai 12
4601 Olten, Switzerland
Tel.: (41) 62 286 71 11
Web Site: www.alpiq.com
Securities Brokerage Services
S.I.C.: 6211
N.A.I.C.S.: 523120

Alpiq Management Ltd. (1)
Bahnhofquai 12
4601 Olten, Switzerland
Tel.: (41) 62 286 75 60
Fax: (41) 62 286 76 69
E-Mail: info@alpiq.com
Web Site: www.alpiq.cz/en/news-stories/press-releases/press_releases.jsp?news=tcm:123-93144
Business Management Consulting Services
S.I.C.: 8742
N.A.I.C.S.: 541611
Hans Schweickardt *(Chm)*

Alpiq Suisse Ltd. (1)
Ch de Mornex 10 CP 570
1001 Lausanne, Switzerland
Tel.: (41) 21 341 21 11
Fax: (41) 213412049
E-Mail: info.lausanne@alpiq.com
Web Site: www.alpiq.com
Emp.: 200
Electric Power Generation Services
S.I.C.: 4911
N.A.I.C.S.: 221118

Alpiq Suisse SA (1)
Ch De Mornex 10
CP 570
1001 Lausanne, Switzerland CH (100%)
Tel.: (41) 213412111
Fax: (41) 213413412
E-Mail: info.lausanne@alpiq.com
Web Site: www.alpiq.ch
Emp.: 200
Hydro Power, Thermal Energy & Renewable Energy Generation
S.I.C.: 4931
N.A.I.C.S.: 221111

Alpiq Trading Ltd. (1)
Bahnhofquai 12
Olten, 4600, Switzerland
Tel.: (41) 622867111
Fax: (41) 622867373
Electric Power Distribution Services
S.I.C.: 4939
N.A.I.C.S.: 221122

Avenis SA (1)
Chemin de Mornex 10
1003 Lausanne, Switzerland
Tel.: (41) 21 341 28 00
Fax: (41) 21 341 28 01
Emp.: 20
Electric Power Distribution Services
S.I.C.: 4931
N.A.I.C.S.: 221122
Michael Wider *(Mng Dir)*

Birs Wasserkraft AG (1)
Bahnhofstrasse 21
Grellingen, 4203, Switzerland
Tel.: (41) 622867111
Electric Power Generation & Distribution Services
S.I.C.: 4911
N.A.I.C.S.: 221118

Energie Electrique du Simplon SA (1)
12 Place de la Gare
Lausanne, 1001, Switzerland
Tel.: (41) 21 341 21 11
Fax: (41) 21 341 20 49
E-Mail: info@alpiq.com
Hydroelectric Power Generation Services
S.I.C.: 4911
N.A.I.C.S.: 221111
Michael Wider *(Gen Mgr)*

Entegra Wasserkraft AG (1)
Rosenbergstrasse 72
9000 Saint Gallen, Switzerland
Tel.: (41) 81 511 11 70
E-Mail: info@entegra.ch
Emp.: 5
Hydroelectric Power Generation Services
S.I.C.: 4939
N.A.I.C.S.: 221111
Ivo Scherrer *(Gen Mgr)*

Grande Dixence SA (1)
Rue des Creusets 41
1950 Sion, Switzerland
Tel.: (41) 27 328 43 11
Fax: (41) 27 328 43 82
E-Mail: info@grande-dixence.ch
Web Site: www.grande-dixence.ch
Emp.: 4
Electric Power Generation Services
S.I.C.: 4931
N.A.I.C.S.: 221118
Amedee Kronig *(Mng Dir)*

Hydro-Solar Energie AG (1)
Bachmatten 9
4435 Niederdorf, Switzerland
Tel.: (41) 61 963 00 33
Fax: (41) 61 963 00 35
E-Mail: info@hydro-solar.ch
Web Site: hydro-solar.ch
Emp.: 13
Hydroelectric Power Generation Services
S.I.C.: 4939
N.A.I.C.S.: 221111
N. Sriram *(Gen Mgr)*

Nant de Drance SA (1)
Chemin du Gilloud 3
1920 Martigny, Switzerland
Tel.: (41) 27 720 47 30
Fax: (41) 27 720 47 39
E-Mail: info@nant-de-drance.ch
Electric Power Generation Services
S.I.C.: 4939
N.A.I.C.S.: 221118

Nuclear Power Plant Niederamt Ltd. (1)
Bahnhofquai 12
4601 Olten, Switzerland
Tel.: (41) 62 289 48 88
Fax: (41) 62 289 48 90
Emp.: 600
Nuclear Electric Power Generation Services
S.I.C.: 4939
N.A.I.C.S.: 221113
Hans E. Schweickardt *(Gen Mgr)*

Joint Venture:

Aare Energie AG (1)
Solothurnerstrasse 21 Postfach
4601 Olten, Switzerland CH
Tel.: (41) 622055656
Fax: (41) 622055658
E-Mail: info@aen.ch
Web Site: www.aen.ch
Emp.: 80
Energy Services; Owned 50% by Alpiq AG
S.I.C.: 4939
N.A.I.C.S.: 221122
Jost Bitterli *(Pres)*
Caspar Norbert *(Mng Dir-Admin)*

Non-U.S. Subsidiaries:

3CB SAS (1)
Route Departementale 2001 Les Primots 0033
03500 Bayet, France
Tel.: (33) 470355350
Fax: (33) 470353957
Web Site: www.3cb.fr
Emp.: 30
Electric Power Generation Services
S.I.C.: 4911
N.A.I.C.S.: 221118
Jean-Paul Costes *(Gen Mgr)*

Alpiq Csepeli Eromu Kft (1)
Szinesfem Utca 3
1211 Budapest, Hungary
Tel.: (36) 1 278 5440
Fax: (36) 1 278 5465
E-Mail: info.csepel@alpiq.com
Emp.: 80
Electric Power Generator & Distribution Services
S.I.C.: 4911
N.A.I.C.S.: 221118
Ambrovics Denes *(Deputy Gen Mgr)*

Alpiq Csepeli Szolgaltato Kft. (1)
Hoeromu Utca 3
1211 Budapest, Hungary
Tel.: (36) 1 278 3800
Fax: (36) 1 278 3838
E-Mail: info.csepel@alpiq.com
Emp.: 86
Electric Power Generation Services
S.I.C.: 4939
N.A.I.C.S.: 221118
Varga Csaba *(Grp Dir-Production)*

Alpiq Deutschland GmbH (1)
Im Breitspiel 7
Heidelberg, 69126, Germany
Tel.: (49) 62219401
Fax: (49) 62212548
Emp.: 2
Electric Power Generation Services
S.I.C.: 4939
N.A.I.C.S.: 221118

Alpiq EcoPower Scandinavia AS (1)
Dronning Eufemias Gate 6
191 Oslo, Norway
Tel.: (47) 22 81 47 00
Fax: (47) 22 81 47 01
Hydroelectric Power Generation Services
S.I.C.: 4939
N.A.I.C.S.: 221111

Alpiq Energia Espana S.A.U. (1)
c/Balmes 89 2 2
8008 Barcelona, Spain
Tel.: (34) 902 02 02 76
Fax: (34) 93 45 22 472
E-Mail: info.barcelona@alpiq.com
Electric Power Generation & Distribution Services
S.I.C.: 4931
N.A.I.C.S.: 221118

Alpiq Energija BH d.o.o. (1)
Kaptol 5/2
71000 Sarajevo, Bosnia & Herzegovina
Tel.: (387) 33 260 135
Fax: (387) 33 260 136
E-Mail: info.bih@alpiq.com
Emp.: 2
Electric Power Distribution Services
S.I.C.: 4931
N.A.I.C.S.: 221122
Ermina Arnautovic *(Gen Mgr)*

Alpiq Energija Hrvatska d.o.o. (1)
7 Vijenac
Zagreb, 10000, Croatia
Tel.: (385) 16152550
Fax: (385) 16112574
Emp.: 1
Electric Power Distr
S.I.C.: 4911
N.A.I.C.S.: 221122
Peter Dworak *(Mng Dir)*

Alpiq Energy Hellas S.A. (1)
Karistou 5
Ambelokipi, 11523 Athens, Greece
Tel.: (30) 210 6998 201
Fax: (30) 210 6998 202
E-Mail: info.hellas@alpiq.com
Emp.: 2
Electric Power Distribution Services
S.I.C.: 4931
N.A.I.C.S.: 221122
Alexandros Charitos *(Gen Mgr)*

Alpiq Italia S.r.l. (1)
Via Montalbino 3/5
Milan, 20159, Italy

Tel.: (39) 02 366981
Fax: (39) 0236 69 82 66
E-Mail: info.mercato.ita@alpiq.com
Web Site: www.alpiq.com.it
Electric Power Generation & Distribution Services
S.I.C.: 4911
N.A.I.C.S.: 221118

Alpiq Narzole S.r.l. (1)
Via Montalbino 3/5
Milan, 20159, Italy
Tel.: (39) 02366981
Electric Power Generation Services
S.I.C.: 4911
N.A.I.C.S.: 221118

Alpiq Norway AS (1)
Dronning Eufemias Gate 6
PO Box 26
0051 Oslo, Norway
Tel.: (47) 22 81 47 00
Fax: (47) 22 81 47 01
E-Mail: info.nor@alpiq.com
Web Site: www.alpiq.no
Emp.: 30
Energy Consulting Services
S.I.C.: 8999
N.A.I.C.S.: 541690

Alpiq Production France Management S.A.S. (1)
15 Rue Louis Le Grand
75002 Paris, France
Tel.: (33) 1 53 43 49 36
Fax: (33) 1 53 43 49 30
Web Site: www.alpiq.com
Emp.: 8
Business Management Consulting Services
S.I.C.: 8742
N.A.I.C.S.: 541611
Peter Jones *(Gen Mgr)*

Alpiq Vercelli S.r.l. (1)
48 Via Ara Ettore
13100 Vercelli, Italy
Tel.: (39) 016129 991
Electric Power Structure Construction Services
S.I.C.: 1623
N.A.I.C.S.: 237130

Biogas neu Kosenow GmbH & Co KG (1)
Neuer Wall 54
20354 Hamburg, Germany
Tel.: (49) 40 809063100
Electric Power Generation Services
S.I.C.: 4911
N.A.I.C.S.: 221118

Energit S.p.A. (1)
Via Edward Jenner 19/21
9121 Cagliari, Italy
Tel.: (39) 070 7521
Fax: (39) 070 752151
E-Mail: info@energit.it
Web Site: www.energit.it
Emp.: 6
Electric Power Distribution Services
S.I.C.: 4911
N.A.I.C.S.: 221122
Cosimo Aragonese *(Head-Customer Care, Portfolio & Settlement)*

Frankenluk AG (1)
Podeldorfer Str 86
Bamberg, 96052, Germany
Tel.: (49) 9511820
Fax: (49) 951182487
E-Mail: info@frankenluk.de
Web Site: www.frankenluk.de
Emp.: 40
Electric Power Generation Services
S.I.C.: 4939
N.A.I.C.S.: 221118
Otto Traunter *(Gen Mgr)*

GA Austria GmbH (1)
Gewerbestrasse 5
4072 Alkoven, Austria
Tel.: (43) 7274 7333 0
Fax: (43) 7274 7333 33
E-Mail: office@ga-austria.at
Electric Power Structure Construction Services
S.I.C.: 1629
N.A.I.C.S.: 237130

GA-Magyarorszag Kft. (1)
Topark Utca 1/A
2045 Torokbalint, Hungary
Tel.: (36) 23 501 100
Fax: (36) 23 501 125
E-Mail: ga@ga.hu
Emp.: 120
Electric Power Structure Construction Services
S.I.C.: 1629
N.A.I.C.S.: 237130
Laszlo Papp *(Gen Mgr)*

GAH Pensions GmbH (1)
Im Breitspiel 7
69126 Heidelberg, Germany
Tel.: (49) 6221 9401
Fax: (49) 6221 941707
Electric Power Distribution Services
S.I.C.: 4939
N.A.I.C.S.: 221122

Idrovalsesia S.r.l. (1)
Via Montalbino 3/5
Milan, 20159, Italy
Tel.: (39) 02366981
Electric Power Generation Services
S.I.C.: 4931
N.A.I.C.S.: 221118

K+M Fahrleitungstechnik GmbH (1)
Malerstrasse 22
38550 Isenbuttel, Germany
Tel.: (49) 5374 91909 0
Fax: (49) 5374 91909 55
E-Mail: info@kuma-fl.de
Road & Rail Transport Infrastructure Support Services
S.I.C.: 4789
N.A.I.C.S.: 488490

Kraftanlagen Power Plants GmbH (1)
Ridlerstr 31c
Munich, 80339, Germany
Tel.: (49) 8962370
Fax: (49) 896237223
E-Mail: info@ka-muenchen.de
Web Site: www.ka-muenchen.de
Emp.: 35
Power Plant Construction Engineering Services
S.I.C.: 1623
N.A.I.C.S.: 237130

Kraftszer Vallalkozasi Kft. (1)
Pap Karoly u 4-6
1139 Budapest, Hungary
Tel.: (36) 1 465 7031
Fax: (36) 1 350 1063
E-Mail: kraftszer@kraftszer.hu
Web Site: www.kraftszer.hu
Power Plant Construction Engineering Services
S.I.C.: 1623
N.A.I.C.S.: 237130
Istvan Jaszberenyi *(Mng Dir)*

Martin Bohsung GmbH (1)
Im Bonholz 7
71277 Rutesheim, Germany
Tel.: (49) 7152 33116 0
Fax: (49) 7152 33116 11
E-Mail: info@bohsung.de
Pipeline Construction Engineering Services
S.I.C.: 1629
N.A.I.C.S.: 237120

Vetrocom Ltd. (1)
Georgi Rakovski 130
Sofia, 1000, Bulgaria
Tel.: (359) 28 15 75 10
Fax: (359) 29 81 69 64
Wind Farm Electric Power Generation Services
S.I.C.: 4931
N.A.I.C.S.: 221118

ALPITOUR S.P.A.

Via Roccavione 15
12100 Cuneo, Italy
Tel.: (39) 11 0171111
Fax: (39) 0171313219
E-Mail: servizio.informazioni@alpitourworld.it
Web Site: www.gruppoalpitour.it
Sales Range: $1-4.9 Billion
Emp.: 3,500

Business Description:
Tourism Services
S.I.C.: 4725
N.A.I.C.S.: 561520

Personnel:
Gabriele Burgio *(Pres & CEO)*

ALPLA-WERKE ALWIN LEHNER GMBH & CO. KG

Mockenstrasse 34
Hard, 6971, Austria
Tel.: (43) 5574602200
Fax: (43) 557460267
E-Mail: office@alpla.com
Web Site: www.alpla.com
Emp.: 14,000

Business Description:
Mfr. of Plastics
S.I.C.: 3089
N.A.I.C.S.: 326199

Personnel:
Guenth Lahnar *(Gen Mgr)*

U.S. Subsidiary:

Alpla Inc. (1)
289 Hwy 155 S
McDonough, GA 30253
Tel.: (770) 914-1407
Fax: (770) 914-8591
Sls.: $10,600,000
Emp.: 480
Plastics Bottles Mfr
S.I.C.: 3085
N.A.I.C.S.: 326160
Jodok Schaeffler *(Gen Mgr-US)*

ALPOS, D.D.

Ulica Leona Dobrotinska 2
3230 Sentjur pri Celju, Slovenia
Tel.: (386) 37463100
Fax: (386) 37463201
E-Mail: info@alpos.si
Web Site: www.alpos.si
APOG—(LJU)
Sales Range: $150-199.9 Million
Emp.: 980

Business Description:
Steel Pipes & Other Products Mfr
S.I.C.: 3317
N.A.I.C.S.: 331210

Personnel:
Vladimir Sprah *(Chm-Supervisory Bd)*
Mirjan Bevc *(CEO & Gen Mgr)*

Supervisory Board of Directors:
Vladimir Sprah
Stojan Ostir
Milan Pirc
Velimir Plavsteiner
Iztok Sprah
Simon Zidan

Subsidiaries:

Alpos Alu, d.o.o. (1)
Cesta Leona Dobrotinska 2
3230 Sentjur pri Celju, Slovenia
Tel.: (386) 37462750
Fax: (386) 37462770
E-Mail: alu@alpos.si
Web Site: www.alu.alpos.si
Emp.: 100
Aluminium Ladders Mfr
S.I.C.: 3499
N.A.I.C.S.: 332999
Damjana Kozlevca *(Gen Mgr)*

Alpos Ekoloska Pec, D.O.O (1)
Cesta Kozjanskega Odreda 25
3230 Sentjur pri Celju, Slovenia
Tel.: (386) 37463412
Fax: (386) 3 746 34 47
E-Mail: eko.pec@alpos.si
Web Site: www.ekoloska-pec.alpos.si
Waste Management Services
S.I.C.: 4212
N.A.I.C.S.: 562112

Alpos, Industrija Kovinsklh Izdelkov On Opreme, d.d. (1)
Cesta Kozjanskega Odreda 25
3230 Sentjur pri Celju, Slovenia
Tel.: (386) 37463100
Fax: (386) 37463201
E-Mail: info@alpos.si
Emp.: 200
Steel Pipes Mfr
S.I.C.: 3317
N.A.I.C.S.: 331210
Mirjan Bevc *(Gen Mgr)*

Alpos Mizarska Proizvodnja, d.o.o. (1)
Cesta Leona Dobrotinska 2
3230 Sentjur pri Celju, Slovenia
Tel.: (386) 3 7463 182
Fax: (386) 3 7463 243
E-Mail: mizarska-proizvodnja@alpos.si
Web Site: www.mizarska-proizvodnja.alpos.si
Furnitures Mfr
S.I.C.: 3429
N.A.I.C.S.: 332510
Marija Zoric *(Mng Dir)*

Alpos Pohistvo, d.o.o. (1)
Cesta Leona Dobrotinska 2
3230 Sentjur pri Celju, Slovenia
Tel.: (386) 37463123
Fax: (386) 37463212
E-Mail: pohistvo@alpos.si
Web Site: www.pohistvo.alpos.si
Emp.: 115
Metal Furnitures Mfr
S.I.C.: 3429
N.A.I.C.S.: 332510
Zdenko Pinter *(Mng Dir)*

Alpos Posebne Storitve, d.o.o. (1)
Cesta Leona Dobrotinska 2
3230 Sentjur pri Celju, Slovenia
Tel.: (386) 37462702
Fax: (386) 3 7462 720
E-Mail: posebne-storitve@alpos.si
Web Site: www.posebne-storitve.alpos.si
Emp.: 158
Metal Production & Textile Services
S.I.C.: 3429
N.A.I.C.S.: 332510
Matjaz Knez *(Mng Dir)*

Alpos Proizvodnja Orodij, d.o.o. (1)
Cesta Kozjanskega Odreda 25
3230 Sentjur pri Celju, Slovenia
Tel.: (386) 37463406
Fax: (386) 37463422
E-Mail: vinko.gobec@alpos.si
Web Site: www.proizvodnja-orodij.alpos.si
Emp.: 25
Cylinder Mfr
S.I.C.: 3593
N.A.I.C.S.: 333995
Vinko Gobec *(CEO)*

Non-U.S. Subsidiaries:

Alpos d.d. (1)
Predovecka 13
HR - 1000 Zagreb, Croatia
Tel.: (385) 98237897
Web Site: www.alpos.si/default.asp?id=536
Furniture Mfr
S.I.C.: 3429
N.A.I.C.S.: 332510

Alpos d.o.o. Aleksinac (1)
Naselje Aleksinacki Rudnik Bb
18220 Aleksinac, Serbia
Tel.: (381) 18804700
Fax: (381) 18 804 310
E-Mail: info@alpos.co.yu
Web Site: pohistvo.alpos.si/default.asp?id=516
Steel Pipes Mfr
S.I.C.: 3444
N.A.I.C.S.: 332322

Alpos Handels GmbH (1)
Paradeisergasse 92
9020 Klagenfurt, Austria
Tel.: (43) 463502171
Fax: (43) 463502178
E-Mail: stahl@alpos.at
Web Site: www.alpos.si/de/default.asp?id=1423
Furnitures Mfr
S.I.C.: 3429
N.A.I.C.S.: 332510
Stane Flander *(Gen Mgr)*

ALPOS Oprema Trgovin d.o.o. (1)
Hajduk Veljkova 11
21000 Novi Sad, Serbia
Tel.: (381) 21301608
Fax: (381) 21301608

ALPOS, d.d.—(Continued)

E-Mail: oprema-trgovin@alpos.si
Emp.: 2
Steel Pipes Mfr
S.I.C.: 3317
N.A.I.C.S.: 331210
Dragan Musicki *(Gen Mgr)*

Alpos Rohr Und Metallhandel Deutschland GmbH **(1)**
Nordliche Munchner Str
82041 Grunwald, Germany
Tel.: (49) 896252686
Fax: (49) 89 625 2907
E-Mail: info@alpos.de
Web Site: www.alpos.de
Emp.: 10
Steel Pipes Mfr
S.I.C.: 3444
N.A.I.C.S.: 332322
R Rieger *(CEO)*

Alpos Sp. z.o.o. **(1)**
Ul Fabryczna 3
67-320 Malomice, Zagan, Poland
Tel.: (48) 683769313
Fax: (48) 683769311
E-Mail: alpos@alpos.pl
Web Site: www.alpos.pl
Furnitures Mfr
S.I.C.: 3429
N.A.I.C.S.: 332510

ZAO Alpos **(1)**
Moskovsky Prospect 111
196084 Saint Petersburg, Russia
Tel.: (7) 812 369 3960
Fax: (7) 812 388 9787
E-Mail: spb@alpos.ru
Web Site: www.alpos.ru
Furniture Production & Services
S.I.C.: 3429
N.A.I.C.S.: 332510

ALPRINT S.A.

Henry Ford 1000
Maipu, Santiago, Chile
Tel.: (56) 2 5352171
Fax: (56) 29644940
E-Mail: info@alprint.cl
Web Site: www.alprint.cl
Emp.: 27
Business Description:
Mfr of Aluminum Flexible Packaging Products
S.I.C.: 2672
N.A.I.C.S.: 322220
Personnel:
Maria Eugenia Tellez *(Gen Mgr)*

ALPRO A.D.

Njegoseva BB
75440 Vlasenica, Bosnia & Herzegovina
Tel.: (387) 56 733 720
Fax: (387) 56 733 041
E-Mail: office@alpro-vl.com
Web Site: www.alpro-vl.com
Year Founded: 1977
ALPR—(BANJ)
Emp.: 141
Business Description:
Architectural Aluminium Product Mfr
S.I.C.: 3999
N.A.I.C.S.: 339999
Personnel:
Georgios Mylonas *(Chm-Mgmt Bd)*
Konstantinos Akrivopoluos *(Member-Mgmt Bd)*
Dimitrios Koutsoupias *(Member-Mgmt Bd)*
Charikleia Lozinsky *(Member-Mgmt Bd)*
Evangelia Mylonas *(Member-Mgmt Bd)*

ALPS ELECTRIC CO., LTD.

1-7 Yukigaya-otsukamachi Ota-ku
Tokyo, 145 8501, Japan
Tel.: (81) 3 3726 1211
Telex: 246 6076; 246 6649
Fax: (81) 3 3728 1741
E-Mail: irgroup@jp.alps.com
Web Site: www.alps.co.jp
Year Founded: 1948
6770—(TKS)
Sls.: $6,010,653,000
Assets: $4,965,576,000
Liabilities: $2,772,066,000
Net Worth: $2,193,510,000
Earnings: ($77,825,000)
Emp.: 36,199
Fiscal Year-end: 03/31/13
Business Description:
Electronic Components Mfr
S.I.C.: 3679
N.A.I.C.S.: 334419
Personnel:
Masataka Kataoka *(Chm)*
Toshihiro Kuriyama *(Pres)*
Nobuhiko Komeya *(Sr Mng Dir)*
Takashi Kimoto *(Co-Mng Dir)*
Shuji Takamura *(Co-Mng Dir)*
Board of Directors:
Masataka Kataoka
Yoshitada Amagishi
Hitoshi Edagawa
Takash Iida
Shinji Inoue
Takashi Kimoto
Nobuhiko Komeya
Toshihiro Kuriyama
Yasuo Sasao
Motohiro Shimaoka
Shuji Takamura
Junichi Umehara
Transfer Agent:
Mitsubishi UFJ Trust & Banking Corporation
4-5 Marunouchi 1-Chome Chiyoda-ku
Tokyo, 100-8212, Japan
Tel.: (81) 3 3212 1211

Subsidiaries:

Alpine Electronics, Inc. **(1)**
1-1-8 Nishi-Gotanda Shinagawa-Ku
Tokyo, 141-8501, Japan (100%)
Tel.: (81) 334941101
Fax: (81) 334941109
Web Site: www.alpine.com
6816—(OTC TKS)
Sls.: $2,169,735,840
Assets: $1,640,275,360
Liabilities: $566,763,200
Net Worth: $1,073,512,160
Earnings: $17,050,720
Emp.: 11,107
Fiscal Year-end: 03/31/13
Electronic Components & Audio Products
S.I.C.: 3679
N.A.I.C.S.: 334419
Toru Usami *(Pres & CEO)*

Alpine Giken, Inc. **(1)**
1 7 Yukigaya-otsukamachi Ota-ku
Tokyo, 145 8501, Japan (100%)
Tel.: (81) 337261211
Fax: (81) 337281741
E-Mail: alts-hp@jp.alts.com
Web Site: www.agk.jp
Emp.: 600
Electronic & Technology Components Mfr
S.I.C.: 3674
N.A.I.C.S.: 334413

Alpine Manufacturing, Inc. **(1)**
3 10 Yoshima Kogyo Danchi
Iwaki, Fukushima, 970 1144, Japan JP (100%)
Tel.: (81) 246366969
Fax: (81) 246365943
Emp.: 300
Sales of Electrical Appliances
S.I.C.: 5722
N.A.I.C.S.: 443141
Yoshihugu Kanno *(Pres)*

Alpine Electronics Marketing Inc. **(1)**
1 7 Yukigaya Otsukamachi
Ota-ku, Tokyo, 145 0067, Japan (100%)
Tel.: (81) 354994531
Fax: (81) 354994541
Web Site: www.alpine.co.jp
Emp.: 300
Semiconductor & Related Devices
S.I.C.: 3674
N.A.I.C.S.: 334413

Alpine Marketing **(1)**
3 9 5 Hagino Cho Miyagino Ku
Sendai, Miyagi, 983 0043, Japan (100%)
Tel.: (81) 222395331
Fax: (81) 222366740
Web Site: www.alpine.co.jp
S.I.C.: 3674
N.A.I.C.S.: 334413

Alpine Precision, Inc. **(1)**
48 1 Akai Aza Tanmachi Taira
Iwaki, Fukushima, 979 3131, Japan (100%)
Tel.: (81) 246210008
Fax: (81) 246252951
Web Site: www.alpine.com
S.I.C.: 3674
N.A.I.C.S.: 334413

Alpine Technology Manufacturing, Inc. **(1)**
61-1 OHara Aza Shinbori Onahama
Iwaki, Fukushima, 971 8111, Japan (100%)
Tel.: (81) 246545161
Fax: (81) 246535265
Web Site: www.atmi.co.jp
Emp.: 130
S.I.C.: 3674
N.A.I.C.S.: 334413
Izuni Wada *(Pres)*

Alps Accounting Centre **(1)**
1-7 Yukigaya-otsuka-cho Ota-Ku
Tokyo, 145-8501, Japan
Tel.: (81) 337261211
Web Site: www.alps.co.jp
S.I.C.: 3674
N.A.I.C.S.: 334413

ALPS GREEN DEVICES CO., LTD. **(1)**
1-7 Yukigaya-otsukamachi
Ota-ku, Tokyo, 145-8501, Japan
Tel.: (81) 3 5499 3101
Fax: (81) 3 5499 3103
Web Site: www.alpsgd.com
Emp.: 90
Power Control Devices Mfr
S.I.C.: 3699
N.A.I.C.S.: 335999
Yasuhiro Fuji *(Pres & CEO)*

NISHIKI ELECTRONICS CO., LTD. **(1)**
28 Mae Eguri NIshikimachi
Iwaki, Fukushima, 974-8232, Japan
Tel.: (81) 246 631167
Fax: (81) 246 627484
Electronic Components Mfr & Distr
S.I.C.: 3679
N.A.I.C.S.: 334419

Ryosan Company, Limited **(1)**
5-9 Kitafutaba-cho Takasaki chi
Gunma, 370-0842, Japan (100%)
Tel.: (81) 273247321
Fax: (81) 273247574
Web Site: www.alps.com
Electronic Components Distr
S.I.C.: 3674
N.A.I.C.S.: 334413

Tohoku Alps, Co., Ltd. **(1)**
1 7 Yukigaya Otsuka Cho
Ota Ku, Tokyo, 145 8501, Japan (100%)
Tel.: (81) 337261211
Fax: (81) 337281741
Web Site: www.alps.com
Emp.: 6,000
S.I.C.: 3674
N.A.I.C.S.: 334413

Plants:

Alps Electric Co., Ltd. - FURUKAWA PLANT **(1)**
6-3-36 Furukawanakazato
Osaki, Miyagi, 989-6181, Japan
Tel.: (81) 229 23 5111
Fax: (81) 229 24 5782
Web Site: www.alps.com
Electronic Component Mfr
S.I.C.: 3679
N.A.I.C.S.: 334419

Alps Electric Co., Ltd. - KAKUDA PLANT **(1)**
6-1 Nishida Kakuda
Kakuda, Miyagi, 981-1595, Japan
Tel.: (81) 224 63 1211
Fax: (81) 224 63 1399
Electronic Component Mfr
S.I.C.: 3679
N.A.I.C.S.: 334419

Alps Electric Co., Ltd. - NAGAOKA PLANT **(1)**
1-3-5 Higashitakami
Nagaoka, Niigata, 940-8572, Japan
Tel.: (81) 258 24 4111
Fax: (81) 258 24 4110
Web Site: www.alps.com
Electronic Component Mfr
S.I.C.: 3679
N.A.I.C.S.: 334419

Alps Electric Co., Ltd. - ONAHAMA PLANT **(1)**
41-25 Yanagi-machi Noda Onahama
Iwaki, Fukushima, 971-8615, Japan
Tel.: (81) 246 58 6464
Fax: (81) 246 58 5125
Electronic Component Mfr
S.I.C.: 3679
N.A.I.C.S.: 334419

Alps Electric Co., Ltd. - TAIRA PLANT **(1)**
39-1 Sakuhata Oyasaku Yoshima-machi
Iwaki, Fukushima, 970-1193, Japan
Tel.: (81) 246 36 4511
Fax: (81) 246 36 6774
Web Site: www.alps.com
Electronic Component Mfr
S.I.C.: 3679
N.A.I.C.S.: 334419

Alps Electric Co., Ltd. - WAKUYA PLANT **(1)**
230 Shibue
Tohda-gun, Miyagi, 981-1595, Japan
Tel.: (81) 229 43 2711
Fax: (81) 229 43 5729
Web Site: www.alps.com
Electronic Component Mfr
S.I.C.: 3679
N.A.I.C.S.: 334419

U.S. Subsidiaries:

Alpine Electronics of America, Inc. **(1)**
19145 Gramercy Pl
Torrance, CA 90501-1128
Mailing Address:
PO Box 2859
Torrance, CA 90509-2859
Tel.: (310) 326-8000
Fax: (310) 533-0369
Toll Free: (800) ALPINE1
Web Site: www.alpine.com
Emp.: 356
Mfr & Importer of Mobile Electronics Import Export
S.I.C.: 5064
N.A.I.C.S.: 423620
Kaz Watanabe *(Pres)*
Koichi Endo *(CTO-Product Dev)*
Jim O'Neill *(Exec VP-Sls & Mktg)*

Alps Electric (North America), Inc. **(1)**
1500 Atlantic Blvd
Auburn Hills, MI 48326-1500
Tel.: (248) 391-9950
Fax: (248) 391-2500
E-Mail: info@alpsautomotive.com
Web Site: www.alps.com
Emp.: 100
Mfr of Automotive On-Board Electronics
S.I.C.: 7539
N.A.I.C.S.: 811118
Masataka Kataoka *(Pres)*

ALPS ELECTRIC (NORTH AMERICA), INC. **(1)**
910 E Hamilton Ave Ste 500
Campbell, CA 95008
Tel.: (408) 361-6400
Fax: (408) 226-7301
E-Mail: sales@alps.com
Web Site: www.alps.com
Electrical Component Distr
S.I.C.: 5065
N.A.I.C.S.: 423690
Greg Grzywinski *(Acct Mgr)*

Alps Electric (USA), Inc. **(1)**
910 E Hamilton Ave Ste 500
Campbell, CA 95008-0645

Tel.: (408) 361-6400
Fax: (800) 825-1445
E-Mail: info@alpsusa.com
Web Site: www.alpsusa.com
Emp.: 50
S.I.C.: 3674
N.A.I.C.S.: 334413

Cirque Corporation (1)
2463 S 3850 W Ste A
Salt Lake City, UT 84120-2335
Tel.: (801) 467-1100
Fax: (801) 467-0208
E-Mail: info@cirque.com
Web Site: www.cirque.com
Emp.: 28
Input Technology Products Developer
S.I.C.: 7373
N.A.I.C.S.: 541512
Anna Williamson *(CFO)*

Non-U.S. Subsidiaries:

ALCOM ELECTRONICOS DE MEXICO, S.A. DE C.V. (1)
Av Industrial Del Norte Lote 5-1
Reynosa, Tamaulipas, 88730, Mexico
Tel.: (52) 8999210800
Fax: (52) 92100891
Electronic Component Mfr
S.I.C.: 3679
N.A.I.C.S.: 334419

Alpine Electronics Australia Pty. Limited (1)
161 165 Princes Hwy
Hallam, VIC, 3803, Australia (100%)
Tel.: (61) 387871200
Fax: (61) 387871299
E-Mail: info@alpine.com.au
Web Site: www.alpine.com.au
Emp.: 15
S.I.C.: 3674
N.A.I.C.S.: 334413
Joey Thompson *(Mng Dir)*

Alpine Electronics (China) Company Limited (1)
R2-4F China Merchants Tower No 116
Jiangou Street
Chaoyang District, Beijing, 100022, China
Tel.: (86) 10 6566 0308
Fax: (86) 10 6566 0093
E-Mail: Contact-ALPS-Beijing@cn.alps.com
Web Site: www.alpine.com.cn
Mfr of Semiconductors & Related Devices
S.I.C.: 3674
N.A.I.C.S.: 334413

Alpine Electronics de Espana, S.A. (1)
Portal De Gamarra 36
36 Pabellon 32, 01013 Vitoria, Alava, Spain (100%)
Tel.: (34) 945283588
Fax: (34) 945283461
E-Mail: alpine@alpine.es
Web Site: www.alpine.es
Emp.: 19
S.I.C.: 3674
N.A.I.C.S.: 334413
Carlos Vourendes *(Mgr-Sls)*

Alpine Electronics (Europe) GmbH (1)
Kreunerkanp 7
40847 Ratingen, Germany (100%)
Tel.: (49) 21024550
Fax: (49) 2102455149
E-Mail: support@alpine.de
Web Site: www.alpine.de
Emp.: 50
S.I.C.: 3674
N.A.I.C.S.: 334413

Alpine Electronics France S.A.R.L. (1)
98 Rue De La Belle Etoile
PO Box 50016
Z I Paris Nord II, F 95945 Roissy-en-France, Cedex, France (99%)
Tel.: (33) 148638989
Fax: (33) 148632581
E-Mail: mathan.robin@alpine-electronics.fr
Web Site: www.alpine-electronics.fr
Emp.: 20
Mfr. of Semiconductors & Related Devices
S.I.C.: 3674
N.A.I.C.S.: 334413
Mouge Not *(Mng Dir)*

Alpine Electronics GmbH (1)
Willhelm-Wagenfeld Strasse 123
80807 Munich, Germany (100%)
Tel.: (49) 893242640
Fax: (49) 89324264241
E-Mail: support@alpine.de
Web Site: www.alpine.com
Emp.: 170
Mfr. of Semiconductors & Related Devices
S.I.C.: 3674
N.A.I.C.S.: 334413
Hitoshi Kajiwara *(Mng Dir-Production & Pur)*

Alpine Electronics Manufacturing of Europe Ltd. (1)
2051 Biatorbagy
Vendel Park, 2051 Budapest, Hungary
Tel.: (36) 23534111
Fax: (36) 23534112
E-Mail: job@alpine.com
Web Site: www.alpine.com
Emp.: 1,000
Audio Products Mfr
S.I.C.: 3651
N.A.I.C.S.: 334310
Matsuki Yasuki *(Mng Dir)*

Alpine Electronics of Canada, Inc. (1)
777 Supertest Road
Toronto, ON, M3J 2M9, Canada (100%)
Tel.: (416) 736-6211
Fax: (416) 736-7511
Web Site: www.alpine-usa.com
Emp.: 10
S.I.C.: 3674
N.A.I.C.S.: 334413
Stefan Hashinsky *(Sr Mgr)*

Alpine Electronics of U.K. Limited (1)
Alpine House Fletchanstead Hwy
Coventry, CV4 9TW, United Kingdom (100%)
Tel.: (44) 2476719500
Fax: (44) 2476719501
Web Site: www.alpine.com
Emp.: 50
Mfr. of Semiconductors & Related Devices
S.I.C.: 3674
N.A.I.C.S.: 334413

Alpine Italia S.P.A. (1)
Via Colombo 8
20090 Trezzano San Naviglio, Milan, Italy (100%)
Tel.: (39) 02484781
Fax: (39) 0248403555
E-Mail: info@alpine.com
Web Site: www.alpine.com
Emp.: 20
S.I.C.: 3674
N.A.I.C.S.: 334413
Marco Falconi *(Pres)*

ALPS COMMUNICATION DEVICES TECHNOLOGY(SHANGHAI) CO., LTD. (1)
Room 5A Tomson Commercial Bldg 710 Dongfang Rd
Pudong New Area, Shanghai, 200122, China
Tel.: (86) 2150817575
Fax: (86) 2150815252
Web Site: www.alps.com
Communication Device Mfr
S.I.C.: 3669
N.A.I.C.S.: 334290

ALPS ELECTRIC CZECH, s.r.o. (1)
Sebranice 240 Sebranice u
Boskovice, 679 31, Czech Republic
Tel.: (420) 516490111
Fax: (420) 516455980
Web Site: www.alps.com
Emp.: 400
Electromechanical Component Mfr
S.I.C.: 3679
N.A.I.C.S.: 334419
Hideaki Terasaki *(Mng Dir)*

Alps Electric Europa GmbH (1)
Hansaallee 203
D 40549 Dusseldorf, 11, Germany (100%)
Tel.: (49) 21159770
Fax: (49) 2115977146
E-Mail: info@alps.de
Web Site: www.alps.com
Emp.: 80
S.I.C.: 3674
N.A.I.C.S.: 334413
Yoichero Kaga *(Pres)*

ALPS ELECTRIC EUROPE GmbH (1)
Hansaallee 203
40549 Dusseldorf, Germany
Tel.: (49) 211 59770
Fax: (49) 211 5977146
E-Mail: info@alps-europe.com
Web Site: www.alps.com
Emp.: 100
Electrical Component Distr
S.I.C.: 5063
N.A.I.C.S.: 423610
Yoichiro Kega *(Gen Mgr)*

Plant:

Alps Electric Co., Ltd. - DORTMUND PLANT (2)
Giselherstrasse 4
44319 Dortmund, Germany
Tel.: (49) 231 21880
Fax: (49) 231 2188199
Electronic Component Mfr
S.I.C.: 3679
N.A.I.C.S.: 334419

Alps Electric (Ireland) Limited (1)
Clara Rd Millstreet
Cork, Ireland (100%)
Tel.: (353) 2970677
Fax: (353) 2970603
E-Mail: info@alps.ie
Web Site: www.alps.ie
Emp.: 500
S.I.C.: 3674
N.A.I.C.S.: 334413
Brendan Shauthnessy *(Mgr)*

Alps Electric Korea Co., Ltd. (1)
970 1 Jangduk Dong Gwangsan Ku
Kwangju, 506 732, Korea (South) (100%)
Tel.: (82) 629502114
Fax: (82) 629502222
Web Site: www.alps.co.kr
Emp.: 800
S.I.C.: 3674
N.A.I.C.S.: 334413
Kyeong Ho Kong *(Asst Mgr-Products Controlling)*

Alps Electric (Malaysia) Sdn. Bhd. (1)
Nalai Industrial Estate Darul Khusus
71800 Nilai, Negeri Sembilan, Malaysia (100%)
Tel.: (60) 67991515
Fax: (60) 67991654
Web Site: www.alpselectric.com
Emp.: 3,000
S.I.C.: 3674
N.A.I.C.S.: 334413
Yoshitada Amagishi *(Mng Dir)*

Plant:

Alps Electric (Malaysia) Sdn.Bhd. - JENGKA PLANT (2)
LOT3 industrial Estate Phase2
26400 Bandar Pusat Jengka, Pahang Darul Makmur, Malaysia
Tel.: (60) 9 4663388
Fax: (60) 9 4663399
Web Site: www.alps.com
Electronic Component Mfr
S.I.C.: 3679
N.A.I.C.S.: 334419

Alps Electric (S) Pte. Ltd. (1)
28 Genting Ln #09-06 Platinum 28
349585 Singapore, Singapore (60%)
Tel.: (65) 62262933
Fax: (65) 62207479
Web Site: www.alps.com
Sales Range: $150-199.9 Million
Emp.: 12
S.I.C.: 3674
N.A.I.C.S.: 334413
Naoki Hashigasako *(Dir-Sls)*

Alps Electric (Singapore), Pte. Ltd. (1)
168 Changi Road #03-01 Fragrance Building
Singapore, 419730, Singapore (100%)
Tel.: (65) 62262933
Fax: (65) 62207479
Web Site: www.alps.com
Emp.: 42
Electronic Components Mfr & Distr
S.I.C.: 3674
N.A.I.C.S.: 334413

ALPS ELECTRIC (THAILAND) CO., LTD. (1)
24 Prime Building 12th Floor Room No A
Sukhumvit 21 Road
Khet Wattana, Bangkok, Thailand 10110
Tel.: (66) 2665 2866
Fax: (66) 2665 2869
Web Site: www.alps.com
Electronic Component Distr
S.I.C.: 5065
N.A.I.C.S.: 423690

Alps Electric (UK) Limited (1)
Garamonde Drive Wymbush
Milton Keynes, Bucks, MK8 8LW, United Kingdom (100%)
Tel.: (44) 1908555700
Fax: (44) 1908569789
Emp.: 100
Mfr. of Semiconductors & Related Devices
S.I.C.: 3674
N.A.I.C.S.: 334413

Alps Electronics Hong Kong Limited (1)
Unit 5 Fl 9 Mirror Tower 61 Mody Rd Tsim Sha Tsui E
Kowloon, China (Hong Kong) (100%)
Tel.: (852) 23693626
Fax: (852) 23673987
E-Mail: alex.yeung@hk.alps.com
Web Site: www.alps.com
Emp.: 75
Electronic Components Mfr & Sales
S.I.C.: 3679
N.A.I.C.S.: 334419
Yoshino Tatsuo *(Mng Dir)*

ALPS ELECTRONICS TAIWAN CO., LTD. (1)
2F No 130 Sec 3 Nanjing E Rd
Zhongshan District, Taipei, 104, Taiwan
Tel.: (886) 287725969
Fax: (886) 287725869
Web Site: www.alps.com
Electronic Component Distr
S.I.C.: 5065
N.A.I.C.S.: 423690

Alps Logistics (Guang Dong) Co., Ltd. (1)
Wangshui Shan Chong Toucun Chang An Zhen
Dongguan, 523856, China
Tel.: (86) 769 8541 0666
Fax: (86) 769 8541 0633
Web Site: www.alps-logistics.jp/eng/
Emp.: 100
International Forwarding Service of Air & Sea Cargo
S.I.C.: 4491
N.A.I.C.S.: 488320

Alps Electric Europe GmbH (1)
Korta Gatan 7
PO Box 4025
SE 17154 Solna, Sweden (100%)
Tel.: (46) 8404 3200
Fax: (46) 85070 3398
Web Site: www.alps.com
Emp.: 40
Electronic Components Sales
S.I.C.: 3674
N.A.I.C.S.: 334413

Alps Precision (Malaysia) Sdn. Bhd. (1)
PT 10643 Nilai Industrial Estate Nalai Post Office
71800 Nilai, Negeri Sembilan Daru, Malaysia
Tel.: (60) 67991515
Fax: (60) 67901388
Web Site: www.alps.com.my
Emp.: 3,000
S.I.C.: 3674
N.A.I.C.S.: 334413
Mazman Abdul Malik *(CEO)*

Alps Electric Co., Ltd.—(Continued)

ALPS (SHANGHAI) INTERNATIONAL TRADING CO., LTD. **(1)**
Room No 5A Tomson Commercial Bldg 710 Dongfang Rd
Pudong, Shanghai, 200122, China
Tel.: (86) 21 5820 3213
Fax: (86) 21 5820 3183
Web Site: www.alps.com
Electronic Component & Audio Equipment Distr
S.I.C.: 5065
N.A.I.C.S.: 423690

Alps(China)Co., Ltd. **(1)**
Unit 903 IBM Tower Pacific Century Place
2A Gong Ti Bei Lu, Beijing, 100027, China (100%)
Tel.: (86) 1065393690
Fax: (86) 1065393697
E-Mail: contact-alps-beijing@cn.alps.com
Emp.: 25
Electrical Components Mfr & Distr
S.I.C.: 3674
N.A.I.C.S.: 334413

Dalian Alpine Electronics Co., Ltd. **(1)**
2 Yingbin Rd Jinzhou Economic Development Zone
Dalian, Liaoning, 116100, China
Tel.: (86) 411 8768 3131
Fax: (86) 411 8767 5820
Web Site: www.alpine.com
Automobile Communications & Navigation Equipment
S.I.C.: 3674
N.A.I.C.S.: 334413

Dalian Alps Electronics Co., Ltd. **(1)**
No 6 Hanzheng Road Jinzhou
Economic Development Zone, Dalian, China
Tel.: (86) 41187675102
Fax: (86) 411 8767 4427
E-Mail: fang@alpsdl.com
Web Site: www.alpsco.jp
Electronic Products
S.I.C.: 3679
N.A.I.C.S.: 334419

Dan Dong Alpine Electronics, Inc. **(1)**
No 14 Guozhen Rd
Dandong, Liaoning, 51001, China (100%)
Tel.: (86) 4156167836
Fax: (86) 4157683380
Emp.: 800
S.I.C.: 3674
N.A.I.C.S.: 334413

DANDONG ALPS ELECTRONICS CO., LTD. **(1)**
No 14 Guo Zhen Road
Dandong, Liaoning, China 118002
Tel.: (86) 415 6162140
Fax: (86) 415 3196259
Web Site: www.alps.com
Electronic Components Mfr & Distr
S.I.C.: 3679
N.A.I.C.S.: 334419

DONGGUAN ALPS ELECTRONICS CO., LTD. **(1)**
Xinxing Industry Zone Xingfa South Street Wusha
Changan Town, Dongguan, Guangdong, China
Tel.: (86) 769 85333771
Fax: (86) 769 85335776
Electronic Component Mfr & Distr
S.I.C.: 3679
N.A.I.C.S.: 334419

Ningbo Alps Electronics Co., Ltd. **(1)**
81 Ln Huanchen West Rd
Ningbo, Zhejiang, China (100%)
Tel.: (86) 57487508100
Fax: (86) 57487505592
Web Site: www.alps.com
Emp.: 150
S.I.C.: 3674
N.A.I.C.S.: 334413

Tianjin Alps Electronics Co., Ltd. **(1)**
No 1 Wei 7 Rd Micro-Electronics Industrial Park
Jingang Rd, Tianjin, 300385, China
Tel.: (86) 22 839 82577
Fax: (86) 22 839 82599
Web Site: www.alps.com
Mfr & Sales of Electronic Components
S.I.C.: 3679
N.A.I.C.S.: 334419

ALPS INDUSTRIES LIMITED
57/2 Site IV Industrial Area
Sahibabad
Ghaziabad, 201010, India
Tel.: (91) 1204161700
Fax: (91) 1202896041
E-Mail: alps@alpsindustries.com
Web Site: www.alpsindustries.com
ALPSINDUS—(NSE)
Rev.: $135,165,685
Assets: $203,336,579
Liabilities: $245,457,586
Net Worth: ($42,121,007)
Earnings: ($21,472,843)
Emp.: 3,855
Fiscal Year-end: 03/31/13
Business Description:
Fashion Accessories, Home Furnishing & Automotive Fabrics Mfr
S.I.C.: 2399
N.A.I.C.S.: 315990
Personnel:
Sandeep Agarwal *(CEO & Mng Dir)*
A. K. Singhal *(CFO & Pres-Fin & Accts)*
Ajay Gupta *(Compliance Officer, Sec & Gen Mgr-Legal)*
Board of Directors:
Krishan Kumar Agarwal
Sandeep Agarwal
Sonalal Datta
Tilak Raj Khosla
Prabhat Krishna
Pradyuman Kumar Lamba
Pramod Kumar Rajput
Transfer Agent:
Alankit Assignments Ltd
Alankit House 2E/21, Jhandewalan Extension
New Delhi, India

ALRAFAH MICROFINANCE BANK
Al-Masyoun
Ramallah, Palestine
Tel.: (970) 2 294 6090
Fax: (970) 2 294 6114
E-Mail: info@alrafahbank.ps
Web Site: www.alrafahbank.ps
AMB—(PAL)
Business Description:
Commercial Banking Services
S.I.C.: 6029
N.A.I.C.S.: 522110
Personnel:
Talal Kazem Abdullah Naser Aldeen *(Chm)*
Azziz Abed Aljawad *(Deputy Chm)*
Board of Directors:
Talal Kazem Abdullah Naser Aldeen
Kamal Abu-Khdeeja
Eyhab Alashqar
Muhammad Naser Aldeen
Ahmad Alhajhasan
Azziz Abed Aljawad
Basem Makhool
Samer Farid Muhammad

ALROS PRODUCTS LIMITED
(d/b/a Polytarp Products)
350 Wildcat Rd
Toronto, ON, M3J 2N5, Canada
Tel.: (416) 633-2231
Fax: (416) 633-1685
Toll Free: (800) 606-2231
E-Mail: info@polytarp.com
Web Site: www.polytarp.com
Year Founded: 1957
Rev.: $38,960,490
Emp.: 150
Business Description:
Polyethylene Products Supplier
S.I.C.: 3081
N.A.I.C.S.: 326113
Personnel:
Marty Benkiel *(Mgr-Construction & GSD)*

ALROSA CO. LTD.
ul Lenina 6
Mirny, 678170, Sakha
Tel.: (7) 4113630180
Fax: (7) 4113630451
E-Mail: info@alrosa.ru
Web Site: www.alrosa.ru
Year Founded: 1992
Sales Range: $1-4.9 Billion
Emp.: 35,051
Business Description:
Diamond Exploration, Mining, Polishing & Whslr
Export
S.I.C.: 1499
N.A.I.C.S.: 212399
Personnel:
Alexey Leonidovich Kudrin *(Chm-Supervisory Bd)*
Alexander Alikhanovich Akhpolov *(Vice Chm-Supervisory Bd)*
Fyodor Borisovich Andreev *(Pres & CEO)*
Igor Mikhailovich Kulichik *(CFO & VP)*
Supervisory Board of Directors:
Alexander Alikhanovich Akhpolov
Gennady Fyodorovich Alekseev
Fyodor Borisovich Andreev
Yegor Afanasyevich Borisov
Ivan Kirillovich Demyanov
Sergey Konstantinovich Dubinin
Aisen Sergeevich Nikolayev
Vladimir Borisovich Rybkin
Alexey Struchkov
Anatoly Vladimirovich Tikhonov
Vladimir Tikhonov
Yakov Moiseevich Urinson
Victor Petrovich Yefimov
Ilya Yuzhanov

Non-U.S. Subsidiaries:

Arcos Hong Kong Ltd. **(1)**
64th Floor Central Plaza
Harbour Rd No 18, Wanchai, China (Hong Kong)
Tel.: (852) 25219229
Fax: (852) 25219636
E-Mail: info@arcos-hk.com
Web Site: www.alrosa.ru/eng/representative_offices
Emp.: 3
Jewelry, Watch, Precious Stone & Precious Metal Whslr
S.I.C.: 5094
N.A.I.C.S.: 423940

Arcos Limited **(1)**
2nd Floor 86 Hatton Garden
London, EC1N8QQ, United Kingdom
Tel.: (44) 2078313004
Fax: (44) 2072423174
E-Mail: arcos@arcos.ltd.uk
Emp.: 5
Activities for Nonmetallic Minerals
S.I.C.: 1481
N.A.I.C.S.: 213115
Sergey Luchinkin *(Mng Dir)*

ALS LIMITED
Level 2 299 Coronation Drive
Milton, QLD, 4064, Australia
Mailing Address:
PO Box 2191
Milton, QLD, 4064, Australia
Tel.: (61) 7 3367 7900
Fax: (61) 7 3367 8156
E-Mail: investor@campbell.com.au
Web Site: www.campbell.com.au
Year Founded: 1863
ALQ—(ASX OTC)
Rev.: $1,516,880,760
Assets: $1,807,730,870
Liabilities: $768,652,960
Net Worth: $1,039,077,910
Earnings: $240,204,050
Emp.: 12,605
Fiscal Year-end: 03/31/13
Business Description:
Consumer Products; Industrial Chemicals, Including Hygienic; Laboratory Services
S.I.C.: 2899
N.A.I.C.S.: 325998
Personnel:
Greg Kilmister *(CEO & Mng Dir)*
Richard Stephens *(CFO)*
Mike Munro *(CIO)*
Tim Mullen *(Sec)*
Board of Directors:
Nerolie Withnall
Melvyn John Bridges
Bruce R. Brown
Raymond G. Hill
Greg Kilmister
John Mulcahy
Grant Murdoch

Divisions:

Ammtec Limited **(1)**
6 Macadam Place
Balcatta, WA, 6021, Australia
Tel.: (61) 893442416
Fax: (61) 93454688
E-Mail: ammtec@alsglobal.com
Web Site: www.alsglobal.com
Sales Range: $25-49.9 Million
Emp.: 200
Metallurgical & Mineral Testing Consulting Services
S.I.C.: 1481
N.A.I.C.S.: 213115
Sharyn Long *(CFO & Sec)*
Ron Grogan *(CEO-Metallurgy)*

Division:

Ammtec Limited - Burnie Research Laboratory **(2)**
39 River Rd
Burnie, Tasmania, 7320, Australia
Tel.: (61) 364316333
Fax: (61) 364316896
E-Mail: burnie.admin@ilsglobal.com
Web Site: www.burnielab.com.au
Emp.: 36
Metallurgical Testing Laboratory
S.I.C.: 8734
N.A.I.C.S.: 541380
John Glen *(Mgr)*

U.S. Subsidiary:

Purity Systems, Inc. **(2)**
3116 Old Pond Rd
Missoula, MT 59802 CA
Tel.: (406) 532-3237 (72%)
Fax: (406) 327-0879
Web Site: www.puritysystemsinc.com
Ion Exchange Resin Products Mfr
S.I.C.: 2821
N.A.I.C.S.: 325211
Dave Sisto *(Pres)*

Australian Laboratory Services **(1)**
32 Shand St
Stafford, Brisbane, QLD, 4053, Australia (100%)
Tel.: (61) 732437222
Fax: (61) 00732437218
E-Mail: info@als.com.au
Web Site: www.alsglobal.com.au
Emp.: 350
Laboratory Services
S.I.C.: 8734
N.A.I.C.S.: 541380
Greg Kilmister *(CEO & Mng Dir)*

Division:

PearlStreet Limited **(2)**
109 Binnictor Road
Canning Vale, WA, 6155, Australia AU
Tel.: (61) 894769600 (100%)

Fax: (61) 892320397
E-Mail: canningvale@alsglobal.com
Web Site: www.alsglobal.com
Sales Range: $50-74.9 Million
Emp.: 559
Industrial Materials Testing; Power, Oil & Gas, Minerals, Mining, Water & Pipelines
S.I.C.: 8734
N.A.I.C.S.: 541380
Frank Mcginty *(Gen Mgr)*

Subsidiaries:

PearlStreet Accura Pty Ltd (3)
Lot 2073 Collins St
Collie, WA, 6225, Australia
Tel.: (61) 897343622
Fax: (61) 897344174
E-Mail: accura@alsglobal.com
Web Site: www.accura.com
Emp.: 16
Oil & Gas Exploration Services
S.I.C.: 1389
N.A.I.C.S.: 213112
Russel Scrooby *(Mgr-Bus)*

PearlStreet Metlabs Pty Ltd (3)
109 Bannister Road
Canning Vale, WA, 6155, Australia
Tel.: (61) 894769600
Fax: (61) 892320399
Engineering Services
S.I.C.: 8711
N.A.I.C.S.: 541330

Subsidiaries:

Ecowise Environmental Pty Ltd (2)
16B Lithgow St
PO Box 1834
Fyshwick, 2609, Australia
Tel.: (61) 262025400
Fax: (61) 262025455
Web Site: www.ecowise.com.au
Environmental Management Services
S.I.C.: 8999
N.A.I.C.S.: 541620

U.S. Subsidiaries:

ALS Group USA, Corp (2)
3352 128th Ave
Holland, MI 49424-9263
Tel.: (616) 399-6070
Fax: (616) 399-6185
Web Site: www.alsglobal.com
Emp.: 50
Testing Laboratories
S.I.C.: 8734
N.A.I.C.S.: 541380

ALS USA, Inc (2)
4977 Energy Way
Reno, NV 89502-4105
Tel.: (775) 356-5395
Fax: (775) 355-0179
Emp.: 100
Mining & Mineral Exploration Services
S.I.C.: 1241
N.A.I.C.S.: 213113
Joyce Quiroz *(Mgr-Laboratory)*

Analytical Laboratory Services, Inc. (2)
34 Dogwood Ln
Middletown, PA 17057
Tel.: (717) 944-5541
Fax: (717) 944-1430
Toll Free: (800) 794-7709
E-Mail: mfarlling@analyticallab.com
Web Site: www.analyticallab.com
Emp.: 84
Testing Laboratory Services
S.I.C.: 8734
N.A.I.C.S.: 541380
Michael S. Farlling *(Pres)*

Division:

Analytical Laboratory Services - Environmental (3)
978 Loucks Mill Rd
York, PA 17402-1901
Tel.: (717) 505-5280
Fax: (717) 505-5285
Emp.: 25
Testing Laboratory Services
S.I.C.: 8734
N.A.I.C.S.: 541380
Scoot Brunk *(Mgr)*

Subsidiary:

Columbia Analytical Services, Inc. (3)
1317 S 13th Ave
Kelso, WA 98626-2845 CA
Tel.: (360) 577-7222
Fax: (360) 636-1068
E-Mail: contact@caslab.com
Web Site: www.alsglobal.com
Sales Range: $400-449.9 Million
Emp.: 400
Commercial Laboratory Performing Chemical & Biotoxicity Analyses for Industrial, Commercial & Regulatory Customers
S.I.C.: 8732
N.A.I.C.S.: 541720
Stephen W. Vincent *(Chm, Pres & CEO)*

Non-U.S. Subsidiaries:

ALS Canada Ltd (2)
2103 Dollarton Hwy
North Vancouver, BC, V7H 0A7, Canada
Tel.: (604) 984-0221
Fax: (604) 984-0218
Web Site: www.als.ca
Analytical Laboratories Operators
S.I.C.: 8734
N.A.I.C.S.: 541380
Colin Ramshaw *(Gen Mgr)*

ALS Chemex de Mexico S.A. de C.V. (2)
Jazmin No 1140 San Carlos
Guadalajara, 44460, Mexico
Tel.: (52) 3336197438
Emp.: 30
Chemical Testing Laboratory Services
S.I.C.: 8734
N.A.I.C.S.: 541380
Raul Silva *(Gen Mgr)*

ALS Chemex South Africa (Proprietary) Ltd (2)
Gano 3 Friesland Drive
Gauteng, 1609, South Africa
Tel.: (27) 116080555
Fax: (27) 116083163
Testing Laboratories
S.I.C.: 8734
N.A.I.C.S.: 541380

ALS Czech Republic s.r.o (2)
Na Harfe 336/9
190 00 Prague, Czech Republic
Tel.: (420) 226226228
Fax: (420) 284081750
E-Mail: customer.support@alsglobal.com
Web Site: www.alsglobal.cz
Emp.: 300
Testing Laboratories
S.I.C.: 8734
N.A.I.C.S.: 541380
Lubos Holy *(Gen Mgr)*

ALS Finland OY (2)
Ruosilankuja 3 E
00390 Helsinki, Finland
Tel.: (358) 10 470 1200
Fax: (358) 10 470 1201
E-Mail: info.hel@alsglobal.com
Web Site: www.alsglobal.fi
Testing Laboratory Services
S.I.C.: 8734
N.A.I.C.S.: 541380

ALS Laboratory Group (Thailand) Co. Ltd (2)
615 Ramkhamheang Road Bang Kapi
Bangkok, 10240, Thailand
Tel.: (66) 27158700
Fax: (66) 23744030
Food Products Testing Services
S.I.C.: 8734
N.A.I.C.S.: 541380

ALS Patagonia S.A (2)
Los Ebanistas 8521 Parque Industrial
La Reina, Santiago, Chile
Tel.: (56) 24345060
Fax: (56) 26546130
Analytical Laboratory Services
S.I.C.: 8734
N.A.I.C.S.: 541380

ALS Peru S.A. (2)
Calle Uno Mz D Lt 1 A
Callao, 1, Peru
Tel.: (51) 15745700
Fax: (51) 15740721
E-Mail: alsglobal@alsperu.com
Web Site: www.alsglobal.com
Emp.: 20
Laboratory Testing Services
S.I.C.: 8734
N.A.I.C.S.: 541380
Bronwyn Blomefield *(Gen Mgr)*

ALS Poland Sp. z.o.o (2)
ul Zolkiewskiego 17
05-075 Warsaw, Poland
Tel.: (48) 228551031
Fax: (48) 228946084
E-Mail: czsupport.poland@alsglobal.com
Testing Laboratories
S.I.C.: 8734
N.A.I.C.S.: 541380

ALS Taiwan Co. Ltd (2)
530-1 Chung Shan Rd Fl 10 Sec 2
Chungho, Taipei, 23557, Taiwan
Tel.: (886) 282281355
Fax: (886) 282281358
E-Mail: als.taiwan@msa.hinet.net
Web Site: www.alstaiwan.com.tw
Emp.: 70
Laboratory Testing Services
S.I.C.: 8734
N.A.I.C.S.: 541380
Kevin Jeng *(Mng Dir)*

ALS Technichem (HK) Pty Ltd (2)
11 F Chung Shun Knitting Ctr 1-3 Wing Yip St
Kwai Chung, China (Hong Kong)
Tel.: (852) 26101044
Fax: (852) 26102021
Emp.: 90
Testing Laboratories
S.I.C.: 8734
N.A.I.C.S.: 541380
Richard Fung *(Gen Mgr)*

ALS Technichem (Singapore) Pte Ltd (2)
Tropical Industrial Bldg 07-01 14 Little Rd
536987 Singapore, Singapore
Tel.: (65) 62839268
Fax: (65) 62839689
E-Mail: alssg@alsglobal.com
Laboratory Testing Services
S.I.C.: 8734
N.A.I.C.S.: 541380
Yao Kai Wen *(Gen Mgr)*

ALS Testing Services (Thailand) Co. Ltd (2)
75/37 Moo 11 Tumbol Khlong Nueng Amphoe
Khlong Luang, Pathum Thani, Thailand
Tel.: (66) 29081681
Fax: (66) 29081680
E-Mail: alsthai@als.com.au
Food Products Testing Services
S.I.C.: 8734
N.A.I.C.S.: 541380

Witlab (Proprietary) Ltd (2)
1 Gryhoak Str Extension 23 Mpumalanga
Witbank, South Africa
Tel.: (27) 136928000
Fax: (27) 136925609
Mineral Exploration Services
S.I.C.: 1481
N.A.I.C.S.: 213115

Reward Distribution Group (1)
13 Business Street
Yatala, QLD, 4207, Australia
Tel.: (61) 734415800
Fax: (61) 734415803
E-Mail: salesbris@rewarddistribution.com.au
Web Site: www.rewarddistribution.com.au
Emp.: 25
Non-Food Consumables Distr
S.I.C.: 5169
N.A.I.C.S.: 424690
Andrew Ross *(Gen Mgr)*

Subsidiaries:

ACIRL Quality Testing Services Pty Ltd (1)
1 Acirl St
Riverview, 4303, Australia
Tel.: (61) 738105200
Fax: (61) 732170774
Inspection & Testing Services
S.I.C.: 9651
N.A.I.C.S.: 926150
Wes Membrey *(Gen Mgr)*

Ecowise Australia Pty Ltd (1)
22 Dalmore Dr
Scoresby, VIC, 3179, Australia
Tel.: (61) 387568000
Fax: (61) 397631862
E-Mail: canberra@ecowise.com.au
Web Site: www.ecowise.com.au
Agricultural Support Services
S.I.C.: 0851
N.A.I.C.S.: 115310
Geoff Anderson *(Gen Mgr)*

Reward Supply Co. (N.T.) Pty Ltd (1)
81 Mcminn St
Darwin, 0800, Australia
Tel.: (61) 889816488
Fax: (61) 0889816577
Web Site: www.rewarddistribution.com.au
Emp.: 6
Inspection & Testing Services
S.I.C.: 9651
N.A.I.C.S.: 926150
Steve Skinner *(Mgr)*

Subsidiaries:

Pandee Services Pty Ltd (2)
28 Gray Street
Kilkenny, SA, 5009, Australia
Tel.: (61) 8 8347 1999
Fax: (61) 8 444 4944
Web Site: www.pandee.com.au
Logistics Consulting & Distribution Services
S.I.C.: 4731
N.A.I.C.S.: 541614

Non-U.S. Subsidiary:

Reservoir Group Limited (1)
1 Albyn Terrace
Aberdeen, AB10 1YP, United Kingdom UK
Tel.: (44) 1224628970
Fax: (44) 1224628989
Web Site: www.reservoir-group.com
Holding Company; Oil & Gas Drilling, Completion & Production Technologies Mfr & Services
S.I.C.: 6719
N.A.I.C.S.: 551112
C. Christopher Gaut *(Chm)*
Rick Clark *(CFO)*

Subsidiaries:

Corpro Group Limited (2)
Muirtonside
Whitecairns, Aberdeen, AB23 8UP, United Kingdom UK
Tel.: (44) 1651 863 000
Fax: (44) 1651 863 050
E-Mail: ops@corpo.co.uk
Web Site: www.corpo-group.com
Holding Company; Oil & Gas Drilling & Geological Surveying Services
S.I.C.: 6719
N.A.I.C.S.: 551112
Philippe Cravatte *(Dir-Technical)*

Enigma Data Solutions Limited (2)
First Floor Tribune House Bell Lane
Uckfield, E Sussex, TN22 1QL, United Kingdom UK
Tel.: (44) 1825745100
Fax: (44) 1825767031
E-Mail: sales@interica.com
Web Site: www.interica.com
Emp.: 25
Information Management Software & Consultancy Services
S.I.C.: 7371
N.A.I.C.S.: 541511
Simon Howes *(Gen Mgr)*

U.S. Subsidiary:

Enigma Data Systems Inc. (3)
16000 Barkers Point Ln Ste 202
Houston, TX 77079
Tel.: (281) 497-0440
Fax: (281) 497-0402
Web Site: www.Interica.com
Sales Range: $1-9.9 Million
Emp.: 8

ALS Limited—(Continued)

Information Management Software & Consultancy Services
S.I.C.: 7371
N.A.I.C.S.: 541511
Chris Bearce *(VP)*

InfoAsset Limited (2)
5 Swan Business Pk Sandpit Rd
Dartford, Kent, DA1 5ED, United Kingdom UK
Tel.: (44) 1322285921
Fax: (44) 1322285923
E-Mail: enquiries@interica.com
Web Site: www.interica.com
Sales Range: $1-9.9 Million
Emp.: 20
Geotechnical Asset & Information Management Services
S.I.C.: 7389
N.A.I.C.S.: 541990
Simon Kendall *(Mng Dir)*

Kirk Petrophysics Limited (2)
Unit 1A/1B Henley Park
Normandy, Guildford, Surrey, GU3 2DX, United Kingdom UK
Tel.: (44) 1483235183
Fax: (44) 1483 236 779
E-Mail: opslondon@alsglobal.com
Web Site: www.kirkpetrophysics.com
Geophysical Core Analysis Services
S.I.C.: 7389
N.A.I.C.S.: 541990
Jean-Valery Garcia *(Mng Dir)*

Omega Data Services Limited (2)
Unit 45 Howe Moss Avenue
Kirkhill Industrial Estate, Dyce, Aberdeen, AB21 0GP, United Kingdom UK
Tel.: (44) 1224772763
Fax: (44) 1224772783
E-Mail: enquiry@omega-data.com
Web Site: www.omega-data.com
Sales Range: $1-9.9 Million
Emp.: 12
Oil & Gas Downhole Memory Tools & Surveying Gauges Designer, Mfr & Whslr
S.I.C.: 3533
N.A.I.C.S.: 333132
Neil Matheson *(Mng Dir)*

U.S. Subsidiaries:

Diamond Oil Well Drilling Company, Inc. (2)
14103 Interdrive W
Houston, TX 77032 TX
Tel.: (281) 776-5300
Fax: (281) 227-3115
Web Site: www.dowdco.com
Sales Range: $10-24.9 Million
Emp.: 10
Oil & Gas Drilling Services
S.I.C.: 1381
N.A.I.C.S.: 213111
Dennis Yeager *(Pres)*

Empirica Logging (2)
6741 Satsuma Dr
Houston, TX 77041
Tel.: (713) 466-7400
Fax: (713) 466-7595
Web Site: www.empirica-logging.com
Emp.: 135
Oil & Gas Surface Logging & Other Support Services
S.I.C.: 1389
N.A.I.C.S.: 213112
Etienne Roux *(Mng Dir)*

Subsidiary:

Geosearch Logging, Inc. (3)
609 Westland Dr
Edmond, OK 73083 OK
Tel.: (405) 340-5545
Toll Free: (800) 375-5545
E-Mail: geosearch@geosearchlogging.com
Web Site: www.geosearchlogging.com
Sales Range: $10-24.9 Million
Emp.: 232
Support Activities for Oil & Gas Operations
S.I.C.: 1389
N.A.I.C.S.: 213112
Joe Struckel *(Pres & CEO)*

Mudlogging Systems, Inc. (2)
574 Northgate Dr Ste 2
Grand Junction, CO 81505 CO
Tel.: (970) 243-3044
Fax: (970) 243-1272
Web Site: www.mudlogsys.com
Digital Gas Detection Systems & Software Mfr
S.I.C.: 3533
N.A.I.C.S.: 333132
Andy Kelley *(Pres)*

Non-U.S. Subsidiary:

Canada Tech Corp. (2)
#105 1437-47 Avenue NE
Calgary, AB, T2E 6N7, Canada
Tel.: (403) 232-1400
Fax: (403) 232-1401
Toll Free: (866) 815-3421
Web Site: www.canadatech.com
Emp.: 25
Oil & Gas Downhole Measurement Tools Designer, Mfr & Whslr
S.I.C.: 3533
N.A.I.C.S.: 333132
Thomas Gigin *(Gen Mgr)*

ALSACE BOSSUE DISTRIBUTION

Rue Paul Paray
67430 Diemeringen, Bas Rhin, France
Tel.: (33) 388004848
Sales Range: $10-24.9 Million
Emp.: 79
Business Description:
Grocery Stores
S.I.C.: 5411
N.A.I.C.S.: 445110
Personnel:
Georges Noel *(Dir-Pur)*

ALSEA, S.A.B. DE C.V.

Av Paseo de la Reforma No 222 3er Piso Col Juarez
06600 Mexico, DF, Mexico
Tel.: (52) 5552417100
E-Mail: ri@alsea.com.mx
Web Site: www.alsea.com.mx
ALSEA—(MEX)
Sls.: $1,063,714,732
Assets: $768,795,420
Liabilities: $390,936,923
Net Worth: $377,858,497
Earnings: $31,613,467
Emp.: 29,800
Fiscal Year-end: 12/31/12
Business Description:
Fresh Pizzas Mfr
S.I.C.: 2099
N.A.I.C.S.: 311991
Personnel:
Alberto Torrado Martinez *(Chm)*
Fabian Gerardo Gosselin Castro *(CEO)*
Diego Gaxiola *(CFO)*
Xavier Mangino Duenas *(Sec)*
Board of Directors:
Alberto Torrado Martinez
Fabian Gerardo Gosselin Castro
Julio Gutierrez Mercadillo
Leon Kraig
Raul Mendez Segura
Ivan Moguel Kuri
Marcelo Rivero Garza
Federico Tejado Barcena
Armando Torrado Martinez
Cosme Torrado Martinez

Subsidiaries:

Distribuidora e Importadora Alsea, S. A. de C. V. (1)
Avenue Tlahuac 6768
Santiago, Zapotiltic, Jalisco, 13300, Mexico
Tel.: (52) 5558623000
Fax: (52) 5558623082
Fast Food Restaurants Services
S.I.C.: 5812
N.A.I.C.S.: 722513

Especialistas en Restaurantes de Comida Estilo Asiatica, S. A. de C. V. (1)
Boulevard Pureta De Hierro 5225 Sn
Puebla, 72500, Mexico
Tel.: (52) 3336113294
Emp.: 90
Fast Food Distr
S.I.C.: 5812
N.A.I.C.S.: 722513
Miguel Rodrigues *(Mgr)*

Operadora de Franquicias Alsea, S. A. de C. V. (1)
Central Suc I No 243 Estado De Nezahualcoyotl
Bosques De Aragon, Mexico, 57170, Mexico (80%)
Tel.: (52) 5526518586
Fax: (52) 5526518586
Emp.: 21
Fast Food Distr
S.I.C.: 5812
N.A.I.C.S.: 722513
Luis Arenas *(Mgr)*

Non-U.S. Subsidiary:

Fast Food Sudamericana, S. A. (1)
Avenida Del Libertador 1295 Edificio Libertador Park Piso 30
Vicente Lopez, Buenos Aires, 1112, Argentina
Tel.: (54) 1155307000
Fax: (54) 1155307000
Web Site: www.burgerking.com.ar
Fast Food Store Operation Services
S.I.C.: 5812
N.A.I.C.S.: 722513

ALSHARK ELECTRODE CO.

180-Alsalam str
PO Box 09
Ramallah, Palestine
Tel.: (970) 2 2228874
Fax: (970) 2 2229477
E-Mail: info@alshark-co.com
Web Site: www.alshark-co.com
Year Founded: 1972
ELECTRODE—(PAL)
Business Description:
Welding Equipment Mfr
S.I.C.: 3548
N.A.I.C.S.: 333992
Personnel:
Salah Nasereddin Abdelfatiah Nasereddin *(Chm)*
Board of Directors:
Salah Nasereddin Abdelfatiah Nasereddin
Adel Abdul Hafeez Hassouneh
Jawdat Ibrahim Hassouneh
Mansour Hassouneh
Hakam Mohmad Nasereddin
Muhammad Tahir Nasereddin Nasereddin
Yahya Mohamed Yahya Shawar

ALSINCO SA

Nafpliou Str 8
Metamorfosi, 14452 Athens, Greece
Tel.: (30) 210 284 3076
Fax: (30) 210 284 6722
E-Mail: info@alsinco.gr
Web Site: www.alsinco.gr
Year Founded: 1992
ALSIN—(ATH)
Emp.: 32
Business Description:
Footwear & Apparel Retailer
S.I.C.: 5139
N.A.I.C.S.: 424340
Personnel:
George Avramidis *(Founder, Pres & CEO)*

ALSONS CONSOLIDATED RESOURCES, INC.

Alsons Building 2286 Chino Roces Ext
Makati, Philippines 1231
Tel.: (63) 29823000
Fax: (63) 29823077
E-Mail: info@acr.com.ph
Web Site: www.acr.com.ph
ACR—(PHI)
Rev.: $75,258,993
Assets: $343,442,585
Liabilities: $69,023,596
Net Worth: $274,418,990
Earnings: $26,409,988
Emp.: 243
Fiscal Year-end: 12/31/12
Business Description:
Investment Holding Services
S.I.C.: 6799
N.A.I.C.S.: 523920
Personnel:
Tomas I. Alcantara *(Chm & Pres)*
Luis R. Ymson, Jr. *(CFO, Corp Info & Compliance Officer)*
Editha I. Alcantara *(Treas)*
Roberto V. San Jose *(Sec)*
Tirso G. Santillan, Jr. *(Exec VP)*
Board of Directors:
Tomas I. Alcantara
Alejandro I. Alcantara
Conrado C. Alcantara
Editha I. Alcantara
Thomas G. Aquino
Ramon T. Diokno
Carlos G. Dominguez
Jacinto C. Gavino
Jose Ben R. Laraya
Honorio A. Poblador III
Tirso G. Santillan, Jr.

Subsidiary:

Southern Philippines Power Corporation (1)
3rd Floor Solid House Building
2285 Chino Roces Ext, Makati, 1231, Philippines
Tel.: (63) 28120294
Fax: (63) 28120294
Power Generation Services
S.I.C.: 4939
N.A.I.C.S.: 221111

ALSTAR OILFIELD CONTRACTORS LTD.

300 1B Avenue
PO Box 1200
Fox Creek, AB, TOH 1P0, Canada
Tel.: (780) 622-3640
Fax: (780) 622-3595
E-Mail: foxcreek@alstaroc.com
Web Site: www.alstaroc.com
Year Founded: 1969
Rev.: $17,927,800
Emp.: 120
Business Description:
Oil Filed Construction Services
S.I.C.: 1389
N.A.I.C.S.: 213112
Personnel:
Scott Fofonoff *(Pres)*

ALSTOM S.A.

3 Avenue Andre Malraux
92309 Levallois-Perret, France
Tel.: (33) 141492000
Telex: 611938
Fax: (33) 1 41 49 24 85
Web Site: www.alstom.com
Year Founded: 1988
ALO—(EUR)
Sls.: $27,285,519,730
Assets: $42,555,126,040
Liabilities: $35,684,274,360
Net Worth: $6,870,851,680
Earnings: $1,101,167,060
Emp.: 86,252
Fiscal Year-end: 03/31/13
Business Description:
Energy Generation & Distribution Equipment; Thermal & Nuclear Power

Plant Turbogenerators; Industrial Equipment; Railroad Equipment & Shipbuilding Mfr
S.I.C.: 3621
N.A.I.C.S.: 335312

Personnel:
Patrick Kron *(Chm & CEO)*
Nicolas Tissot *(CFO)*
Philippe Cochet *(Pres-Alstom Thermal Power & Exec VP)*
Jerome Pecresse *(Pres-Alstom Renewable Power & Exec VP)*
Henri Poupart-Lafarge *(Pres-Transport Sector & Exec VP)*
Gregoire Poux-Guillaume *(Pres-Alstom Grid Sector & Exec VP)*
Keith Carr *(Gen Counsel)*
Bruno Guillemet *(Sr VP-HR)*
Christine Rahard-Burnat *(Sr VP-Comm)*

Board of Directors:
Patrick Kron
Candace Krugman Beinecke
Olivier Bouygues
Georges Chodron de Courcel
Pascal Colombani
Jean-Martin Folz
Lalita Dileep Gupte
Gerard Hauser
Katrina Landis
James William Leng
Klaus J. Mangold
Philippe Marien
Amparo Moraleda
Alan M. Thomson

Mazars SA
61 rue Henri Regnault
92400 Courbevoie, France

Transfer Agent:
Karvy Computershare Pvt Ltd (Karvy)
17-24 Vithal Rao Nagar Madhapur
Hyderabad, India

Subsidiaries:

Alstom Grid SAS (1)
Tour Galilee Esplanade Du General De Gaulle
92907 Paris, France
Tel.: (33) 149016100
Fax: (33) 6103622005
Electric Grid Mfr
S.I.C.: 3612
N.A.I.C.S.: 335311

Non-U.S. Subsidiaries:

Alstom Grid AB (2)
Garvaren Plan 7
341 60 Ljungby, Sweden
Tel.: (46) 372 134 07
Fax: (46) 372 134 08
Web Site: www.alstom.com
Automation Equipment Mfr
S.I.C.: 3699
N.A.I.C.S.: 335999
Risto Tuominen *(Mng Dir)*

Alstom Grid AS (2)
Drammensveien 165
0277 Oslo, Norway
Tel.: (47) 22 12 70 00
Fax: (47) 22 12 70 01
E-Mail: mail.norway@power.alstom.com
Web Site: www.alstom.com
Electric Grid Mfr
S.I.C.: 3612
N.A.I.C.S.: 335311

Alstom Grid Canada, Inc (2)
1400 Rue Industrielle
La Prairie, QC, J5R 2E5, Canada
Tel.: (450) 659-1399
Fax: (450) 659-3371
Web Site: www.alstom.com
Emp.: 25
Wind Turbine Mfr
S.I.C.: 3511
N.A.I.C.S.: 333611
Robert Gingras *(Gen Mgr)*

Alstom Grid Enerji Endustrisi A.S (2)
Baris Mah Guney Yanyol Cad No 320
41410 Gebze, Kocaeli, Turkey
Tel.: (90) 262 648 33 00
Fax: (90) 262 641 20 36
Web Site: www.alstom.com
Emp.: 110
Electrical Grid Installation Services
S.I.C.: 1629
N.A.I.C.S.: 237130
Volkan Boyali *(Project Mgr)*

Alstom Grid GmbH (2)
Lilienthalstrasse 150
34123 Kassel, Germany
Tel.: (49) 5615020
Fax: (49) 5615022499
Electrical Grid Installation Services
S.I.C.: 1623
N.A.I.C.S.: 237120
Klaus Lingelmann *(Mng Dir-Unit)*

Alstom Grid Japan K.K. (2)
1-5-9 Takatsukadai
Nishi-Ku, Kobe, 651-2271, Japan
Tel.: (81) 789967380
Fax: (81) 789967385
Electric Grid Mfr
S.I.C.: 3612
N.A.I.C.S.: 335311

Alstom Grid Messwandler GmbH (2)
Bauernallee 27
19288 Ludwigslust, Germany
Tel.: (49) 3874454380
Fax: (49) 3874454418
Electronic Component Mfr
S.I.C.: 3679
N.A.I.C.S.: 334419
Benno Besler *(Mng Dir-Unit)*

Alstom Grid Oy (2)
Kaapelikatu 3
PO Box 4
33331 Tampere, Finland
Tel.: (358) 3 3883 11
Fax: (358) 3883360
Emp.: 30
Electric Grid Mfr
S.I.C.: 3999
N.A.I.C.S.: 327110
Risto Peltola *(Dir-Sls-High Voltage Switchgears & Sys)*

Alstom Grid Pte Ltd (2)
31 Kaki Bukit Rd 3 02-05 TechLink
Singapore, 417818, Singapore
Tel.: (65) 6749 0777
Fax: (65) 6841 9555
Electric Grid Mfr
S.I.C.: 3612
N.A.I.C.S.: 335311

Alstom Grid Spa (2)
Viale Giovanni Suzzani 229
20162 Milan, Italy
Tel.: (39) 02 6470445
Fax: (39) 02 6470906
Web Site: www.alstom.com
Electric Grid Mfr
S.I.C.: 3612
N.A.I.C.S.: 335311
Zohir Benhammou *(Gen Mgr)*

Alstom Grid UK LTD (2)
St Leonards Avenue
Stafford, ST17 4LX, United Kingdom
Tel.: (44) 1785 223 251
Fax: (44) 1785 252 540
Web Site: www.alstom.com
Emp.: 130
Electric Grid Mfr
S.I.C.: 3612
N.A.I.C.S.: 335311
Kevin Marriott *(Reg VP-Comml)*

Alstom Holdings (1)
3th Ave Andre Malraux
Levallois-Perret, Cedex 16, France
Tel.: (33) 141492000
Fax: (33) 147552890
Web Site: www.alstom.com
Holding Company
S.I.C.: 6719
N.A.I.C.S.: 551112

Subsidiary:

Alstom Power Holdings (2)
25 Avenue Kleber
Paris, 75116, France (100%)
Tel.: (33) 147552000
Fax: (33) 147553699
Web Site: www.power.alstom.com
Holding Company
S.I.C.: 6719
N.A.I.C.S.: 551112

Subsidiaries:

Alstom Power Hydro SA (3)
82 Ave Leon Blum
PO Box 75
38041 Grenoble, France (100%)
Tel.: (33) 476393000
Fax: (33) 476393001
Web Site: www.power.alstom.com
Emp.: 800
Power Generation Systems & Equipment Design, Engineering & Mfr
S.I.C.: 3511
N.A.I.C.S.: 333611

Alstom Power Service S.A. (3)
3 avenue Andre Malraux
92300 Levallois-Perret, Cedex, France
Tel.: (33) 141493354
Telex: 612046
Fax: (33) 141493887
Web Site: www.service.power.alstom.com
Emp.: 4,000
Power Generation Systems
S.I.C.: 3612
N.A.I.C.S.: 335311
Patrick Kron *(CEO)*

U.S. Subsidiary:

Alstom Inc (2)
200 Great Pond Dr PO Box 500
Windsor, CT 06095
Tel.: (860) 285-3790
Fax: (860) 285-9966
Web Site: www.apcompower.com
Emp.: 1,000
Holding Company
S.I.C.: 8711
N.A.I.C.S.: 541330
Amy Ericson *(Country Pres)*
Tim Curran *(CFO)*

Subsidiaries:

Alstom Power Inc (3)
175 Addison Rd
Windsor, CT 06095
Tel.: (860) 285-5810
Fax: (860) 396-2047
Web Site: www.power.alstom.com
Emp.: 2,000
Boiler Engineering, Services & Research & Development
S.I.C.: 8711
N.A.I.C.S.: 541330
Philippe Joubert *(Pres)*

Divisions:

Alstom Power Inc - Turbine Services (4)
2800 Waterford Lake Dr
Midlothian, VA 23112
Tel.: (804) 763-7000
Telex: 844 464
Web Site: www.power.alstom.com
Emp.: 425
Mfr & Repair of Gas & Steam Industrial Generators
S.I.C.: 8711
N.A.I.C.S.: 541330
John Crean *(Dir-Thermal Svcs)*

Alstom Power Inc. - Air Preheater Company (4)
3020 Truax Rd
Wellsville, NY 14895 TX
Mailing Address: (100%)
PO Box 372
Wellsville, NY 14895-0372
Tel.: (585) 593-2700
Fax: (585) 593-2721
Toll Free: (800) 828-0444 (Outside NY)
E-Mail: info@airpreheaterco.com
Web Site: www.airpreheaterco.com
Emp.: 500
Supplier of Engineered Products, Services & Technologies for Heat Recovery Systems
Import Export
S.I.C.: 3443
N.A.I.C.S.: 332313
David Breckenridge *(Pres)*

Units:

Alstom Power Inc. - Air Preheater Company (5)
1830 E 6 St
Concordia, KS 66901
Tel.: (785) 243-3300
Fax: (785) 243-9201
Web Site: www.airpreheaterco.com
Emp.: 220
Supplier of Engineered Products, Services & Technologies for Heat Recovery Systems
S.I.C.: 3612
N.A.I.C.S.: 335311

Alstom Power Inc. - Air Preheater Company (5)
3020 Terex Rd
Lockport, NY 14095
Tel.: (585) 593-2700
Fax: (585) 593-2721
Toll Free: (877))6615509
E-Mail: info@airpreheaterco.com
Web Site: www.airpreheaterco.com
Emp.: 500
Supplier of Engineered Products, Services & Technologies for Heat Recovery Systems
S.I.C.: 8711
N.A.I.C.S.: 541330

Alstom Power Inc.-Hydro (4)
7921 Southpark Plz Ste 208
Littleton, CO 80120-4506
Tel.: (303) 730-4000
Fax: (303) 730-4113
Web Site: www.power.alstom.com
Emp.: 50
Sells, Installs, Repairs, Upgrades & Retrofits Hydro Electric Generators, Turnkey Hydro Electric Power Plants
S.I.C.: 8711
N.A.I.C.S.: 541330

Alstom Power Inc (4)
1409 Centerpoint Blvd
Knoxville, TN 37932
Fax: (865) 560-9611
Toll Free: (800) 346-8944
Web Site: www.alstom.com
Air Pollution Control Systems Mfr
S.I.C.: 8711
N.A.I.C.S.: 541330

Alstom Power, Inc. (4)
2800 Waterford Lake Dr
Midlothian, VA 23112 (100%)
Tel.: (804) 763-7000
Fax: (804) 763-7395
E-Mail: ron.cox@power.alstom.com
Web Site: www.service.power.alstom.com
Emp.: 60
Repair of Gas & Steam Turbines, Generators & Components
S.I.C.: 8711
N.A.I.C.S.: 541330
Ron Cox *(Dir-Mktg)*

Subsidiaries:

Amstar Surface Technology, Ltd. (4)
9404 Zaka Rd
Houston, TX 77064
Tel.: (832) 467-8300
Fax: (832) 476-8300
Web Site: www.amstar-usa.com
Sales Range: $1-9.9 Million
Emp.: 25
Surface Protection Product Application Services
S.I.C.: 2851
N.A.I.C.S.: 325510

AP Com Power Inc. (4)
200 Great Pond Dr
Windsor, CT 06095-1580
Tel.: (860) 285-3598
Fax: (860) 285-4377
E-Mail: windsorparts@power.alstom.com
Web Site: www.apcompower.com
Boiler & Emission Equipment Installation & Maintenance Services
S.I.C.: 1799
N.A.I.C.S.: 238290
Eric Heuser *(Pres)*

Alstom Signaling, Inc. (3)
1025 John St
West Henrietta, NY 14586 (100%)
Tel.: (585) 783-2000
Fax: (585) 274-8777

Alstom S.A.—(Continued)

Toll Free: (800) 717-4477
E-Mail: info@alstomsignalingsolutions.com
Web Site: www.alstomsignalingsolutions.com
Emp.: 657
Mfr. & Whslr of Transportation Control Equipment for Railroad & Rail Mass Transit Systems
Import Export
S.I.C.: 3669
N.A.I.C.S.: 334290
Jim Heinlein *(Mgr-Mktg)*

Unit:

Alstom Transportation Inc (4)
1 Transit Dr
Hornell, NY 14843
Tel.: (607) 324-4595
Fax: (607) 281-2951
Web Site: www.transport.alstom.com
Emp.: 200
Railroad Stock Mfr
S.I.C.: 3743
N.A.I.C.S.: 336510
Mark Garrow *(Mng Dir)*

Power Systems Manufacturing (3)
1440 W Indiantown Rd Ste 200
Jupiter, FL 33458-7925
Tel.: (561) 354-1100
Fax: (561) 354-1199
Web Site: www.psm.com
Emp.: 400
Gas Turbine & Military Jet Engine Design
S.I.C.: 3519
N.A.I.C.S.: 333618
Alexander Hoffs *(Pres & CEO)*

Non-U.S. Subsidiaries:

Alstom Australia Ltd (2)
16 Giffnock Avenue
North Ryde, NSW, 2113, Australia (100%)
Tel.: (61) 2 8870 6000
Fax: (61) 2 8870 6005
Web Site: www.alstom.com
Emp.: 400
Energy Generation & Distribution Equipment Mfr, Railroad Equipment Mfr & IT Services
S.I.C.: 3511
N.A.I.C.S.: 333611
Chris W. Raine *(Pres)*
Michael Vladimiroff *(CFO)*

Subsidiary:

Alstom Power Ltd (3)
16 Giffnock Ave Macquarie Park
North Ryde, NSW, 2113, Australia (100%)
Tel.: (61) 288706000
Fax: (61) 288706005
Web Site: www.alstom.com.au
Emp.: 200
Power Plant Equipment Design, Mfr & Installation
S.I.C.: 1623
N.A.I.C.S.: 237130
Chris W. Raine *(Pres & Mng Dir)*

Alstom Belgium SA (2)
50 52 Rue Cambier Dupret
6001 Charleroi, Belgium
Tel.: (32) 71445411
Fax: (32) 71445793
E-Mail: info@alstom.com
Web Site: www.alstom.com
Emp.: 1,000
Holding Company
S.I.C.: 6719
N.A.I.C.S.: 551112
Marcel Miller *(Pres)*

Subsidiary:

Alstom Transport Belgium (3)
South Center Titanium Place
Marcel Broodthaers 8, B 6001 Charleroi, B1060, Belgium
Tel.: (32) 71445607
Fax: (32) 71445793
Web Site: www.alstom.com
Emp.: 800
Sales, Marketing & Mfr of Rail & Locomotive Products
S.I.C.: 3743
N.A.I.C.S.: 336510
Marcel Miller *(Pres)*

Alstom Chile S.A (2)
Edificio Birmann Sanchez Fontecilla 310 of 101
Santiago, Chile (100%)
Tel.: (56) 22908500
Fax: (56) 22908555
E-Mail: camila.arrendondo@crn.alstom.com
Web Site: www.alstom.cl
Emp.: 200
Power Generation, Distribution & Transmission Services; Railroad Equipment Mfr
S.I.C.: 4939
N.A.I.C.S.: 221122
Guelu Friedmann *(Pres)*

Alstom (China) Investment Co. Ltd (2)
5 F Entrance C Qian Kun Plaza 6 West Street
San Li Tun District, Beijing, 100027, China
Tel.: (86) 1084609000
Fax: (86) 1084609001
Web Site: www.cn.alstom.com
Holding Company
S.I.C.: 6719
N.A.I.C.S.: 551112
Claude Burckbuchler *(Pres)*

Subsidiaries:

ALSTOM Technical Services (Shanghai) Co., Ltd. (3)
F3 A Mansion Building No 291 Fu Min Road
Shanghai, 200031, China
Tel.: (86) 21 6103 3888
Fax: (86) 21 6170 1036
Power Transmission Engineering & Technical Consulting Services
S.I.C.: 8711
N.A.I.C.S.: 541330
Yuhua Wu *(Gen Mgr)*

Wuhan Boiler Company Limited (3)
No 586 Wu Luo Road
Wuhan, HUB, 430070, China (51%)
Tel.: (86) 27 87652719
Fax: (86) 27 87655152
Web Site: www.wbcl.com.cn/glpage/index.htm
200770—(SSE)
Emp.: 2,335
Development, Production & Sale of Power Station Boilers, Specialty Boilers, Desulfurizing Equipment & Other Pressure Vessels & Related Equipment
S.I.C.: 3559
N.A.I.C.S.: 332410
Kwok Wei Yeung *(Chm)*
Liang Qin *(Sec)*

Alstom Danmark A/S (2)
Ringager 2A
DK-2605 Brondby, Denmark (100%)
Tel.: (45) 46900100
Fax: (45) 46900106
E-Mail: info@alstom.com
Web Site: www.alstom.com
Emp.: 22
Sales & Marketing of Rail & Locomotive Products
S.I.C.: 3743
N.A.I.C.S.: 336510
Torpen Lang *(Dir-Mktg)*

Alstom Deutschland AG (2)
Boveristrasse 22
D 68309 Mannheim, Germany (100%)
Tel.: (49) 6213290
Fax: (49) 6213292660
E-Mail: info.mannheim@power.alstom.com
Web Site: www.de.alstom.com
Emp.: 1
Energy &Transport Infrastructure Services
S.I.C.: 3511
N.A.I.C.S.: 333611
Andreas Wittke *(Pres)*

Subsidiaries:

Alstom Power Service GmbH (3)
Boveristrasse 22
D 68309 Mannheim, Germany (100%)
Tel.: (49) 6213293896
Fax: (49) 6213292660
E-Mail: info.mannheim@power.alstom.com
Web Site: www.de.alstom.com
Emp.: 3,850
Holding Company
S.I.C.: 6719
N.A.I.C.S.: 551112
Carsten Nemitz *(Dir-Comm)*

Subsidiaries:

Alstom Power Boiler GmbH (4)
Augsburgerstrasse 712
D 70329 Stuttgart, Germany
Tel.: (49) 7119171828
Fax: (49) 7119171674
E-Mail: andreas.wittke@power.alstom.com
Web Site: www.power.alstom.com
Emp.: 200
Steam Generation Equipment Mfr
S.I.C.: 3511
N.A.I.C.S.: 333611
Andreas Wittke *(Mng Dir)*

Alstom Power Energy Recovery GmbH (4)
Ellenbacher Str 10
D 34123 Kassel, Germany (100%)
Tel.: (49) 56195270
Fax: (49) 5619527109
E-Mail: ap.recovery.kassel@online.de
Web Site: www.de.alstom.com
Emp.: 200
Mfr of Gas Cooling Systems for the Petrochemical & Chemical Industries; Waste Heat Steam Generation Systems
S.I.C.: 3822
N.A.I.C.S.: 334512
Axel Freitag *(Mng Dir)*

Division:

Alstom Power Energy Recovery GmbH (5)
Parsevalstrasse 9A
D 40468 Dusseldorf, Germany
Tel.: (49) 21147260
Fax: (49) 2114726200
E-Mail: info.stack@power.alstom.com
Web Site: www.de.alstom.com
Emp.: 70
Mfr of Gas Cooling Systems for the Petrochemical & Chemical Industries; Waste Heat Steam Generation Systems
S.I.C.: 3822
N.A.I.C.S.: 334512
Hans-Peter Steffen *(Mng Dir)*

Alstom Power Generation AG (4)
Boveristrasse 22
68309 Mannheim, Germany (100%)
Tel.: (49) 6213298915
Fax: (49) 6213292660
E-Mail: info.mannheim@power.alstom.com
Web Site: www.de.alstom.com
Emp.: 166
Electricity Generation Plant & Equipment Mfr
S.I.C.: 3511
N.A.I.C.S.: 333611
Gerard Brunel *(Chm)*

Division:

Alstom Power Generation AG (Bexbach) (5)
Schaufelfertigung in der Kolling
66540 Bexbach, Germany
Tel.: (49) 68269290
Fax: (49) 6826929150
E-Mail: contact@power.alstom.com
Web Site: www.de.alstom.com
Emp.: 240
Turbine Blade Mfr
S.I.C.: 3511
N.A.I.C.S.: 333611
Christopher Andrews *(Mng Dir)*
Diana Burger *(Sec)*

Non-U.S. Joint Venture:

NTPC Alstom Power Services Private Limited (5)
B-1 J-1 Mohan Co-operative Industrial Estate
Mathura Road, New Delhi, 110 044, India
Tel.: (91) 1151678666
Fax: (91) 1151678675
E-Mail: nasl@nasl-india.com
Web Site: www.nasl-india.com
Electric Power Distr; Owned 50% by NTPC Limited & 50% by Alstom Power Generation AG
S.I.C.: 4939
N.A.I.C.S.: 221122
A. K. Ahuja *(Mng Dir)*
R. N. Sen *(Mng Dir)*

Alstom Transport Deutschland GmbH (3)
Linke-Hofmann-Busch Strasse 1
38239 Salzgitter, Germany
Tel.: (49) 53419000
Fax: (49) 53419006943
Web Site: www.de.alstom.com
Transport Systems Developer, Designer & Mfr
S.I.C.: 3743
N.A.I.C.S.: 336510
Andreas Wittke *(Chm)*

Joint Venture:

Alstom Lokomotiven Service GmbH (4)
Tangermunderstrasse 23A
D 29576 Stendal, Germany
Tel.: (49) 0393125400
Fax: (49) 393125601
E-Mail: koaus.hiller@transport.alstom.com
Web Site: www.transport.alstom.com
Sales Range: $25-49.9 Million
Emp.: 175
Locomotive Refurbishment Services: Joint Venture of Alstom (51%) & Deutsche Bahn AG (49%)
S.I.C.: 3743
N.A.I.C.S.: 336510
Koaus Hiller *(Mng Dir)*

Alstom Espana IB (2)
Paseo de la Castellana 257
28046 Madrid, Spain (100%)
Tel.: (34) 913345800
Fax: (34) 913345880
Web Site: www.es.alstom.com
Emp.: 4,000
Holding Company
S.I.C.: 6719
N.A.I.C.S.: 551112
Antonio Moreno *(Pres)*

Subsidiaries:

Alstom Power S.A. (3)
Paseo de la Castellana 257-6
28046 Madrid, Spain (100%)
Tel.: (34) 913345950
Fax: (34) 913345800
E-Mail: sarah.wilkinson@crn.alstom.com
Web Site: www.es.alstom.com
Emp.: 30
Combined-Cycle & Hydro-Electric Power Plant Design, Manufacture & Installation
S.I.C.: 1623
N.A.I.C.S.: 237130
Lopez Morancho *(Dir-Comm)*

Divisions:

Alstom Power SA (4)
Barrio Galindo S N
Trapagaran, 48510 Bilbao, Spain
Tel.: (34) 944728500
Fax: (34) 944728504
E-Mail: markcom.power@power.alstom.com
Web Site: www.es.alstom.com
Diesel & Hydraulic Generators Mfr
S.I.C.: 3511
N.A.I.C.S.: 333611

Alstom Power S.A (4)
Castellana 257
28046 Madrid, Spain
Tel.: (34) 933761000
Fax: (34) 913345801
E-Mail: markcom.power@power.alstom.com
Web Site: www.es.alstom.com
Emp.: 50
Electrical Generation Equipment Manufacture & Repair
S.I.C.: 3511
N.A.I.C.S.: 333611

Subsidiaries:

Alstom Wind Galicia, S.L.U. (4)
Poligono Industrial Parcela B
15565 As Somozas, A Coruna, Spain
Tel.: (34) 981 40 4090
Fax: (34) 981 40 4137
Web Site: www.alstom.com
Emp.: 65

Wind Turbine Mfr
S.I.C.: 3511
N.A.I.C.S.: 333611
Jose-Luis Blanco *(Gen Mgr)*

Alstom Wind Navarra, S.A.U (4)
Poligono Industrial Parcela G 1
31540 Bunuel, Navarre, Spain
Tel.: (34) 948 83 2012
Web Site: www.alstom.com
Turbine Generator Mfr
S.I.C.: 3511
N.A.I.C.S.: 333611

Alstom Wind, S.L.U. (4)
Roc Boronat 78
8005 Barcelona, Spain
Tel.: (34) 93 225 7600
Fax: (34) 93 221 0939
Wind Farm Research & Development Services
S.I.C.: 8731
N.A.I.C.S.: 541712
Maria-Pau Tomez *(Dir-HR)*

Alstom Transporte SA (3)
Castellana 257 Planta 6
28046 Madrid, Spain (100%)
Tel.: (34) 913345700
Fax: (34) 913345801
E-Mail: recion.castellana@es.alstom.com
Web Site: www.es.alstom.com
Emp.: 300
Locomotive, Train Control Systems & Parts Mfr & Service
S.I.C.: 3743
N.A.I.C.S.: 336510

Alstom Gulf Area (2)
Crescent Twr 4 Fl
Al Buhaira Corniche Rd, 25448 Sharjah, United Arab Emirates (100%)
Tel.: (971) 65563971
Fax: (971) 65562154
E-Mail: alstomcr@emirates.net.ae
Web Site: www.alstrom.com
Emp.: 10
Energy Generation & Distribution Equipment; Thermal & Nuclear Powerplant Turbogenerators; Industrial Equipment; Railroad Equipment
S.I.C.: 3511
N.A.I.C.S.: 333611
Sylvain Hijazi *(Pres)*

Alstom Hydro Canada Inc. (2)
1350 Chemin Saint Roch
Sorel-Tracy, QC, H3A 2R7, Canada ON
Tel.: (450) 746-6500 (100%)
Fax: (450) 746-6511
E-Mail: marylene.fleury@power.alstom.com
Web Site: www.alstom.com
Emp.: 800
Hydro Mfr
S.I.C.: 4911
N.A.I.C.S.: 221111
Francine Gesmarais *(Asst Mgr)*

Subsidiaries:

Alstom Canada Inc., Power Hydro (3)
1350 Chemin St Roch
Sorel, QC, J3R 5P9, Canada (100%)
Tel.: (450) 746-6500
Fax: (450) 746-6510
Emp.: 500
Hydro Turbine Mfr
S.I.C.: 3511
N.A.I.C.S.: 333611
Claude Lembert *(Gen Mgr)*

Alstom Canada Inc., Transport Service (3)
1010 rue Sherbrooke Ouest Suite 2320
Montreal, QC, H3A 2R7, Canada (100%)
Tel.: (514) 281-6200
Fax: (514) 281-6300
Web Site: www.alstom.com
Railroad Stock Mfr
S.I.C.: 3743
N.A.I.C.S.: 336510

Alstom Canada, Inc. (3)
1430 Blair Pl Ste 600
Gloucester, ON, K1J 9N2, Canada (100%)
Tel.: (613) 747-5222
Fax: (613) 747-5888
Web Site: www.power.alstom.com
Emp.: 90
Mfr. of Marketing & Servicing of Steam Generators for Paper & Pulp Mills
S.I.C.: 3511
N.A.I.C.S.: 333611
Adnan Jamali *(CFO)*

Alstom Telecite Inc (3)
5003 Levi St Offce Ste 200
Saint Laurent, QC, H4R 2N9, Canada (100%)
Tel.: (514) 333-0888
Fax: (514) 333-0496
Web Site: www.alstom.com
Emp.: 200
Mfr of Passenger Information Systems for Public Mass Transit & Airport Applications
S.I.C.: 4512
N.A.I.C.S.: 481111
William Crawl *(Gen Mgr)*

Alstom Mexico SA de CV (2)
Montes Urales No 727
Col Lomas de Chapultepec, 11000 Mexico, Mexico (100%)
Tel.: (52) 5511010700
Fax: (52) 5526240144
Web Site: www.alstom.com
Emp.: 30
Holding Company
S.I.C.: 6719
N.A.I.C.S.: 551112
Cintia Angulo *(Pres)*

Subsidiary:

Alstom Transporte SA de CV (3)
Montesurales No 727 Lomis de Chapultepec
11520 Mexico, Mexico (100%)
Tel.: (52) 5511010700
Fax: (52) 5526240144
E-Mail: info@alstom.com
Web Site: www.alstom.com
Emp.: 55
Locomotive, Train Control Systems & Parts Mfr & Service
S.I.C.: 3743
N.A.I.C.S.: 336510

Alstom Netherlands N.V. (2)
Koopmansstraat 7
2288 BC Rijswijk, Netherlands
Tel.: (31) 704132833
Fax: (31) 704132848
Web Site: www.alstom.com
Emp.: 50
Holding Company
S.I.C.: 6719
N.A.I.C.S.: 551112
Leon Lindern *(Mng Dir)*

Subsidiaries:

Alstom Nederland BV (3)
Koopmansstraat 7
2288 BC Rijswijk, Netherlands (50%)
Tel.: (31) 74132833
Fax: (31) 704140094
Web Site: www.alstom.com
Emp.: 50
Equipment for Power Generation; Transmission & Distribution, Railway Systems, Shipbuilding
S.I.C.: 4111
N.A.I.C.S.: 485112
Alphonse Le-Grand *(Reg Mgr)*

Alstom Transport B.V. (3)
Koopmansstraat 7
2288 BC Rijswijk, Netherlands (100%)
Tel.: (31) 704132830
Fax: (31) 704132848
Web Site: www.alstom.com
Emp.: 200
Motors, Generators, Traction Drive Systems, Crane Drive Systems, Power Supplies, Servicing/Refurbishing
S.I.C.: 3621
N.A.I.C.S.: 335312
Leon Linden *(Gen Mgr)*

Alstom Transport BV (3)
Ringdijk 390 A
Ridderkerk, 2983 GS, Netherlands
Tel.: (31) 180453999
Web Site: www.alstom.com
Railroad Electrical Equipment Mfr
S.I.C.: 3743
N.A.I.C.S.: 336510

U.S. Subsidiary:

Alstom Power Inc.- Boiler Services (3)
200 Creek Palm Dr
Windsor, CT 06095-1580 (100%)
Mailing Address:
PO Box 500
Windsor, CT 06095-0711
Tel.: (860) 688-1911
Fax: (860) 285-9611
Web Site: www.power.alstom.com
Emp.: 2,000
Steam Generations, Both Fossil & Nuclear Powered
S.I.C.: 8711
N.A.I.C.S.: 541330
Pierre Gauthier *(Pres)*

Non-U.S. Subsidiaries:

Alstom Ferroviaria S.p.A. (3)
Via Di Corticella 75
40128 Bologna, Italy
Tel.: (39) 0514163111
Fax: (39) 0514163594
Web Site: www.alstom.com
Emp.: 5,000
Locomotive, Train Control Systems & Parts Mfr & Service
S.I.C.: 3743
N.A.I.C.S.: 336510

Branches:

Alstom Ferroviaria S.p.A. (4)
Via Dei Gladioli 5
Modugno Z I BA, Bari, 40128, Italy
Tel.: (39) 0514163111
Web Site: www.alstom.com
Train Detection & Control Systems
S.I.C.: 3743
N.A.I.C.S.: 336510

Alstom Ferroviaria SpA (4)
Via Ottavio Moreno 23
Savigliano, 12038 Cuneo, Italy
Tel.: (39) 0172718111
Fax: (39) 0172718820
Web Site: www.alstom.com
Locomotive Mfr
S.I.C.: 3743
N.A.I.C.S.: 336510
Emilio Gallocchio *(Pres-Europe Div)*

Alstom Ferroviaria S.p.A. (4)
Via Dell Elettronica 19
Z A I Basson, Verona, 37138, Italy
Tel.: (39) 0458393111
Fax: (39) 0458510530
Web Site: www.alstom.com
Emp.: 100
Rail Voice & Data Communications Systems Mfr
S.I.C.: 3669
N.A.I.C.S.: 334290
Lara Borgo *(Mgr-HR)*

Alstom Transport Systems SpA (4)
Via Lago Dei Tartari 14
Rome, Italy
Tel.: (39) 077437741
Fax: (39) 0774353430
Web Site: www.alstom.com
Emp.: 70
Locomotive Mfr
S.I.C.: 3743
N.A.I.C.S.: 336510

Alstom Transport Systems SpA (4)
Via Fosse Ardeatine 120
Sesto San Giovanni, Milan, 20099, Italy
Tel.: (39) 0254144400
Web Site: www.alstom.com
Automatic People Mover Mfr
S.I.C.: 3743
N.A.I.C.S.: 336510

Subsidiary:

Osvaldo Cariboni Lecco Spa (4)
Via Roma 14
23855 Pescate, Lecco, Italy
Tel.: (39) 0341 358711
Fax: (39) 0341 364672
E-Mail: info@cariboni.it
Web Site: www.cariboni.it
Emp.: 80
Electric Power Transmission Services
S.I.C.: 4911
N.A.I.C.S.: 221121

Alstom K.K. (3)
3-4 Minatojima Chuo Ku
Nakamachi 2 Chome
Chuo Ku, 650 0046 Kobe, Japan
Tel.: (81) 78 303 5790
Fax: (81) 78 303 5781
E-Mail: info.japan@power.alstom.com
Web Site: www.jp.alstom.com
Energy Generation & Distribution Equipment; Thermal & Nuclear Powerplant Turbogenerators; Industrial Equipment; Railroad Equipment; Shipbuilding
S.I.C.: 3511
N.A.I.C.S.: 333611

Alstom Power Asia Pacific Sdn Bhd (3)
5th Fl Chulan Tower
3 Jalan Conley, 50450 Kuala Lumpur, Malaysia (100%)
Tel.: (60) 320556071
Fax: (60) 20556333
E-Mail: Info.malaysia@crn.alstom.com
Emp.: 200
Energy Generation & Distribution Equipment; Thermal & Nuclear Powerplant Turbogenerators; Industrial Equipment; Railroad Equipment; Shipbuilding
S.I.C.: 3511
N.A.I.C.S.: 333611
Saji Raghaven *(Pres)*

Alstom Power Centrales (3)
4 Ave Andre Malraux
92309 Levallois-Perret, France (100%)
Tel.: (33) 141493176
Fax: (33) 141493566
Web Site: www.alstom.com
Emp.: 2,000
Power Plant Automation Sys Mfr
S.I.C.: 1629
N.A.I.C.S.: 237130
Patrick Kron *(Chm, Pres & CEO)*

Alstom Power Italia SpA (3)
P Le Lodi 3
Milan, 20137, Italy
Tel.: (39) 0254141
Fax: (39) 0254142288
Web Site: www.alstom.com
Heat Recovery Steam Generator & Industrial Boiler Mfr
S.I.C.: 3823
N.A.I.C.S.: 334513

Alstom Power Sp.z.o.o (3)
Stoczniowa 2
82300 Elblag, Poland (100%)
Tel.: (48) 552324961
Fax: (48) 552324976
E-Mail: info@alstom.pl
Web Site: www.alstom.pl
Emp.: 700
Power Generation Systems & Equipment Design. Engineering & Mfr
S.I.C.: 3511
N.A.I.C.S.: 333611
Jakub Radulski *(Pres & CEO)*

Subsidiary:

Alstom Power Sp. z o.o. (4)
Al Jana Pawla II Ste 12
00 124 Warsaw, Poland
Tel.: (48) 228509600
Fax: (48) 226545590
Web Site: www.alstom.pl
Emp.: 100
Locomotive Mfr
S.I.C.: 3743
N.A.I.C.S.: 336510
Jakub Radulski *(Pres)*

Plant:

Alstom Power Sp. z o.o. - Generator Factory (4)
Ul Fabryczna 10
53-609 Wroclaw, Poland
Tel.: (48) 71 771 25 53
Fax: (48) 71 35 58 560
Web Site: www.alstom.com
Emp.: 500
Electric Power Generation Services
S.I.C.: 4939
N.A.I.C.S.: 221118
Jacek Przygoda *(Dir-Generator Factory)*

Alstom S.A.—(Continued)

Alstom Power s.r.o (3)
Olomoucka 7-9
656 66 Brno, Czech Republic
Tel.: (420) 545102512
Fax: (420) 545213007
E-Mail: petr.brzezina@power.alstom.com
Web Site: www.alstom.cz
Emp.: 250
Combined-Cycle & Hydro-Electric Power Plant Design, Manufacture & Installation
S.I.C.: 1623
N.A.I.C.S.: 237130
Petr Brzezina *(CEO & Pres)*

Non-U.S. Subsidiary:

Alstom Power Slovakia s.r.o (4)
Kukuricna 8
831 03 Bratislava, Slovakia (100%)
Tel.: (421) 249266201
Fax: (421) 249266266
Web Site: www.alstom.cz
Emp.: 11
Combined-Cycle & Hydro-Electric Power Plant Design, Manufacture & Installation
S.I.C.: 1629
N.A.I.C.S.: 237130

Alstom Power Sweden AB (3)
Vastra Jarnvagsgatan 23
111 64 Stockholm, Sweden
Tel.: (46) 1188300
Fax: (46) 87236590
Web Site: www.se.alstom.com
Emp.: 300
Hydro-Electric Generator Systems Mfr
S.I.C.: 3511
N.A.I.C.S.: 333611
Nils Lanneforss *(Pres)*

Divisions:

Alstom Power Sweden AB (4)
Kvrwagan
PO Box 1233
351 12 Vaxjo, Sweden
Tel.: (46) 470762000
Fax: (46) 470762001
E-Mail: mats.thimanson@power.alstom.com
Web Site: www.alstom.com
Emp.: 200
Environmental Control Systems Mfr
S.I.C.: 3823
N.A.I.C.S.: 334513
Mats Thimanson *(Mng Dir)*

Logstor Sweden AB (4)
Verkstadsgatan 1
Box 66
701 41 Orebro, Sweden
Tel.: (46) 19208100
Fax: (46) 19208130
E-Mail: info@logstor.com
Web Site: www.logstor.com
Emp.: 45
Prefabricated Pipe Systems Mfr
S.I.C.: 3498
N.A.I.C.S.: 332996
Peter Jorsal *(Mng Dir)*

Alstom Power Turbomachines (3)
3 Ave Des Trois Chenes
Belfort, 90018, France (100%)
Tel.: (33) 384551000
Fax: (33) 384551058
Web Site: www.alstom.com
Steam Turbines & Parts Mfr
S.I.C.: 3511
N.A.I.C.S.: 333611

Alstom Switzerland Ltd (3)
Brown Boveri Str 7
5401 Baden, Switzerland (100%)
Tel.: (41) 562057733
Fax: (41) 562057171
E-Mail: communicationsbox@alstom.com
Web Site: www.alstom.ch
Emp.: 3,000
Power Generation Systems & Equipment Design, Engineering & Manufacture
S.I.C.: 3511
N.A.I.C.S.: 333611
Walter Granicher *(Pres-Power Svcs)*

Alstom Transport AB (3)
PO Box 739
10135 Stockholm, Sweden
Tel.: (46) 87236581
Fax: (46) 87236590
E-Mail: kerstin.hasselgren@transport.alstom.com
Web Site: www.transport.alstom.com
Emp.: 100
Locomotive Mfr
S.I.C.: 3743
N.A.I.C.S.: 336510

Alstom New Zealand Holdings Ltd (2)
2 A Simpsay Pl
PO Box 20532
3241 Hamilton, New Zealand (100%)
Tel.: (64) 78548734
Fax: (64) 79579252
Emp.: 25
Holding Company
S.I.C.: 6719
N.A.I.C.S.: 551112

Subsidiaries:

Alstom Power New Zealand Ltd (3)
2 A Simsay Pl
PO Box 20532
Hamilton, New Zealand (100%)
Tel.: (64) 78548734
Fax: (64) 79579252
Web Site: www.alstom.co.nz
Emp.: 25
Maintainance & Refurbishment Services to Energy Generation Companies
S.I.C.: 7629
N.A.I.C.S.: 811219

Alstom Transport New Zealand Ltd (3)
Gate 1, Hellaby's Road
Private Box 22430
Otahuhu, Auckland, New Zealand
Tel.: (64) 92720540
Fax: (64) 92737154
Web Site: www.alstom.co.nz
Locomotive Maintainence Services
S.I.C.: 3743
N.A.I.C.S.: 336510

Alstom Power Austria GmbH (2)
Clemens Holz Meister 4
1109 Vienna, Austria (100%)
Tel.: (43) 16088880
Fax: (43) 1608888230
E-Mail: office@power.alstom.com
Web Site: www.at.alstom.com
Rev.: $72,696,000
Emp.: 60
Energy Generation & Distribution Equipment Mfr; Railroad Equipment Mfr
S.I.C.: 3511
N.A.I.C.S.: 333611
Wolfgang Koelliker *(Mng Dir)*

Alstom Power Holdings Ltda (2)
Av Embaixador Macedo Soares 10.001
CEP 05095-035 Sao Paulo, SP, Brazil
Tel.: (55) 11 3612 7000
Web Site: www.alstom.com
Emp.: 1,000
Holding Company: Power Generation
S.I.C.: 6719
N.A.I.C.S.: 551112

Subsidiary:

Alstom Energia e Transporte (Sao Paulo) (3)
Av Embaixador Macedo Soares 10.001Vila Anastacio
CEP 05095-035 Sao Paulo, Brazil (100%)
Tel.: (55) 11 3612 7000
Web Site: www.alstom.com
Emp.: 1,500
Energy Generation, Distribution Equipment & Railroad Equipment Mfr
S.I.C.: 3511
N.A.I.C.S.: 333611

Alstom Power Norway AS (2)
Drammensveien 165
0277 Oslo, Norway (100%)
Tel.: (47) 22127000
Fax: (47) 22127001
E-Mail: post@alstom.com
Web Site: www.alstom.com
Emp.: 250
Power Generation Systems & Equipment Design, Engineering & Manufacture
S.I.C.: 3511
N.A.I.C.S.: 333611
Arne Ellstad *(Pres)*
Einar Sauns *(Mng Dir)*

Alstom Power (Rugby) (2)
Newbold Rd
Rugby, Warks, CV21 2NH, United Kingdom
Tel.: (44) 1788 577 111
Telex: 311 335
Fax: (44) 1788 531 700
Web Site: www.alstom.com
Emp.: 900
Holding Company: Power Generation
S.I.C.: 6719
N.A.I.C.S.: 551112

Subsidiaries:

Alstom Transport (3)
3 Ibstock Rd
Coventry, CV6 6NL, United Kingdom (100%)
Tel.: (44) 1908574400
Fax: (44) 1908574414
Web Site: www.transport.alstom.com
Emp.: 3,000
Railway Rolling Stock Refurbishment; Joint Venture of Babcock International Group Plc (60%) & Siemens plc (40%)
S.I.C.: 3743
N.A.I.C.S.: 336510
Rob Baxter *(Mng Dir)*

Tidal Generation Limited (3)
8th Floor Castlemead
Lower Castle Street, Bristol, BS1 3AG, United Kingdom
Tel.: (44) 117 325 7001
Fax: (44) 117 325 7002
E-Mail: info@tidalgeneration.co.uk
Web Site: www.tidalgeneration.co.uk
Sales Range: $10-24.9 Million
Emp.: 29
Steam Turbine Mfr
S.I.C.: 3511
N.A.I.C.S.: 333611
James Sheppard *(Program Dir)*

Alstom T&D India Ltd. (2)
Magnet House 457 Anna Salai
Teynampet, Chennai, 600 018, India In
Tel.: (91) 4424364575
Fax: (91) 4424323462
Web Site: www.areva-td.co.in
Emp.: 60
Holding Company
S.I.C.: 6719
N.A.I.C.S.: 551112
Rathin Basu *(Mng Dir)*
Vijay Sharma *(CFO)*

Subsidiary:

Alstom Projects India Ltd (3)
IHDP Building Plot #7
Sector 127, Noida, Uttar Pradesh, 201 301, India (100%)
Tel.: (91) 1204731100
Fax: (91) 1204731200
E-Mail: in.corporatecommunications@power.alstom.com
Web Site: www.in.alstom.com
Emp.: 700
Power Generation Systems & Equipment Design, Engineering & Manufacture
S.I.C.: 3511
N.A.I.C.S.: 333611
Francois Carpentier *(Vice Chm & Mng Dir)*
Rathin Basu *(Pres-India & South Asia)*

Alstom (2)
Avenida Raimundo Pereira de Magalhaes 230
05092 040 Sao Paulo, Brazil
Tel.: (55) 1136432347
Fax: (55) 1136432345
Web Site: www.alstom.com.br
Emp.: 1,200
Electrical Transformer Mfr
S.I.C.: 3675
N.A.I.C.S.: 334416
Aloisio Vasconcelos *(Country Pres)*

Alstom Hydro France S.A. (1)
82 Avenue Laon Blum
BP 75
38041 Grenoble, France
Tel.: (33) 4 76 39 30 00
Fax: (33) 4 76 39 30 01
Emp.: 100
Piston Engine Parts Mfr
S.I.C.: 3714
N.A.I.C.S.: 336310
Jacques Quenin *(Gen Mgr)*

Non-U.S. Subsidiaries:

ALSTOM Algerie Spa (1)
153 Rue Ali Khodja El Biar Hydra
Algiers, Algeria
Tel.: (213) 21 92 97 19
Fax: (213) 21 92 95 35
Gas Turbine Mfr & Distr
S.I.C.: 3511
N.A.I.C.S.: 333611

Alstom Asia Pacific Sdn. Bhd. (1)
5th Floor Chulan Tower 3 Jalan Conlay
Kuala Lumpur, 50450, Malaysia
Tel.: (60) 3 2055 6000
Fax: (60) 21617788
Web Site: www.alstom.com
Emp.: 50
Power Plant Construction Engineering Services
S.I.C.: 1623
N.A.I.C.S.: 237130
Beverly Ho *(Dir-Comm)*

Alstom Austria GmbH (1)
Clemens-Holzmeister-Str 4
1109 Vienna, Austria
Tel.: (43) 1608880
Fax: (43) 1608888230
E-Mail: office@power.alstom.com
Web Site: alstom.echonet.at
Sls.: $66,069,500
Emp.: 80
Electric Power Generation & Transmission Services
S.I.C.: 4911
N.A.I.C.S.: 221118
Josef Reisel *(CEO & Exec Dir)*

Alstom Carbon Capture GmbH (1)
Lorenz-Schott-Strasse 4
55252 Mainz-Kastel, Germany
Tel.: (49) 61347120
Fax: (49) 6134712387
E-Mail: ampfang.wiesbaden@power.alstom.com
Emp.: 12
Electric Power Generation Services
S.I.C.: 4939
N.A.I.C.S.: 221118
Kai Uwe Krauel *(Gen Mgr)*

Alstom Finland Oy (1)
Martinkylantie 43
1720 Vantaa, Finland
Tel.: (358) 10 3037 100
Fax: (358) 103037650
E-Mail: info@power.alstom.com
Emp.: 50
Electric Power Generation & Transmission Services
S.I.C.: 4931
N.A.I.C.S.: 221118
Sari Luhanka *(Country Dir-Comm)*

ALSTOM Grid Australia Ltd (1)
Level 3 Quad 3 102 Bennelong Parkway
Olympic Park
Sydney, NSW, 2127, Australia
Tel.: (61) 7 3274 7649
Electric Grid Mfr
S.I.C.: 3999
N.A.I.C.S.: 327110

Alstom Hong Kong Ltd. (1)
Units 1011-1012 10F New Kowloon Plaza
38 Tai Kok Tsui Road
Kowloon, China (Hong Kong)
Tel.: (852) 27246300
Fax: (852) 23818680
Emp.: 10
Electric Power Generation & Transmission Services
S.I.C.: 4911
N.A.I.C.S.: 221118
Vincent Tung *(Gen Mgr)*

Alstom Hydro Spain S.L. (1)
WTC Almeda Park Placa de la Pau s/n Edif 3 - 3
Cornella de Llobregat, Barcelona, 8940, Spain
Tel.: (34) 93 474 88 00
Fax: (34) 93 474 88 01
Emp.: 6
Hydro Power Generation Equipment Mfr & Distr

S.I.C.: 3511
N.A.I.C.S.: 333611
Jordi Ubach *(Controller-Project)*

Alstom Hydro Sweden AB (1)
Finnslatten Building 350
721 76 Vasteras, Sweden
Tel.: (46) 21 32 60 00
Fax: (46) 21 32 62 30
Emp.: 35
Hydroelectric Power Generation Services
S.I.C.: 4911
N.A.I.C.S.: 221111
Fredrik Forsberg *(Gen Mgr)*

Alstom Konstal S.A. (1)
Ul Metalowcow 9
41-500 Chorzow, Poland
Tel.: (48) 32 349 12 66
Fax: (48) 32 349 14 63
Electric Power Generation Services
S.I.C.: 4911
N.A.I.C.S.: 221118

Alstom LLC (1)
18 Shchipok Str Building 2
115093 Moscow, Russia
Tel.: (7) 495 231 29 49
Fax: (7) 495 231 29 45
Emp.: 60
Electric Power Generation & Transmission Services
S.I.C.: 4939
N.A.I.C.S.: 221118
Philippe Pegorier *(Pres)*

Subsidiary:

Alstom Hydro (2)
10 Letnikovskaya Str Bldg 4 7th Floor
115144 Moscow, Russia
Tel.: (7) 495 989 99 09
Fax: (7) 495 989 99 08
E-Mail: info.hydro@alstom.com
Emp.: 10
Hydroelectric Power Generation & Transmission Services
S.I.C.: 4931
N.A.I.C.S.: 221111
Frederic Brochard *(Dir-HR)*

Alstom Ltd. (1)
The Place 175 High Holborn
London, WC1V 7AA, United Kingdom
Tel.: (44) 207 438 92
Fax: (44) 207 438 92
E-Mail: enquiries.uk@alstom.com
Emp.: 650
Electric Power Transmission Services
S.I.C.: 4911
N.A.I.C.S.: 221121
Stephen Burgin *(Pres)*

Alstom Norway AS (1)
Drammensveien 165
277 Oslo, Norway
Tel.: (47) 22 12 70 00
Fax: (47) 22 12 70 01
E-Mail: mail.norway@power.alstom.com
Emp.: 20
Electric Power Generation & Transmission Services
S.I.C.: 4911
N.A.I.C.S.: 221118
Eric Staurset *(Pres & Mng Dir)*

Alstom Power & Transport Canada Inc. (1)
1350 Chemin St-Roch
Sorel-Tracy, QC, J3R 5P9, Canada
Tel.: (450) 746-6500
Fax: (450) 746-7043
Emp.: 500
Wind Turbine Mfr
S.I.C.: 3511
N.A.I.C.S.: 333611
Claude Lambert *(VP)*

Alstom Power GmbH (1)
Friedrich-Ebert-Strasse Technologiepark
51429 Bergisch Gladbach, Germany
Tel.: (49) 2204 84 3270
Fax: (49) 2204 84 3279
E-Mail: standort.bergisch-gladbach@power.alstom.com
Emp.: 3
Electric Power Generation Services
S.I.C.: 4939
N.A.I.C.S.: 221118

Alstom Power Service (HK) Ltd. (1)
Unit 911-912 9/F New Kowloon Plaza 38
Tai Kok Tsui Road
Kowloon, China (Hong Kong)
Tel.: (852) 2611 9181
Fax: (852) 2611 9239
Electric Power Generation Services
S.I.C.: 4939
N.A.I.C.S.: 221118

Alstom Power Uniturbo OOO (1)
Kulakov Pereulok 9 Building 1
129626 Moscow, Russia
Tel.: (7) 495 956 60 17
Fax: (7) 495 956 75 49
Gas Turbine Design Engineering Services
S.I.C.: 3511
N.A.I.C.S.: 333611
Igor Petrov *(Gen Mgr)*

Alstom S&E Africa (Pty) Ltd (1)
Country Club Estates 21 Woodlands Drive
Woodmead, 2191, South Africa
Tel.: (27) 11 518 8100
Fax: (27) 11 518 8210
Web Site: www.alstom.com
Emp.: 200
Electric Power Generation & Transmission Services
S.I.C.: 4911
N.A.I.C.S.: 221118
Jerome Boyet *(Pres)*
Reg Engelbrecht *(Mng Dir & Country Dir-Fin)*

Alstom Services Sdn. Bhd. (1)
5th Floor Chulan Tower 3 Jalan Conlay
Kuala Lumpur, 50450, Malaysia
Tel.: (60) 3 2055 6000
Fax: (60) 3 2055 6333
Web Site: www.alstom.com
Emp.: 50
Industrial Equipment Distr
S.I.C.: 5084
N.A.I.C.S.: 423830
Saji Raghavan *(Gen Mgr)*

ALSTOM Slovakia, s.r.o. (1)
Prievozska 4
821 09 Bratislava, Slovakia
Tel.: (421) 232 251 001
Fax: (421) 232 251 000
Electric Power Generation Services
S.I.C.: 4939
N.A.I.C.S.: 221118
Jiri Filip *(Country Mgr-Comm-Czech Republic)*

Alstom S.p.A. (1)
Viale Regina Margherita 262
198 Rome, Italy
Tel.: (39) 06 42038901
Fax: (39) 06 42038920
Electric Power Generation & Transmission Services
S.I.C.: 4939
N.A.I.C.S.: 221118
Antonino Turicchi *(Pres)*

Alstom s.r.o. (1)
Olomoucka 7/9
656 66 Brno, Czech Republic
Tel.: (420) 545 101 111
Fax: (420) 545 213 007
E-Mail: info.czech@power.alstom.com
Web Site: www.alstom.com
Emp.: 20
Electric Power Generation Services
S.I.C.: 4931
N.A.I.C.S.: 221118
Petr Brzezina *(Pres)*

Alstom Taiwan Ltd (1)
10f 65 Chou Tzu St
Taipei, 11493, Taiwan
Tel.: (886) 226275000
Fax: (886) 226275500
Web Site: www.alstom.com.tw
Electric Power Generation & Transmission Services
S.I.C.: 4911
N.A.I.C.S.: 221113

Alstom Transport Regional Trains (1)
Hoole Bridge Hoole Road
Chester, CH2 3DJ, United Kingdom
Tel.: (44) 1244 605873
Fax: (44) 1244 605876
Emp.: 90
Train Repair & Maintenance Services
S.I.C.: 4789
N.A.I.C.S.: 488210
Angelo Cuffaro *(Mng Dir)*

Alstom Vannkraft AS (1)
Drammensveien 165
277 Oslo, Norway
Tel.: (47) 22 12 70 00
Fax: (47) 22 12 70 01
E-Mail: mail.norway@power.alstom.com
Hydroelectric Power Generation Services
S.I.C.: 4931
N.A.I.C.S.: 221111
Fredrik Forsberg *(Mng Dir)*

Alstom Vietnam Ltd. (1)
2001 Capital Tower 109 Tran Hung Dao St
Hoan Kiem, Hanoi, Vietnam
Tel.: (84) 438243053
Fax: (84) 438247450
Emp.: 2
Electric Power Generation & Transmission Services
S.I.C.: 4931
N.A.I.C.S.: 221118
Hoang Ngoc Tuan *(Gen Dir)*

Nihon Kengyo K.K. (1)
2-3 Shindenasahimachi
Daito, Osaka, 574-0053, Japan
Tel.: (81) 728721581
Electric Power Generation Services
S.I.C.: 4911
N.A.I.C.S.: 221118

Non-U.S. Joint Venture:

CASCO Signal Ltd. (1)
27 Floor Room C D Triumphal Arch Building
No 428 Tian Mu Zhong Road, Shanghai, 200070, China CN
Tel.: (86) 163543654
Fax: (86) 163542837
E-Mail: mkting@casco.com.cn
Web Site: www.casco.com.cn
Emp.: 100
Supplies Complete Signaling Systems, Communications Equipment, Project Design, Engineering & Consulting Services for Railroad & Transit Authorities: Joint Venture of Casco Signal Ltd (50%) & Alstom Signalling Inc (50%)
S.I.C.: 8711
N.A.I.C.S.: 541330

Non-U.S. Units:

Alstom S.A. - Agua Branca Unit (1)
Virgil Wey 150
05036 050 Sao Paulo, Brazil
Tel.: (55) 11 3491 7000
Emp.: 271
Electric Parts Mfr
S.I.C.: 3699
N.A.I.C.S.: 335999

Alstom S.A. - Itajuba Unit (1)
Av N Senhora da Piedade 1021
37504-358 Itajuba, Minas Gerais, Brazil
Tel.: (55) 35 36297000
Web Site: www.alstom.com
Emp.: 495
Switchgear & Electric Transformer Mfr
S.I.C.: 3613
N.A.I.C.S.: 335313

Alstom S.A. - Lapa Unit (1)
Av Raimundo Pereira De Magalhaes 230
05092 040 Sao Paulo, Brazil
Tel.: (55) 1136432000
Fax: (55) 1136432280
Web Site: www.alstom.com
Emp.: 100
Rolling Stock Mfr
S.I.C.: 3743
N.A.I.C.S.: 336510

ALSTON ENERGY INC.

Suite 1100 744 4th Avenue Southwest
Calgary, AB, T2P 3T4, Canada
Tel.: (403) 265-2770
Fax: (403) 265-2775
E-Mail: don.umbach@alstonenergy.ca
Web Site: alstonenergy.ca
Year Founded: 2004
ALO—(TSXV)
Sales Range: $1-9.9 Million

Business Description:
Oil & Gas Exploration Services
S.I.C.: 1389
N.A.I.C.S.: 213112

Personnel:
Dennis Nerland *(Chm)*
Don K. Umbach *(Pres & CEO)*
Neil Burrows *(CFO & VP-Fin)*
Bruce Eckert *(COO & VP-Ops)*

Board of Directors:
Dennis Nerland
Wayne J. Babcock
Jack P. Donhuysen
Bruce Eckert
Don K. Umbach

ALSTRIA OFFICE REIT-AG

Backerbreitergang 75
20355 Hamburg, Germany
Tel.: (49) 40226341300
Fax: (49) 40226341310
E-Mail: info@alstria.de
Web Site: www.alstria.de
Year Founded: 2006
AOX—(DEU)
Rev.: $136,348,175
Assets: $2,405,461,750
Liabilities: $1,289,100,469
Net Worth: $1,116,361,281
Earnings: $53,726,991
Emp.: 59
Fiscal Year-end: 12/31/12

Business Description:
Real Estate Investment Services
S.I.C.: 6726
N.A.I.C.S.: 525990

Personnel:
Alexander Stuhlmann *(Chm-Supervisory Bd)*
Johannes Conradi *(Vice Chm-Supervisory Bd)*
Olivier Elamaine *(CEO & MemberMgmt Bd)*
Alexander Dexne *(CFO & Member-Mgmt Bd)*

Supervisory Board of Directors:
Alexander Stuhlmann
Johannes Conradi
Benoit Herault
Roger Lee
Richard Mully
Marianne Voigt

ALSUWAIKET TRADING & CONTRACTING CO.

PO Box 31800
Al Khobar, 31952, Saudi Arabia
Tel.: (966) 38580509
Fax: (966) 38591563
E-Mail: info@albabtrading.com
Web Site: www.alsuwaiket.com
Sales Range: $900-999.9 Million
Emp.: 750

Business Description:
Holding Company; Oil & Gas, Industrial, Travel, Trading, Agricultural & Catering Services
S.I.C.: 7389
N.A.I.C.S.: 425120

Personnel:
Mobarak A. AlSuwaiket *(Chm & Pres)*

Divisions:

AlSuwaiket Agriculture Division (1)
PO Box 691
Dhahran, 31932, Saudi Arabia
Tel.: (966) 501422680
Fax: (966) 50 310 2971
E-Mail: agriculture@alsuwaiket.com
Web Site: www.alsuwaiket.com
Agricultural Services
S.I.C.: 0139
N.A.I.C.S.: 111998

AlSuwaiket Trading & Contracting Co.—(Continued)

Mobarak A. AlSuwaiket *(Chm)*

AlSuwaiket Education Division (1)
PO Box 691
Dhahran, 31932, Saudi Arabia
Tel.: (966) 38575603
Fax: (966) 38570076
E-Mail: education@alsuwaiket.com
Web Site: www.alsuwaiket.com
Education Services
S.I.C.: 9411
N.A.I.C.S.: 923110
Mobarak A. AlSuwaiket *(Chm)*

AlSuwaiket Furniture & Home Furnishing Division (1)
PO Box 654
Dhahran, 31932, Saudi Arabia
Tel.: (966) 38592170
Fax: (966) 38592427
E-Mail: furnishings@alsuwaiket.com
Emp.: 100
Home Furnishings
S.I.C.: 5023
N.A.I.C.S.: 423220
Mobarak A. AlSuwaiket *(Chm)*

AlSuwaiket Travel & Tourism Division (1)
PO Box 654
Dhahran, 31932, Saudi Arabia
Tel.: (966) 38944100
Fax: (966) 38941615
E-Mail: info@travellers-sa.com
Web Site: www.travellers-sa.com
Emp.: 55
Travel & Tourism Services
S.I.C.: 4724
N.A.I.C.S.: 561510
Mobarak A. AlSuwaiket *(Chm)*

ALTA COMPANY

Lot II-3 Group 2 11th Street Tan Binh Industrial Park Tay Thanh Ward
Tan Phu District, Ho Chi Minh City, Vietnam
Tel.: (84) 8 38162884
Fax: (84) 8 38162887
E-Mail: alta@alta.com.vn
Web Site: www.alta.com.vn
Year Founded: 1989
ALT—(HNX)

Business Description:
Printing & Packaging Products Mfr & Distr
S.I.C.: 2671
N.A.I.C.S.: 326112

Personnel:
Hoang Van Dieu *(Chm & Gen Mgr)*

ALTA-FAB STRUCTURES LTD.

(Formerly 347678 ALBERTA LTD)
504-13 Avenue
Nisku, AB, T9E 7P6, Canada
Tel.: (780) 955-7733
Fax: (780) 955-7851
Toll Free: (800) 252-7990
Web Site: www.altafab.com
Year Founded: 1973
Rev.: $46,167,768
Emp.: 300

Business Description:
Modular Buildings Mfr
S.I.C.: 3448
N.A.I.C.S.: 332311

Personnel:
Hank Van Weelden *(VP-Sls & Mktg)*

ALTA-FAB STRUCTURES LTD.

504 13 Avenue
Nisku, AB, T9E 7P6, Canada
Tel.: (780) 955-7733
Fax: (780) 955-7851
Toll Free: (800) 252-7990
Web Site: www.altafab.com
Year Founded: 1973
Rev.: $17,555,630
Emp.: 150

Business Description:
Modular Buildings Mfr
S.I.C.: 2452
N.A.I.C.S.: 321992

Personnel:
Hank Van Weelden *(VP-Sls & Mktg)*

ALTA FLIGHTS (CHARTERS) INC.

3767 56 Avenue East Edmonton International Airport
Edmonton, AB, T5J 2T2, Canada
Tel.: (780) 890-1333
Fax: (780) 890-1310
Toll Free: (800) 668-4766
Web Site: www.altaflights.com
Year Founded: 1986
Rev.: $20,861,440
Emp.: 40

Business Description:
Air Transportation Services
S.I.C.: 4522
N.A.I.C.S.: 481212

Personnel:
Bob Lamoureux *(Pres)*

ALTA NATURAL HERBS & SUPPLEMENTS LTD.

115 21600 Westminster Hwy
Richmond, BC, Canada
Tel.: (778) 859-1936
Fax: (604) 247-0892
E-Mail: info@altanatural.ca
Web Site: www.altanatural.ca
Year Founded: 1996
AHS—(TSXV)
Sls.: $599,502
Assets: $830,550
Liabilities: $71,643
Net Worth: $758,907
Earnings: ($87,439)
Fiscal Year-end: 10/31/12

Business Description:
Natural Health Products Mfr
S.I.C.: 2834
N.A.I.C.S.: 325412

Personnel:
Jianfang Jin *(Pres & CEO)*
Haofang Song *(CFO)*

Board of Directors:
Yi-Fang Cheng
Jianfang Jin
Haofang Song
William Xiong

ALTAGAS LTD.

1700 355 4th Ave SW
Calgary, AB, T2P 0J1, Canada
Tel.: (403) 691-7575
Fax: (403) 691-7576
Toll Free: (888) 890-2715
E-Mail: feedback@altagas.ca
Web Site: www.altagas.ca
Year Founded: 1994
ALA—(OTC TSX)
Rev.: $1,441,587,445
Assets: $5,876,586,599
Liabilities: $3,888,748,385
Net Worth: $1,987,838,214
Earnings: $119,538,857
Emp.: 1,542
Fiscal Year-end: 12/31/12

Business Description:
Natural Gas Facilities & Services
S.I.C.: 4924
N.A.I.C.S.: 221210

Personnel:
David W. Cornhill *(Chm & CEO)*
Deborah S. Stein *(CFO & Sr VP-Fin)*
David Harris *(Pres-Gas & Power)*
Dennis A. Dawson *(Gen Counsel, Sec & VP)*
Massimiliano Fantuz *(Exec VP)*
John Lowe *(Exec VP-Corp Dev)*
David Wright *(Exec VP)*

Board of Directors:
David W. Cornhill
Catherine M. Best
Allan L. Edgeworth
Hugh A. Fergusson
Daryl Harvey Gilbert
Robert Bruce Hodgins
Myron F. Kanik
David French Mackie
M. Neil McCrank

Transfer Agent:
Computershare Trust Company of Canada
Ste 600 530 8th Ave SW
Calgary, AB, Canada T2P 3S8
Tel.: (800) 558-0046

Subsidiaries:

AltaGas General Partner Inc. (1)
355 4th Avenue SW Suite 1700
Calgary, AB, T2P 0J1, Canada (100%)
Tel.: (403) 691-7575
Fax: (403) 691-7576
Web Site: www.altagas.ca
Emp.: 300
Crude Petroleum & Natural Gas Extraction
S.I.C.: 1311
N.A.I.C.S.: 211111
David W. Cornhill *(Chm & CEO)*

AltaGas Operating Partnership (1)
355 4th Avenue Southwest Suite 1700
Calgary, AB, T2P 0J1, Canada (100%)
Tel.: (403) 691-7575
Fax: (403) 691-7576
Web Site: www.atlagas.com
Emp.: 250
Crude Petroleum & Natural Gas Extraction
S.I.C.: 1311
N.A.I.C.S.: 211111
David W. Cornhill *(Chm & CEO)*

AltaGas Utilities, Inc. (1)
5509 45th St
Leduc, AB, T9E 6T6, Canada (100%)
Tel.: (780) 986-5215
Fax: (780) 986-5220
E-Mail: altagasutilities@agutl.com
Web Site: www.altagasutilities.com
Sales Range: $75-99.9 Million
Emp.: 220
Transmission of Natural Gas
S.I.C.: 4923
N.A.I.C.S.: 486210
Patricia M. Newson *(Pres)*

AltaGas (1)
382 Wellington Street West Ste 201
Chatham, ON, N7M 1K4, Canada (100%)
Tel.: (519) 436-1420
Fax: (519) 436-1574
E-Mail: info@altagas.com
Web Site: www.altagas.com
Emp.: 25
Natural Gas Distribution
S.I.C.: 4924
N.A.I.C.S.: 221210

ECNG Energy Limited Partnership (1)
Ste 1700 355 4th Ave SW
Calgary, AB, T2P 0J1, Canada (100%)
Tel.: (403) 691-7575
Fax: (403) 691-7576
E-Mail: feedback@altagas.ca
Web Site: www.ecng.com
Emp.: 600
Crude Petroleum & Natural Gas Extraction
S.I.C.: 1311
N.A.I.C.S.: 211111
David Cornhill *(Chm & CEO)*
Bill Swan *(Pres)*

Pacific Northern Gas Ltd. (1)
Suite 950 1185 West Georgia Street
Vancouver, BC, V6E 4E6, Canada BC
Tel.: (604) 691-5680
Fax: (604) 697-6210
E-Mail: investors@png.ca
Web Site: www.png.ca
Sales Range: $75-99.9 Million
Emp.: 102
Natural Gas Transmission, Distr & Retail Sales
S.I.C.: 4924
N.A.I.C.S.: 221210
Greg B. Weeres *(Pres)*
Kevin R. Teitge *(Treas & VP-Corp Dev)*
K.E. Stark-Anderson *(Sec)*

Taylor NGL LP (1)
Ste 1700 355-4th Avenue SW
Calgary, AB, T2P 0J1, Canada
Tel.: (403) 691-7575
Fax: (403) 691-7576
E-Mail: info@taylorngl.com
Web Site: www.taylorngl.com
Sales Range: $200-249.9 Million
Emp.: 14
Natural Gas Liquids Extraction Services
S.I.C.: 1321
N.A.I.C.S.: 211112

Subsidiaries:

Taylor Gas Liquids Limited Partnership (2)
800 5th Ave SW Suite 2200
Calgary, AB, Canada
Tel.: (403) 781-8181
Fax: (403) 777-1907
Natural Gas Liquid Extraction
S.I.C.: 1321
N.A.I.C.S.: 211112
Robert Pritchard *(Mng Dir)*

Taylor Gas Processing Limited Partnership (2)
800 5th Ave SW Suite 2200
Calgary, AB, Canada
Tel.: (403) 781-8181
Fax: (403) 777-1907
E-Mail: info@taylorngl.com
Emp.: 18
Natural Gas Liquid Extraction
S.I.C.: 1321
N.A.I.C.S.: 211112
Robert Pritchard *(Mng Dir)*

Taylor Processing Inc. (2)
800 5th Ave SW Suite 2200
Calgary, AB, Canada
Tel.: (403) 781-8181
Fax: (403) 777-1907
E-Mail: info@taylorngl.com
Emp.: 18
Oil & Gas Field Machinery & Equipment Mfr
S.I.C.: 1321
N.A.I.C.S.: 211112
Robert Pritchard *(Mng Dir)*

U.S. Subsidiaries:

Blythe Energy, LLC (1)
301 Hobsonway
Blythe, CA 92225
Tel.: (760) 922-2957
Sales Range: $10-24.9 Million
Emp.: 15
Electric Power Generation
S.I.C.: 4939
N.A.I.C.S.: 221118
Paul Thessen *(Pres)*

SEMCO Energy, Inc. (1)
1411 Third Ave Ste A
Port Huron, MI 48060 MI
Tel.: (810) 987-2200
Toll Free: (866) 473-6261
E-Mail: webmaster@semcoenergy.com
Web Site: www.semcoenergy.com
Sales Range: $600-649.9 Million
Emp.: 570
Natural Gas Distribution
S.I.C.: 4924
N.A.I.C.S.: 221210
James C. Larsen *(Pres)*

Subsidiaries:

ENSTAR Natural Gas Company (2)
3000 Spenard Rd
Anchorage, AK 99503-3606
Mailing Address:
PO Box 190288
Anchorage, AK 99519-0288
Tel.: (907) 277-5551
E-Mail: info@enstarnaturalgas.com
Web Site: www.enstarnaturalgas.com
Emp.: 150
Natural Gas Distribution
S.I.C.: 4924
N.A.I.C.S.: 221210
Daniel M. Dieckgraeff *(Mgr-Fin)*

SEMCO Energy Ventures, Inc. (2)
PO Box 5004
Port Huron, MI 48060 MI

Tel.: (810) 987-2200
Energy Investment Activities
S.I.C.: 6211
N.A.I.C.S.: 523999
James C. Larsen *(Pres)*

ALTAI RESOURCES INC.
2550 Victoria Park Avenue Suite 738
Toronto, ON, M2J 5A9, Canada
Tel.: (416) 383-1328
Fax: (416) 383-1686
E-Mail: info@altairesources.com
Web Site: www.altairesources.com
Year Founded: 1955
ATI—(TSXV)
Rev.: $237,629
Assets: $22,772,165
Liabilities: $200,107
Net Worth: $22,572,058
Earnings: ($56,891)
Fiscal Year-end: 12/31/12
Business Description:
Mineral Exploration
S.I.C.: 1481
N.A.I.C.S.: 213115
Personnel:
Niyazi Kacira *(Chm & Pres)*
Maria Au *(Treas & Sec)*
Board of Directors:
Niyazi Kacira
Jeffrey S. Ackert
Didier Pomerleau
Raymond Savoie
Mehmet F. Taner

ALTAIR GOLD INC.
World Trade Center Suite 404
999 Canada Place, Vancouver, BC, V6C 3E2, Canada
Tel.: (604) 641-1305
Fax: (604) 688-8309
E-Mail: info@altairgold.com
Web Site: www.altairgold.com
Year Founded: 2005
AVX—(TSXV)
Assets: $2,386,078
Liabilities: $106,708
Net Worth: $2,279,370
Earnings: ($880,479)
Fiscal Year-end: 03/31/13
Business Description:
Mineral Exploration Services
S.I.C.: 1081
N.A.I.C.S.: 213114
Personnel:
Robert A. Archer *(Chm)*
Fayyaz Alimohamed *(Pres & CEO)*
Tony M. Ricci *(CFO & Sec)*
Board of Directors:
Robert A. Archer
Fayyaz Alimohamed
Shehzad Bharmal
Legal Counsel:
Bull, Housser & Tupper LLP
Suite 3000 1055 West Georgia Street
Vancouver, BC, Canada
Transfer Agent:
Computershare Investor Services Inc.
3rd Floor 510 Burrard St
V6C 3B9 Vancouver, BC, Canada

ALTAIR SEMICONDUCTOR LTD.
6 Haharash Street
PO Box 7158
Hod Hasharon, 45240, Israel
Tel.: (972) 74 7800800
Fax: (972) 9 7403049
Web Site: www.altair-semi.com
Emp.: 150
Business Description:
Semiconductor Mfr
S.I.C.: 3674
N.A.I.C.S.: 334413
Personnel:
Oded Melamed *(Co-Founder & CEO)*
Yigal Bitran *(Co-Founder & CTO)*
Eran Eshed *(Co-Founder & VP-Mktg)*
Guy Nathanzon *(CFO)*

ALTAIR VENTURES INCORPORATED
(See Under Altair Gold Inc.)

ALTAMIR AMBOISE S.C.A.
(Name Changed to Altamir S.C.A.)

ALTAMIR S.C.A.
(Formerly Altamir Amboise S.C.A.)
45 avenue Kleber
75784 Paris, Cedex 16, France
Tel.: (33) 153650100
Fax: (33) 153650106
E-Mail: altamir-amboise@apax.fr
Web Site: www.altamir-amboise.fr
LTA—(EUR)
Rev.: $114,397,527
Assets: $701,623,804
Liabilities: $39,712,015
Net Worth: $661,911,789
Earnings: $76,804,383
Emp.: 50
Fiscal Year-end: 12/31/12
Business Description:
Private Equity Firm
S.I.C.: 6211
N.A.I.C.S.: 523999
Personnel:
Maurice Tchenio *(Chm)*
Joel Seche *(Chm-Supervisory Bd)*
Monique Cohen *(Deputy CEO)*
Supervisory Board of Directors:
Joel Seche
Jean Besson
Gerard Hascoet
Charles Hochman
Sophie Javary
Jean-Hugues Loyez
Philippe Santini

ALTAN NEVADA MINERALS LIMITED
800 1199 West Hastings St
Vancouver, BC, V6E 3T5, Canada
Tel.: (604) 495-8374
E-Mail: ej@altnev.com
Web Site: www.altnev.com
Year Founded: 2008
ANE—(TSXV)
Rev.: $30,834
Assets: $6,917,387
Liabilities: $188,635
Net Worth: $6,728,752
Earnings: ($985,232)
Fiscal Year-end: 12/31/12
Business Description:
Gold Exploration Services
S.I.C.: 1041
N.A.I.C.S.: 212221
Personnel:
John L. C. Jones *(Chm)*
Evan Jones *(Pres & CEO)*
Board of Directors:
John L. C. Jones
Evan Jones
Aidan Nania
Murray Seitz
Brion Theriault
Legal Counsel:
Venex Law
700-595 Howe Street
Vancouver, BC, V6C 2T5, Canada
Transfer Agent:
Computershare Investor Services
3rd Floor, 510 Burrard Street
Vancouver, BC, Canada

ALTAN RIO MINERALS LIMITED
Ste 1110-1111 W Georgia St
Vancouver, BC, V6E 4M3, Canada
Tel.: (604) 639-5899
E-Mail: info@altanrio.com
Web Site: www.altanrio.com
Year Founded: 2010
AMOP—(TSXV)
Rev.: $1,403
Assets: $9,256,530
Liabilities: $607,476
Net Worth: $8,649,054
Earnings: ($1,452,783)
Fiscal Year-end: 12/31/12
Business Description:
Investment Services
S.I.C.: 6211
N.A.I.C.S.: 523999
Personnel:
John L. C. Jones *(Chm)*
Evan Jones *(Pres & CEO)*
Board of Directors:
John L. C. Jones
J. Kelly Cluer
Evan Jones
Paul O'Brien
Murray Seitz
Legal Counsel:
Venex Law
700-595 Howe Street
Vancouver, BC, V6C 2T5, Canada
Transfer Agent:
Equity Financial Trust Company
1185 West Georgia Street Suite 1620
Vancouver, BC, Canada

ALTAPEX CORPORATION
1741 Blvd Edouard Laurin
Saint Laurent, QC, H4L 5E9, Canada
Tel.: (514) 937-1700
Fax: (514) 937-5682
E-Mail: altapex@altapex.com
Web Site: www.altapex.com
Year Founded: 1992
Rev.: $12,010,500
Emp.: 12
Business Description:
Construction Services
S.I.C.: 1542
N.A.I.C.S.: 236220
Personnel:
Leonardo Soares *(Founder, Pres & CEO)*

ALTAREA SCA
8 avenue Delcasse
75008 Paris, France
Tel.: (33) 156262400
Fax: (33) 144958818
E-Mail: info@altarea.com
Web Site: www.altareacogedim.com
ALTA—(EUR)
Rev.: $215,925,668
Assets: $6,894,813,506
Liabilities: $5,061,329,966
Net Worth: $1,833,483,540
Earnings: $81,039,434
Emp.: 1,232
Fiscal Year-end: 12/31/12
Business Description:
Commercial & Residential Real Estate Investment Services
S.I.C.: 6726
N.A.I.C.S.: 525990
Personnel:
Alain Taravella *(Founder, Chm & CEO)*
Manuel Colleaux *(Co-Chm-Cogedim)*
Philippe Ulivieri *(Co-Chm-Cogedim)*
Jacques Nicolet *(Chm-Supervisory Bd)*
Alain Jodar *(Deputy CEO-Portfolio-France)*
Frederic Laloum *(Deputy CEO-Leasing-France)*
Eric Dumas *(CFO)*
Albert Malaquin *(Chm/CEO-Rue du Commerce & Mng Dir-Altarea Commerce)*
Christophe Bacque *(Chm-Cogedim Residence & Mng Dir-Cogedim)*
Christian Musset *(Chm-Cogedim Vente)*
Fabrice Allouche *(CEO-Cogedim Enterprise Dev)*
Jean-Frederic Heinry *(CEO-Cogedim Entreprise-Promotion)*
Philippe Mauro *(Gen Sec)*
Gilles Boissonnet *(Sr Exec VP-Retail Property-France)*
Christian de Gournay *(Sr Exec VP-Residential Property & Institutional Rels)*
Stephane Theuriau *(Sr Exec VP-Office Property & Private Equity)*
Supervisory Board of Directors:
Jacques Nicolet
Altarea Commerce
Alain Dassas
Francoise Debrus
Olivier Dubreuil
Olivier Esteve
Christophe Kullmann
Alta Patrimoine
Dominique Rongier
Emeric Servin
Gautier Taravella
Matthieu Taravella

A.A.C.E. Ile de France
10 rue de Florence
Paris, France

Subsidiaries:

Alta CRP Aubergenville SNC (1)
Rte Quarante Sous
78410 Aubergenville, Yvelines, France
Tel.: (33) 139297240
Fax: (33) 0139297241
Emp.: 2
Real Estate Management Services
S.I.C.: 6531
N.A.I.C.S.: 531210

Altarea COGEDIM Citalis (1)
8 Avenue Delcasse
Paris, 75008, France
Tel.: (33) 153892120
Real Estate Management Services
S.I.C.: 6531
N.A.I.C.S.: 531210

ALTAREA France SAS (1)
8 Deltassa Avenue
75008 Paris, France
Tel.: (33) 144958810
Fax: (33) 144958818
Web Site: www.altarea.com
Emp.: 400
Real Estate Management Services
S.I.C.: 6531
N.A.I.C.S.: 531210
Dominique Goudard *(Deputy CEO-Dev)*
Alain Jodar *(Deputy CEO-Portfolio)*
Frederic Laloum *(Deputy CEO-Mktg)*
Laurent Campredon *(Pres-Legal)*

COGEDIM Midi-Pyrenees (1)
46 Boulevard De Strasbourg
Toulouse, Haute-Garonne, 31000, France
Tel.: (33) 534414900
Fax: (33) 534411043
E-Mail: infotoulouse@cogedim.com.fr
Emp.: 30
Real Estate Management Services
S.I.C.: 6531
N.A.I.C.S.: 531210
Christophe Brochet *(Mng Dir)*

COGEDIM Savoies-Leman SNC (1)
Parc de la Bouvarde Allee du Parmelan
74 370 Metz-Tessy, Haute-Savoie, France
Tel.: (33) 450058060
Fax: (33) 450052249
E-Mail: infoannecy@cogedim.com
Web Site: www.altarea-cogedim.com
Emp.: 20

Altarea SCA—(Continued)

Real Estate Management Services
S.I.C.: 6531
N.A.I.C.S.: 531210
Laborde Thomas *(Mng Dir)*

Rue du Commerce SA (1)
44/50 avenue du Capitaine Glarner
93400 Saint-Ouen, France FR
Tel.: (33) 1 4166 1800 (96.5%)
Fax: (33) 1 4166 1803
E-Mail: investisseurs@rueducommerce.com
Web Site: www.rueducommerce.com
RDC—(EUR)
Sales Range: $400-449.9 Million
Emp.: 370
E-Commerce Services
S.I.C.: 5961
N.A.I.C.S.: 454111
Albert Malaquin *(Chm)*
Alexandre de Lamarzelle *(Dir Gen)*

Salle Wagram (1)
5 Bis rue de Montenotte
75017 Paris, France
Tel.: (33) 155378686
Fax: (33) 1 43 80 96 95
E-Mail: contact@sallewagram.com
Web Site: www.sallewagram.com
Event Management Services
S.I.C.: 7999
N.A.I.C.S.: 711310

SCCV Clef de Sol (1)
Zone Scolaire Groupe Malbosc Avenue De Fes
Montpellier, Herault, 34080, France
Tel.: (33) 467412790
Fax: (33) 467412790
Real Estate Management Services
S.I.C.: 6531
N.A.I.C.S.: 531210

SNC COGEDIM Atlantique (1)
1 rue de Suffren
44000 Nantes, Loire-Atlantique, France
Tel.: (33) 251860020
Fax: (33) 251860321
E-Mail: infonantes@cogedim.com
Web Site: www.cogedim.ff
Emp.: 15
Real Estate Management Services
S.I.C.: 6531
N.A.I.C.S.: 531210
Gerone Beimzoas *(Gen Mgr)*

SNC COGEDIM Grand Lyon (1)
235 cours Lafayette
69451 Lyon, Rhone, France
Tel.: (33) 4 72 75 40 80
Fax: (33) 4 72 75 40 99
E-Mail: infolyon@cogedim.com
Web Site: www.altarea-cogedim.com
Emp.: 50
Real Estate Investment Trust
S.I.C.: 6726
N.A.I.C.S.: 525990
Zirginia Bernoux *(Mng Dir)*

SNC COGEDIM Grenoble (1)
56 Vdjanbegta
38300 Grenoble, France
Tel.: (33) 476896989
Fax: (33) 476896980
E-Mail: infogrenoble@cogedim.com
Emp.: 15
Real Estate Management Services
S.I.C.: 6531
N.A.I.C.S.: 531210

SNC COGEDIM Mediterranee (1)
400 promenade des Anglais
06200 Nice, Alpes-Maritimes, France
Tel.: (33) 492478000
Fax: (33) 492478019
E-Mail: cogedimmediterranee@cogedim.com
Web Site: www.cogedim-logement.com
Emp.: 50
Real Estate Property Development Services
S.I.C.: 6531
N.A.I.C.S.: 531210
Hugues Duroussy *(Co-Pres)*
Jean-Marie Ebel *(Co-Pres)*

SNC COGEDIM Provence (1)
26 rue Grignan
13001 Marseille, Bouches-du-Rhone, France
Tel.: (33) 496176320
Fax: (33) 496176321
E-Mail: infomarseille@cogedim.com
Emp.: 25
Real Estate Management Services
S.I.C.: 6531
N.A.I.C.S.: 531210
Dominique Gougard *(Mgr)*

SNC COGEDIM Vente (1)
8 Avenue Delcasse
75008 Paris, France
Tel.: (33) 1 60 79 86 70
Real Estate Management Services
S.I.C.: 6531
N.A.I.C.S.: 531210
Christian Musset *(Chm)*

SNC Toulouse Bertillon (1)
46 Boulevard de Strasbourg
31000 Toulouse, Haute-Garonne, France
Tel.: (33) 534414900
Fax: (33) 5 34 41 49 47
Emp.: 28
Real Estate Management Services
S.I.C.: 6531
N.A.I.C.S.: 531210
Brochet Christopha *(Dir Gen)*

Non-U.S. Subsidiaries:

Alta Spain Castellana B.V. (1)
Rokin 55
1012 KK Amsterdam, North Holland, Netherlands
Tel.: (31) 205214777
Real Estate Management Services
S.I.C.: 6531
N.A.I.C.S.: 531210

ALTAREA Espana SL (1)
Calle Orense ed Lexington 85
Madrid, 28020, Spain
Tel.: (34) 913822101
Fax: (34) 915678400
Web Site: www.Altareacogedim.com
Emp.: 5
Real Estate Management Services
S.I.C.: 6531
N.A.I.C.S.: 531210
Asun Sanchez *(Mgr-Mktg)*

ALTAREA Italia s.r.l. (1)
Via Crocefisso 27
20122 Milan, Italy
Tel.: (39) 243331426
Fax: (39) 0243331420
E-Mail: rossi.c@altarea.com
Emp.: 40
Real Estate Management Services
S.I.C.: 6531
N.A.I.C.S.: 531210
Ludovic Castillo *(Pres)*

ALTAVIA

10 Rue Blanqui
93400 Saint-Ouen, France
Tel.: (33) 149480000
Web Site: www.altavia-paris.com
Rev.: $13,700,000
Emp.: 55

Business Description:
Marketing & Publishing Services
S.I.C.: 8742
N.A.I.C.S.: 541613

Personnel:
Raphael Palti *(Chm & Pres)*

Board of Directors:
Raphael Palti
Gilles Maurisset

Subsidiary:

Altavia Victor (1)
Les Hauts De Coueron Rue Des Forgerons
44220 Coueron, Loire Atlantique, France
Tel.: (33) 251802828
Fax: (33) 25180032
Rev.: $31,300,000
Emp.: 80
Marketing & Publishing Services
S.I.C.: 8742
N.A.I.C.S.: 541613
Nicola Gentile *(Gen Mgr)*

ALTAWEST GROUP

11 Rue de Fontenay
92340 Bourg-la-Reine, France
Tel.: (33) 140848834
Fax: (33) 140849202
E-Mail: contact@altawest.net
Web Site: www.altawest.net
Year Founded: 2005
Sales Range: $150-199.9 Billion
Emp.: 700

Business Description:
OEM & Energy, Environmental, Process Industries Service Solutions
S.I.C.: 3612
N.A.I.C.S.: 335311

Personnel:
Philippe Garelli *(Pres)*

Subsidiaries:

Jeumont Electric (1)
367 rue de l'Industrie
PO Box 20109
59572 Jeumont, France FR
Tel.: (33) 3 61 99 96 00
Fax: (33) 3 61 99 97 33
E-Mail: jeumont.contact@jeumontelectric.com
Web Site: www.jeumontelectric.com
Emp.: 450
Designs, Maintains & Mfr Synchronous & Asynchronous Machines for the Energy Generation, Oil, Gas, Industry & Marine Markets.
S.I.C.: 3559
N.A.I.C.S.: 333249

Subsidiary:

Sarelem (2)
5 Rue Du Chateau De Bel Air
PO Box 80203
44472 Carquefou, France (100%)
Mailing Address:
BP 203
44472 Carquefou, France
Tel.: (33) 240251355
Telex: SARELEM 330300 F
Fax: (33) 240251356
E-Mail: bernard.chaillou@sarelem.fr
Web Site: www.sarelem.fr
Emp.: 100
Renovator of Electrical Equipment
S.I.C.: 3699
N.A.I.C.S.: 335999

ALTE LEIPZIGER VERSICHERUNG AG

Alte Leipziger Platz 1
D 61440 Oberursel, Taunus, Germany
Tel.: (49) 61716600
Fax: (49) 6171664311
Web Site: www.al-h.de
Year Founded: 1819
Emp.: 1,700

Business Description:
Fire, Comprehensive Personal Property, Homeowners, Transportation, Automobile (Comprehensive, Accident & Liability), General Accident, General Liability & Technical Insurance for Business & Industry
S.I.C.: 6399
N.A.I.C.S.: 524128

Personnel:
Gesa Adolphs *(Mgr-PR)*

Subsidiaries:

Alte Leipziger Rueckversicherung AG (1)
Alte Leipziger Platz 1
61440 Oberursel, Taunus, Germany (50%)
Tel.: (49) 61 71 66 6967
Fax: (49) 61 71 66 3939
E-Mail: presse@alte-leipziger.de
Web Site: www.alte-leipziger.de
Emp.: 1,800
Reinsurance Services
S.I.C.: 6399
N.A.I.C.S.: 524130

Rechtsschutz Union Versicherungs AG (1)
Sonnenstrasse 33
80331 Munich, Germany (25.01%)
Tel.: (49) 8954853605
Fax: (49) 8954853610
E-Mail: kundendiemst@ru.de
Web Site: www.rechtsschutzunion.de
Insurance
S.I.C.: 6399
N.A.I.C.S.: 524128
Wald Schmidt *(Dir)*

Alte Leipziger Autoversicherung (1)
Alte Leipziger Platz 1
61440 Oberursel, Taunus, Germany (100%)
Tel.: (49) 6171662030
Fax: (49) 6171663611
E-Mail: hehlm@alte-leipziger.de
Web Site: www.alte-leipziger.com
Emp.: 1,200
Automobile Insurance
S.I.C.: 6399
N.A.I.C.S.: 524128
Walter Botermann *(Gen Mgr)*

ALTECH CO., LTD.

Sumitomo Irifune Bldg 2F 1-1 Irifune 2-chome
Chuo-ku, Tokyo, 104-0042, Japan
Tel.: (81) 355426760
Fax: (81) 355426767
E-Mail: information@altech.co.jp
Web Site: www.altech.co.jp
Year Founded: 1976
9972—(TKS)
Sls.: $189,571,778
Assets: $172,774,503
Liabilities: $75,511,898
Net Worth: $97,262,605
Earnings: $290,620
Emp.: 532
Fiscal Year-end: 11/30/12

Business Description:
Industrial Machinery & Equipment Sales
S.I.C.: 5084
N.A.I.C.S.: 423830

Personnel:
Norihiro Chono *(Pres & CEO)*
Kenichi Takigawa *(Mng Dir & Sr Mng Exec Officer)*
Toshishige Ikeya *(Mng Dir)*
Hiroaki Katayama *(Mng Dir)*
Noriyuki Sakaguchi *(Mng Dir)*
Hidehiko Suyama *(Mng Dir)*
Hiroyuki Inoue *(Exec Officer)*

Board of Directors:
Norihiro Chono
Toshishige Ikeya
Hiroaki Katayama
Noriyuki Sakaguchi
Hidehiko Suyama
Kenichi Takigawa

Subsidiaries:

Alpallet Co., Ltd. (1)
68-12 Oguro
Maruoka-cho, Sakai, Fukui, 910-0315, Japan
Tel.: (81) 776681170
Fax: (81) 776681180
Web Site: www.alpallet.co.jp
Emp.: 50
Plastic Products Processing & Mfr & Whslr
S.I.C.: 3086
N.A.I.C.S.: 326150
Isobe Kojiro *(CEO)*

Altech Engineering Co., Ltd. (1)
Sumitomo Fudosan Yotsuya Bldg 1F 13-4 Araki-cho
Shinjuku-ku, Tokyo, 160-0007, Japan
Tel.: (81) 353630864
Fax: (81) 353630867
Web Site: www.altech-engineering.com
Sls.: $6,517,688
Emp.: 45
Industrial Equipment Repair & Maintenance Services
S.I.C.: 7699
N.A.I.C.S.: 811310
Hiroshi Kahata *(Chm)*
Kunihiro Moriwak *(Mng Dir)*
Hiroyuki Inoue *(Mng Dir)*
Hidetoshi Tamura *(Mng Dir)*

Altech IT Inc. (1)
Intec 88 Bldg 8F 20-21 Araki-cho
Shinjuku-ku, Tokyo, 160-0007, Japan
Tel.: (81) 353633007
Fax: (81) 353633008
E-Mail: sales@altech-it.com
Web Site: www.altech-it.com
Emp.: 40
Software Development & Sales
S.I.C.: 7372
N.A.I.C.S.: 511210

Non-U.S. Subsidiary:

Altech IT (Suzhou) Co., Ltd. (2)
5A5 Intl Sci & Tech Park 1355 Jinjihu Ave
Suzhou Indust Park, Suzhou, Jiangsu, 215012, China
Tel.: (86) 512 6262 0305
Fax: (86) 512 6262 0306
Information Processing & Software Development Services
S.I.C.: 7371
N.A.I.C.S.: 541511

Non-U.S. Subsidiaries:

Altech Shanghai Co., Ltd. (1)
3 G Zhaofeng World Trade Bldg
369 Jiangsu Rd, Shanghai, 200050, China
Tel.: (86) 2152400183
Fax: (86) 2152400383
E-Mail: sales@altech.com.cn
Web Site: www.altech-china.com
Emp.: 10
Packing Devices Mfr
S.I.C.: 3053
N.A.I.C.S.: 339991
Inoue Kenji *(Gen Mgr)*

PT. Altech (1)
JL Siliwangi Km 28 Kp Sindangresmi Ds Kutajaya
Kec Cicurug, Sukabumi, 43359, Indonesia
Tel.: (62) 266731888
Fax: (62) 266731887
Web Site: www.altech-china.com
Preforms Mfr & Distr
S.I.C.: 3082
N.A.I.C.S.: 326121
Kimura Nobuyuki *(Mgr)*

ALTECH CORPORATION

Queen's Tower C 18F 2-3-5
Minatomirai
Nishi-ku, Yokohama, Kanagawa, 220-6218, Japan
Tel.: (81) 45 640 3700
Web Site: www.alpsgiken.co.jp
Year Founded: 1968
4641—(TKS)
Emp.: 2,565

Business Description:
Staffing Services
S.I.C.: 7363
N.A.I.C.S.: 561330

Personnel:
Toshio Matsui *(Founder)*
Soichi Ushijima *(Chm & Pres)*
Tadao Ishii *(Mng Dir)*
Tadatoshi Chino *(Corp Officer)*
Atsushi Imamura *(Corp Officer)*
Setsuo Kobayashi *(Corp Officer)*
Minoru Kurihara *(Corp Officer)*
Makoto Makino *(Corp Officer)*
Chikashi Miyasaka *(Corp Officer)*
Hiroshi Oda *(Corp Officer)*
Hiroaki Egoshi *(Exec VP)*

Board of Directors:
Soichi Ushijima
Hiroaki Egoshi
Tadao Ishii
Tetsuji Morikawa
Hiroshi Noda
Masashi Sugai

ALTEK CORPORATION

3F No 10 Li-Hsin Rd Hsinchu
Science-Based Industrial Park
Hsin-chu, Taiwan
Tel.: (886) 35784567
Fax: (886) 35781155
E-Mail: eservice@altek.com.tw
Web Site: www.altek.com.tw
3059—(TAI)
Sales Range: $400-449.9 Million

Business Description:
Digital Camera Mfr
S.I.C.: 3575
N.A.I.C.S.: 334118

Personnel:
Allen Hsu *(Chm)*
Alex Hsia *(Pres & CEO)*

Board of Directors:
Allen Hsu
Sophia Chen
Alex Hsia
James Huang
Kenneth Tai Yen Kai
Jamei Tang
Ching Kuo Ting

U.S. Subsidiary:

Altek Lab Inc. (1)
1411 W 190th St Ste 475
Gardena, CA 90248
Tel.: (310) 225-5688
Photographic Equipment Mfr
S.I.C.: 3579
N.A.I.C.S.: 333316
Qinghua Fu *(Sr Mgr)*

ALTEN S.A.

40 Avenue Andre Morizet
92513 Boulogne-Billancourt, Cedex, France
Tel.: (33) 146087200
Fax: (33) 146087010
E-Mail: comfi@alten.fr
Web Site: www.alten.fr
Year Founded: 1988
ATE—(EUR)
Rev.: $1,612,723,776
Assets: $1,045,116,580
Liabilities: $443,234,550
Net Worth: $601,882,030
Earnings: $103,268,739
Emp.: 15,950
Fiscal Year-end: 12/31/12

Business Description:
Engineering & Technology Consulting Services
S.I.C.: 8711
N.A.I.C.S.: 541330

Personnel:
Simon Azoulay *(Chm & CEO)*
Gerald Attia *(Deputy CEO-Sls, Structured Projects & Intl Zone 2)*
Bruno Benoliel *(Deputy CEO-Fin, Legal & Info Sys)*
Pierre Marcel *(Deputy CEO-France)*
Benoit Maistre *(COO & Head-TCE-Paris)*
Pierre Bonhomme *(Exec VP-France)*
Jean-Francois Guyomar *(Exec VP-NTIS Div-Paris)*
Stephane Ougier *(Exec VP-France)*

Board of Directors:
Simon Azoulay
Gerald Attia
Catherine Behar
Bruno Benoliel
Emily Luna

Subsidiaries:

ALTEN SIR AND TELECOM (1)
130 rue de Silly
92514 Boulogne-Billancourt, France
Tel.: (33) 146087500
Fax: (33) 1 46 08 75 01
E-Mail: communication@alten.fr
Web Site: www.alten.fr
Emp.: 500
Telecommunication Services
S.I.C.: 4899
N.A.I.C.S.: 517919

Alten Sud Ouest SAS (1)
Buroparc 3 Rue de la Decouverte
BP 47533
31675 Labege, France
Tel.: (33) 562882121
Fax: (33) 5 61 73 23 45
Emp.: 300
Engineering Services
S.I.C.: 8711
N.A.I.C.S.: 541330

ANOTECH ENERGY SA (1)
Buroparc III rue de la Decouverte
BP 77536
31675 Labege, France
Tel.: (33) 5 62 19 21 70
Fax: (33) 5 61 73 23 45
E-Mail: rh@anotech.fr
Web Site: www.anotech.fr
Oil & Gas Exploration Services
S.I.C.: 1389
N.A.I.C.S.: 213112

AXEN SARL (1)
2 R Seze
Bordeaux, Gironde, France
Tel.: (33) 556815397
Fax: (33) 5 56 81 87 56
Engineering Services
S.I.C.: 8711
N.A.I.C.S.: 541330

B2I AUTOMOTIVE (1)
1 Rue Galvani Bat C
91300 Massy, France
Tel.: (33) 1 46 84 41 00
Fax: (33) 1 46 08 80 45
Web Site: www.b2i-automotive.com
Emp.: 200
Automotive Engineering Services
S.I.C.: 8711
N.A.I.C.S.: 541330

DIXID (1)
1 rue Ampere
22300 Lannion, France
Tel.: (33) 296484428
Fax: (33) 296486520
E-Mail: contact@dixid.com
Web Site: www.dixid.com
Software Development Services
S.I.C.: 7371
N.A.I.C.S.: 541511
Marcel Pierre *(Gen Mgr)*

ELITYS CONSULTING SARL (1)
115 Boulevard Stalingrad
69100 Villeurbanne, France
Tel.: (33) 4 37 42 13 33
Fax: (33) 4 37 42 13 34
Web Site: www.elitys.fr
Engineering Consultancy Services
S.I.C.: 8711
N.A.I.C.S.: 541330

Extia (1)
1 Avenue de la Cristallerie Bat A 6 Eme Etage
92310 Sevres, France
Tel.: (33) 146999191
Fax: (33) 1 46 99 91 90
E-Mail: contact@extia.fr
Web Site: www.extia.fr
Engineering Consulting Services
S.I.C.: 8711
N.A.I.C.S.: 541330

Non-U.S. Subsidiaries:

Algor, S.L. (1)
Calle Zurbano 8
Madrid, 28010, Spain
Tel.: (34) 913190124
Fax: (34) 913085450
Engineering Services
S.I.C.: 8711
N.A.I.C.S.: 541330

ALTEN GMBH (1)
Rosenauer Strasse 27
96450 Coburg, Germany
Tel.: (49) 9561 5533 0
Fax: (49) 9561 5533 88
E-Mail: contact@de.alten.com
Web Site: www.alten-engineering.com
Emp.: 45
Automotive Engineering Services
S.I.C.: 8711
N.A.I.C.S.: 541330

ALTEN ITALIA SPA (1)
Via Gaetano Crespi 12
Milan, Italy
Tel.: (39) 0236571000
Fax: (39) 0236571090
E-Mail: altenitalia@decinf.it
Web Site: www.alten.it
Business Development Consulting Services
S.I.C.: 7389
N.A.I.C.S.: 561499

ALTEN LTD (1)
The Whitehouse 9A Belvedere Road
South Bank, London, SE1 8AB, United Kingdom
Tel.: (44) 8456585770
Fax: (44) 2074018233
E-Mail: info@alten.co.uk
Web Site: www.alten.co.uk
Emp.: 150
Engineering Consulting Services
S.I.C.: 8711
N.A.I.C.S.: 541330

Alten PCS (1)
Eemnesserweg 26
3741 GA Baarn, Netherlands
Tel.: (31) 356926969
Fax: (31) 356913416
E-Mail: info@pts.nl
Web Site: www.altenpts.nl
Emp.: 170
Software Consulting Services
S.I.C.: 8999
N.A.I.C.S.: 541690
Eric Haesen *(Mng Dir)*

ALTEN SI-TECHNO ROMANIA SRL (1)
Sector 2 73 Bd Dacia
Bucharest, 020062, Romania
Tel.: (40) 213100337
Fax: (40) 213100338
Information Technology Consulting Services
S.I.C.: 7373
N.A.I.C.S.: 541512

BURKE NEWCO S.L. (1)
Paseo Castellana 139-3
Madrid, 28046, Spain
Tel.: (34) 915715550
Fax: (34) 915715602
Engineering Services
S.I.C.: 8711
N.A.I.C.S.: 541330

Electro Mechanical Systems Ltd (1)
Eros House Calleva Park
Aldermaston, Berkshire, RG7 8LN, United Kingdom
Tel.: (44) 118 9817391
Fax: (44) 118 9817613
E-Mail: sales@ems-ltd.com
Web Site: www.ems-limited.co.uk
Precision Motors Mfr & Sales
S.I.C.: 3621
N.A.I.C.S.: 335312

Imp Poland sp. z o.o. (1)
Pilsudskiego 12
50-049 Wroclaw, Poland
Tel.: (48) 713766910
Fax: (48) 713766980
E-Mail: contact@pl.imp-engineering.com
Web Site: www.altens.com
Emp.: 20
Engineering Services
S.I.C.: 8711
N.A.I.C.S.: 541330
Martin Novak *(Gen Mgr)*

ONION S.p.A. (1)
Via L Abbiati n 14
25125 Brescia, Italy
Tel.: (39) 030 3581510
Fax: (39) 030 3581525
Web Site: www.onion.it
Information Technology Consulting Services
S.I.C.: 7373
N.A.I.C.S.: 541512

SD PARTNERS LIMITED (1)
The Whitehouse 9a Belvedere Road
London, SE1 8AB, United Kingdom
Tel.: (44) 2074019399
Fax: (44) 20 7401 8233
E-Mail: info@sd-partners.com
Web Site: www.sd-partners.com
Emp.: 100
Information Technology Consulting Services
S.I.C.: 7373
N.A.I.C.S.: 541512
Benedicte Bunout *(Mgr-HR)*

XDIN AB (1)
A Odhners Gata 41
Vastra Frolunda, 42130, Sweden

Alten S.A.—(Continued)

Tel.: (46) 317251000
Fax: (46) 317251099
E-Mail: info@xdin.com
Web Site: www.xdin.com
Rev.: $72,859,100
Emp.: 700
Mechanical Design & Engineering Services
S.I.C.: 8711
N.A.I.C.S.: 541330
Per Bjorklund *(Mgr-Xdin Stockholm Branch)*

ALTEO ENERGIASZOLGALTATO NYRT
(d/b/a ALTE Energy Group)
Honved u 20/A
1055 Budapest, Hungary
Tel.: (36) 614749790
Fax: (36) 614749791
E-Mail: info@alteo.hu
Web Site: www.alteo.hu
Year Founded: 2008
ALTEO—(BUD)
Sales Range: $1-9.9 Million
Emp.: 90
Business Description:
Electric Power Distr
S.I.C.: 4939
N.A.I.C.S.: 221122
Personnel:
Attila Chikan *(CEO)*
Bea Fodor *(CFO)*

ALTER NRG CORP.
215 4000 - 4th Street SE
Calgary, AB, T2G 2W3, Canada
Tel.: (403) 806-3875
Fax: (403) 806-3721
E-Mail: info@alternrg.ca
Web Site: www.alternrg.ca
NRG—(OTC TSX)
Sls.: $13,617,819
Assets: $57,222,317
Liabilities: $23,290,581
Net Worth: $33,931,736
Earnings: ($11,040,606)
Emp.: 31
Fiscal Year-end: 12/31/12
Business Description:
Clean Energy Producer
S.I.C.: 4911
N.A.I.C.S.: 221118
Personnel:
Kevin M. Bolin *(Chm)*
Richard Fish *(Pres)*
Walter Q. Howard *(CEO)*
Danny Hay *(CFO)*
Brock W. Gibson *(Sec)*
Kent Hicks *(Sr VP-Engrg, Ops & Construction-Westinghouse Plasma Corporation)*
Board of Directors:
Kevin M. Bolin
Brent J. Conway
Paul N. Heagren
Walter Q. Howard
Nancy M. Laird
Mark A. Montemurro
Wayne Sim
Eugene Alexander Tenenbaum
Legal Counsel:
Blake, Cassels & Graydon LLP
Calgary, AB, Canada
Transfer Agent:
Valiant Trust Company
Suite 300 606 4th Street SW
Calgary, AB, Canada
U.S. Subsidiary:

Westinghouse Plasma Corporation (1)
Waltz Mill Site Plasma Ctr I 70 Exit 54
Madison, PA 15663
Tel.: (724) 722-7050
Fax: (724) 722-7057
E-Mail: wpcinfo@westinghouse-plasma.com
Web Site: www.westinghouse-plasma.com
Plasma Technology Products Mfr
S.I.C.: 2836
N.A.I.C.S.: 325414
Mark Wright *(VP-Strategic Alliance & Bus Dev)*

ALTERA WEALTH MANAGEMENT PLC
II/3 43 Benczur Str
1068 Budapest, Hungary
Tel.: (36) 1 442 46 40
E-Mail: iroda@alterart.hu
Web Site: www.alterart.hu
ALTERA—(BUD)
Business Description:
Investment Services
S.I.C.: 6211
N.A.I.C.S.: 523999
Personnel:
Pal Ivancsics *(Chm)*
Barnabas Szabo *(Chm-Mgmt Bd)*
Csaba Bundik *(Member-Mgmt Bd)*
Balazs Faluvegi *(Member-Mgmt Bd)*
Supervisory Board of Directors:
Pal Ivancsics
Zoltan Bodnar
Lajos Jager
Gabor Oblath
Nora Szeles

ALTERNATIFBANK A.S.
(Acquired by Commercial Bank of Qatar Q.S.C.)

ALTERNATIVE EARTH RESOURCES INC.
(Formerly Nevada Geothermal Power, Inc.)
1500 409 Granville Street
Vancouver, BC, V6C 1T2, Canada
Tel.: (604) 688-1553
Fax: (604) 688-5926
Toll Free: (866) 688-0808
E-Mail: info@alternative-earth.com
Web Site: www.alternative-earth.com
AER—(OTC TSXV)
Assets: $4,229,283
Liabilities: $563,542
Net Worth: $3,665,741
Earnings: $78,653,649
Emp.: 35
Fiscal Year-end: 06/30/13
Business Description:
Geothermal Power Services
S.I.C.: 4931
N.A.I.C.S.: 221118
Personnel:
Brian D. Fairbank *(Pres & CEO)*
Edward Low *(CFO)*
Board of Directors:
Gavin John Cooper
Brian D. Fairbank
James Ernest Yates
Legal Counsel:
Miller Thomson
1000 - 840 Howe Street
Vancouver, BC, Canada
Transfer Agent:
Computershare Investor Services Inc.
100 University Ave 9th Floor
Toronto, ON, Canada
Subsidiary:

Blue Mountain Power Company Inc.; (1)
1114 E Vendor Ste 840
v6e 4g1, Vancouver, BC, V6E 4G1, Canada
Tel.: (604) 688-1553
Fax: (604) 688-5926
E-Mail: info@nevadageothermal.com
Emp.: 11
Geothermal Leasing & Drilling Services
S.I.C.: 1623
N.A.I.C.S.: 237110
Bryan Fairbank *(Pres & CEO)*

U.S. Subsidiaries:

Nevada Geothermal Power Company (1)
1755 E Plumb Ln Ste 101
Reno, NV 89052
Tel.: (775) 324-3044
E-Mail: reno@nevadageothermal.com
Web Site: www.nevadageothermal.com
Geothermal Exploration Services
S.I.C.: 4911
N.A.I.C.S.: 221118

NGP Blue Mountain I LLC (1)
595 Double Eagle Crt Ste 2001
Reno, NV 89521
Tel.: (775) 786-3399
Fax: (775) 853-2375
Emp.: 25
Geothermal Power Plant Construction
S.I.C.: 1629
N.A.I.C.S.: 237130
Brian D. Fairbank *(Pres)*

ALTERNATIVE ENERGY LIMITED
1 Science Park Road 02-09 The Capricorn
Singapore Science Park II,
Singapore, 117528, Singapore
Tel.: (65) 6873 7782
E-Mail: info@alternativenergy.com.sg
Web Site: www.alternativeenergy.com.sg
ALR—(AIM)
Sales Range: Less than $1 Million
Business Description:
Energy Alternatives Researcher & Developer
S.I.C.: 8731
N.A.I.C.S.: 541712
Personnel:
Christopher George Edward Nightingale *(Chm)*
Boon Hou Tay *(CTO)*
Lian Seng Yap *(Sec)*
Board of Directors:
Christopher George Edward Nightingale
Yew Chuan Bay
Swee Ming Goh
Richard Anthony Finlayson Lascelles
Noel Meaney
Legal Counsel:
Stamford Law Corporation
9 Raffles Place #32-00 Republic Plaza
Singapore, Singapore

Kerman & Co. LLP
200 Strand
London, EC1V 9EE, United Kingdom

Boardroom Corporate & Advisory Services Pte Ltd.
3 Church Street 08-01 Samsung Hub
Singapore, 049483, Singapore
Tel.: (65) 6536 5355
Fax: (65) 6536 1360
Subsidiary:

Renewable Power Pte Ltd (1)
1 Science Park Road Suite 02-09 The Capricorn
Singapore Science Park II, Singapore, Singapore
Tel.: (65) 68737782
Fax: (65) 68737761
Emp.: 10
Energy Research & Development Services
S.I.C.: 8731
N.A.I.C.S.: 541712
Eric Goh *(Gen Mgr)*

Non-U.S. Subsidiary:

Alternative Energy Technology Pte Ltd (1)
6 Simmonds Way
Atherstone, Warwickshire, CV9 3AX, United Kingdom
Tel.: (44) 8451361000
E-Mail: admin@altntec.com
Web Site: www.altntec.com
Emp.: 5
Solar Cells Mfr
S.I.C.: 3674
N.A.I.C.S.: 334413
Dave Wilkins *(Gen Mgr)*

ALTERNATIVE NETWORKS PLC
Chatfield Court 56 Chatfield Road
London, SW11 3UL, United Kingdom
Tel.: (44) 8003168866
Fax: (44) 8003168867
E-Mail: info@alternativenetworks.com
Web Site: www.alternativenetworks.com
AN—(LSE)
Rev.: $180,565,475
Assets: $112,344,409
Liabilities: $52,723,496
Net Worth: $59,620,913
Earnings: $15,392,230
Emp.: 497
Fiscal Year-end: 09/30/12
Business Description:
Telecommunications Services
S.I.C.: 4812
N.A.I.C.S.: 517911
Personnel:
James Murray *(Founder & Co-Chm)*
Edward Spurrier *(CEO)*
Gavin Griggs *(CFO)*
Board of Directors:
Timothy Holland-Bosworth
James Murray
Ben Mingay
Edward Spurrier
Legal Counsel:
Bird & Bird
15 Fetter Lane
EC4A 1JP London, United Kingdom
Subsidiary:

Aurora Kendrick James Limited (1)
7 Sherwood House Walderslade Ctr
Chatham, Kent, ME 5 9UD, United Kingdom
Tel.: (44) 1634673800
Fax: (44) 1634673919
E-Mail: info@akjl.co.uk
Web Site: www.akjl.co.uk
Emp.: 70
Telecommunication Billing & Consulting Services
S.I.C.: 8748
N.A.I.C.S.: 541618
Matt Atkinson *(Mng Dir)*

ALTERNERGY LIMITED
Swan Business Centre 9 Fishers Lane Chiswick
London, W4 1RX, United Kingdom
Tel.: (44) 20 8996 9560
E-Mail: info@alternergy.co.uk
Web Site: www.alternergy.co.uk
Year Founded: 2006
Sales Range: $50-74.9 Million
Emp.: 20
Business Description:
Solar Energy Product Whslr
S.I.C.: 5065
N.A.I.C.S.: 423690
Personnel:
Rajiv Bhatia *(Founder)*

ALTERRA POWER CORP.
600 - 888 Dunsmuir Street
Vancouver, BC, V6C 3K4, Canada
Tel.: (604) 669-4999
Fax: (604) 682-3727
Toll Free: (877) 669-4999
E-Mail: info@alterrapower.ca
Web Site: www.alterrapower.ca
Year Founded: 2008
AXY—(OTC TSX)
Rev.: $61,112,000
Assets: $712,530,000
Liabilities: $348,483,000

Net Worth: $364,047,000
Earnings: ($20,082,000)
Emp.: 140
Fiscal Year-end: 12/31/12
Business Description:
Geothermal Exploration & Mining Services
S.I.C.: 4911
N.A.I.C.S.: 221118
Personnel:
Ross J. Beaty *(Chm)*
Donald Arthur McInnes *(Vice Chm)*
John B. Carson *(CEO)*
Lynda Freeman *(Interim CFO)*
Bruce Ripley *(COO)*
Rupert Legge *(Sec & Exec VP-Legal)*
Board of Directors:
Ross J. Beaty
James Matthew Ilsley Bruce
John B. Carson
David W. Cornhill
Donald Arthur McInnes
Walter Thomas Segsworth
Donald Myron Shumka
Transfer Agent:
Computershare Investor Services Inc.
510 Burrard Street 2nd Floor
Vancouver, BC, V6C 3B9, Canada

Non-U.S. Subsidiary:

HS Orka hf (1)
Brekkustig 36
260 Reykjanesbae, Iceland IS (75%)
Tel.: (354) 422 5200
Fax: (354) 421 4727
E-Mail: hs@hs.is
Web Site: www.hsorka.is
Emp.: 131
Geothermal Energy Power Plants
S.I.C.: 4911
N.A.I.C.S.: 221118
Julius Jonsson *(CEO)*
Albert Albertsson *(Deputy CEO)*
Agnar Mar Olsen *(CFO)*

ALTERRUS SYSTEMS INC.

120 Columbia Street
Vancouver, BC, V6A 3Z8, Canada
Tel.: (604) 837-2697
Fax: (866) 279-8218
E-Mail: info@alterrus.ca
Web Site: www.alterrus.ca
ASI—(CNSX OTC)
Sls.: $42,016
Assets: $2,626,341
Liabilities: $7,119,157
Net Worth: ($4,492,816)
Earnings: ($1,415,217)
Emp.: 8
Fiscal Year-end: 03/31/13
Business Description:
Life Sciences Products Researcher & Developer
S.I.C.: 8731
N.A.I.C.S.: 541712
Personnel:
Stephen K. Fane *(Chm & Acting CFO)*
Christopher Ng *(CEO)*
Board of Directors:
Stephen K. Fane
Naveen Aggarwal
Christopher Ng
Ray Torresan

U.S. Subsidiary:

Valcent USA, Inc. (1)
20 Park Plz Ste 468
Boston, MA 02116
Tel.: (617) 440-7872
Fax: (888) 413-1877
E-Mail: info@valcent-usa.com
Agricultural Products Mfr
S.I.C.: 3523
N.A.I.C.S.: 333111

ALTIA CONSULTORES SA

(d/b/a Altia Consultants)
Avenida del Pasaje n 32
15006 La Coruna, Spain
Tel.: (34) 981138847
Fax: (34) 981138848
Web Site: www.altia.es
ALC—(MAD)
Sales Range: $25-49.9 Million
Emp.: 365
Business Description:
Computer & IT Consulting Services
S.I.C.: 7379
N.A.I.C.S.: 541519
Personnel:
Constantino Fernadez Pico *(Pres)*

ALTIA OYJ

Porkkalankatu 22
PO Box 350
00101 Helsinki, Finland
Tel.: (358) 207013013
Fax: (358) 207013000
Web Site: www.altia.fi
Year Founded: 1977
Sales Range: $550-599.9 Million
Emp.: 1,108
Business Description:
Mfr, Distr, & Marketer of Finnish Wines & Spirits
S.I.C.: 2084
N.A.I.C.S.: 312130
Personnel:
Antti Pankakoski *(CEO)*
Tomi Tanninen *(CFO)*
Joacim Hultin *(Sr VP-Trading)*
Sirpa Laakso *(Sr VP-HR)*
Hannu Tuominen *(Sr VP-Indus Svcs & Supply Chain)*
Board of Directors:
Catarina Fagerholm
Ainomaija Haarla
Jarmo Leppiniemi
Ilkka Puro
Markku Ronkko
Ulla Sydanoja
Riitta Vermas

Subsidiaries:

Alakari Wines Ltd (1)
Salmisaarenranta 7h
Helsinki, Finland (100%)
Tel.: (358) 91332720
Other Grocery & Related Products Whslr
S.I.C.: 5149
N.A.I.C.S.: 424490

OY Wennerco Ab (1)
Porkkalankatu 22 A
FIN-00180 Helsinki, Finland (100%)
Tel.: (358) 207013012
Fax: (358) 207013200
E-Mail: info@wennerco.fi
Web Site: www.wennerco.fi
Emp.: 20
Beer & Ale Whslr
S.I.C.: 5181
N.A.I.C.S.: 424810

SkyCellar Ltd (1)
Porkkalankatu 22 A
00180 Helsinki, Finland (80.1%)
Tel.: (358) 207013011
Fax: (358) 207013300
Web Site: www.skycellar.fi
Emp.: 11
Winery Production
S.I.C.: 2084
N.A.I.C.S.: 312130

Non-U.S. Subsidiaries:

Altia Eesti AS (1)
Tammi tee 30
Laabi kula Tabasalu, 76901 Harjumaa, Estonia (100%)
Tel.: (372) 6712100
Fax: (372) 6712101
E-Mail: info@altia.ee
Web Site: www.altia.ee
Emp.: 80
Beer & Ale Whslr
S.I.C.: 5181
N.A.I.C.S.: 424810
Kristel Mets *(Mng Dir)*

Altia Norway Services AS (1)
Hoffsveien 70 C
342
0213 Oslo, Norway (100%)
Tel.: (47) 21501800
Fax: (47) 21501801
Web Site: www.altiacorporation.com
Emp.: 70
Wine & Distilled Alcoholic Beverage Whslr
S.I.C.: 5182
N.A.I.C.S.: 424820

Altia Sweden AB (1)
Sandhamnsgatan 63 A
27084
10251 Stockholm, Sweden (100%)
Tel.: (46) 859811000
Fax: (46) 859811129
E-Mail: info@altiacorporation.com
Web Site: www.altiacorporation.com
Emp.: 110
Wine & Distilled Alcoholic Beverage Whslr
S.I.C.: 5182
N.A.I.C.S.: 424820
Joacim Hultin *(Sr VP)*

Subsidiaries:

Altia Sweden Services AB (2)
Samdhamnsgatan 63A
PO Box 27084
10251 Stockholm, Sweden (100%)
Tel.: (46) 859811100
Fax: (46) 859811129
Web Site: www.altiacorporation.com
Emp.: 100
Management Consulting Services
S.I.C.: 8748
N.A.I.C.S.: 541618
Anne Bonnerstig *(Mng Dir)*

Bibendum AB (2)
Sandhamnsgatan 63 A
10251 Stockholm, Sweden (100%)
Tel.: (46) 859811100
Fax: (46) 859811110
E-Mail: info@bibendum.se
Web Site: www.bibendum.se
Emp.: 45
Beer & Ale Whslr
S.I.C.: 5181
N.A.I.C.S.: 424810
Stephen Moss *(Chm)*
Michael Saunders *(Mng Dir)*

Philipson & Soderberg AB (2)
Sandhamnsgatan 63 C
10052 Stockholm, Sweden (100%)
Tel.: (46) 859811200
Fax: (46) 859811241
E-Mail: info@philipson-soderberg.se
Web Site: www.philipson-soderberg.se
Emp.: 30
Beer & Ale Whslr
S.I.C.: 5181
N.A.I.C.S.: 424810
Trik Hultberj *(Pres)*

Best Buys International AS (1)
Harbitzalle 2B
0275 Oslo, Norway (100%)
Tel.: (47) 21501880
Fax: (47) 21501881
E-Mail: bestbuys@bestbuys.no
Web Site: www.bestbuys.no
Emp.: 6
Wine & Distilled Alcoholic Beverage Whslr
S.I.C.: 5181
N.A.I.C.S.: 424810
Dier Gjerdrum *(Mng Dir)*

BevCo AB (1)
Sandhamnsgatan 63 C
PO Box 27084
SE-10251 Stockholm, Sweden (100%)
Tel.: (46) 855779009
E-Mail: bevco@altiacorporation.se
Web Site: www.altiacorporation.com
Emp.: 1
Beer & Ale Whslr
S.I.C.: 5181
N.A.I.C.S.: 424810
Johan Wikren *(Mng Dir)*

Bibendum AS (1)
Hoffsveien 70 C
476
0213 Oslo, Norway (100%)
Tel.: (47) 21501800
Fax: (47) 22128165
E-Mail: info@bibendum.no
Web Site: www.bibendum.no
Emp.: 8
Wine & Distilled Alcoholic Beverage Whslr
S.I.C.: 5182
N.A.I.C.S.: 424820
Pal Helge Kraknes *(Mng Dir)*

Interbev AS (1)
Hoffsveien 70 C
0213 Oslo, Norway (100%)
Tel.: (47) 21501820
Fax: (47) 21501801
E-Mail: froee.hellmann@interbev.no
Web Site: www.altiacorporation.com
Emp.: 15
Drinking Places (Alcoholic Beverages)
S.I.C.: 5813
N.A.I.C.S.: 722410
Froee Hellmann *(Mng Dir)*

SIA Mobil Plus ADV (1)
Kuldigas iela 36A
1083 Riga, Latvia (100%)
Tel.: (371) 67628884
Fax: (371) 67805614
E-Mail: mobilplus@mobilplus.lv
Web Site: www.altiacorporation.com
Emp.: 100
Wine & Distilled Alcoholic Beverage Whslr
S.I.C.: 5181
N.A.I.C.S.: 424810
Igor Silins *(Dir-Comml)*

Strom AS (1)
Hoffsveien 70 C
386
0213 Oslo, Norway (100%)
Tel.: (47) 21501860
Fax: (47) 21501861
E-Mail: info@strom.no
Web Site: www.strom.no
Emp.: 10
Wine & Distilled Alcoholic Beverage Whslr
S.I.C.: 5182
N.A.I.C.S.: 424820
Piilhelge Kiraknes *(Mng Dir)*

Non-U.S. Joint Venture:

Brand Partners AS (1)
Hoffsveien 70c
PB 386, Oslo, Norway (50%)
Tel.: (47) 21501840
Fax: (47) 21501841
Emp.: 14
Wine & Distilled Alcoholic Beverage Whslr
S.I.C.: 5182
N.A.I.C.S.: 424820
Erik Anundsen *(Mng Dir)*

ALTICAST CORP.

10/F Nara Investment Building 1329
2 Seocho 2 Dong
Seocho-gu, Seoul, Korea (South)
Tel.: (82) 2 2007 7827
Web Site: www.alticast.com
085810—(KRS)
Sales Range: $50-74.9 Million
Emp.: 290
Business Description:
Interactive Television Software Solutions
S.I.C.: 7372
N.A.I.C.S.: 511210
Personnel:
Won-Chul Kang *(CEO)*

ALTICE S.A.

3 Boulevard Royal
LU-2449 Luxembourg, Luxembourg
Tel.: (352) 35227858
E-Mail: IR@altice.net
Web Site: www.altice.net
ATC—(EUR)
Rev.: $1,470,556,108
Assets: $3,661,582,400
Liabilities: $2,541,972,811
Net Worth: $1,119,609,589
Earnings: ($255,503,066)
Emp.: 5,647
Fiscal Year-end: 12/31/12

Altice S.A.—(Continued)

Business Description:
Cable & Telecommunication Services
S.I.C.: 4813
N.A.I.C.S.: 517110
Personnel:
Patrick Drahi *(Chm)*
Dexter Goei *(CEO)*
Dennis Okhuijsen *(CFO)*
Max Aaron *(Gen Counsel & Chief Legal Officer)*
Max Blumberg *(CTO)*
Jeremie Bonnin *(Sec & Head-Corp & Bus Dev)*

Non-U.S. Subsidiary:

Tricom S.A. **(1)**
Avenida Lope de Vega 95
Santo Domingo, Dominican Republic DO
Tel.: (809) 4766000 (88%)
Fax: (809) 4766700
E-Mail: sc@tricom.com.do
Web Site: www.tricom.net
Sales Range: $200-249.9 Million
Emp.: 1,723
Telecommunications Services
S.I.C.: 4899
N.A.I.C.S.: 517410
Ricardo Valdez Albizu *(Chm)*

ALTICE VII SARL
(See Under Altice S.A.)

ALTIMA DENTAL CANADA INC.
1 Yorkdale Road Suite 320
Toronto, ON, M6A 3A1, Canada
Tel.: (416) 785-1828
Fax: (416) 785-5561
Toll Free: (888) 817-6453
E-Mail: info@altima.ca
Web Site: www.altimadental.com
Emp.: 300
Business Description:
Dental Clinics Operator
S.I.C.: 8021
N.A.I.C.S.: 621210
Personnel:
Sven Grail *(Co-Founder, Co-CEO & Chm)*
George Christodoulou *(Co-Founder, Pres, Co-CEO & Sr Partner)*

ALTIMA PARTNERS LLP
11 Slingsby Place Saint Martin's Courtyard
London, WC2E 9AB, United Kingdom
Tel.: (44) 20 7968 6400
Fax: (44) 20 7968 6401
Web Site: www.altimapartners.com
Year Founded: 2004
Managed Assets: $1,000,000,000
Business Description:
Investment Advisory & Fund Management Services
S.I.C.: 6799
N.A.I.C.S.: 523920
Personnel:
Mark Robert Donegan *(Mng Partner & Chief Investment Officer-Funds)*
Malcolm Ian Goddard *(Partner & COO)*
Radenko Milakovic *(Partner)*
Mark Foster-Brown *(Partner-IR)*
David Gray *(Partner)*
John Webster *(Partner)*

Non-U.S. Holding:

Banjalucka Pivara a.d., Banja Luka **(1)**
Slatinska 8
7800 Banja Luka, Bosnia & Herzegovina BA
Tel.: (387) 51 334 100
Fax: (387) 51 300 624
E-Mail: info@blpivara.com
Web Site: www.banjaluckapivara.com
BLPV—(BANJ)
Rev.: $23,855,648
Assets: $30,662,749
Liabilities: $31,085,898
Net Worth: ($423,149)
Earnings: ($851,754)
Emp.: 230
Fiscal Year-end: 12/31/12
Beer Brewery Operator
S.I.C.: 2082
N.A.I.C.S.: 312120
Nicholas Penny *(Dir Gen)*
Mirjana Jovanovic *(Vice Chm-Mgmt Bd & CFO)*
Kevin Smith *(Member-Mgmt Bd)*
Ragnar A. Tryggvason *(Member-Mgmt Bd)*
Travis Willis-Davis *(Member-Mgmt Bd)*

ALTIMA RESOURCES LTD.
Box 4 Suite 303 595 Howe Street
Vancouver, BC, V6C 2T5, Canada
Tel.: (604) 336-8610
Fax: (604) 718-2808
E-Mail: info@altimaresources.com
Web Site: www.altimaresources.com
ARH—(TSXV)
Rev.: $100,837
Assets: $25,200,050
Liabilities: $6,190,321
Net Worth: $19,009,729
Earnings: ($1,384,155)
Emp.: 6
Fiscal Year-end: 11/30/12
Business Description:
Oil & Natural Gas Exploration Services
S.I.C.: 1311
N.A.I.C.S.: 211111
Personnel:
Jim O'Byrne *(Chm)*
Richard Switzer *(Pres & CEO)*
Richard Barnett *(CFO & Sec)*
Board of Directors:
Jim O'Byrne
Joe DeVries
Richard Switzer
Stephen Watts
Jurgen Wolf
Legal Counsel:
DuMoulin Black LLP
10th Floor 595 Howe St
Vancouver, BC, Canada

ALTIMO GROUP CORP.
Jozefa Bema 6A
85-001 Bydgoszcz, Poland
Tel.: (48) 601 212 388
E-Mail: altimogroupcorp@gmail.com
Year Founded: 2013
Business Description:
Frozen Yogurt
S.I.C.: 2024
N.A.I.C.S.: 311520
Personnel:
Marek Tomaszewski *(Pres, Treas & Sec)*
Board of Directors:
Marek Tomaszewski

ALTIN AG
Neuhofstrasse 8
Postfach 2262
CH-6342 Baar, Switzerland
Tel.: (41) 417606260
Fax: (41) 417619223
E-Mail: info@altin.ch
Web Site: www.altin.ch
AIA—(LSE)
Rev.: $13,044,000
Assets: $345,938,000
Liabilities: $96,071,000
Net Worth: $249,867,000
Earnings: $7,044,000
Emp.: 3
Fiscal Year-end: 12/31/12
Business Description:
Investment Services
S.I.C.: 6211
N.A.I.C.S.: 523999
Personnel:
Peter Altorfer *(Chm)*
Tony Morrongiello *(CEO)*
Board of Directors:
Peter Altorfer
Andre Pabst
Roger Ruegg
Eric Max Charles Syz

ALTIPLANO MINERALS LTD.
220 9797 45th Avenue
Edmonton, AB, T6E 5V8, Canada
Tel.: (780) 437-6624
Fax: (780) 439-7308
E-Mail: info@altiplanominerals.com
Web Site: www.altiplanominerals.com
Year Founded: 2010
APN—(TSXV)
Int. Income: $9,932
Assets: $931,129
Liabilities: $41,109
Net Worth: $890,019
Earnings: ($396,809)
Fiscal Year-end: 09/30/13
Business Description:
Metal Mining Services
S.I.C.: 1099
N.A.I.C.S.: 212299
Personnel:
John Williamson *(Chm)*
Peter Kleespies *(Pres)*
Brian Budd *(CEO)*
Justin Timms *(CFO)*
Board of Directors:
John Williamson
Brian Budd
Peter Kleespies
Sean Mager
Transfer Agent:
Olympia Trust Company
125 9th Avenue SE Suite 2300
Calgary, AB, T2G 0P6, Canada
Tel.: (403) 261-0900

ALTIS SEMICONDUCTOR S.A.
224 Boulevard John Kennedy
91105 Corbeil-Essonnes, Cedex, France
Tel.: (33) 160885151
Fax: (33) 160909435
E-Mail: info@altissemiconductor.com
Web Site: www.altissemiconductor.com
Sales Range: $200-249.9 Million
Emp.: 1,500
Business Description:
Semiconductor Distr
S.I.C.: 3674
N.A.I.C.S.: 334413
Personnel:
Germain Djouhri *(Chm-Supervisory Bd)*
Jean-Paul Beisson *(CEO)*

ALTISOURCE PORTFOLIO SOLUTIONS S.A.
40 Avenue Monterey
L-2163 Luxembourg, Luxembourg
Tel.: (352) 24697900
Web Site: www.altisource.com
ASPS—(NASDAQ)
Rev.: $768,357,000
Assets: $724,838,000
Liabilities: $567,097,000
Net Worth: $157,741,000
Earnings: $133,793,000
Emp.: 7,747
Fiscal Year-end: 12/31/13
Business Description:
Real Estate & Mortgage Portfolio Management Services
S.I.C.: 6799
N.A.I.C.S.: 523920
Personnel:
William Charles Erbey *(Chm)*
William B. Shepro *(CEO)*
Michelle D. Esterman *(CFO)*
Kevin J. Wilcox *(Chief Admin Officer & Gen Counsel)*
S. P. Ravi *(Chief Risk Officer)*
Board of Directors:
William Charles Erbey
W. Michael Linn
Roland Muller-Ineichen
William B. Shepro
Timo Vatto

U.S. Subsidiaries:

Altisource Solutions, Inc. **(1)**
2002 Summit Blvd Ste 600
Atlanta, GA 30319
Tel.: (888) 255-1791
Fax: (770) 644-7420
Real Estate Management Services
S.I.C.: 6531
N.A.I.C.S.: 531210

The Mortgage Partnership of America, L.L.C. **(1)**
2 Cityplace Dr
Saint Louis, MO 63141
Tel.: (314) 292-7920
Mortgage Brokerage Services
S.I.C.: 6163
N.A.I.C.S.: 522310

Springhouse, L.L.C. **(1)**
2002 Summitt Blvd Ste 600
Atlanta, GA 30319
Tel.: (502) 384-0727
Fax: (314) 754-8111
E-Mail: customerservice@springhouseamc.com
Web Site: www.springhouseamc.com
Real Estate Management Services
S.I.C.: 6531
N.A.I.C.S.: 531320
Brian Levine *(CEO)*

ALTITUDE GROUP PLC
Unit 4 Rhodes Business Park Silburn Way
Middleton, Manchester, M24 4NE, United Kingdom
Tel.: (44) 844 880 2751
E-Mail: info@altitudeplc.com
Web Site: www.altitudeplc.com
ALT—(AIM)
Rev.: $6,434,027
Assets: $11,721,490
Liabilities: $3,337,040
Net Worth: $8,384,451
Earnings: ($792,804)
Emp.: 58
Fiscal Year-end: 12/31/12
Business Description:
Promotional Merchandise, Marketing & Exhibitions
S.I.C.: 7319
N.A.I.C.S.: 541890
Personnel:
Martin Varley *(CEO)*
Richard Sowerby *(CFO)*
Board of Directors:
Stephen Yapp
Martin Varley
Legal Counsel:
DWF LLP
1 Scott Place 2 Hardman Street
Manchester, United Kingdom

Subsidiaries:

Promoserve Business Systems Limited **(1)**
Unit 1 Acorn Business Park Woodseats Close
Sheffield, S8 0TB, United Kingdom
Tel.: (44) 844 509 0030
Fax: (44) 871 433 2518
E-Mail: sales@promoserve.co.uk
Web Site: www.promoserve.co.uk

Emp.: 10
Business Management Software Development Services
S.I.C.: 7371
N.A.I.C.S.: 541511
Andy Barton *(COO)*

Ross Promotional Products Limited (1)
40 Crimea Street
Glasgow, G2 8PW, United Kingdom
Tel.: (44) 141 221 1030
Fax: (44) 141 221 1025
E-Mail: enquiries@rosspromotional.co.uk
Web Site: www.rosspromotional.co.uk
Emp.: 12
Promotional Merchandise Mfr
S.I.C.: 3999
N.A.I.C.S.: 339999

Trade Only Limited (1)
Unit 4 Rhodes Business Park
Middleton, Manchester, M24 4NE, United Kingdom
Tel.: (44) 844 880 2751
Fax: (44) 870 145 3861
E-Mail: sales@tradeonly.co.uk
Web Site: www.tradeonly.co.uk
Catalog & Magazine Publishing Services
S.I.C.: 2721
N.A.I.C.S.: 511120
Vicky Robinson *(Mng Dir)*

Non-U.S. Subsidiary:

Trade Only Inc. (1)
1810 Ave Rd Ste 300
Toronto, ON, M5M 3Z2, Canada
Tel.: (416) 221-4619
Fax: (888) 305-1369
Toll Free: (888) 256-3013
E-Mail: info@tradeonly.com
Web Site: www.tradeonly.com
Business Management Software Development Services
S.I.C.: 7371
N.A.I.C.S.: 541511
Martin Varley *(Pres & CEO)*
Graham Anderson *(CTO)*
Robert Hechler *(Exec VP)*

ALTIUM LIMITED

3 Minna Close
Belrose, NSW, 2085, Australia
Tel.: (61) 286228100
Fax: (61) 299757720
E-Mail: info.au@altium.com
Web Site: www.altium.com
Year Founded: 1985
ALU—(ASX)
Rev.: $62,054,000
Assets: $46,427,000
Liabilities: $41,357,000
Net Worth: $5,070,000
Earnings: $1,366,000
Emp.: 275
Fiscal Year-end: 06/30/13

Business Description:
Computer Software Mfr
S.I.C.: 7372
N.A.I.C.S.: 511210

Personnel:
Phil Adams *(CEO)*
Aram Mirkazemi *(CEO)*
Richard Leon *(CFO)*
Frank Hoschar *(CMO)*
Martin Harris *(Chief Sls Officer)*
Alison Raffin *(Sec)*

Board of Directors:
Samuel Scott Weiss
Aram Mirkazemi
Carl J. Rooke
David M. Warren

Non-U.S. Subsidiaries:

Altium B.V. (1)
Plotterweg 31
3821 BB Amersfoort, Netherlands
Tel.: (31) 334558584
Fax: (31) 334550033
E-Mail: info.nl@altium.com
Web Site: www.tasking.com
Emp.: 45
Electronic Products Mfr
S.I.C.: 3676
N.A.I.C.S.: 334416
Peter Mwmrn *(Gen Mgr)*

Altium Europe GmbH (1)
Technologiepark Karlsruhe
Albert Nestler Strasse 7, 76131 Karlsruhe, Germany
Tel.: (49) 7218244300
Fax: (49) 7218244320
E-Mail: support.eu@altium.com
Emp.: 40
Electronic Products Mfr & Sls
S.I.C.: 3678
N.A.I.C.S.: 334417
Martin Harris *(Gen Mgr)*

Altium Information Technology (Shanghai) Co., Ltd. (1)
9C E Hope Plz No 1777 Century Ave
Shanghai, 200122, China
Tel.: (86) 2161823900
Fax: (86) 2168764015
E-Mail: support.cn@altium.com
Web Site: www.altium.com.cn
Emp.: 200
Electronic Products Mfr
S.I.C.: 3678
N.A.I.C.S.: 334417
Roger Shen *(CEO)*

Altium Japan KK (1)
Resona Gotanda Bldg 7F 1-23-9 Nishi-Gotanda
Shinagawa-ku, Tokyo, 141 0031, Japan
Tel.: (81) 3 5436 2501
Fax: (81) 3 5436 2505
E-Mail: tasking.support.jp@altium.com
Electronic Products Mfr
S.I.C.: 3678
N.A.I.C.S.: 334417

ALTIUS MINERALS CORPORATION

Suite 202 Kenmount Business Center
66 Kenmount Road
Saint John's, NL, A1B 3V7, Canada
Mailing Address:
PO Box 8263
Saint John's, NL, A1B 3N4, Canada
Tel.: (709) 576-3440
Fax: (709) 576-3441
Toll Free: (877) 576-2209
E-Mail: info@altiusminerals.com
Web Site: www.altiusminerals.com
ALS—(TSX)
Rev.: $5,829,927
Assets: $271,208,417
Liabilities: $12,263,225
Net Worth: $258,945,192
Earnings: ($13,072,357)
Emp.: 13
Fiscal Year-end: 04/30/13

Business Description:
Mineral Exploration & Development
S.I.C.: 1081
N.A.I.C.S.: 213114

Personnel:
John Antle Baker *(Chm)*
Brian Francis Dalton *(Pres & CEO)*
Ben Lewis *(CFO)*
Chad S. Wells *(Sec & VP-Corp Dev)*

Board of Directors:
John Antle Baker
Brian Francis Dalton
Frederick Mifflin
Susan Sherk
Jamie Digby Ronald Strauss
Donald J. Warr

Transfer Agent:
Equity Financial Trust Company
Toronto, ON, Canada

Subsidiary:

Altius Resources Inc. (1)
66 Kentmount Rd Ste 202
Saint John's, NL, A1B 3V7, Canada
Tel.: (709) 576-3440
Gold & Copper Exploration Services
S.I.C.: 1081
N.A.I.C.S.: 213114
Brian Francis Dalton *(Pres)*

ALTIUS MINING LIMITED

Level 3 521 Toorak Road
Toorak, VIC, 3142, Australia
Mailing Address:
PO Box 473
Toorak, VIC, 3142, Australia
Tel.: (61) 1300 136453
E-Mail: admin@altiusmining.com.au
Web Site: www.altiusmining.com.au
AYM—(ASX)

Business Description:
Gold & Other Metal Mining
S.I.C.: 1041
N.A.I.C.S.: 212221

Personnel:
Jannie Siew Lee Chan *(Chm)*
Joe Fekete *(CFO)*
Alfonso M.G. Grillo *(Sec)*

Board of Directors:
Jannie Siew Lee Chan
Joe Fekete
Robert McLennan

Legal Counsel:
Websters Solicitors
Level 11 37 Bligh Street
Sydney, NSW, Australia

ALTO PLASTICS LTD.

19 Keeling Road
Henderson, Auckland, New Zealand
Mailing Address:
PO Box 21308
Auckland, New Zealand
Tel.: (64) 98360225
Fax: (64) 98367764
E-Mail: plastics@altoplastics.co.nz
Web Site: www.alto.co.nz
Sales Range: $250-299.9 Million
Emp.: 110

Business Description:
Rigid Plastics Packaging Products
S.I.C.: 3089
N.A.I.C.S.: 326199

Personnel:
Siva Mudaly *(Gen Mgr)*

ALTO VENTURES LTD.

Suite 910 - 475 Howe Street
Vancouver, BC, V6C 2B3, Canada
Tel.: (604) 689-2599
Fax: (604) 689-3609
Toll Free: (866) 689-2599
E-Mail: info@altoventures.com
Web Site: www.altoventures.com
Year Founded: 1987
ATV—(TSXV)
Rev.: $37,117
Assets: $4,060,662
Liabilities: $134,310
Net Worth: $3,926,352
Earnings: ($654,054)
Fiscal Year-end: 06/30/13

Business Description:
Gold Exploration Services
S.I.C.: 1041
N.A.I.C.S.: 212221

Personnel:
Marian Koziol *(Pres)*
Richard Mazur *(CEO)*
Robert Anderson *(CFO)*
Jacqueline Collins *(Sec)*

Board of Directors:
David Cowan
Marian Koziol
Richard Mazur
Gary Frank J. Zak

Legal Counsel:
McMillan LLP
1500 1055 West Georgia Street
V6E4N7 Vancouver, BC, Canada

Transfer Agent:
Computershare Investor Services Inc.
510 Burrard St
Vancouver, BC, V6C 3B9, Canada

ALTON SPORTS CO., LTD.

227-13 Bangi-dong
Songpa- gu, Seoul, Korea (South)
Tel.: (82) 31 858 6770
Fax: (82) 2 423 0506
Web Site: www.altonsports.co.kr
Year Founded: 1994
123750—(KRS)

Business Description:
Bicycle Mfr
S.I.C.: 3751
N.A.I.C.S.: 336991

Personnel:
Chan Wu Park *(CEO)*

ALTONA ENERGY PLC

18 - 19 Pall Mall
London, SW1Y 5LU, United Kingdom
Tel.: (44) 207 024 8391
Fax: (44) 203 272 0093
Web Site: www.altonaenergy.com
A8L—(AIM DEU)
Rev.: $1,579
Assets: $20,075,934
Liabilities: $701,205
Net Worth: $19,374,730
Earnings: ($2,207,847)
Emp.: 10
Fiscal Year-end: 06/30/13

Business Description:
Coal Exploration Services
S.I.C.: 1241
N.A.I.C.S.: 213113

Personnel:
Michael Qiang Zheng *(Chm)*
Christopher Walter Lambert *(CEO)*
Stephen Frank Ronaldson *(Sec)*

Board of Directors:
Michael Qiang Zheng
Peter Michael John Fagiano
Christopher Walter Lambert
Phillip George Sutherland
Qinfu Zhang

Legal Counsel:
Watson, Farley & Williams
15 Appold Street
London, EC2A 2HB, United Kingdom

Ronaldsons
55 Gower Street
London, United Kingdom

ALTONA MINING LIMITED

Ground Floor 1 Altona Street
West Perth, WA, 6005, Australia
Mailing Address:
PO Box 1466
West Perth, 6872, Australia
Tel.: (61) 8 9485 2929
Fax: (61) 8 9486 8700
E-Mail: altona@altonamining.com
Web Site: www.altonamining.com
AOH—(ASX DEU OSL)
Rev.: $66,807,989
Assets: $150,428,177
Liabilities: $42,308,218
Net Worth: $108,119,959
Earnings: $13,179,439
Emp.: 10
Fiscal Year-end: 06/30/13

Business Description:
Copper Exploration, Development & Mining
S.I.C.: 1021
N.A.I.C.S.: 212234

Personnel:
Michael Holbrook *(Pres & CEO)*
Alistair Cowden *(Mng Dir)*
David R. Frank *(CFO & Sec)*
Iain Scott *(COO)*

Board of Directors:

Altona Mining Limited—(Continued)

Kevin Maloney
Alistair Cowden
David R. Frank
Paul Hallam
Michael Holbrook
Tyler Holbrook
Peter Ingram
Steve Scudamore
David L. Wolf

Legal Counsel:
Gilbert & Tobin
1202 Hay Street
West Perth, Australia

Computershare Registry Services Pty Ltd
Level 2 Reserve Bank Building 45 St Georges Terrace
Perth, WA, 6000, Australia

Non-U.S. Subsidiary:

Kylylahti Copper Oy (1)
Kummunkato 34
83500 Outokumpu, Finland
Tel.: (358) 504109552
Fax: (358) 13 830 228
E-Mail: jvesanto@vulcanresources.com.au
Metal Ore Mining
S.I.C.: 1099
N.A.I.C.S.: 212299

ALTOR

Parc Industriel de Tabari
BP 9417
44194 Clisson, France
Tel.: (33) 240361667
Fax: (33) 240361678
Web Site: www.laurent-laugier.fr
Sls.: $23,800,000
Emp.: 200

Business Description:
Plastics Products
S.I.C.: 3089
N.A.I.C.S.: 326199

Personnel:
Bertrand Touzet *(Pres)*

ALTOR EQUITY PARTNERS AB

Jakobsgatan 6
SE 111 52 Stockholm, Sweden
Tel.: (46) 86789100
Fax: (46) 86789101
E-Mail: info@altor.com
Web Site: www.altor.com
Year Founded: 2003
Emp.: 50

Business Description:
Private Equity Firm
S.I.C.: 6211
N.A.I.C.S.: 523999

Personnel:
Johan Cervin *(Partner)*
Reynir Indahl *(Partner)*
Jaakko Kivinen *(Partner)*
Stefan Linder *(Partner)*
Hugo Maurstad *(Partner)*
Harald Mix *(Partner)*
Fredrik Stromholm *(Partner)*
Jesper Eliasson *(CFO)*

Holdings:

BYGGmax Group AB (1)
PO Box 6063
171 06 Solna, Sweden
Tel.: (46) 851493060
Fax: (46) 851493030
E-Mail: info@byggmax.se
Web Site: www.byggmax.com
BMAX—(OMX)
Sales Range: $250-299.9 Million
Emp.: 400
Building Materials Retailer
S.I.C.: 5211
N.A.I.C.S.: 444110
Magnus Agervald *(CEO)*

Carnegie Investment Bank AB (1)
Regeringsgatan 56
SE 111 56 Stockholm, Sweden
Tel.: (46) 86768800
Fax: (46) 858869138
E-Mail: kundtjanst@carnegie.seb
Web Site: www.carnegie.se
Emp.: 758
Investment Banking Services
S.I.C.: 6211
N.A.I.C.S.: 523110
Arne Liljedahl *(Chm)*
Pia Marions *(CFO & Acting CEO)*

Subsidiary:

Carnegie Fonder AB (2)
Regeringsgatan 56
103 38 Stockholm, Sweden
Tel.: (46) 8 5886 88 00
Fax: (46) 8 5886 93 93
E-Mail: fonder@carnegie.se
Web Site: www.carnegie.se
Sales Range: $25-49.9 Million
Mutual Fund Management Services
S.I.C.: 6722
N.A.I.C.S.: 525910
Hans Hedstrom *(Pres)*

U.S. Subsidiary:

Carnegie Inc. (2)
20 W 55th St 10th Fl
New York, NY 10019-5373
Tel.: (212) 262-5800
Fax: (212) 265-3946
E-Mail: webmaster@carnegieinc.com
Web Site: www.carnegieinc.com
Emp.: 17
Investment Banking Services
S.I.C.: 6211
N.A.I.C.S.: 523110

Dustin AB (1)
Augustendalsv 7
Box 27304
131 26 Nacka, Sweden
Tel.: (46) 8 553 44 553
Fax: (46) 8 553 44 330
Web Site: www.dustin.se/pd_5010082500.aspx
Sales Range: $500-549.9 Million
Emp.: 200
Internet Retailer of Computer Equipment
S.I.C.: 5961
N.A.I.C.S.: 454111
Per Eriksson *(CEO)*

Papyrus AB (1)
Kronogardsgatan 3
SE-431 33 Molndal, Sweden SE
Mailing Address:
Box 1004
SE-431 26 Molndal, Sweden
Tel.: (46) 105170000
Fax: (46) 317060987
E-Mail: info@papyrus.com
Web Site: www.papyrus.com
Sales Range: $1-4.9 Billion
Emp.: 2,700
Holding Company; Paper, Office Supplies & Industrial Packaging Whslr
S.I.C.: 6719
N.A.I.C.S.: 551112
Peter Sandberg *(Pres & CEO)*
Stig Johansson *(CFO)*
Dan Andersson *(Sr VP-South & Eastern Reg)*
Christian Carlsson *(Sr VP-HR)*
Soren Gaardboe *(Sr VP-Nordic Reg)*
Michael Hurter *(Sr VP-Central Reg)*
Steffen Karlsson *(Sr VP-Bus Dev)*
Jan Muller *(Sr VP-Western Reg)*
Stefan Syren *(Sr VP-Mktg & Supply)*

Subsidiary:

Papyrus Sverige AB (2)
Kronogardsgatan 3
SE-431 33 Molndal, Sweden SE
Mailing Address:
Box 1004
SE-431 26 Molndal, Sweden
Tel.: (46) 105170000
Fax: (46) 31872428
E-Mail: info.se@papyrus.com
Web Site: www.papyrus.com
Emp.: 300
Paper, Office Supplies & Industrial Packaging Whslr
S.I.C.: 5111
N.A.I.C.S.: 424110
Soren Gaardboe *(CEO)*

Non-U.S. Subsidiaries:

Papyrus A/S (2)
Bredebjergvej 1
Taastrup, DK-2630 Copenhagen, Denmark DK
Tel.: (45) 70223838
Fax: (45) 70223939
E-Mail: info.dk@papyrus.com
Web Site: www.papyrus.com
Paper, Office Supplies & Industrial Packaging Whslr
S.I.C.: 5111
N.A.I.C.S.: 424110
Soren Gaardboe *(CEO)*

Papyrus AS (2)
Betooni 6
14115 Tallinn, Estonia EE
Tel.: (372) 6788670
Fax: (372) 678 8671
E-Mail: info.ee@papyrus.com
Web Site: www.papyrus.com
Emp.: 10
Paper, Office Supplies & Industrial Packaging Whslr
S.I.C.: 5111
N.A.I.C.S.: 424110

Papyrus Deutschland GmbH & Co. KG (2)
Gehrnstrasse 7-11
D-76275 Ettlingen, Germany De
Tel.: (49) 7243730
Fax: (49) 724373171
E-Mail: info.de@papyrus.com
Web Site: www.papyrus.com
Sales Range: $1-4.9 Billion
Emp.: 1,147
Paper, Office Supplies & Industrial Packaging Whslr; Envelope Mfr
S.I.C.: 5111
N.A.I.C.S.: 424110
Michael Hurter *(CEO & Chm-Mgmt Bd)*
Robert Matzke *(Member-Mgmt Bd)*
Stefan Peter *(Member-Mgmt Bd)*

Papyrus Finland Oy (2)
Riihikuja 4
PL 150
FI-01721 Vantaa, Finland FI
Tel.: (358) 20774949
Fax: (358) 20774939
E-Mail: info.fi@papyrus.com
Web Site: www.papyrus.com
Emp.: 60
Paper, Office Supplies & Industrial Packaging Whslr
S.I.C.: 5111
N.A.I.C.S.: 424110
Jyri Rautakoura *(Mng Dir)*

Papyrus Groep Nederland b.v. (2)
Bijsterhuizen Noord 22-02
6604 LD Wijchen, Netherlands NL
Mailing Address:
PO Box 62
6500 AB Nijmegen, Netherlands
Tel.: (31) 886565222
Fax: (31) 88 65 65 223
E-Mail: papyrus.nl@papyrus.com
Web Site: www.papyrus.com
Emp.: 170
Paper, Office Supplies & Industrial Packaging Whslr
S.I.C.: 5111
N.A.I.C.S.: 424110

Papyrus Hungaria Zrt. (2)
Konyves Kalman korut 11/c
HU-1097 Budapest, Hungary HU
Tel.: (36) 14529800
Fax: (36) 13403923
E-Mail: info.hu@papyrus.com
Web Site: www.papyrus.com
Emp.: 60
Paper, Office Supplies & Industrial Packaging Whslr
S.I.C.: 5111
N.A.I.C.S.: 424110
Roland Palko *(Mng Dir)*

Papyrus Norge AS (2)
Soren Bulls vei 2
NO-1051 Oslo, Norway NO
Mailing Address:
PO Box 110 Furuset
NO-1001 Oslo, Norway
Tel.: (47) 22904590
Fax: (47) 22904510
E-Mail: info.no@papyrus.com
Web Site: www.papyrus.com
Emp.: 40
Paper, Office Supplies & Industrial Packaging Whslr
S.I.C.: 5111
N.A.I.C.S.: 424110
Elin Hagen *(Mgr-Customer Svc)*

Papyrus Schweiz AG (2)
Zurcherstrasse 68
CH-8800 Thalwil, Switzerland CH
Tel.: (41) 585805800
Fax: (41) 585805850
E-Mail: info.ch@papyrus.com
Web Site: www.papyrus.com
Sales Range: $250-299.9 Million
Emp.: 240
Paper, Office Supplies & Industrial Packaging Whslr
S.I.C.: 5111
N.A.I.C.S.: 424110
Marco Letta *(CEO)*

Papyrus SIA (2)
Dzelzavas iela 120
LV-1021 Riga, Latvia LV
Tel.: (371) 731 3022
Fax: (371) 731 2268
E-Mail: info.lv@papyrus.com
Web Site: www.papyrus.com
Paper, Office Supplies & Industrial Packaging Whslr
S.I.C.: 5111
N.A.I.C.S.: 424110
Ilmars Lipskis *(Mng Dir)*

Papyrus Sp. z o.o. (2)
Domaniewska 41 bud Saturn
PL-02-672 Warsaw, Poland PL
Tel.: (48) 224490200
Fax: (48) 224490201
E-Mail: info.pl@papyrus.com
Web Site: www.papyrus.com
Emp.: 60
Paper, Office Supplies & Industrial Packaging Whslr
S.I.C.: 5111
N.A.I.C.S.: 424110
Pawel Bielak *(Pres)*

UAB Papyrus Lietuva (2)
R Kalantos St 59
52304 Kaunas, Lithuania LT
Tel.: (370) 37400330
Fax: (370) 37473836
E-Mail: info.lt@papyrus.com
Web Site: www.papyrus.com
Paper, Office Supplies & Industrial Packaging Whslr
S.I.C.: 5111
N.A.I.C.S.: 424110
Vilija Rugieniute *(Gen Dir)*

Relacom AB (1)
Arstaangsvagen 1C
117 43 Stockholm, Sweden
Tel.: (46) 855390000
Fax: (46) 855390303
E-Mail: contact@relacom.com
Web Site: www.relacom.com
Sales Range: $1-4.9 Billion
Emp.: 16,000
Computer Network Design Services
S.I.C.: 7373
N.A.I.C.S.: 541512
Johan Ek *(Pres & CEO)*
Thord Hansson Rivedal *(Sr VP & Head-HR)*

U.S. Holdings:

NorthStar Battery Co. LLC (1)
4000 Continental Way
Springfield, MO 65803
Tel.: (417) 575-8200
Fax: (417) 575-8250
E-Mail: info@northstarbattery.com
Web Site: www.northstarbattery.com
Sales Range: $200-249.9 Million
Emp.: 400
Battery Mfr
S.I.C.: 3692
N.A.I.C.S.: 335912
Larry Hill *(CEO)*

Northstar Marine Electronics (1)
30 Sudbury Rd
Acton, MA 01720
Tel.: (978) 897-6600
Fax: (978) 897-8264
Toll Free: (800) 628-4487
E-Mail: ns-support@navico.com
Web Site: www.northstarcmc.com
Emp.: 45
Electronic Navigation Equipment Mfr
S.I.C.: 3812
N.A.I.C.S.: 334511

Orchid Orthopedic Solutions, LLC (1)
1489 Cedar St
Holt, MI 48842
Tel.: (517) 694-2300
Fax: (517) 694-2340
Web Site: www.orchid-orthopedics.com
Emp.: 1,500
Surgical Instrument & Supplies Mfr
S.I.C.: 3841
N.A.I.C.S.: 339112
Mike Miller *(CEO)*
Jorge Ramos *(CFO)*
Mark Burba *(Exec VP-Machining)*
Matthew Burba *(Exec VP-Implant Mfr)*
Christopher Norbye *(Exec VP-Global Ops)*

Subsidiaries:

Orchid Bio-Coat (2)
21249 Bridge St
Southfield, MI 48034 MI
Tel.: (248) 352-4570
Fax: (248) 352-5543
Emp.: 65
Medical Instrument Coating & Surface Treatment Services
S.I.C.: 3841
N.A.I.C.S.: 339112
Bob Naumann *(Gen Mgr)*

Orchid Macdee Orthopedic Solutions, LLC (2)
13800 Luick Dr
Chelsea, MI 48118 MI
Tel.: (734) 475-9165
Fax: (734) 475-3825
Emp.: 70
Plastic Medical Instrument & Supplies Mfr
S.I.C.: 3841
N.A.I.C.S.: 339112
Patrick Davidson *(Gen Mgr)*

Units:

Orchid Keller (2)
3203 Kashiwa St
Torrance, CA 90505 CA
Tel.: (310) 326-6291
Fax: (310) 326-0417
Emp.: 28
Surgical Appliance & Supplies Mfr
S.I.C.: 3841
N.A.I.C.S.: 339113
Steven Dragovich *(Gen Mgr)*

Orchid Orthopedic Solutions, LLC - Alabama (2)
331 City Park Dr SE
Arab, AL 35016
Tel.: (256) 586-4534
Fax: (256) 586-4533
Emp.: 80
Surgical Instrument & Supplies Mfr
S.I.C.: 3841
N.A.I.C.S.: 339112
Clay Clayton *(Gen Mgr)*

Non-U.S. Subsidiary:

Orchid Orthopedic Solutions Sheffield Ltd. (2)
Unit D, Beighton Business Park Old Colliery Way
Sheffield, S20 1DJ, United Kingdom UK
Tel.: (44) 114 2942300 (100%)
Fax: (44) 114 2942301
E-Mail:
Emp.: 100
Medical Stainless Steel Products & Materials Mfr & Distr
S.I.C.: 3841
N.A.I.C.S.: 339112
Ian Hainsworth *(Gen Mgr)*

Non-U.S. Holdings:

AGR Group ASA (1)
Smalonane 12-14
PO Box 163
5342 Straume, Norway NO
Tel.: (47) 56316000 (76%)
Fax: (47) 56316001
E-Mail: reception@agr.com
Web Site: www.agr.com
AGR—(OSL)
Rev.: $321,784,474
Assets: $392,920,060
Liabilities: $269,582,433
Net Worth: $123,337,626
Earnings: ($18,818,435)
Emp.: 479
Fiscal Year-end: 12/31/12
Oil & Natural Gas Operations Support Services
S.I.C.: 1389
N.A.I.C.S.: 213112
Eivind Reiten *(Chm)*
Age Landro *(CEO)*
Svein Sollund *(CFO)*
Ian Burdis *(Exec VP-UK & West Africa)*
David Hine *(Exec VP-Enhanced Drilling Solutions)*
Patrick McKinley *(Exec VP-Americas)*
Sjur B. Talstad *(Exec VP-Norway & Russia)*
Johan Moller Warmedal *(Exec VP-Tools & Tech)*
Atle Andresen *(Sr VP-AGR Energy)*
Ralph Doughty *(Sr VP-AGR FJ Well Mgmt)*
Tove Magnussen *(Sr VP-HSEQ)*

Constructor Group AS (1)
Kinoveien Ste A
1338 Sandvika, Norway
Tel.: (47) 67807880
Fax: (47) 67807881
Web Site: www.constructordexion.com
Sales Range: $400-449.9 Million
Emp.: 1,000
Material Handling Services
S.I.C.: 4731
N.A.I.C.S.: 541614
Simon Martinsen *(CFO)*
Ad Ewalts *(Sr VP-Mfg)*
Richard Moss *(Sr VP-Sls & Mktg)*
Oddgeir Overli *(Sr VP-Supply Chain)*

Subsidiary:

Constructor Norge AS (2)
Sandviksveien 36
PO Box 363
N 1323 Hovik, N 1363, Norway
Tel.: (47) 67112600
Fax: (47) 67112601
E-Mail: nofirmapost@constructor.no
Web Site: www.constructor.no
Emp.: 30
Provider of Industrial & Office Storage Products
S.I.C.: 2599
N.A.I.C.S.: 337215
Terge Danielsen *(Mng Dir)*

Non-U.S. Subsidiaries:

Bruynzeel Archiv and Buero Sys GmbH (2)
Moselstrasse 18
41464 Neuss, Germany
Tel.: (49) 213140990
Fax: (49) 21314099199
E-Mail: info@bruynzeel.de
Web Site: www.bruynzeel.de
Emp.: 12
Provider of Commercial Storage Products
S.I.C.: 2599
N.A.I.C.S.: 337215
Hogas Wiras *(Gen Mgr)*

Bruynzeel Storage Systems bv (2)
Industrieterrein 7
5981 NK Panningen, Netherlands
Tel.: (31) 773069000
Fax: (31) 773078133
E-Mail: info@bruynzeel.org
Web Site: www.bruynzeelstoragesystems.nl
Emp.: 170
Provider of Commercial Storage Systems
S.I.C.: 2599
N.A.I.C.S.: 337215
A. Ewaos *(Mng Dir)*

Constructor Bruynzeel SA/NV (2)
Buro & Design Ctr Heizel Esplanade B
1020 Brussels, Belgium
Tel.: (32) 24794242
Fax: (32) 24798282
E-Mail: info@bruynzeel.be
Web Site: www.bruynzeel.org
Emp.: 21
Provider of Commercial Storage Products
S.I.C.: 2599
N.A.I.C.S.: 337215
Pearre Pletteu *(Dir-Fin)*

Constructor Danmark A/S (2)
Rorupvej 1
DK 4320 Roskilde, Lejre, Denmark
Tel.: (45) 46328008
Fax: (45) 46328118
E-Mail: constructor.denmark@constructor.dk
Web Site: www.constructor.dk
Emp.: 30
Provider of Industrial & Office Storage Products
S.I.C.: 2599
N.A.I.C.S.: 337215
Michael Sahl *(Mng Dir)*

Constructor Dexion France SARL (2)
PB 101413
F 60500 Survilliers, France
Tel.: (33) 344545200
Fax: (33) 344549828
E-Mail: contact@dexion.fr
Web Site: www.dexion.fr
Emp.: 15
Provider of Industrial & Office Storage Products
S.I.C.: 2599
N.A.I.C.S.: 337215
Paul Richard *(Mgr-Fin)*

Constructor Dexion (Hong Kong) Ltd. (2)
6th Fl MTL Bldg Phase II Berth 1
Container Port Rd, Kwai Chung, China (Hong Kong)
Tel.: (852) 24108383
Fax: (852) 24298700
E-Mail: hk@dexion.co.hk
Web Site: www.constructordexion.com
Emp.: 10
Provider of Industrial & Office Storage Products
S.I.C.: 2599
N.A.I.C.S.: 337215
Wika Ip *(Gen Mgr)*

Constructor Dexion Italia SRL (2)
Via Paracelso 26
I 20864 Agrate Brianza, MI, Italy
Tel.: (39) 0396091952
Fax: (39) 0396091957
E-Mail: info@dexionitalia.it
Web Site: www.dexionitalia.it
Industrial & Office Storage Products
S.I.C.: 4226
N.A.I.C.S.: 493190

Constructor Dexion (Malaysia) Ltd. (2)
9 Jalan Juruanalisis U1/35A Hicorn Glenmarie Industrial Park
Hicorn Glenmarie Industrial Pk
Seksyen U1, 40150 Shah Alam, Selangor Darul Ehsan, Malaysia
Tel.: (60) 3 519 2688
Fax: (60) 3 519 2699
Web Site: www.constructordexion.com
Provider of Industrial & Office Storage Products
S.I.C.: 2599
N.A.I.C.S.: 337215

Constructor Dexion (Singapore) Pte. Ltd. (2)
61 Kaki Bukit Ave 61 Fl 2 Unit No 17 Shun Indus Park
Singapore, 417943, Singapore
Tel.: (65) 68426211
E-Mail: customer@dexion.com.sg
Web Site: www.dexion.com.au
Emp.: 100
Provider of Industrial & Office Storage Products
S.I.C.: 2599
N.A.I.C.S.: 337215

Constructor Dexion (Thailand) Ltd. (2)
51 1 Panich Plz
3rd Fl Rama Rd Huaykwang, Bangkok, 10310, Thailand
Tel.: (66) 26438044
Fax: (66) 26431122
E-Mail: info@tellus.co.th
Web Site: www.tellus.co.th
Provider of Industrial & Office Storage Products
S.I.C.: 2599
N.A.I.C.S.: 337215
Peter Johansson *(Mng Dir)*

Constructor Finland Oy (2)
Kasteninkatu 1
P O Box 100
FI-08151 Lohja, Finland
Tel.: (358) 19 36251
Fax: (358) 19 3625333
Web Site: www.kasten.fi
Emp.: 120
Industrial & Office Storage Products
S.I.C.: 4226
N.A.I.C.S.: 493190

Constructor Lagertechnik GmbH (2)
Alte Papiermuhle 25
PO Box 1280
Werk Wipperfurth, D-51688 Wipperfurth, Hammern, Germany
Tel.: (49) 2267660
Fax: (49) 226766105
Web Site: www.lager-logistik.de/deutsch/anbieter/lief_display.php3/288
Provider of Industrial Storage Solutions
S.I.C.: 2599
N.A.I.C.S.: 337215

Constructor Sverige AB (2)
Berdsjodalen 60
S 40053 Gothenburg, Sweden
Tel.: (46) 317719600
Fax: (46) 317719696
E-Mail: info@constructor.se
Web Site: www.constructor.se
Emp.: 65
Provider of Industrial & Office Storage Products
S.I.C.: 2599
N.A.I.C.S.: 337215
Are Lien *(Chm)*
Ulf Sternebratt *(CEO)*

Dexion (Australia) Pty. Ltd. (2)
23 Tattersall Road
PO Box 6470
Blacktown, NSW, 2148, Australia
Tel.: (61) 298305000
Fax: (61) 298305006
Web Site: www.dexion.com.au
Emp.: 200
Provider of Industrial & Office Storage Products
S.I.C.: 2599
N.A.I.C.S.: 337215
Farhad Nourai *(CEO)*
Mark Barraclough *(Exec Gen Mgr-Logistics Sls)*
Martyn Isbell *(Exec Gen Mgr-Intl Bus)*

Dexion Comino Ltd. (2)
Oak Tree House Waterside
Bromsgrove, Worcs, B60 4FD, United Kingdom
Tel.: (44) 8702240220
Fax: (44) 8702240221
E-Mail: enquiries@dexion.co.uk
Web Site: www.dexion.com
Sls.: $495,355,000
Emp.: 3,200
Shelving & Racking Systems Mfr
Export
S.I.C.: 2599
N.A.I.C.S.: 337215
Richard Moss *(Mng Dir)*

Dexion GmbH (2)
Dexionstrasse 1-5
35321 Laubach, Germany
Tel.: (49) 6405800
Fax: (49) 64051422
E-Mail: kontakt@dexion.de
Web Site: www.dexion.de
Emp.: 250
Provider of Industrial Storage Products
S.I.C.: 2599
N.A.I.C.S.: 337215
Norbach Sulzman *(Mng Dir)*

Dexion Kft. (2)
VIII Rigo utca 3
H-1085 Budapest, Hungary
Tel.: (36) 13138426
Fax: (36) 23428175
Web Site: www.constructordexion.com

Altor Equity Partners AB—(Continued)

Provider of Industrial & Office Storage Products
S.I.C.: 2599
N.A.I.C.S.: 337215

Dexion Polska Sp. z.o.o. (2)
ul Annopol 4A
03 236 Warsaw, Poland
Tel.: (48) 22 210 85 00
Fax: (48) 22 210 85 10
E-Mail: biuro@dexionpolska.pl
Web Site: www.dexionpolska.pl
Industrial & Office Storage Products
S.I.C.: 4226
N.A.I.C.S.: 493190
Oddgeir Overli *(Reg Pres)*

Dexion s.r.o. (2)
Leharova 1066/14
Modrany, CZ-1430 Prague, 4, Czech Republic
Tel.: (420) 2402 6468
Fax: (420) 2402 6474
E-Mail: dexion@dexion.cz
Web Site: www.dexion.cz
Provider of Industrial & Office Storage Products
S.I.C.: 2599
N.A.I.C.S.: 337215

Dexion Storage Equipment (Shanghai) Co. Ltd. (2)
Suite 605 Taipan Business Centre
20 Dong Hu Lu, Shanghai, 200031, China
Tel.: (86) 2154043152
Fax: (86) 2154041831
Web Site: www.constructordexion.com
Provider of Industrial & Office Storage Products
S.I.C.: 2599
N.A.I.C.S.: 337215

Ferrosan A/S (1)
Sydmarken 5
DK 2860 Soborg, Denmark (70%)
Tel.: (45) 39692111
Fax: (45) 39696518
E-Mail: info@ferrosan.com
Web Site: www.ferrosan.com
Sales Range: $200-249.9 Million
Emp.: 700
Developer, Producer & Marketer of Pharmaceuticals
S.I.C.: 2834
N.A.I.C.S.: 325412
Hakan Astrom *(Chm)*
Ola Erici *(Pres & CEO)*
Mogens C. Pedersen *(Sr Mng Dir-Corp Bus Dev)*
Henrik Krxis *(Mng Dir-Medical Devices)*
Jens Mondrup *(Mng Dir-Consumer Health)*
Soren Kristiansen *(CFO & Exec VP)*

U.S. Subsidiary:

Ferrosan International A/S (2)
Ste 300, 8117 Preston Road
Dallas, TX 75225
Tel.: (214) 706-9060
Fax: (214) 706-9061
Developer, Producer & Marketer of Pharmaceuticals
S.I.C.: 2834
N.A.I.C.S.: 325412

Non-U.S. Subsidiaries:

Ferrosan do Brasil Ltda. (2)
Rua Americo Brasiliense No 271 CJ 608
Chacara Sto Antonio, Sao Paulo, 0471 5005, Brazil
Tel.: (55) 1121641400
Fax: (55) 1151840557
E-Mail: imaging@imaging.com.br
Web Site: www.imaging.com.br
Emp.: 25
Developer, Producer & Marketer of Pharmaceuticals
S.I.C.: 2834
N.A.I.C.S.: 325412
Maristela Fieschi *(Country Mgr)*

Ferrosan International A/S (2)
25 Rue d'Hauteville
75 010 Paris, France
Tel.: (33) 153249140
Fax: (33) 147709803
E-Mail: sag@ferrosan.com
Web Site: www.ferrosan.com
Developer, Producer & Marketer of Pharmaceuticals
S.I.C.: 2834
N.A.I.C.S.: 325412
Sabine Granier *(Country Mgr-France)*

Ferrosan Ltd. (2)
21-22 Grosvenor St
London, W1K 4QJ, United Kingdom
Tel.: (44) 2074085080
Fax: (44) 2074082444
Web Site: www.imedeen.co.uk
Provider of Pharmaceuticals
S.I.C.: 2834
N.A.I.C.S.: 325412

Ferrosan Norge AS (2)
Trollasveien 6
PO Box 443
N-1411 Kolbotn, Norway
Tel.: (47) 66995780
Fax: (47) 66995790
Web Site: www.ferrosan.com
Developer, Producer & Marketer of Pharmaceuticals
S.I.C.: 2834
N.A.I.C.S.: 325412

Ferrosan Poland Sp. z.o.o. (2)
ul Wlodarzewska 45D
PL 02 384 Warsaw, Poland
Tel.: (48) 226687676
Fax: (48) 228832353
Developer, Producer & Marketer of Pharmaceuticals
S.I.C.: 2834
N.A.I.C.S.: 325412
Mikolej Lypka *(Country Mgr)*

Ferrosan S.R.L (2)
Calea Turziy 178C
40595 Cluj-Napoca, Romania
Tel.: (40) 264453232
Fax: (40) 264438012
Developer, Producer & Marketer of Pharmaceuticals
S.I.C.: 2834
N.A.I.C.S.: 325412

Oy Ferrosan AB (2)
Vavarsvagen 11
FIN 02630 Espoo, Finland
Tel.: (358) 95259050
Fax: (358) 9520236
E-Mail: phar@ferrosan.com
Web Site: www.ferrosan.fi
Emp.: 17
Developer, Marketer & Producer of Pharmaceuticals
S.I.C.: 2834
N.A.I.C.S.: 325412
Kaj Molin *(Country Mgr)*

Haarslev Industries A/S (1)
Bogensevej 85
5471 Sonderso, Funen, Denmark DK
Tel.: (45) 63831100
Fax: (45) 63831120
E-Mail: info@haarslev.com
Web Site: www.haarslev.com
Sales Range: $200-249.9 Million
Emp.: 650
Mfr of Processing Equipment for the Meat, Pet Food, Fish, Oil, Environmental Protection & Biofuel Industries
S.I.C.: 3559
N.A.I.C.S.: 333249
Claus Ostergaard Nielsen *(CEO)*

U.S. Subsidiary:

Haarslev Inc. (2)
9700 NW Conant Ave
Kansas City, MO 64153
Tel.: (816) 799-0808
Fax: (816) 799-0812
E-Mail: info-usa@haarslev.com
Web Site: www.haarslev.com
Emp.: 20
Sales of Processing Equipment for the Meat, Pet Food, Fish, Oil, Environmental Protection & Biofuel Industries
S.I.C.: 5084
N.A.I.C.S.: 423830
Robert McKay *(VP-Sls)*

Non-U.S. Subsidiaries:

Haarslev Industries GmbH (2)
Hohenbudberger Strasse 33
47829 Krefeld, Germany
Tel.: (49) 2151494690
Fax: (49) 21514946949
E-Mail: info@haarslev.de
Web Site: www.haarslev.com
Emp.: 4
Mfr & Sales of Processing Equipment for the Meat, Pet Food, Fish, Oil, Environmental Protection & Biofuel Industries
S.I.C.: 5084
N.A.I.C.S.: 423830
Juergen Hess *(Mng Dir)*

Haarslev Industries Ltda. (2)
Rua Cyro Correia Pereira 3210
CIC, Curitiba, PR, CEP 81460 050, Brazil
Tel.: (55) 41 3389 0055
Fax: (55) 41 3389 0035
E-Mail: info@haarslev.com.br
Web Site: www.haarslev.com.br
Mfr of Processing Equipment for the Meat, Pet Food, Fish, Oil, Environmental Protection & Biofuel Industries
S.I.C.: 3559
N.A.I.C.S.: 333249

Haarslev Industries Ltd. (2)
10 Beatrice Tinsley Crescent
Albany, Auckland, New Zealand
Tel.: (64) 9415 2330
Fax: (64) 9415 2331
E-Mail: info@haarslev.com
Sales of Processing Equipment for the Meat, Pet Food, Fish, Oil, Environmental Protection & Biofuel Industries
S.I.C.: 5084
N.A.I.C.S.: 423830
Tissa Fernando *(Mng Dir)*

Haarslev Industries SAC (2)
Av Comercial no 13 Urb Las Praderas de Lurin
Lurin, Lima, Peru
Tel.: (51) 1720 7272
E-Mail: info@haarslev.com.pe
Mfr of Processing Equipment for the Meat, Pet Food, Fish, Oil, Environmental Protection & Biofuel Industries
S.I.C.: 3559
N.A.I.C.S.: 333249

Haarslev Industries S.A.U. (2)
Poligon Ind Font del Radium Alfred Nobel 16
Granollers, 08403 Barcelona, Spain
Tel.: (34) 9 3840 4500
Fax: (34) 9 3840 1248
E-Mail: info@haarslev.com.es
Mfr of Processing Equipment for the Meat, Pet Food, Fish, Oil, Environmental Protection & Biofuel Industries
S.I.C.: 3559
N.A.I.C.S.: 333249
Joaquim Latorre *(Mgr-Svc)*

Haarslev Industries Sdn Bhd (2)
2A Jalan Anggerik Vanilla W31/W Kota Kemuning
40460 Shah Alam, Selangor Darul Eshan, Malaysia
Tel.: (60) 3 5122 3763
Fax: (60) 3 5122 9763
E-Mail: info@haarslev.com
Sales of Processing Equipment for the Meat, Pet Food, Fish, Oil, Environmental Protection & Biofuel Industries
S.I.C.: 5084
N.A.I.C.S.: 423830

Haarslev Industries (2)
Level 13 Platinum Techno Park 17 & 18 Sector 30 Vashi
Navi Mumbai, 400705, India
Tel.: (91) 22 6121 4949
Fax: (91) 22 6121 4950
E-Mail: info@haarslev.com
Sales of Processing Equipment for the Meat, Pet Food, Fish, Oil, Environmental Protection & Biofuel Industries
S.I.C.: 5084
N.A.I.C.S.: 423830

Haarslev Machinery Xuzhou Co. (2)
18 Miaoshan Road Jinshanqiao Economic Development Zone
Xuzhou, Jiangsu, China
Tel.: (86) 516 8773 2999
Fax: (86) 516 8789 4999
E-Mail: info@haarslev.com
Mfr of Processing Equipment for the Meat, Pet Food, Fish, Oil, Environmental Protection & Biofuel Industries
S.I.C.: 3559
N.A.I.C.S.: 333249

Haarslev UK Ltd. (2)
Haarslev House West Pimbo Business Park
Paddock Road, Skelmersdale, Lancs, WN8 9PL, United Kingdom
Tel.: (44) 1695455500
Fax: (44) 1695 455 555
E-Mail: info@haarslevuk.com
Web Site: www.haarslevuk.com
Mfr & Sales of Processing Equipment for the Meat, Pet Food, Fish, Oil, Environmental Protection & Biofuel Industries
S.I.C.: 5084
N.A.I.C.S.: 423830

OOO Haarslev Industries (2)
Prospect Lenina 107/49 Office 304
Podolsk, Russia
Tel.: (7) 495 543 94 10
Fax: (7) 4967 55 93 70
E-Mail: info@haarslev.com
Sales of Processing Equipment for the Meat, Pet Food, Fish, Oil, Environmental Protection & Biofuel Industries
S.I.C.: 5084
N.A.I.C.S.: 423830

Navico Holding AS (1)
Nyaskaiveien 2
4370 Egersund, Norway NO
Tel.: (47) 6712 6400
Web Site: www.navico.com
Sales Range: $300-349.9 Million
Emp.: 1,500
Holding Company; Marine Electronics Equipment Mfr & Distr
S.I.C.: 6719
N.A.I.C.S.: 551112
Leif Ottosson *(Pres & CEO)*
Marcel Crince *(CFO & COO-EMEA)*
Louis Chemi *(COO-Americas & Exec VP)*
John Scott *(COO-Asia Pacific & Exec VP)*
Jim Brailey *(Exec VP-Supply Chain Mgmt & Ops)*
Tom Edvardsen *(Exec VP-R&D)*

U.S. Subsidiary:

Navico, Inc. (2)
4500 S 129th East Ave Ste 200
Tulsa, OK 74134 DE
Tel.: (918) 437-6881
Fax: (918) 234-1728
Web Site: www.lowrance.com
Sonar & Navigational Equipment & Accessories Mfr & Distr
Import Export
S.I.C.: 3812
N.A.I.C.S.: 334511
Louis Chemi *(Pres & Grp COO-Americas)*

Non-U.S. Subsidiary:

Brookes & Gatehouse, Ltd. (2)
Premier Way Abbey Pk
Romsey, Hampshire, SO51 9DH, United Kingdom
Tel.: (44) 1794510010
Fax: (44) 1794518077
E-Mail: service.uk@navico.com
Web Site: www.bandg.com
Emp.: 30
Mfr of Marine Navigation Products
S.I.C.: 3812
N.A.I.C.S.: 334511
Christian Olsson *(Gen Mgr)*

Non-U.S. Joint Ventures:

EWOS AS (1)
Tollbodallmenningen 1b
5803 Bergen, Norway NO
Mailing Address:
Postboks 4 Sentrum
5803 Bergen, Norway
Tel.: (47) 55697000
Fax: (47) 55697001
E-Mail: ordre@ewos.no
Web Site: www.ewos.com
Emp.: 20
Fish Feed Mfr
S.I.C.: 2048
N.A.I.C.S.: 311119
Einar Wathne *(COO)*

Subsidiary:

EWOS Innovation AS (2)
Hanaveien 17
4327 Sandnes, Norway

Mailing Address:
Postboks 23
4335 Dirdal, Norway
Tel.: (47) 5569 7800
Fax: (47) 5569 7810
E-Mail: innovation@ewos.com
Web Site: www.ewos.com
Fish Feed Research & Development
S.I.C.: 8731
N.A.I.C.S.: 541711
Adel El-Mowafi *(Mng Dir)*

Non-U.S. Subsidiaries:

EWOS Canada Ltd. **(2)**
7721 132nd Street
Surrey, BC, V3W 4M8, Canada
Tel.: (604) 591-6368
Fax: (604) 591-7232
E-Mail: canada@ewos.com
Web Site: www.ewos.com
Emp.: 90
Fish Feed Mfr
S.I.C.: 2048
N.A.I.C.S.: 311119
Ross Grierson *(Pres & Mng Dir)*

EWOS Chile S.A. **(2)**
Av Benavente 550 Edif Torre Campanario
Puerto Montt, Los Lagos, 1184, Chile CL
Tel.: (56) 65272222
Fax: (56) 65321111
E-Mail: tarl.samsing@ewos.com
Web Site: www.ewos.com
Emp.: 20
Fish Feed Mfr
S.I.C.: 2048
N.A.I.C.S.: 311119
Andres Tagle *(Gen Mgr)*

Subsidiaries:

EWOS Chile Alimentos Ltda. **(3)**
Parque Industrial Escuadron Km 20 Camino
Concepcion Coronel, Coronel, Chile CL
Tel.: (56) 412205700
Fax: (56) 412205776
Web Site: www.ewos.com
Fish Feed Mfr
S.I.C.: 2048
N.A.I.C.S.: 311119
Andres Tagle *(Gen Mgr)*

EWOS Limited **(2)**
Westfield
Bathgate, W Lothian, EH48 3BP, United Kingdom UK
Tel.: (44) 1506 633 966
Fax: (44) 1506 632 730
E-Mail: customersolutions@ewos.com
Web Site: www.ewos.com
Emp.: 60
Fish Feed Mfr
S.I.C.: 2048
N.A.I.C.S.: 311119
Douglas Low *(Mng Dir)*

Lindorff Holding AB **(1)**
Fyrstikkalleen 1
0661 Oslo, Norway
Mailing Address:
PO Box 283-Skoyen
N 0213 Oslo, Norway
Tel.: (47) 23211000
Fax: (47) 23211100
E-Mail: info.norge@lindorff.com
Web Site: www.lindorff.com
Sales Range: $250-299.9 Million
Emp.: 1,200
Credit Reporting & Debt Collection Services; Owned 50% by Altor Equity Partners AB & 50% by Investor AB
S.I.C.: 7323
N.A.I.C.S.: 561450
Hugo Maurstad *(Chm)*
Endre Rangnes *(CEO)*
Petra Hedengrand *(Mng Dir)*
Frederik Zimmer *(CFO)*
Anders Nybo *(COO)*
Lassi Karppinen *(Exec VP-Payment Nordic & Head-Eastern-Central Europe)*

Non-U.S. Subsidiaries:

Lindorff A/S **(2)**
Roskildevej 342 A
2630 Tastrup, Denmark
Tel.: (45) 70268610
Fax: (45) 70268601
E-Mail: Info.danmark@lindorff.com
Web Site: www.lindorff.com
Credit Services
S.I.C.: 6099
N.A.I.C.S.: 522390
Anette Trolle *(Mgr)*

Lindorff Eesti AS **(2)**
Ravala pst 5
10143 Tallinn, Estonia
Tel.: (372) 6161800
Fax: (372) 6161801
E-Mail: info.eesti@lindorff.ee
Credit Services
S.I.C.: 6099
N.A.I.C.S.: 522390

Lindorff Netherlands B.V. **(2)**
Punterweg 12
8042PB Zwolle, Netherlands
Tel.: (31) 384973939
Fax: (31) 384973971
E-Mail: info@lindorff.nl
Web Site: www.lindorff.com
Emp.: 170
Credit Services
S.I.C.: 6099
N.A.I.C.S.: 522390
Martin Van Loon *(Mng Dir)*

Lindorff Oy **(2)**
PO Box 20
20101 Turku, Finland
Tel.: (358) 10270000
Fax: (358) 102700100
E-Mail: turkka.kuusisto@lindorff.com
Web Site: www.lindorff.com
Emp.: 500
Other Activities Related to Credit Intermediation
S.I.C.: 6099
N.A.I.C.S.: 522390
Turkka Kuusisto *(Country Mgr)*

Lindorff Sverige AB **(2)**
Fredsborgsgatan 24
SE-117 43 Stockholm, Sweden
Mailing Address:
Box 472 97
SE-100 74 Stockholm, Sweden
Tel.: (46) 858728100
Fax: (46) 858728101
E-Mail: info.stockholm@lindorff.com
Web Site: www.lindorff.com
Emp.: 200
Credit Services
S.I.C.: 6099
N.A.I.C.S.: 522390
Mikael Inglander *(Country Mgr)*

ALTPLUS INC.

3-12-18 Shibuya
Shibuya-ku, Tokyo, 150-0002, Japan
Tel.: (81) 3 4577 6701
E-Mail: info@altplus.co.jp
Web Site: www.altplus.co.jp
3672—(TKS)
Rev.: $10,061,964
Emp.: 90
Fiscal Year-end: 09/30/12

Business Description:
Mobile Device Social Game Developer
S.I.C.: 7372
N.A.I.C.S.: 511210

Personnel:
Takeshi Ishii *(Pres)*

ALTRAN TECHNOLOGIES S.A.

2 rue Paul Dautier
78457 Velizy-Villacoublay, France
Tel.: (33) 130674800
Fax: (33) 130674810
Web Site: www.altran.com
Year Founded: 1982
ALT—(EUR OTC)
Rev.: $2,009,489,883
Assets: $1,663,303,421
Liabilities: $1,023,070,354
Net Worth: $640,233,067
Earnings: $86,957,197
Emp.: 18,130
Fiscal Year-end: 12/31/12

Business Description:
Engineering & Technology Consulting & Related Services
S.I.C.: 8711
N.A.I.C.S.: 541330

Personnel:
Philippe Salle *(Chm & CEO)*
Olivier Aldrin *(CFO & VP)*
Jose Ramon Magarzo *(Chm/CEO-Iberia)*
Bernard Carrel Billiard *(Gen Counsel & Grp VP)*
Cyril Roger *(Sr Exec VP-Southern Europe)*
Michel Bailly *(Exec VP-Programs & Innovation)*
Michael Blickle *(Exec VP-Northern Europe)*
Pascal Brier *(Exec VP-Indus & Solutions Bus Dev)*
Claude Cohen *(Sr VP-HR)*
Frederic Grard *(Sr VP-Northern Europe)*

Board of Directors:
Philippe Salle
Jean-Pierre Alix
Bernard Carrel Billiard
Christian Bret
Monique Cohen
Jacques-Etienne de T'Serclaes
Thomas de Villeneuve
Hans-Georg Harter
Florence Parly
Nathalie Rachou
Gilles Rigal
Maurice Tchenio

Deloitte & Associes
185 avenue Charles-de-Gaulle
Neuilly-sur-Seine, France

Subsidiaries:

Altran CIS France **(1)**
58 Boulevard Gouvion Saint Cyr
75017 Paris, France
Tel.: (33) 1 48 88 70 00
Fax: (33) 1 48 88 70 01
Information Technology Consulting Services
S.I.C.: 7373
N.A.I.C.S.: 541512

Altran Praxis SAS **(1)**
950 Avenue De Roumanille Batiment Teck
BP 305
6906 Sophia-Antipolis, France
Tel.: (33) 4 92 38 11 11
Fax: (33) 4 92 38 11 12
E-Mail: info@altran-praxis.com
Emp.: 80
Security Software Development Services
S.I.C.: 7371
N.A.I.C.S.: 541511
Karim Alami *(Mgr)*

DATACEP SA **(1)**
Immeuble Le Libertis 2 Rue Paul Vaillant Couturier
92300 Levallois-Perret, France
Tel.: (33) 1 46 17 51 00
Fax: (33) 1 46 17 51 02
Web Site: www.datacep.fr
Information Technology Consulting Services
S.I.C.: 7373
N.A.I.C.S.: 541512

DIOREM **(1)**
2 Rue Paul Vaillant Couturier
92300 Levallois-Perret, France
Tel.: (33) 1 48 88 74 60
Fax: (33) 1 46 17 45 49
Web Site: www.diorem.fr
Emp.: 12
Professional Training Services
S.I.C.: 8299
N.A.I.C.S.: 611430
Bruno Koenig *(Gen Mgr)*

NSI S.A. **(1)**
6 Avenue Du Pre De Challes
74 943 Annecy-le-Vieux, France
Tel.: (33) 450 094 630
E-Mail: nsi@nsi.fr
Web Site: www.nsi.fr
Sales Range: $10-24.9 Million
Electronic Software Development Services
S.I.C.: 7371
N.A.I.C.S.: 541511
Yvan Chabanne *(Mng Dir)*

U.S. Subsidiaries:

Altran Solutions Corp. **(1)**
80 Fargo St
Boston, MA 02210
Tel.: (617) 204-1000
Fax: (617) 204-1010
E-Mail: sales@altransolutions.com
Web Site: www.altransolutions.com
Engineering Services
S.I.C.: 8711
N.A.I.C.S.: 541330
Thomas Foley *(Pres)*
Christopher Caprio *(CFO)*

Altran USA Holdings Inc. **(1)**
451 D St Ste 110
Boston, MA 02210-1988
Tel.: (617) 204-1000
Fax: (617) 204-1010
Investment Management Services
S.I.C.: 6211
N.A.I.C.S.: 523999

Non-U.S. Subsidiaries:

Altran AG **(1)**
Avenue De Savoie 10
1003 Lausanne, Switzerland
Tel.: (41) 21 331 15 30
Fax: (41) 21 989 22 55
E-Mail: info@altran.ch
Information Technology Consulting Services
S.I.C.: 7371
N.A.I.C.S.: 541511

Altran B.V. **(1)**
H Walaardt Sacrestraat 405
Schiphol Oost, 1117 BM Schiphol, Netherlands
Tel.: (31) 20 4498390
Fax: (31) 20 4499999
E-Mail: info@altran.nl
Web Site: www.altran.nl
Emp.: 125
Business Management Consulting Services
S.I.C.: 8742
N.A.I.C.S.: 541611

Altran Canada Inc **(1)**
7575 Rte Transcanadienne Bureau 500
Montreal, QC, H4T 1V6, Canada
Tel.: (514) 331-0155
Fax: (514) 331-6120
Engineering Consulting Services
S.I.C.: 8711
N.A.I.C.S.: 541330

Altran Deutschland Holding GmbH **(1)**
Schillerstr 20
Frankfurt am Main, 60313, Germany
Tel.: (49) 696605530
Fax: (49) 6966055416
Investment Management Services
S.I.C.: 6211
N.A.I.C.S.: 523999

Altran Innovacion S.L.U. **(1)**
Parque Empresarial Las Mercedes
C/Campezo 1 Edificio 1
28022 Madrid, Spain
Tel.: (34) 91 550 41 00
Fax: (34) 91 415 61 53
E-Mail: comunicacion@altran.es
Emp.: 216
Information Technology Consulting Services
S.I.C.: 7373
N.A.I.C.S.: 541512

Altran International B.V. **(1)**
Walaardt Sacrestraat 405
Schiphol, 1117 BM, Netherlands
Tel.: (31) 20 4498390
Fax: (31) 20 4499999
Web Site: www.altran.nl
Emp.: 150
Information Technology Consulting Services
S.I.C.: 7373
N.A.I.C.S.: 541512
Roman Lauzin *(Gen Mgr)*

Altran Italia S.p.A. **(1)**
Via Goito 52
185 Rome, Italy
Tel.: (39) 06 91659500
Fax: (39) 06 91659502

Altran Technologies S.A.—(Continued)

E-Mail: info@altran.it
Web Site: www.altran.it
Emp.: 200
Management Consulting Services
S.I.C.: 8742
N.A.I.C.S.: 541611
Marcel Alain Aetrignani *(Pres)*

Altran Luxembourg S.A.N.V. **(1)**
26-28 Rue Edward Steichen
2540 Luxembourg, Luxembourg
Tel.: (352) 26 30 85 1
Web Site: www.altran.be/altran-in-the-world/countries/country/luxembourg.html
Emp.: 60
Financial Management Services
S.I.C.: 6211
N.A.I.C.S.: 523999
Pascal Laffineur *(CEO)*

Altran Norway AS **(1)**
Ostensjoveien 36
0667 Oslo, Norway
Tel.: (47) 22 20 71 30
Fax: (47) 22 20 70 69
E-Mail: info@altran.no
Web Site: www.altran.se/no/norge/
Emp.: 15
Enterprise Content Management Consulting Services
S.I.C.: 8748
N.A.I.C.S.: 541618
Hans Johansson *(CEO)*
Peter Forsmark *(COO)*

Altran Osterreich GmbH **(1)**
Schottenfeldgasse 23/ 5 OG
1070 Vienna, Austria
Tel.: (43) 1 877 01 20 0
Fax: (43) 1 877 01 20 399
E-Mail: office.at@altran.com
Web Site: www.altran.at
Emp.: 4
Information Technology Consulting Services
S.I.C.: 7373
N.A.I.C.S.: 541512
Michael Haehnle *(Bus Mgr)*

Altran Portugal S.A. **(1)**
Av Das Forcas Armadas Ed Open N 125 - 3
1600-079 Lisbon, Portugal
Tel.: (351) 210 331 600
Fax: (351) 210 331 639
E-Mail: info@altran.pt
Web Site: www.altran.pt
Emp.: 400
Information Technology Consulting Services
S.I.C.: 7373
N.A.I.C.S.: 541512
Celia Reis *(Gen Mgr)*

Altran Praxis Limited **(1)**
22 St Lawwrence Street South Gate
Bath, BA1 1AN, United Kingdom
Tel.: (44) 1225 466991
Fax: (44) 1225 469006
E-Mail: info@altran.com
Web Site: www.altran.com
Emp.: 15
Software Development Services
S.I.C.: 7371
N.A.I.C.S.: 541511
Mike Greenan *(Gen Mgr)*

Altran S.A.N.V. **(1)**
Avenue De Tervuren 142-144 Tervurenlaan 142-144
Tervurenlaan 142-144, 1150 Brussels, Belgium
Tel.: (32) 2 737 68 11
Fax: (32) 2 737 68 36
E-Mail: info@altran.com
Web Site: www.altran.be
Emp.: 15
Engineering Consulting Services
S.I.C.: 8999
N.A.I.C.S.: 541690
Pascal Laffineur *(CEO)*

Altran Shangai Ltd. **(1)**
Unit 1801 Silver Tower 85 Taoyuan Road
Shanghai, 200021, China
Tel.: (86) 21 6407 9499
Web Site: www.altran.com
Business Management Consulting Services
S.I.C.: 8748
N.A.I.C.S.: 541618
David Nicolas *(CEO-China & Southeast Asia)*

Altran Sverige AB **(1)**
Sofierogatan 3A 4 Tr
Gothenburg, 412 51, Sweden
Tel.: (46) 31 746 55 50
Fax: (46) 31 746 55 69
E-Mail: info@altran.se
Web Site: www.altran.se
Emp.: 35
Information Technology Consulting Services
S.I.C.: 7373
N.A.I.C.S.: 541512
Philippe Salle *(CEO)*
Hans Johansson *(Mng Dir)*
Leif Jakobsson *(CFO)*

Altran (Switzerland) S.A. **(1)**
Avenue De Savoie 10
1003 Lausanne, Switzerland
Tel.: (41) 21 331 15 30
Fax: (41) 21 331 15 39
E-Mail: education@altran.ch
Web Site: www.altran.ch
Emp.: 200
Information Technology Consulting Services
S.I.C.: 7373
N.A.I.C.S.: 541512
Nicolas Mayer *(Gen Mgr)*

Altran Technologies India Ltd. **(1)**
A - 1 First Floor Sector - 10
Noida, Uttar Pradesh, 201301, India
Tel.: (91) 120 47 38 900
Fax: (91) 120 47 38 910
E-Mail: business.queries@altran.com
Web Site: www.altran.co.in
Information Technology Consulting Services
S.I.C.: 8999
N.A.I.C.S.: 541690
Sanjay Kumar *(CEO)*

Altran Technologies Sweden AB **(1)**
Lofstroms Alle 5
172 66 Sundbyberg, Sweden
Tel.: (46) 8 705 86 40
Fax: (46) 8 514 949 79
E-Mail: contact@altran-tech.se
Web Site: www.altran.se/en/sweden/Altran-Technologies/
Emp.: 15
Information Technology Consulting Services
S.I.C.: 7373
N.A.I.C.S.: 541512
Sarla Moodley *(Mgr)*

Altran Technologies UK Ltd. **(1)**
2nd Floor Shackleton House 4 Battlebridge Lane
London, SE1 2HP, United Kingdom
Tel.: (44) 203 117 0700
Fax: (44) 203 117 0701
Web Site: www.altran-tech.co.uk
Automotive Information Technology Consulting Services
S.I.C.: 7373
N.A.I.C.S.: 541512
Fabrice Boyer *(Mng Dir & Dir-Acting ASDR Div)*

Altran UK Limited **(1)**
2nd Floor Shackleton House 4 Battlebridge Lane
London, SE1 2HP, United Kingdom
Tel.: (44) 203 117 0700
Fax: (44) 203 117 0701
Web Site: www.altran.be/altran-in-the-world/countries/country/united-kingdom.html
Emp.: 500
Information Technology Consulting Services
S.I.C.: 7373
N.A.I.C.S.: 541512
Mike Simms *(CEO)*
Michael Blickle *(Exec VP-Northern Europe)*

Altran Xype Deutschland GmbH **(1)**
Blohmstrasse 10 Channel 9
21079 Hamburg, Germany
Tel.: (49) 40 30 38 57 84 0
Fax: (49) 40 30 38 57 84 9
E-Mail: contact@xype.com
Web Site: www.altran-xype.com
Emp.: 9
Engineering Consulting Services
S.I.C.: 8999
N.A.I.C.S.: 541690
Thorsten Bartel *(Gen Mgr)*

Altran Xype Ltd **(1)**
Brabazon Park Golf Course Lane
Filton, Bristol, BS34 7PZ, United Kingdom
Tel.: (44) 117 90 62 130
Fax: (44) 117 90 62 131
E-Mail: contact@xype.com
Web Site: www.altran-xype.com
Information Technology Consulting Services
S.I.C.: 7373
N.A.I.C.S.: 541512

Cambridge Consultants Ltd **(1)**
Science Park Milton Road
Cambridge, CB4 0DW, United Kingdom UK
Tel.: (44) 1223420024
Telex: 81481 CCL G
Fax: (44) 1223423373
E-Mail: info@cambridgeconsultants.com
Web Site: www.cambridgeconsultants.com
Emp.: 380
Technology Consulting Services
S.I.C.: 8999
N.A.I.C.S.: 541690
Alan Richardson *(CEO)*
Mammen Eapen *(CFO)*
Eric Wilkinson *(COO)*
Ray Edgson *(CTO & Dir-Ventures)*

U.S. Subsidiary:

Cambridge Consultants, Inc. **(2)**
101 Main St
Cambridge, MA 02142
Tel.: (617) 532-4700
Fax: (617) 532-4747
E-Mail: info@cambridgeconsultants.com
Web Site: www.cambridgeconsultants.com
Business Management Consulting Services
S.I.C.: 8742
N.A.I.C.S.: 541611
Alan Richardson *(CEO)*
Mammen Eapen *(CFO)*
Eric Wilkinson *(COO)*
Ray Edgson *(CTO & Dir-Ventures)*

CHS Data Systems Gesellschaft fur Systementwicklung und Beratung GmbH **(1)**
Bahnhofplatz 18-20
56068 Koblenz, Germany
Tel.: (49) 261 915990
Fax: (49) 261 915778
Information Technology Consulting Services
S.I.C.: 7373
N.A.I.C.S.: 541512

SUTHERLAND CONSULTING LIMITED **(1)**
Hidden Orchard
Market Rasen, Lincolnshire, LN8 6JH, United Kingdom
Tel.: (44) 1507 313400
E-Mail: info@sutherlandconsulting.co.uk
Web Site: www.sutherlandconsulting.co.uk
Information Technology Consulting Services
S.I.C.: 7373
N.A.I.C.S.: 541512

ALTRI, SGPS, S.A.

Rua do General Norton de Matos 68 - r/c
4050-424 Porto, Portugal
Tel.: (351) 228346502
Fax: (351) 228346503
E-Mail: sede@altri.pt
Web Site: www.altri.pt
Year Founded: 2005
ALTR—(EUR)
Sls.: $703,123,989
Assets: $1,518,964,443
Liabilities: $1,271,367,552
Net Worth: $247,596,891
Earnings: $70,276,315
Emp.: 636
Fiscal Year-end: 12/31/12

Business Description:
Paper Pulp Mfr
S.I.C.: 2611
N.A.I.C.S.: 322110

Personnel:
Paulo Jorge dos Santos Fernandes *(Chm)*
Joao Manuel Matos Borges de Oliveira *(CFO)*
Ricardo Mendes Ferreira *(IR Officer)*

Board of Directors:
Paulo Jorge dos Santos Fernandes
Laurentina da Silva Martins
Domingos Jose Vieira de Matos
Pedro Macedo Pinto de Mendonca
Joao Manuel Matos Borges de Oliveira

Subsidiaries:

Celulose Beira Industrial (Celbi), S.A. **(1)**
Leirosa
3081-853 Figueira da Foz, Portugal
Tel.: (351) 233 955 600
Fax: (351) 233 955 648
Web Site: www.celbi.pt
Paper Pulp Mfr
S.I.C.: 2621
N.A.I.C.S.: 322121

Viveiros do Furadouro Unipessoal, Lda. **(1)**
Qta Do Furadouro
Olho Marinho, Leiria, Portugal 2510-582
Tel.: (351) 26 296 5020
Plant Cultivation Services
S.I.C.: 0181
N.A.I.C.S.: 111421

Non-U.S. Subsidiary:

Altri Sales, S.A. **(1)**
Route de Clementy 62
1260 Nyon, Switzerland
Tel.: (41) 22 365 51 60
Fax: (41) 22 365 51 69
Paper Pulp Whlsr
S.I.C.: 5149
N.A.I.C.S.: 424490

Non-U.S. Holding:

Altri, Participaciones Y Trading, S.L. **(1)**
Calle de Orense 25
28020 Madrid, Spain
Tel.: (34) 914 17 44 84
Fax: (34) 914 84 44 84
Emp.: 1
Investment Management Services
S.I.C.: 6282
N.A.I.C.S.: 523920
Alexandra Costa, *(Gen Mgr)*

ALTURA MINING LIMITED

Building 8 22 Magnolia Drive
Brookwater, QLD, 4300, Australia
Tel.: (61) 7 3814 6900
Fax: (61) 7 3814 6911
E-Mail: info@alturamining.com
Web Site: www.alturamining.com
AJM—(ASX)
Rev.: $7,338,468
Assets: $91,022,225
Liabilities: $29,838,449
Net Worth: $61,183,775
Earnings: ($980,616)
Emp.: 12
Fiscal Year-end: 06/30/13

Business Description:
Mining Services
S.I.C.: 1241
N.A.I.C.S.: 213113

Personnel:
James Brown *(Mng Dir)*
Noel Young *(Co-Sec & Controller-Fin)*
Damon Cox *(Co-Sec)*

Board of Directors:
James Brown
Allan Charles Buckler
Beng Teik Kuan
Paul Mantell
Dan O'Neill

ALTURAS MINERALS CORP.

67 Yonge Street Suite 1102
Toronto, ON, M5E 1J8, Canada
Tel.: (416) 363-4900
E-Mail: contact@alturasminerals.com
Web Site: www.alturasminerals.com
ALT—(TSXV)
Sales Range: Less than $1 Million
Emp.: 4

Business Description:
Mineral Exploration Services
S.I.C.: 1081
N.A.I.C.S.: 213114
Personnel:
Walter C. Henry *(Chm)*
Miguel Cardozo *(Pres & CEO)*
Mario A. Miranda *(CFO)*
Kathleen Skerrett *(Corp Counsel)*
Board of Directors:
Walter C. Henry
Augusto Baerti
Miguel Cardozo
Roland Eschle
Paul Pearson
Kathleen Skerrett
Transfer Agent:
Computershare Trust Company of Canada
Calgary, AB, Canada

ALTUS GROUP LIMITED

33 Yonge Street Suite 500
Toronto, ON, M5E 1G4, Canada
Tel.: (416) 641-9500
Fax: (416) 641-9501
E-Mail: info@altusgroup.com
Web Site: www.altusgroup.com
Year Founded: 2005
AIF—(TSX)
Rev.: $320,669,858
Assets: $415,539,127
Liabilities: $291,889,003
Net Worth: $123,650,124
Earnings: ($12,578,329)
Emp.: 1,700
Fiscal Year-end: 12/31/12
Business Description:
Real Estate Development Services
S.I.C.: 6531
N.A.I.C.S.: 531390
Personnel:
Harvey S. Naglie *(Chm)*
Robert Courteau *(CEO)*
Angelo Bartolini *(CFO)*
Mike Abramsky *(CTO)*
Colin Johnston *(Pres-Res, Valuation & Advisory-Canada)*
Daniel Lachance *(Pres-Geomatics)*
Alex Probyn *(Pres-UK)*
Robert K. Ruggles, III *(Pres-Res, Valuation & Advisory-USA)*
Liana Turrin *(Gen Counsel & Sec)*
Michael Commons *(Sr Exec VP-Cost Consulting & Project Mgmt)*
Board of Directors:
Harvey S. Naglie
Robert Courteau
J. Trevor Eyton
Tony Gaffney
Diane MacDiarmid
A. B. McArthur
Raymond Mikulich
Eric W. Slavens
Transfer Agent:
CIBC Mellon Trust
PO Box 700 Station B
Montreal, QC, H3B 3K3, Canada

ALTUS RENEWABLES LIMITED

Suite 4 3974 Pacific Highway
PO Box 4667
Loganholme, QLD, 4109, Australia
Tel.: (61) 738050200
Fax: (61) 738050222
Web Site: www.altusrenewables.com
Business Description:
Biomass-Based Fuel Production
S.I.C.: 1311
N.A.I.C.S.: 211111
Personnel:
Denis P. Waddell *(Chm)*
Ian Sandeman *(CEO & Mng Dir)*
Kim Hogg *(Sec)*
Board of Directors:
Denis P. Waddell
Stephen Mann
Ian Sandeman

ALTUS RESOURCE CAPITAL LIMITED

Anson Place Mill Court La Charroterie
Saint Peter Port, GY1 1EJ, Guernsey
Tel.: (44) 1481 722260
E-Mail: info@altus-cap.com
Web Site: www.altrescap.com
Year Founded: 2009
Business Description:
Investment Services
S.I.C.: 6211
N.A.I.C.S.: 523999
Personnel:
Nicholas J. Falla *(Chm)*
Board of Directors:
Nicholas J. Falla
David M. Gelber
Robert Milroy
David Netherway

ALTWOOD GARAGE DOORS LTD.

140 Ashwarren Road
Downsview, ON, M3J 1Z8, Canada
Tel.: (416) 635-5500
Fax: (416) 636-6929
Toll Free: (877) 786-5500
E-Mail: sales@altwooddoors.com
Web Site: www.altwooddoors.com
Year Founded: 1983
Rev.: $11,215,899
Emp.: 60
Business Description:
Garage Door Products Mfr
S.I.C.: 2431
N.A.I.C.S.: 321911
Personnel:
Mario Urbano *(Owner & Pres)*

ALUCON PUBLIC COMPANY LIMITED

500 Moo 1 Soi Sirikam Sukhumvit Road
Samrong Nua, Samut Prakan, 10270, Thailand
Tel.: (66) 2 3980147
Fax: (66) 2 3983455
E-Mail: alucon@alucon.th.com
Web Site: www.alucon.th.com
Year Founded: 1961
ALUCON—(THA)
Rev.: $163,598,377
Assets: $175,388,942
Liabilities: $63,202,441
Net Worth: $112,186,501
Earnings: $19,889,660
Emp.: 1,528
Fiscal Year-end: 12/31/12
Business Description:
Aluminium Container Mfr & Distr
S.I.C.: 3412
N.A.I.C.S.: 332439
Personnel:
Somchai Aungsanant *(Chm)*
Takaaki Takeuchi *(Mng Dir)*
Eumporn Pamornbutr *(Asst Mng Dir)*
Pitipong Archamongkol *(Sec & Mgr-Legal)*
Board of Directors:
Somchai Aungsanant
Iam Bunchaloemviphas
Krit Indhewat
Toshiyuki Koike
Subpachai Lovanit
Slinee Mahtani
Yoshihiro Mitsuta
Eumporn Pamornbutr
Takaaki Takeuchi
Vrinporn Uer-anant
Legal Counsel:
Pow & Associate Law Office
7th Floor Udom-Vidhya Building No 956 Rama IV Road Silom Sub-district
Bangrak District, Bangkok, 10500, Thailand

ALUM S.A.

Str Isaccei nr 82
280228 Tulcea, Romania
Tel.: (40) 240535022
Fax: (40) 240535495
E-Mail: alum@alum.ro
Web Site: www.alum.ro
BBGA—(BUC)
Rev.: $192,038,922
Assets: $170,138,595
Liabilities: $64,376,582
Net Worth: $105,762,013
Earnings: ($5,065,323)
Emp.: 721
Fiscal Year-end: 12/31/12
Business Description:
Aluminum Mfr
S.I.C.: 3334
N.A.I.C.S.: 331313
Personnel:
Gheorghe Dobra *(Chm & CEO)*
Pavel Machitski *(Vice Chm)*
Board of Directors:
Gheorghe Dobra
Marian Cilianu
Mihaela Duralia
Pavel Machitski
Ioan Popa

THE ALUMASC GROUP PLC

Burton Latimer
Kettering, Northamptonshire, NN15 5JP, United Kingdom
Tel.: (44) 1536383844
Fax: (44) 1536725069
E-Mail: info@alumasc.co.uk
Web Site: www.alumasc.co.uk
ALU—(LSE)
Rev.: $184,412,114
Assets: $125,869,413
Liabilities: $90,425,408
Net Worth: $35,444,005
Earnings: $3,742,917
Emp.: 768
Fiscal Year-end: 06/30/13
Business Description:
Engineering & Building Products Mfr & Sales
S.I.C.: 1542
N.A.I.C.S.: 236220
Personnel:
G. Paul Hooper *(CEO)*
Andrew Magson *(Sec & Dir-Fin)*
Board of Directors:
John S. McCall
Philip H. R. Gwyn
G. Paul Hooper
Andrew Magson
John Pilkington
Jon Peter Pither
Richard C. C. Saville
Keith Walden
Legal Counsel:
Pinsent Masons LLP
3 Colmore Circus
Birmingham, United Kingdom
Herbert Smith LLP
Exchange House Primrose Street
London, EC2A 2HS, United Kingdom
Divisions:

Alumasc Dispense (1)
Unit 3 Acan Business Park Garrard Way
Kettering, NN16 8TD, United Kingdom (100%)
Tel.: (44) 1536311888
Fax: (44) 153631881
E-Mail: sales@alumascdispense.com
Web Site: www.alumascdispense.com
Emp.: 50
Aluminum Die-Casting Foundries
S.I.C.: 3364
N.A.I.C.S.: 331523

Alumasc Interior Building Products (1)
Halesfield 19
Telford, Shropshire, TF7 4QT, United Kingdom (100%)
Tel.: (44) 1952580590
Fax: (44) 1952587805
E-Mail: sales@alumascinteriors.com
Web Site: www.pendock.co.uk
Emp.: 50
Sawmill & Woodworking Machinery Mfr
S.I.C.: 3553
N.A.I.C.S.: 333243
Michael Leaf *(Mng Dir)*

Alumasc Precision Components (1)
Burton Latimer
Kettering, Northants, NN15 5JP, United Kingdom (100%)
Tel.: (44) 1536383849
Fax: (44) 1536723835
E-Mail: info@alumasc.co.uk
Web Site: www.alumasc-precision.co.uk
Emp.: 200
Engineering Services
S.I.C.: 8711
N.A.I.C.S.: 541330
Paul Hooper *(Mng Dir)*

Dyson Diecasting (1)
2nd Ave
Bletchley, MK1 1EA Milton Keynes, United Kingdom (100%)
Tel.: (44) 1908279200
Fax: (44) 1908279201
E-Mail: dyson@alumascprecision.co.uk
Web Site: www.dyson-diecasting.co.uk
Emp.: 90
Aluminum Die-Casting Foundries
S.I.C.: 3364
N.A.I.C.S.: 331523
Les White *(Mng Dir)*

Elkington Gatic (1)
Hammond House
Holmestone Rd Poulton Close, Dover, Kent, CT17 0UF, United Kingdom (100%)
Tel.: (44) 1304203545
Fax: (44) 1304215001
E-Mail: acp@gatic.com
Web Site: www.gatic.com
Emp.: 50
Special Trade Contractors
S.I.C.: 1542
N.A.I.C.S.: 236220
Nick Buckingham *(Mng Dir)*

Roof-Pro (1)
PO Box 505
Kempston, Bedfordshire, MK427LQ, United Kingdom (100%)
Tel.: (44) 1234843790
Fax: (44) 1234856259
E-Mail: info@roof-pro.co.uk
Web Site: www.roof-pro.co.uk
Emp.: 18
Roofing Siding & Insulation Material Merchant Whslr
S.I.C.: 5033
N.A.I.C.S.: 423330
David Gatehouse *(Mng Dir)*

Scaffold & Construction Products (1)
1 Station Ct Girton Rd
Cannock, Staffordshire, WS11 0EJ, United Kingdom
Tel.: (44) 1543467800
Fax: (44) 1543467993
E-Mail: acp@scpburton.co.uk
Web Site: www.scp-props.co.uk
Emp.: 4
Special Trade Contractors
S.I.C.: 1542
N.A.I.C.S.: 236220
Matt Johnson *(Mgr-Comml)*

Subsidiaries:

Alumasc Exterior Building Products Limited (1)
White House Works Bold Rd
Sutton, Saint Helens, Merseyside, WA94JG, United Kingdom (100%)
Tel.: (44) 1744648400
Fax: (44) 1744648401

The Alumasc Group plc—(Continued)

E-Mail: info@alumasc-exteriors.co.uk
Web Site: www.alumasc-exteriors.co.uk
Emp.: 120
Asphalt Shingle & Coating Materials Mfr
S.I.C.: 2952
N.A.I.C.S.: 324122
Paul Hetherington *(Mng Dir)*

Alumasc Precision Limited (1)
APC Kettering Burton Latimer
Kettering, NN15 5JP, United Kingdom
Tel.: (44) 1536383849
Fax: (44) 1536723835
E-Mail: info@alumascprecision.co.uk
Web Site: www.alumasc-precision.co.uk
Emp.: 120
Precision Machining Tools Mfr
S.I.C.: 3559
N.A.I.C.S.: 333249
Les White *(Mng Dir-Dyson Div)*

Blackdown Horticultural Consultants Limited (1)
Street Ash Nursery Combe St Nicholas
Chard
Somerset, TA20 3HZ, United Kingdom
Tel.: (44) 1460 234582
Fax: (44) 845 0760267
E-Mail: enquiries@blackdown.co.uk
Web Site: www.blackdown.co.uk
Emp.: 10
Green Roofing System Installation Services
S.I.C.: 1761
N.A.I.C.S.: 238160
Neil Allan *(Dir-Fin)*

Levolux Limited (1)
Forward Dri
Harrow, Middlesex, HA38NT, United Kingdom
Tel.: (44) 2088639111
Fax: (44) 2088638760
E-Mail: info@levolux.com
Web Site: www.levolux.com
Emp.: 60
Curtain & Drapery Mills
S.I.C.: 2391
N.A.I.C.S.: 314120
Andrew Smith *(Mgr-Pur)*

Subsidiary:

Levolux A.T. Limited (2)
24 Eastville Close
Eastern Avenue, Gloucester, GL4 3SJ, United Kingdom
Tel.: (44) 1452500007
Fax: (44) 1452527496
E-Mail: sales@levoluxat.co.uk
Web Site: www.levolux.com
Emp.: 60
Knit Fabric & Lace Mills
S.I.C.: 2259
N.A.I.C.S.: 313240

Timloc Building Products Ltd. (1)
Rawcliffe Rd
Goole, E Yorkshire, DN14 6UQ, United Kingdom (100%)
Tel.: (44) 1405765567
Fax: (44) 1405720479
E-Mail: sales@timloc.co.uk
Web Site: www.timloc.co.uk
Emp.: 60
Building Products Services
S.I.C.: 7382
N.A.I.C.S.: 561621
Micheal Leaf *(Mng Dir)*

Non-U.S. Subsidiary:

Elkington China Limited (1)
Rm 3 6/F Honour Indl Ctr 6 Sun Yip St
Chai Wan, China (Hong Kong)
Tel.: (852) 23050100
Fax: (852) 27555715
Construction Materials Distr
S.I.C.: 5039
N.A.I.C.S.: 423390

ALUMECO INDIA EXTRUSION LTD.

Kallakal Village Toopran Mandal
Medak, Andhra Pradesh, 502336, India
Tel.: (91) 8454 250530
Fax: (91) 8454 250514
E-Mail: mktg@alumecoindia.com
Web Site: www.alumecoindia.com
513309—(BOM)
Rev.: $12,339,136
Assets: $3,257,972
Liabilities: $4,963,722
Net Worth: ($1,705,749)
Earnings: ($1,013,666)
Fiscal Year-end: 06/30/13

Business Description:
Metal Products Extrusion & Mfr
S.I.C.: 3355
N.A.I.C.S.: 331318

Personnel:
Ashish Kumar Gupta *(Chm)*
Nand Kishore Khandelwal *(CFO & Compliance Officer)*
Ajay Kishen *(Sec)*

Board of Directors:
Ashish Kumar Gupta
Anand Parkash
Hans Schweers

Transfer Agent:
XL Softech Systems Limited
3 Sagar Society Road No. 2 Banjara Hills
Hyderabad, India

ALUMIL ALUMINIUM INDUSTRY S.A.

Kilkis Industrial Area
61100 Kilkis, Greece
Tel.: (30) 23410 79300
Fax: (30) 23410 71988
E-Mail: info@alumil.com
Web Site: www.alumil.com
Year Founded: 1988
ALMY—(ATH)
Sales Range: $250-299.9 Million
Emp.: 2,300

Business Description:
Aluminium Extrusion Services
S.I.C.: 3354
N.A.I.C.S.: 331318

Personnel:
George A. Milonas *(Chm & Co-CEO)*
Evaggelia A. Milona *(Co-CEO & VP)*

Board of Directors:
George A. Milonas
Tasos C. Alexandridis
George J. Doukidis
Eutixia Milona
Evaggelia A. Milona
Hristos A. Sidiras

Non-U.S. Subsidiaries:

Alumil Bulgaria Ltd. (1)
5 Ilia Beshkov str
1528 Sofia, Bulgaria
Tel.: (359) 2 979 0022
Fax: (359) 2 979 0022
E-Mail: officebg@alumil.com
Web Site: www.alumil.bg
Extruded Aluminum Products Mfr
S.I.C.: 3355
N.A.I.C.S.: 331318

Alumil Deutschland GmbH (1)
Wingertstrasse 21
D-64354 Reinheim, Germany
Tel.: (49) 6162 9677 770
Fax: (49) 6162 9688 775
E-Mail: info@alumil.de
Web Site: www.alumil.de
Extruded Aluminum Products Mfr
S.I.C.: 3355
N.A.I.C.S.: 331318

Alumil Gulf fzc (1)
Technology Park
PO Box 54548
Ras al Khaimah, United Arab Emirates
Tel.: (971) 7 2444106
E-Mail: c.hatzigeorgiou@alumil.com
Extruded Aluminum Products Mfr
S.I.C.: 3355
N.A.I.C.S.: 331318

Alumil Hungary K.T.F. (1)
Gyar utca 2
2040 Budaors, Hungary
Tel.: (36) 2342 8498
Fax: (36) 2343 30284
E-Mail: info@alumil.hu
Extruded Aluminum Products Mfr
S.I.C.: 3355
N.A.I.C.S.: 331318

Alumil Industry S.R.L. (1)
Cetatea Bucuriei Street no 7
Chisinau, Moldova
Tel.: (373) 2259 5217
Fax: (373) 2258 2542
E-Mail: office@alumil.ro
Extruded Aluminum Products Mfr
S.I.C.: 3354
N.A.I.C.S.: 331318

Alumil Kosova shpk (1)
Rruga Prishtine-Dushe
Pristina, Serbia
Tel.: (381) 38 601 185
Fax: (381) 38 601 186
E-Mail: info.ks@alumil.com
Extruded Aluminum Products Mfr
S.I.C.: 3354
N.A.I.C.S.: 331318

Alumil Polska sp. z o.o. (1)
Ul Sklodowskiej Curie 65
Torun, Poland
Tel.: (48) 56645 8801
Fax: (48) 56645 8800
E-Mail: dyrekcja@alumil.com.pl
Web Site: alumil.com.pl
Extruded Aluminum Products Mfr
S.I.C.: 3354
N.A.I.C.S.: 331318

Alumil Rom Industry S.A. (1)
Calea Rahovei 286 A Sector 5
Bucharest, Romania
Tel.: (40) 214243456
Fax: (40) 214233932
E-Mail: office@alumil.ro
Web Site: www.alumil.ro
ALU—(BUC)
Sls.: $22,764,057
Assets: $38,082,627
Liabilities: $17,109,613
Net Worth: $20,973,014
Earnings: $980,154
Emp.: 167
Fiscal Year-end: 12/31/12
Aluminum Processor
S.I.C.: 3355
N.A.I.C.S.: 331318
Michail E. Sotiriou *(Pres & CEO)*

Alumil Skopje D.o.o. (1)
Bul Promajska br 74A
1000 Skopje, Macedonia
Tel.: (389) 2 2466 200
E-Mail: info.skopje@alumil.com
Extruded Aluminum Products Mfr
S.I.C.: 3355
N.A.I.C.S.: 331318

Alumil SRB D.o.o. (1)
Dragoslava Bojovica 586
32212 Cacak, Preljina, Serbia
Tel.: (381) 32 320 480
Fax: (381) 32 320 490
E-Mail: alumil@eunet.rs
Extruded Aluminum Products Mfr
S.I.C.: 3355
N.A.I.C.S.: 331318

Alumil Technic D.o.o. (1)
Autoput za Novi Sad 221
11000 Belgrade, Serbia
Tel.: (381) 11 3774 822
Fax: (381) 11 3774 821
E-Mail: office@alumiltechnic.com
Extruded Aluminum Products Mfr
S.I.C.: 3354
N.A.I.C.S.: 331318

Alumil Ukraine Ltd. (1)
77-a Vladimirskaya Str
01033 Kiev, Ukraine
Tel.: (380) 44 377 7357
E-Mail: y.kechagias@alumil.com
Extruded Aluminum Products Mfr
S.I.C.: 3355
N.A.I.C.S.: 331318

Alumil Varna Ltd. (1)
West Industrial Zone 9009
Varna, Bulgaria
Tel.: (359) 5250 3636
Fax: (359) 5250 5663
E-Mail: varna-alumil@abv.bg
Extruded Aluminum Products Mfr
S.I.C.: 3354
N.A.I.C.S.: 331318

Alumil Yu Industry A.D. (1)
Industrijska zona bb
23330 Nova Pazova, Serbia
Tel.: (381) 22 321 302
Fax: (381) 22 321 244
E-Mail: alumilyuindustry@alumil.com
Extruded Aluminum Products Mfr
S.I.C.: 3354
N.A.I.C.S.: 331318

ALUMINA LIMITED

Level 12 IBM Centre 60 City Road
Southbank, VIC, 3006, Australia
Tel.: (61) 3 8699 2600
Fax: (61) 3 8699 2699
E-Mail: chris.thiris@aluminalimited.com
Web Site: www.aluminalimited.com
AWC—(ASX OTC)
Rev.: $100,000
Assets: $3,311,400,000
Liabilities: $682,900,000
Net Worth: $2,628,500,000
Earnings: ($62,100,000)
Emp.: 12
Fiscal Year-end: 12/31/12

Business Description:
Investment Services; Bauxite & Aluminum Mining & Smelting Operations
S.I.C.: 6211
N.A.I.C.S.: 523999

Personnel:
Peter Christopher Wasow *(CEO)*
Chris Thiris *(CFO)*
Stephen Foster *(Gen Counsel & Sec)*

Board of Directors:
George John Pizzey
Michael Peter Ferraro
Emma Rachel Stein
Peter Christopher Wasow

Joint Venture:

Alcoa of Australia Limited (1)
181-205 Davy Street
Booragoon, WA 6154, Australia
Tel.: (61) 893165111
Fax: (61) 893165228
Web Site: www.alcoa.com.au
Emp.: 5,000
Aluminum Mining, Smelting & Refining; Owned 60% by Alcoa Inc. & 40% by Alumina Limited
S.I.C.: 3334
N.A.I.C.S.: 331313
Melanie Brown *(Gen Counsel)*

Subsidiary:

Alcoa World Alumina Australia (2)
181 205 Davy St
Booragoon, 6953, Australia
Tel.: (61) 893165111
Telex: AA30446
Fax: (61) 893165228
Web Site: www.alcoa.com.au
Sales Range: $25-49.9 Million
Emp.: 200
Bauxite Mining & Alumina Refining, Aluminum Smelting & Gold Mining Services Export
S.I.C.: 1099
N.A.I.C.S.: 212299
Alan Cransberg *(VP-Alcoa)*

Non-U.S. Subsidiaries:

Jamalco-Alcoa Minerals of Jamaica, Inc. (2)
May Pen
PO Box 54
Kingston, 10, Jamaica JM
Tel.: (876) 9862561
Fax: (876) 9869637
E-Mail: blossom.laidlaw@alcoa.com
Web Site: www.alcoa.com

Sales Range: $75-99.9 Million
Emp.: 985
Bauxite Mining & Alumina Producer
S.I.C.: 1099
N.A.I.C.S.: 212299
Jerome Maxwell *(Mng Dir)*

Suriname Aluminum Company, L.L.C. **(2)**
13 VH Hogerhuysstraat
PO Box 1810
Paramaribo, Suriname
Tel.: (597) 323281
Fax: (597) 323314
Web Site: www.alcoa.com
Sales Range: $50-74.9 Million
Emp.: 800
Bauxite Mining Operations
S.I.C.: 1099
N.A.I.C.S.: 212299

ALUMINIUM BAHRAIN B.S.C.(C)

PO Box 570
Manama, Bahrain
Tel.: (973) 17 830000
Fax: (973) 17 830083
Web Site: www.albasmelter.com
ALBH—(BAH)
Sls.: $1,927,445,147
Assets: $3,185,355,626
Liabilities: $1,035,309,321
Net Worth: $2,150,046,305
Earnings: $250,206,987
Emp.: 3,000
Fiscal Year-end: 12/31/12
Business Description:
Aluminum Smelter
S.I.C.: 3399
N.A.I.C.S.: 331314
Personnel:
Mahmood Hashim Al-Kooheji *(Chm)*
Tim Murray *(CEO)*
Ali Hassan Al Baqali *(Acting CFO & Chief Supply Officer)*
Isa Abdul Latif Al-Ansari *(COO)*
Jean-Baptiste Lucas *(CMO)*
Elham Al Eid *(Chief Medical Officer)*
Basem Al Sharqi *(Chief Support Functions Officer)*
Bryan Harris *(Chief Risk Mgmt Officer)*
Afshan Akhtar *(Gen Counsel & Sec)*
Board of Directors:
Mahmood Hashim Al-Kooheji
Osama Mohammed Al Arrayedh
Abdul Aziz Al Humaid
Mutlaq Hamad Al Murished
Talaat Aldafer Alqahtani
Fawzi Ahmed Kanoo
Mohammed Khalifa Al Khalifa
David Meen
Yusuf Abdulla Taqi

ALUMINIUM COMPANY OF MALAYSIA BERHAD

No 3 Persiaran Waja Bukit Raja Industrial Estate
41050 Kelang, Selangor Darul Ehsan, Malaysia
Tel.: (60) 333466262
Fax: (60) 333412793
Web Site: www.alcom.com.my
ALCOM—(KLS)
Rev.: $94,539,008
Assets: $70,025,676
Liabilities: $11,438,178
Net Worth: $58,587,499
Earnings: ($960,478)
Fiscal Year-end: 03/31/13
Business Description:
Aluminum Sheet Mfr
S.I.C.: 3353
N.A.I.C.S.: 331315
Personnel:
Vishal Rao *(Mng Dir)*
Lee San Lam *(Co-Sec)*
Ericia Yoke Kuan Tan *(Co-Sec)*
Board of Directors:
Imran Almarhum Ja'afar
Emilio Stefano Lorenzo Braghi
Yunus Kamaruddin
Wee Kiat Kok
Shashi Kant Maudgal
Vishal Rao
Paul Allen Stadnikia

ALUMINUM CORPORATION OF CHINA LIMITED

(d/b/a Chinalco)
No 62 N Xizhimen Street
Haidian District, Beijing, 100082, China
Tel.: (86) 10 8229 8103
Fax: (86) 10 6397 1690
Web Site: www.chalco.com.cn
Year Founded: 2001
ACH—(NYSE)
Rev.: $23,744,710,716
Assets: $27,801,431,706
Liabilities: $19,259,884,528
Net Worth: $8,541,547,178
Earnings: ($1,373,033,160)
Emp.: 97,990
Fiscal Year-end: 12/31/12
Business Description:
Aluminum Producer
S.I.C.: 3334
N.A.I.C.S.: 331313
Personnel:
Weiping Xiong *(Chm & CEO)*
Xie Weizhi *(CFO & VP)*
Liu Qiang *(Sec)*
Board of Directors:
Weiping Xiong
Liu Caiming
Luo Jianchuan
Youqing Lv
Mengkui Wang
Liu Xiangmin
Zhuoyuan Zhang
Demiao Zhu

Non-U.S. Subsidiary:

Peru Copper Inc. **(1)**
625 Howe Street Suite 1050
Vancouver, BC, V6C 2T6, Canada Ca
Tel.: (604) 689-0234
Fax: (604) 688-0094
E-Mail: info@perucopper.com
Web Site: www.perucopper.com
Sales Range: Less than $1 Million
Emp.: 58
Copper Exploration
S.I.C.: 1021
N.A.I.C.S.: 212234
J. David Lowell *(Exec Chm)*
Gerald Wolfe *(Pres & CEO)*
Thomas J. Findley *(CFO)*
Paul M. Stein *(Sec)*

ALUMINUM PRODUCTS COMPANY LTD.

(d/b/a ALUPCO)
Alupco St 7 industrail Area
PO Box 2080
Dammam, 31451, Saudi Arabia
Tel.: (966) 38471300
Fax: (966) 38473010
E-Mail: info@alupco.com
Web Site: www.alupco.com
Year Founded: 1975
Sales Range: $150-199.9 Million
Emp.: 800
Business Description:
Extruded & Surface-Treated Aluminum Products Mfr
S.I.C.: 3354
N.A.I.C.S.: 331318
Personnel:
Hashim S. Hashim *(Chm)*

ALUMTEK CORPORATION

No 7 21st Street Gandi AVE
Tehran, 15178, Iran
Tel.: (98) 21 88797223
Fax: (98) 21 88774955
E-Mail: Info@alumtekcorp.com
Web Site: www.alumtekcorp.com
Year Founded: 1967
ALTK—(THE)
Emp.: 450
Business Description:
Overhead Conductor Mfr
S.I.C.: 3999
N.A.I.C.S.: 339999
Personnel:
M. J. Safavian *(Pres)*

ALUWORKS LIMITED

PO Box 914
Tema, Ghana
Tel.: (233) 22208701
Fax: (233) 22208700
E-Mail: aluworks@aluworks.com
Web Site: www.aluworks.com
ALW—(GHA)
Sales Range: $10-24.9 Million
Emp.: 265
Business Description:
Aluminum Fabricated Products Mfr
S.I.C.: 3355
N.A.I.C.S.: 331318
Personnel:
William Ekroo Inkumsah *(Chm)*
Ernest Kwasi Okoh *(Mng Dir)*
Francis Agboada *(CFO)*
David-Ruthven Adzogble *(COO)*
Board of Directors:
William Ekroo Inkumsah
Togbe Afede
Anthony Fofie
Benjamin Akuete Gogo
Napoleon D. K. Kpoh
Kwadwo Kwarteng
Ernest Kwasi Okoh

ALVARION LTD.

21a Habarzel Street
Tel Aviv, 69710, Israel
Tel.: (972) 36456262
Fax: (972) 36456222
E-Mail: corporate-sales@alvarion.com
Web Site: www.alvarion.com
Year Founded: 1993
ALVRQ—(OTC)
Sls.: $49,949,000
Assets: $96,159,000
Liabilities: $60,628,000
Net Worth: $35,531,000
Earnings: ($55,909,000)
Emp.: 356
Fiscal Year-end: 12/31/12
Business Description:
Point-to-Multipoint Broadband Wireless Access Services
S.I.C.: 4899
N.A.I.C.S.: 517919
Personnel:
Amnon Yacoby *(Chm)*
Assaf Katan *(Pres & CEO)*
Avi Stern *(CFO)*
Mati Wax *(CTO)*
Leor Porat *(Gen Counsel & Exec VP)*
Ulik Broida *(Exec VP-Mktg, Products & Customer Svcs)*
Zeev Farkash *(Exec VP-Sls)*
Moshe Fourier *(Exec VP-R&D)*
Nir Golan *(Exec VP-Sls & Svcs)*
Board of Directors:
Amnon Yacoby
Raphael Amit
Benny Hanigal
Doron R. Inbar
Transfer Agent:
American Stock Transfer & Trust Company
59 Maiden Ln
New York, NY 10038

U.S. Subsidiary:

Alvarion, Inc. **(1)**
2495 Leghorn St
Mountain View, CA 94043
Tel.: (650) 314-2500
Fax: (650) 967-3966
E-Mail: sales-north.america@alvarion.com
Web Site: www.alvarion.com
Emp.: 65
Other Electronic Parts & Equipment Wholesalers
S.I.C.: 5065
N.A.I.C.S.: 423690
Gregory Daily *(Pres)*

Subsidiary:

Wavion, Inc. **(2)**
1190 Saratoga Ave Ste 240
San Jose, CA 95129
Tel.: (408) 261-7000
Sales Range: $1-9.9 Million
Emp.: 65
Management Consulting Services
S.I.C.: 8742
N.A.I.C.S.: 541613
Adi Corem *(VP-Ops)*

Non-U.S. Subsidiary:

Wavion Ltd. **(3)**
5 Ha mada Street
PO Box 580
Yokneam, 20692, Israel Il
Tel.: (972) 4 909 7300
Fax: (972) 4 909 7322
E-Mail: info@wavionnetworks.com
Web Site: www.wavionnetworks.com
Internet Service Providers
S.I.C.: 4899
N.A.I.C.S.: 517919

Non-U.S. Subsidiaries:

Alvarion de Mexico S.A. de C.V. **(1)**
Calle Amores 1120 piso 5 Colonia del Valle Del Benito Juarez, Mexico, DF, CP 03100, Mexico
Tel.: (52) 55 1107 1915
Fax: (52) 55 1107 1635
E-Mail: alvarionmexico@alvarion.com
Web Site: www.alvarion.com
Point-to-Multipoint Broadband Wireless Access Services
S.I.C.: 4899
N.A.I.C.S.: 517919

Alvarion do Brasil Telecomunicacoes Ltda. **(1)**
Rua Floriano Essenfelder 178
Curitiba, Parana, CEP 80060-270, Brazil
Tel.: (55) 41 3024 6665
E-Mail: brazil-sales@alvarion.com
Web Site: www.alvarion.com
Point-to-Multipoint Broadband Wireless Access Services
S.I.C.: 4899
N.A.I.C.S.: 517919

Alvarion Italy SRL **(1)**
Via Cristoforo Colombo 5/C
20094 Corsico, MI, Italy IT
Tel.: (39) 02 45862169
Fax: (39) 02 48689516
E-Mail: sales@alvarion.com
Web Site: www.alvarion.com
Point-to-Multipoint Broadband Wireless Access Services
S.I.C.: 4899
N.A.I.C.S.: 517919

Alvarion Japan KK **(1)**
Shiba Koen Plaza Building 6th Fl 3-6-9
Shiba Minato ku
105-0014 Tokyo, Japan JP
Tel.: (81) 354198321 (100%)
Fax: (81) 354198325
E-Mail: tomoko.kurokaa@alvarion.com
Web Site: www.alvarion.com
Emp.: 10
Point-to-Multipoint Broadband Wireless Access Services
S.I.C.: 4899
N.A.I.C.S.: 517919

Alvarion Philippines Inc. **(1)**
1505 88 Corporate Center
Sedeno St Salcedo Village, 1227 Makati, Philippines (100%)

Alvarion Ltd.—(Continued)

Tel.: (63) 27561730
Fax: (63) 27561731
E-Mail: ph-sales@alvarion.com
Web Site: www.alvarion.com
Emp.: 10
Point-to-Multipoint Broadband Wireless Access Services
S.I.C.: 4899
N.A.I.C.S.: 517919
Udi Bendavid *(Mng Dir)*

Alvarion S.A. **(1)**
Alicia Moreau de Justo 1720 2 G
Buenos Aires, CABA, CP1107, Argentina
Tel.: (54) 11 5648 5021
E-Mail: lasales@alvarion.com
Web Site: www.alvarion.com
Point-to-Multipoint Broadband Wireless Access Services
S.I.C.: 4899
N.A.I.C.S.: 517919

Alvarion SARL **(1)**
45 rue Boissiere
75016 Paris, France
Tel.: (33) 156266371
Fax: (33) 156266380
E-Mail: france-sales@alvarion.com
Web Site: www.alvarion.fr
Emp.: 7
Other Management Consulting Services
S.I.C.: 8748
N.A.I.C.S.: 541618
Michael Bokobzo *(Mng Dir)*

Alvarion Singapore Pte Ltd. **(1)**
8 Shenton Way #05-02 AXA Tower
Singapore, 068811, Singapore SG
Tel.: (65) 6293 3080
Fax: (65) 6293 3086
E-Mail: ap-sales@alvarion.com
Web Site: www.alvarion.com
Emp.: 7
Point-to-Multipoint Broadband Wireless Access Services
S.I.C.: 3663
N.A.I.C.S.: 334220
Udi Shaked *(Mng Dir)*

Alvarion South Africa (Pty) Ltd **(1)**
Hazel Close Building 1 Suite 1C 141 Witch Hazel Avenue
Highveld Park, Centurion, Gauteng, 0157, South Africa ZA
Tel.: (27) 12 665 1424
Fax: (27) 86 659 9548
E-Mail: sales-sa@alvarion.com
Web Site: www.alvarion.com
Point-to-Multipoint Broadband Wireless Access Services
S.I.C.: 4899
N.A.I.C.S.: 517919

Alvarion Spain SL **(1)**
Parque Tecnologico de Boecillo
Edificio Galileo bl modulo ama, 47151
Valladolid, Spain
Tel.: (34) 983148148
Fax: (34) 983148111
E-Mail: nacho.torre@alvarion.com
Emp.: 2
Point-to-Multipoint Broadband Wireless Access Services
S.I.C.: 4899
N.A.I.C.S.: 517919
Jesus Alonso *(Mng Dir)*

Alvarion Srl **(1)**
6A Dimitrie Pompeiu Upground Estates Building 5th Floor
Entrance A Sector 2, 020337 Bucharest, Romania
Tel.: (40) 21 301 8000
Fax: (40) 21 301 8011
E-Mail: sales@alvarion.com
Web Site: www.alvarion.com
Point-to-Multipoint Broadband Wireless Access Services
S.I.C.: 4899
N.A.I.C.S.: 517919

Alvarion Uruguay SA **(1)**
Zonamerica Business & Technology Park
Oficina 703 Ruta 8 Km 17,500
Edificio 700, Montevideo, 91600, Uruguay UY
Tel.: (598) 2 518 2975
Fax: (598) 2 518 2976
E-Mail: lasales@alvarion.com
Web Site: www.alvarion.com
Point-to-Multipoint Broadband Wireless Access Services
S.I.C.: 4899
N.A.I.C.S.: 517919

India 4Motion Broadband Wireless Network Private Limited **(1)**
4th Floor No 345 Udyog Vihar Phase II
Gurgaon, 122 015, India
Tel.: (91) 124 4969868
Fax: (91) 124 4969861
E-Mail: india-sales@alvarion.com
Web Site: www.alvarion.com
Point-to-Multipoint Broadband Wireless Access Services
S.I.C.: 3663
N.A.I.C.S.: 334220

Tadipol ECI Sp. z o.o. **(1)**
ul Jutrzenki 177
02-231 Warsaw, Poland
Tel.: (48) 228739100
Fax: (48) 228739101
E-Mail: sales@alvarion.com
Web Site: www.alvarion.com
Emp.: 6
Point-to-Multipoint Broadband Wireless Access Services
S.I.C.: 4899
N.A.I.C.S.: 517919

ALVOPETRO ENERGY LTD.

Suite 1175 332 6th Avenue Southwest
Calgary, AB, T2P 0B2, Canada
Tel.: (587) 794-4216
Fax: (403) 705-0234
E-Mail: info@alvopetro.com
Web Site: www.alvopetro.com
Year Founded: 2013
ALV—(TSXV)

Business Description:
Oil & Gas Exploration
S.I.C.: 1311
N.A.I.C.S.: 211111

Personnel:
John D. Wright *(Chm)*
Core C. Ruttan *(Pres & CEO)*
Alison Howard *(CFO)*
John Koch *(COO)*

Board of Directors:
John D. Wright
Roderick L. Fraser
Kenneth R. McKinnon
Core C. Ruttan
Firoz Talakshi
Geir Ytreland

ALVOPETRO INC.

(Name Changed to Fortaleza Energy Inc.)

AM GOLD INC.

Suite 305 - 369 Terminal Avenue
Vancouver, BC, V6A 4C4, Canada
Tel.: (604) 646-0067
Fax: (604) 692-0117
Toll Free: (877) 646-0067
E-Mail: info@amgold.ca
Web Site: www.amgold.ca
Year Founded: 1985
AMG—(DEU OTC TSXV)
Int. Income: $515
Assets: $6,403,777
Liabilities: $403,565
Net Worth: $6,000,212
Earnings: ($1,088,460)
Fiscal Year-end: 12/31/12

Business Description:
Gold & Copper Exploration & Mining Services
S.I.C.: 1041
N.A.I.C.S.: 212221

Personnel:
John Fiorino *(CEO)*
Murray Caruth *(Sec)*

Board of Directors:
John Fiorino
Dennis B. Goldstein
Stewart A. Jackson

Legal Counsel:
Lang Michener LLP
1500 1055 West Georgia Street
PO Box 1117
Vancouver, BC, V6E 4N7, Canada
Tel.: (604) 689-9111

Transfer Agent:
Computershare Limited
100 University Avenue 9 Floor
Toronto, ON, M5J 2Y1, Canada

Non-U.S. Subsidiary:

Canper Exploraciones S.A.C. **(1)**
San Borja Sur 793 795
San Borja, Lima, 41, Peru
Tel.: (51) 12264848
Fax: (51) 12259570
E-Mail: info@acero-martin.com
Web Site: www.aceromartin.com
Emp.: 25
Gold Ore Mining Services
S.I.C.: 1041
N.A.I.C.S.: 212221
Ralph Rust Strickler *(Gen Mgr)*

AM PM SYSTEMS

(Formerly 406106 ALBERTA INC)
101 6741 Cariboo Road
Burnaby, BC, V3N 4A3, Canada
Tel.: (604) 421-5677
Fax: (604) 421-6568
Toll Free: (800) 336-2622
E-Mail: mail@ampmservice.com
Web Site: www.ampmservice.com
Year Founded: 1987
Rev.: $14,000,000
Emp.: 200

Business Description:
Point of Sale System & Software Support Services
S.I.C.: 7379
N.A.I.C.S.: 541519

Personnel:
John Chan *(Pres)*

AMA GROUP LIMITED

Suite 1 1233 High Street
Armadale, VIC, 3143, Australia

Mailing Address:
PO Box 122
Margate, QLD, 4019, Australia
Tel.: (61) 7 3897 5743
Fax: (61) 7 3283 1168
E-Mail: info@amagroupltd.com
Web Site: www.amagroupltd.com
AMA—(ASX)
Rev.: $67,641,669
Assets: $70,255,256
Liabilities: $25,073,968
Net Worth: $45,181,288
Earnings: $7,492,699
Emp.: 31
Fiscal Year-end: 06/30/13

Business Description:
Automotive & Electrical Accessories Whslr
S.I.C.: 5012
N.A.I.C.S.: 423110

Personnel:
Raymond Malone *(CEO & Mng Dir-Mr Gloss)*
Ray Smith Roberts *(COO & Mng Dir-East Coast Bullbars)*
Terri Bakos *(Co-Sec)*
Phillip Allen Hains *(Co-Sec)*

Board of Directors:
Duncan Fischer
Simon Doyle
Raymond Malone

Legal Counsel:
Foster Nicholson Jones Lawyers
Level 6 406 Collins Street
Melbourne, Australia

AMACON CONSTRUCTION LTD

Suite 300 911 Homer Street
Vancouver, BC, V6B 2W6, Canada
Tel.: (604) 602-7700
Fax: (604) 602-7110
Web Site: www.amacon.com
Rev.: $12,780,908
Emp.: 50

Business Description:
Real Estate Development & Construction Services
S.I.C.: 6519
N.A.I.C.S.: 531190

Personnel:
Don DeCotiis *(VP)*

AMAD INVESTMENT & REAL ESTATE DEVELOPMENT PLC

Queen Rania Al-Abullah St Building Number 82
PO Box 926179
Amman, 11190, Jordan
Tel.: (962) 6 5156603
Fax: (962) 6 5156603
E-Mail: amadinvestment@hotmail.com
Year Founded: 1996
AMAD—(AMM)
Rev.: $10,812,546
Assets: $25,296,694
Liabilities: $6,598,540
Net Worth: $18,698,154
Earnings: ($1,361,447)
Emp.: 11
Fiscal Year-end: 12/31/12

Business Description:
Real Estate Investment Services
S.I.C.: 6531
N.A.I.C.S.: 531390

Personnel:
Safwan Al-Amad *(Gen Mgr)*

AMADA CO., LTD.

200 Ishida
Isehara, Kanagawa, 259-1196, Japan
Tel.: (81) 463961111
Telex: 3882311 AMADA J
Fax: (81) 463949781
Web Site: www.amada.co.jp
Year Founded: 1948
6113—(TKS)
Sls.: $2,090,198,000
Assets: $5,449,939,000
Liabilities: $1,213,817,000
Net Worth: $4,236,122,000
Earnings: $45,386,000
Emp.: 7,678
Fiscal Year-end: 03/31/13

Business Description:
Metalworking Machines & Bandsaws Mfr
S.I.C.: 3541
N.A.I.C.S.: 333517

Personnel:
Mitsuo Okamoto *(Pres & CEO)*
Yasuhiro Endo *(Sr Corp Officer-Sheet Metal Mfg)*
Nobuyuki Jinbo *(Corp Officer-Sls & Mktg)*
Masaaki Oonuki *(Corp Officer-Engrg Svc Bus)*
Hidehiko Sakai *(Sr Corp Officer-Saw Blade Production)*
Masashi Sato *(Corp Officer-Sheet Metal Solution)*
Kiyoshi Takeo *(Corp Officer-ICT Div)*
Hiroyuki Takeshita *(Corp Officer-Sls Admin Div)*
Koji Yamamoto *(Corp Officer-Corp Mgmt Div)*
Tomohiro Yano *(Corp Officer-Fin)*

Board of Directors:
Atsushige Abe

Tsutomu Isobe
Katsuhide Ito
Mitsuo Okamoto
Kotaro Shibata
Takaya Shigeta
Toshio Takagi

Transfer Agent:

Mitsubishi UFJ Trust & Banking Corporation
7-10-11 Higashisuna Koto-ku
137-8081 Tokyo, Japan

Branch:

Amada Co., Ltd. (1)
1 21 Higashi 18 Chome Kita Jugojo
Sapporo, Higashi Ku, 065 0015, Japan
Tel.: (81) 117817131
Fax: (81) 117812268
Web Site: www.amada.co.jp/english/
Emp.: 16
Sales of Machines & Tools
S.I.C.: 5084
N.A.I.C.S.: 423830

Division:

Amada Co., Ltd. Overseas Division (1)
200 Ishida
Isehara, Kanagawa, 259 1196, Japan (100%)
Tel.: (81) 463963411
Fax: (81) 463963257
E-Mail: amada-overseas@amada.co.jp
Emp.: 800
Sales & Administration
S.I.C.: 5963
N.A.I.C.S.: 454390
Mitsuo Okamoto *(Pres)*

Subsidiaries:

Amada Ailink Service Co., Ltd. (1)
Forum 246 605 350 Ishida
Isehara, Kanagawa, 259-1116, Japan
Tel.: (81) 463 97 2800
Fax: (81) 463 97 2803
E-Mail: info@ai-link.ne.jp
Web Site: www.amada.co.jp/english/corporate/group.html
Electronic Device Information Services
S.I.C.: 7389
N.A.I.C.S.: 519190

Amada Butsuryu Co., Ltd. (1)
200 Ishida
Isehara, Kanagawa, 259 1196, Japan (100%)
Tel.: (81) 463963331
Fax: (81) 463931300
Web Site: www.amadabutsuryu.co.jp
Emp.: 50
Distribution Service & Agency for Importing & Exporting Machines & Tools
S.I.C.: 5084
N.A.I.C.S.: 423830

AMADA DOCUMECH CO., LTD. (1)
200 Ishida
Isehara, Kanagawa, 259-1196, Japan
Tel.: (81) 463 96 3171
Information Editing & Production Services
S.I.C.: 7389
N.A.I.C.S.: 561410

Amada Engineering Co., Ltd. (1)
200 Ishida
Isehara, Kanagawa, 259-1196, Japan
Tel.: (81) 463 91 8090
Web Site: www.amada.co.jp/english/corporate/group.html
Industrial Machinery Mfr
S.I.C.: 3559
N.A.I.C.S.: 333249

Amada Franchise Center Co., Ltd. (1)
200 Ishida
Isehara, Kanagawa, 259 1196, Japan (100%)
Tel.: (81) 463963535
Web Site: amada.co.jp
Sales Range: $1-4.9 Billion
Emp.: 1,652
Agency for Sales Handling, Charge Accounting & Processing of Accounting Documents
S.I.C.: 7322
N.A.I.C.S.: 561440

Amada Lease Co., Ltd. (1)
200 Ishida
Isehara, Kanagawa, 259 1196, Japan (100%)
Tel.: (81) 463963663
Fax: (81) 463931323
E-Mail: amada-overseas@amada.co.jp
Web Site: amada.co.jp
Sales Range: Less than $1 Million
Emp.: 12
Lease of Metalworking Machines, Machine Tools & Related Products
S.I.C.: 7359
N.A.I.C.S.: 532490

Amada Machine Tools Co., Ltd. (1)
200 Ishida
Isehara, Kanagawa, 259 1196, Japan
Tel.: (81) 463963351
Fax: (81) 4463963228
E-Mail: mike_sakurai@amada.co.jp
Web Site: www.amada.co.jp/amt/
Sales & Services for Metal Cutting Machines & Machine Tools
S.I.C.: 5084
N.A.I.C.S.: 423830

Amada Machine Tools Mfg Co., Ltd. (1)
2-158 Nakashima
Shimoobari, Komaki, Aichi, 485 0051, Japan
Tel.: (81) 568718821
Web Site: www1.amada.co.jp/amt/
Mfr & Sales of Metal Cutting Machines & Machine Tools
S.I.C.: 3542
N.A.I.C.S.: 333517

AMADA PLANTECH CO., LTD. (1)
200 Ishida
Isehara, Kanagawa, 259-1196, Japan
Tel.: (81) 463 96 3603
Commercial Building Landscaping Services
S.I.C.: 0782
N.A.I.C.S.: 561730

Amada Soft Service Co., Ltd. (1)
200 Ishida
Isehara, Kanagawa, 259-1196, Japan
Tel.: (81) 463 96 3251
Web Site: www.amada.co.jp
Machine Tool & Metalworking Machine Software Mfr & Sales
S.I.C.: 3541
N.A.I.C.S.: 333517

AMADA TOOL PRECISION CO., LTD. (1)
200 Ishida
Isehara, Kanagawa, 259-1196, Japan
Tel.: (81) 463 91 8050
Machine Tool Mfr & Distr
S.I.C.: 3545
N.A.I.C.S.: 333515

Amada Tool Technica Co., Ltd. (1)
200 Ishida
Isehara, Kanagawa, 259-1196, Japan
Tel.: (81) 463918050
Fax: (81) 463918137
Web Site: www.amada.co.th
Emp.: 200
Punches & Dies Mfr
S.I.C.: 3542
N.A.I.C.S.: 333517

Amada Toyo Co., Ltd. (1)
3-73 Sameganji
Yatomi, Aichi, 490-1415, Japan
Tel.: (81) 567 52 2121
Fax: (81) 567 52 2115
Sheet Metal Processing Machinery Mfr & Distr
S.I.C.: 3559
N.A.I.C.S.: 333249

Miyachi Corporation (1)
2 6 6 Motoasakusa Taito
Tokyo, 111-0041, Japan (91.7%)
Tel.: (81) 352466700
Fax: (81) 3 52466890
Web Site: www.miyachi.com
Sales Range: $250-299.9 Million
Emp.: 965
Electronic Equipment Mfr; Lasers & Welding Equipment Mfr
S.I.C.: 3679
N.A.I.C.S.: 334419
Kunihiko Komiyama *(Pres & CEO)*
Kiyoshi Kouyama *(Mng Dir)*
Takahiro Uchida *(Mng Dir)*

Nicotec Co., Ltd. (1)
1-15-12 Tamagawa Denenchofu
Tokyo, 158 0085, Japan (100%)
Tel.: (81) 337227642
Fax: (81) 337227641
E-Mail: liyang@nccgp.co.jp
Web Site: www.nccgp.co.jp
Emp.: 150
Metal Working Machines & Tools Sales
S.I.C.: 3423
N.A.I.C.S.: 332216

O.I.J. INC. (1)
350 Ishida
Isehara, Kanagawa, 259-1116, Japan
Tel.: (81) 463 96 3711
Fax: (81) 463 96 3707
Web Site: www.oij.co.jp
Restaurant Operating Services
S.I.C.: 5812
N.A.I.C.S.: 722511
Takao Endo *(Pres)*

Plant:

Amada Co., Ltd. - Ono Plant (1)
56 Hata-machi
Ono, Hyogo, Japan
Tel.: (81) 794 62 5931
Fax: (81) 794 62 4351
Band Saw Blade Mfr
S.I.C.: 3425
N.A.I.C.S.: 332216

U.S. Subsidiaries:

Amada Cutting Technologies, Inc. (1)
4070 Winnetka Ave
Rolling Meadows, IL 60008-1374 (100%)
Tel.: (714) 670-1704
Fax: (714) 670-2017
E-Mail: info@amadabandsaw.com
Web Site: www.amadabandsaw.com
Emp.: 45
Cutting Machines Sales & Service
S.I.C.: 5084
N.A.I.C.S.: 423830
Toshi Ichimura *(Pres)*

Amada Laser America Inc. (1)
11100 Alcovy Rd
Covington, GA 30014-6406 (80%)
Tel.: (770) 385-5114
Fax: (770) 788-9051
Toll Free: (800) 262-9080
Web Site: www.amadabandsaw.com
Emp.: 13
Cutting Machines Sales & Service
S.I.C.: 8743
N.A.I.C.S.: 541820

Amada Machine Tools America, Inc. (1)
2324 Palmer Dr
Schaumburg, IL 60173
Tel.: (847) 285-4800
Fax: (847) 519-2127
Web Site: www.amadawasino.com
Sales Range: Less than $1 Million
Emp.: 18
Metalworking Machinery
S.I.C.: 5084
N.A.I.C.S.: 423830
Rod Milliken *(VP-Ops)*

Amada North America, Inc. (1)
7025 Firestone Blvd
Buena Park, CA 90621-1869
Tel.: (714) 739-2111
Fax: (714) 739-4099
E-Mail: allsales@amada.com
Web Site: www.amada.com
Emp.: 310
Cutting Machines Sales & Service
S.I.C.: 5084
N.A.I.C.S.: 423830
Kathy Gonzalez *(Mgr-HR)*

Amada Tool America, Inc. (1)
4A Treadeasy Ave
Batavia, NY 14020
Tel.: (585) 344-3900
Fax: (585) 344-3905
Web Site: www.amada.com
Emp.: 65
Hand Tool Mfr
S.I.C.: 3423
N.A.I.C.S.: 332216
Edward Dries *(COO)*

Non-U.S. Subsidiaries:

Ab LKI Kaldman Oy (1)
Ojesvagen 74
68910 Bennas, Finland
Tel.: (358) 6 781 5424
Fax: (358) 6 781 5433
Emp.: 100
Industrial Machinery Distr
S.I.C.: 5084
N.A.I.C.S.: 423830
Tom Nordstrom *(Gen Mgr)*

AMADA ASIA PTE LTD. (1)
12 Tannery Road 03-07 HB Centre 1
Singapore, 347722, Singapore
Tel.: (65) 6743 3244
Fax: (65) 6743 3844
Machine Tool Mfr
S.I.C.: 3541
N.A.I.C.S.: 333517
Umada Sachiro *(Mng Dir)*

Amada Austria GmbH (1)
Wassergasse 1
2630 Ternitz, Austria (100%)
Tel.: (43) 263035170
Fax: (43) 263035165
E-Mail: info@amada.at
Web Site: www.amada.at
Emp.: 120
Mfr. & Sales of Bandsaw Blades & Punches & Dies
S.I.C.: 3423
N.A.I.C.S.: 332216
Katsuhiko Kawabata *(Gen Mgr)*

Amada Canada Ltd. (1)
885 Ave Geroges Cros
Granby, QC, J2J 1E8, Canada (100%)
Tel.: (450) 378-0111
Fax: (450) 378-4903
Toll Free: (800) 363-1220
E-Mail: info@amada.ca
Web Site: www.amada.ca
Emp.: 30
Cutting Machines Sales & Service
S.I.C.: 3546
N.A.I.C.S.: 333991
Frank Corigliano *(Mgr)*

Amada De Mexico, S. de R.L. de C.V. (1)
Ave Ricardo Margain 575 Parque Corporativo Santa Engracia
Garza Garcia, Nuevo Leon, 66267, Mexico
Tel.: (52) 81 1234 0700
Fax: (52) 8112340705
Web Site: www.amada.com
Machine Tool Distr
S.I.C.: 5084
N.A.I.C.S.: 423830

Amada do Brasil Ltda. (1)
Rua Dr Moises Kahan 55 73
01139 040 Sao Paulo, SP, Brazil (100%)
Tel.: (55) 1136116278
Fax: (55) 1166930663
E-Mail: amadabrasil@amadabrasil.com.br
Web Site: www.amada.com
Emp.: 7
Cutting Machines Sales & Service
S.I.C.: 3554
N.A.I.C.S.: 333243

Amada Engineering Europe S.p.A. (1)
Via Amada I 1/3
29010 Pontenure, Piacenza, Italy
Tel.: (39) 0523 952811
Fax: (39) 0523 952899
E-Mail: info@amada-engineering.eu
Web Site: www.computesweb.com
Machine Tool Software Development Services
S.I.C.: 7371
N.A.I.C.S.: 541511

Amada Europe S.A. (1)
ZI Paris Nord 2 96 Ave de la Pyramide
F 93290 Tremblay, France
Tel.: (33) 149903000
Fax: (33) 149903199

Amada Co., Ltd.—(Continued)

E-Mail: accubeil@amada.fr
Web Site: www.amada.fr
Emp.: 200
Development, Manufacture & Sales of Metalworking Machines & Tools
S.I.C.: 3425
N.A.I.C.S.: 332216
Gilles Bajolet *(Pres)*

Amada Europe Software Center, S.A.S (1)
ZI Paris Nord II 96 Avenue De La Pyramide
93290 Tremblay-les-Gonesse, France
Tel.: (33) 1 4990 7638
Fax: (33) 1 4990 7637
Software Development Services
S.I.C.: 7371
N.A.I.C.S.: 541511

Amada GmbH (1)
Amada Allee 1
D 42781 Haan, Nordrhein Westfalen, Germany
Tel.: (49) 212957901
Fax: (49) 21042126999
E-Mail: info@amada.de
Web Site: www.amada.de
Emp.: 175
Cutting Machines Sales & Service
S.I.C.: 5084
N.A.I.C.S.: 423830
Frank Morchel *(Gen Mgr)*

Amada Hong Kong Co., Ltd. (1)
Unit 1101 11/F Austin Tower 22-26 Austin Ave
Jordan, Kowloon, China (Hong Kong) (100%)
Tel.: (852) 28689186
Fax: (852) 25211363
Emp.: 6
Cutting Machines Sales & Service
S.I.C.: 5084
N.A.I.C.S.: 423830

AMADA (INDIA) PVT. LTD. (1)
D - Wing 115 Floral Deck Plaza MIDC
Andheri East, Mumbai, 400 093, India
Tel.: (91) 22 28395592
Fax: (91) 22 28235405
E-Mail: info@amadaindia.co.in
Web Site: www.amadaindia.co.in
Emp.: 15
Metal Working Machinery Mfr
S.I.C.: 3549
N.A.I.C.S.: 333519
Kuniya Matsumoto *(Pres & CEO)*

Amada International Industry & Trading (Shanghai) Co., Ltd. (1)
629 Xihuan Road
Shanghai, 200235, China (100%)
Tel.: (86) 2162121111
Fax: (86) 2162404105
E-Mail: kojima@amada.com.cn
Web Site: www.amada.com.cn
Sales Range: $10-24.9 Million
Emp.: 70
Cutting Machines Sales & Service
S.I.C.: 5084
N.A.I.C.S.: 423830

Amada International Trading (Shenzhen) Co., Ltd (1)
Rm 801-803 8/F Talfook Chong No 9
Shihua Rord Futian Free Trade Zone
Shenzhen, China
Tel.: (86) 755 8358 0011
Fax: (86) 755 8359 7489
Machine Tool Distr
S.I.C.: 5084
N.A.I.C.S.: 423830

Amada Italia S.r.l. (1)
Via Amada I 1/3
29010 Pontenure, Piacenza, Italy
Tel.: (39) 0523 872111
Fax: (39) 0523 872101
E-Mail: info@amada.it
Web Site: www.amada.it
Machine Tool Distr
S.I.C.: 5084
N.A.I.C.S.: 423830
Mitsuo Okamoto *(Pres)*

Amada Korea Co., Ltd. (1)
123 Block 5 Lot Namdong Industrial Area
693 4 Kojan Dong Namdong Ku, Incheon, Korea (South)
Tel.: (82) 328216010
Fax: (82) 328216015
Web Site: www.amada.co.kr
Emp.: 80
Cutting Machines Sales & Service
S.I.C.: 3423
N.A.I.C.S.: 332216

Amada Lianyungang Machine Tool Co., Ltd (1)
No 3-2 Songtiao Eco & Tech Development Zone
Lianyungang, Jiangsu, China
Tel.: (86) 518 8515 1111
Fax: (86) 518 8515 1777
Machine Tool Mfr
S.I.C.: 3542
N.A.I.C.S.: 333517

Amada Lianyungang Machinery Co., Ltd. (1)
No 18 Hailian West Rd
Xinpu, Lianyungang, Jiangsu, China
Tel.: (86) 518 8515 9215
Fax: (86) 518 8551 3399
Web Site: www.amada.co.th/about_us/group.html
Cutting Machines Sales & Service
S.I.C.: 3554
N.A.I.C.S.: 333243

Amada Machine Tools Europe GmbH (1)
AMADA Allee 3
42781 Haan, Germany
Tel.: (49) 212957903
Fax: (49) 212957339
E-Mail: info@amadamachinetools.de
Web Site: www.amada-mt.de
Emp.: 70
Sales of Cutting Machines & Machine Tools
S.I.C.: 5084
N.A.I.C.S.: 423830

AMADA MACHINE TOOLS (THAILAND) CO., LTD. (1)
700/146 Village No 1
Bankao Sub-District Phan Thong, Chon Buri, 20160, Thailand
Tel.: (66) 3846 8920
Machine Tool Mfr
S.I.C.: 3541
N.A.I.C.S.: 333517

Amada (Malaysia) Sdn. Bhd. (1)
No 38 Jalan Kartunis U1 47 Section U1
Temasya Industrial Park
Glenmarie Darul Eshan, 40150 Shah Alam, Selangor, Malaysia
Tel.: (60) 355991035
Fax: (60) 355991042
E-Mail: amada3@po.jaring.my
Web Site: www.amada.com.au/amadagroup_03.html
Cutting Machines Sales & Service
S.I.C.: 5084
N.A.I.C.S.: 423830

Amada Maquinaria S.I. (1)
Calle Marina N 12/14 Cornella De Llobregat
08940 Barcelona, Spain
Tel.: (34) 93 4742725
Fax: (34) 93 3779 196
Web Site: www.amada.co.jp/english/corporate/group.html
Emp.: 27
Machine Tool Distr
S.I.C.: 5084
N.A.I.C.S.: 423830
Paul Mansfield *(Mng Dir)*

Amada Oceania Pty. Ltd. (1)
Unit 7 16 Lexington Drive Norwest Business Park
Bella Vista, NSW, 2153, Australia (100%)
Tel.: (61) 288871100
Fax: (61) 288871101
E-Mail: mhanson@amada.com.au
Web Site: www.amada.com.au
Emp.: 6
Sales & After-Sales Service of Machines & Tools
S.I.C.: 3554
N.A.I.C.S.: 333243

Amada Outillage S.A. (1)
Zone Industrielle
BP 35
76720 Auffay, France
Tel.: (33) 2 3280 8100
Fax: (33) 2 3532 7646
Web Site: www.amada.co.jp/english/corporate/group.html
Machine Tool Mfr
S.I.C.: 3541
N.A.I.C.S.: 333517

Amada S.A. (1)
ZI Paris Nord 2 96 Ave de la Pyramide
F 93290 Tremblay, France (100%)
Tel.: (33) 149903000
Fax: (33) 149903199
E-Mail: accueal@amada.fr
Web Site: www.amada.fr
Emp.: 150
Cutting Machines Sales & Service
S.I.C.: 5084
N.A.I.C.S.: 423830
Gilles Bajolet *(Pres)*

AMADA SHANGHAI MACHINE TECH CO., LTD. (1)
No 68 Hui Shen Road Nan Xiang High-tech Industry Park
Jia Ding District, Shanghai, China
Tel.: (86) 21 6917 1352
Web Site: www.amada.co.jp/english/corporate/group.html
Machine Tool Mfr
S.I.C.: 3541
N.A.I.C.S.: 333517

Amada Singapore (1989) Pte. Ltd. (1)
12 Tannery Rd
HB Ctr 05 01 02, Singapore, 247722, Singapore
Tel.: (65) 67436334
Fax: (65) 67433134
Web Site: www.amadabandsaw.com
Emp.: 12
Cutting Machines Sales & Service
S.I.C.: 5084
N.A.I.C.S.: 423830
Kozo Makade *(CEO)*

AMADA SOFT (INDIA) PVT.LTD. (1)
Block-6 No 2 2nd Floor IITM Research Park
M G R Film City Road
Taramani, Chennai, 600 113, India
Tel.: (91) 44 66630300
Fax: (91) 4466630308
E-Mail: asi@amadasoft.co.in
Web Site: www.amadasoft.co.in
Emp.: 10
Software Development Services
S.I.C.: 7371
N.A.I.C.S.: 541511
L. J. Hang *(COO)*

Amada Sweden AB (1)
Borgens Gata 16-18
441 39 Alingsas, Sweden
Tel.: (46) 322 20 99 00
Fax: (46) 322 20 99 29
E-Mail: info@amadasweden.se
Web Site: www.amadasweden.se
Emp.: 23
Machine Tool Distr
S.I.C.: 5084
N.A.I.C.S.: 423830
Inger Blom *(Mgr-Admin)*

Amada Taiwan, Inc. (1)
2 Wenming Rd
Linkou 3 Industrial Park Kweis, Taoyuan, Hsien, Taiwan (100%)
Tel.: (886) 33283511
Fax: (886) 33284200
Web Site: www.amada.com.tw
Emp.: 80
Cutting Machines Sales & Service
S.I.C.: 5084
N.A.I.C.S.: 423830
Honda Kuji *(Mgr)*

Amada Techni-Scia S.a.r.l. (1)
Ave De La Pyramide
BP 41040
F 95912 Roissy-en-France, Cedex, France (100%)
Tel.: (33) 149903094
Fax: (33) 149903170
E-Mail: info@amadamachinetools.fr
Web Site: www.amada.com
Emp.: 19
Cutting Machines Sales & Service
S.I.C.: 5072
N.A.I.C.S.: 423710
Osvald Gahdelli *(Mng Dir)*

Amada (Thailand) Co., Ltd. (1)
110/8 Moo 13 Rachatheva Sub-District
Bangplee District, Bangkok, Samutprakam, 10540, Thailand (100%)
Tel.: (66) 27389530
Fax: (66) 27389534
E-Mail: info@amada.co.th
Web Site: www.amada.co.th
Sales Range: $10-24.9 Million
Emp.: 70
Cutting Machines Sales & Service
S.I.C.: 5084
N.A.I.C.S.: 423830
Yuji Fujimoto *(Mng Dir)*

Amada Turkiye Makina Teknoloji Sanayi Ve Ticaret Ltd. (1)
Ikitelli Organize Sanayi Bolgesi Haseyad Kooperatifi
Turgut Ozal Caddesi No 116, 34670 Istanbul, Turkey
Tel.: (90) 212 549 10 70
Fax: (90) 212 549 1076
Web Site: www.amada.co.jp/english/corporate/group.html
Machine Tool Distr
S.I.C.: 5084
N.A.I.C.S.: 423830

Amada United Kingdom Limited (1)
Spennells Valley Road
Kidderminster, Worcs, DY10 1XS, United Kingdom (100%)
Tel.: (44) 1562749500
Fax: (44) 1562749510
E-Mail: info@amada.co.uk
Web Site: www.amada.co.uk
Emp.: 132
Cutting Machines Sales & Service
S.I.C.: 5084
N.A.I.C.S.: 423830
Alan Parrott *(Mng Dir)*

Amada Vietnam Co., Ltd. (1)
469 Ha Huy Tap Yen Vien
Gia Lam, Hanoi, Vietnam
Tel.: (84) 4 6261 4583
Fax: (84) 4 6261 4584
E-Mail: info@amadavietnam.vn
Web Site: www.amadavietnam.vn
Emp.: 10
Machine Tool Distr
S.I.C.: 5084
N.A.I.C.S.: 423830
Kazunori Kojima *(Gen Dir)*

Beijing Amada Machine & Tooling Co., Ltd. (1)
Room 302 Beijing Jingwen Liaoshi Building
114 Chongwenmenwai Da Street, Beijing, 100062, China (100%)
Tel.: (86) 1067118414
Fax: (86) 1067118348
Web Site: www.amada.com
Cutting Machines Sales & Service
S.I.C.: 3425
N.A.I.C.S.: 332216

Crea S.r.l. (1)
Via Asti 43
10026 Santena, Torino, Italy (100%)
Tel.: (39) 011 9496211
Fax: (39) 011 9496296
E-Mail: info@crea-amada.it
Web Site: www.crea-amada.it
Emp.: 40
Mfr. of Metalworking Machines & Bandsaws
S.I.C.: 3554
N.A.I.C.S.: 333243

AMADEUS CAPITAL PARTNERS LTD.

16 St James St
London, SW1A 1ER, United Kingdom
Tel.: (44) 2070246900
Fax: (44) 2070246999
E-Mail: info@amadeuscapital.com
Web Site: www.amadeuscapital.com
Emp.: 30

Business Description:
Private Equity Firm
S.I.C.: 6211
N.A.I.C.S.: 523999

Personnel:
Anne Glover *(CEO)*

AMADEUS ENERGY LIMITED

(Name Changed to Lonestar Resources Limited)

AMADEUS FIRE AG

Darmstadter Landstrasse 116
60598 Frankfurt, Germany
Tel.: (49) 69968760
Fax: (49) 6996876399
E-Mail: frankfurt@amadeus-fire.de
Web Site: www.amadeus-fire.de
AAD—(DEU)
Rev.: $184,429,329
Assets: $80,412,119
Liabilities: $24,805,875
Net Worth: $55,606,244
Earnings: $18,006,370
Emp.: 2,434
Fiscal Year-end: 12/31/12
Business Description:
Staffing Services
S.I.C.: 7363
N.A.I.C.S.: 561320
Personnel:
Christoph Gross *(Chm-Supervisory Bd)*
Peter Haas *(Chm-Mgmt Bd & CEO)*
Michael C. Wisser *(Deputy Chm-Supervisory Bd)*
Robert von Wulfing *(CFO & Member-Mgmt Bd)*
Axel Endriss *(Chief Trng Officer & Member-Mgmt Bd)*
Supervisory Board of Directors:
Christoph Gross
Ulrike Bert
Arno Frings
Karl Graf zu Eltz
Knuth Henneke
Ulrike Hosl-Abramowski
Silke Klarius
Sibylle Lust
Elmar Roth
Hartmut van der Straeten
Mathias Venema
Michael C. Wisser

Subsidiaries:

Amadeus FiRe Interim- und Projektmanagement GmbH **(1)**
Darmstadter Landstrasse 116
60598 Frankfurt am Main, Hesse, Germany
Tel.: (49) 6996876150
Fax: (49) 6996876199
E-Mail: info@amadeus-fire.de
Web Site: www.interim-projektmanagement.de
Emp.: 100
Accounting Services
S.I.C.: 8721
N.A.I.C.S.: 541219
Peter Haas *(Mng Dir)*

Amadeus FiRe Services GmbH **(1)**
Darmstadter Landstr 116
60598 Frankfurt am Main, Germany
Tel.: (49) 6996876477
Fax: (49) 6996876299
E-Mail: info@amadeus-fire.de
Emp.: 9
Accounting & Auditing Services
S.I.C.: 8721
N.A.I.C.S.: 541211

Greenwell Gleeson GmbH **(1)**
Palazzo Michelangelo Gerbermuhlstrasse 9
60594 Frankfurt am Main, Hesse, Germany
Tel.: (49) 6990027720
Fax: (49) 6990027722
E-Mail: info@greenwellgleeson.de
Web Site: www.greenwellgleeson.de
Professionals Recruiting Services
S.I.C.: 8999
N.A.I.C.S.: 541612
Harald H.J Heil *(Mng Dir)*

Steuer-Fachschule Dr. Endriss GmbH & Co. KG **(1)**
Lichtstrasse 45-49
50825 Cologne, Nordrhein-Westfalen, Germany
Tel.: (49) 2219364420
Fax: (49) 22193644233
E-Mail: info@endriss.de
Web Site: www.endriss.de
Emp.: 30
Educational Services
S.I.C.: 8299
N.A.I.C.S.: 611691
Joerg Philippen *(Mng Dir)*

Subsidiary:

Akademie fur Internationale Rechnungslegung Prof. Dr. Leibfried GmbH **(2)**
Lichtstrasse 45-49
50825 Cologne, Nordrhein-Westfalen, Germany
Tel.: (49) 2219364420
Fax: (49) 22193644233
E-Mail: info@academy-international-accounting.com
Web Site: www.academy-international-accounting.com
Emp.: 10
Educational Services
S.I.C.: 8299
N.A.I.C.S.: 611710
Peter Leibfried *(Founder & Mng Dir)*

Non-U.S. Subsidiary:

Greenwell Gleeson Ltd. **(1)**
Cathedral Place 42-44 Waterloo St
Birmingham, B2 5QB, United Kingdom
Tel.: (44) 1212339911
Fax: (44) 1212339912
E-Mail: info@ggltd.co.uk
Web Site: www.greenwell-gleeson.co.uk
Emp.: 20
Accounting Professionals Recruitment Services
S.I.C.: 8999
N.A.I.C.S.: 541612
Rob Lawton *(Mng Dir)*

AMADEUS IT HOLDING S.A.

C Salvador de Madariaga 1
28027 Madrid, Spain
Tel.: (34) 915820100
Fax: (34) 915 820 188
E-Mail: reception.madrid@amadeus.com
Web Site: www.amadeus.com
AMS—(BAR BIL MAD OTC VAL)
Rev.: $3,917,793,551
Assets: $6,940,097,319
Liabilities: $2,061,574,546
Net Worth: $4,878,522,772
Earnings: $668,097,440
Emp.: 9,163
Fiscal Year-end: 12/31/12
Business Description:
Holding Company
S.I.C.: 6719
N.A.I.C.S.: 551112
Personnel:
Jose Antonio Tazon Garcia *(Chm)*
Guillermo de la Dehesa Romero *(Vice Chm)*
Luis Maroto Camino *(Pres & CEO)*
Jacinto Esclapes Diaz *(Vice Sec)*
Holger Taubmann *(Sr VP-Distr)*
Board of Directors:
Jose Antonio Tazon Garcia
Christian Guy Marie Boireau
Guillermo de la Dehesa Romero
Enrique Dupuy De Lome Chavarri
Clara Furse
Stephan Gemkow
Pierre Henri Gourgeon
Bernard Andre Joseph Bourigeaud
Francesco Loredan
Stuart Anderson McAlpine
David Gordon Comyn Webster

Holding:

Amadeus IT Group S.A. **(1)**
Salvador de Madariaga 1
28027 Madrid, Spain ES
Tel.: (34) 915820100
Fax: (34) 915827717
E-Mail: reception.madrid@amadeus.com
Web Site: www.amadeus.com
Sales Range: $1-4.9 Billion
Travel & Tourism Information Solutions
S.I.C.: 7374
N.A.I.C.S.: 518210
Luis Maroto Camino *(Pres & CEO)*
Ana de Pro Gonzalo *(CFO)*
Tomas Lopez Fernebrand *(Gen Counsel & VP)*
Philippe Chereque *(Exec VP-Comml)*
Eberhard Haag *(Exec VP-Ops)*
Jean-Paul Hamon *(Exec VP-Dev)*
Julia Sattel *(Sr VP-Airline IT)*

Subsidiaries:

Amadeus Purchase Debt, S.A. **(2)**
Calle salvador De Madariaga 1
Madrid, 28027, Spain
Tel.: (34) 915820100
Fax: (34) 915827717
Web Site: www.es.amadeus.com
Financial Software Development Services
S.I.C.: 7371
N.A.I.C.S.: 541511
Luis Maroto *(Gen Mgr)*

Amadeus Soluciones Tecnologicas, S.A **(2)**
Ed Apot Ribera del Sena 21 1a Planta
28042 Madrid, Spain
Tel.: (34) 91 329 86 83
Fax: (34) 91 329 86 19
E-Mail: amadeus@es.amadeus.com
Travel Software Development Services
S.I.C.: 7371
N.A.I.C.S.: 541511

U.S. Subsidiary:

Amadeus North America, Inc. **(2)**
9250 NW 36th St
Miami, FL 33178 DE
Tel.: (305) 499-6000
Fax: (305) 499-6889
E-Mail: salesinquiries@amadeus.com
Web Site: www.amadeus.com
Travel & Tourism Information Solutions
S.I.C.: 7379
N.A.I.C.S.: 518210
Scott Gutz *(Pres & CEO)*
Vic Pynn *(COO)*
Scott Alvis *(CMO)*
Stephane Durand *(Chief Comml Officer)*
Jean-Francois Billiard *(Sr VP-Strategic Programs-Americas)*

Subsidiary:

Amadeus Revenue Integrity Inc. **(3)**
3530 E Campo Abierto Ste 200
Tucson, AZ 85718-5876
Tel.: (520) 577-6500
Fax: (520) 577-6600
Tourism Software Development Services
S.I.C.: 7371
N.A.I.C.S.: 541511

Unit:

Amadeus North America, Inc. - E-Travel Business **(3)**
307 Weaverly Oaks Rd Ste 401
Waltham, MA 02452
Tel.: (781) 522-8920
Fax: (781) 522-8901
E-Mail: fgutz@amadeus.com
Web Site: www.amadeus.com
Sales Range: $1-9.9 Million
Emp.: 66
Computer Software Providers
S.I.C.: 4724
N.A.I.C.S.: 561510
Tom Cates *(VP)*

Non-U.S. Subsidiaries:

Amadeus Argentina S.A. **(2)**
Avda del Libertador 1068 5 piso
C1112 ABN Buenos Aires, Argentina
Tel.: (54) 1157772000
Fax: (54) 11 5777 2010
E-Mail: amadeus@amadeus.com.ar
Web Site: www.ar.amadeus.com
Emp.: 12
Information Technology Consulting Services
S.I.C.: 7373
N.A.I.C.S.: 541512
Geoff Erby *(Country Mgr)*

Amadeus Asia Limited **(2)**
21st Floor Capital Tower 87 1 All Season Place Wireless Rd Lumpini
Pathumwan, 10330 Bangkok, Thailand
Tel.: (66) 23058110
Fax: (66) 23058120
Travel & Tourism Information Solutions
S.I.C.: 7374
N.A.I.C.S.: 518210
Angel Gallego *(Pres-Asia Pacific)*

Amadeus Austria Marketing GmbH **(2)**
Alpenstrasse 108a
5020 Salzburg, Austria
Tel.: (43) 662 639 660
Fax: (43) 662 639 668
E-Mail: office.szg@amadeus.at
Web Site: www.at.amadeus.com
Tourism Software Development Services
S.I.C.: 7371
N.A.I.C.S.: 541511

Amadeus Benelux N.V. **(2)**
Medialaan 30
1800 Vilvoorde, Belgium
Tel.: (32) 2 257 99 11
Fax: (32) 2 460 03 84
E-Mail: infobe@benelux.amadeus.com
Emp.: 4
Tourism Software Development Services
S.I.C.: 7371
N.A.I.C.S.: 541511
Luc Pannecoeck *(Gen Mgr)*

Amadeus Bulgaria OOD **(2)**
1 Bulgaria Square 16th Floor
1463 Sofia, Bulgaria
Tel.: (359) 29 532 386
Fax: (359) 29 533 257
E-Mail: info@bg.amadeus.com
Tourism Software Consulting Services
S.I.C.: 7373
N.A.I.C.S.: 541512
Denka Gouneva *(Gen Mgr)*

Amadeus Central and West Africa S.A. **(2)**
7 Ave Nojues Inneuvle Bsic 4 Fl
Abidjan, Cote d'Ivoire
Tel.: (225) 20312240
Fax: (225) 20312250
Tourism Software Development Services
S.I.C.: 7371
N.A.I.C.S.: 541511
Vasken Tokatlien *(Mgr)*

Amadeus Denmark A/S **(2)**
Oldenburg Alle 3 1 tv
2630 Tastrup, Denmark
Tel.: (45) 43 59 20 00
Fax: (45) 43 59 20 01
E-Mail: denmark@sca.amadeus.com
Web Site: www.amadeusdenmark.dk
Tourism Software Development Services
S.I.C.: 7371
N.A.I.C.S.: 541511

Amadeus France SNC **(2)**
Le Seine St Germain Batiment C
28 Ave Du Bas Meudon, F 92445 Issy-les-Moulineaux, France FR
Tel.: (33) 141338300
Fax: (33) 141338045
E-Mail: info@amadeus.com
Web Site: www.amadeus.com
Emp.: 200
Travel Services
S.I.C.: 4724
N.A.I.C.S.: 561510
Arnaud Debuchy *(Mng Dir)*

Subsidiary:

Amadeus France Services S.A. **(3)**
2 Avenue Du Bas Meudon
Issy-les-Moulineaux, 92130, France
Tel.: (33) 141338100
Data Transaction Processing Services
S.I.C.: 7379
N.A.I.C.S.: 518210

Amadeus IT Holding S.A.—(Continued)

Amadeus GDS LLP (2)
86 Gogol Street Rooms 709 712 713 7th Floor
480091 Almaty, Kazakhstan
Tel.: (7) 727 250 7255
Fax: (7) 727 250 7062
E-Mail: info@amadeus.kz
Web Site: www.amadeus.ru/about/worldwide.htm
Software Consulting Services
S.I.C.: 7371
N.A.I.C.S.: 541511

Amadeus GDS Singapore Pte. Ltd. (2)
600 North Bridge Road 15-06 Parkview Square
Singapore, 188778, Singapore
Tel.: (65) 6220 6866
Fax: (65) 6296 6839
E-Mail: cs@sg.amadeus.com
Web Site: www.amadeus.com
Information Technology Consulting Services
S.I.C.: 7373
N.A.I.C.S.: 541512

Amadeus Germany GmbH (2)
Marienbader Platz 1
61348 Bad Homburg, Germany
Tel.: (49) 6172910
Fax: (49) 6172911999
E-Mail: zentrale@de.amadeus.com
Web Site: www.de.amadeus.com
Emp.: 700
Travel & Tourism Information Solutions
S.I.C.: 7379
N.A.I.C.S.: 541519
Petra Euler *(Mgr-HR)*

Amadeus Global Travel Israel Ltd. (2)
1 Ben YehudaTel Aviv
Tel Aviv, 63801, Israel
Tel.: (972) 37950000
Fax: (972) 37950011
Tourism Software Consulting Services
S.I.C.: 7373
N.A.I.C.S.: 541512

Amadeus GTD (Malta) Limited (2)
Birkirkara Road
San Gwann, SGN 4193, Malta
Tel.: (356) 21383873
Fax: (356) 21383885
E-Mail: acomalta@mt.amadeus.com
Web Site: www.mt.amadeus.com
Tourism Software Consulting Services
S.I.C.: 7373
N.A.I.C.S.: 541512
Simon Rossi *(Gen Mgr)*

Amadeus GTD Southern Africa Pty. Ltd. (2)
Rentworks Place Turnberry Office Park 48 Grosvenor Road
Bryanston, Sandton, South Africa
Tel.: (27) 11 548 7300
Fax: (27) 11 548 7320
E-Mail: info@amadeus.co.za
Web Site: www.amadeus.co.za
Software Consulting Services
S.I.C.: 7373
N.A.I.C.S.: 541512
Peter Long *(Gen Mgr)*

Amadeus Hellas S.A. (2)
157 Sygrou Avenue N Smyrni
171 21 Athens, Greece
Tel.: (30) 210 9303000
Fax: (30) 210 9356873
E-Mail: info.gr@amadeus.com
Web Site: www.amadeus.com
Tourism Software Consulting Services
S.I.C.: 7373
N.A.I.C.S.: 541512
Eva Karamanou *(Gen Mgr)*

Amadeus Hong Kong Limited (2)
3/F Henley Building 5 Queen's Road Central, China (Hong Kong)
Tel.: (852) 29130123
Fax: (852) 29130133
E-Mail: sales.hk@amadeus.com
Information Technology Consulting Services
S.I.C.: 7373
N.A.I.C.S.: 541512

Amadeus IT Pacific Pty. Ltd. (2)
Level 12 300 Elizabeth St
Locked Bag A5085
Sydney, NSW, 1235, Australia
Tel.: (61) 2 9903 3933
Fax: (61) 2 9903 3900
Travel & Tourism Software Development Services
S.I.C.: 7371
N.A.I.C.S.: 541511

Amadeus Italia S.P.A. (2)
Via Morimondo 26
20143 Milan, Italy
Tel.: (39) 02 725471
E-Mail: commerciale@it.amadeus.com
Web Site: www.amadeus.com
Software Consulting Services
S.I.C.: 7373
N.A.I.C.S.: 541512

Amadeus Japan K.K. (2)
2-4-9 Ginza Sppginza Bldg 5f
Chuo-Ku, Tokyo, 104-0061, Japan
Tel.: (81) 355243700
Fax: (81) 355243701
E-Mail: info@jp.amadeus.com
Web Site: www.jp.amadeus.com
Travel Arrangement Software Development Services
S.I.C.: 7371
N.A.I.C.S.: 541511

Amadeus Magyaroszag Kft (2)
Madach Imre ut 13-14
1075 Budapest, Hungary
Tel.: (36) 1 880 1100
Fax: (36) 1 239 1829
E-Mail: info@hu.amadeus.com
Emp.: 14
Tourism Software Development Services
S.I.C.: 7371
N.A.I.C.S.: 541511
Mathias Kamolz *(Gen Mgr)*

Amadeus Marketing Ireland Ltd. (2)
10 Coke Lane
Smithfield, Dublin, 7, Ireland
Tel.: (353) 1 879 2555
Fax: (353) 1 878 3929
E-Mail: sales@ie.amadeus.com
Web Site: www.ie.amadeus.com
Emp.: 10
Travel & Tourism Software Development Services
S.I.C.: 7371
N.A.I.C.S.: 541511
Volker Lorenz *(Gen Mgr)*

Amadeus Marketing Phils Inc. (2)
36 Floor Lkg Tower 6801 Ayala Ave
Makati, Philippines 1226
Tel.: (63) 2 857 71 00
Fax: (63) 2 753 17 23
E-Mail: sales@amadeusph.com
Web Site: www.amadeus.com.ph
Information Technology Consulting Services
S.I.C.: 7371
N.A.I.C.S.: 541511

Amadeus Marketing Romania S.R.L. (2)
10-12 Str Maior Gheorghe Sontu
Bucharest, Romania
Tel.: (40) 21 223 03 54
Fax: (40) 21 223 03 60
Web Site: www.amadeus.com
Automated Ticketing Software Development Services
S.I.C.: 7371
N.A.I.C.S.: 541511
Razvan Antoni *(Gen Mgr)*

Amadeus Marketing (Schweiz) A.G. (2)
Pfingstweidstrasse 60
8005 Zurich, Switzerland
Tel.: (41) 44 217 97 97
Fax: (41) 44 217 97 99
E-Mail: admin@ch.amadeus.com
Emp.: 23
Tourism Software Consulting Services
S.I.C.: 7373
N.A.I.C.S.: 541512
Cornel Kung *(Gen Mgr)*

Amadeus Marketing (UK) Ltd. (2)
The Web House 106 High Street
Crawley, West Sussex, RH10 1BF, United Kingdom
Tel.: (44) 870 895 9199
Fax: (44) 870 895 9299
E-Mail: sales@uk.amadeus.com
Web Site: www.amadeus.com
Emp.: 100
Tourism Software Consulting Services
S.I.C.: 7373
N.A.I.C.S.: 541512
Rob Sinclair-Barnes *(Dir-Mktg-UK & Ireland)*

Amadeus Maroc S.A.S. (2)
7 Rue Naguib Mahfouz
Quartier Gauthier, 20000 Casablanca, Morocco
Tel.: (212) 22489800
Fax: (212) 22489814
E-Mail: fbouab@amadeus.co.ma
Web Site: www.ma.amadeus.com
Emp.: 14
Travel Products Distr
S.I.C.: 4724
N.A.I.C.S.: 561510

Amadeus Norway AS (2)
C J Hambros Plass 2C
0164 Oslo, Norway
Tel.: (47) 22 96 70 00
Fax: (47) 22 99 60 10
E-Mail: norway@sca.amadeus.com
Web Site: www.amadeus.com
Information Technology Consulting Services
S.I.C.: 7373
N.A.I.C.S.: 541512
Jesper Soderstrom *(Mng Dir)*

Amadeus Paraguay S.R.L. (2)
Edificio Inter Express 2do Piso Oficina 202
Asuncion, Paraguay
Tel.: (595) 21 450 707
Fax: (595) 21 450 708
Tourism Software Consulting Services
S.I.C.: 7373
N.A.I.C.S.: 541512

Amadeus Peru S.A. (2)
Victor Andres Belaunde 147 T 5 of 902
San Isidro, Lima, Peru
Tel.: (51) 1 2156030
Fax: (51) 1 2222190
Tourism Information Technology Consulting Services
S.I.C.: 7373
N.A.I.C.S.: 541512

Amadeus Polska Sp. Z o.o. (2)
Domaniewska 49
Warsaw, 02-672, Poland
Tel.: (48) 225394200
Fax: (48) 225394230
Web Site: www.amadeus.com
Emp.: 60
Tourism Software Development Services
S.I.C.: 7371
N.A.I.C.S.: 541511

Amadeus Rezervasyon Dagitim Sistemleri A.S. (2)
Muallim Naci Caddesi No 41 Kat 4
Ortakoy, 34347 Istanbul, Turkey
Tel.: (90) 212 310 07 00
Fax: (90) 212 236 50 80
E-Mail: turkey@amadeus.com.tr
Web Site: www.amadeus.com
Travel Software Development Services
S.I.C.: 7371
N.A.I.C.S.: 541511

Amadeus s.a.s. (2)
485 Route du Pin Montard Boite Postale 69
06902 Sophia-Antipolis, Biot, France
Tel.: (33) 4 92 94 60 00
Fax: (33) 4 97 15 41 20
Travel System Software Development Services
S.I.C.: 7371
N.A.I.C.S.: 541511

Amadeus Scandinavia AB. (2)
Gavlegatan 22
Box 6602
113 84 Stockholm, Sweden
Tel.: (46) 84 58 05 00
Fax: (46) 8 32 01 90
E-Mail: sweden@sca.amadeus.com
Emp.: 200
Tourism Software Consulting Services
S.I.C.: 7373
N.A.I.C.S.: 541512

Amadeus Services Ltd. (2)
World Business Centre 3 1208 Newall Road
Heathrow, Middlesex, TW6 2RB, United Kingdom
Tel.: (44) 20 8990 0600
Fax: (44) 20 8990 6501
E-Mail: sales@uk.amadeus.com
Emp.: 40
Tourism Software Consulting Services
S.I.C.: 7373
N.A.I.C.S.: 541512

Amadeus Sweden AB (2)
Gavlegatan 22
Box 6602
113 84 Stockholm, Sweden
Tel.: (46) 8 458 05 00
Fax: (46) 8 32 01 90
E-Mail: sweden@sca.amadeus.com
Web Site: www.amadeus.com
Tourism Software Development Services
S.I.C.: 7371
N.A.I.C.S.: 541511

Amadeus Taiwan Company Limited (2)
12F No 77 Sec3 Nanking E Rd
Taipei, 104, Taiwan
Tel.: (886) 2 25180518
Fax: (886) 2 25070190
Web Site: www.tw.amadeus.com
Software Consulting Services
S.I.C.: 7371
N.A.I.C.S.: 541511

AMADEUSGLOBAL Ecuador S.A. (2)
Av Republica de El Salvador No 35-126 y Portugal Edificio Zante
Piso 2-Oficina 206, Quito, Ecuador
Tel.: (593) 2 3 333 228
Fax: (593) 2 3 333 208
E-Mail: amadeusecuador@ec.amadeus.com
Web Site: www.amadeus.com
Tourism Software Consulting Services
S.I.C.: 7373
N.A.I.C.S.: 541512

NMC Eastern European CRS B.V. (2)
Schouwburgplein 30-34
Rotterdam, 3012 CL, Netherlands
Tel.: (31) 102245333
Fax: (31) 104117894
Computerized Reservation Services
S.I.C.: 7379
N.A.I.C.S.: 541519

Onerail Global Holdings Pty. Ltd. (2)
L 12 300 Elizabeth St
Surry Hills, NSW, 2010, Australia
Tel.: (61) 293215100
Fax: (61) 293215199
Emp.: 150
Online Reservation Software Development Services
S.I.C.: 7371
N.A.I.C.S.: 541511
Juergen Koller *(Gen Mgr)*

Sistemas de Distribucion Amadeus Chile, S.A. (2)
Marchant Pereira 221 Ofi 111 Santiago
Santiago, Chile
Tel.: (56) 23401010
Tourism Software Development Services
S.I.C.: 7371
N.A.I.C.S.: 541511

Sistemas de Reservaciones CRS de Venezuela, C.A. (2)
Av Romulo Gallegos y 1era Av Sta Eduvigis
Torre KLM Piso 8 Ofc 8A y 8B
Urb Los Palos Grandes, Caracas, 1070, Venezuela
Tel.: (58) 212 283 1683
Fax: (58) 212 285 2995
E-Mail: info@ve.amadeus.com
Information Technology Consulting Services
S.I.C.: 7373
N.A.I.C.S.: 541512

Traveltainment AG (2)
Carlo-Schmid-Strasse 12 Aachen
Wurselen, 52080, Germany De
Tel.: (49) 2405 448 40
Fax: (49) 2405 448 490
E-Mail: helpdesk@traveltainment.de
Web Site: www.traveltainment.de
Tourism Software Consulting Services
S.I.C.: 7373
N.A.I.C.S.: 541512
Mona Kronenberg *(VP-Ops)*

Non-U.S. Subsidiaries:

Traveltainment Polska Sp. z o.o. **(3)**
ul Domaniewska 49
02-672 Warsaw, Poland
Tel.: (48) 22 377 17 50
Fax: (48) 22 377 17 99
E-Mail: sales@traveltainment.pl
Web Site: www.traveltainment.pl
Travel & Tour Operating Services
S.I.C.: 4725
N.A.I.C.S.: 561520

Traveltainment UK Ltd. **(3)**
18-20 Tesla Court Innovation Way
Peterborough, PE2 6FL, United Kingdom
Tel.: (44) 1733 361 345
Fax: (44) 1733 394 313
E-Mail: mail@traveltainment.co.uk
Web Site: www.traveltainment.co.uk
Emp.: 25
Online Ticket Booking & Tour Operating Agencies
S.I.C.: 4729
N.A.I.C.S.: 561599
Andrew Nicholson *(Mng Dir)*

UAB Amadeus Lietuva **(2)**
A Juozapaviciaus g 6/2
Vilnius, 9310, Lithuania
Tel.: (370) 5 2726869
Fax: (370) 5 2726870
E-Mail: amadeus@amadeus.lt
Emp.: 7
Information Technology Consulting Services
S.I.C.: 7373
N.A.I.C.S.: 541512

AMADOR GOLD CORP.

711 675 West Hastings Street
Vancouver, BC, V6B 1N2, Canada
Tel.: (604) 685-2222
Fax: (604) 685-3764
E-Mail: info@amadorgoldcorp.com
Web Site: www.amadorgoldcorp.com
AGX—(TSXV)
Assets: $7,840,293
Liabilities: $1,102,374
Net Worth: $6,737,919
Earnings: ($4,321,092)
Fiscal Year-end: 10/31/12

Business Description:
Mineral Exploration Services
S.I.C.: 1081
N.A.I.C.S.: 213114

Personnel:
Richard W. Hughes *(Pres & CEO)*
Alan D. Campbell *(CFO)*
John-Mark Campbell *(Sec)*

Board of Directors:
Alan D. Campbell
Steven Chan
Darcy Hughes
Richard W. Hughes

Legal Counsel:
Stephen Pearce
711-675 West Hastings Street
Vancouver, BC, Canada

Transfer Agent:
Computershare Trust Company of Canada
510 Burrard St
Vancouver, BC, Canada

AMAG AUSTRIA METALL AG

Lamprechthausenerstrasse 61
PO Box 3
A-5282 Ranshofen, Austria
Tel.: (43) 77228010
Fax: (43) 7722809498
E-Mail: holding@amag.at
Web Site: www.amag.at
AMAG—(VIE)
Sls.: $1,096,043,537
Assets: $1,184,644,408
Liabilities: $452,217,542
Net Worth: $732,426,866
Earnings: $95,998,075
Emp.: 1,490
Fiscal Year-end: 12/31/12

Business Description:
Aluminum Semis & Casthouse Products Mfr
S.I.C.: 3355
N.A.I.C.S.: 331318

Personnel:
Josef Krenner *(Chm-Supervisory Bd)*
Michael Junghans *(Deputy Chm-Supervisory Bd)*
Gerhard Falch *(CEO & Member-Exec Bd)*
Gerald Mayer *(CFO & Member-Exec Bd)*
Helmut Kaufmann *(COO & Member-Exec Bd)*

Supervisory Board of Directors:
Josef Krenner
Max Angermeier
Franz Gasselsberger
Robert Hofer
Otto Hofl
Michael Junghans
Patrick F. Prugger
Heinrich Schaller
Georg Schreiner
Herbert Schutzeneder
Sabine Seidler
Peter Uggowitzer

Subsidiaries:

AMAG Metal GmbH **(1)**
Lamprechtshausner Strasse 61
5282 Ranshofen, Austria (100%)
Tel.: (43) 77228013846
Fax: (43) 7722809479
E-Mail: metal@amag.at
Web Site: www.amag.at
Emp.: 5
Alumina Refining
S.I.C.: 3334
N.A.I.C.S.: 331313
Wolfgang Etl *(Mng Dir)*

AMAG Rolling GmbH **(1)**
Postfach 32
5282 Ranshofen, Austria (100%)
Tel.: (43) 77228012686
Fax: (43) 7722809406
E-Mail: rolling@amag.at
Web Site: www.amag.at/
Sales Range: $600-649.9 Million
Emp.: 810
Other Aluminum Rolling & Drawing
S.I.C.: 3354
N.A.I.C.S.: 331318
Anton Eberle *(Mng Dir)*
Georg Weger *(Mng Dir)*

AMAG Service GmbH **(1)**
PO Box 39
5282 Ranshofen, Austria (100%)
Tel.: (43) 77228010
Fax: (43) 7722809418
E-Mail: ars@amag.at
Emp.: 500
Real Estate Agents & Brokers Offices
S.I.C.: 6531
N.A.I.C.S.: 531210
Reinhare Wachter *(Mng Dir)*

AMAG Treasury GmbH **(1)**
Lamprechtshausner Strasse 61
5282 Ranshofen, Austria (100%)
Tel.: (43) 77228010
Fax: (43) 7722809433
E-Mail: empfang@amag.at
Web Site: www.amag.at
Emp.: 1,300
All Other Legal Services
S.I.C.: 7389
N.A.I.C.S.: 541199
Terhart Salth *(Gen Mgr)*

Non-U.S. Subsidiary:

AMAG Benelux B. V. **(1)**
Galgkade 3 b
3133 KN Vlaardingen, Netherlands (100%)
Tel.: (31) 104604499
Fax: (31) 104600809
E-Mail: info@amag.at
Web Site: www.amag.com
Emp.: 3
Industrial Supplies Whslr
S.I.C.: 5085
N.A.I.C.S.: 423840
Marco Nschouwaneer *(Mng Dir)*

AMAGASA CO., LTD.

6-36-2 Asakusa Taito-ku
Tokyo, 111-0032, Japan
Tel.: (81) 3 3871 0111
Fax: (81) 3 3871 0108
Web Site: www.amagasa-co.com
Year Founded: 1990
3070—(JAS)
Sls.: $67,639,000
Assets: $59,587,000
Liabilities: $39,600,000
Net Worth: $19,987,000
Earnings: $2,090,000
Emp.: 110
Fiscal Year-end: 01/31/13

Business Description:
Women's Shoe Retailer & Whslr
S.I.C.: 5661
N.A.I.C.S.: 448210

Personnel:
Ryuzo Amagasa *(Pres)*

AMAGERBANKEN A/S

Amagerbrogade 25
DK 2300 Copenhagen, Denmark
Tel.: (45) 32666666
Fax: (45) 32666601
E-Mail: information@amagerbanken.dk
Web Site: www.amagerbanken.com
Year Founded: 1903
AMAG—(CSE)
Sales Range: $200-249.9 Million

Business Description:
Banking Services
S.I.C.: 6099
N.A.I.C.S.: 522320

Personnel:
N. E. Nielsen *(Chm)*
Villy Rasmussen *(Vice Chm)*
Jorgen Braendstrup *(CEO & Mng Dir)*
Allan Ottsen *(Mng Dir)*

Board of Directors:
N. E. Nielsen
Carsten Ehlers
Henrik Hakonsson
Kent Madsen
Villy Rasmussen
Jesper Reinhardt
Anne Toxvaerd
Henrik Zimino

Subsidiary:

Investeringsanpartsselskabet AMAK **(1)**
Amagerbrogade 25
PO Box 1800
2300 Copenhagen, Denmark
Tel.: (45) 32666666
Fax: (45) 32544534
E-Mail: international@amagerbanken.dk
Web Site: www.amagerbanken.dk
Emp.: 500
Banking Advisory Services
S.I.C.: 6211
N.A.I.C.S.: 523110
Joergen Braendstrup *(CEO & Mng Dir)*

AMAIZEINGLY GREEN PRODUCTS, L.P.

201 MacDonald Rd
Collingwood, ON, L9Y 4J1, Canada
Tel.: (705) 445-1140
Fax: (705) 445-9402
Web Site: www.amaizeinglygreen.com
Emp.: 50

Business Description:
Starches Mfr
S.I.C.: 2046
N.A.I.C.S.: 311221

Personnel:
Daryl Dorchak *(CEO)*

Subsidiary:

Amaizeingly Green Value Products ULC **(1)**
2680 14th Avenue Unit 5
Markham, ON, L3R 5B2, Canada
Tel.: (905) 947-9444
Fax: (905) 477-4449
Toll Free: (888) 614-7336
E-Mail: info@amaizeinglygreen.com
Web Site: www.amaizeinglygreen.com
Natural Fertilizer Mfr
S.I.C.: 2873
N.A.I.C.S.: 325311

AMAL SAMHA CO.

PO Box 25220
Damascus, Syria
Tel.: (963) 0116330890
Fax: (963) 0116330894
E-Mail: amalsamhaco@net.sy
Web Site: www.samha.com
Year Founded: 1980
Sales Range: $10-24.9 Million
Emp.: 550

Business Description:
Knitwear Mfr
S.I.C.: 5699
N.A.I.C.S.: 315220

Personnel:
Ahmad Samha *(Gen Mgr)*

AMALGAMATED APPLIANCE HOLDINGS LTD.

(Acquired by The Bidvest Group Limited)

AMALGAMATED ELECTRONIC CORPORATION LIMITED

Amecor House 14 Richard Road
Industria North
Roodepoort, 1706, South Africa
Tel.: (27) 11 477 2600
Fax: (27) 11 477 2696
Web Site: www.amecor.com
AER—(JSE)
Rev.: $35,684,017
Assets: $32,265,550
Liabilities: $11,815,403
Net Worth: $20,450,148
Earnings: $2,821,542
Emp.: 298
Fiscal Year-end: 03/31/13

Business Description:
Electronic Equipment Mfr
S.I.C.: 3825
N.A.I.C.S.: 334515

Personnel:
Dereck Alexander *(CEO)*
Kerry Colley *(CFO & Sec)*
Keith Vieira *(COO)*

Board of Directors:
Chris Boulle
Dereck Alexander
Kerry Colley
Keith Vieira
Percy Ying

Legal Counsel:
HR Levin Attorneys Notaries & Conveyancers
Kentgate 64 Kent Road
Dunkeld, Johannesburg, South Africa

Transfer Agent:
Link Market Services South Africa (Pty) Limited
11 Diagonal Street
Johannesburg, South Africa

Subsidiaries:

Amecor Power Services (Proprietary) Limited **(1)**
14 Richard Road Industria North
Gauteng, South Africa

Amalgamated Electronic Corporation Limited—(Continued)

Tel.: (27) 112340109
Fax: (27) 114772629
Emp.: 6
Power Generating Equipments Supplier
S.I.C.: 5063
N.A.I.C.S.: 423610
Kerry Colley *(Dir-Fin)*

Subsidiary:

Amecor Property Developments (Proprietary) Limited **(2)**
14 Richard Rd Indus N
Johannesburg, 1709, South Africa
Tel.: (27) 114772600
Fax: (27) 861105961
Web Site: www.amecor.co.za
Emp.: 70
Real Estate Property Development Services
S.I.C.: 6531
N.A.I.C.S.: 531210

Power Development Services (Proprietary) Limited **(1)**
275 Granville Ave N Robertville Ext 10
Roodepoort, Johannesburg, Gauteng, 1709, South Africa
Tel.: (27) 114720669
Fax: (27) 114726008
E-Mail: sales@pdspower.co.za
Web Site: www.pdspower.co.za
Emp.: 40
Power Generating Equipments Supplier
S.I.C.: 5063
N.A.I.C.S.: 423610
Kevin Helfrich *(Mgr-Sls)*

Subsidiary:

Durapower Manufacturing (Proprietary) Limited **(2)**
Dura House 275 Granville Ave N Robertville Ext 10
Florida, Gauteng, 1709, South Africa
Tel.: (27) 116724720
Fax: (27) 116724730
E-Mail: sales@durapower.co.za
Web Site: www.durapower.co.za
Emp.: 8
Uninterruptible Power Supplies Mfr & Distr
S.I.C.: 3699
N.A.I.C.S.: 335999
Rainer Krisch *(Mgr)*

Sabre Radio Networks (Proprietary) Limited **(1)**
14 Richard Rd Industria N
Florida Hills, Johannesburg, Gauteng, 1709, South Africa
Tel.: (27) 114772600
Fax: (27) 114772696
E-Mail: sales@fsk.co.za
Web Site: www.sabreradionetworks.co.za
Emp.: 20
Radio Networks Management & Maintenance Services
S.I.C.: 4832
N.A.I.C.S.: 515111
Terence Kearns *(Dir-Fin)*

AMALGAMATED METAL CORPORATION PLC

55 Bishopsgate
London, EC2N 3AH, United Kingdom
Tel.: (44) 2076264521
Telex: 888701
Fax: (44) 2076236015
E-Mail: maildesk@amcgroup.com
Web Site: www.amcgroup.com
Year Founded: 1929
Rev.: $785,909,264
Emp.: 150

Business Description:
Trades, Distributes & Manufactures Metals, Metal Products & Chemicals
S.I.C.: 6719
N.A.I.C.S.: 551112

Personnel:
H. Stodieck *(Chm)*
V. H. Sher *(CEO)*

Board of Directors:
H. Stodieck
R. Feuerhake
M.C. Roberts
G. C.L. Rowan
V. H. Sher

Subsidiaries:

Amalgamated Metal Trading Ltd **(1)**
55 Bishopsgate
London, EC2N 3AH, United Kingdom (100%)
Tel.: (44) 2076264521
Fax: (44) 2076233982
E-Mail: maildesk@emcgroup.com
Web Site: www.emcgroup.com
Emp.: 120
Commodity Contracts Brokerage
S.I.C.: 6221
N.A.I.C.S.: 523140
J. W. Land *(Mng Dir)*

AMC Physical Trading Ltd **(1)**
55 Bishopsgate
London, EC2N3AH, United Kingdom (100%)
Tel.: (44) 2076264521
Fax: (44) 2076233982
E-Mail: maildesk@amcgroup.com
Web Site: www.amcphysical-trading.co.uk
Emp.: 140
Commodity Contracts Brokerage
S.I.C.: 6221
N.A.I.C.S.: 523140
R. Seibel *(Gen Mgr)*

AMC Treasury Services Ltd **(1)**
55 Bishopsgate
London, EC2N 3AH, United Kingdom (100%)
Tel.: (44) 2076264521
Fax: (44) 2076236015
E-Mail: enquries@amctreasury.co.uk
Web Site: www.amcgroup.co.uk
Commodity Contracts Brokerage
S.I.C.: 6029
N.A.I.C.S.: 522110

AMT Futures Limited **(1)**
55 Bishopsgate
London, EC2N 3AH, United Kingdom (100%)
Tel.: (44) 2076264521
Fax: (44) 2076236015
E-Mail: maildesk@amcgroup.com
Web Site: www.amtfutures.co.uk
Emp.: 140
Commodity Contracts Brokerage
S.I.C.: 6221
N.A.I.C.S.: 523140
C. J. Rigby *(Dir-Futures)*

BKS Surveys Ltd **(1)**
47 Ballycairn Road
Coleraine, Belfast, BT513HZ, United Kingdom (100%)
Tel.: (44) 2870352311
Fax: (44) 2870357637
Web Site: www.bks.co.uk
Emp.: 100
Geophysical Surveying & Mapping Services
S.I.C.: 8713
N.A.I.C.S.: 541360
Alan Campbell *(Gen Mgr)*

Brookside Metal Company Ltd **(1)**
Bilston Lane
Willenhall, West Midlands, WV13 2QE, United Kingdom (100%)
Tel.: (44) 1902365500
Fax: (44) 1902636671
E-Mail: mail@brooksidemetal.com
Web Site: www.brooksidemetal.com
Emp.: 65
Powder Metallurgy Part Mfr
S.I.C.: 3499
N.A.I.C.S.: 332117
Neil Jackson *(Mng Dir)*

Keeling & Walker Ltd **(1)**
Whieldon Rd
Stoke-on-Trent, ST4 4JA, United Kingdom (100%)
Tel.: (44) 1782744136
Fax: (44) 1782744126
E-Mail: sales@keelingwalker.co.uk
Web Site: www.keelingwalker.co.uk
Emp.: 32
Electroplating Plating Polishing Anodizing & Coloring
S.I.C.: 3471
N.A.I.C.S.: 332813
S. Lipiec *(Mng Dir)*

Non-U.S. Subsidiary:

Thermox Zinnoxide GmbH **(2)**
Ruhr Allee 191
45136 Essen, Germany
Tel.: (49) 201125960
Fax: (49) 201125961 3
E-Mail: sales@zinnoxid.de
Web Site: www.zinnoxid.eu
Emp.: 5
Primary Copper Smelting & Refining
S.I.C.: 3339
N.A.I.C.S.: 331410
Steve Lipiec *(Mng Dir)*

Mil-Ver Metal Company Ltd **(1)**
Coronel Avenue
Rowleys Green Industrial Estate, Coventry, CV6 6AP, United Kingdom (100%)
Tel.: (44) 2476667098
Fax: (44) 2476662299
E-Mail: sales@milver.co.uk
Web Site: www.milver.com
Emp.: 107
Nonferrous Metal Mfr
S.I.C.: 3341
N.A.I.C.S.: 331492
Steve Miles *(Mng Dir)*

William Rowland Ltd **(1)**
9-13 Meadow St
Sheffield, S37BL, United Kingdom (100%)
Tel.: (44) 1142769421
Fax: (44) 1142759429
E-Mail: e-mail@william-rowland.co.uk
Web Site: www.william-rowland.com
Emp.: 30
Steel Investment Foundries
S.I.C.: 3324
N.A.I.C.S.: 331512
David P. Cooper *(Mng Dir)*

Non-U.S. Subsidiaries:

Amalgamet (South East Asia) Pte Ltd **(1)**
100 Beach Road
22-07 Shaw Towers, 189702 Singapore, Singapore (100%)
Tel.: (65) 62942058
Fax: (65) 62971776
E-Mail: amc@amalgamet.com.sg
Web Site: www.amcphysical-trading.co.uk
Emp.: 5
Metal Service Centers & Offices
S.I.C.: 5051
N.A.I.C.S.: 423510
Antony Ho *(Mgr)*

British Metal Corporation (India) Pte Ltd **(1)**
Apeejay Ho 1st Floor
Dinsha Wachha Rd Backbay Recla, 400020
Mumbai, MH, India
Tel.: (91) 2222872344
E-Mail: mumbai@britishmetal.com
Web Site: www.hindujagroup.com
Emp.: 8
Metal Service Centers & Metal Merchant Whslr
S.I.C.: 5051
N.A.I.C.S.: 423510
J. Daniel *(CEO)*

Consolidated Alloys (NZ) Ltd **(1)**
Penrose
PO Box 12-387
Auckland, New Zealand (100%)
Tel.: (64) 96229100
Fax: (64) 96229119
E-Mail: enquiries@dlmwallace.co.nz
Web Site: www.consolidatedalloys.co.nz
Emp.: 30
Building Material Dealers
S.I.C.: 5211
N.A.I.C.S.: 444190
B. Mudford *(Gen Mgr)*

Consolidated Alloys Pty Ltd **(1)**
32 Industrial Ave
3034 Thomastown, VIC, Australia (100%)
Tel.: (61) 393595811
Fax: (61) 393594076
E-Mail: info@cagroup.com.au
Web Site: www.cagroup.com.au
Emp.: 75
Plate Work Mfr
S.I.C.: 3443
N.A.I.C.S.: 332313
Nick Hardpastle *(Mng Dir)*

Debro Steel Ltd. **(1)**
7 Blair Drive
Brampton, ON, L6T 2H4, Canada (100%)
Tel.: (905) 457-5235
Fax: (905) 451-1221
E-Mail: sales@debrosteel.com
Web Site: www.debrosteel.com
Emp.: 90
Plate Work Mfr
S.I.C.: 3443
N.A.I.C.S.: 332313
Gunar Zenaitis *(Pres)*

Premetalco Inc. **(1)**
110 Belfield Rd
Rexdale, ON, M9W 1G1, Canada
Tel.: (416) 245-7386
Fax: (416) 242-2839
Emp.: 686
Holding Company
S.I.C.: 6719
N.A.I.C.S.: 551112
V. H. Sher *(Chm)*

Division:

Amalgamet Canada **(2)**
60 Yonge St Suite 1001
Toronto, ON, M5E 1H5, Canada (100%)
Tel.: (416) 366-3954
Fax: (416) 366-0586
E-Mail: info@amalgamet.com
Web Site: www.amalgamet.com
Emp.: 6
Minerals, Metals, Chemicals & High Purity Materials Marketer & Whslr
S.I.C.: 1799
N.A.I.C.S.: 238990
R. Seibel *(Mng Dir)*
Charles A. Merivale *(Sr VP)*

Thailand Smelting & Refining Co Ltd **(1)**
800 Moo Sakdidej Road Tambon Vichit
Amphur Muang, 83000 Phuket, Thailand (75%)
Tel.: (66) 76371111
Fax: (66) 76371120
E-Mail: mspratt@thaisarco.com
Web Site: www.thaisarco.com
Emp.: 260
Primary Copper Smelting & Refining
S.I.C.: 3339
N.A.I.C.S.: 331410
D. M. Spratt *(Gen Mgr)*

AMALGAMATED TELECOM HOLDINGS LIMITED

2nd Flr Harbour Front Rodwell Road
Suva, Fiji
Tel.: (679) 3308700
Fax: (679) 3308044
E-Mail: athl@conncect.com.fj
Web Site: www.ath.com.fj
Year Founded: 1998
ATH—(SPSE)
Rev.: $152,352,483
Assets: $247,323,177
Liabilities: $129,247,454
Net Worth: $118,075,723
Earnings: ($15,703,399)
Emp.: 1,002
Fiscal Year-end: 03/31/13

Business Description:
Telecommunications & Information Services
S.I.C.: 4813
N.A.I.C.S.: 517110

Personnel:
Ajith Kodagoda *(Chm)*
Ivan Fong *(Acting CEO, Sec & Gen Mgr)*

Board of Directors:
Ajith Kodagoda
David Kolitagane
Umarji Musa
Arun Narsey
Tom Ricketts
Taito Waqa

Subsidiaries:

ATH Call Centre Limited (1)
Garden City Raiwai
PO Box 5040
Raiwaqa, Suva, Fiji
Tel.: (679) 679 3310 333
Fax: (679) 112244
Call Center Services
S.I.C.: 4899
N.A.I.C.S.: 517919
Arun Narsey *(Chm)*
Titilia Veiogo *(Sec)*

Fiji Directories Limited (1)
3rd & 4th Floors Telecom New Wing
Building Edward Street
PO Box 16059
Suva, Fiji
Tel.: (679) 3311 000
Fax: (679) 3300 004
Web Site: www.yellowpages.com.fi
Telephone Directory Services
S.I.C.: 2741
N.A.I.C.S.: 511140
Aslam Khan *(Chm)*
Margaret Peters-Whippy *(CEO & Sec)*

Internet Services Fiji Limited (1)
Garden City Raiwai
PO Box 13779
Suva, Fiji
Tel.: (679) 3300 100
Fax: (679) 3307 237
Web Site: www.connect.com.fj
Internet Services
S.I.C.: 4899
N.A.I.C.S.: 517919
Robert Victor Mail *(Chm)*
Samulela Vadei *(Sec)*

Pacific Emerging Technologies Limited (1)
Level 4 General Post Office Building
Edward Street
POBox U43 USP, Suva, Fiji
Tel.: (679) 331 0025
Technology Services
S.I.C.: 7389
N.A.I.C.S.: 561499
Umarji Musa *(Chm)*
Patricia Gock *(Sec)*

Telecom Fiji Ltd (1)
Edward Street
Ganilau House, Suva, Fiji
Tel.: (679) 3304019
Fax: (679) 3305595
Web Site: www.TelecomFiji.com.fj
Emp.: 200
Telecommunications
S.I.C.: 4899
N.A.I.C.S.: 517919
Tom Ricketts *(Chm)*
Mothilal De Silva *(CEO)*
Samuela Vadei *(Sec)*

Transtel Limited (1)
5th Floor Telecom New Wing Guilding
Edward Street
Private Mail Bag, Suva, Fiji
Tel.: (679) 3210 528
Fax: (679) 310153
Web Site: www.transtel.com.fj
Telecommunication Services
S.I.C.: 4899
N.A.I.C.S.: 517919
Rohan Victor Mail *(Chm)*
Samuela Vadei *(Sec)*

Xceed Pasifika Limited (1)
1 Carpenter St
Garden City Raiwai, Suva, Fiji
Tel.: (679) 3216000
Fax: (679) 3216098
E-Mail: info@xceed.com.fj
Web Site: www.xceed.com
Emp.: 8
Telecommunications
S.I.C.: 4899
N.A.I.C.S.: 517919
Rohan Victor Mail *(Chm)*
Samuela Vadei *(Sec)*

AMALPHI AG

Bahnhofstrasse 6
65623 Hahnstatten, Germany
Tel.: (49) 64 30 92 67 0
Fax: (49) 64 30 92 75 37
E-Mail: info@almalphi.de
Web Site: www.amalphi.de
Year Founded: 2003
AMI—(DEU)
Sls.: $5,519,297
Assets: $2,503,876
Liabilities: $2,288,489
Net Worth: $215,387
Earnings: ($2,355,797)
Emp.: 15
Fiscal Year-end: 12/31/12
Business Description:
IT Services
S.I.C.: 7379
N.A.I.C.S.: 541519
Personnel:
Peter Biewald *(Chm-Supervisory Bd)*
Joachim Glaser *(Deputy Chm-Supervisory Bd)*
Siegfried Schmidt *(Member-Exec Bd)*
Supervisory Board of Directors:
Peter Biewald
Joachim Glaser
Markus Kunzle

AMAN BUILDING CORPORATION

20-41 Broadway Blvd
Sherwood Park, AB, T8H 2C1, Canada
Tel.: (780) 449-5825
Fax: (780) 467-3513
E-Mail: info@amanbuilding.com
Web Site: www.amanbuilding.com
Year Founded: 1985
Sales Range: $25-49.9 Million
Emp.: 60
Fiscal Year-end: 01/31/13
Business Description:
Construction Services
S.I.C.: 1541
N.A.I.C.S.: 236210
Personnel:
Shiraz Jiwani *(Pres)*

AMANA AGRICULTURAL & INDUSTRIAL INVESTMENT CO.

41 Yathreb Complex - Wasfi Al- Tal Str
PO Box 2805
Amman, 11953, Jordan
Tel.: (962) 5539100
Fax: (962) 5518323
Year Founded: 1995
AMAN—(AMM)
Sales Range: Less than $1 Million
Emp.: 29
Business Description:
Olive Tree Cultivating Services
S.I.C.: 0721
N.A.I.C.S.: 115112
Personnel:
Abdel Rahman Al-Mougraby *(Gen Mgr)*

AMANA COPPER LTD.

(Formerly Titan Goldworx Resources Inc.)
1 Westmount Square Suite 600
Westmount, QC, H3Z 2P9, Canada
Tel.: (416) 716-8181
Fax: (514) 759-3518
Year Founded: 2011
AMA—(CNSX)
Int. Income: $693
Assets: $994,570
Liabilities: $22,034
Net Worth: $972,535
Earnings: ($248,026)
Fiscal Year-end: 10/31/12
Business Description:
Copper Mining
S.I.C.: 1021
N.A.I.C.S.: 212234
Personnel:
Yaron Conforti *(CEO)*
Jonathan H. Rubin *(CFO)*
Board of Directors:
John King Burns
Yaron Conforti
Henry J. Sandri
Transfer Agent:
Olympia Trust Company
Suite 1003 750 West Pender Street
Vancouver, BC, V6C 2T8, Canada

AMANA HOLDINGS INC.

2-2-43 Higashishinagawa
Shinagawa-ku, Tokyo, Japan
Tel.: (81) 3 3740 4011
E-Mail: info@amana.jp
Web Site: www.amanaholdings.jp
Year Founded: 1979
2402—(TKS)
Sales Range: $1-4.9 Billion
Emp.: 909
Business Description:
Visual Content Designing Services
S.I.C.: 7336
N.A.I.C.S.: 541430
Personnel:
Hironobu Shindo *(Pres)*
Board of Directors:
Keiko Endo
Kazuo Fukasaku
Yoji Horiuchi
Yukihiro Ishigame
Yukihiro Iwanaga
Shinji Koba
Hideaki Kodama
Muneaki Masuda
Yukihiro Sawa
Hironobu Shindo

AMANA TAKAFUL PLC

No 98 Bauddhaloka Mawatha
Colombo, 4, Sri Lanka
Tel.: (94) 117501000
Fax: (94) 112597429
E-Mail: info@takaful.lk
Web Site: www.takaful.lk
ATL—(COL)
Rev.: $16,907,099
Assets: $22,360,365
Liabilities: $13,705,893
Net Worth: $8,654,472
Earnings: $942,970
Emp.: 380
Fiscal Year-end: 12/31/12
Business Description:
Insurance Services
S.I.C.: 6311
N.A.I.C.S.: 524113
Personnel:
Tyeab Akbarally *(Chm)*
M. Fazal Ghaffoor *(CEO)*
A Reyaz Jeffrey *(CEO/Gen Mgr-Family Takaful)*
Board of Directors:
Tyeab Akbarally
Zaid Ibnu Aboobucker
Mohamed Uvais Mohamed Ali Sabry
Radhakrishnan Gopinath
Aboobacker Admani Mohamed Haroon
Ifthikar A. Ismail
Osman Kassim
Aboo Sally Mohamed Muzzammil
Mohamed Haniffa Mohamed Rafiq
Thirugnanasambandar Senthilverl
Mohd Fadzli Yusof
Ehsan Zaheed

AMANAH LEASING PUBLIC COMPANY LIMITED

16-16/1 Soi Kasemsant 1 Phayathai
Road Wangmai Sub-District
Patumwan, Bangkok, 10330, Thailand
Tel.: (66) 2 612 3233
Fax: (66) 2 612 3255
Web Site: www.amanah.co.th
Year Founded: 1992
AMANAH—(THA)
Rev.: $10,764,316
Assets: $107,300,299
Liabilities: $63,360,392
Net Worth: $43,939,906
Earnings: $484,292
Fiscal Year-end: 12/31/12
Business Description:
Finance Services
S.I.C.: 6211
N.A.I.C.S.: 523999
Personnel:
Jaroondech Janjarussakul *(Chm)*
Thongrob Dan-ampai *(Vice Chm)*
Zati Sankhavanija *(Pres)*
Board of Directors:
Jaroondech Janjarussakul
Thongrob Dan-ampai
Pongstorn Kunanusorn
Theerapun Petchsuwan
Surasak Phansaichua
Nantaphol Pongspaibool
Thaphol Ponnaset
Poonnis Sakuntanaga
Zati Sankhavanija
Phaiboon Siripanoosatien
Pramote Yai-aroon

AMANO CORPORATION

275 Mamedocho Kohoku-ku
Yokohama, Kanagawa, 222-8558, Japan
Tel.: (81) 454011441
Fax: (81) 454391150
E-Mail: info@amano.co.jp
Web Site: www.amano.co.jp/english/
Year Founded: 1931
6436—(TKS)
Sls.: $993,245,000
Assets: $1,204,236,000
Liabilities: $360,338,000
Net Worth: $843,898,000
Earnings: $43,846,000
Emp.: 4,240
Fiscal Year-end: 03/31/13
Business Description:
Time Recorder & Time Information Systems; Parking Systems; Environmental Systems & Cleaning Systems
S.I.C.: 3822
N.A.I.C.S.: 334512
Personnel:
Kaoru Haruta *(Chm)*
Izumi Nakajima *(Pres)*
Myeong-Jin Jeon *(Operating Officer)*
Kenji Kohori *(Operating Officer)*
Masamiki Konno *(Mng Operating Officer)*
Minoru Koyama *(Mng Operating Officer)*
Nobuyuki Tabata *(Mng Operating Officer)*
Board of Directors:
Kaoru Haruta
Isao Kishi
Minoru Koyama
Izumi Nakajima
Hiroshi Shiraishi
Nobuyuki Tabata
Isao Terasaki
Toru Ueno
Haruhiko Yamaguchi

Subsidiaries:

Amano Agency Corp. (1)
275 Mamedocho
Kohoku-Ku, Yokohama, Kanagawa, Japan
Tel.: (81) 454391534
Web Site: www.amano.co.jp/English/about_amano/network.html
Vacuum Cleaner Mfr

Amano Corporation—(Continued)

S.I.C.: 3999
N.A.I.C.S.: 335210

Amano Business Solutions Corp. (1)
Amano Galaxy Building 7-3-24 Kikuna
Kohoku, Yokohama, Kanagawa, 222-0011, Japan
Tel.: (81) 454301950
Fax: (81) 454301952
Web Site: www.amano.co.jp
Internet Payroll Services
S.I.C.: 8721
N.A.I.C.S.: 541214

Amano Corporation (1)
2 36 3 Nagatake
Tsukui, Kanagawa, 220 0204, Japan (100%)
Tel.: (81) 427847441
Fax: (81) 427807107
Web Site: www.amano.co.jp/English/factory/index_tsukui.html
Emp.: 130
Mfr. of Electronic Time Recording & Time Information Equipment, P.C.B. & Plastic Components
S.I.C.: 3829
N.A.I.C.S.: 334519

Amano Corporation (1)
8123 Kiga Hosoe Cho Kita-Ku
Hamamatsu, Shizuoka, 431 1305, Japan (100%)
Tel.: (81) 535220951
Fax: (81) 535272109
Web Site: www.amano.co.jp
Emp.: 300
Mfr. of General Purpose Dust Collectors, Large-Scale Dust Collection Equipment, Industrial Vacuum Cleaners, Floor Cleaning Equipment & Air Cleaning Equipment
S.I.C.: 3564
N.A.I.C.S.: 333413
Kaoru Haruta *(Pres)*
Izumi Nakashima *(Pres)*

Amano Corporation (1)
1 6 2 Shinmiyakoda
Hamamatsu, Shizuoka, 431 2103, Japan (100%)
Tel.: (81) 534841051
Fax: (81) 534841081
Web Site: www.amano.co.jp
Emp.: 70
Mfr. of Precision Molds, Cut Parts & Automatic Mold Replacement Equipment
S.I.C.: 3425
N.A.I.C.S.: 332216

Amano Maintenance Engineering Corp. (1)
Amano Second Galaxy Building 7-3-22 Kikuna
Kohoku, Yokohama, Kanagawa, 222-8565, Japan
Tel.: (81) 454301966
Fax: (81) 454392204
Web Site: www.amano.co.jp
Emp.: 35
Environmental & Parking System Engineering Services
S.I.C.: 8711
N.A.I.C.S.: 541330
Fumio Yamada *(Pres & Gen Mgr)*

Amano Management Service Corp. (1)
Amano Second Galaxy Building 7-3-22 Kikuna
Kohoku, Yokohama, Kanagawa, Japan
Tel.: (81) 454331945
E-Mail: ams_soumu@amano.co.jp
Web Site: www.amano.co.jp/English/about_amano/network.html
Parking & Cleaning Business Management Services
S.I.C.: 8748
N.A.I.C.S.: 541618

Environmental Technology Company (1)
1-6-2 Shimmiyakoda
Kita-Ku, Hamamatsu, Shizuoka, 431-2103, Japan
Tel.: (81) 534841475
Fax: (81) 534841476
Web Site: www.amano.co.jp
Emp.: 1
Environmental Consulting Services
S.I.C.: 8999
N.A.I.C.S.: 541620
Izumi Nakajima *(Gen Mgr)*

Plants:

Amano Corporation - HOSOE FACILITY (1)
8123 Kiga Hosoe-cho
Kita-ku, Hamamatsu, Shizuoka, Japan 431-1305
Tel.: (81) 535220951
Fax: (81) 535270002
Web Site: www.amano.co.jp/English/about_amano/ourfacilities.html
Emp.: 280
Cleaning Equipment Mfr
S.I.C.: 3589
N.A.I.C.S.: 333318

Amano Corporation - MIYAKODA FACILITY (1)
1-6-2 Shinmiyakoda
Kita-ku, Hamamatsu, Shizuoka, Japan 431-2103
Tel.: (81) 534841051
Fax: (81) 534841081
Web Site: www.amano.co.jp/English/about_amano/ourfacilities.html
Emp.: 59
Metal Die Mfr
S.I.C.: 3364
N.A.I.C.S.: 331523

Amano Corporation - TSUKUI FACILITY (1)
236-3 Nagatake
Midori-ku, Sagamihara, Kanagawa, Japan 252-0154
Tel.: (81) 427847441
Fax: (81) 427807107
Web Site: www.amano.co.jp/English/about_amano/ourfacilities.html
Emp.: 59
Electronic Time Recorder Mfr
S.I.C.: 3823
N.A.I.C.S.: 334513

Amano Corporation-YOKOHAMA FACILITY (1)
275 Mamedo
Kohoku, Yokohama, Kanagawa, 222-8558, Japan
Tel.: (81) 454011441
Fax: (81) 454391120
Web Site: www.amano.co.jp/English/about_amano/ourfacilities.html
Emp.: 680
Software Development Services
S.I.C.: 7371
N.A.I.C.S.: 541511

U.S. Subsidiaries:

Accu-Time Systems, Inc. (1)
420 Somers Rd
Ellington, CT 06029
Tel.: (860) 870-5000
Fax: (860) 872-1511
Toll Free: (800) 355-4648
E-Mail: info@accu-time.com
Web Site: www.accu-time.com
Biometric Device Mfr
S.I.C.: 3575
N.A.I.C.S.: 334118
James Mchale *(CFO)*

Amano Cincinnati, Inc. (1)
140 Harrison Ave
Roseland, NJ 07068
Tel.: (973) 403-1900
Fax: (973) 364-1086
Toll Free: (800) 526-2559
E-Mail: info@amano.com
Web Site: www.amano.com
Emp.: 50
Development, Mfr & Sales of Time Recording, Time Information & Parking Equipment
Export
S.I.C.: 3829
N.A.I.C.S.: 334519
Michael John Lee *(Pres & CEO)*

Branches:

ACI Cincinnati (2)
130 Commerce Blvd
Loveland, OH 45140-7726
Tel.: (513) 697-9000
Fax: (513) 697-2345
Web Site: www.aci.com
Emp.: 60
Mfr., Developer & Distributor of Time Recording Equipment
S.I.C.: 3559
N.A.I.C.S.: 333249

Subsidiaries:

Amano USA Inc (2)
8 Capitol Dr
Wallingford, CT 06492
Tel.: (203) 265-8100
Fax: (203) 949-4710
E-Mail: info@amano.com
Web Site: www.amano.com
Emp.: 70
Signaling Equipment, Electrical
S.I.C.: 5063
N.A.I.C.S.: 423610
Al Siegel *(Controller)*

Amano McGann, Inc. (1)
651 Taft St NE
Minneapolis, MN 55413
Tel.: (612) 331-2020
Fax: (612) 331-5187
E-Mail: info@mcgannsoft.com
Web Site: www.amanomcgann.com
Sales Range: $25-49.9 Million
Emp.: 70
Designer & Developer of Custom Application Software for the Parking Industry
S.I.C.: 7373
N.A.I.C.S.: 541512
Mike Lee *(Chm)*
Larry Feuer *(Pres)*

Branch:

Amano McGann (2)
8312 Page Ave
Saint Louis, MO 63130-1043 (100%)
Tel.: (314) 426-7727
Fax: (314) 426-1776
Web Site: www.amanomcgann.com
Emp.: 9
Time Clocks & Parking Equipment Distr
S.I.C.: 5999
N.A.I.C.S.: 453998
Jeff Becker *(VP)*

Pioneer Eclipse Corporation (1)
1 Eclipse Rd
Sparta, NC 28675-0909 NC
Tel.: (336) 372-8080
Fax: (336) 372-2895
Toll Free: (800) 334-2246
Web Site: www.pioneer-eclipse.com
Sls.: $30,000,000
Emp.: 136
Development, Manufacture & Sales of Floor Cleaning Chemicals & Equipment for the Industrial & Institutional Markets; Develops High Speed, High Tech Floor Maintenance Systems
Import Export
S.I.C.: 2842
N.A.I.C.S.: 325612
Ledia Sutphin *(VP-Fin)*

Subsidiary:

Amano Business Credit (2)
1865 NE Dixie Hwy
Jensen Beach, FL 34957 (100%)
Tel.: (772) 283-9664
Fax: (772) 334-7999
Toll Free: (800) 625-2455
E-Mail: leaseit@amano-credit.com
Web Site: www.amano-credit.com
Emp.: 10
Floor Cleaning Equipment Leasing
S.I.C.: 3579
N.A.I.C.S.: 339940
Joel D. Ronan *(Founder & Pres)*

Non-U.S. Division:

AMANO UK LTD. - Parking Division (1)
8 Newhouse Business Centre Old Crawley Road
Horsham, West Sussex, RH12 4RU, United Kingdom
Tel.: (44) 7708169135
Fax: (44) 8455576278
E-Mail: parking-uk@amano.eu
Web Site: www.amano-parking.co.uk
Parking Software System Development Services
S.I.C.: 7371
N.A.I.C.S.: 541511

Non-U.S. Subsidiaries:

Accu-Tech Systems, Ltd. (1)
C1 Caerphilly Business Park
Caerphilly, Mid Glamorgan, CF83 3ED, United Kingdom
Tel.: (44) 2920 885599
Fax: (44) 2920 868666
E-Mail: sales@accu-tech.co.uk
Web Site: www.accu-tech.co.uk
Emp.: 2
Biometric & Data Collection Terminal Equipment Mfr
S.I.C.: 3575
N.A.I.C.S.: 334118
Bert Peirsman *(Gen Mgr)*

Advanced Time & Traffic, Pty Ltd. (1)
40 Bridge ST
Rydalmere, NSW, 2116, Australia
Tel.: (61) 296384445
Fax: (61) 296385445
Emp.: 4
S.I.C.: 3579
N.A.I.C.S.: 339940

Amano Cincinnati Canada, Inc. (1)
2740 Matheson Boulevard East Unit 4
Mississauga, ON, L4W 4X3, Canada
Tel.: (905) 624-4085
Fax: (905) 624-5464
Toll Free: (800) 387-3388
Web Site: www.amanomcgann.com
Emp.: 4
Time Recorder & Biometric Device Mfr
S.I.C.: 3577
N.A.I.C.S.: 334118
Thorsten Muller *(Office Mgr)*

Amano Cleantech Malaysia Sdn. Bhd. (1)
No 12 Jalan Pengacara U 1/48 Temasya Industrial Park
40150 Shah Alam, Selangor Darul Ehsan, Malaysia
Tel.: (60) 3 5569 5003
Fax: (60) 3 5569 5893
Web Site: www.amano.com.my/index.html
Emp.: 22
Sales & Service of General Purpose Dust Collectors, Large Scale Dust Collectors, Pneumatic Conveyance Equipment, Industrial Vacuum Cleaners, Floor Cleaning Equipment & Air Cleaning Equipment
S.I.C.: 1799
N.A.I.C.S.: 238290
Osamu Otani *(Mng Dir)*

Amano Electronics Europe, N.V. (1)
Westerring 2
Genk, Limburg, 3600, Belgium (100%)
Tel.: (32) 89323920
Fax: (32) 89306947
E-Mail: info@amano.be
Web Site: www.amano.be
Emp.: 40
Development, Manufacture & Sales of Time Recording, Time Information & Parking Equipment; Sales of Floor Cleaning Equipment & Chemicals
S.I.C.: 3829
N.A.I.C.S.: 334519
Yamaga Hideharue *(Pres)*

Amano Europe Holdings N.V. (1)
Westerring 2
3600 Genk, Belgium
Tel.: (32) 89328741
Fax: (32) 89 30 6947
E-Mail: info@amano.be
Emp.: 3
Investment Management Services
S.I.C.: 6799
N.A.I.C.S.: 523920
Herbert Klawatsch *(Gen Mgr)*

Amano International Trading (Shanghai) Co., Ltd. (1)
Rm 901 Zhongdian Mansion 1029 Laoshan Rd W
Pudong, Shanghai, 200122, China (100%)

Tel.: (86) 158790030
Fax: (86) 2158790029
Web Site: www.amano.com
Emp.: 25
Sales of Time Recording, Time Information, Parking, Floor Cleaning, Environmental & Aqua Equipment
S.I.C.: 5044
N.A.I.C.S.: 423420
Kaoru Haruta *(CEO & Pres)*

Amano Korea Corporation (1)
4 Yang Tyeong Tong 3 Yeong Deung Po Tu
Seoul, 150 103, Korea (South) (100%)
Tel.: (82) 21649900
Fax: (82) 21649400
Web Site: www.amano.co.kr
Emp.: 25
Sales of Time Recording, Time Information, Parking, Floor Cleaning & Environmental Equipment
S.I.C.: 5044
N.A.I.C.S.: 423420

Amano Malaysia Sdn.Bhd. (1)
No 12 Jalan Pengacara U1/48 Temasya Industrial Park
40150 Shah Alam, Selangor Darul Ehsan, Malaysia
Tel.: (60) 3 5569 5002
Fax: (60) 3 5569 5893
E-Mail: am@amano.com.my
Web Site: www.amano.com.my
Emp.: 40
Time Management & Car Parking Control System Mfr
S.I.C.: 3823
N.A.I.C.S.: 334513
Osamu Otani *(Mng Dir)*

Amano Software Engineering (Shanghai) Co., Ltd. (1)
North Nanquan Road No 1029 Room 901 Electric Building Pudong New Area
Shanghai, China (100%)
Tel.: (86) 2158790030
Fax: (86) 2158790029
Web Site: www.amano.com.cn
Emp.: 25
Supplier of Computer Software
S.I.C.: 5731
N.A.I.C.S.: 443142
Rong Qian *(Mgr-Fin)*

Amano Time & Air Singapore Pte. Ltd. (1)
Block 213 Henderson Rd Unit 04-06-07 Henderson Industrial park
Singapore, 159553, Singapore (100%)
Tel.: (65) 62752885
Fax: (65) 62752897
E-Mail: amanosg@amano.com.sg
Web Site: www.amano.com.sg
Emp.: 25
Sales of Time Recording, Time Information, Parking, Floor Cleaning, Environmental & Aqua Equipment
S.I.C.: 5044
N.A.I.C.S.: 423420
Osamu Otami *(Mng Dir)*
Noboru Sugawara *(Mng Dir)*

Amano Time & Parking Spain, S.A. (1)
C/ Plomo n 5 - 7 Planta 2 - Oficina 2
8038 Barcelona, Spain
Tel.: (34) 932 237910
Fax: (34) 932 237911
E-Mail: info@amano-spain.com
Parking Time Control Equipment Mfr
S.I.C.: 3823
N.A.I.C.S.: 334513

Horoquartz S.A. (1)
Tour CIT 3 rue de L'arrivee
75749 Paris, France
Tel.: (33) 169 351 832
Fax: (33) 169 351 833
E-Mail: contact@horoquartz.fr
Web Site: www.horoquartz.fr
Emp.: 300
Electronic Temptation Software Development Services
S.I.C.: 7371
N.A.I.C.S.: 541511
Jean-Francois Bienvenu *(Mng Dir)*

P.T. Amano Indonesia (1)
Gedung Pusat Perfilman H Usmar Ismail Lantai 3 JL HR Rasuna Siad Kav, Jakarta, 12940, Indonesia (100%)
Tel.: (62) 215278832
Fax: (62) 215278834
E-Mail: amanoid@cbn.net.id
Web Site: www.amano.co.id
Emp.: 15
Sales & Service of Time Recording, Time Information, Industrial Dust Collecting & Pneumatic Conveyance Equipment
S.I.C.: 5044
N.A.I.C.S.: 423420
Nobuyuki Umizawa *(Pres)*

Scopus-Omnibadges S.A.S. (1)
39 rue Louveau
92320 Chatillon, France
Tel.: (33) 1 46 54 15 13
Fax: (33) 1 46 54 10 12
E-Mail: info@omnibadges.com
Web Site: www.omnibadges.com
Emp.: 40
Smart Card Mfr
S.I.C.: 3089
N.A.I.C.S.: 326199
Didier Beau *(Acct Mgr)*

AMANTA RESOURCES LTD.

5423 Monte Bre Place
Vancouver, BC, V7W 3A8, Canada
Tel.: (604) 730-9505
Fax: (604) 648-8096
E-Mail: info@amantaresources.com
Web Site: www.amantaresources.com
AMH—(TSXV)
Int. Income: $259
Assets: $2,733,435
Liabilities: $1,719,428
Net Worth: $1,014,007
Earnings: ($731,722)
Fiscal Year-end: 02/28/13

Business Description:
Mineral Exploration Services
S.I.C.: 1081
N.A.I.C.S.: 213114

Personnel:
Gerald D. Wright *(Pres & CEO)*
Pieter J. Bakker *(COO & Exec VP)*

Board of Directors:
Pieter J. Bakker
Patrick Cauley
Thanawut Sirinawin
Manomay Vilayhong
Alfred Wahlstrom
Gerald D. Wright

Legal Counsel:
Morton & Company
Suite 1200-750 W Pender Street
Vancouver, BC, Canada

Transfer Agent:
Computershare
3rd Floor 510 Burrard Street
Vancouver, BC, Canada

AMAR REMEDIES LTD.

B1 G 01 Marathon Innova Off
Ganpatrao Kadam Marg Lower Parel
Mumbai, 400013, India
Tel.: (91) 2230409100
Fax: (91) 2230409120
E-Mail: queries@amarremedies.com
Web Site: www.amarremedies.com
AMAR—(NSE)

Business Description:
Oral Care & Health Care Products Mfr
S.I.C.: 2841
N.A.I.C.S.: 325611

Personnel:
Sagar P. Shah *(Mng Dir)*
Rajiv M. Chitnis *(Compliance Officer)*
Jagdish Nagpal *(Sec)*

Board of Directors:
Pravin N. Shah
Rajiv M. Chitnis
Preeti Balwantrai Desai
Gaurav M. Doshi
Dilip S. Mehta
Natasha S. Shah
Pratima P. Shah
Sagar P. Shah
Jyotirmay Prakash Varma
Yusuf Iqbal Yusuf

Transfer Agent:
Link Intime India Pvt. Ltd
C-13 Pannalal Silk Mills Compound LBS Marg
Bhandup (West)
Mumbai, India

AMARA HOLDINGS LTD.

100 Tras Street 06-01 100 AM
Singapore, 079027, Singapore
Tel.: (65) 68792515
Fax: (65) 62242660
E-Mail: corporate@amaraholdings.com
Web Site: www.amaraholdings.com
Year Founded: 1930
A34—(SES)
Rev.: $73,080,097
Assets: $439,980,922
Liabilities: $213,597,633
Net Worth: $226,383,289
Earnings: $23,807,021
Emp.: 500
Fiscal Year-end: 12/31/12

Business Description:
Investment Services
S.I.C.: 6211
N.A.I.C.S.: 523999

Personnel:
Albert Hock Chuan Teo *(CEO)*
Soon Soo Foo *(Co-Sec)*
Susan Geok Tin Teo *(Co-Sec)*

Board of Directors:
Meng Teng Chang
Alphonsus Chung Mun Chia
Ko Hing Foo
Richard Boo Yeong Khoo
Lawrence Kwok Wah Mok
Albert Hock Chuan Teo
Susan Geok Tin Teo

Subsidiaries:

Amara Hotel Properties Pte Ltd (1)
Amara Corporate Tower 06-01 100 Tras St
Singapore, Singapore
Tel.: (65) 62248866
Fax: (65) 62242660
E-Mail: corporate@amaraholdings.com
Web Site: www.amarahotels.com
Hotel Management Services
S.I.C.: 7011
N.A.I.C.S.: 721110
Eric Brand *(Gen Mgr)*

Amara Sentosa Investments Pte Ltd (1)
Amara Corporate Tower 06-01 100 Tras Street
Singapore, 79027, Singapore
Tel.: (65) 62248866
Fax: (65) 62242660
E-Mail: corporate@amaraholdings.com
Web Site: www.amaraholdings.com
Hotel Management Services
S.I.C.: 7011
N.A.I.C.S.: 721110
Albert Teo *(CEO)*

Amarathai Restaurant Pte Ltd (1)
1 Tanjong Pagar Road Amara Hotel/ shopping Centre 01-06
Singapore, 088539, Singapore
Tel.: (65) 62224688
Fax: (65) 62237183
Restaurant Operators Services
S.I.C.: 5812
N.A.I.C.S.: 722511

Creative Investments Pte Ltd (1)
Amara Hotel 05-03 165 Tanjong Pagar Rd
Singapore, Singapore
Tel.: (65) 62248866
Fax: (65) 62242660
Property Development Services
S.I.C.: 6531
N.A.I.C.S.: 531311

Silk Road Restaurants International Pte Ltd (1)
100 Tras Street 06-01 Amara Corporate Tower
Singapore, 79027, Singapore
Tel.: (65) 68792515
Fax: (65) 6224 2660
E-Mail: silkroad@amaraholdings.com
Web Site: www.silkroadrestaurants.com
Hotel Investment & Management Services
S.I.C.: 7011
N.A.I.C.S.: 721110

TTH Development Pte Ltd (1)
165 Tanjong Pagar Rd 05-03 Amara Hotel
Singapore, 088539, Singapore
Tel.: (65) 68792515
Fax: (65) 62242660
Property Development Services
S.I.C.: 6531
N.A.I.C.S.: 531311

AMARA MINING PLC

(Formerly Cliff Gold plc)
4th Floor 29-30 Cornhill
London, EC3V 3NF, United Kingdom
Tel.: (44) 20 7398 1420
Fax: (44) 20 7398 1421
Web Site: www.amaramining.com
AMA—(AIM)
Rev.: $91,320,000
Assets: $201,032,000
Liabilities: $43,712,000
Net Worth: $157,320,000
Earnings: $2,447,000
Emp.: 643
Fiscal Year-end: 12/31/12

Business Description:
Gold Production Services
S.I.C.: 1041
N.A.I.C.S.: 212221

Personnel:
John McGloin *(Chm)*
Peter Spivey *(CEO)*
Catherine Apthorpe *(Sec & Mgr-Comml)*

Board of Directors:
John McGloin
Peter Cowley
Alexander John Davidson
Hendrik Johannes Faul
Pete Gardner
Peter Hain
Peter Spivey
Geoff Stanley

Legal Counsel:
K&L Gates LLP
One New Change
London, United Kingdom

Fasken Martineau DuMoulin LLP
333 Bay Street Suite 2400 Bay Adelaide Centre
PO Box 20
Toronto, ON, Canada

Subsidiary:

Cliff Gold (UK) Limited (1)
15 Carteret St
London, SW1H 9DJ, United Kingdom
Tel.: (44) 2073409790
Fax: (44) 2072229477
E-Mail: admin@cliffgold.com
Web Site: www.cliffgold.com
Emp.: 10
Gold Mining & Exploration Services
S.I.C.: 1041
N.A.I.C.S.: 212221
Greg Anastasi *(Controller-Fin)*

Non-U.S. Subsidiaries:

Cliff Gold (SL) Limited (1)
58 Charlotte St
Freetown, Sierra Leone
Tel.: (232) 76862525
E-Mail: alimac57@yahoo.co.uk
Gold Exploration Services
S.I.C.: 1041
N.A.I.C.S.: 212221

Cliff Gold (WA) Cote d Ivoire SARL (1)
PO Box 1958
Abidjan, 06, Cote d'Ivoire

Amara Mining plc—(Continued)

Tel.: (225) 22416388
Fax: (225) 22416371
Gold Exploration Services
S.I.C.: 1041
N.A.I.C.S.: 212221
Robert Yobou *(Mng Dir)*

Cliff Mining Burkina SARL (1)
82 Rue Raul Follereau
P O Box 2522
Koulouba, Ouagadougou, 01, Burkina Faso
Tel.: (226) 31 06 06
Fax: (226) 31 06 10
Gold Exploration Services
S.I.C.: 1041
N.A.I.C.S.: 212221
Djeneba Nana *(Country Mgr)*

Kalsaka Mining SA (1)
82 Ave Saye Zerbo
P O Box 2522
Koulouba Sector 4, Ouagadougou, 01, Burkina Faso
Tel.: (226) 50310606
Fax: (226) 50310610
Gold Mining Services
S.I.C.: 1041
N.A.I.C.S.: 212221

Yaoure Mining SA (1)
06 DP 1958
Abidjan, 06, Cote d'Ivoire
Tel.: (225) 22416388
Fax: (225) 22416371
E-Mail: robert.yobou@cluffgold.com
Emp.: 30
Gold Mining Services
S.I.C.: 1041
N.A.I.C.S.: 212221

AMARA RAJA BATTERIES LTD

Renigunta Cuddapah Road
Karakambadi
Hyderabad, Andhra Pradesh, 517 520, India
Tel.: (91) 8772265000
Fax: (91) 8772286999
E-Mail: amararaja@amararaja.co.in
Web Site: www.amararaja.co.in
AMARAJABAT—(NSE)
Rev.: $557,673,374
Assets: $328,245,138
Liabilities: $131,755,622
Net Worth: $196,489,516
Earnings: $53,155,107
Emp.: 3,467
Fiscal Year-end: 03/31/13

Business Description:
Electronic Components Industry
S.I.C.: 3699
N.A.I.C.S.: 335999

Personnel:
Jayadev Galla *(Vice Chm & Mng Dir)*
K. Suresh *(CFO)*
Srinivasa Rao Ganga *(CMO-Indus Battery Div)*
Rajesh Jindal *(CMO-Automotive Battery Div)*
M. R. Rajaram *(Sec)*

Board of Directors:
Ramachandra N. Galla
Ravi Bhamidipati
Raymond J. Brown
Jayadev Galla
Eric Stuart Mitchell
T. R. Narayanaswamy
N. Sri Vishnu Raju
P. Lakshmana Rao
Qing Yang Shu
Nagarjun Valluripalli

Chevuturi Associates
Vijayawada, India

Transfer Agent:
Cameo Corporate Services Limited
Subramanian Building No 1 Club House Road
5th Floor
Chennai, India

Subsidiaries:

Amara Raja Power Systems Limited (1)
MC Design House #27 Rohini Layout Hi-Tech City
Hyderabad, Madhapur, 81, India
Tel.: (91) 40 23633500
Fax: (91) 40 23101999
E-Mail:
Web Site: www.amararajapowersystems.com
Emp.: 3,000
Design & Development of Power Electronic Products, Integration & Testing & Magnetics Mfr
S.I.C.: 3613
N.A.I.C.S.: 335313
Jayadev Galla *(Mng Dir)*
Ramachandra Naidu Galla *(Mng Dir)*

Amaron Batteries (P) Ltd. (1)
Jail Rd
Gurgaon, Haryana, 122001, India
Tel.: (91) 1242311410
E-Mail: yadav_batteryhouse@yahoo.co.in
Emp.: 20
Batteries Mfr
S.I.C.: 3691
N.A.I.C.S.: 335911
S.C Yadav *(Branch Mgr)*

Galla Foods Ltd. (1)
73-75, Dr. Radhakrishnan Salai Mylapore
2nd Fl Ace Tower
Chennai, Tamil Nadu, 600 004, India
Tel.: (91) 4428213270
Fax: (91) 4428284821
E-Mail: sales@gallafoods.com
Web Site: www.gallafoods.com
Emp.: 15
Food Processing & Export Services
S.I.C.: 2034
N.A.I.C.S.: 311423
Asheesh Nigam *(Gen Mgr)*

Unit:

Mangal Precision Products Limited - Works 1 (1)
Karakambadi
517520 Tirupati, Andhra Pradesh, India
Tel.: (91) 877 2285561
Fax: (91) 877 2285599
E-Mail: amararaja@amararaja.co.in
Emp.: 7,000
Automobile Components & Fasteners Mfr
S.I.C.: 3493
N.A.I.C.S.: 332613

AMARILLO GOLD CORPORATION

Suite 1818 - 701 West Georgia Street
Pacific Centre
PO Box 10144
Vancouver, BC, V7Y 1C6, Canada
Tel.: (604) 689-1799
Fax: (604) 689-8199
E-Mail: info@amarillogold.com
Web Site: www.amarillogold.com
AGC—(TSXV)
Int. Income: $14,714
Assets: $28,994,247
Liabilities: $829,946
Net Worth: $28,164,301
Earnings: ($2,278,201)
Fiscal Year-end: 12/31/12

Business Description:
Mineral Exploration Services
S.I.C.: 1081
N.A.I.C.S.: 213114

Personnel:
Buddy Doyle *(Pres & CEO)*
Waldemar Opalka *(CFO)*

Board of Directors:
Robert K. Landis
Richard Brown
Buddy Doyle
Michael Durose
Patrick Power

Non-U.S. Subsidiary:

Amarillo Mineracao do Brasil Limitada (1)
Praca Carlos Chagas 49 - Salas 504 a 506
Bairro Santo Agostinho, Belo Horizonte, Minas Gerais, 30170-020, Brazil
Tel.: (55) 31 32615974
E-Mail: info@amarillogold.com
Emp.: 2
Mineral Mining Services
S.I.C.: 1499
N.A.I.C.S.: 212399
Luiz Carlos Ferreira de Silva *(Gen Mgr)*

AMARIN CORPORATION PLC

2 Pembroke House Upper Pembroke Street 28-32
Dublin, 2, Ireland
Tel.: (353) 1 669 9020
Fax: (353) 1 6699028
E-Mail: investor.relations@amarincorp.com
Web Site: www.amarincorp.com
Year Founded: 1999
AMRN—(NASDAQ)
Rev.: $26,351,000
Assets: $252,476,000
Liabilities: $286,332,000
Net Worth: ($33,856,000)
Earnings: ($166,227,000)
Emp.: 185
Fiscal Year-end: 12/31/13

Business Description:
Pharmaceutical Researcher, Developer & Mfr
S.I.C.: 2834
N.A.I.C.S.: 325412

Personnel:
Lars G Ekman *(Chm)*
John F. Thero *(Pres & CEO)*
Michael Farrell *(CFO, Chief Acctg Officer & Controller)*
Joseph T. Kennedy *(Chief Compliance Officer, Gen Counsel, Sec & Sr VP)*
Paul E. Huff *(Chief Comml Officer & Sr VP)*
Frederick W. Ahlholm *(Chief Acctg Officer, VP-Fin & Admin)*
Declan Doogan *(Chief Medical Officer)*
Steven B. Ketchum *(Pres-R&D & Sr VP)*
Paresh Soni *(Sr VP & Head-Dev)*
Aaron D. Berg *(Sr VP-Mktg & Sls)*
Stuart Sedlack *(Sr VP-Corp Dev)*

Board of Directors:
Lars G Ekman
James I. Healy
Patrick J. O'Sullivan
Kristine Peterson
David M. Stack
G. Jan Van Heek
Joseph S. Zakrzewski

Subsidiaries:

Amarin Pharmaceuticals Company Limited (1)
7 Curzon Street
London, W1J 5HG, United Kingdom
Tel.: (44) 2074999009
Fax: (44) 2074999004
E-Mail: info@amarincorp.com
Pharmaceuticals
S.I.C.: 2834
N.A.I.C.S.: 325412

AMARIN PRINTING & PUBLISHING PUBLIC COMPANY LIMITED

378 Chaiyaphruk Road
Taling Chan, Bangkok, 10170, Thailand
Tel.: (66) 2422 9999
Fax: (66) 2434 3555
E-Mail: info@amarin.co.th
Web Site: www.amarin.co.th
AMARIN—(THA)
Rev.: $72,210,181
Assets: $81,758,115
Liabilities: $15,751,128
Net Worth: $66,006,986
Earnings: $11,562,900
Fiscal Year-end: 12/31/12

Business Description:
Printing, Publishing & Television Broadcasting Services
S.I.C.: 2759
N.A.I.C.S.: 323111

Personnel:
Metta Utakapan *(Chm & Pres)*
Rarin Utakapan Punjarungroj *(CEO)*
Cheewapat Nathalang *(Deputy CEO & Mng Dir-Printing Bus)*
Chokchai Punjarungroj *(Deputy CEO & Mng Dir-Activ Amarin & Amarin Television)*
Ongaj Jira-On *(Asst Mng Dir-Book Publ Bus)*
Titaya Nilrungsee *(Asst Mng Dir-Printing Sls)*
Praphan Prabhasavat *(Deputy Mng Dir-Publ Bus)*
Achara Taesuwan *(Deputy Mng Dir-Magazine Bus-Adv)*
Supawadee Komaradat *(Sr Exec VP)*

Board of Directors:
Metta Utakapan
Supawadee Komaradat
Charoenchit Nasongkhla
Cheewapat Nathalang
Wathanyu Nathalang
Suphap Noi-Um
Somchai Phagaphasvivat
Rarin Utakapan Punjarungroj
Smat Ruangnarong

AMARJOTHI SPINNING MILLS LTD

Amarjothi House 157 Kumaran Road
Tirupur, 641 601, India
Tel.: (91) 4212201980
Fax: (91) 4212201984
E-Mail: sales@amarjothi.net
Web Site: www.melangeonline.net
AMARJOTHI—(NSE)
Sales Range: $25-49.9 Million

Business Description:
Cotton Yarn Mfr & Distr
S.I.C.: 2299
N.A.I.C.S.: 313110

Personnel:
N. Rajan *(Chm)*
R. Jaichander *(Mng Dir)*
R. Premchander *(Mng Dir)*
K. Sriram *(Sec)*

Board of Directors:
N. Rajan
R. Jaichander
R. Premchander
N. Radhakrishnan
S. Sathyanarayan
K. Sriram
V. Subramaniam
V. T. Subramanian

Transfer Agent:
SKDC Consultants Ltd
Kanapathy Towers 3rd Floor 1391 A-1 Sathy Road Ganapathy Post
614008 Coimbatore, India

Division:

Amarjothi Spinning Mills Ltd - Amarjothi Dyeing Division (1)
Plot No E7-E9 & G11-G13 Sipcot Industrial Growth Centre
Perundurai, Erode, 638 052, India
Tel.: (91) 4294 234114
Fax: (91) 4294 234092
E-Mail: dyeing@amarjothi.net
Web Site: www.melangeonline.net
Spinning Yarn Mfr

S.I.C.: 2299
N.A.I.C.S.: 313110

AMAROK ENERGY INC.

(Formerly Drako Capital Corp.)
Standard Life Tower Suite 2500 639 5th Avenue Southwest
Calgary, AB, T2P 0M9, Canada
Tel.: (403) 695-3722
Fax: (403) 266-1395
Web Site: amarokenergy.com
Year Founded: 2010
AMR—(TSXV)
Int. Income: $67,960
Assets: $4,103,843
Liabilities: $311,194
Net Worth: $3,792,650
Earnings: ($721,606)
Fiscal Year-end: 12/31/12
Business Description:
Petroleum & Natural Gas Exploration, Development & Production
S.I.C.: 1311
N.A.I.C.S.: 211111
Personnel:
Murray Hinz *(CFO & VP-Fin)*
William C. Guinan *(Sec)*
Board of Directors:
Robert John Dales
Danny G. Geremia
Massimo M. Geremia
William C. Guinan
Samuel Ingram
Dennis Nerland
Transfer Agent:
Valiant Trust Company
Suite 310 606 4th Street S.W.
Calgary, AB, Canada

AMARU, INC.

62 Cecil Street #06-00 TPI Building
Singapore, Singapore 049710
Tel.: (65) 6332 9287
Fax: (65) 6332 29123
E-Mail: enquiry.us@m2bworld.com
Web Site: www.amaruinc.com
AMRU—(OTC)
Rev.: $19,012
Assets: $2,500,423
Liabilities: $3,280,403
Net Worth: ($779,980)
Earnings: ($975,911)
Emp.: 14
Fiscal Year-end: 12/31/12
Business Description:
Broadband Entertainment Services
S.I.C.: 7374
N.A.I.C.S.: 518210
Personnel:
Sakai Torisawa *(Chm)*
Leong Hin Chua *(Pres, CEO & Acting CFO)*
Board of Directors:
Sakai Torisawa
Leong Hin Chua
Percy Soo Lian Chua
Legal Counsel:
Law Offices of Iwona J. Alami
620 Newport Ctr Dr Ste 1100
Newport Beach, CA 92660
Transfer Agent:
Integrity Stock Transfer
3243 E Warm Springs Rd Ste 103
Las Vegas, NV 89120

AMATA CORPORATION PUBLIC COMPANY LIMITED

700 Moo 1 Klong Tamru Muang
Chon Buri, 20000, Thailand
Tel.: (66) 38213007
Fax: (66) 38213700
E-Mail: marketing@amata.com
Web Site: www.amata.com
Year Founded: 1989
AMATA—(BAK)
Rev.: $125,731,447
Assets: $790,098,022
Liabilities: $419,261,122
Net Worth: $370,836,900
Earnings: $57,145,138
Emp.: 140
Fiscal Year-end: 12/31/12
Business Description:
Industrial Estate Developer & Manager
S.I.C.: 1629
N.A.I.C.S.: 236210
Personnel:
Wissanu Krea-Ngam *(Chm)*
Vikrom Kromadit *(Chm-Exec Bd & CEO)*
Keita Ishii *(Vice Chm)*
Yanyong Phuangrach *(COO)*
Viboon Kromadit *(CMO)*
Vatana Supornpaibul *(Chief Bus Officer)*
Varaporn Vatchranukroh *(Sec & VP-Investment)*
Board of Directors:
Wissanu Krea-Ngam
Keita Ishii
Viboon Kromadit
Vikrom Kromadit
Noppun Muangkote
Chackchai Panichapat
Anucha Sihanatkathakul
Vatana Supornpaibul
Somchet Thinaphong
Legal Counsel:
International Business Lawyers Co., Ltd
23rd Floor Wall Street Tower 33/118-119
Surawongse Road
Bangkok, Thailand

Subsidiaries:

Amata City Co. Ltd. **(1)**
700 Moo 1
Klong Tamru, Chon Buri, 20000, Thailand (83.67%)
Tel.: (66) 38213007
Fax: (66) 38213700
E-Mail: marketing@amata.com
Web Site: www.amata.com
Other Activities Related to Real Estate
S.I.C.: 6531
N.A.I.C.S.: 531390
Aukkares Choochouy *(Mgr)*

Amata Facility Service Co. Ltd. **(1)**
Amata Nakorn Industrial Estate
700-2 Moo 1 Klongtamru Muang, 20000
Chon Buri, Thailand (91%)
Tel.: (66) 382150079
Fax: (66) 38215006
E-Mail: thanapat@amata.com
Web Site: www.amata.com
Emp.: 28
Other Management Consulting Services
S.I.C.: 8748
N.A.I.C.S.: 541618
Aukkares Choochouy *(Mng Dir)*

Amata Natural Gas Distribution Co. Ltd. **(1)**
Amata Nakorn Industrial Estate 700/2 Moo 1 Bangna
Trad Rd Klong Tumru, 20000 Chon Buri, Thailand (10%)
Tel.: (66) 38458601
Fax: (66) 38214255
E-Mail: smattachai@amatangd.com
Natural Gas Distribution
S.I.C.: 4924
N.A.I.C.S.: 221210

Amata Summit Ready Built Co. Ltd. **(1)**
Amata Nakorn Industrial Estate
700-2 Moo 1 Klongtamru Muang, 20000
Chon Buri, Thailand (49%)
Tel.: (66) 38213007
Fax: (66) 38213700
E-Mail: janjira@amata.com
Web Site: www.amata.com
Emp.: 60
Other Construction Material Whslr
S.I.C.: 5039
N.A.I.C.S.: 423390
Janjira Yamyim *(Gen Mgr)*

Amata Water Co. Ltd. **(1)**
Amata Nakorn Industrial Estate
700-2 Moo 1 Klongtamru Muang, 20000
Chon Buri, Thailand (100%)
Tel.: (66) 38 213 213
Fax: (66) 38213214
E-Mail: chuchat@amata.com
Web Site: www.amata.com
Production & Sale of Water Products for Industrial Use
S.I.C.: 4953
N.A.I.C.S.: 562219
Chuchat Saitin *(Mng Dir)*

Non-U.S. Subsidiary:

Amata (Vietnam) Joint Stock Company **(1)**
Long Binh Ward
Bien Hoa, Dong Nai, Vietnam
Tel.: (84) 613991007
Fax: (84) 613891251
E-Mail: amata-mktg@hcm.vnn.vn
Industrial Park Development Services
S.I.C.: 1629
N.A.I.C.S.: 236210

AMATHEON AGRI HOLDING N.V.

Friedrichstrasse 95
10117 Berlin, Germany
Tel.: (49) 30 530009005
Fax: (49) 30 530009020
E-Mail: info@amatheon-agri.com
Web Site: www.amatheon-agri.com
MLAAH—(EUR)
Business Description:
Holding Company; Farming
S.I.C.: 6719
N.A.I.C.S.: 551112
Personnel:
Carl Heinrich Bruhn *(CEO)*
Enno Gloer *(CFO)*

AMATHUS PUBLIC LIMITED

Amathus Building 2 Syntagmatos Sq
PO Box 53023
3300 Limassol, Cyprus
Tel.: (357) 25 745270
Fax: (357) 25 369656
E-Mail: info@amathus.com
Web Site: www.amathus.com
Year Founded: 1943
ANC—(CYP)
Business Description:
Hotel Management Services
S.I.C.: 7011
N.A.I.C.S.: 721110
Personnel:
Platon Lanitis *(Chm)*
Christos Christou *(Gen Dir)*
Achilleas Dorotheou *(Gen Dir)*
Board of Directors:
Platon Lanitis
Ioannis Archontides
Markos Christodoulou
Michalis G. Hadjikyriacos
Costas E. Lanitis
Marios E. Lanitis
Constantinos Mitsides
Savvas Orfanides

AMATO EXPLORATION LTD.

Suite 1402 - 1710 Bayshore Drive
Vancouver, BC, V6G 3G4, Canada
Tel.: (604) 315-2559
Fax: (604) 684-1376
E-Mail: info@amatoexploration.com
Web Site: www.amatoexploration.com
Year Founded: 2007
AMT—(TSXV)
Int. Income: $8,951
Assets: $1,841,772
Liabilities: $23,575
Net Worth: $1,818,197
Earnings: ($230,333)
Emp.: 8
Fiscal Year-end: 11/30/12
Business Description:
Metal Mining & Exploration Services
S.I.C.: 1099
N.A.I.C.S.: 212299
Personnel:
James D. Romano *(Pres & CEO)*
Pamela Egan *(CFO & Sec)*
Board of Directors:
Cameron Andrews
Tim Earle
Kieran Prashad
James D. Romano
Legal Counsel:
DuMoulin Black LLP
10th Floor 595 Howe St
Vancouver, BC, Canada
Transfer Agent:
Computershare Investor Services Inc.
510 Burrard St 2nd Floor
Vancouver, BC, V6C 3B9, Canada
Tel.: (604) 661-9400

AMAX HOLDINGS LIMITED

1503-05A Tower 6 China Hong Kong City
33 Canton Road
Tsim Sha Tsui, Kowloon, China (Hong Kong)
Tel.: (852) 2559 5925
Web Site: www.amaxhldg.com
0959—(HKG)
Sales Range: Less than $1 Million
Emp.: 20
Business Description:
Gaming & Entertainment Services
S.I.C.: 7999
N.A.I.C.S.: 713290
Personnel:
Brian Nam Chung Cheung *(Chm)*
Ronald Chi Keung Ng *(Exec Dir & Sec)*
Board of Directors:
Brian Nam Chung Cheung
Xiaomei Deng
Allen Kai Tai Cheng
Ronald Chi Keung Ng
Yoshida Tsuyoshi
Dingjie Wu
Legal Counsel:
Michael Li & Co.
6 Duddell Street
Central, China (Hong Kong)

AMAYA GAMING GROUP INC.

7600 Trans-Canada Hwy
Pointe-Claire, QC, H9R 1C8, Canada
Tel.: (514) 744-3122
Fax: (514) 744-5114
Toll Free: (866) 744-3122
E-Mail: admin@amayagaming.com
Web Site: www.amayagaming.com
Year Founded: 2004
AYA—(TSX)
Rev.: $75,977,928
Assets: $346,987,138
Liabilities: $202,278,226
Net Worth: $144,708,912
Earnings: ($7,069,820)
Emp.: 800
Fiscal Year-end: 12/31/12
Business Description:
Casino Game Developer & Casino Services
S.I.C.: 7999
N.A.I.C.S.: 713290
Personnel:
David Baazov *(Chm, Pres, CEO, Treas & Sec)*
Daniel Sebag *(CFO)*
Marlon D. Goldstein *(Gen Counsel & Exec VP-Corp Dev)*

Amaya Gaming Group Inc.—(Continued)

Board of Directors:
David Baazov
Wesley K. Clark, Sr.
Divyesh Gadhia
Harlan W. Goodson
Daniel Sebag

Transfer Agent:
Computershare Investor Services Inc.
Toronto, ON, Canada

Subsidiary:

Chartwell Technology Inc. **(1)**
750 11th Street Southwest Suite 400
Calgary, AB, T2P 3N7, Canada AB
Tel.: (403) 261-6619
Fax: (403) 237-5816
E-Mail: info@chartwellgames.com
Web Site: www.chartwellgames.com
Sales Range: $10-24.9 Million
Emp.: 150
Internet Gaming Software Developer
S.I.C.: 7372
N.A.I.C.S.: 511210
Darold H. Parken *(Pres & CEO)*
David Acorn *(COO)*

Non-U.S. Subsidiaries:

Chartwell Games (International) Ltd **(2)**
CostaDelMar
Locker St Slima, SLM 3125 San Giljan, PTM 01, Malta
Tel.: (356) 21373778
Fax: (356) 21373855
E-Mail: info@chartwelltech.com
Web Site: www.chartwelltechnologies.com
Emp.: 10
Online Software Gaming Services
S.I.C.: 2741
N.A.I.C.S.: 519130

U.S. Subsidiaries:

Cadillac Jack, Inc. **(1)**
2450 Satellite Blvd
Duluth, GA 30096 GA
Tel.: (770) 908-2094
Fax: (770) 908-1790
Web Site: www.cadillacjack.com
Sales Range: $75-99.9 Million
Emp.: 350
Gaming Machinery Mfr
S.I.C.: 3589
N.A.I.C.S.: 333318
Roger Maloch *(CFO)*
Mauro Franic *(COO)*
Sigmund Lee *(CTO)*

Diamond Game Enterprises, Inc. **(1)**
9340 Penfield Ave
Chatsworth, CA 91311 DE
Tel.: (818) 727-7286
E-Mail: sales@diamondgame.com
Web Site: www.diamondgame.com
Sales Range: $1-9.9 Million
Emp.: 29
Gaming Products Developer & Mfr
S.I.C.: 3999
N.A.I.C.S.: 339999
Benton Au *(VP-Ops)*

Non-U.S. Subsidiary:

CryptoLogic Limited **(1)**
Marine House Clanwilliam Place
Dublin, 2, Ireland Ca
Tel.: (353) 12340400
Fax: (353) 16619637
E-Mail: info@cryolife.com
Web Site: www.cryptologic.com
Emp.: 103
Internet Gaming Software Developer Export
S.I.C.: 7372
N.A.I.C.S.: 511210
David Baazov *(Pres & CEO)*
Daniel Sebag *(CFO)*

Non-U.S. Subsidiary:

WagerLogic Limited **(2)**
41-49 Agiou Nicolaou Street Block C 1st Floor
Engomi, 2408 Nicosia, Cyprus CY
Tel.: (357) 22552400 (100%)
Fax: (357) 22552500
Web Site: www.wagerlogic.com
Internet Gaming Software Licensing
S.I.C.: 9651
N.A.I.C.S.: 926150

AMAZE CO., LTD.

1-7-17 Nishitsurusaki Oita-shi
Oita, 870-0105, Japan
Tel.: (81) 97 5243301
Fax: (81) 97 5218500
Web Site: www.kamenoi.com
6076—(FKA)
Rev.: $93,555,000
Emp.: 110
Fiscal Year-end: 11/30/12
Business Description:
Food Services
S.I.C.: 5812
N.A.I.C.S.: 722310
Personnel:
Yasuo Anami *(Pres)*

AMAZONIA MINERACAO LTDA

Edificio Aquarius Center
Sala 704 Rua T 36, Goiania, Brazil
Tel.: (55) 62 2550211
Fax: (55) 62 2428299
Web Site:
Business Description:
Gold Mining
S.I.C.: 1041
N.A.I.C.S.: 212221
Personnel:
Douglas Arantes *(Pres & CEO)*

Joint Venture:

Sertao Mineracao Ltda. **(1)**
Av Hermogenes Coelho 65 Setor Central
Goiania, Goias, Brazil BR
Tel.: (55) 6233714533
Fax: (55) 6233712680
Gold Ore Mining Services
S.I.C.: 1041
N.A.I.C.S.: 212221

AMAZONICA, CORP.

Av Presidente Medice 120 Floor 1
Room 1
Osasco, SP, 06268, Brazil
Tel.: (55) 11 78374178
Year Founded: 2010
AMZZ—(OTC OTCB)
Liabilities: $30,387
Net Worth: ($30,387)
Earnings: ($32,846)
Fiscal Year-end: 04/30/13
Business Description:
Hardwood Flooring & Other Construction Materials Distr
S.I.C.: 5031
N.A.I.C.S.: 423310
Personnel:
Michael Soursos *(Pres & Treas)*
Board of Directors:
Michael Soursos

AMBASSADOR OIL & GAS LIMITED

76 East Boundary Road
Bentleigh, VIC, 3165, Australia
Tel.: (61) 3 9570 5451
Fax: (61) 3 9563 7170
E-Mail: info@ambassadorexp.com.au
Web Site: www.ambassadorexp.com.au
AQO—(ASX OTC)
Business Description:
Oil & Gas Exploration
S.I.C.: 1311
N.A.I.C.S.: 211111
Personnel:
David Shaw *(Chm)*
Giustino Guglielmo *(Mng Dir)*
Emmanuel Correia *(Sec)*
Board of Directors:
David Shaw
Emmanuel Correia
Giustino Guglielmo

AMBASSADOR THEATRE GROUP LIMITED

4th Floor Prince Consort House
London, SE1 7TJ, United Kingdom
Tel.: (44) 844 871 7627
E-Mail: customercare@theambassadors.com
Web Site: www.atgtickets.com
Year Founded: 1992
Sales Range: $25-49.9 Million
Emp.: 2,596
Business Description:
Theatre Operator
S.I.C.: 7832
N.A.I.C.S.: 512131
Personnel:
Greg Dyke *(Chm)*
Howard Panter *(Co-CEO & Dir-Creative)*
Rosemary Squire *(Co-CEO)*
Helen Enright *(CFO & Dir-Comml)*
Eddie Kulukundis *(Pres-Life)*
Tim McFarlane *(CEO-Asia Pacific)*
Board of Directors:
Greg Dyke
Peter Beckwith
Bill Benjamin
David Blyth
Simon Davidson
Helen Enright
Chris Graham
Peter Kavanagh
Richard Lenane
Michael Lynas
Tim McFarlane
Howard Panter
Nick Potter
Rosemary Squire

AMBEE PHARMACEUTICALS LIMITED

House 01 Road 71 Gulshan Circle -2
Dhaka, 1212, Bangladesh
Tel.: (880) 2 9896406
Fax: (880) 2 8827777
E-Mail: info@ambeepharma.com
Web Site: www.ambeepharma.com
Year Founded: 1976
AMBEEPHA—(DHA)
Business Description:
Pharmaceutical Products Mfr
S.I.C.: 2834
N.A.I.C.S.: 325412
Personnel:
Aziz Mohammad Bhai *(Chm)*
Naureen Aziz Mohammad Bhai *(Mng Dir)*
Board of Directors:
Aziz Mohammad Bhai
A. F. M. Azim
Khatija Mohammad Bhai
Naureen Aziz Mohammad Bhai
Georgina Gruber
Nurjehan Hudda
Nasrulah Miraly
Sakina Miraly
Laszlo Nemes

AMBER ENERGY LIMITED

Room 706 7th Floor Albion Plaza 2-6
Granville Road
Tsim Sha Tsui, Kowloon, China (Hong Kong)
Tel.: (852) 89271026
Fax: (852) 89271026
Web Site: www.amberenergy.com.hk
0090—(HKG)
Sls.: $97,597,281
Assets: $244,544,810
Liabilities: $158,319,759
Net Worth: $86,225,051
Earnings: $3,090,903
Emp.: 330
Fiscal Year-end: 12/31/12
Business Description:
Power Generation Services
S.I.C.: 4939
N.A.I.C.S.: 221112
Personnel:
Wei Chai *(Chm & Pres)*
Chun Yu Lai *(Sec)*
Board of Directors:
Wei Chai
Chun Yu Lai
Jin Quan Li
Shao Hua Pei
Chi Man Tse
Xian Guo Yao
Wayne W. Yu
Legal Counsel:
DLA Piper Hong Kong
17/F Edinburgh Tower The Landmark 15 Queen's Road
Central, China (Hong Kong)

AMBER TAVERNS LIMITED

The Victory Offices 112 Victory Road
Blackpool, FY1 1QW, United Kingdom
Tel.: (44) 1253 757158
Fax: (44) 1253 757151
Web Site: www.ambertaverns.co.uk
Year Founded: 2005
Sales Range: $25-49.9 Million
Emp.: 24
Business Description:
Pub Operator
S.I.C.: 5813
N.A.I.C.S.: 722410
Personnel:
Clive Preston *(Founder & Chm)*

AMBER WIRELESS GMBH

AlbinKobis Strasse 18
51147 Cologne, Germany
Tel.: (49) 2203691950
E-Mail: info@amber-wireless.de
Web Site: www.amber-wireless.de
Year Founded: 1998
Business Description:
Short Range Radio Module Mfr, Design & Marketing
S.I.C.: 3663
N.A.I.C.S.: 334220
Personnel:
Heinz Brych *(Mng Dir)*

AMBERTECH LIMITED

Unit 1 2 Daydream Street
Warriewood, NSW, 2102, Australia
Mailing Address:
PO Box 955
Mona Vale, NSW, 1660, Australia
Tel.: (61) 2 9998 7600
Fax: (61) 2 9999 0770
Web Site: www.ambertech.com.au
AMO—(ASX)
Rev.: $56,743,387
Assets: $30,093,764
Liabilities: $16,382,854
Net Worth: $13,710,910
Earnings: ($2,305,125)
Emp.: 90
Fiscal Year-end: 06/30/13
Business Description:
Professional Film Recording Equipment Mfr & Distr
S.I.C.: 3579
N.A.I.C.S.: 333316
Personnel:
Peter Andrew Amos *(Mng Dir)*
Robert John Glasson *(CFO & Sec)*
Board of Directors:
Peter Francis Wallace

Peter Andrew Amos
Thomas Robert Amos
Edwin Francis Goodwin
David Rostil Swift

AMBICA AGARBATHIES & AROMA INDUSTRIES LTD.

Shankar Towers
Powerpet, Eluru, Andhra Pradesh, 534 002, India
Tel.: (91) 8812 230216
Fax: (91) 8812 233876
E-Mail: ambicaincense@gmail.com
Web Site: www.ambicaagarbathies.com
Year Founded: 1946
532335—(BOM)
Sales Range: $10-24.9 Million

Business Description:
Incense Sticks Mfr
S.I.C.: 2899
N.A.I.C.S.: 325998

Personnel:
Ambica Krishna *(Chm & Mng Dir)*
P. R. N. V. Prasada Rao *(CFO)*

Board of Directors:
Ambica Krishna
Sreedharan Venkatesan Palasur
Ambica Ramchandra Rao
Puvvada Kishore Thandava

Transfer Agent:
Sathguru Management Consultants Pvt.Ltd.
Plot No.15, Hindi Nagar, Behind Saibaba Temple, Punjagutta
500 034 Hyderabad, India

AMBIKA COTTON MILLS LIMITED

15 Valluvar Street Sivanandha Colony
Coimbatore, Tamil Nadu, 641012, India
Tel.: (91) 422 2491501
Fax: (91) 422 2499623
E-Mail: ambika@acmills.in
Web Site: www.acmills.in
Year Founded: 1988
531978—(BOM)
Rev.: $73,799,256
Assets: $78,335,973
Liabilities: $37,476,230
Net Worth: $40,859,743
Earnings: $5,744,442
Fiscal Year-end: 03/31/13

Business Description:
Cotton Yarn Mfr
S.I.C.: 2299
N.A.I.C.S.: 313110

Personnel:
P. V. Chandran *(Chm & Mng Dir)*
Radheyshyam Padia *(Sec)*

Board of Directors:
P. V. Chandran
Bhavya Chandran
Vidya Jyothish
R. Soundararaja Perumal
K. N. Sreedharan
G. Udayakumar
K. Venkatachalam

Transfer Agent:
SKDC Consultants Limited
Kanapathy Towers 3rd Floor 1391/A-1 Sathy Road Ganapathy
Coimbatore, 641006, India

AMBITION GROUP LIMITED

Level 5 55 Clarence Street
Sydney, NSW, 2000, Australia
Tel.: (61) 292495000
Fax: (61) 2 9249 5050
E-Mail: info@ambition.com.au
Web Site: www.ambition.com.au
AMB—(ASX)
Rev.: $91,248,360
Assets: $20,813,863
Liabilities: $8,173,190
Net Worth: $12,640,673
Earnings: $71,905
Emp.: 275
Fiscal Year-end: 12/31/12

Business Description:
Accounting, Finance Services
S.I.C.: 6141
N.A.I.C.S.: 522291

Personnel:
Nick Waterworth *(Chm)*
Guy Day *(CEO)*
Rick Taylor *(CFO)*
James Ash *(COO)*
Andrew Bursill *(Sec)*

Board of Directors:
Nick Waterworth
Guy Day
Cathy Doyle
Paul Lyons
Paul Young

Divisions:

Ambition Group Limited - Ambition Technology Division (1)
Level 5 55 Clarence St
Sydney, NSW, 2000, Australia
Tel.: (61) 292486200
Fax: (61) 292486250
E-Mail: info@ambition.com.au
Web Site: www.ambition.com.au/
Information Technology Recruiting Services
S.I.C.: 7361
N.A.I.C.S.: 561311
Andrew Cross *(Mng Dir)*

Ambition Group Limited - Finance Division (1)
Level 5 55 Clarence St
Sydney, NSW, 2000, Australia
Tel.: (61) 292495000
Fax: (61) 292495050
E-Mail: info@ambition.com.au
Web Site: www.ambition.com.au
Emp.: 40
Accounting & Financial Professionals Recruitment Services
S.I.C.: 7361
N.A.I.C.S.: 561311
Gavin Houchell *(Mng Dir)*

Subsidiaries:

Ambition Corporate Services Pty Limited (1)
Level 5 65 Clarence St
Sydney, NSW, 2000, Australia
Tel.: (61) 292495000
Fax: (61) 292495059
E-Mail: recruits.ambition@ambition.com.sg
Web Site: www.ambition.com.sg
Emp.: 150
Corporate Services
S.I.C.: 8741
N.A.I.C.S.: 551114
Jidin Houthell *(Mng Dir)*

Ambition Recruit Pty Limited (1)
Level 5 55 Clarance St
Sydney, NSW, 2000, Australia
Tel.: (61) 292495000
Fax: (61) 292495061
E-Mail: info@ambition.com.au
Web Site: www.ambition.com.au
Emp.: 150
Employment Agencies
S.I.C.: 7361
N.A.I.C.S.: 561311
Paul Lyons *(Mng Dir)*

Watermark Search International Pty Limited (1)
Level 1 350 George St
PO Box 2708
Sydney, NSW, 2000, Australia
Tel.: (61) 292331200
Fax: (61) 292214229
E-Mail: search@watermarksearch.com.au
Web Site: www.watermarksearch.com.au
Emp.: 15
Employment Placement Agencies
S.I.C.: 7361
N.A.I.C.S.: 561311
Nick Waterworth *(Mng Dir)*

Non-U.S. Subsidiaries:

The Ambition Group Limited (HK) (1)
Jardine House 3911-17
Central, China (Hong Kong)
Tel.: (852) 31013066
Fax: (852) 31013068
E-Mail: info@ambition.com.hk
Web Site: www.ambition.com.hk
Emp.: 25
Recruitment Services
S.I.C.: 7361
N.A.I.C.S.: 561311
Mathew Hill *(Mng Dir)*

The Ambition Group Limited (UK) (1)
13 Southampton Pl
London, WC1A 2AL, United Kingdom
Tel.: (44) 2074044004
Fax: (44) 2074042865
E-Mail: info@witanjardine.co.uk
Web Site: www.witanjardine.co.uk
Recruitment Services
S.I.C.: 7361
N.A.I.C.S.: 561311
James Ash *(Mng Dir)*

Ambition Group Singapore PTE Limited (1)
65 Chulia St No 39-05
06 OCBC Ctr, Singapore, Singapore
Tel.: (65) 68545600
Fax: (65) 68545650
E-Mail: information@ambition.com.sg
Web Site: www.ambition.com.sg
Emp.: 30
Recruitment Services
S.I.C.: 7361
N.A.I.C.S.: 561311
Guy Day *(Mng Dir)*

AMBITIOUS PLASTOMAC COMPANY LIMITED

608 Gold Crest Business Centre L T Road Opp Manubhai Jewellers
Borivali W, Mumbai, 400092, India
Tel.: (91) 22 28067285
E-Mail: info@ambitiousplastomac.com
Web Site: www.ambitiousplastomac.com
APC—(BOM)
Sales Range: Less than $1 Million
Emp.: 450

Business Description:
Baby Care Product Mfr
S.I.C.: 3069
N.A.I.C.S.: 326299

Personnel:
Dilip B. Sheth *(Compliance Officer)*

Transfer Agent:
Sharex Dynamic (India) Private Limited
Unit No1 Luthra Indus Premises Andheri Kurla Rd Safed Pool Andheri(E)
Mumbai, India

AMBOW EDUCATION HOLDING LTD.

18th Floor Building A Chengjian Plaza
18 BeiTaiPingZhuang Road
Haidian District, Beijing, 100088, China
Tel.: (86) 10 62068000
Fax: (86) 10 62068100
E-Mail: enquiries@ambow.com
Web Site: www.ambow.com
Year Founded: 2000
AMBO—(NYSE)
Sales Range: $250-299.9 Million
Emp.: 5,991

Business Description:
Educational & Career Enhancement Services
S.I.C.: 8299
N.A.I.C.S.: 611710

Personnel:
Jin Huang *(Pres & CEO)*
KJ Tan *(Acting CFO)*
Yisi Gu *(CTO & Sr VP)*
Huimin Jenny Zhan *(Chief Strategy Officer)*

Board of Directors:
Shasha Chang
Mark Robert Harris
Jin Huang
Lisa Lo
Daniel Phillips
Xuejun Xie

Subsidiary:

Beijing Ambow Shida Education Technology Co., Ltd. (1)
2 F West Zone Block B Kelun Building
Chaoyang District, Beijing, 100020, China
Tel.: (86) 1065810099
Fax: (86) 1065831250
Educational Support Services
S.I.C.: 8299
N.A.I.C.S.: 611710

AMBRA S.A.

ul Pulawska 336
02-819 Warsaw, Poland
Tel.: (48) 225663300
Fax: (48) 225663303
E-Mail: warszawa@ambra.com.pl
Web Site: www.ambra.com.pl
AMB—(WAR)
Emp.: 701

Business Description:
Wines & Non Alcoholic Beverages Mfr
S.I.C.: 2084
N.A.I.C.S.: 312130

Personnel:
Nick Gunther Reh *(Chm-Supervisory Bd)*
Robert Piotr Ogor *(Chm-Mgmt Bd)*
Wilhelm Max Ludwig Seiler *(Vice Chm-Supervisory Bd)*
Grzegorz Stanislaw Nowak *(Vice Chm-Mgmt Bd)*
Piotr Dziarski *(Member-Mgmt Bd)*
Piotr Kazmierczak *(Member-Mgmt Bd)*

Supervisory Board of Directors:
Nick Gunther Reh
Oliver Gloden
Rafal Dominik Konieczny
Andreas Meier
Wilhelm Max Ludwig Seiler
Jaroslaw Szlendak

AMBRIAN CAPITAL PLC

(Merged with RFC Ambrian Group Limited & Name Changed to East West Resources plc)

AMBRILIA BIOPHARMA INC.

1010 Sherbrooke Street West Suite 1800
Montreal, QC, H3A 2R7, Canada
Tel.: (514) 751-2003
Fax: (514) 751-2502
E-Mail: ir@ambrilia.com
Web Site: www.ambrilia.com
Year Founded: 1986
Sales Range: $1-9.9 Million
Emp.: 14

Business Description:
Oncology & Infectious Disease Pharmaceutical Products Mfr
S.I.C.: 2834
N.A.I.C.S.: 325412

Personnel:
Frederic Porte *(Chm)*
Richard La Rue *(Interim Pres & CEO)*
Brian L. Davies *(CFO)*

Board of Directors:
Frederic Porte

Ambrilia Biopharma Inc.—(Continued)

Bonabes de Rouge
Faraj Nakhleh
Paul-Henry Schmelck
Philip S. Tabbiner

Transfer Agent:
Computershare Investor Services Inc.
1500 University Street Suite 700
Montreal, QC, H3A 3SB, Canada

AMBROISE BOUVIER TRANSPORTS

Lieu Dit Megaudais Rn 12
53500 Laval, France
Tel.: (33) 243087200
Rev.: $21,700,000
Emp.: 169

Business Description:
Trucking Services
S.I.C.: 4213
N.A.I.C.S.: 484121

Personnel:
Huguette Ambroise *(Chm)*

AMBROISIE CAPITAL HOLDING S.A.S.

(d/b/a Kenmar Olympia Group)
21-25 rue Balzac
75008 Paris, France
Tel.: (33) 1 4953 9038
Fax: (33) 1 4256 7009
E-Mail: clientservices@olympiagroup.com
Web Site: www.olympiagroup.com
Year Founded: 2006

Business Description:
Holding Company; Investment Management Services
S.I.C.: 6719
N.A.I.C.S.: 551112

Personnel:
Sergio Heuer *(Chm)*

Subsidiary:

Olympia Capital Management S.A. (1)
21-25 rue Balzac
75008 Paris, France FR
Tel.: (33) 1 4953 9038
Fax: (33) 1 4256 7009
E-Mail: accuial@olympiagroup.com
Investment Management Services
S.I.C.: 6799
N.A.I.C.S.: 523920
Sergio Heuer *(Chm & Co-Chief Investment Officer)*
Guido Bolliger *(CEO & Co-Chief Investment Officer)*
Karim Benjelloun *(COO)*

U.S. Subsidiary:

Olympia Capital Management Inc. (2)
1211 Ave of the Americas Ste 2701
New York, NY 10036 NY
Tel.: (212) 403-9500
Web Site: www.olympiagroup.com
Investment Management Services
S.I.C.: 6282
N.A.I.C.S.: 523920

U.S. Subsidiary:

Kenmar Group Inc. (1)
900 King St Ste 100
Rye Brook, NY 10573 DE
Tel.: (914) 307-7000
Fax: (914) 307-4044
E-Mail: info@kenmar.com
Web Site: www.kenmar.com
Emp.: 45
Alternative Investment Holding Company
S.I.C.: 6719
N.A.I.C.S.: 551112
Kenneth A. Shewer *(Co-Founder, Chm & Co-Chief Investment Officer)*
Marc S. Goodman *(Co-Founder, Pres, CEO & Co-Chief Investment Officer)*
Esther Goodman *(Exec VP)*

Subsidiaries:

Kenmar Global Investment Management LLC (2)
900 King St Ste 100
Rye Brook, NY 10573 DE
Tel.: (914) 307-7020
Fax: (914) 307-4044
Web Site: www.kenmar.com
Investment Management Services
S.I.C.: 6282
N.A.I.C.S.: 523920
Marc S. Goodman *(Pres & CEO)*

Kenmar Securities Inc. (2)
900 King St Ste 100
Rye Brook, NY 10573 DE
Tel.: (914) 307-7000
Fax: (914) 307-4044
E-Mail: info@kenmar.com
Web Site: www.kenmar.com
Emp.: 42
Securities Brokerage
S.I.C.: 6211
N.A.I.C.S.: 523120
Kenneth A. Shewer *(Chm)*
Marc S. Goodman *(Pres & CEO)*

AMBROMOBILIARE S.P.A.

Corso Venezia 16
20121 Milan, Italy
Tel.: (39) 02 87399069
Fax: (39) 02 87399081
E-Mail: info@ambromobiliare.it
Web Site: www.ambromobiliare.it
AMB—(ITA)

Business Description:
Financial Advisory Services
S.I.C.: 6282
N.A.I.C.S.: 523930

Personnel:
Alberto Franceschini *(Chm)*
Giovanni Natali *(CEO)*

AMBU A/S

Baltorpbakken 13
DK 2750 Ballerup, Denmark
Tel.: (45) 72252000
Fax: (45) 72252050
E-Mail: ambu@ambu.com
Web Site: www.ambu.com
AMBUB—(CSE)
Rev.: $185,673,163
Assets: $171,474,221
Liabilities: $51,042,773
Net Worth: $120,431,448
Earnings: $20,373,029
Emp.: 1,683
Fiscal Year-end: 09/30/12

Business Description:
Mfr. & Developer of Medical Apparatus
Export
S.I.C.: 3845
N.A.I.C.S.: 334510

Personnel:
Jens Bager *(Chm)*
Mikael Worning *(Vice Chm)*
Lars Marcher *(Pres, CEO & Member-Exec Bd)*
Michael Hojgaard *(CFO & Exec VP)*
Jesper Jul *(Chief Comml Officer)*
Bjarne Norgaard Sorensen *(Exec VP-Global Ops)*

Board of Directors:
Jens Bager
Jesper Funding Andersen
Anne-Marie Jensen
Allan Sogaard Larsen
Ingeborg Hojer Riis
Christian Sagild
Mikael Worning

U.S. Subsidiaries:

Ambu Inc. (1)
6740 Baymeadow Dr
Glen Burnie, MD 21060-6412
Tel.: (410) 636-1144
Fax: (410) 768-3993
E-Mail: rca@ambu.com
Web Site: www.ambu.com
Emp.: 50
Sales of Medical Supplies
S.I.C.: 5047
N.A.I.C.S.: 423450
Robert Campbell *(CFO)*

King Systems Corporation (1)
1401 6th Ave S
Clear Lake, IA 50428 (100%)
Tel.: (641) 355-1000
Fax: (641) 355-1099
E-Mail: info@kingland.com
Web Site: www.kingland.com
Emp.: 56
Software Reproducing
S.I.C.: 3652
N.A.I.C.S.: 334614
David J. Kingland *(Pres & CEO)*
Todd Rognes *(CFO)*

Non-U.S. Subsidiaries:

Ambu Australia Pty. Ltd. (1)
Unit 2 1 Prosperity Parade
Warriewood, NSW, 2102, Australia
Tel.: (61) 299995969
Fax: (61) 299996844
E-Mail: aussales@ambu.com
Web Site: www.ambu.com
Emp.: 10
Medical Diagnostic Equipments Distr
S.I.C.: 5047
N.A.I.C.S.: 423450
Anders Kolding *(Mng Dir)*

Ambu BV (1)
Schiphol Boulevard 127
Schiphol Airport, 1118 BG Schiphol, Netherlands
Tel.: (31) 182526060
Fax: (31) 182527073
E-Mail: info@ambu.nl
Web Site: www.ambu.nl
Medical Equipments Distr
S.I.C.: 5047
N.A.I.C.S.: 423450
Floris de Raadt *(Owner)*
Sebastien Piat *(Dir Gen)*

Ambu (China) Trading Ltd. (1)
Complex Bldg No C 5th Fl Xiang Yu FTZ
Xiamen, Fujian, 361006, China
Tel.: (86) 5926025212
Fax: (86) 5926025390
Medical Diagnostic Equipments Distr
S.I.C.: 5047
N.A.I.C.S.: 423450

Ambu (Deutschland) GmbH (1)
In Der Hub 5
61231 Bad Nauheim, Germany (100%)
Tel.: (49) 603292500
Fax: (49) 60329250200
E-Mail: info@ambu.de
Web Site: www.ambu.de
Emp.: 20
Patient Monitoring Equipment, Airway Management & Emergency Products
S.I.C.: 8099
N.A.I.C.S.: 621999

Ambu France S.a.r.l. (1)
Airspace 6 Rue Gagarine
F 33187 Le Haillan, France (100%)
Tel.: (33) 557923150
Fax: (33) 557923159
E-Mail: info@ambu.fr
Web Site: www.ambu.fr
Emp.: 20
S.I.C.: 8732
N.A.I.C.S.: 541720
Sebastien Piat *(Pres)*

Ambu Japan, K.K. (1)
2-4-1 Nishikamakura
Kamakura, Kanagawa, 248-0036, Japan
Tel.: (81) 467391570
Fax: (81) 4 6739 1571
Diagnostic, Life Support & Training Equipment & Solutions to Hospitals & Rescue Services
S.I.C.: 3845
N.A.I.C.S.: 334510

Ambu Ltd. (1)
Unit AB 3 F No C Warehouse 7 Process Complex Bldg
Xiang yu Ftz, Xiamen, China
Tel.: (86) 926025212
Fax: (86) 926025390
Web Site: www.ambu.com
S.I.C.: 8732
N.A.I.C.S.: 541720
Henik Nanaek *(Gen Mgr)*

Ambu Ltd. (1)
Burrel Road
Saint Ives, Cambridgeshire, PE27 3LE, United Kingdom
Tel.: (44) 1480498403
Fax: (44) 1480498405
E-Mail: uksales@ambu.com
Web Site: www.ambu.co.uk
Emp.: 30
Medical Diagnostic Equipments Whslr
S.I.C.: 5047
N.A.I.C.S.: 423450
Keith McCallum *(Mng Dir)*

Ambu S.r.l. (1)
Via Paracelso 18 Centro Direzionale Colleoni
20041 Agrate Brianza, Monza e Brianza, Italy
Tel.: (39) 039657811
Fax: (39) 0396898177
E-Mail: italia@ambu.com
Web Site: www.ambu.it
Emp.: 9
Diagnostic Equipments Distr
S.I.C.: 5047
N.A.I.C.S.: 423450
Lars Marcher *(Pres & Owner)*

AMBUJA CEMENTS LTD

Elegant Business Park MIDC Cross Road B Off Andheri-Kurla Road
Andheri E, Mumbai, Maharashtra, 400059, India
Tel.: (91) 2240667000
Fax: (91) 2222853051
Web Site: www.gujaratambuja.com
500425—(BOM NSE)
Sls.: $2,040,504,984
Assets: $2,309,561,172
Liabilities: $678,365,622
Net Worth: $1,631,195,550
Earnings: $239,761,134
Emp.: 5,814
Fiscal Year-end: 12/31/12

Business Description:
Cement Mfr
S.I.C.: 3255
N.A.I.C.S.: 327120

Personnel:
Ajay L. Kapur *(CEO)*
Onne van der Weijde *(Mng Dir)*
Sanjeev Churiwala *(CFO)*
Rajiv Gandhi *(Compliance Officer & Sec)*
Vinayak Khandekar *(Secretarial Officer)*
Meenakshi Narain *(Pres-HR)*
Sunil Tiwari *(CEO-HSSA)*

Board of Directors:
N. S. Sekhsaria
M. L. Bhakta
Naresh Chandra
Rajendra P. Chitale
Bernard Fontana
Omkar Goswami
Shailesh Haribhakti
Paul Hugentobler
Haigreve Khaitan
Nasser Munjee
B. L. Taparia
Bernard Terver
Onne van der Weijde

Transfer Agent:
Sharepro Services (India) Pvt Ltd
13/ab Samhita Warehousing Complex Near Sakinaka Tel Exchange Andheri E
Andheri Kurla Road Sakinaka, Mumbai, 400072, India

AMCIL LIMITED

Level 21 101 Collins Street
Box 146
Melbourne, VIC, 3000, Australia

Tel.: (61) 396509911
Fax: (61) 396509100
E-Mail: invest@amcil.com.au
Web Site: www.amcil.com.au
AMH—(ASX)
Sales Range: $1-9.9 Million
Business Description:
Investment Services
S.I.C.: 6211
N.A.I.C.S.: 523999
Personnel:
Ross E. Barker *(Mng Dir)*
Andrew J. B. Porter *(CFO & Co-Sec)*
R. Mark Freeman *(Chief Investment Officer)*
Simon M. Pordage *(Co-Sec)*
Board of Directors:
Bruce B. Teele
Ross E. Barker
Peter C. Barnett
Roger Brown
Rupert Myer
Richard B. Santamaria

AMCO INDIA LTD.

C53-54 Sector-57 Phase III
Noida, Uttar Pradesh, 201301, India
Tel.: (91) 11 4581088
Fax: (91) 11 4581288
Web Site: www.amcoindialimited.com
530133—(BOM)
Sales Range: $25-49.9 Million
Business Description:
Leather Cloth Mfr
S.I.C.: 2389
N.A.I.C.S.: 315280
Personnel:
Surendar Kumar Gupta *(Chm & Mng Dir)*
Board of Directors:
Surendar Kumar Gupta
Dharam Aggarwal
Subash Bansal
Suresh Chand Goyal
Devinder Gupta
Neeraj Gupta
Rajeev Gupta
Rakesh Gupta
Surinder Raj Pahwa
Transfer Agent:
Beetal Financial & Computer Services Pvt. Ltd
Beetal House 3rd Floor 99 Madangir Behind L S C Near Dada Harsukh Dass
New Delhi, India

S.C. AMCO OTOPENI S.A.

Sos Bucuresti-Ploiesti Km 13 200
Otopeni, Ilfov, 075100, Romania
Tel.: (40) 21 3519379
Fax: (40) 213505735
E-Mail: amco@amco-otopeni.ro
Web Site: www.amco-otopeni.ro
AMC—(BUC)
Business Description:
Measuring Instrument Mfr
S.I.C.: 3829
N.A.I.C.S.: 334519
Personnel:
Mihai Staicu *(Pres & Gen Mgr)*

AMCO UNITED HOLDING LIMITED

Unit 8 10th Floor Riley House
88 Lei Muk Road
Kwai Chung, NT, China (Hong Kong)
Tel.: (852) 24801398
Fax: (852) 24232525
Web Site:
0630—(HKG)
Sales Range: $50-74.9 Million
Emp.: 260
Business Description:
Computer Printing & Imaging Products Mfr & Sales
S.I.C.: 5044
N.A.I.C.S.: 423420
Personnel:
Wai Lun Yip *(Chm)*
Subsidiaries:

Afex International (HK) Limited **(1)**
5 F Kam Foo Indus Bldg 97-103 Ta Chuen Ping St
Kwai Chung, New Territories, China (Hong Kong)
Tel.: (852) 2427 1891
Fax: (852) 2429 2933
E-Mail: info@afex.cc
Web Site: www.afex.cc
Toner Cartridges Recycling Services
S.I.C.: 7629
N.A.I.C.S.: 811212

Jackin Optical Marketing Company Limited **(1)**
Rm 1008 10th Fl Riley House 88 Lei Muk Rd
Kwai Chung, New Territories, China (Hong Kong)
Tel.: (852) 2 480 1398
Fax: (852) 2 480 4295
Data Media Products Whslr
S.I.C.: 5045
N.A.I.C.S.: 423430

U.S. Subsidiary:

Jackin U.S.A. Inc. **(1)**
15320 Valley View Ave Unit 4 Valley View Bus Ctr
La Mirada, CA 90638-5236
Tel.: (714) 228-0980
Fax: (562) 921-7806
E-Mail: jackinusa@earthlink.net
Emp.: 6
Computer Printing & Imaging Products Sales
S.I.C.: 5045
N.A.I.C.S.: 423430
Mark Duva *(VP)*

AMCOM TELECOMMUNICATIONS LIMITED

Level 22 44 St Georges Terrace
Perth, WA, 6000, Australia
Tel.: (61) 8 9244 6000
Fax: (61) 8 9244 6591
E-Mail: info@amcom.com.au
Web Site: www.amcom.com.au
AMM—(ASX)
Rev.: $164,375,644
Assets: $214,627,790
Liabilities: $88,902,593
Net Worth: $125,725,197
Earnings: $21,623,575
Emp.: 360
Fiscal Year-end: 06/30/13
Business Description:
Internet Service Provider
S.I.C.: 4899
N.A.I.C.S.: 517919
Personnel:
Clive Stein *(CEO & Mng Dir)*
David A. Hinton *(CFO & Sec)*
Michael Knee *(COO)*
Richard Whiting *(CTO)*
Board of Directors:
Anthony J. Grist
Paul Brandling
Peter J. Clifton
Craig Coleman
Anthony Davies
Clive Stein
Ian Warner
Subsidiaries:

Amcom Pty. Ltd. **(1)**
Level 6-97 Pirie St
Adelaide, SA, 5000, Australia
Tel.: (61) 882240552
Fax: (61) 882240510
Web Site: www.amcom.com.au/CONTACTUS/OfficeLocations.aspx
Internet Broadcasting Services
S.I.C.: 2741
N.A.I.C.S.: 519130

Amnet Broadband Pty. Ltd. **(1)**
Level 1 1 Adelaide Tce
Perth, WA, 6000, Australia
Tel.: (61) 892446000
Fax: (61) 892446096
E-Mail: accounts@amnet.com.au
Web Site: www.amnet.com.au
Emp.: 150
Broadband Internet Providers
S.I.C.: 4899
N.A.I.C.S.: 517919

Amnet Internet Services Pty. Ltd. **(1)**
Level 22 44 Saint Georges Terrace
Perth, WA, 6000, Australia
Tel.: (61) 892446000
Fax: (61) 892021333
E-Mail: sales@amnet.com.au
Web Site: www.amnet.com.au
Emp.: 150
Internet Service Provider
S.I.C.: 4899
N.A.I.C.S.: 517919
Shane Mclean *(Mgr-Billing)*

Future Proof Technologies (WA) Pty. Ltd. **(1)**
156 Aberdare Rd
Shenton Park, Perth, WA, 6008, Australia
Tel.: (61) 8 9381 4983
Financial Planning Services
S.I.C.: 6211
N.A.I.C.S.: 523999

AMCOR LIMITED

109 Burwood Road
Hawthorn, VIC, 3122, Australia
Mailing Address:
GPO Box 1643
Melbourne, VIC, 3001, Australia
Tel.: (61) 392269000
Fax: (61) 392269065
E-Mail: head.office@amcor.com
Web Site: www.amcor.com
AMC—(ASX)
Rev.: $12,948,405,130
Assets: $12,944,132,520
Liabilities: $9,087,424,630
Net Worth: $3,856,707,890
Earnings: $654,855,640
Emp.: 33,354
Fiscal Year-end: 06/30/13
Business Description:
Packaging & Containers Mfr
S.I.C.: 2671
N.A.I.C.S.: 322220
Personnel:
Graeme Richard Liebelt *(Chm)*
Kenneth N. MacKenzie *(CEO & Mng Dir)*
Ron Delia *(CFO & Exec VP-Fin)*
Billy Chan *(Chm-AMVIG)*
Peter Brues *(Pres-Flexibles-Europe & Americas)*
Peter Konieczny *(Pres-Tobacco Pkg)*
Michael Schmitt *(Pres-Rigid Plastics)*
Ralf Klaus Wunderlich *(Pres-Flexibles-Asia Pacific)*
Julie F. McPherson *(Gen Counsel & Sec)*
Steve Keogh *(Exec VP-HR)*
Ian Wilson *(Exec VP-Strategy & Dev)*
Board of Directors:
Graeme Richard Liebelt
Paul V. Brasher
Karen Jane Guerra
Kenneth N. MacKenzie
Julie F. McPherson
Armin Meyer
Jeremy L. Sutcliffe
John G. Thorn
Subsidiary:

Amcor Flexibles Group Pty. Ltd. **(1)**
(Formerly Aperio Group Pty. Limited)
109 Burwood Road
Hawthorn, VIC, 3122, Australia AU
Tel.: (61) 3 9226 9000
E-Mail: info.flexible@amcor.com.au
Web Site: www.amcor.com
Sales Range: $300-349.9 Million
Emp.: 1,150
Flexible Packaging Products Mfr
S.I.C.: 2671
N.A.I.C.S.: 322220
Steven MacAleer *(Gen Mgr)*

U.S. Subsidiaries:

Amcor Flexibles Inc. **(2)**
1919 S Butterfield Rd
Mundelein, IL 60060-9735 WA
Tel.: (847) 362-9000
Fax: (847) 918-4665
E-Mail: info@amcor.com
Web Site: www.amcor.com
Sales Range: $125-149.9 Million
Emp.: 300
Coating, Printing & Conversion of Paper & Plastic Films For Flexible Medical Packaging
S.I.C.: 7389
N.A.I.C.S.: 561910
Peter Brues *(Pres)*

Subsidiary:

Amcor Flexibles - Ashland Inc **(3)**
150 Homer Ave
Ashland, MA 01721-0227
Tel.: (508) 881-2440
Fax: (508) 881-7234
Web Site: www.amcor.com
Packaging Materials Whslr
S.I.C.: 5085
N.A.I.C.S.: 423840

Amcor Flexibles Puerto Rico Inc. **(2)**
50 Calle Baldorioty
Cidra, PR 00739-3436
Tel.: (787) 739-8667, ext. 210
Fax: (787) 739-7264
Web Site: www.amcor.com
Packaging Paper Products Mfr
S.I.C.: 2671
N.A.I.C.S.: 322220

Non-U.S. Subsidiaries:

Amcor Flexibles A/S **(2)**
Hatteingvej #10
8700 Horsens, Denmark DK
Tel.: (45) 70131400 (100%)
Fax: (45) 76256020
Web Site: www.amcorflexible.com
Sls.: $350,966,016
Emp.: 350
S.I.C.: 2034
N.A.I.C.S.: 311423
Per Norgaard *(Pres)*

Amcor Flexibles Alzira S.L.U. **(2)**
CTRA Tabernes Cv-50 Km 18 1 Apartado de Correos 15
Alzira, Valencia, 46600, Spain
Tel.: (34) 96 245 89 00
Packaging Material Whslr
S.I.C.: 5085
N.A.I.C.S.: 423840

Amcor Flexibles Bangkok Public Company Limited **(2)**
91 Moo 13 Kingkaew Rd Rachathewa
Bang Phli, Samut Prakan, 10540, Thailand
Tel.: (66) 231241229
Fax: (66) 23124133
Flexible Packaging Services
S.I.C.: 7389
N.A.I.C.S.: 561910

Amcor Flexibles Barcelona **(2)**
Avenida Sant Julia 222
08400 Granollers, Barcelona, Spain
Tel.: (34) 93 860 28 00
Fax: (34) 93 860 28 01
E-Mail: flexibles@amcor.com
Emp.: 200
Packaging Material Whslr
S.I.C.: 5085
N.A.I.C.S.: 423840
Victor Catala *(Gen Mgr)*

Amcor Flexibles Burgdorf Gmbh **(2)**
Kirchbergstrasse 168-170B
3401 Burgdorf, Switzerland
Tel.: (41) 34 421 5111
Fax: (41) 34 421 52 76
Web Site: www.amcor.com

Amcor Limited—(Continued)

Emp.: 220
Packaging Material Mfr & Whslr
S.I.C.: 2671
N.A.I.C.S.: 322220
Roy Van den Oudenhoven *(Gen Mgr)*

Amcor Flexibles Cramlington Ltd (2)
49 Colbourne Avenue Nelson Park
Cramlington, Northumberland, NE23 1WD, United Kingdom
Tel.: (44) 1670730684
Fax: (44) 1670730689
Web Site: www.amcor.com
Emp.: 50
Packaging Products Mfr
S.I.C.: 2672
N.A.I.C.S.: 322220
John Roberts *(Gen Mgr)*

Amcor Flexibles Denmark ApS (2)
Hattingvej 10
8700 Horsens, North Jutland, Denmark
Tel.: (45) 70131400
Fax: (45) 76256040
Web Site: www.amcor.com
Emp.: 300
Plastic Plate & Sheet Mfr
S.I.C.: 3089
N.A.I.C.S.: 326199
Jorgen Winther *(Gen Mgr)*

Amcor Flexibles Europa Sur S.L. (2)
Avenida Sant Julia 222
Granollers, Barcelona, 08403, Spain
Tel.: (34) 938602828
Fax: (34) 938602800
E-Mail: amcor.barcelona@amcor.com
Emp.: 250
Packaging Services
S.I.C.: 7389
N.A.I.C.S.: 561910
Victor Catala *(Gen Mgr)*

Amcor Flexibles Europe (2)
Da Vinci Laan 2
B 1935 Zaventem, Belgium (100%)
Tel.: (32) 24162611
Fax: (32) 324162612
E-Mail: info@amcor-flexibles.com
Web Site: www.amcor.com
Emp.: 45
Mfr. of Flexible, Tobacco & Medical Packaging
S.I.C.: 2672
N.A.I.C.S.: 322220
Peter Brues *(Mng Dir)*

Amcor Flexibles Italia S.r.l. (2)
2 Via Dalmastro
Lugo di Vicenza, 36030, Italy
Tel.: (39) 0445 329 111
Fax: (39) 0445329329
Plastic Packaging Products Mfr
S.I.C.: 3089
N.A.I.C.S.: 326199

Amcor Flexibles (New Zealand) Ltd. (2)
(Formerly Aperio Group (New Zealand) Ltd.)
26-38 Andrew Baxter Drive
Mangere, Auckland, New Zealand NZ
Tel.: (64) 9 275 0169
E-Mail:
Emp.: 350
Flexible Plastic Packaging
S.I.C.: 3081
N.A.I.C.S.: 326113
Ken Jones *(Gen Mgr)*

Amcor Flexibles Phetchaburi Co., Ltd. (2)
32 Moo 1 Petkasem Road
Khao Yoi, Phetchaburi, 76140, Thailand
Tel.: (66) 32 446 649
Web Site: www.amcor.com
Packaging Services
S.I.C.: 7389
N.A.I.C.S.: 561910

Amcor Flexibles Rorschach AG (2)
Langrutistrasse 19
9403 Goldach, Switzerland
Tel.: (41) 718443333
Fax: (41) 718443535
Emp.: 300
Packaging Services
S.I.C.: 7389
N.A.I.C.S.: 561910
Juergen Schwarz *(Gen Mgr)*

Amcor Flexibles Sarrebourg S.A.S. (2)
48 Route de Sarreguemines
BP 50014
Sarrebourg, 57402, France
Tel.: (33) 3 87 24 53 00
Fax: (33) 387036631
Web Site: www.amcor.com
Emp.: 320
Packaging Paper Products Mfr
S.I.C.: 2672
N.A.I.C.S.: 322220
Dominique Lutz *(Gen Mgr)*

Amcor Flexibles Singapore Pte Ltd (2)
4 Tuas Avenue 20
Singapore, 638819, Singapore
Tel.: (65) 68619600
Fax: (65) 68619611
E-Mail: smg.ass@amcor.com
Web Site: www.amcor.com
Emp.: 40
Packaging Materials Mfr & Distr
S.I.C.: 2672
N.A.I.C.S.: 322220
Max Wang *(Gen Mgr)*

Amcor Flexibles Singen GmbH (2)
Alusingen-Platz 1
78224 Singen, Germany
Tel.: (49) 7731804
Fax: (49) 7731802941
E-Mail: singen@amcor.com
Web Site: www.amcor.com
Emp.: 1,100
Aluminum Packaging Mfr
S.I.C.: 3353
N.A.I.C.S.: 331315
Norbert Mauz *(Mng Dir)*

Amcor Flexibles Transpac B.V.B.A (2)
Ottergemsesteenweg Zuid 801
Gent, 9000, Belgium
Tel.: (32) 9 2408 211
Fax: (32) 9 2408 800
Web Site: www.amcor.com
Emp.: 400
Plastic Packaging Products Mfr
S.I.C.: 3089
N.A.I.C.S.: 326199
Thierry de Schryver *(Gen Mgr)*

Amcor Flexibles UK Ltd. (2)
83 Tower Road North
Warmley, Bristol, BS30 8XP, United Kingdom UK
Tel.: (44) 1179753200 (100%)
Fax: (44) 1179753311
Web Site: www.amcor.com
Rev.: $1,000,000
Emp.: 40
Mfr. of Flexible, Tobacco, & Medical Packaging
S.I.C.: 2671
N.A.I.C.S.: 322220
Mark Suitor *(Mng Dir)*
Peter Brues *(Pres-Amcor Flexibles Healthcare)*

Amcor Flexibles Zutphen BV (2)
Finsestraat 1
Zutphen, Gelderland, 7202 AA, Netherlands
Tel.: (31) 575 599 540
Fax: (31) 575599581
Packaging Products Mfr
S.I.C.: 2671
N.A.I.C.S.: 322220

U.S. Subsidiaries:

Amcor Rigid Plastics USA, Inc. (1)
935 Technology Dr Ste 100
Ann Arbor, MI 48108 DE
Tel.: (734) 428-9741 (100%)
Fax: (734) 428-4622
Toll Free: (800) 666-7741
Web Site: www.amcor.com
Emp.: 5,800
Plastic Packaging Products Mfr
S.I.C.: 2652
N.A.I.C.S.: 322219

Plants:

Amcor Rigid Plastics USA, Inc. - Tumwater Plant (2)
3045 32nd Ave SE
Tumwater, WA 98512-6161
Tel.: (360) 943-2527
Fax: (360) 943-2587
Emp.: 570
Plastic Bottles Mfr
S.I.C.: 3085
N.A.I.C.S.: 326160
William J. Long *(Pres)*

Amcor Tobacco Packaging Americas Inc. (1)
445 Dividend Dr
Peachtree City, GA 30269-1940
Tel.: (770) 486-9095
Packaging Paper Products Mfr
S.I.C.: 2671
N.A.I.C.S.: 322220

Non-U.S. Subsidiaries:

Amcor Rentsch Rickenbach AG (1)
Industriestrasse W 6
CH 4613 Rickenbach, Switzerland (100%)
Tel.: (41) 622090111
Fax: (41) 622090112
E-Mail: info@amcor.com
Web Site: www.amcor.com
Emp.: 200
Tobacco Packaging
S.I.C.: 2672
N.A.I.C.S.: 322220
Jerzy Czubak *(Mng Dir)*

Amcor Rigid Plastics de Mexico S.A. de C.V. (1)
Rogelio Gonzalez Caballero No 850 Parque Ind Stiva
Apodaca, Nuevo Leon, 66600, Mexico
Tel.: (52) 811 156 0200
Fax: (52) 811 156 0800
Commercial Packaging Services
S.I.C.: 7389
N.A.I.C.S.: 561910

Amcor Rigid Plastics de Venezuela S.A. (1)
Calle Este-Oeste 4 Con Calle Norte-Sur 5
Valencia, Carabobo, Venezuela
Tel.: (58) 2418391000
Fax: (58) 2418391104
Emp.: 520
Plastic Foam Products Mfr
S.I.C.: 3086
N.A.I.C.S.: 326140
Ernesto Molina *(Gen Mgr)*

Amcor Tobacco Packaging Novgorod (1)
Rabochaya Street 15
Velikiy Novgorod, 173008, Russia
Tel.: (7) 8162643177
Fax: (7) 8162643204
Web Site: www.amcor.com
Packaging Paper Products Whslr
S.I.C.: 5113
N.A.I.C.S.: 424130
Boris Kaploun *(Gen Mgr)*

Amcor Tobacco Packaging Polska Spolka z.o.o (1)
Ul Aleksandrowska 55
Lodz, 91-205, Poland
Tel.: (48) 426138138
Fax: (48) 426138139
Web Site: www.amcor.com
Packaging Container Mfr
S.I.C.: 3499
N.A.I.C.S.: 332439

Amcor Tobacco Packaging Switzerland GmbH (1)
Industriestrasse W6
Rickenbach, 4613, Switzerland
Tel.: (41) 622090111
Fax: (41) 622090112
Emp.: 300
Tobacco Packaging Products Mfr
S.I.C.: 2671
N.A.I.C.S.: 322220
Frank Strube *(Gen Mgr)*

Vinisa Fueguina S.R.L (1)
Perito Moreno 1793
Ushuaia, Tierra Del Fuego, Argentina
Tel.: (54) 2901423444
Fax: (54) 2901423444, ext. 4213
Web Site: www.amcor.com
Emp.: 80
Packaging Materials Mfr
S.I.C.: 2672
N.A.I.C.S.: 322220
Gustavo Suarez *(Gen Mgr)*

Zimmerlund & Co. (1)
Bernt Ankersgt 10B
0183 Oslo, Norway
Tel.: (47) 22416226
Fax: (47) 22364106
S.I.C.: 2621
N.A.I.C.S.: 322122

Non-U.S. Joint Venture:

BERICAP North America, Inc. (1)
835 Syscon Court
Burlington, ON, L7L 6C5, Canada ON
Tel.: (905) 634-2248
Fax: (905) 634-7780
E-Mail: info.na@bericap.com
Web Site: www.bericap.com
Emp.: 140
Plastic Bottle Cap & Other Packaging Enclosure Products Mfr & Distr
S.I.C.: 3089
N.A.I.C.S.: 326199
David Anderson *(Pres)*

U.S. Subsidiary:

BERICAP, LLC (2)
1671 Champagne Ave Ste B
Ontario, CA 91761-3650 CA
Tel.: (909) 390-5518
Fax: (909) 390-5597
E-Mail: info.usa@bericap.com
Web Site: www.bericap.com
Plastic Bottle Cap & Other Packaging Enclosure Products Mfr & Distr
S.I.C.: 3089
N.A.I.C.S.: 326199

AMCORP PROPERTIES BERHAD

2-01 PJ Tower 18 Persiaran Barat
46050 Petaling Jaya, Selangor, Malaysia
Tel.: (60) 3 7966 2628
Fax: (60) 3 7966 2629
Web Site: www.amcorpproperties.com
AMPROP—(KLS)
Rev.: $57,073,820
Assets: $356,790,077
Liabilities: $101,350,234
Net Worth: $255,439,842
Earnings: $31,707,241
Emp.: 1,145
Fiscal Year-end: 03/31/13

Business Description:
Engineering & Construction Services
S.I.C.: 8711
N.A.I.C.S.: 541330

Personnel:
Keen Pong Lee *(Mng Dir)*
Shahman Azman *(Deputy Mng Dir)*
Siew Chuan Chua *(Co-Sec)*
Johnson Choon Seng Yap *(Co-Sec)*

Board of Directors:
Azmi Hashim
Shahman Azman
Shalina Azman
Wing Sum Chen
Md Nawawi Ismail
Keen Pong Lee
Lam Thye Lee
Kamil Ahmad Merican
Soo Theng P'ng
Kim Wai Soo
Robert Bun Poo Tan

Subsidiary:

Blue Star M & E Engineering Sdn Bhd (1)
13 F Bangunan AmAssurance No 1
Jalan Lumut Kompleks Damai, Kuala Lumpur, 50400, Malaysia
Tel.: (60) 340418261
Fax: (60) 340419520
E-Mail: acmv@ambluestar.com
Emp.: 31
Engineering Services
S.I.C.: 8711

N.A.I.C.S.: 541330
A. N. Krishamoorthy *(CEO)*

AMD INDUSTRIES LIMITED

18 Pusa Road 1st Floor
Karol Bagh, New Delhi, 110 005, India
Tel.: (91) 11 257 58650
Fax: (91) 1128753591
E-Mail: amdgroup@amdindustries.com
Web Site: www.aamdindustries.com
Year Founded: 1983
532828—(BOM NSE)
Sales Range: $25-49.9 Million
Emp.: 200

Business Description:
Metal Packaging Services
S.I.C.: 7389
N.A.I.C.S.: 561910

Personnel:
Harswarup S. Gupta *(Chm)*
Ashok Gupta *(Mng Dir)*
Prakash Chandra Prusty *(Sec)*

Board of Directors:
Harswarup S. Gupta
Mahipal Ahluwalia
Adit Gupta
Ashok Gupta
Prabhat Krishna
Seshadri Ratnam

AMDOCS LIMITED

Hirzel House Smith Street
Saint Peter Port, Guernsey GY1 2NG
Tel.: (44) 1481 728444
E-Mail: dox_info@amdocs.com
Web Site: www.amdocs.com
DOX—(NASDAQ)
Rev.: $3,345,854,000
Assets: $4,925,813,000
Liabilities: $1,651,030,000
Net Worth: $3,274,783,000
Earnings: $412,439,000
Emp.: 20,774
Fiscal Year-end: 09/30/13

Business Description:
Holding Company
S.I.C.: 6719
N.A.I.C.S.: 551112

Personnel:
Robert A. Minicucci *(Chm)*
Elizabeth W. McDermon *(Sec)*
Ayal Shiran *(Sr VP & Head-Customer Bus Grp-Amdocs Mgmt Ltd)*

Board of Directors:
Robert A. Minicucci
Julian A. Brodsky
Adrian Gardner
Eli Gelman
James S. Kahan
Richard T. C. LeFave
John Thomas McLennan
Simon Olswang
Giora Yaron
Zohar Zisapel

Corporate Headquarters:

Amdocs Inc. (1)
1390 Timberlake Manor Pkwy
Chesterfield, MO 63017-6041 MO
Tel.: (314) 212-7000
Fax: (314) 212-7500
E-Mail: info@amdocs.com
Web Site: www.amdocs.com
Emp.: 500
Operations Support Software for Networks & Telecommunications Services
S.I.C.: 7372
N.A.I.C.S.: 511210
Brian Shepherd *(Exec VP & Pres-Strategy Grp)*
Elizabeth W. McDermon *(Grp Sec & VP-Corp Strategy/IR)*

Branches:

Amdocs Inc. - San Jose (2)
2545 N 1st St
San Jose, CA 95131-1033
Tel.: (408) 965-7000
Fax: (408) 965-7001
Web Site: www.amdocs.com
Emp.: 400
Supplier of Customer & Business Operations Management Software & Services to the Telecom Industry
S.I.C.: 4899
N.A.I.C.S.: 517919

Amdocs Inc. - Seattle (2)
2211 Elliott Ave Ste 400
Seattle, WA 98121
Tel.: (206) 447-6000
Fax: (206) 447-0669
Web Site: www.amdocs.com
Emp.: 300
Software Publisher
S.I.C.: 7372
N.A.I.C.S.: 511210

Division:

Amdocs Broadband Cable & Satellite Division (2)
1104 Investment Blvd
El Dorado Hills, CA 95762-5710
Tel.: (916) 934-7000
Fax: (916) 934-7054
Toll Free: (800) 835-8389
E-Mail: info@amdocs.com
Web Site: www.amdocs.com
Sales Range: $25-49.9 Million
Emp.: 170
Billing & Customer Management Software for Voice, Video & Data Services Markets
S.I.C.: 7371
N.A.I.C.S.: 541511

Non-U.S. Subsidiaries:

Amdocs Australia Proprietary Limited (2)
Level 25 35 Collins Street
Melbourne, NSW, 3000, Australia
Tel.: (61) 3 9835 3200
Fax: (61) 3 9835 3201
E-Mail:
Web Site: www.amdocs.com
Emp.: 40
Supplies Customer & Business Operations Management Software & Services to the Telecom Industry
S.I.C.: 7371
N.A.I.C.S.: 541511

Amdocs Brazil Limitada (2)
Rua Bandeira Paulista
702 8 Andar Itaim, CEP 04532 002 Sao Paulo, SP, Brazil BR
Tel.: (55) 1130404700
Fax: (55) 1130408999
E-Mail: amdocsbr@amdocs.com
Web Site: www.amdocs.com.br
Sales Range: $10-24.9 Million
Emp.: 200
Supplies Customer & Business Operations Management Software & Services to the Telecom Industry
S.I.C.: 7371
N.A.I.C.S.: 541511
Mario Xavier *(Gen Mgr)*

Amdocs Canada, Inc. (2)
2 Bloor Street East Suite 400
Toronto, ON, M4W 3Y7, Canada Ca
Tel.: (416) 355-4000
Fax: (416) 355-4085
E-Mail: info@amdocs.com
Web Site: www.amdocs.com
Emp.: 210
S.I.C.: 3679
N.A.I.C.S.: 334418

Subsidiaries:

Amdocs Holdings ULC (3)
1705 Tech Avenue Unit 2
Mississauga, ON, L4W 0A2, Canada
Tel.: (416) 355-4001
Fax: (416) 355-4095
Web Site: www.amdocs.com
Emp.: 88
Investment Management Services
S.I.C.: 6211
N.A.I.C.S.: 523999

Bridgewater Systems Corporation (3)
303 Terry Fox Dr Ste 500
Ottawa, ON, K2K 3J1, Canada Ca
Tel.: (613) 591-6655
Fax: (613) 591-6656
Web Site: www.bridgewatersystems.com
Sales Range: $75-99.9 Million
Emp.: 275
Subscriber-Centric Policy Management Software for Fixed, Mobile & Converged Networks Mfr
Export
S.I.C.: 7372
N.A.I.C.S.: 511210
Terence H. Matthews *(Chm)*

Amdocs Development Centre India Private Limited (2)
Cybercity Tower 2
Magarpatta City Hadapsar, Pune, 411013, India
Tel.: (91) 20 40153000
Fax: (91) 20 26824928
Customer Relation Management Software Development Services
S.I.C.: 7371
N.A.I.C.S.: 541511
Sanjay Sharma *(Head-South West Asia & Reg VP)*

Amdocs Japan (2)
Tanbaya Bldg 3F 3 2 4 Kojimachi
Chiyoda Ku, Tokyo, 102 0083, Japan
Tel.: (81) 335141840
Fax: (81) 335141829
E-Mail: info@amdocs.co.jp
Web Site: www.amdocs.co.jp
Emp.: 12
Supplies Customer & Business Operations Management Software & Services to the Telecom Industry
S.I.C.: 7371
N.A.I.C.S.: 541511

Amdocs Management Limited (2)
15 Fetter Lane
London, EC4A 1BW, United Kingdom UK
Tel.: (44) 2073432500
Fax: (44) 2073293066
E-Mail: info@amdocs.com
Web Site: www.amdocs.com
Emp.: 80
Customer & Business Operations, Management Software & Services to the Telecom Industry
S.I.C.: 7371
N.A.I.C.S.: 541511
Tamar Rapaport-Dagim *(CFO & Sr VP)*

Subsidiary:

Amdocs (UK) Limited (3)
Fleetway House
25 Farringdon St, London, EC4A 1BR, United Kingdom UK
Tel.: (44) 2073432500
Fax: (44) 2073293066
Emp.: 100
Supplies Customer & Business Operations Management Software & Services to the Telecom Industry
S.I.C.: 7371
N.A.I.C.S.: 541511
Kevin Picker *(Mng Dir)*
Simon Cassif *(Sr VP)*

Subsidiaries:

Amdocs Systems Group Limited (4)
The Square
Lower Bristol Road, Bath, BA2 3BH, United Kingdom UK
Tel.: (44) 1225471300
Fax: (44) 1225471301
E-Mail: info@amdocs.com
Web Site: www.amdocs.com
Emp.: 200
Telecommunications Software Developer
S.I.C.: 7372
N.A.I.C.S.: 511210

JacobsRimell (4)
Cutler Ct 4th Fl
115 Houndsditch, London, EC3A 7BR, United Kingdom
Tel.: (44) 2070744100
Fax: (44) 2070744104
Web Site: www.jacobsrimell.com
Emp.: 50
Fulfillment Solutions for Broadband Cable Industry
S.I.C.: 7379
N.A.I.C.S.: 541519
David Jacobs *(Co-Founder & CTO)*
David Rice-Jones *(CFO)*
Maurice O'Connor *(COO)*

Non-U.S. Division:

Amdocs Digital Commerce Division (3)
Dammstrasse 4/2
6923 Lauterach, Austria
Tel.: (43) 1532 64640
Fax: (43) 5574 76900 99
Web Site: www.amdocs.com
Software Development Services
S.I.C.: 7371
N.A.I.C.S.: 541511

Non-U.S. Subsidiaries:

Amdocs (CR) S.R.O. (3)
Amdocs PDC Delnicka 12
Rosmarin Business Centre, 170 00 Prague, 7, Czech Republic CZ
Tel.: (420) 266773222
Fax: (420) 266773303
Web Site: www.amdocs.com
Emp.: 50
Supplier of Customer & Business Operations, Management Software & Services to the Telecom Industry
S.I.C.: 7371
N.A.I.C.S.: 541511
Jiri Dite *(Mng Dir)*

Amdocs Development Limited (3)
141 Omonia Ave The Maritime Ctr
PO Box 50483
3045 Limassol, Cyprus CY
Tel.: (357) 25886000
Fax: (357) 25886520
E-Mail: yinannis.tinis@amdocs.com
Web Site: www.amdocs.com
Emp.: 500
Supplier of Customer & Business Operations, Management Software & Services to the Telecom Industry
S.I.C.: 7371
N.A.I.C.S.: 541511
Yinannis Tinis *(Gen Mgr-Ops)*

Amdocs France (3)
10 Ave De Larche
92419 Courbevoie, Cedex, France
Tel.: (33) 146911152
Fax: (33) 146918780
Emp.: 15
S.I.C.: 3679
N.A.I.C.S.: 334418

Amdocs International GmbH (3)
Bahnhofstrasse 25
Zug, 6300, Switzerland
Tel.: (41) 417278696
Fax: (41) 417278699
Software Development Services
S.I.C.: 7371
N.A.I.C.S.: 541511

Amdocs (Israel) Limited (3)
8 Hapnina St
Ra'anana, 43000, Israel Il
Tel.: (972) 97762222
Fax: (972) 97762121
E-Mail: liatko@amdocs.com
Web Site: www.amdocs.com
Emp.: 6,000
Supplies Customer & Business Operations Management Software and Services to the Telecom Industry
S.I.C.: 7371
N.A.I.C.S.: 541511
Eli Gelman *(CEO)*

Amdocs Software GmbH (3)
Forumstrasse 26
41468 Neuss, Germany De
Tel.: (49) 21313480
Fax: (49) 2131348222
E-Mail: info@amdocs.com
Web Site: www.amdocs.com
Emp.: 75
Supplies Customer & Business Operations Management Software & Services to the Telecom Industry
S.I.C.: 7371
N.A.I.C.S.: 541511

Amdocs Software Systems Ltd. (3)
1st Fl Block S East Point Business Park
Dublin, 3, Ireland IE

Amdocs Limited—(Continued)

Tel.: (353) 14393600
Fax: (353) 18239070
E-Mail:
Web Site: www.amdocs.com
Emp.: 70
Supplier of Customer & Business Operations, Management Software & Services to the Telecom Industry
S.I.C.: 7371
N.A.I.C.S.: 541511

Subsidiary:

ChangingWorlds, Ltd. (4)
5th Fl Block A The Atrium Blackthorn Rd
Sandyford, Dublin, 18, Ireland
Tel.: (353) 16933700
Fax: (353) 16933801
E-Mail: camila.chimelo@amdocs.com
Web Site: www.changingworlds.com
Emp.: 50
Personalized Mobile Information Services
S.I.C.: 7389
N.A.I.C.S.: 519190
Olivier Avaro *(VP)*

AMEC PLC

Old Change House 128 Queen Victoria Street
London, EC4V 4BJ, United Kingdom
Tel.: (44) 2074297500
Fax: (44) 2075395900
Web Site: www.amec.com
Year Founded: 1982
AMEC—(LSE)
Rev.: $6,566,687,820
Assets: $3,976,652,220
Liabilities: $2,266,281,150
Net Worth: $1,710,371,070
Earnings: $342,705,930
Emp.: 23,379
Fiscal Year-end: 12/31/12

Business Description:
Construction & Civil Engineering Services
S.I.C.: 8711
N.A.I.C.S.: 541330

Personnel:
Samir Y. Brikho *(CEO)*
Ian McHoul *(CFO)*
Hisham Mahmoud *(Pres-Growth Reg)*
Simon Naylor *(Pres-Americas)*
John Pearson *(Pres-Europe)*
Alison R. Yapp *(Gen Counsel & Sec)*

Board of Directors:
John P. Connolly
Linda L. Adamany
Samir Y. Brikho
Neil Carson
Colin R. Day
Timothy W. Faithfull
Ian McHoul
Simon R. Thompson

Division:

AMEC Upstream Oil & Gas Division (1)
City Gate Altens Farm Rd
Aberdeen, AB12 3LB, United Kingdom (100%)
Tel.: (44) 224291000
Telex: 537034
Fax: (44) 224291001
Emp.: 500
Construction of Offshore Drilling Equipment
S.I.C.: 3532
N.A.I.C.S.: 333131

Subsidiaries:

AMEC Civil Engineering Ltd. (1)
Leonard Fairclough House Church St
Adlington, Chorley, PR7 4LB, United Kingdom (100%)
Tel.: (44) 1257484400
Telex: 67510
Fax: (44) 1257484405
Emp.: 300
Heavy Construction
S.I.C.: 1629
N.A.I.C.S.: 237990

AMEC Environment & Infrastructure UK Limited (1)
Northumbria House Regent Centre
Gosforth, Newcastle upon Tyne, NE3 3PX, United Kingdom
Tel.: (44) 191 272 6100
Fax: (44) 191 272 6592
E-Mail: info.ukenvironment@amec.com
Web Site: www.amec-ukenvironment.com
Emp.: 750
Environmental & Engineering Consulting Services
S.I.C.: 8999
N.A.I.C.S.: 541620
Simon Armes-Reardon *(Mng Dir)*

AMEC Group Limited (1)
Meadowside St
PO Box 1
Renfrew, PA4 8LF, United Kingdom (100%)
Tel.: (44) 418851234
Telex: 778749
Fax: (44) 1418867724
Emp.: 150
Heavy Construction
S.I.C.: 1629
N.A.I.C.S.: 237990

AMEC NNC Limited (1)
Booths Hall
Chelford Rd, Knutsford, Cheshire, WA16 8QZ, United Kingdom UK
Tel.: (44) 565633800 (100%)
Telex: 666000
Fax: (44) 565633659
E-Mail: info@amecnnc.com
Web Site: www.amecnnc.com
Rev.: $150,520,326
Emp.: 500
Engineering Consulting Services
Export
S.I.C.: 8711
N.A.I.C.S.: 541330

AMEC Offshore Services Ltd (1)
Edison Way Gapton Hall Industrial Estate
Great Yarmouth, NR31 0NG, United Kingdom
Tel.: (44) 1493 412200
Fax: (44) 1493 653442
Survey & Offshore Facilities Engineering Services
S.I.C.: 8711
N.A.I.C.S.: 541330

AMEC Process & Energy Ltd. (1)
60 London wall
Isrington, London, EC2M 5TQ, United Kingdom (100%)
Tel.: (44) 32151700
Telex: 23764 MATHAL G
Fax: (44) 2032151701
E-Mail:
Web Site: www.amec.com
Emp.: 250
Offshore Engineering Specialists
S.I.C.: 8711
N.A.I.C.S.: 541330

Amec Project Investments Limited (1)
Sandiway House
Northwich, CW8 2YA, United Kingdom
Tel.: (44) 1606 883885
Project Management & Consulting Services
S.I.C.: 8748
N.A.I.C.S.: 541618

AMEC Property and Overseas Investments Limited (1)
Sandiway House Littledales Lane
Northwich, CW8 2YA, United Kingdom
Tel.: (44) 1606 883885
Project Management & Consulting Services
S.I.C.: 8748
N.A.I.C.S.: 541618

C.V. Buchan Ltd. (1)
Kings Ln
Rudheath, Middlewich, Cheshire, CW10 9NB, United Kingdom (100%)
Tel.: (44) 01606843500
Telex: 666132
Fax: (44) 1606842214
E-Mail: sales@cvbuchan.co.uk
Web Site: www.buchanconcreate.co.uk
Emp.: 150
Precast Concrete Mfr.
S.I.C.: 3271
N.A.I.C.S.: 327331

Performance Improvements (PI) Group Limited (1)
6 Albyn Terrace
Aberdeen, AB10 1YP, United Kingdom
Tel.: (44) 1224 647770
Fax: (44) 1224 647776
E-Mail: info@pi-ltd.com
Web Site: www.pi-ltd.com
Design & Production Optimization Consultancy Services
S.I.C.: 8748
N.A.I.C.S.: 541618
Robin Etherington, *(Mng Dir)*

Performance Improvements (PI) Limited (1)
PI House 6 Albyn Terrace
Aberdeen, AB10 1YP, United Kingdom
Tel.: (44) 1224 647770
Fax: (44) 1224 647776
E-Mail: info@pi-ltd.com
Web Site: www.pi-ltd.com
Emp.: 50
Oil & Gas Engineering Consulting Services
S.I.C.: 8999
N.A.I.C.S.: 541690
Robin Etherington *(Mng Dir)*

Primat Recruitment Limited (1)
Lingfield Point
Darlington, DL1 1RW, United Kingdom
Tel.: (44) 1325 744400
Web Site: www.primatrecruitment.com
Emp.: 20
Human Resource Consulting Services
S.I.C.: 8999
N.A.I.C.S.: 541612
Colin Fleming *(Dir-Fin)*

U.S. Subsidiaries:

AGRA Foundations Inc. (1)
10108 32nd Ave W Bldg C3 Ste A2
Everett, WA 98204 DE
Tel.: (425) 353-5506 (100%)
Fax: (425) 353-4151
E-Mail: corporate@agrafoundations.net
Web Site: www.agrafoundations.com
Emp.: 10
Foundation Pilings
S.I.C.: 1771
N.A.I.C.S.: 238110

AMEC E&C Services, Inc. (1)
1979 Lakeside Pkwy Ste 500
Tucker, GA 30084-5853
Tel.: (404) 370-3200
Fax: (404) 370-3646
Project Management Consulting Services
S.I.C.: 8748
N.A.I.C.S.: 541618
Richard Druyeh *(Sr Project Mgr)*

AMEC Environment & Infrastructure, Inc. (1)
1105 Lakewood Pkwy Ste 300
Alpharetta, GA 30009 GA
Tel.: (770) 360-0600
Emp.: 7,000
Engineering, Environmental & Remedial Construction Services
S.I.C.: 8711
N.A.I.C.S.: 541330
Hisham Mahmoud *(Pres)*
Lawrence J. White *(CIO & Sr VP)*
W. Charles Green *(Sr VP & Dir-Engrg & Science)*
Keith R. McGuinn *(Sr VP & Dir-Sls & Mktg)*
Donald C. Zimmer *(Sr VP & Dir-Govt Affairs)*

Branches:

AMEC Environment & Infrastructure, Inc. - Cincinnati (2)
4460 Lake Forest Dr Ste 200
Cincinnati, OH 45242
Tel.: (859) 581-6031
Fax: (513) 489-6619
Emp.: 20
Civil & Geotechnical Engineering; Environmental Consulting Services
S.I.C.: 8711
N.A.I.C.S.: 541330
Allen Kipler *(Pres)*

AMEC Environment & Infrastructure, Inc. - Greensboro (2)
7347 W Friendly Ave Ste E
Greensboro, NC 27410-6254
Tel.: (336) 294-4221
Fax: (336) 294-4227
Emp.: 35
Environmental Consulting & Engineering Services
S.I.C.: 8711
N.A.I.C.S.: 541330
Steve Fenton *(Gen Mgr)*

AMEC Environment & Infrastructure (2)
2100 Riverchase Ctr Ste 450
Birmingham, AL 35244-1897
Tel.: (205) 733-7600
Fax: (205) 985-2951
Emp.: 16
Engineering, Environmental & Design Consulting Services Company
S.I.C.: 8711
N.A.I.C.S.: 541330
James M. DeLano *(Office Mgr)*

AMEC Environment & Infrastructure (2)
4600 E Washington St Ste 600
Phoenix, AZ 85034
Tel.: (602) 733-6000
Fax: (602) 733-6100
Web Site: www.amec.com
Emp.: 50
Infrastructure Engineering
S.I.C.: 8711
N.A.I.C.S.: 541330
Mellisa Martin *(Acct Mgr)*

AMEC Environment & Infrastructure (2)
3630 E Wier Ave
Phoenix, AZ 85040-2957 AZ
Tel.: (602) 437-0250
Fax: (602) 437-3675
Sales Range: $25-49.9 Million
Emp.: 115
Engineering & Environmental Services
S.I.C.: 8711
N.A.I.C.S.: 541330

AMEC Environment & Infrastructure (2)
4201 Santa Ana St Ste F
Ontario, CA 91761-1554
Tel.: (909) 605-6500
Fax: (909) 605-6502
Emp.: 13
Environmental Services
S.I.C.: 8711
N.A.I.C.S.: 541330
John Thune *(Branch Mgr)*

AMEC Environment & Infrastructure (2)
9210 Sky Park Ct Ste 200
San Diego, CA 92123-3720
Tel.: (858) 300-4300
Fax: (858) 300-4301
Emp.: 30
Engineering Consulting Services
S.I.C.: 8711
N.A.I.C.S.: 541330
Barry Snyder *(Mgr)*

AMEC Environment & Infrastructure (2)
9177 Sky Park Ct A
San Diego, CA 92123-4341 CA
Tel.: (858) 278-3600
Fax: (858) 495-1941
Emp.: 162
Environmental Consulting & Engineering Services
S.I.C.: 8711
N.A.I.C.S.: 541330
Peter Campbell *(Branch Mgr)*

AMEC Environment & Infrastructure (2)
5628 E Slauson Ave
Los Angeles, CA 90040 CA
Tel.: (323) 889-5300
Fax: (323) 721-6700
Emp.: 85
Engineering & Environmental Consulting Services
S.I.C.: 8711

N.A.I.C.S.: 541330

AMEC Environment & Infrastructure (2)
510 Superior Ave Ste 200
Newport Beach, CA 92663 (100%)
Tel.: (949) 642-0245
Fax: (949) 642-4474
Web Site: www.amec.com
Emp.: 25
Consulting Engineering
S.I.C.: 8711
N.A.I.C.S.: 541330
Christine Lundgren *(Mgr-Admin)*

AMEC Environment & Infrastructure (2)
4919 W Laurel St
Tampa, FL 33607-2721 FL
Tel.: (813) 289-0750
Fax: (813) 289-5474
Emp.: 20
Engineering Services
S.I.C.: 8711
N.A.I.C.S.: 541330

AMEC Environment & Infrastructure (2)
4150 N John Young Pkwy
Orlando, FL 32801-2042 FL
Tel.: (407) 522-7570
Fax: (407) 522-7576
Engineering Services
S.I.C.: 8711
N.A.I.C.S.: 541330

AMEC Environment & Infrastructure (2)
2000 E Edgewood Dr Ste 215
Lakeland, FL 33803 FL
Tel.: (863) 667-2345 (100%)
Fax: (863) 667-2662
Toll Free: (877) 550-4224
E-Mail: amec-bci.info@amec.com
Web Site: www.amec.com
Emp.: 150
Engineering & Environmental Consulting Services
S.I.C.: 8711
N.A.I.C.S.: 541330
David Butcher *(Office Mgr)*

AMEC Environment & Infrastructure (2)
404 SW 140 Ter
Newberry, FL 32669 FL
Tel.: (352) 332-3318
Fax: (352) 333-6622
Web Site: www.amec.com
Emp.: 100
S.I.C.: 8711
N.A.I.C.S.: 541330
Mark Dublin *(Mgr)*

AMEC Environment & Infrastructure (2)
9211 N Davis Hwy
Pensacola, FL 32514-5846 FL
Tel.: (850) 478-8100
Fax: (850) 478-0990
Emp.: 15
S.I.C.: 8711
N.A.I.C.S.: 541330
Richard Brown *(Office Mgr)*

AMEC Environment & Infrastructure (2)
5845 NW 158 St
Miami Lakes, FL 33014-3911 PR
Tel.: (305) 826-5588
Fax: (305) 826-1799
Emp.: 30
Engineering Services
S.I.C.: 8711
N.A.I.C.S.: 541330

AMEC Environment & Infrastructure (2)
3901 Carmichael Ave
Jacksonville, FL 32207
Tel.: (904) 396-5173
Fax: (904) 396-5703
Engineering Services
S.I.C.: 8711
N.A.I.C.S.: 541330

AMEC Environment & Infrastructure (2)
2580 Metrocenter Blvd Ste 6
West Palm Beach, FL 33407 FL
Tel.: (561) 242-7713
Fax: (561) 242-5591
Emp.: 12
Environmental Consulting & Engineering Services
S.I.C.: 8711
N.A.I.C.S.: 541330
Bruce Schmitt *(Office Mgr)*

AMEC Environment & Infrastructure (2)
396 Plasters Ave NE
Atlanta, GA 30324-3951 GA
Tel.: (404) 873-4761
Fax: (404) 817-0175
Emp.: 100
Engineering, Environmental & Design Consulting Services Company
S.I.C.: 8711
N.A.I.C.S.: 541330

AMEC Environment & Infrastructure (2)
3200 Town Pt Dr NW Ste 100
Kennesaw, GA 30144-7088 GA
Tel.: (770) 421-3400
Fax: (770) 421-3486
Emp.: 170
Environmental Engineering & Consulting Services
S.I.C.: 8711
N.A.I.C.S.: 541330

AMEC Environment & Infrastructure (2)
5470 Habersham St
Brunswick, GA 31520 GA
Tel.: (912) 265-6709
Fax: (912) 261-0009
Emp.: 4
Engineering, Environmental & Design Consulting Services Company
S.I.C.: 8711
N.A.I.C.S.: 541330
Joe Mizelle *(Mgr)*

AMEC Environment & Infrastructure (2)
1000 Hurricane Shoals Rd NE Bldg B Ste 100
Lawrenceville, GA 30043-4826 GA
Tel.: (770) 962-7435
Fax: (770) 962-7436
Emp.: 20
Environmental Consulting & Engineering Services
S.I.C.: 8711
N.A.I.C.S.: 541330
David Sikes *(Office Mgr)*

AMEC Environment & Infrastructure (2)
8745 W Higgins Rd Ste 300
Chicago, IL 60631 IL
Tel.: (773) 693-6030
Fax: (773) 693-6039
Emp.: 60
Environmental Consulting & Engineering Services
S.I.C.: 8711
N.A.I.C.S.: 541330
Ann Massey *(Pres)*

AMEC Environment & Infrastructure (2)
2056 Ste 100
Lexington, KY 40509-1000 KY
Tel.: (859) 255-3308
Fax: (859) 254-2327
Emp.: 13
Environmental Consulting & Engineering Services
S.I.C.: 8711
N.A.I.C.S.: 541330
Brian Owens *(Mgr-Ops)*

AMEC Environment & Infrastructure (2)
13425 Eastpoint Center Dr Ste 122
Louisville, KY 40223-4161 KY
Tel.: (502) 253-2500
Fax: (502) 253-2501
Emp.: 30
Environmental Consulting & Engineering Services
S.I.C.: 8711
N.A.I.C.S.: 541330

AMEC Environment & Infrastructure (2)
Midwest Plz Bldg 800 Marquette Ave Ste 1200
Minneapolis, MN 55402
Tel.: (612) 332-8326
Fax: (612) 332-2423
Web Site: www.amec.com
Emp.: 100
Engineering Services
S.I.C.: 3845
N.A.I.C.S.: 334510
Tony Wedell *(Dir-Ops)*

AMEC Environment & Infrastructure (2)
4021 Stirrup Creek Dr Ste 100
Durham, NC 27703-1658 NC
Tel.: (919) 876-0416
Fax: (919) 381-9901
Emp.: 84
Environmental Engineering Services
S.I.C.: 8711
N.A.I.C.S.: 541330

AMEC Environment & Infrastructure (2)
1308 C Patton Ave
Asheville, NC 28806-2604 NC
Tel.: (828) 252-8130
Fax: (828) 251-9690
Emp.: 20
Engineering, Environmental & Design Consulting Services Company
S.I.C.: 8711
N.A.I.C.S.: 541330
Matt Wallace *(Principal)*

AMEC Environment & Infrastructure (2)
2801 Yorkmont Rd Ste 100
Charlotte, NC 28208-7305 NC
Tel.: (704) 357-8600
Fax: (704) 357-8638
Emp.: 78
S.I.C.: 8711
N.A.I.C.S.: 541330
Michael Sufnarski *(Office Mgr)*

AMEC Environment & Infrastructure (2)
5710 Oleander Dr Ste 110
Wilmington, NC 28403-4722 NC
Tel.: (910) 452-1185
Fax: (910) 791-1338
Emp.: 20
Providers Of Engineering Services
S.I.C.: 8711
N.A.I.C.S.: 541330
Oceanna Rhew *(Supvr-Warehouse)*

AMEC Environment & Infrastructure (2)
8519 Jefferson St NE
Albuquerque, NM 87113-1603
Tel.: (505) 821-1801
Fax: (505) 821-7371
Sls.: $185,000,000
Emp.: 80
Environmental Consulting & Geotechnical Engineering
S.I.C.: 8711
N.A.I.C.S.: 541330
David Kondziolka *(VP)*

AMEC Environment & Infrastructure (2)
961 Matley Ln Ste 110
Reno, NV 89502-2119 NV
Tel.: (775) 329-6123
Fax: (775) 322-9380
Engineering Services
S.I.C.: 8711
N.A.I.C.S.: 541330

AMEC Environment & Infrastructure (2)
780 Vista Blvd Ste 100
Sparks, NV 89434-6677 (100%)
Tel.: (775) 331-2375
Fax: (775) 331-4153
E-Mail: paulkaplan@amec.com
Web Site: www.amec.com
Emp.: 25
Environmental Consulting & Engineering Services
S.I.C.: 8711
N.A.I.C.S.: 541330

AMEC Environment & Infrastructure (2)
7376 SW Durham Rd
Portland, OR 97224-7307 (100%)
Tel.: (503) 639-3400
Fax: (503) 620-7892
Web Site: www.amec.com
Emp.: 83
Engineering Services
S.I.C.: 8711
N.A.I.C.S.: 541330

AMEC Environment & Infrastructure (2)
720 Gracern Rd Ste 132
Columbia, SC 29210-7657 SC
Tel.: (803) 798-1200
Fax: (803) 750-1303
Emp.: 30
Environmental Consulting & Engineering Services
S.I.C.: 8711
N.A.I.C.S.: 541330
Jim Smith *(Office Mgr)*

AMEC Environment & Infrastructure (2)
555 N Pleasantburg Dr Ste 202
Greenville, SC 29607-2181 SC
Tel.: (864) 288-5116
Fax: (864) 297-7938
Emp.: 10
Construction Material and Environmental Testing Services
S.I.C.: 8711
N.A.I.C.S.: 541330
Paul Johnstone *(Office Mgr)*

AMEC Environment & Infrastructure (2)
9725 Cogdill Rd Ste 101
Knoxville, TN 37932-4301 TN
Tel.: (865) 588-8544
Fax: (865) 588-8026
Environmental Consulting & Engineering Services
S.I.C.: 8711
N.A.I.C.S.: 541330

AMEC Environment & Infrastructure (2)
2525 Perimeter Place Dr
Nashville, TN 37214 TN
Tel.: (770) 360-0600
Fax: (615) 832-0983
Emp.: 15
Environmental Consulting & Engineering Services
S.I.C.: 8711
N.A.I.C.S.: 541330
Janis Brown *(Mgr-Mktg)*

AMEC Environment & Infrastructure (2)
3520 Executive Ctr Dr Ste 200
Austin, TX 78731-1636 TX
Tel.: (512) 795-0360
Fax: (512) 795-8423
Emp.: 23
Engineering, Environmental and Design Consulting Services Company
S.I.C.: 8711
N.A.I.C.S.: 541330
Sam Watson *(Office Mgr)*

AMEC Environment & Infrastructure (2)
125 Montoya Rd
El Paso, TX 79932-1801 (100%)
Tel.: (915) 585-2472
Fax: (915) 585-2626
Web Site: www.amec.com
Emp.: 30
Environmental Consulting & Engineering Services
S.I.C.: 8711
N.A.I.C.S.: 541330

AMEC Environment & Infrastructure (2)
14925 Memorial Dr
Houston, TX 77079 TX
Tel.: (281) 552-2400
Fax: (281) 552-2440
Emp.: 20
Environmental Consulting & Engineering Services
S.I.C.: 8711

AMEC plc—(Continued)

N.A.I.C.S.: 541330

AMEC Environment & Infrastructure (2)
2200 Gravel Dr
Fort Worth, TX 76118 TX
Tel.: (877) 762-2832
Emp.: 33
Environmental Consulting & Engineering Services
S.I.C.: 8711
N.A.I.C.S.: 541330

AMEC Environment & Infrastructure (2)
9865 S 500 W
Sandy, UT 84070-2561
Tel.: (801) 999-2002
Fax: (801) 999-2098
Web Site: www.amec.com
Emp.: 40
Engineering Consulting Services
S.I.C.: 8711
N.A.I.C.S.: 541330
Hisham Mahmoud *(Pres)*

AMEC Environment & Infrastructure (2)
3705 Saunders Ave
Richmond, VA 23227 VA
Tel.: (804) 358-7111
Fax: (804) 358-6646
E-Mail: info@mactec.com
Web Site: www.mactec.com
Emp.: 300
Environmental, Facilities Operation & Maintenance & Construction Engineering Consulting Services
S.I.C.: 8711
N.A.I.C.S.: 541330

AMEC Environment & Infrastructure (2)
14428 Albemarle Point Pl Ste 150
Chantilly, VA 20151 VA
Tel.: (703) 488-3700
Fax: (703) 488-3701
Emp.: 25
Engineering & Consulting Services
S.I.C.: 8711
N.A.I.C.S.: 541330
Steve Jencen *(Principal)*

AMEC Environment & Infrastructure (2)
11810 N Creek Pkwy N
Bothell, WA 98011 (100%)
Tel.: (425) 820-4669
Fax: (425) 368-1001
Web Site: www.amec.com
Emp.: 100
Engineering Consultant Services
S.I.C.: 8711
N.A.I.C.S.: 541330
Doug Smith *(Sr VP)*

AMEC Geomatrix Consultants, Inc. (1)
2101 Webster St 12th Fl
Oakland, CA 94612-3027 CA
Tel.: (510) 663-4100
Fax: (510) 663-4141
Web Site: www.geomatrix.com
Emp.: 160
Engineering & Technical Consulting Services
S.I.C.: 8711
N.A.I.C.S.: 541330
Anthony Daus *(Pres & Principal)*
James C. Price *(CFO)*

AMEC Kamtech, Inc. (1)
1979 Lakeside Pkwy Ste 400
Tucker, GA 30084
Tel.: (770) 688-2500
Fax: (770) 688-2501
E-Mail: tkr.reception@amec.com
Web Site: www.kamtech.com
Emp.: 300
Construction Services
S.I.C.: 2653
N.A.I.C.S.: 322211
Tim Gelbar *(Pres)*

Terra Nova Technologies, Inc. (1)
10770 Rockville St
Santee, CA 92071-8505
Tel.: (619) 596-7400
Fax: (619) 596-7402
Web Site: www.tntinc.net
Emp.: 60
Machinery & Services to the Mining Industry
S.I.C.: 3535
N.A.I.C.S.: 333922
Ronald R. Kelly *(Pres)*

Non-U.S. Subsidiaries:

AMEC Americas Limited (1)
2020 Winston Park Dr Ste 700
Oakville, ON, L6H 6X7, Canada (100%)
Tel.: (905) 829-5400
Fax: (905) 829-5401
Web Site: www.amec.com
Emp.: 500
Electrical & Mechanical Engineering Consultant
S.I.C.: 8711
N.A.I.C.S.: 541330
Samir Brikho *(COO)*

Branches:

AMEC Americas Limited (2)
900 AMEC Pl 801 6th Ave SW
Calgary, AB, T2P 3W3, Canada (100%)
Tel.: (403) 298-4170
Fax: (403) 298-4125
Emp.: 2,000
Engineering Services
S.I.C.: 8711
N.A.I.C.S.: 541330
Peter Madden *(Pres)*

AMEC Americas Limited (2)
7071 Bayers Rd Ste V225
Halifax, NS, B3L 2C2, Canada (100%)
Tel.: (902) 420-8900
Fax: (902) 420-8949
Web Site: www.amec.com
Emp.: 80
Engineering & Consulting Services
S.I.C.: 8711
N.A.I.C.S.: 541330

Subsidiaries:

AMEC Earth & Environmental Limited (2)
140 Quarry Park Blvd SE
Calgary, AB, T2C 3G3, Canada (100%)
Tel.: (403) 248-4331
Fax: (403) 248-2188
Web Site: www.amec.com
Emp.: 250
Provider of Environmental & Geotechnical Engineering Services; Engineering, Scientific & Contracting Services; Air, Water, Soil & Groundwater Assessment, Site Remediation & Materials Testing
S.I.C.: 8711
N.A.I.C.S.: 541330
Roger Jinks *(Pres)*

AMEC Infrastructure Ltd. (2)
140 Quarry Park Blvd Southeast
Calgary, AB, T2C 3G3, Canada (100%)
Tel.: (403) 253-2560
Fax: (403) 248-1016
Web Site: www.amec.com
Emp.: 40
Highway Design & Surveying
S.I.C.: 3829
N.A.I.C.S.: 334519
Jim McClusky *(Pres)*
Kim Turner *(Sec)*

Branch:

AMEC Infrastructure Ltd. (3)
4015 Millar Ave
Saskatoon, SK, S7K 2K6, Canada (100%)
Tel.: (306) 374-6121
Fax: (306) 955-2388
Emp.: 35
Engineering Services
S.I.C.: 8711
N.A.I.C.S.: 541330
Dzien Dzienkowski *(Mgr)*

AMEC Land Surveys Ltd. (2)
5681 70th Street
Edmonton, AB, T6B 3P6, Canada (100%)
Tel.: (780) 436-2152
Fax: (780) 435-8425
E-Mail: david.j.mcarthur@amec.com
Web Site: www.amec.com
Emp.: 400
Surveying Services
S.I.C.: 8713
N.A.I.C.S.: 541360
Ken Kozakewich *(VP)*

AMEC Technologies Limited (2)
210 Colonnade Rd S Ste 300
Ottawa, ON, K2E 7L5, Canada
Tel.: (613) 727-0658
Fax: (613) 727-9465
Web Site: www.amec.com
Environmental Services
S.I.C.: 8999
N.A.I.C.S.: 541620

Teshmont Consultants LP (2)
1190 Waverley St
Winnipeg, MB, R3T 0P4, Canada (100%)
Tel.: (204) 284-8100
Fax: (204) 475-4601
E-Mail: teshmont@teshmont.com
Web Site: www.teshmont.com
Emp.: 50
Electrical Engineering Consultants; Joint Venture with Stantec & Manitoba Hydro
S.I.C.: 8711
N.A.I.C.S.: 541330
Ralph Kurth *(Pres)*

Transtech Interactive Training Inc. (2)
1111 Dunsmuir St Ste 400
Vancouver, BC, V6B 5W3, Canada (100%)
Tel.: (604) 602-8918
Fax: (604) 602-8962
E-Mail: mary.hoekstra@amec.com
Web Site: www.atd.na.amec.com
Emp.: 40
Provider of Training Services
S.I.C.: 8331
N.A.I.C.S.: 624310
Mary Hoesktra *(VP-Fin & Gen Mgr)*

Units:

AMEC Inc. - St. John's (2)
133 Crosbie Rd
Saint John's, NL, A1B 1H3, Canada
Tel.: (709) 724-1900
Fax: (709) 739-5458
Web Site: www.amec.com
Emp.: 125
Engineering Consultancy Services
S.I.C.: 8711
N.A.I.C.S.: 541330
Glen Forbes *(VP)*

AMEC Inc. - Vancouver (2)
111 Dunsmuir Ste 400
Vancouver, BC, V6B 5W3, Canada
Tel.: (604) 664-4315
Fax: (604) 669-9516
E-Mail: shelley.skavinski@amec.com
Web Site: www.amec.com
Emp.: 639
Engineering Services
S.I.C.: 8711
N.A.I.C.S.: 541330

AMEC Australia Pty Limited (1)
Level 3 68 Grenfell Street
Adelaide, SA, 5000, Australia
Tel.: (61) 881773600
Fax: (61) 881 292784
Web Site: www.amec.com
Mechanical Engineering Contracting & Design
S.I.C.: 8711
N.A.I.C.S.: 541330

Amec Azerbaijan (1)
6th Floor Landmark III 96 Nizami St
Baku, AZ1010, Azerbaijan
Tel.: (994) 12 436 43 00
Fax: (994) 12 436 43 20
Project Management Consulting Services
S.I.C.: 8748
N.A.I.C.S.: 541618
Reyhan Talbova *(Mgr-Sls)*

AMEC BDR Limited (1)
801 - 6th Avenue S W Suite 1300
Calgary, AB, T2P 4E1, Canada
Tel.: (403) 283-0060
Fax: (403) 270-2685
Web Site: www.bdreng.com
Project Management Consulting Services
S.I.C.: 8748
N.A.I.C.S.: 541618
Jon Glaser *(Project Engr)*

AMEC Cade Ingenieria y Desarrollo de Proyectos Ltda. (1)
Av Jose Domingo Canas N 2640
Nunoa, Santiago, 7750164, Chile
Tel.: (56) 2 640 6600
Fax: (56) 2 274 5315
Web Site: www.amec.com
Engineering Services
S.I.C.: 8711
N.A.I.C.S.: 541330

AMEC Cade Servicios de Ingenieria Ltda. (1)
Avenida Jose Domingo Canas 2640
Nunoa, Santiago, Chile
Tel.: (56) 2 6406600
Fax: (56) 2 2745315
Emp.: 2,000
Engineering Services
S.I.C.: 8711
N.A.I.C.S.: 541330
Sergio Rosales *(Gen Mgr)*

AMEC Earth & Environmental GmbH (1)
Eschborner Landstr 42-50
Frankfurt, 60489, Germany
Tel.: (49) 69 756 0070
Fax: (49) 69 756 00756
Environmental Consulting Services
S.I.C.: 8999
N.A.I.C.S.: 541620

AMEC Engineering & Consulting (Shanghai) Co., Ltd (1)
29 30/F Shanghai Information Maison No 211 Centural Avenue Pu
Shanghai, 201209, China
Tel.: (86) 21 3861 5599
Fax: (86) 21 5877 0248
Project Management Consulting Services
S.I.C.: 8748
N.A.I.C.S.: 541618

AMEC Environment & Infrastructure GmbH (1)
Kalfjeslaan 56
Delft, 2623 AJ, Netherlands
Tel.: (31) 152154190
Fax: (31) 152154191
Web Site: www.amec.com
Emp.: 3
Engineering Consulting Services
S.I.C.: 8748
N.A.I.C.S.: 541618
Gert Stam *(Gen Mgr)*

AMEC Inc. (1)
2020 Winston Park Drive Suite 700
Oakville, ON, L6H 6X7, Canada ON
Tel.: (905) 829-5400 (100%)
Fax: (905) 829-5401
E-Mail: amectoronto@amec.com
Web Site: www.amec.com
Emp.: 550
Engineering, Construction, Environment & Systems Technology Operations
Export
S.I.C.: 8711
N.A.I.C.S.: 541330

AMEC International Ingenieria y Construccion Limitada (1)
Av Apoquindo 3846 Piso 15
Las Condes, Santiago, Chile
Tel.: (56) 2 2109500
Fax: (56) 2 2109510
E-Mail: amec.chile@amec.com
Emp.: 900
Engineering Services
S.I.C.: 8711
N.A.I.C.S.: 541330
Luis Alberto Garrido *(Gen Mgr)*

AMEC Minproc Ltd. (1)
Level 14 AMP Bldg
140 Saint Georges Terr, Perth, 6000, Australia AU
Mailing Address:
PO Box Z5266
Perth, 6831, Australia
Tel.: (61) 893474777
Fax: (61) 893474747
E-Mail: info@minproc.com
Web Site: www.minproc.com
Sales Range: $150-199.9 Million
Emp.: 654
Engineering & Mineral Processing Services

S.I.C.: 8711
N.A.I.C.S.: 541330
Malcolm Brown *(Pres)*

Subsidiaries:

Global Renewables Australia (2)
Level 5
250 Collins Street, Melbourne, VIC, 3000, Australia
Tel.: (61) 396500560
Fax: (61) 396500559
E-Mail: info@globalrenewables.com.au
Web Site: www.globalrenewables.eu
Urban Waste Treatment Facility Builder, Owner & Operator
S.I.C.: 4212
N.A.I.C.S.: 562111
John White *(Chm)*
Cliff Lawrenson *(CEO)*

Non-U.S. Division:

Global Renewables United Kingdom (3)
Digital World Centre
1 Lowry Plaza The Quays, Salfords, M50 3UB, United Kingdom
Tel.: (44) 1616014920
Fax: (44) 161 6-1 4921
Web Site: www.globalrenewables.eu
Urban Waste Treatment Facility Operator
S.I.C.: 4953
N.A.I.C.S.: 562219

GRD Minproc Limited (2)
Level 14 AMP Building
140 St Georges Terrace, Perth, WA, 6831, Australia
Mailing Address:
PO Box 5266
Perth, WA, 6000, Australia
Tel.: (61) 893474777
Fax: (61) 893474747
E-Mail: info@amec.com.au
Web Site: www.amec.com
Emp.: 300
Mineral Resource & Waste-to-Resource Projects Designer, Engineering & Construction Services
S.I.C.: 8711
N.A.I.C.S.: 541330
Richard Court *(Chm)*
Malcolm Brown *(CEO)*

Non-U.S. Subsidiary:

AMEC Minproc (Johannesburg) (3)
Highbury House Hampton Office Park North
20 Georgian Crescent, Bryanston, 2021, South Africa
Tel.: (27) 115140005
Fax: (27) 115140006
E-Mail: jo-anne.tun@minproc.co.za
Web Site: www.minproc.com
Emp.: 200
Mineral Resource & Waste-to-Resource Projects Designer, Engineering & Construction Services
S.I.C.: 8711
N.A.I.C.S.: 541330
Richard Linnell *(Chm)*
Colin Kubank *(Mng Dir)*

U.S. Subsidiary:

Methane Credit, LLC (2)
PO Box 65837
Tucson, AZ 85728
Tel.: (520) 615-8995
Fax: (520) 615-8997
Web Site: www.methanecredit.com
Methane Producer
S.I.C.: 2899
N.A.I.C.S.: 325998

AMEC NCL Limited (1)
700 University Avenue 4th Floor
Toronto, ON, M5G 1X6, Canada
Tel.: (416) 592-2102
Fax: (416) 592-8284
E-Mail: corporate@amecncl.com
Web Site: www.amecncl.com
Engineering, Project Management & Consulting Services
S.I.C.: 8711
N.A.I.C.S.: 541330

Amec New Zealand Limited (1)
Level 5 21 Pitt St
PO Box 5647
Auckland, 1141, New Zealand
Tel.: (64) 9 300 9700
Fax: (64) 9 300 9701
Engineering Services
S.I.C.: 8711
N.A.I.C.S.: 541330

AMEC NSS Limited (1)
700 University Avenue 4th Floor
Toronto, ON, M5G 1X6, Canada
Tel.: (416) 592-7000
Fax: (416) 592-8284
Web Site: www.amecnss.com
Nuclear Management Consulting Services
S.I.C.: 8999
N.A.I.C.S.: 541690
Jim Rippon *(Pres)*

AMEC (Peru) S.A. (1)
Calle Las Begonias 441 Piso 8
San Isidro, Lima, 27, Peru
Tel.: (51) 1 221 3130
Fax: (51) 1 221 3143
E-Mail: lima.office@amec.com
Web Site: www.amec.com
Project Management Consulting Services
S.I.C.: 8748
N.A.I.C.S.: 541618
Pierre Montauvan *(Gen Mgr)*

AMEC Philippines (1)
Insular Life Corporate Center Level 22
Tower 1 Corporate Corner
Commerce Avenue Filinvest, Muntinlupa, 1780, Philippines
Tel.: (63) 2 4222000
Fax: (63) 2 7711532
Web Site: www.amec.com
Engineering Services
S.I.C.: 8711
N.A.I.C.S.: 541330

Amec Romania (1)
184 Calea Dorobantilor Et 2 Ap 3 Sector 1
Bucharest, 010583, Romania
Tel.: (40) 21 231 63 27
Engineering Services
S.I.C.: 8711
N.A.I.C.S.: 541330

Amec Russia (1)
Bld 72 Block 4 Office 604 Leningradskiy Prospekt
Moscow, 125315, Russia
Tel.: (7) 495 721 30 02
Fax: (7) 495 721 30 02
E-Mail: customerservices@amec.com
Project Management Consulting Services
S.I.C.: 8748
N.A.I.C.S.: 541618
Andrey Pivovarov *(Gen Mgr)*

AMEC Services Ltd. (1)
Insular Life Corporate Center Level 22
Tower 1 Corporate Corner
Alabang, Muntinlupa, 1780, Philippines
Tel.: (63) 0027711576
Fax: (63) 0027711532
Engineering, Project Management & Consulting Services
S.I.C.: 8711
N.A.I.C.S.: 541330

Amec Singapore Pte Ltd (1)
78 Shenton Way 27-02/03 Lippo Centre
Singapore, 079120, Singapore
Tel.: (65) 6423 9180
Fax: (65) 6423 9678
Emp.: 26
Project Management Consulting Services
S.I.C.: 8748
N.A.I.C.S.: 541618
Rosie Hawkridge *(Gen Mgr)*

AMEC South Africa (1)
Highbury House Hampton Office Park North
20 Georgian Crescent
Johannesburg, 2021, South Africa
Tel.: (27) 11 514 0005
Fax: (27) 11 514 0006
Web Site: www.amec.com
Engineering Services
S.I.C.: 8711
N.A.I.C.S.: 541330

AMEC (South Korea) (1)
J-Tower 4/F 538 Sinsa-dong
Gangnam-gu, Seoul, 135-889, Korea (South)
Tel.: (82) 2 3014 8100
Fax: (82) 2 3014 8111
Project Management Consulting Services
S.I.C.: 8748
N.A.I.C.S.: 541618

AMEC s.r.o. (1)
Krenova 58
Brno, 602 00, Czech Republic
Tel.: (420) 543 428 311
E-Mail: amec@amec.cz
Web Site: www.amec.cz
Environmental Consulting Services
S.I.C.: 8999
N.A.I.C.S.: 541620
Petr Vymazal *(Mng Dir & Project Mgr)*
Eliska Smrzova *(Sec & Mgr-Admin)*

AMEC (United Arab Emirates) (1)
Shk Sultan Bin Hamdan Al Nahyan Building
Building No E48-C8 5th Floor
PO Box 63404
Khalifa Park Area, Abu Dhabi, United Arab Emirates
Tel.: (971) 2 622 1155
Fax: (971) 2 622 1179
Project Management Consulting Services
S.I.C.: 8748
N.A.I.C.S.: 541618

AMEC Zektin Pty Limited (1)
Level 15 300 Latrobe St
Melbourne, VIC, 3000, Australia
Tel.: (61) 3 8480 1000
Fax: (61) 3 8480 1055
E-Mail: zektin@amec.com
Web Site: www.zektin.com.au
Emp.: 70
Environmental Consulting Services
S.I.C.: 8999
N.A.I.C.S.: 541620
Joe Gangi *(Mng Dir-Bioprocess & Controlled Environments)*

Aquenta Consulting Pty Limited (1)
Level 6 26 Flinders Street
GPO Box 852
Adelaide, SA, 5000, Australia
Tel.: (61) 8 8231 3330
Fax: (61) 8 8231 3339
E-Mail: adelaide@aquenta.com.au
Web Site: www.aquenta.com.au
Emp.: 30
Business Management Consulting Services
S.I.C.: 8742
N.A.I.C.S.: 541611
Bob McCallum *(Mng Dir)*
Greg Eaton *(Principal & Mgr-Building Sector)*
Stephen Bolt *(Principal)*
Jonathan Brown *(Principal)*
Roger Burman *(Principal)*
David Carter *(Principal)*
Peter Coombs *(Principal)*
Dafydd Griffiths *(Principal)*

Baymont Malaysia Sdn. Bhd. (1)
13th Floor Menara TM Asia Life
189 Jalan Tuk Razak, 50400 Kuala Lumpur, Malaysia
Tel.: (60) 321645233
Fax: (60) 321614116
Web Site: www.amec.com
Emp.: 13
Engineering
S.I.C.: 8711
N.A.I.C.S.: 541330
Nick Smith *(Project Mgr)*

CHANGZHOU AMEC GROUP CO., LTD (1)
No 62 Xinggang Rd
Changzhou, Jiangsu, 213023, China
Tel.: (86) 519 83978019
Fax: (86) 519 83978999
E-Mail: sales@amecco.com
Web Site: www.amecco.com
Emp.: 1,000
Asset Management Services
S.I.C.: 6799
N.A.I.C.S.: 523920

PT AMEC Berca Indonesia (1)
CCM Building 4th Floor Jl Cikini Raya No 95
Jakarta, 10330, Indonesia
Tel.: (62) 21 315 9040
Fax: (62) 21 314 2740
E-Mail: info@amec-berca.co.id
Web Site: www.amec-berca.co.id
Engineering Services
S.I.C.: 8711
N.A.I.C.S.: 541330
Karuna Murdaya *(Chm)*

AMEDES HOLDING AG

Werner von Siemens Str 8 10
37077 Gottingen, Germany
Tel.: (49) 551307500
Fax: (49) 5513075077
E-Mail: info@wagnerstibbe.de
Web Site: www.amedes-group.com
Emp.: 1,800
Business Description:
Medical Diagnostic Services
S.I.C.: 8071
N.A.I.C.S.: 621511
Personnel:
Oliver Gotz *(COO)*
Werner Stibbe *(Chief Medical Officer)*

AMEDIA AS

Akersgata 47/49 6th Floor
0180 Oslo, Norway
Tel.: (47) 22 00 90 00
Fax: (47) 22 33 40 37
E-Mail: kontakt@amedia.no
Web Site: www.amedia.no
Business Description:
Print & Digital Media Services & Distr
S.I.C.: 2759
N.A.I.C.S.: 323111
Personnel:
Thor Gjermund Eriksen *(Mng Dir)*

AMER GROUP HOLDING

11 Cleopatra St
Heliopolis, Cairo, Egypt
Tel.: (20) 224132000
E-Mail: internationalsales@amer-group.com
Web Site: www.amer-group.com
AMER—(EGX)
Emp.: 700
Business Description:
Real Estate Developer, Manager & Operator
S.I.C.: 6531
N.A.I.C.S.: 531390
Personnel:
Mansour A. Amer *(Chm & Mng Dir)*

AMER INTERNATIONAL GROUP CO., LTD.

East Pacific International Center
7888th Shennan Boulevard
Shenzhen, 518040, China
Tel.: (86) 755 82785868
Fax: (86) 755 27118899
Web Site: www.amer.com.cn
Sales Range: $25-49.9 Million
Emp.: 15,000
Business Description:
Non Ferrous Metal Product Mfr
S.I.C.: 3399
N.A.I.C.S.: 331110
Personnel:
Wang Wen Yin *(Chm)*
Liu Jie Hong *(Mng Dir)*

AMER SPORTS CORPORATION

Makelankatu 91
FI-00610 Helsinki, Finland
Mailing Address:
PO Box 130
FI-00601 Helsinki, Finland
Tel.: (358) 97257800
Fax: (358) 972578200
E-Mail: amer.communications@amersports.com
Web Site: www.amersports.com
Year Founded: 1950
AMY—(DEU EUR)

Amer Sports Corporation—(Continued),

Sls.: $2,778,494,880
Assets: $2,507,241,625
Liabilities: $1,485,633,212
Net Worth: $1,021,608,413
Earnings: $77,404,775
Emp.: 7,186
Fiscal Year-end: 12/31/12

Business Description:
Sporting Goods Mfr & Marketer
Import Export
S.I.C.: 3949
N.A.I.C.S.: 339920

Personnel:
Anssi Vanjoki *(Chm)*
Ilkka Brotherus *(Vice Chm)*
Heikki Takala *(Pres & CEO)*
Jussi Siitonen *(CFO & Member-Exec Bd)*
Antti Jaaskelainen *(Chief Dev Officer, Member-Exec Bd & Sr VP-Supply Chain & IT)*
Mikko Moilanen *(Pres-Sports Instruments, Member-Exec Bd & Head-Digital Products)*
Rob Barker *(Pres-Fitness & Member-Exec Bd)*
Michael Dowse *(Pres-Ball Sports & Member-Exec Bd)*
Bernard Millaud *(Pres-Mavic SAS & Member-Exec Bd)*
Jean-Marc Pambet *(Pres-Footwear & Salomon SAS & Member-Exec Bd)*
Michael Schineis *(Pres-Winter Sports Equipment & Member-Exec Bd)*
Andy Towne *(Pres-Apparel & Member-Exec Bd)*
Victor Duran *(Member-Exec Bd & Sr VP-Bus to Consumer & Mktg)*
Terhi Heikkinen *(Member-Exec Bd & Sr VP-HR)*
Matt Gold *(Member-Exec Bd & Gen Mgr-Asia Pacific)*
Michael White *(Member-Exec Bd)*

Board of Directors:
Anssi Vanjoki
Indra Asander
Ilkka Brotherus
Martin Burkhalter
Christian Fischer
Hannu R. Ryopponen
Bruno Salzer

Subsidiaries:

Amer Sport Oy (1)
Valimotie 7
1510 Vantaa, Finland (100%)
Tel.: (358) 987587400
Fax: (358) 987587401
E-Mail: juha.pinoma@suunto.com
Web Site: www.amersport.fi
Emp.: 20
S.I.C.: 3949
N.A.I.C.S.: 339920
Heikki Takala *(CEO & Pres)*

Amer Sports Finance Oy (1)
Makelankatu 91
610 Helsinki, Finland
Tel.: (358) 9 875870
Financial Management Services
S.I.C.: 6211
N.A.I.C.S.: 523999

Amer Sports Suomi Oy (1)
Makelankatu 91
610 Helsinki, Finland
Tel.: (358) 9 7257 800
Fax: (358) 9 7257 8401
Emp.: 20
Sporting Goods Mfr
S.I.C.: 3949
N.A.I.C.S.: 339920
Heikki Takala *(Mng Dir)*

Amer Tobacco Ltd. (1)
Amerintie 1
04300 Tuusula, Finland (100%)
Mailing Address:
PO Box 12
FIN-04301 Tuusula, Finland
Tel.: (358) 9273011
Telex: 123204 amert fi
Fax: (358) 92755627
E-Mail: atinfo@amertobacco.fi
Web Site: www.norway.com
Emp.: 320
Tobacco Products; Manufacturer & Marketer of Philip Morris Cigarettes & Own Brands
S.I.C.: 2131
N.A.I.C.S.: 312230

Suunto OY (1)
Valimotie 7
FIN 01510 Vantaa, Finland FI
Tel.: (358) 9875870 (100%)
Fax: (358) 987587300
E-Mail: press@suunto.com
Web Site: www.suunto.com
Emp.: 250
Mfr. of Diving Equipment, Compasses & Nautical Equipment
S.I.C.: 3949
N.A.I.C.S.: 339920
Mikko Moilanen *(Mng Dir)*

Subsidiary:

Amerb Oy (2)
Makelankatu 91
601 Helsinki, Finland
Tel.: (358) 9 7257800
Web Site: www.amersports.com
Sporting Goods Distr
S.I.C.: 5091
N.A.I.C.S.: 423910
Roger McKenna *(CEO)*

Subsidiary:

Amerc Oy (3)
Makelankatu 91
00610 Helsinki, Finland
Tel.: (358) 9 7257800
Communications Equipment Distr
S.I.C.: 5065
N.A.I.C.S.: 423690

Non-U.S. Subsidiary:

Recta AG (2)
Viaduktstrasse 3 CP 331
2501 Biel, Switzerland
Tel.: (41) 32 333 28 20
Fax: (41) 32 333 28 21
E-Mail: info@recta.ch
Web Site: www.recta.ch
Compass Mfr
S.I.C.: 3812
N.A.I.C.S.: 334511

U.S. Subsidiaries:

Amer Sports Company (1)
8750 W Bryn Mawr Ave
Chicago, IL 60631-3512
Tel.: (773) 714-6400
Fax: (773) 714-4565
Sporting Goods Mfr
S.I.C.: 3949
N.A.I.C.S.: 339920

Subsidiaries:

Amer Sports Winter & Outdoor Company (2)
2030 Lincoln Ave
Ogden, UT 84401
Tel.: (801) 624-7500
Fax: (801) 334-4500
Web Site: www.amersports.com
Emp.: 120
Sporting Goods Mfr & Distr
S.I.C.: 3949
N.A.I.C.S.: 339920
Mick Dowse *(Pres & Gen Mgr)*

ClubCom Holding Company, Inc. (2)
1209 N Orange St
Wilmington, DE 19801
Tel.: (302) 658-7581
Investment Management Services
S.I.C.: 6211
N.A.I.C.S.: 523999

Amer Sports Portland Design Center, Inc. (1)
1111 NE Flanders Ste 205
Portland, OR 97232
Tel.: (503) 236-3473
Fax: (503) 236-0989
Web Site: www.amersports.com
Sports Equipment Mfr & Whslr
S.I.C.: 3949
N.A.I.C.S.: 339920

Atomic Ski USA Inc. (1)
2030 Lincoln Ave
Ogden, UT 84401 (100%)
Tel.: (603) 880-6143
Fax: (801) 334-4503
Toll Free: (800) 258-5020
Web Site: www.atomicsnow.com
Emp.: 50
Ski Equipment Distr
S.I.C.: 5091
N.A.I.C.S.: 423910
Michael Adams *(Pres & Gen Mgr)*

Precor, Inc. (1)
20031 142nd Ave NE
Woodinville, WA 98072-4002 DE
Mailing Address: (100%)
PO Box 7202
Woodinville, WA 98072-4002
Tel.: (425) 486-9292
Fax: (425) 486-3856
Toll Free: (800) 786-8404
E-Mail: customersupport@precor.com
Web Site: www.precor.com
Emp.: 400
Mfr of Exercise Equipment
Export
S.I.C.: 3949
N.A.I.C.S.: 339920
Paul Byrne *(Pres)*
Jim Birrell *(Chief Innovation Officer)*

Salomon & Bonfire Snowboarding, Inc. (1)
1111 NE Flanders Ste 205
Portland, OR 97232
Tel.: (503) 236-3473
Fax: (503) 236-0989
Web Site: www.bonfiresnow.com
Snowboarding Apparels & Accessories Mfr
S.I.C.: 3949
N.A.I.C.S.: 339920
Brad Steward *(Founder, VP & Dir-Creative)*
Phil College *(Mng Dir)*

Salomon North America, Inc. (1)
5055 N Greeley Ave
Portland, OR 97217-3524
Tel.: (971) 234-7001
Fax: (971) 234-7059
Toll Free: (877) 2-SALOMON
Web Site: www.amersports.com
Emp.: 100
Ski & Golf Equipment Mfr
S.I.C.: 5091
N.A.I.C.S.: 423910
Jean-Marc Pambet *(Pres)*

Wilson Sporting Goods Co. (1)
8750 W Bryn Mawr Ave
Chicago, IL 60631 IL
Tel.: (773) 714-6400 (100%)
Fax: (773) 714-4565
Web Site: www.wilson.com
Emp.: 300
Sporting & Athletic Goods
Import Export
S.I.C.: 3949
N.A.I.C.S.: 339920
Steve Millea *(Pres-Golf & Racquet Sports)*

Subsidiary:

Athletic Training Equipment Company, Inc. (2)
655 Spice Islands Dr
Sparks, NV 89431 DE
Tel.: (775) 352-2800
Fax: (775) 352-2822
Toll Free: (800) 998ATEC
E-Mail: askatec@wilson.com
Web Site: www.atecsports.com
Emp.: 31
Mfr. Small Track & Field
S.I.C.: 3949
N.A.I.C.S.: 339920
Mike Jones *(Mgr)*

Plant:

Wilson Sporting Goods Co. (2)
217 Liberty St
Ada, OH 45810-1135
Tel.: (419) 634-9901
Fax: (419) 634-4630
Web Site: www.wilson.com
Emp.: 150
Mfr. of Sporting Goods
S.I.C.: 3949
N.A.I.C.S.: 339920
Dan Riegle *(Mgr-Factory)*

Non-U.S. Subsidiaries:

Amer Sport Malaysia Sdn. Bhd. (2)
Lot 4 And 6 Jalan Anggerik Mokara 31 50
Kota Kemuning Seksyen 31, 40460 Shah Alam, Selangor, Malaysia (100%)
Tel.: (60) 351248000
Fax: (60) 351249000
Web Site: www.amersport.com
Emp.: 46
Sales of Sporting Goods
S.I.C.: 5941
N.A.I.C.S.: 451110

Amer Sports Australia Pty. Ltd. (2)
18 20 Lakewood Blvd
Braeside, VIC, 3195, Australia (100%)
Mailing Address:
PO Box 333
Braeside, VIC, 3195, Australia
Tel.: (61) 385866666
Fax: (61) 85866688
E-Mail: info@amersports.com
Web Site: www.amersports.com
Sales Range: $10-24.9 Million
Emp.: 40
S.I.C.: 3949
N.A.I.C.S.: 339920
Adam Joyce *(Gen Mgr)*

Amer Sports Japan, Inc. (2)
Simomoto Bldg 1 46 3 Hatsudai
Shibiya Ku, Tokyo, 151-0061, Japan (100%)
Tel.: (81) 353024307
Fax: (81) 3 5302 4679
Web Site: www.amerjapan.com
Emp.: 100
Sales of Sporting Goods
S.I.C.: 5941
N.A.I.C.S.: 451110

Amer Sports Korea Ltd. (2)
Rm 301 Nam Do
53 4 Chung Dam Dong Kangnam Gu,
Seoul, 100135, Korea (South) (100%)
Tel.: (82) 25457348
Fax: (82) 25475464
Web Site: www.amersports.com
Emp.: 20
S.I.C.: 3949
N.A.I.C.S.: 339920

Amer Sports Malaysia Sdn Bhd (2)
Suite 19 01 19th Floor Menara IGB No1
The Boulevard Mid Valley City
Lingkaran Syed Putra, 59200 Kuala Lumpur, Malaysia
Tel.: (60) 3 2282 0009
Fax: (60) 3 2287 6541
E-Mail: Marketing.Malaysia@amersports.com
Web Site: www.wilsonsports.com.my
Emp.: 40
Sporting Goods Distr
S.I.C.: 5091
N.A.I.C.S.: 423910

Amer Sports Spain S.A. (2)
Del Atlantic 115
Nave A51, 08040 ZAL08020 Barcelona, Spain (100%)
Tel.: (34) 932625100
Fax: (34) 932625101
E-Mail: info.wilsonspain@amer.de
Web Site: www.amersports.net
Emp.: 25
S.I.C.: 3949
N.A.I.C.S.: 339920
Sergeo Perez *(Gen Mgr)*

Amer Sports Taiwan (2)
26-2 Rd 18th Taichung Industrial Park
Taichung, 40850, Taiwan (100%)
Tel.: (886) 423595363
Fax: (886) 423595702
Web Site: www.amersports.com
Emp.: 50
Mfr of Athletic Apparel & Sporting Equipment
S.I.C.: 3949
N.A.I.C.S.: 339920

Amer Sports UK Ltd. - Logistics Center (2)
North Newmoor Industrial Estate
1-5 Crompton Way, Irvine, Ayrshire, KA11 4HU, United Kingdom (100%)
Tel.: (44) 1294 219 117
Fax: (44) 1294219110
E-Mail: michael.white@amersports.net
Web Site: www.amersports.net
Sales Range: $25-49.9 Million
Emp.: 100
Sporting & Athletic Goods Sales
S.I.C.: 5941
N.A.I.C.S.: 451110
Andy Clift *(Mgr-Health & Safety)*

Amer Sports UK Limited (2)
1 Tanners Yard
London Road, Bagshot, Surrey, GU19 5HD, United Kingdom (100%)
Tel.: (44) 1294316200
Fax: (44) 1294316255
Emp.: 7
Sales of Sporting Goods
S.I.C.: 5941
N.A.I.C.S.: 451110

Amersports Czech Republic (2)
V Chotejne 7 700
Praha 10, 102 00 Prague, Czech Republic (100%)
Tel.: (420) 272700963
Fax: (420) 272704216
E-Mail: ivona.malinova@amersports.com
Web Site: www.amersports.cz
Emp.: 40
S.I.C.: 3949
N.A.I.C.S.: 339920
Pavel Kozuch *(Reg Mgr)*

AmerSports Deutschland GmbH (2)
Parkring 15
85748 Garching, Germany (100%)
Tel.: (49) 898980102
Telex: 5214110 wilson d
Fax: (49) 8989801129
E-Mail: customer.service@amersports.com
Web Site: www.amersports.com
Emp.: 250
Sales of Sporting Goods
S.I.C.: 5941
N.A.I.C.S.: 451110
Thomas Henkeo *(Mng Dir-IT)*

Wilson Brazil (2)
Ave Brigadeiro Faria Lima 2391
11 Andar Conjunto 111 112, Sao Paulo, SP, 01452 000, Brazil
Tel.: (55) 1130941900
Fax: (55) 1130377784
Web Site: www.wilson.com
S.I.C.: 3949
N.A.I.C.S.: 339920

Wilson France S.A.R.L. (2)
ZI Petite Montagne Sud
F-91000 Evry, Cedex, France
Tel.: (33) 160862222
Telex: 681130
Fax: (33) 160860551
Sales of Sporting Goods
S.I.C.: 5941
N.A.I.C.S.: 451110

Wilson Sporting Goods Co. de Mexico (2)
No 495 Ave Sante Fe 18th Fl
Colonia Cruz Manca, Mexico, DF, 05349, Mexico (100%)
Tel.: (52) 5591779100
Fax: (52) 5591779101
E-Mail: ramiro.arregui@amersports.com
Web Site: www.wilson.com
Emp.: 55
S.I.C.: 3949
N.A.I.C.S.: 339920
Ramiro Arregui *(Mgr-Adv)*

Wilson Sporting Goods Company Kaohsiung Branch (2)
14th Fl 2 6 Min Chuan 2nd Rd
Chien Chen, Kaohsiung, 806, Taiwan (100%)
Tel.: (886) 73365088
Fax: (886) 73311090
Web Site: www.wilsongolf.com
Emp.: 10
Sales of Sporting Goods
S.I.C.: 5941
N.A.I.C.S.: 451110
Ann Huang *(Gen Mgr)*

Wilson Sports Equipment Canada Shields (2)
2700 14 Avenue Unit 1
Markham, ON, L3R0J1, Canada (100%)
Tel.: (905) 470-9966
Fax: (905) 470-7315
E-Mail: info@wilsoncanada.com
Web Site: www.wilson.com
Emp.: 25
Sales of Sporting Goods
S.I.C.: 5941
N.A.I.C.S.: 451110
David Deasley *(Pres)*

Non-U.S. Subsidiaries:

Amer Sports Asia Services Limited (1)
Rm 1115 11/F World Commerce Ctr 11 Canton Rd
Tsim Sha Tsui, Kowloon, China (Hong Kong)
Tel.: (852) 21955100
Fax: (852) 28818010
Sporting Goods Distr
S.I.C.: 5091
N.A.I.C.S.: 423910

Amer Sports Austria GMBH (1)
Lackengasse 301
5541 Altenmarkt, Austria
Tel.: (43) 6452 3900 0
Fax: (43) 452 3900 192
E-Mail: info@atomic.com
Emp.: 50
Sporting Goods Distr
S.I.C.: 5091
N.A.I.C.S.: 423910

Amer Sports Canada, Inc. (1)
85 Davy Rd
PO Box 909
Belleville, ON, K8N 5B6, Canada
Tel.: (613) 966-9220
Fax: (613) 966-9366
E-Mail: info@amercanada.com
Web Site: www.amercanada.com
Emp.: 80
Sporting Goods Distr
S.I.C.: 5091
N.A.I.C.S.: 423910
Paul Mckeown *(VP-Fin & Ops)*

Amer Sports China (1)
2F Building 3 YouYou Century Square 428 South Yang Gao Road
Pudong New Area, 200127 Shanghai, China
Tel.: (86) 21 5116 5288
Fax: (86) 21 5116 5299
Sporting Goods Distr
S.I.C.: 5091
N.A.I.C.S.: 423910

Amer Sports Czech Republic s.r.o. (1)
V Chotejne 7/700
102 00 Prague, Czech Republic
Tel.: (420) 272 700 963
Fax: (420) 272 704 216
E-Mail: customer.service.cz@amersports.com
Web Site: www.amersports.com
Sporting Goods Distr
S.I.C.: 5091
N.A.I.C.S.: 423910
Pavel Kozuch *(Gen Mgr)*

Amer Sports Deutschland GmbH (1)
Park Ring 15
85748 Garching, Germany (100%)
Tel.: (49) 898980103
Fax: (49) 8989801129
E-Mail: amer.communication@amersports.com
Web Site: www.atomicsnow.com
Emp.: 115
S.I.C.: 3949
N.A.I.C.S.: 339920
Arming Fox *(Mng Dir)*

Amer Sports Estonia (1)
Herne 28
10135 Tallinn, Estonia
Tel.: (372) 64 59737
Fax: (372) 64 59737
E-Mail: info@amersports.com
Web Site: www.amersports.com
Sporting Goods Distr
S.I.C.: 5091
N.A.I.C.S.: 423910
Ari Alkio *(Country Mgr)*

Amer Sports Europe GmbH (1)
Parkring 15
85748 Garching, Germany
Tel.: (49) 89 89 801 01
Fax: (49) 89 89 801 129
Web Site: www.amersports.com
Emp.: 210
Sporting Goods Distr
S.I.C.: 5091
N.A.I.C.S.: 423910
Michael White *(Chief Sls Officer & Gen Mgr-EMEA & Americas)*

Subsidiary:

Amer Sports Europe Services GmbH (2)
Saar Im Hasfeld 2
66802 Uberherrn, Germany
Tel.: (49) 6836 91903 28
Fax: (49) 6836 91903 30
Web Site: www.amersports.com
Emp.: 110
Sporting Goods Distr
S.I.C.: 5091
N.A.I.C.S.: 423910
Anja Burkhardt *(Dir-HR)*

Amer Sports European Center AG (1)
Bachtalen 33
Cham, 6332, Switzerland
Tel.: (41) 417841212
Fax: (41) 417841213
Emp.: 80
Sporting Goods Distr
S.I.C.: 5091
N.A.I.C.S.: 423910
Andreas Balz *(Gen Mgr)*

Amer Sports France (1)
ZAC Du Parc Technologique
63 Rue Condorcet, FR 38 090 Vaulx-Milieu, France (100%)
Tel.: (33) 474991515
Fax: (33) 474991516
E-Mail: info.atomicfrance@amer.de
Web Site: www.atomicsnow.com
Emp.: 25
S.I.C.: 3949
N.A.I.C.S.: 339920
Tierrt Louis Radius *(Gen Mgr)*

Amer Sports Holding GmbH (1)
Lackengasse 301
Altenmarkt, 5541, Austria
Tel.: (43) 64523900
Fax: (43) 6452390012
Investment Management Services
S.I.C.: 6211
N.A.I.C.S.: 523999

Non-U.S. Subsidiaries:

Amer Sports Denmark ApS (2)
Kokkedal Industripark 14 B
2980 Kokkedal, Denmark
Tel.: (45) 455 655 30
Fax: (45) 455 655 31
Emp.: 1
Sporting Goods Distr
S.I.C.: 5091
N.A.I.C.S.: 423910
Lars Stigmo *(Mgr-Customer Svc)*

Amer Sports Italia S.p.a. (2)
Via Priula 78
31040 Nervesa della Battaglia, Treviso, Italy
Tel.: (39) 0422 5291
Fax: (39) 0422 529199
E-Mail: amersports-italy@amersports.com
Emp.: 7
Sporting Goods Distr
S.I.C.: 5091
N.A.I.C.S.: 423910

Amer Sports Norge A/S (2)
Eyvind Lychesvei 9C
Postboks 293
1338 Sandvika, Norway
Tel.: (47) 67 551 330
Fax: (47) 67 551 331
Sporting Goods Distr
S.I.C.: 5091
N.A.I.C.S.: 423910

Amer Sports Poland Sp. z.o.o. (2)
ul Pilotow 2
31-462 Krakow, Poland
Tel.: (48) 12 328 39 00
Fax: (48) 12 328 39 01
Web Site: www.amersports.com
Sporting Goods Distr
S.I.C.: 5091
N.A.I.C.S.: 423910

Nikita ehf (2)
Skipholti 25
Reykjavik, Iceland
Tel.: (354) 5851000
Sales Range: $10-24.9 Million
Sporting Goods Distr
S.I.C.: 5091
N.A.I.C.S.: 423910

ZAO Amer Sports (2)
Andover Ave Building 18 Block 7 Floor 9
115432 Moscow, Russia
Tel.: (7) 495 641 2646
Fax: (7) 495 641 2645
Web Site: www.amersports.com
Emp.: 100
Sports Equipment Mfr & Whslr
S.I.C.: 3949
N.A.I.C.S.: 339920
Vetrova Tatiana *(Gen Mgr)*

Amer Sports Holding S.A.S. (1)
63 Rue Condorcet
38090 Villefontaine, France
Tel.: (33) 4 74 99 15 15
Investment Management Services
S.I.C.: 6211
N.A.I.C.S.: 523999

Subsidiary:

Salomon S.A. (2)
Les Croiselets
74370 Metz-Tessy, France
Tel.: (33) 4 50 65 4141
Fax: (33) 4 50 65 4260
Sporting Goods Mfr
S.I.C.: 3949
N.A.I.C.S.: 339920

Non-U.S. Subsidiary:

Salomon Canada Sports Ltd (3)
3545 Thimens Blvd
Saint Laurent, QC, H4R1V5, Canada
Tel.: (514) 335-5948
Web Site: www.salomon.com
Sporting Goods Distr
S.I.C.: 5091
N.A.I.C.S.: 423910

Amer Sports Latin America (1)
Av Santa Fe 495 Piso 18 Int 1801 Col Cruz Manca
Mexico, 5349, Mexico
Tel.: (52) 55 9177 9100
Fax: (52) 55 9177 9101
E-Mail: info.latinamerica@amersports.com
Sporting Goods Mfr
S.I.C.: 3949
N.A.I.C.S.: 339920

Amer Sports Netherlands (1)
Plesmanstraat 1
3833 LA Leusden, Netherlands
Tel.: (31) 33 432 0314
Fax: (31) 33 432 02917
Sports Goods Retailer
S.I.C.: 5941
N.A.I.C.S.: 451110
Arjan Buzzer *(Gen Mgr)*

Amer Sports Russia (1)
Kaluzhskoe Shossee 21km D Mamyri
MEGA Mall Office 208
Leninski Rayon, 142704 Moscow, Russia
Tel.: (7) 495 641 26 46
Fax: (7) 495 641 26 45
Web Site: www.amersports.com
Sporting Goods Distr
S.I.C.: 5091
N.A.I.C.S.: 423910

Amer Sports SA (1)
Bachtalen 33
6332 Cham, Switzerland
Tel.: (41) 41 784 26 26
Fax: (41) 800 26 26 26
E-Mail: info.schweiz@amersports.com

Amer Sports Corporation—(Continued)

Web Site: www.amersports.com
Emp.: 30
Sporting Goods Distr
S.I.C.: 5091
N.A.I.C.S.: 423910
Andi Balz *(Gen Mgr)*

Amer Sports Shanghai Trading Ltd. (1)
2/F Bldg 3 Youyou Century Plaza No 428 Yanggao South Road
Pudong New Area, Shanghai, 200127, China
Tel.: (86) 2151165288
Fax: (86) 2151165299
Emp.: 50
Sporting Goods Distr
S.I.C.: 5091
N.A.I.C.S.: 423910
Matt Gold *(Gen Mgr)*

Amer Sports Slovakia (1)
Hattalova 12/A
831 04 Bratislava, Slovakia
Tel.: (421) 2 4464 0011
Fax: (421) 2 4445 0923
E-Mail: customer.service.sk@amersports.com
Web Site: www.amersports.com
Emp.: 3
Sporting Goods Distr
S.I.C.: 5091
N.A.I.C.S.: 423910
Tomas Jezo *(Gen Mgr)*

Amer Sports Sourcing Ltd. (1)
Units 1102-5 11/F World Commerce Centre
11 Canton Road
Tsimshatsui, Kowloon, China (Hong Kong)
Tel.: (852) 21955100
Fax: (852) 28818010
Sporting Goods Distr
S.I.C.: 5091
N.A.I.C.S.: 423910

Amer Sports Sverige AB (1)
Asboholmsgatan 16
Box 966
501 10 Boras, Sweden
Tel.: (46) 0057575747
Fax: (46) 20 86 00 1
Sporting Goods Mfr & Whslr
S.I.C.: 3949
N.A.I.C.S.: 339920

Amer Sports UK & Ireland Ltd (1)
Theta Lyon Way
Frimley, GU16 7ER Camberley, United Kingdom
Tel.: (44) 1276 404 800
Fax: (44) 1294 316 255
Web Site: www.amersports.com
Emp.: 100
Sporting Goods Distr
S.I.C.: 5091
N.A.I.C.S.: 423910
Keith Wishart *(Mng Dir)*

Amer Sports UK Logistics Center (1)
1-5 Crompton Way North Newmoor Industrial Estate
Irvine, Ayrshire, KA11 4HU, United Kingdom
Tel.: (44) 1294 219 117
Fax: (44) 1294 219 130
E-Mail: customer.serviceuk@amersports.com
Web Site: www.amersports.com
Emp.: 50
Logistics Consulting Services
S.I.C.: 4731
N.A.I.C.S.: 541614
Alistair Carey *(Gen Mgr)*

Arc'teryx Equipment, Inc. (1)
100 - 2155 Dollarton Hwy
North Vancouver, BC, V7H 3B2, Canada
Tel.: (604) 960-3001
Fax: (604) 904-3692
Toll Free: (800) 985-6681
E-Mail: propurchase@arcteryx.com
Web Site: www.arcteryx.com
Emp.: 250
Outdoor Apparel & Gear Mfr
S.I.C.: 2389
N.A.I.C.S.: 315990
Jon Hoerauf *(VP & Sr Dir-Global Comml Sls)*

Atomic Austria GmbH (1)
Atomic strasse 1
5541 Altenmarkt, Austria (100%)
Tel.: (43) 645239000
Fax: (43) 64523900120
E-Mail: info.atomic@amersports.com
Web Site: www.atomicsnow.com
Sales Range: $200-249.9 Million
Emp.: 900
S.I.C.: 3949
N.A.I.C.S.: 339920
Wolfgang Mayrhofer *(Pres)*

Atomic Sports Canada (1)
2700 14th Avenue unit 1
Markham, ON, L3R 0J1, Canada (100%)
Tel.: (905) 470-9966
Fax: (905) 470-7315
Web Site: www.atomicsnow.com
Emp.: 15
S.I.C.: 3949
N.A.I.C.S.: 339920
Dave Deasley *(Pres)*

Grupo Wilson, S.A. de C.V. (1)
Av Sante Fe No 495 P-18 Cruz Manca
Cuajimalpa De Morelos
Mexico, 05349, Mexico
Tel.: (52) 5591779100
Fax: (52) 5591779101
Sporting Goods Retailer
S.I.C.: 5941
N.A.I.C.S.: 451110

Subsidiary:

Asesoria Deportiva Especializada, S.A. de C.V. (2)
Cruz Manca San Mateo Tlaltenango
Cuajimalpa De Morelos
Mexico, Mexico
Tel.: (52) 55 9177 9127
Sporting Goods Mfr & Whslr
S.I.C.: 3949
N.A.I.C.S.: 339920

Mavic S.A.S. (1)
Les Croiselets
74370 Metz-Tessy, France
Tel.: (33) 4 50 65 41 41
Fax: (33) 4 50 65 43 95
E-Mail: contact@mavic.fr
Web Site: www.mavic.com
Emp.: 300
Motor Vehicle Parts Mfr & Distr
S.I.C.: 3714
N.A.I.C.S.: 336390

U.S. Subsidiary:

Mavic, Inc. (2)
17 Parkridge Rd
Haverhill, MA 01835
Tel.: (978) 469-8400
Fax: (978) 373-1113
Web Site: www.amersports.com
Sporting Goods Distr
S.I.C.: 5091
N.A.I.C.S.: 423910
Steve Levesque *(CFO)*

Nikita Germany GmbH (1)
Schulterblatt 58
20357 Hamburg, Germany
Tel.: (49) 4053307030
Fax: (49) 4053307053
Emp.: 9
Clothing Accessories Distr
S.I.C.: 5137
N.A.I.C.S.: 424330

AMERICA MOVIL, S.A.B. DE C.V.

Lago Zurich 245 Plaza Carso Edificio Telcel Colonia Granada Ampliacion
Delegacion Miguel Hidalgo, 11529
Mexico, DF, Mexico
Tel.: (52) 55 2581 4449
Fax: (52) 55 2581 4422
E-Mail: daniela.lecuona@americamovil.com
Web Site: www.americamovil.com
Year Founded: 2000
AMX—(MEX NYSE)
Rev.: $60,982,479,669
Assets: $78,986,695,663
Liabilities: $54,413,092,360
Net Worth: $24,573,603,302
Earnings: $7,249,549,786
Emp.: 158,719
Fiscal Year-end: 12/31/12

Business Description:
Wireless Telecommunication Services
S.I.C.: 4812
N.A.I.C.S.: 517210

Personnel:
Carlos Slim Domit *(Co-Chm)*
Patrick Slim Domit *(Co-Chm)*
Daniel Hajj Aboumrad *(CEO)*
Carlos Garcia Moreno Elizondo *(CFO)*
Alejandro Cantu Jimenez *(Gen Counsel & Sec)*

Board of Directors:
Carlos Slim Domit
Patrick Slim Domit
Daniel Hajj Aboumrad
Pablo Roberto Gonzalez Guajardo
Carlos Bremer Gutierrez
Alejandro Soberon Kuri
David Ibarra Munoz
Santiago Cosio Pando
Ernesto Vega Velasco
Mike Viola
Rayford Wilkins, Jr.

Subsidiaries:

AMX USA Holding, S.A. de C.V. (1)
Lago Alberto No 366 Anahuac
Miguel Hidalgo, Mexico, 11320, Mexico
Tel.: (52) 5525813700
Investment Management Services
S.I.C.: 6799
N.A.I.C.S.: 523920

Carso Global Telecom, S.A. de C.V. (1)
Insurgentes Sur 3500
Colonia Pena Pobre, Mexico, DF, 14060, Mexico MX
Tel.: (52) 5552440802 (99.44%)
Fax: (52) 5552440808
Web Site: www.cgtelecom.com.mx
CGTVF—(OTC)
Sales Range: $15-24.9 Billion
Emp.: 76,400
Holding Company; Telecommunications
S.I.C.: 6719
N.A.I.C.S.: 551112
Jamie Chico Pardo *(Chm & CEO)*
Carlos Slim Domit *(Vice Chm)*
Rafael Robles Miaja *(Sec)*

Subsidiaries:

Empresas y Controles en Comunicaciones, S.A. de C.V. (2)
Insurgentes Sur No 3500 P B Penaa Pobre
Tlalpan, Mexico, 14060, Mexico
Tel.: (52) 5552440260
Telecommunication Services
S.I.C.: 4812
N.A.I.C.S.: 517210

Grupo Telvista, S.A. de C.V. (2)
Blvd Agua Caliente No 11606
Tijuana, 22014, Mexico (51.98%)
Tel.: (52) 664 622 6800
Fax: (52) 664 622 6801
Emp.: 3,000
Telemarketing Services
S.I.C.: 7389
N.A.I.C.S.: 561422

Sercotel, S.A. de C.V. (1)
Lago Alberto No 366 Colonia Anahuac
Mexico, 11320, Mexico
Tel.: (52) 55 2 581 4410
Fax: (52) 55 2 581 4440
Wireless Telecommunication Services
S.I.C.: 4812
N.A.I.C.S.: 517210

Non-U.S. Subsidiaries:

America Movil Peru, S.A.C. (2)
Avda Carlos Villaran 140 Piso 12
Santa Catalina La Victoria, Lima, Peru
Tel.: (51) 1 6131000
Fax: (51) 1 6131083
E-Mail: atencionalcliente@claro.com.pe
Web Site: www.claro.com.pe
Wireless Telecommunication Services
S.I.C.: 4812
N.A.I.C.S.: 517210

Claro Chile S.A. (2)
Avenida El Condor 820
Huechuraba, Santiago, Chile
Tel.: (56) 2 4445000
Fax: (56) 2 4445170
Web Site: www.clarochile.cl
Wireless Telecommunication Services
S.I.C.: 4812
N.A.I.C.S.: 517210
Mauricio Escobedo *(CEO)*

Claro Telecom Participacoes, S.A. (2)
Rua Mena Barreto 427
Rio de Janeiro, 22271-100, Brazil
Tel.: (55) 2125289090
Fax: (55) 2125289090
Mobile Telecommunication Services
S.I.C.: 4812
N.A.I.C.S.: 517210

Subsidiary:

Claro S.A. (3)
Rua Florida 1970
Sao Paulo, 04565-001, Brazil
Tel.: (55) 11 5509 6144
Fax: (55) 11 5509 6108
Web Site: www.claro.com.br
Mobile Communication System Distr
S.I.C.: 5065
N.A.I.C.S.: 423690

Comunicacion Celular S.A. (2)
Calle 90 No 14-37 Piso 6
Bogota, Colombia
Tel.: (57) 1 616 9797
Fax: (57) 1 616 9975
Web Site: www.comcel.com.co
Wireless Telecommunication Services
S.I.C.: 4812
N.A.I.C.S.: 517210

Consorcio Ecuatoriano de Telecomunicaciones, S.A. (2)
Av Francisco De Orellana Y Alberto Borges
Edificio Centrum
Guayaquil, Ecuador
Tel.: (593) 4 2693693
Fax: (593) 4 2693611
E-Mail: callcenter@claro.com.ec
Web Site: www.claro.com.ec
Wireless Telecommunication Services
S.I.C.: 4812
N.A.I.C.S.: 517210

Telmex Peru, S.A. (2)
Av Larco 1301 Torre Parque Mar
Miraflores, Lima, Peru
Tel.: (51) 1 6105555
Web Site: www.telmex.com
Wireless Telecommunication Services
S.I.C.: 4812
N.A.I.C.S.: 517210

Telefonos de Mexico S.A.B. de C.V. (1)
Parque Via 190
Colonia Cuauhtemoc, Mexico, 06599, Mexico MX
Tel.: (52) 55 5222 1774 (100%)
Fax: (52) 55 5545 5550
E-Mail: infori@telmex.com
Web Site: www.telmex.com.mx
Emp.: 51,077
Telecommunication Services
S.I.C.: 4812
N.A.I.C.S.: 517210
Carlos Slim Domit *(Chm)*
Juan Antonio Perez Simon *(Vice Chm)*
Hector Slim Seade *(CEO)*
Adolfo Cerezo Perez *(CFO)*
Patrick Slim Domit *(Chief Comml Officer & Dir-Sls)*
Sergio F. Medina Noriega *(Gen Counsel & Sec)*

Telmex Internacional, S.A.B. de C.V. (1)
Avenida de los Insurgentes 3500
Colonia Pena Pobre
Delegacion Tlalpan, Mexico, DF, 14060, Mexico MX
Tel.: (52) 55 5223 3200 (97.5%)
Web Site: www.telmexinternacional.com

Sales Range: $5-14.9 Billion
Emp.: 24,769
Holding Company; International Telecommunications Services
S.I.C.: 6719
N.A.I.C.S.: 551112
Carlos Slim Domit *(Chm)*
Oscar Von Hauske Solis *(CEO)*
Francisco J. Ortega Castaneda *(Chief Comml Officer)*
Eduardo A. Ramirez de Arellano *(Gen Counsel)*

Non-U.S. Subsidiaries:

Embratel Participacoes S.A. (2)
Rua Regente Feijo 166 Sala 1687-B
Centro, Rio de Janeiro, RJ, 20060-060, Brazil
Tel.: (55) 21 212 16474
Fax: (55) 21 216 388
Web Site: www.embratel.com.br
EBTP—(BRAZ)
Sales Range: $1-4.9 Billion
Emp.: 13,888
Telephone Communications
S.I.C.: 4813
N.A.I.C.S.: 517110
Carlos Henrique Moreira *(Chm & Pres)*
Jose Formoso Martinez *(Vice Chm & CEO)*

Affiliate:

Net Servicos de Comunicaco S.A. (3)
Rua Verbo Divino 1356
Sao Paulo, 04719-002, Brazil BR
Tel.: (55) 11 2111 2785 (41.3%)
Fax: (55) 11 21112780
Web Site: ir.netservicos.com.br
NETC4—(BRAZ)
Rev.: $3,905,211,120
Assets: $4,800,443,050
Liabilities: $2,546,828,848
Net Worth: $2,253,614,202
Earnings: $193,658,077
Emp.: 15,441
Fiscal Year-end: 12/31/12
Cable & Broadband Internet Services
S.I.C.: 4841
N.A.I.C.S.: 515210
Marcelo Parraga *(Head-Engrg & Infrastructure)*

Telmex Corp. S.A. (2)
Rinconada El Salto 202 Huechuraba
Santiago, Chile
Tel.: (56) 25820171
Fax: (56) 25825116
Web Site: www.clarochile.cl
Sales Range: $50-74.9 Million
Emp.: 758
Telecommunication Services
Export
S.I.C.: 4813
N.A.I.C.S.: 517110
Alejandro Rojas Pinaud *(Chm, Pres & CEO)*

U.S. Subsidiary:

Telecomunicaciones de Puerto Rico, Inc. (1)
1515 FD Roosevelt Ave
Guaynabo, PR 00968 PR
Mailing Address:
PO Box 360998
San Juan, PR 00936-0998
Tel.: (787) 555-1212
Fax: (787) 282-0958
Web Site: www.telefonicapr.com
Emp.: 4,900
Telephone Communications
S.I.C.: 4813
N.A.I.C.S.: 517110

Subsidiaries:

Coqui.net Corporation (2)
562 Avenida Ponce de Leon
Hato Rey, PR 00918
Tel.: (787) 707-1771
E-Mail: info@coqui.net
Web Site: www.coqui.net
Internet Services
S.I.C.: 4899
N.A.I.C.S.: 517919
Roberto A. Correa *(VP & Gen Mgr)*

PRT Larga Distancia, Inc. (2)
1515 FD Roosevelt Ave
Guaynabo, PR 00968
Mailing Address:
PO Box 360998
San Juan, PR 00936-0998
Tel.: (787) 749-2000
Long Distance Telephone Services
S.I.C.: 4813
N.A.I.C.S.: 517110
Enrique Ortiz de Montellano *(Pres)*

U.S. Affiliate:

TracFone Wireless, Inc. (1)
9700 NW 112 Ave
Miami, FL 33178-1504
Tel.: (305) 640-2000
Fax: (305) 640-2070
Web Site: www.tracfone.com
Sls.: $270,000,000
Emp.: 500
Prepaid Wireless Communication Services
S.I.C.: 4813
N.A.I.C.S.: 517911
F. J. Pollak *(Pres & CEO)*
Derek Hewitt *(Sr VP-Mktg)*

Non-U.S. Subsidiaries:

AM Wireless Uruguay, S.A. (1)
Av San Martin 2460
Montevideo, 11800, Uruguay
Tel.: (598) 22 01 15 00
Fax: (598) 22 01 15 00
Web Site: www.claro.com.uy
Telecommunication Services
S.I.C.: 4899
N.A.I.C.S.: 517919
Horacio Alvarellos *(Mng Dir)*

AMX Paraguay, S.A. (1)
Avenida Mariscal Lopez 1730
Asuncion, Paraguay
Tel.: (595) 21 2499000
Fax: (595) 21 2499099
Web Site: www.claro.com.py
Wireless Telecommunication Services
S.I.C.: 4812
N.A.I.C.S.: 517210

Claro Panama, S.A. (1)
Punta Pacifica Edificio Metrobank Piso 1 Y 7
Panama, Panama
Tel.: (507) 2169701
Fax: (507) 2152004
Web Site: www.claro.com.pa
Wireless Telecommunication Services
S.I.C.: 4812
N.A.I.C.S.: 517210
Oscar Augusto Borda *(Mng Dir)*

Compania de Telecomunicaciones de El Salvador (CTE), S.A. de C.V. (1)
Colonia Y Complejo Roma
San Salvador, El Salvador
Tel.: (503) 2 2717010
Fax: (503) 2 22214849
E-Mail: clientes@claro.com.sv
Web Site: www.claro.com.sv
Emp.: 2,300
Telecommunication Services
S.I.C.: 4899
N.A.I.C.S.: 517919
Antonio Aguilar *(Gen Mgr)*

Subsidiary:

Telecomoda, S.A. de C.V. (2)
Km 10 1/2 Carretera A
Santa Tecla, El Salvador
Tel.: (503) 22717020
Fax: (503) 22717530
Telecommunication Consulting Services
S.I.C.: 8748
N.A.I.C.S.: 541618
Enrique Luna *(Mgr-Fin)*

Non-U.S. Subsidiary:

Cablenet, S.A. (2)
Ave Jean Paul Genie 500 Mts Abajo
Managua, Nicaragua
Tel.: (505) 22557300
Television Broadcasting Services
S.I.C.: 4833
N.A.I.C.S.: 515120

Smart Systems Ltda. (1)
Napoleon 3565 Oficina 412 Las Condes
Santiago, Chile
Tel.: (56) 22037330
Fax: (56) 22030267
E-Mail: gerencia@smart.cl
Web Site: www.smartcom.cl/empresa.php
Wireless Communication Services
S.I.C.: 4812
N.A.I.C.S.: 517210

Telmex Colombia, S.A. (1)
Carrera 7 No 71-52 Torre B Piso 18
Bogota, Colombia
Tel.: (57) 1 606 9606
Fax: (57) 1 312 3148
Web Site: www.telmex.com.co
Telecommunication Services
S.I.C.: 4899
N.A.I.C.S.: 517919

Non-U.S. Holding:

CTI Compania de Telefonos del Interior S.A. (1)
Avda. Presidente Figueroa Alcorta, 3259
Buenos Aires, Argentina
Tel.: (54) 1141098888
Fax: (54) 1148098959
Web Site: www.cti.com.ar
Emp.: 1,300
Telecommunications
S.I.C.: 4813
N.A.I.C.S.: 517110

AMERICAN BONANZA GOLD CORP.

Suite 302 -1620 West 8th Ave
Vancouver, BC, V6J 1V4, Canada
Tel.: (604) 688-7515
Fax: (604) 681-0122
E-Mail: info@americanbonanza.com
Web Site: www.americanbonanza.com
BZA—(OTC TSX)
Assets: $63,236,064
Liabilities: $23,557,739
Net Worth: $39,678,325
Earnings: ($19,026,928)
Emp.: 13
Fiscal Year-end: 12/31/13

Business Description:
Gold Exploration Services
S.I.C.: 1041
N.A.I.C.S.: 212221

Personnel:
Brian P. Kirwin *(Pres & CEO)*
Joe Chan *(CFO & VP)*
Catherine Tanaka *(Sec)*

Board of Directors:
James Bagwell
Giulio T. Bonifacio
Brian P. Kirwin
Robert T. McKnight
Ronald Kort Netolitzky
Jamie Newall

Legal Counsel:
Woodburn and Wedge
Reno, NV 89511-1159

Lang Michener
Vancouver, BC, Canada

Transfer Agent:
Computershare Trust Company of Canada
Vancouver, BC, Canada
Tel.: (604) 661-9400
Fax: (604) 669-1548

U.S. Subsidiary:

Bonanza Explorations Inc. (1)
290 Gentry Way
Reno, NV 89502-4230
Tel.: (775) 824-0707
Fax: (775) 824-0898
E-Mail: info@americanbonanza.com
Emp.: 7
Gold Exploration & Mining Services
S.I.C.: 1041
N.A.I.C.S.: 212221
Brian Kirwin *(Pres & CEO)*

AMERICAN CONSOLIDATED MINERALS CORP.

Suite 750 580 Hornby Street
PO Box 113
Vancouver, BC, V6C 3B6, Canada
Tel.: (604) 602-4935
Fax: (604) 602-4936
Toll Free: (866) 602-4935
E-Mail: info@americanconsolidatedminerals.com
Web Site: www.americanconsolidatedminerals.com
Year Founded: 2006
AJC—(TSXV)
Rev.: $101,514
Assets: $3,324,566
Liabilities: $428,399
Net Worth: $2,896,168
Earnings: ($1,063,448)
Emp.: 28
Fiscal Year-end: 09/30/12

Business Description:
Metals & Minerals Mining Services
S.I.C.: 1099
N.A.I.C.S.: 212299

Personnel:
Al Fabbro *(Pres & CEO)*
Gary Arca *(CFO & Sec)*

Board of Directors:
Gary Arca
Herb Duerr
Robert Eadie
Al Fabbro
David Gunning
Richard Kern
Ken Sumanik

Legal Counsel:
Maitland & Company Barristers & Solicitors
700 - 625 Howe Street
Vancouver, BC, Canada

Transfer Agent:
Computershare Investor Services
3rd Floor, 510 Burrard Street
Vancouver, BC, Canada

AMERICAN CREEK RESOURCES LTD.

53A Broadway North
Box 798
Raymond, AB, T0K 2S0, Canada
Tel.: (403) 752-4040
Fax: (403) 752-4020
E-Mail: info@americancreek.com
Web Site: www.americancreek.com
Year Founded: 2005
AMK—(OTC TSXV)
Assets: $14,326,838
Liabilities: $286,496
Net Worth: $14,040,342
Earnings: ($3,477,669)
Fiscal Year-end: 12/31/12

Business Description:
Gold, Silver & Other Metals Mining Services
S.I.C.: 1041
N.A.I.C.S.: 212221

Personnel:
Allan G. Burton *(Pres & CEO)*
Robert N. Edwards *(CFO)*
Darren R. Blaney *(COO)*

Board of Directors:
Darren R. Blaney
Allan G. Burton
Kirk Harline
Darcy Heggie

Legal Counsel:
Miller Thompson LLP
700 - 9th Avenue SW Suite 3000
Calgary, AB, Canada

Dorsey & Whitney LLP
Republic Plaza Building Suite 4700 370 17th Street
Denver, CO 80202-5647

Transfer Agent:
Olympia Trust
2300 125 9 Avenue S E
Calgary, AB, Canada

AMERICAN CUMO MINING CORPORATION

(Formerly Mosquito Consolidated Gold Mines Limited)
(d/b/a CuMoCo)
638 Millbank Road
Vancouver, BC, V5Z 4B7, Canada
Tel.: (604) 689-7902
Fax: (604) 689-7816
Toll Free: (800) 667-0873
E-Mail: info@cumoco.com
Web Site: www.cumoco.com
MLY—(OTC TSXV)
Assets: $21,945,336
Liabilities: $3,879,087
Net Worth: $18,066,250
Earnings: ($12,158,373)
Fiscal Year-end: 06/30/13

Business Description:
Metal Mining Services
S.I.C.: 1099
N.A.I.C.S.: 212299

Personnel:
Hongxue Fu *(Chm)*
Aurora G. Davidson *(CFO)*
Shaun M. Dykes *(COO)*
Brett A. Kagetsu *(Sec)*
Charles Yuen *(Exec VP)*

Board of Directors:
Hongxue Fu
Joseph Baird
Shaun M. Dykes
John Moeller
Yiming Xie
Charles Yuen

Transfer Agent:
Computershare Investor Services Inc
100 University Avenue 9th Floor
Toronto, ON, Canada

AMERICAN HOTEL INCOME PROPERTIES REIT LP

1690 401 West Georgia Street
Vancouver, BC, V6B 5A1, Canada
Tel.: (604) 684-0444
E-Mail: roneill@oneillhotels.com
Year Founded: 2012
HOT.UN—(OTC TSX)

Business Description:
Real Estate Investment Trust
S.I.C.: 6211
N.A.I.C.S.: 525990

Personnel:
Peter Robert Beverley Armstrong *(Chm)*
Robert Francis O'Neill *(CEO)*
Robert Hibberd *(CFO & Sec)*

Board of Directors:
Peter Robert Beverley Armstrong
Stephen J. Evans
Kevin Grayston
Tamara L. Lawson
W. Michael Murphy
Robert Francis O'Neill
Robert Pratt

Transfer Agent:
Computershare Investor Services Inc.
510 Burrard Street 2nd Floor
Vancouver, BC, V6C 3B9, Canada

AMERICAN LORAIN CORPORATION

Beihuan Road
Junan, Shandong, China 276600
Tel.: (86) 5397318818
Year Founded: 1986
ALN—(NYSEMKT)
Rev.: $239,673,463
Assets: $250,365,233
Liabilities: $69,662,883
Net Worth: $180,702,350
Earnings: $21,743,769
Emp.: 2,005
Fiscal Year-end: 12/31/12

Business Description:
Convenience Foods, Chestnut Products, Frozen, Canned, & Bulk Food Developer, Mfr & Sales
S.I.C.: 2099
N.A.I.C.S.: 311999

Personnel:
Si Chen *(Chm, Pres & CEO)*
David She *(CFO)*
Yundong Lu *(COO)*
Yinglee Tseng *(Corp Sec & Dir-Bus Dev)*

Board of Directors:
Si Chen
Yundong Lu
Maoquan Wei
William Jianxiao Wu
Dekai Yin

AMERICAN MANGANESE INC.

2A 15782 Marine Drive
White Rock, BC, V4B 1E6, Canada
Tel.: (604) 531-9639
Fax: (604) 531-9634
E-Mail: info@amymn.com
Web Site: www.americanmanganesei nc.com
Year Founded: 1987
AMY—(TSXV)
Rev.: $2,139
Assets: $9,839,961
Liabilities: $702,480
Net Worth: $9,137,481
Earnings: ($2,862,142)
Fiscal Year-end: 07/31/13

Business Description:
Metal Exploration Services
S.I.C.: 1081
N.A.I.C.S.: 213114

Personnel:
Larry W. Reaugh *(Pres & CEO)*
Shaheem Ali *(CFO)*
Michael MacLeod *(COO)*
Teresa Piorun *(Sec)*

Board of Directors:
Jan Eigenhuis
Paul Hildebrand
Andris Kikauka
Michael MacLeod
Larry W. Reaugh
Edward Skoda

Legal Counsel:
Fraser & Company
1200 999 West Hastings Street
Vancouver, BC, Canada

Transfer Agent:
Computershare Investor Services Inc.
3rd Floor 510 Burrard St
V6C 3B9 Vancouver, BC, Canada

U.S. Subsidiary:

Rocher Manganese Inc. **(1)**
2613 Empire Ranch Rd
Carson City, NV 89701
Tel.: (775) 841-7120
Mineral Mining Services
S.I.C.: 1481
N.A.I.C.S.: 213115

AMERICAN NANO SILICON TECHNOLOGIES, INC.

Nanchong Shili Industrial Street
Economic & Technology Development
Xiaolong Chunfei Industrial Park,
Nanchong, Sichuan, China 637005
Tel.: (86) 817 363 4888
Year Founded: 1993
ANNO—(OTC)
Rev.: $798,390
Assets: $25,127,319
Liabilities: $17,007,341
Net Worth: $8,119,978
Earnings: ($7,172,094)
Emp.: 122
Fiscal Year-end: 09/30/13

Business Description:
Chemical Mfr
S.I.C.: 2819
N.A.I.C.S.: 325180

Personnel:
Fachun Pu *(Chm, Pres, CEO & CFO)*

Board of Directors:
Fachun Pu
Robert J. Fanella
Ping He
Dechun Liu
Shuming Lu
Changlong Zhang
Qiwei Zhang

AMERICAN OIL & GAS, INC.

Suite 400-601 West Broadway
Vancouver, BC, V5Z 4C2, Canada
Toll Free: (888) 609-1173
E-Mail: americanoilngas@gmail.com
Year Founded: 2012
AOIX—(OTC OTCB)
Rev.: $2,951
Assets: $45,551
Liabilities: $4,800
Net Worth: $40,751
Earnings: ($18,684)
Fiscal Year-end: 01/31/13

Business Description:
Oil & Gas Exploration
S.I.C.: 1311
N.A.I.C.S.: 211111

Personnel:
Robert Gelfand *(Pres, CEO, CFO, Treas & Sec)*

AMERICAN ORIENTAL BIOENGINEERING, INC.

1 Liangshuihe First Ave
Beijing E-Town Economic & Technology Development Area E-Town, Beijing, 100176, China
Tel.: (86) 10 5982 2039
E-Mail: aobosz@bioaobo.com
Web Site: www.bioaobo.com
Year Founded: 1970
AOBI—(OTC)
Rev.: $145,099,627
Assets: $446,308,924
Liabilities: $118,722,218
Net Worth: $327,586,706
Earnings: ($59,725,397)
Emp.: 3,719
Fiscal Year-end: 12/31/12

Business Description:
Nutraceutical & Pharmaceutical Products Developer & Distr
S.I.C.: 2834
N.A.I.C.S.: 325412

Personnel:
Tony Shujun Liu *(Chm & CEO)*
Yanchun Li *(CFO & Sec)*
Xiaopeng Xu *(COO)*
Yan Gao *(Chief Acctg Officer)*

Board of Directors:
Tony Shujun Liu
Yanchun Li
Jun Min
Cosimo J. Patti
Xianmin Wang
Baiqing Zhang

Subsidiary:

Guangxi Boke Pharmaceutical Co., Ltd. **(1)**
No 56 Keyuan Ave
Gaoxin Dist Xixiangtang, Nanning, Guangxi, 530003, China
Tel.: (86) 7713219100
Pharmaceutical Products Mfr & Distr
S.I.C.: 2834
N.A.I.C.S.: 325412

AMERICAN OVERSEAS GROUP LIMITED

Maiden House 1st Floor 131 Front Street
Hamilton, HM 12, Bermuda
Mailing Address:
PO Box HM3302
Hamilton, HM PX, Bermuda
Tel.: (441) 2966501
Fax: (441) 2966509
E-Mail: info@aoreltd.com
Web Site: www.aoreltd.com
Year Founded: 1998
AORE—(OTC)
Premiums: $21,508,357
Assets: $297,396,545
Liabilities: $220,397,405
Net Worth: $76,999,140
Earnings: ($22,901,107)
Emp.: 15
Fiscal Year-end: 12/31/12

Business Description:
Holding Company; Reinsurance Services
S.I.C.: 6399
N.A.I.C.S.: 524130

Personnel:
Steven J. Tynan *(Chm)*
David K. Steel *(Pres & CEO)*
Rochelle P. Fyfe *(CFO)*

Board of Directors:
Steven J. Tynan
Clement Story Dwyer, Jr.
Rochelle P. Fyfe
Debra J. Roberts
David K. Steel
James Lando Zech

Transfer Agent:
BNY Mellon Shareholder Services
480 Washington Blvd
Jersey City, NJ 07310

Subsidiary:

RAM Reinsurance Company Ltd. **(1)**
RAM Re House
Penthouse Suite
46 Reid Street, Hamilton, Bermuda
Tel.: (441) 2966501
Web Site: www.ramre.com
Insurance Services
S.I.C.: 6399
N.A.I.C.S.: 524130
David K. Steel *(Pres & CEO)*

AMERICAN PARAMOUNT GOLD CORP.

141 Adelaide St West Suite 240
Toronto, ON, M5H 3L5, Canada
Tel.: (416) 214-0049
E-Mail: info@americanparamountgo ld.com
Web Site: www.americanparamou ntgold.com
APGAD—(OTC)

Business Description:
Gold Mining Services
S.I.C.: 1041
N.A.I.C.S.: 212221

Personnel:
Wayne Parsons *(CFO)*

Transfer Agent:
Nevada Agency & Transfer Company
50 W Liberty Street Suite 880
Reno, NV 89501

AMERICAN RARE EARTHS & MATERIALS, CORP.

200 Queens Quay East Unit #1
Toronto, ON, M5A 4K9, Canada
Tel.: (416) 362-2121
Fax: (416) 362-2100
Web Site: www.americanrare.com
Year Founded: 2002
AREM—(OTC)
Sales Range: $1-9.9 Million
Emp.: 5

Business Description:
Metal Mining Services
S.I.C.: 1099
N.A.I.C.S.: 212299
Personnel:
Nataliya Hearn *(Chm, Pres & CEO)*
Board of Directors:
Nataliya Hearn
J. Errol Farr

Subsidiary:

Element 21 Golf Canada Inc (1)
200 Queens Quay E Unit 1
Toronto, ON, M5A 4K9, Canada
Tel.: (416) 362-2121
Fax: (416) 362-2100
Scandium Mining Services
S.I.C.: 1479
N.A.I.C.S.: 212393

AMERICAN SAFETY INSURANCE HOLDINGS, LTD.
(Acquired by FAIRFAX FINANCIAL HOLDINGS LIMITED)

AMERICAN SMOOTH WAVE VENTURES, INC.
Jiangtou Industrial Zone Chendai
Jinjiang, Fudian, China
Tel.: (86) 595 851 96329
Year Founded: 2008
ASWV—(OTC)
Business Description:
Candy, Sweets, Food & Bakery Products
S.I.C.: 2064
N.A.I.C.S.: 311340
Personnel:
Baofu Ding *(Chm & CEO)*
Wing Sang Lo *(CFO)*
Baojian Ding *(COO)*
Board of Directors:
Baofu Ding
Baojian Ding
Changming Ding

AMERICAN VANADIUM CORP.
Suite 910 800 W Pender St
Vancouver, BC, V6C 2V6, Canada
Tel.: (604) 681-8588
Fax: (604) 685-9466
E-Mail: info@americanvanadium.com
Web Site: www.americanvanadium.com
Year Founded: 2006
AVC—(OTC TSXV)
Int. Income: $9,641
Assets: $5,832,927
Liabilities: $1,263,592
Net Worth: $4,569,335
Earnings: ($6,016,799)
Emp.: 1
Fiscal Year-end: 12/31/12
Business Description:
Mineral Mining & Exploration Services
S.I.C.: 1499
N.A.I.C.S.: 212399
Personnel:
Ronald J. MacDonald *(Chm)*
William J. Radvak *(Pres & CEO)*
John Downes *(CFO)*
Sandra Lee *(Sec)*
Michael Doyle *(Exec VP-Ops)*
Board of Directors:
Ronald J. MacDonald
Brian Eric Bayley
Alan Branham
George T. Hawes
E. Kelly Hyslop
William J. Radvak
Legal Counsel:
Davis LLP
2800 Park Place 666 Burrard Street
Vancouver, BC, Canada
Transfer Agent:
Computershare Trust Company of Canada
510 Burrard St 2nd Fl
Vancouver, BC, Canada

AMERICAN VIETNAMESE BIOTECH INCORPORATION
No 1251 Highway 14 Tien Thanh Commune
Dong Xoai District, Ho Chi Minh City, Binh Phuoc, Vietnam
Tel.: (84) 8 32908914
E-Mail: amvibiotechinc@gmail.com
Web Site: www.amvibiotech.com
AMV—(HNX)
Business Description:
Diagnostic Test Kit Mfr
S.I.C.: 2835
N.A.I.C.S.: 325413
Personnel:
Thi Phuong Dung Ha *(Supvr-Factory)*
Board of Directors:
Bach Mong Ha
Viet Tan Pham
Huynh Van Giau

AMERICAS DIAMOND CORP.
(Formerly IMPACT EXPLORATIONS INC.)
2nd Floor Berkeley Square House
Berkeley Square, London, W1H 1DP, United Kingdom
Tel.: (44) 207 887 6189
Web Site: www.americasdiamondcorp.com
Year Founded: 2010
ADMC—(OTC OTCB)
Assets: $2,727,808
Liabilities: $2,809,429
Net Worth: ($81,621)
Earnings: ($99,642)
Fiscal Year-end: 01/31/13
Business Description:
Metal Mining
S.I.C.: 1099
N.A.I.C.S.: 212299
Personnel:
Daniel Martinez *(Pres & CEO)*
Thomas L. Crom, III *(CFO, Treas & Sec)*
Board of Directors:
Thomas L. Crom, III
Daniel Martinez
Transfer Agent:
Empire Stock Transfer
1859 Whitney Mesa Dr
Henderson, NV 89014

AMERICAS PETROGAS INC.
3911 Trasimene Cres SW
Calgary, AB, T3E 7J6, Canada
Tel.: (403) 685-1888
Fax: (403) 685-1880
E-Mail: info@americaspetrogas.com
Web Site: americaspetrogas.com
BOE—(OTC TSXV)
Rev.: $53,473,722
Assets: $198,523,289
Liabilities: $20,735,140
Net Worth: $177,788,149
Earnings: ($12,513,184)
Fiscal Year-end: 12/31/12
Business Description:
Oil & Gas Exploration Services
S.I.C.: 1389
N.A.I.C.S.: 213112
Personnel:
Carlos Lau *(Chm)*
Barclay W. Hambrook *(Pres & CEO)*
Douglas Yee *(CFO)*
Board of Directors:
Carlos Lau
Barclay W. Hambrook
Ron Ho
Rakesh Kapur
Ross C. McCutcheon
Easton Wren

Subsidiary:

GrowMax Agri Corp. (1)
3911 Trasimene Cres SW
Calgary, AB, T3E 7J6, Canada
Tel.: (403) 685-1888
E-Mail:
Web Site: www.growmaxagricorp.com
Emp.: 1
Potash Fertilizer Mfr
S.I.C.: 1479
N.A.I.C.S.: 212393
Barclay W. Hambrook *(Co-Chm & CEO)*
Carlos Lau *(Co-Chm)*
Douglas Yee *(CFO)*

Non-U.S. Subsidiaries:

Americas Petrogas Argentina S.A. (1)
Tucuman 1 - Piso 8 B Edificio
Buenos Aires, 1049, Argentina
Tel.: (54) 11 4331 2326
Fax: (54) 11 4331 4754
E-Mail: infoba@americaspetrogas.com
Web Site: www.americaspetrogas.com
Emp.: 4
Oil & Gas Exploration Services
S.I.C.: 1389
N.A.I.C.S.: 213112
Graham Bevington *(Gen Mgr)*

Americas Potash Peru S.A. (1)
Av Carlos Villaran N 860
La Victoria, Lima, Peru
Tel.: (51) 73322742
Potash Mining Services
S.I.C.: 1474
N.A.I.C.S.: 212391

AMERIGO RESOURCES LTD.
Commerce Place Suite 1950 400 Burrard Street
Vancouver, BC, V6C 3A6, Canada
Tel.: (604) 681-2802
Fax: (604) 682-2802
E-Mail: questions@amerigoresources.com
Web Site: www.amerigoresources.com
ARG—(TSX)
Rev.: $181,760,724
Assets: $204,416,319
Liabilities: $72,217,963
Net Worth: $132,198,356
Earnings: ($8,192,396)
Emp.: 198
Fiscal Year-end: 12/31/12
Business Description:
Copper Mining Services
S.I.C.: 1021
N.A.I.C.S.: 212234
Personnel:
Klaus M. Zeitler *(Chm & CEO)*
Robert Duncan Henderson *(Pres & COO)*
Aurora G. Davidson *(CFO)*
Michael Kuta *(Gen Counsel & Sec)*
Board of Directors:
Klaus M. Zeitler
Geoff Castle
Robert J. Gayton
Ruston E. Goepel
Miguel Grau
George Ireland
Sidney P. H. Robinson
Alberto Salas
Transfer Agent:
Computershare Trust Company of Canada
510 Burrard St 2nd Fl
Vancouver, BC, Canada

Non-U.S. Subsidiary:

Minera Valle Central S.A (1)
Colihues Km 13
Rancagua, Chile
Tel.: (56) 72330100
Fax: (56) 72330140
E-Mail: info@mineravallecentral.cl
Web Site: www.mineravallecentral.cl
Emp.: 167
Copper Materials Mfr
S.I.C.: 3351
N.A.I.C.S.: 331420
Raul Poblete *(Gen Mgr)*

AMERISUR RESOURCES PLC
Lakeside Fountain Lane
St Mellons, Cardiff, CF3 0FB, United Kingdom
Tel.: (44) 2920500880
Fax: (44) 2920500701
E-Mail: info@amerisurresources.com
Web Site: www.amerisurresources.com
AMER—(LSE)
Rev.: $42,190,000
Assets: $152,922,000
Liabilities: $27,542,000
Net Worth: $125,380,000
Earnings: $12,792,000
Emp.: 47
Fiscal Year-end: 12/31/12
Business Description:
Gold Mining
S.I.C.: 1041
N.A.I.C.S.: 212221
Personnel:
Giles Clarke *(Chm)*
John Wardle *(CEO)*
Brian James *(Sec)*
Board of Directors:
Giles Clarke
Douglas Ellenor
Nick Harrison
Nigel Luson
Victor M. Valdovinos
John Wardle
George Woodcock
Legal Counsel:
Sanclemente & Fernandez AbogadosS.A
Carrera 9 No. 69-70
Bogota, Colombia

Osborne Clarke
2 Temple Back East Temple Quay
Bristol, United Kingdom

AMERIX PRECIOUS METALS CORPORATION
40 University Avenue Suite 606
Toronto, ON, M5J 1T1, Canada
Tel.: (647) 260-0470
Fax: (416) 479-4371
E-Mail: info@amerixcorp.com
Web Site: www.amerixcorp.com
APM—(TSXV)
Int. Income: $2,725
Assets: $404,123
Liabilities: $255,857
Net Worth: $148,266
Earnings: ($2,162,614)
Fiscal Year-end: 07/31/13
Business Description:
Mineral Exploration Services
S.I.C.: 1081
N.A.I.C.S.: 213114
Personnel:
Jeffrey Reeder *(Chm)*
Steve Brunelle *(Pres & CEO)*
Dan Hamilton *(CFO)*
Board of Directors:
Jeffrey Reeder
Luciano Borges
Steve Brunelle
Robert Crombie
Dan Noone
William Whitehead

AMEROPA AG
Rebgasse 108
CH 4102 Binningen, Switzerland

Ameropa AG—(Continued)

Tel.: (41) 613075011
Fax: (41) 613029863
E-Mail: info@ameropa.com
Web Site: www.ameropa.com
Emp.: 4,875
Business Description:
Grain & Fertilizer Trading
S.I.C.: 9641
N.A.I.C.S.: 926140
Personnel:
Andreas Zivy *(CEO)*

U.S. Subsidiary:

Ameropa North America, Inc. (1)
2502 N Rocky Point Dr
Tampa, FL 33607 FL
Tel.: (813) 282-8228
Emp.: 16
Grain & Fertilizer Trading
S.I.C.: 9641
N.A.I.C.S.: 926140
Nicholas Adamchak *(Mng Dir)*

Non-U.S. Subsidiaries:

Azomures S.A. (1)
300 Gheorghe Doja St
540237 Tirgu Mures, Romania
Tel.: (40) 265 253700
Fax: (40) 265 252627
E-Mail: office@azomures.com
Web Site: www.azomures.com
Sales Range: $550-599.9 Million
Emp.: 2,688
Fertilizer Mfr
S.I.C.: 2873
N.A.I.C.S.: 325311
Andrew Henry Zivy *(Pres)*

Subsidiary:

Chimpex S.A. (2)
54 Incinta Port Dana
900900 Constanta, Romania
Tel.: (40) 241603536
Fax: (40) 241603030
E-Mail: office@chimpex.ro
Web Site: www.chimpex.ro
CHEM—(BUC)
Sales Range: $10-24.9 Million
Cargo Handling Services
S.I.C.: 4491
N.A.I.C.S.: 488320
Suat Surmen *(Pres)*
Liana Constantin *(CFO)*

Impact Fertilisers Pty Ltd (1)
Suite 12 600 Lonsdale St
Melbourne, VIC, 3000, Australia
Tel.: (61) 3 8622 9920
Fax: (61) 3 8622 9939
Fertilizer Mfr
S.I.C.: 2874
N.A.I.C.S.: 325312

AMEROPA GRAINS SA

Theodor Burada Street 25
Constanta, Romania
Tel.: (40) 241625539
Fax: (40) 241638296
E-Mail: office@ameropa.ro
Web Site: www.ameropa.ro
CCRL—(BUC)
Sales Range: $75-99.9 Million
Emp.: 237
Business Description:
Grain Farming
S.I.C.: 0119
N.A.I.C.S.: 111199
Personnel:
Andrew H. Zivy *(Pres)*

AMEX EXPLORATION INC.

1155 University Street Suite 812
Montreal, QC, H3B 3A7, Canada
Tel.: (514) 866-8209
Fax: (514) 866-8096
E-Mail: info@amexexploration.com
Web Site: www.amexexploration.com
Year Founded: 1986
AMX—(TSXV)
Assets: $8,202,901
Liabilities: $1,021,605
Net Worth: $7,181,296
Earnings: ($676,791)
Fiscal Year-end: 12/31/12
Business Description:
Gold Exploration Services
S.I.C.: 1041
N.A.I.C.S.: 212221
Personnel:
Jacques Trottier *(Pres & CEO)*
Martin Nicoletti *(CFO)*
Pierre Carrier *(Sec & Mgr-Ops)*
Board of Directors:
Pierre Carrier
James Hayward Coleman
Andre Gagne
Andre Shareck
Jacques Trottier
Transfer Agent:
Computershare Investor Services Inc.
1500 University Street Suite 700
Montreal, QC, H3A 3SB, Canada

AMEX RESOURCES LIMITED

97 Outram Street
West Perth, WA, 6005, Australia
Mailing Address:
PO Box 1395
West Perth, WA, 6872, Australia
Tel.: (61) 894800455
Fax: (61) 893210320
E-Mail: info@amex.net.au
Web Site: www.amex.net.au
AXZ—(ASX)
Rev.: $260,029
Assets: $18,657,028
Liabilities: $266,725
Net Worth: $18,390,302
Earnings: ($3,620,044)
Fiscal Year-end: 06/30/13
Business Description:
Gold, Nickel & Iron Mining Services
S.I.C.: 1041
N.A.I.C.S.: 212221
Personnel:
Matthew John Collard *(Mng Dir)*
J. Gary Dunlop *(Sec)*
Board of Directors:
Xiao Qin
Matthew John Collard
Yibo Qiu
Alan Senior
Legal Counsel:
Margaret McGuinn
3 Agnew Way
6008 Subiaco, WA, Australia

AMEYA LABORATORIES LTD.

(Formerly Anu's Laboratories Limited)
A-49 Madhura Nagar Vengalarao Nagar
Hyderabad, Andhra Pradesh, 500 038, India
Tel.: (91) 40 2374 1677
Fax: (91) 40 2374 1678
E-Mail: anulabs@anulabs.com
Web Site: www.anulabs.com
532981—(BOM)
Sales Range: $50-74.9 Million
Emp.: 358
Business Description:
Chemical Mfr
S.I.C.: 2899
N.A.I.C.S.: 325998
Personnel:
Haribabu Kosaraju *(Mng Dir)*
N. Nagendra Naidu *(Compliance Officer)*
Board of Directors:
Haribabu Kosaraju
Madhava Rao
M. S. S. V. Satyanarayana
Transfer Agent:
Karvy Computershare Private Limited
Plot No 17 to 24 Vittalrao Nagar Madhapur
Hyderabad, India

AMF GROUP JSC

112 Nekrasov Street
030006 Aktobe, Kazakhstan
Tel.: (7) 7132210025
Fax: (7) 7132214274
E-Mail: info@amf.kz
Web Site: www.amf.kz
AKFI—(KAZ)
Sales Range: $25-49.9 Million
Emp.: 200
Business Description:
Electric & Gas Distr
S.I.C.: 4911
N.A.I.C.S.: 221122
Personnel:
Askarbek A. Mamyrbaev *(Chm)*
Berdibekv Baysirinov *(Pres)*

AMFORGE INDUSTRIES LTD.

108 Raheja Chambers Free Press Journal Marg Nariman Point
Mumbai, Maharashtra, 400021, India
Tel.: (91) 2222821486
Fax: (91) 2266365964
Web Site: www.amforgeindia.com
513117—(BOM)
Rev.: $519,392
Assets: $6,132,763
Liabilities: $2,234,283
Net Worth: $3,898,480
Earnings: ($195,154)
Fiscal Year-end: 03/31/13
Business Description:
Steel Forging Mfr
S.I.C.: 3462
N.A.I.C.S.: 332111
Personnel:
Puneet Makar *(Chm, Mng Dir & Compliance Officer)*
Rajkumar R. Tiwari *(Sec)*
Board of Directors:
Puneet Makar
Sunil K. Aggarwal
Rakesh Khanna
Yogiraj Makar
Fali P. Mama
Sharat Devindra Nath
Legal Counsel:
Mulla & Mulla, Craigie Blunt & Caroe
Mulla House 51 M.G. Road
Mumbai, India
Transfer Agent:
Sharex Dynamic (India) Pvt. Ltd.
Unit-1 Luthra Ind Premises Safed Pool Andheri Kurla Rd Andheri (E)
Mumbai, India

AMG ADVANCED METALLURGICAL GROUP N.V.

WTC Amsterdam Toren C 13th Floor
Strawinskylaan 1343, 1077 XX
Amsterdam, Netherlands
Tel.: (31) 207147140
Fax: (31) 207147163
E-Mail: info@amg-nv.com
Web Site: www.amg-nv.com
AMG—(EUR)
Rev.: $1,215,602,000
Assets: $947,921,000
Liabilities: $730,376,000
Net Worth: $217,545,000
Earnings: $70,000
Emp.: 3,275
Fiscal Year-end: 12/31/12
Business Description:
Metal Processing & Engineering Services
S.I.C.: 1099
N.A.I.C.S.: 212299
Personnel:
Pedro Pablo Kuczynski *(Chm-Supervisory Bd)*
Heinz C. Schimmelbusch *(Chm-Mgmt Bd & CEO)*
Jack L. Messman *(Vice Chm-Supervisory Bd)*
Amy E. Ard *(CFO & Member-Mgmt Bd)*
Eric E. Jackson *(Pres-Advanced Matls & COO)*
Hoy E. Frakes, Jr. *(Pres-Mining)*
Supervisory Board of Directors:
Pedro Pablo Kuczynski
Guy de Selliers
Steve H. Hanke
Martin Hoyos
Jack L. Messman
Norbert Quinkert
Ute Wolf

Corporate Headquarters:

AMG Advanced Metallurgical Group N.V. (1)
435 Devon Park Dr Bldg 200
Wayne, PA 19087 NL
Tel.: (610) 293-2501
Fax: (610) 293-2510
E-Mail: info@amg-nv.com
Web Site: www.amg-nv.com
Specialty Metal Processing & Engineering Services
S.I.C.: 8741
N.A.I.C.S.: 551114
Heinz C. Schimmelbusch *(Chm-Mgmt Bd & CEO)*
William J. Levy *(CFO)*
Eric E. Jackson *(Pres-Advanced Matls)*
Reinhard Walter *(Pres-Engrg Svcs)*

Subsidiaries:

AMG Idealcast Solar Corporation (2)
630 Solarex Ct
Frederick, MD 21703-8624
Tel.: (240) 439-6311
Fax: (240) 459-6320
Emp.: 8
Solar Energy Equipment Distr
S.I.C.: 5074
N.A.I.C.S.: 423720
Roger Clark *(Gen Mgr)*

AMG Vanadium, Inc. (2)
60790 Southgate Rd
Cambridge, OH 43725 (100%)
Tel.: (740) 435-4600
Fax: (740) 432-5937
E-Mail: vanadium@amg-v.com
Web Site: www.amg-v.com
Emp.: 120
Specialty Chemicals Mfr
S.I.C.: 2899
N.A.I.C.S.: 325998
R. James Carter *(VP-Sls-Intl)*

KB Alloys, LLC (2)
2208 Quarry Dr Ste 201
Reading, PA 19609 PA
Tel.: (610) 370-6585
Fax: (610) 370-6571
Toll Free: (800) 523-8457
E-Mail: customerservice@kballoys.com
Web Site: www.kballoys.com
Emp.: 150
Aluminum Master Alloys Mfr
Export
S.I.C.: 2899
N.A.I.C.S.: 325998
Richard J. Malliris *(Pres & CEO)*

Metallurg Holdings Corporation (2)
435 Devon Park Dr Bldg 200
Wayne, PA 19087-1945
Tel.: (610) 293-2501
Fax: (610) 293-2501
Investment Management Services
S.I.C.: 6211
N.A.I.C.S.: 523999

Metallurg, Inc. (2)
435 Devon Park Dr Ste 200
Wayne, PA 19087-1937 DE
Tel.: (610) 293-2501
Fax: (610) 293-2510
Web Site: www.metallurg.com

Mfr of Ferrous Alloys, Ores & Minerals; Aluminum Master Alloys
Import Export
S.I.C.: 3339
N.A.I.C.S.: 331410
Heinz C. Schimmelbusch *(Chm & CEO)*
Eric E. Jackson *(Pres-Advanced Matls)*

Non-U.S. Holdings:

London & Scandinavian Metallurgical Co. Ltd. (3)
Fullerton Road
Rotherham, South Yorkshire, S60 1DL, United Kingdom (100%)
Tel.: (44) 1709828500
Telex: 54581 lsmrhm g
Fax: (44) 1709828367
E-Mail: enquiries@lsm.co.uk
Web Site: www.lsm.co.uk
Emp.: 250
Metallurgical Products Mfr
S.I.C.: 3312
N.A.I.C.S.: 331110
Itamar Resende *(Mng Dir)*

Subsidiary:

The Aluminum Powder Company Limited (4)
Forge Lane
Minworth, Sutton Coldfield, West Midlands, B76 1AH, United Kingdom (100%)
Tel.: (44) 1213516119
Fax: (44) 1213517604
E-Mail: sales@alpoco.co.uk
Web Site: www.alpoco.co.uk
Emp.: 20
Mfr of Atomised Aluminum & Special Alloy Powders
S.I.C.: 3499
N.A.I.C.S.: 332117
Scott Carr *(Mng Dir)*

Non-U.S. Joint Venture:

Benda-Lutz-Alpoco Sp.z o.o. (5)
ul Pilsudskiego 23
32 050 Skawina, Poland
Tel.: (48) 122761110
Fax: (48) 122763661
E-Mail: office@benda-lutz.com.pl
Web Site: www.benda-lutz.com
Emp.: 15
Metal Powders & Pigments Mfr
S.I.C.: 2851
N.A.I.C.S.: 325510
Janusz Jedrusik *(Gen Mgr)*

Non-U.S. Subsidiaries:

Companhia Industrial Fluminense Mineracao S.A. (4)
Brat Tqm 94 Colonie de Marca
Colonia do Giarola, 36302-812 Sao Joao del Rei, Brazil (100%)
Tel.: (55) 32 3379 3500
Telex: 53997
Fax: (55) 32 3379 3505
E-Mail: contatos@cif.ind.br
Web Site: www.cif.ind.br
Emp.: 256
Mineral Mining
S.I.C.: 1499
N.A.I.C.S.: 212399
Sergio Hallaq *(Mgr)*

LSM (Jiaxing) Co., Ltd. (4)
E Building 289 Muyang Road
Jiaxing, Zhejiang, 314033, China CN
Tel.: (86) 57382222125 (100%)
Web Site: www.lsm.co.uk/corporate/locations
Metal
S.I.C.: 3312
N.A.I.C.S.: 331110

Metallurg Mexico, S.A. de CV (3)
Eucken No 16 Piso 5
Colonia Anzures, Mexico, DF, 11590, Mexico
Tel.: (52) 5552546986
Telex: 1763016
Fax: (52) 5555313362
E-Mail: lgarcia@metallurg-mex.com.mx
Web Site: www.metallurg.com.mx
Sales Range: $1-9.9 Million
Emp.: 8
Sales Of Electrometallurgical Products
S.I.C.: 3312
N.A.I.C.S.: 331110
Jorge Gomez *(Gen Mgr)*

Non-U.S. Subsidiaries:

ALD Vacuum Technologies GmbH (2)
Wilhelm-Rohn-Strasse 35
63450 Hanau, Germany De
Tel.: (49) 61813070
Fax: (49) 61813073292
E-Mail: info@ald-vt.de
Web Site: www.ald-vt.com
Sales Range: $200-249.9 Million
Emp.: 380
Vacuum Furnace Systems Mfr & Marketer
S.I.C.: 3567
N.A.I.C.S.: 333994
Reinhard Walter *(Chm & CEO)*
Matthias Haberle *(CFO)*

Subsidiaries:

ALD Industrie- und Montagepark Staaken GmbH (3)
Staakener Strasse 53-63
13581 Berlin, Germany De
Tel.: (49) 30 330 96 93 0 (51%)
Fax: (49) 30 330 96 93 10
E-Mail: info@ald-imp.de
Web Site: www.ald-imp.de
Emp.: 130
Mfr of Heat Treating Furnace Systems
S.I.C.: 3567
N.A.I.C.S.: 333994
Thomas Hess *(Mgr)*

ALD Own & Operate GmbH (3)
Wilhelm-Rohn-Strasse 35
63450 Hanau, Germany De
Tel.: (49) 6181 307 3438 (100%)
Fax: (49) 6181 307 383438
E-Mail: own-operate@ald-vt.de
Web Site: www.ald-vt.com
Design & Manufacture of Vacuum Heat Treating Systems
S.I.C.: 3559
N.A.I.C.S.: 333249
Joerg Molz *(Mgr)*

Subsidiary:

VACUHEAT GmbH (4)
Hohensteiner Str 11-13
09212 Limbach-Oberfrohna, Germany De
Tel.: (49) 372240220 (100%)
Fax: (49) 3722402255
E-Mail: info@vacuheat.net
Web Site: www.vacuheat.net
Emp.: 50
Vacuum Heat Treating
S.I.C.: 3398
N.A.I.C.S.: 332811
Udo Bardelmeier *(Mng Dir)*
Klaus-Juergen Heimbach *(Mng Dir)*

U.S. Subsidiary:

ALD Thermal Treatment, Inc. (4)
2656 24th St
Port Huron, MI 48060 (100%)
Tel.: (810) 357-0680
Fax: (810) 357-0689
E-Mail: info-porthuron@aldtt.net
Web Site: www.aldtt.net
Vacuum Metal Heat Treating
S.I.C.: 3398
N.A.I.C.S.: 332811
Robert Peters *(Mgr)*

Non-U.S. Subsidiary:

ALD Tratamientos Termicos S.A. de C.V. (4)
Blvd Omega 2270
Parque Industrial Santa Maria, Ramos Arizpe, CP, 25901, Mexico MX
Tel.: (52) 844 86697 70 (100%)
Fax: (52) 844 86697 96
E-Mail: info@aldtt-mexico.com
Web Site: www.aldtt-mexico.com
Design & Manufacture of Vacuum Heat Treating Systems
S.I.C.: 3559
N.A.I.C.S.: 333249

U.S. Subsidiary:

ALD Vacuum Technologies, Inc. (3)
18 Thompson Rd
East Windsor, CT 06088 (100%)
Tel.: (860) 386-7227
Fax: (860) 386-7220
Web Site: www.ald-vt.com
Vacuum Heat Treating Furnace Systems Marketer
S.I.C.: 3567
N.A.I.C.S.: 333994
David Esser *(Pres)*

U.S. Joint Venture:

ALD Holcroft Vacuum Technologies Co. (3)
49630 Pontiac Trl
Wixom, MI 48393
Tel.: (248) 668-4130
Fax: (248) 668-2145
E-Mail: sales@ald-holcroft.com
Web Site: www.ald-holcroft.com
Designs & Manufactures Vacuum Furnace Systems Used for Heat Treating; Joint Venture Owned 50% by ALD Vacuum Technologies GmbH & 50% by AFC-Holcroft LLC
S.I.C.: 3559
N.A.I.C.S.: 333249
Jason Sisler *(Pres)*

Non-U.S. Subsidiaries:

ALD Thermo Technologies Far East Co., Ltd. (3)
10F Shinjuku Nomura Bldg 1-26-2 Nishi-Shinjuku
Shinjuku-ku, Tokyo, 163 0558, Japan JP
Tel.: (81) 333403726 (100%)
Fax: (81) 3 3340 37 27
E-Mail: peter.lang@ald-vt.de
Web Site: www.ald-vt.com
Vacuum Heat Treating Furnace Systems Mfr & Marketer
S.I.C.: 3567
N.A.I.C.S.: 333994
Peter Lang *(Mgr)*

ALD Vacuum Technologies Ltd. (3)
1st Floor 276 High Street
Guildford, Surrey, GU1 3JL, United Kingdom UK
Tel.: (44) 1483454434 (100%)
Fax: (44) 1483306641
E-Mail: philip@aldvactech.co.uk
Web Site: www.ald-vt.de
Emp.: 5
Vacuum Heat Treating Furnace Systems Mfr & Marketer
S.I.C.: 3567
N.A.I.C.S.: 333994
Philip Wightman *(Mgr)*

ALD Vacuum Technologies Singapore Pte. Ltd. (3)
18 Enterprise Road
Singapore, 629842, Singapore SG
Tel.: (65) 6305 3689 (100%)
Fax: (65) 6305 3699
E-Mail: jeremy.chee@ald-singapore.com
Web Site: www.ald-vt.com
Vacuum Heat Treating Furnace Systems Mfr & Marketer
S.I.C.: 3567
N.A.I.C.S.: 333994
Jeremy Min Lick Chee *(Mgr)*

ALD Vacuumyje Technologii OOO (3)
ul Bolschaja Ordynka 40 str 2
109017 Moscow, Russia RU
Tel.: (7) 4957876733 (100%)
Fax: (7) 495 7876734
E-Mail: ald@metallurg.com.ru
Web Site: www.ald-vt.com
Vacuum Heat Treating Furnace Systems Mfr & Marketer
S.I.C.: 3567
N.A.I.C.S.: 333994
Dimitrij Korowin *(Mgr)*

Furnaces Nuclear Applications Grenoble S.A. (3)
4 avenue Charles de Gaulle
38800 Le Pont-de-Claix, France FR
Tel.: (33) 4 76 33 64 40 (100%)
Fax: (33) 4 76 33 30 27
E-Mail: info@fnag.eu
Web Site: www.fnag.eu
Furnace Systems for Nuclear Applications
S.I.C.: 3567
N.A.I.C.S.: 333994
Eric Marsat *(Mng Dir)*

Non-U.S. Affiliates:

Dynatech Furnaces Pvt. Ltd. (3)
301/302 Jyoti Estate 14 Anand Nagar S N Road
Andheri E, Mumbai, 400 069, India In
Tel.: (91) 2226826781 (30%)
Fax: (91) 22 2 682 67 84
E-Mail: dynacells@dynatechfurnaces.com
Web Site: www.dynatechfurnaces.com
Emp.: 35
Vacuum Furnaces Mfr
S.I.C.: 3567
N.A.I.C.S.: 333994
S. R. Bhat *(Mng Dir)*
M. S. Ganesh *(Mng Dir)*

Thermique Industrie Vide (3)
ZI Les Iles Cordees RN 532
38113 Veurey Voroize, France FR
Tel.: (33) 476539005 (30%)
Fax: (33) 476539022
E-Mail: info@tiv-fours.fr
Web Site: www.tiv-fours.fr
Emp.: 27
Vacuum Heat Treating Furnace Systems Mfr & Marketer
S.I.C.: 3567
N.A.I.C.S.: 333994
Philippe Segovia *(Gen Mgr)*

The Aluminium Powder Company Limited (2)
Forge Lane Minworth
Sutton Coldfield, West Midlands, B761AH, United Kingdom
Tel.: (44) 121 351 6119
Fax: (44) 121 351 7604
E-Mail: sales@alpoco.co.uk
Web Site: www.alpoco.com
Aluminium Powders Mfr
S.I.C.: 3355
N.A.I.C.S.: 331318

AMG Advanced Metallurgical Group Investment BV (2)
Strawinskylaan 1343
Amsterdam, 1077 XX, Netherlands
Tel.: (31) 207147140
Fax: (31) 7147163
Web Site: www.amg-nv.com
Emp.: 1
Investment Management Services
S.I.C.: 6211
N.A.I.C.S.: 523999
Rainer Steger *(Gen Mgr)*

AMG Brazilian Holding BV (2)
Strawinskylaan 1343
Amsterdam, 1077 XX, Netherlands
Tel.: (31) 207147140
Investment Management Services
S.I.C.: 6211
N.A.I.C.S.: 523999

AMG Coating Technologies GmbH (2)
Wilhelm-Rohn-Str 35
Hanau, 63450, Germany
Tel.: (49) 61813070
Fax: (49) 61813073290
E-Mail: info@ald-vt.de
Web Site: www.ald-vt.de
Emp.: 35
Metallurgical Products Coating Services
S.I.C.: 3479
N.A.I.C.S.: 332812
Reinhard Walter *(Gen Mgr)*

AMG Euro Holdings CV (2)
Strawinskylaan 1343
Amsterdam, 1077 XX, Netherlands
Tel.: (31) 20 7147140
Investment Management Services
S.I.C.: 6211
N.A.I.C.S.: 523999

Branwell Graphite Ltd. (2)
Crown House 3rd Floor 151 High Road
Loughton, IG10 4LG, United Kingdom
Tel.: (44) 1992577334
Fax: (44) 1992575043
E-Mail: sales@graphexel.com
Graphite Products Mfr
S.I.C.: 3624
N.A.I.C.S.: 335991

Edelgraphit GmbH (2)
Friesdorfer Str 242
53175 Bonn, Germany

AMG Advanced Metallurgical Group N.V.—(Continued)

Tel.: (49) 2 28 31 02 36
Fax: (49) 2 28 31 30 26
E-Mail: info@edelgraphit.de
Web Site: www.edelgraphit.de
Graphite Products Mfr
S.I.C.: 3624
N.A.I.C.S.: 335991
Hinnerk Hoff *(Gen Mgr)*

GfE Gesellschaft fur Elektrometallurgie mbH (2)
Hofener Strasse 45
D 90431 Nuremberg, Germany
Tel.: (49) 911931591
Telex: 622-2235
Fax: (49) 9119315429
E-Mail: contact@gfe.com
Web Site: www.gfe.com
Emp.: 400
Holding Company; Electrometallurgical Products Mfr
S.I.C.: 6719
N.A.I.C.S.: 551112
Jacques van den Burg *(Mng Dir)*
Ernst Wallis *(Mng Dir)*

Subsidiaries:

GfE Fremat GmbH (3)
Lessingstrasse 41
09599 Freiburg, Germany
Tel.: (49) 37313750
Fax: (49) 373132857
E-Mail: fremat@gfe.com
Web Site: www.gfe.com
High Performance Metals & Materials Mfr
S.I.C.: 3312
N.A.I.C.S.: 331110
Jacques van den Burg *(Mng Dir)*
Uwe van Osten *(Mng Dir)*
Ernst Wallis *(Mng Dir)*

GfE Metalle und Materialien GmbH (3)
Hofener Strasse 45
90431 Nuremberg, Germany
Tel.: (49) 911931592
Fax: (49) 911 9315 489
E-Mail: contact@gfe.com
Web Site: www.gfe.com
High Performance Metals & Materials Mfr
S.I.C.: 3312
N.A.I.C.S.: 331110
Guido Loeber *(Mng Dir)*
Jacques van den Burg *(Mng Dir)*
Uwe van Osten *(Mng Dir)*
Ernst Wallis *(Mng Dir)*

U.S. Subsidiary:

GfE Materials Technology, Inc. (3)
435 Devon Park Rd Ste 200
Wayne, PA 19087
Tel.: (610) 293-5811
Fax: (610) 675-2599
Web Site: www.gfe.com
Sales & Support Services
S.I.C.: 5051
N.A.I.C.S.: 423510

GK Graphit Kropfmuhl GmbH (2)
Langheinrichstr 1
94051 Hauzenberg, Germany
Tel.: (49) 8586 6090
Fax: (49) 8586 609112
Web Site: www.graphitkropfmuhl.com
Emp.: 13
Nonmetallic Mineral Mining Services
S.I.C.: 1499
N.A.I.C.S.: 212399
Klaus Vetter *(CFO)*

Graphit Kropfmuhl AG (2)
Langheinrichstrasse 1
94501 Hauzenberg, Germany (88%)
Tel.: (49) 85866090
Fax: (49) 8586609111
E-Mail: info@gk-graphite.com
Web Site: www.graphite.de
Sales Range: $50-74.9 Million
Emp.: 699
Graphite Extraction & Processing
S.I.C.: 3624
N.A.I.C.S.: 335991
Heinz C. Schimmelbusch *(Chm-Supervisory Bd)*
Martin Ebeling *(CEO)*
Hans-Detlef Antel *(Mng Dir)*

Subsidiary:

RW Silicium GmbH (3)
Wohlerstrase 30
94060 Pocking, Germany
Tel.: (49) 85317020
Fax: (49) 853170290
E-Mail: info@silicium.de
Web Site: www.silicium.de
Emp.: 110
Silicon Extraction & Processing
S.I.C.: 1099
N.A.I.C.S.: 212299
Hans-Detlef Antel *(Mng Dir)*

Graphite Tyn spol. s r.o. (2)
Pisecka 417
375 01 Tyn nad Vltavou, Czech Republic
Tel.: (420) 385 109 210
Fax: (420) 385 109 213
E-Mail: info@gk-graphite.cz
Web Site: www.graphite.cz
Emp.: 4
Graphite Mining Services
S.I.C.: 1499
N.A.I.C.S.: 212399
Evzen Kroupa *(Mng Dir)*

Societe Industrielle et Chimique de l'Aisne S.A.S. (2)
38 rue Geo Lufbery
Chauny, 02300, France
Tel.: (33) 3 23 40 35 30
Fax: (33) 3 23 39 42 09
Web Site: www.sica-chauny.com
Emp.: 70
Antimony Trioxide Mfr
S.I.C.: 2899
N.A.I.C.S.: 325998

Sudamin Holding SPRL (2)
Lion Office Center
Chaussee de Nivelles 81, 1420 Braine-l'Alleud, Belgium (100%)
Tel.: (32) 23520960
Fax: (32) 23520966
E-Mail:
Web Site: www.sudamin.com
Emp.: 5
Metal Trader
S.I.C.: 7389
N.A.I.C.S.: 425120
Eric Jackson *(Mng Dir)*

Subsidiary:

Sudamin SPRL (3)
Chaussee de Nivelles 81
1420 Braine-l'Alleud, Belgium
Tel.: (32) 23520960
Fax: (32) 23520966
Web Site: www.sudamin.com
Emp.: 5
Metals & Ferro Alloy Distr
S.I.C.: 5051
N.A.I.C.S.: 423510
Lukas Aleksandravicius *(CEO)*

Non-U.S. Subsidiary:

Sudamin France S.A.S (3)
136 Bureaux De La Colline
92210 Saint-Cloud, France
Tel.: (33) 1 47 71 16 16
Fax: (33) 1 47 71 92 82
Web Site: www.sudamin.com
Emp.: 100
Nonferrous Metal Products Distr
S.I.C.: 5051
N.A.I.C.S.: 423510
Charles-Antoine Rougier *(Pres)*

Non-U.S. Holdings:

Produits Chimiques de Lucette S.A.S. (3)
Z I de la Vallee Verte
53940 Le Genest-Saint-Isle, France
Tel.: (33) 243012310
Fax: (33) 2 43 02 49 06
E-Mail: vdrochon@pcdlucette.com
Web Site: www.pcdlucette.com
Antimony Oxide & Other Specialty Chemicals Mfr
S.I.C.: 2899
N.A.I.C.S.: 325998

Sudamin Holdings SA (2)
Les Bureaux de la Colline de Saint-Cloud 136
92213 Saint-Cloud, France
Tel.: (33) 1 47 71 16 16
Fax: (33) 1 47 71 92 82
Web Site: www.sudamin.com
Investment Management Services
S.I.C.: 6211
N.A.I.C.S.: 523999

VACUHEAT Verwaltungs GmbH (2)
Hohensteiner Strasse 11-13
09212 Limbach-Oberfrohna, Germany
Tel.: (49) 3722 40220
Fax: (49) 3722 403355
Non Ferrous Metal Products Distr
S.I.C.: 5051
N.A.I.C.S.: 423510

Non-U.S. Subsidiaries:

LSM Brasil S.A. (1)
Br 383 S/N Km 94
Sao Joao del Rei, Minas Gerais, 36302-812, Brazil
Tel.: (55) 3233793500
Fax: (55) 3233793505
Web Site: www.lsmbrasil.com.br
Emp.: 25
Aluminum Extruded Products Mfr
S.I.C.: 3354
N.A.I.C.S.: 331318
Zdenek Fous *(Mng Dir)*

Metallurg Servicios S.A. de R.L. de C.V. (1)
Eucken No 16 Int 502 Piso 5 Anzures
Miguel Hidalgo, Mexico, 11590, Mexico
Tel.: (52) 5552500136
Fax: (52) 5555313362
E-Mail: laalrcia@amg.com
Web Site: www.amg.com
Metallurgical Services
S.I.C.: 3299
N.A.I.C.S.: 327999

AMG BIOENERGY RESOURCES HOLDINGS LTD.

190 Middle Road 190-05 Fortune Centre
Singapore, Singapore 188979
Tel.: (65) 6223 1098
Fax: (65) 62238258
Year Founded: 2006
ABG—(TSXV)
Assets: $2,053,928
Liabilities: $986,716
Net Worth: $1,067,212
Earnings: ($1,152,579)
Fiscal Year-end: 02/28/13
Business Description:
Tree Plantation Services
S.I.C.: 0181
N.A.I.C.S.: 111421
Personnel:
Shoong Lim Lee *(CEO)*
Tit Khuen Pang *(CFO)*

AMI RESOURCES INC.

Suite 888 609 West Hastings Street
Vancouver, BC, V6B 4W4, Canada
Tel.: (604) 669-2901
Fax: (604) 669-8922
Toll Free: (888) 669-2901
Web Site: www.amiresources.com
AMU—(TSXV)
Assets: $5,546,809
Liabilities: $81,220
Net Worth: $5,465,588
Earnings: ($532,864)
Fiscal Year-end: 02/28/13
Business Description:
Gold Exploration & Development Services
S.I.C.: 1041
N.A.I.C.S.: 212221
Personnel:
Dustin A. Elford *(Pres & CEO)*
William C. Pettigrew *(CFO & Sec)*
Edward Jay Sujir *(Corp Counsel)*
Board of Directors:
Ryan Cheung
Dustin A. Elford
William C. Pettigrew
Legal Counsel:
Lithur & Brew
No 1108 Off Kade Ave Kada Estates PO Box CT3865
Accra, Ghana
Anfield Sujir Kennedy & Durno
Suite 1600 609 Granville Street PO Box 10068 Pacific Centre
Vancouver, BC, Canada

AMIAD WATER SYSTEMS LTD.

D N Galil Elyon 1
Jerusalem, 1233500, Israel
Tel.: (972) 46909500
Fax: (972) 46909391
E-Mail: info@amiad.com
Web Site: www.amiad.com
Year Founded: 1962
AFS—(LSE)
Rev.: $131,091,000
Assets: $122,143,000
Liabilities: $66,771,000
Net Worth: $55,372,000
Earnings: $8,027,000
Emp.: 67
Fiscal Year-end: 12/31/12
Business Description:
Water Filtration Systems Mfr
S.I.C.: 3569
N.A.I.C.S.: 333999
Personnel:
Arik Dayan *(CEO)*
Amir Harel *(CFO)*
Board of Directors:
Tal Yeshua
Izhar Ben-Shlomo
Arik Dayan
Amir Harel
Zeev Holender
Simon Olswang
Michael Rosenberg
Amos Shalev
Legal Counsel:
Speechly Bircham LLP
6 New Street Square
London, EC4A 3LX, United Kingdom
Barnea & Co.
Life Plaza 6 Hachoshlim Street
Herzliya Pituach, Israel

U.S. Subsidiaries:

Amiad USA Inc. (1)
120-J Talbert Rd
Mooresville, NC 28117
Tel.: (704) 662-3133
Fax: (704) 662-3155
E-Mail: info@amiadusa.com
Web Site: www.amiadusa.com
Emp.: 35
Water Filtration Systems Sales & Installation Services
S.I.C.: 5074
N.A.I.C.S.: 423720

PEP Filters, Inc. (1)
120-J Talbert Rd
Mooresville, NC 28117-7119
Tel.: (704) 662-3133
Fax: (704) 662-3155
Toll Free: (800) 243-4583
E-Mail: pepusa@pepfilters.com
Web Site: www.pepfilters.com
Emp.: 50
Water Filtration Systems Mfr
S.I.C.: 3569
N.A.I.C.S.: 333999
Tom Akehurst *(Pres)*

Non-U.S. Subsidiaries:

Amiad Filtration Solutions Ltd. (1)
Prinz-Regent-Str 68a
Bochum, 44795, Germany
Tel.: (49) 234 588082 12
Fax: (49) 234 588082 10
Water Filtration Systems Mfr
S.I.C.: 3569
N.A.I.C.S.: 333999

Amiad Filtration Systems India Pvt Ltd (1)
305 Sai Commercial Building Govandi Stn Rd
Govandi, Mumbai, 400 088, India

Tel.: (91) 22 67997813
Fax: (91) 22 25270864
E-Mail: info@amiadindia.com
Web Site: www.amiadindia.com
Emp.: 15
Water Filtration Systems Sales & Installation Services
S.I.C.: 5074
N.A.I.C.S.: 423720
Sudhir Mehta *(CEO)*

Amiad Water Systems Europe SAS (1)
Zi la Boitardiere
37530 Charge, France
Tel.: (33) 247 23 01 10
Fax: (33) 247 23 80 67
E-Mail: info@amiadfrance.com
Web Site: www.amiadfrance.com
Emp.: 1
Water Filtration Systems Installation Services
S.I.C.: 1629
N.A.I.C.S.: 237110
Bruno Jauneaud *(Gen Mgr)*

Filtration & Control Systems PTE Ltd. (1)
19B Teo Hong Road
88330 Singapore, Singapore
Tel.: (65) 6 337 6698
Fax: (65) 6 337 8180
E-Mail: fcs1071@pacific.net.sg
Emp.: 6
Filtration Systems Sales & Installation Services
S.I.C.: 5074
N.A.I.C.S.: 423720
Lena Ng *(Office Mgr)*

Fitrasyon Aritim Sistemleri Sanayive Ticaret FTS (1)
Istanbul yolu 26 Km Yurt Orta Sanayii
Saray, Ankara, Turkey
Tel.: (90) 312 8155266
Fax: (90) 312 8155248
Water Filtration Systems Mfr
S.I.C.: 3569
N.A.I.C.S.: 333999

Yixing Taixing Environtaec Co. Ltd. (1)
70 Baihe Chang
Xingjie, Yixing, Jiangsu, 214204, China
Tel.: (86) 5108 7134000
Fax: (86) 5108 7134999
E-Mail: marketing@taixing.cc
Water Filters & Filtration Systems Mfr
S.I.C.: 3569
N.A.I.C.S.: 333999

AMICA MATURE LIFESTYLES, INC.

10th Floor 1111 Melville Street
Vancouver, BC, V6E 3V6, Canada
Tel.: (604) 608-6777
Fax: (604) 608-6717
Toll Free: (877) 447-4827
E-Mail: mail@amica.ca
Web Site: www.amica.ca
ACC—(TSX)
Rev.: $97,671,411
Assets: $476,553,068
Liabilities: $312,637,182
Net Worth: $163,915,886
Earnings: ($8,724,514)
Emp.: 706
Fiscal Year-end: 05/31/13
Business Description:
Retirement & Nursing Residence Operator
S.I.C.: 8059
N.A.I.C.S.: 623311
Personnel:
Samir A. Manji *(Chm, Pres & CEO)*
Arthur J. Ayres *(CFO & Sec)*
Colin R. Halliwell *(COO)*
Board of Directors:
Samir A. Manji
Terry M. Holland
Salim A. Manji
Andrew L. Oppenheim
Shant Poladian
Mike Shaikh
Charles W. van der Lee
Transfer Agent:
Computershare Investor Services Inc.
3rd Floor 510 Burrard St
V6C 3B9 Vancouver, BC, Canada

AMICA WRONKI S.A.

Ul Mickiewicza 52
64-510 Wronki, Poland
Tel.: (48) 672546100
Fax: (48) 672540320
E-Mail: contakt@amica.com.pl
Web Site: www.amica.com.pl
Year Founded: 1921
AMC—(WAR)
Sales Range: $50-74.9 Million
Emp.: 2,200
Business Description:
Household Appliance Mfr
S.I.C.: 3639
N.A.I.C.S.: 335228
Personnel:
Tomasz Rynarzewski *(Chm-Supervisory Bd)*
Jacek Rutkowski *(Pres-Mgmt Bd)*
Supervisory Board of Directors:
Tomasz Rynarzewski
Grzegorz Golec
Wojciech Kochanek
Piotr Sawala
Bogna Katarzyna Sikorska

Subsidiaries:

Amica International GmbH (1)
Ul Mickiewicza 52
64 510 Wronki, Poland
Tel.: (48) 672546100
Fax: (48) 67 25 40 320
E-Mail: contact@amica.com.pl
Web Site: www.amica-international.com
Home Appliances Mfr
S.I.C.: 3639
N.A.I.C.S.: 335228

Hansa sp. z o.o (1)
40 Sowlanska
Bialystok, 15 560, Poland
Tel.: (48) 857437280
E-Mail: hansa@hansa.com.pl
Web Site: www.hansa.com.pl
Medical Dressings Mfr
S.I.C.: 3841
N.A.I.C.S.: 339112

Non-U.S. Subsidiary:

Gram A/S (1)
Aage Grams Vej 1
DK 6500, Vojens, Denmark
Tel.: (45) 73201000
E-Mail: heda@gram.dk
Web Site: www.gram.dk
Home Appliances Mfr
S.I.C.: 3639
N.A.I.C.S.: 335228
Peter R. Laugesen *(CEO)*

AMICO GAMES CORP.

Room North-02 9th Floor Flat A
89 Zhongshan Avenue West
Tianhe District, Guangzhou, Canton, 510630, China
Tel.: (86) 20 8556 2666
Web Site: www.amicogames.com
AMCG—(OTC)
Sales Range: $1-9.9 Million
Emp.: 86
Business Description:
Mobile Phone Games Developer & Distr
S.I.C.: 3942
N.A.I.C.S.: 339930
Personnel:
Carter Jun Ho *(Pres & CEO)*
Board of Directors:
Roger Ding
Carter Jun Ho

AMICOGEN, INC.

694-4 Sangchon
Jinsung, Jinju, 660-852, Korea (South)
Tel.: (82) 55 759 6161
Fax: (82) 55 759 6094
E-Mail: master@amicogen.com
Web Site: www.amicogen.com
Year Founded: 2000
092040—(KRS)
Sales Range: $1-9.9 Million
Emp.: 50
Business Description:
Enzymes & Food Ingredients Mfr
S.I.C.: 2899
N.A.I.C.S.: 325998
Personnel:
Yong-Chul Shin *(CEO)*
Seon-Gug Kang *(CFO)*
Kyung-Hwa Jung *(CTO)*

AMICORP SWITZERLAND AG

Bellerivestrasse 17
Zurich, 8008, Switzerland
Tel.: (41) 44 252 0880
Fax: (41) 44 252 0881
E-Mail: switzerland@amicorp.com
Web Site: www.amicorp.com
Business Description:
Outsourcing Services
S.I.C.: 7389
N.A.I.C.S.: 561499
Personnel:
Toine Knipping *(CEO)*
Kin Chi Lai *(CFO)*
Kiran Kumar *(COO)*

Non-U.S. Subsidiary:

Amicorp Netherlands B.V. (1)
(Formerly Advanta Holdings B.V.)
Strawinskylaan 1143
WTC Amsterdam Tower C-11, Amsterdam, North-Holland, 1077 XX, Netherlands
Tel.: (31) 205788388
Fax: (31) 205788389
E-Mail: netherlands@amicorp.com
Web Site: www.amicorp.com
Emp.: 15
Investment Management Services
S.I.C.: 6211
N.A.I.C.S.: 523999
Koenraad Van Baren *(Branch Mgr)*

AMIMON, INC.

2 Maskit St Building D 2nd Fl
PO Box 12618
46733 Herzliyya, Israel
Tel.: (972) 99629222
Fax: (972) 99565467
E-Mail: contact@amimon.com
Web Site: www.amimon.com
Sales Range: $25-49.9 Million
Emp.: 80
Business Description:
Developer of Wireless Transmission Equipment for High Definition Televisions
S.I.C.: 3663
N.A.I.C.S.: 334220
Personnel:
Meir Feder *(Co-Founder & CTO)*
Zvi Reznic *(Co-Founder & VP-R&D)*
Yoav Nissan-Cohen *(Chm & CEO)*

AMINES & PLASTICIZERS LIMITED

D Building Shivsagar Estate 6th Floor
Dr Annie Besant Road
Worli, Mumbai, 400018, India
Tel.: (91) 22 24935282
Fax: (91) 22 24938162
E-Mail: amines@vsnl.com
Web Site: www.amines.com
Year Founded: 1973
506248—(BOM)
Rev.: $35,740,170
Assets: $24,601,208
Liabilities: $19,847,737
Net Worth: $4,753,471
Earnings: $233,363
Fiscal Year-end: 03/31/13
Business Description:
Chemical Product Mfr
S.I.C.: 2899
N.A.I.C.S.: 325998
Personnel:
Hemant Kumar Ruia *(Chm & Mng Dir)*
Pramod Sharma *(CFO)*
Ajay Puranik *(Compliance Officer, Sec & Sr VP-Corp Affairs)*
Board of Directors:
Hemant Kumar Ruia
Brij Mohan Jindel
Arun Suryashanker Nagar
Kailashchandra K. Seksaria
Mithilesh Kumar Sinha
Pandurang Hari Vaidya
Transfer Agent:
Sharepro Services (India) Pvt. Ltd
13AB Samhita Warehousing Complex 2nd Floor
Sakinaka Telephone Exchange Lane Off
Andheri Kurla Road Sakinaka, Mumbai, 400 072, India

AMINEX PLC

10 Bedford Street
London, WC2E 9HE, United Kingdom
Tel.: (44) 20 7240 1600
Fax: (44) 20 7240 0295
E-Mail: info@aminex-plc.com
Web Site: www.aminex-plc.com
AEX—(ISE LSE OTC)
Rev.: $4,914,000
Assets: $107,386,000
Liabilities: $14,949,000
Net Worth: $92,437,000
Earnings: ($5,333,000)
Emp.: 23
Fiscal Year-end: 12/31/12
Business Description:
Oil & Gas Exploration, Development & Production Services
S.I.C.: 1311
N.A.I.C.S.: 211111
Personnel:
Brian Arthur Hall *(Chm)*
Jayanta Bhattacherjee *(CEO)*
Max Williams *(CFO & Dir-Fin)*
Philip Thompson *(COO)*
Board of Directors:
Brian Arthur Hall
Jayanta Bhattacherjee
Andrew N. J. Hay
David Symonds Hooker
Keith J. Phair
Philip Thompson
F. Derek Tughan
Max Williams
Legal Counsel:
Eversheds
One Earlsfort Centre Earlsfort Terrace
Dublin, Ireland
Ashurst
London, United Kingdom

Subsidiaries:

Aminex Petroleum Services Limited (1)
7 Gower Street
London, WC1E 6HA, United Kingdom
Tel.: (44) 2072913100
Fax: (44) 20 7636 9667
E-Mail: info@aminex-plc.com
Emp.: 12
Oil & Gas Exploration Services
S.I.C.: 1311
N.A.I.C.S.: 211111
Brian Hall *(Chm)*

Amossco Limited (1)
7 Gower Street
London, WC1E 6HA, United Kingdom

Aminex PLC—(Continued)

Tel.: (44) 2072913103
Fax: (44) 2076314293
E-Mail: sales@amossco.com
Web Site: www.amossco.com
Emp.: 15
Oil & Gas Exploration Services
S.I.C.: 1311
N.A.I.C.S.: 211111

Halyard Offshore Limited (1)
7 Gower St
London, WC1E 6HA, United Kingdom
Tel.: (44) 2072913100
Fax: (44) 02076314293
Web Site: www.amasco.com
Emp.: 6
Oil & Gas Exploration Services
S.I.C.: 1311
N.A.I.C.S.: 211111
Jonathan Major *(Gen Mgr)*

Korex Limited (1)
52 Stockwell Road
London, SW9 9ER, United Kingdom
Tel.: (44) 2077376864
E-Mail: korex@talktalk.net
Emp.: 5
Property Management Services
S.I.C.: 6531
N.A.I.C.S.: 531311

U.S. Subsidiary:

Aminex U.S.A. Inc. (1)
PO Box 130
Somerset, TX 78069
Tel.: (210) 271-9919
Fax: (210) 271-3302
Web Site: www.aminex-plc.com
Emp.: 16
Petroleum Exploration Services
S.I.C.: 1311
N.A.I.C.S.: 211111
Antonio G. Prado *(Pres)*

Non-U.S. Subsidiaries:

Ndovu Resources Limited (1)
Plot no 5 15 Mkwawa Road
PO Box 105589
Dar es Salaam, Tanzania
Tel.: (255) 22 2667199
Fax: (255) 22 2667284
Web Site: www.aminex-plc.com
Emp.: 5
Oil & Gas Exploration Services
S.I.C.: 1311
N.A.I.C.S.: 211111
Thaerroy Murrcia *(Mgr-Country)*

Tanzoil NL (1)
3rd Fl MPH Bldg 23 Barrack St
Perth, WA, 6000, Australia
Tel.: (61) 892210033
Fax: (61) 892210133
Emp.: 20
Petroleum Exploration Services
S.I.C.: 1311
N.A.I.C.S.: 211111
Didier Murcia *(Mng Dir)*

AMINO TECHNOLOGIES PLC

Buckingway Business Park Anderson Road
Swavesey, Cambs, CB24 4UQ, United Kingdom
Tel.: (44) 1954234100
Fax: (44) 1954234101
E-Mail: info@aminocom.com
Web Site: www.aminocom.com
AMO—(LSE)
Rev.: $65,856,393
Assets: $50,543,597
Liabilities: $15,096,433
Net Worth: $35,447,164
Earnings: $4,488,342
Emp.: 105
Fiscal Year-end: 11/30/12
Business Description:
Electronic Systems Design & Software Services
S.I.C.: 3679
N.A.I.C.S.: 334419
Personnel:
Donald Kevin McGarva *(CEO & COO)*
Julia Hornby *(CFO & Sec)*
Mike Greenall *(Sr VP-Product & Partner Mgmt)*
Gary Hamer *(Sr VP-Global Sls)*
Board of Directors:
Thomas Keith Todd
Michael Bennett
Julia Hornby
Donald Kevin McGarva
Peter Murphy
Colin Richard Smithers
Legal Counsel:
Hewitsons
Shakespeare House 42 Newmarket Road
Cambridge, United Kingdom

Subsidiary:

Amino Communications Limited (1)
Buckingway Bus Pk
Anderson Rd, Swavesey, Cambridge, CB24 4UQ, United Kingdom
Tel.: (44) 1954234100
Fax: (44) 1954234101
E-Mail: info@aminocom.com
Web Site: www.aminocom.com
Emp.: 75
Internet TV & In Home Multimedia Distribution Services
S.I.C.: 2741
N.A.I.C.S.: 519130
Joe Coles *(Sr VP-Product Mgmt & Mktg)*

Non-U.S. Subsidiary:

Amino Communications AB (1)
Finlandsgatan 40
SE 164 74 Kista, Sweden
Tel.: (46) 856251600
Fax: (46) 856251699
E-Mail: info@aminocom.com
Web Site: www.aminocom.com
Emp.: 40
Digital Entertainment Services
S.I.C.: 3572
N.A.I.C.S.: 334112
Bjorn von Haartman *(Mgr)*

AMINOLOGICS CO., LTD.

Jungbu B/D 6th 7th Fl 968-6 Daechi-Dong
Kangnam-gu, Seoul, 135-848, Korea (South)
Tel.: (82) 27614570
Fax: (82) 2764571
Web Site: www.alogics.co.kr
Year Founded: 1997
074430—(KRS)
Business Description:
Biotechnology Services
S.I.C.: 8731
N.A.I.C.S.: 541711
Personnel:
Hoon-Yul Yoon *(Pres & CEO)*
Kwan Mook Kim *(CTO)*

AMIRA NATURE FOODS LTD.

29E AU Tower Jumeirah Lake Towers
Dubai, United Arab Emirates
Tel.: (971) 4 2351755
Web Site: www.amirafoods.com
ANFI—(NYSE)
Rev.: $413,682,574
Assets: $326,531,978
Liabilities: $182,899,243
Net Worth: $143,632,735
Earnings: $19,249,038
Emp.: 326
Fiscal Year-end: 03/31/13
Business Description:
Packaged Indian Specialty Rice Distr & Mfr
S.I.C.: 5149
N.A.I.C.S.: 424490
Personnel:
Karan A. Chanana *(Chm & CEO)*
Ashish Poddar *(CFO)*
Protik Guha *(COO)*
Sanjay Chanana *(Sec)*
Board of Directors:
Karan A. Chanana
Sanjay Chanana
Neal B. Cravens
Daniel I. Malina
Bimal Kishore Raizada
Harash Pal Sethi

AMITA HOLDINGS CO., LTD.

28 Sanbanchou Chiyoda-ku
Tokyo, 102-0075, Japan
Tel.: (81) 352158255
Web Site: www.amita-net.co.jp
Business Description:
Environmental Services Including Recycling & Waste Management
S.I.C.: 5093
N.A.I.C.S.: 423930
Personnel:
Eisuke Kumano *(Pres & CEO)*

AMJ CAMPBELL, INC.

(d/b/a AMJ Campbell Van Lines)
1445 Courtney Park Dr E
Mississauga, ON, L5T 2E3, Canada
Tel.: (905) 795-3785
Fax: (905) 670-3787
E-Mail: info@amjcampbell.com
Web Site: www.amjcampbell.com
Year Founded: 1934
Sales Range: $50-74.9 Million
Emp.: 150
Business Description:
Moving Services for Household & Commercial Office Relocations
S.I.C.: 4214
N.A.I.C.S.: 484210
Personnel:
Bruce D. Bowser *(Pres & CEO)*
Denis M. Frappier *(Pres-Self Storage & Bus Dev)*
Thomas S. Finlay *(Exec VP)*

AML FOODS LTD.

2nd Level Town Center Mall Blue Hill Road
PO Box SS-6322
Nassau, Bahamas
Tel.: (242) 677 7200
Fax: (242) 356 7822
E-Mail: info@amlfoods.com
Web Site: www.amlfoods.com
AML—(BISX)
Sales Range: $75-99.9 Million
Emp.: 700
Business Description:
Stores & Fast Food Restaurant Franchise Owner & Operator
S.I.C.: 5411
N.A.I.C.S.: 445110
Personnel:
Dionisio J. D'Aguilar *(Chm)*
Robert Sands *(Vice Chm)*
Gavin Watchorn *(Pres & CEO)*
Stephen Smollett *(Exec VP)*
Shervin Stuart *(Exec VP)*
Board of Directors:
Dionisio J. D'Aguilar
Franklyn A. Butler, II
Frank Crothers
Michael Moss
Robert Sands
R. Craig Symonette
Legal Counsel:
Callenders & Co
One Millars Court Shirley Street
Nassau, Bahamas
Transfer Agent:
Bahamas Central Securities Depository
Suite 202 Fort Nassau Centre British Colonial Hilton Bay Street
Nassau, Bahamas

AML STEEL LIMITED

AML Towers No 9 6th Cross Street
Gopalapuram, Chennai, 600 086, India
Tel.: (91) 4439170000
Fax: (91) 4439170012
E-Mail: corporate@amlsteel.com
Web Site: www.amlsteel.com
AMLSTEEL—(NSE)
Business Description:
Rolled Steel Mfr
S.I.C.: 3399
N.A.I.C.S.: 331110
Personnel:
Ashok Agarwal *(CEO & Mng Dir)*
Board of Directors:
Ankit Agarwal
Ashok Agarwal
Lalit R. Agarwal
Sai Anantharamakrishnan

AMLIN PLC

St Helen's 1 Undershaft
London, EC3A 8ND, United Kingdom
Tel.: (44) 2077461000
Fax: (44) 2077461696
Web Site: www.amlin.com
Year Founded: 1903
AML—(LSE OTC)
Premiums: $3,662,373,510
Assets: $10,291,601,214
Liabilities: $7,936,248,108
Net Worth: $2,355,353,106
Earnings: $391,190,133
Emp.: 1,628
Fiscal Year-end: 12/31/12
Business Description:
Commercial Insurance & Reinsurance Services
S.I.C.: 6399
N.A.I.C.S.: 524128
Personnel:
Richard H. Davey *(Chm)*
Charles Philipps *(CEO)*
Jayne Styles *(Chief Investment Officer)*
James Illingworth *(Chief Risk Officer)*
Simon C. W. Beale *(Grp Chief Underwriting Officer)*
Andrew Grant *(Grp Ops Officer)*
Francois Martinache *(Chm-France)*
Kim Hvirgel *(CEO-Amlin Corporate Insurance)*
Philippe Regazzoni *(CEO-Amlin AG)*
Andrew Springett *(CEO-Amlin Underwriting Limited)*
Rob Wyatt *(CEO-Bermuda)*
Mark Stevens *(Sec)*
Board of Directors:
Richard H. Davey
Simon C. W. Beale
Nigel Buchanan
Brian D. Carpenter
Julie Chakraverty
Alan Collins
Martin D. Feinstein
Richard A. Hextall
Shonaid C. R. Jemmett-Page
Charles Philipps
Charles Mark Garmondsway Wrightson
Legal Counsel:
Linklaters
1 Silk Street
London, EC2Y 8HQ, United Kingdom

Subsidiaries:

Allied Cedar Insurance Group Limited (1)
Kingfisher House 1 Gilders Way
Norwich, Norfolk, NR3 1UB, United Kingdom
Tel.: (44) 1603 628034
General Insurance Services
S.I.C.: 6411
N.A.I.C.S.: 524210

Amlin Corporate Services Limited (1)
St Helens 1 Undershaft
EC3A 8ND London, United Kingdom
Tel.: (44) 2077461000
Fax: (44) 2077461696
E-Mail: info@amlin.com
Web Site: www.amlin.com
Emp.: 600
Holding Company
S.I.C.: 6719
N.A.I.C.S.: 551112
Charles Philipps *(CEO)*

Amlin Investments Limited (1)
St Helens 1 Undershaft
EC3A 8ND London, United Kingdom
Tel.: (44) 2077461000
Fax: (44) 2077461696
E-Mail: enquries@amlin.com
Emp.: 700
Insurance Related Activities
S.I.C.: 6411
N.A.I.C.S.: 524298
Charles Philipps *(CEO)*

Amlin (Overseas Holdings) Limited (1)
St Helen's 1 Undershaft
London, EC3A 8ND, United Kingdom
Tel.: (44) 2077461000
Fax: (44) 2077461696
Emp.: 600
General Insurance Services
S.I.C.: 6411
N.A.I.C.S.: 524210
Charles Philipps *(CEO)*

Amlin Plus Limited (1)
St Helens 1 Undershaft
EC3A8ND London, United Kingdom
Tel.: (44) 8456050233
Fax: (44) 8456050234
Web Site: www.amlinplus.com
Emp.: 300
Reinsurance Carriers
S.I.C.: 6399
N.A.I.C.S.: 524130
Charles Philipps *(CEO)*

Amlin Underwriting Limited (1)
Helens St 1 Undershaft
London, EC3A 8ND, United Kingdom
Tel.: (44) 2077461000
Fax: (44) 2077461696
E-Mail: info@amlin.co.uk
Web Site: www.amlin.com
Emp.: 700
Insurance Agencies & Brokerages
S.I.C.: 6411
N.A.I.C.S.: 524210
Charles Philipps *(CEO)*

AUT Holdings Limited (1)
12th Floor The International Financial Center
London, United Kingdom
Tel.: (44) 2076211666
Holding Company
S.I.C.: 6719
N.A.I.C.S.: 551112
Charles Philipps *(CEO)*

AUT (No 2) Limited (1)
St Helens 1 Undershaft
EC3A8ND London, United Kingdom
Tel.: (44) 2077461005
Fax: (44) 2077461696
Emp.: 700
Direct Insurance Carriers
S.I.C.: 6399
N.A.I.C.S.: 524128
Charles Philipps *(CEO)*

Crowe Livestock Underwriting Limited (1)
W Farm Office Station Rd Barnham
Norfolk, IP24 2PX, United Kingdom
Tel.: (44) 1842890733
Fax: (44) 1842890735
E-Mail: info@crowelivestock.co.uk
Web Site: www.crowelivestock.co.uk
Emp.: 20
General Insurance Services
S.I.C.: 6411
N.A.I.C.S.: 524210
Emma Stamper *(Mng Dir)*

Delian Beta Limited (1)
St Helens 1 Undershaft
EC3A8ND London, United Kingdom
Tel.: (44) 2077461000
Fax: (44) 2077461696
Emp.: 300
Direct Life Insurance Carriers
S.I.C.: 6311
N.A.I.C.S.: 524113
Charles Philipps *(CEO)*

Non-U.S. Subsidiaries:

Amlin AG (1)
Kirchenweg 5
8008 Zurich, Switzerland
Tel.: (41) 44 389 4000
Fax: (41) 443894099
Web Site: www.amlinre.ch
Reinsurance Operation Services
S.I.C.: 6399
N.A.I.C.S.: 524130

Amlin Bermuda Ltd (1)
141 Front Street
HM 19 Hamilton, Bermuda (100%)
Tel.: (441) 248 1500
Fax: (441) 296 1413
E-Mail: info@amlin.bm
Web Site: www.amlin.bm
Emp.: 30
Insurance Agencies & Brokerage Services
S.I.C.: 6411
N.A.I.C.S.: 524210
Robert Wyatt *(Mng Dir)*

Amlin Corporate Insurance N.V. (1)
Prof JH Bavincklaan 1
NL-1183 AT Amstelveen, Netherlands NL
Mailing Address:
Postbus 2190
NL-1180 ED Amstelveen, Netherlands
Tel.: (31) 205031100
Fax: (31) 205031900
Web Site: www.aci.amlin.com
Emp.: 350
Reinsurance & Property Insurance Products & Services
S.I.C.: 6399
N.A.I.C.S.: 524130
Kim Hvirgel *(CEO)*
Yves Warlop *(CFO)*
Andreas Luberichs *(Pres-Non Marine)*
Bert Nelen *(Pres-Marine)*
Philippe van Oosterzee *(Exec VP & Country Mgr-Belgium)*
Jaap Gispen *(Exec VP-Marine Div)*

Amlin France Holdings SAS (1)
25 Rue De Liege
Paris, 75008, France
Tel.: (33) 144707100
Fax: (33) 142934742
General Insurance Services
S.I.C.: 6411
N.A.I.C.S.: 524210

Subsidiary:

Amlin France SAS (2)
25 Rue De Liege
75008 Paris, France
Tel.: (33) 144707100
Fax: (33) 1 42 93 47 42
E-Mail: contact@amlinfrance.com
Web Site: www.amlinfrance.com
General Insurance Services
S.I.C.: 6411
N.A.I.C.S.: 524210
Alexandre Martinache *(Gen Mgr)*

Amlin Singapore Pte. Ltd. (1)
8 Moroina View #15-01 Asia Square Twr 1
Singapore, 018960, Singapore
Tel.: (65) 65570580
Fax: (65) 66361183
E-Mail: info@amlin.sg
Web Site: www.amlin.sg
Emp.: 9
Insurance Services
S.I.C.: 6399
N.A.I.C.S.: 524130
Simon Clarke *(Mng Dir)*

AMMAN STOCK EXCHANGE

PO Box 212466
Amman, 11121, Jordan
Tel.: (962) 6 5664081
Fax: (962) 6 5664071
E-Mail: info@ase.com.jo
Web Site: www.ase.com.jo
Year Founded: 1999

Business Description:
Stock Exchange Services
S.I.C.: 6231
N.A.I.C.S.: 523210

Personnel:
Mohammad Malallah *(Chm)*
Adel Beno *(Vice Chm)*
Jalil Tarif *(CEO)*
Nader Azar *(Deputy CEO)*

Board of Directors:
Mohammad Malallah
Naser Al-Amad
Marwan Al-Batayneh
Hatem Al-Shahed
Nezar Al-Taher
Adel Beno
Khaled Zakaria

AMMB HOLDINGS BERHAD

(d/b/a AmBank Group)
22nd Floor Bangunan AmBank Group
55 Jalan Raja Chulan
50200 Kuala Lumpur, Malaysia
Tel.: (60) 3 2078 2633
Fax: (60) 3 2078 2842
E-Mail: ir@ambankgroup.com
Web Site: www.ambankgroup.com
AMM—(KLS)
Rev.: $2,440,120,272
Assets: $41,643,639,657
Liabilities: $37,336,990,875
Net Worth: $4,306,648,782
Earnings: $555,234,144
Emp.: 12,770
Fiscal Year-end: 03/31/13

Business Description:
Banking Services
S.I.C.: 6029
N.A.I.C.S.: 522110

Personnel:
Ashok Ramamurthy *(Mng Dir)*
Mandy Jean Simpson *(CFO)*
Ross Neil Foden *(COO)*
Charles Keng Lock Tan *(CIO)*
Fauziah Yacob *(Chief HR Officer)*
Nigel Christopher William Denby *(Chief Risk Officer)*
Kim Mon Thein *(Chief Internal Auditor)*
Tuck Cheong Kok *(CEO/Mng Dir-AmInvestment Bank Berhad)*
Mahdi Murad *(CEO/Mng Dir-AmIslamic Bank Berhad)*
Travis Atkinson *(CEO-AmGeneral Insurance Berhad)*
Paul Hong Ceong Low *(CEO-AmLife Insurance Berhad)*
Datin Maznah Binti Mahbob *(CEO-AmInvest)*
Zamri Zain *(CEO-AmFamily Takaful Berhad)*
Mohamed Azmi Mahmood *(Deputy Mng Dir)*
Phaik Gunn Koid *(Sec)*

Board of Directors:
Azman Hashim
Shayne Cary Elliott
Larry Nyap Liou Gan
Azlan Hashim
Clifford Francis Herbert
Mohammed Hanif Omar
Aris Othman
Gilles Plante
Ashok Ramamurthy
Kim Wai Soo
Rohana Tan Sri Mahmood
Mark David Whelan

Subsidiaries:

Am Ara Reit Managers Sdn Bhd (1)
Level 16 Bangunan Group 55 Jalan Raja Chulan
50200 Kuala Lumpur, Malaysia
Tel.: (60) 320269102
Fax: (60) 327320644
E-Mail: yplim@ambankgroup.com
Web Site: www.amfirstreit.com.my
Emp.: 12
Commercial Banking
S.I.C.: 6029
N.A.I.C.S.: 522110
Lim Yoon Peng *(CEO)*

AM Nominees (Tempatan) Sdn Bhd (1)
Level 9 Bangunan Ambank Group
Kuala Lumpur, Malaysia (51%)
Tel.: (60) 320782788
Commercial Banking
S.I.C.: 6029
N.A.I.C.S.: 522110

AmAssurance Berhad (1)
9th Floor Bangunan AmAssurance
1 Jalan Lumut, 50400 Kuala Lumpur, Malaysia (70%)
Tel.: (60) 340478000
Fax: (60) 340438680
Emp.: 724
Direct Life Insurance Carriers
S.I.C.: 6311
N.A.I.C.S.: 524113
Adrian John Nurse *(Deputy CEO)*

AmBank (M) Berhad (1)
Level 18 Menara am bank Dion Jalan Yat Jwan Seng
50450 Kuala Lumpur, Malaysia
Tel.: (60) 321788888
Fax: (60) 0321713171
E-Mail: customercare@ambamkgroup.com
Web Site: www.ambankgroup.com
Emp.: 250
Banking Services
S.I.C.: 6029
N.A.I.C.S.: 522110
Ross Neil Foden *(COO)*

AmFutures Sdn Bhd (1)
15th Floor Bangunan
AmBank Group 55 Jalan Raja Chu, 50200
Kuala Lumpur, Malaysia (51%)
Tel.: (60) 392353235
Fax: (60) 320323221
E-Mail: amfuturesdealingalliance@ambankgroup.com
Web Site: www.ambankgroup.com
Emp.: 7
Commodity Contracts Brokerage
S.I.C.: 6221
N.A.I.C.S.: 523140
Stephen Kwong *(Dir-eBroking)*

AmG Insurance Berhad (1)
9th Floor Bangunan AmAssurance No 1 Jln Lumut
50400 Kuala Lumpur, Malaysia
Tel.: (60) 3 4047 8000
Fax: (60) 3 4043 8680
E-Mail: amassurance-general@ambankgroup.com
Web Site: www.amassurance.com.my/src/html/am_phase2/general/index.php
Insurance Management Services
S.I.C.: 6411
N.A.I.C.S.: 524298
Azman Hashim *(Chm)*

AmInternational (L) Ltd (1)
Level 12 B Block 4 Office Tower
Financial Park Labuan Complex, 87000
Labuan, Malaysia (51%)
Tel.: (60) 87413133
Fax: (60) 87425211
E-Mail: musa-buang@mbankgroup.com
Web Site: www.ambankgroup.com
Emp.: 14
Commercial Banking
S.I.C.: 6029
N.A.I.C.S.: 522110
Paul Whee Sen Ong *(CEO)*

AmInvestment Bank Group (1)
22nd Floor Bangunan Ambank Group
55 Jalan Raja Chulan, 50200 Kuala Lumpur, Malaysia (51%)
Tel.: (60) 320362633
Fax: (60) 320782842
Holding Company
S.I.C.: 6719
N.A.I.C.S.: 551112

AMMB Holdings Berhad—(Continued)

Subsidiaries:

AmInvestment Management Sdn Bhd (2)
9th Floor Bangunan Arab-Malaysian
No 55 Jalan Raja Chulan, 50200 Kuala Lumpur, Malaysia (100%)
Tel.: (60) 320782633
Fax: (60) 320265630
Web Site: www.ambankgroup.com
Management Consulting Services
S.I.C.: 8748
N.A.I.C.S.: 541618
Maznah Datin Mahbop *(CEO)*

AmInvestment Services Berhad (2)
Level 9 Bangunan AmBank Group
55 Jalan Raja Chulan, 50200 Kuala Lumpur, Malaysia (100%)
Tel.: (60) 320746131
Fax: (60) 320315210
Investment Advice
S.I.C.: 6282
N.A.I.C.S.: 523930

AmIslamic Bank Berhad (1)
Level 45 Menara AmBank
No 8 Jalan Yap Kwan Seng, 50450 Kuala Lumpur, Malaysia (100%)
Tel.: (60) 321673000
Fax: (60) 321665664
Web Site: www.ambg.com.my
Commercial Banking
S.I.C.: 6029
N.A.I.C.S.: 522110
Mahdi Murad *(CEO & Mng Dir)*

AMMB Nominees (Tempatan) Sdn Bhd (1)
11th Floor Bangunan Ambank Group
55 Jalan Raja Chulan, 50200 Kuala Lumpur, Malaysia (51%)
Tel.: (60) 320782633
Fax: (60) 320263946
Securities & Commodity Exchanges
S.I.C.: 6231
N.A.I.C.S.: 523210

AMMerchant Bank Berhad (1)
Ground Floor Bangunan AmBank Group
No 55 Jalan Raja Chulan, 50200 Kuala Lumpur, Malaysia
Tel.: (60) 320782100
Telex: MA 31167
Fax: (60) 320323935
Web Site: www.ambankgroup.com
Emp.: 747
Banking Services
S.I.C.: 6159
N.A.I.C.S.: 522298
Cheah Tek Kuang *(Grp Mng Dir)*

AmPrivate Equity Sdn Bhd (1)
Tingkat 15 Bangunan AmBank Group
No 55 Jalan Raja Chulan, 50200 Kuala Lumpur, Malaysia
Tel.: (60) 320782392
Fax: (60) 320728253
Commercial Banking
S.I.C.: 6029
N.A.I.C.S.: 522110

AmProperty Trust Management Berhad (1)
22nd Floor Bangunan Ambank Group
50200 Kuala Lumpur, Malaysia (51%)
Tel.: (60) 320782633
Fax: (60) 27320644
Real Estate Investment Trusts
S.I.C.: 6726
N.A.I.C.S.: 525990

AmResearch Sdn Bhd (1)
15th Fl Ambank Group Bldg
55 Jalan Raja Chulan, 50200 Kuala Lumpur, Malaysia
Tel.: (60) 320782788
Fax: (60) 320317218
Web Site: www.asecurities.com.my
Emp.: 25
Investment Advice
S.I.C.: 6282
N.A.I.C.S.: 523930
Denny Chew *(Exec Dir-AmResearch)*

Amsec Nominees (Asing) Sdn Bhd (1)
Tingkat 22 Bangunanambank group
55 Jalan Raja Chulan, 50200 Kuala Lumpur, Malaysia (51%)
Tel.: (60) 320782788
Fax: (60) 320263946
E-Mail: info@ambankgroup.com
Web Site: www.ambankgroup.com
Emp.: 100
Securities & Commodity Exchanges
S.I.C.: 6231
N.A.I.C.S.: 523210

Amsec Nominees (Tempatan) Sdn Bhd (1)
55 Jalan Raja Chulan 15th Floor
Kuala Lumpur, Malaysia (51%)
Tel.: (60) 320782788
Securities & Commodity Exchanges
S.I.C.: 6231
N.A.I.C.S.: 523210

AmTrustee Berhad (1)
15 Menara Amfirst No 1 Jalan 19/3
Bangunan Ambank Group, Petaling Jaya, 46300, Malaysia (60.4%)
Tel.: (60) 9546862
Fax: (60) 37953712
Web Site: www.ambg.com.my
Emp.: 30
Trust & Fiduciary Services
S.I.C.: 6091
N.A.I.C.S.: 523991
Tan Kok Cheeng *(CEO)*

Malaysian Ventures Management Incorporated Sdn Bhd (1)
15th Fl Bangunan AmBank Group
No 55 Jalan Raja Chulan, 50200 Kuala Lumpur, Malaysia
Tel.: (60) 320782392
Fax: (60) 320728253
E-Mail: peter-ype@ammbbankgroup.com
Emp.: 5
Management Consulting Services
S.I.C.: 8748
N.A.I.C.S.: 541618
Francis Ng *(CEO)*

MBf Cards (Msia) Sdn. Bhd. (1)
Menara MBf Jalan Sultan Ismail
50250 Kuala Lumpur, Malaysia
Tel.: (60) 321677600
Fax: (60) 321677722
E-Mail: customer.service@mbfcards.com
Web Site: www.mbfcards.com
Credit & Charge Cards Issuing Services
S.I.C.: 6141
N.A.I.C.S.: 522210
John Ding *(Pres)*
Perry Ong *(CEO)*
Choong Beng Hin *(Sr VP-Fin)*
Kiran Jeyabalan *(Sr VP-Bus Dev & IR)*
Kim Lee Mei *(Sr VP-Grp HR & Admin)*
Rajjish Verronn *(Sr VP-Mktg)*

Non-U.S. Subsidiaries:

AmFraser Securities Pte Ltd (1)
4 Shenton Way
13-01 SGX Centre 2, 068807 Singapore, Singapore (51%)
Tel.: (65) 65359455
Fax: (65) 65357879
E-Mail: customerservice@amfraser.com.sg
Web Site: www.amfraser.com.sg
Emp.: 100
Securities Brokerage
S.I.C.: 6211
N.A.I.C.S.: 523120
Ma Wei Tong *(Mng Dir)*

Fraser-Ammb Research Pte Ltd (1)
4 Shenton Way # 12-01
068807 Singapore, Singapore (51%)
Tel.: (65) 62362504
Fax: (65) 65362315
Commercial Banking
S.I.C.: 6029
N.A.I.C.S.: 522110

PT. AmCapital Indonesia (1)
Wisma GKBI 5th Floor Suite 501 Jl Jend Sudirman No 28
Jakarta, 10210, Indonesia
Tel.: (62) 21 5795 7000
Fax: (62) 21 57950698
E-Mail: cs@amcapital.co.id
Web Site: www.amcapital.co.id
Securities Brokerage Services
S.I.C.: 6211
N.A.I.C.S.: 523120

AMMEUX FRANCE

Rue De La Gare
59470 Esquelbecq, Nord, France
Tel.: (33) 328659830
Fax: (33) 328659831
E-Mail: contact@ammeux.fr
Web Site: www.ammeux.fr
Sls.: $23,100,000
Emp.: 90

Business Description:
Fresh Fruits & Vegetables
S.I.C.: 5148
N.A.I.C.S.: 424480

Personnel:
Jozef Muyshondt *(Pres)*

AMOI TECHNOLOGY CO., LTD.

4/F:22 Guan Ri Road Software Park
Siming District, Xiamen, Fujian, 361008, China
Tel.: (86) 5923663088
Fax: (86) 592 366 3081
E-Mail: overseas@amoi.com.cn
Web Site: www.amoi.com.cn
Year Founded: 1981
600057—(SHG)
Sales Range: $200-249.9 Million
Emp.: 1,405

Business Description:
Electronics Mfr
S.I.C.: 3663
N.A.I.C.S.: 334220

Personnel:
Xuehong Liu *(Chm)*
Guoliang Lin *(Vice Chm)*
Shunhua Shi *(Vice Chm)*
Zhenyu Lu *(Pres)*
Dong Lu *(Sec)*

AMONIL S.A.

Calarasi Road Km 4
Slobozia, Romania 920120
Tel.: (40) 243211225
Fax: (40) 243232539
E-Mail: amonil.sl@amonil.ro
Web Site: www.amonil.ro
AMO—(BUC)
Rev.: $2,308,762
Assets: $25,949,303
Liabilities: $6,272,840
Net Worth: $19,676,463
Earnings: $39,627
Emp.: 18
Fiscal Year-end: 12/31/12

Business Description:
Chemical Fertilizers Producer
S.I.C.: 2873
N.A.I.C.S.: 325311

Personnel:
Cristina Matei *(Gen Mgr)*

AMOREPACIFIC CORP.

5F-13F Signature Towers West Wing
100 Cheonggyecheon-ro Jung-gu
Seoul, Korea (South)
Tel.: (82) 27095114
Fax: (82) 27095339
Web Site: eng.amorepacific.co.kr
090430—(KRS)
Sls.: $3,191,511,690
Assets: $4,199,838,150
Liabilities: $820,020,060
Net Worth: $3,379,818,090
Earnings: $321,500,070
Emp.: 10,526
Fiscal Year-end: 12/31/12

Business Description:
Beauty & Health Care Products
S.I.C.: 2844
N.A.I.C.S.: 325620

Personnel:
Kyung-Bae Suh *(Chm & CEO)*

Board of Directors:
Kyung-Bae Suh
Dong-Hyun Bae
Dong-Chul Cho
Dong-Soo Kim
Young-So Kwon
Eon-Oh Lee
Eun Namkung
Sang-Bae Shim
Jae-Yong Song

Non-U.S. Subsidiary:

Annick Goutal S.A.S. (1)
14 Rue De Castiglione
75001 Paris, France
Tel.: (33) 142605282
Fax: (33) 140712070
Web Site: www.annickgoutal.com
Sales Range: $10-24.9 Million
Perfume & Cosmetics Retailer
S.I.C.: 5122
N.A.I.C.S.: 446120
William Bouheret *(Mng Dir)*

AMORFIX LIFE SCIENCES LTD.

3403 American Drive
Mississauga, ON, L4V 1T4, Canada
Tel.: (416) 847-6898
Fax: (416) 847-6899
E-Mail: info@amorfix.com
Web Site: www.amorfix.com
AMF—(TSX)
Rev.: $49,220
Assets: $319,884
Liabilities: $534,838
Net Worth: ($214,955)
Earnings: ($2,217,561)
Emp.: 9
Fiscal Year-end: 03/31/13

Business Description:
Neurodegenerative Diseases Diagnosis & Treatment Products Developer & Mfr
S.I.C.: 3841
N.A.I.C.S.: 339112

Personnel:
Neil Cashman *(Founder, Chm & Chief Scientific Officer)*
Robert Gundel *(Pres & CEO)*
Warren Whitehead *(CFO)*

Board of Directors:
Neil Cashman
Hans Black
William Copeland
Robert Gundel
Aziz Mekouar
William Wyman

Olympia Transfer Services Inc
Toronto, ON, Canada

Transfer Agents:
Olympia Trust Company
Calgary, AB, Canada

Olympia Transfer Services Inc
Toronto, ON, Canada

AMOTECH CO LTD

1 Lot 617 Namchon-Dong
Namdong Gu, Incheon, Korea (South)
Tel.: (82) 328210363
Fax: (82) 82328110283
Web Site: www.amotech.co.kr
52710—(KRS)
Sales Range: $75-99.9 Million

Business Description:
Electronic Appliances
S.I.C.: 3677
N.A.I.C.S.: 334416

Personnel:
Pyung Kyu Kim *(CEO)*

Divisions:

Amotech Co., Ltd. - Antenna Division (1)
5 Bl 1 Lot 617 Namchon-Dong
Namdong-Gu, 405-100 Incheon, Korea (South)
Tel.: (82) 328210363
Fax: (82) 328110283
Web Site: www.amotech.co.kr

Emp.: 120
Antenna Mfr
S.I.C.: 3663
N.A.I.C.S.: 334220
Kim Pyung Kyu *(Pres)*

Amotech Co., Ltd. - Motor Division (1)
Manho-ri Poseung-myun
Pyeongtaek, Gyeonggi-do, Korea (South)
Tel.: (82) 3180537000
Fax: (82) 316819115
E-Mail: yjkim07@amotech.co.kr
Emp.: 50
Motors Mfr
S.I.C.: 3714
N.A.I.C.S.: 336390
Yejin Kim *(Mgr-Sls)*

Amotech Co., Ltd. - Varistor Division (1)
5 Bl 1 Lot 617 Namchon-Dong
Namdong-Gu, 405-100 Incheon, Korea (South)
Tel.: (82) 5 9724578
Fax: (82) 32 811 0283
Electronic Products Mfr
S.I.C.: 3677
N.A.I.C.S.: 334416

Subsidiary:

AMOTECH KOREA Inc. (1)
5 Bl 1 Lot 617 Namchon-Dong Namdong Industrial Complex
617 Bunji, Incheon, 405-846, Korea (South)
Tel.: (82) 42 76 44 68
Fax: (82) 32 811 0283
E-Mail: support@amotech.co.kr
Web Site: www.amotech.co.kr/
Electronic Products Mfr
S.I.C.: 3566
N.A.I.C.S.: 333612

Non-U.S. Plant:

Amotech Co., Ltd. - Shandong Factory (1)
Room 609 West Tianan Hi-Tech Plaza Phase II, Shenzhen, China
Tel.: (86) 75582507984
Fax: (86) 75582507987
E-Mail: shirzh@amotech.com.cn
Web Site: www.amotech.co.kr
Emp.: 400
Electronic Products Mfr
S.I.C.: 3679
N.A.I.C.S.: 334419
Pyung Kyu Kim *(CEO)*

Non-U.S. Subsidiary:

AMOTECH EUROPE Ltd. (1)
Ste 20 Trinity House Heather Pk Dr
Wembley, Middlesex, HAO 1SU, United Kingdom
Tel.: (44) 2089001021
Fax: (44) 2089001844
E-Mail: hhkim@amotech.co.kr
Emp.: 2
Electronic Components Mfr
S.I.C.: 3679
N.A.I.C.S.: 334419
M. Cho *(Gen Mgr)*

AMOUN INTERNATIONAL FOR INVESTMENT P.L.C

Building 85 Sherif Nasser Bin Jamel Street Shmeisani Area
17523 Amman, Jordan
Tel.: (962) 6 556 0511
Fax: (962) 6 556 0514
E-Mail: info@ammouninvest.com
Year Founded: 2008
AMON—(AMM)
Rev.: $33,154
Assets: $14,292,692
Liabilities: $557,019
Net Worth: $13,735,673
Earnings: ($313,515)
Emp.: 6
Fiscal Year-end: 12/31/12

Business Description:
Real Estate Development Services
S.I.C.: 6531
N.A.I.C.S.: 531390

Personnel:
Emad Al Ghannam *(Gen Mgr)*

AMP LIMITED

Level 24 33 Alfred Streey
Sydney, NSW, 2000, Australia
Tel.: (61) 292575000
Fax: (61) 292577178
E-Mail: polinfo@amp.com.au
Web Site: www.amp.com.au
Year Founded: 1849
AMP—(ASX OTC)
Rev.: $4,999,995,800
Assets: $123,750,417,100
Liabilities: $115,902,362,000
Net Worth: $7,848,055,100
Earnings: $715,922,700
Emp.: 5,829
Fiscal Year-end: 12/31/12

Business Description:
Financial Management & Capital Investment Services
S.I.C.: 6211
N.A.I.C.S.: 523999

Personnel:
Simon McKeon *(Chm)*
Craig William Dunn *(CEO & Mng Dir)*
Colin Storrie *(CFO)*
Lee Barnett *(CIO)*
Paul Sainsbury *(Chief Customer Officer)*
Brian Salter *(Gen Counsel)*
Darryl Mackay *(Sec & Head-Secretariat)*

Board of Directors:
Simon McKeon
Patricia Elizabeth Akopiantz
Richard Hugh Allert
Catherine Michelle Brenner
Brian James Clark
Craig William Dunn
Paul Anthony Fegan
Trevor John Matthews
John Leonard Palmer
Nora Lia Scheinkestel
Peter Roger Shergold

Subsidiaries:

AMP Australian Financial Services Holdings Limited (1)
L 24 33 Alfred St
Sydney, NSW, Australia (100%)
Tel.: (61) 292575000
Web Site: www.amp.com.au
Holding Company
S.I.C.: 6719
N.A.I.C.S.: 551112
Craig Don *(CEO)*

AMP Bank Limited (1)
33 Alfred Street
Sydney, NSW, 2000, Australia (100%)
Tel.: (61) 296419641
Fax: (61) 296419090
Web Site: www.amp.com.au
Commercial Banking
S.I.C.: 6029
N.A.I.C.S.: 522110
Andrew Mohl *(CEO & Mng Dir)*

AMP Capital Holdings Limited (1)
L 24 33 Alfred St
2000 Sydney, NSW, Australia (85%)
Tel.: (61) 292575000
E-Mail: polinfo@amp.com.au
Web Site: www.amp.com.au
Emp.: 3,500
Holding Company
S.I.C.: 6719
N.A.I.C.S.: 551112
Craig William Dunn *(CEO)*
Margaret Payn *(CFO)*

AMP Capital Investors International Holdings Limited (1)
L 12 50 Bridge St
Sydney, NSW, Australia (100%)
Tel.: (61) 292575000
Web Site: www.ampcapital.com.au/information/contactus.asp
Holding Company
S.I.C.: 6719
N.A.I.C.S.: 551112

AMP Capital Investors Limited (1)
50 Bridge Street
Sydney, NSW, 2000, Australia
Tel.: (61) 292575000
Fax: (61) 292571234
Web Site: www.ampcapital.com
Emp.: 200
Investment Services
S.I.C.: 6282
N.A.I.C.S.: 523930
Stephen Dunne *(Mng Dir)*
Henry Capra *(CFO)*
Mark Beardow *(Chief Investment Officer-Specialist Investment)*
Andrew Bird *(Chief Investment Officer-Property)*
Mark O'Brien *(Chief Investment Officer)*

Holding:

Jeminex Ltd (2)
Level 20 68 Pitt Street
Sydney, NSW, 2000, Australia
Tel.: (61) 2 9226 2000
Fax: (61) 2 9226 2099
E-Mail: info@jeminex.com
Web Site: www.jeminex.com.au
Emp.: 20
Industrial Safety Component Distr
S.I.C.: 5085
N.A.I.C.S.: 423840
Kevin Clarke *(Chm)*
Geoff Heatley *(Deputy Chm)*

Non-U.S. Subsidiary:

AMP Capital Investors (New Zealand) Limited (2)
Ground Floor PwC Tower 113-119 The Terrace
PO Box 3764
Wellington, New Zealand
Tel.: (64) 44942200
Fax: (64) 44942100
Web Site: www.ampcapital.co.nz
Emp.: 50
Financial & Investment Services
S.I.C.: 6282
N.A.I.C.S.: 523930
Graham Law *(Mng Dir)*
Anthony Beverley *(CIO)*

AMP Capital Office and Industrial Pty Limited (1)
Suite 19 45 Collins Street
Melbourne, Australia
Tel.: (61) 3 9655 3600
Financial Investment Services
S.I.C.: 6211
N.A.I.C.S.: 523999

AMP Finance Services Limited (1)
L24 33 Alfred Street
Sydney, NSW, Australia (100%)
Tel.: (61) 292575000
Fax: (61) 292575001
Web Site: www.amp.com.au
Emp.: 100
Business Support Services
S.I.C.: 7389
N.A.I.C.S.: 561499
Carg Dunn *(CEO)*
Craig Meller *(Mng Dir)*

AMP Financial Planning Pty Limited (1)
33 Alfred St Amp Building
Sydney, NSW, 2000, Australia (100%)
Tel.: (61) 292575000
Investment Advice
S.I.C.: 6282
N.A.I.C.S.: 523930
David Randall *(Mgr-Bus Partnership-North Queensland)*
Craig William Dunn *(Mng Dir)*

AMP Gbs Limited (1)
L 22 Amp Building 33 Alfred St
Sydney, NSW, Australia (100%)
Tel.: (61) 292576273
Business Support Services
S.I.C.: 7389
N.A.I.C.S.: 561499
Andrew Mohl *(CEO)*

AMP Group Finance Services Limited (1)
L24 Amp Sydney Cove Bldg 33 Alfred St
Sydney, NSW, 2000, Australia (100%)
Tel.: (61) 292575453
Fax: (61) 292577178
AQN—(ASX)
Emp.: 3,005
Investment Advice
S.I.C.: 6282
N.A.I.C.S.: 523930
Craig Meller *(Mng Dir)*

AMP Group Holdings Limited (1)
L24 33 Alfred St
Sydney, NSW, Australia (100%)
Tel.: (61) 292575000
Web Site: www.amp.com.au/wps/portal/au
Business Support Services
S.I.C.: 7389
N.A.I.C.S.: 561499
Andrew Mohl *(CEO)*

AMP Group Services Limited (1)
L 24 33 Alfred St
2000 Sydney, NSW, Australia (100%)
Tel.: (61) 292575000
Web Site: www.amp.com.au
Investment Advice
S.I.C.: 6282
N.A.I.C.S.: 523930
Craig Denn *(CEO)*

AMP Holdings Limited (1)
L 24 Amp Sydney Cove Bldg
Sydney, NSW, 2000, Australia (100%)
Tel.: (61) 292575000
Web Site: www.ampcapital.com
Emp.: 10
Holding Company
S.I.C.: 6719
N.A.I.C.S.: 551112
Craig William Dunn *(CEO & Mng Dir)*

AMP Insurance Investment Holdings Pty Limited (1)
L 9 33 Alfred St
Sydney, NSW, 2000, Australia
Tel.: (61) 292578444
Fax: (61) 130036826
Insurance Management Services
S.I.C.: 6411
N.A.I.C.S.: 524298

AMP Investment Services Pty Limited (1)
L 11 Amp Centre 50 Bridge St
Sydney, NSW, Australia (100%)
Tel.: (61) 292575000
Fax: (61) 1300301267
E-Mail: polinfo@amp.com.au
Web Site: amp.com.au
Business Support Services
S.I.C.: 7389
N.A.I.C.S.: 561499
Craig William Dunn *(Mng Dir)*

AMP Private Wealth Management Pty Limited (1)
Level 7 17 Castlereagh Street
Sydney, NSW, 2000, Australia
Tel.: (61) 1300 098 859
Fax: (61) 2 9232 7209
E-Mail: ampprivate@amp.com.au
Web Site: www.ampprivate.com.au
General Insurance Services
S.I.C.: 6411
N.A.I.C.S.: 524210
Doug Webber *(Head-Client Sls & Svc)*

AMP Services Holdings Limited (1)
AMP Bldg 33 Alfred Street
Sydney, NSW, 2000, Australia (100%)
Tel.: (61) 292575000
Fax: (61) 1300301267
E-Mail: polinso@amp.com.au
Web Site: www.amp.com.au
Emp.: 1,000
Nondepository Credit Intermediation
S.I.C.: 6159
N.A.I.C.S.: 522298
Craig William Dunn *(Mng Dir)*

AMP Services Limited (1)
Level 18 33 Alfred Street
2000 Sydney, NSW, Australia (100%)
Tel.: (61) 92575190
Fax: (61) 92577466
Web Site: www.amp.com.au/vgn-ext-templating/v/index.jsp?vgnextoid=f0bb50665a6cc110VgnVCM1000002930410aRCRD
Management Consulting Services
S.I.C.: 8748

AMP Limited—(Continued)

N.A.I.C.S.: 541618

AMP Superannuation Limited (1)
L 14 Amp Sydney Cove Building 33 Alfred St
Sydney, NSW, 2000, Australia
Tel.: (61) 292575000
Financial Management Services
S.I.C.: 6211
N.A.I.C.S.: 523999

AMP Warringah Mall Pty Ltd (1)
Cnr Condamine St Old Pittwater Road
Brookvale, NSW, 2100, Australia
Tel.: (61) 29905 0633
Fax: (61) 29939 2046
E-Mail: warringahmall@ampcapital.com.au
Web Site: www.warringahmall.com.au
Shopping Mall Operating Services
S.I.C.: 5411
N.A.I.C.S.: 445110

Arrive Wealth Management Limited (1)
123 Eagle Street
Level 15 Riverside Centre, Brisbane, NSW, 4000, Australia (100%)
Tel.: (61) 730017000
Fax: (61) 730017001
E-Mail: admin@arrive.com.au
Web Site: www.arrive.com.au
Emp.: 150
Investment Advice
S.I.C.: 6282
N.A.I.C.S.: 523930

AXA Asia Pacific Holdings Limited (1)
750 Collins Street
Docklands, Melbourne, VIC, 3008, Australia AU
Tel.: (61) 396163911
Fax: (61) 386885799
Web Site: www.axa.com.au
Sales Range: $5-14.9 Billion
Holding Company; Insurance Products & Services
S.I.C.: 6719
N.A.I.C.S.: 551112
Geoff Roberts *(CFO)*
Peter Mahler *(Acting CIO-Australia & New Zealand)*
Mark Dutton *(Chief Investment Officer)*
Warren Lee *(CEO-Australia & New Zealand)*
Kevin Keenan *(Gen Counsel & Co-Sec)*
Darryl Mackay *(Co-Sec & Gen Mgr-CEO Office)*

Subsidiaries:

AXA Australia (2)
750 Collins Street
Melbourne, VIC, 3008, Australia
Tel.: (61) 386883911
Fax: (61) 396142240
E-Mail: info@axa.com.au
Web Site: www.axa.com.au
Emp.: 1,000
Insurance & Financial Services
S.I.C.: 6211
N.A.I.C.S.: 523999
Jeiff Roperts *(CFO)*

Genesys Wealth Advisers Limited (2)
14 383 Kent St
Sydney, NSW, 2000, Australia
Mailing Address:
PO Box 3936
Sydney, NSW, 2001, Australia
Tel.: (61) 288763400
Fax: (61) 298690842
Web Site: www.genesyswealth.com.au
Emp.: 25
Miscellaneous Financial Investment Activities
S.I.C.: 6211
N.A.I.C.S.: 523999
John Saint *(CEO)*

National Mutual Funds Management Ltd. (2)
750 Collins Street
Melbourne, VIC, 3000, Australia
Tel.: (61) 396163911
Fax: (61) 386885799
E-Mail: client.enquire@axa.com.au
Web Site: www.axa.com.au
Sales Range: $25-49.9 Million
Financial Management Services
S.I.C.: 8742
N.A.I.C.S.: 541611
Elizabeth Anne Foley *(Head-Summit)*

National Mutual Life Association of Australia Ltd. (2)
750 Collins St
Melbourne, Victoria, 3000, Australia (100%)
Tel.: (61) 396163911
Fax: (61) 386885799
E-Mail: info@axa.com.au
Web Site: www.axa.com.au
Emp.: 2,000
Life Insurance & Finance Services
S.I.C.: 6311
N.A.I.C.S.: 524113
Richard Hugh Allert *(Chm)*

Non-U.S. Subsidiary:

AXA New Zealand (2)
80 The Terrace
PO Box 1692
Wellington, 6140, New Zealand NZ
Tel.: (64) 44744500 (100%)
Fax: (64) 0800161699
E-Mail: askus@axa.co.nz
Web Site: www.axa.co.nz
Emp.: 200
Life Insurance
S.I.C.: 6311
N.A.I.C.S.: 524113
Jack Regon *(CEO)*

Collins Place No. 2 Pty Ltd (1)
Melbourne
Melbourne, VIC, 3000, Australia
Tel.: (61) 396553600
Fax: (61) 396553666
Real Estate Management Services
S.I.C.: 6531
N.A.I.C.S.: 531390

Collins Place Pty Limited (1)
45 Collins Street
Melbourne, 3000, Australia
Tel.: (61) 3 9655 3600
Fax: (61) 3 9655 3666
E-Mail: info@collinsplace.com.au
Web Site: www.collinsplace.com.au
Real Estate Management Services
S.I.C.: 6531
N.A.I.C.S.: 531390

Glendenning Pty Limited (1)
1132 Richmond Rd
Marsden Park, Sydney, NSW, 2765, Australia
Tel.: (61) 296271804
Fax: (61) 296275318
Business Support Services
S.I.C.: 7389
N.A.I.C.S.: 561499

Hillross Alliances Limited (1)
Darling Park Twr 3 L 16 201 Sussex St
Sydney, NSW, 2000, Australia
Tel.: (61) 2 8115 4000
Business Management Consulting Services
S.I.C.: 8742
N.A.I.C.S.: 541611

Hillross Financial Services Limited (1)
Level 11 33 Alfred Street
Sydney, NSW, 2000, Australia
Mailing Address:
PO Box 4134
Sydney, NSW, 2001, Australia
Tel.: (61) 2 9257 4040
Fax: (61) 2 9257 9281
E-Mail: info@hillross.com.au
Web Site: www.hillross.com.au
Financial & Investment Services
S.I.C.: 6282
N.A.I.C.S.: 523930
Seng Wing Chong *(Head-Governance & Risk)*

Hillross Innisfail Pty Limited (1)
Shop 10 27 Owen St
Innisfail, QLD, 4860, Australia
Tel.: (61) 740614588
Fax: (61) 740614977
Business Management Consulting Services
S.I.C.: 8742
N.A.I.C.S.: 541611

Homemaker Megamall Auburn Pty Ltd (1)
265 Parramatta Road Corner Parramatta Rd & Duck St
Auburn, NSW, 2144, Australia
Tel.: (61) 29748 6900
Fax: (61) 29748 4102
Web Site: www.auburnhomemegamall.com.au
Shopping Mall Operating Services
S.I.C.: 5411
N.A.I.C.S.: 445110
Angela Bechara *(Mgr-Mktg-Casual Mall Leasing)*

Marrickville Metro Shopping Centre Pty Limited (1)
34 Victoria Road
Marrickville, NSW, 2204, Australia
Tel.: (61) 295191066
Fax: (61) 295198753
Web Site: www.marrickvillemetro.com.au
Shopping Mall Operating Services
S.I.C.: 5411
N.A.I.C.S.: 445110
Christian Hogg *(Gen Mgr)*

Mowla Pty. Ltd (1)
25 Collins St
Melbourne, VIC, 3000, Australia (100%)
Tel.: (61) 396530000
Fax: (61) 396504261
E-Mail: h1902-co01@accor.com
Web Site: www.sositelmelbourne.com.au
Emp.: 500
Amusement & Recreation Industries
S.I.C.: 7999
N.A.I.C.S.: 713990
Clive Scott *(Gen Mgr)*

Priority One Financial Services Limited (1)
Level 4 33 Alfred St
Sydney, NSW, Australia (100%)
Tel.: (61) 296419641
Financial Services
S.I.C.: 6099
N.A.I.C.S.: 522320
Andrew Mohl *(CEO)*

SPP No. 1 (Mornington) Pty Limited (1)
36 Racecourse Rd
Pakenham, VIC, 3810, Australia
Tel.: (61) 359417439
Fax: (61) 395617126
Emp.: 10
Retirement Home Services
S.I.C.: 8361
N.A.I.C.S.: 623312
Andrew Philip *(Mng Dir)*

SPP No. 3A Investments Pty Limited (1)
L 15 50 Bridge St
Sydney, NSW, 2000, Australia
Tel.: (61) 2 9257 1629
Investment Management Services
S.I.C.: 6211
N.A.I.C.S.: 523999

Sugarland Shopping Centre Pty Limited (1)
115-119 Takalvan Street
West Bundaberg, Bundaberg, QLD, 4670, Australia
Tel.: (61) 7 4152 5788
Fax: (61) 7 4152 6874
Web Site: www.sugarlandshoppingtown.com.au
Emp.: 700
Stationery Products Distr
S.I.C.: 5112
N.A.I.C.S.: 424120

United Equipment Holdings Pty Limited (1)
524 Abernethy Rd
Kewdale, WA, 6105, Australia
Tel.: (61) 894538999
Fax: (61) 894538988
E-Mail: service@unitedequipment.com.au
Web Site: www.unitedequipment.com.au
Emp.: 30
Industrial Truck Distr
S.I.C.: 5084
N.A.I.C.S.: 423830
Peter Court *(Mng Dir)*

U.S. Subsidiary:

AMP Capital Investors (US) Limited (1)
777 3rd Ave 19th Fl
New York, NY 10017
Tel.: (212) 223-7600
Fax: (212) 202-3854
Investment Management Services
S.I.C.: 6211
N.A.I.C.S.: 523999

Non-U.S. Subsidiaries:

AMP Capital Investments Limited (1)
Level 14 HP Tower 171 Featherston Street
Wellington, New Zealand (100%)
Tel.: (64) 44942299
Fax: (64) 44942119
Web Site: www.ampcapital.com.au/institutions/infrastructure/locations.asp
Investment Advice
S.I.C.: 6282
N.A.I.C.S.: 523930

AMP Capital Investors (Luxembourg) S.a r.l. (1)
18-20 Rue Edward Steichen
2540 Luxembourg, Luxembourg
Tel.: (352) 2784 8035
Fax: (352) 2784 8034
Emp.: 3
Investment Management Services
S.I.C.: 6211
N.A.I.C.S.: 523999
Adelaide Care *(Mng Dir)*

AMP Capital Investors Property Japan KK (1)
Otemachi First Square East Tower 4F 1-5-1 Otemachi
Chiyoda-Ku, Tokyo, 100-0004, Japan
Tel.: (81) 3 5219 1328
Fax: (81) 3 5219 1448
Web Site: www.ampcapital.com
Real Estate Management Services
S.I.C.: 6531
N.A.I.C.S.: 531390

AMP Custodian Services (NZ) Limited (1)
86-90 Custom House Quay
Wellington, 6011, New Zealand
Tel.: (64) 44988000
Financial Investment Services
S.I.C.: 6211
N.A.I.C.S.: 523999

AMP Life Ltd. (1)
Level 11 HP Towers 187 Featherstone St
PO Box 1290
Wellington, New Zealand (100%)
Tel.: (64) 44988000
Fax: (64) 093377797
E-Mail: service@amp.co.nz
Web Site: www.amp.co.nz
Emp.: 200
S.I.C.: 6399
N.A.I.C.S.: 524128
Jack Regan *(Mng Dir)*

AMP Services (NZ) Limited (1)
29 Custom St Auckland Central
PO Box 1290
Level 1 AMP Chambers, Auckland, New Zealand (100%)
Tel.: (64) 44988000
Fax: (64) 093377797
E-Mail: service@amp.co.nz
Web Site: www.amp.co.nz
Emp.: 500
Financial Transactions Processing Reserve & Clearinghouse Activities
S.I.C.: 6099
N.A.I.C.S.: 522320
Jack Regan *(Mng Dir)*

AMP Superannuation (NZ) Limited (1)
29 Customs Street
PO Box 55
Auckland, 1140, New Zealand (100%)
Tel.: (64) 44988000
Fax: (64) 800509955
E-Mail: service@amp.co.nz
Web Site: www.amp.co.nz
Reinsurance Carriers
S.I.C.: 6399
N.A.I.C.S.: 524130

Jack Regan *(Mng Dir)*

Arthur Ellis Limited (1)
20 Treffers Road
8004 Christchurch, New Zealand (100%)
Tel.: (64) 33418250
Fax: (64) 33418251
Sporting & Athletic Goods Mfr
S.I.C.: 3949
N.A.I.C.S.: 339920
Mary Devine *(Mng Dir)*

Donaghys Industries Limited (1)
PO Box 20449
8543 Christchurch, New Zealand (75%)
Tel.: (64) 39834100
Fax: (64) 39834191
E-Mail: trm@donaghys.co.nz
Web Site: www.donaghys.com
Emp.: 20
Textile Product Mills
S.I.C.: 2389
N.A.I.C.S.: 314999
Jeremy Silva *(CEO & Mng Dir)*

Donaghys Limited (1)
16 Sheffield Crescent Harewood
8543 Christchurch, New Zealand (75%)
Tel.: (64) 39834100
Fax: (64) 39834191
E-Mail: jsilva@donaghys.co.nz
Web Site: www.donaghys.co.nz
Emp.: 25
Rope Cordage & Twine Mills
S.I.C.: 2296
N.A.I.C.S.: 314994
Jeremy Silva *(CEO & Mng Dir)*

Methven Limited (1)
447 Rosebank Rd
PO Box 19996
Auckland, 1026, New Zealand (100%)
Tel.: (64) 98290429
Fax: (64) 98290439
E-Mail: info@methven.com
Web Site: www.methven.com
Emp.: 120
Tap & Valve Mfr
S.I.C.: 3491
N.A.I.C.S.: 332911
Phil Lough *(Chm)*
Rick Fila *(CEO)*

Roost 2007 Limited (1)
Level 21 AMP Centre 29 Customs St West
Auckland, New Zealand
Tel.: (64) 9 337 7219
E-Mail: admin@roost.co.nz
Web Site: www.roost.co.nz
Mortgage Loan Brokerage Services
S.I.C.: 6163
N.A.I.C.S.: 522310
Blair Vernon *(Gen Mgr)*

AMPCO METAL SA

48 Rte De Chesalles
Marly, Fribourg, 1723, Switzerland
Tel.: (41) 264399310
Fax: (41) 264399301
E-Mail: info@ampcometal.com
Web Site: www.ampcometal.com
Emp.: 150

Business Description:
Mfr. & Producer of Copper Alloys
S.I.C.: 3369
N.A.I.C.S.: 331529

Personnel:
Luis Bento *(Chm)*

U.S. Subsidiary:

Ampco Metal, Inc. (1)
1117 E Algonquin Rd
Arlington Heights, IL 60005-4756
Tel.: (847) 437-6000
Fax: (847) 437-6008
Toll Free: (800) 844-6008
E-Mail: sales@ampcometal.com
Web Site: www.ampcometal.com
Emp.: 75
Mfr. & Producer of Copper Alloys
S.I.C.: 3369
N.A.I.C.S.: 331529
Jason Carter *(Gen Mgr)*

Non-U.S. Subsidiaries:

Ampco Metal SAS (1)
46 Avenue Des Freres Lumiere
Batiment A, 78190 Trappes, France (100%)
Tel.: (33) 130492929
Fax: (33) 130626398
E-Mail: info@ampcometal.com
Web Site: www.ampcometal.com
Sales Range: $25-49.9 Million
Emp.: 7
Mfr. & Producer of Copper Alloys
S.I.C.: 3369
N.A.I.C.S.: 331529
Luis Bento *(CEO)*

Ampco Metal Ltd. (1)
17 Binns Cl Torrington Ave
Coventry, CV4 9TB, United Kingdom
Tel.: (44) 2476467011
Telex: 311415 AMPCOV G
Fax: (44) 2476461455
E-Mail: infouk@ampcometal.com
Web Site: www.ampcometal.com
Sls.: $1,858,335
Emp.: 4
Mfr. & Producer of Copper Alloys
S.I.C.: 3369
N.A.I.C.S.: 331529
Fabrice Podevin *(Mgr-Europe)*

Ampco Metal Portugal Ltda. (1)
Vila Central 360
4475 330 Porto, Milheiros, Portugal
Tel.: (351) 229783080
Fax: (351) 229780912
E-Mail: portugal@ampcometal.com
Web Site: www.ampcometal.com
Emp.: 8
Mfr. & Producer of Copper Alloys
S.I.C.: 3369
N.A.I.C.S.: 331529
Luis Bento *(Pres)*

AMPCONTROL PTY. LTD.

21 Old Punt Road
Tomago, NSW, 2322, Australia
Tel.: (61) 2 4961 9000
Fax: (61) 2 4961 9009
E-Mail: cst@ampcontrolgroup.com
Web Site: www.ampcontrolgroup.com
Year Founded: 1968
Emp.: 900

Business Description:
Electrical & Electronic Products Mfr
S.I.C.: 3699
N.A.I.C.S.: 335999

Personnel:
Peter Cockbain *(Founder & Dir-Tech)*
Robert Douglas Humphris *(Chm)*
Geoff Lilliss *(CEO & Mng Dir)*

Board of Directors:
Robert Douglas Humphris
Peter Cockbain
Terry Lawler
Geoff Lilliss
John Wasik
Robert Gordon Westphal

Subsidiary:

Capacitor Technologies Pty. Ltd. (1)
Unit 13 40 Edina Rd
Ferntree Gully, Melbourne, VIC, 3156, Australia
Tel.: (61) 397585866
Fax: (61) 397522067
E-Mail: sales@captech.com.au
Web Site: www.captech.com.au
Emp.: 12
Computer Aided Design Services
S.I.C.: 7373
N.A.I.C.S.: 541512
Yury Brodsky *(Gen Mgr)*

Non-U.S. Subsidiary:

Ampcontrol UK Ltd. (1)
66 Third Avenue Heatherhouse Industrial Estate Irvine
Irvine, KA12 8HN, United Kingdom
Tel.: (44) 1294 273111
Fax: (44) 1294 274063
Flameproof Electrical Distribution & Motor Control Equipment Mfr
S.I.C.: 3699
N.A.I.C.S.: 335999

AMPELLA MINING LIMITED

Suite 22 513 Hay Street
Subiaco, WA, 6008, Australia
Tel.: (61) 8 6142 0980
Fax: (61) 8 9200 1879
E-Mail: info@ampella.com.au
Web Site: www.ampella.com.au
AMX—(ASX OTC)
Rev.: $22,635
Assets: $35,190,433
Liabilities: $2,636,177
Net Worth: $32,554,256
Earnings: ($39,757,836)
Fiscal Year-end: 12/31/12

Business Description:
Zinc & Gold Exploration Services
S.I.C.: 1031
N.A.I.C.S.: 212231

Personnel:
Paul Anthony Kitto *(CEO & Mng Dir)*
Jean Luc Roy *(COO)*
Neil Hackett *(Sec)*

Board of Directors:
Peter Mansell
Michael Anderson
Ronnie Beevor
Paul Anthony Kitto
Ron Renton

AMPER, S.A.

C/ Marconi 3 Parque Tecnologico de Madrid
Tres Cantos, 28760 Madrid, Spain
Tel.: (34) 917243000
Fax: (34) 917243010
E-Mail: informacion@amper.es
Web Site: www.amper.es
Year Founded: 1956
AMP—(MAD)
Rev.: $468,580,238
Assets: $562,941,371
Liabilities: $520,561,247
Net Worth: $42,380,124
Earnings: ($33,111,743)
Emp.: 2,039
Fiscal Year-end: 12/31/12

Business Description:
Civil & Military Communications Applications & Services
Import Export
S.I.C.: 4812
N.A.I.C.S.: 517210

Personnel:
Jaime Espinosa de los Monteros Pitarque *(Chm)*
Maria Marco *(CFO)*
Antonio Medina Cuadros *(Sec)*

Board of Directors:
Jaime Espinosa de los Monteros Pitarque
Jose Manuel Arrojo Botija
Luis Bastida Ibarguen
Ignacio Bonilla Ganosa
Ignacio Lopez del Hierro
Jose Francisco Mateu Isturiz
Yago Enrique Mendez Pascual
Luis Rivera Novo
Pedro Mateache Sacristan
Juan Jose Toribio Davila

Joint Venture:

Amper Programas de Electronica y Comunicaciones S.A (1)
Avenida Leonardo da Vinci 15 Getafe
28906 Madrid, Spain
Tel.: (34) 914532400
Fax: (34) 914532401
E-Mail: sergeneral@amper.es
Web Site: www.amper.es
Emp.: 200
Developer & Mfr of Military Communications & Electronic Systems; Joint Venture of Amper, S.A. (51%) & Thales Group (49%)
S.I.C.: 4812
N.A.I.C.S.: 517210
Rafael Posada *(Dir Gen)*

U.S. Subsidiary:

eLandia International Inc. (1)
8333 NW 53 rd St
Miami, FL 33166 DE
Tel.: (305) 415-8830 (100%)
Fax: (786) 413-1913
E-Mail: ir@elandiagroup.com
Web Site: www.elandiagroup.com
Sales Range: $150-199.9 Million
Emp.: 800
Information & Communications Technology
S.I.C.: 3663
N.A.I.C.S.: 334220

Subsidiary:

BlueSky Communications (2)
478 Laufou Shopping Ctr
Pago Pago, AS 96799
Tel.: (684) 699-2759
Fax: (684) 699-6593
Telecommunications Services
S.I.C.: 4813
N.A.I.C.S.: 517110
Adolfo Montenegro *(CEO)*

Non-U.S. Subsidiary:

BlueSky Samoa (3)
Chief Post Office Beach Road
Apia, Samoa (Western) (75%)
Tel.: (685) 67788
Fax: (685) 24123
E-Mail: info@blueskysamoa.com
Web Site: www.blueskysamoa.ws
Emp.: 240
Telecommunications Services
S.I.C.: 4813
N.A.I.C.S.: 517110
Adolfo Montenegro *(CEO)*
Tiafau Douglas Creevy *(COO)*

AMPERE LIMITED

15 Torbarrie Road
Toronto, ON, M3L 1G5, Canada
Tel.: (416) 661-3330
Fax: (416) 661-4508
Web Site: www.ampere.ca
Year Founded: 1959
Rev.: $13,911,132
Emp.: 75

Business Description:
Electrical Contractors
S.I.C.: 1731
N.A.I.C.S.: 238210

Personnel:
Mario Bernardini *(Pres & CEO)*

AMPERICO CORP.

42 Rockwood Crescent
Thornhill, ON, L4J 7T2, Canada
Tel.: (775) 461-5130
Web Site: www.amperico.com
Year Founded: 2011
AMPO—(OTC)
Assets: $136
Liabilities: $10,526
Net Worth: ($10,390)
Earnings: ($31,663)
Emp.: 1
Fiscal Year-end: 05/31/13

Business Description:
Website Analytical Software Publisher
S.I.C.: 7372
N.A.I.C.S.: 511210

Personnel:
Nicholas Thompson *(Pres, CEO, CFO, Treas & Sec)*

AMPHION INNOVATIONS PLC

Fort Anne
Douglas, Isle of Man IM1 5PD
Tel.: (44) 2070168821
Fax: (44) 2070169100
E-Mail: info@amphionplc.com
Web Site: www.amphionplc.com
AMP—(AIM)
Rev.: $1,395,806
Assets: $43,679,659
Liabilities: $23,101,128

Amphion Innovations plc—(Continued)

Net Worth: $20,578,531
Earnings: ($6,946,234)
Emp.: 7
Fiscal Year-end: 12/31/12

Business Description:
Operate Life Science & Technology Companies
S.I.C.: 6282
N.A.I.C.S.: 523920

Personnel:
Robert J. Bertoldi *(Pres & CFO)*
Richard C. E. Morgan *(CEO)*
John A. Caruso *(Mng Dir)*
Joseph R. Flicek *(Mng Dir)*
Andrew J. Baker *(Sec)*

Board of Directors:
R. James Macaleer
Robert J. Bertoldi
Anthony W. Henfrey
Richard C. E. Morgan
Gerard M. Moufflet
Jerel Whittingham

Legal Counsel:
Reed Smith
Beaufort House 15 St. Botolph Street
London, United Kingdom

Cains Fiduciaries Limited
Fort Anne
Douglas, Isle of Man

U.S. Subsidiaries:

Amphion Innovations US, Inc. (1)
330 Madison Ave
New York, NY 10017
Tel.: (212) 210-6282
Fax: (212) 210-6271
E-Mail: info@amphionplc.com
Web Site: www.amphionplc.com
Emp.: 6
Operate Life Science & Technology Companies
S.I.C.: 6282
N.A.I.C.S.: 523920
Richard C. E. Morgan *(CEO)*

DataTern, Inc. (1)
330 Madison Ave 31st FL
New York, NY 10017
Tel.: (212) 210-6221
Fax: (212) 210-6271
E-Mail: info@datatern.com
Web Site: www.datatern.com
Emp.: 1
Administrative Software Distr
S.I.C.: 7371
N.A.I.C.S.: 541511
John A. Caruso *(CEO)*

Non-U.S. Subsidiary:

Amphion Innovations UK, Ltd. (1)
10 Gray Coat Place
London, SW1T 1SB, United Kingdom (100%)
Tel.: (44) 2070168821
Fax: (44) 2079606100
E-Mail: info@amphionplc.com
Web Site: www.amphioninnovations.com
Emp.: 5
Operate Life Science & Technology Companies
S.I.C.: 6282
N.A.I.C.S.: 523920
Jerel Whittingham *(Mng Dir)*

AMPHITECH

1 R Robert et Sonia Delaunay
75011 Paris, France
Tel.: (33) 143679377
Web Site: www.amphitech.fr/
Sls.: $24,200,000
Emp.: 128

Business Description:
Telephone & Telegraph Apparatus
S.I.C.: 3661
N.A.I.C.S.: 334210

Personnel:
Alain Wehrbach *(Mng Partner)*

AMPLAST CO

Laresti
117430 Arges, Romania
Tel.: (40) 248512199
Fax: (40) 248549555
E-Mail: amplast@geostar.ro
Web Site: www.amplast.ro
Year Founded: 1993
Emp.: 300

Business Description:
Disposable Plastic Packaging Mfr
S.I.C.: 2671
N.A.I.C.S.: 322220

Personnel:
Jean Jordache *(Pres)*

AMPLEFIELD LTD.

7500A Beach Road 09 316 The Plaza
Singapore, 199591, Singapore
Tel.: (65) 6294 6022
Fax: (65) 6299 2798
Year Founded: 1989
C60—(SES)
Rev.: $4,386,355
Assets: $14,541,077
Liabilities: $3,901,732
Net Worth: $10,639,345
Earnings: ($1,304,569)
Emp.: 220
Fiscal Year-end: 09/30/12

Business Description:
Holding Company; Industrial Components Mfr
S.I.C.: 6719
N.A.I.C.S.: 551112

Personnel:
Weng Yau Yap *(CFO)*
Cindy Caroline Wai Cheng Foo *(Sec)*

Board of Directors:
Albert Saychuan Cheok
Ming Fatt Hoh
Ooi Jin Woon
Yew Tho Yak
Teiong Choon Yap

AMPLEX AB

Fagerstagatan 3
163 08 Spanga, Sweden
Tel.: (46) 8 546 802 20
Fax: (46) 8 546 802 29
Web Site: www.amplexab.se
Sales Range: $350-399.9 Million
Emp.: 700

Business Description:
Holding Company
S.I.C.: 6719
N.A.I.C.S.: 551112

Personnel:
Kenneth Lindqvist *(Chm)*
Roger Lindqvist *(CFO)*
Ulf Sundell *(COO)*

Holding:

Kamic AB (1)
Grimstagatan 160
Box 39
162 11 Vallingby, Sweden
Tel.: (46) 8 759 35 00
Fax: (46) 54 56 25 13
E-Mail: info@kamicgroup.com
Web Site: www.kamicgroup.com
Electrical Components, Lighting & Electrical Power Equipment Mfr
S.I.C.: 3699
N.A.I.C.S.: 335999
Per Blixt *(CEO)*
Matthias Eriksson *(COO & CFO)*

Subsidiaries:

EG Electronics AB (2)
Box 39
162 11 Vallingby, Sweden SE
Tel.: (46) 8 759 35 70
Fax: (46) 8 759 35 90
E-Mail: info@egelectronics.com
Web Site: www.egelectronics.com
Emp.: 40
Electrical & Electronic Equipments Supplier
S.I.C.: 1731
N.A.I.C.S.: 238210
Kenneth Zaar *(VP-Ops)*

Non-U.S. Subsidiaries:

EG Components Finland Oy (3)
Sinikalliontie 5A
02630 Espoo, Finland
Tel.: (358) 20 752 87 00
Fax: (358) 975103599
Emp.: 20
Electrical & Electronic Equipments Supplier
S.I.C.: 1731
N.A.I.C.S.: 238210
Hannu Jarvenkyla *(Acct Mgr)*

EG Componets Norway AS (3)
Hoffsveien 17
N-0275 Oslo, Norway
Tel.: (47) 23 25 46 00
Fax: (47) 23 25 46 01
E-Mail: info@egelectronics.com
Web Site: www.egelectronics.com
Emp.: 8
Electrical & Electronic Equipments Supplier
S.I.C.: 1731
N.A.I.C.S.: 238210

EG (Shanghai) Commercial Co., Ltd. (3)
Room 1808 Shenshi Building
Number 511 Weihai Road, 200041
Shanghai, China
Tel.: (86) 2152130077
Fax: (86) 2152133152
E-Mail: info.cn@etalgroup.com
Web Site: www.etalgroup.com
Emp.: 12
Electonic Components Supplier
S.I.C.: 5065
N.A.I.C.S.: 423690
Taylor Tang *(Gen Mgr)*

ETAL Group AB (2)
PO Box 39
162 11 Vallingby, Sweden
Tel.: (46) 87593500
Fax: (46) 87593540
E-Mail: info.se@etalgroup.com
Web Site: www.etalgroup.com
Emp.: 4
Electronic Transformers Supplier
S.I.C.: 3675
N.A.I.C.S.: 334416
Lars Skog *(Mng Dir)*

Non-U.S. Subsidiaries:

AS ETAL Group (3)
Peterburi tee 2f
11415 Tallinn, Estonia
Tel.: (372) 6143030
Fax: (372) 6143031
E-Mail: info.ee@etalgroup.com
Web Site: www.etalgroup.com
Emp.: 72
Electronic Equipment Supplier
S.I.C.: 5065
N.A.I.C.S.: 423690

ETAL Group (Pvt.) Ltd. (3)
No 7 2nd Ln Maligawa Rd
Ratmalana, Sri Lanka
Tel.: (94) 112623754
Fax: (94) 112623802
E-Mail: info.lk@etalgroup.com
Web Site: www.etalgroup.com
Electronic Components Supplier
S.I.C.: 5065
N.A.I.C.S.: 423690

ETAL (UK) Ltd. (3)
Unit 2 Mid Sussex Business Park
Folders Lane East, Ditchling, East Sussex, BN6 8SG, United Kingdom
Tel.: (44) 1444 871186
Fax: (44) 1444 870582
E-Mail: info.uk@etalgroup.com
Web Site: www.etalgroup.com
Emp.: 6
Electronic Components Supplier
S.I.C.: 5065
N.A.I.C.S.: 423690
Gordon Dunbar *(Mgr-Sls)*

Osterlinds El-Agentur AB (2)
Gribbylundsvagen 11-13
Box 96
183 21 Taby, Sweden
Tel.: (46) 858708800
Fax: (46) 8 587 08 802
E-Mail: info@osterlinds.se
Web Site: osterlinds.verktyget.se
Emp.: 20
Electrical & Electronic Equipments Supplier
S.I.C.: 1731
N.A.I.C.S.: 238210
Lars Aleby *(Pres)*

Scanditron Sverige AB (2)
Grimstagatan 162
162 58 Vallingby, Sweden
Tel.: (46) 8 795 24 00
Fax: (46) 8 795 24 10
E-Mail: info@scanditron.se
Web Site: www.scanditron.se
Emp.: 20
Electronic Components Mfr
S.I.C.: 5065
N.A.I.C.S.: 423690
Anders Lind *(Mng Dir)*

Non-U.S. Subsidiaries:

Scanditron Danmark A/S (3)
Lyshojen 12
8520 Lystrup, Denmark
Tel.: (45) 86741233
Fax: (45) 86741755
E-Mail: info@scanditron.dk
Web Site: www.scanditron.dk
Emp.: 15
Electronic Components Supplier
S.I.C.: 5065
N.A.I.C.S.: 423690
Tage Hausgaard Poulsen *(CEO)*

Scanditron Finland Stencils (3)
PL 89 00381 Helsinki Hoylaamotie 3 b
380 Helsinki, Finland
Tel.: (358) 94393330
Fax: (358) 94558925
E-Mail: stencil@scanditron.fi
Web Site: www.scanditron.fi
Emp.: 5
Electronic Components Supplier
S.I.C.: 5065
N.A.I.C.S.: 423690

Scanditron Sp. z.o.o. (3)
Ul Obywatelska 115
94 104 Lodz, Poland
Tel.: (48) 426860246
Fax: (48) 426860238
E-Mail: info@scanditron.pl
Web Site: www.scanditron.pl
Emp.: 9
Electronic Components Supplier
S.I.C.: 5065
N.A.I.C.S.: 423690
Martin S. Stromberg *(Mng Dir)*

Non-U.S. Holdings:

Dosmar Oy (1)
Tormaniityntie 14
FI 02710 Espoo, Finland
Tel.: (358) 9 8870 230
Fax: (358) 9 8870 2337
E-Mail: dosmar@dosmar.fi
Web Site: www.dosmar.fi
Sales Range: $10-24.9 Million
Office Equipment Supplier
S.I.C.: 5044
N.A.I.C.S.: 423420
Timo Puranen *(Mng Dir)*

Non-U.S. Subsidiary:

Postronic AB (2)
Stensatravagen 9
127 39 Skarholmen, Sweden
Tel.: (46) 8 50 10 84 00
Fax: (46) 8 744 36 95
E-Mail: info@postronic.se
Web Site: www.postronic.se
Office Equipment Supplier
S.I.C.: 5044
N.A.I.C.S.: 423420

Optiscan Oy (1)
Laturinkuja 6
02650 Espoo, Finland
Tel.: (358) 9 4766 766
Fax: (358) 9 4766 7689
E-Mail: info.fi@optiscangroup.com
Web Site: www.optiscangroup.com
Logistics Solutions & Software Developer
S.I.C.: 4731

N.A.I.C.S.: 541614
Mikko Mertjarvi *(Mng Dir)*

Non-U.S. Subsidiary:

Optiscan AB (2)
Fagerstagatan 3
SE 163 53 Spanga, Sweden
Tel.: (46) 8 632 66 50
Fax: (46) 8 632 66 60
E-Mail: info.se@optiscangroup.com
Logistics Solutions & Software Developer
S.I.C.: 4731
N.A.I.C.S.: 541614

AMPLIFON S.P.A.

Via G Ripamonti 133
20141 Milan, Italy
Tel.: (39) 02574721
Fax: (39) 0257300033
E-Mail: assistenza@amplifon.it
Web Site: www.amplifon.com
Year Founded: 1950
AMP—(ITA)
Rev.: $1,139,682,330
Assets: $1,573,493,689
Liabilities: $994,427,895
Net Worth: $579,065,795
Earnings: $58,076,466
Emp.: 5,253
Fiscal Year-end: 12/31/12

Business Description:
Hearing Aid Mfr & Distr
S.I.C.: 3841
N.A.I.C.S.: 339112

Personnel:
Franco Moscetti *(CEO)*
Ugo Giorcelli *(CFO)*
Massimiliano Gerli *(CIO)*
Alberto Baroli *(Chief Dev Officer & Chief Innovation Officer)*
Giovanni Caruso *(Chief HR Officer)*
Paolo Tacciaria *(Compliance Officer & Head-Internal Audit)*
Cristina Vitrani *(Sec)*

Board of Directors:
Susan Carol Holland
Giampio Bracchi
Maurizio Costa
Luca Garavoglia
Andrea Guerra
Franco Moscetti
Giovanni Tamburi

U.S. Subsidiaries:

Amplifon Hearing Aid Center Inc (1)
2501 Lakeview Pkwy
Rowlett, TX 75088-3350 (100%)
Tel.: (214) 607-9714
Web Site: www.amplifonhearing.com
Store Retailer
S.I.C.: 5999
N.A.I.C.S.: 453998

Amplifon USA (1)
5000 Cheshire Ln N
Minneapolis, MN 55446
Tel.: (763) 268-4000
Fax: (763) 268-4323
E-Mail: mary@amplifon.com
Web Site: www.amplifonusa.com
Emp.: 200
Hearing Aids Retailer & Distr
S.I.C.: 3999
N.A.I.C.S.: 339999
Heine Rouch *(Pres)*

Subsidiary:

Miracle-Ear, Inc. (2)
5000 Cheshire Pkwy N
Minneapolis, MN 55446-3706 MN (100%)
Tel.: (763) 268-4000
Fax: (763) 268-4295
Toll Free: (877) 268-4264
Web Site: www.miracle-ear.com
Emp.: 100
Mfr. & Sales of Hearing Aids
S.I.C.: 3845
N.A.I.C.S.: 334510
Herns Runch *(Pres)*

Sonus USA Inc. (1)
1780 Barnes Blvd SW Bldg G
Tumwater, WA 98512 (100%)
Tel.: (763) 268-4000
Fax: (763) 268-4224
Web Site: www.sonusnetwork.com
Hearing Health Services; Testing Centers & Hearing Aids
S.I.C.: 3841
N.A.I.C.S.: 339112
Maho Riemms *(Treas)*

Non-U.S. Subsidiaries:

Amplifon AG (1)
Sihlbruggstrasse 109
6340 Baar, Switzerland (100%)
Tel.: (41) 417267926
Fax: (41) 417267927
E-Mail: infoch@amplifon.com
Web Site: www.amplifon.ch
Emp.: 25
Electronic Parts & Equipment Whslr
S.I.C.: 5064
N.A.I.C.S.: 423620

Amplifon Beheer BV (1)
Leigraafseweg 8
6983 BP Doesburg, Netherlands (100%)
Tel.: (31) 313485555
Fax: (31) 313485567
E-Mail: infonl@amplifon.com
Web Site: www.beterhoren.nl
Emp.: 100
Hearing Aids & Equipment Whslr
S.I.C.: 5047
N.A.I.C.S.: 423450
Peter Peters *(Mng Dir)*

Amplifon Cote d'Azur SAS (1)
Rue Leon Basso
83700 Saint Raphael, France (100%)
Tel.: (33) 494830915
Fax: (33) 490830013
Web Site: www.amplifon.fr
Emp.: 4
Store Retailer
S.I.C.: 5999
N.A.I.C.S.: 453998

Amplifon Deutschland GmbH (1)
Normannenweg 30
20537 Hamburg, Germany (100%)
Tel.: (49) 4069454400
Fax: (49) 40694544090
E-Mail: infode@amplifon.com
Web Site: www.amplifon.de/wps/wcm/connect/SiteCompanyGe/sitecompanyge/ge/amplifon/kontakt/
Emp.: 45
Electromedical & Electrotherapeutic Apparatus Mfr
S.I.C.: 3845
N.A.I.C.S.: 334510
Robert Leitl *(Pres)*

Amplifon Groupe France SA (1)
18 Rue Oberkampf
75011 Paris, France (100%)
Tel.: (33) 156982222
Fax: (33) 156981715
Holding Company
S.I.C.: 6719
N.A.I.C.S.: 551112
Andrea Senaldi *(Chm)*

Amplifon Iberica SA (1)
Paseo Zona Franca 83 95
08038 Barcelona, Spain (100%)
Tel.: (34) 0933945300
Fax: (34) 0932231110
Web Site: www.amplifoniberica.es
Store Retailer
S.I.C.: 5999
N.A.I.C.S.: 453998

Amplifon Magyarorszag Ltd. (1)
Konyves Kalman Krt 12-14 3rd floor
1097 Budapest, Hungary (100%)
Tel.: (36) 13429398
Fax: (36) 13429398
E-Mail: iroda@amplifon.com
Web Site: www.amplifon.hu
Hearing Aids & Audiology Testing Laboratories
S.I.C.: 8049
N.A.I.C.S.: 621340

Amplifon Participaties BV (1)
Leigraafseweg 8
6983BP Doesburg, Netherlands (100%)
Tel.: (31) 313485555
Fax: (31) 313485567
Web Site: www.maryor.nl
Emp.: 80
Store Retailer
S.I.C.: 5999
N.A.I.C.S.: 453998
P. Peters *(Gen Mgr)*

Amplifon Sietech Ltd. (1)
273 Kensington Hogh Street
London, W8 6NA, United Kingdom (100%)
Tel.: (44) 2077063051
Fax: (44) 2076028351
Emp.: 3
Medical Dental & Hospital Equipment & Supplies Whslr
S.I.C.: 5047
N.A.I.C.S.: 423450

Amplifon Sud Ouest SAS (1)
31 Allees Jean Jaures
Toulouse, France (100%)
Tel.: (33) 561993333
Store Retailer
S.I.C.: 5999
N.A.I.C.S.: 453998

Audiogestion 2001 SL (1)
Calle Luis Montoto 61
Seville, 41018, Spain (59%)
Tel.: (34) 95 4576104
Web Site: www.amplifon.es
Electronics Store Retailer
S.I.C.: 5999
N.A.I.C.S.: 453998
Gilbert Ferraroli *(Reg Mktg Dir)*

Auditech BV (1)
Leigraafseweg 8
6983BP Doesburg, Netherlands (100%)
Tel.: (31) 313485522
Fax: (31) 313485567
E-Mail: Wilco.boomkamp@amplifon.com
Emp.: 10
Medical Dental & Hospital Equipment & Supplies Whslr
S.I.C.: 5047
N.A.I.C.S.: 423450
Philippe Robert *(Gen Mgr)*

Beter Horen BV (1)
Misterstraat 14
7101EW Winterswijk, Netherlands (100%)
Mailing Address:
Leigraafseweg 8
6983 BP Doesburg, Netherlands
Tel.: (31) 313485555
Fax: (31) 313485566
Web Site: www.beterhoren.nl
Emp.: 80
Medical Dental & Hospital Equipment & Supplies Whslr
S.I.C.: 5047
N.A.I.C.S.: 423450
Pem Peters *(Pres)*

Centre Auditiu Sant Boi SL (1)
Ramadla Asael Casanova 12
Barcelona, Spain (100%)
Tel.: (34) 936543795
Drugs & Druggists Sundries Whslr
S.I.C.: 5122
N.A.I.C.S.: 424210

Electro Medical Instruments BV (1)
Leigraafseweg 8
6983BP Doesburg, Netherlands (100%)
Tel.: (31) 313485555
Fax: (31) 313485567
E-Mail: info@emid.nl
Web Site: www.emid.nl
Emp.: 100
Surgical & Medical Instrument Mfr
S.I.C.: 3841
N.A.I.C.S.: 339112
Peter Peters *(Gen Mgr)*

Espace de l Audition SAS (1)
19 Place Manigne
87000 Limoges, France (100%)
Tel.: (33) 555324550
Fax: (33) 555347071
E-Mail: marieannick.vallois@amplifon.com
Store Retailer
S.I.C.: 5999
N.A.I.C.S.: 453998
Richard Darmon *(Mng Dir)*

Hearing Supplies SA (1)
Via Soave 2
Lugano, Switzerland (100%)
Tel.: (41) 916409830
Electromedical & Electrotherapeutic Apparatus Mfr
S.I.C.: 3845
N.A.I.C.S.: 334510
Bortesi Emrico *(Gen Mgr)*

Horen Deventer BV (1)
Graaf Florisstraat 1
7415 LK Deventer, Netherlands (100%)
Tel.: (31) 570624880
Fax: (31) 570677094
E-Mail: deventer408@Amplifon.com
Web Site: www.beterhoren.nl
Electromedical & Electrotherapeutic Apparatus Mfr
S.I.C.: 3845
N.A.I.C.S.: 334510

Horen Nederland Beheer BV (1)
Leigraafseweg 8
6983 BP Doesburg, Netherlands (100%)
Tel.: (31) 313485555
Fax: (31) 313485567
E-Mail: klantenservice@amplifon.com
Web Site: www.beterhoren.nl
Emp.: 100
Holding Company
S.I.C.: 6719
N.A.I.C.S.: 551112
P. Peters *(Gen Mgr)*

Laboratoire d Audition de Arceaux Sarl (1)
Res Les Terrasses St Jean 74 Esplanade
34430 Saint-Jean-de-Vedas, France (100%)
Tel.: (33) 467691275
Fax: (33) 467691275
Store Retailer
S.I.C.: 5999
N.A.I.C.S.: 453998

Laide Auditive SA (1)
Rue Du Simplon 40
Vevey, 1800, Switzerland (100%)
Tel.: (41) 219222222
Fax: (41) 219222223
E-Mail: vevey@amplifon.com
Web Site: www.amplifon.ca
Emp.: 100
Electromedical & Electrotherapeutic Apparatus Mfr
S.I.C.: 3845
N.A.I.C.S.: 334510

The London Otological Centre Ltd (1)
66 New Cavendish Street
London, W1G 8TD, United Kingdom (100%)
Tel.: (44) 2076375111
Fax: (44) 2075809749
E-Mail: val.caven@amplifon.com
Emp.: 5
Hearing Equipment Mfr
S.I.C.: 5047
N.A.I.C.S.: 423450

NHC Group Pty. Ltd. (1)
Suite 401a 15 Orion Road
Lane Cove, Sydney, NSW, 2066, Australia
Tel.: (61) 290918440
Fax: (61) 294275261
E-Mail: info@nhc.com.au
Web Site: www.nhc.com.au
Sales Range: $150-199.9 Million
Emp.: 4
Hearing Diagnostic & Rehabilitation Services
S.I.C.: 8049
N.A.I.C.S.: 621399

Non-U.S. Subsidiary:

National Hearing Care (New Zealand) Limited (2)
Smales Farm Tech Off Pk Vodafone Bldg
Level 1 Cnr Taharoto Roads
Northcote, Takapuna, 0622, New Zealand
Tel.: (64) 94470200
Fax: (64) 093031380
E-Mail: info@bayaudiology.co.nz
Web Site: www.bayaudiology.co.nz
Emp.: 30
Hearing Diagnostic & Rehabilitation Services
S.I.C.: 8049
N.A.I.C.S.: 621399
James Whitaker *(Gen Mgr)*

Amplifon S.p.A.—(Continued)

Subsidiary:

Bay Audiology Ltd. (3)
Smales Farm Technology Park Lvl 1 Telstra Clear Bldg
Cnr Northcote & Taharoto Rds, Takapuna, 0622, New Zealand
Tel.: (64) 93031374
Fax: (64) 93031380
E-Mail: info@bayaudiology.co.in.nz
Web Site: www.bayaudiology.co.nz
Emp.: 28
Audiology Services
S.I.C.: 8049
N.A.I.C.S.: 621340
James Whittaker *(Mng Dir)*

SAS S.C.A.M. (1)
Z.A. de Kerbusson
Saint Barnabe, 22600 Paris, France (100%)
Tel.: (33) 296282030
Fax: (33) 296660490
E-Mail: scam@scamsas.fr
Web Site: www.scamsas.fr
Store Retailer
S.I.C.: 5999
N.A.I.C.S.: 453998

Sonus Canada Ltd (1)
1011 Glenmore Trl SW
Calgary, AB, T2V 4R6, Canada (100%)
Tel.: (403) 253-4327
Fax: (403) 253-9190
Web Site: www.sonuscanada.com
Emp.: 7
Medical Dental & Hospital Equipment & Supplies Whslr
S.I.C.: 5047
N.A.I.C.S.: 423450
Mark Richards *(CFO)*

Non-U.S. Joint Ventures:

Acousoft Informatisering BV (1)
Leigraafseweg 8
6983 BP Doesburg, Netherlands (50%)
Tel.: (31) 313485511
Fax: (31) 313485512
E-Mail: info@acousoft.nl
Web Site: www.acousoft.nl
Emp.: 3
Software Reproducing
S.I.C.: 3652
N.A.I.C.S.: 334614
Hans Schneider *(CEO)*

Comfoor BV (1)
Vlijtstraat 60-01
7005 BN Doetinchem, Netherlands (50%)
Tel.: (31) 314362110
Fax: (31) 314361911
E-Mail: sales@comfoor.com
Web Site: www.comfoor.com
Emp.: 45
Surgical Appliance & Supplies Mfr
S.I.C.: 3841
N.A.I.C.S.: 339113
Dick Dazzler *(Mgr-Sls)*

AMPLIO PARTNERS

21 Arlington Street
London, SW1A 1RN, United Kingdom
Tel.: (44) 2073559547
Fax: (44) 2073559549
E-Mail: info@ampliopartners.com
Web Site: www.ampliopartners.com
Emp.: 150
Business Description:
Private Equity Firm
S.I.C.: 6211
N.A.I.C.S.: 523999
Personnel:
Riccardo Segat *(Founder & CEO)*
Alberto Dalla Rosa *(Partner)*
Andrea Davi *(Partner)*
Joanne Kennedy-Reardon *(CFO)*

U.S. Holding:

Envirogen Technologies, Inc. (1)
Two Kingwood Pl 700 Rockmead Dr Ste 105
Kingwood, TX 77339 DE
Fax: (281) 358-2443
Toll Free: (877) 312-8950
E-Mail: info@basinwater.com
Web Site: www.envirogen.com
Sales Range: $10-24.9 Million
Emp.: 103
Design, Build & Implement Systems for the Treatment of Contaminated Water
S.I.C.: 4941
N.A.I.C.S.: 221310
Scott A. Katzmann *(Chm)*
Richard A. Reese *(COO & VP)*
Scott B. Hamilton *(Gen Counsel & Sec)*

AMPLITUDE AUTOMOBILES

7-16 Rue Benjamin Franklin
ZAC de la Vrillonnerie, 37170
Chambray les Tours, Indre Et Loire, France
Tel.: (33) 247272121
Fax: (33) 247278990
Web Site: www.amplitude-automobiles.fr
Sls.: $21,100,000
Emp.: 37
Business Description:
New & Used Car Dealers
S.I.C.: 5511
N.A.I.C.S.: 441110
Personnel:
Dominique Frangolacci *(Dir-Sls)*

AMPLO S.A.

Bd Petrolului nr 10
100521 Ploiesti, Romania
Tel.: (40) 244 573 641
Fax: (40) 244 571 506
E-Mail: marketing@amplo.ro
Web Site: www.amplo.ro
Year Founded: 1962
AMPL—(BUC)
Rev.: $3,349,928
Assets: $6,214,672
Liabilities: $282,752
Net Worth: $5,931,920
Earnings: $296,291
Emp.: 147
Fiscal Year-end: 12/31/12
Business Description:
Measuring Instrument Mfr
S.I.C.: 3825
N.A.I.C.S.: 334515
Personnel:
P. Marica *(Pres)*

AMPOL FOOD PROCESSING LTD.

392/56-57 Soi Preechapanich,
Maharat Rd. Praborommaharajwang
Phranakorn District, Bangkok, 10200, Thailand
Tel.: (66) 26223434
Fax: (66) 22261829
E-Mail: kritsada@ampolfood.com
Web Site: www.ampolfood.com
Year Founded: 1988
Rev.: $21,390,940
Emp.: 600
Business Description:
Agricultural Products Mfr & Distr
S.I.C.: 5149
N.A.I.C.S.: 424490
Personnel:
Jareeporn Theppadungporn *(Chm)*
Kriengsak Theppadungporn *(Mng Dir, Dir-Mktg & Mgr-Intl Sls)*
Board of Directors:
Jareeporn Theppadungporn
Aphisak Theppadungporn
Kaitisak Theppadungporn
Korranat Theppadungporn
Kriengsak Theppadungporn
Thayapol Theppadungporn

AMPRION GMBH

Rheinlanddamm 24
44139 Dortmund, Germany
Tel.: (49) 231 5849 0
Fax: (49) 231 5849 14188
Web Site: www.amprion.net
Emp.: 850
Business Description:
Electric Power Distribution Services
S.I.C.: 4911
N.A.I.C.S.: 221122
Personnel:
Hans-Jurgen Brick *(Mng Dir-Comml)*

AMRADEEP INDUSTRIES LIMITED

24 Laxmi Chambers Navjeevan Press Road Opp Old Gujarat High Court
Ahmedabad, 380014, India
Tel.: (91) 79 26581329
Fax: (91) 79 26579169
E-Mail: amradeepindustries@gmail.com
Web Site: www.amradeepindustries.com
531681—(BOM)
Business Description:
Laminate Sheet Mfr & Distr
S.I.C.: 3083
N.A.I.C.S.: 326130
Personnel:
Shankar Prasad Bhagat *(Compliance Officer)*
Board of Directors:
Shankar Prasad Bhagat
Mahendra Dolatrai Ganatra
Nileshkumar Tribhovandas Kava
Transfer Agent:
PURVA SHAREGISTRY (INDIA) PRIVATE LIMITED
Unite No 9 Shiv Shakti Industrial Estate, Ground Floor JR Boricha Marg
Opp Kasturba Hospital Lower Parel E, Mumbai, 400011, India
Tel.: (91) 22 2301 6761
Fax: (91) 22 2301 2517

AMRAPALI CAPITAL AND FINANCE SERVICES LIMITED

19-20-21 3rd Floor Narayan Chambers
B/h Patang Hotel Asram Road,
Ahmedabad, 380009, India
Tel.: (91) 79 26575105
Fax: (91) 79 26584313
E-Mail: support@amrapali.com
Web Site: www.amrapali.com
536737—(BOM)
Business Description:
Securities Brokerage Services
S.I.C.: 6211
N.A.I.C.S.: 523120
Personnel:
Chirag Yashwant Thakkar *(Chm & Mng Dir)*

AMRAPALI GROUP

C-56/40 Sector-62
Noida, 201301, India
Tel.: (91) 1204055555
Fax: (91) 1204233556
E-Mail: info@amrapali.in
Web Site: www.amrapali.in
Business Description:
Real Estate Developer
S.I.C.: 1531
N.A.I.C.S.: 236117
Personnel:
Anil Kumar Sharma *(Chm)*

AMRAWORLD AGRICO LTD.

803 Samedh Building Adj Associated Petrol Pump C G Road
Ahmedabad, 380006, India
Tel.: (91) 79 2656 2165
Fax: (91) 79 2657 5106
E-Mail: amraworldagrico@gmail.com
Web Site: www.amraworldagrico.com
531991—(BOM)
Sales Range: $1-9.9 Million
Business Description:
Commodities Brokerage Services
S.I.C.: 6221
N.A.I.C.S.: 523140
Personnel:
Ashok H. Shah *(Compliance Officer)*
Board of Directors:
Shambhu Prasad R. Bhagat
Harleen Singh Kathuria
Ashok H. Shah

AMREST HOLDINGS SE

pl Grunwaldzki 25-27
50-365 Wroclaw, Poland
Tel.: (48) 713861000
Fax: (48) 713861060
E-Mail: ir@amrest.eu
Web Site: www.amrest.eu
EAT—(WAR)
Sls.: $746,318,837
Assets: $807,559,811
Liabilities: $468,304,920
Net Worth: $339,254,892
Earnings: $31,044,807
Emp.: 18,000
Fiscal Year-end: 12/31/12
Business Description:
Fast Food Restaurant Owner & Operator
S.I.C.: 5812
N.A.I.C.S.: 722513
Personnel:
Henry McGovern *(Chm-Supervisory Bd)*
Mark Chandler *(CFO & Member-Mgmt Bd)*
Wojciech Mroczynski *(Member-Mgmt Bd)*
Drew O'Malley *(Member-Mgmt Bd)*
Supervisory Board of Directors:
Henry McGovern
Peter A. Bassi
Bradley D. Blum
Per Steen Breimyr
Raimondo Eggink
Robert Feuer
Joseph P. Landy

Subsidiaries:

AmRest Sp. z o.o. (1)
Pl Grunwaldzki 25-27
50-365 Wroclaw, Lower Silesian, Poland
Tel.: (48) 713861000
Fax: (48) 713861060
E-Mail: reception@amrest.eu
Emp.: 200
Restaurant Operation Services
S.I.C.: 5812
N.A.I.C.S.: 722513
Henry Macgovern *(Gen Mgr)*

SCM Sp. z o.o. (1)
Ojca Augustyna Kordeckiego 12
05-123 Chotomow, Masovian, Poland
Tel.: (48) 225951864
Fax: (48) 225865401
Web Site: www.scmpoland.pl
Emp.: 25
Restaurant Meals Delivery Services
S.I.C.: 4215
N.A.I.C.S.: 492210
Cylny Zbigniew Janusz *(Chm-Supervisory Bd)*

U.S. Subsidiary:

AmRest, LLC (1)
2120 Powers Ferry Rd Ste 350
Atlanta, GA 30339 DE
Tel.: (770) 951-0586
Fax: (770) 952-5943
E-Mail: applebeesinfo@amrest.eu
Web Site: www.amrestapplebees.com
Sales Range: $250-299.9 Million
Emp.: 3,500
Franchise Bar-Restaurants Operator
S.I.C.: 5812
N.A.I.C.S.: 722511

Non-U.S. Subsidiaries:

AmRest Kft (1)
Becsi Ut 13
Budapest, 1023, Hungary
Tel.: (36) 14234000
Fax: (36) 14234004
E-Mail: office.budapest@amrest.eu
Web Site: www.amrest.eu/contact_details.php
Emp.: 30
Fast Food Restaurant Management Services
S.I.C.: 5812
N.A.I.C.S.: 722513
Tomas Sallai *(Dir-HR)*

AmRest s.r.o. (1)
Evropska 33/E
16000 Prague, Czech Republic
Tel.: (420) 235013311
Fax: (420) 235013312
E-Mail: katerina.dlabacova@amrest.eu
Emp.: 60
Restaurant Operation Services
S.I.C.: 5812
N.A.I.C.S.: 722513
Tomas Benda *(Product Mgr)*

OOO AmRest (1)
36/40 Sredniy Prospect of Vasilievsky Island
Saint Petersburg, Russia
Tel.: (7) 812 703 0030
Fast Food Restaurant Owner & Operator
S.I.C.: 5812
N.A.I.C.S.: 722513

AMRIT BANASPATI COMPANY LIMITED

Amrit Corporate Centre A-95 Sector-65
Noida, UP, 201 309, India
Tel.: (91) 120 4506900
Fax: (91) 120 4506910
E-Mail: abcl@amritbanaspati.com
Web Site: www.amritbanaspati.com
Rev.: $18,177,304
Assets: $32,282,590
Liabilities: $5,318,131
Net Worth: $26,964,459
Earnings: $563,165
Fiscal Year-end: 03/31/13

Business Description:
Edible Oils
S.I.C.: 2079
N.A.I.C.S.: 311225

Personnel:
N. K. Bajaj *(Chm & Co-Mng Dir)*
V. K. Bajaj *(Co-Mng Dir)*
Mahesh Mittal *(CFO & Pres-Fin & Audit)*
Tushar Goel *(Compliance Officer & Sec)*

Board of Directors:
N. K. Bajaj
Sundeep Agarwal
A. K. Bajaj
V. K. Bajaj
B. S. Bhatia
G. N. Mehra
J. C. Rana
Mohit Satyanand
Sujal Anil Shah
V. K. Sibal

Transfer Agent:
MAS Services Limited
T-34 2nd Floor Okhla Industrial Area Phase - II
New Delhi, India

AMRIT CORP LTD

Amrit Nagar
G T Rd
201009 Ghaziabad, Uttar Pradesh, India
Tel.: (91) 1202866880
Fax: (91) 12024506910
E-Mail: info@amritcorp.com
Web Site: www.amritcorp.com
507525—(BOM)
Sales Range: $1-9.9 Million

Business Description:
Food Processing Services
S.I.C.: 2026
N.A.I.C.S.: 311511

Personnel:
N. K. Bajaj *(Chm & Mng Dir)*
A. K. Bajaj *(Mng Dir)*
A. K. Bagga *(Pres-Tax & CR)*
Mahesh Mittal *(Pres-Fin & Audit)*
Pranab K. Das *(Sec)*

Board of Directors:
N. K. Bajaj
A. K. Bajaj
Vikram Bajaj
Praveen Kumar
Romesh Lal
G. N. Mehra
K. R. Ramamoorthy
Mohit Satyanand

AMRUTANJAN HEALTH CARE LIMITED

103 Old No 42-45 Luz Church Road
Mylapore
Chennai, 600 004, India
Tel.: (91) 4424994465
Fax: (91) 4424994585
E-Mail: customercare@amrutanjan.com
Web Site: www.amrutanjan.com
AMRUTANJAN—(NSE)
Sls.: $26,710,356
Assets: $23,018,819
Liabilities: $7,766,517
Net Worth: $15,252,302
Earnings: $1,875,655
Emp.: 453
Fiscal Year-end: 03/31/13

Business Description:
Pain Balm Mfr
S.I.C.: 2834
N.A.I.C.S.: 325412

Personnel:
S. Sambhu Prasad *(Chm & Mng Dir)*

Board of Directors:
S. Sambhu Prasad
A. Sathis Kumar
Pasumarthi S. N. Murthi
D. Seetharama Rao
H. B. N. Shetty

Transfer Agent:
Cameo Corporate Services Limited
Subramanian Building No 1 Club House Road
5th Floor
Chennai, India

AMS ADVANCED MEDICAL SERVICES GMBH

Am Exerzierplatz 2
D-68167 Mannheim, Germany
Tel.: (49) 6217009100
Fax: (49) 62170095140
E-Mail: ams@ams-europe.com
Web Site: www.ams-europe.com
Year Founded: 1997
Rev.: $15,173,400
Emp.: 170

Business Description:
Clinical Research Services
S.I.C.: 8062
N.A.I.C.S.: 622110

Personnel:
Christian Carls *(CEO)*

AMS AG

Tobelbader Strasse 30
8141 Unterpremstatten, Austria
Tel.: (43) 31365000
Fax: (43) 313652501
E-Mail: info@ams.com
Web Site: www.ams.com
AMS—(SWX)
Rev.: $521,823,954
Assets: $853,461,011
Liabilities: $302,185,549
Net Worth: $551,275,461
Earnings: $110,256,708
Emp.: 1,282
Fiscal Year-end: 12/31/12

Business Description:
Semiconductor Designer & Mfr
S.I.C.: 3674
N.A.I.C.S.: 334413

Personnel:
Hans Jorg Kaltenbrunner *(Chm-Supervisory Bd)*
Gerald Rogers *(Vice Chm-Supervisory Bd)*
Siegfried Selberherr *(Vice Chm-Supervisory Bd)*
Kirk S. Laney *(CEO & Gen Mgr-Opto Sensors & Lighting)*
Michael Wachsler-Markowitsch *(CFO)*
Jann H. Siefken *(Gen Counsel)*
Bernd Gessner *(Exec VP & Gen Mgr-Automotive)*
Thomas Riener *(Exec VP-Mktg Comm & Gen Mgr-Full Svc Foundry)*
Thomas Stockmeier *(Exec VP & Gen Mgr-Indus & Medical)*
Engelbert Liebminger *(Exec VP-HR)*
Walter Mente *(Exec VP-Ops)*
Kambiz Dawoodi *(Sr VP & Gen Mgr-Power & Wireless)*
Eric Janson *(Sr VP-Sls & Mktg)*

Supervisory Board of Directors:
Hans Jorg Kaltenbrunner
Johann C. Eitner
Michael Grimm
Wirtschaftsing Klaus Iffland
Jacob Jacobsson
Gunter Kneffel
Gerald Rogers
Siegfried Selberherr
Vida Uhde-Djefroudi

U.S. Subsidiaries:

austriamicrosystems USA Inc (1)
8601 Six Forks Rd Ste 400
Raleigh, NC 27615 (100%)
Tel.: (919) 676-5292
Fax: (509) 696-2713
E-Mail: sales.americas@austriamicrosystems.com
Web Site: www.austriamicrosystems.com
Emp.: 4
Semiconductor & Related Device Mfr
S.I.C.: 3674
N.A.I.C.S.: 334413

Texas Advanced Optoelectronic Solutions, Inc. (1)
1001 Klein Rd Ste 300
Plano, TX 75074
Tel.: (972) 673-0759
Fax: (972) 943-0610
Web Site: www.taosinc.com
Sales Range: $75-99.9 Million
Emp.: 42
Optoelectronic Equipment Mfr
S.I.C.: 3674
N.A.I.C.S.: 334413
Kirk Laney *(Pres)*

Non-U.S. Subsidiaries:

austriamicrosystems France S.a.r.l. (1)
124 Avenue de Paris
94300 Vincennes, France (100%)
Tel.: (33) 143740090
Fax: (33) 143742098
E-Mail: sales.europe@ams.com
Web Site: www.austriamicrosystems.com
Emp.: 5
Other Electronic Parts & Equipment Whslr
S.I.C.: 5065
N.A.I.C.S.: 423690

austriamicrosystems Germany GmbH (1)
Erdinger Strasse 14
85609 Aschheim, Germany (100%)
Tel.: (49) 896936430
Fax: (49) 8969364366
E-Mail: sales@ams.com
Emp.: 7
Semiconductor & Related Device Mfr
S.I.C.: 3674
N.A.I.C.S.: 334413

austriamicrosystems India Private (1)
01-07 Cyber Pearl Block 2 HITEC City
Madhapur, Hyderabad, Andhra Pradesh, 500081, India
Tel.: (91) 40 4008 2350
Fax: (91) 40 4008 2424
Emp.: 30
Electronic Components Distr
S.I.C.: 5065
N.A.I.C.S.: 423690

austriamicrosystems Italy S.r.l. (1)
Via A Volta 18
20094 Corsico, Italy (100%)
Tel.: (39) 245864364
Fax: (39) 24585773
Web Site: www.austriamicrosystems.com
Emp.: 35
Electrical Apparatus & Equipment Wiring Supplies & Construction Material Whslr
S.I.C.: 5063
N.A.I.C.S.: 423610

austriamicrosystems Japan Co. Ltd (1)
KF Building 5th Floor 4-13-8 Shiba
Minato-ku, 108-0014 Tokyo, Japan (100%)
Tel.: (81) 354846745
Fax: (81) 354846746
E-Mail: salesjp@austriamicrosystems.com
Web Site: www.austriasystems.com
Emp.: 8
Prerecorded Tape Compact Disc & Record Stores
S.I.C.: 5731
N.A.I.C.S.: 443142

austriamicrosystems (Philippines) Inc. (1)
B2-1D Carmelray Industrial Park II Special Economic Zone
Brgy Tulo, Calamba, Laguna, 4027, Philippines
Tel.: (63) 49 508 01 62
Fax: (63) 49 508 16 22
Semiconductor Products Mfr
S.I.C.: 3674
N.A.I.C.S.: 334413
Jose Mariano *(Gen Mgr)*

austriamicrosystems Spain S.L. (1)
austriamicrosystems Spain S.L.
Lado Este, 46022 Valencia, Spain
Tel.: (34) 963726825
Web Site: www.austriamicrosystems.com
Emp.: 10
Electronic Components Distr
S.I.C.: 5065
N.A.I.C.S.: 423690
Jose Vinau *(Mgr)*

austriamicrosystems Switzerland AG (1)
Rietstrasse 4
8640 Rapperswil, Sankt Gallen, Switzerland
Tel.: (41) 55 220 90 00
Fax: (41) 55 220 90 01
E-Mail: info@ams.com
Web Site: www.ams.com
Emp.: 30
Electronic Components Distr
S.I.C.: 5065
N.A.I.C.S.: 423690

AMS GMBH

Bruchstrasse 1-9
57578 Elkenroth, Germany
Tel.: (49) 274780080
Fax: (49) 2747800890
E-Mail: info@ams-mbt.de
Web Site: www.ams-mbt.de
Year Founded: 1972
Rev.: $13,656,060
Emp.: 120

Business Description:
Metal Fitting Mfr
S.I.C.: 3499

AMS GmbH—(Continued)

N.A.I.C.S.: 332999
Personnel:
Thomas Imhauser *(Mng Dir)*

AMS PUBLIC TRANSPORT HOLDINGS LIMITED

11th 12th Floor Abba Commercial Building 223 Aberdeen Main Road
Hong Kong, China (Hong Kong)
Tel.: (852) 28736808
Fax: (852) 28732042
E-Mail: service@amspt.com
Web Site: www.amspt.com
0077—(HKG)
Sls.: $46,258,620
Assets: $63,763,454
Liabilities: $22,957,097
Net Worth: $40,806,356
Earnings: ($5,101,649)
Emp.: 1,273
Fiscal Year-end: 03/31/13
Business Description:
Public Bus Transportation Services
S.I.C.: 4111
N.A.I.C.S.: 485113
Personnel:
Man Kit Wong *(Chm)*
Man Chun Chan *(CEO)*
Ka Yan Wong *(Sec & Controller-Fin)*
Board of Directors:
Man Kit Wong
Dorothy Yuen Tak-fai Chan
Man Chun Chan
Ki Chi Kwong
Allen Peng Fei Lee
Sui Chun Ng
May Wai Sum Wong
Vincent Ling Sun Wong
Transfer Agent:
Union Registrars Limited
18/F Fook Lee Commercial Centre Town Place
33 Lockhart Road
Wanchai, China (Hong Kong)

AMSC CO., LTD.

Yoyogi Community Bldg 1-11-2
Yoyogi Shibuya-ku
151-0053 Tokyo, Japan
Tel.: (81) 3 5302 1556
Fax: (81) 3 5302 1558
Web Site: www.amsc.co.jp
Year Founded: 1975
Sales Range: $200-249.9 Million
Business Description:
Wholesale Traders
S.I.C.: 7389
N.A.I.C.S.: 425120
Personnel:
Shintaro Kurihara *(Pres)*
Kazuaki Hirai *(Co-Mng Dir)*
Toshikazu Mishina *(Co-Mng Dir)*
Kenzo Abe *(Exec Officer)*
Tatsuo Higashihashi *(Exec Officer)*
Board of Directors:
Kazuaki Hirai
Shintaro Kurihara
Toshikazu Mishina
Atushi Nishioka

AMSCO CAST PRODUCTS (CANADA) INC.

224-9738 51 Ave NW
Edmonton, AB, T6E 0A6, Canada
Tel.: (780) 432-6898
Fax: (780) 432-6905
E-Mail: amsco@worldgate.ca
Web Site: www.amscocast.com
Year Founded: 1916
Rev.: $12,921,952
Emp.: 100
Business Description:
Steel Castings Supplier
S.I.C.: 3325
N.A.I.C.S.: 331513
Personnel:
Eddie Chung *(Chm & CEO)*

AMSECO EXPLORATION LTD.

620 rue Saint-Jacques bureau 110
Montreal, QC, H3C 1C7, Canada
Tel.: (514) 284-5111
Fax: (514) 284-6111
E-Mail: info@amsecoexploration.com
Web Site: www.amsecoexploration.com
Year Founded: 1984
AEL—(TSXV)
Sales Range: $1-9.9 Million
Business Description:
Metal Exploration Services
S.I.C.: 1099
N.A.I.C.S.: 212299
Personnel:
Roger Bourgault *(Chm)*
Jean Desmarais *(Pres & CEO)*
Board of Directors:
Roger Bourgault
Jean-Pierre Cloutier
Jean Desmarais
Francois LaComte
Lyne Plante

AMSPHERE LIMITED

90 Fenchurch St
London, EC3M 4BY, United Kingdom
Tel.: (44) 8701208327
Fax: (44) 8701208333
Web Site: www.amsphere.com
Sales Range: $10-24.9 Million
Emp.: 100
Business Description:
Software Testing Services
S.I.C.: 8999
N.A.I.C.S.: 541690
Personnel:
Ricky Shankar *(CEO)*
Ken Campbell *(Sec)*

AMSTERDAM COMMODITIES N.V.

WTC Beursplein 37 10th Floor
PO Box 30156
3001 DD Rotterdam, Netherlands
Tel.: (31) 104051195
Fax: (31) 104055094
E-Mail: info@acomo.nl
Web Site: www.acomo.nl
ACOMO—(EUR)
Sls.: $798,412,839
Assets: $357,878,166
Liabilities: $193,732,738
Net Worth: $164,145,429
Earnings: $36,383,133
Emp.: 541
Fiscal Year-end: 12/31/12
Business Description:
Trade & Distribution of Agricultural Products
S.I.C.: 7389
N.A.I.C.S.: 425120
Personnel:
Bernard H. Stuivinga *(Chm-Supervisory Bd)*
Erik Rietkerk *(CEO & Member-Mgmt Bd)*
Jan ten Kate *(CFO & Member-Mgmt Bd)*
Supervisory Board of Directors:
Bernard H. Stuivinga
Yoav Gottesmann
Machtelt Groothuis
Jan Niessen

Subsidiaries:

Acomo Investments B.V., (1)
Beursplein 378E Etage
3001 DD Rotterdam, South Holland, Netherlands
Tel.: (31) 104051195
Fax: (31) 104055094
Investment Management Services
S.I.C.: 6211
N.A.I.C.S.: 523999
Stephane Holvoet *(Gen Mgr)*

Catz International B.V. (1)
Blakeburg Building Blaak 22
PO Box 180
3000 AD Rotterdam, Netherlands
Tel.: (31) 104113440
Fax: (31) 104118913
E-Mail: info@catz.nl
Web Site: www.catz.nl
Emp.: 42
Food Trading & Distributing Services
S.I.C.: 7389
N.A.I.C.S.: 425120
Henk C. Moerman *(Mng Dir)*

King Nuts & Raaphorst B.V. (1)
Spanjeweg 4
PO Box 1044
2410 CA Bodegraven, South Holland, Netherlands
Tel.: (31) 172632222
Fax: (31) 172 632 233
E-Mail: info@kingnuts-raaphorst.com
Web Site: www.kingnuts-raaphorst.com
Nuts & Dried Fruits Distr
S.I.C.: 5149
N.A.I.C.S.: 424490

King Nuts Holding B.V., (1)
Spanjeweg 4
PO Box 1044
2410 CA Bodegraven, South Holland, Netherlands
Tel.: (31) 172632222
Investment Management Services
S.I.C.: 6211
N.A.I.C.S.: 523999

Red River van Eck B.V. (1)
Huizersdijk 11
PO Box 14
Zevenbergen, Noord-Brabant, 4761 PT, Netherlands
Tel.: (31) 168323555
Fax: (31) 168325294
Emp.: 10
Agricultural Supplements Distr
S.I.C.: 5191
N.A.I.C.S.: 424910
Anton Van Eck *(Gen Mgr)*

TEFCO EuroIngredients B.V. (1)
Italieweg 21
PO Box 1020
2410 CA Bodegraven, South Holland, Netherlands
Tel.: (31) 172650018
Fax: (31) 172 61 54 00
E-Mail: food@tefco.nl
Web Site: www.tefco.nl
Emp.: 11
Natural Ingredients Distr
S.I.C.: 5149
N.A.I.C.S.: 424490
Ton Driessen *(Mng Dir)*

Tefco Food Ingredients B.V. (1)
Italieweg 21
PO Box 1020
2410CA Bodegraven, Netherlands (100%)
Tel.: (31) 172650018
Fax: (31) 172615400
E-Mail: food@tefco.nl
Web Site: www.tefco.nl
Emp.: 10
Grocery & Related Products Whslr
S.I.C.: 5149
N.A.I.C.S.: 424490
Marian Weerdenburg *(Mng Dir)*

Tovano B.V. (1)
Transportwg 47
Maasdijk, 2676 LM Hague, Netherlands (100%)
Tel.: (31) 174528333
Fax: (31) 174528001
E-Mail: info@tovano.nl
Web Site: www.tovano.nl
Emp.: 6
Grocery & Related Products Whslr
S.I.C.: 5149
N.A.I.C.S.: 424490
Toon van Noort *(Mng Dir)*

Van Rees B.V (1)
Wijnhaven 65D
PO Box 914
3011 WJ Rotterdam, South Holland, Netherlands
Tel.: (31) 10 4021750
Fax: (31) 10 4136881
E-Mail: trading@vanrees.com
Emp.: 40
Tea Products Mfr & Distr
S.I.C.: 2095
N.A.I.C.S.: 311920
Flip Van Rijen *(Mng Dir)*

Vriesthee B.V (1)
Wijnhaven 65D
PO Box 1191
3011 WJ Rotterdam, South Holland, Netherlands
Tel.: (31) 10 4655844
Fax: (31) 10 4136881
E-Mail: teadept@vriesthee.nl
Web Site: www.vanrees.com
Tea Products Distr
S.I.C.: 5149
N.A.I.C.S.: 424490

U.S. Subsidiary:

Red River Commodities Inc (1)
PO Box 3022
Fargo, ND 58102
Tel.: (800) 437-5539
Fax: (701) 282-5325
Web Site: www.redriv.com
Emp.: 50
Ingredient Products Mfr
S.I.C.: 2099
N.A.I.C.S.: 311999
Bob Majkrzak *(Pres & CEO)*

Subsidiary:

Sungold Food Inc. (2)
501 42nd St NW
Fargo, ND 58102
Tel.: (701) 282-5325
Fax: (800) 437-5539
E-Mail: info@sunbutter.com
Web Site: www.sunbutter.com
Emp.: 75
Sunflower Kernel Butter Mfr
S.I.C.: 2068
N.A.I.C.S.: 311911
Dan Hofland *(VP-Mktg)*

Non-U.S. Subsidiaries:

P.T. Van Rees Indonesia (1)
Wisma Kemang 4th Floor Jl Kemang Selatan Raya No 1
Jakarta, 12560, Indonesia
Tel.: (62) 217817044
Fax: (62) 217817047
E-Mail: vanrees@vri.co.id
Tea Products Distr
S.I.C.: 5149
N.A.I.C.S.: 424490

Snick EuroIngredients N.V., (1)
Industriepark Saint Jorisstraat 85E
8730 Beernem, West Flanders, Belgium
Tel.: (32) 50361685
Fax: (32) 50372207
E-Mail: info@snick.be
Web Site: www.snick.be
Emp.: 10
Food Ingredients Mfr & Distr
S.I.C.: 2099
N.A.I.C.S.: 311999
Philippe Snick *(Gen Mgr)*

Van Rees Ceylon Ltd. (1)
51/27 New Nuge Road
Peliyagoda, Colombo, Sri Lanka
Tel.: (94) 11 2931698
Fax: (94) 11 2939263
E-Mail: vrc@vanrees.lk
Web Site: www.vanrees.com
Emp.: 26
Tea Mfr
S.I.C.: 2095
N.A.I.C.S.: 311920
Niraj de Mel *(Mng Dir)*

Van Rees LLC (1)
Room 809 Building 16/18 2nd Tverskaya Yamskaya Ulitsa
Moscow, 125047, Russia
Tel.: (7) 4952254504

Fax: (7) 4957559120
E-Mail: vrm@vanrees.ru
Emp.: 7
Tea Whslr
S.I.C.: 5149
N.A.I.C.S.: 424490
Andrey Machavariani *(Gen Dir)*

Van Rees North America Inc (1)
2200 Yonge Street Suite 1006
Toronto, ON, M4S 2C6, Canada
Tel.: (416) 482-7878
Fax: (416) 482-6009
E-Mail: vrnatrading@vanreesna.com
Web Site: www.vanrees.com
Emp.: 6
Tea Products Whslr
S.I.C.: 5149
N.A.I.C.S.: 424490
Peter Scandrett *(Pres)*

Van Rees UK Ltd, (1)
24 Winchester Street
Basingstoke, Hampshire, RG21 7DZ, United Kingdom
Tel.: (44) 1256810020
Fax: (44) 1256354142
E-Mail: tea@vanrees.co.uk
Web Site: www.vanrees.co.uk
Tea Products Distr
S.I.C.: 5149
N.A.I.C.S.: 424490

AMT-SYBEX LTD.

The Spirella Bldg Bridge Rd
Letchworth, Hertfordshire, SG6 4ET, United Kingdom
Tel.: (44) 1462476400
Fax: (44) 1462476401
E-Mail: info@amt-sybex.com
Web Site: www.amt-sybex.com
Sales Range: $50-74.9 Million
Emp.: 150
Business Description:
Consultancy & Systems Technology Provider
S.I.C.: 8999
N.A.I.C.S.: 541690
Personnel:
Andrew Miller *(Mng Dir)*
Board of Directors:
Andrew Miller
Brian Miller

AMTECH ELECTRONICS INDIA LIMITED

E-6 GIDC Electronics Zone
Gandhinagar, Gujarat, 382 028, India
Tel.: (91) 7923289101
Fax: (91) 7923289111
E-Mail: info@amtechelectronics.com
Web Site: www.amtechelectronics.com
Year Founded: 1987
Emp.: 80
Business Description:
Motion Control, Automation, Power Quality & Industrial Electronics Equipment Mfr
S.I.C.: 3559
N.A.I.C.S.: 333249
Personnel:
Piyush Patel *(Mng Dir)*
Subsidiary:

Amtech Power Limited (1)
1st Floor E-6 GIDC Electronics Zone
Gandhinagar, Gujarat, 382 028, India
Tel.: (91) 7923289116
Fax: (91) 7923289111
E-Mail: apl@amtechelectronics.com
Web Site: www.amtechelectronics.com
Emp.: 10
Power Generation Control & Protection Systems Mfr & Installation Services
S.I.C.: 3612
N.A.I.C.S.: 335311
Bhaskar Narayanan *(Mng Dir)*

U.S. Subsidiary:

Amtech Drives, Inc. (1)
3852 Oakcliff Industrial Ct
Doraville, GA 30340
Tel.: (770) 469-5240
Fax: (770) 469-5241
E-Mail: info@amtechdrives.com
Web Site: www.amtechdrives.com
Emp.: 10
Industrial Electronics Mfr
S.I.C.: 3612
N.A.I.C.S.: 335311
Charles Geraldi *(Pres)*

AMTEK AUTO LIMITED

(d/b/a Amtek Auto Group)
3 Local Shopping Centre
Pamposh Enclave GK-1, New Delhi, 110048, India
Tel.: (91) 11 4234 4444
Fax: (91) 11 4234 4000
E-Mail: info@amtek.com
Web Site: www.amtek.com
520077—(BAN NSE)
Business Description:
Automotive & Non-Automotive Components Mfr
S.I.C.: 3714
N.A.I.C.S.: 336390
Personnel:
Arvind Dham *(Chm)*
John Ernest Flintham *(Sr Mng Dir)*
D. S. Malik *(Mng Dir)*
V. K. Pabby *(Mng Dir)*
Rajeev Raj Kumar *(Sec)*
Board of Directors:
Arvind Dham
Raj Narain Bhardwaj
Sanjay Chhabra
John Ernest Flintham
B. Lugani
D. S. Malik
Rajiv Thakur
B. Venugopal

Subsidiaries:

Ahmednagar Forgings Limited (1)
Gat No 614 At Village Kuruli
Tal Khed, Pune, 410 501, India In (54.96%)
Tel.: (91) 202622220
Fax: (91) 20639777
E-Mail: afl@giaspn01.vsnl.net.in
Web Site: www.amtek.com
513335—(BAN NSE)
Steel Forgings Mfr
S.I.C.: 3462
N.A.I.C.S.: 332111
S. Rajagopalan *(CEO)*
Swati Ahuja *(Compliance Officer & Sec)*

Amtek India Limited (1)
3 Local Shopping Centre
Pamposh Enclave GK-1, New Delhi, 110048, India In (61.64%)
Tel.: (91) 1142344444
Fax: (91) 1142344000
E-Mail: info@amtek.com
Web Site: www.amtek.com
532282—(BAN NSE)
Automotive Component Mfr
S.I.C.: 3566
N.A.I.C.S.: 333612
Arvind Dham *(Chm)*
Gautam Malhotra *(Mng Dir)*
Vishal Wason *(Sec)*

AMTEK ENGINEERING LTD.

35 Pioneer Road North
Singapore, 628475, Singapore
Tel.: (65) 62640033
Fax: (65) 62617693
E-Mail: enquires@amtek.com.sg
Web Site: www.amtek.com.sg
Year Founded: 1970
M1P—(SES)
Rev.: $625,966,000
Assets: $471,098,000
Liabilities: $297,391,000
Net Worth: $173,707,000
Earnings: $27,552,000
Emp.: 10,000
Fiscal Year-end: 06/30/13
Business Description:
Metal Stamping Component Mfr
S.I.C.: 3469
N.A.I.C.S.: 332119
Personnel:
Daniel Bou Wai Yeong *(Chm & CEO)*
Sheila Won Lein Ng *(Deputy CEO & CFO)*
Jocelin Swee Har Soon *(Deputy CFO & Sec)*
Keut Wan Soo *(CMO)*
Ka Yew Ling *(CTO)*
Pek Chuan Quek *(Chief Design & Dev Officer)*
Yeng Kwong Yuen *(Supply Chain Officer)*
Board of Directors:
Daniel Bou Wai Yeong
Tong Huat Ang
Horn Kee Leong
Steven Kok Hoong Lim
Seow Juan Low
Willian Edward Alastair Morrison
Sheila Won Lein Ng
Sigit Prasetya

Subsidiaries:

Amlab Services Pte Ltd (1)
1 Kian Teck Drive Level 2
628818 Singapore, Singapore (100%)
Tel.: (65) 66639824
Fax: (65) 62618875
Web Site: www.amlab.com.sg
Emp.: 18
Testing Laboratories
S.I.C.: 8734
N.A.I.C.S.: 541380
William Pang *(Mgr)*

Amtek Precision Technology Pte Ltd (1)
35 Pioneer Road North
Singapore, 628475, Singapore (85%)
Tel.: (65) 6264 0033
Fax: (65) 6265 2510
E-Mail: amtek-tech@amtek.com.sg
Web Site: www.amtek.com.sg
Metal Stamping
S.I.C.: 3466
N.A.I.C.S.: 332119
Doreen Goo *(Mgr-Pur)*

Amtek Technology Pte Ltd (1)
1 Kian Tech Drive
Singapore, 628818, Singapore
Tel.: (65) 62640033
Fax: (65) 62652510
Semiconductor Equipment Mfr
S.I.C.: 3674
N.A.I.C.S.: 334413

U.S. Subsidiaries:

Amtek (USA) Enterprises Inc (1)
830 Stewart Dr #243
Sunnyvale, CA 94085 (100%)
Tel.: (408) 667-1023
Web Site: www.amtek.com.sg/global_contact.html
Emp.: 60
Sales & Technical Services
S.I.C.: 3466
N.A.I.C.S.: 332119

Non-U.S. Subsidiaries:

AE Components Sdn. Bhd. (1)
No 7 Jalan Cj 7
Cheras Jaya, Kajang, Selangor, Malaysia (100%)
Tel.: (60) 360740773
Fax: (60) 390742058
Metal Stamping
S.I.C.: 3466
N.A.I.C.S.: 332119
Toe Peng Ju *(Mng Dir)*

AE Rubber Sdn. Bhd. (1)
12 Jalan Istimewa 1 Taman Perindustrian Cemerlang
Ulu Tiram, 81800 Johor, Malaysia (63.3%)
Tel.: (60) 78616608
Fax: (60) 78616605
E-Mail: aerubber@streamyx.com
Web Site: www.aerubber.com
Emp.: 250
All Other Rubber Product Mfr
S.I.C.: 3069
N.A.I.C.S.: 326299
Tai Nan Ching *(Mng Dir)*

AE Technology Sdn. Bhd (1)
No 7 Jalan Cj 7
Cheras Jaya, Kajang, Selangor, Malaysia (100%)
Tel.: (60) 390740773
Fax: (60) 390742058
Metal Stamping
S.I.C.: 3466
N.A.I.C.S.: 332119
Toe Peng Ju *(Mng Dir)*

Amtek Europe Development SA (1)
22 Rue Guynemer
78600 Maisons-Laffitte, France (74.67%)
Tel.: (33) 134936900
Fax: (33) 139622953
E-Mail: angung@amtek.com.sg
Web Site: www.amtek.com.sg/global_contact.html
Emp.: 25
Engineering Services
S.I.C.: 8711
N.A.I.C.S.: 541330
Ung Ang *(Pres)*

Amtek Huizhou (HK) Industries Ltd. (1)
Unit 612 6th Floor Nan Fung Commercial Centre No 19 Lam Lok Street
Kowloon Bay, Kowloon, China (Hong Kong)
Tel.: (852) 2753 6886
Fax: (852) 2753 9389
Metal Stamping Component Mfr
S.I.C.: 3466
N.A.I.C.S.: 332119

Amtek (Huizhou) Industries Ltd. (1)
No 3 Pingnangzhong Road Pingnan Industrial Park
Xiexia, Huizhou, Guangdong, 516006, China (82%)
Tel.: (86) 7522609511
Fax: (86) 752 260 1036
E-Mail: penny_wu@amtek.com.cn
Web Site: www.amtek.com.sg/global_presence.html
Emp.: 1,000
Metal Stamping
S.I.C.: 3469
N.A.I.C.S.: 332119
Chong Yong Min *(Gen Mgr)*

Amtek Metalforming (Shanghai) Ltd. (1)
No 819 Xuanhuang Highway Nanhui Industrial Park
Shanghai, 201300, China
Tel.: (86) 21 3828 6688
Fax: (86) 21 5818 6008
Metal Stamping Components Mfr
S.I.C.: 3466
N.A.I.C.S.: 332119

Amtek Mexico SA de C.V. (1)
Ave Rubilina 88 Col Palaco
21385 Mexicali, Baja California, Mexico (100%)
Tel.: (52) 6865639088
Fax: (52) 6865636898
E-Mail: rodney@amtek.com.mx
Web Site: www.amtek.com.mx
Emp.: 100
Metal Stamping
S.I.C.: 3466
N.A.I.C.S.: 332119

Amtek Precision Engineering Czech Republic S R O (1)
Za Pazdernou 1531
Pisek, South Bohemia, Czech Republic (100%)
Tel.: (420) 382734411
Fax: (420) 382174410
E-Mail: daniel.soo@amtek.com.sg
Emp.: 700
Trim Manufacturing
S.I.C.: 3432
N.A.I.C.S.: 332913
Dau Yee Liew *(Mng Dir)*

Amtek Precision Engineering France (1)
Parc Mecatronic
03410 Saint-Victor, France (100%)

Amtek Engineering Ltd.—(Continued)

Tel.: (33) 470640710
Fax: (33) 470034319
Web Site: www.amtek.com
Emp.: 60
Metal Stamping
S.I.C.: 3469
N.A.I.C.S.: 332119
Gomis Antoeni *(Mng Dir)*

Amtek Precision Engineering (Shanghai) Co., Ltd. (1)
No 819 Xuanhuang Highway Nanhui Industrial Zone
Pudong New District, Shanghai, 201300, China
Tel.: (86) 2138286688
Fax: (86) 2138286688
Metal Stamping Services
S.I.C.: 3466
N.A.I.C.S.: 332119

Amtek Precision Technology (Hanoi) Co., Ltd. (1)
Log K4-2 Que Vo Industrial Park
Bac Ninh, Vietnam
Tel.: (84) 241 3634 868
Fax: (84) 241 3634 869
Metal Stamping Components Mfr
S.I.C.: 3466
N.A.I.C.S.: 332119

Amtek Precision Technology (India) Private Limited (1)
XXXII/3F Sarovaram Kureekkad Road
Puthiyakavu Jn Ernakulam
Tripunithura PO, 682 301 Kerala, India
Tel.: (91) 484 278 5062
Fax: (91) 484 278 5073
Web Site: www.amtek-india.com
Emp.: 9
Precision Tool Mfr
S.I.C.: 3451
N.A.I.C.S.: 332721
B. E. Mathai *(Mgr)*

Amtek (Suzhou) Precision Engineering Ltd. (1)
No 36 Xing Ming Street CSS Industrial Park
Suzhou, Jiangsu, 215021, China
Tel.: (86) 512 6763 0088
Fax: (86) 512 6761 4655
Metal Stamping Components Mfr
S.I.C.: 3466
N.A.I.C.S.: 332119

Amtek Technology (H.K.) Limited (1)
Unit 612 6/F Nan Fung Commerical Centre
No 19 Lam Lok Street
Kowloon Bay, Kowloon, China (Hong Kong)
Tel.: (852) 2753 6886
Fax: (852) 2753 9389
Web Site: www.amtek.com.sg/global_contact.html
Metal Parts & Tools Whslr
S.I.C.: 5051
N.A.I.C.S.: 423510

Cheval Electronic Enclosure Co. Ltd. (1)
145 Bangplee Ind Estate Soi 4 Moo 7
Teparak Road Bangsaotong
Sub-District Bangsaotong, Samut Prakan, 10540, Thailand
Tel.: (66) 2 315 1504
Fax: (66) 2 315 1506
Electronic Products Mgr
S.I.C.: 3679
N.A.I.C.S.: 334419

Cheval Technology Co. Ltd. (1)
121/4 Moo 4 Chaechang
San Kamphang
Chiang Mai, 50130, Thailand
Tel.: (66) 53 880 788
Fax: (66) 53 880 787
Electronic Products Mfr
S.I.C.: 3679
N.A.I.C.S.: 334419

Huizhou Amtek Technology Ltd. (1)
No 3 Pingnanzhong Road Pingnan Industrial Park
Xiexia, Huizhou, Guangdong, 516006, China
Tel.: (86) 752 260 9542
Fax: (86) 752 260 1879
Metal Stamping Components Mfr
S.I.C.: 3466
N.A.I.C.S.: 332119

Lian Jun Industrial (H.K.) Limited (1)
Rm B31 5th Floor Cambridge Plz Blk B
Sheung Shui, China (Hong Kong) (100%)
Tel.: (852) 35292739
Fax: (852) 35292748
Plastics Materials & Basic Forms & Shapes Wholesalers
S.I.C.: 5162
N.A.I.C.S.: 424610

Lian Jun (Shenzhen) Technology Ltd. (1)
No 12 Da Guang Kan Estate Industrial Area
Ban Tian Bu Ji
Long Gang District, Shenzhen, 518129, China
Tel.: (86) 755 8471 2688
Fax: (86) 755 8471 2989
Metal Stamping Components Mfr
S.I.C.: 3469
N.A.I.C.S.: 332119

PT Amtek Engineering Batam (1)
Block E No 1 Jl Letjen Soeprapto Cammo Industrial Park
Batam Centre, Batam, 29432, Indonesia
Tel.: (62) 778 464 698
Fax: (62) 778 464 697
Engineering Services
S.I.C.: 8711
N.A.I.C.S.: 541330

PT Amtek Engineering Jakarta (1)
Kota Bukit Indah
Kawasan Industri Indotaisei Se, Karawang, Indonesia (100%)
Tel.: (62) 264351139
Fax: (62) 264351138
E-Mail: ptasi@indosat.net.id
Emp.: 400
Engineering Services
S.I.C.: 8711
N.A.I.C.S.: 541330

PT Amtek Plastic Batam (1)
Lot 11 Citra Buana Industrial Park III
Jalan Engku Putri
Batam, 29461, Indonesia
Tel.: (62) 778 471 694
Fax: (62) 778 471 899
Plastics Products Mfr
S.I.C.: 3089
N.A.I.C.S.: 326199

PT Amtek Precision (1)
Lot 1 Citra Buana Industrial Park III Jl Engku
29461 Batam, Indonesia (100%)
Tel.: (62) 778471988
Fax: (62) 778471989
Emp.: 400
Engineering Services
S.I.C.: 8711
N.A.I.C.S.: 541330
K L Lai *(CEO)*

AMTEK HOLDINGS BERHAD

Level 2A No 88 Jalan Perdana
Taman Tasek Perdana
50480 Kuala Lumpur, Malaysia
Tel.: (60) 320927170
Fax: (60) 322732078
Web Site: www.amtek.com.my
AMTEK—(KLS)
Rev.: $15,500,623
Assets: $17,763,315
Liabilities: $9,406,050
Net Worth: $8,357,265
Earnings: ($266,442)
Fiscal Year-end: 06/30/13

Business Description:
Garments & Shoes Mfr
S.I.C.: 2399
N.A.I.C.S.: 315210

Personnel:
Azmin Mohd Nursin *(Chm)*
Muhammad Mohd Taib *(Sec)*

Board of Directors:
Azmin Mohd Nursin
Ahmad Abu Bakar
Rashid Mohamed
Tieh Chuan Ng
Teong Bun Thong

AMTEK INDIA LIMITED

(See Under Amtek Auto Limited)

AMTEL HOLDINGS BERHAD

No 7 Jalan PJS 7/19 Bandar Sunway
46150 Petaling Jaya, Selangor Darul Ehsan, Malaysia
Tel.: (60) 356322449
Fax: (60) 356370042
E-Mail: ahb@amtel.com.my
Web Site: www.amtel.com.my
AMTEL—(KLS)
Rev.: $18,221,162
Assets: $22,383,300
Liabilities: $7,457,910
Net Worth: $14,925,390
Earnings: $1,428,825
Fiscal Year-end: 11/30/12

Business Description:
Electronic & Telecommunications Products Distr
S.I.C.: 1731
N.A.I.C.S.: 238210

Personnel:
Hun Kian Koid *(Mng Dir)*
Phooi Sze Chan *(Co-Sec)*
Yit Foong Hoh *(Co-Sec)*

Board of Directors:
Kamel Rijaludin
Pak Hing Chang
Hun Kian Koid
Ah Chong Ng
Hock Lee Siow
Tuck Kuan Wong

Subsidiaries:

Amtel Cellular Sdn. Bhd. (1)
No 5 Jalan PJS 7/19
Bandar Sunway, 46150 Petaling Jaya, Selangor, Malaysia
Tel.: (60) 356326788
Fax: (60) 356325678
E-Mail: inquiry@mynavi.com.my
Web Site: www.lokatoo.com
Emp.: 50
Global Positioning System Navigator Retailer
S.I.C.: 5065
N.A.I.C.S.: 423690
Woon Huei Tan *(Mng Dir)*

Amtel Communications Sdn. Bhd. (1)
No 9 Jalan PJS 7/19
Bandar Sunway, 46150 Petaling Jaya, Selangor Darul Ehsan, Malaysia
Tel.: (60) 356388738
Fax: (60) 356323217
E-Mail: acsbprod@amtel.com.my
Web Site: www.amtelcomms.com.my
Emp.: 15
Radios Distr & Repairing Services
S.I.C.: 5734
N.A.I.C.S.: 443142
Kenneth Parker *(Owner)*

Amtel Group Sdn. Bhd. (1)
7 Jalan Pjs 7/19
Taman Bandar Sunway, Petaling Jaya, Selangor, 46150, Malaysia
Tel.: (60) 356370113
Fax: (60) 356325678
Investment Management Services
S.I.C.: 6211
N.A.I.C.S.: 523999

Amtel Resources Sdn. Bhd. (1)
255 Lorong Perak 12 Mergong 2
05150 Alor Setar, Kedah, Malaysia
Tel.: (60) 47339809
Fax: (60) 47330994
E-Mail: pschan@amtel.com.my
Web Site: www.amtel.com.my
Emp.: 7
Telecommunication Civil Works Contract Services
S.I.C.: 1629
N.A.I.C.S.: 237130
Wou Chau Chin *(Exec Dir)*

AMTEX LIMITED

1 Km Khurrianwala Jaranwala Rd
Faisalabad, 48000, Pakistan
Tel.: (92) 414361724
Fax: (92) 414361726
E-Mail: info@amtextile.com
Web Site: www.amtextile.com
Emp.: 7,000

Business Description:
Home Textile & Garment Mfr
S.I.C.: 2391
N.A.I.C.S.: 314120

Personnel:
Khurram Iftikhar *(CEO)*

AMTRADA HOLDING B.V.

Herengracht 214
Amsterdam, 1016 BS, Netherlands
Tel.: (31) 205240520
Fax: (31) 25240556
E-Mail: trade@nedcoffee.nl
Web Site: www.nedcoffee.com
Sls.: $816,000,000
Emp.: 7

Business Description:
Holding Company
S.I.C.: 6719
N.A.I.C.S.: 551112

Personnel:
J.W.M. Hendriksen *(CEO)*

Subsidiaries:

Continaf B.V. (1)
Simon Carmiggeltstraat 6-50
1011 DJ Amsterdam, Netherlands
Tel.: (31) 20 524 0 524
E-Mail: trade@continaf.nl
Web Site: www.continaf.com
Cocoa Bean Whslr
S.I.C.: 5159
N.A.I.C.S.: 424590

Daarnhouwer & Co. (1)
Korte Hogendijk 18
1506 MA Zaandam, Netherlands
Mailing Address:
PO Box 2037
1500 GA Zaandam, Netherlands
Tel.: (31) 75 6126388
Fax: (31) 75 6318532
E-Mail: directie@daarnhouwer.nl
Web Site: www.daarnhouwer.com
Cocoa Bean Whslr
S.I.C.: 5159
N.A.I.C.S.: 424590

Nedcoffee BV (1)
Simon Carmiggeltstraat 6-50
1011 DJ Amsterdam, Netherlands
Tel.: (31) 20 524 05 20
E-Mail: trade@nedcoffee.nl
Web Site: www.nedcoffee.com
Emp.: 50
Coffee Bean Distr
S.I.C.: 5149
N.A.I.C.S.: 424490

AMUN EDELMETALL HANDELSKONTOR AG

Sterngasse 3
1010 Vienna, Austria
Tel.: (43) 810 7000 60
E-Mail: office@amunkontor.com
Web Site: www.amunkontor.com
IAM—(DEU)

Business Description:
Precious Metals Trading Services
S.I.C.: 6221
N.A.I.C.S.: 523140

Personnel:
Hans Gogg *(Member-Mgmt Bd)*
Konrad Keil *(Member-Mgmt Bd)*
Andreas Tschanz *(Member-Mgmt Bd)*

AMUR MINERALS CORPORATION

14 Gaidar Street Office 9
Khabarovsk, 680063, Russia
Tel.: (7) 4212755615
E-Mail: rjyoung@amurminerals.com
Web Site: www.amurminerals.com
AMC—(LSE)

Assets: $26,317,000
Liabilities: $119,000
Net Worth: $26,198,000
Earnings: ($3,998,000)
Emp.: 49
Fiscal Year-end: 12/31/12

Business Description:
Mineral Exploration Services
S.I.C.: 1481
N.A.I.C.S.: 213115

Personnel:
Robin Young *(CEO)*

Board of Directors:
Robert Schafer
Brian Savage
Robin Young

Legal Counsel:
Norton Rose Fulbright (Central Europe) LLP
White Square Office Center Butyrsky Val St 10 Bldg A
Moscow, Russia

Maples & Calder
Sea Meadow House Road Town
PO Box 173
Tortola, Virgin Islands (British)

Field Fisher Waterhouse LLP
35 Vine Street
London, United Kingdom

AMUSE INC.

20-1 Sakuragaoka-cho Shibuya-ku
Tokyo, 150-8570, Japan
Tel.: (81) 354573333
Fax: (81) 354573334
Web Site: ir.amuse.co.jp
4301—(TKS)
Rev.: $339,590,669
Assets: $253,475,695
Liabilities: $80,987,027
Net Worth: $172,488,668
Earnings: $27,284,191
Emp.: 255
Fiscal Year-end: 03/31/13

Business Description:
Media Visual & Artist Management Services
S.I.C.: 7336
N.A.I.C.S.: 541430

Personnel:
Kuniko Osato *(Founder)*
Yokichi Osato *(Chm)*
Tatsuro Hatanaka *(Pres)*
Yasuyuki Saito *(Mng Dir)*
Kazuki Aoki *(Corp Officer)*
Hiroyuki Araki *(Corp Officer)*
Nobuhiro Chiba *(Corp Officer)*
Takeshi Fukuoka *(Corp Officer)*
Chiaki Harada *(Corp Officer)*
Rieko Ito *(Corp Officer)*
Yoshinori Kumazawa *(Corp Officer)*
Toshio Miyakoshi *(Corp Officer)*
Shin Sugimoto *(Sr Corp Officer)*
Masaaki Tomaru *(Corp Officer)*

Board of Directors:
Yokichi Osato
Tatsuro Hatanaka
Rumiko Ichige
Muneaki Masuda
Yasuyuki Saito
Yojiro Shiba
Nobuyuki Soma

Subsidiaries:

A-Sketch Inc. (1)
20-1 Sakuragaokacho
Shibuya-ku, Tokyo, 150-0031, Japan
Tel.: (81) 354575566
Fax: (81) 354570233
Web Site: www.a-sketch.com
Music Entertainment Services
S.I.C.: 7929
N.A.I.C.S.: 711510

Amuse Edutainment Inc. (1)
2-34-3 Asakusa
Taito-ku, Tokyo, Japan
Tel.: (81) 358061181
Fax: (81) 358061182
E-Mail: k-matsumoto@amuse.co.jp
Web Site: www.amusemuseum.com
Emp.: 30
Community Museums & Entertainment Services
S.I.C.: 8412
N.A.I.C.S.: 712110
Yokichi Osato *(Pres)*

Amuse Soft Entertainment, Inc. (1)
20-1 Shibuya Infos Tower 13F Sakuragaoka
Shibuya-ku, 150-0031 Tokyo, Japan
Tel.: (81) 354573402
Fax: (81) 354573347
Web Site: www.amuse-s-e.co.jp
Emp.: 60
Audio & Video Production Services
S.I.C.: 7812
N.A.I.C.S.: 512110
Tapsuro Hatanaka *(Pres)*

AZEAL Inc. (1)
Infosutawa 20-1 Sakuragaokacho
Shibuya-ku, Tokyo, 150-8570, Japan
Tel.: (81) 354573398
Fax: (81) 354573466
E-Mail: techesko@azeal.co.jp
Web Site: www.techesko.com
Artists Management Services
S.I.C.: 7389
N.A.I.C.S.: 711410

Brussels Co., Ltd. (1)
1-4 Kanbakineocho Thiyota-ku
Tokyo, 1010051, Japan
Tel.: (81) 332197800
Fax: (81) 332336144
E-Mail: b-info@brussels.co.jp
Web Site: www.brussels.co.jp
Emp.: 30
Beverage Whslr
S.I.C.: 5182
N.A.I.C.S.: 424820
Kenji Takizawa *(Mgr)*

J-Feel Inc. (1)
20-1 Sakuragaokacho
Shibuya-ku, Tokyo, 150-8570, Japan
Tel.: (81) 354573470
Fax: (81) 354573466
E-Mail: info@j-feel.jp
Web Site: www.j-feel.jp
Emp.: 10
Business Consulting Services
S.I.C.: 8742
N.A.I.C.S.: 541611
Katsunori Takahashi *(Pres)*

AMVIG HOLDINGS LIMITED

Room 601-602 6th Floor Top Glory Tower 262 Gloucester Road
Causeway Bay, China (Hong Kong)
Tel.: (852) 2970 7000
Fax: (852) 2970 7070
E-Mail: info@amvig.com
Web Site: www.amvig.com
2300—(HKG)
Sls.: $463,719,287
Assets: $837,250,557
Liabilities: $343,315,319
Net Worth: $493,935,238
Earnings: $58,556,582
Emp.: 2,596
Fiscal Year-end: 12/31/12

Business Description:
Cigarette Packages Printing Services
S.I.C.: 3199
N.A.I.C.S.: 316998

Personnel:
Sai Wai Chan *(Vice Chm)*
Su Ge *(Pres & CEO)*
Guo Min Xu *(Deputy CEO-Dongguan KWG & Kunming Plant)*
Shun Fai Liu *(CFO & Sec)*

Board of Directors:
Billy Chew Keak Chan
Ellis Yeung Tin Wah Au
Sai Wai Chan
Jerzy Czubak
Su Ge
Sai Kit Ng
Eric Choon Gan Oh
Keith Ah Kee Tay
Ralf Klaus Wunderlich

Royal Bank of Canada Trust Company (Cayman) Limited
4th Floor Royal Bank House 24 Shedden Road
Georgetown, Cayman Islands

Transfer Agents:
Tricor Investor Services Limited
26th Floor Tesbury Centre 28 Queens Road East
Wanchai, China (Hong Kong)

Royal Bank of Canada Trust Company (Cayman) Limited
4th Floor Royal Bank House 24 Shedden Road
Georgetown, Cayman Islands

Subsidiary:

World Grand Holdings Limited (1)
Rm 1311 Shun Tak Ctr W Tower 200 Connaught Rd
Central, China (Hong Kong)
Tel.: (852) 25451443
Fax: (852) 25410344
Hot Stamping Foils Whslr
S.I.C.: 3499
N.A.I.C.S.: 332999

Non-U.S. Subsidiary:

Leigh-Mardon Pacific Packaging Pte Ltd. (1)
25J Sungei Kadut St 1
Singapore, 729334, Singapore
Tel.: (65) 63650211
Fax: (65) 6365 5616
Cigarette Packages Printing Services
S.I.C.: 2759
N.A.I.C.S.: 323111

AMWAL INVEST PLC

PO Box 940988
Amman, 11194, Jordan
Tel.: (962) 6 5000360
Fax: (962) 6 5000364
E-Mail: info@amwalinvest.com
Web Site: www.amwalinvest.com
Year Founded: 2005
AMWL—(AMM)
Sales Range: $1-9.9 Million
Emp.: 17

Business Description:
Investment Management Services
S.I.C.: 6211
N.A.I.C.S.: 523999

Personnel:
Qasem Newashi *(Chm)*
Fayiz Al Jundi *(Vice Chm)*
Mutasem Faouri *(CEO)*

Board of Directors:
Qasem Newashi
Qasem Al Dhamsheh
Fayiz Al Jundi
Mohammad Al Rajabi
Mahmmod Al Soudi
Hasan Gareeb
Khader Hunaiti

AN PHAT PLASTIC & GREEN ENVIRONMENT JOINT STOCK COMPANY

Lot CN 11& CN 13 An Dong Industrial Park
Nam Sach Distict, Hai Duong, Vietnam
Tel.: (84) 3203755997
Fax: (84) 3203755113
E-Mail: anphat@anphatplastic.com
Web Site: www.anphatplastic.com
AAA—(HNX)
Sales Range: $10-24.9 Million
Emp.: 1,100

Business Description:
Plastic Products Including Plastic Bags & Films
S.I.C.: 3089
N.A.I.C.S.: 326199

Personnel:
Duong Anh Pham *(Chm & Gen Dir)*

Plant:

An Phat Plastic & Green Environment Joint Stock Company - Factory No 2 (1)
An Dong Industrial Zone
Hai Duong, Vietnam
Tel.: (84) 437555840
Fax: (84) 4375 55841
Plastic Products Mfr
S.I.C.: 3089
N.A.I.C.S.: 326199

AN PHU IRRADIATION J.S.C.

Hamlet 1B
An Phu, Thuan An, Binh Duong, Vietnam
Tel.: (84) 650 3712292
Fax: (84) 650 3712293
Web Site: www.apic.com.vn
Year Founded: 2003
APC—(HOSE)

Business Description:
Food & Fruit Irradiation Services
S.I.C.: 7389
N.A.I.C.S.: 561990

Personnel:
Huu Hiep Vo *(Chm)*
Minh Anh Ngoc Phan *(Vice Chm)*
Canh Duong Le *(Member-Exec Bd)*
Dinh Khoat Vuong *(Member-Exec Bd)*

Board of Directors:
Huu Hiep Vo
Viet Ha Le
Duc Thang Nguyen
Minh Anh Ngoc Phan
Ngoc Thanh Tran

AN POST LIMITED

General Post Office O'Connell Street
Dublin, 1, Ireland
Tel.: (353) 17057000
Fax: (353) 17057466
E-Mail: customer.services@anpost.ie
Web Site: www.anpost.ie
Sls.: $1,086,756,310
Assets: $686,607,278
Liabilities: $669,502,842
Net Worth: $17,104,436
Earnings: ($53,008,136)
Emp.: 10,389
Fiscal Year-end: 12/31/12

Business Description:
Postal Services
S.I.C.: 4311
N.A.I.C.S.: 491110

Personnel:
Christoph Mueller *(Chm)*
Donal Connell *(CEO)*
Peter Quinn *(CFO)*
Jack Dempsey *(Sec)*

Board of Directors:
Christoph Mueller
Noel Adamson
Patrick Compton
Donal Connell
Thomas Devlin
Paul Henry
William Mooney
Martina O'Connell
Peter Ormond
John Quinlivan
William Scally
Lorraine Tormey
James Wrynn

Subsidiaries:

An Post Direct Limited (1)
General Post Office
O'Connell Street, Dublin, 1, Ireland (100%)
Tel.: (353) 17057000
Fax: (353) 18090908
E-Mail: info@anpost.ie

An Post Limited—(Continued)

Web Site: www.anpost.ie/AnPost/MainContent/About+An+Post/
Emp.: 2,000
Direct Title Insurance Carriers
S.I.C.: 6361
N.A.I.C.S.: 524127
Donal Connell *(CEO)*

An Post National Lottery Co. **(1)**
Lower Abbey St
Dublin, Ireland (80%)
Tel.: (353) 18364444
Fax: (353) 18366034
E-Mail: info@lottorey.ie
Web Site: www.lottorey.ie
Emp.: 100
All Other Amusement & Recreation Industries
S.I.C.: 7999
N.A.I.C.S.: 713990
Dermot Jgrissin *(Mng Dir)*

JMC Van Trans Limited **(1)**
Newlands
Naas Road, Dublin, 22, Ireland (100%)
Tel.: (353) 14602555
Fax: (353) 14094111
E-Mail: info@jmcvantrans.ie
Web Site: www.jmcvantrans.ie
General Freight Trucking & Logistics Services
S.I.C.: 4731
N.A.I.C.S.: 541614
Garrett Thornton *(Mng Dir)*

Precision Marketing Information Limited **(1)**
1st Floor 19-24 St Andrews St
Dublin, 2, Ireland (100%)
Tel.: (353) 18584800
Fax: (353) 18584801
E-Mail: info@dataireland.ie
Web Site: www.dataireland.ie
Emp.: 25
Security Systems Services
S.I.C.: 7382
N.A.I.C.S.: 561621
Joseph Houlihan *(Dir-Comml)*

Printpost Limited **(1)**
Unit 4 Broomhill Business Park Tallaght
Dublin, Ireland (100%)
Tel.: (353) 14513355
Fax: (353) 14513742
E-Mail: sales@printpost.ie
Web Site: www.printpost.com
Emp.: 40
All Other Business Support Services
S.I.C.: 7389
N.A.I.C.S.: 561499
Tommy McKane *(Mng Dir)*

Non-U.S. Subsidiary:

Air Business Ltd **(1)**
4 The Merlin Centre
Acrewood Way, Saint Albans, Hertfordshire, AL4 0JY, United Kingdom (100%)
Tel.: (44) 1727890600
Fax: (44) 1727810621
E-Mail: sales@airbusonline.com
Web Site: www.airbusonline.co.uk
Emp.: 100
General Freight Trucking, Local
S.I.C.: 4212
N.A.I.C.S.: 484110
Adam Sherman *(Mng Dir)*

ANA HOLDINGS INC.

(Formerly All Nippon Airways Co., Ltd.)
Shiodome City Center 1-5-2 Higashi-Shimbashi
Minato-ku, Tokyo, 105-7133, Japan
Tel.: (81) 3 6735 1030
Fax: (81) 367351005
Web Site: www.ana.co.jp
Year Founded: 1952
9202—(LSE TKS)
Rev.: $16,319,391,000
Assets: $23,509,662,000
Liabilities: $15,075,555,000
Net Worth: $8,434,107,000
Earnings: $474,540,000
Emp.: 32,634
Fiscal Year-end: 03/31/13

Business Description:
Air Transportation, Hotel & Travel Services
S.I.C.: 4512
N.A.I.C.S.: 481111

Personnel:
Yoji Ohashi *(Chm)*
Shinichiro Ito *(Pres & CEO)*
Yoshinori Maruyama *(Chm-CSR Promotion, PR, Legal & Admin & Exec VP)*
Osamu Shinobe *(Pres-All Nippon Airways Co., Ltd.)*
Shinya Katanozaka *(Sr Exec VP-HR Strategy, Corp Plng & Bus Dev)*
Shigeyuki Takemura *(Sr Exec VP-Govt & Indus Affairs & Strategic Plng-Asia Pacific)*
Kiyoshi Tonomoto *(Exec VP-IR, Fin & Acctg)*
Naoto Ishizaka *(Sr VP & Dir-Govt & Indus Affairs)*
Jun Katagiri *(Sr VP & Dir-Exec Secretariat)*
Koji Shibata *(Sr VP & Dir-Strategic Plng-Asia Pacific)*
Shinzo Shimizu *(Sr VP & Dir-Corp Plng)*

Board of Directors:
Yoji Ohashi
Shinichiro Ito
Shinya Katanozaka
Izumi Kobayashi
Yoshinori Maruyama
Shosuke Mori
Osamu Shinobe
Shigeyuki Takemura
Kiyoshi Tonomoto
Ado Yamamoto

Transfer Agent:
Sumitomo Mitsui Trust Bank, Limited
4-1 Marunouchi 1-chome Chiyoda-ku
Tokyo, Japan

Subsidiaries:

Air Japan Co., Ltd **(1)**
1-5-2 Shimbashi Nittsunittsukoku Bldg
Minato-Ku, Tokyo, 105-0004, Japan
Tel.: (81) 367355900
Fax: (81) 367355902
Web Site: www.air-japan.co.jp
Emp.: 400
Air Transportation Services
S.I.C.: 4512
N.A.I.C.S.: 481111

Air Next Co., Ltd. **(1)**
2-14-6 Minamisaiwai
Nishi-ku, Yokohama, Kanagawa, 220-0005, Japan
Tel.: (81) 453174501
Air Transportation Services
S.I.C.: 4581
N.A.I.C.S.: 488190

Air Nippon Co., Ltd. **(1)**
1-5-2 Higashi-Shimbashi
Minato-ku, Tokyo, 105 7133, Japan JP (100%)
Tel.: (81) 367355411
Fax: (81) 367355481
E-Mail: sh.matsumoto@air.ana-g.com
Web Site: www.air-nippon.co.jp
Emp.: 500
Domestic Air Transportation
S.I.C.: 4512
N.A.I.C.S.: 481111
Koichi Uchizono *(CEO)*

Air Nippon Network Co., Ltd. **(1)**
3-3-2 Hanedakuko
Ota-ku, Tokyo, 144 8515, Japan JP (100%)
Tel.: (81) 357574203
Fax: (81) 357574218
E-Mail: at.yama.yamacuchi@anawings.co.jp
Web Site: www.anawings.co.jp
Emp.: 100
Air Transportation Services
S.I.C.: 4512
N.A.I.C.S.: 481111
Akihiko Sasegawa *(CEO)*

All Nippon Airways Trading Co., Ltd. **(1)**
1-5-2 Higashi-Shimbashi
Minato-ku, Tokyo, 105 7136, Japan JP
Tel.: (81) 367355011
Fax: (81) 367355035
E-Mail: info-ht@anatc.com
Web Site: www.anatc.com
Emp.: 407
Trading & Retail; Development of Airport Stores, Other Stores & Direct Sales Through ANA In-Flight Magazine
S.I.C.: 5999
N.A.I.C.S.: 453998
Tomohiro Hidema *(CEO)*

All Nippon Airways World Tours Co., Ltd. **(1)**
Shiodome City Ctr 1-5-2 Higashi-Shimbashi
Minato-ku, Tokyo, 105 7133, Japan
Tel.: (81) 367352000
Fax: (81) 367352005
Emp.: 260
S.I.C.: 4512
N.A.I.C.S.: 481111
Shiba Yasunobu *(Gen Mgr)*

ANA Aircraft Maintenance Co., Ltd **(1)**
3-8-1 Minowa
Toyonaka, 560-0035, Japan
Tel.: (81) 668583833
Fax: (81) 668583789
Web Site: www.anam.co.jp
Emp.: 400
Aircraft Maintenance Services
S.I.C.: 4581
N.A.I.C.S.: 488190
Izumi Hiroki *(Pres)*

ANA Business Create Co., Ltd **(1)**
1-7-1 Hanedakuko Kukoshisetsu No 2 Sogo Building
Ota-ku, Tokyo, 144-0041, Japan
Tel.: (81) 337478211
Fax: (81) 337470639
E-Mail: info@abc.co.jp
Web Site: www.abc.co.jp
Emp.: 248
Aircraft Staff Recruitment Services
S.I.C.: 4581
N.A.I.C.S.: 488190
Wagat Suma *(Gen Mgr)*

ANA Catering Service Co., Ltd. **(1)**
3-2-8 Hanedakuko
Ota-ku, Tokyo, 144 0041, Japan JP (100%)
Tel.: (81) 357575950
Fax: (81) 357575963
Web Site: www.anac.co.jp
Emp.: 700
In-Flight Meals Preparation
S.I.C.: 4581
N.A.I.C.S.: 488190
Mitsuhiko Kazuta *(Pres & CEO)*

ANA Information Systems Planning Co., Ltd. **(1)**
7th Floor ANA Bijinesusenta Building 6-7-56 Higashi-Kojiya
Ota-ku, Tokyo, 144-0033, Japan (100%)
Tel.: (81) 3 3745 8111
Web Site: www.asp-kk.co.jp
System Consulting & System Integration Services
S.I.C.: 8999
N.A.I.C.S.: 541690

ANA Logistic Service Co., Ltd **(1)**
1-6-6 Hanedakuko No 1 Sogo Bldg 5 F
Ota-ku, Tokyo, 144-0041, Japan
Tel.: (81) 337479850
Fax: (81) 337479851
Web Site: www.als.ana-g.com
Emp.: 700
General Warehousing Storage Services
S.I.C.: 4225
N.A.I.C.S.: 493110
Kiyohisa Nakazawa *(Gen Mgr)*

ANA Sales Co., Ltd. **(1)**
1-5-2 Higashi-Shinbashi
Tokyo, 105 7133, Japan (100%)
Tel.: (81) 367353000
Fax: (81) 362518822
Web Site: www.anas.co.jp
Emp.: 1,700
Travel Services
S.I.C.: 4729
N.A.I.C.S.: 561599
Shiki Takashi *(Pres)*

International Airport Utility Co., Ltd **(1)**
3-3-2 Hanedakuko No 1 Ryokyaku Terminal Building 4f
Ota-ku, Tokyo, 144-0041, Japan
Tel.: (81) 357573300
Fax: (81) 357573314
Web Site: www.iau.co.jp
Airport Operations Services
S.I.C.: 4581
N.A.I.C.S.: 488119

Sky Building Service Co., Ltd **(1)**
1-6-6 Hanedakuko No 1 Sogo Bldg 2 Fl
Ota-ku, Tokyo, 144-0041, Japan
Tel.: (81) 337471110
Fax: (81) 337471198
Web Site: www.sbs.ana-g.com
Emp.: 700
Building Maintenance Consulting Services
S.I.C.: 1542
N.A.I.C.S.: 236220

U.S. Subsidiary:

All Nippon Airways Co., Ltd **(1)**
1251 Ave Of The Americas Ste 820
New York, NY 10020-1104 (100%)
Tel.: (212) 840-3700
Fax: (212) 840-5858
Web Site: www.fly-ana.com
Emp.: 35
Airline Ticket Sales
S.I.C.: 5088
N.A.I.C.S.: 423860

ANABELLE BITS PTY LTD.

8 Lord St
Botany, NSW, 2019, Australia
Tel.: (61) 293848000
Fax: (61) 0296665655
E-Mail: sales@asi.com.au
Web Site: www.asi.com.au
Year Founded: 1995
Emp.: 100

Business Description:
Computer Products Distr
S.I.C.: 5045
N.A.I.C.S.: 423430

Personnel:
Kenneth Ronald Lowe *(Mng Dir)*

ANABOND LIMITED

No 36 Type II Dr VSI Estate
Thiruvanmiyur
Chennai, Tamil Nadu, 600 041, India
Tel.: (91) 44 23460041
Fax: (91) 44 23460048
E-Mail: marketing@anabond.com
Web Site: www.anabond.com
Year Founded: 1979

Business Description:
Developer, Mfr & Marketing of Engineering Adhesives & Sealants
S.I.C.: 2891
N.A.I.C.S.: 325520

Personnel:
J. Vijayakumar *(Chm & Mng Dir)*

Board of Directors:
J. Vijayakumar
Ashok Ahuja
A. V. Ramanujam

Joint Venture:

Anabond Limited **(1)**
No 36 Type 2 Dr VSI Estate
Thiruvanmiyur, Chennai, 600 041, India
Tel.: (91) 4423460041
Fax: (91) 4423460048
E-Mail: sales@anabond.com
Sales Range: $150-199.9 Million
Emp.: 80
Adhesives & Sealants Mfr: Owned 50% by Anabond Limited & 50% by Dow Automotve
S.I.C.: 2891
N.A.I.C.S.: 325520
Vijay Kumar *(Mng Dir)*

ANACAP FINANCIAL PARTNERS LLP

25 Bedford Street
Covent Garden, London, WC2E 9ES, United Kingdom
Tel.: (44) 2070705250
Fax: (44) 2070705290
E-Mail: contact@anacapfp.com
Web Site: www.anacapfp.com
Year Founded: 2005

Business Description:
Private Equity Firm
S.I.C.: 6211
N.A.I.C.S.: 523999

Personnel:
Joe Giannamore *(Founder & Co-Mng Partner)*
Peter Cartwright *(Co-Mng Partner & Head-Bus Svcs)*
Fabrizio Cesario *(Partner & Head-Mergers & Acq)*
Chris Patrick *(Partner & Head-Risk & Liability Mgmt)*
Justin Sulger *(Partner & Head-Credit)*
Amber Hilkene *(Mng Dir & Head-IR & Comm)*
Michael Edwards *(COO)*
Wendy Meharg *(Gen Counsel)*

Holdings:

Aldermore Bank PLC (1)
1st Floor Block B Western House
Peterborough, Lynch Wood, PE2 6FZ, United Kingdom
Tel.: (44) 1733 404 506
E-Mail: contactus@aldermore.co.uk
Web Site: www.aldermore.co.uk
Emp.: 600
Banking Services
S.I.C.: 6029
N.A.I.C.S.: 522110
Phillip Monks *(CEO)*
Damon Walford *(Mng Dir)*
James Mack *(CFO)*

Subsidiary:

Aldermore Invoice Finance Limited (2)
Saint James House
7 Charlotte, Manchester, M1 4DZ, United Kingdom
Tel.: (44) 16 1238 5000
Fax: (44) 8700438569
E-Mail:
Emp.: 100
Financial Investment Activities
S.I.C.: 6211
N.A.I.C.S.: 523999
Nick Smith *(Mng Dir)*
Tony Smedley *(Mng Dir)*

Cabot Financial Group Limited (1)
1 Kings Hill Avenue
Kings Hill, West Malling, Kent, ME19 4UA, United Kingdom UK
Tel.: (44) 1732524600
E-Mail: cabotpr@cabotfinancial.com
Web Site: www.cabotfinancial.com
Sales Range: $100-124.9 Million
Consumer Debt Purchasing Services
S.I.C.: 6099
N.A.I.C.S.: 522390
Neil Clyne *(CEO)*
Glen Crawford *(Mng Dir)*
Chris Bowyer *(COO)*
Steve Mound *(COO)*

Non-U.S. Subsidiary:

Cabot Financial (Ireland) Limited (2)
Block C Cookstown Court Old Belgard Road
Tallaght, Dublin, 24, Ireland
Tel.: (353) 1 6608011
E-Mail: tallaght@cabotfinancial.ie
Web Site: www.cabotfinancial.ie
Consumer Debt Purchasing Services
S.I.C.: 6099
N.A.I.C.S.: 522390
Orla Hughes *(CFO)*
Sean Webb *(COO)*

Xbridge Limited (1)
One Finsbury Square
London, EC2A 1AE, United Kingdom UK
Tel.: (44) 20 7920 8000
Fax: (44) 20 7920 8088
E-Mail:
Web Site: www.simplybusiness.com
Sales Range: $10-24.9 Million
Emp.: 220
Online Business Insurance Brokerage Services
S.I.C.: 6411
N.A.I.C.S.: 524210
Jason Stockwood *(CEO)*
Kevin Fleming *(CFO)*
Chris Slater *(COO)*
Lukas Oberhuber *(CTO)*
Arvinder Mangat *(Sec)*

Non-U.S. Holdings:

Equa bank a.s. (1)
Lazarska 1718 3
111 21 Prague, Czech Republic
Tel.: (420) 224 990 211
Fax: (420) 222 510 099
E-Mail: info@equabank.cz
Web Site: www.equabank.cz
Emp.: 100
Banking Services
S.I.C.: 6029
N.A.I.C.S.: 522110
David Putts *(CEO)*

First Names (Isle of Man) Limited (1)
(Formerly IFG International Limited)
International House Castle Hill Victoria Road
Douglas, IM2 4RB, Isle of Man
Tel.: (44) 1624 630600
Fax: (44) 1624 624469
E-Mail:
Web Site: www.firstnames.com
Sales Range: $10-24.9 Million
Financial Management Consulting Services
S.I.C.: 8742
N.A.I.C.S.: 541611

Subsidiary:

Moore Fund Administration (IOM) Limited (2)
(Formerly IFG Fund Administration (IOM) Limited)
International House Castle Hill Victoria Road
Douglas, Isle of Man IM2 4RB
Tel.: (44) 1624 661020
Fax: (44) 1624 617823
E-Mail:
Business Fund Administration Services
S.I.C.: 6371
N.A.I.C.S.: 524292

Non-U.S. Subsidiaries:

First Names Corporate Services Limited (2)
(Formerly IFG Managed Services Limited)
Universal House
Shannon, Ennis, Ireland
Tel.: (353) 61 364350
Fax: (353) 61 703440
Web Site: www.ifgint.com
Emp.: 18
Financial Management Consulting Services
S.I.C.: 8742
N.A.I.C.S.: 541611
Oonagh Hayes *(Mng Dir)*

First Names (Cyprus) Limited (2)
(Formerly IFG Trust (Cyprus) Limited)
Chapo Central 3rd Floor 20 Spyrou Kyprianou Avenue
Nicosia, 1075, Cyprus
Tel.: (357) 22749000
Fax: (357) 22749100
E-Mail: cyprus@firstnames.com
Web Site: www.firstnames.com
Emp.: 44
Financial Management Services
S.I.C.: 8742
N.A.I.C.S.: 541611
Christof Michael *(Gen Mgr)*

First Names (Jersey) Limited (2)
(Formerly IFG Trust (Jersey) Limited)
15 Union Street
Saint Helier, Jersey
Tel.: (44) 1534714500
Fax: (44) 1534767787
E-Mail:
Emp.: 70
Trustee & Corporate Services
S.I.C.: 7389
N.A.I.C.S.: 541199
Mark Pesco *(Mng Dir)*

First Names (Switzerland) Limited (2)
(Formerly IFG Suisse S.A.)
Am Schanzengraben 25
PO Box 2432
8022 Zurich, Switzerland
Tel.: (41) 44 286 2727
Fax: (41) 227163239
E-Mail: geneva@ifgint.com
Financial Management Services
S.I.C.: 8742
N.A.I.C.S.: 541611

Moore Fund Administration (Jersey) Limited (2)
(Formerly IFG Fund Administration (Jersey) Limited)
IFG House 15 Union Street
Saint Helier, Jersey JE1 1FG
Tel.: (44) 1534 786260
Fax: (44) 1534 786296
E-Mail:
Fund Administration Services
S.I.C.: 6371
N.A.I.C.S.: 524292
Declan Kenny *(Mng Dir)*

Mediterranean Bank plc (1)
10 St Barbara Bastion
Valletta, VLT 1961, Malta
Tel.: (356) 25574400
E-Mail: info@medbank.com.mt
Web Site: www.medbank.com.mt
Emp.: 63
Banking Services
S.I.C.: 6029
N.A.I.C.S.: 522110
Mark A. Watson *(CEO)*

ANACONDA MINING INC.

150 York Street Suite 410
Toronto, ON, M5H 3S5, Canada
Tel.: (416) 304-6622
Fax: (416) 363-4567
E-Mail: info@anacondamining.com
Web Site: www.anacondamining.com
Year Founded: 2007
ANX—(TSX)
Rev.: $24,028,882
Assets: $25,235,786
Liabilities: $4,006,664
Net Worth: $21,229,122
Earnings: $7,394,146
Emp.: 45
Fiscal Year-end: 05/31/13

Business Description:
Gold Ore Mining
S.I.C.: 1041
N.A.I.C.S.: 212221

Personnel:
Tim Casgrain *(Chm)*
Dustin Angelo *(Pres & CEO)*
J. Errol Farr *(CFO & Sec)*

Board of Directors:
Tim Casgrain
Dustin Angelo
Michael Byron
Glenn Dobby
Lewis Lawrick
Maruf Raza

Transfer Agent:
Equity Financial Trust Company
Toronto, ON, Canada

ANADOLU ANONIM TURK SIGORTA SIRKETI

Is Kuleleri Kule 2 Kat 23-26 Levent
34330 Istanbul, Turkey
Tel.: (90) 212 350 0 350
Fax: (90) 212 350 0 355
E-Mail: bilgi@anadolusigorta.com.tr
Web Site: www.anadolusigorta.com.tr
Year Founded: 1925
ANSGR—(IST)
Rev.: $1,105,972,077
Assets: $1,329,239,422
Liabilities: $984,364,060
Net Worth: $344,875,362
Earnings: ($31,529,008)
Emp.: 915
Fiscal Year-end: 12/31/12

Business Description:
Insurance Services
S.I.C.: 6411
N.A.I.C.S.: 524298

Personnel:
Caner Cimenbicer *(Chm & Mng Dir)*
Ahmet Dogan Arikan *(Deputy Chm)*
Erdinc Gokalp *(Deputy CEO-Org Dept, Actuarial Dept & Reinsurance Dept)*
Mehmet Abaci *(Deputy CEO-IT Dept & Info & Comm Tech Software Dev Dept)*
Fatih Goren *(Deputy CEO-Claims Dept, Legal Affairs & Subrogation Dept)*
Mehmet Metin Oguz *(Deputy CEO-TRNC Branch & Motor Insurance Dept)*
Levent Sonmez *(Deputy CEO-Individual & Comml Insurance Dept)*
Filiz Tiryakioglu *(Deputy CEO-Bank Insurance, Agency & Channel Mgmt Dept)*

Board of Directors:
Caner Cimenbicer
Hakan Aran
Ahmet Dogan Arikan
Kubilay Aykol
Turkay Berksoy
R. Semih Nabioglu
Nevzat Burak Seyrek
Fahri Kayhan Soyler
Musa Ulken
Atakan Yalcin
Hasan Hulki Yalcin

ANADOLU EFES BIRACILIK VE MALT SANAYII A.S.

Esentepe Mah Anadolu Cad No 1 Kartal
34870 Istanbul, Turkey
Tel.: (90) 2165868000
Fax: (90) 2163062517
E-Mail: info@efespilsen.com.tr
Web Site: www.anadoluefes.com
AEFES—(IST OTC)
Sls.: $3,626,345,964
Assets: $6,580,827,519
Liabilities: $2,745,408,322
Net Worth: $3,835,419,198
Earnings: $356,183,355
Emp.: 19,036
Fiscal Year-end: 12/31/12

Business Description:
Beer & Soft Drink Bottler & Distr
S.I.C.: 2082
N.A.I.C.S.: 312120

Personnel:
Tuncay Ozilhan *(Chm)*
Damian Paul Gammell *(CEO)*
Huseyin Murat Akin *(Pres-Soft Drink Grp-Intl Ops)*
Burak Basarir *(Pres-Soft Drink Grp-Turkey)*
Alejandro Jimenez *(Pres-Beer Grp)*

Board of Directors:
Tuncay Ozilhan
Recep Yilmaz Arguden
Aycan Avci
Mehmet Mete Basol
Omer Bozer
Alan J. Clark
Ahmet Cemal Dorduncu
Salih Metin Ecevit
Alejandro Jimenez Fonseca
Mehmet Cem Kozlu
Mehmet Hursit Zorlu

Anadolu Efes Biracilik ve Malt Sanayii A.S.—(Continued)

Subsidiary:

Efes Pazarlama ve Dagitim Ticaret A.S. **(1)**
4 Bahcelievler Mahallesi Sehit Ibrahim Koparir Caddesi
Istanbul, 34180, Turkey
Tel.: (90) 2124493600
Fax: (90) 2126429149
Alcoholic Beverages Mfr & Distr
S.I.C.: 5182
N.A.I.C.S.: 424820
Tuncay Ozilhan *(Chm)*

Non-U.S. Subsidiaries:

Central Asian Beverages B.V. **(1)**
Strawinskylaan 1227
Amsterdam, North Holland, 1077, Netherlands
Tel.: (31) 205752290
Fax: (31) 205752291
Investment Management Services
S.I.C.: 6211
N.A.I.C.S.: 523999

Efes Breweries International N.V. **(1)**
Strawinskylaan 1227
1077 XX Amsterdam, Netherlands NL
Tel.: (31) 205752290 (70.2%)
Fax: (31) 205752291
E-Mail: ir@efesholland.nl
Web Site: www.efesinternational.com
Sales Range: $800-899.9 Million
Emp.: 4,704
Breweries
S.I.C.: 2082
N.A.I.C.S.: 312120
Alejandro Jimenez *(CEO)*

Efes Vitanta Moldova Brewery S.A. **(1)**
167 Uzinelor Street
Chisinau, 2023, Moldova
Tel.: (373) 22 40 32 95
Fax: (373) 22 40 32 00
E-Mail: info@vitanta.com
Beer & Soft Drinks Mfr
S.I.C.: 2082
N.A.I.C.S.: 312120
Kamil Yazici *(Gen Mgr)*

ZAO Moscow-Efes Brewery **(1)**
Ulitsa Podolskikh Kursantov 15B
Moscow, 117546, Russia
Tel.: (7) 4957979800
Fax: (7) 4957 97 98 27
Beer Mfr
S.I.C.: 2082
N.A.I.C.S.: 312120

Subsidiary:

OOO Vostok Solod **(2)**
5 Ul Tikhoretskaya
Kazan, 420054, Russia
Tel.: (7) 8432789028
Fax: (7) 8432789017
Beer Mfr
S.I.C.: 2082
N.A.I.C.S.: 312120

ANADOLU GIRISIM SERMAYESI YATIRIM ORTAKLIGI A.S.

Asagi Ovecler Mah 1042 Cadde 1330
Sok 3/3 Cankaya
Ankara, Turkey
Tel.: (90) 312 465 03 82
Fax: (90) 312 465 03 13
E-Mail: info@anadolugirisim.com
Web Site: www.anadolugirisim.com
Business Description:
Venture Capital Investment Services
S.I.C.: 6211
N.A.I.C.S.: 523999
Personnel:
Ozdemir Ucar *(Chm)*
Aydin Baylam *(Vice Chm)*
Board of Directors:
Ozdemir Ucar
Mehmet Dogan Ates
Aydin Baylam

ANAECO LIMITED

3 Turner Avenue Technology Park
Bentley, WA, 6102, Australia
Mailing Address:
PO Box 1287
Bentley, WA, 6983, Australia
Tel.: (61) 893614777
Fax: (61) 893614888
E-Mail: info@anaeco.com
Web Site: www.anaeco.com
ANQ—(ASX)
Rev.: $165,178
Assets: $19,858,911
Liabilities: $12,466,826
Net Worth: $7,392,085
Earnings: ($4,146,936)
Emp.: 21
Fiscal Year-end: 06/30/13
Business Description:
Solid Waste Recycling Solutions
S.I.C.: 4959
N.A.I.C.S.: 562998
Personnel:
Shaun Scott *(Chm)*
David Andrew Lymburn *(CEO)*
Tim Hinton *(Sec)*
Board of Directors:
Shaun Scott
Ian Lindsay Campbell
Gianmario Alessio Capelli

ANALABS RESOURCES BERHAD

Unit 621 6th Floor Block A Kelana Centre Point No 3 Jalan SS7/19
Kelana Jaya, 47301 Petaling Jaya, Selangor Darul Ehsan, Malaysia
Tel.: (60) 378809699
Fax: (60) 378808699
E-Mail: enquiry@analabs.com.my
Web Site: www.analabs.com.my
ANALABS—(KLS)
Rev.: $48,327,538
Assets: $66,983,563
Liabilities: $13,448,327
Net Worth: $53,535,235
Earnings: $3,130,324
Fiscal Year-end: 04/30/13
Business Description:
Paints & Lubricant Products Mfr
S.I.C.: 2851
N.A.I.C.S.: 325510
Personnel:
Yow Kheong Kan *(Chm)*
Irene Mei Ling Chew *(Co-Sec)*
Cynthia Gloria Louis *(Co-Sec)*
Board of Directors:
Yow Kheong Kan
Yew Choong Lai
Yoke Soo Lim
Chin Ann Low
Ganesan Sundaraj

Subsidiaries:

Centralised Waste Treatment Plant Sdn. Bhd. **(1)**
Unit 725 7th Floor Block A Kelana Centre Point No 3 Jalan SS7/19
Kelana Jaya, 47301 Petaling Jaya, Selangor Darul Ehsan, Malaysia (100%)
Tel.: (60) 3 7880 9699
Fax: (60) 3 79814868
Web Site: www.analabs.com.my
Hazardous Waste Disposal Services
S.I.C.: 4953
N.A.I.C.S.: 562211

Inagro Sdn. Bhd. **(1)**
Lot 6493 Batu 5 3/4 Jalan Kapar
Kelang, Selangor, 42100, Malaysia
Tel.: (60) 332918028
Fax: (60) 332918029
Emp.: 14
Agricultural Chemicals Mfr
S.I.C.: 2879
N.A.I.C.S.: 325320

Non-U.S. Subsidiary:

Cleanway Disposal Services Pte. Ltd. **(1)**
40 Penjuru Road
Singapore, 609145, Singapore
Tel.: (65) 62644411
Fax: (65) 62640715
E-Mail: cleanway@singnet.com.sg
Emp.: 40
Waste Collection & Disposal Services
S.I.C.: 4953
N.A.I.C.S.: 562211
S. K. Martin *(Mgr)*

ANALYTICA LIMITED

GPO Box 670
Brisbane, QLD, 4001, Australia
Tel.: (61) 7 3278 1950
Fax: (61) 732598313
E-Mail: Reception@AnalyticaMedical.com
Web Site: www.analyticamedical.com
ALT—(ASX)
Rev.: $564,049
Assets: $440,600
Liabilities: $266,837
Net Worth: $173,763
Earnings: ($1,183,566)
Fiscal Year-end: 06/30/13
Business Description:
Medical Devices & Pharmaceutical Implants Development Services
S.I.C.: 3845
N.A.I.C.S.: 334510
Personnel:
Michael Monsour *(Chm)*
Geoff Daly *(CEO)*
Bryan Dulhunty *(Sec)*
Board of Directors:
Michael Monsour
Warren Stephen Brooks
Ross Mangelsdorf
Carl Stubbings

ANALYTIK JENA AG

Konrad-Zuse-Strasse 1
07745 Jena, Germany
Tel.: (49) 36417770
Fax: (49) 3641779279
E-Mail: info@analytik-jena.com
Web Site: www.analytik-jena.de
AJA—(DEU)
Rev.: $134,212,161
Assets: $173,805,977
Liabilities: $83,318,971
Net Worth: $90,487,006
Earnings: ($4,205,504)
Emp.: 983
Fiscal Year-end: 09/30/13
Business Description:
Analytical & Optical Solutions Provider
S.I.C.: 7379
N.A.I.C.S.: 518210
Personnel:
Klaus Berka *(Co-Founder, Chm-Exec Bd & CEO)*
Jens Adomat *(Co-Founder, Deputy Chm-Exec Bd & COO)*
Andreas Krey *(Chm-Supervisory Bd)*
Stefan Dohmen *(CFO & Member-Exec Bd)*
Supervisory Board of Directors:
Andreas Krey
Franz-Ferdinand von Falkenhausen
Matthias Wierlacher

Subsidiaries:

AJ Blomesystem GmbH **(1)**
Konrad-Zuse-Strasse 1
07745 Jena, Germany
Tel.: (49) 3641779877
Fax: (49) 364177769800
E-Mail: sales@aj-blomesystem.com
Web Site: www.aj-blomesystem.com
Emp.: 17
Laboratory Information Management Services
S.I.C.: 7819
N.A.I.C.S.: 512199
Klaus Berka *(CEO)*
Lothar Korn *(Mng Dir)*

AJ Cybertron Gesellschaft fur Laborautomationssysteme mbH **(1)**
Louis-Bleriot-Str 5
12487 Berlin, Germany
Tel.: (49) 306310631
Fax: (49) 30319891529
E-Mail: info@ag-cybertron.de
Web Site: www.ag-cybertron.de
Emp.: 20
Laboratory Automation Services
S.I.C.: 1542
N.A.I.C.S.: 236220
Matthias Arndt *(Mgr)*

AJ Cybertron GmbH **(1)**
Louis-Bleriot-Strasse 5
12487 Berlin, Germany
Tel.: (49) 306310631
Fax: (49) 306310636
E-Mail: info@aj-cybertron.com
Web Site: www.aj-cybertron.de
Laboratory Automation Services
S.I.C.: 8734
N.A.I.C.S.: 541380
Klaus Berka *(CEO)*
Matthias Arndt *(Mng Dir)*

AJ eBiochip GmbH **(1)**
Fraunhoferstrasse 1
25524 Itzehoe, Schleswig-Holstein, Germany
Tel.: (49) 4821174333
Fax: (49) 4821174250
E-Mail: info@aj-ebiochip.com
Web Site: www.aj-ebiochip.com
Emp.: 8
Diagnostic Product Mfr & Sales
S.I.C.: 2834
N.A.I.C.S.: 325412
Klaus Berka *(Mng Dir)*

AJ Innuscreen GmbH **(1)**
Robert-Rossle-Strasse 10
13125 Berlin, Germany
Tel.: (49) 3094893380
Fax: (49) 3094893381
E-Mail: info@aj-innuscreen.com
Web Site: www.aj-innuscreen.com
Emp.: 20
Diagnostic Products Mfr
S.I.C.: 2835
N.A.I.C.S.: 325413
Klaus Berka *(Mng Dir)*
Timo Hillebrand *(Mng Dir)*

AJ Roboscreen GmbH **(1)**
Delitzscher Strasse 135 Laborgebaude
04129 Leipzig, Saxony, Germany
Tel.: (49) 3419897340
Fax: (49) 341989734199
E-Mail: info@aj-roboscreen.com
Web Site: www.aj-roboscreen.com
Diagnostic Test Kits Mfr & Distr
S.I.C.: 5047
N.A.I.C.S.: 423450
Klaus Berka *(CEO)*

Biometra GmbH **(1)**
Rudolf-Wissell-Str 30
37079 Gottingen, Lower Saxony, Germany
Tel.: (49) 551506860
Fax: (49) 5515068666
E-Mail: info@biometra.de
Web Site: www.biometra.com
Emp.: 45
Laboratory Products Mfr & Distr
S.I.C.: 3826
N.A.I.C.S.: 334516
Alexander Berka *(Mng Dir)*
Volker Grimm *(Mng Dir)*

Unit:

Analytik Jena AG - Optics **(1)**
Seerasen 2
98673 Eisfeld, Thuringia, Germany
Tel.: (49) 3686371100
Fax: (49) 3686322037
E-Mail: info@docter.germany.com
Web Site: www.docter-germany.com
Emp.: 120
Binoculars & Optical Products Mfr
S.I.C.: 3827

N.A.I.C.S.: 333314
Reinhard Jacob *(Gen Mgr)*

Non-U.S. Subsidiaries:

Analytik Jena Japan Co.,Ltd. (1)
Yokohama Bus Park E Tower 11th Fl 134 Goudo-cho
Hodogaya-ku, Yokohama, Kanagawa, 240-0005, Japan
Tel.: (81) 453405740
Fax: (81) 453405745
E-Mail: sales@analytik-jena.co.jp
Web Site: www.analytik-jena.co.jp
Diagnostic Equipments Mfr
S.I.C.: 3845
N.A.I.C.S.: 334510

Analytik Jena Shanghai Instruments Co. Ltd. (1)
Rm B 10th Fl No 91 Bldg No 1122 N Quinzhou Rd
Shanghai, 200233, China
Tel.: (86) 2154261977
Fax: (86) 2154261976
E-Mail: info@analytik-jena.com.cn
Web Site: www.analytikjena.com.cn
Emp.: 18
Analytical Instruments Mfr
S.I.C.: 3826
N.A.I.C.S.: 334516
Zhao Tai *(Gen Mgr)*

CyBio Northern Europe Ltd. (1)
8 James Whatman Ct Turkey Mill Ashford Rd
Maidstone, Kent, ME 14 5SS, United Kingdom
Tel.: (44) 1622662118
Fax: (44) 1622664157
E-Mail: info@cybio-ag.com
Web Site: www.cybio-ag.com
Emp.: 5
Diagnostic Equipments Distr
S.I.C.: 5047
N.A.I.C.S.: 423450

ANAM ELECTRONICS CO., LTD.

213 Manhae-ro Danwon-gu
Ansan, Gyeonggi, Korea (South) 425-834
Tel.: (82) 314902000
Fax: (82) 314959598
E-Mail: remedios@aname.co.kr
Web Site: www.aname.co.kr
Year Founded: 1973
008700—(KRS)
Sls.: $126,340,493
Assets: $112,018,176
Liabilities: $49,300,202
Net Worth: $62,717,974
Earnings: ($3,503,208)
Emp.: 150
Fiscal Year-end: 12/31/12

Business Description:
Consumer Electronics Products Mfr
S.I.C.: 3651
N.A.I.C.S.: 334310

Personnel:
Seong Yeol Choi *(CEO)*

Divisions:

Anam Electronics Co., Ltd - Consumer A/V Division (1)
645 Seonggok-dong Danwon-gu
Ansan, Gyeonggi-do, Korea (South)
Tel.: (82) 3149023519
Fax: (82) 4947413
Web Site: www.anam.co.kr
Audio Equipment Mfr
S.I.C.: 3651
N.A.I.C.S.: 334310
S.L. Choi *(CEO)*

Anam Electronics Co., Ltd - Manufacturing Division (1)
645 Seonggok-dong Danwon-gu
Ansan, Gyeonggi-do, Korea (South)
Tel.: (82) 314902000
Fax: (82) 314959598
E-Mail: remedios@aname.co.kr
Web Site: www.aname.co.kl
Medical Electronic Devices Mfr
S.I.C.: 3845
N.A.I.C.S.: 334510
Joonkoo Park *(Mgr-Sls)*

ANAM INFORMATION TECHNOLOGY CO., LTD.

14th Floor C-dong Woolim Lion's Valley 371-28 Gasan-Dong
GeumCheon-Gu, Seoul, Korea (South)
Tel.: (82) 2 3443 5811
Fax: (82) 2 3443 5815
Web Site: www.anamit.com
Year Founded: 1995
050320—(KRS)

Business Description:
Software Development Services
S.I.C.: 7373
N.A.I.C.S.: 541512

Personnel:
Dong Min Kim *(CEO)*

ANAND CREDIT LTD.

11 Krishna Aparments Bhudarpura Road Ambawadi
Ahmedabad, 380 006, India
Tel.: (91) 79 26460358
E-Mail: anandcredit@yahoo.co.in
Web Site: www.anandcredit.com
531678—(BOM)
Sales Range: Less than $1 Million

Business Description:
Financial Credit Management Services
S.I.C.: 6099
N.A.I.C.S.: 522390

Personnel:
Ramesh Laherchand Shah *(Chm & Mng Dir)*

Transfer Agent:
Sharepro Services (India) Pvt. Ltd.
416-420 4th Floor Devnandan Mall Opp. Sanyash Ashram Ellisbridge
Ahmedabad, India

ANANDA DEVELOPMENT PUBLIC COMPANY LIMITED

99/1 Moo 14 Bangna-Trad Km 10.5 Rd
Bangpleeyai
Bangplee, Samut Prakan, 10540, Thailand
Tel.: (66) 2 3162222
Fax: (66) 2 3171100
E-Mail: information@ananda.co.th
Web Site: www.ananda.co.th
ANAN—(THA)

Business Description:
Residential Housing Developer & Construction
S.I.C.: 1522
N.A.I.C.S.: 236116

Personnel:
Narongchai Akrasanee *(Chm)*
Chanond Ruangkritya *(CEO)*

Board of Directors:
Narongchai Akrasanee
Tanyalak Nunthanavorasiri
Wiboon Rasmeepaisarn
Chanond Ruangkritya
Natthavipha Ruangkritya
Patcharavalai Ruangkritya
Poolsak Tansitthipun
Nopporn Thepsithar

ANANGEL-AMERICAN SHIPHOLDINGS LIMITED

354 Sygrou Ave
GR 176 74 Kallithea, Greece
Tel.: (30) 2109467200
Telex: 214676
Fax: (30) 2109467317
E-Mail: mail@anangelmar.com
Web Site: www.anangelmar.com
Year Founded: 1987
Sales Range: $75-99.9 Million
Emp.: 400

Business Description:
Shipping Services
S.I.C.: 4412
N.A.I.C.S.: 483111

Personnel:
John Platsidakis *(Mng Dir)*
Dimitri A. Stylianou *(CFO & Treas)*

ANANT RAJ INDUSTRIES LIMITED

(Name Changed to Anant Raj Limited)

ANANT RAJ LIMITED

(Formerly Anant Raj Industries Limited)
H-65 Connaught Circus
New Delhi, 110 001, India
Tel.: (91) 1143034400
Fax: (91) 1143582879
E-Mail: info@anantraj.com
Web Site: www.anantraj.com
Year Founded: 1969
ANANTRAJ—(NSE)
Rev.: $107,176,485
Assets: $1,076,710,480
Liabilities: $350,375,262
Net Worth: $726,335,218
Earnings: $19,895,702
Fiscal Year-end: 03/31/13

Business Description:
Property Management Services
S.I.C.: 6531
N.A.I.C.S.: 531311

Personnel:
Ashok Sarin *(Chm)*
Amit Sarin *(CEO)*
Anil Sarin *(Mng Dir)*
Manoj Pahwa *(Compliance Officer & Sec)*
Yogesh Sharma *(Sr Pres-Fin)*
Navneet Singh *(Pres-Admin & Mktg)*

Board of Directors:
Ashok Sarin
Ambarish Chatterjee
Maneesh Gupta
Amit Sarin
Anil Sarin
Brajinder Mohan Singh

Transfer Agent:
Alankit Assignments Ltd
RTA Division 2E/21 First Floor Jhandewalan Extn
New Delhi, 110055, India

ANAP INC.

2-31-16 Jingumae-ku
Tokyo, 150-0001, Japan
Tel.: (81) 3 5772 2717
Web Site: www.anap.co.jp
3189—(JAS)
Rev.: $94,490,220
Emp.: 270
Fiscal Year-end: 08/31/13

Business Description:
Women's & Girls' Clothing Retailer
S.I.C.: 5621
N.A.I.C.S.: 448120

Personnel:
Atsuzo Nakajima *(Chm)*

ANAPASS, INC.

Shinsegae Digital Center 6th Fl
197-12 Guro-dong Guro-gu, Seoul, Korea (South)
Tel.: (82) 2 6922 7400
Fax: (82) 2 6922 7499
E-Mail: webmaster@anapass.com
Web Site: www.anapass.com
123860—(KRS)
Emp.: 40

Business Description:
Integrated Circuit Mfr
S.I.C.: 3674
N.A.I.C.S.: 334413

Personnel:
Sung Dae Joe *(CEO)*

ANATEVKA SA

22-24 Boulevard Royal
L-2449 Luxembourg, Luxembourg
Tel.: (352) 26 26 76 1
Fax: (352) 26 26 76 76
Web Site: www.assya.eu
MLANA—(EUR)

Business Description:
Investment Banking & Insurance Services
S.I.C.: 6211
N.A.I.C.S.: 523110

Personnel:
Thierry Leyne *(Chm)*
Philippe Herve *(CEO)*

ANATOLIA ENERGY LIMITED

140 Colin Street
West Perth, WA, 6005, Australia
Tel.: (61) 864611365
Fax: (61) 864611355
E-Mail: admin@anatoliaenergy.com.au
Web Site: anatoliaenergy.com.au
Year Founded: 1996
AEK—(ASX)

Business Description:
Uranium Exploration Services
S.I.C.: 1094
N.A.I.C.S.: 212291

Personnel:
James J. Graham *(Mng Dir)*
Lee Boyd *(CFO & Sec)*

Board of Directors:
Hikmet Akin
Robert Annett
Lee Boyd
Paul Cronin
James J. Graham
Peter Kausch

Legal Counsel:
Steinepreis Paganin
Level 4 The Read Buildings 16 Milligan Street
Perth, Australia

ANCA PTY LTD

25 Gatwick Road
Bayswater, VIC, 3153, Australia
Tel.: (61) 397518200
Fax: (61) 397517300
E-Mail: ozinfo@anca.com
Web Site: www.anca.com
Year Founded: 1974
Sales Range: $50-74.9 Million
Emp.: 300

Business Description:
Tool Cutting & Grinding Equipment Mfr
S.I.C.: 3545
N.A.I.C.S.: 333515

Personnel:
Patrick Gerard Boland *(Founder & Mng Dir)*
Patrick John McCluskey *(Co-Founder)*
Grant Anderson *(CEO)*

U.S. Subsidiary:

ANCA (USA) Inc (1)
31129 Century Dr
Wixom, MI 48393 (100%)
Tel.: (248) 926-4466
Fax: (248) 926-4475
E-Mail: usainfo@anca.com
Web Site: www.anca.com
Sales Range: $10-24.9 Million
Emp.: 40
Tool Cutting & Grinding Equipment Mfr
S.I.C.: 3545

ANCA Pty Ltd—(Continued)

N.A.I.C.S.: 333515
Russell Riddiford *(CEO)*

Non-U.S. Subsidiaries:

ANCA do Brasil (1)
Rua Francisco Ferreira Leao 377
Sorocaba, 18040-330 Sao Paulo, Brazil (100%)
Tel.: (55) 1532215512
Fax: (55) 1532215512
E-Mail: brinfo@anca.com.au
Emp.: 4
Tool Cutting & Grinding Equipment Mfr
S.I.C.: 3542
N.A.I.C.S.: 333517
Russell Riddiford *(Chm)*

ANCA GmbH (1)
Alois-Senefelder-Str 4
68167 Mannheim, Germany (100%)
Tel.: (49) 621338100
Fax: (49) 621335278
E-Mail: gerinfo@anca.com.au
Web Site: www.ger.anca.com
Emp.: 25
Tool Cutting & Grinding Equipment Mfr
S.I.C.: 3545
N.A.I.C.S.: 333515
Jan Langfelder *(Mng Dir)*

ANCA (UK) Ltd (1)
2 Eastwood Business Village
Harry Weston Road, Coventry, CV3 2UB, United Kingdom (100%)
Tel.: (44) 2476447000
Fax: (44) 2476447333
E-Mail: ukinfo@anca.com
Web Site: www.anca.com
Rev.: $410,543
Emp.: 9
Tool Cutting & Grinding Equipment Mfr
S.I.C.: 3545
N.A.I.C.S.: 333515
Patrick John McCluskey *(Mng Dir)*

ANCHENG PROPERTY & CASUALTY INSURANCE CO., LTD.

1405-1406 Investment Mansion 128 Zhongshan 3 Road
Yuzhong District, Chongqing, 400015, China
Tel.: (86) 2363855290
Fax: (86) 2363855127
Web Site: www.e-acic.com
Business Description:
Property & Casualty Insurance Services
S.I.C.: 6331
N.A.I.C.S.: 524126
Personnel:
Ke Xu *(Gen Mgr)*

ANCHOR CONSTRUCTION INDUSTRIAL PRODUCTS LTD

1810 Dublin Avenue
Winnipeg, MB, R3H 0H3, Canada
Tel.: (204) 633-0064
Fax: (204) 694-1261
Toll Free: (800) 363-0682
E-Mail: wpgsales@anchorproducts.ca
Web Site: www.anchorproducts.ca
Year Founded: 1967
Rev.: $13,857,093
Emp.: 65
Business Description:
Construction & Industrial Products Supplier
S.I.C.: 5085
N.A.I.C.S.: 423840
Personnel:
Fil Fileccia *(Pres)*

ANCHOR LAND HOLDINGS, INC.

11th Floor LV Locsin Building 6752 Ayala Avenue cor Makati Avenue
Makati, Philippines
Tel.: (63) 28886688
Fax: (63) 28857349
Web Site: www.anchorland.com.ph
Year Founded: 2004
ALHI—(PHI)
Rev.: $101,502,187
Assets: $326,239,954
Liabilities: $226,728,580
Net Worth: $99,511,374
Earnings: $25,125,053
Emp.: 365
Fiscal Year-end: 12/31/12
Business Description:
Residential & Commercial Real Estate Construction & Development Services
S.I.C.: 1531
N.A.I.C.S.: 236117
Personnel:
Stephen Lee *(Chm)*
Steve Li *(Vice Chm)*
Elizabeth Ventura *(Pres)*
Neil Chua *(CFO)*
Ronaldo Ortiz *(Compliance Info Officer & Mgr-Corp Affairs)*
Peter Kho *(Treas)*
Christine Base *(Sec)*
Board of Directors:
Stephen Lee
Christine Base
Solita Delantar
Peter Kho
Steve Li
Frances Monje
Elizabeth Ventura

Subsidiary:

Posh Properties Development Corporation (1)
11th Floor Lv Locsin Building 6752 Ayala Avenue Corner Makati Ave
Makati, 1200, Philippines
Tel.: (63) 28517991
Property Management Services
S.I.C.: 6531
N.A.I.C.S.: 531312
Beth Ventura *(VP-Sls & Mktg)*

ANCHOR MINING INC.

(See Under Trident Gold Corp.)

ANCHOR RESOURCES LIMITED

GO2 59 Goulburn St
Sydney, NSW, 2000, Australia
Tel.: (61) 2 8987 3710
Fax: (61) 2 9283 8803
E-Mail: admin@anchorresources.com.au
Web Site: www.anchorresources.com.au
AHR—(ASX)
Rev.: $22,365
Assets: $6,631,386
Liabilities: $4,639,276
Net Worth: $1,992,110
Earnings: ($1,429,097)
Fiscal Year-end: 06/30/13
Business Description:
Mineral Exploration Services
S.I.C.: 1481
N.A.I.C.S.: 213115
Personnel:
Steven Jiayi Yu *(CEO)*
Ian Leslie Price *(Mng Dir)*
Guy Robertson *(Sec)*
Board of Directors:
Jianguang Wang
Ronald Norman Lees
Ian Leslie Price
Vaughan Webber
Steven Jiayi Yu
Legal Counsel:
Gadens Lawyers
Skygarden Building 77 Castlereagh Street
Sydney, NSW, Australia

ANCHORAGE CAPITAL PARTNERS PTY. LIMITED

Level 4 6 Bridge Street
Sydney, NSW, 2000, Australia
Tel.: (61) 282597777
Fax: (61) 282597778
E-Mail: anchorage@anchoragecapital.com.au
Web Site: www.anchoragecapital.com.au
Emp.: 10
Business Description:
Private Equity Firm
S.I.C.: 6211
N.A.I.C.S.: 523999
Personnel:
Michael Briggs *(Partner)*
Phillip Cave *(Partner)*
Daniel Wong *(Partner)*
Dani Sher *(CFO)*

Holding:

Dick Smith Holdings Limited (1)
2 Davidson Street
Chullora, NSW, 2190, Australia
Tel.: (61) 2 9642 9100
Fax: (61) 2 9642 9111
E-Mail: investor@dicksmithholdings.com.au
Web Site: www.dicksmithholdings.com.au
DSH—(ASX)
Holding Company; Consumer Electronics Retailer
S.I.C.: 6719
N.A.I.C.S.: 551112
Phillip Cave *(Chm)*
Nicholas Abboud *(CEO & Mng Dir)*
Michael Potts *(CFO & Sec)*

Subsidiary:

Dick Smith Electronics Limited (2)
2 Davidson Street
Chullora, NSW, 2190, Australia AU
Tel.: (61) 2 9642 9100 (100%)
Fax: (61) 2 9642 9111
E-Mail: feedback@dicksmith.com.au
Web Site: www.dicksmith.com.au
Sales Range: $1-4.9 Billion
Emp.: 4,500
Holding Company; Electronics Stores Owner, Operator & Franchisor
S.I.C.: 6719
N.A.I.C.S.: 551112
Nick Abboud *(CEO)*

Subsidiaries:

Dick Smith Electronics Franchising Pty. Ltd. (3)
2 Davidson Street
Chullora, NSW, 2190, Australia AU
Tel.: (61) 2 9642 9213
Fax: (61) 2 9642 9111
Electronics Store Franchisor
S.I.C.: 6794
N.A.I.C.S.: 533110
Deborah Singh *(Gen Mgr)*

Dick Smith Electronics Pty. Ltd. (3)
2 Davidson Street
Chullora, NSW, 2190, Australia AU
Tel.: (61) 2 9642 9100
Fax: (61) 2 9642 9111
Web Site: www.dicksmith.com.au
Electronics Stores Operator
S.I.C.: 5946
N.A.I.C.S.: 443142
Nick Abboud *(CEO)*

Dick Smith (Wholesale) Pty. Ltd. (3)
2 Davidson Street
Chullora, NSW, 2190, Australia AU
Tel.: (61) 2 9642 9100
Fax: (61) 2 9642 9111
Web Site: www.dicksmith.com.au/help/commercial-content
Electronic Products Distr
S.I.C.: 5065
N.A.I.C.S.: 423690
Deborah Singh *(Gen Mgr)*

ANCOM BERHAD

Level 18 The Gardens North Tower
Mid Valley City
Lingkaran Syed Putra, 59200 Kuala Lumpur, Malaysia
Tel.: (60) 322648888
Fax: (60) 322822733
E-Mail: cosec@ancom.com.my
Web Site: www.ancom.com.my
ANCOM—(KLS)
Rev.: $666,518,387
Assets: $318,463,443
Liabilities: $186,596,646
Net Worth: $131,866,798
Earnings: ($4,109,821)
Fiscal Year-end: 05/31/13
Business Description:
Agricultural Chemicals & Herbicides Mfr
S.I.C.: 0711
N.A.I.C.S.: 115112
Personnel:
Ka Wei Siew *(Mng Dir)*
Cheun Wei Lee *(CFO)*
Se Eng Choo *(Co-Sec)*
Wai Foong Wong *(Co-Sec)*
Board of Directors:
Johari Razak
Mohamed Al Amin Abdul Majid
Thye Seng Chan
Edmond Swee Leng Cheah
Hock Chye Lim
See Yan Lin
Ka Wei Siew

Subsidiaries:

Ancom Crop Care Sdn. Bhd. (1)
Lot 5 Persiaran Selangor Section 15
40000 Shah Alam, Selangor Darul Ehsan, Malaysia
Tel.: (60) 355194022
Fax: (60) 355103888
E-Mail: sales@ancomcropcare.com.my
Web Site: www.ancomcropcare.com.my
Emp.: 120
Agrochemical Products Mfr
S.I.C.: 2873
N.A.I.C.S.: 325311
Shamsuddin Basri *(Mng Dir)*

Subsidiary:

Ancom Bioscience Sdn. Bhd. (2)
Lot 5 Persiaran Selangor
Seksyen 15, 40000 Shah Alam, Selangor, Malaysia
Tel.: (60) 355194022
Fax: (60) 355103888
Web Site: www.ancomcropcare.com.my
Emp.: 120
Agrochemical Products Distr
S.I.C.: 5191
N.A.I.C.S.: 424910
Anthony Tan *(Gen Mgr)*

iEnterprise Online Sdn. Bhd. (1)
Unit 1003 & 1005 Block B Phileo Damansara II No 15 Jalan
16/11 Off Jalan Damansara, 46350 Petaling Jaya, Selangor, Malaysia
Tel.: (60) 376651988
Fax: (60) 376651638
E-Mail: info@ieol.com.my
Web Site: www.ieol.com.my
Enterprise Resource Planning Applications Development Services
S.I.C.: 7371
N.A.I.C.S.: 541511
Diana Quek *(Acct Dir)*

Meru Utama Sdn. Bhd. (1)
Suite E13-21 Block E Plaza Mont Kiara No 2 Jalan Kiara
50480 Kuala Lumpur, Malaysia
Tel.: (60) 362011488
Fax: (60) 362018633
Web Site: www.meruutama.com
Airport Advertising Services
S.I.C.: 7311
N.A.I.C.S.: 541810
Ong Pen Woon *(Gen Mgr)*

RedBerry Sdn. Bhd. (1)
502 Block A Pusat Dagangan Phileo Damansara I No 9 Jalan
16/11 Off Jalan Damansara, 46350 Petaling Jaya, Selangor Darul Ehsan, Malaysia
Tel.: (60) 3 7956 1713
Fax: (60) 3 7956 2676

E-Mail: enquiries@redberry.com.my
Web Site: www.redberry.com.my
Media Advertising Services
S.I.C.: 7313
N.A.I.C.S.: 541840

Wheel Sport Management Sdn. Bhd. (1)
Lot 2A Jalan 13/2 Redberry City
46200 Petaling Jaya, Selangor Darul Ehsan, Malaysia
Tel.: (60) 3 7495 1188
Fax: (60) 3 7495 1191
E-Mail: info@malaysianrally.com
Web Site: www.malaysianrally.com
Emp.: 5
Motor Rally Promoter
S.I.C.: 7999
N.A.I.C.S.: 711310
Shaharin Abu Bakar Suleiman *(Founder)*
Raja Nor Mazli Mohar *(Mng Dir)*

Non-U.S. Subsidiary:

Sinsenmoh Transportation Pte. Ltd. (1)
32 Tanjung Penjuru
Jurong Town, Singapore, 609028, Singapore
Tel.: (65) 62648488
Fax: (65) 68981588
Freight Forwarding Services
S.I.C.: 4731
N.A.I.C.S.: 488510

ANCONIA RESOURCES CORP.

65 Front Street east Suite 200
Toronto, ON, M5E 1B5, Canada
Tel.: (416) 815-9777
Fax: (416) 815-1355
E-Mail: info@anconia.ca
Web Site: www.anconia.ca
Year Founded: 1969
ARA—(TSXV)
Assets: $5,469,851
Liabilities: $814,200
Net Worth: $4,655,651
Earnings: ($562,996)
Fiscal Year-end: 09/30/13

Business Description:
Precious Metal Exploration Services
S.I.C.: 1499
N.A.I.C.S.: 212399

Personnel:
Jason Brewster *(Interim Chm, Pres & CEO)*
Harvey McKenzie *(CFO & Sec)*

Board of Directors:
Jason Brewster
Denis Clement
Michael Florence
James M. Franklin
John Sadowski

Transfer Agent:
Computershare Investor Services Inc
100 University Avenue 11th Floor
Toronto, ON, Canada

ANCORA ENERGISPAR AB

Warfvinges vag 19
112 51 Stockholm, Sweden
Tel.: (46) 8 56256500
Fax: (46) 8 56256501
E-Mail: info@ancoraenergispar.se
Web Site: www.ancoraenergispar.se

Business Description:
Heat Pumps & Air Quality Products Mfr
S.I.C.: 3433
N.A.I.C.S.: 333414

Personnel:
Hans Geisewall *(Chm)*

AND INTERNATIONAL PUBLISHERS NV

Van Vollenhovenstraat 3
3016 BE Rotterdam, Netherlands
Tel.: (31) 108851200
Fax: (31) 108851240
E-Mail: info@and.com
Web Site: www.and.com
Year Founded: 1984
AND—(EUR)
Rev.: $6,032,188
Assets: $17,057,320
Liabilities: $4,135,434
Net Worth: $12,921,886
Earnings: $2,361,182
Emp.: 276
Fiscal Year-end: 12/31/12

Business Description:
Mapping Software Development Services
S.I.C.: 7371
N.A.I.C.S.: 541511

Personnel:
P. W. Middelhoven *(Chm-Supervisory Bd)*
Hugo van der Linde *(Member-Mgmt Bd & CEO)*

Supervisory Board of Directors:
P. W. Middelhoven
M. S. Douma
R. M. Westerhof

ANDATEE CHINA MARINE FUEL SERVICES CORPORATION

24/F Xiwang Tower No 136
Zhongshan Road
Zhongshan District, Dalian, China
Tel.: (86) 21 5015 2581
Fax: (86) 21 50152530
Web Site: www.andatee.com
AMCF—(NASDAQ)
Rev.: $228,813,813
Assets: $120,713,582
Liabilities: $60,252,578
Net Worth: $60,461,004
Earnings: $1,409,965
Emp.: 197
Fiscal Year-end: 12/31/12

Business Description:
Blended Marine Fuel Oil Production, Storage, Distribution & Sales
S.I.C.: 5171
N.A.I.C.S.: 424710

Personnel:
Hao Wang *(CEO)*
Quan Zhang *(Interim CFO)*
Xun Sun *(COO)*
Jinhai Bai *(CTO)*

Board of Directors:
Yudong Hou
Wen Y. Jiang
Zhenyu Wu

Transfer Agent:
Continental Stock Transfer & Trust Company
2 Broadway 19th Fl
New York, NY 10004
Tel.: (212) 509-4000
Fax: (212) 509-5150
Toll Free: (800) 509-5586

ANDEANGOLD LTD.

Suite 1500 - 701 West Georgia Street
Vancouver, BC, V7Y 1C6, Canada
Tel.: (604) 601-5610
Fax: (604) 801-5911
Toll Free: (866) 684-4743
E-Mail: info@andeangoldltd.com
Web Site: www.andeangoldltd.com
Year Founded: 2006
AAU—(TSXV)
Assets: $6,626,479
Liabilities: $316,639
Net Worth: $6,309,840
Earnings: ($906,863)
Fiscal Year-end: 03/31/13

Business Description:
Mineral Exploration Services
S.I.C.: 1099
N.A.I.C.S.: 212299

Personnel:
Dana T. Jurika *(Founder)*
Anthony F. Ciali *(Pres & CEO)*
David Cross *(CFO)*
Graham H. Scott *(Sec)*

Board of Directors:
Anthony F. Ciali
Dana T. Jurika
Thomas Kelly
William F. Lindquist
Fernando Pickman

Legal Counsel:
Vector Corporate Finance Lawyers
Suite 1040 - 999 West Hastings Street
Vancouver, BC, Canada

Transfer Agent:
Computershare Corporate Trust Company
510 Burrard Street 2nd Floor
Vancouver, BC, Canada

ANDERSON ENERGY LTD

2200 Dome Tower 333 - 7th Avenue SW
Calgary, AB, T2P 2Z1, Canada
Tel.: (403) 262-6307
Fax: (403) 261-2792
E-Mail: info@andersonenergy.ca
Web Site: www.andersonenergy.ca
Year Founded: 2002
AXL—(OTC TSX)
Sls.: $77,340,720
Assets: $341,424,002
Liabilities: $209,259,102
Net Worth: $132,164,899
Earnings: ($31,304,672)
Emp.: 32
Fiscal Year-end: 12/31/12

Business Description:
Oil & Gas Exploration Services
S.I.C.: 1389
N.A.I.C.S.: 213112

Personnel:
James C. Anderson *(Chm)*
David J. Sandmeyer *(Vice Chm)*
Brian H. Dau *(Pres & CEO)*
M. Darlene Wong *(CFO, Sec & VP-Fin)*
David M. Spyker *(COO)*

Board of Directors:
James C. Anderson
Brian H. Dau
Christopher L. Fong
Glenn D. Hockley
David J. Sandmeyer
David G. Scobie

Legal Counsel:
Bennett Jones L.L.P.
855 2nd St SW Ste 4500
Calgary, AB, T2P 4K7, Canada
Tel.: (403) 298-3100
Fax: (403) 233-0353

Transfer Agent:
Valiant Trust Company
606 4th Street SW Suite 310
Calgary, AB, T2P 1T1, Canada
Tel.: (403) 233-2801
Fax: (403) 233-2857

ANDERSON GROUP LIMITED

Springfield Lodge
Colchester Rd, Chelmsford, Essex, CM2 5PW, United Kingdom
Tel.: (44) 1245399999
Fax: (44) 1245399950
E-Mail: info@andersongroup.co.uk
Web Site: www.andersongroup.co.uk
Year Founded: 1987
Emp.: 500

Business Description:
Construction & Architectural Services & Consulting
S.I.C.: 1542
N.A.I.C.S.: 236220

Personnel:
Mark Anderson *(Chm)*

Subsidiaries:

3R Limited (1)
Springfield Lodge
Colchester Road, Chelmsford, Essex, CM2 5PW, United Kingdom
Tel.: (44) 1245399977
Fax: (44) 1245399988
E-Mail: info@anderson.co.uk
Web Site: www.threer.co.uk
Emp.: 10
Earthwork & Demolition Services
S.I.C.: 1799
N.A.I.C.S.: 238910
Andrew Jay *(Mng Dir)*

Anderson Construction Ltd (1)
Springfield Lodge Colchester Rd
Chelmsford, Essex, CM2 5PW, United Kingdom
Tel.: (44) 1245399999
Fax: (44) 1245399900
E-Mail: info@andconst.co.uk
Web Site: www.andconst.co.uk
Emp.: 100
Groundworks & Civil Engineering Services
S.I.C.: 1629
N.A.I.C.S.: 237990
Sean Emmett *(Grp Comml Dir)*

Anderson Design & Build (1)
Springfield Lodge
Colchester Road, Chelmsford, Essex, CM2 5PW, United Kingdom
Tel.: (44) 1245399940
Fax: (44) 1245399950
E-Mail: info@anderson-db.co.uk
Web Site: www.anderson-db.co.uk
Emp.: 5
Architectural & Building Design Services
S.I.C.: 8712
N.A.I.C.S.: 541310
Mark Anderson *(Gen Mgr)*

Anderson Developments (1)
Springfield Lodge Colchester Rd
Chelmsford, Essex, CM2 5PW, United Kingdom
Tel.: (44) 8454300304
Fax: (44) 801245399950
Web Site: www.andersondevelopments.co.uk
Emp.: 40
Real Estate Developers
S.I.C.: 6519
N.A.I.C.S.: 531190

Anderson Regenerate (1)
Springfield Lodge
Colchester Road, Chelmsford, Essex, CM2 5PW, United Kingdom
Tel.: (44) 1245399940
Fax: (44) 1245399950
E-Mail: info@andersongroup.co.uk
Web Site: www.andersonregen.co.uk
Emp.: 30
Land Acquisition Corporation
S.I.C.: 6531
N.A.I.C.S.: 531312
Mark Anderson *(Mng Dir)*

EcoAggregates Limited (1)
Springfield Lodge
Colchester Road, Chelmsford, Essex, CM2 5PW, United Kingdom
Tel.: (44) 1245399940
Fax: (44) 1245399950
E-Mail: info@andersongroup.co.uk
Web Site: www.andersongroup.co.uk
Emp.: 300
Environmental Consulting Services For Construction Industry
S.I.C.: 8999
N.A.I.C.S.: 541620
Andrew Jay *(Mng Dir)*

MAP Limited (1)
Brunswick House Ripple Road A13
Barking, Essex, IG11 OSL, United Kingdom
Tel.: (44) 2085927070
Fax: (44) 2085928080
E-Mail: info@mapplant.co.uk
Web Site: www.mapplant.co.uk
Emp.: 20
Heavy Construction Equipment Services
S.I.C.: 5082
N.A.I.C.S.: 423810
Darren Carter *(Mng Dir)*

ANDERSON INDUSTRIAL CORPORATION
7th Fl No 72 Sung-Chiang Rd
Taipei, Taiwan
Tel.: (886) 225237866
Fax: (886) 225236676
Web Site: www.anderson.com.tw
1528—(TAI)
Sales Range: $25-49.9 Million

Business Description:
Industrial Machinery & Construction Plates Mfr
S.I.C.: 1799
N.A.I.C.S.: 238910

Personnel:
Andy Hsieh *(Chm)*

Subsidiaries:

Anderson Taiwan (Central) **(1)**
No 33 Jing 2nd Rd Wuci Township
Taichung, 435, Taiwan
Tel.: (886) 4 2659 5866
Fax: (886) 426595879
Business Support Services
S.I.C.: 7389
N.A.I.C.S.: 561499

Digital Photonics Corp. **(1)**
19F 5 No 81 Section 1 Sintai 5th Rd
Sijhih, Taipei, 221, Taiwan
Tel.: (886) 226984500
Fax: (886) 226980758
E-Mail: service@thinkfly.com.tw
Web Site: www.thinkfly.com.tw
Emp.: 20
Digital Printers Mfr
S.I.C.: 3577
N.A.I.C.S.: 334118
Kai Liu *(Gen Mgr)*

Sogotec Enterprise Co., Ltd. **(1)**
No 11 37th Road Taichung Industrial Area
Taichung, 407, Taiwan
Tel.: (886) 423591131
Fax: (886) 423591580
Numerical Control Machinery Mfr
S.I.C.: 3559
N.A.I.C.S.: 333242
Jeffrey Hou *(Chm & Gen Mgr)*

Plant:

Anderson Industrial Corporation - Houlung Factory **(1)**
No 1498 Chung-Hua Road
Hou-lung, Miaoli, 358, Taiwan
Tel.: (886) 37 726 876
Fax: (886) 37 727 727
Web Site: www.anderson.com.tw
Emp.: 200
Industrial Machinery Mfr
S.I.C.: 3559
N.A.I.C.S.: 333249

U.S. Subsidiary:

Anderson America Corp. **(1)**
10710 Southern Loop Blvd
Pineville, NC 28134-8467
Tel.: (704) 522-1823
Fax: (704) 522-0871
E-Mail: info@andersonamerica.com
Web Site: www.andersonamerica.com
Emp.: 15
Woodworking & Printing Machinery Distr
S.I.C.: 5084
N.A.I.C.S.: 423830
David Steranko *(VP-Sls)*

Non-U.S. Subsidiaries:

Anderson Europe GmbH **(1)**
Am Oberen Feld 5
32758 Detmold, Nordrhein-Westfalen, Germany
Tel.: (49) 523196630
Fax: (49) 5231966311
E-Mail: info@andersoneurope.com
Web Site: www.andersoneurope.com
Emp.: 20
Precision Machines Mfr
S.I.C.: 3451
N.A.I.C.S.: 332721
Tzu-Jen Hsieh *(Co-Mng Dir)*
Yuan-Nan Wang *(Co-Mng Dir)*

Anderson Industrial Hong Kong Limited **(1)**
Mayor of Dongguan Changan Kam new 26th Street
Guangzhou, Guangdong, 530000, China
Tel.: (86) 769 82380598
Fax: (86) 769 82381936
Semiconductor & Electronic Components Distr
S.I.C.: 5065
N.A.I.C.S.: 423690

Anderson Machinery (Singapore) Pte. Ltd. **(1)**
459 Pasir Ris Dr 4 10-257
Singapore, 510459, Singapore
Tel.: (65) 65840749
E-Mail: andi.singapore@gmail.com
Web Site: www.anderson.tw
Emp.: 10
Woodworking Machinery Distr
S.I.C.: 5084
N.A.I.C.S.: 423830
Jiang Wen-Chuan *(Mgr)*

ANDERSON SPRATT GROUP
Anderson House Holywood Rd
Belfast, Northern Ireland, BT4 2GU, United Kingdom
Tel.: (44) 28 9080 2000
Fax: (44) 28 9080 2001
E-Mail: info@asgireland.com
Web Site: www.asgireland.com
Year Founded: 1982
Emp.: 40

Business Description:
Advertising
S.I.C.: 7311
N.A.I.C.S.: 541810

Personnel:
R.J.C. Anderson *(Chm)*
Seamus McKenna *(Deputy CEO)*
Prakash Dhandrabalan *(Sr VP & Dir-Fin)*

Branch

ASG Ltd **(1)**
(Formerly Anderson Spratt Group)
Anderson House
Holywood Rd
Belfast, Northern Ireland, BT4 2GU, United Kingdom
Tel.: (44) 28 9080 2000
Fax: (44) 28 9080 2001
E-Mail: info@asgireland.com
Web Site: www.asgireland.com
Emp.: 20
Advertising
S.I.C.: 7311
N.A.I.C.S.: 541810
Colin Anderson *(Chm)*

Group Companies

Tibus **(1)**
Macken House
Mayer Street Upper, Dublin, 1, Ireland
Tel.: (353) 1 473 1650
Fax: (353) 1 473 1850
E-Mail: belfast@tibus.com
Web Site: www.tibus.com
Emp.: 25
Advertising
S.I.C.: 7311
N.A.I.C.S.: 541810
Rick McKee *(Dir-Comml)*

Tibus **(1)**
Ormeau Rd
BT7 1AB Belfast, 4, Ireland
Tel.: (353) 1 473 1650
Fax: (353) 1 473 1850
E-Mail: dublin@tibus.com
Web Site: www.tibus.com
Advertising
S.I.C.: 7311
N.A.I.C.S.: 541810

ANDES ENERGIA PLC
3rd Floor 16 Dover St
London, W15 4LR, United Kingdom
Tel.: (44) 2074955326
E-Mail: info@andesenergiaplc.com.ar
Web Site: www.andesenergiaplc.com.ar
AEN—(AIM OTC)
Rev.: $4,828,669
Assets: $180,249,217
Liabilities: $58,467,691
Net Worth: $121,781,526
Earnings: ($27,017,104)
Emp.: 730
Fiscal Year-end: 12/31/12

Business Description:
Electricity Generation
S.I.C.: 1623
N.A.I.C.S.: 237130

Personnel:
Ricardo Nicolas Mallo Huergo *(Chm & CEO-JV Ops)*
Alejandro Oscar Jotayan *(CEO)*
German Rantfl *(CFO)*
Nigel John Duxbury *(Sec)*

Board of Directors:
Ricardo Nicolas Mallo Huergo
Javier Francisco Alvarez
Nigel John Duxbury
Juan Carlos Esteban
David Clifford Jackson
Alejandro Oscar Jotayan
Carolina Maria Landi
Matthieu Milandri
German Rantfl

Legal Counsel:
Nabarro
Lacon House Theobald's Road
London, United Kingdom

ANDHRA BANK
Dr Pattabhi Bhavan 5-9-11
Secretariat Road
Saifabad, Hyderabad, 500 004, India
Tel.: (91) 40 23252000
Fax: (91) 40 23231385
E-Mail: customerser@andhrabank.co.in
Web Site: www.andhrabank-india.com
Year Founded: 1923
532418—(BOM)
Rev.: $2,696,141,901
Assets: $27,357,498,466
Liabilities: $25,790,100,669
Net Worth: $1,567,397,797
Earnings: $238,154,458
Emp.: 16,523
Fiscal Year-end: 03/31/13

Business Description:
Banking Services
S.I.C.: 6029
N.A.I.C.S.: 522110

Personnel:
Rajendran C. V. R. *(Chm & Mng Dir)*
T. V. S. Chandra Sekhar *(CFO & Gen Mgr-Accts)*
T. R. Ramabhadran *(Compliance Officer & Sec)*

Board of Directors:
Rajendran C. V. R.
K. R. Ananda
Pankaj Chaturvedi
Manoranjan Das
Satish Kumar Kalra
K. K. Misra
Mustafa Mohammad
K. Raghuraman
N. Rajagopal Reddy
Nandlal L. Sarda
G. R. Sundaravadivel
R Subramanian & Company
Hyderabad, India
Patro & Co
Hyderabad, India
Nataraja Iyer & Co
Hyderabad, India
Nag & Associates
Hyderabad, India
C.R.Sagdeo & Co
Hyderabad, India

Transfer Agent:
MCS Limited
Kashiram Jamnadas Building Office No. 21/22
Ground Fl 5 P Dmello Rd
Mumbai, India

THE ANDHRA PETROCHEMICALS LIMITED
Venkatarayapuram
West Godavari Dist., Tanuku, Andhra Pradesh, 534 215, India
Tel.: (91) 8819 224075
Fax: (91) 8819 224168
E-Mail: info.tnk@andhrapetrochemicals.com
Web Site: www.andhrapetrochemicals.com
500012—(BOM)
Rev.: $104,960,428
Assets: $61,280,021
Liabilities: $21,265,565
Net Worth: $40,014,456
Earnings: $578,207
Emp.: 300
Fiscal Year-end: 03/31/13

Business Description:
Petrochemical Products Mfr
S.I.C.: 2869
N.A.I.C.S.: 325110

Personnel:
B. B. Ramaiah *(Mng Dir)*
K. Raghu Ram *(Compliance Officer, Mgr-Fin & Asst Sec)*

Board of Directors:
M. R. B. Punja
Anirudha Behera
P. Narendranath Chowdary
Surinder Kumar Kapoor
A. A. Krishnan
Ravi Pendyala
Anita Rajendra
B. B. Ramaiah
G. Ramanujam
M. Thimmaraja

THE ANDHRA SUGARS LIMITED
Venkatarayapuram
West Godavari, Tanuku, 534215, India
Tel.: (91) 8819 224911
Fax: (91) 8819 224168
E-Mail: info.tnk@theandhrasugars.com
Web Site: www.theandhrasugars.com
590062—(BOM)
Rev.: $248,771,518
Assets: $259,255,073
Liabilities: $129,362,794
Net Worth: $129,892,278
Earnings: $16,702,093
Emp.: 2,284
Fiscal Year-end: 03/31/13

Business Description:
Sugar Mfr & Distr
S.I.C.: 2063
N.A.I.C.S.: 311313

Personnel:
B. B. Ramaiah *(Chm & Co-Mng Dir)*
P. Narendranath Chowdary *(Co-Mng Dir)*
M. Narendranath *(Co-Mng Dir)*
P. Achuta Ramayya *(Co-Mng Dir)*

M. Thimmaraja *(Co-Mng Dir)*
M. Palachandra *(Compliance Officer & Sec)*
Board of Directors:
B. B. Ramaiah
P. A. Chowdary
P. Narendranath Chowdary
Pamidi Kotaiah
M. Narendranath
V. S. Raju
Anumolu Ramakrishna
G. Ramanujam
P. Achuta Ramayya
A. Ranga Rao
A. V. Rama Rao
Alapaty Appa Rao
P. S. R. V. K. Ranga Rao
M. Thimmaraja

ANDINA ACQUISITION CORPORATION

Carrera 10 28 49 Torre A Oficina 20 05
Bogota, Colombia
Tel.: (57) 1 281 1811
Year Founded: 2011
ANDAU—(NASDAQ)
Int. Income: $27,991
Assets: $42,816,950
Liabilities: $11,025,484
Net Worth: $31,791,466
Earnings: ($11,379,280)
Emp.: 1
Fiscal Year-end: 02/28/13
Business Description:
Investment Services
S.I.C.: 6211
N.A.I.C.S.: 523999
Personnel:
Benjamin Luke Weil *(CEO)*
Board of Directors:
A. Lorne Weil
Martha L. Byorum
Rudolf M. Hommes Rodriguez
Luis Eduardo Robayo Salom
Julio A. Torres Garcia

ANDON HEALTH CO., LTD.

7/F Hua Qiao Chuang Ye Plaza 10 Jing Ping Road
Ya An Street
Nankai District, Tianjin, 300190, China
Tel.: (86) 22 60526081
Fax: (86) 22 60526162
Web Site: www.jiuan.com
Year Founded: 1995
002432—(SSE)
Sales Range: $25-49.9 Million
Emp.: 1,500
Business Description:
Medical Equipment & Product Mfr
S.I.C.: 3845
N.A.I.C.S.: 334510
Personnel:
Yi Liu *(Chm)*

ANDOR TECHNOLOGY PLC

7 Millennium Way Springvale Business Park
Belfast, BT12 7AL, United Kingdom
Tel.: (44) 2890237126
Fax: (44) 2890310792
Web Site: www.andor.com
AND—(AIM LSE)
Rev.: $91,694,609
Assets: $95,966,385
Liabilities: $24,776,930
Net Worth: $71,189,455
Earnings: $11,893,996
Emp.: 341
Fiscal Year-end: 09/30/12
Business Description:
Developer & Mfr of High Performance Digital Cameras
S.I.C.: 3579
N.A.I.C.S.: 333316
Personnel:
Conor Walsh *(CEO)*
Alan Lilley *(Sec & Dir-Fin)*
Board of Directors:
Colin Walsh
Kevin Boyd
Donal Denvir
Mary Duseau
Jonathan Flint
Alan Lilley
Conor Walsh
Legal Counsel:
Elliott Duffy & Garrett
Royston House 34 Upper Queen Street
Belfast, United Kingdom

Addleshaw Goddard
100 Barbirolli Square
Manchester, United Kingdom

U.S. Subsidiaries:

Andor Technology plc (USA) (1)
425 Sullivan Ave Ste 3
South Windsor, CT 06074
Tel.: (860) 290-9211
Fax: (860) 290-9566
Toll Free: (800) 296-1579
Web Site: www.andor.com
Laboratory Equipment Mfr
S.I.C.: 3826
N.A.I.C.S.: 334516
Chris Calling *(Pres)*

Bitplane Inc (1)
425 Sullivan Ave Ste 3
South Windsor, CT 06074
Tel.: (860) 290-9211
Fax: (860) 290-9566
E-Mail: ussales@bitplane.com
Web Site: www.bitplane.com
Emp.: 18
Image Analysis Software Services
S.I.C.: 7372
N.A.I.C.S.: 511210
Chris Calling *(Gen Mgr)*

Non-U.S. Subsidiaries:

Andor Technology plc (Beijing) (1)
1213, Building B Luo Ke Time Square No 103 Huizhongli
Chaoyang, Beijing, 100101, China
Tel.: (86) 1051294977
Fax: (86) 84871580
Web Site: www.andor.com
Emp.: 4
Laboratory Equipment Mfr
S.I.C.: 3826
N.A.I.C.S.: 334516
Erric Chen *(Mgr)*

Andor Technology plc (Tokyo) (1)
4F NE Sarugakucho Bldg 2-7-6 Sarugaku-Cho
Chiyoda-ku, Tokyo, 101 0064, Japan
Tel.: (81) 335186488
Fax: (81) 335186489
E-Mail: sales@andor.com
Web Site: www.andor.com
Emp.: 10
Laboratory Equipment Mfr
S.I.C.: 3826
N.A.I.C.S.: 334516
Philip Moore *(Mgr-Sls)*

Bitplane AG (1)
Badenerstrasse 682
8048 Zurich, Switzerland
Tel.: (41) 444301100
Fax: (41) 444301101
E-Mail: welcome@bitplane.com
Web Site: www.bitplane.com
Image Analysis Software Development Services
S.I.C.: 7372
N.A.I.C.S.: 511210

ANDRADE & CANELLAS ENERGIA S.A.

Rua Alexandre Dumas 2.100 13 andar
Chac Santo Antonio, CEP 04717-004
Sao Paulo, Brazil
Tel.: (55) 1121220400
Fax: (55) 1121220440
E-Mail: info@andradecanellas.com.br
Web Site: www.andradecanellas.com.br
Emp.: 70
Business Description:
Energy Consulting Services
S.I.C.: 8999
N.A.I.C.S.: 541690
Personnel:
Joao Carlos de Oliveira Mello *(CEO)*
Board of Directors:
Ivete Andrade Silva Crisafulli
Andre Crisafulli

ANDRE VOSS ERDBAU UND TRANSPORT GMBH

Am Liepengraben 6
D-18147 Rostock, Germany
Tel.: (49) 381128310
Fax: (49) 3811283119
E-Mail: kontakt@andrevoss.de
Web Site: www.andre-voss.de
Rev.: $12,309,871
Emp.: 60
Business Description:
Paving Materials Mfr
S.I.C.: 2951
N.A.I.C.S.: 324121
Personnel:
Dietmar Gottschalk *(Mgr-Production)*

ANDREAS SIMONSEN GMBH

Ruhrstrasse 90
22761 Hamburg, Germany
Tel.: (49) 408533450
Fax: (49) 408501061
Web Site: www.simonsengmbh.de
Year Founded: 1892
Rev.: $46,588,860
Emp.: 20
Business Description:
Fish & Seafood Distr
S.I.C.: 5146
N.A.I.C.S.: 424460
Personnel:
Andreas Simonsen *(CEO)*

ANDREAS STIHL AG & CO.

Badstrasse 115
D 71336 Waiblingen, Germany
Tel.: (49) 7151260
Fax: (49) 7151261140
E-Mail: info@stihl.de
Web Site: www.stihl.de
Year Founded: 1926
Sales Range: $300-349.9 Million
Emp.: 3,788
Business Description:
Outdoor Power Equipment
S.I.C.: 3546
N.A.I.C.S.: 333991
Personnel:
Hans Peter Stihl *(Chm)*

U.S. Subsidiaries:

Stihl, Inc. (1)
536 Viking Dr
Virginia Beach, VA 23452 (100%)
Tel.: (757) 486-9100
Fax: (757) 631-5745
Toll Free: (800) 467-8445
Web Site: www.stihlusa.com
Emp.: 2,000
Mfr of Chain Saws, Grass Trimmers, Leaf Blowers, Grass Edgers & Augers
Export
S.I.C.: 3546
N.A.I.C.S.: 333991
Fred J. Whyte *(Pres)*

Subsidiary:

Stihl Parts, Inc. (2)
536 Viking Dr
Virginia Beach, VA 23452-7821 (100%)
Tel.: (757) 486-9100
Fax: (757) 486-9197
E-Mail: info@stihlusa.com
Web Site: www.stihlusa.com
Emp.: 1,500
Distribution of Machinery
Import Export
S.I.C.: 3546
N.A.I.C.S.: 333991
Fred J. Whyte *(Pres)*

Non-U.S. Subsidiary:

Stihl Ltd (2)
1515 Sise Rd
PO Box 5666
London, ON, N6A 4L6, Canada (100%)
Tel.: (519) 681-3000
Fax: (519) 681-1603
E-Mail: info.canada@stihl.ca
Web Site: www.stihl.ca
Emp.: 80
Mfr. of Chainsaws & Accessories
S.I.C.: 3546
N.A.I.C.S.: 333991
Greg Quigt *(Gen Mgr)*

USA Zama Inc. (1)
114 Seaboard Ln
Franklin, TN 37067
Tel.: (615) 371-9493
Fax: (615) 371-9496
Toll Free: (888) 233-2272
E-Mail: carb@usazama.com
Web Site: www.zamacarb.com
Emp.: 20
Carburetors Design & Whslr
S.I.C.: 3714
N.A.I.C.S.: 336310
Mamoru Toda *(Pres)*

ANDREW HENDRIKS & SONS GREENHOUSES

5095 North Service Road
Beamsville, ON, L0R 1B3, Canada
Tel.: (905) 563-8132
Fax: (905) 563-9307
Toll Free: (800) 449-1786
Web Site: www.hendriksgreenhouses.com
Year Founded: 1953
Rev.: $10,669,234
Emp.: 50
Business Description:
Gardening Services
S.I.C.: 5261
N.A.I.C.S.: 444220
Personnel:
Andrew Hendriks, Sr. *(Pres)*

ANDREW PELLER LIMITED

697 South Service Road
Grimsby, ON, L3M 4E8, Canada
Tel.: (905) 643-4131
Fax: (905) 643-4944
E-Mail: info@andrewpeller.com
Web Site: www.andrewpeller.com
Year Founded: 1961
ADW.A—(TSX)
Sls.: $287,413,925
Assets: $294,745,816
Liabilities: $166,114,658
Net Worth: $128,631,158
Earnings: $14,670,741
Emp.: 1,189
Fiscal Year-end: 03/31/13
Business Description:
Winery Owner & Wine Retailer
Import Export
S.I.C.: 2084
N.A.I.C.S.: 312130
Personnel:
Joseph A. Peller *(Chm)*
John F. Petch *(Vice Chm)*
John E. Peller *(Pres & CEO)*
Peter B. Patchet *(CFO & Exec VP-HR)*
Anthony M. Bristow *(COO)*
Robert P. Van Wely *(Pres-Global Vintners Inc)*
Shari A. Niles *(Exec VP-Mktg)*
Brendan P. Wall *(Exec VP-Ops)*

Andrew Peller Limited—(Continued)

Board of Directors:
Joseph A. Peller
Mark W. Cosens
Lori C. Covert
Richard D. Hossack
Perry J. Miele
A. Angus Peller
John E. Peller
John F. Petch
Randy A. Powell
Brian J. Short
Transfer Agent:
Computershare Investor Services
100 University Avenue 9th Floor
Toronto, ON, Canada

ANDREW SHERET LIMITED
721 Kings Road
Victoria, BC, V8T 1W4, Canada
Tel.: (250) 287-9571
Fax: (250) 381-4210
Web Site: www.sheret.com
Year Founded: 1989
Rev.: $55,123,098
Emp.: 250
Business Description:
Bathroom Accessories Mfr
S.I.C.: 3269
N.A.I.C.S.: 327110
Personnel:
David Broad *(VP)*

ANDREW YULE & COMPANY LTD.
Yule House 8 Dr Rajendra Prasad Sarani
Kolkata, 700 001, India
Tel.: (91) 33 2242 8210
Fax: (91) 33 2242 9770
E-Mail: fund@andrewyule.com
Web Site: www.andrewyule.com
526173—(BOM)
Rev.: $61,617,801
Assets: $100,834,406
Liabilities: $58,902,006
Net Worth: $41,932,400
Earnings: $2,091,776
Emp.: 15,043
Fiscal Year-end: 03/31/13
Business Description:
Industrial Machinery Mfr & Distr
S.I.C.: 3559
N.A.I.C.S.: 333249
Personnel:
Kallol Datta *(Chm & Mng Dir)*
Sudip Kar *(Chief Vigilance Officer)*
D. Bandopadhyay *(Sec & Controller-Fin)*
Board of Directors:
Kallol Datta
Amitava Dhar
Suresh Kumar Goyal
Sunil Munshi
Harbhajan Singh
S. Swaminathan
Transfer Agent:
MCS Share Transfer Agent Limited
12/1/5 Manoharpukar Road Ground Floor
Kolkata, 700026, India

Subsidiary:

Hooghly Printing Company Ltd. **(1)**
Yule House 8 Dr Rajendra Prasad Sarani
Kolkata, 700 001, India
Tel.: (91) 33 22428210
Fax: (91) 33 22882734
E-Mail: hooghlyprinting@data.in
Web Site: www.hooghlyprinting.com
Emp.: 55
Brochure & Pamphlet Printing Services
S.I.C.: 2759
N.A.I.C.S.: 323113
Kallol Datta *(Chm)*

ANDREWS REALTY LTD
(d/b/ais Re/Max Real Estate Services)
410 650 W 41 Ave North Tower
Vancouver, BC, V5Z 1M9, Canada
Tel.: (604) 263-2823
Fax: (604) 263-1057
Toll Free: (888) 840-2823
Year Founded: 1986
Rev.: $10,694,229
Emp.: 115
Business Description:
Real Estate Services
S.I.C.: 6531
N.A.I.C.S.: 531210
Personnel:
David Andrews *(Owner)*

ANDREWS SYKES GROUP PLC
Premier House Darlington Street
Wolverhampton, WV1 4JJ, United Kingdom
Tel.: (44) 1902328700
Fax: (44) 1902422466
E-Mail: info@andrews-sykes.com
Web Site: www.andrews-sykes.com
ASY—(LSE)
Rev.: $92,198,950
Assets: $95,881,854
Liabilities: $31,385,230
Net Worth: $64,496,624
Earnings: $17,621,718
Emp.: 472
Fiscal Year-end: 12/31/12
Business Description:
Warm Air Heating & Air-Conditioning Equipment Mfr
S.I.C.: 3585
N.A.I.C.S.: 333415
Personnel:
J. G. Murray *(Chm)*
P. T. Wood *(Mng Dir)*
M. J. Calderbank *(Sec)*
Board of Directors:
J. G. Murray
M. Gailer
M. C. Leon
X. Mignolet
J. J. Murray
J. P. Murray
E. D. O. A. Sebag
P. T. Wood

ANDRITZ AG
Stattegger Strasse 18
8045 Graz, Austria
Tel.: (43) 31669020
Fax: (43) 3166902415
E-Mail: investors@andritz.com
Web Site: www.andritz.com
Year Founded: 1852
ANDR—(OTC VIE)
Sls.: $6,968,960,550
Assets: $6,947,536,254
Liabilities: $5,555,872,439
Net Worth: $1,391,663,815
Earnings: $326,047,759
Emp.: 17,865
Fiscal Year-end: 12/31/12
Business Description:
Holding Company; Customized Industrial Plant & Systems Designer & Construction
S.I.C.: 6719
N.A.I.C.S.: 551112
Personnel:
Hellwig Torggler *(Chm-Supervisory Bd)*
Klaus Ritter *(Deputy Chm-Supervisory Bd)*
Wolfgang Leitner *(Pres, CEO & Member-Exec Bd)*
Karl Hornhofer *(Member-Exec Bd-Pulp & Paper)*
Humbert Kofler *(Member-Exec Bd-Pulp, Paper & Separation)*
Friedrich Papst *(Member-Exec Bd-Hydro, Metals, Feed & Biofuel)*
Wolfgang Semper *(Member-Exec Bd-Hydro)*
Supervisory Board of Directors:
Hellwig Torggler
Georg Auer
Isolde Findenig
Andreas Martiner
Peter Mitterbauer, Sr.
Christian Nowotny
Fritz Oberlerchner
Klaus Ritter
Kurt Stiassny

Division:

Andritz Hydro GmbH **(1)**
Penzinger Strasse 76
1141 Vienna, Austria
Tel.: (43) 1891000
Fax: (43) 18946046
E-Mail: contact-hydro@andritz.com
Sales Range: $1-4.9 Billion
Emp.: 200
Hydroelectric Power Plant Turbine & Other Electromechanical Equipment Mfr & Services
S.I.C.: 3511
N.A.I.C.S.: 333611
Harald Heber *(Member-Mgmt Bd)*
Michael Kombock *(Member-Mgmt Bd-Svc & Rehab Bus Div)*
Wolfgang Semper *(Member-Mgmt Bd-Large Hydro)*
Manfred Woergoetter *(Member-Mgmt Bd-Pumps Div)*

Non-U.S. Subsidiary:

Andritz Hydro AG **(2)**
Obernaustrasse 4
CH 6010 Kriens, Switzerland
Tel.: (41) 413295111
Telex: 865578 BELL CH
Fax: (41) 413295152
E-Mail: contact-hydro.ch@andritz.com
Sls.: $71,800,000
Emp.: 460
Hydroelectric Power Plant Turbine & Other Electromechanical Equipment Mfr & Services
S.I.C.: 3511
N.A.I.C.S.: 333611
Christian Dubois *(Mng Dir)*

Subsidiaries:

Andritz Energy & Environment GmbH **(1)**
Waagner Biro Platz 1
Raaba, AT-8074 Graz, Austria AT (100%)
Tel.: (43) 3165010
Fax: (43) 316 501 482
E-Mail: info-aee@andritz.com
Web Site: www.andritz.com
Sales Range: $250-299.9 Million
Emp.: 320
Energy Generation & Environmental Technology Plant System Mfr Engineering Services
S.I.C.: 3511
N.A.I.C.S.: 333611

ANDRITZ PULP & PAPER **(1)**
Stattegger Strasse 18
8045 Graz, Austria
Tel.: (43) 316 69020
Fax: (43) 316 6902415
E-Mail: welcome@andritz.com
Web Site: www.andritz.com
Paper Industry Machinery Mfr
S.I.C.: 3554
N.A.I.C.S.: 333243
Wolfgang Leitner *(Pres & CEO)*

U.S. Subsidiaries:

ANDRITZ HYDRO Corp. **(1)**
10735 David Taylor Dr Ste 500
Charlotte, NC 28262
Tel.: (704) 943-4343
Fax: (704) 943-0200
E-Mail: contact.usa@andritz-hydro.com
Web Site: reports.andritz.com
Electro Mechanical System Distr
S.I.C.: 5065
N.A.I.C.S.: 423690

Andritz Inc. **(1)**
1115 Northmeadow Pkwy
Roswell, GA 30076-3857
Tel.: (770) 640-2500
Fax: (770) 640-9454
Web Site: www.andritz.com
Emp.: 250
Design & Engineering of Products for the Pulp Industry
S.I.C.: 8711
N.A.I.C.S.: 541330
Tim Ryan *(Pres)*

Branches:

Andritz Inc. **(2)**
PO Box 767
Pell City, AL 35125-0767
Tel.: (205) 338-3331
Fax: (205) 338-3334
S.I.C.: 2653
N.A.I.C.S.: 322211

Andritz Inc. **(2)**
1 Namic Pl
Glens Falls, NY 12801 (100%)
Tel.: (518) 793-5111
Fax: (518) 793-1917
Web Site: www.andritz.com
Emp.: 75
Engineering Firm
S.I.C.: 7699
N.A.I.C.S.: 811219
Jack Morphis *(Treas)*

Division:

ANDRITZ Inc. - ANDRITZ Kusters Division **(2)**
201 Zima Park Dr
Spartanburg, SC 29301
Tel.: (864) 587-4848
Fax: (864) 576-2306
E-Mail: kpc@andritz.com
Web Site: www.andritz.com
Non Woven & Paper Products Mfr
S.I.C.: 2297
N.A.I.C.S.: 313230
Tammy Mittag *(Office Mgr)*

ANDRITZ KMPT Inc. **(1)**
8070 Production Dr
Florence, KY 41042
Tel.: (859) 547-1100
Fax: (859) 547-1098
E-Mail: separation.us@andritz.com
Web Site: www.andritz.com
Emp.: 30
Industrial Machinery Mfr & Distr
S.I.C.: 3559
N.A.I.C.S.: 333249
Patrick McCarty *(Gen Mgr)*

ANDRITZ Paper Machinery Ltd. **(1)**
101 S Main St Ste 400
Janesville, WI 53545
Tel.: (608) 758-5920
Fax: (608) 758-5935
E-Mail: tissue.na@andritz.com
Web Site: www.andritz.com
Paper Machinery Mfr
S.I.C.: 3553
N.A.I.C.S.: 333243

Andritz Separation Inc. **(1)**
1600 Boston Providence Hwy
Walpole, MA 02081 DE (100%)
Tel.: (508) 404-1400
Fax: (508) 668-6855
E-Mail: separation.us@andritz.com
Web Site: www.andritz.com
Emp.: 22
Mfr. of Specialized Machinery for the Process Industry
Export
S.I.C.: 3569
N.A.I.C.S.: 333999

Bottom Dollar Food Holding, LLC **(1)**
2110 Executive Dr
Salisbury, NC 28147-9007
Tel.: (704) 310-2221
Investment Management Services
S.I.C.: 6211
N.A.I.C.S.: 523999

Non-U.S. Subsidiaries:

Andritz AB (1)
Gavlegatan 22
11330 Stockholm, Sweden (100%)
Mailing Address:
PO Box 21154
10031 Stockholm, Sweden
Tel.: (46) 858602500
Telex: 17338 alsto s
Fax: (46) 87362529
Web Site: www.andritz.com
Emp.: 10
Mfr. of Equipment for the Pulp & Paper Industry
S.I.C.: 3553
N.A.I.C.S.: 333243
Mihael Forslund *(VP)*

ANDRITZ AG (1)
Profsojusnaja 73
117342 Moscow, Russia
Tel.: (7) 499 75091 83
Fax: (7) 499 940 41 86
E-Mail: separation.ru@andritz.com
Industrial Machinery Distr
S.I.C.: 5084
N.A.I.C.S.: 423830

ANDRITZ AG (1)
3F No 77 Sec 2 Tun Hwa South Road
Taipei, 106, Taiwan
Tel.: (886) 2 2722 7475
Fax: (886) 2 2722 7476
E-Mail: separation.tw@andritz.com
Emp.: 1
Industrial Machinery Distr
S.I.C.: 5084
N.A.I.C.S.: 423830
Eric Hao *(Gen Mgr)*

ANDRITZ Asselin-Thibeau (1)
41 Rue Camille Randoing
76500 Elbeuf, France
Tel.: (33) 232964242
Fax: (33) 232960314
Textile Machinery Distr
S.I.C.: 5084
N.A.I.C.S.: 423830

ANDRITZ AUTOMATION Ltd. (1)
345 Wallace Street Suite 403
Nanaimo, BC, V9R 5B6, Canada
Tel.: (250) 753-5307
E-Mail: automation-sales@andritz.com
Web Site: www.andritz.com
Emp.: 100
Industrial Machinery Distr
S.I.C.: 5084
N.A.I.C.S.: 423830

ANDRITZ Biax S.A.S. (1)
18 Rue du Lac Saint Andre Immeuble Le Dauphin
Savoie Technolac, 73382 Le Bourget du Lac, France
Tel.: (33) 479 268 560
Fax: (33) 479268600
E-Mail: biax@andritz.com
Web Site: www.andritz.com
Industrial Machinery Mfr & Distr
S.I.C.: 3559
N.A.I.C.S.: 333249

ANDRITZ Boisfer Iggesund S.A.S. (1)
ZI de la Tuilliere
01700 Miribel, France
Tel.: (33) 4 785 597 97
Fax: (33) 4 785 597 98
E-Mail: france@iggesundtools.com
Web Site: www.andritz.com
Industrial Machine Tool Distr
S.I.C.: 5084
N.A.I.C.S.: 423830

Andritz Brasil Ltda. (1)
Av Vicente Machado 589 Centro
80420 010 Curitiba, PR, Brazil (100%)
Tel.: (55) 4121037611
Fax: (55) 4121037511
Web Site: www.andritz.com
Emp.: 150
Mfr. of Equipment & Machinery for the Pulp & Paper Industry
S.I.C.: 3554
N.A.I.C.S.: 333243
Diana Ho *(Dir-Fin)*

Subsidiary:

ANDRITZ FEED & BIOFUEL Brasil Ltda. (2)
Av Vicente Machado 589 - Centro
Curitiba, Parana, 80420-010, Brazil
Tel.: (55) 41 2103 7572
Fax: (55) 41 2103 7623
E-Mail: andritz-fb.br@andritz.com
Web Site: www.andritz.com
Industrial Machinery Mfr & Distr
S.I.C.: 3559
N.A.I.C.S.: 333249

ANDRITZ Chile Ltda. (1)
Isidora Goyenechea 3600 Floor 7
Las Condes, Santiago, 7550053, Chile
Tel.: (56) 2 462 4600
Fax: (56) 2 462 4646
E-Mail: separation.cl@andritz.com
Web Site: www.andritz.com
Emp.: 50
Industrial Machinery Equipment Distr
S.I.C.: 5084
N.A.I.C.S.: 423830
Harri Soila *(Gen Mgr)*

ANDRITZ (China) Ltd. (1)
Room 802 Hong Yu Building 7 Xueyuan Road
Haidian District, Beijing, 100083, China
Tel.: (86) 10 5131 3700
Fax: (86) 10 8230 6637
E-Mail: filtration.cn@andritz.com
Web Site: www.andritz.cn/print/index/locations.htm?country=15159&location=15741
Industrial Machinery Distr
S.I.C.: 5084
N.A.I.C.S.: 423830

ANDRITZ DELKOR (Pty) Ltd. (1)
76 Kyalami Boulevard Kyalami Business Park
Kyalami, 1684, South Africa
Tel.: (27) 11 4662361
Fax: (27) 866 362122
E-Mail: separation.za@andritz.com
Emp.: 72
Mining Liquid Separation Equipment Distr
S.I.C.: 5082
N.A.I.C.S.: 423810
Gary Whitford *(Gen Mgr)*

Andritz Dies & Rolls B.V. (1)
Spaarpot 112
5667 KZ Geldrop, Netherlands
Tel.: (31) 40 262 7777
Fax: (31) 40 262 7751
E-Mail: adr.nl@andritz.com
Web Site: reports.andritz.com
Industrial Machinery Distr
S.I.C.: 5084
N.A.I.C.S.: 423830

ANDRITZ FEED & BIOFUEL A/S (1)
Glentevej 5
6705 Esbjerg, Denmark
Tel.: (45) 72 160 300
Fax: (45) 72 160 301
E-Mail: andritz-fb@andritz.com
Web Site: www.andritz.com
Emp.: 200
Feed & Biofuel Processing Equipment Distr
S.I.C.: 5084
N.A.I.C.S.: 423830
Jari Algars *(CEO)*

ANDRITZ FEED & BIOFUEL A/S (1)
Av Carlos Sandda c/c Av Andres Eloy Blanco CC Beverly Center
Nivel 2 2 Urb El Vin, Valencia, 2001, Venezuela
Tel.: (58) 241 842 2515
Fax: (58) 241 842 3709
E-Mail: andritz-fb.ve@andritz.com
Web Site: www.andritz.com
Emp.: 6
Industrial Machinery Mfr & Distr
S.I.C.: 3559
N.A.I.C.S.: 333249

ANDRITZ FEED & BIOFUEL A/S (1)
No 35 1A Street Binh Tri Dong B Ward
Binh Tan District, Ho Chi Minh City, Vietnam
Tel.: (84) 8 6253943 4
Fax: (84) 8 62539436
E-Mail: rep.office@aspvietnam.com
Web Site: www.andritz.com
Emp.: 10
Industrial Machinery Mfr & Distr
S.I.C.: 3559
N.A.I.C.S.: 333249
Quy Ninh Le *(Office Mgr)*

ANDRITZ FEED & BIOFUEL B.V. (1)
Spaarpot 112
5667 KZ Geldrop, Netherlands
Tel.: (31) 40 262 7777
Fax: (31) 40 262 7751
E-Mail: andritz-fb.nl@andritz.com
Web Site: reports.andritz.com
Emp.: 120
Industrial Machinery Distr
S.I.C.: 5084
N.A.I.C.S.: 423830
Christ van den Hoven *(Gen Mgr)*

Andritz Feed & Biofuel Ltd. (1)
Stockholm Road Sutton Fields
Industrial Estate, Hull, HU7 0XL, United Kingdom (100%)
Tel.: (44) 1482825119
Fax: (44) 1482839806
E-Mail: andritz-fb.uk@andritz.com
Emp.: 23
Feed Milling
S.I.C.: 2046
N.A.I.C.S.: 311221
David Tattersfield *(Gen Mgr)*

ANDRITZ FEED & BIOFUEL Mexico (1)
Constitucion No 464 Entre Hidalgo y Bravo Col Centro
91700 Veracruz, Mexico
Tel.: (52) 229 178 3669
Fax: (52) 229 178 3671
E-Mail: andritz-fb.mx@andritz.com
Farm Machinery Mfr & Whslr
S.I.C.: 3523
N.A.I.C.S.: 333111

ANDRITZ FEED & BIOFUEL (1)
Industriestrasse 15A
40822 Mettmann, Germany
Tel.: (49) 2104 9197 0
Fax: (49) 2104 1205 4
E-Mail: andritz-fb.de@andritz.com
Industrial Machinery Distr
S.I.C.: 5084
N.A.I.C.S.: 423830

Andritz Fiber Drying Ltd. (1)
2260 32nd Ave
Lachine, QC, H8T 3H4, Canada (100%)
Tel.: (514) 631-7700
Fax: (514) 631-8355
Web Site: www.andritz.com
Emp.: 60
Paper Treatment Systems
S.I.C.: 3589
N.A.I.C.S.: 333318
Wolfgang Leitner *(Pres & CEO)*

ANDRITZ Fiedler GmbH (1)
Weidener Strasse 9
93057 Regensburg, Germany
Tel.: (49) 941 6401 0
Fax: (49) 941 6241 4
E-Mail: andritz-fiedler@andritz.com
Emp.: 27
Industrial Machinery Mfr
S.I.C.: 3559
N.A.I.C.S.: 333249
Matthias Muller *(Gen Mgr)*

ANDRITZ Fliessbett Systeme GmbH (1)
Goethestrasse 36
88214 Ravensburg, Germany
Tel.: (49) 751 56058 0
Fax: (49) 75 15 60 58 930
E-Mail: separation.ce@andritz.com
Emp.: 4
Fluid Bed System Mfr
S.I.C.: 3492
N.A.I.C.S.: 332912

ANDRITZ Frautech S.r.l. (1)
Via Ravizza 58
20149 Milan, Italy
Tel.: (39) 02 574 3011
Fax: (39) 02 5681425
E-Mail: separation.it@andritz.com
Web Site: www.andritz.com
Emp.: 5
Industrial Machinery & Equipment Mfr & Distr
S.I.C.: 3559
N.A.I.C.S.: 333249

ANDRITZ HYDRO AB (1)
Vaplans Vag 29
PO Box 1
Nalden, 835 05 Krokom, Sweden
Tel.: (46) 640 177 00
Fax: (46) 640 177 80
E-Mail: contact-hydro.se@andritz.com
Emp.: 145
Industrial Machinery Mfr & Distr
S.I.C.: 3559
N.A.I.C.S.: 333249
Roger Nojdh *(Gen Mgr)*

ANDRITZ HYDRO AG ABMB Bulach (1)
Feldstrasse 60
8180 Bulach, Switzerland
Tel.: (41) 44 864 4700
Fax: (41) 44 864 4703
E-Mail: paperfinishing-coating@andritz.com
Web Site: www.andritz.com
Coating & Drying Machinery Mfr
S.I.C.: 3559
N.A.I.C.S.: 333249

ANDRITZ HYDRO AS (1)
Bergermoen
3520 Jevnaker, Norway
Tel.: (47) 61 315 200
Fax: (47) 61 312846
E-Mail: contact-hydro.no@andritz.com
Emp.: 16
Hydro Power Plant Machinery Mfr
S.I.C.: 3559
N.A.I.C.S.: 333249
Erik Pike *(Gen Mgr)*

ANDRITZ HYDRO C.A. (1)
Avenida la Estancia Torre las Mercedes Piso 6 Of 606
Chuao, 1060 Caracas, Venezuela
Tel.: (58) 212 9919159
Fax: (58) 212 9928720
E-Mail: contact-hydro.ve@andritz.com
Industrial Machinery Distr
S.I.C.: 5084
N.A.I.C.S.: 423830

ANDRITZ HYDRO GmbH (1)
Uliza Artema 60 Office 306
4053 Kiev, Ukraine
Tel.: (380) 44 4843939
Fax: (380) 44 4861665
E-Mail: admin@uie.kiev.ua
Electromechanical Equipment Distr
S.I.C.: 5065
N.A.I.C.S.: 423690

ANDRITZ HYDRO GmbH (1)
108 Trieu Viet Vuong Street Hai Ba
Hanoi, Vietnam
Tel.: (84) 4 394 54 765
E-Mail: contact-hydro.vn@andritz.com
Industrial Machinery Distr
S.I.C.: 5084
N.A.I.C.S.: 423830

ANDRITZ HYDRO GmbH (1)
Escher-Wyss-Weg 1
88212 Ravensburg, Germany
Tel.: (49) 751 295 11 0
Fax: (49) 751 295 11 999
E-Mail: contact-hydro.de@andritz.com
Web Site: www.andritz-hydro.de
Emp.: 50
Electromechanical Equipment Mfr & Distr
S.I.C.: 3568
N.A.I.C.S.: 333613
Rudi Resch *(Gen Mgr)*

ANDRITZ HYDRO, Inc. (1)
Unit 3004 88 Corporate Center 141 Valero Street Corner Sedeno St
Salcedo Village, 1227 Makati, Manila, Philippines
Tel.: (63) 2 50150 93
Fax: (63) 2 50150 96
E-Mail: contact-hydro.ph@andritz.com
Hydraulic Power Generation Services
S.I.C.: 4931
N.A.I.C.S.: 221111
May Mercado *(Sec)*

ANDRITZ HYDRO Ltda. (1)
Cra 67 No 100-20 Piso 9
93228 Bogota, Colombia
Tel.: (57) 1 7448200
Fax: (57) 1 7448200

Andritz AG—(Continued)

E-Mail: contact-hydro.co@andritz.com
Industrial Machinery Distr
S.I.C.: 5084
N.A.I.C.S.: 423830

ANDRITZ HYDRO Ltd. Sti. (1)
Hollanda Caddesi 695 Sokak No 1 Hilal Mah
Cankaya, 06550 Ankara, Turkey
Tel.: (90) 312 4088 000
Fax: (90) 312 442 0691
E-Mail: contact-hydro.tr@andritz.com
Web Site: www.andritz.com
Emp.: 60
Industrial Machinery Distr
S.I.C.: 5084
N.A.I.C.S.: 423830
Wolfgang Hofmann *(Mng Dir)*

ANDRITZ HYDRO Ltee/Ltd. (1)
390 Sherbrooke
Lachine, QC, H8S 1G4, Canada
Tel.: (514) 428-6843
Fax: (514) 428-6901
E-Mail: contact-hydro.ca@andritz.com
Web Site: www.andritz.com
Industrial Machinery Distr
S.I.C.: 5084
N.A.I.C.S.: 423830

ANDRITZ HYDRO S.A. de C.V. (1)
Av Ciudad Industrial No 977 Col Ciudad Industrial
58200 Morelia, Michoacan, Mexico
Tel.: (52) 443 323 1530
Fax: (52) 443 323 1538
E-Mail: contact-hydro.mx@andritz.com
Web Site: www.andritz.com
Industrial Machinery Mfr
S.I.C.: 3559
N.A.I.C.S.: 333249

ANDRITZ HYDRO S.A. (1)
Centro Comercial y Empresarial El Polo II Oficina C 304
Avenida El Polo 670, Lima, Peru
Tel.: (51) 1 434 33 33
Fax: (51) 1 564 8202
E-Mail: contact-hydro.pe@andritz.com
Industrial Machinery Distr
S.I.C.: 5084
N.A.I.C.S.: 423830

ANDRITZ HYDRO SA (1)
Rue des Deux Gares 6
1800 Vevey, Switzerland
Tel.: (41) 21 925 7700
Fax: (41) 21 925 7703
E-Mail: contact-hydro.ch@andritz.com
Web Site: www.andritz.com
Emp.: 90
Electromechanical Equipment Distr
S.I.C.: 5065
N.A.I.C.S.: 423690
Roland Cuenod *(Gen Mgr)*

ANDRITZ HYDRO S.A.S. (1)
49-51 Boulevard Paul Langevin
38601 Fontaine, France
Tel.: (33) 476 859 523
Fax: (33) 476 859 698
E-Mail: contact.hydro.fr@andritz.com
Web Site: www.andritz.com
Emp.: 50
Hydro Electric Power Generation Services
S.I.C.: 4911
N.A.I.C.S.: 221111

ANDRITZ HYDRO S.L. (1)
Carretera M-106 KM 2
28046 Madrid, Algete, Spain
Tel.: (34) 91 425 1000
Fax: (34) 91 425 1001
E-Mail: contact-hydro.es@andritz.com
Emp.: 10
Hydraulic Power Generation Equipment Distr
S.I.C.: 5084
N.A.I.C.S.: 423830

ANDRITZ HYDRO S.r.l. Unipersonale (1)
Via Daniele Manin 16/18
36015 Schio, Vicenza, Italy
Tel.: (39) 0445 678 211
Fax: (39) 0445 678 218
E-Mail: contact-hydro.it@andritz.com
Web Site: www.andritz.com
Industrial Machinery Mfr
S.I.C.: 3559
N.A.I.C.S.: 333249

ANDRITZ HYDRO s.r.o. (1)
Ceskobrodska 108n
PO Box 8
130 04 Prague, Czech Republic
Tel.: (420) 2 84 028 411
Fax: (420) 2 84824 313
E-Mail: martin.cejka@andritz.com
Web Site: www.andritz.com
Emp.: 25
Electromechanical Equipment Distr
S.I.C.: 5084
N.A.I.C.S.: 423830
John Matthews *(Mng Dir)*

ANDRITZ Iggesund Tools AB (1)
Forsavagen 7
PO Box 6
825 21 Iggesund, Sweden
Tel.: (46) 650 29100
Fax: (46) 650 291 70
E-Mail: sweden@iggesundtools.com
Web Site: www.iggesundtools.com
Emp.: 10
Industrial Tool Mfr
S.I.C.: 3545
N.A.I.C.S.: 333515
Torbjoern Baecklund *(Gen Mgr)*

ANDRITZ Iggesund Tools Canada Inc. (1)
1405 Stevens Road 10
Kelowna, BC, V1Z 3Y2, Canada
Tel.: (250) 769-1288
Web Site: www.andritz.com
Industrial Machine Tool Mfr
S.I.C.: 3542
N.A.I.C.S.: 333517

ANDRITZ India Private Limited (1)
CB-14 Sector-1 Salt Lake Commercial Complex Salt Lake
Salt Lake, Kolkata, 700064, India
Tel.: (91) 33 23212239
Fax: (91) 33 23211595
E-Mail: contact@andritzindia.com
Emp.: 2
Hydro Electric Power Generation Services
S.I.C.: 4931
N.A.I.C.S.: 221111
Mahadevan Anand *(Mng Dir)*

Andritz Ingenieria S.A. (1)
PO Box 1017
Hospitalet de Llobregat, 08902 Barcelona, Spain
Tel.: (34) 932988598
Fax: (34) 934325997
E-Mail: pulpandpaper.es@andritz.com
Web Site: www.andritz.com
Emp.: 7
Mfr. of Equipment for the Pulp & Paper Industry
S.I.C.: 3553
N.A.I.C.S.: 333243
Anssi Marttila *(Area Mgr)*

ANDRITZ Jochman s.r.o. (1)
Radlinskeho 19
052 01 Spisska Nova Ves, Slovakia
Tel.: (421) 53 4198 111
Fax: (421) 53 4198 122
E-Mail: separation.sk@andritz.com
Emp.: 70
Industrial Steel Machinery Mfr
S.I.C.: 3559
N.A.I.C.S.: 333249
Milos Jochman *(Gen Mgr)*

ANDRITZ Kaiser GmbH (1)
Gewerbestrasse 30
Golshausen, 75015 Bretten, Germany
Tel.: (49) 7252 910 01
Fax: (49) 7252 910 199
E-Mail: andritz.kaiser@andritz.com
Web Site: www.andritz.com
Punching & Metal Forming Presses Mfr
S.I.C.: 3541
N.A.I.C.S.: 333517

ANDRITZ Kft. (1)
Dozsa Telep 69
6060 Tiszakecske, Hungary
Tel.: (36) 76 542 100
Fax: (36) 76 542 199
E-Mail: infoandritzkft@andritz.com
Emp.: 40
Electric Power Equipment Mfr
S.I.C.: 3511
N.A.I.C.S.: 333611
Karoly Mezei *(Mng Dir)*

ANDRITZ K.K. (1)
Harumi Island Triton Square Office Tower Z 29F 1-8-12
Harumi, Tokyo, 104-6229, Japan
Tel.: (81) 3 3536 9700
Fax: (81) 3 3536 9750
E-Mail: pulpandpaper.jp@andritz.com
Web Site: www.andritz.com
Emp.: 50
Pulp & Paper Industry Machinery Distr
S.I.C.: 3554
N.A.I.C.S.: 333243

ANDRITZ KMPT GmbH (1)
Industriestrasse 1-3
Vierkirchen, Germany
Tel.: (49) 8139 80299 902
E-Mail: kmpt@andritz.com
Web Site: www.andritz.com
Solid & Liquid Separation Machinery Mfr
S.I.C.: 3559
N.A.I.C.S.: 333249

Andritz Kuesters GmbH (1)
Eduard Kuesters Strasse 1
D 47805 Krefeld, Germany
Tel.: (49) 2151340
Fax: (49) 2151341206
E-Mail: kuesters.nonwoven@andritz.com
Web Site: www.kuesters.com
Emp.: 400
Nonwoven & Paper Finishing Machines Mfr Export
S.I.C.: 2297
N.A.I.C.S.: 313230
Andreas Lucas *(CEO)*

ANDRITZ Kufferath GmbH (1)
Lommessemstrasse 32-36
52353 Duren, Germany
Tel.: (49) 2421 801 104
Fax: (49) 2421 801 215
E-Mail: kufferath@andritz.com
Web Site: www.kufferath.com
Forming Fabric Mfr & Distr
S.I.C.: 2676
N.A.I.C.S.: 322291
Stefan Schreiner *(Gen Mgr)*

ANDRITZ Kufferath s.r.o. (1)
Ku Bratke 5
934 05 Levice, Slovakia
Tel.: (421) 36 6356 324
Fax: (421) 36 6314 596
E-Mail: kufferath@kufferathlv.sk
Web Site: www.kufferath.com
Emp.: 79
Paper Industry Fabric Mfr & Distr
S.I.C.: 2295
N.A.I.C.S.: 313320

Andritz Ltd./Ltee. (1)
2600 Wentz Avenue
Saskatoon, SK, S7K 2L1, Canada
Tel.: (306) 931-0801
Fax: (514) 631-3995
E-Mail: separation.ca@andritz.com
Industrial Equipment Distr
S.I.C.: 5084
N.A.I.C.S.: 423830

ANDRITZ Ltd. (1)
Suite 5L North Mill Bridgefoot
Belper, Derbyshire, DE56 1YD, United Kingdom
Tel.: (44) 1773 599 540
Fax: (44) 1773 599 541
E-Mail: SeparationUK@andritz.com
Web Site: www.andritz.com
Solid & Liquid Separation Machinery Mfr
S.I.C.: 3559
N.A.I.C.S.: 333249

Andritz MAERZ GmbH (1)
Corneliusstrasse 36
D-40215 Dusseldorf, Germany De
Mailing Address: (100%)
PO Box 103642
40027 Dusseldorf, Germany
Tel.: (49) 211384250
Fax: (49) 2113842520
E-Mail: welcome-maerz@andritz.com
Web Site: www.andritz-maerz.com
Emp.: 40
Industrial Furnace Designer, Mfr & Installation
S.I.C.: 3567
N.A.I.C.S.: 333994

Andritz Oy (1)
Tammasaarenkatu 1
00180 Helsinki, Finland FI
Tel.: (358) 204505555
Fax: (358) 204505109
E-Mail: markku.hanninen@andritz.com
Web Site: www.andritz.fi
Emp.: 60
Design & Engineering of Heat Recovery for the Pulp & Paper Industry
S.I.C.: 8711
N.A.I.C.S.: 541330

Subsidiary:

Savonlinna Works Oy (2)
Lypsyniemenkatu 5
57100 Savonlinna, Finland FI
Tel.: (358) 204506000 (100%)
Telex: 5613 alsav sf
Fax: (358) 204506239
Supplier of Equipment Specializing in Chemical & Heat Recovery for the Pulp & Paper Industry
S.I.C.: 2899
N.A.I.C.S.: 325998
Kaj Lindh *(Mng Dir)*

ANDRITZ Perfojet S.A.S. (1)
ZA Pre-Milliet 530 Rue Aristide Berges
38330 Montbonnot-Saint-Martin, France
Tel.: (33) 4 7652 2311
Fax: (33) 4 7652 2173
E-Mail: perfojet@andritz.com
Industrial Equipment Mfr
S.I.C.: 3559
N.A.I.C.S.: 333249

ANDRITZ Power Sdn. Bhd. (1)
A-9-2D Block A Plaza Mont Kiara 2 Jalan Mont Kiara
Mont Kiara, 50480 Kuala Lumpur, Malaysia
Tel.: (60) 3 6201 1741
Fax: (60) 3 6201 2758
E-Mail: contact-hydro.my@andritz.com
Emp.: 87
Electric Power Generation Services
S.I.C.: 4931
N.A.I.C.S.: 221118
Michael Kalum Moggie *(Gen Mgr)*

ANDRITZ Pty. Ltd. (1)
Suite 13 2nd Floor Granada Centre 22 Chartwell Drive
Umhlanga, 4319 Durban, South Africa
Tel.: (27) 31 561 7271
Fax: (27) 31 561 6265
E-Mail: pulpandpaper.za@andritz.com
Emp.: 50
Pulp & Paper Machinery Whslr
S.I.C.: 5084
N.A.I.C.S.: 423830
Garry Hugh *(Gen Mgr)*

ANDRITZ Ritz GmbH (1)
Guglingstrasse 50
73529 Schwabisch Gmund, Germany
Tel.: (49) 7171 609 0
Fax: (49) 7171 609 287
E-Mail: ritz@andritz.com
Emp.: 20
Centrifugal Pump & Motor Mfr
S.I.C.: 3561
N.A.I.C.S.: 333911
Rainer Schoeller *(Mng Dir)*

ANDRITZ Selas S.A.S. (1)
4 Avenue Laurent Cely Hall A
92600 Asnieres-sur-Seine, France
Tel.: (33) 1 4080 3400
Fax: (33) 1 4080 3438
E-Mail: welcome.selas@andritz.com
Emp.: 35
Industrial Furnace Distr
S.I.C.: 5084
N.A.I.C.S.: 423830
Jurgan Ziemendorff *(Pres)*

Andritz Selas UK Ltd. (1)
Suite 5L Business Centre
North Mill
Bridgefoot, Belper, Derbyshire, DE56 1YD, United Kingdom
Tel.: (44) 1773 829 954
Fax: (44) 1773 829 985
E-Mail: welcome@andritzselas.com
Web Site: www.andritz.com

Emp.: 2
Mfg., Designing, Developing & Engineering of Selas-Heat Processing Equipment, Deuer-Spare Tire Holders & Lifts; Resistance Technology, Microminiature Components & Molded Plastic Parts for Hearing Instruments
S.I.C.: 3567
N.A.I.C.S.: 333994

ANDRITZ SEPARATION GmbH (1)
Dillenburger Strasse 100
51105 Cologne, Germany
Tel.: (49) 221 9856 0
Fax: (49) 221 9856 202
E-Mail: separation.de@andritz.com
Emp.: 15
Mechanical & Thermal Separation System Mfr
S.I.C.: 3589
N.A.I.C.S.: 333318
Markus Ostwald *(Gen Mgr)*

ANDRITZ SEPARATION (India) Private Ltd. (1)
No 6 Vanagaram Road
Ayyanambakkam, Chennai, 600 095, India
Tel.: (91) 44 4399 1111
Fax: (91) 44 2653 5103
E-Mail: separation.in@andritz.com
Web Site: www.andritz.com
Emp.: 70
Industrial Machinery Mfr
S.I.C.: 3559
N.A.I.C.S.: 333249
Robert Stantish *(Mng Dir)*

ANDRITZ SEPARATION Industria e Comercio de Equipamentos de Filtracao Ltda. (1)
Rua Progresso 450
Pomerode, 89107-000, 89107-000, Brazil
Tel.: (55) 47 3387 9100
Fax: (55) 47 3387 9103
E-Mail: separation.bra@andritz.com
Web Site: www.andritz.com
Emp.: 150
Liquid Separation Equipment Distr
S.I.C.: 5084
N.A.I.C.S.: 423830

ANDRITZ SEPARATION Ltda. (1)
Rua Tabapua 627 - Conj 92
Itaim Bibi, Sao Paulo, 04533-012, Brazil
Tel.: (55) 11 2168 0130
Fax: (55) 11 2168 0120
E-Mail: separation.bra@andritz.com
Web Site: www.andritz.com
Emp.: 5
Liquid Separation Machinery Distr
S.I.C.: 5084
N.A.I.C.S.: 423830
Miguel Brito *(Mgr-Sls)*

ANDRITZ SEPARATION (1)
2600 Wentz Avenue
Saskatoon, SK, S7K 2L1, Canada
Tel.: (306) 931-0801
Fax: (306) 931-2442
E-Mail: separation.ca@andritz.com
Web Site: www.andritz.com
Emp.: 45
Industrial Machinery Equipment Distr
S.I.C.: 5084
N.A.I.C.S.: 423830
Minoru Moriwaki *(Gen Mgr)*

ANDRITZ Singapore Pte. Ltd. (1)
Unit 4B MB Aguirre Building III F Reyes St
Balibago Santa Rosa
Laguna, Manila, 4026, Philippines
Tel.: (63) 2 420 8182
Fax: (63) 49 534 3060
E-Mail: separation.sg@andritz.com
Industrial Machinery Distr
S.I.C.: 5084
N.A.I.C.S.: 423830

ANDRITZ Singapore Pte. Ltd. (1)
25 Tuas Ave 4
Singapore, 639375, Singapore
Tel.: (65) 6512 1800
Fax: (65) 6863 4482
E-Mail: separation.sg@andritz.com
Emp.: 5
Industrial Machinery Mfr
S.I.C.: 3559
N.A.I.C.S.: 333249
Matthias Zick *(Mng Dir)*

ANDRITZ S.R.L. (1)
Transilvaniei No 21
555300 Cisnadie, Sibiu, Romania
Tel.: (40) 269 206 053
Fax: (40) 269 561 727
E-Mail: lenser.ro@andritz.com
Web Site: www.lenser.ro
Emp.: 5
Filter Equipment Mfr
S.I.C.: 3564
N.A.I.C.S.: 333413
Cristi Fodor *(Dir Gen)*

ANDRITZ Sundwig GmbH (1)
Stephanopeler Strasse 22
58675 Hemer, Germany
Tel.: (49) 2372 540
Fax: (49) 2372 54200
E-Mail: sundwig_welcome@andritz.com
Emp.: 30
Industrial Machinery Mfr & Distr
S.I.C.: 3559
N.A.I.C.S.: 333249
Paul Krecker *(Gen Mgr)*

ANDRITZ Talcahuano (1)
Av Gran Bretana 4889 Lote A-15 Parque Empresarial Bio-Bio
4290319 Talcahuano, Chile
Tel.: (56) 41 243 4740
Fax: (56) 41 243 44715
E-Mail: service.cl@andritz.com
Web Site: www.andritz.com
Emp.: 30
Pulp Machinery Equipment Whslr
S.I.C.: 5084
N.A.I.C.S.: 423830
Harri Soila *(Gen Mgr)*

ANDRITZ Technologies Pvt. Ltd. (1)
Magnolia Block B Level 4 Manyata Embassy Business Park Outer Ring Road
Nagawara, Bengaluru, 560 045, India
Tel.: (91) 80 2544 4640
E-Mail: atech@andritz.com
Emp.: 12
Industrial Machinery Mfr
S.I.C.: 3559
N.A.I.C.S.: 333249
Suresh Chandra *(Gen Mgr)*

ANDRITZ (Thailand) Ltd. (1)
Lake Rajada Office Complex Unit 22 E
193/96 Ratchadaphisek Road
Klongtoey, Bangkok, 10110, Thailand
Tel.: (66) 2 264 0488
Fax: (66) 2 264 0499
E-Mail: bangkok.office@andritz.com
Web Site: www.andritz.com
Emp.: 5
Industrial Machinery & Equipment Distr
S.I.C.: 5084
N.A.I.C.S.: 423830

ANDRITZ THERMTEC B.V. (1)
Wijnhaven 76
3011 WT Rotterdam, Netherlands
Tel.: (31) 10 280 1660
Fax: (31) 10 404 7356
E-Mail: welcome.thermtec@andritz.com
Emp.: 3
Industrial Furnace Distr
S.I.C.: 5084
N.A.I.C.S.: 423830
Rodney Verkaart *(Gen Mgr)*

PT. ANDRITZ HYDRO (1)
Jl Talang No 3 Pegangsaan
Menteng, Jakarta, 10320, Indonesia
Tel.: (62) 21 390 6929
Fax: (62) 21 390 5006
E-Mail: contact-hydro.id@andritz.com
Electromechanical Equipment Distr
S.I.C.: 5065
N.A.I.C.S.: 423690

PT. Andritz (1)
VA Tech Building 3rd Floor Jl Talang No 3 Pegangsaan
Jakarta, 10320, Indonesia
Tel.: (62) 21 3905001
E-Mail:
Web Site: www.andritz.com
Marketing & Sales of Equipment & Machinery for the Pulp & Paper Industry
S.I.C.: 2611
N.A.I.C.S.: 322110

ANDRY MONTGOMERY LTD.
(d/b/a Montgomery Group)
9 Manchester Sq
London, W1U 3PL, United Kingdom
Tel.: (44) 2078863000
Fax: (44) 2078863001
E-Mail: info@montex.co.uk
Web Site: www.montex.co.uk
Sales Range: $10-24.9 Million
Emp.: 20

Business Description:
Holding Company; Trade Show Organizer
S.I.C.: 6719
N.A.I.C.S.: 551112

Personnel:
Sandy Angus *(Chm)*

Holding:

Montgomery Exhibitions Ltd. (1)
9 Manchester Square
London, W1U 3PL, United Kingdom UK
Tel.: (44) 2078863000
Fax: (44) 2078863001
E-Mail: mel@montex.co.uk
Web Site: www.montex.co.uk
Emp.: 30
Trade Show Organizer
S.I.C.: 7389
N.A.I.C.S.: 561920
Christopher Newton *(Chm)*
George Tsangari *(Sec)*

Division:

Exhibition Consultants Ltd. (2)
9 Manchester Square
London, W1U 3PL, United Kingdom UK
Tel.: (44) 2078863000
Fax: (44) 2078863081
E-Mail: ecl@montex.co.uk
Web Site: www.exhibitionconsultants.com
Emp.: 4
Exhibition Management Consultancy Services
S.I.C.: 8748
N.A.I.C.S.: 541618
Ian Angus *(Chm)*

Non-U.S. Subsidiary:

Specialised Exhibitions (Pty.) Limited (2)
IHS South Africa Bldg Cnr Northern Pkwy & Handel Rd
Ormonde Extension 5, Johannesburg, 2091, South Africa ZA
Mailing Address:
PO Box 82196
Southdale, 2135, South Africa
Tel.: (27) 118351565
Fax: (27) 114961161
E-Mail: specialised@specialised.com
Web Site: www.specialised.com
Emp.: 300
Trade Show Organizer
S.I.C.: 7389
N.A.I.C.S.: 561920
John Kaplan *(Mng Dir)*

ANDULELA INVESTMENT HOLDINGS LIMITED
108 4th street
Parkmore, Sandton, 2196, South Africa
Mailing Address:
PO Box 786 786
Sandton, 2146, South Africa
Tel.: (27) 11 888 8888
Fax: (27) 11 883 2523
E-Mail: info@andulelaholdings.com
Web Site: www.andulelaholdings.com
Year Founded: 1950
AND—(JSE)
Rev.: $164,419,272
Assets: $115,764,986
Liabilities: $63,164,786
Net Worth: $52,600,200
Earnings: ($5,572,266)
Emp.: 461
Fiscal Year-end: 12/31/12

Business Description:
Investment Management Services
S.I.C.: 6799
N.A.I.C.S.: 523920

Personnel:
Ashruf Kaka *(CEO)*
Johannes H. P. Engelbrecht *(CFO)*
Humeira I. Kazi *(Sec)*

Board of Directors:
Mohamed J. Husain
Pieter C. de Jager
Pieter E. du Preez
Johannes H. P. Engelbrecht
Ashruf Kaka
Humeira I. Kazi
Nosipho C.W. Molope
Graham R. Rosenthal

Legal Counsel:
Glyn Marais Incorporated
2nd Floor The Place 1 Sandton Drive
Sandton, South Africa

Transfer Agent:
Link Market Services (Proprietary) Limited
13th Floor Rennie House 19 Ameshoff Street
Braamfontein, 2001, South Africa

ANEK LINES SA
Karamanlis Avenue
73100 Chania, Crete, Greece
Tel.: (30) 2821024000
Fax: (30) 2821027611
E-Mail: anek@anek.gr
Web Site: www.anek.gr
ANEK—(ATH)
Sls.: $268,799,187
Assets: $528,398,648
Liabilities: $465,975,399
Net Worth: $62,423,249
Earnings: ($81,534,825)
Emp.: 907
Fiscal Year-end: 12/31/12

Business Description:
Shipping Transportation & Communication Services
S.I.C.: 4481
N.A.I.C.S.: 483112

Personnel:
Irineos Galanakis *(Chm)*
Georgios Archontakis *(Third Vice Chm)*
Georgios Katsanevakis *(Vice Chm)*
Spiros Protopapadakis *(Second Vice Chm)*
Yannis S. Vardinoyiannis *(Mng Dir)*
Stylianos I. Stamos *(CFO)*
Aristotle Balis *(Deputy Mng Dir)*

Board of Directors:
Irineos Galanakis
Emmanouel Apostolakis
Georgios Archontakis
Aristotle Balis
Georgios Baourakis
Emmanouel Galanakis
Michael Georvasakis
Dimitrios Kantilierakis
Georgios Katsanevakis
Michael Marakakis
Georgios Marinakis
Evagelos Mpairaktaris
Spiros Protopapadakis
Emmanouel Skoulakis
Yannis S. Vardinoyiannis

Crowe Horwath International
3 Fok Negri Street
112 57 Athens, Greece

Subsidiaries:

CHAMPION FERRIES L.T.D. (1)
63 Dragatsaniou Str
18545 Piraeus, Greece
Tel.: (30) 2104619106
Fax: (30) 2104619315
E-Mail: info@championferries.gr
Web Site: www.championferries.gr
Emp.: 14
Shipping Agency Services
S.I.C.: 4731
N.A.I.C.S.: 488510
Kostas Valantasis *(Gen Mgr)*

Anek Lines SA—(Continued)

LEFKA ORI S.A. (1)
Stylos Apokoronou
Kalyves, 73003 Chania, Greece
Tel.: (30) 2825083310
Fax: (30) 2825083312
E-Mail: info@etanap.gr
Web Site: www.etanap.gr
Emp.: 30
Plastic Bottles Mfr
S.I.C.: 3085
N.A.I.C.S.: 326160
Emmanouil Apostolakis *(Mng Dir)*

ANEL ELECTRICAL PROJECT CONTRACTING TRADE INC.

Anel Business Center Saray Mah Site
Yolu Sokak No 5/4
Umraniye, 34768 Istanbul, Turkey
Tel.: (90) 216 636 20 00
Fax: (90) 216 636 25 00
E-Mail: bilgi@anel.com.tr
Web Site: www.anel-elektrik.com
Year Founded: 1986
ANELE—(IST)
Sales Range: $200-249.9 Million
Emp.: 1,193
Business Description:
Engineering Services
S.I.C.: 8711
N.A.I.C.S.: 541330
Personnel:
Ridvan Celikel *(Chm)*
Avniye Mukaddes Celikel *(Vice Chm)*
Cem Ozsen *(CFO)*
Board of Directors:
Ridvan Celikel
Ahmet Bulent Batukan
Avniye Mukaddes Celikel
Mahir Kerem Celikel
Merve Sirin Celikel
Cahit Duzel
Ahmet Munir Ekonomi

ANERGY CAPITAL INC.

600 666 Burrard Street
Vancouver, BC, V6C 2X8, Canada
Tel.: (778) 785-0321
Fax: (604) 648-8031
E-Mail: anergyinfo@anergy.ca
Year Founded: 2008
ACA.P—(TSXV)
Int. Income: $1,057
Assets: $207,740
Liabilities: $37,459
Net Worth: $170,281
Earnings: ($47,737)
Fiscal Year-end: 09/30/12
Business Description:
Investment Services
S.I.C.: 6211
N.A.I.C.S.: 523999
Personnel:
Harley Sinclair *(Pres, CEO & CFO)*
Board of Directors:
Eugene Beukman
Lisa Payne
Harley Sinclair
Transfer Agent:
Computershare Investor Services Inc.
3rd Floor 510 Burrard Street
Vancouver, BC, Canada

ANESCO LIMITED

The Green Easter Park Benyon Road
Reading, Berkshire, RG7 2PQ,
United Kingdom
Tel.: (44) 845 894 4444
E-Mail: info@anesco.co.uk
Web Site: www.anesco.co.uk
Year Founded: 2008
Sales Range: $25-49.9 Million
Emp.: 54
Business Description:
Energy Efficiency Consultancy
Services
S.I.C.: 7389
N.A.I.C.S.: 541350
Personnel:
Steve Shine *(Chm)*
Adrian Pike *(CEO)*
Hedley Mayor *(CFO)*
Tim Payne *(COO)*
Jeremy Cross *(Sec)*
Board of Directors:
Steve Shine
Paul Dowling
Gary Le Sueur
David Sneddon

ANEST IWATA CORPORATION

3176 Shinyoshida-cho Kohoku-ku
Yokohama, 223-8501, Japan
Tel.: (81) 455911111
Fax: (81) 455915962
E-Mail: aijlogi@anest-iwata.co.jp
Web Site: www.anest-iwata.co.jp
Year Founded: 1926
6381—(TKS)
Sales Range: $200-249.9 Million
Emp.: 1,001
Business Description:
Air Compressors, Air Pressure Equipment, Air Driven Equipment, Vacuum Equipment & Systems, Painting Equipment, Liquid Application Equipment & Systems Mfr & Sales
S.I.C.: 3563
N.A.I.C.S.: 333912
Personnel:
Kiyoshi Morimoto *(Chm)*
Takahiro Tsubota *(Pres)*
Shinichi Fukase *(Exec Officer)*
Nobukazu Kamehara *(Exec Officer)*
Masato Suzuki *(Exec Officer)*
Shinya Tsukamoto *(Exec Officer)*
Marco G. Vicentini *(Exec Officer)*
Board of Directors:
Kiyoshi Morimoto
Akira Hirase
Toshiyuki Iida
Hiroshi Koga
Atsumi Machida
Takahiro Tsubota

U.S. Subsidiaries:

Anest Iwata-Medea Inc (1)
1336 N Mason
Portland, OR 97217
Tel.: (503) 253-7308
Fax: (503) 253-0721
E-Mail: info@iwata-medea.com
Web Site: www.iwata-medea.com
Airbrush Materials Distr
S.I.C.: 5085
N.A.I.C.S.: 423840
Gary Glass *(Pres)*

Anest Iwata Usa Inc (1)
5325 Muhlhauser Rd
West Chester, OH 45011
Tel.: (513) 755-3100
Fax: (513) 755-0888
E-Mail: inquiry@anestiwata.com
Web Site: www.anestiwata.com
Air Compressor Mfr
S.I.C.: 3563
N.A.I.C.S.: 333912
Satoru Iwata *(Pres)*

Non-U.S. Subsidiaries:

Air Gunsa S.r.l (1)
Via Degli Aceri 1
Cardano al Campo, Varese, 21010, Italy
Tel.: (39) 0331733120
Fax: (39) 0331262338
E-Mail: info@anest-iwataeu.com
Web Site: www.anest-iwataeu.com
Emp.: 25
Air Compressor & Vacuum Pump Mfr
S.I.C.: 3563
N.A.I.C.S.: 333912
Vicentini Marco *(Mgr-Europe)*

Anest Iwata Australia Pty Ltd (1)
Unit 3 10 Boden Road
Seven Hills, NSW, 2147, Australia
Tel.: (61) 2 9853 2000
Fax: (61) 2 9853 2090
E-Mail: info@anest-iwata.com.au
Web Site: www.anest-iwata.com.au
Emp.: 15
Automotive Coatings Distr
S.I.C.: 5198
N.A.I.C.S.: 424950
Karl Isherwood *(Gen Mgr)*

Anest Iwata Deutschland GmbH (1)
Mommsenstrasse 5
4329 Leipzig, Germany
Tel.: (49) 3412414430
Fax: (49) 34125595
E-Mail: info@anest-iwata.de
Web Site: www.anest-iwata.de
Air Compressor & Vacuum Pump Mfr
S.I.C.: 3563
N.A.I.C.S.: 333912
Marco G. Vicentini *(Gen Mgr)*

ANEST IWATA (DONGGUAN) Corporation (1)
6 Jin Song Road Quan Tang Zone Liao Bu Town
523425 Dongguan, Guandong, China
Tel.: (86) 76981100612
Fax: (86) 76981100523
Web Site: www.anest-iwata.co.jp/english/company/network/overseas.html
Air Compressor Equipment Distr
S.I.C.: 5075
N.A.I.C.S.: 423730
Osawa Kenichi *(Gen Mgr)*

Anest Iwata Europe S.r.l (1)
Corso Vigevano 46
10155 Turin, Italy
Tel.: (39) 0112480868
Fax: (39) 011 85 19 44
E-Mail: info@anest-iwataeu.com
Web Site: www.anest-iwataeu.com
Air Compressor Distr
S.I.C.: 5084
N.A.I.C.S.: 423830

ANEST IWATA France S.A. (1)
25 Rue De Madrid
38070 Saint-Quentin-Fallavier, France
Tel.: (33) 474945969
Fax: (33) 474943439
E-Mail: info@anest-iwata.fr
Web Site: www.anest-iwata.fr
Emp.: 17
Industrial Machinery & Equipment Whslr
S.I.C.: 5084
N.A.I.C.S.: 423830

ANEST IWATA IBERICA S.L. (1)
C/Les Teixidores 3-5
08918 Badalona, Barcelona, Spain
Tel.: (34) 933 205 993
Fax: (34) 933 205 965
E-Mail: info@anest-iwata.es
Web Site: www.anest-iwata.es
Spray Gun & Pump Mfr
S.I.C.: 3546
N.A.I.C.S.: 333991
Santiago Garcia *(Gen Mgr)*

Anest Iwata Italia S.r.l (1)
Corso Vigevano 46
10155 Turin, Italy
Tel.: (39) 011 24 80 868
Fax: (39) 011 85 19 44
E-Mail: info@anest-iwata.it
Web Site: www.anest-iwata.it
Air Compressor Mfr
S.I.C.: 3563
N.A.I.C.S.: 333912

ANEST IWATA Motherson Limited (1)
B 123&124 Sector 63
201301 Noida, India
Tel.: (91) 1206752100
Fax: (91) 1202521866
E-Mail: info@motherson.com
Web Site: www.motherson.com
Emp.: 150
Air & Gas Compressor Mfr
S.I.C.: 3563
N.A.I.C.S.: 333912
Dhrup Mehra *(COO)*

ANEST IWATA Scandinavia Aktierbolag (1)
Ogardesvagen 6C
43330 Partille, Sweden
Tel.: (46) 313402860
Fax: (46) 313402869
Web Site: www.anest-iwata.se
Emp.: 5
Engineering Services
S.I.C.: 8711
N.A.I.C.S.: 541330
Jonas Brick *(Gen Mgr)*

ANEST IWATA SEGI Corporation (1)
148-6 Gajwa-dong Seo-gu
404-250 Incheon, Korea (South)
Tel.: (82) 325780330
Fax: (82) 325786349
E-Mail: jrku@ai-se.co.kr
Web Site: www.ai-se.co.kr/
Emp.: 15
Air & Gas Compressor Mfr
S.I.C.: 3563
N.A.I.C.S.: 333912
Wesely Choi *(Mng Dir)*

ANEST IWATA Shanghai Coating Machinery Co., Ltd. (1)
200 Wan Ping Nan Road
Shanghai, China
Tel.: (86) 2164380190
Fax: (86) 21 6438 4993
Web Site: www.anest-iwata.co.jp/english/company/network/overseas.html
Air Compressor & Vacuum Pump Distr
S.I.C.: 5084
N.A.I.C.S.: 423830

Anest Iwata (Shanghai) Corporation (1)
Room A6130 No 808 Hong Qiao Road
Shanghai, 200030, China
Tel.: (86) 21 6407 9713
Fax: (86) 21 6407 9723
Web Site: www.anest-iwata-sh.com
Industrial Equipment Distr
S.I.C.: 5084
N.A.I.C.S.: 423830

ANEST IWATA Southeast Asia Co., Ltd. (1)
91-1 5A th Floor Chaiyo Building
Room No 5A10 Rama IX Road, Bangkok, Thailand
Tel.: (66) 26432870
Fax: (66) 26432874
E-Mail: hnifhidafianest-iwata@iwata.co.tha
Web Site: www.anest-iwata.co.jp/english/company/network/overseas.html
Emp.: 10
Air & Gas Compressor Mfr
S.I.C.: 3563
N.A.I.C.S.: 333912
Hiroki Nishida *(Mng Dir)*

ANEST IWATA Taiwan Corporation (1)
Sin-Chu Expanding Zone No 31 Kuang Fu North Road
Chung-Hsin Tsun Hu-Kuo, Hsin-chu, Taiwan
Tel.: (886) 35983206
Fax: (886) 35981877
Web Site: www.anest-iwata.co.jp/english/company/network/overseas.html
Emp.: 45
Air & Gas Compressor Mfr
S.I.C.: 3563
N.A.I.C.S.: 333912
Kiyoshi Sato *(Mng Dir)*

Anest Iwata (U.K.) Ltd. (1)
Unit 10 Little End Road Eaton Socon
Saint Neots, Cambridgeshire, PE19 8JH, United Kingdom
Tel.: (44) 1480405419
Fax: (44) 1480 21 76 10
E-Mail: enquiries@anest-iwata.co.uk
Web Site: www.anest-iwata.co.uk
Emp.: 8
Painting Machinery Distr
S.I.C.: 5084
N.A.I.C.S.: 423830
Tony Robson *(Mng Dir)*
Liz Wood *(Sec & Office Mgr)*

Century Trading Co., Ltd (1)
1301 Daeryung Techno-Town 8 Gasan-Dong
Geumcheon-ku, 481-11 Seoul, Korea (South)

Tel.: (82) 52 32 27 10
Fax: (82) 2 2163 0309
Air Compressor Mfr
S.I.C.: 3563
N.A.I.C.S.: 333912

Iwata Service & Sales(M) Sdn. Bhd. (1)
No 54 Jalan Segambut Tengah
51200 Kuala Lumpur, Malaysia
Tel.: (60) 362514757
Fax: (60) 362514813
E-Mail: iwata-malaysia@issm-istl.com
Emp.: 20
Air & Gas Compressor Mfr
S.I.C.: 3563
N.A.I.C.S.: 333912

PT. INA Nusantara Abadi (1)
Jl Mangga dua Raya Kompl Ruko Bahan Bangunan Blok F 7 No 2
Jakarta, Indonesia
Tel.: (62) 21 6011714
Fax: (62) 21 6011717
E-Mail: info@iwata.co.id
Web Site: www.iwata.co.id
Air Compressor Distr
S.I.C.: 5084
N.A.I.C.S.: 423830

Smooth Investment Co., Ltd. (1)
G/F 16 Tai Nan Street
Mongkok, Kowloon, China (Hong Kong)
Tel.: (852) 23955297
Fax: (852) 27892083
E-Mail: enquiry@smooth.imsbiz.com.hk
Web Site: www.smooth.hk
Industrial Equipment Mfr & Distr
S.I.C.: 3559
N.A.I.C.S.: 333249

ANEXCO RESOURCES LTD.

(Formerly Hilltown Resources Inc.)
675 W Hastings Street Suite 810
Vancouver, BC, V6B 1N2, Canada
Tel.: (604) 689-4010
Fax: (604) 684-2349
E-Mail: jmcclusky@telus.net
Web Site: www.hilltownresources.com
Year Founded: 2006
AXO—(CNSX)
Int. Income: $3,135
Assets: $9,283
Liabilities: $33,184
Net Worth: ($23,901)
Earnings: ($253,655)
Fiscal Year-end: 02/28/13

Business Description:
Gold Mining Services
S.I.C.: 1041
N.A.I.C.S.: 212221

Personnel:
Kent E. Ausburn *(Pres & COO)*
Rudy de Jonge *(CEO & CFO)*

Board of Directors:
Kent E. Ausburn
Rudy de Jonge
Matthew Lechtzier
Catherine McClusky

ANF IMMOBILIER

32 rue de Monceau
75008 Paris, France
Tel.: (33) 144150111
Fax: (33) 147660793
E-Mail: investorrelations@anf-immobilier.com
Web Site: www.anf-immobilier.com
Year Founded: 1882
ANF—(EUR)
Rev.: $105,757,808
Assets: $1,240,130,843
Liabilities: $521,897,993
Net Worth: $718,232,849
Earnings: ($87,696,245)
Emp.: 50
Fiscal Year-end: 12/31/12

Business Description:
Real Estate Investment Services
S.I.C.: 6726
N.A.I.C.S.: 525990

Personnel:
Alain Lemaire *(Chm-Supervisory Bd)*
Bruno Keller *(Chm-Exec Bd)*
Patrick Sayer *(Vice Chm-Supervisory Bd)*
Xavier de Lacoste Lareymondie *(COO & Member-Exec Bd)*
Ghislaine Seguin *(Member-Exec Bd & Dir-Real Estate)*

Supervisory Board of Directors:
Alain Lemaire
Philippe Audouin
Sebastien Bazin
Sabine Roux de Bezieux
Fabrice de Gaudemar
Sebastien Didier
Eric Le Gentil
Philippe Monnier
Jean-Pierre Richardson
Patrick Sayer
Isabelle Xoual
Theodore Zarifi

Mazars
61 rue Henri Regnault
Courbevoie, France

ANFIELD NICKEL CORP.

410 - 625 Howe Street
Vancouver, BC, V6C 2T6, Canada
Tel.: (604) 646-1899
Fax: (604) 687-7041
E-Mail: info@anfieldnickel.com
Web Site: www.anfieldnickel.com
ANF—(TSXV)
Rev.: $85,293
Assets: $61,783,348
Liabilities: $907,530
Net Worth: $60,875,818
Earnings: ($2,147,105)
Fiscal Year-end: 12/31/12

Business Description:
Nickel Exploration & Development Services
S.I.C.: 1081
N.A.I.C.S.: 213114

Personnel:
David Strang *(Chm)*
Marshall Koval *(Pres & CEO)*
Martin Rip *(CFO)*
Leo Hathaway *(Chief Geological Officer)*
Robert Parvis Pirooz *(Sec)*

Board of Directors:
David Strang
Lyle Braaten
Marshall Koval
Robert Parvis Pirooz
Aziz Shariff
Donald Myron Shumka
Anish Sunderji

Legal Counsel:
Borden Ladner Gervais LLP
Vancouver, BC, Canada

Transfer Agent:
Computershare Investor Services Inc.
3rd Floor 510 Burrard St
V6C 3B9 Vancouver, BC, Canada

ANFIELD RESOURCES INC.

(Formerly Equinox Copper Corp.)
608 1199 West Pender Street
Vancouver, BC, V6E 2R1, Canada
Tel.: (604) 687-0300
Fax: (604) 687-0151
E-Mail: info@equinoxcopper.com
Web Site: www.equinoxexploration.com
ARY—(OTC TSXV)
Assets: $3,512,432
Liabilities: $914,254
Net Worth: $2,598,178
Earnings: ($945,291)
Fiscal Year-end: 12/31/12

Business Description:
Metal Mining Services
S.I.C.: 1099
N.A.I.C.S.: 212299

Personnel:
Corey A. Dias *(CEO)*
Laara Shaffer *(CFO)*

Board of Directors:
Joshua D. Bleak
H. Kenneth Bond
Steve Butrenchuk
Corey A. Dias
Roy Fuller
Richard Hunter

ANG INDUSTRIES LIMITED

90 Okhla Industrial Estate Phase - III
New Delhi, 110020, India
Tel.: (91) 1140677000
Fax: (91) 1141001946
E-Mail: marketing@angindustries.com
Web Site: www.angindustries.com
ANGIND—(NSE)
Sales Range: $25-49.9 Million

Business Description:
Automotive Component Mfr & Distr
S.I.C.: 3714
N.A.I.C.S.: 336340

Personnel:
Premjit Singh *(CEO & Mng Dir)*
Arun Jain *(CFO)*

Board of Directors:
Sanjay Garg
Gupta A. K.
Om Prakash Sharma
Premjit Singh

Transfer Agent:
Beetal Financial & Computer Services Pvt. Ltd
Beetal House 3rd Floor 99 Madangir Behind Local Shopping Centre
New Delhi, India

ANGEL GOLD CORP.

(Formerly Caerus Resource Corporation)
837 Hastings Street West Suite 408
Vancouver, BC, V6C 3N6, Canada
Tel.: (604) 684-6264
Fax: (604) 684-6242
E-Mail: info@angelgoldcorp.com
Web Site: www.angelgoldcorp.com
Year Founded: 1988
ANG—(TSXV)
Int. Income: $1,792
Assets: $2,058,730
Liabilities: $184,617
Net Worth: $1,874,112
Earnings: ($830,594)
Fiscal Year-end: 12/31/12

Business Description:
Gold Exploration Services
S.I.C.: 1041
N.A.I.C.S.: 212221

Personnel:
Blanca Stella Frias *(Pres & CEO)*
Mark Gelmon *(CFO)*
Marion McGrath *(Sec)*

Board of Directors:
Allen Vernon Ambrose
Jon Lehmann
Paulo Javier Ochoa Silva
Thomas E. Wharton, Jr.

Legal Counsel:
Gowlings
550 Burrard Street Suite 2300
Vancouver, BC, Canada

Transfer Agent:
Computershare Investor Services Inc.
3rd Floor 510 Burrard St
V6C 3B9 Vancouver, BC, Canada

ANGEL GROUP LTD.

The Angel House
225 Marsh Wall, London, E14 9FW, United Kingdom
Tel.: (44) 2075368688
Fax: (44) 2070932193
E-Mail: info@theangelgroup.com
Web Site: www.theangelgroup.com
Sales Range: $50-74.9 Million
Emp.: 220

Business Description:
Property Holding Company
S.I.C.: 6531
N.A.I.C.S.: 531312

Personnel:
Julie A. Davey *(Owner)*

ANGEL HUMAN RESOUCES LTD

Angel House 4 Union Street London Bridge
London, SE1 1SZ, United Kingdom
Tel.: (44) 2079402000
Fax: (44) 2079402001
E-Mail: hq@angelhr.org
Web Site: www.angelhr.org
Year Founded: 1965
Rev.: $21,697,487
Emp.: 58

Business Description:
Recruitment Services
S.I.C.: 7361
N.A.I.C.S.: 561311

Personnel:
Russell Crawford *(Mng Dir)*

ANGEL YEAST COMPANY LIMITED

168 Chengdong Avenue
Yichang, Hubei, 443003, China
Tel.: (86) 717 6369520
Fax: (86) 717 6370680
E-Mail: aie@angelyeast.com
Web Site: www.angelyeast.com
Year Founded: 1986
600298—(SHG)

Business Description:
Yeast Mfr
S.I.C.: 2099
N.A.I.C.S.: 311999

Personnel:
Xuefeng Yu *(Chm & Pres)*

ANGELINI ACRAF S.P.A.

Viale Amelia 70
00181 Rome, Italy
Tel.: (39) 6 78053 1
E-Mail: relazioni.esterne@angelini.it
Web Site: www.angelinipharma.com
Sls.: $1,200,000,000
Emp.: 3,500

Business Description:
Pharmaceutical & Health Care Products Mfr
S.I.C.: 2834
N.A.I.C.S.: 325412

Personnel:
Francesco Angelini *(Pres & Chm)*

Joint Ventures:

Fameccanica Data S.p.A. (1)
Via Aterno 136
San Giovanni Teatino, Chieti, 66020, Italy
Tel.: (39) 08545531
Fax: (39) 0854461422
E-Mail: staff@fameccanica.com
Web Site: www.fameccanica.com
Emp.: 600
Service Establishment Equipment & Supplies
S.I.C.: 5087
N.A.I.C.S.: 423850
Roberto Lemme *(Dir-Customer Svc)*

Fater S.p.A. (1)
Via Alessandro Volta 10
Pescara, 65129, Italy
Tel.: (39) 08545521
Fax: (39) 0854552279
Web Site: www.fater.it
Paper Products Mfr

Angelini ACRAF S.p.A.—(Continued)

S.I.C.: 2676
N.A.I.C.S.: 322291
Roberto Marinucci *(Gen Mgr)*

ANGELO MORATTI S.A.P.A.

SS 195 Sulcitana Km 19
Cagliari, 09018, Italy
Tel.: (39) 0706848465
Business Description:
Holding Company
S.I.C.: 6719
N.A.I.C.S.: 551112
Personnel:
Gian Marco Moratti *(Chm)*
Subsidiary:

Saras S.p.A. (1)
SS Sulcitana n 195 Km 19
09018 Cagliari, Italy (50.02%)
Tel.: (39) 070 90911
Fax: (39) 070 900209
E-Mail: ir@saras.it
Web Site: www.saras.it
SRS—(ITA OTC)
Rev.: $16,004,950,326
Assets: $5,303,804,799
Liabilities: $3,692,845,852
Net Worth: $1,610,958,947
Earnings: ($121,291,263)
Emp.: 1,854
Fiscal Year-end: 12/31/12
Oil Refining & Production & Engineering Services
S.I.C.: 1311
N.A.I.C.S.: 211111
Gian Marco Moratti *(Chm)*
Angelo Moratti *(Vice Chm)*
Massimo Moratti *(CEO)*
Corrado Costanzo *(CFO)*
Alberto Maria Alberti *(Chm/CEO-Sarlux Srl)*
Marco Schiavetti *(CEO-Arcola Petrolifera & Dir-Supply & Trading)*
Giampiero Spanedda *(CEO-Saras Energia)*
Enrico Padova *(Gen Counsel)*
Dario Scaffardi *(Exec VP & Gen Mgr)*

Subsidiaries:

Akhela S.r.l. (2)
Sesta Strada Ovest ZI Macchiareddu
Cagliari, 9010, Italy
Tel.: (39) 07024661000
Fax: (39) 07024661111
E-Mail: info@akhela.com
Web Site: www.akhela.com
Corporate IT Consulting Services
S.I.C.: 8748
N.A.I.C.S.: 541618
Piercarlo Ravasio *(CEO)*

Sarlux S.r.l. (2)
S.S. Sulcitana No. 195 Km 19
09018 Sarroch, Italy
Tel.: (39) 070 909241
Fax: (39) 070 906018
E-Mail: info@sarlux.it
Web Site: www.sarlux.it
Electric Power Generation
S.I.C.: 4939
N.A.I.C.S.: 221118
Domenico Mizzi *(Pres)*

ANGERMAYER, BRUMM & LANGE UNTERNEHMENSGRUPPE GMBH

Grueneburgweg 18
60322 Frankfurt, Germany
Tel.: (49) 69719128000
Fax: (49) 697191280614
E-Mail: info@abl-group.de
Web Site: www.abl-group.de
Business Description:
Investment Services
S.I.C.: 6211
N.A.I.C.S.: 523999
Personnel:
Christian Angermayer *(Mng Dir & Partner)*
Peter Brumm *(Mng Dir & Partner)*
Sebastian Grabmaier *(Partner)*
Ralph Konrad *(Partner)*
Andreas Lange *(Partner)*
Subsidiary:

Altira AG (1)
Grueneburgweg 18
60322 Frankfurt am Main, Germany(61.7%)
Tel.: (49) 69 719 12800
Fax: (49) 69 719 1280999
E-Mail: info@altira-group.de
Web Site: www.altira-group.de
A7A—(DEU)
Rev.: $23,006,045
Assets: $39,351,241
Liabilities: $6,979,891
Net Worth: $32,371,350
Earnings: ($12,087,260)
Emp.: 70
Fiscal Year-end: 12/31/12
Asset Management Services
S.I.C.: 6282
N.A.I.C.S.: 523920
Axel-Gunter Benkner *(Chm-Supervisory Bd)*
David Zimmer *(CEO)*
Juan Rodriguez *(Member-Mgmt Bd)*
Stefan Schutze *(Member-Mgmt Bd)*

ANGIOTECH PHARMACEUTICALS, INC.

355 Burrard Street Ste 1100
Vancouver, BC, V6C 2G8, Canada
Tel.: (604) 221-7676
Fax: (604) 221-2330
E-Mail: info@angio.com
Web Site: www.angiotech.com
Year Founded: 1992
ANPMF—(OTC)
Rev.: $243,825,000
Assets: $608,402,000
Liabilities: $467,734,000
Net Worth: $140,668,000
Earnings: ($6,226,000)
Emp.: 1,364
Fiscal Year-end: 12/31/12
Business Description:
Specialty Pharmaceuticals & Medical Devices
S.I.C.: 2834
N.A.I.C.S.: 325412
Personnel:
Kurt M. Cellar *(Co-Chm)*
Jeffrey D. Goldberg *(Co-Chm)*
Victor Diaz *(Pres & COO)*
Tammy Neske *(Chief Bus Officer)*
Jay Dent *(Principal Acctg Officer & Sr VP-Fin)*
Board of Directors:
Kurt M. Cellar
Jeffrey D. Goldberg
K. Thomas Bailey
Donald M. Casey, Jr.
Bradley S. Karro
Omar Vaishnavi
Transfer Agent:
Computershare Trust Company of Canada
510 Burrard St 3rd Fl
Vancouver, BC, V6C 3B9, Canada
U.S. Branch:

Angiotech Pharmaceuticals, Inc. - Sarasota (1)
600 Tallevast Rd Ste 201
Sarasota, FL 34243-3254
Tel.: (941) 364-3700
Fax: (941) 365-2465
Emp.: 13
Pharmaceutical Mfr
S.I.C.: 2834
N.A.I.C.S.: 325412
Dawn Benson *(Dir-Quality Assurance & Quality Control)*
U.S. Unit:

Angiotech Pharmaceuticals, Inc.-Surgical Specialties (1)
100 Dennis Dr
Reading, PA 19606 PA
Tel.: (610) 404-1000
Fax: (610) 404-4010
Toll Free: (877) 991-1110
E-Mail: AngioCSRDG@angio.com
Web Site: www.surgicalspecialties.com
Emp.: 331
Surgical & Medical Instruments Mfr Import Export
S.I.C.: 3841
N.A.I.C.S.: 339112
Steven Briant *(Sr VP-Sls & Mktg-Medical Device Technologies)*
Non-U.S. Subsidiary:

PBN Medicals Denmark A/S (1)
Knud Bro Alle 3
Fcenlose, 3660 Odense, Denmark
Tel.: (45) 47192700
Fax: (45) 47192701
E-Mail: customer@angio.com
Web Site: www.anpiocech.com
Emp.: 130
Drugs & Druggists Sundries Whslr
S.I.C.: 5122
N.A.I.C.S.: 424210
Phil Hunter *(Mng Dir)*

ANGKOR GOLD CORP.

1188 West Georgia Street Suite 1440
Vancouver, BC, V6E 4A2, Canada
Tel.: (780) 518-0326
E-Mail: mw@angkorgold.ca
Web Site: www.angkorgold.ca
Year Founded: 2008
ANK—(TSXV)
Business Description:
Gold Mining Services
S.I.C.: 1041
N.A.I.C.S.: 212221
Personnel:
Michael Weeks *(Chm & CEO)*
Aaron Triplett *(CFO)*
Don Erno *(Sec & Treas)*
Board of Directors:
Michael Weeks
Adrian G. Mann
Terry Mereniuk
Guillermo Salazar
Transfer Agent:
Computershare Investor Services Inc
100 University Avenue 9 Floor North Tower
Toronto, ON, M5J 2Y1, Canada

ANGLE ENERGY INC.

(Acquired & Absorbed by Bellatrix Exploration Ltd.)

ANGLE PLC

3 Frederick Sanger Road The Surrey Research Park
Guildford, Surrey, GU2 7YD, United Kingdom
Tel.: (44) 1483685830
Fax: (44) 1483685836
E-Mail: enquiries@angleplc.com
Web Site: www.angleplc.com
Year Founded: 1994
AGL—(LSE)
Rev.: $1,530,368
Assets: $11,880,735
Liabilities: $1,163,014
Net Worth: $10,717,721
Earnings: ($1,627,597)
Emp.: 29
Fiscal Year-end: 04/30/13
Business Description:
Consulting, Management & Venture Services
S.I.C.: 8742
N.A.I.C.S.: 541611
Personnel:
Andrew D. W. Newland *(Founder & CEO)*
George Hvichia *(CTO-Parsortix Inc)*
Shane Booth *(Pres/CEO-Parsortix Inc)*
Ian F. Griffiths *(Sec & Dir-Fin)*
Board of Directors:
Garth R. Selvey
Ian F. Griffiths
Brian Howlett
Andrew D. W. Newland
David W. Quysner
Legal Counsel:
Pinsent Masons
30 Crown Place Earl Street
London, United Kingdom
Subsidiaries:

ANGLE Technology Licensing Limited (1)
3 Frederick Singer Rd
The Surrey Research Park, Guildford, GU27YD, United Kingdom (100%)
Tel.: (44) 1483295830
Fax: (44) 1483295836
E-Mail: enquiries@angleplc.com
Web Site: www.angletechnology.com
Emp.: 10
Management Consulting Services
S.I.C.: 8748
N.A.I.C.S.: 541618
Andrew Newland *(Mng Dir)*

ANGLE Technology Limited (1)
3 Frederick Sanger Rd Surrey Research Pk
Guildford, GU2 7YD, United Kingdom
Tel.: (44) 1522 668980
E-Mail: enquiries@angleplc.com
Web Site: www.angleplc.com
Emp.: 40
Business Management Services
S.I.C.: 8742
N.A.I.C.S.: 541611

ANGLE Technology Ventures Limited (1)
3 Frederick Sanger Road
The Surrey Research Park, Guildford, GU27YD, United Kingdom (100%)
Tel.: (44) 1483295830
Fax: (44) 1483685836
E-Mail: info@angletechnologyventures.com
Web Site: www.angletechnologyventures.com
Emp.: 10
Management Consulting Services
S.I.C.: 8748
N.A.I.C.S.: 541618
Andrew Newland *(Founder & CEO)*

Novocellus Limited (1)
3 Frederick Sanger Rd Surrey Research Park
Guildford, Surrey, GU2 7YD, United Kingdom (62.67%)
Tel.: (44) 1483685830
Fax: (44) 1483685836
E-Mail: enquiries@angleplc.com
Web Site: www.novocellus.com
Emp.: 10
Diagnostic Imaging Centers
S.I.C.: 8071
N.A.I.C.S.: 621512
Andrew Newland *(CEO)*

Progeny BioVentures Limited (1)
20 Nugent Road
The Surrey Research Park, Guildford, GU27YG, United Kingdom (96.5%)
Tel.: (44) 1483295830
Fax: (44) 1483295836
Emp.: 10
Business Support Services
S.I.C.: 7389
N.A.I.C.S.: 561499
Andrew Newland *(Mng Dir)*

Synature Limited (1)
3 Frederick Sango Rd
The Surrey Research Park, Guildford, GU2 7YD, United Kingdom (55%)
Tel.: (44) 1483295830
Fax: (44) 1483685836
E-Mail: c.dawes@angleplc.com
Web Site: www.synature.com
Emp.: 40
Internet Publishing & Broadcasting
S.I.C.: 2741
N.A.I.C.S.: 519130
Andrew Newland *(Mng Dir)*
U.S. Subsidiaries:

ANGLE Technology LLC (1)
1000 Research Pk Blvd Ste 103
Charlottesville, VA 22911

Tel.: (434) 974-9700
Fax: (703) 991-2660
Web Site: www.angle.com
Emp.: 2
Consulting, Management & Venture Services
S.I.C.: 8742
N.A.I.C.S.: 541611
Gary Evans *(CEO)*

ANGLESEY MINING PLC

Parys Mountain Anglesey
Amlwch, Wales, LL68 9RE, United Kingdom
Tel.: (44) 1248361333
E-Mail: mail@angleseymining.co.uk
Web Site: www.angleseymining.co.uk
Year Founded: 1984
AYM—(LSE OTC)
Sales Range: Less than $1 Million
Emp.: 3

Business Description:
Copper, Zinc & Lead Mining Services
S.I.C.: 1021
N.A.I.C.S.: 212234

Personnel:
John F. Kearney *(Chm)*
D. William Hooley *(Pres, CEO & COO)*
Robert Ian Cuthbertson *(Sec & Dir-Fin)*

Board of Directors:
John F. Kearney
Robert Ian Cuthbertson
D. William Hooley
David Lean
Howard B. Miller
Roger W. Turner
Danesh Varma

Legal Counsel:
DLA LLP
101 Barbirolli Square
Manchester, United Kingdom

ANGLO ALUMINUM CORP.

(Name Changed to Navasota Resources Inc.)

ANGLO AMERICAN PLC

20 Carlton House Terrace
London, SW1Y 5AN, United Kingdom
Tel.: (44) 2079688888
Fax: (44) 2079688500
E-Mail: investorrelations@angloamerican.com
Web Site: www.angloamerican.com
Year Founded: 1975
AAL—(JSE LSE NAM SWX)
Rev.: $28,761,000,000
Assets: $79,369,000,000
Liabilities: $35,582,000,000
Net Worth: $43,787,000,000
Earnings: ($614,000,000)
Emp.: 106,000
Fiscal Year-end: 12/31/12

Business Description:
Holding Company; Coal, Gold, Diamonds, Platinum, Base Metals & Iron Mining; Steel, Building Materials, Paper & Textiles Mfr
S.I.C.: 6719
N.A.I.C.S.: 551112

Personnel:
Mark Cutifani *(CEO)*
Paulo Castellari-Porchia *(CEO-Iron Ore-Brazil)*
Ruben Fernandes *(CEO-Niobium & Phosphates)*
Seamus G. French *(CEO-Metallurgical Coal)*
Godfrey Gomwe *(CEO-Thermal Coal)*
Christopher Ivan Griffith *(CEO-Anglo American Platinum Limited)*
John MacKenzie *(CEO-Copper)*
Philippe J-C Mellier *(CEO-De Beers Grp)*
Neville F. Nicolau *(CEO-Platinum)*
Nicholas Jordan *(Sec)*

Board of Directors:
John L. Parker
David Challen
Chung-kong Chow
Mark Cutifani
Philip R. Hampton
Rene Medori
Phuthuma Nhleko
Anthony Martin O'Neill
Ray O'Rourke
Mphu Ramatlapeng
Jim Rutherford
Anne L. Stevens
Jack Edward Thompson
Peter Woicke

Equiniti
Aspect House Spencer Road
Lancing, United Kingdom

Subsidiary:

Tarmac Group Ltd. **(1)**
Millfields Rd Effingshall
Wolverhampton, W Midlands, WV4 6JP, United Kingdom (100%)
Tel.: (44) 1902353522
E-Mail: victoria.fletcher@tarmac.co.uk
Web Site: www.tarmac.co.uk
Sls.: $3,866,099,968
Emp.: 12,500
Holding Company
S.I.C.: 6719
N.A.I.C.S.: 551112
Robbie Robertson *(CEO)*
Keith Jackson *(CFO)*
Leon Cook *(Pub Affairs Officer)*
Jane Harte *(Sec)*

Subsidiary:

Tarmac Building Products Limited **(2)**
Millfields Road
Ettingshall, Wolverhampton, West Midlands, WV4 6JP, United Kingdom
Tel.: (44) 1902 353 522
E-Mail: buildingproducts@tarmac.co.uk
Web Site: www.tarmacbuildingproducts.co.uk
Emp.: 800
Building Materials Whslr
S.I.C.: 5032
N.A.I.C.S.: 423320
Ian Lichfield *(CEO)*

Units:

Tarmac Ltd. **(2)**
PO Box 1
Kington, Herefordshire, HR5 3LQ, United Kingdom (100%)
Tel.: (44) 1544230711
Fax: (44) 1544231406
Web Site: www.tarmac.co.uk
Emp.: 100
Mfr. of Asphalt, Aggregates, Concrete Products & Building Materials
S.I.C.: 2951
N.A.I.C.S.: 324121

Tarmac Ltd. **(2)**
N Rd Vellmoor
Retford, Nottinghamshire, DN22 8SG, United Kingdom (100%)
Tel.: (44) 1777703891
Fax: (44) 1777860546
E-Mail: stuarthaines@tarmac.co.uk
Web Site: www.tarmac.co.uk
Emp.: 150
Mfr. of Asphalt, Aggregates, Concrete Products & Building Materials
S.I.C.: 2951
N.A.I.C.S.: 324121
Stuart Haines *(Mng Dir)*

Tarmac Ltd. **(2)**
Millfields Rd Ettingfhall
PO Box 8
Wolverhampton, WV4 6JP, United Kingdom (100%)
Tel.: (44) 1902353522
Fax: (44) 1902353920
Web Site: www.tarmac.co.uk
Emp.: 600
Mfr. of Aggregates, Concrete Products & Building Materials
S.I.C.: 2951
N.A.I.C.S.: 324121

Tarmac Ltd. **(2)**
Millfields Road Ettingshall
Wolverhampton, West Midlands, WV4 6JP, United Kingdom (100%)
Tel.: (44) 1902353522
Web Site: www.tarmac.co.uk
Emp.: 20
Mfr. of Asphalt, Aggregates, Concrete Products & Building Materials
S.I.C.: 2951
N.A.I.C.S.: 324121

Tarmac Ltd. **(2)**
Fell Bank
PO Box 5
Birtley, Chester-le-Street, DH3 2ST, United Kingdom (100%)
Tel.: (44) 1914924000
Fax: (44) 1914108489
Web Site: www.tarmac.co.uk
Mfr. of Asphalt, Aggregates, Concrete Products & Building Materials
S.I.C.: 2951
N.A.I.C.S.: 324121

Non-U.S. Subsidiaries:

Lausitzer Grauwacke GmbH **(2)**
Werkstrasse 1
01920 Dresden, Germany
Tel.: (49) 357925760
Fax: (49) 35 792 576 15
Web Site: www.tarmac-baustoffe.com
Construction Materials; Building Aggregates Production
S.I.C.: 2951
N.A.I.C.S.: 324121
Thomas Lehmann *(Mng Dir)*

Tarmac Polska Sp. z o.o. **(2)**
ul Powstancow Sl 5
53 332 Wroclaw, Poland
Tel.: (48) 713351069
Fax: (48) 713351067
E-Mail: tarmac.polska@tarmac.pl
Web Site: www.tarmac.pl
Construction Aggregates (Gravel, Sand, Granite & Quartzite Chippings) Production
S.I.C.: 1429
N.A.I.C.S.: 212319
Grzegorz Lajca *(Pres)*

Joint Venture:

Midland Quarry Products Ltd. **(1)**
Leicester Rd
Whitwick, Leics, LE67 5GR, United Kingdom UK
Tel.: (44) 1530831000
Fax: (44) 1530832299
E-Mail: info@mqp.co.uk
Web Site: www.mqp.co.uk
Emp.: 30
Aggregates & Crushed Stone Mining & Quarry Operations; Owned 50% by Anglo American plc & 50% by Hanson Limited
S.I.C.: 1429
N.A.I.C.S.: 212319
Simon Willis *(Mng Dir)*
John van Rensburg *(Sec & Dir-Fin)*

Non-U.S. Subsidiaries:

Anglo American Brasil Limitada **(1)**
Paulista 2 300 10 Andar
Sao Paulo, 01310-300, Brazil
Tel.: (55) 1121257555
Fax: (55) 1121257500
E-Mail: augustojuanbernargi@angloamerican.com
Web Site: www.angloamerican.com.br
Nickel Mining Services
S.I.C.: 1021
N.A.I.C.S.: 212234
Augusto Juan Bernargi *(Mgr-Sls)*

Subsidiary:

Anglo Ferrous Brazil S.A. **(2)**
Praia Do Flamengo 154 Sala 501 Parte Flamengo, 22210-030 Rio de Janeiro, Brazil
Tel.: (55) 21 2555 5557
E-Mail: ri@ironx.com.br
Web Site: www.anglo-iron3.com.br
Iron Ore Mining Services
S.I.C.: 1011
N.A.I.C.S.: 212210
Stephan Weber *(CEO)*

Subsidiary:

Anglo Ferrous Minas Rio Mineracao SA **(3)**
Da Americas 3 434 Bloco 03 - Sala 301
Rio de Janeiro, 22631-002, Brazil
Tel.: (55) 2130313434
Fax: (55) 2130313434
Metal Mining Services
S.I.C.: 1099
N.A.I.C.S.: 212299

Anglo American Chile **(1)**
Av Pedro De Valdivia 291
Santiago, Chile
Tel.: (56) 22306000
Fax: (56) 22306700
E-Mail: contacto.chile@angloamerican.com
Web Site: www.angloamerican-chile.cl
Emp.: 700
Copper Ore & Nickel Ore Mining
S.I.C.: 1021
N.A.I.C.S.: 212234
John MacKenzie *(Pres-Topper)*
Marcelo Glavic *(Sr VP)*

Subsidiaries:

Anglo American Norte SA **(2)**
Avenida Pedro de Valdivia 291
Providencia, Santiago, 7500524, Chile CL
Tel.: (56) 22306000 (99.9%)
Fax: (56) 2230 6700
E-Mail: contacto.chile@angloamerican.com
Web Site: www.angloamerican-chile.cl
Emp.: 550
Copper Ore Mining
S.I.C.: 1021
N.A.I.C.S.: 212234
James Beans *(VP-Fin)*

Anglo American Sur SA **(2)**
Av Pedro De Valdivia 291 Providencia
Santiago, 7500524, Chile CL
Tel.: (56) 2 230 6000 (50.1%)
Fax: (56) 2 230 6700
Web Site: www.angloamerican-chile.cl
Holding Company; Copper Mining
S.I.C.: 6719
N.A.I.C.S.: 551112

Joint Venture:

Compania Minera Dona Ines de Collahuasi SCM **(2)**
Av Andres Bello 2687 Piso 11
Las Condes, Santiago, Chile
Tel.: (56) 2 362 6562
Fax: (56) 2 362 6562
E-Mail: contacto@collahuasi.cl
Web Site: www.collahuasi.cl
Emp.: 978
Copper Mining
S.I.C.: 1021
N.A.I.C.S.: 212234
Pieter Louw *(Pres)*
Jon Evans *(CEO)*

Anglo American Metallurgical Coal Holdings Limited **(1)**
Ground Floor 201 Charlotte St
Brisbane, QLD, 4000, Australia
Tel.: (61) 738341333
Fax: (61) 738341390
E-Mail: Seamus.French@angloamerican.com
Web Site: www.angloamerican.com.au
Investment Management Services
S.I.C.: 6211
N.A.I.C.S.: 523999
Seamus French *(CEO)*

Anglo American Platinum Limited **(1)**
55 Marshall Street
2001 Johannesburg, South Africa ZA
Mailing Address: (79.83%)
PO Box 62179
2107 Marshalltown, South Africa
Tel.: (27) 113736111
E-Mail: corporatecommunicati@angloplat.com
Web Site: www.angloplatinum.com
AMS—(JSE)
Rev.: $6,594,585,560
Assets: $11,179,695,200
Liabilities: $3,911,484,330

Anglo American PLC—(Continued)

Net Worth: $7,268,210,870
Earnings: $472,267,830
Emp.: 48,988
Platinum Mining
S.I.C.: 1099
N.A.I.C.S.: 212299
Frederik Tshamano Mohau Phaswana *(Chm)*
Thomas Alexander Wixley *(Deputy Chm)*
Neville Nicolau *(CEO)*

Anglo Base Metals (Ireland) Ltd. **(1)**
Killoran Moyne
Thurles, Tipperary, Ireland
Tel.: (353) 50445600
Fax: (353) 50445700
E-Mail: info@lisheenmine.ie
Web Site: www.lisheenmine.ie
Emp.: 350
Holding Company; Metal Ore Mining
S.I.C.: 6719
N.A.I.C.S.: 551112
Alan Buckley *(Sec & Accountant)*

Subsidiary:

Lisheen Mine **(2)**
Killoran Moyne
Thurles, Tipperary, Ireland (100%)
Tel.: (353) 50445600
Fax: (353) 50445700
E-Mail: info@lisheenmine.ie
Web Site: www.lisheenmine.ie
Emp.: 400
Zinc & Lead Mining
S.I.C.: 1031
N.A.I.C.S.: 212231
John Elems *(Gen Mgr)*

Anglo Coal **(1)**
45 Main Street
Johannesburg, Gauteng, South Africa
Tel.: (27) 11 638 9111
Fax: (27) 11 638 4043
Coal Mining Services
S.I.C.: 1241
N.A.I.C.S.: 213113

AngloGold Ashanti Limited **(1)**
76 Jeppe Street Newtown
Johannesburg, 2001, South Africa (54.5%)
Mailing Address:
PO Box 62117
Marshalltown, 2107, South Africa
Tel.: (27) 11 637 6000
Fax: (27) 11 637 6108
E-Mail: investors@anglogoldashanti.com
Web Site: www.anglogoldashanti.com
AU—(ASX EUR GHA JSE LSE NYSE)
Sls.: $6,428,000,000
Assets: $13,102,000,000
Liabilities: $7,254,000,000
Net Worth: $5,848,000,000
Earnings: $848,000,000
Emp.: 65,822
Fiscal Year-end: 12/31/12
Gold Exploration, Mining & Processing Import Export
S.I.C.: 1041
N.A.I.C.S.: 212221
Srinivasan Venkatakrishnan *(CEO)*
Richard N. Duffy *(CFO)*
Ken Kluksdahl *(Pres-Colombia)*
Maria Sanz Perez *(Gen Counsel, Sec & Exec VP)*
Charles E. Carter *(Exec VP-Strategy & Bus Dev)*
Graham Ehm *(Exec VP-Plng & Tech)*
Robbie L. Lazare *(Exec VP-South Africa)*
Thero Setiloane *(Exec VP-Bus Sustainability)*
Stewart Bailey *(Sr VP-IR)*

U.S. Subsidiary:

AngloGold Ashanti North America Inc. **(2)**
6300 S Syracuse Way Ste 500
Centennial, CO 80111 (100%)
Tel.: (303) 889-0700
Fax: (303) 889-0700
Web Site: www.anglogoldashantina.com
Sls.: $62,500,000
Emp.: 20
Gold Exploration, Mining & Processing
S.I.C.: 1041
N.A.I.C.S.: 212221
Ron Largent *(Exec VP)*

Black Mountain Mining (Proprietary) Limited **(1)**
1 Penge Road
Springbok, Northern Cape, 8893, South Africa
Tel.: (27) 549839648
Fax: (27) 549839243
Lead & Zinc Ore Mining Services
S.I.C.: 1031
N.A.I.C.S.: 212231

Copebras Limitada **(1)**
Rodovia Conego Domenico Rangoni - SP 055 Km 264 2 Oeste
11573 904 Cubatao, Sao Paulo, Brazil
Tel.: (55) 13 3362 7069
Fax: (55) 1333627409
E-Mail: faleconosco@copebras.com.br
Web Site: www.copebras.com.br
Emp.: 120
Phosphate Fertilizer Mfr & Distr
S.I.C.: 2874
N.A.I.C.S.: 325312
Alan Green *(Office Mgr)*

Kumba Iron Ore Ltd. **(1)**
Centurion Gate 124 Akkerboom Street
Centurion, 0175, South Africa (63.4%)
Tel.: (27) 126837000
Fax: (27) 862950746
Web Site: www.kumba.co.za
KIO—(JSE)
Rev.: $5,076,318,200
Assets: $4,081,071,200
Liabilities: $1,924,255,900
Net Worth: $2,156,815,300
Earnings: $1,798,370,000
Emp.: 7,580
Fiscal Year-end: 12/31/12
Iron Ore Mining
S.I.C.: 1011
N.A.I.C.S.: 212210
Norman Bloe Mbazima *(CEO)*
Frikkie Kotzee *(CFO)*
Vusani Malie *(Sec)*

Minera Loma De Niquel, CA **(1)**
Autopista Regional Del Centro Km 54 Via Tiara
Tejerias, Venezuela (91%)
Tel.: (58) 2444000500
E-Mail: info@mldn.com.de
Web Site: www.mineralomadeniquel.com
Emp.: 150
Nickel Mining
S.I.C.: 1021
N.A.I.C.S.: 212234
Walter De Simoni *(Pres)*

Minera Quellaveco S.A. **(1)**
Los Laureles 399
San Isidro, Lima, 27, Peru (80%)
Tel.: (51) 14224121
Fax: (51) 14223264
Copper Mining
S.I.C.: 1021
N.A.I.C.S.: 212234

Scaw Metals Ltd. **(1)**
Union Junction
Germiston, Gauteng, South Africa (100%)
Tel.: (27) 118429000
Fax: (27) 118429721
Web Site: www.scaw.co.za
Earnings: $29,260,000
Emp.: 4,500
Mfr of Rolled & Forged Steel Products
S.I.C.: 3399
N.A.I.C.S.: 331221
Mike Borello *(Head-Sls & Mktg)*

Non-U.S. Subsidiary:

AltaSteel Ltd. **(2)**
9401 E 34th St
PO Box 2348
Edmonton, AB, T5J 2R3, Canada AB
Tel.: (780) 468-1133
Fax: (780) 468-7335
Web Site: www.altasteel.com
Sales Range: $25-49.9 Million
Emp.: 362
Merchant & Special Quality Bars
S.I.C.: 3312
N.A.I.C.S.: 331110
Chris Jager *(Pres)*

ANGLO AUSTRALIAN RESOURCES NL

Ground Floor 63 Hay Street
Subiaco, WA, 6008, Australia
Tel.: (61) 893828822
Fax: (61) 863801904
Web Site: www.anglo.com.au
AAR—(ASX)
Rev.: $26,419
Assets: $5,508,475
Liabilities: $461,763
Net Worth: $5,046,712
Earnings: ($1,359,054)
Fiscal Year-end: 06/30/13
Business Description:
Gold Exploration & Mining
S.I.C.: 1041
N.A.I.C.S.: 212221
Personnel:
John Load Cecil Jones *(Chm)*
Graeme Smith *(Sec)*
Board of Directors:
John Load Cecil Jones
Angus Claymore Pilmer
Peter Stern

ANGLO-BOMARC MINES LTD.

708-1155 West Pender
Vancouver, BC, V6B 2M1, Canada
Tel.: (604) 734-1628
Fax: (604) 484-5615
E-Mail: info@anglo-bomarcmines.com
Web Site: www.anglo-bomarcmines.com
Year Founded: 1967
ANB—(TSXV)
Int. Income: $656
Assets: $830,070
Liabilities: $338,254
Net Worth: $491,816
Earnings: ($88,493)
Fiscal Year-end: 03/31/13
Business Description:
Mineral Exploration Services
S.I.C.: 1081
N.A.I.C.S.: 213114
Personnel:
Russell W. Marshall *(Pres & CEO)*
Nizar Y. Bharmal *(CFO)*
Board of Directors:
Nizar Y. Bharmal
Gordon Guiboche
Russell W. Marshall
Gordon Patterson
Rodney Spence

ANGLO-CANADIAN MINING CORP.

The Marine Building 530 - 355 Burrard Street
Vancouver, BC, V6C 2G8, Canada
Tel.: (604) 669-6807
Fax: (604) 669-5715
Toll Free: (866) 488-3838
E-Mail: info@anglocanex.com
Web Site: www.anglocanex.com
Year Founded: 1979
URA—(TSXV)
Rev.: $7,046
Assets: $2,580,879
Liabilities: $644,851
Net Worth: $1,936,029
Earnings: ($1,450,966)
Fiscal Year-end: 07/31/13
Business Description:
Gold & Uranium Exploration Services
S.I.C.: 1041
N.A.I.C.S.: 212221
Personnel:
Len J. Harris *(Pres & CEO)*
James Turner *(CFO)*
Board of Directors:
Robert L. Card
Len J. Harris
David Hudson
James Turner
Transfer Agent:
Equity Transfer & Trust Company
1185 West Georgia Street Suite 1620
Vancouver, BC, V6E 4E6, Canada

ANGLO CANADIAN OIL CORP.

(Name Changed to Tallgrass Energy Corp.)

ANGLO EASTERN PLANTATIONS PLC

Quadrant House 6th Floor 4 Thomas More Square
London, E1W 1YW, United Kingdom
Tel.: (44) 20 7216 4621
Fax: (44) 2077672602
Web Site: www.angloeastern.co.uk
AEP—(LSE)
Rev.: $237,352,000
Assets: $597,001,000
Liabilities: $97,410,000
Net Worth: $499,591,000
Earnings: $62,703,000
Emp.: 4,819
Fiscal Year-end: 12/31/12
Business Description:
Oilseed Processing
S.I.C.: 0119
N.A.I.C.S.: 111120
Personnel:
John Ewe Chuan Lim *(Dir-Fin & Corp Affairs)*
Board of Directors:
Siew Kim Lim
Jonathan Ngee Song Law
John Ewe Chuan Lim
Kanaka Puradiredja
Din Sulaiman
Legal Counsel:
Withers LLP
16 Old Bailey
EC4M 7EG London, United Kingdom

ANGLO EUROPEAN AVIATION AG

Quaderstrasse 7
CH-7000 Chur, Switzerland
Tel.: (41) 81 5330172
Fax: (41) 81 5330174
E-Mail: sales.ch@angloeuropean.com
Web Site: www.angloeuropean.com
Year Founded: 1989
Sales Range: $10-24.9 Million
Business Description:
Air Charter Services
S.I.C.: 4512
N.A.I.C.S.: 481111
Personnel:
Mark Everts *(Mng Dir)*

ANGLO PACIFIC GROUP PLC

17 Hill Street Mayfair
London, W1J 5LJ, United Kingdom
Tel.: (44) 2034357400
E-Mail: info@anglopacificgroup.com
Web Site: www.anglopacificgroup.com
APF—(LSE TSX)
Rev.: $20,952,440
Assets: $558,228,478
Liabilities: $82,919,042
Net Worth: $475,309,436
Earnings: $15,882,920
Emp.: 11
Fiscal Year-end: 12/31/12
Business Description:
Coal Mining Services
S.I.C.: 1222
N.A.I.C.S.: 212112

Personnel:
Brian M. Wides *(Acting Chm)*
Julian Treger *(CEO)*
Kevin Flynn *(CFO)*
Mark Potter *(Chief Investment Officer)*
Peter T. J. Mason *(Corp Counsel & Sec)*
Board of Directors:
Brian M. Wides
Mike H. Atkinson
Michael Blyth
Paul N. R. Cooke
Mark Potter
Robert Stan
Julian Treger
John G. Whellock
Anthony H. Yadgaroff
Equiniti
Aspect House Spencer Road
Lancing, United Kingdom
Transfer Agent:
Equity Transfer & Trust Company
200 University Avenue Ste 400
Toronto, ON, M5H 4H1, Canada
Tel.: (416) 361-0152
Fax: (416) 361-0470
Subsidiary:

APGM Ltd (1)
17 Hill St
Mayfair, London, W1J 5NZ, United Kingdom
Tel.: (44) 2073186360
Web Site: www.anglopacificgroup.co.uk
Investment Management Services
S.I.C.: 8748
N.A.I.C.S.: 541618

ANGLO PHILIPPINE HOLDINGS CORPORATION

6th Floor Quad Alpha Centrum 125
Pioneer Street
Mandaluyong, Metro Manila,
Philippines 1550
Tel.: (63) 26315139
Fax: (63) 26313113
E-Mail: info@anglophil.com
Web Site: www.anglophil.com
APO—(PHI)
Rev.: $13,358,759
Assets: $133,376,211
Liabilities: $47,798,106
Net Worth: $85,578,105
Earnings: $9,377,731
Emp.: 12
Fiscal Year-end: 12/31/12
Business Description:
Oil & Mining Exploration Services
S.I.C.: 1311
N.A.I.C.S.: 211111
Personnel:
Alfredo C. Ramos *(Chm)*
Christopher M. Gotanco *(Pres)*
Augusto B. Sunico *(Treas)*
Roberto V. San Jose *(Sec)*
Adrian S. Arias *(Exec VP & Asst Sec)*
Board of Directors:
Alfredo C. Ramos
Ramoncito Z. Abad
Christopher M. Gotanco
Roberto V. San Jose
Cecilia R. Licauco
Francisco A. Navarro
Adrian Paulino S. Ramos
Anton S. Ramos
Presentacion S. Ramos
Augusto B. Sunico
Renato C. Valencia

ANGLO SWISS RESOURCES INC.

900-555 Burrard Street
Vancouver, BC, V7X 1M8, Canada
Tel.: (604) 683-0484
Fax: (604) 683-7497
Web Site: www.anglo-swiss.com
ASW—(OTC TSXV)
Rev.: $11,356
Assets: $12,687,709
Liabilities: $196,640
Net Worth: $12,491,069
Earnings: ($1,112,283)
Fiscal Year-end: 12/31/12
Business Description:
Gold Mining Services
S.I.C.: 1041
N.A.I.C.S.: 212221
Personnel:
Jari Paakki *(CEO)*
Christopher C. Robbins *(CFO, Sec & VP)*
Board of Directors:
Todd Keast
Thomas J. Obradovich
Jari Paakki
Christopher C. Robbins
Blair D. Zaritsky
Legal Counsel:
Farris Vaughan Wills & Murphy
25th Floor 700 West Georgia Street
Vancouver, BC, Canada
Transfer Agent:
Computershare Investor Services Inc.
2nd Fl 510 Burrard St
Vancouver, BC, Canada

ANGOSTURA HOLDINGS LIMITED

Corner Eastern Main Rd & Trinity Ave
Laventille, Trinidad & Tobago
Tel.: (868) 6231841
Fax: (868) 6231847
E-Mail: corphq@angostura.com
Web Site: www.angostura.com
Emp.: 300
Business Description:
Alcoholic Beverages
S.I.C.: 5182
N.A.I.C.S.: 424820
Personnel:
Lawrence Andre Duprey *(Chm)*
Robert Wong *(CEO)*
Michael E. Carballo *(Sec & Exec Dir)*
Board of Directors:
Lawrence Andre Duprey
Martin Geoffrey Daly
Nicholas Knollys Inniss
Louis Andre Monteil
Subsidiaries:

Angostura Limited (1)
Eastern Main Road
Laventille, Trinidad & Tobago (100%)
Tel.: (868) 6231841
Fax: (868) 6230788
E-Mail: mecarballo@angostura.com
Web Site: www.angostura.com
Emp.: 250
Wine & Distilled Alcoholic Beverage Merchant Whslr
S.I.C.: 5182
N.A.I.C.S.: 424820
Lawrence Duprey *(Chm)*
Robert Wong *(CEO)*

Trinidad Distillers Limited (1)
Eastern Main Rd & Angostura St
Laventille, Trinidad & Tobago (100%)
Tel.: (868) 623 2101
Fax: (868) 623 1847
Emp.: 40
Wine & Distilled Alcoholic Beverage Merchant Whslr
S.I.C.: 5182
N.A.I.C.S.: 424820

U.S. Subsidiaries:

Servis Limited (1)
2774 Farrington St
Saint Paul, MN 55113-2450 (100%)
Tel.: (651) 486-0178
Emp.: 10
Carpet & Upholstery Cleaning Services
S.I.C.: 7217
N.A.I.C.S.: 561740

Non-U.S. Subsidiaries:

Suriname Alcholic Beverages N.V. (1)
Cornelis Jongbawstraat 18 - 28 141
Paramaribo, Suriname (75%)
Tel.: (597) 473344
Fax: (597) 471201
E-Mail: info@sabrum.com
Web Site: www.sabrum.com
Emp.: 90
Wine & Distilled Alcoholic Beverage Merchant Whslr
S.I.C.: 5182
N.A.I.C.S.: 424820
Stephan Meegong *(Gen Mgr)*

ANGUS MINING INC.

83 Yonge Street Suite 200
Toronto, ON, M5C 1S8, Canada
Tel.: (416) 640-1933
Fax: (416) 640-1928
Year Founded: 2007
ANA—(TSXV)
Rev.: $245
Assets: $365,672
Liabilities: $1,279,241
Net Worth: ($913,569)
Earnings: ($3,303,587)
Fiscal Year-end: 12/31/12
Business Description:
Mineral Exploration Services
S.I.C.: 1099
N.A.I.C.S.: 212299
Personnel:
Fraser A. Buchan *(Pres & CEO)*
Brian Morales *(CFO)*
Board of Directors:
Fraser A. Buchan
Robert Buchan
Cameron Mingay
Carl Pescio
Transfer Agent:
Computershare Investor Services Inc.
100 University Avenue 8th Floor
Toronto, ON, M5J 2Y1, Canada
Tel.: (514) 982-7555

ANGUS RESOURCES INC.

1836 West 5th Avenue Suite 205
Vancouver, BC, V6J 1P3, Canada
Tel.: (604) 318-4053
Fax: (604) 736-2340
E-Mail: ctagencies@hotmail.com
Year Founded: 2008
GUS.P—(TSXV)
Business Description:
Investment Services
S.I.C.: 6211
N.A.I.C.S.: 523999
Personnel:
Craig Taylor *(Pres, CEO, CFO & Sec)*
Board of Directors:
Andrew Rees
Brandon Rook
Craig Taylor
Jeff Tindale

ANHANGUERA EDUCACIONAL PARTICIPACOES S.A.

Al Maria Tereza 4266 - Sala 06
13278181 Valinhos, SP, Brazil
Tel.: (55) 19 3517 3799
Fax: (55) 19 3512 1703
Year Founded: 1994
AEDU3—(BRAZ)
Sales Range: $1-4.9 Billion
Emp.: 18,300
Business Description:
Education Services
S.I.C.: 8299
N.A.I.C.S.: 611710
Personnel:
Vitor Alaga Pini *(Dir-IR)*

ANHEUSER-BUSCH INBEV N.V./S.A.

Brouwerijplein 1
3000 Leuven, Belgium
Tel.: (32) 16276111
Fax: (32) 16506111
Web Site: www.ab-inbev.com
ABI—(EUR)
Rev.: $39,758,000,000
Assets: $122,621,000,000
Liabilities: $77,180,000,000
Net Worth: $45,441,000,000
Earnings: $9,434,000,000
Emp.: 117,632
Fiscal Year-end: 12/31/12
Business Description:
Beer, Malt Beverages & Soft Drinks Mfr & Distr
Import Export
S.I.C.: 2082
N.A.I.C.S.: 312120
Personnel:
Kees J. Storm *(Chm)*
Carlos Brito *(CEO)*
Felipe Dutra *(CFO & CTO)*
Miguel Patricio *(CMO)*
Sabine Chalmers *(Chief Legal & Corp Affairs Officer)*
Bernardo Pinto Paiva *(Chief Sls Officer)*
Jo Van Biesbroeck *(Chief Strategy Officer)*
Claudio Garcia *(Chief People Officer)*
Claudio Braz Ferro *(Chief Supply Officer)*
Tony Milikin *(Chief Procurement Officer)*
Joao Castro Neves *(Pres-Latin America North)*
Michel Doukeris *(Pres-Asia Pacific)*
Luiz Fernando Edmond *(Pres-North America)*
Marcio Froes *(Pres-Latin America South)*
Stuart MacFarlane *(Pres-Europe)*
Ricardo Tadeu *(Pres-Mexico)*
Board of Directors:
Kees J. Storm
Carlos Alberto R. da Veiga Sicupira
Gregoire de Spoelberch
Paul Cornet de Ways Ruart
Stefan Descheemaeker
Olivier Goudet
Jorge Paulo Lemann
Marcel Hermann Telles
Roberto Moses Thompson Motta
Alexandre Van Damme
Mark Winkelman
Subsidiaries:

Brouwerij van Hoegaarden N.V. (1)
Stoopkensstraat 46
Hoegaarden, 3320, Belgium BE
Tel.: (32) 16 76 98 11
Fax: (32) 16 76 76 91
E-Mail: media.relations@inbev.com
Web Site: www.hoegaarden.com
Emp.: 155
Beer Brewer & Whlsr
S.I.C.: 2082
N.A.I.C.S.: 312120
Anne Ghanima *(Plant Mgr)*

COBREW N.V. (1)
Brouwerijplein 1
3000 Leuven, Belgium
Tel.: (32) 16276111
Fax: (32) 16506111
E-Mail: reception.ghq@ab-inbev.com
Web Site: www.inbev.com
Emp.: 40
Business Management Consulting Services
S.I.C.: 8742
N.A.I.C.S.: 541611
Carlos Brito *(CEO)*

Anheuser-Busch InBev N.V./S.A.—(Continued)

U.S. Subsidiaries:

Anheuser-Busch Companies, LLC (1)
1 Busch Pl
Saint Louis, MO 63118-1849 DE
Tel.: (314) 577-2000
Fax: (314) 577-2900
Toll Free: (800) 342-5283
E-Mail: info@anheuser-busch.com
Web Site: www.anheuser-busch.com
Emp.: 30,849
Holding Company; Beer & Malt Beverage Mfr & Distr
Import Export
S.I.C.: 6719
N.A.I.C.S.: 551112
Gary L. Rutledge *(Gen Counsel & VP)*

Subsidiaries:

Anheuser-Busch, Inc. (2)
1 Busch Pl
Saint Louis, MO 63118
Tel.: (314) 577-2000
Fax: (314) 577-2900
Toll Free: (800) 342-5283
Web Site: www.anheuser-busch.com
Beer & Malt Beverage Mfr & Distr
Import Export
S.I.C.: 2082
N.A.I.C.S.: 312120
August A. Busch, IV *(Chm & Pres)*

Subsidiaries:

August A. Busch & Company of Massachusetts, Inc. (3)
440 Riverside Ave
Medford, MA 02155-4948 MA
Tel.: (800) 222-8724
Fax: (781) 306-5694
Emp.: 250
Beer Wholesaler
S.I.C.: 5181
N.A.I.C.S.: 424810
Mark Wahlgren *(Gen Mgr)*

Busch Agricultural Resources, Inc. (3)
3636 S Geyer Rd Fl 2
Saint Louis, MO 63127-1024
Tel.: (314) 984-4680
Fax: (314) 984-4629
Emp.: 23
Agricultural Products Mfr
S.I.C.: 2044
N.A.I.C.S.: 311212

Subsidiary:

Pacific International Rice Mills (4)
845 Kentucky Ave
Woodland, CA 95695-2744
Mailing Address:
PO Box 652
Woodland, CA 95776-0652
Tel.: (530) 666-1691
Fax: (925) 600-6850
Web Site: www.pirmirice.com
Emp.: 100
Rice Mfr
S.I.C.: 2044
N.A.I.C.S.: 311212
Kathleen Santiago *(Supvr-Customer Fulfillment)*

Busch Properties, Inc. (3)
1 Busch Pl
Saint Louis, MO 63118-1849 DE
Tel.: (314) 577-2000
Fax: (314) 577-2900
Web Site: www.anheuser-busch.com
Emp.: 30,000
Real Estate Holding Company
S.I.C.: 2082
N.A.I.C.S.: 312120
W. Randolph Baker *(Chm & Pres)*
Robin D. Carson *(Exec VP)*

Subsidiary:

Kingsmill Realty Inc. (4)
100 Kingsmill Rd
Williamsburg, VA 23185-5579 VA
Tel.: (757) 253-3933
Fax: (757) 345-0018
Toll Free: (800) 392-0026
Web Site: www.kingsmill.com
Emp.: 12
Real Estate Services
S.I.C.: 6531
N.A.I.C.S.: 531210
Robin D. Carson *(Mng Dir & Exec VP)*

Units:

Anheuser-Busch Sales of Hawaii (3)
99-877 Iwaena St
Aiea, HI 96701-3220
Tel.: (808) 487-0055
Fax: (808) 488-1343
Web Site: www.anheuserbusch.com
Emp.: 225
Beer & Other Fermented Malt Liquors Mfr
S.I.C.: 5181
N.A.I.C.S.: 424810
Chad Hoffmeisger *(Pres)*

Anheuser-Busch Sales of Lima (3)
(Formerly C&G Distributing Co., Inc.)
3535 Saint Johns Rd
Lima, OH 45804 OH
Tel.: (419) 221-2337
Fax: (419) 221-2023
Emp.: 100
Beer Distr
S.I.C.: 5181
N.A.I.C.S.: 424810
Fino J. Cecala *(Pres & CEO)*
Gary J. Guagenti *(CFO)*
Mark G. Guagenti *(COO)*

Anheuser-Busch Sales Pomona (3)
2800 S Reservoir St
Pomona, CA 91766
Tel.: (800) 622-2667
Fax: (909) 628-2234
Sls.: $60,300,000
Emp.: 180
Beer & Other Fermented Malt Liquors Mfr
S.I.C.: 5181
N.A.I.C.S.: 424810

Anheuser-Busch International, Inc. (2)
1 Busch Pl
Saint Louis, MO 63118-1849
Tel.: (314) 577-2000
Fax: (314) 577-2900
E-Mail: contactcenter@anheuser-busch.com
Web Site: www.abconference.com
Emp.: 37
International Beer Operations, Sales & Marketing & Equity Investments with International Brewers
S.I.C.: 5181
N.A.I.C.S.: 424810

Manufacturers Railway Company (2)
1 Arsenal St
Saint Louis, MO 63118 MO
Tel.: (314) 577-1749
Fax: (314) 577-3136
Web Site: www.anheuser-busch.com
Sales Range: $1-9.9 Million
Emp.: 70
Switching Services
S.I.C.: 4789
N.A.I.C.S.: 488210
Kurt R. Andrew *(Pres & CEO)*
Barbara Houseworth *(Treas & VP)*

St. Louis Refrigerator Car Company (2)
1 Busch Pl
Saint Louis, MO 63118-1852 MA
Tel.: (314) 577-2000
Fax: (314) 577-2900
Toll Free: (800) 342-5283
Web Site: www.anheuser-busch.com
Emp.: 4,000
Transportation Services
S.I.C.: 4789
N.A.I.C.S.: 488210
Kurt R. Andrew *(Pres & CEO)*
Barbara J. Houseworth *(Treas & VP)*

Anheuser-Busch Packaging Group, Inc. (1)
1 Busch Pl
Saint Louis, MO 63118-1849
Tel.: (314) 821-0599
Packaging & Recycling Services
S.I.C.: 7389
N.A.I.C.S.: 561910
Michael S. Harding *(Pres & CEO)*

Subsidiaries:

Anheuser-Busch Recycling Corporation (2)
1 Busch Pl
Saint Louis, MO 63118-1849 OH
Tel.: (314) 957-0787
Fax: (314) 957-9324
Web Site: www.anheuserbusch.com
Emp.: 25
Beer Can Recycling Services
S.I.C.: 5093
N.A.I.C.S.: 423930
Trevor Hasen *(VP)*

Eagle Packaging Inc. (2)
3219 Rider Trl S
Earth City, MO 63045-1520 DE
Tel.: (314) 298-6700
Fax: (314) 298-6750
Emp.: 20
Food Products Assembling & Packaging Services
S.I.C.: 7389
N.A.I.C.S.: 561990

Longhorn Glass Inc. (2)
4202 Fidelity St
Houston, TX 77029-3550
Tel.: (713) 679-7529
Fax: (713) 679-7556
Emp.: 187
Packing Bottling & Canning Glass Mfr
S.I.C.: 3221
N.A.I.C.S.: 327213

Metal Container Corporation (2)
3636 S Geyer Rd Ste 400
Saint Louis, MO 63127-1237 DE
Tel.: (314) 957-9500
Fax: (314) 957-9515
E-Mail: metal@metal.com
Web Site: www.metal.com
Emp.: 60
Cans Mfr
S.I.C.: 3411
N.A.I.C.S.: 332431

Non-U.S. Subsidiaries:

AB - INBEV FRANCE S.A.S. (1)
Immeuble Crystal Zac Euralille 38 Allee Vauban
59110 La Madeleine, France
Tel.: (33) 3 2048 3030
Fax: (33) 3 2048 3240
Emp.: 30
Alcoholic Beverage Distr
S.I.C.: 5182
N.A.I.C.S.: 424820
Eric Lauwers *(Pres)*

ANHEUSER-BUSCH INBEV GERMANY HOLDING GmbH (1)
Am Deich 18
Bremen, 28199, Germany
Tel.: (49) 42150940
Fax: (49) 42150944060
E-Mail: info@inbev.de
Web Site: www.ab-inbev.com
Investment Management Services
S.I.C.: 6211
N.A.I.C.S.: 523999
Chris Cools *(Mng Dir)*

BRASSERIE DE LUXEMBOURG MOUSEL - DIEKIRCH SA (1)
1 Rue de la Brasserie
9214 Diekirch, Luxembourg
Tel.: (352) 80 21 31 999
Fax: (352) 80 3923
Emp.: 75
Alcoholic Beverage Mfr
S.I.C.: 2082
N.A.I.C.S.: 312120
Karen Couck *(Dir-External Comm-Global & Belux)*

Brasseries Stella Artois (1)
Ave Pierre Brossolette 14 Bte 9
59426 Armentieres, France (100%)
Tel.: (33) 320483030
Fax: (33) 320483140
Emp.: 450
Beer Breweries
S.I.C.: 2082
N.A.I.C.S.: 312120
Eric Lauwers *(Gen Mgr)*

BRAUEREI BECK GmbH & CO. KG (1)
Am Deich 18/19
Bremen, 28199, Germany
Tel.: (49) 421 5094 0
Fax: (49) 421 5094 667
E-Mail: info@becks.de
Web Site: www.becks.de
Alcoholic Beverage Mfr & Distr
S.I.C.: 2082
N.A.I.C.S.: 312120

Brauerei Diebels GmbH & Co. KG (1)
Brauerei Diebels Strasse 1
47661 Issum, Germany (80%)
Tel.: (49) 2835300
Fax: (49) 283530165
E-Mail: info@einschoemer-tag.de
Emp.: 250
Malt Beverages Mfr
Export
S.I.C.: 2082
N.A.I.C.S.: 312120
Andre Castens *(Mgr-PR)*

BRAUERGILDE HANNOVER AG (1)
Hildesheimer Str 132
Hannover, 30173, Germany
Tel.: (49) 51198080
Fax: (49) 5119808467
Alcoholic Beverage Mfr
S.I.C.: 2082
N.A.I.C.S.: 312120
Hans Josef Toussaint *(Mng Dir)*

BUDWEISER WUHAN INTERNATIONAL BREWING COMPANY LIMITED (1)
No 20 Youfang Street
Xiangfang District, Harbin, China
Tel.: (86) 451 55602920
Fax: (86) 451 55602925
Alcoholic Beverage Mfr
S.I.C.: 2082
N.A.I.C.S.: 312120
Yan Chuang *(Gen Mgr)*

CERVECERIA BOLIVIANA NACIONAL S.A. (1)
Ave Montes 400 Casilla 421
La Paz, Bolivia
Tel.: (591) 22454454
Fax: (591) 22455644
E-Mail:
Web Site: www.cbn.bo/contacto.php
Beverage Products Mfr & Distr
S.I.C.: 2082
N.A.I.C.S.: 312120

Cerveceria Cuauhtemoc Moctezuma S.A. de C.V. (1)
Avenida Alfonso Reyes 2202 Nte
Monterrey, Nuevo Leon, 64442, Mexico
Tel.: (52) 83285000
Fax: (52) 83285454
Beer Breweries
S.I.C.: 2082
N.A.I.C.S.: 312120

CERVECERIA PARAGUAYA S.A. (1)
Ruta A Villeta Km 30
Ypane, 2660, Paraguay
Tel.: (595) 215 88 60 00
Fax: (595) 215 88 60 00
Web Site: www.ab-inbev.com
Alcoholic Beverage Mfr
S.I.C.: 2082
N.A.I.C.S.: 312120

Companhia de Bebidas das Americas (1)
Rua Dr Renato Paes de Barrios 1017 4th Floor
04530-001 Sao Paulo, SP, Brazil BR
Tel.: (55) 11 2122 1508 (56%)
Fax: (55) 11 2122 1526
E-Mail: ir@ambev.com.br
Web Site: www.ambev.com.br
AMBV3—(BRAZ)
Sls.: $15,854,106,590
Assets: $26,640,713,211
Liabilities: $11,921,495,229
Net Worth: $14,719,217,982
Earnings: $5,234,988,514
Emp.: 51,217
Fiscal Year-end: 12/31/12

Beer & Ale Mfr
Import Export
S.I.C.: 2082
N.A.I.C.S.: 312120
Carlos Alves de Brito *(Co-Chm)*
Victorio Carlos De Marchi *(Co-Chm)*
Joao M. Castro Neves *(CEO)*
Joao Mauricio Giffoni de Castro Neves *(CEO)*
Nelson Jose Jamel *(CFO & IR Officer)*
Rodrigo Figueiredo de Souza *(Exec Officer-Supply)*
Michel Dimitrios Doukeris *(Exec Officer-Soft Drinks)*
Ricardo Manuel Frangatos Pires Moreira *(Exec Officer-Hispanic Latin America)*
Milton Seligman *(Exec Officer-Corp Affairs)*
Pedro De Abreu Mariani *(Gen Counsel)*

Non-U.S. Subsidiary:

Quilmes Industrial S.A. (2)
84 Grand-Rue
L-1660 Luxembourg, Luxembourg LU
Tel.: (352) 473885 (91.18%)
Fax: (352) 226056
E-Mail: cries@quilvest.com
LQU—(LUX)
Beer, Mineral Water & Soft Drinks Mfr & Distr
S.I.C.: 2082
N.A.I.C.S.: 312120
Miguel Gomez Eiriz *(CFO)*

Non-U.S. Subsidiary:

FNC S.A. (3)
Entre Rios 1060
Montevideo, 11800, Uruguay UY
Tel.: (598) 2 200 1681 (97.89%)
Fax: (598) 2 2001681
Web Site: www.fnc.com.uy
Sales Range: $25-49.9 Million
Emp.: 400
Beer & Soft Drink Mfr & Distr
S.I.C.: 2082
N.A.I.C.S.: 312120

Compania Cervecera AmBev Dominicana (1)
Av San Martin 279
Zona Industrial de Herrera
Santo Domingo, Dominican Republic
Tel.: (809) 540 7777
Fax: (809) 575 77 96
Web Site: www.ab-inbev.com
Emp.: 1,600
Beer Breweries
S.I.C.: 2082
N.A.I.C.S.: 312120

Crown Beers India Limited (1)
8-2-684/A 6th Floor Bhavya Fantastica Plot No 23 Road No 12
Banjara Hills, Hyderabad, Andra Pradesh, 500034, India In
Tel.: (91) 4023324245 (100%)
Fax: (91) 4023324247
Emp.: 30
Beer Brewer & Distr
S.I.C.: 2082
N.A.I.C.S.: 312120
Kapil Agarwal *(CEO)*

Grupo Modelo, S.A. de C.V. (1)
Lago Alberto 156 Col Anahuac
Mexico, DF, 11320, Mexico MX
Tel.: (52) 55 5262 1100 (100%)
Fax: (52) 55 5280 6718
E-Mail: ir@gmodelo.com.mx
Web Site: www.gmodelo.com
Emp.: 37,307
Beer Producer & Distr
S.I.C.: 2082
N.A.I.C.S.: 312120
Margarita Hugues Velez *(Sec)*

HASSERODER BRAUEREI GmbH (1)
Auerhahnring 1
Wernigerode, 38855, Germany
Tel.: (49) 3943 93 60
Fax: (49) 3943 93 60
E-Mail: info@hasseroeder.de
Web Site: hasseroeder.de
Beverage Products Mfr
S.I.C.: 2082
N.A.I.C.S.: 312120

InBev N.V. (1)
Ceresstraat 1
PO Box 3212
4800 MA Breda, Netherlands (100%)
Tel.: (31) 765252424
Telex: 54217 biere
Fax: (31) 765252505
E-Mail: info.netherlands@inbev.com
Web Site: www.vestbro.nl
Emp.: 125
Beer Brewery
S.I.C.: 2082
N.A.I.C.S.: 312120

INBEV SEDRIN BREWERY Co, Ltd (1)
No 660 Gongye Road
Hanjiang District, Putian, 351111, China
Tel.: (86) 5943587303
Fax: (86) 5943597390
Beer Mfr
S.I.C.: 2082
N.A.I.C.S.: 312120

InBev UK Ltd. (1)
Porter Tun House 500 Capability Green
Luton, Beds, LU1 3LS, United Kingdom (100%)
Tel.: (44) 1582391166
Fax: (44) 1582397439
Web Site: www.inbev.co.uk
Emp.: 2,961
Brewing, Packaging, Beer Marketing & Distribution
S.I.C.: 2082
N.A.I.C.S.: 312120
Carlos Brito *(CEO)*
Felipe Dutra *(CFO)*

INTERBREW INTERNATIONAL B.V. (1)
Ceresstraat 1
Breda, 4811 CA, Netherlands
Tel.: (31) 765 25 23 98
Fax: (31) 765252505
E-Mail: info.netherlands@inbev.com
Alcoholic Beverage Mfr & Distr
S.I.C.: 2082
N.A.I.C.S.: 312120

Kamenitza AD (1)
Kapitan Raitcho St 95
BG 4000 Plovdiv, Bulgaria (87%)
Tel.: (359) 32621560
Web Site: www.kamenitza.bg
Brewery
S.I.C.: 2082
N.A.I.C.S.: 312120
Dragan Radovoevich *(Gen Mgr)*

Labatt Brewing Company Limited (1)
207 Queens Quay West Ste 299
Toronto, ON, M5J 1A7, Canada (100%)
Tel.: (416) 361-5050
Fax: (416) 361-5200
Toll Free: (866) 666-6057
E-Mail: guest@labatt.com
Web Site: www.labatt.com
Emp.: 3,000
Brewing Company
S.I.C.: 2082
N.A.I.C.S.: 312120
Christine Hamilton *(Assoc Brand Mgr-Budweiser)*

Plants:

Columbia Brewing Company (2)
1220 Erikson St
PO Box 1950
Creston, BC, V0B 1G0, Canada (100%)
Tel.: (250) 428-9344
Fax: (250) 428-3433
E-Mail: ino@labatt.com
Web Site: www.labatt.com
Emp.: 125
Brewery Services
S.I.C.: 2082
N.A.I.C.S.: 312120
Murray Oswald *(Gen Mgr)*

La Brasserie Labatt (2)
50 Labatt Ave
Montreal, QC, H8R 3E7, Canada (100%)
Tel.: (514) 366-5050
Fax: (514) 364-8045
Web Site: www.labatt.com
Emp.: 1,200
Beer Mfr
S.I.C.: 2082
N.A.I.C.S.: 312120
Yvon Payette *(Mgr-Fin)*

Labatt Breweries Atlantic Region (2)
3055 Aricola St
Halifax, NS, B3K 4G2, Canada (100%)
Tel.: (902) 453-1867
Fax: (902) 453-3847
Web Site: www.labatt.com
Emp.: 275
Beer Distr
S.I.C.: 5181
N.A.I.C.S.: 424810
Kevin Ffearn *(Mgr - HR)*

Labatt Breweries of London (2)
150 Simcoe St Ste A
London, ON, N6A 4M3, Canada (100%)
Tel.: (519) 663-5050
Fax: (519) 667-7532
Web Site: www.labatt.com
Emp.: 450
Beer Mfr
S.I.C.: 2082
N.A.I.C.S.: 312120

Labatt Breweries of Newfoundland (2)
60 Leslie St
Saint John's, NL, A1E 2V8, Canada (100%)
Tel.: (709) 579-0121
Fax: (709) 579-2018
Web Site: www.labatt.com
Emp.: 100
Beer Mfr
S.I.C.: 2082
N.A.I.C.S.: 312120

Labatt Breweries Ontario Ltd. (2)
445 Export Blvd
Mississauga, ON, L5S 0A1, Canada (50%)
Tel.: (905) 696-3300
Web Site: www.labatts.com
Emp.: 50
Beer Mfr
S.I.C.: 2082
N.A.I.C.S.: 312120

Labatt Breweries Prairie Region (2)
4344-99 St
Edmonton, AB, T6E 6K8, Canada
Tel.: (780) 436-6060
Fax: (780) 436-3656
E-Mail: guest@labatt.com
Web Site: www.labatt.com
Emp.: 200
Beer Mfr
S.I.C.: 2082
N.A.I.C.S.: 312120

SPATEN - FRANZISKANER - BRAU GmbH (1)
Marsstrae 46-48
Munich, Germany
Tel.: (49) 89 5122 0
Fax: (49) 89 5222 2400
Web Site: www.spatenbeer.com
Alcoholic Beverage Mfr
S.I.C.: 2082
N.A.I.C.S.: 312120

ANHUI ANKE BIOTECHNOLOGY (GROUP) CO., LTD.

Anke Bio Building 669 Changjiang Road West
Hefei, Anhi, 230088, China
Tel.: (86) 5515319890
Fax: (86) 5515319895
E-Mail: ankebio@mail.hf.ah.cn
Web Site: www.ankebio.com
Business Description:
Biological Products Mfr
S.I.C.: 2836
N.A.I.C.S.: 325414
Personnel:
Lihua Song *(Chm)*

ANHUI ANLI ARTIFICIAL LEATHER CO., LTD.

Anhui Hefei Economic and Technological Development Zone Industrial Par
Hefei, Anhui, 230601, China
Tel.: (86) 551 8991746
Fax: (86) 551 8991640
E-Mail: anli@mail.hf.ah.cn
Web Site: www.chinapuleather.com
300218—(CHIN)
Sales Range: $125-149.9 Million
Emp.: 1,500
Business Description:
Synthetic Leather Mfr
S.I.C.: 3199
N.A.I.C.S.: 316998
Personnel:
Huasheng Yao *(Chm)*

ANHUI CONCH CEMENT COMPANY LIMITED

Conch International Convention Centre 1011 Jiuhuashan South Road
Wuhu, Anhui, China
Tel.: (86) 5538398999
Fax: (86) 5538398753
E-Mail: cement@conch.cn
Web Site: www.conch.cn
600585—(HKG OTC SHG)
Sls.: $7,269,961,347
Assets: $13,903,111,629
Liabilities: $5,833,035,858
Net Worth: $8,070,075,771
Earnings: $1,030,401,017
Emp.: 43,875
Fiscal Year-end: 12/31/12
Business Description:
Cement & Clinker Developer, Producer & Seller
S.I.C.: 3241
N.A.I.C.S.: 327310
Personnel:
Wensan Guo *(Chm)*
Leo Pak Yue Chiu *(Sec)*
Board of Directors:
Wensan Guo
Meicai Ding
Jingbin Guo
Qinying Ji
Woon Kang
Kun Kau Wong
Jianping Wu
Mingjing Zhang
Supervisory Board of Directors:
Feng Ding
Yanmou Wang
KPMG
8th Floor Princes Building 10 Chater Road
Central, China (Hong Kong)
Legal Counsel:
Jingtian & Gongcheng
15/F The Union Plaza 20 Chaoyangmen Wai Dajie
Beijing, 100020, China
Chiu & Partners
41 Floor Jardine House 1 Connaught Place
Central, China (Hong Kong)
Transfer Agent:
Hong Kong Registrars Limited
46/F Hopewell Centre 183 Queens Road East
Wanchai, China (Hong Kong)

Subsidiaries:

Anhui Changfeng Conch Cement Co., Ltd. (1)
Shuangdun Town
Changfeng, Hefei, Anhui, China
Tel.: (86) 5516377090
Cement Mfr
S.I.C.: 3241
N.A.I.C.S.: 327310

Shanghai Conch Cement Co., Ltd. (1)
No 90 Punan Rd
Xidu Town Fengxia, Shanghai, China
Tel.: (86) 2157159100
Cement Mfr
S.I.C.: 3241
N.A.I.C.S.: 327310

Anhui Conch Cement Company Limited—(Continued)

Shanghai Conch Construction Material International Trading Co., Ltd. **(1)**
Rm 1101-1102 Yu an Bldg No 738
Pudong New Area, 200122 Shanghai, China
Tel.: (86) 2158209601
Fax: (86) 2123010307
E-Mail: ld@trade.conch.cn
Emp.: 22
Cement Mfr
S.I.C.: 3241
N.A.I.C.S.: 327310
Yuan Lin *(Gen Mgr)*

Shuangfeng Conch Cement Co., Ltd. **(1)**
Chachong Vlg Santangpu Town
Loudi, Hunan, China
Tel.: (86) 7386625050
Cement Mfr
S.I.C.: 3241
N.A.I.C.S.: 327310

Taicang Conch Cement Co., Ltd. **(1)**
Sangang Vlg Ludu Town
Taicang, Suzhou, Jiangsu, 215400, China
Tel.: (86) 51281606590
Fax: (86) 051281606522
Cement Mfr
S.I.C.: 3241
N.A.I.C.S.: 327310

ANHUI DELI HOUSEHOLD GLASS CO., LTD.

Anhui Fengyang Gate Industrial Park
Chuzhou, 233121, China
Tel.: (86) 5506678862
Fax: (86) 5506679688
Web Site: www.deliglass.com
Year Founded: 1996
002571—(SSE)
Sales Range: $75-99.9 Million
Emp.: 2,100

Business Description:
Household Glass Products Mfr & Sales
S.I.C.: 3221
N.A.I.C.S.: 327213

Personnel:
Wei Dong Shi *(CEO)*

ANHUI EXPRESSWAY COMPANY LIMITED

520 Wangjiang West Road
Hefei, Anhui, China 230088
Tel.: (86) 5515338697
Fax: (86) 5515338696
E-Mail: wtgs@anhui-expressway.net
Web Site: www.anhui-expressway.net
Year Founded: 1996
600012—(HKG OTC SHG)
Rev.: $495,985,298
Assets: $1,818,437,599
Liabilities: $639,693,239
Net Worth: $1,178,744,360
Earnings: $131,684,267
Emp.: 1,946
Fiscal Year-end: 12/31/12

Business Description:
Toll Expressway Construction & Management Services
S.I.C.: 1622
N.A.I.C.S.: 237310

Personnel:
Renqiang Zhou *(Chm)*
Wei Sheng Wang *(Chm-Supervisory Bd)*
Xiao Bei Tu *(Vice Chm)*

Board of Directors:
Renqiang Zhou
Yunfei Cui
Bin Hu
Jiezhi Li
Jun Jie Li
Xianfu Liu
Jie Meng
Xiao Bei Tu
Mianzhi Yang

Supervisory Board of Directors:
Wei Sheng Wang
Wenjie Wang
Yicong Yang

PricewaterhouseCoopers
22nd Floor Prince's Building
Central, China (Hong Kong)
Tel.: (852) 2 826 2111

Legal Counsel:
Gallant Y.T. Ho & Co.
5th Floor Jardine House 1 Connaught Place
Central, China (Hong Kong)
Tel.: (852) 2526 3336
Fax: (852) 2845 9294

Anhui Expressway Lawyer's Office
19th Floor Wangcheng Mansion 248
Changjiang West Road
Hefei, Anhui, China

China Securities Central Clearing and Registration Corporation
36th Floor China Insurance Mansion 166
Lujiazui East Road
Shanghai, China

Transfer Agent:
China Securities Central Clearing & Registration Corporation
China Insurance Mansion 166 Liujiazui East Road
Shanghai, China

ANHUI HELI CO., LTD.

No 15 West Wangjiang Road
Hefei, Anhui, China 230022
Tel.: (86) 551 3648005
E-Mail: heli@helichina.com
Web Site: www.helichina.com
Year Founded: 1958
600761—(SHG)

Business Description:
Industrial Vehicle & Construction Machinery Mfr
S.I.C.: 3537
N.A.I.C.S.: 333924

Personnel:
Dejin Zhang *(Chm)*

ANHUI HONGLU STEEL CONSTRUCTION (GROUP) CO., LTD.

(d/b/a Honglu Group)
Shuangfeng Industry Zone
Hefei, Anhui, China
Tel.: (86) 551 6391405
Fax: (86) 551 6391725
E-Mail: honglu002@hong-lu.cn
Web Site: www.hong-lu.com
002541—(SSE)
Sales Range: $150-199.9 Million

Business Description:
Steel Structure Products Mfr
S.I.C.: 3441
N.A.I.C.S.: 332312

Personnel:
Xiaobo Shang *(Chm)*

ANHUI JIANGHUAI AUTOMOBILE CO., LTD.

176 Dongliu Road
Hefei, Anhui, China 230022
Tel.: (86) 551 62296601
Web Site: www.jac.com.cn
Year Founded: 1964
600418—(SHG)

Business Description:
Automobile Mfr
S.I.C.: 3711
N.A.I.C.S.: 336111

Personnel:
Jin An *(Chm)*

ANHUI JINHE INDUSTRIAL CO., LTD.

East Street No 127
Hefei, Anhui, China 239200
Tel.: (86) 550 5624224
E-Mail: jinheshiye@jinheshiye.com
Web Site: www.jinheshiye.com
002597—(SSE)

Business Description:
Chemical Product Mfr
S.I.C.: 2899
N.A.I.C.S.: 325998

Personnel:
Yingchun Yang *(Chm)*

ANHUI JUAN KUANG ELECTRIC CO., LTD.

No 79 Shanmen South Road
Ningguo, Anhui, 242300, China
Tel.: (86) 5634180988
Fax: (86) 5634180818
E-Mail: ahjk@jkdq.com
Web Site: www.jkdq.com
Emp.: 400

Business Description:
Capacitors Mfr
S.I.C.: 3676
N.A.I.C.S.: 334416

Personnel:
Haito Wen *(Gen Mgr)*

ANHUI SAUNAKING CO., LTD.

34 Hehuan Road High-Tech Development Zone
Hefei, Anhui, China
Tel.: (86) 551 5329292
Fax: (86) 551 5329191
E-Mail: sales@chinasauna.com
Web Site: www.chinasauna.com
Year Founded: 1995
300247—(CHIN)
Sales Range: $25-49.9 Million
Emp.: 380

Business Description:
Saunas & Related Products
S.I.C.: 3999
N.A.I.C.S.: 335210

Personnel:
Daoming Jin *(Chm)*

ANHUI SHENGYUN MACHINERY CO., LTD.

(d/b/a Shengyun Machinery)
265 Tong'an Road
Tongcheng, Anhui, 231400, China
Tel.: (86) 5566207688
Fax: (86) 5566205898
E-Mail: ahsy@sy-168.com
Web Site: www.sy-168.com
300090—(CHIN)

Business Description:
Conveyor Mfr
S.I.C.: 3535
N.A.I.C.S.: 333922

Personnel:
Xioasheng Kai *(CEO)*

ANHUI SHENJIAN NEW MATERIALS CO., LTD.

The National Level Economic Development Zone
Wuhu, 241008, China
Tel.: (86) 553 5316331
Fax: (86) 553 5316330
E-Mail: wang@shen-jian.com.cn
Web Site: www.shen-jian.com.cn
002361—(SSE)
Sales Range: $50-74.9 Million
Emp.: 260

Business Description:
Polyester Resins Mfr & Sales
S.I.C.: 2821
N.A.I.C.S.: 325211

Personnel:
Zhijian Liu *(Chm)*

ANHUI SIERTE FERTILIZER INDUSTRY CO., LTD.

(d/b/a Sierte Fertilizer)
Anhui Province Economic and Technological Development
Ningguo, 242300, China
Tel.: (86) 5634181598
Fax: (86) 5634181525
Web Site: www.sierte.com
002538—(SSE)
Emp.: 1,500

Business Description:
Fertilizer Mfr
S.I.C.: 2873
N.A.I.C.S.: 325311

Personnel:
Guoqing Jin *(Chm)*

ANHUI TAIER HEAVY INDUSTRY CO., LTD.

18 South Hongqi Road Economic & Technological Development Zone
Ma'anshan, Anhui, 243000, China
Tel.: (86) 555 2229303
Fax: (86) 555 2229287
E-Mail: taier@taier.biz
Web Site: www.taier.info
002347—(SSE)

Business Description:
Mechanical Power Transmission Equipment & Shearing Blades Mfr & Distr
S.I.C.: 3568
N.A.I.C.S.: 333613

Personnel:
Zhengbiao Tai *(Chm)*

ANHUI TIANDA OIL PIPE COMPANY LIMITED

Zhengxing Road
Tongcheng, Anhui, China 239311
Tel.: (86) 550 7518892
Fax: (86) 550 7518895
E-Mail: xsk@td-gg.com
Web Site: www.td-gg.com
Year Founded: 1993
TJO—(DEU HKG)
Rev.: $629,133,050
Assets: $427,122,075
Liabilities: $59,889,468
Net Worth: $367,232,607
Earnings: $5,573,411
Emp.: 1,990
Fiscal Year-end: 12/31/12

Business Description:
Oil & Gas Pipe Mfr
S.I.C.: 3498
N.A.I.C.S.: 332996

Personnel:
Shiqu Ye *(Chm)*
Huming Zhang *(Vice Chm & Gen Mgr)*
Shing Kei Shum *(Sec)*

Transfer Agent:
Computershare Hong Kong Investor Services Limited
Shops 1712-1716 17th Floor Hopewell Centre
183 Queens Road East
Wanchai, China (Hong Kong)

ANHUI USTC IFLYTEK CO., LTD.

iFLYTEK Mansion 616 Huangshan Rd Information Industry Base
Hefei, Anhui, China 230088
Tel.: (86) 5515331807
E-Mail: iflytek@iflytek.com
Web Site: www.iflytek.com
002230—(SSE)

Business Description:
Software Development Services
S.I.C.: 7371
N.A.I.C.S.: 541511

Personnel:
Bo Yin *(Dir-Res)*

ANHUI WANTONG TECHNOLOGY CO., LTD.

7 Mengyuan Road Hi Tech Zone
Hefei, 230088, China
Tel.: (86) 551 5318666
Fax: (86) 551 5311668
Web Site: www.wantong-tech.net
002331—(SSE)
Sales Range: $10-24.9 Million
Emp.: 200
Business Description:
IT Services
S.I.C.: 7373
N.A.I.C.S.: 541512
Personnel:
Zhongsheng Wang *(Chm)*

ANHUI WANWEI UPDATED HI-TECH MATERIAL INDUSTRY COMPANY LIMITED

56 Wanwei Road
Chaohu, Anhui, 238002, China
Tel.: (86) 565 2317212
Fax: (86) 565 2317447
Web Site: www.wwgf.com.cn
600063—(SHG)
Sales Range: $350-399.9 Million
Emp.: 3,100
Business Description:
Chemical Products Mfr
S.I.C.: 2899
N.A.I.C.S.: 325998
Personnel:
Fusheng Wu *(Chm)*

ANHUI XINHUA MEDIA CO., LTD.

279 Changjiang Middle Road
Hefei, 230001, China
Tel.: (86) 551 2661323
E-Mail: ahtsfx@ahsxhsd.com
Web Site: www.ahsxhsd.com
601801—(SHG)
Business Description:
Textbooks, Books, Video & Audio Products Publisher, Retailer & Whslr
S.I.C.: 2731
N.A.I.C.S.: 511130
Personnel:
Zhimin Ni *(Chm)*

ANHUI XINLONG ELECTRIC COMPANY, LTD.

118 Jiuhua North Road Appliance Parts Park
Eco & Tech Dev Zone, Wuhu, Anhui, 241008, China
Tel.: (86) 5535772627
Fax: (86) 5535312688
E-Mail: sales@ah-xinlong.com
Web Site: www.ah-xinlong.com
002298—(SSE)
Emp.: 840
Business Description:
Voltage Switch Equipment, Components & Automatic Control Products Mfr
S.I.C.: 3613
N.A.I.C.S.: 335313
Personnel:
Longsheng Shu *(Chm)*

ANHUI ZHONGDING HOLDING (GROUP) CO., LTD.

Ningguo Economic & Tech Development Zone
Ningguo, Anhui, 242300, China
Tel.: (86) 563 418 1800
Fax: (86) 563 418 1880
E-Mail: office@zhongdinggroup.com
Web Site: www.zhongdinggroup.com
Year Founded: 1980
Business Description:
Holding Company; Automotive Parts Mfr
S.I.C.: 6719
N.A.I.C.S.: 551112
Personnel:
Dinghu Xia *(Chm)*

U.S. Subsidiary:

Zhongding U.S.A., Inc. **(1)**
400 Detroit Ave
Monroe, MI 48162 MI
Tel.: (734) 241-8870
Holding Company; Industrial Supplies Mfr & Distr
S.I.C.: 6719
N.A.I.C.S.: 551112
Jaison Xia *(Pres)*

Subsidiary:

Zhongding Sealing Parts (USA), Inc. **(2)**
310 Railroad Ave Ext
Strasburg, OH 44680 OH
Tel.: (330) 878-7800
Fax: (330) 878-7850
Holding Company; Rubber Sealant Products Mfr
S.I.C.: 6719
N.A.I.C.S.: 551112
Steve Seketa *(Gen Mgr)*

Subsidiaries:

Allied-Baltic Rubber, Inc. **(3)**
310 Railroad Ave Ext
Strasburg, OH 44680 OH
Tel.: (330) 878-7800
Fax: (330) 878-7850
Emp.: 175
Rubber Products
S.I.C.: 3069
N.A.I.C.S.: 326299
Fred Burgess *(Gen Mgr)*

BRP Hannibal, Inc. **(3)**
5151 Industrial Dr
Hannibal, MO 63401-0998 MO (100%)
Tel.: (573) 221-8933
Fax: (573) 221-7144
Web Site: www.buckhornrubber.com
Sales Range: $125-149.9 Million
Emp.: 300
Rubber Products Mfr
S.I.C.: 3069
N.A.I.C.S.: 326299
Dennis R. Roberts *(Gen Mgr)*

ANICOM HOLDINGS, INC.

1-5-22 Shimoochiai Shinjuku-ku
Tokyo, 161-0033, Japan
Tel.: (81) 353483911
Fax: (81) 359256959
E-Mail: release@ani-com.com
Web Site: www.anicom.co.jp
8715—(TKS)
Sales Range: $100-124.9 Million
Emp.: 247
Business Description:
Insurance Services
S.I.C.: 6411
N.A.I.C.S.: 524298
Personnel:
Nobuaki Komori *(Pres)*

ANIK INDUSTRIES LTD.

610 Tulsiani Chambers Nariman Point
Mumbai, 400 021, India
Tel.: (91) 22 22824851
Fax: (91) 22 22042865
E-Mail: anik@anikgroup.com
Web Site: www.anikgroup.com
519383—(BOM)
Rev.: $241,785,386
Assets: $155,326,542
Liabilities: $110,879,315
Net Worth: $44,447,228
Earnings: $1,977,161
Emp.: 365
Fiscal Year-end: 03/31/13
Business Description:
Dairy Products Mfr
S.I.C.: 2023
N.A.I.C.S.: 311514
Personnel:
Manish Shahra *(Co-Mng Dir)*
Suresh Chandra Shahra *(Co-Mng Dir)*
Shailesh Kumath *(Compliance Officer & Sec)*
Board of Directors:
Kailash Chandra Shahra
Hari Narayan Bhatnagar
K. K. Gupta
Vijay Rathi
Manish Shahra
Suresh Chandra Shahra
Ashok Trivedi
Transfer Agent:
Sarthak Global Limited
170 10 Film Colony R.N.T. Marg
Indore, India

Subsidiary:

Anik Ferro-Alloys Pvt. Ltd **(1)**
2/1 South Tukoganj
Indore, 452 001, India
Tel.: (91) 731 4018009
Fax: (91) 731 4018010
Ferrous Alloy Mfr
S.I.C.: 3399
N.A.I.C.S.: 331110

ANIL LTD.

Anil Road Bapunagar
P O Box 10009
Ahmedabad, 380025, India
Tel.: (91) 79 22203222
Fax: (91) 79 22200731
E-Mail: mktg.apl@anil.co.in
Web Site: www.anil.co.in
532910—(BOM)
Rev.: $135,103,353
Assets: $149,213,220
Liabilities: $102,264,489
Net Worth: $46,948,731
Earnings: $8,499,422
Fiscal Year-end: 03/31/13
Business Description:
Corn Starch Mfr
S.I.C.: 2046
N.A.I.C.S.: 311221
Personnel:
Amol S. Sheth *(Chm & Mng Dir)*
Dipal Palkhiwala *(CFO)*
Chandresh B. Pandya *(Compliance Officer & Sec)*
Board of Directors:
Amol S. Sheth
Shashin Desai
Anurag V. Kothawala
Indiraben J. Parikh
Anish K. Shah
Kamal R. Sheth
Transfer Agent:
Link Intime India Pvt. Ltd.
211 Sudarshan Complex Near Mithakhali Under Bridge Navrangpura
Ahmedabad, India

ANIL SPECIAL STEEL INDUSTRIES LTD.

Kanakpura PO Meenawala
Jaipur, India 302012
Tel.: (91) 141 2470211
Fax: (91) 141 2470863
E-Mail: info@anilspecialsteel.com
Web Site: www.anilspecialsteel.com
504629—(BOM)
Sales Range: $10-24.9 Million
Business Description:
Steel Machinery Equipment Mfr
S.I.C.: 3317
N.A.I.C.S.: 331210
Personnel:
Sudhir Khaitan *(Chm & Mng Dir)*
Board of Directors:
Sudhir Khaitan
Purshottam Lal Bawa
Vipin Behari Lal Mathur
Shiv Shankar Sharma
Transfer Agent:
MCS Limited
Shri Venkatesh Bhawan W-40 Okhla Ind Area Phase II
New Delhi, India

ANIMALCARE GROUP PLC

10 Great North Way York Business Park
Nether Poppleton, York, YO26 6RB, United Kingdom
Tel.: (44) 1904 487687
Fax: (44) 1904 487615
E-Mail: info@animalcaregroup.co.uk
Web Site: www.animalcaregroup.co.uk
ANCR—(AIM)
Rev.: $19,137,836
Assets: $33,932,625
Liabilities: $5,565,418
Net Worth: $28,367,207
Earnings: $2,976,962
Emp.: 57
Fiscal Year-end: 06/30/13
Business Description:
Veterinary Products & Services Development, Marketing & Sales
S.I.C.: 5999
N.A.I.C.S.: 453910
Personnel:
Chris Brewster *(CFO & Sec)*
Board of Directors:
James S. Lambert
Chris Brewster
Nick Downshire
Raymond Bryan Harding
Iain D. Menneer
Stephen M. Wildridge
Legal Counsel:
Langleys LLP
Queens House Micklegate
York, YO1 6WG, United Kingdom

Subsidiaries:

Animalcare Limited **(1)**
10 Great Northway York Business Park
Dunnington, York, YO26 6RB, United Kingdom
Tel.: (44) 1904487687
Fax: (44) 1904487611
E-Mail: office@animalcare.co.uk
Web Site: www.animalcare.co.uk
Emp.: 30
Veterinary Products Mfr & Supplier
S.I.C.: 5999
N.A.I.C.S.: 453910
Stephen M. Wildridge *(Mng Dir)*

ANIMAS RESOURCES LTD.

325 Howe Street Suite 410
Vancouver, BC, V6C 1Z7, Canada
Tel.: (604) 687-6197
Fax: (604) 688-3392
Web Site: www.animasresources.com
Year Founded: 2006
ANI—(TSXV)
Rev.: $119,403
Assets: $14,886,670
Liabilities: $358,921
Net Worth: $14,527,749
Earnings: ($486,757)
Fiscal Year-end: 12/31/12
Business Description:
Mineral Exploration Services
S.I.C.: 1081
N.A.I.C.S.: 213114

Animas Resources Ltd.—(Continued)

Personnel:
Mark Thomas Brown *(Interim Pres & Interim CEO)*
Winnie Wong *(CFO)*
Board of Directors:
Mark Thomas Brown
Gregory Ellis McKelvey
Hugh Miller
Donald E. Ranta
Transfer Agent:
Computershare Trust Company of Canada
510 Burrard St 2nd Fl
Vancouver, BC, Canada

ANIPET ANIMAL SUPPLIES INC.

19038 24th Avenue
Surrey, BC, V3S 3S9, Canada
Tel.: (604) 536-3367
Fax: (604) 536-3379
Toll Free: (888) 926-4738
Web Site: www.anipet.com
Year Founded: 1977
Rev.: $41,388,542
Emp.: 113
Business Description:
Pet Supplies & Pet Food Distr
S.I.C.: 5999
N.A.I.C.S.: 453910
Personnel:
Larry Kellington *(Pres)*

ANISHA IMPEX LIMITED

56/33 Site - IV Industrial Area
Sahibabad, Ghaziabad, Uttar Pradesh, 201010, India
Tel.: (91) 120 4543708
Fax: (91) 120 416 7930
E-Mail: contact@anishaimpex.com
Web Site: www.anishaimpex.com
Rev.: $34,731,827
Emp.: 11
Fiscal Year-end: 12/31/13
Business Description:
Home Textile Products
S.I.C.: 2389
N.A.I.C.S.: 314999
Personnel:
Sunil Kumar Malik *(Mng Dir)*
Ram Mohan Jha *(Compliance Officer & Sec)*
Board of Directors:
Sachin Kumar Agarwal
Puja Malik
Sunil Kumar Malik
Dinesh Singh Patwal

ANITE PLC

353 Buckingham Avenue
Slough, Berkshire, SL1 4PF, United Kingdom
Tel.: (44) 1753 804000
Fax: (44) 1753 804497
E-Mail: publicsector@anite.com
Web Site: www.anite.com
Year Founded: 1984
AIE—(LSE)
Rev.: $209,270,139
Assets: $305,633,677
Liabilities: $133,156,257
Net Worth: $172,477,419
Earnings: $30,530,834
Emp.: 538
Fiscal Year-end: 04/30/13
Business Description:
IT Solutions & Consulting Services to the Finance, Telecommunications, Travel Industry & Public Sector Markets
S.I.C.: 7373
N.A.I.C.S.: 541512
Personnel:
Christopher Humphrey *(CEO)*
Kari Ojala *(CTO-Network Testing Bus)*
Ari Niskanen *(Pres-Singapore Office-Network Testing Bus)*
Neil Bass *(Sec)*
Heikki Koivuaho *(Sr VP-Sls & Mktg-Network Testing Bus)*
Pasi Niemi *(Sr VP-Bus Dev & Product Mgmt-Network Testing Bus)*
Board of Directors:
Clayton Brendish
Nigel Clifford
Patrick De Smedt
Christopher Humphrey
David Hurst-Brown
Paul Taylor
Legal Counsel:
Simmons & Simmons
CityPoint 1 Ropemaker Street
London, ED2Y 9SS, United Kingdom
Subsidiaries:

Anite Business Systems Limited (1)
353 Buckingham Ave
SL1 4PF Slough, Berkshire, United Kingdom (100%)
Tel.: (44) 1753804000
Fax: (44) 1753809735
Emp.: 30
Computer & Computer Peripheral Equipment & Software Merchant Whslr
S.I.C.: 5045
N.A.I.C.S.: 423430

Anite Financial Management Limited (1)
353 Buckingham Ave
Slough, Berkshire, United Kingdom
Tel.: (44) 1753804000
Information Technology Consulting Services
S.I.C.: 7373
N.A.I.C.S.: 541512

U.S. Subsidiaries:

Anite Inc. (1)
6225 N State Hwy 161 Ste 425
Irving, TX 75038 (100%)
Tel.: (469) 951-9106
Fax: (972) 929-9898
E-Mail: wireless@anite.com
Web Site: www.anite.com
Emp.: 25
Cellular & Other Wireless Telecommunications
S.I.C.: 4812
N.A.I.C.S.: 517210
Markku Poibiainen *(Gen Mgr)*

Anite Telecoms Inc (1)
1900 E Golf Rd Centennial Ctr Ste M50
Schaumburg, IL 60173 (100%)
Tel.: (847) 273-3800
Fax: (847) 995-0085
E-Mail: wireless@anite.com
Web Site: www.anite.com
Emp.: 35
Cellular & Other Wireless Telecommunications
S.I.C.: 4812
N.A.I.C.S.: 517210
Kevin Wrinters *(Reg VP)*

Non-U.S. Subsidiaries:

Anite Finland Oy (1)
Kiviharjunlenkki 1 D
90220 Oulu, Finland FI
Tel.: (358) 503957700
Fax: (358) 85516182
E-Mail: nemo@anite.com
Web Site: www.anite.com
Emp.: 50
Mfr & Developer of Solutions for the Measurement Needs of Operators, Network Providers & Consultants for the Wireless Network Life Cycle
S.I.C.: 3699
N.A.I.C.S.: 335999
Kai Ojala *(CTO)*

Subsidiaries:

Anite Travel Systems AB Ltd (2)
Kiviharjunlenkki 1 D
90220 Oulu, Finland (100%)
Tel.: (358) 503957700
Fax: (358) 85516182
E-Mail:
Web Site: www.anite.com
Emp.: 19
Software Publishers
S.I.C.: 7372
N.A.I.C.S.: 511210

Anite Singapore Pte. Ltd. (1)
101 Thomson Rd
No 18-04 United Sq, 307591 Singapore, Singapore (100%)
Tel.: (65) 62549003
Fax: (65) 62549885
E-Mail: nemo_apac@anite.com
Web Site: www.anite.com
Emp.: 10
Computer & Computer Peripheral Equipment & Software Merchant Whslr
S.I.C.: 5045
N.A.I.C.S.: 423430
Ari Niskanen *(Pres)*

Anite Telecoms India Pvt Ltd (1)
1st Fl Kabra Excelilsor No 6/A 7th Main 1st Block koromongala
560035 Bengaluru, India (100%)
Tel.: (91) 8040311800
Fax: (91) 8040311810
Web Site: www.anite.com
Emp.: 23
Software Publishers
S.I.C.: 7372
N.A.I.C.S.: 511210
Mike Bonin *(CEO)*

Anite Telecoms KK (1)
22nd Fl 1-6-1 Kamiookanishi
Konan-ku, Yokohama, Kanagawa, 233-0002, Japan (100%)
Tel.: (81) 458492161
Fax: (81) 458492165
E-Mail: wireless@anite.com
Web Site: www.anite.com
Cellular & Other Wireless Telecommunications
S.I.C.: 4812
N.A.I.C.S.: 517210

Anite Telecoms Korea Ltd (1)
#1803 Korea Teachers Pension Building
27-2 Yoido-Dong, 150-42 Seoul, Korea (South) (100%)
Tel.: (82) 237753661
Fax: (82) 237753662
E-Mail: wonhee.lee@anite.com
Web Site: www.anite.com
Emp.: 30
Cellular & Other Wireless Telecommunications
S.I.C.: 4812
N.A.I.C.S.: 517210
Christopher Humphrey *(CEO)*

Anite Telecoms Ltd (1)
Room 1704 17th Floor No 333 Sec 1
Jilong Rd Xinyi District, 110 Taipei, Taiwan (100%)
Tel.: (886) 227226890
Fax: (886) 227226896
E-Mail: wireless@anite.com
Web Site: www.anitetelecoms.com
Emp.: 4
Cellular & Other Wireless Telecommunications
S.I.C.: 4812
N.A.I.C.S.: 517210
Mike Tonnie *(Mng Dir)*
Paz Anderson *(Mng Dir)*

Anite Wireless Trading (Beijing) Ltd (1)
JB11/09 Jianwai Diplomatic Compound
Jianguomenwai St
Chaoyang District, 100600 Beijing, China
Tel.: (86) 1065678528
Fax: (86) 1065678521
E-Mail: yizhong.yan@anite.com
Web Site: www.anite.com
Emp.: 7
Computer & Computer Peripheral Equipment & Software Merchant Whslr
S.I.C.: 5045
N.A.I.C.S.: 423430
Yan Yizhong *(Gen Mgr)*

Reilrop B.V. (1)
Herculesplein 5
3584 AA Utrecht, Netherlands (100%)
Tel.: (31) 306599200
Fax: (31) 306599201
Emp.: 100
Holding Companies Offices
S.I.C.: 6719
N.A.I.C.S.: 551112

ANITTEL GROUP LIMITED

Level 10/132 Arthur Street
North Sydney, NSW, 2060, Australia
Tel.: (61) 1300 10 11 12
Fax: (61) 1300 88 67 83
E-Mail: enquiries@anittel.com.au
Web Site: www.anittel.com.au
AYG—(ASX)
Rev.: $53,091,869
Assets: $21,060,841
Liabilities: $21,355,755
Net Worth: ($294,914)
Earnings: ($7,703,203)
Emp.: 230
Fiscal Year-end: 06/30/13
Business Description:
IT & Telecommunications Service
S.I.C.: 7379
N.A.I.C.S.: 541519
Personnel:
Peter Kazacos *(Chm & Mng Dir)*
Michael O'Sullivan *(COO)*
Robert Pickering *(CTO)*
Justyn Stedwell *(Sec)*
Board of Directors:
Peter Kazacos
Campbell E. Corfe
Michael O'Sullivan
John Walters

Subsidiaries:

5Star Telecom Pty Ltd. (1)
PO Box 1544
Sydney, NSW, 2060, Australia
Tel.: (61) 1300886784
Fax: (61) 1300886783
E-Mail: enquiries@5startelecom.com.au
Web Site: www.5startelecom.com.au
Emp.: 200
Telecommunication Services
S.I.C.: 4812
N.A.I.C.S.: 517911
Carlos Perez *(Founder)*

Anittel Pty. Ltd. (1)
Unit 3 75 Erindale Rd
Balcatta, WA, 6021, Australia
Tel.: (61) 8 9374 1333
Fax: (61) 8 9374 1334
E-Mail: info@accord.com.au
Web Site: www.anittel.com.au
Emp.: 54
Information Technology Management & Consulting Services
S.I.C.: 7373
N.A.I.C.S.: 541512
Mike Ford *(Mng Dir)*
Steven Crockett *(CTO)*

Anittel (1)
8/82 George St
Bathurst, NSW, 2795, Australia
Tel.: (61) 2 6884 6884
Fax: (61) 1902 243 575
Web Site: www.anittel.com.au
Emp.: 1
Information Technology Services
S.I.C.: 7373
N.A.I.C.S.: 541512
Mathew Dickerson *(Mng Dir)*

OneNetwork Pty Ltd. (1)
71-73 Thistlethwaite St
S Melbourne, Melbourne, VIC, 3205, Australia
Tel.: (61) 383203200
Fax: (61) 383203201
E-Mail: support@onenetwork.com.au
Web Site: www.onenetwork.com.au
Emp.: 30
Voice & Data Communication Services
S.I.C.: 4813
N.A.I.C.S.: 517110
Afshin Mashayekhi *(Gen Mgr)*

Sholl Communications (Aust) Pty Ltd. (1)
71 Thistlethwaite St
S Melbourne, Melbourne, VIC, 3205, Australia
Tel.: (61) 1300 859 879
Fax: (61) 1300 888 829
E-Mail: info@sholl.com.au
Web Site: www.sholl.com.au
Data & Voice Communication Support Services
S.I.C.: 4812
N.A.I.C.S.: 517210

ANJANI PORTLAND CEMENT LTD.
Anjani Cement Centre Plot No 7 & 8
Punjagutta Main Road
Hyderabad, 500 082, India
Tel.: (91) 40 23353038
Fax: (91) 40 2335 3093
E-Mail: info@anjanicement.com
Web Site: www.anjanicement.com
518091—(BOM)
Rev.: $60,633,012
Assets: $76,562,246
Liabilities: $60,795,070
Net Worth: $15,767,176
Earnings: $803,320
Fiscal Year-end: 03/31/13
Business Description:
Cement Mfr
S.I.C.: 3241
N.A.I.C.S.: 327310
Personnel:
K. V. Vishnu Raju *(Chm & Mng Dir)*
A. Siva Sankar Reddy *(Compliance Officer & VP-Fin)*
Board of Directors:
K. V. Vishnu Raju
P. Ramachandra Raju
P. V. R. L. Narasimha Raju
R. A. Rama Raju
P. S. Ranganath
P. V. Subba Rao
Transfer Agent:
Karvy Computershare Private Limited
Plot No 17-24 Vittal Rao Nagar Madhapur
Hyderabad, 500 081, India
Tel.: (91) 40 2342 0818
Subsidiary:

Hitech Print Systems Ltd. (1)
Anjani Cement Centre Plot No 7 & 8 D No 8-2-248/1/7
Nagarjuna Hills Main Road, Hyderabad, 500 082, India
Tel.: (91) 40 2335 1696
Fax: (91) 40 2335 1698
E-Mail: info@hitechprint.com
Web Site: www.hitechprint.com
Business Form Printing Services
S.I.C.: 2759
N.A.I.C.S.: 323111

Unit:

Anjani Portland Cement Ltd. - Nalgonda Works (1)
Anjani Puram Malkapuram Post
Mellacheruvu Mandal
Chintalapalem Village, Nalgonda, Andhra Pradesh, 508 246, India
Tel.: (91) 8683 230 168
Fax: (91) 8683 230 024
E-Mail: works@anjanicement.com
Cement Mfr
S.I.C.: 3241
N.A.I.C.S.: 327310

ANJANI SYNTHETICS LTD.
202 Kaivanna Nr Panchvati Circle
Ellisbridge, Ahmedabad, Gujarat, 380 006, India
Tel.: (91) 79 26462955
Fax: (91) 79 26462960
E-Mail: info@anjanisynthetics.com
Web Site: www.anjanisynthetics.com
531223—(BOM)
Sales Range: $25-49.9 Million
Business Description:
Synthetic Textile Products Mfr
S.I.C.: 2389
N.A.I.C.S.: 314999
Personnel:
Vasudev S. Agarwal *(Chm, CFO & Mng Dir)*
Board of Directors:
Vasudev S. Agarwal
Mahavirprasad Santlal Dalmia
Manoj H. Lunia
Ajaykumar Chinubhai Shah
Transfer Agent:
Sharepro Services (India) Pvt. Ltd.
416-420 Devnandan Mall Opp. Sanyas Ashram Ellisbridge
Ahmedabad, India
Plant:

Anjani Synthetics Ltd. - Ahmedabad Plant (1)
140 Pirana Road
Piplej, Ahmedabad, Gujarat, 382 405, India
Tel.: (91) 79 22173181
Fax: (91) 79 25715553
Bed Sheet & Apparel Mfr
S.I.C.: 2259
N.A.I.C.S.: 313240

ANKA INDIA LIMITED
Village & P O Kherki Daula
Gurgaon, Haryana, 122001, India
Tel.: (91) 124 41539232
E-Mail: response@ankaindia.com
Web Site: www.ankaindia.com
Year Founded: 1997
531673—(BOM)
Sales Range: Less than $1 Million
Business Description:
Shoe Soles Mfr
S.I.C.: 3199
N.A.I.C.S.: 316998
Personnel:
Dinesh Arora *(Sec)*

ANKER-TEPPICHBODEN GEBRUDER SCHOELLER GMBH & CO. KG
Zollhausstrasse 112
D 52353 Duren, Germany
Tel.: (49) 24218040
Fax: (49) 2421804200
E-Mail: ankder@anker-teppichboden.de
Web Site: www.anker-teppichboden.de
Year Founded: 1854
Emp.: 420
Business Description:
Mfr. of Carpets
S.I.C.: 2273
N.A.I.C.S.: 314110
Personnel:
Mark Scheller *(Pres)*
Division:

ANKER-Teppichboden Gebruder Schoeller GmbH & Co. KG - Aviation Division (1)
Zollhausstrasse 112
Postfach 10 19 26
52353 Duren, Germany
Tel.: (49) 24 21 804 0
Fax: (49) 24 21 804 200
E-Mail: export@anker-dueren.de
Emp.: 300
Aircraft Carpet Mfr
S.I.C.: 2273
N.A.I.C.S.: 314110
Markus Schoeller, *(Mng Partner)*

ANKIT METAL & POWER LTD.
35 Chittranjan Avenue
Kolkata, 700 012, India
Tel.: (91) 33 2211 9805
Fax: (91) 33 2211 4134
E-Mail: enquiry@ankitmetal.com
Web Site: www.ankitmetal.com
532870—(BOM)
Rev.: $247,012,925
Assets: $307,059,220
Liabilities: $214,515,401
Net Worth: $92,543,819
Earnings: $9,490,255
Emp.: 538
Fiscal Year-end: 03/31/13
Business Description:
Steel Products Mfr & Distr
S.I.C.: 3312
N.A.I.C.S.: 331110
Personnel:
Ankit Patni *(Mng Dir)*
Chandra Kumar Jain *(Compliance Officer, Sec & Gen Mgr-Fin & Accts)*
Board of Directors:
Suresh Kumar Patni
Jayanta Kumar Chatterjee
Ankit Patni
Jatindra Nath Rudra
Jay Shanker Shukla
Sanjay Singh
Transfer Agent:
Link Intime India Pvt. Ltd.
59-C Chowringhee Road 3rd Floor
Kolkata, 700 020, India
Tel.: (91) 33 2289 0540
Fax: (91) 33 2289 0539

ANKUR DRUGS & PHARMA LIMITED
C-306 Crystal Plaza Andheri Link Road
Andheri West, Mumbai, 400 053, India
Tel.: (91) 22 40682300
Fax: (91) 22 40682323
E-Mail: info@ankurdrugs.com
Web Site: www.ankurdrugs.com
Year Founded: 1995
531683—(BOM)
Emp.: 1,245
Business Description:
Pharmaceutical Preparation Mfr
S.I.C.: 2834
N.A.I.C.S.: 325412
Personnel:
Purnandu Jain *(Chm & Mng Dir)*
Asraf Hossain *(Pres-Technical & Projects)*
S. C. Rane *(Sec)*
Board of Directors:
Purnandu Jain
Ramesh Batham
Dileep Shinde
Giriraj Vijayvargiya
Transfer Agent:
Ajel Limited
106 Link Plaza Commercial Complex 2nd Floor
New Link Road
Oshiwara Jogeshwari West, Mumbai, India

ANKUSH FINSTOCK LIMITED
B-708 Fair Deal House Opp Xavier's Ladies Hostel Off C G Road
Ahmedabad, 380009, India
Tel.: (91) 79 30182613
Fax: (91) 79 26440031
E-Mail: corporate@ankushfinstock.com
Web Site: www.ankushfinstock.com
Year Founded: 1993
531519—(BOM)
Sales Range: Less than $1 Million
Business Description:
Securities Brokerage Services
S.I.C.: 6211
N.A.I.C.S.: 523120
Personnel:
Bharat M. Shah *(Chm & Mng Dir)*
Samir P. Shah *(Compliance Officer)*
R. S. Singh *(Sec)*
Board of Directors:
Bharat M. Shah
Vikesh B. Makvana
Kamlesh H. Mehta
Zalak D. Shah
Nishant B. Vardhamani

ANLIMA YARN DYEING LIMITED
(d/b/a Anlima Group)
Suite 4/3 City Heart 67 Naya Paltan
Dhaka, 1000, Bangladesh
Tel.: (880) 29349881
Fax: (880) 28317184
E-Mail: info@anlima.com
Web Site: www.anlima.com
ANLIMAYARN—(DHA)
Emp.: 264
Business Description:
Yarn Dyeing Services
S.I.C.: 2299
N.A.I.C.S.: 313110
Personnel:
Mahmudul Hoque *(Chm, Pres & Mng Dir)*
M. Abdul Kalam Mazumdar *(CFO & Exec VP)*
M. Jahangir Alom *(Sec)*
Board of Directors:
Mahmudul Hoque
Abul Bashar
Hubbun Nahar Hoque
M. Abdul Kalam Mazumdar
Legal Counsel:
Lee Khan & Associates
67 Naya Paltan
Dhaka, Bangladesh
Subsidiary:

Anlima Textile Limited (1)
Suite 413 City Heart 67 Naya Paltan
Dhaka, 1000, Bangladesh
Tel.: (880) 229349884
Fax: (880) 28317184
E-Mail: info@anlima.com
Knit & Fabrics Mfr
S.I.C.: 2259
N.A.I.C.S.: 313240
Mahmudul Haque *(Mng Dir)*

ANMAR MECHANICAL AND ELECTRICAL CONTRACTORS LTD.
199 Mumford Rd
Lively, ON, P3Y 1L2, Canada
Tel.: (705) 692-0888
Fax: (705) 692-0462
E-Mail: general@anmar.ca
Web Site: www.anmar.ca
Rev.: $12,945,882
Emp.: 150
Business Description:
Heating Systems Repair & Maintenance Services
S.I.C.: 1711
N.A.I.C.S.: 238220
Personnel:
Gianni Grossi *(Pres)*
Giulio Grossi *(CEO)*

ANN JOO RESOURCES BERHAD
Wisma Ann Joo Lot 19391 Batu 8 1/2
Jalan Klang Lama
46000 Petaling Jaya, Selangor Darul Ehsan, Malaysia
Tel.: (60) 378770028
Fax: (60) 378759354
E-Mail: info@annjoo.com.my
Web Site: www.annjoo.com.my
ANNJOO—(KLS)
Rev.: $682,151,317
Assets: $956,321,622
Liabilities: $614,813,601
Net Worth: $341,508,021

Ann Joo Resources Berhad—(Continued)

Earnings: ($6,186,867)
Fiscal Year-end: 12/31/12
Business Description:
Steel & Steel Related Products Mfr
S.I.C.: 3411
N.A.I.C.S.: 332431
Personnel:
Kiam Lam Lim *(Chm)*
Hong Thye Lim *(Mng Dir)*
Oi Wah Leong *(Co-Sec)*
Mabel Mei Peng Tio *(Co-Sec)*
Board of Directors:
Kiam Lam Lim
Naquiyuddin Ibni Jaafar
Hong Thye Lim
Kien Lip Lim
Sin Seong Lim
Kamarudin Md Ali
Kim Hoay Ong
A. Razak Ramli

ANNA INFRASTRUCTURES LIMITED

E-14/6 First Floor Shanta Tower
Sanjay Place
Agra, 282 002, India
Tel.: (91) 562 2526650
E-Mail: annainfra@gmail.com
Web Site: annainfra.com
Year Founded: 1993
530799—(BOM)
Sales Range: Less than $1 Million
Business Description:
Real Estate Management Services
S.I.C.: 6531
N.A.I.C.S.: 531390
Personnel:
Anil Kumar Agarwal *(Compliance Officer)*

ANNAIK LIMITED

52 Tuas Avenue 9
Singapore, 639193, Singapore
Tel.: (65) 62102727
Fax: (65) 68615705
Web Site: www.annaik.com.sg
Year Founded: 1977
A52—(SES)
Rev.: $66,871,471
Assets: $94,424,072
Liabilities: $34,191,167
Net Worth: $60,232,905
Earnings: $1,466,330
Emp.: 189
Fiscal Year-end: 12/31/12
Business Description:
Stainless Steel Piping Products Mfr & Distr
S.I.C.: 3317
N.A.I.C.S.: 331210
Personnel:
Chin Seng Ow *(Chm & CEO)*
Yoen Har Wong *(Co-Sec)*
Caroline Poh Noi Yeo *(Co-Sec)*
Board of Directors:
Chin Seng Ow
Mong Seng Ang
Chow Siong Choong
Beng Leong Koh
Bon Leong Lee
Daniel Wei Lin
Kheng Low
Kim Keang Ng

Subsidiary:

Pioneer Environmental Technology Pte Ltd **(1)**
135 Pioneer Road
639589 Singapore, Singapore
Tel.: (65) 93690986
Fax: (65) 68616919
Water Treatment Equipment Mfr
S.I.C.: 3589
N.A.I.C.S.: 333318

Non-U.S. Subsidiaries:

Shinsei Japan Industry Co Ltd **(1)**
5-11-9 Nishi-Nakajima
Yodogawa-Ku, Osaka, 532-0011, Japan
Tel.: (81) 661005811
Fax: (81) 661005812
E-Mail: info@shinseiindustry.co.jp
Web Site: www.shinseiindustry.co.jp
Emp.: 5
Machine Tools Import & Distr
S.I.C.: 5084
N.A.I.C.S.: 423830
Tatsumi Kiyoshi *(Gen Mgr)*

Shinsei (Jiangyan) Steel Flanges Co Ltd **(1)**
No 688 Tianmu Road Jiangyan Economic Development Zone
Taixian, Jiangsu, 225500, China
Tel.: (86) 52388206028
Fax: (86) 52388206058
E-Mail: shinsei@ssflanges.com.cn
Web Site: www.ssflanges.com.cn
Stainless Steel Flanges Mfr
S.I.C.: 3312
N.A.I.C.S.: 331110
James Ow *(Pres)*

ANNEC GREEN REFRACTORIES CORPORATION

No 5 West Section Xidajie Street
Xinmi, Henan, 452370, China
Tel.: (86) 371 69999012
Web Site: www.annec.com.cn
Year Founded: 2010
ANNC—(OTC)
Rev.: $84,758,095
Assets: $122,281,479
Liabilities: $79,862,368
Net Worth: $42,419,111
Earnings: $5,035,144
Emp.: 1,224
Fiscal Year-end: 12/31/12
Business Description:
Refractory Production & Sales
S.I.C.: 3297
N.A.I.C.S.: 327120
Personnel:
Fuchao Li *(Chm)*
Jiantao Li *(Pres, CEO & CFO)*
Qichang Wu *(CTO)*
Board of Directors:
Fuchao Li
Jiantao Li
Zhaoqing Sun
Yang Zheng

ANNEX PUBLISHING & PRINTING INC.

105 Donly Drive South
PO Box 530
Simcoe, ON, N3Y 4N5, Canada
Tel.: (519) 429-3966
Fax: (519) 429-3112
Toll Free: (888) 599-2228
Web Site: www.annexweb.com
Year Founded: 1997
Sales Range: $25-49.9 Million
Emp.: 100
Business Description:
Online Magazine Publishing & Distr
S.I.C.: 2741
N.A.I.C.S.: 519130
Personnel:
Michael Fredericks *(Pres & CEO)*
Peter Muise *(CFO)*
Diane Kleer *(VP-Production & Grp Publr)*
Scott Jamieson *(Grp Publr & Dir-Editorial)*
Martin McAnulty *(Grp Publr & Dir-Sls)*

ANNIDIS CORPORATION

245-2650 Queensview Drive
Ottawa, ON, K2B 8H6, Canada
Tel.: (613) 596-1800
Fax: (613) 596-9453
E-Mail: geralds@annidis.com
Web Site: www.annidis.com
Year Founded: 2010
RHA—(TSXV)
Rev.: $1,137,611
Assets: $1,576,524
Liabilities: $4,038,173
Net Worth: ($2,461,650)
Earnings: ($4,516,831)
Fiscal Year-end: 12/31/12
Business Description:
Healthcare Investment Services
S.I.C.: 6211
N.A.I.C.S.: 523999
Personnel:
Michael Mueller *(Chm)*
Zeljko Ribaric *(Pres)*
Gerald Slemko *(CEO)*
Brian Baker *(CFO)*
Dave Kahn *(CTO)*
Alan Boate *(Chief Scientific Officer)*
Brian Leonard *(Chief Medical Officer)*
Board of Directors:
Michael Mueller
Michael Crowley
Robert Devenyi
Zeljko Ribaric
Gerald Slemko
Rony Thomas
Transfer Agent:
Equity Financial Trust Company
200 University Avenue Suite 400
Toronto, ON, M5H 4H1, Canada
Tel.: (416) 361-0152
Fax: (416) 361-0470
Toll Free: (866) 393-4891

ANNONA ENERGY INC.

2316 A Willemar Avenue
Courtenay, BC, V9N 3M8, Canada
Tel.: (250) 898-8882
E-Mail: annona.energy@yahoo.com
Year Founded: 2012
Business Description:
Oil & Gas Exploration
S.I.C.: 1311
N.A.I.C.S.: 211111
Personnel:
Lawrence Jean *(Pres, CEO, CFO, Treas & Sec)*
Board of Directors:
Lawrence Jean

ANNUITY & LIFE RE (HOLDINGS), LTD.

16 Burnaby St
Hamilton, HM 11, Bermuda
Mailing Address:
PO Box HM 2904
Hamilton, HM LX, Bermuda
Tel.: (441) 278 7709
Fax: (441) 292 1196
Web Site: www.alre.bm
Year Founded: 1997
Sales Range: Less than $1 Million
Emp.: 10
Business Description:
Life & Annuity Reinsurance Services
S.I.C.: 6311
N.A.I.C.S.: 524113
Personnel:
Martin A. Berkowitz *(Chm)*
Board of Directors:
Martin A. Berkowitz

Subsidiary:

Annuity & Life Reassurance, Ltd. **(1)**
Cumberland House
1 Victoria Street, Hamilton, HM 11, Bermuda
Mailing Address:
PO Box HM 98
Hamilton, HM AX, Bermuda
Tel.: (441) 296 7667
Fax: (441) 296 7665
Web Site: www.annuityandlifere.com
Reinsurance
S.I.C.: 6399
N.A.I.C.S.: 524130

U.S. Subsidiary:

Annuity and Life Re America, Inc. **(1)**
1805 Monument Ave Ste 201
Richmond, VA 23220-7001
Tel.: (860) 285-8252
Fax: (860) 285-0233
Toll Free: (888) 393-5501
Emp.: 5
Reinsurance Services
S.I.C.: 6311
N.A.I.C.S.: 524113

ANNUITY PROPERTIES LIMITED

Boundary Place 18 Rivonia Road
Illovo, Sandton, 2196, South Africa
Mailing Address:
PO Box 55112
Northlands, 2116, South Africa
Tel.: (27) 10 595 3000
Fax: (27) 11 268 0414
E-Mail: info@annuityproperties.co.za
Web Site: www.annuityproperties.co.za
Year Founded: 2011
ANP—(JSE)
Rev.: $12,137,586
Assets: $162,625,246
Liabilities: $156,308,313
Net Worth: $6,316,933
Earnings: $5,403,745
Fiscal Year-end: 03/31/13
Business Description:
Real Estate Investment Services
S.I.C.: 6726
N.A.I.C.S.: 525990
Personnel:
Derek Greenberg *(Co-CEO)*
Panico Theocharides *(Co-CEO)*
Schalk Strydom *(CFO & Dir-Fin)*
Whitney Green *(Sec)*
Board of Directors:
P. Jabu Moleketi
Anthony M. Chait
Martin Ettin
Derek Greenberg
Eugene C. Loubser
Daniel E. Rubenstein
Roland D. E. B. Sassoon
D. Tyrone Soondarjee
Schalk Strydom
Panico Theocharides
Sarah J. Williams
Legal Counsel:
Glyn Marais Incorporated
The Place 1 Sandton Drive
Sandton, 2196, South Africa
Transfer Agent:
Link Market Services South Africa Proprietary Limited
13th Floor Rennies House 19 Ameshoff Street
Braamfontein, South Africa

ANOD BANK

Tourist Street 18
Ulaanbaatar, Mongolia
Tel.: (976) 11315315
Fax: (976) 11315431
Web Site: www.anodbank.com
Emp.: 450
Business Description:
Banking Services
S.I.C.: 6029
N.A.I.C.S.: 522110
Personnel:
N. Davaa *(Pres)*
L. Ulambayar *(Deputy CEO)*
E. Gur-Aranz *(CEO)*
D. Ariunaa *(CFO)*
E. Oyunsuren *(COO)*

ANOORAQ RESOURCES CORPORATION
(Name Changed to Atlatsa Resources Corporation)

ANOTO GROUP AB
Traktorvagen 11
SE-226 60 Lund, Sweden
Mailing Address:
PO Box 4106
SE-227 22 Lund, Sweden
Tel.: (46) 465401200
Fax: (46) 0465401202
E-Mail: info@anoto.com
Web Site: www.anoto.com
ANOT—(OMX)
Sls.: $30,750,401
Assets: $33,546,244
Liabilities: $15,619,939
Net Worth: $17,926,304
Earnings: ($6,939,529)
Emp.: 102
Fiscal Year-end: 12/31/12
Business Description:
Text & Images Capturing & Processing Services
S.I.C.: 7379
N.A.I.C.S.: 541519
Personnel:
Jorgen Durban *(Chm)*
Stein O. Revelsby *(CEO)*
Dan Wahrenberg *(CFO)*
Petter Ericson *(CTO)*
Teruo Yamanaka *(CEO-Anoto Maxell)*
Torgny Hellstroem *(Gen Counsel & Sr VP)*
Magnus Hollstroem *(Exec VP-Tech Licensing)*
Dennis Ladd *(Exec VP-Products & Tech)*
Max Marinissen *(Exec VP-Global Sls)*
Christian Delfin *(Sr VP & Head-Ops)*
Pietro Parravicini *(Sr VP & Mgr-Americas)*
Tim Aughenbaugh *(Sr VP-Bus Dev)*
Hein Haugland *(Sr VP-Mktg)*
Jan Skoglund *(Sr VP-Supply Chain Mgmt)*
Johan Zander *(Sr VP-R&D)*
Board of Directors:
Jorgen Durban
Kjell Brathen
Gunnel Duveblad
Andrew Hur
Subsidiaries:

C Technologies AB (1)
Traktorvagen 11
Box 4106
SE 227 22 Lund, Sweden
Tel.: (46) 46 540 10 00
E-Mail: info@cpen.com
Web Site: www.cpen.com
Mfr & Developer of C-Pen Handheld Scanner & Solutions Software
S.I.C.: 7372
N.A.I.C.S.: 511210

C Technologies (1)
Emdalavagen 18
SE 223 69 Lund, Sweden
Tel.: (46) 465401000
Fax: (46) 0465401202
Web Site: www.cpen.com
Text & Images Capturing & Processing Services
S.I.C.: 7379
N.A.I.C.S.: 541519

U.S. Subsidiary:

Anoto Inc. (1)
200 Friberg Pkwy Ste 3003
Westborough, MA 01581
Tel.: (508) 983-9550
Fax: (508) 983-9551
Toll Free: (866) 552-6686
E-Mail: boston@anoto.com
Web Site: www.anoto.com
Text & Images Capturing & Processing Services
S.I.C.: 7379
N.A.I.C.S.: 541519
Pietro Parravicini *(Pres & CEO)*

Non-U.S. Subsidiary:

Anoto Nippon K.K (1)
7F Dai-3 Nishi Aoyama Bldg
1-8-1 Shibuya, Shibuya-ku, Tokyo, 150-0002, Japan
Tel.: (81) 357741212
Fax: (81) 3057741211
Web Site: www.anoto.com
Emp.: 13
Text & Images Capturing & Processing Services
S.I.C.: 7379
N.A.I.C.S.: 541519

ANOVA METALS LIMITED
(Formerly Kimberley Rare Earths Limited)
Level 1 101 Edward Street
Brisbane, QLD, 4000, Australia
Mailing Address:
GPO Box 363
Brisbane, QLD, 4001, Australia
Tel.: (61) 8 9486 4326
Fax: (61) 8 9486 4327
E-Mail: info@anovametals.com.au
Web Site: www.anovametals.com.au
AWV—(ASX)
Sales Range: Less than $1 Million
Emp.: 4
Business Description:
Gold & Other Metal Mining Services
S.I.C.: 1041
N.A.I.C.S.: 212221
Personnel:
Jon Parker *(Chm)*
Tim Dobson *(Mng Dir)*
Darren Crawte *(Sec)*
Board of Directors:
Jon Parker
Tim Dobson
Bill Fry
Malcolm James
Allan Trench
Legal Counsel:
Steinepreis Paganin Lawyers
Level 4 The Read Buildings 16 Milligan Street
6000 Perth, WA, Australia

ANP HOLDING B.V.
Verrijn Stuartlaan 7
2288 EK Rijswijk, Netherlands
Tel.: (31) 704141414
Fax: (31) 0704141203
E-Mail: recepcie@anp.nl
Web Site: www.anp.nl
Sales Range: $50-74.9 Million
Emp.: 200
Business Description:
News Agency
S.I.C.: 7383
N.A.I.C.S.: 519110
Personnel:
Erik van Gruijthuijsen *(Gen Dir)*

ANPARIO PLC
Manton Wood Enterprise Park
Worksop, Notts, S8O 2RS, United Kingdom
Tel.: (44) 1909 537380
E-Mail: info@anpario.com
Web Site: www.anpario.com
ANP—(AIM)
Rev.: $37,127,529
Assets: $38,545,731
Liabilities: $10,300,129
Net Worth: $28,245,602
Earnings: $3,322,826
Emp.: 88
Fiscal Year-end: 12/31/12
Business Description:
High Performance Natural Feed Additives for Global Agriculture & Aquaculture Markets
S.I.C.: 2899
N.A.I.C.S.: 325998
Personnel:
Richard P. Edwards *(Vice Chm)*
David Michael Alexander Bullen *(CEO)*
Karen L. Prior *(Sec & Dir-Fin)*
Board of Directors:
Richard S. Rose
David Michael Alexander Bullen
Richard P. Edwards
Peter A. Lawrence
Karen L. Prior

ANPHAT SECURITIES JOINT STOCK COMPANY
(d/b/a An Phat Securities)
75A Tran Hung Dao
Hoan Kiem, Hanoi, Vietnam
Tel.: (84) 4 3941 0277
Fax: (84) 4 3941 0273
E-Mail: anphat@apsi.vn
Web Site: www.apsi.com.vn
APG—(HNX)
Emp.: 40
Business Description:
Investment Banking & Securities Brokerage Services
S.I.C.: 6211
N.A.I.C.S.: 523110
Personnel:
Phuong Kim Tran *(Chm)*

ANPULO FOOD DEVELOPMENT, INC.
(Formerly Specializer, Inc.)
Hebaliang Industry Park Hangkong Road
Laifeng, Wuhan, Hubei, China
Tel.: (86) 718 6288576
Year Founded: 2010
ANPL—(OTCB)
Liabilities: $8,831
Net Worth: ($8,831)
Earnings: ($40,001)
Emp.: 1
Fiscal Year-end: 06/30/13
Business Description:
Investment Services
S.I.C.: 6211
N.A.I.C.S.: 523999
Personnel:
Wenping Luo *(CEO, CFO & Chief Acctg Officer)*
Transfer Agent:
TranShare Corporation
4626 S Broadway
Englewood, CO 80113
Tel.: (303) 662-1112
Fax: (303) 662-1113

ANPULO FOOD, INC.
Hangkong Road Xiangfeng Town
Laifeng, Laifenghsien, Hubei, 445700, China
Tel.: (86) 718 628 8576
Web Site: www.anpulo.cn
Year Founded: 2010
Sls.: $20,206,497
Assets: $20,524,370
Liabilities: $16,093,504
Net Worth: $4,430,866
Earnings: ($874,831)
Emp.: 330
Fiscal Year-end: 12/31/13
Business Description:
Meat Processing & Distr
S.I.C.: 5147
N.A.I.C.S.: 311612
Personnel:
Wenping Luo *(Pres & CEO)*
Maochun Kang *(CFO)*
Board of Directors:
Shijia Li
Chunhai Lin
Wenping Luo
Tao Yang
Xinlian Zhang

ANRIKA GROUP SCANDINAVIA AB
Vastra Hamngatan 18
SE-411 17 Gothenburg, Sweden
Tel.: (46) 3113 7110
Fax: (46) 3113 7109
E-Mail: info@anrika.se
Web Site: www.anrika.se
Year Founded: 2010
Business Description:
Holding Company; Infrastructure & Social Development Consulting Services
S.I.C.: 6719
N.A.I.C.S.: 551112
Personnel:
Lars Ake Junelind *(CEO)*
Subsidiaries:

Anrika Quality Services AB (1)
Vastra Hamngatan 18
SE-411 17 Gothenburg, Sweden SE
Tel.: (46) 3113 7110
Fax: (46) 3113 7109
E-Mail: info@anrika.se
Web Site: www.anrika.se
Infrastructure Development Consultancy Services
S.I.C.: 8999
N.A.I.C.S.: 541690
Per Anders Harald Linden *(Mng Dir)*

Indevelop AB (1)
Karlbergsvagen 77 5Fl
SE-113 35 Stockholm, Sweden SE
Tel.: (46) 8 5883 1800 (Toll Free)
Fax: (46) 8678 7217
E-Mail: info@indevelop.se
Web Site: www.indevelop.se
Social Development Consulting Services
S.I.C.: 8748
N.A.I.C.S.: 541618
Catharina Schmitz *(Mng Dir)*

ANRITSU CORPORATION
5 1 1 Onna
Atsugi, Kanagawa, 243 8555, Japan
Tel.: (81) 462231111
Fax: (81) 462258358
Web Site: www.anritsu.com
Year Founded: 1931
6754—(TKS)
Rev.: $1,041,535,000
Assets: $1,265,979,000
Liabilities: $556,105,000
Net Worth: $709,874,000
Earnings: $153,362,000
Emp.: 3,771
Fiscal Year-end: 03/31/13
Business Description:
Optical & Electronic Measuring Instruments, Communication Systems, Computer Peripherals, Industrial Automation Systems, Devices & Inspection Systems Mfr Export
S.I.C.: 3829
N.A.I.C.S.: 334519
Personnel:
Hirokazu Hashimoto *(Pres)*
Kenji Tanaka *(Sr Exec VP)*
Frank Tiernan *(Exec VP)*
Junkichi Shirono *(Sr VP)*
Toshihiko Takahashi *(Sr VP)*
Fumihiro Tsukasa *(Sr VP)*
Board of Directors:
Michikazu Aoi
Hirokazu Hashimoto

Anritsu Corporation—(Continued)

Yasushi Hosoda
Akifumi Kubota
Takaya Seki
Kenji Tanaka
Toshisumi Taniai
Fumihiro Tsukasa

Transfer Agent:
Sumitomo Mitsui Trust Bank Limited
1-4-1 Marunouchi Chiyoda-ku
Tokyo, Japan

U.S. Subsidiaries:

Anritsu Company (1)
490 Jarvis Dr
Morgan Hill, CA 95037-2809 CA
Tel.: (408) 778-2000
E-Mail: infor@us.anritsu.com
Web Site: www.us.anritsu.com
Emp.: 450
Communication & Network Devices Mfr Export
S.I.C.: 5065
N.A.I.C.S.: 423690
Frank Tiernan *(Pres)*

Divisions:

Microwave Measurement Division (2)
490 Jarvis Dr Bldg 12C
Morgan Hill, CA 95037-2809
Tel.: (408) 778-2000
Fax: (408) 776-1744
Web Site: www.global.anritsu.com
Emp.: 600
Microwave Testing Equipment Mfr Export
S.I.C.: 5065
N.A.I.C.S.: 423690
Frank Tiernan *(Pres)*

Non-U.S. Subsidiaries:

Anritsu A/S (1)
Kay Fiskers Plats 9
DK 2300 Copenhagen, Denmark
Tel.: (45) 72112200
Fax: (45) 72112210
E-Mail: info@anritsu.com
Web Site: www.anritsu.com
Emp.: 100
Electronic Measuring Instruments & Systems for Telecommunications
S.I.C.: 3825
N.A.I.C.S.: 334515
Gerald Ostheimer *(Gen Mgr)*

Anritsu AB (1)
Borgarfjordsgatan 13A
Kista, 164 40 Stockholm, Sweden
Tel.: (46) 853470700
Fax: (46) 853470730
Measuring Equipment Sales & Maintenance Services
S.I.C.: 5084
N.A.I.C.S.: 423830

Anritsu Co. Ltd. (1)
1006 10th Fl Greenfield Tower Concordia Plz 1
Science Museum Rd, Kowloon, China (Hong Kong)
Tel.: (852) 23014980
Fax: (852) 23013545
E-Mail: sales_ap@hk.anritsu.com
Web Site: www.anritsu.com
Broadcast & Satellite Services & Sales
S.I.C.: 4899
N.A.I.C.S.: 517410
Waikwok Lo *(Mgr-Bus Dev Center)*

Anritsu Company, S.A. de C.V (1)
Av Ejercito Nacional No 579 Piso 9
Col Granada, Mexico, Mexico
Tel.: (52) 55 1101 2370
Fax: (52) 55 5254 3147
Web Site: www.anritsu.com
Electronic Measuring Equipment Distr
S.I.C.: 5065
N.A.I.C.S.: 423690

Anritsu Electronica, Ltda. (1)
Praca Amadeu Amaral 27 1 andar
Paraiso, 01327 010 Sao Paulo, Brazil BR
Tel.: (55) 1132832511 (100%)
Telex: 2131704ANBRBR
Fax: (55) 1132886940
E-Mail: vendas@anritsu.com
Web Site: www.anritsu.com
Emp.: 50
Sales & Marketing of Test Instruments for Telecommunications
S.I.C.: 3825
N.A.I.C.S.: 334515
Carlos Martins *(Gen Mgr)*

Anritsu Electronics Ltd (1)
700 Silver Seven Road Suite 120
Kanata, ON, K2V 1C3, Canada
Tel.: (613) 591-2003
Fax: (613) 591-1006
Toll Free: (800) 267-4878
Emp.: 12
Electronic Measuring Instruments Mfr
S.I.C.: 3825
N.A.I.C.S.: 334515
Tony Paredes *(Gen Mgr)*

Anritsu EMEA Ltd (1)
200 Capability Green
Luton, Bedfordshire, LU1 3LU, United Kingdom
Tel.: (44) 1582433280
Fax: (44) 1582731303
Web Site: www.anritsu.com
Emp.: 200
Measuring Equipment Sales & Maintenance Services
S.I.C.: 5084
N.A.I.C.S.: 423830

Anritsu GmbH (1)
Konrad Zuseplatz 1
81829 Munich, Germany DE
Tel.: (49) 894423080 (100%)
Telex: 8584904ANRID
Fax: (49) 8944230855
E-Mail: info@anritsu.de
Web Site: www.anritsu.com
Emp.: 25
Sales & Marketing of Anritsu Products
S.I.C.: 5946
N.A.I.C.S.: 443142
Michael Statny *(Gen Mgr)*

Anritsu Limited (1)
200 Capability Green
Luton, Bedfordshire, LU1 3LU, United Kingdom UK
Tel.: (44) 1582433200 (100%)
Telex: 826750ANRSUEG
Fax: (44) 1582 731303
E-Mail: info@eu.anritsu.com
Web Site: www.anritsu.co.uk
Sls.: $9,500,000
Emp.: 100
Sales & Marketing of Wire & Wireless Communication Equipment
S.I.C.: 5063
N.A.I.C.S.: 423610

Anritsu Pte. Ltd (1)
60 Alexandra Ter 02-08 The Comtech Lobby A
Singapore, 118502, Singapore
Tel.: (65) 62822400
Fax: (65) 62822533
E-Mail: acst.sales@anritsu.com
Web Site: www.anritsu.com
Emp.: 20
Electronic Testing & Measuring Instrument Mfr
S.I.C.: 3825
N.A.I.C.S.: 334515
Lin Poh Seng *(Gen Mgr)*

Anritsu Pty. Ltd (1)
Unit 21/270 Ferntree Gully Road
Notting Hill, VIC, 3168, Australia
Tel.: (61) 3 9558 8177
Fax: (61) 3 9558 8255
E-Mail: au-sales@anritsu.com
Web Site: anritsu.com
Emp.: 7
Electronic Measuring Equipment Mfr
S.I.C.: 3825
N.A.I.C.S.: 334515
Ian Fraser *(Gen Mgr)*

Anritsu S.A (1)
12 Avenue du Quebec Silic 720
91961 Courtaboeuf, France
Tel.: (33) 160921550
Fax: (33) 1 64 46 10 65
E-Mail: info.france@anritsu.com
Emp.: 13
Electronic Measuring Equipment Mfr
S.I.C.: 3825
N.A.I.C.S.: 334515
Eric Fauxpoint *(Gen Dir)*

Anritsu Solutions S.r.l (1)
Via Sante Bargellini 4
00157 Rome, Italy
Tel.: (39) 06 43 36 24 00
Telecommunication Services
S.I.C.: 4899
N.A.I.C.S.: 517919

Anritsu S.r.l (1)
Via Elio Vittorini 129
00144 Rome, Italy
Tel.: (39) 065099711
Fax: (39) 65022425
E-Mail: support.acit@anritsu.com
Web Site: www.anritsu.com
Emp.: 15
Communication Equipment Mfr
S.I.C.: 3669
N.A.I.C.S.: 334290

ANS GROUP PLC

Synergy House Manchester Science Park
Manchester, M15 6SY, United Kingdom
Tel.: (44) 161 227 1002
Fax: (44) 161 227 1020
E-Mail: enquries@ansgroup.co.uk
Web Site: www.ansgroup.co.uk
Year Founded: 1996
Sales Range: $50-74.9 Million
Emp.: 120

Business Description:
Computer Systems Design Services
S.I.C.: 7373
N.A.I.C.S.: 541512

Personnel:
Scott Fletcher *(Founder & Chm)*
Paul Sweeney *(Mng Dir)*

ANSA MCAL LIMITED

11th Floor Tatil Building 11 Maraval Road
Port of Spain, Trinidad & Tobago
Tel.: (868) 625 3670
Fax: (868) 624 8753
E-Mail: corporatecommunications@ansamcal.com
Web Site: www.ansamcal.com
AMCL—(TRI)
Rev.: $908,321,630
Assets: $1,744,056,029
Liabilities: $920,138,615
Net Worth: $823,917,414
Earnings: $114,755,734
Emp.: 6,000
Fiscal Year-end: 12/31/12

Business Description:
Holding Company; Diversified Services
S.I.C.: 6719
N.A.I.C.S.: 551112

Personnel:
Anthony Norman Sabga *(Chm & CEO)*
David B. Sabga *(Deputy Chm)*
Gerry C. Brooks *(COO)*
Nicholas V. Mouttet *(Pres/CEO-ANSA McAL (Barbados) Ltd)*
Frances Bain-Cumberbatch *(Sec & Head-Legal)*

Board of Directors:
Anthony Norman Sabga
Steve Bideshi
Gerry C. Brooks
W. David Clarke
Aneal Maharaj
Nicholas V. Mouttet
Anthony E. Phillip
Imtiaz Rahaman
Andrew N. Sabga
Anthony N. Sabga
David B. Sabga
Ray A. Sumairsingh
Teresa White

Subsidiaries:

Alstons Building Enterprises Limited (1)
Building 2 Mingot Street
Mount Hope, Port of Spain, Trinidad & Tobago TT
Tel.: (868) 665-5221 (100%)
Fax: (868) 222-1116
E-Mail: abel.sales@ansamcal.com
Web Site: www.abelbestcrete.com
Emp.: 150
Steel Investment Foundries
S.I.C.: 3324
N.A.I.C.S.: 331512
Nicholas Mouttet *(Mng Dir)*

Division:

ABEL Building Solutions (2)
Maingot Street Ext
Mount Hope, Port of Spain, Trinidad & Tobago
Tel.: (868) 6652235
Fax: (868) 2231115
E-Mail: abel.airconditioning@ansamcal.com
Web Site: abelbestcrete.com
Emp.: 700
Air-Conditioning & Warm Air Heating Equipment & Commercial & Industrial Refrigeration Equipment Mfr
S.I.C.: 3585
N.A.I.C.S.: 333415
Victor Cooper *(Mng Dir)*

Alstons Marketing Company Limited (1)
Uriah Butler Highway & Endeavour Road
Chaguanas, Trinidad & Tobago TT
Tel.: (868) 671-2713 (100%)
Fax: (868) 671-2857
Web Site: www.amcott.info
Sales Range: $25-49.9 Million
Emp.: 300
Distribution & Marketing of a Wide Range of Food/Cold Chain Services, Pharmaceuticals, Wines & Spirits & Consumer Products
S.I.C.: 5141
N.A.I.C.S.: 424410
Rene De Gannes *(Mng Dir)*
Joel Popplewell *(CFO)*
Jose Nivet *(Head-Distr & Chm-AMCO)*

Alstons Shipping Limited (1)
3 Abercromby Street
PO Box 600
Port of Spain, Trinidad & Tobago (100%)
Tel.: (868) 62522015
Fax: (868) 6253691
E-Mail: admin@alstonsshipping.com
Web Site: www.ansamcal.com
Navigational Services to Shipping
S.I.C.: 4499
N.A.I.C.S.: 488330
Mitra Mahabir *(Mng Dir)*

Alstons Travel Limited (1)
67 Independence Sq
Port of Spain, Trinidad & Tobago (100%)
Tel.: (868) 6231980
Fax: (868) 6253682
E-Mail: alstons.travel@ansamcal.com
Web Site: www.ansamcal.com
Emp.: 6
Traveler Accommodation
S.I.C.: 7011
N.A.I.C.S.: 721199
Anthony de Souza *(Mng Dir)*

Ansa Automotive Limited (1)
25 Richmond St
Port of Spain, Trinidad & Tobago (100%)
Tel.: (868) 6246632
Fax: (868) 6243376
Web Site: www.ansaauto.com
Automotive Sales, Repair & Maintenance
S.I.C.: 7539
N.A.I.C.S.: 811198
Jerome Borde *(Mng Dir)*

ANSA McAL Chemicals Ltd. (1)
North Sea Drive Point Lisas Industrial Estate
Savonetta, Trinidad & Tobago (100%)
Tel.: (868) 6365380

Fax: (868) 6369931
E-Mail: roberths.mohammed@ansamcal.com
Web Site: www.ansamcal.com
Emp.: 100
Basic Inorganic Chemical Mfr
S.I.C.: 2819
N.A.I.C.S.: 325180
Sherrine Christopher *(Mgr-Export)*

ANSA Merchant Bank Limited (1)
ANSA Centre 11 Maraval Road
Port of Spain, Trinidad & Tobago
Tel.: (868) 6238672
Fax: (868) 6248763
E-Mail: ansabank@ansamcal.com
Web Site: www.ansabank.com
AMBL—(TRI)
Rev.: $115,174,097
Assets: $852,658,219
Liabilities: $617,243,114
Net Worth: $235,415,105
Earnings: $23,065,773
Fiscal Year-end: 12/31/12
Banking & Financial Services
S.I.C.: 6029
N.A.I.C.S.: 522110
Anthony N. Sabga *(Chm)*
Ray A. Sumairsingh *(Deputy Chm)*
Gregory N. Hill *(Mng Dir)*
Nigel Edwards *(Sec)*

Ansa Polymer Limited (1)
Ansa McAl Industrial Park
51-59 Tumpuna Rd S Guanapo, Arima, Trinidad & Tobago (100%)
Tel.: (868) 643-3137
Fax: (868) 643-1254
Web Site: www.ansamcal.com
Unsupported Plastics Bag Mfr
S.I.C.: 2673
N.A.I.C.S.: 326111
John Charles *(Mng Dir)*

Ansa Technologies Limited (1)
40 Cipero Rd
PO Box 10
San Fernando, Trinidad & Tobago (100%)
Tel.: (868) 6577151
Fax: (868) 6526407
Web Site: www.ansamcal.com
Emp.: 75
Oil & Gas Field Machinery & Equipment Mfr
S.I.C.: 3533
N.A.I.C.S.: 333132
Anthony Beaubum *(Chm)*

Burmac Machinery Ltd. (1)
25 Royal Rd
San Fernando, Trinidad & Tobago (100%)
Tel.: (868) 6572277
Fax: (868) 6526222
Web Site: www.ansamcal.com
Agricultural, Industrial & Construction Equipment Supplier
S.I.C.: 5046
N.A.I.C.S.: 423440
David Gunn *(Gen Mgr)*

Carib Brewery Limited (1)
Eastern Main Rd
Champs Fleurs, Trinidad & Tobago (80%)
Tel.: (868) 662 2231
Fax: (868) 663 7004
E-Mail: carib@caribbeer.com
Web Site: www.caribbeer.com
Emp.: 900
Malt Mfr
S.I.C.: 2083
N.A.I.C.S.: 311213
Derek Waddell *(CEO)*

Carib Glassworks Limited (1)
Eastern Main Rd
Champs Fleurs, Trinidad & Tobago (100%)
Tel.: (868) 662 2231
Fax: (868) 663 1779
E-Mail: carglass@tstt.net.tt
Web Site: www.ansamcal.com
Glass Packaging Producer
S.I.C.: 3221
N.A.I.C.S.: 327213
Roger Mew *(Mng Dir)*

Caribbean Development Company Limited (1)
Eastern Main Rd
Champs Fleurs, Trinidad & Tobago (80%)
Tel.: (868) 662 2231
Fax: (868) 663 1780
Web Site: www.caribbeer.com
Breweries
S.I.C.: 2082
N.A.I.C.S.: 312120
Wayne Choy *(CEO)*

Carmax Limited (1)
Cnr Richmond & Charles St
Port of Spain, Trinidad & Tobago (100%)
Tel.: (868) 6232731
Fax: (868) 6236882
Web Site: www.carmaxtt.com
Automobile Mfr
S.I.C.: 3711
N.A.I.C.S.: 336111
Aloysius Landeau *(Mgr-Automotive Sector)*

Classic Motors Ltd (1)
Cor Richmond & Charles Streets
Port of Spain, Trinidad & Tobago (100%)
Tel.: (868) 627-3714
Fax: (868) 624 3376
E-Mail: classicmotors@tstt.net.tt
Web Site: www.classicmotorstt.net
Automobile Mfr
S.I.C.: 3711
N.A.I.C.S.: 336111
Jerome Borde *(Mng Dir)*

Grand Bazaar Ltd. (1)
The City of Grand Bazaar Churchill Roosevelt
Uriah Butler Highways, Port of Spain, Valsayn, Trinidad & Tobago (100%)
Tel.: (868) 662 2282
Fax: (868) 662 2282
E-Mail: justforbusinezz@yahoo.com
Emp.: 25
Real Estate Property Lessors
S.I.C.: 6519
N.A.I.C.S.: 531190
Edward Ayin *(Gen Mgr)*

McEnearney Business Machines Limited (1)
34 Richmond St
PO Box 1237
Port of Spain, Trinidad & Tobago TT (100%)
Tel.: (868) 625-1044
Fax: (868) 625-0086
E-Mail: tony.Beharrylal@ansamcal.com
Web Site: www.ansamcal.com
Emp.: 90
Industrial Machinery Mfr
S.I.C.: 3559
N.A.I.C.S.: 333249
Mahadeu Beharrylal *(Gen Mgr)*

McEnearney Motors Limited (1)
25 Richmond St
Port of Spain, Trinidad & Tobago (100%)
Tel.: (868) 627-367
Fax: (868) 625-4988
Web Site: www.fordtrinidad.com
Automobile Mfr
S.I.C.: 3711
N.A.I.C.S.: 336111
Jerome Borde *(Mng Dir)*

Penta Paints Caribbean Limited (1)
51-59 Tumpuna Rd S
Arima, Guanapo, Trinidad & Tobago (100%)
Tel.: (868) 643-2425
Fax: (868) 643-2509
Paint & Coating Mfr
S.I.C.: 2851
N.A.I.C.S.: 325510
Bernard Mitchell *(Mng Dir)*

Trinidad & Tobago Insurance Limited (1)
11A Maraval Rd
Port of Spain, Trinidad & Tobago TT (100%)
Tel.: (868) 628-2845
Fax: (868) 628-0035
E-Mail: info@tatil.co.tt
Web Site: www.ansamcal.com
Insurance Related Activities
S.I.C.: 6411
N.A.I.C.S.: 524298
Ray A. Sumairsingh *(Mng Dir)*

Trinidad Match Limited (1)
Corner Gordon & Maingot Streets
Port of Spain, Mount Hope, Trinidad & Tobago TT (100%)
Tel.: (868) 638-1974
Fax: (868) 675-0084
Web Site: www.ansamcal.com
Emp.: 60
Holding Company: Safety Matches
S.I.C.: 6719
N.A.I.C.S.: 551112
Michael Baiz *(Gen Mgr)*

Trinidad Publishing Company Limited (1)
Guardian Building 22-24 St Vincent Street
Port of Spain, Trinidad & Tobago (100%)
Tel.: (868) 6238871
Fax: (868) 625 7211
Web Site: www.ansamcal.com
Newspaper Publishers
S.I.C.: 2711
N.A.I.C.S.: 511110
Gabriel Faria *(Mng Dir)*

Joint Venture:

Caribbean Roof Tile Company Limited (1)
Depot Rd Longdenville
Chaguanas, Trinidad & Tobago (50%)
Tel.: (868) 671-1741
Fax: (868) 672-9370
Web Site: www.ansamcal.com
Piece Goods Notions & Dry Goods Whslr
S.I.C.: 5199
N.A.I.C.S.: 424310
Ernesto Fuentes *(Plant Mgr)*

U.S. Subsidiaries:

ANSA McAL (U.S.) Inc. (1)
11403 NW 39th St
Doral, FL 33178 FL (100%)
Tel.: (305) 599-8766
Fax: (305) 599-8917
Web Site: www.ansamcal.com
Emp.: 30
Wholesale Trade Distr
S.I.C.: 7389
N.A.I.C.S.: 425120
Suresh Dutta *(Chm)*
Wendell Beckles *(Pres)*

DCI Miami, Inc. (1)
11403 NW 39th St
Doral, FL 33178 FL (100%)
Tel.: (305) 591-0885
Fax: (305) 591-3104
E-Mail: caribbeer@caribbeerus.com
Web Site: www.caribbeer.com
Emp.: 5
Beer & Ale Whslr
S.I.C.: 5181
N.A.I.C.S.: 424810
Jose Nivet *(Chm)*

Non-U.S. Subsidiaries:

ANSA McAL Trading (Guyana) Limited (1)
Lot 60 Beterverwagting
East Coast, Demerara, Guyana (100%)
Tel.: (592) 2200455
Fax: (592) 2200796
E-Mail: ansamcaltradinglimited@ansamcal.com
Web Site: www.ansamcal.com
Rev.: $8,300,000
Emp.: 150
Pharmaceutical Preparation Mfr
S.I.C.: 2834
N.A.I.C.S.: 325412
Troy Cadogan *(Dir-Mktg)*

Grenada Breweries Limited (1)
Grand Anse
PO Box 202
Saint George's, Grenada (55.54%)
Tel.: (473) 444 4248
Fax: (473) 444 4842
E-Mail: gbl@spiceisle.com
Emp.: 140
Breweries
S.I.C.: 2082
N.A.I.C.S.: 312120
Ron Antoine *(Mng Dir)*

Non-U.S. Holding:

ANSA McAL (Barbados) Limited (1)
McEnearney Quality Complex
Wildey, St Michael, BB14007, Barbados BB (70.9%)
Tel.: (246) 434-2600 (PBX)
Fax: (246) 228-1619
E-Mail: headoffice@mcalbds.com
Holding Company
S.I.C.: 6719
N.A.I.C.S.: 551112
Nicholas V. Mouttet *(Pres & CEO)*

Subsidiaries:

A.S. Bryden & Sons (Barbados) Ltd. (2)
Bryden Stokes Barbarees Hill
PO Box 403
Saint Michael, 12060, Barbados BB (100%)
Tel.: (246) 431 2600
Fax: (246) 426 0755
E-Mail: barbados@brydens.com
Web Site: www.brydens.com
Sales Range: $50-74.9 Million
Emp.: 200
Wholesale Trade Distr
S.I.C.: 7389
N.A.I.C.S.: 425120
Andrew Lewis *(CEO)*
Christine Dabaiya *(CFO)*
Ricky Nurse *(CEO-Brydens Barbarees)*

Subsidiaries:

Brydens Business Solutions Inc. (3)
Stokes & Bynoe Bldg Wildey Main Rd
Saint Michael, Barbados (100%)
Tel.: (246) 430-7401
Fax: (246) 436-4817
Web Site: www.ansamcal.com
Office Equipment Sales
S.I.C.: 5044
N.A.I.C.S.: 423420
Rachel Duncan *(Gen Mgr)*

Brydens Insurance Inc. (3)
Clapham Ct
Wildey Main Rd, BB 14012 Saint Michael, Barbados (100%)
Tel.: (246) 431-3611
Fax: (246) 429-5675
Web Site: www.ansamcal.com
Emp.: 33
Residential Property Managers
S.I.C.: 6531
N.A.I.C.S.: 531311
Paul Inniss *(Gen Mgr-Fin Sector)*

Affiliates:

Brydens Retail Inc. (3)
Victoria St
Bridgetown, Barbados (100%)
Tel.: (246) 431-2648
E-Mail: pencils@caribsurf.com
Web Site: www.ansamcal.com
Stationery Whslr
S.I.C.: 5112
N.A.I.C.S.: 424120
Harry Lashley *(Mng Dir)*

Brydens Xpress (Office Supplies) Inc. (3)
Lower Estate
Saint Michael, BB 19188, Barbados (52%)
Tel.: (246) 431 2646
Fax: (246) 426 3556
E-Mail: bxi@caribsurf.com
Web Site: www.brydensxpress.com
Emp.: 25
Stationery Whslr
S.I.C.: 5112
N.A.I.C.S.: 424120
Harry Lashley *(Mng Dir)*

Consolidated Finance Company Limited (2)
Hastings Christ Church
BB15150 Saint Michael, W.I., Barbados (100%)
Tel.: (246) 467-2350
Fax: (246) 426-8626
Web Site: www.ansamcal.com
Financial Investment Activities
S.I.C.: 6211
N.A.I.C.S.: 523999
Glen Sobers *(CFO)*
John MacKenzie *(CEO-Fin Sector)*

McEnearney Quality, Inc. (2)
McEnearney Quality Complex
Wildey, St Michael, 14007, Barbados
Tel.: (246) 4672400
Fax: (246) 4270764
E-Mail: autoind@mce.mcalbds.com
Web Site: www.mcenearneyquality.com
Emp.: 85

ANSA McAL Limited—(Continued)

Auto Dealership
S.I.C.: 5511
N.A.I.C.S.: 441110
Margaret Hoyte *(Mgr-Mktg)*

ANSAL BUILDWELL LTD

118 UFF Prakash Deep Building 7
Tolstoy Marg Connaught Place
New Delhi, 110 001, India
Tel.: (91) 1123353051
Fax: (91) 1123359550
E-Mail: info@ansalabl.com
Web Site: www.ansalabl.com
523007—(BOM)
Rev.: $19,697,043
Assets: $66,689,908
Liabilities: $52,657,681
Net Worth: $14,032,227
Earnings: $1,982,194
Emp.: 2,000
Fiscal Year-end: 03/31/13

Business Description:
Real Estate Development Services
S.I.C.: 6531
N.A.I.C.S.: 531210

Personnel:
Gopal Ansal *(Chm, CEO & Mng Dir)*
Ashok Babu *(Compliance Officer, Sec & VP)*

Board of Directors:
Gopal Ansal
K. S. Bakshi
R. L. Gupta
Gaurav Mohan Puri
Subhash Verma
V. P. Verma

Transfer Agent:
Link Intime India Private Limited
44 Community Centre 2nd Floor Naraina
Industrial Area Phase-I
Near PVR Naraina, New Delhi, India

ANSAL HOUSING & CONSTRUCTION LTD

15 UGF Indra Prakash Building 21
Barakhamba Road
New Delhi, 110 001, India
Tel.: (91) 1139913100
Fax: (91) 1123350847
E-Mail: ahcl@ansals.com
Web Site: www.ansals.com
507828—(BOM)
Rev.: $85,954,558
Assets: $316,470,763
Liabilities: $246,722,816
Net Worth: $69,747,947
Earnings: $8,165,663
Emp.: 529
Fiscal Year-end: 03/31/13

Business Description:
Property Development Services
S.I.C.: 1531
N.A.I.C.S.: 236117

Personnel:
Deepak Ansal *(Chm & Mng Dir)*
Mohinder Bajaj *(Compliance Officer, Sec & Sr VP)*
Karun Ansal *(Pres-Projects)*
Sanjay Mehta *(Sr VP-Fin)*

Board of Directors:
Deepak Ansal
Pradeep Anand
Kushagr Ansal
Sham Lal Chopra
S. L. Kapur
Ashok Khanna
Maharaj Krishen Trisal

Transfer Agent:
Link Intime India Pvt Ltd
44 Community Centre 2nd Floor Naraina
Industrial Area Phase-I
New Delhi, 110 28, India

Subsidiary:

ANSAL CLUBS PVT. LIMITED (1)
110 Indra Prakash 21 Barakhamba Rd
New Delhi, 110001, India
Tel.: (91) 1143577100
Fax: (91) 1143577308
Web Site: www.ansals.com
Emp.: 30
Real Estate Agencies
S.I.C.: 6531
N.A.I.C.S.: 531210
Tarun Saldana *(Mgr)*

ANSAL PROPERTIES & INFRASTRUCTURE LIMITED

115 Ansal Bhawan 16 Kasturba
Gandhi Marg
New Delhi, 110 001, India
Tel.: (91) 1123353550
Fax: (91) 1123322009
E-Mail: info@ansalapi.com
Web Site: www.ansalapi.com
500013—(BOM NSE)
Rev.: $230,079,657
Assets: $1,263,946,108
Liabilities: $932,101,355
Net Worth: $331,844,753
Earnings: $882,059
Emp.: 1,350
Fiscal Year-end: 03/31/13

Business Description:
Real Estate Services
S.I.C.: 6552
N.A.I.C.S.: 237210

Personnel:
Sushil Ansal *(Chm)*
Pranav Ansal *(Vice Chm & Co-Mng Dir)*
Anil Kumar *(CEO & Co-Mng Dir)*
Prabhunath Misra *(Co-Mng Dir)*
Lalit Rustagi *(CFO & Pres-Fin & Accts)*
Amitav Ganguly *(Compliance Officer, VP-Corp Affairs & Sec)*

Board of Directors:
Sushil Ansal
Pranav Ansal
Lalit Bhasin
Dharmendar Nath Davar
P. R. Khanna
Anil Kumar
Prabhunath Misra
Prem Singh Rana
R. C. Vaish

Transfer Agent:
Link Intime India Private Limited
44 Community Centre 2nd Floor Naraina
Industrial Area Phase-I
Near PVR Naraina, New Delhi, India

Subsidiary:

Ansal IT City & Parks Ltd. (1)
115 Ansal Bhawan 16 Kasturba Gandhi Marg
New Delhi, 110 001, India
Tel.: (91) 1123353550
Fax: (91) 1123322009
E-Mail: info@apin.com
Commercial Building Construction Services
S.I.C.: 1542
N.A.I.C.S.: 236220
Monika Dhingra *(Sec)*

ANSALDO STS S.P.A.

Via Paolo Mantovani 3 5
16151 Genoa, Italy
Tel.: (39) 0106552111
Fax: (39) 010 655 2939
E-Mail: info@ansaldo-sts.com
Web Site: www.ansaldo-sts.com
STS—(ITA OTC)
Rev.: $1,679,816,888
Assets: $2,511,346,097
Liabilities: $1,879,768,903
Net Worth: $631,577,194
Earnings: $101,899,684
Emp.: 3,991
Fiscal Year-end: 12/31/12

Business Description:
Railway & Mass Transit System Engineering Services
S.I.C.: 4789
N.A.I.C.S.: 488210

Personnel:
Luigi Calabria *(Chm)*
Giancarlo Grasso *(Deputy Chm)*
Sergio De Luca *(CEO)*
Christian Andi *(CFO)*
Emmanuel Viollet *(Pres-Signalling Bus Unit)*
Giovanni Bocchetti *(Sr VP-Innovation & Competitiveness)*
Francesco Di Maio *(Sr VP-Transportation Solutions Bus Unit)*
Marco Fumagalli *(Sr VP-Strategy Quality & Improvement)*
Mauro Giganti *(Sr VP-Internal Audit)*

Board of Directors:
Luigi Calabria
Giovanni Cavallini
Maurizio Cereda
Sergio De Luca
Paola Girdinio
Giancarlo Grasso
Bruno Pavesi
Tatiana Rizzante
Attilio Salvetti

U.S. Subsidiary:

Ansaldo STS USA Inc. (1)
1000 Technology Dr
Pittsburgh, PA 15219-3120
Mailing Address:
PO Box 420
Pittsburgh, PA 15219
Tel.: (412) 688-2400
Fax: (412) 688-2399
Toll Free: (800) 351-1520
Web Site: www.ansaldo-sts.com
Sales Range: $200-249.9 Million
Emp.: 650
Railway Signaling & Automation Equipment Mfr
S.I.C.: 3743
N.A.I.C.S.: 336510
Sergio De Luca *(CEO)*

Non-U.S. Subsidiaries:

Ansaldo STS Ireland (1)
Mona Valley Industrial Estate
Tralee, Kerry, Ireland (100%)
Tel.: (353) 667124411
Fax: (353) 667124413
Web Site: www.ansaldo-sts.ie
Emp.: 30
Railway Signaling & Automation Equipment Mfr
S.I.C.: 3743
N.A.I.C.S.: 336510
Jimmy Laite *(Mng Dir)*

Ansaldo STS Sweden AB (1)
Solna Strandvag 80
PO Box 6066
Solna, 16353 Stockholm, 17106, Sweden
Tel.: (46) 86219500
Fax: (46) 86211424
E-Mail: info@ansaldo-sts.com
Emp.: 50
Railway Signaling & Automation Equipment Mfr
S.I.C.: 3743
N.A.I.C.S.: 336510
Jilles Pascault *(Mng Dir)*

ANSELL CAPITAL CORP.

3rd Floor Bellevue Centre 235 - 15th Street
Vancouver, BC, V7T 2X1, Canada
Tel.: (604) 921-1810
Fax: (604) 921-1898
E-Mail: info@ansellcapital.com
Web Site: www.ansellcapital.com
Year Founded: 2006
ACP—(TSXV)
Int. Income: $17,309
Assets: $9,636,380
Liabilities: $76,267
Net Worth: $9,560,113
Earnings: ($377,631)
Fiscal Year-end: 07/31/13

Business Description:
Mineral Exploration Services
S.I.C.: 1081
N.A.I.C.S.: 213114

Personnel:
Rahoul Sharan *(Chm)*
Jevin Werbes *(Pres & CEO)*
Matthew G. Wright *(CFO)*
Bev Funston *(Sec)*

Board of Directors:
Rahoul Sharan
Hrayr Agnerian
Pat Campling, Jr.
Bev Funston
Christopher Martin Healey
Jevin Werbes

ANSELL LIMITED

Level 3 678 Victoria Street
Richmond, VIC, 3121, Australia
Tel.: (61) 392707270
Fax: (61) 392707300
E-Mail: dgraham@ap.ansell.com
Web Site: www.ansell.com
Year Founded: 1889
ANN—(ASX OTC)
Rev.: $1,396,414,000
Assets: $1,912,670,340
Liabilities: $1,044,288,410
Net Worth: $868,381,930
Earnings: $146,727,680
Emp.: 12,596
Fiscal Year-end: 06/30/13

Business Description:
Latex Medical & Household Gloves, Synthetic Industrial Gloves & Condoms; Automotive & Industrial Batteries & Lead Recycling Mfr; Clothing, Footwear & Sporting Goods; Electrical, Industrial & Automotive Products; Power & Telecommunications Cables, Bedding & Foam Fibre Mfr & Distr
Import Export
S.I.C.: 2295
N.A.I.C.S.: 313320

Personnel:
Magnus R. Nicolin *(CEO & Mng Dir)*
Neil I. Salmon *(CFO)*
Giri Peddinti *(CIO & Sr VP)*
Peter Carroll *(Pres/Gen Mgr-Sexual Wellness GBU)*
Scott Corriveau *(Pres/Gen Mgr-Indus Solutions GBU)*
Thomas Draskovics *(Pres/Gen Mgr-Specialty Markets GBU)*
Anthony Lopez *(Pres/Gen Mgr-Medical GBU & LAC Reg)*
William G. Reilly *(Gen Counsel, Co-Sec & Sr VP)*
Alistair Grant *(Co-Sec & Assoc Gen Counsel-Asia Pacific)*
Peter Dobbelsteijn *(Sr VP & Dir-EMEA)*
Robert Gaither *(Sr VP & Dir-North America)*
Denis Gallant *(Sr VP & Dir-APAC)*
Steve Genzer *(Sr VP-Ops)*
Francois Le Jeune *(Sr VP-Bus Dev & Transformational Initiatives)*

Board of Directors:
Glenn Lawrence Barnes
Ronald J. S. Bell
John Andrew Bevan
L. Dale Crandall
William Peter Day
Annie H. Lo
Magnus R. Nicolin
Marissa T. Peterson

Legal Counsel:
Freehill Hollingdale & Page
Level 43 101 Collins Street
Melbourne, 3000, Australia

Subsidiary:

Ansell International (1)
678 Victoria St Level 3
Richmond, VIC, 3121, Australia AU
Tel.: (61) 3 9270 7270 (100%)
Web Site: www.ansell.com
Emp.: 5,105
Mfr., Marketing & Distribution of Latex Products, Medical, Household & Industrial Gloves & Condoms
S.I.C.: 2399
N.A.I.C.S.: 315990

U.S. Subsidiaries:

Ansell Healthcare LLC (1)
111 Wood Ave S Ste 210
Iselin, NJ 08830
Tel.: (732) 345-5400
Fax: (732) 219-5114
E-Mail: info@ansell.com
Web Site: www.ansellpro.com
Mfr. of Healthcare Products
S.I.C.: 3069
N.A.I.C.S.: 326299
Steve Genzer *(Sr VP-Global Ops)*

Subsidiary:

Ansell Sandel Medical Solutions LLC (2)
19736 Dearborn St
Chatsworth, CA 91311
Tel.: (818) 534-2500
Fax: (818) 534-2510
Toll Free: (866) 764-3327
Web Site: www.sandelmedical.com
Emp.: 32
Surgical Appliance & Supplies Mfr
S.I.C.: 3841
N.A.I.C.S.: 339113
Anthony B. Lopez *(Pres & Gen Mgr-Medical GBU)*

BarrierSafe Solutions International Inc. (1)
150 Field Dr Ste 210
Lake Forest, IL 60045
Tel.: (866) 931-3613
Fax: (847) 735-0410
Web Site: www.barriersafe.com
Sales Range: $250-299.9 Million
Emp.: 250
Disposable Protective Glove Mfr
S.I.C.: 3841
N.A.I.C.S.: 339113
Mike Mattos *(CEO)*

Subsidiaries:

Microflex Corporation (2)
150 Field Dr Ste 210
Lake Forest, IL 60045 NV
Tel.: (866) 931-3613
Fax: (847) 735-0410
Toll Free: (800) 876-6866
E-Mail: sales@microflex.com
Web Site: www.microflex.com
Billings: $5,000,000
Emp.: 112
Rubber Glove Mfr
S.I.C.: 3841
N.A.I.C.S.: 339113
Phil Renfrow *(Dir-Creative)*

Subsidiary:

High Five Products, Corp. (3)
150 Field Dr Ste 210
Lake Forest, IL 60045
Tel.: (312) 266-9030
Fax: (800) 876-6632
Toll Free: (800) 876-6866
Web Site: www.highfivegloves.com
Disposable Glove Whslr
S.I.C.: 5199
N.A.I.C.S.: 424990

ONGUARD Industries LLC (2)
1850 Clark Rd
Havre De Grace, MD 21078 DE
Tel.: (410) 272-2000
Fax: (410) 272-3346
Toll Free: (800) 365-2282
E-Mail: support@onguardindustries.com
Web Site: www.onguardindustries.com
Emp.: 120
Protective Footwear & Apparel Mfr & Distr
S.I.C.: 2389
N.A.I.C.S.: 316210
Doug Ramer *(Pres)*
Chris Maistros *(COO)*

Non-U.S. Subsidiaries:

Ansell Healthcare Europe N.V. (1)
Riverside Business Park Block J
Boulevard International 55, Brussels, 1070, Belgium BE
Tel.: (32) 2528 7400
Fax: (32) 2528 7401
E-Mail: info@eu.ansell.com
Web Site: www.anselleurope.com
Rubber Products Mfr
S.I.C.: 3069
N.A.I.C.S.: 326299

Non-U.S. Subsidiary:

Ansell Protective Solutions AB (2)
(Formerly Trelleborg Protective Products AB)
Johan Kocksgatan 10
231 81 Trelleborg, Sweden SE
Tel.: (46) 410 518 00 (100%)
Fax: (46) 410 518 40
E-Mail: orderprotective@eu.ansell.com
Web Site: protective.ansell.com
Sales Range: $25-49.9 Million
Emp.: 170
Protective Clothing & Related Products Mfr & Whslr
S.I.C.: 3999
N.A.I.C.S.: 339999
Magnus Andersson *(Mng Dir)*

Non-U.S. Subsidiaries:

Ansell Norway AS (3)
(Formerly Trelleborg Industri AS)
Prof Birkelands vej 36 D
PO Box 58
Leirdal, 1008 Oslo, Norway NO
Tel.: (47) 22904900 (100%)
Fax: (47) 22321654
E-Mail: orderprotective@eu.ansell.com
Web Site: protective.ansell.com
Sales Range: $1-9.9 Million
Emp.: 20
Protective Clothing & Related Products Whslr
S.I.C.: 5136
N.A.I.C.S.: 424320
Ellen Slathen *(Mgr-Fin)*

Ansell (Hong Kong) Limited (1)
33 Wang Chiu Road Kowloon Bay
2610B-12A 26/F Exchange Tower, Kowloon, 8523, China (Hong Kong) HK
Tel.: (852) 2185 0600 (100%)
Web Site: www.ansell.com
Rubber Products Mfr
S.I.C.: 3069
N.A.I.C.S.: 326299

Comasec SAS (1)
5 Allee des Bas Tilliers
92238 Gennevilliers, France
Tel.: (33) 1 47 92 92 92
Fax: (33) 1 47 92 92 19
E-Mail: france@comasec.com
Web Site: www.comasec.com
Sales Range: $25-49.9 Million
Emp.: 1,200
Industrial Gloves Mfr
S.I.C.: 2389
N.A.I.C.S.: 315990
Pascal Berend *(Pres)*

U.S. Subsidiary:

Marigold Industrial USA Inc. (2)
141 Old Mill Rd
Greenville, SC 29607
Tel.: (866) 343-7025
Fax: (866) 808-5009
Industrial Gloves Distr
S.I.C.: 5046
N.A.I.C.S.: 423440
Brian Shenton *(Dir-Sls & Mktg-North America)*

Non-U.S. Subsidiaries:

Comasec Italia Srl (2)
Via Torricelli 2
20090 Buccinasco, Milan, Italy
Tel.: (39) 02 45707516
Fax: (39) 02 45703595
E-Mail: italia@comasec.com
Web Site: www.comasec.com
Industrial Gloves Distr
S.I.C.: 5046
N.A.I.C.S.: 423440

Marigold Industrial Gloves Iberia S.L. (2)
Paseo de la Habana 4-1-1
28036 Madrid, Spain
Tel.: (34) 91 561 42 00
Fax: (34) 91 564 85 87
E-Mail: iberia@marigold-industrial.com
Web Site: www.comasec.com
Industrial Gloves Distr
S.I.C.: 5046
N.A.I.C.S.: 423440

Marigold Industrial GmbH (2)
Samannstrasse 2-4
66538 Neunkirchen, Germany
Tel.: (49) 6821 8608 0
Fax: (49) 6821 8608 10
E-Mail: germany@comasec.com
Web Site: www.comasec.com
Emp.: 27
Industrial Gloves Distr
S.I.C.: 5046
N.A.I.C.S.: 423440
Petrus Dobbelsteijn *(Mng Dir)*

Marigold Industrial Ltd (2)
Vantage Park Old Gloucester Road
Hambrook, Bristol, BS16 1GW, United Kingdom
Tel.: (44) 845 075 3355
Fax: (44) 845 075 3356
E-Mail: uk@marigold-industrial.com
Web Site: www.comasec.com
Emp.: 20
Industrial Gloves Distr
S.I.C.: 5046
N.A.I.C.S.: 423440
Mike Credicott *(Gen Mgr)*

Marigold Industrial Sdn. Bhd. (2)
Kulim Industrial Est
Kedah, Kulim, 9000, Malaysia MY
Tel.: (60) 44891973 (100%)
Fax: (60) 44891048
E-Mail:
Web Site: www.ansell.com
Emp.: 900
Industrial & Household Gloves Mfr
S.I.C.: 2389
N.A.I.C.S.: 315990

ANSHAN HEAVY DUTY MINING MACHINERY CO., LTD.

900 Shengli North Road
Lishan District, Anshan, 114042, China
Tel.: (86) 412 5213058
Web Site: www.aszkjqc.com
002667—(SSE)
Sales Range: $25-49.9 Million
Emp.: 530

Business Description:
Mining Machinery Mfr
S.I.C.: 3532
N.A.I.C.S.: 333131

Personnel:
Yongzhu Yang *(Chm)*

ANSHAN IRON & STEEL GROUP CORPORATION

(d/b/a Ansteel)
396 Nan Zhong Hua Lu
Tie Dong District, Anshan, China
Tel.: (86) 4126723090
Fax: (86) 4126723080
E-Mail: office@ansteel.com.cn
Web Site: www.ansteelgroup.com

Business Description:
Steel Producer
S.I.C.: 3399
N.A.I.C.S.: 331110

Personnel:
Zhang Xiaogang *(Chm)*

Non-U.S. Subsidiary:

Angang Group Hong Kong Co. Ltd. (1)
Room 3412-13 Convention Plaza Office Tower 1 Harbour Road
Wanchai, Hong Kong, China (Hong Kong)
Tel.: (852) 28028318
Fax: (852) 28028636
E-Mail: aghk@netvigator.com.hk
Sales Range: $500-549.9 Million
Emp.: 55
Steel Distr & Retailer
S.I.C.: 1081
N.A.I.C.S.: 213114
Da Guang Li *(Chm & Pres)*
Heng Wang *(Mng Dir)*

Subsidiary:

Angang Steel Company Ltd. (1)
Angang Industrial Zone Tiexi District
Anshan, 114021, China CN
Tel.: (86) 4128417273
Fax: (86) 4126727772
E-Mail: ansteel@ansteel.com.cn
Web Site: www.ansteel.com.cn
000898—(HKG SSE)
Sales Range: $5-14.9 Billion
Emp.: 31,576
Steel Products Mfr & Distr
S.I.C.: 3462
N.A.I.C.S.: 332111
Xiaogang Zhang *(Chm)*

ANSHAN SENYUAN ROAD & BRIDGE CO., LTD.

281 Anqian Road East Zone
Anshan, 114051, China
Tel.: (86) 412 5225728
E-Mail: assyrb@assyrb.com
Web Site: www.assyrb.com
300210—(CHIN)
Emp.: 250

Business Description:
Road & Bridge Vehicle & Construction Machinery Mfr
S.I.C.: 3711
N.A.I.C.S.: 336120

Personnel:
Songsen Guo *(Chm)*

ANSHU'S CLOTHING LIMITED

F 103 Shivalik Complex Opp AMA Near IIM
Panjrapol, Ahmedabad, Gujarat, 380015, India
Tel.: (91) 79 3007 1919
E-Mail: investors@gmail.com
Web Site: www.anshusdesigns.com
Year Founded: 2005
534707—(BOM)

Business Description:
Sarees & Other Women's Clothing Mfr
S.I.C.: 2389
N.A.I.C.S.: 315240

Personnel:
Ravi Bhandari *(Mng Dir)*
Pooja Gwalani *(Sec)*

Board of Directors:
Ravi Bhandari
Ajay Jain
Chirag Jagdishbhai Khatri

ANTA SPORTS PRODUCTS LIMITED

Unit 4408 44/F COSCO Tower 183 Queen's Road
Central, China (Hong Kong)
Tel.: (852) 2116 1660
Fax: (852) 2116 1590
E-Mail: ir@anta.com
Web Site: www.anta.com.cn
2020—(HKG OTC)
Sls.: $1,210,883,051
Assets: $1,594,228,608
Liabilities: $492,968,260
Net Worth: $1,101,260,348

ANTA Sports Products Limited—(Continued)

Earnings: $215,370,895
Emp.: 11,900
Fiscal Year-end: 12/31/12

Business Description:
Sportswear Design Distribution & Manufacturing Services
S.I.C.: 5091
N.A.I.C.S.: 423910

Personnel:
Shizhong Ding *(Chm & CEO)*
Shijia Ding *(Deputy Chm)*
Shing Ping Ling *(CFO, Sec & VP)*
Shixian Lai *(COO & VP)*
Jie Zheng *(Pres-Brand)*
Yonghua Wu *(Exec VP)*

Board of Directors:
Shizhong Ding
Zhongchuan Dai
Shijia Ding
Shixian Lai
Hong Te Lu
Wenmo Wang
Yonghua Wu
Chi Tat Yeung
Jie Zheng

Computershare Hong Kong Investor Services Limited
Shops 1712-1716 17th Floor Hopewell Centre
183 Queens Road East
Wanchai, China (Hong Kong)

Transfer Agents:
Royal Bank of Canada Trust Company (Cayman) Limited
4th Floor Royal Bank House 24 Shedden Road
Georgetown, Cayman Islands

Computershare Hong Kong Investor Services Limited
Shops 1712-1716 17th Floor Hopewell Centre
183 Queens Road East
Wanchai, China (Hong Kong)

ANTARCHILE S.A.

150 Av El Golf Piso 21
Las Condes, 7550107 Santiago, Chile
Tel.: (56) 36 461 7710
Fax: (56) 36 461 7717
E-Mail: contacto@antarchile.cl
Web Site: www.antarchile.cl
ANTARCHILE—(SGO)
Sales Range: $5-14.9 Billion
Emp.: 8,400

Business Description:
Diversified Financial Investment Services
S.I.C.: 6211
N.A.I.C.S.: 523999

Personnel:
Roberto Angelini Rossi *(Chm)*
Jose Tomas Guzman Dumas *(Vice Chm)*
Jorge Andueza Fouque *(CEO & Gen Mgr)*

Board of Directors:
Roberto Angelini Rossi
Manuel Enrique Bezanilla Urrutia
Juan Edgardo Goldenberg Penafiel
Arnaldo Gorziglia Balbi
Jose Tomas Guzman Dumas
Felipe Larrain Bascunan
Andres Lyon Lyon

Subsidiary:

Empresas Copec S.A. **(1)**
El Golf 150 Piso 17 Las Condes
Santiago, Chile (60.82%)
Tel.: (56) 24617000
Fax: (56) 24617070
E-Mail: wmaster@empresascopec.cl
Web Site: www.empresascopec.cl
Sales Range: $900-999.9 Million
Emp.: 18
Gasoline & Petroleum By Products Importer & Distr
S.I.C.: 5172
N.A.I.C.S.: 424720
Roberto Angelini Rossi *(Chm)*
Jose Tomas Guzman Dumas *(Vice Chm)*
Eduardo Navarro Beltran *(CEO)*
Rodrigo Huidobro Alvarado *(CFO)*
Jose Tomas Guzman Rencoret *(Sec)*

Subsidiaries:

Abastecedora de Combustibles S.A. **(2)**
Avenida Vicuna Mackenna 55
Santiago, Chile
Tel.: (56) 26939000
Fax: (56) 26939304
Web Site: www.abastible.cl
Gasoline & Petroleum
S.I.C.: 5172
N.A.I.C.S.: 424720
Jose Odone *(CEO)*

Celulosa Arauco y Constitucion S.A. **(2)**
Avenida El Golf 150 14th Floor Las Condes
Santiago, Chile CL
Tel.: (56) 24617200 (99.98%)
Fax: (56) 246985967
E-Mail: info@arauco.cl
Web Site: www.arauco.cl
Rev.: $4,280,302,000
Assets: $13,551,186,000
Liabilities: $6,585,427,000
Net Worth: $6,965,759,000
Earnings: $140,471,000
Emp.: 13,227
Fiscal Year-end: 12/31/12
Holding Company; Forest Plantations, Wood Pulp Mills, Sawmills & Wood Processing Plants Operator
S.I.C.: 6719
N.A.I.C.S.: 551112
Jose Tomas Guzman Dumas *(Chm)*
Roberto Angelini Rossi *(First Vice Chm)*
Manuel Enrique Bezanilla Urrutia *(Second Vice Chm)*
Cristian Infante Bilbao *(Pres & COO)*
Matias Domeyko Cassel *(CEO)*
Gianfranco Truffello *(CFO)*
Felipe Guzman *(Gen Counsel)*
Robinson Tajmuch *(Sr VP & Comptroller)*
Franco Bozzalla *(Sr VP-Woodpulp)*
Charles Kimber *(Sr VP-Comml & Corp Affairs)*
Antonio Luque *(Sr VP-Sawn Timber)*
Camila Merino *(Sr VP-HR)*
Alvaro Saavedra *(Sr VP-Forestry)*
Gonzalo Zegers *(Sr VP-Panels)*

Non-U.S. Subsidiary:

Flakeboard Company Limited **(3)**
80 Tiverton Court Suite 701
Markham, ON, L3R 0G4, Canada
Tel.: (905) 475-9686
Fax: (905) 475-3827
Toll Free: (800) 268-9830
Web Site: www.flakeboard.com
Emp.: 20
Composite Wood Products Mfr
S.I.C.: 2499
N.A.I.C.S.: 321999
Kelly Shotbolt *(Pres & CEO)*
Robert Henry *(CFO & VP-Fin)*

Subsidiaries:

Flakeboard (SSM) Company Limited **(4)**
657 Base Line
Sault Sainte Marie, ON, P6A 5K6, Canada
Tel.: (705) 253-0770
Fax: (705) 253-6888
E-Mail: michael.rosso@flakeboard.com
Web Site: www.flakeboard.com
Emp.: 124
Medium Density Fibreboard Mfr
S.I.C.: 2499
N.A.I.C.S.: 321999
Michael Rosso *(Mng Dir-Mfg)*

Non-U.S. Joint Venture:

Eufores, S.A. **(3)**
Luis Alberto de Herrera 1248 Complejo World Trade Center
Torre 3 Piso 9, Montevideo, Uruguay
Tel.: (598) 2623 6300
E-Mail: contacto@montesdelplata.com.uy
Web Site: www.montesdelplata.com.uy
Emp.: 250
Forest Nurseries & Wood Pulp Mills
S.I.C.: 0831
N.A.I.C.S.: 113210
Erwin Kaufmann *(Gen Mgr)*

Compania de Petroleos de Chile Copec S.A. **(2)**
El Golf 150 Piso 17
Las Condes, Santiago, Chile
Tel.: (56) 24617000
E-Mail: wmaster@empresascopec.cl
Web Site: www.ec.cl
Emp.: 20
Gasoline & Petroleum By-Products Importer & Distr
S.I.C.: 5172
N.A.I.C.S.: 424720
Lorenzo Gazmuri Schleyer *(CEO)*

Empresa Electrica Guacolda S.A. **(2)**
Av Apoquindo 3885 Piso 10
Las Condes, Santiago, Chile
Tel.: (56) 51 546100
Fax: (56) 51 531666
Web Site: www.guacolda.cl
Electrical Engineering Services
S.I.C.: 1731
N.A.I.C.S.: 238210
Jorge Rodriguez Grossi *(Chm)*

MetroGas S.A. **(2)**
El Regidor 54
Las Condes, Santiago, Chile
Tel.: (56) 23378000
Fax: (56) 23320344
Web Site: www.metrogas.cl
Natural Gas Distr
S.I.C.: 4924
N.A.I.C.S.: 221210
Eduardo Morande Montt *(CEO)*

Sociedad Minera Isla Riesco S.A. **(2)**
El Bosque Norte 500 Piso 23
Las Condes, Santiago, Chile
Tel.: (56) 2 429 6300
Web Site: www.minainvierno.cl
Mining Services
S.I.C.: 1099
N.A.I.C.S.: 212299

Sociedad Nacional de Oleoductos S.A. **(2)**
Av Isabel La Catolica 4473 Casilla 243 Correo 34
Las Condes, Santiago, 6761025, Chile
Tel.: (56) 2 2081603
Fax: (56) 2 2081323
E-Mail: asuntoscorporativos@sonocol.cl
Web Site: www.sonacol.cl
Pipeline Engineering Services
S.I.C.: 8711
N.A.I.C.S.: 541330
Fernando Prado Alvarez *(Chm)*

SouthPacific Korp S.A. **(2)**
Avenida El Golf 150 piso 15
Las Condes, Santiago, Chile
Tel.: (56) 2 4764 100
Fax: (56) 2 4764 131
Web Site: www.spk.cl
Food Products from Materials Extracted from Ocean
S.I.C.: 2092
N.A.I.C.S.: 311710
Roberto Angelini Rossi *(Chm)*
Joaquin Cruz Sanfiel *(CEO)*

ANTARES ENERGY LIMITED

Ground Floor 20 Kings Park Road
West Perth, WA, 6005, Australia
Tel.: (61) 4 1717 4773
E-Mail: mail@amityoil.com.au
Web Site: www.antaresenergy.com
AO7—(ASX DEU)
Rev.: $27,653,166
Assets: $153,357,520
Liabilities: $71,938,247
Net Worth: $81,419,273
Earnings: ($8,262,811)
Fiscal Year-end: 12/31/12

Business Description:
Oil & Gas Exploration Services
S.I.C.: 1389
N.A.I.C.S.: 213112

Personnel:
James Andrew Cruickshank *(Chm & CEO)*
Kelli Lynn Roach *(Chief Admin Officer & Gen Counsel)*
Vicky Ann McAppion *(Sec & Mgr-Fin & Admin)*

Board of Directors:
James Andrew Cruickshank
Mark Gerard Clohessy
Vicky Ann McAppion
Kelli Lynn Roach
Gregory David Shoemaker

Legal Counsel:
Allens Arthur Robinson
Level 37 QV1 Building 250 St Georges Terrace
Perth, WA, 6000, Australia

ANTARIA LIMITED

108 Radium Street
Welshpool, WA, 6106, Australia
Tel.: (61) 8 9258 1602
Fax: (61) 8 9285 5800
E-Mail: info@antaria.com
Web Site: www.antaria.com
Year Founded: 1997
BBJ—(ASX DEU)
Rev.: $4,567,449
Assets: $6,299,565
Liabilities: $2,590,176
Net Worth: $3,709,389
Earnings: ($467,068)
Fiscal Year-end: 06/30/13

Business Description:
Specialty Chemical Mfr
S.I.C.: 2899
N.A.I.C.S.: 325998

Personnel:
Deana Cesari *(CFO)*
Brad Goodsell *(Sec)*

Board of Directors:
Rade Dudurovic
Ron Higham
Paul Pisasale

ANTECO SA

str Lamaitei nr 2
Ploiesti, Prahova, 100185, Romania
Tel.: (40) 244 543088
Fax: (40) 244 516571
E-Mail: office@anteco.ro
Web Site: www.anteco.ro
Year Founded: 1886
ANTE—(BUC)

Business Description:
Household Furniture Mfr
S.I.C.: 2519
N.A.I.C.S.: 337125

Personnel:
Mircea Ilisie *(Pres)*

ANTENA 3 TELEVISION, S.A.

Antena 3 Television Avda Avenida Isla Graciosa 13
San Sebastian de los Reyes, 28703 Madrid, Spain
Tel.: (34) 916230500
Fax: (34) 916549204
E-Mail: comunicacion@antena3tv.es
Web Site: www.grupoantena3.com
A3TV—(MAD)
Rev.: $959,245,742
Assets: $1,580,119,538
Liabilities: $1,127,534,492
Net Worth: $452,585,046
Earnings: $42,954,939
Emp.: 537
Fiscal Year-end: 12/31/12

Business Description:
Television & Radio Broadcasting Services
S.I.C.: 4833
N.A.I.C.S.: 515120

Personnel:
Jose Manuel Lara Bosch *(Chm)*
Maurizio Carlotti *(Deputy Chm)*
Silvio Gonzalez Moreno *(CEO)*
Antonio Manso *(CFO)*
Javier Gonzalez Ferrari *(Chm-Uniprex)*
Mikel Lejarza *(Chm-Antena 3 Films)*
Manuel de la Viuda *(Gen Counsel)*
Board of Directors:
Jose Manuel Lara Bosch
Mauricio Casals Aldama
Maurizio Carlotti
Nicolas Abel Bellet de Tavernost
Marco Drago
Josep Maria Benet Ferran
Maria Entrecanales Franco
Elmar Heggen
Jose Creuheras Margenat
Silvio Gonzalez Moreno
Aurora Cata Sala
Jose Miguel Contreras Tejera
Pedro Ramon y Cajal Agueras
Subsidiaries:

ANTENA 3 EVENTOS S.L.U. (1)
Calle Fuerteventura 12-12
San Sebastian de los Reyes, 28703, Spain
Tel.: (34) 916232750
Fax: (34) 916232740
E-Mail: production@a3eventos.es
Web Site: www.a3eventos.es
Emp.: 20
Television Broadcasting Services
S.I.C.: 4833
N.A.I.C.S.: 515120
Alvaro Pitto *(Mng Dir)*

ANTENA 3 FILMS S.L.U. (1)
Calle Isla de Graciosa 13
San Sebastian de los Reyes, 28703, Spain
Tel.: (34) 916230500
Fax: (34) 916230301
Web Site: www.antena3films.com
Motion Picture Production Services
S.I.C.: 7812
N.A.I.C.S.: 512110
Gautier Barbagi *(Gen Mgr)*

ATRES ADVERTISING S.L.U. (1)
Fuerteventura 12
28700 San Sebastian de los Reyes, Spain
Tel.: (34) 916230500
Fax: (34) 916234710
Web Site: www.atresadvertising.com
Advertising Agencies
S.I.C.: 7311
N.A.I.C.S.: 541810

MOVI ERECORD CINE S.A.U. (1)
Calle Isla de Graciosa 13
San Sebastian de los Reyes, 28703, Spain
Tel.: (34) 916230102
Fax: (34) 916234680
E-Mail: movierecord@movierecord.com
Web Site: www.movierecord.com
Cinema Advertising Services
S.I.C.: 7311
N.A.I.C.S.: 541810

MUSICA APARTE S.A.U. (1)
Calle Fuerteventura 12
San Sebastian de los Reyes, 28703, Spain
Tel.: (34) 916232534
Fax: (34) 916234593
Television Broadcasting Services
S.I.C.: 4833
N.A.I.C.S.: 515120

UNIPUBLIC S.A. (1)
Fuerteventura 12
28703 San Sebastian de los Reyes, Madrid, Spain
Tel.: (34) 916232750
Fax: (34) 916232740
E-Mail: info@unipublic.es
Web Site: www.unipublic.es
Emp.: 10
Bicycling Race Organizers
S.I.C.: 7999
N.A.I.C.S.: 711310
Javier Guillen *(Mng Dir)*

Non-U.S. Subsidiary:

A3 MULTIMEDIA S.L.U. (1)
rue des pagannes
49300 Cholet, France
Tel.: (33) 241463855
Fax: (33) 2 41 46 38 45
E-Mail: A3multimed@agena3000.fr
Web Site: www.a3multimedia.com
Barcode Terminals Whslr
S.I.C.: 5065
N.A.I.C.S.: 423690

ANTENNA GROUP
10-12, Kifissias Avenue
15125 Maroussi, Greece
Tel.: (30) 2106886100
Web Site: www.antenna.gr
Year Founded: 1988
Business Description:
Media Group
S.I.C.: 3652
N.A.I.C.S.: 512220
Personnel:
Minos X. Kyriakou *(Pres)*
Theodore Kyriakou *(CEO)*
Pete Smith *(Mng Dir)*
Subsidiary:

Antenna TV S.A. (1)
Kifissias Ave 10 12
Maroussi, 151 25 Athens, Greece
Tel.: (30) 2106886100
Fax: (30) 2106890304
E-Mail: perbena@antenna.gr
Web Site: www.antenna.gr
Sales Range: $200-249.9 Million
Emp.: 750
Broadcast Television Network Services
S.I.C.: 4833
N.A.I.C.S.: 515120
George Levendi *(Mng Dir)*
Jonathan Procter *(Mng Dir)*

ANTENNA HOUSE, INC.
Higashi Nihonbashi Towa Bldg 2-1-6
Higashi Nihonbashi
Chuo-ku, Tokyo, 103-0004, Japan
Tel.: (81) 3 58299021
Fax: (81) 3 58299024
Web Site: www.antennahouse.com
Sales Range: $1-9.9 Million
Emp.: 50
Business Description:
Document Formatting & Processing
S.I.C.: 7389
N.A.I.C.S.: 561410
Personnel:
Tokushige Kobayashi *(Pres)*

ANTEO DIAGNOSTICS LIMITED
4 26 Brandl Street Brisbane
Technology Park
Eight Mile Plains, QLD, 4113, Australia
Tel.: (61) 732190085
Fax: (61) 732190553
E-Mail: contact@anteodx.com
Web Site: www.anteodx.com
ADO—(ASX)
Rev.: $228,811
Assets: $3,413,240
Liabilities: $520,614
Net Worth: $2,892,626
Earnings: ($2,270,968)
Emp.: 18
Fiscal Year-end: 06/30/13
Business Description:
Biological Research Services
S.I.C.: 8731
N.A.I.C.S.: 541712
Personnel:
Geoff Cumming *(CEO)*
N. Joe Maeji *(Chief Scientific Officer)*
Shane Hartwig *(Sec)*
Board of Directors:
Mark Bouris
Sandra Andersen
Geoff Cumming
John Hurrell
Richard Martin
Legal Counsel:
Clarkekann Lawyers
300 Queen Street
Brisbane, Australia

ANTEO GROUP LLC
(Acquired by Recruit Co., Ltd.)

ANTERRA ENERGY INC.
1420 1122 - 4th Street SW
Calgary, AB, T2R 1M1, Canada
Tel.: (403) 215-3280
Fax: (403) 261-6601
Web Site: www.anterraenergy.com
Year Founded: 2005
AE.A—(OTC TSXV)
Rev.: $7,768,316
Assets: $43,137,097
Liabilities: $18,597,910
Net Worth: $24,539,187
Earnings: ($808,648)
Fiscal Year-end: 12/31/12
Business Description:
Oil & Natural Gas Exploration & Production
S.I.C.: 1311
N.A.I.C.S.: 211111
Personnel:
Owen C. Pinnell *(Chm)*
Gang Fang *(Pres & CEO)*
Norman G. Knecht *(CFO)*
Board of Directors:
Owen C. Pinnell
Gary Chang
James Hayward Coleman
Ross O. Drysdale
Gang Fang
ZhenXiang Huo
Hong Lei

ANTEX WESTERN
1375 Church Ave
PO Box 778
Winnipeg, MB, R3C 2L4, Canada
Tel.: (204) 633-4815
Fax: (204) 633-0550
E-Mail: antex@antexwestern.com
Web Site: www.antexwestern.com
Year Founded: 1928
Rev.: $13,801,154
Emp.: 86
Business Description:
Flooring Contractors & Services
S.I.C.: 1752
N.A.I.C.S.: 238330
Personnel:
Mike Kolas *(Pres & CEO)*
Elmer Fakharuddin *(CFO)*
Brian Fedorchuk *(Treas & Mgr-Floorcoverings Div-Winnipeg)*
Joseph Ng *(Sec)*
Board of Directors:
Bryan Demarcke
Brian Fedorchuk
Ken Klohn
Mike Kolas
Joseph Ng

ANTHEM RESOURCES INC.
675 West Hastings Street Suite 611
Vancouver, BC, V6B 1N2, Canada
Tel.: (604) 568-7709
Fax: (604) 669-2543
Web Site: www.anthemresourcesinc.com
AYN—(OTC TSXV)
Int. Income: $242,736
Assets: $13,158,511
Liabilities: $184,082
Net Worth: $12,974,429
Earnings: ($8,972,343)
Emp.: 5
Fiscal Year-end: 06/30/13
Business Description:
Uranium Exploration Services
S.I.C.: 1094
N.A.I.C.S.: 212291
Personnel:
Walter Coles, Jr. *(Pres & CEO)*
Karen A. Allan *(CFO & Sec)*
Board of Directors:
Walter Coles, Jr.
Robert G. Ingram
Robert V. Matthews
Ronald K. Netolitzky
Legal Counsel:
DuMoulin Black
10th Floor, 595 Howe Street
Vancouver, BC, V6C 2T5, Canada
Transfer Agent:
Computershare Trust Company of Canada
510 Burrard St 2nd Fl
Vancouver, BC, Canada

ANTHEM WORKS LTD.
550 Burrard St Ste 300
Vancouver, BC, V6C 2B5, Canada
Tel.: (604) 689-3040
Fax: (604) 689-5642
E-Mail: info@anthemproperties.com
Web Site: www.anthemproperties.com
Year Founded: 1991
Sales Range: $10-24.9 Million
Emp.: 75
Business Description:
Retail, Industrial, Office & Residential Real Estate Management
S.I.C.: 6531
N.A.I.C.S.: 531390
Personnel:
Eric H. Carlson *(Pres & CEO)*
David Ferguson *(Sr VP-Investment Grp)*
Subsidiary:

Anthem Properties Group (1)
Dentall 5 550 Burrard St Ste 300
Vancouver, BC, V6C 2B5, Canada
Tel.: (604) 689-3040
Fax: (604) 689-5642
E-Mail: info@anthemproperties.com
Web Site: www.anthemproperties.com
Emp.: 150
Real Estate Investment, Development & Management Services
S.I.C.: 6726
N.A.I.C.S.: 525990
Eric Carlson *(CEO)*

Subsidiary:

United, Inc. (2)
808 4th Avenue Southwest Ste 200
Calgary, AB, T2P 3E8, Canada
Tel.: (403) 265-6180
Fax: (403) 265-6270
E-Mail: inquiriescgy@unitedcommunities.com
Web Site: www.unitedcommunities.com
Emp.: 28
Real Estate Development & Services
S.I.C.: 6531
N.A.I.C.S.: 531390
Donald J. Douglas *(Pres & CEO)*
B. Paul Simpson *(CFO & Exec VP)*
Chris M. Kolozetti *(COO & Exec VP)*

ANTHONY CLARK INTERNATIONAL INSURANCE BROKERS LTD.
102 7909 Flint Road SE
Calgary, AB, T2H 1G3, Canada
Tel.: (403) 278-8811
Fax: (403) 225-5745
E-Mail: info@aclarkinsurance.com
Web Site: www.anthonyclarkinsurance.com
Year Founded: 1989
ACL—(TSXV)

Anthony Clark International Insurance Brokers Ltd.—(Continued)

Rev.: $12,969,615
Assets: $17,649,303
Liabilities: $20,141,707
Net Worth: ($2,492,404)
Earnings: $1,156,065
Fiscal Year-end: 05/31/13
Business Description:
Insurance Brokerage Services
S.I.C.: 6411
N.A.I.C.S.: 524210
Personnel:
Tony Consalvo *(Chm, Pres & CEO)*
Mahesh Bhatia *(CFO & VP-Fin)*
Mark Hoffinger *(Sec)*
Board of Directors:
Tony Consalvo
Normand Cournoyer
Douglas Owen Farmer
Robert Sadleir
Legal Counsel:
Demiantschuk Lequier Burke & Hoffinger LLP
1200 1015 - 4th Street SW
Calgary, AB, Canada
Transfer Agent:
Canadian Stock Transfer Company Inc.
600 333 - 7th Avenue SW
Calgary, AB, Canada

Subsidiary:

Anthony Clark Insurance Brokers Ltd. **(1)**
Suite 102 7909 Flint Road SE
Calgary, AB, T2H 1G3, Canada
Tel.: (403) 278-8811
Fax: (403) 259-4429
Toll Free: (800) 278-8811
Web Site: www.anthonyclarkinsurance.com
Emp.: 4
Insurance Brokerage Services
S.I.C.: 6411
N.A.I.C.S.: 524210
Mahesh Bhatia *(Mgr-Adv)*

U.S. Subsidiary:

Addison York Insurance Brokers Ltd. **(1)**
154 Newtown Rd Ste B-6
Virginia Beach, VA 23462
Tel.: (757) 499-2598
Insurance Brokerage Services
S.I.C.: 6411
N.A.I.C.S.: 524210

ANTIBE THERAPEUTICS INC.
15 Prince Arthur Avenue
Toronto, ON, M5R 1B2, Canada
Tel.: (416) 473-4095
Web Site: www.antibethera.com
Year Founded: 2009
ATE—(TSXV)
Assets: $733,612
Liabilities: $1,734,469
Net Worth: ($1,000,858)
Earnings: ($1,038,853)
Fiscal Year-end: 03/31/13
Business Description:
Pharmaceutical Mfr
S.I.C.: 2834
N.A.I.C.S.: 325412
Personnel:
Walt Macnee *(Chm)*
Dan Legault *(Pres & CEO)*
Michael Bumby *(CFO)*
David Vaughan *(Chief Dev Officer)*
John L. Wallace *(Chief Scientific Officer)*
Board of Directors:
Walt Macnee
Roderick J. Flower
Jonathan Goodman
Dan Legault
John L. Wallace
Legal Counsel:
Norton Rose
Toronto, ON, Canada
Transfer Agent:
Olympia Transfer Services Inc.
Suite 920 120 Adelaide Street West
Toronto, ON, Canada

ANTIBIOTICE S.A.
1 Valea Lupului Street
Iasi, 707410, Romania
Tel.: (40) 232209000
Fax: (40) 372065633
E-Mail: office@antibiotice.ro
Web Site: www.antibiotice.ro
ATB—(BUC)
Rev.: $93,561,437
Assets: $158,245,340
Liabilities: $51,619,288
Net Worth: $106,626,052
Earnings: $8,341,462
Emp.: 1,440
Fiscal Year-end: 12/31/12
Business Description:
Anti-Infectives & Antibiotics Mfr
S.I.C.: 2833
N.A.I.C.S.: 325411
Personnel:
Valentin Radu *(Chm-Mgmt Bd)*
Ioan Nani *(Deputy Chm-Mgmt Bd & CEO)*
Gabriela Ilie *(Member-Mgmt Bd)*
Gheza-Gheorghe Molnar *(Member-Mgmt Bd)*
Nicolae Stoian *(Member-Mgmt Bd)*

ANTICA DITTA MARCHISIO S.P.A.
Via Cagliari 8
10153 Turin, Italy
Tel.: (39) 0112481766
Fax: (39) 0112481768
E-Mail: info@mattioligioielli.it
Web Site: www.mattioligioielli.it
Sales Range: $10-24.9 Million
Emp.: 100
Business Description:
Jewelry Mfr
S.I.C.: 3914
N.A.I.C.S.: 339910
Personnel:
Luciano Mattioli *(Pres)*

ANTIGOON INVEST NV
Korte Nieuwstraat 4
2000 Antwerp, Belgium
Tel.: (32) 32332207
Fax: (32) 3 2330722
Web Site: www.antigoon.be
ANTG—(EUR)
Sales Range: $1-9.9 Million
Business Description:
Real Estate Investment Services
S.I.C.: 6531
N.A.I.C.S.: 531390
Personnel:
Erik Bogaerts *(Co-CEO)*
Luc Van Weert *(Co-CEO)*
Board of Directors:
Erik Bogaerts
Luc Van Weert

ANTIOQUIA GOLD INC.
200 625 4th Avenue SW
Calgary, AB, T2P 0K2, Canada
Mailing Address:
PO Box 75075
Calgary, AB, T2K 6J8, Canada
Tel.: (403) 457-4653
Fax: (403) 457-4659
E-Mail: info@antioquiagoldinc.com
Web Site: www.antioquiagoldinc.com
Year Founded: 2009
AGD—(OTC TSXV)
Rev.: $11,548
Assets: $15,641,563
Liabilities: $585,883
Net Worth: $15,055,679
Earnings: ($3,033,539)
Fiscal Year-end: 12/31/12
Business Description:
Gold Mining
S.I.C.: 1041
N.A.I.C.S.: 212221
Personnel:
Fernando Jaramillo Escobar *(Pres & CEO)*
Rodger D. Roden *(CFO)*
Cathy Hume *(CEO-CHF IR)*
James H. Decker *(Exec VP)*
Board of Directors:
James H. Decker
Fernando Jaramillo Escobar
Felipe Ferraro
Ernesto Bendezu Flores
Transfer Agent:
Equity Transfer & Trust Company
200 University Avenue Ste 400
Toronto, ON, M5H 4H1, Canada
Tel.: (416) 361-0152
Fax: (416) 361-0470

ANTIPA MINERALS LTD.
21/589 Stirling Highway
Cottesloe, WA, 6011, Australia
Tel.: (61) 9 6365 4850
Fax: (61) 8 6365 5116
E-Mail: contact@antipaminerals.com.au
Web Site: www.antipaminerals.com.au
AZY—(ASX)
Business Description:
Gold, Copper, Uranium & Other Iron Ore Mining Services
S.I.C.: 1041
N.A.I.C.S.: 212221
Personnel:
Stephen Power *(Chm)*
Roger Mason *(Mng Dir)*
Alex Neuling *(Sec)*
Board of Directors:
Stephen Power
Peter Buck
Gary Johnson
Roger Mason
Mark Rodda

ANTIPHON AB
Pappersvagen 1
S 670 40 Amotfors, Sweden
Tel.: (46) 57131800
Telex: 5781
Fax: (46) 57131482
E-Mail: info@antiphon.se
Web Site: www.antiphon.se
Sales Range: $10-24.9 Million
Emp.: 20
Business Description:
Sound Dampening Material Mfr
S.I.C.: 3069
N.A.I.C.S.: 326299
Personnel:
Berit Andersson *(Chm)*
Ingemar Gustavsson *(Mng Dir)*

ANTISENSE THERAPEUTICS LIMITED
Levl 1 6 Wallace Avenue
Toorak, VIC, 3142, Australia
Tel.: (61) 3 9827 8999
Fax: (61) 3 9827 1166
Web Site: www.antisense.com.au
ANP—(ASX OTC)
Rev.: $211,843
Assets: $5,420,125
Liabilities: $577,429
Net Worth: $4,842,696
Earnings: ($2,558,191)
Fiscal Year-end: 06/30/13
Business Description:
Pharmaceutical Mfr
S.I.C.: 2834
N.A.I.C.S.: 325412
Personnel:
Robert William Moses *(Chm)*
Mark Diamond *(Mng Dir)*
Phillip Allen Hains *(CFO & Sec)*
Board of Directors:
Robert William Moses
Christopher Belyea
Mark Diamond
Graham F. Mitchell

ANTISEPTICA CHEM.-PHARM PRODUKTE GMBH
Carl-Friedrich-Gauss-Strasse 7
D-50259 Pulheim, Germany
Tel.: (49) 2234984660
Fax: (49) 22349846611
E-Mail: info@antiseptica.com
Web Site: www.antiseptica.com
Year Founded: 1976
Rev.: $11,035,200
Emp.: 16
Business Description:
Medical Services
S.I.C.: 8071
N.A.I.C.S.: 621511
Personnel:
Hans-Joachim Molitor *(Owner & Gen Mgr)*

ANTISOMA PLC
(Name Changed to Sarossa Capital PLC)

ANTLER HILL OIL & GAS LTD.
(Formerly PrimeWest Exploration Inc.)
708 11th Avenue Southwest Suite 445
Calgary, AB, T2R 0E4, Canada
Tel.: (403) 266-4141
E-Mail: cwchap@chapeng.ab.ca
Web Site:
Year Founded: 2009
AHO—(TSXV)
Assets: $314,292
Liabilities: $59,682
Net Worth: $254,610
Earnings: ($176,796)
Fiscal Year-end: 12/31/12
Business Description:
Oil & Gas Exploration Services
S.I.C.: 1311
N.A.I.C.S.: 211111
Personnel:
Charlie W. Chapman *(Chm, CEO & CFO)*

ANTLER LTD
Alfred St
Bury, Lancashire, BL9 9EF, United Kingdom
Tel.: (44) 1617625000
Fax: (44) 1617640723
E-Mail: customerservice@antler.co.uk
Web Site: www.antler.co.uk
Sales Range: $50-74.9 Million
Emp.: 150
Business Description:
Luggage & Travelware Mfr
S.I.C.: 3199
N.A.I.C.S.: 316998

ANTOFAGASTA PLC
Cleveland House 33 King Street St James
London, SW1Y 6RJ, United Kingdom
Tel.: (44) 2078080988

Fax: (44) 2079307578
E-Mail: info@antofagasta.co.uk
Web Site: www.antofagasta.co.uk
Year Founded: 1982
ANTO—(LSE)
Rev.: $6,740,100,000
Assets: $12,869,900,000
Liabilities: $4,065,100,000
Net Worth: $8,804,800,000
Earnings: $1,733,600,000
Emp.: 5,637
Fiscal Year-end: 12/31/12
Business Description:
Copper Mining
S.I.C.: 1021
N.A.I.C.S.: 212234
Personnel:
Jean-Paul Luksic *(Chm)*
Diego Hernandez Cabrera *(CEO-AMSA)*
Desmond O'Conor *(CEO-UK)*
Board of Directors:
Jean-Paul Luksic
Timothy C. Baker
Juan G. Claro
Manuel Lino Silva De Sousa-Oliveira
Hugo Dryland
William M. Hayes
Ramon F. Jara
Andronico Luksic Craig
Guillermo A. Luksic
Gonzalo S. Menendez
Nelson Pizarro
Transfer Agent:
Computershare Investor Services PLC
The Pavilions Bridgwater Road
PO Box 82
Bristol, United Kingdom

Non-U.S. Division:

Antofagasta Minerals S.A. **(1)**
Apoquindo 4001 piso 18
Santiago, Chile
Tel.: (56) 7987000
Web Site: www.aminerals.cl
Emp.: 150
Mining Operations
S.I.C.: 1021
N.A.I.C.S.: 212234
Jean-Paul Luksic *(Chm)*
Diego Hernandez Cabrera *(CEO)*
Eduardo Tagle *(CFO)*

Non-U.S. Subsidiaries:

Equatorial Mining Limited **(1)**
1 York Street Level 15
Sydney, NSW, 2000, Australia
Tel.: (61) 292473222
Fax: (61) 2 9247 9333
E-Mail: info@equamin.com.au
Web Site: www.equatorial.com.au
Copper Mining & Mineral Exploration Services
S.I.C.: 1021
N.A.I.C.S.: 212234
Sebastian Gil *(CEO)*

Minera Esperanza Ltda. **(1)**
Apoquindo 4001 Piso 13
Las Condes, Santiago, Chile
Tel.: (56) 27987000
Fax: (56) 7987096
E-Mail: contacto@mineraesperanza.cl
Web Site: www.mineraesperanza.cl
Copper & Gold Mining Services
S.I.C.: 1041
N.A.I.C.S.: 212221

Minera Los Pelambres Ltda. **(1)**
Apoquindo 4001 Piso 18
Las Condes, Santiago, 7550162, Chile
Tel.: (56) 27987000
Fax: (56) 27984181
E-Mail: contacto@minera.co
Web Site: www.pelambres.cl
Copper Mining Services
S.I.C.: 1021
N.A.I.C.S.: 212234
Jean-Paul Luksic *(Pres)*

ANTOLINI LUIGI & C. S.P.A.
Via Marconi 101
Sega di Cavaion, 37010 Verona, Italy
Tel.: (39) 045 6836611
Fax: (39) 045 6836666
E-Mail: al.spa@antolini.it
Web Site: www.antolini.com
Sales Range: $100-124.9 Million
Emp.: 180
Business Description:
Dimensional Stone Distr
S.I.C.: 5094
N.A.I.C.S.: 423940
Personnel:
Francesco Antolini *(Pres)*
Alberto Antolini *(Mng Dir)*

ANTON DEBATIN GMBH
Vichystr 6
76646 Bruchsal, Germany
Tel.: (49) 72518009100
Fax: (49) 72518009199
E-Mail: vertrieb@debatin.de
Web Site: www.debatin.de
Rev.: $58,803,251
Emp.: 230
Business Description:
Packaging Bags Mfr
S.I.C.: 2671
N.A.I.C.S.: 322220
Personnel:
Harald Misch *(Co-Mng Dir)*
Juergen Wilhelm *(Co-Mng Dir)*

ANTON OILFIELD SERVICES GROUP LIMITED
(d/b/a Antonoil)
8 Pincui West Road Donhuqu
Chaoyang District, Beijing, China
Tel.: (86) 10 57397788
Fax: (86) 10 57397799
E-Mail: group@antonoil.com
Web Site: www.antonoil.com
3337—(HKG OTC)
Sales Range: $150-199.9 Million
Emp.: 1,262
Business Description:
Oilfield Services
S.I.C.: 1381
N.A.I.C.S.: 213111
Personnel:
Lin Luo *(Chm & CEO)*
Enlong Liu *(Pres & Exec Dir)*
Maurice Wai Fung Ngai *(Sec)*
Wei Chen *(Exec VP)*
Yonghong Fan *(Exec VP)*
Bingnan Li *(Exec VP)*
Enhai Ma *(Exec VP)*
Jian Ma *(Exec VP)*
Zhifeng Pi *(Exec VP)*
Haihong Shen *(Exec VP)*
Bin Zeng *(Exec VP)*
Board of Directors:
Lin Luo
Enlong Liu
Mingcai Wang
Di Wu
Yongyi Zhang
Xiaoping Zhu

ANTONOV PLC
2 Hawkes Drive
Heathcote Industrial Estate
Warwick, CV34 6LX, United Kingdom
Tel.: (44) 1926455800
Web Site: www.antonovplc.com
ATVAM—(EUR)
Sales Range: Less than $1 Million
Emp.: 27
Business Description:
Automotive Transmission Products Mfr
S.I.C.: 3714
N.A.I.C.S.: 336390
Personnel:
Jan Eeuwe Haag *(Chm & CEO)*
Legal Counsel:
Field, Fisher & Waterhouse LLP
35 Vine St
London, EC3N 2AA, United Kingdom
Tel.: (44) 20 7861 4000
Fax: (44) 20 7488 0084

Subsidiaries:

Antonov Automotive Technologies B.V. **(1)**
Keystone Innovation Centre
Croxton Road, Norfolk, IP24 1JD, United Kingdom
Tel.: (44) 1842768320
Fax: (44) 1842768319
Web Site: www.antonovat.com
Emp.: 30
Automotive Components
S.I.C.: 3714
N.A.I.C.S.: 336390
Sam Alexander *(Controller)*

Antonov Automotive Technologies Ltd **(1)**
2 Hawkes Drive Heathcote Industrial Estate
Warwick, CV34 6LX, United Kingdom
Tel.: (44) 1926455800
Fax: (44) 1926312879
E-Mail: enquiries@antonovplc.com
Emp.: 40
Automotive Transmission Equipments Mfr
S.I.C.: 3714
N.A.I.C.S.: 336390

ANTRIM CONSTRUCTION COMPANY LTD
130-134 High Street
Holywood, Down, BT18 9HW, United Kingdom
Tel.: (44) 2890428661
Fax: (44) 2890428841
E-Mail: sales@antrimconstruction.net
Web Site: www.antrimconstruction.net
Rev.: $24,104,817
Emp.: 55
Business Description:
Residential Home Construction Services
S.I.C.: 1522
N.A.I.C.S.: 236116
Personnel:
Jackie Scott *(Mng Dir)*

ANTRIM ENERGY INC.
610 301 - 8th Avenue SW
Calgary, AB, T2P1C5, Canada
Tel.: (403) 264-5111
Fax: (403) 264-5113
E-Mail: info@antrimenergy.com
Web Site: www.antrimenergy.com
AEN—(OTC TSX)
Rev.: $276,000
Assets: $96,520,000
Liabilities: $29,524,000
Net Worth: $66,996,000
Earnings: ($134,544,000)
Emp.: 14
Fiscal Year-end: 12/31/12
Business Description:
Oil & Gas Exploration, Production & Sales
S.I.C.: 1311
N.A.I.C.S.: 211111
Personnel:
Gerry Orbell *(Chm)*
Stephen E. Greer *(Pres & CEO)*
Anthony J. Potter *(CFO)*
Adrian Harvey *(Sec)*
Board of Directors:
Gerry Orbell
Stephen E. Greer
Colin Hunter James MacLean
Erik Mielke
Jim F. Perry
James Cameron Smith
Jay M. Zammit
Legal Counsel:
Burstall Winger LLP
Suite 1600 Dome Tower
333 7th Avenue SW, Calgary, AB, T2P 2Z1, Canada
Tel.: (403) 264-1915
Transfer Agent:
CIBC Mellon Trust Company
Ste 600 333 7th Ave SW
Calgary, AB, T2P 2Z1, Canada
Tel.: (403) 232-2400
Fax: (403) 264-2100
Toll Free: (800) 387-0825
Non-U.S. Subsidiary:

Antrim Resources (N.I.) Limited **(1)**
Ashbourne House The Guildway Old Portsmouth Rd Artington
Guildford, Surrey, United Kingdom
Tel.: (44) 1483307530
Fax: (44) 1483307531
Web Site: www.masterdeed.com
Oil & Gas Field Exploration Services
S.I.C.: 1389
N.A.I.C.S.: 213112

ANUH PHARMA LTD.
3 A Shiv Sagar Estate North Wing
Annie Basant Road
Worli, Mumbai, 400018, India
Tel.: (91) 22 66227575
Fax: (91) 22 66227500
E-Mail: anuh@skageexports.com
506260—(BOM)
Sales Range: $10-24.9 Million
Business Description:
Pharmaceutical Products Mfr
S.I.C.: 2834
N.A.I.C.S.: 325412
Personnel:
G. C. Sharda *(CEO)*
Bipin N. Shah *(Mng Dir)*
Board of Directors:
Bharat N. Shah
Bipin N. Shah
J. G. Shah
J. P. Shah
L. P. Shah
Transfer Agent:
Bigshare Services Pvt. Ltd.
E-2/3 Ansa Industrial Estate Sakivihar Road
Saki Naka Andheri E
Mumbai, India

ANU'S LABORATORIES LTD.
(Name Changed to Ameya Laboratories Ltd.)

ANV SECURITY GROUP, INC.
8th Floor Block B R&D Building
Tsinghua Hi-Tech Park
Nanshan District, Shenzhen, China 518057
Tel.: (86) 755 86656436
E-Mail: info@anvsecuritygroup.com
Web Site: www.anvsecuritygroup.com
Year Founded: 1981
ANVS—(OTC)
Rev.: $185,175
Assets: $2,835,221
Liabilities: $174,363
Net Worth: $2,660,858
Earnings: ($8,324,773)
Emp.: 370
Fiscal Year-end: 12/31/12
Business Description:
Network Video Surveillance & Video Alarm Service Product Developer
S.I.C.: 7382
N.A.I.C.S.: 561621
Personnel:
Weixing Wang *(Co-Founder, Chm & CEO)*
Yan Wang *(Co-Founder & VP)*
Kevin Su *(CFO)*

ANV SECURITY GROUP, INC.—(Continued)

Board of Directors:
Weixing Wang
Yiquan Song
Paul Strickland
Yan Wang

ANVIFISH JOINT-STOCK COMPANY

National Road 91 Thanh An Village
My Thoi Ward
Long Xuyen, An Giang, Vietnam
Tel.: (84) 76 923545
Fax: (84) 76 932554
E-Mail: anvifish@vnn.vn
Web Site: www.anvifish.com
Year Founded: 2004
AVF—(HOSE)
Business Description:
Fish Farming Services
S.I.C.: 0921
N.A.I.C.S.: 112511
Personnel:
Bach Thao Luu *(Chm, Mng Dir & Gen Dir)*
Thi Lai Le *(Vice Mng Dir)*
Minh Giau Truong *(Vice Mng Dir)*

ANWELL TECHNOLOGIES LTD.

8 Wilkie Road 03 01 Wilkie Edge
Singapore, 228095, Singapore
Tel.: (65) 65337600
Fax: (65) 65947855
E-Mail: anwell@anwell.com
Web Site: www.anwell.com
G5X—(SES)
Sls.: $172,333,938
Assets: $696,977,974
Liabilities: $655,678,642
Net Worth: $41,299,332
Earnings: ($33,758,723)
Emp.: 2,375
Fiscal Year-end: 12/31/12
Business Description:
Integrated Optical Disc Replication Systems, Sub-Systems & Peripherals Designer, Mfr & Sales
S.I.C.: 3827
N.A.I.C.S.: 333314
Personnel:
Kai Leung Fan *(Chm & CEO)*
Wai Kin Wu *(CFO)*
Huisen Liu *(COO)*
Sam Ming Sang Yeung *(CTO)*
Peck Khim Yap *(Sec)*
Board of Directors:
Kai Leung Fan
Kun Shuin Chan
Huisen Liu
Bao Naikeng
Ann Ling Ng
Cheng Han Tan
Wai Kin Wu
Subsidiaries:

Anwell Precision Technology (HK) Limited (1)
Unit 10-15 9th Fl Metro Loft No 38 Kwai Hei St
Kwai Chung, New Territories, China (Hong Kong)
Tel.: (852) 24999178
Fax: (852) 24999170
Web Site: www.anwell.com
Emp.: 50
Optical Disc Mfr
S.I.C.: 3572
N.A.I.C.S.: 334112
Fanny Lai *(Mgr-HR)*

Anwell Solar Technologies Limited (1)
Unit 10-15 9th Fl Metro Loft No 38 Kwai Hei St
Kwai Chung, New Territories, China (Hong Kong)
Tel.: (852) 24999178
Fax: (852) 24999170
E-Mail: anwell@anwell.com
Web Site: www.anwell.com
Emp.: 40
Optical Storage Media Disc Mfr
S.I.C.: 3572
N.A.I.C.S.: 334112

Sungen International Limited (1)
Unit 1-7 6 F Metro Loft 38 Kwai Hei St
Kwai Chung, China (Hong Kong)
Tel.: (852) 35835286
Fax: (852) 31062801
E-Mail: sales@sungen.com
Web Site: www.SUNGEN.com
Emp.: 20
Solar Cells Mfr & Mktg Services
S.I.C.: 3674
N.A.I.C.S.: 334413

Umedisc (Holdings) Limited (1)
Rm 601 Metroloft 38 Kwai Hei St
Kwai Chung, China (Hong Kong)
Tel.: (852) 31062822
Fax: (852) 31062801
Web Site: www.umedisc.com
Emp.: 40
Investment Holding Services
S.I.C.: 6719
N.A.I.C.S.: 551112

Umedisc Limited (1)
Rm 601 Metroloft 38 Kwai Hei St
Kwai Chung, New Territories, China (Hong Kong)
Tel.: (852) 31062822
Fax: (852) 31062801
E-Mail: sales@umedisc.com
Web Site: www.umedisc.com
Emp.: 42
Optical Storage Media Disc Mfr
S.I.C.: 3572
N.A.I.C.S.: 334112
Lawrence Luk *(Mgr)*

ANXIN-CHINA HOLDINGS LIMITED

Units 2001-2005 20th Floor Harbour Centre 25 Harbour Road
Wanchai, China (Hong Kong)
Tel.: (852) 23428702
Fax: (852) 23448917
E-Mail: info@anxin-china.com.hk
Web Site: www.anxin-china.com.hk
1149—(HKG)
Sls.: $109,572,684
Assets: $526,385,377
Liabilities: $86,683,672
Net Worth: $439,701,705
Earnings: $70,642,034
Emp.: 516
Fiscal Year-end: 12/31/12
Business Description:
Emergency & Safety Products & Software
S.I.C.: 7382
N.A.I.C.S.: 561621
Personnel:
Zhongkui Liu *(Chm & CEO)*
Bo Wang *(Vice Chm)*
Zhengzhong Han *(CTO)*
Hong Chen *(CEO-Shenzhen Anxin & Jiangsu Hongxin)*
Pui Ki Leung *(Sec)*
He Li *(Sr VP)*
Board of Directors:
Zhongkui Liu
Adiv Baruch
Chuen Chueng
Victor On-kwok Li
Supeng Lin
Bo Wang
John Peter Ben Wang
Baitang Xie
Ma Yang
Royal Bank of Canada Trust Company (Cayman) Limited
4th Floor Royal Bank House 24 Shedden Road
Georgetown, Cayman Islands

Transfer Agents:
Tricor Standard Limited
26/F Tesbury Centre 28 Queen's Road East
Wanchai, China (Hong Kong)
Tel.: (852) 2980 1333
Fax: (852) 2810 8185

Royal Bank of Canada Trust Company (Cayman) Limited
4th Floor Royal Bank House 24 Shedden Road
Georgetown, Cayman Islands

ANY SECURITY PRINTING COMPANY PLC

(Formerly Allami Nyomda Nyrt)
Halom u 5
H-1102 Budapest, Hungary
Tel.: (36) 14311200
Fax: (36) 14311220
E-Mail: info@any.hu
Web Site: www.any.hu
ANY—(BUD)
Sls.: $75,849,790
Assets: $42,916,270
Liabilities: $14,447,235
Net Worth: $28,469,035
Earnings: $2,982,373
Emp.: 857
Fiscal Year-end: 12/31/12
Business Description:
Security Printing Services
S.I.C.: 7382
N.A.I.C.S.: 561621
Personnel:
Akos Erdos *(Chm)*
Tamas Sarkozy *(Chm-Supervisory Bd)*
Gyorgy Gyergyak *(Vice Chm)*
Istvanne Gomori *(Vice Chm-Supervisory Bd)*
Gabor Zsamboki *(CEO)*
Laszlo Balla *(Deputy CEO)*
Gabor Peter *(CIO)*
Zoltan Toth *(CTO & Chief Production Officer)*
Ferenc Berkesi *(Chief Security Officer)*
Lajos Szekelyhidi *(Chief R&D Officer)*
Board of Directors:
Akos Erdos
Tamas Doffek
Gyorgy Gyergyak
Peter Kadocsa
Gyorgy Karady
Gabor Zsamboki
Supervisory Board of Directors:
Tamas Sarkozy
Ferenc Berkesi
Istvanne Gomori
Erzsebet Novotny
Imre Repa
Janos Stumpf

Subsidiaries:

Gyomai Kner Nyomda Zrt. (1)
10-12 Kossuth Street
Gyomaendrod, Bekes, 5500, Hungary
Tel.: (36) 66 887 400
Fax: (36) 66 887 445
E-Mail: knernyomda@gyomaikner.hu
Web Site: www.gyomaikner.hu
Printing Services
S.I.C.: 2759
N.A.I.C.S.: 323111
Peter Fazekas *(Gen Dir)*

Specimen Papir es Nyomdaipari Zrt. (1)
Kozma u 2
1108 Budapest, Hungary
Tel.: (36) 14344720
Fax: (36) 1 43 44 721
E-Mail: nyomda@specimen.hu
Web Site: www.specimen.hu
Security Products Printing Services
S.I.C.: 2759
N.A.I.C.S.: 323111

ANYANG IRON & STEEL GROUP CO., LTD.

Meiyuanzhuang
Yindu District, Anyang, Henan, 455004, China
Tel.: (86) 3723122587
Fax: (86) 3723931892
E-Mail: agjt@angang.com.cn
Web Site: www.angang.com.cn
Year Founded: 1948
Sales Range: $1-4.9 Billion
Emp.: 35,000
Business Description:
Iron & Steel Products Mfr
S.I.C.: 3462
N.A.I.C.S.: 332111
Subsidiary:

Xinyang Iron & Steel Co., Ltd. (1)
34 Xinming Road Minggang
Pingqiao District, Xinyang, Henan, China CN
Tel.: (86) 376 867 2022
Fax: (86) 376 866 2386
Web Site: www.xyisco.com
Iron & Steel Products Mfr
S.I.C.: 3462
N.A.I.C.S.: 332111
Dianzhou He *(Pres & Gen Mgr)*

AO ENERGY LIMITED

(Formerly Australia Oriental Minerals NL)
15 Bentham Street
Adelaide, SA, 5000, Australia
Tel.: (61) 8 8212 0144
Web Site: aoenergy.com.au
AOM—(ASX)
Rev.: $8,000
Assets: $978,731
Liabilities: $452,611
Net Worth: $526,120
Earnings: ($3,430,193)
Fiscal Year-end: 12/31/12
Business Description:
Oil & Gas Exploration & Production Services
S.I.C.: 1311
N.A.I.C.S.: 211111
Personnel:
Donald Stephens *(Sec)*
Board of Directors:
Simon O'Loughlin
Graham Ascough
David Brooks
Donald Stephens
Legal Counsel:
Addisons Lawyers
Level 12 60 Carrington Street
Sydney, Australia

AO WORLD PLC

AO Park 5a The Parklands
Lostock, Bolton, BL6 4SD, United Kingdom
Tel.: (44) 1204 672400
Fax: (44) 1204 672987
E-Mail: cosec@ao.com
Web Site: www.ao.com
AO—(LSE)
Rev.: $457,726,720
Fiscal Year-end: 03/31/13
Business Description:
Home Appliance Online Retailer
S.I.C.: 5961
N.A.I.C.S.: 454111
Personnel:
Richard Rose *(Chm)*
John Roberts *(CEO)*
Stephen Caunce *(CFO & COO)*
Board of Directors:
Richard Rose
Marisa Cassoni
Bill Holroyd
Chris Hopkinson
Rudolf Lamprecht

Brian McBride
John Roberts

AOC HOLDINGS, INC.

(Name Changed to Fuji Oil Company, Ltd.)

AOHATA CORPORATION

1-1-25 Tadanouminaka-Machi
Takehara, Hiroshima, 729 2316, Japan
Tel.: (81) 846260111
Fax: (81) 846250537
E-Mail: aohata@aohata.co.jp
Web Site: www.aohata.co.jp
Year Founded: 1932
Sales Range: $150-199.9 Million
Emp.: 378

Business Description:
Fruit Jellies, Jams & Preserves, Canned Fruits, Pasta Sauces, Cooking Sauces, Soups & Stews Mfr
S.I.C.: 2033
N.A.I.C.S.: 311421

Personnel:
Eiichi Nozawa *(Chm)*

Subsidiaries:

AFC Co., Ltd. (1)
1-1-25 Tadanoumicyo
Takehara City, Hiroshima, 7292316, Japan
Tel.: (81) 846260777
Fax: (81) 846261103
Emp.: 3
Computer Controlled Warehousing of Processed Marine & Farm Produce
S.I.C.: 4221
N.A.I.C.S.: 493130
Masashi Sakai *(Mgr)*

Aohata Corporation, Jam Factory (1)
1-2-43 Tadanouminaka-machi
Takehara, Hiroshima, 729-2316, Japan
Tel.: (81) 846260586
Fax: (81) 846262788
Web Site: www.aohata.co.jp
Production & Sales of Processed Fruit Products, Jams & Jellies
S.I.C.: 3556
N.A.I.C.S.: 333241
Jiro Fukuyama *(Gen Mgr)*

Aohata Kosau Co., Ltd. (1)
1-1-25 Tadanoumicyo
Takehara City, Hiroshima, 792 2316, Japan
Tel.: (81) 846261114
Fax: (81) 0846262676
Web Site: www.aohata.co.jp/ci007_us/network/index.html
Employee Welfare Activities & Commissioned Management of Group Companies, Building Rentals, Accident Insurance Agency, Environmental Planning & Waste Disposal
S.I.C.: 8744
N.A.I.C.S.: 561210

Geinan Shokuhin Co., Ltd. (1)
1678 Takeharacyo
Takehara City, Hiroshima, 725 0021, Japan
Tel.: (81) 846220232
Emp.: 180
Processed Fruit Products & Confectioneries Mfr & Sales
S.I.C.: 2099
N.A.I.C.S.: 311999

Rainbow Shokuhin Co., Ltd. (1)
1-1-25 Tadanoumicyo
Takehara City, Hiroshima, 792 2316, Japan
Tel.: (81) 846262462
Web Site: www.aohata.co.jp/ci007_us/network/index.html
Sales of Local Food Specialties, Canned Goods, Oyster Extract & Other Health Foods
S.I.C.: 5499
N.A.I.C.S.: 445299

Techno-Aid Co., Ltd. (1)
1-2-43 Tadanoumicyo
Takehara City, Hiroshima, 792 2316, Japan
Tel.: (81) 846262570
Fax: (81) 0846261229
Web Site: www.aohata.co.jp/ci007_us/network/index.html
Introduction, Installation & Maintenance of Food Production Equipment; Sales of Food Production Equipment; Pest Extermination & Sanitizing
S.I.C.: 3556
N.A.I.C.S.: 333241

Tohoku Aohata Co., Ltd. (1)
484-1 Takanosu
Ooishidacyo Kitamurayama-gun, Yamagata, 999 4101, Japan
Tel.: (81) 237353611
Web Site: www.aohata.co.jp/ci007_us/network/index.html
Processed Fruit Products, Processed Foods & Confectioneries Production & Sales
S.I.C.: 2099
N.A.I.C.S.: 311999

AOI ADVERTISING PROMOTION INC.

(See Under AOI Pro. Inc.)

AOI ELECTRONICS CO., LTD.

455-1 Kohzai Minamimachi
Takamatsu, Kagawa, 761-8014, Japan
Tel.: (81) 878821131
Fax: (81) 878815575
Web Site: www.aoi-electronics.co.jp
Year Founded: 1969
6832—(TKS)
Sales Range: $300-349.9 Million
Emp.: 1,298

Business Description:
Integrated Circuits, Modules, Thermal Print Heads, Chip Resistors & Resistor Networks Mfr
S.I.C.: 3672
N.A.I.C.S.: 334412

Personnel:
Michiyoshi Onishi *(Chm)*
Koji Nakayama *(Pres)*

Board of Directors:
Michiyoshi Onishi
Masaaki Kawaji
Kazuhiro Kinoshita
Akihiro Miyamoto
Koji Nakayama
Yoshio Okada
Norio Saeki
Kaoru Tada

Subsidiary:

Hayama Industries Co., Ltd. (1)
3 3 5 Asahimachi
Takamatsu, Kagawa, 760 0065, Japan
Tel.: (81) 878512001
Fax: (81) 878236234
Web Site: www.aoi-electronics.co.jp/aoi_e_com_company.html
Electronic Goods Mfr
S.I.C.: 3679
N.A.I.C.S.: 334419

AOI PRO. INC.

Osaki Center Building 1-5-1 Osaki
Shinagawa-ku, Tokyo, 141-8580, Japan
Tel.: (81) 337798000
Fax: (81) 337798029
E-Mail: aoi-ipd@aoi-pro.co.jp
Web Site: www.aoi-pro.com
Year Founded: 1963
Sls.: $280,500,000
Emp.: 568
Fiscal Year-end: 03/31/13

Business Description:
Advertising Services
S.I.C.: 7311
N.A.I.C.S.: 541810

Personnel:
Tsugihiko Fujiwara *(Pres)*
Satoru Yaegashi *(Sr Mng Dir)*
Mitsuhisa Aoyama *(Corp Officer)*
Jin Ebashi *(Corp Officer)*
Akira Hosaka *(Corp Officer)*
Toru Igarashi *(Corp Officer)*
Kohta Kanki *(Corp Officer)*
Kumiko Kitamura *(Corp Officer)*
Shigemasa Murai *(Corp Officer)*
Akira Nagai *(Corp Officer)*
Kunitoshi Natsukuri *(Corp Officer)*
Toshihiko Okubo *(Corp Officer)*
Tomomitsu Sasa *(Corp Officer)*
Toshihiro Seino *(Corp Officer)*
Yoshifumi Seno *(Corp Officer)*
Yusaku Tanaka *(Corp Officer)*
Kota Taniuchi *(Corp Officer)*
Tomoaki Yasaki *(Corp Officer)*

Board of Directors:
Tsugihiko Fujiwara
Norio Kokabu
Yasuhito Nakae
Hirotaka Ogata
Yoshio Sasanuki
Koichiro Tsujino
Hajime Ushioda
Satoru Yaegashi
Satoshi Yuzurihara

Subsidiaries:

Digital Garden Inc. (1)
2-36-13 Ebisu
Shibuya-ku, Tokyo, 150-0013, Japan
Tel.: (81) 3 5791 2215
Fax: (81) 3 5791 2245
E-Mail: dgi@dgi.co.jp
Web Site: www.dgi.co.jp
Emp.: 11
Post Production Services
S.I.C.: 7819
N.A.I.C.S.: 512191
Matsumoto Hirokazu *(Pres)*
Hitoshi Hara *(CEO)*

Media Garden Inc. (1)
2-1-56 Chigasaki-minami
Tsuduki-ku, Yokohama, 224 0037, Japan
Tel.: (81) 45 945 3800
Fax: (81) 45 945 3807
E-Mail: yoko@media-garden.co.jp
Web Site: www.media-garden.co.jp
Emp.: 25
Commercial Film Studio
S.I.C.: 7812
N.A.I.C.S.: 512110
Hitoshi Hara *(Pres)*

AOKI HOLDINGS INC.

24-1 Chigasakichuo Tsuzuki-ku
Yokohama, 224-8588, Japan
Tel.: (81) 459411888
Fax: (81) 334782188
Web Site: www.aoki-hd.co.jp
8214—(TKS)
Sls.: $1,766,479,000
Assets: $2,130,304,000
Liabilities: $903,980,000
Net Worth: $1,226,324,000
Earnings: $108,152,000
Emp.: 2,975
Fiscal Year-end: 03/31/13

Business Description:
Fashion & Menswear Products Sales
S.I.C.: 7389
N.A.I.C.S.: 541490

Personnel:
Hironori Aoki *(Chm)*
Takahisa Aoki *(Vice Chm)*
Akihiro Aoki *(Pres & COO)*
Haruo Tamura *(Exec VP)*

Subsidiaries:

AOKI Inc. (1)
6-56 Kuzugaya
Tsuzuki-ku, Yokohama, Kanagawa, 224-8688, Japan
Tel.: (81) 459413488
Fashion Designing Services
S.I.C.: 7389
N.A.I.C.S.: 541490

ORIHICA Inc. (1)
6-56 Kuzugaya
Tsuzuki-ku, Yokohama, Kanagawa, 224 8688, Japan
Tel.: (81) 459455178
Fax: (81) 459441888
E-Mail: sda@orihica.com
Web Site: www.orihica.com
Emp.: 500
Fashion Designing Services
S.I.C.: 7389
N.A.I.C.S.: 541490

ANNIVERSAIRE Inc. (1)
3-25 Chigasakicyuou Tsuzuki-ku
Yokohama, Kanagawa, 224-0032, Japan
Tel.: (81) 459486388
Web Site: www.anniversaire.co.jp/
Emp.: 499
Bridal Services
S.I.C.: 7299
N.A.I.C.S.: 812990
Akihiro Aoki *(Pres & COO)*

VALIC Co., Ltd. (1)
1-50 Kita-Yamata 3-Chome
Tsuzuki-ku, Yokohama, Kanagawa, 224-0021, Japan
Tel.: (81) 455904888
Fax: (81) 455906488
Web Site: www.valic.co.jp/en/corporate/index1.html
Emp.: 1,000
Entertainment Services
S.I.C.: 5812
N.A.I.C.S.: 722310
Yusuke Nakabayashi *(Pres)*

THE AOMORI BANK, LTD.

9-30 Hashimoto 1-chome
Aomori, 030-0823, Japan
Tel.: (81) 177771111
Web Site: www.a-bank.jp
Year Founded: 1879
8342—(TKS)
Sales Range: $500-549.9 Million
Emp.: 1,461

Business Description:
Commercial Banking Services
S.I.C.: 6029
N.A.I.C.S.: 522110

Personnel:
Yoshisada Kafuku *(Chm)*
Satoshi Hamaya *(Pres)*
Tadashi Takayashiki *(Sr Mng Dir)*
Shoji Adachi *(Mng Dir & Dir-Sls)*
Naomitsu Kikuchi *(Mng Dir)*
Susumu Narita *(Mng Dir)*
Akihiro Kawamura *(Exec Officer)*
Hitoshi Takeuchi *(Exec Officer)*

Board of Directors:
Yoshisada Kafuku
Fumitaka Demachi
Shoji Fukui
Satoshi Hamaya
Mitsuo Hayashi
Naomitsu Kikuchi
Tadashi Takayashiki
Reiji Tatebe

Subsidiaries:

Aogin Business Service Co., Ltd. (1)
1-5-18 Hashimoto
Aomori, Japan
Tel.: (81) 177732479
Business Support Services
S.I.C.: 7389
N.A.I.C.S.: 561499

Affiliates:

Aogin Confidence Guarantee Co., Ltd. (1)
1-16-16 Furukawa
Aomori, Japan
Tel.: (81) 177776661
Credit Bureaus
S.I.C.: 7323
N.A.I.C.S.: 561450

Aogin Credit Card Co., Ltd. (1)
1-16-16 Furukawa
Aomori, Japan
Tel.: (81) 177736511
Credit Card Issuing
S.I.C.: 6141
N.A.I.C.S.: 522210

The Aomori Bank, Ltd.—(Continued)

Aogin DC Card Co., Ltd. **(1)**
5th Fl Aoginshimmachi Bldg
Aomori, Japan
Tel.: (81) 177762161
Web Site: www.aogindc.co.jp
Credit Card Issuing
S.I.C.: 6141
N.A.I.C.S.: 522210

Aogin Lease Co., Ltd. **(1)**
Aoginfurukawa Bldg
Aomori, Japan
Tel.: (81) 177231665
Commercial & Industrial Machinery & Equipment Rental & Leasing
S.I.C.: 7359
N.A.I.C.S.: 532490

AON INC.

PO Box 296
Peterborough, ON, K9J 7M4, Canada
Tel.: (705) 742-5445
Fax: (705) 742-9276
E-Mail: info@aoninc.com
Web Site: www.aoninc.com
Sales Range: $150-199.9 Million
Emp.: 510

Business Description:
Retirement Community Development & Property Management Services
S.I.C.: 6531
N.A.I.C.S.: 531311

Personnel:
Ross A. Smith *(Pres & CEO)*
Brad R. Smith *(Exec VP)*
Tim W. Harrold *(Sr VP)*

AON PLC

8 Devonshire Square
London, EC2M 4PL, United Kingdom
Tel.: (44) 20 7623 5500
E-Mail: investors@asc.aon.com
Web Site: www.aon.com
Year Founded: 1979
AON—(NYSE)
Rev.: $11,815,000,000
Assets: $30,251,000,000
Liabilities: $22,056,000,000
Net Worth: $8,195,000,000
Earnings: $1,148,000,000
Emp.: 66,000
Fiscal Year-end: 12/31/13

Business Description:
Insurance Holding Company
S.I.C.: 6733
N.A.I.C.S.: 525190

Personnel:
Lester B. Knight, III *(Chm)*
Gregory C. Case *(Pres & CEO)*
Dan Morris *(Partner-Investment Consulting)*
Michael C. Barbarita *(Mng Dir & Exec VP-Risk Solutions-Pittsburgh)*
Christa Davies *(CFO & Exec VP-Global Fin)*
Philip B. Clement *(Global CMO & Chief Comm Officer)*
Gregory J. Besio *(Chief HR Officer & Exec VP)*
Stephen P. McGill *(Chm/CEO-Aon Risk Solutions)*
Baljit Dail *(CEO-Aon Consulting Global)*
Peter M. Lieb *(Gen Counsel & Exec VP)*
Ram Padmanabhan *(Sec)*
Michael D. O'Halleran *(Sr Exec VP)*
Matthew C. Levin *(Exec VP & Head-Global Strategy)*
Laurel Meissner *(Sr VP & Controller)*
Roy C. Keller *(Sr VP-Global Real Estate)*
Liam Murphy *(Sr VP-Risk Solutions-Little Rock)*
David Sult *(Sr VP-Transformation Svcs)*
Ronald Young *(Sr VP-Global Product Mgmt-ESolutions)*

Board of Directors:
Lester B. Knight, III
Gregory C. Case
Fulvio Conti
Cheryl A. Francis
Edgar Dalzell Jannotta
J. Michael Losh
Robert S. Morrison
Richard B. Myers
Richard C. Notebaert
Gloria Santona
Carolyn Y. Woo

Transfer Agent:
Computershare Trust Company, N.A.
PO Box 43069
Providence, RI 02940
Tel.: (781) 575-2724

Co-Headquarters:

Aon Corporation **(1)**
200 E Randolph St
Chicago, IL 60601 DE
Tel.: (312) 381-1000
Risk Solutions & Insurance Services
S.I.C.: 6411
N.A.I.C.S.: 524298
Gregory C. Case *(Pres & CEO)*
Maureen McDonald *(Sr VP-Sherman Oaks)*
Max West *(Sr VP-Aon Risk Solutions)*

Branches:

Aon Corp. **(2)**
10461 Mill Run Cir
Owings Mills, MD 21117-5544
Tel.: (410) 363-5000
Fax: (410) 363-5069
Web Site: www.aon.com
Rev.: $260,000
Emp.: 3
Insurance Brokers
S.I.C.: 6411
N.A.I.C.S.: 524210
Frank G. Zarb *(Pres)*

Aon Corp. **(2)**
299 S Main St Ste 1700
Salt Lake City, UT 84111-2279
Tel.: (801) 488-2550
Fax: (801) 488-2559
Web Site: www.ano.com
Sales Range: Less than $1 Million
Emp.: 10
Insurance Agents Brokers & Service
S.I.C.: 6411
N.A.I.C.S.: 524298

Subsidiaries:

A&A Underwriting Services Inc. **(2)**
7230 McGinnis Ferry Rd Ste 300
Suwanee, GA 30024-1289 GA
Tel.: (678) 512-2400
Sales Range: Less than $1 Million
Emp.: 64
Insurance Brokers
S.I.C.: 6411
N.A.I.C.S.: 524210

Subsidiary:

Atlanta International Insurance Company **(3)**
2 Central Sq
Cambridge, MA 02139-3311 GA
Tel.: (678) 512-2486 (100%)
Fax: (770) 813-6363
Rev.: $1,954,413
Emp.: 14
Fire Marine And Casualty Insurance
S.I.C.: 6351
N.A.I.C.S.: 524126
Michael Murphy *(Sr VP)*

Affinity Insurance Services, Inc. **(2)**
159 E County Line Rd
Hatboro, PA 19040-1218 WA
Tel.: (215) 773-4600
Fax: (800) 853-5227
Web Site: www.affinityinsuranceservices.com
Emp.: 420
Insurance Services
S.I.C.: 6411
N.A.I.C.S.: 524210
Bill Vit *(Pres)*
Calvin R. Johnson *(Exec VP & Pres-Affinity Healthcare)*

Subsidiaries:

Access Plans, Inc. **(3)**
900 36th Ave NW Ste 105
Norman, OK 73072 OK
Tel.: (405) 579-8525
Web Site: www.alliancehealthcard.com
Sales Range: $50-74.9 Million
Emp.: 78
Discount Medical Plan Services
S.I.C.: 6411
N.A.I.C.S.: 524298
Robert Hoeffner *(VP-Ops)*

Subsidiaries:

Access Plans USA, Inc. **(4)**
4929 W Royal Ln
Irving, TX 75063 OK
Tel.: (972) 915-3200
Fax: (972) 915-3286
E-Mail: nzalud@accessplansusa.com
Web Site: www.accessplansusa.com
Sales Range: $25-49.9 Million
Emp.: 124
Healthcare Savings Membership Services
S.I.C.: 6411
N.A.I.C.S.: 524298
David E. Huguelet *(Pres)*
Brandon Vining *(CMO)*
Bradley Denison *(Gen Counsel & Exec VP)*

Divisions:

Care Entree **(5)**
4929 W Royal Ln Ste 200
Erving, TX 75063 TX
Tel.: (972) 915-3200
Fax: (972) 915-3283
Toll Free: (888) 411-3888
E-Mail: repsupport@accessplansusa.com
Web Site: www.careentree.com
Sales Range: $75-99.9 Million
Emp.: 60
Non-Insurance Health Care Services
S.I.C.: 7389
N.A.I.C.S.: 561499
Judith Henkels *(Pres & CEO)*

America's Health Care Plan/Rx Agency, Inc. **(4)**
4929 W Royal Ln Fl 2
Irving, TX 75063
Tel.: (972) 915-3200
Fax: (972) 915-3211
Toll Free: (877) 228-8773
E-Mail: info@ahcpsales.com
Web Site: www.ahcpsales.com
Sales Range: $10-24.9 Million
Emp.: 20
Insurance Marketing Consulting Services
S.I.C.: 6411
N.A.I.C.S.: 524298
Charles Harris *(Pres)*

JLT Services Corp. **(3)**
22 Century Hill Dr Ste 102
Latham, NY 12110
Tel.: (518) 782-3000
Fax: (518) 782-3032
Toll Free: (800) 366-5273
E-Mail: terms@jltrena.com
Web Site: www.jltservices.com
Sales Range: $25-49.9 Million
Emp.: 260
Insurance & Employee Benefits Services
S.I.C.: 6311
N.A.I.C.S.: 524298
David Gosstola *(CFO & COO)*
William M. Gordon *(Pres-Protection Advantage)*

Subsidiary:

Professional Dental Reviewers **(4)**
13 Cornell Rd
Latham, NY 12110
Tel.: (518) 782-3000
Toll Free: (800) 637-2526
Rev.: $2,700,000
Emp.: 16
Independent Dental Consultants
S.I.C.: 6411
N.A.I.C.S.: 524291

Allen Insurance Associates, Inc. **(2)**
520 N Harbor City Blvd
Melbourne, FL 32935
Tel.: (321) 259-1998
Toll Free: (877) 870-1998
E-Mail: info@allenins.net
Web Site: www.allenins.net
Advertising Agency
S.I.C.: 7311
N.A.I.C.S.: 541810

Aon Advisors, Inc. **(2)**
200 East Randolph
Chicago, IL 60601 VA
Tel.: (312) 381-3333 (100%)
Fax: (312) 381-0117
Emp.: 750
Insurance-Based Asset Management Programs
S.I.C.: 6282
N.A.I.C.S.: 523930
Michael Conway *(Pres)*

Aon/Albert G. Ruben Insurance Services, Inc. **(2)**
15303 Ventura Blvd Ste 1200
Sherman Oaks, CA 91403-5817
Tel.: (818) 742-1400
Fax: (847) 953-2480
E-Mail: ruben@aon.com
Web Site: www.albertgruben.com
ruben@aon.com
S.I.C.: 6411
N.A.I.C.S.: 524210

Aon Benfield, Inc **(2)**
200 E Randolph St
Chicago, IL 60601 CT
Tel.: (312) 381-1000
Fax: (312) 381-0160
Web Site: www.aonbenfield.com
Rev.: $27,100,000
Emp.: 4,000
Reinsurance Broker
S.I.C.: 6411
N.A.I.C.S.: 524210
Michael Bungert *(Chm)*
William Farmer *(Vice Chm)*
Kelly Smith *(Pres)*
Eric Andersen *(CEO)*
Alan Gregory *(Co-CEO-EMEA)*
Richard Posgate *(Co-CEO-EMEA)*
Maggie Westdale *(CFO & Global COO)*
Steve Betts *(CIO)*
Grahame Chilton *(Chm-Strategy & Mktg & Client Dev)*
Dominic Christian *(Chm-Intl)*
Robert Bredahl *(Pres-Americas)*
Baljit Dall *(CEO-Consulting)*
Bryon Ehrhart *(CEO-Americas)*
Alejandro J. Galazia *(CEO-Latin America)*
Ahmed Rajab *(CEO-Middle East & North Africa)*
Elliot Richardson *(CEO-Aon Benfield Fac)*
Joe Smith *(CEO-Chile)*

Subsidiaries:

Aon Benfield Fac Inc. **(3)**
200 E Randolph
Chicago, IL 60601-6535
Tel.: (312) 381-5300
Risk Management Services
S.I.C.: 6411
N.A.I.C.S.: 524210
Paul Summers *(Global CEO)*

Aon Benfield Inc. **(3)**
5600 W 83rd St 8200 Tower Ste 1100
Bloomington, MN 55437 DE
Tel.: (952) 886-8000
Fax: (952) 886-8010
Web Site: www.aonbenfield.com
Sales Range: $400-449.9 Million
Emp.: 700
Reinsurance Brokerage & Related Risk Management Services
S.I.C.: 6399
N.A.I.C.S.: 524130
Dave Cameron *(Mng Dir)*
Ralph Flum *(COO)*

Aon Benfield Securities, Inc. **(3)**
Aon Ctr 200 E Randolph St
Chicago, IL 60601
Tel.: (312) 381-4488
Risk Management Services
S.I.C.: 6411

N.A.I.C.S.: 524210

Paragon Strategic Solutions Inc. (3)
5600 W 83rd St Ste 1100 8200 Tower
Minneapolis, MN 55437
Tel.: (952) 886-8016
Fax: (952) 886-8001
Toll Free: (800) 854-8523
E-Mail: inquiries@paragon.aonbenfield.com
Web Site: www.paragon.aonbenfield.com
Sales Range: $600-649.9 Million
Emp.: 800
Reinsurance Risk Management Services
S.I.C.: 6399
N.A.I.C.S.: 524130
Patrick Van Wert *(Pres-Reinsurance Practice)*

Non-U.S. Subsidiaries:

Aon Benfield Canada (3)
150 King St W Ste 1900
Toronto, ON, M5H 1J9, Canada
Tel.: (416) 979-3300
Fax: (416) 979-7724
Web Site: www.benfieldgroup.com
Sales Range: $1-4.9 Billion
Emp.: 100
Reinsurance Services
S.I.C.: 6311
N.A.I.C.S.: 524113
Robert McLean *(CEO)*

Aon Benfield Limited (3)
55 Bishopsgate
London, EC2N 3BD, United Kingdom UK
Tel.: (44) 2075223954
Fax: (44) 2075787002
E-Mail: richard.dudley@aonbenfield.com
Web Site: www.aonbenfield.com
Sales Range: $650-699.9 Million
Reinsurance & Risk Intermediary Services
S.I.C.: 6399
N.A.I.C.S.: 524130
Geoffrey Bromley *(Vice Chm-Intl)*
David Ledger *(CEO-UK)*

Aon Benfield (New Zealand) Ltd. (3)
Level 8 70 Shortland St
PO Box 699
Auckland, New Zealand
Tel.: (64) 93029583
Fax: (64) 93098044
E-Mail: richard.trevethick@aonbenfield.com
Web Site: www.benfieldgroup.com
Sales Range: $150-199.9 Million
Emp.: 4
Reinsurance Services
S.I.C.: 6399
N.A.I.C.S.: 524130
Richard Trevethick *(Mng Dir)*

Aon Benfield Pte. Ltd. (3)
60 Anson Road #08-01 Maple Tree
Anson, 079914, Singapore
Tel.: (65) 65356511
Fax: (65) 65623976
E-Mail: neil.mathison@aonbenfield.com
Web Site: www.benfieldgroup.com
Sales Range: $150-199.9 Million
Emp.: 500
Reinsurance Services
S.I.C.: 6399
N.A.I.C.S.: 524130
Neil Mathison *(Mng Dir)*

Aon Benfield Pty. Ltd. (3)
Level 21 Clarence Street
Sydney, NSW, 2000, Australia
Tel.: (61) 2 8209 4200
Fax: (61) 2 9241 2441
E-Mail: info@benfieldgroup.com
Web Site: www.benfieldgroup.com
Sales Range: $25-49.9 Million
Emp.: 50
Reinsurance Services
S.I.C.: 6399
N.A.I.C.S.: 524130

Aon Benfield S.A. de C.V. (3)
Insurgentes 1457 Piso 8 Torre Manacar
Col Insurgentes Mixcoac, 03920 Mexico, DF, Mexico
Tel.: (52) 5555982398
Fax: (52) 55 5563 2601
E-Mail: albert.fischl@aonbenfield.com
Web Site: www.aonbenfield.com
Sales Range: $150-199.9 Million
Reinsurance Services
S.I.C.: 6399
N.A.I.C.S.: 524130
Albert Fischl *(Mng Dir)*

Aon Benfield (South Africa) Pty Ltd. (3)
The Galaxy Ste No 5 70-11 Eton Rd
Parkdown, Johannesburg, South Africa
Tel.: (27) 11 726 5755
Fax: (27) 11 726 5527
E-Mail: bgjohannesburg@benfieldgroup.com
Web Site: www.benfieldgroup.com
Sales Range: $1-4.9 Billion
Reinsurance Services
S.I.C.: 6399
N.A.I.C.S.: 524130
Terry Ray *(Mng Dir)*

Aon Consulting, Inc. (2)
1000 Rockey Ave
New York, NY 10038 NY
Tel.: (212) 441-1000 (100%)
Fax: (212) 441-1919
Web Site: www.aon.com
Sales Range: $150-199.9 Million
Insurance Brokerage & Financial Services
S.I.C.: 8999
N.A.I.C.S.: 541612
Kathryn Hayley *(Co-CEO)*
Piyush Chaudhari *(CEO-EMEA)*
Viq Pervaaz *(Sr VP-Corp Transactions)*

Branches:

Aon Consulting - Chicago (3)
200 E Randolph St
Chicago, IL 60601
Tel.: (312) 381-1000
Fax: (312) 381-0125
Web Site: www.aon.com
Sales Range: $75-99.9 Million
Human Resource & Executive Search Consulting Services
S.I.C.: 8999
N.A.I.C.S.: 541612
Craig Pearlman *(Principal-Galagated Investment Solutions)*
Chuck Longiotti *(Exec VP & Dir-Central West Reg)*
Clint Cary *(Sr VP-Investment Consulting)*
Patricia Smallsreed *(Sr VP)*

Aon Consulting - Tampa (3)
7650 W Courtney Campbell Causeway Ste 1000
Tampa, FL 33607-1462
Tel.: (813) 636-3000
Fax: (813) 636-3010
Web Site: www.aon.com
Sales Range: $10-24.9 Million
Emp.: 90
Business Consulting
S.I.C.: 8748
N.A.I.C.S.: 541618
Brenda Cooper *(Sr VP)*
J. R. Shamley *(Sr VP-Health-Benefits)*

Aon Consulting (3)
400 Atrium
Somerset, NJ 08873-4140
Tel.: (732) 302-2100
Fax: (732) 356-0425
Web Site: www.aonconsulting.com
Rev.: $16,300,000
Emp.: 155
Consultants
S.I.C.: 8742
N.A.I.C.S.: 541611
Daniel Hunger *(CFO)*

Aon Consulting (3)
301 Rt 71 N
Rutherford, NJ 07070 (100%)
Tel.: (201) 460-6700
Fax: (201) 460-6999
Web Site: www.aon.com
Sales Range: $10-24.9 Million
Emp.: 80
Insurance Brokers
S.I.C.: 8999
N.A.I.C.S.: 541612
Lou Monari *(VP-Bus Dev)*

Aon Consulting (3)
555 E Lancaster Ave Ste 300
Radnor, PA 19087 (100%)
Mailing Address:
PO Box 867
Conshohocken, PA 19428-0867
Tel.: (610) 834-2100
Fax: (610) 834-2184
E-Mail: info@aon.com
Web Site: www.aon.com
Rev.: $19,000,000
Emp.: 120
Employee Benefit Consulting Services
S.I.C.: 8999
N.A.I.C.S.: 541612
Tammy Mattson *(Exec VP & Dir-Northeast Reg)*
Jon Rinehimer *(Exec VP)*
Kathleen Childress *(Sr VP)*
Philip Peterson *(Sr VP)*

Subsidiaries:

Aon Consulting & Insurance Services (3)
199 Fremont St Fl 15
San Francisco, CA 94105-2253
Tel.: (415) 486-7500
Fax: (415) 486-7029
Toll Free: (800) 669-9460
Web Site: www.aon.com
Emp.: 250
Risk Management Services
S.I.C.: 6411
N.A.I.C.S.: 524210
Matt Davis *(Mgr-Residential)*

Units:

Aon Consulting - San Francisco (4)
199 Fremont St Ste 1400
San Francisco, CA 94105-2245 (100%)
Tel.: (415) 486-7500
Fax: (415) 486-7029
Sales Range: $75-99.9 Million
Emp.: 250
Provider of Human Resources Consulting Services
S.I.C.: 6411
N.A.I.C.S.: 524210
Karol Nowyarta *(Mgr-Facilities)*

Aon Insurance Services (4)
10880 Wilshire Blvd
Los Angeles, CA 90024-4101 CA
Tel.: (310) 234-6800
Fax: (310) 446-7839
E-Mail: info@aon.com
Web Site: www.aon.com
Sales Range: $10-24.9 Million
Emp.: 90
Insurance Agents & Brokers
S.I.C.: 6411
N.A.I.C.S.: 524210
Scott Milne *(Chm)*
Peter Robey *(Pres & CEO)*

Aon Management Consulting/Rath & Strong Inc. (3)
45 Hayden Ave Ste 2700
Lexington, MA 02421-7951 MA
Tel.: (781) 861-1700
Fax: (781) 861-1424
Sales Range: $1-9.9 Million
Emp.: 10
Consulting Services
S.I.C.: 8748
N.A.I.C.S.: 541618
Daniel L. Quinn *(Pres & CEO)*

McLagan Partners Inc. (3)
1600 Summer St Ste 601
Stamford, CT 06905 DE
Tel.: (203) 359-2878
Fax: (203) 323-9851
E-Mail: info@mclagan.com
Web Site: www.mclagan.com
Emp.: 60
Consulting Services
S.I.C.: 8742
N.A.I.C.S.: 541611
Brian Dunn *(Chm)*
Michael Burke *(Pres)*
Doris Van Beck *(COO)*

Radford (3)
2570 N First St Ste 500
San Jose, CA 95131
Tel.: (408) 321-2500
Fax: (408) 321-2650
E-Mail: sales@radford.com
Web Site: www.radford.com
Emp.: 65
Consulting Services
S.I.C.: 8748
N.A.I.C.S.: 541618
Linda E. Amuso *(Pres)*
John Radford *(Sr VP & Head-Surveys Mgmt)*
Terry Adamson *(Sr VP-Radford Valuation Svcs)*
Ted Buyniski *(Sr VP-Consulting Mgmt)*
Steve Radford *(Sr VP-Surveys Mgmt)*
Donald B. York *(Sr VP-Surveys Mgmt)*

Non-U.S. Subsidiaries:

Aon Consultants (3)
Level 33 Aon Tower 201 Kent St
Sydney, NSW, 2000, Australia AU
Tel.: (61) 292537100 (100%)
Fax: (61) 292537001
E-Mail: interactive@aon.com.au
Web Site: www.aon.com.au
Sales Range: $25-49.9 Million
Emp.: 900
Provider of Human Capital Management Services
S.I.C.: 8742
N.A.I.C.S.: 541611
Stewart Fotheringham *(Mng Dir)*

Aon Consulting Inc. (3)
145 Wellington St W Ste 500
Toronto, ON, M5J 1H8, Canada ON
Tel.: (416) 542-5500 (100%)
Fax: (416) 542-5504
E-Mail: ashim.khemani@aon.ca
Web Site: www.aon.ca
Sales Range: $50-74.9 Million
Emp.: 180
Consulting Services
S.I.C.: 4731
N.A.I.C.S.: 541611

Aon Consulting Inc. (3)
700 De La Gauchetiere St W Ste 1800
Montreal, QC, H3B 0A7, Canada QC
Tel.: (514) 845-6231 (100%)
Fax: (514) 845-0678
Web Site: www.aonhewitt.com
Sales Range: $75-99.9 Million
Emp.: 500
Business Consulting Services
S.I.C.: 8742
N.A.I.C.S.: 541611

Aon Consulting New Zealand Ltd. (3)
29 Customs St W
1184 Auckland, New Zealand NZ
Tel.: (64) 93629820 (100%)
Fax: (64) 93629121
E-Mail: consulting.auck@aon.co.nz
Web Site: www.aon.co.nz
Sales Range: $10-24.9 Million
Emp.: 24
Provider of Human Capital Management Services
S.I.C.: 8742
N.A.I.C.S.: 541611
Mike Glenday *(Mng Dir)*

Aon Hong Kong Ltd. (3)
Aon China Bldg 21st Fl
29 Queen's Rd, Central, China (Hong Kong) HK
Tel.: (852) 28616666 (100%)
Fax: (852) 28616673
E-Mail: info@aon.com.hk
Web Site: www.aon.com.hk
Sales Range: $25-49.9 Million
Emp.: 125
Human Capital Consulting Services
S.I.C.: 8742
N.A.I.C.S.: 541611
Kitty Chan *(Mng Dir-Aon Consulting)*

Aon Reed Stenhouse, Inc. (3)
Reed Stenhouse Towers 20 Bay St
Toronto, ON, M5J 2N9, Canada (100%)
Tel.: (416) 868-5500
Telex: 62 19611
Fax: (416) 868-5580
Web Site: www.aon.ca
Sales Range: $100-124.9 Million
Emp.: 400
International Insurance & Reinsurance Brokering & Risk Management
S.I.C.: 6411
N.A.I.C.S.: 524298
Doug Swartout *(Chm & CEO)*
Christine Lithgow *(Pres)*

Aon eSolutions, Inc. (2)
5000 Executive Pkwy Ste 340
San Ramon, CA 94583-4210

Aon plc—(Continued)

Tel.: (925) 242-4600
Web Site: www.aon-esolutions.com
Risk Management Services
S.I.C.: 6411
N.A.I.C.S.: 524210
Kathy Burns *(CEO)*
Stephen Rhee *(COO)*
Paul Holden *(CIO)*
David Black *(Chief Info Security Officer)*
Don Ameche *(Sr VP-Global Sls & Mktg)*
Ron Young *(Sr VP-Global Product Mgmt)*

Aon Fire Protection Engineering Corporation (2)
1000 Milwaukee Ave 5th Fl
Glenview, IL 60025
Tel.: (847) 953-7700
Fax: (847) 953-7756
Web Site: www.aonfpe.com
Risk Management Services
S.I.C.: 6411
N.A.I.C.S.: 524210
Mark Rochholz *(COO)*

Aon Group, Inc. (2)
200 E Randolph St
Chicago, IL 60601
Tel.: (312) 381-1000
Fax: (312) 381-6032
Risk Management Services
S.I.C.: 6411
N.A.I.C.S.: 524210

Aon Healthcare (2)
199 Fremont St Fl 15
San Francisco, CA 94105-2253
Tel.: (415) 486-6200
Fax: (415) 486-7029
Web Site: www.cicsr.com
Sales Range: $200-249.9 Million
Emp.: 250
S.I.C.: 6399
N.A.I.C.S.: 524128
Matt Davis *(Pres)*

Aon Healthcare (2)
501 Corporate Centre Dr Ste 300
Franklin, TN 37067-2665 TN
Tel.: (615) 771-8100
Fax: (615) 771-8179
Web Site: www.aon.com
Rev.: $2,900,000
Emp.: 35
Insurance Agents Brokers and Service
S.I.C.: 6411
N.A.I.C.S.: 524210

Aon Hewitt (2)
100 Half Day Rd
Lincolnshire, IL 60069 DE
Tel.: (847) 295-5000
Fax: (847) 295-7634
E-Mail:
Web Site: www.aon.com
Emp.: 23,000
Human Resource Consulting
S.I.C.: 7361
N.A.I.C.S.: 561311
Yvan Legris *(Global CEO)*
Pavan Bhalla *(Exec VP & Mng Dir-India Ops)*
Brad Anderson *(Sr VP-Outsourcing)*
John Asencio *(Sr VP-New York)*

Subsidiaries:

Hewitt Associates LLC (3)
100 Bayview Cir
Newport Beach, CA 92660 DE
Tel.: (949) 725-4500
Fax: (949) 725-0668
Sales Range: $450-499.9 Million
Emp.: 242
Human Resource Management Services
S.I.C.: 8748
N.A.I.C.S.: 541618

Non-U.S. Subsidiaries:

Aon Hewitt Belgium (3)
Rue Jules Cockxstraat 8-10
1160 Brussels, Belgium BE
Tel.: (32) 27309511 (100%)
Fax: (32) 27309888
E-Mail: info@aon.de
Web Site: www.aon.de
Emp.: 25
Human Resources Outsourcing & Consulting Services
S.I.C.: 8999
N.A.I.C.S.: 541612
Philip Alliet *(Pres)*

Aon Hewitt GmbH (3)
Radlkoferstr 2
81373 Munich, Germany De
Tel.: (49) 89889870
Fax: (49) 8988987100
Sales Range: $25-49.9 Million
Emp.: 100
Human Capital & Financial Management Consultants
S.I.C.: 8742
N.A.I.C.S.: 541611
Joachim Bode *(Mng Dir)*

Aon Hewitt GmbH (3)
Dante Strasse 4-6
65189 Wiesbaden, Germany (100%)
Tel.: (49) 611928830
Fax: (49) 61192883196
E-Mail:
Emp.: 70
Provider of Human Resources Outsourcing & Consulting Services
S.I.C.: 8999
N.A.I.C.S.: 541612
Andrew Tarrell Cox *(Mng Dir)*
Alfred Ludwig Marchlewski *(Mng Dir)*

Aon Hewitt Korea (3)
7th Fl Gwanghwamun Bldg 211 Sejomgno Kong Noku
Seoul, 110 730, Korea (South) Ks
Tel.: (82) 23993600 (100%)
Fax: (82) 23993636
E-Mail: infoseoul@aonhewitt.com
Emp.: 50
Human Resources Outsourcing & Consulting Services
S.I.C.: 8999
N.A.I.C.S.: 541612
Kris Park *(Mng Dir)*
Stewart Fotheringham *(CEO-Consulting-Asia Pacific)*
Steven Gaffney *(CEO-Consulting-Pacific)*

Aon Hewitt Limited (3)
6 More London Place
London, SE1 2DA, United Kingdom UK
Tel.: (44) 20 7939 4000
Fax: (44) 20 7939 4411
E-Mail: hnbs@aonhewitt.com
Web Site: www.nbsc.co.uk
Management Consulting Services on Executive Pay & Share Plans
S.I.C.: 8748
N.A.I.C.S.: 541618
Rob Burdett *(Principal)*

Aon Hewitt S.A. (3)
Vuelta de Obligado 1878
8vo piso, C1428ADB Buenos Aires, Argentina Ar
Tel.: (54) 1155564900 (100%)
Fax: (54) 1155564901
Human Resources Outsourcing & Consulting Services
S.I.C.: 8999
N.A.I.C.S.: 541612

Aon Hewitt (Thailand) Ltd. (3)
17th Fl Abdulrahim Place 990 Rama IV Road
Silom Bangrak, Bangkok, 10500, Thailand TH
Tel.: (66) 26130900 (100%)
Fax: (66) 26130999
Emp.: 22
Human Resources Outsourcing & Consulting Services
S.I.C.: 8999
N.A.I.C.S.: 541612

Aon Hewitt - Toronto (3)
2 Sheppard Ave E
Toronto, ON, M2N 7A4, Canada Ca
Tel.: (416) 225-5001 (100%)
Fax: (416) 226-8251
E-Mail: canada.info@hewitt.com
Sales Range: $100-124.9 Million
Emp.: 300
Human Resources Outsourcing & Consulting Services
S.I.C.: 8999
N.A.I.C.S.: 541612
Tony Gaffney *(CEO)*
Noula Kondovski *(Sr VP-HR)*
Deron Waldock *(Sr VP-Legal Consulting Practice)*

Aon Poland Sp. z.o.o. (3)
Al Jana Pawla II 12
00 124 Warsaw, Poland PL
Tel.: (48) 22 850 9700 (100%)
Fax: (48) 22 850 9705
Web Site: www.aon.com
Sales Range: $10-24.9 Million
Emp.: 30
Human Resources Outsourcing & Consulting Services
S.I.C.: 8999
N.A.I.C.S.: 541612
Edward Stanoch *(Dir-Eastern Europe)*

Hewitt Associates (Chile) Ltda. (3)
Av Providencia 655 Piso 3
Santiago, 6640305, Chile CL
Tel.: (56) 23600900 (100%)
Fax: (56) 23619523
E-Mail: chileweb@hewitt.com
Web Site: www.hewitt.com
Sales Range: $10-24.9 Million
Emp.: 15
Provider of Human Resources Outsourcing & Consulting Services
S.I.C.: 8999
N.A.I.C.S.: 541612

Hewitt Associates GmbH (3)
Landstrasser Hoppstrasser
A 1030 Vienna, Austria AT
Tel.: (43) 0017129981 (100%)
Fax: (43) 712998135
E-Mail: info@hewitt.at
Web Site: www.hewitt.at
Sales Range: $10-24.9 Million
Emp.: 20
Provider of Human Resources Outsourcing & Consulting Services
S.I.C.: 8999
N.A.I.C.S.: 541612
Bernhard Stieger *(Mng Dir)*

Hewitt Associates Kabushiki Gaisya (3)
Mitakokusai Bldg 24 fl 1-4-28 Mitaminatoku
Tokyo, Minato Ku, 108-0073, Japan JP
Tel.: (81) 345802360 (100%)
Fax: (81) 45802380
E-Mail: Infotokyo@hewitt.com
Web Site: www.hewittasia.com
Sales Range: $10-24.9 Million
Emp.: 20
Human Resources Outsourcing & Consulting Services
S.I.C.: 8999
N.A.I.C.S.: 541612
Jim Humphrey *(Dir)*

Hewitt Associates Ltd. (3)
2601 05 Shell Tower Times Sq 1 Matheson St
Causeway Bay, China (Hong Kong) HK
Tel.: (852) 28778600 (100%)
Fax: (852) 28772701
E-Mail: info@hewittasia.com
Web Site: www.hewittasia.com
Sales Range: $10-24.9 Million
Emp.: 30
Provider of Human Resources Outsourcing & Consulting Services
S.I.C.: 8999
N.A.I.C.S.: 541612
Calo Ieponto *(Gen Mgr)*

Hewitt Associates Pte. Ltd. (3)
The Rutherford Singapore Science Park 1
89 Science Park Dr 03-01-02, Singapore, 118261, Singapore SG
Tel.: (65) 68727668 (100%)
Fax: (65) 67742100
E-Mail: info@hewittasia.com
Web Site: www.aonhewitt.com
Sales Range: $25-49.9 Million
Emp.: 50
Provider of Human Resources Outsourcing & Consulting Services
S.I.C.: 8999
N.A.I.C.S.: 541612

Hewitt Associates S.A. (3)
Edificio Gorbea 5th Floor
Paseo De La Castellana 149, 28046 Madrid, Spain ES
Tel.: (34) 914059350 (100%)
Fax: (34) 914059358
E-Mail: hewittspain@hewitt.com
Web Site: www.hewitt.com
Sales Range: $10-24.9 Million
Emp.: 50
Provider of Human Resources Outsourcing & Consulting Services
S.I.C.: 8999
N.A.I.C.S.: 541612

Hewitt Associates SARL (3)
7 Ave Georges Pompidou
92593 Levallois-Perret, Cedex, France FR
Tel.: (33) 155632323 (90%)
Fax: (33) 155632424
E-Mail: hewittfrance@hewitt.com
Web Site: www.hewittassociates.com
Sales Range: $25-49.9 Million
Emp.: 90
Human Resources Outsourcing & Consulting Services
S.I.C.: 8999
N.A.I.C.S.: 541612

Hewitt Associates Sdn Bhd (3)
Ste 201 Wisma E and C No 2 Lorong Dungun Kiri
Kuala Lumpur, 50490, Malaysia MY
Tel.: (60) 320944088 (100%)
Fax: (60) 320941088
Web Site: www.hewittasia.com
Sales Range: $10-24.9 Million
Emp.: 30
Provider of Human Resources Outsourcing & Consulting Services
S.I.C.: 8999
N.A.I.C.S.: 541612

Hewitt Associates Srl (3)
Via Alessandro Volta 16 Scala H
20093 Cologno Monzese, Milan, Italy IT
Tel.: (39) 022540794 (100%)
Fax: (39) 022538694
Web Site: www.hewitt.com
Sales Range: $100-124.9 Million
Provider of Human Resources Outsourcing & Consulting Services
S.I.C.: 8999
N.A.I.C.S.: 541612

Aon International Holdings, Inc. (2)
200 E Randolph St LI3
Chicago, IL 60601-6408
Tel.: (312) 381-1000
Fax: (312) 381-0118
Risk Management Services
S.I.C.: 6411
N.A.I.C.S.: 524210

Aon of Arizona Inc. (2)
1850 N Central Ave Ste 1700
Phoenix, AZ 85004 AZ
Tel.: (602) 427-3200
Fax: (602) 427-3032
Rev.: $5,800,000
Emp.: 40
Insurance Agents Brokers And Service
S.I.C.: 6411
N.A.I.C.S.: 524210

Aon Premium Finance, LLC (2)
200 E Randolph St
Chicago, IL 60601
Tel.: (312) 381-4628
Insurance Finance Services
S.I.C.: 6411
N.A.I.C.S.: 524298

Aon Risk Services Inc. (2)
200 E Randolph St
Chicago, IL 60601 DE
Tel.: (312) 381-1000 (100%)
Fax: (312) 381-0171
Web Site: www.aon.com
Sales Range: $350-399.9 Million
Emp.: 2,000
Insurance Brokers
S.I.C.: 6411
N.A.I.C.S.: 524210
Dirk P.M. Verbeek *(Chm & CEO)*

Subsidiaries:

Aon Risk Services Companies, Inc. (3)
199 Waters St
New York, NY 10038
Tel.: (212) 441-1000
Web Site: www.aon.com

Sales Range: $75-99.9 Million
Insurance Brokers
S.I.C.: 6411
N.A.I.C.S.: 524210
Steve McGill *(Chm & CEO)*
John Bayeux *(Mng Dir)*
Mike O'Connor *(COO)*
Warren Mula *(Chm-US Retail & CEO-Retail & Specialty Brokering)*
Elliot Richardson *(CEO-Aon Brokering Hubs & Facultative Brokering Ops)*

Subsidiaries:

Aon Risk Insurance Services West, Inc. **(4)**
199 Fremont St Ste 1400
San Francisco, CA 94105-2253
Tel.: (415) 486-7000
Fax: (415) 486-7029
Risk Management Services
S.I.C.: 6411
N.A.I.C.S.: 524210

Aon Risk Service of Texas Inc. **(4)**
301 Commerce St Ste 2101
Fort Worth, TX 76102-4139 TX
Tel.: (817) 810-4000
Fax: (817) 329-2019
E-Mail: info@aon.com
Web Site: www.aon.com
Rev.: $3,000,000
Emp.: 35
Insurance Agents Brokers & Service
S.I.C.: 6411
N.A.I.C.S.: 524210
Jerry Ferreira *(Mng Dir-Resident)*

Aon Risk Services Inc. Florida **(4)**
1001 Brickell Bay Dr Ste 1100
Miami, FL 33131 FL
Tel.: (305) 372-9950
Fax: (305) 372-1423
Web Site: www.aon.com
Sales Range: $25-49.9 Million
Emp.: 180
Insurance Agents Brokers & Service
S.I.C.: 6411
N.A.I.C.S.: 524210
Mike Parrish *(Mng Dir)*

Aon Risk Services Inc. (LA) **(4)**
639 Loyola Ave Ste 2560
New Orleans, LA 70113-7107 LA
Tel.: (504) 522-5341
Fax: (504) 525-6692
Web Site: www.aon.com
Sales Range: $10-24.9 Million
Emp.: 6
Insurance Agents Nec
S.I.C.: 6411
N.A.I.C.S.: 524210

Aon Risk Services, Inc. of Central California **(4)**
1418 S Main St Ste 104
Salinas, CA 93908 CA
Tel.: (831) 422-9831 (100%)
Fax: (831) 422-4856
E-Mail: info@aon.com
Web Site: www.wiredforgrowth.com
Sales Range: Less than $1 Million
Emp.: 15
Insurance Brokers
S.I.C.: 6411
N.A.I.C.S.: 524210
Michael Mahoney *(Mng Dir)*

Aon Risk Services Inc. of Colorado **(4)**
1900 16th St Ste 1000
Denver, CO 80202 CO
Tel.: (303) 758-7688 (100%)
Fax: (303) 758-9458
Web Site: www.aon.com
Rev.: $6,000,000
Emp.: 120
Insurance Brokers Nec
S.I.C.: 6411
N.A.I.C.S.: 524210
Gregory C. Case *(CEO)*

Aon Risk Services Inc. of Indiana **(4)**
201 N Illinois St Ste 1400
Indianapolis, IN 46204-4231 IN
Tel.: (317) 237-2400 (100%)
Fax: (317) 237-2461
E-Mail: info@aon.com
Web Site: www.themilwaukeechannel.com
Sales Range: $1-9.9 Million
Emp.: 36
Insurance
S.I.C.: 6411
N.A.I.C.S.: 524210
John Boss *(Mng Dir)*

Aon Risk Services, Inc. of Massachusetts **(4)**
1 Federal St
Boston, MA 02110-2320 MA
Tel.: (617) 482-3100 (100%)
Fax: (617) 542-2597
Web Site: www.aonriskservices.com
Sales Range: $75-99.9 Million
Emp.: 250
Insurance Agency
S.I.C.: 6411
N.A.I.C.S.: 524210
Paul Healy *(Exec VP & Mng Dir-Natl Contract Surety)*

Aon Risk Services Inc. of NJ **(4)**
10 Lanidex Plz W
Parsippany, NJ 07054-0608 NJ
Tel.: (973) 884-4000 (100%)
Fax: (973) 884-8808
Web Site: www.aon.com
Rev.: $5,900,000
Emp.: 125
Insurance Agents Brokers & Services
S.I.C.: 6411
N.A.I.C.S.: 524210
Gregory C. Case *(Pres & CEO)*
Matthew T. Schneider *(Mng Dir)*

Aon Risk Services Inc. **(4)**
315 W 3rd St
Little Rock, AR 72201-2411 AR
Mailing Address:
PO Box 3870
Little Rock, AR 72203-3870
Tel.: (501) 374-9300
Fax: (847) 953-1800
E-Mail: atgsvcctr@aon.com
Web Site: www.aon.com
Sales Range: $1-9.9 Million
Emp.: 36
Insurance Agents Brokers and Service
S.I.C.: 6411
N.A.I.C.S.: 524210
Mark S. Brockinton *(Mng Dir)*
Greg Golden *(COO)*

Aon Risk Services Inc. **(4)**
707 Wilshire Blvd Ste 2600
Los Angeles, CA 90017-3543 (100%)
Tel.: (213) 630-3200
Fax: (213) 689-4450
Web Site: www.acon.com
Sales Range: $150-199.9 Million
Emp.: 500
Insurance Brokers
S.I.C.: 6411
N.A.I.C.S.: 524210
Sam Cargill *(Pres)*
Reshma Dalia *(Global Mng Dir-Fin-Construction Svcs Grp)*

Aon Risk Services Inc. **(4)**
100 Bayview Cir Ste 100
Newport Beach, CA 92660 CA
Tel.: (949) 608-6300 (100%)
Fax: (949) 608-6451
E-Mail: info@aon.com
Web Site: www.armtech.com
Sales Range: $50-74.9 Million
Emp.: 120
Insurance Broker
S.I.C.: 6411
N.A.I.C.S.: 524298
Art Schuler *(Pres)*

Aon Risk Services Inc. **(4)**
199 Fremont St Fl 15
San Francisco, CA 94105-2245 CA
Tel.: (415) 486-7000 (100%)
Fax: (415) 486-7029
Web Site: www.aon.com
Sls.: $56,000,000
Emp.: 230
Insurance Brokers
S.I.C.: 6411
N.A.I.C.S.: 524210
Curtis Ingram *(VP)*

Aon Risk Services Inc. **(4)**
340 Pemberwick Rd
Greenwich, CT 06831-4240 CT
Mailing Address:
PO Box 900
Old Greenwich, CT 06870
Tel.: (203) 344-3300
Fax: (203) 344-3400
Premiums: $10,900,000
Emp.: 95
Insurance Brokers Nec
S.I.C.: 8742
N.A.I.C.S.: 541611

Aon Risk Services Inc. **(4)**
1120 20th St Northwest Ste 600
Washington, DC 20036-3406 DC
Tel.: (202) 331-3075
Rev.: $14,000,000
Emp.: 70
Insurance Agents Brokers & Service
S.I.C.: 6411
N.A.I.C.S.: 524210

Branch:

Aon Huntington T Block Insurance Agency **(5)**
1120 20th St NW Ste 600
Washington, DC 20036-3406 DC
Tel.: (202) 223-0673
Fax: (202) 331-8409
Rev.: $10,000,000
Emp.: 100
Insurance Brokers
S.I.C.: 6411
N.A.I.C.S.: 524210
Debbie Romos *(Office Mgr)*

Aon Risk Services Inc. **(4)**
200 E Randolph St
Chicago, IL 60601 (100%)
Tel.: (312) 381-1000
Web Site: www.aon.com
Sales Range: $1-4.9 Billion
Emp.: 10,000
Insurance Brokers
S.I.C.: 6411
N.A.I.C.S.: 524298
Greg Cases *(Pres)*
John Sullivan *(CEO)*

Aon Risk Services Inc. **(4)**
200 E Randolph St
Chicago, IL 60601-6436 IL
Mailing Address:
200 E.Randolf
Chicago, IL 60606-1743
Tel.: (312) 381-1000
Fax: (312) 381-0144
Web Site: www.aon.com
Rev.: $1,600,000
Emp.: 2,000
Marketing Consulting Services
S.I.C.: 6411
N.A.I.C.S.: 524210
Gregory C. Case *(CEO)*

Aon Risk Services Inc. **(4)**
1111 Metropolitan Ave Ste 400
Charlotte, NC 28204 NC
Tel.: (704) 343-4100
Fax: (704) 343-0826
E-Mail: bruce.quintana@aon.com
Web Site: www.aon.com
Sales Range: $1-9.9 Million
Emp.: 50
Commercial Insurance Agents & Brokers
S.I.C.: 6411
N.A.I.C.S.: 524210
Bruce Quintana *(Mng Dir)*

Aon Risk Services Inc. **(4)**
300 Jericho Quadrangle Ste 300
Jericho, NY 11753 NY
Tel.: (516) 747-1950
Fax: (516) 342-2727
Rev.: $2,600,000
Emp.: 10
Insurance Agents
S.I.C.: 6411
N.A.I.C.S.: 524210

Aon Risk Services Inc. **(4)**
1660 W 2nd St Ste 650
Cleveland, OH 44113-1419 OH
Tel.: (216) 621-8100 (100%)
Fax: (216) 623-4195
Sales Range: $1-9.9 Million
Emp.: 53
Insurance Agency
S.I.C.: 6411
N.A.I.C.S.: 524210
Jerry Kysela *(Pres)*

Aon Risk Services Inc. **(4)**
1650 Market St Ste 1000
Philadelphia, PA 19103-7301 PA
Tel.: (215) 255-2000
Fax: (215) 255-1887
Premiums: $17,700,000
Emp.: 180
Insurance Brokers
S.I.C.: 6411
N.A.I.C.S.: 524210
Bruce Vassallo *(CEO)*

Aon Risk Services Inc. **(4)**
50 Kennedy Plz Fl 10
Providence, RI 02903-2393 RI
Tel.: (401) 331-7700
Fax: (401) 331-2809
Web Site: www.aon.com
Rev.: $7,000,000
Emp.: 30
Insurance Brokers
S.I.C.: 6411
N.A.I.C.S.: 524210
Peter Caine *(Mng Dir)*

Aon Risk Services Inc. **(4)**
1330 Post Oak Blvd
Houston, TX 77056 OK
Tel.: (918) 496-3900
Fax: (800) 953-4542
Sales Range: Less than $1 Million
Emp.: 50
Insurance Brokers Nec
S.I.C.: 6371
N.A.I.C.S.: 524298
Ernie Joyner *(Mgr-HR)*

Aon Risk Services Inc. **(4)**
10700 Research Dr Ste 450
Milwaukee, WI 53226-3460 (100%)
Tel.: (414) 271-6420
Fax: (414) 271-4103
E-Mail: info@aon.com
Web Site: www.aon.com
Sales Range: $1-9.9 Million
Emp.: 30
Insurance Services
S.I.C.: 6411
N.A.I.C.S.: 524210
Jill Anhalt *(Office Mgr)*

Aon Risk Services of Oregon **(4)**
51 SW 6th Ave
Portland, OR 97204 OR
Tel.: (503) 224-9700 (100%)
Fax: (503) 295-0923
Sales Range: $1-9.9 Million
Emp.: 50
Insurance Agents and Brokers
S.I.C.: 6411
N.A.I.C.S.: 524210
Peter Johnson *(Pres)*

Aon Risk Services of Puerto Rico Inc **(4)**
20304 Ponce De Leon Ave Ste 1000 10th Fl
San Juan, PR 00918-2032 PR
Mailing Address: (100%)
PO Box 191229
San Juan, PR 00919-1229
Tel.: (787) 754-8787
Fax: (787) 753-7990
Web Site: www.aon.com
Sales Range: $1-9.9 Million
Emp.: 77
Insurance Brokers Nec
S.I.C.: 6411
N.A.I.C.S.: 524210
Ivan Mendez *(Pres)*

Aon Risk Services of Texas **(4)**
1330 Post Oak Blvd
Houston, TX 77056 TX
Tel.: (832) 476-6000
Fax: (800) 953-4542
Web Site: www.aon.com
Rev.: $6,300,000
Emp.: 600
Insurance Brokers & Claim Adjusters
S.I.C.: 6411
N.A.I.C.S.: 524210
Phil Pott *(VP)*

Aon Risk Services Southwest, Inc. **(4)**
5555 San Felipe St Ste 1500
Houston, TX 77056-2701

Aon plc—(Continued)

Tel.: (832) 476-6000
Fax: (832) 476-6530
Risk Management Services
S.I.C.: 6411
N.A.I.C.S.: 524210

Aon Risk Services (4)
390 N Broadway
Jericho, NY 11753
Tel.: (516) 733-9200
Fax: (516) 681-7390
Web Site: www.alliedna.com
Sales Range: $10-24.9 Million
Emp.: 105
Surety & Construction Insurance
S.I.C.: 6411
N.A.I.C.S.: 524210
William A. Marino *(Vice Chm-Construction Svcs Grp & Pres-Global Construction Bus)*

Non-U.S. Subsidiaries:

Aon Risk Services, Japan, Ltd. (4)
Bancho Kaikan 3 F
12 1 Gobancho Chiyoda Ku, Tokyo, 102 0076, Japan JP
Tel.: (81) 332375511 (100%)
Fax: (81) 332375599
E-Mail: jp_info@aon-asia.com
Web Site: www.aon.com
Sales Range: $50-74.9 Million
Emp.: 250
Provider of Risk Management Services
S.I.C.: 8742
N.A.I.C.S.: 541611
G. Randall Wada *(CEO)*

Aon Risk Services Singapore (Insurance Brokers) Pte. Ltd. (4)
32nd Floor Singapore Land Tower 50 Raffles Place
Singapore, 48623, Singapore SG
Tel.: (65) 62218222 (100%)
Fax: (65) 62241700
E-Mail: david_lum@aon-asia.com
Web Site: www.aon.com
Sales Range: $100-124.9 Million
Emp.: 400
Provider of Insurance
S.I.C.: 6411
N.A.I.C.S.: 524298
David Lum *(CEO)*

Aon Specialty Re, Inc. (2)
200 East Randolph St
Chicago, IL 60601-1743 IL
Tel.: (312) 381-5300 (100%)
Fax: (312) 381-0160
Web Site: www.aon.com
Sales Range: $300-349.9 Million
Emp.: 500
Broker of Property & Casualty Facultative & Program Reinsurance
S.I.C.: 6411
N.A.I.C.S.: 524298
Gregory C. Case *(Pres)*

Bankers Insurance Service Corp. (2)
200 E Randolph St
Chicago, IL 60601-6436 IL
Tel.: (312) 381-1000
Fax: (312) 381-6199
Web Site: www.bankers.fprsi.com
Rev.: $7,600,000
Emp.: 2,000
Insurance Brokers
S.I.C.: 6371
N.A.I.C.S.: 524298
Tom Delaney *(Mng Dir)*

CD Dextor Inc. (2)
3601 Cedar Springs Rd
Dallas, TX 75219-4905 TX
Mailing Address:
PO Box 8264
Chicago, IL 60680-8264
Tel.: (214) 526-2553
Fax: (214) 526-6926
Web Site: www.dextorcompany.com
Sls.: $84,000
Emp.: 2
Safety & Security Specialization
S.I.C.: 6411
N.A.I.C.S.: 524210

Financial Professional Risk Solutions, Inc. (2)
200 E Randolph St Ste 1100
Chicago, IL 60601 IL
Tel.: (312) 381-3729
Fax: (312) 381-6199
Toll Free: (800) 621-0324
Web Site: www.fprsi.com
Sales Range: $1-9.9 Million
Emp.: 50
Insurance Brokers
S.I.C.: 6411
N.A.I.C.S.: 524210

Hewitt EnnisKnupp, Inc. (2)
10 S Riverside Plz Ste 1600
Chicago, IL 60606
Tel.: (312) 715-1700
Fax: (312) 715-1952
Web Site: www.ennisknupp.com
www.ennisknupp.com
S.I.C.: 6411
N.A.I.C.S.: 524210
Stephen Cummings *(CEO & Principal)*
John Thompson *(Partner & Head-Investment Solutions-Institutional Advisory)*

Impact Forecasting, L.L.C. (2)
200 E Randolph St
Chicago, IL 60601
Tel.: (312) 381-5919
Fax: (312) 381-0181
E-Mail: impact.forecasting@aonbenfield.com
Web Site: www.aon.com
Emp.: 25
Risk Management Services
S.I.C.: 6411
N.A.I.C.S.: 524210

Johnsons Rooney Welch, Inc. (2)
2250 Douglas Blvd Ste 210
Roseville, CA 95661
Tel.: (916) 784-6232
Fax: (916) 784-8151
Toll Free: (800) 631-0311
Sales Range: Less than $1 Million
Emp.: 13
Group Insurance
S.I.C.: 6411
N.A.I.C.S.: 524210
Jan Massara *(VP-Sls)*

K&K Insurance Group Inc. (2)
1712 Magnavox Way
Fort Wayne, IN 46804 IN
Mailing Address:
PO Box 2338
Fort Wayne, IN 46801-2338
Tel.: (260) 459-5000
Fax: (260) 459-5866
Toll Free: (800) 237-2917
E-Mail: KK_General@kandkinsurance.com
Web Site: www.kandkinsurance.com
Sales Range: $100-124.9 Million
Emp.: 300
Property & Casualty Insurance Agent
S.I.C.: 6411
N.A.I.C.S.: 524210
Todd Bixler *(Pres & CEO)*

Premier Auto Finance Inc. (2)
5050 N Broadway St
Chicago, IL 60640-3016 IL
Mailing Address:
PO Box 803403
Chicago, IL 60680-3403
Tel.: (773) 765-1000
Toll Free: (800) 346-9737
Sales Range: $25-49.9 Million
Emp.: 140
Investors
S.I.C.: 7515
N.A.I.C.S.: 532112

Underwriters Marine Services, Inc. (2)
3850 N Causeway Blvd Two Lakeway Ste 1930
Metairie, LA 70002-1752
Tel.: (504) 828-6311
Fax: (504) 828-6686
Web Site: www.umsmarine.com
Emp.: 10
Insurance Agencies Brokerages
S.I.C.: 6411
N.A.I.C.S.: 524210
David Manion *(Pres)*

Wrapid Specialty, Inc. (2)
707 Wilshire Blvd Ste 2600
Los Angeles, CA 90017
Tel.: (877) 616-4777
Fax: (877) 557-2211
E-Mail: wrapups@wrapidspecialty.com
Web Site: www.wrapidspecialty.com
Wrap Administrator
S.I.C.: 6411
N.A.I.C.S.: 524210

Non-U.S. Subsidiaries:

Accuracy SAS (2)
41 rue de Villiers
92523 Neuilly-sur-Seine, France
Tel.: (33) 158757510
Fax: (33) 158757511
E-Mail: contact@accuracy.com
Web Site: www.accuracy.com
Emp.: 100
Financial Advisory Services
S.I.C.: 6282
N.A.I.C.S.: 523930
Frederic Duponchel *(CEO & Partner)*
Nicolas Barsalou *(Partner)*
Nicolas Bourdon *(Partner)*
Xavier Chevreux *(Partner)*
Giovanni Foti *(Partner)*
Xavier Gallais *(Partner)*
Bruno Husson *(Partner)*
Christophe Leclerc *(Partner)*
Frederic Loeper *(Partner)*
Damien Gros *(CFO)*

Accuracy Srl (2)
Piazza Cavour 2
20121 Milan, Italy
Tel.: (39) 236696201
E-Mail: infoitaly@accuracy.com
Emp.: 15
Financial Advisory Services
S.I.C.: 6282
N.A.I.C.S.: 523930
Giovanni Foti *(Partner)*
Pierluca Mezzetti *(Partner)*
Renato Vigezzi *(Partner)*
Alessandro Reitelli *(Mng Dir)*

AIM Sweden AB (2)
Doktor Liborius Gata 20B
Vastra Gotaland, Goteborg, 413 23, Sweden
Tel.: (46) 707353624
Risk Management Services
S.I.C.: 6411
N.A.I.C.S.: 524210

Aon Adjudication Services Ltd (2)
Briarcliff House Kingsmead
Farnborough, Hampshire, GU14 7TE, United Kingdom
Tel.: (44) 1252768000
Fax: (44) 1252522206
Emp.: 500
Risk Management Services
S.I.C.: 6411
N.A.I.C.S.: 524210

Aon Affinity Chile Ltda. (2)
Av Isidora Goyenechea 3477 Of 100-B
Las Condes, Santiago, Chile
Tel.: (56) 2251 99500
Fax: (56) 3315115
Web Site: www.aon.com
Emp.: 140
Risk Management Services
S.I.C.: 6411
N.A.I.C.S.: 524210
Carlos Bello *(CEO)*

Aon Affinity sp zoo (2)
00-12 Al Jana Pawla II
Warsaw, 00-124, Poland
Tel.: (48) 228509700
Fax: (48) 228509705
E-Mail: aonvip@aon.pl
Web Site: www.aon.com
Emp.: 70
Risk Management Services
S.I.C.: 6411
N.A.I.C.S.: 524210
Slawomir Bane *(Gen Mgr)*

Aon Asia Pacific Limited (2)
28 Fl Tower 1 Round Square 1 Matheson St
28 Fl Tower 1 Round Square 1 M, Hong Kong, China (Hong Kong)
Tel.: (852) 28616666
Fax: (852) 28616672
Risk Management Services
S.I.C.: 6411
N.A.I.C.S.: 524210

Aon Belgium NV (2)
Rue Jules Cockxstraat 8-10
Brussels, 1116, Belgium
Tel.: (32) 27309511
Fax: (32) 27309888
Web Site: www.aon.be
Risk Management Services
S.I.C.: 6411
N.A.I.C.S.: 524210

Aon Benfield China Limited (2)
21/F Aon China Bldg 29 Queen S Rd C
Central District, Hong Kong, China (Hong Kong)
Tel.: (852) 28616666
Fax: (852) 28616694
Risk Management Services
S.I.C.: 6411
N.A.I.C.S.: 524210

Aon Benfield Colombia Ltda. Corredores de Reaseguros (2)
Av Carrera 9 No 113-52 Ofc 505
Bogota, Cundinamarca, Colombia
Tel.: (57) 16222222
Fax: (57) 16209112
Web Site: www.aon.com
Risk Management Services
S.I.C.: 6411
N.A.I.C.S.: 524210
Humberto Cabrera *(Gen Mgr)*

Aon Benfield Greece SA (2)
7 Granikou
Maroussi, 15125, Greece
Tel.: (30) 2106386700
Fax: (30) 2106386790
Web Site: www.aon.com
Risk Management Services
S.I.C.: 6411
N.A.I.C.S.: 524210
Panagiotis Galatis *(Gen Mgr)*

Aon Benfield Iberia, Correduria de Reaseguros SA (2)
Calle Rosario Pino 14 - 16
Madrid, 28020, Spain
Tel.: (34) 902114611
Fax: (34) 902309303
Risk Management Services
S.I.C.: 6411
N.A.I.C.S.: 524210

Aon Benfield Italia Spa (2)
Via Andrea Ponti 10
Milan, MI, 20143, Italy
Tel.: (39) 2454341
Fax: (39) 245434810
Risk Management Services
S.I.C.: 6411
N.A.I.C.S.: 524210

Aon Benfield Japan Ltd. (2)
Bancho Kaikan 12-1 Gobancho
Chiyoda-ku, Tokyo, 102-0076, Japan
Tel.: (81) 332376600
Fax: (81) 332376575
Insurance Brokerage Services
S.I.C.: 6411
N.A.I.C.S.: 524210

Aon Benfield Malaysia Limited (2)
Level 11B Block 4 Office Tower Financial Park Labuan Complex
Labuan, WP, 87000, Malaysia
Tel.: (60) 87417672
Fax: (60) 87452333
Risk Management Services
S.I.C.: 6411
N.A.I.C.S.: 524210

Aon Benfield Netherlands CV (2)
Paalbergweg 2-4
1105 AG Amsterdam, Netherlands
Tel.: (31) 204305200
Risk Management Services
S.I.C.: 6411
N.A.I.C.S.: 524210

Aon Benfield Peru Corredores Reaseguros SA (2)
Manuel A Fuentes 355 Lima
San Isidro, 27, Peru
Tel.: (51) 12124210
Fax: (51) 14213309
E-Mail:
Web Site: www.aon.com
Emp.: 18
Risk Management Services
S.I.C.: 6411

N.A.I.C.S.: 524210
Michael Dressen *(Office Mgr)*

Aon Benfield Ruckversicherungsmakler Ges.mbH (2)
Geiselbergstrasse 17
Vienna, 1110, Austria
Tel.: (43) 57800231
Fax: (43) 578006232
Risk Management Services
S.I.C.: 6411
N.A.I.C.S.: 524210

Aon (Bermuda) Ltd. (2)
Aon House 30 Woodbourne Ave
Hpembroke
Hamilton, HM 08, Bermuda (70%)
Tel.: (441) 2950265
Fax: (441) 2923244
E-Mail: venicia.warner@aon.com
Sales Range: $10-24.9 Million
Emp.: 100
S.I.C.: 6411
N.A.I.C.S.: 524298
Paul C. J. Markey *(Chm)*
Joe Rego *(Pres)*
Robert Johnson *(Mng Dir)*

Aon Bolivia SA Corredores de Seguros (2)
Torre Lucia P3 Av Ballivian Esq Calle 13
Calacoto
La Paz, Bolivia
Tel.: (591) 22790955
Fax: (591) 22125858
Web Site: www.aon.com
Risk Management Services
S.I.C.: 6411
N.A.I.C.S.: 524210

Aon Botswana (Pty) Ltd. (2)
Aon House Plot 50368
PO Box 624
Gaborone, Botswana
Tel.: (267) 3617300
Fax: (267) 3914608
Web Site: www.aon.com
Emp.: 90
Risk Management Services
S.I.C.: 6411
N.A.I.C.S.: 524210
Barnabas Mavuma *(Gen Mgr)*

Aon Bulgaria EOOD (2)
Alexander Stamboliyski Blvd 103 Office
Building Sofia Tower 4 Floor
Sofia, 1303, Bulgaria
Tel.: (359) 29337800
Fax: (359) 29835025
E-Mail: office.bulgaria@aon.bg
Web Site: www.aon.com
Emp.: 31
Risk Management Services
S.I.C.: 6411
N.A.I.C.S.: 524210
Hristo Borisov *(Gen Mgr)*

Aon Canada Inc. (2)
20 Bay St
Toronto, ON, M5J 2N9, Canada ON
Tel.: (416) 868-5500 (100%)
Fax: (416) 868-5580
E-Mail: corporate_communications@reed.aon.ca
Web Site: www.aon.ca
Sales Range: $100-124.9 Million
Emp.: 300
Insurance Agents Brokers & Service
S.I.C.: 6411
N.A.I.C.S.: 524298
Craig Gilmour *(Sr VP)*

Subsidiaries:

Aon Tarizeau Inc. (3)
700 de la Gauchetiere W Ste 1800
Montreal, QC, H3B 0A4, Canada QC
Tel.: (514) 842-5000 (100%)
Fax: (514) 842-3456
E-Mail: info@aon.com
Web Site: www.aon.com
Rev.: $1,133,900
Emp.: 200
Insurance Agents Brokers & Service
S.I.C.: 6411
N.A.I.C.S.: 524298
Joan Lepin *(Exec VP)*

Aon Captive Services Group (2)
Aon House 30 Woodbourne Ave
Pembroke, HM 08, Bermuda BM
Tel.: (441) 2952220 (100%)
Fax: (441) 2924910
E-Mail: aoninsurancemanager@agl.aon.com
Web Site: www.aon.bm
Sales Range: $25-49.9 Million
Emp.: 100
Captive Management & Insurance Services
S.I.C.: 8742
N.A.I.C.S.: 541611
Peter Mullen *(Mng Dir)*

Aon Central and Eastern Europe AS (2)
Tylova 57
Plzen, 316 00, Czech Republic
Tel.: (420) 378132309
Fax: (420) 378134169
E-Mail: petr.seiala@aon.cz
Web Site: www.aon.cz
Emp.: 2
Risk Management Services
S.I.C.: 6411
N.A.I.C.S.: 524210
Andy Higgins *(Gen Mgr)*

Aon-Cofco Insurance Brokers Co. Ltd. (2)
42/F Jin Mao Tower 88 Century Boulevard
Pudong, Shanghai, 200121, China
Tel.: (86) 2138658000
Fax: (86) 2150498331
Emp.: 300
Risk Management Services
S.I.C.: 6411
N.A.I.C.S.: 524210

Aon Consulting Argentina SA (2)
Emma de la Barra 353 Dique 4 Puerto
Madero
Buenos Aires, 1107, Argentina
Tel.: (54) 1148148000
Fax: (54) 1148148065
Web Site: www.aon.com
Emp.: 50
Risk Management Services
S.I.C.: 6411
N.A.I.C.S.: 524210
Juan Juan *(Gen Mgr)*

Aon Consulting Lesotho (Pty) Ltd. (2)
PO Box 993
Maseru, 100, Lesotho
Tel.: (266) 22313540
Fax: (266) 22310033
Web Site: www.aon.com
Risk Management Services
S.I.C.: 6411
N.A.I.C.S.: 524210

Aon Consulting (PNG) Ltd. (2)
PO Box 479
Port Moresby, Papua New Guinea
Tel.: (675) 3224544
Fax: (675) 3202562
Risk Management Services
S.I.C.: 6411
N.A.I.C.S.: 524210

Aon Consulting South Africa (Pty) Ltd. (2)
The Place 1 Sandton Drive Sandhurst
Sandton, Johannesburg, 2196, South Africa
Tel.: (27) 119447000
Fax: (27) 114443474
Risk Management Services
S.I.C.: 6411
N.A.I.C.S.: 524210

Aon Consulting (Thailand) Ltd. (2)
989 Siam Tower Bldg 18Fl Rama I Rd
Pathumwan
Bangkok, 10330, Thailand
Tel.: (66) 23054555
Fax: (66) 26580173
Insurance Brokerage Services
S.I.C.: 6411
N.A.I.C.S.: 524210

Aon CR Srl (2)
Corso Andrea Podesta 1
Genoa, 16121, Italy
Tel.: (39) 1057141
Fax: (39) 1057141
Risk Management Services
S.I.C.: 6411
N.A.I.C.S.: 524210

Aon Credit International Insurance Broker GmbH (2)
Caffamacherreihe 16
Hamburg, 20355, Germany
Tel.: (49) 4036053300
Fax: (49) 4036051000
Web Site: www.aon.de
Emp.: 60
Risk Management Service
S.I.C.: 6411
N.A.I.C.S.: 524210

Aon Denmark A/S (2)
Strandgade 4C
1401 Copenhagen, Denmark
Tel.: (45) 32697000
Fax: (45) 32697001
Web Site: www.aon.com
Insurance Brokerage Services
S.I.C.: 6411
N.A.I.C.S.: 524210
Soren Lindbo *(Gen Mgr)*

Aon Direct Group Espana SL (2)
Ayala 10 Fl 2
Madrid, 28001, Spain
Tel.: (34) 914320790
Fax: (34) 914320789
Emp.: 5
Direct Marketing Services
S.I.C.: 6411
N.A.I.C.S.: 524210

Aon Direct Group Inc. (2)
2255 Sheppard Ave E Ste E400
Toronto, ON, M2J 4Y1, Canada ON
Tel.: (416) 756-1573 (100%)
Fax: (416) 756-9290
Web Site: www.aon.ca
Sales Range: Less than $1 Million
Emp.: 14
Insurance Agents Brokers & Service
S.I.C.: 6411
N.A.I.C.S.: 524298

Aon Finland Oy (2)
Oulunkylan Tori 1
Helsinki, 640, Finland
Tel.: (358) 201266200
Fax: (358) 201266201
E-Mail: infofi@aon.fi
Web Site: www.aon.com
Risk Management Services
S.I.C.: 6411
N.A.I.C.S.: 524210
Petri Suni *(Gen Mgr)*

Aon France Finance SA (2)
Du 31 Au 35 31 Rue De La Federation
75015 Paris, France
Tel.: (33) 147831010
Fax: (33) 147831111
Web Site: www.aon.fr
Emp.: 800
Risk Management Services
S.I.C.: 6411
N.A.I.C.S.: 524210
Robert Lublanc *(Gen Mgr)*

Aon Gil y Carvajal Correduria de Seguros SA (2)
Toro 21 2 A
Salamanca, 37002, Spain
Tel.: (34) 923271224
Fax: (34) 983356395
Web Site: www.aon.es
Risk Management Services
S.I.C.: 6411
N.A.I.C.S.: 524210
Rafael Estedan *(CEO)*

Aon Global Risk Consulting Luxembourg Sarl (2)
534 Rue De Neudorf
Luxembourg, 2220, Luxembourg
Tel.: (352) 223422400
Fax: (352) 317174
E-Mail: info@aon.lu
Emp.: 1
Risk Management Services
S.I.C.: 6411
N.A.I.C.S.: 524210

Aon Global Services, Inc. (2)
25 Centurion Dr Fl 2
Markham, ON, L3R 5N8, Canada ON
Tel.: (905) 513-6494 (100%)
Fax: (905) 513-6497
Web Site: www.globalsvr.com
Sales Range: $10-24.9 Million
Emp.: 20
Pension Mutual Insurance
S.I.C.: 6371
N.A.I.C.S.: 524292

Aon Grieg AS (2)
C Sundtsgt 17/19 Postboks 234
Bergen, 5804, Norway
Tel.: (47) 55576800
Fax: (47) 55576790
Risk Management Services
S.I.C.: 6411
N.A.I.C.S.: 524210

Aon Hewitt GmbH (2)
Dantestrasse 4-6
Wiesbaden, 65189, Germany
Tel.: (49) 611928830
Fax: (49) 61192883196
E-Mail: info@aonhewitt.de
Web Site: www.aonhewitt.com
Emp.: 7
Risk Management Services
S.I.C.: 6411
N.A.I.C.S.: 524210
Olaf Peterson *(Gen Mgr)*

Aon Holdings Corretores de Seguros Ltda (2)
Felix Da Cunha 1009 Conj 301
Porto Alegre, Rio Grande Do Sul, 90570-001, Brazil
Tel.: (55) 5133231200
Risk Management Services
S.I.C.: 6411
N.A.I.C.S.: 524210

Aon Holdings Norway AS (2)
Vollsveien 4
Lysaker, 1366, Norway
Tel.: (47) 67112200
Fax: (47) 67112201
Web Site: www.aon.com
Emp.: 120
Risk Management Services
S.I.C.: 6411
N.A.I.C.S.: 524210
Espen Husstad *(Gen Mgr)*

Aon Insurance Brokers (Malaysia) Sdn Bhd (2)
7th Floor Bangunan Malaysian Re No 17
Lorong Dungun
Kuala Lumpur, 50490, Malaysia
Tel.: (60) 320956628
Fax: (60) 320956618
Web Site: www.aon.com
Emp.: 100
Insurance Brokerage Services
S.I.C.: 6411
N.A.I.C.S.: 524210
Ahmed Hairani *(Mgr-HR)*

Aon Insurance Brokers (Pvt) Ltd. (2)
Bahria Complex 3 2nd Floor MT Khan Road
Karachi, 74000, Pakistan
Tel.: (92) 2135615339
Fax: (92) 35615338
Web Site: www.aon.com
Emp.: 3
Risk Management Services
S.I.C.: 6411
N.A.I.C.S.: 524210
Amin Dherani *(Gen Mgr)*

Aon Insurance Managers (Barbados) Ltd. (2)
Sunrise House Wildey Main Road
Saint Michael, Barbados
Tel.: (246) 4364895
Fax: (246) 4369016
Web Site: www.aon.com
Emp.: 13
Risk Management Services
S.I.C.: 6411
N.A.I.C.S.: 524210
Vinston Hampden *(Mng Dir)*

Aon Insurance Managers (Luxembourg) SA (2)
534 Rue De Neudorf
Luxembourg, 2220, Luxembourg
Tel.: (352) 317171
Fax: (352) 317174
E-Mail: info@aon.lu
Web Site: www.aon.lu

Aon plc—(Continued)

Emp.: 48
Risk Management Services
S.I.C.: 6411
N.A.I.C.S.: 524210
John Torrie *(Gen Mgr)*

Aon Italia SpA (2)
Via Andrea Ponti 8/10
Milan, MI, 20143, Italy
Tel.: (39) 02454341
Fax: (39) 0245434811
Risk Management Services
S.I.C.: 6411
N.A.I.C.S.: 524210

Aon Jauch & Huebener Holdings GmbH (2)
Caffamacherreihe 16
20355 Hamburg, Germany DE
Tel.: (49) 4036052580 (100%)
Fax: (49) 403605271000
E-Mail: info@aon-jh.de
Web Site: www.aon-jh.de
Rev.: $118,154,428
Emp.: 750
Holding Company; Owner of Insurance Brokerage & Consulting Service Providers
S.I.C.: 6411
N.A.I.C.S.: 524298
Jurgen Grupe *(Mng Dir)*

Subsidiary:

Aon Jauch & Huebener GmbH (3)
Caffamacherreihe 16
20355 Hamburg, Germany (100%)
Tel.: (49) 4036050
Fax: (49) 4036051000
E-Mail: info-d@aon.de
Web Site: www.aon.de
Sales Range: $125-149.9 Million
Emp.: 1,300
Provider of Insurance Brokerage & Consulting Services
S.I.C.: 6411
N.A.I.C.S.: 524298
Ralph P. Liebke *(CEO)*

Non-U.S. Subsidiaries:

Aon Jauch & Huebener GmbH (3)
Versicherungsmakler Geiselbergstrasse 17
1110 Vienna, Austria AT
Tel.: (43) 578000 (100%)
Fax: (43) 578006138
E-Mail: aon@jahu.at
Web Site: www.aon-jh.at
Sales Range: $25-49.9 Million
Emp.: 150
Insurance Brokerage & Consulting Services
S.I.C.: 6411
N.A.I.C.S.: 524298

Subsidiary:

Aon Jauch & Hubener Employee Benefit Consulting Ges.mbH (4)
Geiselbergstrasse 17
Vienna, 1110, Austria
Tel.: (43) 578000
Fax: (43) 578006139
Risk Management Services
S.I.C.: 6411
N.A.I.C.S.: 524210

Aon (Schweiz) AG (3)
Bederstrasse 66
Zurich, 8027, Switzerland CH
Tel.: (41) 19252211 (100%)
Fax: (41) 19252200
Web Site: www.aon.ch
Sales Range: $50-74.9 Million
Emp.: 100
Provider of Risk Management Services
S.I.C.: 6331
N.A.I.C.S.: 524126
Welson Bolognesi *(Pres)*

Aon Slovakia (3)
7/D Galvaniho
Bratislava, 821 04, Slovakia Sk
Tel.: (421) 244460666 (100%)
Fax: (421) 232604299
E-Mail: info@aonstach.sk
Web Site: www.aonstach.sk
Sales Range: Less than $1 Million
Emp.: 20
Provider of Insurance Brokerage & Consulting Services
S.I.C.: 6411
N.A.I.C.S.: 524298
Rabovan Skultety *(Mng Dir)*

Jauch & Huebener spol. s.r.o. (3)
Sarikova 17
120 00 Prague, Czech Republic CZ
Tel.: (420) 222232288 (100%)
Fax: (420) 222230077
E-Mail: aon@aon.cz
Web Site: www.aon.cz
Sales Range: Less than $1 Million
Emp.: 70
Industrial & Personal Insurance Services
S.I.C.: 6311
N.A.I.C.S.: 524113
Miroslav Matocha *(CEO)*

Aon Korea Inc. (2)
20th Floor Kukdong Bldg 60-1 Chungmuro 3-Ga Jung-Gu
Seoul, 100-705, Korea (South)
Tel.: (82) 222602600
Fax: (82) 222773545
Risk Management Services
S.I.C.: 6411
N.A.I.C.S.: 524210

Aon Latvia Sia (2)
Biekensalas Street 6
Riga, 1004, Latvia
Tel.: (371) 67892551
Fax: (371) 67892552
E-Mail: aonlatvia@aon.lv
Web Site: www.aon.com
Emp.: 12
Risk Management Services
S.I.C.: 6411
N.A.I.C.S.: 524210
Aigars Milts *(CEO)*

Aon Lesotho (Pty) Ltd. (2)
4 Bowker Road
Old Europa, Maseru, Lesotho
Tel.: (266) 22313540
Fax: (266) 22310939
Web Site: www.aon.com
Risk Management Services
S.I.C.: 6411
N.A.I.C.S.: 524210

Aon Luxembourg SA (2)
534 Rue De Neudorf
Luxembourg, 2220, Luxembourg
Tel.: (352) 317235
Fax: (352) 3524751
Emp.: 5
Risk Management Services
S.I.C.: 6411
N.A.I.C.S.: 524210

Aon MacDonagh Boland Group Ltd (2)
Metropolitan Building James Joyce Street
Dublin, Ireland
Tel.: (353) 12666000
Fax: (353) 12666620
E-Mail: info@aon.ie
Web Site: www.aon.ie
Emp.: 50
Risk Management Services
S.I.C.: 6411
N.A.I.C.S.: 524210
Richard Andersen *(CEO)*

Aon Makelaars in Assurantien BV (2)
Admiraliteitskade 62
Rotterdam, 3063 ED, Netherlands
Tel.: (31) 104487100
Fax: (31) 104488700
Risk Management Services
S.I.C.: 6411
N.A.I.C.S.: 524210

Aon Monia Oy (2)
Oulunkylan Tori 1
Helsinki, 640, Finland
Tel.: (358) 201266200
Fax: (358) 201266201
Web Site: www.aon.com
Emp.: 5
Risk Management Services
S.I.C.: 6411
N.A.I.C.S.: 524210

Aon New Zealand (2)
16th Floor AMP Centre 29 Customs Street West
PO Box 1184
Auckland, 1140, New Zealand
Tel.: (64) 93629000
Fax: (64) 93092536
E-Mail: ars-info@aon.co.nz
Web Site: www.aon.co.nz
Risk Management Services
S.I.C.: 6411
N.A.I.C.S.: 524210

Aon Parizeau Inc. (2)
700 de la Gauchetiere Suite 1600
Montreal, QC, Canada
Tel.: (514) 842-5000
Fax: (514) 842-3456
Web Site: www.aon.com
Emp.: 180
Risk Management Services
S.I.C.: 6411
N.A.I.C.S.: 524210
Johanne Oepine *(Exec VP)*

Aon Philippines, Inc. (2)
4/F Tower One & Exchange Plaza
Ayala Triangle Ayala Avenue, Makati, 1200, Philippines (100%)
Tel.: (63) 2759 4283
Fax: (63) 2759 4301
Web Site: www.aon.com
Emp.: 106
Insurance Services
S.I.C.: 6351
N.A.I.C.S.: 524126

Aon Polska sp zoo (2)
Al.Jeroz limskie 96
807 Warsaw, Poland
Tel.: (48) 228509700
Fax: (48) 850229705
E-Mail: aon@aon.pl
Web Site: www.aon.com
Emp.: 20
Risk Management Services
S.I.C.: 6411
N.A.I.C.S.: 524210
Slawomir Bany *(CEO)*

Aon Private Consulting A/S (2)
Strandgade 4C
Copenhagen, 1401, Denmark
Tel.: (45) 70257026
Fax: (45) 70273745
E-Mail: aonpc@aon.dk
Web Site: www.aon.com
Emp.: 15
Pension Saving Services
S.I.C.: 6411
N.A.I.C.S.: 524210
Peter Lindblad *(Mgr)*

Aon Qatar LLC (2)
2nd Floor Office 1 Tatweer Tower West Bay
Doha, Qatar
Tel.: (974) 44213000
Fax: (974) 44213111
E-Mail: aon@qatar.net.qa
Web Site: www.aon.com
Emp.: 5
Insurance Brokerage Services
S.I.C.: 6411
N.A.I.C.S.: 524210
Abdulla Alrayes *(CEO)*

Aon Re Middle East WLL (2)
Impact House Office 41 4th Fl Bldg No 662 Rd 2811 Al Seef District 428
Manama, 30125, Bahrain
Tel.: (973) 17226066
Fax: (973) 17225299
E-Mail: teresita.habib@aon.com.bh
Web Site: www.aon.com
Risk Management Services
S.I.C.: 6411
N.A.I.C.S.: 524210

Aon Re Switzerland (2)
Elisabethenstrasse 15
Basel, 4010, Switzerland
Tel.: (41) 612060606
Fax: (41) 612060699
Web Site: www.aon.com
Emp.: 2
Risk Management Services
S.I.C.: 6411
N.A.I.C.S.: 524210
Markus Hauswirdh *(Gen Mgr)*

Aon Risk Services Australia Ltd. (2)
Level 33 201 Kent Street
Sydney, NSW, 2600, Australia
Tel.: (61) 292537000
Fax: (61) 292537001
E-Mail: au.interactive@aon.com
Web Site: www.aon.com.au
Emp.: 10
Risk Management Services
S.I.C.: 6411
N.A.I.C.S.: 524210
Ronald Friedreich *(Mng Dir)*

Aon Risk Services (Chile) SA (2)
Hendaya 60 Of 602
Las Condes, Santiago, Chile
Tel.: (56) 23365584
Web Site: www.aon.com
Emp.: 125
Risk Management Services
S.I.C.: 6411
N.A.I.C.S.: 524210
Carlos Bello *(COO)*

Aon Risk Services Taiwan Ltd. (2)
9/F No 136 Lotus Building Jen Ai Rd Sec 3
Taipei, Taiwan
Tel.: (886) 223252221
Fax: (886) 223252278
Web Site: www.aon.com
Emp.: 130
Risk Management Services
S.I.C.: 6411
N.A.I.C.S.: 524210
WY C Wei *(Gen Mgr)*

Aon Risk Services (Thailand) Ltd. (2)
18th Floor Siam Tower Building 989 Rama I Road Patumwan
Bangkok, 10330, Thailand
Tel.: (66) 23054555
Fax: (66) 26580175
Risk Management Services
S.I.C.: 6411
N.A.I.C.S.: 524210

Aon Romania Broker de Asigurare - re asigurare SRL (2)
Victoria Center Calea Victoriei 145 7th Floor
Bucharest, 10072, Romania
Tel.: (40) 212125816
Fax: (40) 213155758
Risk Management Services
S.I.C.: 6411
N.A.I.C.S.: 524210
Valentin Tuca *(CEO)*

Aon Rus Insurance Brokers LLC (2)
Moika River Emb 42A Of 28N
Saint Petersburg, 191186, Russia
Tel.: (7) 8125711594
Fax: (7) 8125704386
Risk Management Services
S.I.C.: 6411
N.A.I.C.S.: 524210

Aon Sweden AB (2)
Primusgatan 20
Box 12820
Stockholm, 112 97, Sweden
Tel.: (46) 86974000
Fax: (46) 86974040
Web Site: www.aon.com
Risk Management Services
S.I.C.: 6411
N.A.I.C.S.: 524210
Jacob Schlawitz *(Gen Mgr)*

Aon Taiwan Ltd. (2)
Rm 902 9f 136 Jen Ai Rd Sec 3
Taipei, 10657, Taiwan
Tel.: (886) 223252221
Fax: (886) 223252278
Risk Management Services
S.I.C.: 6411
N.A.I.C.S.: 524210

Aon Tanzania Ltd. (2)
488 Haile Selassie Rd Msasani Peninsula
PO Box 9232
Dar es Salaam, Tanzania
Tel.: (255) 222602441
Fax: (255) 222601910
E-Mail: aon_tanzania@aon.co.tz
Web Site: www.aon.com
Risk Management Services
S.I.C.: 6411
N.A.I.C.S.: 524210
Khamis Sulaiman *(Gen Mgr)*

Aon (Thailand) Ltd. (2)
18th Floor Siam Tower Building 989 Rama I Road Patumwan
Bangkok, 10330, Thailand

Tel.: (66) 23054555
Fax: (66) 26580173
Risk Management Services
S.I.C.: 6411
N.A.I.C.S.: 524210

Aon Turner Reinsurance Services SA (2)
7 Granikou Street
151 25 Athens, Greece
Tel.: (30) 2106386700
Fax: (30) 2106386790
Risk Management Services
S.I.C.: 6411
N.A.I.C.S.: 524210

Aon UK Limited (2)
8 Devonshire Square
London, EC2M 4PL, United Kingdom UK
Tel.: (44) 20 7623 5500
Fax: (44) 20 7621 1511
Web Site: www.aon.co.uk
Risk Management & Insurance Brokerage Services
S.I.C.: 6411
N.A.I.C.S.: 524210

Non-U.S. Subsidiary:

Aon Insurance Managers (Guernsey) Ltd. (3)
Maison Trinity Square
Saint Peter Port, GY1 4AT, Guernsey (100%)
Tel.: (44) 1481707909
Fax: (44) 1481710551
Web Site: www.aon.com
Sales Range: $25-49.9 Million
Emp.: 65
Captive Management
S.I.C.: 4959
N.A.I.C.S.: 562998

Aon Vietnam Limited (2)
14/F Vietcombank Tower 198 Tran Quang Khai Street
Hoan Kiem, Hanoi, Vietnam
Tel.: (84) 438260832
Fax: (84) 438243983
Risk Management Services
S.I.C.: 6411
N.A.I.C.S.: 524210

Aon Zambia Ltd (2)
No 8 11th Avenue Nkana West
Kitwe, Zambia
Tel.: (260) 212230355
Fax: (260) 212230520
Web Site: www.aon.com
Emp.: 10
Risk Management Services
S.I.C.: 6411
N.A.I.C.S.: 524210
Zava Shoko *(Branch Mgr)*

Groupe-Conseil Aon Inc. (2)
2600 Boul Laurier 750
Sainte-Foy, QC, G1V 4W2, Canada
Tel.: (418) 650-1119
Fax: (418) 650-1440
Risk Management Services
S.I.C.: 6411
N.A.I.C.S.: 524210

Hewitt Associates Korea Yuhan Hoesa (2)
Gwanghwamun Building 211 Sejongno Jongno-ku
Seoul, 110-730, Korea (South)
Tel.: (82) 23993600
Fax: (82) 23993636
Risk Management Services
S.I.C.: 6411
N.A.I.C.S.: 524210

K&K Insurance Brokers, Inc. Canada (2)
5800 Explorer Dr Ste 101
Mississauga, ON, L4W 5K9, Canada ON (100%)
Tel.: (905) 602-9339
Fax: (905) 602-9141
E-Mail: kk_canada@kandkcanada.com
Web Site: www.kandkcanada.com
Sales Range: Less than $1 Million
Emp.: 10
Insurance Agents & Brokers
S.I.C.: 6411
N.A.I.C.S.: 524298
Tom Butler *(VP & Gen Mgr)*

Minet Inc. (2)
700 Rue De La Gauchetiere O
Montreal, QC, H3B 0A7, Canada
Tel.: (514) 288-2273
Fax: (514) 982-5175
Emp.: 30
Risk Management Services
S.I.C.: 6411
N.A.I.C.S.: 524210
Christopher Mathews *(VP & Principal)*

PT Aon Indonesia (2)
Menara Sudirman 3rd FloorJl Jend Sudirman Kav 60
Jakarta, Indonesia
Tel.: (62) 215220123
Fax: (62) 215220111
Risk Management Services
S.I.C.: 6411
N.A.I.C.S.: 524210

AONIX S.A.

Batiment B 66/68 Ave Pierre Brossolette
92247 Malakoff, Cedex, France
Tel.: (33) 141481000
Fax: (33) 141481020
E-Mail: info@aonix.fr
Web Site: www.aonix.fr
Emp.: 60

Business Description:
Software Developer
S.I.C.: 3652
N.A.I.C.S.: 334614

U.S. Subsidiary:

Aonix North America Inc. (1)
5930 Cornerstone Ct W Ste 250
San Diego, CA 92121
Tel.: (858) 457-2700
Fax: (858) 824-0212
Toll Free: (800) 97-AONIX
E-Mail: info@aonix.com
Web Site: www.aonix.com
Emp.: 35
Software Developer
S.I.C.: 3652
N.A.I.C.S.: 334614
Shawn Fanning *(Dir-Ops)*

AORTECH INTERNATIONAL PLC

Level Two Springfield House 23 Oatlands Drive
Weybridge, Surrey, KT13 9LZ, United Kingdom
Tel.: (44) 8708508286
Fax: (44) 2083993897
E-Mail: info@aortech.com
Web Site: www.aortech.com
AOR—(LSE)
Rev.: $3,795,000
Assets: $4,651,000
Liabilities: $540,000
Net Worth: $4,111,000
Earnings: ($847,000)
Emp.: 18
Fiscal Year-end: 03/31/13

Business Description:
Polyurethane Mfr
S.I.C.: 3086
N.A.I.C.S.: 326150

Personnel:
Frank Maguire *(CEO)*
David Parsons *(Sec)*

Board of Directors:
William Donald Brown
Frank Maguire
Edward McDaid
Roy Walter Mitchell
Gordon Wright

Legal Counsel:
Brodies LLP
2 Blythswood Square
Glasgow, United Kingdom

THE AOT GROUP PTY. LTD.

Level 8 420 Saint Kilda Rd
Melbourne, VIC, 3004, Australia
Tel.: (61) 398677233
Fax: (61) 398677244
Web Site: www.aot.com.au
Year Founded: 1987
Emp.: 100

Business Description:
Holding Company; Tour Operator & Travel Services
S.I.C.: 6719
N.A.I.C.S.: 551112

Personnel:
Andrew Burnes *(Founder, Co-Owner, CEO & Chm-Exec Bd)*
Cinzia Burnes *(Co-Owner & Mng Dir-AOT Inbound)*
Des Fielding *(Grp CFO)*

Subsidiary:

Australian Online Travel Pty. Ltd. (1)
Level 4 18-22 Pitt St
Circular Quay, Sydney, NSW, 2000, Australia AU
Tel.: (61) 282482350
Fax: (61) 292517568
E-Mail: mark.campbell@aot.com.au
Web Site: www.aot.com.au
Travel Arrangement Services
S.I.C.: 4729
N.A.I.C.S.: 561599
Russell Farr *(Mng Dir)*

Division:

Travelmate.com.au Pty. Ltd. (2)
Level 4 18-22 Pitt Street
Circular Quay, Sydney, NSW, 2000, Australia
Tel.: (61) 282482350
Fax: (61) 292517568
Web Site: www.travelmate.com.au
Travel Agencies
S.I.C.: 4724
N.A.I.C.S.: 561510
Des King *(Mng Dir)*

AOYAMA TRADING CO. LTD.

3-5 Ohji-cho 1-chome
Fukuyama, Hiroshima, 721-8556, Japan
Tel.: (81) 849200025
Web Site: www.aoyama-syouji.co.jp
8219—(TKS)
Sls.: $2,336,400,000
Assets: $3,788,103,000
Liabilities: $1,147,806,000
Net Worth: $2,640,297,000
Earnings: $138,831,000
Emp.: 3,493
Fiscal Year-end: 03/31/13

Business Description:
Men's Apparel Sales
S.I.C.: 2389
N.A.I.C.S.: 315210

Personnel:
Shozo Miyamae *(Chm)*
Hiroaki Miyamae *(Vice Chm)*
Osamu Aoyama *(Pres & CEO)*

Board of Directors:
Shozo Miyamae
Osamu Aoyama
Yoshiyuki Matsukawa
Hiroaki Miyamae
Makoto Miyatake
Shinji Okano
Seishi Uchibayashi

Transfer Agent:
Sumitomo Mitsui Trust Bank Limited
5-33 Kitahama 4-chome Chuo-ku
Osaka, 5400041, Japan

AOYAMA ZAISAN NETWORKS CO., LTD.

18F Shinjuku NS Bldg
2 4 1 Nishishinjuku
Shinjuku ku, 1630818 Tokyo, Japan
Tel.: (81) 53217020
Web Site:
8929—(TKS)
Sales Range: $50-74.9 Million
Emp.: 766

Business Description:
Asset Consulting & Management Services
S.I.C.: 8742
N.A.I.C.S.: 541611

Personnel:
Hideo Murakami *(Chm)*
Masazumi Hasumi *(Pres & CEO)*
Hisao Nakatsuka *(Mng Dir)*

AP COMPANY

18F, Akasaka Twin Tower East Wing
2-17-22 Akasaka
Minato-ku, Tokyo, 107-0052, Japan
Tel.: (81) 3 6277 8738
Fax: (81) 362778754
Web Site: www.apcompany.jp
3175—(TKS)
Sls.: $125,257,000
Assets: $81,884,000
Liabilities: $61,644,000
Net Worth: $20,240,000
Earnings: $4,730,000
Emp.: 411
Fiscal Year-end: 03/31/13

Business Description:
Chicken & Fish Production & Distribution
S.I.C.: 5146
N.A.I.C.S.: 424460

Personnel:
Hisashi Yoneyama *(Pres & CEO)*

Board of Directors:
Yuji Kawamata
Nobutaka Ohkubo
Junko Satomi
Hisashi Yoneyama
Katsumi Yoshino

A.P. EAGERS LIMITED

80 McLachlan Street
PO Box 199
Fortitude Valley, Brisbane, QLD, 4006, Australia
Tel.: (61) 7 3248 9455
Fax: (61) 7 3248 9459
E-Mail: corporate@apeagers.com.au
Web Site: www.apeagers.com.au
APE—(ASX)
Rev.: $2,753,785,724
Assets: $1,227,675,084
Liabilities: $739,413,718
Net Worth: $488,261,366
Earnings: $57,889,697
Emp.: 3,000
Fiscal Year-end: 12/31/12

Business Description:
Motor Vehicle Retailer
S.I.C.: 5012
N.A.I.C.S.: 423110

Personnel:
Martin Andrew Ward *(CEO & Mng Dir)*
Stephen Graham Best *(CFO)*
Denis Gerard Stark *(Gen Counsel & Sec)*

Board of Directors:
Timothy Boyd Crommelin
David Arthur Cowper
Peter William Henley
Nicholas George Politis
Daniel Thomas Ryan
Martin Andrew Ward

Legal Counsel:
Herbert Geer
Level 26 240 Queen Street
Brisbane, QLD, 4000, Australia

Subsidiaries:

Adtrans Group Ltd. (1)
4 Greenhill Road
1st Fl, Wayville, SA, 5034, Australia
Tel.: (61) 883731991

A.P. Eagers Limited—(Continued)

Fax: (61) 8 8373 3712
E-Mail: corporate@adtransgroup.com.au
Web Site: www.adtrans.com.au
Sales Range: $600-649.9 Million
Emp.: 837
Motor Vehicles & Trucks Retailer
S.I.C.: 5511
N.A.I.C.S.: 441110
Shaun A. Swift *(Mng Dir)*
Teresa J. Colliver *(Sec)*

Subsidiaries:

Adtrans Australia Pty Ltd (2)
198 Whitehall St
Footscray, VIC, 3011, Australia
Tel.: (61) 396877244
Fax: (61) 396877278
Web Site: www.whitehorsetruckandbus.com.au
Emp.: 30
Truck Repair & Maintenance Services
S.I.C.: 7549
N.A.I.C.S.: 811198
Steve Evans *(Branch Mgr)*

Adtrans Automotive Group Pty. Ltd. (2)
28-30 Tikalara St
5010 Regents Park, SA, Australia (100%)
Tel.: (61) 883731991
Fax: (61) 883733712
Emp.: 100
Used Car Dealers
S.I.C.: 5521
N.A.I.C.S.: 441120
Shaun A. Swist *(Mng Dir)*

Adtrans Corporate Pty. Ltd. (2)
4 Greenhill Rd
Wayville, SA, Australia (100%)
Tel.: (61) 883731991
Fax: (61) 883733712
E-Mail: corporate@adtransgroup.com.au
Web Site: www.adtrans.com.au
Emp.: 14
Used Car Dealers
S.I.C.: 5521
N.A.I.C.S.: 441120
Shaun A. Swist *(Mng Dir)*

Adtrans Hino Pty Ltd (2)
253-259 Coward St
Mascot, NSW, 2020, Australia
Tel.: (61) 2 9598 9444
Fax: (61) 2 9598 9477
E-Mail: enquiries@adtranshino.com.au
Web Site: www.adtranshino.com.au
New & Used Truck Distr
S.I.C.: 5012
N.A.I.C.S.: 423110
Jeff Morgan *(Gen Mgr)*

Adtrans Truck Centre Pty. Ltd. (2)
4 Greenhill Rd level 1
5034 Wayville, SA, Australia (100%)
Tel.: (61) 883731991
Fax: (61) 0883731989
Web Site: www.adtransgroup.com.au
Emp.: 900
Automobile & Motor Vehicle Whslr
S.I.C.: 5012
N.A.I.C.S.: 423110
Shaun A. Swist *(Mng Dir)*

Adtrans Used Cars Pty. Ltd. (2)
1115 South Road
5042 Saint Marys, SA, Australia (100%)
Tel.: (61) 882763333
Fax: (61) 82764343
Web Site: www.adtrans.com.au
Emp.: 7
Used Car Dealers
S.I.C.: 5521
N.A.I.C.S.: 441120
David Pallant *(Mgr)*

Graham Cornes Motors Pty. Ltd. (2)
46 Belair Road
Hawthorn, SA, Australia (90%)
Tel.: (61) 882721488
Fax: (61) 883731989
Web Site: www.adtrans.com.au
Emp.: 70
Used Car Dealers
S.I.C.: 5521
N.A.I.C.S.: 441120
Graeme D. Bignell *(Chm)*

Stillwell Trucks Pty Ltd (2)
20 Ashford Avenue
Milperra, NSW, 2214, Australia
Tel.: (61) 29748500
Fax: (61) 297742379
E-Mail: trucks@stillwelltrucks.com.au
Web Site: www.stillwelltrucks.com.au
Sales Range: $25-49.9 Million
Emp.: 100
Truck Retailer
S.I.C.: 5599
N.A.I.C.S.: 441228
Henry Eggers *(Mng Dir)*

Whitehorse Trucks Pty Ltd (2)
67 75 Princess Highway
VIC, Dandenong, SA, 3175, Australia
Tel.: (61) 397916533
Fax: (61) 397913077
E-Mail: whitehorse@whitehorsetrucks.com.au
Web Site: www.whitehorsetrucks.com.au
Emp.: 100
Truck Retailer
S.I.C.: 5571
N.A.I.C.S.: 441228
David McQueen *(Mgr-Fin)*

Adtrans Trucks Pty Ltd (1)
Cnr Raymond & Boundary Rds
Laverton North, Melbourne, VIC, 3026, Australia
Tel.: (61) 3 9360 9922
Fax: (61) 3 9360 9363
E-Mail: adetrad@adtranstrucks.com.au
Web Site: www.adtranstrucks.com.au
Emp.: 6
Truck Repair & Maintenance Services
S.I.C.: 7539
N.A.I.C.S.: 811198
Marcus Prato *(Gen Mgr)*

A.P. Ford Pty Ltd (1)
80 Mclachlan St
Fortitude Valley, QLD, 4006, Australia
Tel.: (61) 732489455
Fax: (61) 732489459
E-Mail: corporate@apeagers.com.au
Emp.: 15
Automotive Spare Parts Distr
S.I.C.: 5013
N.A.I.C.S.: 423120
Martin Ward *(CEO)*

A.P. Motors (No.2) Pty Ltd (1)
692 Curtin Ave East Eagle Farm
Brisbane, QLD, 4009, Australia
Tel.: (61) 732602722
Fax: (61) 732602733
Motor Vehicle Spare Parts Distr
S.I.C.: 5013
N.A.I.C.S.: 423120

A.P. Motors (No.3) Pty Ltd (1)
314 Gympie Rd
Strathpine, QLD, 4500, Australia
Tel.: (61) 732054244
Fax: (61) 732489459
Automotive Spare Parts Distr
S.I.C.: 5013
N.A.I.C.S.: 423120

Austral Pty Ltd (1)
80 Mclachlan St
Fortitude Valley, QLD, 4006, Australia
Tel.: (61) 732489455
Fax: (61) 732489459
Motor Vehicle Spare Parts Distr
S.I.C.: 5013
N.A.I.C.S.: 423120

Bill Buckle Autos Pty Ltd (1)
571 Pittwater Rd
Brookvale, NSW, 2100, Australia
Tel.: (61) 299382255
Fax: (61) 299386686
E-Mail: service@billbuckle.com.au
Web Site: www.billbuckle.com.au
Emp.: 14
Automotive Spare Parts Distr
S.I.C.: 5013
N.A.I.C.S.: 423120
Michael Beris *(Gen Mgr)*

Bill Buckle Holdings Pty Ltd (1)
Cnr Pittwater & Harbord Rds
Brookvale, NSW, 2100, Australia
Tel.: (61) 299397766
Fax: (61) 299396868
Motor Vehicle Spare Parts Distr
S.I.C.: 5013
N.A.I.C.S.: 423120

Bill Buckle Leasing Pty Ltd (1)
59 Whiting St
Artarmon, NSW, 2064, Australia
Tel.: (61) 732489455
Motor Vehicle Spare Parts Distr
S.I.C.: 5013
N.A.I.C.S.: 423120

City Automotive Group Pty Ltd (1)
Corner Breakfast Creek Rd Evelyn St
Newstead, 4006, Australia
Tel.: (61) 730007777
Fax: (61) 730007788
Web Site: www.city-automotive.com.au
Automotive Spare Parts Diistr
S.I.C.: 5013
N.A.I.C.S.: 423120

Eagers Nominees Pty Ltd (1)
80 Mclachlan St
Fortitude Valley, QLD, 4006, Australia
Tel.: (61) 732489400
Automotive Dealers
S.I.C.: 5511
N.A.I.C.S.: 441110

Eagers Retail Pty Ltd (1)
143 Newmarket Rd
Windsor, QLD, 4030, Australia
Tel.: (61) 733641199
Fax: (61) 731096750
E-Mail: admin@eagers.com
Web Site: www.eagers.com
Emp.: 15
Motor Vehicle Spare Parts Distr
S.I.C.: 5013
N.A.I.C.S.: 423120
Akos Horvath *(Gen Mgr)*

A.P. MOLLER-MAERSK A/S

Esplanaden 50
1098 Copenhagen, K, Denmark
Tel.: (45) 3363 3363
Fax: (45) 3363 4108
E-Mail: cphcorpir@maersk.com
Web Site: www.maersk.com
Year Founded: 1904
MAERSKB—(CSE OTC)
Rev.: $61,693,580,880
Assets: $75,875,828,760
Liabilities: $35,737,792,920
Net Worth: $40,138,035,840
Earnings: $4,219,522,200
Emp.: 121,105
Fiscal Year-end: 12/31/12

Business Description:
Holding Company; Cargo Transportation, Oil Production & Shipbuilding
S.I.C.: 6719
N.A.I.C.S.: 551112

Personnel:
Michael Pram Rasmussen *(Chm)*
Niels Jacobsen *(Vice Chm)*
Ane Maersk Mc-Kinney Uggla *(Vice Chm)*
Nils Smedegaard Andersen *(Grp CEO)*
Trond O. Westlie *(CFO & Member-Exec Bd)*
Stephanie Fell *(IR Officer)*
Johan Mortensen *(Sr IR Officer)*
Kim Fejfer *(CEO-APM Terminals & Member-Exec Bd)*
Claus V. Hemmingsen *(CEO-Maersk Drilling & Member-Exec Bd)*
Soren Skou *(CEO-Maersk Line & Member-Exec Bd)*
Jakob Thomasen *(CEO-Maersk Oil & Member-Exec Bd)*

Board of Directors:
Michael Pram Rasmussen
John Reginald Hartnell Bond
Niels Jacobsen
Arne Karlsson
Jan Leschly
Leise Maersk Mc-Kinney Moller
Lars Pallesen
John Axel Poulsen
Erik Rasmussen
Robert J. Routs, III
Jan Topholm
Ane Maersk Mc-Kinney Uggla

KPMG
Copenhagen, Denmark

Division:

Maersk Line Agency Holding A/S (1)
Esplanaden 50
DK-1098 Copenhagen, Denmark DK
Tel.: (45) 33633363
Fax: (45) 33634108
Web Site: www.maerskline.com
Sales Range: $25-49.9 Billion
Emp.: 17,000
Holding Company; Marine Freight Shipping Services
S.I.C.: 6719
N.A.I.C.S.: 551112
Soren Skou *(CEO)*
Jakob Stausholm *(CFO)*
Stephen Richard Schueler *(Chief Comml Officer)*
Morten Engelstoft *(CEO-Svcs & Other Shipping Segment)*
Lars Reno Jakobsen *(Member-Mgmt Bd & Head-Network & Product)*
Peter S. Linnemann *(Head-HR & Member-Mgmt Bd)*

Subsidiaries:

APM Terminals - Cargo Service A/S (1)
Osthavnsvej 43
Box 165
8100 Arhus, Denmark
Tel.: (45) 8934 8800
Fax: (45) 8934 8882
E-Mail: planner@apmterminals.com
Emp.: 30
Marine Cargo Handling Services
S.I.C.: 4491
N.A.I.C.S.: 488320
Johan Uggla *(Mng Dir)*

Damco A/S (1)
Sletvej 2e
8310 Tranbjerg, Denmark
Tel.: (45) 89316600
Fax: (45) 89316660
Freight Forwarding Services
S.I.C.: 4731
N.A.I.C.S.: 488510
Hanne Birgitte Breinbjerg Sorensen *(CEO)*
Tommy Molgaard *(Global CFO)*
Helmut Kaspers *(Chief Comml Officer-West Europe)*

Damco International A/S (1)
Dampfaergevej 21
DK 2100 Copenhagen, Denmark (100%)
Tel.: (45) 33635600
Fax: (45) 33635541
Web Site: www.damco.com
Sales Range: $1-9.9 Million
Emp.: 10,000
Freight Transportation & Storage Services
S.I.C.: 4731
N.A.I.C.S.: 488510
Rolf Habben-Jansen *(CEO)*

U.S. Subsidiaries:

Damco Customs Services, Inc. (2)
3100 Broadway Ste 300
Kansas City, MO 64111
Tel.: (816) 221-6800
Fax: (816) 960-3721
Web Site: www.damco.com
Sales Range: $10-24.9 Million
Emp.: 40
Customs House Brokers
S.I.C.: 4731
N.A.I.C.S.: 488510
Brenda Merrick *(Office Mgr)*

Damco USA Inc. (2)
Giralda Farms Madison Ave Bldg 2
Madison, NJ 07940
Tel.: (973) 514-2076
Fax: (973) 514-5227
E-Mail: info@damco.com
Logistics Consulting Services
S.I.C.: 4731
N.A.I.C.S.: 541614

Anthony A. Chiarello *(Pres)*
Samuel Israel *(CEO-Latin America)*

Danbor Service AS (1)
Kanalen 1
6700 Esbjerg, Denmark (100%)
Tel.: (45) 79111900
Fax: (45) 79111901
E-Mail: danbor@danbor.dk
Web Site: www.danbor.dk
Rev.: $3,279,080
Emp.: 120
Logistics & Transportation Services
S.I.C.: 4731
N.A.I.C.S.: 488510
Soeren Floe Knudsen *(CEO)*
Johnnie La Fontaine *(COO & Dir-Sls)*

Dansk Industri Syndikat A/S (1)
Hojager 8
2730 Tastrup, Denmark
Tel.: (45) 44505050
Fax: (45) 44945225
E-Mail: disa.industries@disagroup.com
Web Site: www.disagroup.com
Emp.: 2,600
Industrial Foundry Equipment
Import Export
S.I.C.: 5084
N.A.I.C.S.: 423830
Peter Holm Larsen *(Pres & COO)*
Rob Joyce *(CEO)*
Anders Dommerby Kristensen *(CFO & Exec VP)*
Bo Bugge *(CIO)*
Erich Brunner *(Exec VP)*

U.S. Subsidiary:

DISA Goff Inc. (2)
PO Box 1607
Seminole, OK 74818-1607
Tel.: (405) 382-6900
Fax: (405) 382-7013
Web Site: www.goff-inc.com
Emp.: 100
Plastics Product Manufacturing
S.I.C.: 3089
N.A.I.C.S.: 326199

Non-U.S. Subsidiary:

DISA Industrie AG (2)
Solenbergstrasse 5
Schaffhausen, 8207, Switzerland (100%)
Tel.: (41) 526311717
Fax: (41) 526314858
E-Mail: info@disagroup.com
Web Site: www.disagroup.com
Sls.: $39,755,296
Emp.: 200
Mfr. of Foundry Systems; Joint Venture of A.P. Moller Group & Georg Fischer AG
S.I.C.: 3499
N.A.I.C.S.: 332999
Erich Brunner *(Exec VP)*

Dansk Supermarked A/S (1)
Bjodstrupvej 18
D-8270 Hojbjerg, Denmark (68%)
Tel.: (45) 89303030
Fax: (45) 86276563
E-Mail: henrik.kirkeperp@dsg.dk
Web Site: www.dsg.dk
Sls.: $7,800,000,000
Emp.: 21,600
Retail Supermarket Chain
S.I.C.: 5411
N.A.I.C.S.: 445110
Erling Jensen *(CEO)*
Chris Nicholas *(CFO)*

Lindo Industripark A/S (1)
Kystvejen 100
5330 Munkebo, Denmark
Tel.: (45) 30 10 77 10
E-Mail: contact@lindo-industripark.dk
Web Site: www.lindo-industripark.dk
Storage & Transportation Services
S.I.C.: 4225
N.A.I.C.S.: 493110
Lars-Erik Brenoe *(Chm)*
Michael Nymark Hansen *(Sr VP)*

Maersk A/S (1)
Esplanaden 50
1098 Copenhagen, Denmark
Tel.: (45) 3363 3363
Fax: (45) 3363 4108
Emp.: 1,500
Container Terminal Operating Services
S.I.C.: 4226
N.A.I.C.S.: 493190
Nils Smedegaard *(CEO)*

Maersk Container Industri AS (1)
Bjerndrupvej 47
DK 6360 Tinglev, Denmark (100%)
Tel.: (45) 73643400
Fax: (45) 736434569
E-Mail: mci@maerskbox.com
Web Site: www.maerskbox.com
Emp.: 65
Mfr. of Intermodal Dry Cargo & Reefer Containers
S.I.C.: 3499
N.A.I.C.S.: 332439
Peter Nyman *(Gen Mgr)*

Maersk Drilling (1)
50 Esplanaden
1098 Copenhagen, Denmark (100%)
Tel.: (45) 33633363
Fax: (45) 33633182
Web Site: www.maersk-drilling.com
Emp.: 3,200
Drilling & Production of Oil & Gas
S.I.C.: 1311
N.A.I.C.S.: 211111
Claus V. Hemmingsen *(CEO)*
Martin Fruergaard *(Chief Comml Officer)*

Non-U.S. Subsidiary:

Maersk Drilling Norge AS (2)
Christian August Thorings Veg 9
PO Box 134
Forus, 4065 Stavanger, Norway
Tel.: (47) 5201 7000
Fax: (47) 5201 7001
Oil & Gas Wells Drilling Services
S.I.C.: 1381
N.A.I.C.S.: 213111
Jakob Korsgaard *(Mng Dir)*

Maersk FPSOs A/S (1)
Esplanaden 50
1098 Copenhagen, Denmark
Tel.: (45) 3363 3363
Fax: (45) 3363 3182
Web Site: www.maersk-fpsos.com
Emp.: 60
Oil & Gas Exploration Services
S.I.C.: 1389
N.A.I.C.S.: 213112
Stig Hoffmeyer *(CEO & Chief Comml Officer)*
David McLean *(COO)*
Birgitte Brinch Madsen *(CTO)*

Maersk FPSOs Australia A/S (1)
Esplanaden 50
1263 Copenhagen, Denmark
Tel.: (45) 33633363
Web Site: www.maersk-fpsos.com
Oil & Gas Exploration Services
S.I.C.: 1389
N.A.I.C.S.: 213112
Jakob Thomasen *(CEO-Maersk Oil)*

Maersk Oil (1)
Esplanaden 50
1263 Copenhagen, Denmark
Tel.: (45) 33 63 40 00
E-Mail:
Web Site: www.maerskoil.com
Oil & Gas Exploration Services
S.I.C.: 1389
N.A.I.C.S.: 213112
Jakob Thomasen *(Chm & CEO)*
Kevin Manser *(COO)*

U.S. Subsidiary:

Maersk Oil America Inc (2)
2500 City W Blvd Ste 100
Houston, TX 77042
Tel.: (713) 346-5800
Oil Wells Drilling Services
S.I.C.: 3291
N.A.I.C.S.: 327910
Bruce Laws *(Pres)*

Non-U.S. Subsidiary:

Maersk FPSOs UK Ltd (2)
City Wharf Shiprow
Aberdeen, AB11 5BY, United Kingdom
Tel.: (44) 1224 243100
Fax: (44) 1224 59245
Emp.: 8
Freight Transportation Services
S.I.C.: 4412
N.A.I.C.S.: 483111
David Cannon *(Gen Mgr)*

Maersk Olie og Gas AS (1)
Esplanade 50
1263 Copenhagen, Denmark (100%)
Tel.: (45) 33634000
Fax: (45) 33633806
E-Mail: cphinfo@maersk.com
Web Site: www.maersk.com
Emp.: 500
Exploration & Production of Oil & Gas
S.I.C.: 1311
N.A.I.C.S.: 211111
Mills S. Andersen *(Chm)*

Maersk Supply Service (1)
Esplanaden 50
DK 1098 Copenhagen, Denmark (100%)
Tel.: (45) 33633363
Fax: (45) 33633353
E-Mail: cphsupply@maersk.com
Web Site: www.maersksupplyservice.com
Emp.: 200
Transportation of Equipment to Offshore Platforms & Drilling Rigs
S.I.C.: 4449
N.A.I.C.S.: 483211
Carsten Plougmann Andersen *(CEO)*
Nils S. Andersen *(Mng Dir)*

Maersk Tankers (1)
Esplanaden 50
DK 1098 Copenhagen, Denmark (100%)
Tel.: (45) 33633363
Fax: (45) 33634878
E-Mail: cphtank@maersk.com
Web Site: www.maersktankers.com
Emp.: 160
Oil & Natural Gas Transport Services
S.I.C.: 4731
N.A.I.C.S.: 488510
Henrik Kvist-Jacobsen *(CFO)*
Henrik Ramskov *(COO)*
Klaus Rud Sejling *(Chief Comml Officer)*

Odense Steel Shipyard Ltd. (1)
Lintoealleen 150
PO Box 176
5100 Odense, Denmark (100%)
Tel.: (45) 63971234
Fax: (45) 63972345
E-Mail: info@oss.dk
Web Site: www.oss.dk
Emp.: 2,000
Shipyard
S.I.C.: 3731
N.A.I.C.S.: 336611
Peter Jann Nielsen *(Mng Dir)*

Rederiet A.P. Moller A/S (1)
Esplanaden 50
1263 Copenhagen, Denmark
Tel.: (45) 33 63 33 63
Shipping Transportation Services
S.I.C.: 4412
N.A.I.C.S.: 483111

SVITZER A/S (1)
Pakhus 48 Sundkaj 9
2100 Copenhagen, Denmark (100%)
Tel.: (45) 39193919
Fax: (45) 39193909
E-Mail: info@svitzer.com
Web Site: www.svitzer.com
Emp.: 40
Marine Towage, Salvage & Offshore Services
S.I.C.: 4491
N.A.I.C.S.: 488310
Robert Uggla *(CEO)*

Non-U.S. Subsidiary:

SVITZER Australasia (2)
Level 23 201 Elizabeth St
Sydney, NSW, 2000, Australia AU
Tel.: (61) 293699200
Fax: (61) 293699288
E-Mail: gm.hrTony.wilkes@svitzer.com
Web Site: www.svitzer.com
Sales Range: $250-299.9 Million
Emp.: 26
Marine Towage, Salvage & Offshore Services
S.I.C.: 4491
N.A.I.C.S.: 488310
Mark Malone *(Mng Dir)*
Alan Bradley *(Chief Comml Officer)*

U.S. Subsidiaries:

Maersk Drilling USA Inc. (1)
2500 City W Blvd Ste 1850
Houston, TX 77042
Tel.: (713) 346-4300
Fax: (713) 783-9409
Web Site: www.maerskdrilling.com
Oil & Gas Well Drilling Services
S.I.C.: 1381
N.A.I.C.S.: 213111
Lars Kasueske *(Reg Mgr)*

Maersk Inc. (1)
2 Giralda Farms Madison Ave
Madison, NJ 07940 DE
Mailing Address: (100%)
PO Box 880
Madison, NJ 07940-0880
Tel.: (973) 514-5000
Fax: (973) 514-5410
Toll Free: (800) 321-8807
E-Mail: grf@maersk.com
Web Site: www.maersk.com
Emp.: 750
Sea & Land Transporter Containerized Cargo
S.I.C.: 4731
N.A.I.C.S.: 488510
J. Russell Bruner *(Chm)*
John Boudreau *(Pres)*
Morten K. Nicolaisen *(CFO)*
Bob Copaldo *(CIO & VP-Bus Process & Quality)*
Gene Pentimonti *(Sr VP-Govt Affairs)*
William Woodhour *(Sr VP)*

Maersk Line, Limited (1)
1 Commercial Pl Fl 20
Norfolk, VA 23510-2126
Tel.: (757) 857-4800
Fax: (757) 852-3232
Web Site: www.maersklinelimited.com
Marine Shipping Services
S.I.C.: 4499
N.A.I.C.S.: 488390
Steven E. Hadder *(CFO & VP)*
William Kenwell *(Chief Comml Officer & Sr VP)*
Mike Hopkins *(Gen Counsel & Sr VP-Contracts/Procurement)*

Non-U.S. Division:

APM Terminals International B.V. (1)
Anna van Saksenlaan 71
2593 HW Hague, Netherlands
Tel.: (31) 703043100
Fax: (31) 703043199
E-Mail: cenapmtcfo@apmterminals.com
Web Site: www.apmterminals.com
Emp.: 150
Container Terminal Operator
S.I.C.: 4731
N.A.I.C.S.: 488510
Kim Fejfer *(CEO)*
Christian Moller Laursen *(CFO)*
Peder Sondergaard *(Sr VP & Head-New Terminals)*

Subsidiaries:

APM Terminals B.V. (2)
Anna Van Saksenlaan 71
Hague, 2593 HW, Netherlands
Tel.: (31) 703043100
Container Terminal Operating Services
S.I.C.: 4225
N.A.I.C.S.: 493110

APM Terminals Management B.V. (2)
Anna van Saksenlaan 71
2593 HW Hague, Netherlands
Tel.: (31) 70 304 3100
Fax: (31) 703043199
Web Site: www.apmterminals.com
Rev.: $4,682,320,000
Container Terminal Operating Services
S.I.C.: 4226
N.A.I.C.S.: 493190
Kim Fejfer *(CEO)*
Christian Moller Laursen *(CFO & VP)*
Martin Gaard Christiansen *(Chief Comml Officer)*
Henrik L. Pedersen *(CEO-Asia Pacific Reg)*
Peder Sondergaard *(CEO-Africa & Middle East Reg)*

A.P. Moller-Maersk A/S—(Continued)

APM Terminals Rotterdam B.V. (2)
Coloradoweg 50 Port Number 8203
Maasvlakte, 3199 LA Rotterdam, Netherlands
Tel.: (31) 181 372 222
Fax: (31) 181 372 414
E-Mail: rot.marketing@apmterminals.com
Emp.: 750
Container Terminal Operating Services
S.I.C.: 4226
N.A.I.C.S.: 493190
Hans van Kerkhof *(Mng Dir)*

U.S. Subsidiaries:

APM Terminal Pacific Ltd. (2)
1002 Milwaukee Way
Tacoma, WA 98421
Tel.: (253) 680-4439
Fax: (253) 680-4403
Emp.: 33
Freight Transportation Services
S.I.C.: 4731
N.A.I.C.S.: 488510
Kim Fejfer *(CEO)*
Alan McCorkle *(Mng Dir)*
Christian Laursen *(CFO)*
Richard Mitchell *(Chief Comml Officer)*
Eric Sisco *(Pres-Americas)*
Peder Sondergaard *(Sr VP)*

APM Terminals North America, Inc. (2)
6000 Carnegie Blvd
Charlotte, NC 28209
Tel.: (704) 571-2768
Fax: (704) 571-4967
Web Site: www.apmterminals.com
Sales Range: $25-49.9 Million
Emp.: 500
Container Terminal Operator
S.I.C.: 4731
N.A.I.C.S.: 488510
Anthony Scioscia *(Pres & CEO)*
John Loepprich *(CFO & Sr VP)*

Non-U.S. Subsidiaries:

APM Terminals Algeciras S.A. (2)
Muelle Juan Carlos I
PO Box 160
12011 Algeciras, Spain
Tel.: (34) 956 671900
Fax: (34) 956 671907
Web Site: www.apmterminals.com
Emp.: 200
Container Terminal Operating Services
S.I.C.: 4226
N.A.I.C.S.: 493190
Anders Kjeldsen *(Mng Dir)*
Javier Lancha *(CFO)*
Laurids Uglvig *(COO)*

Gujarat Pipavav Port Limited (2)
Pipavav Port At Post Uchchaiya via Rajula District Amreli, Gandhinagar, Gujarat, 365 560, India (57.9%)
Tel.: (91) 2794302400
Fax: (91) 2794302402
Web Site: www.pipavav.com
Emp.: 500
Port Operations
S.I.C.: 4491
N.A.I.C.S.: 488310
Prakash Tulsiani *(Mng Dir)*
Manish Agnihotri *(Sec & Compliance Officer)*

Non-U.S. Subsidiaries:

Addicks & Kreye Container Logistik GmbH & Co (1)
Amerikaring 21
27580 Bremerhaven, Germany
Tel.: (49) 471 98395 0
Fax: (49) 471 98395 49
E-Mail: zentrale@addicks.de
Web Site: www.addicks.de/index_en.html
Logistics Consulting Services
S.I.C.: 4731
N.A.I.C.S.: 541614
Ruediger Rempe *(Mgr)*

Addicks & Kreye Container Service GmbH & Co. KG (1)
Amerikaring 21
27580 Bremerhaven, Germany
Tel.: (49) 471 98395 0
Fax: (49) 471 98395 19
Web Site: www.addicks.de
Container Trucking Services
S.I.C.: 4214
N.A.I.C.S.: 484110
Thomas Woehlken *(Gen Mgr)*

Addicks & Kreye Holding GmbH (1)
Windhukstr 20-26
28237 Bremen, Germany
Tel.: (49) 421 69 435 13
Fax: (49) 421 69 435 10
E-Mail: zentrale@addicks.de
Web Site: www.addicks.de
Emp.: 32
Container Trucking Services
S.I.C.: 4214
N.A.I.C.S.: 484110
Ruediger Rempe *(Mgr)*

Addicks & Tally Union GmbH & Co (1)
Container-Terminal Gatehouse II
27568 Bremerhaven, Germany
Tel.: (49) 471 413065
Fax: (49) 471 4191523
E-Mail: tallyunion@addicks.de
Cargo Handling Services
S.I.C.: 4491
N.A.I.C.S.: 488320
Ruediger Rempe *(Mgr)*

A.P. Moller Singapore Pte. Ltd. (1)
3 Harbourfront Place 13-01 Harbourfront Tower 2
Singapore, 099254, Singapore
Tel.: (65) 6323 8323
Fax: (65) 6223 7191
E-Mail: asishipfin@maersk.com
Web Site: www.apmsingapore.com
Emp.: 3,300
Marine Vessel Services
S.I.C.: 4499
N.A.I.C.S.: 488330
Morten H. Engelstoft *(Chm)*
Thomas Riber Knudsen *(CEO-Asia Pacific Reg)*

APM Terminals Liberia Ltd (1)
Freeport Monrovia Bushrod Island
PO Box 1929
1000 Monrovia, Liberia
Tel.: (231) 880649068
Fax: (231) 77086015
Container Terminal Operating Services
S.I.C.: 4226
N.A.I.C.S.: 493190

APM Terminals North America B.V. (1)
Turfmarkt 107
Hague, 2511 DP, Netherlands
Tel.: (31) 703043100
Fax: (31) 703043199
Container Terminal Operating Services
S.I.C.: 4226
N.A.I.C.S.: 493190
Jim Pfeiffer *(Gen Mgr)*

Brostrom AB (1)
Molndalsvagen 24
412 63 Gothenburg, Sweden
Tel.: (46) 31616100
Fax: (46) 317118030
E-Mail: info@brostrom.se
Web Site: www.brostrom.se
Sales Range: $500-549.9 Million
Emp.: 1,526
Logistic Services
S.I.C.: 4731
N.A.I.C.S.: 541614
Robert Uggla *(Mng Dir)*

Subsidiaries:

Brostrom Holding BV (2)
Molndalsvagen 24
40523 Gothenburg, Sweden (100%)
Tel.: (46) 31616000
Fax: (46) 31616012
E-Mail: brotank@brostrom.se
Web Site: www.brostrom.se
Emp.: 110
Process Physical Distribution & Logistics Consulting Services
S.I.C.: 4731
N.A.I.C.S.: 541614
Robert Uggla *(CEO)*

Brostrom Tankers AB (2)
Molndalsvagen 24
40330 Gothenburg, Sweden (100%)
Tel.: (46) 31616000
Fax: (46) 317118030
Web Site: www.brostrom.se
Emp.: 80
Other Support Activities for Water Transportation
S.I.C.: 4499
N.A.I.C.S.: 488390

Wintria AB (2)
Ostra Hamngatan 7
Gothenburg, Sweden (100%)
Tel.: (46) 31616100
Emp.: 110
Other Accounting Services
S.I.C.: 8721
N.A.I.C.S.: 541219
Robert Uggla *(Gen Mgr)*

Non-U.S. Subsidiaries:

Brostrom Tankers SAS (2)
52 avenue Champs Elysees
75008 Paris, France (100%)
Tel.: (33) 142996666
Fax: (33) 142996620
E-Mail: brotank.paris@brostrom.fr
Web Site: www.brostrom.no/Contact/Organisation/Offices/
Emp.: 54
Process Physical Distribution & Logistics Consulting Services
S.I.C.: 4731
N.A.I.C.S.: 541614
Bruno Caillard *(Mng Dir)*

Coman S.A. (1)
Maersk House Zone OCBN Lot 531
Parcelle B 01
BP 2826
Cotonou, Benin
Tel.: (229) 21 316092
Fax: (229) 21 316097
Marine Cargo Handling Services
S.I.C.: 4491
N.A.I.C.S.: 488320

Container Operators S.A. (1)
Av Las Factorias 8150 Malvilla
San Antonio, Chile
Tel.: (56) 35 202700
Fax: (56) 35 202727
E-Mail: info@contopsa.com
Web Site: www.contopsa.cl
Emp.: 186
Container Terminal Operating Services
S.I.C.: 4226
N.A.I.C.S.: 493190
Hector Espinoza *(Gen Mgr)*

Damco China Limited (1)
3&5/F Tian'An Center No 338 Nanjing West Road
Shanghai, 200003, China
Tel.: (86) 2123062000
Fax: (86) 2123061038
Freight Forwarding Services
S.I.C.: 4731
N.A.I.C.S.: 488510

Damco France S.A.S. (1)
40 Rue De La Vague
59650 Villeneuve d'Ascq, France
Tel.: (33) 328765252
Fax: (33) 328765253
Freight Forwarding Services
S.I.C.: 4731
N.A.I.C.S.: 488510

Damco India Private Limited (1)
3rd Floor Shobhan Building 6-3-927/ A & B
Somajiguda Raj Bhavan Road
Hyderabad, Andhra Pradesh, India
Tel.: (91) 40 66567200
Fax: (91) 40 66567205
Emp.: 15
Freight Forwarding Services
S.I.C.: 4731
N.A.I.C.S.: 488510
Lars Sorensen *(CEO)*

Damco Italy S.R.L. (1)
Street 7 Bldg T3 Rozzano
Milan, 20089, Italy
Tel.: (39) 01020921
Fax: (39) 02 26944539
E-Mail: SalesItaly@damco.com
Web Site: www.damco.com
Emp.: 14
Freight Forwarding Services
S.I.C.: 4731
N.A.I.C.S.: 488510

Damco Sweden AB (1)
Terminalvagen 17
418 79 Gothenburg, Sweden
Tel.: (46) 31 751 2400
E-Mail: info@granslosttullager.se
Logistics Consulting Services
S.I.C.: 4731
N.A.I.C.S.: 541614

Ers Railways B.V. (1)
A Plesmanweg 61 K-L
3088 Rotterdam, Netherlands
Tel.: (31) 104285220
Fax: (31) 104286140
E-Mail: info@ersrail.com
Web Site: www.ersrail.com
Deep Sea Freight Transportation

Maersk Australia Pty. Ltd. (1)
201 Elizabeth Street Level 26
Sydney, NSW, 2000, Australia AU
Mailing Address:
GPO Box 4323
Sydney, NSW, 2001, Australia
Tel.: (61) 296969696
Fax: (61) 296969688
E-Mail: sydsaldir@maersklines.com
Web Site: www.maersklines.com
Emp.: 450
Freight Transportation Services
S.I.C.: 4412
N.A.I.C.S.: 483111
Nicolaj Noes *(Mng Dir)*

Maersk Benelux B.V. (1)
Boompjes 40
3011 XB Rotterdam, Netherlands
Mailing Address:
PO Box 487
3000AL Rotterdam, Netherlands
Tel.: (31) 107127000
Fax: (31) 107127999
E-Mail: nlasaltel@maersk.com
Web Site: www.maersklines.com
Holding Company; Container Shipping Services
S.I.C.: 6719
N.A.I.C.S.: 551112
Lodewijk Christiaan van Wachem *(Chm)*
Jacob den Arend *(Mng Dir)*

Non-U.S. Joint Venture:

Port of Tianjin Commercial Bonded Warehousing & Service Co. Ltd. (2)
No 46 5th Coastal Way Free Trade Zone
Tanggu, Tianjin, 300461, China
Tel.: (86) 2225763392
Fax: (86) 2225763391
E-Mail: iqgl@cbwxg.com
Web Site: www.cbwxg.com
Emp.: 90
Warehousing & Logistics Services
S.I.C.: 4731
N.A.I.C.S.: 488510
Jihua Li *(CFO)*

Maersk Brasil Ltda. (1)
Praca Rua Barbosa 26/27 Centro
Santos, SP, CEP 11010-130, Brazil
Tel.: (55) 13 3211 7800
Fax: (55) 13 3219 4754
Web Site: www.maersk.com
Emp.: 30
Freight Transportation Services
S.I.C.: 4412
N.A.I.C.S.: 483111
Viggo Andersen *(Mng Dir)*

The Maersk Company Limited (1)
Maersk House Braham Street
London, E1 8EP, United Kingdom (100%)
Tel.: (44) 2077125000
Fax: (44) 2077125100
E-Mail: gbrcorpprj@maersk.com
Web Site: www.maersklines.com
Sales Range: $1-4.9 Billion
Emp.: 150
Freight Transportation & Logistics Services
S.I.C.: 4731
N.A.I.C.S.: 488510
John William Baker *(Chm)*

Maersk Container Industry Dongguan Ltd. (1)
Machong Town
Dasheng District, Dongguan, Guangdong, 523146, China

Tel.: (86) 769 888 26668
Fax: (86) 769 888 24251
Emp.: 200
Container Mfr
S.I.C.: 3412
N.A.I.C.S.: 332439

Maersk Denizcilik A.S. (1)
Buyukdere Cad No 121 Ercan Han A Blok Kat 3-6
Gayrettepe, Istanbul, 34350, Turkey
Tel.: (90) 212 444 06 75
Fax: (90) 212 336 95 53
Storage & Warehousing Services
S.I.C.: 4226
N.A.I.C.S.: 493190

Maersk Deutschland A/S & Co.KG (1)
Am Santorkai 70-73
20457 Hamburg, Germany
Tel.: (49) 40235210
Telex: 215004
Fax: (49) 4023521725
E-Mail: info@maerskline.com
Web Site: www.maerskline.com
Emp.: 800
Freight Transportation Services
S.I.C.: 4731
N.A.I.C.S.: 488510
Soren Toft *(Gen Mgr)*

Maersk France S.A. (1)
Immeuble Europrogramme 6-7 Floor
40 boulevard de Dunkerque, 13002 Marseilles, France
Mailing Address:
PO Box 125
13473 Marseilles, Cedex 2, France
Tel.: (33) 491399696
Fax: (33) 491399653
Web Site: www.maerskline.com
Emp.: 42
Freight Transportation Services
S.I.C.: 4731
N.A.I.C.S.: 488510
Thomas Riber *(Mgr)*

Maersk Global Service Centres (India) Private Limited (1)
4th Floor Prudential Bldg Hiranandani Business Park Powai
Central Avenue Road, 400 076 Mumbai, India
Tel.: (91) 22 66799999
Fax: (91) 22 66799030
Emp.: 2,400
Container Terminal Operating Services
S.I.C.: 4226
N.A.I.C.S.: 493190
Sreenivasan Geetha *(Mng Dir)*

Maersk Holding B.V. (1)
Boompjes 40
Rotterdam, 3011 XB, Netherlands
Tel.: (31) 107127000
Fax: (31) 107127999
Investment Management Services
S.I.C.: 6211
N.A.I.C.S.: 523999

Maersk (Hong Kong) Ltd. (1)
25th Fl PCCW Twr
Taikoo Place
979 Kings Rd, Quarry Bay, China (Hong Kong)
Tel.: (852) 28566100
Fax: (852) 28561705
Web Site: www.maerskline.com
Emp.: 350
Freight Transportation Services
S.I.C.: 4412
N.A.I.C.S.: 483111

Maersk Italia spa (1)
Via Magazzini del Cotone 17
16128 Genoa, Italy
Tel.: (39) 01020961
Fax: (39) 0102096236
E-Mail: italintopsec@maersk.com
Web Site: www.maerskline.com
Emp.: 380
Freight Transportation Services
S.I.C.: 4412
N.A.I.C.S.: 483111
Norman Todd Pigeon *(Mng Dir)*
Todd Pigeon *(Mng Dir)*

Maersk Kenya Ltd. (1)
Maritime Centre
Archbishop Makarios Close, Mombasa, Kenya
Mailing Address:
PO Box 80149
Mombasa, Kenya
Tel.: (254) 412221273
Fax: (254) 202220086
E-Mail: mbamng@maersk.com
Web Site: www.maerskline.com
Emp.: 95
Freight Transportation Services
S.I.C.: 4412
N.A.I.C.S.: 483111
Rols Niensen *(Mng Dir)*

Branch:

Maersk Kenya Ltd. (2)
Kamsons House
PO Box 43986 00100 GPO
Mombasa Road, Nairobi, Kenya
Tel.: (254) 20828910
Fax: (254) 20828921
E-Mail: kenlinmng@maersk.com
Web Site: www.maersklines.com
Freight Services
S.I.C.: 4412
N.A.I.C.S.: 483111

Maersk K.K. (1)
Omori Bellport D-Wing 13th Fl
6-26-3 Minami-ohi
Shinagawa-Ku, Tokyo, 140-8554, Japan
Tel.: (81) 352132098
Fax: (81) 3 52132131
Web Site: www.maersklines.com
Emp.: 120
Freight Transportation Services
S.I.C.: 4412
N.A.I.C.S.: 483111
Jorgen H. Madose *(Mng Dir)*

Maersk Line Peru S.A.C. (1)
Chinchon St 1018 4th Fl
San Isidro, Lima, L27, Peru
Tel.: (51) 1 6160202
Fax: (51) 1 6289085
E-Mail: prucs@maersk.com
Web Site: www.maerskline.com
Emp.: 35
Shipping Container Operating Services
S.I.C.: 4499
N.A.I.C.S.: 488330
Jose Antonio Duarte *(Mgr-Fin)*

Maersk Malaysia Sdn Bhd (1)
Bangunan Palm Grove II, 3rd Fl, No.12 Jalan Glenmarie
Section U1, 40150 Shah Alam, Malaysia
Tel.: (60) 0356390588
Fax: (60) 355699880
E-Mail: lpkopsgen@maersk.com
Web Site: www.maerskline.com
Emp.: 100
Freight Transportation Services
S.I.C.: 4412
N.A.I.C.S.: 483111
Bjrne Foldager *(Mng Dir)*

Maersk New Zealand Ltd. (1)
The CPO Level 3 12 Queen St
1142 Auckland, New Zealand
Tel.: (64) 93593499
Fax: (64) 6493593488
Web Site: www.maerskline.com
Emp.: 110
Freight Transportation Services
S.I.C.: 4412
N.A.I.C.S.: 483111
Julian Bevis *(Country Mgr)*

Maersk Oil N. Sea UK (1)
Maersk House Crawpeel Road Altens Industrial Estate
Aberdeen, AB12 3LG, United Kingdom
Tel.: (44) 1224 242 000
Fax: (44) 12 2424 2235
Emp.: 500
Oil & Gas Exploration Services
S.I.C.: 1389
N.A.I.C.S.: 213112
Martin Rune Pedersen, *(Mng Dir)*

Maersk Oil Norway AS (1)
Chr August Thoringsvej 7
PO Box 8014
Forus, 4033 Stavanger, Norway
Tel.: (47) 5200 2800
Fax: (47) 5200 2801
Web Site: www.maerskoil.com
Oil & Gas Exploration Services
S.I.C.: 1389
N.A.I.C.S.: 213112

Maersk Oil Qatar A/S (1)
Al Jazi Tower 950 Asia Street
PO Box 22050
Doha, Qatar
Tel.: (974) 4401 3301
Fax: (974) 4401 3403
E-Mail:
Web Site: www.maerskoil.com
Emp.: 100
Oil & Gas Exploration Services
S.I.C.: 1389
N.A.I.C.S.: 213112
Lewis Affleck *(Mng Dir)*

Maersk Singapore Pte. Ltd. (1)
200 Cantonment Rd
Ste 10-00 Southpoint, Singapore, 089763, Singapore
Tel.: (65) 63238323
Fax: (65) 62247191
E-Mail: apms_maersk@pacific.net.sg
Web Site: www.maerskline.com
Emp.: 100
Freight Transportation Services
S.I.C.: 4412
N.A.I.C.S.: 483111
Jan Holm *(Mng Dir)*

Maersk Spain, S.L.U. (1)
Aqua Calle del Pintor Maella
46023 Valencia, Spain
Tel.: (34) 963 24 13 00
Container Terminal Operating Services
S.I.C.: 4226
N.A.I.C.S.: 493190

Maersk Supply Service Canada Ltd. (1)
100 New Gower Street Suite 803
Saint John's, NL, A1C 6K3, Canada
Tel.: (709) 753-4792
Fax: (709) 753-8640
E-Mail: msscomnor@maersk.com
Web Site: www.maersksupplyservice.com
Emp.: 7
Marine Vessel Operating Services
S.I.C.: 4499
N.A.I.C.S.: 488330
Chris Bailey *(Gen Mgr)*

Maersk Supply Service Holdings UK Limited (1)
Maersk House Brahman Street
London, E1 8EP, United Kingdom
Tel.: (44) 2077125000
Investment Management Services
S.I.C.: 6211
N.A.I.C.S.: 523999

Maersk Supply Service UK Limited (1)
City Wharf Ship Row
Aberdeen, AB11 5BY, United Kingdom
Tel.: (44) 1224 243243
E-Mail: abzmss@maersk.com
Web Site: www.maersksupplyservice.com
Emp.: 2
Ship Chartering Services
S.I.C.: 4412
N.A.I.C.S.: 483111
Robin Critchard *(Gen Mgr)*

Maersk Tankers Singapore Pte. Ltd (1)
3 Harbourfront Place 12-01 Harbourfront Tower 2
Singapore, 99254, Singapore
Tel.: (65) 63238323
Fax: (65) 62237191
Web Site: www.maersktankers.com
Emp.: 10
Container Terminal Operating Services
S.I.C.: 4226
N.A.I.C.S.: 493190
Erik V. Brodersen *(Mgr-Chartering)*

Maersk Vietnam Ltd. (1)
28 Phung Khac Khoan St Dakao Ward
Dist 1, Ho Chi Minh City, Vietnam
Tel.: (84) 88243252
Fax: (84) 88231395
Marine Vessel Services
S.I.C.: 4499
N.A.I.C.S.: 488330

NTS International Transport Services Co. Ltd. (1)
8/F Shartex Plaza 88 Zunyi Road South
Shanghai, China
Tel.: (86) 21 61206222
Freight Transportation Services
S.I.C.: 4731
N.A.I.C.S.: 488510

Safmarine Container Lines N.V. (1)
De Gerlacjekaay 20
B 2000 Antwerp, Belgium (100%)
Tel.: (32) 32442999
Fax: (32) 32442900
E-Mail: safmarine@linernet.com
Web Site: www.safmarine.com
Emp.: 180
International Liner Shipping
S.I.C.: 4412
N.A.I.C.S.: 483111
Lode Dheedene *(CEO)*

Non-U.S. Subsidiary:

SATI Container Services (Pty) Ltd. (2)
5 Sati Road Potsdam Killarney Gardens
Cape Town, 8000, South Africa
Tel.: (27) 21 550 8840
Fax: (27) 21 550 8843
Emp.: 90
Container Handling & Storage Services
S.I.C.: 4225
N.A.I.C.S.: 493110
Kevin Jacques *(Mgr-Ops)*

Safmarine (Pty) Ltd. (1)
Safemarine Quay The Clocktower Precinct Victoria & Alfred
Cape Town, 8001, South Africa (100%)
Tel.: (27) 214086911
Fax: (27) 214086370
E-Mail: safmarine@linernet.com
Web Site: www.safmarine.com
Emp.: 400
International Liner Shipping
S.I.C.: 4412
N.A.I.C.S.: 483111
Grant Daly *(CEO)*
Gail Kelly *(CEO)*

Terminal 4 S.A. (1)
Avenida Tomas Edison Y Prefectura Naval Argentina
Ciudad De, Buenos Aires, Argentina
Tel.: (54) 1145900900
Fax: (54) 1145900991
Container Terminal Operating Services
S.I.C.: 4226
N.A.I.C.S.: 493190

UTi (Dubai) Fze. (1)
Emirates Sky Cargo Mega Terminal Building Module E 4th Floor Suite
PO Box 293822
No 4009 Dubai Cargo Village, Dubai, United Arab Emirates
Tel.: (971) 4 283 4990
Fax: (971) 4 283 4991
Web Site: www.go2uti.com
Logistics Consulting Services
S.I.C.: 4731
N.A.I.C.S.: 541614

AP OIL INTERNATIONAL LTD.

30 Gul Crescent Jurong
Singapore, 629535, Singapore
Tel.: (65) 68615503
Fax: (65) 68619162
E-Mail: enquiry@apoil.com.sg
Web Site: www.apoil.com.sg
Year Founded: 1975
5AU—(SES)
Rev.: $72,922,210
Assets: $35,139,302
Liabilities: $5,533,353
Net Worth: $29,605,949
Earnings: $4,665,376
Emp.: 100
Fiscal Year-end: 12/31/12

Business Description:
Lubricating Oils & Specialty Chemicals Mfr
S.I.C.: 2992
N.A.I.C.S.: 324191

Personnel:
Leng Woon Ho *(Chm, CEO & Mng Dir)*
Chee Hon Ho *(Deputy CEO)*
Woon Chan Lau *(Sec)*

AP Oil International Ltd.—(Continued)

Board of Directors:
Leng Woon Ho
Kwok Wah Chang
Chee Hon Ho
Woon Chan Lau
Ban Huat Quah
Woon Hum Tan

Subsidiaries:

A.I.M. Chemical Industries Pte Ltd (1)
19 Tractor Road
Jurong, Singapore, 627977, Singapore (100%)
Tel.: (65) 62654700
Fax: (65) 62665082
E-Mail: enquiry@aimchem.com.sg
Web Site: www.aimchem.com.sg
Emp.: 45
Chemicals Manufacturing
S.I.C.: 2899
N.A.I.C.S.: 325998
Kwok Wah Chang *(Mng Dir)*

Alpha Pacific Petroleum (S) Pte Ltd (1)
18 Pioneer Sector 1
Jurong, Singapore, 628428, Singapore (100%)
Tel.: (65) 68622765
Fax: (65) 68610259
Web Site: www.apoil.com.sg/contact.html
Emp.: 10
Lubricating Oils & Greases Mfg
S.I.C.: 2992
N.A.I.C.S.: 324191
Leng Woon Ho *(Mng Dir)*

GB Chemicals Pte Ltd (1)
18 Pioneer Sector 1
Jurong, Singapore, 628428, Singapore
Tel.: (65) 68630220
Fax: (65) 68630200
E-Mail: enquiry@gbchemicals.com.sg
Web Site: www.gbchemicals.com.sg
Cleaning Chemicals Mfr & Distr
S.I.C.: 2833
N.A.I.C.S.: 325411
Alphonsus Chue *(Mng Dir)*

APA-AUSTRIA PRESSE AGENTUR EG

(d/b/a APA-Gruppe)
Laimgrubengasse 10
1060 Vienna, Austria
Tel.: (43) 1 360 60 0
E-Mail: apa@apa.at
Web Site: www.apa.at
Emp.: 511

Business Description:
News Agency
S.I.C.: 7383
N.A.I.C.S.: 519110

Personnel:
Konrad Tretter *(Mng Dir)*

Subsidiary:

Gentics Software GmbH (1)
Gonzagagasse 11/25
A-1010 Vienna, Austria
Tel.: (43) 1 7109904 0
Fax: (43) 1 7109904 4
E-Mail: office@gentics.com
Web Site: www.gentics.com
Content Management Software
S.I.C.: 7372
N.A.I.C.S.: 511210
Gunter Kaminger *(Co-CEO & Mng Dir)*
Alexander Szlezak *(Co-CEO & Chief Sls Officer)*
Klaus M. Schremser *(CFO)*
Haymo Meran *(CTO, CMO & Dir-Product Experience)*
Clemens Prerovsky *(Chief Dev Officer)*

APA FINANCIAL SERVICES LIMITED

Level 1 41 Edward Street
Brisbane, QLD, 4000, Australia
Tel.: (61) 7 3020 3020
Fax: (61) 7 3020 3080
E-Mail: info@apafs.com.au
Web Site: www.apafs.com.au
APP—(ASX)
Rev.: $89,058
Assets: $754,163
Liabilities: $14,719
Net Worth: $739,444
Earnings: $104,769
Fiscal Year-end: 06/30/13

Business Description:
Financial Investment Services
S.I.C.: 6211
N.A.I.C.S.: 523999

Personnel:
Jerome Jones *(Sec)*

Board of Directors:
Michael Hackett
Graham Anderson
Adrian Rowley

APA GROUP

Level 19 580 George Street
Sydney, NSW, 2000, Australia
Tel.: (61) 296930000
Fax: (61) 296930093
Web Site: www.apa.com.au
APA—(ASX)
Sales Range: $800-899.9 Million

Business Description:
Natural Gas Infrastructure Business
S.I.C.: 1311
N.A.I.C.S.: 211111

Personnel:
Leonard Bleasel *(Chm)*
Michael McCormack *(CEO & Mng Dir)*
Peter Fredricson *(CFO)*
Mark Knapman *(Sec)*

Board of Directors:
Leonard Bleasel
Steven Crane
John Fletcher
Russell Higgins
Michael McCormack
Patricia McKenzie
Muri Muhammad
Robert Wright

Subsidiaries:

APA GasNet Australia (Operations) Pty. Ltd. (1)
180 Greens Rd
3175 Dandenong, Victoria, Australia
Tel.: (61) 397975277
Fax: (61) 397975220
Web Site: www.apa.com.au
Emp.: 150
Gas Transmission Services
S.I.C.: 4922
N.A.I.C.S.: 486210
Mick McCormick *(CEO)*

APA GasNet Australia Pty Limited (1)
180 Greens Rd
Dandenong, Victoria, 3175, Australia
Tel.: (61) 397975222
Fax: (61) 397975211
Web Site: www.apa.com.au
Gas Transmission Services
S.I.C.: 4922
N.A.I.C.S.: 486210
Ed Deprince *(Mgr)*

APT Facility Management Pty. Ltd. (1)
Level 19 HSBC Bldg 580 George St
Sydney, New South Wales, 2000, Australia
Tel.: (61) 296930000
Fax: (61) 296930093
E-Mail: feedback@pipelinetrust.com.au
Web Site: www.apa.com.au
Emp.: 100
Gas Transmission Services
S.I.C.: 4922
N.A.I.C.S.: 486210
Michael McCormack *(Mng Dir)*

APT Goldfields Pty. Ltd. (1)
Level 8 Australia Pl 15-17 William St
6000 Perth, Western Australia, Australia
Tel.: (61) 894224100
Fax: (61) 893223631
Emp.: 70
Gold Mining Services
S.I.C.: 1041
N.A.I.C.S.: 212221

APT O&M Services Pty Ltd. (1)
Level 19 HSBC Bldg 580 George St
Sydney, NSW, 2000, Australia
Tel.: (61) 296930000
Natural Gas Transportation Services
S.I.C.: 4922
N.A.I.C.S.: 486210

APT Parmelia Pty. Ltd. (1)
Level 5 233 Adelaide Ter
Perth, WA, 6000, Australia
Tel.: (61) 893205600
Fax: (61) 894349
Web Site: www.apa.com.au
Gas Transmission Services
S.I.C.: 4923
N.A.I.C.S.: 486210

APT Pipelines (Qld) Pty Limited (1)
Level 5 Airport Central Tower
241 O Riordan St, Mascot, New South Wales, 2020, Australia
Tel.: (61) 296930000
Natural Gas Transportation Services
S.I.C.: 4922
N.A.I.C.S.: 486210

Central Ranges Pipeline Pty. Ltd. (1)
5 Phoenix St
Westdale, Tamworth, New South Wales, 2340, Australia
Tel.: (61) 267615522
Fax: (61) 267615577
E-Mail: gary.green@apa.com.au
Web Site: www.centralranges.com.au
Emp.: 4
Gas Transmission Services
S.I.C.: 4923
N.A.I.C.S.: 486210
Gary Green *(Mgr)*

Goldfields Gas Transmission Pty. Ltd. (1)
Level 8 Australia Pl 15 17 William St
Perth, Western Australia, 6000, Australia
Tel.: (61) 894224100
Fax: (61) 893223631
E-Mail: ggt@ggt.com.au
Web Site: www.ggt.com.au
Gas Transmission Services
S.I.C.: 4922
N.A.I.C.S.: 486210
David A. King *(Gen Mgr)*

NT Gas Pty Limited (1)
16 Georgina Crescent
PO Box 7
Palmerston, Darwin, Northern Territory, 0831, Australia
Tel.: (61) 889248100
Fax: (61) 889321663
E-Mail: contactus@ntgas.com.au
Web Site: www.ntgas.com.au
Emp.: 50
Natural Gas Pipeline Transportation Services
S.I.C.: 4922
N.A.I.C.S.: 486210
Michael McCormack *(Chm)*

APAC COAL LIMITED

Level 1 981 Wellington Street
West Perth, WA, 6005, Australia
Tel.: (61) 865552950
Fax: (61) 893213102
E-Mail: info@apaccoal.com
Web Site: www.apaccoal.com
AAL—(ASX)
Rev.: $210,374
Assets: $4,431,580
Liabilities: $1,865,868
Net Worth: $2,565,713
Earnings: ($290,366)
Fiscal Year-end: 06/30/13

Business Description:
Coal Exploration Services
S.I.C.: 1241
N.A.I.C.S.: 213113

Personnel:
Zane Lewis *(Sec)*

Board of Directors:
Idris Abdullah
Sam di Giacomo
Teng Kiat Koh
Kuan Yew Lim
Boon Ban Quah

Legal Counsel:
Steinepreis Paganin
Level 4 The Read Building 16 Milligan Street
Perth, WA, 6000, Australia
Tel.: (61) 8 9321 4000
Fax: (61) 8 9321 4333

Soebagio, Jatim Djarot
Plaza DM, 17 Floor Jalan Jenderal Sudirmankav.25
Jakarta, Indonesia

APAC RESOURCES LIMITED

32/F China Online Centre 333 Lockhart Road
Wanchai, China (Hong Kong)
Tel.: (852) 2541 0338
Fax: (852) 2541 9133
E-Mail: info@apacresources.com
Web Site: www.apacresources.com
1104—(SHG)
Rev.: $142,440,362
Assets: $325,896,753
Liabilities: $34,646,028
Net Worth: $291,250,725
Earnings: ($268,175,639)
Emp.: 25
Fiscal Year-end: 06/30/13

Business Description:
Investment Management Services
S.I.C.: 6282
N.A.I.C.S.: 523920

Personnel:
Sok Un Chong *(Chm)*
Andrew Ferguson *(CEO)*
Frederick Wai Keung Wong *(CFO & Sec)*

Board of Directors:
Sok Un Chong
Johnson Francis Chu Fai Chang
Peter Anthony Curry
Andrew Ferguson
Muk Yin Kong
Seng Hui Lee
Kwok Hoo So
Robert Moyse Willcocks
Albert Wing Kuen Wong

Butterfield Fulcrum Group (Bermuda) Limited
26 Burnaby Street
Hamilton, HM 11, Bermuda

Transfer Agents:
Tricor Secretaries Limited
26th Floor Tesbury Centre 28 Queen's Road East
Wanchai, China (Hong Kong)

Butterfield Fulcrum Group (Bermuda) Limited
26 Burnaby Street
Hamilton, HM 11, Bermuda

APACER TECHNOLOGY INC.

4F 75 Sec 1 Xintai 5th Rd
Xizhi City, Taipei, 221, Taiwan
Tel.: (886) 2 26982888
Fax: (886) 2 26982889
E-Mail: public@apacer.com
Web Site: www.apacer.com
Year Founded: 1997
8271—(TAI)
Sales Range: $350-399.9 Million
Emp.: 500

Business Description:
Memory Modules, Flash Memory Related Application Products, Dynamic Random Access Memory (DRAMs) Products & Flash Memory Products Mfr
S.I.C.: 3572

N.A.I.C.S.: 334112
Personnel:
Lee-da Lu *(Chm)*
Wan-Yuan Lin *(CFO)*

U.S. Subsidiary:

Apacer Memory America, Inc. (1)
386 Fairview Way Ste 102
Milpitas, CA 95035
Tel.: (408) 518-8699
Fax: (408) 935-9611
Storage Devices Mfr
S.I.C.: 3572
N.A.I.C.S.: 334112
Pei-Fen Chen *(Mgr-Sls)*

Non-U.S. Subsidiaries:

Apacer Electronic (Shanghai) Co., Ltd. (1)
Room G 20 Floor No 2 Lane 600 Jieyun Plaza Tianshan Road
Shanghai, 200051, China
Tel.: (86) 2162412741
Web Site: www.eu.apacer.com
Emp.: 10
Storage Devices Mfr
S.I.C.: 3572
N.A.I.C.S.: 334112

Apacer Technologies Pvt Ltd. (1)
Door No. 535, 1st Floor, 8th cross, JP Nagar 3rd Phase, Bengaluru, Karnataka, 560 078, India
Tel.: (91) 8041529061
Fax: (91) 8041700215
Web Site: in.apacer.com
Emp.: 8
Storage Devices Mfr
S.I.C.: 3572
N.A.I.C.S.: 334112
Naveen Peter *(Country Mgr)*

Apacer Technology Corp (1)
5F Matsura Building 1-9-6 Shiba
Minato-Ku, Tokyo, 105-0014, Japan
Tel.: (81) 354192668
Fax: (81) 354190018
Web Site: jp.apacer.com
Storage Devices Mfr
S.I.C.: 3572
N.A.I.C.S.: 334112

APACS

Mercury House Triton Ct 14 Finsbury Sq
London, EC2A 1LQ, United Kingdom
Tel.: (44) 2077116200
Fax: (44) 2072565527
E-Mail: corpcomms@apacs.org.uk
Web Site: www.apacs.org.uk
Sales Range: $50-74.9 Million
Emp.: 150
Business Description:
Market Research & Payment Delivery Services
S.I.C.: 8732
N.A.I.C.S.: 541910
Personnel:
Paul Smee *(CEO)*

APAR INDUSTRIES LTD.

Apar House Build No 5 Corporate Park Sion Trombay Road
Chembur, Mumbai, Maharashtra, 400 071, India
Tel.: (91) 22 25263400
Fax: (91) 22 67800400
E-Mail: corporate@apar.com
Web Site: www.apar.com
532259—(BOM)
Rev.: $929,519,586
Assets: $604,114,776
Liabilities: $487,607,562
Net Worth: $116,507,214
Earnings: $20,292,030
Fiscal Year-end: 03/31/13
Business Description:
Power Transmission Equipment Mfr
S.I.C.: 3568
N.A.I.C.S.: 333613
Personnel:
Kushal N. Desai *(CEO & Mng Dir)*
Chaitanya N. Desai *(Mng Dir)*
Sanjaya Kunder *(Compliance Officer & Sec)*
Board of Directors:
Narendra D. Desai
Chaitanya N. Desai
Kushal N. Desai
Sanjiv Maheshwari
Rajesh Sehgal
H. N. Shah
N. K. Thingalaya
F. B. Virani
Transfer Agent:
MCS Limited
Neelam Apartment 88 Sampatrao Colony B/H Standard Chartered Bank
Vadodara, India

APATOR S.A.

ul Gdanska 4a Lok C4
87-100 Torun, Poland
Tel.: (48) 566191111
Fax: (48) 566191295
E-Mail: apator@apator.com.pl
Web Site: www.apator.torun.pl
APT—(WAR)
Rev.: $212,104,155
Assets: $159,975,594
Liabilities: $64,965,983
Net Worth: $95,009,611
Earnings: $30,355,684
Emp.: 1,919
Fiscal Year-end: 12/31/12
Business Description:
Switchgear & Metering Equipment Mfr
S.I.C.: 3613
N.A.I.C.S.: 335313
Personnel:
Janusz Niedzwiecki *(Chm-Supervisory Bd)*
Andrzej Szostak *(Chm-Exec Bd & Mng Dir)*
Mariusz Lewicki *(Deputy Chm-Supervisory Bd)*
Tomasz Habryka *(Member-Exec Bd & Dir-Strategic Dev & Mktg)*
Jerzy Kus *(Member-Exec Bd & Dir-Metering Equipment & Sys)*
Supervisory Board of Directors:
Janusz Niedzwiecki
Danuta Guzowska
Krzysztof Kwiatkowski
Mariusz Lewicki
Janusz Marzyglinski

Subsidiaries:

APATOR CONTROL Sp. z o.o. (1)
ul Zolkiewskiego 21/29
87 100 Torun, Kuyavian-Pomeranian, Poland
Tel.: (48) 566191601
Fax: (48) 566191337
E-Mail: info@acontrol.com.pl
Web Site: www.acontrol.com.pl
Emp.: 100
Electrical Equipment Mfr & Distr
S.I.C.: 3825
N.A.I.C.S.: 334515
Ryszard Trabala *(Gen Mgr)*

APATOR KFAP Sp. z o.o. (1)
ul Wroclawska 53
30 011 Krakow, Lesser Poland, Poland
Tel.: (48) 126374222
Fax: (48) 12 637 34 97
E-Mail: biuro@apator-kfap.pl
Web Site: www.kfap.pl
Emp.: 40
Metering Equipments Mfr
S.I.C.: 3829
N.A.I.C.S.: 334514
Adam Kulwik *(Mgr-Sls)*

APATOR METRIX S.A (1)
ul Piaskowa 3
83 110 Tczew, Poland
Tel.: (48) 585309200
Fax: (48) 585309300
E-Mail: metrix@metrix.pl
Web Site: www.metrix.com.pl
Emp.: 100
Metering Instruments Mfr
S.I.C.: 3613
N.A.I.C.S.: 335313
Maciej Zalewski *(Mgr-Electronic Sys Dept)*

APATOR MINING Sp. z o.o. (1)
Al Rozdzienskiego 188
40 203 Katowice, Silesian, Poland
Tel.: (48) 32 735 88 07
Fax: (48) 32 258 20 48
E-Mail: biuro@apator-mining.com.pl
Web Site: www.apator-mining.com.pl
Mechanical Equipment Mfr & Distr
S.I.C.: 3563
N.A.I.C.S.: 333912
Korneliusz Kuczera *(Asst Head-Sls Dept)*

Apator Powogaz S.A. (1)
23/25 Klemensa Janickiego St
60 542 Poznan, Wielkopolska, Poland
Tel.: (48) 618418100
Fax: (48) 618470192
E-Mail: sekretariat@powogaz.com.pl
Web Site: www.powogaz.com.pl
Metering Instruments Mfr
S.I.C.: 3823
N.A.I.C.S.: 334513
Michael Lisiecki *(Gen Mgr)*

Subsidiaries:

APATOR TELEMETRIA Sp. z o.o. (2)
Filmowa 2-6/a
76 200 Slupsk, Pomeranian, Poland
Tel.: (48) 597205114
Fax: (48) 59 720 51 27
E-Mail: office@telemetria.eu
Web Site: www.telemetria.eu
Emp.: 17
Telemetric Products Mfr & Support Services
S.I.C.: 3829
N.A.I.C.S.: 334514

WODPOL Sp. z o.o. (2)
ul Ks Slonki 24
34 300 Zywiec, Silesian, Poland
Tel.: (48) 338618527
Fax: (48) 338666716
E-Mail: sekretariat@wodpol.zywiec.pl
Web Site: www.wodpol.zywiec.pl
Emp.: 100
Building Architectural Design Services
S.I.C.: 8712
N.A.I.C.S.: 541310
Wo Chjanucv *(Chm)*

APATOR RECTOR Sp. z o.o. (1)
Sulechowska 1
Zielona Gora, Lubusz, Poland
Tel.: (48) 684514499
Fax: (48) 684514498
E-Mail: rector@rector.com.pl
Web Site: www.rector.com.pl
Computing Equipment Services & Mfr
S.I.C.: 7389
N.A.I.C.S.: 561990

Non-U.S. Subsidiary:

APATOR GmbH (1)
Aroser Allee 78
D-13407 Berlin, Germany
Tel.: (49) 3081799740
Fax: (49) 3081799742
E-Mail: info@apator.de
Web Site: www.apator.de
Emp.: 2
Office Equipment Whslr
S.I.C.: 5044
N.A.I.C.S.: 423420
Tomasz Habryka *(Mng Dir)*
Miroslaw Klepacki *(Mng Dir)*

APAX PARTNERS LLP

33 Jermyn Street
London, SW1Y 6DN, United Kingdom
Tel.: (44) 2078726300
Fax: (44) 2076666441
E-Mail: fmenquiry@apax.com
Web Site: www.apax.com
Year Founded: 1972
Emp.: 300
Business Description:
Private Equity Advisory Firm
S.I.C.: 6211
N.A.I.C.S.: 523999
Personnel:
Martin Halusa *(Chm & Partner)*
Andrew Sillitoe *(Co-CEO & Partner)*
Mitchell L. Truwit *(Co-CEO & Partner-United States)*
Ralf Gruss *(Partner & COO)*
Simon Cresswell *(Partner & Gen Counsel)*
Emilio Voli *(Partner & Co-Head-IR)*
Giancarlo Alberti *(Partner)*
Gabriele Cipparrone *(Partner)*
Steven Dyson *(Partner)*
Frank Ehmer *(Partner)*
Rohan Haldea *(Partner)*
Tom Hall *(Partner)*
Nico Hansen *(Partner)*
David Marks *(Partner & Advisor-Tax)*
Salim Nathoo *(Partner)*
Christian Stahl *(Partner)*

Holdings:

Incisive Media Limited (1)
Haymarket House
28-29 Haymarket, London, SW1Y 4RX, United Kingdom
Tel.: (44) 2074849700
Fax: (44) 2074849797
E-Mail: customerservices@incisivemedia.com
Web Site: www.incisivemedia.com
Sales Range: $75-99.9 Million
Emp.: 500
Business Information Publishing through Magazines, Web Sites, Newsletters & Databases
S.I.C.: 2721
N.A.I.C.S.: 511120
Tim Weller *(Grp CEO)*
James Hanbury *(Grp Mng Dir)*
Jamie Campbell-Harris *(CFO)*
Matthew McGowan *(VP-Publr)*
George Dillehay *(Sr VP-Legal)*
Kevin Vermeulen *(Sr VP-Events)*

Subsidiaries:

Global Professional Media Limited (2)
28/29 Haymarket House
SW1Y4RX London, United Kingdom UK
Tel.: (44) 2074849700
Fax: (44) 2074849797
Web Site: www.incisivemedia.com
Emp.: 82
Book Publishers
S.I.C.: 2731
N.A.I.C.S.: 511130
Tim Weller *(CEO)*

Incisive Media Investment Limited (2)
28/29 Haymarket House
London, SW1Y4RX, United Kingdom UK
Tel.: (44) 2074849700
Fax: (44) 2074849797
Web Site: www.incisivemedia.com
Book Publishers
S.I.C.: 2731
N.A.I.C.S.: 511130
Tim Weller *(CEO)*

Incisive Media Limited (2)
32-34 Broadwick St
London, W1A 2HG, United Kingdom UK
Tel.: (44) 2073169000
Fax: (44) 2073169003
E-Mail:
Web Site: www.incisivemedia.com
Emp.: 600
Publisher of Finance & Technology Trade Magazines
S.I.C.: 2721
N.A.I.C.S.: 511120
Tim Weller *(CEO)*
James Hanbury *(Grp Mng Dir)*

Incisive RWG Limited (2)
28/29 Haymarket House
SW1Y4RX London, United Kingdom UK
Tel.: (44) 2074849700
Fax: (44) 2079302238

Apax Partners LLP—(Continued)

E-Mail: customerservices@incisivemedia.com
Web Site: www.incisivemedia.com
Emp.: 700
Book Publishers
S.I.C.: 2731
N.A.I.C.S.: 511130
Tim Weller *(CEO)*

U.S. Subsidiaries:

American Lawyer Media, Inc. (2)
120 Broadway 5th Fl
New York, NY 10271 DE
Tel.: (212) 457-9400
Fax: (646) 417-7705
Toll Free: (800) 888-8300
E-Mail: customer.service@alm.com
Web Site: www.alm.com
Emp.: 777
Legal & Business Publishing
S.I.C.: 2721
N.A.I.C.S.: 511120
Bill Carter *(Pres & CEO)*
Eric F. Lundberg *(CFO & Sr VP)*
Kevin Michielsen *(Chief Strategy Officer & Sr VP-Info/Res Solutions Bus)*
Jeffrey K. Whittle *(CTO & Sr VP)*
Ron Spinner *(Publr-Verdictsearch & ALM Experts)*
Lenny Izzo *(Sr VP-Mktg)*
Jeffrey S. Litvack *(Sr VP-Digital Media)*
Kevin Vermeulen *(Sr VP-Conferences & Trade Shows)*

Subsidiaries:

Law.com (3)
1035 Market St Ste 500
San Francisco, CA 94103-1650
Tel.: (415) 633-2500
Toll Free: (800) 903-9872
Web Site: www.law.com
Emp.: 42
Online Legal News, Information, Related Products & Services
S.I.C.: 4899
N.A.I.C.S.: 517919
Larry W. Sonsini *(Chm)*
Bill Pollak *(Pres)*

The New York Law Publishing Company (3)
120 Broadway 5th Fl
New York, NY 10271
Tel.: (212) 457-9545
Fax: (212) 696-4514
Toll Free: (800) 888-8300
Web Site: www.newyorklawjournal.com
Sales Range: $100-124.9 Million
Emp.: 250
Publishing Newspapers for Lawyers
S.I.C.: 2711
N.A.I.C.S.: 511110
William L. Pollak *(Pres & CEO)*
Eric Lundberg *(CFO)*
Stephen P. Lincoln *(Publr)*

Incisive RWG Inc (2)
120 Broadway 5th Fl
New York, NY 10271-0096
Tel.: (212) 457-7788
Web Site: www.structuredproductsonline.com
Emp.: 70
Periodical Publishers
S.I.C.: 2721
N.A.I.C.S.: 511120
Gary Lynch *(Mng Dir)*

Non-U.S. Subsidiaries:

Incisive Financial Publishing Limited (2)
Tower 2 20th Floor Admiralty Centre
18 Harcourt Road Admiralty, Wanchai, China (Hong Kong)
Tel.: (852) 25452710
Fax: (852) 25457317
Emp.: 70
All Other Publishers
S.I.C.: 2741
N.A.I.C.S.: 511199
Harjeet Singh *(Mng Dir)*

Incisive Media (2)
20/F Tower 2 Admiralty Centre
18 Harcourt Road, Hong Kong, China (Hong Kong)
Tel.: (852) 3411 4983
Web Site: www.incisivemedia.com
Media Marketing
S.I.C.: 8742
N.A.I.C.S.: 541613
Jonathon Whiteley *(Mng Dir)*

Sophos Ltd. (1)
The Pentagon
Abingdon Science Park, Abingdon, OX14 3YP, United Kingdom
Tel.: (44) 1235559933
Fax: (44) 1235559935
E-Mail: sales@sophos.com
Web Site: www.sophos.com
Sales Range: $250-299.9 Million
Emp.: 1,000
Computer Security & Data Protection Software Publisher
S.I.C.: 7372
N.A.I.C.S.: 511210
Jan Hruska *(Co-Founder)*
Peter Lammer *(Co-Founder)*
Kris Hagerman *(CEO)*
Nicholas Bray *(CFO)*
Gerhard Eschelbeck *(CTO)*
Ken Paul *(Dir-HR)*
Jan Hichert *(Sr VP & Gen Mgr-Network Security)*
Wendy Dean *(Sr VP-Engrg & Tech Ops)*
Michael McGuinness *(Sr VP-Worldwide Sls & Field Ops)*

U.S. Subsidiary:

Sophos Inc. (2)
3 Van de Graaff Dr 2nd Fl
Burlington, MA 01803
Tel.: (781) 494-5800
Fax: (781) 494-5801
Toll Free: (866) 866-2802
Web Site: www.sophos.com
Computer Security & Data Protection Software Publisher
S.I.C.: 7372
N.A.I.C.S.: 511210
Steve Munford *(CEO)*
Matt Fairbanks *(CMO)*
Ari Buchler *(Gen Counsel & VP-Corp Dev)*
Mike McGuinness *(Sr VP-Worldwide Sls & Field Ops)*
Michael Valentine *(Sr VP-Sls)*
Mary Winfield *(Sr VP-Global Technical Svcs-Silicon Valley)*

Non-U.S. Subsidiaries:

Astaro GmbH & Co. KG (2)
Amalienbadstr 41/Bau 52
76227 Karlsruhe, Germany De
Tel.: (49) 721 25516 0
Fax: (49) 721 25516 200
E-Mail: emea@astaro.com
Web Site: www.astaro.com
Emp.: 220
Computer Security Services
S.I.C.: 7373
N.A.I.C.S.: 541512
Jan Hichert *(CEO)*
Frank Nellissen *(CFO)*
Markus Hennig *(CTO)*
Gunter Junk *(Sr VP-Sls & Mktg-Global)*

U.S. Subsidiary:

Astaro Corporation (3)
3 Van de Graaff Dr 2nd Fl
Burlington, MA 01803
Tel.: (781) 494-5800
Fax: (781) 494-5801
Toll Free: (888) 767-4679
E-Mail: americas@astaro.com
Web Site: www.astaro.com
Emp.: 225
Software Publishers
S.I.C.: 7372
N.A.I.C.S.: 511210
Jan Hichert *(CEO)*

Sophos AB (2)
Farogatan 33
164 51 Kista, Sweden
Tel.: (46) 8 584 00 600
Fax: (46) 8 584 00 610
E-Mail: info.nordic@sophos.com
Web Site: www.sophos.com
Security Software Publisher
S.I.C.: 7372
N.A.I.C.S.: 511210

Sophos Anti-Virus Asia Pte Ltd. (2)
2 Shenton Way SGX Centre 1 17 01
Singapore, 068804, Singapore
Tel.: (65) 6224 4168
Fax: (65) 6224 0191
Security Software Publisher
S.I.C.: 7372
N.A.I.C.S.: 511210
Stuart Fisher *(Mng Dir-Asia Pacific)*

Sophos B.V. (2)
Hoevestein 11B
4903 SE Oosterhout, Netherlands
Tel.: (31) 162 480 240
Fax: (31) 162 430 330
Web Site: www.sophos.com
Emp.: 15
Security Software Publisher
S.I.C.: 7372
N.A.I.C.S.: 511210
Pieter Lacroix *(Mng Dir)*

Sophos GmbH (2)
Gustav Stresemann Ring 1
65189 Wiesbaden, Germany
Tel.: (49) 611 5858 0
Fax: (49) 611 5858 1042
E-Mail: info@sophos.de
Web Site: www.sophos.de
Security Software Publisher
S.I.C.: 7372
N.A.I.C.S.: 511210

Sophos Italy S.r.l. (2)
Via Tonale 26
20125 Milan, Italy
Tel.: (39) 02 91 18 08
Fax: (39) 02 91 18 08 99
E-Mail: sales@sophos.it
Web Site: www.sophos.it
Security Software Publisher
S.I.C.: 7372
N.A.I.C.S.: 511210

Sophos K.K. (2)
Nisseki Yokohama Building 15F
1 1 8 Sakuragicho Naka ku, Yokohama, Kanagawa, 231 0062, Japan
Tel.: (81) 45 227 1800
Fax: (81) 45 227 1818
E-Mail: sales@sophos.co.jp
Web Site: www.sophos.co.jp
Security Software Publisher
S.I.C.: 7372
N.A.I.C.S.: 511210

Sophos Pty Ltd. (2)
One Elizabeth Plaza
North Sydney, NSW, 2060, Australia
Tel.: (61) 2 9409 9100
Fax: (61) 2 9409 9191
E-Mail: sales@sophos.com.au
Web Site: www.sophos.com
Emp.: 5
Security Software Publisher
S.I.C.: 7372
N.A.I.C.S.: 511210
Ashley Wearne *(Gen Mgr-Australia & New Zealand)*

Sophos Sarl (2)
80 Quai Voltaire
95870 Bezons, France
Tel.: (33) 1 34 34 80 00
Fax: (33) 1 34 34 80 01
E-Mail: sales@sophos.fr
Web Site: www.sophos.fr
Security Software Publisher
S.I.C.: 7372
N.A.I.C.S.: 511210

Trader Media Group Ltd. (1)
41-47 Hartfield Rd
London, Wimbledon, SW19 3RQ, United Kingdom (100%)
Tel.: (44) 2085447000
Fax: (44) 85447018
E-Mail: customersuppot@autotrader.co.uk
Web Site: www.autotrader.co.uk
Emp.: 170
Newspaper Publisher; Owned by Guardian Media (50.1%) Group plc & Apax Partners Ltd (49.9%)
S.I.C.: 2711
N.A.I.C.S.: 511110
Trevor Mather *(CEO)*

Joint Venture:

Top Right Group Limited (1)
Greater London House
Hampstead Road, London, NW1 7EJ, United Kingdom UK
Tel.: (44) 207 728 5000
E-Mail: contact@topright-group.com
Web Site: www.topright-group.com
Sales Range: $1-4.9 Billion
Emp.: 600
Holding Company; Magazine Publisher & Trade Exhibition Organizer
Export
S.I.C.: 6719
N.A.I.C.S.: 551112
Duncan Painter *(CEO)*
Malcolm Gough *(Deputy CEO)*
John Gulliver *(CFO)*

Subsidiary:

EMAP Limited (2)
Greater London House
Hampstead Road, London, NW1 7EJ, United Kingdom UK
Tel.: (44) 20 3033 2600
E-Mail: reception.glh@topright-group.com
Web Site: www.emap.com
Emp.: 10
Magazine Publisher
S.I.C.: 2721
N.A.I.C.S.: 511120
Natasha Christie-Miller *(CEO)*

Subsidiaries:

EMAP Construction Networks Ltd. (3)
Greater London House Hampstead Road
London, NW1 7EJ, United Kingdom
Tel.: (44) 2077285000
E-Mail: alex.koster@construct.emap.com
Emp.: 200
Magazine Publisher
S.I.C.: 2721
N.A.I.C.S.: 511120
Alex Koster *(Mgr-Trng)*

Subsidiaries:

Construction Research Communications Ltd. (4)
151 Rosebery Ave
London, EC1R 4GB, United Kingdom
Tel.: (44) 2075056600
Fax: (44) 2075056606
Emp.: 250
Publishers for the UK Building Research Establishment
S.I.C.: 2721
N.A.I.C.S.: 511120
Simon Middleboe *(Mng Dir)*

EMAP Construct Ltd. (4)
151 Roseberry Ave
London, EC1R 4QX, United Kingdom
Tel.: (44) 2074056600
Fax: (44) 2075056606
Web Site: www.emapconstruct.co.uk
Emp.: 220
Magazine & Directory Publisher
S.I.C.: 2721
N.A.I.C.S.: 511120

EMAP Maclaren (4)
19th And 20th Floor Leon House
Croydon, Surrey, CR0 9XT, United Kingdom
Tel.: (44) 2082775000
Fax: (44) 2082775650
Web Site: www.emapmaclaren.com
Emp.: 150
Magazine & Directory Publisher
S.I.C.: 2721
N.A.I.C.S.: 511120

Glenigan (4)
41 47 Seabourne Rd
Bournemouth, Dorset, BH5 2HU, United Kingdom
Tel.: (44) 202432121
Fax: (44) 1202431204
E-Mail: info@glenigan.emap.com
Web Site: www.glenigan.com
Emp.: 100
Sales Leads & Contract Information Magazines & Directories
S.I.C.: 2721
N.A.I.C.S.: 511120

EMAP Public Sector Management Ltd. (3)
Greater London House Hampstead Road
London, NW1 7EJ, United Kingdom
Tel.: (44) 2078740200
Fax: (44) 2073471831

E-Mail: sonia.liffen@emap.com
Web Site: www.emap.com
Emp.: 1,300
Magazine & Directory Publisher & Online Information Service
S.I.C.: 2721
N.A.I.C.S.: 511120
Simon Middleboe *(Mng Dir)*

U.S. Subsidiary:

EMAP Communications USA **(3)**
420 Lexington Ave Ste 244
New York, NY 10170-0299
Tel.: (212) 599-5209
Fax: (212) 599-5202
Provider of Business Services
S.I.C.: 2741
N.A.I.C.S.: 511199

Non-U.S. Subsidiary:

EMAP Communications BV **(3)**
Zonnebaan 27
3606 CH Maarssen, Netherlands
Mailing Address:
PO Box 1888
3600BW Maarssen, Netherlands
Tel.: (31) 302411088
Fax: (31) 302413287
E-Mail: info@emapbv.nl
Web Site: www.emap.nl
Emp.: 12
Magazine Publisher
S.I.C.: 2721
N.A.I.C.S.: 511120

Non-U.S. Subsidiaries:

AME Info FZ LLC **(2)**
Dubai Media City Phase II Building 4 Office 204-205
PO Box 502100
Dubai, United Arab Emirates AE
Tel.: (971) 43902700
Fax: (971) 4 3908015
Web Site: www.ameinfo.com
Business & Financial Information Services
S.I.C.: 2741
N.A.I.C.S.: 519130
Peter J. Cooper *(Owner)*
Erik Stensgaard *(CTO)*
Youssef Bazzi *(Pub Rel Officer)*

Bounty Services Pty Ltd. **(2)**
54-58 Park St
Sydney, NSW, 2000, Australia
Tel.: (61) 292828000
Fax: (61) 292674361
E-Mail: info@acpmagazines.com.au
Web Site: www.acpmagazines.com.au
Magazine Publisher
S.I.C.: 2721
N.A.I.C.S.: 511120

Media Corporation Publishing (M) **(2)**
137 Jalan SS 25 2 311 Pont 01 11th Fl
Jaya Mewah, Petaling Jaya, 46500, Malaysia
Tel.: (60) 379579698
Fax: (60) 379571060
Web Site: www.corporate.mediacorp.sg/career/job_1147250879.htm
Emp.: 30
Magazine Publisher
S.I.C.: 2721
N.A.I.C.S.: 511120

U.S. Subsidiary:

Apax Partners, L.P. **(1)**
601 Lexington Ave
New York, NY 10022 DE
Tel.: (212) 753-6300
Fax: (212) 319-6155
E-Mail: info@apax.com
Web Site: www.apax.com
Emp.: 65
Private Equity Advisory Firm
S.I.C.: 6211
N.A.I.C.S.: 523999
John F. Megrue, Jr. *(CEO, Partner & Head-USA)*
Seth Brody *(Partner)*
Marcelo Gigliani *(Partner)*
Buddy Gumina *(Partner)*
Ashish Karandikar *(Partner)*
David Kim *(Partner)*
Roy Mackenzie *(Partner)*
Alex Pellegrini *(Partner)*
Jason Wright *(Partner)*
Ameya Agge *(Principal)*
Michael Bergen *(Principal)*
Will Chen *(Principal)*
Adil Haque *(Principal)*
Vivek Vyas *(Principal)*
Robert Whipple *(Principal)*

U.S. Holdings:

Advantage Sales & Marketing LLC **(1)**
18100 Von Karman Ave Ste 1000
Irvine, CA 92612-1539
Tel.: (949) 797-2900
Fax: (949) 797-9112
E-Mail: info@asmnet.com
Web Site: www.asmnet.com
Sales Range: $750-799.9 Million
Emp.: 20,000
Sales & Marketing Services for the Consumer Packaged Goods Industry
S.I.C.: 5141
N.A.I.C.S.: 424410
Sonny King *(Chm & CEO)*
Tanya Domier *(Pres & COO)*
Todd Baird *(Pres-Sls)*

Subsidiaries:

Advantage Sales & Marketing **(2)**
50 Commerce Dr Ste 170
Schaumburg, IL 60173
Tel.: (630) 339-7600
Fax: (847) 519-3486
Emp.: 100
Food Brokers
S.I.C.: 5141
N.A.I.C.S.: 424410
Jeff Clegg *(Gen Mgr)*

Advantage Sales & Marketing **(2)**
56 Grandville SW
Grand Rapids, MI 49503
Tel.: (616) 784-3308
Fax: (616) 242-2600
Web Site: www.asmnet.com
Sls.: $11,600,000
Emp.: 30
Provider of Sales & Marketing Services for the Consumer Packaged Goods Industry
S.I.C.: 5141
N.A.I.C.S.: 424410
Kurt Johnson *(Mgr-Bus Dev)*

Advantage Sales & Marketing **(2)**
123 Tice Blvd Ste 300
Woodcliff Lake, NJ 07677
Tel.: (201) 825-9400
Fax: (201) 825-8556
Web Site: www.asmnet.com
Emp.: 1,200
Sales & Marketing Services for the Consumer Packaged Goods Industry
S.I.C.: 5141
N.A.I.C.S.: 424410
Karen Pitts *(Dir-HR)*

Advantage Sales & Marketing **(2)**
140 Heimer Rd Ste 500
San Antonio, TX 78232
Tel.: (210) 494-8226
Fax: (210) 494-0916
Web Site: www.asmnet.com
Sls.: $110,900,000
Emp.: 265
Sales & Marketing Services for the Consumer Packaged Goods Industry
S.I.C.: 5141
N.A.I.C.S.: 424410

Advantage Sales & Marketing **(2)**
841 Powell Ave SW Ste 150
Renton, WA 98057
Tel.: (425) 572-3250
Web Site: www.asmnet.com
Emp.: 25
Food Brokers
S.I.C.: 5141
N.A.I.C.S.: 424410
Sonny King *(Chm & CEO)*

Associated Independent Agencies, Inc. **(1)**
375 S Grand Ave
Pullman, WA 99163 WA
Tel.: (509) 332-3535
Fax: (509) 332-2914
Web Site: www.hubinternational.com
Sales Range: $1-9.9 Million
Emp.: 17
Insurance Agencies & Brokerages
S.I.C.: 6411
N.A.I.C.S.: 524210
Ashley Allred *(Mgr-Ops)*

Bankrate, Inc. **(1)**
11760 US Hwy One Ste 200
North Palm Beach, FL 33408 DE
Tel.: (561) 630-2400
Fax: (561) 625-4540
E-Mail: info@bankrate.com
Web Site: www.bankrate.com
RATE—(NYSE)
Rev.: $457,432,000
Assets: $1,296,811,000
Liabilities: $457,849,000
Net Worth: $838,962,000
Earnings: ($10,002,000)
Emp.: 488
Fiscal Year-end: 12/31/13
Internet Consumer Banking Marketplace
S.I.C.: 6726
N.A.I.C.S.: 525990
Peter Christopher Morse *(Chm)*
Edward J. DiMaria *(CFO & Sr VP)*
Kenneth S. Esterow *(COO & Sr VP)*
Bruce J. Zanca *(CMO, Chief Comm Officer & Sr VP)*
Daniel P. Hoogterp *(CTO & Sr VP)*
Michael J. Ricciardelli *(Sr VP-Bus Dev & Consumer Mktg)*
Donaldson M. Ross *(Chief Revenue Officer & Sr VP)*

Subsidiaries:

InsWeb Corporation **(2)**
10850 Gold Center Dr Ste 250
Rancho Cordova, CA 95670 CA
Tel.: (916) 853-3300
Fax: (916) 853-3325
Web Site: www.insweb.com
Sales Range: $75-99.9 Million
Insurance Lead Generation & Marketing Services
S.I.C.: 6411
N.A.I.C.S.: 524298
Hussein A. Enan *(Chm & CEO)*

LinkOffers, Inc. **(2)**
8920 Business Park Dr Ste 350
Austin, TX 78759
Tel.: (855) 889-5465
E-Mail: support@LinkOffers.com
Web Site: www.linkoffers.com
Online Publishing Services
S.I.C.: 2741
N.A.I.C.S.: 511199

NetQuote, Inc. **(2)**
1860 Blake St Ste 900
Denver, CO 80202
Tel.: (800) 795-2886
Fax: (303) 291-1934
Web Site: www.netquote.com
Online Insurance Services
N.A.I.C.S.: 524298
Scott Axcell *(VP-Mktg)*

Non-U.S. Subsidiary:

Freedom Marketing Limited **(2)**
5 Beacon End Courtyard
London Road, Colchester, Essex, CO3 0NU, United Kingdom
Tel.: (44) 2071951970
E-Mail: contactus@freedommarketing.co.uk
Web Site: www.freedommarketing.co.uk
Online Publishing Services
S.I.C.: 2741
N.A.I.C.S.: 511199

Cengage Learning, Inc. **(1)**
200 1st Stamford Pl Ste 400
Stamford, CT 06902-6800 DE
Tel.: (203) 965-8600
Fax: (203) 965-8556
Web Site: www.cengage.com
Sales Range: $1-4.9 Billion
Emp.: 5,800
Library Reference & Educational Materials Publishing & Learning Solutions
S.I.C.: 2731
N.A.I.C.S.: 511130
Ronald G. Dunn *(Chm)*
Michael E. Hansen *(CEO)*
Dean D. Durbin *(CFO)*
Kevin Stone *(Chief Sls & Mktg Officer & Exec VP)*
Sandi Kirshner *(CMO)*
Fernando Bleichmar *(Chief Strategy Officer & Exec VP)*
George Moore *(CTO)*
Mark Howe *(Chief People Officer)*
William D. Rieders *(Chief Bus Dev Officer)*
Julian Drinkall *(Pres/CEO-EMEA & India)*
Ken Carson *(Gen Counsel)*
Susan Aspey *(Sr VP-Pub Affairs)*
Josef Blumenfeld *(Sr VP-Corp Affairs)*
Torsten Geers *(Sr VP-Corp Dev, Mergers & Acq)*

Branch:

Cengage Learning, Inc. - Boston **(2)**
20 Channel Center St
Boston, MA 02210
Tel.: (617) 289-7700
Fax: (617) 289-7844
Toll Free: (800) 354-9706
Web Site: www.cengage.com
Emp.: 500
ESL & Other Language Educational Materials Publisher
S.I.C.: 2731
N.A.I.C.S.: 511130
Ronald G. Dunn *(Chm)*
Kevin Stone *(Chief Sls & Mktg Officer & Exec VP)*
Sandi Kirshner *(CMO)*
Alexander Broich *(Pres-Intl)*

Division:

Cengage Higher Education **(2)**
20 Davis Dr
Belmont, CA 94002
Tel.: (650) 595-2350
Web Site: www.academic.cengage.com
Educational Book Publishing
S.I.C.: 2731
N.A.I.C.S.: 511130
Charles Siegel *(CEO)*

Units:

South-Western Cengage Learning **(3)**
5191 Natorp Blvd
Mason, OH 45040
Tel.: (513) 229-1000
Fax: (513) 229-1002
Toll Free: (800) 543-0487
Web Site: www.cengagelearning.com
Emp.: 700
Accounting, Marketing & Management Education Book Publisher
S.I.C.: 2731
N.A.I.C.S.: 511130
Ron Dunn *(CEO)*

Wadsworth Cengage Learning **(3)**
10 Davis Dr
Belmont, CA 94002-3002
Tel.: (650) 595-2350
Fax: (650) 637-7544
Toll Free: (800) 354-9706
Web Site: www.academic.cengage.com
Educational Software & Textbook Publisher
S.I.C.: 2731
N.A.I.C.S.: 511130

Subsidiaries:

Delmar Cengage Learning **(2)**
5 Maxwell Dr Executive Woods
Clifton Park, NY 12065-2919
Mailing Address:
PO Box 8007
Clifton Park, NY 12065-8007
Tel.: (518) 348-2300
Fax: (518) 881-1258
Toll Free: (800) 648-7450
Web Site: www.cengage.com
Emp.: 294
Educational, Technical & Vocational Publishers
S.I.C.: 2731
N.A.I.C.S.: 511130
Manuel Guzman *(Interim CEO & CFO)*

Gale Group Inc. **(2)**
27500 Drake Rd
Farmington Hills, MI 48331-3535
Tel.: (248) 699-4253
Fax: (248) 699-8064
Toll Free: (800) 877-4253

Apax Partners LLP—(Continued)

Web Site: www.gale.com
Emp.: 1,000
Reference Book & Electronic Reference Materials Publisher
Import Export
S.I.C.: 2741
N.A.I.C.S.: 511140
Dennis Stepaniak *(COO)*
Frank Menchaca *(Exec VP-Publ)*

Divisions:

Macmillan Reference USA (3)
12 Lunar Dr
Woodbridge, CT 06525-2322
Tel.: (203) 397-2600
Fax: (203) 397-8296
Toll Free: (800) 444-0799
Web Site: gale.cengage.com
Emp.: 55
Publisher of Academic & Professional Reference Materials, Newspapers & U.S. & Foreign Patents
S.I.C.: 2731
N.A.I.C.S.: 511130
Frank Menchaca *(Exec VP-Publ)*

Non-U.S. Subsidiaries:

Cengage Learning Asia (2)
151 Lorong Chuan 02-08 New Tech Park
UIC Bldg, Singapore, 556741, Singapore
Tel.: (65) 64101200
Fax: (65) 64101208
E-Mail: asia.info@cengage.com
Web Site: www.cengageasia.com
Emp.: 70
Educational & Reference Book Publisher
S.I.C.: 2731
N.A.I.C.S.: 511130
Tat Chu Tan *(Pres)*

Cengage Learning Australia Pty. Limited (2)
80 Dorcas St Level 7
Victoria, VIC, 3205, Australia AU
Tel.: (61) 396854111
E-Mail: aust.customerservice@cengage.com
Web Site: www.cengage.com.au
Emp.: 200
Educational & Reference Book Publishing
S.I.C.: 2731
N.A.I.C.S.: 511130
Michael Vella *(CFO)*
Tat Chu Tan *(Pres-Asia Pacific)*

Nelson Education Ltd. (2)
1120 Birchmount Rd
Scarborough, ON, M1K 5G4, Canada
Tel.: (416) 752-9448
Fax: (800) 430-4445
Toll Free: (800) 268-2222
E-Mail: inquire@nelson.com
Web Site: www.nelson.com
Emp.: 400
Education & Reference Book Publishing
S.I.C.: 2731
N.A.I.C.S.: 511130
Greg Nordel *(Pres)*
James Reeve *(Mng Dir & Sr VP-Higher Education Div)*
Michael Andrews *(CFO)*
Susan Cline *(Sr VP-Media Svcs)*
Linda Rushford *(Sr VP-Product)*

Cole Haan LLC (1)
Roundwood Business Park 6 Ashley Dr
Scarborough, ME 04074 DE
Tel.: (207) 510-5100 (100%)
Toll Free: (800) 695-8945
Web Site: www.colehaan.com
Sales Range: $550-599.9 Million
Emp.: 200
Footwear, Accessories & Outerwear Retailer
Import Export
S.I.C.: 5139
N.A.I.C.S.: 424340
Jack A. Boys *(CEO)*
J. Michael Prince *(COO & CFO)*

Subsidiary:

Cole Haan Company Store (2)
109 Newbury St
Boston, MA 02116-2902 ME
Tel.: (617) 536-7826
Fax: (617) 437-7031
Web Site: www.colehaan.com
Rubber & Plastics Footwear Mfr
S.I.C.: 2389
N.A.I.C.S.: 316210
Gina Nieves *(Gen Mgr)*

Non-U.S. Subsidiary:

Cole Haan Japan, Inc. (2)
Rene Aoyama Bldg 3F 3-3-11 Kita
Minato-Ku, Tokyo, 107-0061, Japan
Tel.: (81) 3 3470 7700
Fax: (81) 3 3470 7716
Web Site: www.colehaan.co.jp
Emp.: 240
Footwear Retailer
S.I.C.: 5139
N.A.I.C.S.: 424340

Contech Construction Products Inc. (1)
9025 Ctr Pointe Dr Ste 400
West Chester, OH 45069 OH
Tel.: (513) 645-7000
Fax: (513) 645-7933
Toll Free: (800) 338-1122
E-Mail: info@contech-cpi.com
Web Site: www.contech-cpi.com
Sales Range: $700-749.9 Million
Emp.: 1,800
Civil Engineering Services
S.I.C.: 1629
N.A.I.C.S.: 237990
Patrick Harlow *(Chm)*
Ronald C. Keating *(Pres & CEO)*
Jeff Lee *(CFO & Exec VP)*
Richard G. Stepien *(Pres-Mktg)*
Rebecca Appenzeller *(Gen Counsel)*

Subsidiaries:

Contech Inc. (2)
710 SW Armco Ave
Hillsboro, OR 97123
Tel.: (503) 640-2783
Fax: (503) 640-8325
Emp.: 7
Metal Culvert Pipe Mfr & Distr
S.I.C.: 3498
N.A.I.C.S.: 332996
Mike Roche *(Gen Mgr)*

ConTech (2)
6523 188th St NE
Arlington, WA 98223-8707
Tel.: (360) 435-2181
Fax: (360) 435-9436
Web Site: www.contech-cpi.com
Emp.: 15
Mfr of Metal Culvert Pipe
S.I.C.: 5051
N.A.I.C.S.: 423510
Bob Showalter *(Plant Mgr)*

Epicor Software Corporation (1)
4120 Dublin Blvd Ste 300
Dublin, CA 94568 DE
Tel.: (925) 361-9900
Fax: (925) 361-9999
Toll Free: (800) 999-1809
E-Mail: info@epicor.com
Web Site: www.epicor.com
Rev.: $961,731,000
Assets: $2,429,942,000
Liabilities: $1,918,133,000
Net Worth: $511,809,000
Earnings: ($40,373,000)
Emp.: 4,600
Fiscal Year-end: 09/30/13
Integrated Enterprise & E-Business Software Solutions Designer, Developer & Marketer
S.I.C.: 3652
N.A.I.C.S.: 334614
Joseph L. Cowan *(Pres & CEO)*
Kathleen Crusco *(CFO)*
John D. Ireland *(Gen Counsel & VP)*
Craig McCollum *(Exec VP & Gen Mgr-Retail Distr Solutions Bus)*
Donna Troy *(Exec VP & Gen Mgr-Enterprise Resource Plng-Americas)*
Lauri Klaus *(Exec VP-Worldwide Sls & Consulting)*
Noel Goggin *(Sr VP & Gen Mgr-Retail Solutions Bus)*

Branches:

Epicor Software Corporation-Minneapolis (2)
600 S Hwy 169 Ste 2000 Interchange Tower
Minneapolis, MN 55426
Tel.: (952) 417-5000
Fax: (952) 544-8253
E-Mail: info@epicor.com
Web Site: www.epicor.com
Sales Range: $25-49.9 Million
Emp.: 175
Integrated Enterprise & E-Business Software Solutions Designer, Developer & Marketer
S.I.C.: 7372
N.A.I.C.S.: 511210

Subsidiaries:

Internet Autoparts, Inc. (2)
7600 N Capital Of Texas H
Austin, TX 78731
Tel.: (512) 527-8966
E-Mail: sales@iapshop.com
Web Site: www.iapshop.com
Sales Range: $10-24.9 Million
Emp.: 15
Internet Services
S.I.C.: 4899
N.A.I.C.S.: 517919
Glenn Staats *(Pres)*

Non-U.S. Subsidiaries:

Epicor Scala ECE Overseas Ltd. (2)
12 Andrea Zakou St
2404 Nicosia, Engomi, Cyprus
Mailing Address:
P.O. Box 25149
CY-1307 Nicosia, Engomi, Cyprus
Tel.: (357) 22674741
Fax: (357) 22674277
Web Site: www.epicor.com
Emp.: 6
Integrated Enterprise & E-Business Software Solutions Designer, Developer & Marketer
S.I.C.: 3652
N.A.I.C.S.: 334614

Epicor Software (Asia) Pte. Ltd. (2)
238A Thomson Road 23-06
Novena Square Tower A, 307684
Singapore, Singapore SG
Tel.: (65) 6333 8121
Fax: (65) 6333 8131
E-Mail: asiamarketing@epicor.com
Web Site: www.epicor.com
Integrated Enterprise & E-Business Software Solutions Designer, Developer & Marketer
S.I.C.: 3652
N.A.I.C.S.: 334614

Epicor Software (Beijing) Company, Ltd. (2)
Rm B 4F Office Bldg Tower A
E Gate Plz No 9 Dongzhong, Beijing, 100027, China
Tel.: (86) 1064182998
Fax: (86) 64183988
Emp.: 7
Integrated Enterprise & E-Business Software Solutions Designer, Developer & Marketer
S.I.C.: 3652
N.A.I.C.S.: 334614

Epicor Software Czech s.r.o (2)
Gemini Budova B
Na Pankraci 1724-129, 140 00 Prague, Czech Republic CZ
Tel.: (420) 225992255
Fax: (420) 225 992 387
E-Mail: cz.sales@epicor.com
Integrated Enterprise & E-Business Software Solutions Designer, Developer & Marketer
S.I.C.: 3652
N.A.I.C.S.: 334614

Epicor Software Deutschland GmbH (2)
Hanauer Landstr 291 A
60314 Frankfurt am Main, Germany
Tel.: (49) 69 800 76600
Fax: (49) 69 800 76605
E-Mail: info.germany@epicor.com
Integrated Enterprise & E-Business Software Solutions Designer, Developer & Marketer
S.I.C.: 3652
N.A.I.C.S.: 334614

Epicor Software Estonia OU (2)
Sopruse pst 151
13417 Tallinn, Estonia
Tel.: (372) 6997640
Fax: (372) 6 997 641
E-Mail: info.estonia@epicor.com
Web Site: www.epicor.com
Integrated Enterprise & E-Business Software Solutions Designer, Developer & Marketer
S.I.C.: 3652
N.A.I.C.S.: 334614
Thomas Grouse *(District Mgr)*

Epicor Software Finland Oy (2)
Metsanneidonkuja 10
Espoo, FI-02130, Finland
Tel.: (358) 207 410 850
Fax: (358) 207 410 851
E-Mail: info.finland@epicor.com
Web Site: www.epicor.com
Integrated Enterprise & E-Business Software Solutions Designer, Developer & Marketer
S.I.C.: 3652
N.A.I.C.S.: 334614
Patrick Nordling *(Dir-Sls)*

Epicor Software Hungary Kft (2)
Vaci U 76 VI Torony 2 EM
Budapest, H-1133, Hungary
Tel.: (36) 1 452 7600
Fax: (36) 1 452 7510
E-Mail: info.hungary@epicor.com
Web Site: www.epicor.com
Emp.: 60
Integrated Enterprise & E-Business Software Solutions Designer, Developer & Marketer
S.I.C.: 3652
N.A.I.C.S.: 334614
Timothy Newton *(Mng Dir)*

Epicor Software Italia s.r.l. (2)
Via di Vigna Murata 30
00143 Rome, Italy
Tel.: (39) 0654832093
Fax: (39) 0654834000
Web Site: www.epicor.com
Emp.: 3
Integrated Enterprise & E-Business Software Solutions Designer, Developer & Marketer
S.I.C.: 3652
N.A.I.C.S.: 334614
Tim Newton *(Gen Dir)*

Epicor Software Japan K.K. (2)
16F Holland Hills Mori Tower 5-11-2 Toranomon
Minato-ku, 105-0001 Tokyo, Japan
Tel.: (81) 357334792
Fax: (81) 357334796
E-Mail: asiamarketing@epicor.com
Web Site: www.epicor.com
Integrated Enterprise & E-Business Software Solutions Designer, Developer & Marketer
S.I.C.: 3652
N.A.I.C.S.: 334614

Epicor Software Latvija SIA (2)
120G Dzelzavas Street
LV 1021 Riga, Latvia
Tel.: (371) 67549497
Fax: (371) 7549498
E-Mail: lv@epicor.com
Web Site: www.epicor.com
Integrated Enterprise & E-Business Software Solutions Designer, Developer & Marketer
S.I.C.: 3652
N.A.I.C.S.: 334614

Epicor Software (M) Sdn Bhd (2)
Unit 1101C Level 11 Tower C Uptown 5
No 5 Jalan SS21/39
Damansara Uptown, 47400 Petaling Jaya, Selangor, Malaysia
Tel.: (60) 3 7962 8800
Fax: (60) 3 7722 4633
E-Mail: asiamarketing@epicor.com
Web Site: www.epicor.com

Emp.: 100
Integrated Enterprise & E-Business Software Solutions Designer, Developer & Marketer
S.I.C.: 3652
N.A.I.C.S.: 334614

Epicor Software (North Asia) Ltd. Guangzhou (2)
Level 10 HNA 8 Linhe Zhong Rd
Tianhe Distr, Guangzhou, 510610, China
Tel.: (86) 2028317348
Fax: (86) 2028317000
E-Mail: asiamarketing@epicor.com
Web Site: www.epicor.com
Integrated Enterprise & E-Business Software Solutions Designer, Developer & Marketer
S.I.C.: 3652
N.A.I.C.S.: 334614

Epicor Software (North Asia) Ltd. (2)
18/F Rm 1806 Tower 2
33 Canton Road Tsimshatsui, Hong Kong, China (Hong Kong)
Tel.: (852) 25639930
Fax: (852) 25658599
E-Mail: asiamarketing@epicor.com
Web Site: www.epicor.com
Emp.: 11
Integrated Enterprise & E-Business Software Solutions Designer, Developer & Marketer
S.I.C.: 3652
N.A.I.C.S.: 334614
Luice Lai *(Office Mgr)*

Epicor Software Poland Sp. z o.o. (2)
Ul Obornicka 229
60-650 Poznan, Poland
Tel.: (48) 618484495
Fax: (48) 616561908
E-Mail: info@epicor.pl
Web Site: www.epicor.com
Emp.: 30
Integrated Enterprise & E-Business Software Solutions Designer, Developer & Marketer
S.I.C.: 3652
N.A.I.C.S.: 334614
Danuta Jakubowski *(Dir-Fin)*

Epicor Software (SEA) Pte Ltd. (2)
8th Floor Leema Building
146-1 Soosong-Dong, Seoul, Chongro-Gu, 110-140, Korea (South)
Tel.: (82) 2 398 5875
Fax: (82) 2 398 58 79
E-Mail: asiamarketing@epicor.com
Web Site: www.epicor.com
Integrated Enterprise & E-Business Software Solutions Designer, Developer & Marketer
S.I.C.: 3652
N.A.I.C.S.: 334614

Epicor Software (Shanghai) Co., Ltd. (2)
Suite 2008 Cross Tower
318 Fuzhou Road, Shanghai, 2401-200001, China CN
Tel.: (86) 2163912808
Fax: (86) 21639102809
E-Mail: asiamarketing@epicor.com
Web Site: www.epicor.com
Emp.: 100
Integrated Enterprise & E-Business Software Solutions Designer, Developer & Marketer
S.I.C.: 3652
N.A.I.C.S.: 334614
Susan Tao *(Mgr-Mktg)*

Epicor Software Slovakia, s.r.o. (2)
Dvorakovo Nabrezie 4
81109 Bratislava, Slovakia
Tel.: (421) 2 3500 2300
Fax: (421) 2 5245 1500
E-Mail: info@epicor.com
Web Site: www.epicor.com
Emp.: 50
Integrated Enterprise & E-Business Software Solutions Designer, Developer & Marketer
S.I.C.: 3652
N.A.I.C.S.: 334614
Marian Janci *(Gen Mgr)*

Epicor Software SRL (2)
69 Dacia Blvd
020051 Bucharest, Romania
Tel.: (40) 21 212 1024
Fax: (40) 21 212 1124
E-Mail: info.ro@epicor.com
Web Site: www.epicor.com
Emp.: 15
Integrated Enterprise & E-Business Software Solutions Designer, Developer & Marketer
S.I.C.: 3652
N.A.I.C.S.: 334614
Luliana Cojanu *(Gen Mgr)*

Epicor Software UK, Ltd. (2)
No 1 The Arena Downshire Way
Bracknell, RG12 1PU, United Kingdom
Tel.: (44) 1344 468468
Fax: (44) 1344 468020
E-Mail: europemarketing@epicor.com
Web Site: www.epicor.com
Emp.: 15
Integrated Enterprise & E-Business Software Solutions Designer, Developer & Marketer
S.I.C.: 3652
N.A.I.C.S.: 334614
Keith Deane *(Sr VP & Gen Mgr-EMEA)*

Kinetic Concepts, Inc. (1)
8023 Vantage Dr
San Antonio, TX 78230-4769 TX
Mailing Address:
PO Box 659508
San Antonio, TX 78265-9508
Tel.: (210) 524-9000
Fax: (210) 255-6998
Toll Free: (800) 275-4524
Web Site: www.kci1.com
Sales Range: $1-4.9 Billion
Emp.: 6,900
Wound Treatment Solution, Clinical Beds & Medical Devices Designer, Mfr & Marketer
Export
S.I.C.: 3841
N.A.I.C.S.: 339112
Joseph F. Woody *(Pres & CEO)*
Stephen D. Seidel *(Pres-Therapeutic Support Sys Bus)*
Peter Arnold *(Sr VP-Innovation & Strategic Mktg)*
James Cunniff *(Sr VP-Americas)*
David Lillback *(Sr VP-HR)*
Mike Mathews *(Sr VP-Intl)*

Subsidiary:

LifeCell Corporation (2)
1 Millennium Way
Branchburg, NJ 08876 DE
Tel.: (908) 947-1100
Fax: (908) 947-1200
E-Mail: corporatecommunications@lifecell.com
Web Site: www.lifecell.com
Sales Range: $150-199.9 Million
Emp.: 443
Skin Graft Materials for Reconstructive, Urogynecologic & Orthopedic Surgery
S.I.C.: 2836
N.A.I.C.S.: 325414
Joseph F. Woody *(Interim CEO)*

Non-U.S. Subsidiaries:

KCI Australia Pty. Ltd. (2)
15 Orion Road Level 7 West
Lane Cove, NSW, 2066, Australia
Mailing Address:
PO Box 1541
Lane Cove, NSW, 1595, Australia
Tel.: (61) 294224322
Fax: (61) 294224344
E-Mail: postmasterau@kci-medical.com
Web Site: www.kci-medical.com
Sales Range: $100-124.9 Million
Patient Bedding & Medical Device Developer & Mfr
S.I.C.: 3841
N.A.I.C.S.: 339112
Jim Stack *(Mng Dir)*

KCI Austria GmbH (2)
Lembockgasse 49
Stiege A, 1230 Vienna, Austria AT
Tel.: (43) 1 86 330
E-Mail: austria@kci-medical.com
Web Site: www.kci-medical.at
Sales Range: $100-124.9 Million
Clinical Bedding & Patient Therapy System Developer & Mfr
S.I.C.: 3841
N.A.I.C.S.: 339112
Torsten Van Steelanvt *(Gen Mgr)*

KCI Clinic Spain S.L. (2)
Centro Empresarial Arco Edificio 4 Modulo A C/ Virgilio
No 2 Ciudad de la Imagen Pozue, 28223 Madrid, Spain
Tel.: (34) 902100835
Fax: (34) 916333058
E-Mail: postmastES@kci-medical.com
Web Site: www.kci-medical.com
Sales Range: $100-124.9 Million
Emp.: 15
Clinical Bedding & Medical Device Developer, Mfr & Whslr
S.I.C.: 3841
N.A.I.C.S.: 339112
Jose Antonio Lombardero *(Gen Mgr)*

KCI KK (2)
Kioicho Building 5F 3 12 Kioicho
Chiyoda Ku, Tokyo, 102 0094, Japan
Tel.: (81) 3 3230 3853
Fax: (81) 332303853
Sales Range: $100-124.9 Million
Emp.: 50
Clinical Bedding & Medical Device Developer, Mfr & Whslr
S.I.C.: 3841
N.A.I.C.S.: 339112

KCI Medical AB (2)
Automatakveg 1
2570 Ballerup, Denmark
Tel.: (45) 3990 0180
Fax: (45) 854499691
E-Mail: postmasterse@kci-medical.com
Web Site: www.kci-medical.com
Sales Range: $1-9.9 Million
Emp.: 10
Clinical Bedding & Medical Device Developer, Mfr & Whslr
S.I.C.: 3841
N.A.I.C.S.: 339112

KCI Medical ApS (2)
Telegrafvej 4 3 Flr
2750 Ballerup, Denmark
Tel.: (45) 39900180
Fax: (45) 39901498
E-Mail: postmasterdk@kci-medical.com
Web Site: www.kci-medical.com
Sales Range: $10-24.9 Million
Emp.: 50
Clinical Bedding & Medical Device Developer, Mfr & Whslr
S.I.C.: 3841
N.A.I.C.S.: 339112
Sigve Skimmeland *(Mng Dir)*

KCI Medical Asia Pte. Ltd. (2)
50 Ubi Crescent 01 01
Singapore, 408568, Singapore
Tel.: (65) 67426686
Fax: (65) 67496686
E-Mail: postmasterSG@kci-medical.com
Web Site: www.kcimedical.com
Sales Range: $100-124.9 Million
Emp.: 20
Clinical Bedding & Medical Device Developer, Mfr & Whslr
S.I.C.: 3841
N.A.I.C.S.: 339112

KCI Medical Belgium BVBA (2)
The Crescent Wetenschapspark Erasmus Lenniksebaan 451E, 1070 Brussels, Belgium
Tel.: (32) 2 528 05 11
Fax: (32) 2 528 05 14
E-Mail: infobe@kci-medical.com
Web Site: www.kci-medical.com
Sales Range: $100-124.9 Million
Clinical Bedding & Medical Device Developer, Mfr & Whslr
S.I.C.: 3841
N.A.I.C.S.: 339112

KCI Medical B.V. (2)
Duikboot 1
3991 CK Houten, Netherlands
Tel.: (31) 306355885
Fax: (31) 306377690
E-Mail: infonl@kci-medical.com
Web Site: www.kci-medical.com
Sales Range: $100-124.9 Million
Emp.: 65
Clinical Bedding & Medical Device Developer, Mfr & Whslr
S.I.C.: 3841
N.A.I.C.S.: 339112
Linda Mulder *(Mng Dir)*

KCI Medical Canada, Inc. (2)
75 Courtneypark Drive W Unit 2
Mississauga, ON, L5W 0E3, Canada
Tel.: (905) 565-7187
Fax: (905) 565-7270
E-Mail: postmastca@kci-medical.com
Sales Range: $100-124.9 Million
Clinical Bedding & Medical Device Developer, Mfr & Whslr
S.I.C.: 3841
N.A.I.C.S.: 339112

KCI Medical GmbH (2)
Ifangstrasse 91
8153 Rumlang, Switzerland
Tel.: (41) 434553100
Fax: (41) 43455300
E-Mail: postmasterCH@kci-medical.com
Web Site: www.kci-medical.com
Sales Range: $100-124.9 Million
Clinical Bedding & Medical Device Developer, Mfr & Whslr
S.I.C.: 3841
N.A.I.C.S.: 339112

KCI Medical Ltd. (2)
2050 Orchard Avenue
Citywest Business Campus, Dublin, 24, Ireland
Tel.: (353) 14659510
Fax: (353) 14213901
E-Mail: postmastIE@kci-medical.com
Web Site: www.kci-medical.com
Sales Range: $100-124.9 Million
Emp.: 15
Clinical Bedding & Medical Device Developer, Mfr & Whslr
S.I.C.: 3841
N.A.I.C.S.: 339112

KCI Medical South Africa Pty. Ltd. (2)
Thornhill Office Park Unit 24
94 Bekker Road, Midrand, 1685, South Africa
Tel.: (27) 113150445
Fax: (27) 113151757
E-Mail:
Sales Range: $10-24.9 Million
Emp.: 40
Clinical Bedding & Medical Device Developer, Mfr & Whslr
S.I.C.: 3841
N.A.I.C.S.: 339112
Charl Louw *(Gen Mgr)*

KCI Medical S.R.L. (2)
via Meucci 1
Assago, 20090, Italy
Tel.: (39) 02 457 1721
Fax: (39) 02457174210
E-Mail: info_italy@kci-medical.com
Web Site: www.kci-medical.it
Sales Range: $25-49.9 Million
Emp.: 150
Clinical Bedding & Medical Device Developer, Mfr & Whslr
S.I.C.: 3841
N.A.I.C.S.: 339112
Lioniardo Borghese *(Mng Dir)*

KCI Medizinproduckte GmbH (2)
Hagenauer Strasse 47
65203 Wiesbaden, Germany
Tel.: (49) 611335440
Fax: (49) 6113388408
E-Mail: postmasterde@kci-medical.com
Web Site: www.kci-medical.com
Sales Range: $100-124.9 Million
Clinical Bedding & Medical Device Developer, Mfr & Whslr
S.I.C.: 3841
N.A.I.C.S.: 339112

Laboratoire KCI Medical (2)
Parc Technopolis 17 Ave du Parc
Chilly-Mazarin, 91380 Paris, France
Tel.: (33) 169747171
Fax: (33) 169747172
E-Mail: kcifrance@kci-medical.com
Web Site: www.kci-medical.com

Apax Partners LLP—(Continued)

Sales Range: $25-49.9 Million
Emp.: 100
Clinical Bedding & Medical Device Developer, Mfr & Whslr
S.I.C.: 3841
N.A.I.C.S.: 339112

One Call Care Management, Inc. (1)
20 Waterview Blvd PO Box 614
Parsippany, NJ 07054
Tel.: (973) 394-8461
Fax: (973) 257-3687
Toll Free: (800) 872-2875
E-Mail: pressinquiries@onecallmedical.com
Web Site: www.onecallcm.com
Sales Range: $500-549.9 Million
Emp.: 340
Diagnostic Imaging & Electrodiagnostic Scheduling Services Network Operator
S.I.C.: 8049
N.A.I.C.S.: 621399
Don Duford *(Chm)*
Joseph P. Delaney *(Pres & CEO)*
Kevin English *(CFO)*
Anthony Cuva *(CIO)*
Robert Zeccardi *(CMO & Chief Sls Officer)*
Steven Davis *(Chief Legal Officer)*
Robert A. Cook *(Pres-One Call Care Court Reporting)*
Joe McCullough *(Pres-One Call Care Transport/Translate)*
James Phifer *(Pres-One Call Care Grp Health)*
Will Smith *(Pres-One Call Care Equipment/Complex Care)*
John Stanzi *(Pres-One Call Care Diagnostics)*
Chris Toepke *(Pres-One Call Care Dental/Doctor/Physical Therapy)*
Brent Haines *(Sr VP-Sls-West)*

Subsidiaries:

Express Dental Care, LLC (2)
4350 W Cypress St Ste 1000
Tampa, FL 33607 FL
Tel.: (813) 549-7131
Fax: (888) 539-0579
Toll Free: (888) 539-0577
E-Mail: info@expresshealthservices.com
Web Site: www.expresshealthservices.com
Sales Range: $1-9.9 Million
Emp.: 30
Administrative Management & General Management Consulting Service
S.I.C.: 8742
N.A.I.C.S.: 541611
Stacey Whidden *(CEO)*
Bob Dombroski *(CIO)*

STOPS, Inc. (2)
8855 Grissom Pkwy
Titusville, FL 32780
Tel.: (321) 383-4111
Fax: (321) 383-9332
Toll Free: (800) 487-0521
E-Mail: customercare@stopsinc.com
Web Site: www.stopsinc.com
Emp.: 75
Transportation & Interpretation Services for Patients
S.I.C.: 8099
N.A.I.C.S.: 621999
James Williams *(Pres)*
Bob Cook *(CEO)*

Pictage, Inc. (1)
1580 Francisco St Ste 101
Torrance, CA 90501
Tel.: (310) 525-1600
Fax: (310) 525-1565
Toll Free: (877) 742-1960
E-Mail: support@pictage.com
Web Site: www.pictage.com
Sales Range: $25-49.9 Million
Emp.: 150
Online Photographer Support Services
S.I.C.: 2741
N.A.I.C.S.: 519130
Michael Grant *(CEO)*
Craig Cochrane *(Exec VP-Mktg)*
Jennifer Henriksen *(Exec VP-Client Rels)*

rue21, inc. (1)
800 Commonwealth Dr
Warrendale, PA 15086-7527 DE
Tel.: (724) 776-9780
Fax: (724) 776-4111
Web Site: www.rue21.com
Sls.: $901,886,000
Assets: $399,509,000
Liabilities: $221,198,000
Net Worth: $178,311,000
Earnings: $43,901,000
Emp.: 2,807
Fiscal Year-end: 02/02/13
Apparel & Fragrance Retailer & Mfr Import Export
S.I.C.: 5699
N.A.I.C.S.: 448190
Robert N. Fisch *(Pres & CEO)*
Keith A. McDonough *(CFO & Sr VP)*
Michael A. Holland *(CIO & Sr VP)*
Stacy B. Siegal *(Chief Admin Officer & Sr VP)*
Kim A. Reynolds *(Sr VP & Gen Mgr-Mdse)*
John P. Bugnar *(Sr VP & Dir-Stores)*
Mark K.J. Chrystal *(Sr VP-Plng & Allocation)*
Robert R. Thomson *(Sr VP-Real Estate)*

The TriZetto Group, Inc. (1)
6061 S Willow Dr
Greenwood Village, CO 80111 DE
Tel.: (303) 495-7000
Fax: (303) 495-7001
E-Mail: salesinfo@trizetto.com
Web Site: www.trizetto.com
Sales Range: $450-499.9 Million
Emp.: 2,000
Healthcare Technology Services
S.I.C.: 7379
N.A.I.C.S.: 518210
Jeffrey H. Margolis *(Founder)*
Jude Dieterman *(Pres & COO)*
R. Andrew Eckert *(CEO)*
Douglas E. Barnett *(CFO)*
Alan Cullop *(CIO & Sr VP)*
Dan Spirek *(CMO, Chief Strategy Officer & Exec VP-Enterprise Strategy & Comm)*
Pierre Samec *(CTO & Exec VP)*
Jeffrey Rideout *(Chief Medical Officer & Sr VP)*
Patricia E. Gorman *(Chief Quality Officer)*
Larry Bridge *(Pres-Govt & Intl Markets)*
John Jordan *(Pres-Healthcare Market)*
Rick M. Fitzgerald *(Sr VP)*

Branches:

The TriZetto Group, Inc. - Union Regional Office (2)
1085 Morris Ave
Union, NJ 07083
Tel.: (908) 351-0700
Fax: (908) 351-8964
Web Site: www.trizetto.com
Emp.: 240
Client/Server Software Provider to Health Care & Managed Care Organizations
S.I.C.: 7299
N.A.I.C.S.: 812990
Richard Kerian *(Sr VP)*

Subsidiaries:

Gateway EDI, LLC (2)
1 Financial Plz 501 N Broadway 3rd Fl
Saint Louis, MO 63102 DE
Tel.: (314) 802-6700
Fax: (866) 203-4587
Toll Free: (800) 556-2231
Web Site: www.gatewayedi.com
Medical Industry Electronic Data Interchange Services
S.I.C.: 7379
N.A.I.C.S.: 518210
Timothy R. Fogerty *(CEO)*
Dave Cheli *(CIO)*
Robert E. Strickland *(Exec VP-Sls)*
Kelly A. Triska *(Exec VP-Client Svcs)*

Subsidiary:

National Healthcare Exchange Services, Inc. (3)
629 J St
Sacramento, CA 95814 DE
Tel.: (916) 231-0670
Fax: (916) 231-0220
Toll Free: (800) 753-3638
E-Mail: investorrelations@nhxs.com
Web Site: www.nhxs.com
Sales Range: $1-9.9 Million
Medical Billing & Revenue Recovery Software
S.I.C.: 7372
N.A.I.C.S.: 511210
Mark W. Rieger *(CEO)*

Xerium Technologies, Inc. (1)
14101 Capital Blvd
Youngsville, NC 27596 DE
Tel.: (919) 526-1400 (51.2%)
Fax: (919) 556-1063
Toll Free: (800) 932-8399
E-Mail: ir@xerium.com
Web Site: www.xerium.com
XRM—(NYSE)
Sls.: $546,892,000
Assets: $624,064,000
Liabilities: $635,513,000
Net Worth: ($11,449,000)
Earnings: $4,153,000
Emp.: 3,200
Fiscal Year-end: 12/31/13
Paper Production
S.I.C.: 2299
N.A.I.C.S.: 313210
James F. Wilson *(Chm)*
Harold C. Bevis *(Pres & CEO)*
Clifford E. Pietrafitta *(CFO & Exec VP)*
Bill Butterfield *(CTO)*
Eduardo Fracasso *(Pres-South America)*
Thomas C. Johnson *(Pres-Asia)*
David Pretty *(Pres-Europe & North America)*
Kevin McDougall *(Corp Counsel & Exec VP)*

Subsidiaries:

Stowe Woodward LLC (2)
14101 Capital Blvd Ste 201
Youngsville, NC 27596
Tel.: (919) 556-7235
Fax: (919) 556-2432
Paper Production Consumable Product Mfr & Supplier
S.I.C.: 2299
N.A.I.C.S.: 313210

Weavexx Corporation (2)
51 Flex Way
Youngsville, NC 27596-9433 DE
Tel.: (919) 556-7235
Fax: (919) 556-2432
E-Mail: suzette.defranco@xerium.com
Web Site: www.xerium.com
Emp.: 60
Specialty Paper Machine Clothing Fabrics Developer, Mfr & Distr
S.I.C.: 2299
N.A.I.C.S.: 313210
David Pretty *(Pres)*

Weavexx, LLC (2)
51 Flex Way
Youngsville, NC 27596
Tel.: (919) 556-7235
Fax: (919) 556-2432
Web Site: www.xerium.com
Emp.: 100
Paper Machine Clothing Mfr & Supplier
S.I.C.: 3589
N.A.I.C.S.: 333318

Xerium Asia, LLC (2)
8537 6 Forks Rd Ste 300
Raleigh, NC 27615
Tel.: (919) 526-1406
Fax: (919) 526-1430
Paper Production Consumable Product Mfr & Supplier
S.I.C.: 2299
N.A.I.C.S.: 313210
Tom Johnson *(Pres)*

Non-U.S. Subsidiaries:

Fa. Huyck.Wangner UK Ltd. (2)
2nd Floor Suite 6 The Links
Herne Bay, Kent, CT6 7GQ, United Kingdom
Tel.: (44) 1227 744030
Telex: 96150 Huyxkq f
Fax: (44) 1227 744039
Web Site: www.xerium.com
Emp.: 4
Mfr Paper Forming Fabrics
S.I.C.: 2269
N.A.I.C.S.: 313310
Russell Bird *(CEO)*

Huyck Argentina SA (2)
Calle 7 881
Berazategui, Buenos Aires, B1884BCQ, Argentina
Tel.: (54) 1142756836
Fax: (54) 1142757209
E-Mail: huyck@huyck.wangner.com.ar
Emp.: 70
Paper Production Consumable Product Mfr & Supplier
S.I.C.: 2299
N.A.I.C.S.: 313210
Carlos Fioramonti, *(Mgr-Sls)*

Huyck.Wangner Australia Pty. Limited (2)
36-40 Fellmongers Rd Breakwater
Geelong, VIC, 3219, Australia
Tel.: (61) 352237000
Paper Production Consumable Product Mfr & Supplier
S.I.C.: 2299
N.A.I.C.S.: 313210
Mikel Dean *(Country Mgr)*

Huyck.Wangner Austria GmbH (2)
Huyckstrasse 1
2640 Gloggnitz, Austria
Tel.: (43) 26624100
Fax: (43) 2662410159
Web Site: www.xerium.com
Paper Production Consumable Product Mfr & Supplier
S.I.C.: 2299
N.A.I.C.S.: 313210
Mario Schimanko *(Dir-IT)*

Huyck.Wangner Germany GmbH (2)
Fohrstrasse 39
72760 Reutlingen, Baden-Wurttemberg, Germany
Tel.: (49) 71213060
Fax: (49) 7121306396
Web Site: www.xerium.com
Paper Production Consumable Product Mfr & Supplier
S.I.C.: 3553
N.A.I.C.S.: 333243
Jurgen Hartmann *(VP-Forming Fabric Ops PMC Europe)*

Huyck.Wangner Italia S.p.A (2)
Via Persicara 70
04100 Latina, Italy
Tel.: (39) 077342711
Fax: (39) 0773629008
Paper Production Consumable Product Mfr & Supplier
S.I.C.: 3554
N.A.I.C.S.: 333243
Daniele Giordani *(Mgr-Fin)*

Huyck.Wangner Japan Limited (2)
Sumitomo Fudosan Ningyocho Bldg 2-2-1 Nihonbashi Horidome-cho
Chuo-Ku, Tokyo, 103-0012, Japan
Tel.: (81) 336643392
Fax: (81) 336670986
E-Mail: info@huyck.wangner.jp
Web Site: www.xerium.com
Emp.: 25
Paper Machine Clothing Mfr & Supplier
S.I.C.: 2299
N.A.I.C.S.: 313210

Stowe Woodward Finland Oy (2)
Sementtitehtaankatu 10
Kerava, 04260, Finland
Tel.: (358) 207299400
Fax: (358) 207299480
Emp.: 60
Paper Machine Clothing Mfr & Supplier
S.I.C.: 2299
N.A.I.C.S.: 313210
Janne Nuopponen *(Controller-Plant)*

Xerium Canada Inc. (2)
1 Boulevard Lee
Warwick, QC, J0A 1M0, Canada
Tel.: (819) 358-7100
Fax: (819) 358-7149
Emp.: 126
Paper Production Consumable Product Mfr & Supplier
S.I.C.: 2299
N.A.I.C.S.: 313210
Pierre Rajotte, *(Gen Mgr)*

Xerium Germany Holding GmbH (2)
Fohrstresse 39
72760 Reutlingen, Germany
Tel.: (49) 7121306301
Fax: (49) 7121306315
Investment Management Services

S.I.C.: 6719
N.A.I.C.S.: 551112

Xerium Technologies Brasil Industria e Comercio S.A. (2)
Via Anhanguera Km 107 3-Parte-Bairro Matao
Sumare, Sao Paulo, 13181-030, Brazil
Tel.: (55) 1938548800
Fax: (55) 1938548834
Paper Production Consumable Product Mfr & Supplier
S.I.C.: 2299
N.A.I.C.S.: 313210

Xerium Technologies Limited (2)
100 New Bridge Street
Fleet Street, London, EC4V 6JA, United Kingdom
Tel.: (44) 1227744030
Paper Production Consumable Product Mfr & Distr
S.I.C.: 2299
N.A.I.C.S.: 313210

U.S. Joint Venture:

Norcraft Companies, Inc. (1)
3020 Denmark Ave Ste 100
Eagan, MN 55121 DE
Tel.: (651) 234-3300
Fax: (651) 234-3398
Toll Free: (800) 297-0661
NCFT—(NYSE)
Sales Range: $250-299.9 Million
Emp.: 1,892
Holding Company
S.I.C.: 6719
N.A.I.C.S.: 551112
Mark Buller *(Chm & CEO)*
Leigh Ginter *(CFO)*
Simon Solomon *(Pres-UltraCraft)*
John Swedeen *(Pres-Starmark)*
Kurt Wanninger *(Pres-Mid Continent)*

Subsidiary:

Norcraft Holdings, L.P. (2)
3020 Denmark Ave Ste 100
Eagan, MN 55121-2417 DE
Tel.: (651) 234-3300
Fax: (651) 234-3398
Toll Free: (800) 297-0661
Web Site: www.norcraftcompanies.com
Sales Range: $250-299.9 Million
Emp.: 1,630
Holding Company; Wood Kitchen Cabinets Mfr & Distr
S.I.C.: 6719
N.A.I.C.S.: 551112
Mark Buller *(Chm & CEO)*
Leigh Ginter *(CFO)*
Simon Solomon *(Pres-UltraCraft)*
John Swedeen *(Pres-StarMark)*
Kurt Wanninger *(Pres-Mid Continent)*

Subsidiary:

Norcraft Companies, L.P. (3)
3020 Denmark Ave Ste 100
Eagan, MN 55121-2417 DE
Tel.: (651) 234-3300
Fax: (651) 234-3398
Toll Free: (800) 297-0661
Web Site: www.norcraftcompanies.com
Wood Kitchen Cabinets Mfr & Distr
S.I.C.: 2434
N.A.I.C.S.: 337110
Mark Buller *(Chm & CEO)*
Leigh Ginter *(CFO)*
Simon Solomon *(Pres-UltraCraft)*
John Swedeen *(Pres-Starmark)*
Kurt Wanninger *(Pres-Mid Continent)*

Subsidiaries:

Mid Continent Cabinetry Inc. (4)
1 Mill Race Dr
Lynchburg, VA 24502-4343
Tel.: (434) 385-7500
Fax: (434) 385-6848
Toll Free: (800) 594-9444
Web Site: www.midcontinentcabinetry.com
Sales Range: $10-24.9 Million
Emp.: 230
Kitchen Cabinetry Mfr
S.I.C.: 2434
N.A.I.C.S.: 337110
Kurt Wanninger *(Pres)*

Plant:

Mid Continent Cabinetry (5)
831 S Columbus Ave
Newton, KS 67114-5200 KS
Tel.: (316) 283-8804
Fax: (316) 283-0216
Web Site: www.norcraftcompanies.com
Sales Range: $50-74.9 Million
Emp.: 800
Manufacturing Plant
S.I.C.: 2434
N.A.I.C.S.: 337110
Jay Pennick *(Supvr-Production-Door Plant)*

StarMark, Inc. (4)
700 E 48th St N
Sioux Falls, SD 57104-0622
Tel.: (605) 335-8600
Fax: (605) 336-5586
Web Site: www.starmarkcabinetry.com
Sales Range: $25-49.9 Million
Wooden Cabinets Mfr
S.I.C.: 2434
N.A.I.C.S.: 337110
John Swedeen *(Pres & CEO)*

Non-U.S. Subsidiaries:

Apax Partners Beteiligungsberatung Gmbh (1)
Possartstrasse 11
Kopernikusstrasse, D 81679 Munich, Germany De
Tel.: (49) 899989090 (100%)
Fax: (49) 8999890932
E-Mail: info@apax.com
Web Site: www.apax.com
Emp.: 40
Private Equity Advisory Firm
S.I.C.: 6211
N.A.I.C.S.: 523999
Nico Hansen *(Partner)*
Michael Phillips *(Partner)*
Arthur Brothag *(Principal)*

Apax Partners Espana, S.L. (1)
Diagonal 640 5 andar
08017 Barcelona, Spain ES
Tel.: (34) 93 545 6500 (100%)
Fax: (34) 93 545 6510
Web Site: www.apax.com
Emp.: 5
Private Equity Advisory Firm
S.I.C.: 6211
N.A.I.C.S.: 523999
Borja Martinez *(Partner)*
Oriol Pinya *(Partne)*

Apax Partners (Israel) Ltd. (1)
Museum Tower 4 Berkowitz Street
Tel Aviv, 64238, Israel
Tel.: (972) 318889
Fax: (972) 37774411
Web Site: www.apax.com
Emp.: 60
Private Equity Advisory Firm
S.I.C.: 6211
N.A.I.C.S.: 523999
Zehavit Cohen *(Partner & Head-Israel)*
Shay Aba *(Principal)*

Apax Partners S.A. (1)
45 avenue Kleber
75784 Paris, Cedex 16, France FR
Tel.: (33) 153650100
Fax: (33) 153650106
E-Mail: partners@apax.fr
Web Site: www.apax.fr
Sales Range: $25-49.9 Million
Emp.: 50
Private Equity Firm
S.I.C.: 6211
N.A.I.C.S.: 523999
Maurice Tchenio *(Founder)*
Martine Clavel *(Partner)*
Monique Cohen *(Partner)*
Patrick de Giovanni *(Partner)*
Bertrand Pivin *(Partner)*
Gilles Rigal *(Partner)*
Claude Rosevegue *(Partner)*
Eddie Misrahi *(Mng Dir)*
Bruno Candelier *(Principal)*
Thomas de Villeneuve *(Principal)*
Franck Hagege *(Principal)*
Geoffrey Leland *(Principal)*
Vincent Rondot *(Principal)*

Subsidiary:

Itefin Participations SAS (2)
45 Avenue Kleber
Paris, 75016, France
Tel.: (33) 1 44 04 50 00
Holding Company
S.I.C.: 6719
N.A.I.C.S.: 551112

Holding:

GFI Informatique S.A. (3)
Immeuble La Porte du Parc 145 Boulevard Victor Hugo
93400 Saint-Ouen, France
Tel.: (33) 144045000
Fax: (33) 144045900
Web Site: www.gfi.fr
GFI—(EUR)
Rev.: $898,343,665
Assets: $798,990,934
Liabilities: $545,321,351
Net Worth: $253,669,582
Earnings: $16,257,695
Emp.: 9,011
Fiscal Year-end: 12/31/12
Information Technology Services
S.I.C.: 7373
N.A.I.C.S.: 541512
Vincent Rouaix *(Pres)*

Subsidiaries:

GFI Chrono Time S.A.S. (4)
12 rue Rouget-de-Lisle
Issy-les-Moulineaux, Hauts-de-Seine, France
Tel.: (33) 146623333
Fax: (33) 549795339
Business & Human Resources Management Software Development Services
S.I.C.: 7371
N.A.I.C.S.: 541511

GFI Consulting S.A.S. (4)
15 rue Beaujon
75008 Paris, France
Tel.: (33) 153934444
Fax: (33) 153934401
E-Mail: ce-gfic@yahoo.fr
Web Site: www.ce-gfic.com
Human Resource Management Software Development Services
S.I.C.: 7371
N.A.I.C.S.: 541511

GFI Infogen Systems S.A.S. (4)
3 rue Collange
92300 Levallois-Perret, Hauts-de-Seine, France
Tel.: (33) 141400656
Fax: (33) 144045907
E-Mail: contact@gfi.fr
Web Site: www.infogen.gfi.fr
Emp.: 90
Enterprise Resource Planning Software Publishing Services
S.I.C.: 7372
N.A.I.C.S.: 511210

GFI Informatique-Production S.A. (4)
158 Avenue de Verdun
92130 Issy-les-Moulineaux, Hauts-de-Seine, France
Tel.: (33) 2 40321818
Fax: (33) 2 40321899
Database Management Software Development Services
S.I.C.: 7371
N.A.I.C.S.: 541511

GFI Progiciels S.A.S. (4)
12 rue Rouget-de-Lisle
92130 Issy-les-Moulineaux, Hauts-de-Seine, France
Tel.: (33) 146623000
Fax: (33) 146620688
Business Management Software Development Services
S.I.C.: 7371
N.A.I.C.S.: 541511

Informatique et Services S.A.S. (4)
145 Boulevard Victor Hugo
93400 Saint-Ouen, Seine-Saint-Denis, France
Tel.: (33) 144045000
Fax: (33) 144045900
Emp.: 8,000
Data Processing Services
S.I.C.: 7379
N.A.I.C.S.: 518210
Yves Roy *(Pres)*

Nemausic S.A. (4)
151 rue Gilles Roberval CS72023
30900 Nimes, Gard, France
Tel.: (33) 466287878
Fax: (33) 466287879
E-Mail: contact@nemausic.fr
Web Site: www.nemausic.fr
Financial & Business Management Software Development Services
S.I.C.: 7371
N.A.I.C.S.: 541511

Non-U.S. Subsidiaries:

GFI Benelux S.A. (4)
Technologielaan 11,
3001 Heverlee, Walloon Brabant, Belgium
Tel.: (32) 10237311
Fax: (32) 16381100
E-Mail: info@gfi.be
Web Site: www.gfi.be
Emp.: 100
Business Management Software Development Services
S.I.C.: 7371
N.A.I.C.S.: 541511
Bruno Hannon *(Mgr-Fin)*

GFI Business Solutions Inc. (4)
75 Queen Street
Montreal, QC, H3C 2M6, Canada
Tel.: (514) 288-7161
Fax: (514) 843-4095
E-Mail: info@gfisolutions.com
Web Site: www.gfisolutions.com
Sales Range: $25-49.9 Million
Emp.: 1,000
Integrated Enterprise Resource Planning Software Mfr
S.I.C.: 3652
N.A.I.C.S.: 334614

GFI Informatica (4)
56 Calle de Serrano Galvache Edificio Encina Planta 7
28033 Madrid, Spain
Tel.: (34) 91 383 63 20
Fax: (34) 91 383 28 65
E-Mail:
Web Site: www.gfi.es
Emp.: 1,500
Biometrics Software Development & Consulting Services
S.I.C.: 7371
N.A.I.C.S.: 541511
Carlos Munoz *(CEO & Dir Gen)*

GFI Informatique Maroc (4)
Casablanca Nearshore Parc 2 2 - 3eme etage
Casablanca, 20190, Morocco
Tel.: (212) 522949779
Fax: (212) 522 36 94 14
E-Mail: gfimaroc@gfimaroc.com
Web Site: www.gfimaroc.com
Financial Software Development Services
S.I.C.: 7371
N.A.I.C.S.: 541511
Saloua Karkri-Belkeziz *(Mng Dir)*

GFI International S.A. (4)
Chemin des Aulx 10
1228 Plan-les-Ouates, Geneva, Switzerland
Tel.: (41) 227062711
Fax: (41) 22 706 27 00
E-Mail: info@gfi.ch
Web Site: www.gfi.ch
Emp.: 15
Business & Human Resources Management Software Development Services
S.I.C.: 7371
N.A.I.C.S.: 541511
Vincent Rouaix *(Chm)*

GFI Maroc Offshore (4)
Parc Casa Nearshore Sh 1 3 1100 Bd Al Qods
Sidi Maarouf, 20190 Casablanca, Morocco
Tel.: (212) 522949780
Fax: (212) 522369414
Software Development & Consulting Services
S.I.C.: 7371

Apax Partners LLP—(Continued)

N.A.I.C.S.: 541511
Saloua Karkri-Belkeziz *(Mgr)*

GFI Portugal (4)
Edificio Atlantis Ave D Joao II Lote 1 06 2 2
Piso 4 Parque das Nacoes
1050-047 Lisbon, Portugal
Tel.: (351) 499950
Fax: (351) 210435586
E-Mail: geral@gfi.pt
Web Site: www.gfi.pt
Emp.: 600
Public Administration, Healthcare, Media & Communications, Financial Services, Industry & Utilities, Transportation & Logistics Consulting & Outsourcing Services
S.I.C.: 4731
N.A.I.C.S.: 541614
Nuno Santos *(Mng Dir)*

Grupo Corporativo GFI Informatica S.A. (4)
C/ Serrano Galvache 56 Planta septima
Edificio Encina
28033 Madrid, Spain
Tel.: (34) 913836320
Fax: (34) 913832865
E-Mail: reception@gfi.es
Web Site: www.gfi.es/web/gfi-es/contactolegal
Emp.: 150
Business Management Software Development Services
S.I.C.: 7371
N.A.I.C.S.: 541511
Angel Alonso *(Dir Gen)*

Grupo Corporativo GFI Norte S.L. (4)
C Licenciado Poza 55 - 2a pta
48013 Bilbao, Vizcaya, Spain
Tel.: (34) 944241825
Fax: (34) 944354186
E-Mail: norte@gfi-info.com
Web Site: www.gfi.es
Emp.: 250
Software Consulting Services
S.I.C.: 7372
N.A.I.C.S.: 511210
Jose Echezarra *(Dir Gen)*

Savac Consultores S.L. (4)
Maximo Aguirre 18 Bis 3
48011 Bilbao, Vizcaya, Spain
Tel.: (34) 94 439 54 38
Fax: (34) 94 427 26 53
E-Mail: gestion@savac.es
Web Site: www.savac.es
Healthcare Software Development Services
S.I.C.: 7371
N.A.I.C.S.: 541511
Blanca Tato *(Project Mgr)*

Non-U.S. Holdings:

Capio AB (2)
Lillapommon 5
PO Box 1064
405 22 Gothenburg, Sweden
Tel.: (46) 317324000
Fax: (46) 317324099
E-Mail: info@capio.se
Web Site: www.capio.se
Sales Range: $1-4.9 Billion
Emp.: 14,500
Owner & Operator of Hospital & Healthcare Facilities
S.I.C.: 6324
N.A.I.C.S.: 524114
Thomas Berglund *(Pres & CEO)*
Hakan Winberg *(CFO)*
Olof Bengtsson *(Sr VP-Fin & Treasury)*

Divisions:

Actica Omsorg AB (3)
Gardatorget 1
Gothenburg, 41250, Sweden
Tel.: (46) 317737500
Fax: (46) 31833845
E-Mail: info@actica.se
Web Site: www.actica.se
Emp.: 15
Elderly Care Services
S.I.C.: 8082
N.A.I.C.S.: 621610

Capio Healthcare Nordic (3)
Gullbergs Strandgata 9
PO Box 1064
SE40522 Gothenburg, Sweden
Tel.: (46) 317324000
Fax: (46) 317324099
E-Mail: info@capio.com
Web Site: www.capio.com
Emp.: 35
Provider of Healthcare Services
S.I.C.: 6321
N.A.I.C.S.: 524114
Gunnrr Nemech *(CEO)*

Non-U.S. Subsidiaries:

La Metaire Clinic (3)
Av De Bois Bougy
CH 1260 Nyon, Switzerland
Tel.: (41) 223632020
Fax: (41) 223632001
E-Mail: contact@lametaire.ch
Web Site: www.lametaire.ch
Medical Clinic
S.I.C.: 8011
N.A.I.C.S.: 621493
Catherine Colin *(Gen Mgr)*

Unilabs S.A. (2)
Place Cornavin 12
1201 Geneva, Switzerland
Tel.: (41) 229097777
Fax: (41) 229097734
Web Site: www.unilabs.com
Sales Range: $450-499.9 Million
Emp.: 3,600
Laboratory & Radiology Services
S.I.C.: 8071
N.A.I.C.S.: 621512
Paul Hokfelt *(Chm)*
Jean-Paul Rigaudeau *(CEO)*
Raffi Asadorian *(CFO)*
Franck Simon *(CIO)*

Non-U.S. Subsidiary:

Unilabs AB (3)
Ekonomi V3
PO Box 1061
40522 Gothenburg, Sweden
Tel.: (46) 317253000
Fax: (46) 031636560
Web Site: www.unilabs.se
Emp.: 35
Laboratory & Radiology Services
S.I.C.: 8071
N.A.I.C.S.: 621512
Martin Swegmark *(Regional Head)*

Non-U.S. Holdings:

Garda World Security Corporation (1)
1390 Barre Street
Montreal, QC, H3C 1N4, Canada
Tel.: (514) 281-2811
Fax: (514) 281-2860
E-Mail: info@garda.ca
Web Site: www.gardaglobal.com
Rev.: $1,345,763,917
Assets: $931,579,640
Liabilities: $903,685,450
Net Worth: $27,894,189
Earnings: ($39,721,039)
Emp.: 35,000
Fiscal Year-end: 01/31/13
Risk Consulting & Security Services
S.I.C.: 7382
N.A.I.C.S.: 561621
Stephan D. Cretier *(Founder, Chm, Pres & CEO)*
Patrick Prince *(CFO & Sr VP)*
Jean-Francois Leduc *(CIO & VP)*
Guy Cote *(Chief Security Officer & VP)*
Christopher W. Jamroz *(Pres/COO-Cash Svcs)*
Oliver Westmacott *(Pres/COO-Intl Protective Svcs)*
Patrice Boily *(Sr VP-CEO Office)*
Alain Dumont *(Sr VP-Strategic Corp Dev)*
Jean Talbot *(Sr VP-Pre-Employment, Corp & Insurance Investigations-Canada)*

Subsidiaries:

G4S Cash Solutions (Canada) Limited (2)
150 Ferrand Dr Ste 600
Toronto, ON, M3C 3E5, Canada
Tel.: (888) 717-4447
E-Mail: media@ca.g4s.com
Web Site: www.g4s.ca
Emp.: 250
Security System Services
S.I.C.: 7382
N.A.I.C.S.: 561621
Ed Jamieson *(CEO)*
Alain Roy *(CFO)*
Han Koren *(COO)*
Mark Burton *(Gen Counsel)*

Garda Security Screening Inc. (2)
36 Scarsdale Rd
Toronto, ON, M3B 2R7, Canada
Tel.: (416) 915-9500
Fax: (416) 915-9700
Web Site: www.garda.com
Emp.: 400
Airport Preboarding Screening Services
S.I.C.: 7382
N.A.I.C.S.: 561621
Bill Lukewich *(Gen Mgr)*

Service de Securite et de Protection Cagero Inc. (2)
25 Besville Bois
Gatineau, QC, J8T 8J7, Canada
Tel.: (819) 770-9438
Fax: (819) 776-5665
Emp.: 200
Security Consulting Services
S.I.C.: 8999
N.A.I.C.S.: 541690
Eric Simard *(Gen Mgr)*

U.S. Subsidiaries:

Garda CL Atlantic, Inc. (2)
4200 Governor Printz Blvd
Wilmington, DE 19802-2315
Tel.: (302) 762-5444
Web Site: www.garda.com
Cash Logistics Services
S.I.C.: 6099
N.A.I.C.S.: 522320

Garda CL Great Lakes, Inc. (2)
2100 W 21st St
Chicago, IL 60608
Tel.: (708) 343-2200
Fax: (708) 344-5476
Web Site: www.garda.com
Cash Logistics Services
S.I.C.: 6099
N.A.I.C.S.: 522320

Garda CL New England, Inc. (2)
201 Schofield Dr
Whitehall, OH 43213
Tel.: (626) 564-4284
Fax: (626) 792-5597
Web Site: www.garda.com
Cash Logistics Services
S.I.C.: 6099
N.A.I.C.S.: 522320

Garda CL Northwest, Inc. (2)
1401 E Yesler Way
Seattle, WA 98122-5545
Tel.: (206) 322-8848
Fax: (206) 323-8408
Web Site: www.garda.com
Cash Logistics Services, Including Armored Car Services
S.I.C.: 7381
N.A.I.C.S.: 561613

Garda CL Southwest, Inc. (2)
201 Schofield Dr
Whitehall, OH 43213
Tel.: (626) 564-4284
Fax: (626) 792-5597
Web Site: www.garda.com
Cash Logistics Services, Including Armored Car Services
S.I.C.: 7381
N.A.I.C.S.: 561613
Chris Jamroz *(Pres)*

Garda CL West, Inc. (2)
301 N Lake Ave Ste 600
Pasadena, CA 91101-5129
Tel.: (626) 564-4284
Web Site: www.garda.com
Cash Logistics Services, Including Armored Car Services
S.I.C.: 6099
N.A.I.C.S.: 522320

GW Investments Sarl LLC (2)
824 N Market St
Wilmington, DE 19801
Tel.: (302) 397-5209
Fax: (302) 425-5159
Security Services
S.I.C.: 8999
N.A.I.C.S.: 541690
Tom Laskaris *(Gen mgr)*

Psagot Ofek Investment House Ltd. (1)
4 Ahad Ha am Street
Tel Aviv, 65142, Israel
Tel.: (972) 3 796 8888
Web Site: www.psagot.co.il/heb/EnglishContent/Homepage/.aspx
Emp.: 50
Investment Management Services
S.I.C.: 6211
N.A.I.C.S.: 523110
Ronen Tov *(CEO)*

Takko ModeMarkt GmbH & Co KG (1)
Alfred Krupp Str 21
48291 Berlin, Germany
Tel.: (49) 25049230
Fax: (49) 2504923277
E-Mail: info@takko.de
Web Site: www.takko-fashion.com
Sls.: $1,585,696,000
Emp.: 7,235
Clothing Retailer
S.I.C.: 5699
N.A.I.C.S.: 448190
Stephan Swinka *(CEO & Mng Dir-Mktg, HR & Strategy)*
Erika Tertilt *(CFO & Mng Dir-Fin & IT)*

TIVIT Terceirizacao de Processos, Servicos e Tecnologia S.A. (1)
Av Brigadeiro Faria Lima 1355 22nd Floor Pinheiros
Sao Paulo, 01452 002, Brazil
Tel.: (55) 1137572222
Fax: (55) 1137572902
E-Mail: comercial@tivit.com.br
Web Site: tivit.com.br
Sales Range: $550-599.9 Million
Business Process & IT Outsourcing Services
S.I.C.: 7373
N.A.I.C.S.: 541512
Luiz Roberto Novaes Mattar *(Chm)*
Paulo Henrique de Oliveira Santos *(Vice Chm)*

Trader Corporation (1)
405 The West Mall Ste 110
Etobicoke, ON, M9C 5J1, Canada
Tel.: (416) 784-5200
Web Site: www.autotrader.com
Automotive, Real Estate, General Merchandise & Employment Publications & Website Publisher
S.I.C.: 2741
N.A.I.C.S.: 519130
Sebastian Baldwin *(Pres)*

Non-U.S. Joint Ventures:

Nordic Telephone Company ApS (1)
C/o Bech-Bruun
Langelinie Alle 35
Copenhagen, 2100, Denmark DK
Tel.: (45) 72270027
Sales Range: $250-299.9 Million
Holding Company; Owned by Apax Partners Ltd., The Blackstone Group L.P., Kohlberg Kravis Roberts & Co., Permira Advisers Limited & Providence Equity Partners, Inc.
S.I.C.: 6719
N.A.I.C.S.: 551112

Subsidiary:

TDC A/S (2)
Teglholmsgade 1-3
0900 Copenhagen, Denmark DK
Tel.: (45) 7011 0330
Fax: (45) 6663 7680
E-Mail: tdc@tdc.dk
Web Site: www.tdc.com
TDC—(CSE)
Rev.: $4,710,281,760
Assets: $11,455,745,760
Liabilities: $7,575,661,080
Net Worth: $3,880,084,680
Earnings: $648,033,480
Emp.: 9,143
Fiscal Year-end: 12/31/12
Telecommunications & Internet Services

S.I.C.: 4813
N.A.I.C.S.: 517110
Vagn Ove Sorensen *(Chm)*
Pierre Danon *(Vice Chm)*
Carsten Dilling *(Pres & CEO)*
Pernille Erenbjerg *(CFO & Sr Exec VP)*
Martin Lippert *(COO & Sr Exec VP-Bus)*
Marianne Jensen *(Sec)*
Eva Merete Sofelde Berneke *(Sr Exec VP-Bus)*
Niels Breining *(Sr Exec VP)*
Miriam Igelso Hvidt *(Sr Exec VP-Stakeholder Rels & HR)*
Jens Munch-Hansen *(Sr Exec VP-Nordic & Wholesale)*

Division:

YouSee A/S (3)
Teglholmsgade 1
DK-0900 Copenhagen, Denmark
Tel.: (45) 70 70 40 40
Web Site: yousee.dk
Sales Range: $300-349.9 Million
Emp.: 900
Cable Television & Internet Services
S.I.C.: 4841
N.A.I.C.S.: 515210
Niels Breining *(CEO)*

Subsidiaries:

Connect Partner A/S (4)
Transformerjev 18
2730 Herlev, Denmark
Tel.: (45) 44542000
Fax: (45) 44542001
E-Mail: info@connectpartner.dk
Web Site: www.connectpartner.dk
Sales Range: $25-49.9 Million
Emp.: 140
Cable Television Installation Services
S.I.C.: 4841
N.A.I.C.S.: 515210
Niels Breining *(Chm)*

Dansk Kabel TV A/S (4)
Taastrupgardsvej 20
Hoje Taastrup, 2620 Copenhagen, Denmark
Tel.: (45) 43324700
Fax: (45) 43324701
E-Mail: info@dk-tv.dk
Web Site: www.dk-tv.dk
Sales Range: $75-99.9 Million
Cable Television & Internet Services
S.I.C.: 4841
N.A.I.C.S.: 515210
John Jensen *(CEO)*

Subsidiary:

Dansk Kabel TV A/S (5)
Ravnevej 7
6705 Esbjerg, Denmark
Tel.: (45) 76950695
Fax: (45) 75210390
E-Mail: info@dk-tv.dk
Web Site: www.dk-tv.dk
Sales Range: $25-49.9 Million
Emp.: 50
Cable Television & Internet Services
S.I.C.: 4841
N.A.I.C.S.: 515210
Flemming Graversen *(Gen Mgr)*

Division:

TDC Mobile International A/S (3)
Telegade 2
Hoje Taastrup, 2630 Copenhagen, Denmark DK
Tel.: (45) 80808020
Web Site: www.tdcmobil.dk
Sales Range: $1-4.9 Billion
Emp.: 2,434
Mobile Telecommunications Services
S.I.C.: 4812
N.A.I.C.S.: 517210

Subsidiary:

TDC Mobile A/S (4)
Telegade 2
Hoje Taastrup, 2630 Copenhagen, Denmark DK
Tel.: (45) 80808020
Fax: (45) 33202033
Web Site: tdc.com
Sales Range: $200-249.9 Million
Mobile Telecommunications Services
S.I.C.: 4812
N.A.I.C.S.: 517210

Subsidiaries:

DK Hostmaster A/S (3)
Kalvebod Brygge 45 3 Sal
1560 Copenhagen, Denmark
Tel.: (45) 33646000
Fax: (45) 33646001
E-Mail: info@dk-hostmaster.dk
Web Site: www.dk-hostmaster.dk
Sales Range: $10-24.9 Million
Emp.: 30
Internet Domain Name Registration & Hosting Services
S.I.C.: 7374
N.A.I.C.S.: 518210
John Schweitzer *(CEO & Mng Dir)*

TDC ADSB Invest A/S (3)
Norregade 21
0900 Copenhagen, Denmark
Tel.: (45) 80808080
Fax: (45) 70227608
E-Mail: alder@tdc.dk
Web Site: www.tdc.com
Sales Range: $1-4.9 Billion
Emp.: 16,000
S.I.C.: 1731
N.A.I.C.S.: 238210

TDC Services A/S (3)
Norredage 21
DK 0900 Copenhagen, C, Denmark DK
Tel.: (45) 80808080
Web Site: www.tdc.com
Sales Range: $50-74.9 Million
Information Technology, Procurement & Billing Services
S.I.C.: 4731
N.A.I.C.S.: 541614

Tele Danmark Connect 1 A/S (3)
Norregade 21
0900 Copenhagen, Denmark
Tel.: (45) 80808080
Fax: (45) 33437608
Web Site: www.tdc.dk
Sales Range: $150-199.9 Million
Telecommunications Services
S.I.C.: 1731
N.A.I.C.S.: 238210

Tele Danmark Internet A/S (3)
Norregade 21
0900 Copenhagen, Denmark
Tel.: (45) 70256525
Fax: (45) 70256425
Web Site: www.tdc.dk
Sales Range: $200-249.9 Million
Telecommunications
S.I.C.: 4812
N.A.I.C.S.: 517210
Jens Alder *(Chm)*

Tele Danmark TMN A/S (3)
Norregade 21
1165 Copenhagen, Denmark
Web Site: tdc.com
Sales Range: $150-199.9 Million
Telecommunications Services
S.I.C.: 1731
N.A.I.C.S.: 238210

Non-U.S. Joint Venture:

Nordic Satellite Distribution AS (3)
PO Box 1726
1201 Oslo, Norway
Tel.: (47) 22208061
Sales Range: $150-199.9 Million
Satellites
S.I.C.: 1731
N.A.I.C.S.: 238210

Division:

TDC Solutions A/S (3)
Teglholmsgade 1 G 455
0900 Copenhagen, C, Denmark DK
Tel.: (45) 70110330
Web Site: tdc.com
Emp.: 12,231
Telecommunications, Internet & Business Management Services
S.I.C.: 4813
N.A.I.C.S.: 517110
Kim Frimer *(Pres)*
Martin Lippert *(Exec VP-Bus)*
Dan Sorensson *(Exec VP-Networks)*
Christian Lanng Nielsen *(Sr VP-Installation)*

Subsidiaries:

NetDesign A/S (4)
Hormarken 2
3520 Farum, Denmark
Tel.: (45) 44358000
Fax: (45) 44358001
E-Mail: info@netdesign.dk
Web Site: www.netdesign.dk
Sales Range: $25-49.9 Million
Emp.: 171
Network Infrastructure Services
S.I.C.: 7374
N.A.I.C.S.: 518210
Peter Rasm *(Mng Dir)*

TDC Call Center Europe A/S (4)
Ellegardvej 23 A
6400 Sonderborg, Denmark DK
Tel.: (45) 74181818
Fax: (45) 74181819
E-Mail: sales@cce.dk
Web Site: www.cce.dk
Rev.: $16,000,000
Emp.: 350
Call Center Services Outsourcer
S.I.C.: 7389
N.A.I.C.S.: 561421
Lene Krakau Larsen *(Gen Mgr)*

TDC Erhvervscenter (4)
Sivmosevaenget 2
5260 Odense, Denmark
Tel.: (45) 70106000
Fax: (45) 66191521
E-Mail: info@tdc.dk
Web Site: www.tdc.dk
Sales Range: $75-99.9 Million
Telecommunications & Data Management Services
S.I.C.: 7379
N.A.I.C.S.: 518210

Telecom Invest A/S (4)
Teglholmsgade 1 G 455
2630 Copenhagen, Denmark
Tel.: (45) 7011 0330
Web Site: www.tdc.dk
Emp.: 1
Financial Services
S.I.C.: 6726
N.A.I.C.S.: 525990

Non-U.S. Subsidiaries:

TDC Dotcom AB (4)
Norra Malmvagen 143
191 62 Sollentuna, Sweden
Tel.: (46) 851981000
Fax: (46) 851981001
E-Mail: direkt@tdcdotcom.se
Sales Range: $200-249.9 Million
Emp.: 760
Network Integration Services
S.I.C.: 7389
N.A.I.C.S.: 561499
Erik Heilborn *(Mgr)*

TDC Sverige AB (4)
Norra Malmvagen 143
191 62 Sollentuna, Sweden SE
Tel.: (46) 856310000
Fax: (46) 51981001
E-Mail: info@tdc.se
Web Site: www.tdc.se
Rev.: $7,531,072,512
Emp.: 800
Telecommunications & Internet Services
S.I.C.: 4899
N.A.I.C.S.: 517919
Erik Heilborn *(CEO)*

Subsidiary:

TDC Song Svenska AB (5)
Gustav III Boulevard 18
SE 169 27 Solna, Sweden
Tel.: (46) 8 5631 0527
Fax: (46) 8 5631 07 04
Sales Range: $75-99.9 Million
Telecommunications & Internet Network Services
S.I.C.: 4899
N.A.I.C.S.: 517919

Non-U.S. Subsidiaries:

TDC Song AS (5)
Sandakerveien 130
0484 Oslo, Norway
Tel.: (47) 21502100
Fax: (47) 21502151
E-Mail: ketil.kivedahl@tdc.no
Web Site: www.tdc.no
Sales Range: $50-74.9 Million
Emp.: 220
Telecommunications & Internet Network Services
S.I.C.: 4899
N.A.I.C.S.: 517919
Ketil Kivedahl *(Mng Dir)*

TDC Song Oy (5)
Mechelinikatu 1A
FI 00180 Helsinki, Finland
Tel.: (358) 309941
Fax: (358) 309943100
Web Site: www.tdc.fi
Sales Range: $75-99.9 Million
Emp.: 240
Telecommunications & Internet Network Services
S.I.C.: 4899
N.A.I.C.S.: 517919
Timo Levoranta *(Mng Dir)*

NXP Semiconductors N.V. (1)
High Tech Campus 60
5656 AG Eindhoven, Netherlands NL
Mailing Address:
PO Box 80073
5600 KA Eindhoven, Netherlands
Tel.: (31) 402728686
Fax: (31) 402729658
E-Mail: jean.schreurs@nxp.com
Web Site: www.nxp.com
NXPI—(NASDAQ)
Rev.: $4,815,000,000
Assets: $6,449,000,000
Liabilities: $4,903,000,000
Net Worth: $1,546,000,000
Earnings: $415,000,000
Emp.: 25,691
Fiscal Year-end: 12/31/13
Semiconductors, Wireless Communication Components, Audio & Video Components, Radio Frequency Identification Technologies & Mobile Handset Software; Owned by 80.1% by Kohlberg Kravis Roberts & Co., Bain Capital, Silver Lake Partners, AlpInvest Partners & Apax Partners
S.I.C.: 3674
N.A.I.C.S.: 334413
Peter L. Bonfield *(Chm)*
Richard L. Clemmer *(Pres & CEO)*
Peter Kelly *(CFO & Exec VP)*
Hans Rijns *(Interim CTO)*
Robert Rigby-Hall *(Chief HR Officer & Exec VP)*
Guido Dierick *(Gen Counsel & Sr VP)*
Alexander Everke *(Exec VP & Gen Mgr-High-Performance Mixed-Signal Bus)*
Sean Hunkler *(Exec VP & Gen Mgr-Ops)*
Frans Scheper *(Exec VP & Gen Mgr-Standard Products Applications)*
Kurt Sievers *(Exec VP & Gen Mgr-High-Performance Mixed-Signal Bus)*
Kin Wah Loh *(Exec VP-Sls & Mktg)*
Hai Wang *(Exec VP-R&D)*
Peter Kleij *(Sr VP-HR Mgmt)*

Subsidiary:

NXP Software (2)
High Tech Campus 41
5656 AE Eindhoven, Netherlands
Mailing Address:
PO Box 80021
5600 JZ Eindhoven, Netherlands
Tel.: (31) 4027000
Fax: (31) 402725500
E-Mail: info.software@nxp.com
Web Site: www.nxpsoftware.com
Sales Range: $25-49.9 Million
Mobile Communications Software
S.I.C.: 7372
N.A.I.C.S.: 511210

U.S. Subsidiary:

NXP Semiconductors (2)
1109 McKay Dr
San Jose, CA 95131
Tel.: (408) 434-3000
Fax: (408) 474-8103
Toll Free: (800) 447-1500
Web Site: www.nxp.com
Sales Range: $600-649.9 Million
Emp.: 700
Semiconductor Mfr

Apax Partners LLP—(Continued)

Import Export
S.I.C.: 3674
N.A.I.C.S.: 334413
Dave French *(Exec VP & Gen Mgr-Indus & Infrastructure Bus Unit)*
Frans Scheper *(Sr VP & Gen Mgr-Standard Products Applications)*

Divisions:

NXP Semiconductors (3)
8375 S River Pkwy
Tempe, AZ 85284-2616 AZ
Tel.: (480) 752-8574
Fax: (480) 752-6025
Web Site: www.nxp.com
Sales Range: $1-9.9 Million
Mfr of Semiconductors
S.I.C.: 3674
N.A.I.C.S.: 334413

NXP Semiconductors (3)
15501 Weston Pkwy
Cary, NC 27513 NC
Tel.: (919) 677-7900
Fax: (919) 677-7929
Sales Range: Less than $1 Million
Emp.: 30
Mfr & Marketer of Semiconductors & Related Devices
S.I.C.: 3674
N.A.I.C.S.: 334413
Mike Bruno *(Dir)*

Non-U.S. Subsidiary:

NXP Semiconductors GmbH (2)
Bayerwaldstrasse 11
81737 Munich, Germany
Tel.: (49) 8962706100
Fax: (49) 8962706101
E-Mail: pasquale.langlois@nxp.com
Web Site: www.nxp.com
Sales Range: $1-9.9 Million
Emp.: 40
Marketer of Semiconductors
S.I.C.: 3674
N.A.I.C.S.: 334413

Paradigm B.V. (1)
WTC A Tower 7th Floor Strawinskylaan 717
1077 XX Amsterdam, Netherlands
Mailing Address:
PO Box 87400
1080JK Amsterdam, Netherlands
Tel.: (31) 203337570
Fax: (31) 203337579
E-Mail: info@pdgm.com
Web Site: www.pdgm.com
Emp.: 7
Software Solutions for Oil & Gas Exploration
S.I.C.: 7371
N.A.I.C.S.: 541511
Eldad Weiss *(CEO)*
Jake Pyles *(CFO)*
Duane Dopkin *(Exec VP-Tech)*
Ofra Kalechstain *(Exec VP-Product Dev)*
James Lamb *(Exec VP-Ops)*

U.S. Subsidiary:

Paradigm Geophysical Corp. (2)
2 Memorial Plz 820 Gessner Rd Ste 400
Houston, TX 77024
Tel.: (713) 393-4800
Fax: (713) 393-4802
Toll Free: (888) 223-6631
E-Mail: info@pdgm.com
Web Site: www.pdgm.com
Emp.: 100
Oil & Natural Gas Software Systems
S.I.C.: 7372
N.A.I.C.S.: 511210
David Betty *(Reg VP-North America)*

Non-U.S. Subsidiaries:

Paradigm FZ-LLC (2)
Building 2 Office 101
PO Box 500148
Dubai Internet City, Dubai, United Arab Emirates
Tel.: (971) 43910673
Fax: (971) 43918657
E-Mail: info@pdgm.com
Web Site: www.pdgm.com
Emp.: 35
Software Services for Oil & Gas Production Industry
S.I.C.: 7372
N.A.I.C.S.: 511210
Jim Stewart *(Gen Mgr)*

Paradigm Geophysical Canada Limited (2)
125 9th Avenue SE Suite 2110
Calgary, AB, T2G 0P6, Canada
Tel.: (403) 571-1555
Fax: (403) 750-3536
Toll Free: (877) 570-1555
E-Mail: info@pdgm.com
Web Site: www.pdgm.com
Emp.: 22
Software Services for Oil & Gas Production Industry
S.I.C.: 7372
N.A.I.C.S.: 511210
James Lamb *(Exec VP-Ops)*

Paradigm Geophysical LLC (2)
4th Floor Building 20
6 Leninsky Avenue, Moscow, 119049, Russia
Tel.: (7) 4959334440
Fax: (7) 4959334449
E-Mail: info@pdgm.com
Web Site: www.pdgm.com
Emp.: 100
Software Services for Oil & Gas Production Industry
S.I.C.: 7372
N.A.I.C.S.: 511210
Mikhail Porechenkov *(Mng Dir)*

Paradigm Geophysical S.A. (2)
Carlos Pellegrini 713 Piso 9
Buenos Aires, C1009ABO, Argentina
Tel.: (54) 1143225735
Fax: (54) 1143225515
E-Mail: info@pdgm.com
Web Site: www.pdgm.com
Emp.: 12
Software Services for Oil & Gas Production Industry
S.I.C.: 7372
N.A.I.C.S.: 511210

Paradigm Geophysical Sdn Bhd (2)
Level 12 Tower 1 Etiqa Twins 11 Jalan Pinang
11 Jalan Pinang, Kuala Lumpur, 50540, Malaysia
Tel.: (60) 321638111
Fax: (60) 321638881
E-Mail: info@pdgm.com
Web Site: www.pdgm.com
Emp.: 25
Software Services for Oil & Gas Production Industry
S.I.C.: 7372
N.A.I.C.S.: 511210
Jonathan Ling *(Reg VP-Asia Pacific)*

Paradigm Geophysical (UK) Limited (2)
Dukes Court Bldg C 3rd Flr
Dukes Street, Woking, Surrey, GU21 5BH, United Kingdom
Tel.: (44) 1483758000
Fax: (44) 1483758001
E-Mail: info@pdgm.com
Web Site: www.pdgm.com
Emp.: 40
Software Services for Oil & Gas Production Industry
S.I.C.: 7372
N.A.I.C.S.: 511210
Christa Fitzgibbons *(VP-Technical Svcs)*

Paradigm Technology (Beijing) Co., Ltd. (2)
1803 Capital Mansion No 6 Xin Yan South Road
Chao Yang District, Beijing, 100004, China
Tel.: (86) 1064654870
Fax: (86) 1064654845
E-Mail: info@pdgm.com
Web Site: www.pdgm.com
Emp.: 20
Software Services for Oil & Gas Production Industry
S.I.C.: 7372
N.A.I.C.S.: 511210

Truvo NV/SA (1)
Uitbreidingstraat 80 bus 3
2600 Berchem, Belgium BE
Tel.: (32) 32856411
Fax: (32) 32856400
E-Mail: info@truvo.com
Web Site: www.truvo.com
Sales Range: $500-549.9 Million
Emp.: 2,200
Online & Print Directory Publisher
S.I.C.: 2741
N.A.I.C.S.: 511140
Andrew Day *(Chm)*
Donat Retif *(CEO & Mng Dir)*
Pierre Gatz *(CTO)*
Wim van Neutegem *(Treasury & VP-Tax)*

U.S. Subsidiary:

Axesa Servicios de Informacion, S. en C. (2)
1001 San Roerto St Ste 500
San Juan, PR 00926
Tel.: (787) 758-2828
Fax: (787) 771-6451
E-Mail: newmedia@axesa.com
Web Site: www.axesa.com
Sales Range: $25-49.9 Million
Emp.: 250
Directory Publisher; Owned 39.6% by Truvo & 59.4% by Local Insight Media
S.I.C.: 2741
N.A.I.C.S.: 511140
Linda Martin *(Mng Dir)*

Non-U.S. Subsidiaries:

Gouden Gids B.V. (2)
Harkerbergweg 88
1101 CM Amsterdam, Zuidoost, Netherlands NL
Tel.: (31) 205676767
Fax: (31) 205676950
Web Site: www.truvo.nl
Emp.: 400
Business & Services Contact Information Directory
S.I.C.: 2741
N.A.I.C.S.: 511140
Ian Harrison *(Mng Dir)*

Paginas Amarelas S.A. (2)
Ave D Joao II No 1 17 01 74 Piso
1990 083 Lisbon, Portugal PT
Tel.: (351) 218989500
Fax: (351) 218989510
E-Mail: pa@paginasamarelas.pt
Web Site: www.paginasamarelas.pt
Emp.: 200
Yellow Pages for Telephone Directories Export
S.I.C.: 4899
N.A.I.C.S.: 517919
Marco Goncalvaf *(Dir-Mktg)*

Publitec B.V. (2)
Herikerberweg 88
1101 CM Amsterdam, Netherlands NL
Tel.: (31) 205676869
Fax: (31) 206910374
E-Mail: info@publitec.nl
Web Site: www.publitec.nl
Emp.: 100
Marketing, Media Measurement, Business & Directory Information
S.I.C.: 2741
N.A.I.C.S.: 511140
Peter Gatz *(Gen Mgr)*

APB RESOURCES BERHAD

No 47 Lot 540 Jalan TUDM Kampung Baru Subang Seksyen U6
40150 Kuala Lumpur, Selangor Darul Ehsan, Malaysia
Tel.: (60) 378461389
Fax: (60) 378463795
Web Site: www.apb-resources.com
APB—(KLS)
Rev.: $74,551,723
Assets: $66,893,785
Liabilities: $10,305,925
Net Worth: $56,587,860
Earnings: $2,899,543
Fiscal Year-end: 09/30/12

Business Description:
Fabrication & Non Destructive Testing Services
S.I.C.: 1799
N.A.I.C.S.: 238390

Personnel:
Kim Fah Yap *(Chm & Mng Dir)*
Teng Khuan Tan *(COO)*
Kim Chee Cheok *(Sec)*

Board of Directors:
Kim Fah Yap
Eng Seng Chua
Hong Liang Lim
Fong Ching Mak
Teng Khuan Tan
Yeow Ho Yap

Subsidiary:

Era Julung Sdn. Bhd. (1)
47 Jalan Tudm Subang New Village
Shah Alam, Selangor, 40150, Malaysia
Tel.: (60) 378461389
Fax: (60) 378463795
Emp.: 100
Management Services
S.I.C.: 8741
N.A.I.C.S.: 551114
Yap Kow *(Mng Dir)*

Subsidiaries:

Amalgamated Metal Corporation (M) Sdn. Bhd. (2)
No 47 Lot 540 Jalan TUDM Kampung Baru Subang
Seksyen U6, 40150 Shah Alam, Selangor, Malaysia
Tel.: (60) 378461389
Fax: (60) 378463795
E-Mail: amcsubg@amcsb.com.my
Web Site: www.amcsb.com.my
Emp.: 200
Fabricated Steel Products Mfr & Industrial Engineering Services
S.I.C.: 3441
N.A.I.C.S.: 332312
Swee Sang Yap *(Deputy Gen Mgr)*

Prescan Sdn. Bhd. (2)
No 24 Jalan Tabla 33/21 Shah Alam Technology Park
Shah Alam, Selangor, 40640, Malaysia
Tel.: (60) 351215951
Fax: (60) 351212906
Inspection Services
S.I.C.: 9651
N.A.I.C.S.: 926150

APC GROUP, INC.

10/F Philcom Bldg 8755 Paseo de Roxas
1226 Makati, Philippines
Tel.: (63) 28450614
Fax: (63) 28450259
Web Site: www.apcaragorn.com
APC—(PHI)
Sales Range: $700-749.9 Million
Emp.: 1,855

Business Description:
Oil & Gas Exploration Services
S.I.C.: 1311
N.A.I.C.S.: 211111

Personnel:
Willy N. Ocier *(Chm, Pres & CEO)*
Bernardo D. Lim *(CFO & Exec VP)*
Edmundo L. Tan *(Sec & Compliance Officer)*

Board of Directors:
Willy N. Ocier
Jose T. Gabionza
Manuel A. Gana
Jose Ben R. Laraya
Bernardo D. Lim
Edmundo L. Tan
Jerry Tiu

Subsidiary:

Environment and General Services, Inc. (1)
2nd Fl Ln Bldg Shaw Blvd
Mandaluyong, 1552, Philippines
Tel.: (63) 26333439
Fax: (63) 26332413
E-Mail: operations@egsicnean.com
Web Site: www.egsiclean.com
Emp.: 2,000

Building Cleaning & Janitorial Services
S.I.C.: 7349
N.A.I.C.S.: 561720
Paul Magaziner *(Principal)*

APCB INC.

6 Lane 84 Chun-Ying Street Shu-Lin
Taipei, 238, Taiwan
Tel.: (886) 2 26832626
Fax: (886) 2 26831332
E-Mail: market@apcb.com.tw
Web Site: www.apcb.com.tw
Year Founded: 1981
6108—(TAI)
Sales Range: $150-199.9 Million
Emp.: 3,150
Business Description:
Printed Circuit Board Mfr
S.I.C.: 3672
N.A.I.C.S.: 334412
Personnel:
Yueh-Hsia Tsao *(Chm)*

APCO INDUSTRIES CO. LIMITED

10 Industrial Street
Toronto, ON, M4G 1Z1, Canada
Tel.: (416) 421-6161
Fax: (416) 421-1096
E-Mail: info@apcoindustries.com
Web Site: www.apcoindustries.com
Year Founded: 1935
Rev.: $12,292,321
Emp.: 33
Business Description:
Metals & Chemical Products Mfr
S.I.C.: 3479
N.A.I.C.S.: 332812
Personnel:
James Grierson *(Pres)*

APCO SERVICE STATIONS PTY. LTD.

343 Thompson Road
Geelong, VIC, 3215, Australia
Tel.: (61) 352779379
Fax: (61) 352786768
Web Site: www.apco.com.au
Sales Range: $75-99.9 Million
Emp.: 11
Business Description:
Petroleum Whslr, Convenience Store Retailing
S.I.C.: 5172
N.A.I.C.S.: 424720

APCOTEX INDUSTRIES LIMITED

Plot 3/1 MIDC Industrial Area Taloja
District Raigad, Mumbai,
Maharashtra, 410208, India
Tel.: (91) 2227403500
Fax: (91) 2227412052
E-Mail: info@apcotex.com
Web Site: www.apcotex.com
523694—(BOM)
Rev.: $56,106,619
Assets: $32,860,685
Liabilities: $18,362,795
Net Worth: $14,497,891
Earnings: $2,374,103
Emp.: 170
Fiscal Year-end: 03/31/13
Business Description:
Synthetic Rubber Mfr
S.I.C.: 2822
N.A.I.C.S.: 325212
Personnel:
Abhiraj A. Choksey *(Mng Dir)*
Anand V. Kumashi *(Compliance Officer, Sec & Gen Mgr-Acct & Fin)*
Board of Directors:
Atul C. Choksey
T. N. V. Ayyar
Abhiraj A. Choksey
Amit C. Choksey
Girish C. Choksey
Bipin V. Jhaveri
Manubhai G. Patel
S. Sivaram
Shailesh S. Vaidya
Kamlesh S. Vikamsey
Transfer Agent:
Link Intime India Pvt. Ltd.
C-13 Pannalal Silk Mills Compound
LBS Marg
Bhandup, Mumbai, 400 078, India
Tel.: (91) 22 2596 3838
Fax: (91) 22 2594 6969

APD COMMUNICATIONS LIMITED

Newlands Ctr Unit 2 Inglemire Ln
Kingston upon Hull, HU6 7TQ, United Kingdom
Tel.: (44) 1482808300
Fax: (44) 1482803901
E-Mail: head.office@apdcomms.com
Web Site: www.apdcomms.com
Sales Range: $10-24.9 Million
Emp.: 150
Fiscal Year-end: 12/31/12
Business Description:
Mobile IT Solutions
S.I.C.: 7371
N.A.I.C.S.: 541511

APE PTACEK ENGINEERING GMBH

Bayerwaldstrasse 9
81737 Munich, Germany
Tel.: (49) 896302090
Fax: (49) 8963020990
E-Mail: info@ape.de
Web Site: www.ape.de
Year Founded: 1989
Rev.: $11,173,140
Emp.: 30
Business Description:
Programming & Hardware Integration Service
S.I.C.: 7371
N.A.I.C.S.: 541511
Personnel:
Helmut Ptacek *(Founder)*

APELLA RESOURCES INC.

(Name Changed to PacificOre Mining Corp.)

APEN LTD.

Industriestrasse 13c
6304 Zug, Switzerland
Tel.: (41) 417107060
Fax: (41) 417107064
E-Mail: info@apen.com
Web Site: www.apen.com
APEN—(SWX)
Rev.: $62,616,750
Assets: $501,720,823
Liabilities: $230,711,126
Net Worth: $271,009,697
Earnings: $1,190,490
Emp.: 4
Fiscal Year-end: 12/31/12
Business Description:
Private Equity Investment Services
S.I.C.: 6211
N.A.I.C.S.: 523999
Personnel:
Eduardo Leemann *(Chm)*
Antonio Bonchristiano *(Vice Chm)*
Board of Directors:
Eduardo Leemann
Antonio Bonchristiano
David Emery
Alvaro Lopes
David B. Pinkerton

APERAM SA

12C rue Guillaume Kroll
L-1882 Luxembourg, Luxembourg
Tel.: (352) 27 36 27 00
E-Mail: contact@aperam.com
Web Site: www.aperam.com
APAM—(EUR OTC)
Sls.: $5,261,000,000
Assets: $5,909,000,000
Liabilities: $2,719,000,000
Net Worth: $3,190,000,000
Earnings: $108,000,000
Emp.: 9,815
Fiscal Year-end: 12/31/12
Business Description:
Steel Products Mfr
S.I.C.: 3399
N.A.I.C.S.: 331110
Personnel:
Lakshmi Niwas Mittal *(Chm)*
Philippe Darmayan *(CEO)*
Sandeep Jalan *(CFO)*
Timoteo Di Maulo *(Chief Commercial & Sourcing Officer)*
Laurent Beauloye *(Sec)*
Board of Directors:
Lakshmi Niwas Mittal
Romain Bausch
Joseph Greenwell
Kathryn A. Matthews
Aditya Mittal
Laurence Mulliez
Gonzalo Urquijo

Non-U.S. Subsidiary:

Aperam Stainless Europe S.A. **(1)**
1 a 5 Rue Luigi Cherubini
93212 Paris, France
Tel.: (33) 1 71 92 06 52
Fax: (33) 1 71 92 07 91
E-Mail: stainless.europe@arcelormittal.com
Web Site: www.arcelormittal-stainless-europe.com
Sales Range: $5-14.9 Billion
Emp.: 5,500
Stainless Steel Sheet Mfr; Special Strip Products; Leaded Steels
S.I.C.: 3399
N.A.I.C.S.: 331221
Bernard Tonnelle *(CFO & Chief Controlling Officer)*
Bernard Hebeisen *(CTO)*

Subsidiaries:

Aperam Alloys Imphy **(2)**
Innovatis 5 Rue Luigi Cherubini
F-93212 Saint Denis, Cedex, France
Tel.: (33) 171920000
Fax: (33) 171922549
Web Site: www.imphyalloys.com
Sales Range: $650-699.9 Million
Emp.: 1,030
Nickel & Cobalt Alloys Mfr
S.I.C.: 3341
N.A.I.C.S.: 331492
Bourrier Herze *(Gen Mgr)*

Aperam Alloys Rescal SAS **(2)**
Avenue de la Couronne des Pres
78680 Epone, France FR
Tel.: (33) 130900400
Web Site: www.aperam.com
Sls.: $26,400,000
Emp.: 135
Electric Housewares & Fans
S.I.C.: 3639
N.A.I.C.S.: 335210
Raymond Stone *(Pres)*

Aperam Stainless Precision Europe **(2)**
2 Place du General DeGaulle
BP 9
F-25150 Pont-de-Roide, France
Tel.: (33) 381996412
Fax: (33) 381996330
E-Mail: commercial@aperam.com
Web Site: www.iup-stainless.com
Sales Range: $125-149.9 Million
Emp.: 247
Stainless Steel Precision Strips Mfr
S.I.C.: 3399
N.A.I.C.S.: 331221
Lode Colson *(Gen Mgr)*

Aperam Stainless Services & Solutions Tubes Europe **(2)**
1 Rue Prele
F 55170 Ancerville, France
Tel.: (33) 329797474
Fax: (33) 329799040
E-Mail: marc.nicolas@arpelormittal.com
Web Site: www.meusienne.com
Sales Range: $75-99.9 Million
Emp.: 170
Stainless Steel Tubes Mfr
S.I.C.: 3317
N.A.I.C.S.: 331210
Olivier Raynao *(Pres)*

Non-U.S. Subsidiary:

ArcelorMittal Genk Stainless Service Belgium N.V. **(2)**
Bosgel 87
Zone 5, B 3600 Genk, Belgium
Tel.: (32) 89365600
Telex: 39 058 ALDOZG
Fax: (32) 89365631
Sls.: $929,000,000
Emp.: 100
Stainless Steel Flat Products Mfr
Import Export
S.I.C.: 3312
N.A.I.C.S.: 331221
Olivier Benoit *(Gen Mgr)*

APETIT PLC

(Formerly Lannen Tehtaat Plc)
Maakunnantie 4
27801 Sakyla, Finland
Tel.: (358) 1040200
Fax: (358) 104024022
Web Site: www.apetitgroup.fi
APETI—(HEL)
Sls.: $509,121,494
Assets: $313,522,993
Liabilities: $123,039,938
Net Worth: $190,483,055
Earnings: $9,019,339
Emp.: 721
Fiscal Year-end: 12/31/12
Business Description:
Frozen Foods, Jams, Marmalades & Fish Product Developer, Producer & Marketer
S.I.C.: 2038
N.A.I.C.S.: 311412
Personnel:
Aappo Kontu *(Chm)*
Timo Miettinen *(Chm-Supervisory Bd)*
Veijo Merilainen *(Deputy Chm)*
Marja-Liisa Mikola-Luoto *(Deputy Chm-Supervisory Bd)*
Matti Karppinen *(CEO)*
Eero Kinnunen *(Deputy CEO & CFO)*
Asmo Ritala *(Sec & Corp Counsel)*
Board of Directors:
Aappo Kontu
Tuomo Lahdesmaki
Veijo Merilainen
Samu Pere
Helena Wallden
Supervisory Board of Directors:
Timo Miettinen
Heikki Aaltonen
Harri Eela
Matti Eskola
Mari Hakanpera
Jaakko Halkilahti
Laura Hamalainen
Jussi Hantula
Timo Kaila
Risto Korpela
Markku Lanninki
Jonas Laxaback
Mika Leikkonen
Ilkka Markkula
Marja-Liisa Mikola-Luoto
Jari Nevavuori
Markku Parssinen
Tuomo Raininko

Apetit Plc—(Continued)

Kirsi Roos
Timo Ruippo
Esa Ruohola
Heikki Vesanto
Mauno Ylinen

Subsidiaries:

Apetit Kala Oy (1)
Mastotie 7
70460 Kuopio, Finland
Tel.: (358) 104024500
Fax: (358) 104024520
Web Site: www.apetit.fi
Emp.: 300
Fish & Seafood Markets
S.I.C.: 5421
N.A.I.C.S.: 445220
Matti Karppinen *(CEO)*

Apetit Pakaste Oy (1)
Maakunnanpie 4
PO Box 130
27801 Sakyla, Finland
Tel.: (358) 104024300
Fax: (358) 104024333
E-Mail: antti.kerttula@apetit.fi
Web Site: www.apetit.com
Emp.: 100
Food Mfr
S.I.C.: 2099
N.A.I.C.S.: 311999
Vesa Moisio *(Mng Dir)*

Apetit Suomi Oy (1)
Upseerinkatu 1
PO Box 403
02601 Espoo, Finland
Tel.: (358) 104024300
Fax: (358) 10 402 4455
Frozen Food Products Mfr
S.I.C.: 2038
N.A.I.C.S.: 311412

Avena Nordic Grain Oy (1)
Upseerinkatu 1
Espoo, 02600, Finland
Tel.: (358) 1040202
E-Mail: avena@avena.fi
Web Site: www.avena.fi
Emp.: 20
Oilseed & Grain Combination Farming
S.I.C.: 0119
N.A.I.C.S.: 111191
Kaija Viljanen *(Mng Dir)*

Non-U.S. Subsidiaries:

OU Avena Nordic Grain (2)
Tehnika 3
72213 Turi, Estonia
Tel.: (372) 5038151
Fax: (372) 384 7006
E-Mail: info@ang.ee
Web Site: www.ang.ee
Grains & Oilseeds Distr
S.I.C.: 5159
N.A.I.C.S.: 424590
Margus Marrandi *(Country Mgr)*

Too Avena Astana (2)
Raion Almaty Baraeva Str 16
010000 Astana, Kazakhstan
Tel.: (7) 7172592679
Fax: (7) 7172592676
Web Site: www.lannen.fi/en/default2.asp?active_page_id=267
Grains & Oilseeds Distr
S.I.C.: 5159
N.A.I.C.S.: 424590

Mildola Oy (1)
Satamatie 64
Kantvik, Finland
Tel.: (358) 104022300
Web Site: www.mildola.fi
Emp.: 100
Oilseed & Grain Combination Farming
S.I.C.: 0119
N.A.I.C.S.: 111191
Kaija Viljanen *(Mng Dir)*

Non-U.S. Subsidiaries:

Sandanger AS (1)
Industritomta Sor
6083 Gjerdsvika, Norway
Tel.: (47) 70026440
Fax: (47) 70026441
E-Mail: info@sunnmoere.com
Web Site: www.sunnmoere.com
Emp.: 50
Processed Seafood Distr
S.I.C.: 5146
N.A.I.C.S.: 424460
Anne-Britt Sandanger *(Mng Dir)*

SIA Baltic Feed (1)
PO Box 34
3101 Tukums, Latvia
Tel.: (371) 3181127
Fax: (371) 3181132
Web Site: www.balticfeed.com
Food Mfr
S.I.C.: 2099
N.A.I.C.S.: 311999

UAB Avena Nordic Grain (1)
Odminiu g 9-9
01122 Vilnius, Lithuania
Tel.: (370) 52430290
Fax: (370) 52430291
E-Mail: office@ang.lt
Web Site: www.avena.si
Emp.: 5
Oilseed & Grain Combination Farming
S.I.C.: 0119
N.A.I.C.S.: 111191
Arunas Kibickas *(Gen Mgr)*

Zao Avena St.Petersburg (1)
1 Artillerijskaja Str Europa House
191104 Saint Petersburg, Russia
Tel.: (7) 8127188090
Fax: (7) 812 718 8071
Emp.: 4
Grains & Oilseeds Distr
S.I.C.: 5159
N.A.I.C.S.: 424590

APEX ADELCHI FOOTWEAR LIMITED

House No 06 Road 137 Block SE D
Gulshan-1
Dhaka, 1212, Bangladesh
Tel.: (880) 28820300
Fax: (880) 28813038
E-Mail: info@apexadelchi.com
Web Site: www.apexadelchi.com
APEXADELFT—(DHA)
Rev.: $120,684,931
Assets: $101,123,217
Liabilities: $72,813,488
Net Worth: $28,309,729
Earnings: $3,204,624
Emp.: 5,500
Fiscal Year-end: 12/31/12

Business Description:
Leather Footwear Mfr
S.I.C.: 2389
N.A.I.C.S.: 316210

Personnel:
Manzur Elahi *(Chm)*
Gias Hussain *(Mng Dir)*
Nasim Manzur *(Mng Dir)*
Dilip Kajur *(CFO)*
Abdul Momen Bhuiyan *(Deputy Mng Dir)*
S. M. Shahjahan *(Sec)*

Board of Directors:
Manzur Elahi
Nihad Kabir
Golam Mainuddin
Munize Manzur
Nasim Manzur

APEX BIOTECHNOLOGY CORP.

No 7 Li-Hsin Rd V Hsinchu Science Park
Hsin-chu, Taiwan
Tel.: (886) 35641952
Fax: (886) 35678302
E-Mail: info@apexbio.com
Web Site: www.apexbio.com
1733—(TAI)
Sales Range: $25-49.9 Million

Business Description:
Testing Strips & Monitoring System Mfr & Distr
S.I.C.: 3845
N.A.I.C.S.: 334510

Personnel:
Thomas Y. S. Shen *(CEO)*

APEX DEVELOPMENT PUBLIC COMPANY LIMITED

10/53-56 The Trendy Building 2nd Floor Sukhumvit Road Soi 13
Wattana District, Bangkok, 10110, Thailand
Tel.: (66) 2 168 7200
Fax: (66) 2 168 7190
E-Mail: info@apexpcl.com
Web Site: www.apexpcl.com
Year Founded: 1988
APX—(THA)
Rev.: $148,422
Assets: $44,181,837
Liabilities: $36,882,966
Net Worth: $7,298,870
Earnings: ($3,831,484)
Fiscal Year-end: 12/31/12

Business Description:
Real Estate Development Services
S.I.C.: 6531
N.A.I.C.S.: 531390

Personnel:
Pongphan Sampawakoop *(Chm, CEO & Member-Exec Bd)*
Kamolwan Ajjmavara *(Member-Exec Bd & VP-Sls & Mktg)*
Jamnong Singha *(Member-Exec Bd & VP-Gen Mgmt)*
Anong Srisawadampai *(Member-Exec Bd & VP-Fin & Acctg)*
Pattamas Tavornmas *(Member-Exec Bd & VP-Construction Supervision)*
Jitra Chaichan *(Member-Exec Bd & Dir-Acctg & Fin)*
Virat Lertsumpuncharoen *(Member-Exec Bd & Dir-Legal)*
Khanyanat Oumlomyong *(Sec)*

Board of Directors:
Pongphan Sampawakoop
Padungpan Chantaro
Prakai Cholahan
Penpannee Horrungruang
Prawim Horrungruang
Apinan Na Ranong
Yuthana Santikul
Chalit Sathitthong
Anong Srisawadampai

APEX EQUITY HOLDINGS BERHAD

6th Floor Menara Apex Off Jalan Semenyih Bukit Mewah
43000 Kajang, Selangor Darul Ehsan, Malaysia
Tel.: (60) 387361118
Fax: (60) 387373261
E-Mail: enquiry@apexis.com
Web Site: www.apexequity.com.my
APEX—(KLS)
Rev.: $15,535,538
Assets: $109,661,039
Liabilities: $22,181,165
Net Worth: $87,479,874
Earnings: $8,554,449
Fiscal Year-end: 12/31/12

Business Description:
Stock Broking Services
S.I.C.: 6211
N.A.I.C.S.: 523120

Personnel:
Guan Seng Chan *(Chm)*
Yoke Kum Soh *(Co-Sec)*
Cheng Han Tan *(Co-Sec)*
Wei Fong Wong *(Co-Sec)*

Board of Directors:
Guan Seng Chan
Azizan Abdul Rahman
Vijaya Kumar
Tony Cheow Fui Lee
Yan Seong Leow

Subsidiaries:

AEH Capital Sdn. Bhd. (1)
6th Floor Menara Apex Off Jalan Semenyih
Bukit Mewah, 43000 Kajang, Selangor
Darul Ehsan, Malaysia
Tel.: (60) 387341323
Fax: (60) 387373261
E-Mail: info@aehcapital.com
Web Site: www.aehcapital.com
Emp.: 300
Property Development Services
S.I.C.: 6531
N.A.I.C.S.: 531311
Chan Guan Seng *(Mng Dir)*

Apex Investment Services Berhad (1)
7th Floor Menara Apex Off Jalan Semenyih
Bukit Mewah
43000 Kajang, Selangor Darul Ehsan, Malaysia
Tel.: (60) 387361118
Fax: (60) 387377924
E-Mail: enquiry@apexut.com
Web Site: www.apexequity.com.my
Emp.: 25
Investment Advisory Services
S.I.C.: 6282
N.A.I.C.S.: 523930
Keah Huat Tan *(CEO)*

JF Apex Nominees (Asing) Sdn. Bhd. (1)
6F Menara Apex Jalan Semenyir Bukit Mewas
Kajang, Selangor, 43000, Malaysia
Tel.: (60) 387361118
Fax: (60) 387374532
E-Mail: apexetrade@jfapex.com.my
Emp.: 100
Business Support Services
S.I.C.: 8742
N.A.I.C.S.: 541611
Lim Teck Seng *(Gen Mgr)*

JF Apex Securities Berhad (1)
3rd Floor Menara Apex Off Jalan Semenyih
Bukit Mewah
43000 Kajang, Selangor, Malaysia
Tel.: (60) 387391118
Fax: (60) 387363122
E-Mail: apexetrade@jfapex.com.my
Web Site: www.apexetrade.com
Emp.: 120
Securities Brokerage Services
S.I.C.: 6211
N.A.I.C.S.: 523120
Lim Teck Seng *(Deputy Mng Dir)*

APEX HEALTHCARE BERHAD

134/2 Kompleks Periagaan Munshi Abdullah Jalan Munshi Abdullah
75100 Melaka, Malaysia
Tel.: (60) 62847381
Fax: (60) 62832140
Web Site: www.apexpharmacy.com
AHEALTH—(KLS)
Rev.: $130,710,216
Assets: $95,141,166
Liabilities: $24,162,113
Net Worth: $70,979,053
Earnings: $9,531,513
Emp.: 2,600
Fiscal Year-end: 12/31/12

Business Description:
Pharmaceutical & Consumer Healthcare Products Mfr
S.I.C.: 2834
N.A.I.C.S.: 325412

Personnel:
Kirk Chin Kee *(Chm & CEO)*
Felicia Lien Wah Kwong *(CFO)*
Lien Wah Kwong *(Co-Sec)*
Chong Keat Yeoh *(Co-Sec)*

Board of Directors:
Kirk Chin Kee
Tah Peng Kee
Khai Cheong Leong
Heng Su-Ling Mae

Ahmad Kamal Md Alif
Robert Dobson Millner
Jackson Chevalier Yap-Kit-Siong

Legal Counsel:
Chee Siah Le Kee & Partners
105 Taman Melaka Raya
75000 Melaka, Malaysia

Subsidiaries:

ABio Marketing Sdn. Bhd. (1)
No 2 Jalan SS 13/5
47500 Subang Jaya, Selangor Darul Ehsan, Malaysia
Tel.: (60) 356293688
Fax: (60) 356368025
Web Site: www.apexpharmacy.com
Emp.: 100
Pharmaceutical Products Distr
S.I.C.: 5122
N.A.I.C.S.: 424210
Foo Peng Choong *(Mgr-Bus Unit)*

Apex Pharmacy Corporate Sdn. Bhd. (1)
No 2 Jalan SS 13/5
47500 Subang Jaya, Selangor Darul Ehsan, Malaysia
Tel.: (60) 356376888
Fax: (60) 356369280
E-Mail: lkee@apexpharmacy.com.my
Web Site: www.apexpharmacy.com
Pharmaceutical Products Distr
S.I.C.: 5122
N.A.I.C.S.: 424210

Apex Pharmacy Marketing Sdn. Bhd. (1)
No 2 Jalan SS 13/5
47500 Subang Jaya, Selangor Darul Ehsan, Malaysia
Tel.: (60) 356293688
Fax: (60) 356368200
E-Mail: feedback@apexpharma.com.my
Web Site: www.apexpharma.com.my
Emp.: 100
Pharmaceutical Products Distr
S.I.C.: 5122
N.A.I.C.S.: 424210
Kirk Chin Kee *(Mng Dir)*

Xepa-Soul Pattinson (Malaysia) Sdn. Bhd. (1)
1-5 Cheng Industrial Estate
75250 Melaka, Malaysia
Tel.: (60) 63351515
Fax: (60) 63355829
E-Mail: enq@xepasp.com
Web Site: www.xepasp.com
Emp.: 275
Pharmaceutical Products Mfr
S.I.C.: 2834
N.A.I.C.S.: 325412
Tah Peng Kee *(Founder & Chm)*

Non-U.S. Subsidiary:

Xepa-Soul Pattinson (S) Pte. Ltd. (2)
12 Harper Road 06-00 Sulisam Building
Singapore, Singapore
Tel.: (65) 67438648
Fax: (65) 67462029
Web Site: www.xepasp.com
Emp.: 12
Pharmaceuticals Distr
S.I.C.: 5122
N.A.I.C.S.: 424210
Willie Woon *(Reg Mgr)*

Non-U.S. Subsidiary:

Apex Pharma Marketing Pte. Ltd. (1)
12 Harper Rd 06-00 Sulisam Bldg
Singapore, Singapore
Tel.: (65) 67413803
Fax: (65) 67493839
E-Mail: enquiry@apexpharmacy.com.sg
Web Site: www.apexpharmacy.com.sg
Pharmaceuticals & Personal Care Products Distr
S.I.C.: 5122
N.A.I.C.S.: 424210

APEX HOLDING LIMITED

Rupayan Golden Age 5th & 6th Floors
99 Gulshan Avenue Gulshan, Dhaka, 1212, Bangladesh
Tel.: (880) 2 9883358
Fax: (880) 2 9861685
Web Site: www.apexholdings.com
Year Founded: 1998

Business Description:
Holding Company
S.I.C.: 6719
N.A.I.C.S.: 551112

Personnel:
Zafar Ahmed *(Chm)*

Holdings:

Apex Foods Limited (1)
Rupayan Golden Age 5th & 6th Floor 99 Gulshan Avenue
Gulshan, Dhaka, 1212, Bangladesh BD
Tel.: (880) 2 9883358
Fax: (880) 2 9861685
E-Mail: apex@apexfoods.com
Web Site: www.apexfoods.com
APEXFOODS—(DHA)
Sls.: $40,924,780
Assets: $21,772,122
Liabilities: $15,361,022
Net Worth: $6,411,100
Earnings: $179,436
Emp.: 518
Fiscal Year-end: 06/30/13
Seafood Processing Services
S.I.C.: 2092
N.A.I.C.S.: 311710
Zafar Ahmed *(Chm & Mng Dir)*
Zahur Ahmed *(Vice Chm & Deputy Mng Dir)*
S. K. Halder *(CFO)*

Apex Lingerie Limited (1)
Rupayan Golden Age 5th & 6th Floor
99 Gulshan Avenue Gulshan, Dhaka, 1212, Bangladesh
Tel.: (880) 2 9883358
Fax: (880) 2 9861685
Lingerie Mfr
S.I.C.: 5699
N.A.I.C.S.: 315240

Apex Spinning & Knitting Mills Limited (1)
Rupayan Golden Age 5th & 6th Floor 99 Gulshan Avenue Gulshan
Dhaka, 1212, Bangladesh
Tel.: (880) 2 9883358
Fax: (880) 2 9861685
E-Mail: askml@apexknitting.com
Web Site: www.apexknitting.com
APEXSPINN—(DHA)
Sls.: $30,276,597
Assets: $14,628,107
Liabilities: $9,499,172
Net Worth: $5,128,935
Earnings: $228,874
Emp.: 4,690
Fiscal Year-end: 03/31/13
Knitted Garment Mfr
S.I.C.: 2399
N.A.I.C.S.: 314999
Zafar Ahmed *(Chm)*
Zahur Ahmed *(Mng Dir)*
M. Kamruzzaman *(CFO)*

Apex Textile Printing Mills Limited (1)
Rupayan Golden Age 5th & 6th Floors 99 Gulshan Avenue
99 Gulshan Avenue gulshan, Dhaka, 1212, Bangladesh
Tel.: (880) 2 9883358
Fax: (880) 2 9861685
Web Site: www.apextextileprinting.com
Knit Garments & Lingerie Mfr
S.I.C.: 2259
N.A.I.C.S.: 315190
Zahur Ahmed *(Mng Dir)*

Apex Yarn Dyeing Limited (1)
Rupayan Golden Age 5th & 6th Floors
99 Gulshan Avenue Gulshan, Dhaka, 1212, Bangladesh
Tel.: (880) 2 9883358
Fax: (880) 2 9861685
E-Mail: admin@apexthreads.com
Web Site: www.apexthreads.com
Yarn & Thread Producer
S.I.C.: 2299
N.A.I.C.S.: 313110
Zahur Ahmed *(Mng Dir)*

Matex Bangladesh Limited (1)
Rupayan Golden Age 5th & 6th Floors
99 Gulshan Avenue Gulshan, Dhaka, 1212, Bangladesh
Tel.: (880) 2 9883358
Fax: (880) 2 9861685
Web Site: www.matexbd.com
Chemicals & Dyes Mfr
S.I.C.: 2819
N.A.I.C.S.: 325130

APEX LIMITED PARTNERSHIP

1710 14th Ave NW Ste 300 &200
Calgary, AB, T2N 1M5, Canada
Tel.: (403) 264-3232
Fax: (403) 263-0502
E-Mail: info@excelhomes.net
Web Site: www.apexland.com
Year Founded: 1991
Sales Range: $25-49.9 Million
Emp.: 150

Business Description:
Commercial Real Estate Acquirer, Developer & Retailer
S.I.C.: 6531
N.A.I.C.S.: 531210

Personnel:
Frank Boyd *(Chm)*
Greg Lefebre *(Pres & CEO)*
Evelyn Fulton *(CFO)*

Subsidiaries:

Centrex Homes (1)
1710-14th Avenue Northwest Suite 200
Calgary, AB, T2N 1M5, Canada
Tel.: (403) 282-4446
Fax: (403) 264-3258
E-Mail: info@centrexhomes.ca
Web Site: www.centrexhomes.ca
Residential Home Building
S.I.C.: 1521
N.A.I.C.S.: 236115

Excel Homes LP (1)
1710 14th Avenue NW Suite 200
Calgary, AB, T2N 1M5, Canada
Tel.: (403) 253-1433
Fax: (403) 253-1687
E-Mail: info@excelhomes.net
Web Site: www.excelhomes.net
Emp.: 120
Residential Builders
S.I.C.: 1521
N.A.I.C.S.: 236115
Greg Lefebre *(Pres & CEO)*

APEX MINERALS NL

Level 1 10 Ord Street
West Perth, WA, 6005, Australia
Tel.: (61) 863115555
Fax: (61) 863115556
E-Mail: admin@apexminerals.com.au
Web Site: www.apexminerals.com.au
AXM—(ASX)

Business Description:
Mineral Exploration
S.I.C.: 1481
N.A.I.C.S.: 213115

Personnel:
Eduard Eshuys *(Chm)*
Michael Ilett *(Sec)*

Board of Directors:
Eduard Eshuys
Ross Hutton
Brice Mutton
Kim Robinson

Legal Counsel:
Steinepreis Paganin
Level 4 The Read Buildings 16 Milligan Street
Perth, Australia

Subsidiary:

Apex Gold Pty. Ltd. (1)
Level 1 10 Ord St
West Perth, WA, 6005, Australia
Tel.: (61) 8 9981 8200
Fax: (61) 8 9980 6026
Gold Ore Mining & Exploration Services
S.I.C.: 1041
N.A.I.C.S.: 212221
Corey Doust *(Gen Mgr)*

APEX MINING CO., INC.

Unit 1704 17th Floor Prestige Tower
Condominium F Ortigas Jr Road
Ortigas Center, Pasig, 1605, Philippines
Tel.: (63) 27062805
Fax: (63) 7062804
Web Site: www.apexmines.com
APX—(PHI)
Rev.: $44,506,205
Assets: $98,824,147
Liabilities: $40,143,885
Net Worth: $58,680,262
Earnings: $1,391,470
Emp.: 1,023
Fiscal Year-end: 12/31/12

Business Description:
Gold Mining Services
S.I.C.: 1041
N.A.I.C.S.: 212221

Personnel:
Benoit de Galbert *(Chm & Exec VP)*
Reynato S. Puno *(Vice Chm)*
Baiverth M. Diabo *(Pres)*
Rodolfo G. Bravo *(CFO, Treas, VP & Head-Fin)*
Rosanna A. Parica *(Corp Info Officer & Sec)*

Board of Directors:
Benoit de Galbert
Javier Del Ser
Baiverth M. Diabo
Bienvenido E. Laguesma
Reynato S. Puno
Richard Benedict S. So
Graciano P. Yumul, Jr.

APEX REFORESTATION LTD

PO Box 34156
Vancouver, BC, V6J 4N1, Canada
Tel.: (604) 736-0063
Rev.: $21,253,210
Emp.: 2

Business Description:
Forestry Service
S.I.C.: 0851
N.A.I.C.S.: 115310

Personnel:
Marc Hobday *(Pres)*

APEX TANNERY LIMITED

127 Hazaribagh
Dhaka, 1209, Bangladesh
Tel.: (880) 2 8625635
Fax: (880) 2 8616567
E-Mail: apex@accesstel.net
Web Site: www.apextannery.com
Year Founded: 1976
APEXTANRY—(DHA)

Business Description:
Leather Goods Mfr
S.I.C.: 3199
N.A.I.C.S.: 316998

Personnel:
Syed Manzur Elahi *(Chm)*
A. K. M. Rahmatullah *(Mng Dir)*

Board of Directors:
Syed Manzur Elahi
Mohammad Hedayetullah
M. A. Majed
Syed Nasim Manzur
A. K. M. Rahmatullah

APFT BERHAD

Suite 50-5-5 5th Floor Wisma UOA
Damansara 50 Jalan Dungun
Damansara Heights, 50490 Kuala Lumpur, Malaysia
Tel.: (60) 320923177
Fax: (60) 320939218
E-Mail: info@apft.com.my
Web Site: www.apft.edu.my

APFT Berhad—(Continued)

APFT—(KLS)
Rev.: $7,352,093
Assets: $20,119,397
Liabilities: $9,820,606
Net Worth: $10,298,791
Earnings: ($1,598,102)
Emp.: 111
Fiscal Year-end: 12/31/12

Business Description:
Flight Training & Education Services
S.I.C.: 8249
N.A.I.C.S.: 611512

Personnel:
Faruk Othman *(Chm)*
Yim Kong Ng *(Co-Sec)*
Seiw Ling Tan *(Co-Sec)*

Board of Directors:
Faruk Othman
Azmi Abdullah
Arif Faruk
Din Sulaiman
Tony Nyap Keong Tan

APG/SGA SA

(Formerly Affichage Holding SA)
23 Rue Des Vollandes
1211 Geneva, 6, Switzerland
Tel.: (41) 58 220 70 00
Fax: (41) 58 220 70 97
E-Mail: investors@apgsga.ch
Web Site: www.apgsga.ch
APGN—(SWX)
Rev.: $345,490,332
Assets: $310,189,013
Liabilities: $194,644,569
Net Worth: $115,544,444
Earnings: $56,186,161
Emp.: 652
Fiscal Year-end: 12/31/12

Business Description:
Holding Company; Outdoor Advertising Services
S.I.C.: 6719
N.A.I.C.S.: 551112

Personnel:
Jean-Francois Decaux *(Chm)*
Paul-Henry Binz *(Vice Chm)*
Daniel Hofer *(CEO)*
Beat Holenstein *(Head-Partner & Product Mgmt)*
Beat Hermann *(CFO)*

Board of Directors:
Jean-Francois Decaux
Paul-Henry Binz
Gilles Samyn
Markus Scheidegger
Robert Schmidli

Subsidiary:

APG, Allgemeine Plakatgesellschaft APG (1)
Rue des Vollandes 23
1211 Geneva, Switzerland
Tel.: (41) 58 220 72 20
E-Mail: info.digital@apgsga.ch
Web Site: www.apgsga.ch
Emp.: 56
Advertising Agency Services
S.I.C.: 7311
N.A.I.C.S.: 541810
Jean-Francois Decaux *(Chm)*
Paul-Henry Binz *(Vice Chm)*
Daniel Hofer *(CEO)*
Beat Holenstein *(Partner)*
Beat Hermann *(CFO)*

Holdings:

Allgemeine Plakatgesellschaft APG (1)
23 rue des Vollandes
Postfach 6195
1211 Geneva, Switzerland (100%)
Tel.: (41) 227370200
Fax: (41) 582207096
E-Mail: marketing@apg.ch
Web Site: www.apg.ch
Emp.: 600
Display Advertising
S.I.C.: 7312
N.A.I.C.S.: 541850
Ulrich Von Bassewitz *(CFO)*

APG-SGA Traffic SA (1)
Muhlemattstr 50
Postfach 2222
5001 Aarau, Switzerland (100%)
Tel.: (41) 628341073
Fax: (41) 628341078
E-Mail: info@traffic.ch
Web Site: www.traffic.ch
Emp.: 33
Advertising Agencies
S.I.C.: 7311
N.A.I.C.S.: 541810
Daniel Sluopk *(Gen Mgr)*

Bercher SA Publicite Generale (1)
Rte de Pre-boise 20
Postfach 1895
1215 Geneva, 15, Switzerland (100%)
Tel.: (41) 223473388
Fax: (41) 223462047
E-Mail: mail@bercher.ch
Web Site: www.bercher.ch
Emp.: 6
Advertising Agencies
S.I.C.: 7311
N.A.I.C.S.: 541810
Pierre Alain Mettreau *(Mng Dir)*

Paron AG (1)
Giesshuibil St No 4
8045 Zurich, Switzerland (100%)
Tel.: (41) 443875300
Fax: (41) 443875301
E-Mail: info@paron.ch
Web Site: www.paron.ch
Emp.: 7
Outdoor Power Equipment Stores
S.I.C.: 7389
N.A.I.C.S.: 561491
Ernst Fuhrer *(Head-Acq)*

Swiss Poster Research Plus AG (1)
Hoschgasse 70
8008 Zurich, Switzerland (100%)
Tel.: (41) 443858060
Fax: (41) 443858061
E-Mail: info@spr-plus.ch
Web Site: www.spr-plus.ch
Emp.: 3
Marketing Research and Public Opinion Polling
S.I.C.: 8732
N.A.I.C.S.: 541910
Urf Hofmann *(Mng Dir)*

Non-U.S. Subsidiaries:

Amco Srl (1)
Careat 100
Brasov, 500002, Romania
Tel.: (40) 268415591
Fax: (40) 372873978
Web Site: www.amcosrl.com
Emp.: 7
Advertising Agency Services
S.I.C.: 7311
N.A.I.C.S.: 541810
Mircea Chiru *(Gen Mgr)*

International Metropolis Media d.o.o. (1)
Dositejeva 20/3
11000 Belgrade, Serbia
Tel.: (381) 11 202 89 20
Fax: (381) 112028016
E-Mail: office@aqyu.com
Web Site: www.aqyu.com
Emp.: 5
Outdoor Advertising Services
S.I.C.: 7312
N.A.I.C.S.: 541850
Vincent Caille *(Gen Mgr)*

Neonlight Kft (1)
Beg u 3-5
1022 Budapest, Hungary
Tel.: (36) 1 786 3146
Fax: (36) 1 786 3150
E-Mail: office@neonlight.hu
Web Site: www.neonlight.hu
Outdoor Display Advertising Services
S.I.C.: 7312
N.A.I.C.S.: 541850

RBN Romanian Billboard Network Srl (1)
Str Bucium 17
Iasi, Romania
Tel.: (40) 232 276000
Fax: (40) 232211843
Outdoor Advertising Services
S.I.C.: 7312
N.A.I.C.S.: 541850

Non-U.S. Holdings:

Affichage Romania Srl (1)
Biharea No 67/77 Districtt 1
Bucharest, Romania (70%)
Tel.: (40) 213128313
Fax: (40) 213128363
E-Mail: office@affichage.ro
Web Site: www.affichage.ro
Emp.: 30
Advertising Agencies
S.I.C.: 7311
N.A.I.C.S.: 541810
Rene Rosanbarg *(Pres & CEO)*

Alma Quattro d.o.o. (1)
Dositejeva 20-3 Beograd
11000 Belgrade, Serbia (100%)
Tel.: (381) 113285093
Fax: (381) 2028916
E-Mail: office@aqyu.com
Web Site: www.aqyu.com
Other Services Related to Advertising
S.I.C.: 7319
N.A.I.C.S.: 541890
Bojana Novakovic *(Dir-Sls)*

Churchill Media Srl (1)
Gigaro Mora no 31 Strada Comandor Eugen Botez Nr 1
Sector 1, 020232 Bucharest, Romania (70%)
Tel.: (40) 212339333
Fax: (40) 212339333
Emp.: 30
Advertising Agencies
S.I.C.: 7311
N.A.I.C.S.: 541810
Lucian Talaz *(Mng Dir)*

Europlakat d.o.o. (1)
Zagorska 2
10000 Zagreb, Croatia (51%)
Tel.: (385) 13031000
Fax: (385) 13031001
E-Mail: office@europlakat.hr
Web Site: www.europlakat.hr
Emp.: 50
Display Advertising
S.I.C.: 7312
N.A.I.C.S.: 541850
Hrvoje Prtacin *(CEO)*

Non-U.S. Subsidiaries:

Europlakat Bulgaria OOD (2)
Schiptschenski prochod 42 Block 248
BG-1113 Sofia, Bulgaria (65%)
Tel.: (359) 28707280
Fax: (359) 28707280
E-Mail: europlakat.bg@techno-link.com
Web Site: www.europlakat.com
Display Advertising
S.I.C.: 7312
N.A.I.C.S.: 541850
Krassimir Petkov *(Mng Dir)*

Europlakat Kft (2)
Alkotas u 1719
1123 Budapest, Hungary (67.57%)
Tel.: (36) 14888440
Fax: (36) 14888447
E-Mail: office@europlakat.hu
Web Site: www.europlakat.hu
Display Advertising
S.I.C.: 7312
N.A.I.C.S.: 541850
Attila Vamos *(Gen Mgr)*

Europlakat Yugoslavia d.o.o. (2)
Dositejeva 20-3
11000 Belgrade, Serbia (100%)
Tel.: (381) 113285093
Fax: (381) 1132028916
E-Mail: office@aqyu.com
Web Site: www.aqyu.com
Emp.: 50
Other Services Related to Advertising
S.I.C.: 7319
N.A.I.C.S.: 541890
Bojana Novakovic *(Dir-Sls)*

Proreklam-Europlakat d.o.o. (2)
Koprska ul 98
1000 Ljubljana, Slovenia (33%)
Tel.: (386) 12001550
Fax: (386) 12001555
E-Mail: info@europlakat.si
Web Site: www.europlakat.si
Emp.: 50
Advertising Agencies
S.I.C.: 7311
N.A.I.C.S.: 541810
Marko Kolbl *(Mng Dir)*

Interflash d.o.o. (1)
Gubceva cesta 28
8210 Trebnje, Slovenia (100%)
Tel.: (386) 73482222
Fax: (386) 73482237
E-Mail: info@interflash.si
Web Site: www.interflash.si
Emp.: 3
All Other Business Support Services
S.I.C.: 7389
N.A.I.C.S.: 561491
Dejan Smuk *(Mng Dir)*

Publifutura Affichage Italia Srl (1)
Via Rodari 9
22100 Como, Italy (100%)
Tel.: (39) 313371661
Fax: (39) 313371695
E-Mail: info@publifutura.it
Web Site: www.publifutura.it
Emp.: 4
Advertising Agencies
S.I.C.: 7311
N.A.I.C.S.: 541810
Renato Belotti *(Mng Dir)*

Visiorama AG (1)
Messinastrasse 30
FL-9495 Triesen, Liechtenstein (100%)
Tel.: (423) 3880588
Fax: (423) 3880589
E-Mail: info@visiorama.ch
Web Site: www.visiorama.ch
Emp.: 7
Advertising Agencies
S.I.C.: 7311
N.A.I.C.S.: 541810
Christian Vonach *(CEO)*

APHRODITE GOLD LIMITED

45 Ventnor Avenue
West Perth, WA, 6005, Australia
Tel.: (61) 8 9389 4421
Fax: (61) 8 9389 4400
E-Mail: info@aphroditegold.com.au
Web Site: www.aphroditegold.com.au
Year Founded: 2009
AQQ—(ASX)
Rev.: $430,068
Assets: $24,622,765
Liabilities: $4,131,115
Net Worth: $20,491,650
Earnings: ($1,292,790)
Fiscal Year-end: 06/30/13

Business Description:
Gold Mining Services
S.I.C.: 1041
N.A.I.C.S.: 212221

Personnel:
Peter Buttigieg *(Chm & Acting CEO)*
Michael Beer *(Sec)*

Board of Directors:
Peter Buttigieg
Paul Buttigieg
Angus Middleton
Roger Mitchell
Paul Maurice Weston

Legal Counsel:
GTP Legal
Level 1 28 Ord Street
West Perth, Australia

API FINANCE LIMITED

Chipledhunga
Post Box No 168
Kaski, Pokhara, Nepal
Tel.: (977) 61 528325
Fax: (977) 61 528324

E-Mail: info@apifinance.com
Web Site: www.apifinance.com
AFL—(NEP)
Business Description:
Financial Services
S.I.C.: 6211
N.A.I.C.S.: 523999
Personnel:
Surendra Raj Adhikari *(Chm)*
Dhruba Raj Tiwari *(Mng Dir)*
Board of Directors:
Surendra Raj Adhikari
Babu Ram Adhikari
Basanta Raj Adhikari
Ananda Baral
Bhagwan Kunwar
Rajendra Prasad Poudel
Dhruba Raj Tiwari

API GROUP PLC
Second Avenue Poynton Industrial Estate Poynton
Stockport, Cheshire, SK12 1ND, United Kingdom
Tel.: (44) 1625858700
Fax: (44) 1625858701
E-Mail: enquiries@apigroup.com
Web Site: www.apigroup.com
Year Founded: 1920
API—(LSE OTC)
Rev.: $177,553,258
Assets: $108,490,906
Liabilities: $72,279,365
Net Worth: $36,211,540
Earnings: $9,120,400
Emp.: 543
Fiscal Year-end: 03/31/13
Business Description:
Holding Company; Paper Coating & Packaging; Security Systems; Foil Printing
S.I.C.: 6719
N.A.I.C.S.: 551112
Personnel:
Andrew Turner *(Grp CEO)*
Wendy Baker *(Sec)*
Board of Directors:
Richard Wright
Max W. Batzer
Christopher Lan Charles Smith
Andrew Turner
Andrew Walker
Luke Wiseman
Legal Counsel:
Eversheds LLP
Eversheds House 70-76 Great Bridgewater Street
Manchester, United Kingdom
Transfer Agent:
Capita IRG plc
Bourne House 34 Beckenham Road
Beckenham, Kent, BR3 4TU, United Kingdom
Subsidiaries:

API Foils Limited (1)
Firth Rd Houstoun Industrial Estate
Livingston, EH54 5DJ, United Kingdom (100%)
Tel.: (44) 1506438611
Fax: (44) 1506438262
Web Site: www.apigroup.com
Emp.: 100
Metal Stamping
S.I.C.: 3469
N.A.I.C.S.: 332119
Tom Hyland *(Mgr-Mfg)*

API Holographics Limited (1)
Astor Road Eccles New Rd
Salford, Manchester, M50 1BB, United Kingdom (100%)
Tel.: (44) 1617898131
Fax: (44) 1617890564
E-Mail: info@apiholographics.com
Web Site: www.apigroup.com
Emp.: 100
Laminated Aluminum Foil Mfr for Flexible Packaging Uses
S.I.C.: 2672
N.A.I.C.S.: 322220
Stephen Clarke *(Mng Dir)*

API Laminates (1)
2nd Ave Poynton Industrial Est
Poynton, Cheshire, SK12 1ND, United Kingdom (100%)
Tel.: (44) 1625650500
Fax: (44) 1625650580
E-Mail: laminates@apigroup.com
Web Site: www.apigroup.com
Emp.: 85
Metallized Packaging & Tape Mfr
S.I.C.: 2671
N.A.I.C.S.: 322220

U.S. Division:

API Foils Inc. (1)
3841 Greenway Cir
Lawrence, KS 66046-5444
Tel.: (785) 842-7674
Fax: (785) 842-9748
E-Mail: apifoils-na@apigroup.com
Web Site: www.api-worldwide.com
Emp.: 65
Hot Stamping Foils & Application Machinery Mfr
S.I.C.: 3499
N.A.I.C.S.: 332999
Rick Stanwicks *(Gen Mgr)*

U.S. Subsidiary:

API (USA) Holdings Limited (1)
329 New Brunswick Ave
Rahway, NJ 07065-2928
Tel.: (732) 382-6800
Packaging Material Mfr
S.I.C.: 2671
N.A.I.C.S.: 322220

Non-U.S. Subsidiaries:

API Foils (New Zealand) Limited (1)
PO Box 11182
Ellerslie, Auckland, 1542, New Zealand (100%)
Tel.: (64) 95799262
Fax: (64) 95253859
E-Mail: enquiries@apigroup.com
Web Site: www.apigroup.com
Emp.: 6
Metal Service Centers
S.I.C.: 5051
N.A.I.C.S.: 423510
Warren Hadler *(Gen Mgr)*

API Foils Pty Limited (1)
3-25 George St
Homebush, NSW, 2140, Australia (100%)
Tel.: (61) 297432511
Metal Service Centers
S.I.C.: 5051
N.A.I.C.S.: 423510
Andrew Turner *(CEO)*

API Foils SAS (1)
14-16 Boulevard Arago
Z1 Villemilan, 91320 Wissous, France (100%)
Tel.: (33) 169754321
Fax: (33) 169203094
E-Mail: enquiries@apigroup.com
Web Site: www.apigroup.com
Emp.: 24
Industrial Machinery & Equipment Whslr
S.I.C.: 5084
N.A.I.C.S.: 423830
Olivier Dubly *(Mng Dir)*

APIC YAMADA CORPORATION
90 Kamitokuma
Chikuma, Nagano, 389-0898, Japan
Tel.: (81) 262767806
Fax: (81) 262764102
Web Site: www.apicyamada.co.jp
Year Founded: 1950
6300—(TKS)
Sls.: $95,084,000
Assets: $111,804,000
Liabilities: $66,187,000
Net Worth: $45,617,000
Earnings: ($4,334,000)
Emp.: 402
Fiscal Year-end: 03/31/13
Business Description:
Automated Equipment & Dies Mfr
S.I.C.: 3544
N.A.I.C.S.: 333514
Personnel:
Masaki Nonaka *(Chm)*
Hirohito Oshimori *(Pres)*
Board of Directors:
Masaki Nonaka
Atsushi Koide
Masao Nshizawa
Hirohito Oshimori
Hidetoshi Oya
Subsidiaries:

Apic Assist Corporation (1)
90 Kamitokuma
Chikuma, Nagano, 389-0805, Japan (100%)
Tel.: (81) 262768114
Fax: (81) 262768131
Web Site: www.apicyamada.co.jp/english/sales/main01.htm
Emp.: 2
All Other Legal Services
S.I.C.: 7389
N.A.I.C.S.: 541199
Masaki Nonaka *(Pres)*

APIC Yamada Distributors Inc. (1)
90 Kamitokuma
Chikuma, Nagano, 389-0805, Japan (100%)
Tel.: (81) 262768102
Fax: (81) 262767886
Web Site: www.ayd.co.jp
Emp.: 36
Industrial Machinery & Equipment Merchant Wholesalers
S.I.C.: 5084
N.A.I.C.S.: 423830

Plant:

APIC Yamada Corporation - Yoshino Plant (1)
80 Haneo
Chikuma, Nagano, 389-0812, Japan
Tel.: (81) 262763211
Fax: (81) 262762205
Web Site: www.apicyamada.co.jp/english/sales/main01.html
Emp.: 450
Semiconductor Device Mfr
S.I.C.: 3674
N.A.I.C.S.: 334413

U.S. Plant:

APIC YAMADA CORPORATION - Apic Yamada America Plant (1)
Southgate Business Park 104 S 54th St
Chandler, AZ 85226
Tel.: (480) 820-0078
Fax: (480) 820-0079
Web Site: www.apicyamada.co.jp/english/sales/main02.html
Semiconductor Mfr
S.I.C.: 3674
N.A.I.C.S.: 334413

Non-U.S. Subsidiaries:

APIC YAMADA SINGAPORE PTE. LTD. (1)
5 Kallang Sector No 04-02
Kolam Ayer Industrial Park, 349279
Singapore, Singapore
Tel.: (65) 67489300
Fax: (65) 67483600
Web Site: www.apicyamada.com.sg
Emp.: 30
Construction Machinery Mfr
S.I.C.: 3531
N.A.I.C.S.: 333120
William Ho *(Mng Dir)*

Plant:

Apic Yamada Singapore Pte. Ltd - Factory (2)
1 Kallang Sector 01-06 Kolam Ayer Industrial Park
Singapore, 349276, Singapore
Tel.: (65) 67412962
Fax: (65) 67483606
Web Site: www.apicyamada.com.sg/Contact_us.htm
Emp.: 35
Precision Machining Tools Mfr
S.I.C.: 3451
N.A.I.C.S.: 332721

APIC YAMADA TECHNOLOGY (SHANGHAI) CO., LTD. (1)
8950 SongZe DaDao QingPu Industrial Zone
201707 Shanghai, China (100%)
Tel.: (86) 2169212244
Fax: (86) 2169212566
E-Mail: zx@apicyamada.com.cn
Web Site: www.apicyamada.co.jp/english/sales/main02.html
Emp.: 86
Printing Machinery & Equipment Mfr
S.I.C.: 3555
N.A.I.C.S.: 333244
Hu Yong Gang *(Gen Mgr)*

APIC YAMADA (THAILAND) COMPANY LIMITED (1)
1/52 Moo 5 Rojana Industrial Park T Kanharm A U-Tai Pranakorn
13210 Ayutthaya, Sriayutthaya, Thailand
Tel.: (66) 35226328
Fax: (66) 35226317
E-Mail: anong@ayt.th.com
Web Site: www.ayt.th.com
Emp.: 260
Nonferrous Metal (except Copper & Aluminum) Rolling, Drawing, & Extruding
S.I.C.: 3356
N.A.I.C.S.: 331491
Mishida Medumi *(Mng Dir)*

Shanghai Apic Yamada Co.,Ltd. (1)
Unit 502 XinHongQiao Building No 55
Lou Shan Guan Road, 200336 Shanghai, China (100%)
Tel.: (86) 2163293882
Fax: (86) 2163292317
E-Mail: huang_bill@apicyamada.com.cn
Web Site: www.apicyamada.co.jp
Emp.: 10
Industrial Machinery & Equipment Wholesalers
S.I.C.: 5084
N.A.I.C.S.: 423830
Qu Wei Min *(Gen Mgr)*

APICAL LIMITED
Suite 343 162-168 Regent Street
London, W1B 5TD, United Kingdom
Tel.: (44) 20 7439 1000
Fax: (44) 20 7734 3358
E-Mail: info@apical.co.uk
Web Site: www.apical.co.uk
Year Founded: 1999
Sales Range: $10-24.9 Million
Emp.: 39
Business Description:
Software Development Services
S.I.C.: 7371
N.A.I.C.S.: 541511
Personnel:
Michael Tusch *(CEO)*

APIS INDIA LIMITED
18/32 East Patel Nagar
New Delhi, 110 008, India
Tel.: (91) 11 25737038
Fax: (91) 11 25713631
E-Mail: investor.relations@apisindia.com
Web Site: www.apisindia.com
Year Founded: 1924
506166—(BOM)
Sales Range: $10-24.9 Million
Business Description:
Honey Mfr & Distr
S.I.C.: 2099
N.A.I.C.S.: 311999
Personnel:
Vimal Anand *(Mng Dir & Compliance Officer)*
Vikas Aggarwal *(Co-Sec)*
Ruchika Chopra *(Co-Sec)*
Board of Directors:
Sunita Chaddha
Shalini Malik

APLAB LIMITED
Aplab House A-5 Wagle Industrial Estate
Thane, 400 604, India
Tel.: (91) 2267395555
Fax: (91) 2225823137
E-Mail: response@aplab.com
Web Site: www.aplab.com
APLAB—(BOM NSE)
Rev.: $13,675,082
Assets: $24,596,991
Liabilities: $20,196,405
Net Worth: $4,400,586
Earnings: ($2,606,911)
Emp.: 130
Fiscal Year-end: 03/31/13
Business Description:
Electronic Products Mfr
S.I.C.: 3699
N.A.I.C.S.: 335999
Personnel:
Nishith P. Deodhar *(Mng Dir)*
Rajesh K. Deherkar *(Sec & Controller-Fin)*
Board of Directors:
Prabhakar Shankar Deodhar
Jayant Deo
Amrita Prabhakar Deodhar
Nishith P. Deodhar
Amit Goenka
Mukund Gulgali
Shailendra K. Hajela
A. G. Joshi
Transfer Agent:
Adroit Corporate Services Pvt. Ltd.
19, Jaferbhoy Industrial Estate 1st Floor
Makwana Road
Marol Naka Andheri E, 400 059 Mumbai, India
Subsidiaries:

Intel Instruments and Systems Limited (1)
37 Sdf 2 Seepz Andheri
400096, Mumbai, Maharastra, India
Tel.: (91) 2228290843
Fax: (91) 2228290842
E-Mail: iisl@hotmail.com
Emp.: 100
Oscilloscopes Mfr
S.I.C.: 3827
N.A.I.C.S.: 333314
John Jacob *(Mgr)*

Sprylogic Technologies Ltd (1)
A 1 Aplab House Wagle Estate
Thane, Maharastra, 400 604, India
Tel.: (91) 2225821861
Fax: (91) 2225823137
E-Mail: info@sprylogic.com
Web Site: www.sprylogic.com
Emp.: 42
Software Services
S.I.C.: 7372
N.A.I.C.S.: 511210

APLISENS S.A.
ul Morelowa 7
03-192 Warsaw, Poland
Tel.: (48) 228140777
Fax: (48) 228140778
E-Mail: aplisens@aplisens.pl
APN—(WAR)
Sales Range: Less than $1 Million
Business Description:
Measuring Instruments Mfr
S.I.C.: 3812
N.A.I.C.S.: 334511
Personnel:
Miroslaw Karczmarczyk *(Chm-Supervisory Bd)*
Adam Zurawski *(Chm-Mgmt Bd)*
Robert Kozaczuk *(Vice Chm-Supervisory Bd)*
Grzegorz Glowacki *(Member-Mgmt Bd)*
Supervisory Board of Directors:
Miroslaw Karczmarczyk
Andrzej Kobialka
Robert Kozaczuk
Agnieszka Kultys-Zurawska
Rafal Tuzimek
Piotr Zubkow

APLIX IP HOLDINGS CORPORATION
(Formerly GAIA Holdings Corporation)
13F Shinjuku Eastside Square 6-27-30
Shinjuku-ku, Tokyo, 160-0022, Japan
Tel.: (81) 50 3786 1715
Web Site: www.aplix-ip.com
Year Founded: 1986
3727—(TKS)
Sales Range: $25-49.9 Million
Emp.: 495
Business Description:
Software Developer & Sales
S.I.C.: 7372
N.A.I.C.S.: 511210
Personnel:
Ryu Koriyama *(CEO)*
Transfer Agent:
Mitsubishi UFJ Trust & Banking Corporation
4-5 Marunouchi 1-Chome Chiyoda-ku
Tokyo, 100-8212, Japan
Tel.: (81) 3 3212 1211
Non-U.S. Subsidiary:

iaSolution Inc. (1)
7F No 100 Sec 4 Civic Blvd
Daan Dist, Taipei, Taiwan
Tel.: (886) 227761680
Fax: (886) 227761380
E-Mail: net-inquiry@aplix.co.jp
Web Site: www.iasolution.net
Emp.: 200
Software Development Services
S.I.C.: 7372
N.A.I.C.S.: 511210
Ryu Koriyama *(CEO)*

U.S. Subsidiary:

Aplix Corporation of America (2)
5201 Great America Pkwy Ste 446
Santa Clara, CA 95054
Tel.: (415) 558-8800
Web Site: www.aplixcorp.com
Emp.: 10
Software Development Services
S.I.C.: 7372
N.A.I.C.S.: 511210
Ryu Koriyama *(Pres)*

Non-U.S. Subsidiaries:

Aplix Korea Corporation (2)
2302 Trade Tower 159-1 Samsung-dong
Gangnam-ku, Seoul, 135-090, Korea (South)
Tel.: (82) 220510884
Fax: (82) 220510877
E-Mail:
Web Site: www.aplix.co.jp
Emp.: 9
Software Development Services
S.I.C.: 7372
N.A.I.C.S.: 511210
Aaron Pang *(Pres)*

APM AUTOMOTIVE HOLDINGS BERHAD
Lot 600 Pandamaran Industrial Estate
Locked Bag No 218
42009 Port Klang, Selangor Darul Ehsan, Malaysia
Tel.: (60) 33161 8888
Fax: (60) 33161 8833
E-Mail: apmah@apm.com.my
Web Site: www.apm-automotive.com
APM—(KLS)
Rev.: $393,003,922
Assets: $373,472,351
Liabilities: $75,568,508
Net Worth: $297,903,843
Earnings: $41,051,321
Fiscal Year-end: 12/31/12
Business Description:
Automotive Parts Mfr
S.I.C.: 5013
N.A.I.C.S.: 441310
Personnel:
Heng Chew Tan *(Chm)*
Yoke-Lin Chan *(Co-Sec)*
Kwee Cheng Lee *(Co-Sec & Sr Gen Mgr-Fin & Admin)*
Board of Directors:
Heng Chew Tan
Azman Badrillah
Woh Peng Fun
Ji Keng Heng
Seng Chee Low
Abas Nordin
N. Sadasivan
Eng Hwa Tan
Eng Soon Tan
Subsidiaries:

APM Auto Electrics Sdn. Bhd. (1)
Lot 20A-C Jalan Jelawai 2 PC 4 Proton City
35900 Tanjung Malim, Perak Darul Ridzuan, Malaysia
Tel.: (60) 54583333
Fax: (60) 54583366
E-Mail: apmae@apm-automotive.com
Web Site: www.apm-automotive.com
Electronic Component Mfr
S.I.C.: 3679
N.A.I.C.S.: 334419

APM Climate Control Sdn. Bhd. (1)
Lot 3 Jalan 6/3 Kawasan Perusahaan Seri Kembangan
4330 Seri Kembangan, Selangor Darul Ehsan, Malaysia
Tel.: (60) 389463333
Fax: (60) 389426886
E-Mail: apmcc@apm-automotive.com
Web Site: www.apm-automotive.com
Emp.: 220
Air Conditioners & Radiators Mfr
S.I.C.: 3433
N.A.I.C.S.: 333414
Siew Ming Goh *(Gen Mgr)*

APM Coil Springs Sdn. Bhd. (1)
Lot 1 Jalan Raja Lumu
Pandamaran Industrial Area, 42008 Port Klang, Selangor Darul Ehsan, Malaysia
Tel.: (60) 331685007
Fax: (60) 331682371
E-Mail: ksk@apm.com.my
Emp.: 111
Coil Springs Mfr
S.I.C.: 3495
N.A.I.C.S.: 332613
Kam Sim Kwang *(Gen Mgr)*

APM Plastics Sdn. Bhd. (1)
No 8 Jalan Jasmine 3 Kawasan Perindustrian Bukit Beruntung
Seksyen BB10, 48300 Rawang, Selangor Darul Ehsan, Malaysia
Tel.: (60) 360997700
Fax: (60) 360285102
E-Mail: apmpl@apm-automotive.com
Emp.: 1,200
Injection Molded Plastic Products Mfr
S.I.C.: 3082
N.A.I.C.S.: 326121
Low Seng Chee *(Gen Mgr)*

Auto Parts Manufacturers Co. Sdn. Bhd. (1)
No 4 Jalan Jasmine 3 Kawasan Perusahaan Bukit Beruntung
Bandar Bukit Beruntung, 48300 Rawang, Selangor Darul Ehsan, Malaysia
Tel.: (60) 360997700
Fax: (60) 360284620
E-Mail: apmsd@apm-automotive.com
Emp.: 1,000
Automotive Seats Mfr
S.I.C.: 2396
N.A.I.C.S.: 336360
Heng Chew Tan *(Chm)*
Wong Peng Fun *(CEO)*

APM Auto Parts Marketing Sdn. Bhd. (1)
Lot 1 Jalan Raja Lumu Pandamaran Industrial Estate
PO Box 144
42008 Port Klang, Selangor Darul Ehsan, Malaysia
Tel.: (60) 3 3168 5007
Fax: (60) 3 3167 9188
E-Mail: apmex@apm.com.my
Web Site: www.apm-automotive.com
Automotive Parts & Accessories Distr
S.I.C.: 5013
N.A.I.C.S.: 423120
Sim Kwang Kam *(Mng Dir)*

Non-U.S. Subsidiaries:

P.T. APM Armada Suspension (1)
Suryacipta City of Industry Jl Surya Utama Kav 1-15A Ciampel
Karawang, Jawa Barat, 41361, Indonesia
Tel.: (62) 2678610174
Fax: (62) 2189115885
Emp.: 70
Automotive Coil Springs Mfr & Distr
S.I.C.: 3495
N.A.I.C.S.: 332613
Sow Soon Hock *(Pres)*

Radiators Australia (2000) Pty. Ltd. (1)
11-13 Redwood Drive
Notting Hill, VIC, Australia
Tel.: (61) 395433788
Fax: (61) 395432388
Web Site: www.ra2000.com.au
Emp.: 35
Radiators Mfr & Distr
S.I.C.: 3714
N.A.I.C.S.: 336390
Albert Chang *(Mgr)*

APM GROUP LTD.
Sword House Totteridge Road
High Wycombe, Buckinghamshire, HP13 6DG, United Kingdom
Tel.: (44) 1494 452450
Fax: (44) 1494 459 559
Web Site: www.apmgroupltd.com
Year Founded: 1993
Sales Range: $25-49.9 Million
Emp.: 131
Business Description:
Management Consulting Services
S.I.C.: 4731
N.A.I.C.S.: 541614
Personnel:
Alan Harpham *(Chm)*
Richard Pharro *(CEO)*
Board of Directors:
Alan Harpham
Rod Baker
Michael F. Dallas
Adrian Dooley
Richard Pharro

APN EUROPEAN RETAIL PROPERTY GROUP
Level 30 101 Collins St
Melbourne, VIC, 3000, Australia
Tel.: (61) 386561000
Fax: (61) 386561010
E-Mail: apnpg@apngroup.com.au
Web Site: www.apngroup.com.au
Sales Range: $50-74.9 Million
Emp.: 60
Business Description:
Retail Properties Management
S.I.C.: 5961
N.A.I.C.S.: 454111
Personnel:
John Harvey *(Chm)*
David Blight *(Mng Dir)*
John Freemantle *(CFO & Sec)*
Howard Brenchley *(Chief Investment Officer)*
Paul Anderson *(CEO-Europe)*
Board of Directors:
John Harvey
David Blight
Howard Brenchley
Geoff Brunsdon
Michael Johnstone

APN NEWS & MEDIA LTD.
Level 4 100 William Street
Sydney, NSW, 2011, Australia

Tel.: (61) 293334999
Fax: (61) 293334900
E-Mail: info@apn.com.au
Web Site: www.apn.com.au
APN—(ASX NZE OTC)
Rev.: $903,841,467
Assets: $1,403,545,090
Liabilities: $735,662,158
Net Worth: $667,882,932
Earnings: ($450,142,390)
Fiscal Year-end: 12/31/12

Business Description:
Producer of Media & News Publications: Owned 39.1% by Independent News & Media PLC
S.I.C.: 2711
N.A.I.C.S.: 511110

Personnel:
Peter Maxwell Cosgrove *(Chm)*
Albert Edward Harris *(Deputy Chm)*
Michael Miller *(CEO)*
Jeff Howard *(CFO)*
Tim Catley *(CIO)*
Matthew Crockett *(Chief Dev Officer)*
Neil Monagha *(CEO-Media-Australian Reg)*
Martin Simons *(CEO-Media-New Zealand)*
Yvette Lamont *(Gen Counsel & Sec)*

Board of Directors:
Peter Maxwell Cosgrove
Paul Connolly
Vincent Conor Crowley
Peter Damian Cullinane
Albert Edward Harris
Kevin J. Luscombe
Anne Templeman-Jones

Legal Counsel:
Allen, Allen & Hemsley
Chiffley Centre 1 Chiffley Square
Sydney, NSW, 2000, Australia

Link Market Services Limited
Level 12 680 George Street
PO Box 20013
Sydney, Australia

Subsidiaries:

Adhoc Pty Ltd (1)
Whitsunday Business Centre Suite 2 4 230 Shute Harbour Road
Cannonvale, QLD, 4802, Australia
Tel.: (61) 7 4940 2100
Fax: (61) 7 4940 2101
Emp.: 11
Newspaper Publishing Services
S.I.C.: 2711
N.A.I.C.S.: 511110
Leanne Abernethy *(Mng Editor)*

Adshel Street Furniture (1)
The Forum Level 9 205 Pacific Hwy
Saint Leonards, NSW, 2065, Australia (50%)
Tel.: (61) 284257200
Fax: (61) 284257222
E-Mail: adshel@adshel.com.au
Web Site: www.adshel.com.au
Emp.: 51
S.I.C.: 2721
N.A.I.C.S.: 511120
Steve McCarthy *(CEO)*

APN AP National Sales Pty Ltd (1)
L 3 33 Park Rd
Milton, QLD, 4064, Australia
Tel.: (61) 733070333
Fax: (61) 733273377
Newspaper Publishing Services
S.I.C.: 2711
N.A.I.C.S.: 511110
Warren Bright *(Gen Mgr)*

APN Braeside Pty Ltd (1)
L 4 100 William St
Woolloomooloo, NSW, 2011, Australia
Tel.: (61) 293334999
Fax: (61) 293334900
Closed End Management Services
S.I.C.: 6726
N.A.I.C.S.: 525990

APN Educational Media (1)
Level 6 110 Waker Street
Sydney, NSW, 2060, Australia (100%)
Tel.: (61) 299368666
Fax: (61) 299368631
E-Mail: subs@apned.com.au
Web Site: www.apned.com.au
Emp.: 20
Publishing Services
S.I.C.: 7389
N.A.I.C.S.: 561410

APN Newspapers (1)
Level 3 33 Park Rd
Milton, QLD, 4000, Australia (100%)
Tel.: (61) 733070300
Fax: (61) 733070307
E-Mail: info@apn.com.au
Web Site: www.apn.com.au
Emp.: 100
Publishing Services
S.I.C.: 7389
N.A.I.C.S.: 561410
Martin Simons *(CEO)*

APN Online (Australia) Pty Limited (1)
L 4 100 Willian St
Sydney, NSW, 2011, Australia
Tel.: (61) 282898450
Online Publishing Services
S.I.C.: 2741
N.A.I.C.S.: 519130

APN Outdoor (Trading) Pty Ltd (1)
L 4 33 Saunders St
Pyrmont, NSW, 2009, Australia
Tel.: (61) 285693000
Fax: (61) 285693001
Outdoor Advertising Services
S.I.C.: 7312
N.A.I.C.S.: 541850
David Pullinger *(Grp Dir-Sls-New South Wales)*

APN Superannuation Pty Ltd (1)
L 3 33 Park Rd
Milton, QLD, 4064, Australia
Tel.: (61) 7 3307 0333
E-Mail: milton.reception@apn.com.au
Newspaper Publishing Services
S.I.C.: 2711
N.A.I.C.S.: 511110
Wendy Umstad *(Gen Mgr)*

The Australasian Advertising Company Pty Limited (1)
Level 4 33 Saunders Street
Pyrmont, NSW, 2009, Australia
Tel.: (61) 285693000
Fax: (61) 293334900
Advertising Services
S.I.C.: 7319
N.A.I.C.S.: 541890

Australian Provincial Newspapers International Pty Limited (1)
L-4 100 William Street
Sydney, NSW, 2011, Australia
Tel.: (61) 293334999
Fax: (61) 293334900
Newspaper Publishing Services
S.I.C.: 2711
N.A.I.C.S.: 511110

Australian Provincial Newspapers Ltd (1)
Level 4 100 William Street
Sydney, NSW, 2011, Australia
Tel.: (61) 2 9333 4999
Newspaper Publishing Services
S.I.C.: 2711
N.A.I.C.S.: 511110

Biffin Pty Limited (1)
L 4 100 William St
Woolloomooloo, 2011, Australia
Tel.: (61) 293334999
Fax: (61) 293334900
Web Site: www.apn.com.au
Newspaper Publishing Services
S.I.C.: 2711
N.A.I.C.S.: 511110
Brett Chenoweth *(CEO)*
Michael Miller *(CEO)*

The Bundaberg Newspaper Company Pty Limited (1)
36 - 38 Woondooma Street
PO Box 3006
Bundaberg, QLD, 4670, Australia
Tel.: (61) 7 4153 8555
Fax: (61) 7 4153 1028
E-Mail: info@news-mail.com.au
Web Site: www.news-mail.com.au
Emp.: 50
Newspaper Publishing Services
S.I.C.: 2711
N.A.I.C.S.: 511110
Wayne Tomkins *(Gen Mgr)*

Buspak Advertising Group Pty Ltd (1)
L4 33 Saunders St
Pyrmont, NSW, 2009, Australia
Tel.: (61) 293334999
Fax: (61) 293334900
Newspaper Publishing Services
S.I.C.: 2711
N.A.I.C.S.: 511110

Byron Shire News Pty Ltd (1)
Suite 5/75 Jonson Street
Byron Bay, 2481, Australia
Tel.: (61) 2 6685 6358
Fax: (61) 2 6685 6965
E-Mail: admin@byronnews.com.au
Web Site: www.byronnews.com.au
Emp.: 10
Newspaper Publishing Services
S.I.C.: 2711
N.A.I.C.S.: 511110
Alf Boston *(Mgr-Sls)*

Campus Review Pty Ltd (1)
PO BOX 6097
North Sydney, NSW, 2060, Australia
Tel.: (61) 299368666
Fax: (61) 299368631
Web Site: www.campusreview.com.au
Magazine Publishing Services
S.I.C.: 2721
N.A.I.C.S.: 511120

Capricornia Newspapers Pty Ltd (1)
162-164 Quay Street
PO Box 397
Rockhampton, QLD, 4700, Australia
Tel.: (61) 7 4930 4222
Fax: (61) 7 4930 4360
Newspaper Publishing Services
S.I.C.: 2711
N.A.I.C.S.: 511110

Central Queensland News Publishing Company Pty Ltd (1)
62 Egerton Street
PO Box 259
Emerald, QLD, 4720, Australia
Tel.: (61) 7 4980 0800
Fax: (61) 7 4982 2833
E-Mail: cqn@cqnews.com.au
Web Site: www.cqnews.com.au
Emp.: 15
Newspaper Publishing Services
S.I.C.: 2711
N.A.I.C.S.: 511110
Angela Duffy *(Gen Mgr)*

Central Telegraph Pty Ltd (1)
Cnr Kroombit & Washpool Street
PO Box 120
Biloela, QLD, 4715, Australia
Tel.: (61) 7 4992 1533
Fax: (61) 7 4992 2214
E-Mail: editor@centraltelegraph.com.au
Web Site: www.centraltelegraph.com.au
Emp.: 6
Newspaper Publishing Services
S.I.C.: 2711
N.A.I.C.S.: 511110
Cameron Mccrohon *(Gen Mgr)*

Chinchilla Newspapers Pty Ltd (1)
12 Mayne St
Chinchilla, QLD, 4413, Australia
Tel.: (61) 746627368
Newspaper Publishing Services
S.I.C.: 2711
N.A.I.C.S.: 511110

The Daily Examiner Pty Ltd (1)
55 Fitzroy St
Grafton, NSW, 2460, Australia
Tel.: (61) 266430500
Fax: (61) 266427156
E-Mail: help@dailyexaminer.com.au
Web Site: www.dailyexaminer.com.au
Emp.: 30
Newspaper Publishing Services
S.I.C.: 2711
N.A.I.C.S.: 511110
Judy Lewis *(Gen Mgr)*

Eastcott Investments Pty Ltd (1)
L 4 100 William St
Woolloomooloo, NSW, 2011, Australia
Tel.: (61) 293334999
Fax: (61) 733070307
Investment Management Services
S.I.C.: 6211
N.A.I.C.S.: 523999

Gatton Star Pty Ltd (1)
45 North Street
Gatton, QLD, 4343, Australia
Tel.: (61) 7 5462 2266
Fax: (61) 7 5462 2491
E-Mail: admin@gattonstar.com.au
Web Site: www.gattonstar.com.au
Newspaper Publishing Services
S.I.C.: 2711
N.A.I.C.S.: 511110
Bruce Horrocks *(Mgr-Sls)*

Gladstone Newspaper Company Pty Ltd (1)
27-29 Goondoon St
Gladstone, QLD, Australia
Tel.: (61) 749703030
Fax: (61) 749703047
Web Site: www.gladstonepacific.com.au
Emp.: 30
Newspaper Publishing Services
S.I.C.: 2711
N.A.I.C.S.: 511110
Carl Carter *(Gen Mgr)*

The Gold Coast Press Pty Limited (1)
333 Park Rd
Milton, QLD, 4064, Australia
Tel.: (61) 733273300
Newspaper Publishing Services
S.I.C.: 2711
N.A.I.C.S.: 511110

GSP Print Pty Ltd (1)
19 Ash Road
Prestons, Sydney, NSW, 2170, Australia
Tel.: (61) 2 8784 5111
Fax: (61) 2 8784 5155
E-Mail: info@gspprint.com.au
Web Site: www.gspprint.com.au
Outdoor Banner Printing Services
S.I.C.: 2759
N.A.I.C.S.: 323111
Peter Piccione *(Gen Mgr)*

Gulgong Pty Limited (1)
L 4 100 William St
Woolloomooloo, NSW, 2011, Australia
Tel.: (61) 293334999
Fax: (61) 293334900
Emp.: 20
Newspaper Publishing Services
S.I.C.: 2711
N.A.I.C.S.: 511110
Brett Chenoweth *(Pres)*

Gympie Times Pty Ltd (1)
197 Mary Street
Gympie, QLD, 4570, Australia
Tel.: (61) 7 5482 1011
E-Mail: help@gympietimes.com
Web Site: www.gympietimes.com.au
Newspaper Publishing Services
S.I.C.: 2711
N.A.I.C.S.: 511110
Andrew Smith *(Gen Mgr)*

Haswell Pty Limited (1)
L 10 300 Ann St
Brisbane, QLD, 4000, Australia
Tel.: (61) 733070300
Fax: (61) 733070307
Emp.: 60
Newspaper Publishing Services
S.I.C.: 2711
N.A.I.C.S.: 511110

The Mackay Printing and Publishing Company Pty Limited (1)
38-40 Wellington St
Mackay, QLD, 4740, Australia
Tel.: (61) 749570444
Fax: (61) 749570406
E-Mail: news@dailymercury.com
Web Site: www.dailymercury.com.au
Emp.: 5
Newspaper Printing & Publishing Services
S.I.C.: 2711
N.A.I.C.S.: 511110

APN News & Media Ltd.—(Continued)

Darren McVean *(Gen Mgr)*

The Maryborough Hervey Bay Newspaper Company Pty Ltd (1)
131 Bazaar Street
Maryborough, QLD, 4650, Australia
Tel.: (61) 7 4120 1000
Fax: (61) 7 4122 4734
E-Mail: help@frasercoastchronicle.com.au
Web Site: www.frasercoastchronicle.com.au
Emp.: 60
Newspaper Publishing Services
S.I.C.: 2711
N.A.I.C.S.: 511110
Darren Bosley *(Gen Mgr)*

Melbourne Independent Newspapers Pty Ltd (1)
L 4 100 William St
North Sydney, NSW, 2055, Australia
Tel.: (61) 293334999
Fax: (61) 293334900
Newspaper Publishing Services
S.I.C.: 2711
N.A.I.C.S.: 511110

Nettlefold Advertising Pty Ltd (1)
L4 33 Saunders St
Pyrmont, NSW, 2009, Australia
Tel.: (61) 293334999
Outdoor Display Advertising Services
S.I.C.: 7312
N.A.I.C.S.: 541850

Northern Star Ltd (1)
Media Centre Ballina Road
Goonellabah, Lismore, NSW, Australia
Tel.: (61) 2 6620 0500
E-Mail: help@northernstar.com.au
Web Site: www.northernstar.com.au
Newspaper Publishing Services
S.I.C.: 2711
N.A.I.C.S.: 511110
Paul Spotswood *(Gen Mgr)*

PanTV (1)
14 Herbert St
Artarmon, NSW, 2064, Australia (40%)
Tel.: (61) 297772777
Fax: (61) 297773450
E-Mail: worldmovies@pantv.com.au
Web Site: www.worldmovies.net
Emp.: 15
Television Broadcasting Services
S.I.C.: 4833
N.A.I.C.S.: 515120
Linda Hickey *(CEO)*

The Queensland Times Pty Limited (1)
260 Brisbane Street
Ipswich, QLD, 4305, Australia
Tel.: (61) 7 3817 1717
Fax: (61) 7 3817 1775
E-Mail: qt@qt.com.au
Web Site: www.qt.com.au
Emp.: 100
Newspaper Publishing Services
S.I.C.: 2711
N.A.I.C.S.: 511110
Steve Portas *(Gen Mgr)*

The South Burnett Times Pty Ltd (1)
176 Haly St
Kingaroy, QLD, 4610, Australia
Tel.: (61) 741629733
Fax: (61) 741624905
Newspaper Publishing Services
S.I.C.: 2711
N.A.I.C.S.: 511110
Brett Hanwright *(Gen Mgr)*

Toowoomba Newspapers Pty Ltd (1)
618 Ruthven Street
PO Box 40
Toowoomba, QLD, 4350, Australia
Tel.: (61) 7 4690 9300
Fax: (61) 7 4690 9301
E-Mail: news@thechronicle.com.au
Web Site: www.thechronicle.com.au
Newspaper Publishing Services
S.I.C.: 2711
N.A.I.C.S.: 511110

The Tweed Newspaper Company Pty Ltd (1)
13-17 Rivendell
PO Box 6336
Tweed Heads, NSW, 2486, Australia
Tel.: (61) 7 5524 6400
Fax: (61) 7 5524 6222
E-Mail: help@mydailynews.com.au
Web Site: www.tweednews.com.au
Newspaper Publishing Services
S.I.C.: 2711
N.A.I.C.S.: 511110

The Warwick Newspaper Pty Limited (1)
PO Box 358
Warwick, QLD, 4370, Australia
Tel.: (61) 7 4660 1303
Fax: (61) 7 4661 9427
E-Mail: admin@warwickdailynews.com.au
Web Site: www.warwickdailynews.com.au
Emp.: 2
Newspaper Publishing Services
S.I.C.: 2711
N.A.I.C.S.: 511110
Nick Inmon *(Mgr-Media Adv)*

Western Star Pty Ltd (1)
120 Mcdowell St
Roma, QLD, 4455, Australia
Tel.: (61) 746221411
Fax: (61) 462234433
Emp.: 6
Newspaper Publishing Services
S.I.C.: 2711
N.A.I.C.S.: 511110
Ben Balestrieri *(Mgr-Sls)*

Joint Venture:

Australian Radio Network Pty. Limited (1)
3 Byfield Street
North Ryde, NSW, 2113, Australia AU
Tel.: (61) 2 8899 9888
Fax: (61) 2 8899 9566
E-Mail: info@arn.com.au
Web Site: www.arn.com.au
Emp.: 500
Radio Network Operator
S.I.C.: 4832
N.A.I.C.S.: 515111
Ciaran Davis *(CEO)*
Michael Harvey *(CFO)*
Geraint Davies *(COO)*

Non-U.S. Subsidiary:

APN New Zealand Limited (1)
46 Albert Street
Auckland, 1010, New Zealand
Tel.: (64) 9 379 5050
Fax: (64) 93736443
Web Site: www.apn.com
Emp.: 70
Multimedia Holding Company; Newspaper & Online Publishing, Radio Broadcasting & Outdoor Advertising Services
S.I.C.: 6719
N.A.I.C.S.: 551112
Kursten Shalfoon *(CMO)*
Martin Simons *(CEO-Media)*

Subsidiaries:

APN Media (NZ) Limited (2)
46 Albert Street
Auckland, 1010, New Zealand NZ
Tel.: (64) 9 373 6400
Fax: (64) 93736443
Web Site: www.nzherald.co.nz
Emp.: 800
Newspaper Publisher
S.I.C.: 2711
N.A.I.C.S.: 511110
James Fazzino *(CEO)*

Subsidiaries:

APN Educational Media (NZ) Limited (3)
Level 1 Saatchi & Saatchi Building 101-103 Courtenay Place
Box 200
Wellington, 6011, New Zealand NZ
Tel.: (64) 4 471 1080
Fax: (64) 4 471 1080
Web Site: www.apn-ed.co.nz
Emp.: 18
Education & Health Materials Publisher
S.I.C.: 2731
N.A.I.C.S.: 511130
Bronwen Wilkins *(Gen Mgr & Publr)*

APN Online (New Zealand) Limited (3)
46 Albert Street
Auckland, New Zealand
Tel.: (64) 9 373 6400
E-Mail: advertising@nzherald.co.nz
Web Site: www.advertise.nzherald.co.nz
Online Publishing & Advertising Services
S.I.C.: 2741
N.A.I.C.S.: 519130
Hayden Lee *(Head-Adv Strategy & Ops)*

APN Specialist Publications NZ Limited (3)
4th Floor NZ Herald Building 46 Albert Street
Auckland, 6400, New Zealand NZ
Tel.: (64) 9 373 6400
Fax: (64) 9 373 9401
Business Directories Publisher
S.I.C.: 2741
N.A.I.C.S.: 511140
A. J. O'Reilly *(Gen Mgr)*

APN Print NZ Limited (2)
Ruataniwha Street
Ellerslie, Waipukurau, 4200, New Zealand NZ
Tel.: (64) 6 858 8166
Fax: (64) 6 858 8959
Web Site: www.apnprint.co.nz
Commercial Printing Services
S.I.C.: 2759
N.A.I.C.S.: 323111
Brian Hood *(COO)*

APN PROPERTY GROUP LIMITED

Level 30 101 Collins Street
Melbourne, VIC, 3000, Australia
Tel.: (61) 386561000
Fax: (61) 386561010
E-Mail: apnpg@apngroup.com.au
Web Site: www.apngroup.com.au
Year Founded: 1996
APD—(ASX)
Rev.: $19,317,408
Assets: $39,315,307
Liabilities: $6,886,197
Net Worth: $32,429,110
Earnings: $1,425,593
Fiscal Year-end: 06/30/13

Business Description:
Real Estate Investment Services
S.I.C.: 6531
N.A.I.C.S.: 531390

Personnel:
Christopher Aylward *(Chm)*
John Freemantle *(CFO & Sec)*
Howard Brenchley *(Chief Investment Officer)*
Michael Doble *(CEO-Real Estate Securities)*
Stephen Finch *(CEO-Asia)*
Miles Wentworth *(CEO-Generation Healthcare REIT)*

Board of Directors:
Christopher Aylward
Clive Appleton
Howard Brenchley
John Lim

Subsidiary:

APN Funds Management Limited (1)
Level 30 101 Collins Street
Melbourne, VIC, 3000, Australia
Tel.: (61) 3 8656 1000
Fax: (61) 3 8656 1010
E-Mail: apnpg@apngroup.com.au
Web Site: www.apngroup.com.au
Emp.: 34
Investment Fund Management Services
S.I.C.: 6282
N.A.I.C.S.: 523920
Howard Benchley *(CIO)*

Non-U.S. Subsidiaries:

APN Funds Management (Asia) Pte Limited (1)
7 Temasek Boulevard 04-02A Suntec Tower One
Singapore, 38987, Singapore
Tel.: (65) 6500 8180
Fax: (65) 6500 8181
E-Mail: sgoperations@apngroup.com.sg
Web Site: www.apngroup.com.sg
Emp.: 4
Fund Management Services
S.I.C.: 6282
N.A.I.C.S.: 523920
Howard Brenchley *(CIO)*

APN Funds Management (UK) Limited (1)
Level 11 East Centre Point 103 New Oxford Street
London, WC1A 1DD, United Kingdom
Tel.: (44) 20 7535 8770
Fax: (44) 20 7535 8771
Emp.: 14
Investment Fund Management Services
S.I.C.: 6799
N.A.I.C.S.: 523920
David Blight *(Grp Mng Dir)*
Howard Brenchley *(CIO)*

APOGEE SILVER LTD.

65 Queen Street West Suite 815
PO Box 75
Toronto, ON, M5H 2M5, Canada
Tel.: (416) 309-2694
Fax: (416) 861-8165
E-Mail: info@apogeesilver.com
Web Site: www.apogeesilver.com
Year Founded: 1987
APE—(TSXV)
Int. Income: $22,842
Assets: $44,994,885
Liabilities: $1,970,705
Net Worth: $43,024,180
Earnings: ($3,521,718)
Fiscal Year-end: 06/30/13

Business Description:
Mineral Exploration Services
S.I.C.: 1081
N.A.I.C.S.: 213114

Personnel:
G. Scott Paterson *(Chm)*
Neil Ringdahl *(CEO)*
Greg Duras *(CFO)*
Jennifer Wagner *(Sec)*

Board of Directors:
G. Scott Paterson
Peter Bojtos
David Patrick Gower
Chantal Lavoie
Francois Perron
Neil Ringdahl

APOLLO 8 MAINTENANCE SERVICES LTD.

1502 Danforth Avenue
Toronto, ON, M4J 1N4, Canada
Tel.: (416) 461-8748
Fax: (416) 461-1294
Web Site: www.apolloeight.com
Year Founded: 1972
Rev.: $16,954,265
Emp.: 900

Business Description:
Building Cleaning & Maintenance Services
S.I.C.: 7349
N.A.I.C.S.: 561720

Personnel:
Jim Gallos *(Pres)*
James Izzett *(Exec VP)*
Ron Campbell *(Sr VP)*

APOLLO BELL INTERNATIONAL PLC

Schadowstrasse 11e
40212 Dusseldorf, Germany
Tel.: (49) 211 36 116 0
Fax: (49) 211 36 116 116
E-Mail: info@apollobell.com
Web Site: www.apollobell.com
AVC5—(DEU)

Business Description:
GPS Software
S.I.C.: 7372
N.A.I.C.S.: 511210
Personnel:
Norbert Wollnik *(CEO)*
Heiko Piossek *(CFO)*

APOLLO CONSOLIDATED LIMITED

Level 3 3 Ord Street
West Perth, WA, 6005, Australia
Mailing Address:
PO Box 1028
West Perth, WA, 6872, Australia
Tel.: (61) 8 9226 0714
Fax: (61) 8 6314 1557
E-Mail: info@apolloconsolidated.com.au
Web Site: www.apolloconsolidated.com.au
Year Founded: 2002
AOP—(ASX)
Rev.: $76,291
Assets: $5,751,031
Liabilities: $626,374
Net Worth: $5,124,657
Earnings: ($990,103)
Fiscal Year-end: 06/30/13
Business Description:
Gold Exploration Services
S.I.C.: 1041
N.A.I.C.S.: 212221
Personnel:
Nick Castleden *(Mng Dir)*
Alex Neuling *(Sec)*
Board of Directors:
Roger Steinepreis
Nick Castleden
Robert Gherghetta
George Ventouras
Stephen West
Legal Counsel:
Steinepreis Paganin
Level 4 The Read Building 16 Milligan Street
Perth, WA, 6000, Australia
Tel.: (61) 8 9321 4000
Fax: (61) 8 9321 4333

APOLLO FOOD HOLDINGS BERHAD

No 70 Jalan Langkasuka Larkin Industrial Area
PO Box 90
80350 Johor Bahru, Johor, Malaysia
Tel.: (60) 72365096
Fax: (60) 72374748
E-Mail: apollof@apollofood.com.my
Web Site: www.apollofood.com.my
APOLLO—(KLS)
Rev.: $73,042,858
Assets: $84,037,015
Liabilities: $8,555,484
Net Worth: $75,481,531
Earnings: $10,520,705
Fiscal Year-end: 04/30/13
Business Description:
Confectionery Products Mfr
S.I.C.: 2066
N.A.I.C.S.: 311351
Personnel:
Chiang Heng Liang *(Chm & Mng Dir)*
Terence Wang *(Sr Exec-Sls)*
Min Fong Woo *(Co-Sec)*
Wai Bing Yap *(Co-Sec)*
Board of Directors:
Chiang Heng Liang
Abdul Rahim Bunyamin
Aminah Hashim
Kim Poh Liang
Chet Chiang Ng
P. Venugopal

APOLLO FOREST PRODUCTS LTD

2555 Tachie Road
PO Box 129
Fort Saint James, BC, Canada
Tel.: (250) 996-8297
Fax: (250) 996-8730
Web Site: www.apolloforest.com
Year Founded: 1969
Rev.: $33,560,751
Emp.: 140
Business Description:
Lumber Products Supplier & Mfr
S.I.C.: 5031
N.A.I.C.S.: 423310
Personnel:
Brian Ramage *(Plant Mgr)*

APOLLO HOSPITALS ENTERPRISE LIMITED

No. 21 Grames Lane Off Greams Road
Chennai, 600006, India
Tel.: (91) 4428290200
Fax: (91) 4428294429
E-Mail: enquiry@apollohospitals.com
Web Site: www.apollohospitals.com
508869—(BOM)
Rev.: $704,312,352
Assets: $897,162,280
Liabilities: $384,694,988
Net Worth: $512,467,292
Earnings: $54,515,201
Emp.: 35,348
Fiscal Year-end: 03/31/13
Business Description:
Hospital Owner & Operator
S.I.C.: 8062
N.A.I.C.S.: 622110
Personnel:
Prathap C. Reddy *(Chm)*
K. Padmanabhan *(Pres)*
S. Premkumar *(CEO)*
P. Preetha Reddy *(Mng Dir)*
Suneeta Reddy *(Mng Dir)*
Krishnan Akhileswaran *(CFO)*
S. K. Venkataraman *(Chief Strategy Officer)*
S. M. Krishnan *(Compliance Officer, Sec & Sr Gen Mgr-Project & Fin)*
Board of Directors:
Prathap C. Reddy
Khairil Anuar Abdullah
Rafeeque Ahamed
Habibullah Badsha
T. K. Balaji
Shobana Kamineni
Rajkumar Menon
Sanjay Nayar
P. Preetha Reddy
Sangita Reddy
Suneeta Reddy
N. Vaghul
Deepak Vaidya
G. Venkatraman
Transfer Agent:
Integrated Enterprises (India) Ltd
2nd Floor Kences Towers 1 Ramakrishna Street North Usman Road T Nagur, Chennai, 600017, India

Joint Venture:

Apollo Gleneagles PET-CT Limited **(1)**
Apollo Hospital Campus
Jubilee Hills, Hyderabad, India
Tel.: (91) 4023607777
Fax: (91) 4023607530
E-Mail: apollohealthcity@apollohospitals.com
Web Site: www.apollohealthcity.com
Health & Allied Services
S.I.C.: 8082
N.A.I.C.S.: 621610
Prathap Chandra Reddy *(Chm)*

APOLLO MACHINE & WELDING LTD.

4141 93 St
Edmonton, AB, Canada
Tel.: (780) 463-3060
Fax: (780) 463-6348
Web Site: www.apollomachine.com
Year Founded: 1971
Rev.: $11,164,130
Emp.: 75
Business Description:
Machine Equipment Supplier
S.I.C.: 3545
N.A.I.C.S.: 333515
Personnel:
Robert Norton *(Founder)*
Wayne Norton *(Pres)*
Laurie Willis *(CEO)*

APOLLO MINERALS LIMITED

Level 9 50 Margaret Street
Sydney, NSW, 2000, Australia
Mailing Address:
PO Box R933
Royal Exchange, Sydney, NSW, 1225, Australia
Tel.: (61) 2 9078 7665
Fax: (61) 2 9078 7661
E-Mail: info@apollominerals.com.au
Web Site: www.apollominerals.com.au
AON—(ASX)
Rev.: $112,613
Assets: $19,083,142
Liabilities: $631,282
Net Worth: $18,451,859
Earnings: ($1,679,775)
Fiscal Year-end: 06/30/13
Business Description:
Minerals Exploration
S.I.C.: 1481
N.A.I.C.S.: 213115
Personnel:
Dominic Tisdell *(CEO)*
Guy Robertson *(CFO & Sec)*
Board of Directors:
Anthony Ho
Matthew Rimes
Richard Shemesian
Dominic Tisdell
Legal Counsel:
DLA Phillips Fox
Level 32 St Martins Tower 44 St Georges Terrace
Perth, Australia

Subsidiary:

Southern Exploration Pty Limited **(1)**
262-266 Pirie St
Adelaide, SA, 5001, Australia
Tel.: (61) 883424914
Iron Ore Exploration Services
S.I.C.: 1011
N.A.I.C.S.: 212210

APOLLO SOLAR ENERGY, INC.

485 Tengfei 3rd Shuangliu Southwest Airport Economic Development Zone
Shuangliu, Chengdu, China 610207
Tel.: (86) 2885623888
Web Site: www.apollosolarenergy.com.cn
ASOE—(OTC)
Sls.: $4,484,708
Assets: $27,171,027
Liabilities: $12,434,393
Net Worth: $14,736,634
Earnings: ($5,227,750)
Emp.: 92
Fiscal Year-end: 12/31/12
Business Description:
Tellurium-Based Metals Processing & Refining Services
S.I.C.: 3351
N.A.I.C.S.: 331420
Personnel:
Jingong Pan *(Chm & CEO)*
Hua Hui *(Interim CFO)*
Haukang Zhou *(Sec)*
Board of Directors:
Jingong Pan
Zhimin Cao
Yijun Li
Cheng Liu

APOLLO TYRES LTD.

VI Floor Cherupushpam Building
Shanmugham Road
Cochin, Kerala, 682031, India
Tel.: (91) 484 2381902
Fax: (91) 1242383020
E-Mail: info@apollotyres.com
Web Site: www.apollotyres.com
500877—(BOM)
Sls.: $2,547,404,714
Assets: $1,580,823,853
Liabilities: $950,303,668
Net Worth: $630,520,186
Earnings: $113,576,967
Emp.: 16,000
Fiscal Year-end: 03/31/13
Business Description:
Tire Mfr
S.I.C.: 3011
N.A.I.C.S.: 326211
Personnel:
Onkar S. Kanwar *(Chm & Mng Dir)*
Neeraj R. S. Kanwar *(Vice Chm & Mng Dir)*
Sunam Sarkar *(CFO)*
Marco Paracciani *(CMO)*
P. N. Wahal *(Compliance Officer & Sec)*
Luis C. Ceneviz *(CEO-Apollo Vredestein BV)*
Riaz Haffejee *(CEO-Apollo Tyres South Africa (Pty) Ltd)*
Board of Directors:
Onkar S. Kanwar
V. P. Joy
Nimesh N. Kampani
Neeraj R. S. Kanwar
Vikram S. Mehta
S. Narayan
U. S. Oberoi
M. R. B. Punja
Arun Kumar Purwar
Sunam Sarkar
Shardul S. Shroff
K. S. Srinivas
Robert Steinmetz
K. Jacob Thomas

Non-U.S. Subsidiary:

Apollo Vredestein B.V. **(1)**
Ir ELC Schiffstraat 370
NL-7547 RD Enschede, Netherlands NL
Tel.: (31) 534888888
Fax: (31) 534888800
E-Mail: info.apollo@vredestein.com
Web Site: www.apollovredestein.com
Sales Range: $400-449.9 Million
Emp.: 1,300
Motor Vehicle Tire Mfr
Export
S.I.C.: 3011
N.A.I.C.S.: 326211
Robert Henk Oudshoorn *(CEO)*

Subsidiary:

Vredestein Consulting B.V. **(2)**
ELC Schiff Sr Straat 370
NL-7547 RD Enschede, Netherlands NL
Mailing Address:
PO Box 27
NL-7500 AA Enschede, Netherlands
Tel.: (31) 534888880
Fax: (31) 534 888 890
E-Mail: consulting@vredestein.com
Web Site: www.apollovredestein.com
Emp.: 6
Technological Consulting Services

Apollo Tyres Ltd.—(Continued)

S.I.C.: 8999
N.A.I.C.S.: 541690
Kornelis Tetman Hettema *(Mng Dir)*

Non-U.S. Subsidiaries:

NV Vredestein SA (2)
Heysel Esplanade
1020 Brussels, Belgium
Tel.: (32) 22168100
Fax: (32) 22164575
E-Mail: customer.be@apollovredestein.com
Web Site: www.apollovredestein.com
Emp.: 8
Motor Vehicle Tire Distr
S.I.C.: 5014
N.A.I.C.S.: 423130

Vredestein Dack AB (2)
Flojelbergsgatan 18
431 37 Molndal, Sweden
Tel.: (46) 31580010
Fax: (46) 31580019
E-Mail: customer.se@apollovredestein.com
Web Site: www.vredestein.se
Emp.: 10
Motor Vehicle Tire Distr
S.I.C.: 5014
N.A.I.C.S.: 423130
Bo Christer Manssom *(CEO)*

Vredestein France S.A. (2)
59 Avenue Victor Hugo
F-75116 Paris, France
Tel.: (33) 820838281
Fax: (33) 800838281
E-Mail: customer.fr@vredestein.com
Emp.: 10
Motor Vehicle Tire Distr
S.I.C.: 5014
N.A.I.C.S.: 423130

Vredestein GmbH (2)
Seybellgasse 10-12
1230 Vienna, Austria
Tel.: (43) 186933250
Fax: (43) 1869332534
E-Mail: customer.at@vredestein.com
Web Site: www.vredestein.com
Motor Vehicle Tire Distr
S.I.C.: 5014
N.A.I.C.S.: 423130

Vredestein GmbH (2)
Rheinstrasse 103
PO Box 1370
56173 Vallendar, Germany
Tel.: (49) 26180760
Fax: (49) 261807699
E-Mail: customer.de@vredestein.com
Web Site: www.vredestein.com
Emp.: 30
Motor Vehicle Tire Distr
S.I.C.: 5014
N.A.I.C.S.: 423130
Michael Lutz *(Gen Mgr)*

Vredestein Iberica S.A. (2)
Cityparc Edificio Bruselas Carretera De Hospitalet 147
Cornella De Llobregat, 08940 Barcelona, Spain
Tel.: (34) 934745141
Fax: (34) 934745505
E-Mail: customer.es@vredestein.com
Web Site: www.vredestein.es
Emp.: 10
Motor Vehicle Tire Distr
S.I.C.: 5014
N.A.I.C.S.: 423130
Ludovic Billot *(Gen Mgr)*

Vredestein (Schweiz) AG (2)
Mellenger St 2 A
PO Box 2112
5400 Baden, Switzerland
Tel.: (41) 562033030
Fax: (41) 562033049
E-Mail: customer.ch@apollovredestein.com
Web Site: www.vredestein.com
Emp.: 11
Motor Vehicle Tire Distr
S.I.C.: 5014
N.A.I.C.S.: 423130
Markus Blunner *(Gen Mgr)*

APOSENSE LTD.

5-7 Odem St
PO Box 7119
49170 Petah Tiqwa, Israel
Tel.: (972) 39247211
Fax: (972) 39215714
E-Mail: info@aposense.com
Web Site: www.aposense.com
Emp.: 30

Business Description:
Molecular Imaging & Drug Development
S.I.C.: 8731
N.A.I.C.S.: 541711

Personnel:
Eli Hurvitz *(Chm)*
Ilan Ziv *(Vice Chm)*
Yoram Ashery *(CEO)*
Eli Frydman *(COO & VP)*

Board of Directors:
Eli Hurvitz
Morry Blumenfeld
Joseph Dobrowski
Alon Dumanis
Yaacov Gotenstein
Ilan Ziv

APOTEX INC.

150 Signet Dr
Toronto, ON, M9L 1T9, Canada
Tel.: (416) 749-9300
Fax: (416) 401-3849
Toll Free: (800) 268-4623
Web Site: www.apotex.com
Year Founded: 1974
Emp.: 6,800

Business Description:
Pharmaceuticals Mfr
S.I.C.: 2834
N.A.I.C.S.: 325412

Personnel:
Bernard C. Sherman *(Chm & CEO)*
Jacob M. Kay *(Pres & COO)*
Jeff Watson *(Chief Comml Officer)*

Non-U.S. Subsidiary:

Apotex Pty Ltd. (1)
Level 3 16 Giffnock Ave
Macquarie Park, NSW, 2113, Australia
Mailing Address:
PO Box 280
North Ryde Business Centre, North Ryde, NSW, 1670, Australia
Tel.: (61) 288778333
Fax: (61) 288778377
E-Mail: customerservice.aus@apotex.com
Web Site: www.apotex.com.au
Emp.: 70
Pharmaceuticals Marketing & Sales
S.I.C.: 5122
N.A.I.C.S.: 424210
Roger Millichamp *(Mng Dir)*

APP SYSTEMS SERVICES PTE. LTD.

11 Toh Guan Road East
No 03-01 APP Enterprise Bldg, Singapore, 608603, Singapore
Tel.: (65) 64256611
Fax: (65) 65606616
E-Mail: sales@appsystems.com.sg
Web Site: www.appsystems.com.sg
Year Founded: 1982
Sales Range: $10-24.9 Million
Emp.: 80

Business Description:
Distr of Individual Components & Vacuum Systems
S.I.C.: 5084
N.A.I.C.S.: 423830

Personnel:
Song Lin Lee *(Mng Dir)*

Non-U.S. Subsidiaries:

APP Engineering Sdn Bhd (1)
No 18 & 18-1 Block 1A Jalan Kuchai Maju 1 Dynasty 3
Kuchai Entrepreneurs Park, Kuala Lumpur, 58200, Malaysia
Tel.: (60) 380701611
Fax: (60) 379846616
E-Mail: admin_kl@app-msia.com
Web Site: www.app-msia.com
Emp.: 10
Mfr of Individual Components & Vacuum Systems
S.I.C.: 3999
N.A.I.C.S.: 335210
N. G. Chng *(Pres)*
Lee Wc *(Mng Dir)*

APP Systems Services Pte. Ltd. (1)
Bintaro Trade Center Blok D2 No 7
Bintaro Jaya Sektor 7, Jakarta, Tangerang, 15224, Indonesia
Tel.: (62) 21 745 1687
Fax: (62) 21 745 3337
E-Mail: admin.jkt@appsystems.com.sg
Web Site: www.appsystems.com.sg/
Mfr of High Technology Products; Plasma, Thin Films, Vacuum Technology, Cryogenics, Thermal & Bioscience Related Technologies Delivering Solutions
S.I.C.: 8731
N.A.I.C.S.: 541711

APP Systems Services (Thailand) Co. Ltd. (1)
29/4 Moo 9 Taladkwan
Muang Nontaburi, 11000 Nonthaburi, Thailand
Tel.: (66) 25269700
Fax: (66) 25265797
E-Mail: admin.bkk@appsystems.com.sg
Web Site: www.appsystems.com.sg
Rev.: $885,619
Emp.: 10
Mfr of Individual Components & Vacuum Systems
S.I.C.: 3999
N.A.I.C.S.: 335210
Sura Chart *(Gen Mgr)*

APPENINN NYRT.

(d/b/a Appeninn Holding)
Beg u 3-5
1022 Budapest, Hungary
Tel.: (36) 1 3468869
Fax: (36) 1 3468868
E-Mail: info@appeninnholding.com
Web Site: www.appeninn.hu
APPENINN—(BUD)

Business Description:
Property Development
S.I.C.: 6552
N.A.I.C.S.: 237210

Personnel:
Gabor Szekely *(Chm)*

Board of Directors:
Gabor Szekely
Monika Altmann
Lorinc Eder
Gyozo Szekelyi
Seregely Zsolt

APPIAN CAPITAL ADVISORY LLP

5th Floor 33 Saint James's Street
London, SW1A 1HD, United Kingdom
Tel.: (44) 207 004 0952
E-Mail: info@appiancapitaladvisory.com
Web Site: www.appiancapitaladvisory.com
Year Founded: 2011

Business Description:
Private Equity Investment Advisory & Portfolio Management Services
S.I.C.: 6799
N.A.I.C.S.: 523920

Personnel:
Verne Grinstead *(Mng Partner)*
Vincent Jacheet *(Mng Partner)*
Michael W. Scherb *(Gen Partner)*
Jos Haumann *(Sr Technical Partner)*
Robin Mills *(Sr Technical Partner)*
Tony Redman *(Sr Technical Partner)*

APPIPHANY TECHNOLOGIES HOLDINGS CORP.

PO Box 21101
Orchard Park, Kelowna, BC, V1Y 9N8, Canada
Tel.: (205) 864-5377
Web Site: www.appiphanytech.com
Year Founded: 2009
APHD—(OTC OTCB)
Rev.: $689
Assets: $23,056
Liabilities: $239,388
Net Worth: ($216,332)
Earnings: ($120,839)
Emp.: 2
Fiscal Year-end: 04/30/13

Business Description:
Mobile Phone Applications Developer
S.I.C.: 7372
N.A.I.C.S.: 511210

Personnel:
Jesse Keller *(Pres, CEO, CFO, Treas & Sec)*

APPLABS TECHNOLOGIES LIMITED

(Formerly AACL Holdings Limited)
Suite 5 Level 1 12-20 Railway Road
Subiaco, WA, 6008, Australia
Tel.: (61) 8 9388 9968
E-Mail: enquiry@applabs.com.au
Web Site: www.applabsaustralia.com.au
Year Founded: 1997
ALA—(ASX)
Sales Range: $25-49.9 Million

Business Description:
Software Developer
S.I.C.: 7372
N.A.I.C.S.: 511210

Personnel:
Stuart Kidd *(CEO)*
Damon Sweeny *(Sec)*

Board of Directors:
Patrick Glovac
Stuart Kidd
Rocco Tassone
Charles Thomas

Legal Counsel:
Clayton Utz
Level 27 250 St Georges Terrace
Perth, WA, 6000, Australia

APPLEONE SERVICES LTD

120 Adelaide Street West
Toronto, ON, M5H 1T1, Canada
Tel.: (416) 363-1663
Fax: (416) 363-1330
E-Mail: toronto@appleone.com
Web Site: www.appleone.ca
Sales Range: $75-99.9 Million
Emp.: 175

Business Description:
Employment Services
S.I.C.: 7361
N.A.I.C.S.: 561311

Personnel:
Gary Gregg *(Pres & CEO)*

APPLETON EXPLORATION INC.

(Name Changed to Cornerstone Metals Inc.)

APPLICATION SERVICES LTD.

(Acquired by Matchtech Group plc)

APPLICHEM GMBH

Ottoweg 4
64291 Darmstadt, Germany
Tel.: (49) 615193570
Fax: (49) 6151935711
E-Mail: service@applichem.de
Web Site: www.applichem.com
Year Founded: 1992
Rev.: $22,070,400
Emp.: 80

Business Description:
Chemical Products Mfr
S.I.C.: 2899
N.A.I.C.S.: 325998
Personnel:
Markus Frasch *(Co-Mng Dir)*
Johannes Oeler *(Co-Mng Dir)*

APPLIED BIOLOGY COMPANY SAS

(d/b/a CiToxLAB Group)
BP 563
27005 Evreux, Cedex, France
Tel.: (33) 2 3229 2626
Fax: (33) 2 3267 8705
Web Site: www.citoxlab.com
Sales Range: $100-124.9 Million
Emp.: 800
Business Description:
Holding Company; Pre-Clinical Research, Biopharmaceutical Development, Non-Clinical Medical & Testing Laboratories
S.I.C.: 6719
N.A.I.C.S.: 551112
Personnel:
Jean-Francois Le Bigot *(Chm & CEO)*
Patrick Spies *(CFO & Sec)*

Subsidiary:

CiT SAS (1)
BP 563
27005 Evreux, Cedex, France FR
Tel.: (33) 2 3229 2626
Fax: (33) 2 3267 8705
E-Mail: contact.france@citoxlab.com
Web Site: www.citoxlab.com
Pre-Clinical Research & Biopharmaceutical Development
S.I.C.: 8731
N.A.I.C.S.: 541711
Olivier Foulon *(Deputy Mng Dir & Dir-Toxicology & Ops)*

Non-U.S. Subsidiaries:

CiToxLAB Scantox A/S (1)
Hestehavevej 36A
Ejby, 4623 Lille Skensved, Denmark DK
Tel.: (45) 5686 1500
Fax: (45) 5682 1202
E-Mail: contact.scantox@citoxlab.com
Web Site: www.citoxlab.com
Emp.: 130
Non-Clinical Medical Laboratory
S.I.C.: 8071
N.A.I.C.S.: 621511
Andrew Makin *(Mng Dir)*

CiToxLAB North America Inc. (1)
445 Armand Frappier Blvd
Laval, QC, H7V 4B3, Canada Ca
Tel.: (450) 973-2240
Fax: (450) 973-2259
Toll Free: (888) 353-2240
E-Mail: contact.northamerica@citoxlab.com
Web Site: www.citoxlab.com
Emp.: 300
Non-Clinical Biological Research & Testing Laboratory
S.I.C.: 8731
N.A.I.C.S.: 541711
Andrew Graham *(VP-Ops)*

CiToxLAB Hungary Ltd. (1)
Szabadsagpuszta
8200 Veszprem, Hungary HU
Tel.: (36) 88 545 300
Fax: (36) 88 545 301
E-Mail: contact.hungary@citoxlab.com
Web Site: www.citoxlab.com
Emp.: 140
Pre-Clinical Research & Biopharmaceutical Development
S.I.C.: 8731
N.A.I.C.S.: 541711
Christopher Martin Banks *(Mng Dir)*

APPLIED DEVELOPMENT HOLDINGS LIMITED

Unit 3402-03 34/F China Merchants Tower Shun Tak Centre
168-200 Connaught Rd, Central, China (Hong Kong)
Tel.: (852) 25538267
Fax: (852) 28734676
E-Mail: info@applieddev.com
Web Site: www.applieddev.com
0519—(HKG)
Rev.: $63,959
Assets: $75,728,853
Liabilities: $21,575,527
Net Worth: $54,153,326
Earnings: ($293,232)
Emp.: 10
Fiscal Year-end: 06/30/13
Business Description:
Resort & Property Development Services
S.I.C.: 7011
N.A.I.C.S.: 721110
Personnel:
Marcus Kai Mau Hung *(Chm)*
Raymond Kin Sang Hung *(Mng Dir)*
Kit Ling Ng *(Sec)*
Board of Directors:
Marcus Kai Mau Hung
Terence Ming Fai Chan
Raymond Kin Sang Hung
Yun Tai Lo
Tsan Kau Lun
Kit Ling Ng
Ru Jia Su
Butterfield Fulcrum Group (Bermuda) Limited
26 Burnaby Street
Hamilton, HM 11, Bermuda

Subsidiaries:

Applied Investment (Asia) Limited (1)
Rm 3402-3 34 F China Merchants Tower
Shun Tak Ctr 168-200 Connaught Rd
Sheung Wan, China (Hong Kong)
Tel.: (852) 25538267
Fax: (852) 28734676
Investment Holding Services
S.I.C.: 6211
N.A.I.C.S.: 523999

Applied Toys Limited (1)
Rm 4103-4105 Far E Fin Ctr 16 Harcourt Rd
Admiralty, Central, China (Hong Kong)
Tel.: (852) 25538267
Fax: (852) 28734676
Investment Management Services
S.I.C.: 6799
N.A.I.C.S.: 523920

APPLIED GRAPHENE MATERIALS PLC

The Wilton Centre
Redcar, Cleveland, TS10 4RF, United Kingdom
Tel.: (44) 1642 438214
E-Mail: info@appliedgraphenematerials.com
Web Site: www.appliedgraphenematerials.com
Year Founded: 2010
AGM—(AIM)
Business Description:
Graphene Mfr
S.I.C.: 3624
N.A.I.C.S.: 335991
Personnel:
Bryan Dobson *(Chm)*
Jon Mabbitt *(CEO)*
Oliver Lightowlers *(CFO)*
Board of Directors:
Bryan Dobson
Karl Coleman
Oliver Lightowlers
Jon Mabbitt
Claudio Marinelli

APPLIED TECHNOLOGIES INTERNET SAS

(d/b/a AT Internet)
Parc d'Activites La Deveze
8 Impasse Rudolph Diesel, 33700 Merignac, France
Tel.: (33) 1 56 54 14 30
Fax: (33) 1 46 52 73 69
E-Mail: atcontact@atinternet.com
Web Site: www.atinternet.com
Year Founded: 1996
Sales Range: $10-24.9 Million
Emp.: 130
Business Description:
Web Analytics Software
S.I.C.: 7372
N.A.I.C.S.: 511210
Personnel:
Alain Llorens *(Chm)*
Mathieu Llorens *(CEO)*
Cyril Mazeau *(CFO)*
Sebastien Carriot *(CTO)*

Non-U.S. Subsidiaries:

AT Internet Brazil (1)
Av Egenheiro Luis Carlos Berrini 550 4 andar
Itaim Bibi, Sao Paulo, 04571-000, Brazil
Tel.: (55) 11 3192 3991
Web Analytics Software
S.I.C.: 7372
N.A.I.C.S.: 511210

AT Internet GmbH (1)
Schleissheimer Str 4
80333 Munich, Germany
Tel.: (49) 89 324927 0
Fax: (49) 89 324927 444
E-Mail: contact@atinternet.com
Web Site: www.atinternet.com
Emp.: 12
Web Analytics Software
S.I.C.: 7372
N.A.I.C.S.: 511210
Julio Manavella *(Gen Mgr)*

AT Internet Inc. (1)
33 rue Prince
Montreal, QC, H3C 2M7, Canada
Tel.: (514) 658-3571
Web Analytics Software
S.I.C.: 7372
N.A.I.C.S.: 511210

AT Internet Ltd (1)
Gilmoora House 57-61 Mortimer Street
London, W1W 8HS, United Kingdom
Tel.: (44) 20 3178 5356
Fax: (44) 20 7101 7120
Web Analytics Software
S.I.C.: 7372
N.A.I.C.S.: 511210

AT Internet Pte. Ltd (1)
100 Beach Road #16-09 Shaw Towers
Singapore, 189702, Singapore
Tel.: (65) 6295 6053
Web Analytics Software
S.I.C.: 7372
N.A.I.C.S.: 511210

AT Internet SL (1)
Avenida de Concha Espina 8 1a izq
28036 Madrid, Spain
Tel.: (34) 91 1105829
Web Analytics Software
S.I.C.: 7372
N.A.I.C.S.: 511210

APPLY ASA

Koppholen 6
PO Box 8040
4068 Sandnes, Norway
Tel.: (47) 51639000
Fax: (47) 51639275
E-Mail: apply@apply.no
Web Site: www.apply.no
Sales Range: $500-549.9 Million
Emp.: 2,000
Business Description:
Oil & Gas Industry Services & Technology Products
S.I.C.: 1389
N.A.I.C.S.: 213112
Personnel:
Christian Brinch *(Chm)*
Peder Sortland *(CEO)*
Pal Selboe Valseth *(CFO)*
Frederik Hvistendahl *(Exec VP)*
Rolf Nipe *(Exec VP)*
Geir Ove Saltvedt *(Exec VP)*
Lars Solberg *(Exec VP)*

Subsidiaries:

Apply Leirvik AS (1)
Storhaugvegen 130
N 5402 Stord, Norway
Tel.: (47) 53 49 62 00
Fax: (47) 53 49 62 01
Web Site: www.applyleirvik.no
Emp.: 275
Offshore Living Quarters Mfr
S.I.C.: 3448
N.A.I.C.S.: 332311
Lars Solberg *(Mng Dir)*
Kjell Arne Halleraker *(COO)*

Apply LQ Partner AS (1)
Haugesund Offshore Base
Killingoy, 5501 Haugesund, Norway
Tel.: (47) 52708700
Fax: (47) 52708701
E-Mail: firmapost@reanco.no
Web Site: www.reanco.no
Emp.: 15
Offshore Living Quarters Refurbishment Products & Services
S.I.C.: 3448
N.A.I.C.S.: 332311
Bjarne Halleraker *(Gen Mgr)*

Apply Sorco AS (1)
Koppholen 6
Forus, Sandnes, 4313, Norway
Tel.: (47) 51639000
Fax: (47) 4751639275
E-Mail: firmapost@applysorco.no
Web Site: www.applysorco.no
Emp.: 300
Offshore Oil & Gas Facility Engineering, Construction & Support Services
S.I.C.: 8711
N.A.I.C.S.: 541330
Frederik Hvistendahl *(Pres)*
Tove H. Tybero *(Sr VP-Bus Dev)*

APPRECIA TECHNOLOGY, INC.

(Acquired by Tazmo Co., Ltd.)

APPS CARTAGE INC.

(d/b/a APPS Transport Group)
275 Orenda Road
Brampton, ON, L6T 3T7, Canada
Tel.: (905) 451-2720
Fax: (905) 451-2778
Toll Free: (800) 465-2513
Web Site: www.appsexpress.com
Year Founded: 2008
Rev.: $24,746,320
Emp.: 150
Business Description:
Transportation Services
S.I.C.: 4212
N.A.I.C.S.: 484110
Personnel:
Robert M. McDonald *(Pres)*

APPSENSE LTD.

3300 Daresbury Business Park
Daresbury, Warrington, WA4 4BU, United Kingdom
Tel.: (44) 8452232100
Fax: (44) 8452232101
E-Mail: info@appsense.com
Web Site: www.appsense.com
Sales Range: $50-74.9 Million
Emp.: 285
Business Description:
User Virtualization Technology & Services
S.I.C.: 7372
N.A.I.C.S.: 511210
Personnel:
Charles Sharland *(Chm)*

AppSense Ltd.—(Continued)

Darron Antill *(CEO)*
Peter Rawlinson *(CMO)*
Ajay Arora *(CTO-Mobile)*
Jon Rolls *(CTO-Enterprise)*
Keith Turnbull *(Chief Dev Officer)*
Jon Wallace *(CTO-Cloud & Emerging Technologies)*
Michelle Denman *(Chief People Officer)*
Carl Cross *(Sr VP & Gen Mgr-Americas)*
Nick Lowe *(Sr VP-Sls & Gen Mgr-EMEA & APAC)*

APPULSE CORPORATION

3504 - 64 Avenue SE
Calgary, AB, T2C 1P4, Canada
Tel.: (403) 236-2883
Web Site: www.appulsecorp.net
Year Founded: 2001
APL—(TSXV)
Rev.: $7,164,351
Assets: $6,087,467
Liabilities: $3,217,025
Net Worth: $2,870,442
Earnings: $150,153
Fiscal Year-end: 12/31/12
Business Description:
Industries Equipment Sales & Maintenance
S.I.C.: 7699
N.A.I.C.S.: 811310
Personnel:
Franklin T. Bailey *(Chm)*
Douglas A. Baird *(Pres & CEO)*
Dennis R. Schmidt *(CFO & Sec)*
Board of Directors:
Franklin T. Bailey
Douglas A. Baird
Laurie E. Gauthier
James A. Maldaner
Robert D. Richards
Dennis R. Schmidt
Legal Counsel:
Morris McManus Professional Corporation
Calgary, AB, Canada
Transfer Agent:
Computershare Trust Company of Canada
Calgary, AB, Canada
Subsidiaries:

Centrifuges Unlimited Inc. **(1)**
3504 - 64 Avenue SE
Calgary, AB, T2C 1P4, Canada
Tel.: (403) 236-2883
Fax: (403) 279-3342
Toll Free: (877) 336-2883
E-Mail: infocui@centrifuges.net
Web Site: www.centrifuges.net
Emp.: 3
Separation Equipment Distr
S.I.C.: 5084
N.A.I.C.S.: 423830
Kyle Brooks *(Mgr-Matl)*

Design Machining Unlimited Inc. **(1)**
3504 - 64 Avenue SE
Calgary, AB, Canada T2C 1P4
Tel.: (403) 236-4020
Fax: (403) 279-3342
E-Mail: contact@designmachining.com
Web Site: www.designmachining.com
Industrial Equipment Distr
S.I.C.: 5084
N.A.I.C.S.: 423830

APRISO CORPORATION

(Acquired by Dassault Systemes S.A.)

APROMAT SA

Calea Aurel Nr 29-31
Arad, Romania
Tel.: (40) 257 202158
Fax: (40) 257 252602
APRB—(BUC)
Emp.: 8
Business Description:
Metals & Metal Ores Distr
S.I.C.: 5051
N.A.I.C.S.: 423510
Personnel:
Radu Marcovici *(Pres)*

APS TECHNOLOGY GROUP, INC.

(Acquired by ABB Ltd.)

APT SATELLITE INTERNATIONAL COMPANY LIMITED

22 Dai Kwai St
Tai Po, New Territories, China (Hong Kong)
Tel.: (852) 26002100
Fax: (852) 25220419
Web Site: www.apstar.com
Business Description:
Holding Company
S.I.C.: 6719
N.A.I.C.S.: 551112
Personnel:
Xiaowu Rui *(Chm)*
Holding:

APT Satellite Holdings Limited **(1)**
22 Dai Kwai Street Tai Po Industrial Estate
Tai Po, New Territories, China (Hong Kong) BM (51.83%)
Tel.: (852) 26002100
Fax: (852) 25220419
E-Mail: aptmk@apstar.com
Web Site: www.apstar.com
1045—(HKG OTC)
Sls.: $116,133,788
Assets: $648,353,895
Liabilities: $250,340,048
Net Worth: $398,013,846
Earnings: $45,704,393
Emp.: 103
Fiscal Year-end: 12/31/12
Satellite Telecommunications Services
S.I.C.: 4899
N.A.I.C.S.: 517410
Guangren Cheng *(Pres)*
Brian Kin Hang Lo *(Sec & VP)*

APT SYSTEMS, INC.

3400 Manulife Place 10180 -101 Street
Edmonton, AB, T5J 3S4, Canada
Tel.: (780) 270-6048
Web Site: www.aptsys.net
Year Founded: 2010
APTY—(OTC OTCB)
Rev.: $11
Assets: $14,106
Liabilities: $23,981
Net Worth: ($9,875)
Earnings: ($63,708)
Emp.: 1
Fiscal Year-end: 01/31/13
Business Description:
Business Software Publisher
S.I.C.: 7372
N.A.I.C.S.: 511210
Personnel:
Glenda Dowie *(Pres & CEO)*
Carl Hussey *(CFO & Treas)*
Joseph Gagnon *(CTO & Sec)*
Board of Directors:
Glenda Dowie
Joseph Gagnon
Carl Hussey

APTE AMALGAMATIONS LIMITED

14A - The Club Near Mangal Anand Hospital Swastik Park
Chembur, Mumbai, 400071, India
Tel.: (91) 22 2527 7504
Fax: (91) 22 2491 9184
E-Mail: info@apteindia.com
Web Site: www.apteindia.com
Year Founded: 1933
507265—(BOM)
Rev.: $7,210
Assets: $5,937,149
Liabilities: $8,039,701
Net Worth: ($2,102,552)
Earnings: ($304,028)
Fiscal Year-end: 03/31/13
Business Description:
Property Development & Securities Trading Services
S.I.C.: 6531
N.A.I.C.S.: 531390
Personnel:
V. M. Apte *(Chm)*
Board of Directors:
V. M. Apte
M. L. Apte
Rajesh M. Loya
Chetan J. Mehta
Jashwant B. Mehta
Maneesh Taparia
Transfer Agent:
Sharex Dynamic (India) Private Limited
Unit No1 Luthra Indus Premises Andheri Kurla Rd Safed Pool Andheri(E)
Mumbai, India

APTECH LIMITED

Aptech House A-65 MIDC Marol Andheri E
Mumbai, 400 093, India
Tel.: (91) 2228272300
Fax: (91) 2228272399
Web Site: www.aptech-worldwide.com
532475—(BOM NSE)
Rev.: $33,779,713
Assets: $73,076,967
Liabilities: $9,849,764
Net Worth: $63,227,203
Earnings: $5,821,838
Emp.: 434
Fiscal Year-end: 03/31/13
Business Description:
Educational Services
S.I.C.: 8243
N.A.I.C.S.: 611420
Personnel:
Ninad Karpe *(CEO & Mng Dir)*
Ketan H. Shah *(Compliance Officer & Sec)*
Board of Directors:
Rakesh Jhunjhunwala
Rajiv Agarwal
Vijay Aggarwal
Ramesh S. Damani
Anuj Kacker
Ninad Karpe
Asit Koticha
Yash Mahajan
C. Y. Pal
Maheshwer Peri
Walter Saldanha
Utpal Sheth
Transfer Agent:
Sharepro Services (India) Private Limited
13 AB Samhita Warehousing Complex II Floor Sakinaka Telephone Lane
Off Andheri Kurla Rd Sakinaka, Mumbai, India
Subsidiaries:

Avalon Aviation Academy Private Limited **(1)**
Aptech House A-65 M I D C Marol Andheri E, Mumbai, Maharashtra, 400093, India
Tel.: (91) 2228272300
Fax: (91) 2228272399
Web Site: www.avalonacademy.in
Aviation & Hospitality Training School Management Services
S.I.C.: 8221
N.A.I.C.S.: 611310
Ravi Dighe *(VP)*

First English Education Institutes Limited **(1)**
No 79 100 Feet Rd Banashankari 3rd Stage
Bengaluru, Karnataka, 560 065, India
Tel.: (91) 80 6530 4231
Fax: (91) 80 6530 4230
E-Mail: devashishm@aptech.ac.in
Emp.: 7
English Training & Exam Preparation Services
S.I.C.: 8299
N.A.I.C.S.: 611630
Preeti Mallik *(Sr VP)*

Non-U.S. Subsidiary:

AGLSM Sdn. Bhd. **(1)**
3 03d 3rd Fl Kompleks Antarabangsa Jalan Sultan Ismail
50250 Kuala Lumpur, Malaysia
Tel.: (60) 327110373
Fax: (60) 327110372
E-Mail: enquiry_msia@aptech.ac.in
Web Site: www.aptech-globaltraining.com
Emp.: 5
Information Technology Training & Educational Services
S.I.C.: 8243
N.A.I.C.S.: 611420
Saravanan R. Perumal *(Mgr-Center)*

U.S. Subsidiary:

Aptech Worldwide Corporation **(1)**
969-G Edgewater Blvd Ste 240
Foster City, CA 94404
Tel.: (650) 520-6667
Fax: (650) 403-1135
Information Technology Training Services
S.I.C.: 8243
N.A.I.C.S.: 611420

APTILON CORPORATION

460 St Catherine St West Suite 801
Montreal, QC, Canada H3B 1A7
Tel.: (514) 844-8866
Fax: (514) 844-8267
Toll Free: (888) 544-8866
E-Mail: info@aptilon.com
Web Site: www.aptiloncorp.com
APZ—(TSXV)
Sales Range: $25-49.9 Million
Business Description:
Healthcare Services
S.I.C.: 8099
N.A.I.C.S.: 621999
Personnel:
Denis Martineau *(Pres)*
Mark Benthin *(COO)*
Board of Directors:
Justin Beckett
Mark Benthin
Robert Boisjoli
Tommy Boman
Andre Brosseau
Denis Martineau
Robert H. Steinfeld
Legal Counsel:
BCF s.e.n.c.r.l. / LLP
1100 Rene-Levesque Blvd West 25th Floor
Montreal, QC, Canada
Transfer Agent:
Computershare Investor
1500 University St Suite 700
Montreal, QC, Canada
U.S. Subsidiary:

Direct Medical Data Marketing Corp. **(1)**
10255 W Higgins Rd Ste 280
Rosemont, IL 60018
Tel.: (847) 813-1170
Fax: (847) 759-0987
E-Mail: info@dmdconnects.com
Web Site: www.dmdconnects.com

Digital Publishing & Marketing Communication Services
S.I.C.: 2741
N.A.I.C.S.: 511199
Roger Korman *(Pres)*
Raymond Lacy *(CFO)*
Mark Gleason *(COO)*
Jermaine Ransom *(Sr VP-Ops)*
Jim Ufheil *(Sr VP-Corporate Dev)*

APTUS INDUSTRIES LIMITED
501 MCR Complex Sri Ayyappa Society
Madhapur, Hyderabad, 500 081, India
Tel.: (91) 40 64643093
Fax: (91) 40 40266738
E-Mail: csaptus@gmail.com
Web Site: www.aptusindustries.in
Year Founded: 1993
534920—(BOM)
Rev.: $4,805,698
Assets: $4,117,813
Liabilities: $1,570,997
Net Worth: $2,546,816
Earnings: $357,769
Fiscal Year-end: 03/31/13
Business Description:
Software Development & Highway Construction Services
S.I.C.: 7371
N.A.I.C.S.: 541511
Personnel:
Puppala Obul Reddy *(Mng Dir)*
Rajesh Kumar Yadav *(Compliance Officer & Sec)*
Board of Directors:
Kattekola Ravi Babu
Chinmaya Hegde
Jagadeeswar Reddy Rangareddigari
A. Prabhakara Rao
Puppala Obul Reddy
Ganga Reddy S.
Kirtikmar Laxmishanker Upadhyaya
Ch Veeranjaneyulu
Transfer Agent:
Aarthi Consultants Private Limited
1-2-285, Domalguda
Hyderabad, India

AQ GROUP AB
(Formerly Aros Quality Group AB)
Regattagatan 16
SE 723 48 Vasteras, Sweden
Tel.: (46) 2140 4700
Fax: (46) 21804650
Web Site: www.aqg.se
AQ—(OMX)
Sales Range: $200-249.9 Million
Emp.: 1,900
Business Description:
Industrial Components & Systems
S.I.C.: 3559
N.A.I.C.S.: 333249
Personnel:
P. O. Andersson *(Co-Founder & Chm)*
Claes Mellgren *(Co-Founder & CEO)*
Goran Eriksson *(CFO)*
Board of Directors:
P. O. Andersson
Leif Andersson
Rune Glavare
Ulf Gundemark
Claes Mellgren

AQM COPPER INC.
Suite 1500 - 701 W Georgia Street
Vancouver, BC, V7Y-1C6, Canada
Tel.: (604) 669-3113
E-Mail: info@aqmcopper.com
Web Site: www.aqmcopper.com
Year Founded: 2005
AQM—(TSXV)
Sales Range: Less than $1 Million
Business Description:
Copper Ore Exploration & Mining Services
S.I.C.: 1021
N.A.I.C.S.: 212234
Personnel:
Alan R. Edwards *(Chm)*
Bruce L. Turner *(Pres & CEO)*
Erick J. Underwood *(CFO)*
Board of Directors:
Alan R. Edwards
Stephen J. Altmann
Jasper Bertisen
James Gilbert
Bruce L. Turner
Tom Vehrs
Transfer Agent:
Computershare Investor Services Inc.
100 University Ave 9th Floor
Toronto, ON, Canada
Non-U.S. Subsidiaries:

Minera AQM Copper Peru S.A.C. **(1)**
Calle Amador Merino Reyna 339 Officina 401-A
San Isidro, Lima, 27, Peru
Tel.: (51) 1 200 1800
Fax: (51) 1 2429641
Copper Mining Services
S.I.C.: 1021
N.A.I.C.S.: 212234

Sociedad Contractual Minera AQM Copper Chile **(1)**
Avenida El Bosque Norte 0107 Suite 82
Las Condes, Santiago, 7550198, Chile
Tel.: (56) 2 2246 8080
Copper Mining Services
S.I.C.: 1021
N.A.I.C.S.: 212234

AQUA GUARDIAN GROUP LIMITED
Level 9 175 Collins St
Melbourne, VIC, 3000, Australia
Tel.: (61) 3 8530 2000
Fax: (61) 3 8530 2020
E-Mail: info@aquaguardiangroup.com
Web Site: www.aquaguardiangroup.com
Business Description:
Water Conservation Technology & Related Services
S.I.C.: 8999
N.A.I.C.S.: 541620
Personnel:
Alan Cornell *(Chm)*
Tim Grogan *(CEO & Mng Dir)*
Board of Directors:
Alan Cornell
Diane Bettess
Alwyn Davey
Tim Grogan
Ian Woodfield

AQUA LOGISTICS LIMITED
5th Floor B Wing Trade Star Andheri Kurla Road Andheri East
Mumbai, Maharashtra, 400 059, India
Tel.: (91) 2267770200
Fax: (91) 2228353976
Web Site: www.aqualogistics.com
Year Founded: 1999
AQUA—(NSE)
Rev.: $48,330,053
Assets: $112,022,054
Liabilities: $20,406,756
Net Worth: $91,615,299
Earnings: ($5,266,639)
Emp.: 154
Fiscal Year-end: 03/31/13
Business Description:
Logistics & Supply Chain Services
S.I.C.: 4731
N.A.I.C.S.: 541614
Personnel:
Rajesh G. Uchil *(Chm)*
M. S. Sayad *(Vice Chm)*
Harish G. Uchil *(CEO & Mng Dir)*
C. R. Karikal Valavan *(CFO)*
Board of Directors:
Rajesh G. Uchil
B. S. Radhakrishnan
M. S. Sayad
Ravi Sharma
Harish G. Uchil
Transfer Agent:
Link Intime India Pvt. Ltd.
C-13 Pannalal Silk Mills Compound
LBS Marg
Bhandup, Mumbai, 400 078, India
Tel.: (91) 22 2596 3838
Fax: (91) 22 2594 6969

AQUA-PURE VENTURES INC.
135 Commercial Drive Unit 1
Calgary, AB, T3Z 2A7, Canada
Tel.: (403) 301-4123
Fax: (403) 301-4126
Toll Free: (888) 218-9999
E-Mail: info@aqua-pure.com
Web Site: www.fountainquail.com
Year Founded: 1992
AQE—(TSXV)
Rev.: $6,459,757
Assets: $17,271,168
Liabilities: $19,168,332
Net Worth: ($1,897,164)
Earnings: ($5,272,636)
Fiscal Year-end: 12/31/12
Business Description:
Waste Water Management Services
S.I.C.: 4959
N.A.I.C.S.: 562998
Personnel:
Richard Magnus *(Chm)*
Harold Lauman *(Pres)*
Jacob Halldorson *(CEO)*
Karim Teja *(CFO)*
Brent Halldorson *(COO)*
Richard Broderick *(Pres-Fountain Quail Water Mgmt)*
Board of Directors:
Richard Magnus
Brent Halldorson
Jacob Halldorson
Alan Hallman
Harold Lauman
Randal Oberlag
Richard Stroupe
Subsidiary:

Salsnes North America Inc **(1)**
Unit 1 135 Commercial Drive
Calgary, AB, T3Z 2A7, Canada
Tel.: (403) 301-4125
Fax: (403) 301-4126
E-Mail: info@salsnes.ca
Web Site: www.salsnes.ca
Emp.: 1
Water Treatment Equipment Mfr
S.I.C.: 3589
N.A.I.C.S.: 333318
Ivar Solvi *(CEO)*

AQUA SIGNAL GMBH
Von Thunen Strasse 12
28307 Bremen, Germany
Tel.: (49) 42148930
Fax: (49) 4214893210
E-Mail: info@aquasignal.de
Web Site: www.aquasignal.de
Rev.: $56,000,000
Emp.: 230
Business Description:
Light Mfr
S.I.C.: 3648
N.A.I.C.S.: 335129
Personnel:
Joerg Koch-Losekamm *(Mng Dir)*

AQUAINT CAPITAL HOLDINGS LIMITED
Clifford Centre 24 Raffles Place #07-04
Singapore, 048621, Singapore
Tel.: (65) 6532 2920
Web Site: www.aquaintcapital.com.au
AQU—(ASX)
Business Description:
Investment Management, Advice & Coaching
S.I.C.: 6282
N.A.I.C.S.: 523930
Personnel:
Po Tan Yang *(CEO)*
Sherman Tan *(CFO)*
Ming Chiang Soo *(COO)*

AQUALIS ASA
(Formerly Clavis Pharma ASA)
Sjolyst Plass 2 3 etg
0278 Oslo, Norway
Tel.: (47) 24 11 09 50; (47) 2301 4990
Fax: (47) 47 24 11 09 51
E-Mail: mail@aqualis.no
Web Site: www.aqualis.no
AQUA—(DEU OSL)
Rev.: $13,985,278
Assets: $42,720,699
Liabilities: $17,104,460
Net Worth: $25,616,239
Earnings: ($17,321,829)
Emp.: 34
Fiscal Year-end: 12/31/12
Business Description:
Pharmaceutical Drug Mfr
S.I.C.: 2834
N.A.I.C.S.: 325412
Personnel:
Gunnar Manum *(Acting CEO)*
Christian Opsahl *(CFO)*
Ole Henrik Eriksen *(Chief Bus Officer-Healthcare)*
David Wells *(CEO-Offshore)*
Board of Directors:
Glen Ole Rodland
Martin Nes
Yvonne Litsheim Sandvold
Reuben Segal
Oystein Stray Spetalen
Synne Syrrist

AQUARIUS COATINGS INC.
7700 Pine Valley Drive Unit 206
Woodbridge, ON, L4L 2X4, Canada
Tel.: (905) 264-1168
Fax: (905) 264-1169
Toll Free: (800) 661-2298
E-Mail: sales@paintcoatings.com
Web Site: www.paintcoatings.com
Year Founded: 1988
AQC—(TSXV)
Sls.: $183,840
Assets: $247,016
Liabilities: $4,080,250
Net Worth: ($3,833,234)
Earnings: ($287,017)
Fiscal Year-end: 03/31/13
Business Description:
Protective Coating Mfr
S.I.C.: 2851
N.A.I.C.S.: 325510
Personnel:
David J. Hennigar *(Chm & Acting CEO)*
Lorne S. MacFarlane *(CFO & Sec)*
Board of Directors:
David J. Hennigar
J. Thomas MacQuarrie
N. Gary Van Nest
Michael G. Ryan

Aquarius Coatings Inc.—(Continued)

Legal Counsel:
Bennett Jones LLP
Toronto, ON, Canada

Transfer Agent:
Equity Transfer & Trust Company
Toronto, ON, Canada

AQUARIUS PLATINUM LIMITED

Level 4 Suite 5 South Shore Centre
85 The Esplanade, Perth, WA, 6151, Australia
Tel.: (61) 893675211
Fax: (61) 893675233
E-Mail: info@aquariusplatinum.com
Web Site: www.aquariusplatinum.com
Year Founded: 1996
AQP—(ASX)
Rev.: $370,548,000
Assets: $764,921,000
Liabilities: $468,979,000
Net Worth: $295,942,000
Earnings: ($287,913,000)
Emp.: 7,261
Fiscal Year-end: 06/30/13

Business Description:
Platinum, Palladium, Rhodium & Gold Mining Services
S.I.C.: 1099
N.A.I.C.S.: 212299

Personnel:
Jean Nel *(CEO)*
William M. P. Boehm *(Sec)*

Board of Directors:
Nicholas Theobald Sibley
Sonja de Bruyn Sebotsa
David R. Dix
Timothy Freshwater
G. Edward Haslam
Zwelakhe Solomon Mankazana
Kofi Morna
Jean Nel

Computershare Investor Services Pty Limited
Level 2 Reserve Bank Building 45 St Georges Terrace
Perth, 6000, Australia
Tel.: (61) 8 9323 2000

Computershare Investor Services 2004 (Pty) Ltd
8th Floor 70 Marshall Street
Johannesburg, South Africa

Subsidiary:

Aquarius Platinum (Australia) Limited (1)
L 4 Suite 5 85 The Esplanade
South Perth, Perth, WA, 6151, Australia
Tel.: (61) 8 9367 5211
Fax: (61) 8 9367 5233
E-Mail: info@aquariusplatinum.com
Web Site: www.aquariusplatinum.com
Emp.: 3
Platinum Mining Services
S.I.C.: 1099
N.A.I.C.S.: 212299
Jean Nel *(CEO)*

Subsidiary:

Aquarius Platinum Corporate Services Pty Ltd (2)
Level 4 Suite 5 South Shore Centre
85 The Esplanade South, 6151 Perth, WA, Australia (100%)
Tel.: (61) 893675211
Fax: (61) 893675233
E-Mail: info@aquariusplatinum.com
Web Site: www.aquariusplatinum.com
Emp.: 5
All Other Metal Ore Mining
S.I.C.: 1099
N.A.I.C.S.: 212299
Willi Boehm *(Sec)*

Non-U.S. Subsidiary:

Aquarius Platinum (South Africa) (Pty) Ltd (1)
1st Floor Building 5 Harrowdene Office Park
Western Service Road, 2191 Woodmead, South Africa (100%)
Tel.: (27) 116561140
Fax: (27) 118020990
E-Mail: info@aquariusplatinum.com
Web Site: www.aquariusplatinum.com
Emp.: 50
All Other Metal Ore Mining
S.I.C.: 1099
N.A.I.C.S.: 212299
Sonja de Bruyn Sebotsa *(Chm)*
Anton Lubbe *(Mng Dir)*

Subsidiary:

Aquarius Platinum (SA) Corporate Services (Proprietary) Limited (2)
1st Floor Building 5 Harrowdene Office Park
Western Service Road
PO Box 76575
Woodmead, Johannesburg, Gauteng, 2191, South Africa
Tel.: (27) 116561140
Fax: (27) 11 802 0990
E-Mail: info@aquariusplatinum.com
Emp.: 4
Platinum Mining Services
S.I.C.: 1099
N.A.I.C.S.: 212299
Anton Lubbe *(Mng Dir)*

AQUASITION CORP.

8-10 Paul Street
London, EC2A 4JH, United Kingdom
Tel.: (44) 207 426 1155
Year Founded: 2012
AQUUU—(NASDAQ)
Int. Income: $3,785
Assets: $57,497,020
Liabilities: $54,984,229
Net Worth: $2,512,791
Earnings: ($3,108,717)
Fiscal Year-end: 12/31/12

Business Description:
Investment Services
S.I.C.: 6211
N.A.I.C.S.: 523999

Personnel:
Leonidas S. Polemis *(Chm)*
Matthew C. Los *(CEO)*
Stylianos Stergios Sougioultzoglou *(CFO)*

Board of Directors:
Leonidas S. Polemis
Nicholas John Frangos
Themistoklis Kalapotharakos
Matthew C. Los
Stylianos Stergios Sougioultzoglou

AQUASIUM TECHNOLOGY LIMITED

Denny Industrial Ctr
Waterbeach, Cambs, CB25 9QX, United Kingdom
Tel.: (44) 1223863481
Fax: (44) 1223862812
E-Mail: info@aquasium.com
Web Site: www.aquasium.com
Year Founded: 1995
Sales Range: $10-24.9 Million
Emp.: 50

Business Description:
Technology Investment Firm
S.I.C.: 6211
N.A.I.C.S.: 523999

Personnel:
John Peter Cumberland *(Chm)*

Division:

Cambridge Vacuum Engineering Limited (1)
Denny Industrial Center
Pembroke Avenue, CB25 9QX Waterbeach, Cambs, United Kingdom
Tel.: (44) 1223863481
Fax: (44) 1223862812
E-Mail: info@camvaceng.co.uk
Web Site: www.camvaceng.co.uk
Sales Range: $100-124.9 Million
Emp.: 60
Vacuum Furnaces & Electron Beam Welding Systems Mfr
S.I.C.: 3567
N.A.I.C.S.: 333994
John Cumberland *(Chm)*
Bob Nicolson *(Mng Dir)*
Robert Nicholson *(Mng Dir)*

U.S. Subsidiary:

Cambridge Vacuum Engineering Inc. (2)
630 Silver St Unit 7A PO Box 867
Agawam, MA 01001-0867
Tel.: (413) 789-4600
Fax: (413) 786-0508
Web Site: www.camvaceng.com
Emp.: 4
Vacuum Furnaces & Electron Beam Welding Systems Mfr
S.I.C.: 3567
N.A.I.C.S.: 333994
Geoffrey Young *(Mng Dir)*

U.S. Holding:

EBTEC Corporation (1)
120 Shoemaker Ln
Agawam, MA 01001
Tel.: (413) 786-0393
Fax: (413) 789-2851
E-Mail: info@ebteccorp.com
Web Site: www.ebteccorp.com
Emp.: 70
Laser Processing, Electron Beam Welding, Heat-Treating, Abrasive Waterjet Processing, Manual Welding & General Machining Services
S.I.C.: 3398
N.A.I.C.S.: 332811
John Leveille *(Pres)*

AQUILA GROUP HOLDINGS LIMITED

Aquila House 35 London Rd
Redhill, Surrey, RH1 1NJ, United Kingdom
Tel.: (44) 1737859859
Fax: (44) 1737857191
E-Mail: enquiries@aquilauk.co.uk
Web Site: www.aquilauk.co.uk
Year Founded: 1998
Sales Range: $10-24.9 Million
Emp.: 137

Business Description:
Pension & Financial Management Software
S.I.C.: 3652
N.A.I.C.S.: 334614

Personnel:
Finlay Ross *(Chm)*
David E. Ackroyd *(CEO)*

Subsidiaries:

AquilaHeywood Ltd (1)
Aquila House 35 London Road
Redhill, Surrey, RH1 1NJ, United Kingdom (100%)
Tel.: (44) 1737859859
Fax: (44) 1737857191
E-Mail: enquiries@aquilauk.co.uk
Web Site: www.aquilaheywood.co.uk
Emp.: 200
Software Reproducing
S.I.C.: 3652
N.A.I.C.S.: 334614
David E. Ackroyd *(CEO)*

Heywood Limited (1)
Victoria House 2 Victoria St
Altrincham, Cheshire, WA14 1ET, United Kingdom
Tel.: (44) 1616134200
Fax: (44) 1616144012
E-Mail: enquiries@heywood.co.uk
Web Site: www.heywood.co.uk
Emp.: 100
Software-based Pension Administration Services
S.I.C.: 6371
N.A.I.C.S.: 524292
David Ackroyd *(CEO)*

AQUILA RESOURCES INC.

65 Queen Street West Suite 530
Toronto, ON, M5H 2M5, Canada
Tel.: (416) 203-1404
Fax: (416) 955-4771
E-Mail: info@aquilaresources.com
Web Site: www.aquilaresources.com
Year Founded: 1997
AQA—(DEU OTC TSX)
Rev.: $265,059
Assets: $30,902,031
Liabilities: $44,882
Net Worth: $30,857,149
Earnings: ($2,477,661)
Emp.: 8
Fiscal Year-end: 12/31/12

Business Description:
Zinc Mining Services
S.I.C.: 1031
N.A.I.C.S.: 212231

Personnel:
Mark Alexander Burridge *(Chm)*
Barry Hildred *(CEO)*
Louis Robert Nagy *(CFO)*
Nadim Wakeam *(Sec)*

Board of Directors:
Mark Alexander Burridge
Peter M. D. Bradshaw
Stephen L. Fabian
Barry Hildred
Edward J. Munden
Peter Anthony Secker

Legal Counsel:
Blaney McMurtry LLP
2 Queen Street East Suite 1500
Toronto, ON, Canada

Transfer Agent:
Trans Canada Transfer Inc.
25 Adelaide St E Suite 1301
Toronto, ON, M5C 3A1, Canada

U.S. Subsidiary:

HudBay Michigan Inc. (1)
807 E Gerue St
Stephenson, MI 49887
Tel.: (906) 753-9602
Metal Mining Services
S.I.C.: 1081
N.A.I.C.S.: 213114

AQUILA RESOURCES LIMITED

Level 2 Aquila Centre 1 Preston Street
Como, WA, 6152, Australia
Tel.: (61) 894230111
Fax: (61) 894230133
E-Mail: mail@aquilaresources.com.au
Web Site: www.aquilaresources.com.au
AQA—(ASX)
Rev.: $533,762,578
Assets: $1,048,573,525
Liabilities: $188,556,532
Net Worth: $860,016,993
Earnings: $330,875,087
Emp.: 78
Fiscal Year-end: 06/30/13

Business Description:
Exploration for Coal, Iron Ore & Manganese Resources
S.I.C.: 1241
N.A.I.C.S.: 213113

Personnel:
Tony Poli *(Chm & CEO)*
Howard Rae *(CFO)*
May Chan *(Sec)*

Board of Directors:
Tony Poli
Gordon Thomas Galt
Denise Goldsworthy
Zhaoming Lu

Tim Netscher
Steve Scudamore
Legal Counsel:
King & Wood Mallesons
Level 10 Central Park 152 158 St Georges Terrace
Perth, Australia

AQUILINI INVESTMENT GROUP
Standard Building Suite 200 510 W Hastings
Vancouver, BC, V6B 1L8, Canada
Tel.: (604) 687-8813
Fax: (604) 682-6183
E-Mail: enquiry@aquilini.com
Web Site: www.aquilini.com
Emp.: 50
Business Description:
Equity Investment Firm
S.I.C.: 6211
N.A.I.C.S.: 523999
Personnel:
Francesco Aquilini *(Partner)*
Paolo Aquilini *(Partner)*
Roberto Aquilini *(Partner)*
Holding:

Canucks Sports & Entertainment **(1)**
800 Griffiths Way
Vancouver, BC, V6B 6G1, Canada (100%)
Tel.: (604) 899-7400
Fax: (604) 899-7401
Web Site: canucks.nhl.com
Sales Range: $10-24.9 Million
Emp.: 200
Holding Company; Professional Hockey Franchise & Sports Arena Owner & Operator
S.I.C.: 6719
N.A.I.C.S.: 551112
Francesco Aquilini *(Chm & Governor)*
Mike Gillis *(Pres & Gen Mgr-Vancouver Canucks)*
Todd Kobus *(CFO & VP-Fin)*
Victor P. de Bonis *(COO & Alternate Governor)*

Unit:

Vancouver Canucks **(2)**
800 Griffiths Way
Vancouver, BC, V6B 6G1, Canada
Tel.: (604) 899-4600
Fax: (604) 899-7401
Web Site: www.canucks.nhl.com
Professional Hockey Franchise
S.I.C.: 7941
N.A.I.C.S.: 711211
Mike Gillis *(Pres & Gen Mgr-NHL)*
Todd Kobus *(CFO & VP-Fin)*
Victor de Bonis *(COO)*
Francesco Aquilini *(Chm-NHL)*
Chris Gear *(VP & Gen Counsel)*
Michael Doyle *(Exec VP & Gen Mgr-Arena)*
Trent Caroll *(Exec VP-Sls & Mktg)*

AQUINOX PHARMACEUTICALS, INC.
450-887 Great Northern Way
Vancouver, BC, V5T 4T5, Canada
Tel.: (604) 629-9223
Fax: (778) 331-4486
E-Mail: info@aqxpharma.com
Web Site: www.aqxpharma.com
Year Founded: 2003
AQXP—(NASDAQ)
Assets: $15,649,106
Liabilities: $81,342,814
Net Worth: ($65,693,708)
Earnings: ($8,729,371)
Emp.: 12
Fiscal Year-end: 12/31/13
Business Description:
Pharmaceutical Mfr
S.I.C.: 2834
N.A.I.C.S.: 325412
Personnel:
David J. Main *(Pres & CEO)*
Kamran Alam *(CFO & VP-Fin)*
Stephen Shrewsbury *(Chief Medical Officer & Sr VP-Clinical Dev)*
Board of Directors:
Gary Bridger
Elaine Jones
Daniel J. Levitt
David J. Main
Robert Pelzer
Todd Simpson

A.R. MEDICOM INC.
(d/b/a Medicom)
1200 55th Avenue
Lachine, QC, H8T 3J8, Canada
Tel.: (514) 636-6262
Fax: (514) 636-6266
Toll Free: (800) 308-6589
E-Mail: cserviceemail@medicom.ca
Web Site: www.medicom.com
Year Founded: 1988
Sales Range: $10-24.9 Million
Emp.: 100
Business Description:
Disposable Dental & Medical Supplies Mfr
S.I.C.: 3843
N.A.I.C.S.: 339114
Personnel:
Ronald Reuben *(Owner & CEO)*
Guillaume Laverdure *(COO)*

ARA ASSET MANAGEMENT LIMITED
6 Temasek Boulevard Suntec Tower 4 16 02
Singapore, 038986, Singapore
Tel.: (65) 68359232
Fax: (65) 68359672
E-Mail: enquiry@ara-asia.com
Web Site: www.ara-asia.com
D1R—(SES)
Rev.: $108,116,570
Assets: $234,070,391
Liabilities: $34,387,919
Net Worth: $199,682,472
Earnings: $60,100,117
Emp.: 800
Fiscal Year-end: 12/31/12
Business Description:
Real Estate Services
S.I.C.: 6531
N.A.I.C.S.: 531210
Personnel:
John Hwee Chiang Lim *(CEO)*
Moses Song *(Chief Investment Officer & Head-Australia)*
Yvonne Choo *(Sec)*
Board of Directors:
Justin Kwok Hung Chiu
Moses Mo Chi Cheng
Edmond Tak Chuen Ip
Yock Suan Lee
How Teck Lim
John Hwee Chiang Lim
Colin Stevens Russel
Transfer Agent:
Boardroom Corporate & Advisory Services Pte. Ltd.
50 Raffles Place 32-01 Singapore Land Tower
Singapore, Singapore
Subsidiaries:

ARA Trust Management (Suntec) Limited **(1)**
6 Temasek Boulevard 16-02 Suntec Tower Four
Singapore, 038986, Singapore
Tel.: (65) 6835 9232
Fax: (65) 6835 9672
E-Mail: hr@ara.com.hk
Web Site: www.ara-asia.com
Emp.: 80
Trust Management Services
S.I.C.: 8748
N.A.I.C.S.: 541618
Pauline Lim *(Mgr-HR)*

Suntec International Convention and Exhibition Services Pte Ltd **(1)**
1 Raffles Place Tower 1 16-00
Singapore, 048616, Singapore
Tel.: (65) 63372888
Fax: (65) 68252222
Web Site: www.suntecinternational.com
Emp.: 300
Convention & Exhibition Center Management Services
S.I.C.: 6512
N.A.I.C.S.: 531120
Arun Madphok *(CEO)*

Suntec Singapore International Convention & Exhibition Services Pte. Ltd. **(1)**
1 Raffles Boulevard
Suntec City, Singapore, Singapore
Tel.: (65) 6337 2888
Fax: (65) 6825 2222
E-Mail: sales@suntecsingapore.com
Web Site: www.suntecsingapore.com
Emp.: 300
Exhibition Venue Rental & Operation Services
S.I.C.: 7389
N.A.I.C.S.: 561990
Arun Madhok *(CEO)*

Non-U.S. Subsidiary:

ARA Asset Management (Prosperity) Limited **(1)**
Rm 5508-9 55/F The Ctr 99 Queens Rd Central, China (Hong Kong)
Tel.: (852) 21690928
Fax: (852) 21690968
Emp.: 35
Real Estate Investment Trust Management Services
S.I.C.: 4225
N.A.I.C.S.: 531130

ARAB AFRICAN INTERNATIONAL BANK
5 Midan al Saraya al Koubra
Garden City, Cairo, Egypt
Tel.: (20) 27920692
Fax: (20) 27953732
E-Mail: inquiry@aaib.com
Web Site: www.aaibank.com
Sales Range: $25-49.9 Million
Emp.: 575
Business Description:
Banking Services
S.I.C.: 6029
N.A.I.C.S.: 522110
Personnel:
Mahmoud A. Al Nouri *(Chm)*
Hassan E. Abdalla *(Vice Chm & Mng Dir)*
Salah El-Din El Baroudi *(Sec)*
Board of Directors:
Mahmoud A. Al Nouri
Hassan E. Abdalla
Adel M. Al Roumi
Ali H. Alsayegh
Abdullah R. Bou-Qammaz
Salah El-Din El Baroudi
Hala Helmy El Said
Ali A. Khajah
Mahmoud Abdel Aziz Mahmoud
Gamal H. Mubarak
Joint Venture:

Power Generation Engineering And Services Company **(1)**
41 Al Salam Ave
Heliopolis, Cairo, 56356, Egypt
Tel.: (20) 226176497
Fax: (20) 2261855415
E-Mail: info@pgesco.com
Web Site: www.pgesco.com
Sales Range: $25-49.9 Million
Engineering & Construction Management Services; Joint Venture of the Ministry of Electricity & Energy of Egypt (40%), Bechtel Group, Inc. (40%) & Arab African International Bank (20%)
S.I.C.: 8711
N.A.I.C.S.: 541330

ARAB ALUMINIUM INDUSTRY CO. LTD.
Ain El-Basha
PO Box 35042
Amman, 11180, Jordan
Tel.: (962) 6 5343965
Fax: (962) 6 5347145
E-Mail: aral@accessme.com
Year Founded: 1976
AALU—(AMM)
Rev.: $20,051,278
Assets: $23,865,855
Liabilities: $6,839,090
Net Worth: $17,026,765
Earnings: $777,189
Emp.: 297
Fiscal Year-end: 12/31/12
Business Description:
Aluminum Product Mfr
S.I.C.: 3353
N.A.I.C.S.: 331315
Personnel:
Osamah Hussein Al-aqqad *(Gen Mgr)*

THE ARAB ASSURERS P.L.C
Queen Rania St Bld No 32
PO Box 96262
Amman, 11110, Jordan
Tel.: (962) 65100081
Fax: (962) 65100082
E-Mail: info@arabassures.jo
Year Founded: 1996
ARAS—(AMM)
Rev.: $14,363,586
Assets: $17,355,042
Liabilities: $13,673,918
Net Worth: $3,681,124
Earnings: $10,427
Emp.: 70
Fiscal Year-end: 12/31/12
Business Description:
Insurance Agency Services
S.I.C.: 6411
N.A.I.C.S.: 524210
Personnel:
Haitham Khatatneh *(Gen Mgr)*

ARAB BANK PLC
PO Box 950545
Amman, 11195, Jordan
Tel.: (962) 65600000
Fax: (962) 65606793
Web Site: www.arabbank.com
ARBK—(AMM)
Int. Income: $1,765,242,000
Assets: $45,646,524,000
Liabilities: $37,947,358,000
Net Worth: $7,699,166,000
Earnings: $352,050,000
Emp.: 9,012
Fiscal Year-end: 12/31/12
Business Description:
Banking Services
S.I.C.: 6029
N.A.I.C.S.: 522110
Personnel:
Sabih Taher Masri *(Chm)*
Samir Farhan Kawar *(Deputy Chm)*
Nemeh Elias Sabbagh *(CEO)*
Randa Muhammad Sadik *(Deputy CEO)*
Dawod Al Ghoul *(CFO)*
Mohamed Ghanameh *(Chief Credit Officer)*
Andrew Cobb *(Chief Projects Officer)*
Samer Tamimi *(Exec VP & Head-Corp & Institutional Banking)*
Board of Directors:
Sabih Taher Masri
Nazek Al Hariri
Omar Al Razaz

Arab Bank plc—(Continued)

Mohammed Ahmad Al-Hariri
Saleh Sa'ad Al-Muhanna
Khaled Anis Moh'd Zand Irani
Ibrahim Izzeddin
Riad Burhan Taher Kamal
Bassam Wael Rushdi Kanaan
Samir Farhan Kawar
Wahbeh Abdullah Tamari

Subsidiaries:

Al Arabi Investment Group Co. (1)
Al-Rabieh Abdullah Bin Rawaha St
PO Box 143156
Amman, 11814, Jordan
Tel.: (962) 6 5522239
Fax: (962) 6 5519064
E-Mail: research@ab-invest.net
Web Site: www.ab-invest.net
Commercial Banking Services
S.I.C.: 6029
N.A.I.C.S.: 522110
Adel Kasaji *(CEO)*

AL-NISR AL-ARABI INSURANCE (1)
Abdali-Amman Commercial Center
Amman, 11191, Jordan
Tel.: (962) 65685171
Fax: (962) 65685890
E-Mail: al-nisr@al-nisr.com
Web Site: www.al-nisr.com
AAIN—(AMM)
Sales Range: $25-49.9 Million
Emp.: 141
Insurance Services
S.I.C.: 6411
N.A.I.C.S.: 524298
Muneer Butros Al-Muasher *(Chm)*
Yacoub Manawil Sabella *(Vice Chm & Gen Mgr)*

Arab National Leasing Company Ltd (1)
Al-Madina Al-Monawara St
PO Box 720
Tla Al-Ali, Amman, Jordan
Tel.: (962) 6 553 1640
Financial Leasing Services
S.I.C.: 6211
N.A.I.C.S.: 523999

Islamic International Arab Bank plc (1)
PO Box 925802
Amman, 11190, Jordan (100%)
Tel.: (962) 65694901
Fax: (962) 65694681
Web Site: www.iiabank.com
Emp.: 150
Banking Services
S.I.C.: 6029
N.A.I.C.S.: 522110
Tayseer Al-Smadi *(Chm)*
Ghassan Al-Bondukji *(CEO)*

Non-U.S. Subsidiaries:

Arab Bank Australia Ltd (1)
200 George St
Sydney, NSW, 2000, Australia
Tel.: (61) 293778900
Fax: (61) 292215428
E-Mail: admin@arabbank.com.au
Web Site: www.arabbank.com.au
Emp.: 50
Banking Services
S.I.C.: 6029
N.A.I.C.S.: 522110
Joseph Rizk *(Mng Dir)*

Arab Bank (Switzerland) Ltd. (1)
Bahnhofstrasse 46
PO Box 2023
CH 8022 Zurich, Switzerland
Tel.: (41) 44 265 7111
Fax: (41) 44 265 7330
E-Mail: pbanking@arabbank.ch
Web Site: www.arabbank.ch
Emp.: 60
Banking & Financial Services
S.I.C.: 6029
N.A.I.C.S.: 522110
Antoine Raphael *(CEO)*

Arab Investment Bank S.A.L. (1)
Riad El Solh Squar Banks Street BCD
PO Box 11-1015
Beirut, 1107 2070, Lebanon (66.65%)
Tel.: (961) 1985111
Fax: (961) 1987333
E-Mail: arbing@arabbank.com.lb
Emp.: 5
Banking Services
S.I.C.: 6029
N.A.I.C.S.: 522110
Nadim Ghantous *(Gen Mgr)*

Arab Sudanese Bank Limited (1)
Khartoum East-Block 1DE-Building No 7
PO Box 955
Khartoum, Sudan
Tel.: (249) 1565 50001
Fax: (249) 1551 19533
Web Site: www.arabbank.com
Commercial Banking Services
S.I.C.: 6029
N.A.I.C.S.: 522110

Arab Tunisian Bank (1)
9 Rue Hedi Nouira
Tunis, 1001, Tunisia (64.24%)
Tel.: (216) 713 51155
Fax: (216) 713 42852
Web Site: www.atb.com.tn/atb/site/contact.jsp
Banking Services
S.I.C.: 6029
N.A.I.C.S.: 522110

Europe Arab Bank Plc (1)
Mahlerstrasse 7 Top 15 & 16
1010 Vienna, Austria
Tel.: (43) 15134240
Fax: (43) 151342409
E-Mail: info@eabplc.com
Web Site: www.eabplc.com
Emp.: 216
Banking Services
S.I.C.: 6029
N.A.I.C.S.: 522110

Finance Accountancy Mohassaba SA (1)
24 Rue Neuve -Vu-Molard
PO Box 3155
1211 Geneva, 3, Switzerland (100%)
Tel.: (41) 229083000
Fax: (41) 227387229
E-Mail: sam@finance-accountancy.com
Web Site: www.arabbank.ch/OfficesNetwork/InternationalNetwork/Pages/Europenew.aspx
Emp.: 8
Banking Services
S.I.C.: 6029
N.A.I.C.S.: 522110

Non-U.S. Joint Venture:

Oman Arab Bank S.A.O.C. (1)
Muttrah Business District
PO Box 2010
112 Ruwi, Oman
Tel.: (968) 24706265
Fax: (968) 24797736
E-Mail: oabmkt@omantel.net.om
Web Site: www.omanab.com
Emp.: 100
Banking Services; Owned 51% by Oman International Development & Investment Co. SAOG & 49% by Arab Bank plc
S.I.C.: 6029
N.A.I.C.S.: 522110
Amin Rasheed Al Husseini *(CEO)*

ARAB BANKING CORPORATION B.S.C.

ABC Tower Diplomatic Area
PO Box 5698
Manama, Bahrain
Tel.: (973) 17543000
Fax: (973) 533163
E-Mail: webmaster@arabbanking.com
Web Site: www.arabbanking.com
Year Founded: 1980
ABC—(BAH NZE)
Sls.: $1,061,000,000
Assets: $24,527,000,000
Liabilities: $20,305,000,000
Net Worth: $4,222,000,000
Earnings: $263,000,000
Emp.: 15
Fiscal Year-end: 12/31/12

Business Description:
Banking & Investment Services
S.I.C.: 6029
N.A.I.C.S.: 522110

Personnel:
Saddek O. El Kaber *(Chm)*
Hilal Mishari Al-Mutairi *(Deputy Chm)*
Khaled Kawan *(Pres & CEO)*
Roy Gardner *(CFO)*
Sael Al Waary *(Grp COO & Exec VP)*
Vijay Srivastava *(Chief Credit Officer & Chief Risk Officer)*
Ray Ferguson *(Grp Chief Banking Officer & Exec VP)*
Andrew Wilson *(Head-Ops)*
Vernon Handley *(Legal Counsel)*
Ali Mirza *(Asst Treas)*
Kareem Dashti *(Treas-Bahrain)*
Amr Gadallah *(Treas)*

Board of Directors:
Saddek O. El Kaber
Abdallah Saud Al Humaidhi
Yousef Al-Awadi
Anwar Ali Al-Mudhaf
Hilal Mishari Al-Mutairi
Isam Ghellai
Khaled Kagigi

Subsidiary:

ABC Islamic Bank EC (1)
ABC Tower Diplomatic Area
PO Box 2808
Manama, Bahrain
Tel.: (973) 17543342
Fax: (973) 17536379
Banking Servcies
S.I.C.: 6211
N.A.I.C.S.: 523110
Naveed Khan *(Gen Mgr)*

Non-U.S. Subsidiaries:

ABC International Bank plc (1)
Arab Banking Corporation House
1-5 Moorgate, London, EC2R 6AB, United Kingdom
Tel.: (44) 2077764000
Fax: (44) 2076069987
Web Site: www.arabbanking.com
Sales Range: $150-199.9 Million
Emp.: 100
Trade Finance & Investment Services
S.I.C.: 6159
N.A.I.C.S.: 522293
William Playle *(CEO)*
Paul Jennings *(Co-Deputy CEO & Head-Global Trade Fin)*
Alexander Ashton *(Co-Deputy CEO)*

ABC (IT) Services Ltd. (1)
Arab Banking Corporation House 1 5 Moorgate
London, EC2R 6AB, United Kingdom
Tel.: (44) 20 7776 4050
Fax: (44) 20 7606 2708
E-Mail: abcits@arabbanking.com
Web Site: www.arabbanking.com
Commercial Banking Services
S.I.C.: 6029
N.A.I.C.S.: 522110

Banco ABC Brasil S.A. (1)
Avenida Presidente Juscelino Kubitschek 1 400 8s andar
Vila Nova Conceicao, Sao Paulo, SP, Brazil 04543000 (55.9%)
Tel.: (55) 1131702000
Fax: (55) 1131702001
Web Site: www.abcbrasil.com.br
ABCB3—(BRAZ)
Int. Income: $723,189,467
Assets: $6,265,537,415
Liabilities: $5,411,871,666
Net Worth: $853,665,749
Earnings: $118,505,647
Fiscal Year-end: 12/31/12
Banking Services
S.I.C.: 6159
N.A.I.C.S.: 522293
Anwar Ali Al Mudhaf *(Chm)*
Tito Enrique da Silva Neto *(Vice Chm)*
Anis Chacur Neto *(CEO)*
Sergio Ricardo Borejo *(CFO & COO)*
Sergio Lulia Jacob *(VP-Treasury & IR)*

ARAB BANKING CORPORATION (JORDAN)

ABJC Building Shmeisani Queen Noor Street
PO Box 926691
11190 Amman, Jordan
Tel.: (962) 6 5633 500
Fax: (962) 6 5686 291
E-Mail: info@arabbanking.com.jo
Web Site: www.arabbanking.com.jo
ABCO—(AMM)
Sales Range: $50-74.9 Million

Business Description:
Financial & Banking Services
S.I.C.: 6211
N.A.I.C.S.: 523110

Personnel:
Khaled Kagigi *(Chm)*
Sael Fayez Al Waary *(Deputy Chm)*
Simona Sabella Bishouty *(CEO & Mng Dir)*
Khaled Kawan *(Deputy CEO)*
Suleiman Al Mbaidin *(Sec, Exec VP & Head-HR)*
Othman Al Shwaimat *(Exec VP & Head-Treasury)*
Nuha Matar *(Exec VP & Head-Credit & Risk)*
Adnan Shobaki *(Exec VP & Head-Support Grp)*
George Sofia *(Exec VP & Head-Retail Banking Grp)*
Othman Azhari *(Sr VP & Head-IT)*
Nidal Basha *(Sr VP & Head-Consumer Banking)*
Nour Jarrar *(Sr VP & Head-Trade Fin & Fin Institutions)*
Rana Naddeh *(Sr VP & Head-Ops)*
Mohammed Naser *(Sr VP & Head-Corp Banking)*

Board of Directors:
Mona Al Dairy
Marwan Mamdouh Al Sayeh
Sael Fayez Al Waary
Suleiman Azzabi
Khaled Kagigi
Simona Sabella Bishouty
Shafiq Zawaideh

ARAB BUSINESS MACHINES LTD.

Beniyas St 21 Fl Arbist Tower
PO Box 55563
Dubai, United Arab Emirates
Tel.: (971) 42233438
Fax: (971) 42227670
E-Mail: abn@appleme.ae
Web Site: www.appleme.ae
Year Founded: 1986
Sales Range: $100-124.9 Million
Emp.: 200

Business Description:
Computer Hardware & Software Products Distr
S.I.C.: 5045
N.A.I.C.S.: 423430

Personnel:
Joe Sefeir *(VP Mktg)*

ARAB CENTER FOR PHARMACEUTICAL & CHEMICAL INDUSTRIES CO.

King Abdullah II Industrial City
PO BOX 22
Sahab, 11512, Jordan
Tel.: (962) 6 4022470
Fax: (962) 6 4022473
E-Mail: info@acpc.com.jo
Web Site: www.acpc.com.jo
APHC—(AMM)
Sales Range: $1-9.9 Million
Emp.: 115

Business Description:
Pharmaceutical Product Mfr
S.I.C.: 2834

N.A.I.C.S.: 325412
Personnel:
Ata Al-Nazer *(Mng Dir)*

ARAB COMPANY FOR INVESTMENT PROJECTS

Barees St Commercial Al-Zytonah Building
PO Box 3335
Amman, 11953, Jordan
Tel.: (962) 6 5811778
Fax: (962) 6 5826662
APCT—(AMM)
Rev.: $705,526
Assets: $17,606,428
Liabilities: $9,941,400
Net Worth: $7,665,028
Earnings: ($800,636)
Emp.: 2
Fiscal Year-end: 12/31/12
Business Description:
Financial Investment Services
S.I.C.: 6211
N.A.I.C.S.: 523999
Personnel:
Jamal Al-Khattab *(Gen Mgr)*

ARAB EAST FOR REAL ESTATE INVESTMENTS CO. PLC

Complex Real Estate Development Nr 145
PO Box 851322
Fl Nr 402 Wasfi Al Tal Street,
Amman, 11185, Jordan
Tel.: (962) 6 5510355
Fax: (962) 6 5510353
Year Founded: 2004
REAL—(AMM)
Rev.: $2,634,807
Assets: $74,599,644
Liabilities: $43,550,063
Net Worth: $31,049,581
Earnings: ($1,193,177)
Emp.: 1
Fiscal Year-end: 12/31/12
Business Description:
Real Estate Development Services
S.I.C.: 6531
N.A.I.C.S.: 531390
Personnel:
Maein A. Suhaimat *(Gen Mgr)*

ARAB EAST INVESTMENT COMPANY

Um Othaineh
PO Box 851322
Amman, 11185, Jordan
Tel.: (962) 6 551122 7
Fax: (962) 6 5511914
E-Mail: info@aeivco.com
Web Site: www.aeivco.com
Year Founded: 1996
AEIV—(AMM)
Rev.: $5,056,903
Assets: $150,268,427
Liabilities: $38,465,508
Net Worth: $111,802,919
Earnings: ($7,738,366)
Emp.: 19
Fiscal Year-end: 12/31/12
Business Description:
Real Estate Investment Services
S.I.C.: 6531
N.A.I.C.S.: 531390
Personnel:
Mae'n Al-Suhiamat *(Gen Mgr)*

ARAB ELECTRICAL INDUSTRIES

Sahab Industrial Estate
PO Box 3
Amman, 11518, Jordan
Tel.: (962) 5859124
Fax: (962) 5826124
E-Mail: info@aei-jo.com
Web Site: www.aei-jo.com
Year Founded: 1983
AEIN—(AMM)
Sales Range: $10-24.9 Million
Emp.: 108
Business Description:
Electrical Equipment Mfr
S.I.C.: 3699
N.A.I.C.S.: 335999
Personnel:
Mohammed El Kaysi *(Mng Dir)*

Non-U.S. Subsidiary:

ITALCLEM S.p.A. **(1)**
Via Creta 15
25124 Brescia, Italy
Tel.: (39) 030 2422281
Fax: (39) 030 224468
E-Mail: info@italclem.com
Web Site: www.italclem.com
Electrical Component Mfr
S.I.C.: 3699
N.A.I.C.S.: 335999

THE ARAB FINANCIAL INVESTMENT CO.

PO Box 922634
Amman, 11192, Jordan
Tel.: (962) 65002000
Fax: (962) 65692423
E-Mail: info@arabinvestco.com
Web Site: www.arabinvestco.com
AFIN—(AMM)
Sales Range: $10-24.9 Million
Emp.: 30
Business Description:
Portfolio Management & Brokerage Services
S.I.C.: 6282
N.A.I.C.S.: 523920
Personnel:
Osama M. Khater *(Chm)*
Raed M. Shraim *(Vice Chm)*
Tareq Mohammad Khater *(CEO)*
Board of Directors:
Osama M. Khater
Abdullah S. Al-Janabi
Tareq Mohammad Khater
Nabil Makahleh
Zakariya M. Musleh
Raed M. Shraim

ARAB GERMAN INSURANCE CO. LTD.

Al-Shmeissani Abed Al Hameed Sharaff St
PO Box 212640
Amman, 11121, Jordan
Tel.: (962) 65200000
Fax: (962) 65200025
E-Mail: agi@agi.com.jo
Web Site: www.agi.com.jo
Year Founded: 1996
AGICC—(AMM)
Sales Range: $25-49.9 Million
Emp.: 100
Business Description:
Insurance Services
S.I.C.: 6411
N.A.I.C.S.: 524298
Personnel:
Ra'ed Al-Reimouny *(Gen Mgr)*

ARAB HEAVY INDUSTRIES P.J.S.C

PO Box 529
Ajman, United Arab Emirates
Tel.: (971) 65263232
Fax: (971) 65263233
E-Mail: ahiaeme@emirates.net.ae
Web Site: www.ahi-uae.com
AHI—(EMI)
Sales Range: $25-49.9 Million
Business Description:
Ship Repair Services
S.I.C.: 3731
N.A.I.C.S.: 336611
Personnel:
Obaid Ali Al Muhairi *(Chm)*
Ali Abdullah Al Hamrani *(Vice Chm)*
Board of Directors:
Obaid Ali Al Muhairi
Khalid Abdullah Al Futaim
Salem Abdulla Al Ghurair
Ali Abdullah Al Hamrani
Saleh Al Matrooshi
Rashid Humaid Ali Al Mazroei
Abdul Rahman Mohammed Nasser Al Owais
Kok Seng Foo
Ahmad Zaki Ahmad Haroon
Soun Fah Loh
Nelson Chien Sheng Yeo

THE ARAB HOTELS COMPANY

Irsal Street
PO Box 3852
Alberah, Ramallah, Palestine
Tel.: (970) 22965240
Fax: (970) 22965242
E-Mail: info@ahc-pal.com
Web Site: www.ahc-pal.com
Year Founded: 1996
AHC—(PAL)
Rev.: $4,711,086
Assets: $32,194,064
Liabilities: $12,797,694
Net Worth: $19,396,370
Earnings: ($994,006)
Fiscal Year-end: 12/31/12
Business Description:
Hotel Management Services
S.I.C.: 7011
N.A.I.C.S.: 721110
Personnel:
Anan Takrouri *(Deputy Gen Mgr)*

ARAB INFORMATION MANAGEMENT SERVICES

PO Box 23906
Kuwait, 13100, Kuwait
Tel.: (965) 2444070
Fax: (965) 2444078
E-Mail: recruit@aims-kw.com
Web Site: www.aims-kw.com
Year Founded: 1980
Sales Range: $25-49.9 Million
Emp.: 430
Business Description:
Information Technology Consulting Services
S.I.C.: 7373
N.A.I.C.S.: 541512
Personnel:
Anwar A. Al-Nouri *(Partner & Mgr)*
Abdul Wahid Akil Zaman *(Partner & Mgr)*

ARAB INSURANCE GROUP B.S.C.

Arig House Building 131 Road 1702
Diplomatic Area 317
PO Box 26992
Manama, Bahrain
Tel.: (973) 17544444
Fax: (973) 17531155
E-Mail: info@arig.com.bh
Web Site: www.arig.com.bh
Year Founded: 1980
ARIG—(BAH KUW LSE)
Premiums: $238,642,000
Assets: $999,932,000
Liabilities: $696,518,000
Net Worth: $303,414,000
Earnings: $12,385,000
Emp.: 800
Fiscal Year-end: 12/31/12
Business Description:
Insurance Services
S.I.C.: 6331
N.A.I.C.S.: 524126
Personnel:
Khalid Ali Al Bustani *(Chm)*
Khalid Jassim Kalban *(Vice Chm)*
Yassir Albaharna *(CEO)*
Christian Ladoux *(Principal Officer & Gen Mgr-Singapore)*
Board of Directors:
Khalid Ali Al Bustani
Sultan Ahmed Al Ghaith
Majed Omran Al Shamsi
Saif Abdulrahman Al Shamsi
Abdulaziz Abdullah Al Zaabi
Mariam Mohamed Alameeri
Fuad A. A. Alfalah
Fathi M. A. Elhagie
Khalid Jassim Kalban

Bahrain Shares Registering Company WLL
Al-Hedaya Building 2 PO Box 710
Manama, Bahrain

Subsidiary:

Arima Insurance Software W.L.L. **(1)**
PO Box 15642
Manama, Bahrain (100%)
Tel.: (973) 17544111
Fax: (973) 17918111
E-Mail: arima@arima.com.bh
Web Site: www.arima.com.bh
Emp.: 30
Investment Advice
S.I.C.: 6282
N.A.I.C.S.: 523930
Simon Cox *(Gen Mgr)*

Non-U.S. Subsidiaries:

Arig Insurance Company Limited **(1)**
Avava House
2 Cathedral Hill, Guildford, Surrey, GU2 7YL, United Kingdom (100%)
Tel.: (44) 1483452622
Fax: (44) 1483452644
Web Site: www.enstargroup.com
Emp.: 90
Investment Advice
S.I.C.: 6282
N.A.I.C.S.: 523930

Gulf Warranties W.L.L. **(1)**
PO BOX 5209
Dubai, United Arab Emirates (100%)
Tel.: (971) 43355347
Fax: (971) 43355679
E-Mail: meher@gulfwarranties.ae
Web Site: www.gulfwarranties.com
Emp.: 13
Investment Advice
S.I.C.: 6282
N.A.I.C.S.: 523930
John Forester *(Gen Mgr)*

Takaful Re Limited **(1)**
DIFC Dubai International Financial Ctr The Gate Dist Precinct Bldg 3
Level 4 Tenancy 3, Dubai, United Arab Emirates (100%)
Mailing Address:
PO Box 211181
Dubai, United Arab Emirates
Tel.: (971) 43600535
Fax: (971) 43637197
E-Mail: takaful-re@takaful-re.ae
Web Site: www.takaful-re.ae
Investment Advice
S.I.C.: 6282
N.A.I.C.S.: 523930
Khalid Al Bustani *(Chm)*
Sachin Sahni *(Sr Mgr-Compliance & Sec)*

ARAB INTERNATIONAL CO. FOR EDUCATION & INVESTMENT PLC

Al-Madinah Al-Monawarah St - Masaken Capital Complex- building num 156
PO Box 926296
2nd floor - office num 205, Amman, 11190, Jordan

Arab International Co. For Education & Investment Plc—(Continued)

Tel.: (962) 65534121
Fax: (962) 65539103
E-Mail: shareholder@asu.edu.jo
Year Founded: 1989
AIEI—(AMM)
Rev.: $68,847,660
Assets: $139,958,391
Liabilities: $30,435,760
Net Worth: $109,522,631
Earnings: $20,116,515
Emp.: 867
Fiscal Year-end: 12/31/12
Business Description:
Educational Services
S.I.C.: 8299
N.A.I.C.S.: 611710
Personnel:
Haithm Abdullah Abu Khadeajeh *(Gen Mgr)*

ARAB INTERNATIONAL FOOD FACTORIES & INVESTMENT COMPANY

Al- Madina Al-Monawara St
PO Box 926065
Al-Haitham Complex- Building num 156- 2nd floor, Amman, 11190, Jordan
Tel.: (962) 65522581
Fax: (962) 65532683
Year Founded: 1994
AIFF—(AMM)
Rev.: $1,919,597
Assets: $34,543,789
Liabilities: $567,298
Net Worth: $33,976,491
Earnings: $1,722,368
Emp.: 2
Fiscal Year-end: 12/31/12
Business Description:
Baby Food Mfr
S.I.C.: 2032
N.A.I.C.S.: 311422
Personnel:
Sahar Abo khadijah *(Gen Mgr)*

ARAB INTERNATIONAL HOTELS PLC.

Al-Shmeisani Alal Al-Fasi St
PO Box 941676
Amman, 11194, Jordan
Tel.: (962) 65674852
Fax: (962) 65662930
E-Mail: aihc@btc.com.jo
Web Site: www.aiho-group.com
Year Founded: 1975
AIHO—(AMM)
Sales Range: $10-24.9 Million
Emp.: 376
Business Description:
Tourism & Hotel Management Services
S.I.C.: 7011
N.A.I.C.S.: 721110
Personnel:
Bassam Ma'aya'eh *(Gen Mgr)*

ARAB INVESTORS UNION CO. FOR REAL ESTATES DEVELOPING P.L.C

Al Nabilsi Commercial Complex
PO Box 850906
Marj Al Hamam, Amman, 11185, Jordan
Tel.: (962) 65736407
Fax: (962) 65736408
Year Founded: 2006
UNAI—(AMM)
Assets: $3,644,216
Liabilities: $11,970
Net Worth: $3,632,246
Earnings: ($52,218)
Emp.: 3
Fiscal Year-end: 12/31/12
Business Description:
Real Estate Investment Services
S.I.C.: 6531
N.A.I.C.S.: 531390
Personnel:
Jibril Abu Eisha *(Gen Mgr)*

ARAB ISLAMIC BANK

PO Box 631
Al-Bireh, Palestine
Tel.: (970) 22407060
Fax: (970) 22407065
Web Site: www.aibnk.com
AIB—(PAL)
Sales Range: $10-24.9 Million
Business Description:
Commercial Banking Services
S.I.C.: 6029
N.A.I.C.S.: 522110
Personnel:
Walid Fakhouri *(Chm)*
Yahia Zakariah Alqadamani *(Vice Chm)*
Board of Directors:
Walid Fakhouri
Basem Abdulhalim
Atef Alawneh
Yahia Zakariah Alqadamani
Salah Eddien Alsharif
Sam Bahour
Haytham Barakat
Shaker Tawfiq Fakhouri
Fadi Qattan

ARAB JORDAN INVESTMENT BANK

Shmeisani Al Thaqafah Street Building No 7
PO Box 8797, Amman, 11121, Jordan
Tel.: (962) 6 5607126
Fax: (962) 6 5681482
E-Mail: info@ajib.com
Web Site: www.ajib.com
Year Founded: 1978
AJIB—(AMM)
Int. Income: $76,798,965
Assets: $1,451,118,803
Liabilities: $1,233,195,847
Net Worth: $217,922,956
Earnings: $21,069,038
Emp.: 365
Fiscal Year-end: 12/31/12
Business Description:
Commercial & Investment Banking Services
S.I.C.: 6029
N.A.I.C.S.: 522110
Personnel:
Abdulkadir Al-Qadi *(Chm)*
Ali Al-Suheimat *(Vice Chm)*
Hani Al-Qadi *(CEO & Gen Mgr)*
Board of Directors:
Abdulkadir Al-Qadi
Mohammed Shareef Al Zoubi
Hussein Al-Dabbas
Mohammed Al-Okar
Hani Al-Qadi
Samer Al-Qadi
Ali Al-Suheimat
Al-Faitouri Al-Mishat Al-Theeb
Ibrahim Almazyad
Shabib Ammari
Mahmoud Abul Rubb

ARAB JORDANIAN INSURANCE GROUP

Wadi Saqrah Street Toward Optical Signals Of Rabia
PO Box 840657
Amman, 11184, Jordan
Tel.: (962) 65666219
Fax: (962) 65669664
E-Mail: insure@ajig.com
Web Site: www.ajig.com
Year Founded: 1996
ARGR—(AMM)
Sales Range: $10-24.9 Million
Emp.: 61
Business Description:
Insurance Services
S.I.C.: 6411
N.A.I.C.S.: 524298
Personnel:
Sami Jamil Barakat *(Chm)*
Salman A. Abbassi *(Vice Chm)*
Board of Directors:
Sami Jamil Barakat
Salman A. Abbassi
Hilal R. Abdilrahman
Jamal N. Abu Obaid
Osama H. Ali
Yassir Baharneh
Hani J. Barakat
Audeh J. Habash
Rami J. Hadeed

ARAB LIFE & ACCIDENT INSURANCE COMPANY P.S.C.

Abdul Hamid Sharaf St
PO Box 925250
Shmeisani, Amman, 11190, Jordan
Tel.: (962) 65693180
Fax: (962) 65693188
E-Mail: ala@wanadoo.jo
Year Founded: 1981
ARIN—(AMM)
Rev.: $17,099,908
Assets: $30,455,257
Liabilities: $17,933,499
Net Worth: $12,521,758
Earnings: $461,186
Emp.: 136
Fiscal Year-end: 12/31/12
Business Description:
General Insurance Services
S.I.C.: 6411
N.A.I.C.S.: 524298
Personnel:
Daoud Al-Kurd *(Gen Mgr)*

ARAB NATIONAL BANK

PO Box 56921
Riyadh, 11564, Saudi Arabia
Tel.: (966) 14029000
Fax: (966) 14027747
E-Mail: info@anb.com.sa
Web Site: www.anb.com.sa
Year Founded: 1979
1080—(SAU)
Rev.: $998,109,177
Assets: $36,387,039,199
Liabilities: $31,617,716,181
Net Worth: $4,769,323,018
Earnings: $631,403,958
Emp.: 4,627
Fiscal Year-end: 12/31/12
Business Description:
Banking Services
S.I.C.: 6029
N.A.I.C.S.: 522110
Personnel:
Salah Rashed Al-Rashed *(Chm)*
Robert Eid *(CEO & Mng Dir)*
Board of Directors:
Salah Rashed Al-Rashed
Nader Hassan Al Amri
Hesham Abdulatif Al Jabbar
Ahmed Abdullah Al-Akeil
Rashid Saad Al-Rashid
Khaled M. Saad Albawardi
Mohammed A. Alghanamah
Robert Eid
Nemeh Sabbagh

Deloitte & Touche Bakr Abulkhair & Co.
PO Box 213
Riyadh, 11411, Saudi Arabia
Tel.: (966) 1463 0018
Fax: (966) 96614630865

Subsidiary:

ANB Invest (1)
PO Box 220009
11311 Riyadh, Saudi Arabia
Tel.: (966) 14062500
Fax: (966) 1 406 2548
E-Mail: info@anbinvest.com.sa
Web Site: www.anbinvest.com.sa
Investment Banking Services
S.I.C.: 6211
N.A.I.C.S.: 523110

THE ARAB PESTICIDES & VETERINARY DRUGS MFG. CO.

King Abdullah II Str Building No 150
1st Floor Office 101-104
PO Box 930103
Amman, 11193, Jordan
Tel.: (962) 65354161
Fax: (962) 65354949
E-Mail: sales@mobedco.com
Web Site: www.mobedco.com
Year Founded: 1991
MBED—(AMM)
Sales Range: $10-24.9 Million
Emp.: 123
Business Description:
Pesticides & Veterinary Drugs Marketing & Mfr
S.I.C.: 2899
N.A.I.C.S.: 325998
Personnel:
Mohmad Aqal Awees *(Gen Mgr)*

ARAB POTASH COMPANY PLC

PO Box 1470
Amman, 11118, Jordan
Tel.: (962) 65200520
Fax: (962) 65200080
E-Mail: info@arabpotash.com
Web Site: www.arabpotash.com
Year Founded: 1956
APOT—(AMM)
Sls.: $823,642,051
Assets: $1,522,132,285
Liabilities: $167,937,741
Net Worth: $1,354,194,544
Earnings: $279,323,040
Emp.: 2,066
Fiscal Year-end: 12/31/12
Business Description:
Potassium Chloride Fertilizer Producer
S.I.C.: 2874
N.A.I.C.S.: 325312
Personnel:
Jamal Ahmad Mofleh Al-Sarayrah *(Chm)*
Mansour Sulaiman Ibrahim Al-Mebrek *(Vice Chm)*
Board of Directors:
Jamal Ahmad Mofleh Al-Sarayrah
Ahmad Jamal Nawwaf Al Bataineh
Fahid Majid Al Sultan Al Salim
Adbul Al-Hakeem Ali Al-Ajnaff
Abdul Wadoud Abdul-Sattar Mahmoud Al-Dulaimi
Rami Saleh Abdulkareem Wraikat Al-Edwan
Duried Mohammad Abd Al Hameed Al-Mahasneh
Imad Jamal Ahmed Al-Qudah
Adnan Ahmen Rashed Al-Rashdan
George David Delaney
Michael Terence Hogan
Jamal Mohammad Hijazi Sa'ed Salah
Mansour Sulaiman Ibrahim Al-Mebrek

Subsidiaries:

Arab Fertilizers and Chemicals Industries Ltd. (1)
PO Box 2564
Al Aqabah, 77110, Jordan

Tel.: (962) 3 2017174
Fax: (962) 3 2017181
E-Mail: kemapco@kemapco.com.jo
Web Site: www.kemapco.com
Emp.: 220
Fertilizers & Chemicals Mfr
S.I.C.: 2819
N.A.I.C.S.: 325180
Jamal Sarayrah *(Chm)*

Jordan Magnesia Company **(1)**
Extrema Al Quraishi Building No 7 Behind Ministry Of Industry & Trade
PO Box 941701
Amman, 11194, Jordan
Tel.: (962) 65691201
Fax: (962) 65691156
E-Mail: jormag@orange.jo
Magnesium Oxide Mfr
S.I.C.: 2819
N.A.I.C.S.: 325180
Eyad Qudah *(Chm)*

Numeira Mixed Salts & Mud Co. **(1)**
Amman Airport Street Building No 24 3rd Floor
PO Box 941681
Amman, 11118, Jordan (52.7%)
Tel.: (962) 65826889
Fax: (962) 65826901
E-Mail: info@numeira.com
Web Site: www.numeira.com.jo
Emp.: 60
Cosmetics & Skin Care Products
S.I.C.: 2844
N.A.I.C.S.: 325620
Issac Deeki *(Mgr-Fin)*

Plant:

Arab Potash Company PLC - Potash Plant **(1)**
PO Box 1470
Amman, 11118, Jordan
Tel.: (962) 32397100
Fax: (962) 65200090
E-Mail: info@arabpotash.com
Potash Mfr
S.I.C.: 2899
N.A.I.C.S.: 325998

ARAB REAL ESTATE COMPANY K.S.C.C.

7th Floor Emad Commercial Complex
Ahmed Al Jaber Street Sharq
Kuwait, 13130, Kuwait
Tel.: (965) 1840004
Fax: (965) 22420040
E-Mail: info@arec-kwt.com
Web Site: www.arec-kwt.com
Year Founded: 1976
ARABREC—(KUW)
Rev.: $13,008,519
Assets: $603,515,900
Liabilities: $357,098,195
Net Worth: $246,417,705
Earnings: $800,851
Emp.: 125
Fiscal Year-end: 12/31/12
Business Description:
Real Estate Services
S.I.C.: 6531
N.A.I.C.S.: 531390
Personnel:
Emad Jawad Bukhamseen *(Chm & Mng Dir)*
Anwar Ali Al-Naki *(Vice Chm)*
Hamdi S. Mahmoud *(CFO)*
Board of Directors:
Emad Jawad Bukhamseen
Tawfiq Shamlan Al-Bahar
Mohammed W. Al-Muhanna
Anwar Ali Al-Naki
Raed Jawad Bukhamseen

ARAB SATELLITE COMMUNICATIONS ORGANIZATION

Diplomatic Quarter Alfazari Square
Abdulla bin Huthafa Al Sahmy Street
PO Box 1038
Pub Pension Agcy Complex C-6,
Riyadh, 11431, Saudi Arabia
Tel.: (966) 1 482 0000
Fax: (966) 1 488 7999
E-Mail: info@arabsat.com
Web Site: www.arabsat.com
Year Founded: 1976
Business Description:
Satellite Telecommunications Services
S.I.C.: 4899
N.A.I.C.S.: 517410
Personnel:
Khalid A. Balkheyour *(Pres & CEO)*

Non-U.S. Subsidiary:

Hellas Sat Consortium Limited **(1)**
Hellas Sat Space Centre Panagias Galaktotrofousas 1
Kofinou, 7735 Larnaca, Cyprus CY
Mailing Address: (99.05%)
PO Box 27556
2435 Nicosia, Cyprus
Tel.: (357) 22 861400
Fax: (357) 22 861510
E-Mail: sales@hellas-sat.net
Web Site: www.hellas-sat.net
Emp.: 15
Satellite Communication Services
S.I.C.: 4899
N.A.I.C.S.: 517410
Khalid Ahmad Balkheyour *(Chm)*

Non-U.S. Subsidiary:

Hellas Sat S.A. **(2)**
99 Kifissias Avenue
GR 151 24 Maroussi, Athens, Greece GR
Tel.: (30) 210 6100600
Fax: (30) 210 6111545
E-Mail: sales@hellas-sat.net
Web Site: www.hellas-sat.net
Emp.: 50
Satellite Telecommunications Services
S.I.C.: 4899
N.A.I.C.S.: 517410
Christodoulos A. Protopapas *(Mng Dir)*

ARAB SHIPBUILDING & REPAIR YARD CO.

PO Box 50110
Hidd, Bahrain
Tel.: (973) 17671111
Fax: (973) 17670236
E-Mail: asryco@batelco.com.bh
Web Site: www.asry.net
Sales Range: $100-124.9 Million
Emp.: 1,700
Business Description:
Ship Building & Repairing Services
S.I.C.: 3731
N.A.I.C.S.: 336611
Personnel:
Zeyad Humood Al Zahrani *(Deputy Chm)*
Nils Kristian Berge *(Acting CEO)*
Board of Directors:
Awatif Mohamed Al Ali
Khalid Ali Al Hosani
Mohamed Mohsin Al Jenaibi
Zeyad Humood Al Zahrani
Adel Abdulla Al-Baker
Saleh Bin Mohamed Al-Rasheed
Salman Humoud Al-Sabah
Abduljabbar M. Al-Waqqaa
Abdul Raoof Ebrahim
Hussain Mohamed Ibrahim
Sameer Micheal Jerjes
Aref Saleh Khamis
Salem Mohamed Salem

Non-U.S. Subsidiary:

ASRY Marketing Services Ltd. **(1)**
28 Bolton Street
Mayfair, London, W1J 8BP, United Kingdom
Tel.: (44) 2073189800
E-Mail: suhairz@asry.net
Emp.: 3
Marketing Services for Arab Shipbuilding & Repair Yard
S.I.C.: 7389
N.A.I.C.S.: 561499

ARAB SUPPLY & TRADING CO.

(d/b/a ASTRA)
Prince Sultan Bin Abdul Aziz St
PO Box 254
71411 Tabuk, Saudi Arabia
Tel.: (966) 14771488
Fax: (966) 44281584
E-Mail: astra@astra.com.sa
Web Site: www.astra.com.sa
Year Founded: 1976
Sales Range: $500-549.9 Million
Emp.: 5,500
Business Description:
Diversified Holding Company; Trading, Agriculture, Manufacturing, Contracting, Medical & Healthcare & Real Estate Services
S.I.C.: 6719
N.A.I.C.S.: 551112
Personnel:
Sabih Taher Masri *(Chm)*
Khaled Sabih Masri *(Pres)*
Kamil Sadeddin *(Mng Dir)*
Mouin Bitar *(CFO)*
Samer Hendawi *(Chief Investment Officer)*

Subsidiaries:

ASTRA Agricultural Co. Ltd. **(1)**
PO Box 54061
Riyadh, Saudi Arabia
Tel.: (966) 14772346
Fax: (966) 14782102
E-Mail: info@astra-agri.com.sa
Web Site: www.astra-agri.com.sa
Emp.: 180
Farm Supplies Whslr
S.I.C.: 5191
N.A.I.C.S.: 424910
Yehia Elazab *(Gen Mgr)*

ASTRA Food Processing Co. **(1)**
Jordan Road
PO Box 1485
Tabuk, Saudi Arabia
Tel.: (966) 44226661
Fax: (966) 044223172
E-Mail: info@afppco.com.sa
Web Site: www.astra.com.sa/manu_food.asp
Emp.: 100
Food Processing Services
S.I.C.: 2099
N.A.I.C.S.: 311999

Nour Communication Company **(1)**
PO Box 21557
11485 Riyadh, Saudi Arabia
Tel.: (966) 14776555
Fax: (966) 14787171
E-Mail: info@nour.com.sa
Web Site: www.nour.com.sa
Emp.: 900
Telecommunication System Contractor
S.I.C.: 4813
N.A.I.C.S.: 517110
Sobaih Taher Al Masri *(Chm & Mng Dir)*

Saudi Mais Company for Medical Products **(1)**
PO Box 3900
14335-55599 Riyadh, Saudi Arabia
Tel.: (966) 12650184
Fax: (966) 12650139
E-Mail: medical@mais.com.sa
Web Site: www.mais.com.sa
Emp.: 300
Medical Products Mfr & Distr
S.I.C.: 3841
N.A.I.C.S.: 339112
M.A. Mahayni *(Chm)*

Non-U.S. Subsidiaries:

Agricultural Plastic Industrial Company (APICO) **(1)**
PO Box 9
11512 Amman, Jordan
Tel.: (962) 64022555
Fax: (962) 64022557
E-Mail: apico@apico-jo.com
Web Site: www.apico-jo.com
Emp.: 60
Agricultural Plastic Products Mfr
S.I.C.: 3089
N.A.I.C.S.: 326199
Ahmad Al Bitar *(Gen Mgr)*

Cairo Amman Bank **(1)**
PO Box 950661
Amman, 11195, Jordan
Tel.: (962) 6 500 6000
Fax: (962) 6 500 7100
E-Mail: cainfo@ca-bank.com.jo
Web Site: www.ca-bank.com
Emp.: 1,500
Banking Services
S.I.C.: 6029
N.A.I.C.S.: 522110
Khaled Sabih Al Masri *(Chm)*
Mohammad Kamal Eddin Barakat *(Vice Chm)*

Golden Wheat Mills Company **(1)**
PO Box 641
Burnham Village, Ramallah, Palestine
Tel.: (970) 22818013
Fax: (970) 2281014
E-Mail: info@gwmc.ps
Web Site: www.gwmc.ps
Emp.: 55
Wheat Product Production & Marketing Services
S.I.C.: 2041
N.A.I.C.S.: 311211
Barran Walweel *(Gen Mgr)*

Jordan Vegetable Oil Industries Company **(1)**
PO Box 128
11512 Amman, Jordan
Tel.: (962) 64023601
Fax: (962) 64023356
E-Mail: vegoil@vegoils.com
Web Site: www.vegoils.net
Vegetable Oil Producer & Exporter
S.I.C.: 2075
N.A.I.C.S.: 311224
Basel Al Rimawl *(Gen Mgr)*

Palestine Development & Investment Ltd. **(1)**
PO Box 1708
Ramallah, Palestine
Tel.: (970) 22403332
Fax: (970) 22403363
E-Mail: lina@padico.com
Web Site: www.padico.com
PADICO—(PAL)
Sales Range: $100-124.9 Million
Emp.: 100
Economic Development & Investment Services
S.I.C.: 6211
N.A.I.C.S.: 523999
Munib R. Masri *(Chm)*
Nabil G. Sarraf *(Vice Chm)*
Samir Hulileh *(CEO)*
Ziad M. Turk *(Sec)*

Subsidiaries:

Palestine Industrial Investment Co. Ltd. **(2)**
Al Najah St Abu Raad Bldg
PO Box 1769
Nablus, Palestine
Tel.: (970) 92386180
Fax: (970) 92384354
E-Mail: piico@palnet.com
Web Site: www.piico.ps
Emp.: 7
Holding Company
S.I.C.: 6719
N.A.I.C.S.: 551112
Nidal Sukhtian *(Chm)*

Subsidiaries:

Palestine Electrical & Electronics Co. Ltd. **(3)**
PO Box 1769
Nablus, Palestine
Tel.: (970) 92397680
Fax: (970) 92397683
Electronics Mfr & Sales
S.I.C.: 5064

Arab Supply & Trading Co.—(Continued)

N.A.I.C.S.: 423620
Nidal Sukhtian *(Chm)*

Palestine Plastic Industries Co. Ltd. **(3)**
Palestine west bank Nablus deersharf Ind zone
PO Box 1949
Nablus, Palestine
Tel.: (970) 92398716
Fax: (970) 92398715
E-Mail: info@ppic-pal.com
Web Site: www.ppic-pal.com
Emp.: 23
Plastic Products Mfr
S.I.C.: 3089
N.A.I.C.S.: 326199
Nidal Sukhtian *(Chm)*

Palestine Poultry Co. Ltd. **(3)**
PO Box 1835
Nablus, Palestine
Tel.: (970) 92683177
Fax: (970) 92946180
E-Mail: info@aziza-ppc.com
Emp.: 250
Poultry Feed & Hatchery
S.I.C.: 0254
N.A.I.C.S.: 112340
Abad Hakim *(Mng Dir)*

The Palestine Securities Exchange, Ltd. **(2)**
Al-Qaser Building 3rd Floor
PO Box 128
Nablus, Palestine
Tel.: (970) 92345555
Fax: (970) 92341341
E-Mail: pse@p-s-e.com
Web Site: www.p-s-e.com
Stock Exchange Services
S.I.C.: 6231
N.A.I.C.S.: 523210

ARAB UNION INTERNATIONAL INSURANCE CO. LTD.

Shmaisani-Sharif Naser Ben Jamil St
PO Box 7241
Amman, 11118, Jordan
Tel.: (962) 65684459
Fax: (962) 65684085
E-Mail: info@aiui-jo.com
Web Site: www.aiui-jo.com
AIUI—(AMM)
Sales Range: $1-9.9 Million
Emp.: 44

Business Description:
Insurance Services
S.I.C.: 6411
N.A.I.C.S.: 524298

Personnel:
Jamal Nazeh Elawamleh *(Chm)*

Board of Directors:
Jamal Nazeh Elawamleh

ARABI HOLDING GROUP COMPANY K.S.C.C.

Forth Ring Road Shuwaikh Industrial Area Plot 175/176C Behind Ali
PO Box 4090
Abdulwahab Furniture Showroom,
Kuwait, 13041, Kuwait
Tel.: (965) 24817878
Fax: (965) 24816138
E-Mail: arabiho@qualitynet.net
Web Site: www.arabigroup.com
Year Founded: 1981
AGHC—(KUW)
Rev.: $194,801,773
Assets: $247,767,813
Liabilities: $171,219,182
Net Worth: $76,548,631
Earnings: $3,093,554
Emp.: 1,915
Fiscal Year-end: 12/31/12

Business Description:
Holding Company
S.I.C.: 6719
N.A.I.C.S.: 551112

Personnel:
Tareq M. Al Maousherji *(Chm & Mng Dir)*
Hamed Al Bassam *(Vice Chm)*

Board of Directors:
Tareq M. Al Maousherji
Hamed Al Bassam
Yousef Al Jassim
Salah M. Al Maousherji
Abdula Mutlaq Al Osaimi
Faisal Al Zamel

Subsidiaries:

Arabi Agriculture Co. **(1)**
PO Box 4090
Safat, Kuwait, 13041, Kuwait (100%)
Tel.: (965) 4817878
Fax: (965) 4811274
Web Site: www.arabigroup.com
Emp.: 20
Landscaping & Irrigation Services
S.I.C.: 0781
N.A.I.C.S.: 541320

Arabi Company W.L.L. **(1)**
PO Box 4090
Safat, Kuwait, 13041, Kuwait (100%)
Tel.: (965) 4724058
Fax: (965) 4724059
E-Mail: service@arabigroup.com
Web Site: www.arabigroup.com
Emp.: 175
Distr of Oil, Petrochemicals, Water Equipment, Irrigation Equipment, Agricultural Materials, Power Tools, Garage Equipment, Building Systems & Safety Equipment
S.I.C.: 4924
N.A.I.C.S.: 221210

Arabi Engineering Co. **(1)**
PO Box 9831
Ahmadi, 61009, Kuwait (100%)
Tel.: (965) 3986083
Fax: (965) 3986522
Web Site: www.arabienertech.com
Emp.: 734
Engineering Services
S.I.C.: 8711
N.A.I.C.S.: 541330
Sagar Ali *(Mng Dir)*

Arabi Industrial Services & Supplies Co. **(1)**
PO Box 4090
Safat, Kuwait, 13041, Kuwait (100%)
Tel.: (965) 4817878 77
Fax: (965) 4811274
E-Mail: arabico@ncc.moc.kw
Web Site: www.arabigroup.com
Emp.: 25
Construction & Maintenance Services Specializing in Heating, Ventilation & Air Conditioning
S.I.C.: 3433
N.A.I.C.S.: 333414

Arabi Medical & Scientific Equipment Co. W.L.L. **(1)**
E Ahmadi
PO Box 9831
Ahmadi, 61009, Kuwait (100%)
Tel.: (965) 3986083
Fax: (965) 3986522
Web Site: www.arabigroup.com
Emp.: 10
Sales & Service of Medical & Scientific Equipment
S.I.C.: 5999
N.A.I.C.S.: 446199

Hasibat Information Technologist Company **(1)**
PO Box 27728
Kuwait, 13138, Kuwait
Tel.: (965) 22240601
Fax: (965) 22240612
E-Mail: info@hasibat.com
Web Site: www.hasibat.com
COMP—(KUW)
Emp.: 70
Information Technology Solutions & Services
S.I.C.: 7373
N.A.I.C.S.: 541512
Hamed Al-Bassam *(Chm)*
Siraj Al-Baker *(Vice Chm)*

Non-U.S. Subsidiary:

Arabi Gulf Services & Industrial Supplies Co. **(1)**
PO Box 2250
Ruwi, 112, Oman
Tel.: (968) 24811238
Fax: (968) 24816146
E-Mail: gsiscom@omantel.net.om
Web Site: www.arabigsis.com
Emp.: 150
Provider of Industrial Products
S.I.C.: 3823
N.A.I.C.S.: 334513
Salah M. Al Maousherji *(Mng Dir)*

ARABIA INSURANCE CO.

FL5-6-7 Bldg Arabia House Phoenicia St
PO Box 11-2172
Beirut, Lebanon
Tel.: (961) 1363610
Fax: (961) 1365139
E-Mail: arabia@arabia-ins.com.lb
Web Site: www.arabiainsurance.com
Emp.: 120

Business Description:
Provider of Insurance Services
S.I.C.: 6411
N.A.I.C.S.: 524298

Personnel:
Wahbe A. Tamari *(Chm)*
Hani Freij *(Vice Chm)*
Fady Shammas *(CEO)*
Nabih Baaklini *(COO)*
Carlos Saba *(Chief Resources Officer)*

Subsidiaries:

AL MASHRIQ FINANCIAL INVESTMENT CO. s.a.l. **(1)**
PO Box 4068
Beirut, Lebanon
Tel.: (961) 1 364700
Fax: (961) 1 367087
Life Insurance Services
S.I.C.: 6411
N.A.I.C.S.: 524298
Hani Atallah Freij, *(Chm & Gen Mgr)*

ARABIA s.a.l. Holding Company **(1)**
PO Box 11-2172
Beirut, Lebanon
Tel.: (961) 1 363610
Fax: (961) 1 362975
E-Mail: arabia@arabiainsurance.com
Investment Management Services
S.I.C.: 6282
N.A.I.C.S.: 523920
Hani Atallah Freij, *(Chm)*
Fady Shammas *(CEO)*

Non-U.S. Subsidiary:

ARABIA INSURANCE COMPANY - SYRIA S.A. **(1)**
PO Box 34801
Damascus, Syria
Tel.: (963) 11 6627745
Fax: (963) 11 6627750
E-Mail: arabia-insurance@arabiasyria.com
Web Site: www.arabiasyria.com
Life Insurance Services
S.I.C.: 6411
N.A.I.C.S.: 524298
Farouk Joud *(Chm)*
Fady Shammas *(Vice Chm)*
Nabih Baaklini *(Mng Dir)*
Hisham Bsat *(Sec)*

ARABIAN AGRICULTURAL SERVICES CO.

(d/b/a ARASCO)
Office 625 at Akaria Center #2 Olaya Street
PO Box 53845
Riyadh, 11593, Saudi Arabia
Tel.: (966) 14191933
Fax: (966) 14191520
E-Mail: info@arasco.com
Web Site: www.arasco.com
Year Founded: 1983
Sales Range: $150-199.9 Million
Emp.: 1,800

Business Description:
Animal Feed Producer
S.I.C.: 2048
N.A.I.C.S.: 311119

Personnel:
Abdul-Latif Salah Al Shaikh *(Chm)*
Abdullah S. Al Rubaian *(Mng Dir)*
Mohammed Wail Al Kelani *(Sr VP)*

Divisions:

Arasco Chemical Co. **(1)**
Industrial City
PO Box 6977
31452 Dammam, Saudi Arabia
Tel.: (966) 38123456
Fax: (966) 38123133
E-Mail: archem@arasco.com
Web Site: www.arasco.com
Emp.: 30
Organic Chemical Mfr
S.I.C.: 2869
N.A.I.C.S.: 325199
Abdulsalam Al-Salam *(VP)*

Arasco Cold Store Co. **(1)**
Second Industrial City Alkharj Hwy
PO Box 53845
11593 Riyadh, Saudi Arabia
Tel.: (966) 14982039
Fax: (966) 14980455
Web Site: www.arasco.com
Emp.: 25
Refrigerated Warehousing & Storage
S.I.C.: 4222
N.A.I.C.S.: 493120
Adel Younes *(Gen Mgr-Logistics)*

Arasco Feed Mill Co. **(1)**
Alkhobar Costal Road Near King Abdulaziz Port
PO Box 6977
31452 Dammam, Saudi Arabia
Tel.: (966) 38591171
Fax: (966) 38594474
Emp.: 700
Farm Product Raw Material Whslr
S.I.C.: 5159
N.A.I.C.S.: 424590
Abdullah Sulayman Al-Rabian *(CEO)*

Arasco Transport, Handling and Shipping Co. **(1)**
Alkhobar Costal Road Near King Abdulaziz Port
PO Box 6977
31452 Dammam, Saudi Arabia
Tel.: (966) 38591171
Fax: (966) 38594474
Emp.: 200
Freight Transportation Arrangement ,
S.I.C.: 4731
N.A.I.C.S.: 488510
Abdullah Sulayman Al-Rabian *(CEO)*

ARABIAN CEMENT COMPANY LTD.

Malik Road Cement Building
PO Box 275
Jeddah, 21411, Saudi Arabia
Tel.: (966) 26949700
Fax: (966) 24232179
Web Site: www.arabiacement.com
Year Founded: 1956
3010—(SAU)
Sales Range: $200-249.9 Million
Emp.: 900

Business Description:
Cement Mfr
S.I.C.: 3241
N.A.I.C.S.: 327310

Personnel:
Abdullah Mohammad Al Issa *(Chm)*

ARABIAN OUD COMPANY

Malaz St
Riyadh, Saudi Arabia
Tel.: (966) 14742222
Fax: (966) 14743111
Web Site: www.arabianoud.com
Year Founded: 1982

Business Description:
Perfume Mfr & Retailer
S.I.C.: 2844
N.A.I.C.S.: 325620
Personnel:
Abdulaziz Al-Jasser *(Chm)*

ARABIAN SCANDINAVIAN INSURANCE COMPANY P.L.C.

(d/b/a ASCANA)
PO Box 1993
Dubai, United Arab Emirates
Tel.: (971) 42824403
Fax: (971) 42825586
E-Mail: ascana@emirates.net.ae
Web Site: www.ascana.net
Year Founded: 1978
ASCANA—(DFM)
Rev.: $18,246,293
Assets: $102,429,388
Liabilities: $23,671,298
Net Worth: $78,758,090
Earnings: $8,846,826
Fiscal Year-end: 12/31/12
Business Description:
Insurance Services
S.I.C.: 6411
N.A.I.C.S.: 524298
Personnel:
Butti Maktoum Juma Al Maktoum *(Chm)*
Ahmad Mohammed Amin Al Kazim *(Mng Dir)*
Board of Directors:
Butti Maktoum Juma Al Maktoum
Faisal Aqeel Mohammed Noor Al Bastaky
Ahmad Mohammed Amin Al Kazim
Majed Mohammed Amin Al Kazim
Khaled Habib Mohammed Al Redha
Mahmoud Mohammed Hadi Hassan

ARABIAN SHIELD COOPERATIVE INSURANCE COMPANY

3rd Floor No 15 Cercon Bldg Olaya Main Road
PO Box 61352
11565 Riyadh, Saudi Arabia
Tel.: (966) 12505400
Fax: (966) 14631294
E-Mail: riyadh@arabianshield.com
Web Site: www.arabianshield.com
8070—(SAU)
Premiums: $88,288,569
Assets: $148,655,850
Liabilities: $86,173,082
Net Worth: $62,482,768
Earnings: $1,079,314
Fiscal Year-end: 12/31/12
Business Description:
General Insurance Services
S.I.C.: 6351
N.A.I.C.S.: 524126
Personnel:
Mohammed Saud Al Kabeer *(Chm)*
John Clifford Davies *(CEO)*
Board of Directors:
Mohammed Saud Al Kabeer
Ammar Al Khudairy
Abdullah Abdulrahman Thaneyan Al Obeikan
Nasser Mohammed Humoud Al-Mutawa Al-Otaibi
Sulaiman N. Alhatlan
Christopher James Ledwidge
Joseph Rizzo
Abdullah Sulaiman Al Rubaian

ARABIAN STEEL PIPES MFG CO. LTD

Amman Industrial Estate Sahab
PO Box 13
11512 Amman, Jordan
Tel.: (962) 64022136
Fax: (962) 64022890
E-Mail: info@asp-jo.com
Web Site: www.asp-jo.com
ASPMM—(AMM)
Sales Range: $10-24.9 Million
Emp.: 162
Business Description:
Steel Pipes & Tubes Mfr
S.I.C.: 3312
N.A.I.C.S.: 331110
Personnel:
Mazen Khanji *(Gen Mgr)*

ARABIAN STORES COMPANY LTD.

PO Box 53868
Jeddah, 21592, Saudi Arabia
Tel.: (966) 26982290
Fax: (966) 2 698 2604
Year Founded: 1981
Emp.: 400
Business Description:
Grocery Stores
S.I.C.: 5411
N.A.I.C.S.: 445110

ARABTEC HOLDING PJSC

Al Muhairy Centre Zayed the First Street Khalidiya
PO Box 7340
Abu Dhabi, United Arab Emirates
Tel.: (971) 23336666
Fax: (971) 23336600
E-Mail: info@arabtecuae.com
Web Site: www.arabtecholding.com
ARTC—(DFM)
Rev.: $1,540,523,558
Assets: $2,436,464,996
Liabilities: $1,525,928,994
Net Worth: $910,536,002
Earnings: $51,231,625
Emp.: 42,000
Fiscal Year-end: 12/31/12
Business Description:
Holding Company; Construction Services
S.I.C.: 6719
N.A.I.C.S.: 551112
Personnel:
Khadem Abdulla Al Qubaisi *(Chm)*
Riad Burhan Kamal *(Vice Chm)*
Hasan Abdulla Ismaik *(CEO & Mng Dir)*
Gordon Jack *(CIO)*
David Doyle *(Chief Risk Officer)*
Peter Roche *(Chief HR Officer-Construction Bus)*
Sami Haider Asad *(CEO-Construction Grp)*
Board of Directors:
Khadem Abdulla Al Qubaisi
Mohamed Ali Al Fahim
Wassel Issa Al Fakhoury
Khalifa Hamad Al Mehairi
Mohamed Hamad Al Mehairi
Raja Hani Ghanma
Hasan Abdulla Ismaik
Riad Burhan Kamal
Tareq Ahmad Abu Shreehah

ARAFURA RESOURCES LIMITED

Level 5 16 St Georges Terrace
Perth, WA, 6000, Australia
Mailing Address:
PO Box 5773
St George's Terrace, Perth, WA, 6831, Australia
Tel.: (61) 862107666
Fax: (61) 892217966
E-Mail: arafura@arafuraresources.com.au
Web Site: www.arafuraresources.com.au
ARU—(ASX)
Rev.: $1,399,698
Assets: $150,064,119
Liabilities: $3,064,345
Net Worth: $146,999,774
Earnings: ($12,257,334)
Emp.: 19
Fiscal Year-end: 06/30/13
Business Description:
Exploration & Mining of Minerals
S.I.C.: 1481
N.A.I.C.S.: 213115
Personnel:
Gavin John Lockyer *(CEO & Mng Dir)*
Peter Sherrington *(CFO & Sec)*
Board of Directors:
Ian John Kowalick
Terence Grose
Gavin John Lockyer
Shasha Lu
Christopher Stephen Tonkin
Legal Counsel:
Johnson Winter & Slattery
Level 4 167 St Georges Terrace
Perth, Australia

ARAGON HOLDING GMBH

Kormoranweg 1
65201 Wiesbaden, Germany
Tel.: (49) 611 890575 0
Fax: (49) 611 890575 99
Web Site:
Year Founded: 2012
Business Description:
Holding Company
S.I.C.: 6719
N.A.I.C.S.: 551112
Personnel:
Sebastian Grabmaier *(Co-Owner, CEO & Chm-Mgmt Bd)*
Ralph Konrad *(Co-Owner, CFO & Member-Mgmt Bd)*

Holding:

Aragon Aktiengesellschaft (1)
Kormoranweg 1
65201 Wiesbaden, Germany De (23%)
Tel.: (49) 6118905750
Fax: (49) 61189057599
E-Mail: ir@aragon-ag.de
Web Site: www.aragon-ag.com
A8A—(DEU)
Rev.: $145,433,476
Assets: $126,601,904
Liabilities: $79,100,949
Net Worth: $47,500,955
Earnings: ($16,298,080)
Emp.: 370
Fiscal Year-end: 12/31/12
Investment Banking, Advisory & Other Financial Services
S.I.C.: 6211
N.A.I.C.S.: 523110
Herbert Walter *(Chm-Supervisory Bd)*
Sebastian Grabmaier *(CEO & Chm-Mgmt Bd)*
Christian Waigel *(Deputy Chm-Supervisory Bd)*
Ralph Konrad *(CFO & Member-Mgmt Bd)*

Subsidiary:

Jung, DMS & Cie. AG (2)
Ludwig Ganghofer Strasse 1
82031 Grunwald, Germany
Tel.: (49) 896935130
Fax: (49) 8969351315
E-Mail: info@jungdms.de
Web Site: www.jungdms.de
Emp.: 15
Investment Services
S.I.C.: 6282
N.A.I.C.S.: 523930
Sebastian Grabmaier *(CEO)*

ARAKAWA CHEMICAL INDUSTRIES, LTD.

1-3-7 Hiranomachi Chuo-ku
Osaka, 541-0046, Japan
Tel.: (81) 662098581
Fax: (81) 662098542
E-Mail: info@arakawachem.co.jp
Web Site: www.arakawachem.co.jp/e
Year Founded: 1976
4968—(TKS)
Sls.: $745,734,000
Assets: $862,092,000
Liabilities: $420,882,000
Net Worth: $441,210,000
Earnings: $10,802,000
Emp.: 1,334
Fiscal Year-end: 03/31/13
Business Description:
Chemicals Mfr
S.I.C.: 2899
N.A.I.C.S.: 325998
Personnel:
Shozo Tanioku *(Pres)*
Takashi Une *(Mng Dir & Gen Mgr-Mgmt Plng Dept & Pur)*
Masaya Inaba *(Officer)*
Yoichi Kajihara *(Officer)*
Tamotsu Otani *(Officer)*
Board of Directors:
Toshimasa Arakawa
Yoshiteru Manabe
Yasutomo Miyashita
Manabu Nishikawa
Toru Nobuhiro
Tetsuro Sanoh
Nagahiro Suemura
Shozo Tanioku
Junichi Tatsumi
Takashi Une

Subsidiaries:

KAKUTAMA SERVICE CO., LTD. (1)
1-2-2 Awajimachi
Chuo-Ku, Osaka, 541-0047, Japan
Tel.: (81) 662098605
Fax: (81) 662316676
Web Site: www.arakawachem.co.jp/e/profile/pro_network.html
Industrial Chemical Mfr
S.I.C.: 2819
N.A.I.C.S.: 325180

KOATSU CHEMICAL INDUSTRIES, Ltd. (1)
1-12 Tsurumati 5 Chome
Taishou-ku, Osaka, 551-0023, Japan
Tel.: (81) 665520151
Fax: (81) 665510019
E-Mail: info@koatsuchem.co.jp
Web Site: www.koatsuchem.co.jp
Industrial Chemical Mfr
S.I.C.: 2819
N.A.I.C.S.: 325180

Pelnox, Ltd. (1)
8-7 Bodai
Hadano, Kanagawa, 259-1302, Japan
Tel.: (81) 463868000
Fax: (81) 463868021
Resin Compounds Mfr
S.I.C.: 2821
N.A.I.C.S.: 325211

Plants:

Arakawa Chemical Industries, Ltd - Fuji Plant (1)
366 Atsuhara
Fuji, Shizuoka, 419-0201, Japan
Tel.: (81) 545 71 1201
Fax: (81) 545 71 6621
Web Site: www.arakawachem.co.jp/e/profile/pro_network.html
Industrial Chemicals Mfr
S.I.C.: 2819
N.A.I.C.S.: 325180

Arakawa Chemical Industries, Ltd - Kushiro Plant (1)
1-2-68 Otanoshike-minami
Kushiro, Hokkaido, 084-0915, Japan
Tel.: (81) 154578236
Fax: (81) 154 57 5102
Web Site: www.arakawachem.co.jp/e/profile/pro_network.html
Papermaking Chemical Mfr
S.I.C.: 2819

Arakawa Chemical Industries, Ltd.—(Continued)

N.A.I.C.S.: 325180

Arakawa Chemical Industries, Ltd. - Mizushima Plant (1)
1-1 Matsue 4-chome
Kurashiki, Okayama, 712-8052, Japan
Tel.: (81) 864557611
Fax: (81) 864555217
Web Site: www.arakawachem.co.jp/e/profile/pro_network.html
Papermaking Chemical Mfr
S.I.C.: 2819
N.A.I.C.S.: 325180

Arakawa Chemical Industries, Ltd. - Onahama Plant (1)
399-5 Aza Otsurugi Shimokawa Izumi-Cho
Iwaki, Fukushima, 971-8183, Japan
Tel.: (81) 246567731
Fax: (81) 246567739
Web Site: www.arakawachem.co.jp/e/profile/pro_network.html
Emp.: 100
Papermaking Chemical Mfr
S.I.C.: 2819
N.A.I.C.S.: 325180
Hidemichi Shingu *(Mgr)*

Arakawa Chemical Industries, Ltd - Osaka Plant (1)
1-1-9 Tsurumi
Tsurumi-ku, Osaka, 538-0053, Japan
Tel.: (81) 669115881
Fax: (81) 669130852
Web Site: www.arakawachem.co.jp/e/profile/pro_network.html
Emp.: 100
Industrial Chemical Mfr
S.I.C.: 2819
N.A.I.C.S.: 325180

Arakawa Chemical Industries, Ltd. - Tokushima Plant (1)
1577 Nakashima Nakagawa-Cho
Anan, Tokushima, 779-1245, Japan
Tel.: (81) 884420573
Fax: (81) 884 42 1162
Web Site: www.arakawachem.co.jp/e/profile/pro_network.html
Papermaking Chemical Mfr
S.I.C.: 2819
N.A.I.C.S.: 325180

Arakawa Chemical Industries, Ltd - Tsurusaki Plant (1)
1120-3 Aza Higashi Matsuura Oaza
Iejima, Oita, 870-0113, Japan
Tel.: (81) 975273682
Fax: (81) 97 522 2258
Papermaking Chemical Mfr
S.I.C.: 2819
N.A.I.C.S.: 325180

U.S. Subsidiary:

Arakawa Chemical (USA) Inc. (1)
625 N Michigan Ave Ste 1700
Chicago, IL 60611
Tel.: (312) 642-1750
Fax: (312) 642-0089
Web Site: www.arakawa-usa.com
Emp.: 5
Chemical Product & Preparation Mfr
S.I.C.: 2899
N.A.I.C.S.: 325998

Non-U.S. Subsidiaries:

ARAKAWA CHEMICAL (CHINA) INC. (1)
Room 2304 Metro Plaza 555 Lou Shan Guan Road
Chang Ning Ward, Shanghai, 200051, China
Tel.: (86) 21 62375326
Fax: (86) 21 62375345
E-Mail: fxie@arakawachem.com.cn
Web Site: www.arakawachem.com.cn
Emp.: 200
Industrial Chemicals Mfr
S.I.C.: 2819
N.A.I.C.S.: 325180

Guangxi Arakawa Chemical Industries, Ltd. (1)
No 1 5th Road Wuzhou Export Oriented Industrial Zone
Wuzhou, Guangxi, 543100, China
Tel.: (86) 774 5819611
Fax: (86) 774 5819616
Web Site: www.arakawachem.co.jp/e/profile/pro_network.html
Papermaking Chemical Distr
S.I.C.: 5169
N.A.I.C.S.: 424690

Guangxi Wuzhou Arakawa Chemical Industries, Ltd. (1)
No 1 5th Road Wuzhou Export Oriented Industrial Zone
Wuzhou, Guangxi, 543100, China
Tel.: (86) 774 5819611
Fax: (86) 774380386
Web Site: www.gxwzarakawa.com
Emp.: 277
Industrial Chemicals Mfr
S.I.C.: 2819
N.A.I.C.S.: 325180

Nantong Arakawa Chemical Industries, Ltd. (1)
No 18 Jianghe Road Nantong Economic And Technological Development Zone
Nantong, Jiangsu, 226017, China
Tel.: (86) 513 85996390
Fax: (86) 513 85996398
Web Site: www.arakawachem.co.jp
Industrial Chemical Distr
S.I.C.: 5169
N.A.I.C.S.: 424690

Taiwan Arakawa Chemical Industries, Ltd. (1)
No 4 Kung Chien Nang Road
Liu-Tu Industrial District, Keelung, Taiwan
Tel.: (886) 2 2451 5236
Fax: (886) 2 2451 5082
Web Site: www.arakawachem.co.jp/e/profile/pro_network.html
Chemical Mfr
S.I.C.: 2819
N.A.I.C.S.: 325180

Wuzhou Arakawa Chemical Industries, Ltd. (1)
1 Xidi Road 3
Wuzhou, Guangxi, 543002, China
Tel.: (86) 7743830388
Fax: (86) 774 3830386
E-Mail: wzarakawa@wzarakawa.com.cn
Web Site: www.wzarakawa.com.cn
Rosin Derivatives Mfr
S.I.C.: 2821
N.A.I.C.S.: 325211

Xiamen Arakawa Chemical Industries, Ltd. (1)
No 10 Dong Ren Road Xingbei Industrial District
Xinglin Town Jimei District, Xiamen, Fujian, 361022, China
Tel.: (86) 592 6253951
Fax: (86) 592 6253953
Industrial Chemicals Mfr
S.I.C.: 2869
N.A.I.C.S.: 325199

Non-U.S. Joint Venture:

Arakawa Europe GmbH (1)
Dusseldorfer strasse 13
65824 Eschborn, Germany
Tel.: (49) 6196503830
Fax: (49) 61965038310
E-Mail: info@arakawaeurope.de
Web Site: www.arakawaeurope.com
Emp.: 6
Resins Marketer; Owned 60% by The Dow Chemical Company & 40% by Arakawa Chemical Industries, Ltd.
S.I.C.: 2821
N.A.I.C.S.: 325211
Tamotsu Otani *(Mng Dir)*

ARAMEX PJSC

18 Khalil Al Salem Street Tla Al Ali Khalda
11181 Amman, Jordan
Tel.: (962) 6 5358855
Fax: (962) 6 5337733
Web Site: www.aramex.com
Year Founded: 1982
ARMX—(DFM)
Rev.: $4,362,725,738
Assets: $3,814,509,562
Liabilities: $940,004,875
Net Worth: $2,874,504,687
Earnings: $381,444,494
Emp.: 13,900
Fiscal Year-end: 12/31/12

Business Description:
Transportation Services & Solutions
S.I.C.: 4513
N.A.I.C.S.: 492110

Personnel:
Abdullah M. Mazrui *(Chm)*
Hussein Hachem *(CEO)*
Bashar Obeid *(CFO)*
Iyad Kamal *(COO)*
Samer Awajan *(CTO)*
Safwan Tannir *(Chief Freight Officer)*
Othman Aljeda *(CEO-Asia)*
Samer Gharaibeh *(CEO-Africa)*
Tommy Kelly *(CEO-Europe)*
Emad Shishtawi *(Sr VP-Fin)*

Board of Directors:
Abdullah M. Mazrui
Ahmed Al-Badi
Helal Al-Marri
Mana Al-Mulla
Ayed Aljeaid
Charles El Hage
Hussein Hachem
Arif Naqvi

Subsidiaries:

Aramex Amman (1)
18 Khalil Al Salem St
PO Box 3371
Khalda, Amman, 11181, Jordan
Tel.: (962) 65358855
Fax: (962) 65337733
Logistics & Distribution Services
S.I.C.: 4731
N.A.I.C.S.: 541614

Aramex International Limited (1)
18 Khalil Al Salem St
PO Box 3371
Amman, Jordan
Tel.: (962) 65358855
Fax: (962) 65337733
E-Mail: info@aramex.com
Web Site: www.aramex.com
Emp.: 3,000
Transportation & Logistics Services
S.I.C.: 4789
N.A.I.C.S.: 488999
Fadi Ghandour *(Founder, Pres & CEO)*
Abdullah Al Mazrui *(Chm)*

Non-U.S. Subsidiaries:

Arab American International Express Company (1)
Courier Ground - 1st - 4th - 6th Fl
Autostrade Chalouhi Sin El-Fil
PO Box 55606
Beirut, Lebanon
Tel.: (961) 1517012
Fax: (961) 1495404
E-Mail: info@aramex.com.lb
Freight Forwarding Services
S.I.C.: 4731
N.A.I.C.S.: 488510
Asmahane Habib Zain *(Branch Mgr)*

Aramex Emirates LLC (1)
Building No DIC 14 Office No S11
PO Box 3841
Dubai, United Arab Emirates
Tel.: (971) 43900365
Fax: (971) 43908592
Freight Transportation Arrangement
S.I.C.: 4731
N.A.I.C.S.: 488510
Samer Hajjar *(Mng Dir)*

Aramex India Private Limited (1)
Plot No A 60/61 1st MIDC Rd MIDC
Andheri East, Mumbai, Maharashtra, 400093, India
Tel.: (91) 2233003300
Fax: (91) 2228248760
E-Mail: customersupport@aramex.com
Logistics & Transportation Services
S.I.C.: 4731
N.A.I.C.S.: 541614

Aramex International Egypt (1)
31 Musadak Str
PO Box 12311
Dokki, Giza, Egypt
Tel.: (20) 2 33388466
Fax: (20) 2 37482990
Transportation Services
S.I.C.: 4512
N.A.I.C.S.: 481112

Aramex Kuwait KSE (1)
PO Box 22751
Kuwait, Kuwait
Tel.: (965) 8200110
Fax: (965) 346190
Web Site: www.aramex.com
Freight Transportation Arrangement
S.I.C.: 4731
N.A.I.C.S.: 488510
Ashraf Al-Shakaa *(Gen Mgr)*

Memo Express Services LLC (1)
PO Box 13001
Dubai, United Arab Emirates
Tel.: (971) 42118111
Fax: (971) 43364628
Freight Transportation Arrangement
S.I.C.: 4731
N.A.I.C.S.: 488510

Aramex Ireland (1)
Bellinstown
Ballyboughal, Dublin, Ireland
Tel.: (353) 1 8078000
Fax: (353) 1 8078090
E-Mail: info@aramex.com
Web Site: www.aramex.com
Emp.: 50
Logistics & Freight Forwarding Services
S.I.C.: 4731
N.A.I.C.S.: 541614
Frank Kilbride *(Country Mgr)*

Two Way Holland BV (1)
Capronilaan 33-35
1119 NP Schiphol-Rijk, Noord-Holland, Netherlands
Tel.: (31) 206558080
Fax: (31) 206558022
E-Mail: nlinfo@aramex.com
Emp.: 65
Air Freight Transportation Services
S.I.C.: 4512
N.A.I.C.S.: 481112

ARANETA PROPERTIES, INC.

21st Fl Citibank Tower Paseo de Roxas
Makati, Philippines 1700
Tel.: (63) 28481501
Fax: (63) 28481495
E-Mail: ara@info.com.ph
Web Site: www.aranetaproperties.com
ARA—(PHI)
Rev.: $3,920,611
Assets: $36,567,377
Liabilities: $7,451,534
Net Worth: $29,115,843
Earnings: $648,749
Emp.: 44
Fiscal Year-end: 12/31/12

Business Description:
Property Development Services
S.I.C.: 6531
N.A.I.C.S.: 531311

Personnel:
Gregorio Ma. Araneta, III *(Chm & CEO)*
Crisanto Roy B. Alcid *(Pres)*
Carlos R. Araneta *(Treas)*
Christine P. Base *(Sec)*

Board of Directors:
Gregorio Ma. Araneta, III
Crisanto Roy B. Alcid
Carlos R. Araneta
Alfredo de Borja
Jorge Del Rosario
Perry L. Pe
Alfredo D. Roa III
Cesar Zalamea

ARANIKO DEVELOPMET BANK LTD.

Bus Stop Dhulikhel Municipality 6
Kavrepalanchowk, Kathmandu, 45206, Nepal

Tel.: (977) 11 490193
Fax: (977) 11 490195
E-Mail: araniko@ntc.net.np
Web Site: www.aranikobank.com
Year Founded: 2005
ARDBL—(NEP)
Business Description:
Banking Services
S.I.C.: 6029
N.A.I.C.S.: 522110
Personnel:
Dil Sundar Shrestha *(Chm)*
Naranayn Kapoor Pathak *(CEO & Mng Dir)*
Board of Directors:
Dil Sundar Shrestha
Krishna Prasad Adhikari
Govinda Prasad Nepal
Naranayn Kapoor Pathak
Murali Prasad Sharma
Banth Kaji Shrestha
Bhim Prasad Timilsina

ARATA CORPORATION
1389 Kaijinchominami 1-Chome
Funabashi, Chiba, 273-0024, Japan
Tel.: (81) 474951233
Fax: (81) 474951243
Web Site: www.arata-gr.jp
Year Founded: 2002
2733—(TKS)
Sales Range: $5-14.9 Billion
Emp.: 3,010
Business Description:
Pet Supplies, Household Products & Cosmetics Distr
S.I.C.: 5199
N.A.I.C.S.: 424990
Personnel:
Nobuyuki Hatanaka *(Pres)*

ARAX HOLDINGS CORP.
Salvador Diaz Miron 87 Colonia
Santa Maria La Ribera
Mexico, 06400, Mexico
Tel.: (52) 1 55 3223 5259
Year Founded: 2012
ARAT—(OTC OTCB)
Assets: $4,209
Liabilities: $4,221
Net Worth: ($12)
Earnings: ($30,933)
Emp.: 1
Fiscal Year-end: 10/31/13
Business Description:
Hot Dog Stand Operator
S.I.C.: 5963
N.A.I.C.S.: 722330
Personnel:
Steven J. Keough *(Pres, CEO, Treas & Sec)*
Board of Directors:
Steven J. Keough

ARB CORPORATION LIMITED
42-44 Garden Street
Kilsyth, VIC, 3137, Australia
Tel.: (61) 3 9761 6622
Fax: (61) 3 9761 6807
E-Mail: sales@arb.com.au
Web Site: www.arb.com.au
Year Founded: 1975
ARP—(ASX)
Rev.: $306,907,829
Assets: $228,273,047
Liabilities: $43,255,487
Net Worth: $185,017,560
Earnings: $44,141,272
Fiscal Year-end: 06/30/13
Business Description:
Motor Vehicle Parts Mfr & Distr
S.I.C.: 3714
N.A.I.C.S.: 336390
Personnel:
Roger G. Brown *(Chm)*
Andrew H. Brown *(Mng Dir)*
John R. Forsyth *(Sec)*
Board of Directors:
Roger G. Brown
Andrew H. Brown
John R. Forsyth
Robert D. Fraser
Ernest E. Kulmar
Andrew P. Stott

ARB HOLDINGS LIMITED
11 Larch Nook Zwartkop Ext 4
Centurion, 0046, South Africa
Tel.: (27) 12 663 5244
Fax: (27) 12 663 7910
E-Mail: info@arbhold.co.za
Web Site: www.arbhold.co.za
ARH—(JSE)
Rev.: $217,205,227
Assets: $128,052,428
Liabilities: $35,443,395
Net Worth: $92,609,032
Earnings: $13,815,089
Emp.: 754
Fiscal Year-end: 06/30/13
Business Description:
Electrical Products Whslr
S.I.C.: 5063
N.A.I.C.S.: 423610
Personnel:
Alan R. Burke *(Founder)*
Byron Nichles *(CEO)*
William R. Neasham *(Sec & Dir-Fin)*
Board of Directors:
Alan R. Burke
Simon T. Downes
Jacob R. Modise
William R. Neasham
Byron Nichles
Ralph B. Patmore
Gerrit Pretorius
Legal Counsel:
Brink Falcon Hume Inc
2nd Floor 8 Melville Road
Illovo, South Africa
Transfer Agent:
Computershare Investor Services (Pty) Limited
Ground Floor 70 Marshall Street
Johannesburg, South Africa

ARBITRON INC.
(Acquired by Nielsen Holdings N.V.)

ARBURG GMBH & CO.
Arthur Hehl Strasse
72290 Lossburg, Germany
Tel.: (49) 7446330
Fax: (49) 7446333365
E-Mail: contact@arburg.com
Web Site: www.arburg.com
Year Founded: 1923
Emp.: 1,700
Business Description:
Mfr. of Injection Molding Machinery & Equipment
S.I.C.: 3559
N.A.I.C.S.: 333249
Personnel:
Eugen Hehl *(Mng Partner)*
Michael Hehl *(Mng Dir)*
U.S. Subsidiary:

Arburg, Inc. (1)
125 Rockwell Rd
Newington, CT 06111 CT
Tel.: (860) 667-6500 (100%)
Fax: (860) 667-6522
E-Mail: usa@arburg.com
Web Site: www.arburg.com
Emp.: 57
Plastic Processing Equipment; Injection Molding Machines Mfr
Import Export
S.I.C.: 5084
N.A.I.C.S.: 423830
Friedrich Kanz *(Pres)*

ARBUTHNOT BANKING GROUP PLC
Arbuthnot House 20 Ropemaker Street
London, EC2Y 9AR, United Kingdom
Tel.: (44) 2070122400
Fax: (44) 2070122401
E-Mail: info@arbuthnotgroup.co.uk
Web Site: www.arbuthnotgroup.com
ARBB—(AIM)
Int. Income: $98,389,767
Assets: $1,579,304,214
Liabilities: $1,470,889,114
Net Worth: $108,415,100
Earnings: $17,558,546
Emp.: 559
Fiscal Year-end: 12/31/12
Business Description:
Financial Services
S.I.C.: 6029
N.A.I.C.S.: 522110
Personnel:
Henry Angest *(Chm & CEO)*
Andrew Alfred Salmon *(COO & Head-Bus Dev)*
James Fleming *(CEO-Arbuthnot Latham & Co Limited)*
Paul Anthony Lynam *(CEO-Secure Trust Bank PLC)*
Jeremy Robin Kaye *(Sec)*
Board of Directors:
Henry Angest
James Cobb
James Fleming
Ruth Lea
Paul Anthony Lynam
Christopher Meyer
Andrew Alfred Salmon
Robert Wickham
Subsidiaries:

Arbuthnot Latham & Co. Limited (1)
20 Ropemaker Street
London, EC2Y 9AR, United Kingdom
Tel.: (44) 2070122500
Fax: (44) 2070122501
E-Mail: banking@arbuthnot.co.uk
Web Site: www.arbuthnot.co.uk
Emp.: 50
Private Banking & Wealth Management Services
S.I.C.: 6211
N.A.I.C.S.: 523999
John L. Reed *(Vice Chm)*
James Fleming *(CEO)*

Secure Trust Bank plc (1)
One Arleston Way
Solihull, B90 4LH, United Kingdom
Tel.: (44) 1216939100
Fax: (44) 1216939101
E-Mail: customerservices@securetrustbank.com
Web Site: www.securetrustbank.com
STB—(AIM)
Emp.: 240
Banking & Financial Services
S.I.C.: 6029
N.A.I.C.S.: 522110
Henry Angest *(Chm)*
Paul Anthony Lynam *(CEO)*
Neeraj Kapur *(CFO)*

ARC EXPLORATION LIMITED
Level 14 19-31 Pitt Street
Sydney, NSW, 2000, Australia
Mailing Address:
PO Box R1294
Royal Exchange, Sydney, NSW, 1225, Australia
Tel.: (61) 2 9241 3451
Fax: (61) 294198099
E-Mail: management@arcexploration.com.au
Web Site: www.arcexploration.com.au
ARX—(ASX)
Rev.: $1,092,259
Assets: $9,751,150
Liabilities: $370,424
Net Worth: $9,380,726
Earnings: ($1,248,753)
Emp.: 40
Fiscal Year-end: 12/31/12
Business Description:
Gold Exploration
S.I.C.: 1041
N.A.I.C.S.: 212221
Personnel:
John C. Carlile *(Mng Dir)*
Cahyono Halim *(CFO)*
Andrew J. Cooke *(Sec)*
Board of Directors:
Bruce J. Watson
John C. Carlile
George S. Tahija
Robert Moyse Willcocks
Legal Counsel:
Soebagjo, Roosdiono, Jatim & Djarot
Plaza Mashill 17th Floor Jalan Jend Sudirman Kav 25
12920 Jakarta, Indonesia

ARC FINANCIAL CORP.
400 3rd Ave SW Devon Tower
Calgary, AB, T2P 4H2, Canada
Tel.: (403) 292-0680
Fax: (403) 292-0693
E-Mail: genfeedback@arcfinancial.com
Web Site: www.arcfinancial.com
Year Founded: 1989
Managed Assets: $2,700,000,000
Emp.: 50
Business Description:
Private Equity Firm
S.I.C.: 6211
N.A.I.C.S.: 523999
Personnel:
Kevin J. Brown *(CEO)*
Nancy V. Lever *(Mng Dir)*
Brian P. Boulanger *(Sr VP)*
Holding:

Ember Resources Inc. (1)
32400 300W Ave SW
Calgary, AB, T2P 3C4, Canada
Tel.: (403) 270-0803
Fax: (403) 270-2850
E-Mail: info@emberresources.com
Web Site: www.emberresources.com
Sales Range: $25-49.9 Million
Emp.: 31
Gas Production
S.I.C.: 4924
N.A.I.C.S.: 221210
Doug A. Dafoe *(Pres & CEO)*
Bruce Ryan *(CFO & VP-Fin)*
Kent D. Kufeldt *(Sec)*

ARC RESOURCES LTD.
1200 308 4th Ave SW
Calgary, AB, T2P 0H7, Canada
Tel.: (403) 503-8600
Fax: (403) 503-8607
Toll Free: (888) 272-4900
E-Mail: ir@arcresources.com
Web Site: www.arcresources.com
ARX—(TSX)
Rev.: $1,381,091,388
Assets: $5,593,449,942
Liabilities: $2,217,062,208
Net Worth: $3,376,387,734
Earnings: $138,367,584
Emp.: 545
Fiscal Year-end: 12/31/12
Business Description:
Oil & Gas Exploration & Production Services
S.I.C.: 1311

ARC Resources Ltd.—(Continued)

N.A.I.C.S.: 211111
Personnel:
Mac H. Van Wielingen *(Chm)*
Walter DeBoni *(Vice Chm)*
Myron M. Stadnyk *(Pres & CEO)*
P. Van R. Dafoe *(CFO & Sr VP)*
Terry M. Anderson *(COO & Sr VP)*
Allan R. Twa *(Sec)*
David P. Carey *(Sr VP-Capital Markets)*
Terry Gill *(Sr VP-Corp Svcs)*
Board of Directors:
Mac H. Van Wielingen
Walter DeBoni
John P. Dielwart
Frederick J. Dyment
Tim Hearn
James C. Houck
Harold N. Kvisle
Kathleen M. O'Neill
Herbert C. Pinder
William Sembo
Legal Counsel:
Burnet, Duckworth & Palmer
Calgary, AB, Canada
Transfer Agent:
Computershare Trust Company of Canada
Calgary, AB, Canada

ARCA CONTINENTAL, S.A.B. DE C.V.

Ave San Jeronimo 813 Pte
64640 Monterrey, Nuevo Leon, Mexico
Tel.: (52) 81 8151 1400
Fax: (52) 81 8151 1500
E-Mail: info@arcacontal.com
Web Site: www.arcacontal.com
Year Founded: 1922
AC—(MEX)
Sls.: $4,427,223,912
Assets: $5,070,972,736
Liabilities: $1,836,985,627
Net Worth: $3,233,987,109
Earnings: $415,116,860
Fiscal Year-end: 12/31/12
Business Description:
Soft Drinks Bottler
S.I.C.: 2086
N.A.I.C.S.: 312111
Personnel:
Manuel L. Barragan Morales *(Chm)*
Miguel Angel Rabago Vite *(Vice Chm & Deputy CEO)*
Francisco Garza Egloff *(CEO)*
Emilio Marcos Charur *(CFO)*
Arturo Gutierrez Hernandez *(COO)*
Jaime Sanchez Fernandez *(Gen Counsel)*
Board of Directors:
Manuel L. Barragan Morales
Alejandro M. Elizondo Barragan
Ernesto Lopez de Nigris
Estuardo Alvelais Destarac
Jaime Sanchez Fernandez
Felipe Cortes Font
Jose Antonio Rodriguez Fuentes
Tomas Alberto Fernandez Garcia
Eduardo Raul Arrocha Gio
Jesus Viejo Gonzalez
Bruce E. Grossman
Cynthia H. Grossman
Luis Arizpe Jimenez
Jorge Humberto Santos Reyna
Ulrich Guillermo Fiehn Rice
Armando Solbes Simon
Carlos Enriquez Terrazas
Juan Manuel Barragan Trevino
Roberto Garza Velazquez
Miguel Angel Rabago Vite

Subsidiaries:

Grupo Continental, S.A. **(1)**
Avenida Hidalgo 2303 Col Smith
89140 Tampico, Tamaulipas, Mexico
Mailing Address:
Apartado Postal 664
89000 Tampico, Tamaulipas, Mexico
Tel.: (52) 8332412500
Fax: (52) 8332412577
E-Mail: tampico@contal.com
Web Site: www.contal.com
Sales Range: $1-4.9 Billion
Carbonated & Non-Carbonated Soft Drinks Production & Distribution Services
S.I.C.: 2086
N.A.I.C.S.: 312111
Julian Guzman Luna *(COO)*
Roberto Martinez Garza *(Chief Legal Officer, Sec & HR Officer)*
Baldomero Ponce Cruz *(Sr Exec Officer)*
Fred Daniel Acosta *(Treas & Dir-Comptroller)*

Subsidiaries:

Concentrados Industriales, S.A. de C.V. **(2)**
Eje 118 y Av Producto Terminado S/N
Zona Indust, 78320 San Luis Potosi, Mexico
Tel.: (52) 14448245055
Fax: (52) 14448245192
E-Mail: coinsa@e-coinsa.com.mx
Web Site: www.e-coinsa.com.mx
Emp.: 55
Chemical Development Services
S.I.C.: 2899
N.A.I.C.S.: 325199
Francisco Dal Poso *(Production Mgr)*

Embotelladora Guadiana, S.A. de C.V. **(2)**
Carretera Durango Mezquital km 3
Real del Mezquital, Durango, 34199, Mexico
Tel.: (52) 6188260330
Fax: (52) 6188260444
E-Mail: embguad@embguadiana.com
Emp.: 12,500
Soft Drink Mfr
S.I.C.: 2086
N.A.I.C.S.: 312111
Sergio Aldape *(Gen Mgr)*

Embotelladora Lagunera, S.A. de C.V. **(2)**
Mexico 222 Col Ex-Ejido Cuba
Gomez Palacio, 35140, Mexico
Tel.: (52) 8717492500
Fax: (52) 8717523146
E-Mail:
Web Site: www.emblagunera.com
Soft Drink Mfr
S.I.C.: 2086
N.A.I.C.S.: 312111

Embotelladora San Luis, S.A. de C.V. **(2)**
Lado Oriente Glorieta Juarez s/n
Col Hogares Ferrocarrileros, San Luis Potosi, 78070, Mexico
Tel.: (52) 4448348700
Fax: (52) 4448186241
E-Mail: emendezz@embanluis.com
Soft Drink Mfr
S.I.C.: 2086
N.A.I.C.S.: 312111
Fernado Gonzalez *(Gen Mgr)*

Embotelladora Zacatecas, S.A. de C.V. **(2)**
Carr 54 Via Corta Zacatecas Guad Km 306.2
Cieneguillas, Zacatecas, 98170, Mexico
Tel.: (52) 4929256290
Fax: (52) 4929256299
Soft Drink Mfr
S.I.C.: 2086
N.A.I.C.S.: 312111
Samuel Casas *(Gen Mgr)*

Grossman y Asociados, S.A. de C.V. **(2)**
Ave Hidalgo 2303
Smith, 89140 Tampico, Tamaulipas, Mexico
Tel.: (52) 8332412500
Business Consulting Services
S.I.C.: 7389
N.A.I.C.S.: 561499

Petstar, S.A. de C.V. **(1)**
Rio Papaloapan 153 Sta Cruz
Atzcapotzaltongo
Toluca, 07850, Mexico
Tel.: (52) 722 272 6617
Web Site: www.avaicg.com
Waste Collection Services
S.I.C.: 4212
N.A.I.C.S.: 562111
Leo Nava *(Mgr-Natl Accounts)*

U.S. Subsidiary:

Wise Foods, Inc. **(1)**
228 Raseley St
Berwick, PA 18603-4533
Tel.: (570) 759-4000
Toll Free: (888) 759-4401
Web Site: www.wisesnacks.com
Emp.: 2,000
Mfr & Retailer of Snack Foods
S.I.C.: 2052
N.A.I.C.S.: 311919

ARCA IMPRESA GESTIONI SGR S.P.A.

Via Borrome 5
Milan, 20123, Italy
Tel.: (39) 2 29 02 29 85
Fax: (39) 2 29 00 54 11
Business Description:
Private Equity Firm
S.I.C.: 6211
N.A.I.C.S.: 523999
Personnel:
Gianluca Banfi *(Mng Dir)*

ARCA REGLER GMBH

(d/b/a The ARCA Flow Group)
Kempener Strasse 18
D-41918 Tonisvorst, Germany
Tel.: (49) 215677090
Fax: (49) 2156770950
E-Mail: sales@arca-valve.de
Web Site: www.arca.de
Emp.: 300
Business Description:
Control Valve Mfr
S.I.C.: 3491
N.A.I.C.S.: 332911
Personnel:
Joachim Lukoschek *(Co-CEO & Mng Dir)*

Subsidiary:

FELUWA Pumpen GmbH **(1)**
Beulertweg
Murlenbach, 54570 Eifel, Germany
Tel.: (49) 6594 10 0
Fax: (49) 6594 1640
E-Mail: info@feluwa.de
Web Site: www.feluwa.de
Emp.: 125
Control Valve, Pumps & Level Indicator Mfr
S.I.C.: 3491
N.A.I.C.S.: 332911
Rudiger Kaspers *(Chm)*

Non-U.S. Subsidiaries:

ARCA Valvulas S.A. de C.V. **(1)**
Edif 42C Depto 305
11200 Mexico, Mexico
Tel.: (52) 5553959836
Fax: (52) 5555806346
E-Mail: arca@axtel.net
Web Site: www.arca-Valvulas.com
Emp.: 7
Control Valve Mfr
S.I.C.: 3491
N.A.I.C.S.: 332911
Roberto Gonzalez *(Mng Dir)*

Guangzhou ARCA Valve Ltd. **(1)**
Room 807 Building 2 Industrial Plaza
No 730 Ying Bin Road, 511400 Guangzhou, Panyu, China
Tel.: (86) 203921186
Fax: (86) 2039211985
Web Site: www.arca-valve.com.cn
Control Valve Mfr
S.I.C.: 3491
N.A.I.C.S.: 332911
Wei Tao *(Office Mgr)*

von Rohr Armaturen AG **(1)**
Fichtenhagstr 4
CH-4132 Muttenz, Switzerland
Tel.: (41) 61 4614848
Fax: (41) 61 4611827
Web Site: www.von-rohr.ch
Pneumatic & Electrical Control Valves
S.I.C.: 3491
N.A.I.C.S.: 332911
Helga Kuhnert *(Mgr-HR)*

WEKA AG **(1)**
Schuerlistrasse 8
CH-8344 Hinwil, Switzerland
Tel.: (41) 43 8334343
Fax: (41) 43 8334329
E-Mail: info@weka-ag.ch
Web Site: www.weka-ag.ch
Emp.: 60
Valves & Actuators Mfr
S.I.C.: 3491
N.A.I.C.S.: 332911
Marcel Fuerst *(Mng Dir-Sls)*

ARCADIAN WOOL BROKERS LTD.

16 18 Brougham St
Geelong, VIC, 3220, Australia
Tel.: (61) 352221022
Fax: (61) 352222691
Web Site: www.arcadianwool.com.au
Year Founded: 1985
Sales Range: $50-74.9 Million
Emp.: 15
Business Description:
Wool Retailer
S.I.C.: 2299
N.A.I.C.S.: 314999
Personnel:
Ian Shawcross *(Mgr-Geelong Office)*

ARCADIS N.V.

Gustav Mahlerplein 97-103
1082 MS Amsterdam, Netherlands
Mailing Address:
PO Box 33
1008 AB Arnhem, Netherlands
Tel.: (31) 20 2011 011
Telex: 45623 hymy nl
Fax: (31) 20 2011 002
E-Mail: info@arcadis.com
Web Site: www.arcadis.com
Year Founded: 1888
ARCAD—(EUR)
Rev.: $3,425,278,411
Assets: $2,383,892,068
Liabilities: $1,661,452,437
Net Worth: $722,439,631
Earnings: $121,415,111
Emp.: 21,696
Fiscal Year-end: 12/31/12
Business Description:
Engineering, Consulting, Design, Architectural, Urban Planning, Project Management & Contracting Services
S.I.C.: 8711
N.A.I.C.S.: 541330
Personnel:
Rijnhard W.F. van Tets *(Chm-Supervisory Bd)*
Neil McArthur *(CEO)*
Renier Vree *(CFO & Member-Exec Bd)*
Gary Coates *(Pres-Environment Div & COO-Arcadis US)*
Gerard Spans *(CIO)*
Lance Josal *(Pres/CEO-RTKL Associates Inc)*
John Hensley, Jr. *(Pres-Environment)*
Manoel da Silva *(CEO-Arcadis Logos)*
Joseph Lee *(CEO-Langdon & Seah)*
Rob Mooren *(CEO-Arcadis Nederland BV)*

Phillip Youell *(CEO-EC Harris)*
Stephanie Hottenhuis *(Member-Exec Bd)*
Friedrich M. T. Schneider *(Member-Exec Bd)*
Zack Smith *(Member-Exec Bd)*
Bartheke Weerstra *(Gen Counsel & Sec)*
Richard Clare *(Sr VP-Arcadis NV)*

Supervisory Board of Directors:
Rijnhard W.F. van Tets
Ian M. Grice
Niek Hoek
Ruth Markland
George R. Nethercutt, Jr.
Armando Perez
Maarten Schonfeld

Transfer Agent:
The Bank of New York
101 Barclay St Fl 21W
New York, NY 10286
Tel.: (212) 815-5741
Fax: (212) 815-5915
Toll Free: (800) 524-4458

Subsidiary:

ARCADIS Nederland BV (1)
Nieuwe Sta Straat 10
PO Box 33
6800 LE Arnhem, Netherlands (100%)
Tel.: (31) 263778911
Fax: (31) 263515235
E-Mail: info@arcadis.nl
Web Site: www.arcadis.nl
Emp.: 350
Engineering Services
S.I.C.: 8711
N.A.I.C.S.: 541330
Rob Mooren *(Mng Dir)*

Subsidiaries:

ARCADIS Bouw BV (2)
Piat Mondriaanlaan 26
PO Box 220
GH 38112 GG Amersfoort, Netherlands (100%)
Tel.: (31) 334771000
Fax: (31) 306052000
Web Site: www.arcadisbouw.com
Emp.: 800
Engineering Services
S.I.C.: 8711
N.A.I.C.S.: 541330

Subsidiaries:

VOF Stationseiland (3)
Piatmondreaan 26
PO Box 220
3800 AE Amersfoort, Netherlands (100%)
Tel.: (31) 334771200
Fax: (31) 334772000
Emp.: 800
Engineering Services
S.I.C.: 8711
N.A.I.C.S.: 541330
Zaanne Michellin *(Mgr)*

ARCADIS Infra B.V. (2)
Piet Mondrianlaan 26
3812 CV Amersfoort, Netherlands (100%)
Mailing Address:
PO Box 220
3000 AE Amersfoort, Netherlands
Tel.: (31) 334771000
Fax: (31) 334771595
E-Mail: info@arcardis.nl
Web Site: www.arcardis.nl
Emp.: 800
Engineering Services
S.I.C.: 8711
N.A.I.C.S.: 541330
Rob Mooren *(Mng Dir)*

ARCADIS Ruiwitelijke Ohtwilleling BV (2)
2130 Hoosdvorp Jupitarstraat 122
PO Box 410
NL 6800 AG Arnhem, Netherlands (100%)
Tel.: (31) 235668411
Fax: (31) 235611575
E-Mail: info@arcadis.nl
Web Site: www.arcadis.com
Emp.: 200
S.I.C.: 8621
N.A.I.C.S.: 813920
Kees Slingerland *(Mng Dir)*

Subsidiary:

Dynamicon BV (3)
Ucertghtwej 58
PO Box 264
Arnhem, 6812 A8, Netherlands (100%)
Tel.: (31) 263778917
Fax: (31) 264457950
E-Mail: dynamicon@dynamicon.nl
Web Site: www.dynamicon.nl
Emp.: 18
Engineering Services
S.I.C.: 8711
N.A.I.C.S.: 541330

ARCADIS Spatial Information (2)
Hetrietveld 59 A
PO Box 882
7301 BC Apeldoorn, Netherlands (100%)
Tel.: (31) 555815900
Fax: (31) 555815570
Web Site: www.arcadis.nl
Emp.: 100
Engineering Services
S.I.C.: 8711
N.A.I.C.S.: 541330
Jaap Van Gelder *(Mng Dir)*

Subsidiaries:

Kafi BV (3)
Bontemolanlaan 19A
PO Box 114
3448 AC Woerden, Netherlands (100%)
Tel.: (31) 348485400
Fax: (31) 348485498
Emp.: 30
Engineering Services
S.I.C.: 8711
N.A.I.C.S.: 541330

Subsidiary:

Cannock Chase B.V. (4)
Klappashaeda 3
PO Box 103
6650 AC Druten, 6651 KM, Netherlands (100%)
Tel.: (31) 487515123
Fax: (31) 487516505
E-Mail: postbus@cannockchase.nl
Web Site: www.cannockchase.nl
Emp.: 105
Engineering Services
S.I.C.: 8711
N.A.I.C.S.: 541330
Gos Lowek *(Mng Dir)*

Non-U.S. Subsidiaries:

ARCADIS Gedas N.V. (4)
Posthofbrug 12
B 2600 Berchem, Belgium (100%)
Tel.: (32) 33608300
Fax: (32) 33608301
E-Mail: info@arcadisbelgium.be
Web Site: www.arcadisbelgium.be
Emp.: 150
Engineering Services
S.I.C.: 8711
N.A.I.C.S.: 541330
Luc Hellemans *(Mng Dir)*

U.S. Subsidiary:

ARCADIS U.S., Inc. (1)
630 Plz Dr Ste 100
Highlands Ranch, CO 80129 DE (100%)
Tel.: (720) 344-3500
Fax: (720) 344-3535
E-Mail: arcadis@arcadis-us.com
Web Site: www.arcadis-us.com
Emp.: 157
Environmental Engineering & Design Services
S.I.C.: 8999
N.A.I.C.S.: 541690
Wassim Selman *(Pres)*
Gary Coates *(CEO & COO)*
Pete Dyke *(CFO & Exec VP)*
Mark Endry *(CIO & Sr VP)*
Suthan S. Suthersan *(CTO)*
Charles H. Leichner *(Chief Strategy & Sls Officer)*
John Hensley *(Pres-Environment)*
Steven Niparko *(Gen Counsel)*
Robert J. Anderson *(Sr VP)*
Scott Davies *(Sr VP-Raleigh)*
Patrick T. Farr *(Sr VP)*
Geoffrey Germann *(Sr VP-Raleigh)*
Amy Hoeksema *(Sr VP-Brighton)*
Sean P. O'Brien *(Sr VP-Wakefield)*
Thomas E. Rodriguez *(Sr VP)*

Divisions:

ARCADIS U.S., Inc. - Tampa (2)
14025 Riveredge Dr Ste 600
Tampa, FL 33637
Tel.: (813) 903-3100
Fax: (813) 903-9115
Web Site: www.arcadis-us.com
Emp.: 150
Engineering Services
S.I.C.: 8711
N.A.I.C.S.: 541330
Mary Ann Nespolinia *(Office Admininstrator)*

Subsidiaries:

ARCADIS G&M, Inc. (2)
2929 Briarpark Dr Ste 300
Houston, TX 77042-3709 (100%)
Tel.: (281) 496-9737
Fax: (281) 496-2936
Web Site: www.arcadis-us.com
Emp.: 40
Buildings & Infrastructure Projects
S.I.C.: 8711
N.A.I.C.S.: 541330

ARCADIS Geraghty & Miller, Inc. (2)
1717 W 6th St Ste 210
Austin, TX 78703
Tel.: (512) 451-1188
Fax: (512) 451-2930
Web Site: www.arcadis-us.com
Emp.: 15
Environmental Engineering Consulting & Construction
S.I.C.: 8999
N.A.I.C.S.: 541690

Malcolm Pirnie, Inc. (2)
44 S Broadway
White Plains, NY 10602-3804 NY
Tel.: (914) 694-2100
Fax: (914) 694-9286
Toll Free: (800) 759-5020
Web Site: www.pirnie.com
Sales Range: $350-399.9 Million
Emp.: 1,700
Environmental Engineering Services
S.I.C.: 8711
N.A.I.C.S.: 541330
William Dee *(Pres & CEO)*
Douglas Owen *(CTO)*
Gerard P. Cavaluzzi *(Gen Counsel)*

Non-U.S. Subsidiaries:

Malcolm Pirnie Consulting Engineers India Pvt. Ltd (3)
Office No 405 E Ct Bldg A Phoenix Market City Viman Nagar
Pune, 411014, India
Tel.: (91) 2040024494
Emp.: 9
Environmental Engineering Services
S.I.C.: 8711
N.A.I.C.S.: 541330
Ketan Maroo *(Mgr-Sls)*

Malcolm Pirnie Middle East FZC (3)
Abu Dhabi
Abu Dhabi, United Arab Emirates
Tel.: (971) 558841216
Fax: (971) 26994848
Web Site: www.arcadisglobal.com
Emp.: 3
Environmental Engineering Services
S.I.C.: 8711
N.A.I.C.S.: 541330

Rise International L.L.C. (2)
120 S LaSalle St Ste 1350
Chicago, IL 60603
Tel.: (312) 917-1000
Fax: (312) 917-1572
Web Site: www.risegroup.com
Emp.: 50
Technical Management Consulting Services
S.I.C.: 8999
N.A.I.C.S.: 541690
David Crowell *(COO)*
Sonia Y. Cooke *(Sr Vice Pres & HR)*

RTKL Associates Inc. (2)
901 S Bond St
Baltimore, MD 21231 MD
Tel.: (410) 537-6000
Fax: (410) 276-2136
E-Mail: baltimore-info@rtkl.com
Web Site: www.rtkl.com
Sales Range: $75-99.9 Million
Emp.: 700
Architectural, Engineering & Planning Services
Export
S.I.C.: 8712
N.A.I.C.S.: 541310
Paul F. Jacob, III *(Chm)*
Randall S. Pace *(CFO)*
Ardeshir Alaiandust *(CIO)*

Branch:

RTKL Associates Inc. (3)
1717 Pacific Ave Ste 100
Dallas, TX 75201-4655
Tel.: (214) 871-8877
Fax: (214) 468-7601
Web Site: www.rtkl.com
Emp.: 237
Engineering Services
S.I.C.: 8741
N.A.I.C.S.: 561110
Brad T. Barker *(Exec VP)*
Wayne W. Barger *(Sr VP)*

Non-U.S. Subsidiaries:

RTKL International Ltd. (3)
Suite 2106 Platinum 233 Taicang Road
Shanghai, 200020, China
Tel.: (86) 21 6122 7922
Fax: (86) 21 6157 2801
E-Mail: Shanghai-Info@rtkl.com
Web Site: www.arcadis.com
Architectural Design Services
S.I.C.: 8712
N.A.I.C.S.: 541310

RTKL UK Ltd. (3)
22 Torrington Place
London, WC1E 7HP, United Kingdom
Tel.: (44) 20 7306 0404
Fax: (44) 2073060405
E-Mail: london-Info@rtkl.com
Web Site: www.rtkl.com
Emp.: 6
Architecture Design Services
S.I.C.: 8712
N.A.I.C.S.: 541310

Non-U.S. Subsidiaries:

ARCADIS Asia (1)
Zhongrong Plaza Unit 1203 1088 South Pudong Rd
Pudong New Area, Shanghai, 200122, China
Tel.: (86) 21587 61 451
Fax: (86) 21 587 82 738
E-Mail: info@arcadis.cn
Web Site: www.arcadis.com
Construction Engineering Services
S.I.C.: 8711
N.A.I.C.S.: 541330
Thomas Kustusch *(Exec Dir)*

ARCADIS Belgium Holding NV (1)
Posthofbrug 12 City Link
Antwerp, 2600, Belgium
Tel.: (32) 495044146
Fax: (32) 33608301
Investment Management Services
S.I.C.: 6211
N.A.I.C.S.: 523999

ARCADIS CZ a.s. (1)
Na Strzi 1702/65
140 62 Prague, Czech Republic
Tel.: (420) 296 330 111
Fax: (420) 224 236 313
E-Mail: info@arcadis.cz
Emp.: 4
Construction Engineering Services
S.I.C.: 8711
N.A.I.C.S.: 541330
Vaclav Horejsi *(Mng Dir)*

ARCADIS Deutschland Gmbh (1)
Europaplatz 3
D 64293 Darmstadt, Germany De
Tel.: (49) 61513880
Fax: (49) 6151388999

ARCADIS N.V.—(Continued)

E-Mail: info@arcadis.de
Web Site: www.arcadis.de
Sales Range: $1-4.9 Billion
Emp.: 200
Engineering Services
S.I.C.: 8711
N.A.I.C.S.: 541330
Stephanie Hottenhuis *(CEO)*

ARCADIS ESG (1)
9 Avenue Reaumur
92354 Le Plessis-Robinson, France
Tel.: (33) 1 46 01 24 00
Fax: (33) 1 46 01 35 80
E-Mail: direction@arcadis-fr.com
Web Site: www.arcadis.com
Emp.: 700
Engineering Services
S.I.C.: 8711
N.A.I.C.S.: 541330
Paul Souaid *(Mng Dir)*

ARCADIS Eurometudes S.A. (1)
Calea Grivitei Nr 136 Corp B Etaj 2 Sector 1
Bucharest, 33697, Romania
Tel.: (40) 21 31 22699
Fax: (40) 21 31 33697
E-Mail: office@arcadis-ro.com
Emp.: 32
Infrastructure Construction Engineering Services
S.I.C.: 8711
N.A.I.C.S.: 541330
Nicolae Micu *(Mng Dir)*

ARCADIS Geotecnica (1)
Eliodoro yanez
1893 Santiago, Providencia, Chile (67%)
Tel.: (56) 23816000
Fax: (56) 23816001
E-Mail: arcadis@arcadis.cl
Web Site: www.arcadis.cl
Emp.: 600
Engineering Services
S.I.C.: 8711
N.A.I.C.S.: 541330
Hernan Bezimat *(CEO)*

ARCADIS Holding France S.A.S. (1)
9 Avenue Reaumur
92350 Le Plessis-Robinson, France
Tel.: (33) 1 46 23 77 77
Investment Management Services
S.I.C.: 6211
N.A.I.C.S.: 523999

ARCADIS ITALIA Srl (1)
Via G Galilei 16
20090 Assago, Milan, Italy
Tel.: (39) 0248841600
Fax: (39) 0248849056
E-Mail: info@arcadis.it
Web Site: www.arcadis.com
Emp.: 50
Construction Engineering Services
S.I.C.: 8711
N.A.I.C.S.: 541330
Domenico Santi *(Mng Dir)*

ARCADIS Logos Ltda. (1)
Rua Libero Badaro 377 - 11
01009 906 Sao Paulo, Brazil
Tel.: (55) 11 3117 3161
Fax: (55) 11 3115 1009
E-Mail: contata@logoseng.com.br
Web Site: www.logoseng.com.br
Power Plant Construction Engineering Services
S.I.C.: 1629
N.A.I.C.S.: 237130
Celso de Oliveira Azevedo Filho *(Pres)*
Manoel Antonio da Silva *(CEO)*

ARCADIS Sp. z.o.o. (1)
Woloska 22A
02-670 Warsaw, Poland
Tel.: (48) 22 203 2000
Fax: (48) 22 203 2001
E-Mail: arcadis@arcadis.pl
Construction Engineering Services
S.I.C.: 8711
N.A.I.C.S.: 541330

ARCADIS UK Ltd. (1)
10 Furnival Street
London, EC4A 1YH, United Kingdom UK
Tel.: (44) 20 72161000
Fax: (44) 20 72161001
Web Site: www.arcadis-uk.com
Consulting Engineering Services
S.I.C.: 8711
N.A.I.C.S.: 541330
Mike Carroll *(CEO)*
Mark O'Brien *(Interim Mng Dir-Buildings)*
Andrew Smith *(Sec)*

EC Harris LLP (1)
Regent Quarter 34 York Way
London, N19 AB, United Kingdom UK
Tel.: (44) 20 7812 2000
Fax: (44) 20 7812 2001
E-Mail: information@echarris.com
Web Site: www.echarris.com
Sales Range: $400-449.9 Million
Emp.: 3,000
Property & Infrastructure Consulting Services
S.I.C.: 8999
N.A.I.C.S.: 541690
Philip Youell *(CEO)*
Neil Morling *(CFO)*

Eptisa Servicios De Ingenieria S.A. (1)
Arapiles 14 5th Fl
28015 Madrid, Spain (100%)
Tel.: (34) 915949500
Fax: (34) 914465546
E-Mail: eptisa@eptisa.es
Web Site: www.eptisa.es
Sls.: $76,521,624
Emp.: 1,000
Engineering Services
S.I.C.: 8711
N.A.I.C.S.: 541330
Felipe Gabcia Berrio *(Pres)*
Luis Villarroya Alonso *(CEO)*
A. Catena Asunsola *(CFO)*

EurAsia Consult (1)
c/o Centre of Economic Conjuncture & Analysis
Dzhandosov 59 3rd Fl, 480035 Almaty, Kazakhstan
Tel.: (7) 3272551319
Web Site: www.euroconsult.nl
Engineering Services
S.I.C.: 8711
N.A.I.C.S.: 541330

Geotecnicos Peru S.A. (1)
Calle Camino Real Lope 2
Mvn Ate, 03 Lima, Peru
Tel.: (51) 14366040
Fax: (51) 14363100
E-Mail: peruana@geocetnia.net
Emp.: 40
Engineering Services
S.I.C.: 8711
N.A.I.C.S.: 541330

Logos Engenharia S.A. (1)
Rua Libero Badaro 377 11
01009 Sao Paulo, SP, Brazil (100%)
Tel.: (55) 131053171
Fax: (55) 1131057351
E-Mail: arcadis@logoneng.com.br
Web Site: www.logoseng.com.br
Emp.: 400
Engineering Services
S.I.C.: 8711
N.A.I.C.S.: 541330
Jair Roxo *(Fin Dir)*

Ukron (1)
Serpova st 3
252115 Kiev, Ukraine
Tel.: (380) 444441014
Fax: (380) 444521811
E-Mail: valery@ukron.kiev.ua
Engineering Services
S.I.C.: 8711
N.A.I.C.S.: 541330

Non-U.S. Affiliate:

Darwish Consulting Engineers (1)
27 Nazih Khalifa St Ex Baroon
Heliopolis, Cairo, Egypt (26%)
Tel.: (20) 22581559
Fax: (20) 22586639
Web Site: www.dce-ltd.com
Engineering Services
S.I.C.: 8711
N.A.I.C.S.: 541330

ARCAM AB

Krokslatts Fabriker 27A
SE-431 37 Molndal, Sweden
Tel.: (46) 31 710 32 00
Fax: (46) 31 710 32 01
E-Mail: info@arcam.com
Web Site: www.arcam.com
Year Founded: 1997
ARCM—(OMX OTC)
Emp.: 40
Business Description:
Metal Parts Mfr
S.I.C.: 3499
N.A.I.C.S.: 332999
Personnel:
Magnus Rene *(Pres & CEO)*

ARCAN RESOURCES LTD.

Suite 2200 500 - 4th Avenue SW
Calgary, AB, T2P 2V6, Canada
Tel.: (403) 262-0321
Fax: (403) 262-4636
E-Mail: info@arcanres.com
Web Site: www.arcanres.com
Year Founded: 2003
ARN—(OTC TSXV)
Rev.: $132,780,198
Assets: $609,720,934
Liabilities: $363,216,896
Net Worth: $246,504,038
Earnings: ($48,691,076)
Emp.: 28
Fiscal Year-end: 12/31/12
Business Description:
Oil & Gas Exploration Services
S.I.C.: 1389
N.A.I.C.S.: 213112
Personnel:
Michael J. Laffin *(Chm & Sec)*
Douglas N. Penner *(Pres)*
James Terry McCoy *(CEO)*
Graeme Ryder *(CFO & VP-Fin)*
Andy Fisher *(Exec VP)*
Board of Directors:
Michael J. Laffin
Robert John Dales
Murray Hinz
James Terry McCoy
Douglas N. Penner
Transfer Agent:
Valiant Trust Company
Calgary, AB, Canada

ARCAPITA BANK B.S.C. (C)

PO Box 1406
Manama, Bahrain
Tel.: (973) 017218333
Fax: (973) 17217555
Web Site: www.arcapita.com
Emp.: 268
Business Description:
Banking & Investment Services
S.I.C.: 6211
N.A.I.C.S.: 523110
Personnel:
Mohammed Abdulaziz Aljomaih *(Chm)*
Abdulaziz Hamad Aljomaih *(Vice Chm)*
Atif A. Abdulmalik *(CEO)*
Board of Directors:
Mohammed Abdulaziz Aljomaih
Atif A. Abdulmalik
Khalifa Mohamed Al Kindi
Abdulla Abdullatif Al-Fozan
Abdulrahman Abdulaziz Al-Muhanna
Khalid Thani A. Al-Thani
Abdulaziz Hamad Aljomaih
Ghazi Fahad Alnafisi
Khalid Mohammed Boodai

U.S. Subsidiary:

Arcapita, Inc. (1)
75 14th St 24th Fl
Atlanta, GA 30309
Tel.: (404) 920-9000
Fax: (404) 920-9001
Web Site: www.arcapita.com
Emp.: 30
Financial Management & Investment Services
S.I.C.: 6211
N.A.I.C.S.: 523999
Scott A. Buschmann *(Principal)*
William A. Lundstrom *(Principal)*
Lex McGraw *(Principal)*
William C. Miller, Jr. *(Principal)*
Andrea L. Malik Roe *(Principal)*

Holdings:

American Pad & Paper LLC (2)
3001 E George Bush Hwy Ste 210
Richardson, TX 75082
Tel.: (972) 578-2000
Fax: (972) 424-7493
Toll Free: (800))426-1368
Web Site: www.ampad.com
Emp.: 65
Office Supplies Mfr & Distr
S.I.C.: 2678
N.A.I.C.S.: 322230
Donald Meltzer *(Pres & CEO)*
Ed Byrne *(CFO & VP)*
Kevin Coughlin *(Sr VP-Sls)*

Church's Chicken, Inc. (2)
980 Hammond Dr NE Ste 1100
Atlanta, GA 30328-8187 TX
Tel.: (770) 350-3800
Fax: (770) 512-3920
E-Mail: info@churchs.com
Web Site: www.churchs.com
Sales Range: $1-4.9 Billion
Emp.: 75
Fast Food Restaurants Operator
S.I.C.: 5812
N.A.I.C.S.: 722513
Jim Hyatt *(Pres & CEO)*
Louis J. Profumo *(CFO)*
Tony Moralejo *(Chief Dev Officer)*
Edward Brett *(Chief People Officer & Exec VP)*
Steve Davis *(Chief Concept Officer)*
Zack Kollias *(Exec VP-Intl Ops)*
John Barnett *(Sr VP-Global Supply Chain & Pur)*
Joel Bulger *(Sr VP-Brand Mktg)*
Michael Mader *(Sr VP-Global Strategy, Plng & Alliances)*

The J. Jill Group, Inc. (2)
4 Batterymarch Park
Quincy, MA 02169 DE
Tel.: (617) 376-4300
Fax: (617) 769-0177
Web Site: www.jjill.com
Sales Range: $400-449.9 Million
Emp.: 3,400
Women's Apparel & Accessories Mail Order Catalog Whslr, Online Retailer & Store Retailer
S.I.C.: 5621
N.A.I.C.S.: 448120
Paula J. Bennett *(Pres & CEO)*
Avra Myers *(Sr VP & Gen Mgr-Mdsg)*
Sue Walsh *(Sr VP-Stores)*

Tensar Corporation (2)
2500 Northwinds Pkwy Ste 500
Alpharetta, GA 30009-2247 DE
Tel.: (770) 344-2090
Fax: (770) 344-2089
Toll Free: (888) 828-5126
E-Mail: info@tensarcorp.com
Web Site: www.tensarcorp.com
Sales Range: $150-199.9 Million
Emp.: 715
Specialty Products & Engineering Services for the Mining, Erosion Prevention & Solid Waste Industries
Import Export
S.I.C.: 8711
N.A.I.C.S.: 541330
Don Meltzer *(CEO)*
Robert F. Vevoda *(COO)*
Robert F. Briggs *(Gen Counsel, Sec & Exec VP)*

Subsidiary:

North American Green Inc. (3)
14649 Hwy 41 N
Evansville, IN 47725
Tel.: (812) 867-6632
Fax: (812) 867-0427
Toll Free: (800) 772-2040

Web Site: www.nagreen.com
Sls.: $15,400,000
Emp.: 15
Erosion Control Products Distr
S.I.C.: 2875
N.A.I.C.S.: 325314
Tim Lancaster *(Pres)*

Varel International, Inc. (2)
1625 W Crossway Ste 124
Carrollton, TX 75006 DE
Tel.: (972) 242-1160
Fax: (972) 242-9570
Web Site: www.varelintl.com
Sls.: $60,200,056
Emp.: 115
Oil & Gas Well Drill Bit Mfr
S.I.C.: 3545
N.A.I.C.S.: 333515
Jim Nixon *(Pres & CEO)*
John Capasso *(CFO)*

Non-U.S. Holdings:

Freightliner Group Ltd. (1)
3rd Fl The Podium
Eversholt St, London, NW1 2FL, United Kingdom
Tel.: (44) 207 200 3967
E-Mail: enquiries@freightliner.co.uk
Web Site: www.freightliner.co.uk
Freight Transportation Services
S.I.C.: 4011
N.A.I.C.S.: 482111

profine GmbH (1)
Muelheimer Strasse 26 Tor 3
D 53840 Troisdorf, Germany De
Tel.: (49) 224199530
Fax: (49) 224199533561
E-Mail: info@profine-group.com
Web Site: www.profine-group.com
Sales Range: $800-899.9 Million
Emp.: 300
Plastic Floor Coverings, Wall Panels, Windows, Doors & Motor Vehicle Parts
S.I.C.: 3089
N.A.I.C.S.: 326199
Marco von Maltzan *(CEO)*
Achim Judt *(COO & Member-Mgmt Bd)*
Albrecht P. Lange *(Chief Sls Officer & Member-Mgmt Bd)*
Dieter Mayer *(Member-Mgmt Bd)*

U.S. Subsidiary:

Kommerling USA, Inc. (2)
3402 Stanwood Blvd
Huntsville, AL 35811
Tel.: (256) 851-4099
Fax: (256) 859-7562
Toll Free: (800) 330-2239
Web Site: www.kommerlingusa.com
Emp.: 100
Plastics Mfr; PVC Sheets Mfr
S.I.C.: 3089
N.A.I.C.S.: 326199
Teresa Heckaman *(Office Mgr)*

Non-U.S. Subsidiaries:

Koemmerling Tianjin Kunststoff Co. Ltd. (2)
No 2 Zhonghong Road Jinnan Economic Development Area
Tianjin, 300350, China
Tel.: (86) 2288515188
Fax: (86) 2288516618
E-Mail: info@koemmerling.com.cn
Web Site: www.koemmerling.com.cn
Plastic Products Mfr
S.I.C.: 3089
N.A.I.C.S.: 326199
Yves Baracco *(Gen Mgr)*

profine Austria GmbH (2)
Kaerntnerstrasse 155
8053 Graz, Austria
Tel.: (43) 31626167014
Fax: (43) 31626167020
E-Mail: heinz.doppler@profine-group.com
Web Site: www.profine-group.de
Emp.: 50
Mfr of Plastic Profiles for Windows & Doors; Supplier of Shutter Solutions & PVC Sheets
S.I.C.: 3089
N.A.I.C.S.: 326199
Heinz Doppler *(Mgr)*

profine Belux BVBA (2)
Zone 3 Doornveld 110
1731 Zellik, Belgium
Tel.: (32) 24669960
Fax: (32) 2 466 76 27
E-Mail: info@profine-group.be
Web Site: www.profine-group.be
Plastic Profiles for Windows & Doors; Supplier of Shutter Solutions & PVC Sheets
S.I.C.: 5162
N.A.I.C.S.: 424610

profine BH d.o.o. (2)
Magistralni put-A br 33
Zivinice, 75270 Tuzla, Bosnia & Herzegovina
Tel.: (387) 35304600
Fax: (387) 35304601
E-Mail: profine.bh@profine-group.com
Web Site: www.profine.ba
Mfr of Plastic Profiles for Windows & Doors; Supplier of Shutter Solutions & PVC Sheets
S.I.C.: 3089
N.A.I.C.S.: 326199

profine Croatia doo (2)
Vukomericka bb
10410 Velika Gorica, Croatia
Tel.: (385) 16253100
Fax: (385) 16253101
E-Mail: profine@profine-croatia.hr
Web Site: www.profine-croatia.hr
Emp.: 15
Mfr of Plastic Profiles for Windows & Doors; Supplier of Shutter Solutions & PVC Sheets
S.I.C.: 3089
N.A.I.C.S.: 326199
Aleksandar Terer *(Gen Mgr)*

profine France SAS (2)
ZI rue Gutleutfeld
BP 50
67441 Marmoutier, Alsace, Cedex, France
Tel.: (33) 388715050
Fax: (33) 3 88 71 40 50
E-Mail: service.commerical@profine-group.com
Web Site: www.profine-group.fr
Emp.: 100
Mfr of Plastic Profiles for Windows & Doors; Supplier of Shutter Solutions & PVC Sheets
S.I.C.: 3089
N.A.I.C.S.: 326199

profine Iberia S.A. (2)
Poligono Industrial Alcamar S/N
Camarma de Esteruelas, 28816 Madrid, Spain
Tel.: (34) 918866045
Fax: (34) 918866005
E-Mail: info@kommerling.es
Web Site: www.profine-group.com
Mfr of Plastic Profiles for Windows & Doors; Supplier of Shutter Solutions & PVC Sheets
S.I.C.: 3089
N.A.I.C.S.: 326199
Jose-Ramon Navarro *(Gen Mgr)*

profine Italia SRL (2)
Via Casilini 65 loc
03018 Paliano, FR, Italy
Tel.: (39) 0775538149
Fax: (39) 0775538130
E-Mail: info@profine_italia.com
Web Site: www.kbaitalia.it
Mfr of Plastic Profiles for Windows & Doors; Supplier of Shutter Solutions & PVC Sheets
S.I.C.: 3089
N.A.I.C.S.: 326199

profine Nederland b.v. (2)
Regterweistraat 13
4181 CW Waardenburg, Netherlands
Tel.: (31) 418651717
Fax: (31) 418652286
E-Mail: info@profine-nederland.nl
Web Site: www.kbe-online.nl
Emp.: 8
Plastic Profiles for Windows & Doors; Supplier of Shutter Solutions & PVC Sheets
S.I.C.: 5162
N.A.I.C.S.: 424610
Bart de Weger *(Gen Mgr)*

profine Polska Sp. z o.o. (2)
ul Strachowicka 40
54512 Wroclaw, Poland
Tel.: (48) 713471160
Fax: (48) 71 354 71 62
E-Mail: biuro@profine.pl
Web Site: www.profine.pl
Plastic Profiles for Windows & Doors; Supplier of Shutter Solutions & PVC Sheets
S.I.C.: 5162
N.A.I.C.S.: 424610

profine Romania SRL (2)
Soseaua de Centura
Alexandriei 152-156, 077025 Bragadiru, Romania
Tel.: (40) 214932145
Fax: (40) 214932155
E-Mail: koemmerling@profine.ro
Web Site: www.profine-group.com
Mfr of Plastic Profiles for Windows & Doors; Supplier of Shutter Solutions & PVC Sheets
S.I.C.: 3089
N.A.I.C.S.: 326199

profine Schweiz AG (2)
Herblingerstrasse 119
8207 Schaffhausen, Switzerland
Tel.: (41) 526440544
Fax: (41) 526440540
E-Mail: info@profine-group.ch
Web Site: www.profine-group.ch
Plastic Profiles for Windows & Doors; Supplier of Shutter Solutions & PVC Sheets
S.I.C.: 5162
N.A.I.C.S.: 424610

profine Ukraine (2)
Jaroslawiw Wal 5-a
UA 01034 Kiev, Ukraine
Tel.: (380) 442341184
Fax: (380) 442356437
E-Mail: info.ua@profine-group.com
Web Site: www.profine.ua
Emp.: 25
Mfr of Plastic Profiles for Windows & Doors; Supplier of Shutter Solutions & PVC Sheets
S.I.C.: 3089
N.A.I.C.S.: 326199

profine UK Ltd. (2)
Lancaster Road Fradley Park
Fradley, Lichfield, Staffs, WS13 8RY, United Kingdom
Tel.: (44) 1543444900
Fax: (44) 1543444990
E-Mail: enquiries@profine-group.com
Web Site: www.kbe-online.com
Emp.: 18
Mfr of Plastic Profiles for Windows & Doors; Supplier of Shutter Solutions & PVC Sheets
S.I.C.: 3089
N.A.I.C.S.: 326199
Robert Khiross *(Mng Dir)*

SAO profine RUS (2)
2 Roschinski pr 8
115419 Moscow, Russia
Tel.: (7) 4952329330
Fax: (7) 4952329331
E-Mail: marketing.russland@profine-group.com
Web Site: www.profine-group.ru
Mfr of Plastic Profiles for Windows & Doors; Supplier of Shutter Solutions & PVC Sheets
S.I.C.: 3089
N.A.I.C.S.: 326199
Daskovvski Andrie *(Gen Mgr)*

Viridian Group Ltd. (1)
Greenwood House 64 Newforge Lane
Belfast, BT9 5NF, United Kingdom UK
Tel.: (44) 28 9038 3765
Fax: (44) 2890689128
E-Mail: contact@viridiangroup.co.uk
Web Site: www.viridiangroup.co.uk
Sales Range: $1-4.9 Billion
Emp.: 1,554
Electricity Generation & Distribution Services
S.I.C.: 4939
N.A.I.C.S.: 221122
Asim Zafar *(Chm)*
Patrick Haren *(Deputy Chm)*
Patrick Bourke *(CEO)*
Harry McCracken *(Grp Mng Dir-Electricity-Ireland)*

ARCELORMITTAL

19 Avenue de la Liberte
L-2390 Luxembourg, Luxembourg
Tel.: (352) 4792 2484
Fax: (352) 4792 2675
Web Site: www.arcelormittal.com
Year Founded: 2007
MT—(BAR EUR LUX MAD NYSE)
Sls.: $79,440,000,000
Assets: $112,308,000,000
Liabilities: $59,135,000,000
Net Worth: $53,173,000,000
Earnings: ($2,575,000,000)
Emp.: 232,353
Fiscal Year-end: 12/31/13

Business Description:
Holding Company; Steel Production & Steel Products Mfr
S.I.C.: 3312
N.A.I.C.S.: 331221

Personnel:
Lakshmi Niwas Mittal *(Chm & CEO)*
Aditya Mittal *(CFO)*
Pierre Gugliermina *(CTO & Exec VP)*
Vijay Bhatnagar *(CEO-India & China & Exec VP)*
Gerhard Renz *(Exec VP & CEO-Long Europe)*
William Scotting *(CEO-Mining)*
Davinder Chugh *(Member-Grp Mgmt Bd)*
Gonzalo Urquijo Fernandez *(Member-Grp Mgmt Bd)*
Sudhir Maheshwari *(Member-Grp Mgmt Bd)*
Lou Schorsch *(Member-Grp Mgmt Bd)*
Michel Wurth *(Member-Grp Mgmt Bd)*
Bhikam Agarwal *(Exec VP & Head-Fin)*
Henri Blaffart *(Exec VP & Head-HR)*
Michael Pfitzner *(Exec VP & Head-Mktg & Comml Coordination)*
Jefferson De Paula *(Exec VP)*
Robrecht Himpe *(Exec VP)*
Kleber Silva *(Exec VP)*

Board of Directors:
Lakshmi Niwas Mittal
Prince Guillaume de Luxembourg
Lewis B. Kaden
Vanisha Mittal Bhatia
Suzanne P. Nimocks
Wilbur L. Ross, Jr.
Antoine Spillmann
Narayanan Vaghul

Subsidiaries:

Arcelor International Export S.A. (1)
19 Ave de la Liberte
L 2930 Luxembourg, Luxembourg
Tel.: (352) 47921
Fax: (352) 47922675
E-Mail: info@arcelormittal.com
Web Site: www.arcelormittal.com
Emp.: 900
Sales & Distr of Steel Products; Beams, Sections, Bars, Rods, Plates, Sheets, Tubes & Other Products
Import Export
S.I.C.: 7389
N.A.I.C.S.: 425120
Lakshmi Mittal *(CEO)*

Non-U.S. Subsidiaries:

Arcelor International Antwerp (2)
Noordlaan 147
2030 Antwerp, Belgium
Tel.: (32) 32440800
Telex: 31279 metal b
Fax: (32) 32386069
Web Site: www.arcelormittal.com
Emp.: 20
Steel Mfr
Export
S.I.C.: 3325
N.A.I.C.S.: 331513

Arcelor International Venezuela (2)
Av Veracruz Edificio Keope Torre A Piso 4 Oficina 45A
1060 Caracas, Venezuela
Tel.: (58) 2129934635
Fax: (58) 2129921342
E-Mail: ventas@arcelorvenezuela.com
Web Site: www.arcelorvenezuela.com
Emp.: 3
Steel Mfr
S.I.C.: 3325

ArcelorMittal—(Continued)

N.A.I.C.S.: 331513

Arcelor RPS (1)
66 Rue De Luxembourg
L 4221 Esch-sur-Alzette, Luxembourg
Tel.: (352) 53131
Fax: (352) 53133291
E-Mail: emile.reuter@arcelor.com
Web Site: www.rps.arcelor.com
Emp.: 100
Rails & Special Sections Sheet Piling
S.I.C.: 3444
N.A.I.C.S.: 332322
Neco Raoter *(Mng Dir)*

ArcelorMittal Belval & Differdange S.A. (1)
66 Rue De Luxembourg
L 4221 Esch-sur-Alzette, Luxembourg
Tel.: (352) 53131
Fax: (352) 53133299
Web Site: www.arcelor.com
Emp.: 600
Long Carbon Steel Sheet & Bearing Piles Mfr
S.I.C.: 3399
N.A.I.C.S.: 331221

ArcelorMittal Bettembourg S.A. (1)
Krakelshaff Industrial Zone
Krakelshaff, L 3235 Bettembourg, Luxembourg
Tel.: (352) 5150211
Fax: (352) 519163
E-Mail: steel.sales@trefil.arcelormittal.com
Web Site: www.trefilarbed.com
Emp.: 30
Steelcord & Hose Wire Mfr
S.I.C.: 3496
N.A.I.C.S.: 332618
Jos Gacque *(Pres)*

ArcelorMittal Bissen S.A. (1)
Rte Finsterthal
PO Box 16
L 7703 Bissen, Luxembourg
Tel.: (352) 8357721
Fax: (352) 835698
E-Mail: tahcal.genest@arcelormittal.com
Sls.: $340,058,176
Emp.: 60
Sales of Steel Products; Beams, Sections, Bars, Rods, Sheet, Plates, Tubes & other Products
S.I.C.: 1791
N.A.I.C.S.: 238120
Romain Claerbaut *(Dir-Fin)*

ArcelorMittal Dudelange S.A. (1)
Zone Industrielle Wolser
BP 92
L 3401 Dudelange, Luxembourg
Tel.: (352) 5186861
Fax: (352) 5186862222
E-Mail: info@arcelormittal.com
Web Site: www.galvalange.lu
Sls.: $196,000,000
Emp.: 350
Strip Coating of Steel
S.I.C.: 3479
N.A.I.C.S.: 332812
Christian Brugnera *(Gen Mgr)*

ArcelorMittal Flat Carbon Europe S.A. (1)
19 Avenue de la Liberte
Luxembourg, Luxembourg
Tel.: (352) 47922629
Fax: (352) 47924283
E-Mail: press@arcelormittal.com
Web Site: www.arcelormittal.com
Rolled Steel Products Mfr
S.I.C.: 3312
N.A.I.C.S.: 331221

ArcelorMittal International Luxembourg S.A. (1)
19 Avenue de la Liberte
2930 Luxembourg, Luxembourg
Tel.: (352) 4792 1
Fax: (352) 4907 49
E-Mail: international@arcelormittal.com
Web Site: www.arcelormittal.com
Emp.: 40
Steel Slab & Bar Distr
S.I.C.: 5051
N.A.I.C.S.: 423510
Sahib Aliyev *(Reg Mgr-Sls)*

ArcelorMittal Rodange & Schifflange S.A. (1)
2 rue de l'Industrie
L 4823 Rodange, Luxembourg
Tel.: (352) 50191
Fax: (352) 50192587
E-Mail: marea.blanco@arcelormittal.com
Emp.: 318
Industrial Products Mfr
S.I.C.: 3823
N.A.I.C.S.: 334513
Bastian Roland *(Mgr-Site)*

Circuit Foil Luxembourg S.a.r.l. (1)
Rue Salzbach
PO Box 9
L-9501 Wiltz, Luxembourg (90%)
Tel.: (352) 9575511
Telex: 2358 cirfo lu
Fax: (352) 957551249
E-Mail: office@circuitfoil.com
Web Site: www.circuitfoil.com
Emp.: 350
Electro-Deposited Copper Foils Mfr
S.I.C.: 3351
N.A.I.C.S.: 331420
Luc Helsen *(CEO)*

Subsidiary:

Circuit Foil Service S.A. (2)
Rue Salzbach
PO Box 19
L-9501 Wiltz, Luxembourg
Tel.: (352) 957907
Fax: (352) 957491
E-Mail: office@circuitfoilservice.com
Web Site: www.circuitfoil.com
Emp.: 12
Copper Foil Mfr
S.I.C.: 3351
N.A.I.C.S.: 331420
Didier Mauve *(Mng Dir)*

MecanARBED Dommeldange S.a.r.l. (1)
Rue de La Cimenterie
L 1337 Dudelange, Luxembourg
Tel.: (352) 4363621
Telex: 3449 mado lu
Fax: (352) 436362209
E-Mail: joseph.hollman@arcelormittal.com
Web Site: www.arcelor-dommdldanje.com
Emp.: 150
Engineering & Steel Construction; Equipment , Systems & Processes Mfr for Steelmaking; Construction of Buildings & Industrial Complexes
S.I.C.: 8711
N.A.I.C.S.: 541330
Joseph Hollman *(Mng Dir)*

U.S. Subsidiaries:

ArcelorMittal Coatesville (1)
139 Modena Rd
Coatesville, PA 19320
Tel.: (610) 383-2000
Fax: (610) 383-2992
E-Mail: coatesvilleinfo@arcelormittal.com
Web Site: www.arcelormittal.com
Emp.: 800
Construction Machinery Mfr
S.I.C.: 3531
N.A.I.C.S.: 333120
Dennis Newhart *(Sr Engr)*

ArcelorMittal East Chicago (1)
3001 E Columbus Dr 9-000
Chicago, IL 46312
Tel.: (219) 399-6007
Engineering Research & Development Services
S.I.C.: 8731
N.A.I.C.S.: 541712

Arcelormittal Georgetown Inc. (1)
420 S Hazard St
Georgetown, SC 29440
Tel.: (843) 546-2525
Fax: (843) 546-6627
E-Mail: georgetown.sales@arcelormittal.com
Web Site: www.arcelormittal.com
Carbon Wire Rod Mfr & Distr
S.I.C.: 3315
N.A.I.C.S.: 331222
Danie Devapiriam *(Gen Mgr)*

ArcelorMittal Piedmont, LLC (1)
2027 Mclin Creek Rd
Newton, NC 28658
Tel.: (828) 464-9214
Fax: (828) 464-9218
E-Mail: info@arcelormittal.com
Web Site: www.arcelormittal.com
Emp.: 11
General Warehousing Services
S.I.C.: 4225
N.A.I.C.S.: 493110
Debbie McCurry *(Mgr-Admin)*

ArcelorMittal Steel North America (1)
1 S Dearborn
Chicago, IL 60603
Tel.: (312) 899-3991
Fax: (312) 899-3562
Web Site: www.arcelormittal.com
Sales Range: $125-149.9 Million
Emp.: 2
Steel Distrubution
S.I.C.: 5051
N.A.I.C.S.: 423510
Louis L. Schorsch *(CEO)*
Narendra Chaudhary *(Exec VP)*
Andy Harshaw *(Exec VP-Ops)*

Subsidiary:

ArcelorMittal Steel USA Inc. (2)
1 S Dearborn Ste 1800
Chicago, IL 60603 DE
Tel.: (312) 899-3351
Fax: (219) 399-5544
Web Site: www.arcelormittal.com
Emp.: 20,500
Bar & Flat-Rolled Steel Mfr
Import Export
S.I.C.: 3312
N.A.I.C.S.: 331110
Michael G. Rippey *(CEO-USA & Exec VP)*

Subsidiaries:

ArcelorMittal Burns Harbor LLC (3)
250 W US Hwy 12
Burns Harbor, IN 46304 IL
Tel.: (219) 787-2120
Fax: (219) 787-2597
Emp.: 4,000
Mfr. Steel Products
S.I.C.: 7389
N.A.I.C.S.: 425120
John D. Mengel *(VP & Gen Mgr)*

ArcelorMittal Cleveland Inc. (3)
3060 Eggers Rd
Cleveland, OH 44105 DE
Tel.: (216) 429-6000
Fax: (216) 429-6019
Emp.: 3,100
Steel, Energy Products & Aerospace Defense
Import Export
S.I.C.: 3325
N.A.I.C.S.: 331513
Adam Beckler *(Mgr-Acctg)*

ArcelorMittal LaPlace (3)
138 Hwy 3217
La Place, LA 70068 DE
Mailing Address:
PO Box 5000
La Place, LA 70069-1156
Tel.: (985) 652-4900
Fax: (985) 652-8450
Toll Free: (800) 535-7692
Web Site: www.bayousteel.com
Sales Range: $250-299.9 Million
Emp.: 524
Light Structural & Merchant Bar Products Mfr
S.I.C.: 3399
N.A.I.C.S.: 331221
Sally Buckner *(Dir-HR & Labor Rels)*

Plant:

Bayou Steel Corporation (Tennessee) (4)
2404 S Roane St
Harriman, TN 37748
Tel.: (865) 882-5100
Fax: (865) 590-5026
Web Site: www.bayousteel.com
Emp.: 130
Light Structural & Merchant Bar Products Mfr
S.I.C.: 3312
N.A.I.C.S.: 331221
Bob Kenedey *(Plant Mgr)*

ArcelorMittal Minorca Mine Inc. (3)
5950 Old US Hwy 53
Virginia, MN 55792 DE
Tel.: (218) 749-5910
Fax: (218) 749-5256
Emp.: 369
Producer of Iron Ore Fluxed Pellets
S.I.C.: 1011
N.A.I.C.S.: 212210
Jonathan Holmes *(Gen Mgr-Minorca Mines)*

ArcelorMittal Plate LLC (3)
139 Modena Rd
Coatesville, PA 19320-0911 DE
Tel.: (610) 383-2000
Fax: (610) 383-2436
Toll Free: (800) 441-9839
Web Site: www.arcelor.mittal.com
Emp.: 1,000
Mfr of Carbon Alloy & Clad Plate Steels
Import Export
S.I.C.: 3399
N.A.I.C.S.: 331110
Ed Frey *(Gen Mgr)*

ArcelorMittal Steelton LLC (3)
215 S Front St
Steelton, PA 17113
Tel.: (717) 986-2000
Web Site: www.arcelormittal.com
Emp.: 700
Railroad Rails Products & Large Expanded Pipe Mfr
S.I.C.: 8631
N.A.I.C.S.: 813930
Allen Grow *(Mgr-Scrap Sourcing)*

ArcelorMittal Vinton, Inc (3)
Interstate Hwy 10 & Vinton Rd
Canutillo, TX 79835 TX
Tel.: (915) 886-2000
Fax: (915) 886-2218
Toll Free: (800) 669-8464
Web Site: www.bordersteel.com
Sales Range: $75-99.9 Million
Emp.: 360
Steel Making Operations
S.I.C.: 3312
N.A.I.C.S.: 331110
Gerardo Salinas *(Pres)*

ArcelorMittal Weirton Inc. (3)
100 Pennsylvania Ave
Weirton, WV 26062-4950 DE
Tel.: (304) 797-2000
Telex: 710-936-8300 Wsx Weir
Fax: (304) 797-2171
Emp.: 900
Mfr. of Flat Rolled Steel
Import Export
S.I.C.: 3312
N.A.I.C.S.: 331110
Brian James *(Gen Mgr)*

Astralloy Steel Products Inc. (3)
1550 Red Hollow Rd
Birmingham, AL 35215
Tel.: (205) 853-0300
Fax: (205) 853-7321
Toll Free: (800) 633-6635
E-Mail: sales@astralloy.com
Web Site: www.astralloy.com
Sales Range: $25-49.9 Million
Emp.: 60
Metals Service Centers & Offices
S.I.C.: 5051
N.A.I.C.S.: 423510
Edward Moses *(COO)*

Joint Venture:

Double G Coatings Company, L.P. (3)
1096 Mendell Davis Dr
Jackson, MS 39272-9109
Tel.: (601) 371-3460
Fax: (601) 371-3466
Sales Range: $10-24.9 Million
Emp.: 78
Steel Sheeting Mfr
S.I.C.: 3479
N.A.I.C.S.: 332812

Non-U.S. Subsidiaries:

Mittal Canada Inc. (2)
4000 Rte des Acieries
Contrecoeur, QC, JOL 1CO, Canada
Tel.: (450) 587-8600
Fax: (450) 587-8625

Toll Free: (800) 361-2605
E-Mail: info@mittalsteel.com
Web Site: www.mittalsteel.com
Emp.: 2,000
Steel Mfr
S.I.C.: 3462
N.A.I.C.S.: 332111
Daniel Robert *(VP-HR)*

Plants:

Mittal Canada Contrecoeur-Ouest Inc. **(3)**
2050 Rte des Acieries
Contrecoeur, QC, J0L 1CO, Canada
Tel.: (450) 587-2012
Fax: (450) 587-1102
E-Mail: info@arcelormittal.com
Web Site: www.arcelormittal.com
Sales Range: $50-74.9 Million
Emp.: 430
Billets, Merchant Bars & Special Quality Bar Products Mfr
S.I.C.: 3399
N.A.I.C.S.: 331110
Tom Dulok *(Pres)*

Subsidiary:

Fers et Metaux Recycles Ltee. **(4)**
1975 J M Langlois Rd
La Prairie, QC, G5R5Z8, Canada QC
Tel.: (450) 444-4424
Fax: (450) 444-4499
Sales Range: $25-49.9 Million
Emp.: 55
Recycled Metals Whslr
S.I.C.: 3499
N.A.I.C.S.: 332439
Lakshmi Mittal *(Pres)*

Mittal Canada Hamilton Inc. **(3)**
690 Strathearne Ave N
Hamilton, ON, L8N 7N7, Canada
Mailing Address:
PO Box 2030
Hamilton, ON, L8N 3T1, Canada
Tel.: (905) 528-9473
Fax: (905) 777-4481
Toll Free: (800) 461-9473
Emp.: 600
Steel Wire Products
S.I.C.: 3496
N.A.I.C.S.: 332618

Mittal Canada Saint-Patrick Inc. **(3)**
5900 Rue St. Patrick
Montreal, QC, H4E 1B3, Canada
Tel.: (514) 762-5260
Fax: (514) 762-5218
Toll Free: (800) 361-7887
E-Mail: dany.nadeau@mittalsteel.com
Web Site: www.mittalsteel.com
Emp.: 120
Steel Wire Production
S.I.C.: 3315
N.A.I.C.S.: 331222
Danny Nadeau *(Mng Dir)*

ArcelorMittal Tailored Blanks **(1)**
2 Kexon Dr
Pioneer, OH 43554
Tel.: (419) 737-3180
Web Site: www.arcelormittal.com
Automotive Welded Blank Mfr
S.I.C.: 3448
N.A.I.C.S.: 332311
Rodger Swank *(Mgr-Quality)*

Mid-Vol Coal Sales, Inc. **(1)**
640 Clover Dew Dairy Rd
Princeton, WV 24740 WV
Tel.: (304) 325-5719
Fax: (304) 325-5724
Sales Range: $50-74.9 Million
Emp.: 600
Coal Mining & Merchant Whslr
S.I.C.: 5052
N.A.I.C.S.: 423520
Greg Jessee *(Pres)*

U.S. Joint Venture:

AM/NS Calvert **(1)**
(Formerly ThyssenKrupp Steel USA, LLC)
1 Thyssenkrupp Dr
Calvert, AL 36513
Tel.: (251) 289-3000
E-Mail:
Web Site: usa.arcelormittal.com
Emp.: 4,000
Coiled Carbon Steel Mfr & Distr
S.I.C.: 3462
N.A.I.C.S.: 332111
Chris Richards *(Pres)*
Markus Boening *(CFO & VP)*

Non-U.S. Subsidiaries:

Arcelor FCS Commercial S.A. **(1)**
John Kennedylaan 51
9041 Zelzate, Belgium
Tel.: (32) 93422424
Fax: (32) 039474907
E-Mail: fcs@arcelormittal.be
Web Site: www.fcs.arcelor.com
Emp.: 200
Steel Producer
S.I.C.: 3462
N.A.I.C.S.: 332111

Arcelor Logistics Belgium **(1)**
Atlantic House Noordelaan 147
2030 Antwerp, Belgium
Tel.: (32) 33030600
Telex: anvers 31200
Fax: (32) 33030700
E-Mail: logistics@arcelor-mittal.com
Emp.: 60
Steel Producer
S.I.C.: 1011
N.A.I.C.S.: 212210
William Moeyersoen *(Mng Dir)*

ArcelorMittal Ambalaj Celigi Sanayi ve Ticaret A.S. **(1)**
Nispetiye Cad Ozden Is Merkezi No 22-Kat 3
Levent, 34330 Istanbul, Turkey
Tel.: (90) 212 325 27 18
Fax: (90) 212 325 27 23
Web Site: www.arcelormittal.com
Steel Sheet & Slitted Coil Mfr
S.I.C.: 3399
N.A.I.C.S.: 331221

ArcelorMittal Ancenis **(1)**
Zac de l'Aeropole
Ancenis, 44150, France
Tel.: (33) 4 78 97 62 30
Metal Sheet Mfr
S.I.C.: 3499
N.A.I.C.S.: 332999

ArcelorMittal Annaba Spa **(1)**
Sidi Amar El-Hadjar Complex
B P 2055
Annaba, 23000, Algeria
Tel.: (213) 38871525
Fax: (213) 38 876 585
Web Site: www.mittalsteel.com
Iron & Steel Mills
S.I.C.: 3312
N.A.I.C.S.: 331110
Sanjay Kumar *(CEO)*

Arcelormittal Asturias S.A. **(1)**
Lugar Trasona 90
Aviles, Spain
Tel.: (34) 985 12 60 00
Fax: (34) 985 12 66 30
E-Mail: comunicaespana@arcelormittal.com
Web Site: www.arcelormittal.com
Heavy Plate Steel Rod & Rail Mfr
S.I.C.: 3399
N.A.I.C.S.: 331110

ArcelorMittal Atlantique et Lorraine S.A.S. **(1)**
2 Rue Bidet
62240 Desvres, France
Tel.: (33) 3 21 99 28 00
Fax: (33) 3 21 99 28 39
Emp.: 120
Steel Product Mfr
S.I.C.: 3312
N.A.I.C.S.: 331221
Bernard Maille *(Mgr)*

ArcelorMittal Belgium N.V. **(1)**
John Kennedylaan 51
9042 Gent, Belgium
Tel.: (32) 9 347 31 11
Fax: (32) 9 347 49 07
E-Mail: info.sidmar@arcelormittal.com
Emp.: 450
Rolled Steel Products Mfr
S.I.C.: 3399
N.A.I.C.S.: 331221
Wim van Gerven *(CEO)*

ArcelorMittal Beryslav **(1)**
Kirova Str 52
Beryslav, Ukraine
Tel.: (380) 554672285
Limestone Mfr
S.I.C.: 1422
N.A.I.C.S.: 212312

ArcelorMittal Brasil S.A. **(1)**
Avenida Carandai 1115 20/26 Andar
30130-915 Belo Horizonte, MG, Brazil
Tel.: (55) 3132191122
Fax: (55) 3132191358
E-Mail: eimar.magalhaes@arcelormittal.com.br
Web Site: www.arcelor.com
ARCE3—(BRAZ)
Emp.: 10,229
Holding Company; Steel Mfr
S.I.C.: 3462
N.A.I.C.S.: 332111
Jose Armando de Figueiredo Campos *(Chm)*
Benjamin Mario Baptista Filho *(CEO)*

Subsidiary:

Companhia Siderurgica de Tubarao S.A. **(2)**
Ave Brigadeiro Eduardo Gomes
PO Box 930
Jardim Limoeiro, Serra, 29163-970, Brazil
Tel.: (55) 2733481002
Fax: (55) 2733481488
E-Mail: diretoria.amt@arcelormittal.com.br
Web Site: www.arcelormittal.com.br
Emp.: 3,593
Iron & Steel Mills
S.I.C.: 3399
N.A.I.C.S.: 331110
Benjamin Baptista *(CEO)*

Non-U.S. Subsidiary:

Acindar Industria Argentina de Aceros S.A. **(2)**
Estanislao Zeballos 2739
1643 Buenos Aires, Argentina
Tel.: (54) 1147198500
Fax: (54) 1147198501
E-Mail: tomas.acevedo@acindar.com.ar
Web Site: www.acindar.com.ar
Sales Range: $700-749.9 Million
Emp.: 6
Steel Products Mfr
S.I.C.: 3462
N.A.I.C.S.: 332111
Arturo Tomas Acevedo *(Pres)*

ArcelorMittal Bremen GmbH **(1)**
Carl Benz-Strasse 30
D 28237 Bremen, Germany
Mailing Address:
Postfach 21 02 20
D-28222 Bremen, Germany
Tel.: (49) 4216480
Fax: (49) 4216482251
E-Mail: info.amb@arcelormittal.com
Web Site: www.arcelor-bremen.com
Emp.: 3,700
Hot & Cold Rolled Sheet in Coils & Plates Mfr
S.I.C.: 3399
N.A.I.C.S.: 331221
Ditmar Ringel *(Pres & CFO)*
Manfred F. Flearvraghe *(COO)*

Subsidiary:

Bremer Galvanisierungs GmbH **(2)**
Carl Den Str 30
D 28237 Bremen, Germany
Tel.: (49) 4216481500
Fax: (49) 4216481512
Web Site: www.bregal.de
Emp.: 131
Hot Dip Galvanizing Line
S.I.C.: 1011
N.A.I.C.S.: 212210
Bernd Wischnewski *(Mng Dir)*

ArcelorMittal Cariacica **(1)**
Leopoldina Avenue 900 - Vasco da Gama
Cariacica, Espirito Santo, 29140-080, Brazil
Tel.: (55) 27 3246 6000
E-Mail: arcelomittalnet@arcelomittal.com.br
Web Site: www.arcelormittal.com
Rolled Steel Products Mfr
S.I.C.: 3312
N.A.I.C.S.: 331221

Arcelormittal Celaya S.a. De C.v. **(1)**
Av Francisco J Mujica No 1 Int T Col Centro
Lazaro Cardenas, 60950, Mexico
Tel.: (52) 461 618 8980
Fax: (52) 461 618 8982
Steel Product Mfr
S.I.C.: 3399
N.A.I.C.S.: 331110
Victor Cairo *(CEO)*

ArcelorMittal Chevillon **(1)**
1 Rue de la Marne
52170 Chevillon, France
Tel.: (33) 6 29 23 50 25
Fax: (33) 3 25 04 49 15
E-Mail: chevillon.tubularproducts@arcelormittal.com
Precision Tube Mfr
S.I.C.: 3312
N.A.I.C.S.: 331110

ArcelorMittal Commercial RPS Deutschland GmbH **(1)**
Subbelrather Strasse 13
D-50672 Cologne, Germany
Tel.: (49) 352 53 133213
Web Site: www.arcelormittal.com
Emp.: 1,000
Mfr of Sheet Piles, Rails & Special Sections
S.I.C.: 3441
N.A.I.C.S.: 332312
Marc Blum *(Mgr)*

ArcelorMittal Commercial UK FCE Ltd. **(1)**
Arcelor House 4 Prince's Way
Solihull, W Midlands, United Kingdom
Tel.: (44) 1217055444
Fax: (44) 1217030580
E-Mail: John.dyer@arcelormittal.com
Web Site: www.fcs.arcelor.com
Emp.: 55
Integrated Steel Mfr
S.I.C.: 3325
N.A.I.C.S.: 331513
John Dyer *(Mng Dir)*

ArcelorMittal Distribution S.A.S. **(1)**
16 Avenue de la Malle
Saint Brice Courcelles, F-51076 Reims, Cedex, France
Tel.: (33) 326846565
Fax: (33) 3 2684 6650
Steel Products Distr
S.I.C.: 4731
N.A.I.C.S.: 541614
Jacques Dham *(Pres & CEO)*
Gerry Stoll *(Deputy CEO)*
Francois Savage *(CFO)*
Vincent Gillet *(Sr Exec VP)*

Non-U.S. Unit:

Arcelor Distribution **(2)**
19 Ave Be La liberpe
2930 Luxembourg, Luxembourg
Tel.: (352) 47924730
Fax: (352) 4792675
E-Mail: info@arcelormittal.com
Web Site: www.arcelormittal.com
Emp.: 800
Steel Products Distr
S.I.C.: 4731
N.A.I.C.S.: 541614
Lakshmi N. Mittal *(Chm & CEO)*

ArcelorMittal Dofasco Inc. **(1)**
1330 Burlington St E
PO Box 2460
Hamilton, ON, L8N 3J5, Canada
Tel.: (905) 544-3761
Fax: (905) 548-4935
Toll Free: (800) 363-2726
E-Mail:
Web Site: www.dofasco.ca
Sales Range: $5-14.9 Billion
Emp.: 7,400
Galvanized, Tinplate & Chromium-Coated Flat Rolled Steels & Tubular Products Mfr
S.I.C.: 3312
N.A.I.C.S.: 331110
Juergen G. Schachler *(Pres & CEO)*
Raymond P. d'Andrade *(Treas)*
Urmas Soomet *(Sec & Dir-Legal Svcs)*

Subsidiaries:

ArcelorMittal Mines Canada Inc. **(2)**
1801 Mcgill College Suite 1400
Montreal, QC, H3A 2N4, Canada

ArcelorMittal—(Continued)

Tel.: (514) 285-1464
Fax: (514) 285-1978
Web Site: www.arcelormittal.com
Iron Ore Products Distr
S.I.C.: 5051
N.A.I.C.S.: 423510
Alain Cauchon *(VP-Operational Excellence & HR)*

Dosfasco Tubular Products (2)
193 Givins Street
PO Box 1589
Woodstock, ON, N4S 0A7, Canada
Tel.: (519) 537-6671
Fax: (519) 539-0778
E-Mail: info@dofascotube.com
Web Site: www.dofascotube.com
Emp.: 400
Steel Tubing Mfr
S.I.C.: 3317
N.A.I.C.S.: 331210
William Chisholm *(Pres)*

Plant:

ArcelorMittal Brampton (3)
14 Holtby Ave
Brampton, ON, L6X 2M3, Canada
Tel.: (905) 451-2400
Fax: (905) 451-2795
Toll Free: (800) 268-3005
E-Mail: info@dofascotube.com
Web Site: www.dofascotube.com
Emp.: 450
Mfr of Automotive Steel Tubing
S.I.C.: 3317
N.A.I.C.S.: 331210
Bill Chisholm *(Pres)*
Jerome Granboulan *(CEO)*

U.S. Subsidiary:

Dofasco Tubular Products (3)
2105 Four Gateway Center
Pittsburgh, PA 15222-1211
Tel.: (412) 263-3200
Fax: (412) 263-6996
E-Mail: info@dofascotube.com
Web Site: www.dofascotube.com
Retailer of Tubular Steel Products
S.I.C.: 3317
N.A.I.C.S.: 331210

Quebec Cartier Mining Co. (2)
24 Des Iles Blvd Ste 201
Port-Cartier, QC, G5B 2H3, Canada
Tel.: (418) 766-2000
Fax: (418) 768-2154
E-Mail: duval.johanne@arcelormittal.com
Web Site: www.qcmines.com
Emp.: 1,800
Iron Ore Products Mfr
S.I.C.: 1011
N.A.I.C.S.: 212210
Francois Pelletier *(Pres, CEO & COO)*

Joint Ventures:

Baycoat Ltd. (2)
244 Lanark Street
Hamilton, ON, L8N 3K7, Canada
Tel.: (905) 561-0965
Fax: (905) 560-0189
Web Site: www.dofasco.ca
Sales Range: $75-99.9 Million
Emp.: 250
Paint Services to Rolled Steel Coils; Owned 50% by Dofasco, Inc. & 50% by Stelco Incorporated
S.I.C.: 1721
N.A.I.C.S.: 238320
Lionel T. Motl *(Pres & Gen Mgr)*

DJ Galvanizing (2)
300 Sprucewood Avenue
Windsor, ON, N9C 3Y6, Canada
Tel.: (519) 250-2100
Fax: (519) 250-2199
Emp.: 100
Hot-Dip Galvanizing Services; Owned 50% by Dofasco, Inc. & 50% by JFE Steel Corporation
S.I.C.: 3312
N.A.I.C.S.: 331221
Paul Dunmore *(Pres)*

U.S. Subsidiary:

Dofasco USA Inc. (2)
26899 Northwestern Hwy
Southfield, MI 48034-2195
Tel.: (248) 357-3090
Fax: (248) 357-9888
Toll Free: (800) DOFSUSA
Web Site: www.dofasco.ca
Emp.: 10
Steel Whslr
S.I.C.: 5051
N.A.I.C.S.: 423510

U.S. Joint Venture:

Gallatin Steel Company (2)
4831 US Hwy 42 W
Ghent, KY 41045-9704
Tel.: (859) 567-3100
Fax: (859) 567-3165
Toll Free: (800) 581-3853
E-Mail: feedback@gallatinsteel.com
Web Site: www.gallatinsteel.com
Sales Range: $75-99.9 Million
Emp.: 500
Flat-Rolled Carbon Steel Mfr; Owned 50% by Dofasco, Inc. & 50% by Gerdau AmeriSteel Corporation
S.I.C.: 3399
N.A.I.C.S.: 331221
Tobin Pospisil *(Pres)*

ArcelorMittal Duisburg GmbH (1)
Vohwinkelstrasse 107
47137 Duisburg, Germany
Tel.: (49) 203 606 67353
Fax: (49) 203 606 66332
Web Site: www.arcelormittalduisburg.de
Rolled Steel Products Mfr
S.I.C.: 3312
N.A.I.C.S.: 331221

ArcelorMittal Eisenhuttenstadt GmbH (1)
Werkstrasse 1
Eisenhuttenstadt, 15888, Germany
Tel.: (49) 33 64 37 0
Fax: (49) 33 64 44 02 0
E-Mail: info@arcelormittal-ehst.com
Web Site: www.arcelormittal-ehst.com
Rev.: $1,637,202,210
Emp.: 3,000
Rolled Steel Products Mfr
S.I.C.: 3312
N.A.I.C.S.: 331221
Matthieu Jehl *(CEO)*
Ralf-Peter Boesler *(COO-Primary)*
Pierre Jacobs *(COO-Finishing)*
Joachim Niebur *(Dir-Labour)*
Jean-Marie Barthel *(Member-Mgmt Bd)*

ArcelorMittal Escazu (1)
2-1251 San Rafael de Escazu
San Rafael, San Jose, Costa Rica
Tel.: (506) 22058900
Fax: (506) 22058999
Web Site: www.arcelormittal.com
Business Process Consulting Services
S.I.C.: 8742
N.A.I.C.S.: 541611

ArcelorMittal Espana S.A. (1)
Residencia La Granda 1
33440 Gozon, Asturias, Spain ES
Tel.: (34) 985 126 153
Fax: (34) 985 126 088
Emp.: 200
Flat Carbon Steel Products Mfr & Distr
S.I.C.: 3312
N.A.I.C.S.: 331221
Guillermo Ulacia *(Sr Exec VP)*

ArcelorMittal France S.A. (1)
1 Rue Luigi Cherubini
93200 Saint Denis, France FR
Tel.: (33) 141256010
Telex: 614730 usinr f
Sales Range: $600-649.9 Million
Emp.: 577
Steel Mfr
Import Export
S.I.C.: 3325
N.A.I.C.S.: 331513

ArcelorMittal Frydek-Mistek a.s. (1)
Krizikova 1377
738 01 Frydek-Mistek, Czech Republic
Tel.: (420) 558 48 11 11
Fax: (420) 558 48 23 09
E-Mail: info@vpfm.cz
Web Site: www.vpfm.cz
Rolled Steel Products Mfr
S.I.C.: 3312
N.A.I.C.S.: 331221
Dirk Stroo *(Chm & CEO)*
Ashok Patil *(Vice Chm)*

ArcelorMittal Galati S.A. (1)
Str Smardan nr 1
6200 Bucharest, Romania
Tel.: (40) 236407633
Fax: (40) 236 407635
Web Site: www.arcelormittal.com
Emp.: 16,500
Iron & Steel Mills
S.I.C.: 3312
N.A.I.C.S.: 331110
K. A.P. Singh *(CEO)*

ArcelorMittal Gandrange S.A (1)
Site Industriel
57175 Amenville, France
Tel.: (33) 387706000
Fax: (33) 387707272
Web Site: www.ispat.com
Emp.: 1,000
Mfr. of Wire Rods, Rails, Light Girders, Steel Piling & Rolled Steel
S.I.C.: 3312
N.A.I.C.S.: 331221
Bernard Laupretre *(CEO)*

ArcelorMittal Geel (1)
10 Lammerdries Industriezone Geel W Zone 4
B 2440 Geel, Belgium
Tel.: (32) 014563050
Fax: (32) 014590839
E-Mail: info@mittal.arcelor.com
Web Site: www.arcelormittal.nl
Rev.: $125,809,296
Emp.: 70
Coil Coating Services
Import Export
S.I.C.: 2999
N.A.I.C.S.: 324199
Hermen Steenhaut *(Gen Mgr)*

ARCELORMITTAL GENK N.V. (1)
Kanaaloever 3
3600 Genk, Belgium
Tel.: (32) 89 30 18 05
Fax: (32) 89 30 18 00
E-Mail: info.arcelor.genk@arcelormittal.com
Emp.: 15
Cold Rolled Steel Mfr
S.I.C.: 3399
N.A.I.C.S.: 331221
Johan Aelter *(Gen Mgr)*

ArcelorMittal Gent N.V. (1)
John Kennedylaan 51
9042 Gent, Belgium
Tel.: (32) 93473111
Telex: Gent 11 491
Fax: (32) 93474907
E-Mail: info.sidmar@arcelormittal.com
Web Site: www.arcelormittal.com
Emp.: 5,500
Flat Steel Products & Wide High Quality Cold Rolled Sheet Steel Mfr
Import Export
S.I.C.: 3399
N.A.I.C.S.: 331221
Wim Van Gerven *(CEO)*

ArcelorMittal Gent (1)
John Kennedylaan 51
9042 Gent, Belgium
Tel.: (32) 93473111
Fax: (32) 93474907
E-Mail: info.arcelor.shank@arcelor.com
Web Site: www.arcelormittal.com
Emp.: 5,500
Steel Electro-Galvanizing
Import Export
S.I.C.: 3471
N.A.I.C.S.: 332813
Wim Van Gerven *(CEO)*

ArcelorMittal Gipuzkoa S.L. (1)
Artiz Auzotegia 34
Zumarraga, Spain
Tel.: (34) 943720011
Fax: (34) 943722509
Rolled Steel Products Mfr
S.I.C.: 3312
N.A.I.C.S.: 331221

Arcelormittal guapiles (1)
2-1251 San Rafael de Escazu
Guapiles, Limon, Costa Rica
Tel.: (506) 27135001
Rolled Steel Product Mfr & Distr
S.I.C.: 3399
N.A.I.C.S.: 331221

ArcelorMittal Hamburg GmbH (1)
Dradenaustrasse 33
D 21129 Hamburg, Germany De
Tel.: (49) 4074080
Fax: (49) 4074081213
E-Mail: britta.hempel@arcelormittal.com
Sls.: $532,155,808
Emp.: 700
S.I.C.: 1011
N.A.I.C.S.: 212210
Lutz Bandusch *(CEO)*

ARCELORMITTAL HAMILTON INC. (1)
1330 Burlington St E
Po Box 2460
Hamilton, ON, L8N 3J5, Canada
Tel.: (905) 548-6411
Rolled Steel Product Mfr & Distr
S.I.C.: 3312
N.A.I.C.S.: 331221

ArcelorMittal Hautmont (1)
12 Rue des Usines
59330 Hautmont, France
Tel.: (33) 6 29 23 50 25
Fax: (33) 3 27 69 20 55
E-Mail: hautmont.tubularproducts@arcelormittal.com
Precision Tube Mfr
S.I.C.: 3399
N.A.I.C.S.: 331110

ArcelorMittal Hunedoara S.A. (1)
Str Plata Iancu de Hunedoara nr 1
2750 Hunedoara, Romania
Tel.: (40) 254712783
Fax: (40) 254715311
Emp.: 2,200
Iron & Steel Mills
S.I.C.: 3312
N.A.I.C.S.: 331110
Regie Paul Aikaravelil *(CEO)*

ArcelorMittal Itauna (1)
Clara Chaves Street 150 Sao Judas Tadeu, Itauna, Minas Gerais, 35681-168, Brazil
Tel.: (55) 37 3249 4400
E-Mail: arcelormittalnet@arcelormittal.com.br
Steel Bar & Beam Mfr
S.I.C.: 3399
N.A.I.C.S.: 331221

ArcelorMittal Jubail (1)
Cross Cut Road of 308 & 305 Jubail 2 Industrial City
Po Box 10090
31961 Al Jubayl, Saudi Arabia
Tel.: (966) 33 67 14 22
Fax: (966) 33 67 00 24
Precision Tube Mfr
S.I.C.: 3312
N.A.I.C.S.: 331110

ArcelorMittal Juiz de Fora. (1)
Br-040 km 769 Dias Tavares
Juiz de Fora, Minas Gerias, 36105-000, Brazil
Tel.: (55) 32 3229 1000
E-Mail: arcelomittalnet@arcelomittal.com.br
Rolled & Drawn Steel Product Mfr
S.I.C.: 3312
N.A.I.C.S.: 331221

ArcelorMittal Kryviy Rih (1)
1 Ordzhonikidze Street
Krivoy Rog, 50095, Ukraine
Tel.: (380) 564783009
Fax: (380) 564745449
Iron & Steel Mills
S.I.C.: 3312
N.A.I.C.S.: 331110
Jean Robert Jeot *(CEO)*
Rinat Starkov *(CEO)*
Igor Schetinin *(Chief Mining Production Officer)*

ArcelorMittal Lazaro Cardenas S.A. de C.V. (1)
Francisco J Mujica No 1 B Apartado Postal No 19-A
CP 60950 Michoacan, Lazaro Cardenas, Mexico MX
Tel.: (52) 753 533 2606
Fax: (52) 753 532 2723

Web Site: pc.arcelormittal.com
Emp.: 1,100
Produces, Sells & Exports Steel & Slab Products
S.I.C.: 3496
N.A.I.C.S.: 332618
P. S. Venkataramanan *(CEO)*

ARCELORMITTAL LESAKA S.A. (1)
Barrio Arratzubi N 5
31770 Lesaka, Navarra, Spain
Tel.: (34) 948 62 83 00
Fax: (34) 948 62 83 77
Web Site: www.arcelormittal.com
Steel Products Mfr
S.I.C.: 3312
N.A.I.C.S.: 331110

ArcelorMittal Liege SA (1)
Rue de la Digue 22
4400 Flemalle, Belgium
Tel.: (32) 42 36 11 11
Fax: (32) 42 36 29 75
E-Mail: infoliege@arcelormittal.com
Web Site: www.arcelormittal.com
Rolled Steel Products Mfr
S.I.C.: 3399
N.A.I.C.S.: 331221

ArcelorMittal London (1)
2440 Scanlan Street
London, ON, NSW 6H7, Canada
Tel.: (519) 451-7701
Fax: (519) 539-6804
Toll Free: (800) 265-4082
E-Mail: london.tubularproducts@arcelomittal.com
Web Site: www.arcelormittal.com
Emp.: 33
Steel Product Mfr
S.I.C.: 3312
N.A.I.C.S.: 331221
Gregory West *(Gen Mgr)*

ArcelorMittal Madrid S.L. (1)
Carretera da Toledo Km 9 2
Vilaverde, 28021 Madrid, Spain
Tel.: (34) 917972300
Fax: (34) 915053103
E-Mail: comunicaespana@arcelomittal.com
Rolled Steel Products Mfr
S.I.C.: 3312
N.A.I.C.S.: 331221

ArcelorMittal Mediterranee S.A.S. (1)
1 Rue Luigi Cherubini
Saint Denis, 93210, France
Tel.: (33) 171920000
Web Site: www.arcelormediterranee.com
Rolled Steel Products Mfr
S.I.C.: 3399
N.A.I.C.S.: 331221

ArcelorMittal Monlevade S.A. (1)
Getulio Vargas Avenue 100
Joao Monlevade, Minas Gerais, 35930-900, Brazil
Tel.: (55) 31 38591212
E-Mail: arcelormittalnet@arcelormittal.com.br
Web Site: www.arcelormittal.com
Rolled Steel Products Mfr & Distr
S.I.C.: 3312
N.A.I.C.S.: 331221

ArcelorMittal Monterrey (1)
Saltilo km 28 2 Col Arco Vial
Monterrey, 66050, Mexico
Tel.: (52) 81 8220 80 42
Steel Tube & Pipe Mfr
S.I.C.: 3317
N.A.I.C.S.: 331210

ArcelorMittal Montreal Inc. (1)
4000 Route Des Acieries
Contrecoeur, QC, J0L 1C0, Canada
Tel.: (450) 587-8600
Fax: (514) 587-8777
Web Site: www.arcelormittal.com
Emp.: 2,300
Producer of Semi-Finished Products, Slabs, Billets & Other Steel Products
S.I.C.: 3312
N.A.I.C.S.: 331221

U.S. Subsidiary:

Walker Wire & Steel Company (2)
660 East 10 Mile Rd
Ferndale, MI 48220-1036 MI
Tel.: (248) 399-4800
Fax: (248) 399-7881
Web Site: www.mittalsteel.com
Emp.: 150
Mfr. of Steel Wiredrawing
S.I.C.: 3315
N.A.I.C.S.: 331222

ARCELORMITTAL OLABERRIA S.L. (1)
Ctra Madrid - Irun KM 417
Olaberria, Guipuzcoa, 20212, Spain
Tel.: (34) 94 380 5000
Fax: (34) 94 388 0404
E-Mail: comunicaespana@arcelomittal.com
Rolled Steel Products Mfr
S.I.C.: 3399
N.A.I.C.S.: 331221

ArcelorMittal Ostrava a.s. (1)
Vratimovska 689
Ostrava, Kuncice, 707 02, Czech Republic (82.55%)
Tel.: (420) 597331111
Fax: (420) 595684232
Web Site: www.mittal-steel.pl
Emp.: 8,900
Iron & Steel Mills
S.I.C.: 3312
N.A.I.C.S.: 331110
Augustine Koshuparampil *(Chm & CEO)*
Josef Buryan *(Vice Chm & Dir-Production & Tech)*
Gerhard Renz *(Vice Chm-Supervisory Bd)*
Sanjay Samaddar *(Pres & CEO)*
Hana Cubonova *(CIO)*
Peter Baranek *(Chief Green Officer)*
Jiri Michalek *(Chief Health & Safety Officer)*

ArcelorMittal Piombino S.p.A. (1)
Via Portovecchio 34
57025 Piombino, Livorno, Italy
Tel.: (39) 0565 65111
Fax: (39) 0565 65399
E-Mail: infopiombino@arcelor.com
Web Site: www.magona.it
Rolled Steel Products Mfr
S.I.C.: 3399
N.A.I.C.S.: 331221
Jean Luc Maurange *(Pres)*
Leandro Nannipieri *(Mng Dir & Gen Mgr)*

ArcelorMittal Point Lisas Ltd (1)
Mediterranean Drive
Point Lisas, Couva, Trinidad & Tobago
Tel.: (868) 636 2211
Fax: (868) 636 5696
S.I.C.: 1011
N.A.I.C.S.: 212210
Nelson Berros *(Mng Dir & CEO)*

ArcelorMittal Projects Belgium NV (1)
Industrielaan 2 Nolimpark 1323
3900 Overpelt, Belgium
Tel.: (32) 11 800 890
Fax: (32) 11 800 895
E-Mail: projects.europe@arcelormittal.com
Web Site: www.arcelormittal.com
Emp.: 3
Rolled Steel Products Mfr
S.I.C.: 3312
N.A.I.C.S.: 331221

ArcelorMittal Projects Netherlands BV (1)
Mannesmannweg 5
4794 SL Heijningen, Netherlands
Tel.: (31) 88 0083 700
Fax: (31) 88 0083 800
E-Mail: projects.europe@arcelormittal.com
Web Site: www.damwand.nl
Emp.: 150
Rolled Steel Products Mfr
S.I.C.: 3312
N.A.I.C.S.: 331221
Jacobus Paesschen *(Mng Dir)*

ArcelorMittal Rongcheng (1)
No 36 Chengshan Dadao W
Rongcheng, Shandong, 264300, China
Tel.: (86) 6317523619
Web Site: www.arcelormittal.com
Steel Cord & Bead Wire Mfr
S.I.C.: 3399
N.A.I.C.S.: 331221

ArcelorMittal Ruhrort GmbH (1)
Vohwinkelstrasse 107
D 47137 Duisburg, Germany De
Tel.: (49) 2035267353
Fax: (49) 2035266332
Emp.: 950
S.I.C.: 1011
N.A.I.C.S.: 212210
Bernd Webersinke *(Mng Dir)*

ARCELORMITTAL SAGUNTO SL (1)
Carretera de Acceso IV Planta KM 3 9
46520 Sagunto, Spain
Tel.: (34) 962 65 81 00
Fax: (34) 962 65 81 93
E-Mail: comunicaespana@arcelormittal.com
Web Site: www.arcelormittal.com
Cold Rolled Coil Mfr
S.I.C.: 3676
N.A.I.C.S.: 334416

ARCELORMITTAL SESTAO S.L.U (1)
Chavarri 6
48910 Sestao, Spain
Tel.: (34) 944 89 44 11
Fax: (34) 944 89 44 14
Web Site: www.arcelormittal.com
Rolled Steel Products Mfr
S.I.C.: 3312
N.A.I.C.S.: 331221

ArcelorMittal Shipping Ltd. (1)
7th Fl Berkeley Square House
London, W1J 6DA, United Kingdom
Tel.: (44) 2073980720
Fax: (44) 02076297993
E-Mail: reception@arcelormittal.com
Sales Range: $10-24.9 Million
Emp.: 20
Management of Cargo Vessels; Chartering Services; Freight Forwarding
S.I.C.: 4491
N.A.I.C.S.: 488320
Viral Vora *(VP)*

ArcelorMittal Skopje (CRM) AD (1)
Str 16 Makedonska Brigada No 18
MK 1000 Skopje, Macedonia
Tel.: (389) 2 3247 300
Fax: (389) 2 3247 304
Web Site: www.arcelormittal.com
Rolled Steel Products Mfr
S.I.C.: 3312
N.A.I.C.S.: 331221
Aleksandar Rankovic *(Mng Dir)*

ArcelorMittal South Africa Ltd. (1)
Vanderbijlpark Steel 3rd Floor Main Bldg
Delfos Boulevard, Vanderbijlpark, Gauteng, 1900, South Africa ZA
Mailing Address:
PO Box 2
Vanderbijlpark, 1900, South Africa
Tel.: (27) 168899111
Fax: (27) 168892097
Web Site: www.mittalsteelsa.com
Sales Range: $1-4.9 Billion
Emp.: 9,000
Steel & Steel Products
Import Export
S.I.C.: 3325
N.A.I.C.S.: 331513
Hans Ludwig Rosenstock *(Acting CEO)*
Matthias Wellhausen *(CFO)*

Units:

ArcelorMittal South Africa Ltd. - Newcastle Works (2)
Iscor Road
Newcastle, 2940, South Africa
Tel.: (27) 34 314 7911
Fax: (27) 34 318 1341
Web Site: www.arcelormittalsa.com
Emp.: 1,850
Rolled Steel Products Mfr
S.I.C.: 3312
N.A.I.C.S.: 331221
Fanie Conradie *(Mgr-Rolling & Quality)*

ArcelorMittal South Africa Ltd. - Pretoria Works (2)
Frikkie Meyer Road
Pretoria West, 0001 Pretoria, South Africa
Tel.: (27) 12 380 2510
Fax: (27) 12 380 2117
Web Site: www.arcelormittalsa.com
Rolled Steel Products Mfr
S.I.C.: 3399
N.A.I.C.S.: 331221

ArcelorMittal South Africa Ltd. - Saldanha Works (2)
Ystervarkensrug
7395 Saldanha, South Africa
Tel.: (27) 22 709 4000
Fax: (27) 22 709 4200
Web Site: www.arcelormittalsa.com
Rolled Steel Products Mfr
S.I.C.: 3312
N.A.I.C.S.: 331221
Dhesan Moodley *(Gen Mgr)*

ArcelorMittal South Africa Ltd. - Vanderbijlpark Works (2)
Delfos Boulevard
Vanderbijlpark, South Africa
Tel.: (27) 16 889 9111
Fax: (27) 16 889 4318
Web Site: www.arcelormittalsa.com
Emp.: 4,500
Rolled Steel Products Mfr
S.I.C.: 3312
N.A.I.C.S.: 331221
Hayder Dalwai *(Mgr-HR)*

ArcelorMittal South Africa Ltd. - Vereeniging Works (2)
273 General Hertzog Road Peacehaven
Leeuwkuil, 1930 Vereeniging, South Africa
Tel.: (27) 16 440 3000
Fax: (27) 16 454 3139
Web Site: www.arcelormittalsa.com
Emp.: 908
Rolled Steel Products Mfr
S.I.C.: 3399
N.A.I.C.S.: 331221
Roelof Jansen *(Acting Gen Mgr)*

Non-U.S. Joint Venture:

Macsteel International Holdings B.V. (2)
Zuidplein 164
World Trade Ctr, Amsterdam, 1077 XV, Netherlands NL
Tel.: (31) 206424361
Fax: (31) 204044307
Web Site: www.macsteelinternational.com
Emp.: 4
Holding Company; Steel Production & Distr; Owned 50% by ArcelorMittal & 50% by Macsteel Holdings (pty) Ltd. S.A.
S.I.C.: 6719
N.A.I.C.S.: 551112
Leon Price *(CEO)*

Non-U.S. Subsidiaries:

Macsteel International Australia Pty., Ltd. (3)
Suite 1 Level 22
141 Walker Street
Sydney, NSW 2060, Australia
Tel.: (61) 2 9955 7566
Fax: (61) 2 9955 5870
Web Site: www.macsteelinternational.com
Steel Products Distr
S.I.C.: 3325
N.A.I.C.S.: 331513
Les Isaacs *(Mng Dir)*

Macsteel International FZCO (3)
Jumairah Lake Towers
AG Silver Tower 25 Fl, Dubai, United Arab Emirates
Tel.: (971) 44402100
Fax: (971) 4402150
Web Site: www.macsteelinternational.com
Emp.: 25
Steel Products Distr
S.I.C.: 3325
N.A.I.C.S.: 331513
Stuart Lever *(Mng Dir)*

Macsteel Service Centres SA (Pty) Ltd. (3)
7 Brook Rd
Lilianton, Boksburg, South Africa
Tel.: (27) 118710000
Fax: (27) 118233860
Web Site: www.macsteel.co.za
Emp.: 160
Steel Product Mfr & Distr
S.I.C.: 3325
N.A.I.C.S.: 331513
Michael R. Pimstein *(CEO)*

ArcelorMittal—(Continued)

U.S. Subsidiary:

Macsteel International USA Corporation (4)
333 Westchester Ave Ste S101
White Plains, NY 10604
Tel.: (914) 872-2700
Fax: (914) 872-2722
E-Mail: miusa@miusacorp.com
Web Site: www.miusacorp.com
Emp.: 21
Steel Alloy, Carbon Rod & Wire Distr
S.I.C.: 5039
N.A.I.C.S.: 423390
Salvatore Purpura *(Pres & CEO)*

ArcelorMittal SSC UK Ltd (1)
Strawberry Ln
Willenhall, Wolverhampton, WV13 3SE, United Kingdom
Tel.: (44) 902365200
Fax: (44) 902365201
Sales Range: $125-149.9 Million
Emp.: 130
S.I.C.: 1011
N.A.I.C.S.: 212210

ArcelorMittal Tallinn OU (1)
Koorma 5 Muuga Harbor
Viimsi, 74004, Estonia
Tel.: (372) 6056 600
Fax: (372) 6056 601
E-Mail: amt.info@arcelormittal.com
Steel Sheet Mfr
S.I.C.: 3444
N.A.I.C.S.: 332322

ArcelorMittal Temirtau (1)
1 Republic Avenue
472319 Temirtau, Kazakhstan
Tel.: (7) 3213969935
Fax: (7) 3213969835
Web Site: www.arcelormittal.com
Iron & Steel Mills
S.I.C.: 3312
N.A.I.C.S.: 331110
Frank Pannier *(CEO)*

ArcelorMittal Tubarao (1)
Av Brigadeiro Eduardo Gomes 930 - Jardim Limoeiro
29163-970 Serra, Espirito Santo, Brazil
Tel.: (55) 27 3348 1333
Fax: (55) 27 3348 1488
E-Mail: comum@cst.com.br
Web Site: www.cst.com.br/english/
Steel Product Mfr
S.I.C.: 3312
N.A.I.C.S.: 331221

ArcelorMittal Tubular Products Iasi SA (1)
Calea Chisinaului Street
700180 Iasi, Romania
Tel.: (40) 232203103
Fax: (40) 232203300
Web Site: www.arcelormittal.com
Iron & Steel Mills; Welded Carbon Steel Tubes Mfr
S.I.C.: 3312
N.A.I.C.S.: 331110
Alina Prahoveanu *(Mng Dir)*

ArcelorMittal Tubular Products Karvina a.s. (1)
Rude armady 471
733 23 Karvina, Czech Republic
Tel.: (420) 596 391 111
Fax: (420) 596 311 373
E-Mail: jakl@jakl.cz
Web Site: www.jakl.cz
Emp.: 421
Steel Product Mfr
S.I.C.: 3399
N.A.I.C.S.: 331221
Stanislav Konkolski *(CEO)*

ArcelorMittal Tubular Products Roman S.A. (1)
246 Stefan cel Mare Street
5550 Roman, Neamt, Romania
Tel.: (40) 233 748089
Fax: (40) 233 748465
Emp.: 3,100
Iron & Steel Mills
S.I.C.: 3312
N.A.I.C.S.: 331110
Regie Paul Aikaravelil *(Mng Dir)*

ArcelorMittal Warszawa Sp. z.o.o. (1)
ul Kasprowicza 132
01-949 Warsaw, Poland
Tel.: (48) 22 835 8000
Fax: (48) 22 835 4222
Web Site: www.arcelormittal-warszawa.com
Steel Products Mfr
S.I.C.: 3312
N.A.I.C.S.: 331110
Henryk Hulin *(Chm-Mgmt Bd)*
Alina Bielecka *(Dir-Personnel)*
Dariusz Marchewka *(Dir-Fin)*
Jan Nowicki *(Dir-Production)*

ArcelorMittal Zaragoza S.A. (1)
Parque Tecnologico de Reciclado Lopez Soriano Parcela c1-11 Ctra
KM 1 95 La Cartuja Baja, Zaragoza, 50720, Spain
Tel.: (34) 976 46 61 71
Fax: (34) 976 51 76 48
E-Mail: comunicaespana@arcelormittal.com
Rolled Steel Products Mfr
S.I.C.: 3399
N.A.I.C.S.: 331221

Baffinland Iron Mines Corporation (1)
120 Adelaide Street W Ste 1016
Toronto, ON, M5H 1T1, Canada ON
Tel.: (416) 364-8820 (70%)
Fax: (416) 364-0193
E-Mail: info@baffinland.com
Web Site: www.baffinland.com
Sales Range: $1-9.9 Million
Emp.: 20
Iron Ore Mining
S.I.C.: 1011
N.A.I.C.S.: 212210
Tom Paddon *(Pres & CEO)*
Stephaine Anderson *(CFO)*
Michael T. Zurowski *(Exec VP)*

Cockerill Sambre S.A. (1)
Quai du Halage 10
Flemalle, 4400, Belgium
Tel.: (32) 42361111
Fax: (32) 4236 2860
E-Mail:
Emp.: 3,000
Iron & Steel Industry
Import Export
S.I.C.: 3312
N.A.I.C.S.: 331110
Dehut Bernard *(CEO)*

Subsidiaries:

Cockerill Mecanique Prestations (2)
14 Quai d'Ougnee
4102 Seraing, Belgium
Tel.: (32) 43302793
Fax: (32) 43302389
Sales Range: $10-24.9 Million
Emp.: 105
Steel Producer
S.I.C.: 3399
N.A.I.C.S.: 331110
Patrick Bardet *(Mng Dir)*

Colorprofil N.V. (1)
8 Lammerdries Industrieterrein Geel W
2440 Geel, Belgium
Tel.: (32) 14563943
Fax: (32) 14592710
E-Mail: info@arcelormittal.com
Web Site: www.colorprofil.arcelor.com
Sales Range: Less than $1 Million
Emp.: 67
Steel Roof Producer
S.I.C.: 1791
N.A.I.C.S.: 238120

Etilam S.A. (1)
52 Avenue du General Sarrail
52115 Saint Dizier, Cedex, France
Tel.: (33) 325556800
Fax: (33) 325069131
E-Mail: concettina.dalba@arcelormittal.com
Web Site: www.etilam.fr
Sls.: $37,587,000
Emp.: 150
Cold Rolling & Coating of Steel; Fastening Devices for the Building Industry
S.I.C.: 3312
N.A.I.C.S.: 331221

Ferrometalli Safem S.p.A. (1)
97 Viale Sicilia
20052 Monza, Italy
Tel.: (39) 03928121
Fax: (39) 02 61864010
Emp.: 150
Steel Service Center
S.I.C.: 5051
N.A.I.C.S.: 423510

Galtec N.V. (1)
51 John Kennedylaan
B 9042 Gent, Belgium
Tel.: (32) 93473111
Fax: (32) 93474907
E-Mail: arcelormittal@arcelormittal.com
Emp.: 10,000
Iron Ore Mining
S.I.C.: 1011
N.A.I.C.S.: 212210

Industeel Belgium S.A. (1)
266 Rue de Chatelet
6030 Charleroi, Belgium
Tel.: (32) 71 44 16 99
Fax: (32) 71 44 17 14
Web Site: www.industeel.info/about/industrial-presence/belgium.aspx
Emp.: 950
Steel Products Mfr
S.I.C.: 3312
N.A.I.C.S.: 331110
Alex Nick *(CEO)*

Industeel France S.A. (1)
Le Creusot Plant 56 Rue Clemenceau
BP 19
71201 Le Creusot, France
Tel.: (33) 3 85 80 55 55
Fax: (33) 3 85 80 55 00
E-Mail: contact@industeel.info
Web Site: www.arcelormittal.com
Emp.: 1,000
Steel Products Distr
S.I.C.: 5051
N.A.I.C.S.: 423510
Alex Nick *(CEO)*

Kiswire ArcelorMittal Ltd. (1)
134 Yoosan-dong
Yangsan, Kyungnam, 626 230, Korea (South)
Tel.: (82) 55 380 3404
Fax: (82) 55 380 3490
E-Mail: trefilko@soback.kornet.nm.kr
Web Site: www.kiswire.com
Sales Range: $10-24.9 Million
Emp.: 500
Steel Cord Producer
S.I.C.: 3399
N.A.I.C.S.: 331221

U.S. Branch:

ArcelorMittal-Kiswire LLC (2)
7901 Cleveland Ave Nw Ste A
North Canton, OH 44720-8386
Tel.: (330) 670-8310
Fax: (330) 670-8429
Web Site: www.kiswire.com
Emp.: 4
Steel & Wire Products Mfr
S.I.C.: 8742
N.A.I.C.S.: 541613

Laserflash S.A. (1)
Industriestrasse 34
4700 Eupen, Belgium
Tel.: (32) 3287596800
Fax: (32) 87552172
E-Mail: info@laserflash.be
Web Site: www.laserflash.be
Emp.: 40
Steel
S.I.C.: 3325
N.A.I.C.S.: 331513
Frances Brixhe *(Gen Mgr)*

S.A. du Train Universel de Longwy (STUL) (1)
2 route de Moulaine
CS 11 405 Longwy, Cedex, France
Tel.: (33) 382259600
Fax: (33) 382259696
S.I.C.: 1011
N.A.I.C.S.: 212210

Segal S.C. (1)
50 Chaussee De Ramioul
B 4400 Ivoz-Ramet, Belgium
Tel.: (32) 42737373
Fax: (32) 42738080
E-Mail: segal@skynet.be
Emp.: 161
Import Export
S.I.C.: 3312
N.A.I.C.S.: 331110

Siderurgica del Mediterraneo (1)
Carretera Acceso IV Planta Punto
Apartado 91
Sagunto, E-46520, Spain
Tel.: (34) 962658100
Telex: 62336
Fax: (34) 96 265 8193
Steel Mfr
S.I.C.: 3325
N.A.I.C.S.: 331513

SMR (Societe Metallurgique de Revigny) (1)
Route de Contrisson
PO Box 24
55800 Revigny, France
Tel.: (33) 329797991
Fax: (33) 329797999
Web Site: www.smr.fr
Sls.: $81,396,000
Emp.: 90
Steel, Torsion Bars & Industrial Engineering
S.I.C.: 3325
N.A.I.C.S.: 331513
Stephane Billaut *(Pres)*

Societe Nationale de Siderurgie S.A. (1)
Twin Center angle Bd Zerktouni et Massira Al Khadra Tour A 18eme etage
Casablanca, Morocco
Tel.: (212) 5 22 95 41 00
Fax: (212) 5 22 95 86 43
Rolled Steel Product Mfr & Distr
S.I.C.: 3312
N.A.I.C.S.: 331221

Sorevco & Co. Ltd. (1)
25 Rue De L'Acier Industrial Pk
Coteau du Lac, QC, J0P 1B0, Canada
Tel.: (450) 763-0915
Fax: (450) 763-0922
E-Mail: reception@arcelormittal.com
Emp.: 65
Hot-Dip Galvanized Steel Mfr; Owned 50% by Dofasco, Inc. & 50% by Ispat Sidbec Inc.
S.I.C.: 3312
N.A.I.C.S.: 331221
Gilles Lahaie *(Gen Mgr)*

Willenhall Steel Stockholders Ltd (1)
Cakemore Road
Rowley Regis, Warley, B65 0QI, United Kingdom
Tel.: (44) 1215327787
Fax: (44) 1215596200
E-Mail:
Sales Range: $150-199.9 Million
Emp.: 200
Iron Ore Mining
S.I.C.: 1011
N.A.I.C.S.: 212210
Lee Farnell *(Gen Mgr)*

Non-U.S. Plants:

ArcelorMittal - ArcelorMittal Avellino Mill (1)
Via Zona Industriale
83040 Luogosano, Avellino, Italy
Tel.: (39) 082 77 91 11
Fax: (39) 082 77 92 49
E-Mail: info@arcelormittal.com
Web Site: www.arcelormittal.com
Steel Building Construction Services
S.I.C.: 1791
N.A.I.C.S.: 238120

ArcelorMittal - ArcelorMittal Basse-Indre Mill (1)
Route des Sables Rd 107 Rond Point des Forges
BP 5
44610 Indre, France
Tel.: (33) 2 40 38 19 00
Fax: (33) 2 40 38 27 25
Web Site: www.arcelormittal.com
Steel Coil Sheet Mfr
S.I.C.: 3312
N.A.I.C.S.: 331221

ArcelorMittal - ArcelorMittal Canossa Mill (1)
Via Alcide De Gasperi 43
42026 Canossa, Reggio Emilia, Italy
Tel.: (39) 05 22 87 27 11
Fax: (39) 05 22 87 27 46
E-Mail: info@arcelormittal.com
Web Site: www.arcelormittal.com
Metal Product Mfr
S.I.C.: 2672
N.A.I.C.S.: 322220

ArcelorMittal - ArcelorMittal Desvres Mill (1)
Rue Bidet 65
62240 Desvres, France
Tel.: (33) 3 21 99 28 00
Fax: (33) 3 21 99 28 37
Web Site: www.arcelormittal.com
Steel Mfr
S.I.C.: 3399
N.A.I.C.S.: 331110

ArcelorMittal - ArcelorMittal Dunkerque Mill (1)
Rue du Comte Jean Grande Synthe 2508
59381 Dunkerque, France
Tel.: (33) 3 28 29 30 00
Fax: (33) 3 28 29 30 60
Web Site: www.arcelormittal.com
Rolled Steel Products Mfr
S.I.C.: 3312
N.A.I.C.S.: 331221

ArcelorMittal - ArcelorMittal Etxebarri Mill (1)
Egetiaga Uribarri 34 Apto 20
48450 Etxebarri, Biscay, Spain
Tel.: (34) 944 89 40 00
Fax: (34) 944 89 41 60
Web Site: www.arcelormittal.com
Rolled Steel Products Mfr
S.I.C.: 3312
N.A.I.C.S.: 331221

ArcelorMittal - ArcelorMittal Mardyck Mill (1)
Route de Spycker 1
59792 Grande-Synthe, France
Tel.: (33) 3 28 29 52 00
Fax: (33) 3 28 27 90 90
Cold Rolled Steel Mfr
S.I.C.: 3312
N.A.I.C.S.: 331221

ArcelorMittal - ArcelorMittal Montataire Mill (1)
Route de Saint Leu
60761 Montataire, France
Tel.: (33) 3 44 55 70 01
Fax: (33) 3 44 55 77 22
Web Site: www.arcelormittal.com
Steel Galvanizing & Sheet Mfr
S.I.C.: 3312
N.A.I.C.S.: 331110

ArcelorMittal - ArcelorMittal Mouzon Mill (1)
7 Rue Albert Ollivet
08210 Mouzon, France
Tel.: (33) 3 24 29 87 00
Fax: (33) 3 24 29 87 40
Web Site: www.arcelormittal.com
Emp.: 130
Steel Products Mfr
S.I.C.: 3312
N.A.I.C.S.: 331221
Delphine Fauville *(Mgr-HR)*

ArcelorMittal St. Chely d'Apcher Mill (1)
Rue des Martyrs du Maquis
48200 Saint-Chely-d'Apcher, France
Tel.: (33) 4 66 49 57 00
Fax: (33) 4 66 49 57 10
Web Site: www.arcelormittal.com
Emp.: 190
Steel Products Mfr
S.I.C.: 3312
N.A.I.C.S.: 331110
Serge Pugeault *(Mgr-Production & Comml)*

ARCH BIOPARTNERS INC.

27 St Clair Avenue East
PO Box 305
Toronto, ON, M4T 2M5, Canada
Tel.: (647) 428-7031
Fax: (905) 770-4454
Web Site: www.archbiopartners.com
ACH—(CNSX)
Assets: $33,119
Liabilities: $415,674
Net Worth: ($382,555)
Earnings: ($170,832)
Fiscal Year-end: 09/30/13

Business Description:
Pharmaceutical Mfr
S.I.C.: 2834
N.A.I.C.S.: 325412

Personnel:
Jerry McElroy *(Co-Founder & Chm)*
Richard Muruve *(Co-Founder & CEO)*
Daniel Muruve *(Co-Founder & Chief Science Officer)*
Andrew Bishop *(Acting CFO)*

Board of Directors:
Jerry McElroy
Andrew Bishop
Conor Gunne
Richard Muruve
Richard Rossman

Transfer Agent:
Equity Financial Trust Company
200 University Avenue Suite 400
Toronto, ON, Canada

ARCH CAPITAL GROUP LTD.

Waterloo House Ground Floor 100
Pitts Bay Road
Pembroke, HM 08, Bermuda
Tel.: (441) 2789250
Fax: (441) 2789255
E-Mail: investorrelations@archcapgroup.bm
Web Site: www.archcapgroup.bm
ACGL—(NASDAQ)
Rev.: $3,526,157,000
Assets: $19,566,094,000
Liabilities: $13,918,598,000
Net Worth: $5,647,496,000
Earnings: $709,731,000
Emp.: 1,820
Fiscal Year-end: 12/31/13

Business Description:
Insurance Carrier
S.I.C.: 6399
N.A.I.C.S.: 524130

Personnel:
Constantine P. Iordanou *(Chm, Pres & CEO)*
John M. Pasquesi *(Vice Chm)*
Mark Donald Lyons *(CFO, Exec VP & Treas)*
Nasri Toutoungi *(CIO-Fixed Income & Sr VP)*
W. Preston Hutchings *(Chief Investment Officer & Sr VP)*
David J. Mulholland *(Chief Admin Officer & Sr VP)*
Tim Peckett *(Gen Counsel-Arch Reinsurance)*

Board of Directors:
Constantine P. Iordanou
John L. Bunce, Jr.
Eric W. Doppstadt
Kewsong Lee
Yiorgos Lillikas
James J. Meenaghan
Deanna M. Mulligan
John M. Pasquesi
Brian S. Posner
John D. Vollaro
Robert F. Works

Subsidiaries:

Alternative Re Limited (1)
5th Floor Wessex House 45 Reid Street
PO Box 929
Hamilton, HM HX, Bermuda
Tel.: (441) 278 9245
Fax: (441) 278 9249
Web Site: www.alternativegroup.bm
Emp.: 10
Financial Management Services
S.I.C.: 6211
N.A.I.C.S.: 523999
Arthur Cronin *(Pres & COO)*

Alternative Underwriting Services, Ltd. (1)
Wessex House 45 Reid Street
Hamilton, HM 12, Bermuda
Tel.: (441) 441 278 9245
Fax: (441) 441 278 9249
Financial Management Services
S.I.C.: 6211
N.A.I.C.S.: 523999
Arthur Cronin *(Pres)*

Arch Reinsurance Ltd. (1)
Wessex House 3rd Floor
PO Box HM 339
45 Reid Street, Hamilton, HM 12, Bermuda
Tel.: (441) 278 9200
Fax: (441) 278 9230
Web Site: www.archreinsurance.bm
Business Support Services
S.I.C.: 7389
N.A.I.C.S.: 561499
Nicolas Papadopoulo *(Pres & CEO)*
Michelle Seymour-Smith *(CFO)*
Maamoun Rajeh *(Chief Underwriting Officer)*

U.S. Divisions:

Arch Insurance Group, Inc. (1)
1 Liberty Plz 53rd Fl
New York, NY 10006
Tel.: (212) 651-6500
Fax: (212) 651-6499
Toll Free: (866) 413-5550
Web Site: www.archinsurance.com
Insurance Related Activities
S.I.C.: 6411
N.A.I.C.S.: 524298
Michael Murphy *(Pres & Chief Underwriting Officer-Worldwide Insurance Grp)*
Fred S. Eichler *(CFO & Sr VP)*
Scott McClintock *(CIO & Sr VP)*
Thomas McMahon *(CMO & Exec VP)*
David McElroy *(Pres-Fin & Pro Liability Products Grp)*
Roy Mahlstedt *(Exec VP-Programs)*
John Mentz *(Exec VP-Construction, Natl Accts Casualty)*
Steven D. Nelson *(Exec VP-Healthcare)*
Elaine A. Trischetta *(Exec VP-Casualty)*
Mark C. Vonnahme *(Exec VP-Surety)*
Mark G. Wade *(Exec VP & Chief Claims Officer)*

Arch Reinsurance Company Inc. (1)
360 Mt Kemble Ave PO Box 1988
Morristown, NJ 07962-1988
Tel.: (973) 898-9575
Fax: (973) 889-6495
Web Site: www.archreco.com
Emp.: 50
Insurance Related Activities
S.I.C.: 6411
N.A.I.C.S.: 524298
John Rathgeber *(Chm)*
Timothy Olson *(Pres & CEO)*
Barry Golub *(CFO)*
Dale Vincent *(Chief Underwriting Officer)*

Subsidiary:

Arch Re Facultative Underwriters Inc. (2)
10 Waterside Dr Ste 201
Farmington, CT 06032
Tel.: (860) 255-5400
Fax: (800) 553-5245
E-Mail: facsubmissions@archrefac.com
Web Site: www.archrefac.com
Emp.: 80
Reinsurance Services
S.I.C.: 6399
N.A.I.C.S.: 524130
Steve Franklin *(Pres & CEO)*
Philip Augur *(COO)*

U.S. Subsidiaries:

Arch Capital Group (U.S.) Inc. (1)
1 Liberty Plz 53rd Fl
New York, NY 10006
Tel.: (212) 651-6500
Fax: (201) 743-4005
Reinsurance Services
S.I.C.: 6399
N.A.I.C.S.: 524130
David McElroy *(CEO)*

Arch Capital Services Inc. (1)
360 Hamilton Ave Ste 600
White Plains, NY 10601
Tel.: (914) 872-3600
Insurance Agencies Services
S.I.C.: 6411
N.A.I.C.S.: 524210
Louis T. Petrillo *(Pres & Gen Counsel)*
Debra Connor *(CFO)*
Donald Watson *(Exec VP-Fin Svcs)*

Arch Excess & Surplus Insurance Company (1)
300 Plaza Three
Jersey City, NJ 07311
Tel.: (201) 743-4013
Fax: (212) 650-6499
Emp.: 1,000
Direct Property Insurance Services
S.I.C.: 6331
N.A.I.C.S.: 524126
David McElroy *(Chm & CEO)*

Arch Indemnity Insurance Company (1)
300 Plaza Three
Jersey City, NJ 07311
Tel.: (201) 743-4013
Fax: (201) 743-4005
Emp.: 1,000
Direct Property Insurance Services
S.I.C.: 6351
N.A.I.C.S.: 524126
David McElroy *(Chm & CEO)*

Arch Insurance Company (1)
3100 Broadway Ste 511
Kansas City, MO 64111
Tel.: (816) 410-3020
Fax: (816) 531-0189
Toll Free: (800) 821-5546
Web Site: www.archinsurancegroup.com
Emp.: 24
General Insurance Services
S.I.C.: 6411
N.A.I.C.S.: 524210
Mark Donald Lyons *(CFO & Exec VP)*
Dennis R. *(Sr Exec VP-Admin)*
Glenn Ballew *(Exec VP)*

Arch Specialty Insurance Agency Inc. (1)
3100 Broadway St Ste 511
Kansas City, MO 64111-2413
Tel.: (816) 531-7668
Toll Free: (800) 821-5546
Insurance Brokerage Services
S.I.C.: 6411
N.A.I.C.S.: 524210

Arch Specialty Insurance Company (1)
300 Plaza Three Fl 3
Jersey City, NJ 07311
Tel.: (201) 743-4013
Fax: (212) 651-6499
Web Site: www.archinsurance.com
Direct Property Insurance Services
S.I.C.: 6331
N.A.I.C.S.: 524126
David McElroy *(Chm & CEO)*

CMG Mortgage Insurance Company (1)
595 Market St Ste 400
San Francisco, CA 94105 WI
Tel.: (415) 284-2500
Fax: (888) 763-2264
Toll Free: (800) 909-4264
E-Mail: cmgmortgage.insuranceco@cmgmi.com
Web Site: www.cmgmi.com
Mortgage Guaranty Insurance; Joint Venture Owned by CUNA Mutual Insurance Society & PMI Mortgage Insurance Co.
S.I.C.: 6351
N.A.I.C.S.: 524126
Joe Dillon *(Sr VP & Gen Mgr)*

First American Services Corporation (1)
2600 S Douglas Rd Ste 1003
Coral Gables, FL 33134
Tel.: (305) 442-8420
Financial Management Services
S.I.C.: 6211

Arch Capital Group Ltd.—(Continued)

N.A.I.C.S.: 523999

Non-U.S. Subsidiaries:

Arch Insurance Company (Europe) Ltd. (1)
6th Fl Plantation Pl S 60 Great Tower St
London, EC3R 5AZ, United Kingdom
Tel.: (44) 2076214500
Fax: (44) 2076214501
E-Mail: info@archinsurance.co.uk
Web Site: www.archinsurance.co.uk
Emp.: 120
Insurance Related Activities
S.I.C.: 6411
N.A.I.C.S.: 524298
James Weatherstone *(Pres & CEO)*
Knud Christensen *(Sr VP)*

Arch Re Accident & Health ApS (1)
Frederiksgade 19
1265 Copenhagen, Denmark
Tel.: (45) 8888 7660
Fax: (45) 8888 7669
E-Mail: info@archre.dk
Web Site: www.archre.dk
Emp.: 4
Accident & Health Insurance Services
S.I.C.: 6399
N.A.I.C.S.: 524130
Jakob Kolbye *(Co-Gen Mgr)*

Arch Reinsurance Europe Underwriting Limited (1)
Level 2 Block 3 The Oval 160 Shelbourne Road Ballsbridge
Dublin, Ireland
Tel.: (353) 1 669 9700
Fax: (353) 1 664 3749
E-Mail: info@archre.eu
Web Site: www.archre.eu
Reinsurance Services
S.I.C.: 6399
N.A.I.C.S.: 524130
Maamoun Rajeh *(Pres & CEO)*

Arch Underwriting at Lloyd's (Australia) Pty Ltd (1)
Level 1 332 Kent St
Sydney, NSW, 2000, Australia
Tel.: (61) 2 9248 6305
Web Site: www.archinsurance.com.au
Emp.: 5
Reinsurance Services
S.I.C.: 6399
N.A.I.C.S.: 524130
Bruce Row *(Mgr-Technical Underwriting)*

Arch Underwriting at Lloyd's Ltd (1)
60 Great Tower Street
London, EC3R 5AZ, United Kingdom
Tel.: (44) 20 7621 4500
Fax: (44) 20 7621 4501
Emp.: 130
Insurance Brokerage Services
S.I.C.: 6411
N.A.I.C.S.: 524210
Martin John Nilsen *(Mgr)*

ARCHANA SOFTWARE LIMITED

Land Marvel Nest First Floor No 3
First Main Road Indira Nagar
Chennai, Tamil Nadu, 600020, India
Tel.: (91) 44 64555955
Fax: (91) 44 24405166
E-Mail: archanainvestors@gmail.com
Web Site: www.archanasoftware.com
Year Founded: 1994
530565—(BOM)
Business Description:
Software Development Services
S.I.C.: 7371
N.A.I.C.S.: 541511
Personnel:
Thirumalai Kumar *(CEO)*
Board of Directors:
Thirumalai Kumar
Chikalpat Yogesh Pai
Vasanth Kumar S.
M. B. Sekar
S. Ravi Shankar
S. Sonaachalam
Ramani V.
Transfer Agent:
Sharex (India) Pvt. Ltd.
No 17/B Dena Bank Building 2nd Floor
Horniman Circle Fort
Mumbai, Maharashtra, 400001, India

ARCHEAN STAR RESOURCES INC.

410 744 West Hastings Street
Vancouver, BC, V6C 1A5, Canada
Tel.: (604) 684-3394
Fax: (888) 282-7763
Web Site: www.archeanstar.com
ASP—(TSXV)
Business Description:
Gold Mining Services
S.I.C.: 1041
N.A.I.C.S.: 212221
Personnel:
Aidan Nania *(Pres & Interim CEO)*
Anthony Jackson *(CFO)*
Board of Directors:
Philip Francis Bruce
Michael England
Marvin Mitchell
John Pegg

ARCHER CAPITAL PTY. LTD.

Suite 7 Pier 2 3 13 Hickson Road
Dawes Point, Sydney, NSW, 2000, Australia
Tel.: (61) 282433333
Fax: (61) 292413151
Web Site: www.archercapital.com.au
Year Founded: 1996
Emp.: 30
Business Description:
Private Equity Firm
S.I.C.: 6211
N.A.I.C.S.: 523999
Personnel:
Greg Minton *(Mng Partner)*
Peter Wiggs *(Mng Partner)*
Holding:

Keycorp Pty. Limited (1)
22 30 Chifley Drive
Fairfield, Preston, VIC, 3072, Australia AU
Mailing Address:
PO Box 199
Chatswood, NSW, 2057, Australia
Tel.: (61) 394031777
Fax: (61) 394031688
E-Mail: info@keycorp.net
Web Site: www.keycorp.net
Sales Range: $25-49.9 Million
Emp.: 130
Secure Electonic Transaction Services
S.I.C.: 7373
N.A.I.C.S.: 541512
Joe Bonin *(CEO)*
Shane Greenan *(CFO)*

Subsidiaries:

Fox Technology Pty Limited (2)
L 5 Keycorp Tower 799 Pacific Hwy
Chatswood, NSW, Australia (100%)
Tel.: (61) 294145500
Emp.: 60
Software Reproducing
S.I.C.: 3652
N.A.I.C.S.: 334614
Ken Carr *(Mng Dir)*

Keycorp Investments Pty Limited (2)
L 5 Keycorp Tower 799 Pacific Hwy
Chatswood, NSW, Australia (100%)
Tel.: (61) 294145200
E-Mail: info@keycorp.com
Web Site: www.keycorp.com
Emp.: 60
Software Reproducing
S.I.C.: 3652
N.A.I.C.S.: 334614
Ken Carr *(Mng Dir)*

ARCHER EXPLORATION LIMITED

Level 1 28 Greenhill Road
Wayville, SA, 5034, Australia
Tel.: (61) 8 8272 3288
Fax: (61) 8 8272 3888
E-Mail: info@archerexploration.com.au
Web Site: www.archerexploration.com.au
AXE—(ASX)
Rev.: $569,594
Assets: $17,125,746
Liabilities: $515,006
Net Worth: $16,610,741
Earnings: ($374,719)
Emp.: 8
Fiscal Year-end: 06/30/13
Business Description:
Graphite, Magnesite, Manganese, Copper, Gold & Uranium Exploration Services
S.I.C.: 1021
N.A.I.C.S.: 212234
Personnel:
Gerard Anderson *(CEO & Mng Dir)*
Craig Gooden *(Sec)*
Board of Directors:
Gregory English
Gerard Anderson
Alice McCleary
Thomas Phillips
Legal Counsel:
Norman Waterhouse
Level 15 45 Pirie Street
Adelaide, SA, Australia

ARCHER LIMITED

Travbaneveien 3
PO Box 338
4002 Stavanger, Norway
Tel.: (47) 51308000
Fax: (47) 51308001
Web Site: www.archerwell.com
ARCHER—(OSL OTC)
Rev.: $2,188,700,000
Assets: $2,587,300,000
Liabilities: $1,661,100,000
Net Worth: $926,200,000
Earnings: ($375,800,000)
Emp.: 8,300
Fiscal Year-end: 12/31/12
Business Description:
Offshore Drilling Services
S.I.C.: 1389
N.A.I.C.S.: 213112
Personnel:
John T. Reynolds *(Chm)*
David S. King *(CEO)*
Christoph Bausch *(CFO & Exec VP)*
Ronney Coleman *(Pres-North America & Exec VP)*
Carlos F. Etcheverry *(Pres-Latin America & Exec VP)*
John Lechner *(Pres-North Sea & Exec VP)*
Olivier Muller *(Pres-Emerging Markets & Tech & Exec VP)*
Max L. Bouthillette *(Gen Counsel & Exec VP)*
Lars Bethuelsen *(Sr VP-Mergers & IR)*
Board of Directors:
John T. Reynolds
Saad Bargch
Kate Blankenship
Giovanni Dell'Orto
Cecilie Astrup Fredriksen
Tor Olav Troim
Transfer Agent:
Nordea Bank Norge ASA
Verdipapirservice Middelthungsgt 17
Oslo, Norway
U.S. Subsidiaries:

Allis-Chalmers Energy Inc. (1)
10613 W Sam Houston Pkwy N
Houston, TX 77064 DE
Tel.: (713) 856-4222
Fax: (713) 856-4246
Web Site: www.alchenergy.com
Sales Range: $650-699.9 Million
Emp.: 3,750
Oilfield Services
S.I.C.: 1389
N.A.I.C.S.: 213112
Jorgen P. Rasmussen *(Chm, Pres & CEO)*
Thorleif Egeli *(COO & Sr VP)*
Max Bouthillette *(Gen Counsel & Sec)*
Lars Bethuelsen *(Sr VP-Mergers & Acq)*
Terrence P. Keane *(Sr VP-Oilfield Svcs)*

Divisions:

Allis-Chalmers Compressed Air Drilling Services (2)
911 Regional Park Dr
Houston, TX 77060
Tel.: (281) 951-4040
Fax: (713) 934-9067
E-Mail: info@alchenergy.com
Web Site: www.alchenergy.com
Sales Range: $125-149.9 Million
Emp.: 170
Compressed Air Drilling Services
S.I.C.: 1381
N.A.I.C.S.: 213111
Terry P. Keane *(Pres)*

Allis-Chalmers Directional Drilling Services (2)
911 Regional Park Dr
Houston, TX 77060
Tel.: (713) 934-9600
Fax: (713) 934-9067
Web Site: www.alchenergy.com
Sales Range: $50-74.9 Million
Emp.: 50
Oilfield Drilling Services
S.I.C.: 1381
N.A.I.C.S.: 213111
Jerod Furr *(Pres)*

Allis-Chalmers Production Services (2)
10613 w Sam Houston Pkwy N Ste 600
Houston, TX 77064
Tel.: (713) 856-4222
Fax: (713) 856-4246
Web Site: www.archerwell.com
Sales Range: $150-199.9 Million
Emp.: 100
Oil Production Services
S.I.C.: 1311
N.A.I.C.S.: 211111
Ronney Coleman *(Pres)*

Subsidiary:

American Well Control, Inc. (2)
11376 Fm 2854 Rd
Conroe, TX 77304 TX
Tel.: (936) 441-3433
Sales Range: $10-24.9 Million
Emp.: 25
Industrial Valve Mfr
S.I.C.: 3491
N.A.I.C.S.: 332911
Richard Mitchell *(Pres)*

Gray Wireline Service, Inc. (1)
6000 Western Pl Ste 375
Fort Worth, TX 76107 (60%)
Tel.: (817) 546-4970
Fax: (817) 546-1102
E-Mail: sales@archerwell.com
Web Site: www.graywireline.com
Emp.: 400
Oil & Gas Cased-Hole Wireline Services
S.I.C.: 1389
N.A.I.C.S.: 213112
Mark Harris *(Pres & CEO)*

Great White Energy Services, Inc. (1)
14201 Caliber Dr Ste 300
Oklahoma City, OK 73134 DE
Tel.: (405) 285-5812
E-Mail: webmaster@greatwhiteenergy.com
Web Site: www.greatwhiteenergy.com
Sales Range: $75-99.9 Million
Emp.: 569
Drilling Oil & Gas Wells
S.I.C.: 1381
N.A.I.C.S.: 213111
Phillip G. Lancaster *(CEO)*
David W. Sparkman *(CFO & VP)*
Randall J. Holder *(Gen Counsel & VP)*
William E. Haley *(Sr VP-Pressure Pumping Svcs)*

Ronald G. Roles *(Sr VP-Pressure Control Svcs)*
Daniel Ward *(Sr VP-Directional Drilling Svcs)*

ARCHER PETROLEUM CORP.

Suite 880-609 Granville Street
Vancouver, BC, V7Y 1G5, Canada
Tel.: (604) 683-7588
Fax: (604) 683-7588
E-Mail: info@archerpetroleum.com
Web Site: www.archerpetroleum.com
ARK—(OTC TSXV)
Assets: $123,015
Liabilities: $1,544,124
Net Worth: ($1,421,109)
Earnings: ($264,845)
Fiscal Year-end: 11/30/12
Business Description:
Oil & Gas Exploration Services
S.I.C.: 1389
N.A.I.C.S.: 213112
Personnel:
Colin Bowkett *(Pres)*
Claude V. Perrier, III *(CEO)*
Robert G. McMorran *(CFO)*
James L. Harris *(Sec)*
Board of Directors:
Victor Barcot
Colin Bowkett
Joe Mike McKinney
Robert G. McMorran
Claude V. Perrier, III
Joanne Yan
Legal Counsel:
James Harris Law Corporation
Suite 300-576 Seymour Street
Vancouver, BC, V6B 3K1, Canada
Transfer Agent:
Computershare Investor Services Inc.
510 Burrard St 2nd Floor
Vancouver, BC, V6C 3B9, Canada
Tel.: (604) 661-9400

ARCHER TRUCK SERVICES LIMITED

260 Dunkirk Rd RR 6
Saint Catharines, ON, L2R 7K6, Canada
Tel.: (905) 685-6532
Fax: (905) 685-6119
E-Mail: stcathirinesparts@archertruckcenter.com
Year Founded: 1958
Rev.: $21,168,197
Emp.: 46
Business Description:
Truck Dealers
S.I.C.: 5599
N.A.I.C.S.: 441228
Personnel:
George R. Ball *(Pres)*

ARCHIDPLY INDUSTRIES LTD

29/2 GK Manor 1st Floor Nehru Nagar Circle
Seshadripuram, Bengaluru, 560020, India
Tel.: (91) 8023445607
Fax: (91) 8023348463
E-Mail: info@archidply.com
Web Site: www.archidply.com
Year Founded: 1976
532994—(BOM)
Rev.: $38,227,619
Assets: $40,911,872
Liabilities: $20,928,711
Net Worth: $19,983,160
Earnings: $382,801
Emp.: 30
Fiscal Year-end: 03/31/13
Business Description:
Plywood Mfr
S.I.C.: 2435
N.A.I.C.S.: 321211
Personnel:
Deen Dayal Daga *(Chm)*
Shyam D. Daga *(Co-Mng Dir)*
Rajiv D. Daga *(Co-Mng Dir)*
Rajneesh Sharma *(Compliance Officer & Sec)*
Board of Directors:
Deen Dayal Daga
Mohammed Shahid Aftab
Rajiv D. Daga
Shyam D. Daga
Bharathkumar Hukumchand Rathi
Kamal Kishore Taparia
Transfer Agent:
Karvy Computershare Private Limited
Plot No 17-24 Vittal Rao Nagar Madhapur
Hyderabad, 500 081, India
Tel.: (91) 40 2342 0818

ARCHIES LIMITED

C-113 Naraina Industrial Area
Phase I, New Delhi, 110028, India
Tel.: (91) 1141410000
Fax: (91) 1141412222
E-Mail: helpdesk@archiesonline.com
Web Site: www.archiesonline.com
ARCHIES—(NSE)
Sls.: $37,461,108
Assets: $27,460,540
Liabilities: $6,934,980
Net Worth: $20,525,560
Earnings: $1,299,191
Emp.: 1,538
Fiscal Year-end: 03/31/13
Business Description:
Greeting Cards, Stationery & Gift Products Retailer
S.I.C.: 5947
N.A.I.C.S.: 453220
Personnel:
Anil Moolchandani *(Chm & Mng Dir)*
Pramod Arora *(Mng Dir)*
Vikas Kumar Tak *(Sec)*
Board of Directors:
Anil Moolchandani
Pramod Arora
Sunil Behl
Prem Kumar Chadha
Vijayant Chhabra
Jagdish Moolchandani
Dilip Seth
Ajit Ganpatlal Shah
Arun Singhal
Transfer Agent:
Link Intime India Private Limited
44 Community Centre 2nd Floor Naraina Industrial Area Phase-I
Near PVR Naraina, New Delhi, India

ARCHITECTS STUDIO JAPAN INC.

3-23-14 Takanawa Minato-ku
Tokyo, 108-0074, Japan
Tel.: (81) 3 3448 1231
Web Site: www.asj-net.com
6085—(TKS)
Rev.: $14,840,969
Emp.: 60
Fiscal Year-end: 03/31/13
Business Description:
Architectural Services
S.I.C.: 8712
N.A.I.C.S.: 541310
Personnel:
Yuhei Maruyama *(Pres)*

ARCHON MINERALS LIMITED

Suite 2801 323 Jervis Street
Vancouver, BC, V6P 3P8, Canada
Tel.: (604) 682-3303
Fax: (604) 682-2919
Year Founded: 1985
ACS—(TSXV)
Business Description:
Mineral Exploration Services
S.I.C.: 1499
N.A.I.C.S.: 212399
Personnel:
Stewart Blusson *(CEO)*

ARCHOS S.A.

12 Rue Ampere
91430 Igney, France
Tel.: (33) 169331690
Fax: (33) 169331699
E-Mail: durand@archos.com
Web Site: www.archos.com
JXR—(EUR)
Sales Range: $125-149.9 Million
Emp.: 172
Business Description:
Multimedia Devices Mfr
Export
S.I.C.: 3651
N.A.I.C.S.: 334310
Personnel:
Henri Crohas *(Founder & Chm)*
Loic Poirier *(CEO)*
Board of Directors:
Henri Crohas
Loic Poirier

U.S. Subsidiary:

Archos Inc. (1)
7951 E Maplewood Ave #260
Greenwood Village, CO 80111
Tel.: (303) 962-3350
Fax: (630) 579-3515
E-Mail: us-info@archos.com
Web Site: www.archos.com
Emp.: 50
Consumer Electronics Mfr
S.I.C.: 3679
N.A.I.C.S.: 334419

Non-U.S. Subsidiaries:

Archos GmbH (1)
Business Park Vierwinden
Konrad Zuse Strasse 22
41516 Grevenbroich, Germany
Tel.: (49) 2182570410
Fax: (49) 2182 570 4170
E-Mail: vertrieb@archos.com
Web Site: www.archos.com
Consumer Electronics Mfr
S.I.C.: 3679
N.A.I.C.S.: 334419

Archos UK Ltd. (1)
PO Box 1420
Southampton, SO15 1WF, United Kingdom
Tel.: (44) 2380711778
Fax: (44) 2380839259
E-Mail: uk-info@archos.com
Web Site: www.archos.com
Emp.: 15
Consumer Electronics Mfr
S.I.C.: 3679
N.A.I.C.S.: 334419
Chris Leigh *(Mng Dir)*

ARCLAND SERVICE CO., LTD.

New-Chiyoda Building 5F 1-8-4 Kandasakuma-cho
Chiyoda-ku, Tokyo, 101-0025, Japan
Tel.: (81) 352985281
Fax: (81) 352985271
Web Site: www.arcland.co.jp
Year Founded: 1993
3085—(JAS)
Sales Range: $75-99.9 Million
Emp.: 70
Business Description:
Restaurant Chain Operator
S.I.C.: 5812
N.A.I.C.S.: 722511
Personnel:
Kenichiro Usui *(Pres)*

ARCO-IRIS GOLD CORPORATION

Suite 22 Postnet
PO Box 1006
6600 Plettenberg Bay, South Africa
Tel.: (27) 764965865
E-Mail: info@arco-iris.co.za
Web Site: www.arco-iris.co.za
Year Founded: 2012
Business Description:
Gold Mining
S.I.C.: 1041
N.A.I.C.S.: 212221
Personnel:
Stacey Aaron *(Pres, CEO & CFO)*
Board of Directors:
Stacey Aaron

ARCO RESOURCES CORP.

Suite 1200 - 570 Granville Street
Vancouver, BC, V6C 3P1, Canada
Tel.: (604) 639-2866
Fax: (604) 909-1818
Toll Free: (800) 705-4737
Web Site: www.arcoresources.com
Year Founded: 2006
ARR—(TSXV)
Assets: $175,775
Liabilities: $544,010
Net Worth: ($368,236)
Earnings: ($1,000,430)
Fiscal Year-end: 04/30/13
Business Description:
Gold & Silver Exploration Services
S.I.C.: 1041
N.A.I.C.S.: 212221
Personnel:
Warren McIntyre *(Pres & CEO)*
Simon J. Anderson *(CFO)*
Jeffrey Sheremeta *(Sec & VP)*
Board of Directors:
Anthony Dutton
Warren McIntyre
Jeffrey Sheremeta
Ben Whiting

Non-U.S. Subsidiaries:

Arco Exploraciones, SA de CV (1)
1a Cerrada Dec Gardenias No 104 Reforma
68050 Oaxaca, Mexico
Tel.: (52) 9515151314
Fax: (52) 95151513146
Emp.: 1
Metal Mining Services
S.I.C.: 1081
N.A.I.C.S.: 213114
Juan Lopez Luque *(Gen Mgr)*

Predilecta Exploration SA de CV (1)
Primera Cerrada De Gardenias No 104 Reforma
Oaxaca, 68050, Mexico
Tel.: (52) 9515133424
Fax: (52) 95151329182
Emp.: 3
Gold Mining Services
S.I.C.: 1041
N.A.I.C.S.: 212221
Juan Lopez Luque *(Gen Mgr)*

ARCO VARA AS

Joe 2b
10151 Tallinn, Estonia
Tel.: (372) 614 4600
Fax: (372) 614 4601
E-Mail: info@arcovara.ee
Web Site: www.arcorealestate.com
Year Founded: 1992
AV1—(DEU)
Rev.: $27,908,796
Assets: $42,039,543
Liabilities: $37,506,989
Net Worth: $4,532,554
Earnings: ($24,276,830)
Emp.: 86
Fiscal Year-end: 12/31/12
Business Description:
Real Estate Development Services
S.I.C.: 6531
N.A.I.C.S.: 531390

Arco Vara AS—(Continued)

Personnel:
Richard Tomingas *(Chm-Supervisory Bd)*
Tarmo Sild *(CEO)*
Supervisory Board of Directors:
Richard Tomingas
Stephan David Balkin
Rain Lohmus
Hillar-Peeter Luitsalu
Arvo Noges
Aivar Pilv
Toomas Tool

ARCOMET & CO.
Industrieaweg 139
Paal, 3583 Beringen, Belgium
Tel.: (32) 11450950
Fax: (32) 11450952
E-Mail: info@arcomet.com
Web Site: www.arcomet.com
Sales Range: $75-99.9 Million
Emp.: 200
Business Description:
Crane Mfr
S.I.C.: 3536
N.A.I.C.S.: 333923
Personnel:
Dirk Theyskens *(CEO)*
Dirk Vanschoonbeek *(COO)*

Non-U.S. Subsidiary:

Mobile Tower Cranes (MTC) B.V. (1)
MTC De Amert 210
PO Box 53
5460 AB Veghel, 5462 GH, Netherlands (100%)
Tel.: (31) 413311977
Fax: (31) 4130311970
E-Mail: info@mtc-cranes.com
Web Site: www.mtc-cranes.com
Sls.: $9,985,072
Emp.: 35
Mfr. of Construction Machinery
S.I.C.: 3531
N.A.I.C.S.: 333120
Marshall Prysers *(Gen Mgr)*

ARCONTECH GROUP PLC
Finsbury Tower 103-105 Bunhill Row
London, EC1Y 8LZ, United Kingdom
Tel.: (44) 2072562300
Fax: (44) 2072562301
E-Mail: mail@arcontech.com
Web Site: www.arcontech.com
ARC—(AIM)
Rev.: $2,891,233
Assets: $5,070,754
Liabilities: $2,976,581
Net Worth: $2,094,173
Earnings: ($651,993)
Emp.: 22
Fiscal Year-end: 06/30/13
Business Description:
Stock Market Data Services
S.I.C.: 7373
N.A.I.C.S.: 541512
Personnel:
Matthew Jeffs *(CEO)*
Michael Levy *(Sec & Dir-Fin)*
Board of Directors:
Richard Last
Louise Barton
Matthew Jeffs
Michael Levy
Legal Counsel:
TLT LLP
1 Redcliff St
Bristol, United Kingdom

Subsidiary:

Arcontech Ltd. (1)
8th Fl Finsbury Tower
103-105 Bunhill Row, London, EC1Y 8LZ, United Kingdom
Tel.: (44) 2072562300
Fax: (44) 2072562301
E-Mail: mail@arcontech.com
Web Site: www.arcontech.com
Real-Time Market Data Distribution & Trading Systems
S.I.C.: 7374
N.A.I.C.S.: 518210

ARCOR SOCIEDAD ANONIMA, INDUSTRIAL Y COMERCIAL
Maipu 1210 2nd, 3rd & 6th Floor
Buenos Aires, 1006, Argentina
Tel.: (54) 11 4310 9500
E-Mail: info@arcor.com
Web Site: www.arcor.com
Year Founded: 1951
Sales Range: $1-4.9 Billion
Emp.: 13,000
Business Description:
Food Product Mfr & Sales
S.I.C.: 2099
N.A.I.C.S.: 311999
Personnel:
Luis Alejandro Pagani *(Chm)*
Alfredo Gustavo Pagani *(Vice Chm)*
Jorge Luis Seveso *(Sec)*
Board of Directors:
Luis Alejandro Pagani
Luis Maria Blaquier
Alejandro Fabian Fernandez
Hugo Enrique Lafaye
Jose Enrique Martin
Victor Daniel Martin
Alfredo Gustavo Pagani
Fulvio Rafael Pagani
Lilia Maria Pagani
Joao Alves Queiroz Filho
Jorge Luis Seveso

Subsidiaries:

Cartocor S.A. (1)
Calle Hernan Darias S/N Parque Industrial Gral
Belgrano, Parana, Entre Rios, E3100AJB, Argentina
Tel.: (54) 343 420 6000
Fax: (54) 343 426 0296
Web Site: www.cartocor.com
Emp.: 654
Corrugated Cardboard Mfr
S.I.C.: 2653
N.A.I.C.S.: 322211
Ileana Goldentair *(Dir-Admin)*

Converflex S.A. (1)
Maipu 1300 Piso 4
Buenos Aires, 1006, Argentina
Tel.: (54) 11 4310 9859
Fax: (54) 11 4310 9830
Web Site: www.converflex.net
Flexible Packaging Mfr
S.I.C.: 2671
N.A.I.C.S.: 326112

La Campagnola S.A.C.I. (1)
Av Fulvio Salvador Pagani 493
Arroyito, 2434, Argentina
Tel.: (54) 11 4310 9500
Web Site: www.lacampagnola.com
Fresh & Frozen Seafood Producer
S.I.C.: 2092
N.A.I.C.S.: 311710

Joint Venture:

Bagley Latinoamerica S.A. (1)
Edificio International Plaza
Moreno 877 Piso 12, 1091 Buenos Aires, Argentina
Tel.: (54) 114 341 4000
Fax: (54) 114 341 4042
Sales Range: $250-299.9 Million
Emp.: 4,900
Cookies & Cereals Mfr
S.I.C.: 2051
N.A.I.C.S.: 311812

U.S. Subsidiary:

Arcor U.S.A. Inc. (1)
6205 Blue Lagoon Dr Ste 350
Miami, FL 33126
Fax: (305) 592-1081
Toll Free: (800) 572-7267
E-Mail: infousa@arcor.com
Food Products Mfr & Sales
S.I.C.: 2099
N.A.I.C.S.: 311999
Andres Alarcon, *(VP)*

Non-U.S. Subsidiaries:

Arcopar S.A. (1)
Ruta Mariscal Estigarribia Km 10 1/2 Nro 740
San Lorenzo, Paraguay
Tel.: (595) 21 509943
E-Mail: info@arcor.com
Food Products Mfr
S.I.C.: 2099
N.A.I.C.S.: 311999

Arcor A.G. (1)
Tarragona 107-109 18th Floor
Barcelona, 08014, Spain
Tel.: (34) 93 2294 560
Fax: (34) 93 229457
Food Products Sales
S.I.C.: 5141
N.A.I.C.S.: 424410

Arcor Canada Inc. (1)
5659 McAdam Road Unit A3
Mississauga, ON, L4Z 1N9, Canada
Tel.: (905) 502-0012
Fax: (905) 502-0052
Food Products Sales
S.I.C.: 2099
N.A.I.C.S.: 311999

Arcor de Peru S.A. (1)
Av Guillermo Prescott 325
San Isidro, 027 Lima, Peru
Tel.: (51) 1 422 8088
Confectionery Products Mfr
S.I.C.: 2064
N.A.I.C.S.: 311340

Arcor do Brasil Limitada (1)
Edificio Continental Square 16 andar Rua Olimpiadas
205 Vila Olimpia, 04551-000 Sao Paulo, Brazil
Tel.: (55) 11 3046 6800
Fax: (55) 11 3046 6104
E-Mail: info@arcor.com
Food Products Mfr & Sales
S.I.C.: 2099
N.A.I.C.S.: 311999

Arcor Trading (Shanghai) Co. Ltd. (1)
Unit 909 No 1101 Pudong Nan Lu
Shanghai, 200120, China
Tel.: (86) 21 5835 1716
Food Products Sales
S.I.C.: 5149
N.A.I.C.S.: 424490
Jose Chiu *(Mgr-Comml)*

Industria Dos en Uno de Colombia Ltda (1)
Calle 109 #18B 31 Oficina 401
Bogota, Colombia
Tel.: (57) 1619 6492
Fax: (57) 1619 6850
Food Products Mfr & Sales
S.I.C.: 2099
N.A.I.C.S.: 311999

La Serrana S.A. (1)
Av Dole Via a La Guardia 5055 y 5to anillo
Santa Cruz, Bolivia (100%)
Tel.: (591) 3 354 0047
Food Products Mfr & Sales
S.I.C.: 2099
N.A.I.C.S.: 311999

Unidal Ecuador S.A. (1)
Av de las Americas & Eugenio Almazan
Las Americas Building Mecanos 1st Fl Of 101-104, Guayaquil, Ecuador
Tel.: (593) 4229 0014
Food Products Mfr & Sales
S.I.C.: 2099
N.A.I.C.S.: 311999

Unidal Venezuela S.A. (1)
Calle Guaicaipuro y Calle Mohedano Torre Hener Piso 6
El Rosal, Caracas, Venezuela
Tel.: (58) 212 740 581074
Food Products Sales
S.I.C.: 2099
N.A.I.C.S.: 311999

Van Dam S.A. (1)
Br Batile y Ordonez 6791
Montevideo, Uruguay
Tel.: (598) 2359 7013
Fax: (598) 2355 6481
Food Products Mfr & Sales
S.I.C.: 2099
N.A.I.C.S.: 311999

Non-U.S. Joint Venture:

Mundo Dulce S.A. de C.V. (1)
Juan Salvador Agraz N 50 Piso 3
Santa Fe, Mexico, DF, Mexico
Tel.: (52) 1 5552 926231
Confectionery Products Mfr
S.I.C.: 2066
N.A.I.C.S.: 311351

ARCOS DORADOS HOLDINGS INC.
Roque Saenz Pena 432 Olivos
B1636FFB Buenos Aires, Argentina
Tel.: (54) 11 4711 2000
Web Site: www.mcdonalds.com.ar
ARCO—(NYSE)
Rev.: $3,797,394,000
Assets: $2,049,163,000
Liabilities: $1,302,853,000
Net Worth: $746,310,000
Earnings: $114,588,000
Emp.: 94,282
Fiscal Year-end: 12/31/12
Business Description:
Fast Food Restaurant Owner & Operator
S.I.C.: 5812
N.A.I.C.S.: 722513
Personnel:
Woods Staton *(Chm & CEO)*
Alejandro German Lemonnier *(CFO)*
Sergio Daniel Alonso *(COO)*
Juan Carlos Paba *(Pres-Caribbean)*
Marcelo Rabach *(Pres-NOLAD)*
Jose Manuel Valledor Rojo *(Pres-Brazil)*
Alejandro Yapur *(Pres-SLAD)*
Juan David Bastidas *(Chief Legal Counsel)*
Board of Directors:
Woods Staton
Sergio Daniel Alonso
Alfredo Elias Ayub
Michael Siu Yin Chu
Jose Fernandez
Annette Franqui
Carlos Hernandez-Artigas
Alejandro German Lemonnier
Alejandro Ramirez Magana
Jose Alberto Velez Cadavid
Transfer Agent:
Continental Stock Transfer & Trust Company
New York, NY 10001

ARCOTECH LTD.
F-701 A Lado Sarai
New Delhi, 110030, India
Tel.: (91) 11 32503334
Fax: (91) 11 29523020
E-Mail: contact@arcotech.in
Web Site: www.arcotech.in
532914—(BOM)
Sls.: $76,451,503
Assets: $61,986,598
Liabilities: $42,536,519
Net Worth: $19,450,078
Earnings: $4,246,774
Fiscal Year-end: 03/31/13
Business Description:
Nonferrous Metal Mfr
S.I.C.: 3339
N.A.I.C.S.: 331410
Personnel:
Arvind Kumar Saraf *(Chm)*
Amit Sharma *(Compliance Officer, Sec & Mgr-Fin)*

Board of Directors:
Arvind Kumar Saraf
Gautam Khaitan
R. N. Pattanayak
R. D. Tayal

Transfer Agent:
Maheswari Datamatics Private Limited
6 Mangoe Lane 2nd Floor
Kolkata, India

ARCTIC CO-OPERATIVES LIMITED

1645 Inkster Blvd
Winnipeg, MB, R2X 2W7, Canada
Tel.: (204) 697-2243
Fax: (204) 697-1880
E-Mail: info@arcticco-op.com
Web Site: www.arcticco-op.com
Year Founded: 1972
Sales Range: $75-99.9 Million
Emp.: 70

Business Description:
General Merchandise Retailer
S.I.C.: 5399
N.A.I.C.S.: 452990

Personnel:
Andy Morrison *(CEO)*
Mary Nirlungayuk *(Sec)*

Subsidiary:

Nunavut Sealink & Supply Incorporated (1)
1088 E Airport Rd
Iqaluit, NU, X0A 0H0, Canada
Tel.: (867) 979-3799
Fax: (867) 979-2535
Web Site: www.arcticsealift.com
Emp.: 3
Domestic Sea Freight Transportation Services
S.I.C.: 4731
N.A.I.C.S.: 488510

ARCTIC GOLD AB

PO Box 275
751 05 Uppsala, Sweden
Tel.: (46) 18156423
E-Mail: claesson@arcticgold.se
Web Site: www.arcticgold.se
Year Founded: 1999
ARCT—(OMX)

Business Description:
Gold Mining Services
S.I.C.: 1041
N.A.I.C.S.: 212221

Personnel:
Torsten Borjemalm *(Chm)*
Lars-Ake Claesson *(Mng Dir)*

Board of Directors:
Torsten Borjemalm
Tomas Bjorklund
Lars-Ake Claesson
Gunnar Farjsjo
Peter Hjorth
Ulf Tillman

ARCTIC HUNTER ENERGY INC.

501-675 West Hastings Street
Vancouver, BC, V6B 1N2, Canada
Tel.: (604) 681-3131
Fax: (604) 408-3884
E-Mail: rthall@shaw.ca
Web Site: www.arctichunter.com
Year Founded: 2006
AHU—(TSXV)
Rev.: $364,739
Assets: $398,690
Liabilities: $79,079
Net Worth: $319,611
Earnings: ($220,567)
Fiscal Year-end: 06/30/13

Business Description:
Oil & Gas Exploration Services
S.I.C.: 1311
N.A.I.C.S.: 211111

Personnel:
Timothy Andrew Coupland *(Pres, CEO & Sec)*
Gordon Steblin *(CFO)*

Board of Directors:
Edward Burylo
Timothy Andrew Coupland
Robert T. Hall
Ray Lee

Legal Counsel:
Morton & Company
Suite 1200-750 W Pender Street
Vancouver, BC, Canada

Transfer Agent:
Computershare Investor Services Inc
100 University Avenue 9th Floor North Tower
Toronto, ON, Canada

ARCTIC PAPER S.A.

Ul Fabryczna 1
66-470 Kostrzyn, Poland
Tel.: (48) 957210600
Fax: (48) 957524196
E-Mail: info-kostrzyn@arcticpaper.com
Web Site: www.arcticpaper.com
ATC—(OMX WAR)
Sales Range: $300-349.9 Million
Emp.: 1,600

Business Description:
Paper Mfr
S.I.C.: 2621
N.A.I.C.S.: 322121

Personnel:
Olle Grundberg *(Chm)*
Michal Jarczynski *(CEO)*
Per Skoglund *(Mng Dir)*
Sverker Andreasson *(Deputy CFO)*
Michal Bartkowiak *(CFO)*
Bjarne Bjork *(COO)*

Supervisory Board of Directors:
Olle Grundberg
Rune Roger Ingvarsson
Kjell Olsson
Thomas Onstad
Fredrik Plyhr
Wiktorian Zbigniew Tarnawski
Dariusz Witkowski

Non-U.S. Subsidiary:

Rottneros AB (1)
World Trade Center Kungsbron 1
Stockholm, Sweden
Mailing Address:
PO Box 70 370
107 24 Stockholm, Sweden
Tel.: (46) 859001000
Fax: (46) 859001001
E-Mail: info@rottneros.com
Web Site: www.rottneros.com
RROS—(OMX)
Rev.: $232,045,200
Assets: $200,311,200
Liabilities: $46,594,800
Net Worth: $153,716,400
Earnings: ($2,012,400)
Emp.: 275
Fiscal Year-end: 12/31/12
Pulp & Paper Producer
S.I.C.: 2611
N.A.I.C.S.: 322110
Rune Ingvarsson *(Chm)*
Carl-Johan Jonsson *(CEO)*
Krister Lindgren *(Interim CFO)*

Subsidiaries:

Rottneros Bruk AB (2)
Box 70370
68694 Stockholm, Sweden (100%)
Tel.: (46) 56517600
Fax: (46) 56517680
E-Mail: info@rottneros.com
Emp.: 130
Pulp Mills
S.I.C.: 2611
N.A.I.C.S.: 322110
Ole Terland *(Pres & CEO)*
Olle Dahlin *(Mng Dir)*

Rottneros Packaging AB (2)
Box 70 370
107 24 Stockholm, Sweden
Tel.: (46) 859001000
Fax: (46) 859001001
Food Packaging Products Mfr
S.I.C.: 2671
N.A.I.C.S.: 322220

Utansjo Bruk AB (2)
Timmervagen
Utansjo, 87015 Harnosand, Sweden(100%)
Tel.: (46) 612716200
Fax: (46) 61242118
Pulp Mills
S.I.C.: 2611
N.A.I.C.S.: 322110
Olle Dahlin *(Mng Dir)*

Vallviks Bruk AB (2)
Ronnvagen 17
Vallvik, 82021 Soderhamn, Sweden (100%)
Tel.: (46) 859001033
Fax: (46) 27069210
Web Site: www.rottneros.com
Emp.: 160
Pulp Mills
S.I.C.: 2611
N.A.I.C.S.: 322110
Robert Yensen *(Mng Dir)*

Non-U.S. Subsidiaries:

Aspen Tree Re AG (2)
Baarerstrasse 75
Zug, Switzerland (100%)
Tel.: (41) 417272040
Fax: (41) 417272044
E-Mail: joanna.tyra@aon.ch
Web Site: www.aon.com
Emp.: 2
Insurance Agencies & Brokerages
S.I.C.: 6411
N.A.I.C.S.: 524210
Jurgen Hahn *(Mng Dir)*

Rottneros Miranda SA (2)
Carretera de Logrono S-N
PO Box 6
Miranda de Ebro, 09200 Vitoria, Spain (100%)
Tel.: (34) 947310245
Fax: (34) 947347244
Pulp Mills
S.I.C.: 2611
N.A.I.C.S.: 322110

SIA Rottneros Baltic AB (2)
Locu street 1
Ventspils, LV3601 Tukums, Latvia (100%)
Tel.: (371) 3629273
Fax: (371) 3629275
Emp.: 13
Pulp Mills
S.I.C.: 2611
N.A.I.C.S.: 322110
Varis Vezis *(Mng Dir)*

ARCTIC STAR EXPLORATION CORP.

Pacific Centre Suite 1818 701 West Georgia Street
PO Box 10144
Vancouver, BC, V7Y 1C6, Canada
Tel.: (604) 689-1799
Fax: (604) 689-8199
E-Mail: info@arcticstar.ca
Web Site: www.arcticstardiamond.com
Year Founded: 2001
ADD—(TSXV)
Int. Income: $6,947
Assets: $1,761,077
Liabilities: $243,168
Net Worth: $1,517,909
Earnings: ($3,106,677)
Fiscal Year-end: 12/31/12

Business Description:
Diamond Exploration & Development Services
S.I.C.: 1499
N.A.I.C.S.: 212399

Personnel:
Patrick Power *(Pres & CEO)*
Binny Jassal *(CFO)*

Board of Directors:
John Buckle
Christopher Campbell
Sean Charland
Buddy Doyle
Patrick Power
Thomas Yingling

Legal Counsel:
Boughton Law Corporation
1000- 595 Burrard Street
Vancouver, BC, Canada

Transfer Agent:
Computershare
200 - 510 Burrard Street
Vancouver, BC, Canada

ARCTURUS VENTURES INC.

141- 757 Hastings St W
Vancouver, BC, V6C 1A1, Canada
Tel.: (604) 688-2000
Fax: (250) 339-0986
E-Mail: info@arcturusventuresinc.com
Web Site: www.arcturusventuresinc.com
AZN—(TSXV)
Assets: $1,804,796
Liabilities: $252,646
Net Worth: $1,552,150
Earnings: ($294,566)
Fiscal Year-end: 06/30/13

Business Description:
Gold & Copper Exploration Services
S.I.C.: 1021
N.A.I.C.S.: 212234

Personnel:
Blake Macdonald *(Pres)*
Brandon Macdonald *(CFO, Sec & VP-Bus Dev)*

Board of Directors:
Tom Adamson
Blake Macdonald
Brandon Macdonald
Jack McClintock

Legal Counsel:
Fang & Associates
3rd Floor, 576 Seymour Street
Vancouver, BC, Canada

Transfer Agent:
Computershare Trust Company of Canada
510 Burrard St 2nd Fl
Vancouver, BC, Canada

ARCUS DEVELOPMENT GROUP INC.

Suite 1016 - 510 West Hasting Street
Vancouver, BC, Canada V6B 1L8
Tel.: (604) 687-2522
Fax: (604) 688-2578
Toll Free: (888) 688-2522
E-Mail: info@arcusdevelopmentgroup.com
Web Site: www.arcusdevelopmentgroup.com
Year Founded: 2006
ADG—(TSXV)

Business Description:
Mineral Exploration Services
S.I.C.: 1081
N.A.I.C.S.: 213114

Personnel:
Ian J. Talbot *(Pres & CEO)*
James Gray *(CFO)*

Board of Directors:
Marc Blythe
James Gray
Grant Longhurst
P. Gary Paulson
Ian J. Talbot
William Wengzynowski

Legal Counsel:
Morton & Company
1200 - 750 West Pender Street
Vancouver, BC, Canada

Arcus Development Group Inc.—(Continued)

Transfer Agent:
Computershare Trust Company of Canada
510 Burrard St 3rd Fl
Vancouver, BC, V6C 3B9, Canada

ARCUS INFRASTRUCTURE PARTNERS LLP

6 St Andrew Street
London, EC4A 3AE, United Kingdom
Tel.: (44) 2078323400
Fax: (44) 2079363227
E-Mail: info@arcusip.com
Web Site: www.arcusip.com
Year Founded: 2009
Sales Range: $1-4.9 Billion
Emp.: 40

Business Description:
Fund Management Services
S.I.C.: 6211
N.A.I.C.S.: 523999

Personnel:
Antonino Lo Bianco *(Mng Partner)*

Holding:

Forth Ports PLC (1)
1 Prince Of Wales Dock
Edinburgh, EH6 7DX, United Kingdom UK
Tel.: (44) 1315558700
Fax: (44) 1315537462
E-Mail: reception@forthports.co.uk
Web Site: www.forthports.co.uk
Sales Range: $250-299.9 Million
Emp.: 1,120
Commercial Port Operator
S.I.C.: 4491
N.A.I.C.S.: 488310
Charles G. Hammond *(CEO)*
Stuart Paterson *(CFO)*
Morag McNeill *(Sec)*

Subsidiaries:

Forth Estuary Towage Limited (2)
1 Prince of Wales Dock
Edinburgh, VEX 67DX, United Kingdom (100%)
Tel.: (44) 1315558700
Fax: (44) 1315550911
E-Mail: info@forthports.co.uk
Web Site: www.forthports.co.uk
Emp.: 100
Real Estate Agents & Managers
S.I.C.: 6531
N.A.I.C.S.: 531210
Charles Hammond *(Mng Dir)*

Forth Properties Limited (2)
1 Prince of Wales Dock
Edinburgh, EH6 7DX, United Kingdom
Tel.: (44) 1315558700
Fax: (44) 1315537462
E-Mail: reception@forthports.co.uk
Web Site: www.forthports.co.uk
Real Estate Agents & Managers
S.I.C.: 6531
N.A.I.C.S.: 531210
Stuart Paterson *(Head-Fin)*

Forth Property Developments Ltd (2)
1 Prince Of Wales Dock
Edinburgh, EH6 7DX, United Kingdom
Tel.: (44) 1315558700
Fax: (44) 1315550911
E-Mail: info@forthports.co.uk
Web Site: www.forthports.co.uk
Emp.: 100
Real Estate Agents & Managers
S.I.C.: 6531
N.A.I.C.S.: 531210
Charles Hammond *(CEO)*

FP Newhaven Two Limited (2)
1 Prince Of Wales Dock
Edinburgh, United Kingdom
Tel.: (44) 1313431000
Fax: (44) 1315550911
Emp.: 100
Real Estate Agents & Managers
S.I.C.: 6531
N.A.I.C.S.: 531210
Nethen Thompson *(Mng Dir)*

Ocean Terminal Developments Limited (2)
98 Ocean Dr
Edinburgh, EH6 6JJ, United Kingdom
Tel.: (44) 1315558888
Fax: (44) 1314759407
E-Mail: info@oceanterminal.com
Web Site: www.oceanterminal.com
Emp.: 8
Real Estate Agents & Managers
S.I.C.: 6531
N.A.I.C.S.: 531210
Dennis Jones *(Mng Dir)*

Ocean Terminal Limited (2)
98 Ocean Dr Leith
Edinburgh, EH6 6JJ, United Kingdom
Tel.: (44) 1315558888
E-Mail: info@oceanterminal.com
Web Site: www.oceanterminal.com
Emp.: 6
Business Service Centers
S.I.C.: 7334
N.A.I.C.S.: 561439
Dennis Jones *(Mng Dir)*

Port of Dundee Ltd (2)
Port Office Spanner Gate Rd
Dundee, D1 3LU, United Kingdom (100%)
Tel.: (44) 1382224121
Fax: (44) 1382200834
Web Site: www.dundeerenewables.com
Freight Transportation Arrangement
S.I.C.: 4731
N.A.I.C.S.: 488510

Port of Tilbury London Limited (2)
Neptune House
RM187EH Tilbury, United Kingdom
Tel.: (44) 1375852424
Fax: (44) 1375852280
E-Mail: morton.training@potll.com
Web Site: www.potll.com
Emp.: 500
Freight Transportation Arrangement
S.I.C.: 4731
N.A.I.C.S.: 488510
Pary Jliding *(Mng Dir)*

ARCUTTIPORE TEA COMPANY LIMITED

4A Council House Street M M S Chambers 1st Floor
Kolkata, 700001, India
Tel.: (91) 33 32591972
E-Mail: kolkataho@arcuttiporetea.com
Web Site: www.arcuttiporetea.com
Year Founded: 1869
530261—(BOM)
Rev.: $834,618
Assets: $1,867,640
Liabilities: $1,393,781
Net Worth: $473,859
Earnings: ($57,355)
Fiscal Year-end: 03/31/13

Business Description:
Tea Farming Services
S.I.C.: 0191
N.A.I.C.S.: 111998

Personnel:
Harsh Kumar Bajoria *(Mng Dir)*
Naresh Shah *(Compliance Officer)*

Board of Directors:
Harsh Kumar Bajoria
Shalakya Bajoria
Chandi Prasad Poddar
Naresh Shah

Transfer Agent:
MCS Share Transfer Agent Limited
12/1/5 Monoharpukur Road
Kolkata, 700026, India

ARDAGH PACKAGING GROUP LIMITED

4 Richview Office Park
Clonskeagh, Dublin, 14, Ireland
Tel.: (353) 16052400
Fax: (353) 12690832
E-Mail: iedub.reception@ardaghgroup.com
Web Site: www.ardaghgroup.com
Sales Range: $400-449.9 Million
Emp.: 17,700

Business Description:
Glass & Metal Packaging Mfr
S.I.C.: 3221
N.A.I.C.S.: 327213

Personnel:
Paul Coulson *(Chm)*
Niall Wall *(CEO)*
David Matthews *(CFO)*

U.S. Subsidiaries:

Ardagh Metal Packaging USA, Inc. (1)
Carnegie Office Park 600 N Bell Ave Bldg 1 Ste 200
Carnegie, PA 15106
Tel.: (412) 429-5290
Fax: (412) 429-5295
Toll Free: (866) 205CANS
Web Site: www.ardaghgroup.com
Emp.: 30
Metal Packaging
S.I.C.: 7389
N.A.I.C.S.: 561910
Linda Zottola *(Head-Oper)*

Ardagh Group - Bridgeton (1)
443 S East Ave
Bridgeton, NJ 08302-3461
Tel.: (856) 455-2000
Fax: (856) 455-1905
E-Mail:
Web Site: www.ardaghgroup.com
Emp.: 350
Glass Containers Mfr
Import Export
S.I.C.: 3221
N.A.I.C.S.: 327213
David Childers *(Plant Mgr)*

Non-U.S. Subsidiaries:

Ardagh Glass Limited (1)
Headlands Lane
Knottingley, W Yorkshire, WF11 0HP, United Kingdom UK
Tel.: (44) 1977674111
Telex: 556401
Fax: (44) 1977635821
Web Site: www.ardaghgroup.com
Emp.: 300
Glass Container Mfr
S.I.C.: 3221
N.A.I.C.S.: 327213
John Passant *(Mng Dir)*
John Riordan *(Pres-North America)*

U.S. Subsidiary:

Anchor Glass Container Corporation (2)
401 E Jackson St Ste 2800
Tampa, FL 33602 DE
Tel.: (813) 884-0000
Fax: (813) 882-7709
Web Site: www.anchorglass.com
Sales Range: $800-899.9 Million
Emp.: 2,840
Glass Container Products Mfr
Export
S.I.C.: 3221
N.A.I.C.S.: 327213
Jim Fredlake *(CEO)*

Ardagh Metal Packaging Netherlands B.V. (1)
Zutphenseweg 51
7418 AH Deventer, Netherlands NL
Tel.: (31) 570682000
Fax: (31) 570682068
E-Mail: ssc.reception@ardaghgroup.com
Web Site: www.ardaghgroup.com
Emp.: 7,000
Aluminum Can Mfr
S.I.C.: 3411
N.A.I.C.S.: 332431
Niall Wall *(CEO)*

Ardagh Metal Packaging UK Limited (1)
Salhouse Road
Norwich, Norfolk, NR7 9AT, United Kingdom UK
Tel.: (44) 1603 427 313
Fax: (44) 1603 408 571
Sales Range: $25-49.9 Million
Emp.: 45
Mfrs. Cans
S.I.C.: 3411
N.A.I.C.S.: 332431

Plant:

Ardagh Metal Packaging UK Ltd. - Sutton-in-Ashfield Plant (2)
Coxmoor Road
Sutton in Ashfield, Notts, NG17 5LA, United Kingdom
Tel.: (44) 1623518030
Fax: (44) 1623518031
Emp.: 200
Metal Food Packaging Product Mfr
S.I.C.: 3411
N.A.I.C.S.: 332431
David Horton *(Plant Mgr)*

ARDEL STEEL

455 Longman Crescent
Regina, SK, S4N 6G3, Canada
Tel.: (306) 721-2995
Fax: (306) 721-2510
Toll Free: (866) 732-2748
E-Mail: info@ardelsteel.com
Web Site: www.ardelsteel.com
Year Founded: 1980
Rev.: $11,553,274
Emp.: 35

Business Description:
Reinforcing Steel & Fabricator Distr
S.I.C.: 5046
N.A.I.C.S.: 423440

Personnel:
Arnie Matt *(Founder)*

ARDEN PARTNERS PLC

Arden House 17 Highfield Road Edgbaston
Birmingham, B15 3DU, United Kingdom
Tel.: (44) 1214238900
Fax: (44) 1214238901
E-Mail: reception@arden-partners.com
Web Site: www.arden-partners.co.uk
ARDN—(LSE)
Rev.: $16,785,528
Assets: $51,203,919
Liabilities: $32,208,676
Net Worth: $18,995,244
Earnings: $1,644,826
Emp.: 39
Fiscal Year-end: 10/31/13

Business Description:
Securities
S.I.C.: 6211
N.A.I.C.S.: 523120

Personnel:
Jonathan Keeling *(Deputy Chm)*
James Reed-Daunter *(CEO)*
Steve Wassell *(COO & Sec)*

Board of Directors:
Peter Moon
Mark Ansell
Jonathan Keeling
James Reed-Daunter
Steve Wassell

Legal Counsel:
Eversheds LLP
One Wood Street
EC2V 7WS London, United Kingdom

ARDENT LEISURE GROUP

Level 16 61 Lavender Street
Milsons Point, Sydney, NSW, 2061, Australia
Tel.: (61) 294093670
Fax: (61) 29409 3679
Web Site: www.ardentleisure.com.au
AAD—(ASX)
Rev.: $471,809,733
Assets: $833,411,138
Liabilities: $325,606,229

Net Worth: $507,804,909
Earnings: $37,116,476
Emp.: 7,200
Fiscal Year-end: 06/30/13

Business Description:
Theme Park & Entertainment Services
S.I.C.: 7996
N.A.I.C.S.: 713110

Personnel:
Greg Shaw *(CEO & Mng Dir)*
Richard Johnson *(CFO)*
Marcus Anketell *(CEO-d'Albora Marinas)*
Lee Chadwick *(CEO-AMF Bowling Div)*
Craig Davidson *(CEO-Theme Parks Div)*
Tim Innes *(CEO-Kingpin Bowling)*
Charlie Keegan *(CEO-Main Event Entertainment)*
Roy Menachemson *(CEO-Dev)*
Greg Oliver *(CEO-Goodlife Health Clubs Bus)*
Alan Shedden *(Sec)*

Board of Directors:
Neil Balnaves
Roger Andrew Davis
Anne Jillian Keating
Don Morris
Greg Shaw
George Venardos

Subsidiaries:

Ardent Leisure Limited (1)
Level 16 61 Lavender Street
Milsons Point, NSW, 2061, Australia
Tel.: (61) 2 9409 3670
Fax: (61) 2 9409 3679
Entertainment Event Organizers
S.I.C.: 7999
N.A.I.C.S.: 711310

Ardent Leisure Management Health Clubs Pty Limited (1)
Level 16 61 Lavender Street
Milsons Point, NSW, 2061, Australia
Tel.: (61) 294093670
Fax: (61) 264093679
Web Site: www.ardentleisure.com.au
Health Club Management Services
S.I.C.: 7999
N.A.I.C.S.: 713940
Greg Shaw *(CEO)*

Ardent Leisure Management Limited (1)
Level 16 61 Lavender Street
Milsons Point, NSW, 2061, Australia
Tel.: (61) 2 9409 3608
Fax: (61) 2 9929 9488
General Management Services
S.I.C.: 8748
N.A.I.C.S.: 541618

BowlAustralia Holdings Pty Limited (1)
3 Salisbury Road Castle Hill
Sydney, NSW, 2154, Australia
Tel.: (61) 296807677
Fax: (61) 296595388
Emp.: 50
Bowling Centers Operating Services
S.I.C.: 7933
N.A.I.C.S.: 713950

Bowling Centres Australia Pty Limited (1)
Level 12 61 Lavender St
Milsons Point, NSW, 2061, Australia
Tel.: (61) 299293777
Fax: (61) 299299488
E-Mail: amfcustomerservice@amfbowling.com.au
Web Site: www.amfbowling.com.au
Emp.: 2,000
Bowling Centers
S.I.C.: 7933
N.A.I.C.S.: 713950
Jordan Rodgers *(CEO)*

Goodlife Carseldine Pty Limited (1)
16 Graham Rd
Carseldine, Brisbane, QLD, 4034, Australia
Tel.: (61) 732639333
Fax: (61) 33635936
Web Site: www.goodlifehealthclub.com.au
Health Clubs
S.I.C.: 7941
N.A.I.C.S.: 711211

Goodlife Chermside Pty Limited (1)
Level 1 Westfield Shopping Ctr Cnr Gympie & Hamilton Rd
Chermside, Brisbane, QLD, 4302, Australia
Tel.: (61) 733265555
Fax: (61) 733265599
E-Mail: cgmchermside@goodlifehealthclubs.com.au
Web Site: www.goodlifehealthclubs.com.au
Health Clubs
S.I.C.: 7941
N.A.I.C.S.: 711211
Leon Mcneice *(Mng Dir)*

Goodlife Helensvale Pty Limited (1)
92 Junction Rd
Morningside, Brisbane, QLD, 4170, Australia
Tel.: (61) 738992626
Fax: (61) 733996680
Web Site: www.goodlifehealthclubs.com.au
Emp.: 15
Health Clubs
S.I.C.: 7941
N.A.I.C.S.: 711211
Bruce Morris *(Mng Dir)*

Goodlife Hyperdome Pty Limited (1)
Logan Hyperdome Shopping Ctr
Cnr Pacific Hwy Bryants Rd, Loganholme, QLD, 4129, Australia
Tel.: (61) 738065999
Fax: (61) 0738062733
E-Mail: czm@goodlifehealthclub.com.au
Web Site: www.goodlifehealthclubs.com.au
Emp.: 40
Health Clubs
S.I.C.: 7941
N.A.I.C.S.: 711211
Thomas Dux Grocer *(Mgr-Club)*

Goodlife Wintergarden Pty Limited (1)
Level 3 Wintergarden Queen St Mall
Brisbane, QLD, 4000, Australia
Tel.: (61) 732319955
Fax: (61) 732319999
E-Mail: cgqueensc@goodlifehealthclubs.com.au
Web Site: www.goodlifehealthclubs.com.au
Emp.: 25
Health Club Services
S.I.C.: 7941
N.A.I.C.S.: 711211
Luke Marino *(Mgr)*

Holland Park Health Clubs Service Pty Limited (1)
201 Nursery Road
Holland Park, Brisbane, QLD, 4121, Australia
Tel.: (61) 733497003
Health Club Management Services
S.I.C.: 7941
N.A.I.C.S.: 711211

My Boatie Pty Limited (1)
Shed 1 C/o d'Albora Marinas The Spit
Mosman, NSW, 2088, Australia
Tel.: (61) 2 9960 7606
Fax: (61) 2 9960 4501
E-Mail: info@myboatie.com.au
Web Site: www.myboatie.com.au
Boating, Concierge & Skippering Services
S.I.C.: 7999
N.A.I.C.S.: 713990

U.S. Subsidiary:

Main Event Entertainment LP (1)
2070 S Stemmons Fwy
Lewisville, TX 75067-8761
Tel.: (972) 459-7770
Fax: (972) 451-7710
Web Site: www.maineventusa.net
Emp.: 100
Entertainment Services
S.I.C.: 7999
N.A.I.C.S.: 711310
Charlie Keegan *(CEO)*

ARDENT SPORTSWEAR INC

125 W 3rd Ave
Vancouver, BC, V5Y 1E6, Canada
Tel.: (604) 879-3268
Fax: (604) 879-9968
Rev.: $13,690,320
Emp.: 60

Business Description:
Sportswear Retailer
S.I.C.: 5699
N.A.I.C.S.: 448150

Personnel:
Raymond Wong *(Pres)*

ARDEPRO CO. LTD.

2nd Floor Keio Shinjuku 3-chome Building
3-1-24 Shinjuku
Shinjuku-ku, Tokyo, Japan
Tel.: (81) 353672001
Web Site: www.ardepro.co.jp
8925—(TKS)
Sales Range: $600-649.9 Million

Business Description:
Leasing Building & Real Estate
S.I.C.: 6514
N.A.I.C.S.: 531110

Personnel:
Yasuo Takahashi *(Pres)*

ARDEW WOOD PRODUCTS LTD.

1195 Houston Street
Merritt, BC, Canada
Tel.: (250) 378-6161
Fax: (250) 378-6313
E-Mail: info@ardew.com
Web Site: www.ardew.com
Year Founded: 1966
Rev.: $15,932,170
Emp.: 75

Business Description:
Wood Products Mfr
S.I.C.: 2499
N.A.I.C.S.: 321999

Personnel:
Erik Norgaard *(Pres)*

ARDIAN S.A.R.L.

(Formerly AXA Investment Managers Private Equity S.A.)
20 Place Vendome
75001 Paris, France
Tel.: (33) 1 4445 9200
Fax: (33) 1 4445 9300
Web Site: www.ardian-investment.com
Managed Assets: $36,000,000,000
Emp.: 1,000

Business Description:
Private Equity Firm
S.I.C.: 6211
N.A.I.C.S.: 523999

Personnel:
Dominique Senequier *(CEO)*
Dominique Gaillard *(Mng Partner & Head-Direct Funds)*
Vincent Gombault *(Mng Partner & Head-Fund of Funds & Private Debt)*
Benoit Verbrughe *(Mng Partner & Head-USA)*
Frederic Collard *(Mng Dir)*

Holdings:

DIANA S.A.S. (1)
BP 244
56007 Vannes, Cedex, France FR
Tel.: (33) 2 9748 4900
Fax: (33) 2 9748 4910
E-Mail: contact@diana-group.com
Web Site: www.diana-group.com
Sales Range: $500-549.9 Million
Emp.: 1,500
Organic Ingredients & Concentrates Mfr
S.I.C.: 2869
N.A.I.C.S.: 325199
Yves Boisdron *(Chm-Supervisory Bd)*
Oliver Caix *(Chm-Mgmt Bd, Pres & CEO)*
Steve Lawson *(VP & CFO)*
Jean-Yves Parisot *(Exec VP & Pres-Food Div)*
Jean-Pierre Rivery *(Exec VP & Pres-Pet Food Div)*
Miriam Fedida *(VP & Gen Counsel)*

U.S. Subsidiary:

Pacific Pure-Aid Company (2)
1702 Eska Way
Silverton, OR 97381-1294 OR
Mailing Address:
PO Box 157
Silverton, OR 97381
Tel.: (503) 873-3600
Fax: (503) 873-7807
Sales Range: $10-24.9 Million
Emp.: 50
Vegetable Extracts & Concentrates Mfr
S.I.C.: 2087
N.A.I.C.S.: 311930
Bob Acheson *(Gen Mgr)*

Gerflor SA (1)
50 cours de la Republique
69627 Villeurbanne, Cedex, France FR
Tel.: (33) 4 7265 1000
Fax: (33) 4 7265 1060
E-Mail: gerflor@gerflor.com
Web Site: www.gerflorgroup.com
Sales Range: $400-449.9 Million
Emp.: 30
Flooring Products
S.I.C.: 3089
N.A.I.C.S.: 326199
Bertrand Chammas *(Chm & CEO)*

PHOTONIS Technologies S.A.S. (1)
Domaine de PELUS Axis Business Park Bat 5E
18 Avenue de Pythagore, 33700 Merignac, France FR
Tel.: (33) 556164050
Fax: (33) 556164062
E-Mail: holding@photonis.com
Web Site: www.photonis.com
Sales Range: $200-249.9 Million
Electro-Optic Components Mfr
S.I.C.: 3827
N.A.I.C.S.: 333314
Goossen Boers *(CEO)*
Bruno Manac'h *(CFO)*
Kees Brouwer *(COO)*
Geoffroy Deltel *(CTO)*
Celiene Bellejarde *(Gen Counsel)*

Subsidiary:

PHOTONIS France S.A.S. (2)
Avenue Roger Roncier
Avenue Ariane Parc Cabera Sgd, 19100 Brive-la-Gaillarde, France FR
Tel.: (33) 555863700
Fax: (33) 556164062
E-Mail: ism@photonis.com
Web Site: www.photonis.com
Photo Sensor Technology Designer, Developer, Producer & Marketer
S.I.C.: 5043
N.A.I.C.S.: 423410
Goossen Boers *(CEO)*
Kees Brouwer *(COO)*

U.S. Subsidiaries:

PHOTONIS USA, Inc. (2)
Sturbridge Business Pk
Sturbridge, MA 01566 DE
Tel.: (508) 347-4000
Fax: (508) 347-3849
Toll Free: (800) 648-1800
E-Mail: sales@usa.photonis.com
Web Site: www.photonis.com
Electro-Optical Products Mfr
S.I.C.: 3812
N.A.I.C.S.: 334511
Gregory W. Bell *(Pres & CEO)*

PHOTONIS USA Pennsylvania, Inc. (2)
1000 New Holland Ave
Lancaster, PA 17601-5606 PA
Tel.: (717) 295-6000
Fax: (717) 295-6096
Toll Free: (800) 366-2875
E-Mail: info@photonisusa.com
Web Site: www.photonisusa.com
Sales Range: $75-99.9 Million
Emp.: 50

Ardian S.a.r.l.—(Continued)

Electron Tubes & Electro-Optical Devices Mfr
Import Export
S.I.C.: 3679
N.A.I.C.S.: 334419
Ronald L. Minnier *(Pres & CEO)*

Non-U.S. Subsidiary:

PHOTONIS Netherlands B.V. (2)
Dwazziewegen 2
9301 ZR Roden, Netherlands NL
Mailing Address:
PO Box 60
9300 AB Roden, Netherlands
Tel.: (31) 505018808
Fax: (31) 50 501 1456
E-Mail: sales@dep.nl
Web Site: www.photonis.com
Emp.: 370
Image Intensifiers Mfr & Distr
S.I.C.: 3823
N.A.I.C.S.: 334513
Goossen Boers *(CEO)*
Hans Velthuis *(Mng Dir)*
Kees Brouwer *(COO)*

Joint Ventures:

Saur SA (1)
1 Ave Eugene Freyssinet
78064 Saint-Quentin-en-Yvelines, France
Tel.: (33) 130602260
Fax: (33) 130602789
Web Site: www.saur.com
Sales Range: $1-4.9 Billion
Emp.: 12,400
Water Treatment & Sanitation Services
S.I.C.: 4953
N.A.I.C.S.: 562219
Joel Seche *(Chm)*
Olivier Brousse *(Mng Dir & Pres)*
Patrick Barthelemy *(Deputy Mng Dir)*

Subsidiaries:

Coved (2)
1 rue Antoine Lavoisier
78064 Guyancourt, France
Tel.: (33) 130602260
Fax: (33) 130606569
E-Mail: dircom@saur.fr
Web Site: www.saur.com
Sales Range: $550-599.9 Million
Emp.: 2,800
Sanitation Management Services
S.I.C.: 4959
N.A.I.C.S.: 562998
Brousse Olivier *(Mng Dir)*

Stereau SAS (2)
1 rue Antoine Lavoisier
78064 Saint-Quentin-en-Yvelines, France
Tel.: (33) 130606491
Fax: (33) 130606439
Web Site: www.stereau.fr
Emp.: 30
Water Treatment Services
S.I.C.: 4953
N.A.I.C.S.: 562219
Christophe Peltzer *(CFO)*
Jacques Tessier *(COO)*

SPIE SA (1)
Parc Saint-Christophe
10 avenue de l'Enterprise, 95863 Cergy, Cedex, France
Tel.: (33) 134226931
E-Mail: communication@spie.com
Web Site: www.spie.com
Sales Range: $1-4.9 Billion
Emp.: 29,000
Engineering Services
Import Export
S.I.C.: 8711
N.A.I.C.S.: 541330
Gauthier Louette *(Chm & CEO)*
Denis Chene *(CFO)*
Emmanuel Martin *(CEO-Sud-Est)*

Subsidiaries:

SPIE Communications SA (2)
10 avenue de l'Enterprise
Pole Vinci, 95800 Cergy-Pontoise, France
Tel.: (33) 141464146
Fax: (33) 141464147
E-Mail: infos@spie.fr
Web Site: www.spiecom.globalsysteme.com
Emp.: 2,200
Telecommunications Mfr
S.I.C.: 4812
N.A.I.C.S.: 517210
Gilles Brazey *(Mng Dir)*

SPIE Communications (2)
ZA Pre Catelan 1 rue Delesalle
F 59110 La Madeleine, France
Tel.: (33) 320125900
Fax: (33) 320125989
E-Mail: p.spriet@spie.com
Web Site: www.spie.com
Emp.: 2,000
Telephone Equipment Distr
S.I.C.: 5065
N.A.I.C.S.: 423690

TDF S.A.S. (1)
106 avenue Marx Dormoy
92541 Montrouge, France
Tel.: (33) 155951000
Web Site: www.tdf-group.com
Sales Range: $1-4.9 Billion
Emp.: 4,500
Television, Radio, Telecommunications & Satellite Communications Infrastructure Operator
S.I.C.: 4833
N.A.I.C.S.: 515120
Olivier Huart *(CEO)*

U.S. Subsidiary:

AXA Private Equity US, LLC (1)
1370 Avenue of the Americas
New York, NY 10019 DE
Tel.: (212) 641-8604
Fax: (212) 641-8616
Web Site: www.axaprivateequity.com
Emp.: 20
Private Equity Firm
S.I.C.: 6211
N.A.I.C.S.: 523999
Benoit Verbrugghe *(Mng Partner & Head-USA)*
Mathias Burghardt *(Sr Mng Dir & Head-Infrastructure)*
Vladimir Colas *(Mng Dir)*

Non-U.S. Subsidiaries:

AXA Private Equity Asia Pte. Ltd. (1)
1 Temasek Avenue Unit 20-02A Millenia Tower
39192 Singapore, Singapore SG
Tel.: (65) 65133410
Fax: (65) 65133426
Emp.: 1
Private Equity Firm
S.I.C.: 6211
N.A.I.C.S.: 523999
Jenhao Han *(Mng Dir)*

AXA Private Equity Eastern Europe GmbH (1)
Wipplinger Strasse 35
1010 Vienna, Austria AT
Tel.: (43) 153753700
Fax: (43) 153753707
Web Site: www.axaprivateequity.com
Private Equity Firm
S.I.C.: 6211
N.A.I.C.S.: 523999
Thomas Wilfling *(Mng Dir)*

AXA Private Equity Germany GmbH (1)
An der Welle 4
60322 Frankfurt, Germany De
Tel.: (49) 69 50 50 41 500
Fax: (49) 69 50 50 41 550
Private Equity Firm
S.I.C.: 6211
N.A.I.C.S.: 523999
Stephan Illenberger *(Mng Dir)*
Jens Schuster *(CFO)*

AXA Private Equity Italy S.r.l. (1)
Via Priavata Fratelli Gabba N 1/A
20121 Milan, Italy IT
Tel.: (39) 02 5844 2401
Fax: (39) 02 5844 2450
E-Mail: milano.pe@axa-im.com
Private Equity Firm
S.I.C.: 6211
N.A.I.C.S.: 523999
Stefano Mion *(Mng Dir)*

AXA Private Equity Switzerland AG (1)
Affolternstrasse 42
PO Box 6961
8050 Zurich, Switzerland CH
Tel.: (41) 43 299 11 99
Fax: (41) 43 299 11 20
Web Site: www.axaprivateequity.com
Private Equity Firm
S.I.C.: 6211
N.A.I.C.S.: 523999
Martin Kessi *(Mng Dir)*

AXA Private Equity UK Limited (1)
1 Grafton Street
London, W1S 3HY, United Kingdom UK
Tel.: (44) 20 7003 1350
Fax: (44) 20 7575 8309
Web Site: www.axaprivateequity.com
Emp.: 3
Private Equity Firm
S.I.C.: 6211
N.A.I.C.S.: 523999
Andrew Liau *(Co-Mng Dir)*
Stefano Mion *(Co-Mng Dir)*

Non-U.S. Holding:

RIEMSER Pharma GmbH (1)
(Formerly Riemser Arzneimittel AG)
An der Wiek 7
17493 Greifswald, Germany
Tel.: (49) 38351 76 0
Fax: (49) 38351 76 48
E-Mail: info@riemser.com
Web Site: www.riemser.com
Sales Range: $125-149.9 Million
Emp.: 500
Pharmaceuticals Mfr
S.I.C.: 2834
N.A.I.C.S.: 325412
Michael Mehler *(CEO)*
Beatrice von Buchwaldt *(CFO)*

Non-U.S. Joint Venture:

Opodo Limited (1)
Waterfront
Hammersmith Emban, London, W6 9RU, United Kingdom
Tel.: (44) 8703525000
Web Site: www.opodo.com
Internet Travel Agency Services
S.I.C.: 2741
N.A.I.C.S.: 519130
Caroline Noble *(Mng Dir)*

ARDMORE CONSTRUCTION LIMITED

Byrne House Jeffreys Road
Brimsdown
Enfield, Middlesex, EN3 7UB, United Kingdom
Tel.: (44) 20 8344 0300
Fax: (44) 20 8344 0377
E-Mail: info@ardmoregroup.co.uk
Web Site: www.ardmoregroup.co.uk
Year Founded: 1974
Sales Range: $450-499.9 Million
Emp.: 280
Business Description:
Construction Engineering Services
S.I.C.: 8711
N.A.I.C.S.: 541330
Personnel:
Alan Edgar *(Dir-Construction)*

ARDMORE SHIPPING CORPORATION

City Gate Building 1000
Mahon, Cork, Ireland
Tel.: (353) 21 240 9500
Fax: (353) 21 240 9501
E-Mail: info@ardmoreshipping.com
Web Site: www.ardmoreshipping.com
Year Founded: 2010
ASC—(NYSE)
Rev.: $25,172,654
Assets: $179,960,468
Liabilities: $71,569,479
Net Worth: $108,390,989
Earnings: ($453,993)
Fiscal Year-end: 12/31/12
Business Description:
Petroleum Products & Chemical Transportation Services
S.I.C.: 4412
N.A.I.C.S.: 483111
Personnel:
Reginald L. Jones, III *(Chm)*
Anthony Gurnee *(Pres & CEO)*
Paul Tivnan *(CFO, Treas & Sec)*
Mark Cameron *(COO)*
Board of Directors:
Reginald L. Jones, III
Brian Dunne
Anthony Gurnee
Niall McComiskey

ARDO N.V.

Wezestraat 61
8850 Ardooie, Belgium
Tel.: (32) 51310621
Fax: (32) 51305997
E-Mail: info@ardo.be
Web Site: www.ardo.com
Year Founded: 1973
Sales Range: $800-899.9 Million
Emp.: 2,500
Business Description:
Frozen Vegetables Producer & Whslr
S.I.C.: 5431
N.A.I.C.S.: 445230
Personnel:
Gan Haspeslagh *(CEO)*

Non-U.S. Subsidiaries:

Ardo A/B (1)
Enhagsvagen 7
187 40 Taby, Sweden
Tel.: (46) 8 768 1550
Fax: (46) 8 768 1552
Frozen Vegetable & Fruit Mfr & Distr
S.I.C.: 2037
N.A.I.C.S.: 311411

Ardo A/S (1)
Slipshavnsvej 2
5800 Nyborg, Denmark
Tel.: (45) 65310310
Fax: (45) 63315519
E-Mail: info@frigodan.dk
Emp.: 50
Frozen Vegetable & Fruit Whslr
S.I.C.: 5142
N.A.I.C.S.: 424420
AnneMette Thomsen *(Sec)*

Ardo Austria Frost GmbH (1)
Marchfelder Strasse 2
2301 Gross-Enzersdorf, Austria
Tel.: (43) 2249 3535 0
Fax: (43) 2249 3883
E-Mail: info@austriafrost.at
Emp.: 215
Frozen Vegetable & Fruit Mfr & Distr
S.I.C.: 2037
N.A.I.C.S.: 311411
Roman Gabriel, *(Dir-Sls-Retail)*

Ardo B.V. (1)
Industrieweg 9-11
4881 EW Zundert, Netherlands
Tel.: (31) 765 999999
Fax: (31) 765 999900
E-Mail: info@ardobv.nl
Frozen Vegetable & Fruit Mfr & Distr
S.I.C.: 2037
N.A.I.C.S.: 311411
Paul Wortel *(Mgr-Investments)*

Ardo GmbH (1)
Gothaer Strasse 2
40880 Ratingen, Germany
Tel.: (49) 2102 20280
Fax: (49) 2102 202826
E-Mail: Info@Ardo-GmbH.de
Emp.: 20
Frozen Vegetable & Fruit Whslr
S.I.C.: 5142
N.A.I.C.S.: 424420

Ardo Italia SRL (1)
Via PO 134 A
43100 Parma, Italy

Tel.: (39) 0521 929 912
Fax: (39) 0521 256 992
E-Mail: ardoitalia@ardo.be
Emp.: 50
Frozen Vegetable & Fruit Mfr & Distr
S.I.C.: 2037
N.A.I.C.S.: 311411

ARDO Mochov s.r.o. (1)
Sezemicka 2757/2
Horni Pocernice, 193 00 Prague, Czech Republic
Tel.: (420) 326 597 045
Fax: (420) 226015292
Frozen Vegetable & Fruit Whslr
S.I.C.: 5142
N.A.I.C.S.: 424420

Ardo SA (1)
Route de Carhaix
56110 Gourin, France
Tel.: (33) 297 234876
Fax: (33) 297 235149
E-Mail: commercial@ardo.fr
Web Site: www.ardo.com.pl
Frozen Vegetable & Fruit Mfr & Distr
S.I.C.: 2037
N.A.I.C.S.: 311411

Ardo Shangai Marketing Co. Ltd (1)
Zhao Jia Bang Lu 680 Room 906
200031 Shanghai, China
Tel.: (86) 21 6473 8068
Frozen Vegetable & Fruit Mfr & Distr
S.I.C.: 2037
N.A.I.C.S.: 311411

Ardo Sp.Z.o.o. (1)
Ul Chlopickiego 17/19
04-314 Warsaw, Poland
Tel.: (48) 510 080 311
E-Mail: info@ardo.be
Emp.: 1
Frozen Vegetable & Fruit Whslr
S.I.C.: 5142
N.A.I.C.S.: 424420

Ardo UK Ltd. (1)
Ashford Road
Charing, TN27 0DF, United Kingdom
Tel.: (44) 1233 714714
Fax: (44) 1233 714777
E-Mail: info@ardouk.com
Web Site: www.ardouk.com
Emp.: 130
Frozen Vegetable & Fruit Whslr
S.I.C.: 5142
N.A.I.C.S.: 424420
Debbie Henry *(Bus Mgr-Ardo Food Ingredients Sector)*

Ardofoods Ireland Ltd. (1)
Murphystown Road 100 Leopardstown Heights
18 Dublin, Ireland
Tel.: (353) 12 957355
Fax: (353) 12 952636
Frozen Vegetable & Fruit Whslr
S.I.C.: 5142
N.A.I.C.S.: 424420

Ardovries Espana S.A. (1)
Avenida Ramon Y Cajal 4
Dos Hermanas, 41700 Seville, Spain
Tel.: (34) 955 66 06 48
Fax: (34) 955 66 09 36
E-Mail: Ardovries@ardo.es
Frozen Vegetable & Fruit Mfr & Distr
S.I.C.: 2037
N.A.I.C.S.: 311411

ARDOR SA LIMITED

Waterkloof
PO Box 95079
Pretoria, 0145, South Africa
Tel.: (27) 11 467 8889
Fax: (27) 86 681 4213
E-Mail: info@ardorsa.co.za
Web Site: www.ardorsa.co.za
ARD—(JSE)
Sales Range: Less than $1 Million
Business Description:
Real Estate Development Services
S.I.C.: 6531
N.A.I.C.S.: 531390
Personnel:
Mark MacNamara Smith *(CEO)*
Board of Directors:
Barry John Havenga
Modilati Gustav Mahlare
Kgaogelo Richard Molewa
Morrison Etienne Smit
Mark MacNamara Smith

ARDOUR WORLD LIMITED

York House 8th Floor Empire Way
Wembley, Middlesex, HA9 0PA, United Kingdom
Tel.: (44) 208 782 8744
Fax: (44) 208 795 0711
E-Mail: info@ardourworld.com
Web Site: www.ardourworld.com
Year Founded: 2003
Sales Range: $100-124.9 Million
Emp.: 10
Business Description:
Metal Product Whslr
S.I.C.: 5051
N.A.I.C.S.: 423510
Personnel:
Ashish Chaudhari *(Co-Founder)*
Sundip Goyal *(Co-Founder)*

AREALINK CO. LTD.

3-1 Kanda Ogawamachi Chiyoda-ku
Tokyo, 101-0052, Japan
Tel.: (81) 355779222
Fax: (81) 355779215
E-Mail: info@arealink.co.jp
Web Site: www.arealink.co.jp
8914—(TKS)
Sls.: $111,364,000
Assets: $204,732,000
Liabilities: $84,447,000
Net Worth: $120,285,000
Earnings: $10,428,000
Emp.: 89
Fiscal Year-end: 12/31/12
Business Description:
Real Estate Services
S.I.C.: 6513
N.A.I.C.S.: 531110
Personnel:
Naomichi Hayashi *(Pres & CEO)*
Board of Directors:
Naomichi Hayashi
Setsu Kobayashi
Kazuki Kurino
Minoru Nishizawa
Yasuteru Otaki
Shohei Wakasugi

AREEYA PROPERTY PUBLIC COMPANY LIMITED

67/4 Dynasty Complex 2 Ladprao 71 Road Khwang Wangthonglang
Khet Wangthonglang, Bangkok, 10310, Thailand
Tel.: (66) 29330333
Fax: (66) 29559766
Web Site: www.areeya.co.th
Year Founded: 2000
A—(THA)
Rev.: $60,798,791
Assets: $227,472,900
Liabilities: $144,795,283
Net Worth: $82,677,617
Earnings: $3,125,922
Fiscal Year-end: 12/31/12
Business Description:
Residential Building Construction Services
S.I.C.: 1531
N.A.I.C.S.: 236117
Personnel:
Wisit Laohapoonrungsee *(Chm & CEO)*
Archawan Eiampaiboomphans *(Exec VP-Construction Dept)*
Chumpolpat Puldrapaya *(Exec VP-Fin & Acctg Dept)*
Vanchai Srihiranrassamee *(Exec VP-Project Mgmt)*
Chernchin Cherdchoochai *(Sr VP-Brand Corp Dept)*
Board of Directors:
Wisit Laohapoonrungsee
Preecha Boonyakida
Piroj Ratanasopa
Niphapat Romerattanaphun
Wanchai Tantikul
Thun Thiensuwan
Legal Counsel:
Kunnatham Law Office
72/2-3 Sutthisanwinitchai Road Samsen-Nok Huay-Kwang
Bangkok, Thailand

Subsidiary:

One Up Co., Ltd. (1)
No 184 Forum Tower Fl 37 Kwang Huay Kwang Khet Huay Kwang
No 184 236 Ratchadapisek Rd, 10310 Bangkok, Thailand
Tel.: (66) 2 6453535
Fax: (66) 2 6453539
Web Site: www.oneup.co.th
Construction Management Services
S.I.C.: 1522
N.A.I.C.S.: 236116
Dennis Ong Boon Seong *(CEO)*

ARENA BILGISAYAR SANAYI VE TICARET A.S.

Merkez Mahallesi Gokturk Caddesi 4
34077 Istanbul, Turkey
Tel.: (90) 212 364 64 64
Fax: (90) 212 310 46 80
E-Mail: ir@arena.com.tr
Web Site: www.arena.com.tr
Year Founded: 1991
ARENA—(IST)
Sls.: $505,146,000
Assets: $185,886,000
Liabilities: $131,705,000
Net Worth: $54,181,000
Earnings: $8,765,000
Emp.: 243
Fiscal Year-end: 12/31/12
Business Description:
Computer Peripheral Whslr
S.I.C.: 5045
N.A.I.C.S.: 423430
Personnel:
Servet Topaloglu *(Chm)*
Raj Shankar *(Deputy Chm)*
Serkan Celik *(CFO)*
Board of Directors:
Servet Topaloglu
Sriram Ganeshan
Cuneyt Genc
Raj Shankar
Ramanathan Srinivasan

ARENA GROUP

Needingworth Road
Saint Ives, Cambs, PE27 3ND, United Kingdom
Tel.: (44) 1480 46 88 88
Fax: (44) 1480 46 28 88
Web Site: www.arenagroup.com
Business Description:
Holding Company; Event Design, Engineering & Project Planning
S.I.C.: 7999
N.A.I.C.S.: 713990
Personnel:
Greg Lawless *(CEO)*
Grahame Muir *(CEO-UK & Europe)*

Divisions:

Arena Overlay (1)
2nd Floor 53-54 Haymarket
London, SW1Y 4RP, United Kingdom
Tel.: (44) 20 7484 5003
E-Mail: info@arenagroup.com
Web Site: www.arenagroup.com
Temporary Event Overlay Services, Including Budgeting, Designs, Sourcing Materials to Construction & Maintenance of Temporary Environment
S.I.C.: 7999
N.A.I.C.S.: 713990

Arena Scaffolding (1)
Needingworth Road
Saint Ives, Cambs, PE27 3ND, United Kingdom
Tel.: (44) 1480 46 88 88
Fax: (44) 1480 46 28 88
E-Mail: info@arenascaffolding.com
Web Site: www.arenagroup.com
Design & Installation of Temporary Modular Event Scaffolding Systems
S.I.C.: 7999
N.A.I.C.S.: 713990

Subsidiaries:

Arena Event Services Group Ltd. (1)
Needingworth Road
Saint Ives, PE27 3ND, United Kingdom
Tel.: (44) 1480 46 88 88
Fax: (44) 1480 46 28 88
Event Interior Services
S.I.C.: 7999
N.A.I.C.S.: 713990
Christopher Piggott, *(Mng Dir)*

Subsidiary:

Spaceworks Furniture Hire Ltd. (2)
4 Deer Park Road
South Wimbledon, London, SW19 3GY, United Kingdom
Tel.: (44) 845 634 0000
Fax: (44) 845 634 0022
E-Mail: sales@spaceworks.co.uk
Web Site: www.spaceworks.co.uk
Event Furniture for Hire
S.I.C.: 7999
N.A.I.C.S.: 532292
Christopher Piggott, *(Mng Dir)*

Arena Seating Limited (1)
Arena House Membury
Lambourn Woodlands, Hungerford, RG17 7TQ, United Kingdom
Tel.: (44) 1488 67 48 00
Fax: (44) 1488 67 48 22
E-Mail: info@arenaseating.com
Web Site: www.arenagroup.com
Sale & Rental of Permanent & Temporary Event Seating
S.I.C.: 7999
N.A.I.C.S.: 713990
Niall Gaffney *(Mng Dir)*

Arena Structures Limited (1)
Needingworth Road
Saint Ives, Cambridgeshire, PE27 3ND, United Kingdom UK
Tel.: (44) 1480468888
Fax: (44) 1480462888
E-Mail: info@arenastructures.com
Web Site: www.arenastructures.com
Emp.: 100
Marquee & Temporary Structure Rental & Management Services
S.I.C.: 7359
N.A.I.C.S.: 532310
Loren Johnson *(Mng Dir)*

U.S. Subsidiary:

Karl's Event Services, Inc. (1)
7000 S 10th St
Oak Creek, WI 53154
Tel.: (414) 831-7000
Toll Free: (800) 383-6332
Web Site: www.karls.com
Sales Range: $25-49.9 Million
Emp.: 300
Event Related Services
S.I.C.: 7999
N.A.I.C.S.: 532292
John Haener *(Pres & CEO)*
Keith Eismann *(Exec VP-Event Rentals)*

ARENA HOLDING S.P.A.

Piazza Marconi 25
00144 Rome, Italy
Tel.: (39) 065919341
Fax: (39) 06591934222
E-Mail: info@arenaholding.com

Arena Holding S.p.A.—(Continued)

Web Site: www.arenaholding.com
Business Description:
Holding Company; Food Products
S.I.C.: 6719
N.A.I.C.S.: 551112
Personnel:
Dante Di Dario *(Chm)*

Subsidiaries:

Avicola Molisana Srl (1)
Localita Monteverde
Bojano, 3000 Naples, Italy
Tel.: (39) 08747501
Fax: (39) 0874782874
Broilers & Meat Type Chicken Production
S.I.C.: 0251
N.A.I.C.S.: 112320

Non-U.S. Holdings:

Roncadin S.A. (1)
Le Labour
PO Box 13
33870 Vayres, France
Tel.: (33) 557553900
Fax: (33) 557553929
E-Mail: contact@fr.rr-icecream.eu
Web Site: www.rr-icecream.fr
Emp.: 115
Mfr. of Frozen Food Products
S.I.C.: 2034
N.A.I.C.S.: 311423
James Lambert *(Gen Mgr)*

ARENA REIT

Level 20 600 Bourke Street
Melbourne, VIC, 3000, Australia
Tel.: (61) 3 9093 9000
Fax: (61) 3 9093 9093
E-Mail: info@arenainvest.com.au
Web Site: www.arenainvest.com.au
ARF—(ASX)
Business Description:
Real Estate Investment Services
S.I.C.: 6211
N.A.I.C.S.: 523999
Personnel:
David Ross *(Chm)*
James Goodwin *(Mng Dir)*
Bryce Mitchelson *(Mng Dir)*
Gareth Winter *(CFO)*
Board of Directors:
David Ross
James Goodwin
Bryce Mitchelson
Simon Parsons
Dennis Wildenburg

ARENA STRUCTURES

(See Under Arena Group)

ARENDALS FOSSEKOMPANI ASA

Langbryggen 5
4841 Arendal, Norway
Mailing Address:
PO Box 280
4803 Arendal, Norway
Tel.: (47) 37 23 44 00
Fax: (47) 37 23 44 01
E-Mail: firmapost@arendalsfoss.no
Web Site: www.arendalsfoss.no
AFK—(OSL)
Rev.: $482,338,350
Assets: $1,178,588,781
Liabilities: $641,555,253
Net Worth: $537,033,528
Earnings: $58,242,582
Emp.: 1,391
Fiscal Year-end: 12/31/12
Business Description:
Electricity Generation & Distr
S.I.C.: 4931
N.A.I.C.S.: 221122
Personnel:
Sverre Valvik *(CEO)*
Thor R. Gabrielsen *(CFO)*

Holding:

Glamox ASA (1)
Glamox Luxo Lighting
Drammensveien 175, NO-0277 Oslo, Norway NO
Mailing Address: (62.6%)
PO Box 163
Skoyen, Torshov, NO-0212, Norway
Tel.: (47) 22021100
Fax: (47) 22021102
E-Mail: info.no@glamox.com
Web Site: www.glamox.com
Sales Range: $150-199.9 Million
Emp.: 1,100
Lighting Mfr
S.I.C.: 3646
N.A.I.C.S.: 335122
Kjell Stamnes *(Pres & CEO)*
Thomas Lindberg *(CFO)*
Jan Berner *(Sr VP-Global Marine & Offshore)*
Knut S. Rusten *(Sr VP-Mktg)*
Hakan Westin *(Sr VP-Mktg)*

Subsidiary:

Luxo ASA (2)
Drammensveien 175
277 Oslo, Norway (97%)
Mailing Address:
PO Box 163
212 Oslo, Norway
Tel.: (47) 22 06 09 00
Fax: (47) 22021072
E-Mail: info@glamox.com
Web Site: www.glamox.com
Sales Range: $1-9.9 Million
Emp.: 354
Functional Lighting for Offices, Industry & Health Care Mfr
Export
S.I.C.: 3646
N.A.I.C.S.: 335122
Thomas Lindberg *(CFO & VP-Fin)*
Kjetil Gjerdalen *(COO & VP-Ops)*

Subsidiaries:

Stokkan Lys (3)
Gjerdrumsvei 16 B
484 Oslo, Norway
Tel.: (47) 95858803
E-Mail: post@stokkanlys.no
Web Site: www.stokkanlys.no
Sales Range: $75-99.9 Million
Emp.: 19
Functional Lighting for Offices, Industry & Health Care Services
S.I.C.: 3646
N.A.I.C.S.: 335122

U.S. Subsidiary:

Luxo Corporation (3)
5 Westchester Plz
Elmsford, NY 10523
Tel.: (914) 345-0067
Fax: (914) 345-0068
E-Mail: office@luxous.com
Web Site: www.luxous.com
Emp.: 20
Functional Lighting for Offices Industry and Health Care Services
Export
S.I.C.: 3646
N.A.I.C.S.: 335122
Samuel Gumins *(Pres & CEO)*

Non-U.S. Subsidiaries:

Glamox Luxo Lighting A/S (3)
Baldershoj 5
DK 2635 Ishoj, Denmark
Tel.: (45) 43 550 260
Fax: (45) 43 550 270
E-Mail: info.dk@glamox.com
Web Site: www.glamoxluxo.com
Sales Range: $1-9.9 Million
Emp.: 15
Functional Lighting for Offices, Industry & Health Care Services
S.I.C.: 3646
N.A.I.C.S.: 335122

Glamox Luxo Lighting Limited (3)
Unit 3 Capital Business Park
Manor Way, Borehamwood, Hertfordshire, WD6 1GW, United Kingdom
Tel.: (44) 208 9530540
Fax: (44) 208 9539580
E-Mail: ukoffice@glamoxluxo.com
Web Site: www.glamox.com
Emp.: 20
Functional Lighting for Offices, Industry & Health Care Services
S.I.C.: 3646
N.A.I.C.S.: 335122

Glamox Luxo Lighting OY (3)
Orevagen 8
01510 Vantaa, Finland
Tel.: (358) 1 0841 0440
Fax: (358) 1 0841 0464
E-Mail: office@luxo.fi
Web Site: www.luxo.fi
Sales Range: $1-9.9 Million
Emp.: 10
Functional Lighting for Offices, Industry & Health Care Services
S.I.C.: 3646
N.A.I.C.S.: 335122

Glamox Luxo Lighting GmbH (3)
Von Thunen Strasse 12
28307 Bremen, Germany
Tel.: (49) 421 4857 05
Fax: (49) 421 4857 022
E-Mail: info.de@glamoxluxo.com
Web Site: www.glamox.com
Emp.: 25
Functional Lighting for Offices, Industry & Health Care Services
S.I.C.: 3646
N.A.I.C.S.: 335122

Glamox Luxo Lighting AB (3)
Gardveda
570 82 Malilla, Sweden
Tel.: (46) 49 524 99 00
Fax: (46) 49 524 99 24
E-Mail:
Web Site: www.glamox.com
Emp.: 100
Functional Lighting for Offices, Industry & Health Care Services
S.I.C.: 3646
N.A.I.C.S.: 335122
Tomas Kjellberd *(Mgr-Sls)*

ARES ASIA LIMITED

Unit 1602 LHT Tower 31 Queen's Road
Central, China (Hong Kong)
Tel.: (852) 2273 3888
Fax: (852) 2273 3880
E-Mail: ir@aresasialtd.com
Web Site: www.aresasialtd.com
0645—(HKG)
Sls.: $44,639,000
Assets: $32,050,000
Liabilities: $1,089,000
Net Worth: $30,961,000
Earnings: ($4,256,000)
Emp.: 14
Fiscal Year-end: 03/31/13
Business Description:
Footwear Mfr
S.I.C.: 2389
N.A.I.C.S.: 316210
Personnel:
Adwin Haryanto Suryohadiprojo *(Chm)*
Junaidi Yap *(CEO)*
Kin Yee Poon *(Sec)*
Board of Directors:
Adwin Haryanto Suryohadiprojo
Chun Kay Chua
Frank Pun Yuen Lam
Hing Hon Ngan
Junaidi Yap
Sydney Kin Bond Yeung
Legal Counsel:
Conyers, Dill & Pearman
2901 One Exchange Square
8 Connaught Place, Central, China (Hong Kong)
Butterfield Fulcrum Group (Bermuda) Limited
26 Burnaby Street
Hamilton, HM 11, Bermuda
Transfer Agents:
Computershare Hong Kong Investor Services Limited
17th Floor, Hopewell Centre 183 Queens Road East
Hong Kong, China (Hong Kong)
Butterfield Fulcrum Group (Bermuda) Limited
26 Burnaby Street
Hamilton, HM 11, Bermuda

ARES INTERNATIONAL CORPORATION

3F No 111 Sec 2 Zhongshan N Rd
104 Taipei, Taiwan
Tel.: (886) 225221351
Fax: (886) 225601735
E-Mail: www@ares.com.tw
Web Site: www.ares.com.tw
2471—(TAI)
Sales Range: $10-24.9 Million
Emp.: 310
Business Description:
Information Technology Services
S.I.C.: 7372
N.A.I.C.S.: 511210
Personnel:
Hung-Yang Yu *(Chm)*

ARES LIFE SCIENCES SA

Avenue Giuseppe-Motta 31-33
CH-1211 Geneva, Switzerland
Tel.: (41) 58 944 0400
E-Mail: info@areslifesciences.com
Web Site: www.areslifesciences.com
Year Founded: 2008
Business Description:
Life Sciences Investment Holding Company
S.I.C.: 6719
N.A.I.C.S.: 551112
Personnel:
Jacques Theurillat *(CEO & Partner)*
Maria-Gabriella Camboni *(Partner)*
Christian Chavy *(Partner)*
Emmanuel Floret *(Partner)*
Patrick P. Lee *(Partner)*
Giulia Nobili *(Partner)*
Paola Ricci *(Partner)*
Juan Vidal *(Partner)*

Non-U.S. Holding:

Stallergenes S.A. (1)
6 rue Alexis de Tocqueville
92183 Antony, Cedex, France FR
Tel.: (33) 1 5559 2000 (73.18%)
Fax: (33) 1 5559 2002
E-Mail:
Web Site: www.stallergenes.com
GENP—(EUR)
Sls.: $322,868,105
Assets: $377,397,413
Liabilities: $123,205,517
Net Worth: $254,191,896
Earnings: $50,335,989
Emp.: 1,057
Fiscal Year-end: 12/31/12
Allergen Biopharmaceutical Developer, Mfr & Distr
S.I.C.: 2834
N.A.I.C.S.: 325412
Roberto Gradnik *(CEO)*
Peter Buhler *(CFO)*
Thomas Lang *(Sr VP & Gen Mgr-US)*
Pierre Catignol *(Sr VP-Indus Ops)*
Olivier de Beaumont *(Sr VP-Medical Affairs-Global)*
Paul-Louis Gayrel *(Sr VP-Regulatory & Compliance)*

Cecile Hilaire *(Sr VP-Strategic Mktg & Market Access)*
Richard Lejosne *(Sr VP-HR)*
Philippe Moingeon *(Sr VP-Res & Pharmaceutical Dev)*
Poul Sorensen *(Sr VP-Strategic Dev)*
Cyril Tavier *(Sr VP-Ops-Southern Europe)*
Philippe Verez *(Sr VP-Ops-Intl)*
Robert Zeldin *(Sr VP-Clinical Dev-Global)*

U.S. Subsidiary:

Stallergenes, Inc. (2)
600 Cordwainer Dr
Norwell, MA 02061 DE
Tel.: (781) 878-0018 (100%)
Fax: (781) 878-0063
Allergen Biopharmaceutical Distr
S.I.C.: 5122
N.A.I.C.S.: 424210
Thomas Lang *(Pres)*

AREVA SA

(d/b/a Areva Group)
33 rue La Fayette
75442 Paris, Cedex 9, France
Tel.: (33) 134960647
Fax: (33) 134960001
E-Mail: press@areva.com
Web Site: www.areva.com
AREVA—(EUR)
Rev.: $579,411,761
Assets: $23,624,147,333
Liabilities: $14,415,322,789
Net Worth: $9,208,824,543
Earnings: $325,346,404
Emp.: 46,513
Fiscal Year-end: 12/31/12

Business Description:
Power Generation & Distribution
Import Export
S.I.C.: 4931
N.A.I.C.S.: 221113

Personnel:
Pierre Blayau *(Chm-Supervisory Bd)*
Luc Oursel *(Chm-Exec Bd, Pres & CEO)*
Bernard Bigot *(Vice Chm-Supervisory Bd)*
Pierre Aubouin *(CFO & Member-Exec Bd)*
Philippe Knoche *(COO & Member-Exec Bd)*
Pierre Charreton *(Chief Admin Officer & Gen Counsel)*
Tarik Choho *(Sr Chief Comml Officer & Member-Exec Mgmt Bd)*
Christian Barandas *(Chief Indus Officer & Chief Performance Officer)*
Olivier Wantz *(Member-Exec Bd & Sr Exec VP-Mining Bus)*
Claire Terrazas *(Gen Counsel-Corp Governance & Fin & VP-Corp Legal Dept)*
Anne-Marie Choho *(Sr Exec VP-Engrg & Projects)*
Guillaume Dureau *(Sr Exec VP-Front End Bus Grp)*
Louis-Francois Durret *(Sr Exec VP-Renewable Energies Bus Grp)*
Carolle Foissaud *(Sr Exec VP-Safety, Security & Ops Support)*
Benjamin Fremaux *(Sr Exec VP-Strategy & Mergers/Acq)*
Jacques Gerault *(Sr Exec VP-Pub Affairs)*
Charles Hufnagel *(Sr Exec VP-Comm & Member-Exec Mgmt Bd)*
Claude Jaouen *(Sr Exec VP-Reactors & Svcs Bus Grp)*
Dominique Mockly *(Sr Exec VP-Back End Bus Grp)*
Veronique Rouzaud *(Sr Exec VP-HR & Member-Exec Mgmt Bd)*
Jean-Luc Andrieux *(Sr VP-Safety, Health, Security & Sustainable Dev)*
Raphael Berger *(Sr VP-Strategy & Economic Studies)*
Patrick Champalaune *(Sr VP-Pur)*
Jean-Michel Chereau *(Sr VP-Protection)*
Martha Crawford-Heitzmann *(Sr VP-R&D & Innovation)*
Helene Derrien *(Sr VP-Executives Career Mgmt)*
Thierry Noircler *(Sr VP-Audit)*

Supervisory Board of Directors:
Pierre Blayau
Christophe Behar
Bernard Bigot
Sophie Boissard
Claire Cheremetinski
Francois David
Pascal Faure
Christophe Gegout
Marion Guillou
Jean-Michel Lang
Agnes Lemarchand
Francoise Pieri
Philippe Pinson
Guylaine Saucier
Pierre Sellal

Deloitte & Associes
185 avenue Charles-de-Gaulle
Neuilly-sur-Seine, France

Subsidiaries:

Areva NC (1)
33 rue La Fayette
75 442 Paris, Cedex, France FR
Tel.: (33) 134960000 (100%)
Fax: (33) 134960001
Web Site: www.areva-nc.com
Emp.: 19,600
Nuclear Fuel Production, Mining & Waste Recycling Services
S.I.C.: 1623
N.A.I.C.S.: 237110
Didier Benedetti *(COO)*

Division:

Commox GIE (2)
33 Rue Lasayette
75442 Paris, Cedex 09, France (100%)
Tel.: (33) 0139263000
Fax: (33) 134960001
Web Site: www.cogema.fr
Marketer of Nuclear Fuel Products
S.I.C.: 4911
N.A.I.C.S.: 221118

U.S. Subsidiaries:

Areva, Inc (2)
4800 Hampden Ln Ste 1100
Bethesda, MD 20814
Tel.: (301) 841-1600
Fax: (301) 841-1610
E-Mail: arevainc@areva.com
Web Site: www.areva.com
Emp.: 50
Nuclear Power, Energy Distribution & Transmission Industries Services
S.I.C.: 8742
N.A.I.C.S.: 541613
Jacques Besnainou *(Pres & CEO)*
David Jones *(Sr VP-Backend)*

Areva NC, Inc. (2)
4800 Hampden Ln Ste 1100
Bethesda, MD 20814-3400 (100%)
Tel.: (301) 841-1600
Fax: (301) 841-1610
E-Mail: info@areva.com
Web Site: www.areva-nc.com
Emp.: 80
Nuclear Fuel Production, Mining & Waste Recycling Services
Export
S.I.C.: 1094
N.A.I.C.S.: 212291
Jacques Besnainou *(CEO)*

Subsidiaries:

AFS Packaging Projects (3)
1102 Broadway Plaza Ste 300
Tacoma, WA 98402-3526 WA
Tel.: (509) 383-9000 (100%)
Fax: (509) 383-9002
Web Site: www.pactec-tn.com
Emp.: 26
Domestic Supplier of Packaging Engineering & Licensing Services & High Level Waste Management
S.I.C.: 7389
N.A.I.C.S.: 561910
Richard Smith *(Chief Engr)*

AREVA Enrichment Services LLC (3)
4800 Hampden Ln 1100
Bethesda, MD 20814-2969
Tel.: (301) 841-1600
Electric Power Generation Services
S.I.C.: 4911
N.A.I.C.S.: 221118

Canberra Industries, Inc. (3)
800 Research Pkwy
Meriden, CT 06450 (100%)
Tel.: (203) 238-2351
Fax: (203) 235-1347
Toll Free: (800) 243-3955
E-Mail: customersupport@canberra.com
Web Site: www.canberra.com
Emp.: 400
Mfr of Radiation Detection & Analysis Instruments
Export
S.I.C.: 3674
N.A.I.C.S.: 334413
Frederic Vanheems *(Pres)*

Subsidiaries:

Areva NP (4)
One Park Square 6501 Americas Pkway NE Ste 810
Albuquerque, NM 87110 (100%)
Tel.: (505) 828-9100
Fax: (505) 828-9115
Web Site: www.us.areva-np.com
Measurement Solutions for Nuclear Safety & Security
Import Export
S.I.C.: 3823
N.A.I.C.S.: 334513

Canberra (4)
107 Union Valley Rd
Oak Ridge, TN 37830 (100%)
Tel.: (865) 220-6300
Fax: (865) 483-0406
Web Site: www.canberra.com
Mfr of Nuclear Radiation & Testing Apparatus, Search & Navigation Systems Backplane Circuit Cards, Printed Wire Board, Attenuators, Delay Lines & Radio Frequency RF Filters
Export
S.I.C.: 3829
N.A.I.C.S.: 334519
Ann Rivera *(Gen Mgr)*

Transnuclear, Inc. Millstone (4)
Dominion Nuclear Connecticut Rope Ferry Road
Waterford, CT 06385
Tel.: (860) 447-1791
Fax: (860) 447-1791
Web Site: www.transnuclear.com
Spent Nuclear Waste Management Svcs
S.I.C.: 4931
N.A.I.C.S.: 221118

Transnuclear, Inc. (4)
7135 Minstrel Way Ste 300
Columbia, MD 21045-5295 DE
Tel.: (410) 910-6932 (100%)
Fax: (410) 910-6900
Web Site: www.transnuclear.com
Spent Nuclear Fuel Waste Management Dry Storage & Transportation Services
S.I.C.: 8711
N.A.I.C.S.: 541330
Jean Merveilleux du Vignaux *(CFO & VP)*
Robert Grubb *(Sr VP-Engrg)*

Transnuclear, Inc. (4)
310 Woodward Dr
Aiken, SC 29803 (100%)
Tel.: (803) 649-3511
Fax: (803) 295-5153
Web Site: www.transnuclear.com
Emp.: 70
Spent Nuclear Fuel Waste Management Services
S.I.C.: 4212
N.A.I.C.S.: 562112
Tara Neiver *(Pres & CEO)*

Non-U.S. Subsidiary:

Canberra UK Limited (4)
Bldg 528 10 Unit 1 Harwell Intl Bus Ctr
Didcot, Oxfordshire, OX11 0DF, United Kingdom UK
Tel.: (44) 1235838300 (100%)
Fax: (44) 1235838363
E-Mail: uksales@canberra.com
Web Site: www.canberra.com
Emp.: 115
Supplier of Instrumentation Covering a Diverse Range of Applications in the Nuclear Industry
Export
S.I.C.: 3823
N.A.I.C.S.: 334513
Sarah Greenwald *(Mng Dir)*

Subsidiaries:

AREVA NC Australia Pty Ltd (2)
Level 1 12 St Georges Ter
Perth, WA, 6000, Australia
Tel.: (61) 892021100
Fax: (61) 892021122
E-Mail: info@mineraus.com.au
Web Site: www.cogema.com
Emp.: 18
Holding Company
S.I.C.: 6719
N.A.I.C.S.: 551112

Subsidiaries:

Afmeco Mining & Exploration Pty Ltd (Afmex) (3)
68 Greenhill Rd
Wayville, SA, 5034, Australia
Tel.: (61) 882929300
Fax: (61) 883514500
E-Mail: leanne.wooding@afmex.com.au
Web Site: www.areva-nc.com
Emp.: 12
Uranium Exploration
S.I.C.: 1094
N.A.I.C.S.: 212291

Koongarra Resources Pty Ltd (3)
1st Fl 12 St Georges Ter
Perth, WA, 6000, Australia
Tel.: (61) 892021100
Fax: (61) 892021122
Web Site: www.koongarra.com
Mining Operations
S.I.C.: 1099
N.A.I.C.S.: 212299

Canberra Eurisys Benelux NV/SA (2)
Research Park 80
B 1731 Zellik, Belgium
Tel.: (32) 24818530
Fax: (32) 24818550
E-Mail: info.be@canberra.com
Web Site: www.cogema.com
Emp.: 20
Marketing of Radiation Detection & Analysis Instrumentation
S.I.C.: 3829
N.A.I.C.S.: 334519
Luc De Baerdemaeker *(Gen Mgr)*

Canberra Eurisys SA (2)
1 Rue Des Herons
78182 Saint-Quentin-en-Yvelines, Cedex, France (100%)
Tel.: (33) 139485000
Fax: (33) 139486061
Web Site: www.canberra.com
Emp.: 250
Mfr of Radiation Detection & Analysis Instrumentation
S.I.C.: 3829
N.A.I.C.S.: 334519
Bennour Ahmed *(Pres)*

Cogema Deutschland GmbH (2)
Solmsstrasse 18
60486 Frankfurt am Main, Germany (100%)
Mailing Address:
Postfach 900241
60486 Frankfurt am Main, Germany
Tel.: (49) 692470240
Fax: (49) 6924702466
Web Site: www.cogema.com
Emp.: 3
Nuclear Fuel Production, Mining & Waste Recycling Services

Areva SA—(Continued)

S.I.C.: 1499
N.A.I.C.S.: 212399

Subsidiary:

UG (Urangesellschaft GmbH) (3)
Solmsstrasse 12
Postfach 900428
60486 Frankfurt am Main, Germany(69.4%)
Tel.: (49) 697950050
Fax: (49) 697950550
E-Mail: info@ugtrading.com
Emp.: 7
Uranium Trading
S.I.C.: 1094
N.A.I.C.S.: 212291
Gean Michel Guiheux *(Gen Mgr)*

U.S. Subsidiary:

Urangesellschaft USA, Inc (4)
4800 Hampden Ln Ste 1100
Bethesda, MD 20814
Tel.: (301) 841-1636
Emp.: 2
Uranium Trading
S.I.C.: 1081
N.A.I.C.S.: 213114

Cogema Korea Ltd. (2)
Rm 513 City Air Terminal 159 6 Samsung Dong
Seoul, 139 090, Korea (South) (100%)
Tel.: (82) 25510166
Fax: (82) 25510169
Web Site: www.areva.com
Emp.: 6
Nuclear Engineering Services
S.I.C.: 4939
N.A.I.C.S.: 221118
Remy Autebert *(Pres)*

Cogema Resources, Inc. (2)
817 45th Street West
PO Box 9204
Saskatoon, SK, S7K 3X5, Canada (100%)
Tel.: (306) 244-2554
Fax: (306) 653-3883
E-Mail: publicrelations@cogema.ca
Web Site: www.cogema.ca
Emp.: 300
Uranium Mining
S.I.C.: 1094
N.A.I.C.S.: 212291
Vincent Martin *(Pres & CEO)*

U.S. Branch:

Cogema Resources Inc (3)
935 Pendell Blvd
Mills, WY 82644
Tel.: (307) 234-5019
Fax: (307) 473-7306
E-Mail: info@areva.com
Web Site: www.cogema.com
Emp.: 6
Uranium Mining
S.I.C.: 1094
N.A.I.C.S.: 212291

COMURHEX (2)
Z I Du Tricastin
PO Box 29
26701 Pierrelatte, Cedex, France FR
Tel.: (33) 475502999 (100%)
Fax: (33) 475502901
Web Site: www.comurhex.com
Sls.: $350,000,000
Emp.: 360
Uranium Conversion Services
S.I.C.: 1094
N.A.I.C.S.: 212291
Christian Barandas *(CEO & Exec VP-Chemistry Bus Unit)*

ESI (2)
ZI Euro Chanel
76378 Dieppe, France (100%)
Tel.: (33) 235060866
Fax: (33) 235061875
Web Site: www.esi.fa
Emp.: 400
Nuclear Materials Transportation Services; Industrial Cleaning Services
S.I.C.: 4119
N.A.I.C.S.: 485999

Eurodif SA (2)
4 rue Paul Dautier
BP 35
F-78142 Velizy-Villacoublay, Cedex, France
Tel.: (33) 475505400
Fax: (33) 475505705
Web Site: www.areva.com
Emp.: 1,150
Mining of Enriched Uranium
S.I.C.: 1094
N.A.I.C.S.: 212291
Ann Lauvirgeon *(Pres)*

Melox (2)
PO Box 93124
Melox, 30203 Bagnols-sur-Ceze, Cedex, France (100%)
Tel.: (33) 466903600
Fax: (33) 466906934
E-Mail: kmedeleff@cogema.fr
Web Site: www.cogema.com
Emp.: 1,000
Mfr of MOX Fuel Assemblies for Nuclear Power Plants
S.I.C.: 3699
N.A.I.C.S.: 335999

SGN (2)
1 Rue Des Herons
78182 Saint-Quentin-en-Yvelines, France (100%)
Tel.: (33) 139485000
Fax: (33) 139486061
E-Mail: communication@sgn.fr
Web Site: www.sgn.fr
Nuclear Engineering Services
S.I.C.: 8711
N.A.I.C.S.: 541330

Societe Industrielle de Combustible Nucleaire Annecy (SICN) SA (2)
ZA d'Armanville 3 rue des Entrepreneurs
50700 Valognes, Cedex, France
Tel.: (33) 2 33 88 69 88
Web Site: www.cogema.fr
Design & Mfr of Nuclear Components
S.I.C.: 8711
N.A.I.C.S.: 541330

Subsidiaries:

MECAGEST (3)
ZA D Armanville PB 60
P O Box 60
5700 Valognes, France (100%)
Tel.: (33) 233216565
Fax: (33) 233216550
Web Site: www.velognemecagest.fr
Emp.: 60
Mfr of Welded Equipment for the Nuclear & Chemical Industries
S.I.C.: 3548
N.A.I.C.S.: 333992

Subsidiaries:

Mecachimie (4)
Rue du Millecent
50442 Beaumont-Hague, Cedex, France (100%)
Tel.: (33) 233100606
Fax: (33) 0134964782
Web Site: www.areva-nc.fr
Emp.: 200
Mfr of Protective Equipment for Nuclear & Chemical Industries
S.I.C.: 4939
N.A.I.C.S.: 221118
Stefan Lemonier *(Pres & CEO)*

Mecachimie (4)
Route de Bagnols
BP 3
Codolet, 30200 Bagnols-sur-Ceze, France
Tel.: (33) 466505300
Fax: (33) 466900420
E-Mail: mecachimie@wanadoo.fr
Web Site: www.cogema.com
Mfr of Protective Products for the Nuclear & Chemicals Industries
S.I.C.: 4911
N.A.I.C.S.: 221118

MECAGEST (3)
Route De Portbail
50390 Saint Sauveur, France (100%)
Tel.: (33) 233216440
Fax: (33) 233216459
E-Mail: sgsauveur@mecagest.fr
Web Site: www.cogema.com
Sls.: $3,610,016
Emp.: 130
Mfr of Welded Equipment for the Nuclear & Chemical Industries
S.I.C.: 3548
N.A.I.C.S.: 333992
Louzeau Dominique *(Mng Dir)*

STMI Societe Generale pour les Techniques Milieu Ionisant (STMI) (2)
ZAC De Courcelle 1 Rte De La Noue
Montigny Le Bretonneux, 91196 Gif-sur-Yvette, Cedex, France (100%)
Tel.: (33) 169184227
Fax: (33) 169184252
E-Mail: stmi@stmi.fr
Web Site: www.stmi.fr
Emp.: 800
Nuclear Waste Treatment, Processing & Decontamination Svcs
S.I.C.: 4911
N.A.I.C.S.: 221118

Divisions:

Societe des Techniques en Milieu Ionisant (STMI) (3)
Direction Regionale Nord
BP 176
ZI Digulleville, 50447 Beaumont, Cedex, France (100%)
Tel.: (33) 233016600
Fax: (33) 233526126
E-Mail: stmi@stmi.fr
Web Site: www.stmi.fr
Nuclear Waste Treatment, Processing & Decontamination Svcs
S.I.C.: 4931
N.A.I.C.S.: 221118

Societe des Techniques Milieu Ionisant (STMI) (3)
Direction Regionale Sud
Site Du Sactar, 84500 Bollhene, France (100%)
Tel.: (33) 490405607
Fax: (33) 49040509
E-Mail: stmi@stmi.fr
Web Site: www.stmi.fr
Nuclear Waste Treatment, Processing & Decontamination Svcs
S.I.C.: 4931
N.A.I.C.S.: 221118

TN International SA (2)
1 rue des herons
78180 Montigny-le-Bretonneux, France
Tel.: (33) 1 34 96 50 00
Fax: (33) 1 34 96 50 54
Web Site: www.areva.com
Freight Transportation & Storage Services
S.I.C.: 4212
N.A.I.C.S.: 484110

AREVA TA SA (1)
33 Rue La Fayette
91192 Paris, France
Tel.: (33) 1 34 96 00 00
Fax: (33) 1 34 96 00 01
Automatic Train Control System Mfr
S.I.C.: 3679
N.A.I.C.S.: 334419

Euriware Group (1)
1 Place des Freres Montgolfier
78067 Guyancourt, Cedex, France FR
Tel.: (33) 139484000 (100%)
Fax: (33) 139484001
E-Mail: com@euriware.fr
Web Site: www.euriware.fr
Sales Range: $400-449.9 Million
Emp.: 2,250
Consulting & Information Technology Services
Export
S.I.C.: 8742
N.A.I.C.S.: 541611
Khaled Draz *(CEO)*

Subsidiary:

PEA Consulting (2)
Tour Opus 12 77 Esplanade du General de Gaulle
92914 Paris, La Defense, Cedex, France FR
Tel.: (33) 134964900 (100%)
Fax: (33) 134964999
E-Mail: luc.chauevt@pea.fr
Web Site: www.pea.fr
Emp.: 50
Business Consultancy Services
S.I.C.: 8742
N.A.I.C.S.: 541611
Luc Chauevt *(Mgr-Fin)*

Helion SAS (1)
Domaine du Petit Arbois
13545 Aix-en-Provence, France
Tel.: (33) 4 42908150
Fax: (33) 4 42907197
Web Site: www.areva.com
Emp.: 6
Hydro Electric Power Generation Services
S.I.C.: 4911
N.A.I.C.S.: 221111
Jerome Gosset *(CEO)*

Sfarsteel SAS (1)
70 Rue de La Paix
BP 8
71210 Montchanin, France
Tel.: (33) 3 85 73 09 20
Fax: (33) 385739749
E-Mail: info@sotralentz.com
Web Site: www.sotralentz.com
Emp.: 10
Steel Machinery Fabrication Services
S.I.C.: 3441
N.A.I.C.S.: 332312
Pascal Lacour *(Gen Mgr)*

Somair SA (1)
Zi De La Grande Marine
84800 L'Isle-sur-la-Sorgue, France
Tel.: (33) 4 90 38 05 88
Fax: (33) 4 80 20 80 10
Building Materials Machinery & Equipment Mfr
S.I.C.: 3531
N.A.I.C.S.: 333120

Joint Venture:

Areva NP SAS (1)
Tour Areva 1 Place Jean Millier
92084 Paris, La Defense, France
Tel.: (33) 134966000
Telex: FRAMA 630635 F
Fax: (33) 134960001
Web Site: www.framatome-anp.com
Emp.: 14,200
Nuclear Power Plant Construction Services; Joint Venture of Areva (66%) & Siemens AG (34%)
Export
S.I.C.: 1623
N.A.I.C.S.: 237130
Olivier Wantz *(CFO)*
Claude Jaouen *(Sr Exec VP-Plants)*
Guillaume Dureau *(Exec VP)*
Paul Felten *(Sr VP-Mktg)*

Subsidiaries:

Cerca (2)
Tour Framatome
92 084 Paris, Cedex, France (51%)
Tel.: (33) 147965880
Fax: (33) 147965892
E-Mail: helios.nadal@framatome-anp.com
Web Site: www.cerca.fr
Emp.: 100
Nuclear Industry Support Services
S.I.C.: 4939
N.A.I.C.S.: 221113

Branch:

Cerca Romans (3)
ZI Les Berauds
PO Box 1114
26 104 Romans-sur-Isere, France (100%)
Tel.: (33) 475056092
Fax: (33) 47505550
E-Mail: pierre.maccioni@framatome-anp.com
Web Site: www.cerca.fr
Emp.: 150
Supplier of Support Services to the Nuclear Industry
S.I.C.: 4931
N.A.I.C.S.: 221113

FBFC (2)
10 Rue Juliette Recamier
69456 Lyon, Cedex, France (51%)
Tel.: (33) 472747652
Fax: (33) 472747194
Web Site: www.areva.com
Emp.: 16

Mfr of Fuel Assemblies for Nuclear Reactors
S.I.C.: 2999
N.A.I.C.S.: 324199

Intercontrole SA (2)
76 rue des Jumeaux Parc Affaires Silic
30433 Rungis, France
Tel.: (33) 149 78 40 40
Fax: (33) 146 75 92 59
Web Site: www.intercontrole.fr
Emp.: 300
Nuclear Power Plant Testing Services
S.I.C.: 8734
N.A.I.C.S.: 541380
Olivier Moulin *(Dir-Mktg)*

JSPM SA (2)
27 Rue De l Industrie
59573 Jeumont, France
Tel.: (33) 3 27 69 90 00
Fax: (33) 327699150
Electronic Component Mfr & Whslr
S.I.C.: 3679
N.A.I.C.S.: 334419

Joint Ventures:

Cezus (2)
Cezus 2 Areva
PO Box 02
92084 Montreuil, France (100%)
Tel.: (33) 147961414
Telex: 61 44 93
Fax: (33) 147965872
E-Mail: cezus@framatome-anp.com
Web Site: www.framatome-anp.com
Emp.: 1,126
Producer of Primary Non-Ferrous Metals
S.I.C.: 3339
N.A.I.C.S.: 331410
Jean-Pierre Gros *(Sr VP)*

Zircotube (2)
Tour Framatome
1 Place de la Coupole, 92400 Courbevoie, France (50%)
Tel.: (33) 147965920
Telex: 61 40 20
Fax: (33) 147963031
Emp.: 300
Zirconium Alloy Tubing for Nuclear Fuel Sheathing Mfr
S.I.C.: 3356
N.A.I.C.S.: 331491

U.S. Subsidiary:

Areva NP, Inc. (2)
3315 Old Forest Rd
Lynchburg, VA 24501
Mailing Address:
PO Box 10935
Lynchburg, VA 24506-0935
Tel.: (434) 832-3000
Fax: (434) 832-2997
Web Site: www.framatome-anp.com
Emp.: 1,200
Nuclear Power Plant Equipment Mfr
S.I.C.: 3823
N.A.I.C.S.: 334513
Michael W. Rencheck *(Pres & CEO)*
George Beam *(Sr VP-Nuclear Svcs)*
Carl Fisher *(Sr VP-I & C & Electrical Sys)*
Tom Weir *(Sr VP-I & C & Electrical Sys)*

Non-U.S. Subsidiary:

AREVA NP Canada Ltd. (3)
925 Brock Road
Pickering, ON, L1W 2X9, Canada
Tel.: (905) 421-2600
Fax: (905) 421-2605
Nuclear Power Services
S.I.C.: 1629
N.A.I.C.S.: 237130
Steve Seitz *(VP)*

Non-U.S. Subsidiaries:

AREVA NP GmbH (2)
Paul-Gossen Str 100
91052 Erlangen, Germany (100%)
Tel.: (49) 91319000
Fax: (49) 311897073
Web Site: www.areva-np.com
Emp.: 2,000
Nuclear Power Plant Equipment Mfr
S.I.C.: 1629
N.A.I.C.S.: 237130
Stefan vom Scheidt *(Mng Dir)*
Olivier Wantz *(Sr Exec VP-Ops Support)*

Subsidiary:

Advanced Nuclear Fuels GmbH (3)
Am Seitenkanal 1
49811 Lingen, Germany (100%)
Tel.: (49) 919145210
Fax: (49) 2036003309
E-Mail: Karin.Reiche@framatome-anp.com
Web Site: www.de.framatome-anp.com
Nuclear Power Services
S.I.C.: 1629
N.A.I.C.S.: 237130

Lesedi Nuclear Services Ltd (2)
6 Edison Way Century Gate
Century City, Cape Town, 7441, South Africa
Tel.: (27) 215251300
Fax: (27) 215251333
E-Mail: lesedi@lesedins.co.za
Web Site: www.lesedins.co.za
Emp.: 30
Engineering Services
S.I.C.: 8711
N.A.I.C.S.: 541330
Francis Carruthers *(CEO & Mng Dir)*

Non-U.S. Subsidiaries:

Areva Japan Co., Ltd (1)
Urban Toranomon Bldg 5 F 1-16-4 Toranomon
Tokyo, 105 0001, Japan (100%)
Tel.: (81) 335978791
Fax: (81) 335978795
E-Mail: info@areva.com
Emp.: 20
Solutions & Services to the Nuclear Power, Energy Distribution & Transmission Industries
S.I.C.: 4911
N.A.I.C.S.: 221118
Remmy Autebert *(Pres)*

Areva Korea Ltd (1)
Rm 513 City Air Terminal 159-6 Samsung-Dong Kangnam-Ku
Seoul, 135 090, Korea (South) (100%)
Tel.: (82) 25510166
Fax: (82) 25510169
E-Mail: insoon.choi@areva.com
Web Site: www.areva.com
Emp.: 6
Solutions & Services to the Nuclear Power, Energy Distribution & Transmission Industries
S.I.C.: 4931
N.A.I.C.S.: 221113
Insoon Choi *(Sec)*

AREVA Renewables GmbH (1)
Julius-Bamberger-Str 8
Bremen, 28279, Germany
Tel.: (49) 421436800
Fax: (49) 4214368099
Web Site: www.areva.com
Electric Power Generation Services
S.I.C.: 4939
N.A.I.C.S.: 221118
Markus Hamann *(Gen Mgr)*

AREVA Resources Canada Inc. (1)
817 45th St W
Saskatoon, SK, S7L 5X2, Canada
Tel.: (306) 343-4500
Fax: (306) 653-3883
Web Site: www.arevaresources.ca
Emp.: 50
Metal Mining Services
S.I.C.: 1099
N.A.I.C.S.: 212299
Vincent Martin *(Pres & CEO)*

Areva Resources Southern Africa (1)
Block A Ground Floor 204 Rivonia Road
Morningside, Sandton, Gauteng, 2057, South Africa
Tel.: (27) 11 7835 056
Uranium Mining Services
S.I.C.: 1094
N.A.I.C.S.: 212291
John Stalker *(CEO)*

Areva Taiwan (1)
3Fl 3 189 Keelung Rd Sec 2
Taipei, 110, Taiwan
Tel.: (886) 223782102
Fax: (886) 223770142
E-Mail: info@areva.com
Web Site: www.areva.com
Emp.: 3
Solutions & Services to the Nuclear Power, Energy Distribution & Transmission Industries
S.I.C.: 4911
N.A.I.C.S.: 221113
Amanda Wang *(Country-Mgr)*

AREVA Wind GmbH (1)
Am Lunedeich 156
27572 Bremerhaven, Germany
Tel.: (49) 471 80 04 0
Fax: (49) 471 80 04 100
E-Mail: info.arevawind@areva.com
Web Site: www.areva-wind.com
Wind Energy Converter Mfr
S.I.C.: 3511
N.A.I.C.S.: 333611
Jean Huby *(Mng Dir)*
Jens-Karkov Jakobsen *(Mng Dir)*
Michael Munder-Oschimek *(Mng Dir)*
Wolfgang Wilms *(Mng Dir)*

AREX INDUSTRIES LIMITED

612 GIDC Industrial Estate Chhatral
Kalol, Gandhinagar, Gujarat, 382729, India
Tel.: (91) 2764 233636
Fax: (91) 2764 233635
E-Mail: mail@arex.co.in
Web Site: www.arex.co.in
Year Founded: 1989
526851—(BOM)
Rev.: $4,914,365
Assets: $4,830,683
Liabilities: $2,474,158
Net Worth: $2,356,525
Earnings: $132,376
Fiscal Year-end: 03/31/13

Business Description:
Woven Fabric Mfr
S.I.C.: 2299
N.A.I.C.S.: 313210

Personnel:
Dinesh A. Bilgi *(Chm & Co-Mng Dir)*
Chirag D. Bilgi *(Co-Mng Dir)*
Neel D. Bilgi *(Co-Mng Dir)*
Narendra B. Shah *(Sec)*

Board of Directors:
Dinesh A. Bilgi
Chirag D. Bilgi
Neel D. Bilgi
Balkrishna I. Makwana
Dinesh H. Pande
Pragnesh K. Shah
Vasant R. Shah
Laxman C. Tilani

Transfer Agent:
Sharepro Services (India) Pvt. Ltd.
416-420 4th Floor Devnandan Mall Opp.
Sanyash Ashram Ellisbridge
Ahmedabad, India

AREZZO INDUSTRIA E COMERCIO S.A.

Rua Fernandes Tourinho 147 Rooms 1 301 to 1303 Bairro dos Funcionarios
Belo Horizonte, Minas Gerais, 30112-000, Brazil
Tel.: (55) 3121211000
Fax: (55) 1138478971
E-Mail: ri@arezzoco.com.br
Web Site: www.arezzoco.com.br
Year Founded: 1972
ARZZ3—(BRAZ)
Rev.: $423,190,183
Assets: $313,132,747
Liabilities: $89,864,368
Net Worth: $223,268,379
Earnings: $47,651,352
Emp.: 1,879
Fiscal Year-end: 12/31/12

Business Description:
Women's Footwear & Accessories Mfr & Sls
S.I.C.: 5621
N.A.I.C.S.: 448120

Personnel:
Anderson Lemos Birman *(Chm)*
Jose Ernesto Beni Bolonha *(Vice Chm)*
Alexandre Cafe Birman *(CEO)*
Thiago Lima Borges *(CFO, IR Officer & VP)*

Board of Directors:
Anderson Lemos Birman
Jose Ernesto Beni Bolonha
Alexandre Cafe Birman
Welerson Cavalieri
Carolina Villa de Andrade Faria
Jose Murilo Procopio de Carvalho
Guilherme Affonso Ferreira
Rodrigo Galindo
Fabio Hering
Juliana Rozenbaum

ARGAN BEAUTY CORP.

Faraday Str 31
04159 Leipzig, Germany
Tel.: (49) 173 8264 717
Year Founded: 2013
ABXX—(OTC OTCB)

Business Description:
Skin Care Products Distr
S.I.C.: 5169
N.A.I.C.S.: 424690

Personnel:
Vitaliy Gorelik *(Pres, CEO, CFO, Tres & Controller)*
Caroline Bastidas *(Sec)*

Board of Directors:
Vitaliy Gorelik

ARGAN SA

10 rue Beffroy
92200 Neuilly-sur-Seine, France
Tel.: (33) 147470546
Fax: (33) 147470550
E-Mail: contact@argan.fr
Web Site: www.argan.fr
ARG—(EUR)
Sales Range: $25-49.9 Million
Emp.: 9

Business Description:
Warehouse Construction & Rental Services
S.I.C.: 1629
N.A.I.C.S.: 236210

Personnel:
Jean-Claude Le Lan *(Chm-Supervisory Bd)*
Ronan Le Lan *(Chm-Mgmt Bd)*
Francis Albertinelli *(CFO)*

Supervisory Board of Directors:
Jean-Claude Le Lan
Florence Soule de Lafont
Bernard Thevenin

ARGENT ENERGY TRUST

Suite 500 321 6th Avenue SW
Calgary, AB, T2P 3H3, Canada
Tel.: (403) 770-4809
Fax: (403) 770-4850
E-Mail: info@argentenergytrust.com
Web Site: www.argentenergytrust.com
Year Founded: 2012
AET.UN—(TSX)

Business Description:
Investment Services
S.I.C.: 6211
N.A.I.C.S.: 523999

Personnel:
Eric Tremblay *(Chm)*
Rick Louden *(Pres)*
Brian Prokop *(CEO)*
Sean Bovingdon *(CFO)*
John Elzner *(Sr VP)*

Board of Directors:

Argent Energy Trust—(Continued)

Eric Tremblay
John Brussa
Scott Butler
Rick Louden
Brian Prokop
William Robertson
Glen C. Schmidt

Transfer Agent:
Computershare Trust Company of Canada
Calgary, AB, Canada

ARGENT GROUP EUROPE LIMITED

Level 5 9 Hatton Street
London, NW8 8PL, United Kingdom
Tel.: (44) 20 7723 5458
Fax: (44) 20 7724 8950
Web Site: www.argentgroup.com
Year Founded: 1997
Sales Range: $750-799.9 Million
Emp.: 854

Business Description:
Investment Management Services
S.I.C.: 6282
N.A.I.C.S.: 523920

Personnel:
David Gray *(Founder & Mng Dir)*

ARGENT INDUSTRIAL LIMITED

First Floor Ridge 63 8 Sinembe Crescent Sinembe Park
La Lucia Ridge Office Estate,
Durban, 4019, South Africa
Tel.: (27) 315847702
Fax: (27) 315662533
Web Site: www.argent.co.za
ART—(JSE)
Rev.: $206,693,031
Assets: $230,301,496
Liabilities: $78,515,159
Net Worth: $151,786,338
Earnings: $8,519,582
Emp.: 3,172
Fiscal Year-end: 03/31/13

Business Description:
Steel Trading Services
S.I.C.: 3312
N.A.I.C.S.: 331110

Personnel:
Treve Robert Hendry *(CEO)*
Mark du Toit *(Sec)*

Board of Directors:
Teunis Scharrighuisen
Marc Peter Allen
Clayton Dean Angus
Sue Joan Cox
Patrick Arthur Day
Jennifer Ann Etchells
Treve Robert Hendry
Alfred Franz Litschka
Khathutshelo Mapasa

Legal Counsel:
Webber Wentzel
10 Fricker Road Illovo Boulevard
Johannesburg, South Africa

Transfer Agent:
Link Market Services South Africa
13th Floor Rennie House 19 Ameshoff Street
Braamfontein, South Africa

Subsidiaries:

Allan Maskew (Pty) Ltd (1)
11 Barnsley Road
PO Box 653
Benoni south, Benoni, 1502, South Africa
Tel.: (27) 119742941
Fax: (27) 114201824
E-Mail: allanmaskew1@argent.co.za
Web Site: www.allanmaskew.co.za
Emp.: 52
Rubber Mouldings Mfr
S.I.C.: 3061
N.A.I.C.S.: 326291
Rian hugo *(Mng Dir)*

Argent Steel Group (Pty) Ltd (1)
87 Boford Circle
Epping, Western Cape, 7460, South Africa
Tel.: (27) 215077100
Fax: (27) 215077111
E-Mail: gammidct1@argent.co.za
Emp.: 50
Steel Products Whslr
S.I.C.: 5051
N.A.I.C.S.: 423510
Aidan Bain *(Gen Mgr)*

Atomic Office Equipment (Pty) Ltd (1)
30 Coronation Rd
PO Box 254
Maitland, Cape Town, Western Cape, 7405, South Africa
Tel.: (27) 215102145
Fax: (27) 215102181
E-Mail: enquiries@atomicoffice.com
Web Site: www.atomicofficefurniture.co.za
Emp.: 100
Steel Furniture Mfr
S.I.C.: 2522
N.A.I.C.S.: 337214
Gloria Jonathan *(Gen Mgr)*

Barrier Angelucci (Pty) Ltd (1)
130 Terrace Rd
Sebenza, Edenvale, Gauteng, South Africa
Tel.: (27) 116092148
Fax: (27) 0116095842
E-Mail: ba2@argent.co.za
Web Site: www.barrierangelucci.co.za
Emp.: 33
Electronic Security Products Maintenance & Sales
S.I.C.: 3669
N.A.I.C.S.: 334290
Burger Pretorius *(Gen Mgr)*

Excalibur Vehicle Accessories (Pty) Ltd (1)
105 Main Reef Rd
Roodepoort, Gauteng, 1700, South Africa
Tel.: (27) 117644632
Fax: (27) 11 7643199
E-Mail: excaliburaales@argent.co.za
Web Site: www.excaliburacc.co.za
Emp.: 100
Vehicle Parts Mfr
S.I.C.: 3429
N.A.I.C.S.: 332510
Jan Taljaard *(Mng Dir)*

Gammid Trading (Pty) Ltd (1)
7 Borax Rd
Alrode, Alberton, Gauteng, 1450, South Africa
Tel.: (27) 118647610
Fax: (27) 118647705
E-Mail: gammidjhb@argent.co.za
Web Site: www.gammid.co.za
Aluminum & Steel Products Whslr
S.I.C.: 3354
N.A.I.C.S.: 331318
Elaine Midgley *(Founder)*

Giflo Engineering (Pty) Ltd (1)
Stand 245 4th St
Ga-Rankuwa, North-West, 0208, South Africa
Tel.: (27) 127033346
Fax: (27) 127033347
Web Site: www.giflo.co.za
Automobile Parts Mfr
S.I.C.: 3429
N.A.I.C.S.: 332510
Jan Taljaard *(Mng Dir)*

Hendor Mining Supplies (Pty) Ltd (1)
56 Mullet Rd
Wadeville, Gauteng, 1407, South Africa
Tel.: (27) 118241148
Fax: (27) 118241139
Emp.: 150
Metal Scrapers Mfr
S.I.C.: 3423
N.A.I.C.S.: 332216
Mike Daniel *(Mng Dir)*

Jetmaster (Pty) Ltd (1)
Corner Main Reef & Wilgespruit Roads
Thornton, Cape Town, 7460, South Africa
Tel.: (27) 117644632
E-Mail: jetmaster6@argent.co.za
Web Site: ww.jetmaster.co.za
Emp.: 13
Fireplaces & Barbecues Mfr
S.I.C.: 3499
N.A.I.C.S.: 332999

Koch's Cut & Supply Steel Centre (Pty) Ltd (1)
22 Kyalami Rd
Westmead, Pinetown, Kwazulu-Natal, 3610, South Africa
Tel.: (27) 317004422
Fax: (27) 317003333
E-Mail: kochs@argent.co.za
Web Site: www.argent.co.za
Emp.: 70
Steel Processing Services
S.I.C.: 5051
N.A.I.C.S.: 423510
Justin Cadle *(Mng Dir)*

Megamix (Proprietary) Limited (1)
11 Prima Dr Helderberg Indus Park
Cape Town, 7140, South Africa
Tel.: (27) 218458189
Fax: (27) 218458192
E-Mail: megamix@argent.co.za
Emp.: 60
Readymix Concrete Mfr
S.I.C.: 3273
N.A.I.C.S.: 327320
Mark Vonk *(Mgr)*

U.S. Subsidiary:

New Joules Engineering North America Inc. (1)
4401 Clary Blvd
Kansas City, MO 64130 MO
Tel.: (816) 921-7441
Fax: (816) 921-7443
E-Mail: newjoules@aol.com
Web Site: www.newjoules.com
Emp.: 18
Industrial Engineering Services
S.I.C.: 8711
N.A.I.C.S.: 541330
Hans Thyssen *(Mgr)*

Non-U.S. Subsidiaries:

Burbage Iron Craft Services Limited (1)
Unit 16 Sketchley Lane Indust Estate
Hinckley, Leicestershire, LE10 3ER, United Kingdom
Tel.: (44) 1455251656
Fax: (44) 1455614136
E-Mail: sales@burbageironcraft.co.uk
Web Site: www.burbageironcraft.co.uk
Emp.: 10
Gates & Fencing Distr
S.I.C.: 5211
N.A.I.C.S.: 444190

Fencing and Gates (1)
Unit 16 Sketchley Ln Indus Estate
Hinckley, Leicestershire, LE9 3ER, United Kingdom
Tel.: (44) 844 8920130
Fax: (44) 145 5614136
E-Mail: admin@fencing-and-gates.co.uk
Web Site: www.fencing-and-gates.co.uk
Emp.: 20
Iron & Steel Gates & Fence Mfr
S.I.C.: 3446
N.A.I.C.S.: 332323
David Ison *(Mgr)*

ARGENT MINERALS LIMITED

Level 1 115 Cambridge Street
PO Box 1305
Leederville, WA, 6901, Australia
Tel.: (61) 893226600
Fax: (61) 893226610
E-Mail: admin@argentminerals.com.au
Web Site: www.argentminerals.com.au
ARD—(ASX)
Rev.: $69,910
Assets: $1,444,339
Liabilities: $430,890
Net Worth: $1,013,450
Earnings: ($3,606,475)
Fiscal Year-end: 06/30/13

Business Description:
Mineral Exploration
S.I.C.: 1481
N.A.I.C.S.: 213115

Personnel:
David Busch *(Mng Dir)*
Marcus Michael *(Sec)*

Board of Directors:
Stephen Gemell
David Busch
Marcus Michael

Legal Counsel:
Steinepreis Paganin
Level 4 The Read Building 16 Milligan Street
Perth, WA, 6000, Australia
Tel.: (61) 8 9321 4000
Fax: (61) 8 9321 4333

Jones Day
Sydney, Australia

ARGENTEX MINING CORPORATION

Suite 835 1100 Melville Street
Vancouver, BC, V6E 4A6, Canada
Tel.: (604) 568-2496
Fax: (604) 568-1540
Toll Free: (866) 594-7687
E-Mail: info@argentexmining.com
Web Site: www.argentexmining.com
Year Founded: 2001
ATX—(OTC TSXV)
Int. Income: $65,562
Assets: $3,443,763
Liabilities: $455,277
Net Worth: $2,988,486
Earnings: ($7,927,950)
Emp.: 14
Fiscal Year-end: 01/31/13

Business Description:
Metal Mining Services
S.I.C.: 1099
N.A.I.C.S.: 212299

Personnel:
Kenneth E. Hicks *(Chm & Sec)*
Michael James Paterson Brown *(Pres & CEO)*
Jeffrey Finkelstein *(CFO & Treas)*
Peter A. Ball *(Exec VP-Corp Dev)*

Board of Directors:
Kenneth E. Hicks
Michael James Paterson Brown
Patrick G. Downey
Stephen Hanson
Jenna Hardy
Robert Duncan Henderson
Richard A. Thibault

Legal Counsel:
Clark Wilson LLP
800-885 West Georgia Street
Vancouver, BC, Canada V6C 3H1

ARGENTIL CAPITAL PARTNERS LIMITED

8th Floor The Octagon
13A AJ Marinho Drive
Victoria Island, Lagos, Nigeria
Tel.: (234) 1 2710710 3
Fax: (234) 14616221
E-Mail: info@argentilcp.com
Web Site: www.argentilcp.com

Business Description:
Investment Services
S.I.C.: 6211
N.A.I.C.S.: 523999

Personnel:
Adekunle Adedeji *(Mng Partner)*
Olumide Ogunfowora *(Sr Partner)*
Afolashade Ashiru *(Admin Officer)*
Gbenga Hassan *(Sr VP)*

ARGENTINA MINING LIMITED

Unit 9 44 Belmont Ave
Belmont, WA, 6104, Australia
Tel.: (61) 861402567
Fax: (61) 8 6316 3311

E-Mail: info@argentinamining.com.au
Web Site: www.argentinamining.com.au
AVK—(ASX)
Business Description:
Gold & Copper Mining Services
S.I.C.: 1041
N.A.I.C.S.: 212221
Personnel:
Steve Shedden *(Chm)*
Eduardo Videla *(Mng Dir)*
Board of Directors:
Steve Shedden
Tim Kennedy

ARGENTIUM RESOURCES INC.

8th King Street East 4th Floor
Toronto, ON, M5C 1B5, Canada
Tel.: (416) 729-4416
E-Mail: investorrelations@argentiumresources.com
Web Site: www.argentiumresources.com
AOK—(CNSX)
Assets: $3,026,586
Liabilities: $2,300,068
Net Worth: $726,518
Earnings: ($1,106,694)
Fiscal Year-end: 12/31/12
Business Description:
Gold & Silver Mining Services
S.I.C.: 1041
N.A.I.C.S.: 212221
Personnel:
John Ross Moses *(Chm)*
John Arthur Carter *(Pres & CEO)*
Robin Pilkey *(CFO)*
Board of Directors:
John Ross Moses
John Arthur Carter
Scott Jobin-Bevans
Bob Leshchyshen
Peter Tassiopoulos

ARGENTUM SILVER CORP.

Suite 1200 - 570 Granville St
Vancouver, BC, V6C 3P1, Canada
Tel.: (604) 661-2110
Fax: (604) 909-1818
Web Site: www.argentumsilvercorp.com
Year Founded: 2007
ASL—(TSXV)
Rev.: $15,043
Assets: $1,717,498
Liabilities: $189,158
Net Worth: $1,528,340
Earnings: ($4,069,746)
Fiscal Year-end: 06/30/13
Business Description:
Mineral Exploration Services
S.I.C.: 1081
N.A.I.C.S.: 213114
Personnel:
Warren McIntyre *(Pres & CEO)*
Simon Anderson *(CFO)*
Jeff Sheremeta *(Sec)*
Board of Directors:
Geoff Balderson
Lawrence Cyna
Warren McIntyre
Andrew Thomson
Ben Whiting
Transfer Agent:
Computershare
3rd Floor 510 Burrard Street
Vancouver, BC, Canada
Non-U.S. Subsidiary:

Plata de Argentum SA de CV (1)
Cerrada De Gardenias 104 Reforma
Oaxaca, Mexico
Tel.: (52) 951 5151 314
Silver Ore Mining Services
S.I.C.: 1044
N.A.I.C.S.: 212222
Juan Lopez Luque *(Gen Mgr)*

ARGEX TITANIUM INC.

Suite 410 630 Sherbrooke St W
Montreal, QC, H3A 1E4, Canada
Tel.: (514) 843-5959
Fax: (514) 843-9208
Toll Free: (855) 843-5959
E-Mail: info@argex.ca
Web Site: www.argex.ca
Year Founded: 2005
RGX—(OTC TSX)
Rev.: $41,881
Assets: $30,016,363
Liabilities: $2,446,546
Net Worth: $27,569,818
Earnings: ($5,944,352)
Fiscal Year-end: 12/31/12
Business Description:
Mineral Exploration Services
S.I.C.: 1099
N.A.I.C.S.: 212299
Personnel:
Robert Guilbault *(Chm)*
George Roy MacKay Bonnell *(Pres & CEO)*
Glen Kayll *(CFO)*
Enrico Di Cesare *(COO & VP-Tech)*
Genevieve Marchand *(Gen Counsel & Sec)*
Richard Poulin *(Exec VP)*
Mark Anthony Billings *(Sr VP-Corp Dev)*
Board of Directors:
Robert Guilbault
Normand Bergeron
Mark Anthony Billings
George Roy MacKay Bonnell
Anthony W. Garson
Mazen Haddad
Transfer Agent:
Canadian Stock Transfer Company Inc
320 Bay Street B1 Level
Toronto, ON, Canada

ARGIS-GALAC SEA

15 Rue Florian Laporte
56100 Lorient, Morbihan, France
Tel.: (33) 297831000
Fax: (33) 297832500
E-Mail: herve.lemeunier@argisgalacsea.fr
Web Site: www.argisgalacsea.com
Sales Range: $25-49.9 Million
Emp.: 15
Business Description:
Groceries, General Line
S.I.C.: 5141
N.A.I.C.S.: 424410
Personnel:
Regis Prive *(Owner)*

ARGO EXPLORATION LIMITED

Level 4 100 Albert Road
Melbourne, VIC, 3205, Australia
Tel.: (61) 396927222
Fax: (61) 395298057
E-Mail: admin@argoexploration.com.au
Web Site: www.argoexploration.com.au
AXT—(ASX)
Rev.: $13,296
Assets: $2,469,973
Liabilities: $106,553
Net Worth: $2,363,420
Earnings: ($8,105,659)
Emp.: 5
Fiscal Year-end: 06/30/13
Business Description:
Mineral Exploration & Development
S.I.C.: 1481
N.A.I.C.S.: 213115
Personnel:
Melanie J. Leydin *(CFO & Co-Sec)*
Justin Mouchacca *(Co-Sec)*
Board of Directors:
Justin Hondris
Christopher Martin
Andrew Van Der Zwan
Legal Counsel:
Holman Fenwick Willan
Level 39 Bourke Place 600 Bourke Street
Melbourne, VIC, 3000, Australia
Subsidiary:

Athena Mines Limited (1)
Ste 304 22 St Kilda Rd
Saint Kilda, Victoria, 3182, Australia
Tel.: (61) 396927222
Fax: (61) 395298057
E-Mail: info@argoexploration.com.au
Web Site: www.argoexploration.com.au/contact.php
Emp.: 20
Mineral Exploration & Mining Services
S.I.C.: 1481
N.A.I.C.S.: 213115
Justin Mouchacca *(Mgr-Corp Acct)*

ARGO GRAPHICS INC.

ARGO Nihombashi Building 5-14
Nihombashi-hazozaki-cho Chuo-ku
Tokyo, 103-0015, Japan
Tel.: (81) 356412020
Fax: (81) 356412010
E-Mail: m.fukunaga@keeo.argo-graph.co.jp
Web Site: www.argo-graph.co.jp
Year Founded: 1985
7595—(TKS)
Sls.: $329,956,000
Assets: $277,442,000
Liabilities: $92,741,000
Net Worth: $184,701,000
Earnings: $13,992,000
Emp.: 440
Fiscal Year-end: 03/31/13
Business Description:
Advanced Graphics Systems for CAD/CAM Applications
S.I.C.: 7336
N.A.I.C.S.: 541430
Personnel:
Yoshimaro Fujisawa *(Chm & CEO)*
Yoneo Sawada *(Pres & COO)*
Seiichiro Saito *(Sr Mng Dir)*
Takanori Nakai *(Mng Dir)*
Yoshijiro Hamano *(Corp Officer)*
Takemi Inotsuka *(Corp Officer)*
Yoshihiro Nakata *(Corp Officer)*
Masaru Watanabe *(Corp Officer)*
Board of Directors:
Yoshimaro Fujisawa
Takeshi Fujimori
Tetsuya Fukunaga
Hirohiko Igata
Kiyoshi Ishikawa
Toshihiko Kato
Takanori Nakai
Muneshi Ozaki
Seiichiro Saito
Yoneo Sawada

ARGO GROUP INTERNATIONAL HOLDINGS, LTD.

110 Pitts Bay Rd
Pembroke, HM 08, Bermuda
Mailing Address:
PO Box HM 1282
Hamilton, HM FX, Bermuda
Tel.: (441) 2965858
Fax: (441) 2966162
Web Site: www.argolimited.com
AGII—(NASDAQ)
Rev.: $1,470,200,000
Assets: $6,591,000,000
Liabilities: $5,028,000,000
Net Worth: $1,563,000,000
Earnings: $143,200,000
Emp.: 1,249
Fiscal Year-end: 12/31/13
Business Description:
Holding Company; Insurance Services
S.I.C.: 6399
N.A.I.C.S.: 524130
Personnel:
Gary V. Woods *(Chm)*
Mark E. Watson, III *(Pres & CEO)*
Jay S. Bullock *(CFO & Exec VP)*
Mark H. Rose *(Chief Investment Officer & Sr VP)*
Anastasios Omiridis *(Chief Acctg Officer & Sr VP)*
Josh Betz *(Pres-Argo Surety)*
Andrew J. Carrier *(Pres-Agro Re)*
Craig S. Comeaux *(Sec, VP & Gen Counsel)*
Barbara C. Bufkin *(Exec VP)*
George Luecke *(Grp Treas & Sr VP-IR)*
Board of Directors:
Gary V. Woods
F. Sedgwick Browne
Harvey Berry Cash
Hector De Leon
Nabil N. El-Hage
Mural R. Josephson
Kathleen Anne Nealon
John R. Power, Jr.
John H. Tonelli
Mark E. Watson, III
Transfer Agent:
American Stock Transfer & Trust Company LLC
59 Maiden Ln
New York, NY 10007
Tel.: (718) 921-8200
U.S. Division:

Argo Group International Holdings, Ltd. - Alteris Public Risk Solutions Division (1)
1901 W Kettleman Ln Ste 103
Lodi, CA 95242
Tel.: (949) 450-5000
Fax: (949) 450-5005
Toll Free: (888) 919-0001
General Insurance Services
S.I.C.: 6411
N.A.I.C.S.: 524210
U.S. Subsidiaries:

AGI Properties Inc. (1)
10101 Reunion Pl Ste 500
San Antonio, TX 78216
Tel.: (210) 321-8400
Fax: (210) 377-2637
Web Site: www.argogroupus.com
Rev.: $420,000
Emp.: 1,000
Real Estate Managers
S.I.C.: 6531
N.A.I.C.S.: 531390
Mark Watson, III *(Pres & CEO)*

Alteris Insurance Services, Inc. (1)
250 Summer St 3rd Fl
Boston, MA 02210
Tel.: (866) 650-4016
Fax: (617) 235-6108
Toll Free: (866) 650-4016
Web Site: arsolimited.com
Emp.: 20
Insurance Providing Services
S.I.C.: 6411
N.A.I.C.S.: 524298

Argo Group US, Inc. (1)
10101 Reunion Pl Ste 500
San Antonio, TX 78216
Tel.: (210) 321-8400
Fax: (210) 377-2637
E-Mail: grocersinsurance@argonautgroup.com
Web Site: www.argonautgroup.com
Property Insurance Management Services
S.I.C.: 6411

Argo Group International Holdings, Ltd.—(Continued)

N.A.I.C.S.: 524298
Michael Fleischer *(Chief Underwriting Officer-Ops)*
Arthur Davis *(Pres-Excess & Surplus Lines)*
Kevin J. Rehnberg *(Pres-Ops)*

Argo Group (1)
379 Thornall St 2nd Fl 379 Thornall St 2nd Fl
Edison, NJ 08837-2236
Tel.: (732) 906-8100
Fax: (732) 906-9283
Emp.: 50
Reinsurance Company
S.I.C.: 6399
N.A.I.C.S.: 524130
Susan Spivak Bernstein *(Sr VP-IR)*

Argo Pro (1)
101 Hudson St 12th Fl
Jersey City, NJ 07302
Tel.: (732) 906-6718
General Insurance Services
S.I.C.: 6411
N.A.I.C.S.: 524210
Laurie Banez *(Chief Underwriting Officer & Sr VP)*

Argonaut Claims Management, LLC (1)
10101 Reunion Pl Ste 500
San Antonio, TX 78216-4156
Tel.: (210) 321-8400
Fax: (210) 321-8407
Insurance Management Services
S.I.C.: 6411
N.A.I.C.S.: 524298

Argonaut Claims Services, Ltd. (1)
5100 N O'Connor Blvd Ste 200
Irving, TX 75039
Tel.: (972) 506-2400
Fax: (303) 773-7249
Toll Free: (800) 678-6766
Web Site: www.argolimited.com
Emp.: 2
Online Advertisement Services
S.I.C.: 7311
N.A.I.C.S.: 541810
Mark Musa *(Mgr-Client)*

Argonaut Great Central Insurance Company (1)
8325 N Allen Rd PO Box 807
Peoria, IL 61615
Tel.: (309) 688-8571
Fax: (309) 690-3918
Web Site: www.argonautgreatcentral.com
Sales Range: $100-124.9 Million
Emp.: 30
Property & Casualty Insurance
S.I.C.: 6331
N.A.I.C.S.: 524126
Dean Parker *(Dir-Mktg)*

Argonaut Insurance Company (1)
100 Marine Pkwy
Redwood City, CA 94065 (100%)
Tel.: (650) 508-5400
Fax: (650) 508-5499
Web Site: www.argogroupus.com
Sales Range: $450-499.9 Million
Emp.: 29
Property & Casualty Insurance
S.I.C.: 6351
N.A.I.C.S.: 524126

Argonaut Limited Risk Insurance Company (1)
175 E Houston
San Antonio, TX 78205
Tel.: (210) 321-8400
Fax: (210) 377-2637
Insurance Management Services
S.I.C.: 6411
N.A.I.C.S.: 524298
Mark Watson *(CEO)*

Argonaut Management Services, Inc. (1)
175 E Houston
San Antonio, TX 78205
Tel.: (210) 321-8400
Fax: (210) 377-2637
Business Management Consulting Services
S.I.C.: 8742
N.A.I.C.S.: 541611

Argonaut-Midwest Insurance Company (1)
10101 Reunion Pl Ste 500
San Antonio, TX 78246
Tel.: (210) 321-8400
Toll Free: (800) 470-7958
Insurance Management Services
S.I.C.: 6411
N.A.I.C.S.: 524298

Argonaut-Southwest Insurance Company (1)
175 E Houston St
San Antonio, TX 78205
Mailing Address:
PO Box 469012
San Antonio, TX 78246
Tel.: (210) 321-8400
Fax: (303) 773-7373
Toll Free: (800) 456-8458
Emp.: 300
Insurance Management Services
S.I.C.: 6411
N.A.I.C.S.: 524298
Mark Watson *(CEO)*

ARIS Title Insurance Corporation (1)
610 Broadway 4th Fl
New York, NY 10012
Tel.: (212) 563-3600
Fax: (212) 563-3700
Web Site: www.aristitle.com
Insurance Brokerage Services
S.I.C.: 6411
N.A.I.C.S.: 524210
Judith L. Pearson *(Co-Founder & Pres)*
Lawrence M. Shindell *(Chm)*

Central Insurance Management (1)
3625 N Sheridan Rd
Peoria, IL 61633
Tel.: (309) 682-2334
Fax: (309) 685-4335
Toll Free: (800) 325-8299
E-Mail: cim@argogroupus.com
Web Site: www.argonautgreatcentral.com
Rev.: $490,000
Emp.: 5
Insurance Agents, Brokers, & Service
S.I.C.: 6411
N.A.I.C.S.: 524210
Bill Meisen *(Pres & CEO)*

Colony Agency Services, Inc. (1)
8720 Stony Point Pkwy Ste 300
Richmond, VA 90017
Tel.: (804) 560-2000
Fax: (804) 327-3173
Toll Free: (800) 577-6614
Web Site: www.colonyins.com
Insurance Brokerage Services
S.I.C.: 6411
N.A.I.C.S.: 524210
Samuel C. Anderson *(CEO)*
Craig S. Comeaux *(Sec)*

Colony Insurance Group (1)
8720 Stony Pte Pkwy Ste 300
Richmond, VA 23235-6865
Tel.: (804) 327-1700
Fax: (804) 327-1792
E-Mail: vamarketing@colonyspecialty.com
Web Site: www.colonyins.com
Emp.: 250
Environmental Insurance Management
S.I.C.: 6351
N.A.I.C.S.: 524126

Colony Management Services (1)
8520 Stoney Pt Ste 300
Richmond, VA 23235 (100%)
Tel.: (804) 327-1700
Fax: (804) 327-1792
Web Site: www.colonyins.com
Emp.: 300
Property & Casualty Underwriting
S.I.C.: 8742
N.A.I.C.S.: 541611

Subsidiary:

Colony Insurance Company (2)
8720 Stony Point Pkwy Ste 300
Richmond, VA 23235-6865
Tel.: (804) 327-1700
Fax: (804) 327-1792
E-Mail: marketing@colonyins.com
Web Site: www.colonyins.com
Emp.: 250
Property & Casualty Underwriting
S.I.C.: 6331
N.A.I.C.S.: 524126
Louis Levinson *(Pres)*

Colony National Insurance Company (1)
8720 Stony Point Pkwy Ste 300
Richmond, VA 23235-6865
Tel.: (804) 560-2000
Fax: (804) 327-3173
E-Mail: marketing@colonyins.com
Web Site: www.colonyins.com
Insurance Management Services
S.I.C.: 6351
N.A.I.C.S.: 524126

Colony Specialty (1)
8720 Stony Point Pkwy Ste 300
Richmond, VA 23235-6865
Mailing Address:
PO Box 469012
San Antonio, TX 78246
Tel.: (804) 560-2000
Fax: (804) 327-1802
Toll Free: (800) 577-6614
Web Site: www.argolimited.com
Emp.: 150
Property & Casualty Underwriting
S.I.C.: 6411
N.A.I.C.S.: 524210
Kevin Rehnberg *(Pres-U.S. Ops)*

Grocers Insurance Agency, Inc. (1)
6400 Se Lk Rd Ste 190
Portland, OR 97222-2189
Tel.: (503) 833-1600
Fax: (800) 872-3548
Web Site: www.grocersinsurance.com
Emp.: 100
General Insurance Services
S.I.C.: 6411
N.A.I.C.S.: 524210
Eric Wilcoxen *(Gen Mgr)*

Insight Insurance Services, Inc. (1)
2000 S Batavia Ave Ste 300
Geneva, IL 60134
Tel.: (630) 208-1900
Fax: (630) 208-7550
Toll Free: (800) 447-4626
E-Mail: info@insightinsurance.com
Web Site: www.insightinsurance.com
General Insurance Services
S.I.C.: 6411
N.A.I.C.S.: 524210

Mid-State Insurance Underwriters, Inc. (1)
654 Main St
Rockwood, PA 15557
Tel.: (814) 926-4661
Fax: (814) 926-3027
General Insurance Services
S.I.C.: 6411
N.A.I.C.S.: 524210

Rockwood Casualty Insurance Co. (1)
654 Main St
Rockwood, PA 15557-1029 PA
Tel.: (814) 926-4661
Fax: (814) 926-3027
Web Site: www.argolimited.com
Emp.: 120
Property & Casualty Insurance Products & Services
S.I.C.: 6351
N.A.I.C.S.: 524126
John P. Yediny *(Pres & CEO)*
David Hay *(CFO)*

Somerset Casualty Insurance Company (1)
654 Main St
Rockwood, PA 15557
Tel.: (814) 926-4661
Fax: (814) 926-3249
Toll Free: (800) 837-9062
Web Site: www.rockwoodcasualty.com
Emp.: 100
Insurance Policy Services
S.I.C.: 6411
N.A.I.C.S.: 524298
John Yediny *(Gen Mgr)*

Trident Insurance Services, LLC (1)
175 E Houston St
San Antonio, TX 78205
Tel.: (210) 342-8808
Fax: (210) 342-8193
Emp.: 350
Insurance Agencies
S.I.C.: 6411
N.A.I.C.S.: 524210
Ron Vindivich *(Pres)*
Mark Watson *(CEO)*

Non-U.S. Subsidiaries:

Argo Direct, Ltd. (1)
Exchequer Court 33 St Mary Axe
London, EC3A 8AA, United Kingdom
Tel.: (44) 2077 127 600
Fax: (44) 2077 127 601
Web Site: www.argo-int.com
Emp.: 15
Insurance Policy Providing Services
S.I.C.: 6411
N.A.I.C.S.: 524298

Argo Management Holdings, Ltd. (1)
Exchequer Court 33 St Mary Axe
London, EC3A 8AA, United Kingdom
Tel.: (44) 20 7712 7600
Fax: (44) 20 7712 7601
E-Mail: it@argo-int.com
Business Support Services
S.I.C.: 7389
N.A.I.C.S.: 561499

Argo Managing Agency, Ltd. (1)
Exchequer Court 33 St Mary Axe
London, EC3A 8AA, United Kingdom
Tel.: (44) 20 77 12 76 00
Fax: (44) 20 77 12 76 01
Web Site: www.argo-int.com
Emp.: 15
General Insurance Services
S.I.C.: 6331
N.A.I.C.S.: 524126

Argo Re DIFC, Ltd. (1)
Al Fattan Currency House Level 1 Unit 11
PO Box 482067
Dubai, United Arab Emirates
Tel.: (971) 4 389 4 000
Fax: (971) 3894010
Emp.: 6
General Insurance Services
S.I.C.: 6411
N.A.I.C.S.: 524210

Argo Seguras Brasil, SA (1)
Avenida Nacoes Unidas 12 399 Floor 14
04578-000 Sao Paulo, Brazil
Tel.: (55) 11 3056 5530
Fax: (55) 11 3044 3018
Web Site: www.argolimited.com
Emp.: 50
Insurance Providing Services
S.I.C.: 6411
N.A.I.C.S.: 524298

Argo Solutions, SA (1)
Avenue Marcel Thiry 79 BTE 3
Brussels, Belgium 1200
Tel.: (32) 2 777 0909
Fax: (32) 2 777 0900
Web Site: www.argolimited.com
Insurance & Reinsurance Service Providers
S.I.C.: 6411
N.A.I.C.S.: 524298

Argo Underwriting Agency, Ltd. (1)
Exchequer Court 33 Saint Mary Axe
London, EC3A 8AA, United Kingdom
Tel.: (44) 20 7712 7600
Fax: (44) 20 7712 7601
Web Site: www.argo-int.com
Emp.: 15
Underwriting Agencies
S.I.C.: 6211
N.A.I.C.S.: 523110

Subsidiaries:

Argo Re, Ltd. (1)
110 Pitts Bay Road
Pembroke, HM08, Bermuda
Tel.: (441) 296 5858
Fax: (441) 296 6162
Web Site: www.argogroup.com
Emp.: 3
General Business Insurance Services
S.I.C.: 6351
N.A.I.C.S.: 524126
Mark Watson *(CEO)*

Non-U.S. Subsidiary:

ArgoGlobal SE (2)
Strand Tower Floor 1 36 Strand
Sliema, SLM 1022, Malta
Tel.: (356) 234 23000
Web Site: www.argolimited.com
Insurance Underwriting Services
S.I.C.: 6361
N.A.I.C.S.: 524127
Mark Peeters *(Gen Mgr)*

Peleus Reinsurance, Ltd. (1)
110 Pitts Bay Road
P.O. Box HM 1282 HM FX
Pembroke, HM08, Bermuda
Tel.: (441) 296 5858
Fax: (441) 296 6162
Commercial Property Reinsurance
S.I.C.: 6399
N.A.I.C.S.: 524130

ARGO GROUP LIMITED

33-37 Athol Street
Douglas, IM1 1LB, Isle of Man
Tel.: (44) 2075354000
Fax: (44) 2074935691
E-Mail: info@argogrouplimited.com
Web Site: www.argogrouplimited.com
ARGO—(AIM)
Rev.: $8,932,000
Assets: $28,382,000
Liabilities: $668,000
Net Worth: $27,714,000
Earnings: ($14,404,000)
Emp.: 40
Fiscal Year-end: 12/31/12

Business Description:
Investment Management Services
S.I.C.: 6211
N.A.I.C.S.: 523110

Personnel:
Kyriakos Rialas *(CEO)*
Andreas Rialas *(Chief Investment Officer)*

Board of Directors:
Michael Kloter
David Fisher
Andreas Rialas
Kyriakos Rialas
Kenneth Watterson

Legal Counsel:
Berwin Leighton Paisner LLP
Adelaide House London Bridge
London, United Kingdom

Appleby
33 Athol Street
Douglas, Isle of Man

Non-U.S. Subsidiaries:

Argo Capital Management (Asia) Pte. Ltd. (1)
1 Raffles Pl 43-02 OUB Ctr
048616 Singapore, Singapore
Tel.: (65) 65132880
Fax: (65) 65326480
Web Site: www.agrogm.com
Emp.: 2
Investment Management Services
S.I.C.: 8748
N.A.I.C.S.: 541618

Argo Capital Management (Cyprus) Limited (1)
10 Vasilissis Freiderikis Jacky Ct Ofc 401
1066 Nicosia, Cyprus
Tel.: (357) 22668900
Fax: (357) 22445177
E-Mail: info@argocm.com
Web Site: www.argocm.com
Emp.: 20
Investment Management Services
S.I.C.: 8748
N.A.I.C.S.: 541618
Kyriakos Rialas *(CEO)*

Argo Capital Management Limited (1)
24-25 New Bond St
London, W1S 2RR, United Kingdom
Tel.: (44) 2075354000
Fax: (44) 2074935691
E-Mail: info@argofunds.com
Web Site: www.argofunds.com
Emp.: 15
Investment Management Services
S.I.C.: 8748
N.A.I.C.S.: 541618
Kyriakos Rialas *(CEO)*

ARGO Real Estate Opportunities Fund (1)
(Formerly North Asset Management S.R.L.)
51-53 Clucerului St
Bucharest, Romania
Tel.: (40) 212232160
Fax: (40) 0213159506
E-Mail: office@argocapitalproperty.com
Web Site: www.argocapitalproperty.com
Emp.: 25
Investment Advisory Services
S.I.C.: 6282
N.A.I.C.S.: 523930
Lucian Gheorghescu *(Mgr-Mktg)*

ARGO INVESTMENTS LIMITED

Level 12 19 Grenfell Street
Adelaide, SA, 5000, Australia
Mailing Address:
GPO Box 2692
Adelaide, SA, 5001, Australia
Tel.: (61) 8 8212 2055
Fax: (61) 8 8212 1658
E-Mail: invest@argoinvestments.com.au
Web Site: www.argoinvestments.com.au
Year Founded: 1946
ARG—(ASX)
Rev.: $195,460,444
Assets: $4,410,875,828
Liabilities: $490,496,670
Net Worth: $3,920,379,158
Earnings: $182,403,974
Fiscal Year-end: 06/30/13

Business Description:
Investment Management Services
S.I.C.: 6282
N.A.I.C.S.: 523920

Personnel:
Jason Beddow *(CEO)*
Andrew B. Hill *(CFO)*
Brenton R. Aird *(COO)*
Christopher C. Hall *(Sr Investment Officer)*
Timothy C. A. Binks *(Sec)*

Board of Directors:
G. Ian Martin
Anne B. Brennan
Roger Andrew Davis
Russell A. Higgins
Joycelyn C. Morton
Robert J. Patterson
Robert T. Rich

ARGONAUT EXPLORATION INC.

268 McKinnon Place NE
Calgary, AB, T2E 7B9, Canada
Tel.: (403) 969-7903
Fax: (403) 276-5422
Web Site: www.argonautexploration.com
Year Founded: 2005
AGA—(TSXV)
Int. Income: $2,331
Assets: $3,333,142
Liabilities: $73,389
Net Worth: $3,259,752
Earnings: ($453,249)
Fiscal Year-end: 06/30/13

Business Description:
Mineral Exploration Services
S.I.C.: 1081
N.A.I.C.S.: 213114

Personnel:
Raymond A. Cook *(Pres & CEO)*
Oleh Wowkodaw *(CFO & COO)*

Board of Directors:
Raymond A. Cook
Guillermo Salazar
Tell Stephen
Dale Vitone
Oleh Wowkodaw

ARGONAUT RESOURCES NL

Suite 4 Level 9 341 George Street
Sydney, NSW, 2000, Australia
Tel.: (61) 2 9299 9690
Fax: (61) 2 9299 9629
E-Mail: sydney@argonautresources.com
Web Site: www.argonautresources.com
ARE—(ASX)
Rev.: $152,421
Assets: $16,609,064
Liabilities: $876,861
Net Worth: $15,732,202
Earnings: ($11,881,161)
Fiscal Year-end: 06/30/13

Business Description:
Mineral Exploration
S.I.C.: 1481
N.A.I.C.S.: 213115

Personnel:
Andrew William Bursill *(CFO, Sec & Acting Gen Mgr)*

Board of Directors:
Patrick J. D. Elliott
Andrew William Bursill
Lindsay J. Owler
Malcom Ross Richmond

Legal Counsel:
Addisons Lawyers
Level 12 60 Carrington Street
Sydney, Australia

Non-U.S. Subsidiary:

Argonaut Resources Laos Co Limited (1)
Unit 3 Level 5 ANZ Vientiane Comml Bldg
PO Box 10982
33 Lane Xang Ave, Vientiane, Laos
Tel.: (856) 21222731
Fax: (856) 21 240 281
E-Mail: laos@argonautresources.com
Web Site: www.argonautresources.com
Emp.: 6
Gold Ore Mining Services
S.I.C.: 1041
N.A.I.C.S.: 212221
Lindsay Owler *(Gen Mgr)*

ARGOS CARPETS & FLOORING

1914 Merivale Road
Ottawa, ON, K2G 1E8, Canada
Tel.: (613) 226-6573
Fax: (613) 226-6577
E-Mail: reception@argoscarpets.ca
Web Site: www.argoscarpets.ca
Year Founded: 1978
Rev.: $14,320,800
Emp.: 30

Business Description:
Carpet & Rug Dealers
S.I.C.: 2273
N.A.I.C.S.: 314110

Personnel:
Peter A. Foustanellas *(Pres)*

ARGOS RESOURCES LIMITED

Argos House H Jones Road
Stanley, Falkland Islands FIQQ 1ZZ
Tel.: (500) 22685
Fax: (500) 22687
E-Mail: info@argosresources.com
Web Site: www.argosresources.com
Year Founded: 1995
ARG—(AIM)
Rev.: $37,000
Assets: $34,191,000
Liabilities: $637,000
Net Worth: $33,554,000
Earnings: ($1,582,000)
Emp.: 6
Fiscal Year-end: 12/31/12

Business Description:
Oil & Gas Exploration Services
S.I.C.: 1311
N.A.I.C.S.: 211111

Personnel:
Ian Thomson *(Chm)*
John Hogan *(Mng Dir)*
Kevin Kilmartin *(Sec)*

Board of Directors:
Ian Thomson
Dennis Carlton
Christopher Fleming
John Hogan
Andrew Irvine
James Ragg

Legal Counsel:
Peachey & Co LLP
95 Aldwych
London, WC2B 4JF, United Kingdom

ARGOS SODITIC S.A.

Rue du Rhone 118
CH 1204 Geneva, Switzerland
Tel.: (41) 228496633
Fax: (41) 228496627
Web Site: www.argos-soditic.com
Year Founded: 1989

Business Description:
Private Equity Firm
S.I.C.: 6211
N.A.I.C.S.: 523999

Personnel:
Cedric Bruix *(Partner)*
Guy Semmens *(Partner)*

Non-U.S. Subsidiaries:

Argos Soditic France SAS (1)
14 Rue de Bassano
75783 Paris, France FR
Tel.: (33) 153672050
Fax: (33) 153672055
E-Mail: info@argos-soditic.com
Web Site: www.argos-soditic.com
Private Equity Firm
S.I.C.: 6211
N.A.I.C.S.: 523999
Louis Godron *(Partner)*
Karel Kroupa *(Partner)*
Gilles Lorang *(Partner)*

Holding:

Axyntis SAS (2)
45 rue de Pommard
F-75012 Paris, France
Tel.: (33) 1 44 06 77 00
Fax: (33) 1 44 06 76 99
E-Mail: contact@axyntis.com
Web Site: www.axyntis.com
Specialty Chemicals Mfr
S.I.C.: 2899
N.A.I.C.S.: 325199
David Simonnet *(Mng Editor)*

Subsidiary:

Synthexim SAS (3)
Rue des Mouettes
ZI des Dunes, Calais, 61 200, France
Tel.: (33) 3 21 96 85 00
Fax: (33) 3 21 96 04 25
Organic Chemical Mfr
S.I.C.: 2899
N.A.I.C.S.: 325199

Subsidiary:

Calaire Chimie S.A.S. (4)
1 Quai d'Amerique
62100 Calais, France
Tel.: (33) 321 462121
Fax: (33) 321 462120
E-Mail: calaire-chimie-sas@wanadoo.fr
Web Site: www.ic-investors.com
Chemical Products Mfr & Distr
S.I.C.: 2899
N.A.I.C.S.: 325199
Christian Chartoex *(Mgr-Comml)*

Argos Soditic S.A.—(Continued)

Argos Soditic Italia S.p.A. (1)
Piazza Diaz 5
20123 Milan, Italy IT
Tel.: (39) 0200660700
Fax: (39) 0200660799
E-Mail:
Web Site: www.argos-soditic.com
Private Equity Firm
S.I.C.: 6211
N.A.I.C.S.: 523999
Jean-Pierre de Benedetto *(Partner)*
Mirco Dilda *(Partner)*

ARGOSY ENERGY INC.

500 1414 8th Street SW
Calgary, AB, T2P 1J6, Canada
Tel.: (403) 269-8846
Fax: (403) 269-8366
E-Mail: info@argosyenergy.com
Web Site: www.argosyenergy.com
Sales Range: $1-9.9 Million
Emp.: 16
Business Description:
Oil & Gas Exploration Services
S.I.C.: 1311
N.A.I.C.S.: 211111
Personnel:
Peter Salamon *(Pres & CEO)*
Ray Dobek *(Exec VP-Exploration)*
Board of Directors:
Ray Dobek
Kenneth Faircloth
Brian J. Mellum
Jake Roorda
Peter Salamon
Legal Counsel:
Borden Ladner Gervais LLP
Scotia Plaza 40 King Street West Suite 1000
Toronto, ON, Canada
Transfer Agent:
Valiant Trust Company
606 4th Street SW Suite 310
Calgary, AB, T2P 1T1, Canada
Tel.: (403) 233-2801
Fax: (403) 233-2857

ARGOSY MINERALS LIMITED

9/154 Hampden Road
Nedlands, WA, 6009, Australia
Tel.: (61) 893895803
Fax: (61) 893895879
E-Mail: admin@argosyminerals.com.au
Web Site: www.argosyminerals.com.au
AGY—(ASX)
Rev.: $29,228
Assets: $1,012,670
Liabilities: $64,119
Net Worth: $948,551
Earnings: ($981,010)
Emp.: 2
Fiscal Year-end: 12/31/12
Business Description:
Metals Exploration Services
S.I.C.: 1011
N.A.I.C.S.: 212210
Personnel:
Peter Lloyd *(CEO)*
Alan Edward Thomas *(Sec)*
Board of Directors:
Phillip Thick
Peter Lloyd
Danie Van Den Bergh
Legal Counsel:
Allion Legal Pty Ltd
Level 2 50 Kings Park Road
West Perth, WA, Australia

ARGUS GROUP HOLDINGS LIMITED

The Argus Building 14 Wesley Street
Hamilton, HM 11, Bermuda
Mailing Address:
PO Box HM 1064
Hamilton, HM EX, Bermuda
Tel.: (441) 2980838
Fax: (441) 2953456
E-Mail: insurance@argus.bm
Web Site: www.argus.bm
Year Founded: 1962
AGH—(BERM)
Rev.: $171,911,000
Assets: $1,909,164,000
Liabilities: $1,812,228,000
Net Worth: $96,936,000
Earnings: $12,926,000
Emp.: 202
Fiscal Year-end: 03/31/13
Business Description:
Insurance Services
S.I.C.: 6411
N.A.I.C.S.: 524298
Personnel:
Sheila E. Nicoll *(Chm)*
Alan R. Thomson *(Deputy Chm)*
Alison S. Hill *(CEO)*
David W. Pugh *(CFO)*
Andrew I. Baker *(CEO-Argus Insurance Company Europe Limited)*
George N. H. Jones *(Sec)*
Larry A. Peck *(Exec VP & Grp Actuary)*
Lauren M. Bell *(Exec VP-Life & Pensions)*
Andrew H. Bickham *(Exec VP-Broking)*
John Doherty *(Exec VP-Property & Casualty)*
Martin N. Gutteridge *(Exec VP-Info Sys)*
Michelle Brock Jackson *(Exec VP-Grp Insurance)*
Board of Directors:
Sheila E. Nicoll
Wendall S. F. Brown
Peter R. Burnim
John D. Campbell
Alison S. Hill
James S. Jardine
Reginald S. Minors
Everard Barclay Simmons
Robert D. Steinhoff
Alan R. Thomson
Paul C. Wollmann
Non-U.S. Subsidiary:

Data Communications Ltd (1)
1st Floor Cnr Mgr Gonin And Lislet
Geoffroy Street, Port Louis, Mauritius
Tel.: (230) 2101327
Fax: (230) 2119467
E-Mail: info@insodclweb.org
Web Site: www.dclweb.org
Emp.: 60
All Other Information Services
S.I.C.: 7389
N.A.I.C.S.: 519190
Ganesh Ramlingun *(Mng Dir)*

ARGUS MEDIA LTD.

Argus House 175 Saint John Street
London, EC1 V4LW, United Kingdom
Tel.: (44) 2077804200
Fax: (44) 2077804201
E-Mail: sales@argusmediagroup.com
Web Site: www.argusmediagroup.com
Year Founded: 1970
Emp.: 150
Business Description:
Price & Availability Information for Energy Related Products
S.I.C.: 2741
N.A.I.C.S.: 519130
Personnel:
Adrian Binks *(Chm & CEO)*
U.S. Subsidiary:

Argus Media, Inc. (1)
3040 Post Oak Blvd Ste 550
Houston, TX 77056 DE
Tel.: (713) 622-3996 (100%)
Fax: (713) 622-2991
E-Mail: sales@argusmediagroup.com
Web Site: www.argusmediagroup.com
Emp.: 40
Price & Availability Information for Energy Related Products
S.I.C.: 2741
N.A.I.C.S.: 511199
Euan Craik *(CEO)*

Branches:

Argus Media, Inc. - Washington, D.C. (2)
1012 14th St NW Ste 1500
Washington, DC 20005
Tel.: (202) 775-0240
Fax: (202) 872-8045
E-Mail: info@argusmedia.com
Web Site: www.argusmedia.com
Emp.: 300
Price & Availability Information for Energy Related Products
S.I.C.: 7929
N.A.I.C.S.: 711510
Adrian Binks *(Publr)*

Argus Media, Inc. - New York (2)
500 5th Ave Ste 2400
New York, NY 10110
Tel.: (646) 376-6130
Fax: (646) 376-6143
E-Mail: newyork@argusmedia.com
Web Site: www.argusmedia.com
Emp.: 12
Price & Availability Information for Energy Related Products
S.I.C.: 2741
N.A.I.C.S.: 511199
Miles Weigel *(Gen Mgr)*

Subsidiary:

DeWitt & Company Incorporated (2)
601 Sawyer St Ste 750
Houston, TX 77007 TX
Tel.: (713) 360-7500
Fax: (713) 360-7510
E-Mail: info@dewittworld.com
Web Site: www.dewittworld.com
Emp.: 50
Petrochemical Consulting Services
S.I.C.: 8999
N.A.I.C.S.: 541690
Earl H. Armstrong *(Mng Dir & Dir-Olefins & Derivatives)*

Non-U.S. Subsidiaries:

Argus Media Ltd. - Russia (1)
Ul Prechistenka 40/2 Entr 2 Fl 7
119034 Moscow, Russia
Tel.: (7) 959337571
Fax: (7) 9337572
E-Mail: argsales@argus.girmet.ru
Web Site: www.argus.ru
Emp.: 100
Price & Availability Information for Energy Related Products
S.I.C.: 7389
N.A.I.C.S.: 519190

Argus Media Ltd. - Japan (1)
22 Malacca St
10-02 Royal Brothers Bldg, Singapore, 48980, Singapore
Tel.: (65) 65333638
Fax: (65) 65334181
Web Site: www.argusmediagroup.com
Emp.: 20
Price & Availability Information for Energy Related Products
S.I.C.: 7389
N.A.I.C.S.: 519190
Adrias Binks *(Mng Dir)*

ARGUS METALS CORP.

350-580 Hornby St
Vancouver, BC, V6C 3B6, Canada
Tel.: (604) 687-2471
Fax: (604) 687-2472
E-Mail: info@Argusmetalscorp.com
Web Site: www.argusmetalscorp.com
Year Founded: 2009
AML—(TSXV)
Int. Income: $89
Assets: $30,867
Liabilities: $287,882
Net Worth: ($257,015)
Earnings: ($4,282,436)
Fiscal Year-end: 04/30/13
Business Description:
Mineral Exploration Services
S.I.C.: 1081
N.A.I.C.S.: 213114
Personnel:
Paul D. Gray *(Pres & CEO)*
Simon Anderson *(CFO)*
Board of Directors:
Simon Clarke
Michael Collins
Paul D. Gray
Jason K. McLaughlin
Robert van Staten
Legal Counsel:
Maitland & Company
Suite 700 625 Howe Street
Vancouver, BC, Canada V6C 2T6
Transfer Agent:
Computershare
3rd Floor 510 Burrard Street
V6C 3B9 Vancouver, BC, Canada

ARGUS S.A.

1 Industriala St
900147 Constanta, Romania
Tel.: (40) 241676840
Fax: (40) 241634367
E-Mail: secretariat@argus-oil.ro
Web Site: www.argus-oil.ro
UARG—(BUC)
Sales Range: $50-74.9 Million
Emp.: 291
Business Description:
Vegetable Oils Producer
S.I.C.: 2079
N.A.I.C.S.: 311225
Personnel:
Leu Vasile *(Gen Dir)*

ARGYLL PARTNERS LTD.

15 South Molton Street
London, W1K 5QR, United Kingdom
Tel.: (44) 2074093508
Fax: (44) 2074093240
E-Mail: enquiries@argyllpartners.co.uk
Web Site: www.argyllpartners.co.uk
Emp.: 6
Business Description:
Private Equity Firm
S.I.C.: 6211
N.A.I.C.S.: 523999
Personnel:
Christopher Steed *(Founder & CEO)*
Roy Convoy *(Partner)*
Adrian Richmond *(Partner)*
Non-U.S. Holding:

DWW Woolworth Deutschland GmbH & Co. KG (1)
Lyoner Strasse 52
60528 Frankfurt am Main, Germany
Tel.: (49) 6966010
Fax: (49) 6966012399
E-Mail: info@woolworth.de
Web Site: www.woolworth.de
Emp.: 500
Variety Stores
S.I.C.: 5399
N.A.I.C.S.: 452990
Robert Brech *(CEO)*
Dieter Stukenbrok *(CFO)*

ARIA INSURANCE SERVICES LIMITED

(Formerly Europ Assistance Holdings Ltd.)
(d/b/a Aria Assistance)
Sussex House Perrymount Road
Haywards Heath, W Sussex, RH16 1DN, United Kingdom
Tel.: (44) 1444442442
Fax: (44) 1444416348

E-Mail: commercial@aria-assistance.co.uk
Web Site: www.aria-assistance.co.uk
Year Founded: 1973
Emp.: 80
Business Description:
Holding Company; Medical, Travel & Automobile Assistance Services
S.I.C.: 6719
N.A.I.C.S.: 551112
Personnel:
Tim Ablett *(Chm)*
Patrick Leroy *(CEO)*

Subsidiary:

Aria Insurance Limited **(1)**
(Formerly Europ Assistance Insurance Ltd.)
Sussex House Perrymount Rd
Haywards Heath, West Sussex, RH16 1DN, United Kingdom (100%)
Tel.: (44) 1444442900
Fax: (44) 1444412653
Web Site: www.aria-assistance.co.uk
Medical, Travel & Automobile Assistance Services
S.I.C.: 7389
N.A.I.C.S.: 541990
Patrick Leroy *(CEO)*

ARIA SOLUTIONS INC.

525 28th St SE Ste 250
Calgary, AB, T2A 6W9, Canada
Tel.: (403) 235-0227
Fax: (866) 235-1181
Toll Free: (866) 550-2742
Web Site: www.ariasolutions.com
Year Founded: 1996
Rev.: $41,700,000
Emp.: 70
Business Description:
Customer Care Service
S.I.C.: 7389
N.A.I.C.S.: 519190
Personnel:
Robert Church *(Pres & COO)*
Noel Roberts *(CTO & VP-Client Dev)*

ARIADNE AUSTRALIA LIMITED

Level 12 300 Queen Street
Brisbane, QLD, 4000, Australia
Mailing Address:
PO Box 286
Brisbane, QLD, 4001, Australia
Tel.: (61) 7 3225 4800
Fax: (61) 7 3221 5959
E-Mail: info@ariadne.com.au
Web Site: www.ariadne.com.au
ARA—(ASX)
Rev.: $31,121,274
Assets: $92,321,723
Liabilities: $9,229,880
Net Worth: $83,091,844
Earnings: $3,981,864
Emp.: 52
Fiscal Year-end: 06/30/13
Business Description:
Investment Company; Car Park Infrastructure Operations, Property Development, Resorts & Apartments Management, Asset & Financial Services Management, Maritime Infrastructure Ownership & Operation
S.I.C.: 6211
N.A.I.C.S.: 523999
Personnel:
Murray R. Boyte *(CEO)*
Natt M. McMahon *(CFO & Sec)*
D. A. Weiss *(Investment Officer)*
Board of Directors:
David Zalmon Baffsky
Maurice William Loomes
John William Murphy
Kevin Will Seymour
Gary Hilton Weiss

ARIAKE JAPAN CO., LTD.

3-2-17 Ebisu-Minami
Shibuya-ku, Tokyo, 150-0022, Japan
Tel.: (81) 337913301
Web Site: www.ariakejapan.com
2815—(TKS)
Sls.: $369,501,231
Assets: $601,285,905
Liabilities: $89,232,022
Net Worth: $512,053,883
Earnings: $41,669,045
Emp.: 356
Fiscal Year-end: 03/31/13
Business Description:
Natural Seasonings, Agricultural & Livestock Products & Marine Products Mfr & Marketer; Restaurants Management
S.I.C.: 2099
N.A.I.C.S.: 311999
Personnel:
Kineo Okada *(Chm & CEO)*
Tomoki Tagawa *(Pres & COO)*
Katsutoshi Iwaki *(Sr Mng Dir & Gen Mgr-Internal Control Office)*
Taisuke Tsukiashi *(Mng Dir & Head-Kyushu Plant)*
Hitoshi Izumi *(Mng Dir & Gen Mgr-Engrg Dept)*
Board of Directors:
Kineo Okada
Katsutoshi Iwaki
Hitoshi Izumi
Kouichi Matsumoto
Naoki Okada
Naoki Shirakawa
Tomoki Tagawa
Taisuke Tsukiashi
Yoshikazu Uchida
Transfer Agent:
Mitsubishi UFJ Trust & Banking Corporation
1-3-4 Marunouchi, Chiyoda-ku
Tokyo, Japan

Subsidiary:

Ariake Farm Co., Ltd. **(1)**
235 Tsuzura Kozasa-cho
Sasebo, Nagasaki, Japan
Tel.: (81) 956683951
E-Mail: info@ariake-farm.co.jp
Web Site: www.ariake-farm.co.jp
Vegetable Farming Services
S.I.C.: 0161
N.A.I.C.S.: 111219

Plant:

ARIAKE JAPAN Co Ltd - Kyushu Plant **(1)**
1572-21 Aza Kourahama Kouramen Saza-Cho
Kita-Matsuura-gun, Nagasaki, 857-0361, Japan
Tel.: (81) 956635500
Fax: (81) 956635755
E-Mail: m-haraguchi@ariakejapan.com
Web Site: www.ariakejapan.com
Emp.: 500
Food Products Mfr & Supplier
S.I.C.: 5146
N.A.I.C.S.: 424460
Tomoki Tagawa *(Pres)*

U.S. Subsidiary:

ARIAKE U.S.A., Inc. **(1)**
1711 N Liberty St
Harrisonburg, VA 22802-4518
Tel.: (540) 432-6550
Fax: (540) 432-6549
Toll Free: (888) 201-5885
Web Site: www.ariakeusa.com
Emp.: 80
Processed Meat Producers
S.I.C.: 0251
N.A.I.C.S.: 112320
Joe Brisby *(Mgr-Sls)*

Non-U.S. Subsidiaries:

F. P. Natural Ingredients S.A.S **(1)**
6 Arou slo chet
Monitaouge, Paris, 92120, France
Tel.: (33) 145383582
Fax: (33) 145383569
E-Mail: europesales@ariakejapan.com
Web Site: www.ariake-europe.com
Emp.: 8
Food Products Mfr & Supplier
S.I.C.: 5142
N.A.I.C.S.: 424420

F.P.N.I. BELGIUM N.V. **(1)**
Oude Bunders Leemkuilstraat 5
Maasmechelen, Limburg, 3630, Belgium
Tel.: (32) 89460150
Fax: (32) 89460155
E-Mail: fpnib@ariakejapan.com
Web Site: www.ariakejapan.com
Emp.: 25
Food Products Mfr & Supplier
S.I.C.: 5146
N.A.I.C.S.: 424460
Tomoki Tagawa *(Pres)*

Qingdao Ariake Foodstuff Co., Ltd. **(1)**
138 Xining Rd Jiaonan
Qingdao, Shandong, China
Tel.: (86) 53288163152
Fax: (86) 532 8816 3151
Web Site: www.ariakejapan.com
Emp.: 107
Natural Seasonings Mfr & Whslr
S.I.C.: 2087
N.A.I.C.S.: 311942

Taiwan Ariake Foods Co., Ltd. **(1)**
No 188 Ln 53 Sec 2 Hur Sheng Rd
Ping-tung, Taiwan
Tel.: (886) 87550525
Fax: (886) 87530087
E-Mail: service@ariake.com.tw
Web Site: www.ariake.com.tw
Emp.: 63
Food Products Mfr & Supplier
S.I.C.: 5142
N.A.I.C.S.: 424420
Kuramoto Kanya *(Pres)*

ARIAN RESOURCES CORP.

(Formerly Golden Touch Resources Corp.)
1199 West Hastings Street Suite 800
Vancouver, BC, V6E 3T5, Canada
Tel.: (604) 248-5175
Fax: (888) 241-5996
E-Mail: info@arianresources.com
Web Site: www.arianresources.com
Year Founded: 2007
ARC—(DEU TSXV)
Int. Income: $292
Assets: $1,827,619
Liabilities: $601,824
Net Worth: $1,225,795
Earnings: ($2,268,344)
Fiscal Year-end: 05/31/13
Business Description:
Investment Services
S.I.C.: 6211
N.A.I.C.S.: 523999
Personnel:
Zahir Dhanani *(Pres & CEO)*
Anthony Jackson *(CFO)*
Board of Directors:
Kenneth Chapple
Anthony Jackson
Ramon Mahanta
Robert J. Naso
Chad Ulansky

Non-U.S. Subsidiary:

JAB Resources Limited **(1)**
91-93 Commercial Road
Teneriffe, Brisbane, QLD, 4006, Australia
Tel.: (61) 4 1871 2011
Fax: (61) 7 3854 2399
E-Mail: rob@goldentouchresources.com
Gold Exploration Services
S.I.C.: 1041
N.A.I.C.S.: 212221

ARIAN SILVER CORPORATION

Berkeley Square House Berkeley Square
London, W1J 6BD, United Kingdom
Tel.: (44) 20 7887 6599
Fax: (44) 20 7887 6598
E-Mail: info@ariansilver.com
Web Site: www.ariansilver.com
AGQ—(AIM OTC TSXV)
Rev.: $4,588,000
Assets: $14,119,000
Liabilities: $1,116,000
Net Worth: $13,003,000
Earnings: ($4,031,000)
Emp.: 58
Fiscal Year-end: 12/31/12
Business Description:
Silver Mining
S.I.C.: 1044
N.A.I.C.S.: 212222
Personnel:
Anthony Joseph Williams *(Chm)*
James Thomas Williams *(CEO)*
Dean Friday *(CFO)*
David H. Taylor *(Sec)*
Board of Directors:
Anthony Joseph Williams
Thomas Anstey Bailey
James Seymour Cable
James Arnott Crombie
James Thomas Williams
Computershare Investor Services Inc.
100 University Ave 9th Floor
Toronto, ON, Canada
Transfer Agents:
Computershare Investor Services PLC
The Pavilions Bridgewater Road
PO Box 82
Bristol, BS13 8AE, United Kingdom
Tel.: (44) 870 702 0000
Fax: (44) 870 703 6119
Computershare Investor Services Inc.
100 University Ave 9th Floor
Toronto, ON, Canada

Non-U.S. Subsidiary:

Arian Silver Mexico S.A. de C.V.Mexico **(1)**
Mina El Eden 128 Lomas de Bernardez
Guadalupe, Zacatecas, 98610, Mexico
Tel.: (52) 4929279410
Fax: (52) 4929233798
E-Mail: aldoarechiga@ariansilver.net
Web Site: ariansilver.net
Emp.: 8
Silver Products Mfr
S.I.C.: 3914
N.A.I.C.S.: 339910

ARIANA RESOURCES PLC

Bridge House London Bridge
London, SE1 9QR, United Kingdom
Tel.: (44) 207 407 3616
Fax: (44) 207 403 1605
E-Mail: info@arianaresources.com
Web Site: www.arianaresources.com
AAU—(LSE)
Rev.: $14,214
Assets: $11,334,564
Liabilities: $1,174,992
Net Worth: $10,159,573
Earnings: ($1,866,721)
Emp.: 26
Fiscal Year-end: 12/31/12
Business Description:
Mining Industry
S.I.C.: 1041
N.A.I.C.S.: 212221
Personnel:
Michael de Villiers *(Chm)*
Kerim Sener *(Mng Dir)*
William Payne *(CFO)*
Board of Directors:
Michael de Villiers
William Payne
Kerim Sener
Legal Counsel:
Gowlings (UK) LLP
15th Floor 125 Old Broad Street
London, EC2N 1AR, United Kingdom

ARIANA RESOURCES PLC—(Continued)

Non-U.S. Subsidiary:

Galata Madencilik San. ve Tic. Ltd. (1)
Farabi Sokak No 7 5
Cankaya, 06680 Ankara, Turkey
Tel.: (90) 3124681365
Fax: (90) 3124681385
Emp.: 9
Gold Mining Services
S.I.C.: 1041
N.A.I.C.S.: 212221
Erhan Sener *(Mng Dir)*

ARIANESPACE SA

Blvd de l'Europe
BP 177
91006 Evry, France
Tel.: (33) 160876000
Telex: ARESP 602-392
Fax: (33) 160876304
E-Mail: p.serry@arianespace.com
Web Site: www.arianespace.com
Year Founded: 1980
Sales Range: $900-999.9 Million
Emp.: 380
Business Description:
Commercial Space Transportation Services
S.I.C.: 3724
N.A.I.C.S.: 336412
Personnel:
Stephane Israel *(Chm & CEO)*
Alain Deschartes *(Treas & Mgr-Ops)*
Louis Laurent *(Sr VP-Programs)*
Jean-Max Puech *(Sr VP-Fin)*

Joint Venture:

Starsem (1)
2 Rue Francois Truffaut
91042 Evry, France
Tel.: (33) 169870110
Fax: (33) 160783199
E-Mail: communication@starsem.com
Web Site: www.starsem.com
Emp.: 12
Commercial Rocket Launch Services
S.I.C.: 9661
N.A.I.C.S.: 927110
Stephane Israel *(Chm & CEO)*
Victor Nikolaev *(COO)*

U.S. Subsidiary:

Arianespace, Inc. (1)
601 13th St NW Ste 710 N
Washington, DC 20005-3854 (100%)
Tel.: (202) 628-3936
Fax: (202) 628-3949
Web Site: www.arianespace.com
Emp.: 4
Marketing & Sales Office for Launching of Satellites
S.I.C.: 8742
N.A.I.C.S.: 541613
Clayton Mowry *(Pres)*

ARIANNE RESOURCES INC.

30 Racine Street East Suite 160
Chicoutimi, QC, G7H 1P5, Canada
Tel.: (418) 549-7316
Fax: (418) 549-5750
Web Site: www.arianne-inc.com
Year Founded: 1997
DAN—(TSXV)
Rev.: $37,682
Assets: $23,795,613
Liabilities: $4,608,947
Net Worth: $19,186,666
Earnings: ($5,370,280)
Fiscal Year-end: 12/31/12
Business Description:
Mineral Exploration Services
S.I.C.: 1081
N.A.I.C.S.: 213114
Personnel:
Pierre Lortie *(Chm)*
Jim Cowley *(Pres)*
Bernard Lapointe *(CEO)*
Derek L. Lindsay *(CFO)*
Guthrie J. Stewart *(Sec)*
Board of Directors:
Pierre Lortie
Luc Boivin
Jim Cowley
Dave DeBiasio
Marco Gagnon
Bernard Lapointe
Siva J. Pillay
Guthrie J. Stewart
Transfer Agent:
Computershare Investor Services Inc.
Montreal, QC, Canada

ARICENT INFRA LIMITED

1003 10th Floor Ganesh Tower CHS
Dada Patil Wadi
Thane West, Thane, 400601, India
Tel.: (91) 22 25407401
E-Mail: tcltechnologies@yahoo.com
Web Site: www.aricentinfra.co.in
Year Founded: 1991
530967—(BOM)
Business Description:
Construction Engineering Services
S.I.C.: 8711
N.A.I.C.S.: 541330
Personnel:
Tushar Patil *(Chm)*
Mansi B Thakkar *(Compliance Officer)*
Board of Directors:
Tushar Patil
Narendra P. Doshi
Dipesh Joshi
Harish Joshi
Neeta Joshi
Dhananjay R. Kale
Vaibhav V. Patil
Keyur Prakash Shah
Paresh V. Shah
Transfer Agent:
Sharex Dynamic (India) Pvt. Ltd.
Unit-1 Luthra Ind Premises Safed Pool Andheri Kurla Rd Andheri (E)
Mumbai, India

ARIES AGRO LIMITED

Aries House Plot No 24 Deonar
Govandi East
Mumbai, 400 043, India
Tel.: (91) 2225564052
Fax: (91) 2225564054
E-Mail: ariesagro@ariesagro.com
Web Site: www.ariesagro.com
ARIES—(NSE)
Rev.: $47,171,375
Assets: $79,623,314
Liabilities: $46,061,186
Net Worth: $33,562,128
Earnings: $2,523,270
Emp.: 748
Fiscal Year-end: 03/31/13
Business Description:
Fertilizer Mfr & Distr
S.I.C.: 2874
N.A.I.C.S.: 325312
Personnel:
Jimmy Mirchandani *(Chm & Mng Dir)*
S. Ramamurthy *(CFO)*
Qaiser Parvez Ansari *(Compliance Officer & Sec)*
Board of Directors:
Jimmy Mirchandani
Chakradhar Bharat Chhaya
Bhumitra V. Dholakia
R. S. S. Mani
Akshay Mirchandani
Rahul Mirchandani
Transfer Agent:
Aarthi Consultants Private Limited
1-2-285, Domalguda
Hyderabad, India

Non-U.S. Subsidiary:

Golden Harvest Middle East FZC (1)
P3-04 SAIF Zone
PO Box 9267
Sharjah, United Arab Emirates
Tel.: (971) 65578812
Fax: (971) 65578065
E-Mail: gharvest@eim.ae
Web Site: www.ghmefzc.com
Emp.: 15
Chelated Chemical Mfr
S.I.C.: 2899
N.A.I.C.S.: 325998

Subsidiary:

Amarak Chemicals FZC (2)
Al Hayl Fujairah Free Zone
PO Box 5283
Fujairah, United Arab Emirates
Tel.: (971) 9 2774831
Fax: (971) 9 2774832
E-Mail: sales@amarakfzc.com
Web Site: www.amarakfzc.com
Emp.: 25
Sulphur Bentonite Mfr
S.I.C.: 2899
N.A.I.C.S.: 325998

ARIF HABIB CORPORATION LIMITED

(d/b/a The Arif Habib Group)
Arif Habib Centre 23 MT Khan Road
Karachi, 74000, Pakistan
Tel.: (92) 2132460717
Fax: (92) 2132429653
E-Mail: info@arifhabibcorp.com
Web Site: www.arifhabibcorp.com
Year Founded: 1994
AHCL—(KAR LAH LSE)
Rev.: $16,466,967
Assets: $242,301,256
Liabilities: $88,177,001
Net Worth: $154,124,254
Earnings: $11,087,777
Fiscal Year-end: 06/30/13
Business Description:
Financial Holding Company; Commercial & Investment Banking, Securities Brokerage, Private Equity & Asset Management Services
S.I.C.: 6712
N.A.I.C.S.: 551111
Personnel:
Asadullah Khawaja *(Chm)*
Arif Habib *(CEO)*
Basit Habib *(CFO & Sec)*
Board of Directors:
Asadullah Khawaja
Nasim Beg
Sirajuddin Cassim
Muhammad Ejaz
Arif Habib
Kashif A. Habib
Samad A. Habib
Legal Counsel:
Bawaney & Partners
4th Floor Beaumont Plaza Civil Lines
Karachi, Pakistan
Transfer Agent:
Central Depository Company of Pakistan Limited
CDC House 99 B Block B SMCHS Main Shahra-e-Faisal
Karachi, 74400, Pakistan

Subsidiary:

Summit Bank Limited (1)
Arif Habib Centre 23 MT Khan Road
Karachi, 74000, Pakistan PK
Tel.: (92) 21 111124725
Fax: (92) 21 32435736
E-Mail: info@summitbank.com.pk
Web Site: www.summitbank.com.pk
SMBL—(KAR LAH)
Int. Income: $103,959,125
Assets: $1,360,348,239
Liabilities: $1,329,896,901
Net Worth: $30,451,337
Earnings: ($27,526,057)
Emp.: 2,461
Fiscal Year-end: 12/31/12
Banking Services
S.I.C.: 6029
N.A.I.C.S.: 522110
Nasser Abdullah Hussain Lootah *(Chm)*
Husain Lawai *(Pres & CEO)*
Aziz Adil *(CFO)*
Mohammad Zahir Esmail *(COO)*
Muhammad Siddique Memon *(Sec)*

ARIGATOU SERVICES CO., LTD.

30-6-3 Hacchonishi
Imabari, Ehime, 794-0832, Japan
Tel.: (81) 898 23 2243
Fax: (81) 898 23 2099
E-Mail: info@arigatou-s.com
Web Site: www.arigatou-s.com
3177—(JAS)
Sales Range: $75-99.9 Million
Emp.: 160
Business Description:
Used Good Recycling Stores; Restaurants; DVD Rental Stores; Real Estate Rentals
S.I.C.: 5399
N.A.I.C.S.: 452990
Personnel:
Masayuki Imoto *(Pres)*

ARIGENE CO., LTD

83 25 Nonhyun-Dong
Gangnam Gu, Seoul, 135 818, Korea (South)
Tel.: (82) 25 11 77 47
Fax: (82) 25 11 66 36
067850—(KRS)
Business Description:
Holding Company
S.I.C.: 6719
N.A.I.C.S.: 551112
Personnel:
Sang-Baek Park *(CEO)*

ARIHANT CAPITAL MARKETS LTD.

67 Nehru Road 3rd Floor Krishna Bhavan
Vile Parle E, Mumbai, 400057, India
Tel.: (91) 22 42254800
Fax: (91) 22 42254880
E-Mail: contactus@arihantcapital.com
Web Site: www.arihantcapital.com
511605—(BOM)
Rev.: $9,444,312
Assets: $21,975,255
Liabilities: $9,654,159
Net Worth: $12,321,096
Earnings: $1,022,353
Emp.: 167
Fiscal Year-end: 03/31/13
Business Description:
Financial Services
S.I.C.: 6211
N.A.I.C.S.: 523999
Personnel:
Ashok Kumar Jain *(Chm, CEO & Mng Dir)*
Tarun Goyal *(CFO)*
Mahesh Pancholi *(Compliance Officer & Sec)*
Board of Directors:
Ashok Kumar Jain
Anita Surendra Gandhi
Pankaj Kumar Gupta
Rakesh Jain
Sunil Kumar Jain
Akhilesh Rathi
Paragbhai Rameshbhai Shah
Transfer Agent:
Ankit Consultancy Pvt. Ltd
Plot No 60 Electronic Complex Pardeshipura
Indore, India

ARIHANT FOUNDATIONS & HOUSING LIMITED
New No 3 Old No 25 Ganapathy
Colony 3rd Street Off Cenotaph Road
Teynampet, Chennai, 600 018, India
Tel.: (91) 4442244444
Fax: (91) 4442244440
E-Mail: info@arihants.co.in
Web Site: www.arihantfoundations.com
ARIHANT—(NSE)
Rev.: $22,890,994
Assets: $85,425,119
Liabilities: $58,366,751
Net Worth: $27,058,367
Earnings: ($2,995,687)
Fiscal Year-end: 09/30/13
Business Description:
Property Development Services
S.I.C.: 6531
N.A.I.C.S.: 531390
Personnel:
Kamal Lunawath *(Chm & Mng Dir)*
J. Meenakshi *(Compliance Officer & Sec)*
Board of Directors:
Kamal Lunawath
Karan Bhasin
Ravikant M. Choudhary
A. Damodaran
Bharat M. Jain
A. L. Jayabhanu
Vimal Lunawath
Harish Trivedi
Transfer Agent:
Cameo Corporate Services Ltd.
V Fl Subramanian Bldg No 1 Club House Rd
Chennai, Tamil Nadu, India
Tel.: (91) 4428460390
Fax: (91) 44 28460129

ARIHANT SUPERSTRUCTURES LIMITED
302 Persepolis Building Sector 17
Plot No 74
Vashi, Navi Mumbai, 400 703, India
Tel.: (91) 22 4111 3333
E-Mail: info@asl.net.in
Web Site: www.asl.net.in
506194—(BOM)
Rev.: $13,280,563
Assets: $48,828,528
Liabilities: $39,133,022
Net Worth: $9,695,507
Earnings: ($533,629)
Emp.: 100
Fiscal Year-end: 03/31/13
Business Description:
Real Estate Development Services
S.I.C.: 6531
N.A.I.C.S.: 531390
Personnel:
Ashok Chhajer *(Chm & Mng Dir)*
Naveen Ranka *(Compliance Officer)*
Nimesh Shah *(Chief Project Officer)*
Board of Directors:
Ashok Chhajer
Dinesh Babel
Virendra Kumar Mital
Vinayak V. Nalavde
Nimesh Shah
Transfer Agent:
Adroit Corporate Services Pvt. Ltd
19/20 Jaferbhoy Industrial Estate 1st Floor
Makwana Road Marol Naka
Andheri East, Mumbai, 400 059, India
Subsidiary:

Arihant Vatika Realty Private Limited (1)
302 Persipolis Building Plot No 74 Sector 17
Vashi, Mumbai, 400 703, India
Tel.: (91) 22 4111 3333
Fax: (91) 22 2788 2946
E-Mail: info@asl.net.in
Emp.: 200
Real Estate Development Services
S.I.C.: 6531
N.A.I.C.S.: 531390

ARIMA PHOTOVOLTAIC & OPTICAL CORP.
6th Floor No 758 Sector 4 Bade Road
Songshan District, Taipei, Taiwan
Tel.: (886) 2 2749 5588
Fax: (886) 2 2749 5577
E-Mail: info@arima.com.tw
Web Site: www.arima.com.tw/english/
Year Founded: 1987
2381—(TAI)
Sales Range: $800-899.9 Million
Emp.: 10,126
Business Description:
Optoelectronics Products Developer
S.I.C.: 3679
N.A.I.C.S.: 334419
Personnel:
Stephen Lee *(Chm)*
David Su *(CEO)*
Subsidiaries:

Arima Communications Corporation (1)
No 16 Lane 658 Yingtao Rd
Yingge Taipei, 23943, Taiwan
Tel.: (886) 282277755
Fax: (886) 26705511
E-Mail: sales@arimacomm.com.tw
Web Site: www.arimacomm.com.tw
Sales Range: $900-999.9 Million
Emp.: 3,500
Mobile Communications Products Mfr
S.I.C.: 3669
N.A.I.C.S.: 334290
Stephen Lee *(Chm)*

Arima Display Corporation (1)
No 248-47 Shin-Sheng Rd
L.E.P.Z. Kaohsiung, Taiwan
Tel.: (886) 78115388
Fax: (886) 78310555
Web Site: www.arimadisp.com
Emp.: 2,050
Flat Panel Display Mfr
S.I.C.: 3823
N.A.I.C.S.: 334513
Stephen Lee *(Chm, Pres & CEO)*

Arima Optoelectronics Corporation (1)
349 Jen Ho Rd
Dashi, Taoyuan, 335, Taiwan TW
Tel.: (886) 33803801
Fax: (886) 33803786
E-Mail: aocepi@aocepi.com.tw
Web Site: www.aocepi.com.tw
AOC—(TAI)
Sales Range: $50-74.9 Million
Electronic Component Mfr
S.I.C.: 3679
N.A.I.C.S.: 334419
Stephen Lee *(Chm)*

ARIO S.A.
10 Industriei St
420063 Bistrita, Romania
Tel.: (40) 263 234 160
Fax: (40) 263 234 008
E-Mail: info@ario.ro
Web Site: www.ario.ro
Year Founded: 1981
ARIO—(BUC)
Rev.: $1,651,335
Assets: $7,607,827
Liabilities: $4,829,818
Net Worth: $2,778,009
Earnings: ($558,690)
Emp.: 96
Fiscal Year-end: 12/31/12
Business Description:
Casting, Taps & Valves Mfr
S.I.C.: 3494
N.A.I.C.S.: 332919
Personnel:
Muresan Ioan Adrian *(Gen Mgr)*

ARION BANK HF.
Borgartun 19
105 Reykjavik, Iceland
Tel.: (354) 4446000
Fax: (354) 4446009
E-Mail: arionbanki@arionbanki.is
Web Site: www.arionbanki.is
Int. Income: $462,115,080
Assets: $7,043,278,500
Liabilities: $6,019,812,540
Net Worth: $1,023,465,960
Earnings: $133,377,920
Emp.: 1,158
Fiscal Year-end: 12/31/12
Business Description:
Banking Services
S.I.C.: 6029
N.A.I.C.S.: 522110
Personnel:
Monica Birgitte Caneman *(Chm)*
Gudrun Johnsen *(Vice Chm)*
Hoskuldur H. Olafsson *(CEO)*
Stefan Petursson *(CFO)*
Sigurjon Palsson *(COO)*
Gisli S. Ottarsson *(Chief Risk Officer)*
Gudni Adalsteinsson *(Treas)*
Board of Directors:
Monica Birgitte Caneman
Jon G. Briem
Thora Hallgrimsdottir
Mans Hoglund
Gudrun Johnsen
Agnar Kofoed-Hansen
Subsidiary:

Kaupthing Bank (1)
Borgartuni 19
105 Reykjavik, Iceland
Tel.: (354) 4446000
Fax: (354) 4446119
E-Mail: info@kbbanki.is
Web Site: www.kaupthing.com
Emp.: 1,200
Banking Services
S.I.C.: 6029
N.A.I.C.S.: 522110
Finnur Sveinbjornsson *(CEO)*

U.S. Subsidiary:

Kaupthing New York Inc. (2)
230 Park Ave Ste 1528
New York, NY 10169 (100%)
Tel.: (212) 457-8700
Fax: (212) 457-8725
E-Mail: info@kaupthing.us
Web Site: www.kaupthing.us
Emp.: 9
Banking Services; Institutional Sales & Services
S.I.C.: 6029
N.A.I.C.S.: 522110

Non-U.S. Subsidiaries:

Kaupthing Singer & Friedlander Group Limited (2)
21 New St
London, EC2M 48R, United Kingdom UK
Tel.: (44) 2032055000
Fax: (44) 2032055001
E-Mail: groupweb@singer-friedlander.com
Web Site: www.kaupthingsingers.co.uk/
Sales Range: $300-349.9 Million
Emp.: 643
Merchant Banking
S.I.C.: 6099
N.A.I.C.S.: 522320

ARION ENTREPRISE SAS
(Merged with SILKAN)

ARION TECHNOLOGY INC.
3F Pica Bldg 894 Hogye 2-dong
Dongan-gu, Anyang, Gyeonggi-Do, Korea (South) 431-836
Tel.: (82) 31 361 3000
Fax: (82) 31 361 3099
E-Mail: info@arion.co.kr
Web Site: www.arion.co.kr
Year Founded: 1999
058220—(KRS)
Business Description:
Broadcasting Equipment Mfr
S.I.C.: 3663
N.A.I.C.S.: 334220
Personnel:
Jason Lee *(Pres & CEO)*
Thomas Roh *(Sr VP-Sls & Mktg Div)*

ARIP PUBLIC COMPANY LIMITED
99/16-20 Ratchadapisek Road
Din-Daeng, Bangkok, Thailand
Tel.: (66) 2642 3400
Fax: (66) 26412331
E-Mail: webmaster@arip.co.th
Web Site: www.arip.co.th
ARIP—(THA)
Sales Range: $1-9.9 Million
Emp.: 130
Business Description:
Magazine & Internet Publishing Services
S.I.C.: 2721
N.A.I.C.S.: 511120
Personnel:
Manu Leopairote *(Chm)*

ARIS INTERNATIONAL LIMITED
21 1st Floor Princep Street
Kolkata, 700072, India
Tel.: (91) 33 22378520
Fax: (91) 33 2261009
E-Mail: adityagearsltd@gmail.com
Web Site: www.adityagears.in
Year Founded: 1995
531677—(BOM)
Rev.: $10,161
Assets: $168,869
Liabilities: $154,685
Net Worth: $14,184
Earnings: ($21,328)
Fiscal Year-end: 03/31/13
Business Description:
Automobile Parts Mfr
S.I.C.: 3714
N.A.I.C.S.: 336350
Personnel:
Ashok Kumar Harlalka *(Chm & Mng Dir)*
Lokanath Mishra *(Compliance Officer)*
Board of Directors:
Ashok Kumar Harlalka
Anant Veer Harlalka
Sunita Harlalka
Transfer Agent:
Maheshwari Datamatics Pvt Ltd
6 Mangoe Lane 2nd Floor
Kolkata, India

ARISAWA MANUFACTURING CO., LTD.
Minami Honcho 1-5-5
Joetsu, Niigata, 943 8610, Japan
Tel.: (81) 255245121
Fax: (81) 255241117
Web Site: www.arisawa.co.jp
5208—(TKS)
Sls.: $296,989,000
Assets: $535,249,000
Liabilities: $125,224,000
Net Worth: $410,025,000
Earnings: $10,263,000
Emp.: 578
Fiscal Year-end: 03/31/13
Business Description:
Plastics & Resins Mfr
S.I.C.: 2821
N.A.I.C.S.: 325211

Arisawa Manufacturing Co., Ltd.—(Continued)

Personnel:
Sanji Arisawa *(Pres & CEO)*
Yuta Arisawa *(Sr Mng Operating Officer-Sls Div, Tokyo & Osaka Branches)*
Yutaka Hayakawa *(Operating Officer-Electronic Matl Sls Div)*
Tetsuro Iizuka *(Sr Operating Officer-Corp Plng & Human Capital Dept)*
Yasunori Kihara *(Operating Officer-Procurement Dept)*
Takeshi Masuda *(Operating Officer-Corp Plng Dept)*
Takashi Miwa *(Sr Operating Officer-R&D, Gen Affairs & Production Engrg Dept)*
Yukio Takashima *(Sr Operating Officer-Gen Affairs, Mfg Engrg & Procurement Dept)*
Yoshihiko Toda *(Operating Officer-3D Matl Sls & Circuit Matl Sls Div)*
Yuichi Watanabe *(Sr Mng Operating Officer-Mfg Dept)*
Yoshihiro Yoshihara *(Operating Officer-R&D & 3D Material Div)*
Board of Directors:
Sanji Arisawa
Yuta Arisawa
Katsuchika Goto
Tetsuro Iizuka
Etsujiro Koge
Takashi Miwa
Yukio Takashima
Yuichi Watanabe
Transfer Agent:
Mitsubishi UFJ Trust & Banking Corporation
10-11 Higashisuna 7-Chome Koto-Ku
Tokyo, Japan

Divisions:

Arisawa Manufacturing Co., Ltd. - 3D Material Division (1)
2-12-5 Yanagibashi
Taito-ku, Tokyo, Japan
Tel.: (81) 338613625
Fax: (81) 338612140
E-Mail: 3dproducts@arisawa.co.jp
Web Site: www.arisawa.co.jp
Emp.: 50
Electronic Materials Mfr
S.I.C.: 3823
N.A.I.C.S.: 334513
Sanji Prisawa *(Pres)*

Arisawa Manufacturing Co., Ltd. - Circuit Material Division (1)
2-12-5 Yanagibashi
Taito-ku, Tokyo, 111-0052, Japan
Tel.: (81) 338613509
Fax: (81) 338612140
E-Mail: circuit@arisawa.co.jp
Web Site: www.arisawa.co.jp
Emp.: 35
Electronic Materials Mfr
S.I.C.: 3823
N.A.I.C.S.: 334513
Sanji Arisawa *(Pres)*

Arisawa Manufacturing Co., Ltd. - Electrical Insulating & Composite Material Division (1)
2-12-5 Yanagibashi
Taito-ku, Tokyo, Japan
Tel.: (81) 338612141
Fax: (81) 338612140
E-Mail: denzetsu-t@arisawa.co.jp
Web Site: www.arisawa.co.jp
Emp.: 60
Electronic Materials Mfr
S.I.C.: 3823
N.A.I.C.S.: 334513
Sanji Arisawa *(Pres)*

Arisawa Manufacturing Co., Ltd. - Electronic Material Division (1)
2-20-5 Taito-ku
Yanagibashi-ku, Tokyo, Japan
Tel.: (81) 338613562
Fax: (81) 338612140
E-Mail: fpc-t@arisawa.co.jp
Web Site: www.arisawa.co.jp
Emp.: 40
Electronic Materials Mfr
S.I.C.: 3823
N.A.I.C.S.: 334513
Arisawa Sanji *(Pres)*

Subsidiaries:

Arisawa Jushi Kogyo Co., Ltd. (1)
1-5-5 Minami-honcho
Joetsu, Niigata, 943-0841, Japan
Tel.: (81) 482224981
Fax: (81) 255241117
Web Site: www.arisawa.co.jp
Emp.: 700
Plastic Products Mfr
S.I.C.: 3089
N.A.I.C.S.: 326199
Toda Yoshishiko *(Pres)*

Arisawa Kenpan Co., Ltd. (1)
Minami-senba 4-12-12
Chuo-ku, Osaka, 542-0081, Japan
Tel.: (81) 6 6244 4134
Fax: (81) 662441468
Electronic Materials Mfr
S.I.C.: 3679
N.A.I.C.S.: 334419

Arisawa Sogyo Co., Ltd. (1)
1-5-5 Minamihon-cho
Joetsu, Niigata, 943-0841, Japan
Tel.: (81) 255242313
Fax: (81) 255242316
Web Site: www.arisawa-sogyo.co.jp
Emp.: 150
Plastic Products Mfr
S.I.C.: 3089
N.A.I.C.S.: 326199
Tetsuro Iizuka *(Pres)*

Asuna Co., Ltd. (1)
Nana Bldg 6f Taito-Ku
Tokyo, 111-0052, Japan
Tel.: (81) 338616415
Fax: (81) 338616416
E-Mail: info@asuna-3d.com
Web Site: www.asuna-3d.com
Emp.: 5
Electronic Material Mfr
S.I.C.: 3679
N.A.I.C.S.: 334419
Kenji Matsuhiro *(Pres)*

Colorlink Japan Co., Ltd. (1)
Iwamoto Cho Kita Bldg 4F 1-8-15
Chiyoda-Ku, Tokyo, 101-0032, Japan
Tel.: (81) 3 3861 3254
Fax: (81) 3 3861 2146
E-Mail: info@colorlink.co.jp
Web Site: www.colorlink.co.jp
Precision Optics Mfr
S.I.C.: 3827
N.A.I.C.S.: 333314
Yoshitaka Sato *(Pres & CEO)*

Quality Experience Design Co., Ltd. (1)
Waseda Incubation Ctr 09 1-22-3 Nishi-waseda
Shinjuku, Tokyo, 169-0051, Japan
Tel.: (81) 363803092
Fax: (81) 363803092
E-Mail: info@qxd.co.jp
Web Site: www.qxd.co.jp
Emp.: 12
Media Technology Services
S.I.C.: 7374
N.A.I.C.S.: 518210
Keiji Ohta *(CEO)*

Plants:

Arisawa Manufacturing Co., Ltd. - Nakadahara Factory (1)
Oaza-Nakadahara 1
Joetsu, Niigata, 943-8610, Japan
Tel.: (81) 255247487
Fax: (81) 255245155
E-Mail: h-mafumura@arisawa.co.jp
Emp.: 700
Electronic Materials Mfr
S.I.C.: 3823
N.A.I.C.S.: 334513
Hisashi Mafumura *(Mgr)*

Arisawa Manufacturing Co., Ltd. - Nakadahara-Nishi Factory (1)
Oaza-Nakadahara 55
Joetsu, Niigata, 943-8610, Japan
Tel.: (81) 255241646
Fax: (81) 255242444
E-Mail: fpc-p@arisawa.co.jp
Web Site: www.arisawa.co.jp
Electronic Materials Mfr
S.I.C.: 3823
N.A.I.C.S.: 334513
Sanji Arisawa *(Pres)*

ARISE AB

(Formerly Arise Windpower AB)
Kristian IV:s vag 3
Box 808
301 18 Halmstad, Sweden
Tel.: (46) 35 2020900
Fax: (46) 35 227800
E-Mail: info@arisewindpower.se
Web Site: www.arise.se
Year Founded: 2006
A4W—(DEU)
Rev.: $32,508,000
Assets: $496,443,600
Liabilities: $318,114,000
Net Worth: $178,329,600
Earnings: ($2,476,800)
Emp.: 39
Fiscal Year-end: 12/31/12
Business Description:
Wind Power Generation & Turbine Mfr
S.I.C.: 4911
N.A.I.C.S.: 221118
Personnel:
Pehr G. Gyllenhammar *(Chm)*
Peter Nygren *(CEO)*
Lars Froding *(Deputy CEO & COO)*
Thomas Johansson *(CFO)*
Gary Ericsson *(CMO)*
Ulf Edberg *(Exec VP-Project Construction)*
Board of Directors:
Pehr G. Gyllenhammar
Joachim Gahm
Peter Nygren
Maud Olofsson
Birger von Hall

Subsidiaries:

Arise Service & Projektering AB (1)
Industrigatan 18
Laholm, Halland, 312 34, Sweden
Tel.: (46) 430685000
E-Mail: info@arisewindpower.se
Electric Power Generation Services
S.I.C.: 4931
N.A.I.C.S.: 221118

Arise Wind Farm 3 AB (1)
PO Box 808
301 18 Halmstad, Halland, Sweden
Tel.: (46) 430685008
Fax: (46) 435227800
E-Mail: info@arisewindpower.se
Emp.: 30
Electric Power Generation Services
S.I.C.: 4931
N.A.I.C.S.: 221118
Peter Nygren *(CEO)*

Arise Wind Farm 4 AB (1)
Kristian IV S Vaeg 3
302 50 Halmstad, Halland, Sweden
Tel.: (46) 352020900
Electric Power Generation Services
S.I.C.: 4931
N.A.I.C.S.: 221118

ARISE TECHNOLOGIES CORPORATION

65 Northland Rd
Waterloo, ON, N2V 1Y8, Canada
Tel.: (519) 725-2244
Fax: (519) 725-8907
E-Mail: info@arisetech.com
Web Site: www.arisetech.com
Sales Range: $75-99.9 Million
Emp.: 135
Business Description:
Solar Systems Mfr
S.I.C.: 3433
N.A.I.C.S.: 333414
Personnel:
Ian MacLellan *(Founder)*
Doug McCollam *(CFO)*
William White *(Exec VP)*
Sjouke Zijlstra *(Sr VP-Advanced Mfg)*
Board of Directors:
Harold H. Alexander
Peter William Currie
Hal Merwald
Garry J. West
Judson Whiteside
Transfer Agent:
Equity Financial Trust Company
Toronto, ON, Canada

Plant:

ARISE Technologies Corp. - PV Silicon Plant (1)
95 Washburn Drive
Kitchener, ON, N2R 1S1, Canada
Tel.: (877) 274-7383
Fax: (519) 725-8907
E-Mail: info@arisetech.com
Emp.: 50
Photovoltaic Cells Mfr
S.I.C.: 3674
N.A.I.C.S.: 334413
Jeff Dawkins *(VP & Gen Mgr)*

Non-U.S. Subsidiary:

ARISE Technologies Deutschland GmbH (1)
Thormeyerstrasse 1
Bischofswerda, 01877 Bautzen, Saxony, Germany
Tel.: (49) 3594 7179 0
Fax: (49) 3594 7179 111
Emp.: 150
Photovoltaic Cells Mfr
S.I.C.: 3674
N.A.I.C.S.: 334413
Klaus Gotsch *(Mng Dir)*

ARISE WINDPOWER AB

(Name Changed to Arise AB)

ARISON HOLDINGS (1998) LTD.

(d/b/a Arison Group)
Goulda Center 23 Shaul Hamelech Boulevard
Tel Aviv, 64367, Israel
Tel.: (972) 36073100
Fax: (972) 36073101
E-Mail: info@arison.co.il
Web Site: www.arison.co.il
Business Description:
Holding Company
S.I.C.: 6719
N.A.I.C.S.: 551112
Personnel:
Shari Arison *(Owner)*

Divisions:

Arison Investments Ltd. (1)
Goulda Ctr 23 Shaul Hamelech Blvd
Tel Aviv, 63467, Israel
Tel.: (972) 37180200
Fax: (972) 37180222
Web Site: www.arison.co.il/investments/en
Investment Holding Company
S.I.C.: 6719
N.A.I.C.S.: 551112
Efrat Peled *(Chm & CEO)*

Holdings:

Salt of The Earth Ltd. (2)
7 Melach Haaretz Street
Atlit, 30300, Israel
Tel.: (972) 4 9549 535
Fax: (972) 4 8130 735
E-Mail: marketing@salt.co.il
Web Site: www.salt.co.il
Emp.: 142
Salt Production
S.I.C.: 1479
N.A.I.C.S.: 212393

Shikun & Binui Ltd. (2)
1a HaYarden Street
PO Box 1133
Airport City, Ben-Gurion Airport, 70151, Israel II
Tel.: (972) 3 6301 111 (48%)
Fax: (972) 3 6301 595
E-Mail: info@shikunbinui.com
Web Site: en.shikunbinui.co.il
SKBN—(TAE)
Rev.: $1,628,973,255
Assets: $2,847,305,939
Liabilities: $2,541,202,308
Net Worth: $306,103,631
Earnings: $119,458,890
Fiscal Year-end: 12/31/12
Holding Company; Construction, Infrastructure & Real Estate Services
S.I.C.: 6719
N.A.I.C.S.: 551112
Moshe Luhmani *(Chm)*
Ofer Kotler *(CEO)*
Amit Segev *(Deputy CEO)*
Ronit Rosensweig *(Deputy CFO & Head-Monetary Reporting)*
Tal Raz *(CFO)*
Orry Ben-Porath *(CEO-Water)*
Tamir Dagan *(CEO-Real Estate)*
Yehuda Elimelech *(CEO-SBI)*
Yaron Karisi *(CEO-Solel Boneh-Infrastructure)*
Ami Landau *(CEO-Concession Div)*
Rony Paluch *(CEO-SBI Infrastructure)*
Yaron Szilas *(CEO-Renewable Energy)*
Hezi Katan *(Legal Counsel & VP)*

The Ted Arison Family Foundation (Israel) A Public Benefit Company Ltd. (1)
Goulda Center 23 Shaul Hamelech Boulevard
Tel Aviv, 64367, Israel II
Tel.: (972) 36073100
Fax: (972) 36073101
E-Mail: info@arison.com
Web Site: www.arison.co.il/AFFAbout.aspx
Grantmaking & Giving Services
S.I.C.: 8399
N.A.I.C.S.: 813219
Jason Arison *(Chm)*

ARISTOCRAT LEISURE LIMITED

Building A Pinnacle Office Park 85 Epping Road
North Ryde, NSW, 2133, Australia
Mailing Address:
PO Box 361
North Ryde, NSW, 1670, Australia
Tel.: (61) 2 9013 6000
Fax: (61) 2 9013 6200
E-Mail: info@ali.com.au
Web Site: www.aristocrat.com.au
Year Founded: 1953
ALL—(ASX)
Rev.: $725,403,928
Assets: $783,353,214
Liabilities: $446,585,892
Net Worth: $336,767,322
Earnings: $96,160,544
Emp.: 2,173
Fiscal Year-end: 09/30/13
Business Description:
Gaming Technology, Systems & Services
S.I.C.: 7999
N.A.I.C.S.: 713290
Personnel:
Jamie R. Odell *(CEO & Mng Dir)*
Toni Korsanos *(CFO & Sec)*
Manjit Gombra Singh *(CTO)*
Jason Walbridge *(Chief Supply Officer)*
Atul Bali *(Pres-Americas)*
Mark Dunn *(Gen Counsel & Exec VP)*
Victor Blanco *(Sr VP-Platform Architecture)*
Board of Directors:
Ian D. Blackburne
David C. P. Banks
Roger Andrew Davis
Rosalind Dubs
Stephen W. Morro
Jamie R. Odell

Division:

Aristocrat Leisure Australia (1)
Ln Cove 1595
P O Box 808
1445 Rosebery, NSW, 2018, Australia (100%)
Tel.: (61) 296974000
Fax: (61) 297008149
Web Site: www.aristrocatgaming.com
Emp.: 260
S.I.C.: 5941
N.A.I.C.S.: 451110
David Hughes *(Gen Mgr)*

Subsidiaries:

Aristocrat International Pty Ltd (1)
Bldg A Pinnacle Off Park 85 Epping Rd
North Ryde, NSW, 2113, Australia
Tel.: (61) 290136000
Fax: (61) 290136200
Electronic Gaming Machines Mfr
S.I.C.: 3679
N.A.I.C.S.: 334419

Non-U.S. Subsidiaries:

Aristocrat Leisure Cyprus Limited (2)
Eagle Star House 5th Floor 35 Theklas Lysioti Street
Limassol, 3030, Cyprus
Tel.: (357) 25817411
Fax: (357) 25817412
Electronic Gaming Machines Mfr
S.I.C.: 3679
N.A.I.C.S.: 334419

Aristocrat Research & Development (Africa) Pty Ltd (2)
70 Saturn Crescent Cnr Milky Way Linbro Business Park
Linbro Park, Johannesburg, South Africa
Tel.: (27) 11 997 4200
Fax: (27) 11 608 0060
E-Mail: info@aristocratsa.co.za
Electronic Gaming Machine Mfr
S.I.C.: 3589
N.A.I.C.S.: 333318

Aristocrat Service Mexico, S.A. DE C.V. (2)
Av de las Palmas 425 of 1401 Col
Lomas de Chapultepec, Mexico, 11000, Mexico
Tel.: (52) 55 5282 4800
Emp.: 5
Electronic Gaming Machine Mfr
S.I.C.: 3679
N.A.I.C.S.: 334419
Carlos Carrion *(Gen Mgr)*

Aristocrat Technologies Europe (Holdings) Limited (2)
25 Riverside Way
Uxbridge, Middlesex, UB8 2YF, United Kingdom
Tel.: (44) 1895 618500
Fax: (44) 1895 618501
E-Mail: info@aristocrat.co.uk
Emp.: 25
Electronic Gaming Machine Mfr
S.I.C.: 3679
N.A.I.C.S.: 334419
William Wilsnagh *(Mng Dir)*

Aristocrat Technologies India Private Ltd (2)
7th Floor ETT Building Film City 24 Sector 16A Gautam Budh Nagar
Noida, Uttar Pradesh, India
Tel.: (91) 120 467 7400
Fax: (91) 120 467 7444
E-Mail: info@ali.com.au
Electronic Game Machine Mfr
S.I.C.: 3679
N.A.I.C.S.: 334419

Aristocrat Properties Pty Ltd (1)
Building A Pinnacle Office Park 85 Epping Rd
North Ryde, NSW, 2066, Australia
Tel.: (61) 2 9013 6000
Casino Operators
S.I.C.: 7999
N.A.I.C.S.: 713210

Aristocrat Technical Services Pty Ltd (1)
Building A Pinnacle Office Park 85 Epping Rd
North Ryde, NSW, 2113, Australia
Tel.: (61) 290136000
Electronic Gaming Equipment Mfr
S.I.C.: 3679
N.A.I.C.S.: 334419

Aristocrat Technologies Australia Pty. Ltd. (1)
60 62 Commercial Dr
Brisbane, QLD, 4128, Australia (100%)
Tel.: (61) 738014444
Fax: (61) 7 3801 4403
Emp.: 22
Sporting Goods
S.I.C.: 5941
N.A.I.C.S.: 451110

Subsidiary:

Aristocrat Technology Gaming Systems Pty Limited (2)
85 Epping Rd
North Ryde, NSW, 2113, Australia
Tel.: (61) 290136000
Electronic Gaming Machines Mfr
S.I.C.: 3679
N.A.I.C.S.: 334419

Aristocrat Technologies Australia (1)
672 Lorimer St
Melbourne, VIC, 3207, Australia
Tel.: (61) 396441000
Fax: (61) 396441032
Web Site: www.aristocrattechnologies.com.au
Emp.: 22
S.I.C.: 5941
N.A.I.C.S.: 451110
Jodie Scott *(Mgr-Admin)*

U.S. Subsidiary:

Aristocrat Technologies, Inc. (1)
7230 Amigo St
Las Vegas, NV 89119
Tel.: (702) 270-1000
Fax: (702) 270-1001
Toll Free: (800) 748-4156
Web Site: www.aristocrattechnologies.com
Emp.: 100
Hobby, Toy & Game Shops
S.I.C.: 5945
N.A.I.C.S.: 451120
Atul Bali *(Pres-Americas)*

Non-U.S. Subsidiary:

Aristocrat Argentina S.A. (2)
San Vladimiro 3056 1 Piso of 7 San Isidro
Buenos Aires, 1107, Argentina
Tel.: (54) 1147085400
Fax: (54) 1147085454
E-Mail: contact@aristocrat-inc.com
Web Site: www.aristocratgaming.com
Emp.: 1
Electronic Gaming Machine Mfr
S.I.C.: 3569
N.A.I.C.S.: 333999
Petr Strof *(Office Mgr)*

Non-U.S. Subsidiaries:

Aristocrat Argentina Pty Ltd (1)
San Vladimiro 3056 1 piso Of 7
San Isidro, 1642 Buenos Aires, Argentina
Tel.: (54) 1147085400
Fax: (54) 11470854418
E-Mail: atruci@aristocrat-inc.com
Web Site: www.aristocrat-gaming.com
Emp.: 10
Slot Machines, Gaming Development, Production & Sales
S.I.C.: 3577
N.A.I.C.S.: 334118

Aristocrat (Macau) Pty Limited (1)
35-341 Alameda Dr Carlos Assumpcao 17th Floor Hotline Centre
Macau, China (Macau)
Tel.: (853) 2872 2777
Fax: (853) 2872 2777
Electronic Game Machine Mfr
S.I.C.: 3679
N.A.I.C.S.: 334419
David Punter *(Gen Mgr-Asia Pacific)*

Aristocrat Technologies Africa Pty. Ltd. (1)
70 Saturn Cresent Coboner Milky Way
Linbro Park, Johannesburg, South Africa (100%)
Tel.: (27) 115792900
Fax: (27) 116080030
Sales Range: $10-24.9 Million
Emp.: 30
Gaming Systems, Technologies & Solutions
S.I.C.: 3575
N.A.I.C.S.: 334118
William Wilsnagh *(Mng Dir)*

Aristocrat Technologies Europe Limited (1)
25 Riverside Way
Uxbridge, Middlesex, UB8 2YF, United Kingdom
Tel.: (44) 1895618500
Fax: (44) 1895618501
E-Mail: info@aristocrat.co.uk
Web Site: www.aristocrat.com.au/contact/contact/Pages/OfficeLocations.aspx
Emp.: 35
S.I.C.: 5941
N.A.I.C.S.: 451110

Non-U.S. Subsidiary:

Aristocrat Technologies Spain S.L (2)
Centre d Empreses de Noves Tecnologies
Avinguda del Parc Tecnologic 3, 08290
Cerdanyola del Valles, Spain
Tel.: (34) 93 5824444
Web Site: www.aristocratgaming.co.uk/?p=contacts
Emp.: 3
Electronic Gaming Machine Mfr
S.I.C.: 3679
N.A.I.C.S.: 334419
Jaime Riera *(Gen Mgr)*

Aristocrat Technologies NZ Limited (1)
22 Vestey Dr Mt Wellington
Auckland, 1060, New Zealand (100%)
Tel.: (64) 92592000
Fax: (64) 92592001
E-Mail: info@alinz.co.nz
Web Site: www.aristocratgaming.com
Emp.: 80
Gaming Technologies, Systems & Solutions
S.I.C.: 3575
N.A.I.C.S.: 334118

K.K. Aristocrat Technologies (1)
7th Floor Ryukakusan Building 2-5-12 Higashi-kanda
Chiyoda-ku, Tokyo, 101 0031, Japan JP
Tel.: (81) 358350521
Fax: (81) 358350523
E-Mail: info@aristocrat.co.jp
Web Site: www.aristocrat.co.jp
Sales Range: $75-99.9 Million
Emp.: 79
Slot Machines, Gaming Development, Production & Sales
S.I.C.: 3575
N.A.I.C.S.: 334118
Minoru Itaya *(Gen Mgr)*

ARISTON THERMO S.P.A.

Viale Aristide Merloni 45
60044 Fabriano, Italy
Tel.: (39) 07326011
Fax: (39) 0732602331
E-Mail: marketing@mts.it
Web Site: www.aristonthermo.com
Sales Range: $1-4.9 Billion
Emp.: 6,800
Business Description:
Air Conditioners, Boilers & Water Heaters
S.I.C.: 3585
N.A.I.C.S.: 333415
Personnel:
Francesco Merloni *(Chm)*
Paolo Merloni *(CEO)*
Non-U.S. Subsidiary:

Elcotherm AG (1)
Sarganserstrasse 100
CH 7324 Vilters, Switzerland

Ariston Thermo S.p.A.—(Continued)

Tel.: (41) 817252525
Fax: (41) 817231359
E-Mail: vilters@ch.elco.net
Web Site: www.elco.ch/d/
Electric Services
S.I.C.: 4931
N.A.I.C.S.: 221122
Rene Schuermann *(Mng Dir)*

ARIUS3D INC.

755 The Queensway East Unit 20
Mississauga, ON, L4Y 4C5, Canada
Tel.: (905) 270-7999
Fax: (905) 270-6888
E-Mail: info@arius3d.com
Web Site: www.arius3d.com
Year Founded: 2007
Sales Range: $1-9.9 Million

Business Description:
Investment Services
S.I.C.: 6211
N.A.I.C.S.: 523999

Personnel:
Dan Arnold *(VP-Software Dev)*

Subsidiaries:

Arius 3D Canada Inc **(1)**
755 Queensway E Unit 20
Mississauga, ON, L4Y 4C5, Canada
Tel.: (905) 270-7999
Fax: (905) 270-6888
Web Site: www.arius3d.com
Emp.: 18
Three Dimensional Imaging System Distr
S.I.C.: 5065
N.A.I.C.S.: 423690

Arius 3D Inc **(1)**
755 The Queensway E Unit 20
Mississauga, ON, L4Y 4C5, Canada
Tel.: (905) 270-7999
Fax: (905) 270-6888
E-Mail: info@arius3d.com
Three Dimensional Imaging Services
S.I.C.: 7379
N.A.I.C.S.: 518210

Hall Train Studios Ltd. **(1)**
1050 Kamato Rd Unit 10-11
Mississauga, ON, L4W 2W4, Canada
Tel.: (905) 238-0381
Fax: (905) 238-5631
E-Mail: studio@halltrainstudios.com
Web Site: www.halltrainstudios.com
Animation Studios Operating Services
S.I.C.: 7819
N.A.I.C.S.: 512191

ARK MINES LTD

Level 33 Australia Square 264
George Street
Sydney, NSW, 2000, Australia
Tel.: (61) 292581989
Fax: (61) 2 9258 1111
E-Mail: info@arkmines.com.au
Web Site: www.arkmines.com.au
Year Founded: 2007
AHK—(ASX)

Business Description:
Gold & Base Metal Mining Services
S.I.C.: 1041
N.A.I.C.S.: 212221

Personnel:
Antony Corel *(Chm)*
Roger Alan Jackson *(Mng Dir)*
Ian Burnham Mitchell *(Sec)*

Board of Directors:
Antony Corel
Roger Alan Jackson
Robert McLennan
Ian Burnham Mitchell
John Slade

Legal Counsel:
Websters Solicitors
Level 11 37 Bligh Street
Sydney, NSW, Australia

ARK RESOURCES BERHAD

Suite 3A 02 Level 3A Wisma E&C No
2 Lorong Dungun Kiri
Damansara Heights, 50490 Kuala
Lumpur, Malaysia
Tel.: (60) 320940888
Fax: (60) 320954746
E-Mail: info@ark-resources.com.my
Web Site: www.ark-resources.co
m.my
ARK—(KLS)
Rev.: $4,208,047
Assets: $9,110,453
Liabilities: $1,994,689
Net Worth: $7,115,764
Earnings: $30,082
Emp.: 17
Fiscal Year-end: 12/31/12

Business Description:
Engineering & Construction Services
S.I.C.: 8711
N.A.I.C.S.: 541330

Personnel:
Rashidi Aly Abdul Rais *(Mng Dir)*
Mei Ling Chew *(Co-Sec)*
Cynthia Gloria Louis *(Co-Sec)*

Board of Directors:
Mohd Salleh Yeop Abdul Rahman
Rashidi Aly Abdul Rais
Azlan Aziz
Rosthman Ibrahim
Nasir Safar
Gary Wai Choong Wong

ARK THERAPEUTICS GROUP PLC

85 Tottenham Court Road
London, W1T 4TQ, United Kingdom
Tel.: (44) 207 002 1005
Fax: (44) 207 268 3100
E-Mail: arkplc@outlook.com
Web Site: www.arktherapeutics.com
AKT—(LSE)
Rev.: $2,871,149
Assets: $9,016,167
Liabilities: $4,668,381
Net Worth: $4,347,785
Earnings: ($20,110,679)
Emp.: 64
Fiscal Year-end: 12/31/12

Business Description:
Medical Products
S.I.C.: 3841
N.A.I.C.S.: 339112

Personnel:
Russell Banks *(CFO)*
John Martin *(Chief Scientific Officer)*
Sue Steven *(Sec)*

Board of Directors:
Iain Ross
David Bloxham
Charles Spicer
David Venables

Legal Counsel:
Ashurst LLP
Broadwalk House 5 Appold Street
London, EC2A 2HA, United Kingdom

Subsidiary:

Ark Therapeutics Limited **(1)**
4 th Fl 44-46 Whitfield
London, W1T @RJ, United Kingdom
Tel.: (44) 2073887722
Fax: (44) 2073887805
E-Mail: info@arktherapeutics.com
Emp.: 15
Medicine Research & Development Services
S.I.C.: 8731
N.A.I.C.S.: 541712

Non-U.S. Subsidiary:

Ark Therapeutics Oy **(1)**
Microkatu 1 S
FI 70210 Kuopio, Pohjois-Savo, Finland
Tel.: (358) 17240875
Fax: (358) 17240876
E-Mail: info.fi@arktherapeutics.com
Web Site: www.arktherapeutics.com
Emp.: 60
Medicine Research & Development Services
S.I.C.: 8731
N.A.I.C.S.: 541712
Auli Harvima *(Acct Mgr)*

ARKADIA CAPITAL CORP.

2800 715 5th Avenue SW
Calgary, AB, T2P 2X6, Canada
Tel.: (403) 299-9605
Fax: (403) 299-9601
E-Mail: dln@snclaw.com
Year Founded: 2011
AKC.P—(TSXV)

Business Description:
Investment Services
S.I.C.: 6211
N.A.I.C.S.: 523999

Personnel:
Dennis Nerland *(Pres, CEO & CFO)*
Dave Drover *(Sec)*

Board of Directors:
Dave Drover
Edward J. Kalthoff
Dennis Nerland
Wilson Olive

Transfer Agent:
Olympia Trust Company
125 9th Avenue SE Suite 2300
Calgary, AB, T2G 0P6, Canada
Tel.: (403) 261-0900

ARKAN AL-KUWAIT REAL ESTATE COMPANY KSCC

PO Box 20678
Safat, Kuwait, 13067, Kuwait
Tel.: (965) 2232 2282
Fax: (965) 2232 2281
E-Mail: realestate@arkanalkuwait.
com
Web Site: www.arkanalkuwait.com
ARKAN—(KUW)
Sales Range: $1-9.9 Million
Emp.: 20

Business Description:
Real Estate Services
S.I.C.: 6531
N.A.I.C.S.: 531390

Personnel:
Waleed Ahmad Al-Mannai *(Chm)*
Bader Abdulla Al-Ali *(Vice Chm)*
Bader Salem Al-Amiri *(Mng Dir)*

Board of Directors:
Waleed Ahmad Al-Mannai
Fawaz Othman Al-Aayar
Bader Abdulla Al-Ali
Bader Salem Al-Amiri
Ahmad A. Al-Farhan
Saleh Turki Al-Khamees
Meshal Yousef Al-Zaid

ARKAN BUILDING MATERIALS COMPANY PJSC

Al Bateen Area Opposite of The
National Bank of Abu Dhabi
PO Box 40307
Abu Dhabi, United Arab Emirates
Tel.: (971) 26666724
Fax: (971) 26666872
E-Mail: info@arkan.ae
Web Site: www.arkan.ae
Year Founded: 2005
ARKAN—(EMI)
Rev.: $107,981,427
Assets: $881,997,657
Liabilities: $431,215,046
Net Worth: $450,782,611
Earnings: $12,785,383
Fiscal Year-end: 12/31/12

Business Description:
Construction Products Mfr
S.I.C.: 3999
N.A.I.C.S.: 339999

Personnel:
Suhail Mubarak Al Ameri *(Chm)*
Khaled Mohammed Salem Al Tamimi *(Vice Chm)*

Board of Directors:
Suhail Mubarak Al Ameri
Dhafar Ayedh Hussein Al Ahbabi
Rashed Abdul Jalil Al Fahim
Khaled Mohammed Salem Al Tamimi
Tariq Ahmed Al Wahedi
Jasim Saleh Bousbia
Khalifa Yousef Khouri

ARKEMA S.A.

420 rue d'Estienne d'Orves
92705 Colombes, France
Tel.: (33) 149008080
Telex: ATO 611 922 F
Fax: (33) 149008396
Web Site: www.arkema.com
Year Founded: 1953
ARKAY—(EUR)
Sls.: $8,608,757,150
Assets: $7,459,127,970
Liabilities: $4,348,129,100
Net Worth: $3,110,998,870
Earnings: $297,503,570
Emp.: 13,925
Fiscal Year-end: 12/31/12

Business Description:
Vinyl Products, Industrial Chemicals & Performance Chemicals Mfr
S.I.C.: 2821
N.A.I.C.S.: 325211

Personnel:
Thierry Le Henaff *(Chm & CEO)*
Thierry Lemonnier *(CFO)*
Florence Schlegel *(Gen Counsel-Arkema Grp)*
Bernard Boyer *(Exec VP-Strategy)*
Pierre Chanoine *(Exec VP-Bus)*
Michel Delaborde *(Exec VP-HR & Corp Comm)*
Marc Schuller *(Exec VP-Bus)*

Board of Directors:
Thierry Le Henaff
Patrice Breant
Victoire de Margerie
Francois Enaud
Bernard L.M. Kasriel
Laurent Mignon
Thierry Morin
Marc Pandraud
Claire Pedini
Jean-Pierre Seeuws
Philippe Vassor

Ernst & Young Audit
1/2 place des Saisons
92400 Courbevoie, Paris-La Defense, 1, France

Subsidiaries:

Altuglas International S.A.S. **(1)**
89 boulevard National
F-92257 La Garenne-Colombes, Cedex, France FR
Tel.: (33) 1 7866 2300
Fax: (33) 1 7899 2397
Web Site: www.altuglas.com
Sales Range: $700-749.9 Million
Acrylic Resin & Sheet Products
S.I.C.: 3083
N.A.I.C.S.: 326130

U.S. Subsidiary:

Altuglas International **(2)**
100 P.A. Route 413
Bristol, PA 19007
Tel.: (215) 419-5013
Fax: (215) 419-5512
Toll Free: (800) 523-7500
Web Site: www.plexiglas.com
Mfr of Acrylic Resin & Sheet Products
S.I.C.: 3083
N.A.I.C.S.: 326130

Units:

Altuglas International (3)
4350 Camp Ground Rd
Louisville, KY 40216-4604
Tel.: (502) 449-6100
Fax: (502) 449-6116
Web Site: www.arkema-inc.com
Emp.: 72
Mfr of Acrylic Resin Sheet Products
S.I.C.: 3083
N.A.I.C.S.: 326130

Non-U.S. Subsidiary:

Maquiladora General de Matamoros S.A. de C.V (3)
Poniente 2 No 17
Matamoros, 87470, Mexico MX
Tel.: (52) 8688128065
Fax: (52) 8688128150
Web Site: www.altuglasint.com
Emp.: 150
Mfr of Acrylic Sheets & Plastic Modifiers
S.I.C.: 3083
N.A.I.C.S.: 326130
Rigoberto Camacho *(Plant Mgr)*

Non-U.S. Subsidiary:

Altuglas International (2)
7FL DongSung Building 17-8 Yoipo Dong
Young Teung To Gu
Seoul, 100 718, Korea (South)
Tel.: (82) 237036700
Fax: (82) 237036893
E-Mail: trevor.bridgman@arkema.com
Web Site: www.altuglas.com
Emp.: 10
Mfr of Acrylic Resin & Sheet Products
S.I.C.: 3083
N.A.I.C.S.: 326130
Trevor Bridgman *(Pres-Korea)*

ARKEMA EUROPE SA (1)
420 Rue d'Estienne d'Orves
92705 Colombes, Cedex, France
Tel.: (33) 1 49 00 80 80
Fax: (33) 1 49 00 83
E-Mail: arkema.phil-oc-customer-service@arkemagroup.com
Web Site: www.arkema.com
Emp.: 60
Chemical Products Mfr
S.I.C.: 2869
N.A.I.C.S.: 325199

Non-U.S. Subsidiary:

ARKEMA Gmbh (2)
Tersteegenstrasse 28
Dusseldorf, 40474, Germany
Tel.: (49) 2 11 45 52 0
Fax: (49) 11 4552112
E-Mail: info@arkema.com
Emp.: 4
Chemical Products Mfr
S.I.C.: 2899
N.A.I.C.S.: 325998
Heike Laustroer *(Mgr-Sls)*

Ceca S.A. (1)
89 Boulevard National
92257 La Garenne-Colombes, France FR
Tel.: (33) 149003800
Fax: (33) 149003801
E-Mail: info.ceca@ceca.fr
Web Site: www.ceca.fr
Sales Range: $250-299.9 Million
Emp.: 832
Mfr of Absorbents, Additives, Filter Aids & Surfactants
S.I.C.: 2899
N.A.I.C.S.: 325998

Non-U.S. Subsidiaries:

Ceca Italiana S.p.A (2)
Via Galileo Galilei 51 53
20096 Pioltello, MI, Italy
Tel.: (39) 02929191
Fax: (39) 029269507
E-Mail: sales.caca.italy@ceca.it
Web Site: www.cecachemicals.com
Emp.: 60
Chemical Products
S.I.C.: 2819
N.A.I.C.S.: 325180
Mario Schiavone *(Gen Mgr)*

Febex S.A. (2)
Route Des Placettes Case Postale 189
CH-1880 Bex, Switzerland
Tel.: (41) 44630550
Fax: (41) 44630589
E-Mail: info@atofina.com
Web Site: www.ceca.fr
Sls.: $17,056,200
Emp.: 45
Mfr of Chemicals
S.I.C.: 2899
N.A.I.C.S.: 325998
Thierry Vassalo *(Dir Gen)*

COATEX SAS (1)
35 rue Ampere
BP 8
ZI Lyon Nord, 69730 Genay, France
Tel.: (33) 4 72 08 20 00
Fax: (33) 4 72 08 20 40
E-Mail: contact@coatex.com
Web Site: www.coatex.com
Rheological Additives Mfr
S.I.C.: 2899
N.A.I.C.S.: 325998

Dorlyl SNC (1)
297 Rue Des Chantiers
BP 1152
76063 Le Havre, France
Tel.: (33) 235536850
Fax: (33) 235536851
Web Site: www.dorlyl.com
Emp.: 70
Mfr of Vinyl Compounds
S.I.C.: 2821
N.A.I.C.S.: 325211

Non-U.S. Subsidiary:

Rionil Compostos Vinilcos Ltda (2)
Rodovia Washington Luiz 14 235
Duque de Caxias, 25240-000 Rio de Janeiro, Brazil
Tel.: (55) 2126761731
Fax: (55) 2126761298
E-Mail: sede@rionil.com.br
Web Site: www.rionil.com.br
Mfr of Vinyl Compounds
S.I.C.: 2821
N.A.I.C.S.: 325211

MLPC International SA (1)
209 Avenue Charles Despiau
Rion-des-Landes, France
Tel.: (33) 558570200
Fax: (33) 157674418
Web Site: www.mlpc.intl.com
Emp.: 25
Synthetic Products Mfr
S.I.C.: 2816
N.A.I.C.S.: 325130
Jean-Marc Espinosa *(Gen Mgr)*

U.S. Subsidiary:

Arkema Inc. (1)
2000 Market St
Philadelphia, PA 19103-3231 PA
Tel.: (215) 419-7000
Fax: (215) 419-7591
Toll Free: (800) 225-7788
Web Site: www.arkema-inc.com
Sales Range: $1-4.9 Billion
Emp.: 800
Producer & Marketer of Commodity Chemicals, Chemical Intermediates, Specialties & Agrichemicals Including Plastics, Specialized Process Equipment & Health Products Consisting of Ethical & Proprietary Drugs
Import Export
S.I.C.: 2899
N.A.I.C.S.: 325998
Patricia McCarthy *(CFO & Sr VP)*
Mike Keough *(CIO)*
Gary Dee *(Grp Pres-Fluorochemicals-Americas)*
Richard Rowe *(Pres-Additives)*
William Hamel *(Gen Counsel & VP)*
Bernard Leconte *(Sr VP-Mfg & Regulatory Svcs)*

Subsidiaries:

Coatex Inc. (2)
547 Ecology Ln
Chester, SC 29706-4722
Tel.: (803) 377-6200
Fax: (803) 581-5995
Web Site: www.coatex.com
Emp.: 41
Chemical Products Mfr
S.I.C.: 2869
N.A.I.C.S.: 325199
Amber Goodyear *(Mgr-Mktg)*

Delaware Chemicals Corporation (2)
1105 N Market St Ste 1300
Wilmington, DE 19801-1241
Tel.: (302) 427-0263
Chemical Products Mfr
S.I.C.: 2899
N.A.I.C.S.: 325998

ODOR-TECH LLC (2)
7591 Esler Field Rd
Pineville, LA 71360
Tel.: (318) 767-0821
Fax: (318) 767-0874
Toll Free: (800) 636-7832
Web Site: www.odor-tech.com
Natural Gas Distribution Services
S.I.C.: 4924
N.A.I.C.S.: 221210

Sartomer USA, LLC (2)
502 Thomas Jones Way
Exton, PA 19341-2530 PA
Tel.: (610) 363-4100
Fax: (610) 363-4140
Toll Free: (800) 727-8663
Web Site: www.sartomer.com
Emp.: 150
Specialty Chemicals Mfr & Supplier
S.I.C.: 2899
N.A.I.C.S.: 325998
Doug Sharp *(Pres & CEO)*

Plants:

Sartomer USA, LLC (3)
610 S Bolmar St
West Chester, PA 19382-3797 PA
Tel.: (610) 692-8401
Fax: (610) 692-8636
Web Site: www.sartomer.com
Emp.: 90
Mfr Inorganic Chemicals, Plastic Materials & Resins
S.I.C.: 2899
N.A.I.C.S.: 325998

Sartomer USA, LLC (3)
601 Tightsqueeze Industrial Rd
Chatham, VA 24531-3678 VA
Tel.: (434) 432-3705
Fax: (434) 432-3712
Web Site: www.sartomer.com
Emp.: 100
Mfr of Industrial Inorganic Chemicals
S.I.C.: 2899
N.A.I.C.S.: 325998
Marcel Dewols *(CEO)*

Non-U.S. Subsidiaries:

Sartomer Asia Limited (3)
Unit 1106 11/F DCH Commercial Centre
25 Westlands Road, Quarry Bay, China (Hong Kong)
Tel.: (852) 2161 0600
Fax: (852) 2101 0070
E-Mail: info@sartomer.com.cn
Web Site: www.sartomerasia.com
Inorganic Chemicals Mfr
S.I.C.: 2899
N.A.I.C.S.: 325998

Viking chemical company (2)
157 Hwy Ave N
Blooming Prairie, MN 55917
Tel.: (507) 583-6641
Fax: (507) 583-2804
Chemical Products Mfr
S.I.C.: 2869
N.A.I.C.S.: 325199

Joint Venture:

American Acryl LP (2)
12100 Port Rd
Pasadena, TX 77507
Tel.: (281) 909-2600
Fax: (281) 909-2601
E-Mail: webmaster@americanacryl.com
Web Site: www.americanacryl.com
Sales Range: $10-24.9 Million
Emp.: 120
Mfr of Amines, Acids, Salts & Esters. Joint Venture of Arkema S.A. (50%) & NA Industries, Inc. (50%).
S.I.C.: 2899
N.A.I.C.S.: 325199
Shoji Nanda *(Gen Mgr)*

Units:

Arkema Coating Resins (2)
410 Gregson Dr
Cary, NC 27511-6445
Tel.: (919) 469-6700
Fax: (919) 469-6797
Toll Free: (866) 837-5532
Web Site: www.arkemacoatingresins.com
Emp.: 1,650
Specialty Coating Resins Developer & Mfr
S.I.C.: 3087
N.A.I.C.S.: 325991
Richard D. Jenkins *(Pres)*

Plants:

Arkema Coating Resins - Alsip (3)
12840 S Pulaski Rd
Alsip, IL 60803-1917
Tel.: (708) 396-3000
Fax: (708) 396-3051
E-Mail:
Sales Range: $10-24.9 Million
Emp.: 40
Specialty Coating Resins Developer & Mfr
S.I.C.: 3087
N.A.I.C.S.: 325991

Arkema Coating Resins - Torrance Plant (3)
19206 Hawthorne Blvd
Torrance, CA 90503-1505
Tel.: (310) 214-5300
Fax: (310) 542-3898
Sales Range: $25-49.9 Million
Emp.: 60
Specialty Coating Resins Developer & Mfr
S.I.C.: 3087
N.A.I.C.S.: 325991

Arkema Research Center (2)
900 First Ave
King of Prussia, PA 19406
Tel.: (610) 878-6500
Fax: (610) 878-6400
E-Mail: info@arkema.com
Web Site: www.arkema-inc.com
Emp.: 600
Chemical Research & Development Services
S.I.C.: 8731
N.A.I.C.S.: 541712
Ryan Dirkx *(VP-R&D)*

Non-U.S. Subsidiary:

Arkema Canada Inc. (2)
1100 Burloak Dr Ste 107 Berlington
Oakville, ON, L7L 6B2, Canada
Tel.: (905) 827-9841
Fax: (905) 827-7913
Toll Free: (800) 567-5726
E-Mail: arkema.oakv-canada-cf@arkema.com
Web Site: www.arkema.ca
Emp.: 3
Distr of Hydrogen Peroxide
S.I.C.: 2819
N.A.I.C.S.: 325180
Yves Hamelin *(Pres & CEO)*

Division:

Arkema Canada Inc. (3)
655 Alphonse Deshaies Blvd
Becancour, QC, G9H 2Y8, Canada QC
Tel.: (819) 294-9965
Fax: (819) 294-9588
E-Mail: info.becancour@arkema.com
Web Site: www.arkema-inc.com
Emp.: 65
Mfr of Hydrogen Peroxide
S.I.C.: 2819
N.A.I.C.S.: 325180
Yves Hamelin *(Pres & Plant Mgr)*

Non-U.S. Subsidiaries:

Altuglas International Denmark A/S (1)
Industrivej 16
9700 Bronderslev, Denmark

Arkema S.A.—(Continued)

Tel.: (45) 96464646
Fax: (45) 96464647
Emp.: 81
Acrylic Sheet Mfr & Distr
S.I.C.: 3081
N.A.I.C.S.: 326113
Aage Larsen *(Mgr-Supply Chain)*

Arkema Beijing Chemicals Co. Ltd (1)
No 1 Wutong Rd Industrial Development Zone
Tongzhou Dist, Beijing, 101113, China
Tel.: (86) 1061564749
Fax: (86) 1061564746
Chemical Products Mfr
S.I.C.: 2899
N.A.I.C.S.: 325199

Arkema B.V. (1)
Ottho Heldringstraat 41
1066 XT Amsterdam, Netherlands
Mailing Address:
Postbus 90181
1006 BD Amsterdam, Netherlands
Tel.: (31) 204089400
Fax: (31) 206691909
Web Site: www.arkema.com
Emp.: 20
Distr & Retailer of Chemical Products
S.I.C.: 5169
N.A.I.C.S.: 424690
Melt De Haas *(Mng Dir)*

Subsidiaries:

Arkema Rotterdam BV (2)
Tankhoofd 10
Vondelingenplaat, 3196 KE Rotterdam, Netherlands
Tel.: (31) 104725100
Fax: (31) 104382613
E-Mail: info@arkema.com
Web Site: www.arkema.com
Emp.: 50
Chemicals & Fungicides Mfr
S.I.C.: 2899
N.A.I.C.S.: 325998
Melt De Haas *(Mng Dir)*

Arkema Vlissingen B.V. (2)
Haven
9850 Vlissingen, Netherlands NL
Mailing Address: (100%)
PO Box 70
4380 AB Vlissingen, Netherlands
Tel.: (31) 113617000
Fax: (31) 113612984
Web Site: www.arkema.com
Emp.: 110
Mfr of Plastic Heat Stabilizers, Glass Coatings & Fertilizers
S.I.C.: 2821
N.A.I.C.S.: 325211

Arkema Changshu Chemicals Co. Ltd (1)
Fluorin Chemical Industrial Park Economic Development Zone
Changshu, 215522, China
Tel.: (86) 51252322538
Fax: (86) 51252322538
Chemical Products Mfr
S.I.C.: 2819
N.A.I.C.S.: 325180

ARKEMA CHINA INVESTMENT Co. Ltd (1)
Unit 1901-02 Block B Jianwai Soho No 39 East Third Ring Road
Chaoyang District, 100022 Beijing, China
Tel.: (86) 10 5869 5620
Fax: (86) 10 5869 5637
Investment Management Services
S.I.C.: 6211
N.A.I.C.S.: 523999

Subsidiary:

ARKEMA (Changshu) Fluorochemical Co. Ltd (2)
Fluorin Chemical Industrial Park Economic Development Zone
Changshu, 215522, China
Tel.: (86) 51252322538
Fax: (86) 51252322538
Chemical Products Mfr
S.I.C.: 2819
N.A.I.C.S.: 325180

ARKEMA COATINGS RESINS, S.A.U (1)
Olzinelles S/N Sant Celoni
28036 Barcelona, Spain
Tel.: (34) 91 334 34 34
Fax: (34) 938672454
Emp.: 11
Chemical Products Distr
S.I.C.: 5169
N.A.I.C.S.: 424690
Peter Heerwegh *(Mng Dir)*

Arkema Co. Ltd (1)
Suite 3212 32/F Tower 1 The Gateway 25 Canton Road
Tsim Sha Tsui, Kowloon, China (Hong Kong)
Tel.: (852) 2629 1826
Fax: (852) 2629 1878
Chemical Products Distr
S.I.C.: 5169
N.A.I.C.S.: 424690

Arkema Deutschland GmbH (1)
Tersteegen Strasse 28
Dusseldorf, 40474, Germany
Tel.: (49) 21145520
Fax: (49) 2114552112
E-Mail: empsang.empsang@arkemagroup.com
Web Site: www.arkema.com
Emp.: 80
Chemical Distr
S.I.C.: 5169
N.A.I.C.S.: 424690
Wulf Sauer *(Mng Dir)*

Arkema Iniciadores SA de CV (1)
Via Gustavo Baz 2160 Edificio 3 Fracc Industrial La Loma
54070 Tlalnepantla, Mexico
Tel.: (52) 55 5002 7101
Fax: (52) 55 5002 7137
Chemical Products Mfr
S.I.C.: 2899
N.A.I.C.S.: 325998

ARKEMA K.K. (1)
Fukoku-Seimei Bldg 15F 2-2-2 Uchisaiwaicho
Chiyoda-Ku, Tokyo, 100-0011, Japan
Tel.: (81) 352519900
Fax: (81) 352519930
Web Site: www.arkema.co.jp
Sls.: $219,516,410
Specialty Chemicals Distr
S.I.C.: 5169
N.A.I.C.S.: 424690
Jean-Luc Jouk *(Pres)*

Subsidiary:

Akishima Chemical Industries Co. Ltd (2)
Fukokuseimei Bldg 15f 2-2-2 Uchisaiwaicho
Chiyoda-Ku, Tokyo, 100-0011, Japan
Tel.: (81) 3 5251 9940
Fax: (81) 3 5251 9933
Sls.: $15,245,100
Chemical Products Distr
S.I.C.: 5169
N.A.I.C.S.: 424690
Jean-Luc Jouk *(Pres)*

Arkema Ltd (1)
Whitewall Way
Strood, Kent, ME2 4ES, United Kingdom
Tel.: (44) 1634718588
Fax: (44) 1634716774
Emp.: 12
Chemical Products Distr
S.I.C.: 5169
N.A.I.C.S.: 424690
Aude Morel *(Mgr)*

Arkema Mexico SA de CV (1)
Via Gustavo Baz 2160 Edificio 3 Fracc Industrial La Loma
54070 Tlalnepantla, Mexico
Tel.: (52) 5550027101
Fax: (52) 5550027137
Web Site: www.arkema.com
Industrial Chemical Import & Distr
S.I.C.: 5169
N.A.I.C.S.: 424690

ARKEMA NORTH EUROPE BV (1)
Tankhoofd 10
Vondelingenplaat, 3196 KE Rotterdam, Netherlands
Tel.: (31) 10 472 51 00
Fax: (31) 10 438 26 13
Web Site: www.arkema.com
Chemical Products Distr
S.I.C.: 5169
N.A.I.C.S.: 424690

Arkema Pte Ltd (1)
10 Science Park Road 01-01A The Alpha
Singapore, 117684, Singapore
Tel.: (65) 6419 9199
Fax: (65) 6419 9188
Web Site: www.arkema.com
Emp.: 4
Chemical Products Mfr
S.I.C.: 2899
N.A.I.C.S.: 325199
Kay Kellerhoff *(Mng Dir)*

Arkema Pty. Ltd. (1)
313 Centerbury Road Suite 103
Canterbury, VIC, 3126, Australia
Tel.: (61) 392 115 000
E-Mail: info.australia@atofina.com
Web Site: www.arkema.com
Emp.: 15
Chemical Distr
S.I.C.: 5169
N.A.I.C.S.: 424690
Brian Jecks *(Mng Dir)*

Arkema Quimica Ltda (1)
Avda Ibirapuera 2033 44 Andar
04029 901 Sao Paulo, Brazil BR
Tel.: (55) 121488522
Fax: (55) 1150517797
E-Mail: contato.brasil@arkema.com
Web Site: www.arkema.com
Mfr of Organic Peroxides & Distr of Chemicals
S.I.C.: 2869
N.A.I.C.S.: 325199

Arkema Quimica S.A (1)
Avenida de Burgos 12 7
28036 Madrid, Spain
Tel.: (34) 913343434
Fax: (34) 913343470
Web Site: www.arkema.com
Emp.: 30
Chemical Distr
S.I.C.: 5169
N.A.I.C.S.: 424690
Patricia Martine Merello *(Mng Dir)*

Arkema Shanghai Distribution Co. Ltd (1)
D Part No 28 Warehouse No 500 Fu Te Road No 2 East
Shanghai, 200131, China
Tel.: (86) 21 5046 1605
Fax: (86) 21 5046 1732
Chemical Products Distr
S.I.C.: 5169
N.A.I.C.S.: 424690

Arkema sp Z.o.o (1)
ul Przemyslowa
88-100 Inowroclaw, Poland
Tel.: (48) 52 3555710
Fax: (48) 52 3555720
Chemical Products Distr
S.I.C.: 5169
N.A.I.C.S.: 424690

Arkema Srl (1)
Via Pregnana 63
Rho, Milan, 20017, Italy
Tel.: (39) 02939251
Fax: (39) 0293925200
Web Site: www.arkema.com
Chemical Products Mfr
S.I.C.: 2899
N.A.I.C.S.: 325199

Changshu Coatex Additives Co. Ltd (1)
No 18 Haining Rd Fushan Haiyu Town
Changshu, Jiangsu, 215522, China
Tel.: (86) 512 5232 5580
Fax: (86) 512 5232 5509
Emp.: 4
Chemical Products Mfr
S.I.C.: 2819
N.A.I.C.S.: 325180

Coatex Central Eastern Europe s.r.o. (1)
Tomasikova 30
821 01 Bratislava, Slovakia
Tel.: (421) 2 48250 870
Fax: (421) 2 48250 876
Web Site: www.coatex.com
Chemical Products Mfr
S.I.C.: 2869
N.A.I.C.S.: 325199

Coatex Netherlands BV (1)
Middenweg 47a Haven M312
Moerdijk, 4782 PM, Netherlands
Tel.: (31) 168409020
Fax: (31) 168409024
Emp.: 2
Chemical Products Distr
S.I.C.: 5169
N.A.I.C.S.: 424690
Patrick Baud *(Gen Mgr)*

Luperox Iniciadores SA de CV (1)
Km 6 5 Carr Nanchital-Las Choapas El Chapo
Ixhuatlan del Sureste, Veracruz, 96360, Mexico
Tel.: (52) 921 216 07 39
Fax: (52) 9212162741
Web Site: www.luperox.com
Emp.: 25
Chemical Products Mfr
S.I.C.: 2899
N.A.I.C.S.: 325998

SEKI Arkema Co Ltd (1)
79 Gyenae-Ri Chilseo-Myeon
Haman-gun, Gyenae, 637-941, Korea (South)
Tel.: (82) 55 587 8055
Fax: (82) 55 587 8061
Web Site: www.sekiarkema.co.kr
Chemical Products Mfr
S.I.C.: 2899
N.A.I.C.S.: 325199

Shanghai Arkema Gaoyuan Chemicals Co. Ltd (1)
No 3 Workshop No 8999 Hunan Highway
Xuanqiao Town
Pudong New, Shanghai, 201314, China
Tel.: (86) 2158188821
Fax: (86) 2158188200
Web Site: www.arkema.com.cn/en/china/greater_china_plants_gaoyuan.php
Emp.: 60
Chemical Products Mfr
S.I.C.: 2869
N.A.I.C.S.: 325199
Ming Eau Jean *(Gen Mgr)*

Sunclear Srl (1)
Via Per Villapia 27
20010 Casorezzo, Milan, Italy
Tel.: (39) 02 90 35 661
Fax: (39) 02 90 29 67 05
E-Mail: info@sunclear.it
Web Site: www.sunclear.it
Plastic Sheet Distr
S.I.C.: 5162
N.A.I.C.S.: 424610

ARKLE PRINT LTD

17 Gatelodge Close, Round Spinney
Northampton, NN3 8RJ, United Kingdom
Tel.: (44) 1604499506
Fax: (44) 1604645581
E-Mail: mail@arkleprint.co.uk
Web Site: www.arkleprint.co.uk
Rev.: $11,448,096
Emp.: 72

Business Description:
Printing Services
S.I.C.: 2759
N.A.I.C.S.: 323111

Personnel:
Tony Lawson *(Mng Dir)*

ARKOON NETWORK SECURITY SA

(Acquired by Airbus Group N.V.)

ARKRAY, INC.

Kyoto Mliyuki Bldg 10F 689 Takanna-cho Nakagyo-ku
Kyoto, 601-8153, Japan
Tel.: (81) 5055279301

Fax: (81) 756628977
E-Mail: ehpmanager@arkray.co.jp
Web Site: www.arkray.co.jp
Year Founded: 1960
Sales Range: $400-449.9 Million
Emp.: 1,306
Business Description:
Medical & Health Diagnostic Products & Services
S.I.C.: 3841
N.A.I.C.S.: 339112
Personnel:
Shigeru Doi *(Pres & CEO)*
U.S. Subsidiaries:

ARKRAY USA, Inc. (1)
5198 W 76th St
Edina, MN 55439
Tel.: (952) 646-3200
Fax: (952) 646-3210
Toll Free: (800) 818-8877
E-Mail: info@arkrayusa.com
Web Site: www.arkrayusa.com
Sls.: $22,000,000
Creates, Acquires, Markets, & Supports Diagnostic & Medical Testing Equipment
S.I.C.: 5047
N.A.I.C.S.: 423450
Jonathan Chapman *(Pres)*

ARKU MASCHINENBAU GMBH
Siemensstrasse 11
76532 Baden-Baden, Germany
Tel.: (49) 722150090
Fax: (49) 7221500911
E-Mail: info@arku.de
Web Site: www.arku.de
Year Founded: 1928
Rev.: $16,960,000
Emp.: 120
Business Description:
Sheet Metal Mfr
S.I.C.: 3444
N.A.I.C.S.: 332322
Personnel:
Albert Reiss *(Pres)*

ARLA FOODS AMBA
Sonderhoj 14
8260 Viby, Denmark
Tel.: (45) 89381000
Fax: (45) 86281691
E-Mail: arla@arlafoods.com
Web Site: www.arla.com
Year Founded: 1970
Rev.: $11,383,241,040
Assets: $7,841,692,080
Liabilities: $1,969,170,480
Net Worth: $5,872,521,600
Earnings: $341,782,200
Emp.: 18,112
Fiscal Year-end: 12/31/12
Business Description:
Holding Company; Dairy Products Mfr & Distr
Import Export
S.I.C.: 6719
N.A.I.C.S.: 551112
Personnel:
Ake Hantoft *(Chm)*
Peder Tuborgh *(CEO)*
Povl Krogsgaard *(Vice CEO)*
Peter Tibourg *(Mng Dir)*
Frederik Lotz *(CFO)*
Ola Arvidsson *(Chief HR Officer)*
Christer Aberg *(Exec VP)*
Peter Giortz-Carlsen *(Exec VP)*
Finn S. Hansen *(Exec VP)*
Tim Orting Jorgensen *(Exec VP)*
Peter Lauritzen *(Exec VP)*
Jais Valeur *(Exec VP)*
Board of Directors:
Ake Hantoft
Viggo O. Bloch
Palle Borgstrom
Oliver Brandes
Jonas Carlgren
Leif Eriksson
Manfred Graff
Helene Gunnarson
Bjorn Jepsen
Thomas Johansen
Klaus Land
Steen Norgaard Madsen
Torben Myrup
Bjerglund Nielsen
Jan Toft Norgaard
Johnnie Russell
Harry Shaw
Manfred Sievers
Peter Winstone
Subsidiaries:

Arla Foods Ingredients amba (1)
Sonderhoj 14
DK-8260 Viby, Denmark (100%)
Tel.: (45) 89381000
Fax: (45) 89381290
E-Mail: ingredients@arlafoods.com
Web Site: www.arlafoodsingredients.com
Sales Range: $900-999.9 Million
Emp.: 600
Lactose-Based Proteins & Other Basic Organic Food Ingredient Chemicals Developer, Mfr & Whslr
S.I.C.: 2899
N.A.I.C.S.: 325199
Henrik Andersen *(CEO)*

Subsidiary:

Danmark Protein A/S (2)
Norre Vium Sonderupvej 26
6920 Videbaek, Denmark DK
Tel.: (45) 72 17 77 77 (100%)
Telex: 60921
Fax: (45) 72 17 77 70
E-Mail: hjl@arlafoods.com
Emp.: 200
Mfr of Whey Protein Concentrates, Permeate/Lactose & Functional Milk Proteins
S.I.C.: 2023
N.A.I.C.S.: 311514
Erik Veslov *(Plant Mgr)*

U.S. Subsidiary:

Arla Foods Ingredients, Inc. (2)
645 Martinsville Rd
Basking Ridge, NJ 07920 NJ
Tel.: (908) 604-8551 (100%)
Fax: (908) 604-9310
Web Site: www.arlafoodsingredients.com
Lactose-Based Proteins & Other Basic Organic Food Ingredient Chemicals Whslr
S.I.C.: 5169
N.A.I.C.S.: 424690

Non-U.S. Subsidiaries:

Arla Foods Ingredients AB (2)
Lindhagensgatan 126
SE-105 46 Stockholm, Sweden SE
Tel.: (46) 87895000 (100%)
Fax: (46) 87895444
Web Site: www.arlafoodsingredients.com
Lactose-Based Proteins & Other Basic Organic Food Ingredient Chemicals Whslr
S.I.C.: 5169
N.A.I.C.S.: 424690

Arla Foods Ingredients GmbH (2)
Am Bahnhof 1
31097 Harbarnsen, Germany De
Tel.: (49) 5060 6090 (Biolac) (100%)
Fax: (49) 506060939
E-Mail: raineoltmanns@arlafoods.com
Web Site: www.arlafoodsingredients.com
Emp.: 90
Holding Company; Lactose-Based Proteins & Other Basic Organic Food Ingredient Chemicals Mfr & Whslr
S.I.C.: 6719
N.A.I.C.S.: 551112
Luis Cubel *(Mgr)*

Affiliate:

Biolac GmbH & Co. KG (3)
Am Bahnhof 1
D-31097 Harbarnsen, Germany De
Tel.: (49) 50606090 (50%)
Telex: 9-27-268 MILCH
Fax: (49) 506060939
E-Mail: biolac@t-online.de
Web Site: www.biolac.com
Emp.: 70
Lactose-Based Proteins & Other Basic Organic Food Ingredient Chemicals Mfr & Whslr
S.I.C.: 2869
N.A.I.C.S.: 325199
Heinrich Buchholz *(Gen Mgr)*

Arla Foods Ingredients K.K. (2)
Hamamatsucho SS Bldg 3rd Fl 12-9 Shiba-Daimon 2-chome
Minato-ku, Tokyo, 105-0012, Japan JP
Tel.: (81) 334350295 (100%)
Fax: (81) 334317535
Web Site: www.arlafoodsingredients.com
Emp.: 10
Lactose-Based Proteins & Other Basic Organic Food Ingredient Chemicals Whslr
S.I.C.: 5169
N.A.I.C.S.: 424690
Nels Gaardahl *(Gen Mgr)*

Arla Foods Ingredients Korea Co., Ltd. (2)
837-36 Yeoksam-Dong Landmark Tower 21st Fl
Gangnam-gu, Seoul, 135-080, Korea (South) Ks
Tel.: (82) 234529488 (100%)
Fax: (82) 25563802
Web Site: www.arlafoodsingredients.com
Emp.: 2
Lactose-Based Proteins & Other Basic Organic Food Ingredient Chemicals Whslr
S.I.C.: 5169
N.A.I.C.S.: 424690
Seung Joo Lee *(Dir-Sls)*

Arla Foods Ingredients S.A. de C.V. (2)
Cto Luxma 116
Poligono Industrial Milenio, CP 37290 Leon, Guanajuato, Mexico MX
Tel.: (52) 477 167 6300 (100%)
Fax: (52) 477 167 6301
Web Site: www.arlafoodsingredients.com
Lactose-Based Proteins & Other Basic Organic Food Ingredient Chemicals Whslr
S.I.C.: 5169
N.A.I.C.S.: 424690

Non-U.S. Affiliate:

Arla Foods Ingredients S.A. (2)
Avenida Fondo de la Legua 1380
Martinez, B1640FTX Buenos Aires, Argentina Ar
Tel.: (54) 1153684100 (50%)
Fax: (54) 1153684141
E-Mail: afisa@arlafoods.com
Web Site: www.arlafoodsingredients.com
Emp.: 100
Lactose-Based Proteins & Other Basic Organic Food Ingredient Chemicals Mfr Export
S.I.C.: 2869
N.A.I.C.S.: 325199
Bjarne S. Pedeson *(Gen Mgr)*

Cocio Chokolademaelk A/S (1)
Oresundsvej 15
6715 Esbjerg, Denmark DK
Tel.: (45) 76140888
Fax: (45) 76140889
E-Mail: cocio@cocio.dk
Web Site: www.cocio.dk
Emp.: 55
Flavored Milk Mfr
S.I.C.: 2026
N.A.I.C.S.: 311511
Jorgen Spraarup Christensen *(CEO)*

Danapak Holding A/S (1)
Strudsbergsvej 3
DK-4200 Slagelse, Denmark DK
Tel.: (45) 6548 0000 (100%)
Fax: (45) 5853 2060
Web Site: www.danapak.dk
Emp.: 300
Holding Company; Flexible Packaging Products Mfr
S.I.C.: 6719
N.A.I.C.S.: 551112
Lars Wiggers Hyldgaard *(Mng Dir)*

Subsidiaries:

Danapak Flexibles A/S (2)
Strudsbergsvej 3
DK-4200 Slagelse, Denmark DK
Tel.: (45) 65480000 (100%)
Fax: (45) 58532060
E-Mail: info@danapakflex.com
Web Site: www.danapakflex.com
Emp.: 150
Flexible Packing Products Mfr
S.I.C.: 2671
N.A.I.C.S.: 322220
Lars Wiggers Hyldgaard *(Mng Dir)*

Rynkeby Foods A/S (1)
Vestergade 30
5750 Ringe, Denmark (100%)
Tel.: (45) 63623200
Fax: (45) 63623201
E-Mail: info@rynkeby.dk
Web Site: www.rynkeby.dk
Sales Range: $100-124.9 Million
Emp.: 250
Fruit Juice & Fruit Product Mfr
S.I.C.: 2037
N.A.I.C.S.: 311411
Jorgen Dirksen *(Mng Dir)*

U.S. Subsidiary:

Arla Foods Inc. (1)
645 Martinsville Rd
Basking Ridge, NJ 07920 NJ
Tel.: (908) 604-6551
Fax: (908) 604-8220
Web Site: www.arlafoodsusa.com
Cheese & Butter Mfr & Dairy Product Distr Import
S.I.C.: 5143
N.A.I.C.S.: 424430
Susie Moller Hjorth *(Gen Mgr)*

Non-U.S. Subsidiaries:

Arla Foods AB (1)
Lindhagensgatan 126
SE-105 46 Stockholm, Sweden SE
Tel.: (46) 87895000 (100%)
Fax: (46) 87895444
E-Mail: info.sverige@arlafoods.com
Web Site: www.arlafoods.com
Emp.: 3,800
Milk Production; Dairy Products Mfr & Distr Import Export
S.I.C.: 0241
N.A.I.C.S.: 112120
Hans-Ake Hammarstrom *(CEO)*

Arla Foods AS (1)
Jerikovejen 10
Postboks 49
Lindeberg Gard, NO-1007 Oslo, Norway NO
Tel.: (47) 23141860 (100%)
Fax: (47) 22304295
E-Mail: norge@arlafoods.com
Web Site: www.arla.no
Emp.: 22
Cheese & Other Dairy Products Whslr Import
S.I.C.: 5143
N.A.I.C.S.: 424430

Arla Foods Financial Services Centre Sp. z o.o. (1)
Centrum Biurowe Heweliusz
ul Heweliusza 9, 80-890 Gdansk, Poland PL
Tel.: (48) 587638400 (100%)
Fax: (48) 58 763 8491
E-Mail: reception.arla.gdansk@arlafoods.com
Web Site: www.arla.pl/o-arla/arla-foods-w-polsce/globalne-centrum-finansowe
Emp.: 120
Internal Corporate Finance & Accounting Services
S.I.C.: 8721
N.A.I.C.S.: 541219

Arla Foods GmbH (1)
Wahler Street 2
D 40472 Dusseldorf, Germany De
Tel.: (49) 211472310 (100%)
Fax: (49) 2114723166
E-Mail: info.de@arlafoods.com
Web Site: www.arlafoods.de
Emp.: 75
S.I.C.: 2026

Arla Foods amba—(Continued)

N.A.I.C.S.: 311511
Torpen Olsen *(Mng Dir)*

Arla Foods Hellas S.A. (1)
Leoforos Kifisias Ave 6-8 Caracas Ctr
15121 Maroussi, Greece GR
Tel.: (30) 2108196100 (100%)
Fax: (30) 2106209462
E-Mail: arlahellas@arlafoods.com
Web Site: www.arlafoods.gr
Emp.: 35
Cheese & Other Dairy Products Whslr Import
S.I.C.: 5143
N.A.I.C.S.: 424430
Richard Johansen *(Mgr-Sls)*

Arla Foods Inc. (1)
675 Rivermede Road
Concord, ON, L4K 2G9, Canada Ca
Tel.: (905) 669-9393 (100%)
Fax: (905) 669-4110
Web Site: www.arlafoods.ca
Emp.: 200
Cheese & Other Dairy Products Mfr & Distr Import
S.I.C.: 2022
N.A.I.C.S.: 311513
Doug C. Smith *(Pres)*

Arla Foods S.A. (1)
Calle Ochandiano 10 1 dcha
Centro Empresarial El Plantio, 28023
Madrid, Spain ES
Tel.: (34) 91 710 2112 (100%)
Fax: (34) 91 710 2113
E-Mail: arla.es@arlafoods.com
Web Site: www.arlafoods.es
Emp.: 26
Dairy Products Whslr Import
S.I.C.: 5143
N.A.I.C.S.: 424430
Ignacio Cuadrado *(Gen Mgr)*

Arla Foods SA (1)
ul Klobucka 25
02-699 Warsaw, Poland PL
Tel.: (48) 2273 75 473 (100%)
Fax: (48) 2273 75 490
E-Mail: kontakt.polska@arlafoods.com
Web Site: www.arla.pl
Emp.: 130
Holding Company; Regional Managing Office
S.I.C.: 6719
N.A.I.C.S.: 551112
Erik Folden *(CEO)*

Subsidiary:

Arla Foods Sp. z o.o. (2)
ul Lipowa 15
78-120 Goscino, Poland PL
Tel.: (48) 943549100 (100%)
Fax: (48) 943549101
Web Site: www.arla.pl
Emp.: 300
Cheese & Other Dairy Products Mfr & Distr
S.I.C.: 2022
N.A.I.C.S.: 311513
Eric Folden *(Gen Mgr)*

Arla Foods S.A.R.L. (1)
97 Cours Gambetta
69481 Lyon, Cedex 03, France FR
Tel.: (33) 472 848 810 (100%)
Fax: (33) 472 848 815
Emp.: 7
Dairy Products Whslr Import
S.I.C.: 5143
N.A.I.C.S.: 424430
Marian Buzdugan *(Country Mgr)*

Arla Foods S.r.l. (1)
Via Piave 1
Cirimido, IT-22070 Lomazzo, CO, Italy IT
Tel.: (39) 0313525011 (100%)
Fax: (39) 031935218
E-Mail: customer.service@arlafoods.com
Web Site: www.arlafoods.com
Emp.: 5
Dairy Products Whslr Import
S.I.C.: 5143
N.A.I.C.S.: 424430
Andrea Casetta *(Gen Mgr)*

Arla Foods UK plc (1)
Arla House 4 Savannah Way
Leeds Valley Park, Leeds, LS10 1AB, United Kingdom UK
Tel.: (44) 1133827000 (93.7%)
Fax: (44) 1133827030
Web Site: www.arlafoods.co.uk
Emp.: 2,900
Holding Company; Dairy Products Mfr & Distr
S.I.C.: 6719
N.A.I.C.S.: 551112
Peter Lauritzen *(CEO)*
Hanne Sondergaard *(Deputy CEO)*
Jan E. Pedersen *(CFO)*

Subsidiaries:

Arla Foods Limited (2)
Arla House 4 Savannah Way Leeds Valley Park
Leeds, LS10 1AB, United Kingdom UK
Tel.: (44) 113 382 7000 (100%)
Fax: (44) 113 382 7030
Web Site: www.arlafoods.co.uk/company-information
Emp.: 400
Butter, Milk & Other Dairy Products Mfr & Distr
S.I.C.: 2021
N.A.I.C.S.: 311512
Jessica Hardcastle *(Sr Brand Mgr-Lurpak)*

Branch:

Arla Foods (3)
Plym House
3 Longbridge Road, Plymouth, Devon, PL6 8LT, United Kingdom
Tel.: (44) 1752 331871
Fax: (44) 1752 331812
E-Mail:
Emp.: 2,400
Co-Operative Milk Processor, Marketer, Purchaser & Distr
S.I.C.: 5143
N.A.I.C.S.: 424430

The Cheese Company Limited (2)
Maes y Clawdd Maesbury Rd
Oswestry, Shropshire, SY10 8NL, United Kingdom (100%)
Tel.: (44) 1691654564
Fax: (44) 1691671295
Web Site: www.arlafoods.co.uk/about/our-sites/
Emp.: 400
Cheese Mfr
S.I.C.: 2022
N.A.I.C.S.: 311513
Neil Kennedy *(CEO)*

Danya Foods Ltd. (1)
PO Box 3164
Riyadh, 11583, Saudi Arabia (75%)
Tel.: (966) 14981414
Fax: (966) 14980628
E-Mail: danya.foods.ltd@arlafoods.com
Emp.: 200
Provider of Dairy Products
S.I.C.: 2026
N.A.I.C.S.: 311511

ARLE CAPITAL PARTNERS LIMITED

12 Charles II Street
London, SW1Y 4QU, United Kingdom
Tel.: (44) 2079790000
E-Mail: info@arle.com
Web Site: www.arle.com
Emp.: 42

Business Description:
Private Equity & Investment Management Firm
S.I.C.: 6211
N.A.I.C.S.: 523999

Personnel:
John Arney *(Mng Partner)*
Javier Abad *(Partner)*
Mark Dickinson *(Partner)*
Peter Goode *(Partner)*
Quentin Nason *(Partner)*
Nils Stoesser *(Partner)*
Philip Price *(COO)*

Holding:

Innovia Films Ltd. (1)
Station Road
Wigton, Cumbria, CA7 9BG, United Kingdom (100%)
Tel.: (44) 16973 42281
Fax: (44) 1697341417
E-Mail: filmsinfo@innoviafilms.com
Web Site: www.innoviafilms.com
Sales Range: $500-549.9 Million
Emp.: 1,350
Industrial Film Mfr
S.I.C.: 2671
N.A.I.C.S.: 326112
David Beeby *(CEO)*

U.S. Subsidiary:

Innovia Films, Inc. (2)
290 Interstate North Cir SE Ste 100
Atlanta, GA 30339-2401
Tel.: (770) 818-3000
Toll Free: (877) 822-3456
E-Mail: info.films@innoviafilms.com
Web Site: www.innoviafilms.com
Emp.: 30
Industrial Film Mfr
S.I.C.: 2671
N.A.I.C.S.: 326112
Joe Piccione *(Pres)*

Non-U.S. Subsidiaries:

Innovia Films (Asia Pacific) Pty. Ltd. (2)
19 Potter St
PO Box 341
Craigieburn, VIC, 3064, Australia (100%)
Tel.: (61) 393030600
Fax: (61) 393030670
E-Mail: apac@innoviafilms.com
Web Site: www.innoviafilms.com
Sales Range: $25-49.9 Million
Emp.: 100
Industrial Film Mfr
S.I.C.: 2671
N.A.I.C.S.: 326112
Barend van den Hoek *(Dir-APAC)*

Innovia Films BVBA (2)
Sluisweg 8
9820 Merelbeke, Belgium
Tel.: (32) 9 241 1211
E-Mail: merelbeke2@innoviafilms.com
Industrial Film Mfr
S.I.C.: 2671
N.A.I.C.S.: 326112
Vorst Frans *(Gen Mgr)*

Innovia Films (Commercial) Ltd. (2)
Av Ibirapuera 2907 sala 1407
Sao Paulo, 04029-200, Brazil
Tel.: (55) 11 5094 9945
E-Mail: innoviabrazil@innoviafilms.com
Industrial Film Mfr
S.I.C.: 2671
N.A.I.C.S.: 326112

ARM CEMENT LIMITED

(Formerly Athi River Mining Limited)
Rhino House Chiromo Road
PO 41908
Westlands, 00100 Nairobi, Kenya
Tel.: (254) 20 2692 978
Fax: (254) 20 2667 677
E-Mail: info@armafrica.com
Web Site: www.armkenya.com
ARM—(NAI)
Sls.: $128,028,390
Assets: $302,683,313
Liabilities: $222,719,873
Net Worth: $79,963,440
Earnings: $13,988,515
Fiscal Year-end: 12/31/12

Business Description:
Cement Mfr
S.I.C.: 3241
N.A.I.C.S.: 327310

Personnel:
Pradeep H. Paunrana *(Mng Dir & CEO)*
Surendra L. Bhatia *(Deputy Mng Dir)*
Ramesh R. Vora *(Sec)*

Board of Directors:
Rick Ashley
Surendra L. Bhatia
Stella Kilonzo
Atul Mathur
Wilfred Murungi
Daniel Ndonye
Pradeep H. Paunrana
Michael Turner
Ramesh R. Vora

Legal Counsel:
Walker Kontos Advocates
Hakika House Bishops Road
PO Box 60680
Nairobi, Kenya

ARM HOLDINGS PLC

110 Fulbourn Road
Cambridge, CB1 9NJ, United Kingdom
Tel.: (44) 1223 400400
Fax: (44) 1223 400 700
Web Site: www.arm.com
Year Founded: 1990
ARM—(LSE)
Rev.: $1,187,265,024
Assets: $2,722,103,296
Liabilities: $543,290,880
Net Worth: $2,178,812,416
Earnings: $174,118,912
Emp.: 2,833
Fiscal Year-end: 12/31/13

Business Description:
Holding Company; Semiconductors & Other Electronic Components Designer & Mfr
S.I.C.: 6719
N.A.I.C.S.: 551112

Personnel:
John Buchanan *(Chm)*
Simon Segars *(CEO)*
Tim Score *(CFO)*
Graham Budd *(COO)*
Mike Muller *(CTO)*
Patricia Alsop *(Sec)*
Mike Inglis *(Exec VP-Sls, Gen Mgr-Processor Div & Mktg)*
Ian Drew *(Exec VP-Strategy)*
Lance Howarth *(Exec VP-Mktg)*

Board of Directors:
John Buchanan
Andy Green
Larry Hirst
Mike Inglis
Mike Muller
Kathleen Anne O'Donovan
Janice M. Roberts
Philip Rowley
John Scarisbrick
Tim Score
Simon Segars

Legal Counsel:
Linklaters LLP
One Silk Street
London, EC2Y 8HQ, United Kingdom
Tel.: (44) 2074562000
Fax: (44) 2074562222

Subsidiary:

ARM Ltd. (1)
110 Fulbourne Rd
Cambridge, CB1 9NJ, United Kingdom (100%)
Tel.: (44) 223400400
Fax: (44) 223400410
E-Mail: info@arm.com
Web Site: www.arm.com
Emp.: 650
Microprocessor Solutions Provider
S.I.C.: 3674
N.A.I.C.S.: 334413
Simon Segars *(CEO)*

Branches:

ARM Ltd. - Maidenhead (2)
Liberty House Moorbridge Rd
Maidenhead, Berkshire, SL6 8LT, United Kingdom
Tel.: (44) 1628427800

Fax: (44) 1628427701
E-Mail: info@arm.com
Web Site: www.arm.com
Emp.: 40
Microprocessor Solutions Provider
S.I.C.: 3674
N.A.I.C.S.: 334413
Bill Parsons *(Mgr-HR)*

ARM Ltd. - Sheffield (2)
Rockingham Court 152 Rockingham Street
Sheffield, S1 4EB, United Kingdom
Tel.: (44) 1142828000
Fax: (44) 1142828001
E-Mail: info@arm.com
Web Site: www.arm.com
Emp.: 60
Microprocessor Solutions Provider
S.I.C.: 3674
N.A.I.C.S.: 334413
Lotte Aweimrin *(Office Mgr)*

Subsidiary:

Geomerics Limited (2)
City House 126-130 Hills Road
Cambridge, CB2 1RE, United Kingdom UK
Tel.: (44) 1223450170
Fax: (44) 1223361362
E-Mail: info@geomerics.com
Web Site: www.geomerics.com
Emp.: 25
Software Publishers
S.I.C.: 7372
N.A.I.C.S.: 511210
Denise Line *(Office Mgr)*

U.S. Subsidiary:

ARM, Inc. (1)
150 Rose Orchard Way
San Jose, CA 95134-1358 DE
Tel.: (408) 576-1500
Fax: (408) 576-1501
Web Site: www.arm.com
Semiconductor Developer & Mfr
S.I.C.: 3674
N.A.I.C.S.: 334413
Simon Segars *(CEO)*

Branches:

ARM, Inc. (2)
5 East St
Franklin, MA 02038 (100%)
Tel.: (508) 520-1905
Fax: (508) 520-1907
E-Mail: mark.lewin@arm.com
Web Site: www.arm.com
Emp.: 1
Microprocessor Solutions Provider
S.I.C.: 7313
N.A.I.C.S.: 541840
Mark Lewin *(Gen Mgr)*

ARM, Inc. (2)
3711 S Mo Pac Expy Bldg 1
Austin, TX 78746-6015
Tel.: (512) 327-9249
Fax: (512) 314-1078
E-Mail: info@arm.com
Web Site: www.arm.com
Emp.: 250
Microprocessor Solutions Provider
S.I.C.: 7379
N.A.I.C.S.: 518210

Non-U.S. Branches:

ARM Germany (1)
Luherwirthstrasse 4
81829 Munich, Germany (100%)
Tel.: (49) 499286150
Fax: (49) 4992861519
E-Mail: info@arm.com
Web Site: www.arm.com
Emp.: 25
Microprocessor Solutions Provider
S.I.C.: 3674
N.A.I.C.S.: 334413

ARM Israel (1)
3 Hagavish St
Kafr Saba, 44424 Tel Aviv, Israel (100%)
Tel.: (972) 97644888
Fax: (972) 97644884
E-Mail: Shlomo.Rosenberg@arm.com
Web Site: www.arm.com
Microprocessor Solutions Provider
S.I.C.: 3674
N.A.I.C.S.: 334413

Non-U.S. Subsidiaries:

ARM Belgium NV (1)
Geldenaaksebaan 329 1st Fl
3001 Leuven, Belgium (100%)
Tel.: (32) 016391411
Fax: (32) 16406076
E-Mail: armbelgium@arm.com
Web Site: www.arm.com
Emp.: 32
Microprocessor Solutions Provider
S.I.C.: 3674
N.A.I.C.S.: 334413

ARM Consulting (Shanghai) Co. Ltd. (1)
Rm 1601 Metro Plz 555 Loushanguan Rd
Changning Dist, Shanghai, 200051, China (100%)
Tel.: (86) 2162290729
Fax: (86) 2162290725
E-Mail: info-china@arm.com
Web Site: www.arm.com
Emp.: 60
Microprocessor Solutions
S.I.C.: 3674
N.A.I.C.S.: 334413
Hellen Wu *(Gen Mgr)*

ARM Embedded Technologies Pvt. Limited (1)
Level III Salarpuria Touchstone Marthahalli-Sarajapur Outer Ring Road
Varthur Hobli, Bengaluru, 560 103, India
Tel.: (91) 80 2518 5000
Fax: (91) 80 2844 0914
Web Site: www.arm.com
Emp.: 450
Consumer Entertainment Software Development Services
S.I.C.: 7371
N.A.I.C.S.: 541511
Guru Ganeshaan *(Gen Mgr)*

ARM France SAS (1)
25 Allee Pierre Ziller Le Paros
06560 Sophia-Antipolis, France (100%)
Tel.: (33) 497235100
Fax: (33) 497235199
E-Mail: info@arm.com
Web Site: www.arm.com
Emp.: 40
Microprocessor Solutions Provider
S.I.C.: 3674
N.A.I.C.S.: 334413
Peru Pascal *(Mng Dir)*

Branch:

ARM France (2)
12 Ave Des Pres
PO Box 204
78180 Montigny-le-Bretonneux, France (100%)
Tel.: (33) 139304789
Fax: (33) 139304788
Web Site: www.arm.com
Emp.: 6
Microprocessor Solutions Provider
S.I.C.: 3674
N.A.I.C.S.: 334413

ARM KK (1)
Daini Ueno Bldg 8 F 3 7 18 Shin Yokohama
Yokohama, Kanagawa, 222 0033, Japan (100%)
Tel.: (81) 454775260
Fax: (81) 454775261
E-Mail: info-armkk@arm.com
Web Site: www.arm.com
Emp.: 1,500
Microprocessor Solutions Provider
S.I.C.: 3674
N.A.I.C.S.: 334413
Takafumi Nishijima *(Pres)*

ARM Korea Limited (1)
8th Floor Kyungdong B/D
4-4 Sucae
Dong Bundang-Gu, Seongnam, Gyeonggi-Do, 463-020, Korea (South) (100%)
Tel.: (82) 317128234
Fax: (82) 317138225
Web Site: www.arm.com
Microprocessor Solutions Provider
S.I.C.: 3674
N.A.I.C.S.: 334413

ARM Taiwan Limited (1)
8F No 36 Ruihu St
Taipei, Nei-Hu, 11494, Taiwan (100%)
Tel.: (886) 226271681
Fax: (886) 226271682
E-Mail: info@arm.com
Web Site: www.arm.com
Emp.: 15
Microprocessor Solutions Provider
S.I.C.: 3674
N.A.I.C.S.: 334413
Philip Lu *(Pres)*

ARMADA DATA CORPORATION

5710 Timberlea Blvd Suite 201
Mississauga, ON, L4W 4W1, Canada
Tel.: (905) 624-3144
Fax: (905) 629-3299
Toll Free: (866) 453-6995
E-Mail: info@armadadatacorp.ca
Web Site: www.armadadatacorp.ca
ARD—(TSXV)
Rev.: $2,572,446
Assets: $1,569,775
Liabilities: $624,177
Net Worth: $945,598
Earnings: ($492,583)
Emp.: 20
Fiscal Year-end: 05/31/13

Business Description:
Business Information Services
S.I.C.: 7389
N.A.I.C.S.: 561499

Personnel:
R. James Matthews *(Pres, CEO & Sec)*
Elizabeth A. Matthews *(CFO)*
Eli Oszlak *(CTO & VP)*

Board of Directors:
Gregory Harris
Glen Hrabovsky
Fred Marotta
R. James Matthews
Rob Montemarano
Eli Oszlak

Legal Counsel:
Harris & Harris LLP
2355 Skymark Drive Suite 300
Mississauga, ON, Canada

Transfer Agent:
Computershare Trust Company of Canada
510 Burrard St 3rd Fl
Vancouver, BC, V6C 3B9, Canada

ARMADA TOOLWORKS LIMITED

6 Lof Dr
Lindsay, ON, K9V 4S5, Canada
Tel.: (705) 328-9599
Fax: (705) 328-9718
Web Site: www.armadatoolworks.com
Year Founded: 2000
Emp.: 120

Business Description:
Special Dies, Tools Jigs & Fixtures Mfr
S.I.C.: 3544
N.A.I.C.S.: 333514

Personnel:
Ross Chandler *(CEO)*

ARMADILLO RESOURCES LTD.

411 470 Granville Street
Vancouver, BC, V6C 1V5, Canada
Tel.: (604) 408-6500
Fax: (604) 408-3335
E-Mail: les@armadilloresources.com
Web Site: www.armadilloresources.com
Year Founded: 2007
ARO—(CNSX)
Emp.: 2

Business Description:
Investment Services
S.I.C.: 6211
N.A.I.C.S.: 523999

Personnel:
Les Kjosness *(Pres)*
Cherry Cai *(CFO)*

Board of Directors:
Les Kjosness
Corey Klassen
Anthony Pickett
James Turner
Stephen Wetherup

Legal Counsel:
James L. Harris Law Corp
Suite 300 - 576 Seymour Street
Vancouver, BC, Canada

Transfer Agent:
Computershare Investor Services Inc.
2nd Fl 510 Burrard St
Vancouver, BC, Canada

ARMAEC ENERGY GROUP PLC

3 Queen St Mayfair
London, W1J 5PA, United Kingdom
Tel.: (44) 2034 05 19 50
Fax: (44) 8700 34 00 09
E-Mail: info@armaecenergy.com
Web Site: www.armaecenergy.com
Year Founded: 2007

Business Description:
Wind Farms Developer
S.I.C.: 4931
N.A.I.C.S.: 221118

Personnel:
Peter Hughes *(Chm)*
Chandra Raman *(CEO)*

Board of Directors:
Peter Hughes
John French
Allen Hovsepian
Chris Morris
Suchit Punnose
Chandra Raman

ARMAN FINANCIAL SERVICES LTD.

502-3-4 Skar III Opp Old High Court
Off Ashram Road
Ahmedabad, Gujarat, 380 014, India
Tel.: (91) 79 30005000
Fax: (91) 79 27541738
E-Mail: finance@armanindia.com
Web Site: www.armanindia.com
531179—(BOM)
Rev.: $3,149,023
Assets: $15,282,501
Liabilities: $11,065,554
Net Worth: $4,216,946
Earnings: $619,900
Fiscal Year-end: 03/31/13

Business Description:
Financial Services
S.I.C.: 6211
N.A.I.C.S.: 523999

Personnel:
Jayendra B. Patel *(Vice Chm & Mng Dir)*
B. J. Vaghela *(Sec)*

Board of Directors:
Chinubhai R. Shah
Aditya Bhandari
Amit R. Manakiwala
Aakash J. Patel
Aalok J. Patel
Jayendra B. Patel
Ritaben J. Patel
Kaushikbhai D. Shah
Lokesh Kumar Singh

Transfer Agent:
Sharepro Services (India) Pvt. Ltd.
416-420 4th Floor Devnandan Mall Opp. Sanyash Ashram Ellisbridge
Ahmedabad, India

ARMANDO TESTA S.P.A.

Via Luisa del Carretto 58
10131 Turin, Italy
Tel.: (39) 011 88 10111
Fax: (39) 011 88 10468
E-Mail: info@armandotesta.it
Web Site: www.armandotesta.it
Year Founded: 1946
Billings: $791,310,000
Emp.: 150

Business Description:
Advertising Services
S.I.C.: 7311
N.A.I.C.S.: 541810

Personnel:
Marco Testa *(Chm & CEO)*

Branches:

Armando Testa S.p.A. (1)
Via Washington 17
20146 Milan, Italy IT
Tel.: (39) 02 48 08 21
Fax: (39) 02 48 00 8206
E-Mail: info@armandotesta.it
Web Site: www.armandotesta.com
Advertising Services
S.I.C.: 7311
N.A.I.C.S.: 541810
Marco Testa *(Chm & CEO)*

Armando Testa S.p.A. (1)
Via Giovanni da Castells Bolognese 81
00153 Rome, Italy
Tel.: (39) 06 58 31 71
Fax: (39) 06 58 31 72 64
E-Mail: info@armandotesta.it
Web Site: www.armandotesta.com
Advertising Services
S.I.C.: 7311
N.A.I.C.S.: 541810
Vincenzo Vigo *(Dir-Creative)*

Joint Venture:

Bitmama S.r.l. (1)
Via Luisa del Carretto 58
10131 Turin, Italy
Tel.: (39) 0118810711
Fax: (39) 0118810610
E-Mail: info.bitmama@bitmama.it
Web Site: www.bitmama.it
Advertising Services
S.I.C.: 7311
N.A.I.C.S.: 541810
Claudio Papetti *(CEO)*

Non-U.S. Branches:

Armando Testa Brussels NV (1)
Dreve de Willerieken 20 Willerieksedreef 20
1160 Brussels, Belgium
Tel.: (32) 2 678 0606
Fax: (32) 2 678 0607
E-Mail: info@armandotesta.eu
Web Site: www.armandotesta.com
Emp.: 10
Advertising Services
S.I.C.: 7311
N.A.I.C.S.: 541810
Philppe Gelder *(CEO & Founding Partner)*
Douglas Levitt *(Founding Partner)*

Armando Testa GmbH (1)
Lindleystr 12
60314 Frankfurt, Germany
Tel.: (49) 69 13 38 860
Fax: (49) 69 13 38 86 11
E-Mail: cbosset@armandotesta.it
Web Site: www.armandotesta.com
Emp.: 4
Advertising Services
S.I.C.: 7311
N.A.I.C.S.: 541810
Claude Bosset *(Dir-Opers-Intl)*

Armando Testa Ltd. (1)
81 Oxford Street
Gainsborough House, London, W1D 2EU, United Kingdom
Tel.: (44) 207 851 4800
Fax: (44) 207 851 3638
E-Mail: info@armandotesta.co.uk
Emp.: 20
Advertising Services
S.I.C.: 7311
N.A.I.C.S.: 541810
Alexis Jacobs *(Mgr)*

Armando Testa SL (1)
Avda de Brasil 30 Posterior
28020 Madrid, Spain
Tel.: (34) 91 4183300
Fax: (34) 91 4183333
E-Mail: info@armandotesta.es
Web Site: www.armandotesta.es
Emp.: 10
Advertising Services
S.I.C.: 7311
N.A.I.C.S.: 541810
Ignacio Muguerza Pecker *(Dir)*

Armando Testa (1)
12 Rue Rougemont
75009 Paris, France
Tel.: (33) 1 53302 880
Fax: (33) 1 53302 896
E-Mail: info@armandotesta.fr
Web Site: www.armandotesta.fr/main.jsp
Advertising Services
S.I.C.: 7311
N.A.I.C.S.: 541810

Units:

Little Bull (1)
Via Giovanni De Castle Bolognese 81
00153 Rome, Italy
Tel.: (39) 06 58317700
Fax: (39) 06 58317327
E-Mail: info@littlebull.it
Advertising Services
S.I.C.: 7311
N.A.I.C.S.: 541810
Marco Guidone *(Mng Dir)*

Media Italia HQ (1)
Via Luisa del Carretto 58
10131 Turin, Italy
Tel.: (39) 011 8109 311
Fax: (39) 011 8109 500
E-Mail: mediaitalia@mediaitalia.it
Web Site: www.mediaitalia.it
Emp.: 115
Advertising Services
S.I.C.: 7319
N.A.I.C.S.: 541870
Eugenio Bona *(Dir)*

Max Information (1)
Via Rizzoli
Galleria Aquaderni 5, 40126 Bologna, Italy
Tel.: (39) 051 235 001
Fax: (39) 051 235 482
E-Mail: info@maxinformation.com
Web Site: www.maxinformation.com
Advertising Services
S.I.C.: 7311
N.A.I.C.S.: 541810
Giorgio Sandri *(Pres)*

In Testa HQ (1)
Washington Street 17
20146 Milan, Italy
Tel.: (39) 02 480 12776
Fax: (39) 02 49 84750
E-Mail: info@intesta.it
Advertising Services
S.I.C.: 7311
N.A.I.C.S.: 541810
Antonella Testa *(Chm)*
Sergio Fiarelli *(Mng Dir)*

ARMARDA GROUP LTD.

Room 3501 35 Floor West Tower Shun Tak Centre 168-200 Connaught Road
Hong Kong, China (Hong Kong)
Tel.: (852) 3101 2800
Fax: (852) 3101 2801
E-Mail: enquiry@armarda.com
Web Site: www.armarda.com
Year Founded: 2001
5EK—(HKG SES)
Rev.: $1,861,780
Assets: $34,190,319
Liabilities: $4,185,717
Net Worth: $30,004,602
Earnings: ($5,332,340)
Emp.: 109
Fiscal Year-end: 03/31/13

Business Description:
IT Consulting, Systems, Application Architecture & Project Management for Financial Industry
S.I.C.: 8999
N.A.I.C.S.: 541690

Personnel:
Terence Chung Po Luk *(Deputy Chm & CEO)*
Karen Yin Ling Chu *(CFO & Sec)*

Board of Directors:
Joseph Tao-Hsiung Chou
Richard Xiangjun Gao
Joo Hai Lee
Terence Chung Po Luk
Tin Sang Mak
Lian Heng Phuah

Transfer Agents:
M & C Services Private Limited
112 Robinson Road 05-01
Singapore, 068902, Singapore

Appleby Management (Bermuda) Ltd.
Canon's Court 22 Victoria Street
HM 12 Hamilton, Bermuda

Non-U.S. Subsidiaries:

Armarda Technology (Hong Kong) Limited (1)
Room 3501 35/F West Tower Shun Tak Tower Center
168-200 Connaught Road, Central, China (Hong Kong)
Tel.: (852) 31012800
Fax: (852) 31012801
E-Mail: connie.siu@armarda.com
Emp.: 20
IT Consulting Services
S.I.C.: 8999
N.A.I.C.S.: 541690
Edmond Wong *(Mgr-Mktg)*

Non-U.S. Division:

Armarda Technology (2)
Floor 19 Commercial Bank Mansion
Jiuzhou Dadao Dongduan
Jida, Zhuhai, 519015, China
Tel.: (86) 756 322 1818
Fax: (86) 756 322 1801
Web Site: www.armarda.com
IT Consulting Services
S.I.C.: 8999
N.A.I.C.S.: 541690

Brilliant Time Limited (1)
16 F Jardine House 1 Connaught Place
Central, China (Hong Kong)
Tel.: (852) 25070507
Fax: (852) 25301441
Information Technology Consulting Services
S.I.C.: 7373
N.A.I.C.S.: 541512

ARMATURE DNS 2000 INC.

11001 Jean Meunier
Montreal, QC, H1G 4S7, Canada
Tel.: (514) 324-1141
Fax: (514) 324-8212
Toll Free: (800) 363-7996
E-Mail: sales@dns-2000.com
Web Site: www.dns-2000.com
Year Founded: 1977
Rev.: $23,996,806
Emp.: 250

Business Description:
Alternators, Starters, Water Pumps & Calipers Mfr
S.I.C.: 3825
N.A.I.C.S.: 334515

Personnel:
Joe Rinaldi *(Pres)*

ARMATURES BOIS-FRANCS INC.

249 Bonaventure Blvd
Victoriaville, QC, G6T 1V5, Canada
Tel.: (819) 758-7501
Fax: (819) 758-2544
E-Mail: abf@abf-inc.com
Web Site: www.abf-inc.com
Year Founded: 1976
Rev.: $66,044,000
Emp.: 500

Business Description:
Reinforcing Steel & Wire-Mesh Mfr
S.I.C.: 1791
N.A.I.C.S.: 238120

Personnel:
Eric Bernier *(Pres & CEO)*

ARMCO CAPITAL INC.

84 Chain Lake Drive Suite 500
Halifax, NS, B3S 1A2, Canada
Tel.: (902) 423-4000
Fax: (902) 423-9663
E-Mail: sales@armcocap.com
Web Site: www.armcocapital.com
Year Founded: 1982
Rev.: $33,802,335
Emp.: 60

Business Description:
Residential & Industrial Building Construction & Services
S.I.C.: 8361
N.A.I.C.S.: 623990

Personnel:
Robert MacPherson *(Pres)*
Neil Morley *(CFO)*

ARMISTICE RESOURCES CORP.

(Name Changed to Kerr Mines Inc.)

ARMOIRES FABRITEC LTEE.

80 Boulevard de l'Aeroport
Bromont, QC, J2L 1S9, Canada
Tel.: (450) 359-1659
Fax: (450) 534-0406
E-Mail: nathalie.lemieux@fabritec.ca
Web Site: www.groupefabritec.com
Sales Range: $25-49.9 Million
Emp.: 400

Business Description:
Kitchen & Bathroom Cabinet Mfr
S.I.C.: 2434
N.A.I.C.S.: 337110

Personnel:
Clovis Bourgeois *(Pres)*

Branch:

Armoires Fabritec Ltee.-Cookshire (1)
705 Rue Pope
Cookshire, QC, J0B1M0, Canada
Tel.: (819) 875-5421
Fax: (819) 875-5424
E-Mail: info@fabritec.ce
Web Site: www.fabritec.ce
Emp.: 100
Kitchen Cabinet Components Mfr
S.I.C.: 2434
N.A.I.C.S.: 337110
Josee Frechette *(Gen Mgr)*

ARMOUR ENERGY LIMITED

Level 13 145 Eagle Street
Brisbane, QLD, 4000, Australia
Tel.: (61) 7 3303 0620
Fax: (61) 7 3303 0681
E-Mail: info@armourenergy.com.au
Web Site: www.armourenergy.com.au
AJQ—(ASX)

Business Description:
Gas Exploration
S.I.C.: 1311
N.A.I.C.S.: 211111

Personnel:
Nicholas Mather *(Chm)*
Philip McNamara *(CEO & Mng Dir)*
Karl Schlobohm *(Sec)*

Board of Directors:
Nicholas Mather
Jeremy Barlow
Stephen Bizzell
Philip McNamara
Roland Sleeman
William Stubbs

ARMOUR GROUP PLC
Lonsdale House 7/9 Lonsdale Gardens
Tunbridge Wells, Kent, TN1 1NU, United Kingdom
Tel.: (44) 1892502700
Fax: (44) 1892502707
E-Mail: info@armourgroup.uk.com
Web Site: www.armourgroup.uk.com
AMR—(AIM)
Rev.: $53,322,255
Assets: $51,963,197
Liabilities: $23,844,987
Net Worth: $28,118,211
Earnings: $66,458
Emp.: 180
Fiscal Year-end: 08/31/13
Business Description:
Home & Automobile Audio & Visual Entertainment Products Mfr
S.I.C.: 3651
N.A.I.C.S.: 334310
Personnel:
George L. Dexter *(CEO)*
John Harris *(Sec & Dir-Fin)*
Board of Directors:
Bob Morton
Steve Bodger
George L. Dexter
John Harris
Legal Counsel:
Arnold & Porter (UK) LLP
Tower 42 25 Old Broad Street
London, United Kingdom
Subsidiaries:

Alphason Designs Limited (1)
244 Swan Lane Hindley Green
Wigan, WN2 4EY, United Kingdom
Tel.: (44) 845 130 6686
Fax: (44) 1942 521 159
E-Mail: info@alphasondesigns.com
Web Site: www.alphasondesigns.com
Emp.: 20
Consumer Electronic Products Mfr & Distr
S.I.C.: 3651
N.A.I.C.S.: 334310

Armour Automotive Group Limited (1)
Lonsdale House 7-9 Lonsdale Gardens
Tunbridge Wells, Kent, TN1 1NU, United Kingdom
Tel.: (44) 1892 502700
Fax: (44) 1892 502707
Automobile Equipments Mfr
S.I.C.: 3663
N.A.I.C.S.: 334220
George Dexter *(CEO)*

Armour Automotive Ltd. (1)
Lonsdale House 7-9 Lonsdale Gardens
Tunbridge Wells, Kent, TN1 1NU, United Kingdom
Tel.: (44) 1892502700
Fax: (44) 1892502707
Web Site: www.armourautomotive.uk.com
Holding Company; Mfr of Automotive Parts & Accessories
S.I.C.: 7549
N.A.I.C.S.: 811198

Armour Home Electronics Limited (1)
Units 7 & 8 Stortford Hall Industrial Park
Dunmow Road, Bishop's Stortford, United Kingdom
Tel.: (44) 1279501111
Fax: (44) 1279501080
E-Mail: info@armourhome.co.uk
Web Site: www.armourhome.co.uk
Emp.: 70
Specialist Hi-Fi & Home Entertainment Equipment Designer, Mfr & Distr
S.I.C.: 3663
N.A.I.C.S.: 334220
Paul McCarthy *(Dir-Sls)*

Non-U.S. Subsidiaries:

Armour Hong Kong Limited (1)
55 Hoi Yuen Road Suite 14 7 F Block A Hoi Luen Industrial Centre
Kwun Tong, Kowloon, China (Hong Kong)
Tel.: (852) 28106886
Fax: (852) 28106992
E-Mail: sales@armourasia.com
Web Site: www.armourasia.com
Emp.: 500
Household Furniture & Electronic Appliances Mfr & Sales
S.I.C.: 3651
N.A.I.C.S.: 334310
Victor Yuen *(Mgr-Ops)*

Armour Nordic AB (1)
Brodalsvagen 1 B
Partille, Vastra Gotaland, 433 38, Sweden
Tel.: (46) 31444412
Fax: (46) 31446324
Automotive Products Mfr
S.I.C.: 3714
N.A.I.C.S.: 336390

Armour Nordic AS (1)
Tuneveien 97
Gralum, Sarpsborg, Ostfold, Norway
Tel.: (47) 21424121
Automotive Products Mfr
S.I.C.: 3714
N.A.I.C.S.: 336390

ARMOUR PLASTICS LIMITED
Pennywell Industrial Estate
Sunderland, Tyne & Wear, SR4 9EN, United Kingdom
Tel.: (44) 1915346061
Fax: (44) 1905343626
E-Mail: info@armour-plastics.com
Web Site: www.armour-plastics.com
Year Founded: 1971
Sales Range: $25-49.9 Million
Emp.: 50
Business Description:
Mfr. of Sanitary Ware in Vacuum-Formable Materials; Manufacturer of Thermoformed Products & Machinery
S.I.C.: 3089
N.A.I.C.S.: 326199
Personnel:
John Mulloy *(Chm)*
Sean Mulloy *(Mng Dir)*
Divisions:

Armour Plastics Limited - Engineering Division (1)
Alston Road Pattinson Ind Est
Washington, Tyne & Wear, NE38 8QH, United Kingdom
Tel.: (44) 191 416 7786
Fax: (44) 191 416 7109
E-Mail: sales@armour-engineering.com
Web Site: www.armour-engineering.com
Plastic Thermoforming Machinery Mfr
S.I.C.: 3559
N.A.I.C.S.: 333249
Sean Mulloy *(Mng Dir)*

Armour Plastics Limited - Renaissance Baths Division (1)
Pennywell Industrial Estate
Sunderland, Tyne & Wear, SR4 9EN, United Kingdom
Tel.: (44) 191 534 6061
Fax: (44) 191 534 3626
Web Site: www.renaissance-baths.co.uk
Sanitary Ware Mfr
S.I.C.: 3499
N.A.I.C.S.: 332999
Paul Lindley, *(Dir-Sls)*

ARMOUR TRANSPORTATION SYSTEMS
689 Edinburgh Dr
Moncton, NB, E1E 2L4, Canada
Tel.: (506) 857-0205
Fax: (506) 859-9339
Toll Free: (800) 561-7987
Web Site: www.armour.ca
Sales Range: $150-199.9 Million
Emp.: 1,300
Business Description:
Transportation & Logistics Management Services
S.I.C.: 7359
N.A.I.C.S.: 532411
Personnel:
Wesley Armour *(Pres)*
Vicki McKibbon *(Pres-Transportaion Ops)*

ARMS PAPER LTD.
415 Advailt Complex Nr Sandesh Press Vastrapur
Ahmedabad, Gujarat, 380052, India
Tel.: (91) 79 26762109
E-Mail: armspaperltd@gmail.com
Web Site: www.armspapers.com
532397—(BOM)
Rev.: $8,851,680
Assets: $3,786,474
Liabilities: $2,445,672
Net Worth: $1,340,802
Earnings: $41,172
Fiscal Year-end: 03/31/13
Business Description:
Packaging Paper Products Distr
S.I.C.: 5085
N.A.I.C.S.: 423840
Personnel:
Rushal Patel *(Chm)*
Alpesh Gandhi *(Compliance Officer & Sec)*
Board of Directors:
Rushal Patel
Nishant Kumar
Pawanjit Singh Negi
Nikhil Rajpuria
Yogesh Varia
Transfer Agent:
Sharepro Services (India) Pvt. Ltd.
416-420 4th Floor Devnandan Mall Opp. Sanyash Ashram Ellisbridge
Ahmedabad, India

ARMSTRONG INDUSTRIAL CORPORATION LTD.
531 Bukit Batok St 23
Singapore, 659547, Singapore
Tel.: (65) 66658588
Fax: (65) 66658665
E-Mail: aicl@armstrong.com.sg
Web Site: www.armstrong.com.sg
Sls.: $175,083,584
Assets: $137,107,163
Liabilities: $49,160,531
Net Worth: $87,946,632
Earnings: $10,142,861
Emp.: 1,940
Fiscal Year-end: 12/31/12
Business Description:
Dampening, Insulation, Sealing & Cushion Products Designer, Marketer & Mfr
S.I.C.: 3559
N.A.I.C.S.: 333249
Personnel:
Gilbert Peng Koon Ong *(Chm & CEO)*
Steven Gim Hoe Koh *(Deputy CEO)*
Wan Lin Sin *(Grp CFO)*
Glenn Kim Teck Wee *(Pres-Ops-Armstrong Rubber & Chemical Products Co Ltd)*
Tin Fook Koo *(Deputy Mng Dir-Foamline Industries Sdn Bhd & Hardyflex Industries)*
Sheue Ling Chuang *(Co-Sec)*
Swee Oi Lo *(Co-Sec)*
Board of Directors:
Patricia Goon Chau Chow
Legal Counsel:
Tan Peng Chin LLC
30 Raffles Place #11-00 Chevron House
Singapore, Singapore
Subsidiaries:

Armstrong-Odenwald (Asia) Pte Ltd (1)
531 Bukit Batok St 23
659547 Singapore, Singapore
Tel.: (65) 66658588
Fax: (65) 66658665
E-Mail: aicl@armstrong.com.sg
Emp.: 400
Industrial Engineering Services
S.I.C.: 8711
N.A.I.C.S.: 541330
Gilbert Ong *(Mng Dir)*

Armstrong Rubber Manufacturing Pte Ltd (1)
531 Bukit Batok St 23
Singapore, 659547, Singapore
Tel.: (65) 66658588
Fax: (65) 66658665
E-Mail: aicl@armstrong.com.sg
Web Site: www.armstrong-arm.com.sg
Emp.: 500
Rubber Products Mfr
S.I.C.: 3061
N.A.I.C.S.: 326291
Gilbert Ong *(Gen Mgr)*

Non-U.S. Subsidiaries:

Armstrong Mechanical Components Company Limited (1)
Rojana Industrial Park Estate 2 42 9 Moo 4 Tambol Baanchang
Amphur U-Thai, Ayutthaya, 13210, Thailand
Tel.: (66) 3595034043
Fax: (66) 35950344
Web Site: www.armstrong.co.th
Emp.: 300
Industrial Engineering Services
S.I.C.: 8711
N.A.I.C.S.: 541330
Glenn Wee *(Pres)*

Armstrong Odenwald Changchun (AOC) Technology Co Ltd (1)
No 48 Hongmian St Huadu Zone
510800 Guangzhou, Guangdong, China
Tel.: (86) 2036872881
Fax: (86) 2036872883
Industrial Engineering Services
S.I.C.: 8711
N.A.I.C.S.: 541330

Armstrong Odenwald Technology (Tianjin) Co Ltd (1)
No B3-3 Aida International Industry Area
Xiqing Eco Techno Develop Zone, 300385
Tianjin, China
Tel.: (86) 2223870777
Fax: (86) 2223870776
Industrial Engineering Services
S.I.C.: 8711
N.A.I.C.S.: 541330

Armstrong Odenwald Technology (Wuhan) Co Ltd (1)
No 101 Dazhuan Rd Dajijie Industrial Area
Caidian, Wuhan, Hubei, 430113, China
Tel.: (86) 2769160770
Fax: (86) 2769160190
Web Site: www.armstrong.com.sg/manuf.asp
Industrial Engineering Services
S.I.C.: 8711
N.A.I.C.S.: 541330

Armstrong Rubber & Chemical Products Company Limited (1)
591 Moo 17 Soi Bangplee-Phattana Theparuk Rd
Amphur, Ban Sao Thong, Samutprakarn, 10540, Thailand
Tel.: (66) 7052021 30
Fax: (66) 7053661 5
Web Site: www.armstrong.co.th/
Rubber & Chemicals Mfr
S.I.C.: 2822
N.A.I.C.S.: 325212
Glenn Wee *(Pres)*

Armstrong Rubber Technology (Thailand) Company Limited (1)
42 10 Moo 4 Rojana Industrial Park Tambol Baanchang
Amphur U-Thai, Ayutthaya, Thailand
Tel.: (66) 35 950160 3
Fax: (66) 35 950159
E-Mail: arc@armstrong.co.th
Web Site: www.armstrong-mc.co.th
Emp.: 40
Industrial Engineering Services
S.I.C.: 8711
N.A.I.C.S.: 541330

Armstrong Industrial Corporation Ltd.—(Continued)

Armstrong Technology (Suzhou) Co Ltd (1)
No 2 Bao Da Rd Suzhou Industrial Park
KuaTang Sub-District, 215122 Suzhou, JiangSu, China
Tel.: (86) 51262750285
Fax: (86) 51262750295
E-Mail: rpcoliew@armstrong.com.sg
Web Site: www.armstrong.com.sg/manuf.asp
Emp.: 150
Industrial Engineering Services
S.I.C.: 8711
N.A.I.C.S.: 541330
Liew Chieton *(Gen Mgr)*

Armstrong Technology (Wuxi) Co Ltd (1)
No 5 Xing Chuang Rd Wuxi
Singapore Industrial Park, Wuxi, JiangSu, China
Tel.: (86) 51085282400
Fax: (86) 51085281456
E-Mail: atwnet05@pub.wx.jsinfo.net
Web Site: www.armstrong.com.sg/manuf.asp
Industrial Engineering Services
S.I.C.: 8711
N.A.I.C.S.: 541330

Hardyflex Industries Sdn Bhd (1)
No 70 Jalan TSB 9 Taman Industry
47000 Sungai Buloh, Sclangor Darul Ehsan, Malaysia
Tel.: (60) 3 6157 0318
Fax: (60) 3 6157 0078
E-Mail: enquiry@armstrong.net.my
Web Site: www.armstrong.net.my
Rubber Products Mfr
S.I.C.: 3061
N.A.I.C.S.: 326291
Loke Weng Keong *(Mgr)*

ARMTEC INFRASTRUCTURE INC.

370 Speedvale Avenue West
PO Box 3000
Guelph, ON, N1H 6P2, Canada
Tel.: (519) 822-0210
Fax: (519) 822-1160
Web Site: www.armtec.com
ARF—(TSX)
Rev.: $454,679,658
Assets: $359,537,034
Liabilities: $379,609,280
Net Worth: ($20,072,246)
Earnings: ($35,892,074)
Emp.: 1,626
Fiscal Year-end: 12/31/12

Business Description:
Polyethylene & Corrugated Steel Pipe Mfr; Precast Concrete Product Mfr; Sound Barrier Mfr
S.I.C.: 3317
N.A.I.C.S.: 331210

Personnel:
Robert J. Wright *(Chm)*
Mark Anderson *(Pres & CEO)*
Malcolm Buxton-Forman *(CFO)*
Dennis Lattimore *(Pres-Precast Concrete Solutions)*
Jason Redman *(Pres-Drainage Solutions)*
Carrie Boutcher *(Sec & VP)*

Board of Directors:
Robert J. Wright
Ron V. Adams
Farouk M. Ahamed
Mark Anderson
Don W. Cameron
Brian W. Jamieson
J. Mark Richardson
John E. Richardson
Michael S. Skea

Legal Counsel:
Fraser Milner Casgrain LLP
77 King Street West Suite 400 Toronto Dominion Centre
Toronto, ON, M5K 0A1, Canada

Transfer Agent:
Computershare Investor Services Inc.
100 University Ave 9th Floor
Toronto, ON, Canada

Subsidiaries:

A.E. Concrete Precast Products Ltd. (1)
19060 54th Ave
Surrey, BC, V3S 8E5, Canada
Tel.: (604) 576-1808
Fax: (604) 576-2454
Web Site: www.ae-concrete.com
Emp.: 70
Civil Engineering Services
S.I.C.: 1629
N.A.I.C.S.: 237990
Dave Orton *(Office Mgr)*

Durisol Inc. (1)
505 York Blvd Ste 2
Hamilton, ON, L8R 3K4, Canada
Tel.: (905) 521-0999
Fax: (905) 521-8658
E-Mail: info@durisol.com
Web Site: www.durisol.com
Emp.: 40
Noise Barrier Installation Services
S.I.C.: 8999
N.A.I.C.S.: 541620
Chuck Phillips *(CEO)*

ARMY & NAVY DEPARTMENT STORES LIMITED

74 W Cordova St
Vancouver, BC, V6B 1C9, Canada
Tel.: (604) 683-9660
Fax: (604) 683-5985
E-Mail: info@armyandnavy.ca
Web Site: www.armyandnavy.ca
Emp.: 1,000

Business Description:
Clothing Retailer
Export
S.I.C.: 5699
N.A.I.C.S.: 448190

Personnel:
Jacqui Cohen *(Pres & CEO)*

ARMY WELFARE TRUST LLC

AWT Plaza The Mall
Rawalpindi, 46000, Pakistan
Tel.: (92) 5192724004
Fax: (92) 519272394
E-Mail: infoawt@awt.com.pk
Web Site: www.awt.com.pk
Year Founded: 1971
Emp.: 3,375

Business Description:
Military Pension Trust Management & Financial Investment Services
S.I.C.: 6371
N.A.I.C.S.: 524292

Personnel:
Javed Iqbal *(Chm)*
Tahir Mahmood *(Vice Chm & Mng Dir)*
Muhammad Ibrahim Khan *(Sec)*

Board of Directors:
Javed Iqbal
Masuood Ahmed
Mukhtar Ahmed
Asif Akhtar
Muhammad Farooq
Noor Hussain
Malik Riffat Mahmood
Tahir Mahmood
Junaid Rehmat

ARNES WELDING LTD.

835 Mission Street
Winnipeg, MB, R2J 0A4, Canada
Tel.: (204) 233-7111
Fax: (204) 231-1252
Toll Free: (800) 661-1975
E-Mail: arnes@arnes.com
Web Site: www.arnes.com
Sales Range: $10-24.9 Million
Emp.: 80

Business Description:
Truck Trailer Mfr
S.I.C.: 3715
N.A.I.C.S.: 336212

Personnel:
Gerald Bouchard *(Pres)*

ARNOLD BAUER SA

23 Avenue De Stalingrad
92700 Colombes, Hauts De Seine, France
Tel.: (33) 147805461
Fax: (33) 147862972
E-Mail: commercial@abauer.fr
Web Site: www.abauer.fr
Sales Range: $10-24.9 Million
Emp.: 25

Business Description:
Automobile Dealership
S.I.C.: 5511
N.A.I.C.S.: 441110

Personnel:
Anne-Sophie Bauer *(Dir-Fin)*

ARNOLD BROS. TRANSPORT LTD

739 Lagimodiere Blvd
Winnipeg, MB, R2J 0T8, Canada
Tel.: (204) 257-6666
Fax: (204) 257-2213
Toll Free: (800) 665-8085
Web Site: www.arnoldbros.com
Sales Range: $75-99.9 Million
Emp.: 750

Business Description:
Transportation & Delivery Services
S.I.C.: 4213
N.A.I.C.S.: 484121

Personnel:
Fred Arnold *(Pres & CEO)*
Gary Arnold *(Exec VP)*

ARNOLD CLARK AUTOMOBILES LIMITED

134 Nithsdale Dr
Pollokshaws, Glasgow, G41 2PP, United Kingdom
Tel.: (44) 1414222700
Fax: (44) 1414222790
Web Site: www.arnoldclark.com
Sales Range: $1-4.9 Billion
Emp.: 7,500

Business Description:
Automobile Dealership Operator
S.I.C.: 5511
N.A.I.C.S.: 441110

Personnel:
Arnold Clark *(Chm & CEO)*

ARNON CORPORATION

1801 Woodward Drive
Ottawa, ON, K2C 0R3, Canada
Tel.: (613) 226-2000
Fax: (613) 225-0391
Web Site: www.arnon.ca
Year Founded: 1960
Rev.: $71,303,750
Emp.: 250

Business Description:
Commercial & Residential Building Construction & Services
S.I.C.: 8361
N.A.I.C.S.: 623990

Personnel:
Arnon Vered *(Pres)*

ARNOTTS LTD.

12 Henry St
Dublin, 1, Ireland
Tel.: (353) 18050400
Fax: (353) 18721403
E-Mail: info@arnotts.ie
Web Site: www.arnotts.ie
Year Founded: 1843
Sales Range: $200-249.9 Million
Emp.: 1,200

Business Description:
Department Store Owner & Operator
Import
S.I.C.: 5311
N.A.I.C.S.: 452111

Personnel:
Nigel Blow *(Chm)*
Ray Hernan *(CEO)*

Board of Directors:
Nigel Blow
Stephen Hegarty
Tobais Nanda
Richard L. Nesbitt

Legal Counsel:
William Fry
Fitzwilton House Wilton Place
Dublin, 2, Ireland

Transfer Agent:
Capita Corporate Registrars plc
Unit 5 Manor Street Business Park
Manor Street, Dublin, 7, Ireland
Tel.: (353) 1 810 2400
Fax: (353) 1 810 2422

Subsidiaries:

Asgard Financial Services Ltd (1)
104 Middle Abbey St
Dublin, 1, Ireland (100%)
Tel.: (353) 18732410
Telex: 25558
Fax: (353) 18050535
Emp.: 5
S.I.C.: 7334
N.A.I.C.S.: 561499

Boyers & Co. Limited (1)
19-22 North Earl Street
Dublin, 1, Ireland (100%)
Tel.: (353) 18050403
Telex: 32524 Arno EL
Fax: (353) 18745380
E-Mail: boyers@arnotts.ie
Web Site: www.boyers.ie
Emp.: 100
Department Store & Boutiques
Import
S.I.C.: 5311
N.A.I.C.S.: 452112

ARO GRANITE INDUSTRIES LTD.

S16 II Floor Green Park Extension
New Delhi, 110 016, India
Tel.: (91) 1126511021
Fax: (91) 1126511022
E-Mail: arogil@del2.vsnl.net.in
Web Site: www.arotile.com
AROGRANITE—(NSE)
Rev.: $34,717,411
Assets: $46,172,906
Liabilities: $23,439,399
Net Worth: $22,733,507
Earnings: $2,087,474
Fiscal Year-end: 03/31/13

Business Description:
Granite Tiles & Slabs Mfr & Distr
S.I.C.: 3089
N.A.I.C.S.: 326199

Personnel:
Sunil K. Arora *(Mng Dir & Head-Mktg)*
Sabyasachi Panigrahi *(Compliance Officer & Sec)*

Board of Directors:
Kasturi Lal Arora
Sujata Arora
Sunil K. Arora
Rahul Gupta
Pradeep Kumar Jain
Dinesh Chandra Kothari

Transfer Agent:
Alankit Assignments Limited
Alankit House 2E/21Jhandewalan Extention
New Delhi, India

Units:

Aro Granite Industries Ltd. - Unit I (1)
103 SIPCOT Industrial Complex
Hosur, Tamilnadu, 635 126, India
Tel.: (91) 4344276860
Fax: (91) 4344276460
E-Mail: aro@arotile.com
Emp.: 950
Granite Tile & Slab Mfr
S.I.C.: 3281
N.A.I.C.S.: 327991
Sunil Kumar Arora *(Mng Dir)*

Aro Granite Industries Ltd. - Unit II (1)
Koneripalli Village
Shoolagiri, Hosur, Tamilnadu, 635 117, India
Tel.: (91) 4344252100
Fax: (91) 4344252217
E-Mail: aro@arotile.com
Emp.: 800
Granite Tile & Slab Mfr
S.I.C.: 3281
N.A.I.C.S.: 327991
Sunil Kumar Arora *(Mng Dir)*

AROMA AD

12 Kiril Blagoev Str
Sofia, 1271, Bulgaria
Tel.: (359) 2 9350304
Fax: (359) 2 9350320
E-Mail: aroma@aroma.bg
Web Site: www.aroma.bg
Year Founded: 1927
6AR—(BUL)
Business Description:
Cosmetics Products Mfr
S.I.C.: 5122
N.A.I.C.S.: 446120
Personnel:
Maria Dimitrova Andreeva *(Chm)*
Dimitar Lukanov Lukanov *(CEO)*
Board of Directors:
Maria Dimitrova Andreeva
Anita Ivanova Aleksieva
Dimitar Lukanov Lukanov

AROMA COSMETICS AD

12 Kiril Blagoev Str
Sofia, 1271, Bulgaria
Tel.: (359) 2 9350304
Fax: (359) 2 9350320
E-Mail: aroma@aroma.bg
Web Site: aroma.bg
ACZ—(BUL)
Business Description:
Cosmetic Products Mfr
S.I.C.: 5122
N.A.I.C.S.: 446120
Personnel:
Lukan Dimitrov Lukanov *(Chm)*
Dimitar Lukanov Lukanov *(Vice Chm & CEO)*
Board of Directors:
Lukan Dimitrov Lukanov
Anita Ivanova Aleksieva
Evgeni Spasov Ivanov
Dimitar Lukanov Lukanov

AROMASOFT CORP.

13th floor Daeryong post tower 1 cha
Guro 3 dong
Guro gu, Seoul, Korea (South)
Tel.: (82) 2 2082 2800
Fax: (82) 2 2082 2803
E-Mail: biz@aromasoft.com
Web Site: www.aromasoft.com
Year Founded: 1998
072770—(KRS)
Sls.: $5,559,540
Assets: $19,060,350
Liabilities: $9,005,190
Net Worth: $10,055,160
Earnings: $304,110
Fiscal Year-end: 12/31/12
Business Description:
Wireless Internet Services
S.I.C.: 4812
N.A.I.C.S.: 517210
Personnel:
Hyun Jin Lee *(CEO)*

AROMATHERAPY ASSOCIATES LTD.

(Acquired by B&B Investment Partners LLP)

ARONI COMMERCIALS LTD.

209-210 Arcadia Building 2nd Floor
195 Nariman Point
Mumbai, 400021, India
Tel.: (91) 22 66708600
Fax: (91) 22 66708650
E-Mail: aroni.investor@gcvl.in
Web Site: www.aronicommercials.com
512273—(BOM)
Rev.: $273,907
Assets: $11,294,538
Liabilities: $80,514
Net Worth: $11,214,024
Earnings: $49,037
Fiscal Year-end: 03/31/13
Business Description:
Investment Management Services
S.I.C.: 6211
N.A.I.C.S.: 523999
Personnel:
Anoop Chatuvedi *(CFO)*
Avani Jani *(Compliance Officer & Sec)*
Board of Directors:
V. V. Sureshkumar
Bhagwati Prasad Kejariwal
Ashish Mohta
Ritesh Zaveri
Transfer Agent:
Link Intime India Private Limited
C-13 Pannalal Silk Mills Compound L.B.S. Marg
Bhandup
Mumbai, India

ARORA HOTELS LIMITED

Southgate Avenue
Crawley, RH10 6LW, United Kingdom
Tel.: (44) 1293 530 000
E-Mail: Gatwick@arorahotels.com
Web Site: www.arorahotels.com
Year Founded: 1999
Sales Range: $10-24.9 Million
Emp.: 995
Business Description:
Hotel Management Services
S.I.C.: 7011
N.A.I.C.S.: 721110
Personnel:
Bruno Delrieux *(Gen Mgr)*

AROS QUALITY GROUP AB

(Name Changed to AQ Group AB)

AROWANA INTERNATIONAL LIMITED

(Formerly Intelligent Solar Limited)
Level 11 Matisse Tower 110 Mary Street
Brisbane, QLD, 4000, Australia
Tel.: (61) 7 3182 3200
Web Site: arowanainternational.com
AWN—(ASX)
Rev.: $12,583,790
Assets: $81,469,029
Liabilities: $37,119,841
Net Worth: $44,349,188
Earnings: $1,825,969
Fiscal Year-end: 06/13/13
Business Description:
Investment Services
S.I.C.: 6211
N.A.I.C.S.: 523999
Personnel:
David Malcolm Keefe *(Chm)*
Kevin Tser Fah Chin *(Mng Dir & Dir-Fin)*
Board of Directors:
David Malcolm Keefe
Kevin Tser Fah Chin
John Colinton Moore
Subsidiaries:

Cool or Cosy (QLD) Pty. Ltd. (1)
36 Computer Rd
Yatala, Gold Coast, QLD, 4207, Australia
Tel.: (61) 7 3804 6666
Fax: (61) 7 3297 4455
E-Mail: enquiries@coolorcosy.com.au
Web Site: www.coolorcosy.com.au
Air Condition Equipment Whslr
S.I.C.: 5075
N.A.I.C.S.: 423730
Robert Nicholls *(Mng Dir)*

Cool or Cosy Perth (1)
109 Garling St O'Connor Unit 2
Perth, Western Australia, 6163, Australia AU
Tel.: (61) 893389000
Fax: (61) 89314 7755
E-Mail: info@coolorcosyperth.com.au
Web Site: www.coolorcosyperth.com.au/
Supplier & Installer of Environmentally Friendly Cellulose Fiber Insulation
S.I.C.: 5033
N.A.I.C.S.: 423330
Piera West *(Mgr-Sls)*

Morcanna Holdings Pty. Ltd. (1)
65 Stephensons Ave
Torrensville, South Australia, 5031, Australia
Tel.: (61) 882345101
Fax: (61) 82345201
E-Mail: enquiries@ccsa.com.au
Web Site: www.coolorcosysa.com.au
Emp.: 20
Building Material Whslr
S.I.C.: 5039
N.A.I.C.S.: 423390
Glenn Morelli *(Pres)*

AROWAY ENERGY INC.

Suite 1100-888 Dunsmuir Street
Vancouver, BC, V6C 3K4, Canada
Tel.: (604) 304-4087
Fax: (604) 909-2679
E-Mail: info@arowayenergy.com
Web Site: www.arowayenergy.com
Year Founded: 1980
ARW—(OTC TSXV)
Rev.: $5,356,827
Assets: $10,274,262
Liabilities: $8,268,769
Net Worth: $2,005,493
Earnings: ($8,059,875)
Emp.: 1
Fiscal Year-end: 06/30/13
Business Description:
Oil & Gas Exploration Services
S.I.C.: 1389
N.A.I.C.S.: 213112
Personnel:
Christopher R. Cooper *(Pres & CEO)*
Daryn Gordon *(CFO & Sec)*
Board of Directors:
Desmond M. Balakrishnan
Christopher R. Cooper
Daryn Gordon
Brad Nichol
Mike K. Veldhuis
Transfer Agent:
Equity Transfer & Trust Company
1185 West Georgia Street Suite 1620
Vancouver, BC, V6E 4E6, Canada

ARPADIS GROUP

Parc Industriel - Zone D rue Jean Perrin 5A
7170 Manage, Belgium
Tel.: (32) 64 51 76 13
Fax: (32) 64 51 76 14
E-Mail: benelux@arpadis.com
Web Site: www.arpadis.com
ARPA—(EUR)
Sales Range: $75-99.9 Million
Business Description:
Investment Management Services
S.I.C.: 6282
N.A.I.C.S.: 523920
Personnel:
Laurent Abergel *(CEO)*
Chantal Vanderveken *(CFO)*

ARPETROL LTD.

Suite 700 815 8th Avenue SW
Calgary, AB, T2P 3P2, Canada
Tel.: (403) 263-6738
Fax: (403) 263-6913
E-Mail: info@arpetrol.com
Web Site: www.arpetrol.com
Year Founded: 2007
RPT—(TSXV)
Rev.: $5,690,323
Assets: $40,331,163
Liabilities: $16,088,405
Net Worth: $24,242,758
Earnings: ($25,618,441)
Emp.: 31
Fiscal Year-end: 12/31/12
Business Description:
Oil & Gas Exploration Services
S.I.C.: 1389
N.A.I.C.S.: 213112
Personnel:
Claudio A. Ghersinich *(Chm)*
Timothy J. Thomas *(Pres & CEO)*
Ian Habke *(CFO)*
Board of Directors:
Claudio A. Ghersinich
Abdel F. Badwi
Jeffrey S. Boyce
Michelle Gahagan
Timothy J. Thomas
Ronald A. Williams
Transfer Agent:
Canadian Stock Transfer Company
Vancouver, BC, Canada
Non-U.S. Subsidiary:

ArPetrol Argentina S.A. (1)
Cerrito 1186 4th Floor
C1010AAX Buenos Aires, Argentina
Tel.: (54) 11 4819 2150
Fax: (54) 11 4819 2151
E-Mail: a.argentina@arpetrol.com
Web Site: www.arpetrol.com
Oil & Gas Exploration Services
S.I.C.: 1311
N.A.I.C.S.: 211111
Pedro Sanchez *(VP-Argentina)*

ARPICO FINANCE COMPANY PLC

146 Havelock Road
Colombo, 5, Sri Lanka
Tel.: (94) 112553663
Fax: (94) 112500259
E-Mail: info@arpicofinance.com
Web Site: www.arpicofinance.com
ARPI—(COL)
Int. Income: $6,411,528
Assets: $36,131,792
Liabilities: $32,626,456
Net Worth: $3,505,336
Earnings: $334,914
Fiscal Year-end: 03/31/13
Business Description:
Leasing & Financial Services
S.I.C.: 6719
N.A.I.C.S.: 551112
Personnel:
Bri Ponnambalam *(Chm)*
Hafeez Rajudin *(Mng Dir)*
D. V. Dharshan Silva *(COO)*
Board of Directors:
Bri Ponnambalam

Arpico Finance Company PLC—(Continued)

Lyle Dennis Peiris
Nilanka Mevan Pieris
Hafeez Rajudin
Ruwini E. Weerasinghe

ARPLAMA N.V.

Industriezone De Heze
Hagelberg 8, B 2250 Olen, Belgium
Tel.: (32) 14 23 73 92
Fax: (32) 14 23 73 95
E-Mail: info@arplamagroup.com
Web Site: www.arplamagroup.com
Sales Range: $10-24.9 Million
Emp.: 120
Business Description:
Thermosets Mfr & Distr
S.I.C.: 3823
N.A.I.C.S.: 334513
Subsidiary:

Pla-Ma Belgium NV (1)
Industriezone De Heze
Hagelberg 8, B 2550 Olen, Belgium
Tel.: (32) 14 23 73 92
Fax: (32) 14 23 73 95
E-Mail: info@arplamagroup.com
Web Site: www.arplamagroup.com
Polyurethane Processing
S.I.C.: 3089
N.A.I.C.S.: 326199

Non-U.S. Subsidiary:

S.C. Arplama Romania S.R.L. (1)
Mun Fagaras Str Tudor Vladimirescu 86
Jud Brasov, RO 505200 Fagaras, Romania
Tel.: (40) 268280322
Fax: (40) 268280327
E-Mail: info@arplama.ro
Web Site: www.arplama.ro
Emp.: 100
Polyester Processing
S.I.C.: 3089
N.A.I.C.S.: 326199
Bcabirlat Micolas *(Mgr)*

ARQUATI S.P.A.

Via San Vitale 3
43038 Sala Baganza, Italy
Tel.: (39) 05218321
Fax: (39) 0521832378
E-Mail: info@arquati.it
Web Site: www.arquati.it
Sls.: $18,174,000
Emp.: 200
Business Description:
Fabrics & Furnishings
S.I.C.: 5023
N.A.I.C.S.: 423220
Personnel:
Stefano Talza *(Pres)*

ARQUEONAUTAS WORLDWIDE - ARQUEOLOGIA SUBAQUATICA S.A.

Rua das Murcas 88 3rd Fl
9000-058 Funchal, Portugal
Tel.: (351) 214663040
Fax: (351) 214662769
E-Mail: info@arq.de
Web Site: www.arq.de
Year Founded: 1995
QOW—(DEU)
Sales Range: Less than $1 Million
Emp.: 30
Business Description:
Marine Archeological Services
S.I.C.: 8731
N.A.I.C.S.: 541712
Personnel:
Isaias Gomes Teixeira *(Chm-Supervisory Bd)*
Nikolaus Graf Sandizel *(CEO)*
Miguel Rocha de Moura *(CFO)*
Alejandro Mirabal Jorge *(COO)*
Howard Strouth *(Member-Mgmt Bd)*
Supervisory Board of Directors:
Isaias Gomes Teixeira
Tristao da Cunha
Rita Delgado
Clemens Pflanz
Antonio Portugal Catalao

ARR CRAIB TRANSPORT LTD.

Howe Moss Dr Kirkhill Industrial Estate
Dyce, Aberdeen, AB21 OGL, United Kingdom
Tel.: (44) 1224771122
Fax: (44) 1224794160
E-Mail: info@arr-craib.co.uk
Web Site: www.arr-craib.co.uk
Sales Range: $50-74.9 Million
Emp.: 300
Business Description:
Road Transportation Services
S.I.C.: 4212
N.A.I.C.S.: 484110
Personnel:
George F. Craib *(Chm)*
Edward S. Anderson *(Mng Dir)*

ARRAY MARKETING GROUP INC.

45 Progress Ave
Toronto, ON, M1P 2Y6, Canada
Tel.: (416) 299-4865
Fax: (416) 292-9759
E-Mail: inquiry@arraymarketing.com
Web Site: www.arraymarketing.com
Sales Range: $25-49.9 Million
Emp.: 600
Business Description:
Store & Office Display Cases & Fixtures
S.I.C.: 2541
N.A.I.C.S.: 337212
Personnel:
Thomas Hendren *(Pres & CEO)*

Division:

Array Marketing Group Inc. - Array Bradford Fixture Division (1)
35 Reagens Industrial Parkway
Bradford, ON, L3Z 2A4, Canada
Tel.: (416) 213-5740
Fax: (905) 775-4232
Emp.: 75
Fixture & Floor Stand Mfr
S.I.C.: 2599
N.A.I.C.S.: 337215
Ken Simpson, *(Pres)*

U.S. Subsidiary:

Array New York (1)
200 Madison Ave Ste 2121
New York, NY 10016
Tel.: (212) 750-3367
Fax: (212) 750-3369
Marketing Services
S.I.C.: 8742
N.A.I.C.S.: 541613
Robert Thiry, *(VP-Sls)*

Non-U.S. Subsidiary:

Array Asia Ltd. (1)
Suite 1409 14/F XinHua Insurance Building
MinTian Road
FuTian Center, Shenzhen, China 518026
Tel.: (86) 755 3333 6835
Fax: (86) 755 3333 6836
Marketing Services
S.I.C.: 8742
N.A.I.C.S.: 541613
Chung Ng, *(Gen Mgr)*

ARRIA NLG PLC

Space One 1 Beadon Road
Hammersmith, London, W6 0EA, United Kingdom
Tel.: (44) 20 7100 4540
E-Mail: info@arria.com
Web Site: www.arria.com
NLG—(AIM)
Business Description:
Software Developer
S.I.C.: 7372
N.A.I.C.S.: 511210
Personnel:
Stuart Rogers *(Chm & CEO)*
Simon Small *(Pres)*
Wayne Thornhill *(CFO)*
Sharon Daniels *(CMO)*
Robert Dale *(CTO)*
Matthew Gould *(Chief Strategy Officer)*
Thomas Makeig *(Gen Counsel & Sec)*
Board of Directors:
Stuart Rogers
Sharon Daniels
Michael Higgins
Paul Kidney
Simon Small
Wayne Thornhill

ARRICANO REAL ESTATE PLC

13th Floor 33 T Schevchenko Boulevard
01032 Kiev, Ukraine
Tel.: (380) 44 569 67 08
Fax: (380) 44 569 67 09
Web Site: www.arricano.com
ARO—(AIM)
Business Description:
Commercial Real Estate Development & Management
S.I.C.: 6552
N.A.I.C.S.: 237210
Personnel:
Rupert Cottrell *(Chm)*
Yarema Kovaliv *(Acting CEO)*
Tatiana Burkatskaya *(COO)*

ARRIS HOLDINGS INC.

Suite 200 8338 120th Street
Surrey, BC, V3W 3N4, Canada
Tel.: (604) 685-2542
Fax: (604) 408-9301
E-Mail: info@arrisholdingsinc.com
Web Site: www.arrisholdingsinc.com
Year Founded: 2009
AAF—(CNSX)
Assets: $730
Liabilities: $28,411
Net Worth: ($27,681)
Earnings: ($59,540)
Fiscal Year-end: 09/30/13
Business Description:
Investment Holding Company
S.I.C.: 6719
N.A.I.C.S.: 551112
Personnel:
Charles Larsen *(Pres & CEO)*
Larry Tsang *(CFO)*
Board of Directors:
Mikhail Gurfinkel
Navchand Jagpal
Lucky Janda
Sandy Janda
Charles Larsen
Transfer Agent:
Valiant Trust
600 - 750 Cambie Street
Vancouver, BC, Canada

ARRIUM LIMITED

Level 40 259 George Street
Sydney, NSW, 2000, Australia
Tel.: (61) 292396666
Fax: (61) 292513042
E-Mail: investorenquiries@arrium.com
Web Site: www.arrium.com
Year Founded: 2000
ARI—(ASX OTC)
Rev.: $6,341,074,290
Assets: $8,974,148,360
Liabilities: $5,083,468,010
Net Worth: $3,890,680,350
Earnings: ($721,758,460)
Emp.: 10,078
Fiscal Year-end: 06/30/13
Business Description:
Holding Company; Steel Products Mfr; Mining & Metal Recycling Services
S.I.C.: 6719
N.A.I.C.S.: 551112
Personnel:
Peter J. Smedley *(Chm)*
Andrew G. Roberts *(CEO & Mng Dir)*
Robert Canvin Bakewell *(CFO)*
Naomi James *(Chief Legal Officer & CEO-ATM & Mdsg)*
Bill Gately *(Chief HR Officer)*
John Barbagallo *(CEO-Mining Consumables)*
Geoff Feurtado *(CEO-Recycling)*
Steve Hamer *(CEO-Steel)*
Leo Selleck *(CEO-Ops Excellence)*
Greg Waters *(CEO-Mining)*
Kara Nicholls *(Sec)*
Board of Directors:
Peter J. Smedley
Robert Bryan Davis
Colin Robert Galbraith
Peter G. Nankervis
Dean Antony Pritchard
Graham Joseph Smorgon
Rosemary Warnock
Subsidiaries:

Australian Tube Mills Pty. Limited (1)
146 Ingram Road
Acacia Ridge, Brisbane, QLD, 4110, Australia AU
Tel.: (61) 2 4935 4498
Fax: (61) 7 3909 6660
Web Site: www.austubemills.com
Emp.: 300
Structural Steel Pipe & Tube Mfr
S.I.C.: 3317
N.A.I.C.S.: 331210
Tony Schreiber *(CEO)*

OneSteel Manufacturing Pty Limited (1)
105-123 Dohertys Road
Laverton, Victoria, 3026, Australia
Tel.: (61) 393602360
Fax: (61) 393602345
E-Mail: deglaitisg@onesteel.com
Web Site: www.onesteel.com
Emp.: 500
Steel Mfr
S.I.C.: 3325
N.A.I.C.S.: 331513
Shine Murphy *(Gen Mgr)*

Subsidiaries:

Smorgon Grinding Media (2)
Maud St
Po Box 14
Waratah, NSW, 2298, Australia AU
Tel.: (61) 249670200
Fax: (61) 249670210
E-Mail: grinding.media@smorgansteel.com.au
Web Site: www.molycop.com.au/grindingmedia
Emp.: 600
Railway Wheels, Axles & Grinding Media Mfr
S.I.C.: 3714
N.A.I.C.S.: 336350
Rick Dunn *(Gen Mgr)*

Plants:

OneSteel Market Mills (2)
PO Box 245c
Newcastle, NSW, 2300, Australia AU
Tel.: (61) 249355635
Fax: (61) 249355640

E-Mail: onesteeldirect@onesteel.com
Web Site: www.onesteel.com
Emp.: 1,000
S.I.C.: 3317
N.A.I.C.S.: 331210
Dave Taylor *(CEO)*

OneSteel Whyalla Steelworks (2)
Port Augusta Rd
Whyalla, SA, 5600, Australia
Tel.: (61) 886404206
Fax: (61) 886404746
E-Mail: kellys@onesteel.com
Web Site: www.onesteel.com
Emp.: 1,800
S.I.C.: 3317
N.A.I.C.S.: 331210
Theuns Victor *(Gen Mgr)*

U.S. Subsidiary:

OneSteel Recycling, Inc. (2)
25 Ayer St
Oakland, ME 04963 DE
Tel.: (207) 465-2212
Fax: (207) 465-3512
Web Site: www.onesteelrecycling.com
Sales Range: $10-24.9 Million
Emp.: 30
Recycling of Metal Scrap & Waste Materials
S.I.C.: 5093
N.A.I.C.S.: 423930
Geoff Feurtado *(CEO)*

ARRK CORPORATION

10F Tatsuno Minami Hommachi
Building 2-2-9 Minami Hommachi
Chuo-ku, Osaka, 541-0054, Japan
Tel.: (81) 6 6260 1801
Fax: (81) 6 6260 1802
Web Site: www.arrk.co.jp
Year Founded: 1989
7873—(JAS)
Sls.: $898,601,000
Assets: $699,259,000
Liabilities: $441,991,000
Net Worth: $257,268,000
Earnings: ($8,855,000)
Emp.: 4,931
Fiscal Year-end: 03/31/13
Business Description:
Industrial Design Model Mfr
S.I.C.: 7389
N.A.I.C.S.: 541420
Personnel:
Yasuo Suzuki *(Pres)*
Takao Fujita *(Exec Officer-Product Dev Bus)*
Yoshiharu Fushiya *(Exec Officer-Product Dev Bus)*
Yasunori Hirata *(Exec Officer-Mass Production Bus)*
Toshihiro Minagawa *(Exec Officer-Product Dev Bus)*
Naruto Murata *(Exec Officer-Intl Bus)*
Shin Ujihara *(Exec Officer-Product Dev Bus)*
Minoru Yoshida *(Exec Officer-Mass Production Bus)*
Board of Directors:
Satoru Nakagiri
Masaya Nakanishi
Koichi Sakurada
Yasuo Suzuki
Kazushige Takahashi
Koji Tsujino
Masaaki Yoshida

ARROW CAPITAL MANAGEMENT, INC.

36 Toronto St Ste 750
Toronto, ON, M5C 2C5, Canada
Tel.: (416) 323-0477
Fax: (416) 323-3199
Toll Free: (877) 327-6048
E-Mail: info@arrow-capital.com
Web Site: www.arrow-capital.com
Business Description:
Private Investment Firm
S.I.C.: 6211
N.A.I.C.S.: 523999
Personnel:
James McGovern *(Mng Dir & CEO)*
Robert Maxwell *(Mng Dir & CFO)*
Robert Parsons *(Mng Dir & COO)*
Mark Purdy *(Mng Dir & CIO)*
Subsidiary:

BluMont Capital Inc. (1)
70 University Ave Ste 1200
PO Box 16
Toronto, ON, M5J 2M4, Canada ON
Tel.: (416) 216-3566
Fax: (416) 360-1102
Toll Free: (866) 473-7376
E-Mail: service@blumontcapital.com
Web Site: www.blumontcapital.com
Sales Range: $25-49.9 Million
Emp.: 35
Investment Services
S.I.C.: 6282
N.A.I.C.S.: 523930
Victor Koloshuk *(Chm & Pres)*
James Wanstall *(CEO)*
David Scobie *(Mng Dir & COO)*
Pierre Novak *(Mng Dir)*
Veronika Hirsch *(Chief Investment Officer)*
Richard Goode *(Sr VP-Natl Sls)*

ARROW CARS INTERNATIONAL INC.

Calle del Escritor Herrera Santaolalla 2
Churriana, 29140 Malaga, Spain
Tel.: (34) 952623297
Web Site: www.autooasiseurope.com
Sales Range: Less than $1 Million
Emp.: 8
Business Description:
Car Dealership
S.I.C.: 5511
N.A.I.C.S.: 441110
Personnel:
Jeremy Dean Harris *(Pres & CEO)*
Sergio Perez Conejo *(CFO & Dir-Legal)*
Board of Directors:
Jeremy Dean Harris
Sergio Perez Conejo

ARROW COATED PRODUCTS LIMITED

5/D Laxmi Industrial Estate New Link Road
Andheri W, Mumbai, 400 053, India
Tel.: (91) 22 2635 2500
Fax: (91) 22 6692 3377
E-Mail: info@arrowcoated.com
Web Site: www.arrowcoated.com
Year Founded: 1960
516064—(BOM)
Rev.: $2,858,052
Assets: $4,639,246
Liabilities: $1,472,298
Net Worth: $3,166,947
Earnings: $480,149
Fiscal Year-end: 03/31/13
Business Description:
Coated Packaging Product Mfr
S.I.C.: 2671
N.A.I.C.S.: 326112
Personnel:
Shilpan P. Patel *(Chm & Mng Dir)*
Poonam Bansal *(Compliance Officer & Sec)*
Board of Directors:
Shilpan P. Patel
Haresh Mehta
Harish Mishra
Neil Patel
Anil Saxena
Transfer Agent:
System Support Services
209 Shivai Industrial Estate Near Park Davis
89-Andheri Kurla Road
Sakinaka, Mumbai, 400 072, India

ARROW CONSTRUCTION PRODUCTS LIMITED

50 Gervais Court
PO Box 760
Fredericton, NB, E3B 5B4, Canada
Tel.: (506) 458-9610
Fax: (506) 458-0192
Web Site: www.arrowco.ca
Year Founded: 1979
Rev.: $15,302,311
Emp.: 45
Business Description:
Construction Materials Supplier
S.I.C.: 3531
N.A.I.C.S.: 333120
Personnel:
Edgar Goguen *(Pres-Dartmouth)*

ARROW SYNDICATE PUBLIC COMPANY LIMITED

31 Moo 1 Phanthong
Chon Buri, Thailand
Tel.: (66) 38740371
Fax: (66) 38740150
Web Site: www.arrowpipe.com
ARROW—(THA)
Sales Range: $10-24.9 Million
Business Description:
Electrical Conduits & Fittings Mfr
S.I.C.: 3498
N.A.I.C.S.: 332996
Personnel:
Siridech Poolruang *(Chm)*
Lertchai Vongchaiyasit *(CEO)*

ARROW TEXTILES LTD.

Plot No 101 103 MIDC 19th Street
Satpur
Nasik, 422007, India
Tel.: (91) 253 3918200
Fax: (91) 253 3918220
Web Site: www.arrowtextiles.com
533068—(BOM)
Rev.: $692,375,985
Assets: $814,242,798
Liabilities: $403,912,755
Net Worth: $410,330,042
Earnings: $55,188,723
Fiscal Year-end: 03/31/13
Business Description:
Fabric Woven Label Mfr
S.I.C.: 2299
N.A.I.C.S.: 313310
Personnel:
Chand Arora *(Mng Dir)*
Sushama Vesvikar *(Compliance Officer & Sec)*
Board of Directors:
Jaydev Mody
Chand Arora
Aditya Mangaldas
Aurobind Patel
Harshvardhan Piramal
Transfer Agent:
Freedom Registry Limited
Plot No 101/102 19th Street MIDC Satpur
Nasik, Maharashtra, 422 007, India
Tel.: (91) 235 4032
Fax: (91) 235 1892

ARROWCREST GROUP PTY. LTD.

34 Burleigh Avenue
Woodville, SA, 5012, Australia
Mailing Address:
PO Box 3466
Regents Park, SA, 5942, Australia
Tel.: (61) 884684000
Fax: (61) 884684101
E-Mail: rohautomatic@roh.com.au
Web Site: www.roh.com.au
Year Founded: 1946
Sales Range: $100-124.9 Million
Emp.: 300
Business Description:
Holding Company; Automotive Operations & Industrial & Farm Equipment
S.I.C.: 6719
N.A.I.C.S.: 551112
Personnel:
Andrew Gwinnett *(Chm)*
Cheng Huah Hong *(CEO)*
Division:

ROH Wheels Australia (1)
28 Sheffield Street
Woodville, SA, 5012, Australia
Tel.: (61) 884684140
Fax: (61) 884684101
E-Mail: sales@roh.com.au
Web Site: www.roh.com.au
Emp.: 250
Alloy & Steel Wheel Mfr for Aftermarket
S.I.C.: 3714
N.A.I.C.S.: 336390
Andrew Gwinnett *(CEO)*

Subsidiaries:

John Shearer (Holdings) Limited (1)
Share Street
Kilkenny, SA, 5009, Australia
Tel.: (61) 882689555
Fax: (61) 882684099
E-Mail: admin@johnshearer.com.au
Web Site: www.johnshearer.com.au
SHR—(ASX)
Rev.: $23,474,345
Assets: $45,707,548
Liabilities: $6,593,367
Net Worth: $39,114,181
Earnings: ($1,601,708)
Emp.: 30
Fiscal Year-end: 06/30/13
Holding Company; Farming Machinery
S.I.C.: 6719
N.A.I.C.S.: 551112
Andrew William Grinnett *(Chm)*
Allen Elliot Bolaffi *(Sec)*

Subsidiaries:

Brownbuilt Pty Limited (2)
Lot 1 Boc Rd
Caringbah, NSW, 2229, Australia
Tel.: (61) 295260555
Fax: (61) 295251980
E-Mail: nswsales@brownbuilt.com.au
Web Site: www.brownbuilt.com.au
Emp.: 70
Steel Office Shelving & Storage Systems
S.I.C.: 2522
N.A.I.C.S.: 337214
Amit Misra *(Gen Mgr)*

John Shearer Limited (2)
Share Street
Kilkenny, SA, Australia
Mailing Address:
PO Box 32
Welland, SA, 5007, Australia
Tel.: (61) 882689555
Fax: (61) 882684099
E-Mail: admin@johnshearer.com.au
Web Site: www.johnshearer.com.au
Emp.: 30
Farming Machinery Mfr
S.I.C.: 3523
N.A.I.C.S.: 333111
Franco Perrotta *(Mgr-Ops)*

Kockums Industries (Australia) Pty Ltd (2)
188 Northbourne Road
Campbellfield, VIC, 3061, Australia
Tel.: (61) 393054001
Fax: (61) 393053191
Web Site: www.kockumsindustries.com
Emp.: 20
Transport Equipment Mfr
S.I.C.: 3711
N.A.I.C.S.: 336120
Colin Bildock *(Gen Mgr)*

Subsidiaries:

Flocast Australia Pty Ltd (1)
Factory 2 105 Newlands Road
PO Box 650
3058 Reservoir, VIC, 3073, Australia

Arrowcrest Group Pty. Ltd.—(Continued)

Tel.: (61) 393506333
Fax: (61) 393506999
Web Site: www.flocast.com.au
Emp.: 32
Iron & Steel Forgings
S.I.C.: 3462
N.A.I.C.S.: 332111
Jawahar Mahri *(Mng Dir)*

Nonferral Pty Ltd (1)
6-8 Dunstans Court
Reservoir, VIC, 3073, Australia
Tel.: (61) 3 9460 1211
Fax: (61) 3 9460 4519
Emp.: 60
Aluminum Rolling & Drawing
S.I.C.: 3354
N.A.I.C.S.: 331318

ARROWEDGE LTD.

Unit 7/8 The Concept Centre
Innovation Close
Poole, Dorset, BH12 4QT, United Kingdom
Tel.: (44) 1202 763539
Fax: (44) 208 902 0882
E-Mail: buyer@arrowedge.co.uk
Web Site: www.arrowedge.co.uk
Year Founded: 1982
Sales Range: $50-74.9 Million
Emp.: 40
Business Description:
Pharmaceuticals Product Whslr
S.I.C.: 5122
N.A.I.C.S.: 424210
Personnel:
Ullas Patel *(Founder & Mng Dir)*
Nitesh Patel *(Partner)*

ARROWHEAD PROPERTIES LIMITED

2nd Floor 18 Melrose Boulevard
Melrose, South Africa
Mailing Address:
PO Box 685
Melrose, 2076, South Africa
Tel.: (27) 10 100 0076
Fax: (27) 86 614 4329
E-Mail: info@arrowheadproperties.co.za
Web Site: www.arrowheadproperties.co.za
Year Founded: 2011
ARROW—(JSE)
Rev.: $30,184,225
Assets: $274,733,277
Liabilities: $90,382,073
Net Worth: $184,351,204
Earnings: $21,055,807
Fiscal Year-end: 09/30/12
Business Description:
Real Estate Development Services
S.I.C.: 6531
N.A.I.C.S.: 531390
Personnel:
Gerald Leissner *(CEO)*
Imraan Suleman *(CFO)*
Mark Kaplan *(COO)*
Board of Directors:
Taffy Adler
Matthew Nell
Selwyn Noik
Elize Stroebel
Legal Counsel:
Java Capital (Pty) Ltd
2 Arnold Road
Rosebank, 2196, South Africa
Transfer Agent:
Computershare Investor Services (Proprietary) Limited
70 Marshall Street
Johannesburg, South Africa

ARROWHEAD WATER PRODUCTS LTD.

(Acquired & Absorbed by Ice River Springs Water Company Inc.)

ARROWSTAR RESOURCES LTD.

Suite 507 - 475 Howe Street
Vancouver, BC, V6C 2B3, Canada
Tel.: (604) 687-7828
Fax: (604) 687-7848
E-Mail: info@arrowstarresources.com
Web Site: www.arrowstarresources.com
AWS—(TSXV)
Int. Income: $7,601
Assets: $895,151
Liabilities: $177,323
Net Worth: $717,828
Earnings: ($2,116,060)
Fiscal Year-end: 12/31/12
Business Description:
Iron Ore Exploration Services
S.I.C.: 1011
N.A.I.C.S.: 212210
Personnel:
Robert L. Card *(Pres)*
Blaine Y. Bailey *(CFO)*
Betty Anne Loy *(Sec)*
Board of Directors:
Robert L. Card
Andrew Jarvis
Phillip Thomas
Legal Counsel:
McMillan LLP
1500 Royal Centre 1050 West Georgia Street
PO Box 11117
Vancouver, BC, Canada
Transfer Agent:
Computershare Trust Company of Canada
4th Floor, 510 Burrard Street
V6C3B9 Vancouver, BC, Canada

ARSENAL ENERGY INC.

Suite 1900 639-5th Avenue SW
Calgary, AB, T2P 0M9, Canada
Tel.: (403) 262-4854
Fax: (403) 265-6877
Toll Free: (866) 405-4854
E-Mail: info@arsenalenergy.com
Web Site: www.arsenalenergy.com
Year Founded: 2002
AEI—(OTC TSX)
Rev.: $81,676,635
Assets: $181,365,907
Liabilities: $126,667,969
Net Worth: $54,697,939
Earnings: ($111,330)
Emp.: 33
Fiscal Year-end: 12/31/12
Business Description:
Oil & Natural Gas Services
S.I.C.: 4924
N.A.I.C.S.: 221210
Personnel:
R. Neil MacKay *(Chm)*
Tony Van Winkoop *(Pres & CEO)*
J. Paul Lawrence *(CFO & VP-Fin)*
Donald B. Edwards *(Sec)*
Board of Directors:
R. Neil MacKay
William Charles Hews
R. Harley Kempthorne
Derek Petrie
Bill Powers
Tony Van Winkoop
Transfer Agent:
Computershare Trust Company of Canada
Ste 600 530 8th Ave SW
Calgary, AB, Canada T2P 3S8
Tel.: (800) 558-0046
Subsidiary:

Geocan Energy Inc. (1)
639 5th Avenue SW Suite 1900
Calgary, AB, T2P 0M9, Canada AB
Tel.: (403) 262-4854
Fax: (403) 265-6877
E-Mail: info@arsenalenergy.com
Web Site: www.arsenalenergy.com
Sales Range: $25-49.9 Million
Emp.: 25
Oil & Gas Exploration Services
S.I.C.: 1311
N.A.I.C.S.: 211111

ARSEUS NV

Textielstraat 24
8790 Waregem, Belgium
Tel.: (32) 883311211
Fax: (32) 883311210
E-Mail: info@arseus.com
Web Site: www.arseus.com
Year Founded: 1988
RCUS—(EUR)
Rev.: $737,166,731
Assets: $1,008,138,636
Liabilities: $677,810,057
Net Worth: $330,328,579
Earnings: $58,990,516
Emp.: 2,370
Fiscal Year-end: 12/31/12
Business Description:
Professional Health Services; Owned 24.19% by Omega Pharma NV
S.I.C.: 6321
N.A.I.C.S.: 524114
Personnel:
Robert Peek *(Chm)*
Gerardus van Jeveren *(CEO)*
Jan Peeters *(CFO)*
Mario Huyghe *(CEO-Arseus Dental en Arseus Medical)*
Dirk Van Lerberghe *(CEO-Corilus)*
Board of Directors:
Robert Peek
Marc Coucke
Julien De Wilde
Jan Peeters
Johannes Stols
Cedric Van Cauwenberghe
Gerardus van Jeveren
Luc A. C. P. Vandewalle
Frank Vlayen
Subsidiaries:

Arseus BV (1)
Kralingseweg 207-211
3062 Rotterdam, Netherlands
Tel.: (31) 883311211
Fax: (31) 883311201
E-Mail: info@arseus.com
Emp.: 40
Pharmaceuticals Whslr
S.I.C.: 5912
N.A.I.C.S.: 446110
Gerardus van Jeveren *(CEO)*

Arseus Medical BV (1)
Gelderlandhaven 4
3433 PG Nieuwegein, Netherlands
Tel.: (31) 306060330
Fax: (31) 306062047
E-Mail: info@schinkelmedical.nl
Web Site: www.schinkelmedical.nl
Emp.: 22
Medical & Surgical Instruments Mfr
S.I.C.: 3841
N.A.I.C.S.: 339112
Frans A. W. Bours *(Mng Dir)*

De Collegiale Bereiding BV (1)
Hinmanweg 13 A
7575 BE Oldenzaal, Netherlands
Tel.: (31) 541573240
Fax: (31) 541573241
E-Mail: c.arkes@spruyt-hillen.nl
Web Site: www.spruyt-hillen.nl
Emp.: 6
Pharmaceuticals Whslr & Distr
S.I.C.: 5122
N.A.I.C.S.: 424210
John Kohler *(Gen Mgr)*

Fagron Group BV (1)
Venkelbaan 101
2908 KE Capelle aan den IJssel, Netherlands
Tel.: (31) 883311200
Fax: (31) 883311111
E-Mail: industry@fagron.com
Web Site: www.fagron.com
Emp.: 60
Pharmaceutical Raw Materials Mfr
S.I.C.: 2834
N.A.I.C.S.: 325412
Ger van Jeveren *(Founder & CEO)*

Subsidiary:

Fagron BV (2)
Hoogeveenenweg 210
2913 LV Nieuwerkerk, Netherlands
Tel.: (31) 180331133
Fax: (31) 180331111
E-Mail: wavanlatum@fagron.com
Web Site: www.fagron.nl
Pharmaceuticals Mfr
S.I.C.: 2834
N.A.I.C.S.: 325412

U.S. Subsidiary:

Fagron, Inc. (2)
(Formerly Gallipot, Inc.)
2400 Pilot Knob Rd
Saint Paul, MN 55120 MN
Tel.: (651) 681-9517
Fax: (800) 339-1596
E-Mail: info@fagron.us
Web Site: www.fagron.us
Sales Range: $10-24.9 Million
Emp.: 29
Pharmaceutical Preparations Mfr
S.I.C.: 2834
N.A.I.C.S.: 325412
Mellisa Urban *(Mgr-Ops)*

Subsidiary:

B&B Pharmaceuticals, Inc. (3)
17200 E Ohio Dr
Aurora, CO 80017
Tel.: (303) 755-5110
Fax: (303) 755-5242
Toll Free: (800) 499-3100
E-Mail: bbpharm@mindspring.com
Web Site: www.bandbpharmaceuticals.com
Active Pharmaceuticals Ingredients Mfr
S.I.C.: 2834
N.A.I.C.S.: 325412
Bonnie Dassinger *(Pres)*

Non-U.S. Subsidiaries:

Fagron GmbH & Co KG (2)
Von Bronsart St 12
22885 Barsbuttel, Germany
Tel.: (49) 40670675
Fax: (49) 4067067670
E-Mail: info@fagron.de
Web Site: www.fagron.de
Pharmaceutical Mfr
S.I.C.: 2834
N.A.I.C.S.: 325412
Kristina Frost *(Mgr-Mktg)*

Fagron Iberica SAU (2)
Carrer de Josep
Tapiolas 15, Terrassa, Spain
Tel.: (34) 937310722
Fax: (34) 937311644
E-Mail: info@fagron.es
Web Site: www.fagron.com
Emp.: 50
Pharmaceuticals Mfr
S.I.C.: 2834
N.A.I.C.S.: 325412
Manuel Martin *(Mgr)*

Fagron Services BVBA (2)
Industrieweg 2
2850 Boom, Belgium
Tel.: (32) 34440720
Fax: (32) 34440729
Web Site: www.fagron.be
Emp.: 11
Pharmaceuticals Mfr
S.I.C.: 2834
N.A.I.C.S.: 325412
Marc Lenssens *(Mgr)*

Fagron UK Ltd (2)
Fifth Fl 1 Pink Ln
Newcastle upon Tyne, NE1 5DW, United Kingdom
Tel.: (44) 8456522525
Fax: (44) 191 211 1159
E-Mail: info@fagron.co.uk
Web Site: www.fagron.co.uk
Pharmaceuticals Mfr & Distr

S.I.C.: 2834
N.A.I.C.S.: 325412

Lamoral BV (1)
Cartografenweg 18
5141 MT Waalwijk, Netherlands
Tel.: (31) 416650010
Fax: (31) 416650025
E-Mail: info@lamoral.nl
Web Site: www.lamoral.nl
Emp.: 52
Pharmaceuticals Mfr
S.I.C.: 2834
N.A.I.C.S.: 325412
Louis Van De Mortel *(Gen Mgr)*

Spruyt hillen BV (1)
Tinbergenlaan 1
NL-3401 MT IJsselstein, Netherlands
Mailing Address:
Postbus 46
3400 AA IJsselstein, Netherlands
Tel.: (31) 302814411
Fax: (31) 302814444
E-Mail: algemeen@spruyt-hillen.nl
Web Site: www.spruyt-hillen.nl
Emp.: 52
Pharmaceuticals Products Mfr
S.I.C.: 2834
N.A.I.C.S.: 325412
John Korler *(Mgr)*

Timm Health Care BV (1)
Lorentzlaan 4
NL-3401 MX IJsselstein, Netherlands NL
Mailing Address:
Postbus 46
NL-3400 AA IJsselstein, Netherlands
Tel.: (31) 302814472
Fax: (31) 302814464
E-Mail: info@timmhealthcare.nl
Web Site: www.timmhealthcare.nl
Emp.: 8
Health Care Services
S.I.C.: 8099
N.A.I.C.S.: 621999
Jeroen Slooter *(Gen Mgr)*

XO CARE The Netherlands BV (1)
Bijsterhuizen 20-18A
6604 LJ Wijchen, Netherlands
Tel.: (31) 246778776
E-Mail: info@xo-care.nl
Web Site: www.xo-care.nl
Dental Equipments Mfr
S.I.C.: 3843
N.A.I.C.S.: 339114

Non-U.S. Subsidiaries:

APPEG SA (1)
Rue de la Sambre 6
6032 Charleroi, Belgium
Tel.: (32) 71362929
Fax: (32) 7147 2142
Pharmaceuticals Distr
S.I.C.: 5912
N.A.I.C.S.: 446110

Arseus Hospital NV (1)
Rigksweg 10
2610 Bornem, Belgium
Tel.: (32) 38307300
Fax: (32) 38252370
E-Mail: info@arseusmedical.be
Web Site: www.arseus.com
Emp.: 30
Hospital Services
S.I.C.: 8062
N.A.I.C.S.: 622110
Mario Huyghe *(CEO)*

Arseus Tec NV (1)
Textielstraat 24
Waregem, Belgium
Tel.: (32) 56628866
Fax: (32) 50 310574
Pharmaceuticals Mfr
S.I.C.: 2834
N.A.I.C.S.: 325412
Andres Depoorter *(Mgr)*

Denteco 2000 SA (1)
ZAC du Pre Catelan
Rue Delesalle, La Madeleine, France
Tel.: (33) 320061515
Fax: (33) 320744343
Pharmaceuticals Mfr
S.I.C.: 2834
N.A.I.C.S.: 325412

Dorge Medic SA (1)
Chausse de Nivelles 351
5020 Namur, Belgium
Tel.: (32) 81742884
Fax: (32) 81742558
Emp.: 12
Medical Services
S.I.C.: 5047
N.A.I.C.S.: 423450
Collin Christine *(Mng Dir)*

Eurotec Dental GmbH (1)
Forumstrasse 12
4468 Neuss, Germany
Tel.: (49) 21311257872
Fax: (49) 21311333480
E-Mail: info@eurotec-dental.info
Web Site: www.eurotec-dental.info
Emp.: 4
Dental Equipment Mfr
S.I.C.: 3843
N.A.I.C.S.: 339114

Hader SA (1)
Rue Jardiniere 153
2300 La Chaux-de-Fonds, Switzerland
Tel.: (41) 329259050
Fax: (41) 329259069
E-Mail: info@hader-swiss.com
Web Site: www.hader-swiss.com
Emp.: 100
Medical Instruments Mfr
S.I.C.: 3841
N.A.I.C.S.: 339112
Olivier Zaugg *(Gen Mgr)*

JPG Pharma NV (1)
Ondernemersstraat 4
2500 Lier, Belgium
Tel.: (32) 34800980
Fax: (32) 34887764
E-Mail: info@jpgpharma.be
Web Site: www.jpgpharma.be
Emp.: 10
Pharmaceuticals Whslr
S.I.C.: 5122
N.A.I.C.S.: 424210
Joeri Van *(Mng Dir)*

Lamoral NV (1)
Textielstraat 20
8790 Waregem, Belgium
Tel.: (32) 56628953
Fax: (32) 56628899
E-Mail: dental@lamoral.be
Web Site: www.lamoral.be
Emp.: 20
Dental Care Services
S.I.C.: 8072
N.A.I.C.S.: 339116
Edi Droogmans *(Mgr-Sls)*

Multident GmbH (1)
Pelikanplatz 25
30177 Hannover, Germany
Tel.: (49) 511530050
Fax: (49) 51155470833
E-Mail: info@multident.de
Web Site: www.multident.de
Emp.: 100
Pharmaceuticals Mfr
S.I.C.: 2834
N.A.I.C.S.: 325412
Lars Johnsen *(CEO)*

Nolte GmbH (1)
Konrad-Nolte-St 40
76726 Germersheim, Germany
Tel.: (49) 727494700
Fax: (49) 72749470220
E-Mail: info@nolte-hws.de
Web Site: www.rheinspan.de
Pharmaceuticals Mfr
S.I.C.: 2834
N.A.I.C.S.: 325412
Rolf Stadler *(Mgr)*

Owandy SAS (1)
Allee Kepler 4 5
77447 Champs-sur-Marne, France
Tel.: (33) 164111818
Fax: (33) 164111810
E-Mail: info@owandy.com
Web Site: www.owandy.com
Dental Equipment & Instrument Mfr
S.I.C.: 3843
N.A.I.C.S.: 339114
Boris Loyez *(Gen Mgr)*

U.S. Subsidiary:

Owandy Inc (2)
c o Jade Associates 192 Lexington Ave
New York, NY 10016
Tel.: (212) 673-1200
Fax: (212) 504-0871
E-Mail: info.usa@owandy.com
Digital Cameras Mfr
S.I.C.: 3577
N.A.I.C.S.: 334118

Non-U.S. Subsidiaries:

Owandy Iberia SL (2)
C General Margallo 25
28020 Madrid, Spain
Tel.: (34) 912 534 332
Fax: (34) 912 534 098
E-Mail: informacion@owandy.com
Web Site: www.owandy.es/
Digital Cameras Mfr
S.I.C.: 3575
N.A.I.C.S.: 334118

Owandy Radiologie Italia Srl (2)
Via del Guado 57
Desio, Monza, 20033, Italy
Tel.: (39) 0362621106
Fax: (39) 0362627707
Dental Equipment & Instruments Mfr
S.I.C.: 3843
N.A.I.C.S.: 339114

Pharmaflore SA (1)
Rue Botrieux 7
7864 Lessines, Belgium
Tel.: (32) 68332105
Fax: (32) 68336937
E-Mail: pharmaflore@skynet.be
Web Site: www.pharmaflore.be
Emp.: 15
Medicinal Products Mfr
S.I.C.: 2834
N.A.I.C.S.: 325412
Failures Elke *(Gen Mgr)*

Van Hopplynus Ophtalm SA (1)
Rue Colonel Bourg 105
1030 Brussels, Belgium
Tel.: (32) 27022828
Fax: (32) 27022829
E-Mail: info@vho.be
Web Site: www.vho.be
Emp.: 50
Medical Instruments & Apparatus Mfr
S.I.C.: 3841
N.A.I.C.S.: 339112
Gui Van de Wever *(Mng Dir)*

ARSHIYA INTERNATIONAL LTD.

301 Ceejay House Level 3 Shiv
Sagar Estate F-Block
Dr Annie Besant Road Worli,
Mumbai, Maharashtra, 400 018, India
Tel.: (91) 2242305500
Fax: (91) 2242305555
E-Mail: info@arshiyainternational.com
Web Site: www.arshiyainternational.com
ARSHIYA—(NSE)
Rev.: $212,549,168
Assets: $757,001,294
Liabilities: $595,679,516
Net Worth: $161,321,778
Earnings: ($23,574,211)
Fiscal Year-end: 03/31/13

Business Description:
Logistics Consulting Services
S.I.C.: 4731
N.A.I.C.S.: 541614

Personnel:
Ajay S. Mittal *(Chm & Co-Mng Dir)*
Archana A. Mittal *(Co-Mng Dir)*
Shyam Rathi *(CFO)*
Uday Pimprikar *(Chief Comml Officer & Chief Plng Officer)*
Suhas Thakar *(Chief Infrastructure & Regulatory Officer)*
S. Maheshwari *(Pres-Fin & Corp Affairs)*

Board of Directors:
Ajay S. Mittal
Ashish Bairagra
Mukesh Kacker
Archana A. Mittal
G. Raghuram
Rishabh P. Shah
Suhas Thakar

Transfer Agent:
Bigshare Services Pvt. Ltd.
E-2/3 Ansa Industrial Estate Sakivihar Road
Saki Naka Andheri E
Mumbai, India

ARSS INFRASTRUCTURE PROJECTS LIMITED

Plot-no-38 Sector-A Zone-D
Mancheswar Industrial Estate
Bhubaneswar, Odisha, 751 010, India
Tel.: (91) 6742588552
Fax: (91) 6742585074
E-Mail: response@arssgroup.in
Web Site: www.arssgroup.in
ARSSINFRA—(BOM)
Rev.: $144,704,973
Assets: $381,947,900
Liabilities: $313,496,364
Net Worth: $68,451,536
Earnings: ($11,974,345)
Emp.: 1,700
Fiscal Year-end: 03/31/13

Business Description:
Railway Infrastructure, Roads, Highways, Bridges & Irrigation Construction Services
S.I.C.: 1622
N.A.I.C.S.: 237310

Personnel:
Subash Agarwal *(Chm)*
Sunil Agarwal *(Pres & CEO)*
Rajesh Agarwal *(Mng Dir)*
Soumendra Keshari Pattanaik *(CFO & Dir-Fin)*
Anil Agarwal *(COO & Sr VP)*
Sushanta Pradhan *(Compliance Officer & Sec)*
Balvir Singh *(Exec VP-Northern)*

Board of Directors:
Subash Agarwal
Rajesh Agarwal
Bommana Ramesh Babu
Upendra Nath Challu
Swarup Chandra Parija
Soumendra Keshari Pattanaik
Krishna Chandra Rout
Parmod Kumar Sharma

Transfer Agent:
Bigshare Services Private Limited
E-2 Ansa Industrial Estate Sakivihar Road Saki Naka Andheri (E)
Mumbai, India

ART ADVANCED RESEARCH TECHNOLOGIES INC.

2300 Alfred Nobel Boulevard
Saint Laurent, QC, H4S 2A4, Canada
Tel.: (514) 832-0777
Fax: (514) 832-0778
E-Mail: info@art.ca
Web Site: www.art.ca
Year Founded: 1993
Sales Range: $1-9.9 Million
Emp.: 58

Business Description:
Optical Imaging Products Developer, Mfr & Marketer
S.I.C.: 3827
N.A.I.C.S.: 333314

Personnel:
Sebastien Gignac *(Pres & CEO)*
Jacques Bedard *(CFO)*
Joseph G. Kozikowski *(Chief Medical Officer)*
Marie-France Nantel *(Sec)*

ART Advanced Research Technologies Inc.—(Continued)

Legal Counsel:
Osler, Hoskin & Harcourt, LLP
1000 de la Gauchetiere Street West
Suite 2100
Montreal, QC, H3B 4W5, Canada

Transfer Agent:
National Bank Trust
1100 University Fl 12
Montreal, QC, H3B 2J7, Canada
Tel.: (514) 871-7240
Fax: (514) 871-7587

ART & FRAGRANCE S.A.
Buhlstrasse 1
CH 8125 Zolikerberg, Switzerland
Tel.: (41) 434994500
Fax: (41) 434994501
E-Mail: info@art-fragrance.com
Web Site: www.art-fragrance.com
ARTN—(SWX)
Rev.: $120,118,602
Assets: $202,453,449
Liabilities: $127,057,550
Net Worth: $75,395,899
Earnings: $10,461,849
Emp.: 436
Fiscal Year-end: 12/31/12
Business Description:
Perfumes & Cosmetic Products Developer & Distr
S.I.C.: 5122
N.A.I.C.S.: 446120
Personnel:
Silvio Denz *(Chm)*
Roland Weber *(Vice Chm)*
Roger von der Weid *(CEO)*
Claudio Denz *(COO)*
Board of Directors:
Silvio Denz
Claudio Denz
Marc Roesti
Roger von der Weid
Roland Weber

Non-U.S. Subsidiary:

Lalique S.A. (1)
11 Rue Royale
75008 Paris, France (99.3%)
Tel.: (33) 153051212
Fax: (33) 153051282
E-Mail: shop.paris.rueroyale@lalique.fr
Web Site: www.lalique.com
Sales Range: $75-99.9 Million
Emp.: 650
Crystal Mfr
S.I.C.: 3679
N.A.I.C.S.: 334419
Catherine Vincent Dolor *(Dir-Press)*

U.S. Affiliate:

Lalique North America (2)
25 Branca Rd
East Rutherford, NJ 07073 NY
Tel.: (201) 939-4199
Fax: (201) 939-4492
Toll Free: (800) 993-2580
E-Mail: info@lalique.com
Web Site: www.cristallalique.fr/v2/
Emp.: 60
French Crystal Distr
Import
S.I.C.: 5023
N.A.I.C.S.: 423220
James Munn *(Controller)*

THE ART SHOPPE LTD.
2131 Yonge Street
Toronto, ON, M4S 2A7, Canada
Tel.: (416) 487-3211
Fax: (416) 487-3221
Web Site: www.theartshoppe.com
Year Founded: 1934
Rev.: $10,626,605
Emp.: 75
Business Description:
Furniture Mfr
S.I.C.: 2521
N.A.I.C.S.: 337211
Personnel:
Martin Offman *(Pres & CEO)*

ARTAFLEX INC.
96 Steelcase Rd W
Markham, ON, L3R 8T9, Canada
Tel.: (905) 470-0109
Fax: (905) 470-0621
Toll Free: (866) 502-3378
Web Site: www.artaflex.com
Year Founded: 1985
Sales Range: $50-74.9 Million
Emp.: 385
Business Description:
Electronic Equipments Instruments & Components Mfr
S.I.C.: 3669
N.A.I.C.S.: 334290
Personnel:
Paul Walker *(Chm, Pres & CEO)*
Jonathan Szczur *(CFO)*
Phil Woodard *(COO & Sec)*
Trent Carruthers *(Exec VP)*
Gerardo Iuliano *(Exec VP)*
Board of Directors:
Paul Walker
Derek D'Andrade
Paul Langston
David McKee
Peter Tolnai
Phil Woodard

ARTAL LUXEMBOURG S.A.
105 Rue Grand
L 1661 Luxembourg, Luxembourg
Tel.: (352) 224259
Fax: (352) 22425922
Emp.: 50
Business Description:
Holding Company
S.I.C.: 6719
N.A.I.C.S.: 551112

U.S. Holding:

Weight Watchers International, Inc. (1)
675 Ave of the Americas 6th Fl
New York, NY 10010 VA
Tel.: (212) 589-2700
Fax: (212) 589-2601
Toll Free: (800) 651-6000
Web Site: www.weightwatchersinternational.com
WTW—(NYSE)
Rev.: $1,724,123,000
Assets: $1,408,931,000
Liabilities: $2,883,553,000
Net Worth: ($1,474,622,000)
Earnings: $204,725,000
Emp.: 25,000
Fiscal Year-end: 12/28/13
Weight-Control Classes & Related Services
S.I.C.: 7299
N.A.I.C.S.: 812990
Raymond Debbane *(Chm)*
James R. Chambers *(Pres & CEO)*
Nicholas P. Hotchkin *(CFO)*
Dan Crowe *(CTO)*
Ann Hollins *(Chief HR Officer)*
Michael Basone *(Pres-WeightWatchers.com)*
Lesya Lysyj *(Pres-North America)*
Bruce Rosengarten *(Pres-Asia Pacific)*
Melanie Stack *(Pres-Europe)*
Amy Kossover *(Sr VP-Corp Fin & Controller)*
Colin F. Watts *(Sr VP-Health Solutions & Global Innovation)*

Subsidiary:

WeightWatchers.Com, Inc. (2)
11 Madison Ave 17th Fl
New York, NY 10010
Tel.: (212) 817-4214
Fax: (212) 315-0709
Toll Free: (800) 651-6000
Web Site: www.weightwatchers.com
Weight Management Services
S.I.C.: 7299
N.A.I.C.S.: 812191
David P. Kirchoff *(Pres & CEO)*
Karen Miller-Kovach *(Chife Scientific Officer)*
Alexandra Alexkovsky *(Sr VP & Gen Mgr)*

Non-U.S. Subsidiaries:

Centro de Cuidado Del Peso, S. de R.L. de C.V. (2)
Calle Barranca Del Muerto 210 P B Alvaro Obregon
Mexico, Mexico
Tel.: (52) 5556118303
Fax: (52) 5555985495
Emp.: 10
Weight Management Services
S.I.C.: 7299
N.A.I.C.S.: 812191

Weight Watchers Canada, Ltd. (2)
2295 Bristol Circle Suite 200
Oakville, ON, L6H 6P8, Canada
Tel.: (800) 387-8227
Fax: (902) 468-3039
Weight Management Services
S.I.C.: 7299
N.A.I.C.S.: 812191

Weight Watchers Continental Europe (2)
Millennium House
Ludlow Road, Maidenhead, Berkshire, SL6 2SL, United Kingdom (100%)
Tel.: (44) 01628415286
Fax: (44) 1628415242
E-Mail: carnstrong@weight-watchers.co.uk
Web Site: www.weight-watchers.co.uk
Emp.: 150
Weight Loss Seminars; Manufacturer & Marketing of Diet Foods
S.I.C.: 7299
N.A.I.C.S.: 812191
Melanie Stubbing *(Pres-Europe)*

Weight Watchers Denmark APS (2)
Toldbodgade 51b Sal 2
Copenhagen, 1253, Denmark
Tel.: (45) 33110141
Weight Management Services
S.I.C.: 7299
N.A.I.C.S.: 812191

Weight Watchers (Deutschland) Gmbh (2)
Derendorfer Allee 33
40476 Dusseldorf, Germany
Tel.: (49) 2119686180
Fax: (49) 211686260
E-Mail: marketing@weight-watchers.de
Web Site: www.weightwatchers.de
Weight Management Services
S.I.C.: 7299
N.A.I.C.S.: 812191

Weight Watchers European Holding AB (2)
Fredriksbergsgatan 16
212 11 Malmo, Sweden
Tel.: (46) 424900900
Investment Management Services
S.I.C.: 6211
N.A.I.C.S.: 523999

Weight Watchers (Exercise) Ltd. (2)
Kidswell Park House
Maidenhead, SL6 8YT, United Kingdom
Tel.: (44) 8453451500
Weight Management Services
S.I.C.: 7299
N.A.I.C.S.: 812191

Weight Watchers International Pty. Ltd (2)
Level 5 1-3 Smail St
Ultimo, NSW, 2007, Australia
Tel.: (61) 2992281300
Fax: (61) 292114600
E-Mail: custmerservice@weightwatchers.com.au
Web Site: www.weightwatchers.com.au
Weight Management Services
S.I.C.: 7299
N.A.I.C.S.: 812191
David Kirchoff, *(CEO)*

Weight Watchers Operations Spain S.L. (2)
Calle Joan D Austria 39 - Piso 4 B
Barcelona, 08005, Spain
Tel.: (34) 933556600
Web Site: ww.entulinea.es
Weight Management Services
S.I.C.: 7299
N.A.I.C.S.: 812191

Weight Watchers Polska Spz.o.o. (2)
Ostroroga 24a
01-163 Warsaw, Poland
Tel.: (48) 223123223
Weight Management Services
S.I.C.: 7299
N.A.I.C.S.: 812191

Weight Watchers Services Pty Ltd (2)
Level 5 1-3 Smail St
Ultimo, NSW, 2007, Australia
Tel.: (61) 131997
E-Mail: customerservice@weightwatchers.com.au
Web Site: www.weightwatchers.com.au
Weight Management Services
S.I.C.: 7299
N.A.I.C.S.: 812191

Weight Watchers Sweden ViktVaktarna Akiebolag (2)
Hyllie Boulevard 17
215 32 Malmo, Sweden
Tel.: (46) 200113116
E-Mail: info@viktvaktarna.se
Web Site: www.viktvaktarna.se
Weight Management Services
S.I.C.: 7299
N.A.I.C.S.: 812191

Weight Watchers (U.K.) Limited (2)
Millennium House Ludlow Road
Maidenhead, Berkshire, SL6 2SL, United Kingdom
Tel.: (44) 1628415200
Fax: (44) 1628415263
E-Mail: uk.help@weightwatchers.co.uk
Web Site: www.weightwatchers.co.uk
Emp.: 160
Weight Management Services
S.I.C.: 7299
N.A.I.C.S.: 812191
Andrew Knight, *(Sr VP)*

WeightWatchers.fr S.A.R.L. (2)
Parc Ariane - Batiment Mars
78284 Guyancourt, France
Tel.: (33) 130147000
E-Mail: legal@weightwatchers.fr
Web Site: www.weightwatchers.fr
Weight Management Services
S.I.C.: 7299
N.A.I.C.S.: 812191
Corinne Polier *(Gen Mgr)*

WeightWatchers.nl B.V. (2)
Bijster 12
4817 HX Breda, Netherlands
Tel.: (31) 765234000
Web Site: www.weightwatchers.nl
Weight Management Services
S.I.C.: 7299
N.A.I.C.S.: 812191

Non-U.S. Subsidiary:

Artal Holland B.V. (1)
Ijsselburcht 3
Arnhem, Gelderland, 6825, Netherlands
Mailing Address:
Postbus 5486
Arnhem, 6802, Netherlands
Tel.: (31) 263653523
Fax: (31) 263653524
Holding Company
S.I.C.: 6719
N.A.I.C.S.: 551112

Non-U.S. Joint Venture:

AFG Company Limited (2)
Food Town Industrial Port Area
Shaping Town, Heshan, Guangdong, China
Tel.: (86) 7508821028
Fax: (86) 7508820790
Sales Range: $250-299.9 Million
Emp.: 562
Processed Meat Producer, Seller & Distr
S.I.C.: 2099
N.A.I.C.S.: 311999

ARTEFACT PROJECTS LTD.

Artefact Tower 54/3 Chhatrapati Square Wardha Road
Nagpur, 440 015, India
Tel.: (91) 712 3025120
Fax: (91) 712 3025128
E-Mail: artefactngp@artefactprojects.com
Web Site: www.artefactprojects.com
531297—(BOM)
Rev.: $7,465,112
Assets: $15,332,126
Liabilities: $8,473,898
Net Worth: $6,858,227
Earnings: $338,469
Emp.: 221
Fiscal Year-end: 03/31/13
Business Description:
Engineering & Architectural Services
S.I.C.: 8711
N.A.I.C.S.: 541330
Personnel:
Manoj B. Shah *(CEO & Mng Dir)*
Lucky A. Popli *(Compliance Officer & Sec)*
Board of Directors:
Mohandas S. Adige
Sandeep M. Batta
Girish R. Dhabalia
Ashok P. Mehta
Deepak B. Mehta
Manoj B. Shah
Pankaj B. Shah
Siddharth P. Shah

Chaturvedi & Shah
Mumbai, India
Transfer Agent:
Link Intime India Pvt Ltd
C-13 Kantilal Maganlal Estate Pannalal Silk Mills Compound L B S Marg
Bhandup West, Mumbai, India

Subsidiary:

Artefact Infrastructure Ltd. **(1)**
Chhatrapati Square Wardha Road
Nagpur, Maharashtra, 440 015, India
Tel.: (91) 712 3025120
Fax: (91) 712 3025127
E-Mail: artefactngp@artefactprojects.com
Emp.: 100
Bridge & Building Construction Services
S.I.C.: 1611
N.A.I.C.S.: 237310

ARTEK EXPLORATION LTD.

Suite 2300 520 5th Avenue SW
Calgary, AB, T2P 3R7, Canada
Tel.: (403) 532-1888
Fax: (403) 532-1890
E-Mail: info@artekexploration.com
Web Site: www.artekexploration.com
Year Founded: 2004
RTK—(TSX)
Rev.: $40,859,192
Assets: $179,387,807
Liabilities: $64,887,638
Net Worth: $114,500,170
Earnings: ($2,159,011)
Emp.: 14
Fiscal Year-end: 12/31/12
Business Description:
Oil & Gas Exploration Services
S.I.C.: 1311
N.A.I.C.S.: 211111
Personnel:
M. Bruce Chernoff *(Chm)*
Darryl F. Metcalfe *(Pres & CEO)*
Darcy Anderson *(CFO & VP-Fin)*
Michael Sandrelli *(Sec)*
Board of Directors:
M. Bruce Chernoff
Gary F. Aitken
Darryl F. Metcalfe
Rafi G. Tahmazian
David J. Wilson
Legal Counsel:
Burnet, Duckworth & Palmer LLP
Calgary, AB, Canada
Transfer Agent:
Valiant Trust Company
606 4th Street SW Suite 310
Calgary, AB, T2P 1T1, Canada
Tel.: (403) 233-2801
Fax: (403) 233-2857

ARTEL SOLUTIONS GROUP HOLDINGS LIMITED

Unit A 8th Floor St John's Building 33 Garden Road
Central, China (Hong Kong)
Tel.: (852) 3691 9988
Fax: (852) 3691 8282
Web Site: artelgroup.todayir.com
931—(HKG)
Emp.: 5
Business Description:
Investment Management Services
S.I.C.: 6282
N.A.I.C.S.: 523920
Personnel:
Billy Albert Che Kin Kan *(Chm & CEO)*
Ying Seto *(CFO & Sec)*
Board of Directors:
Billy Albert Che Kin Kan
Woon Lai Ip
Kong Leong Lee
Arthur Albert Kai Yien Li
Eleanor Stella Shu Han Li
Siu Yui Li

ARTEMIS OPTICAL LIMITED

1 Western Wood Way Langage Science Park
Plympton, Plymouth, Devon, PL7 5BG, United Kingdom
Tel.: (44) 1752 341 943
Fax: (44) 1752 342 467
Web Site: www.artemis-optical.co.uk
Emp.: 35
Business Description:
Optical Thin Film Coatings Mfr
S.I.C.: 3827
N.A.I.C.S.: 333314
Personnel:
Ian Moyes *(Chm)*

ARTEMIS RESOURCES LTD

Level 9 50 Margaret Street
Sydney, NSW, 2000, Australia
Tel.: (61) 2 9078 7670
Fax: (61) 2 9078 7661
E-Mail: info@artemisresources.com.au
Web Site: www.artemisresources.com.au
ARV—(ASX)
Rev.: $16,989
Assets: $9,503,086
Liabilities: $904,320
Net Worth: $8,598,766
Earnings: ($1,177,427)
Fiscal Year-end: 06/30/13
Business Description:
Mining industry
S.I.C.: 8711
N.A.I.C.S.: 541330
Personnel:
Guy Robertson *(COO & Sec)*
Board of Directors:
Shannon Coates
George Frangeskides
Guy Robertson

ARTEMIS U.S. CAPITAL APPRECIATION FUND

(Formerly Omega Advisors U.S. Capital Appreciation Fund)
5 Hazelton Avenue Suite 200
Toronto, ON, M5R 2E1, Canada
Tel.: (647) 477-4883
Fax: (416) 934-7459
E-Mail: rosten@artemisfunds.ca
Year Founded: 2011
AUF—(TSX)
Rev.: $645,284
Assets: $38,136,257
Liabilities: $328,557
Net Worth: $37,807,700
Earnings: ($761,001)
Fiscal Year-end: 12/31/12
Business Description:
Investment Services
S.I.C.: 6211
N.A.I.C.S.: 523999
Personnel:
Miles S. Nadal *(Chm)*
Conor Bill *(Pres & CEO)*
Trevor Maunder *(CFO & Sec)*
Board of Directors:
Miles S. Nadal
Trevor Maunder
Transfer Agent:
Valiant Trust Company
Toronto, ON, Canada

ARTEON PLC

3rd Floor 38 Bow Lane
London, EC4M 9AY, United Kingdom
Tel.: (44) 20 7148 7700
Fax: (44) 20 7148 7701
E-Mail: info@arteonplc.com
Web Site: www.arteonplc.com
ARTO—(LSE)
Sales Range: $1-9.9 Million
Business Description:
Holding Company; Data & Data Products for Horse Racing & Betting; Owned 38% by IPGL Ltd
S.I.C.: 7999
N.A.I.C.S.: 713290
Personnel:
Peter John Hagerty *(Chm)*
Board of Directors:
Peter John Hagerty
Patrick Aisher
David MacFarlane

ARTERIA S.A.

ul Jana Rosola 10
02-797 Warsaw, Poland
Tel.: (48) 226488072
Fax: (48) 226484073
E-Mail: recepcja@arteriasa.com
ARR—(WAR)
Sales Range: $25-49.9 Million
Business Description:
Marketing Services
S.I.C.: 7389
N.A.I.C.S.: 561422
Personnel:
Dariusz Stokowski *(Chm-Supervisory Bd)*
Wojciech Bienkowski *(Chm-Mgmt Bd)*
Cezary Kubacki *(Vice Chm-Supervisory Bd)*
Marcin Marzec *(Vice Chm-Mgmt Bd)*
Wojciech Glapa *(Member-Mgmt Bd)*
Grzegorz Grygiel *(Member-Mgmt Bd)*
Supervisory Board of Directors:
Dariusz Stokowski
Tomasz Filipiak
Cezary Kubacki
Piotr Kulikowski
Grzegorz Leszczynski

ARTEX FABRICATORS LTD.

27050 Gloucester Way
Langley, BC, V4W 3Y5, Canada
Tel.: (604) 857-2600
Fax: (604) 857-2650
Web Site: www.artexfab.com
Rev.: $13,602,054
Emp.: 50
Business Description:
Farm Equipment Mfr
S.I.C.: 3523
N.A.I.C.S.: 333111
Personnel:
John DeJonge *(Pres)*

ARTGO MINING HOLDINGS LIMITED

13 & 23F Tower B Haifu Center 599 Sishui Road
Huli District, Xiamen, 361000, China
Tel.: (86) 592 2103888
Fax: (86) 592 2132888
E-Mail: info@artgo.cn
Web Site: www.artgo.cn
3313—(HKG)
Business Description:
Marble Mining, Production & Supply
S.I.C.: 1422
N.A.I.C.S.: 212312
Personnel:
Chuanjia Liu *(Chm & CEO)*

ARTHA RESOURCES CORPORATION

Suite 1502 - 543 Granville St
Vancouver, BC, V6C 1X8, Canada
Tel.: (604) 648-6242
Fax: (604) 642-0604
Toll Free: (888) 648-6242
E-Mail: info@artharesources.com
Web Site: www.artharesources.com
Year Founded: 2006
AHC—(TSXV)
Int. Income: $3,639
Assets: $5,650,574
Liabilities: $715,786
Net Worth: $4,934,788
Earnings: ($754,637)
Fiscal Year-end: 12/31/12
Business Description:
Mineral Exploration Services
S.I.C.: 1081
N.A.I.C.S.: 213114
Personnel:
W. Todd McMurray *(Pres & Sec)*
Charles Straw *(CEO)*
Richard Holstein *(CFO)*
Board of Directors:
W. Todd McMurray
Stephen Pearce
Charles Straw
Christine Thomson
Legal Counsel:
Morton & Company
Suite 1200-750 W Pender Street
Vancouver, BC, Canada
Transfer Agent:
Computershare Trust Company
510 Burrard Street
Vancouver, BC, Canada

ARTHALAND CORPORATION

8Floor Picadilly Star Building 4th Avenue corner 27th Street
Bonifacio Global City, Taguig, Philippines
Tel.: (63) 24036910
Web Site: www.arthaland.com
ALCO—(PHI)
Sls.: $35,590,431
Assets: $89,177,607
Liabilities: $56,806,557
Net Worth: $32,371,050
Earnings: $6,514,192
Emp.: 51
Fiscal Year-end: 12/31/12
Business Description:
Property Development Services
S.I.C.: 6531
N.A.I.C.S.: 531312

ArthaLand Corporation—(Continued)

Personnel:
Ernest K. Cuyegkeng *(Chm)*
Ricardo S. Po, Sr. *(Vice Chm)*
Angela de Villa-Lacson *(Pres)*
Ponciano S. Carreon, Jr. *(CFO)*
Riva Khristine V. Maala *(Corp Info Officer & Asst Sec)*
Dennis Omar T. Salvo *(Compliance Officer)*
Leonardo Arthur T. Po *(Treas)*
Daisy P. Arce *(Sec)*
Board of Directors:
Ernest K. Cuyegkeng
Angela de Villa-Lacson
Jaime C. Gonzalez
Jaime Enrique Y. Gonzalez
Fernan Victor P. Lukban
Christopher Paulus Nicolas T. Po
Ricardo Gabriel T. Po, Jr.
Ricardo S. Po, Sr.
Dennis Omar T. Salvo

ARTHUR D. LITTLE SAS

51 rue Francois 1er
75008 Paris, France
Tel.: (33) 155742900
Fax: (33) 155742803
E-Mail: info.adl@adlittle.com
Web Site: www.adlittle.com
Year Founded: 1968
Sales Range: $25-49.9 Million
Emp.: 60
Business Description:
Management Consulting Services
S.I.C.: 8742
N.A.I.C.S.: 541611
Personnel:
Ignacio Garcia Alves *(CEO)*
Francois Valraud *(COO)*

U.S. Subsidiary:

Arthur D. Little, Inc. **(1)**
1 Federal St Ste 2810
Boston, MA 02110 (100%)
Tel.: (617) 532-9550
Fax: (617) 261-6630
Web Site: www.adlittle-us.com
Emp.: 1,000
Management Consulting Services
S.I.C.: 8742
N.A.I.C.S.: 541611
John W. Brennan *(Mng Dir-Americas)*

Non-U.S. Subsidiaries:

Arthur D. Little AB **(1)**
Kungsgatan 12-14
PO Box 70434
107 25 Stockholm, Sweden (100%)
Tel.: (46) 850306500
Fax: (46) 850306502
E-Mail: lenerius.bo@adlittle.com
Web Site: www.adlittle.se
Management Consulting Services
S.I.C.: 8742
N.A.I.C.S.: 541611
Bo Lenerius *(Mng Dir)*

Branch:

Arthur D. Little AB **(2)**
Lila Bommen 1
SE 411 04 Gothenburg, Sweden (100%)
Tel.: (46) 317581000
Fax: (46) 317581002
E-Mail: info@adlitte.com
Web Site: www.adlittle.se
Emp.: 40
Management Consulting Services
S.I.C.: 8742
N.A.I.C.S.: 541611
Bo Lenerius *(Mng Dir)*

Arthur D. Little Asia Pacific Ltd. **(1)**
Suite 41F Tower 2 Grand Gateway Plaza
No 3 Hong Qiao Road, Central, China (Hong Kong) (100%)
Tel.: (852) 2164478866
Fax: (852) 2164470506
E-Mail: chow.doren@cwccppa.com
Web Site: www.adlittle.cn
Emp.: 10
Management Consulting Services
S.I.C.: 8742
N.A.I.C.S.: 541611
Jian Xu *(Mng Dir)*

Unit:

Arthur D. Little Hong Kong **(2)**
21/F Icbc Twr 3 Garden Rd
Central, China (Hong Kong)
Tel.: (852) 28456221
Fax: (852) 22735999
Management Consulting Services
S.I.C.: 8748
N.A.I.C.S.: 541618

Non-U.S. Subsidiaries:

Arthur D. Little Asia Ptd. Ltd. **(2)**
Level 21 Centennial Tower 3 Temasek Avenue
Singapore, 039190, Singapore
Tel.: (65) 62972300
Fax: (65) 62927631
E-Mail: marketing.seasia@adlittle.com
Web Site: www.adlittle.com.sg
Management Consulting Services
S.I.C.: 8742
N.A.I.C.S.: 541611
Thomas Kuruvilla *(Mng Partner)*

Arthur D. Little China Limited **(2)**
Suite 41/F Tower 2 Grand Gateway Plaza
No 3 Hong Qiao Road
Shanghai, 200030, China
Tel.: (86) 21 6447 8866
Fax: (86) 21 6447 0506
E-Mail: info.china@adlittle.com
Web Site: www.adlittle.cn
Management Consulting Services
S.I.C.: 8748
N.A.I.C.S.: 541618
Jian Xu *(Mng Partner)*

Arthur D. Little Japan, Inc. **(2)**
Toranomon 37 Mori Building 13F 3-5-1 Toranomon
Minato-ku, Tokyo, 105 0001, Japan JP (100%)
Tel.: (81) 334362196
Fax: (81) 334362197
Web Site: www.adl.co.jp
Emp.: 50
Management Consulting Services
S.I.C.: 8742
N.A.I.C.S.: 541611
Yusuke Harada *(Mng Dir)*

Arthur D. Little Korea **(2)**
9th Floor Leema Building 146-1 Susong-dong
Chongro-ku, Seoul, 110 755, Korea (South) (100%)
Tel.: (82) 27202040
Fax: (82) 27202100
E-Mail: kang.hyewon@adlittle.com
Web Site: www.adl.co.kr
Emp.: 40
Management Consulting Services
S.I.C.: 8742
N.A.I.C.S.: 541611
Sukgeun Lee *(Mng Dir)*

Arthur D. Little (M) Sdn Bhd **(2)**
Office Suite 19-13-2 Level 13 UOA Centre 19
19 Jalan Pinang, 50450 Kuala Lumpur, Malaysia (100%)
Tel.: (60) 321646063
Fax: (60) 321646067
E-Mail: noor.joanna@adlittle.com
Web Site: www.adlittle.com.my
Emp.: 10
Management Consulting Services
S.I.C.: 8742
N.A.I.C.S.: 541611
Thomas Kuruvilla *(Mng Partner)*

Arthur D. Little Austria GmbH **(1)**
Schottengasse 1
1010 Vienna, Austria (100%)
Tel.: (43) 1 515 41 0
Fax: (43) 1 515 41 23
E-Mail: adlittle.vienna@adlittle.com
Web Site: www.adlittle.at
Emp.: 40
Management Consulting Services
S.I.C.: 8742
N.A.I.C.S.: 541611
Karim Taga *(Mng Partner)*
Ralf Baron *(Partner)*
Wilhelm Lerner *(Partner)*
Matthias von Bechtolsheim *(Partner)*

Arthur D. Little Benelux N.V. **(1)**
Strawinskylaan 10
1077 XZ Amsterdam, Netherlands (100%)
Tel.: (31) 20 301 6500
Fax: (31) 20 301 6501
E-Mail: adlittle.netherlands@adlittle.com
Web Site: www.adlittle.nl
Emp.: 7
Management Consulting Services
S.I.C.: 8748
N.A.I.C.S.: 541618
Ignacio Garcia Alves *(Mng Partner)*

Arthur D. Little Benelux S.A. **(1)**
Avenue de Tervurenlaan 270
B 1150 Brussels, Belgium (100%)
Tel.: (32) 27617200
Telex: 22812 LITTLE B
Fax: (32) 27620758
E-Mail: adlittle.belgium@adlittle.com
Web Site: www.adlittle.be
Emp.: 50
Management Consulting Services
S.I.C.: 8742
N.A.I.C.S.: 541611
Ignacio Garcia Alves *(Mng Dir)*

Arthur D. Little GmbH **(1)**
The Squaire
60600 Frankfurt am Main, Germany (100%)
Tel.: (49) 69 450098 0
Fax: (49) 69 450098 290
E-Mail: info.germany@adlittle.com
Web Site: www.adlittle.de
Management Consulting Services
S.I.C.: 8742
N.A.I.C.S.: 541611
Fabian Doemer *(Partner & Mng Partner-Central Europe)*
Matthias von Bechtolsheim *(Partner & Dir-Global Utilities Practice Leader)*

Branches:

Arthur D. Little GmbH **(2)**
Bernhard-Wicki-Str. House 3
80636 Munich, Germany (100%)
Tel.: (49) 8938088700
Fax: (49) 8938088750
E-Mail: info@adlttle.com
Web Site: www.adlittle.com
Emp.: 40
Management Consulting Services
S.I.C.: 8742
N.A.I.C.S.: 541611
Diethard Buhler *(Pres)*

Arthur D. Little Limited **(1)**
Unit 300 Science Park
Milton Road, Cambridge, CB4 0XL, United Kingdom (100%)
Tel.: (44) 1223 427 100
Fax: (44) 1223 427 101
Web Site: www.adlittle.co.uk
Management Consulting Services
S.I.C.: 8742
N.A.I.C.S.: 541611
Nick White *(Mng Partner-Energy Practice Leader-UK)*
Richard Eagar *(Partner-Tech & Innovation Mgmt)*
Stuart Keeping *(Partner-TIME Practice)*

Branch:

Arthur D. Little **(2)**
1 Bedford Avenue
London, WC1B 3AU, United Kingdom (100%)
Tel.: (44) 207 7660 200
Telex: 261109 LITTLE G
Fax: (44) 207 7660 201
E-Mail:
Web Site: www.adlittle.uk.com
Management Consulting Services
S.I.C.: 8742
N.A.I.C.S.: 541611

Arthur D. Little Middle East FZ LLC **(1)**
Office 606 6th Floor Arjaan Tower Al Sufouh Road
PO Box 112687
Dubai Media City, Dubai, United Arab Emirates
Tel.: (971) 4 4335401
Fax: (971) 4 4290679
E-Mail: executiveoffice.me@adlittle.com
Web Site: www.adlittle.ae
Emp.: 5
Management Consulting Services
S.I.C.: 8742
N.A.I.C.S.: 541611
Thomas Kuruvilla *(Mng Partner)*

Non-U.S. Branch:

Arthur D. Little Saudi Arabia **(2)**
Suite 502 5th Floor Entrance D The Plaza
PO Box 305005
Akaria Complex Olaya Road, Riyadh, 11361, Saudi Arabia
Tel.: (966) 1 293 0023
Fax: (966) 1 293 0490
Web Site: www.adl.com.sa
Management Consulting Services
S.I.C.: 8742
N.A.I.C.S.: 541611

Arthur D. Little (Schweiz) AG **(1)**
Seestrasse 513
Wollishsen, CH 8038 Zurich, Switzerland (100%)
Tel.: (41) 447228989
Fax: (41) 447228999
E-Mail: info.switzerland@adlittle.com
Web Site: www.adlittle.ch
Sales Range: $25-49.9 Million
Emp.: 20
Management Consulting Services
S.I.C.: 8742
N.A.I.C.S.: 541611
Caraten Vollrath *(Mng Dir)*

Arthur D. Little S.L. **(1)**
C/Ortega y Gasset 20 Planta 3a
28006 Madrid, Spain ES (100%)
Tel.: (34) 91 702 7400
Fax: (34) 917027499
E-Mail: ugarte.pedro@adlittle.com
Web Site: www.adlittle.es
Emp.: 30
Management Consulting Services
S.I.C.: 8742
N.A.I.C.S.: 541611
Carlos Abad *(Mng Partner)*
David Borras *(Partner)*
Jesus Porpal *(Partner)*
Salman Ali *(Principal)*
Alejandro Gonzalez *(Principal)*
Pedro Ugarte *(Principal)*

Non-U.S. Branch:

Arthur D. Little **(2)**
Edificio Mira Lisboa Av Fontes Pereira de Melo no 21 8
1050-116 Lisbon, Portugal
Tel.: (351) 210091500
Fax: (351) 210091599
E-Mail: adlittle.lisbon@adlittle.com
Web Site: www.adlittle.pt
Management Consulting Services
S.I.C.: 8742
N.A.I.C.S.: 541611
Grant Greatrex *(Mng Dir)*

Arthur D. Little S.p.A. **(1)**
Corso Monforte 54
20122 Milan, Italy (100%)
Tel.: (39) 02 67 37 61
Fax: (39) 02 67 37 62 51
Web Site: www.adlittle.it
Emp.: 80
Management Consulting Services
S.I.C.: 8742
N.A.I.C.S.: 541611
Saverio Caldani *(Mng Partner)*

ARTIFICIAL LIFE, INC.

26/F 88 Hing Fat Street
Causeway Bay, China (Hong Kong)
Tel.: (852) 3102 2800
E-Mail: info@artificial-life.com
Web Site: www.artificial-life.com
Year Founded: 1999
ALIF—(OTC)
Sales Range: $50-74.9 Million
Emp.: 45
Business Description:
Intelligent Robot Developer for the Internet

S.I.C.: 7372
N.A.I.C.S.: 511210
Personnel:
Eberhard Schoneburg *(Chm, CEO & CFO)*
Ernest Axelbank *(CTO)*
Board of Directors:
Eberhard Schoneburg
Gert Hensel
Rene Jaeggi
Katzutoshi Miyake

Subsidiary:

Artificial Life Asia Limited **(1)**
26F 88 Hing Fat St
Causeway Bay, Hong Kong, China (Hong Kong)
Tel.: (852) 31022800
Fax: (852) 31020690
E-Mail: info@artifical-life.com
Web Site: www.artifical-life.com
Emp.: 50
Mobile Phone Applications Mktg & Distr
S.I.C.: 4812
N.A.I.C.S.: 517210
Eberhard Schoneburg *(CEO)*

Non-U.S. Subsidiary:

Artificial Life Source Holding PLC **(1)**
Kurfurstendamm 30
10719 Berlin, Germany
Tel.: (49) 30 886200 117
Fax: (49) 30 886200 200
E-Mail: info@alife-source.com
Web Site: www.alife-source.com
ALF—(DEU)
Mobile Phone Applications Mktg & Distr
S.I.C.: 4812
N.A.I.C.S.: 517210
Devan Nair *(Chm & CEO)*

ARTIFICIAL MIND & MOVEMENT

416 Maisonneuve Ouest Bureau 600
Montreal, QC, H3A 1L2, Canada
Tel.: (514) 843-4484
Fax: (514) 843-4234
E-Mail: nathalie.carom@a2m.com
Web Site: www.a2m.com
Year Founded: 1992
Sales Range: $25-49.9 Million
Emp.: 450
Business Description:
Software Developer
S.I.C.: 7372
N.A.I.C.S.: 511210
Personnel:
Jamie Leece *(Sr VP-Bus Dev)*

ARTIFICIAL SOLUTIONS HOLDING ASH AB

Osterlanggatan 43 4 fl
111 31 Stockholm, Sweden
Tel.: (46) 8 663 54 50
Fax: (46) 8 663 67 77
Web Site: www.artificial-solutions.com
Year Founded: 2001
Emp.: 200
Business Description:
Language Interaction Software Developer
S.I.C.: 7372
N.A.I.C.S.: 511210
Personnel:
Lawrence Flynn *(CEO)*
Chris Bushnell *(CFO)*
Peter Roost *(COO)*
Andy Peart *(CMO)*
Andreas Wieweg *(CTO)*

ARTILIUM PLC

MoFo Notices Limited CityPoint 1
Ropemaker Street
London, EC2Y 9AW, United Kingdom
Tel.: (44) 20 8133 3858
E-Mail: info@artilium.com
Web Site: www.artilium.com
Year Founded: 1995
ARTA—(LSE)
Rev.: $15,130,951
Assets: $30,160,939
Liabilities: $11,096,479
Net Worth: $19,064,460
Earnings: ($316,350)
Emp.: 55
Fiscal Year-end: 06/30/13
Business Description:
Developer of Mobile Internet Application Software
S.I.C.: 7372
N.A.I.C.S.: 511210
Personnel:
Willem van den Brink *(CEO)*
Wim Seynaeve *(Acting CFO)*
Board of Directors:
Patrick Morley
Jan Paul Menke
Willem van den Brink
Legal Counsel:
Morrison & Foerster (UK) LLP
CityPoint One Ropemaker Street
London, United Kingdom

Non-U.S. Subsidiary:

Artilium N.V. **(1)**
Autobaan 20
8210 Brugge, West Flanders, Belgium
Tel.: (32) 50230300
Fax: (32) 50230309
E-Mail: info@artilium.com
Emp.: 33
Mobile Software Design Services
S.I.C.: 7371
N.A.I.C.S.: 541511
Sofie De Coninck *(Office Mgr)*

ARTINI CHINA CO., LTD.

44/F-47/F World Finance Centre Tower A
4003 Shen Nan Road East,
Shenzhen, 518000, China
Tel.: (86) 75525833018
Fax: (86) 75522163696
E-Mail: info@artini-china.com
Web Site: www.artini-china.com
789—(HKG)
Sales Range: $25-49.9 Million
Emp.: 1,900
Business Description:
Fashion Accessories Mfr, Marketer, Distr & Sales
S.I.C.: 2399
N.A.I.C.S.: 315990
Personnel:
Hoi Chau Tse *(Chm)*
Ying Kam Yip *(Vice Chm, CEO & COO)*
Wah Wai Lo *(Sec)*
Board of Directors:
Hoi Chau Tse
Joseph Shu Hung Chan
Lawrenece Fai Lau
Yiu Kit Lau
Ying Kam Yip
Legal Counsel:
Richards Butler
Reed Smith 20th Floor Alexandra House 18 Chater Road
Central, China (Hong Kong)

Guangdong Zhiming Lawfirm
17/F West Block Xincheng Building No 1027 Shennan Road C.
Shenzhen, China

Conyers, Dill & Pearman
2901 One Exchange Square
8 Connaught Place, Central, China (Hong Kong)

Butterfield Fulcrum Group (Bermuda) Limited
Rosebank Centre 11 Bermudiana Rd
Pembroke, Bermuda

Transfer Agents:
Union Registrars Limited
18/F Fook Lee Commercial Centre Town Place
33 Lockhart Road
Wanchai, China (Hong Kong)

Butterfield Fulcrum Group (Bermuda) Limited
Rosebank Centre 11 Bermudiana Rd
Pembroke, Bermuda

ARTINOVA AB

Hokedalen 50
668 92 Vastra Gotaland, Sweden
Tel.: (46) 313393390
Fax: (46) 317017545
E-Mail: klh@artinova.com
Web Site: www.artinova.se
Year Founded: 1923
Sales Range: $1-9.9 Million
Emp.: 2
Business Description:
Paper Coating & Converting Services Import Export
S.I.C.: 2672
N.A.I.C.S.: 322220
Personnel:
Klas Hellerstrom *(Chm, CEO, Sls & Dir-Mktg)*

Non-U.S. Subsidiaries:

Artin Papiervertriebs GmbH **(1)**
Wilhelm Strasse 42
47807 Krefeld, Germany (100%)
Tel.: (49) 151301961
Fax: (49) 2151306190
E-Mail: artinova@freenet.com
S.I.C.: 2672
N.A.I.C.S.: 322220

Artinova Poland Sp. z o.o. **(1)**
T Dzialynskiego 1d/13
62 020 Swarzedz, Poland
Tel.: (48) 618159170
Fax: (48) 618159170
E-Mail: edd@artinova.se
Web Site: www.artinova.se/Poland.htm
Paper Coating & Converting Services
S.I.C.: 2679
N.A.I.C.S.: 322299

ARTIO GLOBAL INVESTORS INC.

(Acquired & Absorbed by Aberdeen Asset Management PLC)

ARTIS REAL ESTATE INVESTMENT TRUST

300-360 Main Street
Winnipeg, MB, R3C 3Z3, Canada
Tel.: (204) 947-1250
Fax: (204) 947-0453
E-Mail: Investorinquiries@artisreit.com
Web Site: www.artisreit.com
Year Founded: 2004
AX—(TSX)
Rev.: $370,241,635
Assets: $4,355,710,154
Liabilities: $2,318,112,293
Net Worth: $2,037,597,861
Earnings: $338,303,773
Fiscal Year-end: 12/31/12
Business Description:
Real Estate Investment Services
S.I.C.: 6211
N.A.I.C.S.: 523999
Personnel:
Edward Warkentin *(Chm)*
Armin Martens *(Pres & CEO)*
Jim Green *(CFO)*
Kirsty Stevens *(Chief Admin Officer)*
Dave Johnson *(Sr VP-Asset Mgmt-Central Canada & United States)*
John Mah *(Sr VP-Asset Mgmt-Eastern Reg)*
Douglas McGregor *(Sr VP-Leasing-Western Reg)*
Armin Martens *(Trustees:)*
Frank Sherlock *(Sr VP-Property Mgmt)*
Dennis Wong *(Sr VP-Asset Mgmt-Western Reg)*
Transfer Agent:
CIBC Mellon Trust Company
600 333 7th Avenue S W
Calgary, AB, Canada

ARTISAN ENERGY CORPORATION

(Formerly Exito Energy Inc.)
555 4th Avenue Southwest Suite 800
Calgary, AB, T2R 1J6, Canada
Tel.: (403) 984-9275
Fax: (403) 453-1609
E-Mail: info@artisanenergy.ca
Web Site: www.artisanenergy.ca
Year Founded: 2010
AEC—(TSXV)
Rev.: $572,597
Assets: $16,085,491
Liabilities: $6,354,770
Net Worth: $9,730,721
Earnings: ($2,156,219)
Fiscal Year-end: 12/31/12
Business Description:
Investment Services
S.I.C.: 6211
N.A.I.C.S.: 523999
Personnel:
David Evans *(Chm)*
Rick Ironside *(Pres & CEO)*
John Bell *(CFO)*
Rick Young *(COO)*
Board of Directors:
David Evans
Richard Cooper
Tim Dunne
Warren Waldegger
Ron Wanner
Transfer Agent:
Valiant Trust Corporation
310 606 4th Street SW
Calgary, AB, T2P 1T1, Canada

ARTISAN (UK) PLC

Vantage House Vantage Park
Washingley Road
Huntingdon, Cambs, PE29 6SR, United Kingdom
Tel.: (44) 1480436666
Fax: (44) 1480436231
E-Mail: email@artisan-plc.co.uk
Web Site: www.artisan-plc.co.uk
Rev.: $8,429,075
Assets: $33,718,129
Liabilities: $21,853,560
Net Worth: $11,864,569
Earnings: ($4,034,928)
Emp.: 46
Fiscal Year-end: 06/30/13
Business Description:
Real Estate Development Services
S.I.C.: 6531
N.A.I.C.S.: 531390
Personnel:
Christopher P. Musselle *(CEO & Dir-Fin)*
Philip Speer *(Sec)*
Board of Directors:
Geoffrey Melamet
Michael Eyres
John Jones
Christopher P. Musselle
Legal Counsel:
Thomson Webb & Corfield
16 Union Rd
Cambridge, United Kingdom

Subsidiaries:

Artisan (UK) Developments Limited **(1)**
Vantage House Vantage Park
Washingley Road, Huntingdon, Cambs, PE29 6SR, United Kingdom

Artisan (UK) plc—(Continued)

Tel.: (44) 1480436777
Fax: (44) 1480436230
E-Mail: general@artisandevelopments.co.uk
Web Site: www.artisan-plc.co.uk
Emp.: 6
Residential House Building Services
S.I.C.: 6513
N.A.I.C.S.: 531110
Michael Eyres *(Mng Dir)*

Artisan (UK) Projects Limited (1)
Vantage Park Washingley Rd
Huntingdon, Cambridgeshire, PE29 6SR, United Kingdom
Tel.: (44) 1480436666
Fax: (44) 1480436231
E-Mail: email@artisan-plc.co.uk
Emp.: 6
Residential House Building Services
S.I.C.: 6514
N.A.I.C.S.: 531110
Chris Musselle *(Gen Mgr)*

Artisan (UK) Properties Limited (1)
Vantage Park, Washingley Rd
Huntingdon, PE29 6SR, United Kingdom
Tel.: (44) 1480436777
Fax: (44) 1480436230
E-Mail: general@artisandevelopment.co.uk
Web Site: www.artisandevelopment.co.uk
Emp.: 6
Residential House Building Services
S.I.C.: 6513
N.A.I.C.S.: 531110
Michael Eyres *(Mng Dir)*

Rippon Homes Limited (1)
Leeming Lane South
Mansfield Woodhouse, Notts, NG19 9AQ, United Kingdom
Tel.: (44) 1623659000
Fax: (44) 1623420807
E-Mail: info@ripponhomes.co.uk
Web Site: www.ripponhomes.co.uk
Residential House Building Services
S.I.C.: 6513
N.A.I.C.S.: 531110
John Jones *(Mng Dir)*

ARTIST & ENTERTAINMENT GROUP LIMITED

Level 2 131 Macquarie Street
Sydney, NSW, 2000, Australia
Tel.: (61) 292589900
Fax: (61) 292476225
AEM—(ASX)
Rev.: $46,774
Assets: $931,847
Liabilities: $431,512
Net Worth: $500,335
Earnings: ($1,837,016)
Fiscal Year-end: 06/30/13

Business Description:
Mineral Mining Services
S.I.C.: 1481
N.A.I.C.S.: 213115

Personnel:
Ross Hill *(Chm)*
Eric Kam *(Co-Sec)*
Graham Kavanagh *(Co-Sec)*

Board of Directors:
Ross Hill
Wei DingMin
David Hickie
Siew Hong Koh

Legal Counsel:
HWL Ebsworth Lawyers
Level 14 Australia Sq 264 278 George St
Sydney, Australia

ARTIST HOUSE HOLDINGS INC.

Minami Aoyama Building 2F 2-27-7
Minami Aoyama
Minato-ku, Tokyo, Japan
Tel.: (81) 366737080
Fax: (81) 354132523
E-Mail: info@artisthouse.co.jp
Web Site: www.artisthouse.co.jp
Year Founded: 2000
Sales Range: $25-49.9 Million
Emp.: 93

Business Description:
Entertainment Content Copyright, Licensing & Merchandising; Interactive Services Focused on E-Commerce
S.I.C.: 7389
N.A.I.C.S.: 561499

Personnel:
Kouichi Hirahara *(Pres & CEO)*

Board of Directors:
Kouichi Hirahara
Takayuki Suzuki
Nozomu Wada

Subsidiaries:

ArtistHouse Investment, Inc. (1)
Yushin Building 3F
3-27-11 Shibuya
Shibuya-ku, Tokyo, Japan
Tel.: (81) 357669315
Entertainment Industry Intellectual Property Investments
S.I.C.: 6211
N.A.I.C.S.: 523999

Music Land KEY Co., Ltd. (1)
Yushin Building 3F
3-27-11 Shibuya
Shibuya-ku, Tokyo, Japan
Tel.: (81) 357669315
Web Site: www.musicland.co.jp
Entertainment Media Retailer
S.I.C.: 5999
N.A.I.C.S.: 453998

TwoTop Co., Ltd. (1)
Yushin Blsd 3F
3-27-11 Shibuya
Shibuya-ku, Tokyo, Japan
Tel.: (81) 3 5468 8100
Fax: (81) 3 3499 2984
Entertainment Media Distr
S.I.C.: 2741
N.A.I.C.S.: 512230

ARTISTIC DENIM MILLS LIMITED

Plot No 5-9 23-26 Sector-16 Korangi Industrial Area
74900 Karachi, Pakistan
Tel.: (92) 2135054629
Fax: (92) 2135054652
E-Mail: sales@admdenim.com
Web Site: www.admdenim.com
ADMM—(KAR)
Sls.: $62,165,713
Assets: $60,541,621
Liabilities: $19,406,578
Net Worth: $41,135,043
Earnings: $7,672,320
Fiscal Year-end: 06/30/13

Business Description:
Cotton Fabric Garments Mfr
S.I.C.: 2299
N.A.I.C.S.: 313210

Personnel:
Faisal Ahmed *(Chm & CEO)*
Sagheer Ahmed *(CFO & Sec)*

Board of Directors:
Faisal Ahmed
Hajra Ahmed
Muhammad Ali Ahmed
Muhammad Yousuf Ahmed
Sarah Faisal Ahmed
Maliha Faisal
Muhammad Iqbal-ur-Rahim

ARTITALIA GROUP INC.

11755 Rodolphe Forget
Montreal, QC, H1E 7J8, Canada
Tel.: (514) 643-0114
Fax: (514) 643-4973
Toll Free: (800) 644-7595
E-Mail: info@artitalia-group.com
Web Site: www.artitalia.ca
Year Founded: 1984
Rev.: $37,978,840
Emp.: 400

Business Description:
Display Fixtures Mfr
S.I.C.: 3646
N.A.I.C.S.: 335122

Personnel:
Antonio Vardaro *(Co-Pres)*
Tony Vardaro *(Co-Pres)*

Board of Directors:
Jeff Kastner
Antonio Vardaro
Josy Vardaro
Tony Vardaro

ARTIVISION TECHNOLOGIES LTD.

67 Ubi Ave 1 Starhub Green Building
North Wing Unit 06-02/ 06-03
Singapore, 408942, Singapore
Tel.: (65) 65351233
Fax: (65) 65345031
E-Mail: david.yim@arti-vision.com
Web Site: www.arti-vision.com
5NK—(SES)
Rev.: $191,286
Assets: $4,963,348
Liabilities: $2,560,914
Net Worth: $2,402,434
Earnings: ($3,923,807)
Emp.: 27
Fiscal Year-end: 03/31/13

Business Description:
Video Management Products & Solutions
S.I.C.: 3651
N.A.I.C.S.: 334310

Personnel:
Ofer Miller *(Co-Founder & CTO)*
Philip Sai Kiang Soh *(Co-Founder)*
Kenneth Tzu Seoh Goh *(COO)*
Nathaniel Chelvarajah Vanniasingham *(Sec)*

Board of Directors:
Philip Sai Kiang Soh
Chiat Kwong Ching
Kenneth Tzu Seoh Goh
Alan Boon Liang Koh
Ofer Miller
Harry Weng Sui Ng
Khee Giap Tan
Lawrence Chee Meng Wong

ARTIZA NETWORKS, INC.

Faret Tachikawa Centre Square
2-36-2 Akebono-cho
Tachikawa, Tokyo, 190-0012, Japan
Tel.: (81) 425293494
Fax: (81) 425293495
E-Mail: contact@artiza.co.jp
Web Site: www.artiza.co.jp
Year Founded: 1990
6778—(TKS)
Sales Range: $25-49.9 Million
Emp.: 75

Business Description:
Communication Test Equipment Developer & Sales
S.I.C.: 3669
N.A.I.C.S.: 334290

Personnel:
Takashi Tokonami *(Pres & CEO)*
Masahito Shimizu *(CFO)*
Naoyuki Tokonami *(CTO)*

ARTLANT PTA, S.A.

Zona Industrial e Logistica de Sines
Zona 2 Lote 2E1
Monte Feio, 7520-064 Sines, Portugal
Tel.: (351) 269189000
Fax: (351) 269189099
E-Mail: info@artlantpta.com
Web Site: www.artlantpta.com
Emp.: 150

Business Description:
Purified Terephtalic Acid Mfr
S.I.C.: 2899
N.A.I.C.S.: 325199

Personnel:
Jose Luis Morlanes Galindo *(Pres)*

ARTMETCO INC.

(Acquired by MEP Technologies, Inc.)

ARTNATURE INC.

3-40-7 Yoyogi Shibuya-ku
Tokyo, 151-0053, Japan
Tel.: (81) 3 3379 3334
Web Site: www.artnature.co.jp
Year Founded: 1967
7823—(TKS)
Sls.: $386,001,000
Assets: $357,984,000
Liabilities: $163,328,000
Net Worth: $194,656,000
Earnings: $25,410,000
Fiscal Year-end: 03/31/13

Business Description:
Wigs & Hairpieces Mfr
S.I.C.: 3999
N.A.I.C.S.: 339999

Personnel:
Yoshikata Igarashi *(Chm & Pres)*
Keisuke Igarashi *(Co-Mng Dir)*
Hisakazu Moriyasu *(Co-Mng Dir)*

Board of Directors:
Yoshikata Igarashi
Shunichi Hayashi
Keisuke Igarashi
Hisayuki Kawazoe
Hisakazu Moriyasu
Isao Naito
Keisuke Satake
Shunji Tanefusa

ARTNER CO., LTD.

2-18 Nakanoshima 3-chome Kita-ku
Osaka, 530-0005, Japan
Tel.: (81) 664457551
Fax: (81) 664491334
E-Mail: ir@artner.co.jp
Web Site: www.artner.co.jp
Year Founded: 1962
2163—(JAS)
Sales Range: $50-74.9 Million
Emp.: 810

Business Description:
Employment Services
S.I.C.: 7361
N.A.I.C.S.: 561311

Personnel:
Sozo Sekiguchi *(Pres)*

ARTNET AG

Oranienstrasse 164
10969 Berlin, Germany
Tel.: (49) 3020917820
Fax: (49) 3020917829
E-Mail: info@artnet.com
Web Site: www.artnet.com
AYD—(EUR)
Rev.: $18,156,534
Assets: $8,089,796
Liabilities: $4,901,439
Net Worth: $3,188,358
Earnings: ($3,266,744)
Emp.: 118
Fiscal Year-end: 12/31/12

Business Description:
Online Art Sales
S.I.C.: 5999
N.A.I.C.S.: 453920

Personnel:
John D. Hushon *(Chm-Supervisory Bd)*

Jacob Pabst *(Chm-Mgmt Bd & CEO)*
Walter Rust *(Deputy Chm-Supervisory Bd)*

U.S. Subsidiary:

artnet Worldwide Corporation (1)
61 Broadway 23rd Fl
New York, NY 10006-2701
Tel.: (212) 497-9700
Fax: (212) 497-9707
E-Mail: scox@artnet.com
Web Site: www.artnet.com
Emp.: 100
Research Services for Fine & Decorative Arts
S.I.C.: 3291
N.A.I.C.S.: 327910
Hans Neuendorf *(Chm & CEO)*
Jacob Pabst *(CIO)*

ARTPRICE.COM

Domaine de la Source
BP 69
69270 Saint-Romain, France
Tel.: (33) 4 78 22 00 00
Fax: (33) 4 78 22 06 06
E-Mail: artinvestment@artprice.com
Web Site: www.artprice.com
PRC—(EUR)
Business Description:
Online Auction Services
S.I.C.: 5961
N.A.I.C.S.: 454112
Personnel:
Thierry Ehrmann *(Chm & CEO)*
Nabila Arify *(CFO)*
Nadege Ehrmann *(Gen Sec)*

ARTQUEST INTERNATIONAL ALLIANCES, INC.

2525 Daniel Johnson Blvd Suite 290
Laval, QC, H7T 1S9, Canada
Tel.: (450) 681-1150
Fax: (450) 681-1037
E-Mail: info@artquest.ca
Business Description:
Computer Programming, Data Processing & Printing Services
S.I.C.: 7371
N.A.I.C.S.: 541511
Personnel:
Guy Le Henaff *(Chm & CTO)*
Board of Directors:
Guy Le Henaff

ARTS OPTICAL INTERNATIONAL HOLDINGS LTD

Unit 308 3rd Floor Sunbeam Centre
27 Shing Yip Street Kwun Tong
Kowloon, China (Hong Kong)
Tel.: (852) 23435223
Fax: (852) 27978418
Web Site: www.artsgroup.com
1120—(HKG)
Rev.: $190,263,404
Assets: $211,561,044
Liabilities: $46,615,812
Net Worth: $164,945,232
Earnings: $6,492,890
Emp.: 10,200
Fiscal Year-end: 12/31/12
Business Description:
Optical Products Design, Sales & Mfr
S.I.C.: 3572
N.A.I.C.S.: 334112
Personnel:
Michael Hoi Ying Ng *(Founder & Chm)*
Wai Chung Lee *(Sec & Controller-Fin)*
Board of Directors:
Michael Hoi Ying Ng
Eric Hil Lan Chung
Yu Lung Lam
Wai Chung Lee
Kim Ying Ng
Chi Wai Wong

HSBC Securities Services (Bermuda) Limited
6 Front Street
Hamilton, Bermuda

Subsidiaries:

Argent Optical Manufactory Limited (1)
Rm 308 3 F Sunbeam Center
Kwun Tong, Kowloon, China (Hong Kong)
Tel.: (852) 23435223
Fax: (852) 27978418
E-Mail: arksgroup@arksgroup.com
Web Site: www.arksgroup.com
Emp.: 100
Optical Frames Mfr
S.I.C.: 3851
N.A.I.C.S.: 339115
Hoi Ying Ng *(Mng Dir)*

Arts Optical Company Limited (1)
Unit 308 3 F Sunbeam Ctr 27 Shing Yip St
Kwun Tong, Kowloon, China (Hong Kong)
Tel.: (852) 23435223
Fax: (852) 27978418
E-Mail: sales@artsgroup.com
Emp.: 100
Optical Frames Mfr
S.I.C.: 3851
N.A.I.C.S.: 339115
Hoi Ying Ng *(Chm)*

Eyeconcept Limited (1)
Rm 308 3 F Sunbeam Ctr 27 Shing Yip St
Kwun Tong, Kowloon, China (Hong Kong)
Tel.: (852) 23435223
Fax: (852) 29517680
E-Mail: info@eyeconcept.com.hk
Web Site: www.eyeconcept.com.hk
Emp.: 10
Optical Frames Mfr
S.I.C.: 3851
N.A.I.C.S.: 339115
Hans Stetter *(Gen Mgr)*

ARTSANA S.P.A.

Div Medical Center via Saldarini Catelli 1
22070 Grandate, CO, Italy
Tel.: (39) 031382000
Fax: (39) 031382400
Web Site: www.artsana.com
Sales Range: $1-4.9 Billion
Emp.: 6,900
Business Description:
Health & Infant Products
S.I.C.: 5499
N.A.I.C.S.: 446191
Personnel:
Michele Catelli *(Founder, Chm & CEO)*
Subsidiary:

Prenatal SpA (1)
Centro Colleoni
Palazzo Pegaso 1, 20041 Agrate Brianza, Italy (100%)
Tel.: (39) 3965571
Fax: (39) 0396058043
E-Mail: prenatal@prenatal.it
Web Site: www.prenatal.it
Rev.: $217,294,758
Emp.: 200
Mfr. of Maternity & Infant Wear
S.I.C.: 5699
N.A.I.C.S.: 448190

Non-U.S. Subsidiary:

Prenatal, S.A. (2)
Botanica 29-31
Hospitalet De Llobregat, 08908 Barcelona, Spain
Tel.: (34) 932606000
Telex: 50046
Fax: (34) 932630010
E-Mail: prenatal@prenatal.com
Web Site: www.prenatal.com
Emp.: 350
Maternity Clothes & Infant Clothing Mfr
S.I.C.: 2399
N.A.I.C.S.: 315210
Rasael Tena *(Mng Dir)*

U.S. Subsidiary:

The Boppy Company (1)
560 Golden Rdg Rd Ste 150
Golden, CO 80401
Tel.: (720) 746-3820
Fax: (720) 746-3838
Toll Free: (888) 77-BOPPY
E-Mail: info@boppy.com
Web Site: www.boppy.com
Emp.: 20
Mfr. & Sales of Baby Products & Clothing
S.I.C.: 5137
N.A.I.C.S.: 424330
Susan M. Brown *(Pres)*
Nancy Bartley *(CEO)*

ARTSON ENGINEERING LTD

11th Floor Hiranandani Knowledge Park Technology Street
Powai, Mumbai, 400 076, India
Tel.: (91) 2266255600
Fax: (91) 2266255614
E-Mail: artson@artson.net
Web Site: www.artson.net
522134—(BOM)
Rev.: $11,240,524
Assets: $11,929,711
Liabilities: $22,197,256
Net Worth: ($10,267,545)
Earnings: ($7,304,371)
Emp.: 97
Fiscal Year-end: 03/31/13
Business Description:
Tankage Construction & Services
S.I.C.: 8711
N.A.I.C.S.: 541330
Personnel:
Vinayak Deshpande *(Chm)*
Shailesh Jain *(CFO)*
Anuja Bhate *(Sec)*
Board of Directors:
Vinayak Deshpande
Michael Bastian
Arun Kumar Misra
Pralhad Pawar
Nalin Shah
Transfer Agent:
Sharepro Services (India) Private Limited
912 Raheja Centre Free Press Journal Road
Nariman Point
Mumbai, India

ARTSPARK HOLDINGS INC.

2F Pacific Marks Shinjuku 4-15-7 Nishi-Shinjuku
Shinjuku-ku, Tokyo, 160-0023, Japan
Tel.: (81) 3 3372 3156
Fax: (81) 3 3372 3157
Web Site: www.artspark.co.jp
Year Founded: 2012
3663—(TKS)
Business Description:
Holding Company
S.I.C.: 6719
N.A.I.C.S.: 551112
Personnel:
Kazuo Kawabata *(Chm)*
Tadato Murakami *(Pres)*
Board of Directors:
Kazuo Kawabata
Tomonobu Aoyama
Kazuhiko Hoshi
Ken Ito
Yosuke Kawakami
Tadato Murakami
Subsidiaries:

CELSYS, Inc. (1)
Pacific Marks Shinjuku 4-15-7 Nishi-Shinjuku
Shinjuku-ku, Tokyo, 160-0023, Japan
Tel.: (81) 3 3372 3156
Fax: (81) 368213202
E-Mail: international_sales@artspark.co.jp
Web Site: www.celsys.co.jp
Sales Range: $25-49.9 Million
Emp.: 117
Software Developer
S.I.C.: 7372
N.A.I.C.S.: 511210
Shinya Nozaki *(Pres)*

HI Corporation (1)
Meguro Higashiyama Building 5th Floor
1-4-4 Higashiyama Meguro-ku, Tokyo, 153-0043, Japan
Tel.: (81) 3 3710 2843
Fax: (81) 3 5773 8909
E-Mail: press@hicorp.co.jp
Web Site: www.hicorp.co.jp
Sales Range: $10-24.9 Million
Emp.: 160
Computer Software & 3D Content Developer & Distr
S.I.C.: 7372
N.A.I.C.S.: 511210
Kazuo Kawabata *(Pres & CEO)*
Hirotaka Suzuki *(Sr Mng Dir & CTO)*
Kazuhiko Hoshi *(CFO)*

U.S. Subsidiary:

HI Corporation America, Inc. (2)
1525 McCarthy Blvd Ste 1000
Milpitas, CA 95035
Tel.: (408) 876-6079
Web Site: www.hicorp.co.jp/english/corporate/profile.html
Embedded Design Services
S.I.C.: 7389
N.A.I.C.S.: 541490
Ken Xu *(VP)*

Non-U.S. Subsidiaries:

HI Corporation Singapore Pte. Ltd. (2)
2 Intl Bus Park No 10 01 Tower 1
Singapore, 609930, Singapore
Tel.: (65) 62679870
Fax: (65) 62678982
Web Site: www.hicorp.com.sg
Emp.: 8
Embedded Design Services
S.I.C.: 7389
N.A.I.C.S.: 541490

HI Korea & Co. (2)
2 19 Yeajang Dong Chung gu
Seoul, 100 250, Korea (South)
Tel.: (82) 222808154
Fax: (82) 2 2284 8115
Embedded Design Services
S.I.C.: 7389
N.A.I.C.S.: 541490

ARUJ GARMENT ACCESSORIES LIMITED

(Name Changed to Aruj Industries Ltd.)

ARUJ INDUSTRIES LTD.

(Formerly Aruj Garment Accessories Limited)
2-Km Off Raiwind-Manga Rd
Raiwind
53700 Lahore, Pakistan
Tel.: (92) 4235393125
Fax: (92) 4235393127
E-Mail: info@aruj.com
Web Site: www.aruj.com
ARUJ—(KAR LAH)
Sales Range: $1-9.9 Million
Business Description:
Woven Fusible Interlining Mfr
S.I.C.: 2299
N.A.I.C.S.: 313210
Personnel:
Maqsood Ahmad Butt *(CEO)*
Board of Directors:
Ali Maqsood Butt
Durray Zara Butt
Maqsood Ahmad Butt
Naseem Maqsood
Naheed Muneer
Sheikh Ghulam Mustafa

ARUMA RESOURCES LIMITED
Suite 33 18 Stirling Highway
Nedlands, WA, 6009, Australia
Tel.: (61) 8 6389 1799
Fax: (61) 8 6389 0112
E-Mail: info@arumaresources.com
Web Site: www.arumaresources.com
AAJ—(ASX)
Rev.: $81,184
Assets: $3,944,021
Liabilities: $415,142
Net Worth: $3,528,879
Earnings: ($1,909,332)
Emp.: 4
Fiscal Year-end: 06/30/13
Business Description:
Gold Mining Services
S.I.C.: 1041
N.A.I.C.S.: 212221
Personnel:
Peter Schwann *(Mng Dir)*
Phillip MacLeod *(Sec)*
Board of Directors:
Paul Boyatzis
Ki Keong Chong
Peter Schwann
Legal Counsel:
Fairweather Corporate Lawyers
595 Stirling Highway
Cottesloe, Australia

ARUN VALLEY HYDROPOWER DEVELOPMENT CO. LTD.
Milan Chowk
GPO Box 11039
Baneshwor, Kathmandu, Nepal
Tel.: (977) 1 4475234
Fax: (977) 1 4474895
E-Mail: arunvalley@wlink.com.np
Web Site: www.arunhydro.com.np
Year Founded: 1997
AHPC—(NEP)
Business Description:
Hydroelectric Power Generation Services
S.I.C.: 4911
N.A.I.C.S.: 221111
Personnel:
Guru Prasad Neupane *(Chm)*
Ranju Adhikary *(Accts Officer)*
Sarita Ghimire *(RTS Officer)*
Pramod Lama *(Fin Officer)*
Board of Directors:
Guru Prasad Neupane
Shailendra Guragain
Ramesh Prasad Neupane
Sanjeev Neupane
Jeevan Raj Shakya
Bachchha Raj Tater
Bhej Prasad Timilsina

ARUN VARUN TRADE & INVESTMENT LTD.
1/204 Navjivan Society 2nd Floor
Lamington Road
Mumbai, 400 008, India
Tel.: (91) 22 23071996
Fax: (91) 22 23087980
E-Mail: info@avtradeinvest.com
Web Site: www.avtradeinvest.com
Year Founded: 1982
504390—(BOM)
Rev.: $441,671
Assets: $4,755,517
Liabilities: $533,623
Net Worth: $4,221,893
Earnings: $300,887
Fiscal Year-end: 03/31/13
Business Description:
Financial Services
S.I.C.: 6211
N.A.I.C.S.: 523999
Personnel:
Gautam R. Bhandari *(Compliance & Investor Grievance Officer)*
Board of Directors:
Amit Ashokbhai Bhagat
Gautam R. Bhandari
Jayanti R. Bhandari
Ameet Muljibhai Brahmbhatt
Transfer Agent:
Purva Sharegistry (India) Pvt Ltd
9 Shivshakti Industrial Estate J R Boricha Off N M Joshi Marg
Near Lodha Excelus Tower Lower Parel East, Mumbai, 400 011, India

ARUNJYOTI ENTERPRISES LIMITED
Level II Prabhas Arcade Plot No 132
Ganesh Colony Bapuji Nagar
New Bowenpally, Secunderabad, AP, 500 011, India
Tel.: (91) 40 30 228 228
Fax: (91) 40 30 229 229
E-Mail: info@taazastores.com
Web Site: www.taazastores.com
590114—(BOM)
Sales Range: $10-24.9 Million
Business Description:
Grocery Store Operator
S.I.C.: 5411
N.A.I.C.S.: 445110
Personnel:
P. Ravinder Rao *(Mng Dir)*
Abhishek Shukla *(Compliance Officer & Sec)*

ARUNTA RESOURCES LIMITED
(Formerly Transol Corporation Limited)
Level 14 31 Queen Street
Melbourne, VIC, 3000, Australia
Tel.: (61) 386108633
Fax: (61) 386108666
Web Site: www.aruntaresources.com.au
AJR—(ASX)
Sales Range: $1-9.9 Million
Business Description:
Iron, Copper & Gold Mining
S.I.C.: 1011
N.A.I.C.S.: 212210
Personnel:
Adrien Wing *(Sec)*
Board of Directors:
Neil Biddle
Angus Edgar
Adrien Wing
Legal Counsel:
Quinert Rodda & Associates
Level 19 500 Collins St
Melbourne, Australia

ARUP GROUP LTD.
13 Fitzroy Street
London, W1T 4BQ, United Kingdom
Tel.: (44) 2076361531
Fax: (44) 2075803924
E-Mail: london@arup.com
Web Site: www.arup.com
Sales Range: $800-899.9 Million
Emp.: 9,934
Fiscal Year-end: 03/31/13
Business Description:
Engineering Services
S.I.C.: 8711
N.A.I.C.S.: 541330
Personnel:
Philip Dilley *(Chm)*
Andrew Chan *(Deputy Chm)*
Peter Bailey *(Chm-Australasia)*
Robert Care *(Chm-UK, Middle East & Africa)*
Greg Hodkinson *(Chm-Europe)*
L. M. Lui *(Chm-East Asia)*
Mahadev Raman *(Chm-Americas)*
M. J. Ansley-Young *(Sec)*
Board of Directors:
Philip Dilley
Peter Bailey
Jenny Baster
Michael Bear
Alan Belfield
Robert Care
Tristram Carfrae
Andrew Chan
Greg Hodkinson
Michael Kwok
L. M. Lui
Mahadev Raman
David Whittleton
Ngaire Woods

U.S. Subsidiary:

Arup Americas, Inc. **(1)**
155 Avenue of the Americas
New York, NY 10013
Tel.: (212) 229-2669
E-Mail: newyork@arup.com
Emp.: 1,000
Engineering Services
S.I.C.: 8711
N.A.I.C.S.: 541330
Mahadev Raman *(Chm)*
Susan M. Baer *(Principal)*

ARVAL SERVICE LEASE POLSKA SP. Z O.O.
Ul Domaniewska 49 Trinity Pk III
02 672 Warsaw, Poland
Tel.: (48) 224545500
Fax: (48) 224545510
E-Mail: arval@arval.pl
Web Site: www.arval.pl
Emp.: 120
Business Description:
Long Term Vehicle Rental Company for Businesses
S.I.C.: 7519
N.A.I.C.S.: 532120
Personnel:
Janusz Kowalik *(Gen Mgr)*

ARVIND INTERNATIONAL LTD.
131 Vrindavan Vihar DCM Ajmer Road
Jaipur, Rajasthan, 302 019, India
Tel.: (91) 141 3267846
Fax: (91) 141 5176036
E-Mail: contactus@arvindinternational.com
Web Site: www.arvindinternational.com
524760—(BOM)
Business Description:
Polystyrene Foam Mfr
S.I.C.: 3086
N.A.I.C.S.: 326140
Personnel:
Arvind Bajoria *(Mng Dir)*
Board of Directors:
Anupama Bajoria
Arvind Bajoria
Rajiv Chamaria
Suvobrata Ganguly
Sushil Kumar Podddar
Transfer Agent:
Niche Technologies Pvt Ltd
D-511 Bagree Market 5th Fl 71 BRB Basu Rd
Kolkata, India

ARVIND MAFATLAL GROUP
5th Floor Mafatlal House
H.T. Parekh Marg
Backbay Reclamation, Mumbai, 400 020, India
Tel.: (91) 22 40083636
Fax: (91) 22 66345154
E-Mail: marketing@mafatlals.com
Web Site: www.mafatlals.com
Business Description:
Holding Company: Textiles
S.I.C.: 6719
N.A.I.C.S.: 551112
Personnel:
Hrishikesh A. Mafatlal *(Chm & Mng Dir)*
Rajiv Ranjan *(Pres)*

Subsidiaries:

Mafatlal Industries Limited **(1)**
Asarwa Road
Ahmedabad, Gujarat, 380 016, India
Tel.: (91) 7922123944
Fax: (91) 7922123045
E-Mail: marketing@mafatlals.com
Web Site: www.mafatlals.com
500264—(BOM)
Rev.: $155,833,391
Assets: $117,326,311
Liabilities: $50,860,374
Net Worth: $66,465,937
Earnings: $6,892,950
Emp.: 3,407
Fiscal Year-end: 03/31/13
Textile Products Mfr
S.I.C.: 2269
N.A.I.C.S.: 313310
Hrishikesh A. Mafatlal *(Chm)*
Vishad P. Mafatlal *(Vice Chm)*
Rajiv Dayal *(CEO & Mng Dir)*
Rasesh Shah *(Compliance Officer & Sec)*
Rajiv Ranjan *(Pres-Textiles)*
K. R. Jethani *(Sr VP-Fin)*
Suresh Kumar *(Sr VP-HR)*
R. R. Likhite *(Grp Sr VP-HR & Admin)*
Manoj Pandya *(Sr VP-Fin & Accts)*
Rajeev Patil *(Sr VP-Ops & Mktg-Denim)*
M. B. Raghunath *(Sr VP-Mktg & Sls)*

NOCIL Ltd **(1)**
Mafatlal House H T Parekh Marg Backbay Reclamation
Churchgate, Mumbai, 400020, India
Tel.: (91) 2266364062
Fax: (91) 2266364060
Web Site: www.natocil.com
500730—(BOM)
Sls.: $97,679,158
Assets: $122,148,324
Liabilities: $54,478,863
Net Worth: $67,669,461
Earnings: $7,811,718
Emp.: 430
Fiscal Year-end: 03/31/13
Rubber Chemicals Mfr
S.I.C.: 2822
N.A.I.C.S.: 325212
C. R. Gupte *(Mng Dir)*
Vikas K. Gupte *(Compliance Officer, Sec & Gen Mgr-Legal)*
Sudhir Ramchandra Deo *(Pres-Technical)*
R. M. Gadgil *(Sr VP-Mktg)*

Joint Venture:

Dow AgroSciences India Pvt. Ltd. **(2)**
Corporate Park Unit No 1
VN Purav Marg
Chembur, Mumbai, 400 071, India
Tel.: (91) 2267985700
Fax: (91) 2267985790
Web Site: www.dowagro.com
Sales Range: $150-199.9 Million
Agricultural Chemicals Mfr & Sales; Owned 76% by The Dow Chemical Company & 24% by National Organic Chemical Industries Limited
S.I.C.: 2879
N.A.I.C.S.: 325320

ARVIND REMEDIES LTD
190 Poonamalle High Road
Chennai, Tamilnadu, 600 084, India
Tel.: (91) 4443439595
Fax: (91) 4426423296
E-Mail: arl@arvindremedies.com
Web Site: www.arvindremedies.com
Year Founded: 1988
531823—(BOM NSE)
Sales Range: $75-99.9 Million
Business Description:
Ayurvedic Pharmaceutical Products Mfr & Distr
S.I.C.: 2834
N.A.I.C.S.: 325412

Personnel:
Rashik Shah *(Pres)*
B. Arvind Shah *(CEO & Mng Dir)*
G. Ramachandran *(CFO)*
P.R. Krishnan *(Sec)*
G. Ramesh Kumar *(Sr VP-Technical)*
Board of Directors:
Ankur Agarwal
Sudhir Chandra
V. R. Mehta
Raja Mohan
Chandra Ravindran
C.M.K. Reddy
V. Santhanaraman
B. Arvind Shah
Transfer Agent:
Cameo Corporate Services Limited
Subramanian Building No 1 Club House Road
5th Floor
Chennai, India
Plant:

Arvind Remedies Ltd - Thiruvallur Factory (1)
38 39 & 40 SIDCO Industrial Estate
Kakkalur, 602 003 Tiruvallur, India
Tel.: (91) 44 27662144
Fax: (91) 44 27662144
E-Mail: factory@arvindremedies.com
Emp.: 20
Pharmaceutical Products Mfr
S.I.C.: 2834
N.A.I.C.S.: 325412
Ankur Agarwal *(Exec Dir)*

ARX GOLD CORPORATION

(Formerly DAULTON CAPITAL CORP.)
Level 13 40 Creek Street
Brisbane, QLD, 4000, Australia
Toll Free: 8883871403
Web Site: arxgold.net
Year Founded: 2008
DUCP—(OTC)
Assets: $6,802
Liabilities: $769,776
Net Worth: ($762,974)
Earnings: ($1,148,471)
Emp.: 1
Fiscal Year-end: 04/30/13
Business Description:
Gold Exploration Services
S.I.C.: 1041
N.A.I.C.S.: 212221
Personnel:
Brian James Smith *(CEO)*
Board of Directors:
Brian James Smith
Tom Verdon

ARYAMAN FINANCIAL SERVICES LTD

60 Khataou Building Alkesh Dinesh Marg
Fort, Mumbai, 400 001, India
Tel.: (91) 22 2261 8264
Fax: (91) 22 2263 0434
E-Mail: info@afsl.co.in
Web Site: www.afsl.co.in
Year Founded: 1994
530245—(BOM)
Rev.: $37,489,148
Assets: $150,329,534
Liabilities: $11,110,378
Net Worth: $139,219,156
Earnings: $4,466,844
Fiscal Year-end: 03/31/13
Business Description:
Merchant Banking Services
S.I.C.: 6211
N.A.I.C.S.: 523110
Personnel:
Ambreen Khan *(Compliance Officer, Sec & Sr Mgr-Merchant Banking Div)*
Board of Directors:
Ram Gaud
Darshit Parikh
Shreyas Shah
Shripal Shah
Tejal Vala
Transfer Agent:
Adroit Corporate Services (P) Limited.
19 Jaferbhoy Industrial Estate 1st Floor
Makwana Road Marol Naka
Andheri E, Mumbai, 400059, India
Tel.: (91) 22 28590942
Fax: (91) 22 28581132

ARYZTA AG

Talacker 41
8001 Zurich, Switzerland
Tel.: (41) 445834200
Fax: (41) 445834249
E-Mail: info@aryzta.com
Web Site: www.aryzta.com
Year Founded: 2008
ARYN—(ISE SWX)
Rev.: $6,062,732,367
Assets: $7,849,673,426
Liabilities: $4,133,397,485
Net Worth: $3,716,275,941
Earnings: $209,722,517
Emp.: 15,595
Fiscal Year-end: 07/31/13
Business Description:
Bakery Products Mfr & Distr
S.I.C.: 2052
N.A.I.C.S.: 311812
Personnel:
Owen Killian *(CEO)*
Patrick McEniff *(CFO & COO)*
Pat Morrissey *(Chief Admin Officer, Gen Counsel & Sec)*
John Yamin *(Global Food Offier & CEO-Americas)*
Paul Meade *(Comm Officer)*
Board of Directors:
Denis Lucey
Charles Adair
Hugh Cooney
J. Brian Davy
Shaun B. Higgins
Owen Killian
Patrick McEniff
Andrew Morgan
Gotz-Michael Muller
Wolfgang Werle
John Yamin

Subsidiaries:

Hiestand Holdings (Switzerland) AG (1)
Talacker 41
Zurich, 8001, Switzerland
Tel.: (41) 44 755 25 25
Investment Management Services
S.I.C.: 6211
N.A.I.C.S.: 523999

HIESTAND INTERNATIONAL AG (1)
Ifangstrasse 11
8952 Schlieren, Switzerland
Tel.: (41) 44 738 46 11
Fax: (41) 44 755 20 01
E-Mail: info@hiestand.ch
Frozen Food Products Mfr
S.I.C.: 2038
N.A.I.C.S.: 311412

Hiestand Schweiz AG (1)
Ifangstrasse 9
CH-8952 Schlieren, Switzerland (100%)
Tel.: (41) 447384343
Fax: (41) 447384613
E-Mail: info@hiestand.ch
Web Site: www.hiestand.ch
Sales Range: $650-699.9 Million
Emp.: 3,233
Frozen Bakery Products Mfr
S.I.C.: 2053
N.A.I.C.S.: 311813
J. P. McGrath *(CFO)*

Non-U.S. Subsidiary:

Fricopan GmbH (2)
Nobelstrasse 66
12057 Berlin, Germany
Tel.: (49) 306839830
Fax: (49) 3068398322
E-Mail: info@fricopan.de
Web Site: www.fricopan.de
Emp.: 2
Frozen Bakery Products Mfr
S.I.C.: 2053
N.A.I.C.S.: 311813

U.S. Subsidiary:

Fresh Start Bakeries Inc. (1)
145 S State College Blvd No 200
Brea, CA 92821 CA
Tel.: (714) 256-8900
Fax: (714) 256-8916
Web Site: www.freshstartbakeries.com
Emp.: 100
Bread & Other Bakery Products Mfr & Distr
S.I.C.: 5149
N.A.I.C.S.: 424490
Craig Olson *(Pres & CEO)*

Non-U.S. Subsidiaries:

ARYZTA Holdings Asia Pacific BV (1)
Paasheuvelweg
Amsterdam, 1105 BH, Netherlands
Tel.: (31) 20 5646160
Investment Management Services
S.I.C.: 6211
N.A.I.C.S.: 523999

ARYZTA Ltd. (1)
151 Thomas St
Dublin, 8, Ireland UK
Tel.: (353) 1 612 1200
Fax: (353) 1 612 1321
E-Mail: info@iaws.com
Web Site: www.iaws.com
Sales Range: $1-4.9 Billion
Emp.: 4,973
Bakery Products Mfr & Distr
S.I.C.: 2051
N.A.I.C.S.: 311812
Owen Killian *(CEO)*
Patrick McEniff *(CFO)*
Hugo Kane *(COO)*
Pat Morrissey *(Sec)*

Subsidiary:

Cuisine de France Limited (2)
Grange Castle Business Park
Clondalkin, Dublin, 22, Ireland
Tel.: (353) 14057200
Fax: (353) 14647498
E-Mail: info@cuisinedefrance.com
Web Site: www.cuisinedefrance.ie
Sales Range: $200-249.9 Million
Emp.: 600
Specialty Breads, Pastries & Baked Confectionery Mfr & Whslr
S.I.C.: 2052
N.A.I.C.S.: 311812
Dave O'Donoghue *(Mng Dir)*

U.S. Subsidiary:

Cuisine de France Inc. (3)
350 S NW Hwy Ste 302
Park Ridge, IL 60068
Tel.: (847) 692-1916
Fax: (847) 692-1917
Web Site: www.cuisinedefrance.com
Specialty Breads, Pastries & Baked Confectionery Mfr & Whslr
S.I.C.: 2052
N.A.I.C.S.: 311812

Non-U.S. Subsidiary:

Cuisine de France (UK) Limited (3)
Grange Castle Business Park Clondalkin
Dublin, 22, Ireland
Tel.: (353) 2892603222
E-Mail: info@cuisinedefrance.com
Web Site: www.cuisinedefrance.com
Emp.: 700
Specialty Breads, Pastries & Baked Confectionery Mfr & Whslr
S.I.C.: 2051
N.A.I.C.S.: 311812
David O'Donoghue *(CEO)*

U.S. Subsidiaries:

La Brea Bakery, Inc. (2)
15963 Strathern St
Van Nuys, CA 91406
Tel.: (818) 742-4242
Fax: (818) 742-4276
Web Site: www.labreabakery.com
Bread Mfr & Retailer
S.I.C.: 2052
N.A.I.C.S.: 311812
John Yamin *(CEO)*
Rick Anderson *(CMO & Chief Comml Officer)*

Otis Spunkmeyer, Inc. (2)
14490 Catalina St
San Leandro, CA 94577 CA
Tel.: (510) 357-9836
Fax: (510) 352-5680
Toll Free: (888) 275-6847
Web Site: www.spunkmeyer.com
Sales Range: $300-349.9 Million
Emp.: 1,208
Cookie Mfr
S.I.C.: 2052
N.A.I.C.S.: 311821
Gerald P. Reardon *(Exec VP-Sls & Mktg)*

Non-U.S. Subsidiary:

Delice de France plc (2)
Delice House
149 Brent Rd Southall, London, UB2 5LJ, United Kingdom
Tel.: (44) 2089179600
Fax: (44) 2089179704
Web Site: www.delicedefrance.co.uk
Emp.: 150
Frozen Bakery Product Mfr
S.I.C.: 2053
N.A.I.C.S.: 311813
Nick Dint *(Gen Mgr)*

Dalgety Agra Polska Sp. z.o.o. (1)
ul Heleny Szafran 6
60-693 Poznan, Poland
Tel.: (48) 61 842 94 66
Fax: (48) 61 842 94 67
Seeds & Fertilizer Distr
S.I.C.: 5191
N.A.I.C.S.: 424910

France Distribution SAS (1)
Zac De Bel Air N 14 16 14 Avenue Joseph Paxton
Ferrieres en Brie, 77164, France
Tel.: (33) 164116401
Fax: (33) 164116402
Emp.: 200
Bakery Food Products Distr
S.I.C.: 5142
N.A.I.C.S.: 424420

Fresca SAS (1)
29 rue Helene Boucher ZA de la Butte Au Berger
Chilly Mazarin, Paris, 91380, France
Tel.: (33) 1 64 54 54 00
Fax: (33) 1 60 10 07 98
Food Products Distr
S.I.C.: 5142
N.A.I.C.S.: 424420

Fresh Start Bakeries Industrial LTDA (1)
Avenida das Comunicacoes 333 - Industrial Anhanguera
Osasco, 06278-080, Brazil
Tel.: (55) 1136872744
Bakery Food Products Mfr
S.I.C.: 2053
N.A.I.C.S.: 311813

Hiestand & Suhr Handels und Logistik GmbH (1)
Auf der Haid 1
Achkarren, 79235 Vogtsburg, Germany
Tel.: (49) 7662 9303 16
Fax: (49) 7662 9303 30
E-Mail: bestellung@hiestand-suhr.de
Emp.: 50
Frozen Bakery Products Mfr
S.I.C.: 2053
N.A.I.C.S.: 311813
Pedro Rodriguez *(Gen Mgr)*

Hiestand Beteiligungsholding GmbH & Co. KG (1)
Albert Einstein Strasse 1
97447 Gerolzhofen, Germany

ARYZTA AG—(Continued)

Tel.: (49) 9382 9711 0
Fax: (49) 9382 9711 598
E-Mail: info@hiestand.de
Frozen Food Products Mfr
S.I.C.: 2038
N.A.I.C.S.: 311412

Subsidiary:

HIESTAND DEUTSCHLAND GMBH (2)
Albert Einstein Str 1
97447 Gerolzhofen, Germany
Tel.: (49) 9382 9711 0
Fax: (49) 829712562
E-Mail: bestellung@hiestand.de
Web Site: www.hiestand.de
Emp.: 35
Bakery Food Products Mfr & Distr
S.I.C.: 2053
N.A.I.C.S.: 311813

Non-U.S. Subsidiaries:

HIESTAND AUSTRIA GMBH (2)
Industriezentrum No Sud Str 3 Obj 74
2351 Wiener Neudorf, Austria
Tel.: (43) 2236 677 277 0
Fax: (43) 2236 677 277 770
E-Mail: info@hiestand.at
Emp.: 17
Frozen Food Products Distr
S.I.C.: 5142
N.A.I.C.S.: 424420
Dettrech Alexander *(Gen Mgr)*

HIESTAND JAPAN CO., LTD (2)
Yoyogi Yoshino Building 2 F 1-58-5 Yoyogi
Shibuya-ku, Tokyo, 151-0053, Japan
Tel.: (81) 3 5358 6777
Fax: (81) 3 5358 6711
E-Mail: info@hiestand.co.jp
Web Site: www.hiestand.co.jp
Emp.: 6
Baked Goods Mfr
S.I.C.: 2053
N.A.I.C.S.: 311813
Oliver Ryf *(Mng Dir)*

HIESTAND MALAYSIA SDN BHD (2)
Lot 2 Jalan P 10/14 Seksyen 10
43650 Bandar Baru Bangi, Selangor Darul Ehsan, Malaysia
Tel.: (60) 3 8925 7771
Fax: (60) 3 8925 7779
E-Mail: info@hiestand.com.my
Web Site: www.hiestand.com.my
Frozen Bakery Food Mfr
S.I.C.: 2053
N.A.I.C.S.: 311813
Herwig Franz Nickl *(Mng Dir & Head-Sls)*

Masstock Group Holdings Limited (1)
Andoversford
Cheltenham, Gloucestershire, GL54 4LZ, United Kingdom
Tel.: (44) 1242 821 100
Fax: (44) 1242 820 807
Emp.: 40
Investment Management Services
S.I.C.: 6211
N.A.I.C.S.: 523999

Origin Enterprises plc (1)
151 Thomas Street
Dublin, 8, Ireland (68.8%)
Tel.: (353) 1 612 1311
Fax: (353) 1 612 1321
E-Mail: investorrelations@originenterprises.com
Web Site: www.originenterprises.ie
OIZ—(AIM ISE)
Rev.: $1,909,101,947
Assets: $1,208,227,960
Liabilities: $838,588,524
Net Worth: $369,639,436
Earnings: $98,286,564
Emp.: 1,428
Fiscal Year-end: 07/31/13
Agricultural Products, Cereal & Food Mfr
S.I.C.: 2873
N.A.I.C.S.: 325311
Thomas O'Mahony *(CEO)*
Brendan Fitzgerald *(CFO)*
Derek Wilson *(CIO)*
John O'Connell *(Treas)*
Pat Morrissey *(Sec)*

Subsidiaries:

Goulding Chemicals Limited (2)
Centre Pk Rd Marina
Cork, Ireland
Tel.: (353) 214911611
Fax: (353) 214911660
E-Mail: info@gouldings.ie
Web Site: www.gouldings.ie
Emp.: 30
Nitrogenous Fertilizer Mfr
S.I.C.: 2873
N.A.I.C.S.: 325311

R. & H. Hall Limited (2)
151 Thomas Street
Dublin, 8, Ireland
Tel.: (353) 16121234
Fax: (353) 16121213
E-Mail: info@rhhall.ie
Web Site: www.rhhall.ie
Animal Feed Raw Material Supplier
S.I.C.: 2048
N.A.I.C.S.: 311119

Joint Venture:

Valeo Foods Group Limited (2)
Merrywell Industrial Estate
Ballymount, Dublin, 12, Ireland
Tel.: (353) 1 4051500
Fax: (353) 1 460 1336
E-Mail: info@valeofoods.ie
Web Site: www.valeofoods.ie
Sales Range: $400-449.9 Million
Emp.: 50
Grocery Product Mfr; Owned by CapVest Limited (55%) & Origin Enterprises plc (45%)
S.I.C.: 2033
N.A.I.C.S.: 311421
Seamus Fitzpatrick *(Chm)*

Subsidiaries:

Batchelors Ltd. (3)
72 74 Bannow Rd Cabra W
PO Box 88
Dublin, 7, Ireland
Tel.: (353) 18380133
Fax: (353) 18385963
E-Mail: enquiries@bachelors.ie
Web Site: www.batchelors.ie
Emp.: 200
Canned Vegetables & Fruit Juice & Distr Import Export
S.I.C.: 2032
N.A.I.C.S.: 311422
Eugene Heary *(Mng Dir)*

Jacob Fruitfield Food Group Ltd. (3)
Belgard Road
Tallaght, Dublin, 24, Ireland IE
Tel.: (353) 14141111
Fax: (353) 14511898
Web Site: www.jacobfruitfield.com
Sales Range: $125-149.9 Million
Emp.: 70
Candies, Chocolates, Biscuits, Jams & Sauces Mfr & Distr
S.I.C.: 2064
N.A.I.C.S.: 311340
Michael Carey *(Chm)*
Seamus Kearney *(Mng Dir & COO)*

Non-U.S. Subsidiary:

Irish Biscuits (N.I.) Limited (4)
PO Box 3
Hillsborough, Co Down, United Kingdom UK
Tel.: (44) 2892682644
Fax: (44) 2892 683 804
Biscuits, Food & Drinks Products Distr
S.I.C.: 5499
N.A.I.C.S.: 445299

Shamrock Foods Limited (3)
Marywell Industrial Estate
Ballymount Road, Dublin, Ireland
Tel.: (353) 14051500
Fax: (353) 14601336
E-Mail: info@valeofoods.ie
Web Site: www.valeofoods.ie
Emp.: 200
Dried & Dehydrated Food Mfr
S.I.C.: 2034
N.A.I.C.S.: 311423
Seamus Kearney *(Mng Dir)*

Non-U.S. Subsidiary:

Origin Fertilisers (UK) Limited (2)
1-3 Freeman Court
Jarman Way, Royston, Herts, SG8 5HW, United Kingdom
Tel.: (44) 1763255500
Fax: (44) 1763245686
E-Mail: enquiries@originfertilisers.co.uk
Web Site: www.originfertilisers.co.uk
Emp.: 15
Fertilizer Mfr
S.I.C.: 2875
N.A.I.C.S.: 325314
Michael Redden *(Mng Dir)*

Subsidiary:

Origin Fertilisers 2011 Limited (3)
Old Croft
Carlisle, CA3 9BA, United Kingdom
Tel.: (44) 1228 554 600
Agricultural Fertilizer Mfr
S.I.C.: 2875
N.A.I.C.S.: 325314

Non-U.S. Joint Venture:

Welcon AS (2)
Ruselokkveien 6
Oslo, 0251, Norway
Tel.: (47) 2212 2540
Web Site: www.welcon.no
Rev.: $222,932,500
Fish Meal & Fish Oil Mfr; Joint Venture of Origin Enterprises plc (50%) & Austevoll Seafood ASA (50%)
S.I.C.: 2092
N.A.I.C.S.: 311710
Arne Stang *(CEO)*
Tom Tynan *(COO)*

Non-U.S. Subsidiary:

United Fish Industries (UK) Limited (3)
Gilbey Road
Grimsby, Lincs, DN31 2SL, United Kingdom
Tel.: (44) 1472263450
Fax: (44) 1472263333
Sales Range: $50-74.9 Million
Emp.: 35
Animal Aquaculture
S.I.C.: 0273
N.A.I.C.S.: 112519
Thomas Tynan *(COO)*

R & H Hall Trading Limited (1)
Clarendon Ho 23 Clarendon Rd
Belfast, BT1 3BG, United Kingdom
Tel.: (44) 28 9031 3360
Bakery Food Products Distr
S.I.C.: 5142
N.A.I.C.S.: 424420

ARZON LIMITED

4485 Mainway
Burlington, ON, L7L 7P3, Canada
Tel.: (905) 561-2424
Fax: (905) 332-5627
E-Mail: sales@arzonlimited.com
Web Site: www.arzonlimited.com
Rev.: $16,814,700
Emp.: 45

Business Description:
Welded Tube Mfr
S.I.C.: 3317
N.A.I.C.S.: 331210

Personnel:
Jeff Carubba *(Pres)*

AS BALTIKA

(d/b/a Baltika)
Veerenni 24
EE-10135 Tallinn, Estonia
Tel.: (372) 630 2731
Fax: (372) 630 2814
E-Mail: baltika@baltikagroup.com
Web Site: www.baltikagroup.com
BLT1T—(TAL)
Rev.: $75,832,448
Assets: $31,656,534
Liabilities: $17,944,446
Net Worth: $13,712,088
Earnings: $1,083,667
Emp.: 1,288
Fiscal Year-end: 12/31/12

Business Description:
Clothing Mfr & Retailer
S.I.C.: 5651
N.A.I.C.S.: 448140

Personnel:
Jaakko Sakari Mikael Salmelin *(Chm-Supervisory Bd)*
Meelis Milder *(Chm-Mgmt Bd & CEO)*
Maigi Parnik-Pernik *(CFO & Member-Mgmt Bd)*
Kati Kusmin *(Member-Mgmt Bd & Dir-Sls & Mktg)*
Maire Milder *(Member-Mgmt Bd & Dir-Branding & Retail Dev)*
Andrew Paterson *(Member-Mgmt Bd & Dir-Product Div)*

Supervisory Board of Directors:
Jaakko Sakari Mikael Salmelin
Lauri Kustaa Aima
Valdo Kalm
Tiina Mois
Reet Saks

Subsidiaries:

OU Baltika Tailor (1)
Kuuli 4
Tallinn, Harju, Estonia
Tel.: (372) 6302700
Fax: (372) 6302814
Clothing Retail Stores Operation Services
S.I.C.: 5699
N.A.I.C.S.: 448150

OU Baltman (1)
Veerenni 24
Tallinn, Harju, 10135, Estonia
Tel.: (372) 6302806
Fax: (372) 6302814
E-Mail: baltman@baltikagroup.com
Web Site: www.baltman.ee
Emp.: 217
Formal Wear Retailer
S.I.C.: 5611
N.A.I.C.S.: 448110

Non-U.S. Subsidiaries:

Baltika Poland Sp.z.o.o. (1)
Nalewki 8/62
00-158 Warsaw, Poland
Tel.: (48) 228318490
Fax: (48) 228318709
Emp.: 25
Fashion Apparels Retailer
S.I.C.: 5699
N.A.I.C.S.: 448150
Alexander Mlynarska *(Mng Dir)*

Baltika Ukraina Ltd (1)
Frunze 1-3 3rd Floor Office 32
04080 Kiev, Ukraine
Tel.: (380) 445314314
Fax: (380) 445314352
E-Mail: baltika@baltikagroup.com
Emp.: 100
Clothing Retail Stores Operation Services
S.I.C.: 5699
N.A.I.C.S.: 448150
Meelis Milder *(Mng Dir)*

OY Baltinia AB (1)
Etelaesalmentie 7
21620 Kuusisto, Finland
Tel.: (358) 400784505
Clothing Retail Stores Operation Services
S.I.C.: 5699
N.A.I.C.S.: 448150

SIA Baltika Latvija (1)
12 Udens Street
Riga, LV-1007, Latvia
Tel.: (371) 67807540
Fax: (371) 67807541
E-Mail: info.latvia@baltikagroup.com
Emp.: 101
Clothing Retail Stores Operation Services
S.I.C.: 5699
N.A.I.C.S.: 448150
Maruth Eagle *(Mng Dir)*

AS COMPANY S.A.
2klm Palais Simmaxikis Odou
Diastavrosi Pros Oreokastro
Oreokastro, 570 13 Thessaloniki, Greece
Tel.: (30) 2310 572 000
Fax: (30) 2310 572 072
Web Site: ir.ascompany.gr
Year Founded: 1990
ASCO—(ATH)
Emp.: 70
Business Description:
Toy & Electronic Games Mfr
S.I.C.: 3942
N.A.I.C.S.: 339930
Personnel:
Andreadis Efstratios *(Co-Founder, Chm & CEO)*
Andreadou Anastasia *(Co-Founder & Vice Chm)*
Board of Directors:
Andreadis Efstratios
Andreadou Anastasia
Andreadhs Konstantinos
Vasilakeris Morfis
Iakovou Petros
Mehteridis Theofilos

A.S. CREATION TAPETEN AG
Soedstrasse 47
D-51645 Gummersbach, Germany
Tel.: (49) 22615420
Fax: (49) 226155883
E-Mail: contact@as-creation.de
Web Site: www.as-creation.de
ACW—(DEU)
Sls.: $267,765,893
Assets: $217,739,957
Liabilities: $90,070,170
Net Worth: $127,669,787
Earnings: $9,905,484
Emp.: 820
Fiscal Year-end: 12/31/12
Business Description:
Paper & Paper Products Industry
S.I.C.: 2671
N.A.I.C.S.: 322220
Personnel:
Franz Jurgen Schneider *(Chm-Supervisory Bd)*
Jorn Kamper *(Chm-Mgmt Bd)*
Rudiger Liebs *(Vice Chm-Supervisory Bd)*
Maik-Holger Kramer *(Member-Mgmt Bd-Fin & Controlling & Dir-Fin)*
Antonios Suskas *(Member-Mgmt Bd-Production & Logistics)*
Supervisory Board of Directors:
Franz Jurgen Schneider
Jella Susanne Benner-Heinacher
Rudiger Liebs
Peter Mourschinetz
Dieter Schadt
Rolf Schmuck
Subsidiary:

A.S. Creation Textil GmbH (1)
Eichendorffstrasse 2
51709 Marienheide, Germany
Tel.: (49) 22615420
Fax: (49) 226155883
E-Mail: Info@as-creation.de
Furnishing Fabrics Whslr
S.I.C.: 5023
N.A.I.C.S.: 423220

Subsidiary:

Indes Wontextil GmbH (2)
Eichendorffstr 2
51709 Marienheide, Germany
Tel.: (49) 226420135700
Fax: (49) 226420135600
E-Mail: contact@indesfuggerhaus.de
Web Site: www.indes.de
Emp.: 80
Furnishing & Decoration Fabrics Whslr
S.I.C.: 5023
N.A.I.C.S.: 423220
Karsten Hombaeh *(Mgr-Sls)*

Non-U.S. Subsidiaries:

A.S. Creation (France) SAS **(1)**
13-15 rue Jean Bart
69003 Lyon, France
Tel.: (33) 478545417
Fax: (33) 478435508
E-Mail: contact@as-creation.fr
Web Site: www.as-creation.fr
Emp.: 35
Wallpapers Mfr & Decorative Fabrics Sales
S.I.C.: 2671
N.A.I.C.S.: 322220
Thierry Maertens *(Mgr)*

Subsidiary:

MCF Investissement SA **(2)**
17 rue Eugene Pereire
91610 Ballancourt, Essonne, France
Tel.: (33) 169907200
Fax: (33) 164932627
Wallpapers Whslr
S.I.C.: 5198
N.A.I.C.S.: 424950

A.S. Creation (NL) B.V. **(1)**
Calandstraat 20
4251 NZ Werkendam, North Brabant, Netherlands
Tel.: (31) 183504700
Fax: (31) 183504457
E-Mail: contact@as-creation.nl
Web Site: www.as-creation.nl
Emp.: 12
Home Furnishings & Wallpapers Whslr
S.I.C.: 5023
N.A.I.C.S.: 423220
Roth Messer *(Mng Dir)*

AS Creation (UK) Limited **(1)**
Mayflower House 67 Liverpool Rd
Formby, Liverpool, Merseyside, L37 6BU, United Kingdom
Tel.: (44) 1704830555
Fax: (44) 1704830088
E-Mail: ascreation.uk@btinternet.com
Web Site: www.ascreation.de
Emp.: 8
Wallcoverings & Fabrics Distr
S.I.C.: 5198
N.A.I.C.S.: 424950
Stuart Wilson *(Mgr)*

AS EKSPRESS GRUPP
Narva mnt 11E
10151 Tallinn, Estonia
Tel.: (372) 669 8381
Fax: (372) 669 8180
E-Mail: egrupp@egrupp.ee
Web Site: www.egrupp.ee
EEG1T—(TAL)
Rev.: $80,374,426
Assets: $108,001,873
Liabilities: $52,675,632
Net Worth: $55,326,241
Earnings: $3,399,079
Emp.: 1,713
Fiscal Year-end: 12/31/12
Business Description:
Internet, Newspaper, Magazine & Book Publisher
S.I.C.: 2741
N.A.I.C.S.: 519130
Personnel:
Viktor Mahhov *(Chm-Supervisory Bd)*
Gunnar Kobin *(Chm-Mgmt Bd & CEO)*
Pirje Raidma *(CFO & Member-Mgmt Bd)*
Madis Tapupere *(Chief IT Officer & Member-Mgmt Bd)*
Andre Veskimeister *(Chief Innovation Officer & Member-Mgmt Bd)*
Supervisory Board of Directors:
Viktor Mahhov
Ville Jehe
Aavo Kokk
Hans H. Luik
Harri Helmer Roschier
Kari Sakari Salonen
Subsidiaries:

AS Printall **(1)**
Peterburi tee 64a
Tallinn, Harju, 11415, Estonia
Tel.: (372) 6698400
Fax: (372) 6698421
E-Mail: printall@printall.ee
Web Site: www.printall.ee
Emp.: 1,971
Newspaper Printing Services
S.I.C.: 2759
N.A.I.C.S.: 323111
Margus Liivamaegi *(Dir-Sls)*

Delfi AS **(1)**
NW St 11E
Tallinn, Harju, 10150, Estonia
Tel.: (372) 6807800
Fax: (372) 6814719
E-Mail: delfi@delfi.ee
Web Site: www.delfi.ee
Emp.: 30
Newspaper Publishing Services
S.I.C.: 2741
N.A.I.C.S.: 519130
Sven Nuutmann *(CEO)*

Eesti Ajalehed AS **(1)**
Narva mnt 11E
10151 Tallinn, Harju, Estonia
Tel.: (372) 6698080
Fax: (372) 6698154
E-Mail: ekspress@ekspress.ee
Web Site: www.lehet.com
Emp.: 200
Newspaper Publishing Services
S.I.C.: 2711
N.A.I.C.S.: 511110
Taiko Juga *(Mgr-IT)*

Non-U.S. Subsidiaries:

Delfi AS **(1)**
Mukusalas iela 41
Riga, 1004, Latvia
Tel.: (371) 67784050
Fax: (371) 67784051
E-Mail: info@delfi.lv
Web Site: www.delfi.lv
Emp.: 50
Newspaper Publishing Services
S.I.C.: 2741
N.A.I.C.S.: 519130
Egmonts Grzibovskis *(Mgr)*

Subsidiary:

Mango.lv SIA **(2)**
Mukusalas 41
Riga, 1004, Latvia
Tel.: (371) 67784070
Fax: (371) 67784050
Emp.: 50
Internet Entertainment Site Publishing Services
S.I.C.: 2741
N.A.I.C.S.: 519130
Arnis Ozols *(Mng Dir)*

Delfi UAB **(1)**
Gyneju G 16
01109 Vilnius, Lithuania
Tel.: (370) 52045400
Fax: (370) 52045403
E-Mail: delfi@delfi.lt
Web Site: www.delfi.lt
Emp.: 60
Newspaper Publishing Services
S.I.C.: 2741
N.A.I.C.S.: 519130
Vytautas Benokraitis *(Asst Mgr-Advertisment)*

TOV Delfi. **(1)**
Bud 28/2 N P N 43 Vul Mikhaila Grushevskogo, Kiev, 01021, Ukraine
Tel.: (380) 442211950
E-Mail: irina.gil@delphi.ua
Web Site: www.delphi.ua
Online Advertising Agencies
S.I.C.: 7311
N.A.I.C.S.: 541810

AS ENERGOFIRMA JAUDA
Krustpils Street 119
LV-1057 Riga, Latvia
Tel.: (371) 7725789
Fax: (371) 7725770
E-Mail: info@jauda.com
Web Site: www.jauda.com
Year Founded: 1961
Sls.: $36,426,625
Assets: $18,830,042
Liabilities: $2,692,794
Net Worth: $16,137,249
Earnings: $3,514,406
Emp.: 229
Fiscal Year-end: 12/31/12
Business Description:
Electrical Equipment Producer
S.I.C.: 3699
N.A.I.C.S.: 335999
Personnel:
Janis Simins *(Pres)*

AS MERKO EHITUS
Parnu mnt 141
11314 Tallinn, Estonia
Tel.: (372) 650 1250
Fax: (372) 650 1251
E-Mail: tallinn@merko.ee
Web Site: www.merko.ee
Year Founded: 1990
MKS—(DEU)
Rev.: $335,372,678
Assets: $302,952,866
Liabilities: $143,745,379
Net Worth: $159,207,487
Earnings: $10,248,392
Emp.: 900
Fiscal Year-end: 12/31/12
Business Description:
Construction Engineering Services
S.I.C.: 8711
N.A.I.C.S.: 541330
Personnel:
Toomas Annus *(Chm-Supervisory Bd)*
Andres Trink *(Chm-Mgmt Bd)*
Viktor Moisja *(Member-Mgmt Bd)*
Supervisory Board of Directors:
Toomas Annus
Indrek Neivelt
Teet Roopalu
Olari Taal
Tonu Toomik
Subsidiary:

AS Merko Ehitus Eesti **(1)**
Jarvevana tee 9g
11314 Tallinn, Estonia (100%)
Tel.: (372) 680 5105
Fax: (372) 680 5106
E-Mail: merko@merko.ee
Web Site: www.merko.ee
Construction Engineering Services
S.I.C.: 1629
N.A.I.C.S.: 237990

Subsidiaries:

AS Gustaf **(2)**
Ringi 10
80010 Parnu, Estonia (92.5%)
Tel.: (372) 443 1300
Fax: (372) 443 1302
E-Mail: gustaf@gustaf.ee
Web Site: www.gustaf.ee
Construction Engineering Services
S.I.C.: 1629
N.A.I.C.S.: 237990

AS Merko Infra **(2)**
Jarvevana tee 9g
11314 Tallinn, Estonia (100%)
Tel.: (372) 680 5015
Fax: (372) 680 5106
E-Mail: merko@merko.ee
Web Site: www.merko.ee
Construction Engineering Services
S.I.C.: 1629
N.A.I.C.S.: 237990

AS Merko Tartu **(2)**
Raekoja plats 20
51004 Tartu, Estonia (66%)
Tel.: (372) 730 2890
Fax: (372) 730 2891

AS Merko Ehitus—(Continued)

E-Mail: merkotartu@merkotartu.ee
Web Site: www.merkotartu.ee
Construction Engineering Services
S.I.C.: 1629
N.A.I.C.S.: 237990

AS Tallinna Teed (2)
Betooni 24
11415 Tallinn, Estonia (100%)
Tel.: (372) 606 1901
Fax: (372) 606 1925
E-Mail: info@talteede.ee
Web Site: www.talteede.ee
Construction Engineering Services
S.I.C.: 8711
N.A.I.C.S.: 541330

OU Fort Ehitus (2)
Tare tee 2-5
74001 Viimsi, Estonia (75%)
Tel.: (372) 50 27165
Fax: (372) 600 5008
E-Mail: peeter.luks@mail.ee
Construction Engineering Services
S.I.C.: 1629
N.A.I.C.S.: 237990

OU Gustaf Tallinn (2)
Sopruse pst 145
13417 Tallinn, Estonia (80%)
Tel.: (372) 656 3523
Fax: (372) 656 3525
E-Mail: info@gustaf-tallinn.ee
Web Site: www.gustaf-tallinn.ee
Construction Engineering Services
S.I.C.: 1629
N.A.I.C.S.: 237990

Non-U.S. Subsidiaries:

SIA Merks (1)
Skanstes iela 50
LV-1013 Riga, Latvia (100%)
Tel.: (371) 6737 3380
Fax: (371) 6737 3379
E-Mail: merks@merks.lv
Web Site: www.merks.lv
Construction Engineering Services
S.I.C.: 8711
N.A.I.C.S.: 541330

UAB Merko Statyba (1)
Laisves pr 3
LT-03150 Vilnius, Lithuania (100%)
Tel.: (370) 5210 5330
Fax: (370) 5210 5333
E-Mail: merko@merko.lt
Web Site: www.merko.lt
Construction Engineering Services
S.I.C.: 1629
N.A.I.C.S.: 237990

AS OLAINFARM

Rupnicu iela 5
Olaine, 2114, Latvia
Tel.: (371) 67013705
Fax: (371) 67013777
E-Mail: olainfarm@olainfarm.lv
Web Site: www.olainfarm.lv
Year Founded: 1972
UUK—(DEU)
Sls.: $100,502,433
Assets: $95,679,497
Liabilities: $26,641,187
Net Worth: $69,038,309
Earnings: $18,523,973
Emp.: 1,083
Fiscal Year-end: 12/31/12

Business Description:
Pharmaceutical Product Mfr
S.I.C.: 2834
N.A.I.C.S.: 325412

Personnel:
Valentina Andrejeva *(Chm-Supervisory Bd)*
Valerijs Maligins *(Chm-Mgmt Bd)*
Jelena Dudko *(Deputy Chm-Supervisory Bd)*
Jelena Borcova *(Member-Mgmt Bd)*
Veranika Dubickaja *(Member-Mgmt Bd)*
Salvis Lapins *(Member-Mgmt Bd)*
Inga Liscika *(Member-Mgmt Bd)*

Supervisory Board of Directors:
Valentina Andrejeva
Jelena Dudko
Volodimirs Krivozubovs
Aleksandrs Raicis

AS PAREX BANKA

(Name Changed to AS Reverta)

AS REVERTA

(Formerly AS Parex Banka)
2A Republikas laukums
LV-1522 Riga, Latvia
Tel.: (371) 6 777 9100
Fax: (371) 6 777 9101
E-Mail: info@parexgroup.com
Web Site: www.parexgroup.com
Year Founded: 1992
Int. Income: $14,114,592
Assets: $687,521,327
Liabilities: $850,744,440
Net Worth: ($163,223,112)
Earnings: ($184,117,017)
Emp.: 159
Fiscal Year-end: 12/31/12

Business Description:
Banking Services
S.I.C.: 6029
N.A.I.C.S.: 522110

Personnel:
Michael Joseph Bourke *(Chm-Supervisory Bd)*
Christopher Gwilliam *(Chm-Mgmt Bd & CEO)*
Solvita Deglava *(CFO & Member-Mgmt Bd)*
Ruta Amtmane *(Chief Legal Officer & Member-Mgmt Bd)*

Supervisory Board of Directors:
Michael Joseph Bourke
Kaspars Abolins
Mary Ellen Collins
Andris Ozolins

Subsidiaries:

Parex Asset Management (1)
ZAMeierovica Blvd 14
1010 Riga, Latvia
Tel.: (371) 7010810
Fax: (371) 7778622
E-Mail: pam@parex.lv
Web Site: www.parex.lv
Emp.: 70
Asset Management Services
S.I.C.: 6211
N.A.I.C.S.: 523999
Roberts Idelsons *(Pres & CEO)*

Non-U.S. Subsidiaries:

Parex Asset Management Russia (2)
40/4 B Ordinka Street
Moscow, Russia
Tel.: (7) 4959336226
E-Mail: pam@parexam.ru
Web Site: www.parexam.ru
Emp.: 10
Asset Management Services
S.I.C.: 6211
N.A.I.C.S.: 523999
Popemko Aleksey *(Mng Dir)*

Parex Asset Management Ukraine (2)
172 Gorkogo Street
03150 Kiev, Ukraine
Tel.: (380) 445691088
Fax: (380) 445691085
E-Mail: pam@parex.ua
Web Site: www.parex.ua
Asset Management Services
S.I.C.: 6211
N.A.I.C.S.: 523999

UAB Parex Investiciju Valdymas (2)
K Kalinausko Street 13
03107 Vilnius, Lithuania
Tel.: (370) 52649730
Fax: (370) 52649731
E-Mail: invest@parex.lt
Web Site: www.parexinvest.lt
Emp.: 16
Investment Banking
S.I.C.: 6211
N.A.I.C.S.: 523110
Renata Bagaviciene *(VP)*

Parex Brokerage System (1)
Citadeles Street 2
1010 Riga, Latvia
Tel.: (371) 7323835
Fax: (371) 7323948
E-Mail: pbs@dtc.lv
Web Site: www.dtc.lv
Emp.: 40
Securities Brokerage Services
S.I.C.: 6211
N.A.I.C.S.: 523120
Ramond Krasnais *(Exec Dir)*

Parex Leasing & Factoring (1)
Brivibas Street 224
1039 Riga, Latvia
Tel.: (371) 7001100
Fax: (371) 7514455
E-Mail: lizings@parex.lv
Web Site: www.parexgroup.com
Leasing & Factoring Services
S.I.C.: 6726
N.A.I.C.S.: 525990

Parex Open Pension Fund (1)
K Barona Street 20 22 Republikas lautuns 2A
1010 Riga, Latvia
Tel.: (371) 7064717
Fax: (371) 7064669
E-Mail: pfonds@parex.lv
Web Site: www.parex.lv
Emp.: 6
Pension Fund Management Services
S.I.C.: 6371
N.A.I.C.S.: 525110
Juris Poncols *(Chm)*

Non-U.S. Subsidiaries:

AB Parex Bankas (1)
K Kalinausko Street 13
03107 Vilnius, Lithuania
Tel.: (370) 852664600
Fax: (370) 8 52664602
E-Mail: info@parex.lt
Web Site: www.parex.lt
Sales Range: $1-9.9 Million
Emp.: 186
Banking Services
S.I.C.: 6029
N.A.I.C.S.: 522110

AP Anlage und Privatbank AG (1)
Kantonstrasse 1
8807 Freienbach, Switzerland
Tel.: (41) 447876200
Fax: (41) 447876210
E-Mail: info@apbank.ch
Web Site: www.apbank.ch
Emp.: 20
Banking Services
S.I.C.: 6029
N.A.I.C.S.: 522110
Joachim Bodschwinna *(Mng Dir)*
Valery Hudorozhkov *(Deputy Mng Dir)*

Parex Bank Sweigniederlassung Berlin (1)
Franzosische Strasse 15
10117 Berlin, Germany
Tel.: (49) 3030345870
Fax: (49) 30779077456
E-Mail: info@parexbank.de
Web Site: www.parexbank.de
Banking Services
S.I.C.: 6029
N.A.I.C.S.: 522110
Signe Kalnina *(Gen Mgr)*

Parex Pank (1)
Roosikrantsi Street 2
10119 Tallinn, Estonia
Tel.: (372) 6110200
Fax: (372) 7700001
E-Mail: info@citadele.ee
Web Site: www.parex.ee
Emp.: 60
Banking Services
S.I.C.: 6029
N.A.I.C.S.: 522110
Sophia Krist *(Gen Mgr)*

AS SANGAR

Sopruse Pst 2
50050 Tartu, Estonia
Tel.: (372) 7307300
Fax: (372) 7307301
E-Mail: sangar@sangar.ee
Web Site: www.sangar.ee
Sales Range: $10-24.9 Million
Emp.: 300

Business Description:
Apparel & Accessories
S.I.C.: 2389
N.A.I.C.S.: 315990

Personnel:
Gunnar Kraft *(Chm)*

Subsidiary:

Sangar Valga Vabrik AS (1)
7 Sepa
68203 Valga, Estonia
Tel.: (372) 7666500
Fax: (372) 7666501
Emp.: 220
Men's & Boys' Suits & Coats Mfr
S.I.C.: 5699
N.A.I.C.S.: 315220

Non-U.S. Subsidiary:

SIA Sangar Trading (1)
Krasta 46
1003 Riga, Latvia (100%)
Tel.: (371) 7030382
Fax: (371) 67113139
Emp.: 3
Clothing & Furnishings Merchant Whslr
S.I.C.: 5136
N.A.I.C.S.: 424320

AS TALLINK GRUPP

(d/b/a/ Tallink Group)
Sadama 5 7
10111 Tallinn, Estonia
Tel.: (372) 6409800
Fax: (372) 6409810
E-Mail: info@tallink.ee
Web Site: www.tallink.com
TAL1T—(TAL)
Sales Range: $1-4.9 Billion
Emp.: 6,612

Business Description:
Maritime Passenger, Vehicle & Goods Transportation & Storehouse Services
S.I.C.: 4482
N.A.I.C.S.: 483114

Personnel:
Toivo Ninnas *(Chm-Supervisory Bd)*
Enn Pant *(Chm-Mgmt Bd)*
Andres Hunt *(Vice Chm-Mgmt Bd)*
Lembit Kitter *(Member-Mgmt Bd)*
Janek Stalmeister *(Member-Mgmt Bd)*

Supervisory Board of Directors:
Toivo Ninnas
Lauri Kustaa Aima
Ain Hanschmidt
Kalev Jarvelill
Eve Pant
Ashwin Roy

Subsidiaries:

AS Tallink Baltic (1)
Sadama 5/7
10111 Tallinn, Harju, Estonia
Tel.: (372) 6409800
Fax: (372) 6409810
E-Mail: info@tallink.ee
Web Site: www.tallink.ee
Emp.: 500
Marine Passenger Transport Services
S.I.C.: 4481
N.A.I.C.S.: 483112

AS Tallink Duty Free (1)
Sadama 5/7
10111 Tallinn, Harju, Estonia
Tel.: (372) 6409813
Fax: (372) 6409830
E-Mail: dutyfree@tallink.ee

Web Site: www.tallink.ee
Emp.: 20
Shipping Goods Supplier
S.I.C.: 5199
N.A.I.C.S.: 424990

OU Hansaliin (1)
Sadana 5/7
10111 Tallinn, Harju, Estonia
Tel.: (372) 6409800
Fax: (372) 6409810
E-Mail: info@tallink.ee
Web Site: www.tallink.ee
Marine Crewing Services
S.I.C.: 4481
N.A.I.C.S.: 483112

OU Hansatee Kinnisvara (1)
Sadama 5/7
10111 Tallinn, Harju, Estonia
Tel.: (372) 6 409 800
Fax: (372) 6 409 810
Vehicle Leasing Services
S.I.C.: 7515
N.A.I.C.S.: 532112

OU Hera Salongid (1)
Sadama 11A
10145 Tallinn, Harju, Estonia
Tel.: (372) 6301024
E-Mail: herasalongid.spa@tallink.ee
Web Site: www.herasalongid.ee
Emp.: 15
Body Massaging Services
S.I.C.: 7299
N.A.I.C.S.: 812199
Krista Ilvis *(Gen Mgr)*

OU HT Laevateenindus (1)
Sadama 5/7
10111 Tallinn, Harju, Estonia
Tel.: (372) 6 40 9945
Fax: (372) 6 40 9947
E-Mail: info@tallink.ee
Crewing & Ship Management Services
S.I.C.: 4481
N.A.I.C.S.: 483112

OU HT Meelelahutus (1)
Sadama 5-7
10111 Tallinn, Harju, Estonia
Tel.: (372) 6 409 954
E-Mail: entertainment@tallink.ee
Web Site: www.tallink.ee
Emp.: 10
Cruise Ship Entertainment Services
S.I.C.: 4489
N.A.I.C.S.: 487210
Kyri Maidla *(Mng Dir)*

OU Tallink Travel Club (1)
Sadama 5/7
10145 Tallinn, Harju, Estonia
Tel.: (372) 6300841
Fax: (372) 6409888
E-Mail: info@travelclub.tallink.ee
Web Site: www.travelclub.tallink.com
Travel & Tour Operating Agencies
S.I.C.: 4724
N.A.I.C.S.: 561510
Tiina Mander *(Mgr)*

OU TLG Hotell (1)
Sadama 5/7
10111 Tallinn, Harju, Estonia
Tel.: (372) 6 30 0800
Fax: (372) 6 40 9810
E-Mail: hotelbooking@tallink.ee
Web Site: www.tallinkhotels.com
Emp.: 110
Hotel Management Services
S.I.C.: 7011
N.A.I.C.S.: 721110
Taavi Tiivel *(Pres)*

SIA HT Shipmanagement (1)
Tartu Maantee 13
10145 Tallinn, Harju, Estonia
Tel.: (372) 6 40 9948
Fax: (372) 6 40 9947
Crewing & Ship Management Services
S.I.C.: 4481
N.A.I.C.S.: 483112

Non-U.S. Subsidiaries:

HTG Stevedoring OY (1)
PL 28
02151 Espoo, Finland
Tel.: (358) 91804472
Fax: (358) 972793684
Stevedoring Services
S.I.C.: 4491
N.A.I.C.S.: 488320

OOO Tallink-Ru (1)
Kazanskaya Street 7 2nd Floor Office 10
191186 Saint Petersburg, Russia
Tel.: (7) 812 322 6754
Fax: (7) 812 322 6936
E-Mail: info@tallink.spb.ru
Web Site: www.tallinksilja.ru/ru
Cargo Shipping & Passenger Transportation Services
S.I.C.: 4481
N.A.I.C.S.: 483112
Aleksei Salumaa *(Gen Dir)*

SIA TLG Hotell Lalvija (1)
Elizabetes Str 24/1
1050 Riga, Latvia
Tel.: (371) 67099760
Fax: (371) 6 709 9762
Web Site: www.hotels.tallink.com
Hotel Management Services
S.I.C.: 7011
N.A.I.C.S.: 721110
Anactija Mozira *(Mgr)*

Tallink Silja Oy (1)
Tyynennerenkatu 9
00200 Helsinki, Finland
Tel.: (358) 918041
Fax: (358) 91804402
Web Site: www.tallinksilja.com
Marine Passenger Transportation Services
S.I.C.: 4481
N.A.I.C.S.: 483112

Non-U.S. Subsidiaries:

Tallink Silja AB (2)
Sodra Hamnvagen 50A, 10253 Stockholm, Sweden
Mailing Address:
PO Box 27295
10253 Stockholm, Sweden
Tel.: (46) 86663330
Fax: (46) 092316066
E-Mail: international.sales@tallinksilja.com
Web Site: www.tallinksilja.com
Marine Cargo Containers Leasing
S.I.C.: 4491
N.A.I.C.S.: 488320

Tallink Silja GmbH (2)
Zeissstrasse 6
23560 Lubeck, Germany
Tel.: (49) 4515899222
Fax: (49) 4515899203
E-Mail: info.eu@tallinksilja.com
Web Site: www.tallinksilja.de
Passenger Transportation & Cargo Shipping Services
S.I.C.: 4481
N.A.I.C.S.: 483112

AS TALLINNA VESI

Adala 10
10614 Tallinn, Estonia
Tel.: (372) 62 62 200
Fax: (372) 62 62 300
E-Mail: tvesi@tvesi.ee
Web Site: www.tallinnavesi.ee
A1T—(DEU)
Rev.: $71,244,701
Assets: $270,214,012
Liabilities: $156,229,760
Net Worth: $113,984,252
Earnings: $30,422,096
Emp.: 301
Fiscal Year-end: 12/31/12
Business Description:
Water Treatment Services
S.I.C.: 4941
N.A.I.C.S.: 221310
Personnel:
Robert John Gallienne *(Chm-Supervisory Bd)*
Ian John Alexander Plenderleith *(Chm-Mgmt Bd & CEO)*
Riina Kai *(CFO)*
Ilona Nurmela *(Gen Counsel)*
Supervisory Board of Directors:
Robert John Gallienne
Steven Richard Fraser
Simon Roger Gardiner
Valdur Laid
Priit Lello
Mart Magi
Brendan Francis Murphy
Rein Ratas
Toivo Tootsen

AS TRIGON CAPITAL GROUP

(d/b/a Trigon Capital)
Metro Plaza Viru Valjak 2
10111 Tallinn, Estonia
Tel.: (372) 6679200
Fax: (372) 6679201
E-Mail: trigon@trigoncapital.com
Web Site: www.trigoncapital.com
Year Founded: 1994
Rev.: $6,927,391
Assets: $45,184,196
Liabilities: $16,045,000
Net Worth: $29,139,196
Earnings: $22,885
Fiscal Year-end: 12/31/12
Business Description:
Investment Services
S.I.C.: 6211
N.A.I.C.S.: 523999
Personnel:
Joakim Helenius *(Founder & Chm-Supervisory Bd)*
Ulo Adamson *(COO & Member-Mgmt Bd)*
Supervisory Board of Directors:
Joakim Helenius
Peter Fagernas
Kai Helenius
Timo Jouhki
Pertti Laine

ASA GROUP HOLDING LTD.

3888 Hong Mei Nan Lu
Min Hang Qu
201108 Shanghai, China
Tel.: (86) 65365355
A25—(HKG SES SHG)
Emp.: 2,644
Business Description:
Holding Company
S.I.C.: 6719
N.A.I.C.S.: 551112
Personnel:
Hang-Pu Yu *(Sec-Intl Bus Dept)*
Board of Directors:
Koh Ngin Joo
Soo Choon Kiat
Hoi Yin Ng
Ivan Shieh Tzong Yih
Jian Gen Zhang

ASA HOLDING D.O.O.

(d/b/a ASA Group)
Bulevar Mese Selimovica 16
71 000 Sarajevo, Bosnia & Herzegovina
Tel.: (387) 33770900
Fax: (387) 33770967
E-Mail: info@asa-holding.ba
Web Site: www.asa.ba
Emp.: 470
Business Description:
Holding Company; New Automobile & Motor Vehicle Parts Distr
S.I.C.: 6719
N.A.I.C.S.: 551112
Personnel:
Nihad Imamovic *(Chm & Pres)*
Board of Directors:
Nihad Imamovic
Emir Ahmetagic
Damir Ferovic
Janko Gojkovic
Eldin Hadziselimovic
Samir Redzepovic
Adnan Smailbegovic

A'SAFFA FOODS S.A.O.G

PO Box 3436
112 Ruwi, Oman
Tel.: (968) 24591800
Fax: (968) 24592800
Web Site: www.asaffa.com
Year Founded: 2001
SPFI—(MUS)
Rev.: $66,944,503
Assets: $100,170,615
Liabilities: $40,358,366
Net Worth: $59,812,250
Earnings: $18,814,285
Fiscal Year-end: 12/31/12
Business Description:
Poultry Services
S.I.C.: 0259
N.A.I.C.S.: 112390
Personnel:
Saleh Mohammed Al Shanfari *(Chm)*
Fahad Al-Abdul Kader *(Vice Chm)*
Nasser Zahir Nasser Al Maawali *(CEO)*
Mohamed Ahmed Al Shanfari *(Asst CEO-Admin Affairs)*
Muhammad Rafique Chaudhry *(CFO)*
Board of Directors:
Saleh Mohammed Al Shanfari
Saeed Ali Al Araimi
Mohammed Hassan Al Assiri
Areej Al Kulaib
Mubarak Suleiman Al Mantheri
Fahad Al-Abdul Kader
Suleiman Nasser Al Lamki

ASAGAMI CORPORATION

Kokusai Bldg 6F 3-1-1 Marunouchi
Chiyoda-ku, Tokyo, 100-0005, Japan
Tel.: (81) 3 6880 2200
Fax: (81) 3 6880 2230
Web Site: www.asagami.co.jp
9311—(TKS)
Business Description:
Logistics Services
S.I.C.: 4212
N.A.I.C.S.: 484110
Personnel:
Kenichi Kimura *(COO)*

ASAHI DIAMOND INDUSTRIAL CO. LTD.

The New Otani Garden Court 11th Floor 4-1 Kioi-cho Chiyoda-Ku
Tokyo, 102 0094, Japan
Tel.: (81) 332226311
Fax: (81) 332226305
Web Site: www.asahidia.co.jp
6140—(TKS)
Sls.: $422,158,000
Assets: $680,482,000
Liabilities: $128,128,000
Net Worth: $552,354,000
Earnings: $35,783,000
Emp.: 2,059
Fiscal Year-end: 03/31/13
Business Description:
Diamond & Jewelry Tool Mfr
S.I.C.: 3911
N.A.I.C.S.: 339910
Personnel:
Susumu Kida *(Chm)*
Kazuo Kawashima *(Pres)*
Kazuki Kataoka *(Exec Mng Dir)*
Kazuo Kogawa *(Mng Dir)*
Takeo Okui *(Mng Dir)*
Hideo Abe *(Exec Officer)*
Toshimasa Hagiwara *(Exec Officer)*
Tomohiko Hara *(Exec Officer)*
Osami Imoto *(Exec Officer)*
Junichi Matsuda *(Exec Officer)*
Masashi Mochizuki *(Exec Officer)*
Takao Okouchi *(Exec Officer)*
Akira Takiguchi *(Exec Officer)*

Asahi Diamond Industrial Co. Ltd.—(Continued)

Board of Directors:
Susumu Kida
Kazuki Kataoka
Kazuo Kawashima
Kazuo Kogawa
Ming-Shong Lan
Takeo Okui
Toru Suzuki
Kazuaki Taniguchi

Transfer Agent:
Sumitomo Mitsui Trust Bank Limited
1-4-1 Marunouchi Chiyoda-ku
Tokyo, Japan

Subsidiary:

Yamanashi Asahi Diamond Industrial Co., Ltd. (1)
800 Wakaoshinden Tatsuoka-cho
Nirasaki, Yamanashi, 407-0031, Japan
Tel.: (81) 551227501
Fax: (81) 551227069
Web Site: www.asahidia.co.jp/co_joffice_en.shtml
Diamond Mfr
S.I.C.: 1499
N.A.I.C.S.: 212399

Plants:

Asahi Diamond Industrial Co. Ltd. - Chiba No.2 Factory (1)
1-35 Miharadai Chonan-machi
Chosei-gun, Chiba, 297-0143, Japan
Tel.: (81) 475463101
Fax: (81) 475405221
E-Mail: tursomu@asahidia.co.jp
Web Site: www.asahidia.co.jp
Emp.: 100
Diamond Tools Mfr
S.I.C.: 3544
N.A.I.C.S.: 333514
Soji Horie *(Mng Dir)*

Asahi Diamond Industrial Co. Ltd. - Chiba Tsurumai Factory (1)
787 Tabi
Ichihara, Chiba, 290-0515, Japan
Tel.: (81) 436883221
Fax: (81) 436883274
Diamond Jewelry Mfr
S.I.C.: 3914
N.A.I.C.S.: 339910

Asahi Diamond Industrial Co. Ltd. - Mie Factory (1)
7-8-1 Yumegaoka
Iga, Mie, 518-0131, Japan
Tel.: (81) 595267321
Fax: (81) 595267272
E-Mail: nakauchi@asahidia.co.jp
Emp.: 400
Diamond Jewelry Mfr
S.I.C.: 3914
N.A.I.C.S.: 339910
Takeo Okui *(Gen Mgr)*

Asahi Diamond Industrial Co. Ltd. - Tamagawa Factory (1)
3-4-35 Kuji
Takatsu-ku, Kawasaki, Kanagawa, 213-0032, Japan
Tel.: (81) 448336221
Fax: (81) 448336702
Web Site: www.asahidia.co.jp/co_joffice_en.shtml
Diamond Jewelry Mfr
S.I.C.: 3914
N.A.I.C.S.: 339910

Non-U.S. Subsidiaries:

Asahi Diamond Industrial Australia Pty., Ltd. (1)
No 81 Bassett St
Mona Vale, NSW, 2103, Australia
Tel.: (61) 299977033
Fax: (61) 299978313
E-Mail: asahi@tpgi.com.au
Web Site: www.asahi-diamond.com.au
Emp.: 10
Diamond Tool Suppliers
S.I.C.: 5085
N.A.I.C.S.: 423840

Asahi Diamond Industrial Europe SAS (1)
47 Avenue dOrleans
BP 841
28011 Chartres, Eure-et-Loir, France
Tel.: (33) 237244040
Fax: (33) 237244099
E-Mail: contact@asahidia.eu
Web Site: www.asahidia.eu
Emp.: 108
Diamond & Cutting Tools Mfr
S.I.C.: 3545
N.A.I.C.S.: 333515
Dominique Bourges *(CEO)*

P.T. Asahi Diamond Industrial Indonesia (1)
Jln Jababeka XI Blok H No 1 H Kawasan Industri Jababeka Cikarang
Bekasi, West Java, 17520, Indonesia
Tel.: (62) 218936217
Fax: (62) 218936342
E-Mail: asahidi@cbn.net.id
Web Site: www.asahi-indonesia.com
Emp.: 80
Diamond Tools Mfr & Sales
S.I.C.: 3544
N.A.I.C.S.: 333514
Joe Fisher *(Pres)*

Taiwan Asahi Diamond Industrial Co., Ltd. (1)
248 Hwa kong St
33464, Taoyuan, Taiwan
Tel.: (886) 33636971
Fax: (886) 33620709
E-Mail: sales@taiwandiamond.com
Web Site: www.taiwandiamond.com
Emp.: 350
Diamond Tools & Cutting Tools Mfr & Sales
S.I.C.: 3291
N.A.I.C.S.: 327910
Ming Hsiung Lan *(Pres)*

U.S. Subsidiary:

Asahi Diamond America, Inc. (1)
9872 Windisch Rd
West Chester, OH 45069
Tel.: (513) 759-5222
Fax: (513) 759-2885
Web Site: www.asahidiamond.com
Emp.: 9
Diamond Tool Mfr
S.I.C.: 3544
N.A.I.C.S.: 333514
Hedikki Matsukawa *(Pres)*

ASAHI GLASS CO., LTD.

1 5 1 Marunouchi Chiyoda ku
Tokyo, 100 8405, Japan
Tel.: (81) 332185741
Telex: J24616 ASAGLAS
Fax: (81) 332187815
E-Mail: info-agchp@agc.co.jp
Web Site: www.agc.co.jp
Year Founded: 1907
5201—(TKS)
Sls.: $13,089,516,000
Assets: $20,893,103,000
Liabilities: $9,926,664,000
Net Worth: $10,966,439,000
Earnings: $481,690,000
Emp.: 49,961
Fiscal Year-end: 12/31/12

Business Description:
Glass Products, Chemicals, Silica Products & Plastics Mfr
S.I.C.: 3211
N.A.I.C.S.: 327211

Personnel:
Kazuhiko Ishimura *(Pres & CEO)*
Masahiro Sakane *(Sr Exec Officer)*
Hajime Sawabe *(Sr Exec Officer)*
Jean-Francois Heris *(Pres-Glass Company-Europe & Pres/CEO-AGC Glass Europe)*
Kimikazu Ichikawa *(Pres-Glass Company-Japan & Asia Pacific)*
Marehisa Ishiko *(Pres-Glass Company)*
Shinji Miyaji *(Pres-Glass Company-North America)*
Masao Nemoto *(Pres-Chemicals Company)*
Takuya Shimamura *(Pres-Chemicals Company)*
Akinobu Shimao *(Pres-AGC Ceramics Co ltd)*
Yuji Nishimi *(Sr Exec VP-Bus Dev & Electronics Bus)*
Yoshiaki Tamura *(Exec VP-Bus Mgmt & Gen Mgr-Tech Gen Div)*
Kei Yonamoto *(Exec VP)*

Board of Directors:
Takashi Fujino
Kazuhiko Ishimura
Hiroshi Kimura
Yuji Nishimi
Masahiro Sakane
Hajime Sawabe
Yoshiaki Tamura

Legal Counsel:
Graham & James
885 Third Ave.
New York, NY 10022
Tel.: (212) 848-1000

Transfer Agent:
Mitsubishi UFJ Trust & Banking Corporation
4-5 Marunouchi 1-Chome Chiyoda-ku
Tokyo, 100-8212, Japan
Tel.: (81) 3 3212 1211

Subsidiaries:

AGC Amenitech Co., Ltd. (1)
NBF Ueno Building 4-24-11 Higashiueno
Taito-ku, Tokyo, 110-0015, Japan
Tel.: (81) 3 5806 6210
Fax: (81) 3 5806 6270
E-Mail: info@agac.co.jp
Web Site: www.agac.co.jp
Information Technology Consulting Services
S.I.C.: 7373
N.A.I.C.S.: 541512

AGC Ceramics Co., Ltd. (1)
Mita NN Building Floor 6 4-1-23 Shiba
Minato-ku, Tokyo, 1080014, Japan
Tel.: (81) 3 5442 9172
Fax: (81) 3 5442 9190
E-Mail: info@agcc.jp
Web Site: www.agcc.jp
Emp.: 230
Ceramic Products Whslr
S.I.C.: 5032
N.A.I.C.S.: 423320
Akinobu Shimao *(Pres & CEO)*

AGC Coat-Tech Co., Ltd. (1)
101-0054 Comfort Yasuda Bldg 5FL 2-9 Kandanishiki-cho
Chiyoda-ku, Tokyo, Japan
Tel.: (81) 3 5217 5100
Fax: (81) 3 5217 5105
E-Mail: info@agccoat-tech.co.jp
Web Site: www.agccoat-tech.co.jp
Paint Mfr & Distr
S.I.C.: 2851
N.A.I.C.S.: 325510
Seiichi Kabasawa *(Chm)*

AGC Display Glass Yonezawa Co., Ltd. (1)
4-2837-11 Hachimanpara
Yonezawa, Yamagata, 992-1128, Japan
Tel.: (81) 238 28 8301
Fax: (81) 238 28 8317
Web Site: www.agft.jp
Emp.: 520
Flat Panel Display Glass Mfr
S.I.C.: 3211
N.A.I.C.S.: 327211

AGC Electronics Co., Ltd. (1)
1-8 Machiikedai
Koriyama, Fukushima, 963-0215, Japan
Tel.: (81) 24 959 1890
Fax: (81) 24 959 5275
Web Site: www.agcel.co.jp
Electronic Component & Semiconductor Mfr
S.I.C.: 3674
N.A.I.C.S.: 334413

AGC Engineering Co., Ltd. (1)
WBG Marive West 19F 2-6-1 Nakase
Mihama-ku, Chiba, 261-7119, Japan
Tel.: (81) 43 350 3366
Fax: (81) 43 350 3383
E-Mail: supply@agec.co.jp
Web Site: www.agec.co.jp
Emp.: 420
Anti Pollution Plant Engineering Services
S.I.C.: 8711
N.A.I.C.S.: 541330
Kazuhisa Takahashi *(Pres & CEO)*

AGC Fabritech Co., Ltd. (1)
6th Floor Akusesuooimachi Building 1-49-15 Ooi
Shinagawa-ku, Tokyo, 140-0014, Japan
Tel.: (81) 3 5742 5851
Fax: (81) 3 5742 5866
Web Site: www.agc-fabritech.com
Emp.: 50
Processed Glass Products Whslr
S.I.C.: 5093
N.A.I.C.S.: 423930
Tomonori Imada *(Pres)*

AGC Finance Co., Ltd. (1)
1-5-1 Marunouchi
Chiyoda-Ku, Tokyo, 100-6530, Japan
Tel.: (81) 332013395
Fax: (81) 332014148
Web Site: www.agc.com
Emp.: 4
Financial Management Services
S.I.C.: 6211
N.A.I.C.S.: 523999
Toshio Onuma *(Gen Mgr)*

AGC Glass Kenzai Co., Ltd. (1)
NBF Ueno Bldg 6-7F 4-24-11 Higashiueno
Taito-Ku, Tokyo, 110-0015, Japan
Tel.: (81) 358066500
Building Glass Material Installation Services
S.I.C.: 1793
N.A.I.C.S.: 238150

AGC Glass Products Co., Ltd (1)
NBF Ueno Bldg 4F-5F 4-24-11 Higashiueno
Taito-Ku, Tokyo, 110-0015, Japan
Tel.: (81) 358066300
Flat Glass Mfr & Distr
S.I.C.: 3211
N.A.I.C.S.: 327211

AGC Green-Tech Co., Ltd. (1)
3-5-8 Iwamotocho Iwamotocho City Plaza Bldg 9f
Chiyoda-Ku, Tokyo, 101-0032, Japan
Tel.: (81) 3 5833 5451
Fax: (81) 3 5833 5457
E-Mail: info@f-clean.com
Web Site: www.f-clean.com
Fluororesin Film Distr
S.I.C.: 5162
N.A.I.C.S.: 424610

AGC Insurance Management Co., Ltd. (1)
4-10-4 Hacchobori
Chuo-ku, Tokyo, 104-0032, Japan
Tel.: (81) 3 6222 5011
Fax: (81) 3 3206 7111
Web Site: www.agim.co.jp
Insurance Management Services
S.I.C.: 6411
N.A.I.C.S.: 524298

AGC Logistics Co., Ltd. (1)
Shin-Marunouchi Bldg 1-5-1 Marunouchi
Chiyoda-ku, Tokyo, 100-6530, Japan
Tel.: (81) 3 3218 5476
Fax: (81) 3 3218 7062
Web Site: www.agcl.co.jp
Logistics Consulting Services
S.I.C.: 4731
N.A.I.C.S.: 541614

AGC Matex Co., Ltd. (1)
1-2-27 Miyashita
Chuo-ku, Sagamihara, Kanagawa, 252-0212, Japan
Tel.: (81) 42 772 1171
Fax: (81) 42 773 0167
E-Mail: info@agm.co.jp
Web Site: www.agm.co.jp
Plastic Products Mfr & Distr
S.I.C.: 3089
N.A.I.C.S.: 326199

AGC Micro Glass Co., Ltd. (1)
3-22-28 Morooka
Hakata-ku, Fukuoka, 812-0894, Japan
Tel.: (81) 92 502 8380
Fax: (81) 92 502 8382

E-Mail: info-amgc@agc.com
Web Site: www.amgc.co.jp
Aspherical Glass Lense Mfr & Distr
S.I.C.: 3231
N.A.I.C.S.: 327215

AGC Polycarbonate Co., Ltd. (1)
1 Azaasahi Taketoyocho
Chita, Aichi, 470-2514, Japan
Tel.: (81) 569737181
Polycarbonate Sheet Mfr & Distr
S.I.C.: 2671
N.A.I.C.S.: 326112

AGC Polymer Material Co., Ltd. (1)
1-3-8 Ningyocho Nihonbashi
Chuo-ku, Tokyo, 103-0013, Japan
Tel.: (81) 3 6667 8427
Web Site: www.agc-polymer.com
Polyurethane Coating Mfr
S.I.C.: 2851
N.A.I.C.S.: 325510

AGC Research Institute, Inc. (1)
Shin-Marunouchi Bldg 1-5-1 Marunouchi
Chiyoda-ku, Tokyo, 100-6530, Japan
Tel.: (81) 332185663
Engineering Research & Development Services
S.I.C.: 8731
N.A.I.C.S.: 541712

AGC Seimi Chemical Co., Ltd. (1)
3-2-10 Chigasaki
Chigasaki, Kanagawa, 253-8585, Japan
Tel.: (81) 467 82 4131
Fax: (81) 467 86 2767
E-Mail: tky-info@seimichemical.co.jp
Web Site: www.seimichemical.co.jp
Rev.: $155,448,000
Emp.: 348
Liquid Crystal & Cathode Material Mfr
S.I.C.: 3679
N.A.I.C.S.: 334419
Kouichi Yokoyama *(Chm)*
Shigenori Ishizuki *(Mng Dir)*

AGC Si-Tech Co., Ltd. (1)
13-1 Kitaminato-machi
Wakamatsu-ku, Kitakyushu, Fukuoka, 808-0027, Japan
Tel.: (81) 93 761 1135
Fax: (81) 93 771 6161
E-Mail: info@agc-si.com
Web Site: www.agc-si.com
Emp.: 114
Silica Products Mfr
S.I.C.: 2819
N.A.I.C.S.: 325180
Yasuhiro Sanada *(Pres)*

AGC Sunsmile, Inc. (1)
1-1 Suehirocho
Tsurumi-Ku, Yokohama, Kanagawa, 230-0045, Japan
Tel.: (81) 455037132
Building Waste Management Services
S.I.C.: 4959
N.A.I.C.S.: 562998

AGC Techno Glass Co., Ltd. (1)
3583-5 Kawashiri Yoshidacho
Haibara, Shizuoka, 421-0302, Japan
Tel.: (81) 548321211
Fax: (81) 548324811
Web Site: www.atgc.co.jp
Electronic Glass Products Mfr
S.I.C.: 3231
N.A.I.C.S.: 327215

AGC Techno Glass Corporation (1)
1-50-1 Gyoda
Funabashi, 273-0044, Japan
Tel.: (81) 474212115
Fax: (81) 474212207
Glass Product Mfr
S.I.C.: 3231
N.A.I.C.S.: 327215

AGC Technology Solutions Co., Ltd. (1)
Cube-Kawasaki Bldg 1F 1-14 Nisshin-cho
Kawasaki-Ku, Kawasaki, Kanagawa, 210-0024, Japan
Tel.: (81) 44 230 5620
Fax: (81) 44 230 5640
Web Site: www.agmc.co.jp
Sls.: $282,744,000
Emp.: 188
Glass Plant Engineering Services
S.I.C.: 8711
N.A.I.C.S.: 541330
Hitoshi Chosokabe *(Pres)*

AGC Wakasa Chemicals Co., Ltd. (1)
24-26-1 Hansei
Obama, Fukui, 917-0044, Japan
Tel.: (81) 770 53 1403
Fax: (81) 770 53 1403
Pharmaceutical Products Mfr
S.I.C.: 2834
N.A.I.C.S.: 325412

Hokkaido Soda Co., Ltd. (1)
134-122 Numanohata
Tomakomai, 059-1364, Japan
Tel.: (81) 1 4455 7862
Fax: (81) 1 4455 1193
Web Site: www.hokkaido-soda.co.jp
Inorganic Chemicals Mfr
S.I.C.: 2819
N.A.I.C.S.: 325180

Kashima Chlorine and Alkali Co., Ltd. (1)
3 Touwada
Kamisu, Ibaraki, 314-0102, Japan
Tel.: (81) 299962311
Fax: (81) 299967729
Web Site: www.agc-group.com
Caustic Soda & Chlorine Mfr
S.I.C.: 2899
N.A.I.C.S.: 325998

Kashima South Joint Power Corp. (1)
33 Touwada
Kamisu, Ibaraki, 314-0102, Japan
Tel.: (81) 299964112
Fax: (81) 299964121
Web Site: www.nankyo.co.jp
Electric Power Generation Services
S.I.C.: 4911
N.A.I.C.S.: 221118

Keiyo Monomer Co., Ltd. (1)
11-6 Goiminamikaigan
Ichihara, Chiba, 290-0045, Japan
Tel.: (81) 436248535
Fax: (81) 436248529
Web Site: www.agc-group.com
Industrial Inorganic Chemical Mfr
S.I.C.: 2819
N.A.I.C.S.: 325180

Kyoei Shoji Co., Ltd. (1)
2-16-1 Minamikamata
Ohta-ku, Tokyo, 144-0035, Japan
Tel.: (81) 357140725
Fax: (81) 357140729
Web Site: www.kyoeishoji.co.jp
Warehousing & Transportation Services
S.I.C.: 4225
N.A.I.C.S.: 493110

La Foret Engineering Co., Ltd. (1)
Roppongi Annex 7F 6-7-6 Roppongi
Minato-ku
Tokyo, 106 0032, Japan
Tel.: (81) 364066720
Fax: (81) 364066723
E-Mail: info-e9@himawari-net.co.jp
Web Site: www.himawari-net.co.jp
Emp.: 9
Solar-Light Collection & Transmission Systems Mfr & Sales
S.I.C.: 4931
N.A.I.C.S.: 221121

Optical Coatings Japan (1)
32F Shinmarunouchi Bldg 1-5-1 Marunouchi
Chiyoda-ku, Tokyo, 100-6530, Japan
Tel.: (81) 3 3218 7998
Fax: (81) 3 3218 7063
E-Mail: info@ocj.co.jp
Web Site: www.ocj.co.jp
Emp.: 127
Film Coated Optical Products Mfr & Distr
S.I.C.: 3827
N.A.I.C.S.: 333314
Norihira Yoneyama *(Pres & CEO)*

Tokai Kogyo Co., Ltd. (1)
Shiba Boat Bldg 6F Shiba 3-1-15
Minato-ku, Tokyo, 105-0014, Japan
Tel.: (81) 354199010
Fax: (81) 354199018
E-Mail: info@tokai-kc.co.jp
Web Site: www.tokai-kc.co.jp
Emp.: 50
Commercial Building Construction Services
S.I.C.: 1541
N.A.I.C.S.: 236210

Joint Venture:

Kashima Chemical Co., Ltd. (1)
30 Towada
Kamisu, Ibaraki, Japan JP
Tel.: (81) 299 96 2271 (78.75%)
Fax: (81) 299 96 9286
Web Site: www.kashima-chemical.com
Emp.: 60
Chemicals Mfr
S.I.C.: 2899
N.A.I.C.S.: 325998
Masayoshi Nanba *(Pres)*

Plants:

AGC Seimi Chemical Co., Ltd. - Kashima Plant (1)
2276-2 Nada Hirai
Kashima, Ibaraki, 314-0012, Japan
Tel.: (81) 299 84 0808
Fax: (81) 299 84 0217
Liquid Crystal & Cathode Material Mfr
S.I.C.: 3679
N.A.I.C.S.: 334419

Asahi Glass Co., Ltd. - Aichi Plant (Taketoyo) (1)
1 Asahi Taketoyo-cho
Chita, Aichi, 470-2394, Japan
Tel.: (81) 569 73 1110
Web Site: www.agc.com
Emp.: 1,055
Flat Glass Mfr
S.I.C.: 3211
N.A.I.C.S.: 327211

Asahi Glass Co., Ltd. - Aichi Plant (Toyota) (1)
9-30-1 Umetsubocho
Toyota, Aichi, 471-0064, Japan
Tel.: (81) 565 32 7331
Flat Glass Mfr
S.I.C.: 3211
N.A.I.C.S.: 327211

Asahi Glass Co., Ltd. - Chiba Plant (1)
10 Goikaigan
Ichihara, Chiba, Japan
Tel.: (81) 436 23 3121
Web Site: www.agc.com
Emp.: 883
Specialty Chemical Mfr
S.I.C.: 2899
N.A.I.C.S.: 325998

Asahi Glass Co., Ltd. - Kansai Plant (1)
2 Nishimukoujima-cho
Amagasaki, Hyogo, 660-0857, Japan
Tel.: (81) 6 6413 3325
Web Site: www.agc.com
Emp.: 314
Glass Products Mfr
S.I.C.: 3231
N.A.I.C.S.: 327215

Asahi Glass Co., Ltd. - Kashima Plant (1)
25 Touwada
Kamisu, Ibaraki, 314-0195, Japan
Tel.: (81) 299 96 2215
Emp.: 499
Glass Products Mfr
S.I.C.: 3231
N.A.I.C.S.: 327215

Asahi Glass Co., Ltd. - Keihin Plant (1)
1-1 Suehiro-cho
Tsurumi-ku, Yokohama, 230-0045, Japan
Tel.: (81) 45 503 7100
Web Site: www.agc.com
Emp.: 831
Glass Products Mfr
S.I.C.: 3231
N.A.I.C.S.: 327215

Asahi Glass Co., Ltd. - Kitakyushu Plant (1)
5-1-1 Makiyama
Tobata-ku, Kitakyushu, 804-8520, Japan
Tel.: (81) 93 871 1551
Web Site: www.agc.com
Automotive Glass Mfr
S.I.C.: 3231
N.A.I.C.S.: 327215

Asahi Glass Co., Ltd. - Sagami Plant (1)
Kakuta 426-1 Aikawa-cho
Aiko-gun, Koza, Kanagawa, 243-0301, Japan
Tel.: (81) 46 286 1254
Emp.: 474
Automotive Safety Glass Mfr
S.I.C.: 3231
N.A.I.C.S.: 327215

Asahi Glass Co., Ltd. - Takasago Plant (1)
5-6-1 Umei
Takasago, Hyogo, 676-8655, Japan
Tel.: (81) 794 47 1882
Web Site: www.agc.com
Emp.: 444
Liquid Crystal Display Glass Mfr
S.I.C.: 3231
N.A.I.C.S.: 327215

U.S. Subsidiaries:

AGC America, Inc. (1)
11175 Cicero Dr Ste 400
Alpharetta, GA 30022-1167 (100%)
Tel.: (404) 446-4200
Fax: (704) 357-6328
Web Site: www.agc.co.jp/english/company/group_world_02.html
Emp.: 23
Holding Company; Glass Products & Chemicals Manufacturing & Distributing
Import Export
S.I.C.: 6719
N.A.I.C.S.: 551112

Subsidiary:

AGC Flat Glass North America, Inc. (2)
11175 Cicero Dr Ste 400
Alpharetta, GA 30022 DE
Mailing Address:
PO Box 929
Kingsport, TN 37662
Tel.: (404) 446-4200
Fax: (404) 446-4221
Toll Free: (800) 251-0441
E-Mail: webmaster@afgglass.com
Web Site: www.afgglass.com
Emp.: 4,300
Flat Glass & Rolled Glass Mfr
Export
S.I.C.: 3211
N.A.I.C.S.: 327211
Mark Ishiko *(Pres & CEO)*
Tadayuki Oi *(CTO & VP-Tech Dev)*

Subsidiary:

AGC Automotive Americas Co. (3)
2300 Litton Ln Ste 100
Hebron, KY 41048 (100%)
Tel.: (859) 334-8900
Fax: (859) 334-8761
E-Mail: sales@us.agc-automotive.com
Web Site: www.agc-automotive.com
Emp.: 75
Automotive Glass Mfr
S.I.C.: 3231
N.A.I.C.S.: 327215
Lea Amburgey *(Office Mgr)*

Plant:

AGC Automotive (4)
1465 W Sandusky Ave
Bellefontaine, OH 43311-0819
Tel.: (937) 599-3131
Fax: (937) 599-3322
Web Site: www.us.agc.com
Emp.: 600
Mfr of Automotive Glass
S.I.C.: 3231
N.A.I.C.S.: 327215
Kevin Terando *(Controller)*

Joint Venture:

SCHOTT Gemtron Corporation (3)
615 Hwy 68
Sweetwater, TN 37874-1911 TN
Tel.: (423) 337-3522

Asahi Glass Co., Ltd.—(Continued)

Fax: (423) 337-7979
E-Mail: salesinfo@gemtron.net
Web Site: www.gemtron.net
Emp.: 250
Mfr. of Tempered & Decorative Glass For Uses Including Shower Doors, Ovens & Shelving; Joint Venture of Schott Glaswerke & AFG Industries, Inc.
Export
S.I.C.: 3211
N.A.I.C.S.: 327211
Mark Delp *(Exec VP)*

Subsidiary:

SCHOTT Gemtron Corporation **(4)**
2000 Chestnut St
Vincennes, IN 47591-1760
Mailing Address:
PO Box 317
Vincennes, IN 47591-0317
Tel.: (812) 882-2680
Fax: (812) 882-7679
Web Site: www.gemtron.com
Emp.: 500
Glass Tempering & Tempered Glass; Ceramics
Import Export
S.I.C.: 3231
N.A.I.C.S.: 327215
Tim Kiger *(Gen Mgr)*

Plants:

AGC Flat Glass North America, Inc. - Abingdon Plant **(3)**
18370 Oak Park Dr
Abingdon, VA 24210
Tel.: (276) 619-6000
Fax: (276) 619-6039
Web Site: www.afgglass.com
Glass Products Mfr
S.I.C.: 3231
N.A.I.C.S.: 327215

AGC Flat Glass North America, Inc. - AGC-Alvarado Plant **(3)**
1201 Hwy 67 E
Alvarado, TX 76009
Tel.: (817) 477-1144
Fax: (817) 783-7123
Toll Free: (800) 777-5171
Web Site: www.afgglass.com
Glass Products Mfr
S.I.C.: 3231
N.A.I.C.S.: 327215

AGC Flat Glass North America, Inc. - AGC-Baton Rouge Plant **(3)**
1414 Julia St
Baton Rouge, LA 70802
Tel.: (225) 344-9401
Fax: (225) 343-2318
Toll Free: (800) 695-2341
Web Site: www.afgglass.com
Glass Products Mfr
S.I.C.: 3231
N.A.I.C.S.: 327215

AGC Flat Glass North America, Inc. - AGC-Carbondale Plant **(3)**
Clidco Dr
Carbondale, PA 18407
Tel.: (800) 233-4170
Fax: (570) 282-1382
Web Site: www.afgglass.com
Glass Products Mfr
S.I.C.: 3231
N.A.I.C.S.: 327215

AGC Flat Glass North America, Inc. - AGC-Fall River Plant **(3)**
575 Currant Rd
Fall River, MA 02720
Tel.: (508) 675-9220
Fax: (508) 677-3212
Toll Free: (800) 666-2343
Web Site: www.afgglass.com
Flat Glass Mfr
S.I.C.: 3211
N.A.I.C.S.: 327211

AGC Flat Glass North America, Inc. - AGC-Hebron Plant **(3)**
160 N High St
Hebron, OH 43025
Tel.: (888) 480-2343
Fax: (740) 929-2440
Web Site: www.afgglass.com
Glass Products Mfr
S.I.C.: 3231
N.A.I.C.S.: 327215
Rich Vaughn *(Gen Mgr)*

AGC Flat Glass North America, Inc. - AGC-Houston Plant **(3)**
5909 Milwee St
Houston, TX 77292-4767
Tel.: (713) 686-2509
Fax: (713) 686-7650
Toll Free: (800) 897-7992
Web Site: www.afgglass.com
Glass Products Mfr
S.I.C.: 3231
N.A.I.C.S.: 327215

AGC Flat Glass North America, Inc. - AGC-Jacksonville Plant **(3)**
6600 Suemac Pl
Jacksonville, FL 32254
Tel.: (904) 786-6611
Fax: (904) 781-9779
Toll Free: (800) 627-2341
Web Site: www.afgglass.com
Flat Glass Mfr
S.I.C.: 3211
N.A.I.C.S.: 327211

AGC Flat Glass North America, Inc. - AGC-Knoxville Plant **(3)**
2522 Westcott Blvd
Knoxville, TN 37931
Tel.: (865) 691-2040
Fax: (865) 691-2585
Toll Free: (800) 395-2343
Web Site: www.afgglass.com
Emp.: 40
Glass Products Mfr
S.I.C.: 3231
N.A.I.C.S.: 327215
Bill Evers *(Gen Mgr)*

AGC Flat Glass North America, Inc. - AGC-Opelousas Plant **(3)**
710 W Landry St
Opelousas, LA 70570
Tel.: (800) 489-3386
Fax: (337) 942-5005
Web Site: www.afgglass.com
Glass Products Mfr
S.I.C.: 3231
N.A.I.C.S.: 327215
Danny Guilbeau *(Gen Mgr)*

AGC Flat Glass North America, Inc. - AGC-Richmond Plant **(3)**
6200 Gorman Rd
Richmond, VA 23231
Tel.: (804) 222-0120
Fax: (804) 226-1859
Web Site: www.afgglass.com
Glass Products Mfr
S.I.C.: 3231
N.A.I.C.S.: 327215

AGC Flat Glass North America, Inc. - AGC-Salt Lake City Plant **(3)**
3515 S 300 W
Salt Lake City, UT 84115
Tel.: (801) 268-2521
Fax: (801) 284-6421
Toll Free: (800) 453-6226
Web Site: www.afgglass.com
Glass Products Mfr
S.I.C.: 3231
N.A.I.C.S.: 327215

AGC Flat Glass North America, Inc. - AGC-San Antonio Plant **(3)**
5807 Business Park
San Antonio, TX 78218
Tel.: (210) 653-7790
Fax: (210) 655-3945
Toll Free: (800) 727-7790
Web Site: www.afgglass.com
Glass Products Mfr
S.I.C.: 3231
N.A.I.C.S.: 327215

AGC Flat Glass North America, Inc. - Blue Ridge Plant **(3)**
1400 Lincoln St
Kingsport, TN 37660
Tel.: (423) 229-7200
Fax: (423) 229-7321
Web Site: www.afgglass.com
Flat Glass Mfr
S.I.C.: 3211
N.A.I.C.S.: 327211

AGC Flat Glass North America, Inc. - Boardman Plant **(3)**
365 McClurg Rd- Ste E
Boardman, OH 44512
Tel.: (330) 965-1000
Fax: (330) 965-1011
Web Site: www.afgglass.com
Emp.: 60
Glass Products Mfr
S.I.C.: 3231
N.A.I.C.S.: 327215
Jared Rastetter *(Gen Mgr)*

AGC Flat Glass North America, Inc. - Carbondale **(3)**
Clidco Dr
Carbondale, PA 18407-0313
Tel.: (570) 282-6711
Fax: (570) 282-1382
Toll Free: (800) 233-4170
Web Site: www.afg.com
Emp.: 26
Mfr of Laminated Glass
S.I.C.: 3231
N.A.I.C.S.: 327215
Jeff Nabraski *(Controller)*

AGC Flat Glass North America, Inc. - Greenland Plant **(3)**
AGC Road Hwy 11 W
Church Hill, TN 37642
Tel.: (423) 357-2400
Fax: (423) 357-2476
Web Site: www.afgglass.com
Flat Glass Mfr
S.I.C.: 3211
N.A.I.C.S.: 327211

AGC Flat Glass North America, Inc. - Marietta **(3)**
3200 Austell Rd
Marietta, GA 30008-6836
Tel.: (770) 434-2041
Fax: (770) 436-2654
Emp.: 80
Glass Fabricator
S.I.C.: 3211
N.A.I.C.S.: 327211
Billy Blair *(Branch Mgr)*

AGC Flat Glass North America, Inc. - Quakertown Plant **(3)**
480 California Rd
Quakertown, PA 18951
Tel.: (215) 538-9424
Fax: (215) 538-9438
Web Site: www.afgglass.com
Emp.: 40
Flat Glass Mfr
S.I.C.: 3211
N.A.I.C.S.: 327211
Dave Goulette *(Gen Mgr)*

AGC Flat Glass North America, Inc. - Richmond Plant **(3)**
201 Duncannon Ln
Richmond, KY 40475
Tel.: (859) 625-9002
Fax: (859) 625-9050
Web Site: www.afgglass.com
Emp.: 175
Flat Glass Mfr
S.I.C.: 3211
N.A.I.C.S.: 327211
Glan Brieter *(Plant Mgr)*

AGC Flat Glass North America, Inc. - Spring Hill Plant **(3)**
20400 N Webster
Spring Hill, KS 66083
Tel.: (913) 592-6100
Fax: (913) 592-6110
Web Site: www.afgglass.com
Flat Glass Mfr
S.I.C.: 3211
N.A.I.C.S.: 327211

Non-U.S. Plants:

AGC Flat Glass North America, Inc. - AGC-Calgary Plant **(3)**
4015 7th St S E
Calgary, AB, T2G 2Y9, Canada
Tel.: (403) 243-2501
Fax: (403) 243-4753
Flat Glass Mfr
S.I.C.: 3211
N.A.I.C.S.: 327211

AGC Flat Glass North America, Inc. - AGC-Edmonton Plant **(3)**
9845 42nd Ave
Edmonton, AB, T6E 0A3, Canada
Tel.: (780) 462-5252
Fax: (780) 462-4355
Emp.: 40
Flat Glass Mfr
S.I.C.: 3211
N.A.I.C.S.: 327211
Mark Jackson *(Gen Mgr)*

AGC Flat Glass North America, Inc. - AGC-Regina Plant **(3)**
500 10th Ave E
Regina, SK, S4N 6G7, Canada
Tel.: (306) 525-2341
Fax: (306) 757-4862
Web Site: www.afgglass.com
Emp.: 37
Flat Glass Mfr
S.I.C.: 3211
N.A.I.C.S.: 327211
Cheryl Johnson *(Mgr)*

AGC Flat Glass North America, Inc. - AGC-Winnipeg Plant **(3)**
450 Deschambault St
Winnipeg, MB, R2H 0K1, Canada
Tel.: (204) 233-0229
Fax: (204) 233-0762
Web Site: www.afgglass.com
Emp.: 60
Glass Products Mfr
S.I.C.: 3231
N.A.I.C.S.: 327215

Joint Ventures:

Belletech Corp. **(2)**
700 W Lake Ave
Bellefontaine, OH 43311-0790
Mailing Address:
PO Box 790
Bellefontaine, OH 43311
Tel.: (937) 599-3774
Fax: (937) 599-5478
E-Mail: info@belletechcorp.com
Web Site: www.belletechcorp.com
Sales Range: $75-99.9 Million
Emp.: 150
Automotive Glass Assemblies; Owned 60% by Asahi Glass Co., Ltd. & 40% by PPG Industries, Inc.
S.I.C.: 3231
N.A.I.C.S.: 327215
Mark McIntyre *(VP)*

AGC Automotive Americas R&D, Inc. **(1)**
1401 S Huron St
Ypsilanti, MI 48197
Tel.: (734) 547-2370
Fax: (734) 547-2368
Web Site: www.agc.com
Processed Automotive Glass Mfr
S.I.C.: 3231
N.A.I.C.S.: 327215
Thomas Throop *(Pres & CEO)*
Kazuhiro Sako *(Treas)*

AGC Automotive California, Inc. **(1)**
19301 Pacific Gateway Dr Ste 200
Torrance, CA 90502
Tel.: (310) 817-8700
Fax: (310) 817-8716
Web Site: www.agc.com
Automotive Glass Parts Whslr
S.I.C.: 5013
N.A.I.C.S.: 423120
Toshiaki Yamashita *(Pres)*

AGC Capital, Inc. **(1)**
11175 Cicero Dr Ste 400
Alpharetta, GA 30022
Tel.: (404) 446-4272
Fax: (404) 446-4295
Web Site: www.agc.com
Financial Management Services
S.I.C.: 6211
N.A.I.C.S.: 523999

AGC Chemicals Americas, Inc. **(1)**
55 E Uwchlan Ave Ste 201
Exton, PA 19341
Tel.: (610) 423-4300

Fax: (610) 423-4301
Toll Free: (800) 424-7833
E-Mail: finechemicals@agcchem.com
Web Site: www.agcchem.com
Emp.: 120
Flat Glass & Chemical Products Mfr
S.I.C.: 3211
N.A.I.C.S.: 327211
Gary Trupe *(Mgr-IT)*

Plant:

AGC Chemicals Americas, Inc. - Thorndale Manufacturing Plant **(2)**
255 S Bailey Rd
Downingtown, PA 19335
Tel.: (610) 380-6200
Web Site: www.agcce.com
Chemical Products Mfr
S.I.C.: 2899
N.A.I.C.S.: 325998

AGC Electronics America, Inc. **(1)**
4375 NW 235 Ave
Hillsboro, OR 97124
Tel.: (503) 844-9689
Fax: (503) 844-7207
E-Mail: info@agem-usa.com
Web Site: www.agpr-usa.com
Electronic Machinery & Component Mfr & Distr
S.I.C.: 3679
N.A.I.C.S.: 334419
Dean Owens *(Supvr-CAM)*

Non-U.S. Subsidiaries:

AGC Automotive Canada, Inc. **(1)**
120 Artesian Ind Pkwy
PO Box 1225
Bradford, ON, L3Z 2B6, Canada
Tel.: (905) 778-8224
Fax: (905) 778-8226
Automotive Glass Mfr
S.I.C.: 3231
N.A.I.C.S.: 327215

AGC Automotive Europe S.A **(1)**
Batiment Bleu Ave du Marquis
Fleurus, Belgium
Tel.: (32) 71 826 411
Fax: (32) 71 826 499
E-Mail: comuto@au.agc.com
Web Site: www.agc.com
Emp.: 150
Automotive Glass Mfr
S.I.C.: 3231
N.A.I.C.S.: 327215
Meunier Jeanmarc *(CEO)*

AGC Automotive Foshan Co., Ltd **(1)**
Huasha Road Songxia C Area Nanhai Economic Development Zone
Foshan, Guangdong, China
Tel.: (86) 757 8588 8000
Fax: (86) 757 8588 7000
Web Site: www.agc.com
Automotive Glass Distr
S.I.C.: 5013
N.A.I.C.S.: 423120

AGC Automotive Italy S.r.l **(1)**
Via Genova 31
12100 Cuneo, Italy
Tel.: (39) 0171 3401
Fax: (39) 0171 340 333
Web Site: www.agc.com
Automotive Glass Mfr
S.I.C.: 3231
N.A.I.C.S.: 327215

AGC Automotive Philippines Inc. **(1)**
Bldg No 1 Daystar Sta Rosa Industrial Park Brgy
Pulong, Santa Rosa, Laguna, 4026, Philippines
Tel.: (63) 25208490
Fax: (63) 25208489
Automotive Glass Assembly Services
S.I.C.: 7536
N.A.I.C.S.: 811122
Marilyn Encinares *(Pres)*

AGC Automotive (Thailand) Co., Ltd. **(1)**
700/366 Moo 6 Bangpakong Industrial Park 2 Bangna-Trad km 57
Nongmaidaeng Amphur Muang, Chon Buri, 20000, Thailand
Tel.: (66) 38 214840
Fax: (66) 38 214853
Web Site: www.th.agc-automotive.com
Automotive Glass Products Distr
S.I.C.: 5013
N.A.I.C.S.: 423120
Kihachiro Okamoto *(Pres)*

AGC Automotive U.K. Ltd. **(1)**
Unit B Edgemead Close Round Spinney
Northampton, NN3 4RG, United Kingdom
Tel.: (44) 1604671150
Fax: (44) 1604671140
Emp.: 100
Automotive Glass Mfr
S.I.C.: 3231
N.A.I.C.S.: 327215

AGC Chemicals Asia Pacific Pte. Ltd. **(1)**
460 Alexandra Road 30-02 PSA Building
Singapore, 119963, Singapore
Tel.: (65) 6273 5656
Fax: (65) 6276 8783
Chemical Products Distr
S.I.C.: 5169
N.A.I.C.S.: 424690

AGC Chemicals Europe, Ltd. **(1)**
York House Hillhouse International
PO Box 4
Thornton Cleveleys, Thornton, Lancashire, FY5 4QD, United Kingdom
Tel.: (44) 1 253 861951
Fax: (44) 1 253 861950
E-Mail: enquiries@agcce.com
Web Site: www.agcce.com
Chemical Products Whslr
S.I.C.: 5169
N.A.I.C.S.: 424690
Kazuhiko Ishimura *(Pres & CEO)*

AGC Chemicals Trading (Shanghai) Co., Ltd. **(1)**
Room 2701-2705 Metro Plaza No 555 Lou Shan Guan Road
Chang Ning Ward, Shanghai, 200051, China
Tel.: (86) 21 63862211
Fax: (86) 21 63865377
E-Mail: acs-info@agc.com
Web Site: www.agcsh.com
Emp.: 30
Specialty Chemicals Whslr
S.I.C.: 5169
N.A.I.C.S.: 424690
H. Zuwki *(Gen Mgr)*

AGC (China) Holdings Co., Ltd. **(1)**
Unit 3511 China World Office 2 No 1 Jianguomenwai Ave
Beijing, China
Tel.: (86) 1065058029
Fax: (86) 1065050270
Web Site: www.agc.com
Emp.: 9
Investment Management Services
S.I.C.: 6282
N.A.I.C.S.: 523920
Masayuki Kamiya *(Gen Mgr)*

AGC Electronics Singapore Pte. Ltd. **(1)**
460 Alexandra Road 30-02 PSA Building
Singapore, 119963, Singapore
Tel.: (65) 6273 5656
Fax: (65) 6271 3370
Emp.: 8
Glass & Electronic Materials Distr
S.I.C.: 5065
N.A.I.C.S.: 423690
Takako Kanoh *(Gen Mgr)*

AGC Europe S.A. **(1)**
Chaussee de La Hulpe 166
1170 Brussels, Belgium
Tel.: (32) 26743384
Fax: (32) 26743355
Web Site: www.agc-group.com
Glass Products Mfr
S.I.C.: 3231
N.A.I.C.S.: 327215

AGC Flat Glass Asia Pacific Pte. Ltd. **(1)**
PSA Bldg 460 Alexandra Rd Fl 30 Ste 2
Singapore, 119963, Singapore (100%)
Tel.: (65) 62735656
Telex: RS39855 AGCSIN
Fax: (65) 62789281
E-Mail: inqury@sg.agc-flatglass.com
Web Site: www.agc-flatglass.sg
Rev.: $58,245,164
Emp.: 32
S.I.C.: 3211
N.A.I.C.S.: 327211
Tosio Atsumi *(Mng Dir)*

AGC Flat Glass Czech A.S. **(1)**
Sklarska 450
416 74 Teplice, Czech Republic
Tel.: (420) 417 501 111
Fax: (420) 417 502 121
E-Mail: czech@eu.agc-group.com
Emp.: 200
Float & Automotive Glass Mfr
S.I.C.: 3231
N.A.I.C.S.: 327215
Zuzana Zimova *(Mgr-Sls)*

AGC Flat Glass (Dalian) Co., Ltd. **(1)**
No 5 West Tieshan Road Development Zone
Dalian, 116600, China
Tel.: (86) 411 87614190
Fax: (86) 411 87614197
E-Mail: Inquiry@cn.agc-flatglass.com
Web Site: www.agc-flatglass.cn
Emp.: 700
Automotive Glass Products Mfr & Distr
S.I.C.: 7536
N.A.I.C.S.: 811122
Masahiro Takeda *(Pres)*

AGC Flat Glass Europe **(1)**
Chausee De La Hulpe 166
1170 Brussels, Brabant, Belgium
Tel.: (32) 26743111
Telex: 21097
Fax: (32) 26724462
E-Mail: peter.vanrhede@au-agc.com
Web Site: www.agc.com
Emp.: 300
Mfr. of Flat Glass
S.I.C.: 3211
N.A.I.C.S.: 327211
Jean-Francois Heris *(Pres & CEO)*
Marc Van Den Neste *(CTO & VP)*

AGC Flat Glass (Hong Kong) Co., Ltd. **(1)**
11/F Workington Tower 78 Bonhan Strand East
Sheung Wan, China (Hong Kong)
Tel.: (852) 2541 0789
Fax: (852) 2815 0943
Web Site: www.agc.com
Flat Glass Distr
S.I.C.: 5039
N.A.I.C.S.: 423390

AGC Flat Glass Iberica S.A. **(1)**
Calle Mallorca 272-274 6 5a
8037 Barcelona, Spain
Tel.: (34) 93 467 07 60
Fax: (34) 93 467 07 70
Float Glass Distr
S.I.C.: 5039
N.A.I.C.S.: 423390
Recuerdo Montserrat *(Country Mgr)*

AGC Flat Glass Italia S.r.l **(1)**
Via Genova 31
12100 Cuneo, Italy
Tel.: (39) 0171 3401
Fax: (39) 0171 340 333
Float Glass Mfr
S.I.C.: 3211
N.A.I.C.S.: 327211

AGC Flat Glass Nederland B.V. **(1)**
PB 6025
4000 HA Tiel, Netherlands
Tel.: (31) 344679911
Fax: (31) 344679506
Web Site: www.agc.com
Emp.: 190
Float Glass Mfr
S.I.C.: 3211
N.A.I.C.S.: 327211

AGC Flat Glass Philippines Inc. **(1)**
Bo Pinagbuhatan
Pasig, Philippines 1600
Tel.: (63) 26411981
Fax: (63) 26411988
E-Mail: inquiries@ph.agc-flatglass.com
Web Site: www.agc-flatglass.ph
Flat Glass Mfr
S.I.C.: 3211
N.A.I.C.S.: 327211

AGC Flat Glass Protech (Shenzhen) Co., Ltd. **(1)**
1st Floor of Block A And Block C Haitian Industrial Garden Qisan Road
Pingshan New Zone, Shenzhen, China
Tel.: (86) 755 2682 6802
Fax: (86) 755 2682 5406
Soda Lime Glass Mfr
S.I.C.: 3231
N.A.I.C.S.: 327215

AGC Flat Glass (Suzhou) Co., Ltd. **(1)**
No 158 Wang- Jiang Road Suzhou Industrial Park
Suzhou, 215121, China
Tel.: (86) 512 6285 2501
Fax: (86) 512 6285 2502
Automotive Float Glasses Mfr & Distr
S.I.C.: 3211
N.A.I.C.S.: 327211

AGC Flat Glass (Thailand) Public Co., Ltd. **(1)**
200 Moo 1 Suksawad Road Phra Samut Chedi
Samut Prakan, Thailand 10290
Tel.: (66) 2425 8970
Fax: (66) 2425 8816
Web Site: www.agc-flatglass.co.th
Flat Glass Mfr
S.I.C.: 3211
N.A.I.C.S.: 327211
Toshikazu Adachi *(Pres)*

Plant:

AGC Flat Glass (Thailand) Public Co., Ltd. - Chon Buri Factory **(2)**
700/22 Moo 5 Bangna Trad Road Amata Nakorn Industrial Estate
Amphur Muang, Chon Buri, Thailand 20000
Tel.: (66) 3821 3063
Fax: (66) 3821 3066
Web Site: www.agc-flatglass.co.th/en/job/body_location.asp
Automotive Parts Mfr
S.I.C.: 3714
N.A.I.C.S.: 336390

AGC Glass Europe S.A. **(1)**
166 Chaussee de la Hulpe
1170 Brussels, Belgium
Tel.: (32) 2 674 31 11
Fax: (32) 2 672 44 62
E-Mail: headquarters@eu.agc-group.com
Web Site: www.agc-glass.eu
Emp.: 30
Flat Glass Mfr & Distr
S.I.C.: 3211
N.A.I.C.S.: 327211
Jean-Francois Heris *(Pres & CEO)*
Michel Grandjean *(CFO & VP)*
Marc van den Neste *(CTO & VP)*

AGC Micro Glass (Thailand) Co., Ltd **(1)**
Saha Group Industrial Park Lamphun 99/39 Moo 5 T Pasak
A Muang Lamphun, Lamphun, 51000, Thailand
Tel.: (66) 53 584300
Fax: (66) 53 597326
Molded Aspherical Glass Lenses Mfr
S.I.C.: 3231
N.A.I.C.S.: 327215

AGC Shanghai Co., Ltd. **(1)**
Unit 15A 398 Huai Hai Zhong Road
Lu Wan District, Shanghai, China 200020
Tel.: (86) 21 53830808
Fax: (86) 21 53825722
Business Support Services
S.I.C.: 7389
N.A.I.C.S.: 561499

AGC Singapore Services Pte. Ltd. **(1)**
460 Alexandra Road 30-02 PSA Building
Singapore, 119963, Singapore
Tel.: (65) 6273 5656
Fax: (65) 6278 1709
Web Site: www.agc.com
Financial Management Services
S.I.C.: 6211

Asahi Glass Co., Ltd.—(Continued)

N.A.I.C.S.: 523999
Hiromasa Kondo *(Mng Dir)*

AGC Techno Glass (Thailand) Co., Ltd. (1)
700/322 Moo 6 Amata Nakorn Industrial Estate Bangna-Trad Rd KM 57
T Donhuaroh A Muang, Chon Buri, 20000, Thailand
Tel.: (66) 38 214497
Fax: (66) 38 214496
Glass Tableware & Products Mfr
S.I.C.: 3231
N.A.I.C.S.: 327215

AGC Technology Solutions (Kunshan) Co., LTD. (1)
Mp Bldg A-12F Room 1211 Weiye Road 18
Development Zone
Kunshan, Jiangsu, China 215300
Tel.: (86) 512 5518 1759
Fax: (86) 512 5518 1780
Web Site: www.agc.com
Glass Plant Engineering Services
S.I.C.: 8711
N.A.I.C.S.: 541330

AGC Technology Solutions (Thailand) Co., Ltd. (1)
Kulab Building 7th Floor 12/555 Bangna-Trad Road Bangkaew
Bang Phli, Samut Prakan, 10540, Thailand
Tel.: (66) 2 316 1423
Fax: (66) 2 316 1424
Web Site: www.agc.com
Glass Plant Engineering Services
S.I.C.: 8711
N.A.I.C.S.: 541330

Asahi Glass Europe B.V. (1)
Strawinskylaan 1525
Amsterdam, 1077XX, Netherlands (100%)
Tel.: (31) 205736040
Fax: (31) 208804188
E-Mail: info@asahi.com
Web Site: www.asahi.com
Emp.: 20
S.I.C.: 3211
N.A.I.C.S.: 327211
Y. Narita *(Gen Mgr)*

Asahi India Glass Ltd. (1)
Unit No 203 to 208 Tribhuwan Complex
Ishwar Nagar Mathura Road
New Delhi, 110065, India
Tel.: (91) 1149454900
Fax: (91) 1149454970
Web Site: www.asahiindia.com
515030—(BOM)
Rev.: $402,475,590
Assets: $432,842,256
Liabilities: $416,527,056
Net Worth: $16,315,200
Earnings: ($18,076,500)
Emp.: 1,042
Fiscal Year-end: 03/31/13
Automotive Glass Mfr
S.I.C.: 3211
N.A.I.C.S.: 327211
Sanjay Labroo *(CEO & Mng Dir)*
Shailesh Agarwal *(CFO)*
Gopal Ganatra *(Chief Legal Officer, Compliance Officer & Sec)*
Hideaki Nohara *(CTO-Auto & Deputy Mng Dir)*

Units:

Asahi India Glass, Ltd. - AIS (Auto) Haryana Works. (2)
94 4 Kms Stone Delhi - Jaipur Highway
NH-8 Village Jaliawas
Tehsil Bawal, Rewari, Haryana, 123 501, India
Tel.: (91) 1284264367
Fax: (91) 1284264185
Glass Product Mfr
S.I.C.: 3231
N.A.I.C.S.: 327215

Asahi India Glass, Ltd. - AIS (Float) Works (2)
Plot No F-76 to 81 SIPCOT Industrial Park
Irungattukottai Sriperumpdur
Taluk Kancheepuram, Chennai, Tamilnadu, 602105, India
Tel.: (91) 4447103442
Fax: (91) 4447100441
Emp.: 150
Glass Product Mfr
S.I.C.: 3231
N.A.I.C.S.: 327215
Rui Neves *(Gen Mgr)*

Asahi PD Glass Korea Co., Ltd. (1)
5 Block Gumi 4th National Indusutrial Complex Sandong-Myeon
Bonsan-Ri, Gumi, Kyung-Buk, Korea (South)
Tel.: (82) 54 478 0001
Fax: (82) 54 478 0018
Plasma Display Panel Glass Mfr
S.I.C.: 3231
N.A.I.C.S.: 327215

Hankuk Electric Glass Co., Ltd. (1)
150 Gongdan-Dong
Gumi, Kyung-Buk, Korea (South)
Tel.: (82) 544681156
Fax: (82) 544635055
Web Site: www.heg.co.kr
Color Television Glass Mfr
S.I.C.: 3231
N.A.I.C.S.: 327215

Hanwook Techno Glass Co., Ltd. (1)
11 Block 4-Complex Gumi Industrial Complex
Okgye-Dong, Gumi, Kyungbuk, Korea (South)
Tel.: (82) 544753953
Fax: (82) 54 475 3958
Web Site: www.htg.co.kr
Display Glass Panel Mfr
S.I.C.: 3231
N.A.I.C.S.: 327215

MCIS Safety Glass Sdn. Bhd. (1)
Lot 1 Lorong Senawang 2/1 Senawang Industrial Estate
70450 Seremban, Negeri Sembilan, Malaysia
Tel.: (60) 66775367
Fax: (60) 66772076
E-Mail: sales@mcissafetyglass.com.my
Web Site: www.mcissafetyglass.com.my
Emp.: 400
Automotive Glass Products Distr
S.I.C.: 5013
N.A.I.C.S.: 423120
Mukhtar Mohamad *(Gen Mgr)*

P.T. Asahimas Chemical (1)
9th Fl Summitmas I Jl Jend Sudirman Kav 61-62
Jakarta, 12190, Indonesia
Tel.: (62) 215202111
Fax: (62) 215202110
E-Mail: helpline@asc.co.id
Web Site: www.asc.co.id
Emp.: 70
Specialty Chemicals Mfr
S.I.C.: 2899
N.A.I.C.S.: 325998
Jun Miyazaki *(Pres)*

Plant:

P.T. Asahimas Chemical - Cilegon Factory (2)
Desa Gunung Sugih Jl Raya Anyer Km 122
Cilegon, Baten, 42447, Indonesia
Tel.: (62) 254 601 252
Fax: (62) 254 602 014
Web Site: www.asc.co.id/?idm=10
Chemical Products Mfr
S.I.C.: 2899
N.A.I.C.S.: 325998

Siam Asahi Technoglass Co., Ltd. (1)
87/12 Moo 2 Sukhumvit Road
Laemchabang Industrial Estate
Thung Sukhla, Si Racha, Chon Buri, 20230, Thailand
Tel.: (66) 38490680
Fax: (66) 38490708
Web Site: www.agc.co.jp/english/company/group_world_01.html
Emp.: 1,400
Television Glass Bulbs Mfr
S.I.C.: 3699
N.A.I.C.S.: 335999

Zibo Asahi Glass Alumina Materials Co., Ltd. (1)
60 Wulinglu Boshan
Zibo, Shandong, 255200, China
Tel.: (86) 533 428 1441
Fax: (86) 533 428 2807
Glass Products Whslr
S.I.C.: 1793
N.A.I.C.S.: 238150

Non-U.S. Plants:

AGC Chemicals (Thailand) Co., Ltd. - Phrapradaeng Plant (1)
202 Moo 1 Suksawasdi Road Km17 Tambol Pak Klong Bang Plakod
Amphur Prasamutjedi, Samut Prakan, 10290, Thailand
Tel.: (66) 2 463 6345
Fax: (66) 2 463 3728
Web Site: www.acth.co.th/contact.html
Chemical Products Mfr
S.I.C.: 2899
N.A.I.C.S.: 325998

AGC Chemicals (Thailand) Co., Ltd. - Rayong Plant (1)
4 Soi G-12 Eastern Industrial Estate Pakorn Songkrohrad Road
Tambol Mab Ta Put Amphur Muang, Rayong, 21150, Thailand
Tel.: (66) 3 868 3573
Fax: (66) 3 8 683576
Chemical Products Mfr
S.I.C.: 2899
N.A.I.C.S.: 325998

ASAHI GROUP HOLDINGS LTD.

1-23-1 Azumabashi
Sumida-ku, Tokyo, 130-8602, Japan
Tel.: (81) 356085126
Fax: (81) 356087121
E-Mail: ir@asahigroup-holdings.com
Web Site: www.asahigroup-holdings.com
Year Founded: 1949
2502—(OTC TKS)
Sls.: $17,369,847,000
Assets: $19,054,068,000
Liabilities: $11,058,399,000
Net Worth: $7,995,669,000
Earnings: $629,013,000
Emp.: 17,956
Fiscal Year-end: 12/31/12

Business Description:
Beer & Soft Drinks Mfr; Food Products & Nutritional Supplements Mfr
Import Export
S.I.C.: 2082
N.A.I.C.S.: 312120

Personnel:
Hitoshi Ogita *(Chm & CEO)*
Naoki Izumiya *(Pres & COO)*
Katsuyuki Kawatsura *(Sr Mng Dir & Sr Mng Corp Officer)*
Fumio Yamasaki *(Mng Dir)*
Takayoshi Kanaya *(Mng Corp Officer)*
Akira Matsunobu *(Mng Corp Officer)*
Hideaki Takemoto *(Mng Corp Officer)*
Kenji Taniguchi *(Mng Corp Officer)*
Masafumi Tanino *(Mng Corp Officer)*
Shiro Ikeda *(Corp Officer)*
Toshio Kodato *(Corp Officer)*
Kiminari Maruta *(Corp Officer)*
Yasuyuki Ohtake *(Corp Officer)*
Yoshihide Okuda *(Corp Officer)*
Yasutaka Sugiura *(Corp Officer)*
Katsutoshi Takahashi *(Corp Officer)*

Board of Directors:
Hitoshi Ogita
Mariko Bando
Shiro Ikeda
Ichiro Ito
Naoki Izumiya
Katsuyuki Kawatsura
Toshio Kodato
Akiyoshi Koji
Yoshihide Okuda
Katsutoshi Takahashi
Naoki Tanaka

Subsidiaries:

Asahi Food & Healthcare Co., Ltd. (1)
1-23-1 Azumabashi
130 8602 Tokyo, Sumida-ku, Japan JP
Tel.: (81) 356085116 (100%)
Fax: (81) 356087122
Web Site: www.asahibeer.com
Sales Range: $300-349.9 Million
Health Care Products, Including Yeast Extract, Organic Foods & Freeze-Dried Foods Mfr
S.I.C.: 2034
N.A.I.C.S.: 311423

Asahi Soft Drinks Co., Ltd. (1)
1-23-1 Azumabashi
Sumida-ku, Tokyo, 130 8602, Japan JP
Tel.: (81) 356085331 (97.4%)
Fax: (81) 356087228
Web Site: www.asahiinryo.co.jp
Sales Range: $1-4.9 Billion
Emp.: 1,400
Soft Drinks, Coffee & Tea Mfr
S.I.C.: 2086
N.A.I.C.S.: 312111
Shirou Kikuchi *(Pres)*
Masaaki Okada *(Pres)*

Subsidiary:

Asahi Calpis Beverages Co., Ltd. (2)
1-23-1 Azumabashi
Sumida-ku, Tokyo, 130-8602, Japan (80%)
Tel.: (81) 3 5619 5670
Distribution of Soft Drinks Through Vending Machines
S.I.C.: 5962
N.A.I.C.S.: 454210

Subsidiary:

Calpis Beverages Co., Ltd. (3)
1F Daikanyama CA Building
2-20-3 Ebisu-nishi
Shibuya Ku, Tokyo, 150 0021, Japan
Tel.: (81) 33780 2240
Fax: (81) 337705374
Emp.: 200
Importer of Soft Drinks
S.I.C.: 2086
N.A.I.C.S.: 312111

Calpis Co., Ltd. (1)
3F Calpis Building 2-4-1 Ebisu-minami
Shibuya-ku, Tokyo, 150-0022, Japan (100%)
Tel.: (81) 3 5721 3111
Fax: (81) 337705374
Web Site: www.calpis.net
Sales Range: $50-74.9 Million
Emp.: 797
Mfr & Distr of Fruit Beverages, Health Functioning Beverages, Dairy Products, Liquors & Feedstuff Additives
S.I.C.: 2026
N.A.I.C.S.: 311511
Fujio Yamada *(CEO & Pres)*
Shunsuke Fuji *(Sr Officer)*
Takeshi Ichiki *(Sr Officer)*
Yukio Itagaki *(Sr Officer)*
Katsuhiko Kishigami *(Sr Officer)*
Youichi Marunaga *(Sr Officer)*
Hideki Obata *(Exec Officer)*
Makoto Utena *(Sr Officer)*
Minoru Yamasaki *(Exec Officer)*

Subsidiaries:

Calpis Foods Service Co., Ltd. (2)
3F Calpis Building 2-4-1 Ebisu-minami
Shibuya-ku, Tokyo, 150-0022, Japan
Tel.: (81) 3 5768 7481
Fax: (81) 3 5768 8060
Web Site: www.calpis-cfs.co.jp
Milk & Dairy Products Mfr & Distr
S.I.C.: 2026
N.A.I.C.S.: 311511
Megumi Nakayama Tsukasa *(Pres)*

U.S. Subsidiary:

Calpis U.S.A. Inc. (2)
970 W 190th St Suite 110
Torrance, CA 90502
Tel.: (310) 324-5900
Fax: (310) 324-5959
E-Mail: info@calpisusa.com
Web Site: www.calpis.net

Emp.: 6
Milk Beverages, Soft Drinks & Animal Feed Products Distr
S.I.C.: 5149
N.A.I.C.S.: 424490
Jun Kuranari *(Pres)*

Non-U.S. Subsidiaries:

PT Calpis Indonesia (2)
EJIP Industrial Park Plot 7C
Cikarang Selatan, Bekasi, 17550, Indonesia
Tel.: (62) 218970240
Fax: (62) 218970241
Web Site: www.calpis.net
Soft Drinks Mfr & Distr
S.I.C.: 2086
N.A.I.C.S.: 312111

Taiwan Calpis Co., Ltd. (2)
3F No 125 Sung Chiang Road
Taipei, 10485, Taiwan
Tel.: (886) 225172194
Lactic Acid Drinks, Nutritional Supplements & Fruit Juice Distr
S.I.C.: 5149
N.A.I.C.S.: 424490

LB Co., Ltd. (1)
69 2 Shirabyoshi
Kagiya Machi Tokai Shi, Nagoya, Aichi, 477 0032, Japan JP
Tel.: (81) 562333181
Fax: (81) 562333170
E-Mail: kavuhiro.hayashi@asahibeer.co.jp
Web Site: www.elbee.co.jp
Emp.: 100
Health Drinks & Other Long Shelf-Life Beverage Products Mfr & Distr
S.I.C.: 2099
N.A.I.C.S.: 311999
Kavuhiro Hayashi *(Mgr)*

LB Co., Ltd. (1)
3469 1 Kurohama
Hasuda, Saitama, 349-0101, Japan JP
Tel.: (81) 487691133
Fax: (81) 48763440
Emp.: 25
Chilled Tea & Fruit Juice Mfr & Distr
S.I.C.: 2037
N.A.I.C.S.: 311411
Yoshi Hirotonavuka *(Pres)*

The Nikka Whisky Distilling Co., Ltd. (1)
5-4-31 Minami-Aoyama
Minato-ku, Tokyo, 107 8616, Japan JP
Tel.: (81) 334980331
Fax: (81) 334981783
Web Site: www.nikka.com
Emp.: 440
Distilled & Blended Liquors
S.I.C.: 2085
N.A.I.C.S.: 312140
Hiroshi Yamashita *(Pres)*

Wakodo Co., Ltd. (1)
2-14-3 Kandatsukasamachi
Chiyoda-ku, Tokyo, 101 0048, Japan
Tel.: (81) 352966806
Fax: (81) 352966817
E-Mail: sakatay@wakodo.co.jp
Web Site: www.wakodo.co.jp
Emp.: 600
Baby Food & Powdered Milk Mfr
S.I.C.: 2099
N.A.I.C.S.: 311999

U.S. Subsidiary:

Asahi Beer U.S.A., Inc. (1)
3625 Del Amo Blvd Ste 250
Torrance, CA 90503-1670 (92.2%)
Tel.: (310) 214-9051
Fax: (310) 542-5108
E-Mail: info@asahibeerusa.com
Web Site: www.asahibeerusa.com
Emp.: 15
Import & Distribution of Beer Import
S.I.C.: 5181
N.A.I.C.S.: 424810
Hitoshi Ogita *(Pres & COO)*

Non-U.S. Subsidiaries:

Asahibeer (Shanghai) Product Services Co., Ltd (1)
No 712 Room City Square No 1168 Nanjing Road West
Jing An District, Shanghai, China
Tel.: (86) 2152929952
Fax: (86) 2152925308
Alcoholic Beverage Distr
S.I.C.: 5182
N.A.I.C.S.: 424820

Beijing Beer Asahi Co., Ltd. (1)
No 1 N Yanqi Roa Yanqi Industrial Economic Development Zone
Beijing, 101407, China
Tel.: (86) 1065677001
Fax: (86) 1065666885
Alcoholic Beverage Distr
S.I.C.: 5182
N.A.I.C.S.: 424820
Yamasaki Fumio *(CEO)*

Boon Rawd Brewery Co, Ltd (1)
999 Samsen Road Dusit
Bangkok, 10300, Thailand
Tel.: (66) 2 242 4000
Fax: (66) 2 669 2089
E-Mail: pr_relations@boonrawd.co.th
Web Site: www.boonrawd.co.th
Alcoholic Beverage Distr
S.I.C.: 5182
N.A.I.C.S.: 424820
Chamnong Bhirombhakdi *(Chm)*
Piya Bhirombhakdi *(Vice Chm)*
Vapee Bhirombhakdi *(Vice Chm)*
Vudha Bhirombhakdi *(Vice Chm)*
Santi Bhirombhakdi *(Pres)*
Santi Bhirombhakdi *(Pres)*
Chutinant Bhirombhakdi *(Exec VP)*
Rojrit Debhakam *(Exec VP)*

Buckinghamshire Golf Company, Ltd. (1)
Denham Court Drive
Denham, Buckinghamshire, UB9 5PG, United Kingdom (100%)
Tel.: (44) 1895835777
Fax: (44) 1895835210
Web Site: www.buckinghamshiregolfclub.co m.uk
Emp.: 200
Golf Course & Clubhouse
S.I.C.: 7999
N.A.I.C.S.: 713910
Motohiro Suzuki *(Mng Dir)*

Schweppes Australia Pty Ltd (1)
Level 5 111 Cecil Street
South Melbourne, VIC, 3205, Australia
Tel.: (61) 388663888
E-Mail: consumerrelations@schweppes.co m.au
Web Site: www.schweppesaustralia.com.au
Emp.: 1,500
Carbonated Soft Drinks Mfr & Distr
S.I.C.: 2086
N.A.I.C.S.: 312111
Carissa Ward *(Mgr-Natl Sls)*

Non-U.S. Joint Ventures:

Hangzhou Xihu Beer Asahi Co., Ltd. (1)
545 Xixi Road
Xihu District, Hangzhou, Zhejiang, China (55%)
Tel.: (86) 57185021919
Fax: (86) 57185122654
E-Mail: siwo@xihubeer.com
Web Site: www.xihubeer.com
Emp.: 900
Beer Mfr
S.I.C.: 2082
N.A.I.C.S.: 312120

Qingdao Tsingtao Beer & Asahi Beverage Co., Ltd. (1)
97 Laoshan Road
Qingdao, Shandong, 266100, China
Tel.: (86) 53288807400
Fax: (86) 532 8880 7401
Sls.: $4,444,039
Soft Drink Sales & Production: Owned 60% by Asahi Breweries Ltd. & 40% by Tsingtao Brewery Group Company Ltd.
S.I.C.: 2086
N.A.I.C.S.: 312111

Yantai Beer Asahi Co., Ltd. (1)
100 Huanshan Road
Zhifu District, Yantai, Shandong, 264001, China (53%)
Tel.: (86) 535 608 2283
Fax: (86) 535 608 6279
Emp.: 1,327
Brewery
S.I.C.: 2082
N.A.I.C.S.: 312120
Ji Guang Qu *(Gen Mgr)*

ASAHI HOLDINGS INC

Nissay Sannomiya Building 16F 4-4-17 Kano-cho Chuo-ku
Kobe, Hyogo, 650-0001, Japan
Tel.: (81) 78 333 5600
Fax: (81) 78 333 5681
Web Site: www.asahiholdings.com
5857—(TKS)
Sls.: $1,060,048,000
Assets: $684,860,000
Liabilities: $222,728,000
Net Worth: $462,132,000
Earnings: $49,698,000
Emp.: 1,344
Fiscal Year-end: 03/31/13

Business Description:
Metal Recycle & Environmental Conservation
S.I.C.: 3339
N.A.I.C.S.: 331410

Personnel:
Tsutomu Sakurai *(Pres)*
Mitsuharu Terayama *(CEO)*

Board of Directors:
Tomoya Higashiura
Masaki Hirano
Shoji Morii
Keitaro Shigemasa
Yoshikatsu Takeuchi

Transfer Agent:
Mitsubishi UFJ Trust & Banking Corporation
3-6-3 Fushimimachi, Chuo-ku
Osaka, Japan

Subsidiaries:

Asahi Pretec Corporation (1)
4-4-17 Nissay Sannomiya Bldg Kano-cho
Chuo-ku, Kobe, Hyogo, 650-0001, Japan
Tel.: (81) 783335600
Fax: (81) 783335681
E-Mail: m-horiuchi@asahiholdings.com
Web Site: www.asahipretec.com
Metal Refining Services
S.I.C.: 5082
N.A.I.C.S.: 423810
Yoshikatsu Takeuchi *(Pres)*
Mitsuharu Terayama *(CEO)*

Japan Waste Corporation (1)
1 7 12 Marunouchi Chiyoda-ku
Sapia Tower, 100-0005 Tokyo, Japan
Tel.: (81) 362701828
Fax: (81) 362701839
E-Mail: kankyo@japanwaste.co.jp
Web Site: www.japanwaste.co.jp
Emp.: 1,200
Environmental Services
S.I.C.: 8999
N.A.I.C.S.: 541620
Takeuti Yoshikatsu *(Pres)*

Subsidiaries:

Shioiri Kenzai Co., Ltd. (2)
478-1 Minaminagaike
Nagano, 381-0024, Japan
Tel.: (81) 262441608
Fax: (81) 262592986
Industrial Waste Treatment Services
S.I.C.: 4953
N.A.I.C.S.: 562211

Taiyo Chemical Co., Ltd. (2)
1-1-1 Nishiura
Funabashi, Chiba, 273-0017, Japan
Tel.: (81) 474351817
Fax: (81) 47 431 6045
Waste Water Treatment Services
S.I.C.: 4953
N.A.I.C.S.: 562211

Non-U.S. Subsidiaries:

Asahi G&S Sdn. Bhd. (1)
Plot 65 Zon Perdagangan Bebas Fasa 4
Bayan Lepas, Pulau Pinang, 11900, Malaysia
Tel.: (60) 46461292
Fax: (60) 46462292
Web Site: www.asahiholdings.com
Emp.: 5
Metal Refinining Services
S.I.C.: 5082
N.A.I.C.S.: 423810
Maseeki Pakeuthi *(Mng Dir)*

Asahi Pretec Korea Co., Ltd. (1)
501 City Air Tower 159 9 Samsung-Dong
Gangnam-Gu, Seoul, 135-973, Korea (South)
Tel.: (82) 25517447
Fax: (82) 25517456
Emp.: 8
Metal Refining Services
S.I.C.: 5082
N.A.I.C.S.: 423810
Kunaki Gondo *(CEO)*

ASAHI INDUSTRIES CO., LTD.

49F Sunshine 60 Building 1-1
Higashi-Ikebukuro 3-chome Toshima-ku
Tokyo, 170-6049, Japan
Tel.: (81) 3 3987 2161
Fax: (81) 3 3987 5326
Web Site: www.asahi-kg.co.jp
Year Founded: 1935
5456—(JAS)
Sls.: $441,932,942
Assets: $454,833,797
Liabilities: $273,524,174
Net Worth: $181,309,623
Earnings: ($16,284,268)
Emp.: 579
Fiscal Year-end: 03/31/13

Business Description:
Structural Steel Production & Sale
S.I.C.: 1791
N.A.I.C.S.: 238120

Personnel:
Kiyoshige Akamatsu *(Pres)*
Isao Iijima *(Co-Mng Dir)*
Naoki Machida *(Co-Mng Dir)*
Noriyuki Nakamura *(Co-Mng Dir)*

Board of Directors:
Pran Agarwal
Kiyoshige Akamatsu
Kiyoshi Hirose
Susumu Inaba
Naoki Machida
Noriyuki Nakamura
Makoto Sato
Makoto Yaguchi

Subsidiaries:

EAC Corporation (1)
Ikebukuro KS Building 23-13 Higashi-ikebukuro 3-chome
Toshima-ku, Tokyo, 171-0013, Japan
Tel.: (81) 3 3987 2182
Fax: (81) 3 3988 1060
E-Mail:
Environmental Consulting Services
S.I.C.: 8999
N.A.I.C.S.: 541620

Jobu Co,. Ltd. (1)
3092-1 Kanezawa Minano-machi
Chichibu-gun, Saitama, 369-1601, Japan
Tel.: (81) 494 62 1321
Fax: (81) 494 62 1377
E-Mail:
Crushed Stone & Sand Whslr
S.I.C.: 5032
N.A.I.C.S.: 423320

Plant:

Jobu Co,. Ltd. - Material Recycling Plant (2)
162-2 Ofuchi Minano-machi
Chichibu-gun, Saitama, 369-1623, Japan
Tel.: (81) 494 62 0522
Fax: (81) 494 62 0523
Steel Recycling Services
S.I.C.: 4953
N.A.I.C.S.: 562920

ASAHI INDUSTRIES CO., LTD.—(Continued)

Plants:

ASAHI INDUSTRIES CO., LTD. - Chiba Plant (1)
13 Sakuradai 1-chome
Asahi-shi, Chiba, 289-050, Japan
Tel.: (81) 479 68 1600
Fax: (81) 479 68 1621
E-Mail:
Fertilizer Mfr
S.I.C.: 2875
N.A.I.C.S.: 325314

ASAHI INDUSTRIES CO., LTD. - Kansai Plant (1)
6776 Minakuchi Minakuchi-cho
Koka, Shiga, 528-0005, Japan
Tel.: (81) 748 62 8171
Fax: (81) 748 62 9847
E-Mail:
Fertilizer Mfr
S.I.C.: 2875
N.A.I.C.S.: 325314

ASAHI INDUSTRIES CO., LTD. - Saitama Plant (1)
222 Wataruse Kamikawa-machi
Kodama-gun, Saitama, 367-0394, Japan
Tel.: (81) 274 52 2713
Fax: (81) 274 52 6019
E-Mail:
Steel Recycling Services
S.I.C.: 4953
N.A.I.C.S.: 562920

ASAHI INTECC CO., LTD.

1703 Wakita-cho Moriyama-ku
Nagoya, Aichi, 463-0024, Japan
Tel.: (81) 527681211
Fax: (81) 527681221
Web Site: www.asahi-intecc.com
Year Founded: 1976
7747—(TKS)
Sales Range: $200-249.9 Million
Emp.: 2,678

Business Description:
Medical Devices, Ultra-Thin Stainless Steel Wire Ropes & Terminal Processing Products Mfr
S.I.C.: 3841
N.A.I.C.S.: 339112

Personnel:
Masahiko Miyata *(Pres & CEO)*

Subsidiaries:

Asahi Intecc GMA Co., Ltd. (1)
3898-1 Asaba
Fukuroi, Shizuoka, 437-1101, Japan
Tel.: (81) 537 48 0151
Fax: (81) 538 30 0153
Medical Device Mfr
S.I.C.: 3841
N.A.I.C.S.: 339112

Asahi Intecc J-sales, Inc. (1)
13/F Shinjuku-Sanei Building 1-22-2 Nishi-Shinjuku
Shinjuku-ku, Tokyo, 160-0023, Japan
Tel.: (81) 3 5339 6290
Fax: (81) 3 5339 6291
Medical Device Sales
S.I.C.: 3841
N.A.I.C.S.: 339112

Filmecc Co., Ltd. (1)
3-109 Amakoda
Moriyama-ku, Nagoya, Aichi, 463-0027, Japan
Tel.: (81) 52 773 7031
Fax: (81) 52 773 7781
Medical Device Mfr
S.I.C.: 3841
N.A.I.C.S.: 339112

Non-U.S. Subsidiaries:

Asahi Intecc Hanoi Co., Ltd. (1)
G03 Thang Long Industrial Park
Dong Anh District, Hanoi, Vietnam
Tel.: (84) 4 3955 0038
Fax: (84) 4 3955 0037
Medical Device Mfr
S.I.C.: 3841
N.A.I.C.S.: 339112

Asahi Intecc Thailand Co., Ltd. (1)
158-1 Moo 5 Bangkadi Industrial Park
Tiwanon Road
Tambol Bangkadi Amphur Muang, Pathumthani, 1200, Thailand
Tel.: (66) 2 501 1302
Fax: (66) 2 501 1305
Medical Device Mfr
S.I.C.: 3841
N.A.I.C.S.: 339112

ASAHI KASEI CORPORATION

1-105 Kanda Jinbocho Chiyoda-ku
Tokyo, 101-8101, Japan
Tel.: (81) 332963008
Fax: (81) 332963162
Web Site: www.asahi-kasei.co.jp
Year Founded: 1931
3407—(TKS)
Sls.: $18,333,040,000
Assets: $19,801,870,000
Liabilities: $10,732,909,000
Net Worth: $9,068,961,000
Earnings: $590,832,000
Emp.: 28,363
Fiscal Year-end: 03/31/13

Business Description:
Holding Company; Chemicals, Plastics, Fibers & Textiles, Housing & Construction Materials & Special Products Mfr & Marketer
Import Export
S.I.C.: 6719
N.A.I.C.S.: 551112

Personnel:
Ichiro Itoh *(Chm)*
Taketsugu Fujiwara *(Pres)*
Toshio Asano *(Exec Officer)*
Masahito Hirai *(Exec Officer)*
Hiroshi Kobayashi *(Sr Exec Officer)*
Yuji Kobayashi *(Exec Officer)*
Hideki Kobori *(Sr Exec Officer)*
Makoto Konosu *(Exec Officer)*
Ryo Matsui *(Sr Exec Officer)*
Yuji Mizuno *(Sr Exec Officer)*
Masafumi Nakao *(Exec Officer)*
Shinichiro Nei *(Exec Officer)*
Naoki Okada *(Exec Officer)*
Hiroshi Sawayama *(Exec Officer)*
Shoichiro Tonomura *(Exec Officer)*
Yoshihiro Wada *(Exec Officer)*

Board of Directors:
Ichiro Itoh
Taketsugu Fujiwara
Norio Ichino
Hiroshi Kobayashi
Hideki Kobori
Yukiharu Kodama
Masafumi Nakao
Hiroshi Sawayama
Masumi Shiraishi
Yoshihiro Wada

Transfer Agent:
Sumitomo Mitsui Trust Bank Limited
1-4-1 Marunouchi Chiyoda-ku
Tokyo, Japan

Subsidiaries:

Asahi Kasei Amidas Co., Ltd. (1)
3-21-1 Nihombashihamacho Nihombashi Hamacho F Tower 12f
Chuo-Ku, Tokyo, 103-0007, Japan
Tel.: (81) 356956602
Human Resource Consulting Services
S.I.C.: 8999
N.A.I.C.S.: 541612

Asahi Kasei Chemicals Corporation (1)
1-105 Kanda Jinbocho
Chiyoda-ku, Tokyo, 101-8101, Japan JP
Tel.: (81) 332963200 (100%)
Fax: (81) 332963438
E-Mail: chemicals@on.asahi-kasei.co.jp
Web Site: www.asahi-kasei.co.jp
Emp.: 6,851
Organic & Inorganic Industrial Chemicals, Synthetic Resins, Synthetic Rubber, Fertilizer, Coating Materials, Food Additives & Plastic Film, Sheet & Foam Mfr
S.I.C.: 2819
N.A.I.C.S.: 325180
Taketsugu Fujiwara *(Pres)*
Masaki Fakanoto *(Pres-Asahi Kasei Chemicals Corp)*

Subsidiary:

Asahi Kasei Finechem Co., Ltd. (2)
1-8-7 Fukumachi
Nishiyodogawa-ku, Osaka, Japan JP
Tel.: (81) 664723155
Fax: (81) 664723704
E-Mail: hamasuna.yg@on.asahi-kasei.co.jp
Web Site: www.asahikasei-fc.jp
Emp.: 140
Chemical Products Mfr & Marketer
S.I.C.: 2899
N.A.I.C.S.: 325998
Naoki Moriyama *(Pres)*

U.S. Subsidiary:

Asahi Kasei Plastics North America, Inc. (2)
900 E Van Riper
Fowlerville, MI 48836 (100%)
Tel.: (517) 223-2000
Fax: (517) 223-2002
Toll Free: (800) 444-4408
E-Mail: generalinfo@asahikaseiplastics.com
Web Site: www.asahikaseiplastics.com
Emp.: 180
Resins Mfr
S.I.C.: 2821
N.A.I.C.S.: 325211
John Moyer *(Pres)*

Non-U.S. Subsidiaries:

Asahi Kasei Plastics Ltd. (2)
78 Shenton Way 07-02
Singapore, 04079120, Singapore SG
Tel.: (65) 63243001 (100%)
Fax: (65) 63243808
Web Site: www.asahi-kasei.co.jp
Emp.: 10
Mfr. & Marketer of Chemicals, Plastics, Fibers & Textiles, Housing & Construction Materials & Special Products & Services
S.I.C.: 2821
N.A.I.C.S.: 325211
Sato Seinosuke *(Mng Dir)*

Asahi Photoproducts Europe n.v./s.a. (2)
Paepsem Business Park
Boulevard Paepsem 22, 1070 Brussels, Belgium (100%)
Tel.: (32) 25260530
Fax: (32) 25260545
E-Mail: planning@asahi-photoproducts.be
Web Site: www.asahi-photoproducts.com
Emp.: 7
Liquid & Solid Photopolymers & Printing Plate Making Systems Mfr
S.I.C.: 2899
N.A.I.C.S.: 325998
Tatsuya Tajima *(Mng Dir)*

Tongsuh Petrochemical Corp., Ltd. (2)
22nd Fl 1 IFC Gookjegeumyoongro 10
Yoido dong
Youngdungpro gu, Seoul, 150-742, Korea (South) Ks
Tel.: (82) 232150700 (100%)
Fax: (82) 232150770
E-Mail: tspcmail@tspc.co.kr
Web Site: www.tspc.co.kr
Emp.: 174
Chemicals Mfr
S.I.C.: 2899
N.A.I.C.S.: 325998
Jong Pil Huh *(Pres)*

Asahi Kasei Construction Materials (1)
1-105 Kanda Jinbocho
Chiyoda-ku, Tokyo, 101-8101, Japan JP
Tel.: (81) 332963000 (100%)
Fax: (81) 332963162
E-Mail: asahi@om.asahi-kasei.co.jp
Web Site: www.asahi-kasei.co.jp/asahi/en/construction/index.html
Emp.: 25,000
Construction Materials Mfr
S.I.C.: 3086
N.A.I.C.S.: 326140
Taketsugu Fujiwara *(Pres)*

Asahi Kasei E-materials Corp. (1)
Jinbocho-Mitsui Building 1-105 Kanda Jinbocho
Chiyoda-ku, Tokyo, 101-8101, Japan
Tel.: (81) 3 3296 3235
Fax: (81) 3 3296 3453
Web Site: www.asahi-kasei.co.jp/ake-mate/
Electronic Device Mfr
S.I.C.: 3679
N.A.I.C.S.: 334419

Asahi Kasei EMD Corporation (1)
1 105 Kanda Jinbocho
Chiyoda-ku, Tokyo, 101 8101, Japan JP
Tel.: (81) 3296 3961 (100%)
Fax: (81) 3296 3962
Web Site: www.asahi-kasei.co.jp/akm
Emp.: 2,603
Electronics Materials & Products Mfr
S.I.C.: 3679
N.A.I.C.S.: 334419
Makoto Konosu *(Pres)*

U.S. Subsidiary:

AKM Semiconductor, Inc. (2)
1731 Technology Dr Ste 500
San Jose, CA 95110
Tel.: (408) 436-8580
Fax: (408) 436-7591
Toll Free: (888) 256-7364
E-Mail: icinfo@akm.com
Web Site: www.akm.com
Emp.: 50
Electronic Devices Sales
S.I.C.: 5065
N.A.I.C.S.: 423690

Asahi Kasei Epoxy Co., Ltd. (1)
1-2 Yuraku-cho 1-chome
Chiyoda-ku, Tokyo, Japan
Tel.: (81) 332963354
Fax: (81) 335077637
Epoxy Resin Chemical Mfr
S.I.C.: 2899
N.A.I.C.S.: 325998

Asahi Kasei Geotechnologies Co., Ltd. (1)
Nihonbashi Kakigaracho
Tokyo, 103-0014, Japan
Tel.: (81) 356376711
Web Site: www.asahi-kasei.co.jp/agt/
Civil Engineering Construction Material Whslr
S.I.C.: 5039
N.A.I.C.S.: 423390

Asahi Kasei Home Products Corp. (1)
1-105 Kanda Jinbo-cho
Chiyoda-ku, Tokyo, 101-8101, Japan
Tel.: (81) 3 3296 3400
Web Site: www.asahi-kasei.co.jp/saran/recipe/index.html
Household Products Distr
S.I.C.: 5023
N.A.I.C.S.: 423220

Asahi Kasei Homes Corp. (1)
1-24-1 Nishi-shinjuku
Shinjuku-ku, Tokyo, 160-8345, Japan
Tel.: (81) 3 3344 7111
Web Site: www.asahi-kasei.co.jp/asahi/en/homes/index.html
Real Estate Management Services
S.I.C.: 6531
N.A.I.C.S.: 531390
Masahito Hirai *(Pres)*

Asahi Kasei Kuraray Medical Co., Ltd. (1)
1-105 Kanda Jinbocho
Tokyo, Chiyoda-ku, 101-8101, Japan (93%)
Tel.: (81) 332963727
Fax: (81) 332963722
Web Site: www.asahi-kasei.co.jp/medical/en
Emp.: 1,500
Artificial Kidney & Therapeutic Apheresis Device Mfr
S.I.C.: 3841
N.A.I.C.S.: 339112
Yasuyuki Yoshida *(Pres)*

Asahi Kasei Medical Co., Ltd. (1)
1-105 Kanda Jinbocho
Chiyoda-ku, Tokyo, 101-8101, Japan JP
Tel.: (81) 332963795 (100%)

Fax: (81) 332963792
Emp.: 500
Leukocyte Reduction Filters & Virus Removal Filters Mfr
S.I.C.: 3841
N.A.I.C.S.: 339112
Yutaka Shibata *(Pres)*

Asahi Kasei Microdevices Corp. **(1)**
1-105 Kanda Jinbocho
Chiyoda-Ku, Tokyo, 101-0051, Japan
Tel.: (81) 3 3296 3941
Fax: (81) 3 3296 2274
E-Mail: sales@akmj.co.jp
Web Site: www.asahi-kasei.co.jp/akm/
Electronic Equipment Mfr
S.I.C.: 3679
N.A.I.C.S.: 334419
Hideki Kobori *(Pres & CEO)*

Asahi Kasei Microsystems Co., Ltd. **(1)**
1-24-1 Nishi-shinjuku
Shinjuku, 160-8345, Japan
Tel.: (81) 332963911
Fax: (81) 359082723
Information Technology Consulting Services
S.I.C.: 7373
N.A.I.C.S.: 541512

Asahi Kasei Mortgage Corporation. **(1)**
2-3-1 Nishishinjuku Shinjuku Monoris 17f
Shinjuku-Ku, Tokyo, 160-0023, Japan
Tel.: (81) 333447015
Web Site: www.asahi-kasei.co.jp/mortgage/
Mortgage Business Management Services
S.I.C.: 6159
N.A.I.C.S.: 522294

Asahi Kasei Pharma **(1)**
1-105 Kanda Jinbocho Chiyoda-ku
Tokyo, 101-8101, Japan JP
Tel.: (81) 332963000 (100%)
Fax: (81) 332963161
Web Site: www.Asahi-Kasei.com
Emp.: 4,028
Pharmaceuticals, Pharmaceutical Intermediates, Diagnostic Reagents, Nutritional Products & Animal Health Products
S.I.C.: 2834
N.A.I.C.S.: 325412
Toshio Asano *(Pres)*
Taketsugu Fujiwara *(Pres)*

Asahi Kasei Reform Co., Ltd. **(1)**
2-3-10 5th Floor
Shinjuku-ku, Tokyo, 1600022, Japan
Tel.: (81) 3 3356 6110
Home Maintenance & Remodeling Services
S.I.C.: 1522
N.A.I.C.S.: 236118

Asahi Kasei Technoplus Co., Ltd. **(1)**
26-3 Shinkawa 2-Chome
Chuo-Ku, Tokyo, Japan
Tel.: (81) 3 3552 5200
Fax: (81) 3 3552 5210
Web Site: www.aktp.co.jp
Plastic & Fiber Products Mfr & Distr
S.I.C.: 3089
N.A.I.C.S.: 326199

Asahi Kasei Trading Co., Ltd. **(1)**
3-23 Nakanoshima 3-chome
Kita-ku, Osaka, 530-8205, Japan
Tel.: (81) 648037870
Fax: (81) 648037750
Web Site: www.asahi-kasei.co.jp/akt/
Sls.: $525,096,000
Emp.: 132
Textile Fabric Distr
S.I.C.: 5199
N.A.I.C.S.: 424310
Yasushi Asano *(Pres)*

Asahi Research Center Co., Ltd. **(1)**
Jinbocho PR-Ex Bldg 3-7-5 Kanda Ogawamachi
Chiyoda-ku, Tokyo, 101-0052, Japan
Tel.: (81) 3 5577 6771
Fax: (81) 3 3259 5411
Web Site: www.asahi-kasei.co.jp/arc/
Emp.: 37
Biotechnology Research & Development Services
S.I.C.: 8731
N.A.I.C.S.: 541711
Yoshihiko Nagasato *(Pres)*

Asahi SKB Co., Ltd. **(1)**
2511-5 Kamiichibara
Kasama, Ibaraki, 309-1731, Japan
Tel.: (81) 296 72 1515
Fax: (81) 296 72 1522
Web Site: www.asahiskb.com
Shotgun Cartridges Mfr
S.I.C.: 3482
N.A.I.C.S.: 332992

Japan Elastomer Co., Ltd. **(1)**
1-105 Kandajimbocho Mitsui Bldg
Chiyoda-Ku, Tokyo, 101-0051, Japan
Tel.: (81) 332963250
Fax: (81) 332963454
Synthetic Rubber Mfr
S.I.C.: 2822
N.A.I.C.S.: 325212

Kyokuyo Sangyo Co., Ltd. **(1)**
5F Meiji Yasuda Seimei Fukui Bldg 2-7-15 Ohte
Fukui, 910-8558, Japan
Tel.: (81) 776220120
Fax: (81) 776220129
Web Site: www.kyokuyo-sangyo.co.jp
Sls.: $204,408,000
Emp.: 109
Textile Yarn Mfr & Distr
S.I.C.: 2299
N.A.I.C.S.: 314999
Manabu Haneda *(Pres)*

PS Japan Corp. **(1)**
4-1 Koishikawa 1-chome
Bunkyo-ku, Tokyo, 112-0002, Japan
Tel.: (81) 356896540
Fax: (81) 356896544
Web Site: www.psjp.com
Polystyrene Mfr & Distr
S.I.C.: 3086
N.A.I.C.S.: 326140
Hoshino Tetsuya *(Gen Mgr)*

Sanyo Petrochemical Co., Ltd. **(1)**
Jimbochomitsui Bldg
Chiyoda-Ku, Tokyo, 101-0051, Japan
Tel.: (81) 332963221
Fax: (81) 332963446
Web Site: www.asahikasei.co.jp
Emp.: 10
Petrochemical Mfr
S.I.C.: 2869
N.A.I.C.S.: 325110
Tetsuya Shibari *(Gen Mgr)*

Sun Trading Co., Ltd. **(1)**
4-10-1 Shiba Hanfa Bldg 7f
Minato-Ku, Tokyo, 108-0014, Japan
Tel.: (81) 3 5476 9941
Chemical Products Whslr
S.I.C.: 5169
N.A.I.C.S.: 424690

U.S. Subsidiaries:

Asahi Kasei America, Inc. **(1)**
535 Madison Ave Fl 33
New York, NY 10022-4212 (100%)
Tel.: (212) 371-9900
Fax: (212) 371-9050
Web Site: www.ak-america.com
Emp.: 12
Mfr. & Research of Chemicals
S.I.C.: 5169
N.A.I.C.S.: 424690

Asahi Kasei Bioprocess, Inc. **(1)**
1855 Elmdale Ave
Glenview, IL 60026
Tel.: (847) 556-9700
Fax: (800) 293-5059
Toll Free: (800) 865-4100
Web Site: www.ak-bio.com
Emp.: 30
Laboratory Equipment Mfr
S.I.C.: 3826
N.A.I.C.S.: 334516
Katsunori Horikoshi *(Gen Mgr-Planova Div)*

Asahi Kasei Medical America Inc. **(1)**
3570 Winchester Rd Ste 103
Memphis, TN 38118
Tel.: (888) 362-6105
Fax: (901) 362-6180
Web Site: www.akmamerica.com
Medical & Surgical Equipment Distr
S.I.C.: 5047
N.A.I.C.S.: 423450
Mike Jackson *(Chm)*

Asahi Kasei Spandex America, Inc. **(1)**
1566 Bushy Park Rd
Goose Creek, SC 29445-6336
Tel.: (843) 820-6513
Textile Machinery Mfr
S.I.C.: 3559
N.A.I.C.S.: 333249

Asahikasei Plastics (America) Inc. **(1)**
900 E Van Riper Rd
Fowlerville, MI 48836
Tel.: (517) 223-2000
Fax: (517) 223-2002
Plastics Materials & Resin Mfr
S.I.C.: 2821
N.A.I.C.S.: 325211

Crystal Is, Inc. **(1)**
70 Cohoes Ave
Green Island, NY 12183 NY
Tel.: (518) 276-3325
Fax: (518) 276-3857
Web Site: www.crystal-is.com
Sales Range: $1-9.9 Million
Emp.: 22
Semiconductor & Related Device Mfr
S.I.C.: 3674
N.A.I.C.S.: 334413
Leo J. Schowalter *(CTO)*

Sun Plastech Inc. **(1)**
1055 Parsippany Blvd Ste 205
Parsippany, NJ 07054
Tel.: (973) 257-1999
Fax: (973) 257-1011
Toll Free: (800) 787-4348
E-Mail: sales@asaclean.com
Web Site: www.asaclean.com
Asaclean Purging Compound Mfr & Distr
S.I.C.: 2821
N.A.I.C.S.: 325211
Joseph T. Serell *(VP & Mgr-Sls)*

Zoll Medical Corporation **(1)**
269 Mill Rd
Chelmsford, MA 01824-4105 MA
Tel.: (978) 421-9655
Fax: (978) 421-0025
Toll Free: (800) 348-9011
E-Mail: info@zoll.com
Web Site: www.zoll.com
Sales Range: $500-549.9 Million
Emp.: 1,908
Cardiac Resuscitation Devices Mfr
S.I.C.: 3845
N.A.I.C.S.: 334510
Benson F. Smith *(Chm)*
Jonathan A. Rennert *(Pres)*
Richard A. Packer *(CEO)*
Patrice Blechet *(Mng Dir-France)*
A. Ernest Whiton *(CFO & VP-Admin)*
Aaron M. Grossman *(VP, Gen Counsel & Sec)*
Steven K. Flora *(Sr VP & VP-North America Sls)*
Ward M. Hamilton *(Sr VP & VP-Mktg)*

Subsidiaries:

Bio-Detek, Inc. **(2)**
525 Narragansett Pk Dr
Pawtucket, RI 02861-4323 MA
Tel.: (401) 729-1400 (100%)
Fax: (401) 729-1408
Toll Free: (800) 225-1310
E-Mail: sales@bio-detek.com
Web Site: www.bio-detek.com
Sales Range: $100-124.9 Million
Emp.: 160
Medical Equipment
S.I.C.: 3841
N.A.I.C.S.: 339112
Mark Totman *(Pres)*

Zoll Data Systems **(2)**
11802 Ridge Pkwy Ste 400
Broomfield, CO 80021 DE
Tel.: (303) 801-0000 (100%)
Fax: (303) 801-0001
Toll Free: (800) 474-4489
E-Mail: info@zolldata.com
Web Site: www.zolldata.com
Sales Range: $50-74.9 Million
Emp.: 160
Cardiac Resuscitation Equipment
S.I.C.: 6531
N.A.I.C.S.: 531210
Greg Mears *(Dir-Medical-Data Mgmt Products)*

Non-U.S. Subsidiaries:

Zoll Medical Australia Pty. Ltd. **(2)**
Unit 10 39 Herbert St
Saint Leonards, NSW, 2065, Australia AU
Tel.: (61) 284248700 (100%)
Fax: (61) 284248711
E-Mail: info@zoll.com.au
Web Site: www.zoll.com.au
Sales Range: $10-24.9 Million
Emp.: 21
Medical Equipment
S.I.C.: 3841
N.A.I.C.S.: 339112

Zoll Medical Canada, Inc. **(2)**
1750 Sismet Rd
Mississauga, ON, L4W 1Z7, Canada Ca
Tel.: (905) 629-5005 (100%)
Fax: (905) 629-0575
Web Site: www.zoll.com
Sales Range: $1-9.9 Million
Emp.: 6
Medical Equipment
S.I.C.: 3841
N.A.I.C.S.: 339112
Richard A. Packer *(Chm & CEO)*

Zoll Medical Deutschland (GmbH) **(2)**
Emil-Hoffmann Strasse 47
50996 Cologne, Germany De
Tel.: (49) 2213989340 (100%)
Fax: (49) 2236878777
E-Mail: info@zollmedical.de
Web Site: www.zollmedical.de
Sales Range: $10-24.9 Million
Emp.: 20
Medical Equipment
S.I.C.: 3841
N.A.I.C.S.: 339112
Alexander Aegner *(Gen Mgr)*

Zoll Medical France S.A. **(2)**
189 Rte Nationale 10
781310 Coignieres, France FR
Tel.: (33) 130051498 (100%)
Fax: (33) 130490693
E-Mail: zms2@wanadoo.fr
Sales Range: $1-9.9 Million
Emp.: 9
Medical Equipment
S.I.C.: 3841
N.A.I.C.S.: 339112

Zoll Medical International Holding BV **(2)**
Newtonweg 18
6662 PV Elst, Netherlands NL
Tel.: (31) 481366410 (100%)
Fax: (31) 481366411
E-Mail: info.benelux@zoll.com
Web Site: www.zoll.com
Sales Range: $1-9.9 Million
Emp.: 15
Medical Equipment
S.I.C.: 3841
N.A.I.C.S.: 339112
Ronald Melieste *(VP-Intl Bus Dev)*

Zoll Medical New Zealand Pty. Ltd. **(2)**
Fl 1 Unit 1 29 Acheron Dr Riccarton
Christchurch, New Zealand (100%)
Tel.: (64) 33415016
Fax: (64) 3415010
E-Mail: asorokotut@zoll.com
Web Site: www.zoll.co.nz
Sales Range: $1-9.9 Million
Emp.: 2
Medical Equipment
S.I.C.: 3841
N.A.I.C.S.: 339112
Scott Rogers *(Gen Mgr)*

Zoll Medical U.K. Ltd. **(2)**
16 Seymour Court
Tunor Road Manor Park, Runcorn, Cheshire, WA7 1SY, United Kingdom UK
Tel.: (44) 1928595160 (100%)
Fax: (44) 1928595161
E-Mail: custamerservice-uk@Zoll.com
Sales Range: $10-24.9 Million
Emp.: 25
Medical Equipment

Asahi Kasei Corporation—(Continued)

S.I.C.: 3841
N.A.I.C.S.: 339112
Richard Knell-Mllre *(Gen Mgr)*

Non-U.S. Subsidiaries:

Asahi Chemical (H.K.) Ltd. **(1)**
Prudential Tower The Gtwy
Tsim Sha Tsui, Kowloon, China (Hong Kong) HK
Tel.: (852) 25227875 (100%)
Fax: (852) 28459230
Web Site: www.asahi-kasei.co.jp
Emp.: 30
Mfr. & Marketer of Chemicals, Plastics, Fibers & Textiles, Housing & Construction Materials & Special Products & Services
S.I.C.: 2821
N.A.I.C.S.: 325211

Asahi Glass Fine Techno Korea Co., Ltd. **(1)**
5 Block Gumi 4th National Industrial Complex Sandong-Myeon
Bonsan-Ri, Gumi, Kyung-Buk, Korea (South)
Tel.: (82) 57874000
Fax: (82) 54 478 0577
Web Site: www.afk.co.kr
Display Glass Mfr
S.I.C.: 3231
N.A.I.C.S.: 327215

Asahi Kasei-Beijing **(1)**
Room 1407 New China Insurance Tower No 12
Jian Guo Men Wai Ave, Beijing, 100022, China (100%)
Tel.: (86) 1065693939
Fax: (86) 1065693938
Emp.: 30
Mfr. & Marketer of Chemicals, Plastics, Fibers & Textiles, Housing & Construction Materials & Special Products & Services
S.I.C.: 2821
N.A.I.C.S.: 325211

Asahi Kasei Bioprocess Europe SA/NV **(1)**
Rue Colonel Bourg 122
1140 Brussels, Belgium
Tel.: (32) 2 526 0500
Fax: (32) 2 526 0510
Emp.: 6
Bio Process Virus Removal Products Whslr
S.I.C.: 5047
N.A.I.C.S.: 423450

Asahi Kasei Business Management (Shanghai) Co., Ltd. **(1)**
8/F One ICC Shanghai International Commerce Centre No 999
Huai Hai Zhong Road, Shanghai, 200031, China
Tel.: (86) 21 6391 6111
Fax: (86) 21 6391 6686
Business Management Consulting Services
S.I.C.: 8748
N.A.I.C.S.: 541618

Asahi Kasei Chemicals Korea Co., Ltd. **(1)**
27 - 2 Youido-Dong
Yongdungpo-Gu, Seoul, 150880, Korea (South)
Tel.: (82) 32782599
Fax: (82) 2 3775 0119
Web Site: www.asahi-kasei.co.jp
Chemical Products Whslr
S.I.C.: 5169
N.A.I.C.S.: 424690
Masahiro Abe *(Gen Mgr)*

Asahi Kasei Deutschland GmbH **(1)**
Herriot Strasse 1
60528 Frankfurt am Main, Germany De
Tel.: (49) 6966371200 (100%)
Fax: (49) 696666016
E-Mail: deutsch.db@om.asahi-kasei.co.jp
Web Site: www.asahi-kasei.co.jp
Emp.: 4
Mfr. & Marketer of Chemicals, Plastics, Fibers & Textiles, Housing & Construction Materials & Special Products & Services
S.I.C.: 2821
N.A.I.C.S.: 325211

Asahi Kasei Fibers Deutschland GmbH **(1)**
Herriotstr 1
Frankfurt am Main, Hessen, 60528, Germany
Tel.: (49) 6966371200
Fax: (49) 696666016
Web Site: www.ak-fibers.jp
Artificial Suede Distr
S.I.C.: 5137
N.A.I.C.S.: 424330
Junpei Seki *(Gen Mgr)*

Asahi Kasei Fibers Italy SRL **(1)**
Via Raffaello Sanzio 2
21013 Gallarate, Italy
Tel.: (39) 0331 21 3716
Fax: (39) 0331 70 5666
E-Mail: info@asahikaseifibersitaly.com
Web Site: www.asahi-kasei.co.jp/fibers/en/seni_subsidiaries.html
Yarn Fiber Mfr
S.I.C.: 2299
N.A.I.C.S.: 314999
Hiroshi Yamamoto *(Pres)*

Asahi Kasei Medical Europe GmbH **(1)**
Herriotstr 1
Frankfurt am Main, Hessen, 60528, Germany
Tel.: (49) 6966371500
Fax: (49) 696665193
E-Mail: info@asahi-kasei.de
Emp.: 20
Medical Devices Whslr
S.I.C.: 5047
N.A.I.C.S.: 423450
Yasumasa Shizume *(Mng Dir)*

Asahi Kasei Medical (Hangzhou) Co., Ltd. **(1)**
M10-19-7 Hangzhou Economic & Technological Development Zone
Hangzhou, Zhejiang, 310018, China
Tel.: (86) 571 8673 7228
Fax: (86) 571 8671 4121
Medical & Surgical Equipment Distr
S.I.C.: 5047
N.A.I.C.S.: 423450

Asahi Kasei Medical Trading (Korea) Co., Ltd. **(1)**
Room 303 Keumkang-Tower 889-13 Daechi 4-dong
Gangnam-gu, Seoul, 135-570, Korea (South)
Tel.: (82) 2 3468 7661
Fax: (82) 2 3468 7664
Web Site: www.asahi-kasei.co.jp/medical/en/profile/index.html
Medical Device Whslr
S.I.C.: 5047
N.A.I.C.S.: 423450

Asahi Kasei Microdevices Europe SAS **(1)**
Bureaux de la Colline Batime 1 Rue Royale
92210 Saint-Cloud, Hauts De Seine, France
Tel.: (33) 141128040
Fax: (33) 147110835
Emp.: 8
Electronic Component Distr
S.I.C.: 5065
N.A.I.C.S.: 423690
Takagi Kazumoto *(Gen Mgr)*

Asahi Kasei Microdevices Korea Corp. **(1)**
27-2 Yeouido-Dong
Yeongdeungpo-Gu, Seoul, 150742, Korea (South)
Tel.: (82) 237750990
Fax: (82) 237751991
Electronic Component Distr
S.I.C.: 5065
N.A.I.C.S.: 423690

Asahi Kasei Microza (Hangzhou) Co., Ltd. **(1)**
No 435 Avenue 23 Hangzhou Economic & Technological Development Zone
Hangzhou, 310018, China
Tel.: (86) 571 8679 3958
Fax: (86) 571 8687 5187
Web Site: www.asahi-kasei.co.jp/membrane/microza/en/ask.html
Industrial Filtration Membranes & System Mfr
S.I.C.: 3559
N.A.I.C.S.: 333249

Asahi Kasei Plastics (Hong Kong) Co., Ltd. **(1)**
Suite 1606 16/F One Peking No1 Peking Road
Tsim Tsa Tsui, Kowloon, China (Hong Kong)
Tel.: (852) 21514000
Plastic Resin Whslr
S.I.C.: 5162
N.A.I.C.S.: 424610

Asahi Kasei Plastics Singapore Pte. Ltd. **(1)**
20 Sakra Road Jurong Island
Singapore, 627889, Singapore
Tel.: (65) 63161777
Fax: (65) 63161730
Web Site: www.asahikaseiplastics.com
Emp.: 100
Plastic Resin Whslr
S.I.C.: 5162
N.A.I.C.S.: 424610
Seinosuke Sato *(Mng Dir)*

Asahi Kasei-Shanghai **(1)**
Rm 1811 Shanghai International Trade Ctr
2200 Yan An Rd W, Shanghai, 200335, China (100%)
Tel.: (86) 2162780408
Fax: (86) 2162780407
Web Site: www.asahi-kasei.co.jp
Emp.: 9
Mfr. & Marketer of Chemicals, Plastics, Fibers & Textiles, Housing & Construction Materials & Special Products & Services
S.I.C.: 2821
N.A.I.C.S.: 325211

Asahi Kasei Spandex Europe GmbH **(1)**
Chempark Dormagen Building E 4
41538 Dormagen, Germany
Tel.: (49) 2133 4798 201
Fax: (49) 2133 4798 282
Web Site: www.dorlastan.com
Emp.: 160
Spandex Fiber Mfr
S.I.C.: 2652
N.A.I.C.S.: 322219
Werner Nahl *(Co-Mng Dir)*
Masakazu Sawada *(Co-Mng Dir)*

Asahi Pharma Spain, SL **(1)**
Calle Paris 207 Piso 1 Pta 1
Barcelona, 08008, Spain
Tel.: (34) 93 322 40 54
Fax: (34) 93 588 57 31
Pharmaceuticals Products Mfr
S.I.C.: 2834
N.A.I.C.S.: 325412

Asahi Photoproducts (UK) Ltd. **(1)**
1 Prospect Way Hutton Industrial Estate
Shenfield, CM 13 1XA, United Kingdom
Tel.: (44) 1277232877
Fax: (44) 1277224414
E-Mail: mail@asahi-photoproducts.co.uk
Web Site: www.asahi-photoproducts.com
Emp.: 10
Specialty Chemicals Distr
S.I.C.: 5169
N.A.I.C.S.: 424690
David Galton *(Gen Mgr)*

Asahi-Schwebel (Taiwan) Co., Ltd. **(1)**
330 Min Tsu Rd Sec 6
Chung-li, Taoyuan, 32050, Taiwan
Tel.: (886) 34901121
Fax: (886) 34904466
Textile Fabric Products Mfr
S.I.C.: 2389
N.A.I.C.S.: 314999

Asahikasei Plastics (Shanghai) Co., Ltd. **(1)**
Room 2309 Shanghai Central Plaza 381 Huahai Zhong Road
Shanghai, 200020, China
Tel.: (86) 2163915222
Fax: (86) 21 63916607
Plastic Resin Whslr
S.I.C.: 5162
N.A.I.C.S.: 424610

Hangzhou Asahikasei Textiles Co., Ltd. **(1)**
No M10-5-2 Xiasha Economic Technology Development Zone
Hangzhou, Zhejiang, 310018, China
Tel.: (86) 57186910286
Fax: (86) 57186912040
Broadwoven Fabric Products Mfr
S.I.C.: 2299
N.A.I.C.S.: 313210

Polyxylenol Singapore Pte. Ltd. **(1)**
20 Sakra Road
Singapore, 627889, Singapore
Tel.: (65) 63161777
Fax: (65) 63161730
Specialty Chemicals Mfr
S.I.C.: 2899
N.A.I.C.S.: 325998
Seinosuke Sato *(Mng Dir)*

Thai Asahi Kasei Spandex Co., Ltd. **(1)**
19/194 Chamman Phenjati Bldg 23rd Floor Rama 9 RD
Huaykwang, Bangkok, Thailand 10310
Tel.: (66) 2 643 2857
Fax: (66) 2 643 2859
E-Mail: marketing@taspandex.co.th
Web Site: www.taspandex.co.th
Spandex Bare Yarn Mfr & Distr
S.I.C.: 5131
N.A.I.C.S.: 424310

Tong Suh Petrochemical Corp., Ltd. **(1)**
8th Floor KTP Building 27-2 Yoido-dong
Youngdungpo-gu, Seoul, 150742, Korea (South)
Tel.: (82) 232150700
Fax: (82) 232150770
E-Mail: tspcmail@tspc.co.kr
Web Site: www.tspc.co.kr
Rev.: $760,680,000
Emp.: 174
Chemical Products Mfr & Distr
S.I.C.: 2899
N.A.I.C.S.: 325998
Pil Huh Jong *(Pres)*

Non-U.S. Joint Venture:

Formosa Asahi Spandex Co., Ltd. **(1)**
Rm 386 12F Tun Hwa N Rd
Taipei, Taiwan
Tel.: (886) 227122211
Fax: (886) 227128718
Web Site: www.formosa.com
Emp.: 12
Elastic Products Mfr; Owned 50% by Formosa Plastics Corporation & 50% by Asahi Kasei Corporation
S.I.C.: 3089
N.A.I.C.S.: 326199
Y.C. Wang *(Chm)*

Non-U.S. Plant:

Thai Asahi Kasei Spandex Co., Ltd. - Amphur Sriracha Factory **(1)**
919 Moo 11 Tambon Nongkhaam
Amphur Sriracha, Chon Buri, Thailand 20230
Tel.: (66) 38 483 005
Fax: (66) 38 482 969
Web Site: www.taspandex.co.th/contact1.php
Spandex Bare Yarn Mfr
S.I.C.: 2299
N.A.I.C.S.: 313110

ASAHI KOGYOSHA CO., LTD.

1-25-7 Hamamatsucho
Minato-ku, Tokyo, 105-8543, Japan
Tel.: (81) 3 3432 5711
Web Site: www.asahikogyosha.co.jp
Year Founded: 1925
1975—(TKS)
Emp.: 920

Business Description:
Air Conditioning System Installation Services
S.I.C.: 1711
N.A.I.C.S.: 238220

Personnel:
Yasutomo Takasu *(Pres)*

ASAHI NET, INC.

Asahi Bldg 8F Ginza 6-6-7
Chuo-ku, Tokyo, 104-0061, Japan

Tel.: (81) 3 3569 3511
Fax: (81) 3 3569 3501
Web Site: www.asahi-net.co.jp
Year Founded: 1990
3834—(TKS)
Sls.: $79,575,243
Assets: $117,350,750
Liabilities: $12,192,829
Net Worth: $105,157,921
Earnings: $6,018,100
Fiscal Year-end: 03/31/13
Business Description:
Internet Connection Services
S.I.C.: 2741
N.A.I.C.S.: 519130
Personnel:
Jiro Hijikata *(Pres)*
Board of Directors:
Satoshi Mizokami
Kouichi Nakano
Transfer Agent:
Mitsubishi UFJ Trust & Banking Corporation
1 4 5 Marunouchi Chiyoda ku
Tokyo, 1008212, Japan

ASAHI ORGANIC CHEMICALS INDUSTRY CO., LTD.

2-5955 Nakanose-cho
Nobeoka, Miyazaki, 882-8688, Japan
Tel.: (81) 982350880
Fax: (81) 982359350
Web Site: www.asahi-yukizai.co.jp
Year Founded: 1945
4216—(TKS)
Sales Range: $350-399.9 Million
Emp.: 1,043
Business Description:
Industrial Resins & Plastic Piping Materials Mfr
S.I.C.: 2821
N.A.I.C.S.: 325211
Personnel:
Yoichi Saji *(Chm)*
Keiji Kamei *(Pres)*
Yasushi Kishimoto *(Sr Mng Dir)*
Masahiro Kinoshita *(Mng Dir)*
Masayuki Kuwata *(Exec Officer)*
Kyoji Tominaga *(Exec Officer)*
Board of Directors:
Yoichi Saji
Keiji Kamei
Masahiro Kinoshita
Yasushi Kishimoto
Masayuki Kuwata
Kyoji Tominaga

Subsidiaries:

AOC Techno Co., Ltd. (1)
15-9-2 Uchikanda Furukawa Chiyoda Bldg 3rd Floor
Chiyoda-Ku, Tokyo, Japan JP
Tel.: (81) 332562451 (100%)
Fax: (81) 332543473
E-Mail: info@aoc-techno.co.jp
Web Site: www.aoc-techno.co.jp
Industrial Supplies Whslr
S.I.C.: 5085
N.A.I.C.S.: 423840

Asahi AV Trading Co ,Ltd (1)
No 2-12 Kandatsukasamachi 2-Chome Chiyoda-Ku
Chiyoda-Ku, Tokyo, 101-0048, Japan
Tel.: (81) 332547958
Fax: (81) 332549022
Web Site: www.asahi-avt.com
Emp.: 30
Industrial Machinery & Equipment Whslr
S.I.C.: 5084
N.A.I.C.S.: 423830
Nobuhiro Suzuki *(Gen Mgr)*

Asahi Organic Chemicals Industry Co., Ltd. - Aichi Plant (1)
1-4-16 Nishiki
Naka-ku, Nagoya, Aichi, 460-0003, Japan
Tel.: (81) 522228533
Fax: (81) 522228233
Phenolic Resins Mfr
S.I.C.: 2821
N.A.I.C.S.: 325211

Asahi Yuki Hanbai Nishi-Nihon K.K. (1)
2-11-29 Shiohama
Koto-Ku, Tokyo, Japan
Tel.: (81) 336998621
Fax: (81) 369982699
E-Mail: hiroshi.hesagawa@asahiyukizai.co.jp
Emp.: 20
Chemical & Allied Products Merchant Whslr
S.I.C.: 5169
N.A.I.C.S.: 424690
Hiroshi Hesegewa *(Gen Mgr)*

Plant:

Asahi Organic Chemicals Industry Co., Ltd. - Hirosima Plant (1)
88-61 Aza Ouji Shinjo-cho
Shobara, Hiroshima, 727-0004, Japan
Tel.: (81) 824728011
Fax: (81) 824728003
Phenolic Resins Mfr
S.I.C.: 2821
N.A.I.C.S.: 325211

U.S. Subsidiary:

Asahi/America, Inc. (1)
35 Green St
Malden, MA 02148-0134 MA
Mailing Address:
PO Box 653
Malden, MA 02148
Tel.: (781) 321-5409
Fax: (781) 321-4421
E-Mail: asahi@asahi-america.com
Web Site: www.asahi-america.com
Emp.: 100
Mfr. & Distributor of Thermoplastic Valves, Actuation & Piping Systems & Flow Meter Devices
Import Export
S.I.C.: 3084
N.A.I.C.S.: 326122
Hidetoshi Hashimoto *(Chm & CEO)*
Stephen P. Harrington *(CFO, Treas & Sr VP)*

Non-U.S. Subsidiaries:

ASAHI AV VALVE (SHANGHAI) CO., LTD. (1)
No 16 Shanghai Malu Fengdeng Industry City 615 Fengdeng Road
Malu Town Jiading District, Shanghai, 201818, China
Tel.: (86) 2161392600
Fax: (86) 2161392606
Industrial Valves Mfr
S.I.C.: 3491
N.A.I.C.S.: 332911

Asahi Organic Chemicals (Nantong) Co., Ltd. (1)
No 21 Tong Wang Road Nantong ETDZ
Nantong, Jiangsu, 226017, China
Tel.: (86) 51383592400
Fax: (86) 51383593400
Web Site: www.asahi-yukizai.co.jp/en/about-corp/office/index.html
Phenolic Resins Mfr
S.I.C.: 2821
N.A.I.C.S.: 325211
Hiroshi Furusawa *(Mgr)*

Asahi Organic Chemicals Trading (Shanghai) Co., Ltd. (1)
Room 405 East Tower Sun Plaza No 88 Xianxia Road
Changning District, Shanghai, 200336, China
Tel.: (86) 2162787862
Fax: (86) 21 6278 7892
Web Site: www.asahi-yukizai.co.jp/en/about-corp/office/index.html
Emp.: 10
Organic Chemicals Distr
S.I.C.: 5169
N.A.I.C.S.: 424690

ASAHI ORIKOMI INC.

5-3-2 Tukiji
Chuo-ku, Tokyo, 104-8011, Japan
Tel.: (81) 335447621
Fax: (81) 335448071
Web Site: www.asaori.co.jp
Year Founded: 1959
Billings: $379,700,000
Emp.: 187
Business Description:
Advertising Agency
S.I.C.: 7311
N.A.I.C.S.: 541810
Personnel:
Hitoshi Kuroda *(Gen Mgr)*

ASAHI RUBBER INC.

2-7-2 Dote-cho Omiya-ku Saitama-shi
Saitama, 330-0801, Japan
Tel.: (81) 48 650 6051
Fax: (81) 48 650 5201
E-Mail: info@asahi-rubber.co.jp
Web Site: www.asahi-rubber.co.jp
Year Founded: 1976
5162—(JAS)
Sls.: $52,679,000
Assets: $82,687,000
Liabilities: $50,072,000
Net Worth: $32,615,000
Earnings: $836,000
Emp.: 247
Fiscal Year-end: 03/31/13
Business Description:
Industrial Rubber Products Mfr
S.I.C.: 3061
N.A.I.C.S.: 326291
Personnel:
Shigeyoshi Yokoyama *(Chm)*
Jun Ito *(Pres)*
Shoji Nakazawa *(Mng Dir)*
Board of Directors:
Shigeyoshi Yokoyama
Iwao Ito
Jun Ito
Masashi Kamemoto
Shoji Nakazawa
Youichiro Watanabe
Transfer Agent:
Mitsubishi UFJ Trust & Banking Corporation
7-10-11 Higashisuna Koto-ku
Tokyo, Japan

Subsidiary:

ASAHI FR R&D Co., Ltd. (1)
2-7-2 Dote-cho Omiya-ku
Saitama, 330-0801, Japan
Tel.: (81) 48 650 6051
Fax: (81) 48 650 5201
E-Mail:
Industrial Rubber Mfr
S.I.C.: 3069
N.A.I.C.S.: 326299

Plants:

Asahi Rubber Inc. - Fukushima Factory (1)
1 Bozukubo Oaza Izumizaki Izumizaki-mura Nishi-Shirakawa-gun
Fukushima, 969-0101, Japan
Tel.: (81) 248 53 3491
Fax: (81) 248 53 3493
Industrial Rubber Mfr
S.I.C.: 3069
N.A.I.C.S.: 326299

Asahi Rubber Inc. - Shirakawa Factory (1)
1-21 Tsukinoiri Kayane
Shirakawa-shi, Fukushima, 961-0004, Japan
Tel.: (81) 248 21 1401
Fax: (81) 248 21 1404
Industrial Rubber Mfr
S.I.C.: 3069
N.A.I.C.S.: 326299

U.S. Subsidiary:

ARI INTERNATIONAL CORPORATION (1)
2015 S Arlington Heights Rd Ste 109
Arlington Heights, IL 60005
Tel.: (847) 364-1000
Fax: (847) 364-1270
E-Mail:
Web Site: www.ari-corp.com
Industrial Rubber Whslr
S.I.C.: 5085
N.A.I.C.S.: 423840

ASAHI-SEIKI MANUFACTURING CO., LTD.

Asahimae-cho Owariasahi
Nagoya, 488-8655, Japan
Tel.: (81) 561533119
Fax: (81) 561542439
Web Site: www.asahiseiki-mfg.co.jp
Year Founded: 1953
6111—(NGO)
Sales Range: $100-124.9 Million
Emp.: 482
Business Description:
Precision Metal Components, Automatic Presses, Spring-Forming Machines, Automatic Assembly Machines, Machine Tools, Airplane Parts & Small Arms Ammunition Mfr
S.I.C.: 3499
N.A.I.C.S.: 332999
Personnel:
Hiroshi Yamaguchi *(Pres)*

Divisions:

Asahi-Seiki Manufacturing Co., Ltd Machinery Division (1)
Asahimae-cho
Owariasahi, Aichi, Japan
Tel.: (81) 561533119
Fax: (81) 0561542439
Web Site: www.asahiseiki-mfg.co.jp/
Emp.: 480
Spring & Metal Mfr
S.I.C.: 3493
N.A.I.C.S.: 332613
Hiroshi Yamaguchi *(Pres)*

Asahi-Seiki Manufacturing Co., Ltd. Precision Engineering Division (1)
Asahimae cho
Owariasahi, Aichi, 4888655, Japan
Tel.: (81) 561533118
Fax: (81) 561542438
E-Mail: kazuo-ikuta@asahiseiki-mfg.co.jp
Web Site: www.asahiseiki-mfg.co.jp/eg/corpf/corp01.htm
Emp.: 500
Spring & Metal Mfr
S.I.C.: 3495
N.A.I.C.S.: 332613
Hiroshi Yamaguchi *(Pres)*

ASAHI SEIREN CO., LTD.

9-37 Ota
Yao, 581 0037, Japan
Tel.: (81) 72 953 2212
E-Mail: info@asahiseiren.com
Web Site: www.asahiseiren.com
Business Description:
Aluminum Alloy Mfr
S.I.C.: 3334
N.A.I.C.S.: 331313
Personnel:
Keizo Taniyama *(Pres)*

THE ASAHI SHIMBUN COMPANY

5-3-2 Tsukiji
Chuo-ku, Tokyo, 104-8011, Japan
Tel.: (81) 335450131
Fax: (81) 355407618
E-Mail: info@asahi.com
Web Site: www.asahi.com
Emp.: 5,000
Business Description:
Holding Company
Export
S.I.C.: 6719
N.A.I.C.S.: 551112

The Asahi Shimbun Company—(Continued)

Personnel:
Michiko Murayama *(Co-Owner)*
Shoichi Ueno *(Co-Owner)*
Kotaro Akiyama *(Pres & CEO)*
Board of Directors:
Kotaro Akiyama
Yuzo Ito
Michiko Murayama
Shoichi Ueno
Yoshibumi Wakamiya
Subsidiaries:

Asahi Airport Service Co., Ltd. (1)
3-2-7 Minowa Toyonaka
Osaka, 560-0035, Japan
Tel.: (81) 668565002
Fax: (81) 668536954
Web Site: www.aas.co.jp
Emp.: 100
Newsstand Operator
S.I.C.: 5994
N.A.I.C.S.: 451212
Akihito Abukawa *(Pres)*

Asahi Building Co., Ltd. (1)
Shinasahi Bldg 7F 2-3-1 Nakanoshima
Kita-ku, Osaka, 530-0005, Japan
Tel.: (81) 662317501
Fax: (81) 662314063
Web Site: www.asahibuilding.co.jp
Non-Residential Building Operator
S.I.C.: 6531
N.A.I.C.S.: 531312

Asahi Culture Center K.K. (1)
Izutsuya Jimuto 2nd Fl 1-3-9 Bashadku
Kokurakita-ku
Kitakyushu, Fukuoka, 802-0077, Japan
Tel.: (81) 935218381
Culture Center
S.I.C.: 9411
N.A.I.C.S.: 923110

Asahi Family News Co., Ltd. (1)
Shinasahi Bldg 3F 2-3-18 Nakanoshima
Kita-ku, Osaka, 530-0005, Japan
Tel.: (81) 662013328
Periodical Publisher
S.I.C.: 2721
N.A.I.C.S.: 511120

Asahi Gakusei Shimbun Publishing Company K.K. (1)
Nakagawa Tukiji Building 7F 3-5-4 Tsukiji
Chuo-ku, Tokyo, 104-0045, Japan
Tel.: (81) 335455221
Fax: (81) 35450978
Web Site: www.asagaku.com
Newspaper Publisher
S.I.C.: 2711
N.A.I.C.S.: 511110
H. Yamamoto *(Pres)*

Asahi Service Kosan K.K. (1)
2-1-8 Daimon Kokurakita-ku
Kitakyushu, Fukuoka, 803-0811, Japan
Tel.: (81) 935610231
Web Site: www.asahiservicekosan.co.jp
Building Maintenance Services
S.I.C.: 7349
N.A.I.C.S.: 561720

Asahi Tatemono Kanri K.K. (1)
3-2-4 Nakanoshima
Kita-ku, Osaka, 530-0005, Japan
Tel.: (81) 662030521
Fax: (81) 662030525
Web Site: www.asahitatemonokanri.co.jp
Building Maintenance Services
S.I.C.: 7349
N.A.I.C.S.: 561720

Hokkaido Nikkan Sports Shimbunsha K.K. (1)
3-1-30 Kita Johigashi
Chuo-ku, Hokkaido, 060-0033, Japan
Tel.: (81) 112423900
Fax: (81) 112721754
Web Site: www.nikkansports.com
Emp.: 46
Newspaper Publisher
S.I.C.: 2711
N.A.I.C.S.: 511110
Yoshitaka Suzuki *(Pres)*

Nagoya Nikkan Sports Shimbunsha K.K. (1)
1-3-3 Sakae
Naka-ku, Nagoya, 460-8488, Japan
Tel.: (81) 52 2318131
Web Site: www.asahi.com
Newspaper Publisher
S.I.C.: 2711
N.A.I.C.S.: 511110

Nikkan Sports Newspaper (1)
3-5-10 Tsukiji
Chuo-ku, Tokyo, 104-0045, Japan
Tel.: (81) 355508888
Web Site: www.nikkansports.com
Newspaper Publisher
S.I.C.: 2711
N.A.I.C.S.: 511110

U.S. Subsidiary:

Asahi Shimbun America, Inc. (1)
620 8th Ave
New York, NY 10018-1618
Tel.: (212) 317-3000
News Services
S.I.C.: 7383
N.A.I.C.S.: 519110
Y. Naito *(Pres)*

Branch:

Asahi Shimbun America, Inc. (2)
529 14th St NW Ste 1022
Washington, DC 20045
Tel.: (202) 783-0523
Fax: (202) 783-0039
Web Site: www.asahi.com
News Services
S.I.C.: 7383
N.A.I.C.S.: 519110

Non-U.S. Subsidiaries:

Asahi Shimbun International Ltd. (1)
6th Floor Halton House
20 23 Holborn, London, EC1N 2JD, United Kingdom
Tel.: (44) 20 78311114
News Services
S.I.C.: 7383
N.A.I.C.S.: 519110

ASAHI SONGWON COLORS LTD.
Asahi House Chhatral-Kadi Road
Mehsana, Gujarat, 382 721, India
Tel.: (91) 2764 233007
Fax: (91) 2764 233550
E-Mail: mktg@asahisongwon.com
Web Site: www.asahisongwon.com
532853—(BOM)
Rev.: $43,129,397
Assets: $44,314,958
Liabilities: $22,011,424
Net Worth: $22,303,534
Earnings: $1,920,067
Fiscal Year-end: 03/31/13
Business Description:
Color Pigments Mfr
S.I.C.: 2819
N.A.I.C.S.: 325130
Personnel:
Paru M. Jaykrishna *(Chm & Co-Mng Dir)*
Gokul M. Jaykrishna *(Co-Mng Dir)*
Munjal M. Jaykrishna *(Co-Mng Dir)*
Saji V. Joseph *(Sec)*
Board of Directors:
Paru M. Jaykrishna
Arvind Goenka
Gokul M. Jaykrishna
Munjal M. Jaykrishna
Pradeep J. Jha
H. K. Khan
Guarang N. Shah
R. K. Sukhdevsinhji
Transfer Agent:
Link Intime India Private Limited
C 133 Pannalal Silk Mills Compound Kantilal Maganlal Ind Estate
L. B. S. Marg Bhandup West, Mumbai, India

ASAKA RIKEN CO., LTD.
47 Azamaseguchi Kaneya
Tamuramachi
Koriyama, Fukushima, 963-0725, Japan
Tel.: (81) 249444744
E-Mail: grmatsus@asaka.co.jp
Web Site: www.asaka.co.jp
Year Founded: 1969
5724—(JAS)
Sales Range: $125-149.9 Million
Emp.: 138
Business Description:
Metal Products Collection, Recycling & Sales
S.I.C.: 5051
N.A.I.C.S.: 423510
Personnel:
Keita Yamada *(Pres)*
Yukio Sakuma *(Exec Officer & Dir-Metal Bus)*
Takashi Shimura *(Exec Officer & Dir-Environ Bus)*
Shinobu Suzuki *(Exec Officer & Dir-Ops/Admin)*
Board of Directors:
Ko Kumagai
Hideo Misaki
Yukio Sakuma
Masataka Sakurai
Takashi Shimura
Shinobu Suzuki
Keita Yamada
Takayuki Yoshida

ASANKO GOLD INC.
(Formerly Keegan Resources Inc.)
700-1199 West Hastings Street
Vancouver, BC, V6E 3T5, Canada
Tel.: (604) 683-8193
Fax: (604) 683-8194
Toll Free: (800) 863-8655
E-Mail: info@asanko.com
Web Site: www.asanko.com
Year Founded: 1999
AKG—(NYSEMKT TSX)
Business Description:
Gold Mining & Exploration Services
S.I.C.: 1041
N.A.I.C.S.: 212221
Personnel:
Colin Henri Steyn *(Chm)*
Peter Binsteed Breese *(Pres & CEO)*
Gregory J. McCunn *(CFO)*
Tony Devlin *(COO)*
Board of Directors:
Colin Henri Steyn
Peter Bradford
Peter Binsteed Breese
Marcel H. de Groot
Gordon J. Fretwell
Michael Price
Shawn Kristen Wallace
Transfer Agent:
Computershare Trust Company of Canada
510 Burrard St 3rd Fl
Vancouver, BC, V6C 3B9, Canada
Non-U.S. Subsidiary:

Keegan Resources (Ghana) Limited (1)
No 15 Senchi Loop
Airport Residential Area, Accra, Ghana
Tel.: (233) 243690224
Fax: (233) 302761454
E-Mail: info@keeganresources.com
Gold Mfr
S.I.C.: 3911
N.A.I.C.S.: 339910
Ben Adoo *(Mng Dir)*

ASANTE GOLD CORPORATION
595 Howe Street Suite 206
Vancouver, BC, V6C 2T5, Canada
Tel.: (604) 558-1134
Fax: (604) 558-1136
E-Mail: douglas@asantegold.com
Web Site: www.asantegold.com
Year Founded: 2011
ASE—(TSXV)
Business Description:
Gold Mining
S.I.C.: 1041
N.A.I.C.S.: 212221
Personnel:
Douglas MacQuarrie *(Pres & CEO)*
Philip Gibbs *(CFO)*
Board of Directors:
Mark Holcombe
Douglas MacQuarrie
Florian Riedl-Riedenstein
Jagtar Sandhu
Transfer Agent:
Computershare Investor Services Inc.
510 Burrard St
Vancouver, BC, V6C 3B9, Canada

ASANTE INCORPORATED
1-33-15 Shinjuku
Shinjuku-ku, Tokyo, 160-0022, Japan
Tel.: (81) 3 3226 5511
Fax: (81) 3 32265370
Web Site: www.asante.co.jp
6073—(TKS)
Sales Range: $100-124.9 Million
Emp.: 840
Business Description:
Construction, Home Improvement & Repair Services
S.I.C.: 1522
N.A.I.C.S.: 236118
Personnel:
Makoto Munemasa *(Pres)*

ASANUMA CORPORATION
12-6 Higashikouzu-cho
Tennoji-ku, Osaka, 543-8688, Japan
Tel.: (81) 667685222
Fax: (81) 667686336
Web Site: www.asanuma.co.jp
1852—(TKS)
Sls.: $1,333,112,000
Assets: $1,178,210,000
Liabilities: $1,082,818,000
Net Worth: $95,392,000
Earnings: ($37,598,000)
Emp.: 1,426
Fiscal Year-end: 03/31/13
Business Description:
Construction Services
S.I.C.: 1542
N.A.I.C.S.: 236220
Personnel:
Kenichi Asanuma *(Pres)*
Toshiyuki Morimoto *(Sr Mng Officer)*
Kazuo Asanuma *(Mng Officer)*
Takeshi Hashimoto *(Mng Officer)*
Shinji Hirota *(Mng Officer)*
Hidefumi Naito *(Mng Officer)*
Takashi Ueda *(Mng Officer)*
Morio Yamakoshi *(Mng Officer)*
Sho Asanuma *(Exec Officer)*
Tetsuo Fukuchi *(Exec Officer)*
Hidekazu Kawai *(Exec Officer)*
Hiroaki Kawasaki *(Exec Officer)*
Tatsuyuki Kojima *(Exec Officer)*
Takashi Maeda *(Exec Officer)*
Takeo Miura *(Exec Officer)*
Yoshio Omori *(Exec Officer)*
Takuya Sato *(Exec Officer)*
Shigefumi Tajima *(Exec Officer)*
Shigeru Takeda *(Exec Officer)*
Ryoji Tatsuishi *(Exec Officer)*
Board of Directors:
Kazuo Asanuma
Kenichi Asanuma
Sho Asanuma
Shinji Hirota
Tatsuyuki Kojima
Toshiyuki Morimoto
Hidefumi Naito
Morio Yamakoshi

Plant:

Asanuma Corporation - Precast Concrete Plant (1)
Shiraoka-cho
Minami-ku, Saitama, Japan
Tel.: (81) 480 92 1881
Fax: (81) 480 92 1883
Web Site: www.asanuma.co.jp
Precast Concrete Products Mfr
S.I.C.: 3271
N.A.I.C.S.: 327331
Kenichi Asanuma *(Pres)*

U.S. Subsidiary:

Asanuma Construction Ltd. (1)
PO Box 22108
Barrigada, GU 96921
Tel.: (671) 646-4243
Fax: (671) 646-5180
Emp.: 18
Construction Engineering Services
S.I.C.: 8711
N.A.I.C.S.: 541330
Tsutomu Higa *(Gen Mgr)*

ASAPLUS RESOURCES LIMITED

21 Bukit Batok Crescent #15-74
Wcega Tower
Singapore, 658065, Singapore
Tel.: (65) 6602 8140
Fax: (65) 6491 6407
Web Site: www.asaplusresources.com
AJY—(ASX)
Business Description:
Iron Ore Mining
S.I.C.: 1011
N.A.I.C.S.: 212210
Personnel:
Ir Che Mohamed Hussein Mohamed Shariff *(Chm)*

ASAS DUNIA BERHAD

Wisma Asas No 228-B Lebuh Chulia
10200 Pulau Penang, Malaysia
Tel.: (60) 42631999
Fax: (60) 42632999
E-Mail: enquiries@asasdunia.com
Web Site: www.asasdunia.com.my
ASAS—(KLS)
Rev.: $44,556,075
Assets: $138,459,411
Liabilities: $5,692,874
Net Worth: $132,766,537
Earnings: $8,936,295
Fiscal Year-end: 12/31/12
Business Description:
Building Construction & Property Investment Services
S.I.C.: 1522
N.A.I.C.S.: 236118
Personnel:
Tony Leong Foon Chan *(Chm)*
Jerry Fook Sing Chan *(Mng Dir)*
Ching Ping Lim *(Co-Sec)*
Sook Fun Thum *(Co-Sec)*
Board of Directors:
Tony Leong Foon Chan
Fook Hean Chan
Fook Sun Chan
Jerry Fook Sing Chan
Chin Teck Diong
Shiew Ming Moo
Choo Ee Teoh

Subsidiaries:

Asas Mutiara Sdn. Bhd. (1)
Wisma Asas No 228-B Chulia Street
Pulau Penang, 10200, Malaysia
Tel.: (60) 45881999
Fax: (60) 45881380
E-Mail: enquiries@asasdunia.com
Web Site: www.asasdunia.com
Real Estate Property Development Services
S.I.C.: 6531
N.A.I.C.S.: 531210

Fung Yik Sdn. Bhd. (1)
Wisma Asas 228B Lebuh Chulia
10200 Pulau Penang, Malaysia
Tel.: (60) 42631999
Fax: (60) 42632999
E-Mail: enquiries@asasdunia.com
Emp.: 30
Real Estate Property Development Services
S.I.C.: 6531
N.A.I.C.S.: 531210
Jerry Fook Sing Chan *(Mng Dir)*

ASATSU-DK INCORPORATED

(d/b/a ADK Group)
13-1 Tsukiji 1-chome Chuo-ku
Tokyo, 104-8172, Japan
Tel.: (81) 335472111
Fax: (81) 3 3547 2345
Web Site: www.adk.jp
Year Founded: 1951
9747—(TKS)
Billings: $3,859,042,000
Assets: $2,146,793,000
Liabilities: $941,633,000
Net Worth: $1,205,160,000
Earnings: $30,591,000
Emp.: 3,376
Fiscal Year-end: 12/31/12
Business Description:
Holding Company; Advertising Agencies
S.I.C.: 6719
N.A.I.C.S.: 551112
Personnel:
Koichiro Naganuma *(Chm)*
Shinichi Ueno *(Pres & CEO)*
Yoshihiro Sakai *(CFO)*
Takeshi Kato *(Operating Officer)*
Kazuhiko Narimatsu *(Sr Operating Officer)*
Board of Directors:
Koichiro Naganuma
Takeshi Kato
Hideaki Kido
Kazuhiko Narimatsu
Stuart Neish
Hiroshi Ohbayashi
Yoshihiro Sakai
Shinichi Ueno
Mochio Umeda
Transfer Agent:
Tokyo Securities Transfer Agent Co., Ltd.
6-2 Otemachi 2-chome Chiyoda-ku
Tokyo, 100 0004, Japan

Branches:

Asatsu-DK Incorporated (1)
6-20 Dojima 1-chome
Kita-ku, Osaka, 530-0003, Japan JP
Tel.: (81) 6 4795 0200
Fax: (81) 6 4795 0204
Web Site: www.adk.jp
S.I.C.: 7311
N.A.I.C.S.: 541810

Asatsu-DK Incorporated (1)
16-27 Nishiki 3-chome Naka-ku
Nagoya, 460-8623, Japan JP
Tel.: (81) 52 950 3621
Fax: (81) 152 950 3824
Web Site: www.adk.jp
Emp.: 50
S.I.C.: 7311
N.A.I.C.S.: 541810
Yoji Shimizu *(Pres & Grp CEO)*
Koichiro Naganuma *(Pres)*

Asatsu-DK Incorporated (1)
3-8, Nakasu 5-chome
Hakata-ku, Fukuoka, 810-0801, Japan
Tel.: (81) 92 283 3977
Web Site: www.adk.jp
S.I.C.: 7311
N.A.I.C.S.: 541810
Koichiro Naganuma *(Chm & CEO)*

Asatsu-DK Incorporated (1)
4-22 Nakanohashidori 1-chome
Morioka, 020-0871, Japan
Tel.: (81) 19 626 3150
Web Site: www.adk.jp
S.I.C.: 7311
N.A.I.C.S.: 541810

Asatsu-DK Incorporated (1)
5-8 Higashi-Odori 2-chome
Niigata, 950-0087, Japan
Tel.: (81) 25 241 5177
Web Site: www.adk.jp
S.I.C.: 7311
N.A.I.C.S.: 541810

Asatsu-DK Incorporated (1)
8-45 Nakasangeshita 1-chome
Okayama, 700-0821, Japan JP
Tel.: (81) 86 232 2531
Fax: (81) 86 23 8857
Web Site: www.adk.jp
Emp.: 22
S.I.C.: 7311
N.A.I.C.S.: 541810
Ueno Shoichi *(Pres)*

Asatsu-DK Incorporated (1)
1-1 Nishi 4-chome Kita 3-jo
Chuo-ku, Sapporo, 060-0003, Japan JP
Tel.: (81) 11 231 1797
Fax: (81) 11 221 3837
E-Mail: takamori@adk.jp
Web Site: www.adk.jp
S.I.C.: 7311
N.A.I.C.S.: 541810
Yoji Shimizu *(Pres & Grp CEO)*
Koichiro Naganuma *(Pres)*

Asatsu-DK Incorporated (1)
54 Irie 2-chome
Kanazawa, 921-8011, Japan
Tel.: (81) 76 269 7500
Web Site: www.adk.jp
S.I.C.: 7311
N.A.I.C.S.: 541810
Koichiro Naganuma *(Pres & Group CEO)*

Asatsu-DK Incorporated (1)
3-21 Hanazono
Matsuyama, 790-0005, Japan
Tel.: (81) 89 998 6333
Web Site: www.adk.jp
S.I.C.: 7311
N.A.I.C.S.: 541810
Sameer Ambegaonkar *(Mng Dir)*

Asatsu-DK Incorporated (1)
6 8 Bancho 1 chome
Takamatsu, 760 0017, Japan JP
Tel.: (81) 87 822 5991
Fax: (81) 87 822 8077
Web Site: www.adk.jp
S.I.C.: 7311
N.A.I.C.S.: 541810
Koichiro Naganuma *(Pres)*

Subsidiaries:

ADK Dialog (1)
4th Fl Togeki Bldg
Chuo Ku, Tokyo, 104 0045, Japan
Tel.: (81) 3 3546 9120
Fax: (81) 3 3546 9107
Web Site: www.adk-intl.jp
Emp.: 79
Provider of Marketing Services
S.I.C.: 7389
N.A.I.C.S.: 561499
Takeshi Yamagishi *(Pres & COO)*
Seiji Kazama *(CEO)*

ADK Interactive Inc. (1)
14F ADK Shochiku Square 1-13-1 Tsukiji
Chuo-ku, Tokyo, Japan
Tel.: (81) 3 3547 2780
Fax: (81) 3 3547 2087
Web Site: www.adk-i.jp
Emp.: 80
Online Marketing Services
S.I.C.: 7389
N.A.I.C.S.: 561990
Toshiyuki Inoue *(Chm)*

ADK International (1)
7F Togeki Bldg 1-1 Tsukiji 4-chome
Chuo-ku
Tokyo, 104-0045, Japan
Tel.: (81) 3 3546 9100
Fax: (81) 3 3546 9208
Web Site: www.adk-intl.jp
Emp.: 100
Communication
S.I.C.: 7311
N.A.I.C.S.: 541810
Michael Fujino *(Mng Dir)*

Affiliates:

Kyowa Kikaku Ltd. (1)
1-Gokan Shimbashi-Ekimae Building 20-15
Shimbashi 2-chome
Minato-ku, Tokyo, 105-0004, Japan JP
Tel.: (81) 3 3571 3111
Fax: (81) 3 3571 3314
E-Mail: uketsuke@kk-kyowa.co.jp
Web Site: www.kk-kyowa.co.jp
Emp.: 106
S.I.C.: 7311
N.A.I.C.S.: 541810
Yukio Umeda *(Founder)*
Shogo Sakurai *(Pres)*

U.S. Subsidiary:

ADK America, Inc. (1)
3137 S La Cienega Blvd
Los Angeles, CA 90016 CA
Tel.: (310) 630-3600
Fax: (310) 630-3620
E-Mail: info@adkamerica.com
Web Site: www.adkamerica.com
Billings: $36,000,000
Emp.: 20
Advertising Agency
S.I.C.: 7311
N.A.I.C.S.: 541810
Dwain Taylor *(Pres)*
Marija Kosanovich *(Sr VP-Media & Comm)*

Branch:

ADK America, Inc. - New York Office (2)
515 W 20th St 6th fl
New York, NY 10011
Tel.: (646) 284-9811
Fax: (646) 284-9825
E-Mail: info@adkamerica.com
Web Site: www.adkamerica.com
Emp.: 10
S.I.C.: 7311
N.A.I.C.S.: 541810
Dwain Taylor *(Pres)*
Daniel Yamada *(Sr VP & Dir-Creative)*

Non-U.S. Subsidiaries:

ADK Deutschland GmbH (1)
Waldschmidt Str 19
60316 Frankfurt am Main, Germany
Tel.: (49) 69 9712 08 32
Fax: (49) 69 9712 08 21
E-Mail: info@adk-deutschland.de
Web Site: www.asatsu.de
Emp.: 20
S.I.C.: 7311
N.A.I.C.S.: 541810
Brigitte Danzer *(Office Mgr)*

ADK-FORTUNE PVT. LTD. (1)
B1/B2 Enkay Centre Udyog Vihar Phase-V
Gurgaon, 122016, India
Tel.: (91) 124 453 9723
Web Site: www.adk.jp/english/html/company/oversea.html
Emp.: 25
Advertising Services
S.I.C.: 7311
N.A.I.C.S.: 541810
Hidehito Araki *(CEO & Mng Dir)*

ADK INTEGRA INC (1)
25F Raffles Corporate Center F Ortigas Jr Road Emerald Ave
Pasig, 1605, Philippines
Tel.: (63) 2 914 4297
Fax: (63) 2 914 9001
Web Site: www.adk.jp/english/html/company/oversea.html
Emp.: 80
Advertising Services
S.I.C.: 7319
N.A.I.C.S.: 541890
Richard Yang *(Pres)*

Asatsu Century (Shanghai) Advertising Co.,Ltd. (1)
9F Yongxing Mansion No 887 Huaihai Rd
Shanghai, 200020, China
Tel.: (86) 21 6474 8908
Fax: (86) 21 6474 8909
Web Site: www.adk.jp
S.I.C.: 7311

Asatsu-DK Incorporated—(Continued)

N.A.I.C.S.: 541810

Asatsu-DK Hong Kong Ltd. **(1)**
25F Leighton Centre 77 Leighton Road
Causeway Bay, China (Hong Kong)
Tel.: (852) 2895 8111
Fax: (852) 2576 3322
E-Mail: info@adk.com.hk
Web Site: www.adk.jp
Emp.: 50
S.I.C.: 7311
N.A.I.C.S.: 541810
Yusuf Ismail *(Grp Acct Dir)*

Asatsu-DK Korea Co.,Ltd. **(1)**
7F DaeHeung B/D 4-3 Yangjae-dong
Seocho-gu, Seoul, Korea (South)
Tel.: (82) 2 511 5934
Web Site: www.adk.jp/english/html/company/oversea.html
Advertising Services
S.I.C.: 7319
N.A.I.C.S.: 541890

Asatsu-DK Malaysia Sdn. Bhd. **(1)**
Level 18 Menara Merais No 1 Jalan 19/3
46300 Petaling Jaya, Selangor, Malaysia MY
Tel.: (60) 3 7954 0388
Fax: (60) 3 7954 0266
E-Mail: enquiries@adk.com.my
Web Site: www.adk-asia.com
Emp.: 30
S.I.C.: 7311
N.A.I.C.S.: 541810
Lai Hean Wai *(CFO)*

Asatsu-DK Singapore PTE. LTD. **(1)**
1 Liang Seah St 02-05
Singapore, 189022, Singapore
Tel.: (65) 6333 5115
Fax: (65) 6333 5225
Web Site: www.adk-asia.com
Billings: $23,492,547
Emp.: 60
S.I.C.: 7311
N.A.I.C.S.: 541810
Kazuki Shiobara *(Chm)*
Takamasa Tokumo *(Mng Dir)*

ASATSU-DK VIETNAM INC. **(1)**
28 Nguyen Van Thu St
District 1, Ho Chi Minh City, Vietnam
Tel.: (84) 8 3910 5550
Fax: (84) 8 3910 5551
Emp.: 25
Online Advertising Services
S.I.C.: 7319
N.A.I.C.S.: 541890
Hiromi Kondo *(Mng Dir)*

Asatsu Europe B.V. **(1)**
Emmastraat 36-38
1075 HW Amsterdam, Netherlands
Tel.: (31) 23 5543 530
Fax: (31) 23 5543 553
E-Mail: jong@adk-europe.com
Web Site: www.adk-europe.com
Sales Range: $25-49.9 Million
Emp.: 40
S.I.C.: 7311
N.A.I.C.S.: 541810
Shinya Miyata *(Chm)*
Rob Findlay *(Mng Dir)*

Asatsu (Shanghai) Exposition & Advertising Co., Ltd. **(1)**
23F Jiushifuxing Mansion No 918 Huaihai Road M
Shanghai, 200020, China
Tel.: (86) 21 6415 5881
Online Advertising Services
S.I.C.: 7319
N.A.I.C.S.: 541890

Asatsu (Thailand) Co., LTD. **(1)**
24/F Sirinrat Bldg 3388/86 Rama IV Rd
Klongton Klongtoey, Bangkok, 10110, Thailand TH
Tel.: (66) 2 367 5951
Fax: (66) 2 367 5777
Web Site: www.asatsu.co.th
Emp.: 100
S.I.C.: 7311
N.A.I.C.S.: 541810
Makoto Kawamura *(Chm & CEO)*
Ritsuo Fukazawa *(Pres)*

ASDIK Ltd. **(1)**
6F Shinawatra Tower III 1010 Vibhavadi Rangsit Rd Ladyao
Chatuchak, Bangkok, 10900, Thailand
Tel.: (66) 2 949 2800
Fax: (66) 2 949 2805
Emp.: 100
Advertising Services
S.I.C.: 7319
N.A.I.C.S.: 541890
Keiki Okamoto *(Gen Mgr)*

Beijing Asatsu Advertising Co., Ltd. **(1)**
C-3 Huitong Office Park No. 71 Jianguo Road
Chaoyang District, Beijing, 100025, China CN
Tel.: (86) 10 8599 7788
Fax: (86) 10 8599 7579
Web Site: www.adk.jp
S.I.C.: 7311
N.A.I.C.S.: 541810

Beijing DongFang SanMeng Public Relations Consulting Co., Ltd. **(1)**
Room 1205 Yongxing Mansion No 887 Huaihai Road M
Shanghai, 200020, China
Tel.: (86) 21 6433 9623
Public Relation Consulting Services
S.I.C.: 8743
N.A.I.C.S.: 541820

Beijing Huawen-Asatsu International Advertising Co., Ltd **(1)**
25F Block Winterless Center No 1 West Dawang Road
Chao Yang District, Beijing, 100016, China CN
Tel.: (86) 10 5870 3636
Fax: (86) 10 5870 3628
E-Mail: huawen-adk@adk-bj.com.cn
Web Site: www.adk-bj.com.cn
S.I.C.: 7311
N.A.I.C.S.: 541810
Ono Aiko *(Mng Dir)*

Dai-Ichi Kikaku (Malaysia) Sdn. Bhd. **(1)**
C-13A-3A Dataran 3 Two No 2 Jalan 19/1
46300 Petaling Jaya, Selangor, Malaysia
Tel.: (60) 3 7960 8106
Fax: (60) 3 7960 8103
Online Advertising Services
S.I.C.: 5961
N.A.I.C.S.: 454111

DAI-ICHI KIKAKU (THAILAND) CO., LTD **(1)**
23F Shinawatra Tower III 1010 Vibhavadi Rangsit Rd Ladyao
Chatuchak, Bangkok, 10900, Thailand
Tel.: (66) 2 949 2700
Fax: (66) 2 949 2777
Online Advertising Services
S.I.C.: 7319
N.A.I.C.S.: 541890

DIK-Ocean Advertising Co., Ltd. **(1)**
13F No 287 Nanking East Rd Sec 3
Taipei, 105, Taiwan TW
Tel.: (886) 2 8712 8555
Fax: (886) 2 8712 9555
Web Site: www.adk.com.tw
Emp.: 100
S.I.C.: 7311
N.A.I.C.S.: 541810
Lin Chan *(Mng Dir)*

DK ADVERTISING (HK) LTD **(1)**
25F Leighton Centre 77 Leighton Road
Causeway Bay, China (Hong Kong)
Tel.: (852) 2811 9999
Fax: (852) 2811 9699
Web Site: www.adk.jp/english/html/company/oversea.html
Online Advertising Services
S.I.C.: 7319
N.A.I.C.S.: 541890

Guangdong Guangxu (Asatsu) Advertising Co., Ltd. **(1)**
26F Telecom Phong Shan Er Road
Guangzhou, 510081, China CN
Tel.: (86) 20 8888 9818
Web Site: www.adk.jp
S.I.C.: 7311
N.A.I.C.S.: 541810

IMMG Pte Ltd. **(1)**
213 Henderson Industrial Road 01-09
Henderson Industrial Park
Singapore, 1595535, Singapore
Tel.: (65) 6376 5088
Fax: (65) 6375 2029
Advertising Services
S.I.C.: 7319
N.A.I.C.S.: 541890

KNOTs Research B.V. **(1)**
Neptunusstraat 31
2132 JA Hoofddorp, Netherlands
Tel.: (31) 23 554 3554
Fax: (31) 23 554 3553
E-Mail: info@knotsresearch.com
Web Site: www.knotsresearch.com
Emp.: 30
Online Marketing Services
S.I.C.: 8742
N.A.I.C.S.: 541613
Nimrod Moyal *(Co-Founder & Mng Dir)*

PT. Asta Atria Surya **(1)**
Wisma Slipi Lantai 11 Jl Let Jend S Parman Kav 12
Jakarta, 11480, Indonesia
Tel.: (62) 21 530 7155
Fax: (62) 21 530 7156
Web Site: www.adk.jp/english/html/company/oversea.html
Advertising Services
S.I.C.: 7311
N.A.I.C.S.: 541810

Scoop AD WORLD Pte Ltd. **(1)**
1 Liang Seah Street 02-06
Singapore, 189022, Singapore
Tel.: (65) 6336 2346
Fax: (65) 6333 5225
Web Site: www.adk.jp
Emp.: 60
Advertising Services
S.I.C.: 7319
N.A.I.C.S.: 541890

Shanghai Asatsu Advertising Co., Ltd. **(1)**
10F Yongxing Mansion No 887 Huaihai Zhong Lu
Shanghai, 200020, China CN
Tel.: (86) 21 6467 4118
Fax: (86) 21 6474 7803
Web Site: www.adk.jp
S.I.C.: 7311
N.A.I.C.S.: 541810
Daisy Gu *(Dir-Art)*

Shanghai Dai-Ichi Kikaku Fortune Advertising Co., Ltd. **(1)**
9F Yongxing Mansion No 887 Huaihai Zhong Lu
Shanghai, 200020, China
Tel.: (86) 21 6474 8908
Fax: (86) 21 6474 8909
Web Site: www.adk.jp
Billings: $2,593,210
S.I.C.: 7311
N.A.I.C.S.: 541810
Han Jinke *(Gen Mgr)*

SOL Advertising Company **(1)**
28 Nguyen Van Thu St
District 1, Ho Chi Minh City, Vietnam
Tel.: (84) 8 3910 5550
Fax: (84) 8 3910 5551
Emp.: 25
Advertising Services
S.I.C.: 7319
N.A.I.C.S.: 541890
Hiromi Kondo *(Mng Dir)*

Tiexu Advertising Co., Ltd. **(1)**
18F Golden Land Building No 32 Liangmaqiao Road
Chaoyang District, Beijing, 100016, China
Tel.: (86) 10 6464 2122
Online Advertising Services
S.I.C.: 7319
N.A.I.C.S.: 541890

United Asatsu International Ltd. **(1)**
13F No 287 Nanking East Road Sec 3
Taipei, 105, Taiwan TW
Tel.: (886) 2 8712 8555
Fax: (886) 2 8712 9555
Web Site: www.adk.com.tw
Emp.: 75
S.I.C.: 7311
N.A.I.C.S.: 541810

Huang Yves *(Pres)*

ASB CAPITAL INC.

3357 Queens Street
Vancouver, BC, V5R 4T7, Canada
Tel.: (604) 432-1267
E-Mail: bt35@hotmail.com
Year Founded: 2011
ASB.P—(TSXV)

Business Description:
Investment Services
S.I.C.: 6211
N.A.I.C.S.: 523999

Personnel:
Terry Tang *(Pres, CEO & Sec)*
Matthew Kavanagh *(CFO)*

Board of Directors:
Nathan Eric Fier
Matthew Kavanagh
Ian Mallmann
Terry Tang

Transfer Agent:
Computershare Investor Services Inc.
510 Burrard St
Vancouver, BC, V6C 3B9, Canada

ASBISC ENTERPRISES PLC

43 Kolonakiou Street Diamond Court
Ayios Athanasios
4103 Limassol, Cyprus
Tel.: (357) 25857101
Fax: (357) 25857288
Web Site: www.asbis.com
ASB—(WAR)
Rev.: $1,744,877,804
Assets: $506,713,418
Liabilities: $403,628,271
Net Worth: $103,085,147
Earnings: $9,047,037
Emp.: 1,407
Fiscal Year-end: 12/31/12

Business Description:
Computer Peripheral Equipments Distr
S.I.C.: 5045
N.A.I.C.S.: 423430

Personnel:
Siarhei Kostevitch *(Chm & CEO)*
Marios Christou *(CFO)*
Laurent Journoud *(Exec VP-New Bus Dev)*

Board of Directors:
Siarhei Kostevitch
Marios Christou
Laurent Journoud
Efstathios Papadakis
Chris Pavlou
Constantinos Tziamalis

Legal Counsel:
Costas Tsirides & Co
Grivas Digenis Avenue Panagides Building 2nd Floor
CY-3305 Limassol, Cyprus

Subsidiaries:

ASBIS KYPROS LTD **(1)**
51B Stygos Street
Lemesos, CY-3117, Cyprus
Tel.: (357) 25828241
Fax: (357) 25 322 432
E-Mail: info@asbis.com.cy
Web Site: www.asbis.com.cy
Emp.: 20
Computer Peripheral Equipments & Software Distr
S.I.C.: 5045
N.A.I.C.S.: 423430
Stelios Hadjiionas *(Gen Mgr)*

Prestigio Plaza Ltd. **(1)**
Academias 26
4043 Limassol, Cyprus
Tel.: (357) 70006011
Fax: (357) 25327100
E-Mail: info@prestigioplaza.com
Web Site: www.prestigioplaza.com
Emp.: 2
Online Trading Services

S.I.C.: 5961
N.A.I.C.S.: 454111
Anthony Loukos *(Mgr-Sls)*

Non-U.S. Subsidiary:

Prestigio Europe spol. s.r.o. (2)
Na Dlouhem 79
Jazlovice, 251 01 Ricany, Czech Republic
Tel.: (420) 227186003
E-Mail: info@prestigio.com
Web Site: www.prestigio.cz
Emp.: 10
Computer Peripheral Equipments & Software Distr
S.I.C.: 5045
N.A.I.C.S.: 423430
Martin Zeman *(Gen Mgr)*

Non-U.S. Subsidiaries:

ASBIS-Baltik AS (1)
Luha 34
Tallinn, Harju, 10113, Estonia
Tel.: (372) 6407130
Fax: (372) 6407129
E-Mail: sales@asbis.ee
Web Site: www.asbis.ee
Emp.: 9
Computer Peripheral Equipments & Software Distr
S.I.C.: 5045
N.A.I.C.S.: 423430
Marina Bukovskaja *(CFO)*

ASBIS CZ, spol. s r.o. (1)
Obchodni 103 251 52 Cestilice Praha-vychod
Prague, Czech Republic
Tel.: (420) 2 72 117 111
Fax: (420) 2 72 117 316
E-Mail: info@asbis.cz
Web Site: www.asbis.cz
Computer Peripheral & Software Distr
S.I.C.: 5045
N.A.I.C.S.: 423430

ASBIS D.O.O. (1)
Milutina Milankovica 9G
11070 Belgrade, Serbia
Tel.: (381) 113107700
Fax: (381) 113107710
E-Mail: infosales@asbis.rs
Web Site: www.asbis.rs
Emp.: 30
Computer Peripheral Equipments & Software Distr
S.I.C.: 5045
N.A.I.C.S.: 423430
Ivan Pavlovic *(Dir-Sls)*

ASBIS Europe BV (1)
Haarstraat 27
4201 JA Gorinchem, South Holland, Netherlands
Tel.: (31) 183610190
Fax: (31) 183610199
E-Mail: info@canyon-ch.com
Web Site: www.canyon-ch.com
Emp.: 10
Computer Peripheral & Software Distr
S.I.C.: 5045
N.A.I.C.S.: 423430

ASBIS HUNGARY COMMERCIAL LTD (1)
Vaci Boulevard 81-85
1139 Budapest, Hungary
Tel.: (36) 12361000
Fax: (36) 12361010
E-Mail: infosales@asbis.hu
Emp.: 30
Computer Peripheral & Software Distr
S.I.C.: 5045
N.A.I.C.S.: 423430
Andrez Velsko *(Gen Mgr)*

ASBIS Kazakhstan LLP (1)
8 Nauryzbai Batyra str
050004 Almaty, Kazakhstan
Tel.: (7) 7272959300
Fax: (7) 727 295 93 01
E-Mail: info@asbis.kz
Web Site: www.asbis.kz
Emp.: 25
Computer Peripheral Equipments & Software Distr
S.I.C.: 5045
N.A.I.C.S.: 423430
Igor Golovkin *(Gen Dir)*

ASBIS Ltd. (1)
Gostinichnaya str 4/9
Moscow, 127106, Russia
Tel.: (7) 4957750641
Fax: (7) 4957750641
E-Mail: sales@asbis.ru
Web Site: www.asbis.ru
Computer Peripheral & Software Distr
S.I.C.: 5045
N.A.I.C.S.: 423430

ASBIS LIMITED (1)
Unit 1a Knock Airport Business Park
Knock Airport, Charlestown, Connacht, Ireland
Tel.: (353) 949370010
Fax: (353) 949370011
E-Mail: infosales@asbis.ie
Web Site: www.asbis.ie
Emp.: 30
Computer Peripheral Equipments & Software Distr
S.I.C.: 5045
N.A.I.C.S.: 423430
Una Boyle *(Mgr-Fin)*

ASBIS LV SIA (1)
Bauskas iela 20
LV-1004 Riga, Latvia
Tel.: (371) 67892574
Fax: (371) 67892572
E-Mail: office@asbis.lv
Web Site: www.asbis.lv
Emp.: 20
Computer Peripheral Equipments & Software Distr
S.I.C.: 5044
N.A.I.C.S.: 423420

ASBIS ME FZE (1)
PO Box 17706
Jebel Ali S S10715, Dubai, United Arab Emirates
Tel.: (971) 48863850
Fax: (971) 48857543
E-Mail: info@asbisme.ae
Web Site: www.asbisme.ae
Emp.: 60
Computer Peripheral Equipments & Software Distr
S.I.C.: 5045
N.A.I.C.S.: 423430
Yuri Cherkas *(Gen Mgr)*

Non-U.S. Subsidiary:

ASBIS TR BILGISAYAR LIMITED SIRKETI (2)
Barbaros Mah Evren Caddesi No 56 Kat 1
Yenisahra, 34746 Istanbul, Turkey
Tel.: (90) 2164707440
Fax: (90) 2164707458
E-Mail: office@asbis.com.tr
Web Site: www.asbis.com.tr
Emp.: 20
Computer Peripheral Equipments & Software Distr
S.I.C.: 5045
N.A.I.C.S.: 423430

ASBIS PL SP.Z O.O. (1)
Platan Park II Ul Poleczki 23
02-822 Warsaw, Poland
Tel.: (48) 223371510
Fax: (48) 223371599
E-Mail: welcome@asbispl.pl
Web Site: www.asbis.pl
Emp.: 50
Computer Peripheral & Software Distr
S.I.C.: 5045
N.A.I.C.S.: 423430
Przemyslaw Wierzbicki *(Dir-Sls)*

ASBIS UKRAINE LTD. (1)
30 Gazovaja St
Kiev, 03061, Ukraine
Tel.: (380) 444554411
Fax: (380) 444554410
E-Mail: market@asbis.com.ua
Web Site: www.asbis.ua
Emp.: 50
Computer Peripheral Equipments & Software Distr
S.I.C.: 5045
N.A.I.C.S.: 423430
Viktor Poberezhnik *(Gen Mgr)*

ASBIS VILNIUS UAB (1)
Ateities G 25 B
06326 Vilnius, Lithuania
Tel.: (370) 5 259 5610
Fax: (370) 5 246 1326
E-Mail: info@asbis.lt
Web Site: www.asbis.lt
Computer Peripheral Equipment & Software Distr
S.I.C.: 5045
N.A.I.C.S.: 423430
Sam Kancleriene *(Mgr-Mktg)*

ASBISc-CR d.o.o. (1)
Slavonska avenija 24/6 1 Kat
10000 Zagreb, Croatia
Tel.: (385) 16009900
Fax: (385) 16009988
E-Mail: asbis@asbis.hr
Web Site: www.asbis.hr
Emp.: 50
Computer Peripheral & Software Distr
S.I.C.: 5045
N.A.I.C.S.: 423430
Ozrenka Gacesa *(Mgr-Sls)*

Megatrend d.o.o. Sarajevo (1)
Dzemala Bijedica 162
Sarajevo, 71000, Bosnia & Herzegovina
Tel.: (387) 33770200
Fax: (387) 33770220
E-Mail: info@megatrend.ba
Web Site: www.megatrend.ba
Emp.: 20
Computer Peripheral Equipments & Software Distr
S.I.C.: 5045
N.A.I.C.S.: 423430
Adnan Bajramovic *(Gen Mgr)*

ASC PTY LTD

694 Mersey Road North
Osborne, SA, 5017, Australia
Mailing Address:
GPO Box 2472
Adelaide, SA, 5001, Australia
Tel.: (61) 883487000
Fax: (61) 883487001
E-Mail: reach@asc.com.au
Web Site: www.asc.com.au
Year Founded: 1985
Rev.: $959,320,787
Assets: $645,731,012
Liabilities: $401,265,816
Net Worth: $244,465,197
Earnings: $10,277,190
Emp.: 2,400
Fiscal Year-end: 06/30/13

Business Description:
Naval Ships & Submarine Building
S.I.C.: 3731
N.A.I.C.S.: 336611

Personnel:
Bruce Carter *(Chm)*
Stephen Ludlam *(CEO & Mng Dir)*
John Harris *(CFO & Exec Gen Mgr-Performance)*
Wendy Hoad *(Gen Counsel & Sec)*

Board of Directors:
Bruce Carter
Rosalind Dubs
Kathy Hirschfeld
Stephen Ludlam
Jack O'Connell
Sally Pitkin

ASC TELECOM AG

Seibelstrasse 2 4
63768 Hosbach, Germany
Tel.: (49) 602150010
Fax: (49) 60215001310
E-Mail: hq@asctelecom.com
Web Site: www.asctelecom.com
Year Founded: 1964
Rev.: $35,048,970
Emp.: 131

Business Description:
Software Solution Service
S.I.C.: 7371
N.A.I.C.S.: 541511

Personnel:
Guenther Mueller *(Chm)*
Frank Schaffrath *(CEO)*
Marco Mueller *(Exec VP)*

ASCENCIA LIMITED

5th Floor Rogers House 5 President John Kennedy Street
Port Louis, Mauritius
Tel.: (230) 202 6500
Fax: (230) 213 1097
E-Mail: contact@ascencia-propertyfund.com
Web Site: www.ascencia-propertyfund.com
Year Founded: 2007
ASCE—(MAU)
Rev.: $7,435,667
Assets: $80,754,631
Liabilities: $20,478,507
Net Worth: $60,276,124
Earnings: $6,113,506
Fiscal Year-end: 09/30/12

Business Description:
Real Estate Development Services
S.I.C.: 6531
N.A.I.C.S.: 531390

Personnel:
Tioumitra Maharahaje *(Sec)*

Board of Directors:
Philippe Espitalier-Noel
Marc Ah Ching
Ziyad Bundhun
Gilbert Espitalier-Noel
Dominique Galea
Sanjiv Mihdidin

Transfer Agent:
MCB Registry & Securities Ltd
Raymond Lamusse Building 9-11 Sir William Newton Street
Port Louis, Mauritius

ASCENCIO S.A.

Avenue Jean Mermoz 1 Batiment H Boite 4
6041 Gosselies, Belgium
Tel.: (32) 71919500
Fax: (32) 71344896
E-Mail: info@ascencio.be
Web Site: www.ascencio.be
ASC—(EUR)
Sales Range: $10-24.9 Million
Emp.: 8

Business Description:
Real Estate Investment Services
S.I.C.: 6726
N.A.I.C.S.: 525990

Personnel:
Carl Mestdagh *(Pres)*

Subsidiary:

Etudibel S.A. (1)
Ave Jean Mermoz 1b4
6041 Gosselies, Belgium
Tel.: (32) 71919500
Fax: (32) 71344896
Emp.: 30
Real Estate Investment Services
S.I.C.: 6531
N.A.I.C.S.: 531390
Marc Baresack *(Mng Dir)*

ASCENDANT GROUP LIMITED

27 Serpentine Road
Pembroke, HM 07, Bermuda
Mailing Address:
PO Box HM 3392
Hamilton, HM PX, Bermuda
Tel.: (441) 2986100
Fax: (441) 2928975
E-Mail: info@ascendant.bm
Web Site: www.ascendantgroup.bm
Year Founded: 1995
AGL—(BERM)
Rev.: $263,321,371
Assets: $414,020,567
Liabilities: $86,109,391
Net Worth: $327,911,176
Earnings: $11,531,364
Emp.: 350
Fiscal Year-end: 12/31/12

Ascendant Group Limited—(Continued)

Business Description:
Holding Company; Electric Power Generation & Energy Distribution Services
S.I.C.: 6719
N.A.I.C.S.: 551112

Personnel:
Reginald S. Minors *(Chm)*
Peter C. Durhager *(Deputy Chm)*
Walter M. Higgins, III *(Pres & CEO)*
Christopher A. Coelho *(CFO & Sr VP)*
Denton E. Williams *(COO-Bermuda Electric Light Company Limited & Sr VP)*
Cheryl-Ann Mapp *(Gen Counsel & Sec)*
Abayomi Carmichael *(Treas)*
William C. DeSilva *(Exec VP)*
Jennifer Smatt Adkins *(Sr VP-HR)*
Linda C. Smith *(Sr VP-Corp Relations)*

Board of Directors:
Reginald S. Minors
Gavin R. Arton
James B. Butterfield
A. David Dodwell
Peter C. Durhager
Walter M. Higgins, III
L. A. Joaquin
Stanley A. Oliver
Donna L. Pearman
Michael L. Schrum
Richard D. Spurling
Wilbert N. E. Warner
W. Edward Williams

Legal Counsel:
Marshall Diel & Myers
Hamilton, Bermuda

Conyers, Dill & Pearman
Hamilton, Bermuda

Appleby (Bermuda) Limited
Hamilton, Bermuda

Subsidiaries:

Bermuda Electric Light Company Limited (1)
27 Serpentine Road
Pembroke, HM 07, Bermuda BM
Mailing Address: (100%)
PO Box HM 1026
Hamilton, HM DX, Bermuda
Tel.: (441) 295-5111
Fax: (441) 292-8975
E-Mail: info@belco.com
Web Site: www.belco.bm
Electric Power Distribution
S.I.C.: 4931
N.A.I.C.S.: 221122
Walter Higgins *(Pres & CEO)*

Subsidiary:

BELCO Properties Limited (2)
PO Box HM 1026
Hamilton, Bermuda (100%)
Tel.: (441) 2955111
Fax: (441) 2928975
E-Mail: info@belco.bhl.bm
Web Site: www.belcoholdings.bm/belco/contact-us.html
Residential Property Managers
S.I.C.: 6531
N.A.I.C.S.: 531311
Garry Madeiros *(CEO)*
Christopher A. Coelho *(Sr VP-Fin & Admin)*
Robert B. Steynor *(Sr VP-Ops)*

Bermuda Gas & Utility Company Limited (1)
25 Serpentine Rd
Pembroke, HM 11, Bermuda (100%)
Mailing Address:
PO Box HM 373
Hamilton, HM BX, Bermuda
Tel.: (441) 295 3111
Fax: (441) 295 8311
E-Mail: info@bermudagas.bm
Web Site: www.bermudagas.bm
Emp.: 45
Natural Gas Distribution
S.I.C.: 4924
N.A.I.C.S.: 221210
Judith Uddin *(Gen Mgr)*

BTS Limited (1)
PO Box 1026
HM DX Hamilton, Bermuda
Tel.: (441) 295 5111
Fax: (441) 292 8975
Investment Management Services
S.I.C.: 8741
N.A.I.C.S.: 551114

PureNERGY Renewables, Ltd (1)
25 Serpentine Road
Pembroke, HM 07, Bermuda
Tel.: (441) 2992808
Fax: (441) 2952577
E-Mail: info@purenergy.bm
Web Site: www.purenergy.bm
Emp.: 4
Wind Turbine Mfr
S.I.C.: 3511
N.A.I.C.S.: 333611
Kevon Makell *(VP & Gen Mgr)*

ASCENDAS HOSPITALITY TRUST

61 Science Park Road #04-01 The Galen
Singapore Science Park II, Singapore, 117525, Singapore
Tel.: (65) 6508 4939
Web Site: www.a-htrust.com
Q1P—(SES)

Business Description:
Real Estate Investment Trust
S.I.C.: 6726
N.A.I.C.S.: 525990

Personnel:
Neo Chian Lim *(Chm)*
Juay Hiang Tan *(CEO)*
Susana San San Lim *(CFO)*

Board of Directors:
Neo Chian Lim
Nam Toon Chia
Siak Ching Chong
Steven Kian Koon Choo
Kim Wai Ho
Michael Issenberg
Benson Tuan Soon Puah
Chong Huat Tan
Juay Hiang Tan

Transfer Agent:
Boardroom Corporate & Advisory Services Pte. Ltd.
50 Raffles Place 32-01 Singapore Land Tower
Singapore, Singapore

ASCENDAS INDIA TRUST

61 Science Park Road 04-01 The Galen
Singapore Science Park II, Singapore, 117525, Singapore
Tel.: (65) 6774 1033
Fax: (65) 6774 9563
Web Site: www.a-itrust.com
Year Founded: 2007
CY6U—(OTC SES)
Rev.: $102,235,055
Assets: $862,192,606
Liabilities: $337,035,777
Net Worth: $525,156,829
Earnings: $36,668,788
Fiscal Year-end: 03/31/13

Business Description:
Real Estate Investment Services
S.I.C.: 6211
N.A.I.C.S.: 523999

Personnel:
Jonathan Neng Tong Yap *(CEO)*
Arthur Meng Teck Tan *(CFO)*
Thomas Teo *(Chief Real Estate Dev Officer)*
Fu Nyap Lee *(CEO-India)*
Mary Judith De Souza *(Co-Sec)*
Edwin Wee Tack Kung *(Co-Sec)*

ASCENT RESOURCES PLC

5 Charterhouse Square
London, EC1M 6EE, United Kingdom
Tel.: (44) 2072514905
Fax: (44) 2076812680
E-Mail: info3@ascentresources.co.uk
Web Site: www.ascentresources.co.uk
AST—(LSE)
Rev.: $2,659,524
Assets: $58,256,850
Liabilities: $16,329,859
Net Worth: $41,926,991
Earnings: ($9,513,643)
Emp.: 11
Fiscal Year-end: 12/31/12

Business Description:
Oil & Gas Industry
S.I.C.: 1311
N.A.I.C.S.: 211111

Personnel:
Leonard John Reece *(CEO)*
John Bottomley *(Sec)*

Board of Directors:
Clive Nathan Carver
Cameron Davies
Nigel Moore
Leonard John Reece

Legal Counsel:
Taylor Wessing LLP
5 New Street Square
London, United Kingdom

SGH Martineau LLP
One America Square Crosswall
London, EC3N 2SG, United Kingdom

ASCIANO LIMITED

Level 4/476 St Kilda Road
Melbourne, VIC, 3004, Australia
Tel.: (61) 2 8484 8000
Fax: (61) 2 8484 8154
E-Mail: info@asciano.com.au
Web Site: www.asciano.com.au
AIO—(ASX)
Rev.: $3,843,473,220
Assets: $7,964,874,510
Liabilities: $4,177,049,430
Net Worth: $3,787,825,080
Earnings: $356,710,830
Emp.: 8,891
Fiscal Year-end: 06/30/13

Business Description:
Ports & Rail Assets Management
S.I.C.: 4111
N.A.I.C.S.: 485112

Personnel:
John Mullen *(CEO & Mng Dir)*
Roger Burrows *(CFO)*
Saul Cannon *(Gen Counsel & Dir-Comml & Legal)*
Fiona Mead *(Sec)*

Board of Directors:
Malcolm W. Broomhead
Chris Barlow
Robert John Edgar
Peter George
Shirley In't Veld
Geoff Kleemann
John Mullen
Ralph Graham Waters

Subsidiary:

Pacific National Pty. Ltd. (1)
Level 6 15 Blue St
15 Blue St, North Sydney, NSW, 2060, Australia
Tel.: (61) 284848000
Fax: (61) 284848154
Web Site: www.pacificnational.com.au
Sales Range: $25-49.9 Million
Emp.: 100
Short Line Railroad
S.I.C.: 4013
N.A.I.C.S.: 482112

Non-U.S. Joint Venture:

C3 Limited (1)
Maritime House 10 Rata Street
Mount Maunganui, 12501 Tauranga, New Zealand
Tel.: (64) 75728972
Fax: (64) 75728933
E-Mail: solutions@c3.co.nz
Web Site: www.c3.co.nz
Emp.: 600
Marine Cargo Handling
S.I.C.: 4491
N.A.I.C.S.: 488320
Dean Camplin *(CEO)*
Joe Culling *(CFO)*

ASCO CONSTRUCTION LTD.

381 County Rd 17
Hawkesbury, ON, K6A 2R2, Canada
Tel.: (613) 632-0121
Fax: (613) 632-5244
Web Site: www.ascoconstruction.com
Year Founded: 1988
Rev.: $22,833,381
Emp.: 23

Business Description:
Architectural & Construction Services
S.I.C.: 8711
N.A.I.C.S.: 541330

Personnel:
Anthony Assaly *(Pres)*

ASCO INDUSTRIES NV

Weiveldlaan 2
B-1930 Zaventem, Belgium
Tel.: (32) 27160611
Fax: (32) 27160770
E-Mail: asco@asco.be
Web Site: www.asco.be
Emp.: 705

Business Description:
Slat Actuation Systems Mfr
S.I.C.: 3728
N.A.I.C.S.: 336413

Personnel:
Emile Boas *(Founder)*
Christian Boas *(CEO)*
Go Maes *(CFO)*
Tack Louis *(COO)*

Board of Directors:
Christian Boas
Guy de Marnix
Trudo Motmans
Andree Vangeyte
Francis Vermeiren

U.S. Subsidiary:

ASCO Aerospace USA, LLC (1)
3003 N Perkins Rd
Stillwater, OK 74075
Tel.: (405) 533-5800
Fax: (405) 533-5805
E-Mail: info@ascoaerospaceusa.com
Emp.: 13
Aerospace Equipment Mfr
S.I.C.: 3728
N.A.I.C.S.: 336413
Joe Payne *(Mgr-Trng & Recruiting)*

Non-U.S. Subsidiaries:

ASCO Aerospace Canada Ltd. (1)
8510 River Road
Delta, BC, V4G 1B5, Canada
Tel.: (604) 946-4900
Fax: (604) 946-4671
Aerospace Equipment Mfr
S.I.C.: 3728
N.A.I.C.S.: 336413

ASCO Aerospace do Brasil (1)
Avenida Dr Nelson D Avila 389-Sala 71B Centro
Sao Jose dos Campos, Brazil 12 3204 6632
Tel.: (55) 12 3204 6632
Aerospace Equipment Mfr
S.I.C.: 3728
N.A.I.C.S.: 336413

ASCO Deutschland GmbH (1)
Otto-Mueller Strasse 55
63688 Gedern, Oberhessen, Germany
Tel.: (49) 6045 9612 0
Fax: (49) 6045 9612 20
E-Mail: info@ascodeutschland.de
Emp.: 200
Aerospace Equipment Mfr
S.I.C.: 3728
N.A.I.C.S.: 336413
Kissel Holger *(Sr Program Mgr)*

ASCOM HOLDING AG

(d/b/a Ascom Group)
Belpstrasse 37
CH 3000 Bern, 14, Switzerland
Tel.: (41) 448231369
Fax: (41) 448231321
E-Mail: ask-ascom@ascom.ch
Web Site: www.ascom.com
Year Founded: 1987
ASCN—(SWX)
Rev.: $485,478,136
Assets: $560,275,012
Liabilities: $318,831,128
Net Worth: $241,443,884
Earnings: $18,996,032
Emp.: 1,771
Fiscal Year-end: 12/31/12

Business Description:
Communications Holding Company
Import Export
S.I.C.: 6719
N.A.I.C.S.: 551112

Personnel:
Juhani Anttila *(Chm)*
Paul E. Otth *(Vice Chm)*
Fritz Mumenthaler *(CEO & Member-Exec Bd)*
Bianka Wilson *(CFO)*
Daniel Lack *(Chief Comm Officer & Gen Sec)*
Rikard Lundqvist *(Member-Exec Bd & Gen Mgr-Network Testing)*
Claes Odman *(Member-Exec Bd & Gen Mgr-Wireless Solutions)*
Judith Bischof *(Gen Counsel)*
Kurt Renggli *(Sr VP-HR)*

Board of Directors:
Juhani Anttila
J. T. Bergqvist
Cornelia Gehrig
Kenth-Ake Jonsson
Paul E. Otth
Andreas Vicente Umbach

Subsidiary:

Ascom (Schweiz) AG (1)
Stettbachstrasse 6
8600 Dubendorf, Switzerland (100%)
Tel.: (41) 319991111
Fax: (41) 319992300
E-Mail: ask-ascom@ascom.com
Web Site: www.ascom.ch
Emp.: 100
Communications Equipment
S.I.C.: 3669
N.A.I.C.S.: 334290
Riet Cadonau *(CEO)*

Subsidiaries:

Ascom Immobilien AG (2)
Belpstrasse 37
3000 Bern, 14, Switzerland (100%)
Tel.: (41) 319991111
Fax: (41) 313829142
E-Mail: ascom@ascom.ch
Web Site: www.ascom.ch
Emp.: 30
Communications Equipment
S.I.C.: 3669
N.A.I.C.S.: 334290
Riet Cadonau *(CEO)*

Ascom Network Testing AG (2)
Glutz Blotzheim Strasse 1 3
CH 4503 Solothurn, Switzerland CH
Tel.: (41) 326242121 (100%)
Fax: (41) 326242143
E-Mail: ask-ascom@ascom.ch
Web Site: www.ascom.ch
Emp.: 200
Communications Network Testing Services
S.I.C.: 7389
N.A.I.C.S.: 541990
Rikard Lundqvist *(Gen Mgr)*

Ascom Security Solutions AG (2)
Jewerbe Park
Postfach 500
CH 5506 Magenwil, Switzerland CH
Tel.: (41) 628895901 (100%)
Fax: (41) 628895990
Web Site: www.ascom.ch
Emp.: 50
Telephone Handsets & Military Radio Equipment Development & Mfr
S.I.C.: 3663
N.A.I.C.S.: 334220

Ascom Systec AG (2)
Gewerbepark
Hintermaettlistrasse, 5506 Magenwil, Switzerland CH
Tel.: (41) 628895281 (100%)
Fax: (41) 319991111
E-Mail: ask-ascom@ascom.ch
Web Site: www.ascom.ch
Emp.: 2,500
S.I.C.: 3669
N.A.I.C.S.: 334290

U.S. Subsidiary:

Ascom (US) Inc. (1)
598 Airport Blvd Ste 300
Morrisville, NC 27560
Tel.: (919) 234-2500
Fax: (919) 234-2526
Toll Free: (877) 712-7266
E-Mail: info@ascomwireless.com
Web Site: www.ascom.us
Emp.: 130
Wireless Communications for Hospitals, Manufacturing Industry, Retail & Hotels
S.I.C.: 4812
N.A.I.C.S.: 517210
Chad West *(Pres & CEO)*
Tom McKearney *(Exec VP-Mktg & Bus Dev)*

Non-U.S. Subsidiaries:

Ascom B.V. (1)
Savannaweg 31
3542 AW Utrecht, Netherlands (100%)
Tel.: (31) 302409100
Fax: (31) 302411946
E-Mail: info@ascom.nl
Web Site: www.ascom.nl
Emp.: 350
S.I.C.: 3669
N.A.I.C.S.: 334290
Co Honhout *(Mng Dir)*

Subsidiary:

Ascom (Nederland) BV (2)
Savannahweg 31
Postbus 40242
3504 AA Utrecht, Netherlands
Tel.: (31) 30 240 91 00
Fax: (31) 30 241 19 46
E-Mail: info@ascom.nl
Web Site: www.ascom.nl
Emp.: 33
Telecommunications Peripherals Distr
S.I.C.: 4899
N.A.I.C.S.: 517919
Jacques Van Zyl *(Gen Mgr)*

Subsidiaries:

Ascom Tateco BV (3)
Savannahweg 31
Postbus 40242
3504 AA Utrecht, Netherlands
Tel.: (31) 30 240 91 00
Fax: (31) 302409146
E-Mail: info@ascom.nl
Web Site: www.ascom.nl
Emp.: 33
Radio Communications Equipment & Systems Mfr
S.I.C.: 4832
N.A.I.C.S.: 515111
Potos Janos *(Mng Dir)*

Mocsa Real Estate BV (3)
Savannahweg 31
Postbus 40242
Utrecht, 3542 AW, Netherlands
Tel.: (31) 30 2409100
Fax: (31) 30 2409290
Real Estate Development Services
S.I.C.: 6531
N.A.I.C.S.: 531390

TPA Traffic & Parking Automation Systems (3)
Blankenweg 22
6827 BW Arnhem, Netherlands (100%)
Tel.: (31) 263553535
Fax: (31) 263553533
E-Mail: info@tpa.nl
Web Site: www.tpa.nl
Emp.: 70
S.I.C.: 3669
N.A.I.C.S.: 334290

Non-U.S. Subsidiary:

Ascom (Belgium) NV (2)
Raketstraat 64
1130 Brussels, Belgium BE
Tel.: (32) 27271311 (100%)
Fax: (32) 27271300
E-Mail: info@ascom.be
Web Site: www.ascom.be
Emp.: 160
Mission-Critical Communications Solutions
S.I.C.: 3669
N.A.I.C.S.: 334290

Ascom Colombia S.A. (1)
Apartado Aereo 8539 Calle 37 No 20 51
Bogota, Colombia Co
Tel.: (57) 3239390 (100%)
Fax: (57) 12886251
E-Mail: info@ascom.com.co
Web Site: www.ascom.com.co
Emp.: 50
S.I.C.: 3669
N.A.I.C.S.: 334290

Ascom de Mexico S.A. (1)
Kansas 38 Col Napoles
03810 Mexico, DF, Mexico (99%)
Tel.: (52) 5556823333
Fax: (52) 5556821716
E-Mail: ascommex@data.net.mx
Web Site: www.ascom.com.mx
Sales Range: $25-49.9 Million
Emp.: 30
Communications Holding Company
S.I.C.: 3669
N.A.I.C.S.: 334290

Ascom Denmark A/S (1)
Mavrland 3
2600 Glostrup, Denmark DK
Tel.: (45) 70203883
Fax: (45) 43435354
E-Mail: info@ascom.dk
Web Site: www.ascom.dk
Emp.: 50
S.I.C.: 3669
N.A.I.C.S.: 334290
Aage Andersen *(CEO)*

Ascom Deutschland GmbH (1)
Kruppstrasse 105
60388 Frankfurt am Main, Germany De
Tel.: (49) 69 580057 0 (100%)
Fax: (49) 69 580057 333
E-Mail: info@ascom.de
Web Site: www.ascom.de
Emp.: 30
S.I.C.: 3669
N.A.I.C.S.: 334290
Juergen Veit *(Mng Dir)*

Subsidiaries:

Technologiepark Teningen GmbH (2)
Tscheulinstr 21
Teningen, Baden-Wurttemberg, Germany
Tel.: (49) 76414550
Fax: (49) 7641455480
Emp.: 220
Electric Transformers Converters & Rectifier Mfr
S.I.C.: 3679
N.A.I.C.S.: 334419

Ascom (Finland) OY (1)
Pakkalankuja 6
01510 Vantaa, Finland (100%)
Tel.: (358) 9825901
Fax: (358) 982590279
E-Mail: info@ascom.fi
Web Site: www.ascom.fi
Emp.: 25
Wireless Solutions, Security Communications & Network Testing
S.I.C.: 3669
N.A.I.C.S.: 334290

Ascom HPF SA (1)
BP 29
F 74130 Bonneville, France FR
Tel.: (33) 450970010 (100%)
Fax: (33) 450970926
Web Site: www.ascom.fr
Sales Range: $25-49.9 Million
Emp.: 300
Mfr. & Marketer of Telephones
S.I.C.: 3661
N.A.I.C.S.: 334210

Ascom India Pvt Ltd (1)
34 Udyog Vihar Phase IV
Gurgaon, Haryana, 122016, India In
Tel.: (91) 1246342083 (100%)
Fax: (91) 124 634 9114
E-Mail: ascomindia@ascom.com
Web Site: www.ascom.co.in
S.I.C.: 3669
N.A.I.C.S.: 334290

Ascom Monetel S.A. (1)
Rue Claude Chappe
PO Box 348
07503 Guilherand-Granges, France FR
Tel.: (33) 475814141 (100%)
Fax: (33) 475814100
E-Mail: claude.garoyan@ascom.fr
Web Site: www.ascom.fr
Emp.: 450
S.I.C.: 3669
N.A.I.C.S.: 334290
Claude Garoyan *(CEO)*

Ascom Network Testing AB (1)
Laboratorgrand 3
931 62 Skelleftea, Sweden
Tel.: (46) 10 492 5000
E-Mail: customercare.tems@ascom.com
Web Site: www.ascom.com
Network Testing Services
S.I.C.: 8734
N.A.I.C.S.: 541380

Ascom Nira Pty Ltd. (1)
Ground Fl 53 Balfour Street
Chippendale, NSW, 2008, Australia AU
Tel.: (61) 296989000 (100%)
Fax: (61) 296982749
E-Mail: apsk@integlatedwiless.com.au
Web Site: www.ascom.com.au
Sales Range: $1-9.9 Million
Emp.: 35
S.I.C.: 3669
N.A.I.C.S.: 334290
Leo Silver *(Mng Dir)*

Ascom Nira SA (1)
28 Ave De Ille St Martin
92024 Nanterre, Cedex, France (70%)
Tel.: (33) 147696464
Fax: (33) 147696452
E-Mail: info@ascomnira.fr
Web Site: www.ascomnira.fr
Emp.: 40
S.I.C.: 3669
N.A.I.C.S.: 334290

Ascom Norway (1)
Brobekkveien 2
PO Box 73
0582 Oslo, Norway NO
Tel.: (47) 23247700
Fax: (47) 22647440
Web Site: www.ascom.no
Emp.: 36
S.I.C.: 3669
N.A.I.C.S.: 334290

Ascom Poland Sp. Z.o.o. (1)
UL Fabryczna 16/22 office 24
00-446 Warsaw, Poland (100%)
Tel.: (48) 226226255
Fax: (48) 226226256
E-Mail: ascom@ascom.com.pl
Web Site: www.ascom.com.pl
Emp.: 15
Communications Holding Company
S.I.C.: 3669
N.A.I.C.S.: 334290
Jakub Gowin *(Mgr-Central Europe)*

Ascom (Sweden) AB (1)
Grimbodalen 2
PO Box 8783
402 76 Gothenburg, Sweden

Ascom Holding AG—(Continued)

Tel.: (46) 31 55 93 00
Fax: (46) 31 55 20 31
E-Mail: info@ascom.se
Web Site: www.ascom.se
Wireless Telecommunication Services
S.I.C.: 4812
N.A.I.C.S.: 517210

Subsidiary:

Ascom Tateco AB (2)
Grimbodalen 2
PO Box 8783
40749 Gothenburg, 40276, Sweden SE
Tel.: (46) 31559300 (100%)
Fax: (46) 31552031
E-Mail: info@ascom.se
Web Site: www.ascom.se
Emp.: 200
S.I.C.: 3663
N.A.I.C.S.: 334220
Claes Odman *(Mng Dir)*

Ascom UK Group Ltd. (1)
Enterprise Drive Aldridge Road Streetly
Birmingham, West Midlands, B74 2DY,
United Kingdom
Tel.: (44) 121 353 6151
Fax: (44) 121 352 1424
E-Mail: sales@ascom.co.uk
Wireless Telecommunication Services
S.I.C.: 4812
N.A.I.C.S.: 517210

Subsidiary:

Ascom (UK) Ltd. (2)
Clockhouse Ct 45 Westerham Rd
Sevenoaks, Kent, TN13 2QB, United
Kingdom (100%)
Tel.: (44) 732742014
Fax: (44) 732455865
Web Site: www.ascomtelenova.co.uk
Emp.: 40
S.I.C.: 3669
N.A.I.C.S.: 334290
Robert Wood *(Mng Dir)*

Maticmind (1)
Benedetto Croce 1
20090 Vimodrone, Milan, Italy (100%)
Tel.: (39) 0002274261
Fax: (39) 0227426700
E-Mail: ascomws@maticmind.it
Web Site: www.maticmind.it
Emp.: 80
Communications Holding Company
S.I.C.: 3669
N.A.I.C.S.: 334290

ASCON CONSTRUCTION PUBLIC COMPANY LIMITED

17 Ramkhamhaeng 60/2 Rd
Huamark
Bang kapi, Bangkok, 10240, Thailand
Tel.: (66) 2 735 1999
Fax: (66) 2 735 4771
E-Mail: construction@asconthai.com
Web Site: www.asconthai.com
Year Founded: 1998
ASCON—(THA)
Sales Range: $25-49.9 Million
Business Description:
Property Development Services
S.I.C.: 6519
N.A.I.C.S.: 531190
Personnel:
Pattanapong Tanumathaya *(Chm & CEO)*
Board of Directors:
Pattanapong Tanumathaya
Kamolvis Kaewfaek
Wirach Nimmanwathana
Chairit Simaroj
Suraphan Tanumathaya

ASCOPIAVE S.P.A.

Via Verizzo 1030
31053 Pieve di Soligo, TV, Italy
Tel.: (39) 0438980098
Fax: (39) 0438964779
E-Mail: info@ascopiave.it
Web Site: www.ascopiave.it
ASC—(ITA)
Rev.: $1,451,222,414
Assets: $1,259,959,927
Liabilities: $736,543,454
Net Worth: $523,416,473
Earnings: $37,511,027
Emp.: 625
Fiscal Year-end: 12/31/12
Business Description:
Natural Gas Distr
S.I.C.: 4924
N.A.I.C.S.: 221210
Personnel:
Fulvio Zugno *(Chm)*
Roberto Gumirato *(Mng Dir & Gen Mgr)*
Claudio Fabbi *(Gen Dir-Ascotrade)*
Board of Directors:
Fulvio Zugno
Giovanni Bernardelli
Dimitri Coin
Massimino Colomban
Enrico Quarello

ASCORIA

854 B Boulevard De L Est
50110 Tourlaville, Manche, France
Tel.: (33) 233883388
Web Site:
Sls.: $40,300,000
Emp.: 87
S.I.C.: 5511
N.A.I.C.S.: 441110
Personnel:
Herve Prehu *(Sls Mgr)*

ASCOT CORP.

20 Araki-Cho Shinjuku-Ku
Tokyo, 160-0007, Japan
Tel.: (81) 3 53267762
Fax: (81) 3 53267763
Web Site: www.ascotcorp.co.jp
Year Founded: 1999
3264—(JAS)
Sales Range: $125-149.9 Million
Emp.: 65
Business Description:
Condominium Units & Houses Developer; Real Estate Investment & Property Management Services
S.I.C.: 1522
N.A.I.C.S.: 236116
Personnel:
Shinji Kagaya *(Pres & CEO)*

Subsidiary:

Ascot Asset Consulting Corp. (1)
22-6 Arakicho
Shinjuku-Ku, Tokyo, 160-0007, Japan
Tel.: (81) 3 5312 1057
Fax: (81) 3 5363 7848
Web Site: www.ascotac.co.jp
Real Estate & Asset Management Consulting Services
S.I.C.: 8748
N.A.I.C.S.: 541618

ASCOT LLOYD HOLDINGS LTD.

Units 2 & 4 Forest Court Oakland's Park
Wokingham, Berks, RG41 2FD, United Kingdom
Tel.: (44) 845 345 5111
Fax: (44) 845 345 5311
Web Site: www.ascotlloyd.co.uk
Business Description:
Holding Company; Financial Advisory & Wealth Management Services
N.A.I.C.S.: 551112
Personnel:
Richard Dunbabin *(CEO)*
Pat O'Hara *(Mng Dir)*
Board of Directors:
Richard Dunbabin
Geoff Markham
Neil Methold
David Morgan
Pat O'Hara

Subsidiary:

Ascot Lloyd Financial Services Ltd. (1)
Units 2 & 4 Forest Court Oakland's Park
Wokingham, Berks, United Kingdom UK
Tel.: (44) 845 345 5111 (100%)
Fax: (44) 845 345 5311
E-Mail: info@ascotlloyd.co.uk
Web Site: www.ascotlloyd.co.uk
Financial Advisory & Wealth Management Services
N.A.I.C.S.: 524292
Richard Dunbabin *(CEO)*
Pat O'Hara *(Mng Dir)*

ASCOT MINING PLC

4th Floor 36 Spital Square
London, E1 6DY, United Kingdom
Tel.: (44) 20 7377 2850
E-Mail: info@ascotmining.com
Web Site: www.ascotmining.com
Year Founded: 2006
ASMP—(DEU ISDX OTC)
Rev.: $772,315
Assets: $28,884,502
Liabilities: $11,927,191
Net Worth: $16,957,311
Earnings: ($1,849,391)
Fiscal Year-end: 09/30/12
Business Description:
Gold Mining Services
S.I.C.: 1041
N.A.I.C.S.: 212221
Personnel:
David Brian Jackson *(CEO & Mng Dir)*
Jeffrey Benavides *(CFO)*
Andrew H. von Kursell *(COO)*
Graham May *(Sec)*
Board of Directors:
Jeffrey Benavides
Milo Filgas
David Brian Jackson
Alex Panko
Andrew H. von Kursell

ASCOT RESOURCES LTD.

Suite 605 - 475 Howe Street
Vancouver, BC, V6C 2B3, Canada
Tel.: (604) 379-1170
Fax: (604) 684-9877
E-Mail: info@ascotresources.ca
Web Site: www.ascotresources.ca
AOT—(TSXV)
Rev.: $42,416
Assets: $28,400,373
Liabilities: $4,012,012
Net Worth: $24,388,361
Earnings: ($1,444,117)
Fiscal Year-end: 03/31/13
Business Description:
Mineral Exploration Services
S.I.C.: 1081
N.A.I.C.S.: 213114
Personnel:
Andrew Caruso *(Chm)*
John A. Toffan *(CEO)*
Robert A. Evans *(CFO)*
Board of Directors:
Andrew Caruso
Ken M. Carter
Robert A. Evans
Rick L. Kasum
Paul Kopejtka
John Swann
John A. Toffan
Transfer Agent:
Canadian Stock Transfer Company
Vancouver, BC, Canada

ASCOT RESOURCES LIMITED

(Formerly Epic Resources Limited)
512 Hay Street
Subiaco, WA, 6008, Australia
Tel.: (61) 8 9381 4534
Fax: (61) 8 9380 6440
E-Mail: info@ascotresources.com
Web Site: www.ascotresources.com
Year Founded: 2010
AZQ—(ASX)
Rev.: $107,798
Assets: $5,509,563
Liabilities: $3,340,637
Net Worth: $2,168,926
Earnings: ($2,784,115)
Fiscal Year-end: 06/30/13
Business Description:
Coal Exploration Services
S.I.C.: 1222
N.A.I.C.S.: 212112
Personnel:
Andrew Caruso *(Chm & CEO)*
David Berg *(Legal Counsel & Sec)*
Board of Directors:
Andrew Caruso
Francis De Souza
Paul Kopejtka
Legal Counsel:
Steinepreis Paganin
Level 4 The Read Building 16 Milligan Street
Perth, WA, 6000, Australia
Tel.: (61) 8 9321 4000
Fax: (61) 8 9321 4333

ASCRIBE LTD

Ascribe House Brancker Street
Westhoughton, Bolton, Lancs, BL5 3JD, United Kingdom
Tel.: (44) 161 2808080
Fax: (44) 8700 53 37 77
E-Mail: info@ascribe.com
Web Site: www.ascribe.com
Sales Range: $25-49.9 Million
Emp.: 270
Fiscal Year-end: 12/31/12
Business Description:
Healthcare Information Technology Services
S.I.C.: 7373
N.A.I.C.S.: 541512
Personnel:
Stephen Critchlow *(Founder & CEO)*
Chris Dickson *(COO)*
Board of Directors:
Stephen Critchlow
Neville Davis
Chris Dickson
David Ewing
Marcus Mellor

Branch:

Ascribe (1)
7 Signet Court Swann's Road
Cambridge, CB5 8LA, United Kingdom
Tel.: (44) 1223314855
Fax: (44) 1223312010
E-Mail: sharedcare@ascribe.com
Web Site: www.ascribe.com
Emp.: 20
Custom Computer Programming Services
S.I.C.: 7371
N.A.I.C.S.: 541511

Subsidiaries:

ASC Computer Software Ltd (1)
Ascribe House Brancker Street
Westhoughton, Bolton, Lancs, BL5 3JD,
United Kingdom
Tel.: (44) 8700 53 45 45
Fax: (44) 8700 53 37 77
E-Mail: info@ascribe.com
Web Site: www.ascribe.com
Emp.: 100
Custom Computer Programming Services
S.I.C.: 7371
N.A.I.C.S.: 541511
Stephen Critchlow *(CEO)*

Non-U.S. Subsidiary:

ASC Computer Software Pty Limited (2)
Level 12, 1 Pacific HWY
North Sydney, NSW, 2060, Australia
Tel.: (61) 280815555
E-Mail: infoasc@ascribe.com
Web Site: www.ascribe.com
Emp.: 30
Custom Computer Programming Services
S.I.C.: 7371
N.A.I.C.S.: 541511

Scorpio Information Systems Ltd (1)
20 Pylewell Rd
Hythe, Southampton, SO45 6AR, United Kingdom
Tel.: (44) 2380849315
Fax: (44) 2380 845566
E-Mail: info@scorpio-is.co.uk
Web Site: www.ascribe.com
Custom Computer Programming Services
S.I.C.: 7371
N.A.I.C.S.: 541511

ASE S.P.A.

Via Verdi 33
20010 San Giorgio, Legnano, Italy
Tel.: (39) 331402216
Telex: 316812 BORMI I
Fax: (39) 0331404550
E-Mail: info@ase-spa.com
Web Site: www.ase-spa.com
Sales Range: $10-24.9 Million
Emp.: 80
Business Description:
Industrial Components Mfr
S.I.C.: 3589
N.A.I.C.S.: 333318
Personnel:
Paolo Fantini *(CEO)*

ASEANA PROPERTIES LTD.

12 Castle Street
Saint Helier, JE2 3RT, Jersey
Tel.: (44) 1534847000
Fax: (44) 1534847001
E-Mail: info@aseanaproperties.com
Web Site: www.aseanaproperties.com
ASPL—(LSE)
Rev.: $23,732,000
Assets: $409,674,000
Liabilities: $213,027,000
Net Worth: $196,647,000
Earnings: ($18,429,000)
Fiscal Year-end: 12/31/12
Business Description:
Real Estate
S.I.C.: 6726
N.A.I.C.S.: 525990
Personnel:
Lai Voon Hon *(Pres/CEO-Ireka Development Management Sdn Bhd)*
Board of Directors:
Mohammed Azlan Hashim
David Harris
John Lynton Jones
Christopher Henry Lovell
Gerald Chong Keng Ong
Ismail Shahudin

ASECO INTEGRATED SYSTEMS LTD.

635 Fourth Line Unit 16
Oakville, ON, L6L 5B3, Canada
Tel.: (905) 339-0059
Fax: (905) 339-3857
Toll Free: (800) 387-0467
E-Mail: consulting@aseco.net
Web Site: www.aseco.net
Year Founded: 1988
Rev.: $16,245,544
Emp.: 90
Business Description:
Manufacturing Consulting & Systems Integration Services Provider
S.I.C.: 8999
N.A.I.C.S.: 541690
Personnel:
Robert Peters *(Founder & CEO)*
Brad Walker *(Pres)*
Jeff Peters *(CTO)*

ASEEM GLOBAL LTD.

5476 South Basti Harphool Singh
Sadar Thana Road Sadar Bazar
Delhi, 110006, India
Tel.: (91) 11 23528157
Fax: (91) 11 23528187
E-Mail: contactus@aseemglobal.com
Web Site: www.aseemglobal.com
Year Founded: 1983
534564—(BOM)
Rev.: $63,886,504
Assets: $16,237,406
Liabilities: $11,828,854
Net Worth: $4,408,552
Earnings: $253,497
Fiscal Year-end: 03/31/13
Business Description:
Metal Product Whslr
S.I.C.: 5051
N.A.I.C.S.: 423510
Personnel:
Ira Rastogi *(Chm & Mng Dir)*
Pallavi Agarwal *(Compliance Officer & Sec)*
Board of Directors:
Ira Rastogi
Rajeev Kumar Goel
Mudit Rastogi
Tanuj Rastogi
Motia Sharma
Rajni Sharma
Yogesh Sharma
Transfer Agent:
Skyline Financial Services Pvt Ltd.
D 153A 1st Floor Okhla Industrial Area Phase 1
New Delhi, India

ASETEK A/S

Saltumvej 27
DK-9700 Bronderslev, Denmark
Tel.: (45) 9645 0047
Fax: (45) 9645 0048
Web Site: www.asetek.com
Year Founded: 2000
ASETEK—(OSL)
Sales Range: $1-9.9 Million
Emp.: 60
Business Description:
Data Centers, Servers, Work Stations, Gaming & High Performance PCs Energy Efficient Liquid Cooling Systems
S.I.C.: 3571
N.A.I.C.S.: 334111
Personnel:
Sam Szteinbaum *(Chm)*
Andre Eriksen *(CEO)*
Peter Dam Madsen *(CFO)*
Board of Directors:
Sam Szteinbaum
Chris J. Christopher
Andre Eriksen
Gregers Kronborg
Henri P. Richard
Jorgen Smidt
Ib Sonderby
Alex Wong

ASETRONICS AG

Freiburgstrasse 251
3018 Bern, Switzerland
Tel.: (41) 313293111
Fax: (41) 3132931999
E-Mail: info@asetronics.ch
Web Site: www.asetronics.ch
Sales Range: $75-99.9 Million
Emp.: 180
Business Description:
Electronic Components Mfr
S.I.C.: 3679
N.A.I.C.S.: 334419
Personnel:
Andre Maurer *(Chm & CEO)*
Guido Perrelet *(CTO)*

ASF GROUP LIMITED

Suite 2 3b Macquarie St
Sydney, NSW, 2000, Australia
Tel.: (61) 292519088
Fax: (61) 292519066
E-Mail: info@asfgroupltd.com
Web Site: www.asfgroupltd.com
AFA—(ASX)
Rev.: $1,752,623
Assets: $13,416,459
Liabilities: $12,208,531
Net Worth: $1,207,928
Earnings: ($31,825,500)
Fiscal Year-end: 06/30/13
Business Description:
Mineral Resources
S.I.C.: 5052
N.A.I.C.S.: 423520
Personnel:
Min Yang *(Chm)*
William Chi Yuen Kuan *(Sec)*
Board of Directors:
Min Yang
Geoff Baker
David Quan Fang
Wai Sang Ho
Alan Humphris
Yong Jiang
Nga Fong Lao
Xin Zhang
Legal Counsel:
Thomsons Lawyers
Level 25 1 O'Connell Street
Sydney, NSW, 2000, Australia

Clayton Utz
1 Bligh Street
Sydney, Australia

ASG GROUP LIMITED

Level 1 267 St Georges Terrace
Perth, WA, 6000, Australia
Tel.: (61) 894205420
Fax: (61) 894205422
E-Mail: info@asggroup.com.au
Web Site: www.asggroup.com.au
Year Founded: 1996
ASZ—(ASX)
Rev.: $158,958,808
Assets: $172,274,762
Liabilities: $83,841,113
Net Worth: $88,433,648
Earnings: ($27,815,733)
Emp.: 447
Fiscal Year-end: 06/30/13
Business Description:
IT Services & Business Solutions
S.I.C.: 7389
N.A.I.C.S.: 541990
Personnel:
Geoffrey Lewis *(CEO & Mng Dir)*
Michael Large *(CFO)*
Dean Langenbach *(COO)*
Michelle Bevan *(Exec-People & Culture)*
Gerald Strautins *(Exec-Strategy)*
Peter Torre *(Sec)*
Board of Directors:
Ronald Baxter
Ian G. Campbell
Stephen Johnston
Geoffrey Lewis
Trevor O'Hoy
Legal Counsel:
Murcia Pestell Hillard
Level 3 23 Barrack Street
Perth, WA, Australia

Subsidiaries:

Capiotech Pty Ltd (1)
Level 4 10 Bridge Street
Sydney, NSW, 2000, Australia
Tel.: (61) 2 8061 1700
Fax: (61) 2 9241 7746
Information Technology Consulting Services
S.I.C.: 7373
N.A.I.C.S.: 541512

Dowling Consulting Pty Ltd (1)
Level 3 312 St Kilda Road
Melbourne, VIC, 3056, Australia
Tel.: (61) 3 8598 5569
Fax: (61) 3 8598 5569
Management Consulting Services
S.I.C.: 8742
N.A.I.C.S.: 541611
Mike Andrews, *(Mgr-Delivery)*

Progress Pacific Pty Ltd (1)
Suite 302 / 161 Walker Street
Sydney, NSW, 2060, Australia
Tel.: (61) 2 9026 8500
Fax: (61) 2 9026 8563
E-Mail: admin@progresspacific.com
Web Site: www.progresspacific.com
Software Development Services
S.I.C.: 7379
N.A.I.C.S.: 541519
Matt Wilkinson, *(Dir-Sls & Mktg)*

ASGENT, INC.

6-4 Akashicho Chuo-ku
Tokyo, 104-0044, Japan
Tel.: (81) 3 6853 7401
Fax: (81) 3 6853 7411
Web Site: www.asgent.co.jp
Year Founded: 1997
4288—(JAS)
Sls.: $38,909,354
Assets: $29,183,605
Liabilities: $7,221,159
Net Worth: $21,962,446
Earnings: $1,481,513
Fiscal Year-end: 03/31/13
Business Description:
Network Security Services
S.I.C.: 7382
N.A.I.C.S.: 561621
Personnel:
Takahiro Sugimoto *(Pres & CEO)*
Takenori Katsuragi *(Mng Dir & CFO)*
Board of Directors:
Takenori Katsuragi
Tsutomu Nambu
Takahiro Sugimoto
Takuya Sugiyama

ASH & LACY BUILDING SYSTEMS LTD

Bromford Lane
B707JJ West Bromwich, United Kingdom
Tel.: (44) 1215251444
Fax: (44) 1215253444
E-Mail: sales@ashandlacy.com
Web Site: www.ashandlacy.com
Sales Range: $25-49.9 Million
Emp.: 150
Business Description:
Commercial & Institutional Building Construction
S.I.C.: 1542
N.A.I.C.S.: 236220
Personnel:
David Wright *(Mng Dir)*

ASHAPURA INTIMATES FASHION LTD

Shop No 3-4 Pacific Plaza
Mahim Division Dadar West, Mumbai, Maharashtra, 400028, India
Tel.: (91) 22 24331552
Web Site: www.valentineloungeweargroup.com
535467—(BOM)

Ashapura Intimates Fashion Ltd—(Continued)

Business Description:
Women's Intimates Mfr
S.I.C.: 5699
N.A.I.C.S.: 315240
Personnel:
Harshad H. Thakkar *(Chm & Mng Dir)*

ASHAPURA MINECHEM LIMITED

(Filed Ch 15 Bankruptcy #11-14668 on 10/06/11 in U.S. Bankruptcy Ct, Southern Dist of NY, Manhattan)
Jeevan Udyog Building 3rd Floor 278 Dr D N Road Fort
Mumbai, 400 001, India
Tel.: (91) 2266221700
Fax: (91) 2222079395
E-Mail: contact@ashapura.com
Web Site: www.ashapura.com
ASHAPURMIN—(NSE)
Rev.: $145,778,956
Assets: $163,531,875
Liabilities: $215,633,625
Net Worth: ($52,101,750)
Earnings: $8,184,169
Emp.: 1,800
Fiscal Year-end: 03/31/13
Business Description:
Mineral Mining Services
S.I.C.: 1499
N.A.I.C.S.: 212399
Personnel:
Navnitlal R. Shah *(Chm)*
Chetan Shah *(CEO & Mng Dir)*
Sachin Polke *(Compliance Officer, Sec & VP-Secretarial)*
Geetha Nerurkar *(CEO-Bentonite, Kaolin & Allied Products)*
Hemul Shah *(CEO-Intl Projects & Investments)*
Board of Directors:
Navnitlal R. Shah
Ashok Kadakia
Harish Motiwalla
Abhilash Munsif
Chetan Shah
Transfer Agent:
Link Intime India Private Limited
C-13 Pannalal Silk Mills Compound L.B.S. Marg
Bhandup
Mumbai, India

Subsidiary:

Ashapura International Limited (1)
Jeevan Udyog Building 3rd Floor 278 Dr D N Road Fort
Mumbai, 400 001, India
Tel.: (91) 22 6665 1700
Fax: (91) 22 2207 9395
E-Mail: ashapura@bsnl.com
Web Site: www.bsnl.com
Emp.: 25
Foundry Grade Bentonite Supplier
S.I.C.: 5052
N.A.I.C.S.: 423520
Suman Mandal *(Mgr)*

ASHBURTON

17 Hilary Street
PO Box 329
Saint Helier, JE4 8SJ, Jersey
Tel.: (44) 1534512000
Fax: (44) 1534512022
E-Mail: enquiries@ashburton.com
Web Site: www.ashburton.com
Emp.: 90
Business Description:
Investment Advice & Management
S.I.C.: 6282
N.A.I.C.S.: 523930
Personnel:
Peter Bourne *(Mng Dir)*

ASHBURTON MINERALS LTD.

(Name Changed to Platypus Minerals Ltd.)

ASHBURTON VENTURES INC.

789 West Pender Street Suite 1220
Vancouver, BC, V6C 1H2, Canada
Tel.: (604) 683-3995
Fax: (604) 683-3988
Toll Free: (888) 945-4770
E-Mail: info@ashburtonventures.com
Web Site: www.ashburtonventures.com
Year Founded: 2006
ABR—(TSXV)
Emp.: 10
Business Description:
Investment Services
S.I.C.: 6211
N.A.I.C.S.: 523999
Personnel:
Kyler Hardy *(Pres)*
Michael England *(CEO)*
Seung Oh *(CFO)*
Board of Directors:
Tom Candless
Michael England
Kyler Hardy
Bill Harris
Lorne McCarthy
Stephen Pearce
Philip Taneda

ASHCO NIULAB INDUSTRIES LIMITED

Lab House Plot No F-13 Opp SEEPZ MIDC
Andheri E, Mumbai, Maharashtra, 400093, India
Tel.: (91) 22 67040800
Fax: (91) 22 2836 8275
Web Site: www.ashconiulab.com
ASHCONIUL—(NSE)
Sales Range: $1-9.9 Million
Emp.: 250
Business Description:
Analytical Instruments Mfr
S.I.C.: 3826
N.A.I.C.S.: 334516
Personnel:
Ashok K. Kotwani *(Chm, Mng Dir, Compliance Officer & Sec)*
Transfer Agent:
System Support Services
209 Shivai Industrial Estate Next to Parke-Davis
89 Andheri-Kurla Rd
Mumbai, India

ASHCOURT ROWAN PLC

60 Queen Victoria Street
London, EC4N 4TR, United Kingdom
Tel.: (44) 20 7871 7250
Fax: (44) 20 7871 7277
E-Mail: enquiries@ashcourtrowan.com
Web Site: www.ashcourtrowan.com
ARP—(AIM)
Rev.: $51,480,116
Assets: $83,547,600
Liabilities: $10,191,158
Net Worth: $73,356,441
Earnings: ($3,387,577)
Emp.: 257
Fiscal Year-end: 03/31/13
Business Description:
Investment Holding Company
S.I.C.: 6719
N.A.I.C.S.: 551112
Personnel:
Jonathan Polin *(CEO)*
Alfio Tagliabue *(CFO & Sec)*
Richard Sinclair *(COO)*
Toni Meadows *(Chief Investment Officer)*
Gaius Jones *(CEO-Fin Plng Bus)*
Board of Directors:
Hugh Ward
Steve Haines
Jonathan Polin
Jim Roberts
Richard Sinclair
Alfio Tagliabue
Legal Counsel:
Memery Crystal
44 Southampton Buildings
WC2A 1AP London, United Kingdom
Subsidiaries:

Ashcourt Holdings Limited (1)
11 Tower View Kings Hill
West Malling, Kent, ME19 4UN, United Kingdom
Tel.: (44) 1732520780
Fax: (44) 1732522422
E-Mail: info@ashcourtrowan.com
Emp.: 60
Investment Management Services
S.I.C.: 6211
N.A.I.C.S.: 523999
Jonathan Tolin *(CEO)*

Subsidiaries:

Ashcourt Investment Advisers Limited (2)
11 Tower View Kings Hill
West Malling, Kent, ME19 4UN, United Kingdom
Tel.: (44) 1732520780
Fax: (44) 1732 522 422
Investment Management Services
S.I.C.: 6211
N.A.I.C.S.: 523999

Ashcourt Rowan Administration Limited (2)
3rd Floor 60 Queen Victoria Street
London, EC4N 4TR, United Kingdom
Tel.: (44) 2078717250
Fax: (44) 2078717279
E-Mail: infolondon@ashcourtrowan.com
Web Site: www.ashcourtrowanadmin.com
Investment Management Services
S.I.C.: 6211
N.A.I.C.S.: 523999
Mark Cheshire *(CEO)*

Ashcourt Rowan Asset Management Limited (2)
2 Redhouse Farm Brighton Road
Newtimber
Hassocks, West Sussex, BN6 9BS, United Kingdom
Tel.: (44) 1273857474
Fax: (44) 1273857434
E-Mail: communication@ashcourtrowan.com
Emp.: 5
Investment Management Services
S.I.C.: 6211
N.A.I.C.S.: 523999
Harry Burnham *(CEO)*
Jonathan Polin *(Grp CEO)*
David Palmer *(Deputy CEO)*

Ashcourt Rowan Financial Planning Limited (2)
60 Queen Victoria Street
London, EC4N 4TR, United Kingdom
Tel.: (44) 2078717250
Fax: (44) 2078717277
E-Mail: enquiry@ashcourtrowan.com
Web Site: www.ashcourtrowanfp.com
Emp.: 120
Financial Management Services
S.I.C.: 8742
N.A.I.C.S.: 541611
Gaius Jones *(CEO)*
Neil Hale *(CFO)*

Independent Financial Solutions Group Limited (2)
Priory Place New London Road
Chelmsford, Essex, CM2 0PP, United Kingdom
Tel.: (44) 1245265444
Fax: (44) 1245265445
Web Site: www.ashcourtrowan.com
Emp.: 12
Financial Management Services
S.I.C.: 8742
N.A.I.C.S.: 541611

Rowan & Company Capital Management plc (2)
37 Gay Street
Bath, Somerset, BA1 2NT, United Kingdom
Tel.: (44) 1225469424
Fax: (44) 1225428760
E-Mail: infobath@ashcourtrowan.com
Emp.: 30
Investment Management Services
S.I.C.: 6211
N.A.I.C.S.: 523999
Jonathan Polin *(CEO)*

Epic Investment Partners Ltd (1)
22 Billiter Street
London, EC3M 2RY, United Kingdom
Tel.: (44) 2075532311
Fax: (44) 02075532301
E-Mail: jo.welman@epicip.com
Web Site: www.epicip.com
Emp.: 20
Private Equity Firm
S.I.C.: 6211
N.A.I.C.S.: 523999
Jo Welman *(Co-Founder, Chm & CEO)*
Ravi Shankar *(Co-Founder, Mng Dir & Chief Investment Officer)*

Subsidiary:

Whittard of Chelsea Plc (2)
Windrush House Windrush Prk Road
Witney, Oxfordshire, 0X29 7DX, United Kingdom
Tel.: (44) 01993893700
Fax: (44) 08704893710
E-Mail: info@whittard.co.uk
Web Site: www.whittard.co.uk
Sales Range: $75-99.9 Million
Emp.: 30
Coffee & Tea Retail Shop Operator
S.I.C.: 5411
N.A.I.C.S.: 445110
Mark Dunhill *(CEO)*
Sara Holton *(Mng Dir)*

Savoy Investment Management Limited (1)
60 Queen Victoria Street
London, EC4N 4TR, United Kingdom
Tel.: (44) 2078717300
Fax: (44) 2078717339
Web Site: www.savoyim.com
Emp.: 120
Investment Management Services
S.I.C.: 6211
N.A.I.C.S.: 523999
Christopher Jeffreys *(CEO)*

ASHER RESOURCES CORPORATION

36 Toronto Street Suite 1000
Toronto, ON, M5C 2C5, Canada
Tel.: (647) 501-3290
Fax: (416) 585-9801
E-Mail: info@asher-resources.com
Web Site: www.asher-resources.com
Year Founded: 2011
ACN.P—(TSXV)
Int. Income: $4,449
Assets: $1,579,976
Liabilities: $69,702
Net Worth: $1,510,274
Earnings: ($496,471)
Fiscal Year-end: 12/31/12
Business Description:
Investment Services
S.I.C.: 6211
N.A.I.C.S.: 523999
Personnel:
John M. Arnold *(Chm)*
Richard Buzbuzian *(Pres & CEO)*
Robert Suttie *(CFO & Sec)*
Board of Directors:
John M. Arnold
Richard Buzbuzian
Terry Christopher
Norman Eyolfson

Rob Montemarano
Kevin D. Sherkin
Transfer Agent:
Computershare Investor Services Inc.
3rd Floor 510 Burrard St
V6C 3B9 Vancouver, BC, Canada

ASHIANA HOUSING LTD
5F Everest 46/C Chowringhee Road
Kolkata, 700 071, India
Tel.: (91) 3322883736
Fax: (91) 3322884774
Web Site: www.ashianahousing.com
ASHIANA—(BOM NSE)
Rev.: $29,927,026
Assets: $76,381,300
Liabilities: $26,936,558
Net Worth: $49,444,742
Earnings: $6,145,511
Emp.: 216
Fiscal Year-end: 03/31/13
Business Description:
Real Estate Development Services
S.I.C.: 6531
N.A.I.C.S.: 531210
Personnel:
Ankur Gupta *(Mng Dir)*
Vishal Gupta *(Mng Dir)*
Bhagwan Kumar *(Compliance Officer, Sec & Gen Mgr-Corp Affairs)*
Board of Directors:
Lalit Kumar Chhawchharia
Abhishek Dalmia
Ankur Gupta
Varun Gupta
Vishal Gupta
Ashok Kumar Mattoo
Sonal Mattoo
Transfer Agent:
Beetal Financial & Computer Services Pvt. Ltd.
Beetal House 99 Madangir Behind Local Shopping Centre
Near Dada Harsukh Dass Mandir, New Delhi, India

ASHIANA ISPAT LTD.
C-9/36 Sector 8
Rohini, Delhi, India 110085
Tel.: (91) 11 27947124
E-Mail: ashianagroup@yahoo.co.in
Web Site: www.ashianaispat.in
513401—(BOM)
Business Description:
Construction Engineering Services
S.I.C.: 1629
N.A.I.C.S.: 237990
Personnel:
Naresh Chand *(Mng Dir)*
Board of Directors:
R. P. Bansal
Naresh Chand
R. K. Garg
Neeraj Kumar Jain
Puneet Jain
Sanjay Jain
Sukhbir Singh Jain
T. C. Kansal
R. K. Pal

ASHIKA CAPITAL LIMITED
1008 Raheja Ctr 214 Nariman Point
Mumbai, 400021, India
Tel.: (91) 2266111700
Fax: (91) 2266111710
E-Mail: mbd@ashikagroup.com
Web Site: www.ashikagroup.com
Emp.: 30
Business Description:
Merchant Banking Services
S.I.C.: 6211
N.A.I.C.S.: 523110
Personnel:
Pawan Jain *(Chm & Mng Dir)*
Rajendra Kanoongo *(Pres)*
Board of Directors:
Pawan Jain
Babulal Bafna
Amit Jain
Daulat Jain
Vikas Jain
Rajendra Kanoongo

ASHIKAGA HOLDINGS CO., LTD.
Ashikaga Ginko Honten 4-1-25 Sakura
Utsunomiya, 320-8610, Japan
Tel.: (81) 28 622 8411
Web Site: www.ashikaga-hd.co.jp
7167—(TKS)
Rev.: $1,082,279,000
Fiscal Year-end: 03/31/13
Business Description:
Banking Services
S.I.C.: 6029
N.A.I.C.S.: 522110
Personnel:
Satoshi Fujisawa *(Pres)*

ASHIMA LTD.
Texcellence Complex Khokhra Mehmedabad
Ahmedabad, 380 021, India
Tel.: (91) 79 6777 7000
Fax: (91) 79 2277 3061
Web Site: www.ashimagroup.com
514286—(BOM)
Rev.: $49,822,950
Assets: $49,365,605
Liabilities: $94,624,934
Net Worth: ($45,259,329)
Earnings: ($2,586,608)
Fiscal Year-end: 03/31/13
Business Description:
Cotton Fabric Mfr
S.I.C.: 2299
N.A.I.C.S.: 313210
Personnel:
Chintan N. Parikh *(Chm & Mng Dir)*
Shrikant S. Pareek *(CEO)*
Hiren S. Mahadevia *(CFO, Compliance Officer & Sec)*
Board of Directors:
Chintan N. Parikh
Jaykant R. Baxi
Bakul H. Dholakia
Pramod Kumar Gupta
Bihari B. Shah
Atul Kumar Singh
Transfer Agent:
Link Intime India Private Limited
Unit No 303 3rd Floor Shoppers Plaza V Opp. Municipal Market
B/h Shoppers Plaza-II, Ahmedabad, India

ASHIMORI INDUSTRY CO., LTD.
10-18 3-chome Kitahorie
Nishi-ku, Osaka, 550-0014, Japan
Tel.: (81) 6 6533 9250
Fax: (81) 6 6533 9291
Web Site: www.ashimori.co.jp
Year Founded: 1878
3526—(TKS)
Emp.: 1,800
Business Description:
Automotive Safety Parts Mfr
S.I.C.: 3714
N.A.I.C.S.: 336390
Personnel:
Fumio Hotogi *(Pres)*
Masaki Kawauchi *(Co-Mng Dir)*
Masao Takahashi *(Co-Mng Dir)*
Isaburo Yagi *(Co-Mng Dir)*
Board of Directors:
Eiichi Dozono
Toshichika Fumoto
Fumio Hotogi
Masaki Kawauchi
Masao Takahashi
Isaburo Yagi
Shigeaki Yamamoto

ASHIRWAD CAPITAL LIMITED
303 Tantia Jogani Industrial Estate Opp Lodha Bellissimo
J R Boricha Marg Lower Parel,
Mumbai, 400 011, India
Tel.: (91) 22 43443555
Fax: (91) 22 23071511
E-Mail: investors@svgcl.com
Web Site: www.ashirwadcapital.in
512247—(BOM)
Rev.: $168,003
Assets: $1,346,241
Liabilities: $246,060
Net Worth: $1,100,181
Earnings: $105,978
Fiscal Year-end: 03/31/13
Business Description:
Securities Brokerage Services
S.I.C.: 6211
N.A.I.C.S.: 523120
Personnel:
Ramprasad Poddar *(Chm)*
Nagabhushan Hegde *(CEO & Compliance Officer)*
Dinesh Poddar *(Mng Dir)*
Board of Directors:
Ramprasad Poddar
Nirmal Jain
Dinesh Poddar
Rajesh Poddar
Sanjiv Rungta
Piyush Shah
Transfer Agent:
Bigshare Services Private Limited
E/2 Ansa Industrial Estate Sakivihar Road
Sakinaka Andheri - East
Mumbai, India

ASHISH POLYPLAST LTD.
A/305 Samudra Near Hotel Klassic Gold Off C G Road
Ahmedabad, Gujarat, 380 006, India
Tel.: (91) 79 26445090
Fax: (91) 79 26562224
E-Mail: info@ashishpolyplast.com
Web Site: www.ashishpolyplast.com
530429—(BOM)
Sales Range: $1-9.9 Million
Business Description:
Pneumatic Hose Mfr
S.I.C.: 3492
N.A.I.C.S.: 332912
Personnel:
Ashish D. Panchal *(Mng Dir)*
Kaplesh Kansara *(Mgr-Accts & Fin & Compliance Officer)*
Board of Directors:
Manish Ravindrabhai Gandhi
Ashish D. Panchal
Kantaben D. Panchal
Keyur Rasiklal Panchal

ASHLEY & HOLMES
22A Papanikoli St
Halandri, 15232 Athens, Greece
Tel.: (30) 2 108 1188 00
Fax: (30) 2168 346 81
E-Mail: info@ashley-holmes.gr
Web Site: www.ashley-holmes.gr
Year Founded: 1988
Emp.: 250
Business Description:
Advertising Services
S.I.C.: 7311
N.A.I.C.S.: 541810
Personnel:
Makis Seriatos *(Pres & Mng Dir)*
Gregory Tsimogiannis *(Mng Dir)*

THE ASHLEY GROUP, LTD.
Nord Centre York St
Aberdeen, Scotland, AB11 5DN, United Kingdom
Tel.: (44) 1224288590
Fax: (44) 224845250
Web Site: www.ashley-group.com
Emp.: 5
Business Description:
Holding Company
S.I.C.: 6719
N.A.I.C.S.: 551112

ASHLEY HOUSE PLC
6 Cliveden Office Village Lancaster Road Cressex Business Park
High Wycombe, HP12 3YZ, United Kingdom
Tel.: (44) 1628600340
Fax: (44) 1628600345
Web Site: www.ashleyhouseplc.com
ASH—(AIM)
Rev.: $24,924,355
Assets: $44,488,599
Liabilities: $13,521,881
Net Worth: $30,966,718
Earnings: $1,997,802
Emp.: 54
Fiscal Year-end: 04/30/13
Business Description:
Health Care
S.I.C.: 8011
N.A.I.C.S.: 621111
Personnel:
Jonathan Holmes *(CEO)*
S. Ronaldson *(Sec)*
Board of Directors:
Christopher Peter Lyons
Richard Darch
Jonathan Holmes
Stephen G. Minion
Antony J. Walters
Andrew J. Willetts
Legal Counsel:
Squire Sanders (UK) LLP
2 Park Lane
Leeds, West Yorkshire, LS3 1ES, United Kingdom

ASHMORE EMERGING MARKETS INCOME FUND
61 Aldwych
London, WC2B 4AE, United Kingdom
Tel.: (44) 20 3077 6000
Business Description:
Investment Services
S.I.C.: 6211
N.A.I.C.S.: 523999
Personnel:
George Grunebaum *(Pres & CEO)*
Chris Tsutsui *(CFO, Principal Acctg Officer & Treas)*

ASHMORE GLOBAL OPPORTUNITIES LTD.
Trafalgar Court Les Banques
Saint Peter Port, GY1 3QL, Guernsey
Tel.: (44) 1481745001
Web Site: www.agol.com
AGOL—(AIM)
Rev.: $28,870,676
Assets: $487,012,182
Liabilities: $6,977,913
Net Worth: $480,034,269
Earnings: ($28,224,178)
Fiscal Year-end: 12/31/12
Business Description:
Financial Services
S.I.C.: 6722
N.A.I.C.S.: 525910
Personnel:
Jonathan Agnew *(Chm)*
Board of Directors:
Jonathan Agnew

Ashmore Global Opportunities Ltd.—(Continued)

Nigel de la Rue
Graeme Dell
Richard Hotchkis
Christopher Legge

Legal Counsel:
Slaughter & May
One Bunhill Row
London, EC1Y 8YY, United Kingdom
Tel.: (44) 20 7600 1200
Fax: (44) 20 7600 0289

Carey Olsen
Carey House Les Banques
PO Box 98
GY1 4BZ Saint Peter Port, Guernsey

Transfer Agent:
Computershare Investor Services PLC
The Pavilions Bridgwater Road
PO Box 82
Bristol, United Kingdom

ASHMORE GROUP PLC
61 Aldwych
London, WC2B 4AE, United Kingdom
Tel.: (44) 20 3077 6000
Fax: (44) 20 3077 6001
E-Mail: ashmore@ashmoregroup.com
Web Site: www.ashmoregroup.com
Year Founded: 1992
ASHM—(LSE)
Rev.: $561,595,524
Assets: $1,284,910,344
Liabilities: $265,004,862
Net Worth: $1,019,905,482
Earnings: $318,384,864
Emp.: 291
Fiscal Year-end: 06/30/13

Business Description:
Emerging Market Debt & Equity Portfolio Management
S.I.C.: 6211
N.A.I.C.S.: 523999

Personnel:
Mark Coombs *(CEO)*
Michael Perman *(Sec)*

Board of Directors:
Michael Benson
Mark Coombs
Melda Donnelly
Simon Fraser
Nick Land
Charles Outhwaite
Dame Anne Pringle
Tom Shippey

Subsidiary:

Ashmore Investment Management Limited **(1)**
61 Aldwych
London, WC2B 4AE, United Kingdom
Tel.: (44) 2030776000
Fax: (44) 2030776001
E-Mail: ashmore@ashmoregroup.com
Web Site: www.ashmoregroup.com
Sls.: $125,797,448
Emp.: 150
Emerging Market Debt & Equity Portfolio Management
S.I.C.: 6211
N.A.I.C.S.: 523999
Mark Coombs *(Mng Dir)*

U.S. Subsidiary:

Ashmore EMM, LLC **(2)**
1001 19th St N
Arlington, VA 22209 (62.9%)
Tel.: (703) 243-8800
Fax: (703) 243-0593
Web Site: www.emiemm.com
Emp.: 56
Portfolio Management
S.I.C.: 6799
N.A.I.C.S.: 523920
Felicia Morrow *(Chm)*

Non-U.S. Subsidiary:

Jasper Investments Limited **(2)**
1 HarbourFront Place #03-01 HarbourFront Tower One
Singapore, 098633, Singapore
Tel.: (65) 63035500
Fax: (65) 65572313
E-Mail: corp@jasperinvests.com
Web Site: www.jasperinvests.com
JASP—(SES)
Rev.: $377,000
Assets: $509,093,000
Liabilities: $185,117,000
Net Worth: $323,976,000
Earnings: ($46,359,000)
Emp.: 255
Fiscal Year-end: 03/31/13
Investment Holding Company
S.I.C.: 6719
N.A.I.C.S.: 551112
Paul Carsten Pedersen *(CEO)*
Choon Sze Tan *(CFO)*
Mee Kium Lee *(Co-Sec & Head-Corp Dev)*
Joo Khin Ng *(Co-Sec)*

Non-U.S. Holdings:

AEI **(2)**
Clifton House 75 Fort Street
PO Box 190GT
Georgetown, Cayman Islands Ky
Tel.: (345) 9494900
Web Site: www.aeienergy.com
Sales Range: $5-14.9 Billion
Emp.: 15,430
Energy Infrastructure Owner & Operator
S.I.C.: 3612
N.A.I.C.S.: 335311
Ronald W. Haddock *(Chm)*
Maureen J. Ryan *(Gen Counsel, Exec VP & Chief Compliance Officer)*
Andrew Parsons *(Exec VP-Admin)*
Emilio Vicens *(Exec VP-Comml)*

U.S. Subsidiary:

AEI Services LLC **(3)**
1600 Smith St Ste 4900
Houston, TX 77002 Ky
Tel.: (713) 345-5200
Fax: (713) 345-5277
E-Mail: john.fulton@aeienergy.com
Web Site: www.aeienergy.com
Earnings: $158,000,000
Emp.: 120
Holding Company; Energy Services
S.I.C.: 6719
N.A.I.C.S.: 551112
Ronald W. Haddock *(Chm)*
Andrew Parsons *(Exec VP-Admin)*
Emilio Vicens *(Exec VP-Comml)*
Brian Zatarain *(Exec VP-Bus Dev)*

Non-U.S. Subsidiary:

Gas Natural de Lima y Callao S.A. **(3)**
Av Primavera 1878 Distrito Ciudad Santiago
Lima, 27, Peru PE
Tel.: (51) 16117500
Web Site: www.calidda.com.pe
Emp.: 186
Natural Gas Supplier
S.I.C.: 4924
N.A.I.C.S.: 221210

ECI Telecom Ltd. **(2)**
30 Hasivim Street
Petah Tiqwa, 49517, Israel Il
Tel.: (972) 39266000
Fax: (972) 39268755
Web Site: www.ecitele.com
Sales Range: $650-699.9 Million
Emp.: 3,032
Telecommunications Systems Marketer & Mfr
Import Export
S.I.C.: 3661
N.A.I.C.S.: 334210
Rafi Maor *(Chm)*
Darryl Alexander Edwards *(Pres & CEO)*
Itzik Zion *(CFO & Exec VP)*
Avi Cohen *(COO)*
Dror Nahumi *(Exec VP & Chief Strategy Officer)*
Tony Scarfo *(Exec VP, Gen Mgr-Network Div & Chief Strategy Officer)*

U.S. Subsidiaries:

ECI Telecom Americas Inc. **(3)**
5100 NW 33rd Ave Ste 150
Fort Lauderdale, FL 33309
Tel.: (954) 772-3070
Fax: (954) 351-4404
Toll Free: (800) 833-4580
E-Mail: sales.na@ecitele.com
Web Site: www.ecitele.com
Emp.: 70
Telecommunication Services
S.I.C.: 7373
N.A.I.C.S.: 541512
John Maguire *(Dir-Customer Support)*

Non-U.S. Holdings:

ECI Telecom GmbH **(3)**
Buropark Oberusel In Der Au 27
61440 Oberursel, Germany De
Tel.: (49) 617162090
Fax: (49) 6171620988
E-Mail: eci.germany@ecitele.com
Web Site: www.ecitele.com
Emp.: 50
Provider of Digital Telecommunications & Data Transmission Systems to Network Service Providers
S.I.C.: 4813
N.A.I.C.S.: 517110
Jehonatan Neuberger *(Mng Dir)*

ECI Telecom Iberica S.A. **(3)**
Josefa Valcarcel 3 5
28027 Madrid, Spain
Tel.: (34) 917434950
Fax: (34) 917434891
Web Site: www.dominion.es
Emp.: 9
Telecom Network Hardware Mfr
S.I.C.: 3679
N.A.I.C.S.: 334418

ECI Telecom Ltd. - China **(3)**
Room 701 Building F Yon He Plaza Eastern Street 28
Dongcheng District, Beijing, 100007, China
Tel.: (86) 1084195260
Fax: (86) 1084195838
Web Site: www.ecitele.com
Emp.: 10
Telecom Network Hardware Mfr
S.I.C.: 3679
N.A.I.C.S.: 334418
Elana Holzman *(VP-IR)*

ECI Telecom (Philippines), Inc. **(3)**
27th Fl Unit 2702 Antel 2000 Bldg 121 Valero St
Salcedo Vlg, Makati, Metro Manila, 1226, Philippines
Tel.: (63) 28452333
Fax: (63) 28438222
Web Site: www.ecitele.com
Sales Range: $1-9.9 Million
Emp.: 50
Telecom Network Hardware Mfr
S.I.C.: 3679
N.A.I.C.S.: 334418
Rondell Cruz *(Gen Mgr)*

ECI Telecom (Singapore) **(3)**
150 Beach Rd Ste 28 07 Gateway W
Singapore, 189720, Singapore
Tel.: (65) 62977335
Fax: (65) 65051999
E-Mail: nikol.tit@ecitele.com
Web Site: www.ecitele.com
Emp.: 14
S.I.C.: 3679
N.A.I.C.S.: 334418

ECI Telecom (UK) Limited **(3)**
ISIS House Reading Rd
Chineham, Basingstoke, Hampshire, RG24 8TW, United Kingdom UK
Tel.: (44) 256388000
Fax: (44) 1256388143
Web Site: www.ecitele.com
Emp.: 50
Telecom Network Hardware Mfr
S.I.C.: 3679
N.A.I.C.S.: 334418
Darren Patterson *(Mng Dir)*

ECI Telecom **(3)**
Espace Velizy Le Nugesser 13 Ave Morane Saulnier
Lathail Beadr, 78140 Velizy Villacoublay, France FR
Tel.: (33) 134630480
Fax: (33) 139462118
E-Mail: support.france@ecitele.com
Web Site: www.ecitele.com
Emp.: 25
Telecom Network Hardware Mfr
S.I.C.: 4899
N.A.I.C.S.: 517919
Barak Eitan *(Pres)*

ASHOK ALCO CHEM LIMITED
104 Venkatesh Chambers 1st flr
Ghanshyam Talwatkar Marg
Fort, Mumbai, 400 001, India
Tel.: (91) 22 6144 6900
Fax: (91) 22 66104355
E-Mail: info@ashokalcochem.com
Web Site: www.ashokalcochem.com
Year Founded: 1992
524594—(BOM)
Rev.: $44,040,123
Assets: $17,754,154
Liabilities: $15,517,115
Net Worth: $2,237,039
Earnings: $1,132,348
Fiscal Year-end: 03/31/13

Business Description:
Specialty Chemical Mfr & Whslr
S.I.C.: 2899
N.A.I.C.S.: 325199

Personnel:
Seema Gangawat *(Compliance Officer, Sec & Deputy Mgr)*

Board of Directors:
Sanjay Bhatia
Sridhar Chari
Manoj Ganatra
Umesh Kulkarni
Sunil Shah

Transfer Agent:
Link Intime India Pvt. Ltd
C-13 Pannalal Silk Mills Compound LBS Marg
Bhandup (West)
Mumbai, India

ASHOKA BUILDCON LTD.
Ashoka House Ashoka Marg Ashoka Nagar
Nasik, 422 011, India
Tel.: (91) 2533011705
Fax: (91) 2532236704
E-Mail: corporate@ashokabuildcon.com
Web Site: www.ashokabuildcon.com
ASHOKA—(BOM NSE)
Rev.: $348,937,150
Assets: $2,306,140,894
Liabilities: $2,059,670,023
Net Worth: $246,470,871
Earnings: $8,391,241
Emp.: 1,089
Fiscal Year-end: 03/31/13

Business Description:
Roads, Bridges, Commercial Buildings Operators & Mfr
S.I.C.: 1611
N.A.I.C.S.: 237310

Personnel:
Ashok M. Katariya *(Chm)*
Satish D. Parakh *(Mng Dir)*
Paresh C. Mehta *(CFO)*
Rajendra Burad *(Co-COO)*
Anil Gandhi *(Co-COO)*
Dilip Kothari *(Co-COO)*
Shrikant P. Shukla *(Co-COO)*
Manoj A. Kulkarni *(Compliance Officer & Sec)*

Board of Directors:
Ashok M. Katariya
Sharad D. Abhyankar
Milap Raj Bhansali
Gyan Chand Daga
Sanjay Londhe
Satish D. Parakh
Michael Pinto
S. G. Shyam Sundar
Albert Tauro

Transfer Agent:
Link Intime India Pvt. Ltd.
C-13 Pannalal Silk Mills Compound
LBS Marg
Bhandup, Mumbai, 400 078, India
Tel.: (91) 22 2596 3838
Fax: (91) 22 2594 6969

ASHS LTD.

(d/b/a Anya Hindmarch)
The Stable Block Plough Brewery
516 Wandsworth Road, London, SW8 3JX, United Kingdom
Tel.: (44) 2075010177
Fax: (44) 2075010170
E-Mail: info@anyahindmarch.com
Web Site: www.anyahindmarch.com
Emp.: 250
Business Description:
Handbag, Shoe & Accessory Designer & Mfr
S.I.C.: 3171
N.A.I.C.S.: 316992
Personnel:
Anya Hindmarch *(Mng Dir)*

ASHTEAD GROUP PLC

Kings House 36-37 King Street
London, EC2V 8BB, United Kingdom
Tel.: (44) 20 7726 9700
Fax: (44) 20 7726 9705
E-Mail: info@ashtead-group.com
Web Site: www.ashtead-group.com
Year Founded: 1982
AHT—(LSE)
Rev.: $2,150,835,051
Assets: $3,589,094,454
Liabilities: $2,511,229,029
Net Worth: $1,077,865,425
Earnings: $219,205,452
Emp.: 8,717
Fiscal Year-end: 04/30/13
Business Description:
Equipment Rental
S.I.C.: 7359
N.A.I.C.S.: 532490
Personnel:
Geoffrey Drabble *(CEO)*
Sat Dhaiwal *(CEO-A-Plant)*
Brendan Horgan *(CEO-Sunbelt)*
Erik Watkins *(Legal Counsel & Sec)*
Board of Directors:
Chris Cole
Michael Burrow
Sat Dhaiwal
Geoffrey Drabble
Wayne Edmunds
Bruce A. Edwards
Hugh Etheridge
Brendan Horgan
Ian Sutcliffe
Suzanne Wood
Legal Counsel:
Travers Smith LLP
10 Snow Hill
EC1A 2AL London, United Kingdom

Skadden, Arps, Slate, Meagher & Flom LLP
155 N Wacker Dr
Chicago, IL 60606

Parker, Poe, Adams & Bernstein LLP
401 South Tryon St
Charlotte, NC 28202
Transfer Agent:
Equiniti
Aspect House Spencer Road
Lancing, United Kingdom
Subsidiaries:

Ashtead Financing Limited (1)
Kings House 36-37 King Street
London, EC2V 8BB, United Kingdom
Tel.: (44) 2077269700
Fax: (44) 2077269705
E-Mail: info@ashtead-group.com
Emp.: 11
Financial Consulting Services
S.I.C.: 8742
N.A.I.C.S.: 541611
Geoff Crabble *(CEO)*

Ashtead Holdings PLC (1)
Kings Court 41-51 Kingston Road
Leatherhead, London, EC2V 8BB, United Kingdom
Tel.: (44) 1372379844
Fax: (44) 1635879401
Emp.: 1,000
Management Services
S.I.C.: 8741
N.A.I.C.S.: 551114
Mark Pudney *(Mng Dir)*

Ashtead Plant Hire Co. Ltd. (1)
102 Dalton Ave
Birch Wood, Warrington, Cheshire, WA3 6YE, United Kingdom (100%)
Tel.: (44) 1925281000
Fax: (44) 1925281001
E-Mail: reception@aplant.com
Web Site: www.aplant.com
Emp.: 120
Equipment Rental
S.I.C.: 7359
N.A.I.C.S.: 532490
Sat Dhaiwal *(CEO)*

U.S. Subsidiary:

Sunbelt Rentals, Inc. (1)
2341 Deerfield Dr
Fort Mill, SC 29715 NC
Tel.: (704) 348-2676 (100%)
Fax: (704) 348-2683
Toll Free: (888) 334-7570
Web Site: www.sunbeltrentals.com
Emp.: 40
Equipment Rentals
S.I.C.: 7353
N.A.I.C.S.: 532412
Brendan Horgan *(CEO)*
Suzanne Wood *(CFO & Exec VP)*
Kurt Kenkel *(Exec VP-Bus Dev)*

Division:

Sunbelt Rentals (2)
12770 Metro Pkwy
Fort Myers, FL 33966
Tel.: (239) 768-3636
Fax: (239) 768-3747
Web Site: www.sunbeltrentals.com
Sales Range: $1-9.9 Million
Emp.: 35
Commercial & Industrial Machinery & Equipment Rental & Leasing
S.I.C.: 7359
N.A.I.C.S.: 532490
Brian Richardson *(Gen Mgr)*

Subsidiaries:

Pacific High Reach & Equipment Services, Inc. (2)
1604 W Collins Ave
Orange, CA 92867 CA
Tel.: (714) 289-8900
Web Site: www.pacifichighreach.net
Sales Range: $1-9.9 Million
Emp.: 12
Construction, Mining & Forestry Machinery & Equipment Rental & Leasing
S.I.C.: 7353
N.A.I.C.S.: 532412
Jeff Davis *(Pres)*

Sunbelt Rentals (2)
2341 Deerfield Dr
Fort Mill, SC 29715 DE
Tel.: (803) 578-5811
Fax: (954) 760-6565
Web Site: www.sunbeltrentals.com
Sales Range: $650-699.9 Million
Emp.: 3,500
Equipment Rental Services
S.I.C.: 7359
N.A.I.C.S.: 532490
Nat Brookhouse *(Dir-Sls Support & Mktg)*

TOPP Construction Services, Inc. (2)
12 Crozerville Rd
Aston, PA 19014
Tel.: (610) 459-5515
Toll Free: (888) 364-8677
Web Site: www.etopp.com
Sales Range: $10-24.9 Million
Emp.: 87
Warm Air Heating, Air-Conditioning Equipment & Supplies Merchant Whslr
S.I.C.: 5075
N.A.I.C.S.: 423730
Daniel P. Topp *(Pres)*
Elizabeth Topp *(Sec)*

ASHUR INTERNATIONAL BANK FOR INVESTMENT

PO Box 3636
Baghdad, Iraq
Tel.: (964) 7187492
Fax: (964) 7193479
E-Mail: info@ashurbank.com
Web Site: www.ashurbank.com
Year Founded: 2005
BASH—(IRAQ)
Sales Range: $10-24.9 Million
Business Description:
Investment Banking Services
S.I.C.: 6211
N.A.I.C.S.: 523110
Personnel:
Wadee N. Al-Handel *(Chm)*
Hardan N. Al-Handel *(Vice Chm)*
Board of Directors:
Wadee N. Al-Handel
Hardan N. Al-Handel
Mohammed N. Al-Handel
Atheer G. Al-Qadi
Jassim Y. Zwier

ASHUTOSH PAPER MILLS LIMITED

D-19 Arya Nagar Apartment 911 P Extension
New Delhi, 110092, India
Tel.: (91) 11 43206710
Fax: (91) 11 22482084
E-Mail: info@ashutoshpapermills.com
Web Site: www.ashutoshpapermills.com
Year Founded: 1988
531568—(BOM)
Business Description:
Paper Product Mfr
S.I.C.: 2621
N.A.I.C.S.: 322121
Personnel:
Amit Agarwal *(Compliance Officer)*
Tapasya Mittal Jain *(Sec)*
Board of Directors:
Sunil Kumar Agarwal
Vinod Kumar Jain
Santosh Kumar Yadav

ASI ENTERTAINMENT, INC.

Level 7 24 Collins Street
Melbourne, VIC, 3000, Australia
Tel.: (61) 3 9016 3021
ASIQ—(OTC)
Rev.: $7,768
Assets: $43,592
Liabilities: $543,007
Net Worth: ($499,415)
Earnings: ($63,055)
Fiscal Year-end: 06/30/13
Business Description:
In-Flight Communications
S.I.C.: 3663
N.A.I.C.S.: 334220
Personnel:
Richard Lukso *(Chm)*
Ronald J. Chapman *(Pres)*
Philip A. Shiels *(CEO & CFO)*
Board of Directors:
Richard Lukso
Ronald J. Chapman
Graham O. Chappell
Philip A. Shiels

ASIA AGRICULTURAL MACHINERY CO., LTD.

168 Geum-dong Yuga-myeon
Dalseong-gun, Daegu, Korea (South)
Tel.: (82) 535807777
Fax: (82) 535807700
Web Site: www.asiakor.com
Year Founded: 1945
050860—(KRS)
Business Description:
Agricultural Machinery Mfr
S.I.C.: 3523
N.A.I.C.S.: 333111
Personnel:
Woong Gil Kim *(CEO)*
Plant:

Asia Agricultural Machinery Co., Ltd. - First Factory (1)
168 Geum-dong Yuga-myeon
Dalseong-gun, Daegu, Korea (South)
Tel.: (82) 12311594
Fax: (82) 53 580 7700
Agriculture Machinery Mfr
S.I.C.: 3523
N.A.I.C.S.: 333111

ASIA ALLIANCE HOLDINGS CO., LTD.

3F LB Building 3-14-4 Shirokanedai
Minato-ku
Tokyo, Japan
Tel.: (81) 356388560
Fax: (81) 356388733
Web Site: www.aah.co.jp
9318—(TKS)
Sls.: $29,022,400
Assets: $28,659,378
Liabilities: $8,914,752
Net Worth: $19,744,626
Earnings: ($6,361,641)
Emp.: 48
Fiscal Year-end: 03/31/13
Business Description:
Investment Services
S.I.C.: 6211
N.A.I.C.S.: 523999
Personnel:
ZiLin Yang *(Chm)*
Yoshinori Funato *(Pres & CEO)*
Board of Directors:
ZiLin Yang
Katsumori Matsushima
Akihiro Nagahara
Hideo Sakamaki
Subsidiaries:

Kosugi Sangyo Co., Ltd. (1)
8-5 Nihonbashi Horidome 2-Chome
Chuo-Ku, Tokyo, 103 8550, Japan JP
Tel.: (81) 336623111
Fax: (81) 336623125
E-Mail: otayori@kosugi.co.jp
Web Site: www.kosugi.jp
Rev.: $224,351,180
Emp.: 566
Wearing Apparel Mfr & Sales
Import Export
S.I.C.: 5611
N.A.I.C.S.: 448110

ASIA ALUMINIUM HOLDINGS LIMITED

12th Floor Railway Plaza
39 Chatham Road South
Kowloon, China (Hong Kong)
Tel.: (852) 21568688
Fax: (852) 85223981808
Web Site: www.asiaalumgroup.com
Sales Range: $400-449.9 Million
Business Description:
Aluminum Extrusion Services
S.I.C.: 3354
N.A.I.C.S.: 331318
Personnel:
Kwong Wui Chun *(Chm)*

Asia Aluminium Holdings Limited—(Continued)

Chan Yiu Tsuan *(Deputy Chm & CEO)*
Gilbert Lau Yu Ching *(CFO)*
Chou Shun Alan *(Treas & Dir-Corp Fin)*
Anita Yee Kit Lin *(Sec)*
Board of Directors:
Kwong Wui Chun
Benby Chan Yiu Tsuan
Ma Tsz Chun
Zhong Jianqiu
Chan Yiu Tsuan
Russell Young

Non-U.S. Subsidiary:

Foshan Nanhai Xinya Aluminum & Stainless Steel Co., Ltd. **(1)**
Guijang Road
Nanhai, Foshan, Guangdong, China(100%)
Tel.: (86) 75785562333
Fax: (86) 75785557721
Aluminum & Stainless Steel Mfr
S.I.C.: 3399
N.A.I.C.S.: 331221

ASIA AVIATION PUBLIC COMPANY LIMITED

Floor 1 OSC Bldg 99 Moo 5
Kingkaew Road
Rachatewa
Bangplee, Samut Prakan, 10540, Thailand
Tel.: (66) 23159800
Fax: (66) 23159801
Web Site: www.aavplc.com
AAV—(THA)
Business Description:
Air Transportation Services
S.I.C.: 4512
N.A.I.C.S.: 481111
Personnel:
Pongsathorn Siriyodhin *(Chm)*

ASIA BIO-CHEM GROUP CORP.

Suite 2105-130 Adelaide Street West
Toronto, ON, M5H 3P5, Canada
Tel.: (416) 603-7500
Fax: (416) 603-8015
E-Mail: info@asiabiochem.com
Web Site: www.asiabiochem.com
Year Founded: 2005
ABC—(TSX)
Sls.: $129,660,120
Assets: $220,169,079
Liabilities: $161,366,722
Net Worth: $58,802,357
Earnings: ($39,044,604)
Emp.: 1,137
Fiscal Year-end: 12/31/12
Business Description:
Corn Starch Mfr
S.I.C.: 2046
N.A.I.C.S.: 311221
Personnel:
Zhiping Wang *(Chm, Pres & CEO)*
Elaine Lanfeng Zhao *(CFO)*
Robert Wilson *(Exec VP)*
Board of Directors:
Zhiping Wang
Jeremy N. Kendall
Brent Majkrzak
William E. Thomson
Robert Wilson
Elaine Lanfeng Zhao

Computershare Investor Services Inc.
510 Burrard Street 2nd Floor
Vancouver, BC, V6C 3B9, Canada

Transfer Agents:
Computershare Investor Services Inc.
510 Burrard Street 2nd Floor
Vancouver, BC, V6C 3B9, Canada

Computershare Investor Services Inc.
Montreal, QC, Canada

ASIA BIOENERGY TECHNOLOGIES BHD

13A06 Lobby 1 Block A Damansara Intan
1 Jalan SS20/27, Petaling Jaya, 47400, Malaysia
Tel.: (60) 3 7726 0668
Fax: (60) 3 7725 0668
E-Mail: mail@bioenergy.com.my
Web Site: www.bioenergy.com.my
ASIABIO—(KLS)
Sales Range: Less than $1 Million
Emp.: 21
Business Description:
Technology Services
S.I.C.: 7379
N.A.I.C.S.: 541519
Personnel:
Kok Keong Leung *(Chm)*
Woah Fen Loh *(Sec)*
Board of Directors:
Kok Keong Leung
Alex Choy
Chong Hoe Lee
Kim Chu Lim
Kem Loong Looi

Subsidiaries:

Grand Inizio Sdn. Bhd. **(1)**
3A-07 Lbby 3 Block C Damansara Intan
No 1 Jalan SS20/27, 47400 Petaling Jaya, Selangor, Malaysia
Tel.: (60) 3 7728 1889
Fax: (60) 3 7727 1998
E-Mail: mail@grandinizio.com.my
Web Site: www.grandinizio.com.my
Emp.: 30
Chemical Process Consulting Services
S.I.C.: 8999
N.A.I.C.S.: 541690
Beh Seng Kee *(CEO)*

Platinum Energy Sdn. Bhd. **(1)**
1st Fl S Wing Block Syed Kechik Found Bldg
Jalan Kapas Bangsar, 59100 Kuala Lumpur, Malaysia
Tel.: (60) 3 2095 1080
Fax: (60) 3 2096 1080
E-Mail: office@platinumenergy.biz
Web Site: www.platinumenergy.biz
Biodiesel Mfr
S.I.C.: 5989
N.A.I.C.S.: 454310
Sushil Singh Sidhu *(CEO)*
Edward Leung Kok Keong *(CFO)*
Anbath Shanmugam *(CFO)*

Subsidiary:

Ganz Biofuels Sdn. Bhd. **(2)**
Jalan Usaha 9
Melaka, Melaka, 75450, Malaysia
Tel.: (60) 6 2323118
Fax: (60) 6 2321218
Biodiesel Mfr
S.I.C.: 5989
N.A.I.C.S.: 454310

STSB Technology Sdn. Bhd. **(1)**
57-1 Persiaran Bayan Indah
Bayan Bay, 11900 Sungai Nibong, Penang, Malaysia
Tel.: (60) 46411887
Fax: (60) 46456698
E-Mail: mail@stsb.biz
Web Site: www.tmf-group.com.my
Online Training Services
S.I.C.: 8243
N.A.I.C.S.: 611420

ASIA BRANDS BERHAD

(Formerly Hing Yiap Group Berhad)
Lot 10449 Batu 4 1/2 Kampung Jawa
41000 Kelang, Selangor Darul Essan, Malaysia
Tel.: (60) 3 5161 8822
Fax: (60) 3 5161 2728
E-Mail: info@asiabrands.com.my
Web Site: www.asiabrands.com.my
Year Founded: 1970
ASIABRN—(KLS)
Rev.: $61,935,739
Assets: $150,579,824
Liabilities: $87,697,540
Net Worth: $62,882,285
Earnings: $5,640,394
Fiscal Year-end: 03/31/13
Business Description:
Textile & Apparel Mfr & Distr
S.I.C.: 2299
N.A.I.C.S.: 313310
Personnel:
Yong Hock Cheah *(CEO)*
Daniel Tai Meng Kok *(CFO)*
Jeannie Ben Cheh Yap *(COO)*
Jasmine Siew Chin Chew *(CEO-Baby Products)*
Yean Fung Lee *(CEO-Casualwear)*
Siew Chuan Chua *(Co-Sec)*
Chooi Peng Mak *(Co-Sec)*
Board of Directors:
Chin Huat Ng
Yong Hock Cheah
Sau Kian Kong
Kim Meng Lim

Subsidiaries:

Bumcity Sdn. Bhd. **(1)**
Lot 59 60 Lorong Kuang Bulan
Taman Kepong, Kuala Lumpur, Malaysia
Tel.: (60) 3 6272 4360
Fax: (60) 3 6275 5036
Specialty Clothing Stores Operator
S.I.C.: 5699
N.A.I.C.S.: 448190

Diesel Marketing Sdn. Bhd. **(1)**
Lot 59 60 Lorong Kuang Butan
Taman Kepong, Kuala Lumpur, 52100, Malaysia
Tel.: (60) 3 6272 4360
Fax: (60) 3 6275 5036
E-Mail: mail@hingyiap.com
Web Site: www.hingyiap.com
Ready-Made Casual Clothing Retail & Distribution
S.I.C.: 5699
N.A.I.C.S.: 448190

VFUSA Marketing Sdn. Bhd. **(1)**
Lot 46 Lorong Kuang Bulan
Taman Kepong, Kuala Lumpur, Malaysia
Tel.: (60) 362726573
Fax: (60) 362726581
E-Mail: hkhoo@hinkyiac.com
Ready-Made Women's Lingerie Retail & Distribution
S.I.C.: 5699
N.A.I.C.S.: 448190

ASIA CAPITAL PLC

21-01 W Tower World Trade Ctr
Echelon Sq
1 Colombo, Sri Lanka
Tel.: (94) 115320000
Fax: (94) 112336018
E-Mail: enquiry@asiacapital.lk
Web Site: www.asiacapital.lk
ACAP—(COL)
Sales Range: $10-24.9 Million
Business Description:
Investment Banking Services
S.I.C.: 6211
N.A.I.C.S.: 523110
Personnel:
H. L. L. Manohan Nanayakkara *(Chm & Mng Dir)*
J. H. Paul Ratnayeke *(Vice Chm)*
Asanga C. Seneviratne *(CEO)*
Andrew D. Ross *(Mng Dir)*
Mayura Fernando *(CFO)*
Stefan Abeyesinhe *(COO)*
Board of Directors:
H. L. L. Manohan Nanayakkara
J. H. Paul Ratnayeke
Andrew D. Ross
Asanga C. Seneviratne

Subsidiary:

Asia Asset Finance Ltd **(1)**
No 76/1 Dharmapala Mw
Colombo, Western Province, 00300, Sri Lanka
Tel.: (94) 11 2574682
Fax: (94) 11 2577477
Web Site: www.asiaassetfinance.lk
Financial Investment Management Services
S.I.C.: 6799
N.A.I.C.S.: 523920
Baya Muthukumarana *(Mng Dir)*

ASIA CARBON INDUSTRIES, INC.

Xi Gu Nan Street
Qing Xu County, Taiyuan, Shanxi, 030407, China
Tel.: (86) 351 5966868
Fax: (86) 351 5966308
E-Mail: ir@asiacarbonindustries.com
Web Site: www.asiacarbonindustries.com
Year Founded: 2008
ACRB—(OTC)
Sls.: $45,937,814
Assets: $39,807,914
Liabilities: $4,237,049
Net Worth: $35,570,865
Earnings: $6,453,248
Emp.: 202
Fiscal Year-end: 12/31/12
Business Description:
Holding Company; Carbon Black Mfr
S.I.C.: 6719
N.A.I.C.S.: 551112
Personnel:
Guoyun Yao *(Chm, Pres, CEO & Sec)*
Elaine Lanfeng Zhao *(CFO)*
Chunde Meng *(COO)*
Board of Directors:
Guoyun Yao
Shi Lei
Chunde Meng
Baozhu Ren
Jianjun Wang

ASIA CASSAVA RESOURCES HOLDINGS LIMITED

Units 612-3 & 617 Houston Centre 63
Mody Road Tsim Sha Tsui
Kowloon, China (Hong Kong)
Tel.: (852) 23699908
Fax: (852) 27214064
E-Mail: acr@asiacassava.com
Web Site: www.asiacassava.com
0841—(HKG)
Rev.: $504,605,206
Assets: $142,972,410
Liabilities: $71,406,320
Net Worth: $71,566,089
Earnings: $3,947,546
Emp.: 75
Fiscal Year-end: 03/31/13
Business Description:
Dried Cassava Chips
S.I.C.: 0191
N.A.I.C.S.: 111998
Personnel:
Ming Chuan Chu *(Chm)*
Shing Kei Shum *(CFO & Sec)*
Board of Directors:
Ming Chuan Chu
Kwok Pui Fung
Ching Fun Lam
Kwan Hung Lee
Yuk Ming Liu
Matthew Man Yiu Yue

Royal Bank of Canada Trust Company (Cayman) Limited
4th Floor Royal Bank House 24 Shedden Road
Georgetown, Cayman Islands

Transfer Agents:
Tricor Investor Services Limited
26th Floor Tesbury Centre 28 Queens Road East
Wanchai, China (Hong Kong)
Royal Bank of Canada Trust Company (Cayman) Limited
4th Floor Royal Bank House 24 Shedden Road
Georgetown, Cayman Islands

Subsidiary:

Artwell Enterprises Limited (1)
Units 612 3 6/F Houston Ctr 63 Mody Rd
Kowloon, China (Hong Kong)
Tel.: (852) 23699908
Fax: (852) 27214064
E-Mail: artwell@artwellgroup.com.hk
Web Site: www.asiacassava.com.hk
Emp.: 20
Real Estate Investment Services
S.I.C.: 6531
N.A.I.C.S.: 531390
Ming-Chuan Chu *(Mgr)*

Non-U.S. Subsidiaries:

Alush (Thailand) Co., Ltd. (1)
59 Moo 1 Pranakorngserayutaya
13190 Ayutthaya, Thailand
Tel.: (66) 35366135
Fax: (66) 8522714064
Chemical Products Mfr
S.I.C.: 2869
N.A.I.C.S.: 325193
Chu Ming Chuan *(Dir-Asia Cassava Resources Holdings Limited)*

Rizhao Yushun Cassava Co. Ltd (1)
No 96 Xinghai Rd
Rizhao, China
Tel.: (86) 6333288028
Fax: (86) 6338028995
Citric Acid Mfr
S.I.C.: 2869
N.A.I.C.S.: 325199

ASIA CEMENT CORPORATION

30Th Floor Taipei Metro Tower 207
Thu Hwa South Re Sec 2
Taipei, 10675, Taiwan
Tel.: (886) 227338000
Fax: (886) 223785191
E-Mail: service@acc.com.tw
Web Site: www.acc.com.tw
1102—(TAI)
Rev.: $398,271,166
Assets: $4,175,433,684
Liabilities: $1,307,686,525
Net Worth: $2,867,747,159
Earnings: $211,185,953
Emp.: 613
Fiscal Year-end: 12/31/12

Business Description:
Cement & Concrete Mfr
S.I.C.: 3273
N.A.I.C.S.: 327320

Personnel:
Douglas Tong Hsu *(Chm)*
K. Y. Lee *(Pres)*
Y. F. Chang *(Chief Exec VP)*
R. H. Shao *(Exec VP)*

Board of Directors:
Douglas Tong Hsu
C. K. Chang
T. H. Chang
C. V. Chen
Ruey Long Chen
Connie Hsu
Peter Hsu
Sheng-cheng Hu
K. Y. Lee
Kao Chao Lee
Chin-Der Ou
Johnny Shih
H. S. Ying

Supervisory Board of Directors:
L. T. Chang
Champion Lee
K. T. Li
T. Y. Tung
S. Y. Wang

Transfer Agent:
Oriental Securities Corporation
3F No 86 Sec 1 Chongqing S Rd Zhongzheng Dist
Taipei, Taiwan

Subsidiaries:

Chiahui Power Corp. (1)
No 688 Sung-Tsai-Chiao Sun Shan village
Ming Hsiung Hsian, Chiayi, 621, Taiwan
Tel.: (886) 52721129
Fax: (886) 5 272 0200
Electric Power Generation Services
S.I.C.: 4931
N.A.I.C.S.: 221112

Fu Da Transportation Co., Ltd. (1)
No 139 Section 1 Datong Road
Xizhi, Taipei, 221, Taiwan
Tel.: (886) 223770788
Fax: (886) 223772984
Freight Trucking Services
S.I.C.: 4214
N.A.I.C.S.: 484110

Fu-Ming Transportation Co. Ltd. (1)
No 139 Section 1 Datong Road
Xizhi, Taipei, 221, Taiwan
Tel.: (886) 223770788
Fax: (886) 223772984
Web Site: www.fu-ming.com.tw
Freight Trucking Services
S.I.C.: 4212
N.A.I.C.S.: 484110

Nan Hwa Cement Corp. (1)
No 90 Section 2 Lin Gaang Road
Longjing, Taichung, 411, Taiwan
Tel.: (886) 426392688
Fax: (886) 4 2639 4505
E-Mail: nanhwa@sparqnet.net
Web Site: www.asiacement.com.tw/en/product/dept_cata.asp?dt_class=5&dt_area=5
Furnace Slag Powder Mfr
S.I.C.: 3295
N.A.I.C.S.: 327992

Ya Tung Ready-Mixed Concrete Corp. (1)
No 139 Section 1 Datong Road
Xizhi, Taipei, 221, Taiwan
Tel.: (886) 286923315
Fax: (886) 2 2690 2494
E-Mail: services@mail.yatung.com.tw
Web Site: www.yatung.com.tw
Ready Mix Concrete Mfr
S.I.C.: 3273
N.A.I.C.S.: 327320

Plants:

Asia Cement Corporation - Hsinchu Plant (1)
No 109 Section 2 Chung-Feng Road
Ta-Tu Hengshan, Hsin-chu, Taiwan
Tel.: (886) 3 5931011
Fax: (886) 3 5932837
E-Mail: acchc@msct.asiacement.com.tw
Web Site: www.acc.com.tw/en/product/dept_cata.asp?dt_class=5&dt_area=5
Cement & Clinker Mfr
S.I.C.: 3241
N.A.I.C.S.: 327310
P. T. Chang *(Mgr)*

Asia Cement Corporation - Hualien Plant (1)
125 Singsing Road
Singcheng, Hua-lien, 97163, Taiwan
Tel.: (886) 38612101
Fax: (886) 3 861 2108
E-Mail: acchl@mshl.asiacement.com.tw
Cement & Clinker Mfr
S.I.C.: 3241
N.A.I.C.S.: 327310

Non-U.S. Subsidiaries:

Asia Cement (China) Holdings Corporation (1)
No 6 Yadong Avenue Ma-Tou Town
Ruichang, Jiangxi, 332207, China
Tel.: (86) 792 4888999
Fax: (86) 792 4886998
Web Site: www.achc.com.cn/en/index.asp
0743—(HKG OTC)
Rev.: $1,061,777,069
Assets: $2,485,837,931
Liabilities: $1,074,665,363
Net Worth: $1,411,172,568
Earnings: $64,589,363
Emp.: 4,148
Fiscal Year-end: 12/31/12
Holding Company; Cement, Concrete & Related Products Mfr & Sales
S.I.C.: 6719
N.A.I.C.S.: 551112
Tsai-hsiung Chang *(Vice Chm)*
Chung-lih Wu *(CEO, Chief Admin Officer & Compliance Officer)*
Seng-chang Lin *(Deputy CEO & CMO)*
Chen-kuen Chang *(Deputy CEO & Chief Technical Officer)*
Ruey-huey Chiang Shao *(CFO)*
Lu-hsing Fang *(Deputy Chief Admin Officer)*
Wai Kit Lo *(Sec)*

Asia Cement (Singapore) Pte. Ltd. (1)
5 Little Road 09-01/02 Cemtex Industrial Building
Singapore, Singapore
Tel.: (65) 62828733
Fax: (65) 62866300
E-Mail: asiacmt@asiacement.com.sg
Web Site: www.asiacement.com.sg
Emp.: 20
Cement Whslr
S.I.C.: 3241
N.A.I.C.S.: 327310
J. H. Lin *(Gen Mgr)*

Asia Continent Investment Holdings Pte. Ltd. (1)
5 Little Road 09-01 Cemtex Industrial Building
Singapore, Singapore
Tel.: (65) 62828733
Fax: (65) 62866300
Emp.: 6
Investment Management Services
S.I.C.: 6282
N.A.I.C.S.: 523920

Nanchang Yadong Cement Co., Ltd. (1)
Industries 2 Road Changdong Industrial Zone
Nanchang, Jiangxi, 330012, China
Tel.: (86) 7918352214
Fax: (86) 7914886998
Cement Mfr
S.I.C.: 3241
N.A.I.C.S.: 327310

Sichuan Yadong Cement Co., Ltd. (1)
No 66 An Peng Road Peng Zhou City
Chengdu, Sichuan, 611930, China
Tel.: (86) 2883731000
Fax: (86) 2883730702
Web Site: www.yadong-sc.com
Cement Mfr
S.I.C.: 3241
N.A.I.C.S.: 327310

Sichuan Yali Transport Co., Ltd. (1)
No 68 An Peng Road
Chengdu, Sichuan, 610000, China
Tel.: (86) 28 8373 1222
Fax: (86) 28 8373 0705
General Freight Trucking Services
S.I.C.: 4214
N.A.I.C.S.: 484110

ASIA CERAMICS HOLDINGS PLC

12 Castle Street
Saint Helier, JE2 3RT, Jersey
Tel.: (44) 7776481237
E-Mail: investor-relations@asiaceramicplc.com
Web Site: www.asiaceramicplc.com
Year Founded: 2010
ACHP—(AIM)
Rev.: $15,124,860
Assets: $4,625,740
Liabilities: $3,149,104
Net Worth: $1,476,636
Earnings: $90,020
Emp.: 65
Fiscal Year-end: 12/31/12

Business Description:
Ceramic Tile & Sanitary Ware Products Distr
S.I.C.: 3259
N.A.I.C.S.: 327120

Personnel:
Dingxin Pu *(CEO)*
Shouyuan Wu *(CFO)*
Dongen Jin *(Sec)*

Board of Directors:
Frank Lewis
Alei Duan
Weifeng Liu
Wenxian Liu
Dingxin Pu
Shouyuan Wu
Yangjing Zhang

Legal Counsel:
Pinsent Masons LLP
CityPoint One Ropemaker Street
London, United Kingdom
HBJ Gateley Wareing LLP
3 Hardman Square Spinningfields
Manchester, United Kingdom
Carey Olsen
47 Esplande
Saint Helier, Jersey
Beijing Yingke Law Firm
2-103 105 Shiqiao World Trade Mission 16B
Dongsanhuan Zhong Road
Chaoyang, Beijing, 100022, China

ASIA COAL LIMITED

Unit A 60th Floor Bank of China Tower 1 Garden Road
Hong Kong, China (Hong Kong)
Tel.: (852) 21520098
Fax: (852) 21520810
E-Mail: info@nubrandsgroup.com
Web Site: www.asiacoallimited.com
0835—(HKG)
Rev.: $1,125,476
Assets: $17,828,498
Liabilities: $5,784,310
Net Worth: $12,044,188
Earnings: ($6,801,081)
Emp.: 56
Fiscal Year-end: 03/31/13

Business Description:
Investment Services; Coal Mining & Personal Care Products
S.I.C.: 6211
N.A.I.C.S.: 523999

Personnel:
Xinjiang Zhu *(Chm)*
Silver Chi Kang Kung *(CEO)*
Kwok Wang Chen *(Sec)*

Board of Directors:
Xinjiang Zhu
Edward John Hill, III
Tony Man Kin Ho
Silver Chi Kang Kung
Peter Kar Fai Li
David Lee Sun
Derek Emory Ting Lap Yeung

Legal Counsel:
Patrick Mak & Tse
16/F Nan Fung Tower 173 Des Voeux Road
Hong Kong, China (Hong Kong)
Butterfield Fulcrum Group (Bermuda) Limited
26 Burnaby Street
Hamilton, HM 11, Bermuda

ASIA COMMERCIAL HOLDINGS LIMITED

19th Floor 9 Des Voeux Road West
Hong Kong, China (Hong Kong)
Tel.: (852) 28196192
Fax: (852) 28179043
Web Site: www.asiacommercialholdings.com
0104—(HKG)
Sls.: $141,663,567
Assets: $135,802,274
Liabilities: $65,263,142
Net Worth: $70,539,132
Earnings: ($26,917,539)
Emp.: 451

Asia Commercial Holdings Limited—(Continued)

Fiscal Year-end: 03/31/13

Business Description:
Watch Whslr
S.I.C.: 5094
N.A.I.C.S.: 423940

Personnel:
Yin Eav *(Founder & Chm)*
Ka Chung Cheng *(Sec & Dir-Fin)*

Board of Directors:
Yin Eav
Henry Ming Chi Duong
Kinson Ming Keong Eav
Si Ming Lai
Vincent Tat Cheung Lee
Andre Francois Meier
Rosaline Wing Yue Wong

Butterfield Fulcrum Group (Bermuda) Limited
Rosebank Centre 11 Bermudiana Road
Pembroke, Bermuda

Subsidiaries:

Accord Watch & Jewellery (International) Limited **(1)**
19th Floor 9 Des Voeux Road West
Hong Kong, China (Hong Kong)
Tel.: (852) 25173008
Fax: (852) 28576700
E-Mail: info@accordinternational.com
Web Site: www.accordinternational.com
Watches & Luxury Products Whslr
S.I.C.: 5094
N.A.I.C.S.: 423940

Juvenia (Hong Kong) Company Limited **(1)**
Room A D 13 F Hk Industrial Building 444 - 452 Des Voeux Road West
Western District, Kowloon, China (Hong Kong)
Tel.: (852) 28196192
Fax: (852) 28179043
Watches & Luxury Products Whslr
S.I.C.: 5094
N.A.I.C.S.: 423940

Time City (Hong Kong) Limited **(1)**
19 F 9 Des Voeux Road West
Western District, Kowloon, China (Hong Kong)
Tel.: (852) 28196192
Fax: (852) 28178741
Watches & Luxury Products Sales
S.I.C.: 5094
N.A.I.C.S.: 423940

Non-U.S. Subsidiary:

Juvenia Montres S.A. **(1)**
rue du Chatelot 21
2300 La Chaux-de-Fonds, Switzerland
Tel.: (41) 329257000
Fax: (41) 329257008
E-Mail: info@juvenia.ch
Web Site: www.juvenia.com
Emp.: 12
Jewelry & Watches Whslr
S.I.C.: 5094
N.A.I.C.S.: 423940
Andre Meier *(Mng Dir)*

ASIA COMMERCIAL JOINT STOCK BANK

442 Nguyen Thi Minh Kha District 3
Ho Chi Minh City, Vietnam
Tel.: (84) 8 3929 0999
Fax: (84) 8 3834 3269
E-Mail: acb-er@acb.com.vn
Web Site: www.acb.com.vn
Year Founded: 1993
ACB—(HNX)
Rev.: $1,113,452,750
Assets: $8,815,380,350
Liabilities: $8,184,157,750
Net Worth: $631,222,600
Earnings: $39,202,000
Emp.: 10,275
Fiscal Year-end: 12/31/12

Business Description:
Commercial Banking Services
S.I.C.: 6029
N.A.I.C.S.: 522110

Personnel:
Hung Huy Tran *(Chm)*
Nghia Hiep Huynh *(Chm-Supervisory Bd)*
Julian Loong Choon Fong *(Vice Chm)*
Van Tu Luong *(Vice Chm)*
Minh Toan Do *(Pres & Member-Mgmt Bd)*
Vijay Maheshwari *(CFO)*
Tan Tai Bui *(Member-Mgmt Bd & VP)*
Van Tuan Dam *(Member-Mgmt Bd & VP)*
Quang Tuan Huynh *(Member-Mgmt Bd & VP)*
Ba Dung Le *(Member-Mgmt Bd & VP)*
Duc Thai Han Nguyen *(Member-Mgmt Bd & VP)*
Thanh Toai Nguyen *(Member-Mgmt Bd & VP)*
Thi Hai Nguyen *(Member-Mgmt Bd & VP)*

Board of Directors:
Hung Huy Tran
Alain Cany
Van Tuan Dam
Thu Thuy Dang
Julian Loong Choon Fong
Stewart Donald Hall
Quang Tuan Huynh
Van Tu Luong
Thanh Long Nguyen
Mong Hung Tran
Trong Kien Tran

Supervisory Board of Directors:
Nghia Hiep Huynh
Ngan Hoang
Thi Tot Phung
Cao Phong Trieu

ASIA DIGITAL HOLDINGS PLC

19 Cavendish Square
London, W1A, United Kingdom
Tel.: (44) 20 7943 4200
Fax: (44) 20 7943 4215
Web Site: www.adhplc.com
Year Founded: 1999
ADH—(AIM)
Sales Range: $1-9.9 Million
Emp.: 97

Business Description:
Online Marketing Services
S.I.C.: 8742
N.A.I.C.S.: 541613

Personnel:
Adrian Moss *(CEO)*
Keith Lassman *(Sec)*

Board of Directors:
David Lees
Keith Lassman
Adrian Moss

Legal Counsel:
Howard Kennedy
19 Cavendish Square
London, W1A 2AW, United Kingdom
Tel.: (44) 20 7636 1616
Fax: (44) 20 7491 2899

Non-U.S. Subsidiaries:

Aktiv Digital Asia Pacific Pte Limited **(1)**
42B Boat Quay
Singapore, 049831, Singapore
Tel.: (65) 65089230
Fax: (65) 65089231
E-Mail: interested@aktivdigital.com
Web Site: www.aktivgroup.com
Emp.: 20
Advertising Agency
S.I.C.: 8742
N.A.I.C.S.: 541613
Mett Sutton *(Mng Dir)*

DGM Asia Pacific Limited **(1)**
42B Boat Quay
Singapore, 049415, Singapore
Tel.: (65) 65089211
Fax: (65) 65089219
E-Mail: interested@dgm-sg.com
Web Site: www.dgmsearchlab.sg/contact-dgmsearchlab.php
Emp.: 10
Online Marketing Services
S.I.C.: 8742
N.A.I.C.S.: 541613
James Hawkins *(Mng Dir)*

ASIA ENERGY LOGISTICS GROUP LIMITED

Unit 1708 17/F International Commerce Centre 1 Austin Road West
Kowloon, China (Hong Kong)
Tel.: (852) 3746 6666
Fax: (852) 3907 0663
E-Mail: enquiries@aelg.com.hk
Web Site: www.aelg.com.hk
0351—(HKG)
Assets: $285,785,051
Liabilities: $174,939,631
Net Worth: $110,845,420
Earnings: ($7,061,560)
Emp.: 135
Fiscal Year-end: 12/31/12

Business Description:
Construction Management Service
S.I.C.: 0762
N.A.I.C.S.: 115116

Personnel:
Pui Man Ho *(Sec)*

Board of Directors:
Baodong Yu
Chi Yuen Chan
David Ka Keung Fung
Jun Liang
Victor Fung Shuen Sit
Wei Sun
On Kin Tse
Sau Lai Yu
Xi Zhang

Transfer Agent:
Tricor Secretaries Limited
26th Floor Tesbury Centre 28 Queen's Road East
Wanchai, China (Hong Kong)

ASIA ENTERPRISES HOLDING LIMITED

3 Pioneer Sector Walk
Singapore, Singapore
Tel.: (65) 62236377
Fax: (65) 68619486
Web Site: www.asiaenterprises.com.sg
A55—(SES)
Rev.: $108,280,126
Assets: $101,717,669
Liabilities: $8,008,545
Net Worth: $93,709,124
Earnings: $1,351,356
Fiscal Year-end: 12/31/12

Business Description:
Steel Mfr
S.I.C.: 3399
N.A.I.C.S.: 331110

Personnel:
Choon Bok Lee *(Chm)*
Yvonne Yih Chyi Lee *(Mng Dir)*
Kok Liang Chew *(Co-Sec)*
Nathaniel Chelvarajah Vanniasingham *(Co-Sec)*

Board of Directors:
Choon Bok Lee
Bon Leong Lee
Yvonne Yih Chyi Lee
Peter Keh Yan Tan
Keng Thwan Teo

Subsidiary:

Asia-Beni Steel Industries (Pte) Ltd **(1)**
3 Pioneer Sector Walk
Singapore, 627897, Singapore
Tel.: (65) 68613677
Fax: (65) 68632468
E-Mail: sales@asiaenterprises.com.sg
Steel Processing Services
S.I.C.: 3399
N.A.I.C.S.: 331110
Yvonne Lee *(Mgr)*

ASIA ENTERTAINMENT & RESOURCES LTD.

Unit 605 East Town Building 16 Fenwick Street
Wanchai, China (Hong Kong)
Tel.: (852) 21119220
Fax: (852) 21109420
E-Mail: info@aerlf.com
Web Site: www.aerlf.com
Year Founded: 2007
AERL—(NASDAQ)
Rev.: $236,300,623
Assets: $377,467,005
Liabilities: $161,400,764
Net Worth: $216,066,241
Earnings: $70,119,242
Emp.: 17
Fiscal Year-end: 12/31/12

Business Description:
Casino Hotels
S.I.C.: 7999
N.A.I.C.S.: 713290

Personnel:
Chien Lee *(Chm)*
Leong Siak Hung *(CEO)*
Chung Ming Li *(CFO)*

Board of Directors:
Chien Lee
Peter Li
Michael Zhang

ASIA ENVIRONMENT HOLDINGS LTD.

77 Robinson Rd
15-01 SIA Building, Singapore, 068896, Singapore
Tel.: (65) 63232343
Fax: (65) 63232423
E-Mail: asiaenv@asiaenv.com
Web Site: www.asiaenv.com
Sales Range: $75-99.9 Million

Business Description:
Integrated Water & Wastewater Treatment Solutions
S.I.C.: 9511
N.A.I.C.S.: 924110

Personnel:
Hongchun Wang *(CEO)*
Koh Poh Yeok *(CFO)*
Huang Zhengxin *(COO)*
Hsueh Ching Long *(Sec)*

Subsidiary:

WB Engineering and Consultancy Pte Ltd **(1)**
65 Chulia St 39-08 OCBC Centre
Singapore, 49513, Singapore
Tel.: (65) 63097488
Fax: (65) 63097480
Environmental Engineering Services
S.I.C.: 8711
N.A.I.C.S.: 541330
Chun Wang Hong *(CEO)*

Non-U.S. Subsidiary:

Yixing Quanxi E.P. Co., Ltd. **(1)**
Xiazhu Street
Zhoutie Town, Yixing, Jiangsu, 214263, China
Tel.: (86) 51087575805
Environmental Protection Equipment Mfr
S.I.C.: 3589
N.A.I.C.S.: 333318

ASIA EURO OIL PLC

77 Gracechurch Street
London, EC3V 0AS, United Kingdom
Tel.: (44) 20 343 28179
Fax: (44) 20 313 75286

E-Mail: info@asiaeurooil.com
Web Site: www.asiaeurooil.com
AEY—(DEU)
Sales Range: Less than $1 Million
Business Description:
Oil & Gas Exploration & Production
S.I.C.: 1311
N.A.I.C.S.: 211111
Personnel:
Mehmet Gulec *(CEO)*

ASIA FIBER PUBLIC COMPANY LIMITED
33 133 Surawongse Road
Bangrak, Bangkok, 10500, Thailand
Tel.: (66) 2632 7071
Fax: (66) 2236 1982
E-Mail: sales@asiafiber.com
Web Site: www.asiafiber.com
Year Founded: 1970
AFC—(THA)
Emp.: 618
Business Description:
Nylon Product Mfr & Distr
S.I.C.: 3999
N.A.I.C.S.: 339999
Personnel:
Namchai Namchaisiri *(Vice Chm)*
Chen Namchaisiri *(Pres)*
Jintana Thanatavee *(Sec)*
Board of Directors:
Tanace Kuvinichkul
Nipon Leelasithorn
Mongkol Mangkornkanok
Montri Mangkornkanok
Chen Namchaisiri
Namchai Namchaisiri
Somsak Puntanakasem
Pira Sirikietsoong
Tira Sirikietsoong
Vira Sirikietsoong
Vitoon Sirikietsoong
Terawat Tachapongvorachai
Vichien Tejapaibul
Jintana Thanatavee
Chaeng Thongthai
Payong U-Prasitwong
Yodjin Uahwatanasakul
Legal Counsel:
Adviser Law & Detective Co Ltd
111/93 Rajdamnern Condominium Nakornsawan Rd Pomprab
Bangkok, Thailand

ASIA FILE CORPORATION BHD.
Plot 16 Kawasan Perindustrian Bayan Lepas Phase 4 Mk12
11900 Bayan Lepas, Penang, Malaysia
Tel.: (60) 46426601
Fax: (60) 46426602
E-Mail: marketing@asia-file.com
Web Site: www.asia-file.com
ASIAFLE—(KLS)
Sales Range: $75-99.9 Million
Business Description:
Stationery Products Mfr
S.I.C.: 3999
N.A.I.C.S.: 327110
Personnel:
Soon Huat Lim *(Chm)*
Voon Kean Lam *(Sec)*
Board of Directors:
Soon Huat Lim
Nurjannah Ali
Khai Hong Khoo
Ean Chin Ooi
Subsidiaries:

ABBA Marketing Sdn. Bhd. **(1)**
Plot 16 Kawasan Perindustrian Phase 4 Mukin
11900 Bayan Lepas, Pulau Pinang, Malaysia
Tel.: (60) 46425199
Fax: (60) 46426602
E-Mail: scmsales@asia-file.com
Emp.: 6
Stationery Products Distr
S.I.C.: 5112
N.A.I.C.S.: 424120
Lim Soon Huat *(Mng Dir)*

Sin Chuan Marketing Sdn. Bhd. **(1)**
No 3 Jln Bp 4/8 Bandar Bukit Puchong
47100 Puchong, Selangor, Malaysia
Tel.: (60) 380685324
Fax: (60) 380685049
E-Mail: scmsales@asia-file.com
Web Site: www.asia-file.com
Stationery Products Distr
S.I.C.: 5112
N.A.I.C.S.: 424120

Non-U.S. Subsidiaries:

Plastoreg Smidt GmbH (Office Supplies Division) **(1)**
Zur Furthmuehle 4
37318 Kirchgandern, Thuringia, Germany
Tel.: (49) 36081640
Fax: (49) 3608164133
E-Mail: info@plastoreg.de
Web Site: www.standardfertigung.plastoreg.de/home-en/
Dividers Mfr
S.I.C.: 2678
N.A.I.C.S.: 322230
Diana Lindemann *(Co-Sec)*
Sandra Schelper *(Co-Sec)*

Plastoreg Smidt GmbH (Specials Division) **(1)**
Kasseler Landstrasse 12
37213 Witzenhausen, Hesse, Germany
Tel.: (49) 55426060
Fax: (49) 554260622
E-Mail: specials@plastoreg.de
Web Site: www.plastoreg.de
Emp.: 60
Dividers Mfr
S.I.C.: 2678
N.A.I.C.S.: 322230
Uwe Smidt *(Mng Dir)*

Premier Stationery Limited **(1)**
Block 2 Gastons Wood
Basingstoke, Hampshire, RG24 8TW, United Kingdom
Tel.: (44) 1256335551
Fax: (44) 1256335552
E-Mail: info@premierstationery.co.uk
Web Site: www.premierstationery.co.uk
Emp.: 20
Stationery Products Import & Distr
S.I.C.: 5112
N.A.I.C.S.: 424120
Rod Martin *(Mng Dir)*

ASIA GREEN AGRICULTURE CORPORATION
Shuinan Industrial Area
Songxi County, Nanping, Fujian, 353500, China
Tel.: (86) 599 2335520
Year Founded: 2008
AGAC—(OTC)
Rev.: $125,736,770
Assets: $165,478,699
Liabilities: $29,842,705
Net Worth: $135,635,994
Earnings: $37,447,047
Emp.: 374
Fiscal Year-end: 12/31/12
Business Description:
Green & Organic Food Mfr & Distr
S.I.C.: 2033
N.A.I.C.S.: 311421
Personnel:
Youdai Zhan *(Chm, Pres & CEO)*
Alex Hon Siang Chin *(CFO & Sec)*
Board of Directors:
Youdai Zhan
Henry Sing Wai Cheng
Pak Sum Lum
Patrick Ka Wing Mak
He Zhang

ASIA GREEN ENERGY PUBLIC COMPANY LIMITED
273/1 Rama 2 Road Samaedam
Bangkhuntien
Bangkok, 10150, Thailand
Tel.: (66) 28940088
Fax: (66) 24531139
Web Site: www.agecoal.com
AGE—(THA)
Rev.: $145,913,874
Assets: $107,501,150
Liabilities: $70,614,874
Net Worth: $36,886,275
Earnings: ($802,819)
Emp.: 230
Fiscal Year-end: 12/31/12
Business Description:
Coal & Palm Shell Distr
S.I.C.: 5052
N.A.I.C.S.: 423520
Personnel:
Boonpen Bumpenboon *(Chm)*
Panom Kuansataporn *(CEO & Mng Dir)*
Somyos Thitisuriyarux *(Asst Mng Dir-Admin)*
Ni-orn Janjamsang *(Sec)*
Board of Directors:
Boonpen Bumpenboon
Panita Kuansataporn
Panom Kuansataporn
Panus Kuansataporn
Pinmanee Makmontana
Sirawit Subtechitmanee
Thawatchai Vorawandthanachai
Amphan Yosamornsuntorn

ASIA GROWTH VENTURE PLC
Chao Yang Men Nei Da Jie
Hua Xi Ge
Dong Cheng Qu Room 318, Beijing, 100010, China
Tel.: (86) 15210696366
E-Mail: chinamine.ew@gmail.com
Web Site: www.asiagrowthventure.com
ARV—(DEU)
Business Description:
Investment Services
S.I.C.: 6211
N.A.I.C.S.: 523999
Board of Directors:
Chengzhou Meng
Eddie Wee
Boa Cheng Zhao
Subsidiary:

Xing Cheng Mining Ltd **(1)**
Chao Yang Men Nei Da Jie Hua Xi Ge
Dongcheng Room 318
100010 Beijing, China
Tel.: (86) 15210696366
E-Mail: chinamine.ew@gmail.com
Web Site: www.asiagrowthventure.com
Shale Mining Services
S.I.C.: 1459
N.A.I.C.S.: 212325

ASIA INSURANCE CO.
No 299 Taleghani St
POB 15815-1885
Tehran, Iran 1599836511
Tel.: (98) 21 88800950
Fax: (98) 21 88898113
E-Mail: info@bimehasia.ir
Web Site: www.bimehasia.com
Year Founded: 1959
ASIA—(THE)
Business Description:
Insurance Services
S.I.C.: 6411
N.A.I.C.S.: 524298
Personnel:
A. Hajfataliha *(Mng Dir)*
Board of Directors:
A. Hajfataliha
F. Khojir
F. M. F. Moazzemi
R. Pirooz
A. Rostami

ASIA INSURANCE LIMITED
T K Bhaban 7th Floor 13 Karwan Bazar
Dhaka, 1215, Bangladesh
Tel.: (880) 2 91372244
Fax: (880) 2 913707
E-Mail: asiainsu@gmail.com
Web Site: www.asiainsurancebd.com
Year Founded: 2000
ASIAINS—(DHA)
Business Description:
Insurance Services
S.I.C.: 6411
N.A.I.C.S.: 524298
Personnel:
Yussuf Abdullah Harun *(Chm)*
Mohammed Jamal Ullah *(Vice Chm)*
A. F. M. Nazrul Islam *(Mng Dir)*
A. M. M. Abdullah-Al-Ziad *(Deputy Mng Dir)*
Mohammad Ali *(Deputy Mng Dir)*
Mohammad Emdadul Haque *(Deputy Mng Dir)*
A. K. M. Showkat Hasan Khan *(Deputy Mng Dir)*
Mohammad Atique Ullah Majumder *(Sec & Exec VP)*
Kazi Zakir Hossain *(Sr Exec VP)*
Board of Directors:
Yussuf Abdullah Harun
Farzana Afroze
Mohammad Jahangir Alam
Khaleda Begum
Abul Bashar Chowdhury
Mohammad Mustafa Haider
Alamgir Kabir
Mohammad Ali Khokan
Zaidi Sattar
Tarik Sujat
Mahbubul Alam Talukder
Mohammed Jamal Ullah

ASIA INTERACTIVE MEDIA INC.
Level 30 Bank of China Tower 1 Garden Road
Central, China (Hong Kong)
Tel.: (852) 9836 2643
Year Founded: 2000
Rev.: $21,785
Assets: $19,463
Liabilities: $21,443
Net Worth: ($1,980)
Earnings: ($17,775)
Fiscal Year-end: 12/31/12
Business Description:
Investment Services
S.I.C.: 6211
N.A.I.C.S.: 523999
Personnel:
Ken Ng *(Pres, CEO, CFO, Treas & Sec)*
Board of Directors:
Ken Ng

ASIA KNIGHT BERHAD
(Formerly Pahanco Corporation Berhad)
9 Jalan Bayu Tinggi 2A/KS6
Taipan 2 Batu Unjur, Kelang, Selangor Darul Ehsan, 41200, Malaysia
Tel.: (60) 333231916
Fax: (60) 3332335584
E-Mail: pahanco@tm.net.my
Web Site: www.pahanco.com.my
9954—(KLS)

Asia Knight Berhad—(Continued)

Rev.: $2,078,650
Assets: $17,077,326
Liabilities: $9,020,196
Net Worth: $8,057,129
Earnings: ($2,348,067)
Emp.: 134
Fiscal Year-end: 12/31/12

Business Description:
Plain & Laminated Particleboard Mfr
S.I.C.: 2434
N.A.I.C.S.: 337110

Personnel:
Teck Wah See *(Chm & Mng Dir)*
King Hua Lim *(Co-Sec)*
Kui Suang Lim *(Co-Sec)*
Paul Ignatius Stanislaus *(Co-Sec)*

Board of Directors:
Teck Wah See
Sukhinderjit Singh Muker
Tse Piao Ooi
Cheong Wei Seah
Hong Liong See
Seng Hong See
Andrew Meng Kit Su
Teng Cheok Tan

ASIA LOGISTICS (CHINA) LIMITED

Unit C 5F Block 1 Wah Fung Industrial Centre 33-39 Kwai Fung Crescent
Kwai Chung, China (Hong Kong)
Tel.: (852) 2545 4500
Fax: (852) 2944 8899
E-Mail: info@asialogistics.com.hk
Web Site: www.asialogistics.com.hk
Year Founded: 2000

Business Description:
Freight & Cargo Shipping Services
S.I.C.: 4731
N.A.I.C.S.: 488510

Personnel:
Stephan Lam *(Mgr)*

ASIA MEDIA CO., LTD.

C607 Shiji Kemao Building 66 Zhongguancun East Road
Haidian District, Beijing, 100190, China
Tel.: (86) 1062670066
Fax: (86) 1062672266
Web Site: www.asiamedia.jp
Emp.: 150

Business Description:
Television Program Guide Services
S.I.C.: 4833
N.A.I.C.S.: 515120

Personnel:
Zhang Kianwei *(CEO)*

ASIA MEDIA GROUP BERHAD

35 1st Floor Jalan Bandar 16
Pusat Bandar Puchong, Puchong, Selangor Darul Ehsan, 47100, Malaysia
Tel.: (60) 3 5882 7788
Fax: (60) 3 5882 6622
Web Site: www.asiamedia.net.my
AMEDIA—(KLS)

Business Description:
Digital Transit Media Services
S.I.C.: 7319
N.A.I.C.S.: 541890

Personnel:
Ricky Wong *(CEO)*

Subsidiary:

Asia Media Sdn Bhd (1)
No 35 1st Floor Jalan Bandar 16
Pusat Bandar Puchong, 47100 Puchong, Selangor Darul Ehsan, Malaysia
Tel.: (60) 3 5882 7788
Fax: (60) 3 5882 6622
E-Mail: hr@asiamedia.net.my
Web Site: www.asiamedia.net.my
Television Broadcasting Network Services
S.I.C.: 4833
N.A.I.C.S.: 515120

ASIA METAL PUBLIC COMPANY LIMITED

55 55/1 moo 2 Soi Watnamdaeng
Srinakarin Rd T Bangkaew
A Bangplee, Samut Prakan, 10540, Thailand
Tel.: (66) 2 383 4100
Fax: (66) 2 383 4102
E-Mail: info@asiametal.co.th
Web Site: www.asiametal.co.th
Year Founded: 1993
AMC—(THA)
Rev.: $243,619,467
Assets: $117,910,001
Liabilities: $61,282,880
Net Worth: $56,627,121
Earnings: $5,430,670
Emp.: 401
Fiscal Year-end: 12/31/12

Business Description:
Steel Product Mfr
S.I.C.: 3999
N.A.I.C.S.: 339999

Personnel:
Virachai Suteerachai *(Chm & Pres)*
Chusak Yongwongpaiboon *(Mng Dir)*
Penchan Yothinupamai *(Deputy Mng Dir)*

Board of Directors:
Virachai Suteerachai
Suree Burathanit
Jumpol Munmai
Taradee Piensumrit
Tisika Praisanguab
Tanakorn Ritthibanrue
Chanathib Trivuth
Chusak Yongwongpaiboon
Penchan Yothinupamai

ASIA MINERAL JOINT STOCK COMPANY

Lot 32C Nam Cam Ind Zone
Nghi Loc District, Vinh, Nghe An, Vietnam
Tel.: (84) 38 3791777
Fax: (84) 38 3791555
E-Mail: amc@amcvina.vn
Web Site: www.amcvina.vn
AMC—(HNX)
Emp.: 100

Business Description:
Stone Powder Mining, Exploration & Processing
S.I.C.: 1422
N.A.I.C.S.: 212312

Personnel:
Dien Trong Hoang *(CEO)*

ASIA NOW RESOURCES CORP.

330 Bay Street Suite 820
Toronto, ON, M5H 2S8, Canada
Tel.: (416) 364-7281
Fax: (416) 364-7711
E-Mail: info@asianow.ca
Web Site: www.asianow.ca
NOW—(TSXV)
Assets: $16,427,870
Liabilities: $1,419,544
Net Worth: $15,008,326
Earnings: ($8,710,464)
Fiscal Year-end: 12/31/12

Business Description:
Mineral Exploration Services
S.I.C.: 1081
N.A.I.C.S.: 213114

Personnel:
Marshall Cooper *(Chm)*
Lukman Wijaya *(Pres & CEO)*
Julio DiGirolamo *(CFO)*
Henry A. Harris *(Sec)*

Board of Directors:
Marshall Cooper
Elliott Jacobson
James Maitland Macintosh
Tai Chiu Ng
Bruce Reid
Alex Tjokrorahardjo
Lukman Wijaya
Wenjin Yang

Legal Counsel:
Gowling Lafleur Henderson LLP
1 First Canadian Place Suite 1600 100 King Street West
Toronto, ON, Canada

Beichuan Law Firm
14F Guangye Building, 2 Huguo Road
Kunming, Yunnan, China 650011
Tel.: (86) 8713116515

Transfer Agent:
Equity Transfer & Trust Company
200 University Avenue Ste 400
Toronto, ON, M5H 4H1, Canada
Tel.: (416) 361-0152
Fax: (416) 361-0470

ASIA OPTICAL CO., INC.

No 22-3 S 2nd Rd Taiwan Export Processing Zone
427 Taichung, Taiwan
Tel.: (886) 425342550
Fax: (886) 425335696
E-Mail: services@aoci.com.tw
Web Site: www.asia-optical.com.tw
3019—(TAI)
Sales Range: $100-124.9 Million
Emp.: 15,657

Business Description:
Optical Components Mfr
S.I.C.: 3851
N.A.I.C.S.: 339115

Personnel:
Robert Lai *(CEO)*
Albert Lin *(CMO)*

Non-U.S. Subsidiaries:

AOF Imaging Technology Limited (1)
2F Continental Electric Bldg 17 Wang Chiu Road
Kowloon Bay, Kowloon, China (Hong Kong)
Tel.: (852) 27508662
Fax: (852) 27508090
Web Site: www.aof-imaging.com
Emp.: 40
Optoelectronic Devices Mfr
S.I.C.: 3679
N.A.I.C.S.: 334419

Non-U.S. Subsidiaries:

AOF Imaging Technology, Japan Ltd. (2)
2F & 3F Benex S-3 Bldg 3-20-8 Shin-Yokohama
Kohoku-ku, Yokohama, Kanagawa, 222-0033, Japan
Tel.: (81) 454759228
Fax: (81) 266788320
Digital Camera & Optical Disk Drives Mfr
S.I.C.: 3572
N.A.I.C.S.: 334112
Masaaki Hino *(Sr Mgr-Sls)*

AOF Imaging Technology (Shenzhen) Co., Ltd. (2)
Li-Song-Lang 2nd Industrial District Gong Ming Street
Guang Ming New Zone, Shenzhen, Guandong, 518106, China
Tel.: (86) 755 2716 5959
Fax: (86) 755 2768 0039
Web Site: www.aof-imaging.com
Digital Camera & Optical Disk Drives Mfr
S.I.C.: 3572
N.A.I.C.S.: 334112

Asia Optical International Ltd. (1)
C/o Shellbourne Trust Company (bvi) Limited Palm Grove House
Wickhams Cay 1, Road Town, Tortola, VG1110, Virgin Islands (British)
Tel.: (284) 494 2616
Fax: (284) 494 2704
Investment Management Services
S.I.C.: 6282
N.A.I.C.S.: 523920
Selina Oneal *(Mgr)*

Scopro Optical Co., Inc. (1)
Boncraft Building Mayon Corner Pinatubo Street
1550 Mandaluyong, Philippines
Tel.: (63) 25347230
Fax: (63) 25315636
Web Site: www.scopro.net
Emp.: 600
Optical Components Mfr
S.I.C.: 3231
N.A.I.C.S.: 327215
Sean Huang *(Gen Mgr)*

ASIA ORIENT HOLDINGS LIMITED

30th Floor Asia Orient Tower Town Place 33 Lockhart Road
Wanchai, China (Hong Kong)
Tel.: (852) 28663336
Fax: (852) 28663722
Web Site: www.asiaorient.com.hk
0214—(HKG)
Sales Range: $150-199.9 Million
Emp.: 608

Business Description:
Property Management Services
S.I.C.: 6531
N.A.I.C.S.: 531311

Personnel:
Clement Siu To Fung *(Chm)*
Yin Cheng Lim *(Deputy Chm)*
Jing Poon *(CEO & Mng Dir)*
Pui Kan Lun *(Sec & Dir-Fin)*

Board of Directors:
Clement Siu To Fung
Kwok Wah Cheung
Yat Ming Hung
Phileas Po Lam Kwan
Yin Cheng Lim
Pui Kan Lun
Hai Poon
Jing Poon
Chi Keung Wong

Legal Counsel:
Stephenson Harwood
35th Floor Bank of China Tower 1 Garden Road
Central, China (Hong Kong)

Appleby
2206-19 Jardine House 1 Connaught Road
Central, China (Hong Kong)

Computershare Hong Kong Investor Services Limited
Shops 1712-1716 17th Floor Hopewell Centre
183 Queens Road East
Wanchai, China (Hong Kong)

Transfer Agent:
Computershare Hong Kong Investor Services Limited
Shops 1712-1716 17th Floor Hopewell Centre
183 Queens Road East
Wanchai, China (Hong Kong)

Subsidiaries:

Asia Orient Company Limited (1)
29-31 F Asia Orient Tower Town Pl 33 Lockhart Rd
Wanchai, China (Hong Kong)
Tel.: (852) 28663336
Fax: (852) 28663772
Web Site: www.asiastandard.com
Emp.: 50
Property Management Services
S.I.C.: 6531
N.A.I.C.S.: 531311
Samuel Fung *(Mgr)*

Prosperity Land Cleaning Service Limited (1)
30 F Asia Orient Tower Town Pl 33 Lockhard Rd
Wanchai, China (Hong Kong)
Tel.: (852) 29729831
Fax: (852) 25294692
E-Mail: alec@asia-standard.com.hk

Emp.: 50
Buildings & Residential Cleaning Services
S.I.C.: 7349
N.A.I.C.S.: 561720
Alec Wong *(Gen Mgr)*

Prosperity Land Estate Management Limited **(1)**
30 F Asia Orient Tower Town Pl 33
Lockhard Rd
Wanchai, China (Hong Kong)
Tel.: (852) 28663336
Fax: (852) 25294692
E-Mail: info@asiastandard.com.hk
Web Site: www.prosperityland.com.hk
Emp.: 10
Property Management Services
S.I.C.: 6531
N.A.I.C.S.: 531311
C. P. Wong *(Mgr)*

ASIA PACIFIC BOILER CORPORATION

(Formerly Panama Dreaming Inc.)
Unit 10 & 11 26th Floor Lippo Centre
Tower 2
89 Queensway Admiralty, Hong Kong, China (Hong Kong)
Tel.: (852) 3875 3362
Web Site:
Year Founded: 2011
PADR—(OTC)
Liabilities: $48,716
Net Worth: ($48,716)
Earnings: ($54,918)
Fiscal Year-end: 06/30/13

Business Description:
Investment Services
S.I.C.: 6211
N.A.I.C.S.: 523999

Personnel:
John Gong Chin Ong *(Chm)*
Qin XiuShan *(Pres)*
Chin Leong Yang *(CFO, Treas & Sec)*

Board of Directors:
John Gong Chin Ong

Transfer Agent:
Quicksilver Stock Transfer
6623 Las Vegas Blvd S 255
Las Vegas, NV 89119

THE ASIA-PACIFIC CENTRE FOR RESEARCH, INC.

(d/b/a ACRE, Inc.)
Rm 425 Cityland Pasong Tamo Tower
2210 Pasong Tamo Street
Makati, 1231, Philippines
Tel.: (63) 27572136
Fax: (63) 28931521
E-Mail: corporate@acreinc.net
Web Site: www.acreinc.net
Year Founded: 1989
Sales Range: $25-49.9 Million
Emp.: 75

Business Description:
Technology Research & Consulting Services; Software Distr
S.I.C.: 8731
N.A.I.C.S.: 541712

Personnel:
Nick B. Fontanilla *(Pres)*

ASIA PACIFIC DATA CENTRE

Level 4 88 Creek Street
Brisbane, QLD, 4000, Australia
Tel.: (61) 2 8072 4916
E-Mail: info@asiapacificdc.com
Web Site: www.asiapacificdc.com
AJD—(ASX)

Business Description:
Data Center Real Estate Investment Services
S.I.C.: 6211
N.A.I.C.S.: 523999

Personnel:
Ian Fraser *(Chm)*
Francina Turner *(CEO & Sec)*

Board of Directors:
Ian Fraser
Greg Baynton
Chris Breach
Francina Turner
John Wright

ASIA PACIFIC GENERAL INSURANCE CO. LIMITED

Green White Bhaban 3rd Floor 28
Bangabandhu Avenue
Dhaka, 1000, Bangladesh
Tel.: (880) 2 9555338
Fax: (880) 2 9558125
E-Mail: apgic@bdcom.com
Web Site: www.apgicl.com
Year Founded: 1999
ASIAPACINS—(DHA)
Sales Range: $1-9.9 Million

Business Description:
Insurance Services
S.I.C.: 6411
N.A.I.C.S.: 524298

Personnel:
Aftab ul Islam *(Chm)*
Kashimiri Kamal *(Vice Chm)*

Board of Directors:
Aftab ul Islam
Shahnaz Begum
Lipika Biswas
Golam Kabir Chowdhury
Iqbal Kabir Chowdhury
Abdul Haque
A. H. M. Mustafa Kamal
Kashfi Kamal
Kashimiri Kamal
Nafisa Kamal
Shah Abul Kashem
Nazma Khan
Animesh Kundu
Mohammad Shahjahan Miah
Wahida Parvin
Moshiur Rahman
Gazi A. Z. M. Shamim
Moynul Haque Sidddiqui
Wahidul Haque Siddiqui
Mohammad Habib Ullah

ASIA - PACIFIC INVESTMENT JOINT STOCK COMPANY

No 14 Le Dai Hanh Street
Hai Ba Trung District, Hanoi, Vietnam
Tel.: (84) 435771983
Web Site: www.apeci.com.vn
Year Founded: 2006
API—(HNX)
Rev.: $437,294
Assets: $21,211,705
Liabilities: $9,589,169
Net Worth: $11,622,537
Earnings: ($1,005,179)
Fiscal Year-end: 12/31/12

Business Description:
Real Estate Investment Services
S.I.C.: 6531
N.A.I.C.S.: 531390

Personnel:
Nguyen Do Lang *(Chm-Mgmt Bd)*
Nguyen Duy Khanh *(Gen Dir & Member-Mgmt Bd)*

ASIA PACIFIC RESOURCES INTERNATIONAL HOLDINGS LTD.

80 Raffles Pl Level 50 Ste 1
UOB Plz 1, Singapore, 048624, Singapore
Tel.: (65) 62169318
Fax: (65) 65384668
E-Mail: info@aprilasia.com
Web Site: www.aprilasia.com
Year Founded: 1994
Emp.: 7,000

Business Description:
Paper & Pulp Manufacturing
S.I.C.: 2611
N.A.I.C.S.: 322110

Personnel:
Sukanto Tanoto *(Chm)*
A. J. Devanesan *(Pres & COO)*
Ratnesh Bedi *(CFO)*

ASIA-PACIFIC SECURITIES JOINT STOCK COMPANY

(d/b/a APEC Securities)
APEC Building 14th Le Dai Hanh Street
Hai Ba Trung District, Hanoi, Vietnam
Tel.: (84) 435771968
Fax: (84) 435771966
Web Site: www.apec.com.vn
Year Founded: 2006
APS—(HNX)
Emp.: 200

Business Description:
Investment Banking & Securities Brokerage Services
S.I.C.: 6211
N.A.I.C.S.: 523110

Personnel:
Lang Do Nguyen *(Pres & CEO)*
Huong Cam La Vu *(Deputy CEO)*
Hao Manh Nguyen *(Member-Mgmt Bd)*

ASIA-PACIFIC STRATEGIC INVESTMENTS LIMITED

1 Scotts Road 20-07 Shaw Centre
Singapore, 228208, Singapore
Tel.: (65) 6735 4118
Fax: (65) 6735 6443
Web Site: www.asiastrategic.com.sg
5RA—(SES)
Rev.: $3,241,817
Assets: $23,568,594
Liabilities: $7,652,669
Net Worth: $15,915,925
Earnings: ($1,133,619)
Fiscal Year-end: 06/30/13

Business Description:
Cemetery Owner & Operator
S.I.C.: 7261
N.A.I.C.S.: 812220

Personnel:
Yeow Ming Choo *(Chm & CEO)*
Keng Mun Lee *(CFO)*
Min-Tze Lean *(Co-Sec)*
Wai Ming Yap *(Co-Sec)*

Board of Directors:
Yeow Ming Choo
Faizal Ahmad Stalin
Soo Lin Chew
Aik Koon Heng
Lee G. Lam
Keng Mun Lee
Hano Maeloa
Lin Mei Qiang
Siean Sin Yap

ASIA PACIFIC TELECOM CO., LTD.

12F No 66 Jingmao 2nd Road
Nangang District, Taipei, 115, Taiwan
Tel.: (886) 2 5555 8888
Fax: (886) 2 5555 9696
Web Site: www.aptg.com.tw
3682—(TAI)
Sls.: $870,871,841
Fiscal Year-end: 12/31/12

Business Description:
Telecommunications Services
S.I.C.: 4899
N.A.I.C.S.: 517919

Personnel:
Sophia Chiu *(Chm)*
Vincent Chih *(CEO & Gen Mgr)*
Annie Hung *(CFO)*

ASIA PACIFIC WIRE & CABLE CORPORATION LIMITED

7/F B No 132 Sec 3 Min-Sheng East Road
Taipei, 105, Taiwan
Tel.: (886) 227122558
Fax: (886) 2712 3557
Web Site: www.apwcc.com
APWC—(NASDAQ)
Sls.: $462,265,000
Assets: $389,384,000
Liabilities: $154,773,000
Net Worth: $234,611,000
Earnings: $18,910,000
Emp.: 1,413
Fiscal Year-end: 12/31/12

Business Description:
Mfr. & Distributor of Power Cable, Telecommunications Cable & Enameled Wire
S.I.C.: 3355
N.A.I.C.S.: 331318

Personnel:
Yuan Chun Tang *(CEO)*
Ivan Hsia *(CFO)*

Board of Directors:
Andy C. C. Cheng
Anson Chan
Fang Hsiung Cheng
Lambert L. Ding
Yichin Le
Michael C. Lee
Ching Roung Shue
David Sun
Yuan Chun Tang

Transfer Agent:
Computershare Limited
Jersey City, NJ 07097

Non-U.S. Subsidiaries:

Australia Pacific Electric Cables Pty., Ltd. **(1)**
89 Platinum St
Crestmead, Queensland, 4132, Australia
Tel.: (61) 738023688
Fax: (61) 7 3803 1955
E-Mail: enquires@apeccables.com.au
Web Site: www.apeccables.com.au
Electric Cables Mfr
S.I.C.: 3357
N.A.I.C.S.: 335921
Patrick Chung *(Gen Mgr)*

Shandong Pacific Fiber Optics Cable Co., Ltd. **(1)**
14 Xihu Yanggu
Liaocheng, Shandong, China
Tel.: (86) 6352151099
Fax: (86) 6356511369
Web Site: www.apwcc.com
Electric Cable Mfr
S.I.C.: 3357
N.A.I.C.S.: 335921

Shandong Pacific Rubber Cable Co., Ltd. **(1)**
14 Xihu Yanggu
Liaocheng, Shandong, China
Tel.: (86) 6356512568
Fax: (86) 635 6511123
Web Site: www.apwcc.com
Electric Cable Mfr
S.I.C.: 3357
N.A.I.C.S.: 335921

Shanghai Yayang Electric Co., Ltd. **(1)**
3 Anxi Rd Wuqiao Fengxian
Shanghai, China
Tel.: (86) 21 5740 3196
Fax: (86) 21 5740 2366
E-Mail: sap@spewc.com
Web Site: www.yayang.com.cn
Emp.: 200
Copper Wire Mfr
S.I.C.: 3351
N.A.I.C.S.: 331420

Sigma Cable Co. (Pte) Ltd. **(1)**
19 Benoi Rd
Sigma Cable High Tech Complex,
Singapore, 629909, Singapore

Asia Pacific Wire & Cable Corporation Limited—(Continued)

Tel.: (65) 62650877
Fax: (65) 68634867
E-Mail: sales@sigmacable.com
Web Site: www.sigmacable.com
Power Cables Mfr
S.I.C.: 3357
N.A.I.C.S.: 335921
Grace Xu *(Mgr-Bus Dev)*

Sigma-Epan International Pte., Ltd. **(1)**
19 Benoi Rd
Sigma Cable High Tech Complex, Singapore, 629909, Singapore
Tel.: (65) 65699100
Fax: (65) 65698460
E-Mail: epanwire@singnet.com.sg
Web Site: www.epanwire.com.sg
Emp.: 10
Electric Cables Mfr
S.I.C.: 3357
N.A.I.C.S.: 335921
Jasper Tan *(Mgr-Sls)*

Subsidiary:

Epan Industries Pte Ltd **(2)**
19 Benoi Rd Level 3 A
Singapore, 629909, Singapore
Tel.: (65) 65699100
Fax: (65) 65698460
E-Mail: epanwire@singnet.com.sg
Web Site: www.epanwire.com.sg
Emp.: 8
Electric Cable Mfr
S.I.C.: 3357
N.A.I.C.S.: 335921
Jasper Tan *(Mgr-Sls)*

ASIA PACK LIMITED

3rd Floor Miraj House
Panchwati, Udaipur, Rajasthan, 313001, India
Tel.: (91) 294 2528435
Fax: (91) 294 2528436
Web Site: www.asiapackltd.com
Year Founded: 1985
530899—(BOM)
Sales Range: Less than $1 Million
Business Description:
Business Management Consulting Services
S.I.C.: 8742
N.A.I.C.S.: 541611
Personnel:
Ashok Ranjan Mishra *(Compliance Officer & Sec)*
Board of Directors:
Pradeep Garg
Revant Purbia
Prakash Chandra Purohit
Anil Kumar Sankhlecha
Transfer Agent:
Ankit Consultancy Pvt. Ltd
Plot No 60 Electronic Complex Pardeshipura
Indore, India

ASIA PACKAGING GROUP INC.

Suite 800 885 West Georgia Street
Vancouver, BC, V6C 3H1, Canada
Tel.: (604) 291-7460
E-Mail: jinkuang@hotmail.com
Web Site: www.htcapital.com
Year Founded: 2010
APX—(TSXV)
Business Description:
Investment Services
S.I.C.: 6211
N.A.I.C.S.: 523999
Personnel:
Wenge Hong *(Pres & CEO)*
Jin Kuang *(CFO & Sec)*
Transfer Agent:
Computershare Investor Services Inc.
510 Burrard St 2nd Floor
Vancouver, BC, V6C 3B9, Canada
Tel.: (604) 661-9400

ASIA PAPER MANUFACTURING CO., LTD.

8F ASEA Tower Bldg 726 Yeoksam-Dong
Gangnam-Gu, Seoul, 135719, Korea (South)
Tel.: (82) 2 527 6882
Fax: (82) 25276859
E-Mail: webmaster@asiapaper.co.kr
Web Site: www.asiapaper.co.kr
Year Founded: 1958
002310—(KRS)
Rev.: $459,461,738
Assets: $439,779,353
Liabilities: $206,259,307
Net Worth: $233,520,046
Earnings: $29,137,556
Emp.: 169
Fiscal Year-end: 12/31/12
Business Description:
Linerboards & Corrugated Boxes Mfr
S.I.C.: 2653
N.A.I.C.S.: 322211
Personnel:
Won Hui Park *(CEO)*

ASIA PAPERTEC, INC.

(Merged with Asia Paper Manufacturing Co., Ltd.)

ASIA PLASTIC RECYCLING HOLDING LIMITED

12F 685 Mingcheng 3rd Rd
Gushan District, Kaohsiung, 804, Taiwan
Tel.: (886) 7 5524591
Web Site: www.asia-recycle.com
1337—(TAI)
Sales Range: $125-149.9 Million
Emp.: 670
Business Description:
Plastic Materials
S.I.C.: 3089
N.A.I.C.S.: 326199
Personnel:
Ding Jin Zao *(Chm)*
Shiue You Wei *(CFO)*

ASIA PLUS SECURITIES PUBLIC COMPANY LIMITED

175 3/1 Floor Sathorn City Tower
South Sathorn Road Thungmahamek
Bangkok, 10120, Thailand
Tel.: (66) 2285 1888
Fax: (66) 2285 1901
E-Mail: public_relations@asiaplus.co.th
Web Site: www.asiaplus.co.th
Year Founded: 1974
ASP—(THA)
Rev.: $68,800,545
Assets: $274,349,462
Liabilities: $135,837,934
Net Worth: $138,511,528
Earnings: $19,982,080
Fiscal Year-end: 12/31/12
Business Description:
Security Brokerage Services
S.I.C.: 6211
N.A.I.C.S.: 523120
Personnel:
Chali Sophonpanich *(Chm)*
Kongkiat Opaswongkarn *(CEO)*
Naruemol Artamnuayvipas *(Mng Dir)*
Pithayain Assavanig *(CFO)*
Choomsai Tantisawetrat *(Sec)*
Pannipa Gulyanon *(Sr Exec VP-Ops Div)*
Board of Directors:
Chali Sophonpanich
Virach Aphimeteetamrong
Satit Chanjavanakul
Jirawat Lewprasert
Kongkiat Opaswongkarn
Sopon Punyaratabandhu
Michael David Roberts
Nintira Sophonpanich
Patchara Surajaras
Subsidiary:

Asset Plus Fund Management Company Limited **(1)**
17th Floor Sathorn City Tower 175 South Sathorn Road
Khet Sathorn, Bangkok, 10120, Thailand
Tel.: (66) 2672 1000
Fax: (66) 2286 4472
Web Site: www.assetfund.co.th
Fund Management Services
S.I.C.: 6722
N.A.I.C.S.: 525910

ASIA POLYMER CORPORATION

12th Floor No 37 Ji-Hu Road
Nei-Hu District, Taipei, 114, Taiwan
Tel.: (886) 287516888
Fax: (886) 226599502
E-Mail: samsontseng@apc.com.tw
Web Site: www.apc.com.tw
1308—(TAI)
Sales Range: $200-249.9 Million
Business Description:
Plastic Tablets & Resins Mfr
S.I.C.: 2821
N.A.I.C.S.: 325211
Personnel:
Quintin Wu *(Chm)*

ASIA POWER CORPORATION LIMITED

24 Raffles Place 27 03 Clifford Building
Singapore, 048621, Singapore
Tel.: (65) 63245788
Fax: (65) 63245766
E-Mail: admin@asiapower.com.sg
Web Site: www.asiapower.com.sg
Year Founded: 1997
A03—(SES)
Rev.: $24,767,892
Assets: $190,902,753
Liabilities: $68,129,018
Net Worth: $122,773,735
Earnings: ($2,840,556)
Emp.: 2,000
Fiscal Year-end: 12/31/12
Business Description:
Power Generation Plants Management & Operation Services
S.I.C.: 3612
N.A.I.C.S.: 335311
Personnel:
Liang Xue *(Chm & CEO)*
Wei Hsiung Lee *(Co-Sec)*
Meng Keong Teo *(Co-Sec)*
Board of Directors:
Liang Xue
Joseph He Jun
Tianfei Li
Victor Fook Ai Ng
Jianping Xu
Non-U.S. Subsidiary:

JAZ Technology Development (Shenzhen) Co., Ltd **(1)**
4/F 5/F 201 Jinzhong Section OCT Eastern Industrial Park
Nanshan District, Shenzhen, Guangdong, 518053, China
Tel.: (86) 75586095518
Fax: (86) 75586106660
Electric Power Generation Services
S.I.C.: 4931
N.A.I.C.S.: 221118

ASIA PRECISION PUBLIC COMPANY LIMITED

700/331 Moo 6 Tambon Donhualor
Amphur Muang, Chon Buri, 20000, Thailand
Tel.: (66) 38468300
Fax: (66) 38458751
E-Mail: info@asiaprecision.com
Web Site: www.asiaprecision.com
Year Founded: 1995
APCS—(THA)
Emp.: 800
Business Description:
Precision Machined Parts
S.I.C.: 3499
N.A.I.C.S.: 332999
Personnel:
Apichart Karoonkornsakul *(Pres)*
Chairoj Vetnaruemarn *(Mng Dir)*
Toyoharu Fujimoto *(Sr Exec VP)*
Ratchadech Vacheesuthum *(Sr Exec VP)*

ASIA RESOURCES HOLDINGS LIMITED

Unit 04 34/F Bank of America Tower
12 Harcourt Road
Central, China (Hong Kong)
Tel.: (852) 3101 0899
Fax: (852) 3102 0899
Web Site: www.asiaresources899.com
899—(HKG)
Rev.: $14,436,855
Assets: $109,523,811
Liabilities: $42,781,225
Net Worth: $66,742,586
Earnings: ($25,702,314)
Emp.: 485
Fiscal Year-end: 03/31/13
Business Description:
Pharmaceutical Product Mfr & Distr
S.I.C.: 2834
N.A.I.C.S.: 325412
Personnel:
Ricky Kim Lun Chim *(Chm & CEO)*
Rosena Lai Si Leung *(Sec)*
Board of Directors:
Ricky Kim Lun Chim
Kai Kwong Cheung
Jesse Hong Yee Kwok
Pak Sum Lum
Leung Sang Tong
Anthony Yiu Bong Yeung
Xianlin Zhang

HSBC Bank Bermuda Limited
Bank of Bermuda Building, 6 Front Street
Hamilton, Bermuda

ASIA SERMKIJ LEASING PUBLIC COMPANY LIMITED

24th Fl Sathorn City Tower 175 S Sathorn Ro Tungmahamek
Sathorn, Bangkok, 10120, Thailand
Tel.: (66) 26796226
Fax: (66) 26796241
Web Site: www.ask.co.th
Sales Range: $10-24.9 Million
Emp.: 315
Business Description:
Automotive Leasing Services
S.I.C.: 7515
N.A.I.C.S.: 532112
Personnel:
Amnuay Viravan *(Chm & CEO)*
Lo Jun Long *(Mng Dir)*
Board of Directors:
Amnuay Viravan
Lo Jun Long
Tientavee Saraton

ASIA STANDARD INTERNATIONAL GROUP LIMITED

30th Floor Asia Orient Tower Town Place
33 Lockhart Road, Wanchai, China (Hong Kong)
Tel.: (852) 28663336

Fax: (852) 28663772
E-Mail: asinfo@asiastandard.com
Web Site: www.asiastandard.com
0129—(HKG)
Sales Range: $125-149.9 Million
Emp.: 468
Business Description:
Commercial, Retail & Residential Property Investment & Development Services
S.I.C.: 6531
N.A.I.C.S.: 531390
Personnel:
Clement Siu To Fung *(Chm)*
Yin Cheng Lim *(Deputy Chm)*
Richard Jing Poon *(CEO & Mng Dir)*
Ricky Pui Kan Lun *(Sec & Dir-Fin)*
Board of Directors:
Clement Siu To Fung
Alan Bok Ming Koon
Phileas Po Lam Kwan
Wai Keung Leung
Yin Cheng Lim
Ricky Pui Kan Lun
Richard Hai Poon
Richard Jing Poon
Chi Keung Wong
Legal Counsel:
Stephenson Harwood
35th Floor Bank of China Tower 1 Garden Road
Central, China (Hong Kong)
Appleby
2206-19 Jardine House 1 Connaught Place
Central, China (Hong Kong)
Butterfield Fulcrum Group (Bermuda) Limited
26 Burnaby Street
Hamilton, HM 11, Bermuda
Transfer Agent:
Computershare Hong Kong Investor Services Limited
Shops 1712-1716 17th Floor Hopewell Centre
183 Queens Road East
Wanchai, China (Hong Kong)
Subsidiary:

Asia Standard Hotel Group Limited **(1)**
30th Floor Asia Orient Tower Town Place
33 Lockhart Road, Wanchai, China (Hong Kong) BM
Tel.: (852) 2866 3336
Fax: (852) 2866 3772
E-Mail: info@asiastandardhotel.com
Web Site: www.asiastandardhotelgroup.com
292—(HKG)
Rev.: $109,084,221
Assets: $608,365,855
Liabilities: $234,943,805
Net Worth: $373,422,050
Earnings: $54,646,044
Emp.: 419
Fiscal Year-end: 03/31/13
Hotel Operator
S.I.C.: 7011
N.A.I.C.S.: 721110
Jing Poon *(Chm)*
Yin Cheng Lim *(Deputy Chm & CEO)*
Dominic Tai Hay Lee *(Sec)*

ASIA TELE-NET & TECHNOLOGY CORPORATION LIMITED

Tai Po Industrial Estate 11 Dai Hei Street
Tai Po, NT, China (Hong Kong)
Tel.: (852) 26662288
Fax: (852) 26640717
E-Mail: info@atnt.biz
Web Site: www.atnt.biz
0679—(HKG)
Rev.: $49,358,707
Assets: $61,173,235
Liabilities: $26,615,280
Net Worth: $34,557,955
Earnings: ($2,731,290)
Emp.: 718
Fiscal Year-end: 12/31/12
Business Description:
Investment Services
S.I.C.: 6719
N.A.I.C.S.: 551112
Personnel:
Kwok Hing Lam *(Chm & Mng Dir)*
Kwok Lun Nam *(Deputy Chm)*
Angela Choi Yiu Lui *(Sec)*
Board of Directors:
Kwok Hing Lam
Kin Wai Cheung
Alan Wang Wai Kwan
Kwok Lun Nam
David Chi Kin Ng
Butterfield Corporate Service Limited
Rosebank Centre 11 Bermudiana Road
Pembroke, HM08, Bermuda
Transfer Agents:
Tricor Secretaries Limited
26th Floor Tesbury Centre 28 Queens Rd E
Hong Kong, China (Hong Kong)
Butterfield Corporate Service Limited
Rosebank Centre 11 Bermudiana Road
Pembroke, HM08, Bermuda

ASIA TIME CORPORATION

Room 1601-1604 16/F CRE Centre
889 Cheung Sha Wan Road,
Kowloon, China (Hong Kong)
Tel.: (852) 2310 0101
Fax: (852) 2310 0032
Web Site: www.asiatimecorp.com
Year Founded: 2006
ATYM—(OTC)
Sales Range: $75-99.9 Million
Emp.: 35
Business Description:
Watches & Watch Movements Components Distr
S.I.C.: 5094
N.A.I.C.S.: 423940
Personnel:
Kai Shun Kwong *(Chm & CEO)*
King Wai Lin *(CFO)*
Board of Directors:
Kai Shun Kwong
Siu Po Lee
Ching Wah Leung
Wu Hok Lun

ASIA TRAVEL CORPORATION

(Formerly Realgold International Inc.)
Unit 1202 Level 12 One Peking
1 Peking Road, Tsim Tsa Tsui,
Kowloon, China (Hong Kong)
Tel.: (852) 3980 9369
ATSR—(OTC OTCB)
Rev.: $121,974
Assets: $816,641
Liabilities: $20,062
Net Worth: $796,579
Earnings: ($240,787)
Emp.: 38
Fiscal Year-end: 03/31/13
Business Description:
Investment Services
S.I.C.: 6211
N.A.I.C.S.: 523999
Personnel:
Lung Lai Tan *(Pres, CEO & CFO)*
Po Hwa Tan *(Sec)*
Board of Directors:
Lung Lai Tan
Po Hwa Tan

ASIA UNITED BANK CORPORATION

Joy Nostalg Center 17 ADB Avenue
Ortigas Center, Pasig, Philippines
Tel.: (63) 26386888
Fax: (63) 26355143
E-Mail: asiaunited@mindgate.net
Web Site: www.aub.com.ph
Year Founded: 1997
AUB—(PHI)
Sales Range: $10-24.9 Million
Emp.: 413
Business Description:
Banking Services
S.I.C.: 6029
N.A.I.C.S.: 522110
Personnel:
Jacinto L. Ng, Jr. *(Chm)*
Ramon Y. Sy *(Vice Chm)*
Abraham T. Co *(Pres)*
Antonio V. Agcaoili, Jr. *(Exec VP)*
Manuel A. Gomez *(Exec VP)*
Isabelita M. Papa *(Exec VP)*
Board of Directors:
Jacinto L. Ng, Jr.
Angelo Patrick Advincula
Adolf S. Azcuna
George T. Chua
Abraham T. Co
Benjamin E. Diokno
Lin Hong Dow
Lily K. Gruba
Jonathan C. Ng
Ramon Y. Sy

ASIA VITAL COMPONENTS CO., LTD.

No 248-27 Sin-Sheng Rd Cian-Jhen District
806 Kaohsiung, Taiwan
Tel.: (886) 78157612
Fax: (886) 78120018
Web Site: www.avc.com.tw
3017—(TAI)
Sales Range: $300-349.9 Million
Emp.: 10,100
Business Description:
Fans & Blowers Mfr
S.I.C.: 1711
N.A.I.C.S.: 238220
Personnel:
Spencer Shen *(Chm & Gen Mgr)*

Plant:

Asia Vital Components Co., Ltd. - AVC Taipei Factory **(1)**
7F-3 No 24 Wucyuan 2 Road
Sinjhuang District, Taipei, 24892, Taiwan
Tel.: (886) 222996930
Fax: (886) 2 2299 6929
E-Mail: sales@avc.com.tw
Thermal Conductivity Instruments Mfr
S.I.C.: 3826
N.A.I.C.S.: 334516

ASIA WATER TECHNOLOGY LTD.

(Name Changed to SIIC Environment Holdings Ltd.)

ASIABASEMETALS INC.

Suite 2560 - 200 Granville Street
P O Box 36
Vancouver, BC, V6C 1S4, Canada
Tel.: (604) 628-1162
Fax: (604) 628-1163
E-Mail: info@asiabasemetals.com
Web Site: www.asiabasemetals.com
Year Founded: 2009
ABZ—(TSXV)
Rev.: $8,994
Assets: $175,728
Liabilities: $18,267
Net Worth: $157,461
Earnings: ($191,115)
Emp.: 5
Fiscal Year-end: 09/30/13
Business Description:
Zinc & Base Metals Mining Services
S.I.C.: 1031
N.A.I.C.S.: 212231
Personnel:
Richard Van Nieuwenhuyse *(Chm)*
Steven Khan *(Interim CEO)*
Wylie Hui *(CFO)*
Board of Directors:
Richard Van Nieuwenhuyse
Gerald G. Booth
Raj I. Chowdhry
Steven Khan
Joe Piekenbrock
Transfer Agent:
Computershare Investor Services Inc
100 University Avenue
Toronto, ON, Canada

ASIAINFO-LINKAGE, INC.

(Acquired by CITIC Group Corporation)

ASIAMEDIC LTD.

350 Orchard Rd 08-00 Shaw House
Singapore, 238868, Singapore
Tel.: (65) 67898888
Fax: (65) 67384136
E-Mail: info@asiamedic.com.sg
Web Site: www.asiamedic.com.sg
Year Founded: 1974
505—(SES)
Rev.: $9,684,325
Assets: $13,719,272
Liabilities: $2,865,643
Net Worth: $10,853,629
Earnings: $27,467
Emp.: 42
Fiscal Year-end: 12/31/12
Business Description:
Medical Facilities Owner & Operator
S.I.C.: 8069
N.A.I.C.S.: 622310
Personnel:
Weng Hong Wong *(CEO)*
Jonathan Joseph Tan *(COO)*
Soon Soo Foo *(Sec)*
Board of Directors:
Wang Cheow Tan
Mark Erhart
Kian Chee Goh
Arthur Boon Chye Ng
Andi Solaiman
Transfer Agent:
KCK CorpServe Pte. Ltd.
333 North Bridge Road 08-00 KH KEA Building
Singapore, Singapore
Subsidiaries:

Aesthetic Medical Centre Pte Ltd **(1)**
350 Orchard Road 08 00
Shaw House, Singapore, 238868, Singapore (100%)
Tel.: (65) 6838 7930
Fax: (65) 6738 4136
Web Site: www.asiamedic.com.sg
Plastic Surgical Medical Facility
S.I.C.: 8069
N.A.I.C.S.: 622310

AsiaMedic Specialist Centre **(1)**
350 Orchard Road #08-00
Shaw House, Singapore, 238868, Singapore (60%)
Tel.: (65) 67898888
Fax: (65) 67384136
E-Mail: info@asiamedic.com.sg
Web Site: www.asiamedic.com.sg/eye_index.html
Eye Treatment & Surgery Center
S.I.C.: 8042
N.A.I.C.S.: 621320
Andi Solaiman *(Acting CEO)*

AsiaMedic PET/CT Centre Pte Ltd **(1)**
350 Orchard Road 08-00
Shaw House, Singapore, 238868, Singapore (100%)
Tel.: (65) 68387900
Fax: (65) 67384220
Web Site: www.asiamedic.com.sg/pet_index.html
Diagnostic Imaging Center
S.I.C.: 8071
N.A.I.C.S.: 621512

AsiaMedic Ltd.—(Continued)

The Orchard Imaging Centre Pte Ltd (1)
350 Orchard Road 08-00
Shaw House, Singapore, 238868, Singapore (100%)
Tel.: (65) 65056092
Web Site: www.asiamedic.com.sg/Imaging-About-Orchard-Imaging-Centre.aspx
Diagnostic Imaging Center
S.I.C.: 8071
N.A.I.C.S.: 621512

Wellness Assessment Centre Pte Ltd (1)
350 Orchard Road 08-00
Shaw House, Singapore, 238868, Singapore (100%)
Tel.: (65) 68387933
Fax: (65) 68387936
E-Mail: info@asiamedic.com.sg
Web Site: www.asiamedic.com.sg/wellness_index.html
Wellness Center
S.I.C.: 8069
N.A.I.C.S.: 622310

ASIAN AMERICAN MEDICAL GROUP LIMITED

6A Napier Road
Gleneagles Hospital Annexe Block #02-07
Singapore, 258500, Singapore
Tel.: (65) 64762088
Fax: (65) 64763088
E-Mail: enquiry@acldt.com
Web Site: www.asianlivercentre.com.sg
Year Founded: 1994
AJJ—(ASX)
Sales Range: $10-24.9 Million
Business Description:
Medical Services
S.I.C.: 8062
N.A.I.C.S.: 622110
Personnel:
Kai Chah Tan *(Chm)*
Pamela Anne Jenkins *(Mng Dir)*
Cherinjit Kumar Shori *(COO)*
Dario Nazzari *(Sec)*
Board of Directors:
Kai Chah Tan
Heng Boo Fong
Pamela Anne Jenkins
Harry Vui Khiun Lee
Wing Kwan Teh
Jeslyn Jacques Kian Leong Wee

ASIAN BAMBOO AG

Stadthausbrucke 1-3
20355 Hamburg, Germany
Tel.: (49) 4037644798
Fax: (49) 4037644500
Web Site: www.asian-bamboo.com
5AB—(DEU)
Rev.: $98,075,215
Assets: $468,945,050
Liabilities: $81,275,014
Net Worth: $387,670,037
Earnings: ($26,662,243)
Emp.: 868
Fiscal Year-end: 12/31/12
Business Description:
Bamboo Producer
S.I.C.: 0181
N.A.I.C.S.: 111421
Personnel:
Hans-Joachim Zwarg *(Chm-Supervisory Bd)*
Lin Zuojun *(Chm-Mgmt Bd & CEO)*
Chris McAuliffe *(Deputy Chm-Supervisory Bd)*
Peter Sjovall *(CFO & Member-Mgmt Bd)*
Richard Haiyan Jiang *(COO & Member-Mgmt Bd)*
Hai Qiu *(Member-Mgmt Bd & Controller-Fin)*
Supervisory Board of Directors:
Hans-Joachim Zwarg
Pan Chaoran
Chris McAuliffe

ASIAN CAPITAL HOLDINGS LIMITED

Suites 1006 & 1203 Bank of America Tower 12 Harcourt Road
Central, China (Hong Kong)
Tel.: (852) 28698861
Fax: (852) 28699660
E-Mail: info@asiancapital.com.hk
Web Site: www.asiancapital.com.hk
Year Founded: 1998
8295—(HKG)
Rev.: $2,599,761
Assets: $15,787,091
Liabilities: $629,663
Net Worth: $15,157,428
Earnings: ($208,770)
Emp.: 22
Fiscal Year-end: 12/31/12
Business Description:
Corporate Finance Advisory & Other Business Related Services
S.I.C.: 6282
N.A.I.C.S.: 523930
Personnel:
Patrick K. C. Yeung *(Founder, Chm & CEO)*
Larry H .L. Chan *(Compliance Officer)*
Elsa Pui Yee Li *(Sec)*
Board of Directors:
Patrick K. C. Yeung
K. N. Chan
Larry H .L. Chan
Andrew P. Y. Tsui
Lawrence Luo Lin Xin
Xiqun Yi
MaplesFS Limited
Queensgate House
PO Box 1093
Georgetown, Cayman Islands
Transfer Agents:
Tricor Investor Services Limited
26/F Tesbury Centre 28 Queen's Road East
Hong Kong, China (Hong Kong)
MaplesFS Limited
Queensgate House
PO Box 1093
Georgetown, Cayman Islands

ASIAN CITRUS HOLDINGS LIMITED

Room 1109-1112 Wayson Commercial Building 28 Connaught Road West
Hong Kong, China (Hong Kong)
Tel.: (852) 25590323
Fax: (852) 25598312
E-Mail: info@asian-citrus.com
Web Site: www.asian-citrus.com
73—(AIM HKG)
Sls.: $236,037,121
Assets: $1,319,851,927
Liabilities: $16,731,194
Net Worth: $1,303,120,733
Earnings: $19,802,559
Emp.: 1,697
Fiscal Year-end: 06/30/13
Business Description:
Orange Plantation Owner & Operator
S.I.C.: 0174
N.A.I.C.S.: 111310
Personnel:
Wang Chow Tong *(Founder)*
Cheuk Lun Ng *(Sec)*
Board of Directors:
Wai Sun Cheung
Koon Yan Chung
Wai Leung Ho
Ming Wah Lui
Hoi Yue Ng
Yi Pang
Tommy Hung Wai Tong
Zhen Han Yang
Legal Counsel:
Zhon Lun Law Firm
10/F Tower A Rongchao Tower 6003 Yitian Road
Futian District, Shenzhen, 518026, China
King & Wood Mallesons
13th Floor Gloucester Tower The Landmark 15 Queens Road Central
Central, China (Hong Kong)
Fladgate LLP
16 Great Queen Street
WC2B5DG London, United Kingdom
Conyers Dill & Pearman
2901 One Exchange Centre 8 Connaught Place
Central, China (Hong Kong)
Computershare Investor Services (Jersey) Limited
Queensway House Hilgrove Street
Saint Helier, JE1 1ES, Jersey
Tel.: (44) 1534 281814
Computershare Hong Kong Investor Services Limited
Shops 1712-1716 17th Floor Hopewell Centre
183 Queens Road East
Wanchai, China (Hong Kong)
Non-U.S. Subsidiary:

Lucky Team Biotech Development (Hepu) Limited (1)
No 51 Mingyuan Rd Wujia
Hepu, Beihai, Guangxi, 536100, China
Tel.: (86) 7797198851
Fax: (86) 7797122059
Emp.: 100
Orange Cultivation & Sales
S.I.C.: 0174
N.A.I.C.S.: 111310
Pang Yi *(Mng Dir)*

Subsidiary:

Asian Citrus (H.K.) Company Limited (1)
Rm 1109 1111 Wayson Comml Bldg 28 Connaught Rd W
Sheung Wan, China (Hong Kong)
Tel.: (852) 25590323
Fax: (852) 25598312
E-Mail: info@asian-citrus.com
Web Site: www.asian-citrus.com
Orange Cultivation & Sales
S.I.C.: 0174
N.A.I.C.S.: 111310
Tony Tong *(CEO)*

ASIAN DEVELOPMENT BANK

6 ADB Avenue
Mandaluyong, Metro Manila, 1550, Philippines
Tel.: (63) 26324444
Telex: 63587 ADB PN etpi
Fax: (63) 26362444
E-Mail: rtayangona@adb.org
Web Site: www.adb.org
Year Founded: 1966
Sales Range: $1-4.9 Billion
Emp.: 2,000
Business Description:
Economic Development Services
S.I.C.: 6211
N.A.I.C.S.: 523999
Personnel:
Takehiko Nakao *(Pres)*
Lakshmi Swaminathan *(Pres-Admin Tribunal)*
Jeremy Hovland *(Gen Counsel)*
Mikio Kashiwagi *(Treas)*
Bruce A. Purdue *(Sec)*
Board of Directors:
Phil Bowen
Howard Brown
Michele Miari Fulcis
Gaudencio Hernandez, Jr.
Ashok K. Lahiri
Robert M. Orr
Masakazu Sakaguchi
Maurin Sitorus
Jaejung Song
Chaiyuth Sudthitanakorn
Eduard Westreicher
Yingming Yang

ASIAN ELECTRONICS LTD

D11 Rd N 28 Wagle Industrial Estate
400604 Thane, India
Tel.: (91) 2225835504
Fax: (91) 2225827636
E-Mail: jp@aelgroup.com
Web Site: www.aelgroup.com
503940—(BOM)
Sales Range: $25-49.9 Million
Business Description:
Electrical Equipments
S.I.C.: 1731
N.A.I.C.S.: 238210
Personnel:
Arun B. Shah *(Chm)*
Charudatta A. Kulkarni *(Sec)*
Board of Directors:
Haresh G. Desai
D. B. Shah
Hardik Shah
Suhas R. Tuljapurkar
Plant:

Asian Electronics Ltd - Plant 1 (1)
68 MIDC Industrial Area
Satpur, Nasik, Maharashtra, 422007, India
Tel.: (91) 2532365000
Fax: (91) 2532365010
E-Mail: info@aelgroup.com
Web Site: www.aelgroup.com
Electrical Light Mfr
S.I.C.: 2899
N.A.I.C.S.: 325998
Neelakanta Iyer *(Mgr)*

ASIAN EUROPEAN FOOTWEAR

Zi De La Croix Rouge
Malville, 44260 Nantes, France
Tel.: (33) 240570300
Fax: (33) 3324057081
Sls.: $21,600,000
Emp.: 20
Business Description:
Womens, Childrens & Infants Clothing
S.I.C.: 5137
N.A.I.C.S.: 424330
Personnel:
Stephane Rohel *(Pres)*

ASIAN GRANITO INDIA LIMITED

202 Dev Arc Opp Iskon Temple S G Highway
Ahmedabad, Gujarat, 380 015, India
Tel.: (91) 7966125500
Fax: (91) 7966125600
E-Mail: info@asiangranito.com
Web Site: www.asiangranito.com
ASIANTILES—(NSE)
Rev.: $131,781,356
Assets: $120,214,380
Liabilities: $71,153,313
Net Worth: $49,061,067
Earnings: $3,171,934
Emp.: 669
Fiscal Year-end: 03/31/13
Business Description:
Building Products Industry
S.I.C.: 3297
N.A.I.C.S.: 327120
Personnel:
Kamleshbhai B. Patel *(Chm, Co-Mng Dir & Dir-Fin)*
Mukeshbhai Patel *(Co-Mng Dir)*
Renuka A. Upadhay *(Compliance Officer & Sec)*
Board of Directors:
Kamleshbhai B. Patel

Premjibhai Chaudhary
Indira Nityanandam
Ajendrakumar Patel
Amrutbhai Patel
Bhaveshbhai Patel
Bhogibhai B. Patel
Kanubhai Patel
Mukeshbhai Patel
Shakarlal Patel
Sureshbhai J. Patel
Maganlal Prajapati

Transfer Agent:
Link Intime India Pvt. Ltd
C-13 Pannalal Silk Mills Compound LBS Marg
Bhandup (West)
Mumbai, India

Unit:

Asian Granito India Limited - Gujarat Unit (1)
Ceramic Zone Dalpur
Sabarkantha Dist, Parantij, Gujarat, 383 120, India
Tel.: (91) 2770 240931
Fax: (91) 2770 240930
E-Mail: vp@asiangranito.com
Ceramic Wall Tiles Mfr
S.I.C.: 3255
N.A.I.C.S.: 327120

ASIAN GROWTH PROPERTIES LIMITED

Portcullis TrustNet Chambers
PO Box 3444
Road Town, Tortola, Virgin Islands (British)
Tel.: (284) 4945296
Fax: (284) 4945283
E-Mail: info@asiangrowth.com
Web Site: www.asiangrowth.com
Year Founded: 2004
AGP—(LSE)

Business Description:
Property Investment, Development & Management Services
S.I.C.: 6531
N.A.I.C.S.: 531390

Personnel:
Lambert Lu *(Exec Dir)*

Board of Directors:
Richard Other Prickett
Donald Ian Fletcher
Sing Tai Lam
Lambert Lu
Lincoln Lu
Wing Chi Lu
David Andrew Runciman

Legal Counsel:
Stephenson Harwood
One St. Paul's Churchyard
London, EC4M 8SH, United Kingdom
Tel.: (44) 81 329 4422

ASIAN HOTELS (EAST) LIMITED

Hyatt Regency Kolkata JA-1 Sector III
Salt Lake City, Kolkata, 700 098, India
Tel.: (91) 33 23351234
Fax: (91) 33 2335 4044
E-Mail: contact@ahleast.com
Web Site: www.ahleast.com
533227—(BOM)
Rev.: $32,496,109
Assets: $239,597,587
Liabilities: $80,870,040
Net Worth: $158,727,546
Earnings: $159,054
Emp.: 304
Fiscal Year-end: 03/31/13

Business Description:
Restaurant Operating Services
S.I.C.: 5812
N.A.I.C.S.: 722511

Personnel:
Arun Kumar Saraf *(Mng Dir)*
Umesh Saraf *(Mng Dir)*
Saumen Chattopadhyay *(Chief Legal Officer, Compliance Officer & Sec)*

Board of Directors:
Radhe Shyam Saraf
Amal Ch. Chakrabortti
Ramesh Kumar Chokhani
Rama Shankar Jhawar
Padam Kumar Khaitan
Arun Kumar Saraf
Umesh Saraf

Transfer Agent:
Karvy Computershare Private Limited
17-24 Vittal Rao Nagar Madhapur
Hyderabad, India

ASIAN HOTELS (NORTH) LIMITED

Bhikaiji Cama Place M G Marg
New Delhi, 110066, India
Tel.: (91) 1126791234
Fax: (91) 11 2679 1033
Web Site: www.asianhotelsnorth.com
500023—(BOM)
Rev.: $65,356,893
Assets: $373,559,827
Liabilities: $209,900,276
Net Worth: $163,659,551
Earnings: $11,076,742
Emp.: 760
Fiscal Year-end: 03/31/13

Business Description:
Hotel Services
S.I.C.: 7011
N.A.I.C.S.: 721120

Personnel:
Shiv Kumar Jatia *(Chm & Mng Dir)*
Dinesh Kumar Jain *(Compliance Officer, Sec & VP)*
Jyoti Subarwal *(Pres-Fin & Ops)*

Board of Directors:
Shiv Kumar Jatia
Lalit Bhasin
P. S. Dasgupta
Gautam R. Divan
Amritesh Jatia
Ramesh Jatia
Dinesh C. Kothari

Transfer Agent:
Karvy Computershare Private Limited
17-24 Vittal Rao Nagar Madhapur
Hyderabad, India

ASIAN HOTELS (WEST) LIMITED

E-Basement Clarion Collection -The Qutab Hotel Shaheed Jeet Singh Marg
New Delhi, 110016, India
Tel.: (91) 1146101210
Fax: (91) 1146101222
Web Site: www.asianhotelswest.com
AHLWEST—(NSE)
Rev.: $25,338,970
Assets: $207,017,492
Liabilities: $140,050,289
Net Worth: $66,967,203
Earnings: ($492,589)
Emp.: 671
Fiscal Year-end: 03/31/13

Business Description:
Hotel Management Services
S.I.C.: 7011
N.A.I.C.S.: 721110

Personnel:
Sushil Gupta *(Chm & Mng Dir)*
Nikhil Sethi *(Compliance Officer & Sec)*

Board of Directors:
Sushil Gupta
Surendra Singh Bhandari
Raj Kumar Bhargava
Lalit Bhasin
S. K. Chhibber
Sunil Diwakar
Sandeep Gupta
Sudhir Gupta

Transfer Agents:
Karvy Computershare Pvt Ltd
Karvy House Plot no 17-24 Vithalrao Nagar
Madhapur
Hyderabad, India

Karvy Computershare Pvt. Ltd
105 108 Arunachal Building 19 Barakhamba Road
New Delhi, India

Subsidiary:

Aria Hotels and Consultancy Services Pvt. Ltd. (1)
E-Basement Clarion Collection The Qutab Hotel shaheed Jeet Singh Marg
New Delhi, 110016, India
Tel.: (91) 11 41200000
Fax: (91) 11 46101213
Hotel Management Services
S.I.C.: 7011
N.A.I.C.S.: 721110

ASIAN INSULATORS PUBLIC COMPANY LIMITED

254 Seri Thai Road Kannayaow
Kannayaow, Bangkok, 10230, Thailand
Tel.: (66) 2517 1451
Fax: (66) 2517 1465
E-Mail: asian@asianinsulators.com
Web Site: www.asianinsulators.com
Year Founded: 1981
AI—(THA)
Rev.: $144,135,624
Assets: $121,761,393
Liabilities: $72,359,177
Net Worth: $49,402,216
Earnings: $6,248,638
Fiscal Year-end: 12/31/12

Business Description:
Electrical Equipment Mfr & Distr
S.I.C.: 3699
N.A.I.C.S.: 335999

Personnel:
Narong Thareratanavibool *(Chm)*
Thanit Thareratanavibool *(CEO)*

Board of Directors:
Narong Thareratanavibool
Pornanong Budsaratragoon
Prayoon Chindapradist
Boonlert Khawcharoenporn
Kovit Thareratanavibool
Thanit Thareratanavibool

ASIAN LIFE INSURANCE COMPANY

Asian Life Bhawan Ma Na Pa Ward
No 33 Maitidevi
PO Box 25943
Kathmandu, Nepal
Tel.: (977) 1 4410115
Fax: (977) 1 4442138
E-Mail: asianlife@asianlife.com.np
Web Site: www.asianlife.com.np
Year Founded: 2008
ALICL—(NEP)

Business Description:
Insurance Services
S.I.C.: 6411
N.A.I.C.S.: 524298

Personnel:
Babulal Agrawal *(Chm)*
Kamal Raj Gautam *(Gen Mgr & Sec)*

Board of Directors:
Babulal Agrawal
Ramesh Kumar Bhattarai
Kamal Raj Gautam
Mohan Raj Joshi
Dinanath Khandelwal
Bijay Kumar Sarawagi
Manoranjan Raman Sharma
Dinesh Lal Shrestha

ASIAN MARINE SERVICES PUBLIC COMPANY LIMITED

128 M00 3 Suksawad Rd Laemfapa
Prasamutjedee
Samut Prakan, 10290, Thailand
Tel.: (66) 2 815 2060
Fax: (66) 2 453 7214
E-Mail: mkd@asimar.com
Web Site: www.asimar.com
Year Founded: 1981
ASIMAR—(THA)
Rev.: $20,963,667
Assets: $22,456,595
Liabilities: $12,369,361
Net Worth: $10,087,234
Earnings: $1,942,259
Emp.: 418
Fiscal Year-end: 12/31/12

Business Description:
Marine & Cargo Handling Services
S.I.C.: 4491
N.A.I.C.S.: 488320

Personnel:
Prakit Pradipasen *(Chm)*
Sutham Tanpaibul *(Chm-Exec Bd)*
Warawan Nganthavee *(Mng Dir)*

Board of Directors:
Prakit Pradipasen
Prwat Chanruang
Bumroong Chinda
Warawan Nganthavee
Nonn Panitvong
Vibul Panitvong
Sribhumi Sukhanetr
Sutham Tanpaibul
Sutsep Tanpaibul
Sutin Tanphaibul
Wannaporn Viravan

ASIAN MICRO HOLDINGS LTD.

No 1 Tech Park Crescent Tuas Tech Park
Singapore, 638131, Singapore
Tel.: (65) 68627777
Fax: (65) 68626277
E-Mail: william@asianmicro.com.sg
Web Site: www.asianmicro.com.sg
Year Founded: 1966
585—(SES)
Rev.: $5,421,137
Assets: $3,348,095
Liabilities: $3,535,073
Net Worth: ($186,979)
Earnings: ($1,044,371)
Emp.: 604
Fiscal Year-end: 06/30/13

Business Description:
Holding Company
S.I.C.: 6719
N.A.I.C.S.: 551112

Personnel:
Kee Liew Lim *(Chm, CEO & Mng Dir)*
Ellen Lee *(Sec)*

Board of Directors:
Kee Liew Lim
Wai Tat Chue
Winchester Xianglong Lin
Chee Wee Ng
Kio Choon Teo

Legal Counsel:
Tan Peng Chin LLC
30 Raffles Place #11-00 Chevron House
Singapore, Singapore

Central Chambers Law Corporation
150, Cecil Street #16-00
Singapore, Singapore

Subsidiaries:

ACI Industries Pte Ltd (1)
1 Tech Park Crescent
Singapore, 638131, Singapore
Tel.: (65) 68627777
Fax: (65) 68626277
E-Mail: info@asianmicro.com.sg
Adhesives, Cleanroom, Industrial & Static Control Products Mfr

Asian Micro Holdings Ltd.—(Continued)

S.I.C.: 2891
N.A.I.C.S.: 325520
Victor Lim *(Gen Mgr)*

Asian Micro (S) Pte Ltd (1)
56 Serangoon N Ave 4 Level 3
Singapore, 555851, Singapore
Tel.: (65) 67526007
Fax: (65) 67529002
Web Site: www.asianmicro.com.sg/contact.htm
Emp.: 40
Hardware Mfr
S.I.C.: 3429
N.A.I.C.S.: 332510
Victor Lim *(CEO)*

Impact Polythene Pte. Ltd. (1)
No 1 Tech Park Crescent
Singapore, 638131, Singapore
Tel.: (65) 68613333
Fax: (65) 68626277
Hard Disk & Electronics Industry Packaging Materials
S.I.C.: 7389
N.A.I.C.S.: 561910

Micro Brite Technology Pte Ltd (1)
1 Tech Park Crescent
Singapore, 638131, Singapore
Tel.: (65) 68627777
Computer Hardware Distr
S.I.C.: 5072
N.A.I.C.S.: 423710

World Circuit Technology Pte. Ltd. (1)
1 Tech Park Crescent
Singapore, Singapore
Tel.: (65) 68627777
Fax: (65) 68626277
Contract Engineering Assemblies & Other Support Services
S.I.C.: 8711
N.A.I.C.S.: 541330
Victor Lam *(Gen Mgr)*

Non-U.S. Subsidiaries:

Asian Micro Co. Ltd. (1)
140 Moo 16 Bangpa-in Industrial Estate
T.Bangkrasan, A. Bangpa-in, Bangkok, 13160, Thailand
Tel.: (66) 35258998
Fax: (66) 35258996
Web Site: asianmicro.listedcompany.com
Contract Engineering Assemblies & Other Support Services
S.I.C.: 8711
N.A.I.C.S.: 541330

Asian Micro Technology Co. Ltd. (1)
Building 1A, Export Processing Zone
No.200 Suhong Middle Road, Suzhou, P.R., 215021, China
Tel.: (86) 51262586877
Fax: (86) 512 6258 6377
Web Site: asianmicro.listedcompany.com
Contract Engineering Assemblies & Other Support Services
S.I.C.: 8711
N.A.I.C.S.: 541330

Asian Micro (Thailand) Co., Ltd. (1)
130/171 130/172 Moo 3 Wang Chula Sub-District
Wang Noi District, Ayutthaya, 13170, Thailand
Tel.: (66) 35 722022
Fax: (66) 35 722018
Web Site: www.asianmicro.com.sg/others/contact_us.htm
Electronic Hardware Mfr
S.I.C.: 3429
N.A.I.C.S.: 332510

Suzhou Asian Micro Recovery Technology Co Ltd (1)
No 288 Lian Yi Road
Lu Zhi, Suzhou, China
Tel.: (86) 51 2660 10238
Fax: (86) 51 2660 10118
E-Mail: chentao@asianmicro.com.cn
Web Site: www.szasianmicro.com
Polyethylene Bags Mfr
S.I.C.: 3089
N.A.I.C.S.: 326199

ASIAN MINERAL RESOURCES LIMITED

120 Adelaide Street West Suite 2500
Toronto, ON, M5H 1T1, Canada
Tel.: (416) 360-3412
Fax: (416) 367-1954
E-Mail: info@asianminres.com
Web Site: www.asianminres.com
ASN—(TSXV)
Int. Income: $58,743
Assets: $38,085,832
Liabilities: $3,703,600
Net Worth: $34,382,231
Earnings: ($4,769,054)
Emp.: 196
Fiscal Year-end: 12/31/12

Business Description:
Mineral Exploration Services
S.I.C.: 1081
N.A.I.C.S.: 213114

Personnel:
Simon Booth *(Pres & CEO)*
Paula Kember *(Co-Sec)*
Ian MacGregor *(Co-Sec)*

Board of Directors:
Jan Castro
James Askew
Michael Brown
Christopher D. Castle
Robin Widdup

Transfer Agent:
Computershare Investor Services inc
3rd Fl 510 Burrard Street
Vancouver, BC, Canada

ASIAN OILFIELD SERVICES LIMITED

29 Payal Complex Sayajigunj Station Road
Sayajigunj, Vadodara, Gujarat, 390020, India
Tel.: (91) 265 2362292
Fax: (91) 265 2226216
E-Mail: mail@asianoilfield.com
Web Site: www.asianoilfield.com
Year Founded: 1992
530355—(BOM)
Rev.: $10,381,581
Assets: $22,326,732
Liabilities: $8,932,984
Net Worth: $13,393,748
Earnings: ($1,908,672)
Emp.: 250
Fiscal Year-end: 03/31/13

Business Description:
Oil & Gas Exploration Services
S.I.C.: 1389
N.A.I.C.S.: 213112

Personnel:
Rahul Talwar *(CEO)*
Avinash Manchanda *(Mng Dir)*
Sudhir Kumar *(CFO)*
Kanika Bhutani *(Compliance Officer & Sec)*
Anil Davadkar *(Compliance Officer & Mgr-Secretarial Svcs)*
Ashwin M. Khandke *(Sr VP-QHSE)*

Board of Directors:
Naresh Chandra Sharma
Rabi Narayan Bastia
Sanjay Bhargava
Gautam Gode
Ajit Kapadia
Avinash Manchanda
Sumeet Narang
Rahul Talwar

Transfer Agent:
Link Intime India Pvt. Ltd
B-102 & 103 Shangrila Complex I Fl Opp HDFC Bank Nr. Radhakrishna Char
Vadodara, India

ASIAN PAC HOLDINGS BERHAD

12th Floor Menara SMI No 6 Lorong P Ramlee
50250 Kuala Lumpur, Malaysia
Tel.: (60) 320781207
Fax: (60) 320704818
E-Mail: query@asianpac.com.my
Web Site: www.asianpac.com.my
ASIAPAC—(KLS)
Rev.: $33,853,805
Assets: $271,793,541
Liabilities: $159,644,573
Net Worth: $112,148,968
Earnings: $5,758,275
Fiscal Year-end: 03/31/13

Business Description:
Property Investment & Development
S.I.C.: 6531
N.A.I.C.S.: 531311

Personnel:
Mustapha Buang *(Mng Dir)*
Yoon Mun Chan *(Co-Sec)*
Mei Ying Ooi *(Co-Sec)*

Board of Directors:
Najmuddin Khas
Mohamed Salleh Bajuri
Mustapha Buang
Siew Poh Tan
Tat Loong Yu

ASIAN PACIFIC TIMBER MARKETING PTY LTD

25 Vallance St
Saint Marys, NSW, 2760, Australia
Mailing Address:
P O Box 1155
Saint Marys, NSW, 1790, Australia
Tel.: (61) 0298334777
Fax: (61) 0298334666
Web Site: www.aptm.com.au
Year Founded: 1986
Sales Range: $50-74.9 Million

Business Description:
New Home Renovation & Commercial Project Timber Whslr
S.I.C.: 2541
N.A.I.C.S.: 337212

Personnel:
Gerry Gardiner *(Chm & Co-Owner)*
Dave Alcock *(Co-Owner)*

Division:

Asian Pacific Timber Marketing Pty Ltd (1)
100 Potassium St
Narangba, QLD, 4504, Australia
Tel.: (61) 738179999
Fax: (61) 738179950
E-Mail: dials@aptm.com.au
Web Site: www.aptm.com.au
Emp.: 27
New Home Renovation & Commercial Project Timber Whslr
S.I.C.: 2499
N.A.I.C.S.: 321999
Dave Alcock *(Mng Dir)*

ASIAN PAINTS LIMITED

Asian Paints House 6A Shantinagar
Santacruz E
Mumbai, 400055, India
Tel.: (91) 2239818000
Fax: (91) 2239818888
E-Mail: proffice@asianpaints.com
Web Site: www.asianpaints.com
500820—(BOM)
Rev.: $2,231,092,476
Assets: $1,258,673,184
Liabilities: $601,419,060
Net Worth: $657,254,124
Earnings: $214,975,008
Emp.: 5,236
Fiscal Year-end: 03/31/13

Business Description:
Paint Mfr
S.I.C.: 2851
N.A.I.C.S.: 325510

Personnel:
K. B. S. Anand *(CEO & Mng Dir)*
Jayesh Merchant *(CFO, Compliance Officer & Sec)*

Board of Directors:
Ashwin Choksi
K. B. S. Anand
Dipankar Basu
Mahendra C. Choksi
Ashwin S. Dani
Malav Dani
S. Ramadorai
Deepak M. Satwalekar
Mahendra Shah
Rajendra Shah
M. K. Sharma
S. Sivaram
Abhay A. Vakil
Amar A. Vakil

B S R & Associates
Bengaluru, India

Sharepro Services (India) Private Limited
13 AB Samhita Warehousing Complex II Floor Sakinaka Telephone Lane
Off Andheri Kurla Rd Sakinaka, Mumbai, India

Transfer Agents:
Sharepro Services (India) Private Limited
912 Raheja Centre Free Press Journal Road
Nariman Point
Mumbai, India

Sharepro Services (India) Private Limited
13 AB Samhita Warehousing Complex II Floor
Sakinaka Telephone Lane
Off Andheri Kurla Rd Sakinaka, Mumbai, India

Subsidiary:

Asian Paints Industrial Coatings Ltd. (1)
Asian Paints House 6A Shantinagar
Santacruz (E), Mumbai, 400 055, India
Tel.: (91) 2239818000
Fax: (91) 2239818888
Web Site: www.asianpaints.com
Industrial Coatings Mfr
S.I.C.: 2851
N.A.I.C.S.: 325510

Non-U.S. Subsidiaries:

Apco Coatings (1)
7-9-11 Ruve Palace
Tavakubu, Lautoka, Fiji
Tel.: (679) 6662799
Fax: (679) 6663959
E-Mail: contact.fiji@apcocoatings.com
Web Site: www.apcocoatings.com
Emp.: 65
Paint & Coatings Mfr
S.I.C.: 2851
N.A.I.C.S.: 325510
Jaideep Nandi *(Mng Dir)*

Asian Paints (Lanka) Limited (1)
81 Koralawella Rd
Moratuwa, Sri Lanka
Tel.: (94) 112658621
Fax: (94) 112658200
E-Mail: contact.lanka@asianpaints.com
Web Site: www.asianpaints.com
Paints & Coating Mfr
S.I.C.: 2851
N.A.I.C.S.: 325510
Channa Hewage *(Mgr-Mktg)*

Asian Paints (Nepal) Pvt. Limited (1)
Balkumari Lalitpur
PO Box 4805
Kathmandu, Nepal
Tel.: (977) 15203045
E-Mail: ccm@asianpaints.com.np
Web Site: www.asianpaints.com
Emp.: 200
Paints & Coatings Mfr
S.I.C.: 2851
N.A.I.C.S.: 325510

Asian Paints (S.I.) Limited (1)
1898-1900 Industrial Estate
Ranadi, Honiara, Solomon Islands
Tel.: (677) 30485

Fax: (677) 30429
E-Mail: contact.solomonislands@abcocoatings.com
Emp.: 10
Paints Mfr & Distr
S.I.C.: 2851
N.A.I.C.S.: 325510
Binay Pal *(Gen Mgr)*

Asian Paints (Vanuatu) Limited (1)
PO Box 253
Port-Vila, Vanuatu
Tel.: (678) 25963
Fax: (678) 25965
Emp.: 6
Paint Mfr & Distr
S.I.C.: 2851
N.A.I.C.S.: 325510

Berger International Ltd. (1)
22 Benoi Sector
Singapore, 629854, Singapore (96.5%)
Tel.: (65) 62615224
Fax: (65) 62656356
E-Mail: berger@bergeronline.com.sg
Web Site: www.bergeronline.com
B64—(SES)
Rev.: $97,369,688
Assets: $55,376,444
Liabilities: $45,303,215
Net Worth: $10,073,229
Earnings: $3,845,170
Emp.: 3,500
Fiscal Year-end: 03/31/13
Specialty Paints & Coatings Mfr
S.I.C.: 2851
N.A.I.C.S.: 325510
Jalaj Ashwin Dani *(Chm)*
Jaideep Nandi *(CEO-Berger Paints Singapore Pte Ltd & Head-Singapore)*
Wei Hsiung Lee *(Co-Sec)*
Joanna Lan Sim Lim *(Co-Sec)*

Subsidiary:

Berger Paints Singapore Pte Ltd (2)
22 Benoi Sector
629854 Singapore, Singapore
Tel.: (65) 62615224
Fax: (65) 62656356
E-Mail: berger@beronline.com.sg
Web Site: www.bergeronline.com
Emp.: 150
Paint Varnish & Supplies Whslr
S.I.C.: 5198
N.A.I.C.S.: 424950
Jaideep Nandi *(CEO)*

Non-U.S. Subsidiaries:

Apco Coatings Ltd. (2)
444 Newman Road
Geebung, Brisbane, QLD, 4034, Australia
Tel.: (61) 733553066
Fax: (61) 32651890
E-Mail: apco@oicoatings.com
Web Site: www.apcocoatings.com
Emp.: 40
Paint & Coating Mfr
S.I.C.: 2851
N.A.I.C.S.: 325510
Daya Shetti *(Mgr)*

Berger Paints Bahrain W.L.L. (2)
PO Box 26688
Manama, Bahrain
Tel.: (973) 17730700
Fax: (973) 17730689
E-Mail: berger@batelco.com.bh
Web Site: www.bergeronline.com
Emp.: 75
Paint & Coating Mfr
S.I.C.: 2851
N.A.I.C.S.: 325510
R. Govindan *(CEO)*

Berger Paints Barbados Ltd. (2)
PO Box 218
Brandons St Michael, Bridgetown, Barbados (100%)
Tel.: (246) 425 9073
Fax: (246) 228 0866
E-Mail: mail@bergerbarbados.com.bb
Emp.: 50
Paint & Coating Mfr
S.I.C.: 2851
N.A.I.C.S.: 325510
Ritesh Doshi *(Mng Dir)*

Berger Paints Emirates Limited (2)
Plot of Land No 22 B Alquoz Industrial Area
PO Box 27524
Dubai, 27524, United Arab Emirates
Tel.: (971) 4 3391 000
Fax: (971) 4 3391 322
E-Mail: customerservice.uae@bergeronline.com
Emp.: 100
Paints Mfr & Distr
S.I.C.: 2851
N.A.I.C.S.: 325510
A. K. Paranthaman *(Mgr-Mktg)*

Berger Paints (Hong Kong) Ltd. (2)
Room 601 Shiu Fung Hong Building
239-241 Wing Lok Street, Sheung Wan,
China (Hong Kong) (100%)
Tel.: (852) 25443768
Fax: (852) 25453984
E-Mail: berger@bergeronline.com.hk
Web Site: www.bergeronline.com
Emp.: 5
Paint Varnish & Supplies Whslr
S.I.C.: 5198
N.A.I.C.S.: 424950
Ken Yen *(Gen Mgr)*

Berger Paints Jamaica Limited (2)
256 Spanish Town Road
PO Box 8
Kingston, Jamaica
Tel.: (876) 923 6226
Fax: (876) 923 5129
E-Mail: bergerja_admin@bergeronline.com
Web Site: www.bergeronline.com
Paint Mfr & Distr
S.I.C.: 2851
N.A.I.C.S.: 325510
Warren A. McDonald *(Reg Mng Dir)*
Mustafa Turra *(Mng Dir)*

Berger Paints Ningbo Co. Ltd. (2)
No 17 Jinqi Road Beilun Shiqiao
Economic & Tech Development Zone,
315821 Ningbo, Zhejiang, China
Tel.: (86) 57486178116
Fax: (86) 57486178205
E-Mail: manish-mehra@bergeronline.com
Web Site: www.bergeronline.com
Emp.: 40
Paint & Coating Mfr
S.I.C.: 2851
N.A.I.C.S.: 325510
Manish Mehra *(CEO)*

Berger Paints (Thailand) Ltd (2)
83 Moo 4 Poochaosamingpral Road
Samrong
Klang Prapradaeng, 10130 Samut Prakan,
Thailand (100%)
Tel.: (66) 275420048
Fax: (66) 27542084
E-Mail: berger@bergerthailand.com
Web Site: www.bergeronline.com
Emp.: 70
Paint & Coating Mfr
S.I.C.: 2851
N.A.I.C.S.: 325510
V. K. Singh *(Mng Dir)*
Pantitsa Suksa *(CFO)*

ASIAN PAY TELEVISION TRUST

10 Marina Boulevard #17-01 Tower 2
Marina Bay Financial Centre
Singapore, 018983, Singapore
Tel.: (65) 66010888
Fax: (65) 66010653
E-Mail: contact@aptt.com.sg
Web Site: www.aptt.com.sg
S7OU—(OTC SES)
Business Description:
Pay TV & Broadband Investment Services
S.I.C.: 6211
N.A.I.C.S.: 523999
Personnel:
Yong Lum Sung *(Chm)*
Robert Neale Thorpe *(CEO)*
Board of Directors:
Yong Lum Sung
Leong Shin Loong
Tri Pham
Robert Neale Thorpe
Benjamin Ian Way
Tan Chung Yaw

ASIAN PHYTOCEUTICALS PUBLIC COMPANY LIMITED

84/3 M4 Northern Region Industrial Estate West
T Banklang
A Muang, Lamphun, 51000, Thailand
Tel.: (66) 53581374
Fax: (66) 53581375
E-Mail: apco@apco.co.th
Web Site: www.apco.co.th
APCO—(THA)
Business Description:
Botanical Extracts Used for Dietary Supplements, Cosmetics & Personal Care Products
S.I.C.: 2833
N.A.I.C.S.: 325411
Personnel:
Maleeratna Plumchitchom *(Chm)*
Pichaet Wiriyachitra *(CEO)*
Board of Directors:
Maleeratna Plumchitchom
Krairit Boonyakiat
Jingjai Hanchanlash
Khunying Chamnongsri Hanchanlash
Praipol Koomsup
Varakorn Samakoses
Chinnakarn Samalapa
Arunee Wiriyachitra
Pichaet Wiriyachitra

Subsidiaries:

Asian Life Co., Ltd. (1)
8/F RS Tower 121/33-34 Ratchadapisek Rd
Dindaeng
Bangkok, 10400, Thailand
Tel.: (66) 2646 4800
Fax: (66) 2646 4898
E-Mail: service@asianlife.co.th
Dietary Supplements & Natural Cosmetics Whslr
S.I.C.: 5122
N.A.I.C.S.: 424210

Green Gold Co., Ltd. (1)
84/3 Moo 4
Muang, Lamphun, 51000, Thailand
Tel.: (66) 53581374
Fax: (66) 53581375
Dietary Supplement Mfr
S.I.C.: 2834
N.A.I.C.S.: 325412

ASIAN PLANTATIONS LIMITED

14 Ann Siang Road 02-10
Singapore, 069694, Singapore
Tel.: (65) 67206812
E-Mail: info@asianplantations.com
Web Site: www.asianplantations.com
PALM—(AIM)
Rev.: $2,820,000
Assets: $196,458,000
Liabilities: $139,428,000
Net Worth: $57,030,000
Earnings: ($6,879,000)
Emp.: 1,200
Fiscal Year-end: 12/31/12
Business Description:
Holding Company; Palm Oil
S.I.C.: 6719
N.A.I.C.S.: 551112
Personnel:
Graeme Iain Brown *(Co-Founder & Co-CEO)*
Dennis Nicholas Melka *(Co-Founder & Co-CEO)*
V. Panirchellvum *(COO)*
Anita Peck Hwa Chew *(Sec)*
Board of Directors:
Amar Leonard Linggi Jugah
Graeme Iain Brown
Amar Leo Moggie
Dennis Nicholas Melka

ASIAN PROPERTY DEVELOPMENT PUBLIC COMPANY LIMITED

170/57 18th Fl Ocean Tower 1
Ratchadapisek Road
Klongtoey, Bangkok, 10110, Thailand
Tel.: (66) 22612518
Fax: (66) 22612548
E-Mail: investor@ap-thai.com
Web Site: www.apthai.com
Year Founded: 1991
AP—(THA)
Rev.: $579,875,607
Assets: $971,114,392
Liabilities: $556,324,794
Net Worth: $414,789,598
Earnings: $77,168,958
Emp.: 1,144
Fiscal Year-end: 12/31/12
Business Description:
Property Development Services
S.I.C.: 1542
N.A.I.C.S.: 236220
Personnel:
Chatchaval Bhanalaph *(Chm)*
Anuphong Assavabhokhin *(Vice Chm & CEO)*
Pichet Vipavasuphakorn *(Mng Dir)*
Pumipat Sinacharoen *(Deputy CFO & Chief People Excellence Officer)*
Kittiya Pongpuchaneekul *(CFO)*
Wason Naruenatpaisan *(COO)*
Vittakarn Chandavimol *(Chief Strategic Mktg Officer)*
Supalak Chanpitak *(Chief Bus Officer-Unit 4)*
Opas Ruangrajitpakorn *(Chief Risk Officer)*
Visanu Suchatlumpong *(Chief Bus Officer-Unit 1)*
Marote Vananan *(Chief Comml Officer)*
Pamorn Prasertsan *(Deputy Chief Bus Officer-Unit 2)*
Boonlert Ratinthorn *(Deputy Chief Bus Officer-Unit 3)*
Somchai Wattanasaowapak *(Chief IT Officer)*
Piyawat Suephaisal *(Exec VP-Bus Liaison Dept)*
Board of Directors:
Chatchaval Bhanalaph
Anuphong Assavabhokhin
Phanporn Dabbaransri
Wason Naruenatpaisan
Kittiya Pongpuchaneekul
Pornwut Sarasin
Shaw Sinhaseni
Siripong Sombutsiri
Visanu Suchatlumpong
Kosol Suriyaporn
Chaiyarat Thampeera
Nontachit Tulayanonda
Pichet Vipavasuphakorn

Subsidiary:

Bangkok CitiSmart Co., Ltd. (1)
170/48 15th Floor Ocean Tower1
Ratchadapisek Rd
Klongtoey, Bangkok, 10110, Thailand
Tel.: (66) 2661 8999
Fax: (66) 2661 8044
E-Mail: info@bkkcitismart.com
Web Site: www.bkkcitismart.com
Property Brokerage Services
S.I.C.: 6531
N.A.I.C.S.: 531390
Sethasit Chanphatree *(COO)*

Non-U.S. Subsidiary:

Trillion Development Co Ltd (1)
Flat 5C 5th Floor Lee Ko Industrial Building
324 Kwun Tong Road Kwun Tong, Kowloon,
China (Hong Kong) (100%)
Tel.: (852) 36111848
Fax: (852) 26317481
E-Mail: info@trillionhk.com

Asian Property Development Public Company Limited—(Continued)

Web Site: www.trillionhk.com
Emp.: 5
Other Real Estate Property Lessors
S.I.C.: 6519
N.A.I.C.S.: 531190
Scott Chan *(Mng Dir)*

ASIAN SEAFOODS COLDSTORAGE PUBLIC COMPANY LIMITED

55/2 Moo 2 Rama II Road Tambol
Bangkrajao Amphoe Mueang
Samut Sakhon, 74000, Thailand
Tel.: (66) 34 822204
Fax: (66) 34 822407
E-Mail: asian2@asianseafoods.co.th
Web Site: www.asianseafoods.co.th
Year Founded: 1982
ASIAN—(THA)
Rev.: $349,740,821
Assets: $231,660,531
Liabilities: $159,705,484
Net Worth: $71,955,047
Earnings: $925,321
Fiscal Year-end: 12/31/12
Business Description:
Frozen Seafood Processing
S.I.C.: 2092
N.A.I.C.S.: 311710
Personnel:
Somsak Amornrattanachaikul *(Pres, CEO & Mng Dir)*
Board of Directors:
Somchai Amornrattanachaikul
Somsak Amornrattanachaikul
Aekarat Punnasung
Apichai Sriarunlucksana
Somsak Sthidthummarong
Chaiphorn Wangnitayasuk

ASIAN STAR ANCHOR CHAIN CO., LTD. JIANGSU

Dongxing Town
Jingjiang, Jiangsu, China 214533
Tel.: (86) 523 8468 1282
Fax: (86) 523 8468 1390
E-Mail: sales@anchor-chain.com
Web Site: www.anchor-chain.com
Year Founded: 1981
601890—(SHG)
Emp.: 2,000
Business Description:
Anchor Chain Mfr
S.I.C.: 3499
N.A.I.C.S.: 332999
Personnel:
Anxiang Tao *(Chm)*

ASIAN STAR COMPANY LTD

114 Mittal Court-C Nariman Point
Mumbai, 400021, India
Tel.: (91) 2222821886
Fax: (91) 2222043747
E-Mail: info@asianstargroup.com
Web Site: www.asianstargroup.com
531847—(BOM)
Rev.: $456,781,438
Assets: $307,054,641
Liabilities: $219,554,740
Net Worth: $87,499,901
Earnings: $8,855,798
Emp.: 2,150
Fiscal Year-end: 03/31/13
Business Description:
Diamond & Jewellery Mfr & Retailer
S.I.C.: 3914
N.A.I.C.S.: 339910
Personnel:
Vipul P. Shah *(CEO & Mng Dir)*
Dharmesh D. Shah *(Mng Dir & CFO)*
Sangeetha Nilesh *(Sec)*
Board of Directors:
Dinesh T. Shah
Hasmukh B. Gandhi
Milind H. Gandhi
K. Mohanram Pai
Nayak M. R.
Apurva R. Shah
Arvind T. Shah
Dharmesh D. Shah
Priyanshu A. Shah
Rahil V. Shah
Vipul P. Shah
Bhupendra K. Shroff
Transfer Agent:
Bigshare Services Pvt. Ltd.
E-2/3 Ansa Industrial Estate Sakivihar Road
Saki Naka Andheri E
Mumbai, India
Subsidiary:

Asian Star Jewels Private Limited **(1)**
G-23 G & J Complex-III Seepz-Sez Andheri
400021 Mumbai, Maharashtra, India
Tel.: (91) 2222821886
Fax: (91) 22043747
E-Mail: info@asianstarco.com
Emp.: 30
Diamond Jewelry Designer
S.I.C.: 5944
N.A.I.C.S.: 448310
Nancy Almeida *(Gen Mgr-Mktg)*

U.S. Subsidiary:

Asian Star Company Limited (USA) **(1)**
551 5th Ave Ste 3502
New York, NY 10176
Tel.: (212) 354-0666
Fax: (212) 354-0606
E-Mail: Mehul@asianstarco.com
Web Site: www.asianstarco.com
Emp.: 10
Diamonds Jewelry Mfr
S.I.C.: 3911
N.A.I.C.S.: 339910
Mehul Shroff *(VP)*

ASIAN TEA & EXPORTS LIMITED

Sikkim Commerce House 4/1
Middleton Street
Kolkata, 700 071, India
Tel.: (91) 33 2287 7334
Fax: (91) 33 2280 3101
E-Mail: info@asianteaexports.com
Web Site: www.asianteaexports.com
519532—(BOM)
Sales Range: $25-49.9 Million
Business Description:
Tea Mfr & Whslr
S.I.C.: 2099
N.A.I.C.S.: 311920
Personnel:
Hariram Garg *(Founder & Chm)*
Board of Directors:
Hariram Garg
Sunil Garg

ASIAN TELEVISION NETWORK INTERNATIONAL LTD.

330 Cochrane Drive
Markham, ON, L3R 8E4, Canada
Tel.: (905) 948-8199
Fax: (905) 948-8108
E-Mail: atn@asiantelevision.com
Web Site: www.asiantelevision.com
SAT—(TSXV)
Rev.: $27,596,942
Assets: $18,834,051
Liabilities: $9,185,828
Net Worth: $9,648,223
Earnings: $2,898,421
Fiscal Year-end: 12/31/12
Business Description:
Television Broadcasting Services
S.I.C.: 4833
N.A.I.C.S.: 515120
Personnel:
Shan Chandrasekar *(Chm, Pres & CEO)*
Kyrill Classen *(CFO)*
Jaya Chandrasekar *(Exec VP & VP-Programming)*
Board of Directors:
Shan Chandrasekar
Prakash Naidoo
Subsidiary:

Asian Television Network Inc. **(1)**
330 Cochrane Drive
Markham, ON, L3R 8E4, Canada
Tel.: (905) 836-6460
Fax: (905) 948-8108
E-Mail: atn@asiantelevision.com
Web Site: www.asiantelevision.com
Television Broadcasting Services
S.I.C.: 4833
N.A.I.C.S.: 515120

ASIAN TRENDS MEDIA HOLDINGS, INC.

203 Hankow Center 5-15 Hankow
Road Tsimshatsui
Kowloon, China (Hong Kong)
Tel.: (852) 28827026
Year Founded: 2002
ATDH.PK—(OTC)
Rev.: $64
Assets: $249
Liabilities: $424,417
Net Worth: ($424,168)
Earnings: ($24,754)
Fiscal Year-end: 12/31/12
Business Description:
Advertising Services
S.I.C.: 7312
N.A.I.C.S.: 541850
Personnel:
Kam Hang Ho *(CEO)*
Cheuk Man Yuki Chong *(CFO)*
Board of Directors:
Fuk Yu Chan
Huang Jian Nan
Cheung Fai Alex Yu
Ka Wai Yu
Lok Man Yu
Zhi Jian Zeng

ASIANLOGIC LIMITED

5F The Workstation 43 Lyndhurst
Terrace
Central, China (Hong Kong)
Tel.: (852) 25810100
Fax: (852) 25810102
E-Mail: info@asianlogic.com
Web Site: www.asianlogic.com
Sales Range: $10-24.9 Million
Emp.: 408
Fiscal Year-end: 12/31/12
Business Description:
Online Gambling Services
S.I.C.: 7999
N.A.I.C.S.: 713290
Personnel:
Thomas Hall *(Co-Founder & Vice Chm)*
Christopher Parker *(Co-Founder & CEO)*
Chi Kan Tang *(Co-Founder & Dir-Global Bus Dev)*
Jong-Dae Lee *(Chm)*
Gary Underwood *(CFO)*
Robert Evans *(COO)*
Nicholas Chappell *(Chief Compliance Officer)*
Itamar Shamshins *(CTO)*
Board of Directors:
Jong-Dae Lee
Robert Evans
Thomas Hall
Jonathan Hubbard
Christopher Parker
Itamar Shamshins
Chi Kan Tang
Gary Underwood
Legal Counsel:
Berwin Leighton
Adelaide House
London Bridge
London, EC4 9HA, United Kingdom
Tel.: (44) 71 623 3144
Subsidiary:

Internet Sports Marketing Limited **(1)**
5Fl The Workstation 43 Lyndhurst Terrace
Central, China (Hong Kong)
Tel.: (852) 25810100
Fax: (852) 25810102
E-Mail: info@ismhongkong.com
Web Site: www.ismhongkong.com
Emp.: 200
Marketing Research Services
S.I.C.: 8732
N.A.I.C.S.: 541910
Nick Chappell *(Mgr)*

Non-U.S. Subsidiaries:

Bayview Technologies, Inc **(1)**
43rd Fl Yuchengco Tower Gil Puyat Ave
RCBC Plz 6819 Ayala Ave cor, Makati,
1200, Philippines
Tel.: (63) 28872525
Fax: (63) 28443098
Web Site: www.bayviewtechnology.com
Emp.: 125
Online Gaming Services
S.I.C.: 2741
N.A.I.C.S.: 519130

Cantonvalley Macau Company Limited **(1)**
Ed AIA Tower
Macau, China (Macau)
Tel.: (853) 28286632
Fax: (853) 28286631
Administrative Management Service Providers
S.I.C.: 8742
N.A.I.C.S.: 541611
Christina Tan *(Mgr-Ops)*

Emphasis Services Limited **(1)**
43 F Yuchengco Tower RCBC Plz 6819
Ayala Ave cor Gil Puyat Ave
Makati, Philippines
Tel.: (63) 28872525
Fax: (63) 28443098
Web Site: www.esl-asia.com
Online Gaming Services
S.I.C.: 7999
N.A.I.C.S.: 713210

Orient Capital Ventures Limited **(1)**
300-1055 W Hastings St
Vancouver, BC, V6E 2E9, Canada
Tel.: (604) 689-0618
Fax: (604) 689-0628
E-Mail: info@orientvc.com
Web Site: www.orientvc.com
Investment Holding Services
S.I.C.: 6719
N.A.I.C.S.: 551112
Mian Kuang *(Gen Mgr)*

ASIAPHARMA HOLDINGS LTD.

International Plaza 10 Anson Road
Suite 23
Singapore, 079903, Singapore
Tel.: (65) 6220 0119
Business Description:
Investment Holding Company
S.I.C.: 6719
N.A.I.C.S.: 551112
Personnel:
Dian Bo Liu *(Chm)*

Holding:

Luye Pharma Group Ltd. **(1)**
137 Telok Ayer Street 05 05
Singapore, 068602, Singapore BM
Tel.: (65) 62200119
Fax: (65) 62200282
E-Mail: info@asiapharm.biz
Web Site: www.luye.cn
A61—(SES)

Sales Range: $250-299.9 Million
Emp.: 1,600
Orthopaedics, Neurology, Gastroenterology & Hepatology Drugs Mfr
S.I.C.: 2834
N.A.I.C.S.: 325412
Dian Bo Liu *(Founder & Chm)*
Rong Bing Yang *(Founder)*
Hui Xian Yuan *(Founder)*
Chin Fan Chong *(CFO)*
Wen De Chen *(COO)*
Caroline Poh Noi Yeo *(Sec)*

ASIAPHOS LIMITED

600 North Bridge Road Parkview Square #12-01
Singapore, 188778, Singapore
Tel.: (65) 6292 3119
Fax: (65) 6292 3122
Web Site: www.asiaphos.com
5WV—(CAT)
Rev.: $3,965,003
Earnings: $991,858
Fiscal Year-end: 12/31/12
Business Description:
Phosphate Mining
S.I.C.: 1475
N.A.I.C.S.: 212392
Personnel:
Hian Eng Ong *(CEO)*

ASIASOFT CORPORATION PUBLIC COMPANY LIMITED

9 UM Tower Room 9/283-5 28th Floor Ramkhamhaeng Road
Suanluang, Bangkok, 10250, Thailand
Tel.: (66) 27698888
Fax: (66) 27174251
E-Mail: corpcom@asiasoft.co.th
Web Site: www.asiasoft.co.th
Year Founded: 2001
AS—(THA)
Rev.: $66,782,669
Assets: $65,937,628
Liabilities: $20,307,364
Net Worth: $45,630,264
Earnings: $10,259,870
Emp.: 808
Fiscal Year-end: 12/31/12
Business Description:
Software Games Development & Publisher
S.I.C.: 3652
N.A.I.C.S.: 334614
Personnel:
Tgow Lim Tan *(Chm)*
Pramoth Sudjitporn *(Vice Chm & CEO)*
Lertchai Kanpai *(Mng Dir)*
Kenny Goh *(CFO)*
Kittipong Prucksa-aroon *(Deputy Mng Dir)*
Chatchawan Triamvicharnkul *(Deputy Mng Dir)*
Vinai Vimukti *(Deputy Mng Dir)*
Board of Directors:
Tgow Lim Tan
Chalermphong Jitkuntivong
Lertchai Kanpai
Surasak Khaoroptham
Thanwa Laohasiriwong
Monluedee Sookpantarat
Pramoth Sudjitporn

Subsidiaries:

Funbox Company Limited **(1)**
No 1168/15 17 Lumpini Tower Rama 4 Road Tungmahamek
Sathorn, Bangkok, 10120, Thailand
Tel.: (66) 2343 1000
Fax: (66) 2679 8772
Web Site: www.funbox.co.th
Online Games Publishing Services
S.I.C.: 7372
N.A.I.C.S.: 511210

Playcybergames Company Limited **(1)**
No 9 UM Tower Room 9/244 24th Floor Ramkhamhaeng Road
Suanluang, Bangkok, 10250, Thailand
Tel.: (66) 2717 3515
Fax: (66) 2717 4254
Web Site: www.playcybergames.com
Online Games Publishing Services
S.I.C.: 7372
N.A.I.C.S.: 511210

Non-U.S. Subsidiaries:

AS Online Sdn. Bhd. **(1)**
Suite 21 01 Level 21 Menara IGB Mid Valley City Lingkaran Syed Putra
59200 Kuala Lumpur, Malaysia
Tel.: (60) 3 2287 1503
Fax: (60) 3 2287 1500
Online Games Publishing Services
S.I.C.: 7372
N.A.I.C.S.: 511210
Sylvia Kheng *(Mgr-HR)*

Asiasoft Online Pte. Ltd **(1)**
5 Tampines Central 1 04-01 Tampines Plaza
Singapore, 529541, Singapore
Tel.: (65) 6825 8500
Fax: (65) 6781 3532
E-Mail: business@asiasoftsea.net
Web Site: www.asiasoftsea.com
Online Games Publishing Services
S.I.C.: 7372
N.A.I.C.S.: 511210
Gerry Wai Ung, *(Mng Dir)*

CIB Development Sdn. Bhd. **(1)**
Suite 6 05-6 07 6th Floor Menara Summit Persiaran Kewajipan USJ I
47600 Subang Jaya, Malaysia
Tel.: (60) 3 8023 8315
Fax: (60) 3 8023 8315
Online Games Publishing Services
S.I.C.: 7372
N.A.I.C.S.: 511210
Ku Foo Keong, *(CEO)*

PT. Asiasoft **(1)**
Cyber Building 6th floor Jl Kuningan Barat No 8
Jakarta, Indonesia
Tel.: (62) 1529 05201
Fax: (62) 1529 05202
Online Games Publishing Services
S.I.C.: 7372
N.A.I.C.S.: 511210
Suyudi Koeswanto, *(Mng Dir)*

ASIASONS CAPITAL LIMITED

22 Cross Street 03-54/61
China Square Central, Singapore, Singapore
Tel.: (65) 6226 3771
Fax: (65) 62261655
E-Mail: enquiry@asiasons.com
Web Site: www.asiasons.com
Year Founded: 1999
ACAP—(SES)
Rev.: $5,116,693
Assets: $157,389,699
Liabilities: $19,383,624
Net Worth: $138,006,075
Earnings: $23,157,668
Emp.: 250
Fiscal Year-end: 12/31/12
Business Description:
Investment Holding Company
S.I.C.: 6211
N.A.I.C.S.: 523999
Personnel:
Mohammed Azlan Bin Hashim *(Chm)*
Lim Chih Li *(Joint Mng Dir)*
Teck Wah Ng *(Joint Mng Dir)*
Board of Directors:
Mohammed Azlan Bin Hashim
Kuan Yew Attlee Hue
Leng Lee Teck
Lim Chih Li
Teck Wah Ng

ASIATIC CARPETS LTD

Oriental Carpet Centre 105 Eade Road
London, N4 1TJ, United Kingdom
Tel.: (44) 2088002000
Fax: (44) 2088008181
E-Mail: mail@asiatic.co.uk
Web Site: www.asiatic.co.uk
Year Founded: 1960
Rev.: $21,882,559
Emp.: 95
Business Description:
Rugs Distr & Mfr
S.I.C.: 7217
N.A.I.C.S.: 561740
Personnel:
Jeremy Nichols *(Dir-Sls)*

ASIATRAVEL.COM HOLDINGS LTD

615 Lorong 4 Toa Payoh 01 01 Storhub
Singapore, 319516, Singapore
Tel.: (65) 67326773
Fax: (65) 67321226
E-Mail: info@asiatravel.com
Web Site: www.asiatravel.com
5AM—(SES)
Rev.: $72,975,241
Assets: $33,490,065
Liabilities: $11,633,340
Net Worth: $21,856,725
Earnings: ($2,815,123)
Fiscal Year-end: 09/30/12
Business Description:
Traveling Services
S.I.C.: 4725
N.A.I.C.S.: 561520
Personnel:
Tuang Poh Boh *(Chm & CEO)*
Chelyn Yen Leng Ang *(CFO)*
Hwa Poh Tan *(CEO-AT Express Pte Ltd)*
Caroline Poh Noi Yeo *(Sec)*
Magdalene Wee Tiang Yeo *(Exec VP-Product Dev & Ops-Singapore, Malaysia, China & India)*
Nicolas J. Rocha *(Sr VP-Philippines, Thailand, Europe & USA)*
Sam Lam Sum Tsui *(Sr VP-Ops-Hong Kong & Macau)*
Lisa Wee Khim Yeo *(Sr VP-Grp Ops)*
Board of Directors:
Tuang Poh Boh
Chin Fan Chong
Heng Su-Ling Mae
Patrick Mia Je Ngiam
Arnold Kheng Lee Tan
Transfer Agent:
Boardroom Corporate & Advisory Services Pte. Ltd.
50 Raffles Place 32-01 Singapore Land Tower
Singapore, Singapore

Subsidiaries:

AT Express Pte. Ltd. **(1)**
22 Cavenagh Orchard Road 01-15A Hotel Grand Central
Singapore, 229617, Singapore
Tel.: (65) 67343933
Fax: (65) 62353933
Emp.: 3
Hotel Reservation Services
S.I.C.: 4729
N.A.I.C.S.: 561599
Hwa Poh Tan *(CEO)*

AT Reservation Pte Ltd **(1)**
111 North Bridge Road 01-33 Peninsula Plaza
Singapore, 179098, Singapore
Tel.: (65) 63383025
Fax: (65) 63386815
Hotel & Travel Reservation Services
S.I.C.: 4729
N.A.I.C.S.: 561599
Irene Leong *(Gen Mgr-Ops)*

Non-U.S. Subsidiaries:

Asiatravel Online Sdn Bhd **(2)**
148-03 3rd Floor Jalan Bukit Bintang
55100 Kuala Lumpur, Malaysia
Tel.: (60) 321436555
Fax: (60) 321436558
E-Mail: evelyne.leong@asiatravel.com
Web Site: www.asiatravel.com
Emp.: 9
Online Air Ticketing Services
S.I.C.: 4729
N.A.I.C.S.: 561599
Evelyne Leong *(Country Mgr)*

AT-Chinese (HK) Limited **(2)**
Room A 7/F No 6 Knutsford Terrace
Tsim Tsa Tsui, Kowloon, China (Hong Kong)
Tel.: (852) 27360922
Fax: (852) 24050922
Travel & Tour Operating Agencies
S.I.C.: 4724
N.A.I.C.S.: 561510
Soon Leong Liu *(Mng Dir)*

AT Phil., Inc. **(2)**
Ground Floor Edgardo Angara Wing IBP Building Jade Street
Ortigas Center, Pasig, Metro Manila, 1605, Philippines
Tel.: (63) 2 634 4220
Fax: (63) 2 635 6699
Web Site: www.asiatravel.com
Travel & Tour Operating Agencies
S.I.C.: 4724
N.A.I.C.S.: 561510

OV International Pte Ltd **(1)**
22 Cavenagh Road Orchard Road 02-05 Hotel Grand Central
Singapore, Singapore
Tel.: (65) 62519688
Fax: (65) 62558998
Web Site: www.asiatravel.com
Travel & Tour Operating Agencies
S.I.C.: 4724
N.A.I.C.S.: 561510
Irene Leong *(Gen Mgr)*

SH Tours Pte Ltd **(1)**
615 Lorong 4 Poa Payoh Unit No X01-01
Singapore, 319516, Singapore
Tel.: (65) 67349923
Fax: (65) 67387955
E-Mail: shtours@asiatours.com.sg
Web Site: www.asiatours.com.sg
Emp.: 100
Travel & Tour Operating Agencies
S.I.C.: 4724
N.A.I.C.S.: 561510
Catherine Khng *(Asst Gen Mgr)*

Non-U.S. Subsidiaries:

Asia Middle East Tours (L.L.C.) **(1)**
Shop Numbers WB21 WB22 WB23
PO Box 112758
Bur Dubai, Dubai, United Arab Emirates
Tel.: (971) 4 396 8787
Fax: (971) 4 397 7889
E-Mail: customerservice@asiatravel.com
Web Site: www.asiatravel.com
Emp.: 17
Travel & Tour Operating Agencies
S.I.C.: 4724
N.A.I.C.S.: 561510
Russell Gonzales *(Gen Mgr)*

Asia Travel Network Ltd. **(1)**
74 Kundmal House 4 Prat Avenue
Tsim Tsa Tsui, Kowloon, China (Hong Kong)
Tel.: (852) 27360922
Fax: (852) 24050922
E-Mail: sam@asiatravel.com
Web Site: www.asiatravel.com
Emp.: 200
Travel & Tour Operating Agencies
S.I.C.: 4724
N.A.I.C.S.: 561510
Sam Tsui *(Mgr)*

ASIATRUST DEVELOPMENT BANK, INC.

(Name Changed to NextGenesis Holdings Corp.)

ASICS CORPORATION

1-1 Minatojima-Nakamachi 7chome
Chuo-ku
Kobe, Hyogo, 650-8555, Japan

ASICS Corporation—(Continued)

Tel.: (81) 783036888
Fax: (81) 783032241
Web Site: www.asics.com
7936—(TKS)
Sls.: $2,862,189,000
Assets: $2,691,975,000
Liabilities: $1,173,117,000
Net Worth: $1,518,858,000
Earnings: $151,503,000
Emp.: 5,937
Fiscal Year-end: 03/31/13
Business Description:
Mfr & Sales of Sports Apparel, Athletic Shoes & Leisure Goods Import Export
S.I.C.: 3949
N.A.I.C.S.: 339920
Personnel:
Motoi Oyama *(Pres & CEO)*
Kousuke Hashimoto *(Mng Exec Officer)*
Masao Hijikata *(Exec Officer)*
Isao Kato *(Exec Officer)*
Katsumi Kato *(Exec Officer)*
Kazuhito Matsuo *(Mng Exec Officer)*
Toshiyuki Sano *(Mng Exec Officer)*
Board of Directors:
Kousuke Hashimoto
Masao Hijikata
Kenji Kajiwara
Isao Kato
Katsumi Kato
Kazuhito Matsuo
Keiji Miyakawa
Motoi Oyama
Toshiyuki Sano
Katsuro Tanaka

U.S. Subsidiary:

ASICS America Corporation (1)
29 Parker Ste 100
Irvine, CA 92618 CA
Tel.: (949) 453-8888
Fax: (949) 453-0292
Toll Free: (800) 333-8404
Web Site: www.asicsamerica.com
Rev.: $150,000,000
Emp.: 180
Sporting Apparel Mfr Import
S.I.C.: 5139
N.A.I.C.S.: 424340
Kevin G. Wulff *(CEO)*

ASIT C.MEHTA FINANCIAL SERVICES LTD.

Nucleus House Saki Vihar Road Andheri East
Mumbai, 400072, India
Tel.: (91) 22 2857 6916
Fax: (91) 22 2857 6918
E-Mail: info@nucleusgis.com
Web Site: www.asitmehta.com
530723—(BOM)
Sales Range: Less than $1 Million
Business Description:
Financial Software Development Services
S.I.C.: 7371
N.A.I.C.S.: 541511
Personnel:
Suupriyo S. Sikdar *(CEO)*
Tushar Kapadia *(Sec)*
Board of Directors:
R. Krishnamurthy
Vijay G. Ladha
Asit C. Mehta
Deena A. Mehta
D. Sunderarajan
Transfer Agent:
Link Intime India Private Limited
C-13 Pannalal Silk Mills Compound L.B.S. Marg Bhandup
Mumbai, India

ASITE SOLUTIONS LTD.

Zetland House 5-25 Scrutton Street
London, EC2A 4HJ, United Kingdom
Tel.: (44) 2077497880
Fax: (44) 2077497890
E-Mail: info@asite.com
Web Site: www.asite.com
Rev.: $2,909,596
Emp.: 120
Business Description:
Data Logistics Technology
S.I.C.: 7389
N.A.I.C.S.: 561499
Personnel:
Tony Ryan *(CEO)*
Board of Directors:
John Egan
Mathew Riley
Peter Rogers
Tony Ryan
Robert Tchenguiz

ASIYA PEARLS, INC.

H 2434 Tengengar Galli near Sheetal Hotel
Belgaum, Karnataka, 590001, India
Tel.: (91) 97 65 24 89 53
E-Mail: asiyapearls@gmail.com
Year Founded: 2013
Business Description:
Pearl Retailer
S.I.C.: 5094
N.A.I.C.S.: 423940
Personnel:
Shabbir Shaikh *(Pres, Treas & Sec)*
Board of Directors:
Asiya Shaikh
Shabbir Shaikh

ASK S.A.

2405 route des Dolines
Sophia-Antipolis, 06560 Nice, France
Tel.: (33) 497214000
Fax: (33) 492389321
E-Mail: info@ask.fr
Web Site: www.ask-rfid.com
Year Founded: 1997
Sales Range: $25-49.9 Million
Emp.: 125
Business Description:
Electronic Documents Mfr
S.I.C.: 3999
N.A.I.C.S.: 339999
Personnel:
Philippe Geyres *(Chm)*
Thierry Lucereau *(CEO)*
Francois Monteil *(COO)*
Philippe Berthault *(Sec & Dir-HR)*
Board of Directors:
Philippe Geyres
Valery Huot
Thierry Lucereau
Bruno Moreau
Ines Sen

ASKA PHARMACEUTICAL CO., LTD.

5 1 Shibaura 2 chome Minato ku
1088532 Tokyo, Japan
Tel.: (81) 354848361
Web Site: www.aska-pharma.co.jp
4514—(TKS)
Sales Range: $300-349.9 Million
Emp.: 1,060
Business Description:
Pharmaceuticals Mfr
S.I.C.: 2834
N.A.I.C.S.: 325412
Personnel:
Takashi Yamaguchi *(Pres)*
Mitsuru Otake *(Mng Dir)*
Toshi Horiuchi *(Exec Officer)*
Akira Naito *(Exec Officer)*
Hirotoshi Yorozuya *(Exec Officer)*
Board of Directors:
Toshi Horiuchi
Hashime Kanazawa
Akira Naito
Mitsuru Otake
Eiji Ueda
Masao Yamaguchi
Takashi Yamaguchi
Hirotoshi Yorozuya

ASKARI GENERAL INSURANCE COMPANY LIMITED

4th Floor AWT Plaza The Mall
Rawalpindi, Pakistan 46000
Tel.: (92) 51 9272425
Fax: (92) 51 9272424
E-Mail: info@agico.com.pk
Web Site: www.agico.com.pk
Year Founded: 1995
AGIC—(ISL)
Rev.: $7,090,468
Assets: $22,539,872
Liabilities: $17,402,404
Net Worth: $5,137,468
Earnings: $759,207
Fiscal Year-end: 12/31/12
Business Description:
Insurance Services
S.I.C.: 6411
N.A.I.C.S.: 524298
Personnel:
Tahir Mahmood *(Chm)*
Abdul Waheed *(Pres & CEO)*
Jamil Ahmed *(CFO)*
Abbas Zaidi *(Chief Health Officer)*
Suleman Khalid *(Sec)*
Board of Directors:
Tahir Mahmood
Mukhtar Ahmed
Irfan Azam
Abdul Hai Mehmood Bhaimia
Khawaja Muhammad Iqbal
Farrukh Iqbal Khan
Suhail Ahmad Rizvi
Tariq Sher
Abdul Waheed
Transfer Agent:
THK Associates (Pvt) Limited
Ground Floor State Life Building 3 Dr Ziauddin Ahmed Road
Karachi, Pakistan

ASKLEPIOS KLINIKEN GMBH

Rubenkamp 226
22307 Hamburg, Germany
Tel.: (49) 18 18 82 66 96
Fax: (49) 18 18 82 67 99
E-Mail: zentrale@asklepios.com
Web Site: www.asklepios.com
Rev.: $4,058,973,130
Assets: $3,555,869,016
Liabilities: $2,409,568,914
Net Worth: $1,146,300,102
Earnings: $152,012,209
Emp.: 44,000
Fiscal Year-end: 12/31/12
Business Description:
Hospital Operator
S.I.C.: 8062
N.A.I.C.S.: 622110
Personnel:
Stephan Witteler *(Chm-Supervisory Bd)*
Ulrich Wandschneider *(Chm-Mgmt Bd & CEO)*
Dominik Schirmer *(Deputy Chm-Supervisory Bd)*
Stephan Leonhard *(CFO & Member-Mgmt Bd)*
Roland Dankwardt *(Member-Mgmt Bd)*
Kai Hankeln *(Member-Mgmt Bd)*
Supervisory Board of Directors:
Stephan Witteler
Erika Harder
Nicolai Jurs
Hans-Otto Koderisch
Karsten Krakow
Rainer Laufs
Michael Lingenfelder
Karl-Heinrich Link
Stefan Murfeld
Monika Paga
Dirk Reischauer
Jochen Repp
Katharina Ries-Heidtke
Dominik Schirmer
Michael Schreder
Martin Simon Schwarzel
Hilke Stein
Andre Stuve
Dirk Volpel-Haus
Stephan Zu Hone

Subsidiary:

MEDICLIN Aktiengesellschaft (1)
Okenstrasse 27
77652 Offenburg, Baden Wurttemberg, Germany (52.73%)
Tel.: (49) 7814880
Fax: (49) 781488133
E-Mail: info@mediclin.de
Web Site: www.mediclin.de
MED—(DEU)
Sls.: $696,784,149
Assets: $430,230,087
Liabilities: $218,854,471
Net Worth: $211,375,616
Earnings: ($1,987,607)
Emp.: 6,256
Fiscal Year-end: 12/31/12
Health Care Services
S.I.C.: 8062
N.A.I.C.S.: 622110
Ulrich Wandschneider *(Chm-Supervisory Bd)*
Frank Abele *(Chm-Mgmt Bd)*
Hans Hilpert *(Vice Chm-Supervisory Bd)*
Jens Breuer *(CFO & Member-Mgmt Bd)*

Subsidiaries:

Cortex Software GmbH (2)
Okenstrasse 27
77652 Offenburg, Germany
Tel.: (49) 781488500
Fax: (49) 781488509
E-Mail: info@cortex-software.de
Web Site: www.cortex-software.de
Emp.: 70
Software Development Services
S.I.C.: 7371
N.A.I.C.S.: 541511
Frank Abele *(Co-CEO)*
Hermann Steppe *(Co-CEO)*

Dr. Hoefer-Janker GmbH & Co. Klinik KG (2)
Villenstrasse 4
53129 Bonn, Nordrhein-Westfalen, Germany
Tel.: (49) 22853060
Fax: (49) 2285306176
E-Mail: info.Robert-janker@mediclin.de
Web Site: www.mediclin.de
Hospital Management Services
S.I.C.: 8062
N.A.I.C.S.: 622110
Muemtaz Koeksal *(Mng Dir)*

Herzzentrum Lahr/Baden GmbH & Co. KG (2)
Hohbergweg 2
77933 Lahr, Germany
Tel.: (49) 78219252501
Fax: (49) 7821925392500
E-Mail: info.herzzentrum-lahr@mediclin.de
Web Site: www.herz-lahr.de
Emp.: 400
Hospital Management Services
S.I.C.: 8062
N.A.I.C.S.: 622110
Jurgen Ennker *(Dir-Medical)*

KB Krankenhausbeteiligungsgesellschaft mbH & Co. KG (2)
Auf der Rotsch 2
45219 Essen, Nordrhein-Westfalen, Germany

Tel.: (49) 2054880
Fax: (49) 2054882001
E-Mail: info@mediclin.de
Web Site: www.fachklinik-rheinruhr.de
Emp.: 300
Hospital Management Services
S.I.C.: 8062
N.A.I.C.S.: 622110
Dirk Schmitz *(Gen Mgr)*

KB Krankenhausbeteiligungsverwaltungs gesellschaft mbH **(2)**
Auf der Rotsch 2
45219 Essen, Nordrhein-Westfalen, Germany
Tel.: (49) 2054880
Fax: (49) 20 54 88 2001
Hospital Management Services
S.I.C.: 8062
N.A.I.C.S.: 622110

KDC-Krankenhaus-Dienstleistungsgesellschaft Crivitz mbH **(2)**
Amtsstr 1
19089 Crivitz, Mecklenburg-Vorpomme, Germany
Tel.: (49) 3863 5200
Fax: (49) 3863 520 158
Hospital Management Services
S.I.C.: 8062
N.A.I.C.S.: 622110

Kraichgau-Klinik Aktiengesellschaft **(2)**
Fritz-Hagner-Promenade 15
74906 Bad Rappenau, Baden-Wurttemberg, Germany
Tel.: (49) 72648020
Fax: (49) 7264802111
E-Mail: Klinikinfo@Kraichgau-Klinik.de
Web Site: www.kraichgau-klinik.de
Emp.: 120
Hospital Management Services
S.I.C.: 8062
N.A.I.C.S.: 622110
Michael Smith *(Gen Mgr)*

Kraichgau-Klinik Bad Rappenau GmbH & Co. KG **(2)**
Fritz-Hagner-Promenade 15
74906 Bad Rappenau, Germany
Tel.: (49) 72648020
Fax: (49) 7264802115
E-Mail: info.kraichgau-klinik@mediclin.de
Web Site: www.kraichgau-klinik.de
Emp.: 120
Hospital Management Services
S.I.C.: 8069
N.A.I.C.S.: 622310
Michael Schmid *(Gen Mgr)*

MC Service GmbH **(2)**
Okenstrasse 27
77652 Offenburg, Baden-Wurttemberg, Germany
Tel.: (49) 7814880
Fax: (49) 781488133
E-Mail: info@mediclin.de
Cleaning & Building Support Services
S.I.C.: 7349
N.A.I.C.S.: 561720
Frank Abele *(Mng Dir)*

MediClin a la Carte GmbH **(2)**
Mainzer Strasse 82
Homburg Homburg, Germany
Tel.: (49) 6841 959 78 93
Fax: (49) 6841959 78 75
Catering & Cafeteria Services
S.I.C.: 5812
N.A.I.C.S.: 722514
Uwe Hektor *(Mng Dir)*

MediClin Catering GmbH **(2)**
Okenstrasse 27
77652 Offenburg, Baden-Wurttemberg, Germany
Tel.: (49) 7814880
Fax: (49) 781488133
E-Mail: info@mediclin.de
Web Site: www.mediclin.de
Emp.: 180
Catering Services
S.I.C.: 5812
N.A.I.C.S.: 722320

MediClin Geschaftsfuhrungs-GmbH **(2)**
Okenstrasse 27
77652 Offenburg, Germany
Tel.: (49) 7814880
Fax: (49) 781488133
E-Mail: info@mediclin.de
Emp.: 130
Hospital Management Services
S.I.C.: 8062
N.A.I.C.S.: 622110
Francesco Cervini *(Gen Mgr)*

MediClin GmbH & Co. KG **(2)**
Okenstrasse 27
77652 Offenburg, Germany
Tel.: (49) 7814880
Fax: (49) 781488133
Emp.: 200
Hospital Management Services
S.I.C.: 8069
N.A.I.C.S.: 622310

MediClin Immobilien Verwaltung GmbH **(2)**
Okenstrasse 27
77652 Offenburg, Germany
Tel.: (49) 7814880
Fax: (49) 781488133
Emp.: 130
Real Estate Property Management Services
S.I.C.: 6531
N.A.I.C.S.: 531312
Ulrich Wandschneider *(Gen Mgr)*

MediClin Krankenhaus am Crivitzer See GmbH **(2)**
Amtsstrasse 1
19087 Crivitz, Mecklenburg-Western, Germany
Tel.: (49) 38635200
Fax: (49) 3863520158
Hospital Management Services
S.I.C.: 8069
N.A.I.C.S.: 622310
Hans-Heinrich Uhlmann *(Mng Dir)*

MediClin Muritz-Klinikum GmbH & Co. KG **(2)**
Weinbergstrasse 19
Muritz Dist, 17192 Waren, Germany
Tel.: (49) 3991770
Fax: (49) 3991772005
E-Mail: info.mueritz-klinikum@mediclin.de
Web Site: www.mueritz-klinikum.de
Hospital Management Services
S.I.C.: 8062
N.A.I.C.S.: 622110
Dirk Schmitz *(Mng Dir)*
Ulrich Wandschneider *(Mng Dir)*

MediClin Pflege GmbH **(2)**
Okenstrasse 27
77652 Offenburg, Baden-Wurttemberg, Germany
Tel.: (49) 781488239
Fax: (49) 781 488 133
Hospital Management Services
S.I.C.: 8062
N.A.I.C.S.: 622110

MediClin Therapie GmbH **(2)**
Okenstrasse 27
77652 Offenburg, Germany
Tel.: (49) 7814880
Fax: (49) 781488133
E-Mail: info@mediclin.de
Web Site: www.mediclin-therapie.de
Emp.: 130
Therapy Services
S.I.C.: 8093
N.A.I.C.S.: 621498

MediServ GmbH **(2)**
Auf der Rotsch 2
45219 Essen, Germany
Tel.: (49) 2054880
Medical Equipments Whslr
S.I.C.: 5047
N.A.I.C.S.: 423450

Medusplus GmbH **(2)**
Auf der Rotsch 2
45219 Essen, Germany
Tel.: (49) 2054880
Fax: (49) 2054882001
Emp.: 400
Catering Services
S.I.C.: 5812
N.A.I.C.S.: 722310
Wiebke Weissmann *(Mng Dir)*

MPS Medizinische Personal- und Servicegesellschaft mbH Kettwig **(2)**
Auf der Rotsch 2
45219 Essen, Nordrhein-Westfalen, Germany
Tel.: (49) 2054880
Fax: (49) 2054882174
E-Mail: angela.sendmer@mediclin.ge
Web Site: www.mediclin.ge
Medical Personnel Recruitment & Placement Services
S.I.C.: 7361
N.A.I.C.S.: 561311

MVZ MediClin Bonn GmbH **(2)**
Villenstr 4-8
53129 Bonn, Germany
Tel.: (49) 22853060
Fax: (49) 2285306205
E-Mail: info.bonn-vset@mediclin.de
Emp.: 76
Hospital Management Services
S.I.C.: 8062
N.A.I.C.S.: 622110
Nenakuc Henmeisper *(Mng Dir)*

Reha-Klinik GmbH & Co. KG **(2)**
Oeninger Weg 59
29614 Soltau, Lower Saxony, Germany
Tel.: (49) 51918000
Fax: (49) 5191800200
E-Mail: ilka.frankenfeod@mediclin.de
Hospital Management Services
S.I.C.: 8062
N.A.I.C.S.: 622110

Rehabilitationszentrum Gernsbach/ Schwarzwald GmbH & Co. KG **(2)**
Langer Weg 3
76593 Gernsbach, Germany
Tel.: (49) 7224 9920
Fax: (49) 7224 992410
E-Mail: info.gernsbach@mediclin.de
Web Site: www.reha-zentrum-gernsbach.de/Home.aspx
Emp.: 100
Hospital Management & Rehabilitation Services
S.I.C.: 8069
N.A.I.C.S.: 622310
Juergen Knosp *(Dir-Comml)*

Vitalisklinik Verwaltungs-GmbH **(2)**
Am Weinberg 3
36251 Bad Hersfeld, Hessen, Germany
Tel.: (49) 66212050
Fax: (49) 6621 205 100
E-Mail: info@vitalisklinik.de
Web Site: www.vitalisklinik.de
Emp.: 130
Hospital Management Services
S.I.C.: 8062
N.A.I.C.S.: 622110
Klaus Warm *(CEO)*

Yvonne Mobilien-Leasing GmbH **(2)**
Okenstr 27
77652 Offenburg, Germany
Tel.: (49) 781 488 189
Fax: (49) 781 488 184
Machinery & Equipment Leasing Services
S.I.C.: 7359
N.A.I.C.S.: 532412

ASKNET AG

Vincenz-Priessnitz-Str 3
76131 Karlsruhe, Germany
Tel.: (49) 721964580
Fax: (49) 7219645899
E-Mail: info@asknet.com
Web Site: www.asknet.com
A5A—(DEU)
Rev.: $101,896,073
Assets: $18,191,510
Liabilities: $13,338,124
Net Worth: $4,853,386
Earnings: ($107,029)
Emp.: 87
Fiscal Year-end: 12/31/12

Business Description:
Online Software Retailing Services
S.I.C.: 7372
N.A.I.C.S.: 511210

Personnel:
Joachim Bernecker *(Chm-Supervisory Bd)*
Thomas Kruger *(Deputy Chm-Supervisory Bd)*
Michael Konrad *(CEO & Member-Exec Bd)*

Supervisory Board of Directors:
Joachim Bernecker
Thomas Kruger
Marc Wurster

U.S. Subsidiary:

asknet Inc. **(1)**
Russ Bldg 235 Montgomery St Ste 1025
San Francisco, CA 94104
Tel.: (415) 352-2610
Fax: (415) 352-2611
Web Site: www.asknet.com
Emp.: 10
Software Distr
S.I.C.: 8741
N.A.I.C.S.: 551114
Mark Begin *(Pres)*

Non-U.S. Subsidiary:

asknet K.K. **(1)**
3F Metlife Kabutocho Bldg 5-1 Nihonbashi Kabutocho Chuo-Ku
Tokyo, 103-0026, Japan
Tel.: (81) 368684900
Fax: (81) 368684950
E-Mail: japan@asknet.com
Web Site: www.asknet.com
Electronic Software Distr
S.I.C.: 7371
N.A.I.C.S.: 541511

ASKUL CORPORATION

2-3 Toyosu 3-chome Koto-ku
Tokyo, 135-0061, Japan
Tel.: (81) 343305001
Fax: (81) 343304100
Web Site: www.askul.co.jp
Year Founded: 1997
2678—(TKS)
Sls.: $2,492,710,000
Assets: $1,211,661,000
Liabilities: $585,365,000
Net Worth: $626,296,000
Earnings: $63,932,000
Emp.: 915
Fiscal Year-end: 05/20/13

Business Description:
Office Supply Mail Order Services
S.I.C.: 5961
N.A.I.C.S.: 454113

Personnel:
Shoichiro Iwata *(Pres & CEO)*
Hitoshi Yoshida *(Co-COO)*
Akira Yoshioka *(Co-COO)*

Board of Directors:
Koji Imaizumi
Toshio Imamura
Shoichiro Iwata
Tadakatsu Saito
Koji Sakamoto
Kazuo Toda
Hiroyuki Toyoda
Masahiko Uotani
Hitoshi Yoshida
Akira Yoshioka

Transfer Agent:
Mizuho Trust & Banking Co., Ltd
1-2-1 Yaesu Chuo-ku
Tokyo, Japan

Subsidiaries:

AlphaPurchase Co., Ltd **(1)**
12F Aoyama Building 2-3 Kita-Aoyama 1-chome
Minato-ku, Tokyo, 107-0061, Japan
Tel.: (81) 3 5772 7801
Fax: (81) 3 5772 7834
E-Mail: po_follow@alphapurchase.co.jp
Web Site: www.alphapurchase.co.jp
Emp.: 140
Business Support Services
S.I.C.: 7389

ASKUL Corporation—(Continued)

N.A.I.C.S.: 561499

ASMARU Corporation (1)
1-1-3 Jingu-mae
Shibuya-ku, Tokyo, Japan
Tel.: (81) 3 5772 6422
Fax: (81) 3 5474 8261
Web Site: www.askul.co.jp/kaisya/english/profile/overview.html
Office Equipment & Supplies Distr
S.I.C.: 5044
N.A.I.C.S.: 423420

Bizex Corporation (1)
3-8-10 Tatsumi
Koto-ku, Tokyo, 135-0053, Japan
Tel.: (81) 3 5569 2055
Office Equipment & Supplies Distr
S.I.C.: 5044
N.A.I.C.S.: 423420

Businessmart Corporation (1)
3-8-10 Tatsumi
Koto-ku, Tokyo, 135-0053, Japan
Tel.: (81) 3 3522 3234
Web Site: www.askul.co.jp/kaisya/english/profile/overview.html
Office Equipment & Supplies Distr
S.I.C.: 5044
N.A.I.C.S.: 423420

SOLOEL Corporation (1)
4F Nittochi Nishi-Shinjuku Building 6-10-1 Nishi-Shinjuku
Shinjuku-ku, Tokyo, 160-0023, Japan
Tel.: (81) 3 6302 4576
Fax: (81) 3 6302 4574
Web Site: www.askul.co.jp
Office Equipment & Supplies Distr
S.I.C.: 5044
N.A.I.C.S.: 423420

Non-U.S. Subsidiary:

ASKUL (Shanghai) Trading Co., Ltd. (1)
A502 Building 4 Mingyuan Business Center
No 118 Jiashan Road
Xuhui District, Shanghai, 200031, China
Tel.: (86) 21 5466 8787
Office Equipment & Supplies Distr
S.I.C.: 5044
N.A.I.C.S.: 423420

ASL DISTRIBUTION SERVICES LIMITED

2160 Buckingham Road
Oakville, ON, L6H 6M7, Canada
Tel.: (905) 829-5141
Fax: (905) 829-8988
Web Site: www.asldistribution.com
Year Founded: 1959
Rev.: $45,037,484
Emp.: 150

Business Description:
Transportation & Warehouse Services
S.I.C.: 4789
N.A.I.C.S.: 488999

Personnel:
Cole Dolny *(Pres & Gen Mgr)*

ASM INTERNATIONAL N.V.

Versterkerstraat 8
1322 AP Almere, Netherlands
Mailing Address:
PO Box 60165
1320 AE Almere, Netherlands
Tel.: (31) 8810 08810
Fax: (31) 8810 08820
E-Mail: general.inquiries@asm.com
Web Site: www.asm.com
Year Founded: 1968
ASMI—(EUR NASDAQ)
Sls.: $1,908,959,253
Assets: $2,018,589,992
Liabilities: $605,127,646
Net Worth: $1,413,462,346
Earnings: $54,426,999
Emp.: 17,404
Fiscal Year-end: 12/31/12

Business Description:
Front-End Chip Making Equipment Mfr
S.I.C.: 3559
N.A.I.C.S.: 333242

Personnel:
Jan C. Lobbezoo *(Chm-Supervisory Bd)*
Charles Dean del Prado *(Chm-Mgmt Bd, Pres & CEO)*
Peter A. M. Van Bommel *(CFO)*
Ivo J.M.M. Raaijmakers *(CTO-Front-End Ops & Dir-R&D)*
Richard W. Bowers *(Chief Legal Officer-Front-End Ops)*

Supervisory Board of Directors:
Jan C. Lobbezoo
Johan M.R. Danneels
Heinrich W. Kreutzer
Ulrich H.R. Schumacher

Transfer Agents:
Citibank, N.A
New York, NY 10105

ABN AMRO Bank NV
Breda, Netherlands

Subsidiaries:

ASM Europe B.V. (1)
Versterkerstraat 8
1322AP Almere, Netherlands (100%)
Tel.: (31) 365406711
Fax: (31) 365406710
Web Site: www.asn.com
Emp.: 300
All Other Business Support Services
S.I.C.: 7389
N.A.I.C.S.: 561499

Non-U.S. Subsidiary:

ASM Belgium N.V. (2)
Kapeldreef 75
3001 Leuven, Belgium
Tel.: (32) 16 281137
Fax: (32) 16 281221
Web Site: www.asm.com
Electronic Component Mfr
S.I.C.: 3679
N.A.I.C.S.: 334419

ASM IP Holding B.V. (1)
Versterkerstraat 8
Almere, 1322 AP, Netherlands
Tel.: (31) 88 1008810
Fax: (31) 36 5406710
Investment Management Services
S.I.C.: 6211
N.A.I.C.S.: 523999

ASM Pacific Holding B.V. (1)
Versterkerstraat 8
Almere, 1322 AP, Netherlands
Tel.: (31) 881008810
Fax: (31) 881008820
Investment Management Services
S.I.C.: 6211
N.A.I.C.S.: 523999

ASM United Kingdom Sales B.V (1)
Versterkerstraat 8
1322AP Almere, Netherlands (100%)
Tel.: (31) 365406711
Fax: (31) 365406710
E-Mail: danielle.van.der.veer@asn.com
Web Site: www.asn.com
Emp.: 150
Other Commercial Equipment Whslr
S.I.C.: 5046
N.A.I.C.S.: 423440

U.S. Subsidiaries:

ASM America Inc. (1)
3440 E University Dr
Phoenix, AZ 85034 (100%)
Tel.: (602) 470-5700
Fax: (602) 437-1403
E-Mail: investor.relations@asm.com
Web Site: www.asm.com
Emp.: 300
Industrial Machinery & Equipment Whslr
S.I.C.: 5084
N.A.I.C.S.: 423830
Per Ove Hansson *(Gen Mgr)*

ASM NuTool, Inc. (1)
3440 E University Dr
Phoenix, AZ 85034
Tel.: (602) 470-5700
Fax: (602) 437-1403
Web Site: www.asm.com
Emp.: 500
Wafer Transfer Device Mfr
S.I.C.: 3674
N.A.I.C.S.: 334413
Homayoun Taliehs *(Founder)*

Non-U.S. Subsidiaries:

ASM China Ltd (1)
A/N 15F No 720 Pudong Avenue
200120 Shanghai, China (100%)
Tel.: (86) 2150368588
Fax: (86) 2150368878
Web Site: www.asm.com
Emp.: 30
Other Electronic Parts & Equipment Whslr
S.I.C.: 5065
N.A.I.C.S.: 423690

ASM Far East Marketing Ltd. (1)
2F No 1 Jinshan 8th St East Dist
300 Hsin-chu, Taiwan (100%)
Tel.: (886) 3 666 7722
Fax: (886) 3 564 8899
Web Site: www.asm.com
Power Boiler & Heat Exchanger Mfr
S.I.C.: 3559
N.A.I.C.S.: 332410

ASM France S.A.R.L. (1)
176 Ave de la Royale
34160 Castries, France (100%)
Tel.: (33) 499136640
Fax: (33) 467642778
Web Site: www.asm.com
Emp.: 11
Relay & Industrial Control Mfr
S.I.C.: 3625
N.A.I.C.S.: 335314
Soghe Fedafic *(Mng Dir)*

ASM Front-End Manufacturing Singapore Pte Ltd (1)
T & A Bldg 543 Yishun Indus Pk A
768765 Singapore, Singapore (100%)
Tel.: (65) 122922
Fax: (65) 122966
Emp.: 450
Wafer & Semiconductor Process Manufacturing
S.I.C.: 3589
N.A.I.C.S.: 333318

ASM Front-End Sales And Services Taiwan Co. Ltd (1)
1 No 38 Jinshan 2nd St
300 Hsin-chu, Taiwan (100%)
Tel.: (886) 6667722
Fax: (886) 36661835
E-Mail: ita.hsu@asm.com
Web Site: www.asm.com
Emp.: 54
Other Electronic Component Mfr
S.I.C.: 3679
N.A.I.C.S.: 334419

ASM Genitech Korea Ltd. (1)
SungKong-Kwan 1 dong Cheonan Valley
514 Sameun-ri Jiksan-eup
Cheonan, Korea (South) (100%)
Tel.: (82) 429352255
Fax: (82) 415890209
Web Site: www.asm.com
Emp.: 85
Semiconductor Machinery Mfr
S.I.C.: 3559
N.A.I.C.S.: 333242
Sang Woo Go *(Mng Dir)*

ASM Germany Sales B.V (1)
Peter-Henlein-Strasse 28
85540 Haar, Germany (100%)
Tel.: (49) 894623650
Fax: (49) 8946236566
E-Mail: harolt.kok@asm.com
Web Site: www.asm.com
Emp.: 37
Space Research & Technology
S.I.C.: 9661
N.A.I.C.S.: 927110
Harolt Kok *(Mng Dir)*

ASM Japan K.K. (1)
23-1-6-chome Nagayama Tama-shi
206-0025 Tokyo, Japan (100%)
Tel.: (81) 423376311
Fax: (81) 4233897555
Web Site: www.ism.com
Emp.: 300
Other Commercial & Service Industry Machinery Mfr
S.I.C.: 3589
N.A.I.C.S.: 333318
Tominori Yoshida *(Gen Mgr)*

Plant:

ASM Japan K.K. - Nagaoka Factory (2)
392-1 Mishimashimbo
Nagaoka, Niigata, 940-2311, Japan
Tel.: (81) 258 42 2400
Fax: (81) 258 41 2490
Web Site: www.asm.com
Semiconductor Device Mfr
S.I.C.: 3674
N.A.I.C.S.: 334413

ASM Pacific Technology Ltd. (1)
12/F Watson Centre 16-22 Kung Yip Street
Kwai Chung, New Territories, China (Hong Kong) (52.8%)
Tel.: (852) 2424 2021
Fax: (852) 2481 3367
Web Site: www.asmpacific.com
0522—(HKG OTC)
Sls.: $1,348,888,954
Assets: $1,318,382,221
Liabilities: $472,899,109
Net Worth: $845,483,112
Earnings: $88,845,776
Emp.: 15,800
Fiscal Year-end: 12/31/12
Semiconductor & Related Device Mfr
S.I.C.: 3674
N.A.I.C.S.: 334413
Arthur H. del Prado *(Chm)*
Wai Kwong Lee *(CEO)*
Robin Gerald Cher Tat Ng *(CFO)*
Eric Koon Hung Tang *(CFO)*
James Chuen Chow *(COO)*
Yam Mo Wong *(CTO)*
Sau Ming So *(Sec)*

Subsidiary:

ASM Assembly Automation Ltd. (2)
4/F Watson Center 16-22 Kung Yip Street
Kwai Chung, New Territories, China (Hong Kong)
Tel.: (852) 26192000
Fax: (852) 26192118
Semiconductor Machinery Mfr
S.I.C.: 3559
N.A.I.C.S.: 333242

U.S. Subsidiary:

ASM Pacific Assembly Products, Inc. (2)
3440 E University Dr
Phoenix, AZ 85034-7200 (54%)
Tel.: (602) 437-4760
Fax: (602) 437-4630
E-Mail: inquire@asmpt.com
Web Site: www.asmpt.com
Emp.: 10
Semiconductor Equipment Mfr
S.I.C.: 3559
N.A.I.C.S.: 333242
Joann Colletti *(Office Mgr)*

Non-U.S. Subsidiaries:

ASM Assembly Equipment Bangkok Limited (2)
51-3 Vibhavadi Tower Ladyao Chatucha
10900 Bangkok, Thailand
Tel.: (66) 29413181
Fax: (66) 29413183
E-Mail: info@asmpacific.com
Web Site: www.asmpacific.com
Emp.: 55
Other Electronic Component Mfr
S.I.C.: 3679
N.A.I.C.S.: 334419
Andy Chan *(Country Mgr)*

ASM Assembly Equipment (M) Sdn. Bhd. (2)
1 Tingkat Satu Jalan Mulia Satu
84000 Penang, Johor, Malaysia
Tel.: (60) 69515713
Fax: (60) 69515786

E-Mail: ccpoh@asmpt.com
Web Site: www.asmpacific.com
Emp.: 30
All Other Industrial Machinery Mfr
S.I.C.: 3559
N.A.I.C.S.: 333249
Po Chin Chong *(Mgr)*

ASM Assembly Products, B.V. (2)
Weltevreden 4A
3731 AL De Bilt, Netherlands
Tel.: (31) 308906310
Fax: (31) 308906320
E-Mail: inquire@asmpt.com
Web Site: www.asmpacific.com
Emp.: 9
Semiconductor & LED Assembly Equipment Manufacturing
S.I.C.: 3674
N.A.I.C.S.: 334413

ASM Assembly Technology Co. Limited (2)
1-7-18 Nishikicho F Bldg 5f
Tachikawa, Tokyo, 190-0022, Japan
Tel.: (81) 42 521 7751
Fax: (81) 42 521 7750
Semiconductor Device Distr
S.I.C.: 5065
N.A.I.C.S.: 423690

ASM Semiconductor Materials (Shenzhen) Co. Ltd. (2)
12-15 Fuqiao Industry Zone 2 Bao'an
Shenzhen, Guangdong, 518103, China
Tel.: (86) 755 29618000
Fax: (86) 755 27335548
Semiconductor Device Mfr
S.I.C.: 3674
N.A.I.C.S.: 334413
Ying Kau *(Mgr-Mfg)*

ASM Technology (Huizhou) Co. Limited (2)
Zone 73 Jiangbeipian
Xiaojinkou Huicheng, Huizhou, 516023, China
Tel.: (86) 7528213000
Fax: (86) 7522297919
Emp.: 210
Semiconductor Equipment Mfr
S.I.C.: 3559
N.A.I.C.S.: 333242

ASM Technology (M) Sdn. Bhd. (2)
Plo 534 Jalan Keluli 3 Kawasan
Perindustrian Pasir Gudang
Pasir Gudang, Johor, 81700, Malaysia
Tel.: (60) 72533500
Fax: (60) 72533533
Semiconductor Equipment Mfr
S.I.C.: 3674
N.A.I.C.S.: 334413

ASM Technology Singapore Pte Ltd (2)
2 Yishun Ave 7
768924 Singapore, Singapore (53.35%)
Tel.: (65) 67526311
Fax: (65) 67582287
E-Mail: inquire@asmpt.com
Web Site: www.asmpacific.com
Emp.: 700
Semiconductor & Related Device Mfr
S.I.C.: 3651
N.A.I.C.S.: 334310
W. K. Lee *(CEO & Exec Dir)*

ASM Services and Support Ireland Ltd. (1)
Unit 23 Hills Industrial Estate
Lucan, Dublin, Ireland (100%)
Tel.: (353) 16219100
Fax: (353) 16280206
Web Site: www.asm.com
Emp.: 40
Semiconductor & Related Device Mfr
S.I.C.: 3651
N.A.I.C.S.: 334310
Dale Robertson *(Mgr-Support)*

ASM Services and Support Israel Ltd (1)
Edwards Building 5 Habarzel St Gat 2000 Industrial Zone
Kiryat Gat, 82107, Israel
Tel.: (972) 8 860 9181
Fax: (972) 8 860 9182
Emp.: 3
Semiconductor Equipment Repair Services
S.I.C.: 7699
N.A.I.C.S.: 811310

ASM Wafer Process Equipment Singapore Pte Ltd (1)
543 Yishun Industrial Park A
768765 Singapore, Singapore (100%)
Tel.: (65) 65122962
Fax: (65) 65122961
Web Site: www.asm.com
Emp.: 15
Engineering Services
S.I.C.: 8711
N.A.I.C.S.: 541330
Roger Su *(Mng Dir)*

ASM RESEARCH INC.
(Acquired by Accenture plc)

ASM TECHNOLOGIES LIMITED
80/2 Lusanne Court Richmond Rd
Bengaluru, 560 0025, India
Tel.: (91) 8066962301
Fax: (91) 8022273606
E-Mail: info@asmltd.com
Web Site: www.asmltd.com
526433—(BOM)
Rev.: $32,848,988
Assets: $19,998,477
Liabilities: $11,969,816
Net Worth: $8,028,662
Earnings: $1,975,658
Emp.: 752
Fiscal Year-end: 03/31/13
Business Description:
Business Consulting & Software Development Services
S.I.C.: 7389
N.A.I.C.S.: 561499
Personnel:
Rabindra Srikantan *(Mng Dir)*
P. N. Lakshmi *(Compliance Officer & Sec)*
Board of Directors:
M. R. Vikram
B. S. Sonde
Rabindra Srikantan
Shekar Viswanathan
Legal Counsel:
IndusLaw
Bengaluru, India
Transfer Agent:
Karvy Computershare Private Limited
Plot 17 to 24 Near Image Hospital Vittalrao Nagar Madhapur
Hyderabad, India

U.S. Subsidiaries:

ESR Associates Inc (1)
7071 W Central Ave
Toledo, OH 43617
Tel.: (419) 843-2571
Fax: (419) 843-2702
E-Mail: inquiries@esr-associates.com
Web Site: www.esr-associates.com
Software System Consulting Services
S.I.C.: 7373
N.A.I.C.S.: 541512
John Seitz *(Principal)*

Pinnacle Talent Inc. (1)
2020 Calamos Ct Ste 200
Naperville, IL 60563-2793
Tel.: (630) 799-1563
Fax: (630) 629-1562
E-Mail: sundar@asmltd.com
Business Consulting & Software Services
S.I.C.: 7389
N.A.I.C.S.: 561499
Sundar Ramanathan *(Office Mgr)*

Non-U.S. Subsidiaries:

Advanced Synergic Pte. Ltd. (1)
Odc Districenter 08-03A 30 Tohguan Rd
30 Tohguan Rd, Singapore, 608840, Singapore
Tel.: (65) 62705737
Fax: (65) 62486076
E-Mail: govindraj@asmltd.com
Web Site: www.asmltd.com
Emp.: 50
Business Consulting & Software Services
S.I.C.: 7389
N.A.I.C.S.: 561499
Govndraj Kumar *(Mgr)*

ASMAR
Edificio Rapa Nui Building Prat 856
Piso 13, Valparaiso, Chile
Tel.: (56) 322260000
Fax: (56) 322260157
Web Site: www.asmar.cl
Year Founded: 1895
Emp.: 4,000
Business Description:
Ship Building & Repair Services
S.I.C.: 3731
N.A.I.C.S.: 336611

ASMEDIA TECHNOLOGY INC.
6F 115 Minquan Rd
Xindian District, New Taipei City, 231, Taiwan
Tel.: (886) 2 2219 6088
Fax: (886) 2 2219 6080
E-Mail: asmedia_investor@asmedia.com.tw
Web Site: www.asmedia.com.tw
Year Founded: 2004
5269—(TAI)
Sales Range: $50-74.9 Million
Business Description:
Integrated Circuit Mfr
S.I.C.: 3674
N.A.I.C.S.: 334413
Personnel:
Zhenlai Shen *(Chm)*

ASML HOLDING N.V.
De Run 6501
5504 DR Veldhoven, Netherlands
Mailing Address:
PO Box 324
NL 5500 AH Veldhoven, Netherlands
Tel.: (31) 480 383 4005
Fax: (31) 480 383 3978
E-Mail: corpcom@asml.com
Web Site: www.asml.com
Year Founded: 1983
ASML—(EUR NASDAQ)
Sls.: $7,061,100,501
Assets: $15,499,437,914
Liabilities: $6,180,674,360
Net Worth: $9,318,763,555
Earnings: $1,367,022,173
Emp.: 10,360
Fiscal Year-end: 12/31/13
Business Description:
Lithography Equipment Mfr
S.I.C.: 3559
N.A.I.C.S.: 333242
Personnel:
Eric Meurice *(Chm)*
Arthur P.M. van der Poel *(Chm-Supervisory Bd)*
Peter T.F.M. Wennink *(Pres & CEO)*
Martin A. Van Den Brink *(Pres & CTO)*
Frits Van Hout *(CMO & Exec VP)*
Supervisory Board of Directors:
Arthur P.M. van der Poel
O. B. Bilous
Fritz W. Frohlich
William T. Siegle
Ieke C.J. van den Burg
Jos W.B. Westerburgen
Transfer Agent:
J.P. Morgan Chase Bank, N.A.
4 New York Plaza
New York, NY 10004
Subsidiaries:

ASML MaskTools B.V. (1)
De Run 6501
Veldhoven, Noord-Brabant, 5504 DR, Netherlands
Tel.: (31) 402683000
Fax: (31) 402682000
Emp.: 5,000
Lithography Equipment Mfr
S.I.C.: 3559
N.A.I.C.S.: 333242

ASML Netherlands B.V. (1)
De Run 6501
5504 DR Veldhoven, Netherlands
Tel.: (31) 40 268 3000
Fax: (31) 40 268 2000
E-Mail: corpcom@asml.com
Web Site: www.asml.com
Lithography Equipment Mfr & Distr
S.I.C.: 3559
N.A.I.C.S.: 333242

ASML Systems B.V. (1)
De Run 6501
Veldhoven, Noord-Brabant, 5504 DR, Netherlands
Tel.: (31) 402683000
Lithography Equipment Mfr
S.I.C.: 3559
N.A.I.C.S.: 333242

U.S. Subsidiaries:

ASML US, Inc. (1)
8555 S River Pkwy
Tempe, AZ 85284-2601
Tel.: (480) 383-4422
Fax: (480) 383-3995
Web Site: www.asml.com
Emp.: 150
S.I.C.: 7389
N.A.I.C.S.: 323120
Craig DeYoung *(VP-IR)*

Branch:

ASML Austin (2)
2324 Ridgepoint Dr Ste G1
Austin, TX 78744-1060 (100%)
Tel.: (512) 443-4244
Fax: (512) 928-0287
Toll Free: (800) 227-6462
Web Site: www.asml.com
Emp.: 50
Distributor of Semicondutor Devices
S.I.C.: 5963
N.A.I.C.S.: 454390
Raul Saleivar *(Gen Mgr)*

Subsidiaries:

ASML Capital US, Inc. (2)
8555 S River Pkwy
Tempe, AZ 85284-2601
Tel.: (480) 383-4422
Investment Management Services
S.I.C.: 6211
N.A.I.C.S.: 523999

ASML MaskTools, Inc. (2)
4211Burton Dr
Santa Clara, CA 95054-1228 DE
Tel.: (408) 653-1500
Fax: (408) 653-1501
E-Mail: info@masktools.com
Web Site: www.masktools.com
Emp.: 3,389
Optical Lithography Extension Solutions Export
S.I.C.: 7371
N.A.I.C.S.: 541511
Stephen Hsu *(Sr Mgr-RET)*

ASML Participation US Inc. (2)
8555 S River Pkwy
Tempe, AZ 85284-2601
Tel.: (480) 383-4422
Lithography Equipment Mfr
S.I.C.: 3559
N.A.I.C.S.: 333242

ASML Ventures 1 Inc. (2)
8555 S River Pkwy
Tempe, AZ 85284-2601
Tel.: (480) 383-4422
Investment Management Services
S.I.C.: 6799
N.A.I.C.S.: 523920

Cymer, Inc. (2)
17075 Thornmint Ct
San Diego, CA 92127-1712 NV
Tel.: (858) 385-7300
Fax: (858) 385-7100
E-Mail: custservice@cymer.com

ASML HOLDING N.V.—(Continued)

Web Site: www.cymer.com
Rev.: $538,625,000
Assets: $1,023,230,000
Liabilities: $273,450,000
Net Worth: $749,780,000
Earnings: ($36,365,000)
Emp.: 1,100
Fiscal Year-end: 12/31/12
Excimer Lasers Mfr for Semiconductor Fabrication
S.I.C.: 3559
N.A.I.C.S.: 333242
Edward J. Brown, Jr. *(Pres & COO)*
Paul B. Bowman *(CFO, Sec & Sr VP)*
Robert P. Akins *(Sr VP)*
Richard L. Sandstrom *(Sr VP)*

Non-U.S. Subsidiaries:

Cymer B.V. (3)
De Run 4312B
5503 LN Veldhoven, Netherlands (100%)
Tel.: (31) 402513684
Fax: (31) 40251319
E-Mail: europe@cymer.com
Rev.: $20,000,000
Emp.: 75
Lasers for Semiconductor Fabrication
S.I.C.: 3559
N.A.I.C.S.: 333242
Marco De Leeuw *(Dir-Fin)*

Cymer Japan, Inc. (3)
Cosmos Motoyawata Building
4-17-8 Minamiyawata, Ichikawa, Chiba, 227-0023, Japan (100%)
Tel.: (81) 473935668
Fax: (81) 473935672
E-Mail: japan@cymer.com
Sales Range: $25-49.9 Million
Emp.: 50
Lasers for Semiconductor Fabrication
S.I.C.: 3559
N.A.I.C.S.: 333242

Cymer Korea, Inc. (3)
Eoyeon Hansan Industrial Park 833 1 Hansan Ri
CheongBook-Myeon Pyungtaek, Seoul, Korea (South)
Tel.: (82) 316801500
Fax: (82) 316801510
Sales Range: $25-49.9 Million
Emp.: 50
Lasers for Semiconductor Fabrication
S.I.C.: 3559
N.A.I.C.S.: 333242
Younghee Chung *(Mgr-HR)*

Cymer Semiconductor Equipment (Shanghai) Co., Ltd. (3)
King Tower 806 No 28 Xinjinqiao Road
Pudong, Shanghai, 201206, China
Tel.: (86) 2150326300
Fax: (86) 2150326301
E-Mail: china@cymer.com
Sales Range: $125-149.9 Million
Emp.: 15
Lasers Mfr
S.I.C.: 3559
N.A.I.C.S.: 333242

Cymer Singapore Pte. Ltd. (3)
51 Goldhill Plaza #10-01
Singapore, 308900, Singapore (100%)
Tel.: (65) 62599792
Fax: (65) 62599036
E-Mail: singapore@cymer.com
Web Site: www.cymer.com
Sales Range: $10-24.9 Million
Emp.: 10
Lasers for Semiconductor Fabrication
S.I.C.: 3559
N.A.I.C.S.: 333242

Cymer Southeast Asia Ltd. (3)
3F No 49 Lane 2
Kuang-Fu Road Sec 2, Hsin-chu, 300 71, Taiwan (100%)
Tel.: (886) 35739960
Fax: (886) 35739961
Sales Range: $125-149.9 Million
Emp.: 40
Lasers Mfr
S.I.C.: 3559
N.A.I.C.S.: 333242

Brion Technologies, Inc (1)
4211 Burton Dr
Santa Clara, CA 95054
Tel.: (408) 653-1500
Fax: (408) 653-1501
Web Site: www.brion.com
Semiconductor Design & Wafer Mfg Optimization Solutions
S.I.C.: 3559
N.A.I.C.S.: 333242
Shauh-Teh Juang *(Sr VP-Mktg & Bus Dev)*

Non-U.S. Divisions:

Brion Technologies KK (2)
Prime Kanda Bldg 10F
8-2 2-chome Kandasuda-cho
Chiyoda-ku, 101-0041 Tokyo, Japan
Tel.: (81) 3 5298 1561
Fax: (81) 3 5298 1562
Web Site: www.brion.com
Semiconductor Design & Wafer Mfg Optimization Solutions
S.I.C.: 3559
N.A.I.C.S.: 333242

Brion Technologies (Shenzhen) Co., Ltd. (2)
2A-3 Bldg B1 Shenzhen Cyber-Tech Zone High-Tech Industrial Pk
Shenzhen, 518057, China
Tel.: (86) 075526037380
Fax: (86) 075526037390
Web Site: www.brion.com
Emp.: 100
Semiconductor Design & Wafer Mfg Optimization Solutions
S.I.C.: 3559
N.A.I.C.S.: 333242
Steve Bisheng Fu *(Gen Mgr-China)*

Non-U.S. Subsidiaries:

ASML Belgium BVBA (1)
Gasthuisstraat 15 B6
2300 Turnhout, Belgium
Tel.: (32) 14 70 66 71
Lithography Equipment Mfr & Distr
S.I.C.: 3559
N.A.I.C.S.: 333242

ASML Equipment Malaysia Sdn. Bhd. (1)
Kulim Hi-Tech Park Suite 2 02 2nd Floor KHTP Business Centre
09000 Kulim, Kedah Darul Aman, Malaysia
Tel.: (60) 4 403 1008
Fax: (60) 4 403 5008
Web Site: www.asml.com
Lithography Equipment Mfr & Distr
S.I.C.: 3559
N.A.I.C.S.: 333242

ASML France S.a.r.l. (1)
Allee Saint Exupery 100
38330 Montbonnot-Saint-Martin, France
Tel.: (33) 4 7604 4040
Fax: (33) 4 7604 4060
Emp.: 30
Lithography Equipment Mfr
S.I.C.: 3559
N.A.I.C.S.: 333242
Brige Leonel *(Dir-Customer Svcs)*

ASML Germany GmbH (1)
An Der Flutrinne 12
01139 Dresden, Germany
Tel.: (49) 351 79 60 0
Fax: (49) 351 79 60 555
Web Site: www.asml.com
Lithography Equipment Mfr
S.I.C.: 3559
N.A.I.C.S.: 333242

ASML Ireland Ltd. (1)
Mail Stop IR4-1-2 Collinstown Industrial Park
Leixlip, Kildare, Ireland
Tel.: (353) 1 606 6635
Industrial Furnace Mfr
S.I.C.: 3567
N.A.I.C.S.: 333994

ASML Japan Co. Ltd. (1)
Gotenyama Trust Tower Bldg 4F
Kitashinagawa 4-7-35
Shinagawa-ku, 140-0001 Tokyo, Japan
Tel.: (81) 3 5793 1800
Web Site: www.asml.com
Lithography Equipment Mfr & Distr
S.I.C.: 3559
N.A.I.C.S.: 333242

ASML Korea Co., Ltd. (1)
372 Chung-Ri Dongtan-Myun
Gyunggi-Do, Hwasun, 445 813, Korea (South) (100%)
Tel.: (82) 313791500
Fax: (82) 313791501
E-Mail: raghi.um@asml.com
Emp.: 200
Lithography Equipment Mfr & Distr
S.I.C.: 7389
N.A.I.C.S.: 323120
Tony Lee *(Mgr-Sls)*

ASML (Shanghai) International Trading Co., Ltd (1)
17F Building A Zhangjiang Hi-tech Park No 560 Song Tao Road
Pudong, 201203 Shanghai, China
Tel.: (86) 21 5027 5858
Fax: (86) 21 5027 0695
Web Site: www.asml.com
Emp.: 70
Lithography Equipment Distr
S.I.C.: 5065
N.A.I.C.S.: 423690
Mark Ting *(Gen Mgr)*

ASML Singapore Pte. Ltd. (1)
10 Ang Mo Kio Street 65 06-09 TechPoint
Singapore, 569059, Singapore
Tel.: (65) 6484 0123
Fax: (65) 6484 0008
Web Site: www.asml.com
Emp.: 150
Lithography Equipment Mfr & Distr
S.I.C.: 3559
N.A.I.C.S.: 333242
Harold Salijo *(Engr-Tech Support)*

ASML Taiwan Ltd. (1)
16F Gongdaowu 5th Rd 101 Sec 2
Hsin-chu, 30070, Taiwan
Tel.: (886) 3 516 6266
Lithography Equipment Mfr & Distr
S.I.C.: 3559
N.A.I.C.S.: 333242

ASML (Tianjin) Co. Ltd. (1)
Ste 1301 Fl 13 Tianjin Tianxin Bldg
He Xi District, 300074 Tianjin, China(100%)
Tel.: (86) 28408718
Fax: (86) 28408719
E-Mail: dae-young.lee@china.asml.nl
Web Site: www.asml.com
Emp.: 10
Lithography Equipment Mfr & Distr
S.I.C.: 7389
N.A.I.C.S.: 323120

ASO FOAM CRETE CO., LTD.

36-1 Kariyado Nakahara-ku
Kawasaki, Kanagawa, 211-0022, Japan
Tel.: (81) 44 422 2061
Fax: (81) 44 411 9927
Web Site: www.asofoam.co.jp
Year Founded: 1961
1730—(JAS)
Emp.: 87
Business Description:
Construction Services
S.I.C.: 3531
N.A.I.C.S.: 333120
Personnel:
Yousuke Kawamura *(Pres)*

ASOCIACION DE COOPERATIVAS ARGENTINAS C.L.

Av E Madero 942 4 5 & 6 Pisos
Capital Federal
1106 Buenos Aires, Argentina
Tel.: (54) 11 4310 1300
Fax: (54) 11 4313 1349
Web Site: www.acacoop.com.ar
Year Founded: 1922
Emp.: 700
Business Description:
Agricultural Cooperative; Grain, Oils & Beef Productiion & Export
S.I.C.: 0212
N.A.I.C.S.: 112111
Personnel:
Hector Zorzon *(Pres)*
Subsidiary:

Aca Salud (1)
Ayacucho 1262
Buenos Aires, Argentina
Tel.: (54) 1148279400
Web Site: www.acasalud.com.ar
Health Care Services
S.I.C.: 8099
N.A.I.C.S.: 621999

ASOLO S.P.A.

Via Delle Industrie 2
Nervesa della Battaglia, 31040, Italy
Tel.: (39) 4228866
Fax: (39) 0422 88 52 82
E-Mail: asolo@asolo.com
Web Site: www.asolo.com
Business Description:
Outdoor Equipment Mfr
S.I.C.: 3949
N.A.I.C.S.: 339920
Personnel:
Marco Zanatta *(Chm)*
U.S. Subsidiary:

Asolo North America Inc. (1)
190 Hanover St
Lebanon, NH 03766
Tel.: (603) 448-8827
Emp.: 7
Outdoor Equipment Distr
S.I.C.: 3949
N.A.I.C.S.: 339920
Bruce Franks *(Pres)*

ASOS PLC

Greater London House Hampstead Road
London, NW1 7FB, United Kingdom
Tel.: (44) 2077561000
Fax: (44) 2077561001
Web Site: www.asosplc.com
ASC—(LSE OTC)
Rev.: $1,215,099,409
Assets: $492,345,237
Liabilities: $239,976,274
Net Worth: $252,368,963
Earnings: $64,634,023
Emp.: 1,352
Fiscal Year-end: 08/31/13
Business Description:
Holding Company; Internet Retailing Services
S.I.C.: 6719
N.A.I.C.S.: 551112
Personnel:
Brian James McBride *(Chm)*
Nicholas Jon Robertson *(CEO)*
Nicholas Beighton *(CFO)*
Pete Marsden *(CIO)*
Board of Directors:
Brian James McBride
Nicholas Beighton
Rita Clifton
Ian Dyson
Karen Jones
Shaun McCabe
Hilary Riva
Nicholas Jon Robertson
Legal Counsel:
Lawrence Graham LLP
4 More London Riverside
London, England, SE1 2AU, United Kingdom

ASPEN GROUP LIMITED

Level 3 129 St Georges Terrace
Perth, WA, 6000, Australia
Mailing Address:
PO Box Z5025
St Georges Terrace, Perth, WA, 6831, Australia
Tel.: (61) 8 9220 8400
Fax: (61) 8 9220 8401

E-Mail: homemail@aspengroup.com.au
Web Site: www.aspengroup.com.au
APZ—(ASX)
Rev.: $66,982,020
Assets: $636,652,237
Liabilities: $338,577,248
Net Worth: $298,074,989
Earnings: ($35,757,577)
Fiscal Year-end: 06/30/13
Business Description:
Commercial, Industrial & Retail Property Management
S.I.C.: 1541
N.A.I.C.S.: 236210
Personnel:
Clem Salwin *(CEO & Mng Dir)*
Brett Fullarton *(CFO)*
Brendan Acott *(CEO-Living)*
Eric Lee *(Sec)*
Board of Directors:
Frank Zipfinger
Clive Appleton
Guy Farrands
Hugh Martin
Clem Salwin
Subsidiaries:

Aspen Funds Management Ltd. **(1)**
Level 3 129 St Georges Tce
256 Adelaide Ter, Perth, WA, 6000, Australia
Tel.: (61) 892208400
Fax: (61) 892208401
E-Mail: funds@aspengroup.com.au
Web Site: www.aspengroup.com.au
Emp.: 120
Fund Management Services
S.I.C.: 6799
N.A.I.C.S.: 523920

Aspen Property Trust **(1)**
Level 8 Septimus Roe Sq
256 Adelaide Ter, Perth, Western Australia, 6000, Australia
Tel.: (61) 892208400
Fax: (61) 892208401
E-Mail: homemail@aspengroup.com.au
Web Site: www.aspengroup.com.au
Emp.: 50
Trust Management Services
S.I.C.: 6282
N.A.I.C.S.: 523920
Jonathan Timms *(CEO)*

ASPEN GROUP RESOURCES CORP.

1000 910 7th Avenue SW
Calgary, AB, T2P 3N8, Canada
Tel.: (805) 693-5800
E-Mail: rmercer@aspengroupresources.com
Sales Range: $1-9.9 Million
Emp.: 9
Business Description:
Oil & Gas Services
S.I.C.: 1389
N.A.I.C.S.: 213112
Personnel:
Robert L. Calentine *(CEO)*
Peter Toy *(CFO)*
Board of Directors:
Robert L. Calentine
Robert C. Cudney
Wayne T. Egan

ASPEN INSURANCE HOLDINGS LIMITED

141 Front Street
Hamilton, HM 19, Bermuda
Mailing Address:
PO Box HM 2729
Hamilton, HMLX, Bermuda
Tel.: (441) 295 8201
Fax: (441) 295 1829
Web Site: www.aspen.bm
Year Founded: 2002
AHL—(NYSE)
Rev.: $2,423,300,000
Assets: $10,230,500,000
Liabilities: $6,930,900,000
Net Worth: $3,299,600,000
Earnings: $329,300,000
Emp.: 945
Fiscal Year-end: 12/31/13
Business Description:
Insurance Services
S.I.C.: 6331
N.A.I.C.S.: 524126
Personnel:
Glyn P. Jones *(Chm)*
Christopher O. O'Kane *(CEO)*
Stephen Postlewhite *(Chief Risk Officer)*
Emil Issavi *(Chief Underwriting Officer-Aspen Re)*
Brian Boornazian *(Chm-Aspen Re & Pres-Aspen Re America)*
Rupert Villers *(Chm/Pres-Intl)*
Julian M. Cusack *(Chm-Bermuda)*
Mario P. Vitale *(Pres/CEO-US)*
James Few *(CEO-Aspen Re)*
Karen Green *(CEO-Aspen UK & AMAL)*
Michael Cain *(Gen Counsel & Head-HR)*
Kerry Calaiaro *(Sr VP-IR)*
Board of Directors:
Glyn P. Jones
Liaquat Ahamed
Albert J. Beer
Richard J. S. Bucknall
John P. Cavoores
Julian M. Cusack
Gary R. Gregg
Heidi E. Hutter
Gordon Ireland
Peter R. O'Flinn
Christopher O. O'Kane
Bret D. Pearlman
Ronald R. Pressman
Subsidiary:

Aspen Insurance Limited **(1)**
Seon Pl 141 Front St 1 Church St
PO Box HM 2729
HM 11 Hamilton, Bermuda (100%)
Tel.: (441) 2958201
Fax: (441) 2951829
E-Mail: info@aspen.bm
Emp.: 50
Insurance Related Activities
S.I.C.: 6411
N.A.I.C.S.: 524298
Tracy Berkeley *(Mgr-HR)*

U.S. Subsidiaries:

Aspen Insurance U.S. Services Inc. **(1)**
600 Atlantic Ave Ste 2100
Boston, MA 02110-2320
Tel.: (617) 531-5100
Fax: (617) 532-7314
Web Site: www.aspenspecialties.com
Emp.: 50
Insurance Agencies & Brokerages
S.I.C.: 6411
N.A.I.C.S.: 524210
Rupert Villers *(CEO)*
Bob Rheel *(Exec VP)*
Douglas Menelly *(Sr VP-Mktg)*

Aspen Specialty Insurance Company **(1)**
600 Atlantic Ave Ste 2100
Boston, MA 02110-2320
Tel.: (617) 531-5100
Fax: (617) 532-7314
E-Mail: info@aspenspecialty.com
Web Site: www.aspenspecialty.com
Emp.: 50
Insurance Agencies & Brokerages
S.I.C.: 6411
N.A.I.C.S.: 524210
Bill Murray *(Pres-US Insurance)*

Aspen Specialty Insurance Solutions, LLC **(1)**
35 N Lake Ave Ste 820
Pasadena, CA 91101
Tel.: (626) 463-7630
General Insurance Services
S.I.C.: 6411
N.A.I.C.S.: 524298

Non-U.S. Subsidiary:

Aspen Risk Management Limited **(1)**
Plantation Place 30 Fenchurch Street
London, EC3M 3BD, United Kingdom
Tel.: (44) 2071848000
Fax: (44) 2071848500
E-Mail:
Web Site: www.aspenriskmanagement.co.uk
Insurance & Reinsurance Services
S.I.C.: 6399
N.A.I.C.S.: 524130
Paul Lee *(Gen Mgr-North England)*

ASPEN PHARMACARE HOLDINGS LIMITED

Aspen Park 98 Armstrong Avenue La Lucia Ridge
Durban, 4019, South Africa
Tel.: (27) 315808600
Fax: (27) 315808647
Web Site: www.aspenpharma.com
APN—(JSE OTC)
Rev.: $2,156,703,600
Assets: $5,073,603,890
Liabilities: $2,526,966,760
Net Worth: $2,546,637,130
Earnings: $392,524,970
Emp.: 8,200
Fiscal Year-end: 06/30/13
Business Description:
Holding Company; Pharmaceutical Products Developer, Mfr & Distr
S.I.C.: 6719
N.A.I.C.S.: 551112
Personnel:
Stephen Bradley Saad *(CEO)*
Michael Guy Attridge *(Deputy CEO)*
Riaan Verster *(Sec)*
Board of Directors:
Judith Dlamini
Roy Cecil Andersen
Michael Guy Attridge
Mogammed Rafique Bagus
John Frederick Buchanan
Douglas Dlamini
Shah Abbas Hussain
Christopher Nattle Mortimer
Stephen Bradley Saad
Sindiswa Victoria Zilwa
Transfer Agent:
Computershare Investor Services (Pty) Ltd.
70 Marshall Street
Johannesburg, 2001, South Africa
Tel.: (27) 11 370 5000
Fax: (27) 11 370 5487
Subsidiaries:

Aspen Nutritionals (Pty) Ltd **(1)**
20 Spanner Rd
Olifantsfontein, Gauteng, 1665, South Africa
Tel.: (27) 113163155
Fax: (27) 113161665
E-Mail: hr@aspenpharma.com
Web Site: nutritionals.aspenpharma.com
Emp.: 100
Infant Nutritional Products Mfr
S.I.C.: 2043
N.A.I.C.S.: 311230
Karyn Purchase *(CEO)*

Fine Chemicals Corporation (Pty) Ltd **(1)**
15 Hawkins Ave Epping Industria
Epping, Cape Town, Western Cape, 7460, South Africa
Tel.: (27) 215316421
Fax: (27) 215314555
E-Mail: administrator@fcc.co.za
Web Site: www.fcc.co.za
Emp.: 290
Pharmaceutical Preparations Mfr
S.I.C.: 2834
N.A.I.C.S.: 325412
Michael Stringer *(Mng Dir)*

Krok Brothers Holdings (Pty) Ltd **(1)**
69 Mellville Rd
Hyde Park, Johannesburg, Gauteng, 2196, South Africa
Tel.: (27) 114474785
Fax: (27) 114474511
Pharmaceutical Preparations Mfr
S.I.C.: 2834
N.A.I.C.S.: 325412

Pharmacare Ltd **(1)**
Aspen Healthcare Park Woodlands Dr
Johannesburg, Gauteng, 2157, South Africa
Tel.: (27) 112396100
Fax: (27) 112396034
Pharmaceutical Preparations Mfr
S.I.C.: 2834
N.A.I.C.S.: 325412
Stephen Saad *(CEO)*

Non-U.S. Subsidiaries:

Aspen Global Incorporated **(1)**
Grand Bay
Riviere du Rempart, Mauritius
Tel.: (230) 427 3966
Fax: (230) 269 1111
Property Management Services
S.I.C.: 6531
N.A.I.C.S.: 531312

Aspen Pharma - Industria Farmaceutica Ltda **(1)**
Avenida das Americas 3 500 - Bloco 03 - 5 Andar - Condominio Le Monde
Barra da Tijuca, Rio de Janeiro, 22640-102, Brazil
Tel.: (55) 2135446900
Fax: (55) 21 35 44 68 00
Web Site: www.aspenpharma.com.br
Pharmaceutical Preparations Mfr
S.I.C.: 2834
N.A.I.C.S.: 325412

Aspen Pharmacare Australia Pty Ltd. **(1)**
Ground Fl 34-36 Chandos St
Saint Leonards, NSW, 2065, Australia
Tel.: (61) 284368300
Fax: (61) 299013540
E-Mail: aspen@aspenpharmacare.com.au
Web Site: www.aspenpharma.com.au
Sales Range: $750-799.9 Million
Emp.: 800
Pharmaceutical Products Mfr & Distr
S.I.C.: 2834
N.A.I.C.S.: 325412
Greg Lan *(CEO)*
Trevor Ziman *(Deputy CEO)*

Aspen Pharmacare Resources Ltd **(1)**
15 Windsor Park
London, SW19 2TJ, United Kingdom
Tel.: (44) 20 84170036
Medicinal Products Distr
S.I.C.: 5122
N.A.I.C.S.: 424210

Beta Healthcare International Ltd **(1)**
Mogadishu Road off Lunga Lunga Road Industrial Area
PO Box 42569
00100 Nairobi, Kenya
Tel.: (254) 20 6530106
Fax: (254) 20 556198
E-Mail: info@ke.betashelys.com
Web Site: www.betacare.co.ke
Pharmaceuticals, Nutraceuticals & Herbal Products Preparations Mfr
S.I.C.: 2834
N.A.I.C.S.: 325412
Sanjay Advani *(CEO)*

Strides Latina S.A. **(1)**
Colonia 810 Escritorio 502
Montevideo, 11100, Uruguay
Tel.: (598) 29016495
Fax: (598) 29016495
Emp.: 2
Pharmaceutical Products Distr
S.I.C.: 5122
N.A.I.C.S.: 424210
Carlos Ruis *(Mgr)*

ASPERMONT LIMITED

613-619 Wellington Street
Perth, WA, 6000, Australia

Aspermont Limited—(Continued)

Mailing Address:
PO Box 78
Leederville, WA, 6902, Australia
Tel.: (61) 862639100
Fax: (61) 862639186
E-Mail: corporate@aspermont.com
Web Site: www.aspermont.com
ASP—(ASX)
Rev.: $41,870,536
Assets: $46,200,461
Liabilities: $34,995,802
Net Worth: $11,204,659
Earnings: $3,686,950
Emp.: 228
Fiscal Year-end: 06/30/13
Business Description:
Media Services
S.I.C.: 7379
N.A.I.C.S.: 518210
Personnel:
Andrew Leslie Kent *(Chm)*
Colm J. O'Brien *(CEO)*
John R. Detwiler *(CFO & Sec)*
Ajit Patel *(CIO)*
David Nizol *(CEO-UK)*
Board of Directors:
Andrew Leslie Kent
Lewis George Cross
Charbel Nader
David Nizol
Colm J. O'Brien
John Stark
Legal Counsel:
Williams & Hughes
Level 1 25 Richardson St
Perth, Australia

Non-U.S. Subsidiary:

Aspermont UK Limited (1)
Albert House 1 Singer St
London, EC2A 4BQ, United Kingdom
Tel.: (44) 2072166060
Fax: (44) 2072166050
E-Mail: info@aspermontuk.com
Web Site: www.aspermontuk.com
Emp.: 40
Mining Journal & Magazine Publishers
S.I.C.: 2731
N.A.I.C.S.: 511130
David Nizol *(CEO)*

ASPIRE INTERNATIONAL, INC.

18 Crown Steel Drive Unit 310
Markham, ON, L3R 9X8, Canada
Tel.: (905) 943-9996
Fax: (905) 943-7560
Web Site: www.aspireinternationalinc.com
Year Founded: 2003
APIT—(OTC)
Emp.: 4
Business Description:
Data Communication Network Connectivity Semiconductor Mfr
S.I.C.: 3674
N.A.I.C.S.: 334413
Personnel:
Bok Wong *(Chm, Pres, CEO & Chief Acctg Officer)*
Board of Directors:
Bok Wong
To-Hon Lam
Eric Wang

ASPIRE MINING LIMITED

Level 2 Suite 20 22 Railway Road
Subiaco, WA, 6008, Australia
Mailing Address:
PO Box 1918
Subiaco, WA, 6904, Australia
Tel.: (61) 8 9287 4555
Fax: (61) 8 9388 1980
E-Mail: info@aspiremininglimited.com
Web Site: www.aspiremininglimited.com
AKM—(ASX)
Rev.: $581,446
Assets: $56,942,617
Liabilities: $4,055,332
Net Worth: $52,887,285
Earnings: ($8,076,697)
Emp.: 2
Fiscal Year-end: 06/30/13
Business Description:
Coal Mining & Exploration
S.I.C.: 1221
N.A.I.C.S.: 212111
Personnel:
David Paull *(Mng Dir)*
Philip Rundell *(Sec)*
Board of Directors:
David McSweeney
Hannah Badenach
Andrew Edwards
Neil Lithgow
David Paull
Mark Read
Sado Demchigsuren Turbat

Deloitte Onch LLC
6th Floor Gurvan Gol Holding Company Building Sukhbaatar District
2nd Khoroo, Ulaanbaatar, Mongolia
Legal Counsel:
Steinepreis Paganin
Level 4 The Read Buildings 16 Milligan Street
Perth, Australia

Corrs Chambers Westgarth
Level 15 Woodside Plaza 240 Saint Georges Terrace
Perth, WA, 6000, Australia

ASPO OYJ

Lintulahdenkuja 10
PO Box 70
00501 Helsinki, Finland
Tel.: (358) 95211
Fax: (358) 95214999
Web Site: www.aspo.fi
Year Founded: 1929
ASU1V—(HEL)
Sls.: $648,304,703
Assets: $418,959,066
Liabilities: $297,574,917
Net Worth: $121,384,149
Earnings: $14,517,097
Emp.: 871
Fiscal Year-end: 12/31/12
Business Description:
Holding Company
S.I.C.: 6719
N.A.I.C.S.: 551112
Personnel:
Gustav Nyberg *(Chm)*
Matti Arteva *(Vice Chm)*
Aki Ojanen *(CEO)*
Arto Meitsalo *(CFO)*
Harri Seppala *(Treas)*
Board of Directors:
Gustav Nyberg
Matti Arteva
Mammu Kaario
Esa Karppinen
Roberto Lencioni
Kristina Pentti-von Walzel
Risto Salo

Subsidiaries:

ESL Shipping Ltd (1)
Lintulahdenkuja 10
00500 Helsinki, Finland
Tel.: (358) 9 75951
Fax: (358) 9 521 9999
E-Mail: operations@eslshipping.com
Web Site: www.eslshipping.com
Marine Cargo Handling Services
S.I.C.: 4491
N.A.I.C.S.: 488320
Aki Ojanen *(Chm)*
Matti-Mikael Koskinen *(Mng Dir)*
Tom Blomberg *(Exec VP-Chartering & Ops-Ships)*

Kaukomarkkinat Oy (1)
Lintulahdenkuja 10
FI 00500 Helsinki, Finland (100%)
Mailing Address:
PO Box 40
02631 Espoo, Finland
Tel.: (358) 95211
Fax: (358) 95216641
E-Mail: info@kaukomarkkinat.fi
Web Site: www.kaukomarkkinat.fi
Sales Range: $25-49.9 Million
Emp.: 779
Industrial Machinery Supplier
S.I.C.: 5084
N.A.I.C.S.: 423830
Jukka Rapeli *(Sr Mgr)*

Non-U.S. Subsidiaries:

Kaukomarkkinat Shanghai Ltd. (2)
Rm 2806-2807 Tower B City Center 100 Zun Yi Road
Shanghai, 200051, China
Tel.: (86) 21 62700640
Fax: (86) 21 62700872
Paper Industry Machinery Mfr
S.I.C.: 3554
N.A.I.C.S.: 333243

OOO Kauko Rus (2)
5 of 4008 Torzhkovskaya Ul
Saint Petersburg, 197342, Russia
Tel.: (7) 8123244062
Fax: (7) 8124494740
Business Support Services
S.I.C.: 7389
N.A.I.C.S.: 561499

Leipurin Oy (1)
Kutojantie 4
PO Box 40
02631 Espoo, Finland
Tel.: (358) 9 521 70
Fax: (358) 9 521 2121
E-Mail: leipurin@leipurin.com
Web Site: www.leipurin.com
Sales Range: $125-149.9 Million
Emp.: 160
Food Product Machinery Distr
S.I.C.: 5046
N.A.I.C.S.: 423440
Matti Vaananen *(Mng Dir)*
Johan Zilliacus *(Deputy Mng Dir)*

Non-U.S. Subsidiaries:

Leipurin Estonia AS (2)
Betooni 6
EE-11415 Tallinn, Estonia
Tel.: (372) 6 201 485
Fax: (372) 6 201 487
Web Site: www.leipurin.com
Food Packaging Machinery Distr
S.I.C.: 5084
N.A.I.C.S.: 423830

OOO Leipurien Tukku (2)
Torzhkovskaya 5
197342 Saint Petersburg, Russia
Tel.: (7) 812 325 2013
Fax: (7) 812 327 4378
E-Mail: spb@leipurin.ru
Web Site: www.leipurin.com
Food Packaging Machinery Distr
S.I.C.: 5084
N.A.I.C.S.: 423830

SIA Leipurin (2)
Dzelzavas Iela 120a
1021 Riga, Latvia
Tel.: (371) 67808080
Fax: (371) 67802774
E-Mail: fvbrcp@leipurin.com
Web Site: www.leipurin.lv
Emp.: 27
Food Products Machinery Distr
S.I.C.: 5084
N.A.I.C.S.: 423830
Yanes Clemens *(Dir-Sls)*

UAB Leipurin (2)
Taikos pr 153c
52119 Kaunas, Lithuania
Tel.: (370) 37 451 450
Fax: (370) 37 452 104
Web Site: www.leipurin.com
Food Processing Machinery Distr
S.I.C.: 5046
N.A.I.C.S.: 423440

Telko Oy (1)
Lintulahdenkuja 10
005800 Helsinki, Finland
Tel.: (358) 9 5211
Fax: (358) 9 521 7270
E-Mail: telko.finland@telko.com
Web Site: www.telko.com
Sales Range: $250-299.9 Million
Emp.: 220
Industrial Chemicals & Plastics Distr
S.I.C.: 5169
N.A.I.C.S.: 424690
Kalle Kettunen *(Mng Dir)*

Subsidiary:

Rauma Terminal Services Oy (2)
Iso-Hakunintie
26100 Rauma, Finland
Tel.: (358) 28220933
Fax: (358) 28226933
Web Site: www.raumastevedoring.fi
Emp.: 7
Liquid Products Storage Services
S.I.C.: 4225
N.A.I.C.S.: 493110
Jarkko Kuusisto *(Gen Mgr)*

Non-U.S. Subsidiaries:

Aspokem International B.V. (2)
Fred Roeskestraat 123
Amsterdam, Noord-Holland, 1076 EE, Netherlands
Tel.: (31) 205771177
Chemical Products Distr
S.I.C.: 5169
N.A.I.C.S.: 424690

FLLC Telko (2)
Dzerzhinskogo Pr 104 Office 1302
220116 Minsk, Belarus
Tel.: (375) 17 271 33 47
Fax: (375) 17 271 65 49
E-Mail: telko.belarus@telko.com
Emp.: 1
Industrial Chemical & Plastic Products Distr
S.I.C.: 5169
N.A.I.C.S.: 424690
Juris Avotins *(Gen Mgr)*

LLC Telko (2)
Stetsenko str 19 Building 68
Kiev, 04128, Ukraine
Tel.: (380) 44 4940838
Fax: (380) 44 4992138
E-Mail: telko.ukraine@telko.com
Web Site: www.telko.com
Emp.: 25
Chemical Products Distr
S.I.C.: 5169
N.A.I.C.S.: 424690

Molub-Alloy AB (2)
E A Rosengrens Gata 19
Vastra Frolunda, 421 31, Sweden
Tel.: (46) 31815990
Fax: (46) 31208210
E-Mail: telko.sweden@telko.com
Web Site: www.moluballoy.se
Emp.: 15
Industrial Lubricants Distr
S.I.C.: 7549
N.A.I.C.S.: 811191

OOO Telko (2)
Bolshoy Sampsonievskiy 32 Building A Office 2B 217
194044 Saint Petersburg, Russia
Tel.: (7) 812 324 1617
Fax: (7) 812 324 8797
E-Mail: rusales@telko.com
Emp.: 50
Chemical Products Distr
S.I.C.: 5169
N.A.I.C.S.: 424690
Sergei Korolev *(Mng Dir)*

Telko Denmark A/S (2)
Frederiksgade 2
3400 Hillerod, Denmark
Tel.: (45) 33 15 28 55
Fax: (45) 33 15 21 61
Web Site: www.telko.com
Chemical & Plastic Products Distr
S.I.C.: 5169
N.A.I.C.S.: 424690

Telko Estonia OU (2)
Moisa 4 / Vabaohumuuseumi Tee 3
13522 Tallinn, Estonia

Tel.: (372) 6 54 88 33
Fax: (372) 6 54 88 34
E-Mail: aspokem@aspokem.ee
Web Site: www.aspokem.ee
Industrial Chemicals Distr
S.I.C.: 5169
N.A.I.C.S.: 424690

Telko Latvia SIA (2)
Viskalu iela 11
Riga, 1026, Latvia
Tel.: (371) 67 84 05 30
Fax: (371) 67 84 05 29
E-Mail: telko.latvia@telko.com
Emp.: 9
Specialty Chemicals Distr
S.I.C.: 5169
N.A.I.C.S.: 424690

Telko Lietuva UAB (2)
Taikos pr 88A 613
Kaunas, 51183, Lithuania
Tel.: (370) 37 742673
Fax: (370) 37 432174
E-Mail: telko.lithuania@telko.com
Chemical & Plastic Products Distr
S.I.C.: 5169
N.A.I.C.S.: 424690

Telko Norway AS (2)
C J Hambrosplass 2C
0164 Oslo, Norway
Tel.: (47) 2299 6293
Fax: (47) 2299 6010
E-Mail: ordre@telkogroup.no
Web Site: www.telko.com
Industrial Lubricant Distr
S.I.C.: 5172
N.A.I.C.S.: 424720

Telko-Poland Sp. z o.o. (2)
Ul Cybernetyki 19
02-677 Warsaw, Poland
Tel.: (48) 22 330 12 00
Fax: (48) 22 330 12 12
E-Mail: telkogroup@telkogroup.com.pl
Web Site: www.telkogroup.com.pl
Emp.: 50
Food Products Mfr & Distr
S.I.C.: 2099
N.A.I.C.S.: 311999
Ewa Brzezik *(Mgr-Mktg)*

Telko Shanghai Ltd. (2)
Room 2804-2807 Tower B City Center 100 Zun Yi Road
Shanghai, 200051, China
Tel.: (86) 216270 0640
Fax: (86) 216270 0872
E-Mail: telko.china@telko.com
Web Site: www.telko.com
Chemical Products Distr
S.I.C.: 5169
N.A.I.C.S.: 424690

Wilfert Chemical Denmark A/S (2)
Frederiksgade 2a
3400 Hillerod, Frederiksborg, Denmark
Tel.: (45) 48251266
Fax: (45) 48251759
Chemical Products Mfr
S.I.C.: 2899
N.A.I.C.S.: 325998

Wilfert Chemical Nordic A/S (2)
Frederiksgade 2
3400 Hillerod, Denmark
Tel.: (45) 48 25 12 66
Fax: (45) 48 25 17 59
Web Site: www.wilfert.dk
Plastic Material Distr
S.I.C.: 5162
N.A.I.C.S.: 424610

Wilfert Chemical Sweden AB (2)
Sorgardsvagen 29
19144 Sollentuna, Sweden
Tel.: (46) 8 594 956 70
Fax: (46) 8 594 956 71
Chemical Products Distr
S.I.C.: 5169
N.A.I.C.S.: 424690

ASPOCOMP GROUP OYJ

Keilaranta 1
02150 Espoo, Finland
Tel.: (358) 207756860
Fax: (358) 207756868
E-Mail: sami.holopainen@aspocomp.com
Web Site: www.aspocomp.com
ACG1V—(HEL)
Sls.: $31,458,647
Assets: $26,372,816
Liabilities: $7,123,932
Net Worth: $19,248,885
Earnings: $5,155,831
Emp.: 150
Fiscal Year-end: 12/31/12

Business Description:
Holding Company; Electronic Component Mfr
S.I.C.: 6719
N.A.I.C.S.: 551112

Personnel:
Tuomo Lahdesmaki *(Chm)*
Johan Hammaren *(Vice Chm)*
Sami Holopainen *(CEO)*
Jouni Kinnunen *(CFO)*
Jari Isoaho *(COO)*

Board of Directors:
Tuomo Lahdesmaki
Johan Hammaren
Paivi Marttila
Kari Vuorialho

Subsidiary:

Aspocomp Oy (1)
Tukijantie 11
90570 Oulu, Finland (100%)
Tel.: (358) 959181
Fax: (358) 207756861
E-Mail: sami.holopainen@aspocomp.com
Web Site: www.aspocomp.com
Emp.: 100
Electronic Component Mfr
S.I.C.: 3679
N.A.I.C.S.: 334419
Sami Holopainen *(CEO)*

Non-U.S. Subsidiaries:

Aspocomp AB (1)
Veddestavagen 3
175 62 Jarfalla, Sweden (100%)
Tel.: (46) 708974269
Web Site: www.aspocomp.com
Electronic Component Mfr
S.I.C.: 3679
N.A.I.C.S.: 334419
Tore Wiberg *(Dir-Mktg)*

Aspocomp (Thailand) Co., Ltd. (1)
684-685 Moo 11 Sukhapibal 8 Road
Si Racha, 20280 Bangkok, Chonburi, Thailand
Tel.: (66) 384805914
Web Site: www.aspocomp.com
Electronic Component Mfr
S.I.C.: 3679
N.A.I.C.S.: 334419

P.C.B. Center (Thailand) Co., Ltd. (1)
600 Sukhapibal 8 Road
Nongkham Sriracha, Chon Buri, Thailand (75%)
Tel.: (66) 38480591
Fax: (66) 38480590
E-Mail: naiunon.thon@pcbc.co.th
Web Site: www.pcb.co.th
Emp.: 649
Printed Circuit Boards Mfr
S.I.C.: 3672
N.A.I.C.S.: 334412

ASPREY

167 New Bond St
London, W1S 4AY, United Kingdom
Tel.: (44) 2074936767
Fax: (44) 8709050768
E-Mail: enquiries@asprey.com
Web Site: www.asprey.com
Emp.: 100

Business Description:
Jewelry, Leather Goods, Clothing & Accessories Mfr
S.I.C.: 3911
N.A.I.C.S.: 339910

Personnel:
Jennifer Heath *(Dir-Legal & HR)*

ASR HOLDINGS LIMITED

Units 1106 1112 on 11th Floor Lu Plaza 2 Wing Yip Street
Kowloon, China (Hong Kong)
Tel.: (852) 3518 7300
Fax: (852) 2331 3311
Web Site: www.asrholdings.com.hk
1803—(HKG)
Rev.: $86,937,703
Assets: $44,461,186
Liabilities: $13,348,001
Net Worth: $31,113,185
Earnings: $11,693,831
Emp.: 174
Fiscal Year-end: 12/31/12

Business Description:
Holding Company; Freight Forwarding
S.I.C.: 6719
N.A.I.C.S.: 551112

Personnel:
Sunny Ho Yuen Yu *(Co-Founder & Chm)*
Niki Kai Lo Law *(Co-Founder & CEO-Gen Sls Agent)*
Richard Chi Hung Mak *(Co-Founder & CEO-Logistics)*
Hoo Cheng *(Co-Sec)*
Chi Keung Ho *(Co-Sec)*

Board of Directors:
Sunny Ho Yuen Yu
Niki Kai Lo Law
Richard Chi Hung Mak
Anthony Kan Hee Tyen
Jin Cai Wei
Xianlin Zhang

Harneys Services (Cayman) Limited
3rd Floor Queensgate House 113 South Church Street
Georgetown, Cayman Islands

Transfer Agent:
Harneys Services (Cayman) Limited
3rd Floor Queensgate House 113 South Church Street
Georgetown, Cayman Islands

Subsidiaries:

AOE Freight (HK) Ltd. (1)
Units 1106-1112 11th Floor Lu Plaza
2 Wing Yip Street, Kowloon, China (Hong Kong)
Tel.: (852) 2331 3022
Fax: (852) 2331 3311
Web Site: www.asrholdings.com.hk
Freight Forwarding
S.I.C.: 4731
N.A.I.C.S.: 488510
Tom Lee *(Gen Mgr)*

Non-U.S. Subsidiary:

AOE Freight (ShenZhen) Ltd. (2)
Unit 9Q Taiyangdao Building Dongmen South Road
Luohu District, Shenzhen, China
Tel.: (86) 755 8207 5085
Fax: (86) 755 8207 6238
Freight Forwarding
S.I.C.: 4731
N.A.I.C.S.: 488510

Subsidiaries:

AOE Freight (ShenZhen) Ltd. (3)
Unit A Level 12 Dongjian Building
121 Fenjiang Middle Road, Foshan, China
Tel.: (86) 757 8801 8261
Fax: (86) 757 8801 8260
Freight Forwarding
S.I.C.: 4731
N.A.I.C.S.: 488510

AOE Freight (ShenZhen) Ltd. (3)
Unit 2213 Level 22 Block 1 Lan Tian Jun Hotel Apartment
Qingyunpu District, Nanchang, China
Tel.: (86) 791 6497 627
Fax: (86) 791 6497 605
Freight Forwarding
S.I.C.: 4731
N.A.I.C.S.: 488510

AOE Freight (ShenZhen) Ltd. (3)
Room 1510 Huai Hai China Tower 885 Renmin Road
Huangpu District, Shanghai, China
Tel.: (86) 21 6335 5303
Fax: (86) 21 6335 5302
Freight Forwarding
S.I.C.: 4731
N.A.I.C.S.: 488510

AOE Freight (ShenZhen) Ltd. (3)
Units 1009-1010 Holdround Plaza 2 Danan Road
Yue Xiu District, Guangzhou, China
Tel.: (86) 20 8372 0085
Fax: (86) 20 8329 9050
Freight Forwarding
S.I.C.: 4731
N.A.I.C.S.: 488510

AOE Freight (ShenZhen) Ltd. (3)
Room 709 Level 7 Yizhong Building 48 Zhongshan Second Road
Shiqi District, Zhongshan, China
Tel.: (86) 760 8881 6281
Fax: (86) 760 8760 0722
E-Mail: hwang.jhs@aoecargo.com.cn
Web Site: www.aoecargo.com.cn
Freight Forwarding
S.I.C.: 4731
N.A.I.C.S.: 488510
K. K. Liu *(Gen Mgr)*

ASR Europe Logistics Ltd. (1)
Units 1106-12 11th Floor Lu Plaza
2 Wing Yip Street, Kowloon, China (Hong Kong)
Tel.: (852) 2331 3022
Fax: (852) 2331 3311
Web Site: www.asreu.com
Logistics
S.I.C.: 4731
N.A.I.C.S.: 541614
Jouni Ritola *(Dir)*

ASR Logistics Ltd. (1)
Units 1106-12 11th Floor Lu Plaza
2 Wing Yip Street, Kowloon, China (Hong Kong)
Tel.: (852) 2331 3022
Fax: (852) 2331 3311
Logistics
S.I.C.: 4731
N.A.I.C.S.: 541614

ASRCO Logistics Ltd. (1)
Units 1106-1112 11th Floor Lu Plaza
2 Wing Yip Street, Kowloon, China (Hong Kong)
Tel.: (852) 3518 7300
Fax: (852) 2331 3311
E-Mail: info@asr.com.hk
Web Site: www.asr.com.hk
Emp.: 5
Logistics
S.I.C.: 4731
N.A.I.C.S.: 541614
Marc Groenewoud *(Dir-Grp Mgmt Performance)*

Star Pacific Logistics Ltd. (1)
Units 1106-1112 11th Floor Lu Plaza
2 Wing Yip Street, Kowloon, China (Hong Kong)
Tel.: (852) 2785 3822
Fax: (852) 3012 1661
Logistics
S.I.C.: 4731
N.A.I.C.S.: 541614

ASR NEDERLAND N.V.

Archimedeslaan 10
3584 BA Utrecht, Netherlands
Mailing Address:
Postbus 2072
3500 HB Utrecht, Netherlands
Tel.: (31) 302579111
Fax: (31) 302578300
Web Site: www.asrverzekeringen.com.nl
Rev.: $5,898,916,940
Assets: $59,881,680,110
Liabilities: $55,930,671,160
Net Worth: $3,951,008,950

ASR Nederland N.V.—(Continued)

Earnings: $333,850,160
Emp.: 4,631
Fiscal Year-end: 12/31/12

Business Description:
Holding Company; Insurance Products & Services
S.I.C.: 6719
N.A.I.C.S.: 551112

Personnel:
Kick van der Pol *(Chm-Supervisory Bd)*
Jos P. M. Baeten *(Chm-Exec Bd & CEO)*
R. T. Wijmenga *(CFO & Member-Exec Bd)*
Karin Bergstein *(Member-Exec Bd)*
Michel Verwoest *(Member-Exec Bd)*

Supervisory Board of Directors:
Kick van der Pol
Annet P. Aris
Margot A. Scheltema
Cor H. van den Bos

Division:

ASR Verzekeringen N.V. (1)
Archimedeslaan 10
NL-3584 BA Utrecht, Netherlands NL
Mailing Address:
Postbus 2072
3500 HB Utrecht, Netherlands
Tel.: (31) 302579111
Fax: (31) 302578302
E-Mail: info@asr.nl
Web Site: www.asrverzekeringen.nl
Emp.: 4,000
Life Insurance & Pension Products & Services
S.I.C.: 6311
N.A.I.C.S.: 524113
Peter Hoitinga *(Dir-Comml)*

Subsidiaries:

Ardanta N.V. (1)
De Ruyterlaan 8
NL-7511 JH Enschede, Netherlands NL
Tel.: (31) 534881122
Fax: (31) 534300326
E-Mail: info@ardanta.nl
Web Site: www.ardanta.nl
Emp.: 60
Funeral Insurance Products & Services
S.I.C.: 6399
N.A.I.C.S.: 524128
Robert Schaaf *(Mng Dir)*

De Amersfoortse Verzekeringen N.V. (1)
Stadsring 15
3811 HM Amersfoort, Netherlands NL
Mailing Address:
Postbus 42
3800 AA Amersfoort, Netherlands
Tel.: (31) 334642911
Fax: (31) 334642930
E-Mail: info@amersfoortse.nl
Web Site: www.amersfoortse.nl
Emp.: 700
Income & Disability Insurance; Pension Products & Services
S.I.C.: 6399
N.A.I.C.S.: 524128
J.P.M. Baeten *(Dir-Insurance)*

Falcon Leven N.V. (1)
Capellalaan 115
2132 JM Hoofddorp, Netherlands NL
Mailing Address: (100%)
Postbus 528
NL-2130 AM Hoofddorp, Netherlands
Tel.: (31) 235648300
Fax: (31) 235637876
Web Site: www.falconleven.nl
Emp.: 125
Flexible & Term Life Insurance Products & Services
S.I.C.: 6311
N.A.I.C.S.: 524113
Gilbert Mattu *(Mng Dir)*

ASSA ABLOY AB

Klarabergsviadukten 90
111 64 Stockholm, Sweden

Mailing Address:
PO Box 70340
SE 107 23 Stockholm, Sweden
Tel.: (46) 850648500
Fax: (46) 850648585
E-Mail: info@assaabloy.com
Web Site: www.assaabloy.com
Year Founded: 1994
ASSAB—(OMX OTC)
Sls.: $7,216,621,200
Assets: $9,265,708,800
Liabilities: $5,128,678,800
Net Worth: $4,137,030,000
Earnings: $793,350,000
Emp.: 42,762
Fiscal Year-end: 12/31/12

Business Description:
Door Opening Solution Products Mfr Export
S.I.C.: 7382
N.A.I.C.S.: 561621

Personnel:
Lars Renstrom *(Chm)*
Carl Douglas *(Vice Chm)*
Johan Molin *(Pres, CEO & Head-Global Tech Div)*
Carolina Dybeck Happe *(CFO & Exec VP)*
Ulf Sodergren *(CTO & Exec VP)*
Denis Hebert *(Exec VP & Head-Global Tech Bus Unit-HID Global)*
Thanasis Molokotos *(Exec VP & Head-Americas Div)*
Tim Shea *(Exec VP & Head-Global Tech Bus Unit-Hospitality)*
Juan Vargues *(Exec VP & Head-Entrance Sys Div)*
Tzachi Wiesenfeld *(Exec VP & Head-EMEA Div)*

Board of Directors:
Lars Renstrom
Carl Douglas
Kurt Hellstrom
Rune Hjalm
Birgitta Klasen
Seppo Liimatainen
Eva Lindqvist
Johan Molin
Sven-Christer Nilsson
Mats Persson
Jan Svensson
Ulrik Svensson

Divisions:

ASSA ABLOY Entrance Systems AB (1)
Lodjursgatan 10
PO Box 131
Landskrona, 26144, Sweden SE
Tel.: (46) 10 47 47 000 (100%)
Fax: (46) 418 284 12
E-Mail: info@aaesg.com
Web Site: www.assaabloyentrance.com
Emp.: 350
Holding Company; Automated Door Systems Mfr & Distr
S.I.C.: 6719
N.A.I.C.S.: 551112
Juan Vargues *(Pres & CEO)*

Subsidiaries:

ASSA ABLOY Entrance Systems Sweden AB (2)
(Formerly Crawford-Allhabo AB)
Redegatan 7
PO Box 5087
SE 426 05 Vastra Frolunda, Sweden (100%)
Tel.: (46) 10 47 47 120
Fax: (46) 31 29 35 19
E-Mail: info@crawfordsolution.com
Web Site: www.crawfordsolution.com
Emp.: 75
Industrial & Garage Doors, Wall Systems, Dock Loading Systems, Storage Cabinets & Lockers Mfr & Whslr
S.I.C.: 3442
N.A.I.C.S.: 332321
Per Henrikson *(Mng Dir)*

Besam Export AB (2)
Lodjursgatan 2
261 44 Landskrona, Sweden (100%)
Tel.: (46) 41851400
Fax: (46) 41851355
E-Mail: general@besam.se
Web Site: www.besam.se
Emp.: 3
Door Automation Systems Mfr
S.I.C.: 3442
N.A.I.C.S.: 332321
Juan Vargues *(Gen Mgr)*

Subsidiary:

Besam Svensk Forsaljning AB (3)
Pilakersgatagan 32
PO Box 353
Landskrona, 26123, Sweden (100%)
Tel.: (46) 41851000
Fax: (46) 41814060
E-Mail: general@besam.com
Web Site: www.besam.se
Emp.: 30
S.I.C.: 6159
N.A.I.C.S.: 522298

Non-U.S. Subsidiary:

Besam, spol. s r.o. (3)
Kapitulska 15
811 01 Bratislava, Slovakia
Tel.: (421) 254 431 045
Fax: (421) 254 431 247
Door Locks Mfr
S.I.C.: 3429
N.A.I.C.S.: 332510

Cardo AB (2)
Roskildevagen 1
PO Box 486
SE 201 24 Malmo, Sweden
Tel.: (46) 40350400
Telex: 32413 cardos
Fax: (46) 40976440
E-Mail: info@cardo.com
Web Site: www.cardo.se
Sales Range: $1-4.9 Billion
Emp.: 5,305
Industrial Doors, Loading Dock Equipment & Braking Systems Mfr
Import Export
S.I.C.: 3442
N.A.I.C.S.: 332321
Peter Aru *(Pres & CEO)*

Subsidiary:

Crawford International AB (3)
Roskildevagen 1
PO Box 171
SE 201 21 Malmo, Sweden (100%)
Tel.: (46) 10 47 47 06
Telex: 32413 Cardo s
Fax: (46) 40976440
E-Mail: info@cardo.se
Web Site: www.cardo.se
Sales Range: $400-449.9 Million
Emp.: 100
Industrial & Garage Doors, Dock Loading Systems, Rapid Action Rolling Doors, Door-Operating Equipment with Attendant Automation Mfr
S.I.C.: 2431
N.A.I.C.S.: 321911

Subsidiaries:

Cardo Door Production AB (4)
Gamla Flygplatsvagen 2 4
PO Box 160
SE 423 21 Torslanda, Sweden (100%)
Tel.: (46) 31566000
Telex: 21437 crawfo s
Fax: (46) 31923468
E-Mail:
Emp.: 150
Mfr. of Industrial & Garage Doors, Wall Systems, Dock Loading Systems, Storage Cabinets & Lockers
S.I.C.: 2431
N.A.I.C.S.: 321911
Juan Vargues *(Gen Mgr)*

Crawford Door Forsaljnings AB (4)
Redegatan 7
PO Box 5087
426 05 Vastra Frolunda, Sweden
Tel.: (46) 317691200
Fax: (46) 31293519
E-Mail: info.se@crawfordsolutions.com
Web Site: www.crawfordsolutions.com
Emp.: 200
Mfr. of Industrial & Garage Doors, Wall Systems, Dock Loading Systems, Storage Cabinets & Lockers
S.I.C.: 2431
N.A.I.C.S.: 321911
Ter Hemritffoom *(Mng Dir)*

Megadoor AB (4)
Servicegatan 6
931 76 Skelleftea, Sweden (100%)
Tel.: (46) 10 47 47 190
Fax: (46) 910 166 20
E-Mail: sales.europe.megadoor@assaabloy.com
Web Site: www.megadoor.se
Emp.: 35
Mfr. of Industrial & Garage Doors, Wall Systems, Dock Loading Systems, Storage Cabinets & Lockers
S.I.C.: 2431
N.A.I.C.S.: 321911
Teter kiu *(Mgr)*

U.S. Subsidiary:

Megadoor Inc. (4)
611 Hwy 74 S
Peachtree City, GA 30269-0957
Tel.: (770) 631-2600
Fax: (770) 631-9086
E-Mail: sales@megadoor.com
Web Site: www.megadoor.com
Emp.: 50
Industrial & Garage Doors, Wall Systems, Dock Loading Systems, Storage Cabinets & Lockers Mfr
S.I.C.: 5039
N.A.I.C.S.: 423390
Ulf Petersson *(Mng Dir)*

Non-U.S. Subsidiaries:

Alsta BV (4)
Glashorst 128
PO Box 8
3925 CK Scherpenzeel, Netherlands (100%)
Tel.: (31) 332776100
Fax: (31) 332774565
E-Mail: info@alsta.nl
Web Site: www.alsta.nl
Emp.: 50
Industrial Door Mfr
S.I.C.: 2431
N.A.I.C.S.: 321911
Jan Van Elsen *(Mng Dir)*

Clever-Crawford SA (4)
1/5 Rue Des Cevennes
I Ge la, 91090 Lisses, Petite Montangne, France
Tel.: (33) 160868900
Fax: (33) 825349180
E-Mail: info@crawfordsolutions.fr
Web Site: www.crawfordsolutions.fr
Emp.: 60
S.I.C.: 2431
N.A.I.C.S.: 321911
Michon Yammick *(Pres)*

Crawford Alfa S.R.L. (4)
Via Maccani 108 21
38100 Trento, Italy (100%)
Tel.: (39) 0461432511
Telex: 400040 crawdr i
Fax: (39) 0461432500
E-Mail: vendite@crawfordsolution.com
Web Site: www.crawfordsolution.com
Sales Range: Less than $1 Million
Emp.: 26
Mfr. of Industrial & Garage Doors, Wall Systems, Dock Loading Systems, Storage Cabinets & Lockers
S.I.C.: 2431
N.A.I.C.S.: 321911
Nicola Fornalli *(Pres)*

Crawford Belux (NV) (4)
Hundelgemsesteenweg 442 444
9820 Merelbeke, Belgium (100%)
Tel.: (32) 92395425
Telex: 85544 crawfo b
Fax: (32) 92325234
E-Mail: info.belux.crawford@assaabloy.com
Web Site: www.crawfordsolutions.com
Emp.: 150

Industrial & Garage Doors, Wall Systems, Dock Loading Systems, Storage Cabinets & Lockers Mfr & Whslr
S.I.C.: 2431
N.A.I.C.S.: 321911
Mark Driscart *(Mng Dir)*

Crawford Combursa S.L.U. (4)
Marie Curie 17-19 Edificio Autocampo II Oficinas B5-B7
28529 Rivas-Vaciamadrid, Madrid, Spain
Tel.: (34) 91 660 10 70
Fax: (34) 91 673 89 20
E-Mail: info@crawfordsolutions.com
Door Locks Mfr
S.I.C.: 3429
N.A.I.C.S.: 332510

Crawford Deur B.V. (4)
kelvinstraat 9 1704RS
PO Box 159
1700 AD Heerhugowaard, Netherlands
Tel.: (31) 725752125
Telex: 57313 crade nl
Fax: (31) 725713376
E-Mail: info.nl.crawford@assaabloy.com
Web Site: www.crawford.nl
Emp.: 230
Industrial & Garage Doors, Wall Systems, Dock Loading Systems, Storage Cabinets & Lockers Mfr
S.I.C.: 2431
N.A.I.C.S.: 321911

Crawford Door (Kunshan) Co., Ltd. (4)
Block L 5th Floor East Hope Plaza No 1777 Shiji Avenue
Pu Dong New District, 200 122 Shanghai, China
Tel.: (86) 21 2025 1196
Fax: (86) 21 5882 6718
E-Mail: marketing.cn.crawford@assaabloy.com
Web Site: www.crawfordsolutions.cn
Emp.: 100
Industrial & Garage Doors, Wall Systems, Dock Loading Systems, Storage Cabinets & Lockers Mfr & Whslr
S.I.C.: 3442
N.A.I.C.S.: 332321
Glen Chen *(Coord-Project)*

Crawford Door M.E. AB (4)
Dubai Investment Park
PO Box 80983
Sharjah, United Arab Emirates
Tel.: (971) 4 885 2888
Fax: (971) 4 885 4919
E-Mail: sales.me@megadoor.com
Web Site: www.megadoor.com
Emp.: 50
Door Mfr, Installer & Distr
S.I.C.: 2431
N.A.I.C.S.: 321911
Derek Salmons *(Sls Mgr)*

Crawford hafa GmbH-Wenningsen (4)
(Formerly Crawford Tor GmbH)
Fangdieckstrasse 64
22547 Hamburg, Germany (100%)
Tel.: (49) 405470060
Fax: (49) 4054700699
E-Mail: info@crawford.de
Web Site: www.crawford.de
Sls.: $15,080,909
Emp.: 30
Garage Doors, Wall Systems, Dock Loading Systems, Storage Cabinets & Lockers Mfr
S.I.C.: 2431
N.A.I.C.S.: 321911

Crawford hafa GmbH (4)
Gottlieb-Daimler-Str 12
30974 Wennigsen, Germany
Tel.: (49) 5103 7014945
Fax: (49) 5103 701496
E-Mail: info.de@crawfordsolutions.com
Web Site: www.crawfordsolutions.de
Emp.: 115
Door Mfr
S.I.C.: 3429
N.A.I.C.S.: 332510
Henning Adams *(Mng Dir)*

Non-U.S. Subsidiaries:

Crawford Hafa AG (5)
Vorstadt 20
PO Box 208
CH 3380 Wangen, Switzerland
Tel.: (41) 326316363
Fax: (41) 326316361
E-Mail: info.ch@crawfordsolutions.com
Web Site: www.crawfordhafa.ch
Emp.: 13
Industrial Door Mfr
S.I.C.: 2431
N.A.I.C.S.: 321911

Crawford-Hafa Kft (5)
Budafoki Ut 209
1117 Budapest, Hungary
Tel.: (36) 1 371 2420
Fax: (36) 1 203 6737
E-Mail: info@crawford-hafa.hu
Web Site: www.iparikapu.net
Door Locks Mfr
S.I.C.: 3429
N.A.I.C.S.: 332510

Crawford-hafa SRL (5)
Via Maccani 108/21
38100 Trento, Italy
Tel.: (39) 0461432511
Fax: (39) 0461432500
Web Site: www.crawford.it
Door Locks Mfr
S.I.C.: 3429
N.A.I.C.S.: 332510

Crawford Normstahl N.V. (4)
Oezerstaat 19
9820 Lokeren, Belgium (100%)
Tel.: (32) 92727100
Fax: (32) 92727109
E-Mail: info@normstahl.be
Web Site: www.normstahl.be
Emp.: 10
Industrial & Garage Doors, Wall Systems, Dock Loading Systems, Storage Cabinets & Lockers Mfr & Whslr
S.I.C.: 2431
N.A.I.C.S.: 321911

Crawford Poland Sp. zo.o. (4)
ul Marecka 49
PL 05 220 Zielonka, Poland
Tel.: (48) 22 750 6245
Fax: (48) 227506245
E-Mail: crawford.pl@crawfordsolutions.com
Web Site: www.crawfordsolutions.pl
Emp.: 17
Industrial & Garage Doors, Wall Systems, Dock Loading Systems, Storage Cabinets & Lockers Mfr & Whslr
S.I.C.: 2431
N.A.I.C.S.: 321911
Micheal Baranowicz *(Mng Dir)*

Crawford (Portugal), Lda. (4)
Quinta da Mata - Sete Casas
2670-350 Loures, Portugal
Tel.: (351) 219 844 840
Fax: (351) 219 844 849
E-Mail: info.pt@crawfordsolutions.com
Web Site: www.crawfordsolutions.com
Industrial & Garage Doors, Wall Systems, Dock Loading Systems, Storage Cabinets & Lockers Mfr & Whslr
S.I.C.: 7699
N.A.I.C.S.: 811490

Crawford Production Romania Srl (4)
Parcul Industrial D J 687/2
331170 Hunedoara, Romania
Tel.: (40) 354808380
Fax: (40) 354808383
E-Mail:
Emp.: 250
Electronic Safety Equipment Mfr
S.I.C.: 3679
N.A.I.C.S.: 334419
Gonzalo Anza *(Mng Dir)*

Crawford Tor GmbH (4)
IZ No-Sud Strasse 2 Objekt M27
2351 Wiener Neudorf, Austria (100%)
Tel.: (43) 22 36 61 66 50
Fax: (43) 223663661
E-Mail:
Emp.: 30
Mfr. & Wholesaler of Industrial & Garage Doors, Wall Systems, Dock Loading Systems, Storage Cabinets & Lockers
S.I.C.: 2431
N.A.I.C.S.: 321911
Hermann Niessler *(Gen Mgr)*

Crawford UK Ltd. (4)
7 Churchill Way 35 A Business Park
Chapel Town, Sheffield, S35 2PY, United Kingdom
Tel.: (44) 1142574330
Fax: (44) 1142574399
E-Mail: sales@assaabloy.com
Web Site: www.crawfordsolutions.uk.com
Emp.: 50
Industrial & Garage Doors, Wall Systems, Dock Loading Systems, Storage Cabinets & Lockers Mfr
S.I.C.: 2431
N.A.I.C.S.: 321911

Normstahl Crawford Tor GmbH (4)
Drautendorf 58
Niederwaldkirchen, AT 4400 Steyr, Austria (100%)
Tel.: (43) 723131280
Fax: (43) 72313123
E-Mail: office@normstahl.at
Web Site: www.normstahl.at
Emp.: 30
S.I.C.: 2431
N.A.I.C.S.: 321911

Normstahl Schweiz AG (4)
Industriestrasse 1
CH 9462 Montlingen, Switzerland (100%)
Tel.: (41) 717639797
Fax: (41) 717612790
E-Mail: info@normstahl.ch
Web Site: www.normstahl.com
Emp.: 20
Industrial Door Mfr
S.I.C.: 2431
N.A.I.C.S.: 321911

Oy Crawford Door AB (4)
Nimismiehenpelto 6
02270 Espoo, Finland (100%)
Tel.: (358) 103869000
Fax: (358) 98037393
E-Mail: info.fi@assaabloy.com
Web Site: www.crawfordsolutions.fi
Emp.: 120
Marketing & Sales of Industrial & Garage Doors
S.I.C.: 5211
N.A.I.C.S.: 444190
Christian Ivars *(Mng Dir)*

P C Henderson Ltd. (4)
Bowburn North Industrial Estate
Durham Rd Bowburn, Durham, DH6 5NG, United Kingdom UK
Tel.: (44) 913770701
Fax: (44) 913771309
E-Mail: sales@pchenderson.com
Web Site: www.pchenderson.com
Emp.: 350
Metal Doors, Sash, Trim, Sliding Door Gear & Garage Doors Mfr
S.I.C.: 3442
N.A.I.C.S.: 332321
Duncan Moncriess *(Mng Dir)*

Non-U.S. Subsidiaries:

Henderson Nederland BV (5)
Rootven 24
PO Box 258
5531 MB Bladel, Netherlands (100%)
Tel.: (31) 497332020
Fax: (31) 497332029
E-Mail: info@henderson.nl
Web Site: www.henderson.nl
Emp.: 8
Door Gear Mfr
S.I.C.: 3442
N.A.I.C.S.: 332321

P.C. Henderson (Ireland) Ltd. (5)
Westlink Industrial Estate Unit 21
Kylemore Road, Dublin, 10, Ireland (100%)
Tel.: (353) 016260444
Telex: 91491 PCH (EI)
Fax: (353) 016260455
Web Site: www.pchenderson.com
Sales Range: $1-9.9 Million
Emp.: 21
Industrial & Garage Doors, Wall Systems, Dock Loading Systems, Storage Cabinets & Lockers Mfr & Whslr
S.I.C.: 3255
N.A.I.C.S.: 327120
Paul Mooney *(Gen Mgr)*

Saudi Crawford Doors Factory Ltd. (4)
Satan Industrial City
PO Box 25960
Riyadh, 11476, Saudi Arabia (60%)
Tel.: (966) 12652225
Telex: 403340 crawdr sj
Fax: (966) 12652226
E-Mail: doors@crawforddoor.com.sa
Web Site: www.crawfordsolutions.com.sa
Emp.: 55
Mfr. of Industrial & Garage Doors, Wall Systems, Dock Loading Systems, Storage Cabinets & Lockers
S.I.C.: 2431
N.A.I.C.S.: 321911
Roger Boogh *(Mng Dir)*

Non-U.S. Subsidiaries:

Cardo Door International AG (3)
Industriestrasse 11
CH 6343 Rotkreuz, Switzerland
Tel.: (41) 417905901
Fax: (41) 417905908
Marketer & Retailer of Industrial & Garage Doors
S.I.C.: 5211
N.A.I.C.S.: 444190

Cardo Door Production B.V. (3)
Postbus 22
3925 ZG Scherpenzeel, Netherlands
Tel.: (31) 725750700
Fax: (31) 725744928
E-Mail:
Emp.: 300
Automatic Door Mfr
S.I.C.: 2431
N.A.I.C.S.: 321911
Remco Witte *(Plant Mgr)*

Cardo Door Production GmbH (3)
Normstahlstrasse 1-3
85366 Moosburg, Germany
Tel.: (49) 8761 6830
Fax: (49) 8761 683210
Door Locks Mfr
S.I.C.: 3429
N.A.I.C.S.: 332510

Cardo Industrial Door Production A/S (3)
Lupinvej 12
9500 Hobro, Denmark (100%)
Tel.: (45) 96574900
Fax: (45) 98525822
Emp.: 50
Industrial & Garage Doors, Wall Systems, Dock Loading Systems, Storage Cabinets & Lockers Mfr & Whslr
S.I.C.: 2431
N.A.I.C.S.: 321911
Henrik Gertz *(Mgr)*

U.S. Subsidiaries:

4Front Engineered Solutions, Inc. (2)
1612 Hutton Dr Ste 140
Carrollton, TX 75006
Tel.: (972) 466-0707
Fax: (972) 323-2661
Toll Free: (877) 778-3625
E-Mail: info@4frontes.com
Web Site: www.4frontes.com
Sales Range: $150-199.9 Million
Emp.: 750
Warehouse & Loading Dock Equipment Mfr
S.I.C.: 3559
N.A.I.C.S.: 333249
Keith Moore *(Pres)*
Paul Venesky *(CFO & VP-Fin)*

Branch:

4Front Engineered Solutions - Muskego (3)
W 183 S 8253 Racine Ave
Muskego, WI 53150-8125
Tel.: (262) 679-6200
Fax: (262) 679-6210
Emp.: 65
Seals & Shelters Mfr for Shipping & Receiving Docks
S.I.C.: 3448
N.A.I.C.S.: 332311
Wayne Straus *(Gen Mgr)*

ASSA ABLOY AB—(Continued)

Subsidiaries:

APS Resources (3)
6219 W Eastwood Ct
Mequon, WI 53092-4479 (100%)
Tel.: (262) 518-1000
Fax: (262) 518-1030
E-Mail: info@apsresource.com
Web Site: www.apsresource.com
Sales Range: $25-49.9 Million
Emp.: 15
Material Handling Industry Aftermarket Solutions & Services
S.I.C.: 7699
N.A.I.C.S.: 811310
Joe Ticcioni *(Reg Mgr-Sls-Northeast)*

TKO Doors (3)
N56 W24701 Corporate Cir
Sussex, WI 53089-9907 WI
Tel.: (262) 820-1217 (100%)
Fax: (262) 820-1273
Toll Free: (877) 408-6788
E-Mail: sales@tkodoors.com
Web Site: www.tkodoors.com
Emp.: 25
Mfr of Doors for Loading Docks
S.I.C.: 3442
N.A.I.C.S.: 332321
Bill Knowten *(Gen Mgr-Mfg)*

Non-U.S. Branch:

Dock Products Canada (3)
600 Orwell Street Unit 6
Mississauga, ON, L5A 3R9, Canada(100%)
Tel.: (905) 276-0565
Fax: (905) 276-6512
Toll Free: (877) 316-6557
E-Mail: info@dockproductscanada.com
Web Site: www.dockproducts.com
Emp.: 25
Loading Dock Equipment Mfr
S.I.C.: 3559
N.A.I.C.S.: 333249
Chris Plaunt *(Mgr-HR)*

Adams Rite Manufacturing Co. (2)
260 Santa Fe St
Pomona, CA 91767 CA
Tel.: (909) 632-2300
Fax: (909) 632-2373
Toll Free: (800) 872-3267
Web Site: www.adamsrite.com
Sales Range: $25-49.9 Million
Emp.: 187
Mfr of Doors & Door Hardware including Maximum Security Locks
Import Export
S.I.C.: 3429
N.A.I.C.S.: 332510
Richard S. Kreidel *(Pres & CEO)*

Subsidiaries:

Markar Architectural Products, Inc. (3)
68 Ward Rd
Lancaster, NY 14086-9779
Tel.: (716) 685-4104
Fax: (716) 685-3919
Toll Free: (800) 866-1688
E-Mail: information@markar.com
Web Site: www.markar.com
Emp.: 90
Mfr of Hardware Products
S.I.C.: 3442
N.A.I.C.S.: 332321
Janet Austin *(Controller)*

Non-U.S. Holding:

Adams Rite Europe Limited (3)
The Meadows Cannock Road
Wolverhampton, WV10 0RR, United Kingdom CA
Tel.: (44) 1902 867 109 (100%)
Fax: (44) 1902 867 118
E-Mail: info@adamsrite.co.uk
Web Site: www.adamsrite.co.uk
Emp.: 40
Distr of Security Door & Window Hardware
S.I.C.: 3429
N.A.I.C.S.: 332510

Albany Door Systems, Inc. (2)
975 A Old Norcross Rd
Lawrenceville, GA 30045
Tel.: (770) 338-5000
Fax: (770) 338-5024
Toll Free: (800) 252-2691
E-Mail: sales@albanydoors.com
Web Site: www.albanydoors.com
Emp.: 80
Mfr of Fast-Acting Roll Up Doors
S.I.C.: 3442
N.A.I.C.S.: 332321
Craig Jones *(Gen Mgr)*

Besam Entrance Solutions Inc (2)
92 N Main St Bldg 19 Unit A
Windsor, NJ 08561
Tel.: (609) 443-5800
Fax: (609) 448-9584
E-Mail: mktg@besam.com
Web Site: www.besam.com
Emp.: 150
Mfr. of Door Automation Systems
S.I.C.: 3699
N.A.I.C.S.: 335999
Karen Maslow *(Mgr-Mktg)*

Besam US Inc. (2)
1900 Airport Rd
Monroe, NC 28110
Tel.: (704) 290-5520
Fax: (704) 290-5555
E-Mail: marketing@besam-usa.com
Web Site: www.besam-usa.com
Emp.: 1,300
Automatic Door Mfr
S.I.C.: 3442
N.A.I.C.S.: 332321
Juan Vargues *(Pres & CEO)*

Non-U.S. Subsidiaries:

Besam A/S (2)
Marielundvej 20
2730 Herlev, Denmark (100%)
Tel.: (45) 44537080
Fax: (45) 44532022
E-Mail: besam@besam.dk
Web Site: www.besam.dk
Sales Range: $1-9.9 Million
Emp.: 30
Mfr. of Door Automation Systems
S.I.C.: 3442
N.A.I.C.S.: 332321
Anders Carlson *(Gen Mgr)*

Besam Automatic Door Systems Trading Co. Ltd. (2)
Suite 1903 Modern Comm Commercial Tower 218 Hengfeng Road
Shanghai, 200070, China (100%)
Tel.: (86) 21 5128 8909
Fax: (86) 21 5128 8919
E-Mail: info@besam.com.cn
Web Site: www.besam.com
Mfr. of Door Automation Systems
S.I.C.: 3699
N.A.I.C.S.: 335999

Besam Belgie N.V. (2)
Centrum Zuid 3042
Houthalen, Limburg, 3530, Belgium (100%)
Tel.: (32) 11609500
Fax: (32) 11604680
E-Mail: info@besam.be
Web Site: www.besam.be
Sales Range: $75-99.9 Million
Emp.: 80
Mfr. of Door Automation Systems
S.I.C.: 3442
N.A.I.C.S.: 332321
Koan Monsieurs *(Dir-Fin)*

Besam Canada Inc. (2)
4020 B Sladeview Crescent
Mississauga, ON, L5L 6B1, Canada
Tel.: (905) 608-9242
Fax: (905) 608-1151
E-Mail: general@besam.ca
Web Site: www.besam.us/en/besam/us/About-us/Contact-Us---Map/?countryid=206797
Door Mfr
S.I.C.: 3429
N.A.I.C.S.: 332510

Besam GmbH (2)
Lagerstrasse 45
Dieburg, 64807, Germany (100%)
Tel.: (49) 60712080
Fax: (49) 6071208111
E-Mail: info@besam.de
Web Site: www.besam.de
Emp.: 50
Mfr. of Door Automation Systems
S.I.C.: 3442
N.A.I.C.S.: 332321
Peter M. Fprick *(Gen Mgr)*

Besam Iberica SA (2)
Sepulveda 7A
28108 Madrid, Spain (100%)
Tel.: (34) 916574860
Fax: (34) 916614380
E-Mail: informacion@besam.es.com
Web Site: www.besam.es
Sls.: $17,124,230
Emp.: 100
Mfr. of Door Automation Systems
S.I.C.: 3442
N.A.I.C.S.: 332321
Gonzalo F. Valladares *(Mng Dir)*

Besam Kft (2)
Nagytetenyi ut 112
1222 Budapest, Hungary (100%)
Tel.: (36) 14247274
Fax: (36) 12261949
E-Mail: besam@besam.hu
Web Site: www.besam.hu
Emp.: 7
Mfr. of Door Automation Systems
S.I.C.: 3442
N.A.I.C.S.: 332321
Csba Banko *(Mng Dir)*

Besam Limited (2)
Unit 39 Navan Enterprice Centre Trim Road
Navan, Meath, Ireland
Tel.: (353) 4690 76747
Fax: (353) 4690 76745
Door Mfr
S.I.C.: 3429
N.A.I.C.S.: 332510

Besam Limited (2)
Washington House Brooklands Close
Sunbury-on-Thames, Middlesex, TW16 7EQ, United Kingdom (100%)
Tel.: (44) 1932765888
Fax: (44) 1932765864
E-Mail: info@besam.co.uk
Web Site: www.besam.com
Emp.: 155
Mfr. of Door Automation Systems
S.I.C.: 3442
N.A.I.C.S.: 332321

Besam (Manufacturing) Pte. Ltd. (2)
33 Ubi Ave 3 No 03-52 Vertex
Singapore, 408868, Singapore (100%)
Tel.: (65) 67456228
Fax: (65) 67457322
E-Mail: info.sg.besam@assaabloy.com
Web Site: www.besam.com
Emp.: 26
Mfr. of Door Automation Systems
S.I.C.: 3442
N.A.I.C.S.: 332321
Kenneth Ng *(Gen Mgr)*

Besam Maschinenhandels GmbH (2)
Hutteldorferstrasse 216 C
1140 Vienna, Austria (100%)
Tel.: (43) 019145537
Fax: (43) 4319149298
E-Mail: general@besam.at
Web Site: www.besam.at
Emp.: 100
Mfr. of Door Automation Systems
S.I.C.: 3442
N.A.I.C.S.: 332321

Besam Nederland BV (2)
Postbus 8155
NL-6710 Ede, Netherlands
Tel.: (31) 318698969
Fax: (31) 318638346
E-Mail: info@besam.nl
Web Site: www.besam.com
Emp.: 200
Door Mfr
S.I.C.: 3442
N.A.I.C.S.: 332321

Besam Oy (2)
Agrnonitti 2
00790 Helsinki, Finland (100%)
Tel.: (358) 972885400
E-Mail: besam@besam.fi
Web Site: www.besam.fi
Rev.: $1,509,712
Emp.: 5
Mfr. of Door Automation Systems
S.I.C.: 3442
N.A.I.C.S.: 332321
Anders Carlson *(Mng Dir)*

Besam Polska Sp. z.o.o. (2)
ul J Olbrachta 94
Warsaw, 01 102, Poland (100%)
Tel.: (48) 223318680
Fax: (48) 223318681
E-Mail: biuro@besam.com.pl
Web Site: www.besam.pl
Sales Range: $1-9.9 Million
Emp.: 26
Mfr of Door Automation Systems
S.I.C.: 3442
N.A.I.C.S.: 332321

Besam SA (2)
10 Rond Pt Du General De Gaulle
94864 Bonneuil, France (100%)
Tel.: (33) 143775566
Fax: (33) 143395600
E-Mail: fxpinglin@besam.fr
Web Site: www.besam.fr
Emp.: 70
Mfr. of Door Automation Systems
S.I.C.: 3442
N.A.I.C.S.: 332321
Juan Vargues *(Pres & CEO)*

Besam S.p.A. (2)
Via Monzoro 142
IT 20010 Milan, Italy (100%)
Tel.: (39) 293611311
Fax: (39) 29362116
Web Site: www.besam.com
Sales Range: $1-9.9 Million
Emp.: 24
Mfr. of Door Automation Systems
S.I.C.: 3442
N.A.I.C.S.: 332321

Besam Spol.s.r.o. (2)
U Blazenky 2155/18
197 00 Prague, Czech Republic (100%)
Tel.: (420) 286001560
Fax: (420) 4286001570
E-Mail: besam@besam.cz
Web Site: www.besam.cz
Emp.: 16
Mfr. of Door Automation Systems
S.I.C.: 3442
N.A.I.C.S.: 332321

Subsidiaries:

AB FAS Lasfabrik (1)
Hejargatan 20
63102 Eskilstuna, Sweden (100%)
Tel.: (46) 16170233
Fax: (46) 16170217
E-Mail: infofas@aasa.se
Web Site: www.assa.se
Emp.: 50
S.I.C.: 3429
N.A.I.C.S.: 332510

Assa AB (1)
Kungsgatan 71
PO Box 371
S 631 05 Eskilstuna, Sweden (100%)
Tel.: (46) 16177000
Fax: (46) 16177005
E-Mail: info@assa.se
Web Site: www.assa.se
Emp.: 600
S.I.C.: 3429
N.A.I.C.S.: 332510
Johan Molin *(Pres & CEO)*

ASSA ABLOY Asia Holding AB (1)
Klarabergsviadukten 90
PO Box 70340
111 64 Stockholm, Sweden
Tel.: (46) 8 5064 8500
Fax: (46) 50648585
E-Mail: info@assaabloy.com
Investment Management Services
S.I.C.: 6282
N.A.I.C.S.: 523920
Johan Molin *(Pres & CEO)*

ASSA ABLOY Forsakrings AB (1)
Klarabergsviadukten 90
111 64 Stockholm, Sweden
Tel.: (46) 8 506 485 00
Fax: (46) 8 506 485 85
Safety Equipment Mfr
S.I.C.: 3429
N.A.I.C.S.: 332510

ASSA ABLOY Hospitality AB (1)
Bruksgatan 17
41451 Gothenburg, Sweden SE
Tel.: (46) 317044095 (100%)
Fax: (46) 317044091
E-Mail: info@vingcard.com
Web Site: www.vingcard.com
Rev.: $1,082,184
Emp.: 2
Hotel Room Locking Systems & In-Room Safe Mfr
S.I.C.: 3429
N.A.I.C.S.: 332510

U.S. Subsidiary:

ASSA ABLOY Hospitality Inc. (2)
631 International Pkwy Ste 100
Richardson, TX 75081 TX
Tel.: (972) 907-2273
Fax: (214) 292-7381
Web Site: www.aah.usa.com
Emp.: 100
Hotel Security Services
S.I.C.: 3429
N.A.I.C.S.: 332510
William J. Oliver *(Pres-North America)*

ASSA ABLOY Identification Technology Group AB (1)
PO Box 70340
10723 Stockholm, Sweden
Tel.: (46) 850648500
Fax: (46) 850648585
Emp.: 70
Safety Equipment Mfr
S.I.C.: 3429
N.A.I.C.S.: 332510
Johan Molin *(Pres & CEO)*

ASSA ABLOY IP AB (1)
Klaradergsviadukten 90
PO Box 70340
107 23 Stockholm, Sweden
Tel.: (46) 8 50648500
Fax: (46) 8 50648585
E-Mail: info@assaabloy.com
Emp.: 70
Security System Services
S.I.C.: 7382
N.A.I.C.S.: 561621
Per Jonas Axel Gardmark *(Corp Treas)*

ASSA ABLOY Kredit AB (1)
Klarabergsviadukten 90
PO Box 7034
107 23 Stockholm, Sweden
Tel.: (46) 850 64 8500
Fax: (46) 850 64 8585
E-Mail: info@assaabloy.com
Emp.: 70
Safety Equipment Mfr
S.I.C.: 3429
N.A.I.C.S.: 332510
Per Jonas Axel Gardmark *(CEO)*

ASSA ABLOY Svensk Fastighets AB (1)
PO Box 70340
107 23 Stockholm, Sweden
Tel.: (46) 8 506 485 00
Door Lock Mfr
S.I.C.: 3429
N.A.I.C.S.: 332510

Assa Industrie AB (1)
Kungsgatan 71
PO Box 371
S 63221 Eskilstuna, Sweden (100%)
Tel.: (46) 16177000
Fax: (46) 16177018
Web Site: www.assa.se
Emp.: 300
S.I.C.: 3429
N.A.I.C.S.: 332510
Joannes Lend *(Mng Dir)*

Fix AB (1)
Bruksgatan 17
Gothenburg, 41451, Sweden (100%)
Tel.: (46) 317044000
Fax: (46) 31142355
E-Mail: info@assaoem.se
Web Site: www.assaoem.se
Emp.: 200
S.I.C.: 3429
N.A.I.C.S.: 332510
Jerry Pull *(Mng Dir)*
Anders Emochssonan *(CFO)*

Solid AB (1)
Sguviksyrahen 24
SE 117 43 Stockholm, Sweden (100%)
Tel.: (46) 86851000
Fax: (46) 86851020
E-Mail: info@solid.se
Web Site: www.solid.se
Emp.: 25
S.I.C.: 3429
N.A.I.C.S.: 332510

Swesafe AB (1)
Kopparbergsvagen 45
PO Box 503
722 09 Vasteras, Vaestmanland, Sweden
Tel.: (46) 21 109630
Web Site: www.swesafe.se
Security Equipment Supplier
S.I.C.: 5072
N.A.I.C.S.: 423710

Timelox AB (1)
Lodjursgatan 2
SE 261 44 Landskrona, Sweden (100%)
Tel.: (46) 41851300
Fax: (46) 41828696
E-Mail: info@timelox.com
Web Site: www.timelox.com
Rev.: $1,846,600
Emp.: 40
Mfr. of Electronic Locking Systems
S.I.C.: 7382
N.A.I.C.S.: 561621
Henrich Mella *(CEO)*

U.S. Division:

ASSA ABLOY, Inc. (1)
110 Sargent Dr
New Haven, CT 06511 OR
Tel.: (203) 624-5225
Fax: (203) 785-8108
Web Site: www.assaabloy.com
Emp.: 7,000
Holding Company; Regional Managing Office
S.I.C.: 6719
N.A.I.C.S.: 551112
Thanasis Molokotos *(Pres)*

Groups:

ASSA ABLOY Door Group, LLC (2)
1502 12th St NW
Mason City, IA 50401 DE
Tel.: (641) 423-1334
Fax: (641) 424-8305
Web Site: www.assaabloydoorgroup.com
Sales Range: $75-99.9 Million
Emp.: 1,200
Holding Company; Metal Door & Window Frame Mfr
S.I.C.: 6719
N.A.I.C.S.: 551112
Thanasis Molokotos *(Pres)*

Subsidiary:

AADG, Inc. (3)
1502 12th St NW
Mason City, IA 50401-5809 DE
Mailing Address: (100%)
PO Box 1648
Mason City, IA 50402-1648
Tel.: (641) 423-1334
Fax: (641) 423-9104
E-Mail: curries@curries.com
Web Site: www.curries.com
Emp.: 700
Mfr. of Steel Doors & Frames
Export
S.I.C.: 3442
N.A.I.C.S.: 332321
Jerry N. Currie *(Pres & CEO)*
Sean Brant *(CFO)*

Units:

Ceco Door Products (4)
9159 Telecom Dr
Milan, TN 38358
Tel.: (731) 686-8345
Fax: (731) 686-4211
Toll Free: (800) 232-6834
E-Mail: cecomarketing@cecodoor.com
Web Site: www.cecodoor.com
Emp.: 500
Side-Hinged Door Systems Mfr
Export
S.I.C.: 3442
N.A.I.C.S.: 332321
Chris Holloway *(VP)*

Graham Wood Doors (4)
525 9th St SE
Mason City, IA 50401
Tel.: (641) 423-2444
Fax: (800) 672-8110
E-Mail: graham@grahamdoors.com
Web Site: www.grahamdoors.com
Wood Doors Mfr
Export
S.I.C.: 2431
N.A.I.C.S.: 321911

ASSA ABLOY Door Security Solutions (2)
110 Sargent Dr
New Haven, CT 06511
Tel.: (203) 624-5225
Fax: (203) 777-9042
Toll Free: (800) 377-3948
E-Mail: info@assaabloydss.com
Web Site: www.assaabloydss.com
Emp.: 600
Holding Company; Door Lock & Other Security Hardware Mfr
S.I.C.: 6719
N.A.I.C.S.: 551112
Thanasis Molokotos *(Pres)*

Subsidiaries:

Abloy Security Inc. (3)
6005 Commerce Dr Ste 330
Irving, TX 75063-2664
Tel.: (972) 753-1127
Fax: (972) 753-0792
E-Mail: info@abloyusa.com
Web Site: www.abloyusa.com
Sales Range: $1-9.9 Million
Emp.: 17
Assembling of Locks
S.I.C.: 5099
N.A.I.C.S.: 423990
Steve Landert *(Pres)*

Arrow Lock Co. Inc (3)
3625 Allegheny Dr
Salem, VA 24153
Tel.: (540) 380-5000
Fax: (800) 421-6615
Toll Free: (800) 839-0915
E-Mail: info@arrowlock.com
Web Site: www.arrowlock.com
Emp.: 56
S.I.C.: 3429
N.A.I.C.S.: 332510
Tom Harris *(Gen Mgr)*

Corbin Russwin, Inc. (3)
225 Episcopal Rd
Berlin, CT 06037-1524
Tel.: (860) 225-7411
Telex: 160917
Fax: (860) 828-7266
E-Mail: contact@corbin-russwin.com
Web Site: www.corbin-russwin.com
Emp.: 400
Mfr. of Residential Commercial & Industrial Locksets & Builders Hardware
S.I.C.: 3429
N.A.I.C.S.: 332510

McKinney Products Company (3)
225 Episcopal Rd # 1
Berlin, CT 06037-1524
Tel.: (570) 346-7551
Fax: (570) 342-4845
Toll Free: (800) 346-7707
Web Site: www.mckinneyhinge.com
Emp.: 14
Mfr. of Door Hinges
S.I.C.: 3429
N.A.I.C.S.: 332510
Thanasis Molokato *(Pres)*

Medeco High Security Locks, Inc. (3)
3625 Alleghany Dr
Salem, VA 24153 VA
Mailing Address: (100%)
PO Box 3075
Salem, VA 24153-0330
Tel.: (540) 380-5000
Fax: (800) 421-6615
Toll Free: (800) 839-3157
E-Mail: comments@medeco.com
Web Site: www.medeco.com
Emp.: 250
High Security Mechanical & Electronic Locks Mfr
Export
S.I.C.: 3429
N.A.I.C.S.: 332510
Tom Kaika *(Pres)*

Sargent Manufacturing Company (3)
100 Sargent Dr
New Haven, CT 06511-5918
Mailing Address:
PO Box 9725
New Haven, CT 06536-0915
Tel.: (203) 562-2151
Fax: (203) 776-5992
E-Mail: webmaster@sargentlock.com
Web Site: www.sargentlock.com
Emp.: 900
Mfr of High Quality Architectural Hardware, Locks, Door Closers & Exit Devices
Import Export
S.I.C.: 3429
N.A.I.C.S.: 332510
David Menn *(VP)*

Security Metal Products Corp (3)
5700 Hannum Ave Ste 250
Culver City, CA 90230
Tel.: (310) 641-6690
Fax: (310) 641-6601
E-Mail: sales@secmet.com
Web Site: www.secmet.com
Emp.: 14
Metal Doors, Sash, & Trim Mfr
S.I.C.: 3442
N.A.I.C.S.: 332321
Jim Hirsch *(Pres)*

ASSA ABLOY Sales & Marketing Group, Inc. (2)
110 Sargent Dr
New Haven, CT 06511-5918 DE
Tel.: (203) 624-5225 (100%)
Fax: (203) 777-9042
Web Site: www.assaabloyiss.com
Sls.: $450,000,000
Emp.: 3,400
Locking Systems, Industrial & Technical Products Distr
Import Export
S.I.C.: 5099
N.A.I.C.S.: 423990
Thanasis Molokotos *(Pres)*
David M. Ambrosini *(CFO)*

Subsidiaries:

Dominion Building Products (2)
6949 Fairbanks N Houston Rd
Houston, TX 77040
Tel.: (713) 466-6790
Fax: (713) 466-8177
E-Mail: info@dominionproducts.com
Web Site: www.dominionproducts.com
Emp.: 50
Mfr. of Steel Doors, Frames & Aluminum Windows
S.I.C.: 3499
N.A.I.C.S.: 332999
Geoff Bennett *(Pres)*

HID Global Corporation (2)
15370 Barranca Pkwy
Irvine, CA 92618-1905 CA
Tel.: (949) 732-2000
Fax: (949) 732-2120
Toll Free: (800) 237-7769
E-Mail: info@hidcorp.com
Web Site: www.hidcorp.com
Emp.: 100
Access Control Cards & Readers Mfr
Import Export
S.I.C.: 3825
N.A.I.C.S.: 334515
Denis Hebert *(Pres & CEO)*
Bridget Burke *(CIO & VP)*
Selva Selvaratnam *(CTO & Sr VP)*
Tam Hulusi *(Sr VP-Strategic Innovation & Intellectual Property)*
Mark Scaparro *(Exec VP-Sls & Mktg)*
Anthony Ball *(Sr VP-Identity & Access Mgmt (IAM))*
Jason Bohrer *(Sr VP-Global Ops)*
Rodney Glass *(Sr VP-Global Quality Ops)*

Subsidiaries:

ActivIdentity Corporation (3)
6623 Dumbarton Cir
Fremont, CA 94555 DE

ASSA ABLOY AB—(Continued)

Tel.: (510) 574-0100
Fax: (510) 574-0101
Toll Free: (800) 529-9499
E-Mail: info@actividentity.com
Web Site: www.actividentity.com
Sales Range: $50-74.9 Million
Emp.: 218
Corporate Security Services
S.I.C.: 7372
N.A.I.C.S.: 511210
Edward J. Treska *(Sr VP & Gen Counsel)*

Non-U.S. Subsidiaries:

ActivIdentity Australia Pty. Ltd. (4)
Unit 3 6 Kennedy Street
Kingston, ACT, 2604, Australia
Tel.: (61) 262084888
Fax: (61) 262817460
E-Mail: info@actividentity.com
Web Site: www.actividentity.com
Sales Range: $100-124.9 Million
Digital Identity Assurance Services
S.I.C.: 7372
N.A.I.C.S.: 511210

ActivIdentity Europe S.A. (4)
24-28 avenue du General de Gaulle
92156 Suresnes, France
Tel.: (33) 142048400
Fax: (33) 142048484
E-Mail: info@actividentity.com
Sales Range: $10-24.9 Million
Emp.: 50
Digital Identity Assurance Services
S.I.C.: 7372
N.A.I.C.S.: 511210
Sandrine Paulin *(Mgr-Logistics)*

ActivIdentity GmbH (4)
Fuerstenrieder Strasse 279a
81377 Munich, Germany
Tel.: (49) 8974120230
Fax: (49) 8974120238
E-Mail: info@actividentity.com
Web Site: www.actividentity.com
Sales Range: $100-124.9 Million
Digital Identity Assurance Services
S.I.C.: 7372
N.A.I.C.S.: 511210

ActivIdentity Japan K.K. (4)
Marunouchi Trust Tower Main Bldg 20th Fl
1 8 3 Marunouchi
Chiyoda-ku, Tokyo, 100-0005, Japan
Tel.: (81) 352885222
Fax: (81) 352885111
Sales Range: $100-124.9 Million
Digital Identity Assurance Services
S.I.C.: 7372
N.A.I.C.S.: 511210

ActivIdentity UK Ltd. (4)
Waterloo Business Centre
117 Waterloo Rd, London, SE1 8UL, United Kingdom
Tel.: (44) 2079600220
Fax: (44) 2079021985
E-Mail: info@actividentity.com
Web Site: www.actividentity.com
Sales Range: $100-124.9 Million
Digital Identity Assurance Services
S.I.C.: 7372
N.A.I.C.S.: 511210

Fargo Electronics Inc. (3)
6533 Flying Cloud Dr
Eden Prairie, MN 55344 DE
Tel.: (952) 941-9470
Fax: (952) 941-7836
Toll Free: (800) 459-5636
Web Site: www.fargo.com
Sales Range: $75-99.9 Million
Emp.: 168
Mfr. Developer & Supplier of Printing Systems & Consumable Supplies
S.I.C.: 3571
N.A.I.C.S.: 334111

LaserCard Corporation (3)
1875 N Shoreline Blvd
Mountain View, CA 94043 DE
Tel.: (650) 969-4428
Fax: (650) 969-3140
E-Mail: investors@lasercard.com
Web Site: www.lasercard.com
Sales Range: $50-74.9 Million
Emp.: 203
Holding Company; Optical Memory Cards & Drives Mfr
Import Export
S.I.C.: 6719
N.A.I.C.S.: 551112

Non-U.S. Subsidiary:

Challenge Card Design Plastikkarten GmbH (4)
Klein Feldhus 23
D 26180 Rastede, Germany
Tel.: (49) 440291190
Fax: (49) 4402911977
E-Mail: ccd@challengecard.de
Web Site: www.challengecard.de
Sales Range: $25-49.9 Million
Emp.: 60
Mfr of Smart Cards
S.I.C.: 3089
N.A.I.C.S.: 326199
Rainer Rettet *(Mng Dir)*

Non-U.S. Subsidiaries:

HID Asia Pacific Ltd. (3)
19 F 625 Kings Rd Island E
North Point, China (Hong Kong) (100%)
Tel.: (852) 31609800
Fax: (852) 31604809
Web Site: www.hidgroval.com
Emp.: 30
Access Control Products Mfr
S.I.C.: 3625
N.A.I.C.S.: 335314
Craig Sandness *(Mng Dir)*

HID China Ltd. (3)
Unit 1503 Chuangxin Science & Technology Plaza Phase Two
Futian Disctrict, Shenzhen, 518040, China
Tel.: (86) 755 8835 3190
Fax: (86) 755 8835 3185
Emp.: 10
Electronic Safety Equipment Mfr
S.I.C.: 3679
N.A.I.C.S.: 334419
Eric Chiu *(Dir-Sls)*

HID Corporation Ltd. (3)
Phoenix Rd
Haverhill, Suffolk, CB9 7AE, United Kingdom
Tel.: (44) 1440714850
Fax: (44) 1440714840
E-Mail: hvhreception@hidglobal.com
Web Site: www.hidglobal.com
Emp.: 60
Mfr. of Access Control Products
S.I.C.: 3625
N.A.I.C.S.: 335314
Harm Radstaak *(Mng Dir)*

HID Corporation Ltd. (3)
35 Boulevard de la Victoire
67000 Strasbourg, France
Tel.: (33) 3 90 22 10 66
Fax: (33) 3 88 36 64 45
Safety Equipment Mfr
S.I.C.: 3429
N.A.I.C.S.: 332510

HID Global GmbH (3)
Ferihumerstrasse 13
4040 Linz, Austria
Tel.: (43) 732 602220
Fax: (43) 732 602220 15
E-Mail: info@hidglobal.com
Emp.: 20
Identification Component Mfr
S.I.C.: 3089
N.A.I.C.S.: 326199

HID Global GmbH (3)
Am Klingenweg 6a
65396 Walluf, Germany
Tel.: (49) 6123 791 0
Fax: (49) 6123 791 199
E-Mail: info-emea@hidglobal.com
Web Site: www.hidglobal.com
Electronic Device Mfr
S.I.C.: 3679
N.A.I.C.S.: 334419
Gerd Hacker *(Dir-HR)*

HID Global Ireland Teoranta Ltd. (3)
Pairc Tionscail Na Tulaigh
Baile na hAbhann, Galway, Ireland
Tel.: (353) 9 150 6900
Fax: (353) 9 150 6901
Emp.: 150
Radio Frequency Identity Card Mfr
S.I.C.: 3089
N.A.I.C.S.: 326199
Rory Noone *(Head-Ops)*

HID Global Sdn. Bhd. (3)
Kawansan Perindustrian Tampoi No 5 Jalan Dewani 1/1
81100 Johor Bahru, Malaysia
Tel.: (60) 7 3342008
Fax: (60) 7 3342003
Electronic Equipment Mfr
S.I.C.: 3679
N.A.I.C.S.: 334419

HID Global Switzerland S.A. (3)
Route de Pra-Charbon 27 Zone Industrielle
1614 Granges-Paccot, Veveyse, Switzerland
Tel.: (41) 21 908 01 00
Fax: (41) 21 908 01 01
E-Mail: info@hidglobal.com
Emp.: 30
Electronic Component Mfr
S.I.C.: 3679
N.A.I.C.S.: 334419
Marc Bielmann *(Gen Mgr)*

HID India Private Ltd (3)
No 1 2 Murphy Road Tower D Annexe
Millenia Towers
Ulsoor, Bengaluru, 560 008, India
Tel.: (91) 80 255 435 66
Fax: (91) 80 255 435 67
Emp.: 25
Electronic Component Mfr
S.I.C.: 3679
N.A.I.C.S.: 334419
Ranjith Nambiar *(Dir-Sls)*

Unit:

YSG Door Security Consultants (2)
1902 Airport Rd
Monroe, NC 28110-7396 (100%)
Tel.: (704) 283-2101
Fax: (800) 338-0965
Web Site: www.ysgsecurity.com
Emp.: 100
Door Hardware Mfr
S.I.C.: 3429
N.A.I.C.S.: 332510
John Davenport *(VP-Fin)*

Non-U.S. Subsidiaries:

Fleming Door Products Ltd (2)
101 Ashbridge Circle
Woodridge, ON, L4L 3R5, Canada (100%)
Tel.: (416) 749-2111
Fax: (905) 851-8346
E-Mail: quotes@flemingbaron.com
Web Site: www.flemingdoor.com
Emp.: 200
Mfr. of Commercial Side-Hinged Steel Doors & Frames
S.I.C.: 3442
N.A.I.C.S.: 332321
Steve Everitt *(Dir-Ops)*

Yale-Corbin Canada Limited (2)
160 4th Valley Drive
Vaughan, ON, L4K 4T9, Canada (100%)
Tel.: (905) 564-5854
Fax: (905) 738-2478
Web Site: www.yalecorbin.ca
Emp.: 50
Distribution of Hardware
S.I.C.: 5072
N.A.I.C.S.: 423710
Carrie Scott *(CFO)*

U.S. Subsidiaries:

ASSA, INC (1)
110 Sargent Dr
New Haven, CT 06511
Tel.: (203) 603-5959
Fax: (800) 892-3256
Toll Free: (800) 235-7482
Lock Mfr
S.I.C.: 3429
N.A.I.C.S.: 332510

Ditec Entrematic US Inc (1)
240 Vista Park Dr
Pittsburgh, PA 15205
Tel.: (412) 200-5750
Fax: (412) 200-5751
Toll Free: (866) 901-4284
E-Mail: info@hunterautomatics.ca
Web Site: www.hunterautomatics.ca
Emp.: 4
Metal Door Mfr
S.I.C.: 3442
N.A.I.C.S.: 332321
Mary Schlegel *(Office Mgr & Mgr-Sls)*

Electronic Security Devices, Inc. (1)
10027 S 51st St Ste 102
Phoenix, AZ 85044
Tel.: (623) 582-4626
Fax: (623) 582-4641
E-Mail: esd@securitypower.com
Web Site: www.securitypower.com
Emp.: 300
Electronic Security Device Mfr
S.I.C.: 3679
N.A.I.C.S.: 334419
Lloyd Lederer *(Pres)*

EMTEK Products, Inc. (1)
15250 E Stafford St
City of Industry, CA 91744
Tel.: (626) 961-0413
Fax: (626) 336-2812
Toll Free: (800) 356-2741
E-Mail: orders@emtek.com
Web Site: www.emtek.com
Emp.: 50
Door Lock Mfr
S.I.C.: 3429
N.A.I.C.S.: 332510
Thomas Miller *(Pres)*

Frameworks Manufacturing Inc. (1)
3801 Yale St
Houston, TX 77018-6565
Tel.: (713) 692-5222
Fax: (713) 692-1391
Toll Free: (877) 278-5222
E-Mail: info@frameworks.com
Web Site: www.frameworks.com
Emp.: 50
Interior Aluminum Door Mfr & Distr
S.I.C.: 3442
N.A.I.C.S.: 332321
Dale Waite *(Pres)*

Hanchett Entry Systems Inc. (1)
10027 S 51st St Ste 102
Phoenix, AZ 85044
Tel.: (623) 582-4626
Fax: (623) 582-4641
E-Mail: sales@hesinnovations.com
Web Site: www.hesinnovations.com
Emp.: 300
Electrical Safety Equipment Mfr
S.I.C.: 3699
N.A.I.C.S.: 335999
Laurie Springer *(Dir-HR)*

IdenTrust, Inc. (1)
55 Hawthorne St Ste 400
San Francisco, CA 94105
Tel.: (415) 486-2900
Fax: (415) 486-2901
Toll Free: (866) 433-6878
E-Mail: helpdesk@identrust.com
Web Site: www.identrust.com
Sales Range: $10-24.9 Million
Emp.: 63
Software Publishers
S.I.C.: 7372
N.A.I.C.S.: 511210
Karen J. Wendel *(CEO)*

Medeco Security Locks Inc (1)
3625 Alleghany Dr
Salem, VA 24153
Tel.: (540) 380-5000
Fax: (540) 380-5010
Security Lock Mfr
S.I.C.: 7699
N.A.I.C.S.: 561622

Securitron Magnalock Corporation (1)
10027 S 51st St Ste 102
Phoenix, AZ 85044
Tel.: (623) 582-4626
Fax: (623) 582-4551
Toll Free: (800) 624-5625
E-Mail: customercare@securitron.com
Web Site: www.securitron.com
Electric Locking System Mfr
S.I.C.: 3699
N.A.I.C.S.: 335999
Don Keith *(Gen Mgr)*

VingCard Elsafe Pacific Corporation (1)
816 N Marine Corps Dr EVA II Bldg Ste 118
Tumon, GU 96921-4493
Tel.: (671) 649-0163
Fax: (671) 646-1770
Web Site: www.vcepacific.com
Electronic Door Lock Sales & Installation Services
S.I.C.: 5065
N.A.I.C.S.: 423690
Yoshimi Tsutaki *(Pres)*

Yale Residential Security Products, Inc. (1)
100 Yale Ave
Lenoir City, TN 37771
Tel.: (678) 728-7400
Fax: (770) 448-1102
Toll Free: (800) 438-1951
E-Mail: sales@yalelock.com
Web Site: www.yalelock.com
Door Locks Mfr
S.I.C.: 3429
N.A.I.C.S.: 332510

Non-U.S. Subsidiaries:

A/S Ruko (1)
Marielundvej 20
PO Box 505
DK-2730 Herlev, Denmark
Tel.: (45) 44544454
Fax: (45) 44544444
E-Mail: ruko@ruko.dk
Web Site: www.ruko.dk
Emp.: 250
Locks & Security Products & Services
S.I.C.: 3429
N.A.I.C.S.: 332510
Tommy Hjulmann *(Dir-Sls)*

Abloy Canada Inc. (1)
9630 Trans Canada
Montreal, QC, H4S 1V9, Canada
Tel.: (514) 335-9500
Fax: (514) 335-0430
E-Mail: info@abloy.ca
Web Site: www.abloy.ca
Emp.: 14
Door Automation Software Development Services
S.I.C.: 7371
N.A.I.C.S.: 541511
Karen Hazlett *(Mgr-Customer Svc)*

Abloy High Security Locks Private Ltd (1)
New 43 Old 20 K B Dasan Road
Teynampet, 600 018 Chennai, India
Tel.: (91) 44 43907100
Fax: (91) 44 43907101
Web Site: www.abloy.in/en/abloy/abloy-in/About-Abloy-High-Security-Locks-Pvt-Ltd/
Emp.: 6
Lock Mfr
S.I.C.: 3429
N.A.I.C.S.: 332510
Ranjana Ravishankar *(Head-Corp Sls)*

Abloy Mul-T-Lock Mexico S.A. de C.V. (1)
Av De los Arcos 36-H Industrial Naucalpan 2 Seccion
53370 Mexico, Mexico
Tel.: (52) 55 5312 2220
Fax: (52) 55 5312 3140
E-Mail: ventas@mul-t-lock.mx
Web Site: www.mul-t-lock.mx
Door Lock Mfr
S.I.C.: 3452
N.A.I.C.S.: 332722
Enrique Margolin *(Pres)*

Abloy Oy (1)
P.O.B. 108
80101 Joensuu, Finland
Tel.: (358) 20 599 2501
Fax: (358) 20 599 2209
E-Mail: export.sales@abloy.com
Web Site: www.abloy.com
Mfr of Architectural Hardware, Locks, Door Closers & Door Automatics
S.I.C.: 3429
N.A.I.C.S.: 332510

AdvanIDe PTE. LTD. (1)
3 Lim Teck Kim Road 11-02 Singapore Technologies Building
88934 Singapore, Singapore
Tel.: (65) 6305 7680
Fax: (65) 6738 0090
E-Mail: info@advanide.com
Web Site: www.advanide.com
Emp.: 15
Silicon Distr
S.I.C.: 5065
N.A.I.C.S.: 423690
Holger Roessner *(Mng Dir)*
Joseph Lian *(Member-Mgmt Bd)*

U.S. Subsidiary:

AdvanIDe Inc. (2)
19 Sylvester Rd
Natick, MA 01760
Tel.: (617) 459-3013
Fax: (866) 870-0802
E-Mail: info@advanide.com
Semiconductor Distr
S.I.C.: 5065
N.A.I.C.S.: 423690

Non-U.S. Subsidiary:

AdvanIDe GmbH (2)
Am Klingenweg 6a
Walluf, Germany
Tel.: (49) 6123 791 30
Fax: (49) 6123 791 328
E-Mail: info@advanide.com
Semiconductor Device Distr
S.I.C.: 5065
N.A.I.C.S.: 423690

Angel Metal Co., Ltd. (1)
908-1 Weolam-dong Dalseo-gu
Daegu, 704-833, Korea (South)
Tel.: (82) 5 3581 0049
Fax: (82) 5 3582 7803
Web Site: www.angellock.co.kr
Lock Mfr
S.I.C.: 3429
N.A.I.C.S.: 332510

ASSA ABLOY Asia Pacific Ltd (1)
35/F Laws Commercial Plaza 788 Cheung Sha Wan Road
Kowloon, China (Hong Kong)
Tel.: (852) 2260 7234
Fax: (852) 2785 1565
E-Mail: info.au@assaabloy.com
Web Site: www.assaabloyasiapacific.com
Electro Mechanical Product Mfr
S.I.C.: 3679
N.A.I.C.S.: 334419

ASSA ABLOY Australia Pacific Pty Ltd (1)
235 Huntingdale Rd
Oakleigh, VIC, 3166, Australia
Tel.: (61) 3 8574 3888
Fax: (61) 1 800 647 673
Emp.: 300
Hardware Mfr
S.I.C.: 3429
N.A.I.C.S.: 332510
Tom Devine *(Gen Mgr)*

ASSA ABLOY Australia Pty Ltd (1)
235 Huntingdale Road
Oakleigh, VIC, 3166, Australia
Tel.: (61) 3 8574 3888
Fax: (61) 3 8574 3400
Web Site: www.assaabloy.com.au
Electronic Safety System Mfr
S.I.C.: 3669
N.A.I.C.S.: 334290

ASSA ABLOY Austria GmbH (1)
Ischlerbahnstrasse 15 Taborstrasse 64
5020 Salzburg, Austria
Tel.: (43) 662 454363
Fax: (43) 662 454363 19
E-Mail: info@assaabloy.at
Web Site: www.assaabloy.at
Emp.: 25
Door Lock Mfr
S.I.C.: 3429
N.A.I.C.S.: 332510
Heinz Schwab *(Dir-Sls-Export)*

ASSA ABLOY Baltic AS (1)
Valdeku 132
EE-11216 Tallinn, Estonia
Tel.: (372) 6 559 101
Fax: (372) 6 559 100
E-Mail: info@assaabloy.ee
Web Site: www.assaabloy.ee/en/local/assaabloyee/About-ASSA-ABLOY/ASSA-ABLOY-Baltic-AS/
Emp.: 15
Safety Equipment Mfr
S.I.C.: 3429
N.A.I.C.S.: 332510
Igor Loos *(Product Mgr)*

ASSA ABLOY Chile Ltda (1)
Jose Joaquin Prieto 395 Buin
Santiago, Chile
Tel.: (56) 2 560 9200
Fax: (56) 2 560 9239
E-Mail: assaabloy@assaabloy.cl
Web Site: www.assaabloy.cl
Door Handle & Lock Mfr
S.I.C.: 3429
N.A.I.C.S.: 332510

ASSA ABLOY Danmark A/S (1)
Marielundvej 20
2730 Herlev, Denmark
Tel.: (45) 44 53 70 80
Fax: (45) 44 53 20 22
Web Site: www.assaabloy.dk
Hardware Mfr
S.I.C.: 3429
N.A.I.C.S.: 332510

ASSA ABLOY Deutschland GmbH (1)
Goerzallee 299
14167 Berlin, Germany
Tel.: (49) 30 8106 2648
Fax: (49) 30 8106 2650
E-Mail: berlin@assaabloy.de
Web Site: www.assaabloy.com
Lock Mfr
S.I.C.: 3429
N.A.I.C.S.: 332510

Assa Abloy Entrance Systems Australia Pty Ltd (1)
Unit 4 18-22 Winterton Road
Clayton, VIC, Australia 3168
Tel.: (61) 1300 13 13 10
Fax: (61) 3 8574 3865
E-Mail: admin@besamaustralia.com
Automatic Door Mfr
S.I.C.: 3442
N.A.I.C.S.: 332321

ASSA ABLOY Entrance Systems Co., Ltd (1)
Suite 1903 Modern Communication Commercial Tower
No 218 Hengfeng Road, Shanghai, 200070, China
Tel.: (86) 21 5218 8909
Fax: (86) 21 5218 8919
E-Mail: info@besam.com.cn
Door Locks Mfr
S.I.C.: 3429
N.A.I.C.S.: 332510

ASSA ABLOY Entrance Systems Denmark A/S (1)
Lupinvej 12
DK-9500 Hobro, Denmark (100%)
Tel.: (45) 7012 7011
Fax: (45) 9852 2055
E-Mail: info.dk.crawford@assaabloy.com
Web Site: www.crawfordsolutions.dk
Emp.: 30
Garage Doors, Wall Systems, Dock Loading Systems, Storage Cabinets & Lockers Mfr & Whlsr
S.I.C.: 2431
N.A.I.C.S.: 321911
Per Henriksson *(Dir-Admin)*

Assa Abloy Entrance Systems Finland Oy (1)
Nimismiehenpelto 6
02770 Espoo, Finland
Tel.: (358) 10 386 9000
Fax: (358) 9 803 7393
E-Mail: asiakaspalvelu.fi@assaabloy.com
Web Site: www.crawfordsolutions.fi
Lock Mfr
S.I.C.: 3429
N.A.I.C.S.: 332510

ASSA ABLOY Entrance Systems GmbH (1)
Hutteldorferstrasse 216 c
1140 Vienna, Austria
Tel.: (43) 1 914 55 37 0
Fax: (43) 1 914 92 98
E-Mail: general@besam.at
Web Site: www.besam.at
Emp.: 50
Security Lock Mfr
S.I.C.: 3452
N.A.I.C.S.: 332722
Sprick Jens Peter *(Mgr)*

ASSA ABLOY Entrance Systems Italy S.p.A. (1)
Via Monzoro 142
20010 Milan, Italy
Tel.: (39) 02 936 11 311
Fax: (39) 02 936 21 16
E-Mail: besamitalia@besam.it
Door Locks Mfr
S.I.C.: 3429
N.A.I.C.S.: 332510

ASSA ABLOY Entrance Systems Norway AS (1)
(Formerly Crawford Door A/S)
Stromsveien 179
Postboks 96
Alnabru, NO 0614 Oslo, Norway
Tel.: (47) 22655450
Telex: 19154 crano
Fax: (47) 22648775
E-Mail: Post.no.aaes@assaabloy.com
Web Site: www.crawfordsolutions.no
Marketing & Sales of Industrial & Garage Doors
S.I.C.: 5211
N.A.I.C.S.: 444190

ASSA ABLOY Entrance Systems, spol. s r.o. (1)
U Blazenky 2155/18
150 00 Prague, Czech Republic
Tel.: (420) 286 001 560
Fax: (420) 286 001 570
E-Mail: besam@besam.cz
Web Site: www.besam.cz
Door Locks Mfr
S.I.C.: 3429
N.A.I.C.S.: 332510

ASSA ABLOY Entrance Systems (Suzhou) Co., Ltd. (1)
Unit 23 Suchun Industrial Sq No 428 Xinglong Street
Suzhou, Jiangsu, 215126, China
Tel.: (86) 512 8818 0100
Fax: (86) 512 8818 0200
E-Mail: info@besam.cn
Web Site: www.assaabloy.com
Emp.: 80
Door Mfr
S.I.C.: 3429
N.A.I.C.S.: 332510

ASSA ABLOY ES Production s.r.o (1)
D5 Logistics Park
349 01 Ostrov u Stribra, Czech Republic
Tel.: (420) 374 634 111
Fax: (420) 371 120 642
Web Site: www.assaabloy.com
Emp.: 150
Hardware Mfr
S.I.C.: 3429
N.A.I.C.S.: 332510

ASSA ABLOY Gecis Sistemleri A.S. (1)
Aydinli Mah Boya Vernik Organize Sanayi Bolgesi 1 No lu Cadde No 17
Tuzla, 34959 Istanbul, Turkey
Tel.: (90) 2165931280
Fax: (90) 2165931284
E-Mail: info@assaabloy.com
Security System Services
S.I.C.: 7382
N.A.I.C.S.: 561621
Kerem Altinoz *(Gen Mgr)*

ASSA ABLOY Holding Italia S.p.A. (1)
Via Modena 68
40017 San Giovanni in Persiceto, Bologna, Italy
Tel.: (39) 05 16 81 24 11
Fax: (39) 05 18 21 89 8
Investment Management Services
S.I.C.: 6211
N.A.I.C.S.: 523999

ASSA ABLOY Holdings (SA) Ltd (1)
176 Progress Rd Technikon
1725 Roodepoort, Gauteng, South Africa
Tel.: (27) 11 761 5000

ASSA ABLOY AB—(Continued)

Fax: (27) 11 766 3573
Emp.: 400
Investment Management Services
S.I.C.: 6282
N.A.I.C.S.: 523920
Thomas Gumede *(Mgr-Fin)*

ASSA ABLOY Hong Kong Limited (1)
Suite 1901 19/F Tower 3
Hong Kong, China (Hong Kong)
Tel.: (852) 22607288
Fax: (852) 26868682
E-Mail: sales@assaabloy.com.hk
Web Site: www.assaabloy.com.hk
Lock Mfr
S.I.C.: 3452
N.A.I.C.S.: 332722

ASSA ABLOY Hospitality (Canada) Ltd. (1)
160 Four Valley Drive
Vaughan, ON, L4K 4T9, Canada
Tel.: (800) 898-2857
Fax: (450) 682-0060
E-Mail: noram@vcegroup.com
Door Locks Mfr
S.I.C.: 3429
N.A.I.C.S.: 332510

ASSA ABLOY Hospitality GmbH (1)
Ostring 13
Nordenstadt, 65205 Wiesbaden, Germany
Tel.: (49) 6122 7033 0
Fax: (49) 6122 7033 29
E-Mail: info.de@assaabloyhospitality.com
Web Site: www.assaabloy.com
Hardware Mfr
S.I.C.: 3429
N.A.I.C.S.: 332510
Marcus Nettelbeck *(Mng Dir)*

ASSA ABLOY Hospitality Iberica, S.L. (1)
Rua Duarte Leite N 43 Palhais
Charneca da Caparica, Almada, Portugal
Tel.: (351) 212 978 790
Fax: (351) 212 978 791
E-Mail: info_es@vcegroup.com
Web Site: www.vingcardelsafe.com
Safety Equipment Mfr
S.I.C.: 3429
N.A.I.C.S.: 332510

ASSA ABLOY Hospitality Ltd (1)
1035/22 Soi KhunVijit Klongton Nua
10110 Bangkok, Thailand
Tel.: (66) 2381 5621 7
Fax: (66) 2381 5628
E-Mail: thailand@vcegroup.com
Web Site: www.assaabloy.com
Hardware Mfr
S.I.C.: 3429
N.A.I.C.S.: 332510

ASSA ABLOY Hospitality Ltd (1)
3/F Culturecom Centre 47 Hung To Road
Kwun Tong, Kowloon, China (Hong Kong)
Tel.: (852) 2316 2200
Fax: (852) 2368 6113
E-Mail: hongkong@vingcard.com
Web Site: www.assaabloy.com
Hardware Mfr
S.I.C.: 3429
N.A.I.C.S.: 332510

ASSA ABLOY Hospitality Ltd (1)
21 Stadium Way Portman Road
Reading, Berkshire, RG30 6BX, United Kingdom
Tel.: (44) 118 945 2200
Fax: (44) 118 945 1375
E-Mail: uksales@vcegroup.com
Emp.: 40
Hardware Mfr
S.I.C.: 3429
N.A.I.C.S.: 332510
Dan Cooper *(Area Mgr-Sls)*

ASSA ABLOY Hospitality Pte Ltd (1)
3 Lim Teck Kim Road 11-02 Genting Centre
Singapore, 088934, Singapore
Tel.: (65) 6305 7670
Fax: (65) 6223 6353
E-Mail: singapore@vcegroup.com
Web Site: www.vingcardelsafe.com
Emp.: 15
Lock Mfr
S.I.C.: 3429
N.A.I.C.S.: 332510

ASSA ABLOY Hospitality sas (1)
37 rue Adam Ledoux
92404 Courbevoie, France
Tel.: (33) 1 41 88 03 03
Fax: (33) 1 41 88 02 88
E-Mail: france@assaabloyhospitality.com
Web Site: www.vingcardelsafe.com
Emp.: 30
Safety Equipment Mfr
S.I.C.: 3429
N.A.I.C.S.: 332510
Christian Henon *(Gen Mgr)*

ASSA ABLOY Hospitality Shanghai Ltd (1)
Building 19-20 No 99 Huajia Road
Songjiang Industrial Zone
Songjiang District, Shanghai, 201613, China
Tel.: (86) 21 37746161
Fax: (86) 21 37746166
Web Site: www.assaabloy.com
Emp.: 200
Electronic Safety System Mfr
S.I.C.: 3669
N.A.I.C.S.: 334290
Dai Grace *(Dir-Fin)*

ASSA ABLOY Hungary Kereskedelmi Kft. (1)
Zahony u 7 Graphisoft park C epulet
Budapest, Hungary
Tel.: (36) 1 226 1616
Fax: (36) 1 226 1303
E-Mail: info@assaabloy.hu
Web Site: www.assaabloy.hu
Door Lock Mfr
S.I.C.: 3429
N.A.I.C.S.: 332510

ASSA ABLOY India Private Ltd. (1)
19th Floor Tower A Building No 5 DLF Cyber Terraces
DLF Cyber City DLF Phase III, Gurgaon, Haryana, 122 002, India
Tel.: (91) 124 4407060
Fax: (91) 124 4407070
E-Mail: info@assaabloy.co.in
Web Site: www.assaabloy.com
Emp.: 40
Hardware Mfr
S.I.C.: 3429
N.A.I.C.S.: 332510
Vikas Gandhi *(Gen Mgr)*

ASSA ABLOY Italia S.p.A. (1)
Via Bovaresa 13
40017 San Giovanni in Persiceto, Bologna, Italy
Tel.: (39) 051 6812411
Fax: (39) 051 827486
E-Mail: info@assaabloy.it
Web Site: www.assaabloy.it
Hardware Mfr
S.I.C.: 3429
N.A.I.C.S.: 332510

ASSA ABLOY Japan Co Ltd (1)
6F IS Alps Bldg 1-16 Kanda Sudacho
Chiyoda-ku, Tokyo, 101-0041, Japan
Tel.: (81) 3 5577 5590
Web Site: www.assaabloy.com
Hardware Mfr
S.I.C.: 3429
N.A.I.C.S.: 332510

ASSA ABLOY Korea Co., Ltd. (1)
iRevo B/D 459-7 Kasan-dong
Geumcheon-gu, Seoul, Korea (South) 153-803
Tel.: (82) 2 2104 6730
Fax: (82) 2 839 2297
Web Site: www.assaabloy.kr
Emp.: 150
Door Lock Mfr
S.I.C.: 3452
N.A.I.C.S.: 332722

ASSA ABLOY Limited (1)
School Street
Willenhall, W Midlands, WV13 3PW, United Kingdom UK
Tel.: (44) 1902 366 911
Fax: (44) 1902 364 666
Web Site: www.assaabloy.co.uk
Holding Company; Locks & Other Door Products Mfr
S.I.C.: 6719
N.A.I.C.S.: 551112
Tzachi Wiesenfeld *(CEO-EMEA)*

Subsidiaries:

Abloy Security Ltd. (2)
2 3 Hatters Lane Croxley Business Pk
Watford, Herts, WD18 8QY, United Kingdom (100%)
Tel.: (44) 1923255066
Fax: (44) 1923230281
Web Site: www.abloy.uk
Sales Range: $10-24.9 Million
Emp.: 50
S.I.C.: 3429
N.A.I.C.S.: 332510

Abloy UK Ltd (2)
Portobello Works School Street
Willenhall, West Midlands, WV13 3PW, United Kingdom
Tel.: (44) 1902 364500
Fax: (44) 1902 364501
E-Mail: marketing@abloy.co.uk
Web Site: www.abloy.co.uk
Door Locks Mfr
S.I.C.: 3429
N.A.I.C.S.: 332510
Roz Graham *(Acct Mgr)*

Assa Ltd. (2)
75 Sumner Rd
Croydon, Surrey, CRO 3LN, United Kingdom (100%)
Tel.: (44) 2086885191
Fax: (44) 2086880285
Web Site: www.assa.co.uk
Emp.: 53
S.I.C.: 3429
N.A.I.C.S.: 332510

Yale UK Ltd. (2)
School St
Willenhall, W Midlands, WV13 3PW, United Kingdom UK
Tel.: (44) 1902366911 (100%)
Telex: 338251
Fax: (44) 08450727211
E-Mail: info@assaabloy.co.uk
Web Site: www.yale.co.uk
Emp.: 500
Locks & Security Products Mfr
S.I.C.: 3429
N.A.I.C.S.: 332510
John Middleton *(Mng Dir)*

Non-U.S. Subsidiaries:

Yale Security Products (Hong Kong) Limited (3)
788 Cheung Sha Wan Road Laichiko
0000 Hong Kong, China (Hong Kong) (100%)
Tel.: (852) 22600888
Fax: (852) 26868682
E-Mail: hongkong@assaabloy.com.hk
Web Site: www.assaabloy.com.hk
Emp.: 50
Holding Company
S.I.C.: 6719
N.A.I.C.S.: 551112
Irene Yip *(Mng Dir)*

Yale Security Products S.p.A. (Italy) (3)
Via Ardeatina 2491 - Km 22,500
40 Santa Palomba, RM, Italy (100%)
Tel.: (39) 0692894250
Telex: 620021
Fax: (39) 0692894580
Web Site: www.yalelock.com
Emp.: 200
Mfr. of Locksets & Padlocks
S.I.C.: 3429
N.A.I.C.S.: 332510
Maurizio Grettierola *(Mng Dir)*

ASSA ABLOY Malaysia Sdn Bhd (1)
No 14 Jalan Wan Kadir 1 Tmn Tun Dr Ismail
Kuala Lumpur, Malaysia 60000
Tel.: (60) 3 7725 3888
Fax: (60) 3 7725 8333
E-Mail: info.au@assaabloy.com
Web Site: www.assaabloy.com
Emp.: 15
Door Lock Mfr
S.I.C.: 3429
N.A.I.C.S.: 332510
Alan Wai Chung San *(Mgr-Fin)*

ASSA ABLOY Nederland B.V. (1)
Meerval 3-5
4941 SK Raamsdonksveer, Netherlands
Tel.: (31) 88 639 46 00
Fax: (31) 88 639 46 75
E-Mail: info@assaabloy.nl
Web Site: www.assaabloy.nl
Hardware Mfr
S.I.C.: 3429
N.A.I.C.S.: 332510

ASSA ABLOY New Zealand Limited (1)
6 Armstrong Road Albany
Auckland, New Zealand 0632
Tel.: (64) 9 415 7111
Fax: (64) 9 415 7222
E-Mail: info.nz@assabloy.com
Web Site: www.assaabloy.co.nz
Door & Window Mfr
S.I.C.: 3429
N.A.I.C.S.: 332510

ASSA ABLOY NV (1)
Canadalaan 73
8620 Nieuwpoort, Belgium
Tel.: (32) 58 234 101
Fax: (32) 58 238 964
E-Mail: info@assaabloy.be
Web Site: www.assaabloy.be
Hardware Mfr
S.I.C.: 3429
N.A.I.C.S.: 332510

ASSA ABLOY Occidente, SA de CV (1)
Av Periferico Sur No 7980 Edif 2B Col
Santa Maria Tequepexpan
Tlaquepaqu, Jalisco, 45601, Mexico
Tel.: (52) 33 3540 5400
Fax: (52) 33 3540 5417
Web Site: www.tesa.com.mx
Emp.: 50
Lock Mfr
S.I.C.: 3429
N.A.I.C.S.: 332510
Juan Pedro Ashida *(CEO)*

ASSA ABLOY Poland Sp. z o.o. (1)
Jana Olbrachta 94
01-102 Warsaw, Poland
Tel.: (48) 22 751 53 54
Fax: (48) 22 751 53 56
E-Mail: biuro@assaabloy.com.pl
Web Site: www.assaabloy.com.pl
Emp.: 35
Door Lock Mfr
S.I.C.: 3452
N.A.I.C.S.: 332722
Rafal Dorywalski *(Mng Dir)*

ASSA ABLOY Portugal, Lda. (1)
Praceta do Comercio 13 B
Alfragide, 2610-042 Amadora, Portugal
Tel.: (351) 21 471 96 23
Fax: (351) 21 471 96 25
E-Mail: geral@assaabloy.pt
Web Site: www.assaport.com
Safety Equipment Mfr
S.I.C.: 3429
N.A.I.C.S.: 332510

ASSA ABLOY Portugal, Unipessoal, Lda (1)
Praceta Do Comercio 13b
Alfragide, 2610-042 Amadora, Portugal
Tel.: (351) 214719623
Fax: (351) 214719625
E-Mail: assa@assaport.com
Web Site: www.assaport.com
Safety Equipment Mfr
S.I.C.: 3429
N.A.I.C.S.: 332510

ASSA ABLOY (SA) (Pty) Ltd (1)
176 Progress Road Technikon
Roodepoort, 1725 Johannesburg, South Africa
Tel.: (27) 11 76 15 000
Fax: (27) 11 76 63 573
E-Mail: info@assaabloy.com
Web Site: www.assaabloy.com
Emp.: 300
Electronic Door Lock Mfr
S.I.C.: 3679
N.A.I.C.S.: 334419
Gerrit Viviers *(Dir-Production)*

ASSA ABLOY Sicherheitstechnik GmbH - IKON (1)
Goerzallee 299
D 14167 Berlin, Germany (100%)

Tel.: (49) 3081060
Fax: (49) 3081062600
E-Mail: berlin@assaabloy.de
Web Site: www.ikon.de
Emp.: 540
Hardware Mfr
S.I.C.: 3429
N.A.I.C.S.: 332510
Stefan Beer *(Mng Dir)*

ASSA ABLOY Sicherheitstechnik GmbH (1)
Bildstockstrasse 20
Albstadt, Germany
Tel.: (49) 7431 123 0
Fax: (49) 7431 123 240
E-Mail: info@assaabloy.de
Web Site: www.assaabloy.de
Electromechanical Lock Mfr
S.I.C.: 3824
N.A.I.C.S.: 334514
Stefan Fischbach *(Chm & Mng Dir)*

Plant:

ASSA ABLOY Sicherheitstechnik GmbH - Berlin plant (2)
Goerzallee 299
14167 Berlin, Germany
Tel.: (49) 30 8106 0
Fax: (49) 30 8106 26 00
E-Mail: berlin@assaabloy.de
Door Lock Mfr
S.I.C.: 3429
N.A.I.C.S.: 332510

ASSA ABLOY Singapore Pte Ltd (1)
10 Arumugam Road 06-00 Lion Building A
Singapore, 409957, Singapore
Tel.: (65) 6880 0000
Fax: (65) 6880 0500
E-Mail: info.au@assaabloy.com
Web Site: www.assaabloy.com.sg
Door Lock Mfr
S.I.C.: 3452
N.A.I.C.S.: 332722

ASSA ABLOY South Asia Pte Ltd (1)
Armorcoat Technologies Building 152 Ubi Avenue 4 03-02
Singapore, Singapore
Tel.: (65) 68800000
Web Site: www.assaabloysouthasia.com
Door Lock Mfr
S.I.C.: 3429
N.A.I.C.S.: 332510

ASSA ABLOY (Switzerland) Ltd. (1)
Untere Schwandenstrasse 22
8805 Richterswil, Switzerland
Tel.: (41) 44 787 3434
Fax: (41) 44 787 3535
E-Mail: info@assaabloy.ch
Web Site: www.assaabloy.ch
Hardware Mfr
S.I.C.: 3429
N.A.I.C.S.: 332510
Rene Walpen *(Chm-Exec Bd & CEO)*
Christian Kaelin *(CFO & Dir-HR & IT)*
Didier Grichting *(COO)*

ASSA ABLOY Thailand Ltd (1)
1919 Preecha Group Building 5th Floor Pattanakarn Rd
Suanluang, 10250 Bangkok, Thailand
Tel.: (66) 2 722 7371
Fax: (66) 2 722 7375
E-Mail: sales@assaabloy.co.th
Web Site: www.assaabloy.co.th
Door Lock Mfr
S.I.C.: 3452
N.A.I.C.S.: 332722

ASSA ABLOY (Zhongshan) Security Technology Company Limited (1)
33-35 Chrysanthemum Road East Xiaolan
Zhongshan, Guangdong, 528415, China
Tel.: (86) 760 2210 2326
Fax: (86) 760 2210 0316
Web Site: www.assaabloy.com
Electrical Equipment Mfr
S.I.C.: 3699
N.A.I.C.S.: 335999

AZBE B.ZUBIA S.A. (1)
C/Basebe 3
20550 Aretxabaleta, Spain
Tel.: (34) 943 71 29 29
Fax: (34) 943 79 86 43
E-Mail: azbe@azbe.com
Web Site: www.azbe.com
Emp.: 6
Security Lock Mfr
S.I.C.: 3452
N.A.I.C.S.: 332722
Agustin Laskurain *(Gen Mgr)*

BAB IKON GmbH Schliesstechnik (1)
Bahlerstrasse 29
Postfach 60 04 19
14469 Potsdam, Germany
Tel.: (49) 33128880
Fax: (49) 3312888140
Web Site: www.babikon.com
Emp.: 100
S.I.C.: 3429
N.A.I.C.S.: 332510

Baodean Security Products Co. Ltd (1)
273 Wenchang Road West
Taizhou, Zhejiang, 318058, China
Tel.: (86) 576 82881688
Fax: (86) 576 82883868
Web Site: www.baodean.com
Sls.: $79,195,000
Emp.: 2,300
Door Lock Mfr & Distr
S.I.C.: 3429
N.A.I.C.S.: 332510

Baron Metal Industries Inc. (1)
101 Ashbridge Circle
Woodbridge, ON, L4L 3R5, Canada
Tel.: (416) 749-2111
Fax: (905) 851-8346
Web Site: www.baronmetal.com
Emp.: 200
Steel Metal Door Mfr & Distr
S.I.C.: 3442
N.A.I.C.S.: 332321
Peter Lawson *(Gen Mgr)*

B.C Lasepartner A/S (1)
Ostbirkvej 7 Seden
5240 Odense, Denmark
Tel.: (45) 66108219
Fax: (45) 66108213
Web Site: www.assaabloy.com
Hardware Mfr
S.I.C.: 3429
N.A.I.C.S.: 332510

CERRADURAS DE COLOMBIA - CERRACOL S.A.S. (1)
Calle 12 No 32 - 39
Bogota, Colombia
Tel.: (57) 1 5962000
Fax: (57) 1 2019912
Web Site: www.cerracol.com
Lock Mfr
S.I.C.: 3429
N.A.I.C.S.: 332510

Cheil Industry Co. Ltd (1)
301-1201 Bucheon Techno Park 365 Samjung-Dong
Ohjung-Gu, 421-741 Bucheon, Korea (South)
Tel.: (82) 32 720 6000
Fax: (82) 32 329 5400
Web Site: www.cheilauto.com
Door Locks Mfr
S.I.C.: 3429
N.A.I.C.S.: 332510
Kui Hwan Lee *(CEO)*

Chubb Union Zimbabwe (Pvt) Ltd (1)
4 Conald Road
Graniteside, Harare, Zimbabwe
Tel.: (263) 4 759 196
Fax: (263) 4 759 194
Hardware Mfr
S.I.C.: 3429
N.A.I.C.S.: 332510

City Lasepartner A/S (1)
Kirkevaenget 7
2500 Valby, Denmark
Tel.: (45) 33 12 12 12
Web Site: www.assaabloy.com
Hardware Mfr
S.I.C.: 3429
N.A.I.C.S.: 332510

Ditec S.p.A. (1)
Via V Pisani 20
20124 Milan, Italy
Tel.: (39) 02 96 39 11
Fax: (39) 02 96 50 314
E-Mail: ditec@ditecva.com
Web Site: www.ditec.it
Sales Range: $100-124.9 Million
Emp.: 550
Automatic Door Distr
S.I.C.: 5031
N.A.I.C.S.: 423310

Subsidiaries:

Ditec D.D. Lazio S.r.l. (2)
Via Casilina 1746/R
00133 Rome, Italy
Tel.: (39) 0620744853
Door Locks Mfr
S.I.C.: 3429
N.A.I.C.S.: 332510

Ditec D.D. Lombardia S.r.l. (2)
Via Piersanti Mattarella 10
20093 Cologno Monzese, Italy
Tel.: (39) 02 27321141
Fax: (39) 02 27307237
Web Site: www.assaabloy.com
Hardware Mfr
S.I.C.: 3429
N.A.I.C.S.: 332510

Non-U.S. Subsidiaries:

DITEC Entrematic Canada Inc. (2)
221A Racco Parkway
Vaughan, ON, L4J 8X9, Canada
Tel.: (416) 674-8880
Fax: (416) 674-8882
Toll Free: (877) 348-6837
E-Mail: info@hunterautomatics.ca
Web Site: www.hunterautomatics.ca
Emp.: 34
Automatic Swinging Door Mfr
S.I.C.: 3699
N.A.I.C.S.: 335999
Frank Cocuzolli *(Gen Mgr)*

DITEC ESPANA S.L.U. (2)
Pol Ind Valldegata Calle Draper 14
08350 Barcelona, Spain
Tel.: (34) 93 795 83 99
Fax: (34) 93 795 90 26
Hardware Mfr
S.I.C.: 3429
N.A.I.C.S.: 332510

Ditec Swiss S.A. (2)
via Passeggiata 24
6828 Balerna, Switzerland
Tel.: (41) 848558855
Fax: (41) 916466127
E-Mail: info@ditecswiss.ch
Web Site: www.ditec.it/en/ditec-worldwide
Door Mfr
S.I.C.: 2431
N.A.I.C.S.: 321911

Ditec Tur GmbH (2)
Erich-Ollenhauer-Str 29
61440 Oberursel, Germany
Tel.: (49) 9321 2307 0
Web Site: www.assaabloy.com
Door Mfr
S.I.C.: 3429
N.A.I.C.S.: 332510

DYNACO Europe NV (1)
Waverstraat 21
9310 Moorsel, Belgium
Tel.: (32) 53 72 98 98
Fax: (32) 53 72 98 50
E-Mail: info@dynaco.eu
Web Site: www.dynacodoor.com
Industrial Door Mfr
S.I.C.: 3442
N.A.I.C.S.: 332321
Olivier Coune *(Mng Dir)*

effeff France S.A.S. (1)
16 Rue de l Industrie
67172 Brumath, France
Tel.: (33) 3 88 59 31 59
Fax: (33) 3 88 59 31 60
E-Mail: info@effeff-France.fr
Web Site: www.effeff-france.fr
Safety Equipment Mfr
S.I.C.: 3429
N.A.I.C.S.: 332510

Flexi Force B.V. (1)
Hanzeweg 19
3771 NG Barneveld, Netherlands
Tel.: (31) 342 427777
Fax: (31) 342 414679
E-Mail: info@flexiforce.nl
Web Site: www.flexiforce.com
Emp.: 100
Hardware Mfr
S.I.C.: 3429
N.A.I.C.S.: 332510
Hans Lubbers *(Mng Dir)*

Non-U.S. Subsidiaries:

Flexi Force Iberica, S.L. (2)
Apartado Correos 403 Ctra Nacional 332 Km 211
46780 Valencia, Spain
Tel.: (34) 96 285 82 50
Fax: (34) 96 285 82 51
Web Site: www.flexiforce.com
Hardware Mfr
S.I.C.: 3429
N.A.I.C.S.: 332510
Julian Lopez Montano *(Mng Dir)*

Flexi Force Italia S.r.l. (2)
Via dei Tigli CNM
25020 Alfianello, Italy
Tel.: (39) 0309936510
Fax: (39) 0309936954
E-Mail: info@flexiforce.it
Web Site: www.flexiforce.com
Emp.: 6
Hardware Mfr
S.I.C.: 3429
N.A.I.C.S.: 332510
Julio Gonzalez Boyle *(Mng Dir)*

Flexi Force Poland Sp. Z.o.o. (2)
Sikorskiego 3
95-015 Glowno, Poland
Tel.: (48) 42 650 04 91
Fax: (48) 42 650 05 20
Web Site: www.flexiforce.com
Hardware Mfr
S.I.C.: 3429
N.A.I.C.S.: 332510
Jan Moszczynski *(Mng Dir)*

FlexiForce Hungary Kft. (2)
Kulso-Hadhazi u 18
Hajduboszormeny, Hungary
Tel.: (36) 52561260
Fax: (36) 52561262
E-Mail: info@flexiforce.hu
Web Site: www.flexiforce.com
Hardware Mfr
S.I.C.: 3429
N.A.I.C.S.: 332510
Imre Olah *(Mng Dir)*

Helton Industries Ltd. (1)
30840 Peardonville Rd
Abbotsford, BC, Canada
Tel.: (604) 854-3660
Fax: (604) 854-3576
Toll Free: (877) 300-7412
E-Mail: info@heltonindustries.com
Web Site: www.heltonindustries.com
Sales Range: $10-24.9 Million
Emp.: 180
Commercial Hardware Mfr
S.I.C.: 3429
N.A.I.C.S.: 332510
Henry Neels *(Co-Founder)*
Gerhard Rauch *(Co-Founder)*

Henderson Nederlands BV (1)
Rootven 24
5531 MB Bladel, Netherlands
Tel.: (31) 497 33 20 20
Fax: (31) 497 33 20 29
E-Mail: sales@henderson.nl
Web Site: www.henderson.nl
Emp.: 7
Door Mfr & Distr
S.I.C.: 3429
N.A.I.C.S.: 332510
A. C. Harpers *(Mng Dir)*

IDD Parts B.V. (1)
Marchandweg 23
3771 ML Barneveld, Netherlands
Tel.: (31) 342 490990
Fax: (31) 342 422280
E-Mail: info@iddparts.nl
Web Site: www.iddparts.nl
Door Lock Mfr
S.I.C.: 3429
N.A.I.C.S.: 332510

ASSA ABLOY AB—(Continued)

JPM S.A. (1)
40 route de Paris Avermes
03021 Moulins, France
Tel.: (33) 4 70 48 40 00
Fax: (33) 4 70 48 40 96
Lock Mfr
S.I.C.: 3429
N.A.I.C.S.: 332510

KESO GmbH (1)
Maurerstrasse 6
21244 Buchholz, Germany
Tel.: (49) 4181 924 0
Fax: (49) 4181 924 100
E-Mail: info@keso.de
Web Site: www.keso.de
Door Lock Mfr
S.I.C.: 3452
N.A.I.C.S.: 332722

Lasepartner A/S (1)
Vesterlundvej 20
2730 Herlev, Denmark
Tel.: (45) 70112211
Fax: (45) 36455858
E-Mail: info@laasepartner.dk
Web Site: www.laasepartner.dk
Emp.: 50
Door Lock Mfr
S.I.C.: 3452
N.A.I.C.S.: 332722
Torben Yde Jensen *(CEO)*

Lasgruppen A.S. (1)
454 Brakeroya
N 3002 Drammen, Norway (100%)
Tel.: (47) 32809800
Fax: (47) 32809850
E-Mail: post@lasgruppen.no
Web Site: www.lasgruppen.no
Emp.: 150
S.I.C.: 3429
N.A.I.C.S.: 332510
Bente Hafredal *(Mgr-Fin)*

Motivation (Traffic Control) Ltd (1)
Unit 5 Horton Court Hortonwood 50
Telford, Shropshire, TF1 7XZ, United Kingdom
Tel.: (44) 1952 670390
Fax: (44) 1952 670379
E-Mail: info@motivation-tc.co.uk
Web Site: www.motivation-tc.co.uk
Emp.: 5
Security Barrier System Mfr
S.I.C.: 3429
N.A.I.C.S.: 332510

Mul-T-Lock Ltd. (1)
PO Box 637
Yavne, 81104, Israel (100%)
Tel.: (972) 89424600
Fax: (972) 89424609
E-Mail: enquiries@mul-t-lock.com
Web Site: www.mul-t-lock.com
Emp.: 350
Develops, Manufactures, Markets & Installs High Security Cylinders & Locks
S.I.C.: 7382
N.A.I.C.S.: 561621
Tzachi Wisenfeld *(Chm)*
Alon Lumbroso *(Pres)*

Subsidiaries:

Alba Locking Products, Ltd (2)
Izhak Ben-Tzvi 42 St Ramat-Elyahou Industrial Area
POB 4594
75633 Rishon le Zion, Israel
Tel.: (972) 3 9615955
Fax: (972) 3 9612889
E-Mail: sales@alba.co.il
Web Site: www.alba.co.il
Emp.: 40
Hardware Mfr & Distr
S.I.C.: 3429
N.A.I.C.S.: 332510
Lior Perets *(Mgr-Sls)*

Mul-T-Lock Machinery Ltd. (2)
Mul-T-Lock Park
81104 Yavne, Israel
Tel.: (972) 8 942 4660
Fax: (972) 8 942 4669
Web Site: www.mul-t-lock.com
Cutting Tool Mfr & Distr
S.I.C.: 3545
N.A.I.C.S.: 333515

U.S. Subsidiaries:

Mul-T-Lock Machinery Ltd. (2)
300 1 State Route 17 S Ste 7
Lodi, NJ 07644-3821
Tel.: (973) 778-3220
Fax: (973) 778-4007
Toll Free: (800) 562-3511
E-Mail: info@mul-t-lockusa.com
Web Site: www.mul-t-loztusa.com
Emp.: 18
Mfr. of Lock Industry Specialized Machines
S.I.C.: 3429
N.A.I.C.S.: 332510
Sherry Butts *(Customer Svc)*

Mul-T-Lock USA, Inc. (2)
100 Commerce Way Ste 2
Hackensack, NJ 07601
Tel.: (973) 778-3222
Fax: (973) 778-4007
Toll Free: (800) 685-8562
E-Mail: info@mul-t-lockusa.com
Web Site: www.mul-t-lockusa.com
Door Lock & Master Key Mfr
S.I.C.: 3429
N.A.I.C.S.: 332510
Micha Kimchi *(Pres)*

Non-U.S. Subsidiaries:

Mul-T-Lock Czech, s.r.o. (2)
Dolnomecholupska 1418/12
102 00 Prague, Czech Republic
Tel.: (420) 226 806 260
Fax: (420) 26 806 202
E-Mail: info@multlock.cz
Web Site: www.multlock.cz
Emp.: 15
Lock Mfr
S.I.C.: 3429
N.A.I.C.S.: 332510
Vratislav Hanzlik *(Pres)*

Mul-T-Lock Technologies Italy SRL (2)
Strada Del Mescolin 62
31016 Cordignano, Treviso, Italy
Tel.: (39) 0438 912275
Fax: (39) 0438 912255
E-Mail: info@mul-t-lock.it
Web Site: www.mul-t-lock.it
Emp.: 20
Hardware Mfr
S.I.C.: 3429
N.A.I.C.S.: 332510
Bruno Azzalini *(Gen Mgr)*

Nemef B.V. (1)
Papegaaiweg 35
7345 DK Apeldoorn, Wenum-Wiesel, Netherlands NL
Tel.: (31) 553128400
Fax: (31) 553122087
E-Mail: info@nemef.nl
Web Site: www.nemef.nl
Emp.: 130
Marketing of Industrial Products
S.I.C.: 5113
N.A.I.C.S.: 424130
Robert Gos *(Mng Dir)*

Normstahl GmbH (1)
Drautendorf 58
4174 Niederwaldkirchen, Austria
Tel.: (43) 72 31 31 28 0
Fax: (43) 72 31 31 23
E-Mail: office@normstahl.at
Web Site: www.normstahl.at
Safety Equipment Distr
S.I.C.: 5087
N.A.I.C.S.: 423850

P C Henderson (Ireland) Limited (1)
Westlink Industrial Estate Kylemore Road
Dublin, Ireland
Tel.: (353) 1 643 6816
Fax: (353) 1 626 0455
E-Mail: sales@pchenderson.ie
Web Site: www.pchenderson.com
Emp.: 6
Sliding Gear System Mfr
S.I.C.: 3429
N.A.I.C.S.: 332510
Duncan Moncrieff *(Mng Dir)*

Pan Pan DOOR Co LTD (1)
Shuiyuan Town
Yingkou, Liaoning, China 115116
Tel.: (86) 417 5179389
Metal Door Mfr
S.I.C.: 3442
N.A.I.C.S.: 332321
Ken Li *(Gen Mgr)*

PORTAFEU SAS (1)
24 Rue des Hautes-Rives
BP 8206
Romilly-sur-Andelle, 27108 Val-de-Reuil, France
Tel.: (33) 2 32 68 37 37
Fax: (33) 2 32 49 47 44
Web Site: www.portafeu.fr
Door Mfr
S.I.C.: 3429
N.A.I.C.S.: 332510

Productos Metalicos de Seguridad, S.A. de C.V. (1)
Pelicano 242 Del Gustavo A Madero
07460 Mexico, Mexico
Tel.: (52) 55 51 18 06 00
Fax: (52) 55 51 18 06 38
Metal Door Mfr
S.I.C.: 3442
N.A.I.C.S.: 332321

Pyropanel Developments Pty Ltd (1)
Unit 1 97 Lewis Rd
Wantirna South, Wantirna, VIC, 3152, Australia
Tel.: (61) 3 9837 8500
Fax: (61) 3 9837 8550
E-Mail: sales@pyropanel.com.au
Web Site: www.pyropanel.com.au
Emp.: 10
Fire Protection Door Mfr
S.I.C.: 3442
N.A.I.C.S.: 332321
Nikitas Smirnios *(Mgr-Bus Dev)*

Ruko A/S (1)
Marielundvej 20
2730 Herlev, Denmark
Tel.: (45) 44 54 44 54
Fax: (45) 44 54 44 44
E-Mail: ruko@ruko.dk
Web Site: www.ruko.com
Lock Mfr
S.I.C.: 3429
N.A.I.C.S.: 332510

Safeplace Ltd. (1)
POB 637
Yavne, 81104, Israel
Tel.: (972) 8 9424279
Fax: (972) 8 8604884
E-Mail: sales@safeplace.co.il
Web Site: www.safeplace-israel.com
Industrial Safety Equipment Mfr & Distr
S.I.C.: 3679
N.A.I.C.S.: 334419
Ravid Brosh *(Pres)*

Samhwa Precision Co., Ltd. (1)
2 Na-601 Shiwha Industrial Complex 1262 Jeongwang-dong
Siheung, Gyeonggi-do, 429-450, Korea (South)
Tel.: (82) 31 497 8822
Fax: (82) 31 497 8828
E-Mail: samhwa@kingdoorcloser.com
Web Site: www.kingdoorcloser.com
Emp.: 300
Door Closer & Floor Spring Mfr
S.I.C.: 3442
N.A.I.C.S.: 332321
Tim Jin *(Mgr-Export)*

Securistyle Group Holdings Limited (1)
Unit A-F Kingsmead Industrial Estate
Cheltenham, Gloucestershire, GL51 7RE, United Kingdom
Tel.: (44) 1242 221 200
Fax: (44) 1242 520 828
Emp.: 205
Investment Management Services
S.I.C.: 6211
N.A.I.C.S.: 523999

SECURITY MERCHANTS AUSTRALIA PTY LTD. (1)
Axxess Business Park Unit 144/45 Gilby Road
Mount Waverley, VIC, Australia 3149
Tel.: (61) 3 9558 8455
Fax: (61) 9 9558 8466
E-Mail: smvic@assaabloy.com
Web Site: www.security-merchants.com
Electronic Security Equipment Distr
S.I.C.: 5065
N.A.I.C.S.: 423690

Shandong Guoqiang Hardware Technology Co., Ltd. (1)
No 518 Tingjinxi Road
Laoling, Shandong, 253600, China
Tel.: (86) 534 2119505
Fax: (86) 534 2119025
Hardware Mfr
S.I.C.: 3429
N.A.I.C.S.: 332510

Shenzhen Longdian Science Technology Industrial Co., Ltd. (1)
No 26 Dongfa Road Dongkeng Area Gongming Town
Guangming New District Shajing, Shenzhen, 518100, China
Tel.: (86) 755 3395 3606
Fax: (86) 755 3318 3640
E-Mail: sales@szldkj.com
Web Site: www.longdiandoor.com
Metal Door Mfr
S.I.C.: 3442
N.A.I.C.S.: 332321

Sistemas y Technicas de Seguridad, S.A. (1)
Sierra de Segura 15
28830 San Fernando de Henares, Madrid, Spain
Tel.: (34) 916785500
Fax: (34) 91 676 96 71
E-Mail: a.muriel@stslocks.com
Web Site: www.stslocks.com
Emp.: 60
Marketing of Industrial Products
S.I.C.: 5113
N.A.I.C.S.: 424130

Slagelse Laseservice A/S (1)
Bredegade 14
4200 Slagelse, Denmark
Tel.: (45) 58524148
Fax: (45) 58534148
Metal Door Mfr
S.I.C.: 3442
N.A.I.C.S.: 332321

TESA Talleres de Escoriaza S.A.U. (1)
Barrio de Ventas n 35
20305 Irun, Guipuzcoa, Spain
Tel.: (34) 943669100
Fax: (34) 943669218
E-Mail: tesalocks@tesa.es
Web Site: www.tesa.es
Emp.: 600
Lock Mfr
S.I.C.: 3429
N.A.I.C.S.: 332510

Traka Plc (1)
30 Stilebrook Road
Olney, Bucks, MK46 5EA, United Kingdom
Tel.: (44) 1234 712345
Fax: (44) 1234 713366
E-Mail: info@traka.com
Web Site: www.traka.com
Emp.: 100
Electronic Key Mfr
S.I.C.: 3679
N.A.I.C.S.: 334419
Valerie Lindsay *(Dir-HR & Comml)*

TrioVing a.s. (1)
Varnaveien 32
PO Box 510
N 1523 Hoyden, Moss, Norway (100%)
Tel.: (47) 69245200
Fax: (47) 69245250
E-Mail: post@trioving.no
Web Site: www.trioving.no
Emp.: 180
S.I.C.: 3429
N.A.I.C.S.: 332510
Leis Lippspad *(Mng Dir)*

VingCard Elsafe AS (1)
Kaenkuja 8 C 32
00500 Helsinki, Finland
Tel.: (358) 20 599 4200
E-Mail: info@vcegroup.com
Web Site: www.vingcardelsafe.com
Electronic Safety System Mfr
S.I.C.: 3679

N.A.I.C.S.: 334419

VingCard Elsafe Japan Corporation (1)
Kitanomaru Residence 3F 2-3-9
Kudankita Chiyoda-Ku, 1120073 Tokyo, Japan
Tel.: (81) 3 3556 1717
Fax: (81) 3 3556 1718
Web Site: www.vingcardelsafe.com
Electronic Door Lock Distr
S.I.C.: 5065
N.A.I.C.S.: 423690

Yale La Fonte Sistemas de Seguranca LTDA (1)
Rua Augusto Ferreira de Moraes 618
Socorro, 04763-001 Sao Paulo, Brazil
Tel.: (55) 11 5693 4700
Fax: (55) 11 5693 4848
Web Site: www.yalelafonte.com.br
Emp.: 200
Electronic Security System Mfr
S.I.C.: 3679
N.A.I.C.S.: 334419
Luis Augusto Barcelos Barbosa *(Gen Mgr)*

Yale Security (SA) (Pty) Ltd (1)
176 Progress Road
Techikon, Roodepoort, 1724, South Africa
Tel.: (27) 11 781 9110
Fax: (27) 11 766 3573
E-Mail: za.yale.info@assaabloy.com
Emp.: 354
Hardware Mfr
S.I.C.: 3429
N.A.I.C.S.: 332510
Clint Jones *(Product Mgr & Mgr-Mktg)*

Zhejiang FACEA Vehicle Locks Co Ltd. (1)
No 80 Xinze Road Suzhou Industrial Park
Suzhou, Jiangsu, 215006, China
Tel.: (86) 512 87182968
Fax: (86) 571 87182958
E-Mail: info@facea.eu
Door Locks Mfr
S.I.C.: 3429
N.A.I.C.S.: 332510

ASSAM COMPANY INDIA LIMITED

301 Vipps Centre Masjid Moth
Greater Kailash Part II
New Delhi, 110 048, India
Tel.: (91) 33 2283 8306
Fax: (91) 33 2283 8334
Web Site: www.assamco.com
500024—(BOM NSE)
Sales Range: $50-74.9 Million
Emp.: 4,000

Business Description:
Tea Producer; Oil & Gas Exploration Services
S.I.C.: 2099
N.A.I.C.S.: 311920

Personnel:
K. K. Jajodia *(Chm)*
Aditya K. Jajodia *(Mng Dir)*

Board of Directors:
K. K. Jajodia
Umesh Barasia
Amit Kumar Ghosh
Aditya K. Jajodia

ASSAS FOR CONCRETE PRODUCTS CO. LTD.

Al Jeeza
PO Box 248
Amman, 16010, Jordan
Tel.: (962) 64711609
Fax: (962) 64711604
E-Mail: alassasbaton@alassas.com
Web Site: www.alassas.com
Year Founded: 1997
BLOK—(AMM)
Sales Range: $1-9.9 Million
Emp.: 63

Business Description:
Construction Materials Supplier
S.I.C.: 5032
N.A.I.C.S.: 423320

Personnel:
Raja Al Alami *(Founder & CEO)*

ASSECO POLAND S.A.

ul Olchowa 14
35-322 Rzeszow, Poland
Tel.: (48) 178885555
Fax: (48) 178885550
E-Mail: info@asseco.pl
Web Site: www.asseco.pl
ACP—(OTC WAR)
Rev.: $1,753,443,483
Assets: $3,056,942,922
Liabilities: $765,805,524
Net Worth: $2,291,137,398
Earnings: $176,292,567
Emp.: 16,638
Fiscal Year-end: 12/31/12

Business Description:
Holding Company; Software Publisher & Distr
S.I.C.: 6719
N.A.I.C.S.: 551112

Personnel:
Jacek Duch *(Chm-Supervisory Bd)*
Adam Noga *(Vice Chm-Supervisory Bd)*
Adam Goral *(Pres & Member-Mgmt Bd)*
Przemyslaw Borzestowski *(Member-Mgmt Bd & VP)*
Tadeusz Dyrga *(Member-Mgmt Bd & VP)*
Rafal Kozlowski *(Member-Mgmt Bd & VP)*
Marek Panek *(Member-Mgmt Bd & VP)*
Pawel Piwowar *(Member-Mgmt Bd & VP)*
Zbigniew Pomianek *(Member-Mgmt Bd & VP)*
Przemyslaw Seczkowski *(Member-Mgmt Bd & VP)*
Wlodzimierz Serwinski *(Member-Mgmt Bd & VP)*
Robert Smulkowski *(Member-Mgmt Bd & VP)*

Supervisory Board of Directors:
Jacek Duch
Piotr Augustyniak
Dariusz Brzeski
Artur Kucharski
Adam Noga
Dariusz Stolarczyk

Subsidiaries:

ADH Soft Sp. z.o.o. (1)
Ul 17 Stycznia 74
02-146 Warsaw, Poland
Tel.: (48) 22 646 62 02
Fax: (48) 22 646 70 12
E-Mail: Sales.Department@adh.com.pl
Web Site: www.adh.com.pl
Financial Software Development Services
S.I.C.: 7371
N.A.I.C.S.: 541511
Pawel Barchwic *(Chm)*
Wieslawa Ciunczyk *(Vice Chm)*

Asseco South Eastern Europe S.A. (1)
ul Branickiego 13
02-972 Warsaw, Poland (51.96%)
Tel.: (48) 225748630
Fax: (48) 225748690
E-Mail: office@asseco-see.com
Web Site: www.asseco-see.com
ASE—(WAR)
Sls.: $146,658,037
Assets: $240,676,300
Liabilities: $29,831,468
Net Worth: $210,844,832
Earnings: $15,725,525
Emp.: 1,339
Fiscal Year-end: 12/31/12
Software & Computer Applicatons
S.I.C.: 7373
N.A.I.C.S.: 541512
Adam Goral *(Chm-Supervisory Bd)*
Piotr Jelenski *(Chm-Mgmt Bd)*
Hatice Ayas *(Member-Mgmt Bd)*
Calin Barseti *(Member-Mgmt Bd)*
Miljan Malis *(Member-Mgmt Bd)*
Miodrag Mircetic *(Member-Mgmt Bd)*
Drazen Pehar *(Member-Mgmt Bd)*
Marcin Rulnicki *(Member-Mgmt Bd)*

Non-U.S. Subsidiaries:

Asseco SEE d.o.o. (2)
Ulica Grada Vukovara 269d
10000 Zagreb, Croatia
Tel.: (385) 1 30 30 000
Fax: (385) 1 30 30 010
E-Mail: info@asseco-see.hr
Emp.: 10
Financial Software Development Services
S.I.C.: 7371
N.A.I.C.S.: 541511
Drazen Pehar *(Pres-Mgmt Bd)*
Ljiljana Ivanek *(Member-Mgmt Bd)*
Emir Memic *(Member-Mgmt Bd)*
Ivica Petrovic *(Member-Mgmt Bd)*

Asseco SEE d.o.o. (2)
Bulevar Milutina Milankovica 19g
11070 Belgrade, Serbia
Tel.: (381) 11 2013 111
Fax: (381) 11 3015 132
E-Mail: office@asseco-see.rs
Emp.: 40
Software Development & Management Services
S.I.C.: 7371
N.A.I.C.S.: 541511
Miljan Malis *(Member-Mgmt Bd)*
Miodrag Mircetic *(Member-Mgmt Bd)*

Asseco SEE d.o.o. (2)
Kolodvorska 12
71000 Sarajevo, Bosnia & Herzegovina
Tel.: (387) 33 726 230
Fax: (387) 33 726 231
E-Mail: office@asseco-see.ba
Emp.: 5
Financial Software Development Services
S.I.C.: 7371
N.A.I.C.S.: 541511

Asseco SEE d.o.o. (2)
Industrijska Cesta 9
1290 Grosuplje, Slovenia
Tel.: (386) 1 620 52 80
Fax: (386) 1 620 52 81
E-Mail: info@asseco-see.si
Web Site: www.asseco.com
Software Development Services
S.I.C.: 7371
N.A.I.C.S.: 541511
Tamas Pletser *(Gen Mgr)*

Asseco SEE d.o.o. (2)
Admirala Zmajevica Br 11
81000 Podgorica, Montenegro
Tel.: (382) 20 651 951
Fax: (382) 20 651 741
E-Mail: cg_contact@asseco-see.me
Web Site: www.asseco.com
Emp.: 9
Software Development Services
S.I.C.: 7371
N.A.I.C.S.: 541511
Marko Simonovic *(CEO)*

Asseco SEE d.o.o.e.l. (2)
Naroden front 17
1000 Skopje, Macedonia
Tel.: (389) 2 32 48 000
Fax: (389) 2 32 16 621
E-Mail: contact@asseco-see.mk
Software Development & Management Services
S.I.C.: 7371
N.A.I.C.S.: 541511
Slavco Angelovski *(Chm-Mgmt Bd & CEO)*
Dejan Ivanoski *(Member-Mgmt Bd)*
Aleksandar Kormushoski *(Member-Mgmt Bd)*
Marija Mackinovska *(Member-Mgmt Bd)*
Kostadin Slavkoshi *(Member-Mgmt Bd)*

Asseco SEE sh.p.k. (2)
EGT Tower
Tirana, 1000, Albania
Tel.: (355) 4 226 9320
Fax: (355) 4 242 1764
E-Mail: info@asseco-see.al
Web Site: www.asseco.al
Emp.: 9
Software Development Services
S.I.C.: 7371
N.A.I.C.S.: 541511
Fedrico Montilla *(Mgr-Bus Dev)*

Asseco SEE Sh.p.k. (2)
Veternik Zona Industriale Nn
10000 Pristina, Kosovo, Serbia
Tel.: (381) 38 55 77 99
Fax: (381) 38 54 23 93
E-Mail: info@asseco-see-ks.com
Web Site: www.asseco.com
Software Development Services
S.I.C.: 7371
N.A.I.C.S.: 541511
Valon Budima *(Mng Dir)*

Asseco SEE Teknoloji A.S. (2)
Manolyali Sokak No 10
34330 Istanbul, Turkey
Tel.: (90) 212 385 02 02
Fax: (90) 212 281 74 16
E-Mail: marcom@asseco-see.com.tr
Web Site: www.asseco-see.com.tr
Emp.: 86
Banking Software Development Services
S.I.C.: 7371
N.A.I.C.S.: 541511
Hatice Ayas *(Mgr)*

EST A.S. (2)
Podoli 1237
584 01 Ledec nad Sazavou, Czech Republic
Tel.: (420) 569 726 097
Fax: (420) 569 726 096
E-Mail: est@estplus.cz
Web Site: www.estplus.cz
Painting Equipment Distr
S.I.C.: 5198
N.A.I.C.S.: 424950
Miloslav Ciz *(Chm)*

Combidata Poland Sp. z.o.o. (1)
ul Zwirki i Wigury 15
81-387 Gdynia, Poland
Tel.: (48) 58 550 95 50
Fax: (48) 58 550 95 51
E-Mail: biuro@combidata.pl
Educational Software Development Services
S.I.C.: 7371
N.A.I.C.S.: 541511

ZUI Novum Sp. z.o.o. (1)
Ul Spokojna 9a
18-400 Lomza, Poland
Tel.: (48) 86 216 98 00
Fax: (48) 86 216 96 98
E-Mail: info@novum.pl
Emp.: 5
Banking Software Development Services
S.I.C.: 7371
N.A.I.C.S.: 541511
Jaroslaw Kowalewski *(Mng Dir)*

ZUI OTAGO Sp. z o.o. (1)
Ul Heweliusza 11
Gdansk, 80-890, Poland
Tel.: (48) 58 740 4000
Fax: (48) 58 740 4099
E-Mail: info@otago.pl
Software Development Management Services
S.I.C.: 7371
N.A.I.C.S.: 541511

Non-U.S. Subsidiaries:

Asseco Austria GmbH (1)
Pummerinfeld 1b
4490 Sankt Florian, Austria
Tel.: (43) 7224 2005130
Fax: (43) 7224 20051 78 20
E-Mail: info@asseco.at
Web Site: www.asseco.com
Emp.: 40
Software Development Services
S.I.C.: 7371
N.A.I.C.S.: 541511
Markus Haller *(Gen Mgr)*

Asseco Denmark A/S (1)
Kronprinsessegade 54
1306 Copenhagen, Denmark
Tel.: (45) 33 36 46 60
Fax: (45) 33 36 46 61
E-Mail: info@asseco.dk
Web Site: www.asseco.dk

Asseco Poland S.A.—(Continued)

Emp.: 3
Information Technology Consulting Services
S.I.C.: 7373
N.A.I.C.S.: 541512
Torben Falholt *(CEO)*
Bo Orskov *(Chief Scientific Officer)*

Asseco Germany AG (1)
Amalienbadstrabe 41 Bau 54
76227 Karlsruhe, Germany
Tel.: (49) 721 91432 0
Fax: (49) 721 91432 298
E-Mail: info@asseco.de
Software Development & Management Services
S.I.C.: 7371
N.A.I.C.S.: 541511
Aleksander Duch *(Chm-Supervisory Bd)*
Markus Haller *(CEO)*

Asseco South Western Europe S.A. (1)
Julian Camarillo 29 D2
28037 Madrid, Spain
Tel.: (34) 913 756 000
Fax: (34) 913 756 001
E-Mail: asseco@asseco.es
Web Site: www.assecosouthwesterneurope.com
Information Technology Consulting Services
S.I.C.: 7373
N.A.I.C.S.: 541512

Asseco Spain SA (1)
Julian Camarillo 29 D2
28037 Madrid, Spain
Tel.: (34) 913 756 000
Fax: (34) 976736163
E-Mail: asseco@asseco.es
Web Site: www.asseco.com
Emp.: 85
Information Technology Consulting Services
S.I.C.: 7373
N.A.I.C.S.: 541512
Maria Cabrerizo *(Dir-HR)*

Formula Systems (1985) Ltd. (1)
5 Haplada Street
Or Yehud, 60218, Israel IL
Tel.: (972) 3 5389 487 (50.7%)
Fax: (972) 3 5389 645
E-Mail: info@formula.co.il
Web Site: www.formulasystems.com
FORTY—(NASDAQ TAE)
Rev.: $744,731,000
Assets: $880,920,000
Liabilities: $412,502,000
Net Worth: $468,418,000
Earnings: $47,484,000
Emp.: 8,297
Fiscal Year-end: 12/31/12
Holding Company; Software Developer
S.I.C.: 7371
N.A.I.C.S.: 541511

Subsidiaries:

Magic Software Enterprises Ltd. (2)
5 Haplada Street
Or Yehuda, Tel Aviv, 60218, Israel II
Tel.: (972) 3 538 9392 (58%)
Fax: (972) 3 538 9393
E-Mail: sales@magicsoftware.com
Web Site: www.magicsoftware.com
MGIC—(NASDAQ TAE)
Rev.: $144,958,000
Assets: $167,003,000
Liabilities: $37,872,000
Net Worth: $129,131,000
Earnings: $16,856,000
Emp.: 1,302
Fiscal Year-end: 12/31/13
Computer Network & Internet Software Developer
S.I.C.: 7372
N.A.I.C.S.: 511210
Guy Bernstein *(CEO)*
Asaf Berenstin *(CFO)*
Eyal Pfeifel *(CTO)*
Regev Yativ *(Pres/CEO-Magic Software Enterprises Inc)*
Yoram Aharon *(CEO-Israel)*
Amit Birk *(Gen Counsel & VP-M&A)*
Amit Ben-Zvi *(Exec VP & Gen Mgr-Europe & Japan)*

U.S. Subsidiaries:

Magic Software Enterprises Inc. (3)
23046 Avenida de la Carlota Ste 300
Laguna Hills, CA 92653
Tel.: (949) 250-1718
Fax: (949) 250-7404
E-Mail: info@magicsoftware.com
Web Site: www.magicsoftware.com
Sales Range: $1-9.9 Million
Emp.: 100
Developer of Computer Network & Internet Software
S.I.C.: 7372
N.A.I.C.S.: 511210
Regev Yativ *(Pres & CEO)*

Non-U.S. Subsidiaries:

Magic Group (Victoria) (3)
Ste 2 300 Ctr Rd
Bentleigh, VIC, 3204, Australia
Tel.: (61) 395578577
Fax: (61) 395578255
E-Mail: sales@magicgrp.com.au
Web Site: www.magicsoftware.com
Emp.: 5
Developer of Computer Network & Internet Software
S.I.C.: 7373
N.A.I.C.S.: 541512
Eric Lesbirel *(Chm-Australia)*

Magic Software Enterprises France (3)
9 bis rue Henri Martin
92415 Boulogne, Cedex, France
Tel.: (33) 149105858
Fax: (33) 149105859
E-Mail: infofrance@magicsoftware.com
Web Site: www.magicsoftware.com
Emp.: 15
Developer of Computer Network & Internet Software
S.I.C.: 7373
N.A.I.C.S.: 541512
Eric Choppe *(Gen Mgr)*

Magic Software Enterprises GmbH (3)
Lise Meitner Strasse 3
85737 Ismaning, Germany
Tel.: (49) 89962730
Fax: (49) 8996273100
E-Mail: infogermany@magicsoftware.com
Web Site: www.magicsoftware.com
Rev.: $6,058,000
Emp.: 30
Developer of Computer Network & Internet Software
S.I.C.: 7372
N.A.I.C.S.: 511210
Stephan Romeder *(Mng Dir)*

Magic Software Enterprises India Pvt. Ltd. (3)
Office No 8 Tara Icon 22 Mumbai Pune Rd
Pune, 411 003, India
Tel.: (91) 9886455398
Fax: (91) 2025815500
E-Mail: srinivas_reddy@magicsoftware.com
Emp.: 80
Developer of Computer Network & Internet Software
S.I.C.: 7373
N.A.I.C.S.: 541512
Srinivas Reddy *(Reg Mgr)*

Magic Software Enterprises Nederland (3)
Pelmolen 17
3994 XX Houten, Netherlands
Mailing Address:
PO Box 276
3990GB Houten, Netherlands
Tel.: (31) 306566266
Fax: (31) 306566277
E-Mail: info-nl@magicsoftware.com
Web Site: www.magicsoftware.com
Emp.: 9
Developer of Computer Network & Internet Software
S.I.C.: 7373
N.A.I.C.S.: 541512
John Verwaaijen *(Gen Mgr)*

Magic Software Enterprises (Onyx) Hungary Ltd. (3)
Bava 8
Budapest, 1094, Hungary
Tel.: (36) 12169910
Fax: (36) 12167271
E-Mail: info@magicsoftware.hu
Web Site: www.magicsoftware.hu
Emp.: 10
Developer of Computer Network & Internet Software
S.I.C.: 7373
N.A.I.C.S.: 541512
Marton Szluha *(Gen Mgr)*

Magic Software Enterprises UK Ltd. (3)
Lily Hill House Lily Hill Rd
Bracknell, Berkshire, RG12 2SJ, United Kingdom
Tel.: (44) 1344667000
Fax: (44) 1344667001
E-Mail: ukinfo@magicsoftware.com
Web Site: www.magicsoftware.com
Emp.: 12
Developer of Computer Network & Internet Software
S.I.C.: 7373
N.A.I.C.S.: 541512

Magic Software Japan KK (3)
Aioi Sonpo Shinjuku Bldg 14 Fl 3 25 3 Yoyogi
Shibuya Ku, Tokyo, 151 0053, Japan
Tel.: (81) 353651600
Fax: (81) 353651630
E-Mail: japan_info@magicsoftware.com
Web Site: www.magicsoftware.co.jp
Emp.: 60
Developer of Computer Network & Internet Software
S.I.C.: 7373
N.A.I.C.S.: 541512
Tosio Sato *(Pres)*

Magic Software (Thailand) Corp., Ltd. (3)
9/68 Ratchadapisek Rd
Ratchadapisek Rd, Bangkok, 10900, Thailand
Tel.: (66) 29119988
Fax: (66) 29119948
E-Mail: infothailand@magicsoftware.com
Web Site: www.magicsoftware.co.th
Sales Range: Less than $1 Million
Emp.: 30
Software Developer & Sales
S.I.C.: 5045
N.A.I.C.S.: 423430
Boonchuay Sa-nguanvorapong *(Pres)*

Matrix IT Ltd. (2)
Abba Eban Blvd
PO Box 2062
46120 Herzliya Pituach, Israel (50.1%)
Tel.: (972) 99598840
Fax: (972) 99598844
E-Mail: yifatg@matrix.co.il
Web Site: www.matrix.co.il
MTRX—(TAE)
Rev.: $533,048,223
Assets: $405,791,972
Liabilities: $253,762,349
Net Worth: $152,029,623
Earnings: $24,361,753
Emp.: 3,500
Fiscal Year-end: 12/31/12
Information Technology Services
S.I.C.: 7373
N.A.I.C.S.: 541512
Guy Bernstein *(Chm)*
Eliezer Oren *(Vice Chm & Pres)*
Moti Gutman *(CEO)*
Moshe Attias *(CFO)*
Asaf Givati *(COO)*
Ranit Zexer *(CTO)*
Yaron Raz *(CEO-Tangram Soft & Dir-Defense & Strategic Consulting Div)*
Eran Lasser *(CEO-John Bryce Hi-Tech Trng & Assimilation Div)*
Ziv Mandel *(CEO-John Bryce Hi-Tech Trng & Assimilation Div)*

U.S. Subsidiaries:

Exzac, Inc. (3)
Harborside Financial Ctr Plz 5 Ste 2720
Jersey City, NJ 07311 NJ
Tel.: (201) 204-5300
Fax: (201) 503-8179
E-Mail: info@exzac.com
Web Site: www.exzac.com
Sales Range: $10-24.9 Million
Emp.: 80
Management Consulting Services
S.I.C.: 8742
N.A.I.C.S.: 541611
Ruth Ben-Hur *(Controller)*

Xtivia, Inc. (3)
304 S 8th St Ste 201
Colorado Springs, CO 80905
Tel.: (719) 623-5870
Fax: (719) 685-3400
Toll Free: (888) 685-3101
E-Mail: info@xtivia.com
Web Site: www.xtivia.com
Sales Range: $10-24.9 Million
Emp.: 150
IT Solutions
S.I.C.: 7373
N.A.I.C.S.: 541512
Dennis Robinson *(Pres & CEO)*

Subsidiary:

Connect The Knowledge Network Corp. (4)
5602 S Nevada St
Littleton, CO 80120-1116
Tel.: (303) 730-7171
Fax: (303) 797-8369
E-Mail: info@connectknowledge.com
Web Site: www.connectknowledge.com
Emp.: 15
Computer Systems Design Services
S.I.C.: 7373
N.A.I.C.S.: 541512
Maureen Clarry *(Mng Dir)*
Todd Saunders *(Exec VP-Customer Solutions)*

Sapiens International Corporation N.V. (2)
Rabin Science Park
PO Box 4011
Nes Ziyyona, 74140, Israel AN
Tel.: (972) 89382721 (63.4%)
Fax: (972) 89382730
E-Mail: info@sapiens.com
Web Site: www.sapiens.com
SPNS—(NASDAQ TAE)
Rev.: $113,909,000
Assets: $162,584,000
Liabilities: $44,145,000
Net Worth: $118,439,000
Earnings: $11,803,000
Emp.: 791
Fiscal Year-end: 12/31/12
Insurance Software Products & Services
S.I.C.: 7372
N.A.I.C.S.: 511210
Guy Bernstein *(Chm)*
Roni Al-Dor *(Pres & CEO)*
Roni Giladi *(CFO)*
Rami Doron *(COO)*
Osnat Segev-Harel *(CMO & VP-Bus Dev)*
Sagi Schliesser *(CTO & VP-R&D)*
Michael Kupferman *(CTO)*
Hadas Gazit-Kaiser *(Chief Bus Ops Officer)*
Ron Karam *(Pres-North America Insurance Div)*
Dan Sobotincic *(Exec VP & Head-Global Property & Casualty Div)*

Subsidiaries:

Sapiens Israel Software Systems (3)
PO Box 4011
Nes Ziyyona, 74140, Israel
Tel.: (972) 89382888
Fax: (972) 89382855
E-Mail: israel@sapiens.com
Web Site: www.sapiens.com
Emp.: 225
Insurance Software Products & Services
S.I.C.: 7372
N.A.I.C.S.: 511210
Roni Al-Dor *(Pres & CEO)*

Sapiens Technologies Ltd. (3)
Park Amhamada Industrial Ctr Rabin
PO Box 4011
Rehovot, 76120, Israel
Tel.: (972) 89382777
Fax: (972) 89382788
E-Mail: israel@sapiens.com
Insurance Software Products & Services
S.I.C.: 7372
N.A.I.C.S.: 511210

U.S. Subsidiaries:

Sapiens Americas (3)
4000 Centre Green Way Ste 150
Cary, NC 27513

Tel.: (919) 405-1500
Fax: (919) 405-1700
E-Mail: usa@sapiens.com
Web Site: www.sapiens.com
Sales Range: $1-9.9 Million
Emp.: 85
Insurance Software Products & Services
S.I.C.: 7372
N.A.I.C.S.: 511210
Roni Al-Dor *(Pres & CEO)*

Non-U.S. Subsidiaries:

Sapiens Japan (3)
Queens Tower C 17F 2-3-5 Minatomirai
Nishi-ku, Yokohama, 220 6217, Japan
Tel.: (81) 456824777
Fax: (81) 456824780
E-Mail: japan@sapiens.com
Web Site: www.sapiens.com
Sales Range: $1-9.9 Million
Emp.: 25
Insurance Software Products & Services
S.I.C.: 7372
N.A.I.C.S.: 511210
Manabu Okada *(Mng Dir)*

Sapiens (UK) Limited (3)
Harman House
1 George Street, Uxbridge, Mddx, UB8 1QQ, United Kingdom
Tel.: (44) 1895464000
Fax: (44) 1895463098
E-Mail: uk@sapiens.com
Web Site: www.sapiens.com
Sales Range: $10-24.9 Million
Emp.: 40
Insurance Software Products & Services
S.I.C.: 7372
N.A.I.C.S.: 511210
Raj Ghuman *(Dir-Ops)*

U.S. Subsidiary:

nextSource Inc. (2)
3 Park Ave 15th Fl
New York, NY 10016 (100%)
Tel.: (212) 736-5870
Fax: (212) 736-9046
Web Site: www.nextsource.com
Emp.: 35
Workforce Management Software & Services
S.I.C.: 7372
N.A.I.C.S.: 511210
Joseph Musacchio *(Pres & CEO)*
Fern Swiss *(CFO)*
Joanne Bocci *(COO)*
Ed Remus *(Sr VP-Customer Implementations & Procurement)*

ASSETCO PLC

Singleton Court Business Park
Wonastow Road, Monmouth, NP25 5JA, United Kingdom
Tel.: (44) 20 8515 3800
E-Mail: info@assetco.com
Web Site: www.assetco.com
ASTO—(AIM)
Sales Range: $50-74.9 Million
Emp.: 141

Business Description:
Fire & Rescue Services
S.I.C.: 9224
N.A.I.C.S.: 922160

Personnel:
Tudor Davies *(Interim Chm)*
Mark Clissett *(Mng Dir)*
Michael Lavender *(Sec)*

Board of Directors:
Tudor Davies
Alexander Mark Butcher
Christopher Mills
Jeff Ord

Legal Counsel:
Nabarro LLP
Lacon House, 84 Theobald's Road
London, WC1X 8RW, United Kingdom
Tel.: (44) 171 493 9933
Fax: (44) 171 629 7900

Mills Selig
21 Arthur Street
Belfast, United Kingdom

Subsidiaries:

AssetCo Engineering Limited (1)
800 Field End Rd
South Ruislip, London, HA4 0QH, United Kingdom
Tel.: (44) 2085153999
Fax: (44) 2085153987
E-Mail: info@assetco.com
Emp.: 200
Integrated Support & Security Services
S.I.C.: 7382
N.A.I.C.S.: 561621
John Shannon *(Mng Dir)*

AssetCo London Limited (1)
800 Field End Rd
South Ruislip, London, HA4 0QH, United Kingdom
Tel.: (44) 2085153999
Fax: (44) 2085153800
E-Mail: info@assetco.com
Emp.: 150
Integrated Security & Support Services
S.I.C.: 7382
N.A.I.C.S.: 561621

AssetCo Technical Rescue (1)
Unit 3 Dunveth Bus Park
Wadebridge, Cornwall, PL27 7FE, United Kingdom
Tel.: (44) 1208814538
Fax: (44) 8700467265
E-Mail: enquiries@assetcotechnicalrescue.com
Web Site: www.assetcotechnicalrescue.com
Emp.: 6
Rescue Training & Consulting Services
S.I.C.: 8299
N.A.I.C.S.: 611699
Matt Bray *(Mng Dir)*

Nene Whitewater Centre Ltd. (1)
Bedford Road
Northampton, NN4 7AA, United Kingdom
Tel.: (44) 1604634040
Fax: (44) 1604634343
E-Mail: info@nenewhitewatercentre.co.uk
Web Site: www.nenewhitewatercentre.co.uk
Emp.: 4
Sporting Facilities & Training Services
S.I.C.: 7991
N.A.I.C.S.: 713940
Chris Chapman *(Mgr)*

Todd Research Limited (1)
1 Papworth Business Park
Papworth Everard, Cambridge, CB23 3WA, United Kingdom
Tel.: (44) 1480832202
Fax: (44) 1480832233
E-Mail: xray@toddresearch.co.uk
Web Site: www.toddresearch.co.uk
Emp.: 10
X Ray & Security Equipments Mfr & Sales
S.I.C.: 3845
N.A.I.C.S.: 334510
Richard Sheil *(Dir-Sls)*

Non-U.S. Subsidiaries:

AssetCo Managed Services (ROI) Limited (1)
Lisfannon Business Park
Lisfannon, Donegal, Ulster, Ireland
Tel.: (353) 749364800
Fax: (353) 749364888
E-Mail: info@assetco.com
Emp.: 50
Business Support Services
S.I.C.: 7389
N.A.I.C.S.: 561499
John Shannon *(CEO)*

AssetCo UAE (1)
PO Box 62104
Abu Dhabi, United Arab Emirates
Tel.: (971) 25587707
Fax: (971) 4944998
E-Mail: info@assetco.com
Emp.: 172
Emergency Planning & Support Services
S.I.C.: 8322
N.A.I.C.S.: 624230
Brendan McCaffrey *(Chief Fire Officer)*
William Wilson *(Deputy Chief Fire Officer)*

ASSICURAZIONI GENERALI S.P.A.

Piazza Duca degli Abruzzi 2
34132 Trieste, Italy
Tel.: (39) 040671402
Fax: (39) 040671338
E-Mail: press@generali.com
Web Site: www.generali.com
Year Founded: 1831
G—(ITA OTC)
Rev.: $119,199,314,990
Assets: $594,663,866,650
Liabilities: $564,284,848,260
Net Worth: $30,379,018,390
Earnings: $494,044,390
Emp.: 79,454
Fiscal Year-end: 12/31/12

Business Description:
Holding Company; Insurance, Financial & Real Estate Services
S.I.C.: 6719
N.A.I.C.S.: 551112

Personnel:
Mario Greco *(Grp CEO)*
Alberto Minali *(CFO)*
C. Shildknecht *(COO)*
Nikhil Srinivasan *(Chief Investment Officer)*
Sandro Panizza *(Chief Risk Officer)*
Massimo Paltrinieri *(Chief IT Officer & Asst Gen Mgr-Grp IT)*
Sergio Balbinot *(Chief Insurance Officer)*
M. Basso *(Compliance Officer)*
Antonio Cangeri *(Gen Counsel)*

Board of Directors:
Gabriele Galateri di Genola
Ornella Barra
Vincent Bollore
Francesco Gaetano Caltagirone
Alberta Figari
Mario Greco
Lorenzo Pellicioli
Sabrina Pucci
Clemente Rebecchini
Paola Sapienza
Paolo Scaroni

Subsidiaries:

Alleanza Toro S.p.A. (1)
Via Mazzini 53
10123 Turin, Italy
Tel.: (39) 0110029111
Fax: (39) 011 837554
E-Mail: info@toroassicurazioni.it
Web Site: www.toroassicurazioni.it
Emp.: 3,213
Life, Property & Casualty Insurance Services
S.I.C.: 6331
N.A.I.C.S.: 524126
Luigi De Puppi *(Chm & CEO)*
Andrea Simoncelli *(Deputy Dir Gen, Head-Fin & Admin & Control)*
Attilio Invernizzi *(Deputy Dir Gen & Head-HR)*

Subsidiaries:

Alleanza Toro Servizi Assicurativi S.r.l (2)
Piazza Duca degli Abruzzi 1
34132 Trieste, Italy
Tel.: (39) 02 62961
Fax: (39) 02 653718
General Insurance Services
S.I.C.: 6411
N.A.I.C.S.: 524210

ISIM S.p.A. (2)
Louis Pasteur Street 6/D
10146 Turin, Italy
Tel.: (39) 011798194
Marketing Consulting Services
S.I.C.: 8742
N.A.I.C.S.: 541613

Simgenia S.p.A. (2)
Via Machiavelli 4
34132 Trieste, Italy
Tel.: (39) 0407 77 71 11
E-Mail: info@simgenia.it
Web Site: www.simgenia.it
Financial Management Services
S.I.C.: 6211
N.A.I.C.S.: 523999

Banca Generali S.p.A. (1)
Via Machiavelli 4
34132 Trieste, Italy (62.3%)
Tel.: (39) 040 777 7111
Fax: (39) 0269462307
E-Mail: investor.relations@bancagenerali.it
Web Site: www.bancagenerali.it
BGN—(ITA)
Rev.: $211,876,389
Assets: $9,850,282,625
Liabilities: $9,318,383,935
Net Worth: $531,898,690
Earnings: $179,146,957
Emp.: 785
Fiscal Year-end: 12/31/12
Asset Management, Financial Planning & Investment Banking & Advisory Services
S.I.C.: 6211
N.A.I.C.S.: 523110
Paolo Vagnone *(Chm)*
Piermario Motta *(CEO & Gen Mgr)*
Giancarlo Fancel *(CFO & Gen Mgr)*

Subsidiaries:

BG Fiduciaria Sim S.p.A. (2)
Via Ugo Bassi 6
20159 Milan, Italy
Tel.: (39) 0268826511
Fax: (39) 0266804540
Web Site: www.bgfiduciaria.it
Asset Management Services
S.I.C.: 6799
N.A.I.C.S.: 523920

GenerFid S.p.A. (2)
Via Ugo Bassi 6
20159 Milan, Italy
Tel.: (39) 0269964721
Fax: (39) 0415487524
E-Mail: generfid@generfid.it
Web Site: www.generfid.it
Asset Management Services
S.I.C.: 6799
N.A.I.C.S.: 523920
Michele Muscolo *(Gen Mgr)*

Non-U.S. Subsidiary:

Generali Fund Management S.A. (2)
5 Allee Scheffer
2520 Luxembourg, Luxembourg
Tel.: (352) 47 67 22 83
Fax: (352) 47 67 46 75
Web Site: www.generali-fm.lu
Emp.: 30
Investment Management Services
S.I.C.: 6211
N.A.I.C.S.: 523999

Casaletto S.r.l (1)
Via Di Monteverde 244
Rome, 00151, Italy
Tel.: (39) 065344087
Fax: (39) 0653279190
Real Estate Development Services
S.I.C.: 6531
N.A.I.C.S.: 531390

D.A.S. Legal Services S.r.l. (1)
9/b v Fermi
37135 Verona, Italy
Tel.: (39) 045 8372611
Fax: (39) 045 8310523
E-Mail: info.daslegalservices@legalmail.it
Legal Management Services
S.I.C.: 7389
N.A.I.C.S.: 541199

Donatello Intermediazione Srl (1)
Via Giosue Carducci 4
00187 Rome, Italy
Tel.: (39) 0647221
Insurance Management Services
S.I.C.: 6411
N.A.I.C.S.: 524298

Fata Assicurazioni Danni SpA (1)
Via Urbana 169/a
00184 Rome, Italy
Tel.: (39) 06 47 65 1
Fax: (39) 06 48 71 18 7
E-Mail: info@fata-assicurazioni.it
Web Site: www.fata-assicurazioni.it
Insurance Management Services
S.I.C.: 6411
N.A.I.C.S.: 524298

Non-U.S. Subsidiaries:

S.C. FATA Asigurari S.A. (2)
Str Vicotorei 43
820150 Tulcea, Romania

Assicurazioni Generali S.p.A.—(Continued)

Tel.: (40) 240514413
Fax: (40) 240514412
Web Site: www.fata-asigurari.ro
Agriculture Insurance Services
S.I.C.: 6351
N.A.I.C.S.: 524126

Zad Victoria AD (2)
No 65 Ekzarh Josif Str
Sofia, Bulgaria
Tel.: (359) 700 19 577
Fax: (359) 2 981 12 47
E-Mail: office@victoria-insbg.com
Emp.: 45
Life Insurance Services
S.I.C.: 6311
N.A.I.C.S.: 524113

Fata Vita S.p.A. (1)
Via Urbana 169/A
Rome, 00184, Italy
Tel.: (39) 06 47651
Fax: (39) 06 4871187
General Insurance Services
S.I.C.: 6411
N.A.I.C.S.: 524210

Genagricola S.p.A. (1)
Via Mons P L Zovatto 71
Annone Veneto, Venice, 30020, Italy
Tel.: (39) 0422 864511
Fax: (39) 0422 864566
E-Mail: info@letenutedigenagricola.it
Web Site: www.letenutedigenagricola.it
Wine Mfr & Distr
S.I.C.: 2084
N.A.I.C.S.: 312130

Non-U.S. Subsidiary:

S.C. Aqua Mures (2)
Str Morii 9 Sinnicolau Great Way
Sannicolau Mare, 305600, Romania
Tel.: (40) 256370458
Insurance Management Services
S.I.C.: 6411
N.A.I.C.S.: 524298

Generali Asset Management S.p.A. (1)
Via Ugo Bassi 6
20159 Milan, Italy (100%)
Tel.: (39) 0260765711
Fax: (39) 026684022
E-Mail: info@generali.com
Web Site: www.generali.com
Emp.: 200
Investment Fund Management
S.I.C.: 6722
N.A.I.C.S.: 525910
Santo Borsellino *(CEO & Gen Mgr)*

Generali Business Solutions S.c.p.A. (1)
Via Machiavelli 4
34132 Trieste, Italy
Tel.: (39) 040 671111
Fax: (39) 040 671600
Web Site: www.generali.com
Life Insurance Services
S.I.C.: 6311
N.A.I.C.S.: 524113
Mario Grepo *(CEO)*

Generali Immobiliare Italia Sgr S.p.A. (1)
Via Meravigli 2
20123 Milan, Italy
Tel.: (39) 02 725041
Fax: (39) 02 801433
E-Mail: info@gii.generali.com
Web Site: www.generali-immobiliare.it
Asset Management Services
S.I.C.: 6282
N.A.I.C.S.: 523920

Generali Investments Europe S.p.A. (1)
Via Trento 8
34132 Trieste, Italy
Tel.: (39) 040 671 111
Fax: (39) 040 671 40
E-Mail: info@am.generali.com
Web Site: www.generali-investments-europe.com
Insurance Management Services
S.I.C.: 6411
N.A.I.C.S.: 524298

Generali Properties S.p.A. (1)
Piazza Duca Degli Abruzzi 1
Trieste, 34132, Italy
Tel.: (39) 0406 79 91 11
Fax: (39) 0406 79 95 00
E-Mail: info@gre.generali.com
Web Site: www.generaliproperties.com
Real Estate Management Services
S.I.C.: 6531
N.A.I.C.S.: 531390
Gianfranco Scotti *(Gen Mgr)*

Generali Real Estate S.p.A. (1)
Piazza Duca Degli Abruzzi 1 - Cap
34132 Trieste, Italy
Tel.: (39) 040 6799111
Fax: (39) 040 6799500
E-Mail: info@gre.generali.com
Web Site: www.gre.generali.com
Real Estate Management Services
S.I.C.: 6531
N.A.I.C.S.: 531390
Christian Delaire *(CEO-Real Estate & Gen Properties)*

Genertel S.p.A. (1)
Via Machiavelli 4
34132 Trieste, Italy (100%)
Tel.: (39) 0406768666
Fax: (39) 040 370442
E-Mail: info@genertel.it
Web Site: www.genertel.it
Sales Range: $150-199.9 Million
Provider of Insurance Services
S.I.C.: 6399
N.A.I.C.S.: 524128
Aldo Minucci *(Chm)*

Unit:

Risparmio Vita Assicurazioni S.p.A. (2)
Via Machiavelli n 4
34132 Trieste, TS, Italy
Tel.: (39) 0415903755
Fax: (39) 0415905292
E-Mail: direzione@risparmio.it
Web Site: www.risparmio.it
Life Insurance Carrier
S.I.C.: 6311
N.A.I.C.S.: 524113

Genertellife S.p.A. (1)
Via Ferretto 1
31021 Mogliano Veneto, Treviso, Italy
Tel.: (39) 041 5939701
Fax: (39) 041 5939795
E-Mail: genertellife@genertellife.it
Web Site: www.genertellife.it
Emp.: 150
General Insurance Services
S.I.C.: 6411
N.A.I.C.S.: 524210
Davide Passero *(Gen Mgr)*

Subsidiary:

Genertel Servizi Assicurativi S.r.l. (2)
Via Erminio Ferretto 1
Mogliano Veneto, Treviso, 31021, Italy
Tel.: (39) 0415939701
Fax: (39) 0415939701
Insurance Management Services
S.I.C.: 6411
N.A.I.C.S.: 524298

Gruppo Generali Servizi S.r.l. (1)
Piazza Buca Degli Abruzzi 2
Trieste, 34132, Italy (67%)
Tel.: (39) 0040671111
Fax: (39) 0040671600
Emp.: 1,000
Insurance Services
S.I.C.: 6399
N.A.I.C.S.: 524128

Il Tiglio - Societa' Agricola S.r.l. (1)
Via Monsignor Paolo Lino Zovatto 71
30020 Venice, Italy
Tel.: (39) 0422864 511
Wine Mfr
S.I.C.: 2084
N.A.I.C.S.: 312130

Inf - Societa' Agricola S.p.A. (1)
Contrada Colle Cavalieri
00040 Lanuvio, Italy
Tel.: (39) 069374049
Food Product Mfr
S.I.C.: 2099
N.A.I.C.S.: 311999

Non-U.S. Subsidiary:

S.C. La Quercia S.r.l. (2)
Str Drumul Morii 7A
305600 Sannicolau Mare, Romania
Tel.: (40) 256370458
Insurance Management Services
S.I.C.: 6411
N.A.I.C.S.: 524298

Sementi Dom Dotto S.p.A. (1)
Via Iavariano 41
33050 Mortegliano, Udine, Italy
Tel.: (39) 0432 760442
Fax: (39) 0432 761665
E-Mail: info@sementidotto.it
Web Site: www.sementidotto.it
Vegetable Seed & Animal Food Distr
S.I.C.: 5191
N.A.I.C.S.: 424910

Subsidiaries:

Agenzia la Torre S.r.l. (2)
Pratovarino Region 14
Moasca, Asti, Italy
Tel.: (39) 0141832070
Real Estate Development Services
S.I.C.: 6531
N.A.I.C.S.: 531390

Sementi Ross S.r.l. (2)
Str Delle Saline 5
34015 Muggia, Italy
Tel.: (39) 040 232481
Financial Management Services
S.I.C.: 6211
N.A.I.C.S.: 523999

Non-U.S. Subsidiary:

CPM Internacional d.o.o. (2)
Zitnjak Bb
10000 Zagreb, Croatia
Tel.: (385) 12 49 97 00
Fax: (385) 12 49 97 01
Vegetable Farming Services
S.I.C.: 0161
N.A.I.C.S.: 111219

UMS-Generali Marine S.p.A. (1)
Via 12 October 1
16100 Genoa, Italy (97.09%)
Tel.: (39) 01084071
Fax: (39) 0108317336
E-Mail: ums@ums.it
Web Site: www.umsgeneralimarine.it
Emp.: 30
Marine Transport Insurance
S.I.C.: 6399
N.A.I.C.S.: 524128

Uniass Assicurazioni S.p.A. (1)
Via Aurelia 294
00165 Rome, Italy (100%)
Tel.: (39) 06399411
Fax: (39) 0639388114
Emp.: 200
Provider of Insurance
S.I.C.: 6399
N.A.I.C.S.: 524128

Affiliate:

Alleanza Assicurazioni S.p.A. (1)
Viale Luigi Sturzo 35
20154 Milan, Italy IT
Tel.: (39) 0262961 (50.4%)
Fax: (39) 02 62966
Web Site: www.alleanzaassicurazioni.it
Sales Range: $5-14.9 Billion
Emp.: 3,600
Life Insurance Services
S.I.C.: 6311
N.A.I.C.S.: 524113
Amato Luigi Molinari *(Chm & Pres)*
Antoine Bernheim *(Vice Chm)*
Sandro Panizza *(Deouty CEO, Mng Dir & CFO)*

Subsidiaries:

Agricola San Giorgio S.p.A. (2)
Via Zovatto 71 Loncon
Annone, 30020 Venice, Italy (100%)
Tel.: (39) 0422864411
Fax. (39) 422864400
E-Mail: direzione.genagricola@genagricola.it
Web Site: www.genagricola.it
Sales Range: $1-9.9 Million
Emp.: 15
Grower of Bread Wheat, Durum Wheat, Sweet Corn, Rice, Sugar Beets, Wine Grapes, Pears & Actinide
S.I.C.: 0111
N.A.I.C.S.: 111140
Giusette Perissmopto *(Pres)*

Non-U.S. Subsidiary:

S.C. San Pietro Romania (3)
Str Drumul Morii 9
305600 Sannicolau Mare, Romania
Tel.: (40) 256370458
Food Product Mfr
S.I.C.: 2099
N.A.I.C.S.: 311999

Fondi Alleanza S.G.R.p.A. (2)
Via Luigi Sturzo 35
20154 Milan, Italy (100%)
Tel.: (39) 0248248111
Fax: (39) 0248248110
Web Site: www.fondialleanza.it/pagine/pagina.aspx?ID=Contatti001&L=IT
Manager of Mutual Funds
S.I.C.: 6722
N.A.I.C.S.: 525910

La Venezia Assicurazioni S.p.A. (2)
Via Ferretto 1
31021 Mogliano Veneto, Treviso, Italy (100%)
Tel.: (39) 0415939701
Fax: (39) 0415939795
E-Mail: genertellife@genertellife.it
Web Site: www.genertellife.it
Life Insurance
S.I.C.: 6311
N.A.I.C.S.: 524113

Subsidiary:

Semgimenenea S.p.A. (3)
Via Ferretto 1
31021 Mogliano Veneto, TV, Italy (100%)
Tel.: (39) 0415939801
Fax: (39) 0415939899
Toll Free: 800 857007
E-Mail: semgimenenea@semgimenenea.it
Web Site: www.semgimenenea.it
Emp.: 50
Securities Brokerage
S.I.C.: 6211
N.A.I.C.S.: 523120

U.S. Subsidiaries:

Assicurazioni Generali (1)
1 Liberty Plz 29th Fl
New York, NY 10006-1404 (100%)
Tel.: (212) 602-7600
Fax: (212) 587-9537
E-Mail: info@generaliusa.com
Web Site: www.generaliusa.com
Emp.: 100
Holding Company
S.I.C.: 6719
N.A.I.C.S.: 551112

General Securities Corp. (1)
422 Armour Rd
Kansas City, MO 64116
Tel.: (816) 472-7170
Securities Brokerage Services
S.I.C.: 6211
N.A.I.C.S.: 523120

Generali Consulting Solutions LLC (1)
7 World Trade Ctr 250 Greenwich St 33rd Fl
New York, NY 10007-0010
Tel.: (212) 602-7600
Fax: (212) 587-9534
Software Management Consulting Services
S.I.C.: 8748
N.A.I.C.S.: 541618

GNAREI 1 Farragut LLC (1)
2711 Centerville Rd Ste 400
Wilmington, DE 19808
Tel.: (302) 636-5401
Insurance Management Services
S.I.C.: 6411
N.A.I.C.S.: 524298

Transocean Holding Corporation (1)
1 Liberty Plz Fl 37
New York, NY 10006-1414

Tel.: (212) 602-7600
Investment Management Services
S.I.C.: 6211
N.A.I.C.S.: 523999

Non-U.S. Subsidiary:

Participatie Maatschappij Transhol B.V. (2)
Diemerhof 42
Diemen, Noord-Holland, 1112 XN, Netherlands
Tel.: (31) 206604444
Fax: (31) 206601893
Financial Investment Management Services
S.I.C.: 6211
N.A.I.C.S.: 523999

Non-U.S. Subsidiaries:

AM Versicherungsvermittlung GmbH (1)
Aureliusstrasse 2
52064 Aachen, Germany
Tel.: (49) 241 4560
Fax: (49) 241 4564510
Insurance Management Services
S.I.C.: 6411
N.A.I.C.S.: 524298

Aseguradora General S.A. (1)
10A Calle 3 17
Zona 10, 00110 Guatemala, Guatemala (51%)
Tel.: (502) 2285 7200
Fax: (502) 3342093
E-Mail: gerendiciageneral@generali.com.gt
Web Site: www.asegurесemejor.com
Emp.: 145
Provider of Insurance
S.I.C.: 6399
N.A.I.C.S.: 524128

Cafel Inversiones 2008, S.L. (1)
Calle Orense 2 - 7
Madrid, 28020, Spain
Tel.: (34) 981619353
Real Estate Management Services
S.I.C.: 6531
N.A.I.C.S.: 531390

Care Management Network Inc. (1)
Erin Court Suite 1 Upper Bishop's Court Hill
Saint Michael, Barbados
Tel.: (246) 246 467 7120
E-Mail: info@canmednet.com
Elder & Disability Care Services
S.I.C.: 8322
N.A.I.C.S.: 624120

Central Erste Immobilien AG&KG (1)
Hansaring 40-50
50670 Cologne, Germany
Tel.: (49) 221 1636 0
Fax: (49) 221 1636200
Real Estate Development Services
S.I.C.: 6531
N.A.I.C.S.: 531390

City Empiria a.s. (1)
Hvezdova 1716/2b Praha 4 Nusle
Prague, 14078, Czech Republic
Tel.: (420) 26 1141112
Property Leasing Services
S.I.C.: 6513
N.A.I.C.S.: 531110

Flandria Participations Financieres S.A. (1)
149 Ave Louise
1050 Brussels, Belgium (100%)
Tel.: (32) 24038423
Fax: (32) 3224038301
Emp.: 5
Holding Company
S.I.C.: 6719
N.A.I.C.S.: 551112
Luc Vaeremans *(Gen Mgr)*

Generali Allgemeine Versicherungen AG (1)
Avenue Perdtemps 23
Case Postale 3000
1260 Nyon, Switzerland
Tel.: (41) 58 471 01 01
Fax: (41) 58 471 01 02
E-Mail: nonlife@generali.ch
Web Site: www.generali.ch/kontakt/kontakt-center.html
General Insurance Services
S.I.C.: 6411
N.A.I.C.S.: 524298
Peter Herzog *(Chm)*
Alfred Leu *(CEO)*

Generali Argentina S.A. (1)
Reconquista 458 - 3er Piso
C1003ABJ Buenos Aires, Argentina
Tel.: (54) 11 48577942
Fax: (54) 11 48577946
E-Mail: infogenerali@generali.com.ar
Web Site: www.generali.com.ar
Insurance Management Services
S.I.C.: 6411
N.A.I.C.S.: 524298

Generali Belgium S.A. (1)
Av Louise 149
Brussels, 1050, Belgium BE
Tel.: (32) 24038111 (100%)
Fax: (32) 24038899
E-Mail: contact@generali-international.be
Web Site: www.generali.geb.com
Emp.: 35
Provider of Insurance Products
S.I.C.: 6399
N.A.I.C.S.: 524128
Mauro Dugulin *(CEO)*

Subsidiaries:

Bureau d'Assurances et dePrets (2)
Avenue De La Salm 9
6690 Vielsalm, Belgium
Tel.: (32) 80217171
Insurance Brokerage Services
S.I.C.: 6411
N.A.I.C.S.: 524210

Groupe Vervietois d'Assureurs S.A (2)
Rue de Liege 39
4800 Verviers, Belgium
Tel.: (32) 87224742
Fax: (32) 87 22 68 81
E-Mail: info@gva-assur.be
Insurance Management Services
S.I.C.: 6411
N.A.I.C.S.: 524298

Soenen Verzekeringskantoor nv (2)
Gasthuisstraat 81
8970 Poperinge, Belgium
Tel.: (32) 57 33 41 41
Fax: (32) 57 33 74 02
E-Mail: info@soenen-verzekeringen.be
Web Site: www.soenen-verzekeringen.be
General Insurance Services
S.I.C.: 6411
N.A.I.C.S.: 524210

Webbroker S.A. (2)
Rue Defacqz 6
1050 Brussels, Belgium
Tel.: (32) 25334030
Fax: (32) 25334036
E-Mail: mefirst.be@gmail.com
Web Site: www.mefirst.be
Emp.: 4
Insurance Management Services
S.I.C.: 6411
N.A.I.C.S.: 524298
Johan Bertrands *(Gen Mgr)*

Non-U.S. Subsidiaries:

Dedale S.A. (2)
15 Place de la Nation
75011 Paris, France
Tel.: (33) 1 58 39 30 90
Fax: (33) 1 58 39 30 99
E-Mail: dedale@dedale.net
Web Site: www.dedale.net
Emp.: 14
Human Resource Consulting Services
S.I.C.: 8999
N.A.I.C.S.: 541612
Jean Paries *(Pres)*

GENERALI Real Estate Investments B.V. (2)
Diemerhof 42
1112 XN Diemen, Noord-Holland, Netherlands
Tel.: (31) 206601802
Fax: (31) 20 6601602
Web Site: www.grei.be
Real Estate Investment Services
S.I.C.: 6531
N.A.I.C.S.: 531390

Non-U.S. Subsidiary:

MRS Bioul S.A. (3)
Avenue Louise 149
1050 Brussels, Belgium
Tel.: (32) 71 79 70 00
Fax: (32) 71 79 99 51
Real Estate Management Services
S.I.C.: 6531
N.A.I.C.S.: 531390

Generali Bulgaria Holding AD (1)
68 Kniaz Doudukov Blvd
Sofia, 1504, Bulgaria
Tel.: (359) 29267111
Fax: (359) 29267112
E-Mail: information@generali.bg
Web Site: www.generali.bg
Premiums: $37,534,272
Holding Company; Insurance Services
S.I.C.: 6719
N.A.I.C.S.: 551112
Ivaylo Yosifov *(CEO)*

Subsidiaries:

Generali Insurance AD (2)
79 Nikola Gabrovski Blvd Business center Twins Centre
Dianabad District, 1700 Sofia, Bulgaria
Tel.: (359) 2 92 67 111
Fax: (359) 2 92 67 112
E-Mail: information@generali.bg
Insurance Agency
S.I.C.: 6411
N.A.I.C.S.: 524210

Generali Zakrila Health Insurance AD (2)
68 Knyaz Alexander Dondoukov Blvd
1504 Sofia, Bulgaria
Tel.: (359) 2 92 67 111
Fax: (359) 2 92 67 112
E-Mail: information@generali.bg
Web Site: www.generali.bg/en/zakrila/
Health Care Management Services
S.I.C.: 8099
N.A.I.C.S.: 621999
Konstantin Velev *(Chm-Mgmt Bd)*
Luisa Coloni *(Deputy Chm)*
Tudor-Mircea Moldovan *(Member-Mgmt Bd)*
Marcel-Constantin Sarca *(Member-Mgmt Bd)*

Generali Colombia Seguros Generales S.A. (1)
Carrera 7 N 7213
Bogota, DC, Colombia (84%)
Tel.: (57) 16068000
Fax: (57) 12551164
Web Site: www.generali.com.co
Emp.: 40
Provider of Insurance
S.I.C.: 6399
N.A.I.C.S.: 524128

Subsidiary:

Generali Colombia Vida - Compania de Seguros S.A. (2)
Carrera 7 No 72-13
Bogota, DC, Colombia (68%)
Tel.: (57) 1 346 8888
Fax: (57) 1 319 82 80
E-Mail: info@generali.com
Web Site: www.generali.com.co
Emp.: 107
Life Insurance
S.I.C.: 6311
N.A.I.C.S.: 524113

Generali Deutschland Holding AG (1)
Tunisstr 19 23
50667 Cologne, Germany DE
Mailing Address:
Postfach 100251
D 52002 Aachen, Germany
Tel.: (49) 221420301
Telex: 832641 amac d
Fax: (49) 22142031805
E-Mail: info.holding@generali.de
Web Site: www.amb-generali.de
GE1—(DEU)
Sales Range: $1-4.9 Billion
Emp.: 354
Holding Company
S.I.C.: 6719
N.A.I.C.S.: 551112
H.C. Wolfgang Kaske *(Chm-Supervisory Bd)*
Rudolf Winkelmann *(Deputy Chm-Supervisory Bd)*
Dietmar Meister *(CEO- Member-Mgmt Bd)*
Christoph Schmallenbach *(Member-Mgmt Bd)*
Winfried Spies *(Member-Mgmt Bd)*
Torsten Utecht *(Member-Mgmt Bd)*

Subsidiaries:

AachenMunchener Lebensversicherung AG (2)
AachenMuenchener-Platz 1
52064 Aachen, Germany
Tel.: (49) 241 456 0
Fax: (49) 241 456 4510
E-Mail: service@amv.de
Web Site: www.amv.de
Life Insurance Services
S.I.C.: 6311
N.A.I.C.S.: 524113
Michael Westkamp *(Gen Mgr)*

Subsidiaries:

AM Erste Immobilien AG&Co. KG (3)
Aureliusstr 2
52064 Aachen, Germany
Tel.: (49) 241 4560
Fax: (49) 241 4565678
Real Estate Management Services
S.I.C.: 6531
N.A.I.C.S.: 531390

ATLAS Dienstleistungen fur Vermogensberatung GmbH. (3)
Muenchener Str 1
60329 Frankfurt, Germany
Tel.: (49) 69 23 84 0
Fax: (49) 69 23 84 185
Financial Advisory Services
S.I.C.: 6282
N.A.I.C.S.: 523930
Reinfried Pohl *(Gen Mgr)*

Subsidiaries:

AM Vertriebsservice-Gesellschaft Personenversicherungen mbH (4)
Munchener Strasse 1
Frankfurt am Main, 60329, Germany
Tel.: (49) 69 2 38 40
Fax: (49) 69 2 38 43 60
Insurance Management Services
S.I.C.: 6411
N.A.I.C.S.: 524298

AM Vertriebsservice-Gesellschaft Sachversicherungen mbH (4)
Muenchener Strabe 1
60329 Frankfurt am Main, Hesse, Germany
Tel.: (49) 69 23840
Fax: (49) 69 2384185
General Insurance Services
S.I.C.: 6411
N.A.I.C.S.: 524210
Reinfried Pohl *(Mng Dir)*

Schloss Bensberg Management GmbH (3)
Im Schlosspark 10
51429 Bergisch Gladbach, Germany
Tel.: (49) 22 04 830 0
Fax: (49) 22 04 830 200
E-Mail: vermietung@schlossbensberg.de
Web Site: www.schlossbensberg.de
Real Estate Development Services
S.I.C.: 6531
N.A.I.C.S.: 531390

AM Vers Erste Immobilien KG (2)
AachenMunchener Plot 1
52064 Aachen, Germany
Tel.: (49) 241 4560
Fax: (49) 241 4564510
E-Mail: service@amv.de
Real Estate Management Services
S.I.C.: 6531
N.A.I.C.S.: 531390

AMB Generali Immobilien GmbH (2)
Tunisia
01923 Cologne, Germany (100%)
Tel.: (49) 2214203100
Fax: (49) 2214203152
E-Mail: info.infomatic@generali.de
Web Site: www.amb-immobilien.de

Assicurazioni Generali S.p.A.—(Continued)

Emp.: 60
Manager of Real Estate Holdings
S.I.C.: 6531
N.A.I.C.S.: 531210

AMCO Beteiligungs-GmbH (2)
Aachener-und-Muenchener-Allee 9
52074 Aachen, Germany
Tel.: (49) 241 4 61 01
Fax: (49) 241 4 61 1805
Investment Management Services
S.I.C.: 6211
N.A.I.C.S.: 523999

Badenia Bausparkasse AG (2)
Badeniaplatz 1
76114 Karlsruhe, Germany (99.99%)
Tel.: (49) 7219950
Fax: (49) 7219952799
E-Mail: service@badenia.de
Web Site: www.badenia.de
Rev.: $1,500,000,000
Emp.: 600
Construction Services
S.I.C.: 1522
N.A.I.C.S.: 236118
Jochen Petin *(Gen Mgr)*

Deutsche Bausparkasse Badenia AG (2)
Badenia Platz 1
76114 Karlsruhe, Germany (100%)
Tel.: (49) 7219950
Fax: (49) 7219952799
E-Mail: service@badenia.de
Web Site: www.badenia.de
Emp.: 600
Home Remodeling & Fashions
S.I.C.: 5211
N.A.I.C.S.: 444110
Dietrich Schroeger *(Chm-Supervisory Bd)*
Jochen Petin *(CEO)*

Subsidiary:

DBB Vermogensverwaltung GmbH & Co. KG (3)
Badeniaplatz 1
Karlsruhe, 76189, Germany
Tel.: (49) 7219950
Real Estate Management Services
S.I.C.: 6531
N.A.I.C.S.: 531390

ENVIVAS Krankenversicherung AG (2)
Gereonswall 68
50670 Cologne, Germany
Tel.: (49) 221 1636 0
Fax: (49) 221 1636 2561
E-Mail: info@envivas.de
Web Site: www.envivas.de
Insurance Management Services
S.I.C.: 6411
N.A.I.C.S.: 524298
Heinz Teuscher *(Chm)*
Willi Alfter *(Chm-Supervisory Bd)*

Generali Beteiligungs AG (2)
Adenauerring 7
81737 Munich, Germany
Tel.: (49) 8951210
Fax: (49) 8951211000
E-Mail: service@generali.de
Emp.: 1,500
General Insurance Services
S.I.C.: 6411
N.A.I.C.S.: 524210

Subsidiaries:

BBG Beteiligungsgesellschaft m.b.H. (3)
Adenauerring 7
81737 Munich, Bavaria, Germany
Tel.: (49) 89 51210
Investment Management Services
S.I.C.: 6211
N.A.I.C.S.: 523999

Deutscher Lloyd GmbH (3)
Lietzenburger Str 75
10719 Berlin, Germany
Tel.: (49) 30 85 95 34 0
Fax: (49) 30 85 95 34 40
E-Mail: mail@deutscherlloyd.de
Web Site: www.deutscherlloyd.de
General Insurance Services
S.I.C.: 6411
N.A.I.C.S.: 524210

Generali Deutschland Pensor Pensionsfonds AG (3)
Oeder Weg 151
60318 Frankfurt am Main, Germany
Tel.: (49) 69 1502 2473
Fax: (49) 69 1502 2001
E-Mail: info@generali-bav.de
Web Site: www.generali-deutschland.de/online/portal/gdinternet/en/content/311210/311146
Pension Fund Management Services
S.I.C.: 6371
N.A.I.C.S.: 525110
Michael Stille *(CEO)*

Thuringia Versicherungs-vermittlungs-GmbH & Co. (3)
Adenauerring 9
81737 Munich, Germany
Tel.: (49) 89 1234021
Fax: (49) 89 1234022
E-Mail: info@thuringia.de
General Insurance Services
S.I.C.: 6411
N.A.I.C.S.: 524210

Volksfursorge Pensionskasse AG (3)
Besenbinderhof 43
20097 Hamburg, Germany
Tel.: (49) 40 286550 30
Pension Fund Management Services
S.I.C.: 6371
N.A.I.C.S.: 525110

Generali Deutschland Immobilien GmbH (2)
Tunisstrasse 19-23
50354 Cologne, Germany
Tel.: (49) 221 4203 04
Fax: (49) 221 4203 4307
Web Site: www.generali-deutschland.de/online/portal/gdinternet/en/content/311210/311224
Real Estate Development Services
S.I.C.: 6531
N.A.I.C.S.: 531390

Subsidiaries:

Generali European Retail IG KG (3)
Tunisstr 19-23
50667 Cologne, Germany
Tel.: (49) 221 420301
Investment Management Services
S.I.C.: 6211
N.A.I.C.S.: 523999

Verwaltungsgesellschaft Marienplatz-Galerie Schwerin mbH (3)
Am Borsigturm 33
13507 Berlin, Germany
Tel.: (49) 30 2060700
Fax: (49) 30 20607079
Real Estate Management Services
S.I.C.: 6531
N.A.I.C.S.: 531390

Generali Deutschland Informatik Services GmbH (2)
Anton Kurze Allee 16
52064 Aachen, Germany (100%)
Tel.: (49) 24146102
Fax: (49) 241461753481
E-Mail: info.informatik@generali.de
Web Site: www.generali-informatik.de
Emp.: 1,300
Information Technology Services
S.I.C.: 7373
N.A.I.C.S.: 541512

Generali Deutschland Pensionskasse AG (2)
AachenMuenchener-Platz 1
52001 Aachen, Germany
Tel.: (49) 221 3395 7780
Fax: (49) 221 3395 7849
E-Mail: info.pensionskasse@generali.de
Web Site: www.generali-pensionskasse.de
Pension Fund Management Services
S.I.C.: 6371
N.A.I.C.S.: 525110
Johannes Booms *(Gen Mgr)*

Generali Deutschland Schadenmanagement GmbH. (2)
Gereonswall 68
50670 Cologne, Germany
Tel.: (49) 2233 3989 56655
General Insurance Services
S.I.C.: 6411
N.A.I.C.S.: 524210

Generali Deutschland Services GmbH (2)
Maria Theresia Allee 38
52064 Aachen, Germany (51%)
Tel.: (49) 24146101
Fax: (49) 2414613519
E-Mail: info.services@generali.de
Web Site: www.generali-deutschland.de
Insurance Services
S.I.C.: 6311
N.A.I.C.S.: 524113

Generali Deutschland SicherungsManagement GmbH. (2)
Unter Sachsenhausen 27
50667 Cologne, Germany
Tel.: (49) 221 4203 5155
Fax: (49) 221 4203 5158
E-Mail: info.sima@generali.de
Web Site: www.generali-sima.de
Security Management Services
S.I.C.: 7382
N.A.I.C.S.: 561621

Generali Investments Deutschland Kapitalanlagegesellschaft mbH (2)
Unter Sachsenhausen 27
50667 Cologne, Germany (100%)
Mailing Address:
Postfach 10 06 54
50446 Cologne, Germany
Tel.: (49) 2211636412
Fax: (49) 22 1 42 035444
E-Mail: service@geninvest.de
Web Site: www.geninvest.de
Emp.: 110
Fund Investments
S.I.C.: 6722
N.A.I.C.S.: 525910
Heinz Gawlak *(Mng Dir)*

Generali Versicherung AG (2)
Adenauerring 7
81737 Munich, Germany
Tel.: (49) 8951210
Fax: (49) 8951211000
E-Mail: service@generali.de
Web Site: www.generali.de
Sales Range: $1-4.9 Billion
Emp.: 2,580
Financial Services
S.I.C.: 6211
N.A.I.C.S.: 523999
Dietmar Meister *(Chm-Supervisory Bd)*
Winfried Spies *(CEO)*

Subsidiaries:

Aachener und Muenchener Lebensversicherung AG (3)
Aurelius Strasse 2
D 52064 Aachen, Germany DE
Tel.: (49) 2414560 (86.04%)
Fax: (49) 2414564510
E-Mail: service@amv.de
Web Site: www.amv.de
Emp.: 800
Life Insurance Products
S.I.C.: 6311
N.A.I.C.S.: 524113
Michael Westkamp *(CEO)*

Aachener und Munchener Versicherung AG (3)
AachenMunchener-Platz 1
D 52064 Aachen, Germany DE
Tel.: (49) 2414560 (96.99%)
Fax: (49) 2414564510
E-Mail: service@amv.de
Web Site: www.amv.de
Emp.: 1,300
Fire, Marine, Property & Casualty Insurance Services
S.I.C.: 6399
N.A.I.C.S.: 524128
Michael Wistkame *(Mng Dir)*

Cosmos Versicherung AG (3)
Halbergstrasse 52 54
D 66101 Saarbrucken, Germany (100%)
Tel.: (49) 68196660
Fax: (49) 6819666633
E-Mail: info@cosmosdirekt.de
Web Site: www.cosmosdirekt.de
Emp.: 1,500
Provider of Property & Casualty Insurance Products
S.I.C.: 6399
N.A.I.C.S.: 524128
Bernd Andres *(Pres)*

Subsidiaries:

ALLWO GmbH (4)
Lange Laube 7
Hannover, 30159, Germany
Tel.: (49) 221 4203110
Fax: (49) 221 4203145
Real Estate Development Services
S.I.C.: 6531
N.A.I.C.S.: 531390

Cosmos Finanzservice GmbH (4)
Halbergstrasse 50-60
66121 Saarbrucken, Germany
Tel.: (49) 681 9 66 66 66
Fax: (49) 681 9 66 66 33
E-Mail: info@cosmosdirekt.de
Financial Management Services
S.I.C.: 6211
N.A.I.C.S.: 523999

Cosmos Krankenversicherung AG (4)
Halbergstrasse 52 54
D 66121 Saarbrucken, Germany DE
Tel.: (49) 6819666666 (100%)
Fax: (49) 6819666633
E-Mail: info@cosmosdirekt.de
Web Site: www.cosmosdirekt.de
Emp.: 1,200
Health Insurance Products
S.I.C.: 6311
N.A.I.C.S.: 524113
Peter Stockhorst *(Pres)*

Cosmos Lebensversicherungs AG (4)
Halbergstrasse 52 54
D 66121 Saarbrucken, Germany (100%)
Tel.: (49) 68196660
Fax: (49) 6819666633
E-Mail: info@cosmosdirekt.de
Web Site: www.cosmosdirekt.de
Emp.: 1,000
Life Insurance Products
S.I.C.: 6311
N.A.I.C.S.: 524113
Carsten Dageforde *(Exec VP)*
Peter Stockhost *(Pres)*

Subsidiary:

Cosmos Fixed Assets GmbH (5)
Halbergstr 50-60
66121 Saarbrucken, Germany
Tel.: (49) 68196660
Fax: (49) 6819666633
Asset Management Services
S.I.C.: 6282
N.A.I.C.S.: 523920

Dialog Lebensversicherungs-AG (3)
Halder Strasse 29
86150 Augsburg, Germany (100%)
Mailing Address:
Postfach 10 15 43
86005 Augsburg, Germany
Tel.: (49) 8213190
Fax: (49) 8213191533
E-Mail: info@dialog-leben.de
Web Site: www.dialog-leben.de
Emp.: 100
Life Insurance Products
S.I.C.: 6311
N.A.I.C.S.: 524113
Rudiger Burchardi *(Mng Dir)*

Generali Lebensversicherung AG (3)
Oeder Weg 151
60318 Frankfurt am Main, Germany (100%)
Tel.: (49) 6915022000
Fax: (49) 6915022885
E-Mail: info@generali.de
Web Site: www.generali.de
Emp.: 250
S.I.C.: 6399
N.A.I.C.S.: 524128
Michael Stille *(Mng Dir)*

Subsidiaries:

Generali 3. Immobilien AG & Co. KG (4)
Adenauerring 7
81737 Munich, Germany

Tel.: (49) 89 5121 0
Fax: (49) 89 51211000
Financial Management Services
S.I.C.: 6211
N.A.I.C.S.: 523999

Generali Partner GmbH (4)
Adenauerring 7
81737 Munich, Germany
Tel.: (49) 89 51210
Fax: (49) 89 51211000
General Insurance Services
S.I.C.: 6411
N.A.I.C.S.: 524210

Generali Pensionsmanagement GmbH (4)
Besenbinderhof 43
20097 Hamburg, Germany
Tel.: (49) 40 2865 4050
Fax: (49) 40 28654700
Pension Fund Services
S.I.C.: 6371
N.A.I.C.S.: 525110

Generali Properties Fund I GmbH & Co. KG. (4)
Lindwurmstr 76
80337 Munich, Germany
Tel.: (49) 89 726103930
Fax: (49) 89 726103946
E-Mail: info@gll-partners.com
Emp.: 70
Property Management Services
S.I.C.: 6531
N.A.I.C.S.: 531311
Gerd Kremer *(Gen Mgr)*

GLL AMB Generali Properties Fund II GmbH & Co. KG (4)
Lindwurmstrasse 76
80337 Munich, Germany
Tel.: (49) 89 726 100
Property Management Services
S.I.C.: 6531
N.A.I.C.S.: 531311

Thuringia Generali 1. Immobilien AG & Co. KG (4)
Adenauerring 7
81737 Munich, Germany
Tel.: (49) 89 51210
Fax: (49) 89 51211000
E-Mail: service@generali.de
Emp.: 4,000
Real Estate Rental Services
S.I.C.: 6531
N.A.I.C.S.: 531390

Thuringia Generali 2. Immobilien AG & Co. KG (4)
Sonnenstrasse 31
80331 Munich, Germany
Tel.: (49) 89 2103760
General Insurance Services
S.I.C.: 6411
N.A.I.C.S.: 524210

Volksfursorge 1. Immobilien AG & Co. KG (4)
Besenbinderhof 43
20097 Hamburg, Germany
Tel.: (49) 40 2865 0
Fax: (49) 40 28653369
Financial Management Services
S.I.C.: 6211
N.A.I.C.S.: 523999

Volksfursorge Fixed Asset GmbH (4)
Besenbinderhof 43
20097 Hamburg, Germany
Tel.: (49) 40 380781454
Asset Management Services
S.I.C.: 6282
N.A.I.C.S.: 523920

U.S. Subsidiary:

Beacon Capital Strategic L.P. (4)
200 State St 5th Fl
Boston, MA 02109
Tel.: (617) 457-0400
Fax: (617) 457-0499
Real Estate Management Services
S.I.C.: 6531
N.A.I.C.S.: 531390

Verwaltungsgesellschaft Wohnen am Westhafen mbH (3)
Kennedyallee 109
60596 Frankfurt am Main, Germany
Tel.: (49) 69 9636610
Fax: (49) 69 96366188
Emp.: 8
Real Estate Development Services
S.I.C.: 6531
N.A.I.C.S.: 531390
Max Baum *(Gen Mgr)*

Non-U.S. Subsidiaries:

Adriatica Participations Financieres S.A. (3)
149 Avenue Louise
1050 Brussels, Belgium (100%)
Financial Services
S.I.C.: 6099
N.A.I.C.S.: 522320

CA Global Property Internationale Immobilien AG (3)
Herrengasse 17
1010 Vienna, Austria
Tel.: (43) 1 534 73 322
Fax: (43) 1 534 73 235
Investment Management Services
S.I.C.: 6211
N.A.I.C.S.: 523999

Generali Immobilien AG (3)
Landskrongasse 1-3
Vienna, 1010, Austria
Tel.: (43) 1 53401 0
Fax: (43) 1 53401 1226
Real Estate Development Services
S.I.C.: 6531
N.A.I.C.S.: 531390

Non-U.S. Subsidiaries:

Generali Velky Spalicek S.r.o. (4)
Vaclavske namesti 823/33
110 00 Prague, Czech Republic
Tel.: (420) 5 43 23 73 85
Fax: (420) 5 43 23 73 81
E-Mail: velkyspalicek@velkyspalicek.cz
Web Site: www.velkyspalicek.cz
Emp.: 5
Shopping Mall Operator
S.I.C.: 6512
N.A.I.C.S.: 531120

Non-U.S. Subsidiary:

Fortuna Lebens-Versicherungs AG Vaduz (5)
Staedtle 35
LI 9490 Vaduz, Liechtenstein (100%)
Tel.: (423) 2361545
Fax: (423) 2361546
E-Mail: fl.service@fortuna.li
Web Site: www.fortuna.li
Emp.: 25
Life Insurance Products
S.I.C.: 6311
N.A.I.C.S.: 524113

Vaci utca Center Kft (4)
Vaci Utca 81
Budapest, 1056, Hungary
Tel.: (36) 1 411 0442
Fax: (36) 1 235 0007
E-Mail: vaciutca@vaciutcacenter.hu
Web Site: www.vaciutcacenter.hu
Emp.: 2
Real Estate Management Services
S.I.C.: 6531
N.A.I.C.S.: 531390
Marcus Evans *(Gen Mgr)*

Generali Leasing GmbH (3)
Landskrong 1-3
1010 Vienna, Austria
Tel.: (43) 1 51403 4229
Fax: (43) 1 51403 4594
Car Leasing Services
S.I.C.: 7515
N.A.I.C.S.: 532112

Generali Sales Promotion GmbH (3)
Neusetzgasse 1
1100 Vienna, Austria
Tel.: (43) 1 879 54 50 71015
Fax: (43) 1 879 54 50 71022
Web Site: www.generali.at/generali-gruppe/unternehmen/konzerngesellschaften.html
Marketing Consulting Services
S.I.C.: 8742
N.A.I.C.S.: 541613

Subsidiaries:

Car Care Consult Versicherungsmakler GmbH (4)
Neusetzg 1
1100 Vienna, Austria
Tel.: (43) 1 6419977
Fax: (43) 1 6419977 55
E-Mail: office@carcc.at
General Insurance Services
S.I.C.: 6411
N.A.I.C.S.: 524210

Generali TVG Vorsorgemanagement GmbH (4)
Alpenstrasse 102-104
5020 Salzburg, Austria
Tel.: (43) 662 876636 0
Fax: (43) 662 878973
E-Mail: office.tvg@generali.at
Web Site: www.generali-tvg.at
Pension Fund Management Services
S.I.C.: 6371
N.A.I.C.S.: 525110

PSC Insurance-Consulting GmbH (4)
Burggasse 9
Klagenfurt, 9020, Austria
Tel.: (43) 463 58 29 451
E-Mail: office@pscinsurance.at
Web Site: www.pscinsurance.at
Business Management Consulting Services
S.I.C.: 8748
N.A.I.C.S.: 541618

Generali Vermogensberatung GmbH (3)
Landskrongasse 1-3
1010 Vienna, Austria
Tel.: (43) 153401 0
Fax: (43) 153401 1226
General Insurance Services
S.I.C.: 6411
N.A.I.C.S.: 524210

PCS Praha Center Ssro (3)
Vaclavske Namesti c Evid 33 c p 823N
110 00 Prague, Czech Republic
Tel.: (420) 221 091 371
Emp.: 3
Real Estate Management Services
S.I.C.: 6531
N.A.I.C.S.: 531390
Jaroslav Kratochvil *(Gen Mgr)*

RISK-AKTIV Versicherungsservice GmbH (3)
Landskrongasse 1-3
1010 Vienna, Austria
Tel.: (43) 1 534 01 1461 0
Fax: (43) 1 534 01 4699
E-Mail: office@riskaktiv.at
Web Site: www.riskaktiv.at
Emp.: 120
Automotive Inspection Services
S.I.C.: 7539
N.A.I.C.S.: 811198

Louisen-Center Bad Homburg Verwaltungsgesellschaft mbH (2)
Am Borsigturm 33
Berlin, 13507, Germany
Tel.: (49) 30 2060700
Fax: (49) 30 20607079
E-Mail: info@tenkhoff-properties.com
Emp.: 15
Real Estate Management Services
S.I.C.: 6531
N.A.I.C.S.: 531390
Joachim Tenkhoff *(Gen Mgr)*

Volksfursorge AG Vertriebsgesellschaft fur Vorsorge- und Finanzprodukte (2)
Raboisen 38-40
D 20095 Hamburg, Germany DE
Tel.: (49) 40 2865 4477 (100%)
Fax: (49) 40 2865 3369
Web Site: www.volksfuersorge.de
Emp.: 1,800
Life Insurance & Financial Products
S.I.C.: 6311
N.A.I.C.S.: 524113

Subsidiary:

Dein Plus GmbH (3)
Olof-Palme-Strasse 19
60439 Frankfurt am Main, Germany
Tel.: (49) 69 95737556
Fax: (49) 69 95737555
Real Estate Management Services
S.I.C.: 6531
N.A.I.C.S.: 531390

Affiliate:

Central Krankenversicherung AG (3)
Hansaring 40 50
D 50670 Cologne, Germany DE
Tel.: (49) 22116360 (45.9%)
Fax: (49) 2211636200
E-Mail: info@central.de
Web Site: www.central.de
Emp.: 1,000
Health Insurance
S.I.C.: 6311
N.A.I.C.S.: 524113
Joachim Reith *(Chm)*

Holdings:

Engel & Voelkers AG (2)
Stadthaus Brucke 5
Hamburg, 20355, Germany (100%)
Tel.: (49) 40361310
Fax: (49) 4036131222
E-Mail: info@engelvoelkers.com
Web Site: www.engelvoelkers.com
Emp.: 300
Commercial & Residential Real Estate Services
S.I.C.: 6531
N.A.I.C.S.: 531210

Affiliate:

AdvoCard Rechtsschutzversicherung AG (2)
Heidenkampsweg 81
D 20097 Hamburg, Germany DE
Tel.: (49) 40237310 (43.54%)
Fax: (49) 4023731414
E-Mail: nachricht@advocard.de
Web Site: www.advocard.de
Emp.: 150
Provider of Legal Insurance Services
S.I.C.: 6399
N.A.I.C.S.: 524128
Peter Stahl *(Mng Dir)*

Generali do Brasil Partipacoes S.A. (1)
Avenida Rio Branco 128
20040 002 Rio de Janeiro, Brazil (79%)
Tel.: (55) 2125080100
Fax: (55) 2125070059
Web Site: www.generali.com.br
Emp.: 265
Holding Company
S.I.C.: 6719
N.A.I.C.S.: 551112
Claudio Mele *(Pres)*

Subsidiary:

Generali do Brasil Companhia Nacional de Seguros (2)
Avenida Rio Branco 128
Centro, Rio de Janeiro, 20040003, Brazil (99%)
Tel.: (55) 2125080100
Fax: (55) 2125070059
E-Mail: mrea-crestena@generali.com.br
Web Site: www.generali.com.br
Sales Range: $10-24.9 Million
Emp.: 165
Provider of Life, Retirement & Property Insurance
S.I.C.: 6399
N.A.I.C.S.: 524128
Sedereaco Paibrogleo *(Sec)*

Generali Ecuador Compania de Seguros S.A. (1)
Edificio World Trade Ctr Torre B Piso 15
Casilla, Guayaquil, 1085, Ecuador (51.37%)
Tel.: (593) 42630170
Fax: (593) 42630175
E-Mail: info.gye@generali.com.ec
Web Site: www.generali.com.ec
Emp.: 120
Insurance Services
S.I.C.: 6399
N.A.I.C.S.: 524128
Miguel Babra *(Pres)*

Generali Employee Benefits Bruxelles (1)
149 Avenue Louise
1050 Brussels, Belgium

Assicurazioni Generali S.p.A.—(Continued)

Tel.: (32) 2 5372760
Fax: (32) 2 5375266
E-Mail: contact@geb.com
Web Site: www.geb.com
Emp.: 70
Employee Benefit Consulting Services
S.I.C.: 8999
N.A.I.C.S.: 541612
Mauro Dugulin *(CEO)*
Fabiano Rossetto *(CFO)*
Marco Giacomelli *(COO)*
Ludovic Bayard *(Chief Comml Officer)*

Generali Espana, Holding de Entidades de Seguros, S.A. (1)
Orense No 2
28020 Madrid, Spain (81%)
Tel.: (34) 913301400
Fax: (34) 913301508
E-Mail: mpmartin@generali.es
Web Site: www.generali.es
Emp.: 50
Holding Company
S.I.C.: 6719
N.A.I.C.S.: 551112
Monica Monderdane *(CEO)*
Santiago Villa *(CEO)*

Subsidiaries:

Banco Vitalicio de Espana Compania Anonima de Seguros (2)
Paseo De Garcia 11
8007 Barcelona, Spain (60.46%)
Tel.: (34) 934840100
Fax: (34) 934840224
E-Mail: info@vitalicio.es
Web Site: www.vitalicio.es
Sls.: $1,141,705,224
Provider of Insurance Products
S.I.C.: 6399
N.A.I.C.S.: 524128

Generali Espana AIE (2)
Calle Orense 2
28020 Madrid, Spain
Tel.: (34) 91 330 14 00
Fax: (34) 91 590 57 90
E-Mail: info@generali.es
Web Site: www.generali.com
Insurance Management Services
S.I.C.: 6411
N.A.I.C.S.: 524298

Hermes S.L. (2)
C/ Colquide 6-2 3
Madrid, Spain
Tel.: (34) 916407640
Fax: (34) 918035300
Business Management Consulting Services
S.I.C.: 8748
N.A.I.C.S.: 541618

Vitalicio Torre Cerda S.l. (2)
C/ Orense 2
Madrid, 28020, Spain
Tel.: (34) 915244007
Fax: (34) 913301790
Emp.: 15
Real Estate Leasing Services
S.I.C.: 6519
N.A.I.C.S.: 531190

Generali France Holding S.A. (1)
7 Et 9 Blvd Haussmann
75009 Paris, France (75.58%)
Tel.: (33) 0158384000
Fax: (33) 158384005
Web Site: www.generali.fr
Emp.: 100
Holding Company
S.I.C.: 6719
N.A.I.C.S.: 551112
Eric Le Gentil *(Mng Dir-Asset Mgmt)*
Claude Tendil *(Mng Dir)*

Subsidiaries:

Europeenne de Protection Juridique S.A. (2)
7 9 Blvd Haussmann
75442 Paris, Cedex, 09, France (99.98%)
Tel.: (33) 158386951
Fax: (33) 158382867
Web Site: www.epj-assurances.com
Emp.: 50
Provider of Legal Insurance Services
S.I.C.: 6399
N.A.I.C.S.: 524128
Thearry Cassajneas *(Gen Mgr)*

Generali France Assurances S.A. (2)
7 9 Blvd Haussmann
75009 Paris, Cedex 09, France (68.96%)
Tel.: (33) 0158384000
Fax: (33) 158387109
E-Mail: info@gfa.generali.fr
Web Site: www.generali.fr
Emp.: 5,000
Provider of Insurance Products
S.I.C.: 6399
N.A.I.C.S.: 524128
Claude Tendil *(Chm & CEO)*

Subsidiaries:

E-Cie Vie S.A. (3)
7/9 Boulevard Haussmann
75009 Paris, France
Tel.: (33) 1 58 38 81 00
Web Site: www.e-cie-vie.fr
Insurance Management Services
S.I.C.: 6411
N.A.I.C.S.: 524298

Expert & Finance S.A. (3)
Le 6eme Part-Dieu - 23 Boulevard Jules Favre
69456 Lyon, France
Tel.: (33) 4 37 24 52 00
Fax: (33) 4 37 24 52 01
Web Site: www.expertetfinance.fr
Emp.: 90
Financial Management Services
S.I.C.: 6211
N.A.I.C.S.: 523999

Generali France Immobilier SAS (3)
7 Boulevard Haussmann
Paris, 75009, France
Tel.: (33) 1 58 38 23 00
Fax: (33) 1 58 38 23 55
Web Site: www.generali-immobilier.fr
Real Estate Management Services
S.I.C.: 6531
N.A.I.C.S.: 531390
Philippe Depoux *(Pres)*

Generali Habitat SCpl (3)
53 rue La Boeatie
75008 Paris, France
Tel.: (33) 1 70 08 08 08
Real Estate Management Services
S.I.C.: 6531
N.A.I.C.S.: 531390

Generali IARD S.A. (3)
7 Boulevard Haussmann
75456 Paris, France
Tel.: (33) 1 58 38 40 00
Fax: (33) 1 58 38 40 05
General Insurance Services
S.I.C.: 6411
N.A.I.C.S.: 524210

Generali Vie S.A. (3)
11 Boulevard Haussmann 09
Paris, 75311, France
Tel.: (33) 1 58 38 74 00
Fax: (33) 1 58 38 74 01
Web Site: www.generali-patrimoine.fr
Life Insurance Services
S.I.C.: 6311
N.A.I.C.S.: 524113

Subsidiaries:

COSEV@D SAS (4)
7 Boulevard Haussmann
Paris, 75009, France
Tel.: (33) 158388000
Fax: (33) 158387568
Insurance Management Services
S.I.C.: 6411
N.A.I.C.S.: 524298

Generali Gerance S.A. (4)
11 Boulevard Haussmann
75009 Paris, France
Tel.: (33) 1 58 38 74 00
Fax: (33) 1 58 38 74 01
General Insurance Services
S.I.C.: 6411
N.A.I.C.S.: 524210

Risque et Serenite S.A. (4)
41-43 Rue Saint Dominique
75007 Paris, France
Tel.: (33) 1 53 70 77 77
Fax: (33) 1 53 70 77 78
Web Site: www.risqueetserenite.fr
Venture Capital Management Services
S.I.C.: 6799
N.A.I.C.S.: 523910

L'Equite Compagnie d'Assurances et de Reassurances Contre les risques de toute nature S.A. (3)
7 Boulevard Haussmann
75442 Paris, Cedex, France (50.11%)
Tel.: (33) 1 58 38 10 10
Fax: (33) 1 58 38 11 61
Web Site: www.equite.com
Emp.: 134
Non-Life Insurance Products
S.I.C.: 6399
N.A.I.C.S.: 524128
Eric Le Gentil *(Mng Dir)*

L'Equite IARD S.A. (3)
7 Boulvard Haussmann
75009 Paris, France
Tel.: (33) 1 58 38 10 10
Fax: (33) 1 58 38 25 69
E-Mail: contact@cap-equite.com
Web Site: www.equite.com
Emp.: 5,000
Insurance Management Services
S.I.C.: 6411
N.A.I.C.S.: 524298

Suresnes Immobilier S.A. (3)
39 Bis Boulevard Mar de Lattre de Tassigny
92150 Suresnes, France
Tel.: (33) 1 47 72 74 93
Fax: (33) 1 47 72 62 77
Emp.: 2
Real Estate Management Services
S.I.C.: 6531
N.A.I.C.S.: 531390

Affiliate:

Generali Informatique S.A. (3)
7 Blvd Haussmann
75009 Paris, France (41.1%)
Tel.: (33) 158384000
Fax: (33) 1558382569
E-Mail: info@generali.fr
Web Site: www.generali.fr
Emp.: 47
Provider of Data Processing Services
S.I.C.: 7374
N.A.I.C.S.: 518210

Non-U.S. Subsidiaries:

Generali Private Equity S.A.S. (3)
Via Peri 23
6900 Lugano, Switzerland
Tel.: (41) 41 711 55 21
Investment Management Services
S.I.C.: 6211
N.A.I.C.S.: 523999

PRUDENCE CREOLE S.A. (3)
Prudence Creole 32 rue Alexis de Villeneuve
BP 301
Saint-Denis, 97466, Reunion
Tel.: (262) 262 70 95 00
Fax: (262) 262 70 95 94
E-Mail: contacts@prudencecreole.com
Web Site: www.prudencecreole.com
Insurance Management Services
S.I.C.: 6411
N.A.I.C.S.: 524298

Generali France Assurances Vie S.A. (2)
7 Boulevard Haussmann
75009 Paris, Cedex 09, France (100%)
Tel.: (33) 158382700
Fax: (33) 158382999
Web Site: www.assurances.generali.fr/
Insurance Services
S.I.C.: 6411
N.A.I.C.S.: 524210

Subsidiary:

Europ Assistance Holding S.A. (3)
7 Blvd Haussmann
75009 Paris, France FR
Tel.: (33) 158342300 (51.05%)
Fax: (33) 158342399
E-Mail: webmaster@europ-assistance.com
Web Site: www.europ-assistance.com
Sales Range: $550-599.9 Million
Emp.: 3,200
Holding Company; Medical, Travel & Automobile Assistance Services
S.I.C.: 6719
N.A.I.C.S.: 551112
Martin Vial *(CEO)*
Odile Collignon *(Deputy Mng Dir & Dir-Resources Center-Europe Assistance Grp)*

Subsidiaries:

E3 S.a.r.l. (4)
Domaine De Calas 37 Av Picasso
13480 Cabries, France
Tel.: (33) 442692874
Insurance Management Services
S.I.C.: 6411
N.A.I.C.S.: 524298

Europ Assistance France S.A. (4)
Immeuble Chaganne
1 Promenade De La Bonnette, 92230
Gennevilliers, France (100%)
Tel.: (33) 141858585
Web Site: www.europ-assistance.fr
Emp.: 700
Medical, Travel & Automobile Assistance Services
S.I.C.: 7389
N.A.I.C.S.: 541990
Catherine Buffler *(Dir-Comm)*

Europ Assistance IHS Services SAS (4)
7 Boulevard Haussmann
75309 Paris, France
Tel.: (33) 1 58 34 23 79
Fax: (33) 1 58 34 23 51
E-Mail: sales@ea-ihs.com
Web Site: www.ea-ihs.com
Emp.: 25
Health Care Services
S.I.C.: 8099
N.A.I.C.S.: 621999
Emmanuel Legeron *(CEO)*
Florence Jean *(Chief Comml Officer)*
Philippe Belliard *(Exec VP-Bus Dev-Heavy Indus, Mining & Energy)*

Non-U.S. Subsidiaries:

EA-IHS Services Nigeria Ltd (5)
Unicem Calabar Medical Center Bishop Moynagh Avenue
Calabar, Cross River State, Nigeria
Tel.: (234) 706 782 7241
E-Mail: sales@ea-ihs.com
Insurance Management Services
S.I.C.: 6411
N.A.I.C.S.: 524298

Europ Assistance Angola Lda (5)
Rua do Comandante Stona n 144 Bairro Alvalade
Luanda, Angola
Tel.: (244) 222 012 639
Fax: (244) 72 72 90 53
E-Mail: sales@ea-ihs.com
Web Site: www.ea-ihs.com
Emp.: 30
Travel & Medical Assistance Services
S.I.C.: 4729
N.A.I.C.S.: 561599
Immanuel Bouloy *(Gen Mgr)*

Europ Assistance IHS (Pty) Ltd. (5)
Valley View Office Park 680 Joseph Lister Street
Florida, 1709, South Africa
Tel.: (27) 11 991 9032
Fax: (27) 11 991 9027
E-Mail: sales@ea-ihs.com
Health Care Services
S.I.C.: 8099
N.A.I.C.S.: 621999

Icare S.A. (4)
160 bis rue de Paris
92100 Boulogne-Billancourt, France
Tel.: (33) 1 41 10 19 00
Fax: (33) 1 41 10 19 83
E-Mail: commercial@icare.europ-assistance.com
Web Site: www.icare-service.com
Emp.: 70
Automobile Repair & Maintenance Services
S.I.C.: 7539
N.A.I.C.S.: 811198
Pascal Briodin *(Gen Mgr)*

Subsidiary:

Icare Assurance S.A. (5)
160b Rue De Paris
92100 Boulogne-Billancourt, France
Tel.: (33) 141101900
Fax: (33) 141101919
Insurance Management Services
S.I.C.: 6411
N.A.I.C.S.: 524298

U.S. Subsidiaries:

CSA Inc. (4)
11 N 26th St
Billings, MT 59101
Tel.: (406) 252-4357
Fax: (406) 252-7705
Toll Free: (800) 247-1161
Emp.: 60
Business Support Services
S.I.C.: 7389
N.A.I.C.S.: 561499
Guillaume Deybach *(CEO)*

Europ Assistance North America, Inc. (4)
7901 SW 36th St Ste 100
Davie, FL 33328-1914
Tel.: (954) 370-1399
Health Care Services
S.I.C.: 8099
N.A.I.C.S.: 621999

Europ Assistance USA Inc. (4)
4330 EW Hwy Ste 1000
Bethesda, MD 20814
Tel.: (240) 330-1000
Fax: (240) 306-0562
E-Mail: info@europassistance-usa.com
Web Site: www.worldwideassistance.com
Emergency Relief Services
S.I.C.: 8322
N.A.I.C.S.: 624230
Guillaume Deybach *(CEO)*
Donald Vetal, Jr. *(CFO)*

Global Medical Management Inc. (4)
1300 Concord Ter Ste 300
Sunrise, FL 33323
Tel.: (954) 370-6404
Fax: (954) 370-8130
Toll Free: (800) 682-6065
E-Mail: contact@gmmi.com
Web Site: www.gmmi.com
Health Care Management Services
S.I.C.: 8099
N.A.I.C.S.: 621999
Martin B. Smith, Jr. *(Founder)*
Alex Kroon *(Pres & CEO)*
Raija Hoppula Itzchaki *(COO)*

Non-U.S. Subsidiaries:

Europ Assistance A/S (4)
Teglvaerksgade 37
2100 Copenhagen, Denmark
Tel.: (45) 70 20 21 71
Fax: (45) 70 20 21 72
Health Care Services
S.I.C.: 8099
N.A.I.C.S.: 621999

Europ Assistance Argentina S.A. (4)
Calle Carlos Pellegrini 1149 8 Piso
C1009ABW Buenos Aires, Argentina (66%)
Tel.: (54) 11 4322 4700
Fax: (54) 11 4322 4777
E-Mail: marketingcorporativo@europ-assistance.com.ar
Web Site: www.europ-assistance.com.ar
Sales Range: $10-24.9 Million
Emp.: 60
Medical, Travel & Automobile Assistance Services
S.I.C.: 7389
N.A.I.C.S.: 541990

Europ Assistance Belgium S.A. (4)
Blvd Du Triomphe 172
Brussels, 1160, Belgium (100%)
Tel.: (32) 25337575
Fax: (32) 25337807
E-Mail: admin@europ-assistance.be
Web Site: www.europ-assistance.com
Emp.: 200
Medical, Travel & Automobile Assistance Services
S.I.C.: 7389
N.A.I.C.S.: 541990
Devos Nadine *(Sec)*

Subsidiary:

Europ Assistance Services S.A. (5)
Boulevard Du Triomflaan 172
1160 Brussels, Belgium
Tel.: (32) 25337575
Fax: (32) 25337807
Emergency Relief Services
S.I.C.: 8322
N.A.I.C.S.: 624230

Europ Assistance Canada Inc. (4)
9th Floor 150 Commerce Valley Drive West
Thornhill, ON, L3T 7Z3, Canada
Tel.: (905) 532-3669
Fax: (905) 762-5191
E-Mail: info@europ-assistance.ca
Web Site: www.europassistance-canada.ca
Health & Travel Assistance Services
S.I.C.: 9441
N.A.I.C.S.: 923130

Subsidiary:

CMN Global Inc. (5)
150 Commerce Valley Drive West 9th Floor
Thornhill, ON, L3T 7Z3, Canada
Tel.: (905) 669-4333
Fax: (905) 669-2318
Toll Free: (800) 310-6970
E-Mail: info@cmn-global.com
Web Site: www.cmn-global.com
Medical Insurance Services
S.I.C.: 6321
N.A.I.C.S.: 524114
Alex Kroon *(Pres & CEO)*
Ken Gibbons *(CFO)*
Derrick Davidson *(COO)*
Peter Lozier *(Chief Network Officer)*

Europ Assistance CEI OOO (4)
Str Letnikovskaya d 11/10
115114 Moscow, Russia
Tel.: (7) 495 787 21 79
Fax: (7) 495 787 21 77
E-Mail: expat@europ-assistance.ru
Web Site: www.europ-assistance.ru
Medical & Travel Assistance Services
S.I.C.: 9441
N.A.I.C.S.: 923130

Europ Assistance Espana S.A. de Seguros y Reaseguros (4)
Calle Orense 2
28020 Madrid, Spain (95%)
Tel.: (34) 915972125
Fax: (34) 915145950
E-Mail: info@europ-assistance.es
Web Site: www.europ-assistancetechnical.es
Sls.: $3,932,638
Emp.: 275
Medical, Travel & Automobile Assistance Services
S.I.C.: 7389
N.A.I.C.S.: 541990

Subsidiaries:

Coris Gestion S.l. (5)
Calle Santa Engracia 179
Madrid, 28003, Spain
Tel.: (34) 915149804
Fax: (34) 915149892
E-Mail: coris@coris.es
Web Site: www.coris.es
Travel Assistance Services
S.I.C.: 4729
N.A.I.C.S.: 561599

Europ Assistance Travel S.A. (5)
Orense 4 Pl 12
Madrid, 28020, Spain
Tel.: (34) 915 149 900
Fax: (34) 915 550 382
Travel & Medical Assistance Services
S.I.C.: 4729
N.A.I.C.S.: 561599

Europ Assistance Gesellschaft m.b.H. (4)
Kratochwjlestrasse 4
1220 Vienna, Austria
Tel.: (43) 1 3195570 0
Fax: (43) 1 319557032
E-Mail: info@europ-assistance.at
Web Site: www.europ-assistance.at
Emp.: 150
Medical Assistance Services
S.I.C.: 9441
N.A.I.C.S.: 923130
Jean-Francois Diet *(CEO & Gen Mgr)*

Europ Assistance India Pvt. Ltd. (4)
301 C Wing Business Square Andheri Kurla Road Chakala
Andheri East, Mumbai, 400093, India
Tel.: (91) 22 6734 7878
Fax: (91) 22 6734 7888
E-Mail: enquiry@europ-assistance.in
Web Site: www.europ-assistance.in
Emp.: 62
Medical Assistance Services
S.I.C.: 9441
N.A.I.C.S.: 923130
Vikram Mehta *(Gen Mgr)*

Europ Assistance Italia S.p.A. (4)
Piazza Trento 8
20135 Milan, Italy (56.43%)
Tel.: (39) 02583841
Fax: (39) 0258384486
E-Mail: calleura@europassistance.it
Web Site: www.europassistance.it
Emp.: 800
Medical, Travel & Automobile Assistance Services
S.I.C.: 7389
N.A.I.C.S.: 541990

Subsidiaries:

Europ Assistance Service SpA (5)
Piazza Trento 8
Milan, 20135, Italy
Tel.: (39) 02 58 24 1
Fax: (39) 02 58 38 44 54
Travel & Healthcare Assistance Services
S.I.C.: 4729
N.A.I.C.S.: 561599
Paolo Frapiccini *(Gen Dir)*

Europ Assistance Trade S.p.A. (5)
Piazza Trento 8
20135 Milan, Italy
Tel.: (39) 02 58 24 1
Fax: (39) 02 58 47 71 28
Travel & Healthcare Assistance Services
S.I.C.: 4729
N.A.I.C.S.: 561599

Europ Assistance Kft. (4)
Devai St 26 28
1134 Budapest, Hungary (74%)
Tel.: (36) 014743000
Fax: (36) 014584445
E-Mail: info@europ-assistance.hu
Web Site: www.europ-assistance.hu
Emp.: 70
Medical, Travel & Automobile Assistance Services
S.I.C.: 7389
N.A.I.C.S.: 541990
Laszlo Kalmar *(Mng Dir)*

Europ Assistance Nederlands BV (4)
Keulenstraat 13
7418 ET Deventer, Netherlands
Tel.: (31) 570 78 31 00
Fax: (31) 570 78 30 39
E-Mail: info@europ-assistance.nl
Web Site: www.europ-assistance.nl
Emergency Relief Services
S.I.C.: 8322
N.A.I.C.S.: 624230

Europ Assistance NL Holding BV (4)
Keulenstraat 13
7418 ET Deventer, Netherlands
Tel.: (31) 570 78 31 00
Fax: (31) 570 78 30 29
E-Mail: info@vhd.nl
Investment Management Services
S.I.C.: 6211
N.A.I.C.S.: 523999

Subsidiary:

Coris the Netherlands BV (5)
Keulenstraat - 13
7418 ET Deventer, Overijssel, Netherlands
Tel.: (31) 20 6005440
Fax: (31) 20 6982753
Financial Management Services
S.I.C.: 6211
N.A.I.C.S.: 523999

Europ Assistance Oceanie SAS (4)
22 Rue Nansouty
98713 Papeete, French Polynesia
Tel.: (689) 50 78 50
Fax: (689) 50 78 51
Web Site: www.europ-assistance.pf
Medical Assistance Sercives
S.I.C.: 9441
N.A.I.C.S.: 923130

Europ Assistance Polska Sp zoo (4)
ul Woloska 5
Warsaw, 02-675, Poland
Tel.: (48) 22 205 50 00
Fax: (48) 22 205 50 20
E-Mail: marketing@europ-assistance.pl
Web Site: www.europ-assistance.pl
Emp.: 115
Emergency Relief Services
S.I.C.: 8322
N.A.I.C.S.: 624230
Robert Swiergocki *(Mgr-Ops & IT)*

Europ Assistance SA (4)
Los Conquistadores 1700 Piso 8 Oficina 8B
Santiago, Chile
Tel.: (56) 2 583 6800
Fax: (56) 2 583 6810
E-Mail: comercial@europ-assistance.cl
Web Site: www.europ-assistance.cl
Telephonic Advisory Services
S.I.C.: 6282
N.A.I.C.S.: 523930

Non-U.S. Subsidiary:

Europ Servicios S.p.A. (5)
Calle Orense 4
Madrid, 28020, Spain
Tel.: (34) 900 46 02 13
Fax: (34) 915 14 98 92
Business Management Consulting Services
S.I.C.: 8748
N.A.I.C.S.: 541618

Europ Assistance s.r.o. (4)
Pankraci 127
Prague, 140 00, Czech Republic
Tel.: (420) 2 2158 6111
Fax: (420) 2 2158 6100
E-Mail: info@ea.cz.com
Emp.: 70
Claim Assistance Services
S.I.C.: 6411
N.A.I.C.S.: 524291

Europ Assistance (Suisse) S.A. (4)
Chemin Des Coquelicots 16
1214 Vernier, Switzerland
Tel.: (41) 22939 22 44
Fax: (41) 22309 22 45
Emergency Relief Services
S.I.C.: 8322
N.A.I.C.S.: 624230

Europ Assistance Versicherungs-AG (4)
Infanterie Strasse 11
P 80797 Munich, Bavaria, Germany (100%)
Tel.: (49) 89559870
Fax: (49) 8955987155
E-Mail: info@europ-assistance.de
Web Site: www.europ-assistance.de
Rev.: $16,728,484
Emp.: 200
Medical, Travel & Automobile Assistance Services
S.I.C.: 7389
N.A.I.C.S.: 541990
Mann Fall *(Mng Dir)*

Europ Assistance Worldwide Services Pte Ltd. (4)
Nankin Row 3 Pickering St 02-15
Singapore, 048660, Singapore
Tel.: (65) 65572129
Fax: (65) 65570663
Emp.: 10
Health Care Services
S.I.C.: 8099
N.A.I.C.S.: 621999

Europ Assistance Worldwide Services (South Africa) Ltd. (4)
1 Napier Rd
Richmond, Johannesburg, Gauteng, 2001, South Africa (77%)
Mailing Address:
PO Box 5171
Halfway House 1685
Docex 31, Halfway House Midrand, South Africa

Assicurazioni Generali S.p.A.—(Continued)

Tel.: (27) 112541000
Fax: (27) 113883544
E-Mail: claims@europassistance.co.za
Web Site: www.europassistance.co.za
Sales Range: $10-24.9 Million
Emp.: 160
Medical, Travel & Automobile Assistance Services
S.I.C.: 7389
N.A.I.C.S.: 541990
Gys Steyn *(CEO-South Africa)*

Subsidiaries:

24 Fix (Pty) Ltd **(5)**
Valley View Office Park 680 Joseph Lister Road
Constantia Kloof, Johannesburg, South Africa
Tel.: (27) 860 024 349
E-Mail: info@24fix.co.za
Web Site: www.24fix.co.za
Automobile Maintenance Services
S.I.C.: 7549
N.A.I.C.S.: 811198

Access Health Africa Ltd **(5)**
680 Joseph Lister Avenue
Florida, 1709, South Africa
Tel.: (27) 119919000
Fax: (27) 119919576
Health Care Services
S.I.C.: 8082
N.A.I.C.S.: 621610

Labour Assist (Pty) Ltd **(5)**
Randburg
Johannesburg, Gauteng, South Africa
Tel.: (27) 860 767 833
E-Mail: info@labourassist.co.za
Web Site: www.labourassist.co.za
Human Resource Consulting Services
S.I.C.: 8999
N.A.I.C.S.: 541612

MRI Criticare Medical Rescue (Pty) Limited **(5)**
Joseph Lister Road
Florida, South Africa
Tel.: (27) 119918000
Health Care Services
S.I.C.: 8099
N.A.I.C.S.: 621999

VHD Omnicare BV **(4)**
Joop Geesinkweg 801
1096 AZ Amsterdam, Netherlands
Tel.: (31) 570 783100
Insurance Management Services
S.I.C.: 6411
N.A.I.C.S.: 524298

Worldwide Assistance Servicos de Assistencia Personalizados S.A. **(4)**
Avenida Presidente Wilson 231 6 Andar
Rio de Janeiro, 20030 021, Brazil (83.5%)
Tel.: (55) 2125080100
Fax: (55) 215334658
E-Mail: comercial@europ-assistance.com.br
Web Site: www.europ-assistance.com
Provider of Travel, Home, Automobile & Funeral Insurance
S.I.C.: 6399
N.A.I.C.S.: 524128

Non-U.S. Joint Venture:

Europ Assistance - Companhia Portuguesa de Seguros de Assistencia, S.A. **(4)**
Avda Columbano Bordalo Pinheiro 75 10th andar
1070-061 Lisbon, Portugal PT
Tel.: (351) 213860003
Fax: (351) 213860308
E-Mail: velculos.eap@europassistance.pt
Web Site: www.europassistance.pt
Emp.: 2,000
Medical, Travel & Automobile Assistance Services; Owned 53% by Assicurazioni Generali S.p.A. & 47% by Espirito Santo Financial Group S.A.
S.I.C.: 7389
N.A.I.C.S.: 541990
Manrico Iachia *(CEO)*

Subsidiaries:

Europ Assistance Servicos S.A. **(5)**
Av Columbano Bordalo Pinheiro n 75 10 Andar
1070-061 Lisbon, Portugal
Tel.: (351) 213 860 003
Fax: (351) 213 801 770
E-Mail: dcomercial@europ-assistance.pt
Web Site: www.europ-assistance.pt
Medical Assistance Services
S.I.C.: 9441
N.A.I.C.S.: 923130

Generali Patrimoine **(2)**
2-8 rue Luigi Cherubini
La Plaine, 93200 Saint Denis, Cedex, France (60%)
Tel.: (33) 1 58387400
Fax: (33) 1 58387401
E-Mail: info@prudencevie.fr
Web Site: www.generali-patrimoine.fr
Emp.: 40
Life Insurance Products
S.I.C.: 6311
N.A.I.C.S.: 524113

GPA-IARD S.A. **(2)**
18 Pl Des Cinq Martyrs Du Lycee Buffon
75014 Paris, France (100%)
Tel.: (33) 140471515
Fax: (33) 143271090
Web Site: www.gpa.fr
Provider of Insurance Products
S.I.C.: 6411
N.A.I.C.S.: 524298

GPA-Vie S.A. **(2)**
7/9 Blvd Haussmann
75009 Paris, France (100%)
Tel.: (33) 1 58 38 81 00
Fax: (33) 158382569
Web Site: www.gpa.fr
Emp.: 200
Insurance Products
S.I.C.: 6371
N.A.I.C.S.: 524292

Affiliates:

La Federation Continentale Compagnie d'Assurances Sur la Vie S.A. **(2)**
2-8 RueLuigi Cherubini
93200 Paris, cedex 9, France (95%)
Tel.: (33) 158387400
Fax: (33) 1 5838 7401
Web Site: www.federation-continentale.fr
Emp.: 500
Life Insurance
S.I.C.: 6311
N.A.I.C.S.: 524113

Generali Hellas A.E.A.Z. Property & Casualty Insurance Co. **(1)**
Megalou Alexandrou Ave And 1 Vas Sofias
Maroussi, 15124 Athens, Greece (99.22%)
Tel.: (30) 2106142034
Fax: (30) 2106142058
Web Site: www.generali.gr
Property & Casualty Insurance
S.I.C.: 6399
N.A.I.C.S.: 524128

Generali Hellas Insurance Company S.A. **(1)**
Ilia Iliou 35-37 & Pitheou
11743 Athens, Greece
Tel.: (30) 210 8096 300
Fax: (30) 210 8096 367
E-Mail: info@generali.gr
Web Site: www.generali.gr
Insurance Management Services
S.I.C.: 6411
N.A.I.C.S.: 524298
Panos Dimitriou *(Mng Dir)*

Generali Holding Vienna AG **(1)**
Landskrongasse 1-3
A-1010 Vienna, Austria AT
Tel.: (43) 1534010
Fax: (43) 1534011226
E-Mail: headoffice@generali.at
Web Site: www.generali-holding.at
Sales Range: $1-4.9 Billion
Emp.: 4,966
Financial Holding Company; Insurance Products, Banking & Other Financial Services
S.I.C.: 6712
N.A.I.C.S.: 551111
Dietrich Karner *(Chm-Supervisory Bd)*
Guido N. Schmidt-Chiari *(Vice Chm-Supervisory Bd)*
Peter Thirring *(CEO)*
Andreas Haschka *(Member-Mgmt Bd)*
Walter Kupec *(Member-Mgmt Bd)*
Harald Steirer *(Member-Mgmt Bd)*

Subsidiaries:

Allgemeine Immobilien-Verwaltungs GmbH **(2)**
Bauernmarkt 12
1010 Vienna, Austria (63%)
Tel.: (43) 15350101
Fax: (43) 015350250
E-Mail: aiv@generali.ag
Web Site: www.aiv-immo.at
Emp.: 40
Provider of Financial Services
S.I.C.: 6099
N.A.I.C.S.: 522320
Ruess Gerald *(Gen Mgr)*

Subsidiaries:

EA-Generali/AIV Leasing Salzburg GmbH **(3)**
Landskrompasse 123
1010 Vienna, Austria (93%)
Tel.: (43) 15350101
Fax: (43) 15350250
E-Mail: office@wiengenerali.at
Web Site: www.generali.at
Emp.: 500
Provider of Land Management Services
S.I.C.: 0762
N.A.I.C.S.: 115116
Luciano Cirina *(Chm-Mgmt Bd & Gen Mgr)*

EA-Generali/AIV Leasing St. Poelten GmbH **(3)**
Bauernmarkt 12
1010 Vienna, Austria (100%)
Tel.: (43) 15350101
Fax: (43) 153502550
E-Mail: office@generali.at
Web Site: www.generaliconnectionlineholdings.at
Land Management Services
S.I.C.: 0762
N.A.I.C.S.: 115116
Louiciano Cirina *(Mng Dir)*

Interunfall/AIV-Leasing Salzburg GmbH **(3)**
Landskrong St 123
1010 Vienna, Austria (100%)
Tel.: (43) 1514030
Fax: (43) 1514011226
E-Mail: headoffice@generali.at
Web Site: www.generali.at
Emp.: 500
Provider of Real Estate Services
S.I.C.: 6531
N.A.I.C.S.: 531390
Luciano Cirina *(Gen Mgr)*

BAWAG PSK Versicherung AG **(2)**
Kratochwjlestrasse 4
1220 Vienna, Austria
Tel.: (43) 1 54616 74000
Fax: (43) 1 54616 74700
E-Mail: online-beratung@bawagpskvers.at
Web Site: www.bawagpsk-versicherung.at
Insurance Management Services
S.I.C.: 6411
N.A.I.C.S.: 524298

Europaische Reiseversicherungs AG **(2)**
Kratochwjle Strasse 4
1220 Vienna, Austria (75%)
Tel.: (43) 013172500
Fax: (43) 13199367
E-Mail: info@europaeische.at
Web Site: www.europaeische.at
Rev.: $17,564,236
Emp.: 60
Provider of Travel Insurance
S.I.C.: 6399
N.A.I.C.S.: 524128
Martin Sturzlbaum *(Chm-Mgmt Bd & CEO)*
Jean-Francois Diet *(Member-Mgmt Bd)*
Wolfgang Lackner *(Member-Mgmt Bd)*

Subsidiaries:

Care Consult Versicherungsmakler GmbH **(3)**
Kratochwjlestrasse 4
1220 Vienna, Austria (100%)
Tel.: (43) 13172600
Fax: (43) 1317260073498
E-Mail: info@careconsult.at
Web Site: www.careconsult.at
Emp.: 5
Provider of Travel & Legal Insurance Products
S.I.C.: 6399
N.A.I.C.S.: 524128
Franz Perter *(Mng Dir)*

TTC Training Center Unternehmensberatung GmbH **(3)**
Kratochwjlestrasse 4
1220 Vienna, Austria
Tel.: (43) 1 317 25 00 73372
Fax: (43) 1 319 93 67 73372
E-Mail: info@ttc.at
Web Site: www.ttc.at
Emp.: 2
Professional Training Services
S.I.C.: 8299
N.A.I.C.S.: 611430
Christian Widerna *(Office Mgr)*

Generali Bank AG **(2)**
Landskrongasse 1-3
1010 Vienna, Austria
Tel.: (43) 1 26067 0
Fax: (43) 810500111
E-Mail: serviceteam@generalibank.at
Web Site: www.generalibank.at
Financial Advisory Services
S.I.C.: 6282
N.A.I.C.S.: 523930

Subsidiaries:

Generali FinanzService GmbH **(3)**
Landskrongasse 1-3
1010 Vienna, Austria
Tel.: (43) 1 532 19 190
Fax: (43) 1 5320949 760
E-Mail: hq@generali-finanzservice.at
Web Site: www.generali-finanzservice.at
Financial Services
S.I.C.: 6211
N.A.I.C.S.: 523999

Generali Telefon- + Auftragsservice GmbH **(3)**
Landskrongasse 1-3
1010 Vienna, Austria
Tel.: (43) 1 53401 0
Fax: (43) 1 53401 1226
General Insurance Services
S.I.C.: 6411
N.A.I.C.S.: 524210

Generali Capital Management GmbH **(2)**
Landskrongasse 1-3
Vienna, 1010, Austria
Tel.: (43) 1 5340 10
Fax: (43) 1 53401 226
Financial Management Services
S.I.C.: 6211
N.A.I.C.S.: 523999

Generali IT-Solutions GmbH **(2)**
Kratochwjlestrasse 4
1220 Vienna, Austria
Tel.: (43) 1 53401 0
Fax: (43) 1 534 01 3391
Information Technology Consulting Services
S.I.C.: 7373
N.A.I.C.S.: 541512

Generali Pensionskasse AG **(2)**
Landskrongasse 1-3
1010 Vienna, Austria
Tel.: (43) 1 53401 0
Fax: (43) 1 534011641
E-Mail: pensionskasse@generali.at
Pension Fund Management Services
S.I.C.: 6371
N.A.I.C.S.: 525110

Generali Versicherung AG **(2)**
Landskrongasse 1-3
A-1010 Vienna, Austria AT
Tel.: (43) 1534010 (92.19%)
Fax: (43) 1534011226
E-Mail: headoffice@generali.at

Web Site: www.generali.at
Emp.: 500
Life, Health, Property & Casualty Insurance Products & Services
S.I.C.: 6411
N.A.I.C.S.: 524298
Walter Kupec *(Member-Mgmt Bd)*
Harald Steirer *(Member-Mgmt Bd)*

Generali VIS Informatik GmbH (2)
Kratochwjlestr 4
1220 Vienna, Austria
Tel.: (43) 1534 01 33 83
General Insurance Services
S.I.C.: 6411
N.A.I.C.S.: 524210

MLW Beteiligungsverwaltungs GmbH (2)
Katsch An Der Mur 202
8842 Frojach-Katsch, Styria, Austria
Tel.: (43) 358888350
Fax: (43) 3588883520
Investment Management Services
S.I.C.: 6211
N.A.I.C.S.: 523999

Non-U.S. Subsidiaries:

B.V. Algemene Holding en Financierings Maatschappij (2)
Diemerhof 42
1112 XN Diemen, Netherlands (100%)
Tel.: (31) 206604461
Fax: (31) 206604455
E-Mail: info@generali.nl
Web Site: www.generali.nl
Emp.: 500
Holding Company
S.I.C.: 6719
N.A.I.C.S.: 551112
F. Wansink *(Gen Mgr)*

Europai Utazasi Biztosito Rt. (2)
Vaci Ut 3638
1132 Budapest, Hungary (70%)
Tel.: (36) 014523580
Fax: (36) 014523312
E-Mail: info@eub.hu
Web Site: www.eub.hu
Sales Range: $1-9.9 Million
Emp.: 40
Provider of Insurance Products
S.I.C.: 6399
N.A.I.C.S.: 524128

Generali Asigurari S.A. (2)
Strasse Gheorghe Manu 5 Sector 1
010442 Bucharest, Romania (83%)
Tel.: (40) 212122920
Fax: (40) 212122940
E-Mail: info@generali.ro
Web Site: www.generali.ro
Sales Range: $10-24.9 Million
Emp.: 130
Provider of Insurance Products
S.I.C.: 6399
N.A.I.C.S.: 524128

Generali Pojistovna a.s. (2)
Belehradska 132
120 84 Prague, Czech Republic (100%)
Tel.: (420) 221091000
Fax: (420) 221091200
E-Mail: kariera@generali.cz
Web Site: www.generali.cz
Emp.: 700
Insurance Products
S.I.C.: 6399
N.A.I.C.S.: 524128
Petr Kopeck *(CEO & Mng Dir)*

Subsidiaries:

Generali Car Care s.r.o. (3)
Belehradska 132
Prague, 120 84, Czech Republic
Tel.: (420) 221 091 391
Fax: (420) 221 091 385
E-Mail: generali.capital@gcapital.cz
General Insurance Services
S.I.C.: 6411
N.A.I.C.S.: 524210
Kabatova Andrea *(Gen Mgr)*

Generali Development spol sro (3)
Belehradska 132
Prague, 120 84, Czech Republic
Tel.: (420) 221 091 199
Fax: (420) 221 091 508
E-Mail: info@generalidevelopment.com
Web Site: www.generalidevelopment.com
Information Technology Consulting Services
S.I.C.: 7373
N.A.I.C.S.: 541512

Generali Penzijni Fond a.s. (3)
Belehradska 132
120 84 Prague, Czech Republic
Tel.: (420) 221 091 367
Fax: (420) 221 109 810
E-Mail: penzijni.fond@generalipf.cz
Web Site: www.generalipf.cz
Pension Fund Management Services
S.I.C.: 6371
N.A.I.C.S.: 525110

Generali Providencia Biztosito Rt. (2)
Terez Krt 42-44
1066 Budapest, Hungary (100%)
Tel.: (36) 013017100
Fax: (36) 12693996
E-Mail: generali@generali.hu
Web Site: www.generali.hu
Emp.: 5,021
Provider of Insurance Products
S.I.C.: 6399
N.A.I.C.S.: 524128
Matyas Palvolgyi *(CEO)*
Anna Ageadus *(CFO)*

Subsidiaries:

Autotal Biztositasi Szolgaltato Kft. (3)
Hizlalo Ter 1
Budapest, 1107, Hungary
Tel.: (36) 1 277 0514
Fax: (36) 1 431 8386
E-Mail: aimhungary@aiminsurance.eu
Insurance Management Services
S.I.C.: 6411
N.A.I.C.S.: 524298

Generali Epito- es Tervezo Kft (3)
Terez Krt 42-44
Budapest, 1066, Hungary
Tel.: (36) 1 301 7100
Fax: (36) 6 40200250
Real Estate Management Services
S.I.C.: 6531
N.A.I.C.S.: 531390

Genertel Biztosito Zrt (3)
Devai U 26-28
1134 Budapest, Hungary
Tel.: (36) 1 451 3880
Fax: (36) 1 451 3881
E-Mail: genertel@genertel.hu
Web Site: www.genertel.hu
Insurance Management Services
S.I.C.: 6411
N.A.I.C.S.: 524298

Generali Zavarovalnica d.d. (2)
Krziceva 3
1000 Ljubljana, Slovenia (67.06%)
Tel.: (386) 14757100
Fax: (386) 14757101
E-Mail: info@mail.generali.si
Web Site: www.generali.si
Emp.: 350
Provider of Personal Life & Property Insurance Products; Joint Venture of Generali Holding Vienna AG (67.06%) & Interunfall Versicherung AG (32.94%)
S.I.C.: 6311
N.A.I.C.S.: 524113
Mariana Bastar *(Mgr-Mktg)*

Holdux Beteiligungsgesellschaft (2)
St Alban-Vorstadt 17
4052 Basel, Switzerland (100%)
Holding Company
S.I.C.: 6719
N.A.I.C.S.: 551112

Generali Insurance (Thailand) Co., Ltd. (1)
16th Floor Unit 1601-2 CRC Tower All Seasons Place
Bangkok, 10330, Thailand
Tel.: (66) 2 685 3828
Fax: (66) 2 685 3830
E-Mail: info@generali.co.th
Web Site: www.generali.co.th
General Insurance Services
S.I.C.: 6411
N.A.I.C.S.: 524210

Generali Life Hellenic Insurance Company A.E. (1)
Ilia Iliou 35-37 & Pitheou
117 43 Athens, Greece (99.97%)
Tel.: (30) 2108096100
Fax: (30) 2108096400
E-Mail: info@generali.gr
Web Site: www.generali.gr
Emp.: 250
Life Insurance Services
S.I.C.: 6311
N.A.I.C.S.: 524113
Panos Dimitriou *(Mgr-Technical)*

Generali PanEurope Limited (1)
Generali House Navan Business Park
Navan, County Meath, Ireland
Tel.: (353) 46 9099 700
Fax: (353) 46 9099 849
E-Mail: enquiries@generali.ie
Web Site: www.generalipaneurope.ie
Wealth Management Services
S.I.C.: 6799
N.A.I.C.S.: 523920
Leslie Priestley *(Chm)*
Paul Gillett *(CEO)*
John Martin *(CFO)*
Cillin O'Flynn *(COO & Head-Wealth Protection & Investment Plng)*
Barry Kelly *(Chief Risk Officer)*

Generali Powszechne Towarzystwo Emerytalne S.A. (1)
Ul Postepu 15
02-676 Warsaw, Poland
Tel.: (48) 22 5430 500
Fax: (48) 22 5430 894
E-Mail: centrumklienta@generali.pl
Life Insurance Management Services
S.I.C.: 6311
N.A.I.C.S.: 524113

Generali Private Equity Investments GmbH (1)
Unter Sachsenhausen 27
50667 Cologne, Germany
Tel.: (49) 221 4203 5000
Fax: (49) 221 4203 5444
E-Mail: service@geninvest.de
Web Site: www.generali-deutschland.de/online/portal/gdinternet/en/content/311210/311224
Investment Management Services
S.I.C.: 6211
N.A.I.C.S.: 523999

Generali Realties Ltd (1)
16 Levontin
Tel Aviv, Israel
Tel.: (972) 3 5665333
Property Management Services
S.I.C.: 6531
N.A.I.C.S.: 531311

Generali Ruckversicherung AG (1)
Landskrongasse 1-3
Postfach 173
1010 Vienna, Austria
Tel.: (43) 1 53401 0
Fax: (43) 1 53401 0 11637
Web Site: www.generali.com
Reinsurance Services
S.I.C.: 6399
N.A.I.C.S.: 524130

Generali (Schweiz) Holding AG (1)
Soodmattenstrasse 10
CH 8134 Adliswil, Switzerland CH
Tel.: (41) 584724040 (57%)
Fax: (41) 584724425
E-Mail: info@generali.ch
Web Site: www.generali.ch
Emp.: 900
Holding Company; Insurance & Investment Services
S.I.C.: 6399
N.A.I.C.S.: 524128
Martin Zellweger *(Chm)*

Subsidiaries:

Fortuna Investment AG (2)
Soodmattenstr 10
8134 Adliswil, Switzerland
Tel.: (41) 58 472 5306
Fax: (41) 58 472 5339
E-Mail: investment@generali.ch
Web Site: www.generali.ch/kontakt/kontakt-center.html
Emp.: 30
Investment Management Services
S.I.C.: 6211
N.A.I.C.S.: 523999
Rene Schmidli *(Portfolio Mgr)*

Fortuna Rechtsschutz-Versicherung-Gesellschaft AG (2)
Soodmattenstrasse 2
8134 Adliswil, 1, Switzerland (100%)
Tel.: (41) 584727200
Fax: (41) 0584727201
E-Mail: info.rvg@fortuna.ch
Web Site: www.generali.ch
Emp.: 30
Provider of Legal Insurance Products
S.I.C.: 6399
N.A.I.C.S.: 524128
Edi Kruger *(Gen Mgr)*

Generali Assurances Generales (2)
Ep 3000
1260 Nyon, Switzerland (98.98%)
Tel.: (41) 223170232
Fax: (41) 0584710102
E-Mail: dossierstr-4directive@generali.ch
Web Site: www.generali.ch
Emp.: 400
Provider of Insurance
S.I.C.: 6399
N.A.I.C.S.: 524128
Alfred Lau *(Mng Dir)*

Generali Group Partner AG (2)
Soodmattenstrasse 10
8134 Adliswil, Switzerland
Tel.: (41) 44 712 44 00
Fax: (41) 44 712 55 55
General Insurance Services
S.I.C.: 6411
N.A.I.C.S.: 524210

Generali Personenversicherungen AG (2)
Soodmattenstrasse 10
PO Box 1047
CH 8134 Adliswil, Switzerland (80%)
Tel.: (41) 584724444
Fax: (41) 58 472 44 25
E-Mail: life@generali.ch
Web Site: www.generali-life.ch
Emp.: 900
Life Insurance Products
S.I.C.: 6311
N.A.I.C.S.: 524113

Non-U.S. Subsidiary:

Fortuna Investment AG (2)
Staedtle 35
9490 Vaduz, Liechtenstein
Tel.: (423) 232 0592
Fax: (423) 236 1546
Web Site: www.generali.com
Investment Management Services
S.I.C.: 6211
N.A.I.C.S.: 523999

Generali Vida Companhia de Seguros S.A. (1)
Rua Duque de Palmela 11
1269-270 Lisbon, Portugal (99.99%)
Tel.: (351) 213112800
Fax: (351) 213563067
E-Mail: europ@generali.pt
Web Site: www.generali.pt
Emp.: 25
Life Insurance
S.I.C.: 6311
N.A.I.C.S.: 524113

Generali Vietnam Life Insurance Ltd (1)
Floor 17 A&B Tower 76 Le Lai
Dist 1, Ho Chi Minh City, Vietnam
Tel.: (84) 8 6288 6888
Fax: (84) 8 6291 6308
E-Mail: info@generali-life.com.vn
Web Site: www.generali-life.com.vn
Emp.: 80
Insurance Management Services
S.I.C.: 6411
N.A.I.C.S.: 524298
George Kung *(CFO & Actuary)*
Simon Lam *(Gen Dir)*

Generali Zycie Towarzystwo Ubezpieczen S.A. (1)
Ul Postepu 15
02-676 Warsaw, Poland

Assicurazioni Generali S.p.A.—(Continued)

Tel.: (48) 22 5430 500
Fax: (48) 22 5430 894
E-Mail: centrumklienta@generali.pl
Web Site: www.generali.pl
Insurance Management Services
S.I.C.: 6411
N.A.I.C.S.: 524298

GENPAR Empreendimentos e Participacoes S.A. (1)
Avenida Rio Branco 128 Centro
Rio de Janeiro, 2004 0002, Brazil (100%)
Tel.: (55) 2125080100
Fax: (55) 2125070059
Web Site: www.generali.com.br
Emp.: 340
Holding Company
S.I.C.: 6719
N.A.I.C.S.: 551112
Federeco Barogleo *(Pres)*

Landy Courtage S.A.S. (1)
7 Boulevard Haussmann
75009 Paris, France
Tel.: (33) 8 99 54 41 43
Fax: (33) 1 55 32 40 05
Insurance Agency Services
S.I.C.: 6411
N.A.I.C.S.: 524210

Makefet Financial Services - Insurance Agency Ltd. (1)
PO Box 50445
Tel Aviv, 61500, Israel
Tel.: (972) 3 511 1777
Fax: (972) 3 510 2670
Insurance Agency Services
S.I.C.: 6411
N.A.I.C.S.: 524210

Migdal Stock Exchange Services (N.E.) Ltd. (1)
26 Saadia Gaon Street 2nd Floor
Tel Aviv, 65141, Israel
Tel.: (972) 3 519 4111
Fax: (972) 3 517 0288
Securities Brokerage Services
S.I.C.: 6211
N.A.I.C.S.: 523120

Migdal Underwriting Business (1)
26 Saadia Gaon
Tel Aviv, 67135, Israel
Tel.: (972) 3 5190441
E-Mail:
Financial Management Services
S.I.C.: 6211
N.A.I.C.S.: 523999

Mivtach-Simon Insurance Agencies Ltd. (1)
14 Achad Ha Am Street Migdal Africa Israel
Tel Aviv, 65142, Israel
Tel.: (972) 3 796 6666
Fax: (972) 3 796 6667
Web Site: www.mvs.co.il
Insurance Agency Services
S.I.C.: 6411
N.A.I.C.S.: 524210

Participatie Maatschappij Graafschap Holland N.V. (1)
Diemerhof 42
1112 XN Diemen, Netherlands NL (100%)
Tel.: (31) 0206604444
Fax: (31) 0203983000
E-Mail: sdleeuw@generali.nl
Web Site: www.generali.nl
Emp.: 450
Holding Company
S.I.C.: 6719
N.A.I.C.S.: 551112
Sergio Balbinot *(Vice Chm)*

Group:

Generali Verzekeringsgroep N.V. (2)
Diemerhof 42
Diemen, 1112XN, Netherlands (36%)
Mailing Address:
Postbus 1888
1110CL Diemen, Netherlands
Tel.: (31) 206604444
Fax: (31) 203983000
E-Mail: info@generali.nl
Web Site: www.gonorali.nl
Emp.: 450
Holding Company
S.I.C.: 6719
N.A.I.C.S.: 551112
F. Vansink *(Mng Dir)*

Subsidiaries:

ANAC Verzekeringen B.V. (3)
Vaalsebergweg 313
5628 CH Eindhoven, Netherlands
Tel.: (31) 40 2645959
Fax: (31) 40 2971525
E-Mail: info@anacverzekeringen.nl
Web Site: www.anacverzekeringen.nl
Insurance Management Services
S.I.C.: 6411
N.A.I.C.S.: 524298

Generali Insurance Co N.V (3)
Diemerhof 42
Diemen, 1112XN, Netherlands (100%)
Tel.: (31) 206604444
Fax: (31) 23983000
E-Mail: info@generali.nl
Web Site: www.generali.nl
Emp.: 400
Life Insurance
S.I.C.: 6311
N.A.I.C.S.: 524113
F. Wansink *(Mng Dir)*

Generali Levensverzekering Maatschappij N.V. (3)
Diemerhof 42
1112 XN Diemen, Netherlands
Tel.: (31) 206604444
Fax: (31) 206909501
E-Mail: info@generali.com
Emp.: 450
Insurance Management Services
S.I.C.: 6411
N.A.I.C.S.: 524298

Generali Schadeverzekering Maatschappij N.V. (3)
Diemerhof 42
Diemen, 1112 XN, Netherlands (100%)
Tel.: (31) 206604444
Fax: (31) 2063983000
E-Mail: info@generali.nl
Web Site: www.generali.nl
Emp.: 450
Insurance Products
S.I.C.: 6399
N.A.I.C.S.: 524128
G. Nolles *(Mgr-Insurance)*

Subsidiaries:

Generali Asia N.V. (2)
Diemerhof 42
1112 XN Diemen, Netherlands
Tel.: (31) 206604444
Fax: (31) 206601899
Insurance Management Services
S.I.C.: 6411
N.A.I.C.S.: 524298
F. Wansink *(Gen Mgr)*

Non-U.S. Subsidiary:

PT Asuransi Jiwa Generali Indonesia (3)
Cyber 2 Tower - 30th Floor Jalan HR Rasuna Said Blok X-5 No 13
Jakarta, 12950, Indonesia
Tel.: (62) 21 2996 3700
Fax: (62) 21 2902 1616
E-Mail: cs@generali.co.id
Web Site: www.generali.co.id
Financial Management Services
S.I.C.: 6211
N.A.I.C.S.: 523999
Edy Tuhirman *(Pres & CEO)*
Alessandro Martirani, *(CFO)*
Petrus Tatipatta *(COO)*
Maria Elvida Rita Dewi *(Chief Bus Dev Officer)*
Wianto Chen *(Chief Agency Officer)*
Rommy Rukyanto *(Chief IT Officer)*

Generali Finance B.V. (2)
Diemerhof 42
PO Box 1888
1112 XN Diemen, Netherlands (60%)
Tel.: (31) 206604444
Fax: (31) 206601602
Web Site: www.generali.nl
Emp.: 1
Insurance Services
S.I.C.: 6411
N.A.I.C.S.: 524298

Subsidiary:

Generali Capital Finance B.V. (3)
Diemerhof 42
1112 XN Diemen, Netherlands
Tel.: (31) 206604444
Fax: (31) 206601899
E-Mail: info@generali.nl
Emp.: 450
Financial Management Services
S.I.C.: 6211
N.A.I.C.S.: 523999

Generali Kent B.V. (2)
Diemerhof 42
Diemen, North Holland, 1112XN, Netherlands (80%)
Mailing Address:
PO Box 1888
1110 CL Diemen, Netherlands
Tel.: (31) 206601655
Fax: (31) 206601893
E-Mail: info@generali.nl
Web Site: www.generali.nl
Sales Range: $1-4.9 Billion
Emp.: 430
Holding Company
S.I.C.: 6719
N.A.I.C.S.: 551112
F. Von Senk *(Gen Mgr)*

Non-U.S. Subsidiary:

Generali Sigorta A.S. (3)
Bankalar Caddesi 31 33 34420
PO Box 920
Karakoy, Istanbul, 80000, Turkey (97.36%)
Tel.: (90) 2122512788
Fax: (90) 2122521838
Web Site: www.generali.com.tr
Emp.: 150
Provider of Insurance Products
S.I.C.: 6399
N.A.I.C.S.: 524128
Luchyano Dagnato *(Gen Mgr)*

Generali Turkey Holding B.V. (2)
Diemerhof 42
1112 XN Diemen, Netherlands
Tel.: (31) 20 6604444
General Insurance Services
S.I.C.: 6411
N.A.I.C.S.: 524298

Saxon Land B.V. (2)
Diemerhof 42
Diemen, Noord-Holland, 1112 XN, Netherlands
Tel.: (31) 206604444
Investment Management Services
S.I.C.: 3291
N.A.I.C.S.: 327910

Affiliate:

Redoze Holding N.V. (2)
Diemerhof 42
1112 XN Diemen, Netherlands (43.97%)
Holding Company
S.I.C.: 6719
N.A.I.C.S.: 551112

Non-U.S. Subsidiaries:

Belgica Insurance Holding S.A. (2)
149 Avenue Louise
1050 Brussels, Belgium (100%)
Holding Company
S.I.C.: 6719
N.A.I.C.S.: 551112

BSI S.A. (2)
Via Magatti 2
6900 Lugano, Switzerland
Tel.: (41) 588093111
Fax: (41) 588093678
E-Mail: info@bsibank.com
Web Site: www.ch.bsibank.com
Rev.: $272,707,467
Assets: $26,213,370,367
Liabilities: $23,540,849,925
Net Worth: $2,672,520,442
Earnings: $76,643,593
Emp.: 1,962
Fiscal Year-end: 12/31/12
Asset Management & Financial Planning Services
S.I.C.: 6282
N.A.I.C.S.: 523930
Alfredo Gysi *(Chm)*
Eugenio Brianti *(Vice Chm)*
Mario Greco *(Vice Chm)*
Stefano Coduri *(CEO & Member-Exec Bd)*
Gianni Aprile *(Deputy CEO-Strategic Plng & Corp Fin & Member-Exec Bd)*
David Matter *(Exec Officer)*
Nicola Battalora *(Member-Exec Bd & Sr Exec VP-BSI Europe)*
Hanspeter Brunner *(Member-Exec Bd & Sr Exec VP-BSI Asia)*
Rajiv Pradhan *(Member-Exec Bd & Sr Exec VP-Corp Svcs)*
Gerald Robert *(Member-Exec Bd & Sr Exec VP-BSI Latin America & Middle East)*
Renato Santi *(Member-Exec Bd & Sr Exec VP-BSI Switzerland)*
Christian Ferry *(Sr Exec VP-Fin Svcs)*
Francois Noverraz *(Sr Exec VP-Private Banking-Switzerland)*
Alfredo F. Orelli *(Sr Exec VP)*
Agostino Ferrazzini *(Exec VP-Private Banking-Switzerland)*

Subsidiaries:

Banca del Gottardo (3)
Viale Stefano Franscini 8
6901 Lugano, Switzerland
Tel.: (41) 918081111
Telex: 841051
Fax: (41) 919239487
E-Mail: info@gottardo.com
Web Site: www.gottardo.com
Sales Range: $400-449.9 Million
Emp.: 500
Asset Management, Financial Planning & Investment Advisory Services
S.I.C.: 6282
N.A.I.C.S.: 523930
F. Noverraz *(CEO)*

Affiliate:

Dreieck Fiduciaria SA (4)
Viale Bagutti 5
6900 Lugano, Switzerland
Tel.: (41) 919239581
Fax: (41) 919228740
Web Site: www.dreieckfid.ch
Emp.: 17
Asset Management & Investment Advisory Services
S.I.C.: 6282
N.A.I.C.S.: 523930
Karl Kohlbrenner *(Mng Dir)*

Non-U.S. Subsidiaries:

Banca del Gottardo Italia Spa (4)
Via Camozzi 5
24121 Bergamo, Italy
Tel.: (39) 035 3833 311
Fax: (39) 035 3833 324
Asset Management, Financial Planning & Investment Advisory Services
S.I.C.: 6282
N.A.I.C.S.: 523930

BSI Luxembourg SA (4)
6 Ave Mari Terrace
2132 Luxembourg, Luxembourg
Tel.: (352) 4615661
Fax: (352) 461566227
E-Mail: info@bsibank.com
Web Site: www.lux.bsibank.com
Emp.: 50
Asset Management, Banking & Investment Advisory Services
S.I.C.: 6282
N.A.I.C.S.: 523930
Urban Antes *(Gen Mgr)*

Gottardo Trust Co. Ltd. (4)
PO Box CB 10976
Nassau, Bahamas
Tel.: (242) 502 22 00
Fax: (242) 502 23 10
Wealth Management Services
S.I.C.: 6282
N.A.I.C.S.: 523930

Oudart SA (4)
10 Rue de la Paix
75002 Paris, France
Tel.: (33) 142862500
Fax: (33) 142862525
E-Mail: oudart@oudart.com
Web Site: www.oudart.com
Emp.: 50

Asset Management, Financial Planning & Investment Advisory Services
S.I.C.: 6282
N.A.I.C.S.: 523930
Jacqueline Eli-Namer *(Chm & CEO)*

Subsidiaries:

Oudart Gestion S.A. (5)
8 Rue Chateau Trompette
33000 Bordeaux, France
Tel.: (33) 5 57 81 80 00
Fax: (33) 5 56 44 95 59
Financial Management Services
S.I.C.: 6211
N.A.I.C.S.: 523999

Oudart Patrimoine Sarl (5)
10A rue de la Paix
75002 Paris, France
Tel.: (33) 1 42 86 25 00
Fax: (33) 1 42 86 25 25
Financial Advisory Services
S.I.C.: 6282
N.A.I.C.S.: 523930

Solidia Finance et Patrimonie S.A. (5)
10 A Rue de la Paix
75002 Paris, France
Tel.: (33) 1 44 50 58 10
Fax: (33) 1 40 20 99 06
E-Mail: contact@solidia.fr
Web Site: www.solidia.fr
Financial Management Services
S.I.C.: 6211
N.A.I.C.S.: 523999

Convivium S.A. (3)
Franscini Viale 8
6900 Lugano, Ticino, Switzerland
Tel.: (41) 919235314
Financial Management Services
S.I.C.: 6211
N.A.I.C.S.: 523999

Thalia S.A. (3)
Via Trevano 2a
6900 Lugano, Switzerland
Tel.: (41) 91 912 97 00
E-Mail: info@thaliainvest.com
Web Site: www.thaliainvest.com
Emp.: 25
Asset Management Services
S.I.C.: 6282
N.A.I.C.S.: 523920
Ugo Pastori *(CEO)*
Paolo Tamburini *(CFO)*
Margrethe Rokkum-Testi *(Chief Investment Officer)*

Non-U.S. Subsidiaries:

Azur Space Solar Power GmbH (3)
Theresienstr 2
74072 Heilbronn, Germany
Tel.: (49) 7131 67 2603
Fax: (49) 7131 67 2727
E-Mail: info@azurspace.com
Web Site: www.azurspace.com
Emp.: 140
Solar Cell Mfr & Whlsr
S.I.C.: 3674
N.A.I.C.S.: 334413
Klaus-Dieter Rasch *(Mng Dir)*

BSI Bank Ltd. (3)
7 Temasek Blvd
32 01 Suntec Tower One, Singapore, 038987, Singapore
Tel.: (65) 64248350
Fax: (65) 63341955
Web Site: www.bsibank.com
Emp.: 35
Asset Management & Investment Banking Services
S.I.C.: 6282
N.A.I.C.S.: 523930
Nicole Battalora *(CEO)*

BSI Generali Asia Ltd. (3)
3502 Two Exchange Square
8 Connaught Place, Central, China (Hong Kong)
Tel.: (852) 28466600
Fax: (852) 28680261
Web Site: www.bsibank.com
Emp.: 100
Asset Management & Investment Banking Services
S.I.C.: 6282
N.A.I.C.S.: 523930

BSI Ifabanque SA (3)
10 rue de la Paix
75002 Paris, France
Tel.: (33) 153230353
Fax: (33) 1 53230350
E-Mail: email@bsiifabanque.com
Web Site: www.bsiifabanque.com
Asset Management & Investment Banking Services
S.I.C.: 6211
N.A.I.C.S.: 523110

BSI Investment Advisors HK Ltd (3)
20th Floor Two Exchange Square
Central, China (Hong Kong)
Tel.: (852) 31260088
Fax: (852) 31260288
E-Mail: info@bsibank.com
Web Site: www.bsibank.hk
Wealth Management & Investment Advisory Services
S.I.C.: 6282
N.A.I.C.S.: 523920

BSI Investment Advisors (Panama) Inc. (3)
Torre Generali Piso14 Ave Samuel Lewis y Calle 54 Obarrio
PA Apartado WTC, 832 1637 Panama, Panama
Tel.: (507) 2657000
Fax: (507) 2643588
Web Site: www.bsibank.com
Emp.: 9
Asset Management, Financial Planning & Investment Advisory Services
S.I.C.: 6282
N.A.I.C.S.: 523930
Armelle Masseron *(Gen Mgr)*

BSI Monaco SAM (3)
Le St Michel
1 Av St Michel, 98000 Monaco, Monaco
Tel.: (377) 92168989
Fax: (377) 97971130
E-Mail: info@bsi.mc
Web Site: www.mc.bsibank.com
Asset Management, Financial Planning & Investment Advisory Services
S.I.C.: 6282
N.A.I.C.S.: 523930

Subsidiary:

BSI Asset Managers SAM (4)
Le St Michel 1 Av St Michel
98000 Monaco, Monaco
Tel.: (377) 92168989
Fax: (377) 97971130
Asset Management Services
S.I.C.: 6799
N.A.I.C.S.: 523920

BSI Overseas (Bahamas) Ltd. (3)
Goodman's Bay Corporate Center
West Bay Street & Sea View Drive, Nassau, Bahamas BS
Mailing Address:
PO Box N-7130
Nassau, Bahamas
Tel.: (242) 5022200
Fax: (242) 5022300
E-Mail: info@bsibank.com
Web Site: www.bs.bsibank.com
Emp.: 36
Asset Management, Financial Planning & Investment Advisory Services
S.I.C.: 6282
N.A.I.C.S.: 523930

BSI (Panama) S.A. (3)
Av Samuel Lewis y Cl 54
Panama, Panama
Tel.: (507) 2647377
Investment Management Services
S.I.C.: 6211
N.A.I.C.S.: 523999

BSI Trust Corporation (Channel Islands) Limited (3)
Generali House
PO Box 386
Saint Peter Port, GY1 4NG, Guernsey
Tel.: (44) 1481 714444
Fax: (44) 1481 712345
E-Mail: info@bsitrustci.com
Web Site: www.bsitrustci.bsibank.com
Asset Management & Trust Administration Services
S.I.C.: 6099
N.A.I.C.S.: 523991

BSI Trust Corporation (Malta) Limited (3)
No 35 Secharay Str
Valletta, VLT 1132, Malta
Tel.: (356) 21225817
Fax: (356) 21225865
E-Mail: info@bsitrustmalta.com
Web Site: www.bsitrustma.bsibank.com
Emp.: 2
Asset Management & Trust Administration Services
S.I.C.: 6282
N.A.I.C.S.: 523930
Claudio Tonolla *(COO)*

BSI Trust Corp. (Singapore) Ltd (3)
7 Temasek Boulevard 22-01B Suntec Tower One
Singapore, 038987, Singapore
Tel.: (65) 6521 1888
Fax: (65) 6884 6229
E-Mail: info@bsibank.com
Web Site: www.bsitrustsg.bsibank.com
Trust Administration Services
S.I.C.: 6099
N.A.I.C.S.: 523991
Francesco Ceruti *(CEO)*

EOS Servizi Fiduciari SpA (3)
Via Montebello 39
20121 Milan, Italy
Tel.: (39) 02 63 69 62 20
Fax: (39) 02 290 63 197
E-Mail: info@eosfiduciaria.it
Web Site: www.bsibank.com
Emp.: 20
Financial Management Services
S.I.C.: 6211
N.A.I.C.S.: 523999

Generali Worldwide Insurance Company Limited (2)
Hirzel St
PO Box 613
Saint Peter Port, GY1 4PA, Guernsey UK
Tel.: (44) 1481715400 (100%)
Fax: (44) 1481715390
E-Mail: enquiries@generali-guernsey.com
Web Site: www.generali-guernsey.com
Emp.: 100
Provider of Assurance & Investement Products
S.I.C.: 8299
N.A.I.C.S.: 611430
Dick Brennan *(Head-Mktg)*

Subsidiaries:

Generali International Limited (3)
Hirzel St
PO Box 613
South Esplanade, Saint Peter Port, GY1 4PA, Guernsey UK
Tel.: (44) 1481714108 (100%)
Fax: (44) 1481712424
E-Mail: enquiries@generali-guernsey.com
Web Site: www.generali-guernsey.com
Emp.: 80
Assurance & Investment Products
S.I.C.: 6399
N.A.I.C.S.: 524128
Gavin Tradelius *(CEO)*

Generali Portfolio Management (Ci) Limited (3)
Hirzel Street
Saint Peter Port, GY1 4PA, Guernsey
Tel.: (44) 1481 703000
Fax: (44) 1481 740052
E-Mail: enquiries@generali-gpm.com
Emp.: 5
Portfolio Management Services
S.I.C.: 6282
N.A.I.C.S.: 523920
Peter Creed *(Head-Portfolio Mgmt)*

Joint Venture:

Generali PPF Holding BV (2)
Strawinskylaan 933
1077 XX Amsterdam, Netherlands NL
Tel.: (31) 208813120 (76%)
Fax: (31) 208813121
Web Site: www.generalippf.eu
Emp.: 8
Holding Company
S.I.C.: 6719
N.A.I.C.S.: 551112
Sergio Balbinot *(Chm)*
Luciano Cirina *(CEO)*

Subsidiary:

CZI Holdings N.V. (4)
Tower B Level 9 Strawinskylaan 933
Amsterdam, Noord-Holland, 1077 XX, Netherlands
Tel.: (31) 20 8813120
Investment Management Services
S.I.C.: 6211
N.A.I.C.S.: 523999

Non-U.S. Subsidiaries:

Generali Administrare Pensii (5)
58-60 Str Polizu
011052 Bucharest, Romania
Tel.: (40) 213135150
Fax: (40) 213135170
E-Mail: pensii@generali.ro
Pension Fund Management Services
S.I.C.: 6371
N.A.I.C.S.: 525110

Generali Life Insurance CJSC (5)
Business Center Forum Park Plaza 9
Moskovskiy Ave build 1 2nd fl
Kiev, 04073, Ukraine
Tel.: (380) 44 200 0 216
Fax: (380) 44 200 0 215
E-Mail: info@generali.ua
Web Site: www.life.generali.ua
Life Insurance Services
S.I.C.: 6311
N.A.I.C.S.: 524113
Dmytro Dubina *(CEO)*
Serhiy Lohmatov *(Deputy CEO-Insurance Activity Mng)*
Andrii Matiashevych *(Deputy CEO-Corp Sls)*
Victoria Zheglova *(First Deputy CEO)*

Generali PPF General Insurance LLC (5)
219 4th Forest Lane 4
Moscow, 125047, Russia
Tel.: (7) 495 785 82 01
Fax: (7) 95 785 82 02
E-Mail: info@generalippf.ru
Web Site: www.generalippf.ru/ru/eng/inrussia/
Emp.: 350
General Insurance Services
S.I.C.: 6411
N.A.I.C.S.: 524210
Sergey Perelygin *(Gen Mgr)*

Generali PPF Life Insurance, LLC (5)
219 4th Forest Lane 4
Moscow, 125047, Russia
Tel.: (7) 495 785 8200
Fax: (7) 495 785 8209
E-Mail: info@generalippf.ru
Web Site: www.generalippf.ru
Life Insurance Services
S.I.C.: 6311
N.A.I.C.S.: 524113
Vit Sedlacek *(Chm)*
Sergey Perelygin *(CEO)*
Alyona Bukashkina *(Deputy CEO & Head-Customer Sls)*
Vladislav Minar *(Deputy CEO)*

JSC Generali Life (5)
Furmanova 248 5th Floor
050059 Almaty, Kazakhstan
Tel.: (7) 727 244 3680
Fax: (7) 727 244 3684
E-Mail: info@generali.kz
Web Site: www.generali.kz
Emp.: 20
Life Insurance Services
S.I.C.: 6311
N.A.I.C.S.: 524113
Dmitriy Nadirov *(CEO)*

Nadace Ceske pojistovny (5)
Na Pankraci 121
140 00 Prague, Czech Republic
Tel.: (420) 224 550 444
E-Mail: nadace@nadacecp.cz
Web Site: www.ceskapojistovna.cz
General Insurance Services
S.I.C.: 6411

Assicurazioni Generali S.p.A.—(Continued)

N.A.I.C.S.: 524210

Non-U.S. Subsidiaries:

Delta Generali Osiguranje a.d. (3)
Milentija Popovica 7b
11070 Belgrade, Serbia
Tel.: (381) 11 2220555
Fax: (381) 11 3114381
E-Mail: kontakt@deltagenerali.rs
Web Site: www.deltagenerali.rs
Emp.: 85,000
Insurance Management Services
S.I.C.: 6411
N.A.I.C.S.: 524298

Subsidiaries:

Delta Generali RE a.d. (4)
Milentija Popovica 7 b
11000 Belgrade, Serbia
Tel.: (381) 11 2220 555
Fax: (381) 11 2011 789
E-Mail: reosiguranje@deltagenerali.rs
Web Site: www.deltagenerali.rs
Reinsurance Services
S.I.C.: 6399
N.A.I.C.S.: 524130

Voluntary Pension Fund M.Delta (4)
Milentija Popovica 7b
11070 Belgrade, Serbia
Tel.: (381) 11 20 11 764
Fax: (381) 11 20 12 737
E-Mail: penzijskifond@deltagenerali.rs
Web Site: www.penzijskifond.rs
Emp.: 20
Pension Fund Management Services
S.I.C.: 6371
N.A.I.C.S.: 525110
Natasa Marjanovic *(Chm-Mgmt Bd)*
Dragan Filipovic *(Member-Mgmt Bd)*
Mladen Ostojic *(Member-Mgmt Bd)*
Branko Pavlovic *(Member-Mgmt Bd)*

Non-U.S. Subsidiary:

Delta Generali Holding d.o.o. (4)
Kralja Nikole 27a
81000 Podgorica, Montenegro
Tel.: (382) 11 222 3785
E-Mail: kontakt@deltagenerali.me
Web Site: www.generali.com
Emp.: 30
Investment Management Services
S.I.C.: 6211
N.A.I.C.S.: 523999
Dejan Bajic *(Gen Mgr)*

Subsidiary:

Delta Generali Osiguranje ad (5)
Kralja Nikole 27/VI VI Sprat
Podgorica, Montenegro
Tel.: (382) 20 444 800
Fax: (382) 20 444 810
E-Mail: kontakt@deltagenerali.me
Web Site: www.deltagenerali.me
Emp.: 30
General Insurance Services
S.I.C.: 6411
N.A.I.C.S.: 524210
Dejan Bajic *(Gen Mgr)*

Foreign Insurance Close Joint Stock Company Generali (3)
Pobediteley Avenue 59 Office 202
220035 Minsk, Belarus
Tel.: (375) 17 200 45 56
Fax: (375) 17 200 35 19
E-Mail: info@generali.by
Web Site: www.generali.by
Emp.: 8
Insurance Services
S.I.C.: 6411
N.A.I.C.S.: 524298
Radek Votruba *(Chm-Supervisory Bd)*
Sergei Slizovskiy *(Mng Dir)*

Generali Osiguranje d.d. (3)
Bani 110
10010 Zagreb, Croatia
Tel.: (385) 1 4600 400
Fax: (385) 1 4600 600
E-Mail: info@generali.hr
Web Site: www.generali.hr
General Insurance Services
S.I.C.: 6411
N.A.I.C.S.: 524210

Generali Slovensko Poist'ovna a.s. (3)
Plynarenska 7/C
824 79 Bratislava, Slovakia
Tel.: (421) 258276666
Fax: (421) 258276100
E-Mail: gsl@gsl.sk
Web Site: www.gsl.sk
Emp.: 750
Insurance Provider
S.I.C.: 6399
N.A.I.C.S.: 524128
Antonin Nekvinda *(CEO)*

Peltours Insurance Agencies Ltd. (1)
Aurec Building 16 Abba Hillel Road
Ramat Gan, 52506, Israel
Tel.: (972) 3 753 7111
Fax: (972) 3 613 8883
Insurance Management Services
S.I.C.: 6411
N.A.I.C.S.: 524298

REFICOR s.r.o. (1)
Na Pankraci 1658
Prague, 140 21, Czech Republic
Tel.: (420) 234 689 111
Fax: (420) 234 689 398
Business Management Consulting Services
S.I.C.: 8742
N.A.I.C.S.: 541611

S.C. Genagricola Romania (1)
Str Drumul Moril 9
305600 Sannicolau Mare, Romania
Tel.: (40) 256370458
Investment Management Services
S.I.C.: 6211
N.A.I.C.S.: 523999

SCI Parcolog Isle D'Abeau 3 (1)
7 Boulevard Haussmann
75009 Paris, France
Tel.: (33) 8 99 96 77 59
Financial Management Services
S.I.C.: 6211
N.A.I.C.S.: 523999

Univerzalni sprava majetku as (1)
Na Pankraci 1658
140 21 Prague, Czech Republic
Tel.: (420) 556 422 111
Real Estate Management Services
S.I.C.: 6531
N.A.I.C.S.: 531390

Vignadoro S.r.l. (1)
B-Dul Stefan Augustin Doinas 20
Arad, 315600, Romania
Tel.: (40) 257256955
Fax: (40) 256370436
Grape Farming Services
S.I.C.: 2084
N.A.I.C.S.: 312130

Non-U.S. Unit:

Assicurazioni Generali S.p.A. - Generali Global London Unit (1)
100 Leman Street
London, E1 8AJ, United Kingdom
Tel.: (44) 207 265 6200
Fax: (44) 207 702 2544
E-Mail: generali-globaluk@generaliglobal.com
Web Site: www.generali.com
General Insurance Services
S.I.C.: 6411
N.A.I.C.S.: 524298

ASSIETTA PRIVATE EQUITY SGR S.P.A.

1Via Cesare Cantu
Milan, 20123, Italy
Tel.: (39) 2 89096595
Fax: (39) 2 89093704
Business Description:
Private Equity Firm
S.I.C.: 6211
N.A.I.C.S.: 523999
Personnel:
Marco Cornaglia *(Mng Dir)*

ASSIMA PLC

CityPoint 1 Ropemaker Street
London, EC2Y 9AW, United Kingdom
Tel.: (44) 2033283280
Fax: (44) 2033283289
Web Site: www.assima.net
Year Founded: 2002
ALSIM—(EUR)
Rev.: $35,634,149
Assets: $40,472,883
Liabilities: $16,485,962
Net Worth: $23,986,921
Earnings: $3,032,043
Emp.: 188
Fiscal Year-end: 12/31/12
Business Description:
Software Developer & Distr
S.I.C.: 7372
N.A.I.C.S.: 511210
Personnel:
Michel Balcaen *(Co-Founder & Chm)*
Eric Duneau *(Co-Founder & CTO)*
Jeffrey Forwood *(CFO)*
Tony Coates *(Chief Alliance Officer)*
Randall Anderson *(Legal Counsel)*
Board of Directors:
Michel Balcaen
Randall Anderson
Tony Coates
Eric Duneau
Jeffrey Forwood

U.S. Subsidiaries:

Assima, Inc. (1)
3330 Cumberland Blvd Ste 975
Atlanta, GA 30339
Tel.: (877) 927-7462
Software Developer & Distr
S.I.C.: 7372
N.A.I.C.S.: 511210
Jay Kuhlman *(Gen Mgr)*

Non-U.S. Subsidiary:

Assima Canada, Inc. (1)
2070 rue Jules Leger
Saint-Bruno, QC, J3V 5M5, Canada
Tel.: (678) 971-2008
Software Developer & Distr
S.I.C.: 7372
N.A.I.C.S.: 511210

ASSMANN BERATEN + PLANEN GMBH

Nordstrasse 23
D-38106 Braunschweig, Germany
Tel.: (49) 53139010
Fax: (49) 5313901110
E-Mail: kontakt@assmann.info
Web Site: www.assmann.info
Year Founded: 1959
Rev.: $31,859,925
Emp.: 315
Business Description:
Design & Project Management Services
S.I.C.: 8748
N.A.I.C.S.: 541618
Personnel:
Martin Assmann *(Founder)*
Hans-Peter Heller *(Mng Dir)*
Hans-Joachim Luer *(Mng Dir)*
Jochen Scheuermann *(Mng Dir)*
Peter Warnecke *(Mng Dir)*

ASSOCIATED ALCOHOLS & BREWERIES LTD.

Associated Alcohols Breweries Limited 4th Floor Silver Arc Plaza
20/1New Palasia, Indore, 452 001, India
Tel.: (91) 731 2430865
Fax: (91) 731 2432586
E-Mail: gen@associatedalcohols.com
Web Site: www.associatedalcohols.com
507526—(BOM)
Sales Range: $10-24.9 Million
Business Description:
Alcoholic Distilleries Mfr
S.I.C.: 2869
N.A.I.C.S.: 325193
Personnel:
Santosh Kumar Kedia *(Dir-Fin)*
Board of Directors:
H. K. Bhandari
Ashish Gadia
Manish Kumar Kedia
Santosh Kumar Kedia
Surendra Kumar Khetawat
Manish Kumar Tibrewal

ASSOCIATED BRANDS INDUSTRIES LIMITED

Bhagowtie Trace
El Socorro, Trinidad & Tobago
Mailing Address:
PO Box 1138
Port of Spain, Trinidad & Tobago
Tel.: (868) 638 4006
Fax: (868) 674 8089
E-Mail: sales@abil-tt.com
Web Site: www.abil-tt.com
Year Founded: 1974
Emp.: 650
Business Description:
Snack Foods, Chocolate Confectionery, Biscuits & Breakfast Cereals Mfr & Distr
Import Export
S.I.C.: 2096
N.A.I.C.S.: 311919
Personnel:
Barbara Mouttet *(CEO & Gen Mgr)*
Arthur Lok Jack *(Chm-Associated Brands Investments Ltd)*

Division:

Associated Brands Industries Limited - Biscuit Division (1)
Churchill Roosevelt Highway
Arima, Trinidad & Tobago
Tel.: (868) 6421971
Fax: (868) 6421870
E-Mail: cdproduction@cansnack.com
Web Site: www.abil-tt.com
Emp.: 150
Biscuit Mfr & Distr
S.I.C.: 2052
N.A.I.C.S.: 311919
Gregory Lok Jack *(Gen Mgr)*

Subsidiary:

Universal Foods Limited (1)
Point Lisas Industrial Estate
Point Lisas, Trinidad & Tobago
Tel.: (868) 636-7965
Fax: (868) 636-7987
E-Mail: sales@abil-tt.com
Web Site: www.abil-tt.com
Emp.: 120
Breakfast Cereal Mfr & Distr
S.I.C.: 2043
N.A.I.C.S.: 311230
Neil Poon Tip *(Mng Dir)*

ASSOCIATED BRITISH ENGINEERING PLC

9 High Street Little Eversden
Cambridge, CB23 1HE, United Kingdom
Tel.: (44) 1223 260022
Fax: (44) 1223 260022
E-Mail: admin@abeplc.co.uk
Web Site: www.abeplc.co.uk
ABSE—(LSE)
Rev.: $3,929,274
Assets: $8,720,839
Liabilities: $2,792,185
Net Worth: $5,928,655
Earnings: ($200,570)
Emp.: 30
Fiscal Year-end: 03/31/13
Business Description:
Diesel & Engineering Services
S.I.C.: 8711
N.A.I.C.S.: 541330

Personnel:
David A. H. Brown *(Chm)*
Board of Directors:
David A. H. Brown
Andrew Richard Beaumont
Stephen J. Cockburn
Colin Weinburg
Legal Counsel:
Heald
Ashton House 495 Silbury Boulevard
Milton Keynes, United Kingdom
Subsidiary:
British Polar Engines Limited (1)
133 Helen St
Glasgow, Scotland, G51 3HD, United Kingdom
Tel.: (44) 1414452455
Fax: (44) 1414454567
E-Mail: sales@britishpolarengines.co.uk
Web Site: www.britishpolarengines.co.uk
Engine Parts Mfr & Distr & Engines Maintenace Services
S.I.C.: 3724
N.A.I.C.S.: 336412
Stewart Davis *(Mng Dir)*

ASSOCIATED ENGINEERS, LTD.

23/F Stelux House 698 Prince Edward Road East
San Po Kong, Kowloon, China (Hong Kong)
Tel.: (852) 27671000
Telex: AELGN HX
Fax: (852) 27672000
E-Mail: info@ael.hk
Web Site: www.ael.hk
Year Founded: 1961
Sales Range: $150-199.9 Million
Emp.: 500
Business Description:
Airport, Logistic, Construction, Environmental & Material Handling Engineering Services
S.I.C.: 8711
N.A.I.C.S.: 541330
Personnel:
G.T. Chow *(Mng Dir)*

ASSOCIATED FINLEASE LIMITED

D-157 IInd Floor Block D Preet Vihar
New Delhi, 110092, India
Tel.: (91) 11 43008305
Fax: (91) 11 22482084
E-Mail: associatedfinltd@yahoo.com
Web Site: www.associatedfinleaseltd.com
Year Founded: 1994
531192—(BOM)
Rev.: $290,018
Assets: $880,806
Liabilities: $6,595
Net Worth: $874,211
Earnings: $548
Fiscal Year-end: 03/31/13
Business Description:
Financial Services
S.I.C.: 6211
N.A.I.C.S.: 523999
Personnel:
Santosh Kumar Garg *(Mng Dir)*
Board of Directors:
Mamta Agarwal
Nikhil Bansal
Santosh Kumar Garg
Rohit Kumar Singhal
Transfer Agent:
Skyline Financial Services Private Limited
D-153 A Okhla Industrial Area Phase-I
New Delhi, India

ASSOCIATED LIGHTING GROUP LTD.

ALG House Gelderd Road
Leeds, LS12 6NB, United Kingdom
Tel.: (44) 113 276 7676
Fax: (44) 113 263 8708
Year Founded: 2009
Sales Range: $50-74.9 Million
Emp.: 140
Business Description:
Lighting Equipment Mfr
S.I.C.: 3645
N.A.I.C.S.: 335121
Personnel:
Nicholas Jeffrey *(Chm)*
David Gutfreund *(CEO)*
Board of Directors:
Nicholas Jeffrey
Bruce Davidson
Brom Dixon
David Green
David Gutfreund
Subsidiaries:
Ring Lighting Limited (1)
Gelderd Rd
Leeds, LS12 6NB, United Kingdom (100%)
Tel.: (44) 1132767676
Fax: (44) 1132310785
E-Mail: enquiries@ring.ltd.uk
Web Site: www.ring.ltd.uk
Sales Range: $10-24.9 Million
Emp.: 100
Lighting Equipment Mfr
S.I.C.: 3645
N.A.I.C.S.: 335121
Bruce Davidson *(Mng Dir)*

ASSOCIATED LOGISTICS SOLUTIONS, INC.

6090 White Hart Lane
Mississauga, ON, L5R 3Y4, Canada
Tel.: (905) 829-9927
Fax: (905) 568-1329
Web Site: www.accurispix.com
Year Founded: 1994
Rev.: $13,282,870
Emp.: 115
Business Description:
Supply Chain Logistics Solutions
S.I.C.: 4731
N.A.I.C.S.: 541614
Personnel:
Michael Andlauer *(Founder)*
Brian Mascarenhas *(CFO)*

ASSOCIATED RETAILERS LIMITED

169-173 Burnley Street
Richmond, VIC, 3121, Australia
Tel.: (61) 394298266
Fax: (61) 394271582
E-Mail: reception@arl.com.au
Web Site: www.arl.com.au
Sales Range: $125-149.9 Million
Emp.: 75
Business Description:
Independent Retail Stores
S.I.C.: 5999
N.A.I.C.S.: 453998
Personnel:
Chris Morgan *(Mng Dir)*

ASSOCIATED STONE INDUSTRIES (KOTAH) LTD.

Marathon Innova A Wing 7th floor Off Ganpatrao Kadam Marg
Lower Parel, Mumbai, 400 013, India
Tel.: (91) 22 40896100
Fax: (91) 22 40896199
E-Mail: asistone@asistone.com
Web Site: www.asistone.com
Year Founded: 1945
502015—(BOM)
Rev.: $32,790,382
Assets: $52,428,765
Liabilities: $21,139,623
Net Worth: $31,289,142
Earnings: $2,411,924
Emp.: 5,000
Fiscal Year-end: 03/31/13
Business Description:
Stone Quarrying & Shaping Services
S.I.C.: 1411
N.A.I.C.S.: 212311
Personnel:
Deepak Jatia *(Chm & Mng Dir)*
S. C. Agarwal *(Pres)*
R. R. Soni *(CEO)*
Uttam Shetty *(Compliance Officer & Sec)*
Board of Directors:
Deepak Jatia
Tushya Jatia
Pramod G. Lath
Padam Kumar Poddar
Anshul M. Sonawala
Transfer Agent:
Sharepro Services (India) Private Limited
13 AB Samhita Warehousing Complex II Floor
Sakinaka Telephone Lane
Off Andheri Kurla Rd Sakinaka, Mumbai, India

ASSOCIATION DES CENTRES DISTRIBUTEURS E. LECLERC

52 Rue Camille Des Moulins
92451 Issy-les-Moulineaux, France
Tel.: (33) 146625100
Fax: (33) 146625126
E-Mail: mail@e-leclerc.com
Web Site: www.e-leclerc.com
Year Founded: 1949
Emp.: 72,000
Business Description:
Central Supermarket & Hypermarket Import
S.I.C.: 5411
N.A.I.C.S.: 445110
Personnel:
Edouard Leclerc *(Co-Chm & Pres)*
Jacques Gattepaille *(Co-Chm)*

ASSOCIAZIONE DEI FONOGRAFICI ITALIANI

Via Vittor Pissani 6
20124 Milan, Italy
Tel.: (39) 26696263
Telex: 311264 afi i
Fax: (39) 026705059
E-Mail: amministrativo@afi.mi.it
Web Site: www.afi.mi.it
Year Founded: 1948
Sales Range: $10-24.9 Million
Emp.: 5
Business Description:
Sound & Video Media
S.I.C.: 6282
N.A.I.C.S.: 524292
Personnel:
Leopoldo Lombardi *(Pres)*
Franco Donato *(Sec)*
Board of Directors:
Franco Bixio
Silvio Crippa
Franco De Gemini
Piero La Falce
Guido Palma
Alberto Salini

ASSORE LIMITED

Assore House 15 Fricker Road Illovo Boulevard
Johannesburg, South Africa 2196
Mailing Address:
Private Bag X03
Northlands, South Africa 2116
Tel.: (27) 117706800
Fax: (27) 112686040
Web Site: www.assore.com
ASR—(JSE)
Rev.: $1,583,367,048
Assets: $2,261,785,040
Liabilities: $681,071,314
Net Worth: $1,580,713,726
Earnings: $382,948,706
Emp.: 6,905
Fiscal Year-end: 06/30/13
Business Description:
Minerals & Metals Mining Services
S.I.C.: 1479
N.A.I.C.S.: 212393
Personnel:
Desmond Sacco *(Chm)*
Christopher J. Cory *(CEO)*
Patrick E. Sacco *(Deputy Mng Dir-Ore & Metal)*
Board of Directors:
Desmond Sacco
Robert J. Carpenter
Christopher J. Cory
Sydney Mhlarhi
Edward M. Southey
Alastair Duncan Stalker
William Frank Urmson
Bastiaan Hendrikus van Aswegen
Legal Counsel:
Webber Wentzel
10 Fricker Road Illovo Boulevard
Johannesburg, South Africa
Norton Rose Fullbright
15 Alice Lane
Sandton, South Africa
Transfer Agent:
Computershare Investor Services (Proprietary) Limited
70 Marshall Street
Johannesburg, South Africa

ASSUMPTION MUTUAL LIFE INSURANCE COMPANY

(d/b/a Assumption Life)
770 Main St
Moncton, NB, E1C 8L1, Canada
Mailing Address:
PO Box 160
Moncton, NB, E1C 8L1, Canada
Tel.: (506) 853-6040
Fax: (506) 853-5428
Toll Free: (800) 455-7337
E-Mail: e.business@assumption.ca
Web Site: www.assumption.ca
Year Founded: 1903
Rev.: $159,436,832
Assets: $1,288,455,682
Liabilities: $1,189,444,332
Net Worth: $99,011,350
Earnings: $4,821,991
Emp.: 210
Fiscal Year-end: 12/31/12
Business Description:
Life Insurance & Portfolio Management Products & Services
S.I.C.: 6311
N.A.I.C.S.: 524113
Personnel:
Yvon Fontaine *(Chm)*
Andre Vincent *(Pres & CEO)*
Robert Moreau *(CFO & VP)*
Derrick Smith *(CIO)*
Sebastien Dupuis *(Chief Risk Officer & Dir-Fin)*
Genevieve Laforge *(Sr Legal Counsel & Sec)*
Board of Directors:
Yvon Fontaine
Yves Arseneau
Nathalie Godbout
Genevieve Laforge
Denis Larocque
Andree Savoie
Allister Surette
Monique Tremblay
Jacques Valotaire
Andre Vincent
Joint Venture:
Louisbourg Investments Inc. (1)
770 Main Street
Moncton, NB, E1C 1E6, Canada NB

Assumption Mutual Life Insurance Company—(Continued)

Mailing Address:
PO Box 160
Moncton, NB, E1C 8L1, Canada
Tel.: (506) 853-5410
Fax: (506) 853-5457
Toll Free: (888) 608-7070
E-Mail: info@louisbourg.net
Web Site: www.louisbourg.net
Managed Assets: $876,319,710
Emp.: 12
Pension Fund, Endowment & Private Wealth Portfolio Management Services; Owned 51% by Assumption Mutual Life Insurance Company & 49% by Montrusco Bolton Investments Inc.
S.I.C.: 6282
N.A.I.C.S.: 523920
Denis Losier *(Pres)*
Luc Gaudet *(CEO & Head-Private Client Svcs)*

ASSURA GROUP LIMITED

The Brew House Greenalls Avenue
Warrington, WA4 6HL, United Kingdom
Tel.: (44) 1925 420660
Fax: (44) 1925 234503
E-Mail: info@assuragroup.co.uk
Web Site: www.assuragroup.co.uk
AGR—(LSE)
Rev.: $58,591,659
Assets: $990,214,830
Liabilities: $677,357,481
Net Worth: $312,857,349
Earnings: $22,267,989
Emp.: 28
Fiscal Year-end: 03/31/13

Business Description:
Investment Holding Company
S.I.C.: 6719
N.A.I.C.S.: 551112

Personnel:
Graham Roberts *(CEO)*
Jonathan Murphy *(Sec & Dir-Fin)*

Board of Directors:
Simon Laffin
Jenefer Greenwood
Jonathan Murphy
David Richardson
Graham Roberts

Legal Counsel:
Addleshaw Goddard LLP
100 Barbirolli Square
Manchester, United Kingdom

Transfer Agent:
Computershare Investor Services (Jersey) Limited
Queensway House Hilgrove Street
Saint Helier, JE1 1ES, Jersey
Tel.: (44) 1534 281814

Subsidiaries:

Assura Health and Wellness Centres Limited (1)
28 Argyle St
Liverpool, L1 5DL, United Kingdom
Tel.: (44) 8450584750
Fax: (44) 7517037729
Web Site: www.assuramedical.co.uk
Emp.: 10
Health Care Services
S.I.C.: 8011
N.A.I.C.S.: 621491
Debby Hindley *(Dir-Bus)*

Assura Investments Limited (1)
3300 Daresbury Business Park
Warrington, Cheshire, WA4 4HS, United Kingdom
Tel.: (44) 1625529191
Investment Services
S.I.C.: 6799
N.A.I.C.S.: 523920

Assura Pharmacy Limited (1)
Lynstock House Lynstock Way
Lostock, Bolton, Lancashire, BL6 4SA, United Kingdom
Tel.: (44) 1925420660
Fax: (44) 01204473123
Web Site: www.cohenschaminst.co.uk
Emp.: 200
Pharmaceutical Supplies & Services
S.I.C.: 5912
N.A.I.C.S.: 446110
Andrew Butterworth *(Mng Dir)*

Assura Properties Limited (1)
3300 Daresbury Business Park
Warrington, Cheshire, WA4 4HS, United Kingdom
Tel.: (44) 1928737000
Fax: (44) 1928737002
E-Mail: andrew.darke@assuragroup.co.uk
Emp.: 30
Property Investment Services
S.I.C.: 6531
N.A.I.C.S.: 531312
Andrew Darke *(Gen Mgr)*

Subsidiary:

Assura Properties UK Limited (2)
The Brew House
Greenalls Avenue, Warrington, Cheshire, WA4 6HL, United Kingdom
Tel.: (44) 1928737000
Fax: (44) 1925234503
E-Mail: kirsty.brady@assuragroup.co.uk
Emp.: 25
Property Investment Services
S.I.C.: 6531
N.A.I.C.S.: 531312
Andrew Darke *(Mng Dir)*

Assura Property Management Limited (1)
The Brew House Greenalls Ave
Warrington, Cheshire, WA4 6HI, United Kingdom
Tel.: (44) 1925420660
Fax: (44) 1925234503
E-Mail: info@assuragroup.co.uk
Web Site: www.assuragroup.co.uk
Emp.: 35
Property Management Services
S.I.C.: 6531
N.A.I.C.S.: 531311
Grame Robins *(CEO)*

ASSURED GUARANTY LTD.

30 Woodbourne Avenue
Hamilton, HM 08, Bermuda
Tel.: (441) 2795700
Fax: (441) 296-3379
E-Mail: info@assuredguaranty.com
Web Site: www.assuredguaranty.com
Year Founded: 2003
AGO—(NYSE)
Rev.: $1,608,000,000
Assets: $16,287,000,000
Liabilities: $11,172,000,000
Net Worth: $5,115,000,000
Earnings: $808,000,000
Emp.: 326
Fiscal Year-end: 12/31/13

Business Description:
Holding Company
S.I.C.: 6719
N.A.I.C.S.: 551112

Personnel:
Anthony Robin Dominic Monro-Davies *(Chm)*
Dominic J. Frederico *(Pres & CEO)*
Robert A. Bailenson *(CFO)*
Robert B. Mills *(COO)*
Kirk Edmunds *(CIO)*
Howard W. Albert *(Chief Risk Officer)*
Francis J. Coughlin, Jr. *(Deputy Chief Surveillance Officer-Pub Fin)*
James M. Michener *(Gen Counsel & Sec)*

Board of Directors:
Anthony Robin Dominic Monro-Davies
Neil Baron
Francisco L. Borges
G. Lawrence Buhl
Stephen A. Cozen
Dominic J. Frederico
Bonnie L. Howard
Patrick W. Kenny
Simon W. Leathes
Michael T. O'Kane
Wilbur L. Ross, Jr.

Subsidiary:

Assured Guaranty Re Ltd. (1)
30 Woodbourne Ave
Hamilton, HM 08, Bermuda (100%)
Tel.: (441) 2964004
Fax: (441) 2963379
Web Site: www.assuredguaranty.com
Emp.: 75
Reinsurance Carriers
S.I.C.: 6399
N.A.I.C.S.: 524130
David Penchoff *(Pres & CEO)*

Subsidiary:

Assured Guaranty Re Overseas Ltd (2)
30 Woodbourne Ave
Hamilton, HM 08, Bermuda (100%)
Tel.: (441) 279 5700
Fax: (441) 279 5701
Web Site: www.assuredguaranty.com
Emp.: 20
Other Holding Companies Offices
S.I.C.: 6719
N.A.I.C.S.: 551112
Gary Burnet *(COO)*

U.S. Subsidiary:

Assured Guaranty US Holdings Inc (1)
31 W 52nd St
New York, NY 10019 (100%)
Tel.: (212) 974-0100
Fax: (212) 581-3268
E-Mail: info@assuredguaranty.com
Web Site: www.assuredguaranty.com
Direct Life Insurance Carriers
S.I.C.: 6311
N.A.I.C.S.: 524113
Robert B. Mills *(CFO)*

U.S. Subsidiaries:

Assured Guaranty Mortgage Insurance Company (1)
31 W 52nd St
New York, NY 10019
Tel.: (212) 974-0100
Fax: (212) 589-3268
Direct Property & Casualty Insurance Services
S.I.C.: 6331
N.A.I.C.S.: 524126
Dominic J. Frederico *(CEO)*

Subsidiaries:

AG Financial Products Inc. (2)
31 W 52nd St
New York, NY 10019 (100%)
Tel.: (212) 974-0100
Fax: (212) 581-3268
E-Mail: info@assuredguaranty.com
Web Site: www.assuredguaranty.com
Emp.: 15
Financial Services
S.I.C.: 7389
N.A.I.C.S.: 561499
Robert Mills *(CFO)*

Assured Guaranty Corp. (2)
31 W 52nd St 26th Fl
New York, NY 10019
Tel.: (212) 974-0100
Fax: (212) 826-0100
Web Site: www.assuredguaranty.com
Emp.: 300
Other Direct Insurance
S.I.C.: 6399
N.A.I.C.S.: 524128
Stephen Donnarumma *(Chief Credit Officer)*

Assured Guaranty Municipal Holdings Inc. (2)
31 W 52nd St
New York, NY 10019
Tel.: (212) 826-0100
Fax: (212) 688-3101
Investment Management Services
S.I.C.: 6282
N.A.I.C.S.: 523930

Non-U.S. Subsidiaries:

Assured Guaranty Corp. (1)
Level 46 Govenor Philip Tower
1 Farrer Place, Sydney, NSW, 2000, Australia AU
Tel.: (61) 299479738 (100%)
Fax: (61) 299479777
Web Site: www.assuredguaranty.com
Emp.: 3
Insurance Services
S.I.C.: 6311
N.A.I.C.S.: 524113

Assured Guaranty (Europe) Ltd. (1)
1 Finsbury Square
London, EC2A 1AE, United Kingdom
Tel.: (44) 2075621900
Fax: (44) 2075621901
Insurance Brokerage Services
S.I.C.: 6411
N.A.I.C.S.: 524210

Assured Guaranty (UK) Ltd. (1)
1 Finsbury Square
London, EC2A 1AE, United Kingdom UK
Tel.: (44) 2075621900 (100%)
Fax: (44) 2075621901
Web Site: www.assuredguaranty.com
Emp.: 20
Reinsurance Carriers
S.I.C.: 6399
N.A.I.C.S.: 524130
Nick Proud *(Sr Mng Dir)*

ASSURIA N.V.

(d/b/a Assuria Verzekering)
Grote Combeweg 37
PO Box 1030
Paramaribo, Suriname
Tel.: (597) 473400
Fax: (597) 476577
E-Mail: customer.service@assuria.sr
Web Site: www.assuria.sr
Sales Range: $25-49.9 Million
Emp.: 153

Business Description:
Holding Company; Life, Medical, Property & Casualty Insurance Products & Services
S.I.C.: 6719
N.A.I.C.S.: 551112

Personnel:
J.J. Healy, Jr. *(Chm-Supervisory Bd)*
S. Smit *(CEO)*
A.K. Achaibersing *(Mng Dir-Non-Life Insurance)*
D. Wesenhagen *(Mng Dir-Life Insurance)*

Subsidiaries:

Assuria Beleggingsmaatschappij N.V. (1)
Grote Combeweg 37
PO Box 1030
Paramaribo, Suriname SR
Tel.: (597) 473400 (99.67%)
Fax: (597) 472390
E-Mail: customerservice@assuria.sr
Web Site: www.assuria.sr
Investment Services
S.I.C.: 6211
N.A.I.C.S.: 523999
S. Smit *(Grp CEO & Mng Dir)*

Assuria Levensverzekering N.V. (1)
Grote Combeweg 37
PO Box 1030
Paramaribo, Suriname SR
Tel.: (597) 473400 (99.3%)
Fax: (597) 472390
E-Mail: assurialecen@assuria.net
Web Site: www.assuria.sr/cms/nl/contact
Life Insurance Products & Services
S.I.C.: 6311
N.A.I.C.S.: 524113
D. Wesenhagen *(Mng Dir)*

Assuria Medische Verzekering N.V. (1)
Henck Arronstraat 5-7
PO Box 1501
Paramaribo, Suriname SR
Tel.: (597) 477955 (99.48%)

Fax: (597) 472390
E-Mail: customer.service@assuria.sr
Emp.: 80
Medical Insurance Products & Services
S.I.C.: 6324
N.A.I.C.S.: 524114
A. K. Achaibersing *(Mng Dir)*

Assuria Schadeverzekering N.V. **(1)**
Henck Arronstraat 5-7
PO Box 1501
Paramaribo, Suriname SR
Tel.: (597) 477955 (100%)
Fax: (597) 476669
E-Mail: assuria@sr.net
Property & Casualty Insurance Products & Services
S.I.C.: 6331
N.A.I.C.S.: 524126
A.K. Achaibersing *(Mng Dir)*

Affiliate:

De Surinaamsche Bank N.V. **(1)**
Henck Arronstraat 26-30
PO Box 1806
Paramaribo, Suriname SR
Tel.: (597) 471100 (49%)
Telex: 134 287
Fax: (597) 411750
E-Mail: info@dsbbank.sr
Emp.: 350
Retail & Commercial Banking, Asset Management, Loans, Transfer & Treasury Services
S.I.C.: 6029
N.A.I.C.S.: 522110
Martin P. Loor *(CFO)*
John H. Lie-Tjauw *(COO)*
Henri L. Henar *(Chief Comml Officer)*

ASSYSTEM S.A.

70 Boulevard de Courcelles
75017 Paris, France
Tel.: (33) 155650300
Fax: (33) 155650049
E-Mail: presse@assystem.com
Web Site: www.assystem.com
Year Founded: 1966
ASY—(EUR)
Sls.: $1,151,783,052
Assets: $815,105,935
Liabilities: $539,679,553
Net Worth: $275,426,382
Earnings: $45,904,397
Emp.: 10,745
Fiscal Year-end: 12/31/12

Business Description:
Engineering & Innovation Consultancy Services
S.I.C.: 8711
N.A.I.C.S.: 541330

Personnel:
Michel Combes *(Chm-Supervisory Bd)*
Dominique Louis *(Chm-Mgmt Bd)*
Gilbert Lehmann *(Vice Chm-Supervisory Bd)*
Gerard Brescon *(Member-Mgmt Bd & Exec VP-HR Dev)*
Gilbert Vidal *(Member-Mgmt Bd & Exec VP-Fin & Legal Matters)*
Stephane Aubarbier *(Exec VP)*
David Bradley *(Exec VP)*
Jean-Louis Ricaud *(Exec VP)*

Supervisory Board of Directors:
Michel Combes
Myriam Maes
Bruno Angles
Armand Carlier
Stanislas Chapron
Bertrand Finet
Pierre Guenant
Gilbert Lehmann

Deloitte & Associes
185 avenue Charles-de-Gaulle
Neuilly-sur-Seine, France

Subsidiaries:

ANAFI Plus **(1)**
Za Le Pont Rouge
Tremuson, 22440, France
Tel.: (33) 296948888
Fax: (33) 296949900
Engineering Services
S.I.C.: 8711
N.A.I.C.S.: 541330

Assystem Developpement **(1)**
70 Blvd De Courcelles
75017 Paris, France
Tel.: (33) 134525000
Fax: (33) 155650049
Web Site: www.assysstem.com
Engineering Services
S.I.C.: 8711
N.A.I.C.S.: 541330

Assystem Environnement **(1)**
70 Boulevard De Courcelles
75017 Paris, France
Tel.: (33) 155650300
Fax: (33) 155650049
Emp.: 20
Engineering Services
S.I.C.: 8711
N.A.I.C.S.: 541330

Assystem Facilities **(1)**
70 Boulevard De Courcelles
Paris, France (100%)
Tel.: (33) 155650300
Fax: (33) 155650301
Web Site: www.assystem.com
Emp.: 5
Engineering Services
S.I.C.: 8711
N.A.I.C.S.: 541330
Dominique Louis *(Gen Mgr)*

Assystem France **(1)**
70 Boulevard De Courcelles
75017 Paris, France (100%)
Tel.: (33) 155650300
Fax: (33) 155650049
Web Site: www.assytems.com
Emp.: 55
Engineering Services
S.I.C.: 8711
N.A.I.C.S.: 541330
Dominique Louis *(CEO)*

Assystem Innovation **(1)**
70 Boulevard De Courcelles
75017 Paris, France (100%)
Tel.: (33) 134525000
Fax: (33) 15565030049
E-Mail: accuel.courcelles@assystem.com
Management Consulting Services
S.I.C.: 8748
N.A.I.C.S.: 541618
Dominique Louis *(Gen Mgr)*

Assystem Technologies & Services Sa **(1)**
70 Boulevard De Courcelles
75017 Paris, France (100%)
Tel.: (33) 155650300
Fax: (33) 155650049
E-Mail: accueil.courcelles@assystem.com
Web Site: www.assystem.com
Emp.: 50
Engineering Services
S.I.C.: 8711
N.A.I.C.S.: 541330
Dominic Louis *(CEO)*

Athos Aeronautique **(1)**
Immeuble Neos Aeroparc D Entzh 1 Rue Icare
67960 Entzheim, France
Tel.: (33) 534396404
Fax: (33) 388021104
Aircraft Mfr
S.I.C.: 3721
N.A.I.C.S.: 336411

Eurosyn Developpement SAS **(1)**
16 Ave Du Quebec
91140 Villebon-sur-Yvette, France
Tel.: (33) 160926400
Fax: (33) 160926488
Web Site: www.eurosyn.fr
Emp.: 30
Engineering Services
S.I.C.: 8711
N.A.I.C.S.: 541330
Herve Dessi *(Pres)*

Non-U.S. Subsidiaries:

Assystem Deutschland Holding GmbH **(1)**
Sportallee 77
Hamburg, 22335, Germany
Tel.: (49) 405079610
Fax: (49) 4050796199
Engineering Services
S.I.C.: 8711
N.A.I.C.S.: 541330

Assystem Engineering & Consulting (Shanghai) Co , Ltd **(1)**
Tangchen Xongxin
Office A1405
188 Zhangyang Road, Shanghai, Pudong, China (100%)
Tel.: (86) 2158368110
Fax: (86) 2158368112
Web Site: www.assystem.com
Engineering Services
S.I.C.: 8711
N.A.I.C.S.: 541330

Assystem GmbH **(1)**
Sportallee 77
Hamburg, Germany
Tel.: (49) 405079610
Fax: (49) 40 507961 99
E-Mail: info@de.assystem.com
Web Site: www.assystem-germany.com
Emp.: 600
Engineering Services
S.I.C.: 8711
N.A.I.C.S.: 541330

Assystem Group Uk Ltd **(1)**
5B Tower House St Catherine's Court
Sunderland Enterprise Park, SR53XJ
Sunderland, United Kingdom
Tel.: (44) 1915160222
Fax: (44) 1915167979
E-Mail: info@assystem.com
Web Site: www.inbis.com
Emp.: 1,500
Engineering Services
S.I.C.: 8711
N.A.I.C.S.: 541330
David Bradley *(CEO)*

Assystem Iberia **(1)**
Avenida De Espana 23 Planta 3
Alcobendas, Madrid, 28100, Spain
Tel.: (34) 944393550
Fax: (34) 918376850
E-Mail: mpascual@assystem.es
Web Site: www.assystem.es
Emp.: 200
Engineering Services
S.I.C.: 8711
N.A.I.C.S.: 541330
Herbert Hughes *(Mgr)*

Assystem India Pvt Ltd **(1)**
Prestige Blue Chip Software Park 4th Floor
2nd Block No 9 Hosur Road
Bengaluru, 560 029, India
Tel.: (91) 80 4112 3660
Fax: (91) 80 4112 3674
E-Mail: info@assystem-india.com
Web Site: www.assystem-india.com
Emp.: 30
Engineering Services
S.I.C.: 8711
N.A.I.C.S.: 541330
Manirathnam Jabaji *(Pres)*

Assystem (IOM) Ltd **(1)**
11 Spring Valley Estate Cooil Rd
Braddan, Isle of Man
Tel.: (44) 1624638400
Fax: (44) 1624638405
Emp.: 45
Engineering Services
S.I.C.: 8711
N.A.I.C.S.: 541330
Brian Maddrell *(Mgr-Ops)*

Assystem Italia Srl **(1)**
Viale Risorgimento 5
Beinasco, Italy (100%)
Tel.: (39) 0238093582
Fax: (39) 113989419
Engineering Services
S.I.C.: 8711
N.A.I.C.S.: 541330
Massenelerno Mocceno *(CEO)*

Assystem Portugal **(1)**
Travessa Da Telheira 305 Sala 10
Perafita, Matosinhos, 4455-563, Portugal
Tel.: (351) 229997130
Fax: (351) 229997139
E-Mail: geral@assystemportugal.pt
Emp.: 20
Engineering Services
S.I.C.: 8711
N.A.I.C.S.: 541330
George Garcia *(Gen Mgr)*

Assystem Romania Srl **(1)**
Sector 5 48 Mitropolit Dosoftei Street
Bucharest, Romania (100%)
Tel.: (40) 742100219
E-Mail: office@assystemromania.ro
Web Site: www.assystemromania.ro
Emp.: 80
Testing Laboratories
S.I.C.: 8734
N.A.I.C.S.: 541380

Assystem UK Ltd **(1)**
Club Street Bamber Bridge
Preston, Lancashire, PR5 6FN, United Kingdom
Tel.: (44) 1772645000
Fax: (44) 1772645001
Web Site: www.assystemuk.com
Emp.: 400
Engineering Services
S.I.C.: 8711
N.A.I.C.S.: 541330
David Bradley *(CEO)*

Subsidiary:

Silver Atena UK Ltd **(2)**
Cedar House Riverside Business Park
Swindon Road
Malmesbury, Wiltshire, SN16 9RS, United Kingdom
Tel.: (44) 1666580000
Fax: (44) 1666580001
E-Mail: info@silver-atena.com
Web Site: www.silver-atena.com
Emp.: 50
Aerospace Engineering Services
S.I.C.: 8711
N.A.I.C.S.: 541330
Parminder Singh *(CEO)*

AssystemBrime Portugal **(1)**
Sala 10 Travessa Da Telheira 305
Perafita, 4455-563 Porto, Portugal (100%)
Tel.: (351) 229997130
Fax: (351) 229997139
E-Mail: geral@assystemportugal.pt
Emp.: 23
Engineering Services
S.I.C.: 8711
N.A.I.C.S.: 541330
Clara Siguairedo *(Asst Mgr)*

AST GROUPE SA

78 rue Elisee Reclus
69150 Decines-Charpieu, Cedex, France
Tel.: (33) 4 72 81 64 64
Fax: (33) 4 72 81 42 35
E-Mail: contact@ast-groupe.fr
Web Site: www.ast-group.fr
Year Founded: 1993
ASP—(EUR)
Emp.: 268

Business Description:
Real Estate Development Services
S.I.C.: 6531
N.A.I.C.S.: 531390

Personnel:
Sylvain Tur *(Deputy CEO)*

Board of Directors:
Martine Tur
Sylvain Tur

ASTA HOLDINGS, CORP.

14 Zelenaya Street Suite 20
Guryvesk, 238300 Kaliningrad, Russia
Tel.: (7) 9062122773
Year Founded: 2013

Business Description:
Yacht Repairs, Maintenance, Refurbishing, Winterizing, Custom Refinishing, Modifications, Interior Customization & Boat Detailing
S.I.C.: 3731
N.A.I.C.S.: 336611

Asta Holdings, Corp.—(Continued)

Personnel:
Uladzimir Astafurau *(Pres, CEO, CFO, Principal Acctg Officer, Treas & Sec)*
Board of Directors:
Uladzimir Astafurau

ASTAIRE GROUP PLC
46 Worship Street
London, EC2A 2EA, United Kingdom
Tel.: (44) 2074924750
Fax: (44) 2074924777
E-Mail: info@astaire.co.uk
Web Site: www.astairegroup.co.uk
ASTR—(LSE)
Emp.: 168
Business Description:
Investment Banking Services
S.I.C.: 6211
N.A.I.C.S.: 523110
Personnel:
James Julian Noble *(Chm)*
Board of Directors:
James Julian Noble
Chris Roberts
David Snow
Legal Counsel:
Macfarlanes LLP
20 Cursitor Street
London, EC4A 1LT, United Kingdom
Tel.: (44) 20 7831 9222

Fasken Martineau LLP
17 Hanover Square
London, United Kingdom

ASTALDI S.P.A.
Via G V Bona 65
00156 Rome, Italy
Tel.: (39) 06417661
Fax: (39) 0641766720
E-Mail: commercialeitalia@astaldi.com
Web Site: www.astaldi.com
AST—(ITA)
Rev.: $3,307,401,034
Assets: $5,046,106,129
Liabilities: $4,299,580,825
Net Worth: $746,525,304
Earnings: $99,547,925
Emp.: 9,963
Fiscal Year-end: 12/31/12
Business Description:
Civil & Hydraulic, Transportation, Electromechanical, Environmental & Infrastructure Engineering
S.I.C.: 1623
N.A.I.C.S.: 237110
Personnel:
Paolo Astaldi *(Chm)*
Giuseppe Cafiero *(Deputy Chm)*
Ernesto Monti *(Deputy Chm)*
Stefano Cerri *(CEO)*
Board of Directors:
Paolo Astaldi
Caterina Astaldi
Giuseppe Cafiero
Luigi Guidobono Cavalchini
Stefano Cerri
Giorgio Cirla
Paolo Cuccia
Guido Guzzetti
Mario Lupo
Chiara Mancini
Nicoletta Mincato
Ernesto Monti
Eugenio Pinto

Subsidiaries:

Co Meri S.p.A (1)
Via Giulio Vincenzo Bona 65
00156 Rome, Italy (99.99%)
Tel.: (39) 06417661
Fax: (39) 0641766720
E-Mail: astaldi@astaldi.com
Heavy & Civil Engineering Construction
S.I.C.: 1629
N.A.I.C.S.: 237990
Stefano Cerri *(Mng Dir)*

Cospe Srl (1)
Via Madonnina 7
43044 Collecchio, Italy (100%)
Tel.: (39) 0521302730
Fax: (39) 0521305170
Excavation Contractors
S.I.C.: 1799
N.A.I.C.S.: 238910
Stefano Cerri *(CEO)*

Garbi Linea 5 S.c.a.r.l. (1)
Via Racconigi Snc
Milan, 20162, Italy
Tel.: (39) 0291431100
Fax: (39) 0641766720
Underground Station Monitoring Services
S.I.C.: 7382
N.A.I.C.S.: 561621

Infraflegrea Progetto S.p.A. (1)
Via Domenico Giustino 3/c
Naples, 80125, Italy
Tel.: (39) 0815709222
Fax: (39) 0815708299
Construction Engineering Services
S.I.C.: 8711
N.A.I.C.S.: 541330

Ospedale Del Mare Societa Consortile A.R.L. (1)
Via Giulio Vincenzo Bona 65
Rome, Italy (60%)
Tel.: (39) 06417661
Nonresidential Property Managers
S.I.C.: 6531
N.A.I.C.S.: 531312
Stefano Cerri *(CEO)*

Portovesme S.r.l. (1)
Strada Provinciale n2 Carbonia Km16 5
Portoscuso, Cagliari, 9010, Italy (80%)
Tel.: (39) 078151131
Fax: (39) 07 81509575
E-Mail: box@portovesme.it
Web Site: www.portovesme.it/pagine/contact.htm
Primary Smelting & Refining Nonferrous Metal
S.I.C.: 3339
N.A.I.C.S.: 331410
Carlo Lolliri *(Mng Dir)*

Romairport Srl (1)
Via Giulio Vincenzo Bona 65
00156 Rome, Italy (99.26%)
Tel.: (39) 06417661
Web Site: www.astaldi.com
Heavy & Civil Engineering Construction
S.I.C.: 1629
N.A.I.C.S.: 237990
Stefano Cerri *(CEO)*

Sartori Sud S.r.l. (1)
7 Via Artom Alessandro
72100 Brindisi, Italy
Tel.: (39) 831546104
Fax: (39) 0831546065
Construction Engineering Services
S.I.C.: 1629
N.A.I.C.S.: 237990

Scuola Carabinieri S.C.r.l. (1)
Via Giulio Vincenzo Bona 65
Rome, 156, Italy
Tel.: (39) 06 41 7661
Fax: (39) 0641766720
Construction Engineering Services
S.I.C.: 1629
N.A.I.C.S.: 237990
Luciano de Crecchio *(Gen Mgr)*

S.P.T. - Societa Passante Torino S.c.r.l. (1)
Via Giulio Vincenzo Bona 65
Rome, Italy (74%)
Tel.: (39) 06417661
Fax: (39) 0641766720
E-Mail: astaldi@astaldi.com
Web Site: www.astaldi.et
Heavy & Civil Engineering Construction
S.I.C.: 1629
N.A.I.C.S.: 237990
Stefano Cerri *(CEO)*

Joint Venture:

Partenopea Finanza Di Progetto Spa (1)
Via Galileo Ferraris 113B
80142 Naples, Italy
Tel.: (39) 0816585106
Fax: (39) 0816585107
E-Mail: d.prosprara@astaldi.com
Emp.: 100
Engineering Services
S.I.C.: 8711
N.A.I.C.S.: 541330
Attilio Roscia *(Mgr)*

U.S. Subsidiary:

Astaldi Construction Corporation (1)
8220 W State Rd 84 Ste 300
Fort Lauderdale, FL 33324 (100%)
Tel.: (954) 423-8766
Fax: (954) 423-2597
Web Site: astaldiconstruction.com
Emp.: 200
Highway Street & Bridge Construction
S.I.C.: 1611
N.A.I.C.S.: 237310
Paolo Astaldi *(Pres)*

Non-U.S. Subsidiaries:

Astaldi Arabia Ltd. (1)
Al Baaz Street
Sulaimaniyah District, Riyadh, 11625, Saudi Arabia
Tel.: (966) 14631199
Fax: (966) 14641512
Emp.: 50
Construction Engineering Services
S.I.C.: 1629
N.A.I.C.S.: 237990
Marco Toresi *(Mng Dir)*

Consorcio Rio Pallca (1)
Cal Chinchon Nro 1018 Int 2
San Isidro, Lima, Peru
Tel.: (51) 1 206 4300
Construction Engineering Services
S.I.C.: 1629
N.A.I.C.S.: 237990

Constructora Astaldi Fe Grande Cachapoal Limitada (1)
Avenida Apoquindo 3846 piso 11
Santiago, Chile
Tel.: (56) 29236000
Fax: (56) 39 0641766744
E-Mail: commercialeestero@astaldi.com
Hydroelectric Plant Construction Services
S.I.C.: 1629
N.A.I.C.S.: 237990
Fabio Taulon *(Mng Dir)*

Romstrade S.r.l. (1)
Str Buzesti Nr 71 Sector 1
Bucharest, Romania
Tel.: (40) 21 317 58 27
Fax: (40) 21 317 58 26
E-Mail: office@romstrade.ro
Web Site: www.romstrade.ro
Construction Engineering Services
S.I.C.: 1629
N.A.I.C.S.: 237990
Bogdan Trasculescu *(Gen Mgr)*

S.C. ASTALROM S.A. (1)
Str Varianta Nord Nr 1 judetul Calarasi
910053 Calarasi, Romania
Tel.: (40) 242332471
Fax: (40) 242 33 14 85
E-Mail: office@astalrom.eu
Web Site: www.astalrom.eu
Emp.: 500
Construction Machinery Repair & Maintenance Services
S.I.C.: 7699
N.A.I.C.S.: 811310
Riccardo Rizze *(Gen Mgr)*

SCAR S.c.r.l. (1)
rue des Martyrs 23
Herve, 4650 Liege, Belgium (60%)
Tel.: (32) 87692040
Fax: (32) 87698996
Web Site: www.scar.be/content/default.asp?page=4893
Heavy & Civil Engineering Construction
S.I.C.: 1629
N.A.I.C.S.: 237990

ASTANA FINANCE JSC
12 Begelidinov Street
010000 Astana, Kazakhstan
Tel.: (7) 7172591919
Fax: (7) 7172 591051
E-Mail: af@af.kz
Web Site: www.af.kz/en/
ASFI—(KAZ)
Sales Range: $200-249.9 Million
Business Description:
Financial Services
S.I.C.: 6726
N.A.I.C.S.: 525990
Personnel:
Yerlan Shakibayev *(Chm-Mgmt Bd)*
Yerlan Manatayev *(Deputy Chm-Mgmt Bd)*
Bauyrzhan Nugymanov *(Deputy Chm-Mgmt Bd)*
Igor Morozov *(Mng Dir)*
Almas Omarkhanov *(Mng Dir)*
Supervisory Board of Directors:
Marat Duisenbekovich Aytenov
Kintal Kintalyevich Islamov
Karibayeva Ninna Khalielovna

ASTAR MINERALS LTD.
(Formerly Pan Pacific Aggregates Plc)
925 West Georgia Street
Vancouver, BC, V6C 3L2, Canada
Tel.: (604) 884-7550
Fax: (604) 684-6701
Web Site: www.panagg.com
Year Founded: 2004
TAR—(TSXV)
Assets: $255,079
Liabilities: $28,778
Net Worth: $226,302
Earnings: ($89,388)
Fiscal Year-end: 04/30/13
Business Description:
Construction Aggregates & Industrial Minerals Mining Services
S.I.C.: 1442
N.A.I.C.S.: 212321
Personnel:
Stephen Stanley *(Pres & CEO)*
Abdul Allibhai *(CFO)*
Legal Counsel:
Robertson Downe & Mullally
33695 South Fraser Way
Abbotsford, BC, Canada

Memery Crystal LLP
44 Southampton Buildings
London, United Kingdom

ASTARTA HOLDING N.V.
Pochayninska str 38/44
04070 Kiev, Ukraine
Tel.: (380) 445859494
Fax: (380) 206730342
E-Mail: office@astartakiev.com
Web Site: www.astartakiev.com
AST—(WAR)
Rev.: $450,818,473
Assets: $850,437,161
Liabilities: $403,978,283
Net Worth: $446,458,878
Earnings: $56,806,997
Emp.: 10,663
Fiscal Year-end: 12/31/12
Business Description:
Sugar Mfr
S.I.C.: 0133
N.A.I.C.S.: 111991
Personnel:
Viktor Ivanchyk *(Founder & CEO)*
Petro Rybin *(CFO & COO)*
Marc van Campen *(Chief Corp Officer)*
Board of Directors:
Valery Korotkov
Wladyslaw Bartoszewski
Viktor Ivanchyk

Petro Rybin
Marc van Campen

ASTEC LIFESCIENCES LTD

5 5-A Kamanwala Chambers
4th Floor Sir PM Road
Fort, Mumbai, 400001, India
Tel.: (91) 2222618212
Fax: (91) 2222618289
E-Mail: info@astecls.com
Web Site: www.astecls.com
ASTEC—(BOM NSE)
Emp.: 125

Business Description:
Chemical Mfr
S.I.C.: 2899
N.A.I.C.S.: 325998

Personnel:
Ashok V. Hiremath *(Chm)*
Ravindra Inani *(CFO)*
Tejal Jariwala *(Sec)*

Board of Directors:
Ashok V. Hiremath
Mandar K. Patil

ASTEELFLASH

6 rue Van Gogh
93360 Neuilly-Plaisance, France
Tel.: (33) 149445300
Fax: (33) 143812331
E-Mail: info@asteelflash.com
Web Site: www.asteelflash.com
Year Founded: 2008
Rev.: $114,000,000
Emp.: 5,000

Business Description:
Industrial Electronic Mfr
S.I.C.: 3679
N.A.I.C.S.: 334419

Personnel:
Gilles Benhamou *(Pres & CEO)*
Claude Savard *(CFO & Exec VP)*
Georges Garic *(COO & Exec VP)*
Joop Ruijgrok *(Exec VP-Sls & Mktg)*

ASTEK GROUP PLC

Astek House Atlantic St
Altrincham, Cheshire, WA15 5DL, United Kingdom
Tel.: (44) 1619423900
Fax: (44) 1619423901
Web Site: www.astekgroup.co.uk
Sales Range: $1-9.9 Million

Business Description:
Medical Devices & Diagnostics
S.I.C.: 3842
N.A.I.C.S.: 339113

Personnel:
Alan Segal *(CEO)*

Subsidiary:

Astek Innovations Ltd. **(1)**
Astek House Atlantic St
Altrincham, Cheshire, WA14 5DH, United Kingdom
Tel.: (44) 1619423900
Fax: (44) 1619423901
E-Mail: info@astekinnovations.co.uk
Web Site: www.astekinnovations.co.uk
Emp.: 12
Dental Products Mfr & Whslr
S.I.C.: 3843
N.A.I.C.S.: 339114

ASTEL JSC

67 Mametovoy Street
050004 Almaty, Kazakhstan
Tel.: (7) 7272379000
Fax: (7) 7272379100
E-Mail: astel@astel.kz
Web Site: www.astel.kz
Year Founded: 1993
ASTL—(KAZ)
Sales Range: $25-49.9 Million
Emp.: 315

Business Description:
Telecommunications Services
S.I.C.: 4812
N.A.I.C.S.: 517210

Personnel:
Vladimir Breusov *(Pres)*

ASTELLAS PHARMA INC.

2-5-1 Nihonbashi-Honcho
Chuo-ku, Tokyo, 103-8411, Japan
Tel.: (81) 332443000
Telex: 2222656
Fax: (81) 332443272
Web Site: www.astellas.com
Year Founded: 1923
4503—(OTC TKS)
Sls.: $11,061,732,000
Assets: $15,901,171,000
Liabilities: $4,218,885,000
Net Worth: $11,682,286,000
Earnings: $911,361,000
Emp.: 17,454
Fiscal Year-end: 03/31/13

Business Description:
Pharmaceutical Product Developer & Mfr
S.I.C.: 2834
N.A.I.C.S.: 325412

Personnel:
Masafumi Nogimori *(Chm)*
Yoshihiko Hatanaka *(Pres & CEO)*
Yoshiro Miyokawa *(Chief Admin Officer, Chief Comml Officer & Exec VP)*
Masaharu Asano *(Sr Corp Exec)*
Masaru Imahori *(Sr Corp Exec)*
Yasumasa Masuda *(Sr Corp Exec)*
Shinichi Tsukamoto *(Sr Corp Exec)*
Kenji Yasukawa *(Sr Corp Exec)*
Masao Yoshida *(Sr Corp Exec)*
Kiyotaka Hayashi *(Corp Exec)*
Haruhisa Hirosaki *(Corp Exec)*
Takahisa Iizuka *(Corp Exec)*
Toshihiko Iwata *(Corp Exec)*
Atsushi Kamide *(Corp Exec)*
Shinichiro Katayanagi *(Corp Exec)*
Masatoshi Kuroda *(Corp Exec)*
Mitsunori Matsuda *(Corp Exec)*
Yoshihiro Minami *(Corp Exec)*
Kazunori Okimura *(Corp Exec)*
Yukihiko Sato *(Corp Exec)*
Hirofumi Seki *(Corp Exec)*
Hidetoshi Shuto *(Corp Exec)*
Kenji Sumi *(Corp Exec)*
Makoto Takeuchi *(Corp Exec)*
Wataru Uchida *(Corp Exec)*
Chihiro Yokota *(Corp Exec)*
Shoji Yokota *(Corp Exec)*
Claire Thom *(Sr VP-Global Oncology Dev)*

Board of Directors:
Masafumi Nogimori
Naoki Aikawa
Yoshihiko Hatanaka
Yutaka Kase
Yoshiro Miyokawa
Kanoko Oishi
Hironobu Yasuda

Transfer Agent:
Sumitomo Mitsui Trust Bank Limited
1-4-1 Marunouchi Chiyoda-ku
Tokyo, Japan

Subsidiaries:

Astellas Analytical Science Laboratories, Inc. **(1)**
2-1-6 Kashima Astellas Seiyaku Kk Kashima Jigyojo
Yodogawa-Ku, Osaka, 532-0031, Japan
Tel.: (81) 663901231
Fax: (81) 663901240
Pharmaceutical Products Research & Development Services
S.I.C.: 8731
N.A.I.C.S.: 541711

Astellas Business Service Co., Ltd. **(1)**
3-17-1 Hasune
Itabashi-Ku, Tokyo, 174-0046, Japan
Tel.: (81) 359165115
Pharmaceutical Products Mfr
S.I.C.: 2834
N.A.I.C.S.: 325412

Astellas Learning Institute Co., Ltd. **(1)**
2-3-11 Nihombashihoncho
Chuo-Ku, Tokyo, 103-0023, Japan
Tel.: (81) 332443481
Pharmaceutical Products Mfr
S.I.C.: 2834
N.A.I.C.S.: 325412

Astellas Pharma Tech Co., Ltd. **(1)**
2-5-1 Nihonbashi-Honcho
Chuo-Ku, Tokyo, 103-8411, Japan
Tel.: (81) 332446320
Fax: (81) 332441163
Emp.: 24
Pharmaceutical Product Mfr & Whslr
S.I.C.: 5122
N.A.I.C.S.: 424210

Astellas Research Technologies Co., Ltd. **(1)**
Miyukigaoka 21
Tsukuba, Ibaraki, 305-8585, Japan
Tel.: (81) 29 854 1590
Pharmaceutical Products Mfr
S.I.C.: 2834
N.A.I.C.S.: 325412

Astellas Tokai Co., Ltd. **(1)**
180 Ozumi
Yaizu, Shizuoka, 425-0072, Japan
Tel.: (81) 546275111
Fax: (81) 546210107
Emp.: 50
Pharmaceutical Products Mfr
S.I.C.: 2834
N.A.I.C.S.: 325412

Lotus Estate Co., Ltd. **(1)**
2-5-1 Nihombashihoncho
Chuo-Ku, Tokyo, 103-0023, Japan
Tel.: (81) 332443400
Fax: (81) 3352018500
E-Mail: masami.sakurai@astellas.com
Web Site: www.astellas.com
Emp.: 6
Real Estate Management Services
S.I.C.: 6531
N.A.I.C.S.: 531390
Masami Sakurai *(Mgr)*

U.S. Subsidiary:

Astellas Pharma US, Inc. **(1)**
3 Pkwy N
Deerfield, IL 60015-2548 (100%)
Tel.: (847) 317-8800
Fax: (847) 317-7296
Toll Free: (800) 695-4321
E-Mail: business.development@us.astellas.com
Web Site: www.us.astellas.com
Emp.: 850
Pharmaceutical Product Developer & Mfr
S.I.C.: 2834
N.A.I.C.S.: 325412
Masao Yoshida *(Pres & CEO)*
Sef Kurstjens *(Chief Medical Officer)*
Charlotte M. E. Kremer *(Sr VP-Global Medical Affairs)*
Patrick Shea *(Sr VP-Mktg & Sls)*

Subsidiaries:

Agensys, Inc. **(2)**
2225 Colorado Ave
Santa Monica, CA 90404
Tel.: (310) 820-8029
Fax: (310) 382-2828
Web Site: www.agensys.com
Emp.: 100
Cancer Treatment Developer
S.I.C.: 8731
N.A.I.C.S.: 541712
Sef Kurstjens *(Pres & CEO)*

Astellas Pharma Technologies, Inc. **(2)**
3300 Marshall Ave
Norman, OK 73072
Tel.: (405) 217-6400
Toll Free: (800) 888-7704
Web Site: www.astellas.com
Pharmaceutical Products Mfr
S.I.C.: 2834
N.A.I.C.S.: 325412
Pam Maguire *(Mgr-HR)*

Astellas Research Institute of America, Inc. **(2)**
Evanston Research Pk 1801 Maple Ave
Evanston, IL 60201 (100%)
Mailing Address:
PO Box 188
Skokie, IL 60076-0188
Tel.: (847) 467-4470
Fax: (847) 467-4471
Web Site: www.us.astellas.com
Clinical Research
S.I.C.: 2834
N.A.I.C.S.: 325412

Astellas Research Institute of America LLC **(2)**
8045 Lamon Ave
Skokie, IL 60077
Tel.: (847) 933-7400
Pharmaceutical Laboratory Operating Services
S.I.C.: 8071
N.A.I.C.S.: 621511
Laurie Erickson *(Mgr-Transplantation Immunology)*

Astellas US LLC **(2)**
Three Parkway North
Deerfield, IL 60015
Tel.: (847) 317-8800
Fax: (847) 317-7288
Pharmaceutical Products Mfr
S.I.C.: 2834
N.A.I.C.S.: 325412
Masao Yoshida *(CEO)*
Jeffrey Winton *(Chief Comm Officer & Sr VP)*

Astellas US Technologies, Inc. **(2)**
330 Marshall Ave
Norman, OK 73072 (100%)
Mailing Address:
PO Box 1525
Los Altos, CA 94023-1525
Tel.: (405) 217-6400
Fax: (405) 217-6417
Web Site: www.us.astellas.com
Emp.: 86
Developer of Drug Delivery Technologies
S.I.C.: 8731
N.A.I.C.S.: 541711

Astellas Venture Management LLC **(2)**
2882 Sand Hill Rd Ste 121
Menlo Park, CA 94026
Tel.: (650) 926-0731
Fax: (650) 926-0740
Web Site: www.astellasventure.com
Investment Fund Management Services
S.I.C.: 6282
N.A.I.C.S.: 523920
Sakae Asanuma *(Pres & CEO)*

OSI Pharmaceuticals, Inc. **(2)**
41 Pinelawn Rd
Melville, NY 11747-3149 DE
Tel.: (631) 962-2000
Fax: (631) 752-3880
E-Mail: info@osip.com
Web Site: www.osip.com
Sales Range: $400-449.9 Million
Emp.: 512
Pharmaceutical Research & Development Services
S.I.C.: 2835
N.A.I.C.S.: 325413
Naoki Okamura *(Pres)*

Unit:

OSI Oncology Development **(3)**
2860 Wilderness Pl
Boulder, CO 80301-5467 DE
Tel.: (303) 546-7600
Fax: (303) 444-0672
Web Site: www.osip.com
Sales Range: $50-74.9 Million
Emp.: 150
Pharmaceutical Research & Development Services
S.I.C.: 2834

Astellas Pharma Inc.—(Continued)

N.A.I.C.S.: 325412

Perseid Therapeutics LLC (2)
515 Galveston Dr
Redwood City, CA 94063
Tel.: (650) 298-5800
Fax: (650) 298-5899
Pharmaceutical Research & Development Services
S.I.C.: 8731
N.A.I.C.S.: 541712
Grant Yonehiro *(Pres & CEO)*

Non-U.S. Subsidiary:

Astellas Pharma Canada, Inc. (2)
675 Cochrane Dr Ste 500
West Tower, Markham, ON, L3R 0B8, Canada
Tel.: (905) 470-7990
Fax: (905) 470-7799
E-Mail: info@astellas.ca
Web Site: www.astellas.com
Emp.: 130
Marketing of Proprietary Pharmaceuticals
S.I.C.: 5122
N.A.I.C.S.: 424210
Michael Trembley *(Pres)*

U.S. Joint Venture:

GPDC Partnership (1)
87 Cambridge Park Dr
Cambridge, MA 02140-2311
Provider of Pharmaceuticals
S.I.C.: 8299
N.A.I.C.S.: 611610

Non-U.S. Subsidiaries:

Astellas Farma Limitada (1)
Edificio Cinema Rua Jose Fontana n 1 - 1 Andar
2770-101 Paco d'Arcos, Portugal
Tel.: (351) 21 440 13 00
Fax: (351) 21 440 13 01
E-Mail: portugal@pt.astellas.com
Web Site: www.astellas.eu/contact/locations/portugal/
Pharmaceutical Product Mfr
S.I.C.: 2834
N.A.I.C.S.: 325412

Astellas Pharma AE (1)
Thoukididou 1 Ag Stefanos
14565 Athens, Greece
Tel.: (30) 2108189900
Fax: (30) 2108189960
E-Mail: info@gr.astellas.com
Web Site: www.astellas.com
Emp.: 57
Pharmaceutical Product Mfr
S.I.C.: 2834
N.A.I.C.S.: 325412
Laitmer George *(Gen Mgr)*

Astellas Pharma A.G. (1)
Grindelstrasse 6
8304 Wallisellen, Switzerland
Tel.: (41) 43 233 60 20
Fax: (41) 43 233 60 30
E-Mail: office@ch.astellas.com
Pharmaceutical Product Mfr
S.I.C.: 2834
N.A.I.C.S.: 325412

Astellas Pharma B.V. (1)
Sylviusweg 62
2353 EW Leiden, Netherlands
Tel.: (31) 71 5455 854
Fax: (31) 71 5455 850
E-Mail: contct@astellas.com
Pharmaceutical Products Mfr
S.I.C.: 2834
N.A.I.C.S.: 325412

Astellas Pharma Co., Limited (1)
25 The Courtyard Kilcarbery Business Park
Clondalkin, Dublin, Ireland
Tel.: (353) 1 467 1555
Fax: (353) 1 467 1550
Web Site: www.astellas.eu/contact/locations/ireland/
Pharmaceutical Product Mfr
S.I.C.: 2834
N.A.I.C.S.: 325412

Astellas Pharma Europe Ltd. (1)
Lovett House Lovett Road
Staines-upon-Thames, Surrey, TW18 3AZ, United Kingdom UK
Tel.: (44) 01784419400 (100%)
Fax: (44) 01784419401
Web Site: www.inchcape.co
Emp.: 3,200
Pharmaceutical Manufacturing
S.I.C.: 2834
N.A.I.C.S.: 325412
Ken Jones *(Pres & CEO)*

Subsidiaries:

Astellas Ltd. (2)
Lovett House Lovett Rd
Staines-upon-Thames, Surrey, TW1 83AZ, United Kingdom (100%)
Tel.: (44) 1784419400
Fax: (44) 1784419401
E-Mail: astellas.europeian.communication@astellas.com
Emp.: 250
Provider of Pharmaceuticals
S.I.C.: 2834
N.A.I.C.S.: 325412
Mike Crooks *(Gen Mgr)*

Non-U.S. Subsidiaries:

Astallas Pharma Sp (2)
Ulica Poleczki 21
02 822 Warsaw, Poland (100%)
Tel.: (48) 225451111
Fax: (48) 225451110
E-Mail: recepcja@astallas.com
Web Site: www.astallas.com.pl
Emp.: 120
Provider of Pharmaceuticals
S.I.C.: 2834
N.A.I.C.S.: 325412
Tapani Sura *(Gen Mgr)*

Astellas Ireland (2)
Damastown
Damastown Industrial Park Mulh, Dublin, 15, Ireland IE
Tel.: (353) 18030800 (100%)
Fax: (353) 18030801
E-Mail: info4@ie.astellas.com
Web Site: www.astellas.com
Emp.: 70
Pharmaceutical Ingredients Mfr
S.I.C.: 2834
N.A.I.C.S.: 325412
Atsuki Yamazaki *(Pres & CEO)*

Astellas Pharma A/S (2)
Naverland 4
2600 Glostrup, Denmark (100%)
Tel.: (45) 43430355
Fax: (45) 43432224
E-Mail: kkontact@dk.astellas.com
Web Site: www.astellaspharma.dk
Emp.: 40
Provider of Pharmaceuticals
S.I.C.: 2834
N.A.I.C.S.: 325412
Mats Persson *(Mng Dir)*

Astellas Pharma AB (2)
Medeon Science Park
20512 Malmo, Sweden (100%)
Tel.: (46) 406501500
Fax: (46) 406501501
E-Mail: info@astellas.se
Web Site: www.astellas.se
Sls.: $20,003,680
Emp.: 6
Pharmaceutical Manufacturer
S.I.C.: 2834
N.A.I.C.S.: 325412

Astellas Pharma Europe B.V. (2)
Sylviusweg 62
Leiden, 2353 EW, Netherlands
Mailing Address:
PO Box 108
2350 AC Leiderdorp, Netherlands
Tel.: (31) 715455854
Fax: (31) 715455850
E-Mail: contact@nl.astellas.com
Web Site: www.astellas.com
Emp.: 500
Pharmaceutical Mfr & Developer
S.I.C.: 2834
N.A.I.C.S.: 325412

Subsidiaries:

Astellas B.V. (3)
Sylviusweg 62
2353 EW Leiden, Netherlands (100%)
Mailing Address:
PO Box 108
2350 AC Leiderdorp, Netherlands
Tel.: (31) 715455745
Fax: (31) 715455501
E-Mail: contactsnl@astellas.com
Web Site: www.astellas.com
Emp.: 600
Provider of Pharmaceutical Research & Development Services
S.I.C.: 2834
N.A.I.C.S.: 325412

Astellas Pharma Europe (3)
Hogemaat 2
7942 JG Meppel, Netherlands
Mailing Address:
PO Box 43
7940 AA Meppel, Netherlands
Tel.: (31) 522235300
Fax: (31) 522258794
Web Site: www.astellas.eu/contact/affiliates.php?location=manufacturing
Emp.: 300
Mfr. of Pharmaceuticals
S.I.C.: 2834
N.A.I.C.S.: 325412
Freek Kuyber *(Gen Mgr)*

Astellas Pharma GmbH (2)
Georg Brauchle Ring 64-66
80992 Munich, Germany DE
Tel.: (49) 89454401
Fax: (49) 8945441329
E-Mail: info@de.astellas.com
Web Site: www.astellas.de
Emp.: 900
Pharmaceuticals Marketer
S.I.C.: 5122
N.A.I.C.S.: 424210

Astellas Pharma GmbH (2)
Linzerstrasse 221/E02
1140 Vienna, Austria AT
Tel.: (43) 18772668
Fax: (43) 18771636
E-Mail: info@astellas.at
Web Site: www.astellas.at
Emp.: 40
Pharmaceuticals Whslr
S.I.C.: 5122
N.A.I.C.S.: 424210
Berthold Cuach *(Mng Dir)*

Astellas Pharma Ltda (2)
Lagoas Park Edifocio 5 Torre C Piso 6
Edifico Cinema No 1, 2780 605 Porto Salvo, Portugal (100%)
Tel.: (351) 214401300
Fax: (351) 214401301
E-Mail: portugal@pt.astellas.com
Web Site: www.yamanouchi-eu.com
Emp.: 64
Provider of Pharmaceuticals
S.I.C.: 2834
N.A.I.C.S.: 325412

Astellas Pharma, S.A. (2)
Centro Empresarial La Finca Paseo del Club 2nd Planta
Deportivo No 1 Block 14, 28223 Madrid, Pozuelo de Alarcon, Spain (30%)
Tel.: (34) 914952700
Fax: (34) 914952711
E-Mail: esreception@astellas.com
Web Site: www.astellas.com
Emp.: 100
Pharmaceuticals
S.I.C.: 2834
N.A.I.C.S.: 325412

Astellas Pharma Sarl (2)
114 rue Victor Hugo
92300 Levallois-Perret, France FR
Tel.: (33) 155917500
Fax: (33) 130084230
E-Mail: recruitment@flpointastellas.com
Web Site: www.astellaspharma.com
Emp.: 50
Provider of Pharmaceuticals
S.I.C.: 2834
N.A.I.C.S.: 325412
Patrick Errard *(Mng Dir)*

Fujisawa SA (2)
Avenida Bruselas 20 Planta 1
Edificio Gorbea IV, E-28108 Alcobendas, Madrid, Spain ES
Tel.: (34) 914902810
Fax: (34) 914841557
E-Mail: contact@fujisawa.es
Web Site: www.fujisawa.es
Provider of Pharmaceuticals
S.I.C.: 2834
N.A.I.C.S.: 325412

Yabrofarma LDA (2)
Edificio Cinema
Rua Jose Fontana N 1-1
2770-101 Paco d'Arcos, Portugal
Provider of Pharmaceuticals
S.I.C.: 2834
N.A.I.C.S.: 325412

Astellas Pharma Ges.mbH (1)
Linzerstrasse 221/E02
1140 Vienna, Austria
Tel.: (43) 1 877 26 68
Fax: (43) 1 877 16 36
E-Mail: office.at@astellas.com
Emp.: 57
Pharmaceutical Products Mfr
S.I.C.: 2834
N.A.I.C.S.: 325412
Berthold Cvach *(Gen Mgr)*

Astellas Pharma Hong Kong Co., Ltd. (1)
Unit 1103-07 11/F Tower 1 Grand Century Place 193 Prince Edward Road
West Mongkok, Kowloon, China (Hong Kong)
Tel.: (852) 2377 9801
Fax: (852) 2856 1440
E-Mail: info@hk.astellas.com
Web Site: www.astellas.com.hk
Emp.: 18
Pharmaceutical Products Mfr
S.I.C.: 2834
N.A.I.C.S.: 325412
Yasutaka Suzuki *(Gen Mgr)*

Astellas Pharma ilac Ticaret ve Sanayi A.s. (1)
Tekstilkent Koza Place A Blok No 16/60
Esenler, 34235 Istanbul, Turkey
Tel.: (90) 212 440 08 00
Fax: (90) 212 438 36 71
Web Site: www.astellas.com.tr
Emp.: 29
Pharmaceutical Product Mfr
S.I.C.: 2834
N.A.I.C.S.: 325412
Piet Dury *(Gen Mgr)*

Astellas Pharma International B.V. (1)
Sylviusweg 62
2353 EW Leiden, Netherlands
Tel.: (31) 71 5455 854
Fax: (31) 71 5455 850
E-Mail: contact@nl.astellas.com
Web Site: www.astellas.com
Pharmaceutical Products Distr
S.I.C.: 5122
N.A.I.C.S.: 424210

Astellas Pharma Kft. (1)
Csorsz u 49-51
1124 Budapest, Hungary
Tel.: (36) 1 577 8200
Fax: (36) 1 577 8210
E-Mail: marketing@hu.astellas.com
Pharmaceutical Products Mfr
S.I.C.: 2834
N.A.I.C.S.: 325412

Astellas Pharma Korea, Inc. (1)
6F Kumha Building 41 2 Chungdam dong
Gangnam gu, Seoul, 135766, Korea (South) Ks
Tel.: (82) 234480504
Fax: (82) 234480510
Web Site: www.astellas.com.kr
Emp.: 120
Pharmaceutical Mfr & Sales
S.I.C.: 5122
N.A.I.C.S.: 424210
Fujii Matsutaro *(Pres & CEO)*

Astellas Pharma Philippines Inc. (1)
23rd Floor Salcedo Towers 169 HV Dela Costa Street
Makati, Salcedo Village, Philippines
Tel.: (63) 845 1558
Fax: (63) 845 1567
Web Site: www.astellas.com.ph
Pharmaceutical Mfr
S.I.C.: 2834
N.A.I.C.S.: 325412

Marites S. Dimal *(Pres & Gen Mgr)*

Astellas Pharma (Pty) Limited (1)
Gillooly's View Office Park Block A 5
Osborne Lane
Bedfordview, 2007 Johannesburg, South Africa
Tel.: (27) 11 615 9433
Fax: (27) 11 615 9427
Emp.: 28
Pharmaceutical Product Mfr
S.I.C.: 2834
N.A.I.C.S.: 325412
Derek Haynes *(Gen Mgr)*

Astellas Pharma S.A.S (1)
Les Malesherbes 102-116 rue Victor Hugo
92686 Levallois-Perret, France
Tel.: (33) 1 55 91 75 00
Fax: (33) 1 55 91 75 68
Web Site: www.astellas.eu/contact/locations/france/
Emp.: 200
Pharmaceutical Product Mfr & Whslr
S.I.C.: 2834
N.A.I.C.S.: 325412

Astellas Pharma S.p.A. (1)
Via Delle Industrie 1
20061 Carugate, Italy
Tel.: (39) 02 92 138 1
Fax: (39) 02 92 138 200
Web Site: www.astellas.eu/contact/locations/italy/
Emp.: 180
Pharmaceutical Products Mfr
S.I.C.: 2834
N.A.I.C.S.: 325412

Astellas Pharma Sp.zo.o. (1)
Poleczki 21 Str
02-822 Warsaw, Poland
Tel.: (48) 22 545 11 11
Fax: (48) 22 545 11 10
Pharmaceutical Products Distr
S.I.C.: 5122
N.A.I.C.S.: 424210

Astellas Pharma s.r.o (1)
Sokolovska 100/94
Karlin, 186 00 Prague, Czech Republic
Tel.: (420) 236 080 300
Fax: (420) 236 080 330
E-Mail: info@cz.astellas.com
Web Site: www.astellas.eu/contact/locations/czech/
Emp.: 50
Pharmaceutical Products Mfr
S.I.C.: 2834
N.A.I.C.S.: 325412
Pavel Machacek *(Dir-Medical)*

Astellas Pharma Taiwan, Inc. (1)
5F No 10 Sec 3 Min-Sheng E Rd
Taipei, 104, Taiwan
Tel.: (886) 2 2507 5799
Fax: (886) 2 2507 1808
Pharmaceutical Product Mfr & Whslr
S.I.C.: 2834
N.A.I.C.S.: 325412

Fujisawa Taiwan Co., Ltd. (1)
3rd Floor, No. 325, Sec. 1 Tun Hwa South Road
Taipei, 106, Taiwan TW
Tel.: (886) 2 2709 1980
Fax: (886) 2 2700 1330
Provider of Pharmaceuticals
S.I.C.: 2834
N.A.I.C.S.: 325412

P.T. Astellas Pharma Indonesia (1)
11th Floor Wisma Keai Indonesia Jl
Jenderal Sudirman Kav 3
Jakarta, 10220, Indonesia
Tel.: (62) 21 5724344
Fax: (62) 21 5724345
E-Mail: ain.safety@astellas.co.id
Web Site: www.astellas.co.id
Pharmaceutical Products Mfr
S.I.C.: 2834
N.A.I.C.S.: 325412

Yamanouchi (Thailand) Co., Ltd. (1)
10th Fl Wave Pl 55 Wireless Rd
Lumpini
Patumwan, Bangkok, 10330, Thailand
Provider of Pharmaceuticals
S.I.C.: 2834
N.A.I.C.S.: 325412

ZAO Astellas Pharma (1)
Marksistskaya Ulitsa 16
109147 Moscow, Russia
Tel.: (7) 495 737 0755
Fax: (7) 495 737 0753
E-Mail: reception.mascowoffice@ru.astellas.com
Emp.: 400
Pharmaceutical Product Mfr
S.I.C.: 2834
N.A.I.C.S.: 325412

Non-U.S. Joint Venture:

Fujisawa Synthelabo Pharmaceuticals Co., Ltd. (1)
2nd Fl No 325 Sec 1 Tun Hwa South Rd
Taipei, 106, Taiwan
Tel.: (886) 227091980
Fax: (886) 227551596
Provider of Pharmaceuticals; Joint Venture of Fujisawa Pharmaceutical Co., Ltd. (49%) & Sanofi-Synthelabo S.A. (51%)
S.I.C.: 2834
N.A.I.C.S.: 325412

ASTELLIA S.A.

ZA du Plessis Rue du Plessis
CS 27241
35772 Vern-sur-Seiche, France
Tel.: (33) 299048060
Fax: (33) 299048061
E-Mail: info@astellia.com
Web Site: www.astellia.com
ALAST—(EUR)
Sales Range: $25-49.9 Million
Emp.: 200

Business Description:
Wireless Telecommunication Hardware & Software Mfr & Sales
S.I.C.: 3663
N.A.I.C.S.: 334220

Personnel:
Christian Queffelec *(Chm & Mng Dir)*
Rajesh Sharma *(Exec VP-Sls & Customer Ops)*

Board of Directors:
Christian Queffelec
Emmanuel Audousset
Julien Lecoeuvre
Frederic Vergine

U.S. Subsidiary:

Astellia Inc (1)
116 W 23rd St Ste 500
New York, NY 10011
Tel.: (646) 375-2435
E-Mail: sales.us@astellia.com
Web Site: www.astellia.com
Telecommunication Services
S.I.C.: 4899
N.A.I.C.S.: 517919

Non-U.S. Subsidiaries:

Astellia do Brasil Ltda (1)
Praia de Botafogo 501 - 1 andar Botafogo
Rio de Janeiro, 22250-040, Brazil
Tel.: (55) 21 25 86 60 28
Fax: (55) 21 25 96 60 01
Mobile Network Optimization Services
S.I.C.: 4812
N.A.I.C.S.: 517210

Astellia South Africa PTY Ltd (1)
Regus House Country Club Estate Astellia
Building 2 Woodlands Drive
Woodmead, 2157, South Africa
Tel.: (27) 112588885
Fax: (27) 11 258 8511
E-Mail: admin@astellia.com
Web Site: www.astellia.com
Wireless Communication Network Monitoring Solutions
S.I.C.: 4812
N.A.I.C.S.: 517210
Louis Wepener *(Mgr-Sls-Southern & Eastern Africa)*

ASTER SILICATES LIMITED

A-602 Fairdeal House Near Swastik Cross Road
Navrang Pura, Ahmedabad, Gujarat, 380009, India
Tel.: (91) 79 26422840
E-Mail: info@astersilicatesltd.com
Web Site: www.astersilicatesltd.com
ASTERSILI—(BOM NSE)
Sales Range: $1-9.9 Million
Emp.: 30

Business Description:
Chemical Mfr
S.I.C.: 2899
N.A.I.C.S.: 325998

Personnel:
Maheshwari A. Maheshbhai *(Chm & Mng Dir)*
Mahendra Soni *(Sec)*

ASTEX PHARMACEUTICALS, INC.

(Acquired by Otsuka Holdings Co., Ltd.)

ASTI CORPORATION

2804 Yonezu-cho
Minami-ku, Hamamatsu, Shizuoka, 432-8056, Japan
Tel.: (81) 53 444 5111
Web Site: www.asti.co.jp
Year Founded: 1963
6899—(TKS)
Sales Range: $150-199.9 Million
Emp.: 3,897

Business Description:
Telecommunication Equipment Mfr
S.I.C.: 3669
N.A.I.C.S.: 334290

Personnel:
Mikio Uehira *(Chm)*
Nobukazu Suzuki *(Pres)*

Board of Directors:
Mikio Uehira
Masahiko Hachiya
Takeshi Nozue
Nobukazu Suzuki
Yasuhiro Uchiyama

ASTI HOLDINGS LIMITED

Blk 25 Kallang Avenue 06-01 Kallang Basin Industrial Estate
Singapore, 339416, Singapore
Tel.: (65) 6392 6922
Fax: (65) 6329 5522
Web Site: www.astigp.com
575—(SES)
Rev.: $82,537,970
Assets: $208,410,013
Liabilities: $117,620,595
Net Worth: $90,789,418
Earnings: ($12,725,741)
Emp.: 2,000
Fiscal Year-end: 12/31/12

Business Description:
Semiconductor Mfr & Distr
S.I.C.: 3674
N.A.I.C.S.: 334413

Personnel:
Michael Soon Gnee Loh *(Chm)*
Charles Lew Siang Cher *(CEO)*
Kwek Kiong Woo *(CFO & Sec)*
Timothy Boon Liat Lim *(Grp Admin Officer)*
Larry Huat Leong Lim *(Pres-Telford Grp)*
Hoo Shoon Lau *(Sr VP-STI)*
Yu Huat Ong *(Sr VP-Telford Grp)*

Board of Directors:
Michael Soon Gnee Loh
Kriengsak Chareonwongsak
Charles Lew Siang Cher
Mandie Man Sui Chong
Wai Leong Fong
Peter Hock Meng Lai
Timothy Boon Liat Lim

Subsidiary:

Dragon Group International Limited (1)
Blk 25 Kallang Avenue 03-06 Kallang Basin Industrial Estate
Singapore, 339416, Singapore (61.61%)
Tel.: (65) 62129629
Fax: (65) 62129630
Web Site: www.dragongp.com
MT1—(SES)
Rev.: $2,656,000
Assets: $107,476,000
Liabilities: $79,185,000
Net Worth: $28,291,000
Earnings: ($8,758,000)
Fiscal Year-end: 12/31/12
Electronics Distr
S.I.C.: 5065
N.A.I.C.S.: 423690
Michael Soon Gnee Loh *(Chm & CEO)*
Zhigang Zhao *(Deputy Chm-Nanjing DTB)*
Timothy Boon Liat Lim *(Admin Officer)*
Yau Joe *(Pres-Dragon Technology Distribution-HK)*
Ming Fai Yip *(Sec)*

ASTINO BERHAD

Lot 1218 Jalan Serunai Kawasan Perusahaan Valdor Sungai Bakap
Seberang Perai Selantan, 14200 Penang, Malaysia
Tel.: (60) 45829988
Fax: (60) 45828877
E-Mail: feedback@astino.com.my
Web Site: www.astino.com.my
ASTINO—(KLS)
Rev.: $167,840,330
Assets: $135,698,239
Liabilities: $55,303,740
Net Worth: $80,394,499
Earnings: $10,366,732
Fiscal Year-end: 07/31/13

Business Description:
Industrial Metal Roofing Systems Mfr
S.I.C.: 3448
N.A.I.C.S.: 332311

Personnel:
Back Teng Ng *(Chm & CEO)*
Hung Seh Ng *(COO)*
Lay Hoon Ch'ng *(Sec)*

Board of Directors:
Back Teng Ng
Soo Jin Cheah
Kam Hou Khong
Hung Seh Ng
Hung Weng Ng
Mohtar Nong

Subsidiaries:

Astino (Malaysia) Colour Steel Sheet Sdn. Bhd. (1)
Lot 3 Jalan Jasmine 6 Bukit Beruntung Industrial Park
Mukim Serendah, 48000 Rawang, Selangor Darul Ehsan, Malaysia
Tel.: (60) 360283882
Fax: (60) 360285509
E-Mail: acss-pg@astino.com.my
Web Site: www.astino.com.my/html/contact.html
Emp.: 60
Metal Roofing Sheets Mfr & Distr
S.I.C.: 3444
N.A.I.C.S.: 332322
Ng Pak Siong *(Mng Dir)*

Astino Southern Sdn. Bhd. (1)
PT 719 720 & 721 Jalan Seri Emas
Taman Seri Telok Mas, 75460 Teluk Mas, Melaka, Malaysia
Tel.: (60) 62617923
Fax: (60) 62617926
Roofing Sheets & Building Materials Whslr
S.I.C.: 5033
N.A.I.C.S.: 423330

Ooi Joo Kee & Brothers Sdn. Bhd. (1)
Lot 1218 Jalan Serunai Kawasan Perusahaan Valdor
Seberang Perai Selantan, 14200 Sungai Bakap, Penang, Malaysia

Astino Berhad—(Continued)

Tel.: (60) 45829988
Fax: (60) 45828877
Roofing Sheets Whslr
S.I.C.: 5033
N.A.I.C.S.: 423330
Back Teng Ng *(Co-Mng Dir)*
Hung Seh Ng *(Co-Mng Dir)*

ASTIVITA RENEWABLES LIMITED

172 Ingram Road
Acacia Ridge, QLD, 4110, Australia
Tel.: (61) 73262000
Fax: (61) 73262099
E-Mail: sales@astivita.com
Web Site: www.astivita.com
Year Founded: 2004
AIR—(ASX)
Rev.: $13,390,985
Assets: $12,560,431
Liabilities: $2,294,704
Net Worth: $10,265,727
Earnings: ($3,042,932)
Fiscal Year-end: 06/30/13
Business Description:
Bathroom, Kitchen & Solar Products Importer & Distr
S.I.C.: 5074
N.A.I.C.S.: 423720
Personnel:
Lev Mizikovsky *(Chm)*
Geoff B. Acton *(Co-Sec)*
Narelle Lynch *(Co-Sec)*
Board of Directors:
Lev Mizikovsky
Geoff B. Acton
Rade Dudurovic
Robert Lynch

ASTM S.P.A.

(Formerly Autostrada Torino-Milano S.p.A.)
Corso Regina Margherita 165
10144 Turin, Italy
Tel.: (39) 0114392111
Fax: (39) 0114392218
E-Mail: astm@astm.it
Web Site: www.astm.it
Year Founded: 1928
AT—(ITA)
Rev.: $1,741,983,019
Assets: $8,241,283,702
Liabilities: $5,089,431,265
Net Worth: $3,151,852,437
Earnings: $771,420,026
Emp.: 2,908
Fiscal Year-end: 12/31/12
Business Description:
Highway & Road Construction
S.I.C.: 1622
N.A.I.C.S.: 237310
Personnel:
Gian Maria Gros-Pietro *(Chm)*
Daniela Gavio *(Vice Chm)*
Marcello Gavio *(Vice Chm)*
Alberto Sacchi *(CEO)*
Cristina Volpe *(Sec)*
Board of Directors:
Gian Maria Gros-Pietro
Stefania Bariatti
Caterina Bima
Luigi Bomarsi
Flavio Dezzani
Cesare Ferrero
Giuseppe Garofano
Daniela Gavio
Marcello Gavio
Barbara Poggiali
Luigi Piergiuseppe Ferdinando Roth
Alberto Rubegni
Alberto Sacchi
Stefano Viviano
Marco Weigmann

Subsidiaries:

Ativa SPA (1)
Strada della Cebrosa 86
10156 Turin, Torino, Italy (100%)
Tel.: (39) 0113814100
Fax: (39) 0113814101
E-Mail: info@ativa.it
Web Site: www.ativa.it
Other Motor Vehicle Electrical & Electronic Equipment Mfr
S.I.C.: 3714
N.A.I.C.S.: 336320

Finsina SPA (1)
Via lineages F 0001
20124 Milan, Italy
Tel.: (39) 22771191
E-Mail: fina@fina.co.it
All Other Business Support Services
S.I.C.: 7389
N.A.I.C.S.: 561499

Satap SPA (1)
Via Bonzanigo 22
10144 Turin, Torino, Italy (100%)
Tel.: (39) 114392111
Fax: (39) 114392218
Web Site: www.a4torinomilano.it
Highway Street & Bridge Construction
S.I.C.: 1611
N.A.I.C.S.: 237310
Gianni Luciani *(Mng Dir)*

Sav SPA (1)
Via Per Statte 7050 Ctr Lari 7050
Taranto, Italy (100%)
Tel.: (39) 997353754
Fax: (39) 997353758
Emp.: 20
Charter Bus Industry
S.I.C.: 4142
N.A.I.C.S.: 485510

Si.co.gen. SRL (1)
V Arduino Divrea
Settimo Torinese, 10036, Italy (41.17%)
Tel.: (39) 0118012629
Other Automotive Mechanical & Electrical Repair & Maintenance
S.I.C.: 7539
N.A.I.C.S.: 811118

Sina SPA (1)
Via Ponte Roitero 1
Splimbergo, 33097 Pordenone, Italy (100%)
Tel.: (39) 427598111
Fax: (39) 42750956
Web Site: www.sinaauto.com
Emp.: 80
Used Car Dealers
S.I.C.: 5521
N.A.I.C.S.: 441120

Sineco SPA (1)
19020 Ceparana di Follo 5
19020 Trieste, Italy (100%)
Tel.: (39) 187931400
Fax: (39) 187939841
Web Site: www.sineco.ws
Emp.: 20
Iron and Steel Mills
S.I.C.: 3312
N.A.I.C.S.: 331110
Gianluigi Ghezzi *(Mng Dir)*

ASTMAX CO., LTD.

2-10-2 Higashigotanda Shinagawa-ku
Tokyo, Japan
Tel.: (81) 3 5447 8400
Fax: (81) 3 5447 8431
Web Site: www.astmax.com
Year Founded: 2012
7162—(JAS)
Rev.: $21,175,000
Assets: $55,946,000
Liabilities: $11,363,000
Net Worth: $44,583,000
Earnings: ($44,000)
Emp.: 15
Fiscal Year-end: 03/31/13
Business Description:
Asset Management Services
S.I.C.: 8748
N.A.I.C.S.: 541618
Personnel:
Hideaki Ushijima *(Chm & Co-CEO)*
Hiroaki Honda *(Pres & Co-CEO)*
Kentaro Obata *(Mng Dir)*
Board of Directors:
Hideaki Ushijima
Hiroaki Honda
Shinji Kiso
Shoji Kuwashima
Kentaro Obata
Subsidiaries:

Astmax Investments Management, Inc. (1)
2-10-2 Higashigotanda
Shinagawa-ku, Tokyo, Japan JP
Tel.: (81) 3 5447 8411 (100%)
Fax: (81) 3 5447 8426
Web Site: www.astmaxim.com
Managed Assets: $410,445,000
Emp.: 21
Investment Advisory & Management Services
S.I.C.: 6799
N.A.I.C.S.: 523930
Hiroaki Honda *(Pres & Co-CEO)*
Yoshio Suzuki *(Co-CEO & COO)*
Shinichiro Shiraki *(Co-CEO & Chief Investment Officer)*

Astmax Trading, Inc. (1)
2-10-2 Higashigotanda
Shinagawa-ku, Tokyo, Japan JP
Tel.: (81) 3 5447 8435
Fax: (81) 3 5789 9531
Web Site: www.astmax.com
Emp.: 33
Investment Advisory Services
S.I.C.: 6282
N.A.I.C.S.: 523930
Hideaki Ushijima *(Pres)*

ITC Investment Partners Corporation (1)
11-3 Kita-Aoyama 2-chome
Minato-ku, Tokyo, 107-0061, Japan
Tel.: (81) 3 5770 2710
Fax: (81) 3 5770 2711
Web Site: www.itc-ip.com
Sales Range: $10-24.9 Million
Asset Management Services
S.I.C.: 6799
N.A.I.C.S.: 523920

ASTON HILL FINANCIAL, INC.

Suite 500 Energy Plaza 321 6th Avenue SW
Calgary, AB, T2P 3H3, Canada
Tel.: (403) 770-4800
Fax: (403) 770-4850
Toll Free: (866) 870-4800
E-Mail: info@astonhill.ca
Web Site: www.astonhill.ca
AHF—(TSX)
Rev.: $24,424,065
Assets: $64,850,859
Liabilities: $45,587,745
Net Worth: $19,263,114
Earnings: ($579,514)
Emp.: 44
Fiscal Year-end: 12/31/12
Business Description:
Investment Fund Manager
S.I.C.: 6211
N.A.I.C.S.: 523999
Personnel:
Benedict Cheng *(Pres & Chief Investment Officer)*
Eric Tremblay *(CEO)*
Larry W. Titley *(CFO & VP)*
Mike Killeen *(COO)*
Sasha Rnjak *(Chief Compliance Officer)*
Sandy Liang *(Pres-AHF Capital Partners & Mgr-Portfolio)*
Theresa Devost *(Sec)*
Derek Slemko *(Sr VP-Fin & Bus Dev & Controller)*
J. D. Rothstein *(Sr VP & Mgr-Natl Sls)*
Sean Stansfield *(Sr VP-Sls & Mktg)*
Board of Directors:
Catherine M. Best
Andre Bineau
Bruce Calvin
Benedict Cheng
John Fielding
Eldon R. Smith
Eric Tremblay
Transfer Agent:
Computershare Trust Company of Canada
100 University Avenue 11th Floor
Toronto, ON, M5J 2Y1, Canada
Tel.: (416) 891-9633
Toll Free: (800) 663-9097
Subsidiaries:

Aston Hill Investments Inc (1)
321 6 Ave SW Ste 500
Calgary, AB, T2P 3H3, Canada
Tel.: (403) 770-4800
Fax: (403) 770-4850
Emp.: 12
Financial Consulting Services
S.I.C.: 6282
N.A.I.C.S.: 523930
Eric Tremblay *(Pres)*

Catapult Energy 2004, Inc. (1)
6th Avenue SW Suite 321
Calgary, AB, T2P 3H3, Canada
Tel.: (403) 770-4800
Fax: (403) 770-4850
E-Mail: jhruska@catapultenergy.com
Web Site: www.catapultenergy.com
Emp.: 4
Financial Management Services
S.I.C.: 8748
N.A.I.C.S.: 541618
Joanne A. Hruska *(Pres)*

Catapult Energy Limited Partnership (1)
Ste 500 321 6th Ave SW
321 6th Avenue SW, Calgary, AB, T2P 2V7, Canada (100%)
Tel.: (403) 770-4800
Fax: (403) 770-4850
E-Mail: overload@overloadfinancial.com
Web Site: www.astonhill.ca/company_overview/catapult.html
Emp.: 75
Open-End Investment Funds
S.I.C.: 6722
N.A.I.C.S.: 525910
Joann A. Hruska *(Pres)*

ASTON HILL SENIOR GOLD PRODUCERS INCOME CORP.

77 King Street West Suite 2110
Toronto-Dominion Centre
Toronto, ON, M5K 1G8, Canada
Tel.: (416) 583-2300
Fax: (877) 374-7952
Toll Free: (800) 513-3868
Web Site: www.astonhill.ca
Year Founded: 2010
GPC—(TSX)
Sales Range: Less than $1 Million
Business Description:
Investment Services
S.I.C.: 6211
N.A.I.C.S.: 523999
Personnel:
Michael J. Killeen *(Pres)*
Transfer Agent:
Equity Financial Trust Company
Toronto, ON, Canada

ASTON VILLA LIMITED

Villa Park
Birmingham, B6 6HE, United Kingdom
Tel.: (44) 1213275353
E-Mail: enquiries@avfc.co.uk
Web Site: www.avfc.co.uk
Year Founded: 1874
Sales Range: $1-9.9 Million
Emp.: 114

Business Description:
Professional Football Team
S.I.C.: 7941
N.A.I.C.S.: 711211
Personnel:
Randy D. Lerner *(Chm & CEO)*
Paul Faulkner *(CEO)*

Subsidiary:

Aston Villa Football Club Limited **(1)**
Villa Park
Birmingham, B6 6HE, United Kingdom
Tel.: (44) 1213272299
Fax: (44) 1213222107
Web Site: www.avfc.co.uk/
Emp.: 400
Football Clubs
S.I.C.: 7941
N.A.I.C.S.: 711211

ASTORG PARTNERS S.A.S.

68 rue du Faubourg Saint Honore
F-75008 Paris, France
Tel.: (33) 153054050
Fax: (33) 153054057
E-Mail: info@astorg-partners.com
Web Site: www.astorg-partners.com
Year Founded: 1998
Emp.: 25
Business Description:
Private Equity Firm
S.I.C.: 6211
N.A.I.C.S.: 523999
Personnel:
Xavier Moreno *(Co-Founder & Chm)*
Thierry Timsit *(Co-Founder & Mng Partner)*
Christian Couturier *(Partner)*
Catherine Couet *(CFO)*
Sophie Saden *(Gen Counsel)*
Jean Casamayou *(Sec)*

Holdings:

Ethypharm S.A. **(1)**
194 bureaux de la Colline Bat D
F-92213 Saint-Cloud, France FR
Tel.: (33) 141121720 (60%)
Fax: (33) 0141121730
E-Mail: info@ethypharm.com
Web Site: www.ethypharm-pharmaceutical.com
Sales Range: $150-199.9 Million
Emp.: 800
Oral Drug Delivery Systems Developer & Mfr
S.I.C.: 2834
N.A.I.C.S.: 325412
Gerard Leduc *(Founder & Vice Chm-Supervisory Bd)*
Gilles Brisson *(Chm-Supervisory Bd)*
Hugues Lecat *(Chm-Mgmt Bd & CEO)*
Jean-Jacques Bancel *(CFO)*
Roseline Joannesse *(Gen Counsel)*

Linxens **(1)**
6 rue Helene Boucher
78280 Guyancourt, France FR
Tel.: (33) 1 34 98 09 50 (70%)
E-Mail: webmaster@linxens.com
Web Site: www.linxens.com
Sales Range: $250-299.9 Million
Emp.: 700
Smart Card Flexible Tape Material Mfr
S.I.C.: 3678
N.A.I.C.S.: 334417
Christophe Duverne *(CEO)*
Cuong Duong *(CFO)*

Financiere Ofic **(1)**
35 rue Baudin
F-92593 Levallois-Perret, Cedex, France FR
Tel.: (33) 1 5563 8010
Fax: (33) 1 4134 3054
Web Site: www.onduline.com
Sales Range: $450-499.9 Million
Holding Company; Lightweight Building Materials Mfr & Distr
S.I.C.: 6719
N.A.I.C.S.: 551112
Jean-Louis Roques *(Chm-Supervisory Bd)*
Herve Claquin *(Vice Chm-Supervisory Bd)*
Jean-Noel Fourel *(CEO)*
Antoine Rebois *(CFO)*

Subsidiary:

Onduline **(2)**
35 rue Baudin
F-92593 Levallois-Perret, Cedex, France FR
Tel.: (33) 155638010 (100%)
Fax: (33) 1 4134 3054
E-Mail: info@onduline.com
Web Site: www.onduline.com
Sales Range: $450-499.9 Million
Emp.: 1,300
Lightweight Roofing, Insulation & Other Building Materials Mfr & Distr
S.I.C.: 2952
N.A.I.C.S.: 324122
Jean-Noel Fourel *(CEO)*
Antoine Rebois *(CFO)*

Non-U.S. Subsidiaries:

Onduline Belgique SA/NV **(3)**
Parc Industriel Avenue Andre Ernst 1
4800 Petit-Rechain, Belgium BE
Tel.: (32) 87325560
Fax: (32) 873255556
E-Mail: info@onduline.be
Web Site: www.onduline.be
Emp.: 7
Lightweight Roofing, Insulation & Other Building Materials Mfr & Distr
S.I.C.: 2952
N.A.I.C.S.: 324122
Paul Callewaert *(Gen Mgr)*

Onduline Building Products Limited **(3)**
Eardley House 182-184 Campden Hill Road
Kensington, London, W8 7AS, United Kingdom UK
Tel.: (44) 2077270533
Fax: (44) 2077921390
E-Mail: enquiries@onduline.net
Web Site: www.onduline.com
Roofing & Insulation Materials Distr
S.I.C.: 5033
N.A.I.C.S.: 423330

Onduline GmbH **(3)**
Ostring 11
D-65205 Wiesbaden, Germany De
Tel.: (49) 61229900
Fax: (49) 612299060
E-Mail: info@onduline.de
Web Site: www.onduline.de
Roofing & Insulation Materials Distr
S.I.C.: 5033
N.A.I.C.S.: 423330
Holger Wiegmann *(Mng Dir)*
Ralf Wiegmann *(Mng Dir)*

Onduline Italia S.p.A. **(3)**
Via Sibolla 52/53 Loc Cerbaia
Altopascio, IT-55011 Lucca, Italy IT
Tel.: (39) 058325611
Fax: (39) 0583264582
Web Site: www.onduline.it
Lightweight Roofing, Insulation & Other Building Materials Mfr & Distr
S.I.C.: 2952
N.A.I.C.S.: 324122

Onduline Materiais de Construcao, S.A. **(3)**
Rua das Lages 524
Canelas Vila Nova de Gaia, PT-4410 272
Porto, Portugal PT
Tel.: (351) 227151230
Fax: (351) 227 123 788
E-Mail: info@onduline.pt
Web Site: www.onduline.pt
Lightweight Roofing, Insulation & Other Building Materials Distr
S.I.C.: 5033
N.A.I.C.S.: 423330

Onduline Material de Constructii S.r.l. **(3)**
Str Navodarinr 30-32 sector 1
Bucharest, Romania RO
Tel.: (40) 212331264
Fax: (40) 212331267
E-Mail: office@onduline.ro
Web Site: www.onduline.ro
Emp.: 15
Lightweight Roofing, Insulation & Other Building Materials Distr
S.I.C.: 5033
N.A.I.C.S.: 423330
Doina Perv *(Mng Dir)*

Onduline Materiales de Construccion, S.A. **(3)**
Apartado 25
ES-48500 Gallarta, Vizcaya, Spain ES
Tel.: (34) 946369444
Fax: (34) 946369103
E-Mail: comercial-onduline@onduline.es
Web Site: www.onduline.es
Lightweight Roofing, Insulation & Other Building Materials Mfr & Distr
S.I.C.: 2952
N.A.I.C.S.: 324122
Andre Blazquez *(CEO)*

Onduline Materialy Budowlane Sp. z o.o. **(3)**
ul Kolobrzeska 8
02 923 Warsaw, Poland PL
Tel.: (48) 226518508
Fax: (48) 226511985
Web Site: www.onduline.com.pl
Lightweight Roofing, Insulation & Other Building Materials Distr
S.I.C.: 5033
N.A.I.C.S.: 423330

Onduline S.M., o.z. **(3)**
Bulharska 38
821 04 Bratislava, Slovakia Sk
Tel.: (421) 243422732
Fax: (421) 243422735
E-Mail: info@onduline.sk
Web Site: www.onduline.sk
Lightweight Roofing, Insulation & Other Building Materials Distr
S.I.C.: 5033
N.A.I.C.S.: 423330

Onduline S.M., s.r.o. **(3)**
Zakourilova 28/1096
14900 Prague, Czech Republic CZ
Tel.: (420) 267913949
Fax: (420) 272937451
E-Mail: info@onduline.cz
Web Site: www.onduline.cz
Emp.: 10
Lightweight Roofing, Insulation & Other Building Materials Distr
S.I.C.: 5033
N.A.I.C.S.: 423330
Pavel Petlak *(Gen Mgr)*

OGF, S.A. **(1)**
31 rue de Cambrai
Paris, 75019, France FR
Tel.: (33) 155265400
Fax: (33) 155265776
Web Site: www.ogf.fr
Sales Range: $700-749.9 Million
Emp.: 5,500
Holding Company; Funeral Services; Funeral Parlor & Crematorium Operator; Coffin, Headstone & Monument Mfr
S.I.C.: 6719
N.A.I.C.S.: 551112
Philippe Lerouge *(Chm & Dir Gen)*

Division:

Pompes Funebres Generales - Roblot **(2)**
31 rue de Cambrai
F-75019 Paris, France
Tel.: (33) 155265400
Fax: (33) 1 5526 5776
E-Mail: contact-pfg@pfg-roblot.fr
Web Site: www.pfg.fr
Funeral Services & Funeral Home Operator
S.I.C.: 7261
N.A.I.C.S.: 812210

Unit:

Societe des Bois et Panneaux Industriels **(2)**
Zone Industrielle de Reyrieux
F-01600 Reyrieux, France
Tel.: (33) 474089544
Fax: (33) 474089549
E-Mail: infos@sbpibois.com
Web Site: www.sbpibois.com
Emp.: 100
Wood Panel & Flooring Mfr
S.I.C.: 5031
N.A.I.C.S.: 321113

SCT Telecom S.A.S. **(1)**
ZAC de Nozal Chaudron
17/19 Avenue de la Metallurgie, F-93210 La Plaine Saint-Denis, France FR
Tel.: (33) 892 020 220 (52%)
Fax: (33) 892 020 221
Web Site: www.sct-mobile.fr
Emp.: 239
Integrated Commercial Telecommunications Services
S.I.C.: 4812
N.A.I.C.S.: 517911
Pascal Chaboisseau *(Founder & CEO)*

STACI **(1)**
Avenue des Gros Chevaux
ZI du Vert Galant, F-95310 Paris, France FR
Tel.: (33) 134402900 (60%)
Fax: (33) 134402903
E-Mail: accueil-client@staci.com
Web Site: www2.staci.com
Sales Range: $200-249.9 Million
Emp.: 600
Advertising & Promotional Logistics Services
S.I.C.: 7319
N.A.I.C.S.: 541870
Jean-Pierre Masse *(Founder & Chm-Exec Bd)*
Xavier Moreno *(Chm-Supervisory Bd)*
Brigitte Andreolis-Clavier *(Dir-Fin & Admin)*
Michel Thomas *(Gen Dir)*
Charles-Albert Ponce *(Sec)*

Non-U.S. Holding:

Metalor Technologies International SA **(1)**
Avenue du Vignoble
PO Box 9
CH-2009 Neuchatel, Switzerland CH
Tel.: (41) 327206111
Fax: (41) 327206625
E-Mail: info@metalor.com
Web Site: www.metalor.com
Sls.: $409,734,696
Assets: $696,471,165
Liabilities: $248,403,339
Net Worth: $448,067,825
Earnings: $50,357,833
Emp.: 1,665
Fiscal Year-end: 12/31/12
Holding Company; Precious Metal Refiner, Coater & Specialty Product Mfr
S.I.C.: 6719
N.A.I.C.S.: 551112
Scott Morrison *(Chm & Mng Dir-Mergers)*
Hubert Angleys *(CEO)*
Patrick Arnegger *(Grp CFO)*
Kenji Kasuga *(Exec-Asia Pacific)*
Ricky Lau *(Exec-Greater China)*
Janet McCarthy *(Gen Counsel)*
John Reid *(Treas)*
Philippe Bayeux *(Exec VP-Electrotechnics)*
Jacques Michel *(Exec VP-Advanced Coatings Div)*
Yuxing Shang *(Exec VP-Refining Div)*

Subsidiary:

Metalor Technologies SA **(2)**
Avenue du Vignoble
PO Box 9
CH-2009 Neuchatel, Switzerland CH
Tel.: (41) 327206111 (100%)
Fax: (41) 327206605
E-Mail: corporate@metalor.com
Web Site: www.metalor.com
Emp.: 400
Precious Metal Refiner, Coater & Specialty Product Mfr
S.I.C.: 3339
N.A.I.C.S.: 331410
Scott Morrison *(CEO & Head-Electrotechnics Div)*

Branch:

Metalor Technologies - Marin **(3)**
Rue des Perveuils 8
CH-2074 Marin, Switzerland
Tel.: (41) 327206111
Fax: (41) 327206602
E-Mail: corporate@metalor.com
Web Site: www.metalor.com
Emp.: 400
Precious Metal Refining & Coating Services
S.I.C.: 3339
N.A.I.C.S.: 331410
Scott Morrison *(Gen Mgr)*

Astorg Partners S.A.S.—(Continued)

Subsidiary:

Metalor Finance SA (3)
Avenue du Vignoble
PO Box 9
CH-2009 Neuchatel, Switzerland CH
Tel.: (41) 327206111 (100%)
Fax: (41) 327206601
E-Mail: corporate@metalor.com
Web Site: www.metalor.com
Emp.: 100
International Trade Financing Services
S.I.C.: 6159
N.A.I.C.S.: 522293

U.S. Subsidiary:

Metalor Technologies USA Corporation (2)
255 John L Dietsch Blvd
North Attleboro, MA 02763 DE
Tel.: (508) 699-8800 (100%)
Fax: (508) 695-1603
Toll Free: (800) 829-9999
Web Site: www.metalor.com
Precious Metal Refiner, Coater & Specialty Product Mfr
S.I.C.: 3479
N.A.I.C.S.: 332812
Laurence Drummond *(Gen Mgr)*

Subsidiaries:

Metalor Electrotechnics (U.S.A.) Corp. (3)
1003 Corporate Ln
Export, PA 15632 DE
Tel.: (724) 733-8332
Fax: (724) 733-8341
Web Site: www.metalor.com
Sales Range: $50-74.9 Million
Emp.: 200
Electrical Contact Products Mfr
Export
S.I.C.: 3643
N.A.I.C.S.: 335931
Gail W. Haas *(Controller)*

Subsidiaries:

Metalor Electrotechnics (Puerto Rico) LLC (4)
KM 3 Hwy 992
Luquillo, PR 00773 DE
Tel.: (787) 889-2400
Fax: (787) 889-3400
E-Mail: pablo.gonzalez@metalor.com
Web Site: www.metalor.com
Sales Range: $25-49.9 Million
Emp.: 100
Electrical Contact Products Mfr
S.I.C.: 3643
N.A.I.C.S.: 335931
Pablo Gonzalez *(Mgr-Mfg)*

Metalor USA Refining Corporation (3)
255 John L Dietsch Blvd
North Attleboro, MA 02763 MA
Tel.: (508) 699-8800 (100%)
Fax: (508) 695-1603
Web Site: www.metalor.com
Precious Metal Refining Services
S.I.C.: 3339
N.A.I.C.S.: 331410
Laurence Drummond *(Gen Mgr)*

Non-U.S. Plant:

Metalor USA Refining Corporation Succursal del Peru (4)
Avenida Produccion Nacional 268 Edif Hermes Urb
LaVilla Chorillos, Lima, 09, Peru
Tel.: (51) 12515456
Fax: (51) 12515472
Web Site: www.metalor.com
Emp.: 4
Precious Metal Refining Services
S.I.C.: 3339
N.A.I.C.S.: 331410
Gonzalo De Cossio *(Gen Mgr)*

Non-U.S. Subsidiaries:

Metalor Technologies (Deutschland) GmbH (2)
Kronacher Strasse 66
D-96257 Redwitz an der Rodach, Germany De
Tel.: (49) 9574 624 0 (100%)
Fax: (49) 9574 624 804
Web Site: www.metalor.com
Precious Metal Coater & Specialty Product Mfr
S.I.C.: 3643
N.A.I.C.S.: 335931

Metalor Technologies (France) S.A.S. (2)
Rue des Aquees
BP 29
F-28190 Courville-sur-Eure, France FR
Tel.: (33) 237237844 (100%)
Fax: (33) 237237467
Web Site: www.metalor.com
Precious Metal Coater & Specialty Product Mfr
S.I.C.: 3643
N.A.I.C.S.: 335931

Metalor Technologies (Hong Kong) Ltd. (2)
Ste 1705-9 The Metropolis Tower 10 Metropolis Dr
Hung Hom, Kowloon, China (Hong Kong) HK
Tel.: (852) 25214131 (100%)
Fax: (852) 28451791
Web Site: www.metalor.com
Emp.: 60
Precious Metal Refining & Coating Services
S.I.C.: 3339
N.A.I.C.S.: 331410
Kenneth W. Beilstein *(Gen Mgr)*

Metalor Technologies (Iberica) SA (2)
Espronceda 183 - 1 1 andar
ES-08018 Barcelona, Spain ES
Tel.: (34) 933030112 (100%)
Fax: (34) 933073795
Web Site: www.metalor.com
Precious Metal Refining & Coating Services
S.I.C.: 3339
N.A.I.C.S.: 331410

Metalor Technologies (Italia) S.R.L. (2)
Via G Di Vittorio 28
Peschiera Borromeo, IT-20068 Milan, Italy IT
Tel.: (39) 25165181 (100%)
Fax: (39) 0255301021
Web Site: www.metalor.com
Precious Metal Coating Services
S.I.C.: 3479
N.A.I.C.S.: 332812

Metalor Technologies (Singapore) Pte. Ltd. (2)
67 Tech Park Crescent
TUAS, Singapore, 638074, Singapore SG
Tel.: (65) 68631600 (100%)
Fax: (65) 68630102
Web Site: www.metalor.com
Emp.: 20
Precious Metal Coating Services
S.I.C.: 3479
N.A.I.C.S.: 332812

Metalor Technologies (Suzhou) Ltd. (2)
8 Zhao Yang Road
Suzhou Industrial Park, Suzhou, Jiansu, 215123, China CN
Tel.: (86) 51265936181 (100%)
Fax: (86) 51265936171
Web Site: www.metalor.com
Emp.: 200
Precious Metal Refiner, Coater & Specialty Product Mfr
S.I.C.: 3339
N.A.I.C.S.: 331410
Kenneth W. Beilstein *(Gen Mgr)*

Metalor Technologies (Sweden) AB (2)
Sagagatan 22
SE-50635 Boras, Sweden SE
Tel.: (46) 33444250 (100%)
Fax: (46) 33444260
Web Site: www.metalor.com
Precious Metal Coating Services
S.I.C.: 3479
N.A.I.C.S.: 332812

Metalor Technologies (UK) Ltd. (2)
74 Warstone Lane
Birmingham, B18 6NG, United Kingdom UK
Tel.: (44) 1212363241 (100%)
Fax: (44) 1212363568
Web Site: www.metalor.com
Emp.: 34
Precious Metal Coater & Specialty Product Mfr
S.I.C.: 3643
N.A.I.C.S.: 335931
Stephanie Burling *(Mng Dir)*

ASTORIUS RESOURCES LTD.

Suite 2300-1066 West Hastings Street
Vancouver, BC, V6E 3X2, Canada
Tel.: (604) 618-1758
Fax: (604) 277-0815
E-Mail: info@astoriusresources.com
Web Site: www.astoriusresources.com
Year Founded: 2007
ASQ—(TSXV)
Int. Income: $423
Assets: $260,892
Liabilities: $25,887
Net Worth: $235,006
Earnings: ($170,897)
Fiscal Year-end: 09/30/13

Business Description:
Copper & Gold Exploration Services
S.I.C.: 1021
N.A.I.C.S.: 212234

Personnel:
Theodore James Malcolm Powell *(Pres & CEO)*
Carl Roland Jonsson *(CFO & Sec)*

Board of Directors:
Carl Roland Jonsson
Jason Powell
Theodore James Malcolm Powell
Arthur G. Troup

ASTRA INDUSTRIAL GROUP COMPANY

PO Box 1560
Riyadh, 11441, Saudi Arabia
Tel.: (966) 14752002
Fax: (966) 14752001
E-Mail: info@astraindustrial.com.sa
Web Site: www.astraindustrial.com.sa
1212—(SAU)
Sls.: $398,472,481
Assets: $954,095,009
Liabilities: $459,528,480
Net Worth: $494,566,529
Earnings: $64,623,175
Fiscal Year-end: 12/31/12

Business Description:
Pharmaceutical Products, Fertilizers & Agricultural Pesticides Mfr
S.I.C.: 2873
N.A.I.C.S.: 325311

Personnel:
Sabih Taher Al Masri *(Chm)*
Khaled Sabih Al Masri *(Deputy Chm)*
Khalid Al-Gwaiz *(Pres)*

Board of Directors:
Sabih Taher Al Masri
Farraj Mansour Abuthenain
Ghassan Ibraheem Akeel
Selman Fares Al Fares
Sameer Mohammad Al Hamaidi
Khaled Sabih Al Masri
Mohammad Nejr Al Utaibi
Kamil Abdulrahman Sadeddin
Ghiath Sukhtian

Subsidiaries:

ASTRA Industrial Complex Co. for Fertilizers & Agrochemicals (1)
PO Box 30447
31952 Al Khobar, Saudi Arabia
Tel.: (966) 38121406
Fax: (966) 38121347
E-Mail: astra-agri@compuserve.com
Web Site: www.astra-agri.com.sa
Emp.: 80
Fertilizer & Agrochemical Producer
S.I.C.: 2873
N.A.I.C.S.: 325311
Sabin Taher Darwish Al Masri *(Mng Dir)*

ASTRA Polymer Compounding Co. Ltd. (1)
PO Box 3863
11481 Al Khobar, Saudi Arabia
Tel.: (966) 38123459
Fax: (966) 3 812 1342
E-Mail: info@astra-polymers.com
Web Site: www.astra-polymer.com
Polymers & Thermoplastic Compound Mfr
S.I.C.: 3089
N.A.I.C.S.: 326199

International Building Systems Factory Co. Ltd. (1)
PO Box 1737
11441 Riyadh, Saudi Arabia
Tel.: (966) 12650004
Fax: (966) 12651756
E-Mail: mail@absf.com
Web Site: www.ibsf.com
Emp.: 500
Pre-Engineered Steel Building Mfr
S.I.C.: 3448
N.A.I.C.S.: 332311

Tabuk Pharmaceutical Manufacturing Company (1)
PO Box 14861
Tabuk, Saudi Arabia
Tel.: (966) 44282964
Fax: (966) 44283031
Web Site: www.tpmc.com.sa
Generic Pharmaceuticals Mfr
S.I.C.: 2834
N.A.I.C.S.: 325412
Ghiath Sukhtian *(CEO & Mng Dir)*

Non-U.S. Subsidiary:

Astrachem Turkey (1)
Cemalpasa Mah Ataturk Cad Ogretmenler Sitesi Cigdem Apt E
E Block K 2 D 4, Adana, Turkey
Tel.: (90) 322 457 1060
Fax: (90) 322 457 1088
Emp.: 11
Agrochemicals Mfr & Sales
S.I.C.: 2879
N.A.I.C.S.: 325320
S. Ihsan Yildirim *(Country Mgr)*

ASTRA MICROWAVE PRODUCTS LIMITED

Astra Towers Survey No 12P
Kothaguda Pos Kondapur Hitechcity
Hyderabad, Andhra Pradesh, India 500084
Tel.: (91) 4030618000
Fax: (91) 4030618048
E-Mail: info@astramwp.com
Web Site: www.astramwp.com
532493—(BOM)
Rev.: $44,179,029
Assets: $92,474,801
Liabilities: $55,231,209
Net Worth: $37,243,592
Earnings: $6,894,192
Emp.: 550
Fiscal Year-end: 03/31/13

Business Description:
Consumer Electronics Industry
S.I.C.: 3663
N.A.I.C.S.: 334220

Personnel:
Shiban K. Koul *(Chm)*
B. Malla Reddy *(Mng Dir)*
P. A. Chitrakar *(COO)*
T. Anjaneyulu *(Compliance Officer & Sec)*

Board of Directors:
Shiban K. Koul
P. A. Chitrakar
Atim Kabra
C. Prameelamma
B. Malla Reddy
Maram Venkateshwar Reddy

S. Gurunatha Reddy
J. Venkatadas

Transfer Agent:
Purva Sharegistry (India) Pvt Ltd
Shiv Shakti Industrial Estate Unit No 9 Ground Floor
7 B J R Boricha Marg, Mumbai, 400011, India

Subsidiary:

Komoline Electronics Private Limited (1)
110-124 Om Towers Satellite Rd
Ahmedabad, Gujarat, 380 015, India
Tel.: (91) 7926746179
Fax: (91) 7926746324
E-Mail: info@komoline.com
Web Site: www.komoline.com
Emp.: 80
Automated Weather Monitoring Components Mfr
S.I.C.: 3829
N.A.I.C.S.: 334519
Sanjay Attara *(Owner)*

Units:

Astra Microwave Products Limited - Unit-I (1)
Plot No 12 Anrich Indus Estate IDA Bollarum
Miyapur Medak Dist, 502 325 Hyderabad, Andhra Pradesh, India
Tel.: (91) 4030618100
Fax: (91) 4030618101
Emp.: 500
Microwave Systems Mfr
S.I.C.: 3679
N.A.I.C.S.: 334419

Astra Microwave Products Limited - Unit-II (1)
Plot No 56A Anrich Indus Estate IDA Bollarum
Miyapur Medak Dist, Hyderabad, Andhra Pradesh, 502325, India
Tel.: (91) 4030618200
Fax: (91) 4030618048
E-Mail: info@astramwp.com
Emp.: 60
Defense & Telecommunication Devices Mfr
S.I.C.: 3669
N.A.I.C.S.: 334290
B. Malla Reddy *(Mng Dir)*

ASTRA VENTURES, INC.

10/F Building B No 329 Tianyaoqiao Road
Xuhui District, Shanghai, China
Tel.: (86) 21 3363 3050, ext. 763
Year Founded: 2010
AAVC—(OTC OTCB)
Assets: $25,064
Liabilities: $44,930
Net Worth: ($19,866)
Earnings: ($32,877)
Fiscal Year-end: 02/28/13

Business Description:
Investment Services; Television & Film Distr
S.I.C.: 6211
N.A.I.C.S.: 523999

Personnel:
Chau To Chan *(Chm & Pres)*
Mao Zhao *(CEO)*
Qinzhen Li *(CFO, Treas & Sec)*

Board of Directors:
Chau To Chan
Yong Li
Mao Zhao

ASTRAL ASIA BERHAD

No 67 69 Jalan SBC 1 Taman Sri Batu Caves
68100 Batu Caves, Selangor Darul Ehsan, Malaysia
Tel.: (60) 361857307
Fax: (60) 361856799
E-Mail: enquiry@astralasia.com
Web Site: www.astralasia.com
AASIA—(KLS)
Rev.: $12,085,597
Assets: $96,592,344
Liabilities: $23,259,478
Net Worth: $73,332,866
Earnings: $2,600,558
Fiscal Year-end: 12/31/12

Business Description:
Civil Engineering & Building Construction Services
S.I.C.: 8711
N.A.I.C.S.: 541330

Personnel:
Kang Poh Lim *(Deputy Chm)*
Md Adanan Abdul Manap *(Deputy CEO)*
Hoon Ping Chua *(Co-Sec)*
Leonard Hui Kit Hoon *(Co-Sec)*

Board of Directors:
Husein Ahmad
Md Adanan Abdul Manap
Misran Jamain
Guan Shiun Lim
Kang Poh Lim
Md Adnan Sulaiman
En Chong Tan

ASTRAL FOODS LIMITED

92 Koranna Avenue
Doringkloo, Centurion, 0157, South Africa
Tel.: (27) 12 667 5468
Fax: (27) 86 504 2002
E-Mail: Olga.Hansen@astralfoods.com
Web Site: www.astralfoods.com
ARL—(JSE)
Rev.: $1,045,224,391
Assets: $456,618,947
Liabilities: $252,191,022
Net Worth: $204,427,925
Earnings: $42,589,925
Emp.: 7,737
Fiscal Year-end: 09/30/12

Business Description:
Animal Feeds, Animal Feed Pre-Mixes, Broiler Genetic Breeding & Broiler Operations; Broilers & Hatching Eggs Producer & Sales
S.I.C.: 2048
N.A.I.C.S.: 311119

Personnel:
Christiaan Ernst Schutte *(CEO)*
Evert Potgieter *(Exec-Audit & Risk)*
Willem Stander *(Exec-Procurement)*
Phil Tozer *(Exec-Sls & Mktg-Poultry Div-Astral Foods)*
Maryna A. Eloff *(Sec)*

Board of Directors:
Jurie Johannes Geldenhuys
Gary Arnold
Theo Delport
Theunis Eloff
Daniel Dirk Ferreira
Izak Stephanus Fourie
Obed Mooki Lukhele
Malcolm MacDonald
Christiaan Ernst Schutte
Nombasa Tsengwa

Transfer Agent:
Computershare Investor Services (Pty) Ltd.
70 Marshall Street
Johannesburg, 2001, South Africa
Tel.: (27) 11 370 5000
Fax: (27) 11 370 5487

Subsidiaries:

Astral Operations Limited (1)
92 Koranna Avenue
Centurion, Centurion, 157, South Africa
Tel.: (27) 126675468
Fax: (27) 126676665
Web Site: www.astralfoods.com
Emp.: 1,200
Broiler Chicken Production & Distr
S.I.C.: 0251
N.A.I.C.S.: 112320
Nick Borain *(CEO)*

Division:

Astral Operations Limited - Earlybird Farm Division (2)
15 Industry Road
PO Box 237
Olifantsfontein, 1665, South Africa
Tel.: (27) 11 206 0600
Fax: (27) 11 316 4989
Web Site: www.earlybirdfarm.com
Emp.: 3,839
Broiler Chicken Production Services
S.I.C.: 0251
N.A.I.C.S.: 112320
Theo Delport *(Mng Dir-Poultry Div)*

Subsidiary:

County Fair Foods (Pty) Ltd (2)
Bofors Circle Epping Industria 7475
Cape Town, Western Cape, 7475, South Africa
Tel.: (27) 21 505 8000
Fax: (27) 21 505 8102
Web Site: www.countyfair.co.za
Rev.: $153,708,000
Emp.: 200
Broiler Chicken Production & Distr
S.I.C.: 0251
N.A.I.C.S.: 112320
Kay Allsop *(Mgr-Customer Svc Liaison)*

Earlybird Farm (Pty) Ltd. (1)
15 Industry Road
Olifantsfontein, 1665, South Africa
Tel.: (27) 0112060723
Fax: (27) 113164989
Web Site: www.earlybirdfarm.com
Emp.: 4,000
Poultry Products Mfr
S.I.C.: 0259
N.A.I.C.S.: 112390
Chris Chutte *(Chm)*
Theo Belport *(Mng Dir)*
Faan Greyling *(COO)*

Meadow Feeds Pty. Ltd. (1)
Warich Close Ofc Pk Blk 2 39 Van Vuuren St
Allen's Nek Ext 47, Roodepoort, South Africa
Tel.: (27) 119916000
Fax: (27) 114755752
E-Mail: info@meadowfeeds.co.za
Web Site: www.meadowfeeds.co.za
Animal Feeds Mfr
S.I.C.: 2048
N.A.I.C.S.: 311119
Pierre Scharneck *(Reg Mgr-Logistics)*

Divisions:

Meadow Feeds Cape (2)
Westhoven Street
PO Box 262
Dal Josafat, 7620 Paarl, 7646, South Africa
Tel.: (27) 218078700
Fax: (27) 218078710
E-Mail: gary.arnold@meadowcape.co.za
Web Site: www.meadowcape.co.za
Emp.: 111
Animal Feed Mfr
S.I.C.: 2048
N.A.I.C.S.: 311119
James Berry *(COO)*

Meadow Feeds Delmas (2)
1 Sarel Cilliers St
PO Box 11
Delmas, 2210, South Africa
Tel.: (27) 136655011
Fax: (27) 136655035
E-Mail: eugene.viljoen@meadowfeeds.com
Web Site: www.meadowfeeds.com
Emp.: 94
Animal Feeds Mfr
S.I.C.: 2048
N.A.I.C.S.: 311119
Eugene Viljoen *(COO)*

Meadow Feeds Kwa-Zulu Natal (2)
56 Ohrtmann Road
Pietermaritzburg, 3201, South Africa
Tel.: (27) 333872403
Fax: (27) 3873115
E-Mail: reception@meadowfeeds.co.za
Web Site: www.meadowfeeds.co.za
Emp.: 80
Animal Feed Mfr
S.I.C.: 2048
N.A.I.C.S.: 311119
Michael Schmitz *(COO)*

Meadow Feeds Port Elizabeth (2)
5B Lindsay Rd
Neave, Port Elizabeth, East Cape, 6014, South Africa
Tel.: (27) 414025000
Fax: (27) 0414535317
E-Mail: receptionpe@meadowcape.co.za
Web Site: www.meadowfeeds.co.za
Emp.: 90
Animal Feed Mfr
S.I.C.: 2048
N.A.I.C.S.: 311119
Andy Crocker *(COO)*

Meadow Feeds Randfontein (2)
144 Main Reef Road
Private Bag X39
Randfontein, 1760, South Africa
Tel.: (27) 116935120
Fax: (27) 116933111
E-Mail: info@meadowfeeds.co.za
Web Site: www.meadowfeeds.co.za
Emp.: 100
Animal Feeds Mfr
S.I.C.: 2048
N.A.I.C.S.: 311119
Theresa De Villiers *(Mgr-Fin)*

Meadow Feeds Welkom (2)
15 2nd Street
PO Box 102
Welkom, 9460, South Africa
Tel.: (27) 573914000
Fax: (27) 573532241
E-Mail: fusinvinniekerk@meadowfeeds.co.za
Web Site: www.meadowfeeds.co.za
Emp.: 19
Animal Feed Mfr
S.I.C.: 2048
N.A.I.C.S.: 311119
Kobus Smit *(Mgr-Sls)*

Non-U.S. Divisions:

Meadow Feed Mauritius (2)
Richeterre Road
Port Louis, Mauritius
Tel.: (230) 9230 249 3860
Web Site: www.meadowfeeds.co.za/Regions/Natal/Natal_Content.htm
Animal Feed Mfr
S.I.C.: 2048
N.A.I.C.S.: 311119

Meadow Feeds Zambia (2)
Plot 8537 Mwembeshi Road
31712
Lusaka Light Industrial Area, 10101 Lusaka, Zambia
Mailing Address:
PO Box 31712
Plot 8537, Lusaka, Zambia
Tel.: (260) 01286262
Fax: (260) 211286266
E-Mail: info@tigerfeeds.com.zm
Web Site: www.tigerfeeds.com
Emp.: 100
Animal Feed Mfr
S.I.C.: 2048
N.A.I.C.S.: 311119
Roedolf Steenkamp *(Mng Dir)*

Meadow Mozambique LDA (2)
Av Abel Babtista
1277 RC
Bairro Sicauma NT, 40009 4047 Matola, Mozambique
Tel.: (258) 21747022
Fax: (258) 21747023
E-Mail: meadowmoz@intra.co.mz
Emp.: 38
Animal Feed Mfr
S.I.C.: 2048
N.A.I.C.S.: 311119
Mark Stratford *(Mgr-Ops)*

National Chick Limited (1)
Devertin Farm D 3234 Umlas Road
PO Box 105 Umlas Road
Kwa-Zulu Natal, 3730, South Africa
Tel.: (27) 317859100
Fax: (27) 317851788
E-Mail: celeste.vanwyk@natchix.co.za

Astral Foods Limited—(Continued)

Web Site: www.natchix.co.za
Emp.: 753
Poultry Mfr
S.I.C.: 0254
N.A.I.C.S.: 112340
David Stuock *(COO)*

Ross Poultry Breeders (Pty) Ltd. **(1)**
PO Box 297
1960 Meyerton, South Africa
Tel.: (27) 163660249
Fax: (27) 163660931
E-Mail: insie@rpb.co.za
Emp.: 270
Poultry Breeding Services
S.I.C.: 0259
N.A.I.C.S.: 112390

Joint Venture:

NuTec Southern Africa (Pty) Ltd. **(1)**
234 Royston Road
Willowton, 3201 Pietermaritzburg, South Africa ZA
Mailing Address:
PO Box 11387
Dorpspruit, 3206, South Africa
Tel.: (27) 333979405
Fax: (27) 333875354
E-Mail: technical@nutecsa.co.za
Web Site: www.nutecsa.co.za
Emp.: 50
Animal Vitamin & Mineral Premix Mfr
S.I.C.: 2048
N.A.I.C.S.: 311119
Gudo Klein Gebbink *(COO)*

ASTRAL MEDIA INC.

(Acquired by BCE INC.)

ASTRAL POLY TECHNIK LIMITED

Astral House 207/1 Bh Rajpath Club
Off S G Highway
Ahmedabad, 380059, India
Tel.: (91) 7966212000
Fax: (91) 7966212121
E-Mail: info@astralcpvc.com
Web Site: www.astralcpvc.com
532830—(BOM)
Rev.: $167,548,817
Assets: $101,218,518
Liabilities: $56,404,223
Net Worth: $44,814,295
Earnings: $11,237,335
Emp.: 50
Fiscal Year-end: 03/31/13
Business Description:
Plastics Industry
S.I.C.: 3084
N.A.I.C.S.: 326122
Personnel:
Sandeep P. Engineer *(Mng Dir)*
Hiranand A. Savlani *(CFO)*
Zankhana V. Trivedi *(Compliance Officer & Sec)*
Board of Directors:
K. R. Shenoy
Pradip N. Desai
Jagruti S. Engineer
Sandeep P. Engineer
Kyle A. Thompson
Transfer Agent:
Bigshare Services Private Limited
E 2/3 Ansa Industrial Estate Sakivihar Road
Sakinaka Andheri(E)
Mumbai, India

ASTRAL SUPREME BERHAD

Level 7 Menara Milenium Jalan
Damanlela Pusat Bandar Damansara
Damansara Heights Wilayah
Persekutuan, 50490 Kuala Lumpur, Malaysia
Tel.: (60) 3 2084 9000
Fax: (60) 3 2094 9940
E-Mail: info@astral-supreme.com
Web Site: www.astral-supreme.com
ASUPREM—(KLS)
Rev.: $3,595,903
Assets: $8,314,937
Liabilities: $1,929,682
Net Worth: $6,385,255
Earnings: $124,343
Fiscal Year-end: 12/31/12
Business Description:
Electronic Products Mfr
S.I.C.: 3812
N.A.I.C.S.: 334511
Personnel:
Tai Chin Ong *(Mng Dir)*
Mun Yee Chin *(Co-Sec)*
Siew Chuan Chua *(Co-Sec)*
Board of Directors:
Chi Keong Yap
Chin Guan Cherng
Heng Khen Lee
Tai Chin Ong
Boon Yeong Siew
Tiew Toon Wee

Subsidiary:

Singatronics (Malaysia) Sdn. Bhd. **(1)**
Lot 20 Kulim Indus Estate
09000 Kulim, Kedah, Malaysia
Tel.: (60) 44892288
Fax: (60) 44891088
E-Mail: kttan@singatronics.com
Web Site: www.singatronics.com.my
Emp.: 300
Electronic Printed Circuit Assemblies Mfr
S.I.C.: 3679
N.A.I.C.S.: 334418
Qui Koh Lai *(Mng Dir)*

ASTRAPAK LIMITED

No 5 Kruger Street Denver
Johannesburg, 2094, South Africa
Mailing Address:
PO Box 75769
Gardenview, 2047, South Africa
Tel.: (27) 116158011
Fax: (27) 116159790
E-Mail: craig@astrarepro.co.za
Web Site: www.astrapak.co.za
APK—(JSE)
Rev.: $292,093,601
Assets: $268,602,868
Liabilities: $128,501,467
Net Worth: $140,101,401
Earnings: $16,595,716
Emp.: 3,975
Fiscal Year-end: 02/28/13
Business Description:
Packaging Services
S.I.C.: 7389
N.A.I.C.S.: 561910
Personnel:
Robin Moore *(CEO)*
Manley Diedloff *(Mng Dir)*
Gene Lapan *(Acting CFO & Dir-Fin)*
Sandile Ngwabi *(Sec)*
Board of Directors:
Phumzile Langeni
Paul Botha
Manley Diedloff
Gugu Pride Duda
Gene Lapan
Craig McDougall
Robin Moore
Gunter Steffens
Legal Counsel:
Cliffe Dekker
1 Protea Place
Sandown, Sandton, South Africa
Transfer Agent:
Computershare Investor Services (Pty) Ltd
70 Marshall Street
Johannesburg, South Africa

Divisions:

Astrapak Limited - Cinqplast Plastop Denver Division **(1)**
5 Kruger Street Denver
Johannesburg, 2094, South Africa
Tel.: (27) 11 417 6300
Fax: (27) 11 622 4428
E-Mail: admin@astrapak.co.za
Emp.: 20
Packaging Plastic Products Mfr
S.I.C.: 2671
N.A.I.C.S.: 322220
Grant Matthews *(Gen Mgr)*

Astrapak Limited - City Packaging Division **(1)**
Corner Hilston Tanjovan Roads
Kya Sands, Randburg, South Africa
Tel.: (27) 11 708 1110
Fax: (27) 11 708 1114
E-Mail: mail@citypack.co.za
Web Site: www.astrapak.co.za/astrapak/GroupCompanies.jsp?id=49
Shrink Film Packaging Products Mfr
S.I.C.: 2672
N.A.I.C.S.: 322220
Andre Smit *(Gen Mgr)*

Astrapak Limited - East Rand Plastics Division **(1)**
87 Uranium Road Vulcania Brakpan
Johannesburg, 1540, South Africa
Tel.: (27) 11 817 9000
Fax: (27) 11 813 3793
Emp.: 20
Packaging Plastic Products Mfr
S.I.C.: 2671
N.A.I.C.S.: 322220
Craig Lowe *(Gen Mgr)*

Astrapak Limited - Packaging Consultants Division **(1)**
1 Imvubu Park Close Riverhorse Valley
Durban, South Africa
Mailing Address:
PO Box 74043
Rochedale Park, Durban, 4034, South Africa
Tel.: (27) 31 569 6100
Fax: (27) 31 569 6063
E-Mail: pacon@pacon.co.za
Emp.: 300
Plastic Packaging Products Mfr
S.I.C.: 2671
N.A.I.C.S.: 322220
Rory van Zyl *(Gen Mgr)*

Astrapak Limited - Peninsula Packaging Division **(1)**
Proton Crescent Stikland
Bellville, 7530, South Africa
Tel.: (27) 21 948 0717
Fax: (27) 21 949 9788
E-Mail: sales@penpak.co.za
Packaging Plastic Products Mfr
S.I.C.: 2671
N.A.I.C.S.: 322220
Andre Adonis *(Acct Mgr)*

Astrapak Limited - Plastform Division **(1)**
Flamindo Crescent Lansdowne
7780 Cape Town, South Africa
Tel.: (27) 21 763 0400
Fax: (27) 21 763 0401
Web Site: www.plastform.co.za
Emp.: 19
Packaging Plastic Products Mfr
S.I.C.: 2671
N.A.I.C.S.: 322220
Neil Jones *(Gen Mgr)*

Astrapak Limited - Plastop Bronkhorstspruit Division **(1)**
197/1 Manganese Street
Ekandustria, Bronkhorstspruit, South Africa
Tel.: (27) 13 933 3205
Fax: (27) 13 933 3410
Emp.: 400
Plastic Packaging Products Mfr
S.I.C.: 2671
N.A.I.C.S.: 322220
Grant Matthews *(Gen Mgr)*

Astrapak Limited - Tristar Plastics Division **(1)**
104 Adcock Ingram Avenue Aeroton
Johannesburg, 2013, South Africa
Tel.: (27) 11 494 2103
Fax: (27) 11 494 3012
E-Mail: tristar@tristarplastics.co.za
Web Site: www.astrapak.co.za/astrapak/contact.jsp#148
Plastic Packaging Products Mfr
S.I.C.: 2672
N.A.I.C.S.: 322220
Andre Smit *(Gen Mgr)*

Astrapak Limited - Ultrapak Division **(1)**
Dick King Place Wilsonia
East London, South Africa
Tel.: (27) 43 745 2233
Fax: (27) 43 745 2218
Web Site: www.astrapak.co.za/astrapak/contact.jsp#148
Emp.: 150
Plastic Packaging Products Mfr
S.I.C.: 2672
N.A.I.C.S.: 322220
Reinard van Deventer *(Gen Mgr)*

Subsidiaries:

Astraflex (Pty) Ltd **(1)**
6 Mahogany Road Mahogany Ridge
Pinetown, 3610, South Africa
Tel.: (27) 31 792 8350
Fax: (27) 31 792 8360
Web Site: www.astrapak.co.za
Commercial Packaging Services
S.I.C.: 7389
N.A.I.C.S.: 561910
James Hynd *(Gen Mgr)*

Astrapak Gauteng (Pty) Ltd **(1)**
87 Uraium Road Volcania
Brakpan, Gauteng, South Africa (100%)
Tel.: (27) 118179000
Fax: (27) 118179068
E-Mail: info@astrapak.co.za
Web Site: www.astrapak.co.za/astrapak/GroupCompanies.jsp?id=46
Emp.: 426
Plastics Product Mfr
S.I.C.: 3089
N.A.I.C.S.: 326199
Heman Jacobs *(Mng Dir)*

Subsidiary:

Coralline Investments (Pty) Ltd **(2)**
13 Bussing Road
Randfontein, Gauteng, 1759, South Africa
Tel.: (27) 114123954
Fax: (27) 116937743
Emp.: 2
Packaging Plastic Products Mfr
S.I.C.: 2671
N.A.I.C.S.: 322220
Piet Buitendag *(Gen Mgr)*

Astrapak KwaZulu-Natal (Pty) Ltd **(1)**
Riverhouse Walley Estate
1 Imvumbu Park Close, Durban, South Africa (100%)
Tel.: (27) 315696100
Fax: (27) 315696063
E-Mail: lea@pacon.co.za
Web Site: www.astrapak.co.za/astrapak/GroupCompanies.jsp?id=48
Emp.: 230
Plastics Material & Resin Mfr
S.I.C.: 2821
N.A.I.C.S.: 325211
Jeff Cuttler *(Mng Dir)*

Astrapak Manufacturing Holdings (Pty) Ltd **(1)**
5 Kruger Street
Johannesburg, Gauteng, 2094, South Africa
Tel.: (27) 116158011
Fax: (27) 116158011
E-Mail: info@astrapak.co.za
Web Site: www.astrapak.co.za
Emp.: 20
Plastic Packaging Products Mfr
S.I.C.: 2671
N.A.I.C.S.: 322220

Astrapak Western Cape Pty Ltd **(1)**
8 Proton Crescent
7532 Bellville, South Africa (100%)
Tel.: (27) 219480717
Fax: (27) 219499788
Web Site: www.astrapak.com
Emp.: 300

Plastics Material & Resin Mfr
S.I.C.: 2821
N.A.I.C.S.: 325211

Consupaq (Pty) Ltd (1)
Unit 2 40 52 Marseilles Cres
Briardene Industrial Pk, 4051 Durban, South Africa (100%)
Tel.: (27) 315711050
Fax: (27) 315643320
E-Mail: enquiries@consupaq.co.za
Web Site: www.consupaq.co.za
Emp.: 150
Packaging & Labeling Services
S.I.C.: 7389
N.A.I.C.S.: 561910
Robin Rigney *(Mng Dir)*

Diverse Labelling Consultants (Pty) Ltd (1)
29 Gillitz Road
Westmead, Durban, 4001, South Africa
Tel.: (27) 31 702 0521
Fax: (27) 31 709 3972
Flexible Packaging Services
S.I.C.: 7389
N.A.I.C.S.: 561910
Greg Petzer *(Gen Mgr)*

Durpak (Pty) Ltd (1)
Proton Cresent Stikland
Cape Town, Western Cape, 7530, South Africa
Tel.: (27) 219480717
Fax: (27) 219499788
Plastic Products Mfr
S.I.C.: 3089
N.A.I.C.S.: 326199
Alan Booth *(Gen Mgr)*

Hilfort Plastics (Pty) Ltd (1)
3 Electron Street
Stikland, Cape Town, 7530, South Africa
Tel.: (27) 21 941 5060
Fax: (27) 21 948 0698
E-Mail: sales@hilfort.co.za
Web Site: www.hilfort.co.za
Emp.: 30
Plastic Container Mfr
S.I.C.: 3089
N.A.I.C.S.: 326199
Ivana Ruzickova *(Gen Mgr)*

International Tube Technology (Pty) Ltd (1)
16 Nourse Avenue Epping Industria
Cape Town, 7460, South Africa
Tel.: (27) 21 534 4779
Fax: (27) 21 534 4805
Industrial Cores & Tubes Mfr & Distr
S.I.C.: 2652
N.A.I.C.S.: 322219
Peter Jooste *(Mng Dir)*

JJ Precision Plastics (Pty) Ltd (1)
Unit 8 Valley View Industrial Park
Otto Volek Road, New Germany, South Africa (100%)
Tel.: (27) 317051585
Fax: (27) 317052600
E-Mail: john@jjpp.co.za
Web Site: www.astrapak.co.za/astrapak/GroupCompanies.jsp?id=54
Emp.: 40
Plastics Material & Resin Mfr
S.I.C.: 2821
N.A.I.C.S.: 325211
John Hall *(Gen Mgr)*

Knilam Packaging (Pty) Ltd (1)
63 Bell Cresent
Westlake Business Park, 7945 Cape Town, South Africa (70%)
Tel.: (27) 217021822
Fax: (27) 217021779
E-Mail: info@knilam.co.za
Web Site: www.knilam.co.za
Emp.: 30
Packing & Crating
S.I.C.: 4783
N.A.I.C.S.: 488991
Bremen Sharp *(Mng Dir)*

Marcom Plastics (Pty) Ltd (1)
100 Pepler St Rossly
Pretoria, 0200, South Africa (50%)
Tel.: (27) 125412784
Fax: (27) 125412787
E-Mail: marcomgp@marcomplastics.co.za
Web Site: www.marcomplastics.co.za
Emp.: 110
Plastics Material & Resin Mfr
S.I.C.: 2821
N.A.I.C.S.: 325211

Pack-Line Holdings (Pty) Ltd (1)
5 Belfast Road Gately
East London, South Africa (100%)
Tel.: (27) 437311696
Fax: (27) 437312090
E-Mail: packline@mweb.co.za
Web Site: www.astrapak.co.za/astrapak/contact.jsp
Emp.: 80
Packing & Crating
S.I.C.: 4783
N.A.I.C.S.: 488991
Wally Ben Rensburg *(Mng Dir)*

PAK 2000 (Pty) Ltd (1)
20 Mahogany Road
Mahogany Ridge, 3610 Pinetown, South Africa (100%)
Tel.: (27) 317009771
Fax: (27) 317009855
E-Mail: gareth@pak2k.co.za
Web Site: www.astrapak.co.za/astrapak/GroupCompanies.jsp?id=53
Packing & Crating
S.I.C.: 4783
N.A.I.C.S.: 488991
Gareth Elcox *(Mng Dir)*

PETech (Pty) Ltd (1)
2 Osmond Road
East London, Eastern Cape, 5247, South Africa
Tel.: (27) 437452207
Fax: (27) 437451184
Web Site: www.astrapak.co.za
Emp.: 3
Packaging Plastic Products Mfr
S.I.C.: 2672
N.A.I.C.S.: 322220

Plas-Top (Pty) Ltd (1)
197/1 Manganese Street
Ekandustria, Bronkhorstspruit, 1028, South Africa
Tel.: (27) 13 933 3205
Fax: (27) 13 933 3410
Emp.: 400
Rigid Plastic Packaging Component Mfr
S.I.C.: 3089
N.A.I.C.S.: 326199
John Painter *(Gen Mgr)*

Plastech Moulders (Pty) Ltd (1)
2 Osmond Street
East London, Eastern Cape, 5247, South Africa
Tel.: (27) 437452207
Fax: (27) 437450014
Web Site: www.astrapak.co.za
Emp.: 15
Plastic Packaging Products Mfr
S.I.C.: 3089
N.A.I.C.S.: 326199
Carlo Westaway *(Gen Mgr)*

Plastop KwaZulu-Natal (Pty) Ltd (1)
3 Mack Rd
Prospecton, Durban, 4110, South Africa
Tel.: (27) 319121270
Fax: (27) 319121279
Plastic Products Mfr
S.I.C.: 3089
N.A.I.C.S.: 326199
Dave Tyler *(Gen Mgr)*

Saflite Packaging (Pty) Ltd (1)
Unit 17 River Park
77 De Waal Road Diep River, Cape Town, 7800, South Africa (75%)
Tel.: (27) 217055882
Fax: (27) 217054090
E-Mail: saflite@mweb.co.za
Web Site: www.astrapak.co.za/astrapak/GroupCompanies.jsp?id=64
Emp.: 13
Packing & Crating
S.I.C.: 4783
N.A.I.C.S.: 488991
Brennan Sharp *(Mng Dir)*

Thermopac (Pty) Ltd (1)
6th Ave
Elsies River, 7490 Cape Town, South Africa (100%)
Tel.: (27) 215921100
Fax: (27) 215921108
E-Mail: lgray@thermopac.co.za
Web Site: www.thermopac.co.za
Emp.: 400
Packaging & Labeling Services
S.I.C.: 7389
N.A.I.C.S.: 561910
Henk Klerk *(Mng Dir)*

ASTRAZENECA PLC

2 Kingdom Street
London, W2 6BD, United Kingdom
Tel.: (44) 20 7604 8000
Telex: 94014000 ZENE G
Fax: (44) 20 7604 8151
E-Mail: ir@astrazeneca.com
Web Site: www.astrazeneca.com
Year Founded: 1999
AZN—(LSE NYSE OMX)
Rev.: $27,973,000,000
Assets: $53,534,000,000
Liabilities: $29,582,000,000
Net Worth: $23,952,000,000
Earnings: $6,327,000,000
Emp.: 30,200
Fiscal Year-end: 12/31/12

Business Description:
Pharmaceuticals Researcher, Developer, Mfr & Marketer
S.I.C.: 2834
N.A.I.C.S.: 325412

Personnel:
Pascal Soriot *(CEO)*
Marc Dunoyer *(CFO)*
Katarina Ageborg *(Chief Compliance Officer)*
Howard Hutchinson *(Chief Medical Officer)*
Jeffrey Pott *(Gen Counsel)*
David Smith *(Exec VP-Global Ops & IS)*
Lynn Tetrault *(Exec VP-HR & Corp Affairs)*

Board of Directors:
Leif Johansson
Louis Schweitzer
Bruce Burlington
Jean-Philippe Courtois
Rudolph Harold Peter Markham
Dame Nancy Rothwell
Shriti Vadera
John Silvester Varley
Marcus Wallenberg

Subsidiaries:

AstraZeneca Corporate IS (1)
Kings Court Water Lane
Wilmslow, Cheshire, SK9 5AZ, United Kingdom (100%)
Tel.: (44) 1625582828
Fax: (44) 1625516658
Emp.: 100
Investor Services
S.I.C.: 6211
N.A.I.C.S.: 523110

AstraZeneca Treasury Limited (1)
15 Stanhope Gate
London, W1K 1LN, United Kingdom
Tel.: (44) 904 049 8229
Investment Management Services
S.I.C.: 6211
N.A.I.C.S.: 523999

AstraZeneca UK Ltd. (1)
Horizon Place 600 Capability Green
Luton, Beds, LU1 3LU, United Kingdom (100%)
Tel.: (44) 582836000
Telex: 923442 ASTRAG G
Fax: (44) 1582838000
Web Site: www.astrazeneca.co.uk
Rev.: $560,000,000
Emp.: 600
Pharmaceuticals Mfr & Whslr
S.I.C.: 2834
N.A.I.C.S.: 325412

AstraZeneca UK Manufacturing (1)
Hurdsfield Industrial Estate
Macclesfield, Cheshire, SK10 2NA, United Kingdom (100%)
Tel.: (44) 1625582828
Telex: 669095 ZENPHA G
Fax: (44) 1625422266
Web Site: www.astrazeneca.com
Mfr. of Pharmaceuticals
S.I.C.: 2834
N.A.I.C.S.: 325412
David Brennan *(CEO)*

U.S. Subsidiary:

AstraZeneca Pharmaceuticals LP (1)
1800 Concord Pike
Wilmington, DE 19850-5437 (100%)
Tel.: (302) 886-3000
Fax: (302) 886-2972
Toll Free: (800) 456-3669
Web Site: www.astrazeneca-us.com
Sales Range: $5-14.9 Billion
Emp.: 12,500
Pharmaceuticals & Specialty Products Mfr & Distr
S.I.C.: 2834
N.A.I.C.S.: 325412
Glenn M. Engelmann *(Gen Counsel & VP)*

Subsidiaries:

Ardea Biosciences, Inc. (2)
4939 Directors Pl
San Diego, CA 92121 DE
Tel.: (858) 652-6500
Fax: (858) 625-0760
E-Mail: info@ardeabiosciences.com
Web Site: www.ardeabio.com
Emp.: 107
Pharmaceutical Mfr
S.I.C.: 2834
N.A.I.C.S.: 325412
Kimberly J. Manhard *(Sr VP-Regulatory Affairs & Ops)*
Colin E. Rowlings *(Sr VP-Pharmaceutical Sciences)*

AstraZeneca LP (2)
1800 Concord Pike
Wilmington, DE 19850-5437
Tel.: (302) 886-3000
Fax: (302) 456-3669
E-Mail: information.center@astrazeneca.com
Web Site: www.astrazeneca-us.com
Development & Marketing of Pharmaceuticals
S.I.C.: 2834
N.A.I.C.S.: 325412
Graham Baker *(CFO-North America & VP)*

AstraZeneca LP (2)
50 Otis St
Westborough, MA 01581-3323 (100%)
Tel.: (508) 366-1100
Fax: (508) 366-7406
Web Site: www.astrazeneca-us.com
Emp.: 1,390
Pharmaceuticals, Local & Topical Anesthetics, Tocalytics, Critical Care Drugs, Dopamine & Syringes Mfr
S.I.C.: 2834
N.A.I.C.S.: 325412
Bob Ward *(VP & Head-Strategy & Alliances & New Opportunities)*

IPR Pharmaceutical Inc. (2)
Rd 188 Lot 17 San Isidro Industrial Park
Canovanas, PR 00729
Mailing Address:
PO Box 1624
Canovanas, PR 00729
Tel.: (787) 957-1400
Fax: (787) 957-1001
Web Site: www.iprpharmaceuticals.com
Emp.: 500
Pharmaceuticals Mfr
S.I.C.: 2834
N.A.I.C.S.: 325412
Ileana Quinones *(Gen Mgr)*

MedImmune LLC (2)
1 MedImmune Way
Gaithersburg, MD 20878-4021 DE
Tel.: (301) 398-0000
Fax: (301) 398-9000
E-Mail: info@medimmune.com
Web Site: www.medimmune.com
Sales Range: $1-4.9 Billion
Emp.: 3,000
Pharmaceuticals, Biotechnologies & Medicinal Products Developer, Mfr & Marketer

AstraZeneca PLC—(Continued)

Export
S.I.C.: 8732
N.A.I.C.S.: 541720
Tim Gray *(CFO)*
Scott Carmer *(Exec VP-Comml Ops)*
Max Donley *(Exec VP-HR)*
Bahija Jallal *(Exec VP)*
Andrew D. Skibo *(Exec VP-Ops)*
Shou-Bai Chao *(Sr VP-Mfg)*
Gail Folena-Wasserman *(Sr VP-Dev)*

Subsidiaries:

MedImmune Oncology, Inc. **(3)**
1 MedImmune Way
Gaithersburg, MD 20878-4021 DE
Tel.: (301) 398-0000 (100%)
Fax: (301) 990-9000
Web Site: www.medimmune.com
Emp.: 155
Oncological Research & Development
S.I.C.: 8732
N.A.I.C.S.: 541720

MedImmune Vaccines, Inc. **(3)**
319 N Bernardo Ave
Mountain View, CA 94043-5205 DE
Tel.: (650) 603-2000
Web Site: www.medimmune.com
Emp.: 400
Vaccine Research & Development
S.I.C.: 8732
N.A.I.C.S.: 541720

MedImmune Ventures, Inc. **(3)**
1 MedImmune Way
Gaithersburg, MD 20878 DE
Tel.: (301) 398-0000 (100%)
Fax: (303) 398-9000
Web Site: www.medimmune.com
Emp.: 1,000
Equity Investment Firm Focused on Therapeutic Products & Technologies Development Companies
S.I.C.: 6211
N.A.I.C.S.: 523999
Ron Laufer *(Sr Mng Dir)*

Non-U.S. Subsidiaries:

MedImmune Limited **(3)**
Milstein Bldg Granta Park
Cambridge, CB1 6GH, United Kingdom UK
Tel.: (44) 1223471471
Fax: (44) 1223471472
E-Mail: info@medimmune.com
Web Site: www.medimmune.com
Sls.: $337,130,752
Emp.: 500
Biopharmaceuticals Mfr
S.I.C.: 2834
N.A.I.C.S.: 325412
Max Donley *(Sr VP-HR)*

MedImmune Pharma B.V. **(3)**
Lagelandseweg 78
NL-6545 CG Nijmegen, Netherlands NL
Tel.: (31) 243717310
Fax: (31) 243731519
E-Mail: info@medimmune.com
Web Site: www.medimmune.com
Emp.: 65
Pharmaceutical Research & Development
S.I.C.: 8732
N.A.I.C.S.: 541720
Louis van de Wiel *(Sr Dir-Site Ops)*

Omthera Pharmaceuticals, Inc. **(2)**
707 State Rd
Princeton, NJ 08540 DE
Tel.: (908) 741-4399
Fax: (908) 741-6524
E-Mail: info@omthera.com
Web Site: www.omthera.com
Emp.: 14
Pharmaceuticals Mfr
S.I.C.: 2834
N.A.I.C.S.: 325412
Stephen F. Mohr *(Chm & Pres)*
Mark S. Uhle *(CFO & VP-Fin)*
Bernardus N. Machielse *(COO & Exec VP)*
Michael H. Davidson *(Chief Medical Officer & Exec VP)*

Non-U.S. Branches:

AstraZeneca Belgium **(1)**
Rue Egide Van Ophem 110
B 1180 Brussels, Belgium (100%)
Tel.: (32) 23704811
Fax: (32) 23322969
E-Mail: info.be@astrazeneca.com
Web Site: www.astrazeneca.be
Emp.: 250
Pharmaceuticals & Medical Equipment Mfr & Distr
S.I.C.: 2834
N.A.I.C.S.: 325412

AstraZeneca Clinical Research Region CEE (HU) **(1)**
Park U 3
H 2045 Torokbalint, Hungary (100%)
Tel.: (36) 23517300
Fax: (36) 23418300
Web Site: www.astrazeneca.hu
Emp.: 75
Research Services
Export
S.I.C.: 8731
N.A.I.C.S.: 541712
Jan Baer *(Mng Dir)*

AstraZeneca Czech Republic **(1)**
Bldg Smichov Gate Prague St
Ptzenska 3217 3218, CZ 15000 Prague, 5, Czech Republic (100%)
Tel.: (420) 222807111
Fax: (420) 222807221
E-Mail: recepce@astrazeneca.com
Web Site: www.aztrazeneca.cz
Emp.: 180
Pharmaceuticals & Medical Equipment Mfr & Distr
S.I.C.: 5047
N.A.I.C.S.: 423450
Robert Weigl *(Pres & Mng Dir)*

AstraZeneca France **(1)**
1 Pl Louis Renault
F 92844 Rueil-Malmaison, Cedex, France (100%)
Tel.: (33) 141294000
Telex: ASTRAPH 613315 F
Fax: (33) 141294001
E-Mail: robert.dahan@astrazeneca.com
Web Site: www.astrazeneca.fr
Emp.: 300
Pharmaceuticals & Medical Equipment Mfr & Distr
S.I.C.: 2834
N.A.I.C.S.: 325412
Francoise Bartoli *(Gen Mgr)*

AstraZeneca (Korea) **(1)**
Hae Sung Bldg No 2 11th Fl 942 10 Daechi 3 Dong
Kangnam-Ku, Seoul, 135 725, Korea (South) (100%)
Tel.: (82) 221880800
Fax: (82) 221880852
E-Mail: info@astrazeneca.co.kr
Web Site: www.astrazeneca.co.kr
Emp.: 100
Pharmaceuticals & Medical Equipment Distr
S.I.C.: 5122
N.A.I.C.S.: 424210
Jake Hwang *(Dir-Fin)*

AstraZeneca New Zealand **(1)**
Level 5 15 Hope Town St
Shortland, 1140 Auckland, New Zealand (100%)
Tel.: (64) 96236300
Fax: (64) 96236301
Web Site: www.astrazeneca.co.nz
Emp.: 65
Pharmaceuticals & Medical Equipment Distr
S.I.C.: 5122
N.A.I.C.S.: 424210
Lance Gravatt *(Pres-Mktg)*

AstraZeneca Romania **(1)**
Sos Pipera-Tunari 2C
Comuna Voluntari Judetul Ilfov, 077190
Bucharest, Romania (100%)
Tel.: (40) 212432520
Telex: 11672 ICI
Fax: (40) 212432358
Web Site: www.astrazeneca.com
Emp.: 90
Pharmaceuticals & Medical Equipment Distr
S.I.C.: 5047
N.A.I.C.S.: 423450

AstraZeneca South Africa **(1)**
5 Leeuwkop Road
PO Box X30
Sunninghill, Johannesburg, 2157, South Africa (100%)
Tel.: (27) 117976000
Fax: (27) 117976001
E-Mail: sainfo@astrazeneca.com
Web Site: www.astrazeneca.co.za/521910/521914/?itemId=827164
Emp.: 200
Pharmaceuticals & Medical Equipment Distr
S.I.C.: 5122
N.A.I.C.S.: 424210
Guni Goolab *(Pres)*

AstraZeneca **(1)**
Calle Roberto Pastoriza Esq Manuel de Jesus Troncoso
Edificio Plaza Dorada Piso 3, Santo Domingo, Dominican Republic (100%)
Tel.: (809) 5496639
Fax: (809) 4734691
Pharmaceuticals & Medical Equipment Distr
S.I.C.: 5047
N.A.I.C.S.: 423450

Non-U.S. Subsidiaries:

AstraZeneca - Produtos Farmaceuticos, Lda. **(1)**
Rua Humberto Madeira 7 Valejas
Barcarena, P 2745 663 Lisbon, Portugal (100%)
Tel.: (351) 214346100
Fax: (351) 214346192
E-Mail: dr.portugal@astrazeneca.com
Emp.: 110
Pharmaceuticals & Medical Equipment Distr
S.I.C.: 5122
N.A.I.C.S.: 424210

AstraZeneca A/S **(1)**
Roskildevej 22
DK 2620 Albertslund, Denmark (100%)
Tel.: (45) 6462454366
Telex: 33457 ASTRA DK
Fax: (45) 43666100
Web Site: www.astrazeneca.dk
Emp.: 100
Pharmaceuticals & Medical Equipment Mfr & Distr
S.I.C.: 2834
N.A.I.C.S.: 325412
Heneric Asmussen *(Mng Dir)*

AstraZeneca AB, o.z. **(1)**
Lazaretska 8
SK 811 08 Bratislava, Slovakia (100%)
Tel.: (421) 257377777
Fax: (421) 257377778
E-Mail: reception@astrazeneca.com
Web Site: www.astrazeneca.sk
Emp.: 84
Pharmaceuticals & Medical Equipment Distr
S.I.C.: 5047
N.A.I.C.S.: 423450
Szilard Both *(Dir-Sls)*

AstraZeneca AB **(1)**
Astraallen
SE 151 85 Sodertalje, Sweden SE
Tel.: (46) 855326000 (100%)
Fax: (46) 855329000
Web Site: www.astrazeneca.se
Sales Range: $250-299.9 Million
Emp.: 8,000
Pharmaceuticals & Medical Equipment Mfr & Distr
S.I.C.: 2834
N.A.I.C.S.: 325412
Jan M. Lundberg *(CEO)*

Divisions:

AstraZeneca R&D Lund **(2)**
Scheelevagen 2
S 221 87 Lund, Sweden (100%)
Tel.: (46) 463360000
Telex: 32763 DRACO S
Fax: (46) 46336666
E-Mail: contact@astrazeneca.se
Web Site: www.astrazeneca.se
Emp.: 1,400
Pharmaceuticals R&D
S.I.C.: 8731
N.A.I.C.S.: 541712

AstraZeneca R&D Molndal **(2)**
Pepparedleden 1
43183 Molndal, Sweden (100%)
Tel.: (46) 0317761000
Telex: 20887 ASTTEC S
Fax: (46) 0317763700
Web Site: www.astrazeneca.se
Emp.: 16,000
Pharmaceuticals R&D
S.I.C.: 8731
N.A.I.C.S.: 541712
Thomas Niosson *(Dir-IT)*

AstraZeneca R&D Sodertalje **(2)**
43183
S 151 85 Gothenburg, Sweden (100%)
Tel.: (46) 855326000
Telex: 10974 ALAB S
Fax: (46) 317763700
E-Mail: info@astrazeneca.com
Web Site: www.astrazeneca.se
Emp.: 8,000
Pharmaceuticals R&D
S.I.C.: 8731
N.A.I.C.S.: 541712

AstraZeneca AG **(1)**
Grafenauweg 10
CH-6301 Zug, Switzerland (100%)
Tel.: (41) 41 725 70 00
Telex: 822114 APH CH
Fax: (41) 41 725 71 71
E-Mail: info@astrazeneca.ch
Web Site: www.astrazeneca.ch
Emp.: 74
Pharmaceuticals & Medical Equipment Mfr & Distr
S.I.C.: 2834
N.A.I.C.S.: 325412
Rolf Zwygart *(Dir-Corp Affairs)*

AstraZeneca Argentina S.A. **(1)**
Argerich 536
1706 Haedo, Buenos Aires, Argentina (100%)
Tel.: (54) 146504071
Telex: 18103 ASTRA AR
Fax: (54) 1144432166
E-Mail: astrazenecaar@astrazeneca.com
Web Site: www.astrazeneca.com
Emp.: 217
Pharmaceuticals & Medical Equipment Mfr & Distr
S.I.C.: 2834
N.A.I.C.S.: 325412

AstraZeneca AS **(1)**
Innspurten 15 Etterstad
N 0601 Oslo, Norway (100%)
Mailing Address:
Postboks 200
Vinderen, N-0319 Oslo, Norway
Tel.: (47) 21006400
Telex: 78722 ASTRA N
Fax: (47) 21006401
E-Mail: firmapost@astrazeneca.com
Web Site: www.astrazeneca.no
Emp.: 106
Pharmaceuticals & Medical Equipment Mfr & Distr
S.I.C.: 2834
N.A.I.C.S.: 325412
Elisabeth Ohlsson *(Mgr-Sls)*

AstraZeneca Bulgaria **(1)**
36 Dragan Tzankov Blvd
Sofia, 1057, Bulgaria
Tel.: (359) 2 971 25 33
Fax: (359) 2 971 11 24
E-Mail: reception.sofia@astrazeneca.com
Web Site: www.astrazeneca.bg
Emp.: 200
Pharmaceutical Product Mfr
S.I.C.: 2834
N.A.I.C.S.: 325412
Zoya Paunova *(CFO)*

AstraZeneca B.V. **(1)**
Louis Pasteurlaan 5
NL 2719 EE Zoetermeer, Netherlands (100%)
Mailing Address:
PO Box 599
2700 AN Zoetermeer, Netherlands
Tel.: (31) 793632222
Telex: 32159 ASTRA NL
Fax: (31) 793632444
E-Mail: info@astrazeneca.com
Web Site: www.astrazeneca.com
Emp.: 400
Marketer of Prescription Drugs
S.I.C.: 5122
N.A.I.C.S.: 424210

AstraZeneca Canada Inc. **(1)**
1004 Middlegate Rd
Mississauga, ON, L4Y 1M4, Canada (100%)

Tel.: (905) 277-7111
Fax: (905) 270-3248
Toll Free: (800) 565-5877
E-Mail: canadianmediainquiries@astrazeneca.com
Web Site: www.astrazeneca.ca
Emp.: 750
Pharmaceuticals & Medical Equipment Mfr & Distr
S.I.C.: 2834
N.A.I.C.S.: 325412
Neil Maresky *(VP-Medical Affairs)*

ASTRAZENECA CHILE S.A. (1)
Isidora Goyenechea No 3477 Las Condes
Santiago, Chile
Tel.: (56) 2 7980800
Fax: (56) 2 7980811
Pharmaceutical Product Mfr
S.I.C.: 2834
N.A.I.C.S.: 325412

AstraZeneca Colombia S.A. (1)
Cra 7 No 71 - 21 Piso 15 Torre A
Santafe, Bogota, Colombia (100%)
Tel.: (57) 1 317 3020
Fax: (57) 1 317 3009
Web Site: www.astrazeneca.com
Pharmaceuticals & Medical Equipment Mfr & Distr
S.I.C.: 2834
N.A.I.C.S.: 325412

AstraZeneca do Brasil Ltda. (1)
Rodovia Raposo Tavares Km 26 9
CEP 06707 000 Cotia, SP, Brazil (100%)
Tel.: (55) 1146131200
Fax: (55) 1146122574
Web Site: www.astrazeneca.com.br
Emp.: 800
Provider of Pharmaceuticals
S.I.C.: 2834
N.A.I.C.S.: 325412

AstraZeneca Dunkirk (1)
224 Ave De La Dordogne
F 59944 Dunkirk, Cedex, France (100%)
Tel.: (33) 328584800
Fax: (33) 328584851
Web Site: www.astrazeneca.fr
Emp.: 650
Pharmaceuticals Mfr
S.I.C.: 2834
N.A.I.C.S.: 325412

AstraZeneca Farmaceutica Spain S.A. (1)
C Serrano Galvache 56 CE Parque Norte
Edificio Roble, 28033 Madrid, Spain (100%)
Tel.: (34) 913019100
Fax: (34) 913019101
E-Mail: compress.spain@astrazeneca.com
Web Site: www.astrazeneca.com
Emp.: 200
Pharmaceuticals & Medical Equipment Mfr & Distr
S.I.C.: 2834
N.A.I.C.S.: 325412

AstraZeneca GmbH (1)
Tinsdaler Weg 183
22880 Wedel, Holstein, Germany (100%)
Tel.: (49) 41037080
Telex: 2189539 APH D
Fax: (49) 41037083293
E-Mail: info@astrazeneca.com
Web Site: www.astrazeneca.de
Emp.: 300
Pharmaceuticals & Medical Equipment Mfr & Distr
S.I.C.: 2834
N.A.I.C.S.: 325412
Henning Wrotemann *(Mng Dir)*
Doris Maier *(CFO)*

AstraZeneca Gulf FZ LLC (1)
Dubai Health Care City D-Block 2nd floor
Oud Metha Road
PO Box 505070
Dubai, United Arab Emirates
Tel.: (971) 4 3624888
Fax: (971) 4 3624899
Pharmaceutical Product Mfr
S.I.C.: 2834
N.A.I.C.S.: 325412

AstraZeneca Holding GmbH (1)
Tinsdaler Weg 183
22880 Wedel, Germany
Tel.: (49) 41037080
Fax: (49) 41037083293
E-Mail: info@astrazeneca.com
Emp.: 1,000
Investment Management Services
S.I.C.: 6211
N.A.I.C.S.: 523999

AstraZeneca Hong Kong Ltd. (1)
Rm 2301 Casco Tower
183 Queens Road, Central, China (Hong Kong)
Tel.: (852) 24207388
Telex: 50683 APIHK HX
Fax: (852) 24226788
Web Site: www.astrazeneca.com.hk
Emp.: 80
Pharmaceuticals & Medical Equipment Distr
S.I.C.: 2834
N.A.I.C.S.: 325412

AstraZeneca Iceland (1)
Horgatuni 2
210 Gardabaer, Iceland
Tel.: (354) 535 7151
Fax: (354) 565 7366
E-Mail: vistor@vistor.is
Web Site: www.vistor.is
Emp.: 6
Pharmaceutical Product Distr
S.I.C.: 5122
N.A.I.C.S.: 424210
Hreggviour Jonsson *(Chm)*

AstraZeneca India Pvt Limited (1)
Bellary Rd Hebbal
560 024 Bengaluru, India (100%)
Tel.: (91) 8023621212
Telex: 845 2409 AIDL IN
Fax: (91) 8023621214
E-Mail: astrazeneca.India@astrazeneca.com
Web Site: www.astrazenecaindia.com
Emp.: 120
Pharmaceuticals & Medical Equipment Mfr & Distr
S.I.C.: 2834
N.A.I.C.S.: 325412
David Haywood *(Chm)*
Jayasri Prasad *(Sec)*

AstraZeneca Kft. (1)
Park U 3
H 2045 Torokbalint, Hungary (100%)
Tel.: (36) 23517300
Fax: (36) 236418312
E-Mail: info@astrazeneca.hu
Web Site: www.astrazeneca.hu
Emp.: 200
Pharmaceuticals & Medical Equipment Distr
S.I.C.: 5047
N.A.I.C.S.: 423450

AstraZeneca KK (1)
Osaka Kitaku Oayodonaka
531 0076 Osaka, Japan (100%)
Tel.: (81) 664537500
Telex: J6427 ASTRA J
Fax: (81) 664537894
Web Site: www.astrazeneca.co.jp
Sls.: $240,000,000
Emp.: 3,000
Pharmaceuticals & Medical Equipment Distr
S.I.C.: 2834
N.A.I.C.S.: 325412
Masuhiro Kato *(Pres)*

AstraZeneca KK (1)
Koraku Mori Bldg 11 Fl 1 4 14 Koraku
Bunkyo-Ku, 112 004 Tokyo, Japan (100%)
Tel.: (81) 358401112
Fax: (81) 358401151
E-Mail: info@astrazeneca.co.jp
Web Site: www.astrazeneca.co.jp
Pharmaceuticals & Medical Equipment Distr
S.I.C.: 5047
N.A.I.C.S.: 423450

AstraZeneca kontor Eestis (1)
Jarvevana tee 9 IV korrus
11314 Tallinn, Estonia
Tel.: (372) 654 9600
Fax: (372) 654 9601
E-Mail: estonia@astrazeneca.com
Web Site: www.astrazeneca.ee
Emp.: 20
Pharmaceutical Product Mfr
S.I.C.: 2834
N.A.I.C.S.: 325412
Mart Levo *(Gen Mgr)*

AstraZeneca Latvia (1)
Skanstes iela 54 3 stavs
Riga, 1013, Latvia
Tel.: (371) 67377100
Fax: (371) 67377004
E-Mail: latvia@astrazeneca.com
Web Site: www.astrazeneca.lv
Emp.: 25
Pharmaceutical Product Mfr
S.I.C.: 2834
N.A.I.C.S.: 325412
Mart Levo *(Country Mgr)*

AstraZeneca Ilac Sanayi ve Tic. Ltd. Sti. (1)
Buyukdere Cad Yapi Kredi Plaza B Blok K 3-4 Levent
Istanbul, Turkey
Tel.: (90) 212 317 23 00
Fax: (90) 212 317 24 05
E-Mail: astrazeneca.turkey@astrazeneca.com
Web Site: www.astrazeneca.com.tr
Pharmaceutical Product Mfr
S.I.C.: 2834
N.A.I.C.S.: 325412

AstraZeneca Luxembourg S.A.R.L. (1)
7B De Am Drill
PO Box 62
L 3961 Luxembourg, Ehlange, Luxembourg (100%)
Tel.: (352) 378989
Fax: (352) 379214
E-Mail:
Web Site: www.astrazeneca.lu
Emp.: 9
Pharmaceuticals & Medical Equipment Distr
S.I.C.: 5122
N.A.I.C.S.: 424210
Vincent Depret *(Mng Dir)*

AstraZeneca Osterreich GmbH (1)
Schwarzenbergplatz 7
PO Box 153
1037 Vienna, Austria (100%)
Tel.: (43) 1711310
Telex: 131446 ICIR A
Fax: (43) 171131221
Web Site: www.astrazeneca.com
Emp.: 150
Pharmaceuticals & Medical Equipment Mfr & Distr
S.I.C.: 2834
N.A.I.C.S.: 325412
Jonathan Hunt *(Mng Dir)*

AstraZeneca Oy (1)
Itsehallintokuja 6
FIN 02600 Espoo, Finland FI
Tel.: (358) 1023010 (100%)
Fax: (358) 010230500
E-Mail: Jyrki.Lonnfors@astrazeneca.com
Web Site: www.astrazeneca.fi
Emp.: 20
Pharmaceuticals & Medical Equipment Distr
S.I.C.: 5047
N.A.I.C.S.: 423450

ASTRAZENECA PERU S.A. (1)
Av El Derby No 055 Torre 2 Office 501
Santiago de Surco
Lima, Peru
Tel.: (51) 1 610 1515
Fax: (51) 1 610 1516
Pharmaceutical Product Mfr
S.I.C.: 2834
N.A.I.C.S.: 325412

AstraZeneca Pharma India Limited (1)
Avishkar Off Bellary Road
PO Box 2483
Hebbal, Bengaluru, 560 024, India
Tel.: (91) 80 6774 8000
E-Mail:
Web Site: www.astrazenecaindia.com
506820—(BOM NSE)
Rev.: $72,384,053
Assets: $56,751,255
Liabilities: $38,257,068
Net Worth: $18,494,188
Earnings: ($16,599,307)
Fiscal Year-end: 03/31/13
Pharmaceutical Product Mfr
S.I.C.: 2834
N.A.I.C.S.: 325412
D. E. Udwadia *(Chm)*
Sanjay Murdeshwar *(Mng Dir)*
Pawan Singhal *(Sec & VP-Legal)*

AstraZeneca Pharma Poland Sp. z.o.o. (1)
Postepu 18 Neptun
02 676 Warsaw, Poland PL
Tel.: (48) 228743500 (100%)
Fax: (48) 228743510
E-Mail: recepcja@astrazeneca.com
Web Site: www.astrazeneca.pl
Emp.: 100
Pharmaceuticals & Medical Equipment Distr
S.I.C.: 5047
N.A.I.C.S.: 423450
Bartosz Bednarz *(Pres)*

AstraZeneca Pharmaceutical Co. Ltd. (1)
43rd Fl CITIC Sq 1168 Nun Jing Xi Rd
Shanghai, 200041, China (100%)
Tel.: (86) 152564555
Web Site: www.astrazeneca.com.cn
Emp.: 120
Pharmaceuticals & Medical Equipment Mfr & Distr
S.I.C.: 2834
N.A.I.C.S.: 325412
Steve Yang *(Sr VP)*

AstraZeneca Pharmaceuticals (Ireland) Ltd. (1)
College Park House 20 Nassau St
Dublin, 2, Ireland (100%)
Tel.: (353) 16097100
Fax: (353) 16796650
E-Mail: irelandinfo@astrazeneca.com
Web Site: www.astrazeneca.ie
Emp.: 30
Pharmaceuticals & Medical Equipment Distr
S.I.C.: 5047
N.A.I.C.S.: 423450
Gerry Burke *(Pres)*

Astrazeneca Pharmaceuticals Pakistan (private) Limited (1)
Off 124 & 125 1st floor Bahria Complex III
M T Khan Road
Karachi, Pakistan
Tel.: (92) 21 35202931
Fax: (92) 21 35635388
Pharmaceutical Product Mfr
S.I.C.: 2834
N.A.I.C.S.: 325412

AstraZeneca Pharmaceuticals (Pty) Ltd (1)
5 Leeuwkop Road
Sunninghill, Johannesburg, Gauteng, 2157, South Africa
Tel.: (27) 11 797 6000
Fax: (27) 11 797 6001
Pharmaceutical Product Mfr
S.I.C.: 2834
N.A.I.C.S.: 325412

AstraZeneca (Philippines) Inc. (1)
PO Box 7689 Domestic Airport Lock Box
Pasay, Metro Manila, Philippines (100%)
Tel.: (63) 28238169
Telex: 26448 APH PH
Fax: (63) 28241298
Web Site: www.astrazeneca.com
Emp.: 700
Pharmaceuticals & Medical Equipment Distr
S.I.C.: 2834
N.A.I.C.S.: 325412

AstraZeneca Produtos Farmaceuticos, Lda. (1)
Rua Humberto Madeira 7 Queluz-de-Baixo
2730-097 Barcarena, Portugal
Tel.: (351) 214 346 100
Fax: (351) 214346192
E-Mail: pr.portugal@astrazeneca.com
Web Site: www.astrazeneca.pt/Sobre-Nos/AstraZeneca-em-Portugal
Pharmaceutical Product Mfr
S.I.C.: 2834
N.A.I.C.S.: 325412
David Setboun *(Pres)*

AstraZeneca Pty. Ltd. (1)
5 Alma Rd
North Ryde, NSW, 2113, Australia (100%)
Mailing Address:
PO Box 131
North Ryde, NSW, 1670, Australia

AstraZeneca PLC—(Continued)

Tel.: (61) 299783500
Telex: ASTRAUS AA 24461
Fax: (61) 299783700
Web Site: www.astrazeneca.com.au
Emp.: 400
Pharmaceuticals & Medical Equipment Mfr & Distr
S.I.C.: 2834
N.A.I.C.S.: 325412
Josa Vieira *(Mng Dir)*

AstraZeneca Russia (1)
Vavilova Str 24 Block 1
Moscow, 119334, Russia
Tel.: (7) 495 799 56 99
Fax: (7) 495 799 56 98
E-Mail: Moscow.reception@astrazeneca.com
Web Site: www.astrazeneca.ru
Emp.: 300
Pharmaceutical Product Mfr
S.I.C.: 2834
N.A.I.C.S.: 325412

AstraZeneca S.A. de C.V. (1)
Super Avenida Lomas Verdes No 67
Naucalpan, Mexico (100%)
Tel.: (52) 5553749600
Telex: 1771693 ASTRAME
Fax: (52) 5553445086
Web Site: www.astrazeneca.com
Emp.: 500
Pharmaceuticals & Medical Equipment Mfr & Distr
S.I.C.: 2834
N.A.I.C.S.: 325412
Ricardo Alvarez *(Pres)*

AstraZeneca S.A. (1)
4 Theotokopoulou Astronaston
PO Box 62042
GR 15125 Maroussi, Greece (100%)
Tel.: (30) 2106871500
Telex: 220345 ASTR GR
Fax: (30) 2106847968
E-Mail: azgrcontactus@astrazeneca.com
Web Site: www.astrazeneca.gr
Emp.: 400
Pharmaceuticals & Medical Equipment Distr
S.I.C.: 2834
N.A.I.C.S.: 325412
Spiros Tsioutsias *(CFO)*

AstraZeneca SA (1)
Torre De Los Proesionales Yaguaron 1407 Ste 1205
Montevideo, 11100, Uruguay (100%)
Tel.: (598) 29018900
Fax: (598) 29023689
E-Mail: astrazeneca.uruguay@astrazeneca.com
Web Site: www.astrazeneca.com
Emp.: 30
Pharmaceuticals & Medical Equipment Mfr & Distr
S.I.C.: 2834
N.A.I.C.S.: 325412
Jorge Turtturiello *(Mgr-Mktg)*

AstraZeneca Sdn Bhd. (1)
Demansara Heights Wisma Prima 17
PO Box 11221
Jalan Sri Samantan 1, 50490 Kuala Lumpur, Malaysia (100%)
Tel.: (60) 320892288
Telex: APMSB MA 32234
Fax: (60) 320892388
E-Mail: azm@astrazeneca.com
Web Site: www.astrazeneca.com
Sales Range: $25-49.9 Million
Emp.: 150
Pharmaceuticals & Medical Equipment Distr
S.I.C.: 2834
N.A.I.C.S.: 325412

AstraZeneca (Singapore) Pte. Ltd. (1)
8 Wilkie Road #06-01 Wilkie Edge
228095 Singapore, Singapore (100%)
Tel.: (65) 65796500
Fax: (65) 62387815
E-Mail: info@astrazeneca.com
Web Site: www.astrazeneca.com
Emp.: 100
Pharmaceuticals & Medical Equipment Distr
S.I.C.: 2834
N.A.I.C.S.: 325412

AstraZeneca S.p.A. (1)
Palazzo Volta Via Francesco Sforza
Basiglio, 20080 Milan, Italy (100%)
Tel.: (39) 298011
Fax: (39) 0290755630
E-Mail: pasa.cegroni@astrazeneca.com
Web Site: www.astrazeneca.it
Emp.: 300
Pharmaceuticals & Medical Equipment Distr
S.I.C.: 2834
N.A.I.C.S.: 325412
Braggio Nicola *(Pres)*

AstraZeneca Taiwan Limited (1)
21 Fl 207 Tun Hwa S Rd Sector 2
Taipei, 10602, Taiwan (100%)
Tel.: (886) 223782390
Telex: 25014 APTWB
Fax: (886) 223783374
E-Mail: info@astrazeneca.com.tw
Web Site: www.astrazeneca.com.tw
Emp.: 200
Pharmaceuticals & Medical Equipment Distr
S.I.C.: 2834
N.A.I.C.S.: 325412
Paul Wang *(Pres)*

AstraZeneca (Thailand) Ltd. (1)
94 Asia Centre Bldg 173 Flat 20
S Sathorn Rd Thungmahamek, Bangkok, 10120, Thailand (100%)
Tel.: (66) 27397400
Telex: 20017 ASTRA TH
Fax: (66) 27397499
E-Mail: info@astrazeneca.co.th
Web Site: www.astrazeneca.co.th
Emp.: 120
Pharmaceuticals & Medical Equipment Distr
S.I.C.: 2834
N.A.I.C.S.: 325412
Reginald Seeto *(Pres)*

AstraZeneca Ukraine LLC (1)
15/15 V Khvoyki Str
Kiev, 04080, Ukraine
Tel.: (380) 44 391 52 82
Pharmaceutical Product Mfr
S.I.C.: 2834
N.A.I.C.S.: 325412

NV AstraZeneca SA (1)
Egide Van Ophemstraat 110
1180 Brussels, Belgium
Tel.: (32) 2 370 48 11
Fax: (32) 2 332 29 69
E-Mail: info.be@astrazeneca.com
Web Site: www.astrazeneca.be
Emp.: 100
Pharmaceutical Product Distr
S.I.C.: 5122
N.A.I.C.S.: 424210

PT AstraZeneca Indonesia (1)
Deutsche Bank Bldg 12 Fl Jalan Imam Bonjol No 80, Jakarta, 10310, Indonesia (100%)
Tel.: (62) 2139831300
Fax: (62) 2139831302
Emp.: 150
Pharmaceuticals & Medical Equipment Mfr & Distr
S.I.C.: 2834
N.A.I.C.S.: 325412

Zeneca International Ltd. (1)
Calle 4 No 715 Entre 7ma y 6 Miramar
Apartado 16002 Zona 16, Havana, Cuba (100%)
Tel.: (53) 72042449
Fax: (53) 7 204 2029
Pharmaceuticals & Medical Equipment Distr
S.I.C.: 5047
N.A.I.C.S.: 423450

ASTRO ALL ASIA NETWORKS PLC

Technology Park Malaysia
Lebuhraya Puchong-Sg
Besi Bukit Jalil, 57000 Kuala Lumpur, Malaysia
Tel.: (60) 3 9543 4188
E-Mail: info@astroplc.com
Web Site: www.astroplc.com
Sales Range: $1-4.9 Billion
Emp.: 4,659

Business Description:
Television Services
S.I.C.: 5013
N.A.I.C.S.: 441310

Personnel:
Augustus Ralph Marshall *(Deputy Chm & CEO)*
Lakshmi Nadarajah *(Gen Counsel)*
Sharon Liew Wei Yee *(Sec)*

Board of Directors:
Badri Masri
Mohamed Khadar Merican
Augustus Ralph Marshall
Chin Kwai Yoong

PricewaterhouseCoopers
Level 10 1 Sentral Jalan Travers
PO Box 10192
Kuala Lumpur, Malaysia

Subsidiaries:

Airtime Management and Programming Sdn. Bhd. (1)
All Asia Broadcast Center Technology Park Malaysia
Lebuhraya Puchong-Sg Besi Buki, 57000 Kuala Lumpur, Malaysia (100%)
Tel.: (60) 395436688
Fax: (60) 395430566
E-Mail: employees-services@austra.com
Web Site: www.austra.com
Emp.: 4,000
Radio & Television Broadcasting & Wireless Communications Equipment Mfr
S.I.C.: 3663
N.A.I.C.S.: 334220
Borhanuddin Osman *(Pres & Sr VP)*

MEASAT Broadcast Network Systems (BVI) Ltd (1)
All Asia Broadcast Center Technology Park
Kuala Lumpur, Malaysia (100%)
Tel.: (60) 395436688
Fax: (60) 395436876
Web Site: www.astro.com.my
Emp.: 4,000
Television Broadcasting
S.I.C.: 8661
N.A.I.C.S.: 813110
Ralph Marshall *(Chm)*
Rohana Rozhan *(CEO)*
Jake Abdullah *(Sr VP)*

MEASAT Radio Communications Sdn. Bhd. (1)
All Asia Broadcast Centre Technology Park Malaysia
Lebuhraya Puchong - Sungai Bes, 57000 Kuala Lumpur, Malaysia (100%)
Tel.: (60) 395436688
Fax: (60) 395433888
Web Site: www.astro.com.my
Emp.: 4,000
Radio & Television Broadcasting & Wireless Communications Equipment Mfr
S.I.C.: 3663
N.A.I.C.S.: 334220
Borhanuddin Osman *(Mng Dir)*

Tayangan Unggul Sdn. Bhd. (1)
Unit 1 Level 5 Block C Mines Waterfront Bussiness Park
Seri Kembangan, Malaysia (100%)
Tel.: (60) 395436688
Fax: (60) 389457722
Emp.: 2,000
Photographic Film Paper Plate & Chemical Mfr
S.I.C.: 3861
N.A.I.C.S.: 325992
Rohane Rozhan *(CEO)*

Non-U.S. Subsidiaries:

ASTRO Nusantara Holdings B.V. (1)
Claud Debussylaan No24 1082
1079LH Amsterdam, Netherlands (100%)
Tel.: (31) 206446125
Fax: (31) 205222500
Emp.: 4
Religious Organizations
S.I.C.: 8661
N.A.I.C.S.: 813110
Thao Spigram *(Mgr)*

ASTRO Nusantara International B.V. (1)
Claud Debussylaan No24 1082
1079LH Amsterdam, Netherlands (100%)
Tel.: (31) 206446125
Fax: (31) 31205222
Emp.: 4
Religious Organizations
S.I.C.: 8661
N.A.I.C.S.: 813110
Dheo Stikerman *(Pres)*

Celestial Filmed Entertainment Limited (1)
8/F, Exchange Tower 33 Wang Chiu Rd
Kowloon Bay
Kowloon, China (Hong Kong) (100%)
Tel.: (852) 29271111
Fax: (852) 26268111
Web Site: www.celestialpictures.com
Emp.: 75
Motion Picture & Video Production
S.I.C.: 7812
N.A.I.C.S.: 512110
Ross Pollack *(Gen Mgr)*

Celestial Movie Channel Limited (1)
8th Floor Exchange Tower No 33
10 Wang Chiu Road Kowloon Bay, Kowloon, China (Hong Kong) (100%)
Tel.: (852) 29271111
Fax: (852) 26268111
E-Mail: enquiry@celestialmovies.com
Web Site: www.celestialpictures.com
Emp.: 80
Other Motion Picture & Video Industries
S.I.C.: 7819
N.A.I.C.S.: 512199

Celestial Pictures Limited (1)
Shaw Administration Building
Lot 220 Clear Water Bay Road, Kowloon, China (Hong Kong) (100%)
Tel.: (852) 29271111
Fax: (852) 22430088
E-Mail: admin@celestialpictures.com
Web Site: www.celestialpictures.com
Emp.: 70
Motion Picture & Video Production
S.I.C.: 7812
N.A.I.C.S.: 512110
Roff Pollack *(CEO)*

Philippine Animation Studio Inc (1)
A And V Crystal Tower 105 Esteban Street
Legaspi Village Makati City, 1229 Manila, Philippines (100%)
Tel.: (63) 28129920
Fax: (63) 28177792
E-Mail: juncamerino@pasi.com.ph
Web Site: www.pasi.com.ph
Emp.: 12
Photography Studios Portrait
S.I.C.: 7221
N.A.I.C.S.: 541921
Jun Camerino *(CFO & Studio Mgr)*

ASTRO JAPAN PROPERTY GROUP

Suite 1 Level 14 50 Pitt Street
Sydney, NSW, 2000, Australia
Tel.: (61) 2 8987 3900
Fax: (61) 2 8987 3999
E-Mail: investorrelations@astrojapanproperty.com
Web Site: www.astrojapanproperty.com
Year Founded: 2005
AJA—(ASX)
Rev.: $99,348,604
Assets: $1,070,632,698
Liabilities: $800,414,084
Net Worth: $270,218,614
Earnings: $13,743,215
Emp.: 7
Fiscal Year-end: 06/30/13

Business Description:
Real Estate Development Services
S.I.C.: 6531
N.A.I.C.S.: 531390

Personnel:
John Pettigrew *(CFO)*
Rohan Purdy *(Gen Counsel & Sec)*

Board of Directors:
Allan McDonald
Douglas Clemson
Kate McCann
John Pettigrew

ASTRO MALAYSIA HOLDINGS BHD
Lebuhraya Puchong-Sungai Besi
Bukit Jalil, Kuala Lumpur, 57000, Malaysia
Tel.: (60) 3 95436688
Fax: (60) 3 95436877
E-Mail: ir@astromalaysia.com.my
Web Site: www.astromalaysia.com.my
6399—(KLS)
Sales Range: $1-4.9 Billion
Emp.: 4,140
Business Description:
Media Holding Company; Pay-TV, Radio, Publications & Digital Media
S.I.C.: 6719
N.A.I.C.S.: 551112
Personnel:
Yang Amat Berbahagia Zaki Azmi *(Chm)*
Augustus Ralph Marshall *(Deputy Chm)*
Yang Berbahagia Rohana Rozhan *(CEO)*
Ahmad Fuaad Mohd Kenali *(CFO)*
Henry Poh Hock Tan *(COO)*
Swee Lin Liew *(Chief Comml Officer)*
Brian Lenz *(Chief Innovation Officer)*
Board of Directors:
Yang Amat Berbahagia Zaki Azmi
Yvonne Chia
Kwai Yoong Chin
Bernard Anthony Cragg
Augustus Ralph Marshall
Yang Berbahagia Mohamed Khadar Merican
Hisham Zainal Mokhtar
Yang Berbahagia Rohana Rozhan

ASTRO RESOURCES N.L.
Level 9 1 O'Connell Street
Sydney, NSW, 2000, Australia
Mailing Address:
GPO Box 5446
Sydney, NSW, 2001, Australia
Tel.: (61) 2 9237 6525
Fax: (61) 2 8346 6099
E-Mail: admin@aro.com.au
Web Site: www.aro.com.au
ARO—(ASX)
Rev.: $79,641
Assets: $4,266,357
Liabilities: $183,064
Net Worth: $4,083,294
Earnings: ($836,931)
Fiscal Year-end: 06/30/13
Business Description:
Mineral Properties Exploration Services
S.I.C.: 1041
N.A.I.C.S.: 212221
Personnel:
Vincent Fayad *(Sec)*
Board of Directors:
Kris Knauer
Graham Libbesson
Michael Povey

ASTRO STROBEL KOMMUNIKATIONSSYSTEME GMBH
Olefant 1 3
51427 Bergisch Gladbach, Germany
Tel.: (49) 22044050
Fax: (49) 220440510
E-Mail: kontakt@astro-kom.de
Web Site: www.astro-kom.de
Rev.: $31,288,537
Emp.: 180
Business Description:
Radio Reception Components Mfr
S.I.C.: 3663
N.A.I.C.S.: 334220
Personnel:
Herbert Strobel *(Mng Dir)*

ASTRON CORPORATION LIMITED
Level 29 Chifley Plaza 2 Chifley Square
Sydney, NSW, 2000, Australia
Tel.: (61) 2 9375 2361
Fax: (61) 2 9375 2121
E-Mail: info@astronlimited.com
Web Site: www.astronlimited.com
ATR—(ASX)
Rev.: $8,251,221
Assets: $212,518,613
Liabilities: $7,586,507
Net Worth: $204,932,106
Earnings: ($5,695,747)
Emp.: 71
Fiscal Year-end: 06/30/13
Business Description:
Chemical & Metal Products Mfr
S.I.C.: 2819
N.A.I.C.S.: 325180
Personnel:
Alex Brown *(Mng Dir)*
Mark Coetzee *(Exec-Project-Niafarang)*
Boris Matveev *(Exec-Project)*
Simon Peters *(Exec-Project-Donald)*
Joshua Theunissen *(Sec)*
Board of Directors:
Gerald King
Alex Brown
Robert John Flew
Ron McCullough
Kang Rong

Grant Thornton Jingdu Tianhua
20th Floor Sunning Plaza 10 Hysan Avenue
Causeway Bay, China (Hong Kong)

Computershare Hong Kong Investor Services Limited
46th Floor Hopewell Centre 183 Queen's Road East
Hong Kong, China (Hong Kong)

Subsidiary:

Donald Mineral Sands Pty. Ltd. (1)
67-71 Main St
PO Box 49
Minyip, VIC, 3392, Australia
Tel.: (61) 353857088
Fax: (61) 353857050
E-Mail: administration@donaldmineralsands.com.au
Web Site: www.donaldmineralsands.com.au
Emp.: 10
Mineral Exploration Services
S.I.C.: 1499
N.A.I.C.S.: 212399
Alexander Brown *(Mng Dir)*

Non-U.S. Subsidiaries:

Astron Titanium (Yingkou) Co., Ltd. (1)
2105 Block E Fortune Plz 59 Beizhan Rd
Shenhe Dist, Shenyang, Liaoning, China
Tel.: (86) 2431286222
Fax: (86) 2431286823
E-Mail: ying.jing@astron.cn
Web Site: www.astronchem.com
Emp.: 60
Titanium Dioxide Mfr
S.I.C.: 2819
N.A.I.C.S.: 325180
Jing Zhang *(VP)*

Coast Resources Limited (1)
3035 Tutor Dr 2nd Fl
Regina, SK, S4W 1B5, Canada
Tel.: (306) 757-3001
Fax: (306) 757-3003
Mineral Exploration Services
S.I.C.: 1081
N.A.I.C.S.: 213114

Yingkou Astron Mineral Resources Co., Ltd. (1)
Level 18 Building B Fortune Plaza
53 Beizhan Road
Shenhe District, Shenyang, Liaoning, 110016, China
Tel.: (86) 2431286222
Web Site: www.astronlimited.com
Mineral Mining Services
S.I.C.: 1499
N.A.I.C.S.: 212399
Alex Brown *(Mng Dir)*

ASTUR GOLD CORP.
1055 West Hastings Street Suite 300
Vancouver, BC, V6E 2E9, Canada
Tel.: (604) 694-1600
Fax: (604) 694-1663
E-Mail: info@asturgold.com
Web Site: www.asturgold.com
Year Founded: 2007
AST—(DEU TSXV)
Int. Income: $1,903
Assets: $8,732,054
Liabilities: $434,942
Net Worth: $8,297,112
Earnings: ($58,377)
Fiscal Year-end: 12/31/12
Business Description:
Gold Mining Services
S.I.C.: 1041
N.A.I.C.S.: 212221
Personnel:
Cary Pinkowski *(Pres & CEO)*
Nick DeMare *(CFO & Sec)*
Michael Surratt *(Interim COO)*
Board of Directors:
Ignacio Garcia Matos
Patrick Moore
Cary Pinkowski
Sean Roosen
Michael Surratt
Transfer Agent:
Computershare Investor Services Inc
100 University Avenue 9 Floor North Tower
Toronto, ON, M5J 2Y1, Canada

ASUSTEK COMPUTER INC.
15 Li-Te Road
Beitou District, Taipei, Taiwan
Tel.: (886) 228943447
Fax: (886) 228946140
E-Mail: marketing@asus.com.tw
Web Site: www.asus.com
Year Founded: 1989
2357—(TAI)
Rev.: $12,948,368,907
Assets: $7,076,906,895
Liabilities: $2,807,179,572
Net Worth: $4,269,727,324
Earnings: $759,444,317
Emp.: 4,904
Fiscal Year-end: 12/31/12
Business Description:
Computer Products Mfr & Distr
S.I.C.: 3575
N.A.I.C.S.: 334118
Personnel:
Jonney Shih *(Chm)*
Jonathan Tsang *(Vice Chm & Co-Pres)*
Jerry Shen *(Co-Pres & CEO)*
David Chang *(CFO)*
Board of Directors:
Jonney Shih
Yen-Cheng Chen
Min-Chieh Hsieh
Hsien-Yuen Hsu
Samson Hu
Jerry Shen
Jonathan Tsang
Supervisory Board of Directors:
Chung-Jen Cheng
Long-Hui Yang
Tze-Kaing Yang
Transfer Agent:
Grand Cathay Securities Corporation
5F No.2 Section 1 Chongqing South Road
Taipei, Taiwan

Subsidiary:

AAEON Technology Inc. (1)
5F No 135 Ln 235 Pao Chiao Rd
231 Hsin Tien, Taipei, Taiwan
Tel.: (886) 289191234
Fax: (886) 289191056
E-Mail: sales@aaeon.com.tw
Web Site: www.aaeon.com.tw
Sales Range: $25-49.9 Million
Emp.: 400
Single Board Computers Mfr
S.I.C.: 3571
N.A.I.C.S.: 334111
Y. S. Chuang *(Chm)*
I. J. Lee *(Vice Chm)*

U.S. Subsidiaries:

AAEON Electronics, Inc. (2)
3 Crown Plaza
Hazlet, NJ 07730-2441
Tel.: (732) 203-9300
Fax: (732) 203-9311
E-Mail: sales@aaeon.com
Computer Peripheral Equipments Distr
S.I.C.: 5045
N.A.I.C.S.: 423430
Yuhmin Hwang *(Owner)*

AAEON Systems, Inc. (2)
324 W Blueridge Ave
Orange, CA 92865
Tel.: (714) 996-1800
Fax: (714) 996-1811
E-Mail: info@aaeon.com
Web Site: www.aaeon.com
Emp.: 30
Computer Peripheral Equipments Distr
S.I.C.: 5045
N.A.I.C.S.: 423430
Alan Chow *(Mgr-Bus Dev)*

Non-U.S. Subsidiaries:

AAEON Technology (Europe) B.V. (2)
Ekkersrijt 4002
5692 DA Son, North Brabant, Netherlands
Tel.: (31) 499462020
Fax: (31) 499 462 010
E-Mail: saleseurope@aaeon.com
Computer Circuit Boards Distr
S.I.C.: 5065
N.A.I.C.S.: 423690

AAEON Technology GmbH (2)
An der Trift 65d
63303 Dreieich, Hesse, Germany
Tel.: (49) 61033747900
Fax: (49) 61033747949
Web Site: www.aaeon.com.tw/OM_Contact_Offices_US_utf-8.html
Emp.: 10
Computer Circuit Boards Distr
S.I.C.: 3679
N.A.I.C.S.: 334418

AAEON Technology Singapore PTE LTD (2)
57 Genting Lane 07-00
Singapore, 349564, Singapore
Tel.: (65) 67498749
Fax: (65) 67461595
E-Mail: sales@aaeon.com.sg
Emp.: 8
Computer Circuit Boards Distr
S.I.C.: 5065
N.A.I.C.S.: 423690
Seng Kim Soon *(Gen Mgr)*

AAEON Technology (Suzhou) Inc. (2)
Room 12 2F Building B No 5 Xing Han Street Suzhou Industrial Park
Suzhou, Jiangsu, 215021, China
Tel.: (86) 51267625700
Fax: (86) 51267617337
E-Mail: sales@aaeon.com.cn
Web Site: www.aaeon.com.cn
Computer Circuit Boards Distr
S.I.C.: 5045
N.A.I.C.S.: 423430

U.S. Subsidiary:

Asus Computer International, Inc. (1)
800 Corporate Way
Fremont, CA 94539

ASUSTeK Computer Inc.—(Continued)

Tel.: (510) 739-3777
Fax: (510) 608-4555
Web Site: support.asus.com
Emp.: 300
Computer Peripheral Products Mfr & Distr
S.I.C.: 5045
N.A.I.C.S.: 423430
Ivan Hoe *(CEO)*
Raymond Chen *(Exec VP)*

Non-U.S. Subsidiaries:

Asus Computer GmbH **(1)**
Harkortstrasse 25
40880 Ratingen, Germany
Tel.: (49) 2102959910
Fax: (49) 2102959911
Web Site: www.asus.de
Computer Software Whslr
S.I.C.: 5045
N.A.I.C.S.: 423430
Thorsten Brokopp *(Dir-Mktg)*

Asus Holland B.V. **(1)**
Nw Amsterdamsestraat 44
7814VA Emmen, Netherlands
Tel.: (31) 591570290
Fax: (31) 591666853
Web Site: stw.asus.com
Electronic Computer Mfr
S.I.C.: 3571
N.A.I.C.S.: 334111
Ernst Kasteleijn *(Engr)*

ASX LIMITED

(d/b/a ASX Group)
Exchange Centre 20 Bridge Street
Sydney, NSW, 2000, Australia
Tel.: (61) 2 9338 0000
Fax: (61) 2 9227 0885
E-Mail: investor.relations@asx.com.au
Web Site: www.asx.com.au
Year Founded: 1987
ASX—(ASX)
Rev.: $816,902,190
Assets: $7,678,922,270
Liabilities: $4,217,274,490
Net Worth: $3,461,647,780
Earnings: $362,859,220
Emp.: 529
Fiscal Year-end: 06/30/13

Business Description:
Holding Company; Securities & Derivatives Exchange
S.I.C.: 6719
N.A.I.C.S.: 551112

Personnel:
Elmer Funke Kupper *(CEO & Mng Dir)*
Peter D. Hiom *(Deputy CEO)*
Ramy Aziz *(CFO)*
Tim Thurman *(CIO)*
Kevin A. Lewis *(Chief Compliance Officer)*
Alan J. Bardwell *(Chief Risk Officer)*
Amanda J. Harkness *(Gen Counsel & Sec)*

Board of Directors:
Rick Holliday-Smith
Ken R. Henry
Elmer Funke Kupper
Peter Ralph Marriott
Heather M. Ridout
Jillian S. Segal
Peter H. Warne

Subsidiaries:

ASX Clearing Corporation Limited **(1)**
Exchange Centre 20 Bridge St
Sydney, NSW, 2000, Australia AU
Tel.: (61) 292270027 (100%)
Web Site: www.asxgroup.com.au
Emp.: 500
Securities Exchange Clearing Services
S.I.C.: 6099
N.A.I.C.S.: 522320
Elmer Funke Kupper *(Mng Dir)*

ASX Operations Pty. Limited **(1)**
Exchange Centre 20 Bridge Street
Sydney, NSW, 2000, Australia AU
Tel.: (61) 292270885 (100%)
Fax: (61) 293470005
Stock Market Operation Services
S.I.C.: 7389
N.A.I.C.S.: 561499

ASX Settlement Corporation Limited **(1)**
Exchange Centre 20 Bridge Street
Sydney, NSW, 2000, Australia AU
Tel.: (61) 292270027
Fax: (61) 293380000
E-Mail: investor.relations@asx.com.au
Web Site: www.asxgroup.com.au/settlement.htm
Emp.: 500
Payment Settlement Services
S.I.C.: 6099
N.A.I.C.S.: 522320
Elmer Funke kupper *(Mng Dir)*

Australian Securities Exchange Limited **(1)**
Exchange Centre 20 Bridge Street
Sydney, NSW, 2000, Australia AU
Tel.: (61) 292270027 (100%)
Fax: (61) 292270885
Web Site: www.asx.com.au
Securities & Derivatives Exchange
S.I.C.: 6231
N.A.I.C.S.: 523210
Elmer Funke Kupper *(CEO & Mng Dir)*

ASYA INFRASTRUCTURE & TOURISM CORPORATION LIMITED

4th floor H N House Nidhi Complex
Above Stadium Under Bridge
Navrangpura, Ahmedabad, Gujarat, 380 009, India
Tel.: (91) 79 26462334
Fax: (91) 79 26462335
E-Mail: info@sayait.com
Web Site: www.sayait.com
511144—(BOM)

Business Description:
Information Technology Services
S.I.C.: 7371
N.A.I.C.S.: 541511

Personnel:
Ketan Shah *(Mng Dir)*
Sandip Shah *(Complaint Officer)*
Pinakin Shah *(Sec)*

Board of Directors:
Mahesh Modi
Ashok Patel
Chintu Shah
Ketan Shah
Sandip Shah

ASYA KATILIM BANKASI A.S.

(d/b/a Bank Asya)
Saray Mah Dr Adnan Buyukdeniz Cd No 10 Umraniye
34768 Istanbul, Turkey
Tel.: (90) 2166335000
Fax: (90) 2166335019
E-Mail: ir@bankasya.com.tr
Web Site: www.bankasya.com.tr
ASYAB—(IST)
Rev.: $945,042,598
Assets: $12,088,144,263
Liabilities: $10,760,499,613
Net Worth: $1,327,644,650
Earnings: $107,596,231
Emp.: 5,064
Fiscal Year-end: 12/31/12

Business Description:
Banking Services
S.I.C.: 6029
N.A.I.C.S.: 522110

Personnel:
Erhan Birgili *(Chm)*
Mustafa Talat Katircioglu *(Vice Chm)*
Ahmet Beyaz *(Pres & CEO)*
Ahmet Akar *(Exec VP)*
Hakan Fatih Buyukadali *(Exec VP)*
Murat Demir *(Exec VP)*
Feyzullah Egriboyun *(Exec VP)*
Fahrettin Soylu *(Exec VP)*
Ali Tuglu *(Exec VP)*
Mahmut Yalcin *(Exec VP)*
Talha Salih Yayla *(Exec VP)*

Board of Directors:
Erhan Birgili
Ahmet Beyaz
Ali Celik
Zafer Ertan
Mehmet Gozutok
Ercument Guler
Mustafa Talat Katircioglu
Recep Kocak
Mehmet Uruc

Subsidiary:

Isik Sigorta A.S. **(1)**
Kat 2 6 Kucuksu Caddesi
Akcakoca Sokak, Istanbul, 34768, Turkey
Tel.: (90) 2166337100
Fax: (90) 216 631 84 48
E-Mail: bilgi@isiksigorta.com.tr
Web Site: www.isiksigorta.com
Commercial Banking Services
S.I.C.: 6029
N.A.I.C.S.: 522110

AT&S AUSTRIA TECHNOLOGIE & SYSTEMTECHNIK AG

Fabriksgasse 13
8700 Leoben, Austria
Tel.: (43) 3842 2000
Fax: (43) 683009290
E-Mail: info@ats.net
Web Site: www.ats.net
AUS—(DEU)
Rev.: $729,183,942
Assets: $978,936,170
Liabilities: $558,321,315
Net Worth: $420,614,855
Earnings: $18,983,689
Emp.: 7,011
Fiscal Year-end: 03/31/13

Business Description:
Printed Circuit Boards Mfr
S.I.C.: 3672
N.A.I.C.S.: 334412

Personnel:
Hannes Androsch *(Chm-Supervisory Bd)*
Andreas Gerstenmayer *(Chm-Mgmt Bd & CEO)*
Willi Dorflinger *(First Deputy Chm-Supervisory Bd)*
Regina Prehofer *(Second Deputy Chm-Supervisory Bd)*
Heinz Moitzi *(CTO & Member-Mgmt Bd)*

Supervisory Board of Directors:
Hannes Androsch
Willi Dorflinger
Karl Fink
Albert Hochleitner
Gerhard Pichler
Regina Prehofer
Georg Riedl
Karin Schaupp

Subsidiary:

AT&S Klagenfurt Leiterplatten GmbH **(1)**
Ebentaler Strasse 140
9020 Klagenfurt, Austria
Tel.: (43) 463311000
Fax: (43) 3110019490
E-Mail: sales@ats.net
Emp.: 150
Other Electronic Component Mfr
S.I.C.: 3679
N.A.I.C.S.: 334419
Fleck Christian *(Mng Dir)*

Non-U.S. Subsidiaries:

AT&S China Co. Ltd. **(1)**
5000 Jin Du Road
Xinzhuang Industry Park, Shanghai, China
Tel.: (86) 2124080000
Fax: (86) 2124080599
Web Site: www.ats.net
Emp.: 3,000
Bare Printed Circuit Board Mfr
S.I.C.: 3672
N.A.I.C.S.: 334412

Tofic Co. Ltd **(1)**
452 Mongnae-Dong
Danwon-Gu, Ansan, Korea (South) (86%)
Tel.: (82) 314952277
Emp.: 296
Electron Tube Mfr
S.I.C.: 3679
N.A.I.C.S.: 334419
Sung Youngchur *(CEO)*

AT AUTOMOBILES

Z I Noirefontaine Rn 75
Montagnat, 01250 Bourg-en-Bresse, France
Tel.: (33) 474239330
Fax: (33) 474235536
Web Site: www.at-automobiles.fr
Sls.: $20,900,000
Emp.: 26

Business Description:
New & Used Car Dealers
S.I.C.: 5511
N.A.I.C.S.: 441110

Personnel:
Jean-Luc Guillerminet *(Pres)*

@UK PLC

5 Jupiter House Calleva Park
Aldermaston, Reading, Berkshire, RG7 8NN, United Kingdom
Tel.: (44) 118 963 7000
Fax: (44) 118 963 7012
E-Mail: contact.uk@ukplc.net
Web Site: www.uk-plc.net
Year Founded: 1999
ATUK—(LSE)
Rev.: $3,504,498
Assets: $1,414,407
Liabilities: $1,220,097
Net Worth: $194,310
Earnings: ($1,244,523)
Emp.: 42
Fiscal Year-end: 12/31/12

Business Description:
Software Development Services
S.I.C.: 7371
N.A.I.C.S.: 541511

Personnel:
Ronald Duncan *(Co-Founder & Chm)*
Lyn Duncan *(Co-Founder & Mgr-Bus Dev)*
Dale Stephens *(CEO-Asia Pacific)*
Alice Mary Teresa Morwood-Leyland *(Sec)*

Board of Directors:
Lyn Duncan
Ronald Duncan
David Holloway

Legal Counsel:
Steptoe & Johnson LLP
99 Gresham Street
London, EC2V 7NG, United Kingdom

ATA INC.

8th 12th 16th Flr E Building No 6 Jian Guo Men Nei Gong Yuan Xi Jie
Beijing, 100005, China
Tel.: (86) 10 65181122
E-Mail: liwei@ata.net.cn
Web Site: www.ata.net.cn
Year Founded: 1999
ATAI—(NASDAQ)
Rev.: $58,246,402
Assets: $72,724,466
Liabilities: $13,068,711

Net Worth: $59,655,755
Earnings: $3,686,589
Emp.: 500
Fiscal Year-end: 03/31/13
Business Description:
Computer-Based Testing & Education Services
S.I.C.: 8299
N.A.I.C.S.: 611710
Personnel:
Kevin Xiaofeng Ma *(Co-Founder & Chm)*
Walter Ling Wang *(Co-Founder)*
Cheng-Yaw Sun *(CEO)*
Benson Tsang *(CFO & Chief Acctg Officer)*
Board of Directors:
Kevin Xiaofeng Ma
Hope Ni
Cheng-Yaw Sun
Alec Tsui
Walter Ling Wang
Andrew Y. Yan
Legal Counsel:
Jincheng Tongda & Neal
11/F, Huaxia Bank Plaza, No.22 Jianguomennei Avenue
Beijing, China
Subsidiary:

ATA Testing Authority (Beijing) Limited (1)
8th Floor East Building No 6 Jian Guo Men Nei Gong Yuan Xi Jie
Beijing, 100005, China
Tel.: (86) 10 6518 1122
Fax: (86) 10 6517 9517
Computer Testing & Education Services
S.I.C.: 7379
N.A.I.C.S.: 541519

ATAC CONSTRUCTION AND INDUSTRY INC.

Antalya Organize Sanayi Bolgesi 1
Kisim Ataturk Bulvari No 19
Dosemealti, Antalya, Turkey
Tel.: (90) 242 258 10 10
Fax: (90) 242 258 11 15
E-Mail: insaat@atac.com.tr
Web Site: www.atac.com.tr
Year Founded: 1962
ATAC—(IST)
Rev.: $109,851,710
Assets: $497,936,595
Liabilities: $362,779,608
Net Worth: $135,156,987
Earnings: ($56,296,988)
Fiscal Year-end: 12/31/12
Business Description:
Construction Services
S.I.C.: 1629
N.A.I.C.S.: 236210
Personnel:
A. Sami Aksemsettinoglu *(Chm)*
M. Deniz Ak *(Deputy Chm)*
Board of Directors:
A. Sami Aksemsettinoglu
M. Deniz Ak
A. Engin Ergruder
Murat Uysal
Metin Yuksel

ATAC RESOURCES LTD.

Suite 1016 510 West Hastings Street
Vancouver, BC, V6B 1L8, Canada
Tel.: (604) 687-2522
Fax: (604) 688-2578
E-Mail: info@nordacres.com
Web Site: www.atacresources.com
ATC—(TSXV)
Int. Income: $254,330
Assets: $92,358,119
Liabilities: $11,525,583
Net Worth: $80,832,535
Earnings: ($7,423,945)
Fiscal Year-end: 12/31/12
Business Description:
Metal Exploration Servcies
S.I.C.: 1081
N.A.I.C.S.: 213114
Personnel:
Douglas O. Goss *(Chm)*
Robert C. Carne *(Pres)*
Graham N. Downs *(CEO)*
Larry Donaldson *(CFO)*
Ian J. Talbot *(COO)*
Glenn R. Yeadon *(Sec)*
Board of Directors:
Douglas O. Goss
Robert C. Carne
Bruce J. Kenway
Helmut H. Wober
Glenn R. Yeadon
Bruce Youngman
Transfer Agent:
Computershare Investor Services Inc.
510 Burrard St 2nd Floor
Vancouver, BC, V6C 3B9, Canada
Tel.: (604) 661-9400

ATACAMA PACIFIC GOLD CORPORATION

330 Bay Street Suite 1210
Toronto, ON, M5H 2S8, Canada
Tel.: (416) 861-8267
Fax: (416) 861-9116
E-Mail: info@atacamapacific.com
Web Site: www.atacamapacific.com
Year Founded: 2008
ATM—(OTC TSXV)
Int. Income: $283,938
Assets: $79,123,558
Liabilities: $3,624,535
Net Worth: $75,499,023
Earnings: ($46,166)
Emp.: 3
Fiscal Year-end: 03/31/13
Business Description:
Gold Mining Services
S.I.C.: 1041
N.A.I.C.S.: 212221
Personnel:
Albrecht Schneider *(Chm)*
Carl B. Hansen *(Pres & CEO)*
Thomas Pladsen *(CFO & Sec)*
Board of Directors:
Albrecht Schneider
Scott A. Caldwell
Paul Champagne
Carl B. Hansen
Antonio Ortuzar, Jr.
Transfer Agent:
Equity Transfer & Trust Company
200 University Avenue Ste 400
Toronto, ON, M5H 4H1, Canada
Tel.: (416) 361-0152
Fax: (416) 361-0470

ATALIAN GLOBAL SERVICES

107 rue Edith Cavell
94400 Vitry-sur-Seine, France
Tel.: (33) 155530300
Fax: (33) 155530301
E-Mail: contact@atalian.com
Web Site: www.atalian.com
Year Founded: 1944
Sales Range: $550-599.9 Million
Business Description:
Property Management & Security Services
S.I.C.: 8744
N.A.I.C.S.: 561210
Personnel:
Franck Julien *(Pres)*

ATARI, SA

78 rue Taitbout
75009 Paris, France
Tel.: (33) 4 3764 3000
Fax: (33) 4 3764 3001
E-Mail: investors@atari.com
Web Site: www.atari.com
Year Founded: 1983
ATA—(EUR)
Rev.: $21,134,869
Emp.: 51
Fiscal Year-end: 03/31/13
Business Description:
Holding Company; Interactive Entertainment Software Developer & Licensor
S.I.C.: 6719
N.A.I.C.S.: 551112
Personnel:
Frank Emmanuel Dangeard *(Chm)*
Frederic Chesnais *(CEO)*
Laurence Betito *(CFO)*
Renato Mascardo *(CTO)*
James Wilson *(CEO-US)*
Denis Bunma *(Legal Counsel)*
Anthony Jacobson *(Sr VP-Bus Dev)*
Board of Directors:
Frederic Chesnais
Frank Emmanuel Dangeard
Erik Euvrard
Tom Virden
Alyssa Padia Walles
Deloitte & Associes
Villeurbanne, France
U.S. Subsidiary:

Atari, Inc. (1)
417 5th Ave
New York, NY 10016-2204 DE
Tel.: (212) 726-6500 (60%)
Fax: (212) 679-3424
E-Mail: info@us.infogrames.com
Web Site: www.atari.com
Interactive Entertainment Software Developer & Licensor
S.I.C.: 6794
N.A.I.C.S.: 533110
James Wilson *(CEO)*
Yves Blehaut *(Sr VP)*

ATASAY KUYUMCULUK

Merkez Mahallesi Sedir Sok No 7
34530 Istanbul, Turkey
Tel.: (90) 2126523366
Fax: (90) 212653998
E-Mail: musteri.hizmetleri@atasay.com
Web Site: www.atasay.com
Year Founded: 1989
Emp.: 1,200
Business Description:
Jewelry Mfr
Export
S.I.C.: 3911
N.A.I.C.S.: 339910
Personnel:
Atasay Kamer *(Chm)*
Cihan Kamer *(Pres)*

ATCO LTD.

(d/b/a ATCO Group of Companies)
1400 909 11th Ave SW
Calgary, AB, T2R 1N6, Canada
Tel.: (403) 292-7500
Fax: (403) 292-7532
Web Site: www.atco.com
Year Founded: 1947
ACO—(TSX)
Rev.: $4,335,915,240
Assets: $14,229,396,300
Liabilities: $9,342,793,980
Net Worth: $4,886,602,320
Earnings: $672,951,540
Emp.: 9,428
Fiscal Year-end: 12/31/12
Business Description:
Electric & Natural Gas Distr; Electrical Generation & Transmission
S.I.C.: 4911
N.A.I.C.S.: 221122
Personnel:
Nancy C. Southern *(Chm, Pres & CEO)*
Brian R. Bale *(CFO & Sr VP)*
Alan M. Skiffington *(CIO & VP)*
Susan R. Werth *(Chief Admin Officer & Sr VP)*
Clinton G. Warkentin *(Treas & VP)*
Carol Gear *(Sec)*
Kevin J. Cumming *(Sr VP-Northern Dev)*
Board of Directors:
Nancy C. Southern
Robert T. Booth
Bertrand P. Collomb
David Allison Dodge
Linda A. Heathcott
Helmut M. Neldner
Michael R. P. Rayfield
Robert J. Routs, III
Ronald D. Southern
Charles W. Wilson
Legal Counsel:
Bennett Jones LLP
Calgary, AB, Canada
Transfer Agent:
CIBC Mellon Trust Company
PO Box 700 Station B
Montreal, QC, Canada
Subsidiaries:

ATCO Blue Flame Kitchen (1)
Calgary Learning Centre Main Floor 909 11 Avenue SW
Calgary, AB, T2R 1N6, Canada
Tel.: (403) 245-7625
Fax: (403) 245-7674
Toll Free: (877) 420-9090
Web Site: www.atcoblueflamekitchen.com
Emp.: 35
Natural Gas Distr
S.I.C.: 4924
N.A.I.C.S.: 221210
Sarah Francis *(Mgr)*

ATCO EnergySense (1)
10035 105 St NW
Edmonton, AB, T5J 1C4, Canada
Tel.: (403) 245-7868
Fax: (403) 245-7884
E-Mail: EnergySense@atco.com
Web Site: www.atcoenergysense.com
Energy Efficiency Program Consulting Services
S.I.C.: 8748
N.A.I.C.S.: 541618

ATCO Structures & Logistics Ltd. (1)
5115 Crowchild Trl SW
Calgary, AB, T3E 1T9, Canada (75.5%)
Tel.: (403) 292-7600
Fax: (403) 292-7575
Toll Free: (877) 999-2826 (North America)
E-Mail: atco@atcostructures.com
Web Site: www.atcostructures.com
Emp.: 3,000
Prefabricated Infrastructure Construction, Logistics & Support Services
S.I.C.: 3448
N.A.I.C.S.: 332311
Harry Wilmot *(Pres & COO)*
Michael Clennett *(Exec VP-Bus Dev-Intl)*
George Lidgett *(Exec VP-Ops & Mfg)*
Brian Andrews *(Sr VP-Comml)*

Divisions:

ATCO Emissions Management (2)
(Formerly ATCO Noise Management)
1243 McKnight Blvd NE
Calgary, AB, T2E 5T1, Canada
Tel.: (403) 292-7804
Fax: (403) 292-7816
E-Mail: info@atconoise.com
Web Site: www.atcoem.com
Emp.: 45
Buildings & Acoustic Barriers Mfr
S.I.C.: 3564
N.A.I.C.S.: 333413
Denise LeClaire *(Mgr-Sls & Mktg)*

U.S. Subsidiary:

ATCO Structures & Logistics (USA) Inc. (2)
1106 N Temple Dr
Diboll, TX 75941
Tel.: (936) 829-2325

ATCO Ltd.—(Continued)

Fax: (936) 829-6087
Toll Free: (800) 575-2826
E-Mail: diboll@atcoslusa.com
Web Site: www.atcosl.com
Emp.: 200
Prefabricated Infrastructure Construction, Logistics & Support Services
S.I.C.: 3448
N.A.I.C.S.: 332311
Doug Irving *(Gen Mgr)*

Unit:

ATCO Structures & Logistics (USA) Inc. - Alaska (3)
425 G St Ste 707
Anchorage, AK 99501
Tel.: (907) 677-6983
Emp.: 100
Prefabricated Infrastructure Construction, Logistics & Support Services
S.I.C.: 3448
N.A.I.C.S.: 332311

Non-U.S. Subsidiaries:

ATCO Frontec Europa Kft-Sucursal em Portugal (2)
Avenida Do Infante 50
9004-521 Funchal, Madeira, Portugal
Tel.: (351) 291 239370
Fax: (351) 291 239379
Emp.: 3
Prefabricated Infrastructure Construction, Logistics & Support Services
S.I.C.: 3448
N.A.I.C.S.: 332311
Roland Kemperman *(Gen Mgr)*

ATCO Frontec Europe Ltd. (2)
Esztergaly u 28
Csomad, 2161 Budapest, Hungary
Tel.: (36) 28 566 442
Fax: (36) 28 566 441
Emp.: 13
Prefabricated Infrastructure Construction, Logistics & Support Services
S.I.C.: 3448
N.A.I.C.S.: 332311
Marcel Wanna *(Gen Mgr & Mng Dir)*

ATCO Structures & Logistics Pty Ltd. (2)
149-151 Magnesium Drive
Crestmead, QLD, 4132, Australia
Tel.: (61) 7 3412 8600
Fax: (61) 7 3803 6590
E-Mail: atcosales@atcosl.com.au
Web Site: www.atcosl.com
Emp.: 6
Prefabricated Infrastructure Construction, Logistics & Support Services
S.I.C.: 3448
N.A.I.C.S.: 332311
Adina Esterlin *(Mng Dir)*

ATCO Structures & Logistics UK Ltd. (2)
Clearway House Industrial Estate
Overthorpe Road
Banbury, Oxfordshire, OX16 4US, United Kingdom
Tel.: (44) 129 526 5953
Fax: (44) 129 526 2506
Emp.: 29
Prefabricated Infrastructure Construction, Logistics & Support Services
S.I.C.: 3448
N.A.I.C.S.: 332311
Campbell Rodden *(Gen Mgr)*

ATCO Water, Ltd. (1)
Ste 800 909- 11 Ave SW
Calgary, AB, T2R 1L8, Canada
Tel.: (403) 245-7106
Fax: (403) 292-7982
Web Site: www.atcowater.com
Emp.: 10
Water Treatment & Distribution Services
S.I.C.: 4941
N.A.I.C.S.: 221310
Arnold MacBurnie *(Mng Dir)*

Canadian Utilities Limited (1)
1400 909 11th Ave SW
Calgary, AB, T2R 1N6, Canada (52.7%)
Tel.: (403) 292-7500
Fax: (403) 292-7532
E-Mail: investorrelations@atco.com
Web Site: www.canadian-utilities.com
CU—(OTC TSX)
Rev.: $3,120,228,780
Assets: $13,317,879,960
Liabilities: $8,975,006,580
Net Worth: $4,342,873,380
Earnings: $576,531,600
Emp.: 7,139
Fiscal Year-end: 12/31/12
Utilities Holding Company
S.I.C.: 4931
N.A.I.C.S.: 221122
Nancy C. Southern *(Chm, Pres & CEO)*
Brian R. Bale *(CFO & Sr VP)*
Alan M. Skiffington *(CIO & VP)*
Susan R. Werth *(Chief Admin Officer & Sr VP)*
Clinton G. Warkentin *(Treas & VP)*
Carol Gear *(Sec)*
Kevin Cumming *(Sr VP-Northern Dev)*
Robert J. Myles *(Sr VP-Corp Dev & Plng)*

Subsidiaries:

ATCO Energy Solutions Ltd (2)
800 909-11 Avenue SW
Calgary, AB, T2R 1N6, Canada
Tel.: (403) 245-7106
Fax: (403) 292-7982
E-Mail: info@atcoenergysolutions.com
Web Site: www.atcoenergysolutions.com
Emp.: 25
Electrical & Industrial Pipeline Mfr
S.I.C.: 3498
N.A.I.C.S.: 332996
Jay Park *(Pres)*

ATCO I-Tek Ltd. (2)
500 10035 105 St
Edmonton, AB, T5J 1V6, Canada (100%)
Tel.: (780) 420-7875
Fax: (780) 420-7746
Web Site: www.atcoitek.com
Emp.: 350
Customer Care & Billing Services
S.I.C.: 8721
N.A.I.C.S.: 541214
R. L. Lambright *(Pres)*

ATCO Midstream Ltd. (2)
900 240 4th Ave SW
Calgary, AB, T2P 4H4, Canada (100%)
Tel.: (403) 298-7700
Fax: (403) 513-3750
E-Mail: solutions@atcomidstream.com
Web Site: www.atcomidstream.com
Emp.: 140
Natural Gas Gathering, Processing, Storage & Retail Gas Management Services
S.I.C.: 4923
N.A.I.C.S.: 486210
Mike Dever *(Sr VP & Gen Mgr)*

Subsidiary:

ATCO Midstream NWT Ltd. (3)
900 240 - 4th Avenue SW
Calgary, AB, T2P 4H4, Canada
Tel.: (403) 513-3700
Fax: (403) 513-3750
Natural Gas Distribution Services
S.I.C.: 4924
N.A.I.C.S.: 221210

ATCO Power Ltd. (2)
900 919 11th Ave SW
Calgary, AB, T2R 1P3, Canada (100%)
Tel.: (403) 209-6900
Fax: (403) 209-6970
E-Mail: atcopower@atcopower.com
Web Site: www.atcopower.com
Emp.: 111
Independent Power Projects Developer, Project Manager, Owner & Operator
S.I.C.: 3612
N.A.I.C.S.: 335311
Grant M. Lake *(Sr VP-Comml)*

Subsidiary:

ASHCOR Technologies Ltd. (3)
919 11 Ave Sw Suite 800
Calgary, AB, T2R 1P3, Canada
Tel.: (403) 209-6011
Fax: (403) 292-7611
Coal Combustion Products Distr
S.I.C.: 5052
N.A.I.C.S.: 423520

Non-U.S. Subsidiary:

ATCO Power Generation Ltd. (3)
2 Queen Anne's Gate Buildings Dartmouth Street
London, SW1H 9BP, United Kingdom
Tel.: (44) 20 72223892
Fax: (44) 20 72273185
Emp.: 6
Electric Power Generation Services
S.I.C.: 4939
N.A.I.C.S.: 221118
Michael Jones *(VP)*

CU Inc. (2)
909 11th Ave SW Ste 1500
Calgary, AB, T2R 1N6, Canada (100%)
Tel.: (403) 292-7500
Fax: (403) 292-7623
Web Site: www.canadian-utilities.com
Emp.: 7,000
Utilities Holding Company
S.I.C.: 6719
N.A.I.C.S.: 551112
Ronald D. Southern *(Chm)*
Nancy C. Southern *(Pres & CEO)*
Brian Bale *(CFO)*
Susan R. Werth *(Chief Admin Officer & Sr VP)*
Paul Wright *(VP-Fin & Treas)*
Patricia Spruin *(Sec & VP-Admin)*

Subsidiaries:

ATCO Electric Ltd. (3)
10035 105 Sta Main St
Edmonton, AB, T5J 2V6, Canada (100%)
Tel.: (780) 420-7310
Telex: 3-72848
Fax: (780) 420-7400
E-Mail: info@atcoelectric.com
Web Site: www.atcoelectric.com
Emp.: 900
Electric Utility Services
S.I.C.: 4931
N.A.I.C.S.: 221122

Subsidiaries:

Northland Utilities Enterprises Ltd. (4)
1 66 Woodland Drive
Hay River, NT, X0E 1G1, Canada (76%)
Tel.: (867) 874-6879
Fax: (867) 874-6829
Web Site: www.northlandutilities.com
Emp.: 30
Natural Gas Distr
S.I.C.: 4924
N.A.I.C.S.: 221210

Subsidiaries:

Northland Utilities (NWT) Limited (5)
1 66 Woodland Dr
Hay River, NT, X0E 1G1, Canada (100%)
Tel.: (867) 874-6879
Fax: (867) 874-6829
Web Site: www.northlandutilities.com
Emp.: 20
Natural Gas Distr
S.I.C.: 4924
N.A.I.C.S.: 221210
Sett F. Policicchio *(Pres)*

Northland Utilities (Yellowknife) Limited (5)
481 Range Lake Rd
Yellowknife, NT, X1A 3R9, Canada (100%)
Tel.: (867) 873-4865
Fax: (867) 920-2099
E-Mail: northlandutilities@northlandutilities.ca
Web Site: www.northlandutilities.com
Emp.: 23
Natural Gas Distr
S.I.C.: 4924
N.A.I.C.S.: 221210
Jeff Barbutza *(Gen Mgr)*

The Yukon Electrical Co. Ltd. (4)
100 1100 1st Ave
Whitehorse, YT, Y1A 3T4, Canada (100%)
Tel.: (867) 633-7000
Telex: 3-68229
Fax: (877) 484-9432
E-Mail: info@yukonelectrical.com
Web Site: www.yukonelectrical.com
Emp.: 45
Electricity Distr
S.I.C.: 4939
N.A.I.C.S.: 221122
Dwight Redden *(Gen Mgr)*

ATCO Gas & Pipelines Ltd. (3)
10035 105 Street
Edmonton, AB, T5J 2V6, Canada AB
Tel.: (780) 420-7211
Fax: (780) 420-7400
Web Site: www.atcogas.com
Holding Company; Natural Gas Pipeline Transportation & Distr
S.I.C.: 6719
N.A.I.C.S.: 551112
Siegfried Kiefer *(COO)*

Divisions:

ATCO Gas (4)
10035 105th St
Edmonton, AB, T5J 2V6, Canada (100%)
Tel.: (780) 424-5222
Telex: 37-2848
Fax: (780) 420-7400
E-Mail: hotline@atcogas.com
Web Site: www.atcogas.com
Emp.: 1,800
Natural Gas Transmission & Distribution Services
S.I.C.: 4924
N.A.I.C.S.: 221210
Jerome Engler *(Pres)*

ATCO Pipelines (4)
1200 909 11th Ave SW
Calgary, AB, T2R 1L8, Canada (100%)
Tel.: (403) 245-7060
Fax: (403) 245-7844
E-Mail: humanresources@atcopipelines.com
Web Site: www.atcopipelines.com
Emp.: 50
Natural Gas Pipeline Transportation Services
S.I.C.: 4923
N.A.I.C.S.: 486210
Jim Yaremko *(Sr Mgr-Comm)*

Non-U.S. Subsidiary:

ATCO Australia Pty. Ltd. (2)
Level 12 2 Mill Street
Perth, WA, 6000, Australia AU
Tel.: (61) 8 9320 0200 (100%)
Fax: (61) 8 9320 0208
E-Mail: enquiries@atcoaustralia.com.au
Web Site: www.atcoaustralia.com.au
Emp.: 5
Holding Company; Energy & Infrastructure Services
S.I.C.: 6719
N.A.I.C.S.: 551112
Steven J. Landry *(Mng Dir & COO)*

Subsidiaries:

ATCO Gas Australia Pty. Ltd. (3)
12-14 The Esplanade
Perth, WA, 6000, Australia AU
Tel.: (61) 8 6218 1700
Web Site: www.atcogas.com.au
Natural Gas Pipeline Transportation & Distr
S.I.C.: 4923
N.A.I.C.S.: 486210
Brian Hahn *(Pres)*

ATCO I-Tek Australia (3)
12-14 The Esplanade
Perth, WA, 6000, Australia
Tel.: (61) 8 6213 7000
Fax: (61) 8 6213 7001
Web Site: www.atcoaustralia.com.au/Contact%20Us/
Emp.: 40
Information Technology Consulting Services
S.I.C.: 7373
N.A.I.C.S.: 541512

ATCO Power Australia Pty Ltd (3)
Level 12 2 Mill Street
Perth, WA, 6000, Australia
Tel.: (61) 8 9320 0200
Fax: (61) 8 9320 0208
E-Mail: enquiries@atcoaustralia.com.au
Web Site: www.atcoaustralia.com.au
Emp.: 5
Electric Power Generation Services
S.I.C.: 4939
N.A.I.C.S.: 221118
Tue Mantoni *(Mng Dir)*

ATCOAT GMBH
Frau Dr Monika Schneider
Katharinenstr 61
D -52353 Duren, Germany
Tel.: (49) 2421 9999 230
Fax: (49) 2421 9999 233
Business Description:
Synthetic Resin Mfr
S.I.C.: 2821
N.A.I.C.S.: 325211
Personnel:
Monika Schneider *(CEO)*

Subsidiary:

ATCOAT Hamburg GmbH (1)
Ottensener Strasse 20 22
22525 Hamburg, Germany De (100%)
Tel.: (49) 405472250
Fax: (49) 405472510
Emp.: 30
Resin Mfr
S.I.C.: 2821
N.A.I.C.S.: 325211
Stefan Ogasa *(Plant Mgr)*

ATCOR MEDICAL HOLDINGS LIMITED
Unit 11 West Ryde Corporate Centre
1059-1063 Victoria Road
Ryde, NSW, 2114, Australia
Tel.: (61) 298748761
Fax: (61) 298749022
Web Site: www.atcormedical.com
ACG—(ASX)
Rev.: $9,438,177
Assets: $6,643,395
Liabilities: $1,559,059
Net Worth: $5,084,336
Earnings: $2,849,125
Emp.: 28
Fiscal Year-end: 06/30/13
Business Description:
Medical Devices Mfr & Marketing
S.I.C.: 3845
N.A.I.C.S.: 334510
Personnel:
Duncan R. Ross *(CEO & Mng Dir)*
Peter Manley *(CFO & Sec)*
Douglas Kurschinski *(Sr VP-Comml Ops-US)*
Board of Directors:
Donal P. O'Dwyer
David L. Brookes
Peter Jenkins
Michael O'Rourke
Duncan R. Ross
Legal Counsel:
Dibbs Barker
Level 8 123 Pitt Street
GPO Box 983
Sydney, Australia

Subsidiary:

AtCor Medical Pty Limited (1)
Unit 11 West Ryde Corporate Centre 1059-1063 Victoria Road
Ryde, NSW, 2114, Australia
Tel.: (61) 298748761
Fax: (61) 298749022
E-Mail: enquiry@atcormedical.com
Web Site: www.atcormedical.com
Emp.: 15
Medical Equipment Mfr
S.I.C.: 3845
N.A.I.C.S.: 334510
Duncan Ross *(CEO)*
Peter Manley *(CFO)*
Douglas Kurschinski *(Sr VP)*

U.S. Subsidiary:

AtCor Medical Inc. (1)
1 Pierce Pl Ste 225w
Itasca, IL 60143-2613
Tel.: (630) 228-8871
Fax: (630) 228-8872
Web Site: www.atcormedical.com
Emp.: 15
Biomedical Diagnostic Equipment Suppliers
S.I.C.: 5047
N.A.I.C.S.: 423450
Douglas Kurschinski *(Sr VP-Comml Ops-US)*

ATEA ASA
Brynsalleen 2
NO-0667 Oslo, Norway
Tel.: (47) 22095000
Fax: (47) 22095070
E-Mail: info@atea.com
Web Site: www.atea.com
ATEA—(OSL)
Rev.: $3,788,174,997
Assets: $1,774,190,673
Liabilities: $1,080,130,221
Net Worth: $694,060,452
Earnings: $91,979,118
Emp.: 6,266
Fiscal Year-end: 12/31/12
Business Description:
Consulting, Technology & Outsourcing Services
S.I.C.: 8742
N.A.I.C.S.: 541611
Personnel:
Ib Kunoe *(Chm)*
Claus Hougesen *(Pres & CEO)*
Dag Fodstad *(Mng Dir)*
Rune Falstad *(CFO & Exec VP)*
Steinar Sonsteby *(Exec Sr VP-Sls & Products)*
Peter Trans *(Exec Sr VP-Svcs & Solutions)*
Board of Directors:
Ib Kunoe
Marthe Dyrud
Jorn Goldstein
Morten Jurs
Lisbeth Toftkaer Kvan
Kristine M. Madsen
Sven Madsen
Marianne Urdahl

Subsidiary:

Atea AS (1)
Brynsalleen 2-4
Oslo, 0605, Norway (100%)
Tel.: (47) 22095000
Fax: (47) 22095001
E-Mail: firmapost@atea.com
Web Site: www.atea.com
Emp.: 600
Computer & Peripheral Equipment & Software Whslr
S.I.C.: 5045
N.A.I.C.S.: 423430
Doug Fodstad *(Mng Dir)*

Non-U.S. Subsidiaries:

Atea A/S (1)
Lautrupvang 6
2750 Ballerup, Denmark
Tel.: (45) 70252550
Fax: (45) 70252575
E-Mail: info@atea.dk
Web Site: www.atea.dk
Emp.: 800
Computer & Peripheral Equipment & Software Whslr
S.I.C.: 5045
N.A.I.C.S.: 423430
Peter Trans *(Mng Dir)*

Atea Finland Oy (1)
PL 39
01621 Vantaa, Finland
Tel.: (358) 10613611
Fax: (358) 961367950
E-Mail: customercare@atea.fi
Web Site: www.atea.fi
Enterprise Management Software Development Services
S.I.C.: 7371
N.A.I.C.S.: 541511

Atea Logistics AB (1)
PO Box 159
35104 Vaxjo, Sweden (100%)
Tel.: (46) 470771600
Fax: (46) 47018940
E-Mail: info@atea.se
Web Site: www.atea.se
Emp.: 150
Computer & Peripheral Equipment & Software Whslr
S.I.C.: 5045
N.A.I.C.S.: 423430

Atea Sverige AB (1)
PO Box 18
16493 Kista, Sweden (100%)
Tel.: (46) 84774700
Fax: (46) 84774701
Web Site: www.atea.se
Emp.: 800
Computer & Peripheral Equipment & Software Whslr
S.I.C.: 5045
N.A.I.C.S.: 423430
Carl Johan Hultenheim *(Mng Dir)*

ATEAM INC.
Nagoya Lucent Tower 36F 6-1
Ushijima-cho
Nishi-ku, Nagoya, 451-6032, Japan
Tel.: (81) 52 527 3070
Fax: (81) 52 527 3080
E-Mail: info@a-tm.co.jp
Web Site: www.a-tm.co.jp
Year Founded: 2000
3662—(TKS)
Sls.: $120,879,000
Assets: $51,051,000
Liabilities: $12,496,000
Net Worth: $38,555,000
Earnings: $11,462,000
Emp.: 482
Fiscal Year-end: 07/31/13
Business Description:
Entertainment & Lifestyle Support Computer Products Developer
S.I.C.: 7372
N.A.I.C.S.: 511210
Personnel:
Takao Hayashi *(Pres)*
Hiroyuki Kumazawa *(Corp Officer)*
Fumio Mase *(Corp Officer)*
Brady Mehagan *(Corp Officer)*
Chihiro Sato *(Corp Officer)*
Hiroaki Takahashi *(Corp Officer)*
Board of Directors:
Takao Hayashi
Atsushi Kato
Takahiro Makino
Yukimasa Nakauchi

ATEBA RESOURCES INC.
130 King Street West Suite 3680
Toronto, ON, M5X 1B1, Canada
Tel.: (416) 366-2856
Fax: (416) 366-8179
E-Mail: info@atebaresources.ca
Web Site: www.atebaresources.ca
ATR—(CNSX)
Rev.: $3,892
Assets: $2,844,169
Liabilities: $220,249
Net Worth: $2,623,920
Earnings: ($342,134)
Fiscal Year-end: 12/31/12
Business Description:
Mineral Exploration & Development Services
S.I.C.: 1481
N.A.I.C.S.: 213115
Personnel:
William P. Dickie *(Pres & CEO)*
John Kennedy *(CFO)*
Board of Directors:
William P. Dickie
Peter J. Evans
Robert J. B. H. Holmes
Scott Jobin-Bevans
Legal Counsel:
Irwin Lowy LLP
Suite 1010 130 Adelaide St W
Toronto, ON, Canada
Transfer Agent:
Capital Transfer Agency
105 Adelaide St West Suite 1101
Toronto, ON, M5H 1P9, Canada

ATECT CORPORATION
2-1-36 Sumida
Higashiosaka, Osaka, 578-0912, Japan
Tel.: (81) 72 967 7000
Fax: (81) 72 967 7001
Web Site: www.atect.co.jp
Year Founded: 1959
4241—(JAS)
Sls.: $27,500,000
Assets: $40,711,000
Liabilities: $29,216,000
Net Worth: $11,495,000
Earnings: $2,288,000
Emp.: 57
Fiscal Year-end: 03/31/13
Business Description:
Buttons Mfr
S.I.C.: 3965
N.A.I.C.S.: 339993
Personnel:
Norio Kotaka *(Pres)*
Board of Directors:
Katsuhide Hino
Keiichi Kagawa
Norio Kotaka
Hiroko Namura

Non-U.S. Subsidiary:

atect korea Corporation (1)
452 - 2 Hyungok-Ri Chungbuk-Myeon
Pyeongtaek, Gyeonggi-do, Korea (South)
Tel.: (82) 316826990
Electronic Component Mfr
S.I.C.: 3679
N.A.I.C.S.: 334419

ATELIER DE PRODUCTION ET DE CREATION
(d/b/a APC)
39 rue Madame
75006 Paris, France
Tel.: (33) 144398787
Fax: (33) 144398795
E-Mail: info@apc.fr
Web Site: www.apc.fr
Sales Range: $25-49.9 Million
Emp.: 100
Business Description:
Clothing & Accessories Mfr & Retailer
S.I.C.: 2389
N.A.I.C.S.: 315990
Personnel:
Jean Touitou *(Pres & Mng Dir)*

ATELIERS PERRAULT FRERES
30 Rue Sebastien Cady
CS 60057
St Laurent de la Plaine, 49290
Avignon, France
Tel.: (33) 241223722
Fax: (33) 241223737
E-Mail: contact@ateliersperrault.com
Web Site: www.ateliersperrault.com
Sls.: $23,900,000
Emp.: 42
Business Description:
Carpentry Work, Iron & Locksmith Services
S.I.C.: 2541
N.A.I.C.S.: 337212
Personnel:
Francois Perrault *(Gen Mgr)*

ATEMPO S.A.
Les Boreales 2 Ave De Laponie
91951 Courtaboeuf, Cedex, France
Tel.: (33) 164868300
Fax: (33) 0164868301

Atempo S.A.—(Continued)

E-Mail: press@atempo.com
Web Site: www.atempo.com
Year Founded: 1992
Sales Range: $10-24.9 Million
Emp.: 170

Business Description:
Database Development Services
S.I.C.: 7371
N.A.I.C.S.: 541511

Personnel:
Rick Wojcik *(Pres & CEO)*
Mark P. Williams *(CFO)*
Brian Olson *(CTO)*

U.S. Subsidiary:

Atempo, Inc. (1)
2465 E Bayshore Rd Ste 400
Palo Alto, CA 94303
Tel.: (650) 494-2600
Fax: (650) 493-1600
Web Site: www.atempo.com
Emp.: 20
Data Backup & Recovery Software
S.I.C.: 7372
N.A.I.C.S.: 511210
Neal Ater *(Chm)*
Michael V. Wall *(Pres & CEO)*
Mark Sutter *(CTO & VP-Engrg)*

Non-U.S. Subsidiary:

Atempo Deutschland GmbH (1)
Curiestrasse 2
D-70563 Stuttgart, Germany
Tel.: (49) 71167400331
Fax: (49) 71167400200
E-Mail: info@atempo.com
Web Site: www.atempo.com
Emp.: 20
Data Backup & Recovery Software
S.I.C.: 7372
N.A.I.C.S.: 511210

ATEN INTERNATIONAL CO., LTD.

No 125 Section 2 Datung Rd 3rd Fl
Sijhih Taipei, Taiwan
Tel.: (886) 286926789
Fax: (886) 286926577
E-Mail: eservice@aten.com.tw
Web Site: www.aten.com.tw
Sales Range: $125-149.9 Million
Emp.: 357

Business Description:
Computer Equipment & Peripheral Mfr
S.I.C.: 3577
N.A.I.C.S.: 334118

Personnel:
Shang Zhong Chen *(Chm)*

U.S. Division:

ATEN Technology Inc. (1)
19641 Da Vinci
Foothill Ranch, CA 92610-2603
Tel.: (949) 428-1111
Fax: (949) 428-1100
Toll Free: (888) 999-ATEN
E-Mail: sales@aten-usa.com
Web Site: www.aten-usa.com
Emp.: 70
Computer Peripherals & Software Distr
S.I.C.: 5045
N.A.I.C.S.: 423430
May Wang *(Office Mgr)*

U.S. Subsidiary:

Aten New Jersey Inc (1)
155 Pierce St
Somerset, NJ 08873
Tel.: (732) 356-1703
Fax: (732) 356-1639
E-Mail: sales@aten-usa.com
Web Site: www.aten-usa.com
Emp.: 35
Computer Related Services
S.I.C.: 7379
N.A.I.C.S.: 541519
David Su *(Gen Mgr)*

Non-U.S. Subsidiaries:

Aten Advance Co.,Ltd (1)
Eagle Town 3rd Floor # 303 278-20
Seongsu-dong 2-ga 3-Dong, Seoul, Korea (South) (100%)
Tel.: (82) 24676789
Fax: (82) 24679876
E-Mail: sales@aten.co.kr
Web Site: www.aten.co.kr
Emp.: 15
Computer Related Services
S.I.C.: 7379
N.A.I.C.S.: 541519
Ko Chgugsub *(Mng Dir)*

Aten Infotech N.V. (1)
Mijnwerkerslaan
3550 Heusden, Belgium (100%)
Tel.: (32) 11531543
Fax: (32) 11531544
E-Mail: sales@aten.be
Web Site: www.aten.be
Emp.: 18
Electronic Computer Mfr
S.I.C.: 3571
N.A.I.C.S.: 334111
Jackie Chan *(Mng Dir)*

Aten Japan Co., Ltd (1)
803 Tatsumi Bldg 16-6 Nishi-shinjuku 6-Chome
Shinjuku-ku, 160-0023 Tokyo, Japan
Tel.: (81) 353237170
E-Mail: info@atenjapan.jp
Web Site: www.atenjapan.jp
Emp.: 20
Computer Related Services
S.I.C.: 7379
N.A.I.C.S.: 541519

Aten U.K. Limited (1)
229 Berwick Avenue
Slough, SL1 4QT, United Kingdom (100%)
Tel.: (44) 1753539121
Fax: (44) 1753215253
E-Mail: sales@aten.co.uk
Web Site: www.aten.co.uk
Emp.: 10
Computer Related Services
S.I.C.: 7379
N.A.I.C.S.: 541519
James Liu *(Mng Dir)*

ATENDE S.A.

(Formerly ATM Systemy Informatyczne S.A.)
ul Ostrobramska 86
04-163 Warsaw, Poland
Tel.: (48) 22 29 57 300
Fax: (48) 22 29 57 447
E-Mail: kontakt@atende.pl
Web Site: www.atende.pl
ASI—(WAR)
Sales Range: $50-74.9 Million
Emp.: 210

Business Description:
IT Solutions
S.I.C.: 7379
N.A.I.C.S.: 541519

Personnel:
Tadeusz Czichon *(Chm-Supervisory Bd)*
Roman Szwed *(Chm-Mgmt Bd)*
Iwona Bakula *(Member-Mgmt Bd & CFO)*
Andrzej Slodczyk *(Member-Mgmt Bd)*

Supervisory Board of Directors:
Tadeusz Czichon
Grzegorz Domagala
Slawomir Kaminski
Miroslaw Panek
Piotr Puteczny

ATEVIA AG

Amalienbadstrasse 41
76227 Karlsruhe, Germany
Tel.: (49) 721 5160 2701
Fax: (49) 721 5160 2702
E-Mail: investor.relations@kizoo.com
Web Site: www.atevia.com
CMBT—(DEU)
Sls.: $2,557,723
Assets: $247,829,897
Liabilities: $6,057,765
Net Worth: $241,772,132
Earnings: $2,153,872
Emp.: 4
Fiscal Year-end: 12/31/12

Business Description:
Financial Management Services
S.I.C.: 6211
N.A.I.C.S.: 523999

Personnel:
Hansjorg Reiter *(Chm-Supervisory Bd)*
Michael Greve *(Chm-Exec Bd & CEO)*
Matthias Hornberger *(CFO)*
Frank Schuler *(CMO)*
Heiko Schneefeld *(CTO)*

ATH RESOURCES PLC

Aardvark House Sidings Court
Doncaster, DN4 5NU, United Kingdom
Tel.: (44) 1302760462
Fax: (44) 1302760463
E-Mail: info@ath.co.uk
Web Site: www.ath.co.uk
ATH—(AIM)
Emp.: 394

Business Description:
Coal Mining Services
S.I.C.: 1222
N.A.I.C.S.: 212112

Personnel:
Alistair Black *(CEO)*
Andrew P. Weatherstone *(Sec & Dir-Fin)*

Board of Directors:
Alistair Black
Andrew P. Weatherstone

Legal Counsel:
Eversheds LLP
Bridgewater Pl Water Ln
Leeds, United Kingdom

Subsidiaries:

Aardvark TMC Ltd (1)
Aardvark House Sidings Crt
Doncaster, South Yorkshire, DN4 5NU, United Kingdom
Tel.: (44) 1302760462
Fax: (44) 1302760463
E-Mail: info@ath.co.uk
Emp.: 40
Mine Operating Services
S.I.C.: 1241
N.A.I.C.S.: 213113
Alistair Black *(CEO)*

ATH Garleffan Ltd (1)
Aardvark House
Sidings Ct, Doncaster, South Yorkshire, DN4 5NU, United Kingdom
Tel.: (44) 1302760462
Fax: (44) 1290332698
E-Mail: info@ath.co.uk
Web Site: www.ath.co.uk
Emp.: 20
Coal Mining Services
S.I.C.: 1222
N.A.I.C.S.: 212112

ATHABASCA MINERALS INC.

9524 27 Ave
Edmonton, AB, T6N 1B2, Canada
Tel.: (780) 465-5696
Fax: (780) 430-9865
E-Mail: info@athabascaminerals.com
Web Site: www.athabascaminerals.com
ABM—(TSXV)
Rev.: $16,442,916
Assets: $33,079,020
Liabilities: $16,092,320
Net Worth: $16,986,700
Earnings: $4,682,241
Fiscal Year-end: 11/30/12

Business Description:
Mineral Exploration Services
S.I.C.: 1081
N.A.I.C.S.: 213114

Personnel:
Douglas Murray Stuve *(Chm)*
Dom Kriangkum *(Pres & CEO)*
Don Hruba *(CFO)*

Board of Directors:
Douglas Murray Stuve
Edward Bereznicki
Wylie Hamilton
William Kanters
Dom Kriangkum
Shaun O'Connor-Parsons
Michael Peck
Theodore J. A. Rousseau

Legal Counsel:
Burstall Winger
1600 Dome Tower 333 - 7th Ave SW
Calgary, AB, Canada

Transfer Agent:
Canadian Stock Transfer Company Inc
600 The Dome Tower, 333 7th Ave SW
Calgary, AB, Canada

ATHABASCA OIL SANDS CORP.

Bow Valley Square 4 Suite 2000
250 6th Avenue SW, Calgary, AB, T2P 3H7, Canada
Tel.: (403) 237-8227
E-Mail: info@aosc.com
Web Site: www.aosc.com
Year Founded: 2006
ATH—(TSX)
Sales Range: $10-24.9 Million
Emp.: 106

Business Description:
Oil Exploration Services
S.I.C.: 1311
N.A.I.C.S.: 211111

Personnel:
William M. Gallacher *(Founder)*
Thomas W. Buchanan *(Chm)*
Sveinung Svarte *(CEO)*
Kim Anderson *(CFO)*
Rob Broen *(COO)*
Anne Schenkenberger *(Sec & VP-Legal)*

Board of Directors:
Thomas W. Buchanan
Gary H. Dundas
Ronald J. Eckhardt
Jeff G. Lawson
Marshall McRae

Transfer Agent:
Olympia Trust Company
2300 125 9 Avenue SW
Calgary, AB, Canada

ATHABASCA URANIUM INC.

Suite 1200 570 Granville Street
Vancouver, BC, V6C 3P1, Canada
Tel.: (604) 689-8336
Fax: (888) 691-0529
Toll Free: (866) 869-8072
E-Mail: info@athabascauranium.com
Web Site: www.athabascauranium.com
Year Founded: 2007
UAX—(OTC TSXV)
Int. Income: $2,981
Assets: $9,326,726
Liabilities: $406,955
Net Worth: $8,919,771
Earnings: ($345,890)
Fiscal Year-end: 08/31/13

Business Description:
Uranium Mining Services
S.I.C.: 1094
N.A.I.C.S.: 212291

Personnel:
Gilbert G. Schneider *(Pres & CEO)*
D. Barry Lee *(CFO)*

Board of Directors:
Otis Kim Goheen
D. Barry Lee
Paula Rogers
Gilbert G. Schneider
Transfer Agent:
Computershare Investor Services Inc
100 University Avenue 9th Floor North Tower
Toronto, ON, Canada

ATHEEB GROUP
27 Al Baz Street
PO Box 7947
Sulaimaniya District, Riyadh, 11472, Saudi Arabia
Tel.: (966) 14646142
Fax: (966) 14656257
Web Site: www.atheeb.com
Business Description:
Holding Company
S.I.C.: 6719
N.A.I.C.S.: 551112
Personnel:
Abdulaziz Bin Ahmed Bin Abdulaziz Al-Saud *(Chm)*

Subsidiary:

Etihad Atheeb Telecom Company **(1)**
PO Box 250398
Riyadh, 11391, Saudi Arabia
Tel.: (966) 12882666
Fax: (966) 18111461110
E-Mail: info@go.com.sa
Web Site: www.go.com.sa
Sales Range: $25-49.9 Million
Emp.: 140
Telecommunications Services
S.I.C.: 4813
N.A.I.C.S.: 517110
Abdulaziz Bin Ahmed Bin Abdulaziz Al-Saud *(Chm)*
Zaid Alshabanat *(CEO)*
Mohammed Madan *(Acting COO)*
Abdulrahman Bin Abdulaziz Mutrib *(Chief Bus Support Officer)*

ATHELNEY TRUST PLC
Waterside Court Falmouth Road
Penryn, Cornwall, TR10 8AW, United Kingdom
Tel.: (44) 1326378288
Fax: (44) 1326378077
E-Mail: info@athelneytrust.co.uk
Web Site: www.athelneytrust.co.uk
ATY—(LSE)
Sales Range: Less than $1 Million
Emp.: 4
Business Description:
Investment Trust Services
S.I.C.: 6211
N.A.I.C.S.: 523999
Personnel:
Robin G. Boyle *(Mng Dir)*
John Girdlestone *(Sec)*
Board of Directors:
Hugo B. Deschampsneufs
Jonathan Lancelot Addison
Robin G. Boyle
David A. Horner
Legal Counsel:
McClure Naismith LLP
49 Queen St
Edinburgh, EH12 3NH, United Kingdom

ATHENA RESOURCES LIMITED
24 Colin Street
PO Box 1970
West Perth, WA, 6005, Australia
Tel.: (61) 892225888
Fax: (61) 892225810
E-Mail: ahn@athenaresources.com.au
Web Site: www.athenaresources.com.au
AHN—(ASX)
Sales Range: Less than $1 Million
Emp.: 1
Business Description:
Mineral Exploration Services
S.I.C.: 1481
N.A.I.C.S.: 213115
Personnel:
Edmond William Edwards *(Mng Dir & Co-Sec)*
Peter John Newcomb *(Co-Sec)*
Board of Directors:
David A. Webster
Edmond William Edwards
Raj P. Kandiah

ATHENA S.A.
Amarousiou - Chalandriou 16
Marousi, 15125 Athens, Greece
Tel.: (30) 210 63 75 000
Fax: (30) 210 61 04 380
E-Mail: athena@athena-sa.gr
Web Site: www.athena-sa.gr
Year Founded: 1966
ATHINA—(ATH)
Emp.: 83
Business Description:
Construction Engineering Services
S.I.C.: 1629
N.A.I.C.S.: 237990
Personnel:
Christos Joannou *(Chm)*
Constantinos Mitzalis *(Mng Dir & VP)*
Board of Directors:
Christos Joannou
Georgios Apegitos
Stylianos Georgallides
Constantinos Mitzalis
Apostolos Mytilis
Anastasios Tsakanikas

Non-U.S. Subsidiaries:

Athena Emirates LLC **(1)**
PO Box 54008
Abu Dhabi, United Arab Emirates
Tel.: (971) 2 679 7666
Fax: (971) 2 679 7690
E-Mail: athename@athena-me.ae
Engineering Construction Services
S.I.C.: 1629
N.A.I.C.S.: 237990

Athena Fujairah LLC **(1)**
PO Box 3894
Fujairah, United Arab Emirates
Tel.: (971) 9 228 1838
Fax: (971) 9 228 1056
Engineering Construction Services
S.I.C.: 1629
N.A.I.C.S.: 237990

ATHENEE PALACE HILTON BUCHAREST HOTEL
1-3 Episcopiei St
District 1, Bucharest, Romania 010292
Tel.: (40) 21 303 3777
Fax: (40) 21 315 2121
Web Site: www.hiltonbucharest.com
Year Founded: 1914
ATPA—(BUC)
Business Description:
Hotel & Motel Services
S.I.C.: 7011
N.A.I.C.S.: 721110
Personnel:
Gheorghe Copos *(Pres & Gen Mgr)*

ATHENS MEDICAL CENTERS SA
5-7 Distomou Street
Maroussi, 15125 Athens, Greece
Tel.: (30) 2106198100
Fax: (30) 2106198555
E-Mail: metox@iatriko.gr
Web Site: www.iatriko.gr
IATR—(ATH)
Rev.: $308,964,861
Assets: $678,480,449
Liabilities: $502,525,261
Net Worth: $175,955,188
Earnings: $9,611,654
Emp.: 2,777
Fiscal Year-end: 12/31/12
Business Description:
Hospitals & Healthcare Services
S.I.C.: 8062
N.A.I.C.S.: 622110
Personnel:
George V. Apostolopoulos *(Pres)*
Vassilios G. Apostolopoulos *(CEO)*
Board of Directors:
Christos G. Apostolopoulos
George V. Apostolopoulos
Vassilios G. Apostolopoulos
Nikolaos Koritsas
Konstantinos Pampoukis
Jochen Guenter Paul Schmidt
Vassilios Tountopoulos

Subsidiary:

Iatriki Techniki S.A. **(1)**
1 Filadelfias St
14562 Athens, Greece (100%)
Tel.: (30) 2106287132
Fax: (30) 2106287174
Emp.: 20
Medical Laboratories
S.I.C.: 8071
N.A.I.C.S.: 621511
Dimitrios Babalis *(Mng Dir)*

Non-U.S. Subsidiary:

Medsana Srl **(1)**
Str Dr Muscel Nanu 12 Sector 5
Bucuresti, Bucharest, Romania (78.9%)
Tel.: (40) 214108643
Fax: (40) 214087800
Web Site: www.medsana.ro
Emp.: 150
Other Individual & Family Services
S.I.C.: 8322
N.A.I.C.S.: 624190
Rodeca Amrtle *(Mgr-Ops)*

ATHENS WATER SUPPLY & SEWERAGE S.A.
Oropou Street 156
Galatsi, 11146 Athens, Greece
Tel.: (30) 2102144400
Fax: (30) 2102144437
E-Mail: eydap-met@eydap.gr
Web Site: www.eydap.gr
Year Founded: 1980
EYDAP—(ATH)
Sls.: $451,430,032
Assets: $2,245,174,634
Liabilities: $1,058,525,779
Net Worth: $1,186,648,855
Earnings: $62,937,486
Emp.: 2,512
Fiscal Year-end: 12/31/12
Business Description:
Water Supply & Sewerage Services
S.I.C.: 4941
N.A.I.C.S.: 221310
Personnel:
Antonis Vartholomeos *(Chm & CEO)*
Christina Kontaratou *(Sec)*
Board of Directors:
Antonis Vartholomeos
Emmanouel Aggelakis
Ioannis Chondrogiannos
Panteleimon Kamas
Eleftheria Karachaliou
Christina Kontaratou
Anastasios Kourtis
Christos Mistriotis
Evagelos Moutafis
Epaminondas Sklavenitis
Panayotis Skoularikis
Gregory Zafeiropoulos
Lampros Zografos

ATHEZZA SARL
Zi Pont Des Charrettes
30700 Uzes, Gard, France
Tel.: (33) 466030013
Fax: (33) 466030099
Web Site: www.athezza.com
Sls.: $11,300,000
Emp.: 31
Business Description:
Home Furnishing Distr
S.I.C.: 5023
N.A.I.C.S.: 423220
Personnel:
Bruno Martin *(Pres)*

ATHI RIVER MINING LIMITED
(Name Changed to ARM Cement Limited)

ATHLETIC CLUB AJACCIEN ACA FOOTBALL
Stade Francois Coti Route De Vazzio
20000 Ajaccio, Corse, France
Tel.: (33) 495203252
Fax: (33) 495100165
Web Site: www.ac-ajaccio.com
Rev.: $20,300,000
Emp.: 53
Business Description:
Sports Clubs, Managers & Promoters
S.I.C.: 7389
N.A.I.C.S.: 711410
Personnel:
Alain Orsoni *(Mng Partner)*

ATHON SA
Via Della Posta 10
CP 225
6934 Bioggio, Switzerland
Tel.: (41) 91 6117070
Fax: (41) 91 6117071
E-Mail: info@athon.ch
Web Site: www.athon.ch
Emp.: 15
Business Description:
Information Technology Consulting Services
S.I.C.: 7373
N.A.I.C.S.: 541512
Personnel:
Lorenzo Medici *(CEO)*

ATHRIS HOLDING AG
Bundesplatz 14
63002 Zug, Switzerland
Tel.: (41) 415601100
Fax: (41) 415601119
E-Mail: info@athris.ch
Web Site: www.athris.ch
Sales Range: $100-124.9 Million
Emp.: 700
Business Description:
Investment Services
S.I.C.: 6211
N.A.I.C.S.: 523999
Personnel:
Georg von Opel *(Chm)*
Board of Directors:
Georg von Opel
Markus Dennler
Gregor Joos

ATI AIRTEST TECHNOLOGIES INC.
9 1520 Cliveden Avenue
Delta, BC, V3M 6J8, Canada
Tel.: (604) 517-3888
Fax: (604) 517-3900
Toll Free: (888) 855-8880
E-Mail: info@airtest.com
Web Site: www.airtest.com
Year Founded: 1996

ATI Airtest Technologies Inc.—(Continued)

AAT—(TSXV)
Sls.: $2,781,199
Assets: $794,202
Liabilities: $3,496,722
Net Worth: ($2,702,520)
Earnings: ($535,295)
Fiscal Year-end: 12/31/12

Business Description:
Air Testing Equipment Mfr
S.I.C.: 3699
N.A.I.C.S.: 335999

Personnel:
George Graham *(Founder, Chm, Pres & CEO)*
Murray Graham *(CFO & Mgr-Ops)*

Board of Directors:
George Graham
Darrel Taylor

ATI TELECOM INTERNATIONAL COMPANY

4336 97th St
Edmonton, AB, T6E 5R9, Canada
Tel.: (780) 424-9100
Fax: (780) 424-9777
Web Site: www.altatelecom.com
Sales Range: $100-124.9 Million
Emp.: 550

Business Description:
Telecommunication
S.I.C.: 4813
N.A.I.C.S.: 517911

Personnel:
Ron Edward *(Pres)*

ATIA GROUP LIMITED

Habankim Street 16
Haifa, 33265, Israel
Tel.: (972) 4 8554755
Fax: (972) 4 8527785
E-Mail: contact@atiagroup.com
Web Site: www.atiagroup.com
ATIA—(LSE TAE)
Sales Range: $150-199.9 Million

Business Description:
Real Estate Management & Development Services
S.I.C.: 6531
N.A.I.C.S.: 531390

Personnel:
Yossi Attia *(CEO)*
Danny Offer *(CFO)*

ATICO MINING CORPORATION

501 543 Granville Street
Vancouver, BC, V6C 1X8, Canada
Tel.: (604) 633-9022
Fax: (604) 688-1157
Year Founded: 2010
ATY—(TSXV)

Business Description:
Copper & Gold Mining
S.I.C.: 1021
N.A.I.C.S.: 212234

Personnel:
Jorge A. Ganoza Durant *(Chm)*
Jorge R. Ganoza Aicardi *(Pres)*
Christina Cepeliauskas *(CFO)*
Kim Casswell *(Sec)*

Board of Directors:
Jorge A. Ganoza Durant
Jorge R. Ganoza Aicardi
Luis D. Ganoza Durant
David Miles
Mario Szotlender
Michael D. Winn

Transfer Agent:
Computershare Investor Services Inc.
510 Burrard Street 2nd Floor
Vancouver, BC, V6C 3B9, Canada

Non-U.S. Subsidiary:

Atico Mining Corporation Colombia SAS **(1)**
Carrera 30 10 C 228 Oficina 529 Interplaza
Medellin, Colombia
Tel.: (57) 4 266 2454
Copper & Gold Mining Services
S.I.C.: 1021
N.A.I.C.S.: 212234
Joseph Salas, *(Country Mgr)*

ATIKWA RESOURCES INC.

Suite 201 1401 1st Street SE
Calgary, AB, T2G 2J3, Canada
Tel.: (403) 233-6092
Fax: (403) 269-2686
E-Mail: info@atikwa.com
Web Site: www.atikwaresources.com
ATK—(TSXV)
Sls.: $3,570,418
Assets: $15,802,346
Liabilities: $8,072,684
Net Worth: $7,729,663
Earnings: ($6,583,163)
Emp.: 15
Fiscal Year-end: 02/28/13

Business Description:
Platinum, Gold & Base Metal Mining & Development Services
S.I.C.: 1041
N.A.I.C.S.: 212221

Personnel:
Sean F. Kehoe *(Pres & CEO)*
Kevin Gowland *(CFO)*

Board of Directors:
Sean F. Kehoe
Ian Rogers
Mark F. Ross
H. Vance White

Transfer Agent:
Equity Transfer & Trust Company
Suite 850, 505 - 3rd Street S.W.
Calgary, AB, Canada

ATINUM INVESTMENT CO., LTD

2nd Floor Jeil Building 168-26
Samsung-Dong
Gangnam-Gu, Seoul, Korea (South)
Tel.: (82) 25550781
Fax: (82) 25572570
Web Site: www.atinuminvest.co.kr
Year Founded: 1988
021080—(KRS)

Business Description:
Financial Consulting Services
S.I.C.: 6211
N.A.I.C.S.: 523999

Personnel:
Ki Chun Shin *(CEO)*

U.S. Subsidiary:

Atinum E&P, Inc. **(1)**
333 Clay St Ste 700
Houston, TX 77002-4115
Tel.: (713) 850-1880
Fax: (281) 872-9610
E-Mail: info@atinumep.com
Web Site: atinumep.com
Oil & Gas Energy Services
S.I.C.: 1389
N.A.I.C.S.: 213112
John Brouillette *(VP-Land Legal)*

ATIS GROUP INC.

1111 St Charles West Suite 952 East Tower
Longueuil, QC, J4K 5G4, Canada
Tel.: (450) 928-0101
Fax: (450) 928-9090
E-Mail: info@atisgroup.ca
Web Site: www.atisgroup.ca
Year Founded: 2004
Sales Range: $150-199.9 Million
Emp.: 1,600

Business Description:
Doors & Windows Developer, Mfr, Distr & Installer
S.I.C.: 3442
N.A.I.C.S.: 332321

Personnel:
Leland Lewis *(Chm)*
Robert Doyon *(Pres & CEO)*
Andre Parent *(Treas, Sec & VP-Fin)*

Board of Directors:
Leland Lewis
Robert Doyon
Beth Haas Laschinger
Richard Laflamme
Norman Silberdick

ATKA KUNSTSTOFFVERARBEITUNG GMBH

Suedring 25
49393 Lohne, Germany
Tel.: (49) 444292680
Fax: (49) 4442926811
E-Mail: info@atka.de
Web Site: www.atka.de
Year Founded: 1981
Rev.: $18,621,900
Emp.: 83

Business Description:
Industrial Products Distr
S.I.C.: 5084
N.A.I.C.S.: 423830

Personnel:
Bernd Kuper *(Mng Dir)*
Frank Sieve *(Mng Dir)*
Jurgen Sieve *(Mng Dir)*
Jochen Simon *(Mng Dir)*

ATL TELECOM LIMITED

Lakeside Fountain Ln
Cardiff, St Mellons, CF3 OFB, United Kingdom
Tel.: (44) 2920500700
Fax: (44) 2920500701
Web Site: www.atltelecom.com
Year Founded: 2001
Emp.: 30

Business Description:
Convergent Voice & Data Products Mfr for Telecommunications Industry
S.I.C.: 4812
N.A.I.C.S.: 517210

Personnel:
Johnathan Nicholas Harrison *(CEO)*

ATLAN HOLDINGS BERHAD

16th Floor Menara Atlan 161-B Jalan Ampang
50450 Kuala Lumpur, Malaysia
Tel.: (60) 321792000
Fax: (60) 321792179
E-Mail: info@atlan.com.my
Web Site: www.atlan.com.my
ATLAN—(KLS)
Rev.: $240,303,383
Assets: $289,999,003
Liabilities: $125,444,484
Net Worth: $164,554,519
Earnings: $29,803,337
Fiscal Year-end: 02/28/13

Business Description:
Property Investment & Development Services
S.I.C.: 6531
N.A.I.C.S.: 531311

Personnel:
Bok Siong Ong *(Mng Dir)*
Siew Chuan Chua *(Co-Sec)*
Sook Fun Thum *(Co-Sec)*

Board of Directors:
Adam Sani Abdullah
Abdullah Ahmad
Sze Siang Lee
Bok Siong Ong
Abdul Rahman Sultan Ahmad Shah Al-Mustain Billah
Robin Yeong Ching Tan
Thiam Chai Tan
Shagul Hamid K. R. Williams
Hon Kong Woo
Mohd Sharif Yusof

Subsidiaries:

Blossom Time Sdn. Bhd. **(1)**
Lot 340 Jalan Batu Ferringhi
Bandar Batu Ferringhi, 11100 Penang, Malaysia
Tel.: (60) 48811340
Fax: (60) 48811350
E-Mail: bt2u@bt.atlan.com.my
Web Site: www.blossomtime.com.my
Emp.: 5
Residential Property Development Services
S.I.C.: 6531
N.A.I.C.S.: 531210
B. S. Ong *(Exec Dir)*

Naluri Corporation Berhad **(1)**
16th Floor Menara Naluri 161B Jalan Ampang
Kuala Lumpur, 50450, Malaysia
Tel.: (60) 321792000
Fax: (60) 321792179
E-Mail: customerservice@mpsb.atlan.com.my
Web Site: www.atlan.com.my
Emp.: 70
Real Estate Property Development Services
S.I.C.: 6531
N.A.I.C.S.: 531210
Adam Sani Abdullah *(Chm)*
Lee Sze Siang *(Mng Dir)*
Teo Beewee *(Co-Sec)*

Naluri Properties Sdn. Bhd. **(1)**
161-D Jalan Ampang
50450 Kuala Lumpur, Malaysia
Tel.: (60) 3 2164 8000
Fax: (60) 3 2164 1000
Real Estate Property Development & Hotel Management Services
S.I.C.: 6531
N.A.I.C.S.: 531210
Thiang Yang Hian *(Mng Dir)*

United Industries Holdings Sdn. Bhd. **(1)**
Bangunan United Industries S/B 5 1/2 Miles Jalan Meru
Kelang, Selangor, 41050, Malaysia
Tel.: (60) 333922911
Fax: (60) 333929344
Web Site: www.uisb.com
Management Services
S.I.C.: 8741
N.A.I.C.S.: 551114
Bernard Ng *(Mng Dir)*

Subsidiary:

United Industries Sdn. Bhd. **(2)**
Bangunan United Industries 5 1/2 Miles Jalan Meru
41050 Kelang, Selangor Darul Ehsan, Malaysia
Tel.: (60) 333922911
Fax: (60) 333921632
E-Mail: uimarketing@uisb.com
Web Site: www.uisb.com
Automotive Components Mfr
S.I.C.: 3714
N.A.I.C.S.: 336310

Non-U.S. Subsidiary:

Duty Free International Limited **(1)**
6 Battery Road 10-01
Singapore, 049909, Singapore (81.15%)
Tel.: (65) 6381 6966
Fax: (65) 6381 6967
E-Mail: dfi@listedcompany.com
Web Site: www.dfi.com.sg
5SO—(CAT)
Rev.: $176,811,185
Assets: $191,023,893
Liabilities: $79,179,235
Net Worth: $111,844,658
Earnings: $24,019,484
Fiscal Year-end: 02/28/13
Duty-Free Stores Operator
S.I.C.: 5999
N.A.I.C.S.: 453998

Lip Piau Saw *(CEO)*
Bok Siong Ong *(Mng Dir)*
Shirley Sey Liy Tan *(Sec)*

Non-U.S. Subsidiary:

DFZ Capital Berhad **(2)**
Wisma Atlan
8 Persiaran Kampung Jawa
11900 Bayan Lepas, Penang, Malaysia (100%)
Tel.: (60) 46413200
Fax: (60) 46423200
E-Mail: enquiry@dfzcapital.com.my
Web Site: www.dfzcapital.com.my
Sales Range: $150-199.9 Million
Holding Company; Real Estate & Travel Services
S.I.C.: 6719
N.A.I.C.S.: 551112
Sook Fun Thum *(Sec)*

ATLANTA GOLD INC.

First Canadian Place 5600
100 King Street West, Toronto, ON, M5X 1C9, Canada
Tel.: (416) 777-0013
Fax: (416) 777-0014
E-Mail: info@atgoldinc.com
Web Site: www.atgoldinc.com
ATG—(OTC TSX)
Assets: $44,749,674
Liabilities: $7,307,005
Net Worth: $37,442,669
Earnings: ($3,707,070)
Fiscal Year-end: 12/31/12

Business Description:
Gold Ore Mining
S.I.C.: 1041
N.A.I.C.S.: 212221

Personnel:
James K. Gray *(Chm)*
W. Warren Holmes *(Vice Chm)*
Ernest Simmons *(Pres & CEO)*
William James Charles Baird *(CFO & VP)*
Paul Collins *(Sec)*

Board of Directors:
James K. Gray
William James Charles Baird
Eric J. Berentsen
Allan J. Folk
W. Warren Holmes
John D. Jackson

Legal Counsel:
Lang Michener
BCE Place Box 747
181 Bay St., Ste. 2500
Toronto, ON, M5J 2T7, Canada

Transfer Agent:
Equity Financial Trust Company
200 University Avenue Suite 400
Toronto, ON, M5H 4H1, Canada
Tel.: (416) 361-0152
Fax: (416) 361-0470
Toll Free: (866) 393-4891

U.S. Subsidiary:

Atlanta Gold Idaho **(1)**
2417 Bank Dr Ste 101
Boise, ID 83705
Tel.: (208) 424-3343
Fax: (208) 338-6513
Web Site: www.atgoldinc.com
Gold Mining Services
S.I.C.: 1041
N.A.I.C.S.: 212221
Wm. Ernest Simmons *(Pres & CEO)*

ATLANTA LIMITED

101 Shree Amba Shanti Chambers
Andheri-Kurla Road Opp Hotel Leela
Andheri E, Mumbai, 400059, India
Tel.: (91) 2229252929
Fax: (91) 2229252900
E-Mail: mail@atlantainfra.com
Web Site: www.atlantainfra.co.in
532759—(BOM)
Rev.: $52,612,522
Assets: $257,260,202
Liabilities: $150,710,462
Net Worth: $106,549,740
Earnings: ($719,681)
Emp.: 136
Fiscal Year-end: 03/31/13

Business Description:
Infrastructure Development, Mining & Real Estate Services
S.I.C.: 1542
N.A.I.C.S.: 236220

Personnel:
Rajhoo Bbarot *(Chm & Co-Mng Dir)*
Rikiin Bbarot *(Co-Mng Dir)*
Bakul Desai *(CFO)*
Narayan R. Joshi *(Sec)*

Board of Directors:
Rajhoo Bbarot
Rikiin Bbarot
Arpan Brahmbhatt
Samir Degan
Vipul Desai

Transfer Agent:
Karvy Computershare Private Limited
Plot No 17 to 24 Vittalrao Nagar Madhapur
Hyderabad, India

ATLANTIA S.P.A.

via Antonio Nibby 20
00161 Rome, Italy
Tel.: (39) 0644172699
Fax: (39) 0644172696
E-Mail: investor.relations@atlantia.it
Web Site: www.atlantia.it
Year Founded: 1956
ATL—(ITA OTC)
Rev.: $6,867,148,366
Assets: $40,898,829,434
Liabilities: $33,564,552,001
Net Worth: $7,334,277,433
Earnings: $1,116,750,324
Emp.: 11,411
Fiscal Year-end: 12/31/12

Business Description:
Holding Company; Motorway Concession & Construction Services
S.I.C.: 4789
N.A.I.C.S.: 488490

Personnel:
Fabio Cerchiai *(Chm)*
Giovanni Castellucci *(CEO)*
Giancarlo Guenzi *(CFO)*
Andrea Grillo *(Sec)*

Board of Directors:
Fabio Cerchiai
Gilberto Benetton
Alessandro Bertani
Alberto Bombassei
Stefano Cao
Giovanni Castellucci
Roberto Giovanni Maria Cera
Alberto Clo
Antonio Fassone
Giuliano Mari
Gianni Mion
Monica Mondardini
Giuseppe Piaggio
Antonino Turicchi
Paolo Zannoni

Subsidiaries:

Autostrade per l'Italia S.p.A. **(1)**
Via Bergamini 50
00159 Rome, Italy (100%)
Tel.: (39) 0643631
Fax: (39) 0643634090
Web Site: www.autostrade.it
Toll Motorway Builder & Operator
S.I.C.: 1611
N.A.I.C.S.: 237310
Giovanni Castellucci *(CEO)*

Generale Mobiliare Interessenze Azionarie S.p.A. **(1)**
Via dell'Aeroporto di Fiumicino n 320
Fiumicino, MI, Italy
Tel.: (39) 06659525777
Fax: (39) 06659525790
E-Mail: investor.relator@gemina.it
Web Site: www.gemina.it
Rev.: $755,847,532
Assets: $5,443,418,782
Liabilities: $3,027,567,292
Net Worth: $2,415,851,490
Earnings: $274,599,834
Emp.: 2,232
Fiscal Year-end: 12/31/12
Holding Company
S.I.C.: 6719
N.A.I.C.S.: 551112
Fabrizio Palenzona *(Chm)*
Carlo Bertazzo *(Mng Dir)*

Subsidiaries:

Aeroporti di Roma S.p.A. **(2)**
Via dell Aeroporto di Fiumicino 320
00054 Fiumicino, Italy IT
Tel.: (39) 0665951 (95.89%)
Fax: (39) 0665953646
E-Mail: aeroportidiroma@adr.it
Web Site: www.adr.it
Rev.: $841,249,903
Assets: $3,640,215,990
Liabilities: $2,219,130,283
Net Worth: $1,421,085,707
Earnings: $354,181,366
Emp.: 2,227
Fiscal Year-end: 12/31/12
Airport Management Services
S.I.C.: 4581
N.A.I.C.S.: 488119
Fabrizio Palenzona *(Chm)*
Carlo Bertazzo *(Deputy Chm)*
Lorenzo Lo Presti *(CEO & Mng Dir)*
Antonio Sanna *(Sec)*

Subsidiaries:

ADR Advertising S.p.A. **(3)**
Torre Uffici 1
Aeroporto Leonardo da Vinci, 00054 Fiumicino, Rome, Italy
Tel.: (39) 665951
E-Mail: info@adradvertising.it
Web Site: www.adradvertising.it
Emp.: 7
Airport Advertising Services
S.I.C.: 7311
N.A.I.C.S.: 541810
Massimo Pini *(Pres)*

ADR Tel S.p.A. **(3)**
Via Dell Aeroporto Di Fiumicino 320
00054 Fiumicino, Rome, Italy
Tel.: (39) 665951
E-Mail: info@adrtel.it
Web Site: www.adrtel.it
Emp.: 15
Telecommunications Services
S.I.C.: 4899
N.A.I.C.S.: 517919

Domino S.r.l. **(2)**
Via Pizzoni 3
20151 Milan, Italy
Tel.: (39) 2 3088574
Fax: (39) 2 33431579
E-Mail: info@dominosrl.it
Web Site: www.dominosrl.it
Computer Hardware & Networking Consulting Services
S.I.C.: 7379
N.A.I.C.S.: 541519

ATLANTIC AIRWAYS

Vagar Airport
FO-380 Sorvagur, Faroe Islands
Tel.: (298) 341000
Fax: (298) 341001
E-Mail: info@atlantic.fo
Web Site: www.atlantic.fo
Sls.: $37,881,618
Emp.: 111

Business Description:
Air Transportation Services
S.I.C.: 4512
N.A.I.C.S.: 481111

Personnel:
Kaj Johannesen *(Vice Chm)*
Marius Davidsen *(CFO)*
Joen Remmer *(COO)*

Board of Directors:
Bjarni Askham Bjarnason
Petur J. Eiriksson
Ingi S. Joensen
Kaj Johannesen
Verna Resmussen

ATLANTIC BRIDGE VENTURES

31 Kildare Street
Dublin, 2, Ireland
Tel.: (353) 16034450
Fax: (353) 16425661
E-Mail: info@abzen.com
Web Site: www.abzen.com
Emp.: 10

Business Description:
Private Equity Firm
S.I.C.: 6211
N.A.I.C.S.: 523999

Personnel:
Peter Mcmanamon *(Chm)*

Board of Directors:
Peter Mcmanamon

Non-U.S. Holding:

Acision Ltd. **(1)**
1430 Arlington Business Park
Theale, Reading, RG7 4SA, United Kingdom
Tel.: (44) 845 003 7151
Web Site: www.acision.com
Sales Range: $600-649.9 Million
Emp.: 160
Mobile Data Services
S.I.C.: 4812
N.A.I.C.S.: 517210
Didier Bench *(Chm)*
Adolfo Hernandez *(CEO)*
Karen Griffiths *(CFO)*
J. F. Sullivan *(CMO)*
Andrew Littlejohns *(Gen Counsel & Exec VP-Bus Ops)*
Rob Bellis *(Exec VP-Global Svcs)*
Matt Cockett *(Exec VP-Enterprise Svcs)*
Henk de Boer *(Exec VP-Strategy, Tech & Partners)*
Sherif Hamoudah *(Exec VP-Global Sls)*
Pavel Pokorny *(Exec VP-R&D)*
Jim Saunders *(Exec VP-Engrg)*
Janet Turner *(Exec VP-HR)*
Marco Wanders *(Exec VP-Products)*
Michael Frausing *(Sr VP & Gen Mgr-Asia Pacific)*
Russell Grahame *(Sr VP & Gen Mgr-North America)*
David Huguet *(Sr VP & Gen Mgr-Middle East, Africa & Pakistan)*
Glen Murray *(Sr VP & Gen Mgr-Europe & Russia)*
Fatima Raimondi *(Sr VP & Gen Mgr-Latin America)*

U.S. Subsidiaries:

Acision LLC **(2)**
6404 International Pkwy Ste 2048
Plano, TX 75093-8246
Tel.: (972) 246-5400
Fax: (214) 599-1001
Toll Free: (888) 8AETHOS
Emp.: 142
Mobile Data Services
S.I.C.: 4812
N.A.I.C.S.: 517210
Russell Grahame *(Sr VP & Gen Mgr-North America)*

Acision LLC **(2)**
4870 Sadler Rd Ste 200
Glen Allen, VA 23060
Tel.: (804) 762-5500
Fax: (804) 762-5540
Emp.: 70
Mobile Data Services
S.I.C.: 4812
N.A.I.C.S.: 517210
Debbie Secrist *(Mgr-HR)*

ATLANTIC COAL PLC

43 Old Elvet
Durham, DH1 3HN, United Kingdom
Tel.: (44) 2070168837
Fax: (44) 2070169100
E-Mail: enquiries@atlanticcoal.com
Web Site: www.atlanticcoal.com

Atlantic Coal PLC—(Continued)

ATC—(AIM OTC)
Rev.: $19,657,105
Assets: $27,439,195
Liabilities: $15,984,041
Net Worth: $11,455,154
Earnings: ($2,661,557)
Emp.: 81
Fiscal Year-end: 12/31/12

Business Description:
Mining Industry
S.I.C.: 1499
N.A.I.C.S.: 212399

Personnel:
Stephen Best *(Mng Dir)*

Board of Directors:
Adam Wilson
Stephen Best
Peter Chinneck
Edward Nelson

Legal Counsel:
Norris Mclaughlin & Marcus
721 Route 202-206
Bridgewater, NJ 08807

Kerman & Co. LLP
200 Strand
London, EC1V 9EE, United Kingdom

U.S. Subsidiary:

Coal Contractors (1991) Inc (1)
100 Hasel Brook Rd
Hazleton, PA 18201
Tel.: (570) 450-5086
Fax: (570) 450-5088
Emp.: 70
Anthracite Mining Services
S.I.C.: 1231
N.A.I.C.S.: 212113
Stephen Best *(Pres)*
Raymond Petrilla *(CFO)*

ATLANTIC GOLD NL

Suite 506 815 Pacific Highway
Chatswood, NSW, 2067, Australia
Tel.: (61) 294100993
Fax: (61) 294100958
E-Mail: enquiries@atlanticgold.com.au
Web Site: www.atlanticgold.com.au
ATV—(ASX)
Rev.: $33,098
Assets: $27,124,656
Liabilities: $1,554,886
Net Worth: $25,569,770
Earnings: ($1,858,225)
Emp.: 3
Fiscal Year-end: 12/31/12

Business Description:
Minerals Exploration Services
S.I.C.: 1481
N.A.I.C.S.: 213115

Personnel:
Wally R. Bucknell *(CEO & Mng Dir)*
Julie Fidler *(Sec)*

Board of Directors:
Ronald J. Hawkes
Wally R. Bucknell
Rodney J. Hanson
Robert H. N. Symons

Legal Counsel:
Norton Rose Australia
RACV Tower 485 Bourke Street
Melbourne, Vic, 3000, Australia

ATLANTIC GROUP

Tonningsgt 19
6006 Alesund, Norway

Mailing Address:
Postbox 410
6001 Alesund, Norway
Tel.: (47) 70101800
Fax: (47) 70101810
Web Site: www.atlantic.no
Emp.: 20

Business Description:
Holding Company
S.I.C.: 6719
N.A.I.C.S.: 551112

Personnel:
Ove Godo *(Gen Mgr)*

Subsidiary:

Atlantic Seafood AS (1)
Tonningsgatan 19
6006 Alesund, Norway NO
Tel.: (47) 70101800
Telex: 42758
Fax: (47) 70101820
E-Mail: monika.midtbo@atlantic.no
Web Site: www.atlantic.no
Emp.: 4
Seafood Purchaser & Whslr
S.I.C.: 5421
N.A.I.C.S.: 445220
Karen Folland *(Controller)*

ATLANTIC GRUPA D.D.

Miramarska 23
10000 Zagreb, Croatia
Tel.: (385) 12413900
Fax: (385) 12413901
E-Mail: grupa@atlanticgrupa.com
Web Site: www.atlanticgrupa.com
ATGR-R-A—(ZAG)
Rev.: $889,524,562
Assets: $915,119,600
Liabilities: $655,420,248
Net Worth: $259,699,352
Earnings: $11,748,764
Emp.: 4,247
Fiscal Year-end: 12/31/12

Business Description:
Sports Food & Vitamin Instant Drinks Producer
S.I.C.: 2834
N.A.I.C.S.: 325412

Personnel:
Zdenko Adrovic *(Chm-Supervisory Bd)*
Lada Tedeschi Fiorio *(Vice Chm-Supervisory Bd)*
Emil Tedeschi *(Pres, CEO & Member-Mgmt Bd)*
Mladen Veber *(Member-Mgmt Bd & Sr VP-Bus Ops)*
Zoran Stankovic *(Member-Mgmt Bd & VP-Fin)*
Neven Vrankovic *(Member-Mgmt Bd & VP-Corp Affairs)*

Supervisory Board of Directors:
Zdenko Adrovic
Lada Tedeschi Fiorio
Franz-Josef Flosbach
Vedrana Jelusic-Kasic
Sasa Pekec
Zeljko Peric
Sinisa Petrovic

Subsidiaries:

Cedevita d.o.o. (1)
Planinska bb 15
10000 Zagreb, Croatia
Tel.: (385) 12413600
Fax: (385) 12413506
E-Mail: dr.cedevita@cedevita.hr
Web Site: www.cedevita.hr
Nutritional Drinks Mfr
S.I.C.: 2023
N.A.I.C.S.: 311514

Non-U.S. Subsidiary:

Multivita d.o.o. (2)
Beogradski put bb
Vrsac, Vojvodina, 26300, Serbia
Tel.: (381) 13 803 448
Fax: (381) 13 803 385
E-Mail: info@multivita.co.rs
Web Site: www.multivita.co.rs
Nutrition Products Whslr
S.I.C.: 5149
N.A.I.C.S.: 424490

Farmacia Plus d.o.o. (1)
Avenija Gojka Suska 6
10000 Zagreb, Croatia
Tel.: (385) 12988684
Fax: (385) 1 2902 754
Emp.: 2
Nutritional Drinks Mfr
S.I.C.: 2023
N.A.I.C.S.: 311514
Erinoslav Rantes *(Mgr-Drug Store)*

Fidifarm d.o.o. (1)
Obrtnicka 37
10437 Rakitje, Zagreb, Croatia
Tel.: (385) 12413800
Fax: (385) 12413835
E-Mail: fidifarm@atlantic.hr
Web Site: www.dietpharm.hr
Emp.: 79
Nutritional & Dietary Drinks Mfr
S.I.C.: 2023
N.A.I.C.S.: 311514

ZU Ljekarne Bamapharm (1)
Jurisiceva 3
Zagreb, 10000, Croatia
Tel.: (385) 14882300
Fax: (385) 14882343
E-Mail: dario.kovacic@atlanticgrupa.com
Web Site: www.farmacia.hr
Pharmaceutical Products Distr
S.I.C.: 5122
N.A.I.C.S.: 424210

Non-U.S. Division:

Droga Kolinska d.d. (1)
Kolinska ulica 1
1544 Ljubljana, Slovenia
Tel.: (386) 14721500
Fax: (386) 14721553
E-Mail: info@drogakolinska.com
Web Site: www.atlanticagrupa.com
Sales Range: $250-299.9 Million
Emp.: 447
Food Processing Services
S.I.C.: 2034
N.A.I.C.S.: 311423
Srecko Nakic *(Pres)*

Non-U.S. Subsidiaries:

AKTIVKOST Handelsgesellschaft mbH (1)
Moorfuhrtweg 17
22301 Hamburg, Germany
Tel.: (49) 402986601
Fax: (49) 4029866100
E-Mail: info@atlantic-multipower.de
Web Site: www.atlantic-multipower.de
Emp.: 80
Dietary Products Mfr
S.I.C.: 2023
N.A.I.C.S.: 311514
Alenka Klarica *(Mng Dir)*

Atlantic Multipower GmbH & Co. OHG (1)
Moorfuhrtweg 17
22301 Hamburg, Germany
Tel.: (49) 402986601
Fax: (49) 4029866100
E-Mail: info@atlantic-multipower.de
Web Site: www.atlantic-multipower.de
Sales Range: $75-99.9 Million
Emp.: 200
Sports Food Distr
S.I.C.: 5149
N.A.I.C.S.: 424490
Neven Vrankovic *(Mng Dir)*

Non-U.S. Subsidiaries:

Atlantic Multipower Srl (2)
Via Proflis Don A Dalla Torre 8/5 ZI Levada
31047 Ponte di Piave, Treviso, Italy
Tel.: (39) 0422852076
Fax: (39) 0422852906
E-Mail: info@atlantic-multipower.it
Emp.: 8
Sports Foods Distr
S.I.C.: 5149
N.A.I.C.S.: 424490
Giuseppe Virzi *(Dir-Comml)*

Atlantic Multipower UK Ltd (2)
Robert Denholm House Bletchingley Road
Nutfield, Surrey, RH1 4 HW, United Kingdom
Tel.: (44) 1737821840
Fax: (44) 1737822293
E-Mail: enquiries@multipoweruk.com
Web Site: www.multipoweruk.com
Emp.: 14
Sports Foods Distr
S.I.C.: 5149
N.A.I.C.S.: 424490
David Hannah *(Mng Dir)*

Atlantic s.r.l. (1)
Via Giambologna 1
20096 Pioltello, Milan, Italy
Tel.: (39) 02923671
Fax: (39) 0292161660
Dietary Drinks Distr
S.I.C.: 2023
N.A.I.C.S.: 311514

Atlantic Trade d.o.o., Ljubljana (1)
98 Koprska Ulica
Ljubljana, 1000, Slovenia
Tel.: (386) 15305570
Fax: (386) 15305576
E-Mail: info@atlantic-trade.com
Web Site: www.atlantic.hr/en/kontakt
Emp.: 12
Sports Foods Distr
S.I.C.: 5149
N.A.I.C.S.: 424490
Bogdan Slovnik *(Gen Mgr)*

ATLANTIC INSURANCE COMPANY PUBLIC LTD

15 Esperidon Str
2001 Strovolos, Cyprus
Tel.: (357) 22 886000
Fax: (357) 22 886111
E-Mail: atlantic@atlantic.com.cy
Web Site: www.atlantic.com.cy
Year Founded: 1983
ATL—(CYP)

Business Description:
Insurance Services
S.I.C.: 6411
N.A.I.C.S.: 524298

Personnel:
Emilios Pyrishis *(Chm & Mng Dir)*
Andreas Pirishis *(Sec, VP & Mgr-Corp & HR)*

Board of Directors:
Emilios Pyrishis
Charalambos Alexandrou
Andreas Frangoullis
Triantafyllos Lysimachou
Panayiotis Mallis
Andreas Pirishis
Nina Pyrishi
George Pyrishis
Marios Savvides

ATLANTIC LTD.

Level 29 Bankwest Tower 108 St Georges Terrace
Perth, WA, 6000, Australia
Tel.: (61) 8 6141 7100
Fax: (61) 8 6141 7101
E-Mail: info@atlanticltd.com.au
Web Site: atlanticltd.com.au
ATI—(ASX)
Rev.: $640,892
Assets: $560,033,919
Liabilities: $589,373,202
Net Worth: ($29,339,283)
Earnings: ($130,459,457)
Emp.: 168
Fiscal Year-end: 06/30/13

Business Description:
Mineral Exploration & Mining Services
S.I.C.: 1499
N.A.I.C.S.: 212399

Personnel:
Michael Minosora *(Chm & Mng Dir)*
Scott Nicholas *(CFO)*
Daniel Harris *(COO)*
Terry Bourke *(Gen Counsel)*
Anthony Veitch *(Sec)*

Board of Directors:
Michael Minosora
Michael John Daniel
Phiong Phillipus Darma

Bradley James Ellis
Anthony Veitch
Legal Counsel:
Blake Dawson
Level 32 Exchange Plaza 2 The Esplanade
Perth, Australia

ATLANTIC LOTTERY CORPORATION

922 Main
PO Box 5500
Moncton, NB, E1C 8W6, Canada
Tel.: (506) 867-5800
Fax: (506) 867-5439
Toll Free: (800) 561-3942
Web Site: www.alc.ca
Rev.: $1,041,785,643
Assets: $256,855,762
Liabilities: $321,637,039
Net Worth: ($64,781,277)
Earnings: $360,457,497
Emp.: 600
Fiscal Year-end: 03/31/13
Business Description:
Lottery Gaming Services
S.I.C.: 7999
N.A.I.C.S.: 713990
Personnel:
C. Sean O'Connor *(Chm)*
Patricia J. Mella *(Vice Chm)*
Brent Scrimshaw *(Pres & CEO)*
Patrick Daigle *(CFO)*
Jim Porter *(CTO)*
Michael Foley *(Chief Comml Officer-Lottery & Gaming)*
Doug Clow *(Sec)*
Board of Directors:
C. Sean O'Connor
Peter Au
Kevin Breen
Doug Clow
Wallace Floyd
Jane Garbutt
Gordon Gillis
Patricia J. Mella
Stephen Mont

ATLANTIC PACKAGING PRODUCTS LTD.

111 Progress Ave
Scarborough, ON, M1P 2Y9, Canada
Tel.: (416) 298-8101
Fax: (416) 297-2236
Toll Free: (800) 268-5620
Web Site: www.atlantic.ca
Emp.: 2,500
Business Description:
Manufacturing & Distribution Services
S.I.C.: 7389
N.A.I.C.S.: 561910
Personnel:
Irving Granovsky *(Chm)*
John Cherry *(Pres)*
Dahra Granovsky *(Member-Mgmt Bd)*

ATLANTIC PROMOTIONS INC.

(d/b/a Les Promotions Atlantiques Inc.)
770 boul Guimond
Longueuil, QC, J4G 1V6, Canada
Tel.: (514) 871-1095
Fax: (450) 651-2344
Toll Free: (800) 361-6232
E-Mail: information@starfrit.com
Web Site: www.starfrit.com
Year Founded: 1965
Rev.: $25,000,000
Emp.: 100
Business Description:
Kitchen Products Distr
S.I.C.: 5023
N.A.I.C.S.: 423220
Personnel:
Jacques Gatien *(Founder & Pres)*

ATLANTIC SOC FRANCAISE DEVELOP THERMIQUE S.A.

(d/b/a Atlantic SFDT)
44 Boulevard des Etats Unis
BP 65
F-85000 La Roche-sur-Yon, Cedex, France
Tel.: (33) 251443434
Fax: (33) 251362959
Sales Range: $1-4.9 Billion
Emp.: 3,000
Business Description:
Holding Company; Residential, Commercial & Industrial Heating, Ventilation, Air-Conditioning & Water Heating Equipment Designer & Mfr
Export
S.I.C.: 6719
N.A.I.C.S.: 551112
Personnel:
Jean-Pierre Lamoure *(Chm-Supervisory Bd)*
Pierre-Louis Francois *(Pres)*
Supervisory Board of Directors:
Jean-Pierre Lamoure
Pierre Lavazay

Divisions:

Atlantic SFDT (1)
58 avenue du General Leclerc
F-92340 Bourg-la-Reine, France
Tel.: (33) 146836000
Fax: (33) 146836008
E-Mail: info.atlantic.tm.fr@groupe-atlantic.com
Web Site: www.atlantic.tm.fr
Emp.: 4,000
Residential, Commercial & Industrial Heating, Ventilation, Air-Conditioning & Water Heating Equipment Designer & Mfr
S.I.C.: 3585
N.A.I.C.S.: 333415
Pascale Gimeno *(Mgr-Comm)*

Units:

Atlantic Climatisation (2)
13 Blvd Monge
BP 71
F-69882 Meyzieu, Cedex, France
Tel.: (33) 472451100
Fax: (33) 472451111
Web Site: www.atlantic-climatisation.com
Emp.: 300
Air Conditioning Equipment Mfr & Distr
S.I.C.: 3585
N.A.I.C.S.: 333415
Eric Bataille *(Mgr-Mktg)*

Atlantic Franco Belge (2)
58 Ave du General Leclerc
F-92340 Bourg-la-Reine, France
Tel.: (33) 146836000
Fax: (33) 146836001
E-Mail: contact@atlantic-francobelge.fr
Web Site: www.atlantic-francobelge.fr
Emp.: 150
Hot Water Heaters & Boilers Mfr, Distr & Services
S.I.C.: 3443
N.A.I.C.S.: 332410
Marek Darhol *(Gen Mgr-Intl Dept)*

Atlantic Guillot (2)
58 avenue du General Leclerc
F-92340 Bourg-la-Reine, France
Tel.: (33) 146836000
Fax: (33) 146836001
E-Mail: contact@atlantic-guillot.fr
Web Site: www.atlantic-comfort.com
Emp.: 100
Commercial & Industrial Boilers Mfr, Distr & Services
S.I.C.: 3559
N.A.I.C.S.: 332410
Jilles Romagne *(Mgr-Intl Sls)*

Atlantic Ventilation (2)
13 Boulevard Monge
BP 71
F-69882 Meyzieu, Cedex, France
Tel.: (33) 4 7245 1100
Fax: (33) 4 7245 1111
Web Site: www.atlantic-ventilation.fr
Ventilation Equipment Mfr & Distr
S.I.C.: 3564
N.A.I.C.S.: 333413

Thermor (1)
17 rue Croix Fauchet
BP 46
F-45141 Saint-Jean-de-la-Ruelle, Cedex, France
Tel.: (33) 238713871
Fax: (33) 238713893
E-Mail: pgalloen@tm.thermo.fr
Web Site: www.thermor.tm.fr
Emp.: 100
Electric Heaters & Bathroom Products Mfr & Distr
S.I.C.: 3433
N.A.I.C.S.: 333414
Grereh Ghoult *(Office Mgr)*

Plant:

Ygnis Industrie (1)
Route De Solesmes
59400 Cauroir, Nord, France
Tel.: (33) 327731875
Web Site: www.ygnis.com
Emp.: 200
Residential & Commercial Boilers Mfr
S.I.C.: 3559
N.A.I.C.S.: 332410
Yves Lepelletier *(Mng Dir)*

Non-U.S. Subsidiary:

Hamworthy Heating Limited (1)
Fleets Corner
Poole, Dorset, BH17 7LA, United Kingdom UK
Tel.: (44) 1202662500
Telex: 41226 HELCD G
Fax: (44) 1202662550
E-Mail: sales@hamworthy-heating.com
Web Site: www.hamworthy-heating.com
Sales Range: $25-49.9 Million
Emp.: 150
Commercial Heating Equipment Designer & Mfr
S.I.C.: 3559
N.A.I.C.S.: 332410
Andrew John Moore *(Mng Dir)*

ATLANTIC SUPER MARKET S.A.

516 Vouliagmenis Ave
17456 Alimos Attikis, Greece
Tel.: (30) 2109971500
Fax: (30) 2109934390
Web Site: www.atlantic.gr
Sales Range: $800-899.9 Million
Emp.: 3,400
Business Description:
Supermarket Owner & Operator
S.I.C.: 5411
N.A.I.C.S.: 445110
Personnel:
Manolis Apostolou *(Chm)*
Periclis Apostolou *(Mng Dir)*
Board of Directors:
Manolis Apostolou
Elpida Apostolou
Ioannis Pilidis

Subsidiary:

VITA PI S.A. (1)
13th Klm Thessaloniki-Veria Old National Road
54623 Thessaloniki, Greece
Tel.: (30) 2310722799
Fax: (30) 2310722464
Soft Drinks Whslr
S.I.C.: 5149
N.A.I.C.S.: 424490

ATLANTIC WIND & SOLAR INC.

2 Bloor Street East Suite 3500
Toronto, ON, M4W 1A8, Canada
Tel.: (416) 900-0380
Fax: (416) 900-0381
Toll Free: (800) 891-1657
E-Mail: info@atlanticwindandsolar.com
Web Site: www.atlanticwindandsolar.com
AWSL—(OTC)
Rev.: $1,886,000
Assets: $1,541,000
Liabilities: $1,850,000
Net Worth: ($309,000)
Earnings: ($347,000)
Fiscal Year-end: 12/31/12
Business Description:
Wind & Solar Electric Power
S.I.C.: 4939
N.A.I.C.S.: 221115
Personnel:
Gilles Andre Trahan *(Chm, Pres & CEO)*
Martin W. Baldwin *(CFO & Treas)*
Board of Directors:
Gilles Andre Trahan
Martin W. Baldwin
Luc C. Duchesne

ATLANTIC ZEISER GMBH & CO.

Bogenstrasse 6 8
D 78576 Emmengen, Germany
Tel.: (49) 74652910
Fax: (49) 7465291166
E-Mail: support@atlanticzeiser.com
Web Site: www.atlanticzeiser.com
Year Founded: 1997
Sales Range: $50-74.9 Million
Emp.: 350
Business Description:
Supplier of Technology Solutions for the Numbering, Printing, Encoding & Information Processing Industries
Export
S.I.C.: 7389
N.A.I.C.S.: 561910
Personnel:
Manfred Minich *(CEO)*

U.S. Subsidiary:

Atlantic Zeiser, Inc. (1)
15 Patton Dr
West Caldwell, NJ 07006-6404
Tel.: (973) 228-0800
Fax: (973) 228-9064
E-Mail: Sales@AtlanticZeiserUSA.com
Web Site: www.atlanticzeiserusa.com
Emp.: 100
Supplier of Technology for The Numbering, Printing, Encoding & Information Processing Industries
S.I.C.: 3589
N.A.I.C.S.: 333318
Thomas Coco *(Pres)*

Non-U.S. Subsidiaries:

Atlantic Zeiser Ltd (1)
53 Central Way
Andover, Hampshire, SP10 5AN, United Kingdom
Tel.: (44) 1264324222
Fax: (44) 1264324333
E-Mail: sales@atlanticzeiserUK.com
Web Site: www.atlanticzeiserUK.com
Emp.: 23
Photographic Equipment & Supplies Whslr
S.I.C.: 5043
N.A.I.C.S.: 423410
R. Lewin *(Mng Dir)*

Atlantic Zeiser S.A. (1)
C/ Manuel Pombo Angulo 12 3a Planta Oficina 6
28050 Madrid, Spain
Tel.: (34) 914336661
Fax: (34) 915528916
E-Mail: az_spain@atlanticzeiser.es
Web Site: www.atlanticzeiser.es
Emp.: 10
Industrial Machinery Whslr
S.I.C.: 5084
N.A.I.C.S.: 423830
Georg Schillinger *(Pres)*

Atlantic Zeiser S.A.S. (1)
21-23 rue Eugene Dupuis-Europarc
94043 Creteil, France

Atlantic Zeiser GmbH & Co.—(Continued)

Tel.: (33) 156711309
Fax: (33) 143774430
E-Mail: info@atlanticzeiser.fr
Web Site: www.atlanticzeiser.fr
Emp.: 10
Industrial Machinery Whslr
S.I.C.: 5084
N.A.I.C.S.: 423830
Minich Manfred *(CEO)*

Atlantic Zeiser Srl (1)
Via Varesina 174
20156 Milan, Italy
Tel.: (39) 0233497740
Fax: (39) 0233401413
E-Mail: info@atlanticzeiser.it
Web Site: www.atlanticzeiser.it
Emp.: 12
Durable Goods Merchant Whslr
S.I.C.: 5099
N.A.I.C.S.: 423990
Luigi Rescaldani *(Gen Mgr)*

Beijing Atlantic Zeiser Tech Co. Ltd. (1)
2nd Fl Unit C Jing Chang High-Tech Info Industrial Pk No 97
ChangPing Rd Chang Ping Dist, 102206 Beijing, China
Tel.: (86) 1082893051
Fax: (86) 1082893238
Web Site: www.atlanticzeiser.com
Emp.: 13
Industrial Machinery Mfr
S.I.C.: 3589
N.A.I.C.S.: 333318
Li Fong *(Pres)*

ATLANTIS RESOURCES LIMITED

65 Niven Road
Singapore, 228414, Singapore
Tel.: (65) 6238 6002
Web Site: www.atlantisresourcesltd.com
ARL—(AIM)
Business Description:
Power Generation Structures Mfr & Services
S.I.C.: 1623
N.A.I.C.S.: 237130
Personnel:
Timothy James Cornelius *(CEO)*

ATLANTIS SUBMARINES INTERNATIONAL INC.

(d/b/a Atlantis Adventures)
210 W 6th Ave Ste 200
Vancouver, BC, V5Y 1K8, Canada
Tel.: (604) 875-1367
Fax: (604) 875-0833
E-Mail: resv@atlantissubmarines.com
Web Site: www.atlantissubmarines.com
Year Founded: 1983
Emp.: 10
Business Description:
Holding Company; Undersea Tour Services
S.I.C.: 6719
N.A.I.C.S.: 551112
Personnel:
Dennis Hurd *(Founder, Pres & CEO)*

U.S. Subsidiary:

Atlantis Submarines Hawaii, Inc. (1)
1600 Kapiolani Blvd
Honolulu, HI 96814 OH
Tel.: (808) 973-9800
Fax: (808) 973-9840
Web Site: www.atlantisadventures.com
Sales Range: $25-49.9 Million
Emp.: 200
Undersea Tour Services
Import Export
S.I.C.: 4725
N.A.I.C.S.: 561520
David Runyon *(Chm)*
John A. Kojima *(CFO)*

ATLANTIS SYSTEMS CORP.

(Acquired by Bluedrop Performance Learning Inc.)

ATLANTSKA PLOVIDBA D.D.

Od Svetoga Mihajla 1
PO Box 192
20000 Dubrovnik, Croatia
Tel.: (385) 20 352 333
Fax: (385) 20 356 148
E-Mail: atlant@atlant.hr
Web Site: www.atlant.hr
Year Founded: 1955
ATPL—(ZAG)
Business Description:
Fleet & Cargo Handling Services
S.I.C.: 4491
N.A.I.C.S.: 488320
Personnel:
Ante Jerkovic *(Chm-Supervisory Bd)*
Pero Kulas *(Chm-Mgmt Bd)*
Niko Bratos *(Deputy Chm-Supervisory Bd)*
Marin Matana *(Member-Mgmt Bd-Ship Mgmt & DPA)*
Pavo Sisevic *(Member-Mgmt Bd-Comml Affairs)*
Dusko Vladovic-Relja *(Member-Mgmt Bd-Fin Affairs)*
Ivica Surkovic *(Sec)*
Supervisory Board of Directors:
Ante Jerkovic
Niko Bratos
Bosko Ercegovac
Vlaho Lonza
Boris Rozic
Antun Separovic
Zelimir Uskokovic

ATLAS BANGLADESH LIMITED

256-267 Tongi Industrial Area
Tongi Gazipur, Dhaka, 1710, Bangladesh
Tel.: (880) 2 980 2327
Fax: (880) 2 980 2397
E-Mail: ablhonda@bdcom.com
Web Site: www.atlas.gov.bd
Year Founded: 1966
ATLASBANG—(DHA)
Sales Range: $50-74.9 Million
Emp.: 243
Business Description:
Motor Vehicle Parts Distr
S.I.C.: 5599
N.A.I.C.S.: 441228
Personnel:
Mohammad Ataur Rahman *(Chm)*
Masud Ahmed *(Mng Dir)*
Mohammad Abul Kalam Azad *(Sec)*
Board of Directors:
Mohammad Ataur Rahman
Masud Ahmed
Nasima Akter
Akbar Ali
Mohammad Abul Kalam Azad
Aktar Hossain
Aawar Hosssain
Mohammad Saiful Islam
Mohammad Majibur Rahman
Md. Farhad Uddin

ATLAS BLOCK CO. LTD.

(Acquired by Brampton Brick Limited)

ATLAS CONSOLIDATED MINING & DEVELOPMENT CORPORATION

7th Fl Quad Alpha Centrum
PH 1554 Mandaluyong, Philippines
Tel.: (63) 26352387
Fax: (63) 6326354495
E-Mail: info@atlasphilippines.com
Web Site: www.atlasphilippines.com
Year Founded: 1953
AT—(OTC PHI)
Sales Range: $200-249.9 Million
Emp.: 60
Business Description:
Copper, Silver & Gold Mining
Import Export
S.I.C.: 1021
N.A.I.C.S.: 212234
Personnel:
Alfredo C. Ramos *(Chm & Pres)*
Martin C. Buckingham *(CFO & Exec VP)*
Constante P. Bumanglag *(COO & Sr VP)*
Noel T. Del Castillo *(Treas)*
Roderico V. Puno *(Sec)*
Adrian Paulino S. Ramos *(Exec VP)*
Board of Directors:
Alfredo C. Ramos
Gerard H. Brimo
Martin C. Buckingham
Christopher M. Gotanco
Jose C. Ibazeta
Frank N. Lubbock
Ricardo V. Quintos
Adrian Paulino S. Ramos
Felipe R. Relucio, Jr.
Alfredo R. Rosal, Jr.
Transfer Agent:
Stock Transfer Service, Inc.
Asian Bank Plaza Sen. Gil J. Puyat Avenue
Makati, Metro Manila, Philippines
Tel.: (63) 2 819 3151

Subsidiary:

ACMDC Ventures, Inc. (AVI) (1)
125 Velez Street Corner of Osmena Street
Cebu, Philippines
Tel.: (63) 322530790
E-Mail: abimla@mozcom.com
Mining
S.I.C.: 1021
N.A.I.C.S.: 212234

ATLAS CONVERTING EQUIPMENT LIMITED

Wolseley Court
Woburn Road Industrial Estate,
Kempston, Bedfordshire, MK42 7XT, United Kingdom
Tel.: (44) 1234852553
Fax: (44) 1234851151
E-Mail: sales.atlas@atlasconverting.com
Web Site: www.atlas-converting.co.uk
Year Founded: 1976
Sales Range: $50-74.9 Million
Emp.: 180
Business Description:
Converting Equipment Mfr
S.I.C.: 3553
N.A.I.C.S.: 333243
Personnel:
Stephen Darlington *(Chm)*
Alan Johnson *(Mng Dir)*

U.S. Subsidiary:

Atlas Converting North America, Inc. (1)
9801-F Southern Pine Bvld
Charlotte, NC 28273
Tel.: (704) 587-2450
Fax: (704) 587-2451
E-Mail: sales.usa@atlasconverting.com
Slitter Rewinder Distr
S.I.C.: 3569
N.A.I.C.S.: 333999

Non-U.S. Subsidiaries:

A.C.E. (Shanghai) Trading Co. Ltd. (1)
6P New Shanghai International Tower 360 South Pudong Road
Shanghai, 200120, China
Tel.: (86) 21 6886 2501
Fax: (86) 21 6886 2502
E-Mail: sales.atlas@atlasconverting.com
Emp.: 300
Slitter Rewinder Distr
S.I.C.: 3569
N.A.I.C.S.: 333999
Raymond Chan, *(Reg Mgr-Sls)*

Atlas Converting Equipment (India) Pvt. Ltd. (1)
Plant No 13 Extension Office Building
Eastern Express Highway
Pirojsha Nagar Vikhroli East, Mumbai, 400 079, India
Tel.: (91) 992 081 9791
Fax: (91) 222 623 3009
E-Mail: sales.atlas@atlasconverting.com
Emp.: 4
Slitter Rewinder Distr
S.I.C.: 3569
N.A.I.C.S.: 333999
Kavish Shah, *(Area Mgr-Sls)*

ATLAS COPCO AB

Sikla Industrivag 19
105 23 Stockholm, Sweden
Tel.: (46) 87438000
Telex: 14090 copco s
Fax: (46) 86449045
E-Mail: ir@se.atlascopco.com
Web Site: www.atlascopco.com
Year Founded: 1873
ATCO—(OMX)
Rev.: $14,014,508,400
Assets: $12,561,865,200
Liabilities: $7,123,431,600
Net Worth: $5,438,433,600
Earnings: $2,153,887,200
Emp.: 39,113
Fiscal Year-end: 12/31/12
Business Description:
Compressors, Mining & Construction Equipment & Industrial Production Equipment Mfr & Equipment Rental & Service
Import Export
S.I.C.: 5084
N.A.I.C.S.: 423830
Personnel:
Sune Carlsson *(Chm)*
Ronnie Leten *(Pres & CEO)*
Hans Ola Meyer *(CFO & Sr VP-Controlling & Fin)*
Nico Delvaux *(Pres-Construction Technique & Sr Exec VP)*
Stephan Kuhn *(Pres-Compressor Technique & Sr Exec VP)*
Mats Rahmstrom *(Pres-Indus Technique & Sr Exec VP)*
Johan Halling *(Pres-Mining & Rock Excavation Technique)*
Hakan Osvald *(Gen Counsel & Sr VP)*
Annika Berglund *(Sr VP-Corp Comm)*
Jeanette Livijin *(Sr VP-Org Dev & HR)*
Board of Directors:
Sune Carlsson
Mikael Bergstedt
Staffan Bohman
Johan Forssell
Ronnie Leten
Bengt Lindgren
Ulla Litzen
Gunilla Nordstrom
Margareth Ovrum
Anders Ullberg
Peter Wallenberg, Jr.
Transfer Agent:
Skandinaviska Enskilda Banken
Sergels Torg 2
S-106 40 Stockholm, Sweden

Subsidiaries:

Atlas Copco CMT Sweden AB (1)
Sickla Industrivag 19
Nacka, 131 54, Sweden
Tel.: (46) 87439230
Fax: (46) 86431070
Emp.: 10
Construction & Mining Machinery Distr
S.I.C.: 5082
N.A.I.C.S.: 423810
Anders Hellgren *(Mgr-Bus Line-RDT)*

Atlas Copco Compressor AB (1)
Sicklaw Industry No 19
Nacka, 131 34, Sweden
Tel.: (46) 87 43 90 00
Fax: (46) 86 44 25 45
Emp.: 10
Air Compressor Distr
S.I.C.: 5074
N.A.I.C.S.: 423720
Vladimir Kozlovski *(Gen Mgr)*

Atlas Copco Construction Tools AB (1)
Sickla Industrivag 19
131 54 Nacka, Sweden SE
Tel.: (46) 87439600 (100%)
Fax: (46) 87439650
Web Site: www.atlascopco.com
Emp.: 200
Mfr., Marketer & Distributor of Fuel-Powered Drills
S.I.C.: 3546
N.A.I.C.S.: 333991
Ronnea Leten *(Pres)*

Non-U.S. Subsidiaries:

Atlas Copco Construction Tools GmbH (2)
Helenstrasse 149
45143 Essen, Germany (100%)
Tel.: (49) 2016331569
Fax: (49) 2016331333
Sales Range: $75-99.9 Million
Emp.: 300
S.I.C.: 3325
N.A.I.C.S.: 331513

Atlas Copco Construction Tools sarl (2)
Parc GiP 4 Rue Gustave Eiffel
95190 Goussainville, France (100%)
Tel.: (33) 134047070
Fax: (33) 134047076
Emp.: 50
S.I.C.: 3325
N.A.I.C.S.: 331513

Atlas Copco Craelius (1)
Bristagatan 13
195 82 Marsta, Sweden (100%)
Tel.: (46) 858778500
Fax: (46) 859118782
E-Mail: atlascopco@craelius.com
Web Site: www.atlascopco.com
Sls.: $32,465,520
Emp.: 90
Equipment Supplier for Core Drilling & Ground Engineering Applications
S.I.C.: 3532
N.A.I.C.S.: 333131
Victor Tapia *(Mng Dir)*

Atlas Copco Customer Finance AB (1)
Sickla Industrivag 19 Nacka
105 23 Stockholm, Sweden
Tel.: (46) 8 743 83 00
Fax: (46) 8 702 21 29
E-Mail: customerfinance@atlascopco.com
Financial Management Services
S.I.C.: 6211
N.A.I.C.S.: 523999
Peter Ahlstedt *(Gen Mgr)*

Non-U.S. Subsidiaries:

Atlas Copco Customer Finance Australia Pty Ltd (2)
3 Bessemer St
Blacktown, NSW, v, Australia
Tel.: (61) 2 9621 9999
Fax: (61) 98315925
Emp.: 25
Financial Management Services
S.I.C.: 6211
N.A.I.C.S.: 523999
Joseph Varga *(Mng Dir)*

Atlas Copco Customer Finance Chile Ltda (2)
Panamericana Norte 5001
Conchali, Santiago, 6553935, Chile
Tel.: (56) 2 442 36 00
E-Mail: customerfinance@cl.atlascopco.com
Web Site: www.atlascopco.cl
Financial Management Services
S.I.C.: 6211
N.A.I.C.S.: 523999

Atlas Copco Dynapac AB (1)
Industrivagen 2
371 46 Karlskrona, Sweden SE
Tel.: (46) 455 30 6000
E-Mail: dynapacinfo@dynapac.com
Web Site: www.dynapac.com
Holding Company; Road Construction & Paving Equipment Mfr & Distr
S.I.C.: 6719
N.A.I.C.S.: 551112

Subsidiaries:

Dynapac Compaction Equipment AB (2)
Industrivagen 2
Karlskrona, 371 46, Sweden
Tel.: (46) 4 55 30 60 00
Fax: (46) 4 55 30 60 30
Web Site: www.dynapac.com
Emp.: 55
Construction Equipment Mfr & Distr
S.I.C.: 3531
N.A.I.C.S.: 333120
Wim Moors *(Gen Mgr)*

Non-U.S. Subsidiaries:

Dynapac Brasil Industria e Comercio Ltda (2)
Av Ceci 169
06460-120 Barueri, Sao Paulo, Brazil
Tel.: (55) 11 3797 2150
Fax: (55) 11 3797 2172
Industrial Machinery Distr
S.I.C.: 5084
N.A.I.C.S.: 423830

Dynapac France SNC (2)
2 rue de l Industrie BT-50048
ZI de la Petite Motte, F-77220 Tournan-en-Brie, France
Mailing Address:
BP 22
F-77222 Tournan-en-Brie, Cedex, France
Tel.: (33) 164425900
Fax: (33) 164064168
E-Mail: dynapac.france@dynapac.com
Web Site: www.dynapac.com
Emp.: 25
Compaction & Paving Equipment Mfr
S.I.C.: 3531
N.A.I.C.S.: 333120
Jraime Mckalzie *(Mgr)*

Dynapac GmbH (2)
Im Tiefenbruch 7
D-31275 Lehrte, Germany De
Tel.: (49) 513282870
Fax: (49) 5132828711
E-Mail: germany@dynapac.com
Web Site: www.dynapac.de
Emp.: 2,500
Compaction & Paving Equipment Mfr
S.I.C.: 3531
N.A.I.C.S.: 333120
Ketteler Stephan *(Pres)*

Atlas Copco Rock Drills AB (1)
Klerkgatan 21
Orebro, 702 25, Sweden
Tel.: (46) 196707000
Fax: (46) 196707070
Web Site: www.atlascopco.com
Emp.: 1,800
Rock Drilling Equipment Mfr & Distr
S.I.C.: 3532
N.A.I.C.S.: 333131
Daniel Lindkvist *(Mgr-Personnel)*

Atlas Copco Secoroc AB (1)
Bjornbacksvagan 2
PO Box 521
SE 737 25 Fagersta, Sweden (100%)
Tel.: (46) 22346100
Fax: (46) 22346101
E-Mail: johan.halling@atlascopco.com
Web Site: www.atlascopco.com
Emp.: 650
Rock Drilling Tools
S.I.C.: 3532
N.A.I.C.S.: 333131
Ann Fvensson *(Sec)*

Atlas Copco Tools AB (1)
Sickla Industrivag 17
131 34 Nacka, Sweden
Tel.: (46) 8 743 95 00
Fax: (46) 8 743 93 75
E-Mail: toolsinfo@se.atlascopco.com
Emp.: 200
Machine Tool Distr
S.I.C.: 5084
N.A.I.C.S.: 423830
Lennart Remneback *(Office Mgr)*

U.S. Subsidiary:

Atlas Copco North America LLC (1)
34 Maple Ave
Pine Brook, NJ 07058 DE
Mailing Address: (100%)
PO Box 2028
Pine Brook, NJ 07058-2028
Tel.: (973) 439-3494
Fax: (973) 439-9455
Web Site: www.atlascopco.com
Emp.: 8,200
Holding Company; Industrial, Mining & Construction Equipment & Supplies Distr
S.I.C.: 6719
N.A.I.C.S.: 551112
Mark Cohen *(Pres)*

Subsidiaries:

Atlas Copco CMT USA Inc. (2)
3700 E 68th Ave
Commerce City, CO 80022-2243 DE
Mailing Address:
4446 W 1730 S
Salt Lake City, UT 84104-4703
Tel.: (801) 974-5544
Fax: (801) 974-1012
Emp.: 4
Mining & Drilling Equipment Mfr
Export
S.I.C.: 3532
N.A.I.C.S.: 333131
Torbjorn Redaelli *(Pres & Gen Mgr)*

Atlas Copco Compressors LLC (2)
1800 Over View Dr
Rock Hill, SC 29730 DE
Tel.: (803) 817-7200
Fax: (803) 817-7176
E-Mail: information@us.atlascopco.com
Web Site: www.atlascopco.us
Emp.: 300
Mfr. of Compressors Including Air & Gas, Rotary, High Pressure, Non-Lubricated, Oil-Free, Reciprocating, Screw, Truck Mounted, Motor-Driven, Engine Starting, Portable
S.I.C.: 3563
N.A.I.C.S.: 333912
John Brookshire *(Pres)*

Subsidiaries:

Quincy Compressor Inc. (3)
3501 Wisman Ln
Quincy, IL 62301-1257
Tel.: (217) 222-7700
Fax: (217) 222-5109
E-Mail: trueblue@quincycompressor.com
Web Site: www.quincycompressor.com
Sales Range: $125-149.9 Million
Emp.: 220
Rotary & Reciprocating Air Compressors Mfr
Export
S.I.C.: 3519
N.A.I.C.S.: 333618
John Thompson *(Pres)*

Atlas Copco Comptec LLC (2)
46 School Rd
Voorheesville, NY 12186-9608 DE
Tel.: (518) 765-3344 (100%)
Fax: (518) 765-3357
Toll Free: (800) 334-1237
Web Site: www.atlascopco.com
Emp.: 200
Mfr. of Custom-Built Turbomachinery
Import Export
S.I.C.: 3563
N.A.I.C.S.: 333912
Alan Keybart *(Mgr-Mktg)*

Atlas Copco Construction & Mining Technique USA LLC (2)
3700 E 68th Ave
Commerce City, CO 80022
Tel.: (303) 217-2834
Emp.: 15
Construction & Mining Machinery Rental Services
S.I.C.: 7353
N.A.I.C.S.: 532412
Kerry Hogan *(Mgr-HR)*

Subsidiaries:

Atlas Copco Construction Equipment LLC (3)
3700 E 68th Ave
Commerce City, CO 80022-2243 DE
Tel.: (303) 287-8822 (100%)
Fax: (303) 288-8828
Web Site: www.atlascopco.com
Emp.: 55
Drill Steel
S.I.C.: 3532
N.A.I.C.S.: 333131
Erik Sparby *(Pres & Gen Mgr)*

Atlas Copco Drilling Solutions LLC (3)
7500 Shadwell Dr
Roanoke, VA 24019-5106 DE
Tel.: (540) 362-3321
Fax: (540) 561-4204
Web Site: www.atlascopco.com
Emp.: 33
Mfr of Drilling Equipment
S.I.C.: 3499
N.A.I.C.S.: 332999

Plant:

Atlas Copco Drilling Solutions (4)
2100 N 1st St
Garland, TX 75040-4102
Mailing Address:
PO Box 462288
Garland, TX 75046-2288
Tel.: (972) 496-7400
Fax: (972) 496-7425
Web Site: www.atlascopco.us
Emp.: 400
Mfr. Drills & Drilling Tools
S.I.C.: 3541
N.A.I.C.S.: 333517

Atlas Copco Hurricane LLC (2)
1015 Hurricane Rd
Franklin, IN 46131
Tel.: (317) 736-3800
Toll Free: (800) 754-7408
E-Mail: sales@hurricane-compressors.com
Web Site: www.atlascopco.us
Emp.: 80
Portable Air & Gas Compressors Mfr
S.I.C.: 3563
N.A.I.C.S.: 333912
Judy Miller *(VP-HR)*

Atlas Copco Mafi-Trench Company LLC (2)
3037 Industrial Pkwy.
Santa Maria, CA 93455
Tel.: (805) 928-5757
E-Mail: marketing@mafi-trench.com
Web Site: www.mafi-trench.com
Rev.: $1,500,000
Emp.: 85
Air & Gas Compressor Manufacturing
S.I.C.: 3563
N.A.I.C.S.: 333912
Jim Reilly *(Gen Mgr)*

Atlas Copco Secoroc LLC (2)
1600 S Great SW Pkwy
Grand Prairie, TX 75051 DE
Tel.: (972) 337-9700
Fax: (972) 602-3135
Toll Free: (800) 527-1632
Web Site: www.atlascopco.com
Emp.: 160
Mining Tools Mfr
S.I.C.: 5084
N.A.I.C.S.: 423830
Ron Boyd *(Mgr-Oil & Gas Products)*

Atlas Copco Specialty Rental LLC (2)
5810 Wilson Rd
Humble, TX 77396-2899

Atlas Copco AB—(Continued)

Tel.: (281) 454-2200
Construction Machinery Rental Services
S.I.C.: 7353
N.A.I.C.S.: 532412
Horst Wasel *(Pres)*

Atlas Copco Tools & Assembly Systems LLC (2)
2998 Dutton Rd
Auburn Hills, MI 48326 DE
Tel.: (248) 373-3000 (100%)
Fax: (248) 373-3001
Web Site: www.atlascopco.com
Emp.: 100
Customer Service for the Pneumatic Powered Tools
S.I.C.: 5084
N.A.I.C.S.: 423830
Anders Hedberg *(Pres)*

Subsidiaries:

Atlas Copco Assembly Systems LLC (3)
2998 Dutton Rd
Auburn Hills, MI 48326 DE
Tel.: (248) 373-3000
Fax: (248) 373-3001
E-Mail: info@atlascopco.com
Web Site: www.atlascopco.com
Emp.: 120
Machine Tool Builders
S.I.C.: 3563
N.A.I.C.S.: 333912

Rapid-Torc Inc. (3)
2406 E Pasadena Fwy
Pasadena, TX 77506 DE
Tel.: (281) 448-5900
Fax: (281) 260-0779
E-Mail: sales@rapidtorc.com
Web Site: www.rapidtorc.com
Sales Range: $10-24.9 Million
Emp.: 30
Industrial Torque, Tension & Bolt Heating Technologies Mfr
S.I.C.: 3569
N.A.I.C.S.: 333999
Roger Dischert *(Co-Founder & VP-Technical & Fin)*
Corinne Billard *(Co-Founder & VP-Sls & Mktg)*

Beacon Medical Products LLC (2)
1800 Overview Dr
Rock Hill, SC 29730
Tel.: (803) 817-5600
Fax: (803) 817-5750
E-Mail: medgasinfo@beaconmedaes.com
Web Site: www.beaconmedaes.com
Emp.: 100
Medical Gas Supplying System Distr
S.I.C.: 5047
N.A.I.C.S.: 423450
Curt Clark *(Reg Mgr-Svc)*

Chicago Pneumatic Tool Company LLC (2)
1800 Overview Dr
Rock Hill, SC 29730-7463 (100%)
Tel.: (704) 936-4000
Fax: (800) 228-9096
Toll Free: (800) 624-4735
Web Site: www.chicagopneumatic.com
Emp.: 100
Vehicle Service Tools, Vehicle Assembly Tools, Pneumatic Tools
Import Export
S.I.C.: 3546
N.A.I.C.S.: 333991
Martin Paulsen *(Gen Mgr)*

Non-U.S. Subsidiaries:

Chicago Pneumatic Construction Equipment AB (3)
Sickla Industrivag 19
105 23 Stockholm, Sweden
Tel.: (46) 766 28 40 35
Fax: (46) 86467261
E-Mail: info@cp.com
Emp.: 60
Construction Equipment Distr
S.I.C.: 5082
N.A.I.C.S.: 423810
Kishore Sidhwani *(VP)*

Subsidiary:

CP Scanrotor Aktiebolag (4)
Kville Sandliden 18
Fjallbacka, 457 43 Tanum, Sweden
Tel.: (46) 525 352 55
Fax: (46) 525 350 93
E-Mail: info.seo@cp.com
Plumbing & Heating Equipment Distr
S.I.C.: 5074
N.A.I.C.S.: 423720
Ralf Majchrzak *(Mgr-Sls-Construction Equipment)*

CP Tools Korea Co. Ltd (3)
4/F Phoong Cheon Bldg 949 Hogye-Dong
Dongan-gu, Anyang, Gyeonggi-Do, 431080, Korea (South)
Tel.: (82) 314608463
Fax: (82) 314513650
Emp.: 1
Machine Tool Mfr
S.I.C.: 3541
N.A.I.C.S.: 333517

Non-U.S. Subsidiary:

Atlas Copco Canada Inc. (2)
2555 Avenue Dollard Suite 203
La Salle, QC, H8N 3A9, Canada (100%)
Tel.: (514) 366-2626
Fax: (514) 366-6430
Web Site: www.atlascopco.com
Emp.: 7
Mining Machinery, Compressors & Tools Mfr & Distr
S.I.C.: 3532
N.A.I.C.S.: 333131
Mark Cohen *(Pres)*

Subsidiary:

Atlas Copco Compressor Canada (3)
30 Montrose
Dollard des Ormeaux, QC, H9B 3J9, Canada (100%)
Tel.: (514) 421-4121
Fax: (514) 421-1950
E-Mail: compressors.canada@ca.atlascopco.com
Web Site: www.atlascopco.com
Emp.: 125
Marketing & Sales of Compressors
S.I.C.: 5084
N.A.I.C.S.: 423830
Ronnie Leten *(Pres & CEO)*

Non-U.S. Subsidiaries:

ABAC Aria Compressa S.p.A (1)
Via Cristoforo Colombo 3
10070 Robassomero, Turin, Italy
Tel.: (39) 01 19 24 64 00
Fax: (39) 01 19 24 10 96
E-Mail: abac@abac.it
Emp.: 30
Industrial Air Compressor Mfr & Distr
S.I.C.: 3563
N.A.I.C.S.: 333912
Uwe Schraader *(Gen Mgr)*

U.S. Subsidiary:

ABAC AMERICAN IMC Inc (2)
1623 Cedar Line Dr
Rock Hill, SC 29730
Tel.: (803) 980-6570
Fax: (803) 980-5751
E-Mail: info@abacamerican.com
Air Compressor Mfr
S.I.C.: 3563
N.A.I.C.S.: 333912

Non-U.S. Subsidiaries:

ABAC Air Compressors s.a Pty Ltd. (2)
5 Hesketh Road
Westmead, 4001 Durban, South Africa
Tel.: (27) 31 700 6501
Fax: (27) 31 700 8056
Emp.: 14
Air Compressor Distr
S.I.C.: 5084
N.A.I.C.S.: 423830

ABAC CATALUNYA S.L. (2)
C/Barcelona 21-23
Casserres, 8693, Spain
Tel.: (34) 938 22 51 80
Fax: (34) 938 22 50 07
E-Mail: abac@minorisa.es
Air Compressors Distr
S.I.C.: 5075
N.A.I.C.S.: 423730

ABAC DMS Air Compressors Pte Ltd (2)
25 Defu Ln
539266 Singapore, Singapore
Tel.: (65) 64636531
Fax: (65) 64638717
E-Mail: dmscomp@singnet.com.sg
Air Compressor Mfr
S.I.C.: 3563
N.A.I.C.S.: 333912
C. F. Loh *(Gen Mgr)*

ABAC France S.A.S. (2)
112 Chemin de la Foret Aux Martins ZAC Briffaut Est
BP 179
26000 Valence, France
Tel.: (33) 4 75 41 81 51
Fax: (33) 4 75 41 89 98
E-Mail: standard.abac@abacfrance.fr
Web Site: www.abacfrance.fr
Air Compressor Mfr
S.I.C.: 3563
N.A.I.C.S.: 333912

ABAC UK Ltd (2)
Unit 11 Granville Way Chaucer Business Park
Bicester, Oxfordshire, OX26 4JT, United Kingdom
Tel.: (44) 1869 326 226
Fax: (44) 1869 326 216
E-Mail: abac.enquiries@abac.co.uk
Web Site: www.abac.co.uk
Air Compressor Mfr & Distr
S.I.C.: 3563
N.A.I.C.S.: 333912

ALUP Kompressoren GmbH (2)
Nurtinger Str 50
73257 Kongen, Germany
Tel.: (49) 7024 9612 100
Fax: (49) 7024 9612 199
E-Mail: info@alup.com
Emp.: 15
Air Compressor Mfr
S.I.C.: 3563
N.A.I.C.S.: 333912

ALUP Kompressoren B.V. (1)
Biezenwade 10
Postbus 1312
3430 BH Nieuwegein, Netherlands
Tel.: (31) 30 2809000
Fax: (31) 30 2895675
E-Mail: info@alup.nl
Emp.: 33
Air Compressor Mfr
S.I.C.: 3563
N.A.I.C.S.: 333912
J. Neelen *(Gen Mgr)*

Non-U.S. Subsidiaries:

ALUP CZ spol. S.r.o (2)
U Stadionu 4
690 02 Breclav, Czech Republic
Tel.: (420) 519 322 980
Fax: (420) 519 331 370
E-Mail: info@alup.cz
Web Site: www.alup.cz
Emp.: 8
Air Compressor Mfr
S.I.C.: 3563
N.A.I.C.S.: 333912
Marcela Havlaskova *(Mgr-Sls-Cechy Area)*

ALUP Kompressoren Polska Sp. Z.o.o. (2)
Al Krakowska 26 Janki
Raszyn, 05-090 Warsaw, Poland
Tel.: (48) 22 720 65 90
Fax: (48) 22 720 65 95
E-Mail: alup@alup.pl
Emp.: 7
Air Compressor Sales & Installation Services
S.I.C.: 5075
N.A.I.C.S.: 423730
Waldemar Szymanski *(Gen Mgr)*

Atlas Copco A/S (1)
Berghagan 5
1405 Langhus, Norway
Tel.: (47) 64 86 03 00
Fax: (47) 64 86 02 39
Construction Machinery Rental Services
S.I.C.: 7359
N.A.I.C.S.: 532412

Subsidiaries:

Atlas Copco Anlegg- og Gruveteknikk A/S (2)
Berghagan 5
Langhus, 1405, Norway
Tel.: (47) 64 86 03 00 00
Fax: (47) 64 86 03 30 30
E-Mail: ac.anlegg@atlascopco.com
Emp.: 6
Construction Machinery Rental Services
S.I.C.: 7353
N.A.I.C.S.: 532412
Erik Presthus *(Gen Mgr)*

Atlas Copco Kompressorteknikk AS (2)
Berghagan 5
1405 Langhus, Norway NO
Tel.: (47) 64860860
Fax: (47) 64860239
E-Mail:
Web Site: www.atlascopco.com
Industrial Machinery Maintenance Services
S.I.C.: 7699
N.A.I.C.S.: 811310
Kjell Hognes *(Product Mgr)*

Atlas Copco Tools A/S (2)
Berghagan 5
Langhus, 1405, Norway
Tel.: (47) 64860400
Fax: (47) 64860475
E-Mail: toolsairno@atlascopco.com
Machine Tool Distr
S.I.C.: 5084
N.A.I.C.S.: 423830

Atlas Copco Angola Lda (1)
Parque Industrial Darfo Estrada do Zango
Viana, Luanda, Angola
Tel.: (244) 929 30 31 39
Fax: (244) 222 39 80 38
E-Mail: ct.angola@ao.atlascopco.com
Web Site: www.atlascopco.com
Construction Machinery Mfr & Distr
S.I.C.: 3531
N.A.I.C.S.: 333120

Atlas Copco Assistance Technique (1)
34 Rue Belkacem Amani
BP 161
16035 Hydra, Algeria
Tel.: (213) 21693558
Fax: (213) 21 602 257
E-Mail: atlascopco@wissal.dz
S.I.C.: 3325
N.A.I.C.S.: 331513

Atlas Copco Australia Pty Ltd (1)
3 Bessemer Street
Blacktown, NSW, 2148, Australia
Tel.: (61) 2 9621 9707
Fax: (61) 419 236 706
E-Mail: ausairinfo@au.atlascopco.com
Web Site: www.atlascopco.com.au
Emp.: 1,000
Construction Equipment Mfr & Distr
S.I.C.: 3531
N.A.I.C.S.: 333120
Chris Moloney *(Gen Mgr)*

Atlas Copco Belgium n.v. (1)
Brusselsesteenweg 346
B-3090 Overijse, Belgium BE
Tel.: (32) 26890511
Fax: (32) 26890514
E-Mail: bga.info@be.atlascopco.com
Web Site: www.atlascopco.be
Holding Company
S.I.C.: 6719
N.A.I.C.S.: 551112

Subsidiaries:

Atlas Copco Airpower n.v. (2)
Boomsesteenweg 957
B 2610 Wilrijk, Belgium BE
Tel.: (32) 38702111 (99%)
Fax: (32) 38702443
E-Mail: info@be.atlascopco.com
Web Site: www.atlascopco.com

Sls.: $1,196,467,968
Emp.: 2,300
Develop, Market, & Manufacture of Stationary & Portable Compressors, in Both Standard and Specially Designed Versions
S.I.C.: 3563
N.A.I.C.S.: 333912
Stephan Kuhn *(Pres)*
Geert Follens *(Pres-Vacuum Solutions)*

Divisions:

Atlas Copco Airtec **(3)**
Boomsesteenweg 957
PO Box 101
2610 Wilrijk, Belgium
Tel.: (32) 38702111
Fax: (32) 38702760
E-Mail: info@atlascopco.com
Web Site: www.atlascopco.com
Emp.: 2,500
Production, Development & Sales of Compressors
S.I.C.: 3563
N.A.I.C.S.: 333912
Stephen Kuhn *(Pres)*
Filip Vandenberghe *(Pres)*
Ronnie Leten *(CEO)*

Atlas Copco Industrial Air **(3)**
Boomsesteenweg 957
PO Box 103
BE 2610 Wilrijk, Belgium
Tel.: (32) 38702111
Fax: (32) 38702443
E-Mail: info@atlascopco.com
Web Site: www.meetatlascopco.com
Emp.: 2,300
S.I.C.: 3563
N.A.I.C.S.: 333912
Ray Lofgren *(Pres)*

Atlas Copco Oil-free Air **(3)**
Boomsesteenweg 957
PO Box 101
BE 2610 Wilrijk, Belgium
Tel.: (32) 038702111
Fax: (32) 038702443
E-Mail: info@atlascopco.com
Web Site: www.atlascopco.com
Emp.: 2,300
S.I.C.: 3563
N.A.I.C.S.: 333912
Chris Lybaert *(Pres)*

Atlas Copco Portable Air **(3)**
Boomsesteenweg 957
PO Box 102
2610 Wilrijk, Belgium
Tel.: (32) 34506011
Fax: (32) 34506200
E-Mail: info.be@atlascopco.com
Web Site: www.atlascopco.com
Emp.: 600
S.I.C.: 3563
N.A.I.C.S.: 333912

Atlas Copco ASAP n.v. **(2)**
Boomsesteenweg 957b 93
Antwerp, 2610, Belgium
Tel.: (32) 38702111
Internet Providing Services
S.I.C.: 4899
N.A.I.C.S.: 517919
Anna-Karin Stenberg *(Gen Mgr)*

Atlas Copco Rental Europe n.v. **(2)**
Antwerpsesteenweg 50
2840 Rumst, Belgium
Tel.: (32) 15 30 73 30
Fax: (32) 15 30 73 39
E-Mail: acre@atlascopco.be
Emp.: 43
Industrial Machinery Rental Services
S.I.C.: 7359
N.A.I.C.S.: 532490
Tom Deckers *(Gen Mgr)*

International Compressor Distribution n.v. **(2)**
Boomsesteenweg 957
2610 Wilrijk, Belgium
Tel.: (32) 3 870 25 71
Fax: (32) 3234019888
E-Mail: info@icdcompany.com
Emp.: 1
Air Compressor Distr
S.I.C.: 5075
N.A.I.C.S.: 423730
Amit Sharma *(Gen Mgr)*

Atlas Copco BH d.o.o. **(1)**
Safeta Zajke 266
71000 Sarajevo, Bosnia & Herzegovina
Tel.: (387) 33 67 43 91
Fax: (387) 33 67 43 92
Emp.: 7
Air Compressor Mfr & Distr
S.I.C.: 3563
N.A.I.C.S.: 333912
Armin Kremo *(Mgr-Sls-Construction & Mining Technique)*

Atlas Copco Boliviana SA **(1)**
Av 20 de Octubre 2665 Esquina Campos Edificio
Torre Azul 2do Piso Of 201, La Paz, Bolivia
Tel.: (591) 2 211 20 00
Fax: (591) 2 211 78 01
E-Mail: acbol@cotas.com.bo
Construction Machinery Mfr & Distr
S.I.C.: 3531
N.A.I.C.S.: 333120
Gianfranco Barbera *(Engr-Sls-Construction & Mining-Surface Mining)*

Atlas Copco (Botswana) (Pty) Ltd **(1)**
Unit 1 Plot 175 Gaborone International Commerce Park
Gaborone, Botswana
Tel.: (267) 395 9155
Fax: (267) 395 9150
Emp.: 77
Air Compressor Mfr
S.I.C.: 3563
N.A.I.C.S.: 333912
Ronnie van der Nest *(Country Mgr)*

Atlas Copco Bulgaria Eood **(1)**
414 Ring Road
1532 Sofia, Bulgaria
Tel.: (359) 2 489 3178
Fax: (359) 2 999 9764
E-Mail: office.sofia@bg.atlascopco.com
Web Site: www.atlascopco.com
Emp.: 35
Construction Machinery Mfr & Distr
S.I.C.: 3531
N.A.I.C.S.: 333120
Predrag Ilibasic *(Gen Mgr)*

Atlas Copco Central Asia LLP **(1)**
1st floor 8A Kurmangaliyev St
Almaty, 050010, Kazakhstan
Tel.: (7) 727 258 19 92
Fax: (7) 727 258 89 99
E-Mail: info@kz.atlascopco.com
Web Site: www.atlascopco.kz
Air Compressor Mfr & Distr
S.I.C.: 3563
N.A.I.C.S.: 333912
Kazbek Bektassov *(Product Mgr-CTO)*

Atlas Copco Chilena S.A.C. **(1)**
Panamericana Norte 5001
Conchali, Santiago, Chile
Tel.: (56) 2 4423677
Fax: (56) 2 4423677
E-Mail: alfredo.de.simone@cl.atlascopco.com
Web Site: www.atlascopco.cl
Construction Machinery Mfr & Distr
S.I.C.: 3531
N.A.I.C.S.: 333120

Atlas Copco China/Hong Kong Ltd **(1)**
Unit 1018 Tower 2 Grand Central Plaza No 138
Shatin Rural Committee Road, Sha Tin, New Territories, China (Hong Kong)
Tel.: (852) 27 97 66 00
Fax: (852) 23 41 43 13
E-Mail: cmt.hkg@hk.atlascopco.com
Emp.: 3
Air Compressor Mfr
S.I.C.: 3563
N.A.I.C.S.: 333912
Thomas Kung *(Mng Dir)*

Atlas Copco Colombia Ltda **(1)**
Cra 85 D No 46A-65 Bod 6 y 7
Bogota, Colombia
Tel.: (57) 1 4199200, ext. 102
Fax: (57) 1 4199222
E-Mail:
Air Compressor Mfr
S.I.C.: 3563
N.A.I.C.S.: 333912

Atlas Copco Compressors Slovakia s.r.o **(1)**
Elektricna 6471
911 01 Trencin, Slovakia
Tel.: (421) 32 7438 001
Fax: (421) 32 7438 002
E-Mail: tlascopco.slovakia@sk.atlascopco.com
Air Compressor Mfr & Distr
S.I.C.: 3563
N.A.I.C.S.: 333912

Atlas Copco (Cyprus) Ltd **(1)**
39 Tripoleos Street
Latsia, 2235 Nicosia, Cyprus
Tel.: (357) 22 48 07 40
Fax: (357) 22 48 00 14
Web Site: www.atlascopco.com
Emp.: 10
Compressor & Generator Distr
S.I.C.: 5084
N.A.I.C.S.: 423830
Voudalikas Costas *(Gen Mgr)*

Atlas Copco DRC sprl **(1)**
8 Avenue Lukafu Quartier Golf
Lubumbashi, Katanga, Congo, Democratic Republic of
Tel.: (243) 99 100 44 30
Fax: (243) 99 053 90 01
Emp.: 13
Construction Machinery Distr
S.I.C.: 5082
N.A.I.C.S.: 423810
Lawrence van der Veeken *(Country Mgr)*

Atlas Copco Eastern Africa Ltd **(1)**
PO Box 40090
00100 Nairobi, Kenya
Tel.: (254) 20 6605000
Fax: (254) 20 825472
Web Site: www.atlascopco.com
Emp.: 100
Industrial Machinery Distr
S.I.C.: 5084
N.A.I.C.S.: 423830
Lorne Hunter *(Reg Gen Mgr)*

Atlas Copco Equipment Egypt S.A.E. **(1)**
El Obour City 1st Industrial Zone - Part 7 - Block No 13024
11828 Cairo, Egypt
Tel.: (20) 2 46100337
Fax: (20) 2 46100341
E-Mail: info@atlascopco.com.eg
Web Site: www.atlascopco.com.eg/egus/
Emp.: 3
Compressor & Generator Machinery Distr
S.I.C.: 5084
N.A.I.C.S.: 423830
Ahmed Elshazly *(Reg Mgr-Bus Line-Speciality Rental Div)*

Atlas Copco France Holding S.A. **(1)**
Zone Industrielle du Vert Galant 2 Avenue de l'Eguillette
95310 Saint-Ouen-l'Aumone, France FR
Tel.: (33) 1 3909 3000
Fax: (33) 1 3909 3049
Web Site: www.atlascopco.fr
Holding Company
S.I.C.: 6719
N.A.I.C.S.: 551112

Subsidiaries:

Atlas Copco Applications Industrielles S.A.S. **(2)**
Zone Industrielle du Vert Galant 2 avenue de l'Eguillette
95310 Saint-Ouen-l'Aumone, France
Tel.: (33) 1 39 09 32 50
Fax: (33) 1 39 09 30 80
E-Mail: outils@fr.atlascopco.com
Web Site: www.atlascopco.fr
Industrial Machinery Mfr
S.I.C.: 3559
N.A.I.C.S.: 333249

Atlas Copco Compresseurs S.A.S **(2)**
Zone Industrielle du Vert Galant 2 Avenue de l' Eguillette
95310 Saint-Ouen-l'Aumone, France
Tel.: (33) 1 39 09 31 00
Fax: (33) 1 39 09 31 99
E-Mail: compresseurs@fr.atlascopco.com
Web Site: www.atlascopco.fr
Air Compressor Mfr
S.I.C.: 3563
N.A.I.C.S.: 333912

Subsidiaries:

Compresseurs Mauguiere S.A.S. **(3)**
2 Avenue des Gros Chevaux
95004 Cergy-Pontoise, France
Tel.: (33) 1 34 32 94 50
Fax: (33) 1 34 32 94 60
E-Mail: mauguiere@mauguiere.com
Emp.: 9
Air Compressor Mfr
S.I.C.: 3563
N.A.I.C.S.: 333912
Kiekens Francis *(Gen Mgr)*

Compresseurs Worthington Creyssensac S.A.S. **(3)**
2 Avenue des Gros Chevaux
BP 40616
95004 Saint-Ouen-l'Aumone, France
Tel.: (33) 1 34 32 95 00
Fax: (33) 1 34 32 95 14
E-Mail: wcf.info@airwco.com
Emp.: 100
Air Compressor Mfr
S.I.C.: 3563
N.A.I.C.S.: 333912
Francis Liekens *(Gen Mgr)*

Atlas Copco Crepelle S.A.S. **(2)**
2 Place Guy De Dampierre
BP 29
59000 Lille, France
Tel.: (33) 3 20 52 47 11
Fax: (33) 3 20 53 76 51
Emp.: 92
Air Compressor Mfr
S.I.C.: 3563
N.A.I.C.S.: 333912
Philippe Ernens *(Gen Mgr)*

Atlas Copco Forage et Construction S.A.S. **(2)**
Zone Industrielle du Vert Galant 2 avenue de l'Eguillette
95310 Saint-Ouen-l'Aumone, France
Tel.: (33) 139093222
Fax: (33) 139093249
E-Mail: forage.construction@fr.atlascopco.com
Construction & Mining Machinery Whslr
S.I.C.: 5082
N.A.I.C.S.: 423810

ETS Georges Renault S.A.S. **(2)**
199 Route De Clisson
BP 13627
44236 Saint Sebastien, France
Tel.: (33) 2 40802000
Fax: (33) 2 40332707
Industrial Machinery Mfr
S.I.C.: 3559
N.A.I.C.S.: 333249

Georges Renault S.A. **(2)**
199 Rte De Clisson
BP 13627
44236 Saint Sebastien, Cedex, France (100%)
Tel.: (33) 240802000
Fax: (33) 240802019
Sls.: $22,000,000
Emp.: 200
Industrial Tools & Assembly Systems
S.I.C.: 3546
N.A.I.C.S.: 333991

Techfluid Nord S.A.S. **(2)**
34 Bis rue de la Distillerie - Parc de La Plaine
59650 Villeneuve d'Ascq, France
Tel.: (33) 3 20 41 04 92
Fax: (33) 3 20 64 01 79
E-Mail: commercial@techfluidnord.com
Compressor Mfr
S.I.C.: 3563
N.A.I.C.S.: 333912

Vibratechniques S.A.S. **(2)**
Rue Du Bourgtheroulde
76460 Saint Valery-en-Caux, France
Tel.: (33) 2 35 57 91 91
Fax: (33) 2 35 57 91 99
Construction Machinery Distr
S.I.C.: 5084
N.A.I.C.S.: 423830

Atlas Copco AB—(Continued)

Atlas Copco Ges.m.b.H. (1)
Csokorgasse 11
1111 Vienna, Austria
Tel.: (43) 1 760 12 240
Fax: (43) 1 760 12 271
E-Mail: compressor1@atatlascopco.com
Emp.: 10
Air Compressor Mfr
S.I.C.: 3563
N.A.I.C.S.: 333912
Dirk Ville *(Mng Dir)*

Subsidiaries:

AGRE Kompressoren GmbH (2)
A-4451 Garsten-St
Sankt Ulrich bei Steyr, Austria
Tel.: (43) 7252 52341 0
Fax: (43) 7252 52133
E-Mail: office@agre.at
Air Compressor Mfr
S.I.C.: 3563
N.A.I.C.S.: 333912

Atlas Copco Powercrusher GmbH (2)
Gollensdorf 24
4300 Sankt Valentin, Austria
Tel.: (43) 7238 293 50
Fax: (43) 7238 293 50 40
E-Mail: office@powercrusher.com
Web Site: www.atlascopco.com
Construction Machinery Mfr & Distr
S.I.C.: 3531
N.A.I.C.S.: 333120
Mansoor Eskandanian *(Mgr-Mktg)*

Atlas Copco Ghana Ltd (1)
No 19 Akosombo Street Airport Residential Area
PO Box 10071
Accra, Ghana
Tel.: (233) 302 77 45 12
Fax: (233) 302 77 61 47
E-Mail: info.ghana@gh.atlascopco.com
Web Site: www.atlascopco.com
Emp.: 126
Construction & Mining Equipment Distr
S.I.C.: 5082
N.A.I.C.S.: 423810
George Apostolopoulos *(Reg Gen Mgr)*

Atlas Copco Hellas AE (1)
93 Koropiou - Varis Avenue
Koropi, 194 00 Athens, Greece
Tel.: (30) 210 349 96 00
Fax: (30) 210 345 47 83
E-Mail: info.grc@gr.atlascopco.com
Web Site: www.atlascopco.com.gr
Emp.: 56
Compressor & Generator Equipment Distr
S.I.C.: 5084
N.A.I.C.S.: 423830
Athanasios Markakis *(Mgr-Bus Line-Compressor Technique Svc)*

Atlas Copco Holding GmbH (1)
Langemarckstr 35
Essen, 45141, Germany
Tel.: (49) 20121770
Fax: (49) 201290874
E-Mail: atlascopco.deutschland@de.atlascopco.com
Investment Management Services
S.I.C.: 6211
N.A.I.C.S.: 523999

Subsidiaries:

Atlas Copco Application Center Europe GmbH (2)
Langemarckstr 35
Essen, 45141, Germany
Tel.: (49) 20121770
Fax: (49) 2012177464
E-Mail:
Construction Machinery Mfr
S.I.C.: 3531
N.A.I.C.S.: 333120

Atlas Copco Energas Gmbh (2)
Schlehenweg 15
50999 Cologne, Germany
Tel.: (49) 223696500
Fax: (49) 22369650899
E Mail: atlascopco.energas@de.atlascopco.com
Web Site: www.atlascopco.de
Air & Gas Compressor Manufacturing
S.I.C.: 3563
N.A.I.C.S.: 333912
Peter Wagner *(Gen Mgr)*

Atlas Copco Kompressoren und Drucklufttechnik GmbH (2)
Langemarckstr 35
Essen, 45141, Germany
Tel.: (49) 20121770
Fax: (49) 201216917
E-Mail: info.kompressoren@de.atlascopco.com
Emp.: 200
Construction Machinery Distr
S.I.C.: 5082
N.A.I.C.S.: 423810
Piet Leys *(Gen Mgr)*

Atlas Copco MCT GmbH (2)
Langemarckstr 35
Essen, 45141, Germany
Tel.: (49) 20121770
Fax: (49) 2012177454
E-Mail: mct.personal@de.atlascopco.com
Emp.: 500
Air & Gas Compressor Mfr
S.I.C.: 3563
N.A.I.C.S.: 333912
Anja Kruse *(Mgr-Personnel)*

Atlas Copco Tools Central Europe GmbH (2)
Langemarckstrasse 35
D-45141 Essen, Germany
Tel.: (49) 20121770
Fax: (49) 2012177100
E-Mail: tools.de@de.atlascopco.com
Web Site: www.atlascopco.de
Compressor Machinery Mfr
S.I.C.: 3563
N.A.I.C.S.: 333912
Conny Schade *(Mgr-Personnel)*

IRMER + ELZE Kompressoren GmbH (2)
Mindener Strasse 29
32547 Bad Oeynhausen, Germany
Tel.: (49) 5731 1801 60
Fax: (49) 5731 1801 66
E-Mail: info@irmair.com
Web Site: www.irmair.com
Emp.: 5
Portable Diesel Driven Screw Compressor Mfr & Distr
S.I.C.: 3563
N.A.I.C.S.: 333912
Kai Altvater *(Gen Mgr)*

TBB Industrial Tools Services GmbH (2)
Bayernwerkstrasse 112
84130 Dingolfing, Germany
Tel.: (49) 873137580
Fax: (49) 8731375870
E-Mail: tbb@info.de
Web Site: www.tbb-its.de
Rev.: $7,500,000
Emp.: 87
Tightening Technology Consulting, Testing & Calibration Services
S.I.C.: 3559
N.A.I.C.S.: 333249
Olas Sommer *(Mng Dir)*

Atlas Copco Holdings South Africa (Pty) Ltd (1)
Saligna Str Hughes Business Park
Witfield, Boksburg, 1459, South Africa
Tel.: (27) 11 821 9000
Fax: (27) 11 821 9183
E-Mail: ct.serv@atlascopco.com
Investment Management Services
S.I.C.: 6211
N.A.I.C.S.: 523999

Subsidiaries:

Atlas Copco South Africa (Pty) Ltd (2)
Saligna Street Hughes Business Park
Witfield, Boksburg, South Africa
Tel.: (27) 11 821 9000
Fax: (27) 11 821 9106
E-Mail: atlas.copco@za.atlascopco.com
Web Site: www.atlascopco.co.za/zaus/
Industrial Machinery Mfr & Distr
S.I.C.: 3559
N.A.I.C.S.: 333249

ZAQ Coalfields Drilling Services (Pty) Ltd (2)
Hughes Business Park Salinga Street
Witfield, Boksburg, 1467, South Africa
Tel.: (27) 11 82 19500
Fax: (27) 11 82 19202
Emp.: 14
Coal Drilling Services
S.I.C.: 1241
N.A.I.C.S.: 213113
Harry Joubert *(Gen Mgr)*

Atlas Copco (India) Ltd. (1)
Sveanagar Bombay Pune Road
Dapodi, Pune, 411012, India
Tel.: (91) 2030722222
Fax: (91) 20 3985 2070
Web Site: www.atlascopco.in
526991—(BOM)
Emp.: 1,280
Air & Gas Compressor Mfr
S.I.C.: 3559
N.A.I.C.S.: 333249
Filip Vandenberghe *(Mng Dir)*
S. H. Ghotage *(CFO & VP)*
A. C. Daga *(Sec)*

Atlas Copco Iran AB (1)
236 Avenue Azadi
Tehran, Iran
Tel.: (98) 21 6693 77 11
Fax: (98) 21 6692 73 14
E-Mail: info@ir.atlascopco.com
Web Site: www.atlascopco.ir/irus/
Construction & Mining Equipment Distr
S.I.C.: 5082
N.A.I.C.S.: 423810
Majid Nouriseresht *(Controller-Bus)*

Atlas Copco (Ireland) Ltd (1)
Unit G15 Calmount Business Park
Bluebell, Dublin, 12, Ireland
Tel.: (353) 1 4505978
Fax: (353) 1 456 76 86
E-Mail: info.ireland@ie.atlascopco.com
Web Site: www.atlascopco.ie
Emp.: 35
Industrial Machinery Mfr & Distr
S.I.C.: 3559
N.A.I.C.S.: 333249
Denis Keily *(Mgr-Portable Air-Construction Technique)*

Atlas Copco Italia S.p.A. (1)
Via F lli Gracchi 39
20092 Cinisello Balsamo, Milan, Italy
Tel.: (39) 02 617991
Fax: (39) 026 171949
E-Mail: info.ct@it.atlascopco.com
Web Site: www.atlascopco.it
Air Compressor Mfr
S.I.C.: 3563
N.A.I.C.S.: 333912

Subsidiaries:

Ceccato Aria Compressa S.p.A. (2)
Via Soastene 34
36040 Brendola, Vicenza, Italy
Tel.: (39) 0444 703911
Fax: (39) 0444 703995
E-Mail: infosales@ceccato.com
Web Site: www.ceccato-compressors.com
Air Compressor Mfr & Distr
S.I.C.: 3563
N.A.I.C.S.: 333912

MultiAir Italia S.r.l. (2)
39 Via Gracchi Fratelli
20092 Cinisello Balsamo, Milan, Italy
Tel.: (39) 0266 018 368
Fax: (39) 0261 799520
Emp.: 200
Air Compressor Mfr
S.I.C.: 3563
N.A.I.C.S.: 333912

Atlas Copco Kft (1)
Vendel Park Huber u 1
Biatorbagy, 2051, Hungary
Tel.: (36) 23 803 600
Fax: (36) 23 803 666
E-Mail: informacio.hun@hu.atlascopco.com
Web Site: www.atlascopco.hu
Emp.: 55
Pneumatic Power Tools Mfr
S.I.C.: 3542
N.A.I.C.S.: 333517
Francesco Pinna *(Gen Mgr)*

Atlas Copco KK (1)
Shiba Building 11F 13-4 Shiba 2-chome
Minato-ku, Tokyo, 105-0014, Japan
Tel.: (81) 3 5765 7890
Fax: (81) 3 5765 3199
E-Mail: ackk@jp.atlascopco.com
Emp.: 30
Pneumatic Tool Mfr
S.I.C.: 3546
N.A.I.C.S.: 333991
Toshinori Yashiki *(Gen Mgr)*

Subsidiary:

Fuji Air Tools Co., Ltd (2)
2-1-14 Kamiji
Higashinari-Ku
Osaka, 537-0003, Japan
Tel.: (81) 669722335
Fax: (81) 669722250
Web Site: www.fujiairtools.com
Air Powered Tools & Accessories Mfr & Distr
S.I.C.: 3545
N.A.I.C.S.: 333515

Atlas Copco Kompressorteknik A/S (1)
Naverland 22
2600 Glostrup, Denmark
Tel.: (45) 43 45 46 11
Fax: (45) 43 63 21 20
E-Mail: ndapost@dk.atlascopco.com
Web Site: www.atlascopco.dk
Air Compressor Mfr
S.I.C.: 3563
N.A.I.C.S.: 333912
Lars Siemen *(Country Mgr)*

Atlas Copco Latvija SIA (1)
Martinmuiza
Marupe, 2167, Latvia
Tel.: (371) 67609190
Fax: (371) 67609191
E-Mail: info@lv.atlascopco.com
Web Site: www.atlascopco.lv
Emp.: 12
Construction & Mining Machinery Mfr
S.I.C.: 3531
N.A.I.C.S.: 333120
Inguna Cauka *(Bus Mgr)*

Atlas Copco Lietuva UAB (1)
Kalvarijos g 38
Kaunas, 46346, Lithuania
Tel.: (370) 37 228 861
Fax: (370) 37 228 872
E-Mail: info@lt.atlascopco.com
Emp.: 9
Mining Machinery Distr
S.I.C.: 5082
N.A.I.C.S.: 423810
Remigijus Blockis *(Mgr-Bus Line-Compressor Technigue)*

Atlas Copco Lifton Eood (1)
Tutrakan Boulevard 100
7000 Ruse, Bulgaria
Tel.: (359) 8281 05 55
Fax: (359) 8281 05 50
E-Mail: aclistom@bg.atlascopco.com
Emp.: 120
Construction Machinery Mfr
S.I.C.: 3531
N.A.I.C.S.: 333120
Nick Evans *(Gen Mgr)*

Atlas Copco Makinalari Imalat AS (1)
Istasyon Mah Ibisaga Cad No 6
Tuzla, 34940 Istanbul, Turkey
Tel.: (90) 216 581 0 581
Fax: (90) 216 581 0 582
E-Mail: info@tr.atlascopco.com
Web Site: www.atlascopco.com.tr
Emp.: 250
Construction Machinery Mfr
S.I.C.: 3531
N.A.I.C.S.: 333120
Mehmet Yagcioglu *(Dir-Fin)*

Atlas Copco (Malaysia) Sdn. Bhd. (1)
26 Jalan Anggerik Mokara 31/47 Kota Kemuning Section 31
Shah Alam, Selangor, Malaysia
Tel.: (60) 3 5123 8888
Fax: (60) 3 5123 8999
E-Mail: malaysia.enquiry@my.atlascopco.com

Web Site: www.atlascopco.com.my
Construction & Mining Machinery Distr
S.I.C.: 5082
N.A.I.C.S.: 423810
Lee Ming Phun *(Gen Mgr-Compressors & Generators)*

Atlas Copco Namibia (Pty) Ltd (1)
No 1 Newcastle Str Northern Industrial Area
Windhoek, Namibia
Tel.: (264) 61 26 13 96
Fax: (264) 61 26 25 08
Web Site: www.atlascopco.co.za/zaus/Contactus/contactnamibia/
Emp.: 13
Construction Machinery Mfr
S.I.C.: 3531
N.A.I.C.S.: 333120
Uschi Kuhn *(Controller-Bus)*

Atlas Copco Nederland B.V. (1)
Merwedeweg 7
3336 LG Zwijndrecht, Netherlands
Tel.: (31) 78 623 02 30
Fax: (31) 786104696
E-Mail: info@nl.atlascopco.com
Web Site: www.atlascopco.nl
Emp.: 50
Oil & Gas Industrial Equipment Distr
S.I.C.: 5084
N.A.I.C.S.: 423830
Bob Vianen *(Mgr)*

Subsidiaries:

Atlas Copco Beheer B.V. (2)
Merwedeweg 7
3336 LG Zwijndrecht, Netherlands
Tel.: (31) 786 23 02 30
Fax: (31) 786 10 06 70
Emp.: 140
Air Compressor Mfr
S.I.C.: 3563
N.A.I.C.S.: 333912
Bob van Wijnen *(Gen Mgr)*

Atlas Copco Rental B.V. (2)
Merwedeweg 7
3336 LG Zwijndrecht, Netherlands
Tel.: (31) 10 23 10 110
Fax: (31) 10 23 10 110
E-Mail: verhuur@nl.atlascopco.com
Web Site: www.atlascopco.nl
Emp.: 2
Construction Machinery Rental & Leasing Services
S.I.C.: 7353
N.A.I.C.S.: 532412
Michtl Gasica *(Gen Mgr)*

Cirmac International B.V. (2)
Lan Van Westenenk 541
7334 DT Apeldoorn, Netherlands
Tel.: (31) 55 53 40110
Fax: (31) 55 534 0050
E-Mail: info@cirmac.com
Web Site: www.cirmac.com
Emp.: 45
Gas Treatment & Generation Services
S.I.C.: 1389
N.A.I.C.S.: 213112

Creemers Compressors B.V. (2)
Galliersweg
5340 AH Oss, Netherlands
Tel.: (31) 412 66 79 99
Fax: (31) 412 66 79 80
E-Mail: info@creemers.nl
Web Site: www.creemers.nl
Emp.: 30
Air Compressor Equipment Installation Services
S.I.C.: 1711
N.A.I.C.S.: 238220
John Neelen *(Gen Mgr)*

Grass-Air Holding B.V. (2)
Galliersweg 27
Oss, 5349 AT, Netherlands
Tel.: (31) 412632956
Fax: (31) 412664199
E-Mail: info@grassair.nl
Web Site: www.grassair.nl
Emp.: 6
Investment Management Services
S.I.C.: 6211
N.A.I.C.S.: 523999
John Neelen *(Dir-Fin & Tech)*

Subsidiary:

Grass-Air Compressoren B.V. (3)
Galliersweg 27
5349 AT Oss, Netherlands
Tel.: (31) 412 664100
Fax: (31) 412 664199
E-Mail: info@grassair.nl
Web Site: www.grassair.nl
Emp.: 45
Air Compressor Equipment Installation Services
S.I.C.: 1711
N.A.I.C.S.: 238220
John Neelen *(Gen Mgr)*

Atlas Copco (N.Z.) Ltd (1)
50 Carbine Road Mt Wellington
Private Bag 92-814
Penrose, Auckland, New Zealand
Tel.: (64) 9 5794069
Fax: (64) 9 5252006
E-Mail: service@nz.atlascopco.com
Web Site: www.atlascopco.co.nz
Emp.: 25
Construction & Mining Equipment Rental Services
S.I.C.: 7353
N.A.I.C.S.: 532412
Ian Cherrie *(Mgr-Natl Sls-Aftermarket)*

Subsidiary:

Intermech Ltd (2)
Level 3 Building 10 666 Great South Road
PO Box 204013
Ellerslie Highbrook, 2161 Auckland, New Zealand
Tel.: (64) 9 525 2220
Fax: (64) 9 579 3900
E-Mail: sales@intermech.co.nz
Web Site: www.intermech.co.nz
Compressed Natural Gas Refueling Solution Mfr
S.I.C.: 3559
N.A.I.C.S.: 333249

Atlas Copco Pakistan (Pvt) Ltd (1)
18 XX Khayaban e Iqbal DHA
Lahore, Pakistan
Tel.: (92) 42 35 749 406
Fax: (92) 42 35 749 409
E-Mail: atlascopco.pakistan@pk.atlascopco.com
Web Site: www.atlascopco.com
Emp.: 40
Industrial Machinery Mfr & Distr
S.I.C.: 3559
N.A.I.C.S.: 333249
Munther-Jack Zureikat *(Gen Mgr)*

Atlas Copco Peruana SA (1)
Francisco Grana 150-152 Urb
Santa Catalina, Lima, Peru
Tel.: (51) 1 411 6126
Fax: (51) 1 224 8675
E-Mail:
Web Site: www.atlascopco.com.pe
Emp.: 550
Construction Machinery Mfr & Distr
S.I.C.: 3531
N.A.I.C.S.: 333120
Luciano Wolfarth *(Gen Mgr)*

Atlas Copco (Philippines) Inc. (1)
North Main Avenue Lot 12 Block 2 Laguna Techno Park
Binan, Laguna, 4024, Philippines
Tel.: (63) 2 8430535
Fax: (63) 2 8430237
E-Mail: acpi@ph.atlascopco.com
Web Site: www.atlascopco.com.ph
Air Compressor Mfr & Distr
S.I.C.: 3563
N.A.I.C.S.: 333912
Eric Alfonso *(Mgr-Bus Line-Compressor Technique Oil Free Div)*

Atlas Copco Polska Sp. Z.o.o. (1)
Al Krakowska 61A Sekocin Nowy
05-090 Raszyn, Poland
Tel.: (48) 22 572 68 00
Fax: (48) 22 572 68 09
E-Mail: acpoland@pl.atlascopco.com
Web Site: www.atlascopco.pl
Emp.: 150
Air Compressor Sales & Maintenance Services
S.I.C.: 5075
N.A.I.C.S.: 423730
Tomasz Przeradzki *(Reg Mgr)*

Atlas Copco Reinsurance SA (1)
74 Rue de Merl
2146 Luxembourg, Luxembourg
Tel.: (352) 24 69 53 1
Fax: (352) 26 25 84 39
Emp.: 2
Insurance Management Services
S.I.C.: 6411
N.A.I.C.S.: 524298
Claude Weber *(Mng Dir)*

Atlas Copco Romania S.R.L (1)
Sos Bucuresti-Ploiesti Nr 135 Corp 2 Parter Sector 1
Bucharest, 013686, Romania RO
Tel.: (40) 31 405 71 74
Fax: (40) 21 351 37 64
E-Mail: office.ro@ro.atlascopco.com
Web Site: www.atlascopco.ro/rous/
Emp.: 50
Construction & Mining Machinery Distr
S.I.C.: 5082
N.A.I.C.S.: 423810
Tuluy Yetis *(Gen Mgr)*

Subsidiary:

Atlas Copco Industrial Technique S.R.L. (2)
6 Aleea Tinutul Herta
Pitesti, 110162, Romania
Tel.: (40) 248211638
Fax: (40) 24821163
Air Compressor Mfr
S.I.C.: 3563
N.A.I.C.S.: 333912

Atlas Copco S.A.E. (1)
Avda Jose Garate 3
28823 Coslada, Madrid, Spain
Tel.: (34) 91 6279100
Fax: (34) 91 6713116
E-Mail: ac.spain@es.atlascopco.com
Web Site: www.atlascopco.com
Emp.: 15
Construction Equipment Mfr & Distr
S.I.C.: 3531
N.A.I.C.S.: 333120

Atlas Copco (Schweiz) AG (1)
Buetigenstrasse 80
Studen, 2557, Switzerland
Tel.: (41) 32 374 19 00
Fax: (41) 32 374 12 72
E-Mail: atlascopco.schweiz@ch.atlascopco.com
Emp.: 80
Air Compressor Mfr & Distr
S.I.C.: 3563
N.A.I.C.S.: 333912
Ricardo Timperi *(Gen Mgr)*

Subsidiaries:

GreenField AG (2)
Sternenfeldstrasse 14
4127 Birsfelden, Switzerland
Tel.: (41) 61 827 35 35
Fax: (41) 61 827 34 34
E-Mail: info@ch.greenfield-comp.com
Web Site: www.greenfield-comp.com
Compressor Machinery Installation Services
S.I.C.: 1711
N.A.I.C.S.: 238220

Servatechnik AG (2)
Aeschwuhrstrasse 54
4665 Oftringen, Switzerland
Tel.: (41) 62 789 75 95
Fax: (41) 62 789 76 76
E-Mail: info@servatechnik.ch
Industrial Machinery Distr
S.I.C.: 5084
N.A.I.C.S.: 423830
Peter Jordi *(Mgr-HR)*

Atlas Copco (Shanghai) Equipment Rental Co Ltd (1)
T72-2 No 1100 Jinsui Road Jinqiao Export Processing Zone
Shanghai, 201206, China
Tel.: (86) 21 6108 2388
Fax: (86) 139 1666 6869
Industrial Equipment Rental Services
S.I.C.: 7359
N.A.I.C.S.: 532490

Atlas Copco (Shanghai) Process Equipment Co Ltd (1)
No 899 Cenglin Road Lingang New City
Pudong New Area, 201306 Shanghai, China
Tel.: (86) 21 60 97 81 00
Fax: (86) 21 60 97 81 44
E-Mail: atlascopco.cof@cn.atlascopco.com
Industrial Machinery Mfr
S.I.C.: 3559
N.A.I.C.S.: 333249

Atlas Copco (Shenyang) Construction and Mining Equipment Ltd (1)
No 12 Kunminghu Street Shenyang Economic
Technological Development Zone,
Shenyang, 110027, China
Tel.: (86) 24 25811769, ext. 8903
Fax: (86) 24 25810522
E-Mail: shenyangcm@shenyangcm.com
Web Site: www.shenyangcm.com
Industrial Drilling Machinery Mfr
S.I.C.: 3559
N.A.I.C.S.: 333249
Kobus Malan *(Gen Mgr)*

Atlas Copco (South East Asia) Pte Ltd (1)
25 Tuas Avenue 2
Singapore, 639456, Singapore
Tel.: (65) 62 10 80 00
Fax: (65) 6862 1562
E-Mail: acsea@sg.atlascopco.com
Web Site: www.atlascopco.com.sg
Construction Equipment Mfr & Distr
S.I.C.: 3531
N.A.I.C.S.: 333120
Lee Ming Phun *(Gen Mgr-Compressor Technique-Brunei & Sri Lanka)*

Atlas Copco S.r.o. (1)
Prumyslova 10
102 00 Prague, Czech Republic
Tel.: (420) 225 434 000
Fax: (420) 225 434 343
E-Mail: kompresory@cz.atlascopco.com
Air Compressor Mfr
S.I.C.: 3563
N.A.I.C.S.: 333912

Atlas Copco Taiwan Ltd (1)
No 8 Alley 80 Lane 298 Gong 2nd Road
Longtan, Tao Yuan, 32559, Taiwan
Tel.: (886) 3 479 6838, ext. 230
Fax: (886) 3 479 6820
E-Mail: twn.info@tw.atlascopco.com
Web Site: www.atlascopco.com
Construction Machinery Mfr & Distr
S.I.C.: 3531
N.A.I.C.S.: 333120
Dereck Devlin *(Gen Mgr)*

Atlas Copco Tanzania Ltd (1)
Plot 35 Nyakato Industrial Area
PO Box 505
Mwanza, Tanzania
Tel.: (255) 28 2570289
Fax: (255) 28 257 0290
Web Site: www.atlascopco.com
Construction & Mining Equipment Distr
S.I.C.: 5082
N.A.I.C.S.: 423810
Henry Ngugi *(Country Mgr)*

Atlas Copco (Thailand) Ltd (1)
125 Moo 9 Wellgrow Industry Estate
Bangna-Trad Km 36
Bangwua, Bang Pakong, Chachoengsao, 24130, Thailand
Tel.: (66) 38 56 29 00
Fax: (66) 38 56 29 01
E-Mail: hotline@th.atlascopco.com
Web Site: www.atlascopco.co.th
Emp.: 200
Air Compressor Mfr
S.I.C.: 3563
N.A.I.C.S.: 333912
Apivat Tienpolkrang *(Country Mgr-Construction & Mining Equipment)*

Atlas Copco UK Holdings Ltd (1)
Swallowdale Lane
Hemel Hempstead, Hertfordshire, HP2 7HA, United Kingdom
Tel.: (44) 1442 261201
Fax: (44) 1442 234791
E-Mail: ToolsUK_info@uk.atlascopco.com
Web Site: www.atlascopco.co.uk

Atlas Copco AB—(Continued)

Emp.: 100
Construction & Mining Machinery Distr
S.I.C.: 5082
N.A.I.C.S.: 423810

Subsidiaries:

Atlas Copco Ltd (2)
Swallowdale Lane
Hemel Hempstead, Hertfordshire, HP2 7EA, United Kingdom
Tel.: (44) 845 6010001
Fax: (44) 1442 234791
E-Mail: gba.info@uk.atlascopco.com
Web Site: www.atlascopco.com
Emp.: 7
Compressor Machinery Mfr & Distr
S.I.C.: 3563
N.A.I.C.S.: 333912
Leen van Diggele *(Gen Mgr)*

Atlas Copco (NI) Ltd (2)
Unit 4 Ballinderry Business Park
Lisburn, Antrim, BT28 2BP, United Kingdom
Tel.: (44) 28 92 606400
Fax: (44) 28 92 606404
E-Mail: ac.cmtuk@uk.atlascopco.com
Air Compressor Mfr
S.I.C.: 3563
N.A.I.C.S.: 333912
Harry McDowell *(Mgr-Compressor Technique)*

Medaes Limited (2)
Telford Crescent
Staveley, Chesterfield, Derbyshire, S43 3PF, United Kingdom UK
Tel.: (44) 1246474242 (100%)
Fax: (44) 1246472982
E-Mail: gbn.info@beaconmedaes.com
Web Site: www.medaes.com
Sales Range: $10-24.9 Million
Emp.: 80
Medical Gas Delivery Systems Mfr
S.I.C.: 3841
N.A.I.C.S.: 339112
Steve Parkinson *(Gen Mgr)*

Atlas Copco Venezuela SA (1)
Calle Milan Con Chicago Edificio Alfa Piso 3 ZI La California Sur
Caracas, Venezuela
Tel.: (58) 212 300 83 00
Fax: (58) 212 300 83 48
E-Mail: tencionalcliente@ve.atlascopco.com
Web Site: www.atlascopco.com.ve
Construction & Mining Machinery Whslr
S.I.C.: 5082
N.A.I.C.S.: 423810
Jose Sanchez *(Mgr-Construction & Mining Tech)*

Atlas Copco Vietnam Company Ltd (1)
Lot F Str 12 Song Than II Industrial Zone
Di An, Binh Duong, Vietnam
Tel.: (84) 650 373 8484
Fax: (84) 650 373 8483
E-Mail: viet.ha@vn.atlascopco.com
Web Site: www.atlascopco.com.vn
Emp.: 70
Construction & Mining Equipment Distr
S.I.C.: 5082
N.A.I.C.S.: 423810
David Anderson *(Gen Mgr-Mining & Rock Excavation)*

Atlas Copco (Zambia) Ltd (1)
No 210 Kabundi Road
PO Box 11291
Chingola, Zambia
Tel.: (260) 212 311281
Fax: (260) 212 313877
E-Mail: atlas.zam@atlascopco.com
Web Site: www.atlascopco.co.zm
Emp.: 126
Industrial Machinery Mfr & Distr
S.I.C.: 3559
N.A.I.C.S.: 333249
Patrick Chanda *(Controller-Bus)*

Desoutter GmbH (1)
Edmund-Seng-Str 3-5
63477 Maintal, Germany
Tel.: (49) 6181 411 0
Fax: (49) 6181 411 184
E-Mail: desoutter.gmbh@desouttertools.com
Industrial Machinery Mfr
S.I.C.: 3559
N.A.I.C.S.: 333249

Desoutter Italiana S.r.l. (1)
Viale della Repubblica 65
20035 Lissone, Italy
Tel.: (39) 0 39 244 101
Fax: (39) 0 39 465 5025
E-Mail: desoutter.italiana@cp.com
Web Site: www.desouttertools.com
Pneumatic System & Tool Mfr
S.I.C.: 3546
N.A.I.C.S.: 333991

Desoutter S.A. (1)
Avenida de la Industria 9 Poligono Industrial de Alcobendas
28108 Alcobendas, Spain
Tel.: (34) 915 90 31 52
Fax: (34) 915 90 31 61
Machine Tool Mfr
S.I.C.: 3541
N.A.I.C.S.: 333517

Edwards Group Limited (1)
Manor Royal
Crawley, W Sussex, RH10 9LW, United Kingdom Ky
Tel.: (44) 1293528844
Fax: (44) 1293533453
E-Mail: info@edwardsvacuum.com
Web Site: www.edwardsvacuum.com
Rev.: $940,151,337
Assets: $1,336,079,340
Liabilities: $925,779,798
Net Worth: $410,299,542
Earnings: $61,750,239
Emp.: 3,300
Fiscal Year-end: 12/31/12
Microelectronics Industry Gases, Vacuum & Specialist Equipment Distr
S.I.C.: 3699
N.A.I.C.S.: 335999
Nicholas C. Rose *(Chm)*
David Smith *(CFO)*
Sia Abbaszadeh *(CTO & CMO)*
Neil A. Lavender Jones *(Sr VP-Gen Vacuum)*
Chris Shepherd *(Sr VP-HR)*

U.S. Subsidiary:

Edwards Vacuum, Inc. (2)
6400 Inducon Corporate Dr
Sanborn, NY 14132 DE
Tel.: (978) 658-5410
Fax: (866) 484-5218
Toll Free: (800) 848-9800
E-Mail: info@edwardsvacuum.com
Web Site: www.edwardsvacuum.com
Emp.: 100
Mfr & Marketing of Vacuum Dry Pumps, Turbo Pumps, Instrumentation
S.I.C.: 3825
N.A.I.C.S.: 334515
Phil Blakey *(Pres)*

Non-U.S. Subsidiaries:

Edwards GmbH (2)
Ammerthalstr 36
D85551 Kirchheim, Germany De
Tel.: (49) 899919180
Telex: 482375
Fax: (49) 8999191899
E-Mail: info@edwardsvacuum.com
Web Site: www.edwardsvacuum.com
Microelectronics Industry Gases, Vacuum & Specialist Equipment Distr
S.I.C.: 3559
N.A.I.C.S.: 333249

Edwards Japan Limited (2)
1078-1 Yoshihashi
Yachiyo, Chiba, 276-8523, Japan JP
Tel.: (81) 474588831
Fax: (81) 474588833
E-Mail: info@edwardsvacuum.com
Web Site: www.edwardsvacuum.com
Emp.: 300
Semiconductor & Vacuum-Dependent Processing Products & Services
S.I.C.: 3674
N.A.I.C.S.: 334413

Edwards S.p.A. (2)
Via Carpaccio 35
Trezzano San Naviglio, Milan, 20090, Italy IT
Tel.: (39) 0248447217
Telex: 311345
Fax: (39) 0248401638
E-Mail: info@edwardsvacuum.com
Web Site: www.edwardsvacuum.com
Emp.: 25
Semiconductor & Vacuum-Dependent Processing Products & Services
S.I.C.: 3674
N.A.I.C.S.: 334413
Marinella Varallo *(Mng Dir)*

Edwards Vacuo Ltda (2)
Rua Bernardo Wrona 222
Bairro do Limao, 02710-060 Sao Paulo, SP, Brazil BR
Tel.: (55) 1139525000
Telex: 1130772
Fax: (55) 11-3965-2766
Web Site: www.edwardsvacuum.com
Emp.: 40
Semiconductor & Vacuum-Dependent Processing Products & Services Mfr
S.I.C.: 3674
N.A.I.C.S.: 334413

Industrial Technique s.r.o. (1)
Elektrarenska 4
831 04 Bratislava, Slovakia
Tel.: (421) 264 462 636
Fax: (421) 264 463 464
E-Mail: info@its-ee.com
Emp.: 17
Machine Tool Maintenance Services
S.I.C.: 7699
N.A.I.C.S.: 811310
Wojciech Wroblewski *(Gen Mgr)*

LLC Atlas Copco Ukraine (1)
9 Moskovskiy Ave Building 3
04073 Kiev, Ukraine
Tel.: (380) 44 499 18 70
Fax: (380) 44 499 18 77
E-Mail: ua_atlascopco@ua.atlascopco.com
Web Site: www.atlascopco.com
Emp.: 35
Industrial Machinery Mfr & Distr
S.I.C.: 3559
N.A.I.C.S.: 333249
Kirill Kondratenko *(Controller-Bus)*

Oy Atlas Copco Ab (1)
Tuupakankuja 1
01740 Vantaa, Finland
Tel.: (358) 20 718 9200
Fax: (358) 20 718 9201
E-Mail: kompressori.fi@fi.atlascopco.com
Emp.: 71
Air Compressor Mfr
S.I.C.: 3563
N.A.I.C.S.: 333912
Max Roos *(Mng Dir)*

Subsidiaries:

Oy Atlas Copco Kompressorit Ab (2)
Tuupakankuja 1
01740 Vantaa, Finland
Tel.: (358) 20 718 92 00
Fax: (358) 20 718 92 01
E-Mail: kompressori.fi@fi.atlascopco.com
Web Site: www.atlascopco.com
Emp.: 100
Compressor Machinery Mfr
S.I.C.: 3563
N.A.I.C.S.: 333912
Max Rose *(Gen Mgr)*

Oy Atlas Copco Louhintatekniikka Ab (2)
Tuupakankuja 1
01740 Vantaa, Finland
Tel.: (358) 20 718 93 00
Fax: (358) 20 718 93 01
E-Mail: louhinta.fi@fi.atlascopco.com
Emp.: 25
Mining Machinery Distr
S.I.C.: 5084
N.A.I.C.S.: 423830
Ilkka Eskola *(Gen Mgr-Construction & Mining Technique)*

Oy Atlas Copco Rotex Ab (2)
Pihtisulunkatu 1a
Tampere, 33330, Finland
Tel.: (358) 207189400
Fax: (358) 207189351
Emp.: 20
Machine Tool Mfr
S.I.C.: 3545
N.A.I.C.S.: 333515

Oy Atlas Copco Tools Ab (2)
Tuupakankuja 1
01740 Vantaa, Finland
Tel.: (358) 20 718 9400
Fax: (358) 207189402
E-Mail: tools.fi@fi.atlascopco.com
Web Site: www.atlascopco.fi
Emp.: 10
Construction & Mining Tool Machinery Distr
S.I.C.: 5082
N.A.I.C.S.: 423810
Tom Karlsson *(Gen Mgr)*

PT Atlas Copco Indonesia (1)
Cilandak Commercial Estate Kav 203 Jl Cilandak Kko
Jakarta, 12560, Indonesia
Tel.: (62) 21 7801008
Fax: (62) 21 7801370
E-Mail: atlascopco.indonesia@id.atlascopco.com
Web Site: www.atlascopco.co.id
Emp.: 15
Construction & Mining Equipment Distr
S.I.C.: 5082
N.A.I.C.S.: 423810
Uut Ananta *(Mgr-Bus Line)*

Subsidiary:

PT Atlas Copco Fluidcon (2)
Cilandak Commercial Estate Building 201 Jl Raya Cilandak KKO
Jakarta, 12560, Indonesia
Tel.: (62) 21 7890550
Fax: (62) 21 7890549
E-Mail: jakarta.branch@id.atlascopco.com
Web Site: www.fluidcon.co.id
Oil & Gas Exploration Services
S.I.C.: 1389
N.A.I.C.S.: 213112
Mustafa Dahlan *(Mgr-Personnel)*

Shanghai Bolaite Compressor Co Ltd (1)
No 528 Laodong Road
Jiading Dist, Shanghai, China
Tel.: (86) 2159946511, ext. 6511
Fax: (86) 2159946638
Compressor Machinery Mfr
S.I.C.: 3563
N.A.I.C.S.: 333912

Sociedade Atlas Copco de Portugal Lda (1)
Avenida do Forte n3
2790-073 Carnaxide, Portugal
Tel.: (351) 2 14 16 85 73
Fax: (351) 214 17 09 41
E-Mail: info.portugal@pt.atlascopco.com
Web Site: www.atlascopco.pt
Emp.: 4
Construction & Mining Equipment Distr
S.I.C.: 5082
N.A.I.C.S.: 423810
Milton Carvalho *(Mgr-Svc-Ports Sines, Setubal & Lisboa)*

SPA Atlas Copco Algerie (1)
Route de Sidi Menif Tranche 3 Lot 119
Zeralda, Algiers, Algeria
Tel.: (213) 21 32 83 25
Fax: (213) 21 32 83 19
Emp.: 80
Construction Equipment Mfr & Distr
S.I.C.: 3531
N.A.I.C.S.: 333120
Faouzi Ben Gharbia *(Gen Mgr)*

Tooltec (Qingdao) Tool Co Ltd (1)
No 192 Zhuzhou Road
Qingdao, 266101, China
Tel.: (86) 532 88706530
Fax: (86) 3288706516
Web Site: www.atlascopco.com
Emp.: 6
Machine Tool Mfr
S.I.C.: 3545
N.A.I.C.S.: 333515
Marco Fossataro *(Mgr-Ops)*

Wuxi Pneumatech Air/Gas Purity Equipment Co Ltd (1)
No 36 ZhuJiang Road New District
Wuxi, Jiangsu, 214028, China
Tel.: (86) 510 8521 1442
Fax: (86) 510 8521 7869
E-Mail: sale@cn.pneumatech.com
Web Site: www.pneumatech.com.cn

Emp.: 200
Compressor Machinery Mfr & Distr
S.I.C.: 3563
N.A.I.C.S.: 333912
Shirley Zhang *(Mgr-Personnel)*

ZAO Atlas Copco (1)
15 Vashutinskoe Road
Khimki, Moscow, Russia
Tel.: (7) 495 933 55 50
Fax: (7) 495 933 55 60
E-Mail: info@ru.atlascopco.com
Compressor Machinery Maintenance Services
S.I.C.: 7699
N.A.I.C.S.: 811310

ATLAS CORPORATION S.R.L.

59 Sos Pipera
Bucharest, Romania
Tel.: (40) 21 230 8782 (-8785)
Fax: (40) 21 230 8786
E-Mail: customerservice@atlascorporation.ro
Web Site: www.atlas-corp.ro
Year Founded: 1994
Emp.: 100
Business Description:
Construction Materials Mfr & Distr, Commercial Office Leasing & Electronic Products Distr
S.I.C.: 5032
N.A.I.C.S.: 423320
Personnel:
John Sitinas *(Owner)*
Division:

Atlas Corporation S.R.L. - Apla Division (1)
59 Sos Pipera
Bucharest, Romania
Tel.: (40) 21 230 8777 (-8780)
Fax: (40) 21 230 8760
E-Mail: info@atlascorporation.ro
Web Site: www.apla.ro
Emp.: 20
Construction Materials Mfr & Distr
S.I.C.: 5032
N.A.I.C.S.: 423320

ATLAS CYCLES (HARYANA) LTD.

Atlas Road Atlas Nagar
Post Box No 20
Sonipat, Haryana, 131001, India
Tel.: (91) 1302200001
Fax: (91) 1302200018
Web Site: www.atlascyclesonepat.com
ATLASCYCLE—(NSE)
Sales Range: $150-199.9 Million
Emp.: 1,900
Business Description:
Bicycle & Steel Tube Mfr
S.I.C.: 3751
N.A.I.C.S.: 336991
Personnel:
Rajiv Kapur *(Co-Pres)*
Vikram Kapur *(Co-Pres)*
Board of Directors:
Hari Krishan Ahuja
Hira Lal Bhatia
Prithvi Raj Chawla
I. D. Chugh
Vikram Khosla
Surendra Mohan Mehra
Kartik Roop Rai
Transfer Agent:
MAS Services Limited
T-34 2nd Floor Okhla Industrial Area Phase - II
New Delhi, India

ATLAS ELECTRICA, S.A.

Carretera a Heredia Km 12
Heredia, Costa Rica
Tel.: (506) 22772000
Fax: (506) 22603930
E-Mail: atlaselectrica@atlas.co.cr
Web Site: www.atlas.co.cr
Year Founded: 1961
Sales Range: $100-124.9 Million
Emp.: 1,500
Business Description:
Home Electronics & Appliances Mfr
S.I.C.: 3999
N.A.I.C.S.: 335210
Personnel:
Luis Gamboa Arguedas *(Pres)*
Alvaro Sancho Castro *(Treas)*
Carlos Fischel Mora *(Sec)*
Board of Directors:
Alvaro Cedeno Gomez
Carlos Fischel Mora
Luis Gamboa Arguedas
Andre Garnier Kruse
Rafael Quiros Bustamante
Elias Reifer Grimbaun
Alvaro Sancho Castro
Alberto Trejos Zuniga

ATLAS ESTATES LIMITED

Martello Court Admiral Park
PO Box 119
Saint Peter Port, GY1 3HB, Guernsey
Tel.: (44) 1481211000
Fax: (44) 1481211001
E-Mail: InvestorRelations@atlasestates.com
Web Site: www.atlasestates.com
ATL—(WAR)
Rev.: $58,099,351
Assets: $437,716,599
Liabilities: $338,485,023
Net Worth: $99,231,575
Earnings: ($17,528,480)
Emp.: 318
Fiscal Year-end: 12/31/12
Business Description:
Real Estate Investment Services
S.I.C.: 6211
N.A.I.C.S.: 523999
Personnel:
Andrew Fox *(Chm)*
Board of Directors:
Andrew Fox
Mark Chasey
Guy Indig
Legal Counsel:
Weil Gotshal & Manges-Pawel Rymarz Sp k
Emilii Plater 53Warsaw
Warsaw, Poland
Ozannes
1 Le Marchant Street
PO Box 186
Saint Peter Port, Guernsey
Non-U.S. Subsidiaries:

Atlas Estates Cooperatief U.A. (1)
Rietland Park
PO Box 15651
1019 DT Amsterdam, Netherlands
Tel.: (31) 206704455
Fax: (31) 206706211
Emp.: 12
Real Estate Services
S.I.C.: 6531
N.A.I.C.S.: 531390
Lena Mariam *(Acct Mgr)*

Capital Art Apartments Sp. z o.o. (1)
Stock Exchange 4
02017 Warsaw, Poland
Tel.: (48) 223405400
Fax: (48) 226326020
E-Mail: caa@caapartments.pl
Web Site: www.caapartments.pl
Real Estate Services
S.I.C.: 6531
N.A.I.C.S.: 531390

Grzybowska Centrum Sp. z o.o. (1)
11 Walicow
00 851 Warsaw, Poland
Tel.: (48) 225839253
Real Estate Services
S.I.C.: 6531
N.A.I.C.S.: 531390

Ligetvaros Kft (1)
Damjanich u 11-15
1071 Budapest, Hungary
Tel.: (36) 14795800
Fax: (36) 14795810
E-Mail: info@ligetvaros.hu
Web Site: www.ligetvaros.hu
Emp.: 90
Real Estate Services
S.I.C.: 6531
N.A.I.C.S.: 531390
Sptingold Tibi *(Owner)*

World Real Estate S.R.L. (1)
Via Paolo Emilio 7
00192 Rome, Italy
Tel.: (39) 0632110998
Fax: (39) 063213962
E-Mail: desk@romepower.com
Web Site: www.romepower.com
Emp.: 3
Houses & Flats Rental Services
S.I.C.: 6514
N.A.I.C.S.: 531110
Marco Agretti *(Mgr)*

ATLAS FINANCE PLC

27A Hr Botev blvd
Plovdiv, 4000, Bulgaria
Tel.: (359) 585 886
E-Mail: office@atlasfinance.bg
Web Site: www.atlasfinance.bg
A4F—(BUL)
Business Description:
Financial & Accounting Services
S.I.C.: 8721
N.A.I.C.S.: 541219
Personnel:
Ginka Milusheva-Kalaydzhieva *(Member-Mgmt Bd)*
Supervisory Board of Directors:
Assen Ivanov Konarev
Peter Neychev Neychev
Stefan Georgiev Pronchev

ATLAS GROUP OF COMPANIES

2nd Floor Federation House
Shahrah-e-Firdousi
Karachi, 75600, Pakistan
Tel.: (92) 215369471
Fax: (92) 5879693
E-Mail: agc@atlas.com.pk
Web Site: www.atlasgrouppk.com
Emp.: 7,000
Business Description:
Holding Company
S.I.C.: 6719
N.A.I.C.S.: 551112
Personnel:
Yusuf H. Shirazi *(Chm)*
Subsidiary:

Atlas Engineering Limited (1)
15th Mile National Highway
Landhi, Karachi, 75120, Pakistan
Tel.: (92) 215016921
Fax: (92) 215011709
E-Mail: ael@atlasengineering.com.pk
Web Site: www.atlasengineering.com.pk
Sls.: $23,890,876
Emp.: 228
Fiscal Year-end: 06/30/13
Cast Iron Process Pig Iron & Aluminum Alloys Producer; Automotive Components Mfr
S.I.C.: 3714
N.A.I.C.S.: 336390
Yusuf H. Shirazi *(Chm)*
Sadaqat Ali *(CEO)*
Shakil Ahmed *(CFO)*
Danyal Ahmed Rasheed *(Sec)*
Holding:

Atlas Bank Ltd. (1)
3rd Floor Federation House
Sharah-e-Firdousi
Main Clifton, Karachi, Pakistan
Tel.: (92) 21111745745
ATBL—(KAR)
Sales Range: $10-24.9 Million
Emp.: 105
Banking Services
S.I.C.: 6211
N.A.I.C.S.: 523110
Cyrus Tengra *(CFO)*
Joint Ventures:

Atlas Battery Ltd. (1)
D-181 Central Avenue
SITE, Karachi, 75730, Pakistan
Tel.: (92) 21 2567990
Fax: (92) 21 32564703
E-Mail: info@atlasbattery.com.pk
Web Site: www.atlasbattery.com.pk
ATBA—(KAR LAH)
Sls.: $89,904,905
Assets: $36,844,259
Liabilities: $16,836,161
Net Worth: $20,008,097
Earnings: $5,896,805
Emp.: 58
Fiscal Year-end: 06/30/13
Battery Mfr; Owned by GS Yuasa International Ltd. & by Atlas Group of Companies
S.I.C.: 3691
N.A.I.C.S.: 335911
Yusuf H. Shirazi *(Chm)*
Ali H. Shirazi *(Pres & CEO)*
Talha Saad *(Mng Dir)*
Ahmad Zafaryab Ali *(CFO)*
Rizwan Ahmed *(Sec)*

Atlas Honda Limited (1)
1 Mcleod Road
Lahore, 5400, Pakistan
Tel.: (92) 42111111245
Fax: (92) 4237233518
E-Mail: ahlhr@lhr.atlashonda.com.pk
Web Site: www.atlashonda.com.pk
ATLH—(KAR LAH)
Sls.: $428,754,701
Assets: $121,706,257
Liabilities: $55,251,836
Net Worth: $66,454,421
Earnings: $16,287,055
Fiscal Year-end: 03/31/13
Motorcycle Mfr & Distr; Joint Venture of Atlas Group & Honda Motor Co., Ltd.
S.I.C.: 3751
N.A.I.C.S.: 336991
Yusuf H. Shirazi *(Chm)*
Saquib H. Shirazi *(CEO)*
Kashif Yaseen *(CFO)*

Honda Atlas Cars Pakistan Ltd. (1)
43 - km Multan Road Manga Mandi
Lahore, Pakistan
Tel.: (92) 4235384671
Fax: (92) 4235384691
E-Mail: info@honda.com.pk
Web Site: www.honda.com.pk
HCAR—(ISL KAR LAH)
Sls.: $306,681,739
Assets: $153,296,500
Liabilities: $139,223,225
Net Worth: $14,073,275
Earnings: $2,474,627
Emp.: 1,003
Fiscal Year-end: 03/31/13
Car Mfr; Owned by Honda Motor Co., Ltd. & Atlas Group of Companies
S.I.C.: 3711
N.A.I.C.S.: 336111
Yusuf H. Shirazi *(Chm)*
Takeharu Aoki *(Pres & CEO)*
Ahmed Umair Wajid *(CFO)*
Sardar Abid Ali Khan *(Sec)*

ATLAS IRON LIMITED

Level 18 Raine Square 300 Murray Street
Perth, WA, 6000, Australia
Tel.: (61) 8 6228 8000
Fax: (61) 8 6228 8999
E-Mail: atlas@atlasiron.com.au
Web Site: www.atlasiron.com.au
AGO—(ASX OTC)
Rev.: $724,402,268
Assets: $2,260,602,520
Liabilities: $580,578,920
Net Worth: $1,680,023,599
Earnings: ($255,389,531)

Atlas Iron Limited—(Continued)

Emp.: 311
Fiscal Year-end: 06/30/13

Business Description:
Iron Ore Mining
S.I.C.: 1011
N.A.I.C.S.: 212210

Personnel:
Kenneth Edward Brinsden *(Mng Dir)*
Jeremy Sinclair *(COO)*
Robert Wilson *(Chief Dev Officer)*
Yasmin Broughton *(Gen Counsel & Co-Sec)*
Mark Hancock *(Co-Sec)*

Board of Directors:
David Flanagan
Kenneth Edward Brinsden
Jeff Dowling
Mark Hancock
David Hannon
Kerry Gaye Sanderson
Geoff Simpson
David Smith
Sook Yee Tai

Legal Counsel:
Ashurst
Level 36 Grosvenor Place 225 George Street
Sydney, 2000, Australia

ATLAS PEARLS AND PERFUMES LTD.

(Formerly Atlas South Sea Pearl Ltd.)
Shop 1 47-49 Bay View Terrace
Claremont, WA, 6010, Australia
Mailing Address:
PO Box 1048
Claremont, WA, 6910, Australia
Tel.: (61) 892844249
Fax: (61) 892843031
E-Mail: atlas@atlaspearlsandperfumes.com.au
Web Site: www.atlaspearlsandperfumes.com.au
Year Founded: 1981
ATP—(ASX)
Rev.: $12,304,756
Assets: $33,601,741
Liabilities: $9,385,023
Net Worth: $24,216,718
Earnings: $1,406,150
Emp.: 840
Fiscal Year-end: 12/31/12

Business Description:
Pearl Farming
Export
S.I.C.: 0971
N.A.I.C.S.: 114210

Personnel:
Stephen Paul Birkbeck *(Chm)*
Jan Jorgensen *(COO)*
Stephen Gleeson *(Co-Sec)*
Susan Patricia Hunter *(Co-Sec)*

Board of Directors:
Stephen Paul Birkbeck
Stephen John Arrow
Timothy James Martin
Geoffrey Newman
Joseph James Uel Taylor

Subsidiary:

Essential Oils Of Tasmania Pty Ltd **(1)**
82 Browns Road Kingston
7050 Hobart, Tasmania, Australia
Tel.: (61) 362294222
Fax: (61) 362292957
Essential Oils & Plant Extract Mfr
S.I.C.: 2833
N.A.I.C.S.: 325411

ATLAS S.A GALATI

Soseaua Smardan nr 2
Galati, Romania
Tel.: (40) 236448114
Fax: (40) 236448113
E-Mail: atlas@atlas-sa.ro
Web Site: www.atlas-sa.ro
ATLK—(BUC)
Rev.: $9,348,999
Assets: $14,121,439
Liabilities: $5,034,212
Net Worth: $9,087,226
Earnings: $102,768
Emp.: 364
Fiscal Year-end: 12/31/12

Business Description:
Civil Construction Services
S.I.C.: 1541
N.A.I.C.S.: 236210

Personnel:
Cernega Ovidiu *(Pres)*
Mitru Aurora *(Sec)*

ATLAS SOUTH SEA PEARL LTD.

(See Under Atlas Pearls and Perfumes Ltd.)

ATLASINVEST

Chaussee de la Hulpe 120
Brussels, 1000, Belgium
Tel.: (32) 2663 1750
Fax: (32) 2663 1760
E-Mail: info@atlasinvest.eu
Web Site: www.atlasinvest.eu
Emp.: 20

Business Description:
Private Equity Firm
S.I.C.: 6211
N.A.I.C.S.: 523999

Personnel:
Marcel Q.H. van Poecke *(Chm)*
Walter Van Cauwenberge *(CFO)*
Ruben Clement *(Gen Counsel)*

Non-U.S. Joint Venture:

Varo Energy Holding S.A. **(1)**
c/o Vitol Boulevard du Pont d'Arve 28
CH-1205 Geneva, Switzerland CH
Tel.: (41) 22 322 1111
Web Site: www.varoenergy.com
Holding Company; Petroleum Refining & Marketing Services
S.I.C.: 6719
N.A.I.C.S.: 551112
Jacobus G. Sterken *(Chm)*

Subsidiaries:

Varo Energy Marketing AG **(2)**
Industriestrasse 24
Postfach 4713
CH-6304 Zug, Switzerland CH
Tel.: (41) 41 747 23 00
Fax: (41) 41 747 23 95
E-Mail: info@varoenergy.com
Web Site: www.varoenergy.com
Emp.: 10
Petroleum Wholesale Trade Agency
S.I.C.: 7389
N.A.I.C.S.: 425120

Varo Refining Cressier S.A. **(2)**
Zone Industrielle Les Hugues
Case Postale 72
CH-2088 Cressier, Switzerland CH
Tel.: (41) 32 758 6111
Fax: (41) 32 758 6222
E-Mail: refining@varoenergy.com
Web Site: www.varoenergy.com
Emp.: 240
Petroleum Refinery
S.I.C.: 2911
N.A.I.C.S.: 324110
Jilles Vollin *(Dir-Ops)*

ATLASSIAN PTY. LTD.

173-185 Sussex Street
Sydney, NSW, 2000, Australia
Tel.: (61) 2 9262 1443
Fax: (61) 2 8208 7383
E-Mail: sales@atlassian.com
Web Site: www.atlassian.com
Year Founded: 2002
Sales Range: $100-124.9 Million
Emp.: 450

Business Description:
Collaboration & Development Software Developer
S.I.C.: 7372
N.A.I.C.S.: 511210

Personnel:
Michael Cannon-Brookes *(Co-Founder & Co-CEO)*
Scott Farquhar *(Co-Founder & Co-CEO)*
Doug Burgum *(Chm)*
Jay Simons *(Pres)*
Alex Estevez *(CFO)*
Paul Willard *(CMO)*
Jeffrey W. Diana *(Chief People Officer)*

Board of Directors:
Doug Burgum
Kirk Bowman
Michael Cannon-Brookes
Murray J. Demo
Scott Farquhar
Jay Parikh
Richard Wong

ATLATSA RESOURCES CORPORATION

(Formerly Anooraq Resources Corporation)
4th Floor 82 Grayston Drive
2146 Sandton, South Africa
Mailing Address:
PO Box 782103
2146 Sandton, South Africa
Tel.: (27) 11 779 6800
Fax: (27) 11 883 0836
E-Mail: info@atlatsa.com
Web Site: www.atlatsaresources.co.za
Year Founded: 1983
ATL—(JSE NYSEMKT TSX)
Rev.: $116,854,338
Assets: $809,197,218
Liabilities: $605,167,434
Net Worth: $204,029,785
Earnings: ($94,995,380)
Emp.: 12
Fiscal Year-end: 12/31/12

Business Description:
Platinum Mining
S.I.C.: 1099
N.A.I.C.S.: 212299

Personnel:
Tumelo M. Motsisi *(Chm)*
Asna Chris Harold Motaung *(CEO)*
Kogi Naicker *(Interim CFO)*
Joel Kesler *(Chief Comml Officer)*

Board of Directors:
Tumelo M. Motsisi
Fikile Tebogo De Buck
Anu Dhir
Asna Chris Harold Motaung
Rizelle M. Sampson

Computershare Investor Services (Pty) Limited
Ground Floor 70 Marshall Street
Johannesburg, South Africa

Transfer Agents:
Computershare Trust Company of Canada
9th Floor 100 University Avenue
Toronto, ON, Canada

Computershare Investor Services (Pty) Limited
Ground Floor 70 Marshall Street
Johannesburg, South Africa

Non-U.S. Subsidiaries:

Pelawan Investments (Proprietary) Limited **(1)**
82 Grayston Dr
PO Box 782103
Sandton, Johannesburg, Gauteng, 2196, South Africa
Tel.: (27) 118830831
Fax: (27) 118830836
E-Mail: info@anooraqresources.co.za
Web Site: www.anooraqresources.co.za
Emp.: 16
Platinum Group Metals Exploration & Development Services
S.I.C.: 1099
N.A.I.C.S.: 212299
Kogi Naicker *(CEO)*

Plateau Resources (Proprietary) Limited **(1)**
4th Fl 82 Grayston Dr
PO Box 782103
Sandton, 2196 Johannesburg, South Africa
Tel.: (27) 118830831
Fax: (27) 118830836
E-Mail: info@anooraqresources.co.za
Web Site: www.anooraqresources.co.za
Emp.: 11
Platinum Group Metals Exploration & Development Services
S.I.C.: 1099
N.A.I.C.S.: 212299
T. Motsisi *(Mgr)*

ATM S.A.

Grochowska 21a
04-186 Warsaw, Poland
Tel.: (48) 225156100
Fax: (48) 225156600
E-Mail: contact@atm.com.pl
Web Site: www.atm.com.pl
ATM—(WAR)
Rev.: $57,967,241
Assets: $113,902,948
Liabilities: $39,179,192
Net Worth: $74,723,756
Earnings: $3,993,935
Fiscal Year-end: 12/31/12

Business Description:
Telecommunication Services
S.I.C.: 4812
N.A.I.C.S.: 517210

Personnel:
Slawomir Kaminski *(Chm-Supervisory Bd)*
Maciej Krzyzanowski *(Chm-Mgmt Bd)*
Tomasz Tucholka *(Vice Chm-Supervisory Bd)*
Tadeusz Czichon *(Vice Chm-Mgmt Bd & CFO)*

Supervisory Board of Directors:
Slawomir Kaminski
Grzegorz Domagaa
Miroslaw Panek
Tomasz Tucholka
Marcin Wysocki

ATM SYSTEMY INFORMATYCZNE S.A.

(Name Changed to Atende S.A.)

ATMANCO INC.

(Formerly Biotonix (2010) Inc.)
1050 rue de la Montagne Bureau 300
Montreal, QC, H3G 1Y8, Canada
Tel.: (514) 935-5959
Fax: (514) 935-4949
E-Mail: chevierd@biotonix.com
Web Site: www.biotonix.com
Year Founded: 2007
BTX—(TSXV)

Business Description:
Healthcare Software Developer
S.I.C.: 7372
N.A.I.C.S.: 511210

Personnel:
Michel Guay *(Pres & CEO)*
Edith Bourgeois *(CFO)*

Board of Directors:
W. Brian Edwards
Andre Dorais
Normand Drouin
Susan Kudzman
Catherine Loubier

Alain Morissette
Rene Vachon
Transfer Agent:
Computershare Investor Services
1500 University Street 7th Floor
Montreal, QC, Canada

ATMIRA ESPACIO DE CONSULTORIA S.L.

Santiago de Compostela 94 8th pl
Madrid, 28035, Spain
Tel.: (34) 91 447 18 47
Fax: (34) 91 386 61 20
E-Mail: marketing@atmira.com
Web Site: www.atmira.com
Year Founded: 2005
Sales Range: $25-49.9 Million
Emp.: 350
Business Description:
Information Technology Consulting Services
S.I.C.: 7373
N.A.I.C.S.: 541512
Personnel:
Joan Cardona *(CEO & Mng Partner)*
Esteve Ponsa *(Deputy CEO)*

ATN HOLDINGS, INC.

Unit 902 9th Floor Summit One
Tower 530 Shaw Boulevard
Mandaluyong, 1550, Philippines
Tel.: (63) 2 717 0523
Fax: (63) 2 533 4052
Web Site: www.atnholdings.com
Year Founded: 1961
ATN—(PHI)
Rev.: $552,087
Assets: $44,269,429
Liabilities: $10,987,156
Net Worth: $33,282,273
Earnings: ($139,787)
Fiscal Year-end: 03/31/13
Business Description:
Holding Company; Mining & Oil Exploration & Development Services
S.I.C.: 6719
N.A.I.C.S.: 551112
Personnel:
Arsenio T. Ng *(Chm, Pres & CEO)*
Paul B. Saria *(CFO & Asst Sec)*
Hilario T. Ng *(COO)*
Renato E. Taguiam *(Sec)*
Board of Directors:
Arsenio T. Ng
Santos L. Cejoco
Choong Cheah Chee
Bonifacio Choa
Arturo Magtibay
Manuel R. Moje
Hilario T. Ng
Jose V. Romero
Hyland Si
Ting Guan Yu
Subsidiaries:

Advanced Home Concept Development Corp. **(1)**
9th Floor Summit One Tower Building 530 Shaw Boulevard
Mandaluyong, 1552, Philippines
Tel.: (63) 27170523
Fax: (63) 27170523
Real Estate Management Services
S.I.C.: 6531
N.A.I.C.S.: 531390

Palladian Land Development Inc **(1)**
9th Floor Summit One Tower Building 530 Shaw Boulevard
Mandaluyong, 1552, Philippines
Tel.: (63) 27170523
Fax: (63) 25334052
Emp.: 7
Real Estate Management Services
S.I.C.: 6531
N.A.I.C.S.: 531390

ATN INTERNATIONAL LIMITED

10 Princep Street 2nd Floor
Kolkata, 700 072, India
Tel.: (91) 3340022880
Fax: (91) 3322379053
E-Mail: info@atninternational.co.in
Web Site: www.atninternational.co.in
ATNINTER—(NSE)
Rev.: $73,272
Assets: $3,427,498
Liabilities: $2,261,086
Net Worth: $1,166,412
Earnings: ($852,633)
Fiscal Year-end: 03/31/13
Business Description:
Investment Banking & Television Broadcasting Services
S.I.C.: 6211
N.A.I.C.S.: 523110
Personnel:
Santosh Kumar Jain *(Mng Dir)*
Manisha Lath *(Compliance Officer & Sec)*
Board of Directors:
Hari Ram Agarwal
Pranab Chakraborty
Tarak Nath Datta
Santosh Kumar Jain
Transfer Agent:
Maheshwari Datamatics Private Limited
6 Mangoe Lane
Kolkata, India

ATOCHA RESOURCES INC.

(Name Changed to Durango Resources Inc.)

ATOMIC ENERGY OF CANADA LIMITED

Chalk River Laboratories
Chalk River, ON, K0J 1J0, Canada
Tel.: (613) 584-3311
Fax: (613) 584-8272
E-Mail: info@aecl.ca
Web Site: www.aecl.ca
Year Founded: 1952
Rev.: $86,262,050
Assets: $1,133,000,894
Liabilities: $8,743,121,594
Net Worth: ($7,610,120,700)
Earnings: ($2,569,998,949)
Emp.: 3,285
Fiscal Year-end: 03/31/13
Business Description:
Design & Construction of Nuclear Power Plants & Research Reactors; Servicing All Types of Nuclear Power Plants
Export
S.I.C.: 1629
N.A.I.C.S.: 237130
Personnel:
Peter William Currie *(Chm)*
Robert Walker *(Pres & CEO)*
Steve Halpenny *(CFO & VP)*
Jonathan Lundy *(Chief Legal Officer & VP)*
Randy Lesco *(Chief Nuclear Officer & VP-Ops)*
Richard Fujarczuk *(Gen Counsel, Sec & VP)*
Yvonne Penning *(Gen Counsel & VP-Wrap Up Office)*
Allan A. Hawryluk *(Sr VP-Strategic Contracting)*
Board of Directors:
Peter William Currie
Serge Dupont
James Hall
Gregory Josey
Claude Lajeunesse
John Luxat
Barbara Trenholm
Robert Walker

U.S. Subsidiary:

AECL Technologies Inc. **(1)**
481 N Frederick Ave Ste 405
Gaithersburg, MD 20877
Mailing Address:
PO Box 3933
Frederick, MD 21705-3933
Fax: (301) 417-0746
Toll Free: (866) 344-2325
E-Mail: info@aecltechnologies.com
Web Site: www.aecltechnologies.com
Nuclear Energy Technology
S.I.C.: 4939
N.A.I.C.S.: 221113

Non-U.S. Divisions:

Aecl-Argentina **(1)**
Nunez 1567 Piso 6
C1429BVA Buenos Aires, Argentina
Tel.: (54) 1147013545
Fax: (54) 1147013545
E-Mail: dianad@aecl-br.com.ar
Web Site: www.aecl.ca/About/Offices/Sites.htm
Emp.: 4
Nuclear Electric Power Generation
S.I.C.: 4911
N.A.I.C.S.: 221113
Raul Palou *(Mgr)*

Aecl-China **(1)**
Avic Plaza 1140 B
Dongsanhuan Zhonglu Yi No 10, 100022
Beijing, China
Tel.: (86) 1065669490
Web Site: www.aecl.cn
Emp.: 2
Nuclear Electric Power Generation
S.I.C.: 4931
N.A.I.C.S.: 221113
Yang Q. Ruan *(Mng Dir)*

Aecl-South Korea **(1)**
4th Floor IL Won Building
1001-1 Daechi-dong Kangnam-Ku, Seoul, 135-280, Korea (South)
Tel.: (82) 25393030
Fax: (82) 25670072
E-Mail: kimsh@aecl.ca
Web Site: www.aecl.ca/About/Offices/Sites.htm
Emp.: 150
Nuclear Electric Power Generation
S.I.C.: 4911
N.A.I.C.S.: 221113
Sunho Kim *(Acct Mgr)*

ATOMSYSTEM CO., LTD.

5-9 Minami-Fujisawa Asahi-Seimei Bldg 8-9F
Fujisawa, Kanagawa, 251-8543, Japan
Tel.: (81) 466291248
Fax: (81) 466291212
Web Site: www.atomsystem.co.jp/en
Year Founded: 1981
Sales Range: $1-4.9 Billion
Emp.: 226
Business Description:
System Developer
S.I.C.: 7371
N.A.I.C.S.: 541511
Personnel:
Tetsuya Hosono *(Pres)*
Hideo Hosono *(Gen Counsel)*
Board of Directors:
Susumu Aizawa
Takashi Itamiya
Yasuo Matsuno
Yoshinobu Takayanagi

ATON GMBH

Leopoldstrasse 53
80802 Munich, Germany
Tel.: (49) 89 970515 0
Fax: (49) 89 970515 199
E-Mail: aton.info@aton.de
Web Site: www.aton.de
Sales Range: $1-4.9 Billion
Emp.: 18,571
Business Description:
Investment Holding Company
S.I.C.: 6719
N.A.I.C.S.: 551112
Personnel:
Dagmar Helmig *(Co-Owner)*
Lutz M. Helmig *(Co-Owner)*
Thomas Eichelmann *(CEO & Chm-Mgmt Bd)*
Jorg Fahrenbach *(CFO & Member-Mgmt Bd)*
Subsidiaries:

Deilmann-Haniel International Mining & Tunneling GmbH **(1)**
Haustenbecke 1
D-44319 Dortmund, Germany De
Mailing Address: (100%)
Postfach 13 01 01
D-44311 Dortmund, Germany
Tel.: (49) 23128910
Fax: (49) 2312891352
E-Mail: info@dhimt.com
Web Site: www.dhimt.com
Sales Range: $650-699.9 Million
Emp.: 4,837
Holding Company; Mine & Tunnel Construction
S.I.C.: 6719
N.A.I.C.S.: 551112
Jochen Greinacher *(Mng Dir)*
Dirk Thone *(Mng Dir)*
Detlef Wilmer *(Mng Dir)*

Subsidiaries:

Deilmann-Haniel Mining Systems GmbH **(2)**
Haustenbecke 1
D-44319 Dortmund, Germany De
Tel.: (49) 2312891289 (100%)
Fax: (49) 2312891314
E-Mail: info@dhms.com
Web Site: www.dhms.com
Sales Range: $50-74.9 Million
Emp.: 200
Mining & Civil Engineering Machinery Mfr
S.I.C.: 3532
N.A.I.C.S.: 333131
Frank Bauer *(Head-Sls Dept)*

Deilmann-Haniel Shaft Sinking GmbH **(2)**
Haustenbecke 1
44319 Dortmund, Germany De
Tel.: (49) 2312891396 (100%)
Fax: (49) 2312891352
E-Mail: info@dh-shaftsinking.com
Web Site: www.dh-shaftsinking.com
Emp.: 210
Shaft Sinking for Civil Engineering & Tunneling Projects
S.I.C.: 1629
N.A.I.C.S.: 237990
Jochen Greinacher *(CEO)*

U.S. Subsidiary:

Frontier-Kemper Constructors, Inc. **(2)**
1695 Allen Rd
Evansville, IN 47710 IN
Mailing Address: (98.97%)
PO Box 6690
Evansville, IN 47719
Tel.: (812) 426-2741
Fax: (812) 428-0337
E-Mail: information@frontierkemper.com
Web Site: www.frontierkemper.com
Sales Range: $100-124.9 Million
Emp.: 100
Underground & Heavy Civil Construction Services
Import Export
S.I.C.: 1629
N.A.I.C.S.: 237990
W. David Rogstad *(Pres & CEO)*
Charles McGlothlen *(CFO & Treas)*
Rich Raab *(Pres-Northeast Div & VP)*
Tom Kilmer *(Exec VP)*

Non-U.S. Subsidiary:

J.S. Redpath Holdings Ltd. **(2)**
710 McKeown Ave
North Bay, ON, P1B 8K1, Canada Ca
Tel.: (705) 474-2461 (100%)

ATON GmbH—(Continued)

Fax: (705) 474-9109
E-Mail: info@redpathmining.com
Web Site: www.jsredpath.com
Emp.: 160
Holding Company; Ore Mining Contractor
S.I.C.: 6719
N.A.I.C.S.: 551112
George B. Flumerfelt *(Pres & CEO)*
Martin A. Hunka *(CFO)*
David C. Hansman *(Sr VP-Comml Svcs)*
Michael J. Kelly *(Sr VP-Admin & Mgmt-Canada & Indonesia)*

Subsidiary:

J.S. Redpath Limited (3)
710 McKeown Ave
PO Box 810
North Bay, ON, P1B 8K1, Canada ON
Tel.: (705) 474-2461 (100%)
Fax: (705) 474-9109
E-Mail: info@jsrl.com
Web Site: www.jsredpathmining.com
Emp.: 200
Ore Mining Contractor Services
S.I.C.: 1799
N.A.I.C.S.: 238990
George B. Flumerfelt *(Pres & CEO)*
Martin A. Hunka *(CFO)*
Andy Fearn *(Sr VP)*
David C. Hansman *(Sr VP)*
Michael J. Kelly *(Sr VP)*

Non-U.S. Subsidiary:

Redpath Mining Australia Pty. Ltd. (3)
63 Lavarack Ave
Eagle Farm, QLD, 4009, Australia AU
Mailing Address: (100%)
PO Box 1208
Eagle Farm, QLD, 4009, Australia
Tel.: (61) 738685000
Fax: (61) 732683734
E-Mail: info.australia@redpathmining.com.au
Web Site: www.redpathmining.com
Sales Range: $25-49.9 Million
Emp.: 400
Ore Mining Contractor Services
S.I.C.: 1799
N.A.I.C.S.: 238990
Gordon J. Shannon *(CEO)*
Rob Nichols *(COO)*

W.O.M. World of Medicine GmbH (1)
Salzufer 8
10587 Berlin, Germany De
Tel.: (49) 30 39981 550 (100%)
Fax: (49) 30 39981 545
E-Mail: info.berlin@womcorp.com
Web Site: www.world-of-medicine.com
Sales Range: $25-49.9 Million
Emp.: 230
Medical Devices Mfr & Distr
S.I.C.: 3845
N.A.I.C.S.: 334510
Oliver Kupka *(Member-Exec Bd)*
Clemens Scholz *(Member-Exec Bd)*

U.S. Subsidiary:

W.O.M. World of Medicine USA, Inc. (2)
4531 36th St
Orlando, FL 32811-6527 FL
Tel.: (407) 438-8810
Fax: (407) 859-2425
E-Mail: info.orlando@womcorp.com
Web Site: www.world-of-medicine.com
Sales Range: $1-9.9 Million
Medical Equipment Distr
S.I.C.: 5047
N.A.I.C.S.: 423450
Johannes Tschepe *(Pres)*

ATORKA GROUP HF

Hlidasmari 1
201 Kopavogur, Iceland
Tel.: (354) 5406200
Fax: (354) 5406220
E-Mail: atorka@atorka.is
Web Site: www.atorka.is
Emp.: 2
Business Description:
Investment Services
S.I.C.: 6211
N.A.I.C.S.: 523999
Personnel:
Thordur Olasur Thordarson *(Chm)*

ATORO CAPITAL CORP.

1050 Smithe Street Suite 1606
Vancouver, BC, V6E 4T4, Canada
Tel.: (778) 558-1756
Fax: (866) 404-2609
E-Mail: pleeca@gmail.com
Year Founded: 2011
TTO.P—(TSXV)
Business Description:
Investment Services
S.I.C.: 6211
N.A.I.C.S.: 523999
Personnel:
John Kowalchuk *(CEO)*
Peter Lee *(CFO & Sec)*
Board of Directors:
Robert Culbert
John Kowalchuk
Peter Lee
Transfer Agent:
Smythe Ratcliffe LLP
700-355 Burrard Street
Vancouver, BC, Canada

ATOS S.A.

River Ouest 80 Quai Voltaire
95877 Bezons, France
Tel.: (33) 1732600000
Fax: (33) 155912005
E-Mail: more-info@atos.net
Web Site: www.atos.net
Year Founded: 2000
ATO—(EUR)
Rev.: $11,905,931,331
Assets: $10,025,331,841
Liabilities: $6,822,389,560
Net Worth: $3,202,942,281
Earnings: $306,926,760
Emp.: 76,417
Fiscal Year-end: 12/31/12
Business Description:
Information Technology Services
S.I.C.: 7373
N.A.I.C.S.: 541512
Personnel:
Thierry Breton *(Chm & CEO)*
Gilles Grapinet *(CEO-Worldline & Sr Exec VP-Global Functions)*
Philippe Mareine *(Gen Sec & Head-Siemens Global Partnership)*
Charles Dehelly *(Sr Exec VP-Global Ops)*
Gilles Arditti *(Sr VP-IR & Fin Comm)*
Board of Directors:
Thierry Breton
Nicolas Bazire
Jean-Paul Bechat
Roland Busch
Jean Fleming
Betrand Meunier
Colette Neuville
Aminata Niane
Lynn Sharp Paine
Michel Paris
Pasquale Pistorio
Vernon L. Sankey
Lionel Zinsou-Derlin

Deloitte & Associes
Neuilly-sur-Seine, France
Subsidiaries:

Atos Consulting France (1)
Nous Ecrire River Ouest 80 quai Voltaire
Bezons, Val-d Oise, France
Tel.: (33) 173260000
Fax: (33) 173260001
E-Mail: fr-ac.contact@atosorigin.com
Web Site: www.fr.atosconsulting.com
Emp.: 4,000
Information Technology Consulting Services
S.I.C.: 8742
N.A.I.C.S.: 541611

Atos Multimedia (1)
Rue de la Pointe
Seclin, Nord, 59113, France
Tel.: (33) 320607813
Fax: (33) 320607676
Web Site: www.atos.com
Emp.: 1,500
Software Development Services
S.I.C.: 7373
N.A.I.C.S.: 541512
Christophe Duquenne *(Gen Mgr)*

Atos Origin Formation S.A (1)
13 Rue De Bucarest
Paris, 75008, France
Tel.: (33) 155306200
Fax: (33) 155306230
E-Mail: formation@atos.net
Web Site: www.formation.fr.atos.net
Emp.: 35
Information Technology Training Services
S.I.C.: 8299
N.A.I.C.S.: 611710
Arnaud Ruffat *(Pres)*

Atos Origin Integration SAS (1)
Le Millenium Sophia Antipo
Valbonne, Alpes Maritimes, 06560, France
Tel.: (33) 492952300
Fax: (33) 497157901
General Management Consulting Services
S.I.C.: 8742
N.A.I.C.S.: 541611

Atos Origin Management France SAS (1)
80 quai Voltaire River Ouest
Bezons, 95877, France
Tel.: (33) 173262215
Fax: (33) 173260001
Emp.: 5,000
Information Technology Consulting Services
S.I.C.: 8742
N.A.I.C.S.: 541611

Atos Worldline SAS (1)
Tour Manhattan
5 6 place de l'Iris
La Defense 2, 92926 Paris, Cedex, France (100%)
Tel.: (33) 149009000
Fax: (33) 147730763
E-Mail: dircom-atosworldline@atosorigin.com
Web Site: www.atosworldline.com
Emp.: 5,000
Information Technology Services for Processing of Electronic Transactions
S.I.C.: 7379
N.A.I.C.S.: 541519
Didier Dhennin *(CEO)*
Olivier Flamand *(CFO)*
Willy Walraeve *(CTO)*
Denis Daulle *(Exec VP-Tech Ops)*
Patrick Degryse *(Exec VP-HR)*
Christophe Duquenne *(Exec VP-Southern Europe & eSvcs/CRM & Fin Markets)*
Claude France *(Exec VP-Bus Mktg & Strategy)*
Erik Munk Koefoed *(Exec VP-Issuing Svc Line-Central Europe)*
Frederic Launoy *(Exec VP-Offerings & Dev)*

U.S. Division:

Atos Origin North America (1)
5599 San Felipe Ste 300
Houston, TX 77056-2724
Tel.: (713) 513-3000
E-Mail: info.na@atosorigin.com
Web Site: www.na.atosorigin.com
Emp.: 25
Information Technology Services
S.I.C.: 7373
N.A.I.C.S.: 541512
Paul Stewart *(CEO & Exec VP)*
Jerry Anderson *(CFO)*
J. Michael Hamilton *(Gen Counsel)*

U.S. Subsidiaries:

Atos Origin Inc (1)
5599 San Felipe St Ste 300
Houston, TX 77056
Tel.: (713) 513-3000
Fax: (713) 403-7204
Emp.: 750
Software Development Services
S.I.C.: 7371
N.A.I.C.S.: 541511
Thierry Breton *(Chm & CEO)*
Philippe Mareine *(Sec)*

Non-U.S. Subsidiaries:

Atos Covics Business Solutions Co., Ltd. (1)
Suite 1207 Unicom International Tower No 547
West Tianmu Road, Shanghai, 200070, China
Tel.: (86) 2163171122
Fax: (86) 21 6317 2889
Web Site: www.covics.cn
Software System Consultancy Services
S.I.C.: 7373
N.A.I.C.S.: 541512

Atos IT Servicios do Brazil LTDA (1)
Avenue Maria Coelho Aguiar 215 bl E 5 andar
Sao Luis, Maranhao, 05804-900, Brazil
Tel.: (55) 11 2183 2344
Fax: (55) 11 2183 2330
Software Development Services
S.I.C.: 7371
N.A.I.C.S.: 541511

Atos Origin AG (1)
Industriestrasse 19
Wallisellen, Zurich, 8304, Switzerland
Tel.: (41) 448776969
Fax: (41) 448776999
E-Mail: swiss-info@atosorigin.com
Web Site: www.ch.atosorigin.com
Information Technology Consulting Services
S.I.C.: 8742
N.A.I.C.S.: 541611

Atos Origin (Asia Pacific) Pte Ltd (1)
620 A Lorong 1 Toa Payoh TP 4 Level 5
Singapore, 319762, Singapore
Tel.: (65) 64963888
Fax: (65) 6496 3777
E-Mail: enquire@atosorigin.com
Web Site: www.ap.atosorigin.com
Emp.: 194
Information Technology Services
S.I.C.: 7389
N.A.I.C.S.: 519190

Atos Origin Belgium SA (1)
Leonardo Da Vincilaan 5
1935 Zaventem, Belgium
Tel.: (32) 26902800
Fax: (32) 26902801
Web Site: www.atos.net
Emp.: 500
Information Technology Consulting Services
S.I.C.: 7373
N.A.I.C.S.: 541512
Patrick Gyseling *(Gen Mgr)*

Atos Origin Brasil Ltda (1)
Maria Coelho Aguiar 215 Bloco E 50 Andar
Sao Paulo, 05804-900, Brazil
Tel.: (55) 1121832344
Fax: (55) 1121832366
Software Development Services
S.I.C.: 7372
N.A.I.C.S.: 511210

Atos Origin Consulting Canarias, SA (1)
Paseo Tomas Morales 85 Piso 1
Las Palmas, 35004, Spain
Tel.: (34) 928296006
Fax: (34) 928296007
Web Site: www.atos.es
Emp.: 150
Information Technology Consulting Services
S.I.C.: 8742
N.A.I.C.S.: 541611

Atos Origin GmbH (1)
Theodor-Althoff-Strasse 47
D-45133 Essen, Germany
Tel.: (49) 20143059095
Fax: (49) 2014305689095
E-Mail: de-info@atosorigin.com
Web Site: www.de.atosorigin.com
Information Technology Services
S.I.C.: 7371
N.A.I.C.S.: 541511
Winfried Holz *(CEO)*

Atos Origin Hellas Information Technology Services SA (1)
7 Fragokklisias Street
Maroussi, Athens, 151 25, Greece
Tel.: (30) 2106889000
Fax: (30) 210 6889099
Information Technology Consulting Services
S.I.C.: 7373
N.A.I.C.S.: 541512
Winfried Holz *(Chm)*

Atos Origin Indonesia PT (1)
Wisma Kyoei Price 1707 Jalan Jenderal Sudirman Kav 3
Jakarta, 10220, Indonesia
Tel.: (62) 215724373
Fax: (62) 215724383
E-Mail: enquire@atosorigin.com
Emp.: 12
Credit Card Payment Services
S.I.C.: 6099
N.A.I.C.S.: 522320
Febrianto Siboro *(Country Mgr)*

Atos Origin Information Technology (China) Co. Ltd (1)
11 F Unicom Mansion No 547 Tianmu West Road
Zhabei District, Shanghai, 200070, China
Tel.: (86) 2163541616
Fax: (86) 2163536001
Information Technology Consulting Services
S.I.C.: 8748
N.A.I.C.S.: 541618

Atos Origin Information Technology GmbH (1)
Technologiestrasse 8 Gebaude D
1120 Vienna, Austria
Tel.: (43) 1605431700
Fax: (43) 1605431755
E-Mail: info.austria@atosorigin.com
Web Site: www.at.atosorigin.com
Software Development Services
S.I.C.: 7371
N.A.I.C.S.: 541511

Atos Origin IT Services Ltd (1)
4 Triton Square Regents Place
London, NW1 3HG, United Kingdom
Tel.: (44) 2078304447
Fax: (44) 2078304445
Software Development Services
S.I.C.: 7371
N.A.I.C.S.: 541511

Atos Origin IT Services Private Ltd (1)
Areena House Plot No 103 Road No 12
Marol MIDC Andheri
Mumbai, Maharashtra, 400 093, India
Tel.: (91) 22 67864600
Fax: (91) 22 28314454
Software Development Services
S.I.C.: 7371
N.A.I.C.S.: 541511

Atos Origin IT Services UK Limited (1)
4 Triton Square
Regents Place, London, NW1 3HG, United Kingdom
Tel.: (44) 2078304444
Fax: (44) 2078304445
Toll Free: 8007833040
E-Mail: ukwebenquiries@atosorigin.com
Web Site: www.uk.atosorigin.com
Information Technology Services
S.I.C.: 7379
N.A.I.C.S.: 541519
Keith Wilman *(CEO)*
Jayesh Maroo *(CFO & Sr VP)*
Mark Bounds *(Sr VP & Mng Dir-Govt & Health)*
Paul Bray *(Sr VP, Mng Dir-Enterprise & Fin & Transport Markets)*
Dick Childs *(Sr VP-Strategic Programmes)*
Joe Edwards *(Sr VP-Sls & Mktg)*
Carl Lowson *(Sr VP-Managed Ops)*
Ursula Morgenstern *(Sr VP-Sys Integration)*
Paula Sussex *(Sr VP-Atos Consulting)*
Kevin Wilkinson *(Sr VP-HR)*

Atos Origin Luxembourg PSF S.A (1)
2 Rue Nicolas Bove
1253 Luxembourg, Luxembourg
Tel.: (352) 3136371
Fax: (352) 313883
Information Technology Consulting Services
S.I.C.: 7373
N.A.I.C.S.: 541512

Atos Origin (Malaysia) SDN BHD (1)
Suite F01 1st Floor Block 2310 Central Square
Jalan Usahawan, Cyberjaya, Selangor, 63000, Malaysia
Tel.: (60) 383160288
Fax: (60) 383186001
Emp.: 400
Credit Card Payment Services
S.I.C.: 6099
N.A.I.C.S.: 522320
Kee Ming Tee *(Mgr)*

Atos Origin SAE (1)
Albarracin 25
Madrid, 28037, Spain
Tel.: (34) 912149011
Fax: (34) 917543252
Information Technology Consulting Services
S.I.C.: 7373
N.A.I.C.S.: 541512
Aljosa Pasic *(Gen Mgr)*

Atos Origin Servicos de Tecnologia da Informacao do Brasil Ltda (1)
Avenida Maria Coelho Aguiar 215 Bloco E 50 e 70
Andares Cep Jardim Sao Luis, Sao Paulo, 05804 900, Brazil
Tel.: (55) 11 2183 2344
Fax: (55) 11 2183 2330
Information Technology Consulting Services
S.I.C.: 7373
N.A.I.C.S.: 541512

Atos Origin, Sociedad Anonima Espanola (1)
Calle Albarracin 25
Madrid, 28037, Spain
Tel.: (34) 914408800
Fax: (34) 917543252
E-Mail: es-macrom@atos.net
Emp.: 1,000
Information Technology Consulting Services
S.I.C.: 7373
N.A.I.C.S.: 541512
Patrick Adeva *(CEO)*

Atos Origin (Taiwan) Ltd (1)
5F No 100 Min Sheng East Road Section 3
Taipei, 10546, Taiwan
Tel.: (886) 225142500
Fax: (886) 225142525
E-Mail: enquire.taiwan@atosorigin.com
Web Site: www.ap.atosorigin.com
Information Management Consulting Services
S.I.C.: 8742
N.A.I.C.S.: 541611

Atos Origin UK. Ltd (1)
4 Triton Square
Regents Place, London, NW1 3HG, United Kingdom
Tel.: (44) 2078304444
Fax: (44) 2078304445
E-Mail: ukwebenquiries@atosorigin.com
Web Site: www.uk.atosorigin.com
Information Technology Consulting Services
S.I.C.: 7371
N.A.I.C.S.: 541511

Atos Worldline GmbH (1)
Hahnstrasse 25
60528 Frankfurt, Germany
Tel.: (49) 69665710
Fax: (49) 69 66 57 12 11
E-Mail: info@atosworldline.de
Web Site: www.atosworldline.com
Information Technology Consulting Services
S.I.C.: 7373
N.A.I.C.S.: 541512

Atos Worldline NV (1)
Ligusterbaan 18
Capelle Aan Den Ijssel, Rotterdam, 2908 LW, Netherlands
Tel.: (31) 102642711
Fax: (31) 102642720
Information Technology Services
S.I.C.: 7373
N.A.I.C.S.: 541512

Atos Worldline Processing GmbH (1)
Hahnstr 25
Frankfurt am Main, Hesse, 60528, Germany
Tel.: (49) 69665710
Fax: (49) 6966571211
E-Mail: info@atos.net
Web Site: www.atos.com
Payment Processing Services
S.I.C.: 6099
N.A.I.C.S.: 522320
Johannes Evers *(Chm)*

Cantabria - Mundivia S.A (1)
C Real Consulado s n Poligono Industrial Candina
Santander, Cantabria, 39011, Spain
Tel.: (34) 942355931
Fax: (34) 942321701
Information Technology Consulting Services
S.I.C.: 7373
N.A.I.C.S.: 541512

Cetisa, S.A. (1)
Condesa de Sagasta 6 Entreplanta B
Leon, 24001, Spain
Tel.: (34) 987276910
Fax: (34) 987239719
Information Technology Consulting Services
S.I.C.: 7373
N.A.I.C.S.: 541512

Infoservicios S.A (1)
Calle Albarracin 25
Madrid, 28037, Spain
Tel.: (34) 912148800
Fax: (34) 917543252
E-Mail: es-macrom@atos.net
Emp.: 1,000
Information Technology Consulting Services
S.I.C.: 8742
N.A.I.C.S.: 541611
Patrick Aveva *(CEO)*

Sema GMBH (1)
Kolner Street 9
Langenfeld, Nordrhein-Westfalen, Nordrhein-Westf, Germany
Tel.: (49) 217391750
Fax: (49) 2173917568
Information Technology Consulting Services
S.I.C.: 8742
N.A.I.C.S.: 541611

Atos IT Solutions and Services GmbH (1)
Otto-Hahn-Ring 6
D-81739 Munich, Germany De
Tel.: (49) 89 636 02
E-Mail:
Holding Company; Information Technology Products & Services
S.I.C.: 6719
N.A.I.C.S.: 551112
Christian Oecking *(Chm-Mgmt Bd & Mng Dir)*
Martin Bentler *(CFO)*
Rainer Koppitz *(Member-Mgmt Bd)*
Thomas Zimmermann *(Member-Mgmt Bd)*

Subsidiaries:

Applied International Informatics GmbH (2)
Business Campus Munchen
Garching Parkring 4, Munich, DE-85748, Germany (100%)
Tel.: (49) 89255495215
Fax: (49) 89 255 495 205
E-Mail: doris.brandner@aiinformatics.com
Web Site: www.aiinformatics.com
Sales Range: $75-99.9 Million
Emp.: 200
Information Technology Solutions
S.I.C.: 7373
N.A.I.C.S.: 541512
Josef Durmoser *(Mng Dir)*

Atos IT-Dienstleistung und Beratung GmbH (2)
Bruchstrasse 5
45883 Gelsenkirchen, Germany De
Tel.: (49) 20994560
Fax: (49) 20994563401
Sales Range: $125-149.9 Million
Emp.: 702
Information Technology Services
S.I.C.: 7376
N.A.I.C.S.: 541513
Achim Todeskino *(Chm-Mgmt Bd)*
Martin Bless *(Dir-Comml)*

SM2 Baleares SA (1)
Software Tic Building Sm2 ParcBit
Palma de Mallorca, 07121, Spain
Tel.: (34) 971750324
Fax: (34) 971750794
E-Mail: info@sm2baleares.es
Web Site: www.sm2baleares.es
Emp.: 100
System Integration & Consulting Services
S.I.C.: 7373
N.A.I.C.S.: 541512
Alexandro Pons *(Gen Mgr)*

Tempos21 S.A (1)
Avda Diagonal 200
Barcelona, 08018, Spain
Tel.: (34) 934861818
Fax: (34) 934860766
Web Site: www.tempos21.com
Emp.: 25
Information Technology Consulting Services
S.I.C.: 7373
N.A.I.C.S.: 541512
Santiago Respol *(Gen Mgr)*

ATOSS SOFTWARE AG

Am Moosfeld 3
81829 Munich, Germany
Tel.: (49) 89427710
Fax: (49) 8942771100
E-Mail: info@atoss.com
Web Site: www.atoss.com
AOF—(DEU)
Sls.: $44,430,026
Assets: $44,733,054
Liabilities: $12,844,407
Net Worth: $31,888,647
Earnings: $7,753,526
Emp.: 276
Fiscal Year-end: 12/31/12

Business Description:
Software Consulting & Training Services
S.I.C.: 7373
N.A.I.C.S.: 541512

Personnel:
Andreas F. J. Obereder *(Founder, CEO & Member-Mgmt Bd)*
Peter Kirn *(Chm-Supervisory Bd)*
Richard Hauser *(Deputy Chm-Supervisory Bd)*
Christof Leiber *(CFO & Member-Mgmt Bd)*

Supervisory Board of Directors:
Peter Kirn
Richard Hauser
Rolf Vielhauer von Hohenhau

Subsidiary:

ATOSS CSD Software GmbH (1)
Rodinger Strasse 19
93413 Cham, Bavaria, Germany
Tel.: (49) 997185180
Fax: (49) 9971851899
E-Mail: info@atoss-csd.de
Web Site: www.atoss-csd.de
Emp.: 20
Management Software Solutions
S.I.C.: 7371
N.A.I.C.S.: 541511
Gunter Schmaderer *(Gen Mgr)*

Non-U.S. Subsidiaries:

ATOSS Software AG (1)
Leutschenbachstrasse 95
8050 Zurich, Switzerland
Tel.: (41) 443083956
Fax: (41) 520116219
Emp.: 200
Management Software Solutions
S.I.C.: 7371
N.A.I.C.S.: 541511
Andreas Obereder *(Mgr)*

ATOSS Software Gesellschaft m.b.H. (1)
Am Moosfeld 3
81829 Modling, Munchendorf, Austria
Tel.: (43) 171728334
Fax: (43) 171728110
E-Mail: info@atoss.com
Emp.: 100
Customized Software Solutions
S.I.C.: 7371
N.A.I.C.S.: 541511

ATOSS Software AG—(Continued)

ATOSS Software S.R.L. (1)
Str Diaconu Coresi Nr 31
300588 Timisoara, Timis, Romania
Tel.: (40) 356710182
Fax: (40) 356710246
E-Mail: info@atoss.com
Web Site: www.atoss.ro
Emp.: 70
Workforce Management Software Solutions
S.I.C.: 7371
N.A.I.C.S.: 541511
Dinu Radu-Bogdan *(Mng Dir)*

ATPI LIMITED

Rivercastle House 10 Leake Street
London, SE1 7NN, United Kingdom
Tel.: (44) 207 111 8500
Fax: (44) 207 111 8290
Web Site: www.atpi.com
Year Founded: 1936
Sales Range: $25-49.9 Million
Emp.: 1,244

Business Description:
Travel Management Services
S.I.C.: 4725
N.A.I.C.S.: 561520

Personnel:
Graham Ramsey *(Grp CEO)*
Dag Kristian Amland *(Co-Mng Dir-Divisional)*
Mike Beacher *(Sec)*

ATREM S.A.

4 Czolgowa Street
62-002 Suchy Las, Poland
Tel.: (48) 616406700
Fax: (48) 616406725
E-Mail: atrem@atrem.pl
Web Site: www.atrem.pl
ATR—(WAR)
Sales Range: $25-49.9 Million

Business Description:
Engineering Services
S.I.C.: 8711
N.A.I.C.S.: 541330

Personnel:
Tadeusz Kowalski *(Chm-Supervisory Bd)*
Konrad Sniatala *(Chm-Mgmt Bd)*
Hanna Krawczynska *(Vice Chm-Supervisory Bd)*
Marek Korytowski *(Vice Chm-Mgmt Bd)*

Supervisory Board of Directors:
Tadeusz Kowalski
Hanna Krawczynska
Wojciech Kuspik
Andrzej Rybarczyk

Subsidiary:

DOM-MAR Sp. z o.o. (1)
ul Rzemieslnicza 37
62-081 Przezmierowo, Greater Poland, Poland
Tel.: (48) 616628970
Fax: (48) 616628971
E-Mail: biuro@dom-mar.pl
Web Site: www.dom-mar.pl
Heating Equipment Installation Services
S.I.C.: 1711
N.A.I.C.S.: 238220

ATREYA PETROCHEM LTD.

9th Floor Galav Chamber Opp Sardar Patel Statue Sayajigunj
Vadodara, Gujarat, 390005, India
Tel.: (91) 265 2362000
E-Mail: info@atreyapetrochem.com
Web Site: www.atreyapetrochem.com
Year Founded: 1992
524444—(BOM)
Sales Range: Less than $1 Million

Business Description:
Lubricating Oil Mfr
S.I.C.: 2992
N.A.I.C.S.: 324191

Personnel:
Santosh Ranchhodbhai Kahar *(Chm & Compliance Officer)*
Jayesh Raichandbhai Thakkar *(Mng Dir)*

Board of Directors:
Santosh Ranchhodbhai Kahar
Jigar Premchand Mota
Nikhil Pranay Pednekar
Amit Tarachand Shah
Kiran Jethalal Soni
Bachubhai Shankerlal Thakkar
Jayesh Raichandbhai Thakkar
Sombhai Shankarbhai Thakkar

ATRIA CAPITAL PARTENAIRES S.A.

5-7 rue de Monttessuy
75340 Paris, Cedex 07, France
Tel.: (33) 145266016
Fax: (33) 158192641
E-Mail: atria@atria-partenaires.com
Web Site: www.atria-partenaires.com
Year Founded: 1999
Sales Range: $400-449.9 Million
Emp.: 5

Business Description:
Private Equity Firm
S.I.C.: 6211
N.A.I.C.S.: 523999

Personnel:
Dominique Oger *(Founding Partner & Chm-Mgmt Bd)*
Thibaut de Chassey *(Mng Partner)*
Edouard Thomazeau *(Mng Partner)*
Patrick Bertiaux *(Founding Partner & Mng Dir)*
Sophie Laroussarias *(CFO)*

Board of Directors:
Patrick Bertiaux
Thibaut de Chassey
Dominique Oger

Holdings:

Shark S.A. (1)
ZAC de la Valentine
110 route de la Valentine, 13396 Marseilles, Cedex, 11, France FR
Tel.: (33) 491182323
Fax: (33) 491352923
E-Mail: contact@shark-helmets.com
Web Site: www.shark-helmets.com
Sales Range: $25-49.9 Million
Emp.: 700
Custom Motorcycle Helmet Designer & Mfr
S.I.C.: 3751
N.A.I.C.S.: 336991
Patric Srancois *(Chm)*

Trigo S.A. (1)
20-22 Rue Gambetta
92022 Nanterre, Cedex, France
Tel.: (33) 141440585
Fax: (33) 141440767
E-Mail: contact@trigo.net
Web Site: www.trigo.net
Sales Range: $50-74.9 Million
Emp.: 1,200
Quality Control Outsourcing Services
S.I.C.: 7389
N.A.I.C.S.: 561499
Stephan Pham *(CEO)*
Mireille Trolet *(Deputy Mng Dir)*

ATRIA PLC

Itikanmaenkatu 3 Seinajoki
PO Box 900
FI-60060 Atria, Finland
Tel.: (358) 20 472 8111
Fax: (358) 6 416 8440
Web Site: www.atriagroup.com
ATRAV—(OMX)
Sls.: $1,808,687,089
Assets: $1,402,208,365
Liabilities: $821,407,357
Net Worth: $580,801,008
Earnings: $13,549,201
Emp.: 4,898
Fiscal Year-end: 12/31/12

Business Description:
Food Processing Services
S.I.C.: 5147
N.A.I.C.S.: 311612

Personnel:
Seppo Paavola *(Chm)*
Ari Pirkola *(Chm-Supervisory Bd)*
Timo Komulainen *(Vice Chm)*
Juho Anttikoski *(Vice Chm-Supervisory Bd)*
Juha Grohn *(Pres & CEO)*
Juha Ruohola *(Deputy CEO & Grp VP-Primary Production)*
Heikki Kyntaja *(CFO)*
Mika Ala-Fossi *(Exec VP-Finland)*
Tomas Back *(Exec VP-Scandinavia)*
Olle Horm *(Exec VP-Baltic)*
Jarmo Lindholm *(Exec VP-Russia)*

Board of Directors:
Seppo Paavola
Tuomo Juhani Heikkila
Esa Kaarto
Timo Komulainen
Kjell-Goran Paxal
Maisa Romanainen
Harri Sivula

Supervisory Board of Directors:
Ari Pirkola
Juho Anttikoski
Mika Asunmaa
Lassi-Antti Haarala
Jussi Hantula
Juhani Herrala
Henrik Holm
Veli Hyttinen
Pasi Ingalsuo
Juha Kiviniemi
Teuvo Mutanen
Mika Niku
Heikki Panula
Pekka Parikka
Juho Partanen
Jari Puutio
Juho Tervonen
Tomi Toivanen
Timo Tuhkasaari

Subsidiary:

Atria Finland Ltd. (1)
Atriantie 1 Nurmo
Box 900
60060, Atria, Finland
Tel.: (358) 6 416 8440
E-Mail: info@atria.fi
Web Site: www.atria.fi
Food Processing Services
S.I.C.: 5147
N.A.I.C.S.: 311612
Mika Ala-Fossi *(Exec VP)*

Non-U.S. Subsidiaries:

Atria Eesti AS (1)
Metsa str 19
EE-68206 Valga, Estonia
Tel.: (372) 76 19900
Fax: (372) 76 79901
Web Site: www.atria.ee
Food Processing Services
S.I.C.: 5147
N.A.I.C.S.: 311612
Olle Horm *(Exec VP)*

Atria Scandinavia AB (1)
Augustendalsvagen 19
SE 131 52 Nacka, Sweden
Tel.: (46) ()19300300
Fax: (46) 55630650
E-Mail: kontact@atria.se
Web Site: www.atria.se
Sales Range: $550-599.9 Million
Emp.: 1,691
Food Processing
S.I.C.: 5147
N.A.I.C.S.: 311612
Tomas Back *(Exec VP)*

Subsidiaries:

Atria Foodservice AB (2)
Drottninggatan 14
SE 252 21 Helsingborg, Sweden
Tel.: (46) 42381400
Fax: (46) 42381461
Web Site: www.atriafoodservice.se
Frozen Fish & Meat
S.I.C.: 2092
N.A.I.C.S.: 311710
Martin Skoglosa *(Gen Mgr)*

Subsidiary:

Gourmet Service AB (3)
Vindkraftsvagen 5
S-135 70 Stockholm, Sweden
Tel.: (46) 856649000
Fax: (46) 856649099
E-Mail: info@gourmet-service.se
Web Site: www.gourmet-service.com
Emp.: 25
Fish Pate & Sandwiches
S.I.C.: 2099
N.A.I.C.S.: 311999
Magnus Selin *(Mng Dir)*

Atria Retail AB (2)
Drottninggatan 14
SE-697 80 Skollersta, Sweden
Tel.: (46) 19300300
Fax: (46) 19230022
Deli Products
S.I.C.: 2099
N.A.I.C.S.: 311999

Subsidiaries:

Alf Eliassons Kott & Chark AB (3)
Maskingatan 1, Skene
Box 214
S-511 22 Kinna, Sweden
Tel.: (46) 320 20 58 00
Fax: (46) 320 20 58 10
Deli Products
S.I.C.: 2099
N.A.I.C.S.: 311999

Charkdelikatesser I Halmstad AB (3)
Svetsaregatan 6
Halmstad, 302 50, Sweden
Tel.: (46) 35172600
Fax: (46) 35172601
Web Site: www.charkdelikatesser.se
Deli Products
S.I.C.: 2099
N.A.I.C.S.: 311999
Thomas Back *(Gen Mgr)*

Subsidiaries:

Charkdelikatesser Produktion AB (4)
Svetsaregatan 6
S-302 50 Halmstad, Sweden
Tel.: (46) 35172600
Fax: (46) 35172601
E-Mail: info@atriaretail.se
Web Site: www.charkdelikatesser.se/kontakt/
Food Production
S.I.C.: 2096
N.A.I.C.S.: 311919
Pontus Edner *(Mgr-Mktg)*

Moheda Chark AB (4)
Ostanakravagen 2
S-340 36 Moheda, Sweden
Tel.: (46) 47272660
Fax: (46) 47272661
Web Site: www.atria.com
Emp.: 20
Deli Products
S.I.C.: 2099
N.A.I.C.S.: 311999
Niclas Kanstebt *(Owner)*

G A Carlsson AB - Gea's (3)
Prastkragens vag 9
Box 188
SE-132 26 Saltsjo-Boo, Sweden
Tel.: (46) 19 300 300
Web Site: www.atriagroup.com
Deli Products
S.I.C.: 2099
N.A.I.C.S.: 311999

Pastejkoket AB (3)
c/o Charkdelikatesser Produktion AB
Svetsaregatan 6, 302 50 Halmstad, Sweden

Tel.: (46) 14057300
Fax: (46) 140 172 17
E-Mail: info@atriaretail.se
Web Site: www.pastejkoket.se/
Emp.: 187
Deli Meat Products
S.I.C.: 2099
N.A.I.C.S.: 311999

Subsidiaries:

AB Carl A Carlson Charkuterier (4)
Jadersvagen
Box 11
S-732 21 Arboga, Sweden
Tel.: (46) 589 128 50
Fax: (46) 589 162 63
Deli Products
S.I.C.: 2099
N.A.I.C.S.: 311999

Delikatess Skinkor AB (4)
Grenvagen 1-3
S-577 39 Hultsfred, Sweden
Tel.: (46) 495249600
Fax: (46) 495249609
Deli Products
S.I.C.: 2099
N.A.I.C.S.: 311999

Norrboda Charkuterifabrik AB (4)
Tryckerigatan 12
S-571 34 Nassjo, Sweden
Tel.: (46) 38016993
Fax: (46) 380 153 75
Deli Products
S.I.C.: 2099
N.A.I.C.S.: 311999

Falbygdens Ost AB (2)
Goteborgsvagen 19
SE-52130 Falkoping, Sweden
Tel.: (46) 515776600
Fax: (46) 0104823283
E-Mail: kontakt@atria.se
Web Site: www.falbygdensost.se
Emp.: 130
Cheese Mfr
S.I.C.: 2022
N.A.I.C.S.: 311513
Lars Ohlin *(CEO)*

Sardus Latta Maltider AB (2)
Hanholmsvagen 51
SE 602 28 Norrkoping, Sweden
Tel.: (46) 19 300 300
Fax: (46) 11 36 67 00
Web Site: www.sarduslattamaltider.se
Light Meals & Sandwiches
S.I.C.: 2099
N.A.I.C.S.: 311991
Richard O'Brien *(Mng Dir)*

Subsidiaries:

Allt Smorgas (3)
Speditionsvagen 25
S-142 50 Skogas, Sweden
Tel.: (46) 87715535
Fax: (46) 87715989
Sandwiches & Salads
S.I.C.: 2099
N.A.I.C.S.: 311999

Smorgasfabriken I Norrkoping AB (3)
Hanholmsvagen 51
Box 6015
S-600 06 Norrkoping, Sweden
Tel.: (46) 11368041
Fax: (46) 11128172
Sandwiches & Salad
S.I.C.: 2099
N.A.I.C.S.: 311999

Non-U.S. Subsidiary:

3-STJERNET A/S (2)
Langmarksvej 1
8700 Horsens, Denmark
Tel.: (45) 76282500
Fax: (45) 76282501
E-Mail: 3-stjernet@3-stjernet.dk
Web Site: www.3-stjernet.dk
Emp.: 140
Meat Toppings
S.I.C.: 0251
N.A.I.C.S.: 112320
Anders Laursen *(Gen Mgr)*

OOO Campomos (1)
Ryabinovaya Street 32
RUS 121471 Moscow, Russia
Tel.: (7) 4954486704
Fax: (7) 84954484503
Web Site: www.campomos.ru
Emp.: 300
Processed Food
S.I.C.: 5147
N.A.I.C.S.: 311612
Juha Ruohola *(Grp VP)*

OOO Pit-Product (1)
Pr Obukhovskoy Oborony 70
RUS-192029 Saint Petersburg, Russia
Tel.: (7) 812 3366 888
Fax: (7) 812 346 6176
E-Mail: office@pitproduct.ru
Web Site: www.pitproduct.ru
Food Processing Services
S.I.C.: 5147
N.A.I.C.S.: 311612

ATRIUM EUROPEAN REAL ESTATE LIMITED

11-15 Seaton Place
Saint Helier, Jersey JE4 0QH
Tel.: (44) 1 3188300
Fax: (44) 1 5318844
E-Mail: info@aere.com
Web Site: www.aere.com
ATR—(VIE)
Rev.: $260,450,241
Assets: $4,130,777,838
Liabilities: $1,059,663,293
Net Worth: $3,071,114,545
Earnings: $129,467,900
Emp.: 351
Fiscal Year-end: 12/31/12

Business Description:
Real Estate Investment & Development Services
S.I.C.: 6726
N.A.I.C.S.: 525990

Personnel:
Rachel Lavine *(CEO)*
Josip Kardun *(Deputy CEO & COO)*
David Doyle *(CFO)*
Thomas Schoutens *(Chief Dev Officer)*
Jorg Banzhaf *(Chief Investment Officer)*
Ronen Goldberg *(Chief Dev Officer-Russia)*
Katarzyna Cyz *(CEO-Poland)*
Asi Kahana *(CEO-Romania)*
Eshel Pesti *(CEO-Russia)*
Oldrich Spurek *(CEO-Czech Republic)*

Board of Directors:
Chaim Katzman
Joseph Azrack
Noam Ben-Ozer
Rachel Lavine
Peter D. Linneman
Simon Radford
Dipak Kumar Rastogi
Aharon Soffer
Thomas William Wernink
Andrew Wignall

ATRIUM INNOVATIONS INC.

(Acquired by Permira Advisers LLP)

ATRIUM LJUNGBERG AB

Sickla Industrivag 19
Box 4200
Nacka, 131 04, Sweden
Tel.: (46) 8 615 89 00
Fax: (46) 8 615 89 99
E-Mail: info@atriumljungberg.se
Web Site: www.atriumljungberg.se
Year Founded: 1946
LJGR B—(OMX)
Rev.: $321,627,960
Assets: $3,942,276,120
Liabilities: $2,354,755,680
Net Worth: $1,587,520,440
Earnings: $159,567,840
Emp.: 265
Fiscal Year-end: 12/31/12

Business Description:
Real Estate Development Services
S.I.C.: 6531
N.A.I.C.S.: 531390

Personnel:
Dag Klackenberg *(Chm)*
Ingalill Berglund *(Mng Dir)*
Annica Anas *(CFO)*

Board of Directors:
Dag Klackenberg
Sune Dahlqvist
Thomas Evers
Anna Hallberg
Johan Ljungberg
Anders Nylander

ATRIUM MORTGAGE INVESTMENT CORPORATION

20 Adelaide St East Suite 900
Toronto, ON, M5C 2T6, Canada
Tel.: (416) 867-1053
Fax: (416) 867-1303
E-Mail: ir@atriummic.com
Web Site: www.atriummic.com
Year Founded: 2001
AI—(TSX)
Rev.: $17,131,994
Assets: $211,331,546
Liabilities: $2,478,078
Net Worth: $208,853,468
Earnings: $13,278,444
Emp.: 1
Fiscal Year-end: 12/31/12

Business Description:
Real Estate Mortgage & Investment Services
S.I.C.: 6163
N.A.I.C.S.: 522310

Personnel:
Murray B. Frum *(Chm)*
Robert G. Goodall *(Pres & CEO)*
Jeffrey D. Sherman *(CFO & Sec)*

Board of Directors:
Murray B. Frum
Peter P. Cohos
Michael J. Cooper
Robert H. DeGasperis
Robert G. Goodall
David M. Prussky
Mark L. Silver

Transfer Agent:
Computershare Trust Company of Canada
100 University Avenue 9th Floor North Tower
Toronto, ON, Canada

ATRUM COAL NL

510 Hay Street
Subiaco, WA, 6008, Australia
Tel.: (61) 8 9388 3131
Fax: (61) 8 9388 3132
Web Site: www.atrumcoal.com
ATU—(ASX)

Business Description:
Coal Mining
S.I.C.: 1222
N.A.I.C.S.: 212112

Personnel:
James Chisholm *(Chm)*
Cameron McLean *(CFO)*
Lyle Hobbs *(COO)*
Brad Van Den Bussche *(CTO)*
Glenn Collick *(Chief Relationships Officer)*

Board of Directors:
James Chisholm
Gino D'anna
Eric Lilford
Russell Moran

Legal Counsel:
Steinepreis Paganin
Level 4 The Read Building 16 Milligan Street
Perth, WA, 6000, Australia
Tel.: (61) 8 9321 4000
Fax: (61) 8 9321 4333

ATRYA SAS

Zone Industrielle Le Moulin
F-67110 Gundershoffen, France
Tel.: (33) 3 8880 2929
Fax: (33) 3 8890 1155
E-Mail: info@atrya.fr
Web Site: www.atrya.fr
Year Founded: 1980
Sales Range: $500-549.9 Million
Emp.: 1,800

Business Description:
Holding Company; Window, Door & Other Building Components Mfr & Distr
S.I.C.: 6719
N.A.I.C.S.: 551112

Personnel:
Johannes Tryba *(Founder, Chm & CEO)*

Subsidiary:

Soprofen SAS (1)
ZA Le Bosquet
rue de la Lisiere, F-67580 Mertzwiller, France FR
Tel.: (33) 3 8890 5025
Fax: (33) 3 8890 1675
E-Mail: mail@soprofen.com
Web Site: www.soprofen.com
Roller Shutters & Garage Doors Mfr & Distr
S.I.C.: 3442
N.A.I.C.S.: 332321
Marc Burger *(Dir Gen)*

Subsidiary:

Soprofen Industrie SAS (2)
Zone Industrielle les Noyes
F-70300 Froideconche, France FR
Tel.: (33) 384406205
Web Site: www.soprofen.fr
Sales Range: $10-24.9 Million
Emp.: 49
Industrial Metal Shutters & Doors Mfr
S.I.C.: 3442
N.A.I.C.S.: 332321
Olivier Flajeolet *(Mgr-Personnel)*

ATS AUTOMATION TOOLING SYSTEMS INC.

730 Fountain St N Building 2
Cambridge, ON, N3H 4R7, Canada
Tel.: (519) 653-6500
Fax: (519) 650-6545
E-Mail: info@atsautomation.com
Web Site: www.atsautomation.com
Year Founded: 1978
ATA—(TSX)
Rev.: $587,563,234
Assets: $576,837,758
Liabilities: $180,617,410
Net Worth: $396,220,348
Earnings: $14,992,804
Emp.: 2,400
Fiscal Year-end: 03/31/13

Business Description:
Turnkey Factory Automation Systems Mfr & Designer
Import Export
S.I.C.: 7373
N.A.I.C.S.: 541512

Personnel:
David McAusland *(Chm)*
Anthony Caputo *(CEO)*
Maria Perrella *(CFO)*
Ronald G. Keyser *(CIO)*
Nedim Cen *(Chief Strategy Officer)*
Stewart McCuaig *(Gen Counsel & VP)*
Carl Galloway *(Treas & VP)*
Hans-Dieter Baumtrog *(Sr VP-ASG Life Sciences)*

ATS Automation Tooling Systems Inc.—(Continued)

Helmut Hock *(Sr VP-ASG Transportation)*
Sandra Ketchen *(Sr VP-ASG Products)*
Eric Kiisel *(Sr VP-ASG Energy & Indus)*

Board of Directors:
David McAusland
Neil D. Arnold
Anthony Caputo
Michael E. Martino
Gordon E. Presher
Neale X. Trangucci
Daryl C. F. Wilson

Transfer Agent:
Computershare Trust Company of Canada
100 University Avenue 11th Floor
Toronto, ON, M5J 2Y1, Canada
Tel.: (416) 891-9633
Toll Free: (800) 663-9097

Divisions:

ATS Advanced Manufacturing Division (1)
730 Fountain St N Bldg 2
Cambridge, ON, N3H 4R7, Canada (100%)
Tel.: (519) 650-2332
Fax: (519) 650-8137
E-Mail: info@atsautomation.com
Web Site: atsautomation.com
Emp.: 150
Mfr of Microelectronics Components
S.I.C.: 7373
N.A.I.C.S.: 541512

ATS Machine Tool Division (1)
730 Fountain St N Building #2
Cambridge, ON, N3H 4R7, Canada (100%)
Tel.: (519) 653-6500
Fax: (519) 650-6545
E-Mail: info@atsautomation.com
Web Site: www.atsautomation.com
Emp.: 30
Machine Tooling
S.I.C.: 3541
N.A.I.C.S.: 333517
Jordi Brown *(Gen Mgr)*

Subsidiaries:

ATS Precision Metal Components (1)
80 Alpine Rd
Kitchener, ON, N2E 1A1, Canada (100%)
Tel.: (519) 744-6661
Fax: (519) 744-8285
E-Mail: components@atsautomation.com
Web Site: www.atsautomation.com
Emp.: 150
S.I.C.: 7373
N.A.I.C.S.: 541512

ATS Precision Plastic Components (1)
730 Fountain St Bldg 1
Cambridge, ON, N3H 4R7, Canada (100%)
Tel.: (519) 650-6600
Fax: (519) 650-5925
E-Mail: components@atsautomation.com
Web Site: www.ats.com
Emp.: 250
S.I.C.: 7373
N.A.I.C.S.: 541512
Jordi Brown *(Gen Mgr)*

ATS Test Systems, Inc. (1)
600 Chrislea Rd
Woodbridge, ON, L4L 8K9, Canada (100%)
Tel.: (905) 850-8600
Fax: (905) 850-9336
E-Mail:
Web Site: www.ats.com
Emp.: 60
S.I.C.: 7373
N.A.I.C.S.: 541512

Photowatt Technologies Inc. (1)
25 Reuter Drive
Cambridge, ON, N3E 1A9, Canada Ca
Tel.: (519) 650-6505
Sales Range: $100-124.9 Million
Emp.: 711
Solar Energy Products Mfr
S.I.C.: 3612
N.A.I.C.S.: 335311
Nelson M. Sims *(Chm)*
Gary J. Seiter *(COO)*

U.S. Subsidiary:

Matrix Solar Technologies, Inc. (2)
540-A Silver Creek NW
Albuquerque, NM 87121
Tel.: (505) 833-0100
Solar Energy Products Mfr
S.I.C.: 4931
N.A.I.C.S.: 221118

U.S. Subsidiaries:

ATS Carolina Inc. (1)
1510 Cedar Line Dr
Rock Hill, SC 29730 (100%)
Mailing Address:
PO Box 12650
Rock Hill, SC 29730
Tel.: (803) 324-9300
Fax: (803) 324-9360
Web Site: www.atsautomation.com
Emp.: 100
Mfr. & Designer of Turnkey Factory Automation Systems
S.I.C.: 3569
N.A.I.C.S.: 333999
Steve Vogel *(Gen Mgr)*

ATS Ohio Inc. (1)
425 Enterprise Dr
Lewis Center, OH 43081-8842
Tel.: (614) 888-2344
Fax: (614) 888-3875
Web Site: www.ats-ohio.com
Emp.: 120
Provider of Automated Tooling Systems
S.I.C.: 3569
N.A.I.C.S.: 333999

ATS Sortimat USA LLC (1)
5655 Meadowbrook Industrial Ct
Rolling Meadows, IL 60008-3833
Tel.: (847) 925-1234
Emp.: 40
General Purpose Machinery Mfr
S.I.C.: 3569
N.A.I.C.S.: 333999
Hans D. Baumtrog *(CEO)*

ATS Systems California (1)
2121 Ne Jack London St
Corvallis, OR 97330-6916
Tel.: (925) 606-1302
Fax: (925) 606-1305
Emp.: 60
Mfr. of Robotics for the Semiconductor Industry
S.I.C.: 3559
N.A.I.C.S.: 333249
Mike Ekdahl *(Mgr-Ops)*

ATS Systems Oregon Inc. (1)
2121 NE Jack London St
Corvallis, OR 97330-6916
Tel.: (541) 758-3329
Fax: (541) 758-9022
Emp.: 15
Automation Tooling Systems
S.I.C.: 5044
N.A.I.C.S.: 423420

Automation Tooling Systems Enterprises, Inc. (1)
1510 Cedar Line Dr
Rock Hill, SC 29730-7442
Tel.: (803) 324-9300
Fax: (803) 324-9360
Industrial Machinery Mfr
S.I.C.: 3559
N.A.I.C.S.: 333249

Subsidiary:

ATW Automation Inc. (2)
12841 Stark Rd
Livonia, MI 48150
Tel.: (734) 522-1900
Fax: (734) 522-9344
Web Site: www.atsautomation.com
Industrial Automation Machinery Mfr
S.I.C.: 3559
N.A.I.C.S.: 333249

Automation Tooling Systems Oregon (1)
2121 NE Jack London St
Corvallis, OR 97330-6916 (100%)
Tel.: (541) 758-3329
Fax: (541) 758-9022
Emp.: 100
Factory Automation Systems, Custom Automation Equipment, Standard Automation Products & Turnkey Assembly Machinery, as well as High-Volume Precision Components
S.I.C.: 3569
N.A.I.C.S.: 333999
Kai Carlson *(Gen Mgr)*

Non-U.S. Subsidiaries:

ACE Automation (Tianjin) Co. Ltd. (1)
157 Huang Hai Road TEDA
Tianjin, 300457, China
Tel.: (86) 11 22 532 2007
Fax: (86) 11 22 532 1471
Web Site: www.atsautomation.com
S.I.C.: 7373
N.A.I.C.S.: 541512

Assembly & Test - Europe GmbH (1)
Carl-Borgward Strasse 11
56566 Neuwied, Germany De
Tel.: (49) 26313820
Fax: (49) 2631382151
E-Mail:
Emp.: 80
Mfr of Automated Production Equipment
S.I.C.: 3559
N.A.I.C.S.: 333249
Thomas Wildt *(Mng Dir)*

ATS Automation Asia Pte Ltd (1)
38A Jalan Pemimpin 01 01 Wisdom Ind Bldg
Singapore, 577178, Singapore (100%)
Tel.: (65) 62995988
Fax: (65) 62990688
Web Site: www.atsautomation.com
Emp.: 100
S.I.C.: 7373
N.A.I.C.S.: 541512
Nulson Chen *(CFO)*

ATS Automation Asia (Tianjin) Co., Ltd. (1)
Bldg C3-4 XEDA International Industry Zone Xiqing Economic
Development Area, Tianjin, 300385, China
Tel.: (86) 2223828218
Fax: (86) 2223828211
E-Mail: info@atsautomation.com
Web Site: www.atsautomation.com
Emp.: 130
Electrical Equipment Mfr
S.I.C.: 3699
N.A.I.C.S.: 335999
Andrew Tay *(Gen Mgr)*

ATS Automation Malaysia SDN. BHD. (1)
Plot 221 Lorong Perindustrian Bukit Minyak 11 Mukim 13
Seberang Perai Tengah, 14000 Bukit Mertajam, Penang, Malaysia
Tel.: (60) 45098585
Fax: (60) 45098686
Conveyor Machinery Mfr
S.I.C.: 3535
N.A.I.C.S.: 333922

ATS Automation Tooling Systems GmbH (1)
Marsstrasse 2
85551 Heimstetten, Germany
Tel.: (49) 894272210
Fax: (49) 89427221660
E-Mail: germany@atsautomation.com
Web Site: www.atsmunich.de
Turnkey Factory Automation Systems Mfr & Designer
S.I.C.: 7373
N.A.I.C.S.: 541512
Josef Wildgruber *(Mng Dir)*

Branch:

ATS Automation Tooling Systems GmbH - Winnenden (2)
Birkenstrasse 1-7
Winnenden, 71364, Germany
Tel.: (49) 7195 702 0
Fax: (49) 7195702260
E-Mail: info@sortimat.de
Web Site: www.sortimat.de
Emp.: 475
Cutting Tool Mfr
S.I.C.: 3545
N.A.I.C.S.: 333515

ATS Automation (1)
Plot 221 Lorong Perindustrian Bukit Minyak 11
Mukim 13 Kawasam Perindustrian
Bukit Mertajam Seberang Perind, 14000
Penang, Malaysia (100%)
Tel.: (60) 45098585
Fax: (60) 45098686
Web Site: www.atsautomaton.com
Emp.: 65
S.I.C.: 7373
N.A.I.C.S.: 541512

ATS Wickel-und Montagetechnik AG (1)
Grosszelgstrasse 21
CH 5436 Wurenlos, Switzerland (100%)
Tel.: (41) 564368585
Fax: (41) 564368538
E-Mail: switzerland@atsautomation.com
Web Site: www.switzerland.atsautomation.com
Emp.: 60
S.I.C.: 7373
N.A.I.C.S.: 541512
Konrad Meier *(Gen Mgr)*

IWK Verpackungstechnik GmbH (1)
Lorenzstrasse 6
D-76297 Stutensee, Germany De
Tel.: (49) 72449680 (100%)
Fax: (49) 724496073
E-Mail: info-pharmapackaging@oystar-group.com
Web Site: www.oystar-group.com
Emp.: 300
Packaging Machinery Mfr
S.I.C.: 3565
N.A.I.C.S.: 333993
Marcus Ehl *(Mng Dir)*

Sortimat Technology Pvt. Ltd. (1)
191/A1 Station Road
Chinchwad, Pune, 411 033, India
Tel.: (91) 20 30700333
Fax: (91) 20 30700334
E-Mail: info@sortimat.in
Web Site: www.sortimat.in
Emp.: 6
Cutting Tool Mfr
S.I.C.: 3541
N.A.I.C.S.: 333517
Philippe Lutgen *(Mng Dir)*

ATTARD & CO. LTD.

Canter House
Marsa, MRF 1524, Malta
Tel.: (356) 21237555
Fax: (356) 21220186
E-Mail: info@attardco.com
Web Site: www.attardco.com
Year Founded: 1921
Sales Range: $10-24.9 Million
Emp.: 100

Business Description:
Mfr., Distributor & Provider of High Performance Liquid Chromotograpy (HPLC), Thermal Analysis & Mass Spectrometry (MS) Instruments, Columns & Related Services
S.I.C.: 3826
N.A.I.C.S.: 334516

Personnel:
Cecilia Pellegrini *(Mgr-Mktg)*

Subsidiaries:

Attard & Co. Foodstuffs Ltd. (1)
Canter House Patri Felicjan Bilocca Street
Marsa, MRS 1524, Malta
Tel.: (356) 2123 7555
Fax: (356) 2122 0186
E-Mail: info@attardco.com
Web Site: www.attardcofood.com
Emp.: 50
Food & Alcoholic Beverage Whslr
S.I.C.: 5149
N.A.I.C.S.: 424490
Susanne Fsadni *(Coord Office)*

Attard & Co. Industrial Ltd. (1)
Building Materials Center
Qormi, QRM 3618, Malta
Tel.: (356) 21 485 629
Emp.: 5
Construction Material Whslr
S.I.C.: 5032
N.A.I.C.S.: 423320

Subsidiaries:

Evolve Ltd. (2)
P F Bilocca Street
Marsa, MRS 1524, Malta
Tel.: (356) 25692120
Fax: (356) 21220186
Web Site: www.evolveltd.eu
Laboratory Equipment & Supplies Distr
S.I.C.: 5049
N.A.I.C.S.: 423490
Hugh Arrigo, *(Mng Dir)*

T4B Ltd. (2)
Canter Business Centre Patri Felicja
Bilocca Str
Marsa, MRS 1524, Malta
Tel.: (356) 25 692121
Fax: (356) 21 220186
E-Mail: info@t4bservices.com
Web Site: www.t4bservices.com
Building Contracting & Finishing Services
S.I.C.: 1799
N.A.I.C.S.: 238390

World Express Logistics Ltd. (2)
Canter Business Centre P Felicja Bilocca
Str
Marsa, MRS 1524, Malta
Tel.: (356) 21442295
Fax: (356) 21440418
E-Mail: info@welogistics.com
Web Site: www.welogistics.com
Freight Forwarding Services
S.I.C.: 4731
N.A.I.C.S.: 488510
Alfred Farrugia *(Dir-Ops-North Africa)*

ATTENDA LIMITED

One London Road
Staines-upon-Thames, TW18 4EX,
United Kingdom
Tel.: (44) 1784211100
Fax: (44) 1784211200
E-Mail: info@attenda.net
Web Site: www.attenda.com
Year Founded: 1997
Rev.: $45,071,344
Emp.: 250
Business Description:
Infomation Technology Services
S.I.C.: 7379
N.A.I.C.S.: 518210
Personnel:
Mark Fowle *(CEO)*
Paul Howard *(CFO)*

ATTI-KAT SA

109-111 Mesogion St Politia Business
Center
11526 Athens, Greece
Tel.: (30) 2106971100
Fax: (30) 2106971118
E-Mail: info@attikat.gr
Web Site: www.attikat.gr
Year Founded: 1980
ATTIK—(ATH)
Sales Range: $10-24.9 Million
Emp.: 60
Business Description:
Heavy Construction Services
S.I.C.: 1542
N.A.I.C.S.: 236220
Personnel:
Panagiotis Panoussis *(Chm, Pres & CEO)*
Board of Directors:
Panagiotis Panoussis
Sofia Alexiadou
Domenikos Chinaris
Gerasimos Lallis
Sotirios Panoussis
Konstantinos Papoulias
Konstantinos Tselos

ATTICA BANK S.A.

23 Omirou Street
106-72 Athens, Greece
Tel.: (30) 2103669000
Fax: (30) 2103669418
E-Mail: info@atticabank.gr
Web Site: www.atticabank.gr
TATT—(ATH)
Rev.: $291,070,610
Assets: $5,247,746,429
Liabilities: $5,118,056,634
Net Worth: $129,689,794
Earnings: ($244,463,433)
Emp.: 1,012
Fiscal Year-end: 12/31/12
Business Description:
Banking Services
S.I.C.: 6029
N.A.I.C.S.: 522110
Personnel:
Ioannis P. Gamvrilis *(Chm, CEO & Mng Dir)*
Board of Directors:
Ioannis P. Gamvrilis
Alexandros Antonopoulos
Georgios E. Chortareas
Efthymia P. Deli
Evangelos P. Delis
Konstantinos N. Gouvalas
Ioannis S. Ioannidis
Periklis I. Karaiskos
Ilias P. Pertzinidis
Athanasios E. Presvelos
Antonios G. Sellianakis
Athanasios D. Stathopoulos
Dimitrios N. Voganatsis
Katerina D. Zevgoli

Subsidiaries:

Attica Consulting S.A. (1)
8 Mavromichali Str
106 79 Athens, Greece
Tel.: (30) 210 3667003
Fax: (30) 210 3667003
Web Site: www.atticabank.gr/index.asp?a_id=1323
Financial Investment Advisory Services
S.I.C.: 6282
N.A.I.C.S.: 523930
George Priovolos *(Mng Dir)*

Attica Ventures S.A. (1)
18 Omeru st
10672 Athens, Greece
Tel.: (30) 2103637663
Fax: (30) 2103637859
E-Mail: gp@attica-ventures.gr
Web Site: www.attica-ventures.com
Emp.: 3
Venture Capital Fund Management
Services
S.I.C.: 6799
N.A.I.C.S.: 523910
Giannis Papadopoulos *(CEO & Gen Mgr)*
Sotiris Chinos *(CFO)*

Attica Wealth Management S.A. (1)
Christou Lada 2
10561 Athens, Greece
Tel.: (30) 2103396860
Fax: (30) 2103238697
E-Mail: info@atticawealth.gr
Web Site: www.atticawealth.gr
Emp.: 14
Wealth Management Services
S.I.C.: 6022
N.A.I.C.S.: 522190
Theodoros Krintas *(Mng Dir)*

AtticaBank Properties S.A (1)
113 Vouliagmenis Avenue & Elia Eliou Str
116 36 Athens, Greece
Tel.: (30) 2103256430
Fax: (30) 210 3244621
E-Mail: info@atticabank.gr
Web Site: www.atticabank.gr/index.asp?a_id=1323
Emp.: 30
Investment Banking Services
S.I.C.: 6211
N.A.I.C.S.: 523110
Theodoros Glavas *(Mng Dir)*

ATTICA GROUP

123-125 Syngrou Avenue & 3 Torva
Street
117 45 Athens, Greece
Tel.: (30) 2108919500
Fax: (30) 2108919509
E-Mail: superfast@superfast.com
Web Site: www.attica-group.com
Year Founded: 1918
ATTICA—(ATH)
Rev.: $344,622,212
Assets: $1,054,343,229
Liabilities: $582,684,300
Net Worth: $471,658,929
Earnings: ($71,709,130)
Emp.: 1,009
Fiscal Year-end: 12/31/12
Business Description:
Ferry Transportation Services
S.I.C.: 4481
N.A.I.C.S.: 483112
Personnel:
Kyriakos D. Magiras *(Chm)*
Michael G. Sakellis *(Vice Chm)*
Spiros Ch. Paschalis *(CEO & Mng Dir)*
Board of Directors:
Kyriakos D. Magiras
Efthymios Th. Bouloutas
Alexandros Th. Edipidis
Markos A. Foros
Spiros Ch. Paschalis
Michael G. Sakellis
Areti G. Souvatzoglou
Subsidiary:

Blue Star Maritime S.A. (1)
157 C Karamanli Avenue
Voula, Athens, 166 73, Greece
Tel.: (30) 2108919840
Fax: (30) 2108919849
Web Site: www.attica-group.com
Sales Range: $150-199.9 Million
Emp.: 725
Maritime Transportation Services
S.I.C.: 4481
N.A.I.C.S.: 483112
Michael G. Sakellis *(Mng Dir)*

ATTILA RESOURCES LIMITED

Suite 23 513 Hay Street
Subiaco, WA, 6008, Australia
Mailing Address:
PO Box 1311
Subiaco, WA, 6904, Australia
Tel.: (61) 8 6142 0989
Fax: (61) 8 9388 8824
E-Mail: admin@attilaresources.com
Web Site: www.attilaresources.com
AYA—(ASX)
Rev.: $74,673
Assets: $17,032,251
Liabilities: $16,192,036
Net Worth: $840,215
Earnings: ($14,890,455)
Fiscal Year-end: 06/30/13
Business Description:
Coal & Gold Exploration Services
S.I.C.: 1222
N.A.I.C.S.: 212112
Personnel:
Oonagh Malone *(Sec)*
Board of Directors:
Max Brunsdon
Evan Cranston
Shaun Day
Bryn Hardcastle
Alan Thom

ATTOCK CEMENT PAKISTAN LIMITED

D-70 Block-4 Kehkashan-5 Clifton
Karachi, 75600, Pakistan
Tel.: (92) 2135309773
Fax: (92) 2135309775
E-Mail: acpl@attockcement.com
Web Site: www.attockcement.com
ACPL—(KAR)
Sls.: $116,573,062
Assets: $108,447,687
Liabilities: $27,948,113
Net Worth: $80,499,575
Earnings: $21,638,541
Emp.: 783
Fiscal Year-end: 06/30/13
Business Description:
Cement Mfr & Sales
S.I.C.: 3297
N.A.I.C.S.: 327120
Personnel:
Babar Bashir Nawaz *(CEO)*
Irfan Amanullah *(Sec)*
Board of Directors:
Ghaith Rashad Pharaon
Fakhr-Ul-Islam Baig
Shuaib A. Malik
Babar Bashir Nawaz
Laith G. Pharaon
Wael G. Pharaon
Abdus Sattar

ATTOCK REFINERY LTD

Morgah
Rawalpindi, Pakistan
Tel.: (92) 515487041
Fax: (92) 515487093
E-Mail: info@arl.com.pk
Web Site: www.arl.com.pk
ATRL—(KAR)
Sls.: $1,654,234,389
Assets: $709,623,579
Liabilities: $383,089,654
Net Worth: $326,533,925
Earnings: $44,971,396
Emp.: 669
Fiscal Year-end: 06/30/13
Business Description:
Oil Refinery
S.I.C.: 2911
N.A.I.C.S.: 324110
Personnel:
Shuaib Anwar Malik *(Chm)*
Adil Khattak *(CEO)*
Saif ur Rehman Mirza *(Sec)*
Board of Directors:
Shuaib Anwar Malik
Munaf Ibrahim
Ghaith R. Pharaon
Laith Ghaith Pharaon
Wael Ghaith Pharaon
Abdus Sattar
Agha Sher Shah

Subsidiaries:

Attock Petroleum Limited (1)
6 Faisal Ave Fl 7/1
Islamabad, Pakistan
Tel.: (92) 512611600
Fax: (92) 2611612
Web Site: www.apl.com.pk
Petroleum Refineries
S.I.C.: 2911
N.A.I.C.S.: 324110
Shoiab A. Malik *(CEO)*

Capgas Private Limited (1)
POL House Morgah
Rawalpindi, 46600, Pakistan
Tel.: (92) 515487589
Storage, Filling & Distribution of Liquefied
Petroleum Gas
S.I.C.: 5989
N.A.I.C.S.: 454310

National Refinery Limited (1)
7-B Korangi Industrial Area
Karachi, 74900, Pakistan PK
Tel.: (92) 21 35064135
Fax: (92) 21 35054663
E-Mail: info@nrlpak.com
Web Site: www.nrlpak.com
NRL—(FKA ISL KAR LAH)

Attock Refinery Ltd—(Continued)

Sls.: $2,189,326,415
Assets: $564,007,179
Liabilities: $291,800,363
Net Worth: $272,206,816
Earnings: $28,814,349
Emp.: 1,032
Fiscal Year-end: 06/30/13
Crude Oil Refining Services
S.I.C.: 1311
N.A.I.C.S.: 211111
Shuaib Anwer Malik *(Deputy Chm & CEO)*
Anwar A. Shaikh *(CFO)*
Nouman Ahmed Usmani *(Sec)*

Pakistan Oilfields Limited (1)
POL House Morgah
Rawalpindi, Pakistan
Tel.: (92) 515487589
Fax: (92) 515487598
E-Mail: polcms@pakoil.com.pk
Web Site: www.pakoil.com.pk
POL—(KAR)
Sls.: $324,824,396
Assets: $570,586,554
Liabilities: $211,864,270
Net Worth: $358,722,284
Earnings: $109,320,144
Emp.: 793
Fiscal Year-end: 06/30/13
Oil & Gas Mfr
S.I.C.: 3533
N.A.I.C.S.: 333132
Shuaib A. Malik *(Chm & CEO)*
Khalid Nafees Zaidi *(CFO & Sec)*

ATTRELL AUTO HOLDINGS LIMITED

(d/b/a Attrell Toyota)
100 Canam Crescent
Brampton, ON, L7A 1A9, Canada
Tel.: (905) 451-1699
Fax: (905) 451-4680
Toll Free: (888) 869-6828
Web Site: www.attrelltoyota.com
Rev.: $20,148,043
Emp.: 44
Business Description:
New & Used Car Dealers
S.I.C.: 5511
N.A.I.C.S.: 441110
Personnel:
Robert Attrell *(Owner)*

ATTUNITY LTD

16 Atdir Yeda Street Atir Yeda Industrial Park
Kfar Saba, Israel
Tel.: (972) 98993000
Fax: (972) 98993001
E-Mail: info-il@attunity.com
Web Site: www.attunity.com
Year Founded: 1988
ATTU—(NASDAQ)
Rev.: $25,479,000
Assets: $26,132,000
Liabilities: $16,570,000
Net Worth: $9,562,000
Earnings: $1,486,000
Emp.: 114
Fiscal Year-end: 12/31/12
Business Description:
Technology Solutions for Integrating Disparate Data Sources, Legacy & Mainframe Applications
S.I.C.: 7372
N.A.I.C.S.: 511210
Personnel:
Shimon Alon *(Chm & CEO)*
Dror Harel-Elkayam *(CFO & Sec)*
Board of Directors:
Shimon Alon
Tali Alush-Aben
Dov Biran
Danny Falk
Gil Weiser
Ron Zuckerman

Subsidiaries:

Attunity Israel (1992) Ltd (1)
Moshav
Kfar Netter, 40593, Israel
Tel.: (972) 98993000
Fax: (972) 98993001
Real Time Data Management Software Development Services
S.I.C.: 7371
N.A.I.C.S.: 541511

U.S. Subsidiaries:

Attunity Inc. (1)
70 Blanchard Rd
Burlington, MA 01803
Tel.: (781) 213-5200
Fax: (877) 896-2760
Toll Free: (866) 288-8648
E-Mail: sales@attunity.com
Web Site: www.attunity.com
Technology Solutions for Integrating Disparate Data Sources, Legacy & Mainframe Applications
S.I.C.: 3652
N.A.I.C.S.: 334614
Dror Elkayam *(CFO)*

Non-U.S. Subsidiaries:

Attunity (Hong Kong) Limited (1)
Room 1703 Top Glory Tower 262 Gloucester Road
Causeway Bay, China (Hong Kong)
Tel.: (852) 27569233
Fax: (852) 27070622
E-Mail: info-hk@attunity.com
Real Time Data Management Software Development Services
S.I.C.: 7371
N.A.I.C.S.: 541511

Attunity (UK) Limited (1)
Venture House Arlington Square Downshire Way
Bracknell, RG12 1WA, United Kingdom
Tel.: (44) 1344742805
Fax: (44) 1344 742 869
E-Mail: info-uk@attunity.com
Real Time Data Management Software Development Services
S.I.C.: 7371
N.A.I.C.S.: 541511
Paul Kelly *(VP-Sls-EMEA)*

Non-U.S. Holdings:

Attunity Ltd. (1)
6 Beacontree Plaza
RG2 0BS Reading, United Kingdom
Tel.: (44) 1189753330
Fax: (44) 1189753005
E-Mail: info-uk@attunity.com
Technology Solutions for Integrating Disparate Data Sources, Legacy & Mainframe Applications
S.I.C.: 3652
N.A.I.C.S.: 334614

Attunity Ltd. (1)
8E Tseng Chow Commercial Mansion
1590 Yan'an Road West, Shanghai, China
Tel.: (86) 2162809691
Fax: (86) 2162806762
E-Mail: info@attunity.com.cn
Web Site: www.attunity.com.cn
Emp.: 10
Technology Solutions for Integrating Disparate Data Sources, Legacy & Mainframe Applications
S.I.C.: 3652
N.A.I.C.S.: 334614

Attunity Ltd. (1)
Room 1703 Top Glory Tower
262 Gloucester Road, Causeway Bay, China (Hong Kong)
Tel.: (852) 27569233
Fax: (852) 27070622
E-Mail: info-hk@attunity.com
Web Site: www.attunity.com.hk
Technology Solutions for Integrating Disparate Data Sources, Legacy & Mainframe Applications
S.I.C.: 3652
N.A.I.C.S.: 334614

Attunity S.A. (1)
51 Blvd Bessieres
75017 Paris, France
Tel.: (33) 153068080
Fax: (33) 153068089
E-Mail: info-france@attunity.com
Web Site: www.attunity.fr
Technology Solutions for Integrating Disparate Data Sources, Legacy & Mainframe Applications
S.I.C.: 3652
N.A.I.C.S.: 334614

A.T.U AUTO-TEILE-UNGER HANDELS GMBH & CO. KG

Dr-Kilian-Strasse 11
92637 Weiden, Germany
Tel.: (49) 9613060
Fax: (49) 9613065672
E-Mail: info@de.atu.eu
Web Site: www.atu.de
Year Founded: 1985
Sales Range: $1-4.9 Billion
Emp.: 13,000
Business Description:
Automotive Parts & Accessories Retailer & Repair Services
S.I.C.: 7538
N.A.I.C.S.: 811111
Personnel:
Reinhard J. Gorenflos *(Chm-Supervisory Bd)*
Manfred Ries *(Chm-Mgmt Bd)*
Christian Sailer *(Member-Mgmt Bd)*
Supervisory Board of Directors:
Reinhard J. Gorenflos
Herbert Bierler
Alexander Bruells
Philipp Freise
Manfred Gerlach
Michael Hanses
Helmut Hennecke
Johannes Peter Huth
Karl-Heinz Kremer
Enno Lucht
Dietmar Maier
John L. Pfeffer
Silke Scheiber
Max Simmerl

ATUL AUTO LTD.

8-B National Highway Nr Microwave Tower Shapar
Rajkot, Veraval, India
Tel.: (91) 2827 666000
Fax: (91) 2827 666029
E-Mail: info@atulauto.co.in
Web Site: www.atulauto.co.in
531795—(BOM)
Sls.: $75,543,002
Assets: $22,795,222
Liabilities: $9,019,359
Net Worth: $13,775,863
Earnings: $4,805,399
Fiscal Year-end: 03/31/13
Business Description:
Transportation Services
S.I.C.: 4789
N.A.I.C.S.: 488999
Personnel:
Jayantibai J. Chandra *(Chm & Mng Dir)*
C. S. Purvi Prashant Mehta *(Compliance Officer & Sec)*
Board of Directors:
Jayantibai J. Chandra
Hasmukhbhai H. Adhvaryoo
Hemantkumar J. Bhatt
Niraj J. Chandra
Vijay K. Kedia
Hakubhai Jadavbhai Lalakiya
Mahendra Jamnadas Patel
Subodhchandra T. Shah
Transfer Agent:
Sharex Dynamic (India) Pvt. Ltd.
Unit-1 Luthra Ind Premises Safed Pool Andheri Kurla Rd Andheri (F)
Mumbai, India

ATURMAJU RESOURCES BERHAD

TB 8285 Lot 20C Perdana Square Commercial Centre
Mile 3 1/2 Jalan Apas, 91000 Tawau, Sabah, Malaysia
Tel.: (60) 89911026
Fax: (60) 89911304
E-Mail: aturmaju_arb@yahoo.com
Web Site: www.aturmaju.com.my
ATURMJU—(KLS)
Rev.: $20,282,836
Assets: $27,880,742
Liabilities: $11,620,829
Net Worth: $16,259,913
Earnings: ($7,318,846)
Fiscal Year-end: 12/31/12
Business Description:
Plywood & Wooden Flooring Board Mfr
S.I.C.: 2435
N.A.I.C.S.: 321211
Personnel:
Wang Seng Yeo *(Mng Dir)*
Voon Wah Chong *(Co-Sec)*
Tong Lang Tan *(Co-Sec)*
Board of Directors:
Baharon Talib
Yun Nyen Lim
Kok Wah Ng
Choon Hwa Tan
Gee Kuan Yeo
Wang Seng Yeo
Wang Ting Yeo

ATW HOLDINGS LIMITED

22 Letchworth Centre Avenue
Salter Point, Perth, WA, 6152, Australia
Tel.: (61) 894507411
Fax: (61) 894507422
Web Site:
Sales Range: Less than $1 Million
Emp.: 350
Business Description:
Energy Medicine & Wellness Products & Services
S.I.C.: 7991
N.A.I.C.S.: 713940
Personnel:
Lloyd A. Halvorson *(Chm)*
Ian Edward Gregory *(Sec)*
Legal Counsel:
Cooper Legal
Level 15 251 Adelaide Terrace
Perth, Australia

Non-U.S. Subsidiaries:

Atos Wellness Pte Ltd (1)
No 1 Tannery Road
Singapore, 347719, Singapore
Tel.: (65) 6289 3000
Fax: (65) 6841 9959
E-Mail: enquiries@atos.com.sg
Web Site: www.atoswellness.com.sg
Emp.: 40
Spa Management Services
S.I.C.: 7011
N.A.I.C.S.: 721110
Ananda Rajah *(Gen Mgr)*

Subsidiary:

Atos Consumer Products Pte Ltd (2)
1 Tannery Rd 9-01
Singapore, 347719, Singapore
Tel.: (65) 62893000
Fax: (65) 68419959
Web Site: www.atos.com.sg
Emp.: 40
Spa Management Sertvices
S.I.C.: 7011
N.A.I.C.S.: 721110

Subsidiary:

Slimcare Studio Pte Ltd (3)
1 Coleman Street 03-33 The Adelphi
Singapore, 179803, Singapore

Tel.: (65) 63339018
Fax: (65) 6336 8225
Spa Management Services
S.I.C.: 7011
N.A.I.C.S.: 721110

Body Contours Pte ltd (1)
1 Tannery Rd 04-06
Singapore, 347719, Singapore
Tel.: (65) 62203415
Fax: (65) 62236394
E-Mail: Pauline@bodycontours.com.sg
Web Site: www.bodycontours.com.sg
Emp.: 30
Spa Management Services
S.I.C.: 7011
N.A.I.C.S.: 721110
Pauline Wee *(Gen Mgr)*

Inner Harmony Pte Ltd (1)
2 Handy Rd 03-08
Singapore, 347719, Singapore
Tel.: (65) 67349959
Web Site: www.inahamani.com
Spa Management Services
S.I.C.: 7011
N.A.I.C.S.: 721110

Medec Systems GmbH (1)
Daimlerstr 11
75334 Straubenhardt, Germany
Tel.: (49) 7082925614
Fax: (49) 7082925625
E-Mail: systems@medec.tv
Web Site: www.medec.tv
Emp.: 6
Surgical & Medical Instrument Mfr
S.I.C.: 3841
N.A.I.C.S.: 339112
Frank Lowas *(Mng Dir)*

AU FINANCIERS (INDIA) LIMITED

19-A Dhuleshwar Garden Ajmer Road
Jaipur, 302 001, India
Tel.: (91) 141 391 0000
Fax: (91) 141 2368815
E-Mail: grievances@aufin.in
Web Site: www.aufin.in
Year Founded: 1996
948112—(BOM)

Business Description:
Financial Services
S.I.C.: 6141
N.A.I.C.S.: 522291

Personnel:
Sanjay Agarwal *(Mng Dir)*
Deepak Jain *(CFO)*
Kapish Jain *(Chief Treasury Officer)*
Manmohan Parnami *(Sec & Deputy VP)*

Board of Directors:
Sanjay Agarwal
Krishan Kant Rathi
Uttam Tibrewal
Mannil Venugopalan

AU MINERA CORP

2 Bloor Street East Suite 3500
Toronto, ON, M4W 1A8, Canada
Tel.: (416) 915-4128
Fax: (416) 915-4129
Web Site: www.auminera.com
ZAU—(DEU)

Business Description:
Gold & Copper Mining Services
S.I.C.: 1099
N.A.I.C.S.: 212299

Personnel:
Rodger J. Cowan *(Pres)*

AU OPTRONICS CORP.

No 1 Li-Hsin Road 2
Hsinchu Science Park, Hsin-chu, Taiwan
Tel.: (886) 35008800
Fax: (886) 35643370
E-Mail: info@auo.com
Web Site: www.auo.com
AUO—(NYSE TAI)
Sls.: $12,818,810,568
Assets: $18,283,111,115
Liabilities: $12,754,325,340
Net Worth: $5,528,785,775
Earnings: ($1,893,570,225)
Emp.: 62,847
Fiscal Year-end: 12/31/12

Business Description:
Display Panels Mfr & Developer
S.I.C.: 3674
N.A.I.C.S.: 334413

Personnel:
Kuen-Yao Lee *(Chm)*
Hsuan Bin Chen *(Vice Chm)*
Paul Peng *(Pres)*
Andy Yang *(CFO & VP-Fin Center & Spokesperson)*
Fang-Chen Luo *(CTO & VP)*
Max Cheng *(Exec VP-Global New Bus)*
Fwu-Chyi Hsiang *(Exec VP)*

Board of Directors:
Kuen-Yao Lee
Hsuan Bin Chen
Ronald Jen-Chuan Chwang
Vivien Huey-Juan Hsieh
Hui Hsiung
Tze-Kaing Yang
Ko-Yung Yu

Citibank N.A.
388 Greenwich St 14th Fl
New York, NY 10013

Transfer Agents:
Taishin International Bank
No.96, Jianguo N. Rd, Sec.1, Taipei
Taipei, Taiwan

Citibank N.A.
388 Greenwich St 14th Fl
New York, NY 10013

U.S. Subsidiary:

AU Optronics Corporation America (1)
9720 Cypresswood Dr Ste 241
Houston, TX 77070
Tel.: (281) 807-2630
Fax: (281) 807-2642
E-Mail: usa@auo.com
Web Site: auo.com
Emp.: 5
Plasma Display Panels (PDP) & TFT LCD Modules Sales
S.I.C.: 5065
N.A.I.C.S.: 423690

U.S. Subsidiary:

AUO Green Energy America Corp. (1)
1525 McCarthy Blvd Ste 218
Milpitas, CA 95035
Tel.: (408) 518-8800
Electronic Component Mfr
S.I.C.: 3679
N.A.I.C.S.: 334419

Non-U.S. Subsidiaries:

AFPD Pte., Ltd. (1)
10 Tampines Industrial Avenue 3
Singapore, 528798, Singapore
Tel.: (65) 6424 9888
Fax: (65) 6424 9889
Web Site: www.afpd.com.sg
Electronic Component Mfr
S.I.C.: 3679
N.A.I.C.S.: 334419

AU Optronics Corporation Japan (1)
Level 14 Shinagawa East One Tower 2 16 1 Kounan
Minato-ku, Tokyo, 108-0075, Japan
Tel.: (81) 3 6717 6288
Fax: (81) 3 6717 6289
Web Site: www.auo.com
Emp.: 25
Electronic Appliance Mfr
S.I.C.: 3639
N.A.I.C.S.: 335228
Richard Hsieh *(Gen Mgr)*

AU Optronics (Czech) s.r.o. (1)
Turanka 856/98d
Slatina, Brno, 627 00, Czech Republic
Tel.: (420) 533 445 288
Web Site: www.auo.com
Communication Equipment Mfr
S.I.C.: 3663
N.A.I.C.S.: 334220

AU Optronics Europe B.V. (1)
Zekeringstraat 39B
1014 BV Amsterdam, Netherlands
Tel.: (31) 207940825
Fax: (31) 207940826
E-Mail: info@auo.com
Web Site: auo.com
Emp.: 15
Plasma Display Panels (PDP) & TFT LCD Modules Sales
S.I.C.: 5065
N.A.I.C.S.: 423690
Susan Liu *(Gen Mgr)*

AU Optronics Korea Ltd. (1)
3F MJL B/D 204 5 Non Hyeon 1 Dong
GangNam-Gu, Seoul, Korea (South) 135-011
Tel.: (82) 2 515 8092
Fax: (82) 2 515 8366
Electronic Component Mfr
S.I.C.: 3679
N.A.I.C.S.: 334419

AU Optronics Manufacturing (Shanghai) Corp. (1)
No 3 Lane 58 Sanzhuang Rd Export Processing Zone
Songjiang, Shanghai, China
Tel.: (86) 2137818800
Electronic Component Mfr
S.I.C.: 3679
N.A.I.C.S.: 334419

AU Optronics (Shanghai) Co., Ltd. (1)
No 3 Ln 58 San Zhuang Rd Songjiang Export Processing Zone
Shanghai, 201613, China
Tel.: (86) 21 3781 8800
Electronic Component Mfr
S.I.C.: 3679
N.A.I.C.S.: 334419

AU Optronics (Slovakia) s.r.o. (1)
Bratislavska 517
91105 Trencin, Slovakia
Tel.: (421) 32 657 8800
Web Site: www.auo.com
Liquid Crystal Display Panel Mfr
S.I.C.: 3679
N.A.I.C.S.: 334419

AUO Green Energy Europe B.V. (1)
Zekeringstraat 39B
1014 BV Amsterdam, Netherlands NL
Tel.: (31) 207940825
Electronic Component Mfr
S.I.C.: 3679
N.A.I.C.S.: 334419

Subsidiary:

AUO Green Energy Germany GmbH (2)
Essener Str 5
Oberhausen, Nordrhein-Westfalen, 46047, Germany
Tel.: (49) 2084094242
Emp.: 6
Solar Module Distr
S.I.C.: 5065
N.A.I.C.S.: 423690
Chien-Ping Chen *(Mng Dir)*

BriView (Hefei) Co., Ltd. (1)
Yuner Road Economic and Technological Development Zone
Hefei, Anhui, China
Tel.: (86) 551 279 8800
Fax: (86) 551 279 9618
Electronic Component Mfr
S.I.C.: 3679
N.A.I.C.S.: 334419

Darwin Precisions (Suzhou) Corp. (1)
No 11 Tingxin Street Suzhou Industry Zone
Suzhou, China
Tel.: (86) 51262758800
Electronic Component Mfr
S.I.C.: 3679
N.A.I.C.S.: 334419

Darwin Precisions (Xiamen) Corp. (1)
No 3089 North of Xiang AnRoad
Xiang An Zone, Xiamen, China 361102
Tel.: (86) 592 716 8800
Fax: (86) 592 776 1695
Electronic Component Mfr
S.I.C.: 3679
N.A.I.C.S.: 334419

M.Setek Co., Ltd. (1)
Shinagawa East One Tower 14F 2-16-1 Konan
Minato-ku, Tokyo, 108-0075, Japan JP
Tel.: (81) 3 3474 8800
Fax: (81) 3 3474 8803
Web Site: www.msetek.com
Emp.: 718
Polysilicon & Single Crystal Silicon Wafer Mfr
S.I.C.: 3674
N.A.I.C.S.: 334413
S. J. Shieh *(Pres)*

AU VIET SECURITIES CORPORATION

3F 194 Nguyen Cong Tru
District, Ho Chi Minh City, Vietnam
Tel.: (84) 838216789
Fax: (84) 838213399
Web Site: www.avsc.com.vn
Year Founded: 2007
AVS—(HNX)
Emp.: 80

Business Description:
Investment Banking & Securities Brokerage Services
S.I.C.: 6211
N.A.I.C.S.: 523110

Personnel:
Vinh Duc Doan *(Chm)*

AUBAY SA

13 rue Louis Pasteur
92513 Boulogne-Billancourt, Cedex, France
Tel.: (33) 146106767
Fax: (33) 146106751
E-Mail: infocorp@aubay.com
Web Site: www.aubay.com
Year Founded: 1997
AUB—(EUR)
Rev.: $256,305,383
Assets: $225,101,163
Liabilities: $108,843,229
Net Worth: $116,257,934
Earnings: $9,254,919
Emp.: 2,674
Fiscal Year-end: 12/31/12

Business Description:
Information Technology Services
S.I.C.: 7373
N.A.I.C.S.: 541512

Personnel:
Christian Aubert *(Chm)*
Philippe Rabasse *(CEO)*
Christophe Andrieux *(Deputy CEO-France & Belgium)*
Philippe Cornette *(Deputy CEO-France)*
David Fuks *(Deputy CEO-Fin Affairs)*
Vincent Gauthier *(Deputy CEO-Legal Affairs)*
Gerard Lucente *(CEO-Spain)*

Board of Directors:
Christian Aubert
Christophe Andrieux
Philippe Cornette
Modeste Entrecanales
David Fuks
Vincent Gauthier
Patrick Grumelart
Philippe Rabasse
Paolo Riccardi

Non-U.S. Subsidiaries:

ART (1)
Largo la foppa 2
20121 Milan, Italy

Aubay SA—(Continued)

Tel.: (39) 026556761
Fax: (39) 0265567631
Software Services
S.I.C.: 7371
N.A.I.C.S.: 541511
Paolo Riccardi *(Mgr)*

AUBAY Isalia (1)
C Albacete 5
28027 Madrid, Spain
Tel.: (34) 913 269270
Fax: (34) 914 59381
E-Mail: adorlet@aubay.es
Web Site: www.aubay.es
Consultancy & Training Services
S.I.C.: 7373
N.A.I.C.S.: 541512

Offis (1)
Escherweg 2
26121 Oldenburg, Germany
Tel.: (49) 44197220
Fax: (49) 4419722102
E-Mail: sekretari@offis.de
Web Site: www.offis.de
Emp.: 200
Research & Development of Computer Systems
S.I.C.: 8731
N.A.I.C.S.: 541712
Holger Peinann *(Mgr)*

Promotic Belgium (1)
Rue Chaude Voie 39
Naninne, 5100 Namur, Belgium
Tel.: (32) 81408200
Fax: (32) 81408201
E-Mail: info@aubay.be
Emp.: 60
IT Solutions Provider
S.I.C.: 7371
N.A.I.C.S.: 541511
Michell Soetenf *(Mng Dir)*

AUBRY LOGISTIQUE

Zone Industrielle 4
88700 Rambervillers, Vosges, France
Tel.: (33) 329653246
Fax: (33) 3332965159
E-Mail: aubrylogistique@aubry-logistique.fr
Web Site: www.aubry-logistique.com
Sales Range: $10-24.9 Million
Emp.: 150

Business Description:
Trucking Services
S.I.C.: 4213
N.A.I.C.S.: 484121

Personnel:
Philippe Aubry *(Chm)*

AUCFAN CO., LTD.

1-14-6 Dogenzaka Shibuya-ku
Tokyo, 150-0043, Japan
Tel.: (81) 3 64163652
Web Site: www.aucfan.co.jp
3674—(TKS)
Rev.: $6,817,987
Emp.: 30
Fiscal Year-end: 09/30/12

Business Description:
Electronic Auction Website Operator
S.I.C.: 5961
N.A.I.C.S.: 454112

Personnel:
Shuichi Takenaga *(Pres & CEO)*

AUCHAN S.A.

40 avenue de Flandre
BP 139
59964 Croix, Cedex, France
Tel.: (33) 1 58 65 08 08
Fax: (33) 1 58 65 08 15
Web Site: www.groupe-auchan.com
Year Founded: 1961
Rev.: $63,177,104,270
Assets: $40,461,831,690
Liabilities: $27,242,442,290
Net Worth: $13,219,389,400
Earnings: $967,896,230
Emp.: 287,000
Fiscal Year-end: 12/31/12

Business Description:
Hypermarket & Supermarket Operator
Export
S.I.C.: 5411
N.A.I.C.S.: 445110

Personnel:
Vianney Mulliez *(Chm)*
Xavier de Mezerac *(CFO)*
Benoit Lheureux *(Chm/CEO-Immochan & Dir-Dev)*
Jerome Guillemard *(Chm/CEO-Banque Accord)*

Board of Directors:
Vianney Mulliez
Jean-Louis Clavel
Christophe Dubrulle
Bertrand Leclercq
Arnaud Mulliez
Louis Mulliez
Muriel Van der Wees

Branches:

Auchan (1)
23 Blvd Louis XI
PO Box 1805
ZI Menneton, 37018 Tours, Cedex, France (100%)
Tel.: (33) 247777777
Telex: STAMDOC 750809 F
Fax: (33) 202777710
Emp.: 32,000
Hypermarket & Supermarket Operator
S.I.C.: 5541
N.A.I.C.S.: 447110

Non-U.S. Branches:

Alcampo (1)
Edificio de Oficinas Calle Santiago de Compostela Sur s/n
28029 Madrid, Spain ES
Tel.: (34) 917306666 (100%)
Fax: (34) 917309837
Web Site: www.alcampo.es
Hypermarkets
S.I.C.: 5411
N.A.I.C.S.: 445110
Patrick Coignard *(Chm)*

Auchan Hungary (1)
Bocskai ut 134-136
1113 Budapest, Hungary HU
Tel.: (36) 23886200 (100%)
Fax: (36) 18874599
E-Mail: info.auchan@auchan.hu
Web Site: www.auchan.hu
Emp.: 5,000
Hypermarket & Supermarket Businesses
S.I.C.: 5411
N.A.I.C.S.: 445110
Jean Paul Filliat *(CEO)*

Auchan Polska (1)
Ul Pulawska 46 Piaseczno
05-500 Warsaw, Poland PL
Tel.: (48) 227038200 (100%)
Fax: (48) 227038210
E-Mail: recepcja.dg@auchan.pl
Web Site: www.auchan.pl
Emp.: 150
Hypermarket Business
S.I.C.: 5411
N.A.I.C.S.: 445110

Auchan Shanghai Hypermarket (1)
3rd Floor 1750 Chang Yang Road
Shanghai, 200090, China CN
Tel.: (86) 2165432211 (100%)
Fax: (86) 2155804509
Web Site: www.auchan.com.cn
Hypermarket Business
S.I.C.: 5411
N.A.I.C.S.: 445110
Bruno Mercier *(Pres)*

Auchan Ukraine (1)
Avenue Moskovskiy 15A
Kiev, 04073, Ukraine UA
Tel.: (380) 443913825 (100%)
Fax: (380) 443913829
E-Mail: info@auchan.ua
Web Site: www.auchan.ua
Emp.: 100
Hypermarket Business
S.I.C.: 5411
N.A.I.C.S.: 445110
Oksana Sereda *(Mgr)*

Auchan (1)
Travessa Teixeira Junior No 1
1300-553 Lisbon, Portugal PT
Tel.: (351) 21 360 2100 (100%)
Fax: (351) 21 360 2165
E-Mail: infojumbo@auchan.pt
Web Site: www.auchan.pt
Hypermarket Business
S.I.C.: 5411
N.A.I.C.S.: 445110
Fernando Ereio *(Dir-Logistics)*

Auchan (1)
Verkhnyaya Krasnoselskaya 3A
107140 Moscow, Russia RU
Tel.: (7) 4957212099 (100%)
Fax: (7) 4957211753
E-Mail: reception@auchan.ru
Web Site: www.groupe-auchan.com
Hypermarket Business
S.I.C.: 5411
N.A.I.C.S.: 445110

Auchan (1)
Milanofiori Strada 8 Palazzo N
20089 Rozzano, MI, Italy IT
Tel.: (39) 0257581 (100%)
Fax: (39) 0257583189
E-Mail: info@auchan.it
Web Site: www.auchan.it
Emp.: 300
Hypermarket & Supermarket Business
S.I.C.: 5411
N.A.I.C.S.: 445110
Massimo Romeo *(Mgr)*

Auchan (1)
5 rue Alphonse Weicker
L 2721 Luxembourg, Luxembourg LU
Tel.: (352) 4377431 (100%)
Fax: (352) 429433
E-Mail: contact@auchan.lu
Web Site: www.auchan.lu
Emp.: 800
Hypermarket Business
S.I.C.: 5411
N.A.I.C.S.: 445110

MGV Distri-Hiper S.A. Auchan (1)
Str Barbu Delavrance a 13
Sector 1, 011351 Bucharest, Romania RO
Tel.: (40) 212227887 (100%)
Fax: (40) 212227884
Web Site: www.auchan.ro
Hypermarket Business
S.I.C.: 5411
N.A.I.C.S.: 445110

AUCKLAND INTERNATIONAL AIRPORT LIMITED

4 Leonard Isitt Drive Auckland Airport
Manukau, 2150, New Zealand
Mailing Address:
PO Box 73020
Manukau, 2150, New Zealand
Tel.: (64) 9 275 0789
Fax: (64) 9 275 5835
E-Mail: corporate@aucklandairport.co.nz
Web Site: www.aucklandairport.co.nz
Year Founded: 1987
AIA—(NZE OTC)
Rev.: $375,359,346
Assets: $3,296,568,024
Liabilities: $1,204,480,665
Net Worth: $2,092,087,359
Earnings: $148,958,379
Fiscal Year-end: 06/30/13

Business Description:
International Airport
S.I.C.: 4581
N.A.I.C.S.: 488119

Personnel:
Adrian Littlewood *(CEO)*
Simon Robertson *(CFO)*
Charles Spillane *(Gen Counsel, Sec & Gen Mgr-Corp Affairs)*

Board of Directors:
Henry William van der Heyden
John Alston Brabazon
Richard John Didsbury
Brett Godfrey
Michelle L. Guthrie
James Miller
Justine Gay Bronwyn Smyth
Keith S. Turner

Legal Counsel:
Russell McVeagh
Auckland, New Zealand

Link Market Services Limited
Level 7 Zurich House 21 Queen Street
Auckland, 1010, New Zealand

AUCLERT SAS

Z I Les Rochettes 12 Rue Des Rochettes
91150 Morigny Champigny, Essonne, France
Tel.: (33) 169921260
Web Site: concessions.peugeot.fr/auclert
Sls.: $17,000,000
Emp.: 48
S.I.C.: 5511
N.A.I.C.S.: 441110

Personnel:
William Monin *(Dir-Mktg)*

AUCNET INC.

Sabancho Tokyo Bldg 8-1 Sanban-cho
Chiyoda-ku, Tokyo, 102-8349, Japan
Tel.: (81) 335126111
Fax: (81) 335126100
E-Mail: ir@ns.aucnet.co.jp
Web Site: www.aucnet.co.jp
Year Founded: 1984
Sales Range: $150-199.9 Million
Emp.: 311

Business Description:
Online Used Car Auctions
Export
S.I.C.: 5961
N.A.I.C.S.: 454112

Personnel:
Kiyotaka Fujisaki *(Pres)*
Hisanao Nagashima *(Sr Mng Dir)*

Board of Directors:
Hiroshi Arai
Kiyotaka Fujisaki
Takashi Fujisaki
Yuji Hikino
Akira Iinuma
Koji Nagaki
Hisanao Nagashima
Yasuhiro Nishi

Subsidiaries:

Advance Car Technology Company Limited (1)
Sanbancho Annex Building 1-4 Fl
Sanban-cho Chiyoda-ku, Tokyo, Japan
Tel.: (81) 352169762
Fax: (81) 352169763
E-Mail: info@act-x.co.jp
Web Site: www.act-x.co.jp
Emp.: 20
New Car Dealers
S.I.C.: 5511
N.A.I.C.S.: 441110
Nariyuki Sawanobori *(Gen Mgr)*

Auc Service Inc. (1)
Sanbancho Tokyu Building 8-1
Chiyoda-ku, 102-8349 Tokyo, Sanbancho, Japan
Tel.: (81) 335126111
Fax: (81) 335126100
Web Site: www.aucnet-nyukai.com
Business Auctions of Automobiles, Motorcycles & Other Business Services
S.I.C.: 5961
N.A.I.C.S.: 454112

Aucnet Sales and Support Inc. (1)
Sanbancho Tokyu Building
8-1 Sanban-cho Chiyoda-ku, 102-8349
Tokyo, Japan

Tel.: (81) 335126544
Fax: (81) 0352169679
Web Site: www.aucnet-nyukai.com
Motor Vehicle Supplies & New Parts Whslr
S.I.C.: 5013
N.A.I.C.S.: 423120

Automobile Inspection System Inc. (1)
Sanbancho Tokyu Bldg
8-1 Sanban-cho Chiyoda-ku, 102-8349
Tokyo, Japan
Tel.: (81) 335126118
Fax: (81) 335126108
Web Site: www.ais-inc.jp
Emp.: 40
Commercial Sectors Regulation Licensing & Inspection
S.I.C.: 9651
N.A.I.C.S.: 926150
Hisato Watanabe *(Gen Mgr)*

Hello Net Inc. (1)
Nihonterebi-Yonbancho Building 1 3F
5-6 Yonban-cho Chiyoda-ku, Tokyo, 102-0081, Japan
Tel.: (81) 335126300
Fax: (81) 335126333
E-Mail: e-staff@hellonet.co.jp
Web Site: www.hellonet.co.jp
Emp.: 20
Real Estate Agents & Brokers
S.I.C.: 6531
N.A.I.C.S.: 531210
Hiroshi Uchida *(Gen Mgr)*

I-Auc Inc. (1)
Sanbancho Tokyu Bldg
8-1 Sanban-cho Chiyoda-ku, 102-8349
Tokyo, Japan
Tel.: (81) 335126123
Fax: (81) 0335126100
E-Mail: info@iauc.co.jp
Web Site: www.iauc.co.jp
Emp.: 60
Motor Vehicle Supplies & New Parts Whslr
S.I.C.: 5013
N.A.I.C.S.: 423120
Goto Hirofumi *(Pres)*

I-Links Inc. (1)
Sanbancho Tokyu Building
8-1 Sanban-cho Chiyoda-ku, 102-8349
Tokyo, Japan
Tel.: (81) 335126150
Fax: (81) 335126170
Web Site: www.aucnet.co.jp/e/profile/prof_group.php
Business Support Services
S.I.C.: 7389
N.A.I.C.S.: 561499

Ing Communications Corp (1)
Nikkodo Bldg 2-10-14
Shiroyama-cho Oyama-city, 323-0025
Tochigi, Japan
Tel.: (81) 285203811
Fax: (81) 285203855
Web Site: www.aucnet.co.jp/e/profile/prof_group.php
New Car Dealers
S.I.C.: 5511
N.A.I.C.S.: 441110

Runmart Inc. (1)
Hanamo Bldg 3-12-9
Kita-aoyama Minato-ku, 107-0061 Tokyo, Japan
Tel.: (81) 357668288
Fax: (81) 357668277
E-Mail: info@runmart.co.jp
Web Site: www.runmart.co.jp
Emp.: 250
Motor Vehicle Supplies & Parts Whslr
S.I.C.: 5013
N.A.I.C.S.: 423120
John Cook *(Mng Dir)*

AUCTUS CAPITAL PARTNERS AG

Prenz Regenten Strasse 18
80333 Munich, Germany
Tel.: (49) 89 159 0700 00
Fax: (49) 89 159 0700 49
E-Mail: info@auctus.com
Web Site: www.auctus.com
Year Founded: 2001
Emp.: 900
Business Description:
Private Equity Firm
S.I.C.: 6211
N.A.I.C.S.: 523999
Personnel:
Ingo Krocke *(CEO)*
Nicolas Himmelmann *(Partner)*
Daniel Meuthen *(Partner)*

AUDALIA RESOURCES LIMITED

Unit 4/70 Wittenoom Street
Perth, WA, 6004, Australia
Mailing Address:
PO Box 3438
Nedlands, WA, 6909, Australia
Tel.: (61) 8 9325 9885
Fax: (61) 8 6389 2588
E-Mail: admin@audalia.com.au
Web Site: www.audalia.com.au
ACP—(ASX)
Rev.: $44,855
Assets: $2,074,703
Liabilities: $166,025
Net Worth: $1,908,678
Earnings: ($300,879)
Fiscal Year-end: 06/30/13
Business Description:
Lead, Zinc & Copper Mining Services
S.I.C.: 1031
N.A.I.C.S.: 212231
Personnel:
Soo Kok Lim *(Chm)*
Karen Logan *(Sec)*
Board of Directors:
Soo Kok Lim
Brent Butler
Andrew Boo Lye Kwa
Siew Swan Ong
Legal Counsel:
Steinepreis Paganin
Level 4 The Read Building 16 Milligan Street
Perth, WA, 6000, Australia
Tel.: (61) 8 9321 4000
Fax: (61) 8 9321 4333

AUDASC

La Folie Nord Cd 917
62180 Berck, France
Tel.: (33) 321090800
Sales Range: $10-24.9 Million
Emp.: 49
Business Description:
Grocery Stores
S.I.C.: 5411
N.A.I.C.S.: 445110
Personnel:
Christine Grohin *(Mgr)*

AUDAX-KECK GMBH

Weiherstrasse 10
D-75365 Calw, Germany
Tel.: (49) 705116250
Fax: (49) 7051162550
E-Mail: info@audax.de
Web Site: www.audax.de
Year Founded: 1982
Rev.: $10,847,073
Emp.: 16
Business Description:
Building Protection Products Distr
S.I.C.: 5169
N.A.I.C.S.: 424690
Personnel:
Gunther Keck *(Founder & Mng Dir)*

AUDEMARS PIGUET & CIE

Rte de France 16
CH 1348 Le Brassus, Switzerland
Tel.: (41) 218451400
Fax: (41) 218451401
E-Mail: info@audemarspiguet.com
Web Site: www.audemarspiguet.com
Year Founded: 1875
Emp.: 500
Business Description:
Jewelry & Watches
Export
S.I.C.: 3911
N.A.I.C.S.: 339910
Personnel:
Farncois Bennhamias *(CEO)*
Subsidiary:

Audemars Piguet (Suisse) S.A. (1)
Vignette 3
CH 1167 Morges, Switzerland
Tel.: (41) 218112280
Fax: (41) 218024957
E-Mail: nicolas.kappenverger@audemarspiguet.com
Web Site: www.audemarspiguet.com
Emp.: 20
Jewelry & Watches
S.I.C.: 3911
N.A.I.C.S.: 339910
Nicolas Kappenverger *(Mgr)*

U.S. Subsidiary:

Audemars Piguet (North America) (1)
65 E 57th St
New York, NY 10022
Tel.: (212) 758-8400
Fax: (212) 688-6381
Web Site: www.audemarspiguet.com
Emp.: 33
Jewelry & Watches
S.I.C.: 3911
N.A.I.C.S.: 339910
Francois-Henri Bennahmias *(Pres)*

Non-U.S. Subsidiaries:

Audemars Piguet Deutschland (1)
Bahnhofstrasse 44 46
D 65185 Wiesbaden, Germany (100%)
Tel.: (49) 611341750
Fax: (49) 6113417520
E-Mail: info-de@audemarspiguet.com
Emp.: 15
Jewelry & Watches
S.I.C.: 3914
N.A.I.C.S.: 339910

Audemars Piguet France (1)
19 Rue Marbeuf
F 75008 Paris, France (100%)
Tel.: (33) 153576760
Fax: (33) 153576768
Jewelry & Watches
S.I.C.: 3914
N.A.I.C.S.: 339910

Audemars Piguet Italia S.p.A. (1)
Via Melchiorre Gioia 168
20125 Milan, Italy
Tel.: (39) 0266985117
Fax: (39) 0266985205
E-Mail: info.italia@audemarspiguet.com
Web Site: www.audemarspiguet.com
Emp.: 12
Jewelry & Watches
S.I.C.: 3911
N.A.I.C.S.: 339910
Andrea Cardillo *(Mng Dir)*

AUDERA

Rue Alfred Nobel
Ifs, 14123 Caen, France
Tel.: (33) 231356666
Web Site: www.audera.fr/
Sls.: $21,800,000
Emp.: 28
Business Description:
New & Used Car Dealers
S.I.C.: 5511
N.A.I.C.S.: 441110
Personnel:
Serge Foucher *(Pres)*

AUDIO PIXELS HOLDINGS LIMITED

Suite 2 Level 12 75 Elizabeth Street
Sydney, NSW, 2000, Australia
Tel.: (61) 292333915
Fax: (61) 292323411
Web Site: www.audiopixels.com.au
Year Founded: 2006
AKP—(ASX OTC)
Rev.: $168,806
Assets: $10,267,418
Liabilities: $590,403
Net Worth: $9,677,015
Earnings: ($2,732,489)
Emp.: 9
Fiscal Year-end: 12/31/12
Business Description:
Electronics Product Mfr
S.I.C.: 7699
N.A.I.C.S.: 811211
Personnel:
Fred Bart *(Chm & CEO)*
Ian Alistair Dennis *(Sec)*
Board of Directors:
Fred Bart
Cheryl Sarah Bart
Ian Alistair Dennis
Legal Counsel:
Gye Associates Lawyers
Level 5 6 O'Connell Street
Sydney, Australia

AUDIO-TECHNICA CORPORATION

2206 Naruse
Machida, Tokyo, 194-8666, Japan
Tel.: (81) 3 6801 2001
Fax: (81) 3 6801 2009
Web Site: www.audio-technica.co.jp
Business Description:
Professional Sound Equipment Mfr
S.I.C.: 3651
N.A.I.C.S.: 334310
Personnel:
Hideo Matsushita *(Chm)*
Kazuo Matsushita *(Pres)*
U.S. Subsidiary:

Audio-Technica U.S., Inc. (1)
1221 Commerce Dr
Stow, OH 44244
Tel.: (330) 686-2600
Fax: (330) 688-3752
Web Site: www.audio-technica.com
Sales Range: $10-24.9 Million
Emp.: 115
Professional Sound Equipment Distr
S.I.C.: 3651
N.A.I.C.S.: 334310
Philip Cajka *(Pres & CEO)*

Non-U.S. Subsidiaries:

Audio-Technica (Greater China) Limited (1)
Room K 9th Floor Kaiser Est Ph 2
51 Man Yue Street
Hung Hom, Kowloon, China (Hong Kong)
Tel.: (852) 23569268
Fax: (852) 27730811
E-Mail: info@audio-technica.com.hk
Web Site: www.audio-technica.com.hk
Professional Audio Equipment
S.I.C.: 3651
N.A.I.C.S.: 334310

Audio-Technica Limited (UK) (1)
Technica House
Royal London Industrial Estate
Old Lane, Leeds, LS11 8AG, United Kingdom
Tel.: (44) 1132771441
Fax: (44) 1132704836
Web Site: www.audio-technica.co.uk
Emp.: 30
Professional Audio Equipment
S.I.C.: 3651
N.A.I.C.S.: 334310

Audio-Technica (S.E.A.) Pte. Ltd. (1)
1 Ubi View 01-14 focus 1
Singapore, 408555, Singapore
Tel.: (65) 67495686
Fax: (65) 67495689
E-Mail: sales@audio-technica.com.sg

Audio-Technica Corporation—(Continued)

Web Site: www.audio-technica.com.sg
Emp.: 20
Professional Audio Equipment
S.I.C.: 3651
N.A.I.C.S.: 334310
Vincent Heng Fai Chan *(Mng Dir)*

AUDIO VISUAL ENTERPRISES S.A.

3 Parnonos Str
151 25 Maroussi, Greece
Tel.: (30) 210 8092000
Web Site: www.ave.gr
Year Founded: 1982
AVE—(ATH)
Emp.: 527

Business Description:
Home Video Distr
S.I.C.: 7829
N.A.I.C.S.: 512120

Personnel:
Antonopoulos Charalampos *(CEO)*
Boylgaris I. Apostolos *(Deputy CEO & VP)*
Apostolos Voulgaris *(IR Officer)*

Board of Directors:
Giakou V. Anna-Irini
Boylgaris I. Apostolos
Georgiadis Basileios
Antonopoulos Charalampos
Konsta G. Evaggelo
Bardinogiannis T. Ioannis
Teofanopoulo K. Nikolao

AUDIOCODES LTD.

1 Hayarden Street Airport City
Lod, 7019900, Israel
Tel.: (972) 3 976 4000
Fax: (972) 3 976 4040
E-Mail: info@audiocodes.com
Web Site: www.audiocodes.com
AUDC—(NASDAQ TAE)
Rev.: $127,490,000
Assets: $166,004,000
Liabilities: $67,707,000
Net Worth: $98,297,000
Earnings: ($4,177,000)
Emp.: 579
Fiscal Year-end: 12/31/12

Business Description:
Voice Compression Chips & Related Products Mfr
Export
S.I.C.: 3661
N.A.I.C.S.: 334210

Personnel:
Shabtai Adlersberg *(Chm, Pres & CEO)*
Guy Avidan *(CFO & VP-Fin)*
Lior Aldema *(COO & Head-Global Sls)*

Board of Directors:
Shabtai Adlersberg
Eyal Kishon
Doron Nevo
Osnat Ronen
Joseph Tenne

U.S. Subsidiaries:

AudioCodes California **(1)**
27 Worlds Fair Dr Ste 1
Somerset, NJ 08873-1353 DE
Tel.: (858) 625-2400 (100%)
Fax: (858) 625-2422
Web Site: www.audiocodes.com
Emp.: 100
Designs, Manufactures & Sells Packet Voice Gateways to Communication Services
S.I.C.: 3661
N.A.I.C.S.: 334210
Guy Avidan *(CFO & VP-Fin)*

AudioCodes, Inc. **(1)**
27 Worlds Fair Dr Ste 2
Somerset, NJ 08873-1353 (100%)
Tel.: (408) 441-1175
Fax: (408) 451-9520
E-Mail: info@audiocodes.com
Web Site: www.audiocodes.com
Emp.: 20
Voice Network Solutions
S.I.C.: 4899
N.A.I.C.S.: 517919
Shabtai Aldersberg *(Chm, Pres & CEO)*
Jeffrey Kahn *(Chief Strategy Officer)*

AudioCodes USA **(1)**
27 World's Fair Dr
Somerset, NJ 08873 (100%)
Tel.: (732) 469-0880
Fax: (732) 469-2298
Toll Free: (800) 648-3647
E-Mail: sales@ai-logix.com
Web Site: www.ai-logix.com
Emp.: 60
Designer & Mfr of Computer Hardware & Software Communication Solutions Products
S.I.C.: 3577
N.A.I.C.S.: 334118
Ron Romanchik *(VP-Call Recording Products)*

Non-U.S. Subsidiaries:

AudioCodes Argentina S.A. **(1)**
Manuela Saenz 323
C1107BPA Buenos Aires, Argentina Ar
Tel.: (54) 91160026632 (100%)
Fax: (54) 8608318493
E-Mail: david.peces@audiocodes.com
Web Site: www.audiocodes.com
Emp.: 334
Information Retrieval Services
Export
S.I.C.: 4899
N.A.I.C.S.: 517919

AudioCodes, Beijing **(1)**
Rm 1808 Tower B Tianyuangang Center No C2 Dongsanhuanbeilu
Chaoyang District, 100027 Beijing, China CN
Tel.: (86) 1051299181 (100%)
Fax: (86) 1065974240
E-Mail: tonyzheng@audiocodes.com.cn
Web Site: www.audiocodes.com
Emp.: 5
Manufacturing & Sales of Voice Gateways to Communication Services
S.I.C.: 3669
N.A.I.C.S.: 334290
Tony Zheng *(Dir-Sls)*

AudioCodes Brasil Equipamentos de Voz sobre IP Ltda. **(1)**
Rua Iguatemi 252-5 andar-cj 51
Jd Paulistano, CEP 01451-010 Sao Paulo, SP, Brazil BR
Tel.: (55) 1191171798 (100%)
Web Site: www.audiocodes.com
Equipment Sales of Voice Gateways to Communication Services
Export
S.I.C.: 4899
N.A.I.C.S.: 517919
Ernasto Trunkl *(Mgr)*

AudioCodes Europe Limited **(1)**
Victoria House 50 Victoria Rd
Farnborough, Hants, GU14 7PG, United Kingdom UK
Tel.: (44) 1252548200 (100%)
Fax: (44) 1252548222
Web Site: www.audiocodes.com
Telecommunication Research & Development
S.I.C.: 8731
N.A.I.C.S.: 541712

AudioCodes GmbH **(1)**
Darmstaedter Landsstrasse 125
60598 Frankfurt, Germany De
Tel.: (49) 9118017512 (100%)
Fax: (49) 9118017513
E-Mail: info@audiocodes.com
Web Site: www.audiocodes.com
Manufacturing & Sales of Packet Voice Gateways to Communication Companies
S.I.C.: 4812
N.A.I.C.S.: 517911

AudioCodes India Pvt. Ltd. **(1)**
Unit No 301 3rd Fl Tower B Millennium Plz
Sushant Lok Phase 1, 122002 Gurgaon, Haryana, India In
Tel.: (91) 1244994550 (100%)
Fax: (91) 1244994551
Emp.: 10
Manufacturing & Sales of Packet Voice Gateways to Communication Companies
S.I.C.: 4812
N.A.I.C.S.: 517911
Munish Bhasin *(Country Mgr)*

AudioCodes Korea Ltd. **(1)**
Room 303 3F World Vision Bldg 24-2 Yoido-dong
Youngdeungpo-gu, 150 877 Seoul, Korea (South) Ks
Tel.: (82) 27825377 (100%)
Fax: (82) 27825177
E-Mail: hyen.kim@audiocodes.com
Web Site: www.audiocodes.com.kr
Emp.: 4
Manufacturing & Sales of Packet Voice Gateways Systems
S.I.C.: 4812
N.A.I.C.S.: 517911
H. Kim *(Gen Mgr)*

AudioCodes Ltd. **(1)**
54 route de Sartrouville
Immeuble Le Montreal
78232 Le Pecq, France FR
Tel.: (33) 979510221 (100%)
Fax: (33) 139768961
Web Site: www.audiocodes.com
Manufacturing & Sales of Voice Gateways to Communication Companies
S.I.C.: 4813
N.A.I.C.S.: 517911

AudioCodes Mexico **(1)**
Alfonso Napoles Gandara #50 4 Piso Col Pena Blanca
Santa Fe, Mexico, DF, 01210, Mexico MX
Tel.: (52) 5591711953 (100%)
Fax: (52) 5591711899
E-Mail: info@audiocodes.com
Web Site: www.audiocodes.com
Sales of Voice Gateways Systems
S.I.C.: 4812
N.A.I.C.S.: 517911

AudioCodes Singapore **(1)**
31 Kaki Bukit Rd 3 Techlink 06 19
417818 Singapore, Singapore SG
Tel.: (65) 64936688 (100%)
Fax: (65) 62994925
E-Mail: angela.lin@audiocodes.com
Web Site: www.audiocodes.com
Emp.: 10
Packet Voice Gateways Systems Mfr & Sales
S.I.C.: 4812
N.A.I.C.S.: 517911

Nuera Communications Singapore Pte Ltd. **(1)**
31 Kaki Bt Rd Unit 06-19 Techlink
Singapore, 417818, Singapore
Tel.: (65) 64936688
Fax: (65) 62994925
Electronic Parts & Equipment Mfr
S.I.C.: 3679
N.A.I.C.S.: 334419

AUDIODEV SWEDEN AB

Derbyvagen 4
212 35 Malmo, Sweden
Tel.: (46) 406904900
Fax: (46) 406904990
E-Mail: info@audiodev.com
Web Site: www.audiodev.com
Year Founded: 1987
Sales Range: $10-24.9 Million
Emp.: 20

Business Description:
Optical Media Test Systems Producer
S.I.C.: 3695
N.A.I.C.S.: 334613

Personnel:
Peter Falk *(Pres & CEO)*

U.S. Subsidiary:

AudioDev USA **(1)**
5126 Clareton Dr
Agoura Hills, CA 91301 (100%)
Tel.: (818) 540-3100
Fax: (818) 540-3107
E-Mail: info@audiodev.com
Web Site: www.audiodev.com
Emp.: 6
Optical Media Test Systems Sales & Servicing
S.I.C.: 3695
N.A.I.C.S.: 334613
Eric Pildeilts *(Pres)*

Non-U.S. Affiliate:

AudioDev Far East Ltd. **(1)**
Flat 1210 12/F Premier Centre
20 Cheung Shun Street, Cheung Sha Wan, China (Hong Kong)
Tel.: (852) 23148736
Fax: (852) 23144537
Web Site: www.audiodev.com
Optical Media Test Systems Sales & Servicing
S.I.C.: 3695
N.A.I.C.S.: 334613

AUDIOTECH HEALTHCARE CORPORATION

175 2nd Ave Ste 760
Kamloops, BC, V2C 5W1, Canada
Tel.: (250) 372-5847
Fax: (250) 372-3859
Toll Free: (888) 590-3555
E-Mail: info@audiotech.org
Web Site: www.audiotech.org
Year Founded: 1998
Sales Range: $1-9.9 Million

Business Description:
Hearing Centers Operator & Manager
S.I.C.: 5999
N.A.I.C.S.: 446199

Personnel:
Osvaldo Iadarola *(Pres & CEO)*
Grant Robertson *(CFO & Sec)*

Board of Directors:
Daniel Allen
James T. Gillis
Osvaldo Iadarola
Glen Martin
Gerald Mill
Grant Robertson

Transfer Agent:
Computershare Trust Company of Canada
9th Floor 100 University Avenue
Toronto, ON, Canada

Subsidiary:

Canadian Hearing Care **(1)**
#760 - 175 Second Ave
Kamloops, BC, V2C 5W1, Canada (100%)
Tel.: (250) 372-5847
Fax: (250) 372-3859
Web Site: www.canadianhearingcare.com
Emp.: 4
Hearing Services
S.I.C.: 5999
N.A.I.C.S.: 446199

U.S. Subsidiary:

American Hearing Care **(1)**
3345 Merlin Dr Ste 200
Idaho Falls, ID 83404 (100%)
Tel.: (208) 529-1514
Fax: (208) 529-3170
Web Site: www.americanhearingcare.com
Emp.: 10
Hearing Healthcare Services
S.I.C.: 5999
N.A.I.C.S.: 446199

AUDIX CORPORATION

No 8 Ln 120 Sec 1 Neihu Rd
Taipei, Taiwan
Tel.: (886) 287976688
Fax: (886) 226597116
E-Mail: audixhqa@audix.com
Web Site: www.audix.com
2459—(TAI)
Sales Range: $150-199.9 Million

Business Description:
Optoelectronic Products & Components Mfr

S.I.C.: 3674
N.A.I.C.S.: 334413
Personnel:
Cheng-Huang Chung *(Chm)*
Chien-Chang Chang *(Gen Mgr & COO)*

Subsidiary:

Lily Medical Corporation (1)
No 28-2 Shun Jeau Diann
Chunan Town, Miao-li, 350, Taiwan
Tel.: (886) 37612625
Fax: (886) 37 612720
Web Site: www.lily-medical.com
Emp.: 100
Surgical Supplies Mfr
S.I.C.: 3842
N.A.I.C.S.: 339113
James Chung *(Chm)*

Non-U.S. Subsidiaries:

AHC Warehouse & Trading (Shenzhen) Co., Ltd. (1)
West 4/F 25 Building Kezhixi Road Science Park
Nanshan District, Shenzhen, Guangdong, 518038, China
Tel.: (86) 755 2663 1938
Fax: (86) 755 2655 3814
Web Site: www.audix.com
General Warehousing & Storage Services
S.I.C.: 4225
N.A.I.C.S.: 493110
Kant Wu *(Mgr)*

AHI Electronics Warehouse (Hang Zhou) Co., Ltd. (1)
Room 610 Huadu Building No 137 Qingchun Road
Hangzhou, Zhejiang, 310006, China
Tel.: (86) 571 8724 4671
Fax: (86) 571 8724 4657
Web Site: www.audix.com
Electronic Components Distr
S.I.C.: 5065
N.A.I.C.S.: 423690
Y. H. Hsieh *(Mgr)*

AHI Electronics Warehouse (Shanghai) Co., Ltd. (1)
3-4/F 34 Building No 806 Guiping Road
Caohejing Development Zone
Shanghai, 200233, China
Tel.: (86) 2164950798
Fax: (86) 2164950791
Web Site: www.audix.com
General Warehousing & Storage Services
S.I.C.: 4225
N.A.I.C.S.: 493110
Justin Lin *(Mgr)*

AHI Electronics Warehouse (Wu Jiang) Co., Ltd. (1)
No 1289 Jiang Xing East Road Eastern Wujiang Economic Development Zone
Wujiang, Jiangsu, 215200, China
Tel.: (86) 51263439990
Fax: (86) 51263403339
Web Site: www.audix.com
Electronic Components Distr
S.I.C.: 5065
N.A.I.C.S.: 423690

Audix Hi-Tech Investment Co., Ltd. (1)
Flat B & C 20F Infotech Centre 21 Hung To Road
Kwun Tong, Kowloon, China (Hong Kong)
Tel.: (852) 27997575
Fax: (852) 27956529
Electronic Components Mfr
S.I.C.: 3675
N.A.I.C.S.: 334416
Ken Chung *(Mgr)*

Audix Singapore (PTE) Ltd. (1)
No 1 Ubi View Unit 04-33 Bldg Focus 1
Singapore, Singapore
Tel.: (65) 67490398
Fax: (65) 67483534
E-Mail: audixa@pacific.com.sg
Web Site: www.audix.com
Emp.: 1
Electronic Components Distr
S.I.C.: 5065
N.A.I.C.S.: 423690
Richard Lee *(Mgr)*

Audix Technology (Wujiang) Co., Ltd. (1)
No 1289 Jiang Xing East Road The Eastern Part of Wujiang
Economic Development Zone, Wujiang, Jiangsu, 215200, China
Tel.: (86) 51263403993
Fax: (86) 51263403339
Web Site: www.audix.com
Emp.: 200
Electronic Components Mfr
S.I.C.: 3674
N.A.I.C.S.: 334413
James Chung *(Chm)*

Audix Technology (Xiamen) Co., Ltd. (1)
No 46 Xingnan Rd Jimei
Xiamen, Fujiang, 361022, China
Tel.: (86) 5926663002
Fax: (86) 5926214837
E-Mail: alf_yeh@audix.com.cn
Web Site: www.audix.com
Emp.: 1,100
Electronic Components Mfr
S.I.C.: 3679
N.A.I.C.S.: 334419
James Chung *(Chm)*

Toyo Kuni Electronics Co. Ltd. (1)
Workshop B&C 20/F Infotech Centre No 21 Hung To Road
Kwun Tong, Kowloon, China (Hong Kong)
Tel.: (852) 27997575
Fax: (852) 27956529
E-Mail: toyokuni@audix.com.hk
Emp.: 10
Electronic Components Distr
S.I.C.: 5065
N.A.I.C.S.: 423690
Daniel Diu *(Mgr)*

YUKA Precision (Wujiang) Co., Ltd. (1)
No 66 Jiang Xing East Road Wujiang Economic Development Zone East
Wujiang, Jiangsu, 215200, China
Tel.: (86) 51263439780
Fax: (86) 51263439781
Web Site: www.audix.com
Industrial Molds Mfr
S.I.C.: 3544
N.A.I.C.S.: 333511
Chenghung Chung *(Chm)*

AUFEMININ.COM S.A.

78 Bis Avenue Hoche
75008 Paris, France
Tel.: (33) 153577943
Fax: (33) 0153577901
E-Mail: regieinternationale@aufeminin.com
Web Site: www.aufeminin.com
FEM—(EUR)
Rev.: $74,079,735
Assets: $140,550,917
Liabilities: $39,347,203
Net Worth: $101,203,714
Earnings: $14,856,332
Emp.: 176
Fiscal Year-end: 12/31/12
Business Description:
Cosmetic Whslr
S.I.C.: 5122
N.A.I.C.S.: 446120
Personnel:
Marie-Laure Sauty de Chalon *(CEO)*
Board of Directors:
Agnes Alazard
Florian Baier
Christophe Decker
Cyrille Geffray
Marc Schmitz

AUG. LAUKHUFF GMBH & CO. KG

Aug Laukhuff Strasse 1
D-97990 Weikersheim, Germany
Tel.: (49) 793491600
Fax: (49) 7934616
E-Mail: info@laukhuff.de
Web Site: www.laukhuff.de
Year Founded: 1823
Rev.: $15,173,400
Emp.: 150
Business Description:
Musical Instrument Mfr
S.I.C.: 3931
N.A.I.C.S.: 339992
Personnel:
Hans-Erich Laukhuff *(Mng Dir)*
Peter Laukhuff *(Mng Dir)*
Magnus Windelen *(Mng Dir)*

AUGE TECHNOLOGY CORPORATION

Bldg 1281 Nishi Gotanda 7 Chome
Shinagawa-ku, Tokyo, 141-0031, Japan
Tel.: (81) 368210265
E-Mail: info@auge-tech.com
Web Site: www.auge-tech.com
Year Founded: 2007
Sales Range: Less than $1 Million
Business Description:
Software Product Sales & Support Services
S.I.C.: 7372
N.A.I.C.S.: 511210
Personnel:
Akira Tomitani *(Owner)*

AUGEAN PLC

4 Rudgate Court
Walton, Wetherby, West Yorkshire, LS23 7BF, United Kingdom
Tel.: (44) 1937844980
Fax: (44) 1937844241
E-Mail: contact@augeanplc.com
Web Site: www.augeanplc.com
AUG—(AIM)
Rev.: $66,995,061
Assets: $113,265,100
Liabilities: $34,177,415
Net Worth: $79,087,685
Earnings: $3,126,994
Emp.: 268
Fiscal Year-end: 12/31/12
Business Description:
Hazardous Waste Management Services
S.I.C.: 4953
N.A.I.C.S.: 562211
Personnel:
Richard Allen *(Interim CEO, Sec & Dir-Fin)*
Board of Directors:
Richard Allen
Andrew Bryce
Rory Macnamara
Roger McDowell
Legal Counsel:
Walker Morris
Kings Court 12 King Street
Leeds, LS1 2HL, United Kingdom

Subsidiaries:

Augean North Limited (1)
4 Rudgate Ct
Walton, Wetherby, LS23 7BF, United Kingdom
Tel.: (44) 1937844980
Fax: (44) 1937846674
E-Mail: info@augeanplc.com
Web Site: www.augeanplc.com
Emp.: 30
Industrial Wastage Recycling Services
S.I.C.: 4959
N.A.I.C.S.: 562998
David Stewart *(Mng Dir)*

Augean South Limited (1)
Stamford Road Kings Cliffe
Peterborough, Northants, PE8 6XX, United Kingdom
Tel.: (44) 1780444900
Fax: (44) 1780444901
E-Mail: info@augeanplc.com
Web Site: www.augeanplc.com
Emp.: 350
Waste Disposal Services
S.I.C.: 4953
N.A.I.C.S.: 562219
Paul Blackler *(CEO)*

Augean Treatment Limited (1)
Smoke Ln
Avonmouth, BS11 0YA, United Kingdom
Tel.: (44) 1179820303
Fax: (44) 1179820301
E-Mail: sales.avonmouth@augeanplc.com
Emp.: 25
Industrial Wastage Recycling Services
S.I.C.: 4959
N.A.I.C.S.: 562998
Tim Young *(Gen Mgr)*

AUGEN CAPITAL CORP.

130 King Street W The Exchange Tower Suite 720
Toronto, ON, M5X 1A6, Canada
Tel.: (416) 777-2007
Fax: (416) 777-2008
Toll Free: (888) 442-8436
E-Mail: info@augencc.com
Web Site: www.augencc.com
Year Founded: 1997
AUG—(TSXV)
Business Description:
Financial Services
S.I.C.: 6211
N.A.I.C.S.: 523999
Personnel:
Norman Michael Brewster *(Chm)*
Alan Cruickshank *(Pres & CEO)*
Carmelo Marrelli *(CFO)*
Board of Directors:
Norman Michael Brewster
Conor S. Bill
Alan Cruickshank
Peter Miller
G. Michael Newman

AUGROS COSMETIC PACKAGING

ZA du Londeau rue de l'expansion
Cerise, 61000 Alencon, France
Tel.: (33) 233817200
Fax: (33) 233288083
Web Site: www.augros.fr
Year Founded: 1919
AUGR—(EUR)
Rev.: $19,891,008
Assets: $11,260,712
Liabilities: $16,259,041
Net Worth: ($4,998,329)
Earnings: $741,740
Fiscal Year-end: 12/31/12
Business Description:
Cosmetics Packaging Product Mfr
S.I.C.: 3999
N.A.I.C.S.: 339999
Personnel:
Jacques Bourgine *(Chm-Supervisory Bd)*
Didier Bourgine *(Chm-Exec Bd)*
Genevieve Bourgine *(Vice Chm-Supervisory Bd)*
Martine Esnault *(CFO)*
Claude Philippon *(Member-Exec Bd)*
Supervisory Board of Directors:
Jacques Bourgine
Catherine Bourgine Boucher
Genevieve Bourgine
Tony Heude

AUGUR CAPITAL AG

Westendstrasse 16-22
D-60325 Frankfurt, Germany
Tel.: (49) 69 716 799 0
Fax: (49) 69 716 799 10
E-Mail: info@augurcapital.com
Web Site: www.augurcapital.com

Augur Capital AG—(Continued)

Business Description:
Private Equity Firm
S.I.C.: 6211
N.A.I.C.S.: 523999
Personnel:
Thomas Schmitt *(Co-Founder & Partner)*
Gunther P. Skrzypek *(Co-Founder & Partner)*

Holding:

myLife Lebensversicherung AG **(1)**
Herzberger Landstrasse 25
D-37085 Gottingen, Germany De
Tel.: (49) 55199760
Fax: (49) 5519976777
E-Mail: info@mylife-leben.de
Web Site: www.mylife-leben.de
Emp.: 75
Life Insurance Products & Services
S.I.C.: 6311
N.A.I.C.S.: 524113
Michael Dreibrodt *(CEO & Chm-Mgmt Bd)*

AUGUR RESOURCES LTD

Level 2 66 Hunter Street
Sydney, NSW, 2000, Australia
Tel.: (61) 293003310
Fax: (61) 292216333
E-Mail: info@augur.com.au
Web Site: www.augur.com.au
AUK—(ASX)
Rev.: $112,770
Assets: $7,031,571
Liabilities: $615,440
Net Worth: $6,416,131
Earnings: ($1,071,287)
Fiscal Year-end: 06/30/13
Business Description:
Minerals Exploration Services
S.I.C.: 1481
N.A.I.C.S.: 213115
Personnel:
Norman Alfred Seckold *(Chm)*
Grant Leo Kensington *(Mng Dir)*
Richard James Edwards *(Sec)*
Board of Directors:
Norman Alfred Seckold
Grant Leo Kensington
Peter James Nightingale
Justin Charles Werner
Legal Counsel:
Minter Ellison
88 Phillip Street
Sydney, Australia

AUGUST EQUITY LLP

10 Slingsby Place
St Martin's Courtyard, London, WC2E 9AB, United Kingdom
Tel.: (44) 2076328200
Fax: (44) 2076328201
Web Site: www.augustequity.com
Emp.: 14
Business Description:
Private Equity Firm
S.I.C.: 6211
N.A.I.C.S.: 523999
Personnel:
Richard Green *(Co-Founder & Chm)*
Tim Clarke *(Co-Founder & Partner)*
Ian Grant *(Co-Founder & Partner)*
John Fisher *(Partner)*
Aatif Hassan *(Partner)*
Philip Rattle *(Partner)*
Sam Watkinson *(Partner)*

AUGUST FALLER KG

Freiburger Strasse 25
79183 Waldkirch, Germany
Tel.: (49) 76814050
Fax: (49) 7681405110
E-Mail: info@august-faller.de
Web Site: www.august-faller.de
Sales Range: $100-124.9 Million
Emp.: 950
Fiscal Year-end: 12/31/12
Business Description:
Pharmaceutical Packaging Product Mfr
S.I.C.: 2657
N.A.I.C.S.: 322212
Personnel:
Michael Faller *(Co-CEO)*
Daniel Keesman *(Co-CEO)*

AUGUST HILDEBRANDT GMBH

Siemensplatz 1
19057 Schwerin, Germany
Tel.: (49) 385645300
Fax: (49) 3856453064
Web Site: www.cabledrum.com
Year Founded: 1868
Rev.: $38,456,437
Emp.: 105
Business Description:
Wooden Cable Drums Mfr
S.I.C.: 2499
N.A.I.C.S.: 321999
Personnel:
Mathias Lohraff *(Mng Dir)*
Sabine Lohraff *(Mng Dir)*
Uwe Wenkel *(Mng Dir)*

AUGUST METAL CORPORATION

4005 1011 West Cordova Street
Vancouver, BC, V6C 0B2, Canada
Tel.: (604) 408-1990
Fax: (604) 608-4822
E-Mail: ir@augustmetalcorporation.com
Web Site: www.augustmetal.com
AGP—(TSXV)
Assets: $273,421
Liabilities: $519,030
Net Worth: ($245,608)
Earnings: ($1,467,511)
Fiscal Year-end: 09/30/12
Business Description:
Mineral Exploration Services
S.I.C.: 1081
N.A.I.C.S.: 213114
Personnel:
Clive Brookes *(Pres & CEO)*
Bruno Fruscalzo *(CFO)*
Board of Directors:
Peter Born
Clive Brookes
Bruno Fruscalzo
Sean O'Neill
Christopher R. Verrico
Transfer Agent:
Computershare Trust Company
510 Burrard Street 2nd Floor
Vancouver, BC, Canada

AUGUST RUEGGEBERG GMBH & CO. KG PFERD-WERKZEUGE

Hauptstrasse 13
51709 Marienheide, Germany
Mailing Address:
Postfach 1280
51704 Marienheide, Germany
Tel.: (49) 8042187117
Telex: 884191
Fax: (49) 22649400
E-Mail: pferd@rueggeberg.com
Web Site: www.rueggeberg.com
Year Founded: 1897
Emp.: 1,900
Business Description:
Mfr. of Files, Burs, Mounted Points, Polishing & Fine Grinding Tools, Cutting & Grinding Wheels; Chain Saw Accessories
S.I.C.: 3423
N.A.I.C.S.: 332216
Personnel:
Jan Ruggeberg *(Mng Dir)*

U.S. Subsidiary:

PFERD, Inc. **(1)**
30 Jytek Dr
Leominster, MA 01453-5932 (100%)
Tel.: (978) 840-6420
Telex: ITT 499 1543
Fax: (978) 840-6421
E-Mail: mail@pferd.com
Web Site: www.pferd.com
Emp.: 30
Distributor of Cutting Tools
S.I.C.: 5085
N.A.I.C.S.: 423840
Gene Huegin *(Pres)*

Non-U.S. Subsidiaries:

D.O.O. Tehnoalat **(1)**
Pitagorina 1
21000 Novi Sad, Serbia (100%)
Tel.: (381) 21504273
Fax: (381) 21504274
E-Mail: office@tehnoalat.co.rs
Web Site: www.tehnoalat.rs
Emp.: 10
Sales of Machine Tools, Metal Cutting Types.
S.I.C.: 3541
N.A.I.C.S.: 333517
Baljana Maeskov *(Gen Mgr)*

PFERD Australia (Pty.) Ltd. **(1)**
No 1 3 Coniser Crescent
3172 Dingley, VIC, Australia (100%)
Tel.: (61) 395581177
Fax: (61) 95653299
E-Mail: sales@pferd.com.au
Web Site: www.pferd.com.au
Emp.: 100
Sales of Machine Tools, Metal Cutting Types.
S.I.C.: 3542
N.A.I.C.S.: 333517

PFERD-Rueggeberg B.V. **(1)**
Hekven 15 Bis
P O Box 2070
NL-4800 Breda, Netherlands
Tel.: (31) 765937090
Fax: (31) 765421033
E-Mail: info@pferd.nl
Web Site: www.pferd.nl
Machine Tools Mfr
S.I.C.: 3541
N.A.I.C.S.: 333517

PFERD Rueggeberg France **(1)**
2 Ave De La Concorde
Zone DActivites Economiques, 67129
Molsheim, France (100%)
Tel.: (33) 388495872
Fax: (33) 388387017
E-Mail: info@pferd.fr
Web Site: www.pferd.com
Emp.: 20
Sales of Machine Tools, Metal Cutting Types.
S.I.C.: 3541
N.A.I.C.S.: 333517
Bernard Weber *(Mng Dir)*

PFERD-Rueggeberg Ges.m.b.H **(1)**
Prinz Eugen Str 17
4020 Linz, Austria (100%)
Tel.: (43) 732796411
Fax: (43) 732796422
E-Mail: info@pferdrueggeberg.at
Web Site: www.pferdrueggeberg.at
Emp.: 10
Sales of Machine Tools, Metal Cutting Types.
S.I.C.: 3542
N.A.I.C.S.: 333517
Hoegner Dietmar *(Mgr)*

PFERD-Tools Pvt. Ltd. **(1)**
115/116 MIDC Estate Satpur
422007 Nasik, India
Tel.: (91) 253350665
Fax: (91) 5253351246
Sales of Machine Tools, Metal Cutting Types.
S.I.C.: 3541
N.A.I.C.S.: 333517

PFERD-VSM Sp.z.o.o. **(1)**
Ul Polna 1 A
62025 Kastryzyn Wielkopolski, Kastryzyn Wielkopols, Poland (100%)
Tel.: (48) 618970480
Fax: (48) 618970490
E-Mail: pferdvsm@pferdvsm.pl
Web Site: www.ferdvsm.pl
Emp.: 30
Distributor of Cutting Tools.
S.I.C.: 3545
N.A.I.C.S.: 333515
Grzegorz Koczur *(Pres)*

Rotea D.O.O. **(1)**
Badaliceva 26 b
HR 10000 Zagreb, Croatia
Tel.: (385) 3820113
Fax: (385) 1 3820103
E-Mail: ro-tea@zg.tel.hr
Machine Tools, Metal Cutting Types Sales
S.I.C.: 3542
N.A.I.C.S.: 333517

S.P.R.L. PFERD Rueggeberg B.V.B.A. **(1)**
Rue de La Grenouillette
Waterranonkelstraat 2 A, 1130 Brussels, Belgium (100%)
Tel.: (32) 22160216
Fax: (32) 22163054
E-Mail: info@pferd.be
Web Site: www.pferd.be
Emp.: 10
Sales of Cutting Tools, Machine Tool Accessories & Machinists Precision Measuring Devices.
S.I.C.: 3545
N.A.I.C.S.: 333515

AUGUSTA CAPITAL LIMITED

35 Chancery Street
Auckland, New Zealand
Mailing Address:
PO Box 37953
Parnell, New Zealand
Tel.: (64) 93006161
Fax: (64) 93006162
E-Mail: info@kermadecproperty.co.nz
Web Site: www.augusta.co.nz
AUG—(NZE)
Rev.: $10,237,347
Assets: $89,955,738
Liabilities: $38,088,522
Net Worth: $51,867,216
Earnings: $4,552,443
Emp.: 6
Fiscal Year-end: 03/31/13
Business Description:
Commercial & Industrial Property Management Services
S.I.C.: 6531
N.A.I.C.S.: 531390
Personnel:
Mark E. Francis *(Mng Dir)*
Simon W. J. Woollams *(CFO)*
Board of Directors:
Peter David Wilson
Mark E. Francis
John Loughlin
Legal Counsel:
Chapman Tripp
Level 35, 23 - 29 Albert Street.
1010 Auckland, New Zealand

AUGUSTA INDUSTRIES INC.

151 Randall Street Suite 101
Oakville, ON, L6J1P5, Canada
Tel.: (905) 338-2299
Fax: (905) 338-2335
Toll Free: (866) 915-2288
Web Site: www.fox-tek.com
Year Founded: 1999
AAO—(TSXV)
Sls.: $3,312,075
Assets: $3,337,919
Liabilities: $2,274,318
Net Worth: $1,063,601
Earnings: ($734,581)

Fiscal Year-end: 12/31/12
Business Description:
Fiber Optic Sensor Mfr
S.I.C.: 3357
N.A.I.C.S.: 335921
Personnel:
Allen Lone *(Pres & CEO)*
Momen Rahman *(CFO)*
Board of Directors:
Tony Boogmans
Stephan Nicholas Ewaskiw
Gerry Feldman
Allen Lone
Jay Vieira
Transfer Agent:
Equity Financial Trust Company
200 University Avenue Suite 400
Toronto, ON, Canada

AUGUSTA RESOURCE CORPORATION

837 West Hastings Street Suite 600
Vancouver, BC, V6C 3N6, Canada
Tel.: (604) 687-1717
Fax: (604) 687-1715
E-Mail: info@augustaresource.com
Web Site: www.augustaresource.com
AZC—(DEU NYSEMKT TSX)
Assets: $309,600,442
Liabilities: $96,574,023
Net Worth: $213,026,419
Earnings: ($7,956,126)
Emp.: 58
Fiscal Year-end: 12/31/12
Business Description:
Copper & Other Base Metal Mining & Exploration Services
S.I.C.: 1021
N.A.I.C.S.: 212234
Personnel:
Richard William Warke, Jr. *(Chm)*
Gilmour C. Clausen *(Pres & CEO)*
Joseph M. Longpre *(CFO & Sr VP)*
Rodney O. Pace *(COO & Exec VP)*
Purni Parikh *(Sec & VP)*
James A. Sturgess *(Sr VP-Corp Dev & Govt Affairs)*
Board of Directors:
Richard William Warke, Jr.
Timothy C. Baker
Lenard F. Boggio
Gilmour C. Clausen
William Durand Eppler
Christopher M. H. Jennings
Robert Parvis Pirooz
Robert P. Wares
Legal Counsel:
Faskin Martineau DuMoulin LLP
Suite 2100 1075 West Georgia Street
Vancouver, BC, Canada
Transfer Agent:
Computershare Investor Services inc
3rd Fl 510 Burrard Street
Vancouver, BC, Canada

AUGUSTA TECHNOLOGIE AG

(Acquired by TKH Group N.V.)

AUGUSTINE VENTURES INC.

130 King Street W The Exchange Tower Suite 720
PO Box 137
Toronto, ON, M5X 1A6, Canada
Tel.: (416) 363-2528
Fax: (866) 288-3582
Web Site: www.augustineventures.com
WAW—(CNSX)
Int. Income: $11,710
Assets: $2,776,109
Liabilities: $722,639
Net Worth: $2,053,470
Earnings: ($1,256,779)
Fiscal Year-end: 11/30/12
Business Description:
Gold Mining Services
S.I.C.: 1041
N.A.I.C.S.: 212221
Personnel:
George Michael Newman *(Chm)*
Robert B. Dodds *(Pres & CEO)*
Khurram R. Qureshi *(CFO)*
John V. Tokarsky *(Sec & Controller)*
Board of Directors:
George Michael Newman
Rick G. Bonner
Robert B. Dodds
Dexter D. S. John
John Sadowski
Legal Counsel:
Fogler, Rubinoff LLP
95 Wellington Street West, Suite 1200
Toronto, ON, Canada
Transfer Agent:
Equity Financial Trust Company
200 University Avenue Suite 400
Toronto, ON, Canada

AUGUSTUS MARTIN LTD.

St Andrews Way Bromley By Bow
London, E3 3PB, United Kingdom
Tel.: (44) 2075374200
Fax: (44) 2079870593
E-Mail: enquiry@amartin.co.uk
Web Site: www.augustusmartin.com
Sales Range: $50-74.9 Million
Emp.: 250
Business Description:
Format Printing Services
S.I.C.: 2759
N.A.I.C.S.: 323111
Personnel:
Lascelle Barrow *(Co-Mng Dir)*

AUGYVA MINING RESOURCES INC.

1 Place Ville Bureau 2500
Montreal, QC, H3B 1R1, Canada
Tel.: (416) 309-2197
Fax: (416) 309-2196
E-Mail: AugyvaMiningResources@gmail.com
Web Site: www.augyvamining.com
Year Founded: 1986
AUV—(TSXV)
Int. Income: $264,811
Assets: $13,620,601
Liabilities: $166,626
Net Worth: $13,453,975
Earnings: ($1,512,867)
Fiscal Year-end: 02/28/13
Business Description:
Mineral Exploration Services
S.I.C.: 1081
N.A.I.C.S.: 213114
Personnel:
Peter R. Jones *(Chm & Interim CEO)*
Shannon C. Penney *(CFO)*
Board of Directors:
Peter R. Jones
Farhad Abasov
Kuldeep Billan
Sandy C. K. Chim
C. Nigel Lees
Michael Skutezky
Transfer Agent:
Computershare Trust Company of Canada
1500 University Street Suite 700
Montreal, QC, Canada

AUHUA CLEAN ENERGY PLC

6 Dongyu Street
Tianqiao District, Jinan, Shandong, China
Tel.: (86) 531 85710168
E-Mail: info@auhuacleanenergy.com
Web Site: www.auhuacleanenergy.com
Year Founded: 2002
ACE—(AIM)
Sales Range: $10-24.9 Million
Emp.: 270
Business Description:
Water Heating Appliances
S.I.C.: 3559
N.A.I.C.S.: 332410
Personnel:
Raphael Wai Mun Tham *(Chm)*
David James Sumner *(Vice Chm)*
Anxiang Chen *(CEO)*
Tien Lung Thng *(CFO)*
Board of Directors:
Maxwell Charles Audley
Anxiang Chen
Yiqun Guan
David James Sumner
Raphael Wai Mun Tham
Tien Lung Thng
James Mun Foong Yip

AUJAN INDUSTRIES CO., L.L.C.

PO Box 990
Dammam, 31421, Saudi Arabia
Tel.: (966) 38570777
Fax: (966) 38577923
E-Mail: aujan@aujan.com.sa
Web Site: www.aujan.com
Year Founded: 1905
Sales Range: $150-199.9 Million
Emp.: 1,100
Business Description:
Beverages & Confectionery Products
S.I.C.: 2064
N.A.I.C.S.: 311352
Personnel:
Adel Aujan *(Chm)*
Adnan Aujan *(Vice Chm)*
Kadir Gunduz *(Pres & CEO)*
Non-U.S. Subsidiaries:

Ansari & Aujan Company L.L.C. (1)
PO Box 5721
Doha, Qatar
Tel.: (974) 4601 230
Fax: (974) 4602 026
Beverage Mfr & Distr
N.A.I.C.S.: 312111
Prebaharen Jeevaretnam *(Key Acct Mgr)*

Rani Soft Drinks Private Ltd. (1)
402 Dev Plaza 4th Floor S V Road
Andheri-West, Mumbai, Maharashtra, 400058, India
Tel.: (91) 22 26249783
Fax: (91) 22 26240783
Beverage Mfr & Distr
N.A.I.C.S.: 312111
Atanu Gangoly *(Country Mgr)*

Saud Aujan & Bros. Co. (1)
PO Box 29
Kuwait, Kuwait
Tel.: (965) 4336131
Fax: (965) 4348070
Web Site: www.aujan.com.sa/cont.htm
Emp.: 120
Food, Beverage & Cigarette Importer & Distr
S.I.C.: 5182
N.A.I.C.S.: 424820
Faisal Aujan *(Mng Dir)*

AUK CORP.

802-12 Shinheung-dong
Iksan, Jeonbuk, 530-800, Korea (South)
Tel.: (82) 63 835 7111
Fax: (82) 63 835 2681
Web Site: www.auk.co.kr
Year Founded: 1984
017900—(KRS)
Rev.: $230,106,101
Assets: $249,468,441
Liabilities: $48,771,237
Net Worth: $200,697,204
Earnings: ($12,227,612)
Fiscal Year-end: 12/31/12
Business Description:
Semiconductor Product Mfr
S.I.C.: 3674
N.A.I.C.S.: 334413
Personnel:
Gi Jeong Lee *(CEO)*

AUKETT FITZROY ROBINSON GROUP PLC

36-40 York Way
London, N1 9AB, United Kingdom
Tel.: (44) 2078433000
Fax: (44) 2078433001
E-Mail: london@auckettfitzroyrobinson.com
Web Site: www.aukettfitzroyrobinson.com
AUK—(LSE)
Rev.: $13,966,065
Assets: $12,216,568
Liabilities: $7,184,067
Net Worth: $5,032,502
Earnings: $621,379
Emp.: 104
Fiscal Year-end: 09/30/13
Business Description:
Professional & Management Services
S.I.C.: 0781
N.A.I.C.S.: 541320
Personnel:
David Hughes *(Deputy Chm)*
Nicholas Thompson *(CEO)*
Duncan Harper *(Sec & Grp Dir-Fin)*
Board of Directors:
Anthony Simmonds
Duncan Harper
David Hughes
Andrew James Murdoch
Nick Pell
Nicholas Thompson
John Vincent
Legal Counsel:
Laytons
2 More London Riverside
London, SE1 2AP, United Kingdom
Fox Williams
10 Dominion Street
London, United Kingdom
Subsidiaries:

Aukett Fitzroy Robinson Limited (1)
36-40 York Way
London, N1 9AB, United Kingdom
Tel.: (44) 2076368033
Fax: (44) 2075803996
E-Mail: london@aukettfitzroyrobinson.com
Emp.: 90
Bulding Architectural Designing & Construction Services
S.I.C.: 1542
N.A.I.C.S.: 236220
Nicholas Thompson *(Mng Dir)*

Veretec Limited (1)
36-40 York Way
London, N1 9AB, United Kingdom
Tel.: (44) 2076314836
Fax: (44) 2075803996
E-Mail: london@veretec.co.uk
Web Site: www.veretec.co.uk
Emp.: 80
Architectural & Construction Design Services
S.I.C.: 8712
N.A.I.C.S.: 541310
Keith Morgan *(Mng Dir)*

Non-U.S. Subsidiaries:

Aukett Fitzroy Robinson Sp. z.o.o. (1)
Ul Emilii Plater 18
00688 Warsaw, Poland
Tel.: (48) 223923350
Fax: (48) 223923351
E-Mail: office@aukettfitzroyrobinson.pl
Web Site: www.afr.com.pl

Aukett Fitzroy Robinson Group plc—(Continued)

Emp.: 12
Architectural & Construction Services
S.I.C.: 8712
N.A.I.C.S.: 541310
Rafael Depowski *(Exec Dir)*

Aukett sro **(1)**
Jilska 2 527
110 00 Prague, Czech Republic
Tel.: (420) 224220025
Fax: (420) 224228019
E-Mail: aukett@aukett.cz
Web Site: www.aukett.cz
Emp.: 10
Building Architectural & Construction Services
S.I.C.: 8712
N.A.I.C.S.: 541310
Jnna Lehotska *(Mng Dir)*

AULBACH ENTGRATUNGSTECHNIK GMBH

Kreuzfeldring 5
63820 Miltenberg, Germany
Tel.: (49) 602220880
Fax: (49) 6022208819
E-Mail: aulbach@aulbach-com.de
Web Site: www.aulbach-com.de
Rev.: $12,069,750
Emp.: 27
Business Description:
Indstrial Machinery Mfr
S.I.C.: 3559
N.A.I.C.S.: 333249
Personnel:
Simone Baron *(Sec)*
Anette Schmitt *(Sec)*

AULD PHILLIPS LTD.

46199 Yale Road
Chilliwack, BC, V2P 2P2, Canada
Tel.: (604) 792-0158
Fax: (604) 792-8540
Year Founded: 1965
Rev.: $16,781,424
Emp.: 250
Business Description:
Womens Clothing Distr
S.I.C.: 5621
N.A.I.C.S.: 448120
Personnel:
Roderick A. Cooper *(Pres)*
Jim Gilbert *(COO)*

AUMA RIESTER GMBH & CO. KG

Aumastrasse 1
D-79379 Mullheim, Germany
Tel.: (49) 7631 809 0
E-Mail: Riester@auma.com
Web Site: www.auma.com
Year Founded: 1965
Emp.: 2,200
Business Description:
Electric Actuator & Valve Gearbox Mfr
S.I.C.: 3491
N.A.I.C.S.: 332911
Personnel:
Matthias Dinse *(Mng Dir)*
Subsidiaries:

GFC AntriebsSysteme GmbH **(1)**
Grenzstrasse 5
01640 Coswig, Germany
Mailing Address:
Postfach 1154
01631 Coswig, Germany
Tel.: (49) 3523 94 60
Fax: (49) 3523 7 41 42
E-Mail: info@gfc-antriebe.de
Web Site: www.gfc-antriebe.de
Gear Mfr
S.I.C.: 3566
N.A.I.C.S.: 333612

Haselhofer Feinmechanik GmbH **(1)**
Eichendorffstrasse 42-48
78054 Villingen-Schwenningen, Germany
Tel.: (49) 7720 8540 0
Fax: (49) 7720 8540 50
E-Mail: info@haselhofer.de
Web Site: www.haselhofer.de
Electric Actuator Mfr
S.I.C.: 3625
N.A.I.C.S.: 335314

SIPOS Aktorik GmbH **(1)**
Im Erlet 2
90518 Altdorf, Germany
Tel.: (49) 9187 9227 0
Fax: (49) 9187 9227 5111
E-Mail: info@sipos.de
Web Site: www.sipos.de
Electric Actuator & Control System Mfr
S.I.C.: 3625
N.A.I.C.S.: 335314
Felix Metzenthin *(Dir-Sls)*

Non-U.S. Joint Venture:

Erichs Armatur AB **(1)**
Travbanegatan 8
21377 Malmo, Sweden
Tel.: (46) 40 31 15 50
Fax: (46) 40 94 55 15
E-Mail: info@erichsarmatur.se
Web Site: www.erichsarmatur.se
Valve & Actuator Mfr
S.I.C.: 3491
N.A.I.C.S.: 332911
Ulf Elowsson *(Mng Dir)*

AUMENTO CAPITAL II CORPORATION

(Name Changed to The Intertain Group Limited)

AUMENTO CAPITAL III CORPORATION

320 Bay Street Suite 1600
Toronto, ON, M5H 4A6, Canada
Tel.: (416) 626-6000
E-Mail: ddanziger@mscm.ca
Year Founded: 2011
AUO.P—(TSXV)
Business Description:
Investment Services
S.I.C.: 6211
N.A.I.C.S.: 523999
Personnel:
David Danziger *(Pres, CEO, CFO & Sec)*
Board of Directors:
Roger Daher
David Danziger
Paul Pathak
Transfer Agent:
CIBC Mellon Trust Company
320 Bay Street
PO Box 1
Toronto, ON, M5H 2A6, Canada
Tel.: (416) 643-5500
Fax: (416) 643-5570
Toll Free: (800) 387-0825

AUMENTO CAPITAL IV CORPORATION

320 Bay Street Suite 1600
Toronto, ON, M5H 4A6, Canada
Tel.: (416) 626-6000
Fax: (416) 626-8650
E-Mail: david.danziger@mnp.ca
Year Founded: 2013
ACV.P—(TSXV)
Business Description:
Investment Services
S.I.C.: 6211
N.A.I.C.S.: 523999
Personnel:
David Danziger *(CEO, CFO & Sec)*
Board of Directors:
Roger Daher
David Danziger
Paul Pathak
Transfer Agent:
Olympia Transfer Services Inc.
Suite 920 120 Adelaide Street West
Toronto, ON, Canada

AUN CONSULTING, INC.

Glass City Koraku 2F 1-1-7 Koraku
Bunkyo-ku, Tokyo, 112-0004, Japan
Tel.: (81) 3 5803 2727
Fax: (81) 3 5803 2750
E-Mail: ir@auncon.co.jp
Web Site: www.auncon.co.jp
Year Founded: 1998
2459—(TKS)
Emp.: 89
Business Description:
Information Technology Consulting Services
S.I.C.: 7373
N.A.I.C.S.: 541512
Personnel:
Tetsuichi Fujiwara *(Chm)*
Akira Shida *(Pres & CEO)*
Akira Kikuchi *(Exec Officer)*
Shigeki Nakata *(Exec Officer)*
Takanori Sakata *(Mng Exec Officer)*
Shigeyuki Tanahashi *(Exec Officer)*
Board of Directors:
Tetsuichi Fujiwara
Takanori Sakata
Akira Shida
Shigeyuki Tanahashi

AUNDE ACHTER & EBELS GMBH

Waldnielerstrasse 151
41068 Monchengladbach, Germany
Tel.: (49) 21619350
Fax: (49) 2161935219
E-Mail: info@aunde.com
Web Site: www.aunde.com
Year Founded: 1982
Sales Range: $200-249.9 Million
Emp.: 257
Business Description:
Automotive Parts Mfr & Distr
S.I.C.: 7539
N.A.I.C.S.: 811118
Personnel:
Rolf Konigs *(CEO & Chm)*
Carl Conrad Bolten *(Mng Dir)*
Christian Prause *(CFO)*
Non-U.S. Subsidiary:

De Witte Lietaer International Textiles NV **(1)**
Koningin Astridlaan 48
B 8930 Lauwe, Belgium BE
Tel.: (32) 56430211 (100%)
Fax: (32) 56430290
E-Mail: dwl@dwl.be
Web Site: www.dwl.be
Emp.: 850
Automotive Textiles Mfr
S.I.C.: 2389
N.A.I.C.S.: 314999
Francis Dejong *(Mgr)*

Non-U.S. Joint Venture:

Aunde India Limited **(1)**
102 Shiv Smriti Chambers 49-A Dr Annie Besant Road
Worli, Mumbai, 400 018, India
Tel.: (91) 22 6618 8777
Fax: (91) 22 2493 6811
E-Mail: info@aundeindia.com
Web Site: www.aundeindia.com
532459—(BOM)
Rev.: $21,178,657
Assets: $24,609,930
Liabilities: $17,518,673
Net Worth: $7,091,257
Earnings: $685,428
Fiscal Year-end: 06/30/13
Automotive Fabric Mfr
S.I.C.: 3499
N.A.I.C.S.: 332999
Ajay Anand *(Chm & Mng Dir)*
Reema Jovita Mathias *(Compliance Officer & Sec)*

AUPLATA SAS

13 Lotissement Calimbe
97300 Cayenne, French Guiana
Tel.: (594) 295440
Fax: (594) 298500
E-Mail: presse@auplata.fr
Web Site: www.auplata.fr
ALAUP—(EUR)
Sales Range: $1-9.9 Million
Emp.: 58
Business Description:
Gold Mining Services
S.I.C.: 1041
N.A.I.C.S.: 212221
Personnel:
Christian Aubert *(Co-Founder & Chm)*
Michel Juilland *(Co-Founder & CEO)*
Patrick Schein *(CFO & Dir-Sls)*

AURA ENERGY LIMITED

Level 4 66 Kings Park Road
West Perth, WA, 6005, Australia
Tel.: (61) 8 6141 3570
Fax: (61) 8 6141 3599
E-Mail: info@auraenergy.com.au
Web Site: www.auraenergy.com.au
AEE—(ASX)
Rev.: $32,469
Assets: $17,862,981
Liabilities: $599,020
Net Worth: $17,263,961
Earnings: ($2,872,383)
Emp.: 3
Fiscal Year-end: 06/30/13
Business Description:
Uranium Exploring
S.I.C.: 1094
N.A.I.C.S.: 212291
Personnel:
Robert Beeson *(Mng Dir)*
Stan Zillwood *(Sec)*
Board of Directors:
Peter Reeve
Robert Beeson
Brett Fraser
Julian Perkins
Legal Counsel:
Steinepreis Paganin
Level 4 The Read Building 16 Milligan Street
Perth, WA, 6000, Australia
Tel.: (61) 8 9321 4000
Fax: (61) 8 9321 4333

AURA MINERALS INC.

155 University Avenue Suite 1240
Toronto, ON, M5H 3B7, Canada
Tel.: (416) 649-1033
Fax: (416) 649-1044
E-Mail: info@auraminerals.com
Web Site: www.auraminerals.com
ORA—(TSX)
Rev.: $307,412,000
Assets: $425,683,000
Liabilities: $142,450,000
Net Worth: $283,233,000
Earnings: ($56,809,000)
Emp.: 1,344
Fiscal Year-end: 12/31/12
Business Description:
Mining Exploration & Development of Copper, Gold & Iron
S.I.C.: 1499
N.A.I.C.S.: 212399
Personnel:
Patrick J. Mars *(Chm)*
James M. Bannantine *(Pres & CEO)*
Rory Taylor *(CFO)*
Ryan Goodman *(Gen Counsel & Sec)*
Neil Hepworth *(Sr VP-Ops-Brazil)*
Board of Directors:
Patrick J. Mars

James M. Bannantine
Stephen Keith
Elizabeth A. Martin
William F. Murray
Tom Ogryzlo
Ian Stalker

Legal Counsel:
DuMoulin Black LLP
10th Floor 595 Howe St
Vancouver, BC, Canada

Transfer Agent:
Equity Transfer & Trust Company
200 University Avenue Ste 400
Toronto, ON, M5H 4H1, Canada
Tel.: (416) 361-0152
Fax: (416) 361-0470

Subsidiary:

Aura Minerals (Ontario) Inc. **(1)**
First Canadian Pl
100 King St W Ste 5700, Toronto, ON, M5X 1C7, Canada
Tel.: (416) 913-0204
Fax: (416) 915-3177
Emp.: 25
Gold Exploration Services
S.I.C.: 1041
N.A.I.C.S.: 212221
Megan Lewis *(Mgr)*

Non-U.S. Subsidiary:

Mineracao Vale Verde Ltda **(1)**
Stephen Rua Antonio Silva 274 c
Hope Garden, Arapiraca, Alagoas, Brazil
Tel.: (55) 8235303473
Fax: (55) 558235303473
Emp.: 60
Mineral Exploration Services
S.I.C.: 1041
N.A.I.C.S.: 212221
Neil Hepworth *(Sr VP-Ops)*

AURA SILVER RESOURCES INC.

1128 Clapp Lane
PO Box 279
Manotick, ON, K4M 1A3, Canada
Tel.: (613) 692-7704
Fax: (613) 692-3234
Toll Free: (877) 692-7704
Web Site: www.aurasilver.com
AUU—(TSXV)
Sales Range: Less than $1 Million

Business Description:
Metal Exploration Services
S.I.C.: 1081
N.A.I.C.S.: 213114

Personnel:
Nicholas Tintor *(Chm)*
Robert G. Boaz *(Pres & CEO)*
John McNeice *(CFO & Corp Sec)*

Board of Directors:
Nicholas Tintor
Robert G. Boaz
W. William Boberg
Eric Craigie
James M. Franklin

Legal Counsel:
Fasken Martineau DuMoulin LLP
Ottawa, ON, Canada

Transfer Agent:
Equity Financial Trust Company
Toronto, ON, Canada

AURACLE RESOURCES LTD.

Suite 302 675 West Hastings Street
Vancouver, BC, V6B 1N2, Canada
Tel.: (604) 682-3131
Fax: (604) 682-1816
E-Mail: info@auracleresources.com
Web Site: www.auracleresources.com
AAL—(TSXV)
Int. Income: $168
Assets: $2,933,332
Liabilities: $305,037
Net Worth: $2,628,295
Earnings: ($506,573)
Fiscal Year-end: 01/31/13

Business Description:
Gold & Silver Mining Services
S.I.C.: 1041
N.A.I.C.S.: 212221

Personnel:
Robin Forshaw *(Pres & CEO)*
Mark Gelmon *(CFO)*
E. Louise Davey *(Treas)*

Board of Directors:
Jason Leikam
Ross C. McCutcheon
George Nicholson
Anil Sachedina
Richard S. Simpson

Transfer Agent:
Computershare
510 Burrard St 2nd Floor
Vancouver, BC, Canada

AURAMEX RESOURCE CORP.

750 Grand Boulevard
North Vancouver, BC, V7L 3W4, Canada
Tel.: (604) 924-9376
Fax: (604) 924-9371
E-Mail: admin@auramex.com
Web Site: www.auramex.com
AUX—(TSXV)
Int. Income: $446
Assets: $3,331,696
Liabilities: $240,837
Net Worth: $3,090,858
Earnings: ($360,573)
Fiscal Year-end: 12/31/12

Business Description:
Metal Exploration Services
S.I.C.: 1081
N.A.I.C.S.: 213114

Personnel:
Wayne Crocker *(Pres & CEO)*
Judie Whitby *(CFO & Sec)*

Board of Directors:
Heather Conley
Wayne Crocker
George Farwell
Clive Forth
Robert Lee
Bill Raney
Judie Whitby

AURANIA RESOURCES LTD.

Suite 1010 8 King Street
Toronto, ON, M5C 1B5, Canada
Tel.: (416) 367-3200
Fax: (416) 367-3205
E-Mail: info@auraniaresources.com
Web Site: www.auraniaresources.com
Year Founded: 2007
AOZ—(TSXV)

Business Description:
Gold, Uranium & Copper Mining
S.I.C.: 1041
N.A.I.C.S.: 212221

Personnel:
Keith Barron *(Chm)*
Donna McLean *(CFO)*

Board of Directors:
Keith Barron
Elaine Ellingham
Gerald Harper
Marvin K. Kaiser

Legal Counsel:
Peterson Law
390 Bay Street Suite 806
Toronto, ON, Canada

Transfer Agent:
Capital Transfer Agency Inc.
105 Adelaide St West Suite 1101
Toronto, ON, M5H 1P9, Canada

AURASOUND, INC.

(Acquired & Absorbed by GuoGuang Electric Company Limited)

AURCANA CORPORATION

1188 West Georgia Street Suite 1750
Vancouver, BC, V6E 4A2, Canada
Tel.: (604) 331-9333
Fax: (604) 633-9178
Toll Free: (866) 532-9333
Web Site: www.aurcana.com
AUN—(OTC TSXV)
Rev.: $56,928,792
Assets: $192,367,811
Liabilities: $21,082,698
Net Worth: $171,285,113
Earnings: $9,951,340
Emp.: 5
Fiscal Year-end: 12/31/12

Business Description:
Mining Exploration Services
S.I.C.: 1099
N.A.I.C.S.: 212299

Personnel:
Robert J. Tweedy *(Chm)*
Lenic M. Rodriguez *(Pres & CEO)*
Salvador Huerta *(CFO)*
Andrew F. Kaczmarek *(Interim COO)*
Terese J. Gieselman *(Treas)*
Sandy Hunter *(Sec)*

Board of Directors:
Robert J. Tweedy
Adrian Aguirre
Kenneth W. Collison
Arthur H. Ditto
Andrew F. Kaczmarek
Lenic M. Rodriguez

Legal Counsel:
Axium Law Group
Suite 3350 Four Bentall Centre 1055 Dunsmuir Street PO Box 49222
Vancouver, BC, V7X 1J2, Canada

Transfer Agent:
Equity Transfer & Trust Company
1185 West Georgia Street Suite 1620
Vancouver, BC, V6E 4E6, Canada

AURCREST GOLD INC.

67 Yonge St Suite 808
Toronto, ON, M5E 1J8, Canada
Tel.: (416) 368-2929
Fax: (416) 601-1450
E-Mail: info@aurcrestgold.com
Web Site: www.aurcrestgold.com
AGO—(TSXV)
Rev.: $57,630
Assets: $218,497
Liabilities: $885,987
Net Worth: ($667,490)
Earnings: ($1,972,088)
Fiscal Year-end: 12/31/12

Business Description:
Mineral Mining Exploration Services
S.I.C.: 1081
N.A.I.C.S.: 213114

Personnel:
Ian A. Brodie-Brown *(Pres & CEO)*
Errol Farr *(CFO)*
William R. Johnstone *(Corp Counsel & Sec)*

Board of Directors:
Christopher Angeconeb
Ian A. Brodie-Brown
William R. Johnstone
Richard E. Nemis
Frank Van de Water
Blaine R. Webster

Legal Counsel:
Gardiner Roberts
40 King Street West Suite 3100 Scotia Plaza
Toronto, ON, M5H 3Y2, Canada

Transfer Agent:
Equity Transfer Service
120 Adelaide St W
Toronto, ON, M5H 1T1, Canada

AUREA, S.A.

(d/b/a Groupe Aurea)
3 avenue Bertie Albrecht
F-75008 Paris, France
Tel.: (33) 153838545
Fax: (33) 153838546
Web Site: www.aurea-france.com
Year Founded: 1988
AURE—(EUR)
Sls.: $234,119,156
Earnings: $2,619,647
Emp.: 277
Fiscal Year-end: 12/31/12

Business Description:
Holding Company; Waste Motor Oil, Polyvinyl Chloride & Worn Tire Processing & Recycling Services; Water Decontamination Services
S.I.C.: 6719
N.A.I.C.S.: 551112

Personnel:
Joel Picard *(Chm & Dir Gen)*
Francois Demalander *(CFO)*

Board of Directors:
Joel Picard
Alain Beja
Antoine Diesbecq
Bernard Gallois

Subsidiaries:

Aluminium Regeal Affimet **(1)**
Avenue du Vermandois
PO Box 80419
60204 Compiegne, France FR
Tel.: (33) 344238200 (100%)
Telex: 209 503
Fax: (33) 344238203
Web Site: www.recovco.fr
Sales Range: $100-124.9 Million
Emp.: 100
Aluminum Reprocessing Services
S.I.C.: 3399
N.A.I.C.S.: 331314
Pierre du Baret *(Mng Dir)*

Broplast S.A.R.L **(1)**
Za Pierre Fondelle Route De Perignat
BP 7
1580 Izernore, Ain, France
Tel.: (33) 474 49 10 37
Fax: (33) 474 49 10 27
E-Mail: broplast@broplast.com
Web Site: www.broplast.com
Emp.: 25
Thermoplastic Recycling Services
S.I.C.: 2842
N.A.I.C.S.: 325612

Compagnie Francaise Eco Huile S.A. **(1)**
3 avenue Bertie Albrecht
F-78008 Paris, France FR
Tel.: (33) 153838555 (100%)
Fax: (33) 153838546
Waste Motor Oil Processing & Recycling Services
S.I.C.: 4953
N.A.I.C.S.: 562920
Rene Riper *(Chm & Dir Gen)*

Eco Huile SA **(1)**
Zone Industrielle Avenue De Port Jerome
Lillebonne, Seine Maritime, 76170, France
Tel.: (33) 235395847
Fax: (33) 235395831
Motor Oil Recycling Services
S.I.C.: 7389
N.A.I.C.S.: 561990

M Lego **(1)**
BP 1
72401 La Ferte-Bernard, Sarthe, France
Tel.: (33) 2 43 60 60 65
Fax: (33) 2 43 93 55 03
E-Mail: info@m-lego.com
Web Site: www.m-lego.com
Emp.: 100
Alloys Mfr
S.I.C.: 3399
N.A.I.C.S.: 331110

Roll-Gom S.A. **(1)**
Rue Laennec
F-62217 Tilloy-les-Mofflaines, France FR
Mailing Address: (100%)
BP 58
Beaurains, F-62217 Tilloy-les-Mofflaines, France
Tel.: (33) 321249495

Aurea, S.A.—(Continued)

Fax: (33) 321249139
E-Mail: contact@roll-gom.com
Web Site: www.roll-gom.com
Emp.: 95
Worn Tires Processing & Recycling Services
S.I.C.: 4953
N.A.I.C.S.: 562920
Richard Lett *(Mng Dir)*

Non-U.S. Subsidiary:

Rulo N.V. (1)
Chaussee d'Audenarde 82
BE-7742 Herinnes, Belgium BE
Tel.: (32) 69559371 (80%)
Fax: (32) 69559372
E-Mail: info@rulo.be
Web Site: www.rulo.be
Emp.: 2
Polyvinyl Chloride & Other Plastic Material Recycling Services
S.I.C.: 4953
N.A.I.C.S.: 562920
Joel Picard *(Pres)*

AURELIUS AG

Ludwig-Ganghofer-Strasse 6
82031 Grunwald, Germany
Tel.: (49) 895447990
Fax: (49) 8954479955
E-Mail: info@aureliusinvest.de
Web Site: www.aureliusinvest.com
AR4—(DEU)
Rev.: $1,717,590,419
Assets: $1,579,427,607
Liabilities: $1,101,910,146
Net Worth: $477,517,461
Earnings: $121,168,762
Emp.: 4,578
Fiscal Year-end: 12/31/12

Business Description:
Private Equity Firm
S.I.C.: 6211
N.A.I.C.S.: 523999

Personnel:
Dirk Roesing *(Chm-Supervisory Bd)*
Dirk Markus *(Chm-Exec Bd & CEO)*
Eugen M. Angster *(Vice Chm-Supervisory Bd)*
Donatus Albrecht *(Member-Exec Bd)*
Gert Purkert *(Member-Exec Bd)*

Supervisory Board of Directors:
Dirk Roesing
Eugen M. Angster
Holger Schulze

Subsidiaries:

1.Vermogensverwaltungs GmbH Hannover Lathusenstrasse (1)
Ludwig-Ganghofer-Str 6
Grunwald, Bavaria, Germany
Tel.: (49) 89 5447990
Fax: (49) 89 544799555
Investment Management Services
S.I.C.: 6211
N.A.I.C.S.: 523999
Kan Rehtock *(Gen Mgr)*

Aurelius Active Management Holding GmbH (1)
Ludwig-Ganghofer-Str 6
Grunwald, 82031, Germany
Tel.: (49) 895447990
Fax: (49) 8954479955
Investment Management Services
S.I.C.: 6211
N.A.I.C.S.: 523999

Aurelius Beteiligungsberatungs AG (1)
Unterer Anger 3
Munich, 80331, Germany
Tel.: (49) 895447990
Fax: (49) 8954479955
Investment Management Consulting Services
S.I.C.: 8748
N.A.I.C.S.: 541618

Aurelius Commercial Beteiligungs GmbH (1)
Ludwig-Ganghofer-Str 6
Grunwald, 82031, Germany
Tel.: (49) 89 5447990
Fax: (49) 89 54479955
Consumer Goods Distr
S.I.C.: 5199
N.A.I.C.S.: 424990

Aurelius Transaktionsberatungs AG (1)
Unterer Anger 3
Munich, 80331, Germany
Tel.: (49) 89 5447990
Fax: (49) 89 54479955
Investment Advisory Services
S.I.C.: 6282
N.A.I.C.S.: 523930

BCA Beteiligungs GmbH (1)
Ludwig-Ganghofer-Str 6
Grunwald, 82031, Germany
Tel.: (49) 895447990
Fax: (49) 8954479955
Human Resource Consulting Services
S.I.C.: 8999
N.A.I.C.S.: 541612

ED Enterprises AG (1)
Ludwig-Ganghofer-Str 6
Grunwald, 82031, Germany
Tel.: (49) 8945205270
Fax: (49) 89452052710
Financial Management Services
S.I.C.: 6211
N.A.I.C.S.: 523999
Fritz Seeman *(Gen Mgr)*

European Direct Sales Holding GmbH (1)
Ludwig-Ganghofer-Str 6
Grunwald, 82031, Germany
Tel.: (49) 895447990
Investment Management Services
S.I.C.: 6211
N.A.I.C.S.: 523999

ISOCHEM Holding GmbH (1)
Ludwig-Ganghofer-Str 6
Grunwald, 82031, Germany
Tel.: (49) 895447990
Investment Management Services
S.I.C.: 6211
N.A.I.C.S.: 523999

Subsidiary:

ISOCHEM Beteiligungs GmbH (2)
Ludwig-Ganghofer-Str 6
Grunwald, 82031, Germany
Tel.: (49) 89 5447990
Specialty Chemicals Distr
S.I.C.: 5169
N.A.I.C.S.: 424690

LD Beteiligungs GmbH (1)
Ludwig-Ganghofer-Str 6
Grunwald, 82031, Germany
Tel.: (49) 895447990
Fax: (49) 8954479955
Real Estate Management Services
S.I.C.: 6531
N.A.I.C.S.: 531390

RH Retail Holding GmbH (1)
Ludwig-Ganghofer-Str 6
Grunwald, 82031, Germany
Tel.: (49) 89 5447990
Fax: (49) 89 452052710
Investment Management Services
S.I.C.: 6211
N.A.I.C.S.: 523999

Holdings:

Berentzen-Gruppe AG (1)
Ritterstrasse 7
D 49740 Haselunne, Germany De
Tel.: (49) 59615020 (75%)
Fax: (49) 5961502268
E-Mail: berentzen@berentzen.de
Web Site: www.berentzen-gruppe.de
Sales Range: $600-649.9 Million
Emp.: 700
Alcoholic Beverage Producer & Distr
S.I.C.: 2085
N.A.I.C.S.: 312140
Gert Purkert *(Chm-Supervisory Bd)*
Stefan Blaschak *(CEO)*
Ralf Bruhofner *(Member-Mgmt Bd)*

Subsidiaries:

Die Stonsdorferei W. Koerner GmbH & Co. KG (2)
Ritterstr 7
Haselunne, 49740, Germany
Tel.: (49) 5961502386
Fax: (49) 5961502268
Web Site: www.berentzen-gruppe.de
Alcoholic Beverage Distr
S.I.C.: 5182
N.A.I.C.S.: 424820

Kornbrennerei Berentzen GmbH (2)
Ritterstr 7
Haselunne, 49740, Germany
Tel.: (49) 59615020
Fax: (49) 5961502268
Beverage Mfr
S.I.C.: 2082
N.A.I.C.S.: 312120

LANDWIRTH'S GmbH (2)
Sollingweg 41
Minden, 32427, Germany
Tel.: (49) 5961502386
Fax: (49) 5961502268
Emp.: 10
Beverage Mfr
S.I.C.: 2082
N.A.I.C.S.: 312120
Schmidt Frank *(Gen Mgr)*

Pabst & Richarz Vertriebs GmbH (2)
Sollingweg 41
32427 Minden, Germany
Tel.: (49) 571 40400
Alcoholic Beverage Mfr
S.I.C.: 2082
N.A.I.C.S.: 312120

Strothmann Spirituosen Verwaltung GmbH (2)
Ritterstr 7
Haselunne, 49740, Germany
Tel.: (49) 59615020
Fax: (49) 5961502268
Investment Management Services
S.I.C.: 6211
N.A.I.C.S.: 523999

Vivaris Getranke GmbH & Co. KG (2)
Neuer Grund 24
Haselunne, Germany
Tel.: (49) 5961 502 865
Fax: (49) 5961 502 378
E-Mail: info@vivaris.net
Web Site: www.vivaris.net
Emp.: 80
Beverage Mfr
S.I.C.: 2086
N.A.I.C.S.: 312111
Bernhard Brinkmann *(Gen Mgr)*

Vivaris Getranke Verwaltung GmbH (2)
Neuer Grund 24
49740 Haselunne, Germany
Tel.: (49) 5961 5024
Fax: (49) 59615020
E-Mail: info@berentzen.de
Web Site: www.berentzen-gruppe.de
Emp.: 70
Beverage Mfr
S.I.C.: 2086
N.A.I.C.S.: 312111
Johan Bosch *(CEO)*

Blaupunkt International GmbH & Co. KG (1)
Robert Bosch Strasse 200
31139 Hildesheim, Germany De
Mailing Address:
Postfach 777777
D 31132 Hildesheim, Germany
Tel.: (49) 512199810
Telex: 927151-0 bp d
Fax: (49) 51214154
E-Mail: info@blaupunkt.de
Web Site: www.blaupunkt.de
Sales Range: $250-299.9 Million
Car Radios, Traffic Warning & Routing Systems Mfr
S.I.C.: 3663
N.A.I.C.S.: 334220
Alexander Schramm *(Mng Dir)*

Subsidiaries:

Blaupunkt AudioVision GmbH & Co. KG (2)
Robert-Bosch-Str 200
31139 Hildesheim, Germany
Tel.: (49) 5121 9981 0
E-Mail: info@blaupunkt.com
Web Site: www.blaupunkt.de/index.php?id=977&L=1
Automotive Audio System Mfr
S.I.C.: 3651
N.A.I.C.S.: 334310

Blaupunkt Car Audio Systems GmbH & Co. KG (2)
Robert-Bosch-Str 200
Hildesheim, 31139, Germany
Tel.: (49) 5121 99810
Fax: (49) 5121 9981139
Car Audio System Mfr
S.I.C.: 3651
N.A.I.C.S.: 334310

Blaupunkt International Services AG (2)
Robert-Bosch-Str 200
Hildesheim, Germany
Tel.: (49) 5121 99810
Fax: (49) 5121 494154
Business Management Consulting Services
S.I.C.: 8742
N.A.I.C.S.: 541611

Non-U.S. Subsidiary:

Blaupunkt Malaysia Sdn. Bhd. (2)
Free Industrial Zone 1
11900 Bayan Lepas, Penang, Malaysia
Tel.: (60) 4 6382 222
Fax: (60) 4 6382 545
E-Mail: info@blaupunkt.com
Automotive Audio System Distr
S.I.C.: 5013
N.A.I.C.S.: 423120
Kok Peow Goh *(Gen Mgr)*

brightONE GmbH (1)
(Formerly Tieto Deutschland GmbH)
Dusseldorfer Strasse 40
65760 Eschborn, Germany
Tel.: (49) 6196 93 29 0
Fax: (49) 6196 93 29 800
E-Mail: info.de@tieto.com
Web Site: www.tieto.de
Emp.: 800
Information Technology Consulting Services
S.I.C.: 7373
N.A.I.C.S.: 541512
Michael Ruoff *(Chm-Supervisory Bd)*
Josef Becker *(Mng Dir)*
Alexander Graf *(Mng Dir)*

Non-U.S. Subsidiary:

brightONE Healthcare Solutions B.V. (2)
(Formerly Tieto Netherlands Healthcare B.V.)
Regulierenring 20
Bunnik, 3981 LB, Netherlands
Tel.: (31) 306569777
Fax: (31) 306569770
E-Mail:
Web Site: www.tieto.nl
Emp.: 28
Information Technology Consulting Services
S.I.C.: 7379
N.A.I.C.S.: 541519

DFA - Transport und Logistik GmbH (1)
Brunnenstrasse 82
07580 Ronneburg, Germany
Tel.: (49) 3660239910
Fax: (49) 3660222257
E-Mail: info@dfa-logistik.de
Web Site: www.dfa-logistik.de
Sales Range: $25-49.9 Million
Emp.: 200
Hazardous Waste Transport Services
S.I.C.: 4953
N.A.I.C.S.: 562211
Michael Hulm *(CEO)*

GHOTEL GmbH (1)
Graurheindorfer Str 35 39
53111 Bonn, Germany
Tel.: (49) 2289610980
Fax: (49) 22896109819
E-Mail: info@ghotel.de
Web Site: www.ghotel.de
Emp.: 83
Hotel & Apartment Building Operator
S.I.C.: 7999
N.A.I.C.S.: 713210

Dino Kitzinger *(Member-Mgmt Bd)*
Jens Lehmann *(Member-Mgmt Bd)*

Subsidiaries:

GHOTEL Beteiligungs GmbH (2)
Ludwig-Ganghofer-Str 6
Grunwald, 82031, Germany
Tel.: (49) 895447990
Property Management Services
S.I.C.: 6531
N.A.I.C.S.: 531312

GHOTEL Deutschland GmbH (2)
Graurheindorfer Str 92
Bonn, 53117, Germany
Tel.: (49) 2289610980
Fax: (49) 22896109819
Hotel Management Services
S.I.C.: 7011
N.A.I.C.S.: 721110

GHOTEL Germany GmbH (2)
Graurheindorfer Str 92
Bonn, 53117, Germany
Tel.: (49) 2289610980
Fax: (49) 22896109819
E-Mail: info@ghotel.de
Web Site: www.ghotel.de/
Emp.: 12
Hotel Management Services
S.I.C.: 7011
N.A.I.C.S.: 721110
Jens Lehmann *(Gen Mgr)*

GHOTEL Hotel und Boardinghaus Deutschland GmbH (2)
Graurheindorfer Str 92
Bonn, 53117, Germany
Tel.: (49) 2289610980
Fax: (49) 22896109819
Emp.: 10
Hotel Management Services
S.I.C.: 7011
N.A.I.C.S.: 721110
Jens Lehmann *(Mgr)*

HanseYachts AG (1)
Salinenstrasse 22
D 17489 Greifswald, Germany (73.68%)
Mailing Address:
Postfach 3165
D 17461 Greifswald, Germany
Tel.: (49) 3834 5792 0
Fax: (49) 3834 5792 81
Web Site: www.hansegroup.com
H9Y—(DEU)
Rev.: $108,948,961
Assets: $72,838,756
Liabilities: $49,972,967
Net Worth: $22,865,789
Earnings: ($7,145,373)
Emp.: 701
Fiscal Year-end: 06/30/13
Yacht Builder
S.I.C.: 3732
N.A.I.C.S.: 336612
Gert Purkert *(Chm-Supervisory Bd)*
Frank Forster *(Vice Chm-Supervisory Bd)*
Jens Gerhardt *(CEO & Member-Mgmt Bd)*
Sven Gobel *(CFO & Member-Mgmt Bd)*

LD Didactic GmbH (1)
Leyboldstr 1
50354 Hurth, Germany
Tel.: (49) 22 33 604 430
Fax: (49) 22 33 604 193
E-Mail: info@ld-didactic.de
Web Site: www.ld-didactic.de
Emp.: 130
Educational & Research Equipment Mfr & Whslr
S.I.C.: 3589
N.A.I.C.S.: 333318
Eric Blumenthal *(Gen Mgr)*

U.S. Subsidiary:

Feedback Education, Inc. (2)
437 Dimmocks Mill Rd
Hillsborough, NC 27278-0400 (100%)
Tel.: (919) 644-6466
Fax: (919) 644-6470
E-Mail: info@fbk.com
Web Site: www.fbk.com
Emp.: 10
Educational Electronic Equipment Mfr & Distr
S.I.C.: 5049
N.A.I.C.S.: 423490

Non-U.S. Subsidiary:

Feedback Instruments Limited (2)
Park Road
Units 5 & 6 Warren Court, Crowborough, East Sussex, TN6 2QX, United Kingdom (100%)
Tel.: (44) 1892653322
Telex: 95255 Feedbk G
Fax: (44) 1892663719
E-Mail: sales@feedback-Instruments.com
Web Site: www.feedback-Instruments.com
Rev.: $7,745,000
Emp.: 40
Educational Electronic Equipment Mfr Export
S.I.C.: 3829
N.A.I.C.S.: 334519
David Marks *(Mng Dir)*
Martin Mayer *(Mng Dir)*

Pohland-Herrenkleidung GmbH & Co. KG (1)
Schildergasse 1
50667 Cologne, Germany
Tel.: (49) 2212580232
Fax: (49) 2212580231
E-Mail: koeln@pohland.de
Web Site: www.pohland.de
Sales Range: $75-99.9 Million
Emp.: 468
Men's Clothing Retailer
S.I.C.: 5611
N.A.I.C.S.: 448110
Achim Rovenich *(Mng Dir)*

Reederei Peter Deilmann GmbH (1)
Am Holm 25
23730 Neustadt in Holstein, Germany
Tel.: (49) 4561 396 0
Fax: (49) 4561 8207
Web Site: www.deilmann-kreuzfahrten.de
Emp.: 5
Tour Operating Services
S.I.C.: 4725
N.A.I.C.S.: 561520
Konstantin Bissias *(CEO)*

Subsidiary:

MS Deutschland Beteiligungsgesellschaft mbH (2)
Am Holm 25
Neustadt in Holstein, 23730, Germany
Tel.: (49) 45613960
Fax: (49) 4561396121
Marine Shipping Services
S.I.C.: 4499
N.A.I.C.S.: 488330
Andreas Demel *(Gen Mgr)*

Richard Scherpe GmbH & Co. (1)
Grafische Betriebe
47800 Krefeld, Germany
Tel.: (49) 21515390
Fax: (49) 21505390
E-Mail: info@scherpe.de
Web Site: www.scherpe.de
Sales Range: $10-24.9 Million
Emp.: 91
Forms, Labels & Packaging Printing Services
S.I.C.: 2759
N.A.I.C.S.: 323111
Wilfried Schumacher *(CEO)*

Secop GmbH (1)
Mads Clausen Strasse 7
D 24939 Flensburg, Germany DE
Mailing Address:
PO Box 1443
D-24904 Flensburg, Germany
Tel.: (49) 46149410
Fax: (49) 46144715
E-Mail: contact@secop.com
Web Site: www.secop.com
Emp.: 750
Household Compressor Mfr
S.I.C.: 3563
N.A.I.C.S.: 333912
Mogens Soholm *(Pres & CEO)*

Subsidiaries:

Secop Verwaltungs GmbH (2)
Ludwig-Ganghofer-Str 6
Grunwald, Bavaria, 82031, Germany
Tel.: (49) 89 5447990
Fax: (49) 89 54479955
Investment Management Services
S.I.C.: 6211
N.A.I.C.S.: 523999

Non-U.S. Subsidiaries:

Secop Compressors (Tianjin) Co., Ltd. (2)
Wuqing Development Zone No 27 Kai Yuan Road
Tianjin, 301700, China
Tel.: (86) 22 8219 6766
Fax: (86) 22 8219 6958
Air Compressor Mfr
S.I.C.: 3563
N.A.I.C.S.: 333912

Secop kompresorji d.o.o. (2)
Heroja Stariha 24
8340 Crnomelj, Slovenia (100%)
Tel.: (386) 73361100
Fax: (386) 73361200
E-Mail:
Emp.: 1,100
Household Compressor Mfr
S.I.C.: 3563
N.A.I.C.S.: 333912
Suzana Vrtin *(Mgr-HR)*

Secop s.r.o. (2)
Tovarenska 49
953 01 Zlate Moravce, Slovakia
Tel.: (421) 376 406 200
E-Mail:
Web Site: www.secop.com
Emp.: 730
Air Compressor Mfr
S.I.C.: 3563
N.A.I.C.S.: 333912
Muehlbach Uwe *(Gen Mgr)*

Non-U.S. Holdings:

CalaChem Ltd. (1)
Earls Rd
Grangemouth, FK3 8XG, United Kingdom
Tel.: (44) 1324 498 300
Fax: (44) 1324 498 350
Web Site: www.calachem.com
Emp.: 20
Specialty Chemicals Mfr
S.I.C.: 2819
N.A.I.C.S.: 325180
Ian C. Brown *(Bus Mgr-Svcs)*

connectis AG (1)
Freiburgstrasse 251
3018 Bern, Switzerland
Tel.: (41) 583011111
E-Mail: info@connectis.ch
Web Site: www.connectis.ch
Sales Range: $75-99.9 Million
Emp.: 220
Speech, Data & Video Communication Services
S.I.C.: 7373
N.A.I.C.S.: 541512
Tom Kleiber *(CEO)*

Non-U.S. Subsidiary:

connectis Beteiligungs GmbH (2)
Ludwig-Ganghofer-Str 6
Grunwald, 82031, Germany
Tel.: (49) 895447990
Fax: (49) 89452052710
Investment Management Services
S.I.C.: 6211
N.A.I.C.S.: 523999

Getronics Global Services BV (1)
Claude Debussylaan 46
1082 MD Amsterdam, Netherlands NL
Tel.: (31) 707 703950
Fax: (31) 886604530
E-Mail: info.nl@getronics.com
Web Site: www.getronics.com
Information Systems; Communications Services
S.I.C.: 7389
N.A.I.C.S.: 519190
Mark Cook *(Grp CEO)*
Pom Burie *(CFO)*
Hans-Jorg Tittlbach *(COO)*
Christian Schmehl *(Chief Transformation Officer)*

Non-U.S. Subsidiaries:

Getronics Belgium S.A. (2)
De Kleetlaan 12B 1831 Diegem
Brussels, 1831, Belgium
Tel.: (32) 22299111
Fax: (32) 22299200
E-Mail: info.belgium@getronics.com
Web Site: www.getronics.com
Sales Range: $75-99.9 Million
Emp.: 500
Information Technology & Communications Infrastructure Services
S.I.C.: 7389
N.A.I.C.S.: 561499
Jean Claude Vandenbosch *(Gen Mgr)*

Getronics Deutschland GmbH (2)
Robert-Bosch-Strasse 13
64293 Darmstadt, Germany
Tel.: (49) 6151 1370 0
Fax: (49) 6151 1370 110
E-Mail: informationen@getronics.com
Web Site: www.getronics.de
Information Technology Consulting Services
S.I.C.: 7373
N.A.I.C.S.: 541512
Hans-Jorg Tittlbach *(VP-Intl Accts & Gen Mgr)*

Getronics Hungary Kft (2)
Henger u 2/B
1027 Budapest, Hungary
Tel.: (36) 1 371 7500
Fax: (36) 1 371 7501
Information Technology Consulting Services
S.I.C.: 7373
N.A.I.C.S.: 541512

Getronics (Schweiz) AG (2)
Industriestrasse 50a
8304 Wallisellen, Switzerland
Tel.: (41) 58 301 12 12
Fax: (41) 44 839 17 95
E-Mail: info@connectis.ch
Emp.: 12
Information Technology Consulting Services
S.I.C.: 7373
N.A.I.C.S.: 541512
Kurt Bylang *(Gen Mgr)*

Getronics Solutions (S) Pte Ltd (2)
20 Anson Road 07-03/04
Twenty Anson, Singapore, 079912, Singapore
Tel.: (65) 6890 2828
Fax: (65) 6890 2888
E-Mail: sales.singapore@getronics.com
Emp.: 160
System Integration & Consulting Services
S.I.C.: 7373
N.A.I.C.S.: 541512
John Maloch *(Mng Dir-Asia Pacific)*

Getronics (UK) Limited (2)
200 Brook Drive Green Park
Reading, Berkshire, RG2 6UB, United Kingdom UK
Tel.: (44) 870 906 8000
Fax: (44) 1252547669
E-Mail: webquery@getronics.com
Web Site: www.getronics.com
Emp.: 100
Information Technology & Business Communications Services
S.I.C.: 7389
N.A.I.C.S.: 561499

sit-up Ltd. (1)
11 Acton Park Estate Eastman Road Acton
London, W3 7QE, United Kingdom
Tel.: (44) 20 8600 9700
Fax: (44) 20 8746 0299
E-Mail: contactus@sit-up.tv
Web Site: www.sit-up.tv
Home Shopping Network Retailer
S.I.C.: 4833
N.A.I.C.S.: 515120

Non-U.S. Subsidiary:

sit-up Beteiligungs GmbH (2)
Ludwig-Ganghofer-Str 6
Grunwald, 82031, Germany
Tel.: (49) 895447990
Investment Management Services
S.I.C.: 6211
N.A.I.C.S.: 523999

Steria Iberica S.A.U. (1)
C/ Via de los Poblados 3
Parque Empresarial Cristalia Edificio 5, 28033 Madrid, Spain ES
Tel.: (34) 91 838 25 00
Fax: (34) 91 838 22 99

Aurelius AG—(Continued)

E-Mail: steria@steria.es
Web Site: www.steria.es
Sales Range: $50-74.9 Million
Emp.: 900
Information Technology Consulting Services
S.I.C.: 8999
N.A.I.C.S.: 541690

AUREOS CAPITAL LIMITED

(Acquired & Absorbed by Abraaj Capital Limited)

AURES TECHNOLOGIES

32 Rue du Bois Chaland
CE 2937
Lisses, Essonne, 91029, France
Tel.: (33) 169111660
Fax: (33) 164975838
E-Mail: yannick.waelly@aures.com
Web Site: www.aures.com
AURS—(EUR)
Sales Range: $25-49.9 Million
Emp.: 40

Business Description:
Computerized & Electronic Point-of-Sale Products Distr
S.I.C.: 5065
N.A.I.C.S.: 423690

Personnel:
Patrick Cathala *(Chm & CEO)*
Gilles Bouvart *(Mng Dir)*

Board of Directors:
Patrick Cathala
Gilles Bouvart

U.S. Subsidiary:

Aures USA Inc (1)
8599 Prairie Trail Dr Unit A 300
Englewood, CO 80112
Tel.: (303) 495-5643
Fax: (303) 482-1153
Toll Free: (866) 491-3753
Web Site: www.aures.com
Emp.: 5
Electronic Products Distr
S.I.C.: 5045
N.A.I.C.S.: 423430
Kevin A. Egyed *(Mgr)*

Non-U.S. Subsidiaries:

Aures GmbH (1)
Dr-von-Fromm-Str 12
92637 Weiden, Germany
Tel.: (49) 96129369
Business Support Services
S.I.C.: 7389
N.A.I.C.S.: 561499
Patrick Cathala *(Mng Dir)*

Aures Technologies Ltd. (1)
Unit 2 Chandlers Ct Picow Farm Rd
Runcorn, Cheshire, WA7 4UH, United Kingdom
Tel.: (44) 1928591222
Fax: (44) 1928591333
E-Mail: info@aures.com
Web Site: www.aures.com
Emp.: 12
Computerized & Electronic Point-of-Sale Products Distr
S.I.C.: 5065
N.A.I.C.S.: 423690

AUREUS MINING INC.

355-359 Strand
London, WC2R 0HS, United Kingdom
Tel.: (44) 20 7010 7690
Fax: (44) 20 7010 7699
E-Mail: info@aureus-mining.com
Web Site: www.aureus-mining.com
Year Founded: 2011
AUE—(AIM TSX)
Rev.: $28,570
Assets: $153,122,155
Liabilities: $4,995,027
Net Worth: $148,127,128
Earnings: ($5,874,467)
Fiscal Year-end: 12/31/12

Business Description:
Gold Mining Services
S.I.C.: 1041
N.A.I.C.S.: 212221

Personnel:
David Reading *(CEO)*
Paul Robert Thomson *(CFO)*

Board of Directors:
David Netherway
David M. Beatty
Luis da Silva
Jean-Guy Martin
David Reading
Adrian Reynolds

Legal Counsel:
Norton Rose Canada LLP
Royal Bank Plaza South Tower Suite 3800 200 Bay Street
Toronto, ON, Canada

Cobbetts LLP
70 Grays Inn Road
London, WC1X 8BT, United Kingdom

Computershare Investor Services Inc
510 Burrard Street 3rd Floor
Vancouver, BC, V6C 3B9, Canada

Transfer Agents:
Computershare Investor Services Inc
The Pavilions Bridgwater Road
Bristol, BS99 6ZZ, United Kingdom

Computershare Investor Services Inc.
3rd Floor 510 Burrard St
V6C 3B9 Vancouver, BC, Canada

AURIC PACIFIC GROUP LTD

06-03 OUE Bayfront 50 Collyer Quay
Singapore, 049321, Singapore
Tel.: (65) 63362262
Fax: (65) 63362272
E-Mail: corporate@auricgroup.com
Web Site: www.auric.com.sg
Year Founded: 1988
A23—(SES)
Rev.: $315,772,771
Assets: $293,247,473
Liabilities: $89,066,419
Net Worth: $204,181,054
Earnings: $9,361,520
Emp.: 747
Fiscal Year-end: 12/31/12

Business Description:
Investment Holding Company
S.I.C.: 6719
N.A.I.C.S.: 551112

Personnel:
Phaik Hwa Saw *(CEO)*
Kai Tek Tan *(CFO)*
Timothy Chee Mun Chan *(CEO-Delifrance Asia Ltd)*
Dora Lee Buay Chong *(CEO-Food Grp)*

Board of Directors:
Albert Saychuan Cheok
Bryan Yew Chan Chang
Boh Soon Lim
Edwin Neo
Stephen T. Riady
Phaik Hwa Saw
Ronnie Keh Poo Tan

Subsidiaries:

Auric Asset Management Pte Ltd (1)
78 Shenton Way #22-02
079120 Singapore, Singapore (100%)
Tel.: (65) 63362262
Fax: (65) 63362272
E-Mail: corporate@auricgroup.com
Emp.: 22
Miscellaneous Financial Investment Activities
S.I.C.: 6211
N.A.I.C.S.: 523999
Yao Che Wan *(Mng Dir)*

Auric Pacific Fine Wines Pte Ltd (1)
50 Kallang Avenue
Level No 06
Noel Corporate Building, 339505 Singapore, Singapore (100%)
Tel.: (65) 62911947
Fax: (65) 62941947
E-Mail: sales@apfw.com.sg
Web Site: www.apfw.com.sg
Emp.: 8
Wine & Distilled Alcoholic Beverage Merchant Whslr
S.I.C.: 5182
N.A.I.C.S.: 424820
Ronnie Tan *(Exec Dir)*

Auric Pacific Food Industries Pte Ltd (1)
50 Collyer Quay #06-03 Oue Bay Front
049321 Singapore, Singapore (100%)
Tel.: (65) 63362262
Fax: (65) 63362272
E-Mail: corporate@auricgroup.com
Web Site: www.auricgroup.com
Emp.: 20
Frozen Cakes Pies & Other Pastries Mfr
S.I.C.: 2053
N.A.I.C.S.: 311813
Saw Thaik Hwa *(CEO)*

Auric Pacific Marketing Pte Ltd (1)
2 Enterprise Road
629814 Singapore, Singapore (100%)
Tel.: (65) 68679100
Fax: (65) 62650689
E-Mail: service@auric.com.sg
Web Site: www.auric.com.sg/
Emp.: 200
Food Service Contractors
S.I.C.: 5812
N.A.I.C.S.: 722310
Yao Che Wan *(CEO)*

Delifrance Asia Ltd (1)
230 Pandan Loop
Singapore, 128415, Singapore
Tel.: (65) 6874 9647
Fax: (65) 6874 9662
Web Site: www.delifranceasia.com
Bakeries Operating Services
S.I.C.: 2051
N.A.I.C.S.: 311812

Delifrance Singapore Pte Ltd (1)
230 Pandan Loop
Singapore, Singapore
Tel.: (65) 68749622
Fax: (65) 68749671
E-Mail: cust.service@delifrance.com.sg
Web Site: www.delifrance.com.sg
Commercial Bakeries
S.I.C.: 2051
N.A.I.C.S.: 311812
Timothy Chan *(COO)*

Food Junction Holdings Limited (1)
50 Raffles Place 32-01 Singapore Land Tower
Singapore, 048623, Singapore (93.1%)
Tel.: (65) 65365355
Fax: (65) 65361360
E-Mail: fjh@foodjunction.com
Web Site: www.foodjunction.com
529—(SES)
Rev.: $46,590,607
Assets: $37,186,983
Liabilities: $18,428,317
Net Worth: $18,758,666
Earnings: ($5,549,547)
Fiscal Year-end: 12/31/12
Beverages Mfr
S.I.C.: 2033
N.A.I.C.S.: 311421
Chew Hoon Teo *(CEO & Mng Dir)*
Choon Hong Pek *(Sec & Controller-Fin)*

Subsidiaries:

FNC International Pte Ltd (2)
163 Tanglin Rd 03-18
Singapore, 247933, Singapore
Tel.: (65) 68363112
Fax: (65) 68363118
Bakery Foods Mfr
S.I.C.: 2099
N.A.I.C.S.: 311999

Food Junction Management Pte Ltd (2)
91 Tanglin Road 02-02 Tanglin Place
Singapore, 247918, Singapore
Tel.: (65) 63388213
Fax: (65) 63366108
E-Mail: fjh@foodjunction.com
Web Site: www.foodjunction.com
Food Products Distr
S.I.C.: 5142
N.A.I.C.S.: 424420
David Lim *(Mng Dir)*

Sunshine Manufacturing Pte Ltd (1)
2 Senoko Avenue
758298 Singapore, Singapore (100%)
Tel.: (65) 62578455
Fax: (65) 62577310
Web Site: www.sunshine.com.sg
Emp.: 500
Commercial Bakeries
S.I.C.: 2051
N.A.I.C.S.: 311812
Albert Chan *(Gen Mgr)*

Non-U.S. Subsidiaries:

Auric Chun Yip Sdn Bhd (1)
Lot 35 Jalan Delima 1-3
Subang Hi-Tech Industrial Park, 40000
Shah Alam, Selangor, Malaysia (58.33%)
Tel.: (60) 351636363
Fax: (60) 51636388
E-Mail: hr.recruitment@auric.com.my
Web Site: www.auric.com.sg
Emp.: 80
Other Grocery & Related Products Whslr
S.I.C.: 5149
N.A.I.C.S.: 424490
Chua Kim Leong *(Gen Mgr)*

Auric Pacific Food Processing Sdn Bhd (1)
Lot 35 Jalan Delima 1/3 Subang Hi-Tech Industrial Park Batu Tiga, 40000 Shah Alam, Selangor Darul Ehsan, Malaysia (58.33%)
Tel.: (60) 351636363
Fax: (60) 351636263
E-Mail: info.malaysia@auric.com.my
Web Site: www.auric.com.sg/contactus.htm
Emp.: 130
Food Service Contractors
S.I.C.: 5812
N.A.I.C.S.: 722310
Chong Wai Choong *(Country Mgr)*

Auric Pacific (M) Sdn Bhd (1)
Lot 35 Jalan Delima 1-3
Subang Hi-Tech Industrial Park, 40000
Shah Alam, Selangor, Malaysia (100%)
Tel.: (60) 356213968
Fax: (60) 356213768
Web Site: www.auricgroup.com
Emp.: 3
Dairy Product except Dried or Canned Whslr
S.I.C.: 5143
N.A.I.C.S.: 424430

Delifrance (HK) Limited (1)
Flat A 2/F Tin Fung Industrial Building 63 Wong Chuk Hang Road
Hong Kong, China (Hong Kong)
Tel.: (852) 2873 3893
Fax: (852) 2873 5457
E-Mail: info@delifrance.com.hk
Web Site: www.delifrance.com.hk
Cafeterias Operators
S.I.C.: 5812
N.A.I.C.S.: 722514

Malone's Limited (1)
6 Miami Avenue Waiheke Island
Auckland, 1701, New Zealand
Tel.: (64) 93728011
Food & Beverages Mfr
S.I.C.: 2099
N.A.I.C.S.: 311999

AURICO GOLD INC.

110 Yonge Street Suite 1601
Toronto, ON, M5C 1T4, Canada
Mailing Address:
PO Box 2067
Halifax, NS, B3J 2Z1, Canada
Tel.: (647) 260-8880
Fax: (647) 260-8881
E-Mail: info@auricogold.com
Web Site: www.auricogold.com
AUQ—(NYSE TSX)
Rev.: $227,631,000
Assets: $2,462,408,000
Liabilities: $674,526,000

Net Worth: $1,787,882,000
Earnings: ($176,770,000)
Emp.: 586
Fiscal Year-end: 12/31/13

Business Description:
Gold Mining & Exploration Services
S.I.C.: 1041
N.A.I.C.S.: 212221

Personnel:
Scott Graeme Perry *(Pres & CEO)*
Robert J. Chausse *(CFO & Exec VP)*
Peter Macphail *(COO & Exec VP)*
Trent Mell *(Exec VP-Corp Affairs)*
Chris Bostwick *(Sr VP-Tech Svcs)*
Luis Chavez *(Sr VP-Mexico)*
Charlene Milner *(Sr VP-Fin)*

Board of Directors:
Alan R. Edwards
Luis Chavez
Richard Mark Colterjohn
Mark J. Daniel
Patrick D. Downey
Martha I. Lara-Alatorre
Terrence A. Lyons
Scott Graeme Perry

Legal Counsel:
McInnes Cooper & Robertson
1601 Lower Water Street
P.O. Box 730
Halifax, NS, B3J 2V1, Canada

Transfer Agent:
Computershare Investor Services Inc
100 University Avenue 8th Fl North Tower
Toronto, ON, Canada

Non-U.S. Subsidiary:

Minera Santa Rita, S. de R.L. de C.V. (1)
Lamberto Hernandez No 278
Caborca, Sonora, 83600, Mexico
Tel.: (52) 6373727094
Fax: (52) 6373731070
Emp.: 600
Gold & Silver Ore Mining Services
N.A.I.C.S.: 212221
Hector Araiza, *(Gen Mgr)*

Non-U.S. Holding:

Oro de Altar, S.A. de C.V. (1)
Calle Paseo Rio Sonora Nte 42 211-A
Colonia Centenario, Hermosillo, Sonora, Mexico
Tel.: (52) 662 372 7094
Fax: (52) 662 372 7094
Investment Management Services
S.I.C.: 6282
N.A.I.C.S.: 523920

AURIGA GOLD CORP.

8 King Street East Suite 1300
Toronto, ON, M5C 1B5, Canada
Tel.: (416) 214-2785
Fax: (416) 864-0620
Toll Free: (877) 864-0615
E-Mail: info@aurigagold.ca
Web Site: www.aurigagold.ca
Year Founded: 1992
AIA—(TSXV)
Rev.: $840
Assets: $13,556,138
Liabilities: $6,473,885
Net Worth: $7,082,252
Earnings: ($4,790,814)
Fiscal Year-end: 03/31/13

Business Description:
Gold Exploration & Mining Services
S.I.C.: 1041
N.A.I.C.S.: 212221

Personnel:
Gorden Glenn *(Interim Pres & Interim CEO)*
Victor Hugo *(CFO & Controller-Fin)*

Board of Directors:
Gorden Glenn
Christopher O. Irwin
Brian Robertson
James D. A. White

Transfer Agent:
Equity Financial Trust Company
200 University Avenue Suite 400
Toronto, ON, Canada

AURIGA INDUSTRIES A/S

Thuborunvej 78
DK-7673 Lemvig, Denmark
Mailing Address:
PO Box 9
DK 7620 Lemvig, Denmark
Tel.: (45) 7010 7030
Fax: (45) 7010 7031
E-Mail: info@auriga.dk
Web Site: www.auriga-industries.com
Year Founded: 1938
AURI B—(OMX)
Rev.: $1,129,512,075
Assets: $1,150,887,982
Liabilities: $782,151,160
Net Worth: $368,736,822
Earnings: $22,151,815
Emp.: 2,148
Fiscal Year-end: 12/31/12

Business Description:
Holding Company; Crop Protection Products
S.I.C.: 6719
N.A.I.C.S.: 551112

Personnel:
Jens Due Olsen *(Chm)*
Torben Svejgard *(Deputy Chm)*
Kurt Pedersen Kaalund *(Pres & CEO)*
Rico Toft Christensen *(Pres-North America)*
Jaime Gomez-Arnau *(Pres-Europe)*
Pramod Karlekar *(Pres-Intl)*
Cesar Rojas *(Pres-Latin America)*
Anton Bro *(Sr VP-Dev & Registration)*
Niels Morten Hjort *(Sr VP-Production & Logistics)*

Board of Directors:
Jens Due Olsen
Jutta af Rosenborg
Lars Hvidtfeldt
Jorgen Jensen
Karl Anker Jorgensen
Kapil Kumar Saini
Peder Munk Sorensen
Torben Svejgard
Jorn Sand Tofting

Subsidiary:

Cheminova A/S (1)
PO Box 9
7620 Ringkobing, Denmark (100%)
Tel.: (45) 96909690
Fax: (45) 96909691
E-Mail: info@cheminova.dk
Web Site: www.cheminova.com
Sales Range: $1-4.9 Billion
Emp.: 900
Fine Chemicals Mfr
S.I.C.: 2899
N.A.I.C.S.: 325998
Kurt Pedersen Kaalund *(Mng Dir)*

U.S. Subsidiary:

Cheminova Inc. (2)
One Park Dr Ste 150
Durham, NC 27709
Tel.: (919) 474-6600
Fax: (919) 474-6629
Web Site: www.cheminova.us.com
Emp.: 22
Inorganic Chemical Mfr
S.I.C.: 2819
N.A.I.C.S.: 325180
Mark Bishop *(Area Mgr-Sls)*

Non-U.S. Subsidiaries:

Cheminova Agro de Argentina S.A. (2)
Aldecoa 1277
1870 Avellaneda, Buenos Aires, Argentina
Tel.: (54) 11 4228 7047
Fax: (54) 11 4209 8844
E-Mail: info@cheminova.com.ar
Web Site: www.cheminova.com
Agricultural Chemicals Mfr
S.I.C.: 2879
N.A.I.C.S.: 325320

Cheminova Agro de Mexico S.A. de C.V. (2)
Paseo de la Reforma No 265
Piso 9 Despacho 1801 Colonia, 06500
Cuauhtemoc, Mexico
Tel.: (52) 5555334280
Fax: (52) 5555334281
E-Mail: info@cheminova.com.mx
Web Site: www.cheminova.com.mx
Emp.: 32
Farm Supplies Whslr
S.I.C.: 5191
N.A.I.C.S.: 424910
Manuel Edevez *(Mgr-Mktg)*

Cheminova Agro France S.A.S. (2)
Immeuble L Europeen
19 Blvd Eugene Deruelle Fr, 69003 Lyon, France
Tel.: (33) 437236570
Fax: (33) 478710846
E-Mail: cheminova@cheminova.fr
Web Site: www.cheminova.fr
Emp.: 14
Chemical Products Whslr
S.I.C.: 5169
N.A.I.C.S.: 424690
Marcos Lobo *(Gen Dir)*

Cheminova Agro Italia S.r.l. (2)
Via Fratelli Bronzetti n 32
24124 Bergamo, Italy
Tel.: (39) 035 1990 4468
Fax: (39) 035 1990 4471
E-Mail: info.it@cheminova.com
Crop Protection Chemicals Mfr
S.I.C.: 2879
N.A.I.C.S.: 325320

Cheminova Agro SA (2)
Paseo de la Castellans 276
28046 Madrid, Spain
Tel.: (34) 915530104
Fax: (34) 915538859
Emp.: 44
Organic Chemicals for Plant Manufacturing
S.I.C.: 2899
N.A.I.C.S.: 325199
Guillerno Cegarra *(Mgr-Mktg)*

Cheminova Agroquimica S.A. de C.V. (2)
Paseo de la Reforma No 265 Floor 1
Colonia Cuauhtemoc, Piso, 6500, Mexico
Tel.: (52) 55 5533 4280
E-Mail: alejandra.ramera@cheminova.com
Web Site: www.cheminova.com
Emp.: 35
Crop Protection Product Mfr
S.I.C.: 2875
N.A.I.C.S.: 325314
Ernesto Trejo *(Gen Mgr)*

Cheminova Brasil Ltda. (2)
Rua Alexandre Dumas
Chacara Santo Antonio 2 220 , 04717-004
Sao Paulo, Brazil
Tel.: (55) 1151892100
Fax: (55) 1151892104
E-Mail: alo.cheminova@cheminova.com.br
Web Site: www.cheminova.com.br
Emp.: 50
Pesticide & Agricultural Chemical Mfr
S.I.C.: 2879
N.A.I.C.S.: 325320
Lewis Guimaraes *(Dir-Fin)*

Cheminova Bulgaria EOOD (2)
102 Bulgaria Blvd Bellissimo Business Ctr
Floor 5 Ofc 59, 1404 Sofia, Bulgaria
Tel.: (359) 28185656
Fax: (359) 28548844
E-Mail: Ivan.Rangelov@Cheminova.com
Web Site: www.cheminova.com
Emp.: 6
Chemical & Allied Products Merchant Whslr
S.I.C.: 5169
N.A.I.C.S.: 424690
Ivan Rangelov *(Mgr)*

Cheminova Canada Inc. (2)
Unit No C2
22499 Jefferies Road, N0L 1R0 Kilworth, ON, Canada
Tel.: (519) 472-0600
Fax: (519) 472-0433
Web Site: www.cheminova.com
Emp.: 5
Farm Supplies Whslr
S.I.C.: 5191
N.A.I.C.S.: 424910
Doug McLean *(Mgr-Sls)*

Cheminova Canada Inc. (2)
22499 Jefferies Road Unit C2
Kilworth, ON, N0L 1R0, Canada
Tel.: (519) 472-0600
Fax: (519) 472-0433
Web Site: www.cheminova.com
Emp.: 5
Farm Supplies Whslr
S.I.C.: 5191
N.A.I.C.S.: 424910
Doug McLean *(Mgr-Sls)*

Cheminova China Ltd. (2)
Room 802 Comalong Building 889 Yishan Road
Shanghai, 200233, China
Tel.: (86) 21 6236 6680
Fax: (86) 21 6236 6681
Web Site: www.cheminova.com
Emp.: 9
Crop Protection Products Mfr
S.I.C.: 2875
N.A.I.C.S.: 325314
Roger Ding *(Gen Mgr)*

Cheminova D.O.O. (2)
Ustanicka 128B
11050 Belgrade, Serbia
Tel.: (381) 11 347 4240
Fax: (381) 11 304 8120
Web Site: www.cheminova.com
Crop Protection Chemicals Mfr
S.I.C.: 2879
N.A.I.C.S.: 325320

Cheminova Hungary Ltd (2)
St 16
1022 Budapest, Ganz, Hungary
Tel.: (36) 13362120
Fax: (36) 13362121
E-Mail: cheminova@dportal.hu
Web Site: www.Cheminova.hr
Emp.: 6
Pesticide & Agricultural Chemical Mfr
S.I.C.: 2879
N.A.I.C.S.: 325320
Attila Takacs *(Mng Dir)*

Cheminova India Ltd (2)
Keshava 7th Floor Bandra Kurla Complex
Bandra E, 400051 Mumbai, India
Tel.: (91) 2267045504
Fax: (91) 2267045488
Pesticide & Agricultural Chemical Mfr
S.I.C.: 2879
N.A.I.C.S.: 325320
Ninad D. Gupte *(Mng Dir)*

Cheminova LLC (2)
Floor 8 24 D Smolnaya Str
Moscow, 125445, Russia
Tel.: (7) 495 783 9003
Fax: (7) 495 783 9004
E-Mail: mail@cheminova.ru
Web Site: www.cheminova.ru
Emp.: 25
Crop Protection Chemicals Mfr
S.I.C.: 2879
N.A.I.C.S.: 325320
Tatyana Yurkovska *(Gen Mgr)*

Cheminova MFG Pty. Ltd. (2)
16 Lucca Road
PO Box 68
Wyong, NSW, 2259, Australia
Tel.: (61) 2 4352 4200
Fax: (61) 2 43533092
Web Site: www.cheminova.com.au
Emp.: 3
Crop Protection Chemicals Mfr
S.I.C.: 2869
N.A.I.C.S.: 325199
Paul Galasso *(Mgr-Toll & Plng)*

Cheminova Polska Sp. Z.o.o. (2)
Aleje Jerozolimskie 212A
02-486 Warsaw, Poland
Tel.: (48) 225714050
Fax: (48) 225714051
E-Mail: cheminova@cheminova.com.pl
Web Site: www.cheminova.pl
Emp.: 5
Pesticide & Agricultural Chemical Mfr

Auriga Industries A/S—(Continued)

S.I.C.: 2879
N.A.I.C.S.: 325320
Jerey Mekiel *(Mgr)*

Cheminova Taiwan Ltd (2)
19th Fl-A3 No 760 Chung Ming S Rd
Taichung, Taiwan
Tel.: (886) 422659718
Fax: (886) 422659719
Web Site: www.cheminova.com
Emp.: 6
Pesticide & Agricultural Chemical Mfr
S.I.C.: 2879
N.A.I.C.S.: 325320
Clive Pei *(Mgr-Sls)*

Chemiplant S.A. (2)
Aldecoa 1277
Avallaneda, 1870 Buenos Aires, Argentina
Tel.: (54) 1142287047
Fax: (54) 1142098844
E-Mail: adf@chemiplant.com.ar
Web Site: www.cheminova.com
Emp.: 30
Pesticide & Agricultural Chemical Mfr
S.I.C.: 2879
N.A.I.C.S.: 325320

CropTech S.A (2)
Carrera 11 No 95-75 Oficina 101
Bogota, Colombia
Tel.: (57) 12577004
Fax: (57) 12572096
Web Site: www.cheminova.com
Computer Systems Design Services
S.I.C.: 7373
N.A.I.C.S.: 541512

Headland Agrochemicals Ltd. (2)
Rectors Lane Pentre
Deeside, Flintshire, CH5 2DH, United Kingdom
Tel.: (44) 1244537370
Fax: (44) 1244532097
E-Mail: info@headland-ag.co.uk
Web Site: www.headland-ag.co.uk
Pesticide & Agricultural Chemical Mfr
S.I.C.: 2879
N.A.I.C.S.: 325320

Ospray Pty Ltd. (2)
502/15 Blue St
Ste 502 Level 5, 2060 Sydney, NSW, Australia AU
Mailing Address:
12 Julius Avenue
Building A, North Ryde, NSW, 2113, Australia
Tel.: (61) 289686500
Fax: (61) 299227532
Web Site: www.ospray.com.au
Farm Supplies Whslr
S.I.C.: 5191
N.A.I.C.S.: 424910

Solufeed Ltd. (2)
Highground Orchards Highground Lane
Barnham North, Bognor Regis, W Sussex, PO22 0BT, United Kingdom
Tel.: (44) 1243554090
Fax: (44) 1243554568
E-Mail: enquiries@solufeed.com
Web Site: www.solufeed.com
Emp.: 6
Fertilizer Mfr
S.I.C.: 2875
N.A.I.C.S.: 325314
Richard Holden *(Mng Dir)*

Stahler International GmbH (2)
Stader Elbstrasse
21683 Stade, Germany
Tel.: (49) 41 41 92 04 0
Fax: (49) 41 41 92 04 10
E-Mail: info@staehler.com
Crop Protection Products Mfr & Distr
S.I.C.: 2879
N.A.I.C.S.: 325320

Non-U.S. Subsidiary:

Stahler Austria GmbH (3)
Saint Peter Hauptstrasse 117
8042 Graz, Austria
Tel.: (43) 316 46 020
Fax: (43) 316 46 0217
E-Mail: info@cheminova.at
Web Site: www.cheminova.at
Emp.: 13
Plant Protection Chemicals Mfr
S.I.C.: 2879
N.A.I.C.S.: 325320
Peter Strycek *(Mng Dir)*

Non-U.S. Joint Venture:

Pytech Chemicals GmbH (2)
Seestrasse 122
ZH 8810 Horgen, Switzerland
Tel.: (41) 17283906
Web Site: www.cheminova.com
Sales Range: $150-199.9 Million
Pesticides Mfr; Owned 50% by Dow AgroSciences Switzerland S.A. & Cheminova A/S
S.I.C.: 2879
N.A.I.C.S.: 325320

Non-U.S. Subsidiaries:

Stahler Deutschland GmbH (1)
Stader Elbstrasse
21683 Stade, Germany
Tel.: (49) 41 41 92 04 0
Fax: (49) 41 41 92 04 10
E-Mail: info@cheminova.com
Web Site: www.cheminova.de
Emp.: 12
Agricultural Pesticide Mfr
S.I.C.: 2879
N.A.I.C.S.: 325320
Steven Nevett *(Gen Mgr)*

Stahler Tec Deutschland GmbH (1)
Stader Elbstr 26
21683 Stade, Germany
Tel.: (49) 414192040
Fax: (49) 4141 920411
E-Mail: staehlertec@staehler.com
Industrial Chemical Mfr
S.I.C.: 2899
N.A.I.C.S.: 325998

AURIGA INTERNATIONAL S.A.

Avenue Victor Hugo 32
B-1420 Braine-l'Alleud, Belgium
Tel.: (32) 23845377
Fax: (32) 23841397
E-Mail: info@auriga-int.com
Web Site: www.auriga-int.com
AURI—(EUR)
Sales Range: $350-399.9 Million
Emp.: 30
Business Description:
Cosmetics & Beauty Products Mfr
S.I.C.: 2844
N.A.I.C.S.: 325620
Personnel:
Alfred Marchal *(CEO)*

AURIGEN CAPITAL LIMITED

Chancery Hall 52 Reid Street Top Floor
PO Box HM 3011
Hamilton, HM MX, Bermuda
Tel.: (441) 278 3500
Fax: (441) 278 3501
E-Mail: info@aurigenre.com
Web Site: www.aurigenre.com
Year Founded: 2010
Business Description:
Holding Company; Reinsurance Products & Services
S.I.C.: 6719
N.A.I.C.S.: 551112
Personnel:
Alan Ryder *(Pres & CEO)*
Gregg Clifton *(CFO)*
Atlaf Rahim *(Chief Risk Officer)*
Michael Pado *(Exec VP)*
Board of Directors:
Adam Barron
Felix Chee
Gregg Clifton
Alex Fridlyand
Bruce Gordon
Grant Hardy
Damerval Jean-Claude
Benjamin Johnston
Michael Pado
Gilbert Palter
Alan Ryder
William Spiegel
Philipp Struth
Srjdan Vukovic

Subsidiary:

Aurigen Reinsurance Limited (1)
Chancery Hall 52 Reid Street Top Floor
PO Box HM 3011
Hamilton, HM MX, Bermuda BM
Tel.: (441) 278 3500 (100%)
Fax: (441) 278 3501
E-Mail: info@aurigenre.com
Web Site: www.aurigenre.com
Reinsurance Products & Services
S.I.C.: 6399
N.A.I.C.S.: 524130
Caspar Young *(Mng Dir)*

U.S. Subsidiary:

Aurigen USA Holdings Inc. (1)
2 Bridge Ave Ste 111
Red Bank, NJ 07701 DE
Tel.: (732) 212-6860 (100%)
E-Mail: info@aurigenre.com
Web Site: www.aurigenre.com
Holding Company; Reinsurance Products & Services
S.I.C.: 6719
N.A.I.C.S.: 551112
Michael Pado *(Pres & CEO)*
Cheryl Rogers *(CFO)*
Thomas Hartlett *(Chief Admin Officer)*
Lou Hensley *(Chief Bus Dev Officer & Sr VP)*
Cristina Downey *(Chief Underwriting Officer & VP)*
Vadim Marchenko *(Chief Pricing Officer & VP)*

Subsidiary:

Aurigen Reinsurance Company of America (2)
(Formerly Brokers National Life Assurance Company)
7010 Hwy 71 W Ste 100
Austin, TX 78735
Tel.: (512) 383-0220
Fax: (512) 383-8596
Toll Free: (855) 817-5307
E-Mail:
Web Site: www.aurigenre.com
Sales Range: $25-49.9 Million
Emp.: 60
Dental & Vision Insurance Products & Services
S.I.C.: 6321
N.A.I.C.S.: 524114
Michael Pado *(Pres & CEO)*

AURION RESOURCES LTD.

120 Torbay Road Suite W275
Saint John's, NL, A1A 2G8, Canada
Tel.: (709) 722-2141
Fax: (709) 722-4129
E-Mail: info@aurionresources.com
Web Site: www.aurionresources.com
Year Founded: 2006
AU—(TSXV)
Rev.: $42,554
Assets: $4,663,596
Liabilities: $118,747
Net Worth: $4,544,849
Earnings: ($2,996,652)
Fiscal Year-end: 12/31/12
Business Description:
Mineral Exploration Services
S.I.C.: 1081
N.A.I.C.S.: 213114
Personnel:
Mike Basha *(Pres & CEO)*
David Loveys *(CFO)*
Board of Directors:
Henry Awmack
Mike Basha
Dennis Clarke
Richard A. Graham
David Loveys
Legal Counsel:
Ottenheimer & Baker
Baine Johnston Centre 10 Fort William Place
PO Box 5457
Saint John's, NL, Canada
Transfer Agent:
Computershare Inc.
Halifax, NS, Canada

AURIONPRO SOLUTIONS LIMITED

35th Floor Sunshine Tower Tulsi Pipe Road Near India Bulls Office
Dadar West, Mumbai, Maharashtra, 400013, India
Tel.: (91) 2266172600
Fax: (91) 2266172666
E-Mail: info@aurionpro.com
Web Site: www.aurionpro.com
Year Founded: 1997
AURIONPRO—(NSE)
Rev.: $107,932,019
Assets: $136,022,511
Liabilities: $48,434,860
Net Worth: $87,587,651
Earnings: $8,496,363
Emp.: 1,200
Fiscal Year-end: 03/31/13
Business Description:
Banking Software Development Services
S.I.C.: 7371
N.A.I.C.S.: 541511
Personnel:
Amit R. Sheth *(Founder & Vice Chm)*
Samir Shah *(Global CEO)*
Dusan Jovanovic *(CFO)*
Jonathan Bank *(CMO)*
Mehul Raval *(Compliance Officer & Sec)*
Sanjay Bali *(Pres-Govt Solutions)*
Kashmira Bhayani *(Pres-Banking & Fin Technologies-South Asia)*
Craig Jones *(Pres-North America)*
Swapnil Mehta *(Pres-Aurionpro SENA)*
Shekhar Mullatti *(Pres-Banking & Payments-Asia Pacific)*
Ashish Pujari *(Pres-Aurionpro SCM & Asia Pacific Consulting)*
Robert Levine *(CEO-North America)*
Nirav Shah *(Exec VP-Delivery)*
Board of Directors:
Paresh C. Zaveri
Sandeep Daga
Sanjay A. Desai
Nikunj Kapadia
Mahendra Mehta
Prem Rajani
Samir Shah
Amit R. Sheth
Transfer Agent:
Bigshare Services Private Limited
E-2 Ansa Industrial Estate Sakivihar Road Saki Naka Andheri (E)
Mumbai, India

Subsidiary:

Sena Systems (India) Pvt. Ltd. (1)
A-3 Abhimanshree Society 1st Floor East Wing
Pashan Road, Pune, Maharashtra, India 411 008
Tel.: (91) 20 30641500
Fax: (91) 20 30641504
Emp.: 150
Information Technology Consulting Services
S.I.C.: 7389
N.A.I.C.S.: 561499

Non-U.S. Subsidiaries:

Aurionpro SCM Pte Ltd. (1)
39 Robinson Road 07-01 Robinson Point
Singapore, 068911, Singapore
Tel.: (65) 6536 6438
Fax: (65) 6536 6831
Web Site: www.scmprofit.com

Supply Chain Software Development Services
S.I.C.: 7371
N.A.I.C.S.: 541511

AurionPro Solutions (HK) Ltd. (1)
Suite 4301-5 Tower One Times Square 1 Matheson Street
Causeway Bay, China (Hong Kong)
Tel.: (852) 65014112
Fax: (852) 25987500
E-Mail: info@aurionpro.com
Emp.: 4
Supply Chain Software Publisher
S.I.C.: 7372
N.A.I.C.S.: 511210

Aurionpro Solutions PTY Ltd. (1)
Level 2 215 Spring Street
Melbourne, VIC, 3000, Australia
Tel.: (61) 411 703 688
E-Mail: info@aurionpro.com
Web Site: www.aurionpro.com
Information Technology Consulting Services
S.I.C.: 7373
N.A.I.C.S.: 541512

AurionPro Solutions, SPC (1)
PO Box 11490
Manama, Bahrain
Tel.: (973) 17 217 991
Fax: (973) 17 217 992
E-Mail: info@aurionpro.com
Web Site: www.aurionpro.com
Emp.: 100
Information Technology Consulting Services
S.I.C.: 7373
N.A.I.C.S.: 541512
M. K. Ranjit *(Head-Ops)*

Integro Technologies Pte Ltd. (1)
39 Robinson Road 07-01 Robinson Point
Singapore, 68911, Singapore
Tel.: (65) 6536 6438
Fax: (65) 6536 6831
Web Site: www.integrosys.com
Emp.: 90
Banking Software Development Services
S.I.C.: 7371
N.A.I.C.S.: 541511
Bak Wee Lim *(Chm)*
Shekhar Mullatti *(CEO & Mng Dir)*

AURIS AG

Hirschgasslein 30
4051 Basel, Switzerland
Tel.: (41) 61 271 27 70
Fax: (41) 61 221 27 71
E-Mail: info@aurisag.ch
Web Site: www.aurisag.ch
Year Founded: 2009
1AU—(DEU)

Business Description:
Gold Mining Services
S.I.C.: 1041
N.A.I.C.S.: 212221
Personnel:
Peter Geoggel *(Chm)*

AURIZON HOLDINGS LIMITED

175 Eagle Street
Brisbane, QLD, 4001, Australia
Mailing Address:
GPO Box 456
Brisbane, QLD, 4001, Australia
Tel.: (61) 7 3019 9000
Fax: (61) 7 3235 2188
Web Site: www.aurizon.com.au
AZJ—(ASX OTC)
Rev.: $3,880,884,610
Assets: $10,961,954,110
Liabilities: $4,192,889,350
Net Worth: $6,769,064,760
Earnings: $465,714,490
Emp.: 7,969
Fiscal Year-end: 06/30/13

Business Description:
Rail Freight Services
S.I.C.: 4011
N.A.I.C.S.: 482111
Personnel:
Lance E. Hockridge *(CEO & Mng Dir)*
Keith Neate *(CFO & Exec VP)*
John Stephens *(Chief HR Officer & Exec VP)*
Dominic D. Smith *(Sec)*
Michael Carter *(Exec VP-Network)*
Mike Franczak *(Exec VP-Ops)*
Alex Kummant *(Exec VP-Strategy)*
Andrew MacDonald *(Acting Exec VP-Comml & Mktg)*
Greg P. Pringle *(Exec VP-Enterprise Svcs)*
Greg Robinson *(Exec VP-Bus Sustainability)*
Board of Directors:
John B. Prescott
John Atkin
Russell Ronald Caplan
John D. Cooper
Karen L. Field
Lance E. Hockridge
Graeme T. John
Andrea J. P. Staines
Gene Thomas Tilbrook

Subsidiaries:

CRT Group Pty Ltd (1)
1 Chambers Road
Altona, VIC, 3025, Australia
Tel.: (61) 392901700
Fax: (61) 92901700
E-Mail: email@crtgroup.com.au
Web Site: www.crtgroup.com.au
Sales Range: $50-74.9 Million
Emp.: 300
Logistics Services
S.I.C.: 4789
N.A.I.C.S.: 488999
Cameron Dunn *(CEO)*

QR Limited (1)
305 Edward St
GPO Box 1429
Brisbane, 4001, Australia
Tel.: (61) 131617
Web Site: www.queenslandrail.com.au
Rail Freight Transportation Services
S.I.C.: 4011
N.A.I.C.S.: 482111

AURO LABORATORIES LIMITED

314 TV Industrial Estate S K Ahire Marg
Worli, Mumbai, 400 030, India
Tel.: (91) 22 6663 5456
Fax: (91) 22 6663 5460
E-Mail: auro@aurolabs.com
Web Site: www.aurolabs.com
Year Founded: 1992
530233—(BOM)
Sales Range: $1-9.9 Million

Business Description:
Pharmaceutical Products Mfr
S.I.C.: 2834
N.A.I.C.S.: 325412
Personnel:
Sharart Deorah *(Chm & Mng Dir)*
Board of Directors:
Sharart Deorah
Siddhartha Deorah

AURO RESOURCES CORP.

20th Floor 250 Howe Street
Vancouver, BC, V6C 3R8, Canada
Tel.: (604) 893-8838
Fax: (604) 662-3904
E-Mail: info@auroresources.com
Web Site: www.auroresources.com
ARU—(TSXV)
Int. Income: $2,718
Assets: $3,594,900
Liabilities: $681,356
Net Worth: $2,913,544
Earnings: ($3,055,588)
Fiscal Year-end: 10/31/12

Business Description:
Mineral Exploration Services
S.I.C.: 1081
N.A.I.C.S.: 213114
Personnel:
Peter Frederick Tegart *(Pres & CEO)*
Cyrus H. Driver *(CFO)*
Board of Directors:
Cyrus H. Driver
Antony Harwood
Scott McLean
Peter Frederick Tegart

Transfer Agent:
Computershare Investor Services Inc
100 University Avenue 9th Floor North Tower
Toronto, ON, Canada

Subsidiary:

White Gold Corporation (1)
595 Howe St Suite 600
Vancouver, BC, V6C 2T5, Canada
Tel.: (604) 484-7118
E-Mail: info@whitegoldcorp.com
Web Site: www.whitegoldcorp.com
Gold Ore Mining Services
S.I.C.: 1041
N.A.I.C.S.: 212221
John Gomez *(Pres)*

AUROBINDO PHARMA LTD.

Plot 2 Maitri Vihar Ameerpet
Hyderabad, Andhra Pradesh, 500 038, India
Tel.: (91) 4066725000
Fax: (91) 4023741080
E-Mail: info@aurobindo.com
Web Site: www.aurobindo.com
Year Founded: 1986
524804—(BOM HYD NSE)
Rev.: $1,112,553,882
Assets: $1,349,311,536
Liabilities: $864,164,232
Net Worth: $485,147,304
Earnings: $54,481,644
Emp.: 8,800
Fiscal Year-end: 03/31/13

Business Description:
Generic Pharmaceuticals & Active Pharmaceutical Ingredient Mfr
S.I.C.: 2834
N.A.I.C.S.: 325412
Personnel:
K. Nityananda Reddy *(Vice Chm)*
N. Govindarajan *(Mng Dir)*
Sudhir B. Singhi *(CFO)*
A. Mohan Rami Reddy *(Compliance Officer, Sec & Assoc VP-Legal)*
Arvind Vasudeva *(CEO-Formulations)*
Board of Directors:
K. Raghunathan
N. Govindarajan
M. Sitarama Murthy
C. Channa Reddy
D. Rajagopala Reddy
K. Nityananda Reddy
M. Madan Mohan Reddy
P. Sarath Chandra Reddy
P. V. Ramaprasad Reddy
M. Sivakumaran

Transfer Agent:
Karvy Computershare Private Limited
Plot No 17-24 Vittal Rao Nagar Madhapur
Hyderabad, 500 081, India

Subsidiaries:

APL Chemi Natura Ltd. (1)
Plot No 2 Maitrivihar
Ameerpet, Hyderabad, 500 038, India
Tel.: (91) 40 5572 5000
Fax: (91) 40 2374 1080
E-Mail: cheminatura@aurobindo.com
Pharmaceutical Preparations
S.I.C.: 2834
N.A.I.C.S.: 325412

APL Research Centre Limited (1)
Plot No 2 Maitrivihar
Ameerpet, Hyderabad, 500038, India
Tel.: (91) 40 66725333
Fax: (91) 4023746833
E-Mail: info@aurobindo.com
Web Site: www.aurobindo.com
Pharmaceutical Products Mfr & Whslr
S.I.C.: 2834
N.A.I.C.S.: 325412

U.S. Subsidiaries:

Aurobindo Pharma USA Inc. (1)
2400 Rte 130 N
Dayton, NJ 08810
Tel.: (732) 839-9400
Fax: (732) 355-9940
E-Mail: swhite@aurobindousa.com
Web Site: www.aurobindo.com
Emp.: 200
Pharmaceutical Preparations
S.I.C.: 2834
N.A.I.C.S.: 325412

Aurolife Pharma LLC (1)
2400 Hwy 130 N
Dayton, NJ 08810
Tel.: (732) 839-9400
Fax: (732) 355-9449
Web Site: www.aurolifepharma.com
Pharmaceutical Products Mfr
S.I.C.: 2834
N.A.I.C.S.: 325412

U.S. Joint Venture:

Cephazone Pharma LLC (1)
250 E Bonita Ave
Pomona, CA 91767-1924
Tel.: (909) 392-8900
Fax: (909) 392-8945
Web Site: www.cephazone.com
Pharmaceutical Preparations
S.I.C.: 2834
N.A.I.C.S.: 325412
Gerald Macedo *(Owner)*

Non-U.S. Subsidiaries:

Agile Malta Holdings Limited (1)
Vault-14 Level 2 Valletta Waterfront
Floriana, FLN 1913, Malta
Tel.: (356) 99991441
Fax: (356) 2229 4118
Web Site: www.aurobindo.com
Emp.: 17
Pharmaceutical Products Mfr
S.I.C.: 2834
N.A.I.C.S.: 325412
Frederick Schembri *(Gen Mgr)*

Agile Pharma (Malta) Limited (1)
Vault-14 Level 2 Valletta Waterfront
Floriana, FLN 1913, Malta
Tel.: (356) 99991441
Pharmaceutical Products Mfr & Distr
S.I.C.: 2834
N.A.I.C.S.: 325412

All Pharma (Shanghai) Trading Company Limited (1)
Room 1401 No 319 Xianxia Road
Changning, Shanghai, 200051, China
Tel.: (86) 21 52080525
Fax: (86) 2152080381
E-Mail: ramesh@allpharma.com.cn
Web Site: www.aurobindo.com
Emp.: 10
Pharmaceutical Products Mfr & Whslr
S.I.C.: 2834
N.A.I.C.S.: 325412
Arvind Kumar Chandak *(Gen Mgr)*

APL Pharma Thai Ltd. (1)
438 Phattanakaran 30 Road
Sunluang, Bangkok, 10250, Thailand
Tel.: (66) 27195512
Fax: (66) 23197517
E-Mail: aplpama@hotmail.com
Web Site: www.aurobindo.com
Pharmaceutical Preparations
S.I.C.: 2834
N.A.I.C.S.: 325412

Aurobindo (Datong) Bio-Pharma Co. Ltd. (1)
Economic & Technology Development Zong
Datong, Shanxi, China
Tel.: (86) 3526108710
Fax: (86) 3526108188
E-Mail: gpprasad2k@yahoo.co.uk
Web Site: www.aurobindo.com
Pharmaceutical Preparations
S.I.C.: 2834
N.A.I.C.S.: 325412

Aurobindo Pharma Ltd.—(Continued)

Aurobindo (H.K.) Limited (1)
Warehouse-B Venton Mfg 1 Wo Hing Road
Wo Hop Shek Santsuen, Hong Kong, China (Hong Kong)
Tel.: (852) 23675053
Fax: (852) 27390373
E-Mail: aurohkl@biznetvigator.com
Pharmaceutical Preparations
S.I.C.: 2834
N.A.I.C.S.: 325412

Aurobindo Ilac Sanayi Ve Ticaret Ltd (1)
Egitim Mh Poyraz Sk Sadikoglu Plaza 5 No 27 Kadikoy
Istanbul, Turkey
Tel.: (90) 2163481076
Fax: (90) 216 348 1768
Pharmaceutical Products Mfr & Whslr
S.I.C.: 2834
N.A.I.C.S.: 325412

Aurobindo Pharma (Australia) Pty Limited (1)
Unit 3/277 - 283 Lane Cove Road
North Ryde, Sydney, NSW, 2113, Australia
Tel.: (61) 298056000
Fax: (61) 2 9887 1191
Emp.: 5
Pharmaceutical Products Mfr & Whslr
S.I.C.: 2834
N.A.I.C.S.: 325412
Avinash Ramcharan *(Gen Mgr)*

Aurobindo Pharma BV (1)
Molenvliet 103
Zwijndrecht, South Holland, 3335 LH, Netherlands
Tel.: (31) 786101836
Web Site: www.pharmacin.nl
Pharmaceutical Products Mfr & Whslr
S.I.C.: 2834
N.A.I.C.S.: 325412

Aurobindo Pharma France SARL (1)
22 - 26 rue des Gaudines
78100 Saint Germain-en-Laye, France
Tel.: (33) 609318105
Web Site: www.aurobindo.com
Pharmaceutical Products Mfr & Whslr
S.I.C.: 2834
N.A.I.C.S.: 325412
Florence Bruneval *(Gen Mgr)*

Aurobindo Pharma GmbH (1)
Carl von Linde Strasse 38
85716 Unterschleissheim, Germany
Tel.: (49) 175 438 0231
Fax: (49) 893 700 33822
E-Mail: info@aurobindo-pharma.com
Web Site: www.aurobindo-pharma.de
Emp.: 5
Pharmaceutical Products Mfr & Distr
S.I.C.: 2834
N.A.I.C.S.: 325412
Alexander Fiedel *(Gen Mgr)*

Aurobindo Pharma Industria Pharmaceutica Ltda (1)
VP-06E QD 09 Mod 12/15
Daia, Anapolis, Goias, 75132-135, Brazil
Tel.: (55) 62 4015 3420
Fax: (55) 6240153401
Web Site: www.aurobindo.ind.br
Emp.: 100
Pharmaceutical Products Mfr
S.I.C.: 2834
N.A.I.C.S.: 325412

Aurobindo Pharma (Italia) S.r.l (1)
Via Pergolesi 15
20124 Milan, Italy
Tel.: (39) 289289800
Pharmaceutical Products Mfr & Whslr
S.I.C.: 2834
N.A.I.C.S.: 325412

Aurobindo Pharma Japan K.K (1)
9th Fl Youth Bldg 1-3-8 Nihonbashibakuro-Cho
Chuo-Ku, Tokyo, 103-0002, Japan
Tel.: (81) 332492261
Fax: (81) 332490828
Web Site: www.aurobindo.com
Emp.: 4
Pharmaceutical Products Mfr
S.I.C.: 2834
N.A.I.C.S.: 325412
Novuo Taku *(Mgr)*

Aurobindo Pharma (Malta) Limited (1)
Vault-14 Level 2 Valletta Waterfront
Floriana, FRN 1913, Malta
Tel.: (356) 9999 1441
Fax: (356) 2229 4118
Web Site: www.aurobindo.com
Emp.: 20
Pharmaceutical Products Distr
S.I.C.: 5122
N.A.I.C.S.: 424210
Frederick Schembri *(Gen Mgr)*

Aurobindo Pharma (Portugal) Unipessoal LDA (1)
Av do Forte n 3 Parque Suecia Ed IV 2 ste 4
2794-038 Carnaxide, Portugal
Tel.: (351) 214185104
Fax: (351) 214187398
E-Mail: marialuisa-sousa@Aurobindo.com
Emp.: 9
Pharmaceutical Products Mfr & Distr
S.I.C.: 2834
N.A.I.C.S.: 325412
Pedero Marlene *(Gen Mgr)*

Aurobindo Pharma Productos Farmaceuticos Ltda (1)
Vp-06E Qd 09 Mod 12/15
Daia, Anapolis, Golas, 75132-135, Brazil
Tel.: (55) 62 40153400
Fax: (55) 62 40153401
E-Mail: abfarmo@abfarmo.ind.br
Web Site: www.aurobindo.ind.br
Pharmaceutical Products Mfr & Whslr
S.I.C.: 2834
N.A.I.C.S.: 325412

Aurobindo Pharma (Pty) Limited (1)
53 Philip Engelbrecht Avenue Woodhill Office Park Buiding No 1
Meyersdal, 1448 Johannesburg, South Africa
Tel.: (27) 118679100
Fax: (27) 11 867 9111
Pharmaceutical Products Mfr
S.I.C.: 2834
N.A.I.C.S.: 325412
Veekesh Galal *(Gen Mgr)*

Aurobindo Pharma Romania SRL (1)
Paneologu Street No 24 2nd Floor Room No E02
3rd District, Bucharest, Romania
Tel.: (40) 213118815
Fax: (40) 213118816
Pharmaceutical Products Mfr & Whslr
S.I.C.: 2834
N.A.I.C.S.: 325412
Daniela Iaru *(Mgr-Corp Sec)*

Aurobindo Switzerland AG (1)
Alpenstrasse 15
6304 Zug, Switzerland
Tel.: (41) 41 726 82 06
Fax: (41) 41 041 726 8250
Pharmaceutical Products Mfr & Distr
S.I.C.: 2834
N.A.I.C.S.: 325412
Beat Werder *(Gen Mgr)*

Aurobindo Tongling (Datong) Pharmaceutical Co. Ltd. (1)
Economic & Technology Development Zone
Datong, Shanxi, China
Tel.: (86) 3526108710
Fax: (86) 3526108188
E-Mail:
Web Site: www.aurobindo.com
Pharmaceutical Preparations
S.I.C.: 2834
N.A.I.C.S.: 325412

Auropharma Inc. (1)
1170 Sheppard Avenue Unit 16
Toronto, ON, M3K 2A3, Canada
Tel.: (416) 633-2666
Web Site: www.aurobindo.com
Pharmaceutical Products Distr
S.I.C.: 5122
N.A.I.C.S.: 424210

Helix Healthcare B.V. (1)
Meespierson Interturst
PO Box 990
1000 AZ Amsterdam, Netherlands
Tel.: (31) 205214704
Fax: (31) 205214825
Web Site: www.aurobindo.com
Pharmaceutical Preparations
S.I.C.: 2834
N.A.I.C.S.: 325412

Milpharm Limited (1)
Ares Block Odyssey Business Park
South Ruislip, London, Middlesex, HA4 6QD, United Kingdom
Tel.: (44) 2088458811
Fax: (44) 2088458795
Web Site: www.aurobindo.com
Emp.: 30
Pharmaceutical Products Mfr & Whslr
S.I.C.: 2834
N.A.I.C.S.: 325412
V. Muralidharan *(VP)*

Pharmacin B.V (1)
Molenvliet 103
3335 LH Zwijndrecht, Netherlands
Tel.: (31) 786101836
Fax: (31) 786102882
E-Mail: info@pharmacin.nl
Web Site: www.pharmacin.nl
Emp.: 20
Pharmaceutical Products Mfr & Whslr
S.I.C.: 2834
N.A.I.C.S.: 325412
R. Steenccjes *(Mng Dir)*

AUROMA COKE LIMITED

Suit No 706 Shantiniketan 8 Camac Street
Kolkata, West Bengal, 700 017, India
Tel.: (91) 3322822310
Fax: (91) 3322825759
E-Mail: info@auroma.in
Web Site: www.auroma.in
Year Founded: 1977
531336—(BOM)
Rev.: $5,271,627
Assets: $10,931,295
Liabilities: $4,186,721
Net Worth: $6,744,574
Earnings: $3,597
Fiscal Year-end: 03/31/13

Business Description:
Coal Product Mfr & Whslr
S.I.C.: 2999
N.A.I.C.S.: 324199

Personnel:
Vimal Kumar Tulsyan *(Chm)*
Rajiv Tulsyan *(Mng Dir)*
Subhash Srivastava *(Compliance Officer)*

Board of Directors:
Vimal Kumar Tulsyan
Swapan De Choudhary
Alok Sawa
Binod Kumar Singh
Nawal Kishore Singh
Prashant Tulsyan
Rajiv Tulsyan
Sanjeev Tulsyan

Transfer Agent:
Niche Technologies Pvt. Ltd
D 511 Bagree Market 71 B R B Basu Road
700001 Kolkata, India

AURORA CONTROL TECHNOLOGIES INC.

980 West 1st Street - Suite 210
North Vancouver, BC, V7P 3N4, Canada
Tel.: (778) 241-5000
E-Mail: info@auroracontrol.com
Web Site: www.auroracontrol.com
Year Founded: 2006
ACU—(TSXV)
Rev.: $129,454
Assets: $1,056,874
Liabilities: $111,692
Net Worth: $945,182
Earnings: ($1,204,230)
Fiscal Year-end: 03/31/13

Business Description:
Electronic Component Mfr
S.I.C.: 3679
N.A.I.C.S.: 334419

Personnel:
Michael Heaven *(Co-Founder & Chm)*
Gordon Deans *(Co-Founder, Pres & CEO)*
Grant Macdonald *(CFO)*

Board of Directors:
Michael Heaven
Gordon Deans
Grant Macdonald
Thomas Schmidt
David Toyoda

Transfer Agent:
Computershare Trust Company of Canada
9th Floor 100 University Avenue
Toronto, ON, Canada

AURORA CORPORATION

15th Fl 2 Sec 5 Shinyi Rd
Taipei, Taiwan
Tel.: (886) 2 2345 8088
Fax: (886) 2 2345 8061
E-Mail: gracep@aurora.com.tw
Web Site: www.aurora.com.tw
Year Founded: 1965
2373—(TAI)
Sales Range: $75-99.9 Million
Emp.: 2,003

Business Description:
Office Machinery & Furniture Mfr & Distr
S.I.C.: 3589
N.A.I.C.S.: 333318

Personnel:
Yung Tai Chen *(Chm & Pres)*

Subsidiaries:

Aurora Development Corporation (1)
3rd Fl No 156 Jiankang Rd
Songshan Dist, 105 Taipei, Taiwan
Tel.: (886) 266002168
Fax: (886) 266006262
Web Site: www.adc.aurora.com.tw
Emp.: 10
Waste Management Services
S.I.C.: 4959
N.A.I.C.S.: 562998

Aurora Office Automation Corporation (1)
10th Floor No 2 Sec 5
Shinyi Rd, 110 Taipei, Taiwan
Tel.: (886) 223458018
Fax: (886) 223458075
Web Site: www.oa-world.com.tw
Emp.: 20
Equipment Whslr
S.I.C.: 5044
N.A.I.C.S.: 423420

Aurora Systems Corporation (1)
3rd Floor No 156 Jiankang Road
Songshan District, 105 Taipei, Taiwan
Tel.: (886) 227476789
Fax: (886) 227471999
E-Mail: admin@eosasc.com.tw
Web Site: www.eosasc.com.tw
Emp.: 534
Computer Programming Services
S.I.C.: 7371
N.A.I.C.S.: 541511
Rongxing Lin *(Chm)*

Aurora Telecom Corporation (1)
3rd Floor No 423 Rueiguang Rd
Neihu Dist, 114 Taipei, Taiwan (60%)
Tel.: (886) 226560668
Fax: (886) 226560658
Web Site: www.auroracomm.com.tw
Cellular Telecommunication Retail Stores
S.I.C.: 4812
N.A.I.C.S.: 517210
Donal Hanrahan *(Gen Mgr)*

U.S. Subsidiary:

Aurora Corp. of America (1)
3500 Challenger St
Torrance, CA 90503-1640
Tel.: (310) 793-5650
Fax: (310) 793-5658
Toll Free: (800) 327-8508

E-Mail: info@auroracorp.com
Web Site: www.auroracorp.com
Emp.: 35
Consumer Electronics Mfr
S.I.C.: 5044
N.A.I.C.S.: 423420

Non-U.S. Subsidiaries:

Aurora Japan Corp. **(1)**
Sun Palace Building 2nd Floor
Shinjuku-Ku, Tokyo, Japan
Tel.: (81) 333696171
Fax: (81) 333699057
Web Site: www.aurora-japan.co.jp
Emp.: 9
Electrical Apparatus & Equipment Wiring Supplies & Construction Material Whslr
S.I.C.: 5063
N.A.I.C.S.: 423610
Kent Chan *(Mng Dir)*

Aurora Office Automation Sales Co., Ltd. **(1)**
11th Floor No 99 Fucheng Rd
Pudong New Area, Shanghai, China
Tel.: (86) 2158828999
Fax: (86) 60216859588
E-Mail: marketing@aurora.com.cn
Web Site: www.aurora.com.cn
Emp.: 3,500
Equipment Whslr
S.I.C.: 5044
N.A.I.C.S.: 423420
Yuntai Chen *(Pres & Gen Mgr)*

Aurora Office Furniture Co., Ltd. **(1)**
10th Floor Aurora Plaza No 99
Fucheng Rd Pudong Dist, Shanghai, China
Tel.: (86) 2159161010
Fax: (86) 2159167495
Web Site: www.aurora.com.tw
Emp.: 1,000
Office Furniture Mfr
S.I.C.: 2522
N.A.I.C.S.: 337214
Shuyan Zhao *(Gen Mgr)*

Aurora Singapore Corp. **(1)**
50 Genting Ln UNit 08-01 Cie Eco Industry Complex
349558 Singapore, Singapore
Tel.: (65) 68416641
Fax: (65) 68416640
Web Site: www.aurora.com.sg
Emp.: 7
Machinery Mfr
S.I.C.: 3589
N.A.I.C.S.: 333318

AURORA FUNDS LIMITED

Level 4 1 Alfred Street
Sydney, NSW, 2000, Australia
Tel.: (61) 2 9080 2377
Fax: (61) 2 9080 2378
E-Mail: enquiries@aurorafunds.com.au
Web Site: www.aurorafunds.com.au
AFV—(ASX)
Rev.: $3,551,400
Assets: $8,570,270
Liabilities: $2,709,251
Net Worth: $5,861,019
Earnings: ($529,807)
Fiscal Year-end: 06/30/13
Business Description:
Investment Fund Services
S.I.C.: 6211
N.A.I.C.S.: 523999
Personnel:
Steuart Roe *(Chm & Mng Dir)*
John Corr *(Chief Investment Officer)*
Betty Poon *(Sec)*
Board of Directors:
Steuart Roe
John Corr
Alastair Davidson
Simon Lindsay
Legal Counsel:
Baker & McKenzie
Level 27 AMP Centre 50 Bridge Street
Sydney, Australia

AURORA GOLD CORPORATION

Coresco AG Level 3 Gotthardstrasse 20
6304 Zug, Switzerland
Tel.: (41) 417110281
Fax: (41) 442742828
E-Mail: lars.pearl@aurora-gold.com
Web Site: www.aurora-gold.com
Year Founded: 1995
ARXGD—(OTC)
Int. Income: $133
Assets: $4,129,662
Liabilities: $277,343
Net Worth: $3,852,319
Earnings: $1,200,374
Fiscal Year-end: 12/31/12
Business Description:
Gold Mining Services
S.I.C.: 1041
N.A.I.C.S.: 212221
Personnel:
Agustin Gomez de Segura *(Chm)*
Lars Michael Pearl *(Pres & CEO)*
Ross Michael Doyle *(CFO)*
Board of Directors:
Agustin Gomez de Segura
Vladimir Bernshtein
Gorden Glenn
Lars Michael Pearl
Andrey Ratsko
Legal Counsel:
Sierchio & Company LLP
430 Park Ave 7th Fl
New York, NY 10022
Transfer Agent:
Worldwide Stock Transfer, LLC
433 Hackensack Ave Level L
Hackensack, NJ 07601

AURORA MINERALS LIMITED

271 Great Eastern Highway
Belmont, WA, 6104, Australia
Mailing Address:
PO Box 707
Belmont, WA, 6984, Australia
Tel.: (61) 8 61431840
Fax: (61) 8 61629079
E-Mail: contact@auroraminerals.com
Web Site: www.auroraminerals.com
ARM—(ASX)
Rev.: $618,013
Assets: $12,646,772
Liabilities: $275,782
Net Worth: $12,370,990
Earnings: ($3,859,413)
Emp.: 7
Fiscal Year-end: 06/30/13
Business Description:
Mineral Exploration Services
S.I.C.: 1099
N.A.I.C.S.: 212299
Personnel:
Phillip Sidney Redmond Jackson *(Chm)*
Martin Pyle *(Mng Dir)*
Eric Gordon Moore *(Sec)*
Board of Directors:
Phillip Sidney Redmond Jackson
Peter Cordin
Martin Pyle

AURORA NETWORKS, INC.

(Acquired by Pace plc)

AURORA OIL & GAS LIMITED

Level 1 338 Barker Road
Subiaco, WA, 6008, Australia
Tel.: (61) 8 9380 2700
Fax: (61) 8 9380 2799
E-Mail: info@auroraoag.com.au
Web Site: www.auroraoag.com.au
AUT—(ASX OTC TSX)
Sales Range: Less than $1 Million
Emp.: 15
Business Description:
Oil & Gas Exploration & Production
S.I.C.: 1311
N.A.I.C.S.: 211111
Personnel:
Jonathan Stewart *(Chm)*
Douglas E. Brooks *(CEO)*
J. David Lucke *(CFO)*
Julie Foster *(Sec)*
Darren Wasylucha *(Exec VP-Corp Affairs-Toronto)*
Board of Directors:
Jonathan Stewart
John Atkins
Douglas E. Brooks
Graham Dowland
Fiona Harris
Frederick William Molson
Alan Watson
Transfer Agent:
Computershare Investor Services Inc
100 University Avenue 8th Fl North Tower
Toronto, ON, Canada

Subsidiary:

Eureka Energy Limited **(1)**
Levl 1 16 Ord Street
West Perth, WA, 6005, Australia AU
Tel.: (61) 893219337 (100%)
Fax: (61) 8 93229548
E-Mail: info@eurekaenergy.com.au
Web Site: www.eurekaenergy.com.au
Sales Range: $1-9.9 Million
Resource Exploration & Development Services
S.I.C.: 1389
N.A.I.C.S.: 213112

AURORA RUSSIA LTD

Dorey Court Admiral Park
Saint Peter Port, Guernsey GY1 2HT
Tel.: (44) 2079753138
Web Site: www.aurorarussia.com
AURR—(LSE)
Int. Income: $9,476
Assets: $98,899,878
Liabilities: $2,259,964
Net Worth: $96,639,914
Earnings: ($22,015,303)
Fiscal Year-end: 03/31/13
Business Description:
Securities
S.I.C.: 6282
N.A.I.C.S.: 523920
Personnel:
John McRoberts *(Founder)*
Board of Directors:
Gilbert Chalk
Jonathan Bridel
Peregrine Moncreiffe
Timothy Slesinger
Lyndon Trott
Legal Counsel:
White & Case LLC
4 Romanov Pereulok
125009 Moscow, Russia
SNR Denton UK LLP
One Fleet Place
London, United Kingdom
Carey Olsen
7 New Street
Saint Peter Port, Guernsey Channel Islands
Capita IRG (CI) Limited
2nd Floor No 1 Le Truchot
Saint Peter Port, Guernsey

AUROTEK CORPORATION

1Fl No 60 Jhouzih St Neihu District
114 Taipei, Taiwan
Tel.: (886) 287523311
Fax: (886) 287523347
E-Mail: info@robot.com.tw
Web Site: www.robot.com.tw
6215—(TAI)
Sales Range: $25-49.9 Million
Business Description:
Automation & Safety Systems Mfr & Distr
S.I.C.: 7373
N.A.I.C.S.: 541512
Personnel:
Yung-Chung Chang *(Chm)*

Plant:

Aurotek Corporation - Taoyuan Factory **(1)**
1st Floor No 61 Lioufu Road
Lujhu Township, Taoyuan, 338, Taiwan
Tel.: (886) 33223788
Fax: (886) 33220866
E-Mail: silvie_chen@robot.com.tw
Circuit Board Cutting Machinery Mfr & Distr
S.I.C.: 3542
N.A.I.C.S.: 333517

Non-U.S. Subsidiaries:

Aurotek (Japan) Inc. **(1)**
2nd Floor Akihabara Seishin Building 1-7-8 Kandasuda-cyo
Chiyoda-ku, Tokyo, 101-0041, Japan
Tel.: (81) 352977028
Fax: (81) 352977029
E-Mail: info@aurotek.co.jp
Web Site: www.aurotek.co.jp
Office Equipments Mfr
S.I.C.: 3425
N.A.I.C.S.: 332216
Kishiro Ryoichi *(Pres)*

Plenty Island (Thai) Co., Ltd. **(1)**
3 Soi Charoenrat 10 Charoenrat Road
Bangkhlo Bangkhorlaem, Bangkok, 10120, Thailand
Tel.: (66) 22919933
Fax: (66) 22912065
E-Mail: sales@plenty.co.th
Web Site: www.plenty.co.th
Emp.: 28
Industrial Machinery Whslr
S.I.C.: 5084
N.A.I.C.S.: 423830

AURUBIS AG

Hovestrasse 50
20539 Hamburg, Germany
Tel.: (49) 4078830
Fax: (49) 4078832255
E-Mail: info@aurubis.com
Web Site: www.aurubis.com
NDA—(DEU OTC)
Rev.: $16,957,231,753
Assets: $5,573,859,774
Liabilities: $2,827,197,381
Net Worth: $2,746,662,393
Earnings: ($209,934,579)
Emp.: 6,563
Fiscal Year-end: 09/30/13
Business Description:
Holding Company; Copper Processing & Product Mfr
S.I.C.: 6719
N.A.I.C.S.: 551112
Personnel:
Heinz Jorg Fuhrmann *(Chm-Supervisory Bd)*
Peter Willbrandt *(Chm-Exec Bd & CEO)*
Hans-Jurgen Grundmann *(Deputy Chm-Supervisory Bd)*
Erwin Faust *(CFO & Member-Exec Bd)*
Henning Michaelsen *(Chief Compliance Officer)*
Benjamin Laatzen *(Personnel Officer)*
Petra Ludeke *(Personnel Officer)*
Andre Scharnberg *(Personnel Officer)*
Frank Schneider *(Member-Exec Bd-Recycling & Precious Metals & Dir-Indus Rels)*
Stefan Boel *(Member-Exec Bd-Copper Products Bus Unit)*
Supervisory Board of Directors:
Heinz Jorg Fuhrmann
Burkhard Becker

Aurubis AG—(Continued)

Bernd Drouven
Jan Eulen
Joachim Faubel
Hans-Jurgen Grundmann
Renate Hold
Sandra Reich
Thomas Schultek
Rolf Schwertz
Fritz Vahrenholt
Ernst J. Wortberg

Subsidiaries:

Aurubis Stolberg GmbH & Co. KG (1)
Zweifaller Strasse 150
D 52224 Stolberg, Germany De
Tel.: (49) 240212410
Fax: (49) 240212412926
E-Mail: info-stolberg@aurubis.com
Web Site: www.aurubis-stolberg.com
Emp.: 400
Producer of Semi-Finished Products of Copper & Copper Alloys
S.I.C.: 3369
N.A.I.C.S.: 331529
Artelt Holger *(Mng Dir)*

Aurubis Stolberg Verwaltungs GmbH (1)
Zweifaller Str 150
Stolberg, 52224, Germany
Tel.: (49) 240212410
Fax: (49) 240284750
E-Mail: info-stolberg@aurubis.com
Web Site: www.aurubis.com
Emp.: 40
Copper Products Mfr
S.I.C.: 3339
N.A.I.C.S.: 331410
Christine Larry *(Gen Mgr)*

CABLO Metall-Recycling und Handel GmbH (1)
Flugplatzstrasse 1-2
Fehrbellin, Oranienburg, 16833, Germany (100%)
Tel.: (49) 339326190
Fax: (49) 3393261910
E-Mail: info@cablo.de
Web Site: www.cablo.de
Emp.: 50
Cable Metal Recycling Services
S.I.C.: 5093
N.A.I.C.S.: 423930
Michael Liesegang *(Mng Dir)*
Holger Hubert *(Deputy Mng Dir)*
Thomas Klein *(Deputy Mng Dir)*
Holger Kuhne *(Deputy Mng Dir)*

Deutsche Giessdraht GmbH (1)
Kupferstr 5
46446 Emmerich am Rhein, Germany (60%)
Tel.: (49) 28227800
Fax: (49) 28223166
E-Mail: info@deutsche-giessdraht.de
Web Site: www.deutsche-giessdraht.de
Emp.: 11
Copper Processing & Mfg
S.I.C.: 3351
N.A.I.C.S.: 331420
Stefan Schneider *(Mng Dir)*
Dagmar Mebus *(Sec)*

E.R.N. Elektro-Recycling NORD GmbH (1)
Peutestrasse 21-23
20539 Hamburg, Germany
Tel.: (49) 40 78 04 78 0
Fax: (49) 40 78 04 78 78
E-Mail: info@ern-gmbh.de
Web Site: www.ern-gmbh.de
Emp.: 15
Electronic Equipment Recycling Services
S.I.C.: 4959
N.A.I.C.S.: 562998
Oliver Carstens *(Mng Dir)*

Huttenbau Gesellschaft Peute mbH (1)
Hovestr 50
Hamburg, 20539, Germany
Tel.: (49) 4078830
Fax: (49) 4078832255
Copper Mining Services
S.I.C.: 1021
N.A.I.C.S.: 212234

Peute Baustoff GmbH (1)
Peutestrasse 79
20539 Hamburg, Germany (52%)
Tel.: (49) 407891600
Fax: (49) 4078916019
E-Mail: info@peute-baustoff.de
Web Site: www.peute-baustoff.de
Emp.: 50
Stone Construction Products Mfr & Distr
S.I.C.: 3281
N.A.I.C.S.: 327991
Manfred Hamann *(Mng Dir)*

PHG Peute Hafen- und Industriebetriebsgesellschaft mbH (1)
Harburger Rathausstrasse 40
21073 Hamburg, Germany
Tel.: (49) 40 771261
Industrial Painting & Decorating Services
S.I.C.: 1721
N.A.I.C.S.: 238320

RETORTE GmbH (1)
Sulzbacher Strasse 45
90552 Rothenbach, An der Pegnitz, Germany (100%)
Tel.: (49) 9119533740
Fax: (49) 911576659
E-Mail: selen@retorte.de
Web Site: www.retorte.de
Emp.: 35
Chemical & Metal Products Mfr
S.I.C.: 2819
N.A.I.C.S.: 325180
Bernd Treiber *(Gen Mgr)*

Schwermetall Halbzeugwerk GmbH & Co. KG (1)
Breiniger Berg 165
D 52223 Stolberg, Germany
Tel.: (49) 24027610
Telex: 832 489
Fax: (49) 2402761210
E-Mail: info@schwermetall.de
Web Site: www.schwermetall.de
Emp.: 260
Metal Pre-Rolled Strips Mfr
S.I.C.: 3351
N.A.I.C.S.: 331420
Dirk Harten *(Mng Dir)*

Non-U.S. Subsidiaries:

Aurubis Finland Oy (1)
Kuparitie
PO Box 60
28101 Pori, Finland
Tel.: (358) 2 626 6111
Fax: (358) 2 626 5300
E-Mail: info-pori@aurubis.com
Web Site: www.aurubis.com
Emp.: 50
Steel Copper Mfr
S.I.C.: 3369
N.A.I.C.S.: 331529
Hannu Heiskanen *(Gen Mgr)*

Aurubis Netherlands B.V. (1)
Oostzeestraat 1
7202 CM Zutphen, Netherlands
Tel.: (31) 575 594 531
Fax: (31) 575 594 646
Web Site: www.aurubis.com
Emp.: 130
Casting & Rolling Metal Mfr
S.I.C.: 3369
N.A.I.C.S.: 331529
Theo Mimpen *(Gen Mgr)*

Aurubis nv/sa (1)
Broekstraat 31 Rue du Marais
1000 Brussels, Belgium BE
Tel.: (32) 22271222
Fax: (32) 22271254
E-Mail: info@aurubis.com
Web Site: www.aurubis.com
Sales Range: $1-4.9 Billion
Emp.: 1,443
Holding Company; Copper Smelting, Refining & Recycling
S.I.C.: 6719
N.A.I.C.S.: 551112
Philippe Gothier *(CEO)*

Plant:

Aurubis nv/sa - Olen (2)
Watertorenstraat 35
2250 Olen, Belgium
Tel.: (32) 14243111
Fax: (32) 14243752
E-Mail:
Web Site: www.aurubis.com
Emp.: 530
Copper Processing
S.I.C.: 3339
N.A.I.C.S.: 331410
Jo Rogiers *(Mng Dir)*

Non-U.S. Subsidiaries:

Aurubis Bulgaria AD (2)
Industrial Zone
Pirdop, 2070 Sofia, Bulgaria BG
Tel.: (359) 72862216
Fax: (359) 72862646
E-Mail: info.pirdop@aurubis.com
Web Site: www.aurubis.com
Sales Range: $1-4.9 Billion
Emp.: 800
Copper Smelting & Refining
S.I.C.: 3339
N.A.I.C.S.: 331410
Nicholas Treand *(Mng Dir)*

Aurubis Italia Srl (2)
Pianodardine
83100 Avellino, Italy IT
Tel.: (39) 0825625507
Fax: (39) 0825619121
E-Mail: info-avellino@aurubis.com
Web Site: www.aurubis.com
Emp.: 100
Copper Smelting & Refining
S.I.C.: 3339
N.A.I.C.S.: 331410
Antonio de Blasio *(Mng Dir)*

Aurubis Switzerland S.A. (2)
Rue Galilee 15
1400 Yverdon-les-Bains, Switzerland CH
Tel.: (41) 244239311
Fax: (41) 245241119
E-Mail: thiele@aurubis.com
Web Site: www.sam.cumerio.com
Emp.: 42
Copper Smelting & Refining of
S.I.C.: 3339
N.A.I.C.S.: 331410

Aurubis Slovakia s.r.o. (1)
Mokrad Ska 2931
Dolny Kubin, Zilina, 026 01, Slovakia Sk
Tel.: (421) 435832111
Fax: (421) 435832113
E-Mail: info@aurubis.com
Web Site: www.aurubis.sk
Emp.: 8
Rolled Non-Ferrous Alloy Mfr
S.I.C.: 3351
N.A.I.C.S.: 331420
Tadeusz Kipiel *(Mng Dir & Gen Mgr-Europe)*

Aurubis Sweden AB (1)
Slottsvagen 1-3
61241 Finspang, Sweden
Tel.: (46) 790 80 90 33
Metal Products Mfr
S.I.C.: 3499
N.A.I.C.S.: 332999

Aurubis UK Limited (1)
Rabone Lane
Smethwick, B66 2NN, United Kingdom UK (100%)
Tel.: (44) 1215551199
Fax: (44) 1215551188
E-Mail: info-uk@aurubis.com
Web Site: www.aurubis.co.uk
Emp.: 25
Rolled Copper & Brass Products Mfr
S.I.C.: 3351
N.A.I.C.S.: 331420
Holger Artelt *(Mng Dir)*
Brian Middleton *(Mng Dir)*
Philip Tromans *(Sec & Dir-Fin)*

AURUM, INC.

Level 8 580 St Kilda Road
Melbourne, VIC, 3004, Australia
Tel.: (61) 3 8532 2800
Web Site: www.auruminc.net
Year Founded: 2008
AURM—(OTCB)
Assets: $41,660
Liabilities: $7,961,058
Net Worth: ($7,919,398)
Earnings: ($1,289,689)
Fiscal Year-end: 10/31/13

Business Description:
Mineral Exploration & Development Services
S.I.C.: 1041
N.A.I.C.S.: 212221

Personnel:
Joseph Isaac Gutnick *(Chm, Pres & CEO)*
Simon Lee *(CFO)*
Peter James Lee *(Sec)*

Board of Directors:
Joseph Isaac Gutnick

AURUM MINING PLC

4th Floor 3 Shepherd Street
London, W1J 7HL, United Kingdom
Tel.: (44) 2074994000
Fax: (44) 2074994050
Web Site: www.aurummining.net
AUR—(LSE)
Rev.: $14,214
Assets: $2,771,654
Liabilities: $156,350
Net Worth: $2,615,304
Earnings: ($1,089,710)
Emp.: 4
Fiscal Year-end: 03/31/13

Business Description:
Mining Industry
S.I.C.: 1044
N.A.I.C.S.: 212222

Personnel:
Christopher Eadie *(CEO)*
Haresh Kanabar *(Sec)*

Board of Directors:
Sean Finlay
Christopher Eadie
Mark Jones
Haresh Kanabar

Legal Counsel:
Lawrence Graham LLP
4 More London Riverside
London, England, SE1 2AU, United Kingdom

AURUM SOFT SYSTEMS LIMITED

15 Besant Avenue
Adyar, Chennai, 600020, India
Tel.: (91) 44 4218 7785
Fax: (91) 44 4218 7803
E-Mail: info@aurumsoftsystems.com
Web Site: www.aurumsoftsystems.com
530885—(BOM MDS)
Rev.: $20,666,385
Assets: $9,987,153
Liabilities: $2,984,414
Net Worth: $7,002,739
Earnings: $286,407
Emp.: 1,542
Fiscal Year-end: 03/31/13

Business Description:
Holding Company; Information Technology Products & Services
S.I.C.: 6719
N.A.I.C.S.: 551112

Personnel:
Srikanth Ramanathan *(CEO & Mng Dir)*
S. Arun Kumar *(CFO, Compliance Officer & Sec)*

Board of Directors:
S. Ramakrishnan
K. Balaji
Srikanth Ramanathan
V. Ganapathi Subramanian
K. S. Vaidyanathan

Transfer Agent:
Cameo Corporate Services Limited
Subramanian Bldg No 1 Club House Road
Chennai, 600 002, India
Tel.: (91) 44 2846 0390
Fax: (91) 44 2846 0129

AURVISTA GOLD CORPORATION
250 Place d Youville 2e etage
Montreal, QC, H2Y 2B6, Canada
Tel.: (416) 682-2674
Fax: (514) 439-5716
E-Mail: info@aurvistagold.com
Web Site: www.aurvistagold.com
Year Founded: 2010
AVA—(TSXV)
Rev.: $7,678
Assets: $30,941,611
Liabilities: $3,051,408
Net Worth: $27,890,203
Earnings: ($437,450)
Fiscal Year-end: 12/31/12
Business Description:
Gold Mining Services
S.I.C.: 1041
N.A.I.C.S.: 212221
Personnel:
Richard Adams *(Pres & CEO)*
Bryan Keeler *(CFO)*
David Johnston *(Sec)*
Board of Directors:
Richard Adams
Bryan Keeler
G. Edmund King
Marc L'Heureux
Gerald McCarvill
Robert A. Mitchell
Claude St-Jacques
Transfer Agent:
Olympia Transfer Services Inc.
Suite 920 120 Adelaide Street West
Toronto, ON, Canada

AURYN RESOURCES LTD.
(Formerly Georgetown Capital Corp.)
Suite 600 1199 West Hastings Street
Vancouver, BC, V6E 3T5, Canada
Tel.: (778) 729-0600
Fax: (778) 729-0650
Web Site: www.aurynresources.com
Year Founded: 2008
AUG—(TSXV)
Assets: $1,294,949
Liabilities: $138,828
Net Worth: $1,156,121
Earnings: ($417,228)
Fiscal Year-end: 06/30/13
Business Description:
Mineral Exploration Services
S.I.C.: 1099
N.A.I.C.S.: 212299
Personnel:
Shawn Wallace *(Pres & CEO)*
Peter Rees *(CFO & Sec)*
Board of Directors:
Steve Cook
Gordon J. Fretwell
Keith Minty
Shawn Wallace
Transfer Agent:
Olympia Trust Company
Suite 1003 750 West Pender Street
Vancouver, BC, V6C 2T8, Canada

AUSDRILL LIMITED
6-12 Uppsala Place
Canning Vale, WA, 6155, Australia
Mailing Address:
PO Box 1540
Canning Vale, WA, 6970, Australia
Tel.: (61) 893115666
Fax: (61) 893115667
E-Mail: info@ausdrill.com.au
Web Site: www.ausdrill.com.au
Year Founded: 1987
ASL—(ASX)
Rev.: $1,178,910,014
Assets: $1,604,204,572
Liabilities: $752,406,621
Net Worth: $851,797,951
Earnings: $94,204,798
Emp.: 5,703
Fiscal Year-end: 06/30/13
Business Description:
Mining Industry Supply Services
S.I.C.: 3532
N.A.I.C.S.: 333131
Personnel:
Ronald George Sayers *(Mng Dir)*
Jose Martins *(CFO)*
Gavin Bell *(CIO)*
Strati Gregoriadis *(Gen Counsel & Co-Sec)*
Paul Chase *(Treas & Gen Mgr-Fin)*
Domenic Mark Santini *(Co-Sec & Controller-Fin)*
Board of Directors:
Terence Edward O'Connor
Donald James Argent
Mark Anthony Connelly
Wallace Macarthur King
Ronald George Sayers
Terrence John Strapp
Legal Counsel:
King Wood Mallesons
Level 10 152 St George's Terrace
Perth, Australia

Clifford Chance
Level 7 190 St George's Terrace
Perth, Australia

Subsidiaries:

Ausdrill (Ghana) Pty. Ltd. (1)
6-12 Uppsala Place
Canning Vale, WA, 6155, Australia
Tel.: (61) 893533055
Fax: (61) 893115667
Mining Support Services
S.I.C.: 8711
N.A.I.C.S.: 541330

Ausdrill Mining Services Pty. Ltd. (1)
6-12 Uppsala Place
PO Box 1540
Canning Vale, WA, 6155, Australia
Tel.: (61) 893115666
Fax: (61) 893115856
E-Mail: enquiries@amsaus.com.au
Web Site: www.amsaus.com.au
Emp.: 70
Mining Support Services
S.I.C.: 1081
N.A.I.C.S.: 213114
Peter Lock *(Gen Mgr)*

Ausdrill Northwest Pty. Ltd. (1)
170 Kewdale Road
Kewdale, WA, 6105, Australia
Tel.: (61) 893115600
Fax: (61) 893115603
E-Mail: enquiries@ausdrillnw.com.au
Web Site: www.ausdrillnw.com.au
Emp.: 150
Exploration Drilling Services
S.I.C.: 1381
N.A.I.C.S.: 213111
Wayne Bucknall *(Gen Mgr)*

Brandrill Limited (1)
27 Quill Way
Henderson, WA, 6166, Australia
Tel.: (61) 894946500
Fax: (61) 894946501
E-Mail: corpinfo@brandrill.com
Web Site: www.brandrill.com
Sales Range: $100-124.9 Million
Emp.: 516
Drilling & Blasting Services
S.I.C.: 1381
N.A.I.C.S.: 213111
Philip Werrett *(CFO)*

Subsidiaries:

DT Hi Load Australia Pty. Ltd. (2)
435c Dundas Road
Forrestfield, Perth, WA, 6058, Australia
Tel.: (61) 893656888
Fax: (61) 893656800
E-Mail: info@dthiload.com
Web Site: www.dthiload.com
Emp.: 64
Light Weight Heavy Duty Trays Mfr
S.I.C.: 3711
N.A.I.C.S.: 336211
Steve Turner *(Mgr-Sls)*

RockTek Limited (2)
27 Quill Way
Henderson, WA, 6166, Australia AU
Tel.: (61) 894946570
Fax: (61) 894946501
E-Mail: info@brandrill.com
Web Site: www.rocktek.com
Drilling Equipment Mfr
S.I.C.: 1629
N.A.I.C.S.: 237990
Ken Perry *(Mng Dir)*

Diamond Communications Pty. Ltd. (1)
24 Adams Dr
Welshpool, WA, 6106, Australia
Tel.: (61) 893115888
Fax: (61) 893115889
E-Mail: enquiries@diacom.com.au
Web Site: www.diacom.com.au
Emp.: 120
Power & Telecommunications Cable Installation Services
S.I.C.: 1629
N.A.I.C.S.: 237130
John Wegmann *(Gen Mgr)*

Subsidiary:

Australian Communications Engineering Pty. Ltd. (2)
24 Adams Dr
Welshpool, WA, 6106, Australia
Tel.: (61) 894522388
Fax: (61) 893115889
E-Mail: email@diacom.com.au
Web Site: www.diacom.com.au
Emp.: 100
Utility Line Construction Services
S.I.C.: 1629
N.A.I.C.S.: 237130
Paul Christopher *(Gen Mgr)*

Drill Rigs Australia Pty. Ltd. (1)
6-12 Uppsala Place
Canning Vale, WA, 6155, Australia
Tel.: (61) 893115666
Fax: (61) 893115667
E-Mail: info@ausdrill.com.au
Web Site: www.drillrigsaus.com.au
Drilling Support Equipments Mfr & Maintenance Services
S.I.C.: 3532
N.A.I.C.S.: 333131
Eddie Banner *(Gen Mgr)*

Drilling Tools Australia Pty. Ltd. (1)
24/26 Gauge Circuit
Canning Vale, WA, 6155, Australia
Tel.: (61) 893115656
Fax: (61) 893115657
E-Mail: enquiries@drillingtools.com.au
Web Site: www.drillingtools.com.au
Emp.: 80
Drill Consumables & Drill Spares Mfr
S.I.C.: 3569
N.A.I.C.S.: 333999
Brian Sanfead *(Gen Mgr)*

Subsidiary:

Remet Engineers Pty. Ltd. (2)
Lot 14 Great Eastern Highway
Kalgoorlie, WA, 6430, Australia
Tel.: (61) 890214588
Fax: (61) 890217244
E-Mail: enquiries.kalgoorlie@remet.com.au
Web Site: www.remet.com.au
Emp.: 23
Drilling Equipments Mfr
S.I.C.: 3532
N.A.I.C.S.: 333131
Christopher Terlat *(Gen Mgr)*

Supply Direct Pty. Ltd. (1)
6-12 Uppsala Place
Canning Vale, WA, 6155, Australia
Tel.: (61) 893115777
Fax: (61) 893115778
E-Mail: supplydirect@supplydirect.net
Web Site: www.supplydirect.net
Mining Equipments & Parts Distr
S.I.C.: 5084
N.A.I.C.S.: 423830
Craig Abbott *(Mgr-Ops-United Kingdom)*

Non-U.S. Subsidiaries:

Logistics Direct Ltd. (2)
Office No 16 AFGO Cargo Village Kotoka International Airport
Accra, Ghana
Tel.: (233) 302770418
Fax: (233) 302770420
E-Mail: enquiries@logisticsdirect.com
Web Site: www.logisticsdirect.com
Emp.: 45
Logistics & Freight Forwarding Services
S.I.C.: 4731
N.A.I.C.S.: 488510
Peter Gralla *(Gen Mgr)*

Supply Direct South Africa Pty. Ltd. (2)
Unit 8 Erf 126 Mifa Industrial Park Cnr George 16th Road
Midrand, Gauteng, 1683, South Africa
Tel.: (27) 113147050
Fax: (27) 113147052
E-Mail: supplydirectsa@supplydirect.co.za
Emp.: 14
Mining Equipments & Parts Distr
S.I.C.: 5084
N.A.I.C.S.: 423830
Mike Keegan *(Mng Dir)*

Synegex Holdings Pty. Ltd. (1)
PO Box 2131
Boulder, Kalgoorlie, WA, 6432, Australia
Tel.: (61) 890809170
Fax: (61) 8 9080 9180
E-Mail: enquiries@synegex.com
Web Site: www.ausdrill.com.au/index.php?option=com_content&task=view&id=109&Itemid=167
Blasting Services & Bulk Explosives Mfr
S.I.C.: 1081
N.A.I.C.S.: 213114
Garry Billing *(Gen Mgr)*

Non-U.S. Subsidiary:

African Mining Services (Ghana) Pty Ltd. (1)
No 3 North Airport Road
Airport Residential Area, Accra, Ghana
Tel.: (233) 21763875
Fax: (233) 302763274
E-Mail: enquiries@amsgh.com
Web Site: www.amsgh.com
Sales Range: $10-24.9 Million
Emp.: 40
Mining Industry Supply Services
S.I.C.: 3532
N.A.I.C.S.: 333131
John Kavanagh *(Gen Mgr)*

AUSENCO LIMITED
144 Montague Road
Brisbane, QLD, 4101, Australia
Tel.: (61) 7 3169 7000
Fax: (61) 731697001
Web Site: www.ausenco.com
AAX—(ASX)
Rev.: $660,154,719
Assets: $476,963,960
Liabilities: $191,232,645
Net Worth: $285,731,315
Earnings: $43,137,730
Emp.: 3,440
Fiscal Year-end: 12/31/12
Business Description:
Engineering & Project Management Services
S.I.C.: 8711
N.A.I.C.S.: 541330
Personnel:
George Lloyd *(Chm)*
Zimi Meka *(CEO & Mng Dir)*
Craig Allen *(CFO)*
Nick Bell *(COO)*
Paul Young *(CIO)*
Frank Mellish *(CMO)*
Jeff Hall *(Chief Corp Dev Officer)*
Greg Lane *(CTO)*
Neil Trembath *(Chief People Officer & Chief Sustainability Officer)*
Peter Bokor *(Pres-Environment & Sustainability)*

Ausenco Limited—(Continued)

Simon Cmrlec *(Pres-APAC & Africa)*
Scott Elfen *(Pres-Ausenco Vector)*
Ed Meka *(Pres-Process Infrastructure)*
Ed Skinner *(Pres-Program Mgmt)*
John Zito *(Pres-Energy)*
Patrick O'Connor *(Sec)*
Board of Directors:
George Lloyd
Zimi Meka
Greg Moynihan
Mary L. Shafer-Malicki
Bob Thorpe
Hank Tuten
Legal Counsel:
McCullough Robertson Lawyers
Level 11 Central Plaza Two 66 Eagle Street
Brisbane, Australia

Subsidiaries:

Ascentis Operations Pty. Ltd. **(1)**
144 Montague Rd
Brisbane, QLD, 4101, Australia
Tel.: (61) 731128280
Fax: (61) 731697001
E-Mail: support@ascentisoperations.com
Web Site: www.ascentisoperations.com
Contract Operations & Maintenance Services
S.I.C.: 1799
N.A.I.C.S.: 238990

Ausenco Global Pty. Ltd. **(1)**
144 Montague Rd
Brisbane, QLD, 4101, Australia
Tel.: (61) 731128200
Fax: (61) 731697001
E-Mail: brisbane@ausenco.com
Web Site: www.ausenco.com
Emp.: 600
Engineering Services
S.I.C.: 8711
N.A.I.C.S.: 541330
Frank Mellish *(CMO)*

Ausenco Services Pty. Ltd. **(1)**
144 Montague Rd
Brisbane, QLD, 4101, Australia
Tel.: (61) 731128200
Fax: (61) 731697000
E-Mail: brisbane@ausenco.com
Web Site: www.ausenco.com
Emp.: 500
Engineering Services
S.I.C.: 8711
N.A.I.C.S.: 541330
Simi Mecha *(CEO)*

Pipeline Systems International Australia Pty. Ltd. **(1)**
Level 3 St Martin s Tower
44 St George's Ter, Perth, Western Australia, 6000, Australia
Tel.: (61) 8 94636601
Web Site: www.ausenco.com
Pipeline System Installation Services
S.I.C.: 1623
N.A.I.C.S.: 237120
Mike Turney *(Gen Mgr)*

U.S. Subsidiaries:

Pipeline Systems Incorporated **(1)**
5099 Comml Cir Ste 102
Concord, CA 94520
Tel.: (925) 939-4420
Fax: (925) 937-8875
Toll Free: (888) 774-9774
E-Mail: info@pipesys.com
Web Site: www.ausenco.com
Emp.: 100
Pipeline System Installation Services
S.I.C.: 1623
N.A.I.C.S.: 237120
Ed Meka *(Pres)*

Non-U.S. Subsidiaries:

Pipeline Systems Incorporated (Baotou) Ltd. **(2)**
Beijing Sunflower Tower Ste 2030 No 37 Maizidian St
Chaoyang Dist, Beijing, 100125, China
Tel.: (86) 1085275800
Fax: (86) 1085275638
Web Site: www.pipesys.com
Emp.: 50
Pipeline System Installation Services
S.I.C.: 1629
N.A.I.C.S.: 237120
Yue-guang Che *(Gen Mgr)*

PSI Engineering Ltd. **(2)**
855 Homer St
Vancouver, BC, V6B 2W2, Canada
Tel.: (604) 221-6677
Fax: (604) 221-6633
Web Site: www.pipesys.com
Emp.: 25
Pipeline System Installation Services
S.I.C.: 1629
N.A.I.C.S.: 237120
Gregg Hodges *(Gen Mgr)*

PSI JRI Peru S.A.C. **(2)**
Escaladhe 371
San Isidro, Lima, Peru
Tel.: (51) 17088200
Fax: (51) 14228409
Web Site: www.pipesys.com
Emp.: 25
Pipeline System Installation Services
S.I.C.: 1623
N.A.I.C.S.: 237120
Paul Murphy *(Mgr-Ops)*

Vector Engineering Inc. **(1)**
143E Spring Hill Dr
Grass Valley, CA 95945
Tel.: (530) 272-2448
Fax: (530) 272-8533
E-Mail: vector@vectoreng.com
Web Site: www.vectoreng.com
Emp.: 450
Engineering & Environmental Consulting Services
S.I.C.: 8711
N.A.I.C.S.: 541330
Ed Meka *(Pres)*

Non-U.S. Subsidiaries:

Ausenco Beijing Limited **(1)**
Beijing Sunflower Tower Ste 2030 No 37 Maizidian St
Chaoyang Dist, Beijing, 100025, China
Tel.: (86) 1085275800
Fax: (86) 1085275638
Web Site: www.ausenco.com
Emp.: 41
Engineering Services
S.I.C.: 8711
N.A.I.C.S.: 541330
Jimi Meka *(Pres)*

Global Procurement Services Limited **(1)**
Unit 2113 21st Fl BB Bldg 54 Sukhumvit 21 Asoke Rd Kwaeng Klong
Toey Nua Khet Watthana Dist, Bangkok, 10110, Thailand
Tel.: (66) 22042210
Fax: (66) 22042211
E-Mail:
Web Site: www.ausenco.com
Emp.: 3
Engineering Services
S.I.C.: 8711
N.A.I.C.S.: 541330
Chidchok Panphiphat *(Mgr-Procurement)*

Sandwell Inc. **(1)**
Ste 1580 Park Pl
666 Burrard St, Vancouver, BC, V6E 4G1, Canada
Tel.: (604) 684-0055
Fax: (604) 684-7533
Civil Engineering & Construction
S.I.C.: 1629
N.A.I.C.S.: 237990

U.S. Division:

Sandwell Engineers Corp. **(2)**
1155 Dairy Ashford St Ste 400
Houston, TX 77079-3012
Tel.: (770) 255-1640
Fax: (770) 255-1649
Web Site: www.sandwell.com
Emp.: 10
Design & Engineering Services
S.I.C.: 8711
N.A.I.C.S.: 541330
Tom Marshall *(VP-Ops)*

Non-U.S. Subsidiaries:

Sandwell (Australia) Pty Ltd. **(2)**
Level 7 200 Adelaide Ter
6004 Perth, WA, Australia
Tel.: (61) 862635600
Fax: (61) 862635699
Web Site: www.sandwell.com
Emp.: 30
Engineering Services
S.I.C.: 8711
N.A.I.C.S.: 541330
Angus Jackson *(Gen Mgr)*

Sandwell Engenharia Ltda. **(2)**
Av Brasil 1701 7 andar
30140-009 Belo Horizonte, Brazil
Tel.: (55) 3132544064
Fax: (55) 3132544064
E-Mail: jose.perez@ausencosandwell.com
Web Site: www.sandwell.com
Emp.: 50
Design & Engineering Services
S.I.C.: 8711
N.A.I.C.S.: 541330
Jose Roberto Perez *(Dir-Mining)*

Sandwell Inc. **(2)**
Ariobimo Central Bldg Lt4
Jl HR Rasuna Said Blok X-2 No, 12950 Jakarta, Indonesia
Tel.: (62) 2152909125
Fax: (62) 2525760
E-Mail: jchandra@sandwell.com
Emp.: 5
Engineering Services
S.I.C.: 8711
N.A.I.C.S.: 541330
Jim Chandra *(Country Mgr)*

Sandwell India Consulting Engineers Pvt. Ltd. **(2)**
602/603 Powai Plaza Central Avenue
Hiranandani Gardens Powai, 400076 Mumbai, India
Tel.: (91) 2267726666
Fax: (91) 2267726677
E-Mail: info@sandwell.com
Web Site: www.sandwell.com
Emp.: 55
Engineering Services
S.I.C.: 8711
N.A.I.C.S.: 541330
Peter Leekha *(Mng Dir)*

Sandwell Peru S.A. **(2)**
Calle Esquilache 371 Fl 8
Torre El Pilar Ofc 702, Lima, Peru
Tel.: (51) 17198696
Fax: (51) 17198697
Web Site: www.sandwell.com
Civil Engineering & Construction Services
S.I.C.: 1629
N.A.I.C.S.: 237990
Pierre Montauban Del Solar *(Gen Mgr)*

Vector Argentina SA **(1)**
Besares 941
Chacras De Coria, Mendoza, 5528, Argentina
Tel.: (54) 2614248940
E-Mail: info.argentina@ausencovector.com.ar
Web Site: www.vectorarg.com.ar
Engineering & Environmental Consulting Services
S.I.C.: 8999
N.A.I.C.S.: 541620
Silverio Prota *(Gen Mgr)*

AUSGOLD LIMITED

Level 16 AMP Building 140 St Georges Terrace
Perth, WA, 6000, Australia
Tel.: (61) 892209890
Fax: (61) 892209820
E-Mail: info@ausgoldlimited.com
Web Site: www.ausgoldlimited.com
AUC—(ASX)
Rev.: $65,630
Assets: $39,814,550
Liabilities: $213,982
Net Worth: $39,600,568
Earnings: ($8,639,721)
Fiscal Year-end: 06/30/13
Business Description:
Gold Mining Services
S.I.C.: 1041
N.A.I.C.S.: 212221
Personnel:
Denis Ivan Rakich *(Sec)*
Board of Directors:
Robert James Pett
Richard Lockwood
Denis Ivan Rakich
Legal Counsel:
Squire Saunders
Level 21 300 Murray Street
Perth, WA, 6000, Australia

AUSGROUP LIMITED

36 Tuas Road
Singapore, 638505, Singapore
Tel.: (65) 68625233
Fax: (65) 68625211
E-Mail: info@agc-ausgroup.com
Web Site: www.agc-ausgroup.com
5GJ—(SES)
Rev.: $607,237,923
Assets: $318,664,801
Liabilities: $138,173,081
Net Worth: $180,491,720
Earnings: $10,117,749
Emp.: 3,000
Fiscal Year-end: 06/30/13
Business Description:
Construction Services
S.I.C.: 1541
N.A.I.C.S.: 236210
Personnel:
Stuart Maxwell Kenny *(CEO & Mng Dir)*
Michael Anthony Hardwick *(CFO)*
Grace Chow Pheng Chan *(Co-Sec)*
Corine Bee Eng Lim *(Co-Sec)*
Board of Directors:
Kia Ngee Chew
Barry Alfred Carson
Stuart Maxwell Kenny
Pak Chow Kok
Damien O'Reilly
Grant Pestell
Legal Counsel:
Rajah & Tann
9 Battery Road #25-01 Straits Trading Building
Singapore, Singapore
Transfer Agent:
M & C Services Private Limited
112 Robinson Road 05-01
Singapore, 068902, Singapore

Subsidiary:

AusGroup Singapore Pte Ltd **(1)**
36 Tuas Road
Singapore, 638505, Singapore
Tel.: (65) 68625233
Fax: (65) 68625211
E-Mail: inquiry@ausgroup.com.sg
Web Site: www.ausgroup.com.sg
Emp.: 200
Oilfield Equipment Mfr
S.I.C.: 3533
N.A.I.C.S.: 333132
Gavin Aitken *(Gen Mgr)*

Non-U.S. Subsidiaries:

AGC Australia Pty Ltd **(1)**
251 St Georges Terrace Level 2
Perth, WA, 6000, Australia
Tel.: (61) 862104500
Fax: (61) 8 6210 4501
E-Mail: info@agc-ausgroup.com
Web Site: www.agc-ausgroup.com
Emp.: 200
Construction Engineering Services
S.I.C.: 8711
N.A.I.C.S.: 541330
Laurie Barlow *(CEO)*

AGC Industries Pty Ltd **(1)**
Level 2 251 Saint Georges Terrace
Perth, WA, 6000, Australia
Tel.: (61) 894391934
Fax: (61) 8 6210 4501
Construction Engineering Services
S.I.C.: 8711
N.A.I.C.S.: 541330

Michael Bourke *(Exec Gen Mgr-Ops)*

MAS Australasia Pty Ltd (1)
34 Clune St
Bayswater, Perth, WA, 6053, Australia
Tel.: (61) 893797222
Fax: (61) 893797223
Emp.: 40
Construction Engineering Services
S.I.C.: 8711
N.A.I.C.S.: 541330

AUSMANI LIMITED

16 James Street
Geelong, VIC, 3220, Australia
Tel.: (61) 352255400
Fax: (61) 352213701
Web Site:
Sales Range: $1-9.9 Million
Emp.: 18
Business Description:
Web Entertainment Services
S.I.C.: 2741
N.A.I.C.S.: 519130
Personnel:
Vincent Sweeney *(Chm)*

Subsidiary:

World Wide Entertainment Production & Sales Pty. Ltd. (1)
Level 5 83 Moorabool St
Geelong, VIC, 3220, Australia AU
Tel.: (61) 352255400
Fax: (61) 352213701
E-Mail: wwent@wwent.net
Emp.: 15
Television Program Production & Broadcasting Services
S.I.C.: 4833
N.A.I.C.S.: 515120

Subsidiaries:

Genr8 Digital Media Pty Ltd. (2)
16 James St
Geelong, VIC, 3220, Australia
Tel.: (61) 3 5225 5475
Fax: (61) 3 5221 3701
E-Mail: info@genr8digital.tv
Web Site: www.genr8digital.tv
Online Digital Media Services
S.I.C.: 2741
N.A.I.C.S.: 519130
Tom Allan *(Creative Dir & Production Mgr)*

World Wide Entertainment DVD Production & Sales Pty. Ltd. (2)
16 James St
Geelong, VIC, 3220, Australia AU
Tel.: (61) 3 5225 5400
Fax: (61) 3 5221 3701
Movie Digital Video Discs Production & Sales
S.I.C.: 3652
N.A.I.C.S.: 334614

AUSMON RESOURCES LIMITED

Level 15 370 Pitt Street
Sydney, NSW, 2000, Australia
Tel.: (61) 292643100
Fax: (61) 292830099
E-Mail: office@ausmonresources.com
Web Site: www.ausmonresources.com.au
AOA—(ASX)
Rev.: $5,267
Assets: $3,048,191
Liabilities: $55,165
Net Worth: $2,993,027
Earnings: ($798,585)
Emp.: 50
Fiscal Year-end: 06/30/13
Business Description:
Metal Exploration & Mining Services
S.I.C.: 1099
N.A.I.C.S.: 212299
Personnel:
John Qiang Wang *(Acting Chm, Sec & Dir-Fin)*
King Ming Fan *(CEO)*
Board of Directors:
King Ming Fan
John Qiang Wang
Liubao Qian
Guojian Xu
Gang Zheng
Legal Counsel:
Piper Alderman
Level 23 Governor Macquarie Tower 1 Farrer Place
Sydney, NSW, 2000, Australia

AUSNUTRIA DAIRY CORPORATION LTD

9th Floor Xin Da Xin Building
168 Huangxing Middle Road,
Changsha, Hunan, 410005, China
Tel.: (86) 73182229278
Fax: (86) 73192229708
E-Mail: info@ausnutria.com
Web Site: www.ausnutria.com.hk
Sales Range: $75-99.9 Million
Emp.: 512
Business Description:
Dairy Products Mfr
S.I.C.: 0241
N.A.I.C.S.: 112120
Personnel:
Yueshi Wu *(Chm)*
Yuanrong Chen *(CEO)*
Wei Hua Wong *(CFO)*
Shihu Xiao *(CMO)*
Siu Hung Ng *(Sec)*
Board of Directors:
Yueshi Wu
Yuk Tong Chan
Yuanrong Chen
Siu Hung Ng
Weifa Qiu
Jason Wan
Weibin Yan

Codan Trust Company (Cayman) Limited
Cricket Square Hutchins Drive
PO Box 2681
Georgetown, Grand Cayman, Cayman Islands
Transfer Agent:
Codan Trust Company (Cayman) Limited
Cricket Square Hutchins Drive
PO Box 2681
Georgetown, Grand Cayman, Cayman Islands

AUSOM ENTERPRISE LIMITED

606-Swagat Building Near Lal Bunglow C G Road
Ahmedabad, 380 006, India
Tel.: (91) 7926421455
Fax: (91) 7926569898
E-Mail: ausom.ael@gmail.com
Web Site: www.ausom.in
AUSOMENT—(NSE)
Rev.: $126,142,259
Assets: $63,108,417
Liabilities: $58,568,694
Net Worth: $4,539,722
Earnings: $326,694
Fiscal Year-end: 03/31/13
Business Description:
Gold & Silver Distr
S.I.C.: 5052
N.A.I.C.S.: 423520
Personnel:
Kishor Pranjivandas Mandalia *(CEO & Mng Dir)*
Rupesh Shah *(CFO)*
Ravikumar Pasi *(Compliance Officer & Sec)*
Board of Directors:
Zaverilal Virjibhai Mandalia
Hitesh Adeshara
Mukesh Adeshara
Ghanshyambhai Akbari
Kishor Pranjivandas Mandalia
Vipul Zaverilal Mandalia
Transfer Agent:
Link Intime India Private Limited
303 3rd Floor Shopper's Plaza 5 Near 5 Government Society
Opp Municipal Market C G Road, Ahmedabad, 380009, India

AUSON AB

Verkstadsgatan 3
SE-434 42 Kungsbacka, Sweden
Tel.: (46) 300562000
Fax: (46) 300562001
E-Mail: info@auson.se
Web Site: www.auson.se
Year Founded: 1928
Business Description:
Mfr of Rust Protection, Sound Damping, Roof Care & Wood Protection Products
S.I.C.: 2865
N.A.I.C.S.: 325194

AUSQUEST LIMITED

8 Kearns Crescent
Ardross, Perth, WA, 6153, Australia
Tel.: (61) 8 9364 3866
Fax: (61) 8 9364 4892
Web Site: www.ausquest.com.au
AQD—(ASX)
Rev.: $202,441
Assets: $14,576,958
Liabilities: $459,459
Net Worth: $14,117,500
Earnings: ($8,583,514)
Emp.: 8
Fiscal Year-end: 06/30/13
Business Description:
Mineral Exploration Services
S.I.C.: 1481
N.A.I.C.S.: 213115
Personnel:
Graeme Drew *(CEO & Mng Dir)*
Darren Crawte *(Sec)*
Board of Directors:
Gregory Hancock
John Ashley
Graeme Drew
Chris Ellis
Legal Counsel:
Nexia Perth
Level 3 88 William Street
Perth, WA, 6000, Australia

AUST & HACHMANN E.K.

Neumann Reichardt Strasse 27 33
DE-22041 Hamburg, Germany
Tel.: (49) 403116700
Fax: (49) 4031167051
E-Mail: info@hachmann-vanilla.de
Web Site: www.hachmann-vanilla.de
Year Founded: 1881
Rev.: $16,925,238
Emp.: 16
Business Description:
Vanilla Beans Distr
S.I.C.: 5153
N.A.I.C.S.: 424510
Personnel:
Berend Hachmann *(Owner)*

AUSTAL LIMITED

100 Clarence Beach Road
Henderson, WA, 6166, Australia
Tel.: (61) 894101111
Fax: (61) 894102564
Web Site: www.austal.com
Year Founded: 1988
ASB—(ASX OTC)
Rev.: $940,821,427
Assets: $984,386,418
Liabilities: $560,056,845
Net Worth: $424,329,573
Earnings: $37,246,738
Emp.: 4,269
Fiscal Year-end: 06/30/13
Business Description:
Commercial & Naval Ship Designer & Builder
S.I.C.: 3731
N.A.I.C.S.: 336611
Personnel:
Andrew Bellamy *(CEO)*
Greg Jason *(CFO)*
Graham Backhouse *(Pres-Australia)*
Craig Perciavalle *(Pres-USA)*
Joey Turano *(Pres-Philippines)*
Adrian Strang *(Sec)*
Board of Directors:
John Rothwell
Dario Amara
Andrew Bellamy
Charles Roland Giles Everist
David Patrick Alexander Singleton

AUSTBROKERS HOLDINGS LIMITED

Level 21 111 Pacific Highway
North Sydney, NSW, 2060, Australia
Mailing Address:
PO Box 1978
North Sydney, NSW, 2059, Australia
Tel.: (61) 299352222
Fax: (61) 299290320
Web Site: www.austbrokers.com.au
AUB—(ASX)
Rev.: $148,165,778
Assets: $587,811,094
Liabilities: $347,713,339
Net Worth: $240,097,756
Earnings: $49,538,308
Emp.: 1,700
Fiscal Year-end: 06/30/13
Business Description:
Insurance brokers
S.I.C.: 6351
N.A.I.C.S.: 524126
Personnel:
Mark Searles *(CEO & Mng Dir)*
Stephen S. Rouvray *(CFO, Sec & Mgr-IR)*
Sunil Vohra *(COO)*
Theo Stevens *(CIO)*
Keith McIvor *(Chief Broking Officer)*
Board of Directors:
Richard Longes
Ray J. Carless
David J. Harricks
Mark Searles
Legal Counsel:
Clayton Utz
1 Bligh Street
Sydney, Australia
Subsidiaries:

AHL Insurance Brokers Pty. Ltd. (1)
Level 1 64 Henley Beach Rd
Mile End, South Australia, 5031, Australia
Tel.: (61) 882389200
Fax: (61) 882389299
E-Mail: insura@abterrace.com.au
Emp.: 21
Insurance Brokerage Services
S.I.C.: 6411
N.A.I.C.S.: 524210
Rob Morrell *(Mgr)*

Austbrokers AEI Transport Pty. Ltd. (1)
Level 10 1 Elizabeth Plz
Sydney, NSW, 2060, Australia
Tel.: (61) 289131600
Fax: (61) 299299975
E-Mail: info@aeitransport.com.au
Web Site: www.aeitransport.com.au
Emp.: 25
Automobile Insurance & Mortgage Services
S.I.C.: 6411
N.A.I.C.S.: 524298
Tim Wedlock *(Mng Dir)*

Austbrokers Canberra Pty. Ltd. (1)
Unit 1 Lyell Ctr Cnr Lyell & Newcastle St
Fyshwick, ACT, 2609, Australia AU
Tel.: (61) 262805477 (85%)

Austbrokers Holdings Limited—(Continued)

Fax: (61) 262807561
Web Site: www.austbrokers.com.au
Brokerage Services
S.I.C.: 6411
N.A.I.C.S.: 524210
Greg Johnston *(Mng Dir)*

Austbrokers CE McDonald Pty. Ltd. **(1)**
280 Montague Rd
West End, Geraldton, Queensland, 4101, Australia
Tel.: (61) 730076700
Fax: (61) 732552765
Automobile Insurance Services
S.I.C.: 6411
N.A.I.C.S.: 524298
Jackie MacDonald *(CEO)*

Austbrokers Central Coast Pty. Ltd. **(1)**
Unit 4 3 Pioneer Ave
PO Box 3009
Tuggerah, NSW, 2259, Australia
Tel.: (61) 243559999
Fax: (61) 243559977
E-Mail: service@abcentralcoast.com.au
Web Site: www.abcentralcoast.com.au
Emp.: 20
Insurance & Brokerage Services
S.I.C.: 6411
N.A.I.C.S.: 524210
Bob White *(Mng Dir)*

Austbrokers Financial Solutions (Syd) Pty. Ltd. **(1)**
Level 10 1 Elizabeth Plz
PO Box 103
Sydney, NSW, 2060, Australia
Tel.: (61) 289131600
Fax: (61) 295705328
Mortgage Brokerage Services
S.I.C.: 6163
N.A.I.C.S.: 522310

Austbrokers Premier Pty. Ltd. **(1)**
280 Montague Rd
PO Box 3290
West End, Brisbane, QLD, 4101, Australia
Tel.: (61) 730101821
Fax: (61) 738441275
E-Mail: premier@premier.austbrokers.com
Web Site: www.premier.austbrokers.com
Emp.: 20
Insurance Brokerage Services
S.I.C.: 6411
N.A.I.C.S.: 524210
Scott Hastings *(Gen Mgr)*

Austbrokers Professional Services Pty. Ltd. **(1)**
Level 10 1 Elizabeth Plz
2060 Sydney, NSW, Australia
Tel.: (61) 289131637
Fax: (61) 299299972
E-Mail: nick.codd@aps.austb.com.au
Web Site: www.austbrokers.com.au/Content_Common/pg-AB-Professional-Services.seo
Brokerage Services,
S.I.C.: 6211
N.A.I.C.S.: 523120

Austbrokers RWA Pty. Ltd. **(1)**
22 Darley Rd
PO Box 485
Manly, NSW, 2095, Australia
Tel.: (61) 299762511
Fax: (61) 299762507
E-Mail: rwa@rwa.austbrokers.com
Web Site: www.austbrokersrwa.com.au
Emp.: 20
Insurance Services
S.I.C.: 6411
N.A.I.C.S.: 524210
John Hallman *(Mng Dir)*

Austbrokers Sydney Pty. Ltd. **(1)**
Level 10 1 Elizabeth Plz
Sydney, NSW, 2060, Australia
Tel.: (61) 289131600
Fax: (61) 299299971
Web Site: www.absyd.com.au
Emp.: 50
Brokerage Services
S.I.C.: 6211
N.A.I.C.S.: 523120
Jeff Howells *(Gen Mgr)*

Austbrokers Terrace Insurance Brokers Pty. Ltd. **(1)**
64 Henley Beach Rd
Mile End, South Australia, 5031, Australia
Tel.: (61) 882389200
Fax: (61) 882389299
E-Mail: insure@abterrace.com.au
Web Site: www.austbrokers.com.au
Emp.: 18
Insurance Services
S.I.C.: 6411
N.A.I.C.S.: 524210
Rob Morrell *(Mgr)*

Carriers Insurance Brokers Pty. Ltd. **(1)**
Suite 404 4th Floor 20 Bungan Street
Mona Vale, NSW, 2103, Australia
Tel.: (61) 299132002
Fax: (61) 299132007
E-Mail: cover@carriers-ins.com.au
Web Site: www.carriersinsurancebrokers.com.au
Emp.: 8
Automobile Insurance & Mortage Services
S.I.C.: 3291
N.A.I.C.S.: 327910
Kevin Hill *(Mng Dir)*
Lisa Tierney *(Fin Officer)*

Finsura Holdings Pty. Ltd. **(1)**
Unit 1 8 Mcmullen Ave
Castle Hill, NSW, 2154, Australia
Tel.: (61) 298992999
Fax: (61) 96803023
E-Mail: info@finsura.com.au
Web Site: www.finsura.com.au/
Emp.: 25
Insurance & Financial Planning Services
S.I.C.: 6211
N.A.I.C.S.: 523999
Matthew Driscoll *(Mng Dir)*

McNaughton Gardiner Insurance Brokers Pty. Ltd. **(1)**
109 Beach Rd
Bunbury, Western Australia, 6230, Australia
Tel.: (61) 897223700
Fax: (61) 897911635
E-Mail: info@mgib.com.au
Web Site: www.mgib.com.au
Emp.: 20
Insurance Brokerage Services
S.I.C.: 6411
N.A.I.C.S.: 524210
Antony Gallagher *(Mng Dir)*

SGP Insurance Brokers Pty. Ltd. **(1)**
Centric Park Cent Ste 105 Level 1
4 Hyde Parade, Campbelltown, New South Wales, 2560, Australia
Tel.: (61) 246265022
Fax: (61) 246283399
E-Mail: info@sgp.com.au
Web Site: www.sgp.com.au
Emp.: 20
Insurance Brokerage Services
S.I.C.: 6411
N.A.I.C.S.: 524210
Paul Murphy *(Mng Dir)*

SPT Financial Services Pty. Ltd. **(1)**
Ste 5 18 Gibbs St
Miranda, New South Wales, 2228, Australia
Tel.: (61) 295404240
Fax: (61) 0295242938
Emp.: 5
Financial Planning Services
S.I.C.: 6211
N.A.I.C.S.: 523999
Philip Budin *(Gen Mgr)*

AUSTEVOLL SEAFOOD ASA

Alfabygget
N 5392 Storebo, Norway
Tel.: (47) 56181000
Fax: (47) 56181003
E-Mail: info@auss.no
Web Site: www.auss.no
AUSS—(OSL)
Rev.: $57,444,416
Assets: $1,212,044,783
Liabilities: $404,169,131
Net Worth: $807,875,652
Earnings: $28,626,102
Emp.: 5,284
Fiscal Year-end: 12/31/12

Business Description:
Commercial Fishing & Fish Processing
S.I.C.: 0919
N.A.I.C.S.: 114119

Personnel:
Helge Singelstad *(Chm)*
Oddvar Skjegstad *(Deputy Chm)*
Arne Mogster *(CEO)*
Britt Kathrin Drivenes *(CFO)*
Erling Mogster *(COO)*
Henning Beltestad *(CEO-Leroy Seafood Group ASA)*
Adriana Giudice *(CEO-Austral Group S A A)*
Esteban Urcelay *(CEO-Foodcorp SA)*

Board of Directors:
Helge Singelstad
Heldge Mogster
Lill Maren Mogster
Inga Lise L. Moldestad
Oddvar Skjegstad
Hilde Waage

Subsidiaries:

Austevoll Fiskeindustri AS **(1)**
Alfabygget
5392 Storebo, Norway
Tel.: (47) 5618 1000
Fax: (47) 5618 1005
E-Mail: info@aufi.no
Web Site: www.aufi.no
Processing of Salmon & Pelagic Products
S.I.C.: 2092
N.A.I.C.S.: 311710

Leroy Seafood Group ASA **(1)**
Bontelabo 2
PO Box 7060
5020 Bergen, Norway (74.93%)
Tel.: (47) 55 21 36 50
Fax: (47) 55 21 36 32
E-Mail: leroy.seafood.group@leroy.no
Web Site: www.leroy.no
LSG—(OSL)
Rev.: $65,492,136
Assets: $898,406,307
Liabilities: $260,351,943
Net Worth: $638,054,363
Earnings: $42,309,308
Emp.: 1,883
Fiscal Year-end: 12/31/12
Distribution, Sales, Marketing & Processing of Seafood; Production of Salmon, Trout & Other Fish
S.I.C.: 2092
N.A.I.C.S.: 311710
Helge Singelstad *(Chm)*
Henning Beltestad *(CEO)*
Sjur Malm *(CFO)*
Stig Nilsen *(Exec VP-Farming)*

Subsidiary:

Sjotroll Havbruk AS **(2)**
C-O Sjotroll AS
5397 Bekkjarvik, Hordaland, Norway (50.7%)
Tel.: (47) 91911800
Fax: (47) 56181801
E-Mail: firmapost@sjotroll.no
Web Site: www.sjotroll.no
Emp.: 120
Salmon & Trout Farming
S.I.C.: 0921
N.A.I.C.S.: 112511
Hans Jorgen Runshaug *(CEO)*

Joint Venture:

Welcon AS **(1)**
Ruselokkveien 6
Oslo, 0251, Norway
Tel.: (47) 2212 2540
Web Site: www.welcon.no
Rev.: $222,932,500
Fish Meal & Fish Oil Mfr; Joint Venture of Origin Enterprises plc (50%) & Austevoll Seafood ASA (50%)
S.I.C.: 2092
N.A.I.C.S.: 311710
Arne Stang *(CEO)*
Tom Tynan *(COO)*

Non-U.S. Subsidiary:

United Fish Industries (UK) Limited **(2)**
Gilbey Road
Grimsby, Lincs, DN31 2SL, United Kingdom
Tel.: (44) 1472263450
Fax: (44) 1472263333
Sales Range: $50-74.9 Million
Emp.: 35
Animal Aquaculture
S.I.C.: 0273
N.A.I.C.S.: 112519
Thomas Tynan *(COO)*

Non-U.S. Subsidiaries:

Austral Group S.A.A. **(1)**
Av Victor Andres Belaunde No 147
Torre Real 7 Centro Empresarial
San Isidro, Lima, Peru (89.26%)
Tel.: (51) 1 710 7000
Fax: (51) 1 442 1660
E-Mail: info@austral.com.pe
Web Site: www.austral.com.pe
Production of Fishmeal, Fish Oil, Canned Fish & Frozen Fish
S.I.C.: 0912
N.A.I.C.S.: 114111

FoodCorp S.A. **(1)**
Reyes Lavalle 3340 Of 1103
Las Condes, Santiago, Chile (100%)
Tel.: (56) 2 445 8700
Fax: (56) 2 445 8701
E-Mail: santiago@fcc.cl
Web Site: www.fcc.cl
Production of Fishmeal, Fishoil, Canned Fish & Frozen Fish
S.I.C.: 0912
N.A.I.C.S.: 114111

AUSTEX OIL LIMITED

Level 7 207 Kent Street
Sydney, NSW, 2000, Australia
Mailing Address:
GPO Box 4246
Sydney, NSW, 2001, Australia
Tel.: (61) 292382363
Fax: (61) 280887280
E-Mail: info@austexoil.com
Web Site: www.austexoil.com
AOK—(ASX OTC TSXV)
Rev.: $6,943,266
Assets: $43,977,641
Liabilities: $5,852,740
Net Worth: $38,124,901
Earnings: ($3,460,061)
Emp.: 13
Fiscal Year-end: 12/31/12

Business Description:
Oil & Gas Producer
S.I.C.: 1389
N.A.I.C.S.: 213112

Personnel:
Richard A. Adrey *(Chm)*
Daniel Lanskey *(Mng Dir)*
Tom Bloomfield *(Co-Sec)*
Justin B. Clyne *(Co-Sec)*

Board of Directors:
Richard A. Adrey
Kwang Hou Hung
Russell Krause
Daniel Lanskey
Patricia Kay Philip
Nicholas J. Stone
Luis F. Vierma

U.S. Subsidiary:

Well Enhancement Services LLC **(1)**
1544 Sawdust Rd Ste 100
The Woodlands, TX 77380
Tel.: (281) 367-0386
Fax: (281) 596-7212
Web Site: www.wellenhancement.com
Emp.: 11
Well Enhancement & Oil Recovery Technologies Provider
S.I.C.: 1381
N.A.I.C.S.: 213111
Keith Phipps *(Pres)*
Chris D Nelson *(CFO)*
Steven Bowen *(COO)*

AUSTIN ENGINEERING CO. LTD.
Village Patla Taluka Bhesan
Junagadh, 362 030, India
Tel.: (91) 2873 252223
Fax: (91) 285 2661505
E-Mail: info@aec.com
Web Site: www.aec-bearings.com
522005—(BOM)
Rev.: $16,636,813
Assets: $16,467,928
Liabilities: $6,586,204
Net Worth: $9,881,724
Earnings: $588,316
Fiscal Year-end: 03/31/13
Business Description:
Roller Bearing Mfr
S.I.C.: 3562
N.A.I.C.S.: 332991
Personnel:
Narottam C. Vadgama *(Chm)*
Rajan R. Bambhania *(Co-Mng Dir)*
Shashikant M. Thanki *(Co-Mng Dir)*
Kaushik Shah *(Sec)*
Board of Directors:
Narottam C. Vadgama
Rajan R. Bambhania
Jayshankar R. Bhogayta
K. J. Mehta
D. B. Nakum
B. R. Sureja
Shashikant M. Thanki
S. V. Vaishnav
Transfer Agent:
Sharepro Services (India) Pvt. Ltd.
13 AB Samhita Warehousing Complex Near Sakinaka Telephone Ex Andheri
Mumbai, India

U.S. Subsidiary:

Accurate Engineering Inc. (1)
555 Old Stage Rd Unit 2D
Auburn, AL 36830
Tel.: (334) 524-3362
Fax: (334) 460-1920
E-Mail: sales@aec.com
Industrial Ball & Roller Bearing Whslr
S.I.C.: 5085
N.A.I.C.S.: 423840

AUSTIN ENGINEERING LTD.
173 Cobalt Street
PO Box 64
Carole Park, QLD, 4300, Australia
Tel.: (61) 732712622
Fax: (61) 732713689
E-Mail: enquiry@austineng.com.au
Web Site: www.austineng.com.au
ANG—(ASX)
Rev.: $300,998,080
Assets: $289,951,820
Liabilities: $130,043,659
Net Worth: $159,908,161
Earnings: $29,639,408
Emp.: 100
Fiscal Year-end: 06/30/13
Business Description:
Industrial Machinery Manufacturing, Repair & Support Services
S.I.C.: 7699
N.A.I.C.S.: 811310
Personnel:
Michael Buckland *(Mng Dir)*
Scott Richardson *(CFO & Co-Sec)*
Steve Shellenberger *(Pres/CEO-Western Technology Services Inc)*
Warren Arthur *(CEO-COR Cooling Grp)*
Jessica Neale *(Co-Sec)*
Board of Directors:
Paul Reading
Michael Buckland
Eugene Fung
Peter Pursey
Legal Counsel:
Thomsons Lawyers
Level 16 Waterfront Place 1 Eagle Street
Brisbane, Australia
Subsidiary:

Austbore Pty. Ltd. (1)
12-16 Progress Dr
PO Box 5726
Paget, Mackay, Queensland, 4740, Australia
Tel.: (61) 749526222
Fax: (61) 749526223
E-Mail: sales@austbore.com.au
Web Site: www.austbore.com.au
Emp.: 50
Mining Engineering Services
S.I.C.: 8711
N.A.I.C.S.: 541330
Kathy Holstead *(Mgr-Admin)*

U.S. Subsidiary:

Western Technology Services Inc. (1)
415 1st St
Mills, WY 82644
Tel.: (307) 235-6475
Fax: (307) 265-8554
Toll Free: (888) 235-6475
E-Mail: sales@westech.com
Web Site: www.wstch.com
Emp.: 175
Industrial Machinery Manufacturing, Repair & Support Services
S.I.C.: 7699
N.A.I.C.S.: 811310
Steve Shellenberger *(Pres & CEO)*
Shane Fox *(CFO)*

AUSTIN EXPLORATION LIMITED
Level 1 160 Queen Street
Melbourne, VIC, 3000, Australia
Mailing Address:
GPO Box 2850
Melbourne, VIC, 3001, Australia
Tel.: (61) 3 9606 3888
Fax: (61) 3 9606 3800
E-Mail: guyg@austinexploration.com
Web Site: www.austinexploration.com
AKK—(ASX OTC)
Business Description:
Oil & Gas Exploration
S.I.C.: 1311
N.A.I.C.S.: 211111
Personnel:
William Mark Hart *(Pres)*
Guy Thomas Goudy *(CEO)*
Board of Directors:
Richard Cottee
Guy Thomas Goudy
William Mark Hart
Nigel Denis Richard Hartley
Dominic Pellicano

AUSTIN FRASER LIMITED
One Forbury Square The Forbury
Reading, Berkshire, RG1 3BB, United Kingdom
Tel.: (44) 118 959 6689
E-Mail: info@austinfraser.com
Web Site: www.austinfraser.com
Year Founded: 2007
Sales Range: $10-24.9 Million
Emp.: 47
Business Description:
Employee Recruitment Services
S.I.C.: 7361
N.A.I.C.S.: 561311
Personnel:
Tom Chapman *(Mgr-Engrg Contracts)*

AUSTIN REED GROUP LIMITED
100 Regent Street
London, W1B 5SR, United Kingdom
Tel.: (44) 2075347777
Fax: (44) 2075347741
Web Site: www.austinreedgroup.co.uk
Year Founded: 1920
Business Description:
Holding Company; Men's & Women's Branded Apparel Licensing & Retailer
S.I.C.: 6719
N.A.I.C.S.: 551112
Personnel:
Nick Hollingworth *(CEO)*
Francesca Mitchell *(Sec)*
Subsidiaries:

Austin Reed Limited (1)
103 / 113 Regent Street Floors 4 & 5
London, W1B 4HL, United Kingdom UK (100%)
Tel.: (44) 2077346789
Telex: 58498
Fax: (44) 2072872137
E-Mail: customerservices@austinreed.co.uk
Web Site: www.austinreed.co.uk
Sales Range: $250-299.9 Million
Emp.: 700
Men's & Women's Branded Apparel Licensing & Store Operator
S.I.C.: 5611
N.A.I.C.S.: 448110
Nick Hollingworth *(CEO)*

Country Casuals Limited (1)
2 Waterhouse Square 138-142 Holborn
London, W1B 4HL, United Kingdom UK
Tel.: (44) 2075347777
E-Mail: customerservices@ccfashion.co.uk
Web Site: www.ccfashion.co.uk
Emp.: 300
Women's Branded Apparel Licensing & Store Operator
S.I.C.: 5621
N.A.I.C.S.: 448120
Nick Hollingworth *(CEO)*

Units:

Austin Reed Group Support Services Center (1)
Station Road
Thirsk, N Yorkshire, YO7 1QH, United Kingdom
Tel.: (44) 1845573000
Fax: (44) 1845573102
E-Mail: itenquiries@austinreedgroup.co.uk
Emp.: 100
Customer Service Call & Corporate Support Center
S.I.C.: 7389
N.A.I.C.S.: 561421

Viyella (1)
2 Waterhouse Square 138-142
London, W1B 4HL, United Kingdom
Tel.: (44) 2075347777
Fax: (44) 2075347741
E-Mail: customer.services@viyella.co.uk
Web Site: www.viyella.co.uk
Emp.: 100
Women's Branded Apparel Licensing & Store Operator
S.I.C.: 5621
N.A.I.C.S.: 448120
Nick Hollingworth *(CEO)*

AUSTIN-SMITH:LORD LLP
Varnish Works 3 Bravingtons Walk
London, N1 9AJ, United Kingdom
Tel.: (44) 20 7843 6161
E-Mail: info@austinsmithlord.com
Web Site: www.austinsmithlord.com
Sales Range: $10-24.9 Million
Emp.: 300
Business Description:
Architectural Services
S.I.C.: 8712
N.A.I.C.S.: 541310
Personnel:
Ian Brebner *(Partner)*
Neil Chapman *(Partner)*
Jennifer Dixon *(Partner)*
Joe Emanuele *(Partner)*
Maggie Mullan *(Partner)*
Neil Musgrove *(Partner)*
Chris Pritchett *(Partner)*
Martin Roe *(Partner)*
Graham Ross *(Partner)*
Alistair Sunderland *(Partner)*
Iain Wylie *(Partner)*
Branches:

Austin-Smith:Lord LLP (1)
One Dunleavy Drive
Cardiff, CF11 0SN, United Kingdom
Tel.: (44) 2920 225 208
E-Mail: cardiff@austinsmithlord.com
Web Site: www.austinsmithlord.com
Emp.: 15
Architectural Services
S.I.C.: 8712
N.A.I.C.S.: 541310

Austin-Smith:Lord LLP (1)
296 St Vincent Street
Glasgow, G2 5RU, United Kingdom
Tel.: (44) 141 223 8500
Fax: (44) 1412238501
E-Mail: glasgow@austinsmithlord.com
Web Site: www.austinsmithlord.com
Emp.: 15
Architectural Services
S.I.C.: 8712
N.A.I.C.S.: 541310
Munirah Khairuddin *(Partner)*

Austin-Smith:Lord LLP (1)
Port of Liverpool Building
Pier Head, Liverpool, L3 1BY, United Kingdom
Tel.: (44) 151 227 1083
Fax: (44) 3970003
E-Mail: liverpool@austinsmithlord.com
Web Site: www.austinsmithlord.com
Emp.: 5
Architectural Services
S.I.C.: 8712
N.A.I.C.S.: 541310

Austin-Smith:Lord LLP (1)
4 Jordan Street
Manchester, M15 4PY, United Kingdom
Tel.: (44) 161 228 7569
E-Mail: manchester@austinsmithlord.com
Architectural Services
S.I.C.: 8712
N.A.I.C.S.: 541310

Non-U.S. Subsidiary:

Austin-Smith:Lord Abu Dhabi (1)
Al Nasr Street Qasr Al Hosn Cultural Quarter
PO Box 129743
Abu Dhabi, United Arab Emirates
Tel.: (971) 2 631 7072
Fax: (971) 2 633 2114
E-Mail: abudhabi@austinsmithlord.com
Web Site: www.austinsmithlord.com
Architectural Services
S.I.C.: 8712
N.A.I.C.S.: 541310
Nadim Khattar *(Gen Mgr)*

AUSTOCK GROUP LIMITED
Level 12 15 William Street
Melbourne, VIC, 3000, Australia
Tel.: (61) 3 8601 2000
Fax: (61) 3 9200 2270
E-Mail: info@austock.com
Web Site: www.austock.com
Year Founded: 1991
ACK—(ASX)
Sales Range: $1-9.9 Million
Business Description:
Financial Investment Services
S.I.C.: 6211
N.A.I.C.S.: 523999
Personnel:
William Eric Bessemer *(CEO)*
Enzo Silverii *(CFO & Sec)*
Board of Directors:
Frederick George Albion Beaumont
William Eric Bessemer
Martin Edward Ryan
Jonathan James Tooth

AUSTOFIX GROUP LIMITED
18 Kinkaid Ave
Plympton, SA, 5037, Australia

Austofix Group Limited—(Continued)

Tel.: (61) 883510644
Fax: (61) 883510855
E-Mail: info@austofix.com.au
Web Site: www.austofix.com.au
Rev.: $1,002,779
Assets: $7,268,977
Liabilities: $3,984,369
Net Worth: $3,284,607
Earnings: ($4,026,107)
Fiscal Year-end: 06/30/13

Business Description:
Specialty Medical Device Designer, Mfr & Distr
S.I.C.: 3841
N.A.I.C.S.: 339112

Personnel:
Mark Neilson Balnaves *(Chm)*
Mark Andrew *(CFO)*
Dion Silvy *(Sec)*

Board of Directors:
Mark Neilson Balnaves
Anthony Mark Ingman
John Nielsen
Victor Previn

Legal Counsel:
Kelly & Co.
Adelaide, Australia

Johnson, Winter & Slattery
Level 10 211 Victoria Square
Adelaide, SA, 5000, Australia

Subsidiaries:

Austofix Surgical Pty Ltd **(1)**
18 Kinkaid Ave
Plympton, South Australia, 5037, Australia
Tel.: (61) 883510644
Fax: (61) 883510855
E-Mail: austofix@austofix.com.au
Web Site: www.austofix.com
Emp.: 20
Surgical Instruments Suppliers
S.I.C.: 3841
N.A.I.C.S.: 339113
Chris Mauriello *(Mgr-Mktg)*

Australian Orthopaedic Fixations Pty Ltd **(1)**
18 Kinkaid Ave
Plympton, SA, 5037, Australia
Tel.: (61) 883510644
Fax: (61) 883510855
E-Mail: austofix@austofix.com.au
Web Site: www.austofix.com.au
Emp.: 15
Medical Orthopaedic Services
S.I.C.: 8062
N.A.I.C.S.: 622110
Chris Henry *(Mgr-Mktg)*

AUSTPAC RESOURCES N.L.

Level 3 62 Pitt Street
Sydney, NSW, 2000, Australia
Mailing Address:
GPO Box 5297
Sydney, NSW, 2001, Australia
Tel.: (61) 292522599
Fax: (61) 292528299
E-Mail: apgtio2@ozemail.com.au
Web Site: www.austpacresources.com
APG—(ASX)
Rev.: $6,773,327
Assets: $38,386,339
Liabilities: $2,803,442
Net Worth: $35,582,897
Earnings: $3,881,335
Emp.: 6
Fiscal Year-end: 06/30/13

Business Description:
Mineral Processing & Exploration Services
S.I.C.: 1481
N.A.I.C.S.: 213115

Personnel:
Michael J. Turbott *(Mng Dir)*
Nicholas J. Gaston *(Sec)*

Board of Directors:
Terry Cuthbertson
Robert J. Harrison
Michael J. Turbott

Legal Counsel:
Gadens Lawyers
77 Castlereagh Street
Sydney, Australia

Emil Ford
580 George Street
Sydney, NSW, 2000, Australia

Plant:

Austpac Resources NL - Newcastle Demonstration Plant **(1)**
240 Cormorant Rd
Kooragang Island, Newcastle, NSW, 2304, Australia
Tel.: (61) 249284338
Fax: (61) 249284644
E-Mail: apgtio2@ozemail.com.au
Web Site: www.austpacresources.com
Emp.: 20
Mineral Exploration Services
S.I.C.: 1481
N.A.I.C.S.: 213115
John Winter *(Gen Mgr)*

AUSTRAL GOLD LIMITED

Terrace Towers Suite 206 Level 2 80 William Street
Sydney, NSW, 2011, Australia
Tel.: (61) 2 9380 7233
Fax: (61) 2 8354 0992
E-Mail: info@australgold.com.au
Web Site: www.australgold.com.au
AGD—(ASX)
Rev.: $65,524,499
Assets: $109,899,370
Liabilities: $76,954,351
Net Worth: $32,945,019
Earnings: ($7,734,662)
Fiscal Year-end: 06/30/13

Business Description:
Metal Mining & Exploration Servcies
S.I.C.: 1099
N.A.I.C.S.: 212299

Personnel:
Catherine Lloyd *(CFO & Sec)*
Stabro Kasaneva *(COO)*

Board of Directors:
Eduardo Elsztain
Pablo Vergara del Carril
Wayne Hubert
Ben Jarvis
Stabro Kasaneva
Robert Trzebski
Saul Zang

AUSTRALASIAN FOOD HOLDINGS PTY. LTD.

830 Wellington Rd
Rowville, VIC, 3178, Australia
Tel.: (61) 397643377
Fax: (61) 397645356

Business Description:
Holding Company
S.I.C.: 6719
N.A.I.C.S.: 551112

Joint Venture:

Fonterra Brands Australia (P&B) Pty Ltd. **(1)**
22 Geddes Street
Locked Bag 3
Balcatta, WA, 6021, Australia AU
Tel.: (61) 894417777
Fax: (61) 894417700
E-Mail: pbflinfo@pbfoods.com.au
Web Site: www.fonterra.com.au
Emp.: 300
Mfr. & Distributor of Ice Cream, Milk & Dairy Products
Import Export
S.I.C.: 2024
N.A.I.C.S.: 311520
Theo Spierings *(CEO)*
Jonathan Mason *(CFO)*

AUSTRALASIAN RESOURCES LTD

Level 7 218 St Georges Terrace
Perth, WA, 6000, Australia
Tel.: (61) 862167400
Fax: (61) 893242164
E-Mail: info@austresources.com.au
Web Site: www.austresources.com.au
ARH—(ASX)
Rev.: $14,129
Assets: $31,504,423
Liabilities: $796,185
Net Worth: $30,708,238
Earnings: ($24,084,373)
Emp.: 10
Fiscal Year-end: 06/30/13

Business Description:
Mineral Exploration
S.I.C.: 1481
N.A.I.C.S.: 213115

Personnel:
Zhenya Wang *(CEO & Mng Dir)*
Grant Ryan *(CFO & Sec)*

Board of Directors:
Domenic Martino
Clive Mensink
Paul Piercy
Vimal Sharma
Zhenya Wang

Legal Counsel:
Jackson McDonald
140 St Georges Terrace
Perth, Australia

Subsidiaries:

International Minerals Pty Ltd. **(1)**
Level 4 5 Mill St
Perth, WA, 6000, Australia
Tel.: (61) 862167400
Fax: (61) 893242164
E-Mail: info@austresources.com.au
Emp.: 5
Iron Ore Mining Services
S.I.C.: 1011
N.A.I.C.S.: 212210

Lefroy Gold Mines Limited **(1)**
L 4 5 Mill St
Perth, WA, 6000, Australia
Tel.: (61) 862167400
Fax: (61) 893242164
E-Mail: info@austresources.com.au
Emp.: 6
Gold Ore Exploration Services
S.I.C.: 1041
N.A.I.C.S.: 212221
Doy Diowing *(Mng Dir)*

AUSTRALIA & NEW ZEALAND BANKING GROUP LIMITED

(d/b/a ANZ Banking Group Limited)
ANZ Centre Melbourne Level 9 833 Collins Street
PO Box 254
Docklands, Melbourne, VIC, 3008, Australia
Tel.: (61) 3 9273 5555
Telex: AA 139920 ANZBNK
Fax: (61) 3 8542 5252
E-Mail: investor.relations@anz.com
Web Site: www.anz.com
Year Founded: 1970
ANZ—(ASX)
Int. Income: $31,823,649,800
Assets: $669,160,546,700
Liabilities: $626,205,184,700
Net Worth: $42,955,362,000
Earnings: $5,905,580,700
Emp.: 48,239
Fiscal Year-end: 09/30/12

Business Description:
Bank Holding Company
S.I.C.: 6712
N.A.I.C.S.: 551111

Personnel:
Michael R. P. Smith *(CEO)*
Graham Hodges *(Deputy CEO)*
Alistair Currie *(Grp COO)*
Anne Weatherston *(CIO)*
Jennifer Evans *(Co-Chief Risk Officer)*
Nigel Williams *(Co-Chief Risk Officer)*
Joyce A. Phillips *(CEO-Wealth & Private Banking & Mng Dir-Mktg, Innovation & Digital)*
Philip Chronican *(CEO-Australia)*
Andrew Geczy *(CEO-Intl & Institutional Banking)*
David Hisco *(CEO-New Zealand)*
Shayne Cary Elliott *(Member-Mgmt Bd)*
Bob Santamaria *(Gen Counsel & Co-Sec)*
John W. Priestley *(Co-Sec)*

Board of Directors:
John P. Morschel
G. J. Clark
Paula Jane Dwyer
Peter Algermon Franc Hay
Hsien Yang Lee
I. J. Macfarlane
D. E. Meiklejohn
Michael R. P. Smith
Alison Mary Watkins

Computershare Investor Services Pty Ltd
GPO Box 2975
Melbourne, VIC, Australia VIC

Computershare Investor Services Limited
Private Bag 92119
Auckland, New Zealand

The Bank of New York Mellon Corporation
BNY Mellon Shareowner Services PO Box 358516
Pittsburgh, PA 15252

Divisions:

ANZ Asia Pacific Division **(1)**
Level 6 100 Queen Street
Melbourne, VIC, 3000, Australia
Tel.: (61) 392736141
Web Site: www.anz.com
Sales Range: $900-999.9 Million
Emp.: 4,394
Banking Operations Management Services
S.I.C.: 8741
N.A.I.C.S.: 551114
Sean West *(Mng Dir-Wealth Asia)*
Wayne Stevenson *(CFO)*

Non-U.S. Groups:

ANZ International Pte. Ltd. **(2)**
1 Raffles Place
#32-00 OUB Centre, Singapore, 049315, Singapore SG
Tel.: (65) 65358355 (100%)
Telex: 23336
Fax: (65) 6539 6111
Web Site: www.anz.com
Bank Holding Company; Commercial Banking Services
S.I.C.: 6712
N.A.I.C.S.: 551111
Joseph Abrahams *(Acting CEO)*

Subsidiary:

ANZ Singapore Limited **(3)**
1 Raffles Place
#32-00 OUB Centre, Singapore, 048616, Singapore (100%)
Tel.: (65) 65358355
Telex: 23336
Fax: (65) 65396111
Web Site: www.anz.com
Financial Services
S.I.C.: 6159
N.A.I.C.S.: 522298
Bill Foo *(Gen Mgr)*

Non-U.S. Subsidiary:

P.T. ANZ Panin Bank **(3)**
ANZ Tower Jl Jend Sudirman Kav 33A
Jakarta, 10220, Indonesia (85%)
Tel.: (62) 215750300

Fax: (62) 215727447
E-Mail: wiharjf@anz.com
Web Site: www.anz.com
Emp.: 140
Banking Services
S.I.C.: 6159
N.A.I.C.S.: 522298

Non-U.S. Units:

ANZ Malaysia (3)
Wisma Genting 4th Floor
Jalan Sultan Ismail, 50250 Kuala Lumpur, Malaysia (100%)
Tel.: (60) 321616088
Telex: 31054
Fax: (60) 3 2161 3210
Web Site: www.anz.com
Emp.: 3
Personal & Commercial Banking Services
S.I.C.: 6029
N.A.I.C.S.: 522110
Fauziah Hisham *(Dir-Institutional Relationships)*

ANZ Philippines (3)
23/F GT Tower International 6813 Ayala Avenue
Corner HV Dela Costa Street, Makati, Philippines
Tel.: (63) 28188117
Fax: (63) 28188112
Web Site: www.anz.com
Personal & Commercial Banking Services
S.I.C.: 6029
N.A.I.C.S.: 522110
Panadda Manoleehakul *(CEO)*

ANZ Thailand (3)
9th Floor GPF Witthayu Tower A
93-1 Wireless Road, Bangkok, 10330, Thailand
Tel.: (66) 22566350
Telex: 21583
Fax: (66) 22566347
Emp.: 3
Trade Financing Services
S.I.C.: 6159
N.A.I.C.S.: 522293
Hintana Kittividoolnas *(Gen Mgr)*

ANZ Vietnam (3)
14 Le Thai To Street
Hoan Kiem, Hanoi, Vietnam
Tel.: (84) 438258190
Fax: (84) 438258188
Web Site: www.anz.com
Emp.: 50
Personal & Commercial Banking Services
S.I.C.: 6029
N.A.I.C.S.: 522110
Thuy Quynh Vu *(Head-Corp & Institutional Banking-Hanoi)*

ANZ International (Hong Kong) Ltd. (2)
Fl 31 One Exchange Sq
8 Connaught Pl, Central, China (Hong Kong) HK
Tel.: (852) 28437111 (100%)
Telex: 86019 ANZ GK MX
Fax: (852) 28680089
Web Site: www.anz.com
Emp.: 400
Bank Holding Company; Commercial Banking Services
S.I.C.: 6712
N.A.I.C.S.: 551111
Alistair Bulloch *(CEO)*
Megan Wong *(CFO & COO-North East Asia)*
Nigel Christopher William Denby *(Chief Risk Officer-Asia Pacific Grp)*

Subsidiaries:

ANZ Asia Limited (3)
Suites 3101-5 One Exchange Square
8 Connaught Place, Central, China (Hong Kong) HK
Tel.: (852) 28437111 (100%)
Telex: 86019
Fax: (852) 28680089
Web Site: www.anz.com
Emp.: 4
Personal & Commercial Banking Services
S.I.C.: 6029
N.A.I.C.S.: 522110
Peter Chan *(Head-Corp & Institutional Relationship Mgmt)*

Non-U.S. Subsidiary:

ANZ Bank (Vanuatu) Limited (3)
ANZ House Kumul Highway
9003 Port-Vila, Vanuatu (100%)
Mailing Address:
PO Box 9003
Port-Vila, Vanuatu
Tel.: (678) 26355
Telex: 21012
Fax: (678) 22814
E-Mail: vanuatu@anz.com
Web Site: www.anz.com
Emp.: 100
Banking Services
S.I.C.: 6029
N.A.I.C.S.: 522110
Paul Mason *(Gen Mgr)*

Non-U.S. Units:

ANZ Japan (3)
33rd Fl Marunouchi Bldg 2-4-1 Marunochi 2-chome
Chiyoda-ku, Tokyo, 100-6333, Japan (100%)
Tel.: (81) 362127702
Telex: 24157
Fax: (81) 362127719
Web Site: www.anz.com
Emp.: 300
Personal & Commercial Banking Services
S.I.C.: 6029
N.A.I.C.S.: 522110

ANZ Korea (3)
22nd Fl Kyobo Building 1 Chongro 1
Seoul, Korea (South) (100%)
Tel.: (82) 27303151
Telex: 27338
Fax: (82) 27376325
E-Mail: kimhe6@anz.com
Web Site: www.anz.com
Emp.: 70
Corporate Banking
S.I.C.: 6029
N.A.I.C.S.: 522110
Heung-Je Kim *(CEO)*

ANZ Shanghai (3)
22nd Floor Raffles City 268 Xizang Middle Road
Peoples Square, Shanghai, 200001, China (100%)
Tel.: (86) 2161366000
Fax: (86) 2161366050
Web Site: www.anz.com
Emp.: 200
Personal & Commercial Banking Services
S.I.C.: 6029
N.A.I.C.S.: 522110

ANZ Taiwan (3)
Suite 1208 12/F International Trade Bldg
333 Keelung Rd, Section 1, Taipei, 11012, Taiwan (100%)
Tel.: (886) 227577299
Telex: 11894
Fax: (886) 237252780
E-Mail: anztaiwan@anz.com
Web Site: www.anz.com
Emp.: 40
Personal & Commercial Banking Services
S.I.C.: 6029
N.A.I.C.S.: 522110
Andrew Leong *(CEO)*

Non-U.S. Subsidiaries:

ANZ Bank (Samoa) Limited (2)
Corner of Beach Road & Post Office Street
PO Box L1855
Apia, Samoa (Western) WS
Tel.: (685) 69999 (100%)
Telex: 258 BWS SX
Fax: (685) 24595
E-Mail: samoa@anz.com
Web Site: www.anz.com
Personal & Commercial Banking Services
S.I.C.: 6029
N.A.I.C.S.: 522110
Saitoria Hanipale *(Mgr-Rural Banking)*

ANZ Bank Solomon Islands (2)
PO Box 10
Honiara, Solomon Islands (100%)
Tel.: (677) 21111
Telex: 66321
Fax: (677) 26937
E-Mail: solomons@anz.com
Web Site: www.anz.com
Personal & Commercial Banking Services
S.I.C.: 6029
N.A.I.C.S.: 522110
Brian Robb *(CEO)*

ANZ Cook Islands (2)
ANZ House Avarua
PO Box 907
Rarotonga, Cook Islands
Tel.: (682) 21750
Telex: 6200038
Fax: (682) 21760
E-Mail: anzcooks@anz.com
Web Site: www.anz.com
Emp.: 40
Personal & Commercial Banking Services
S.I.C.: 6029
N.A.I.C.S.: 522110
David Dennis *(Gen Mgr)*

ANZ Fiji (2)
ANZ House 25 Victoria Parade
PO Box 179
Suva, Fiji (100%)
Tel.: (679) 132411
Telex: 2194
Fax: (679) 3213 756
E-Mail: ebusfj@anz.com
Web Site: www.anz.com
Personal & Commercial Banking Services
S.I.C.: 6029
N.A.I.C.S.: 522110
John Velegrinis *(Gen Mgr)*

ANZ Tonga (2)
Taufa'ahau Road
PO Box 910
Nuku'alofa, Tonga (100%)
Tel.: (676) 67620500
Fax: (676) 67623870
Web Site: www.anz.com
Emp.: 80
Personal & Commercial Banking Services
S.I.C.: 6029
N.A.I.C.S.: 522110
Paul Pelzer *(Gen Mgr)*
Noleen Blake *(COO)*

Australia & New Zealand Banking Group (PNG) Limited (2)
Level 2 ANZ Hauf Harbour city
PO Box 1152
Port Moresby, Papua New Guinea (100%)
Tel.: (675) 3223203
Telex: 22178
Fax: (675) 3211775
E-Mail: cshdpg@anz.com
Web Site: www.anz.com
Emp.: 500
S.I.C.: 6159
N.A.I.C.S.: 522298
Mark Baker *(Mng Dir)*

ANZ Institutional Division (1)
Level 6 100 Queen Street
Melbourne, VIC, 3000, Australia
Tel.: (61) 392736141
Web Site: www.anz.com
Sales Range: $5-14.9 Billion
Emp.: 6,051
Corporate & Institutional Banking Services
S.I.C.: 6029
N.A.I.C.S.: 522110
Michael Rowland *(CFO & Gen Mgr-Mktg/Customer Segmentation)*
Peter Laurent *(Chief Risk Officer)*
Shayne Cary Elliott *(Member-Mgmt Bd)*

Esanda Finance Corporation Limited (1)
85 Spring Street
Melbourne, Vic, 3000, Australia AU
Tel.: (61) 396669100
Telex: 154226 ESNDA
Fax: (61) 396669626
E-Mail: info@esanda.com
Web Site: www.esanda.com
Emp.: 600
Financial Services
S.I.C.: 6282
N.A.I.C.S.: 523930
Moray McDonald *(Mng Dir)*

Subsidiaries:

ANZ Australian Capital Territory (1)
25 Petrie Plaza
Canberra, ACT, 2600, Australia
Mailing Address:
GPO Box 371
Canberra, ACT, 2601, Australia
Tel.: (61) 6 276 4100
Fax: (61) 6 276 4240
S.I.C.: 6159
N.A.I.C.S.: 522298

ANZ Northern Territory (1)
69 Smith St
Darwin, NT, 0800, Australia (100%)
Mailing Address:
GPO Box 1
Darwin, NT, 0801, Australia
Tel.: (61) 889823510
Fax: (61) 889823527
Web Site: www.anz.com
Emp.: 30
Banking Services
S.I.C.: 6159
N.A.I.C.S.: 522298
Steve Straub *(Reg Mgr)*

ANZ Private Bank (1)
Fl 1 324 Queen St
Brisbane, QLD, 4000, Australia (100%)
Mailing Address:
GPO Box 1051
Brisbane, QLD, 4001, Australia
Tel.: (61) 732285513
Fax: (61) 732285516
E-Mail: info@anz.com
Web Site: www.anz.com
Emp.: 30
Investment Banking Services
S.I.C.: 6211
N.A.I.C.S.: 522298

ANZ Securities Limited (1)
Level 12 530 Collins Street
Melbourne, VIC, 3000, Australia (100%)
Tel.: (61) 36401400
Fax: (61) 3 9273 1983
Toll Free: 800 658 793
Stock Brokerage & Related Services
S.I.C.: 6211
N.A.I.C.S.: 523120

ANZ Trustees Limited (1)
Level 43 55 Collins Street
Melbourne, VIC, 3000, Australia
Tel.: (61) 1800 011 047
Fax: (61) 3 9273 6411
Wealth Management Services
S.I.C.: 6799
N.A.I.C.S.: 523920

Australian Commercial Property Management Limited (1)
Level 6 492 Saint Kilda Road
Melbourne, VIC, 3004, Australia AU
Tel.: (61) 398677200 (100%)
Fax: (61) 398200677
E-Mail: info@ribinob.com.au
Web Site: www.ribinob.com.au
Emp.: 35
Property Management Services
S.I.C.: 6531
N.A.I.C.S.: 531312
Ken Lynch *(Chm)*
Andrew Macha *(Co-Sec)*
Viola Pythas *(Co-Sec)*

ETRADE Australia Limited (1)
Level 6 347 Kent Street
Sydney, NSW, 2000, Australia
Tel.: (61) 3 8541 0458
E-Mail: activetrader@etrade.com.au
Web Site: www.etrade.com.au
Online Securities Trading Services
S.I.C.: 7374
N.A.I.C.S.: 518210

OnePath Funds Management Limited (1)
L 13 347 Kent St
Sydney, NSW, 2000, Australia
Tel.: (61) 292348111
Fax: (61) 292346668
Investment Management Services
S.I.C.: 6211
N.A.I.C.S.: 523999

U.S. Subsidiary:

ANZ (Delaware) Inc. (1)
277 Park Ave
New York, NY 10172 DE
Tel.: (212) 801-9800 (100%)
Fax: (212) 801-9859

Australia & New Zealand Banking Group Limited—(Continued)

Web Site: www.anz.com
Sales Range: $1-4.9 Billion
Emp.: 105
Bank Holding Company
S.I.C.: 6712
N.A.I.C.S.: 551111
Douglas Stolberg *(CEO-America)*
John Wade *(CEO-American Territories & Guam)*

Subsidiary:

ANZ Securities Inc. **(2)**
277 Park Ave
New York, NY 10172 (100%)
Tel.: (212) 801-9800
Telex: 607559
Fax: (212) 801-9859
Web Site: www.anz.com
Emp.: 85
Investment Banking
S.I.C.: 6029
N.A.I.C.S.: 522110
John Wade *(Head-Ops & Infrastructure & Deputy Gen Mgr)*

Non-U.S. Division:

ANZ National Bank Ltd. **(1)**
Level 14 ANZ Tower 215-229 Lambton Quay
PO Box 1492
Wellington, 6011, New Zealand NZ
Tel.: (64) 44967000 (100%)
Telex: NZ 3385
Fax: (64) 44968074
Web Site: www.anz.co.nz
Emp.: 9,178
Bank Holding Company
S.I.C.: 6712
N.A.I.C.S.: 551111
David Duncan Hisco *(CEO)*
Nick Freeman *(CFO)*
Craig Sims *(COO)*
Peter Lawrence *(CIO)*
Bob Santamaria *(Gen Counsel & Sec)*

Co-Headquarters:

ANZ National Bank Ltd. **(2)**
Level 24 ANZ Centre 23-29 Albert Street
Auckland, New Zealand
Tel.: (64) 93744051
Fax: (64) 93746160
Web Site: www.anznational.co.nz
Corporate Office; Banking Services
S.I.C.: 8741
N.A.I.C.S.: 551114
Wayne Besant *(Mng Dir-Retail Distr)*

Subsidiaries:

ANZ Investment Services (New Zealand) Limited **(3)**
Level 6 1 Victoria Street
Wellington, 6011, New Zealand
Tel.: (64) 44967000
Fax: (64) 44736919
Financial Investment Services
S.I.C.: 6211
N.A.I.C.S.: 523999

Arawata Assets Limited **(3)**
Level 6 1 Victoria Street
Wellington, 6011, New Zealand
Tel.: (64) 44968071
Fax: (64) 44968074
Financial Management Services
S.I.C.: 6211
N.A.I.C.S.: 523999
Craig Plim *(Head-Property)*

Direct Broking Limited **(3)**
Ground Floor 1 Victoria Street
Wellington, 6011, New Zealand
Tel.: (64) 44996655
Fax: (64) 44987064
E-Mail: help@directbroking.co.nz
Web Site: www.directbroking.co.nz
Emp.: 3
Online Securities Trading Services
S.I.C.: 7379
N.A.I.C.S.: 518210
Mark Peterson *(Mng Dir)*

The National Bank of New Zealand Ltd. **(3)**
Level 14 ANZ Tower 215-229 Lambton Quay
PO Box 1492
Wellington, 6011, New Zealand (100%)
Tel.: (64) 44967000
Telex: 31388 NBNZHO NZ
Fax: (64) 44968074
E-Mail: info@nationalbank.co.nz
Web Site: www.nationalbank.co.nz
Emp.: 2,000
Personal & Commercial Banking Services
S.I.C.: 6029
N.A.I.C.S.: 522110
Jennifer Anne Fagg *(Mng Dir)*

Unit:

National Bank of New Zealand - Rural Banking **(4)**
170-186 Featherstone St
PO Box 1393
Wellington, 6006, New Zealand
Tel.: (64) 44944700
Fax: (64) 44986092
Web Site: www.nationalbank.co.nz
Rural Sector Banking Services
S.I.C.: 6029
N.A.I.C.S.: 522110
Charlie Graham *(Mng Dir)*

UDC Finance Ltd. **(3)**
UDC House Level 2 107 Carlton Gore Rd
New Market
PO Box 91145
6330 Auckland, 1142, New Zealand NZ
Mailing Address: (100%)
PO Box 1616
Wellington, New Zealand
Tel.: (64) 93595030
Telex: 3507
Fax: (64) 92554903
E-Mail: udcinz@inz.com
Web Site: www.udc.co.nz
Emp.: 150
International Banking
S.I.C.: 6159
N.A.I.C.S.: 522293
Tessa Price *(CEO)*

Non-U.S. Subsidiary:

ANZ Bank (Kiribati) Limited **(3)**
PO Box 66
Bairiki, Tarawa, Kiribati
Tel.: (686) 21095
Fax: (686) 21200
Emp.: 7
Commercial Banking Services
S.I.C.: 6029
N.A.I.C.S.: 522110
Isikeli Tuituku *(CEO)*
Veilawa Rereiwasaliwa *(COO)*

Non-U.S. Subsidiaries:

ANZ Bank (Europe) Limited **(1)**
40 Bank Street
London, E14 5EJ, United Kingdom
Tel.: (44) 203 229 2121
Fax: (44) 203 229 2378
Commercial Banking Services
S.I.C.: 6029
N.A.I.C.S.: 522110

OnePath (NZ) Limited **(1)**
Level 17 23-29 ANZ Centre Albert Street
Auckland, 1010, New Zealand
Tel.: (64) 9 356 4000
Fax: (64) 9 356 4005
E-Mail: service@anzinvestments.co.nz
Web Site: www.investments.anz.co.nz
Emp.: 13
Investment Management Services
S.I.C.: 6211
N.A.I.C.S.: 523999
Mike Weiss *(Mng Dir)*
Philip Houghton-Brown *(Chief Investment Officer)*

Non-U.S. Units:

ANZ Germany **(1)**
Mainzer Landstrasse 61
D-60329 Frankfurt am Main, Germany (100%)
Tel.: (49) 697100080
Telex: 4185126 ANZBD
Fax: (49) 6971000821
E-Mail: andreas.wodniok@anz.com
Web Site: www.anz.com
Emp.: 10
Corporate Banking Services
S.I.C.: 6029
N.A.I.C.S.: 522110
Andreas Wodniok *(Gen Mgr)*

ANZ UK **(1)**
40 Bank St
Canary Wharf, London, E14 5EJ, United Kingdom
Tel.: (44) 2032292121
Web Site: www.anz.com
Emp.: 250
Personal, Commercial & Investment Banking Services
S.I.C.: 6029
N.A.I.C.S.: 522110
Tim L'Estrange *(Mng Dir-Europe & America)*

AUSTRALIA CHINA HOLDINGS LIMITED

Level 11 32 Martin Place
Sydney, NSW, 2000, Australia
Tel.: (61) 292622822
Fax: (61) 292623912
E-Mail: sec@aakch.com
Web Site: www.aakch.com
AAK—(ASX)
Rev.: $1,253,646
Assets: $79,177,716
Liabilities: $3,106,500
Net Worth: $76,071,216
Earnings: $333,472
Fiscal Year-end: 03/31/13

Business Description:
Investment Holding Services
S.I.C.: 6799
N.A.I.C.S.: 523920

Personnel:
Nelson Chiu *(Chm & Mng Dir)*
Stonely W. T. Sek *(Sec)*

Board of Directors:
Nelson Chiu
Michael Meen Foh Chai
Henry Xiao B. Qin

AUSTRALIA MINERALS AND MINING GROUP LIMITED

3 Bay Road
Claremont, WA, 6010, Australia
Tel.: (61) 8 9389 5557
Fax: (61) 8 9389 5510
E-Mail: info@ammg.com.au
Web Site: www.ammg.com.au
Year Founded: 2007
AKA—(ASX)
Rev.: $748,995
Assets: $7,732,966
Liabilities: $270,999
Net Worth: $7,461,966
Earnings: ($1,413,894)
Emp.: 7
Fiscal Year-end: 06/30/13

Business Description:
Mineral Mining & Exploration Services
S.I.C.: 1099
N.A.I.C.S.: 212299

Personnel:
Ric Dawson *(Mng Dir)*
Piers Lewis *(CFO & Sec)*
Summer Qi *(R&D Officer)*

Board of Directors:
Luke Frederick Atkins
Peter Bailey
Ric Dawson
Daniel Lewis Tenardi

Legal Counsel:
Steinepreis Paganin
Level 4 The Read Buildings 16 Milligan Street
Perth, Australia

AUSTRALIA NEW AGRIBUSINESS & CHEMICAL GROUP LIMITED

(Formerly Daton Group Australia Limited)
Suite 21 Level 1 7 Clunies Ross Court BTP
Eight Mile Plains, QLD, 4113, Australia
Mailing Address:
PO Box 4554
Eight Mile Plains, QLD, 4113, Australia
Tel.: (61) 7 3147 8010
Fax: (61) 7 3147 8001
E-Mail: queries@newagri.com.au
Web Site: www.newagribusiness.com.au
ANB—(ASX)
Rev.: $12,163,156
Assets: $43,207,514
Liabilities: $10,086,319
Net Worth: $33,121,195
Earnings: $11,244,733
Emp.: 15
Fiscal Year-end: 12/31/12

Business Description:
Holding Company; Coal & Fertilizer Mining
S.I.C.: 6719
N.A.I.C.S.: 551112

Personnel:
Yinan Zhang *(Mng Dir)*
Yi Yang *(Sec)*

Board of Directors:
Jun Xiao
Yiming Cui
James Naiming Li
Yinan Zhang
Julia Yan Zhu

AUSTRALIA ORIENTAL MINERALS NL

(Name Changed to AO Energy Limited)

AUSTRALIA SANDSTONE MERCHANTS PTY. LTD.

465 Halcrows Road
Glenorie, Sydney, NSW, 2157, Australia
Mailing Address:
PO Box 790
Round Corner, Dural, NSW, 2158, Australia
Tel.: (61) 2 9980 7941
Fax: (61) 2 9651 7742
E-Mail: info@australiansandstone.com.au
Web Site: www.australiansandstone.com.au
Sales Range: $10-24.9 Million

Business Description:
Sandstone Quarrying, Processing & Distr
S.I.C.: 1411
N.A.I.C.S.: 212311

Personnel:
Buddy Francis *(Co-Mng Dir)*
Tony Francis *(Co-Mng Dir)*

AUSTRALIA ZOO PTY LTD

163A Steve Irwin Way
Beerwah, QLD, 4519, Australia
Tel.: (61) 754362000
Fax: (61) 754948604
E-Mail: info@australiazoo.com.au
Web Site: www.australiazoo.com.au
Year Founded: 1970
Emp.: 400

Business Description:
Zoo Operations
S.I.C.: 8422
N.A.I.C.S.: 712130

Personnel:
Terri Irwin *(Owner)*

AUSTRALIAN AGRICULTURAL COMPANY LIMITED

Level 1 299 Coronation Drive
Milton, QLD, 4064, Australia
Tel.: (61) 733684400

Fax: (61) 733684401
E-Mail: info@aaco.com.au
Web Site: www.aaco.com.au
AAC—(ASX)
Rev.: $506,004,160
Assets: $1,216,620,487
Liabilities: $551,094,785
Net Worth: $665,525,702
Earnings: ($8,763,019)
Emp.: 432
Fiscal Year-end: 12/31/12
Business Description:
Beef & Agricultural Products
S.I.C.: 0212
N.A.I.C.S.: 112111
Personnel:
Jason Strong *(CEO & Mng Dir)*
Craig White *(CFO)*
Troy Setter *(COO)*
Stuart Carmichael *(Chief Risk Officer)*
Bruce Bennett *(Gen Counsel & Sec)*
Board of Directors:
Donald McGauchie
Adil Allana
Stuart Black
David Crombie
Shehan Dissanayake
Mohd Emir
Tom Keene
Legal Counsel:
King & Wood Mallesons
Level 33 Waterfront Place 1 Eagle Street
Brisbane, Australia
Subsidiary:

Chefs Partner Pty Ltd. **(1)**
30 Manton St
Morningside, Brisbane, QLD, 4170, Australia
Tel.: (61) 7 3902 5900
Fax: (61) 7 3902 5999
E-Mail: info@chefspartner.com.au
Web Site: www.chefspartner.com.au
Emp.: 30
Meat Products Whslr
S.I.C.: 5142
N.A.I.C.S.: 424420
Grant Taylor *(Plant Mgr)*

AUSTRALIAN AGRICULTURAL PROJECTS LTD
(Formerly redisland Australia Ltd.)
79 Broadway
Nedlands, WA, 6009, Australia
Tel.: (61) 8 6389 2688
Fax: (61) 8 6389 2588
E-Mail: info@redisland.com
Web Site: www.redisland.com
AAP—(ASX)
Rev.: $3,407,396
Assets: $14,767,968
Liabilities: $9,608,088
Net Worth: $5,159,880
Earnings: $2,005,864
Fiscal Year-end: 06/30/13
Business Description:
Olive Oil Mfr
S.I.C.: 2075
N.A.I.C.S.: 311224
Personnel:
Paul Robert Challis *(CEO, Mng Dir & Dir-Fin)*
Kimberley Arnold Hogg *(Sec)*
Board of Directors:
Paul Robert Challis
Phillip John Grimsey
Anthony Ho
Legal Counsel:
Steinepreis Paganin
Level 4 16 Milligan St
Perth, Australia
Subsidiary:

AOX Pty Ltd **(1)**
31 Lakewood Blvd
Braeside, VIC, 3195, Australia
Tel.: (61) 385871400
Fax: (61) 385871444
E-Mail: info@redisland.com
Emp.: 10
Olive Oil Mfr & Distr
S.I.C.: 2079
N.A.I.C.S.: 311225
Mike Konowalous *(Mgr)*

AUSTRALIAN ALLIANCE INSURANCE COMPANY LIMITED
Level 4 440 Collins St
Melbourne, VIC, 3000, Australia
Tel.: (61) 385201895
Fax: (61) 3 9520 7926
Web Site: www.aai.com.au
Sales Range: $75-99.9 Million
Emp.: 1,200
Business Description:
General Insurance Services
S.I.C.: 6411
N.A.I.C.S.: 524210
Personnel:
Andrew Mulvogue *(Gen Mgr-Suncorp Personal Insurance)*

AUSTRALIAN-AMERICAN MINING CORPORATION LTD.
572 Hay Street
Perth, WA, 6000, Australia
Mailing Address:
PO Box 1788
West Perth, WA, 6872, Australia
Tel.: (61) 8 9481 0799
Fax: (61) 8 9481 1927
E-Mail: info@ausamerican.com
Web Site: www.ausamerican.com
AIW—(ASX DEU OTC)
Rev.: $62,757
Assets: $7,903,327
Liabilities: $1,132,719
Net Worth: $6,770,608
Earnings: ($5,968,375)
Fiscal Year-end: 06/30/13
Business Description:
Mineral Exploration Services
S.I.C.: 1094
N.A.I.C.S.: 212291
Personnel:
James Malone *(Chm, CFO & Sec)*
Richard Holmes *(Mng Dir)*
Board of Directors:
James Malone
Donald James Wentworth Falconer
Richard Holmes
Peter Neil Landau
Benjamin Warren Mead

AUSTRALIAN ASSOCIATED MOTOR INSURERS LIMITED
PO Box 14180
Melbourne, Victoria, 8001, Australia
Tel.: (61) 61385201300
Fax: (61) 385201950
E-Mail: aami@aami.com.au
Web Site: www.aami.com.au
Sales Range: $1-4.9 Billion
Emp.: 2,900
Business Description:
Insurance Services
S.I.C.: 6411
N.A.I.C.S.: 524298

AUSTRALIAN ASSOCIATED PRESS PTY LTD
AAP News Ctr 3 Rider Blvd Rhodes Waterside
Rhodes, NSW, 2138, Australia
Tel.: (61) 293228000
Fax: (61) 293228889
Web Site: www.aap.com.au
Year Founded: 1935
Sales Range: $125-149.9 Million
Emp.: 600
Business Description:
News Syndicate
S.I.C.: 7383
N.A.I.C.S.: 519110
Personnel:
Bruce Davidson *(CEO)*
Robert Davies *(CFO)*

AUSTRALIAN BANC CAPITAL SECURITIES TRUST
181 University Avenue Suite 300
Toronto, ON, M5H 3M7, Canada
Tel.: (416) 364-2839
Fax: (416) 363-2089
E-Mail: nmurdoch@cclgroup.com
Year Founded: 2010
AUZ.UN—(TSX)
Sales Range: Less than $1 Million
Business Description:
Investment Services
S.I.C.: 6211
N.A.I.C.S.: 523999
Personnel:
Michael W. Freund *(Chm)*
W. Neil Murdoch *(Pres & CEO)*
Darren N. Cabral *(CFO & VP)*
Board of Directors:
Michael W. Freund
Darren N. Cabral
W. Neil Murdoch
Transfer Agent:
Computershare Investor Services Inc.
Montreal, QC, Canada

AUSTRALIAN BANC INCOME FUND
181 University Avenue Suite 300
Toronto, ON, M5H 3M7, Canada
Tel.: (416) 364-2839
Fax: (416) 363-2089
E-Mail: nmurdoch@cclgroup.com
Year Founded: 2011
AUI.UN—(TSX)
Business Description:
Investment Services
S.I.C.: 6211
N.A.I.C.S.: 523999
Personnel:
Michael W. Freund *(Chm & CFO)*
W. Neil Murdoch *(Pres & CEO)*
Board of Directors:
Michael W. Freund
Darren N. Cabral
W. Neil Murdoch
Transfer Agent:
Computershare Investor Services Inc.
Montreal, QC, Canada

AUSTRALIAN BAUXITE LIMITED
(d/b/a ABx)
Level 2 131 Macquarie Street
Sydney, NSW, 2000, Australia
Tel.: (61) 292517177
Fax: (61) 292517500
E-Mail: corporate@australianbauxite.com.au
Web Site: www.australianbauxite.com.au
Year Founded: 2009
ABZ—(ASX)
Rev.: $789,778
Assets: $15,128,652
Liabilities: $258,090
Net Worth: $14,870,563
Earnings: ($1,150,163)
Fiscal Year-end: 12/31/12
Business Description:
Bauxite Mining Services
S.I.C.: 1099
N.A.I.C.S.: 212299
Personnel:
Peter J. Meers *(Deputy Chm)*
Ian Levy *(CEO & Mng Dir)*
Francis Choy *(CFO)*
Leon Hawker *(COO)*
David Laurence Hughes *(Co-Sec)*
Henry Kinstlinger *(Co-Sec)*
Board of Directors:
John S. Dawkins
Ken Boundy
Ian Levy
Peter J. Meers
Rado Jacob Rebek
Huang Wei
Legal Counsel:
Piper Alderman
Level 23 Governor Macquarie Tower 1 Farrer Place
Sydney, NSW, 2000, Australia

AUSTRALIAN CENTRAL CREDIT UNION LTD
(d/b/a People's Choice Credit Union)
GPO Box 1942
Adelaide, SA, 5001, Australia
Tel.: (61) 883058305
Fax: (61) 883058388
Web Site: www.peopleschoicecu.com.au
Year Founded: 1949
Rev.: $441,113,635
Assets: $6,041,492,424
Liabilities: $5,583,842,746
Net Worth: $457,649,678
Earnings: $30,038,533
Emp.: 1,000
Fiscal Year-end: 06/30/13
Business Description:
Banking & Credit Services
S.I.C.: 6062
N.A.I.C.S.: 522130
Personnel:
William Raymond Cossey *(Chm)*
John Leonard Cossons *(Vice Chm)*
Peter Hans Torsten Evers *(Mng Dir & Sec)*
Steve Laidlaw *(CFO & Exec Gen Mgr-Corp Svcs)*
Board of Directors:
William Raymond Cossey
Rosemary Helen Simon Brooks
John Leonard Cossons
Stephen Mark Day
Peter Hans Torsten Evers
Edward Terrence McGuirk
Jan McMahon
Kathryn Anne Skipper

AUSTRALIAN ENERGY MARKET OPERATOR (AEMO)
Level 22 530 Collins St
Melbourne, VIC, 3000, Australia
Tel.: (61) 396098000
Fax: (61) 396098080
Web Site: www.aemo.com.au
Year Founded: 1996
Sales Range: $50-74.9 Million
Emp.: 230
Business Description:
Electricity Administrative Services
S.I.C.: 4939
N.A.I.C.S.: 221118
Personnel:
Thomas Parry *(Chm)*
Matt Zema *(CEO & Mng Dir)*
Karen Olesnicky *(CFO & Dir-Bus Svcs)*
Chris Ford *(CIO)*
Brett Hausler *(Sec & Dir-Corp Affairs)*
Board of Directors:
Thomas Parry
Ian Fraser
Leslie V. Hosking
Michael Lavarch
Greg Martin
Patricia McKenzie
Karen Moses
Michael Sargent

Australian Energy Market Operator (AEMO)—(Continued)

Kathryn Spargo

AUSTRALIAN ETHICAL INVESTMENT LIMITED

Trevor Pearcey House Block E
Traeger Court 34 Thynne Street
Bruce, WA, 2617, Australia
Tel.: (61) 262011988
Fax: (61) 262011987
E-Mail: enquiries@australianethical.com.au
Web Site: www.australianethical.com.au
AEF—(ASX)
Rev.: $17,067,917
Assets: $10,711,132
Liabilities: $3,107,319
Net Worth: $7,603,813
Earnings: $1,107,791
Fiscal Year-end: 06/30/13

Business Description:
Investment Managing
S.I.C.: 6799
N.A.I.C.S.: 523920

Personnel:
Phillip Vernon *(Mng Dir)*
David Barton *(CFO)*
David Macri *(Chief Investment Officer)*
Tom May *(Gen Counsel & Sec)*

Board of Directors:
Steve Gibbs
Mara Bun
Tony Cole
Kate Greenhill
Andre Morony
Phillip Vernon

Subsidiary:

Australian Ethical Superannuation Pty Limited **(1)**
PO Box 1916
Wollongong, NSW, 2500, Australia
Tel.: (61) 1300134337
Fax: (61) 262011959
E-Mail: aes@australianethical.com.au
Pension Funds Management Services
S.I.C.: 6282
N.A.I.C.S.: 523920
Howard Pender *(Exec Dir)*

AUSTRALIAN FILM INSTITUTE

236 Dorcas St
Melbourne, VIC, 3205, Australia
Tel.: (61) 396961844
Fax: (61) 396967972
E-Mail: info@afi.org.au
Web Site: www.afi.org.au
Year Founded: 1958
Sales Range: $1-9.9 Million
Emp.: 11

Business Description:
Film Promoter
S.I.C.: 7819
N.A.I.C.S.: 512199

Personnel:
Damian Trewhella *(CEO)*

Board of Directors:
Eve Ash
Mikael Borglund
Geoff Brown
David Chambers
Edwin Emery
Maggie Gerrand
Russell Howcroft
Denny Lawrence
Alaric McAusland
David Muir
Ian Sutherland

AUSTRALIAN FOOD & FIBRE LTD.

Suite 3 50 Auburn Street
Moree, 2400, Australia
Tel.: (61) 2 6752 5795

Business Description:
Cotton & Miscellaneous Agricultural Product Production Services
S.I.C.: 0131
N.A.I.C.S.: 111920

Personnel:
David Robinson *(Exec Chm)*

Subsidiary:

PrimeAg Australia Limited **(1)**
78 West Street
PO Box 1312
Toowoomba, QLD, 4350, Australia
Tel.: (61) 746884588
Fax: (61) 746130230
E-Mail: info@primeag.com.au
Web Site: www.primeag.com.au
Rev.: $84,813,393
Assets: $267,345,545
Liabilities: $17,370,765
Net Worth: $249,974,780
Earnings: ($32,285,300)
Emp.: 46
Fiscal Year-end: 06/30/13
Agriculture Industry
S.I.C.: 0711
N.A.I.C.S.: 115112
Peter James Corish *(CEO & Mng Dir)*
Samantha J. Macansh *(CFO & Sec)*

AUSTRALIAN FOUNDATION INVESTMENT COMPANY LIMITED

Level 21 101 Collins Street
Melbourne, VIC, 3000, Australia
Tel.: (61) 396509911
Fax: (61) 396509100
E-Mail: invest@afi.com.au
Web Site: www.afi.com.au
Year Founded: 1928
AFI—(ASX)
Rev.: $272,205,899
Assets: $5,962,035,425
Liabilities: $1,140,559,692
Net Worth: $4,821,475,733
Earnings: $252,999,996
Emp.: 17
Fiscal Year-end: 06/30/13

Business Description:
Provider of Investment Services
S.I.C.: 6282
N.A.I.C.S.: 523930

Personnel:
Ross E. Barker *(Mng Dir)*
Andrew J. B. Porter *(CFO & Co-Sec)*
R. Mark Freeman *(Chief Investment Officer)*
Simon M. Pordage *(Co-Sec)*

Board of Directors:
Terrence A. Campbell
Ross E. Barker
Jacqueline C. Hey
Graeme R. Liebelt
John Paterson
David Peever
Fergus D. Ryan
Catherine M. Walter
Peter J. Williams

Computershare Investor Services Pty Ltd
Level 2 159 Hurstmere Road Takapuna North Shore City
Auckland, New Zealand

Subsidiary:

Australian Investment Company Services Limited **(1)**
Level 21 101 Collins St
Melbourne, Victoria, 3000, Australia
Tel.: (61) 396509911
Fax: (61) 396509100
E-Mail: invest@afi.com.au
Financial Investment Services
S.I.C.: 6211
N.A.I.C.S.: 523999
Ross Barker *(Mng Dir)*

AUSTRALIAN GEMSTONE HOUSE PTY LTD

Level 34 50 Bridge St
2000 Sydney, NSW, Australia
Tel.: (61) 282160777
Fax: (61) 282160788
E-Mail: info@agil.com.au
Web Site: www.ozgemstones.com.au
Sales Range: $25-49.9 Million
Emp.: 100

Business Description:
Gemstone Producer, Exporter & Marketer
S.I.C.: 3281
N.A.I.C.S.: 327991

Personnel:
Pnina Feldman *(Chm)*
Sholom Dovber Feldman *(Sec)*

AUSTRALIAN GRAND PRIX CORPORATION PTY. LTD.

Level 5 616 St Kilda Road
Melbourne, VIC, 3004, Australia
Mailing Address:
PO Box 577
South Melbourne, VIC, 3205, Australia
Tel.: (61) 392587100
Fax: (61) 396820410
E-Mail: enquiries@grandprix.com.au
Web Site: www.grandprix.com.au
Rev.: $126,720,402
Assets: $33,196,096
Liabilities: $17,131,082
Net Worth: $16,065,014
Earnings: $1,079,616
Emp.: 57
Fiscal Year-end: 06/30/13

Business Description:
Sports Club Managers & Promoters
S.I.C.: 7941
N.A.I.C.S.: 711211

Personnel:
Ronald J. Walker *(Chm)*
John Harnden *(Deputy Chm)*
Andrew Westacott *(CEO)*
Prataal Raj *(Gen Counsel)*

Board of Directors:
Ronald J. Walker
Laura Anderson
William Bowness
Patrick J. Flannigan
Gillian Franklin
John Harnden
Alan Oxley
Kenneth John Ryan

AUSTRALIAN INDUSTRIAL REIT

c/o Fife Capital Funds Ltd Level 12
89 York Street
Sydney, NSW, 2000, Australia
Tel.: (61) 2 9251 2777
Fax: (61) 2 9251 2877
E-Mail: admin@aireit.com.au
Web Site: www.aireit.com.au
ANI—(ASX)

Business Description:
Real Estate Investment Services
S.I.C.: 6211
N.A.I.C.S.: 523999

Personnel:
Rod Pearse *(Chm)*
Allan Fife *(Mng Dir & Co-Sec)*
Keir Barnes *(CFO & Co-Sec)*

Board of Directors:
Rod Pearse
Michael Allen
Peter Dransfield
Allan Fife
John Hudson

AUSTRALIAN JOCKEY CLUB

(See Under Australian Turf Club)

AUSTRALIAN MINES LIMITED

Level 1 83 Havelock Street
West Perth, WA, 6005, Australia
Mailing Address:
PO Box 883
West Perth, WA, 6872, Australia
Tel.: (61) 8 9481 5811
Fax: (61) 8 9481 5611
E-Mail: office@australianmines.com.au
Web Site: www.australianmines.com.au
AUZ—(ASX)
Rev.: $3,043
Assets: $5,432,696
Liabilities: $558,366
Net Worth: $4,874,330
Earnings: ($8,576,112)
Emp.: 3
Fiscal Year-end: 06/30/13

Business Description:
Nickel Mining Services
S.I.C.: 1021
N.A.I.C.S.: 212234

Personnel:
Michael Ramsden *(Chm & Sec)*
Benjamin Bell *(Mng Dir)*

Board of Directors:
Michael Ramsden
Benjamin Bell
Mick Elias
Dominic Marinelli
Neil F. Warburton

Legal Counsel:
Fairweather Corporate Lawyers
595 Stirling Highway
Cottesloe, Australia

AUSTRALIAN NATURAL PROTEINS LIMITED

21 Wells Road
Mordialloc, VIC, 3187, Australia
Tel.: (61) 3 9580 4328
Fax: (61) 3 9580 2294
Web Site: www.australiannaturalproteins.com.au
Year Founded: 2001
AYB—(ASX)
Rev.: $2,507,179
Assets: $19,683,316
Liabilities: $10,626,933
Net Worth: $9,056,384
Earnings: ($4,631,428)
Fiscal Year-end: 06/30/13

Business Description:
Farming Services
S.I.C.: 0214
N.A.I.C.S.: 112410

Personnel:
Raymond Taylor *(Mng Dir)*
Justyn Stedwell *(Sec)*

Board of Directors:
Paul Duckett
Raymond Taylor
Pun Yan Wu
Lidi Xu

Legal Counsel:
Hardymans Lawyers
Suite 3 6 Walker Street
Torquay, VIC, 3228, Australia

AUSTRALIAN OIL COMPANY LIMITED

Suite 1 45 Ord Street
West Perth, WA, 6005, Australia
Tel.: (61) 8 9226 0866
Fax: (61) 8 9486 7375
E-Mail: info@australianoilcompany.com
Web Site: www.australianoilcompany.com
AOC—(ASX)
Rev.: $172,978
Assets: $987,344
Liabilities: $400,286

Net Worth: $587,058
Earnings: ($1,225,578)
Fiscal Year-end: 06/30/13
Business Description:
Oil & Gas Exploration
S.I.C.: 1389
N.A.I.C.S.: 213112
Personnel:
Andrew Childs *(Chm)*
Gary Jeffery *(Mng Dir)*
Mark Ohlsson *(Sec)*
Board of Directors:
Andrew Childs
Gary Jeffery
Keith Martens

AUSTRALIAN PACIFIC COAL LTD.

Level 7 10 Felix Street
Brisbane, QLD, 4000, Australia
Tel.: (61) 732210679
Fax: (61) 7 3252 2111
E-Mail: info@aqcltd.com
Web Site: www.aqcltd.com
Year Founded: 1999
AQC—(ASX)
Rev.: $430,793
Assets: $3,403,036
Liabilities: $916,369
Net Worth: $2,486,667
Earnings: ($1,955,564)
Fiscal Year-end: 06/30/13
Business Description:
Coal Exploration Services
S.I.C.: 1222
N.A.I.C.S.: 212112
Personnel:
Paul James Byrne *(CEO & Mng Dir)*
Kevin John Mischewski *(Sec)*
Board of Directors:
Peter Alexander Ziegler
Paul James Byrne
Paul Anthony Ingram
Paul Bradley Ryan
Legal Counsel:
Hopgood Ganim
Level 8 Waterfront Place 1 Eagle Street
Brisbane, QLD, 4000, Australia

AUSTRALIAN PHARMACEUTICAL INDUSTRIES LIMITED

11 Grand Avenue
Camellia, NSW, 2142, Australia
Tel.: (61) 288442000
Fax: (61) 288442896
E-Mail: mail@api.net.au
Web Site: www.api.net.au
Year Founded: 1910
API—(ASX)
Rev.: $3,320,279,620
Assets: $1,433,881,663
Liabilities: $825,170,211
Net Worth: $608,711,452
Earnings: $25,314,693
Fiscal Year-end: 08/31/13
Business Description:
Pharmaceutical Products Whlsr
S.I.C.: 5122
N.A.I.C.S.: 424210
Personnel:
Stephen P. Roche *(CEO & Mng Dir)*
Graeme Fallet *(CFO)*
Peter Sanguinetti *(Legal Counsel & Sec)*
Board of Directors:
Peter R. Robinson
Lee Ausburn
Esther Carol Holley
Gerard J. Masters
Robert Dobson Millner
Stephen P. Roche
Michael R. Wooldridge

AUSTRALIAN PLASTIC PROFILES PTY. LTD.

12 Cawarra Rd
Caringbah, NSW, 2229, Australia
Tel.: (61) 0295278800
Fax: (61) 0295278811
E-Mail: sales@app.net.au
Web Site: www.app.net.au
Year Founded: 1972
Sales Range: $25-49.9 Million
Emp.: 120
Business Description:
Plastics, Metal & Electronics Mfr
S.I.C.: 3052
N.A.I.C.S.: 326220
Personnel:
John Hills *(Pres & CEO)*

AUSTRALIAN POSTAL CORPORATION

(d/b/a Australia Post)
111 Bourke Street
Melbourne, VIC, 3000, Australia
Mailing Address:
GPO Box 1777
Melbourne, VIC, 3001, Australia
Tel.: (61) 392047171
Fax: (61) 396631160
Web Site: www.auspost.com.au
Rev.: $6,141,303,720
Assets: $4,586,803,150
Liabilities: $2,833,990,950
Net Worth: $1,752,812,200
Earnings: $325,030,990
Emp.: 32,464
Fiscal Year-end: 06/30/13
Business Description:
Postal Services
S.I.C.: 4311
N.A.I.C.S.: 491110
Personnel:
Ahmed Fahour *(CEO & Mng Dir)*
Ewen Stafford *(COO)*
Greg Sutherland *(CMO)*
Board of Directors:
John Stanhope
Penelope Bingham-Hall
Susan Bitter
Peter Carne
Michael D'Ascenzo
Ahmed Fahour
Brendan Fleiter
Trish White
Talal Yassine
Subsidiary:

Star Track Express Pty. Ltd. (1)
51 Sargents Road
Minchinbury, Sydney, NSW, 2770, Australia AU
Tel.: (61) 2 8801 4000 (100%)
Fax: (61) 2 8801 4001
Web Site: www.startrackexpress.com.au
Sales Range: $100-124.9 Million
Freight Transportation & Logistics Services
S.I.C.: 4731
N.A.I.C.S.: 488510
Stephen Cleary *(CEO)*

Joint Venture:

Australian Air Express Pty. Ltd. (1)
440 Elizabeth St Level 7
Melbourne, 3000, Australia AU
Mailing Address:
PO Box 1324L
Melbourne, 3001, Australia
Tel.: (61) 386333100
Fax: (61) 386333141
Web Site: www.aae.com.au
Freight Air Transportation Services
S.I.C.: 4512
N.A.I.C.S.: 481112

AUSTRALIAN RENEWABLE FUELS LTD

Level 5 409 St Kilda Road
Melbourne, VIC, 3004, Australia
Tel.: (61) 3 9981 0010
Fax: (61) 3 9981 0020
E-Mail: info@arfuels.com.au
Web Site: www.arfuels.com.au
ARW—(ASX)
Rev.: $61,059,107
Assets: $57,720,634
Liabilities: $32,669,419
Net Worth: $25,051,215
Earnings: $2,341,204
Fiscal Year-end: 06/30/13
Business Description:
Bio Diesel Producer
S.I.C.: 2911
N.A.I.C.S.: 324110
Personnel:
Andrew White *(CEO & Mng Dir)*
Michael Burgess *(CFO)*
Christopher Attwood *(COO)*
Mark Licciardo *(Sec)*
Board of Directors:
Philip Garling
Michael Costello
Michael Iwaniw
Deborah Page
Julien Playoust
Andrew White
Legal Counsel:
Gadens Lawyers
Level 25 Bourke Place 600 Bourke Street
Melbourne, Australia
Baker & McKenzie
Level 19 181 William Street
Melbourne, Australia
Subsidiary:

Australian Renewable Fuels Adelaide Pty Ltd (1)
166 Elder Rd
Largs Bay, Adelaide, SA, 5016, Australia
Tel.: (61) 882428600
Fax: (61) 882428626
E-Mail: admin@arfuels.com.au
Emp.: 5
Biodiesel Mfr
S.I.C.: 2999
N.A.I.C.S.: 324199
Tom Engelsman *(Mng Dir)*

U.S. Subsidiary:

American Renewable Fuels Inc (1)
1601 Elm St
Dallas, TX 75201-4701
Tel.: (214) 954-0900
Fax: (214) 954-0966
Biodiesel Mfr
S.I.C.: 2911
N.A.I.C.S.: 324110

AUSTRALIAN RUGBY UNION

Ground Floor 29-57 Christie Street
Saint Leonards, NSW, 2065, Australia
Mailing Address:
PO Box 115
Saint Leonards, NSW, 1590, Australia
Tel.: (61) 280055555
Fax: (61) 280055699
E-Mail: aru@rugby.com.au
Web Site: www.rugby.com.au
Emp.: 100
Business Description:
Management of the Australian National Rugby Team
S.I.C.: 7941
N.A.I.C.S.: 711211
Personnel:
Michael Hawker *(Chm)*
Bill Pulver *(CEO)*

AUSTRALIAN SMALL SCALE OFFERINGS BOARD LIMITED

Level 15 Corporate Centre One
2 Corporate Court, Bundall, QLD, 4217, Australia
Tel.: (61) 1300 722 954
Fax: (61) 1300 722 593
E-Mail: info@assob.com.au
Web Site: www.assob.com.au
AOB—(NSXA)
Sales Range: Less than $1 Million
Business Description:
Investment Services
S.I.C.: 6211
N.A.I.C.S.: 523999
Personnel:
Anthony Puls *(Chm)*
Paul Niederer *(CEO & Mng Dir)*
Susan Williams *(Sec)*
Board of Directors:
Anthony Puls
Paul Niederer
Terrina Planincic

THE AUSTRALIAN SOCIAL INFRASTRUCTURE FUND

Level 12 15 Williams Street
Melbourne, VIC, 3000, Australia
Tel.: (61) 3 8601 2668
Fax: (61) 3 9200 2282
E-Mail: asif@folkestone.com.au
Web Site: www.asifund.com.au
Year Founded: 2000
AZF—(ASX)
Rev.: $15,013,535
Assets: $111,787,109
Liabilities: $38,244,028
Net Worth: $73,543,081
Earnings: $8,457,684
Fiscal Year-end: 06/30/13
Business Description:
Child Care Center Investment Services
S.I.C.: 6531
N.A.I.C.S.: 531390
Personnel:
Travis Butcher *(CFO)*
Nicholas Anagnostou *(CEO-Folkestone Social Infrastructure Funds)*
Scott Nicholas Martin *(Sec)*
Board of Directors:
Victor David Cottren
Warner Kenneth Bastian
Michael Francis Johnstone
Legal Counsel:
Tress Cox
Level 4 40 Creek Street
Brisbane, QLD, 4000, Australia

AUSTRALIAN TRADE COMMISSION

(d/b/a Austrade)
Level 23 AON Tower 201 Kent Street
Sydney, NSW, 2000, Australia
Mailing Address:
GPO Box 5301
Sydney, NSW, 2001, Australia
Tel.: (61) 293922102
Fax: (61) 293922777
E-Mail: info@austrade.gov.au
Web Site: www.austrade.gov.au
Rev.: $185,012,350
Assets: $122,552,002
Liabilities: $56,410,957
Net Worth: $66,141,045
Earnings: ($15,268,849)
Emp.: 1,003
Fiscal Year-end: 06/30/13
Business Description:
Australian Export & International Business Facilitation Services
S.I.C.: 9611
N.A.I.C.S.: 926110
Personnel:
Bruce Gosper *(CEO)*
Marcia Kimball *(Chief HR Officer & Chief Change Mgmt Officer)*
U.S. Division:

Australian Consulate General (1)
150 E 42nd St 34th Fl
New York, NY 10017

Australian Trade Commission—(Continued)

Tel.: (646) 344-8111
Fax: (212) 867-7710
E-Mail: newyork@austrade.gov.au
Web Site: www.austrade.gov.au/usa
Emp.: 15
Consular & Trade Services
Export
S.I.C.: 9199
N.A.I.C.S.: 921190
Anjali Jain *(Sr Dir-US Market Dev)*

AUSTRALIAN TURF CLUB

Royal Randwick Racecourse Alison Rd
Locked Bag 3
Randwick, NSW, 2031, Australia
Tel.: (61) 1300 729 668
Fax: (61) 2 9662 6292
E-Mail: info@australianturfclub.com.au
Web Site: www.australianturfclub.com.au
Year Founded: 1840
Emp.: 150
Business Description:
Racetrack Operator
S.I.C.: 7948
N.A.I.C.S.: 711212
Personnel:
John Cornish *(Chm)*
Michael Crismale *(Vice Chm)*
Darren Pearce *(CEO)*
James Van Beak *(CFO)*
Livia Bartoletti *(Gen Counsel & Gen Mgr-Legal & Regulatory)*
Board of Directors:
John Cornish
John Camilleri
Michael Crismale
Laurie Macri
Mark McInnes
Wilf Mula
Alan Osburg
Darren Pearce

AUSTRALIAN UNITED INVESTMENT COMPANY LTD

Level 20 101 Collins Street
Melbourne, VIC, 3000, Australia
Tel.: (61) 396540499
Fax: (61) 396543499
E-Mail: info@aui.com.au
Web Site: www.aui.com.au
AUI—(ASX)
Rev.: $43,798,579
Assets: $939,988,951
Liabilities: $205,276,406
Net Worth: $734,712,545
Earnings: $36,983,461
Fiscal Year-end: 06/30/13
Business Description:
Investments Management
S.I.C.: 6799
N.A.I.C.S.: 523920
Personnel:
Andrew J. Hancock *(Sec)*
Board of Directors:
Charles B. Goode
James S. Craig
John B. Rose
Peter J. Wetherall

AUSTRALIAN UNITED RETAILERS LIMITED

(d/b/a FoodWorks)
Level 1 1601 Malvern Road
Glen Iris, Melbourne, VIC, 3146, Australia
Tel.: (61) 398098600
Fax: (61) 398098699
E-Mail: vicinfo@foodworks.com.au
Web Site: www.foodworks.com.au
Sales Range: $1-4.9 Billion
Business Description:
Food Stores Owner & Operator
S.I.C.: 5411
N.A.I.C.S.: 445110
Personnel:
Rick Wight *(CEO)*

Subsidiaries:

Australian United Grocers Pty Ltd **(1)**
Level 1 378 Kingston Road
Slacks Creek, Logan, QLD, 4127, Australia
Tel.: (61) 733405200
Groceries Retailer
S.I.C.: 5141
N.A.I.C.S.: 424410

FoodWorks Retail Pty Ltd **(1)**
1601 Malvern Road
Glen Iris, Melbourne, VIC, 3146, Australia
Tel.: (61) 398098600
Fax: (61) 398098699
E-Mail: info@foodworks.com.au
Emp.: 80
Supermarket Operations Services
S.I.C.: 5411
N.A.I.C.S.: 445110

AUSTRALIAN UNITY LIMITED

114 Albert Road
Melbourne, VIC, 3205, Australia
Tel.: (61) 386827000
Fax: (61) 386825493
Web Site: www.australianunity.com.au
Year Founded: 1840
AYU—(ASX)
Rev.: $1,189,856,233
Assets: $3,993,887,850
Liabilities: $3,493,775,723
Net Worth: $500,112,127
Earnings: $30,648,161
Emp.: 1,805
Fiscal Year-end: 06/30/13
Business Description:
Health Insurance
S.I.C.: 9311
N.A.I.C.S.: 921130
Personnel:
Rohan Mead *(CEO & Mng Dir)*
Kevin McCoy *(Deputy CFO & Exec-Strategic Bus Dev)*
Anthony Connon *(CFO)*
David Bryant *(Chief Investment Officer & CEO-Investments)*
Sharon Beaumont *(Exec-HR)*
Steve Davis *(Exec-Personal Fin Svcs)*
Kimina Lyall *(Exec-Corp Dev)*
Tahir Tanveer *(Exec-Bus Tech)*
Amanda Hagan *(CEO-Healthcare)*
Derek McMillan *(CEO-Retirement Living)*
Kirsten Mander *(Gen Counsel & Sec)*
Board of Directors:
Glenn Barnes
John Butler
Eve Crestani
Ian Ferres
Stephen Maitland
Rohan Mead
Peter Promnitz
Warren Stretton
Greg Willcock

Subsidiaries:

Australian Unity Bowral Development Pty Ltd **(1)**
149 Castlereagh Street
Sydney, NSW, 2000, Australia
Tel.: (61) 386826801
Fax: (61) 86825555
Financial Advisory Services
S.I.C.: 6211
N.A.I.C.S.: 523999

Australian Unity Care Services Pty Ltd **(1)**
114 Albert Road
South Melbourne, VIC, 3205, Australia
Tel.: (61) 386826237
Fax: (61) 386826299
Web Site: www.australianunity.com.au
Financial Advisory Services
S.I.C.: 6282
N.A.I.C.S.: 523930
Rohan Mead *(Mng Dir)*

Australian Unity Funds Management Limited **(1)**
L 14 114 Albert Road
South Melbourne, VIC, 3205, Australia
Tel.: (61) 386827000
Fax: (61) 386825493
E-Mail: enquiries@australianunity.com.au
Web Site: www.australianunity.com.au
Emp.: 30
Financial Management Services
S.I.C.: 6211
N.A.I.C.S.: 523999
Frank Salmann *(Gen Mgr)*

Australian Unity Group Services Proprietary Limited **(1)**
114 Albert Road
South Melbourne, VIC, 3205, Australia
Tel.: (61) 386827000
Fax: (61) 86825555
Financial Management Services
S.I.C.: 6211
N.A.I.C.S.: 523999
Rohan Mead *(CEO)*

Australian Unity Health Care Limited **(1)**
L 14 114 Albert Road
South Melbourne, VIC, 3205, Australia
Tel.: (61) 386824288
Web Site: www.Australianunity.com.au
Financial Management Services
S.I.C.: 6211
N.A.I.C.S.: 523999

Australian Unity Health Limited **(1)**
114 Albert Rd
South Melbourne, VIC, 3205, Australia
Tel.: (61) 386827000
Fax: (61) 386825493
Web Site: www.AustralianUnity.com
Health Insurance Services
S.I.C.: 6321
N.A.I.C.S.: 524114
Bishop Grbic *(Head-Health Ops)*

Australian Unity Investment Bonds Limited **(1)**
114 Albert Rd
South Melbourne, VIC, 3205, Australia
Tel.: (61) 386825000
Fax: (61) 0386825057
Financial Advisory Services
S.I.C.: 6211
N.A.I.C.S.: 523999

Australian Unity Nominees Pty Ltd **(1)**
114 Albert Road
South Melbourne, VIC, 3205, Australia
Tel.: (61) 386825000
Fax: (61) 386825057
Funds Management Services
S.I.C.: 6371
N.A.I.C.S.: 524292

Australian Unity Property Limited **(1)**
114 Albert Road
South Melbourne, VIC, 3205, Australia
Tel.: (61) 3 86827000
Fax: (61) 3 86825057
Financial Management Services
S.I.C.: 6211
N.A.I.C.S.: 523999
Rohan Mead *(Gen Mgr)*

Australian Unity Retirement Living Services Limited **(1)**
Unit 30 Karagi Ct 2 Pheasant Ave
Bateau Bay, Wyong, NSW, 2261, Australia
Tel.: (61) 243342602
Fax: (61) 243341283
Web Site: www.australianunity.net
Financial Advisory Services
S.I.C.: 6211
N.A.I.C.S.: 523999
Kevin Fitock *(Gen Mgr)*

The Governor s Retirement Resort Pty Ltd **(1)**
166 River Park Road
Port Macquarie, NSW, 2444, Australia
Tel.: (61) 265834400
Fax: (61) 65834949
Emp.: 12
Financial Management Services
S.I.C.: 6211
N.A.I.C.S.: 523999
Lynette Eiston *(Mgr-Village)*

Lifeplan Australia Building Society Limited **(1)**
111 Gawler Place
Adelaide, SA, 5000, Australia
Tel.: (61) 882123838
Fax: (61) 882319181
Emp.: 13
Financial Management Services
S.I.C.: 6211
N.A.I.C.S.: 523999
Matthew Walsh *(CEO)*

Lifeplan Australia Friendly Society Limited **(1)**
111 Gawler Pl
Adelaide, SA, 5000, Australia
Tel.: (61) 882123838
Fax: (61) 882122790
Web Site: www.lifeplan.com.au
Funds Management Services
S.I.C.: 6371
N.A.I.C.S.: 524292
Matthew Walsh *(Gen Mgr)*

Remedy Healthcare Group Pty Ltd **(1)**
114 Albert Rd
South Melbourne, VIC, 3205, Australia
Tel.: (61) 1300224334
Fax: (61) 0386824270
E-Mail: Remedy@remedyhealthcare.com.au
Web Site: www.remedyhealthcare.com.au
Health Care Management Services
S.I.C.: 8099
N.A.I.C.S.: 621999
Alan Baldwin *(Head-Clinical Governance)*

Willandra Village Management Pty Ltd **(1)**
81 Willandra Road
Cromer, NSW, 2099, Australia
Tel.: (61) 299718035
Fax: (61) 299812385
Financial Management Services
S.I.C.: 6211
N.A.I.C.S.: 523999

AUSTRALIAN VINTAGE LTD.

275 Sir Donald Bradman Drive
Cowandilla, Adelaide, SA, 5033, Australia
Tel.: (61) 8 8172 8333
Fax: (61) 8 8172 8399
E-Mail: headoffice@mswl.com.au
Web Site: www.australianvintage.com.au
Year Founded: 2002
AVG—(ASX)
Rev.: $217,328,913
Assets: $462,501,696
Liabilities: $211,460,848
Net Worth: $251,040,848
Earnings: $7,367,647
Fiscal Year-end: 06/30/13
Business Description:
Wine Producer
S.I.C.: 2084
N.A.I.C.S.: 312130
Personnel:
Neil A. McGuigan *(CEO)*
Michael H. Noack *(CFO & Sec)*
Flora Sarris *(Gen Counsel)*
Board of Directors:
Ian D. Ferrier
Richard H. Davis
Perry R. Gunner
Brian J. McGuigan
Neil A. McGuigan
Legal Counsel:
Johnson, Winter & Slattery
Level 10 211 Victoria Square
Adelaide, SA, 5000, Australia
Subsidiary:
Miranda Wines Pty. Ltd. **(1)**
57 Jondaryan Avenue
Griffith, 2680, Australia (100%)

Tel.: (61) 269624033
Fax: (61) 2 69626944
E-Mail: info@mirandawines.com
Web Site: www.mirandawines.com.au
Sales Range: $25-49.9 Million
Emp.: 65
Beverage Mfr
S.I.C.: 5182
N.A.I.C.S.: 424820
Salvatore Miranda *(Pres & CEO)*
Genaro Miranda *(Mng Dir)*

AUSTRALIAN WOOL INNOVATION LIMITED (AWI)

Level 30 HSBC Centre 580 George St
Sydney, NSW, 2000, Australia
Mailing Address:
GPO Box 4177
Sydney, NSW, 2001, Australia
Tel.: (61) 282953100
Fax: (61) 82954100
E-Mail: apparel@wool.com
Web Site: www.wool.com
Rev.: $72,172,720
Assets: $123,637,870
Liabilities: $22,136,288
Net Worth: $101,501,582
Earnings: ($6,527,714)
Emp.: 100
Fiscal Year-end: 06/30/13
Business Description:
Wool Production & Marketing Services
S.I.C.: 0214
N.A.I.C.S.: 112410
Personnel:
Walter B. Merriman *(Chm)*
Stuart K. McCullough *(CEO)*
Jim Story *(Sec)*
Board of Directors:
Walter B. Merriman
Paul Cocking
Colette Garnsey
James Morgan
Meredith Sheil
Brian P. van Rooyen
David A. A. Webster

AUSTRALIAN WOOL TESTING AUTHORITY LTD.

70 Robertson St
Kensington, VIC, 3031, Australia
Tel.: (61) 3 9371 4100
Fax: (61) 3 9371 4191
E-Mail: wtainfo@awta.com.au
Web Site: www.awta.com.au
Business Description:
Agricultural Product Testing Services
S.I.C.: 8734
N.A.I.C.S.: 541380
Personnel:
Donald McGauchie *(Chm)*
Gordon Dickinson *(Deputy Chm)*
Michael Jackson *(Mng Dir)*
Peter Walsh *(CFO)*
Charles Englander *(Gen Counsel & Sec)*
Board of Directors:
Donald McGauchie
Mike Avery
Gordon Dickinson
Michael Jackson
Peter Morgan
Geoff Power
David Ritchie
Gary Turner
David Webster
Chris Wilcox

Subsidiary:

Agrifood Technology Pty Ltd. (1)
260 Princes Hwy
PO Box 728
Werribee, VIC, 3030, Australia (100%)
Tel.: (61) 397420555
Fax: (61) 397424228
E-Mail: info@agrifood.com.au
Web Site: www.agrifood.com.au
Emp.: 25
Agricultural Product Testing Services
S.I.C.: 8734
N.A.I.C.S.: 541380
Doreen Fernandez *(Div Mgr)*

AUSTRALIAN ZIRCON NL

Level 8 22 King William Street
PO Box 5242 Station Arcade
Adelaide, SA, 5000, Australia
Tel.: (61) 884108884
Fax: (61) 8 8410 8885
E-Mail: info@auzircon.com.au
Web Site: www.auzircon.com.au
AZC—(ASX)
Sales Range: $1-9.9 Million
Business Description:
Zircon & Titanium Mining
S.I.C.: 1099
N.A.I.C.S.: 212299
Personnel:
Jeremy David Shervington *(Chm)*
Johann Van Zyl *(Mng Dir)*
Steve McEwen *(Sec)*
Board of Directors:
Jeremy David Shervington
Giga Bedineishvili
David Brian Clarke
Johann Jacobs
Michael Kiernan
Steve McEwen
Johann Van Zyl

AUSTRIA HOTELS INTERNATIONAL BETRIEBS-GMBH

Hessgasse 7
1010 Vienna, Austria
Tel.: (43) 1 316 65 0
Fax: (43) 1 316 65 42
E-Mail: office@austria-hotels.at
Web Site: www.austria-hotels.at
Year Founded: 1955
Emp.: 700
Business Description:
Hotel Management Services
S.I.C.: 7011
N.A.I.C.S.: 721110
Personnel:
Oliver W. Braun *(Owner & CEO)*

AUSTRO GROUP LIMITED

1125 Leader Avenue Stormill Extension 4
Roodepoort, Gauteng, 1724, South Africa
Mailing Address:
PO Box 1914
Florida, Gauteng, 1710, South Africa
Tel.: (27) 112228300
Fax: (27) 112228500
E-Mail: austro@austro.co.za
Web Site: www.austrogrouplimited.com
ASO—(JSE)
Rev.: $45,912,413
Assets: $42,254,920
Liabilities: $8,948,148
Net Worth: $33,306,772
Earnings: $702,784
Emp.: 344
Fiscal Year-end: 08/31/13
Business Description:
Industrial & Construction Products Sales
S.I.C.: 5084
N.A.I.C.S.: 423830
Personnel:
Paul D. Mansour *(CEO)*
Christian Neuberger *(CEO-Wood)*
Hyram Serretta *(CEO-New Way Power)*
Board of Directors:
Anthony John Phillips
Paul C. Baloyi
David S. Brouze
Jarrord S. Friedman
Nopasika V. Lila
P. Mpho Makwana
Paul D. Mansour
Gordon S. Nzalo
Paul S. O'Flaherty
Uli Schackermann
Legal Counsel:
Java Capital (Pty) Ltd
2nd Floor 2 Arnold Road
2196 Rosebank, South Africa
Transfer Agent:
Computershare Investor Services 2004 (Pty) Ltd
Ground Floor 70 Marshall Street
Johannesburg, South Africa
Subsidiaries:

Austro (Pty) Limited (1)
Unit 4 Brand Park 32 Brand Rd
Durban, Westmead, 3605, South Africa
Tel.: (27) 31 700 1820
Fax: (27) 31 700 4640
E-Mail: austrokzn@austro.co.za
Web Site: www.austro.co.za
Emp.: 10
Woodworking Machinery & Tools Distr
S.I.C.: 5084
N.A.I.C.S.: 423830
Colin Wilkie *(Mgr)*

AUSTRO WOOD (PTY) LIMITED (1)
1125 Leader Avenue Stormill ext 4
Roodepoort, Gauteng, 2148, South Africa
Tel.: (27) 11 222 8300
Fax: (27) 11 222 8500
E-Mail: austro@austro.co.za
Web Site: www.austro.co.za
Emp.: 140
Woodworking Machinery Distr
S.I.C.: 5084
N.A.I.C.S.: 423830
Peter Ivanoff *(VP-Mktg)*

Divisions:

Austro Woodworking Machines & Tools (2)
1125 Leader Avenue Stormill Ext 4
Roodepoort, Gauteng, 1724, South Africa
Tel.: (27) 112228300
Fax: (27) 112228500
E-Mail: austro@austro.co.za
Web Site: www.austro.co.za
Emp.: 100
Woodworking Machinery & Tools Distr
S.I.C.: 5084
N.A.I.C.S.: 423830
Peter Ivanoff *(Mgr-Mktg)*

Gearing Moss Supplies (Pty) Ltd (2)
1127 Leader Ave Stormill Ext 8
Roodepoort, Johannesburg, Gauteng, 1710, South Africa
Tel.: (27) 11 222 8350
Fax: (27) 11 222 8360
E-Mail: sales@gearingmoss.co.za
Web Site: www.gearingmoss.co.za
Portable Sawmills Distr
S.I.C.: 2421
N.A.I.C.S.: 321113

NEW WAY POWER (PTY) LIMITED (1)
No 30 CNR Jacoba and Bloutulp Street
Alberton, 1449, South Africa
Tel.: (27) 116805632
Fax: (27) 119025233
E-Mail: newway@icon.co.za
Web Site: www.newway.co.za
Emp.: 100
Power Turbines Mfr
S.I.C.: 3511
N.A.I.C.S.: 333611
Jonathan Freed *(Mgr)*

Subsidiary:

Austro Engineering Cape (Pty) Limited (1)
18 Manfield Cresent
Cape Town, Western Cape, 7150, South Africa
Tel.: (27) 218564370
Fax: (27) 218564269
E-Mail: austrocpt@austro.co.za
Web Site: www.austro.co.za
Emp.: 15
Woodworking Machinery & Tools Distr
S.I.C.: 5084
N.A.I.C.S.: 423830
Gary Miles *(Mgr)*

Divisions:

Neptune Plant Hire (Pty) Limited (2)
23 Neptune St
Paarden Eiland, Cape Town, Western Cape, 7405, South Africa
Tel.: (27) 215112733
Fax: (27) 215105568
E-Mail: info@neptuneplanthire.co.za
Web Site: www.neptuneplanthire.co.za
Emp.: 7
Generator Leasing Services
S.I.C.: 7359
N.A.I.C.S.: 532490
Reggie Hare *(Mgr-Ops)*

New Way Motor & Diesel Engineering (Pty) Ltd (2)
30 Jacoba Street Alberton North
Johannesburg, Excom, 2023, South Africa
Tel.: (27) 116805632
Fax: (27) 0119025233
E-Mail: newway@icon.co.za
Web Site: www.newway.co.za
Generators Mfr & Distr
S.I.C.: 3484
N.A.I.C.S.: 332994
Jonathan Freed *(Mng Dir)*

Quad Technical Services (Pty) Limited (2)
1626 Harriet Ave
Driehoek, Germiston, Gauteng, 1401, South Africa
Tel.: (27) 117768320
Fax: (27) 117768378
E-Mail: diane@qts.co.za
Web Site: www.qts.co.za
Electrical Control Panels & Generators Mfr & Distr
S.I.C.: 3621
N.A.I.C.S.: 335312

AUSY SA

88 boulevard Gallieni
92445 Issy-les-Moulineaux, Cedex, France
Tel.: (33) 1 41 08 65 65
Fax: (33) 1 46 44 65 08
E-Mail: investors@ausy.fr
Web Site: www.ausy.com
Year Founded: 1989
OSI—(EUR)
Sls.: $432,659,038
Assets: $305,445,973
Liabilities: $192,636,927
Net Worth: $112,809,046
Earnings: $15,884,806
Emp.: 3,760
Fiscal Year-end: 12/31/12
Business Description:
Information Technology Services
S.I.C.: 7373
N.A.I.C.S.: 541512
Personnel:
Jean-Marie Magnet *(Chm & CEO)*
Philippe Morsillo *(Deputy CEO)*
Fabrice Dupont *(Gen Sec)*

AUTECH CORPORATION

930 Houmri Goduk-Myun
Yesan, Choongchungnam-Do, Korea (South)
Tel.: (82) 41 338 8261
Fax: (82) 41 338 8265
Web Site: www.autech.co.kr
Year Founded: 2000
067170—(KRS)
Business Description:
Motor Vehicle Body Mfr
S.I.C.: 3711
N.A.I.C.S.: 336211

Autech Corporation—(Continued)

Personnel:
Sung-hee Kang *(CEO)*

AUTEV AG
Carl-Reichstein-Str 6
D-14770 Brandenburg, Germany
Tel.: (49) 33818043630
Fax: (49) 33818043635
E-Mail: info@autev.com
Web Site: www.autev.com
Year Founded: 2001
LDP—(DEU)
Emp.: 120
Business Description:
Engineering Services; Lighting Mfr
S.I.C.: 8711
N.A.I.C.S.: 541330
Personnel:
Uwe Maiberg *(Chm)*
Non-U.S. Subsidiaries:

AUTEV Asia Pacific Pte., Ltd. **(1)**
6001 Beach Road 18-01 Golden Mile Tower
Singapore, 199589, Singapore
Tel.: (65) 62978641
Fax: (65) 62998238
Web Site: www.autev.com
Light Emitting Diodes Mfr
S.I.C.: 3674
N.A.I.C.S.: 334413
Michael Vender *(Mgr)*

AUTEV Engineering AE **(1)**
Apostolou Pavlou 27
85100 Rhodes, Dodecanese, Greece
Tel.: (30) 22410 63563
Fax: (30) 22410 61548
E-Mail: info@autev-engineering.eu
Web Site: www.autev-engineering.eu
Emp.: 6
Environmental Engineering & Consulting Services
S.I.C.: 8711
N.A.I.C.S.: 541330
Carsten Hoeldtke *(VP)*

AUTHEN-TECH COMMUNICATIONS CANADA INC.
895 Edgeley Boulevard
Concord, ON, L4K 4V9, Canada
Tel.: (905) 738-3528
Fax: (905) 738-0152
E-Mail: info@authentech.ca
Web Site: www.authentech.ca
Rev.: $17,041,210
Emp.: 100
Business Description:
Telecommunications Services
S.I.C.: 4899
N.A.I.C.S.: 517919
Personnel:
Bill Clarke *(Pres)*
Len Stanmore *(CEO)*

AUTHENTIC TEAS INC.
Suite 1801 1 Yonge Street
Toronto, ON, M5E 2A3, Canada
Tel.: (416) 306-2493
E-Mail: info@authentic-teas.com
Web Site: www.authentic-teas.com
Year Founded: 2010
AUTT—(OTC OTCB)
Rev.: $4,267
Assets: $5,320
Liabilities: $103,462
Net Worth: ($98,142)
Earnings: ($42,099)
Fiscal Year-end: 04/30/13
Business Description:
Premium Loose-Leaf Teas Developer, Marketer & Retailer
S.I.C.: 2095
N.A.I.C.S.: 311920
Personnel:
Hrant Isbeceryan *(Pres, CEO, Treas & Sec)*
David Lewis Richardson *(CFO)*
Board of Directors:
Evan Michael Hershfield
Hrant Isbeceryan
David Lewis Richardson
Transfer Agent:
Nevada Agency & Transfer Company
50 W Liberty Street Suite 880
Reno, NV 89501

AUTO CLEARING (1982) LTD
(d/b/a Auto Clearing Chrysler Dodge Jeep)
331 Circle Drive West
Saskatoon, SK, S7L5S8, Canada
Tel.: (306) 244-2186
Fax: (306) 244-0870
Toll Free: (888) 253-2987
E-Mail: info@autoclearing.com
Web Site: www.autoclearing.com
Year Founded: 1926
Rev.: $37,065,600
Emp.: 77
Business Description:
New & Used Car Dealers
S.I.C.: 5511
N.A.I.C.S.: 441110
Personnel:
Henry Savoie *(Owner & Pres)*
Linda Savoie *(Treas & Sec)*

AUTO COLLECTION DE QUEBEC
175 Rue Marais
Vanier, QC, G1M 3C8, Canada
Tel.: (418) 683-4451
Fax: (418) 683-5751
Web Site: www.autocollectiondequebec.com
Year Founded: 1992
Sales Range: $10-24.9 Million
Emp.: 145
Business Description:
New & Used Car Dealers
S.I.C.: 5511
N.A.I.C.S.: 441110
Personnel:
Jean-Luc Desjardins *(Pres)*

AUTO ESCAPE SA
137 rue Jacquard
84120 Pertuis, France
Tel.: (33) 820150300
Fax: (33) 490095187
E-Mail: jean-christophe.brun@autoescape.com
Web Site: www.autoescape.com
Year Founded: 1999
ALAUT—(EUR)
Sales Range: $25-49.9 Million
Emp.: 54
Business Description:
Car Rental Services
S.I.C.: 7514
N.A.I.C.S.: 532111
Personnel:
Bruno Couly *(Chm, CEO & Mng Dir)*
Jean-Christophe Brun *(CFO & Dir-Fin)*
Non-U.S. Subsidiary:

Auto Escape UK **(1)**
Wilberforce House Station Road
London, NW4 4QE, United Kingdom
Tel.: (44) 844 369 0109
E-Mail: info@autoescape.co.uk
Web Site: www.autoescape.co.uk
Car Rental Services
S.I.C.: 7514
N.A.I.C.S.: 532111

AUTO GROUP AURORA INC
(d/b/a Aurora Toyota)
669 Wellington St E
Aurora, ON, L4G 0C9, Canada
Tel.: (905) 727-1948
Fax: (905) 727-0026
Toll Free: (866) 979-3750
E-Mail: info@auroratoyota.ca
Web Site: www.auroratoyota.ca
Rev.: $13,602,054
Emp.: 30
Business Description:
New & Used Car Dealers
S.I.C.: 5511
N.A.I.C.S.: 441110
Personnel:
Allen Trimble *(Bus Mgr)*

AUTO NETWORKS INTERNATIONAL CORPORATION
81 Fu Hsing Road
Section 1 South District, Taichung, 403, Taiwan
Tel.: (886) 963080887
Year Founded: 2009
Business Description:
Automobile Wheels Distr
S.I.C.: 5013
N.A.I.C.S.: 423120
Personnel:
Chi Shing Huang *(Pres, CEO, CFO, Treas & Sec)*
Board of Directors:
Chi Shing Huang
Meng Hann Tsai
Lien Fang Yang

AUTO RELAIS SAGLIO
232 Avenue De Colmar
67100 Strasbourg, Bas Rhin, France
Tel.: (33) 388791679
Sales Range: $10-24.9 Million
Emp.: 27
Business Description:
New & Used Car Dealers
S.I.C.: 5511
N.A.I.C.S.: 441110
Personnel:
Jean-Pierre Wolf *(Pres)*

AUTO SENATEUR INC
(d/b/a Vimont Toyota Laval)
255 boul Saint Martin Est
Laval, QC, H7M 1Z1, Canada
Tel.: (450) 668-2710
Fax: (450) 668-9944
Toll Free: (888) 692-3903
Web Site: www.vimonttoyotalaval.com
Rev.: $68,274,666
Emp.: 70
Business Description:
New & Used Car Dealers
S.I.C.: 5511
N.A.I.C.S.: 441110
Personnel:
Sylvain Lahaie *(Mgr-Lease Renewal)*

AUTO TOOL TECHNOLOGIES INC.
101 1/2 Mary Street West
Whitby, ON, L1N 2R4, Canada
Tel.: (905) 430-6433
Year Founded: 2011
ATOT—(OTCB)
Rev.: $885,561
Assets: $591,039
Liabilities: $415,777
Net Worth: $175,262
Earnings: ($30,898)
Fiscal Year-end: 12/31/12
Business Description:
Hand Tool Distr
S.I.C.: 5072
N.A.I.C.S.: 423710
Personnel:
Cindy Lee Kelly *(Pres, CEO, CFO, Treas & Sec)*
Board of Directors:
Cindy Lee Kelly

AUTOAIR HOLDINGS BERHAD
802 8th Floor Block C Kelana Square
17 Jalan SS7/26, 47301 Petaling Jaya, Selangor Darul Ehsan, Malaysia
Tel.: (60) 37803 1126
Fax: (60) 37806 1387
E-Mail: autoair@autoairgroup.com
Web Site: www.autoairgroup.com
AUTOAIR—(KLS)
Rev.: $3,527,301
Assets: $9,035,146
Liabilities: $3,867,455
Net Worth: $5,167,691
Earnings: ($245,357)
Emp.: 400
Fiscal Year-end: 06/30/13
Business Description:
Automotive Components Mfr
S.I.C.: 3822
N.A.I.C.S.: 334512
Personnel:
Choo Liew *(Grp Mng Dir)*
Oi Wah Leong *(Sec)*
Board of Directors:
Suffian Othman
Keng Ee Chuang
Ah Lek Leong
Choo Liew
Jee Min Liew
Li Ching Liew
Chee Kong Yeow
Subsidiary:

Autoair Manufacturing Sdn Bhd **(1)**
Lot 1735 Batu 29
Jalan Kl-Ipoh, 44300 Batang Kali, Selangor Darul Ehsan, Malaysia
Tel.: (60) 360753333
Fax: (60) 360753402
E-Mail: autoair@autoairgroup.com
Web Site: www.autoairgroup.com
Air Conditioning Systems Mfr
S.I.C.: 3585
N.A.I.C.S.: 333415
Choo Liew *(Mng Dir)*

AUTOBACS SEVEN CO., LTD.
NBF Toyosu Canal Front 6-52 Toyosu 5-chome Koto-ku
Tokyo, 135-8717, Japan
Tel.: (81) 3 6219 8718
Fax: (81) 3 6219 8762
E-Mail: investors@autobacs.co.jp
Web Site: www.autobacs.co.jp
Year Founded: 1947
9832—(TKS)
Sls.: $2,531,848,000
Assets: $2,260,797,000
Liabilities: $684,486,000
Net Worth: $1,576,311,000
Earnings: $83,490,000
Emp.: 4,678
Fiscal Year-end: 03/31/13
Business Description:
Holding Company; Automotive Accessories Stores Owner & Operator
S.I.C.: 6719
N.A.I.C.S.: 551112
Personnel:
Setsuo Wakuda *(CEO & Chief Chain Officer)*
Yasuhiro Tsunemori *(Vice CEO & Vice Chief Chain Officer)*
Yoshihiro Emoto *(Officer-Chubu)*

Shinichi Fujiwara *(Officer-Mktg & Mdse Dev)*
Isao Hirata *(Exec Officer-Corp Plng, IR, PR & Bus Dev)*
Kazushige Hojo *(Officer-HR, Gen Affairs & IT Strategy)*
Yugo Horii *(Officer-Internal Control & Legal)*
Eiji Kaminishizono *(Exec Officer-Kansai)*
Tetsuya Kato *(Officer-Car Goods & Svcs)*
Kosuke Kaya *(Officer-Store Dev & Land Use & Dev)*
Naoyuki Koyama *(Officer-Overseas Bus Plng)*
Eiichi Kumakura *(Officer-Kanto)*
Shinya Kurahayashi *(Officer-Car Sls)*
Katsuhito Matani *(Officer-Car Maintenance & Insurance Svcs)*
Masaru Sasaki *(Officer-Southern Japan)*
Yoshiki Tateuchi *(Officer-Northern Japan)*
Board of Directors:
Norio Hattori
Kiomi Kobayashi
Teruyuki Matsumura
Hironori Morimoto
Noriaki Shimazaki
Tatsuya Tamura
Yasuhiro Tsunemori
Setsuo Wakuda

AUTOBANK AG

Ungargasse 64 3 Top 403
1030 Vienna, Austria
Tel.: (43) 1601901
Fax: (43) 160190590
E-Mail: office@autobank.at
Web Site: www.autobank.at
AW2—(DEU VIE)
Emp.: 50
Business Description:
Motor Vehicle Financing & Leasing Services
S.I.C.: 6153
N.A.I.C.S.: 522220
Personnel:
Eduard Unzeitig *(Chm-Supervisory Bd)*
Michael Kirchner *(Deputy Chm-Supervisory Bd)*
Martin Feith *(Member-Mgmt Bd)*
Gerhard Fischer *(Member-Mgmt Bd)*
Supervisory Board of Directors:
Eduard Unzeitig
Michael Kirchner
Frank Norenberg

AUTOCANADA INC.

200 15505 Yellowhead Trail
Edmonton, AB, T5V 1E5, Canada
Tel.: (780) 482-3503
Fax: (780) 447-0651
Toll Free: (888) 717-3558
Web Site: www.autocan.ca
Year Founded: 2009
ACQ—(TSX)
Rev.: $1,097,311,600
Assets: $408,014,395
Liabilities: $284,258,905
Net Worth: $123,755,490
Earnings: $24,091,069
Emp.: 1,227
Fiscal Year-end: 12/31/12
Business Description:
Holding Company; Car Dealerships Owner & Operator
S.I.C.: 6719
N.A.I.C.S.: 551112
Personnel:
Gordon R. Barefoot *(Chm)*
Thomas Orysiuk *(Pres & CFO)*
Patrick J. Priestner *(CEO)*
Stephen R. E. Rose *(Gen Counsel, Sec & Exec VP-Corp Svcs)*
Board of Directors:
Gordon R. Barefoot
Christopher Cumming
Dennis S. DesRosiers
Thomas Orysiuk
Patrick J. Priestner
Michael Ross
Robin Salmon
Transfer Agent:
Valiant Trust Company
Vancouver, BC, Canada
Subsidiary:

Saskatoon Motor Products **(1)**
715 Circle Drive East
Saskatoon, SK, S7K 0V1, Canada
Tel.: (306) 242-0276
Fax: (306) 242-8821
Toll Free: (877) 203-4222
Web Site: www.smpchev.ca
Rev.: $36,100,070
Emp.: 75
New & Used Car Dealers
S.I.C.: 5511
N.A.I.C.S.: 441110
Joe Yates *(Treas & Sec)*

AUTOCHINA INTERNATIONAL LIMITED

27/F Kai Yuan Center No 5 East Main Street
Shijiazhuang, Hebei, China
Tel.: (86) 311 83827688
Fax: (86) 311 83819636
Web Site: www.autochinaintl.com
Year Founded: 2007
Rev.: $333,112,000
Assets: $439,306,000
Liabilities: $210,946,000
Net Worth: $228,360,000
Earnings: $23,549,000
Emp.: 3,369
Fiscal Year-end: 12/31/12
Business Description:
Holding Company; Car Dealership Owner & Operator
S.I.C.: 6719
N.A.I.C.S.: 551112
Personnel:
Hui Li Yong *(Chm & CEO)*
Jason Wang *(CFO)*
Wei Xing *(COO)*
Ka Yan Hui *(Sec)*
Chen Lei *(Sr VP)*
Board of Directors:
Hui Li Yong
Ka Yan Hui
Thomas Luen-Hung Lau
Diana Chia-Huei Liu
James Cheng-Jee Sha
Legal Counsel:
Loeb & Loeb
345 Park Ave.
New York, NY 10154
Tel.: (212) 408-4800
Transfer Agent:
American Stock Transfer & Trust Company
59 Maiden Ln Plz Level
New York, NY 10038
Tel.: (212) 936-5100
Toll Free: (800) 937-5449

AUTOCONT CONTROL SYSTEMS, S.R.O.

Technologicka 374/6
70 800 Ostrava, Czech Republic
Tel.: (420) 595691150
Fax: (420) 595691199
E-Mail: obchod.ostrava@accs.cz
Web Site: www.accs.cz
Sales Range: $10-24.9 Million
Emp.: 25
Business Description:
Information & Communication Technologies Supplier
S.I.C.: 3575
N.A.I.C.S.: 334118
Personnel:
Richard Altmann *(CEO)*
Tomas Tomala *(Mng Dir)*
Subsidiary:

AutoCont Online A/S **(1)**
Podebradska 88 55
190 02 Prague, 9, Czech Republic CZ
Tel.: (420) 251022102
Fax: (420) 251022129
E-Mail: info@acol.cz
Web Site: www.acol.cz
Emp.: 100
Provider of Telecommunications Services
S.I.C.: 4812
N.A.I.C.S.: 517210
Non-U.S. Subsidiary:

AutoCont a.s. **(1)**
Schneidra Trnavskeho 6
84101 Bratislava, Slovakia (100%)
Tel.: (421) 264287881
Fax: (421) 264287891
E-Mail: bratislava@autocont.sk
Web Site: www.autocont.sk
Emp.: 30
Information & Communication Technologies Distr
S.I.C.: 3577
N.A.I.C.S.: 334118

THE AUTODROME PLC

Autodrome Bldg 304 Union Pl
2 Colombo, Sri Lanka
Tel.: (94) 112326181
Fax: (94) 112338611
E-Mail: info@autodrome.lk
Web Site: www.autodrome.lk
AUTO—(COL)
Sales Range: $1-9.9 Million
Business Description:
Automotive Parts Distr
S.I.C.: 5014
N.A.I.C.S.: 441320
Personnel:
Joseph Aloysius *(Chm)*
Bernadette Aloysius *(Deputy Chm & Dir-Mktg)*
Rajeev A. J. Aloysius *(Mng Dir)*
Board of Directors:
Joseph Aloysius
Bernadette Aloysius
Rajeev A. J. Aloysius
M. Suresh Dominic
M. Raviraj Ratnasabapathy
C. Lakshman Sirimanne
Sarath C. Weerasooria
Subsidiary:

Tourama (Pvt) Ltd. **(1)**
Level 3 304 Union Place
Colombo, Western Province, 00200, Sri Lanka
Tel.: (94) 112326181
Fax: (94) 11 2314805
E-Mail: info@tourama.net
Web Site: www.tourama.net
Emp.: 20
Travel & Tour Operating Agencies
S.I.C.: 4725
N.A.I.C.S.: 561520
Rajeev Aloysius *(Mng Dir)*

AUTOFEED CORPORATION

1288 Osprey Dr
Ancaster, ON, L9G 4V5, Canada
Tel.: (905) 648-8200
Fax: (905) 648-0593
Web Site: www.autofeed.ca
Sales Range: $150-199.9 Million
Emp.: 16
Business Description:
Feeder Equipment Mfr & Service
S.I.C.: 3699
N.A.I.C.S.: 335999
Personnel:
Kenneth Giles *(Pres)*

AUTOHAUS HANSA NORD GMBH

Berliner Strasse 10
D-23560 Lubeck, Germany
Tel.: (49) 451 58375 0
Fax: (49) 451 58375 75
E-Mail: info@autohaus-hansa-nord.de
Web Site: www.autohaus-hansa-nord.de
Business Description:
New & Used Car Dealer
S.I.C.: 5511
N.A.I.C.S.: 441110
Personnel:
Wolfgang Mehte *(Chm-Mgmt Bd)*
Hardy Maas *(Mng Dir & Member-Mgmt Bd)*

AUTOHAUS HEINRICH SENDEN GMBH

Sittarder Str 25-29
52511 Geilenkirchen, Germany
Tel.: (49) 245162080
Fax: (49) 2451620833
E-Mail: info@ah-senden.de
Web Site: www.ah-senden.de
Rev.: $41,382,000
Emp.: 102
Business Description:
Used Car Dealers
S.I.C.: 5521
N.A.I.C.S.: 441120
Personnel:
Ingo Diapers *(Co-Mng Dir)*
Tobias Rulle *(Co-Mng Dir)*

AUTOHAUS KRETTER GMBH

Otto-von-Guericke-Strasse 1
07552 Gera, Germany
Tel.: (49) 365437700
Fax: (49) 3654377040
E-Mail: info@autohaus-kretter.de
Web Site: www.autohaus-kretter.de
Rev.: $64,170,011
Emp.: 75
Business Description:
New & Used Car Dealers
S.I.C.: 5511
N.A.I.C.S.: 441110
Personnel:
Jurgen Munzel *(Mng Dir)*

AUTOHAUS WIDMANN + WINTERHOLLER GMBH

Rudolf-Diesel-Str 18
85221 Dachau, Germany
Tel.: (49) 8131 3121 0
E-Mail: info@widmann-winterholler.de
Web Site: www.widmann-winterholler.de
Business Description:
Motor Vehicle Dealership Operator
S.I.C.: 5511
N.A.I.C.S.: 441110
Personnel:
Andreas Hagenreiner *(Mng Dir)*
Erwin Winterholler *(Mng Dir)*
Subsidiary:

Autohaus Widmann + Winterholler GmbH - Farchant **(1)**
Partenkirchner Str 34
82490 Farchant, Bavaria, Germany
Tel.: (49) 8821 96676 0
Fax: (49) 8821 96676 29
E-Mail: info@oberlandautomobile.de
Web Site: www.oberlandautomobile.de
Emp.: 18

Autohaus Widmann + Winterholler GmbH—(Continued)

Car Dealers
S.I.C.: 5511
N.A.I.C.S.: 441110

AUTOHELLAS S.A.

Viltanioti 31 Str
14564 Kifissia, Greece
Tel.: (30) 2106264000
Fax: (30) 2106264409
E-Mail: info@hertz.gr
Web Site: www.hertz.gr
OTOEL—(ATH)
Sls.: $204,594,170
Assets: $560,640,539
Liabilities: $376,629,866
Net Worth: $184,010,672
Earnings: $10,902,512
Emp.: 506
Fiscal Year-end: 12/31/12
Business Description:
Car Rental Services
S.I.C.: 7514
N.A.I.C.S.: 532111
Personnel:
Theodore E. Vassilakis *(Chm)*
Eftichios T. Vassilakis *(Vice Chm & Mng Dir)*
Board of Directors:
Theodore E. Vassilakis
Spyridon Flegas
Stefanos A. Kotsolis
Dimitrios Magioros
Garyfallia A. Pelekanou
Ioannis Protopapadakis
Eftichios T. Vassilakis
Emmanuella T. Vassilakis
Georgios T. Vassilakis

Non-U.S. Subsidiaries:

Autotechnica Fleet Services S.R.L. (1)
Drumul Garii Odaii 1A Airport Plaza 2Fl
032258 Otopeni, Ilfov, Romania
Tel.: (40) 214078200
Fax: (40) 214078229
E-Mail: sales@hertzlease.ro
Web Site: www.hertzlease.ro
Emp.: 20
Car Rental Services
S.I.C.: 7514
N.A.I.C.S.: 532111
Catalin Tihon *(Gen Mgr)*

Autotechnica Ltd. (1)
53 Nikola Vaptsarov Boulevard
1407 Sofia, Bulgaria
Tel.: (359) 2 439 0 222
Fax: (359) 2 439 0 148
E-Mail: office@hertz.bg
Web Site: www.hertz.bg
Car Rental Services
S.I.C.: 7514
N.A.I.C.S.: 532111

Demstar Rentals 2005 Ltd. (1)
PO Box 27752
Engomi, 2433 Nicosia, Cyprus
Tel.: (357) 22208888
Fax: (357) 22347040
E-Mail: info@hertz.com.cy
Web Site: www.hertz.com.cy
Emp.: 25
Car Rental Services
S.I.C.: 7514
N.A.I.C.S.: 532111
Pambos Danos *(Gen Mgr)*

AUTOKRAZ HOLDING CO.

2 Yaroslavskiy proyezd Str
Kremenchuk, Poltava, 39631, Ukraine
Tel.: (380) 536 76 6210
Fax: (380) 536 77 1673
E-Mail: office@ftfkraz.poltava.ua
Web Site: www.autokraz.com.ua
Sales Range: $10-24.9 Million
Emp.: 17,800
Business Description:
Heavy-Duty Trucks & Special-Purpose Vehicles Mfr
S.I.C.: 3711
N.A.I.C.S.: 336120
Personnel:
Sergey Sazonov *(Gen Dir)*
Fyodor Babich *(Chief Legal Counsel)*

Subsidiary:

FTF KrAZ (1)
9 V Boyko Str
Kremenchuk, Poltavskaya, 39602, Ukraine
Tel.: (380) 536798221
Fax: (380) 536798221
E-Mail: office@ftfkraz.poltava.ua
Web Site: www.autokraz.com.ua/old/eng/ftf/ftfkraz.htm
Heavy-Duty Trucks Exporter
S.I.C.: 3711
N.A.I.C.S.: 336120

AUTOKUHLER GMBH & CO. KG

PO Box 1346
D 34363 Hofgeismar, Germany
Tel.: (49) 56718830
Fax: (49) 56713582
E-Mail: info@akg-gruppe.de
Web Site: www.akg-gruppe.de
Year Founded: 1919
Emp.: 1,200
Business Description:
Heat Exchanger Mfr
S.I.C.: 3559
N.A.I.C.S.: 332410
Personnel:
Hartwig Pietzcker *(CEO)*

AUTOLINE INDUSTRIES LIMITED

S No 313 314 320 to 323
Nanekarwadi Chakana Taluka Khed
Pune, 410501, India
Tel.: (91) 2135 664865
Fax: (91) 2135 664864
Web Site: www.autolineind.com
Year Founded: 1996
532797—(BOM NSE)
Rev.: $156,456,303
Assets: $128,513,150
Liabilities: $69,888,351
Net Worth: $58,624,799
Earnings: $1,978,476
Emp.: 3,450
Fiscal Year-end: 03/31/13
Business Description:
Design, Engineering & Manufacturing of Automotive Mechanical Systems
S.I.C.: 3714
N.A.I.C.S.: 336390
Personnel:
Shivaji Tukaram Akhade *(Co-Founder, CEO & Mng Dir)*
Sudhir Vitthal Mungase *(Co-Founder)*
Mariappasamy Radhakrishnan *(Co-Founder)*
Ravi E. Ketkar *(CFO)*
Digambar C. Pargaonkar *(COO)*
Ashutosh B. Kulkarni *(Compliance Officer & Sec)*
Board of Directors:
Prakash B. Nimbalkar
Shivaji Tukaram Akhade
Amit Kishankumar Goela
Sudhir Vitthal Mungase
Mariappasamy Radhakrishnan
Vijay K. Thanawala
Transfer Agent:
Link Intime India Private Limited
Block No 202 2nd Floor Akshay Complex Near Ganesh Temple
Pune, India

U.S. Plant:

Autoline Industries USA Inc. (1)
100 Commerce St
Butler, IN 46721-0100
Tel.: (260) 868-2147
Fax: (260) 868-5718
Web Site: www.autolineind.com
Emp.: 200
Mfr of Jacks & Tool Kits for Motor Vehicles
S.I.C.: 3714
N.A.I.C.S.: 336390
Sri Bramadesam *(Pres)*

AUTOLITE (INDIA) LIMITED

D-469 Road No 9A VKI Area
Jaipur, 302013, India
Tel.: (91) 1412333994
Fax: (91) 1412330426
E-Mail: info@autopal.com
Web Site: www.autopal.com
AUTOLITIND—(NSE)
Rev.: $22,837,757
Assets: $13,063,303
Liabilities: $7,178,540
Net Worth: $5,884,763
Earnings: $133,062
Fiscal Year-end: 03/31/13
Business Description:
Automotive Head Lamp Mfr
S.I.C.: 3646
N.A.I.C.S.: 335122
Personnel:
Mahi Pal Gupta *(Chm & Mng Dir)*
Vishal Agarwal *(Compliance Officer & Sec)*
Board of Directors:
Mahi Pal Gupta
Sooraj Prakash Batra
Gauri Shankar Das
Adarsh Mahipal Gupta
Amit Mahipal Gupta
Kuldeep Kumar Gupta
Rajendra Singh Mehta
Transfer Agent:
MCS Limited
F-65 Okhla Industrial Area Phase-I
New Delhi, India

Subsidiary:

Autolite Manufacturing Limited (1)
D-469 Road No 9a VKI Area
302013 Jaipur, India
Tel.: (91) 1412333994
Fax: (91) 1412330426
Automotive Lighting Product Mfr
S.I.C.: 3714
N.A.I.C.S.: 336320

U.S. Subsidiary:

Autopal Inc (1)
7316 Lavery Dr
Plano, TX 75025
Tel.: (214) 227-1762
Automotive Lighting Parts Distr
S.I.C.: 5013
N.A.I.C.S.: 423120

AUTOLIV, INC.

Vasagatan 11 7th Floor SE-111 20
PO Box 70381
SE 107 24 Stockholm, Sweden
Tel.: (46) 858720600
Fax: (46) 84117025
E-Mail: info@autoliv.com
Web Site: www.autoliv.com
Year Founded: 1997
ALV—(NYSE OMX)
Sls.: $8,803,400,000
Assets: $6,983,000,000
Liabilities: $2,982,600,000
Net Worth: $4,000,400,000
Earnings: $489,900,000
Emp.: 46,900
Fiscal Year-end: 12/31/13
Business Description:
Automotive Safety Equipment Mfr & Sales
Export
S.I.C.: 3589
N.A.I.C.S.: 333318
Personnel:
Lars Dayton Nyberg *(Chm)*
Jan Carlson *(Pres & CEO)*
Mats Wallin *(CFO & VP-Fin)*
Gunter Brenner *(Pres-Europe)*
Steven Fredin *(Pres-Americas)*
Anthony Nellis *(Interim Gen Counsel & Interim VP-Legal Affairs-Global Bus)*
Board of Directors:
Lars Dayton Nyberg
Robert W. Alspaugh
Jan Carlson
Xiaozhi Liu
George A. Lorch
James M. Ringler
Kazuhiko Sakamoto
Transfer Agent:
EquiServe Trust Company N.A
PO Box 43076
Providence, RI 02940-3076

Subsidiaries:

Autoliv AB (1)
Klarabergsviadukten 70
PO Box 70381
SE 107 24 Stockholm, Sweden (100%)
Tel.: (46) 858720600
Fax: (46) 846244493
E-Mail: info@autoliv.com
Automotive Safety Equipment Designer, Mfr & Whslr
S.I.C.: 3714
N.A.I.C.S.: 336390
Jan Carlson *(Pres & CEO)*
Mats Wallin *(CFO & VP-Fin)*

Autoliv Development AB (1)
Wallentinsvagen 22
S 447 83 Vargarda, Sweden (100%)
Tel.: (46) 322626300
Telex: 2430 Autolivs
Fax: (46) 322620118
Web Site: www.autoliv.com
Emp.: 50
Car-Seat Belts
S.I.C.: 3714
N.A.I.C.S.: 336340
Jan Olsson *(Mng Dir)*

Autoliv Electronics AB (1)
Medevivagen 55
PO Box 383
SE 591 24 Motala, Sweden (100%)
Tel.: (46) 141223000
Fax: (46) 14152857
E-Mail: info@autoliv.com
Web Site: www.autoliv.se
Emp.: 350
Automotive Safety Equipment Designer, Mfr & Whslr
S.I.C.: 3714
N.A.I.C.S.: 336320
Leis Lundberg *(Mng Dir)*

Autoliv Electronics AB (1)
Teknikringen 9
SE 583 30 Linkoping, Sweden (100%)
Tel.: (46) 134804400
Fax: (46) 134804401
Web Site: www.autoliv.com
Emp.: 70
Automotive Safety Equipment Designer, Mfr & Whslr
S.I.C.: 3714
N.A.I.C.S.: 336320
Mats Sundin *(Gen Mgr)*

Autoliv Holding AB (1)
Vasagatan 11
Stockholm, 11120, Sweden
Tel.: (46) 858720600
Motor Vehicle Body Mfr
S.I.C.: 3711
N.A.I.C.S.: 336211
Jan Carlson *(CEO)*

Autoliv Mekan AB (1)
N Kringelvagen 13-15
PO Box 34
SE 281 21 Hassleholm, Sweden (100%)
Tel.: (46) 45142500
Fax: (46) 45115913
E-Mail: info@autoliv.com
Web Site: www.autoliv.com
Sls.: $72,696,000
Emp.: 150
Automotive Safety Equipment Designer, Mfr & Whslr

Import Export
S.I.C.: 3714
N.A.I.C.S.: 336390
Roger Parnestahl *(Mng Dir)*

Autoliv Research (1)
Wallentinsvagen 22
SE 447 83 Vargarda, Sweden (100%)
Tel.: (46) 322626300
Fax: (46) 322620118
E-Mail: info@autoliv.com
Web Site: www.autoliv.com
Emp.: 40
Automotive Safety Equipment Designer & Tester
S.I.C.: 8734
N.A.I.C.S.: 541380
Jan Carlson *(VP)*

Svensk Airbag AB (1)
Smedmastaregatan 3
SE 442 34 Kungalv, Sweden
Tel.: (46) 303204500
Fax: (46) 303204550
Web Site: www.autoliv.com
Emp.: 20
Automotive Airbags Mfr & Whslr
S.I.C.: 3714
N.A.I.C.S.: 336390
Rudi Pech *(Mng Dir)*

U.S. Subsidiaries:

Aerotest Operations, Inc. (1)
3455 Fostoria Way
San Ramon, CA 94583-1317 CA
Tel.: (925) 866-1212 (100%)
Fax: (925) 866-1716
Web Site: www.aerotestoperations.com
Sales Range: $50-74.9 Million
Provides Services for Neutron Radiography, Activation Analysis & Irradiation
S.I.C.: 8734
N.A.I.C.S.: 541380

Autoliv North America (1)
3350 Airport Rd
Ogden, UT 84405
Tel.: (801) 625-4800
Fax: (801) 625-4964
E-Mail: firstname.lastname@autoliv.com
Web Site: www.autoliv.com
Emp.: 10,500
Motor Vehicle Parts & Accessories
S.I.C.: 3711
N.A.I.C.S.: 336340
Mike Ward *(Pres)*

Divisions:

Autoliv - Airbag Inflator Facility (2)
250 American Way
Brigham City, UT 84302
Tel.: (435) 734-6100
Fax: (435) 734-7070
E-Mail: webmaster@autoliv.com
Web Site: www.alliedsecurity.com
Emp.: 1,200
Mfr. of Car Safety Equipment Airbags
S.I.C.: 7389
N.A.I.C.S.: 561499

Autoliv ASP, Inc. (2)
3350 Airport Rd
Ogden, UT 84405-1563
Tel.: (801) 625-8200
Fax: (801) 625-4911
E-Mail: hr@autoliv.com
Web Site: www.autoliv.com
Emp.: 4,000
Mfr. of Air Bags
S.I.C.: 8734
N.A.I.C.S.: 541380
Linda Boyer *(Mgr-Benefits)*

Autoliv Electronics America (2)
1320 Pacific Dr
Auburn Hills, MI 48326-1569
Tel.: (248) 475-9000
Emp.: 300
Automotive Safety Equipment Designer, Mfr & Whslr
S.I.C.: 3714
N.A.I.C.S.: 336320
Wendell Lane *(VP)*

Autoliv Inflators (2)
250 American Way
Brigham City, UT 84302
Tel.: (435) 734-6849
Fax: (435) 734-7070
E-Mail: hr@autoliv.com
Web Site: www.autoliv.com
Emp.: 900
Air Bags & Inflators Mfr
S.I.C.: 8734
N.A.I.C.S.: 541380
Brian Hyde *(Gen Mgr)*

Autoliv Initiators (2)
1360 N 1000 W
Tremonton, UT 84337-9336 (100%)
Tel.: (435) 257-1000
Fax: (435) 257-1010
E-Mail: info@autoliv.com
Web Site: www.autoliv.com
Emp.: 400
Mfr. of Automotive Safety Products & Propellant
S.I.C.: 3714
N.A.I.C.S.: 336390
Kevin Fox *(Gen Mgr)*

Autoliv North America Airbag Inflator Facility (2)
3350 Airport Rd
Ogden, UT 84405-1563
Tel.: (801) 625-8200
E-Mail: webmaster@autoliv.com
Web Site: www.autoliv.com
Emp.: 700
Mfr.of Air Bags
S.I.C.: 8734
N.A.I.C.S.: 541380
Steve Fredin *(Pres)*

Autoliv North America Airbag Module Facility (2)
1000 W 3300 S
Ogden, UT 84401
Tel.: (801) 629-9800
Fax: (801) 629-9619
Emp.: 4,000
Car Safety Equipment Mfr
S.I.C.: 2396
N.A.I.C.S.: 336360

Autoliv North America, American Technical Center (2)
1320 Pacific Dr
Auburn Hills, MI 48326-1569 DE
Tel.: (248) 475-9000
Fax: (248) 475-9011
E-Mail: info@autoliv.com
Web Site: www.autoliv.com
Emp.: 300
Automotive Safety Systems Developer, Mfr & Seller
S.I.C.: 3714
N.A.I.C.S.: 336390
Lars Westerberg *(Chm)*
Jan Carlson *(Pres & CEO)*

Autoliv North America Seat Belt Facility (2)
410 Autoliv Belt Way
Madisonville, KY 42431
Tel.: (270) 326-3300
Fax: (270) 326-3301
Web Site: www.autoliv.com
Emp.: 310
Mfr & Distr of Automotive Seat Belts
Import Export
S.I.C.: 2396
N.A.I.C.S.: 336360
Tammy Johnson *(Mgr-HR)*

Autoliv North America Service Parts Facility (2)
3250 Pennsylvania Ave
Ogden, UT 84401-3309
Tel.: (801) 629-9800
Fax: (801) 629-9199
E-Mail: hr@autoliv.com
Web Site: www.autoliv.com
Mfr. Car Safety Equipments
S.I.C.: 5013
N.A.I.C.S.: 423120
Bryan Crowell *(Plant Mgr)*

Autoliv North America Steering Wheel Facility (2)
4720 E Park 30 Dr
Columbia City, IN 46725-8861
Tel.: (260) 244-4941
Fax: (260) 244-4951
E-Mail: webmaster@autoliv.com
Web Site: www.autoliv.com
Emp.: 26
Mfr. of Steering Wheels
S.I.C.: 3714
N.A.I.C.S.: 336390
Kim Weinman *(Mgr)*

Autoliv Safety Technology (2)
2375 Paseo de la Americas PO Box 2303
San Diego, CA 92154
Tel.: (619) 662-8000
Emp.: 900
Automotive Safety Equipment Mfr
S.I.C.: 3714
N.A.I.C.S.: 336390
Ken Henehan *(Mng Dir)*

Pyrotechnic Processing Facility (2)
167000 W Hwy 83
Promontory, UT 84307
Tel.: (435) 471-3001
Fax: (435) 471-3007
Emp.: 200
Mfr of Pyrotechnic Products for the Airbag Industry
Import Export
S.I.C.: 3711
N.A.I.C.S.: 336111
Mike Ward *(Pres)*

Non-U.S. Subsidiaries:

3G Yatirim ve Gayrimenkul Ticaret A.S (1)
30 Haziran 2005
Persembe, Turkey
Tel.: (90) 212 347 06 47
Automotive Safety System Mfr
S.I.C.: 3714
N.A.I.C.S.: 336390

Airbags International Ltd. (1)
Viking Way
Congleton, Cheshire, CW12 1TT, United Kingdom UK
Tel.: (44) 1260294300 (100%)
Fax: (44) 1260294301
E-Mail: john.bonney@autoliv.com
Web Site: www.autoliv.com
Emp.: 250
Mfr & Distr of Automotive Airbags
Import Export
S.I.C.: 3711
N.A.I.C.S.: 336111
John Bonney *(Mgr-Fin)*

Autoliv Argentina S.A. (1)
Parque Industrial Pilar 1629 Lote 7 Fraccion 7
Calle 7 y del Canal
Pilar, Mar del Plata, Argentina
Tel.: (54) 2322 537400
Fax: (54) 2322 537401
Web Site: www.autoliv.com
Automobile Parts & Accessories Mfr
S.I.C.: 3714
N.A.I.C.S.: 336340

Autoliv Asia Pacific (1)
Unit 1405 7 14th Fl 2 Pacific Pl 142
Sukhumvit Rd Klongtoey
Bangkok, 10110, Thailand (100%)
Tel.: (66) 26598500
Fax: (66) 26532282
E-Mail: info@autoliv.com
Web Site: www.autoliv.com
Emp.: 15
Mfr of Seatbelt Webbing Products
Import Export
S.I.C.: 3711
N.A.I.C.S.: 336111
Gunnar Dahlen *(Pres)*

Autoliv ASP B.V. (1)
Schouwrooij 15
5281 RE Boxtel, Noord-Brabant, Netherlands
Tel.: (31) 411617961
Fax: (31) 411617969
Automobile Component Mfr & Distr
S.I.C.: 3714
N.A.I.C.S.: 336390

Autoliv Australia Pty. Ltd. (1)
1521 Hume Hwy
Campbellfield, VIC, 3061, Australia (100%)
Tel.: (61) 393555500
Fax: (61) 393555511
E-Mail: chris.tmon@autoliv.com
Web Site: www.autoliv.com
Emp.: 310
Mfr & Distr of Seat Belts, Passenger & Side Impact Airbags & Steering Wheels
S.I.C.: 3714
N.A.I.C.S.: 336340

Autoliv Beijing Safety Systems (1)
38 Yongan Rd Chang Ping Park of Zhong Cun Science & Technology Park
Beijing, Changping District, 102200, China (45%)
Tel.: (86) 10 588 23890
E-Mail:
Web Site: www.autoliv.com
Emp.: 80
Seatbelt Production
S.I.C.: 3052
N.A.I.C.S.: 326220

Autoliv BKI S.A. (1)
Poligono La Pobla La Eliana Calle 1 No 5 P.O.Box 87
La Pobla de Vallbona, 46185 Valencia, Spain
Mailing Address:
Apartado 87
La Pobla de Vallbona, 46185 Valencia, Spain
Tel.: (34) 962799600
Fax: (34) 962744450
E-Mail: reception.fax@autoliv.com
Web Site: www.autoliv.com
Emp.: 120
Mfr of Automotive Seat Belts
Import Export
S.I.C.: 2396
N.A.I.C.S.: 336360
Ambaro Vercher *(Mng Dir)*

Autoliv B.V. & Co. KG, Werk Nord (1)
Otto Hahn Strasse 4
PO Box 109
D 25333 Elmshorn, Germany (100%)
Tel.: (49) 41217970
Telex: 218302 AULIV D
Fax: (49) 412175776
E-Mail: info@autoliv.com
Web Site: www.autoliv.com
Emp.: 1,200
Automotive Seat Belts Mfr
Export
S.I.C.: 2396
N.A.I.C.S.: 336360

Autoliv Canada, Inc. (1)
20 Autoliv Dr
PO Box 1090
Tilbury, ON, N0P 2L0, Canada (100%)
Tel.: (519) 682-1083
Fax: (519) 682-2562
E-Mail: hr.canada@autoliv.com
Web Site: www.autoliv.com
Emp.: 200
Automotive Air Bags Mfr
S.I.C.: 3714
N.A.I.C.S.: 336390
Sherry Vasa *(Plant Mgr)*

Autoliv Cankor Otomotiv Emniyet Sistemleri Sanayi Ve Ticaret A.S. (1)
Gebze Organize Sanayi Bolgesi Ihsan Dede Cad 800 Sokak No 801
Gebze, Kocaeli, 41480, Turkey
Tel.: (90) 2626484600
Fax: (90) 2626484601
Automotive Equipments Mfr
S.I.C.: 3711
N.A.I.C.S.: 336211

Autoliv Cankor (1)
Gebze Organize Sanayi Bolgesi Ihsan Dede Cad 800 SK NO 801
41480 Gebze, Kocaeli, Turkey (100%)
Tel.: (90) 2626484600
Fax: (90) 7511928
E-Mail: leyla.irten@autoliv.com
Web Site: www.autoliv.com
Emp.: 460
Mfr of Automotive Seat Belts & Airbags
Import Export
S.I.C.: 2396
N.A.I.C.S.: 336360
Mustafa Alaca *(Mng Dir)*

Autoliv (Changchun) Mawhung Vehicle Safety Systems Co., Ltd. (1)
1831 Century St Economic & Technology Development Zone
Changchun, 130033, China (59%)

Autoliv, Inc.—(Continued)

Tel.: (86) 431 464 2688
Fax: (86) 431 463 4688
Web Site: www.autoliv.com
Emp.: 120
Mfr & Distr of Automotive Safety Systems
Import Export
S.I.C.: 3714
N.A.I.C.S.: 336340
Gunnar Dahlen *(Pres-Autoliv Asia)*

Autoliv (China) Electronics Co., Ltd. (1)
No 318 Huancheng East Road Fengxian District
Shanghai, 201401, China
Tel.: (86) 2167109300
Motor Vehicle Body Mfr
S.I.C.: 3711
N.A.I.C.S.: 336211
Thierry Masson *(Gen Mgr)*

Autoliv (China) Steering Wheel Co., Ltd. (1)
No 1808 Chenqiao Rd Fengpu Development Zone
Fengxian Distric, Shanghai, 201401, China
Tel.: (86) 2167107660
Motor Vehicle Parts Mfr
S.I.C.: 5013
N.A.I.C.S.: 423120

Autoliv Corporation (1)
Song Ri 436-1 Dong Tan-Myun
Hwaseong, Kyung Ki-Do, Korea (South)
Tel.: (82) 313796500
Fax: (82) 313796699
Automotive Safety Equipments Mfr
S.I.C.: 3714
N.A.I.C.S.: 336390

Autoliv de Mexico S.A. de C.V. (1)
Av De Los Sauces 9 Parque Industrial Lerma
CP 52000 Lerma, Mexico (100%)
Tel.: (52) 7282827600
Fax: (52) 7282827659
E-Mail:
Emp.: 1,200
Mfr of Automotive Airbags & Other Safety Systems
Import Export
S.I.C.: 2396
N.A.I.C.S.: 336360
Raul Armenta *(Mng Dir)*

Autoliv do Brasil (1)
Av Marginal a Rodovia Floriano Area Ind do Piracangagua
Rodrigues Pinheiro 551, 12043-000
Taubate, SP, Brazil
Tel.: (55) 1236271077
Fax: (55) 1236271069
E-Mail: damires.satos@autoliv.com
Web Site: www.autoliv.com
Emp.: 6,000
Mfr of Automotive Seats
Import Export
S.I.C.: 2396
N.A.I.C.S.: 336360
Araken Junior *(Gen Mgr)*

Autoliv Electronics Canada, Inc. (1)
7455 Birchmount Rd
Markham, ON, L3R 5C2, Canada (100%)
Tel.: (905) 475-8510
Fax: (905) 470-3296
Web Site: www.autoliv.com
Sales Range: $25-49.9 Million
Emp.: 370
Mfr. of Automotive Parts
S.I.C.: 3714
N.A.I.C.S.: 336340
Steve Brohm *(Branch Mgr)*

Autoliv Electronics, Pontoise (1)
Rue du Petit Albi Parc Silic Batiment D
95801 Cergy, Cedex, France (100%)
Tel.: (33) 0130178500
Fax: (33) 130178501
Web Site: www.autoliv.com
Emp.: 150
Mfr of Automotive Electronic Systems
Import Export
S.I.C.: 7549
N.A.I.C.S.: 811198

Autoliv Electronics SAS, Rouen (1)
Bd Lenine
PO Box 506
76807 Saint Etienne-du-Rouvray, France (100%)
Tel.: (33) 232914343
Fax: (33) 232914344
Web Site: www.autoliv.com
Emp.: 500
Mfr of Automotive Electrical Systems
Import Export
S.I.C.: 3711
N.A.I.C.S.: 336111
Coyote Phiery *(Plant Mgr)*

Autoliv France, Gournay (1)
Z I Ave de l' Europe
BP 99
76220 Gournay-en-Bray, France (100%)
Tel.: (33) 232894000
Fax: (33) 235901250
E-Mail: info@autoliv.com
Web Site: www.autoliv.com
Emp.: 1,100
Mfr of Car Safety Equipment
Import Export
S.I.C.: 3714
N.A.I.C.S.: 336340
Scott Olson *(Mng Dir)*

Autoliv France (1)
2 Rue Villaret de Joyeuse
PO Box 99
75017 Paris, France (100%)
Tel.: (33) 153812100
Fax: (33) 0033235901250
E-Mail: info@autoliv.com
Web Site: www.autoliv.com
Emp.: 30
Mfr of Automotive Airbags & Seat Belts
Import Export
S.I.C.: 2396
N.A.I.C.S.: 336360
Stethane Tuis *(Mng Dir)*

Autoliv GmbH, Braunschweig (1)
Hansestrasse 46
D 38112 Braunschweig, Germany (100%)
Tel.: (49) 5312181152
Fax: (49) 5312181111
E-Mail: helmunt.straden@autoliv.com
Web Site: www.autoliv.com
Emp.: 400
Mfr & Distr of Automotive Airbag Systems
Import Export
S.I.C.: 3711
N.A.I.C.S.: 336111

Autoliv GmbH, Werk Sud (1)
Theodor Heuss Strasse 2
85203 Dachau, Germany (100%)
Mailing Address:
Postfach 1320
85203 Dachau, Germany
Tel.: (49) 81312951183
Fax: (49) 81312951136
Web Site: www.autoliv.com
Emp.: 850
Development & Production of Automotive Airbags
Import Export
S.I.C.: 3711
N.A.I.C.S.: 336111

Autoliv Holding Ltd. (1)
44 Welbeck St
London, W1G 8DY, United Kingdom (100%)
Tel.: (44) 2074874867
Fax: (44) 2074869727
Web Site: www.autoliv.com
Taxation & Financial Matters
S.I.C.: 7291
N.A.I.C.S.: 541213

Autoliv Isodelta (1)
ZI Chire En Montreuil
86190 Vouille, France (100%)
Tel.: (33) 549396000
Fax: (33) 549518185
E-Mail: info@autoliv.com
Web Site: www.autoliv.com
Sls.: $149,026,800
Emp.: 800
Mfr of Automotive Safety Systems
Import Export
S.I.C.: 3714
N.A.I.C.S.: 336111
Geanlut kwantes *(Gen Mgr)*

Autoliv Italia SpA (1)
Strada Torino 27
I 10043 Orbassano, TO, Italy
Tel.: (39) 0119022511
Fax: (39) 0119000133
E-Mail: patrizia.vincenzi@autoliv.com
Web Site: www.autoliv.com
Emp.: 20
Mfr of Automotive Safety Systems
Import Export
S.I.C.: 3711
N.A.I.C.S.: 336111

Autoliv Izumi Ltd. (1)
704 1 Kami Echi
Atsugi, Kanagawa, 243 0801, Japan (100%)
Tel.: (81) 462041200
Fax: (81) 462456731
Web Site: www.autoliv.jp
Emp.: 200
Mfr. of Steering Wheels & Components
S.I.C.: 3714
N.A.I.C.S.: 336340
Hiroyuki Okamura *(Gen Mgr)*

Autoliv Izumi Philippines, Inc. (1)
Third Street Mactan Economic Zone
Lapu-Lapu, Cebu, 6015, Philippines (100%)
Tel.: (63) 323400502
Fax: (63) 323400504
E-Mail: cherryl.castil@autolive.com
Web Site: www.autolivasp.com
Emp.: 936
Mfr of Automotive Safety Systems
Import Export
S.I.C.: 3714
N.A.I.C.S.: 336111
Ronald Modlin *(Gen Mgr)*

Autoliv Japan Ltd. (1)
23-3 Jinta Taketoyo-cho
Chita, Aichi, 470-2372, Japan (100%)
Tel.: (81) 569740862
Fax: (81) 569740852
E-Mail: yasuyuki.Shibato@autoliv.com
Web Site: www.autoliv.com
Emp.: 150
Mfr of Automotive Safety Systems
Export
S.I.C.: 3711
N.A.I.C.S.: 336111
Yasuyuki Shibato *(Pres)*

Autoliv Kft. (1)
Sopronkovesd Iskola u 38-50
9483 Sopron, Ujmajor, Hungary (100%)
Tel.: (36) 99536300
Web Site: www.autoliv.com
Sls.: $22,000,000
Emp.: 1,000
Mfr of Automotive Belt Assemblies
Import Export
S.I.C.: 3052
N.A.I.C.S.: 326220
Martin Rumpf *(Gen Mgr)*

Autoliv KK (1)
33-17546 Shinyokohama Kohoku Ku
Yokohama, 222-8580, Japan (100%)
Tel.: (81) 454753501
Fax: (81) 454753502
E-Mail: info@autoliv.com
Emp.: 30
Mfr & Assembly of Automotive Night Vision Safety Systems
Import Export
S.I.C.: 3711
N.A.I.C.S.: 336111
Jan Carlson *(Pres & CEO)*
Brad Murray *(Pres)*

Division:

Autoliv Japan Ltd. - Fujisawa Facility (2)
12 Kiriharacho
Fujisawa, Kanagawa, 252 0811, Japan
Tel.: (81) 466441711
Fax: (81) 466455808
Web Site: www.autoliv.com
Emp.: 100
Mfr & Distr of Automotive Locking Seat Belt Retractors
Export
S.I.C.: 2396
N.A.I.C.S.: 336360

Autoliv KLE S.A. (1)
Carretera C 170 Km 17 5
PO Box 242
Poligono Industrial Batzacs, E 08403
Granollers, Barcelona, Spain (100%)
Tel.: (34) 938615000
Fax: (34) 938498582
E-Mail: info@autoliv.com
Web Site: www.autoliv.com
Sls.: $190,000,000
Emp.: 300
Mfr of Automotive Seat Belts & Buckles
Import Export
S.I.C.: 2396
N.A.I.C.S.: 336360
Eloe Ruez *(CFO)*

Autoliv Mando Corporation (1)
Song Ri 436-3 Dong Tan Myun
Kangnam-ku
Seoul, 445-810, Korea (South)
Tel.: (82) 313796500
Fax: (82) 313796698
Web Site: www.autoliv.com
Emp.: 500
Mfr of Automotive Safety Systems
S.I.C.: 3714
N.A.I.C.S.: 336340

Autoliv N.Z. Ltd. (1)
306 Rosebank Rd
PO Box 1761
Avondale, Auckland, New Zealand (100%)
Tel.: (64) 98200049
Fax: (64) 98200062
E-Mail: info@autoliv.com
Web Site: www.autoliv.com
Emp.: 6
Mfr of Automotive Safety Systems
Import Export
S.I.C.: 3711
N.A.I.C.S.: 336111
Ray Pekar *(Dir-IR-Bus Dev)*

Autoliv Poland Restraint Systems (1)
Ul Belgijska 2
555 230 Jelcz-Laskowice, Poland (100%)
Tel.: (48) 713810700
Fax: (48) 713810720
E-Mail: info@autoliv.com
Web Site: www.autoliv.com
Emp.: 600
Mfr of Automotive Passenger Seat Restraints
Import Export
S.I.C.: 2396
N.A.I.C.S.: 336360
Jack Till *(Plant Mgr)*

Autoliv Poland Sp.zo.o. (1)
Ul Polna 49
PL 55 200 Olawa, Poland (100%)
Tel.: (48) 713010100
Fax: (48) 713010220
Emp.: 1,500
Mfr of Automotive Power Trains & Safety Systems
Export
S.I.C.: 3714
N.A.I.C.S.: 336350
Sebastian Galka *(Gen Mgr)*

Autoliv Protektor GmbH (1)
Wesloer Str 112
Schleswig-Holstein, Lubeck, 23568, Germany
Tel.: (49) 451619800
Fax: (49) 4516198030
Motor Vehicle Body Mfr
S.I.C.: 3711
N.A.I.C.S.: 336211

Autoliv QB, Inc. (1)
Blk 7 Lot 8 LIIP Ave Laguna International Industrial Park
Mampalasan, Binan Laguna, 4024, Philippines (100%)
Tel.: (63) 495390119
Fax: (63) 495390118
Web Site: www.autoliv.com
Sales Range: $1-9.9 Million
Emp.: 100
Mfr of Automotive Safety Systems
Import Export
S.I.C.: 3711
N.A.I.C.S.: 336111
Ferdinand Raquelsantos *(Mng Dir)*

Autoliv Romania S.A. (1)
8 Bucegi St
2200 Brasov, Romania (100%)
Tel.: (40) 268477850
Fax: (40) 268477925
Web Site: www.autoliv.com
Emp.: 1,100

Automobile Mfr
Export
S.I.C.: 3711
N.A.I.C.S.: 336111
Ionel Fierbinteanu *(Mng Dir)*

Autoliv (Shanghai) Management Co., Ltd. **(1)**
No 1000 Beihe Highway Jiading Industrial Zone
Shanghai, 201807, China
Tel.: (86) 2169928000
Fax: (86) 2169928899
Motor Vehicle Body Mfr
S.I.C.: 3711
N.A.I.C.S.: 336211

Autoliv Sicherheitstechnik GmbH, Werk Ost **(1)**
Eichbergstrasse 10 13
04720 Dobeln, Germany (100%)
Tel.: (49) 343166010
Fax: (49) 3431660114
E-Mail: info@autoliv.com
Web Site: www.autoliv.com
Sales Range: $25-49.9 Million
Emp.: 250
Mfr of Automotive Safety Systems
Import Export
S.I.C.: 3711
N.A.I.C.S.: 336111
Pelle Malmhagen *(Mng Dir)*

Autoliv Southern Africa (Pty) Ltd. **(1)**
19 Fransen Street
Chamdor, Krugersdorp, Gauteng, 1739, South Africa (100%)
Mailing Address:
PO Box 3058
Kenmare, 1745 Gauteng, South Africa
Tel.: (27) 112792600
Fax: (27) 117621468
E-Mail: info@autoliv.com
Web Site: www.autoliv.com
Sales Range: $10-24.9 Million
Emp.: 150
Mfr of Automotive Safety Systems
Import Export
S.I.C.: 3711
N.A.I.C.S.: 336340
David Kretschmer *(Gen Mgr)*

Autoliv Spring Dynamics **(1)**
Maidstone Road
Milton Keynes, Bucks, MK10 0BH, United Kingdom (100%)
Tel.: (44) 1908286900
Fax: (44) 1908286938
Web Site: www.autoliv.com
Emp.: 120
Mfr of Automotive Seat Springs
Import Export
S.I.C.: 2396
N.A.I.C.S.: 336360

Autoliv Stakupress GmbH **(1)**
In De Tarpen 71 99
D 22848 Norderstedt, Germany (100%)
Tel.: (49) 405230600
Fax: (49) 4052306019
E-Mail: info@autoliv.com
Web Site: www.autoliv.com
Rev.: $37,742,792
Emp.: 200
Motor Vehicle Brake
S.I.C.: 3714
N.A.I.C.S.: 336340
Torsten Gross *(Mng Dir)*

Autoliv Steering Wheels S.R.L. de C.V. **(1)**
1 Tepeyac 1120 Carretara
Chichimequallas Km 4 5, 76240 Queretaro, Mexico (100%)
Tel.: (52) 4422781100
Fax: (52) 4422781104
Emp.: 800
Mfr of Automotive Steering Wheels & Other Safety Systems
Import Export
S.I.C.: 3714
N.A.I.C.S.: 336330

Autoliv Textiles **(1)**
Viking Way
Congleton, Cheshire, CW12 1TT, United Kingdom (100%)
Tel.: (44) 1260294300
Fax: (44) 1260294301
E-Mail:
Web Site: www.autoliv.com
Emp.: 250
Automotive Fabrics Mfr
Import Export
S.I.C.: 2269
N.A.I.C.S.: 313310
Francois Maistrelli *(Mng Dir)*

Autoliv Thailand Limited **(1)**
700 415 M 7 Amata Nakorn Industrial Estate
Chon Buri, 20000, Thailand (100%)
Tel.: (66) 38456000
Fax: (66) 38456080
E-Mail: ukos.Surapipongpunp@autoliv.com
Web Site: www.autoliv.com
Emp.: 900
Mfr. & Sales of Automotive Components
S.I.C.: 3714
N.A.I.C.S.: 336330

Autoliv Thailand Limited **(1)**
700 415 Moo 7 Amata Nakorn Industrial Estate Moo 7 Bangna Trad Rd T Do
Chon Buri, 20000, Thailand (100%)
Tel.: (66) 38456000
Fax: (66) 38456080
E-Mail: robert.franklin@autoliv.com
Web Site: www.autoliv.com
Sls.: $61,125,000
Emp.: 1,000
Mfr of Automotive Safety Systems
S.I.C.: 3711
N.A.I.C.S.: 336111
Natthakij Iatikanvhanakoinkij *(Program Mgr)*

Autoliv Tunisia Zriba **(1)**
Z I Zriba
1152 Hammam, Zriba, Tunisia
Tel.: (216) 72677524
Fax: (216) 72677840
Web Site: www.autoliv.com
Emp.: 380
Mfr of Automotive Steering Wheels & Seat Belts
Import Export
S.I.C.: 3714
N.A.I.C.S.: 336330

EAK-Composants Pour l'Automobile **(1)**
Zac Des Combottes
F 25700 Valentigney, France (49%)
Tel.: (33) 381362020
Fax: (33) 381362004
E-Mail: armame.peyron@faurecia.com
Web Site: www.autoliv.com
Emp.: 94
Mfr of Automotive Safety Systems
Import Export
S.I.C.: 3711
N.A.I.C.S.: 336111
Peyron Armame *(Mng Dir)*

Livbag SAS **(1)**
Rte du Beuzit
F 29590 Pont-de-Buis-les-Quimerch, France (100%)
Tel.: (33) 298813000
Fax: (33) 298730504
E-Mail: liv.reception@autoliv.com
Web Site: www.autoliv.com
Emp.: 1,300
Mfr of Automotive Safety Systems
Import Export
S.I.C.: 3714
N.A.I.C.S.: 336111

Mei-An Autoliv Co., Ltd. **(1)**
No 706 Fu Kuo Rd
330 Taoyuan, Taiwan (100%)
Tel.: (886) 33012612
Fax: (886) 33020304
Web Site: www.autoliv.com.tw
Sales Range: $10-24.9 Million
Emp.: 90
Mfr of Automotive Seat Belts & Other Safety Systems
Import Export
S.I.C.: 2396
N.A.I.C.S.: 336360
Amber Wang *(Mng Dir)*

Nanjing Hongguang Autoliv Ltd. **(1)**
18 Hengda Rd Nanjing Economic Devolpment zone
Nanjing, 210038, China (70%)
Tel.: (86) 2585803990
Fax: (86) 2585803660
Emp.: 515
Mfr of Automotive Safety Systems
Import Export
S.I.C.: 3714
N.A.I.C.S.: 336111
Jennfer Gen *(Gen Mgr)*

N.C.S. Pyrotechnie et Technologies SAS **(1)**
Rue de la Cartoucherie
Survilliers, France
Tel.: (33) 134317000
Fax: (33) 134685762
Emp.: 5
Motor Vehicle Body Mfr
S.I.C.: 3711
N.A.I.C.S.: 336211
Ciril Cousin *(Gen Dir)*

N.C.S. Survilliers **(1)**
Rue de la Cartoucherie
PO Box BP10
F 95471 Survilliers, France (100%)
Tel.: (33) 134317000
Fax: (33) 134685762
E-Mail: Cyril.Cousin@autoliv.com
Web Site: www.autoliv.com
Sales Range: $125-149.9 Million
Emp.: 800
Mfr of Automotive Safety Systems
Import Export
S.I.C.: 3711
N.A.I.C.S.: 336111
Bertrand Dambricourt *(Mgr-Logistics)*

Norma A/S **(1)**
Laki 14
EE 10621 Tallinn, Estonia (100%)
Tel.: (372) 6500442
Fax: (372) 6500134
E-Mail: norma@autoliv.com
Web Site: www.norma.ee
Sales Range: $75-99.9 Million
Emp.: 600
Mfr of Automotive Safety Systems
Import Export
S.I.C.: 3714
N.A.I.C.S.: 336111

P.T. Autoliv Indonesia **(1)**
BPSP Bldg 2nd Fl No.8 Pulo Buaran V Blok JJ4
Jakarta Industrial Estate
Pulo Gadung, Jakarta, 13920, Indonesia
Tel.: (62) 214604245
Fax: (62) 214604246
Web Site: www.autoliv.com
Emp.: 105
S.I.C.: 3714
N.A.I.C.S.: 336340
KuKua Kumara *(Gen Mgr)*

Taicang van Oerle Alberton Shenda Special Type Textile Products Co., Ltd. **(1)**
Taicang van Oerle Alberton Shenda Special Type Textile Products Co., L
Taicang, Jiangsu, 215400, China
Tel.: (86) 51253129188
Fax: (86) 51253129119
Motor Vehicle Body Mfr
S.I.C.: 3711
N.A.I.C.S.: 336211

Van Oerle Alberton B.V. **(1)**
Schouwrooij 15
PO Box 52
N 5280 AB Boxtel, Netherlands (100%)
Tel.: (31) 411617961
Fax: (31) 411617969
Web Site: www.autoliv.com
Emp.: 170
Mfr of Safety Belts Webbing
Export
S.I.C.: 3052
N.A.I.C.S.: 326220
Mats Odman *(VP-Corp Comm)*

VOA Canada **(1)**
190 MacDonald Rd
Collingwood, ON, L9Y 4N6, Canada Ca (100%)
Tel.: (705) 444-2561
Fax: (705) 444-7209
E-Mail: david.helm@autoliv.com
Emp.: 100
Mfr of Automotive Seat Belt Webbing
Import Export
S.I.C.: 2396
N.A.I.C.S.: 336360
Jill Stewart *(Dir-Fin)*

ZAO Norma-Osvar **(1)**
Zheleznodorozhnaya Str 13
Vyazniki, Vladimir, Russia 601446
Tel.: (7) 4923331123
Fax: (7) 4923331123
Web Site: www.rubelts.ru
Automotive Safety System Mfr
S.I.C.: 3714
N.A.I.C.S.: 336390

Non-U.S. Joint Venture:

Autoliv Hirotako Sdn. Bhd. **(1)**
Lot 1989 Lebuh Tanming Taman Tanming Jaya
Jalan Balakong, 43300 Seri Kembangan, Selangor Darul Ehsan, Malaysia
Tel.: (60) 389612020
Fax: (60) 389613030
E-Mail: ahsb@autolivhirotako.com.my
Web Site: www.hirotako.com.my/div_ahsb_intro.htm
Emp.: 400
Automotive Restraint Systems Mfr
Export
S.I.C.: 2396
N.A.I.C.S.: 336360
Chow Wing Loke *(Gen Mgr-Comml)*

Subsidiary:

Autoliv Hirotako Safety Sdn. Bhd. **(2)**
Lot 1989 Lebuh Tanming Taman Tanming
Jalan Balakong, 43300 Seri Kembangan, Selangor Darul Ehsan, Malaysia
Tel.: (60) 389612020
Fax: (60) 389613030
E-Mail:
Emp.: 500
Mfr of Automotive Airbags & Other Safety Systems
Export
S.I.C.: 3714
N.A.I.C.S.: 336390
Looi Kok Loon *(Mng Dir)*

Subsidiary:

Autoliv Hirotako SRS Sdn. Bhd. **(3)**
Lot 1989 Lebuh Tanming Taman Tanming Jaya
Jalan Balakong, 43300 Seri Kembangan, Selangor Darul Ehsan, Malaysia
Tel.: (60) 389612020
Fax: (60) 389613030
E-Mail:
Emp.: 400
Mfr of Automotive Safety Restraint Systems
Export
S.I.C.: 3714
N.A.I.C.S.: 336390
Tony Sun Hock Leow *(Mng Dir)*

AUTOMAKEDONIJA A.D.

Ul Mito Hagivasilev br 20
1000 Skopje, Macedonia
Tel.: (389) 2 3 121 423
Fax: (389) 2 3 111 680
E-Mail: automak@automakedonija.com.mk
Web Site: www.automakedonija.com.mk
Year Founded: 1946
AUMK—(MAC)
Emp.: 87

Business Description:
Motor Vehicle Whslr
S.I.C.: 5012
N.A.I.C.S.: 423110

Personnel:
Dimitar Mojsovski *(Pres)*

AUTOMATED BENEFITS CORPORATION

(Name Changed to Symbility Solutions, Inc.)

AUTOMATED TOUCHSTONE MACHINES LIMITED

7th Bldg Nangang 1st Industry Park
Xili Songbai Rd
Nashan, Shenzhen, 518057, China

Automated Touchstone Machines Limited—(Continued)

Tel.: (86) 75526711320
Fax: (86) 75526710324
E-Mail: touchstone@tis.com.cn
Web Site: www.tis.com.cn
Emp.: 197

Business Description:
Banking Equipment & Software Services
S.I.C.: 7389
N.A.I.C.S.: 561499

Personnel:
George Y. Filmeridis *(Chm)*
Kok Teo Chee *(Mng Dir)*
Hun Teo Chin *(Sec)*

Board of Directors:
George Y. Filmeridis
Kah Hong Chan
Kok Teo Chee
Cher Lin Lim

AUTOMOBILE & PCB INC.

254-5 Dodang-Dong
Wonmi-Gu, Bucheon, Kyeonggi-Do, 420-130, Korea (South)
Tel.: (82) 326769700
Fax: (82) 326751044
Web Site: www.anpcb.co.kr
Year Founded: 1977
015260—(KRS)

Business Description:
Printed Circuit Board Mfr & Sales
S.I.C.: 3672
N.A.I.C.S.: 334412

Personnel:
Sang Jo Seo *(CEO)*

AUTOMOBILE CORPORATION OF GOA LTD

Honda Sattari
Goa, 403530, India
Tel.: (91) 832 6731227
Fax: (91) 832 6731262
Web Site: www.acglgoa.com
505036—(BOM)
Rev.: $52,715,996
Assets: $42,003,139
Liabilities: $11,475,031
Net Worth: $30,528,108
Earnings: $2,898,515
Emp.: 585
Fiscal Year-end: 03/31/13

Business Description:
Sheet Metal Components Mfr
S.I.C.: 3444
N.A.I.C.S.: 332322

Personnel:
V. Krishnamurthi *(Mng Dir)*
Pravin Satardekar *(Compliance Officer & Sec)*

Board of Directors:
S. V. Salgaocar
S. B. Borwankar
P. F. X. D'Lima
A. Gajendragadkar
V. Krishnamurthi
Steven A. Pinto
R. Ramakrishnan

Transfer Agent:
TSR Darashaw Limited
6-10 Haji Moosa Patrawala Industrial Estate 20 Dr. E Moses Road
Near Famous Studio Mahalaxmi, Mumbai, India

AUTOMOBILE PROVENCE INNOVATION

Route De Miramas 870 Allee De Szentendre
13300 Avignon, Provence, France
Tel.: (33) 490423939
Fax: (33) 490535083
Web Site: www.citroen.fr/salon-de-provence/
Sales Range: $10-24.9 Million
Emp.: 32

Business Description:
New & Used Car Dealers
S.I.C.: 5511
N.A.I.C.S.: 441110

Personnel:
Jean-Luc Rousselet *(Sls Mgr)*

AUTOMOBILES CHATENET

Pierre Buffiere
BP 9
87260 Limoges, France
Tel.: (33) 555009158
Fax: (33) 555009117
Web Site: www.automobiles-chatenet.com
Sls.: $23,400,000
Emp.: 39

Business Description:
Motor Vehicles & Car Bodies
S.I.C.: 3711
N.A.I.C.S.: 336111

Personnel:
Louis-Georges Chatenet *(Mng Dir)*

Board of Directors:
Louis-Georges Chatenet
Yannick Tourat

AUTOMOBILES DU VAL D'ALLIER

Route De Clermont
63500 Issoire, Puy De Dome, France
Tel.: (33) 473897197
Sls.: $20,500,000
Emp.: 60

Business Description:
New & Used Car Dealers
S.I.C.: 5511
N.A.I.C.S.: 441110

Personnel:
Michel Laurent *(Personnel Dir)*

AUTOMOBILES MAUGER FORD

119 Grande Allee Est
Grande-Riviere, QC, G0C1V0, Canada
Tel.: (418) 385-2118
Web Site: www.mauger.dealerconnection.com
Rev.: $32,517,411
Emp.: 65

Business Description:
New & Used Car Dealers
S.I.C.: 5511
N.A.I.C.S.: 441110

Personnel:
Jean Louis Mauger *(Pres)*
Suzie Beaudin *(Dir Gen)*

AUTOMOBILES ORTHEZIENNES

Route De Pau Avenue Pierre Mendes France
64300 Orleans, France
Tel.: (33) 559670000
Fax: (33) 559670877
Web Site: www.edenauto.com
Sls.: $20,900,000
Emp.: 47

Business Description:
New & Used Car Dealers
S.I.C.: 5511
N.A.I.C.S.: 441110

Personnel:
Pierre Aratto *(Pres)*

AUTOMOBILES ULSAN LTEE

1625 boulevard Hymus
Dorval, QC, H9P 1J5, Canada
Tel.: (514) 683-5702
Fax: (514) 683-2255
E-Mail: service@ulsanhyundai.com
Web Site: www.ulsanhyundai.com
Rev.: $12,954,798
Emp.: 28

Business Description:
New & Used Car Dealers
S.I.C.: 5511
N.A.I.C.S.: 441110

Personnel:
Peter Croft *(Mgr)*

AUTOMODULAR CORPORATION

235 Salem Road South Unit 6
Ajax, ON, L1Z 0B1, Canada
Tel.: (905) 619-4200
Fax: (905) 619-9466
E-Mail: info@automodular.com
Web Site: www.automodular.com
AM—(TSX)
Sls.: $115,259,601
Assets: $49,126,456
Liabilities: $8,591,315
Net Worth: $40,535,142
Earnings: $16,679,656
Emp.: 525
Fiscal Year-end: 12/31/12

Business Description:
Parts Assembly for the Automotive Industry
S.I.C.: 3714
N.A.I.C.S.: 336340

Personnel:
Rae E. Wallin *(Chm)*
Christopher S. Nutt *(Pres & CEO)*
Melinda Diebel *(CFO & VP-Fin)*
Diane C. Erlingher *(Sec)*

Board of Directors:
Rae E. Wallin
Len Crispino
Parsa Kiai
R. Peter McLaughlin
Ralph T. Neville
Christopher S. Nutt

Legal Counsel:
Sheldon Huxtable
Toronto, ON, Canada

Transfer Agent:
Computershare Investor Services Inc.
100 University Avenue 8th Floor
Toronto, ON, M5J 2Y1, Canada
Tel.: (514) 982-7555

Subsidiary:

Automodular Assemblies, Inc. **(1)**
200 Montecorte St
Whitby, ON, L1N 9V8, Canada (100%)
Tel.: (905) 665-0060
Fax: (905) 665-1451
Web Site: www.automodular.net
Emp.: 480
Provider of Parts Assembly for the Automotive Industry
S.I.C.: 3714
N.A.I.C.S.: 336340
Michael F. Blair *(Pres & CEO)*
Christopher S. Nutt *(CFO & VP-Fin)*

AUTOMOTIVE COMPONENTS LIMITED

253-293 George Town Rd
Rocherlea, TAS, 7248, Australia
Tel.: (61) 397940324
Fax: (61) 363244680
Web Site: www.acl.com.au
Year Founded: 1930
Sales Range: $125-149.9 Million
Emp.: 200

Business Description:
Automobile Parts Mfr
S.I.C.: 3711
N.A.I.C.S.: 336111

Personnel:
Chris Brooks *(Gen Mgr)*

AUTOMOTIVE HOLDINGS GROUP LIMITED

21 Old Aberdeen Place
West Perth, WA, 6005, Australia
Tel.: (61) 8 9422 7676
Fax: (61) 8 9422 7686
E-Mail: info@ahg.com.au
Web Site: www.ahgir.com.au
Year Founded: 1952
AHE—(ASX)
Rev.: $4,457,637,981
Assets: $1,647,554,890
Liabilities: $1,140,597,208
Net Worth: $506,957,682
Earnings: $72,849,043
Emp.: 5,700
Fiscal Year-end: 06/30/13

Business Description:
Automotive Retailer
S.I.C.: 5511
N.A.I.C.S.: 441110

Personnel:
Bronte Howson *(Mng Dir)*
Philip Mirams *(CFO)*
David Rowland *(Gen Counsel & Sec)*

Board of Directors:
David Griffiths
Giovanni Groppoli
Tracey Horton
Bronte Howson
Robert McEniry
Michael Smith
Peter Stancliffe

Subsidiaries:

360 Finance Pty Ltd **(1)**
1032 Beaudesert Road
Coopers Plains, QLD, 4108, Australia
Tel.: (61) 1300 361 360
Fax: (61) 7 3336 3300
E-Mail: info@360financial.com.au
Web Site: www.360finance.com.au
Automobile Financing Services
S.I.C.: 6153
N.A.I.C.S.: 522220
Madelyne Prowse *(Mgr-Fin & Settlements)*

AHG 1 Pty Ltd **(1)**
43-63 Princes Hwy
Dandenong, VIC, 3175, Australia
Tel.: (61) 392125555
New & Used Car Dealer
S.I.C.: 5511
N.A.I.C.S.: 441110

Allpike Autos Pty Ltd **(1)**
274 Scarborough Beach Rd
Osborne Park, WA, 6017, Australia
Tel.: (61) 8 6365 4057
Automotive Parts Distr
S.I.C.: 5013
N.A.I.C.S.: 423120

AUT 6 Pty Ltd **(1)**
101 Sterling Hwy
Nedlands, WA, 6009, Australia
Tel.: (61) 892733131
Fax: (61) 892733130
New & Used Car Dealer
S.I.C.: 5511
N.A.I.C.S.: 441110

Big Rock 2005 Pty Ltd **(1)**
445 Wanneroo Rd
Balcatta, WA, 6021, Australia
Tel.: (61) 893440111
Fax: (61) 893443246
New & Used Car Dealer
S.I.C.: 5511
N.A.I.C.S.: 441110

Big Rock Pty Ltd **(1)**
Persival St
Lilyfield, Sydney, NSW, 2040, Australia
Tel.: (61) 2 9552 6663
New & Used Car Dealer
N.A.I.C.S.: 441110

Butmac Pty Ltd **(1)**
13 39 Pilbara St
Welshpool, WA, 6106, Australia
Tel.: (61) 893514833
Fax: (61) 893516694
Emp.: 20

Logistics Consulting Services
S.I.C.: 4731
N.A.I.C.S.: 541614
Jeff Leisk, *(Gen Mgr)*

City Motors (1981) Pty Ltd (1)
505 Newcastle Street
Wangara, WA, 6065, Australia
Tel.: (61) 8 9309 9003
New & Used Car Dealer
S.I.C.: 5511
N.A.I.C.S.: 441110

Duncan Autos 2005 Pty Ltd (1)
501 Albany Hwy
Victoria Park, WA, 6100, Australia
Tel.: (61) 892620000
Fax: (61) 893614419
E-Mail: accounts@duncannissan.com.au
Emp.: 50
New & Used Car Dealer
S.I.C.: 5511
N.A.I.C.S.: 441110
Lee Trant, *(Mgr-Showroom)*

Falconet Pty Ltd (1)
24-26 Kewdale Rd
Welshpool, WA, 6106, Australia
Tel.: (61) 8 9351 2000
New & Used Car Dealer
S.I.C.: 5511
N.A.I.C.S.: 441110

Geraldine Nominees Pty Ltd (1)
268 Great Eastern Hwy
Belmont, WA, 6104, Australia
Tel.: (61) 893331888
New & Used Car Dealer
S.I.C.: 5511
N.A.I.C.S.: 441110

Giant Autos (1997) Pty Ltd (1)
460 Scarborough Beach Rd
Osborne Park, WA, 6017, Australia
Tel.: (61) 894455666
Fax: (61) 894455600
New & Used Car Dealer
S.I.C.: 5511
N.A.I.C.S.: 441110
Ben Dalgliesh, *(Gen Mgr)*

Grand Autos 2005 Pty Ltd (1)
Corner Wanneroo Rd & Lancaster Rd
Wangara, WA, 6065, Australia
Tel.: (61) 894039000
Fax: (61) 894039099
Emp.: 100
New & Used Car Dealer
S.I.C.: 5511
N.A.I.C.S.: 441110

Highland Kackell Pty Ltd (1)
52 Sunnyholt Rd
Blacktown, NSW, 2148, Australia
Tel.: (61) 288844888
New & Used Car Dealer
S.I.C.: 5511
N.A.I.C.S.: 441110

Janetto Holdings Pty Ltd (1)
435 Scarborough Beach Rd
Osborne Park, WA, 6017, Australia
Tel.: (61) 892732333
Emp.: 500
New & Used Car Dealer
S.I.C.: 5511
N.A.I.C.S.: 441110
Andy Diamantis, *(Gen Mgr)*

MCM Autos Pty Ltd (1)
511 Princes Hwy
Sutherland, NSW, 2232, Australia
Tel.: (61) 295457344
New & Used Car Dealer
S.I.C.: 5511
N.A.I.C.S.: 441110

Melborne City Autos (2012) Pty Ltd (1)
32-48 Johnson St
South Melbourne, VIC, 3205, Australia
Tel.: (61) 386092240
New & Used Car Dealer
S.I.C.: 5511
N.A.I.C.S.: 441110

Melville Autos Pty Ltd (1)
174 Leach Hwy
Melville, WA, 6156, Australia
Tel.: (61) 893643346
New & Used Car Dealer
S.I.C.: 5511
N.A.I.C.S.: 441110

Newcastle Commercial Vehicles Pty Ltd (1)
1 Kinta Dr
Beresfield, NSW, 2322, Australia
Tel.: (61) 2 4964 3888
New & Used Car Dealer
S.I.C.: 5511
N.A.I.C.S.: 441110

North City (1981) Pty Ltd (1)
345 Scarborough Beach Rd
Osborne Park, WA, 6017, Australia
Tel.: (61) 892732278
New & Used Car Dealer
S.I.C.: 5511
N.A.I.C.S.: 441110

Nuford Ford Pty Ltd (1)
6 Automotive Dr
Wangara, WA, 6947, Australia
Tel.: (61) 893098888
New & Used Car Dealer
S.I.C.: 5511
N.A.I.C.S.: 441110
Cameron Reed, *(Gen Mgr)*

Rand Transport (1986) Pty Ltd (1)
1248 Lytton Rd
Hemmant, QLD, 4174, Australia
Tel.: (61) 7 3907 8888
Logistics Consulting Services
S.I.C.: 4731
N.A.I.C.S.: 541614

Rand Transport Pty Ltd (1)
20 Vale Rd
Hazelmere, Perth, WA, 6055, Australia
Tel.: (61) 8 9353 7099
Fax: (61) 8 9374 1848
Logistics Consulting Services
N.A.I.C.S.: 541614
David Cole, *(Gen Mgr)*

Southeast Automotive Group Pty Ltd (1)
1310 Logan Rd
Mount Gravatt, QLD, 4122, Australia
Tel.: (61) 738770000
New & Used Car Dealer
S.I.C.: 5511
N.A.I.C.S.: 441110

Southside Autos (1981) Pty Ltd (1)
1261-1273 Albany Hwy
Cannington, WA, 6107, Australia
Tel.: (61) 893589555
New & Used Car Dealer
S.I.C.: 5511
N.A.I.C.S.: 441110

Total Autos (1990) Pty Ltd (1)
1251 Albany Hwy
Cannington, WA, 6107, Australia
Tel.: (61) 893514444
Fax: (61) 893505970
E-Mail: info@totalnissan.com.au
Emp.: 80
New & Used Car Dealer
S.I.C.: 5511
N.A.I.C.S.: 441110
Graham Hampson, *(Gen Mgr)*

Zupps Aspley Pty Ltd (1)
1454 Gympie Road
Aspley, Brisbane, QLD, 4034, Australia
Tel.: (61) 7 3246 8044
Fax: (61) 7 3246 8055
New & Used Car Dealer
N.A.I.C.S.: 441110
James Malone, *(Gen Mgr)*

Zupps Mt Gravatt Pty Ltd (1)
143 Marshall Rd
Rocklea, QLD, 4106, Australia
Tel.: (61) 733207777
Fax: (61) 732758770
E-Mail: info@daimlertrucksbrisbane.com.au
New & Used Car Dealer
S.I.C.: 5511
N.A.I.C.S.: 441110

Non-U.S. Subsidiary:

Auckland Auto Collection Limited (1)
Quigg Partners
Wellington, New Zealand
Tel.: (64) 93769829
New Car Dealer
S.I.C.: 5511
N.A.I.C.S.: 441110

AUTOMOTIVE TRIM DEVELOPMENTS

Priory Mill Charter Avenue
Coventry, Warwickshire, CV4 8AF, United Kingdom
Tel.: (44) 2476 695 150
Fax: (44) 2476 695 156
E-Mail: info@autotrimdev.com
Web Site: www.autotrimdev.com
Year Founded: 2000
Sales Range: $10-24.9 Million
Emp.: 85

Business Description:
Leather Product Mfr
S.I.C.: 3199
N.A.I.C.S.: 316998

Personnel:
Brett Townsend *(Founder & Mng Dir)*

AUTONAVI HOLDINGS LIMITED

16/F Section A Focus Square No 6
Futong East Avenue
Wangjing Chaoyang District, Beijing, 100102, China
Tel.: (86) 10 84107000
Fax: (86) 10 8410 7777
Web Site: www.autonavi.com
Year Founded: 2002
AMAP—(NASDAQ)
Rev.: $163,241,000
Assets: $351,804,000
Liabilities: $57,750,000
Net Worth: $294,054,000
Earnings: $38,184,000
Emp.: 2,825
Fiscal Year-end: 12/31/12

Business Description:
Digital Map Content, Navigation & Location-Based Solutions
S.I.C.: 8713
N.A.I.C.S.: 541360

Personnel:
Congwu Cheng *(Co-Founder, Chm & CEO)*
Jun Hou *(Chm)*
Qin Zhang *(Pres & COO)*
Jun Xiao *(COO & Sr VP-Sls & Mktg)*
June Jun Jin *(CMO)*
Yongqi Yang *(Exec VP-Automotive Bus)*
Derong Jiang *(Sr VP-Quality Control)*
Xiyong Tang *(Sr VP-Ops & Mgmt)*

Board of Directors:
Congwu Cheng
Jun Hou
Derong Jiang
Daqing Qi
Jun Xiao
Jeffrey Zhijie Zeng
Qin Zhang

Subsidiary:

AutoNavi Software Co., Ltd. (1)
1-5 F Suite B1 Cec China Electronic Base
No 18 Changsheng R Changping
High-Tech Park, Beijing, 102200, China
Tel.: (86) 1059855500
Fax: (86) 1059855501
Navigation Software Development Services
S.I.C.: 7371
N.A.I.C.S.: 541511

Subsidiary:

Beijing ADF Navigation Technology Co., Ltd. (2)
South Tower F18 DaHeng Technology
Building No 3 Su Zhou Jie
Hai Dian District, Beijing, 100080, China
Tel.: (86) 10 5985 9800
Fax: (86) 10 5985 9900
Navigation Software Development Services
S.I.C.: 7371
N.A.I.C.S.: 541511
Hou Jun *(CEO)*

AUTONEUM HOLDING AG

Schlosstalstr 43
CH-8406 Winterthur, Switzerland
Tel.: (41) 52 208 82 82
Fax: (41) 52 244 83 37
E-Mail: info@autoneum.com
Web Site: www.autoneum.com
AUTN—(SWX)
Sls.: $2,059,018,764
Assets: $1,036,039,268
Liabilities: $709,329,104
Net Worth: $326,710,164
Earnings: $30,976,484
Emp.: 9,820
Fiscal Year-end: 12/31/12

Business Description:
Motor Vehicle Acoustic & Thermal Management Material & Measurement Equipment Mfr
S.I.C.: 2396
N.A.I.C.S.: 336360

Personnel:
Hans-Peter Schwald *(Chm)*
Rainer Schmuckle *(Vice Chm)*
Martin Hirzel *(CEO & Member-Exec Bd)*
Urs Leinhauser *(Deputy CEO, CFO & Member-Exec Bd)*
Richard Derr *(Member-Exec Bd & Head-North America)*
Volker Eimertenbrink *(Member-Exec Bd & Head-SAMEA)*
Matthias Holzammer *(Member-Exec Bd & Head-Europe)*
Uwe Trautmann *(Member-Exec Bd & Head-Asia)*

Board of Directors:
Hans-Peter Schwald
Michael W. Pieper
Rainer Schmuckle
This E. Schneider
Peter Spuhler
Ferdinand Stutz

Subsidiaries:

Autoneum Management AG (1)
Schlosstalstrasse 43
CH 8406 Winterthur, Switzerland (100%)
Tel.: (41) 522088282
Fax: (41) 522088599
Web Site: www.autoneum.com
Emp.: 100
Motor Vehicle Interior Product Mfr
S.I.C.: 2396
N.A.I.C.S.: 336360
Wolsgang Drees *(Mng Dir)*

Autoneum Switzerland AG (1)
Bahnweg Sud 43
CH 9475 Sevelen, Switzerland CH (100%)
Tel.: (41) 817860100
Fax: (41) 817860101
Web Site: www.autoneum.com
Emp.: 400
Motor Vehicle Interior Product Mfr
S.I.C.: 2396
N.A.I.C.S.: 336360
Harold Zender *(Mng Dir)*

Autoneum Technologies AG (1)
Schlosstalstrasse 43
Winterthur, Zurich, 8406, Switzerland
Tel.: (41) 522087171
Fax: (41) 522088419
Automotive Component Mfr
S.I.C.: 3714
N.A.I.C.S.: 336390

Rieter Automotive (International) AG (1)
Schlosstalstrasse 43
Winterthur, Zurich, 8406, Switzerland
Tel.: (41) 522087171
Fax: (41) 522087060
Holding Company
S.I.C.: 6719
N.A.I.C.S.: 551112

Autoneum Holding AG—(Continued)

U.S. Subsidiary:

Autoneum North America, Inc. (1)
38555 Hills Tech Dr
Farmington Hills, MI 48331 DE
Tel.: (248) 848-0100 (100%)
Fax: (248) 848-0130
E-Mail:
Web Site: www.autoneum.com
Sls.: $175,000,000
Emp.: 120
Automotive & Commercial Sound Control Materials Mfr
S.I.C.: 3714
N.A.I.C.S.: 336390
Richard Derr *(Pres & CEO)*

Joint Venture:

UGN, Inc. (2)
2638 E 126th St
Chicago, IL 60487
Tel.: (773) 437-2400
Web Site: www.ugnusa.com
Sales Range: $300-349.9 Million
Emp.: 1,300
Automotive Acoustic, Interior Trim & Thermal Management Product Mfr
S.I.C.: 3714
N.A.I.C.S.: 336390
Peter Anthony *(Pres & CEO)*
Randy Khalaf *(CFO)*

Plant:

UGN, Inc. - Chicago Heights (3)
1001 State St
Chicago Heights, IL 60411-2907
Tel.: (708) 758-0211
Fax: (708) 758-0213
Web Site: www.ugnusa.com
Emp.: 236
Automotive Acoustic, Interior Trim & Thermal Management Product Mfr
S.I.C.: 3714
N.A.I.C.S.: 336390
David Passmore *(Plant Mgr)*

Plants:

Autoneum North America, Inc. - Aiken (2)
1103 Powderhouse Rd SE
Aiken, SC 29803
Tel.: (803) 649-1371
Web Site: www.autoneum.com
Emp.: 50
Automotive & Commercial Sound Control Materials Mfr
S.I.C.: 3714
N.A.I.C.S.: 336390

Autoneum North America, Inc. - Bloomsburg (2)
480 W Fifth St
Bloomsburg, PA 17815-1563
Tel.: (570) 784-4100
Web Site: www.autoneum.com
Emp.: 700
Automobile Carpeting & Acoustical Parts
S.I.C.: 3714
N.A.I.C.S.: 336390

Non-U.S. Subsidiary:

Autoneum Canada Ltd. (2)
1451 Bellmill Road
PO Box 400
Tillsonburg, ON, N4G 4H8, Canada (100%)
Tel.: (519) 842-6411
Fax: (519) 842-4644
E-Mail: info@autoneum.com
Emp.: 350
Motor Vehicle Interior Product Mfr
S.I.C.: 2396
N.A.I.C.S.: 336360
Jeff Miller *(Controller)*

Non-U.S. Subsidiaries:

Autoneum Belgium N.V. (1)
Oosterring 14
Genk, Limburg, 3600, Belgium
Tel.: (32) 89620100
Fax: (32) 89620119
Web Site: www.autoneum.com
Emp.: 250
Automotive Interior Materials Mfr
S.I.C.: 2396
N.A.I.C.S.: 336360
Mireille Martens *(Mgr)*

Autoneum (Chongqing) Sound-Proof Parts Co. Ltd. (1)
West of Fada Rd Economic Development Zone
Taicang, Jiangsu, 215400, China
Tel.: (86) 51233337798
Fax: (86) 51253372690
Web Site: www.autoneum.com
Motor Vehicle Interior Product Mfr
S.I.C.: 2396
N.A.I.C.S.: 336360

Autoneum CZ s.r.o. (1)
U Dvoriska 1721
Chocen, 56501, Czech Republic
Tel.: (420) 465515111
Fax: (420) 465515247
Web Site: www.autoneum.com
Emp.: 200
Automotive Interior Materials Mfr
S.I.C.: 2396
N.A.I.C.S.: 336360
Aens Schulze *(Gen Mgr)*

Autoneum France S.A.S.U. (1)
Zachges Chevries Ruegs Chevries
F 78416 Aubergenville, France (100%)
Tel.: (33) 130950960
Fax: (33) 130957439
E-Mail: aubergenville.accueim@autoneum.com
Web Site: www.autoneum.com
Emp.: 180
Motor Vehicle Interior Product Mfr
S.I.C.: 2396
N.A.I.C.S.: 336360
Jerome Olivar *(Mng Dir)*

Autoneum Germany GmbH (1)
Werk Gundernhausen Im Mittelbruch
D 64380 Rossdorf, Germany (100%)
Tel.: (49) 60714910
Fax: (49) 6071491369
Web Site: www.autoneum.com
Emp.: 300
Supplier of Noise Control & Thermal Insulation Systems for Motor Vehicles
S.I.C.: 2396
N.A.I.C.S.: 336360
Heinz Walter *(Gen Mgr)*

Autoneum Great Britain Ltd. (1)
Keller House Hereward Rise
Halesowen, W Midlands, B62 8AN, United Kingdom (100%)
Tel.: (44) 1215044500
Fax: (44) 1215500960
Web Site: www.autoneum.com
Emp.: 150
Supplier of Noise Control & Thermal Insulation Systems for Motor Vehicles
S.I.C.: 2396
N.A.I.C.S.: 336360
Lucas Van Der Schalk *(Pres)*

Plant:

Autoneum Great Britain Ltd. - Heckmondwike (2)
Flush Mills
PO Box 22
Heckmondwike, WF16 0EP, United Kingdom (100%)
Tel.: (44) 8706066608
Fax: (44) 924236340
Web Site: www.autoneum.com
Emp.: 150
Automotive Interiors Mfr
S.I.C.: 2396
N.A.I.C.S.: 336360

Autoneum Netherlands B.V. (1)
Graafschap Hornelaan 140
Weert, Limburg, 6004 HT, Netherlands
Tel.: (31) 654222691
Automotive Interior Materials Mfr
S.I.C.: 2396
N.A.I.C.S.: 336360

Autoneum Poland Sp. z.o.o. (1)
Owsiana 60/A
Katowice, 40-780, Poland
Tel.: (48) 322015828
Fax: (48) 322063356
Automotive Interior Materials Mfr
S.I.C.: 2396
N.A.I.C.S.: 336360
Waldemar Miklaszewicz *(Gen Mgr)*

Autoneum Portugal Lda. (1)
Alto da Guerra - en 10 km 44 2
Setubal, 2910-021, Portugal (86%)
Tel.: (351) 265730420
Fax: (351) 265730438
Web Site: www.autoneum.com
Motor Vehicle Interior Product Mfr
S.I.C.: 2396
N.A.I.C.S.: 336360
Liliana Deolindo *(Mgr-Acctg)*

Autoneum Spain Northwest S.L.U. (1)
Pol Ind As Pedreiras Pista de Roblido
A Rua, Spain
Tel.: (34) 988 336 134
Fax: (34) 988 336 148
Motor Vehicle Interior Product Mfr
S.I.C.: 2396
N.A.I.C.S.: 336360

Autoneum Spain S.A.U. (1)
Calle Venus P I Can Parellada 1
08228 Terrassa, Spain
Tel.: (34) 937363030
Fax: (34) 937363048
Motor Vehicle Interior Product Mfr
S.I.C.: 2396
N.A.I.C.S.: 336360

Non-U.S. Joint Ventures:

Autoneum Feltex (Pty) Ltd. (1)
30 Helium Street Autom Supplier Park
Pretoria, Gauteng, South Africa
Tel.: (27) 125643100
Fax: (27) 125643102
Motor Vehicle Interior Product Mfr
S.I.C.: 2396
N.A.I.C.S.: 336360
Robert Gooch *(Mng Dir)*

Tianjin Rieter Nittoku Automotive Sound-Proof Co. Ltd (1)
No 9 Saida5 Sub Rd Xiqing Economic Development Zone
Tianjin, 300385, China
Tel.: (86) 2223889388
Fax: (86) 2223889588
Motor Vehicle Interior Product Mfr
S.I.C.: 2396
N.A.I.C.S.: 336360

AUTOPORT LIMITED

1180 Main Road
Eastern Passage, NS, B3G 1M4, Canada
Tel.: (902) 465-6050
Fax: (902) 465-6007
E-Mail: reception@autoport.ca
Rev.: $42,081,356
Emp.: 450
Business Description:
Transshipment & Vehicle Processing Services
S.I.C.: 4226
N.A.I.C.S.: 493190
Personnel:
Emery Robidoux *(Gen Mgr)*

AUTOPREVOZ AD BANJA LUKA

Bulevar Srpske Vojske 17
78 000 Banja Luka, Bosnia & Herzegovina
Tel.: (387) 51 306 855
E-Mail: info@autoprevoz.org
Web Site: www.autoprevoz.org
Year Founded: 1945
APBL—(BANJ)
Emp.: 8
Business Description:
Transportation Services
S.I.C.: 4789
N.A.I.C.S.: 488999
Personnel:
Dragoslav Mihajlovic *(Gen Mgr)*

AUTORIDERS INTERNATIONAL LTD.

104 Vikas Centre S V Road
Santacruz West, Mumbai, 400 054, India
Tel.: (91) 22 66777394
Fax: (91) 22 66944057
E-Mail: enquiry@autoriders.net
Web Site: www.autoriders.net
512277—(BOM)
Sales Range: $1-9.9 Million
Business Description:
Car Rental Services
S.I.C.: 7514
N.A.I.C.S.: 532111
Board of Directors:
Chintan A. Patel
Tapan Patel

AUTOSTRADA TORINO-MILANO S.P.A.

(Name Changed to ASTM S.p.A.)

AUTOTEHNA A.D

Bulevar Kralja Aleksandra 94
11000 Belgrade, Serbia
Tel.: (381) 11 2433 314
E-Mail: info@autotehna.com
Web Site: www.autotehna.com
Year Founded: 1969
ATHN—(BEL)
Business Description:
Car Rental Services
S.I.C.: 7514
N.A.I.C.S.: 532111
Personnel:
Milisav Rasic *(Founder)*

AUTOVENTIL A.D.

Milosa Obrenovica 2
31000 Uzice, Serbia
Tel.: (381) 31 563 401
Fax: (381) 31 563 483
E-Mail: autoventil@verat.net
Web Site: www.autoventil.co.rs
Year Founded: 1957
AVEN—(BEL)
Business Description:
Valves & Valve Guide Mfr
S.I.C.: 3714
N.A.I.C.S.: 336310
Personnel:
Goran Pijevic *(Owner)*

AUV ENTERPRISES LIMITED

Level 29 66 Goulburn Street
Sydney, NSW, 2060, Australia
Tel.: (61) 2 8263 4000
Fax: (61) 2 8263 4111
AUV—(ASX)
Assets: $36,474
Liabilities: $26,053
Net Worth: $10,421
Earnings: ($11,612,120)
Fiscal Year-end: 06/30/13
Business Description:
Financial Investment Services
S.I.C.: 6211
N.A.I.C.S.: 523999
Personnel:
Peter Dykes *(Sec)*
Board of Directors:
Robert Whitton
Anthony Damianos
Peter Dykes

AUXELLENCE HEALTH CORPORATION

2922 Mount Seymour Parkway
North Vancouver, BC, V7H 1E9, Canada
Tel.: (604) 329-8593
Web Site: www.auxellence.com

Year Founded: 2011
AID—(CNSX)
Business Description:
Pharmaceutical Mfr
S.I.C.: 2834
N.A.I.C.S.: 325412
Personnel:
Ron Ozols *(CEO & CFO)*

AV CONCEPT HOLDINGS LTD

6th Floor Enterprise Square 39 Wang Chiu Road
Kowloon, China (Hong Kong)
Tel.: (852) 23347333
Fax: (852) 27730766
E-Mail: ir.dept@avconcept.com
Web Site: www.avconcept.com
0595—(HKG)
Rev.: $317,734,734
Assets: $191,211,315
Liabilities: $107,751,394
Net Worth: $83,459,922
Earnings: ($886,918)
Emp.: 379
Fiscal Year-end: 03/31/13
Business Description:
Electronic Products & Internet Appliances Semiconductors Distr, Designer & Mfr
S.I.C.: 3679
N.A.I.C.S.: 334419
Personnel:
Yuk Kwan So *(Founder & Chm)*
Chi On So *(CEO)*
Christopher Choi Yan Ho *(CFO & Sec)*
Joon Yun Choi *(Pres/CEO-AV Concept Limited)*
Jong Keun Kweon *(Pres-AV Concept Limited)*
Jun Hyog Lee *(Pres-AV Concept Singapore Pte Ltd)*
Andrew Chiu Ki Tsang *(Pres-AVC Technology (International) Limited)*
Board of Directors:
Yuk Kwan So
Charles Edward Chapman
Christopher Choi Yan Ho
Ming Wah Lui
Chi On So
Ka Kit Wong
HSBC Bank (Cayman) Limited
68 West Bay Road
Georgetown, Cayman Islands
Transfer Agent:
Tricor Tengis Limited
26th Floor Tesbury Centre 28 Queen's Road East
Wanchai, China (Hong Kong)
Tel.: (852) 29801333
Fax: (852) 28108185

Subsidiaries:

AV Concept Limited (1)
6 F Enterprise Square Three 39 Wang Chiu Road
Kowloon, China (Hong Kong)
Tel.: (852) 23347333
Fax: (852) 2764 3108
E-Mail: information@avconcept.com
Electronic Components Distr
S.I.C.: 5065
N.A.I.C.S.: 423690

AVC Technology (International) Limited (1)
6 F Enterprise Square Three 39 Wang Chiu Road
Kowloon, China (Hong Kong)
Tel.: (852) 23347334
Fax: (852) 23347948
E-Mail: sales.avct@avconcept.com
Web Site: www.avconcept.com
Electronic Component Distr
S.I.C.: 5065
N.A.I.C.S.: 423690

Non-U.S. Subsidiary:

AV Concept Singapore Pte Ltd. (1)
219 Henderson Road 10-01 Henderson Industrial Park
159556 Singapore, Singapore (100%)
Tel.: (65) 62765130
Fax: (65) 62765132
E-Mail: avsingapore@avconcept.com
Web Site: www.avconcept.com
Emp.: 30
Semiconductor & Related Device Mfr
S.I.C.: 3651
N.A.I.C.S.: 334310
John Lee *(Pres)*

AV TECH CORPORATION

10F E Bldg No 19-11 San Chung Rd
115 Taipei, Taiwan
Tel.: (886) 226553866
Fax: (886) 226553855
E-Mail: support@avtech.com.tw
Web Site: www.avtech.com.tw
8072—(TAI)
Sales Range: $50-74.9 Million
Business Description:
Video Surveillance Systems Mfr & Distr
S.I.C.: 3663
N.A.I.C.S.: 334220
Personnel:
Shih Chung Chen *(Chm)*
Chen Pin Tien *(Pres & Gen Mgr)*

Division:

Av Tech Corporation - CCTV Product Division (1)
10 F E Building No 19-11 San Chung Road
Nankang, Taipei, 115, Taiwan
Tel.: (886) 2 2655 3866
Fax: (886) 2 2655 3855
E-Mail: support@avtech.com.tw
Closed Circuit Television Mfr
S.I.C.: 3812
N.A.I.C.S.: 334511

Subsidiary:

Chieftron International Inc. (1)
12F B Building No 106 Hsin Tai Wu Road Sec1
Hsi-chieh, Taiwan
Tel.: (886) 226961696
Fax: (886) 2 2696 1988
Web Site: www.chieftron.com.tw
Emp.: 35
Electronic Components Distr
S.I.C.: 5065
N.A.I.C.S.: 423690
Kevin Yang *(Mgr)*

Plant:

Av Tech Corporation - Sanchong Factory (1)
No 193-2 Zhongxing North Street
Sanchong, Taipei, Taiwan
Tel.: (886) 2 8511 2266
Fax: (886) 2 8511 2266
E-Mail: marketing@avtech.com.tw
Web Site: www.avtech.com.tw
Emp.: 300
Surveillance Equipments Mfr
S.I.C.: 3669
N.A.I.C.S.: 334290

AVAC, LTD.

220 6815-8 St NE
Calgary, AB, T2E 7H7, Canada
Tel.: (403) 274-2774
Fax: (403) 274-0101
E-Mail: avacinfo@avacltd.com
Web Site: www.avacltd.com
Business Description:
Investment Firm
S.I.C.: 6211
N.A.I.C.S.: 523999
Personnel:
Rob Rennie *(Chm)*
Michael Raymont *(Pres & CEO)*
Board of Directors:
Rob Rennie
Jerry Bouma
Robert Church
Art Froehlich
Myles Hamilton
Bill McKenzie
Colette Miller
Michael Raymont
Sandy Slator
Rick Smith
Rick Thacker

Subsidiary:

Botaneco Specialty Ingredients Inc. (1)
2985 23rd Ave NE Ste 134
Calgary, AB, T1Y 7L3, Canada
Tel.: (403) 668-6685
Fax: (403) 668-4789
Web Site: www.botaneco.ca
Pharmaceutical Products Mfr
S.I.C.: 2834
N.A.I.C.S.: 325412
James Szarko *(Pres)*

AVACO CO., LTD

1107 Wol-am Dong Seongseo Industrial Complex
Talseo-gu, Taegu, Korea (South)
Tel.: (82) 535838150
Fax: (82) 535889229
E-Mail: avaco@avaco.co.kr
Web Site: www.avaco.co.kr
Year Founded: 2000
083930—(KRS)
Emp.: 310
Business Description:
Flat Panel Display Equipment Mfr
S.I.C.: 3679
N.A.I.C.S.: 334419
Personnel:
Deug-Gi Seong *(Pres)*

Subsidiary:

DaeMyong ENG Co., Ltd (1)
912-8 Wolam-dong
Dalseo-gu, Daegu, Korea (South)
Tel.: (82) 53 583 4050
Fax: (82) 53 583 9132
E-Mail: dmeng@dmeng.kr
Web Site: www.daemyung-eng.co.kr
Vacuum Equipment Mfr
S.I.C.: 3559
N.A.I.C.S.: 333249
Kyung Keun Choi *(CEO)*

Plant:

DaeMyong ENG Co., Ltd - Gumi Factory (2)
1360 Sindang-ri San Dong Myeon Gumisi Shandong-Myeon, Gumi, Gyeongbuk, 730-853, Korea (South)
Tel.: (82) 70 8660 8848
Fax: (82) 54 715 9132
Emp.: 13
Vacuum Equipment Mfr
S.I.C.: 3559
N.A.I.C.S.: 333249

Plant:

AVACO CO., Ltd - Daegu 1st Factory (1)
1107 bunji Woram-dong
Dalseo-gu, Daegu, Korea (South)
Tel.: (82) 53 583 8150
Fax: (82) 53 588 9209
Web Site: www.avaco.co.kr/en/about_08.html
Vacuum Equipment & Clean Transfer System Mfr
S.I.C.: 3559
N.A.I.C.S.: 333249

AVACTA GROUP PLC

Unit 706 Avenue E Thorp Arch Estate
Wetherby, LS23 7GA, United Kingdom
Tel.: (44) 8444140452
Fax: (44) 8444140453
E-Mail: info@avacta.com
Web Site: www.avacta.com
AVCT—(AIM)
Rev.: $4,264,083
Assets: $27,882,365
Liabilities: $3,321,247
Net Worth: $24,561,118
Earnings: ($2,402,100)
Emp.: 73
Fiscal Year-end: 07/31/13
Business Description:
Bio-Analytical Technology Services
S.I.C.: 8731
N.A.I.C.S.: 541712
Personnel:
Alastair Smith *(CEO)*
Timothy J. Sykes *(CFO & Sec)*
Craig Slater *(COO)*
Board of Directors:
Gwyn O. Humphreys
Alan Aubrey
Trevor Nicholls
Tony Robards
Alastair Smith
Timothy J. Sykes
Legal Counsel:
Walker Morris
Kings Court 12 King Street
Leeds, LS1 2HL, United Kingdom

Subsidiary:

Oxford Medical Diagnostics Limited (1)
Oxford University Begbroke Science Park Woodstock Rd
Sandy Ln Yarnton, Begbroke, OX5 1PF, United Kingdom
Tel.: (44) 1865854888
Fax: (44) 1865854889
E-Mail: info@omdiagnostics.com
Web Site: www.omdiagnostics.com
Emp.: 10
Medical Diagnostics Equipment Mfr
S.I.C.: 3841
N.A.I.C.S.: 339112
Ian Campbell *(CEO)*

AVAGO TECHNOLOGIES LIMITED

1 Yishun Avenue 7
Singapore, 768923, Singapore
Tel.: (65) 67557888
E-Mail: press.relations@avagotech.com
Web Site: www.avagotech.com
Year Founded: 2005
AVGO—(NASDAQ)
Rev.: $2,520,000,000
Assets: $3,415,000,000
Liabilities: $529,000,000
Net Worth: $2,886,000,000
Earnings: $552,000,000
Emp.: 4,800
Fiscal Year-end: 11/03/13
Business Description:
Semiconductor Mfr
S.I.C.: 3674
N.A.I.C.S.: 334413
Personnel:
James V. Diller, Sr. *(Chm)*
Hock E. Tan *(Pres & CEO)*
Anthony E. Maslowski *(CFO & VP)*
Bryan T. Ingram *(COO & Sr VP)*
Andy Nallappan *(CIO & VP-Global IT)*
Patricia H. McCall *(Gen Counsel & VP)*
Boon Chye Ooi *(Sr VP-Global Ops)*
Board of Directors:
James V. Diller, Sr.
John T. Dickson
Bruno Guilmart
Kenneth Y. Hao
Justine F. Lien
Donald Macleod
Peter J. Marks
Hock E. Tan

Avago Technologies Limited—(Continued)

Transfer Agent:
Computershare Investor Services
PO Box 43078
Providence, RI 02940-3078
Tel.: (781) 575-3005

Subsidiary:

Avago Technologies ECBU IP (Singapore) Pte. Ltd. **(1)**
1 Yishun Avenue 7
Singapore, 768923, Singapore
Tel.: (65) 67557888
Fax: (65) 67557000
Semiconductor Device Mfr
S.I.C.: 3674
N.A.I.C.S.: 334413
Hock E. Tan *(Gen Mgr)*

U.S. Subsidiaries:

Avago Technologies U.S. Inc. **(1)**
350 W Trimble Rd Bldg 90
San Jose, CA 95131
Tel.: (408) 435-7400
Fax: (408) 435-4172
Toll Free: (877) 673-9442
Web Site: www.avagotech.com
Semiconductor Device Mfr
S.I.C.: 3674
N.A.I.C.S.: 334413
Hock E. Tan *(Pres & CEO)*

Avago Technologies Wireless (U.S.A.) Manufacturing Inc. **(1)**
4380 Ziegler Rd
Fort Collins, CO 80525-9631
Tel.: (970) 288-2575
Semiconductor Device Mfr
S.I.C.: 3674
N.A.I.C.S.: 334413
Brian Ingram *(Pres)*

CyOptics, Inc. **(1)**
9999 Hamilton Blvd
Breinigsville, PA 18031 DE
Tel.: (484) 397-2000
Fax: (484) 397-2014
E-Mail: pr@cyoptics.com
Web Site: www.cyoptics.com
Sales Range: $200-249.9 Million
Emp.: 550
Optical Chips & Components Mfr
S.I.C.: 3674
N.A.I.C.S.: 334413
Ettore J. Coringrato, Jr. *(Pres & CEO)*

East Texas Integrated Circuits, Inc. **(1)**
275 W Campbell Rd Ste 310
Richardson, TX 75080
Tel.: (972) 234-5656
Fax: (972) 234-5657
E-Mail: sales08@easttexasic.com
Web Site: www.easttexasic.com
Integrated Circuits Mfr
S.I.C.: 3674
N.A.I.C.S.: 334413

Non-U.S. Subsidiaries:

Avago Technologies Canada Corporation **(1)**
199 Bay St 5300 Commerce Ct W
Toronto, ON, M5L 1B9, Canada
Tel.: (416) 869-5500
Fax: (416) 947-0866
Semiconductor Device Mfr
S.I.C.: 3674
N.A.I.C.S.: 334413

Avago Technologies Japan, Ltd. **(1)**
7th Fl HillSumitomdosan Aobadais 4-7-7
Aobadai Chromeo-Fu
Meguro-Ku, Tokyo, 1530042, Japan
Tel.: (81) 364072727
Fax: (81) 34676664
E-Mail: support.japan@avagotech.com
Web Site: www.avagotech.co.jp
Emp.: 3
Semiconductor Device Mfr
S.I.C.: 3674
N.A.I.C.S.: 334413
Itaru Yoneyama *(Gen Mgr)*

Avago Technologies Sweden AB **(1)**
Kronborgsgrand 23
Kista, 164 46, Sweden
Tel.: (46) 705441388
Semiconductor Device Mfr
S.I.C.: 3674
N.A.I.C.S.: 334413

Nemicon Corporation **(1)**
Orix Shimbashi Bldg 6F 5-8-11 Shimbashi
Minato-ku, Tokyo, Japan JP
Tel.: (81) 357761711
Fax: (81) 357761720
Web Site: www.nemicon.co.jp
Emp.: 90
Semiconductor Device Mfr
S.I.C.: 3674
N.A.I.C.S.: 334413
Michifumi Mishima *(Pres)*

AVALANCHE SEARCH MARKETING INC.

(d/b/a Avalanche Networks)
34219 Neil Rd
Lucan, ON, N0M 2J0, Canada
Tel.: (519) 964-3738
Toll Free: (888) 994-2223
E-Mail: info@avalanchenetworks.com
Web Site: www.avalanchesearch.com
Sales Range: $10-24.9 Million
Business Description:
Software Developer, Marketer & Sales
S.I.C.: 3652
N.A.I.C.S.: 334614
Personnel:
Bruce Lamb *(Pres & CEO)*

AVALDATA CORPORATION

1-25-10 Asahi-machi Machida-shi
Tokyo, 194-0023, Japan
Tel.: (81) 42 732 1030
Fax: (81) 42 732 1032
E-Mail: lsales@avaldata.co.jp
Web Site: www.avaldata.co.jp
Year Founded: 1959
6918—(JAS)
Sls.: $54,571,000
Assets: $106,854,000
Liabilities: $13,486,000
Net Worth: $93,368,000
Earnings: $187,000
Emp.: 170
Fiscal Year-end: 03/31/13
Business Description:
Industrial Embedded Computer & Electronics Equipment Mfr
S.I.C.: 3571
N.A.I.C.S.: 334111
Personnel:
Isao Hiromitsu *(Pres)*

AVALON FORD SALES LTD.

621 Kenmount Rd
Saint John's, NL, A1B3N9, Canada
Tel.: (709) 754-7500
Fax: (709) 754-7530
E-Mail: sales@avalonford.com
Web Site: www.avalon.dealerconnection.com
Rev.: $54,601,429
Emp.: 125
Business Description:
New & Used Car Dealers
S.I.C.: 5511
N.A.I.C.S.: 441110
Personnel:
David Wilkins *(Owner)*

AVALON MINERALS LTD

65 Park Rd
Milton, QLD, 4064, Australia
Tel.: (61) 7 3368 9888
Fax: (61) 7 3368 9899
E-Mail: info@avalonminerals.com.au
Web Site: www.avalonminerals.com
AVI—(ASX)
Rev.: $110,829
Assets: $40,952,030
Liabilities: $2,790,064
Net Worth: $38,161,966
Earnings: ($6,452,679)
Emp.: 8
Fiscal Year-end: 06/30/13
Business Description:
Mineral Exploration
S.I.C.: 1481
N.A.I.C.S.: 213115
Personnel:
Malcolm Norris *(CEO & Mng Dir)*
Roslynn Shand *(Sec)*
Board of Directors:
Graham Ascough
Crispin Henderson
Don Hyma
Paul Niardone
Legal Counsel:
GRT Lawyers
Level 1 400 Queen St
Brisbane, QLD, 4000, Australia

Non-U.S. Subsidiaries:

Avalon Minerals Adak AB **(1)**
Kasern gatan 6-981-37
98138 Kiruna, Vasterbotten, Sweden
Tel.: (46) 98010910
E-Mail: info@avalonminerals.com
Web Site: www.avalonminerals.com
Mineral Mining Services
S.I.C.: 1459
N.A.I.C.S.: 212325

Avalon Minerals Viscaria AB **(1)**
Hogstromsgatan 16
931 33 Skelleftea, Vasterbotten, Sweden
Tel.: (46) 98010910
Metal Ores Mining Services
S.I.C.: 1099
N.A.I.C.S.: 212299

AVALON RARE METALS INC.

130 Adelaide Street West Suite 1901
Toronto, ON, M5H 3P5, Canada
Tel.: (416) 364-4938
Fax: (416) 364-5162
E-Mail: office@avalonraremetals.com
Web Site: www.avalonventuresraremetals.com
AVL—(NYSEMKT TSX)
Int. Income: $372,043
Assets: $111,177,107
Liabilities: $2,861,417
Net Worth: $108,315,690
Earnings: ($11,132,193)
Emp.: 21
Fiscal Year-end: 08/31/13
Business Description:
Metal Exploration & Mining Services
S.I.C.: 1099
N.A.I.C.S.: 212299
Personnel:
Donald S. Bubar *(Pres & CEO)*
R. James Andersen *(CFO & VP-Fin)*
David Anthony Marsh *(Interim COO & Sr VP-Metallurgy)*
Charlotte May *(Sec)*
Board of Directors:
Brian D. MacEachen
Donald S. Bubar
Alan L. H. Ferry
Larry Philip Fontaine
Sergio Marchi
Peter N. McCarter
Kenneth G. Thomas
Legal Counsel:
Cassels, Brock & Blackwell LLP
2100 Scotia Plaza 40 King St W
Toronto, ON, M5H 3C2, Canada
Tel.: (416) 869-5300
Telex: 6-23415
Fax: (416) 360-8877

Transfer Agents:
TMX Equity Transfer Services Inc
200 University Avenue Suite 400
Toronto, ON, M5H 4H1, Canada

Registrar & Transfer Company
10 Commerce Dr
Cranford, NJ 07016
Tel.: (800) 368-5948

AVALOQ EVOLUTION AG

Zurcherstrasse 59
CH 8800 Thalwil, Switzerland
Tel.: (41) 583161010
Fax: (41) 583163003
Web Site: www.avaloq.com
Sales Range: $75-99.9 Million
Emp.: 600
Business Description:
Developer of Banking Software
S.I.C.: 7372
N.A.I.C.S.: 511210
Personnel:
Didier Sangiorgio *(Chm)*
Francisco Fernandez *(CEO)*
Enrico Ardielli *(CFO)*
Peter Schopfer *(CMO)*
Ronald Strassler *(Chief Special Tasks Officer)*
Board of Directors:
Didier Sangiorgio
Philipp E. Achermann
Dominik S. Koechlin

AVANCO RESOURCES LIMITED

Level 1 330 Churchill Avenue
Subiaco, WA, 6008, Australia
Tel.: (61) 893216600
Fax: (61) 892004469
E-Mail: info@avancoresources.com
Web Site: www.avancoresources.com
AVB—(ASX)
Int. Income: $376,698
Assets: $43,718,501
Liabilities: $634,641
Net Worth: $43,083,860
Earnings: ($2,337,865)
Emp.: 13
Fiscal Year-end: 06/30/13
Business Description:
Copper & Gold Mining
S.I.C.: 1041
N.A.I.C.S.: 212221
Personnel:
Anthony Polglase *(Mng Dir)*
Scott Funston *(Co-Sec)*
David McEntaggart *(Co-Sec)*
Board of Directors:
Matthew Wood
Luis Mauricio Ferraiuoli de Azevedo
Scott Funston
Colin Jones
Simon Mottram
Wayne Phillips
Anthony Polglase
Legal Counsel:
Steinepreis Paganin
Level 4 The Read Buildings 16 Milligan Street
6000 Perth, WA, Australia

FFA Legal
Av Jornalista Ricardo Marinho 360 Sala 113 Ed
Cosmopolitan Barra da
Rio de Janeiro, CEP, 22631-350, Brazil

AVANGARDCO INVESTMENTS PUBLIC LIMITED

121 V Prospect Peremohy
03115 Kiev, Ukraine
Tel.: (380) 443934050
Fax: (380) 443934054
E-Mail: secretar@avangard.co.ua
Web Site: www.avangard.co.ua
Year Founded: 2003
AVGR—(LSE)

Rev.: $629,306,000
Assets: $1,578,328,000
Liabilities: $411,133,000
Net Worth: $1,167,195,000
Earnings: $228,233,000
Emp.: 5,575
Fiscal Year-end: 12/31/12
Business Description:
Shell Eggs Production & Sales
S.I.C.: 0252
N.A.I.C.S.: 112310
Personnel:
Nataliya Vasylyuk *(Chm)*
Iryna Marchenko *(CEO)*
Iryna Melnik *(CFO)*
Natalya Martynenko *(COO)*
George Givishvili *(CMO)*
Oleg Solovei *(Chief Legal Officer)*
Board of Directors:
Nataliya Vasylyuk
Oleg Bakhmatyuk
Iryna Marchenko
Oleg M. Pohotsky
Oksana Prosolenko
Legal Counsel:
Freshfields Bruckhaus Deringer LLP
65 Fleet Street
London, United Kingdom

Avellum Partners LLC
Leonardo Business Center 19-21 Bohdana Khmelnytskoho Str 11th floor
01030 Kiev, Ukraine

AVANQUEST SOFTWARE SA

89-91 Boulevard National
Immeuble Vision La Defense
92250 La Garenne-Colombes, France
Tel.: (33) 141271970
Fax: (33) 1 4127 1971
E-Mail: tbonnefoi@avanquest.com
Web Site: www.avanquest.com
AVQ—(EUR OTC)
Sales Range: $100-124.9 Million
Emp.: 500
Business Description:
Communications Software Mfr
S.I.C.: 7372
N.A.I.C.S.: 511210
Personnel:
Bruno Vanryb *(Co-Founder, Pres & CEO)*
Roger Politis *(Co-Founder & CTO)*
Thierry Bonnefoi *(CFO)*
Roger Bloxberg *(CEO-North America)*
David Wright *(CEO-Software Dev)*

Subsidiary:

Avanquest France (1)
89-91 Boulevard National Immeuble Vision La Defense
92250 La Garenne-Colombes, France
Tel.: (33) 156765800
Fax: (33) 156765810
Web Site: www.avanquest.fr
Emp.: 90
Computer Software Mfr
S.I.C.: 7372
N.A.I.C.S.: 511210

U.S. Subsidiaries:

Avanquest Publishing USA (1)
7031 Koll Center Pkwy Ste 150
Pleasanton, CA 94566
Tel.: (925) 474-1700
Fax: (925) 474-1800
Web Site: www.avanquestusa.com
Emp.: 23
Computer Software Mfr
S.I.C.: 7372
N.A.I.C.S.: 511210
Sharon Chiu *(CFO)*

Avanquest Software USA (1)
1333 W 120th Ave Ste 314
Westminster, CO 80234
Tel.: (720) 330-1400
Fax: (303) 450-1154
Web Site: www.avanquest.com
Computer Software Mfr
S.I.C.: 7372
N.A.I.C.S.: 511210

Nova Development Corp. (1)
23801 Calabasas Rd Ste 2005
Calabasas, CA 91302
Tel.: (818) 591-9600
Fax: (818) 591-8885
Web Site: www.novadevelopment.com
Sales Range: $25-49.9 Million
Emp.: 76
Computer Software Developer
S.I.C.: 7371
N.A.I.C.S.: 541511
Todd Helfstein *(Pres)*
Roger Bloxberg *(CEO)*

Non-U.S. Subsidiaries:

Avanquest China (1)
Huitong Building Room 1201 569 East JinLing Lu
Shanghai, 200021, China
Tel.: (86) 2153066033
Software Publishing Services
S.I.C.: 7372
N.A.I.C.S.: 511210

Avanquest Deutschland GmbH (1)
Sckellstrasse 6
81667 Munich, Germany
Tel.: (49) 897909790
Fax: (49) 897909791
Web Site: www.avanquest.de
Software Distr
S.I.C.: 5045
N.A.I.C.S.: 423430

Avanquest Iberica S.L. (1)
C Peru 6 EdificiosTwin Golf Bloque B Oficina 4 2a Pl
Las Matas, 28290 Madrid, Spain
Tel.: (34) 916307023
Fax: (34) 916368485
E-Mail: amellizo@avanquest.es
Web Site: www.avanquest.es
Emp.: 2
Software Distr
S.I.C.: 5045
N.A.I.C.S.: 423430
Bruno Vanryb *(Co-Founder, Pres & CEO)*

Avanquest Italia Srl (1)
Via E Sacchi 8
26100 Cremona, Italy
Tel.: (39) 0372 38791
Fax: (39) 0372 410596
Web Site: www.avanquest.it
Computer Software Mfr
S.I.C.: 7372
N.A.I.C.S.: 511210

Avanquest UK Ltd (1)
Sheridan House
40-43 Jewry Street, Winchester, Hants, SO23 8RY, United Kingdom
Tel.: (44) 01962835000
Fax: (44) 1962835100
E-Mail: info@avanquest-solutions.co.uk
Web Site: www.avanquest.co.uk
Emp.: 80
Computer Software Mfr
S.I.C.: 7372
N.A.I.C.S.: 511210
Bruno Vanryb *(Co-Founder, Pres & CEO)*

AVANT CORPORATION

(Formerly DIVA CORPORATION)
Shinagawa Intercity Tower B 13F 2 15 2 Konan Minato-ku
Tokyo, 108-6113, Japan
Tel.: (81) 3 5782 8600
Fax: (81) 3 5782 8614
Web Site: www.avantcorp.com
Year Founded: 1997
3836—(JAS)
Sls.: $68,285,850
Assets: $48,542,844
Liabilities: $29,479,734
Net Worth: $19,063,110
Earnings: $3,679,805
Emp.: 399
Fiscal Year-end: 06/30/13
Business Description:
Software Package Development & Consulting Services
S.I.C.: 7372
N.A.I.C.S.: 511210
Personnel:
Tetsuji Morikawa *(Pres & CEO)*
Naoyoshi Kasuga *(CFO)*
Hiroki Takemura *(CIO & Chief HR Officer)*
Ichiro Kawamoto *(CEO-Diva Bus Innovation & Chief Strategy Officer)*
Masaoki Kobayashi *(CTO)*
Hiroshi Takizawa *(CEO-Internet Disclosure)*
Board of Directors:
Naohisa Fukutani
Naoyoshi Kasuga
Ichiro Kawamoto
Tetsuji Morikawa
Takahiro Okabe
Hiroshi Takizawa

AVANT IMAGING & INFORMATION MANAGEMENT, INC.

205 Industrial Parkway North
Aurora, ON, L4G 4C4, Canada
Tel.: (416) 798-7110
Fax: (905) 841-2177
Toll Free: (877) 841-2446
E-Mail: help@aiim.com
Web Site: www.aiim.com
Year Founded: 1990
Sales Range: $10-24.9 Million
Emp.: 100
Business Description:
Commercial Printing Services
S.I.C.: 2759
N.A.I.C.S.: 323111
Personnel:
Mario Giorgio *(Chm & CEO)*
Frank Giorgio *(Pres)*
Emilio Ciampini *(Sr VP-Sls & Mktg)*

AVANTAZH GROUP

20- Kultury Str
61058 Kharkiv, Ukraine
Tel.: (380) 577004410
Fax: (380) 577004414
Web Site: www.avantazh.eu
Year Founded: 1998
Business Description:
Residential & Commercial Real Estate Development, Construction, Ownership, Management, Sales & Leasing Services
S.I.C.: 6514
N.A.I.C.S.: 531390
Personnel:
Anatoliy Denisenko *(Pres)*

AVANTE LOGIXX INC.

1959 Leslie Street
Toronto, ON, M3B 2M3, Canada
Tel.: (416) 923-6984
Fax: (416) 923-5198
E-Mail: info@avantesecurity.com
Web Site: www.avantesecurity.com
Year Founded: 1996
XX—(TSXV)
Rev.: $6,706,095
Assets: $2,212,049
Liabilities: $2,031,520
Net Worth: $180,529
Earnings: $368,602
Fiscal Year-end: 03/31/13
Business Description:
Security Systems Services
S.I.C.: 7382
N.A.I.C.S.: 561621
Personnel:
Emmanuel Mounouchos *(Founder & Co-CEO)*
Leland Verner *(Chm)*
George Rossolatos *(Co-CEO)*
Raghu Sampath *(CFO)*
Board of Directors:
Leland Verner
Bruce Bronfman
W. Wesley De Shane
James Joseph Leeder
Emmanuel Mounouchos
George Rossolatos
Transfer Agent:
Equity Financial Trust Company
200 University Avenue Suite 400
Toronto, ON, Canada

AVANTE SYSTEMS, INC.

Room 709-710 7/F Tower 1
Silvercord Centre Tsim Sha Tsui, Kowloon, China (Hong Kong)
Tel.: (852) 311 3951
Year Founded: 2010
AVTS.OB—(OTCB)
Int. Income: $13
Assets: $61,810
Liabilities: $6,070
Net Worth: $55,740
Earnings: ($32,632)
Emp.: 1
Fiscal Year-end: 10/31/13
Business Description:
Video Camera Mfr & Whslr
S.I.C.: 3651
N.A.I.C.S.: 334310
Personnel:
Yuen Hong Sezto *(Pres, CEO & CFO)*
Board of Directors:
Yuen Hong Sezto

AVANTEC ZERSPANTECHNIK GMBH

Gerokstrasse 22
75428 Illingen, Germany
Tel.: (49) 704282220
Fax: (49) 7042822233
E-Mail: info@avantec.de
Web Site: www.avantec.de
Year Founded: 1989
Rev.: $20,049,979
Emp.: 30
Business Description:
Cutting Tool Mfr
S.I.C.: 3545
N.A.I.C.S.: 333515
Personnel:
Gustav Werthwein *(Founder)*

AVANTEL LTD.

Plot No 16 Sector-III HUDA Techno Enclave Opp K Raheja IT Park
Madhapur, Hyderabad, 500 081, India
Tel.: (91) 4066305000
Fax: (91) 4066305004
E-Mail: info@avantel.in
Web Site: www.avantel.in
532406—(BOM)
Rev.: $8,001,256
Assets: $6,109,450
Liabilities: $1,688,294
Net Worth: $4,421,156
Earnings: $1,208,664
Fiscal Year-end: 03/31/13
Business Description:
Communication Equipment Mfr
S.I.C.: 3669
N.A.I.C.S.: 334290
Personnel:
A. Vidya Sagar *(CEO & Mng Dir)*
M. S. S. Prasad *(Compliance Officer & Gen Mgr-Fin & Accts)*
Karra S. V. S. Sastry *(Sec)*
Board of Directors:
Rajinder Kumar Bagga
Y. Kishore
N. Naveen
A. Vidya Sagar

Avantel Ltd.—(Continued)

Transfer Agent:
Karvy Computershare Private Limited
Plot No 17 to 24 Vittalrao Nagar Madhapur
Hyderabad, India

AVANTHA GROUP
First India Place Tower-C 5th Floor
Mehrauli - Gurgaon Road, Gurgaon, Haryana, 122 022, India
Tel.: (91) 1244099436
Fax: (91) 1242804260
E-Mail: corpcom@avanthagroup.com
Web Site: www.avanthagroup.com
Sales Range: $1-4.9 Billion
Emp.: 22,000
Business Description:
Holding Company
S.I.C.: 6719
N.A.I.C.S.: 551112
Personnel:
Gautam Thapar *(Chm & CEO)*

Subsidiary:

Avantha Power & Infrastructure Limited **(1)**
6th & 7th floor Vatika City Point
MG Road, Gurgaon, Haryana, 122 002, India
Tel.: (91) 1244392000
Fax: (91) 1244376496
E-Mail: info@avanthapower.com
Web Site: www.avanthapower.com
Power Generation & Distribution Services
S.I.C.: 4939
N.A.I.C.S.: 221118
Sudhir Mohan Trehan *(Chm)*
Anil Bhargava *(Mng Dir)*

U.S. Subsidiary:

Pyramid Healthcare Solutions, Inc. **(1)**
14141 46th St N Ste 1212
Clearwater, FL 33762
Tel.: (727) 431-3000
Fax: (727) 431-3099
Web Site: www.pyramidhs.com
Emp.: 300
Health Information Management & Revenue Cycle Services
S.I.C.: 8748
N.A.I.C.S.: 541618
Manoj Malhotra *(Pres)*
Jay Hutchinson *(COO)*

AVANTI CAPITAL PLC
25 Harley Street
London, W1G 9BR, United Kingdom
Tel.: (44) 20 7299 1459
Fax: (44) 20 7299 1451
Web Site: www.avanticap.com
AVA—(AIM)
Rev.: $33,476,210
Assets: $29,543,778
Liabilities: $11,404,053
Net Worth: $18,139,725
Earnings: ($198,991)
Emp.: 526
Fiscal Year-end: 06/30/13
Business Description:
Investment Services
S.I.C.: 6282
N.A.I.C.S.: 523930
Personnel:
Richard H. Kleiner *(Sec)*
Board of Directors:
Philip J. Crawford
William A. H. Crewdson
Richard H. Kleiner
Legal Counsel:
Berwin Leighton Paisner
Adelaide House London Bridge
London, EC4R 9HA, United Kingdom
Tel.: (44) 71 623 3144
Telex: 886420 (lond)
Fax: (44) 71 623 3144

AVANTI COMMUNICATIONS GROUP PLC
Cobham House 20 Black Friars Lane
London, EC4V 6EB, United Kingdom
Tel.: (44) 2077491600
E-Mail: satellite.broadband@avantiplc.com
Web Site: www.avantiplc.com
AVN—(AIM)
Rev.: $32,533,374
Assets: $757,915,485
Liabilities: $376,602,231
Net Worth: $381,313,253
Earnings: ($48,684,773)
Emp.: 174
Fiscal Year-end: 06/30/13
Business Description:
Holding Company; Satellite Communications Services
S.I.C.: 6719
N.A.I.C.S.: 551112
Personnel:
Paul Walsh *(Deputy Chm)*
David J. Williams *(CEO)*
Matthew J. O'Connor *(COO)*
Patrick Willcocks *(Sec)*
Board of Directors:
Frederick Edwin John Gedge Brackenbury
David J. Bestwick
D. Alan Foster
Nigel A. D. Fox
Paul Johnson
Matthew J. O'Connor
Charles Richard Vos
Michael Walker
Paul Walsh
David J. Williams
William P. Wyatt
Legal Counsel:
Osborne Clarke
Apex Plaza Forbury Road
Reading, United Kingdom

Subsidiaries:

Avanti Broadband Limited **(1)**
74 Rivington St
EC2A 3AY London, United Kingdom
Tel.: (44) 2077491600
Fax: (44) 2077491633
E-Mail: reception@avanteplc.com
Web Site: www.avanteplc.com
Emp.: 100
Broadband Service Provider
S.I.C.: 4899
N.A.I.C.S.: 517919
David Williams *(Mng Dir)*

Avanti Communications Limited **(1)**
20 Black Friars Lane
London, EC4V 6EB, United Kingdom
Tel.: (44) 2077491600
Fax: (44) 2077491633
E-Mail: reception@avantiplc.com
Web Site: www.avantiplc.com
Emp.: 100
Satellite Communication Services
S.I.C.: 4899
N.A.I.C.S.: 517410
David Williams *(CEO)*

Avanti Space Limited **(1)**
74 Rivington St
London, EC2A 3AY, United Kingdom
Tel.: (44) 2077491600
Fax: (44) 2877491633
Web Site: www.avantplc.com
Emp.: 100
Satellite Television Network Services
S.I.C.: 4833
N.A.I.C.S.: 515120
David Williams *(CEO)*

AVANTI FEEDS LTD.
G-2 Concorde Apartment 6-3-658
Somajiguda
Hyderabad, Andhra Pradesh, 500 082, India
Tel.: (91) 4023310260
Fax: (91) 4023311604
E-Mail: avantiho@avantifeeds.com
Web Site: www.avantifeeds.com
AVANTI—(NSE)
Rev.: $120,624,614
Assets: $44,677,080
Liabilities: $22,806,091
Net Worth: $21,870,989
Earnings: $5,595,502
Fiscal Year-end: 03/31/13
Business Description:
Shrimp & Fish Feed Mfr
S.I.C.: 2048
N.A.I.C.S.: 311119
Personnel:
C. Ramachandra Rao *(Mng Dir, Compliance Officer & Sec)*
Alluri Indra Kumar *(Mng Dir)*
Board of Directors:
A. V. Achar
Alluri Indra Kumar
B. V. Kumar
Paco Wai Yat Lee
N. Ram Prasad
Anita Rajendra
C. Ramachandra Rao
K. Ram Mohan Rao
M. S. P. Rao
Bunluesak Sorajjakit
Transfer Agent:
Karvy Computershare Private Limited
Plot No 17 to 24 Vittalrao Nagar Madhapur
Hyderabad, India

Subsidiary:

Avanti Thai Aqua Feeds Private Limited **(1)**
Block-498/1 & 501 Balda Village
Valsad Dist, Pardi, 396125, India
Tel.: (91) 2602995480
Fax: (91) 2602370064
E-Mail: avanti@avantifeeds.com
Shrimp Feed Mfr
S.I.C.: 2048
N.A.I.C.S.: 311119

Plant:

Avanti Feeds Ltd. - Prawn Feed/Fish Feed Factories **(1)**
15-11-24 Near Railway Station
West Godavari District, Kovvur, India 534 350
Tel.: (91) 8813 231541
Fax: (91) 8813 231421
E-Mail: feedunit1@avantifeeds.com
Web Site: www.avantifeeds.com
Fish Feed Mfr
S.I.C.: 2048
N.A.I.C.S.: 311119

AVAPLAS LIMITED
19 Changi South Street 1
Changi South Industrial Estate, Singapore, 486779, Singapore
Tel.: (65) 6546 2655
Fax: (65) 6546 2455
E-Mail: avaplas@pacific.net.sg
Web Site: www.avaplas.com.sg
Year Founded: 1993
598—(SES)
Sales Range: $25-49.9 Million
Emp.: 408
Business Description:
Engineered Plastic Components
S.I.C.: 3089
N.A.I.C.S.: 326199
Personnel:
Howe Sear Boone Quek *(Chm & CEO)*
Ching Chek Tan *(Sec)*
Board of Directors:
Howe Sear Boone Quek

Non-U.S. Subsidiaries:

Avaplas Sdn. Bhd. **(1)**
PTD 37441 Jalan Perindustrian 3 Kawasan Perindustrian Fasa 2
Senai, 81400 Johor Bahru, Johor, Malaysia
Tel.: (60) 75985100
Fax: (60) 75987800
Web Site: www.avaplas.com.sg/contactus_worldwide.cfm
Emp.: 200
Plastic Mfr
S.I.C.: 3089
N.A.I.C.S.: 326199

Avaplas (Thailand) Ltd **(1)**
Hi Tech Industrial Estate EPZ 130 Moo 1
Tambol Baanlane
Amphur, Ayutthaya, 13160, Thailand
Tel.: (66) 35351984
Fax: (66) 35351886
Web Site: www.avaplas.com.sg/contactus_worldwide.cfm
Emp.: 140
Plastic Mfr
S.I.C.: 3089
N.A.I.C.S.: 326199
Wong Vee Tong *(Mng Dir)*

AVARAE GLOBAL COINS PLC
Ground Floor West Suite Exchange House 54-58 Athol Street
Douglas, Isle of Man IM1 1JD
Tel.: (44) 1624631693
Web Site: www.avarae.com
AVR—(LSE)
Sls.: $1,740,378
Assets: $18,465,059
Liabilities: $91,599
Net Worth: $18,373,460
Earnings: $560,648
Fiscal Year-end: 03/31/13
Business Description:
Financial Services
S.I.C.: 6211
N.A.I.C.S.: 523110
Personnel:
Chris Shimmin *(Sec)*
Board of Directors:
August Johannes Francisca Maria Berting
Clement Hadrian Chambers
Diane Jane Clarke
Matthew Wood
Legal Counsel:
Appleby
33 Athol Street
Douglas, Isle of Man

AVARONE METALS INC.
(Formerly Remstar Resources Ltd.)
507 700 West Pender Street
Vancouver, BC, V6C 1G8, Canada
Tel.: (604) 669-9788
Fax: (604) 669-9768
E-Mail: info@avarone.com
Web Site: www.avarone.com
Year Founded: 1993
AVM—(TSXV)
Assets: $70,856
Liabilities: $144,464
Net Worth: ($73,608)
Earnings: ($299,096)
Fiscal Year-end: 07/31/13
Business Description:
Metal Exploration Services
S.I.C.: 1099
N.A.I.C.S.: 212299
Personnel:
Marc Levy *(Pres & CEO)*
Nilda Rivera *(CFO)*
Max Pinsky *(Sec)*
Board of Directors:
Anita Algie
Michael Hunter
Marc Levy
Lawrence W. Talbot
Legal Counsel:
Max Pinsky Personal Law Corporation
Suite 1780 - 400 Burrard Street
Vancouver, BC, Canada

Transfer Agent:
Computershare Investor Services Inc.
510 Burrard St 2nd Floor
Vancouver, BC, V6C 3B9, Canada
Tel.: (604) 661-9400

Subsidiary:

V Interactions, Inc. (1)
85 Rue St-Paul W
Montreal, QC, H2Y 3V4, Canada (100%)
Tel.: (514) 390-6100
Fax: (514) 390-6056
E-Mail:
Web Site: www.vtele.ca
Emp.: 250
Television Broadcasting Services
S.I.C.: 3663
N.A.I.C.S.: 334220
Tony Porrello *(Chief Enterprise Officer)*

AVAST SOFTWARE B.V.

Prins Bernhardplein 200
1097 JB Amsterdam, Netherlands
Tel.: (31) 20 521 4777
Web Site: www.avast.com
Year Founded: 2006
Sales Range: $25-49.9 Million
Emp.: 191
Business Description:
Software Publisher
S.I.C.: 7372
N.A.I.C.S.: 511210
Personnel:
Eduard Kucera *(Chm)*
Vincent Steckler *(CEO)*
William Salisbury *(CFO)*
Kenneth Gonzalez *(Chief Strategy Officer)*
Ondrej Vlcek *(CTO)*
Board of Directors:
Eduard Kucera
Pavel Baudis
Scott Collins
Kenneth A. Goldman
Vincent Steckler

AVATAR ENERGY LTD.

Suite 850 633 6th Ave SW
Calgary, AB, T2P 2Y5, Canada
Tel.: (403) 517-8818
Fax: (403) 517-8815
E-Mail: info@avatarenergy.ca
Web Site: www.avatarenergy.ca
Year Founded: 2009
AVG—(TSXV)
Sales Range: $1-9.9 Million
Business Description:
Investment Services
S.I.C.: 6211
N.A.I.C.S.: 523999
Personnel:
Alan D. Jack *(Pres & CEO)*
Lorie J. Hynes *(CFO)*
Neville Jugnauth *(Sec)*
Gerald J. Wendland *(Exec VP)*
Board of Directors:
Timothy Bacon
R. D. Bowman
Alan D. Jack
Paul K. O'Donoghue
Legal Counsel:
Burnet, Duckworth & Palmer LLP
Suite 1400 350 7th Avenue Southwest
Calgary, AB, T2P 3N9, Canada
Tel.: (403) 263-3050
Transfer Agent:
Computershare Investor Services
100 University Avenue 9th Floor
Toronto, ON, Canada

AVATAR VENTURES CORP.

Ming De Road
Chao Yang, Changchun, 1300006, China
Tel.: (86) 13596051170
ATAR—(OTC)
Business Description:
Motor Vehicle Aftermarket Electronic Accessories Mfr
S.I.C.: 3714
N.A.I.C.S.: 336320
Personnel:
Edward Minnema *(Pres)*

AVATEC CO., LTD.

100 Dalseodaero 85-Gil Dalseo-Gu
Daegu, 704240, Korea (South)
Tel.: (82) 535924060
Fax: (82) 535921030
Web Site: www.avatec.co.kr
149950—(KRS)
Sales Range: $25-49.9 Million
Emp.: 420
Business Description:
Electronic Components Mfr
S.I.C.: 3679
N.A.I.C.S.: 334419
Personnel:
Jae Gon Wi *(Chm)*

AVATION PLC

510 Thomson Road 12-04 SLF Building
Singapore, 298135, Singapore
Tel.: (65) 6252 2077
Web Site: www.avation.net
Year Founded: 2006
AVAP—(LSE)
Rev.: $42,739,991
Assets: $394,383,300
Liabilities: $296,146,941
Net Worth: $98,236,359
Earnings: $11,964,993
Fiscal Year-end: 06/30/13
Business Description:
Aircraft Leasing Services
S.I.C.: 7359
N.A.I.C.S.: 532411
Personnel:
Robert Jeffries Chatfield *(Chm)*
Roderick Douglas Mahoney *(COO)*
Duncan Gerard Stephen Scott *(Gen Counsel & Co-Sec)*
Siobhan Mary Macgroarty Cool *(Co-Sec)*
Jason Francis Gollogly *(Co-Sec)*
Board of Directors:
Robert Jeffries Chatfield
Roderick Douglas Mahoney
Legal Counsel:
Speechly Bircham LLP
6 New Street Square
London, EC4A 3LX, United Kingdom

AVC MEDIA ENTERPRISES LTD

Wellington Cir
Altens
Aberdeen, Scotland, AB12 3JG, United Kingdom
Tel.: (44) 1224248007
Fax: (44) 1224248407
E-Mail: info@avcmedia.com
Web Site: www.avcmedia.com
Year Founded: 1976
Emp.: 85
Business Description:
Advertising
S.I.C.: 7311
N.A.I.C.S.: 541810
Personnel:
Keith Main *(Chm)*

AVCON INFORMATION TECHNOLOGY CO., LTD.

22-23F 2 Building 335 Guoding Road
Shanghai, 200433, China
Tel.: (86) 21 55666588
Fax: (86) 21 55666998
Web Site: www.avcon.com.cn
300074—(CHIN)
Sales Range: $10-24.9 Million
Emp.: 300
Business Description:
Video Conferencing & Video Monitoring Control Systems & Software
S.I.C.: 3663
N.A.I.C.S.: 334220
Personnel:
Xiaodan Liu *(Chm)*

AVCORP INDUSTRIES, INC.

10025 River Way
Delta, BC, V4G 1M7, Canada
Tel.: (604) 582-6677
Fax: (604) 582-2620
E-Mail: info@avcorp.com
Web Site: www.avcorp.com
Year Founded: 1986
AVP—(TSX)
Rev.: $88,802,765
Assets: $68,224,563
Liabilities: $43,784,593
Net Worth: $24,439,970
Earnings: $20,517,567
Emp.: 476
Fiscal Year-end: 12/31/12
Business Description:
Aircraft Parts Mfr
S.I.C.: 3728
N.A.I.C.S.: 336413
Personnel:
David Levi *(Chm)*
Mark van Rooij *(Pres & CEO)*
Ed Merlo *(Sec & VP-Fin)*
Board of Directors:
David Levi
Ray Castelli
Kees de Koning
Jaap Rosen Jacobson
Eric Kohn
Elizabeth Otis
Mark van Rooij
Legal Counsel:
McMillan LLP
Vancouver, BC, Canada
Transfer Agent:
CIBC Mellon Trust Company
1177 W Hastings St - Mall Level
Vancouver, BC, V6E 3XI, Canada
Tel.: (604) 891-3024
Toll Free: (800) 387-0825

Divisions:

Avior Integrated Products (1)
1001 Autoroute 440 W
Laval, QC, Canada (100%)
Tel.: (450) 629-6200
Fax: (514) 324-6241
Web Site: www.avior.ca
Emp.: 140
Mfr. of Aircraft Parts
S.I.C.: 3728
N.A.I.C.S.: 336413
Karanjit Dulat *(VP-Engrg-Six Sigma)*

Subsidiary:

Comtek Advanced Structures Ltd (1)
1360 Artisans Ct
Burlington, ON, L7L 5Y2, Canada
Tel.: (905) 331-8121
Fax: (905) 331-8125
Toll Free: (800) 473-0730
E-Mail: contact@comtekadvanced.com
Web Site: www.comtekadvanced.com
Emp.: 80
Aircraft Components Mfr
S.I.C.: 3812
N.A.I.C.S.: 334511
Brent Collver *(Pres)*

AVECIA LTD.

Hexagon House Old Market St
PO Box 42
Blackley, Manchester, M9 8ZS, United Kingdom
Tel.: (44) 1617211013
Fax: (44) 1617215202
E-Mail: biotech@avecia.com
Web Site: www.avecia.com
Year Founded: 1999
Sales Range: $350-399.9 Million
Emp.: 2,529
Business Description:
Specialty Chemical Mfr
Import Export
S.I.C.: 2834
N.A.I.C.S.: 325412
Personnel:
Adrian Buckmaster *(CEO)*

Non-U.S. Subsidiaries:

Avecia NV/SA (1)
Av De Tervueren 13 B
1040 Brussels, Belgium BE
Tel.: (32) 27430090 (100%)
Fax: (32) 27361144
Web Site: www.avecia.com
S.I.C.: 2899
N.A.I.C.S.: 325998

Avecia Spain S.L. (1)
Palou 2 Y 4 Poligono Industrial
Parets Del Valles, Barcelona, Spain (100%)
Tel.: (34) 935620047
Basic Inorganic Chemical Mfr
S.I.C.: 2819
N.A.I.C.S.: 325180

AVECTO LIMITED

Hobart House Cheadle Royal Business Park
Cheadle, Cheshire, SK8 3SR, United Kingdom
Tel.: (44) 845 519 0114
Fax: (44) 845 519 0115
E-Mail: info@avecto.com
Web Site: www.avecto.com
Year Founded: 2008
Sales Range: $10-24.9 Million
Emp.: 59
Business Description:
Security Software Development Services
S.I.C.: 7371
N.A.I.C.S.: 541511
Personnel:
Mark Austin *(Co-Founder & CEO)*
Paul Kenyon *(Co-Founder & Exec VP-Sls)*

AVEDA TRANSPORTATION AND ENERGY SERVICES INC.

300 435 4th Avenue Southwest
Calgary, AB, T2P 3A8, Canada
Tel.: (403) 264-4950
Fax: (403) 262-9195
Web Site: www.avedaenergy.com
Year Founded: 1994
AVE—(TSXV)
Rev.: $82,832,681
Assets: $67,708,666
Liabilities: $43,679,227
Net Worth: $24,029,439
Earnings: ($1,270,358)
Emp.: 204
Fiscal Year-end: 12/31/12
Business Description:
Oilfield Transportation Services
S.I.C.: 4212
N.A.I.C.S.: 484220
Personnel:
David P. Werklund *(Chm)*
Kevin Roycraft *(Pres & CEO)*
Bharat Mahajan *(CFO & VP-Fin)*
Board of Directors:
David P. Werklund
Martin Cheyne
Stefan Erasmus
Douglas McCartney
Paul Shelley

Aveda Transportation and Energy Services Inc.—(Continued)

Transfer Agent:
Olympia Trust Company of Canada
Calgary, AB, Canada

AVEGA GROUP AB
Grev Turegatan 11A
11446 Stockholm, Sweden
Tel.: (46) 84076500
Fax: (46) 84076501
E-Mail: info@avegagroup.se
Web Site: www.avegagroup.se
Year Founded: 2000
AVEG B—(OMX)
Sales Range: $25-49.9 Million
Emp.: 280
Business Description:
IT & Business Development Consulting Services
S.I.C.: 7379
N.A.I.C.S.: 541519
Personnel:
Lars-Erik Eriksson *(Chm)*
January Rosenholm *(Pres & CEO)*
Elizabeth Jarnbring *(CFO)*
Board of Directors:
Lars-Erik Eriksson
Goran E. Larsson
January Rosenholm
Anna Soderblom
Gunnel Tolfes

AVENG LIMITED
(d/b/a Aveng Group)
204 Rivonia Road
Morningside, Sandton, 2057, South Africa
Tel.: (27) 11 779 2800
Fax: (27) 11 784 5030
Web Site: www.aveng.co.za
AEG—(JSE)
Rev.: $5,775,336,800
Assets: $3,397,132,100
Liabilities: $1,910,963,600
Net Worth: $1,486,168,500
Earnings: $51,270,300
Emp.: 28,296
Fiscal Year-end: 06/30/13
Business Description:
Construction & Engineering Services
S.I.C.: 1542
N.A.I.C.S.: 236220
Personnel:
Kobus Verster *(CEO & Dir-Fin)*
John Arron *(Exec-IR & Special Projects)*
Michelle Nana *(Sec)*
Board of Directors:
Angus W. B. Band
Peter J. Erasmus
May Hermanus
Rick Hogben
Michael James Kilbride
Juba J. A. Mashaba
Thoko Martha Mokgosi-Mwantembe
David Robinson
Myles J. D. Ruck
Mahomed Ismail Seedat
Nkululeko Sowazi
Peter Ward
Legal Counsel:
Webber Wentzel
10 Fricker Road Illovo Boulevard
Illovo, South Africa
Transfer Agent:
Computershare Investor Services (Pty) Ltd
70 Marshall Street
Johannesburg, South Africa
Subsidiaries:

Aveng (Africa) Limited **(1)**
S Bldg Grinaker LTA Park Jurgens St
Boksburg, Gauteng, 1469, South Africa
Tel.: (27) 119235000
Fax: (27) 119235447
Web Site: www.avengrinakerlta.com
Emp.: 600
Construction Steel & Concrete Materials Mfr
S.I.C.: 3273
N.A.I.C.S.: 327320
Kobus Verster *(Gen Mgr)*

Division:

Keyplan (Pty) Limited **(2)**
Bldg 30 The Woodlands Woodlands Dr
Woodmead, Sandton, Gauteng, 2128, South Africa
Tel.: (27) 102051800
Fax: (27) 866835758
E-Mail: info@avengwater.co.za
Web Site: www.aveng.co.za
Emp.: 40
Water Treatment Plant Installation Services
S.I.C.: 1629
N.A.I.C.S.: 237110
Gavin Young *(Mng Dir)*

Aveng E+PC Engineering & Projects Company Limited **(1)**
The Highlands Bldg 30 The Woodlands
Woodlands Dr Woodmead, 2191 Sandton, Gauteng, South Africa
Tel.: (27) 10 205 1000
Fax: (27) 87 807 0143
Web Site: www.avenge-pc.co.za
Emp.: 550
Industrial Engineering, Design & Project Delivery Services
S.I.C.: 8711
N.A.I.C.S.: 541330
Peter Du Plessis *(Acting Mng Dir)*
Frank Saieva *(Mng Dir)*

Fraser & Chalmers Siyakha (Pty) Limited **(1)**
1 Belfast Rd
Bayhead, Durban, Kwazulu-Natal, 4026, South Africa
Tel.: (27) 312051525
Fax: (27) 312053611
Industrial Engineering Services
S.I.C.: 8711
N.A.I.C.S.: 541330
Tony Strickland *(Gen Mgr)*

Grinaker-LTA Construction and Development Limited **(1)**
Block A Grinaker LTA Park Jurgens St
Jet Park, Johannesburg, Gauteng, 1620, South Africa
Tel.: (27) 115786000
Fax: (27) 115786161
E-Mail: info@grinaker-lta.co.za
Web Site: www.grinaker-lta.co.za
Emp.: 60
Commercial Building Construction Services
S.I.C.: 1542
N.A.I.C.S.: 236220
Brian Wilmot *(Mng Dir)*

Grinaker-LTA Engineering and Mining Services Limited **(1)**
Jet Park Road
Boksburg, Gauteng, 1459, South Africa
Tel.: (27) 119235802
Fax: (27) 119235222
E-Mail: nblom@grinaker-lta.co.za
Web Site: www.avenggrinaker-lta.co.za
Industrial & Mining Engineering Services
S.I.C.: 8711
N.A.I.C.S.: 541330

Trident Steel Intellectual Property (Pty) Limited **(1)**
Marthunisen Rd
Germiston, Gauteng, 1401, South Africa
Tel.: (27) 118617111
Fax: (27) 118652042
Web Site: www.trident.co.za
Steel Warehousing Services
S.I.C.: 4225
N.A.I.C.S.: 493110

Trident Steel (Pty) Limited **(1)**
Marthunisen Rd
Roodekop, Germiston, Gauteng, 1401, South Africa
Tel.: (27) 118617111
Fax: (27) 118652042
E-Mail: trident@trident.co.za
Web Site: www.trident.co.za
Steel Processing Services
S.I.C.: 3399
N.A.I.C.S.: 331110
Tipten Terblanche *(Mng Dir)*
Craig Werner *(CFO)*
Bright Mtemererwa *(Sec)*

Non-U.S. Subsidiaries:

Built Environs Holdings (Pty) Limited **(1)**
100 Hutt St
Adelaide, SA, 5000, Australia
Tel.: (61) 882321882
Fax: (61) 882321883
E-Mail: de@builtenvirons.com.au
Web Site: www.builtenvirons.com.au
Emp.: 200
Management Services
S.I.C.: 8741
N.A.I.C.S.: 551114
Scott Penhall *(Mng Dir)*

Subsidiary:

Built Environs (Pty) Limited **(2)**
100 Hutt St
Adelaide, SA, 5000, Australia
Tel.: (61) 882321882
Fax: (61) 882321883
E-Mail: be@builtenvirons.com.au
Web Site: www.builtenvirons.com.au
Emp.: 50
Industrial Engineering Services
S.I.C.: 8711
N.A.I.C.S.: 541330
Michael O' Connor *(Chm)*
Jim Frith *(Mng Dir)*

Grinaker-LTA (Namibia) (Pty) Limited **(1)**
27 Kalie Roodt St Northern Industria
PO Box 5801
Windhoek, Namibia
Tel.: (264) 61220600
Fax: (264) 61228411
E-Mail: grinnam@gcl.com.na
Web Site: www.grinaker-lta.com
Emp.: 200
Construction Engineering Services
S.I.C.: 8711
N.A.I.C.S.: 541330

McConnell Dowell Corporation Limited **(1)**
Level 3 109 Burwood Rd
Hawthorn, VIC, 3122, Australia
Tel.: (61) 398162400
Fax: (61) 398183553
E-Mail: macdow_corp@macdow.com.au
Web Site: www.macdow.com.au
Emp.: 200
Construction Engineering Services
S.I.C.: 1629
N.A.I.C.S.: 237990
David G. Robinson *(CEO)*
Dale Morrison *(CFO)*

Subsidiaries:

Electrix Pty Limited **(2)**
208 Hall St
Spotswood, VIC, 3015, Australia
Tel.: (61) 393994688
Fax: (61) 393994730
E-Mail: info@electrix.com.au
Web Site: www.electrix.com.au
Emp.: 500
Electrical Contracting Services
S.I.C.: 1731
N.A.I.C.S.: 238210
Joe Warren *(Gen Mgr-Ops)*

McConnell Dowell Constructors (Aust.) Pty Limited **(2)**
Tech Ofc Park Bldg 10 G&H 107 Miles Platting Rd
Eight Mile Plains, QLD, 4113, Australia
Tel.: (61) 734218200
Fax: (61) 732197244
Web Site: www.mcconnelldowell.com
Emp.: 100
Construction Engineering Services
S.I.C.: 1629
N.A.I.C.S.: 237990
Dale Morrison *(CFO)*

Non-U.S. Subsidiaries:

Dutco McConnell Dowell Qatar LLC **(2)**
Ofc No 12 2 Fl Al Hilal Bldg 114 Dring Rd
PO Box 30933
Doha, Qatar
Tel.: (974) 4675 491
Fax: (974) 4986 778
E-Mail: me@macdow.com.au
Emp.: 29
Commercial Building Construction Services
S.I.C.: 1542
N.A.I.C.S.: 236220
Coles Coles *(Gen Mgr)*

Electrix Limited **(2)**
2 George Bourke Dr
Mt Wellington, Auckland, 1060, New Zealand
Tel.: (64) 92701700
Fax: (64) 92701701
E-Mail: info@electrix.co.nz
Web Site: www.electrix.co.nz
Emp.: 100
Electrical Contracting Services
S.I.C.: 1731
N.A.I.C.S.: 238210
Gavan R. Jackson *(Mng Dir)*

McConnell Dowell Constructors Limited **(2)**
510 Mt Wellington Hwy
Mt Wellington, Auckland, 1060, New Zealand
Tel.: (64) 95735891
Fax: (64) 95735831
E-Mail: nz@macdow.com.au
Web Site: www.macdow.com.au
Mining Engineering Services
S.I.C.: 8711
N.A.I.C.S.: 541330
Roger McRae *(Gen Mgr)*

McConnell Dowell Constructors Thai Limited **(2)**
22nd Fl Unit 2202 Bangkok Bus Ctr Bldg 29
Sukhumvit 63 Rd
Klongton-Nua Wattana, Bangkok, 10110, Thailand
Tel.: (66) 23915406
Fax: (66) 23818400
E-Mail: thai@macdow.com.au
Web Site: www.macdow.com.au
Emp.: 200
Oil & Gas Pipeline Construction Services
S.I.C.: 1623
N.A.I.C.S.: 237120
David Ash *(Mgr-Fabrication)*

McConnell Dowell Philippines Inc. **(2)**
Level 4 NOL Tower Commerce Ave
Madrigal Bus Park
Alabang, Muntinlupa, 1770, Philippines
Tel.: (63) 28096328
Fax: (63) 28096331
Web Site: www.mcconnelldowell.com
Emp.: 500
Industrial Engineering Services
S.I.C.: 8711
N.A.I.C.S.: 541330
Colin Jenner *(Country Mgr)*

PT. McConnell Dowell Indonesia **(2)**
1st Floor Parama Building Jl Achmad Dahlan 69 A-B
Kebayoran Baru, Jakarta, 12130, Indonesia
Tel.: (62) 217253051
Fax: (62) 217253054
Web Site: www.macdow.com.au
Emp.: 50
Construction Engineering Services
S.I.C.: 1629
N.A.I.C.S.: 237990
Yayan Mulyanah *(Mgr-Fin, Acctg, Payroll & Tax)*

Moolman Mining Botswana (Pty) Limited **(1)**
Private Bag F449
Francistown, Botswana
Tel.: (267) 2418849
Fax: (267) 2440888
Web Site: www.aveng.com
Emp.: 500
Mining Support Services
S.I.C.: 1241
N.A.I.C.S.: 213113

Brian Wilmot *(Mng Dir)*

Steeledale Reinforcing & Trading Namibia (Pty) Limited (1)
21 Iscor St Northern Indus Area
Windhoek, Namibia
Tel.: (264) 61262117
Fax: (264) 61261709
Emp.: 7
Steel Reinforcing Contract Services
S.I.C.: 1791
N.A.I.C.S.: 238120
Noble Clark *(Mgr)*

AVENIR ELECTRIQUE DE LIMOGES
99 Rue Henri Giffard
BP 1522
87020 Limoges, Haute Vienne, Cedex 9, France
Tel.: (33) 555358383
Fax: (33) 555358380
Web Site: www.avenirelec.fr
Rev.: $22,600,000
Emp.: 170
Business Description:
Electrical Work
S.I.C.: 1731
N.A.I.C.S.: 238210
Personnel:
Daniel Marie *(Mng Dir)*
Board of Directors:
Daniel Marie
Patrick Dumain

AVENIR ENERGIE SA
13 rue Emmanuel Chabrier
Valence, 26905, France
Tel.: (33) 475822890
Fax: (33) 0475822891
E-Mail: contact@avenir-energie.com
Web Site: www.avenir-energie.com
Sales Range: $10-24.9 Million
Emp.: 50
Business Description:
Geothermal Heating Systems
S.I.C.: 3433
N.A.I.C.S.: 333414

AVENIR FINANCE S.A.
51 Rue de Saint-Cyr
69009 Lyon, France
Tel.: (33) 427705400
Fax: (33) 427705401
E-Mail: contact@avenirfinance.fr
Web Site: www.avenirfinance.fr
AVF—(EUR)
Sales Range: $50-74.9 Million
Emp.: 140
Business Description:
Investment & Financial Services
S.I.C.: 6211
N.A.I.C.S.: 523999
Personnel:
Danyel Blain *(Chm & CEO)*
Cyril Lureau *(Deputy CEO)*
Board of Directors:
Danyel Blain
Gerard Auffray
Frederic Boute
Christian Lauriere
Cyril Lureau
Jean-Pierre Morin
Jean-Noel Vignon
Subsidiaries:

Avenir Finance Corporate (1)
53 rue La Boetie
75008 Paris, France
Tel.: (33) 170080805
Fax: (33) 170080806
E-Mail: info@avenirfinance.fr
Web Site: www.corporate.avenirfinance.fr/
Emp.: 50
Financial Management Services
S.I.C.: 8748
N.A.I.C.S.: 541618

Avenir Finance Gestion (1)
53 Rue La Boetie
75008 Paris, France
Tel.: (33) 1 70 08 08 08
Web Site: www.gestion.avenirfinance.fr
Financial Management Services
S.I.C.: 8748
N.A.I.C.S.: 541618

Avenir Finance Investment Managers (AFIM) (1)
53 Rue La Boetie
75008 Paris, France
Tel.: (33) 170080800
Fax: (33) 170080802
E-Mail: contact@avenirfinance.fr
Web Site: www.im.avenirfinance.fr
Emp.: 30
Mutual Funds Management
S.I.C.: 6722
N.A.I.C.S.: 525910
Thibault Delahaye *(Chm)*

Avenir Finance Partenaires (1)
53 Rue La Boetie
Paris, France
Tel.: (33) 170080885
Web Site: www.partenaires.avenirfinance.fr
Investment Advisory Services
S.I.C.: 6282
N.A.I.C.S.: 523930

Avenir Finance Securities (1)
53 Rue La Boetie
75008 Paris, France
Tel.: (33) 170080808
Fax: (33) 1 70 08 08 09
Web Site: www.securities.avenirfinance.fr
Financial Management Services
S.I.C.: 8748
N.A.I.C.S.: 541618

Sicavonline (1)
53 Rue La Boetie
75008 Paris, France
Tel.: (33) 170080808
Fax: (33) 170080809
E-Mail: info@sicavonline.fr
Web Site: www.sicavonline.fr
Emp.: 70
Investment Management Services
S.I.C.: 6722
N.A.I.C.S.: 525910
Eric Moreau *(Mng Dir)*

AVENIR TELECOM S.A.
(d/b/a Groupe Avenir)
208 bd Plombieres
13581 Marseilles, Cedex 20, France
Tel.: (33) 4 88 00 63 98
Fax: (33) 488006070
E-Mail: actionnaire@avenir-telecom.fr
Web Site: www.avenir-telecom.com
AVT—(EUR)
Rev.: $555,429,742
Assets: $283,772,636
Liabilities: $197,348,522
Net Worth: $86,424,114
Earnings: ($3,903,893)
Emp.: 1,982
Fiscal Year-end: 03/31/13
Business Description:
Mobile Phones & Cellular Accessories Distr
S.I.C.: 5065
N.A.I.C.S.: 423690
Personnel:
Jean-Daniel Beurnier *(Co-Founder, Chm, Pres & CEO)*
Robert Schiano-Lamoriello *(Co-Founder & CEO-France)*
Agnes Tixier *(CFO & Dir-Fin)*
Board of Directors:
Jean-Daniel Beurnier
Pierre Baduel
Robert Schiano-Lamoriello
Agnes Tixier
Subsidiary:

Avenir Telecom France (1)
208 bd de Plombieres
Marseille, 13581 Marseilles, Cedex 20, France
Tel.: (33) 488006000
Fax: (33) 488006180
Emp.: 25
Mobile Telephony Products Distr
S.I.C.: 3663
N.A.I.C.S.: 334220

Non-U.S. Subsidiaries:

Avenir Telecom Romania (1)
Sos Bucuresti Ploiesti
No 67 Sector 1, 013685 Bucharest, Romania
Tel.: (40) 212012900
Fax: (40) 212012917
E-Mail: office@avenir-telecom.ro
Web Site: www.avenir-telecom.ro
Emp.: 500
Mobile Telephony Products Mfr
S.I.C.: 3663
N.A.I.C.S.: 334220
Philippe Auga *(Gen Mgr)*

Avenir Telecom Spain (1)
Pine Ave s n The Oak Park
48170 Zamudio, Biscay, Spain
Tel.: (34) 944521516
Fax: (34) 944 523 535
Web Site: www.avenir-telecom.com
Telecom Distr
S.I.C.: 3663
N.A.I.C.S.: 334220
Bosco Souto *(Mng Dir)*

AVENUE CARS OF GLOUCESTER LIMITED
City Business Centre
Hempsted, Gloucester, GL2 5JH, United Kingdom
Tel.: (44) 1452528181
E-Mail: retail@avenuecars.com
Web Site: www.avenuecars.com
Year Founded: 1989
Rev.: $13,299,495
Emp.: 9
Business Description:
Car Retailers
S.I.C.: 5521
N.A.I.C.S.: 441120
Personnel:
Nick Broady *(Mng Dir)*

AVENUE MOVING AND STORAGE LIMITED
992 Rangeview Road
Mississauga, ON, L5E 1H3, Canada
Tel.: (905) 891-2041
Fax: (905) 891-2044
E-Mail: info@avenuemoving.com
Web Site: www.avenuemoving.com
Year Founded: 1914
Rev.: $21,253,210
Emp.: 30
Business Description:
Transportation & Storage Services
S.I.C.: 4213
N.A.I.C.S.: 484122
Personnel:
Ron Stone *(Pres)*

AVENUE NISSAN SALES LTD.
1661 Avenue Road
Toronto, ON, M5M 3Y2, Canada
Tel.: (416) 783-3303
Fax: (416) 783-5009
E-Mail: sales@avenuenissan.com
Web Site: www.avenuenissan.com
Year Founded: 1980
Rev.: $14,367,170
Emp.: 32
Business Description:
New & Used Car Dealers
S.I.C.: 5511
N.A.I.C.S.: 441110
Personnel:
John Esplen *(Owner)*

AVENUE RESOURCES LIMITED
Level 1 330 Churchill Avenue
Subiaco, WA, 6008, Australia
Tel.: (61) 8 9200 1847
Fax: (61) 8 9200 4469
E-Mail: info@avenueresources.com.au
Web Site: www.avenueresources.com.au
AVY—(ASX)
Rev.: $98,550
Assets: $1,889,478
Liabilities: $83,899
Net Worth: $1,805,579
Earnings: ($8,248,118)
Fiscal Year-end: 06/30/13
Business Description:
Gold Exploration & Mining Services
S.I.C.: 1041
N.A.I.C.S.: 212221
Personnel:
Scott Funston *(Sec)*
Board of Directors:
Anthony Polglase
Luis Mauricio Ferraiuoli de Azevedo
Simon Mottram

AVENZA HOLDINGS INC.
124 Merton Street Suite 400
Toronto, ON, M4S 2Z2, Canada
Tel.: (416) 487-5116
Fax: (416) 487-7213
Web Site: www.avenza.com
Business Description:
Holding Company; Mapping & Spatial Imaging Software Developer, Publisher & Marketer
S.I.C.: 6719
N.A.I.C.S.: 551112
Personnel:
Ted Florence *(Pres & CEO)*
Subsidiary:

Avenza Systems Inc. (1)
124 Merton Street Suite 400
Toronto, ON, M4S 2Z2, Canada
Tel.: (416) 487-5116
Fax: (416) 487-7213
Toll Free: (800) 884-2555 (Sls)
E-Mail: info@avenza.com
Web Site: www.avenza.com
Mapping & Spatial Imaging Software Developer, Publisher & Marketer
S.I.C.: 7372
N.A.I.C.S.: 511210
Ted Florence *(Pres & CEO)*

AVER INFORMATION INC.
5F 135 Jian Yi Rd
Chung Ho City, Taipei, Hsien, Taiwan
Tel.: (886) 222263630
Fax: (886) 232344842
Web Site: www.aver.com
3669—(TAI)
Sales Range: $100-124.9 Million
Emp.: 1,000
Business Description:
Multimedia Surveillance Products Mfr
S.I.C.: 3812
N.A.I.C.S.: 334511
Personnel:
Michael Kuo *(Chm)*
James Chang *(Pres)*
Jenny Kang *(CFO)*
U.S. Subsidiary:

AVer Information, Inc. (1)
423 Dixon Landing Rd
Milpitas, CA 95035
Tel.: (408) 263-3828
Fax: (408) 263-8132
E-Mail: tammy.stephenson@aver.com
Web Site: www.averusa.com
Emp.: 25
Surveillance Product Mfr & Distr
S.I.C.: 3679
N.A.I.C.S.: 334419
Arthur S. Pait *(Pres)*

Non-U.S. Subsidiary:

AVer Information Inc. (1)
Rotterdamseweg 402 A2
2629 HH Delft, Netherlands

AVer Information Inc.—(Continued)

Tel.: (31) 157112337
Fax: (31) 15 711 2339
Electronic Products Mfr & Distr
S.I.C.: 3571
N.A.I.C.S.: 334111

AVERNA TECHNOLOGIES INC.

87 Prince St Ste 140
Montreal, QC, H3C 2M7, Canada
Tel.: (514) 842-7577
E-Mail: info@averna.com
Web Site: www.averna.com
Year Founded: 1999
Sales Range: $25-49.9 Million
Emp.: 100

Business Description:
Test Engineering Solutions from Design to Manufacturing
Export
S.I.C.: 8731
N.A.I.C.S.: 541712

Personnel:
Pascal Pilon *(Chm, Pres & CEO)*
Joseph Cavalancia *(CFO)*
Richard Maltais *(COO)*
Lori Seidman *(Chief Legal Officer)*

Board of Directors:
Pascal Pilon
Mark E. Burton
Andre Gauthier
Jean-Francois Grou
Richard Maltais
Brian Piccioni
William Wignall

AVEROX INC.

House 381Street 13 Sector F-10/2
Islamabad, Pakistan
Tel.: (92) 51 211 0755
E-Mail: pk@averox.com
Web Site: www.averox.com
AVRI—(OTC)
Sales Range: Less than $1 Million
Emp.: 80

Business Description:
Software Solutions, Engineering, Telecommunications Network Deployment Services, Systems Integration & Related Support Services
S.I.C.: 8999
N.A.I.C.S.: 541690

Personnel:
Salmon Mahmood *(Pres & CEO)*
Yasser Ahmad *(CFO & Sec)*

Subsidiary:

Averox (Pvt.) Ltd. (1)
509-B St 9 F 10/2
Islamabad, 44000, Pakistan
Tel.: (92) 51 211 0755
Fax: (92) 51 835 7573
E-Mail: pk@averox.com
Telecommunication Software Development Services
S.I.C.: 7371
N.A.I.C.S.: 541511

AVERTEX UTILITY SOLUTIONS INC.

205235 County Road 109
Amaranth, ON, L9W 2Z3, Canada
Tel.: (519) 942-3030
Fax: (519) 924-2383
Toll Free: (888) 837-3030
E-Mail: info@avertex.ca
Web Site: www.avertex.ca
Year Founded: 2003
Rev.: $18,123,139
Emp.: 85

Business Description:
Construction & Network Installation Services
S.I.C.: 8711
N.A.I.C.S.: 541330

Personnel:
Jack A. Kottelenberg *(Pres & CEO)*
Grant Kottelenberg *(CFO & Mgr-Fin)*
Andrew Blokker *(COO & VP)*

AVESCO GROUP PLC

Unit E2 Sussex Manor Business Park
Gatwick Road
Crawley, Surrey, RH10 9NH, United Kingdom
Tel.: (44) 1293583400
Fax: (44) 1293583410
E-Mail: info@avesco.com
Web Site: www.avesco.com
Year Founded: 1984
AVS—(LSE)
Rev.: $206,073,388
Assets: $215,679,834
Liabilities: $94,064,087
Net Worth: $121,615,747
Earnings: $58,326,513
Emp.: 765
Fiscal Year-end: 09/30/13

Business Description:
Holding Company; Specialist Services to the Corporate, Presentation, Entertainment & Broadcast Markets
S.I.C.: 6719
N.A.I.C.S.: 551112

Personnel:
Richard Murray *(Chm)*
Nicholas Conn *(Sec)*

Board of Directors:
Richard Murray
Graham Andrews
John Christmas
David Crump
Ami Giniger
Carmit Hoomash

Legal Counsel:
Norton Rose LLP
3 More London Riverside
London, SE1 2AQ, United Kingdom
Tel.: (44) 20 7283 6000
Fax: (44) 20 7283 6500

Transfer Agent:
Capita Asset Services
The Registry 34 Beckenham Road
Beckenham, BR3 4TU, United Kingdom

Subsidiaries:

Avesco plc (1)
Unit E2 Sussex Manor Business Park
Gatwick Rd, Crawley, RH10 9NH, United Kingdom UK
Tel.: (44) 1293583400 (100%)
Fax: (44) 1293583412
E-Mail: info@avesco.com
Web Site: www.avesco.com
Sales Range: $25-49.9 Million
Emp.: 39
Holding Company; Office Administrative Services
S.I.C.: 6719
N.A.I.C.S.: 551112
Ian Martin *(CEO)*

Subsidiary:

Avesco Finance Limited (2)
Unit E2 Sussex Manor Business Pk
Gatwick Rd
Crawley, West Sussex, RH10 9NH, United Kingdom
Tel.: (44) 1293 582000
Fax: (44) 1293 582010
Emp.: 120
Financial Management Services
S.I.C.: 6211
N.A.I.C.S.: 523999

Creative Technology Ltd. (1)
Unit E2 Sussex Manor Business Park
Gatwick Rd, Crawley, RH10 9NH, United Kingdom (100%)
Tel.: (44) 1293582000
Fax: (44) 01293582010
E-Mail: info@ctlondon.com
Web Site: www.ctlondon.com
Emp.: 130
Specialist Services Provider to the Corporate, Presentation, Entertainment & Broadcast Markets
S.I.C.: 8741
N.A.I.C.S.: 561110
Dave Crump *(CEO)*

U.S. Branches:

Creative Technology Chicago (2)
1455 Estes Ave
Elk Grove Village, IL 60176-1701
Tel.: (847) 671-9670
Fax: (847) 671-9676
E-Mail: info@ctus.com
Web Site: www.ctus.com
Emp.: 55
Specialist Audio & Video Staging Services
S.I.C.: 7389
N.A.I.C.S.: 561499
Dominic Tosterud *(Dir-Ops)*

Creative Technology Los Angeles (2)
14000 Arminta St
Panorama City, CA 91402 (100%)
Tel.: (818) 464-7500
Fax: (818) 464-7502
E-Mail: info@ctus.com
Web Site: www.ctus.com
Emp.: 50
Specialist Services Provider to the Corporate, Presentation, Entertainment & Broadcast Markets
S.I.C.: 7359
N.A.I.C.S.: 532299
Graham Andrews *(CEO)*

Creative Technology San Francisco (2)
14072 Catalina St
San Leandro, CA 94577-5037
Tel.: (510) 217-2700
Fax: (510) 618-5118
E-Mail: info@ctsanfrancisco.com
Web Site: www.ctus.com
Emp.: 100
Specialist Services Provider to the Corporate, Presentation, Entertainment & Broadcast Markets
S.I.C.: 7389
N.A.I.C.S.: 561499
Graham Andrews *(CEO)*
Stephen Gray *(COO)*

Non-U.S. Branch:

Creative Technology GmbH Co. KG (2)
In der Au 11
72622 Nurtingen, Stuttgart, Germany (100%)
Tel.: (49) 70222530
Fax: (49) 7022253100
E-Mail: info@ctgermany.com
Web Site: www.ctgermany.com
Sls.: $8,891,407
Emp.: 40
Specialist Services Provider to the Corporate, Presentation, Entertainment & Broadcast Markets
S.I.C.: 7389
N.A.I.C.S.: 561990
George Roessler *(Mng Dir)*

Dimension Audio (1)
9 Brunel Centre Newton Road
Gatwick Rd, Crawley, RH10 9TU, United Kingdom (100%)
Tel.: (44) 1293582005
Fax: (44) 1293582006
E-Mail: info@dimension.co.uk
Web Site: www.dimension.co.uk
Emp.: 20
Specialist Services to the Corporate, Presentation, Entertainment & Broadcast Markets
S.I.C.: 3651
N.A.I.C.S.: 334310

Fountain Television Limited (1)
128 Wembley Park Drive
Wembley, HA9 8HP, United Kingdom
Tel.: (44) 2089005800
Fax: (44) 2089005802
E-Mail: enquiries@ftv.co.uk
Web Site: www.ftv.co.uk
Emp.: 40
Television Studio Operators
S.I.C.: 7389
N.A.I.C.S.: 512240
Mariana Spater *(Mng Dir & Dir-Fin)*

Media Control Limited (1)
Venture House Davis Rd
Chessington, Surrey, KT9 1TT, United Kingdom UK
Tel.: (44) 2083919700 (100%)
Fax: (44) 2083919740
E-Mail:
Emp.: 10
Specialist Services Provider to the Corporate, Presentation, Entertainment & Broadcast Markets
S.I.C.: 8741
N.A.I.C.S.: 561110

Subsidiary:

Media Control (Europe) Limited (2)
14 Ockham Drive Greenford Park
Greenford, London, UB6 0FD, United Kingdom
Tel.: (44) 2088397010
Fax: (44) 2088397011
E-Mail: london@mcl-av.com
Web Site: www.mcl-av.com
Emp.: 30
Event Organizing Services
S.I.C.: 7999
N.A.I.C.S.: 711310
Jon Dasent *(Gen Mgr)*

Presteigne Limited (1)
Unit 4 Mnr Gate Mnr Royal
Crawley, Surrey, RH10 9SX, United Kingdom UK
Tel.: (44) 2083362345 (100%)
Fax: (44) 2093651031
E-Mail: hire@presteigne.co.uk
Web Site: www.presteigne.co.uk
Emp.: 25
Rental of Broadcast Equipment
S.I.C.: 3663
N.A.I.C.S.: 334220
Mike Ransome *(CEO-Presteigne Charter)*

Subsidiary:

Presteigne Charter Limited (2)
Unit 2/3 Manor Gate Manor Royal
Crawley, RH10 9SX, United Kingdom
Tel.: (44) 1293 651 300
Fax: (44) 1293 651 301
E-Mail: info@presteignecharter.com
Web Site: www.presteignecharter.com
Emp.: 54
Broadcasting Equipment Rental Services
S.I.C.: 7359
N.A.I.C.S.: 532490
Mike Ransome *(Mng Dir)*

Non-U.S. Subsidiaries:

Presteigne Charter BV (2)
Franciscusweg 10-8
1216 SK Hilversum, Netherlands
Tel.: (31) 356260190
Fax: (31) 356260191
E-Mail: verhuur@presteignecharter.com
Audio Visual Equipment Rental Services
S.I.C.: 7359
N.A.I.C.S.: 532490

Presteigne Charter GmbH (2)
Koeln Innungstrasse 6
50354 Hurth, Germany
Tel.: (49) 2233808050
Fax: (49) 2233 80805 99
E-Mail: koeln@presteignecharter.com
Emp.: 12
Audio Visual Equipment Rental Services
S.I.C.: 7359
N.A.I.C.S.: 532490
Tom Gehring *(Gen Mgr)*

Presteigne Charter Pte Ltd (2)
No 15 Changi N St 1 Unit 01-01
Singapore, 498765, Singapore
Tel.: (65) 62722320
Fax: (65) 62721293
E-Mail: info@presteignecharter.com
Web Site: www.presteignecharter.com
Broadcasting Equipment Rental Services
S.I.C.: 7359
N.A.I.C.S.: 532490

U.S. Subsidiaries:

Creative Technology Group, Inc (1)
1455 Estes Ave Elk Grove Vlg
Chicago, IL 60007

Tel.: (847) 671-9670
Fax: (847) 671-7699
E-Mail: info@ctus.com
Web Site: www.ctus.com
Emp.: 50
Audio & Video Equipment Rental Services
S.I.C.: 7359
N.A.I.C.S.: 532490
Graham Andrews *(CEO-Los Angeles)*

Screenworks LLC (1)
1580 Magnolia Ave
Corona, CA 92879-2073 CA
Tel.: (805) 497-7160
Fax: (805) 497-8301
E-Mail:
Web Site: www.screenworksnep.com
Emp.: 1
Large Scale Video Screen Provider
S.I.C.: 7359
N.A.I.C.S.: 532210

Unit:

Screenworks LLC - Operations & Technical Support (2)
1580 Magnolia Ave
Corona, CA 92879-1350
Tel.: (951) 279-8877
Fax: (951) 279-1460
Web Site: www.screenworksnep.com
Emp.: 40
Large Scale Video Screen Provider
S.I.C.: 7812
N.A.I.C.S.: 512110

Non-U.S. Subsidiaries:

Creative Technology (Asia Pacific) Co., Limited (1)
Unit 1007 10/F Cyberport 1
Hong Kong, China (Hong Kong)
Tel.: (852) 29899300
Fax: (852) 29899360
E-Mail: info@ctasiapacific.com
Audio Visual Equipment Rental Services
S.I.C.: 7359
N.A.I.C.S.: 532490
Charlie Whittock *(Mng Dir)*

Creative Technology-Emirates LLC (1)
Unit 5 Building 11 Dubai Investment Park
PO Box 282572
Jebel Ali, Dubai, United Arab Emirates
Tel.: (971) 4 885 6020
Fax: (971) 4 885 6131
E-Mail: info@ctdubai.com
Web Site: www.ctdubai.com
Audio Visual Equipment Distr
S.I.C.: 5046
N.A.I.C.S.: 423440
Damien McGurn *(Gen Mgr)*

CT Creative Technology GmbH & Co KG (1)
In der Au 11
72622 Nurtingen, Germany
Tel.: (49) 70222530
Fax: (49) 7022253100
E-Mail: info@ctgermany.com
Web Site: www.ctgermany.com
Emp.: 50
Event Staging Services
S.I.C.: 7999
N.A.I.C.S.: 711320
Georg Roessler *(Gen Mgr)*

International Action S.A.M. (1)
7 rue du Gabian
Monaco, 98000, Monaco
Tel.: (377) 97 77 78 79
Fax: (377) 97 77 78 78
E-Mail: info@action.mc
Web Site: www.action.mc
Emp.: 2
Video Equipment & Display Screens Suppliers
S.I.C.: 5084
N.A.I.C.S.: 423830
Philip Paeleman *(Mng Dir)*

JVR Audiovisual B.V. (1)
Rucphensebaan 52
4706 PJ Roosendaal, Netherlands NL
Tel.: (31) 165581000 (100%)
Fax: (31) 165581347
E-Mail: christ.elsten@jvr.nl
Web Site: www.jvr.nl
Emp.: 65
Specialist Services Provider to the Corporate, Presentation, Entertainment & Broadcast Markets
S.I.C.: 8741
N.A.I.C.S.: 561110
Christ Elsten *(Mng Dir)*

Branch:

JVR Audiovisual B.V. - Lijnden (2)
Madridstraat 21-31
1175 RK Lijnden, Netherlands
Tel.: (31) 203581150
Fax: (31) 20 358 11 51
E-Mail: info@jvr.nl
Web Site: www.jvr.nl
Audio Visual Equipment Suppliers
S.I.C.: 5064
N.A.I.C.S.: 423620
Christ Elsten *(Mng Dir)*

AVESCO MARKETING CORPORATION

810 AVESCO Building Aurora Blvd
Cor Yale St
PO Box 3531
Cubao, Quezon City, 1109, Philippines
Tel.: (63) 29128881
Fax: (63) 29122999
E-Mail: cubao@avesco.com.ph
Web Site: www.avesco.com.ph
Year Founded: 1948
Sales Range: $10-24.9 Million
Emp.: 500
Business Description:
Measuring & Controlling Devices Distr
S.I.C.: 3823
N.A.I.C.S.: 334513

AVESTHAGEN LIMITED

Discoverer 9th Fl International Technology Park
Whitefield Rd, Bengaluru, 560066, India
Tel.: (91) 8028411665
Fax: (91) 8028418780
E-Mail: info@avesthagen.com
Web Site: www.avesthagen.com
Year Founded: 1998
Emp.: 650
Business Description:
Biopharmaceuticals & Nutritional Products Mfr
S.I.C.: 2834
N.A.I.C.S.: 325412
Personnel:
Villoo Morawala-Patell *(Founder, Chm & Mng Dir)*
Parag Shah *(CEO-BioNutrition Ops)*
Pierre Socha *(CEO-BioNutrition Div)*
Manan Bhatt *(Sr VP-External Rels)*
Board of Directors:
Villoo Morawala-Patell
David Robert Atkinson
Farah Morawala-Patell
Sanaya Morawala-Patell
Falguni K. Sen
Marc Van Montagu
Jacques Vincent

AVEVA GROUP PLC

High Cross Madingley Road
Cambridge, CB3 0HB, United Kingdom
Tel.: (44) 1223556655
Fax: (44) 1223556666
E-Mail: support@aveva.com
Web Site: www.aveva.com
AVV—(LSE OTC)
Rev.: $347,807,037
Assets: $560,049,399
Liabilities: $162,690,559
Net Worth: $397,358,840
Earnings: $71,878,226
Emp.: 1,317
Fiscal Year-end: 03/31/13
Business Description:
Engineering Software for Plant, Power & Marine Industries
S.I.C.: 8711
N.A.I.C.S.: 541330
Personnel:
Richard Longdon *(CEO)*
James Kidd *(CFO)*
Derek Middlemas *(COO & Head-Enterprise Solutions)*
Dave Wheeldon *(CTO & Head-Engrg & Design Sys)*
Helen Barrett-Hague *(Sec)*
Paul Eveleigh *(Exec VP & Head-Asia Pacific)*
Helmut Schuller *(Exec VP-Sls-Europe, Middle East & Africa)*
Mat Truche-Gordon *(Exec VP-Bus Strategy & Mktg)*
Hans Van Der Drift *(Exec VP-Sls)*
Hilary Wright *(Exec VP-HR & Bus Svcs)*
Board of Directors:
Philip S. Aiken
Jennifer Allerton
Jonathan Brooks
Philip Dayer
James Kidd
Richard Longdon
Legal Counsel:
Mills & Reeve LLP
Francis House 112 Hills Road
Cambridge, CB2 1PH, United Kingdom
Ashurst LLP
Broadwalk House 5 Appold Street
London, EC2A 2HA, United Kingdom

Subsidiaries:

AVEVA Solutions Limited (1)
High Cross Madingley Road
Cambridge, CB3 0HB, United Kingdom
Tel.: (44) 1223556655
Fax: (44) 1223556666
Web Site: www.aveva.com
Emp.: 300
Software Development Services
S.I.C.: 7371
N.A.I.C.S.: 541511
Richard Longdon *(CEO)*

U.S. Subsidiary:

Global Majic Software, Inc. (2)
6767 Old Madison Pike NW
Huntsville, AL 35806-2172 AL
Tel.: (256) 922-0222
Web Site: www.globalmajic.com
Emp.: 14
Software Developer
S.I.C.: 7372
N.A.I.C.S.: 511210

Cadcentre Property Limited (1)
CAD Centre
Cambridge, Cambridgeshire, CB3 0HB, United Kingdom
Tel.: (44) 1223 556655
Fax: (44) 1223 556666
Computer Software Development Services
S.I.C.: 7371
N.A.I.C.S.: 541511

Non-U.S. Subsidiaries:

AVEVA AB (1)
Drottninggatan 18
SE 202 15 Malmo, Sweden (100%)
Mailing Address:
PO Box 50555
SE-202 15 Malmo, Sweden
Tel.: (46) 406680300
Fax: (46) 406680301
E-Mail: sales.no@aveva.com
Web Site: www.tribon.com
Emp.: 50
Internet-Based Service Linking Shipyards
S.I.C.: 7373
N.A.I.C.S.: 541512
Ulf Kall *(VP-Fin & Admin)*

Non-U.S. Subsidiaries:

AVEVA Asia Pacific - Shanghai (2)
Unit 1503 1506 YouYou International Plaza
No 76 Pu Jian Road, Shanghai, 200127, China
Tel.: (86) 2161659118
Fax: (86) 2161659119
E-Mail: sales.china.marine@aveva.com
Web Site: www.aveva.com
Emp.: 15
Computer Technology Solutions for Ships & Submarines
S.I.C.: 7373
N.A.I.C.S.: 541512

AVEVA GmbH (2)
Rugersbart 48
22529 Hamburg, Germany (100%)
Tel.: (49) 40611560
Fax: (49) 4061156160
E-Mail: sales.germany@aveva.com
Web Site: www.aveva.com
Emp.: 4
Internet-Based Service Linking Shipyards
S.I.C.: 7373
N.A.I.C.S.: 541512
Andrew Gorton *(Reg Mgr)*

AVEVA Pte Limited (2)
Mewah Building 02-00 5 International Business Park
Singapore, 609914, Singapore
Tel.: (65) 65694933
Fax: (65) 656 48 700
E-Mail: sales.singapore@aveva.com
Web Site: www.aveva.com
Computer Software Development Services
S.I.C.: 7371
N.A.I.C.S.: 541511

Aveva (2)
Informatics Bldg Level 2
5 International Business Park, Singapore, 609914, Singapore (100%)
Tel.: (65) 65694933
Fax: (65) 65648700
E-Mail: info.singapore@aveva.com
Web Site: www.tribon.com
Emp.: 5
Computer Systems for Submarines & Ships
S.I.C.: 7373
N.A.I.C.S.: 541512
Pam Hanno *(VP)*

Nippon Tribon K.K. (2)
6 F Shin Osaka Hashimoto Building
1 2 6 Miyahara Yodogawa Ku, Osaka, 532 0003, Japan (100%)
Tel.: (81) 663997091
Fax: (81) 663997092
E-Mail: info.japan@aveva.com
Web Site: www.tribon.com
Emp.: 20
Internet-Based Service Linking Shipyards
S.I.C.: 7373
N.A.I.C.S.: 541512

Tribon Solutions (UK) Ltd. (2)
3rd Fl Ctr For Advanced Industry
Coble Dene Royal Quays, North Shields, Tyne And Wear, NE29 6DE, United Kingdom
Tel.: (44) 1912010000
Fax: (44) 1912010001
E-Mail: info.uk@tribon.com
Web Site: www.tribon.com
Emp.: 12
Computer Systems for Submarines & Ships
S.I.C.: 7373
N.A.I.C.S.: 541512

AVEVA AS (1)
Vingveien 2
4050 Sola, Norway
Tel.: (47) 51 64 71 00
Fax: (47) 51 64 71 40
E-Mail: info.no@aveva.com
Computer Software Development Services
S.I.C.: 7371
N.A.I.C.S.: 541511

AVEVA Asia Pacific Sendirian Berhad (1)
Level 59 Tower 2 Petronas Twin Towers KLCC
50088 Kuala Lumpur, Malaysia
Tel.: (60) 3 2176 1234
Fax: (60) 3 2176 1334

AVEVA Group plc—(Continued)

Engineering Software Development Services
S.I.C.: 7371
N.A.I.C.S.: 541511

AVEVA Denmark A/S (1)
Sofiendalsvej 5A
9200 Aalborg, Denmark
Tel.: (45) 9930 1100
Fax: (45) 9930 1101
E-Mail: aveva.denmark@aveva.com
Web Site: www.aveva.com
Emp.: 39
Computer Software Development Services
S.I.C.: 7371
N.A.I.C.S.: 541511
Lars Riisberg *(Gen Mgr)*

AVEVA do Brasil Informatica Ltda (1)
Torre Rio Sul Rua Lauro Muller 116 sala 902
Botafogo, Rio de Janeiro, 22290-160, Brazil
Tel.: (55) 21 3094 9850
E-Mail: suporte.brasil@aveva.com
Web Site: www.aveva.com
Computer Software Development Services
S.I.C.: 7371
N.A.I.C.S.: 541511

AVEVA East Asia Limited (1)
8 f Henley Bldg 5 Queen's Rd
Central, China (Hong Kong)
Tel.: (852) 28544544
Fax: (852) 25435555
Business Software Development Services
S.I.C.: 7371
N.A.I.C.S.: 541511

AVEVA Information Technology India Private Limited (1)
Level 5 Centrepoint 34 SV Road Santacruz West
Mumbai, 400054, India
Tel.: (91) 22 6710 3212
Fax: (91) 22 6710 3257
E-Mail: sales.india@aveva.com
Web Site: www.aveva.com
Emp.: 7
Computer Software Development Services
S.I.C.: 7371
N.A.I.C.S.: 541511
Hanno Tam *(VP)*

AVEVA KK (1)
YBP West Tower 11 F 134 Godo-Cho
Hodogaya-ku, Yokohama, 240-0005, Japan
Tel.: (81) 45 335 7401
E-Mail: sales.japan@aveva.com
Marine Software Development Services
S.I.C.: 7371
N.A.I.C.S.: 541511

AVEVA Pty Limited (1)
Ste 5 Level 28 AMP Pl 140 Saint Georges Terrace
Perth, WA, 6000, Australia
Tel.: (61) 892782428
Fax: (61) 892782727
E-Mail: sales.australasia@aveva.com
Web Site: www.aveva.com
Emp.: 8
Computer Software Development Services
S.I.C.: 7371
N.A.I.C.S.: 541511
David Hill *(VP & Country Mgr-Australasia Reg)*

AVEVA SA (1)
5 Sq Felix Nadar Bat C
94300 Vincennes, France
Tel.: (33) 158641440
Fax: (33) 158641459
E-Mail: sales.se@aveva.com
Web Site: www.aveva.com
Emp.: 30
Computer Software Development Services
S.I.C.: 7371
N.A.I.C.S.: 541511
Fredy Ktourza *(Mgr)*

AVEVA Software and Services S.A. de C.V. (1)
Montecito No 38 Piso 37 Oficina 35 Col
Napoles Del Benito Juarez
03810 Mexico, Mexico
Tel.: (52) 55 9000 4415
Fax: (52) 55 9000 4416
Web Site: www.aveva.com
Emp.: 100
Computer Software Development Services
S.I.C.: 7371
N.A.I.C.S.: 541511
Santiago Pena *(Pres)*

AVEX GROUP HOLDINGS INC.

3-1-30 Minami Aoyama Minato-ku
Tokyo, 107-8577, Japan
Tel.: (81) 354138550
Fax: (81) 354138837
Web Site: www.avex.co.jp
Year Founded: 1988
7860—(TKS)
Sls.: $1,526,404,000
Assets: $1,196,316,000
Liabilities: $658,658,000
Net Worth: $537,658,000
Earnings: $80,542,000
Emp.: 1,397
Fiscal Year-end: 03/31/13

Business Description:
Holding Company; Music & Visual Media Publishing, Production & Distribution Services; Music Artist Management Services
S.I.C.: 6719
N.A.I.C.S.: 551112

Personnel:
Masato Matsuura *(CEO)*
Shigekazu Takeuchi *(CFO)*
Ryuhei Chiba *(Chief Scientific Officer)*
Shinji Hayashi *(Chief Bus Officer)*
Masahiro Anan *(Exec Officer)*
Takahiro Miura *(Exec Officer)*
Toshiki Shida *(Exec Officer)*

Board of Directors:
Ryuhei Chiba
Shinji Hayashi
Toru Kenjo
Masato Matsuura
Yuichi Sato
Shigekazu Takeuchi
Tomohiro Toyama

Transfer Agent:
Mitsubishi UFJ Trust & Banking Corporation
7-10-11 Higashisuna Koto-ku
Tokyo, Japan

Subsidiaries:

Avex Entertainment Inc. (1)
3-1-30 Minami-Aoyama
Minato-Ku, Tokyo, 107-8577, Japan
Tel.: (81) 354138550
Fax: (81) 354138837
Web Site: www.avexnet.jp
Emp.: 1,500
Music & Visual Media Publishing, Production & Distribution Services
S.I.C.: 2741
N.A.I.C.S.: 512230
Masato Matsuura *(Pres)*

Subsidiary:

Binyl Records Inc. (2)
3-1-30 Minamiaoyama
Minato-ku, Tokyo, Japan
Tel.: (81) 354138550
Fax: (81) 354138826
E-Mail: international@av.avex.co.jp
Web Site: bri.binylrecords.com
Emp.: 9
Music Publisher
S.I.C.: 2741
N.A.I.C.S.: 512230
Hiroki Hasegawa *(Pres)*

Avex Management Inc. (1)
3-1-30 Minami-Aoyama
Minato-ku, Tokyo, 107-0062, Japan JP
Tel.: (81) 354138557
Fax: (81) 337465801
Emp.: 400
Music Artist Management Services
S.I.C.: 7389
N.A.I.C.S.: 711410
Masato Matsuura *(CEO)*

Avex Marketing Inc. (1)
NBF Minamiaoyama Bldg 4 5F 3-1-31 Minamiaoyama
Minata-ku, Minami, Tokushima, Japan JP
Tel.: (81) 354138670
Fax: (81) 57729191
Web Site: www.avexnet.jp
Emp.: 1,000
Music & Entertainment Marketing Services
S.I.C.: 7999
N.A.I.C.S.: 711320
Masato Matsuura *(CEO)*

Subsidiary:

Para. TV Inc. (2)
Oriental Bldg 1-2-22 Mita 4F
Minato-ku, Tokyo, 108-0073, Japan JP
Tel.: (81) 354844736
Fax: (81) 354844736
E-Mail: support@paratv.co.jp
Web Site: www.paratv.co.jp
Internet & Mobile Broadcasting Services
S.I.C.: 2741
N.A.I.C.S.: 519130
Tooru Akizuki *(Pres)*

Non-U.S. Subsidiary:

Avex Hong Kong Ltd. (1)
Ste 03 11 F Exchange Tower 33 Wang Chiu Rd
Kowloon Bay, Kowloon, China (Hong Kong)
Tel.: (852) 25042181
Fax: (852) 25042007
E-Mail: info@avexasia.com
Web Site: www.avexasia.com
Emp.: 320
Music & Entertainment Services
S.I.C.: 7929
N.A.I.C.S.: 711130
Puddy Marini *(Mng Dir)*

AVEXA LIMITED

Suite 8 Level 1 61-63 Camberwell Road
Hawthorn East, VIC, 3123, Australia
Tel.: (61) 388881040
Fax: (61) 388881049
E-Mail: reception@avexa.com.au
Web Site: www.avexa.com.au
AVX—(ASX)
Rev.: $1,114,005
Assets: $14,602,947
Liabilities: $493,955
Net Worth: $14,108,992
Earnings: ($3,102,332)
Emp.: 6
Fiscal Year-end: 06/30/13

Business Description:
Pharmaceutical Research & Development Services
S.I.C.: 2834
N.A.I.C.S.: 325412

Personnel:
Jonathan Coates *(Interim CEO & Chief Scientific Officer)*
Lee Mitchell *(Sec)*

Board of Directors:
Iain M. C. Kirkwood
Bruce Hewett
Allan Tan

AVG TECHNOLOGIES N.V.

Gatwickstraat 9-39
1043 GL Amsterdam, Netherlands
Tel.: (31) 205226210
Fax: (31) 205226211
Web Site: www.avg.com
Year Founded: 1991
AVG—(NYSE)
Rev.: $355,966,000
Assets: $323,466,000
Liabilities: $346,036,000
Net Worth: ($22,570,000)
Earnings: $45,817,000
Emp.: 915
Fiscal Year-end: 12/31/12

Business Description:
Security Software Developer
S.I.C.: 7372
N.A.I.C.S.: 511210

Personnel:
Dale L. Fuller *(Chm-Supervisory Bd)*
Gary Kovacs *(Mng Dir & CEO)*
John Little *(CFO & Mng Dir)*
Harvey Anderson *(Chief Legal Officer)*
Yuval Ben-Itzhak *(CTO)*
Todd G. Simpson *(Chief Strategy Officer)*
Siobhan M. MacDermott *(Chief Policy Officer)*
Rob Blasman *(Member-Mgmt Bd, Sr VP-Fin & Controller)*
Christophe Francois *(Gen Counsel & Sec)*
Judith Bitterli *(Sr VP-Mktg)*
Mike Foreman *(Sr VP-Sls)*
Donald A. MacLennan *(Sr VP-Product Mgmt)*
Martin Wheatcroft *(Sr VP-Fin & Grp Controller-Fin)*

Supervisory Board of Directors:
Dale L. Fuller
Rafal W. Bator
Gabriel Eichler
Jan G. Haars
Jonathan Meeks
Dariusz R. Pronczuk
J.R. Smith
Colin John Tenwick

U.S. Subsidiary:

Sana Security, Inc. (1)
2121 S El Camino Real Ste 700
San Mateo, CA 94403
Tel.: (650) 292-7100
Fax: (650) 292-7110
Toll Free: (866) 900-7262
Emp.: 49
Security Software Developer
S.I.C.: 7372
N.A.I.C.S.: 511210
Dale Fuller *(Chm)*
Bob Gagnon *(Mng Dir)*
John Little *(CFO)*

Non-U.S. Subsidiaries:

AVG Technologies CZ s.r.o. (1)
Holandska 4
639 00 Brno, Czech Republic
Tel.: (420) 549524011
Fax: (420) 541211432
Web Site: www.avg.com
Security Software Developer
S.I.C.: 7372
N.A.I.C.S.: 511210

AVG Mobilation (1)
Levinstin Tower
23 Menachem Begin St, Tel Aviv, 66182, Israel
Tel.: (972) 73 249 5000
Fax: (972) 73 249 5200
E-Mail: info-mobilation@avg.com
Web Site: www.avgmobilation.com
Mobile Device Security Software Developer
S.I.C.: 7372
N.A.I.C.S.: 511210
Eran Pfeffer *(Co-Founder & CEO)*
Dror Shalev *(Co-Founder & CTO)*
Omri Sigelman *(Co-Founder & VP-Mktg & Product)*

AVI LIMITED

2 Harries Road
Illovo, Johannesburg, South Africa
Tel.: (27) 115021300
Fax: (27) 115021301
E-Mail: info@avi.co.za
Web Site: www.avi.co.za
AVI—(JSE)
Rev.: $1,029,684,110
Assets: $733,734,960
Liabilities: $322,947,040
Net Worth: $410,787,920
Earnings: $121,283,860
Emp.: 7,668
Fiscal Year-end: 06/30/13

Business Description:
Food, Beverage & Apparels Mfr
S.I.C.: 2023
N.A.I.C.S.: 311514
Personnel:
Simon L. Crutchley *(CEO)*
Owen P. Cressey *(CFO)*
Gordon Christie *(Exec-IT Shared Svcs)*
Catherine Makin *(Exec-Grp Mktg Shared Svcs)*
Tania Naude *(Exec-HR Shared Svcs)*
John Jankovich-Besan *(CEO-I&J)*
Sureya Naidoo *(Sec)*
Board of Directors:
Gavin R. Tipper
Michael J. Bosman
Owen P. Cressey
Simon L. Crutchley
Neo Phakama Dongwana
James R. Hersov
Andisiwe Kawa
Michael Koursaris
Adriaan Nuhn
Barry J. K. Smith
Abe M. Thebyane
Transfer Agent:
Computershare Investor Services Proprietary Limited
70 Marshall Street
Johannesburg, South Africa
Subsidiaries:

A&D Spitz (Pty) Limited (1)
30 Sloane St
Bryanston, Gauteng, 2191, South Africa
Tel.: (27) 117077300
Fax: (27) 117077763
E-Mail: talk2us@spitz.co.za
Web Site: www.spitz.co.za
Emp.: 60
Apparel & Accessories Distr
S.I.C.: 5699
N.A.I.C.S.: 448150
Robert Lunt *(Mng Dir)*

AVI Financial Services (Pty) Limited (1)
2 Harries Road
PO Box 1897
Illovo, Johannesburg, Gauteng, 2196, South Africa
Tel.: (27) 115021300
Fax: (27) 115021301
Web Site: www.avi.co.za
Emp.: 30
Financial Investment Advisory Services
S.I.C.: 6282
N.A.I.C.S.: 523930
Simon Crutchley *(CEO)*

Hampton Sportswear (Pty) Limited (1)
2 Harries Rd
Illovo, Johannesburg, Gauteng, 2196, South Africa
Tel.: (27) 115021340
Fax: (27) 115021302
Emp.: 6
Sportswear Whslr
S.I.C.: 5136
N.A.I.C.S.: 424320
Tami Vinokur *(Mng Dir)*

Indigo Brands (1)
16-20 Evans Ave
Epping, Cape Town, 7460, South Africa
Mailing Address:
PO Box 3460
Cape Town, 8000, South Africa
Tel.: (27) 21 5078500
Fax: (27) 21 5078501
E-Mail: taniaL@indigobrands.com
Web Site: www.indigobrands.com
Emp.: 450
Yardley Cosmetics Mfr & Distr
S.I.C.: 2844
N.A.I.C.S.: 325620
Humsha Ramgobin *(Dir-HR)*

Irvin & Johnson Holding Company (Pty) Limited (1)
I&J House 1 Davidson St
Woodstock, Cape Town, Western Cape, 7925, South Africa
Tel.: (27) 214407800
Fax: (27) 214029282
Web Site: www.ij.co.za
Emp.: 2,000
Convenience Food Mfr & Distr
S.I.C.: 2038
N.A.I.C.S.: 311412
Ronald Fasol *(Mng Dir)*
Chris Schoeman *(Sec)*

National Brands Limited (1)
30 Sloane St
Bryanston, Gauteng, 2021, South Africa
Tel.: (27) 117077000
Fax: (27) 117077804
E-Mail: info@avi.com
Web Site: www.avi.com
Emp.: 200
Chips & Snacks Mfr & Distr
S.I.C.: 2052
N.A.I.C.S.: 311919
Simon L. Crutchley *(CEO)*

AVI-TECH ELECTRONICS LIMITED

19A Serangoon North Avenue 5
Singapore, 554859, Singapore
Tel.: (65) 64826168
Fax: (65) 64826123
E-Mail: enquiry@avi-tech.com.sg
Web Site: www.avi-tech.com.sg
CT1—(SES)
Rev.: $25,799,644
Assets: $46,949,295
Liabilities: $7,556,743
Net Worth: $39,392,551
Earnings: ($3,063,829)
Emp.: 260
Fiscal Year-end: 06/30/13
Business Description:
Semiconductor Circuits Mfr
S.I.C.: 3674
N.A.I.C.S.: 334413
Personnel:
Eng Hong Lim *(Founder & CEO)*
Joseph Nin Choon Wang *(CFO)*
Alvin Tai Meng Lim *(COO)*
Board of Directors:
Thiam Beng Khor
Chung Meng Goh
Michael L. Grenville Gray
Eng Hong Lim

AVIA HEALTH INFORMATICS PLC

(Name Changed to Cientifica Plc)

AVIA SOLUTIONS GROUP AB

Smolensko St 10
LT-03201 Vilnius, Lithuania
Tel.: (370) 5 2525500
Fax: (370) 5 2525501
E-Mail: info@aviasg.com
Web Site: www.aviasg.com
ASG—(WAR)
Rev.: $205,920,281
Assets: $115,013,083
Liabilities: $71,360,796
Net Worth: $43,652,287
Earnings: $7,330,525
Emp.: 1,095
Fiscal Year-end: 12/31/12
Business Description:
Integrated Fleet Management, Crew Training, Charter Flight Management, Aircraft Rental, Aircraft Maintenance & Other Related Services
S.I.C.: 4581
N.A.I.C.S.: 488190
Personnel:
Gediminas Ziemelis *(Chm-Mgmt Bd)*
Daumantas Lapinskas *(Deputy CEO & Memebr-Mgmt Bd)*
Aurimas Sanikovas *(CFO & Member-Mgmt Bd)*
Saulius Batavicius *(CEO-Baltic Ground Services-Memeber-Mgmt Bd)*
Jonas Butautis *(CEO-FL Technics & Member-Mgmt Bd)*
Supervisory Board of Directors:
Vladas Bagavicius
Dziuginta Balciune
Hubert Bojdo
Dariusz Marek Formela
Irtaute Scerbaviciene

AVIAAM LEASING AB

Smolensko St 10
LT-03201 Vilnius, Lithuania
Tel.: (370) 5 252 55 25
Fax: (370) 5 252 55 24
E-Mail: info@aviaam.com
Web Site: www.aviaam.com
AAL—(WAR)
Sales Range: $1-9.9 Million
Business Description:
Aircraft Leasing & Management
S.I.C.: 7359
N.A.I.C.S.: 532411
Personnel:
Gediminas Ziemelis *(Chm)*
Tadas Goberis *(CEO)*
Gediminas Siaudvytis *(Deputy CEO)*
Justinas Gilys *(COO)*
Board of Directors:
Gediminas Ziemelis
Linas Dovydenas
Justinas Gilys
Aurimas Sanikovas
Gediminas Siaudvytis

AVIAOK INTERNATIONAL LLC

Shmidta Str 19
347922 Taganrog, Russia
Tel.: (7) 8634311770
Fax: (7) 8634393717
E-Mail: a.camychov@aviaok.com
Web Site: www.aviaok.com
Year Founded: 1998
Emp.: 200
Business Description:
Aviation Equipment Mfr
S.I.C.: 3812
N.A.I.C.S.: 334511
Personnel:
Oleg Spiridonov *(Dir Gen)*

AVIAREPS MARKETING GARDEN LTD.

International Place 26-3 Sanei-cho
Shinjuku-ku, Tokyo, 160-0008, Japan
Tel.: (81) 3 3225 0008
Fax: (81) 3 5363 1118
E-Mail: japan@aviareps.com
Web Site: www.aviareps.com
Emp.: 40
Business Description:
Public Relations & Advertising Services
S.I.C.: 8743
N.A.I.C.S.: 541820
Personnel:
Yoichi Hayase *(Gen Mgr)*

Branches

Marketing Garden Ltd. (1)
Novel Plz Ste 1605 128 Nanjing Rd W
Shanghai, 200003, China
Tel.: (86) 21 6359 1535
Fax: (86) 21 6359 1571
E-Mail: china@aviareps.com
Web Site: www.aviareps.com
Public Relations & Advertising Services
S.I.C.: 8743
N.A.I.C.S.: 541820
Tina Yao *(Gen Mgr)*

AVIAREPS Marketing Garden (1)
Dongwha Building 14F 58-7 Seosomun-Dong
Joong-Gu, Seoul, 100-814, Korea (South)
Tel.: (82) 2 777 8178
Fax: (82) 2 777 8179
E-Mail: korea@aviareps.com
Web Site: www.aviareps.com
Public Relations & Advertising Services
S.I.C.: 8743
N.A.I.C.S.: 541820
Emily Kim *(Country Mgr-Korea)*

AVIAREPS Marketing Garden Ltd. (1)
8F No 271 Sinyi Road
Section 2, Taipei, 100, Taiwan
Tel.: (886) 2 2377 5630
Fax: (886) 2 2377 4375
E-Mail: taiwan@aviareps.com
Web Site: www.aviareps.com
Public Relations & Advertising Services
S.I.C.: 8743
N.A.I.C.S.: 541820
Jemy See *(Gen Mgr-Taiwan)*

AVIATION INDUSTRY CORPORATION OF CHINA

(d/b/a AVIC)
AVIC Plaza No 128 Jianguo Road
Chaoyang District, Beijing, 100022, China
Tel.: (86) 1058356984
Fax: (86) 1058356518
Web Site: www.avic.com.cn
Sales Range: $250-299.9 Billion
Emp.: 390,254
Business Description:
Aircraft, Helicopter, Attack Aircraft & General Aviation Aircraft Mfr
S.I.C.: 3721
N.A.I.C.S.: 336411
Personnel:
Zuoming Lin *(Pres & CEO)*
U.S. Subsidiaries:

Cirrus Design Corporation (1)
4515 Taylor Cir
Duluth, MN 55811
Tel.: (218) 727-2737
Fax: (218) 727-2148
Toll Free: (800) 279-4322
E-Mail: info@cirrusaircraft.com
Web Site: www.cirrusaircraft.com
Emp.: 500
Aircraft Mfr
S.I.C.: 3721
N.A.I.C.S.: 336411
Dale Klapmeier *(Co-Founder & CEO)*
Patrick Waddick *(COO & Exec VP)*
Todd Simmons *(Exec VP-Sls & Mktg)*

Continental Motors, Inc. (1)
2039 S Broad St
Mobile, AL 36615
Mailing Address:
PO Box 90
Mobile, AL 36601-0090
Tel.: (251) 438-3411
Fax: (251) 432-7352
Toll Free: (800) 718-3411
Web Site: www.genuinecontinental.aero
Sales Range: $125-149.9 Million
Emp.: 375
Manned & Unmanned Aircraft, New & Rebuilt General Aviation Piston Engines Mfr
S.I.C.: 3724
N.A.I.C.S.: 336412
Rhett C. Ross *(Pres)*
Stephen Ginger *(Gen Counsel & Sr VP)*

AVIC INTERNATIONAL HOLDINGS LIMITED

33/F Hangkong Building Catic Zone
Shennan Road Central
Shenzhen, China 518031
Tel.: (86) 755 83688956
Fax: (86) 755 83688209
Web Site: www.avic161.com
Year Founded: 1997
161—(HKG)
Rev.: $4,964,471,062
Assets: $6,367,509,398
Liabilities: $4,530,934,465
Net Worth: $1,836,574,933
Earnings: $201,005,295

AVIC International Holdings Limited—(Continued)

Emp.: 25,516
Fiscal Year-end: 12/31/12
Business Description:
Investment Management Services
S.I.C.: 6799
N.A.I.C.S.: 523920
Personnel:
Guang Quan Wu *(Chm)*
Yong Feng Huang *(Sec)*
Board of Directors:
Guang Quan Wu
Hong Liang Chen
Jun Liu
Lin Wu Pan
Wai Ling Wong
Wei Wu
Lei You
Ping Zhang
Transfer Agent:
Hong Kong Registrars Limited
Rooms 1712-1716 17th Floor Hopewell Centre
183 Queen's Road East
Wanchai, China (Hong Kong)

AVICHINA INDUSTRY & TECHNOLOGY CO., LTD.

Unit B 15/F United Ctr Queensway 95
Hong Kong, China (Hong Kong)
Tel.: (852) 1064094837
Fax: (852) 1064094836
Web Site: www.avichina.com
2357—(HKG)
Rev.: $2,668,710,023
Assets: $5,702,097,391
Liabilities: $3,082,090,937
Net Worth: $2,620,006,454
Earnings: $183,788,179
Emp.: 36,824
Fiscal Year-end: 12/31/12
Business Description:
Aviation Products Development & Mfr
S.I.C.: 3721
N.A.I.C.S.: 336411
Personnel:
Zuoming Lin *(Chm)*
Ping Bai *(Chm-Supervisory Bd)*
Ruisong Tan *(Vice Chm & Pres)*
Jun Wang *(CFO & VP)*
Lingxi Yan *(Sec)*
Board of Directors:
Zuoming Lin
Jianshe Gao
Huizhong Gu
Chongqing Guo
Louis Chung Man Lau
Xianzong Li
Maurice Savart
Mingchuan Sheng
Ruisong Tan
Supervisory Board of Directors:
Ping Bai
Jing Li
Guanghai Yu

PricewaterhouseCoopers
22nd Floor Princes Building 10 Chater Road
Central, China (Hong Kong)
Legal Counsel:
Linklaters
10th Floor Alexandra House Chater Road
Hong Kong, China (Hong Kong)

Beijing Jiayuan Law Firm
F407 Ocean Plaza 158 Fuxingmennei Street
Xicheng Distric
Beijing, China

AVICOLA BRASOV SA

Str Cucului Nr 5
500484 Brasov, Romania
Tel.: (40) 268257741
Fax: (40) 268257989
E-Mail: office@avicolabrasov.ro
Web Site: www.avicolabrasov.ro
AVLE—(BUC)
Sales Range: $25-49.9 Million
Emp.: 490
Business Description:
Poultry Raising & Processing
S.I.C.: 0254
N.A.I.C.S.: 112340
Personnel:
Simion Ovidiu Oprita *(Pres)*

AVICOR CONSTRUCTION

5325 Jean Talcon East St Suite 256
Saint Leonard, QC, H1S 1L4, Canada
Tel.: (514) 744-1700
Fax: (514) 744-1474
Web Site: www.avicor.ca
Rev.: $20,372,500
Emp.: 13
Business Description:
General Building Contracting Services
S.I.C.: 1542
N.A.I.C.S.: 236220
Personnel:
Rode Callegari *(Pres)*
Aldo Vicenzo *(CEO)*

AVID LIFE MEDIA INC.

20 Eglinton Ave Ste 1200
Toronto, ON, M4R 1K8, Canada
Tel.: (416) 480-2334
Fax: (416) 545-1510
E-Mail: inquiries@avidlifemedia.com
Web Site: www.avidlifemedia.com
Sales Range: $25-49.9 Million
Emp.: 90
Business Description:
Dating, Social & Other Websites Owner & Operator
S.I.C.: 2741
N.A.I.C.S.: 519130
Personnel:
Noel Biderman *(Pres & CEO)*

AVIGILON CORPORATION

4th Floor 858 Beatty St
Vancouver, BC, V6B 1C1, Canada
Tel.: (604) 629-5182
E-Mail: sales@avigilon.com
Web Site: www.avigilon.com
Year Founded: 2004
AVO—(TSX)
Sls.: $99,662,433
Assets: $86,450,913
Liabilities: $15,982,848
Net Worth: $70,468,066
Earnings: $7,126,129
Emp.: 255
Fiscal Year-end: 12/31/12
Business Description:
HD Surveillance Systems
S.I.C.: 3651
N.A.I.C.S.: 334310
Personnel:
Alexander Fernandes *(Founder, Chm, Pres & CEO)*
Bradley Bardua *(CFO)*
Bryan Schmode *(COO)*
Joel Schuster *(Sec & VP-Legal)*
Danny Kam *(Exec VP-Engrg)*
Terry Neely *(Sr VP-Emerging Tech)*
Pedro Simoes *(Sr VP-Global Sls)*
Board of Directors:
Alexander Fernandes
Larry Berg
Harry A. Jaako
Wan H. Jung
Bruce Marginson
Murray Tevlin
Transfer Agent:
Computershare Investor Services Inc.
510 Burrard St 2nd Floor
Vancouver, BC, V6C 3B9, Canada
Tel.: (604) 661-9400

AVINCO LTD.

Adelaide House 7 Haddington Ter
Dun Laoghaire
Dublin, Ireland
Tel.: (353) 1 6637440
Fax: (353) 1 2020491
E-Mail: info@awnainc.com
Web Site: www.avinco.net
Year Founded: 2003
Sales Range: $10-24.9 Million
Business Description:
Aircraft Operating Services
S.I.C.: 4581
N.A.I.C.S.: 488119
Personnel:
Francois Gautier *(Founder & CEO)*
Patrick J. Dewez *(Chm)*

AVINGTRANS PLC

Precision House Derby Road
Sandiacre, Nottingham, NG10 5HU, United Kingdom
Tel.: (44) 115 949 9020
Fax: (44) 115 949 9024
E-Mail: info@avingtrans.plc.uk
Web Site: www.avingtrans.plc.uk
AVG—(LSE)
Rev.: $71,510,251
Assets: $91,155,040
Liabilities: $42,963,005
Net Worth: $48,192,034
Earnings: $11,839,937
Emp.: 679
Fiscal Year-end: 05/31/13
Business Description:
Mfr of Components & Systems for Aerospace, Energy & Medical Industries
S.I.C.: 3499
N.A.I.C.S.: 332999
Personnel:
Steve McQuillan *(CEO)*
Stephen M. King *(CFO & Sec)*
Board of Directors:
Roger S. McDowell
Jeremy J. Hamer
Stephen M. King
Steve McQuillan
Graham K. Thornton
Legal Counsel:
Shakespeares Legal LLP
Somerset House Temple Street
Birmingham, B2 5DJ, United Kingdom
Subsidiaries:

C & H Precision Limited **(1)**
Derby Rd Indust Estate
Sandiacre, Nottingham, NG10 5HU, United Kingdom
Tel.: (44) 1159394707
Fax: (44) 1159490146
Web Site: www.chprecision.co.uk
Emp.: 100
Machinery Tools Mfr
S.I.C.: 3545
N.A.I.C.S.: 333515
Philip Akrill *(Gen Mgr)*

Crown UK Limited **(1)**
Unit 24 Old Mill Rd Portishead
Bristol, BS20 7BX, United Kingdom
Tel.: (44) 1275818008
Fax: (44) 1275818288
E-Mail: mark.satcey@crown-international.co.uk
Web Site: www.crown-international.co.uk
Emp.: 7
Fabrication Units Mfr
S.I.C.: 7389
N.A.I.C.S.: 541420
Mark Satcey *(Mng Dir)*

Maloney Metalcraft Ltd. **(1)**
(Formerly Exterran (UK) Ltd.)
Westgate
Aldridge, Walsall, West Midlands, WS9 8EX, United Kingdom UK
Tel.: (44) 1922 450200
Fax: (44) 1922450210
E-Mail: sales@maloney-metalcraft.com
Web Site: www.maloney-metalcraft.com
Sales Range: $10-24.9 Million
Emp.: 85
Mfr of Equipment for Oil & Natural Gas Production
S.I.C.: 5084
N.A.I.C.S.: 423830
Austen Adams *(Mng Dir)*

AVINO SILVER & GOLD MINES LTD.

570 Granville Street Suite 900
Vancouver, BC, V6C 3P1, Canada
Tel.: (604) 682-3701
Fax: (604) 682-3600
E-Mail: ir@avino.com
Web Site: www.avino.com
ASM—(DEU NYSEMKT TSXV)
Rev.: $2,241,889
Assets: $26,034,982
Liabilities: $4,218,850
Net Worth: $21,816,133
Earnings: ($1,255,624)
Emp.: 85
Fiscal Year-end: 12/31/12
Business Description:
Silver & Gold Mining Services
S.I.C.: 1044
N.A.I.C.S.: 212222
Personnel:
David Wolfin *(Pres & CEO)*
Lisa Sharp *(CFO)*
Jose Carlos Rodriguez Moreno *(COO)*
Dorothy Chin *(Sec)*
Board of Directors:
Michael Baybak
Gary R. Robertson
David Wolfin
Jasman Yee

AVINOR AS

Dronning Eufemias gate 6
0154 Oslo, Norway
Tel.: (47) 81530550
Fax: (47) 64812001
E-Mail: post@avinor.no
Web Site: www.avinor.no
Rev.: $1,656,438,579
Assets: $5,094,144,540
Liabilities: $3,219,685,407
Net Worth: $1,874,459,133
Earnings: $167,723,433
Emp.: 3,109
Fiscal Year-end: 12/31/12
Business Description:
Airport Operator
S.I.C.: 4581
N.A.I.C.S.: 488119
Personnel:
Ola Morkved Rinnan *(Chm)*
Kristin Vangdal *(Vice Chm)*
Petter Johannessen *(CFO)*
Board of Directors:
Ola Morkved Rinnan
Christian Berge
Anne Breiby
Dag H. Harstad
Helge Lobergsli
Grete Ovnerud
Eli Skrovset
Heide A. Sorum
Oddbjorg A. Starrfelt
Ola H. Strand
Kristin Vangdal
Subsidiary:

Oslo Lufthavn AS **(1)**
PO Box 100
2061 Gardermoen, Norway
Tel.: (47) 64812000
Fax: (47) 64812001
E-Mail: nic.nilsen@oslo.no
Web Site: www.oslo.no
Emp.: 500
Other Airport Operations
S.I.C.: 4581

N.A.I.C.S.: 488119
Nick Nilsen *(CEO)*

AVIOANE CRAIOVA S.A.
10 Aviatorilor Street
207280 Ghercesti, Dolj, Romania
Tel.: (40) 251 402 000
Fax: (40) 251 402 040
E-Mail: office@acv.ro
Web Site: www.acv.ro
Year Founded: 1972
AVIO—(BUC)
Business Description:
Military Aircraft & Related Machinery Mfr
S.I.C.: 3721
N.A.I.C.S.: 336411
Personnel:
Ioan Sava *(Gen Mgr)*

AVION CONSTRUCTION LTD.
6125 1 Street SE Suite 200
Calgary, AB, T2H 2L6, Canada
Tel.: (403) 287-0144
Fax: (403) 287-2193
Rev.: $14,536,800
Emp.: 15
Business Description:
General Building Contracting Services
S.I.C.: 1542
N.A.I.C.S.: 236220
Personnel:
Alar Poldaas *(Pres)*

AVION-MULTIPLEX CONSTRUCTION INC.
13500 Maycrest Way Ste 240
Richmond, BC, V6V 2N8, Canada
Tel.: (604) 207-9967
Fax: (604) 207-9973
E-Mail: romanp@avionmultiplex.com
Web Site: www.avionmultiplex.com
Sales Range: $10-24.9 Million
Emp.: 10
Business Description:
Construction Services
S.I.C.: 1521
N.A.I.C.S.: 236115
Personnel:
Roman Portnoy *(Pres & Gen Mgr)*

AVISEN PLC
51-53 Great Marlborough Street
London, W1F 7JT, United Kingdom
Tel.: (44) 8708 802978
Fax: (44) 8708 802979
E-Mail: info@avisen.com
Web Site: www.avisen.com
AVI—(AIM)
Sales Range: $1-9.9 Million
Emp.: 2
Business Description:
Investment Services
S.I.C.: 6211
N.A.I.C.S.: 523999
Personnel:
Mark Bernard Battles *(Interim Chm)*
Marcus Hanke *(CEO)*
Nic Snape *(Mng Dir)*
Claire Milverton *(CFO)*
Jonathan Hill *(COO)*
Board of Directors:
Mark Bernard Battles
Stephen Berry
Marcus Hanke
Claire Milverton
Michael Sanderson
Nic Snape
Marcus Yeoman
Legal Counsel:
Brown Rudnick LLP
8 Clifford Street
London, W1K 3SQ, United Kingdom

Subsidiaries:

1Spatial Holdings Limited **(1)**
Tennyson House
Cambridge Business Park, Cambridge, CB4 0WZ, United Kingdom UK
Tel.: (44) 1223420414
Fax: (44) 1223 420044
E-Mail: info@1spatial.com
Web Site: www.1spatial.com
Emp.: 86
Holding Company; Market Research Services
S.I.C.: 6719
N.A.I.C.S.: 551112
Duncan Guthrie *(Dir-Sls)*

Subsidiary:

IQ Research Limited **(2)**
1st Fl 44 46 New Inn Yard
London, EC2A 3EY, United Kingdom
Tel.: (44) 2080990560
Fax: (44) 2080990589
Business Management Consulting Services
S.I.C.: 8748
N.A.I.C.S.: 541618
Julian Green *(Mng Dir)*

Non-U.S. Subsidiary:

STAR-APIC SA **(2)**
Avenue du Prey Aily 24
Liege, Angleur, 4031, Belgium
Tel.: (32) 43675313
Fax: (32) 43671711
E-Mail: info@star-apic.com
Web Site: www.star-apic.com
Emp.: 60
Geographic Information Systems Software Products & Related Services
S.I.C.: 8713
N.A.I.C.S.: 541360
Issan Tannous *(Mng Dir)*

Non-U.S. Subsidiary:

STAR-APIC SAS **(3)**
191 Ave Aristide Briand
94230 Cachan, France
Tel.: (33) 0171330100
Fax: (33) 171330106
E-Mail: info@star-apic.com
Web Site: www.star-apic.com
Emp.: 35
Geographic Information Systems Software Products & Related Services
S.I.C.: 8713
N.A.I.C.S.: 541360
Issam Danous *(Mng Dir)*

Avisen UK Limited **(1)**
51-53 Great Marlborough Street
London, W1F 7JT, United Kingdom
Tel.: (44) 8708802978
Fax: (44) 8708 802 979
E-Mail: info@avisen.com
Web Site: www.avisen.com
Business Management Consulting Services
S.I.C.: 8742
N.A.I.C.S.: 541611
Bruce French *(Mgr-Solutions)*

Solution Minds (UK) Limited **(1)**
16 Devonshire Street
London, W1G 7AF, United Kingdom
Tel.: (44) 8708802978
Business Management Services
S.I.C.: 8741
N.A.I.C.S.: 561110

Storage Fusion Ltd. **(1)**
Wentworth Lodge Great N Rd
Welwyn Garden City, AL8 7SR, United Kingdom
Tel.: (44) 1707387100
Fax: (44) 1707387102
E-Mail: sales@storagefusion.com
Web Site: www.storagefusion.com
Emp.: 10
Software Development Services
S.I.C.: 7371
N.A.I.C.S.: 541511

Non-U.S. Subsidiary:

Avisen BV **(1)**
Strawinskylaan 3051
Amsterdam, North Holland, 1077ZX, Netherlands
Tel.: (31) 20 3012105
Business Administration Software Development Services
S.I.C.: 7371
N.A.I.C.S.: 541511

AVISION INC.
No 20 Creation Rd 1 Science-Based Industrial Park
300 Hsin-chu, Taiwan
Tel.: (886) 35782388
Fax: (886) 35777017
Web Site: www.avision.com.tw
2380—(TAI)
Sales Range: $25-49.9 Million
Business Description:
Computer Equipments Mfr & Distr
S.I.C.: 3577
N.A.I.C.S.: 334118
Personnel:
Thomas Sheng *(Chm & Gen Mgr)*

U.S. Subsidiary:

Avision Labs., Inc. **(1)**
6815 Mowry Ave
Newark, CA 94560
Tel.: (510) 739-2369
Fax: (510) 739-6060
E-Mail: service@avision-labs.com
Emp.: 25
Office Equipments Distr
S.I.C.: 5044
N.A.I.C.S.: 423420
Jun Huang *(Mgr-OEM)*

Non-U.S. Subsidiaries:

Avision Europe GmbH **(1)**
Bischofstr 101
47809 Krefeld, Nordrhein-Westfalen, Germany
Tel.: (49) 2151 56981 40
Fax: (49) 2151 56981 42
E-Mail: info@avision-europe.com
Web Site: www.avision.de
Emp.: 6
Scanners Sales & Support Services
S.I.C.: 5047
N.A.I.C.S.: 423450
Thomas Wulle *(Mgr)*

Avision (Suzhou) Co., Ltd. **(1)**
No 9 Suhong West Road Suzhou Industrial Park
Suzhou, Jiangsu, 215021, China
Tel.: (86) 51262565888
Fax: (86) 512 6256 0307
Office Equipment Distr
S.I.C.: 5044
N.A.I.C.S.: 423420

AVISON YOUNG (CANADA) INC.
18 York Street Suite 400
Toronto, ON, M5J 2T8, Canada
Tel.: (416) 955-0000
Fax: (416) 955-0725
Web Site: www.avisonyoung.com
Year Founded: 1978
Emp.: 800
Business Description:
Real Estate Brokerage Services
S.I.C.: 6531
N.A.I.C.S.: 531210
Personnel:
Mark E. Rose *(Chm & CEO)*
Jim Becker *(Principal & Mng Dir-Detroit)*
Drew Koivu *(Principal & Mng Dir-Apartment Fund-US)*
Scott Pickett *(Principal & Mng Dir-Coumbus)*
Tim Grant *(Sr VP)*

U.S. Subsidiaries:

Avison Young (USA) Inc. **(1)**
120 N LaSalle Ste 850
Chicago, IL 60602 IL
Tel.: (312) 957-7600
Web Site: www.avisonyoung.com
Real Estate Brokerage Services
S.I.C.: 6531
N.A.I.C.S.: 531210
Rick Kimball *(Mng Dir & Principal-Boston)*
Joseph Kupiec *(Mng Dir & Principal-Las Vegas)*
Marc Lunde *(Mng Dir & Principal-Denver)*
Greg Kraut *(Mng Dir & Principal-New York)*
Earl E. Webb *(Pres-Ops-US)*
David Gonzales *(Principal & Mng Dir-Project Mgmt-Northern California)*
Randy Keller *(Principal & Mng Dir-San Mateo)*
Nick Slonek *(Principal & Mng Dir-Northern California)*
Keith Gurtler *(Principal-Boston)*
Mike Hillis *(Principal-Las Vegas)*
Lee Jones *(Principal-Houston)*
Adam Rappaport *(Principal-New York)*
John Ryan, III *(Principal-New York)*
Art Waldrop *(Principal-Atlanta)*
David Krasnoff *(Sr VP-Capital Markets Grp-New York)*

Branches:

Avison Young (USA) Inc. - Los Angeles, North **(2)**
6711 Forest Lawn Dr
Los Angeles, CA 90068
Tel.: (323) 851-6666
Fax: (323) 851-2022
Web Site: www.avisonyoung.com
Emp.: 10
Real Estate Brokerage Services
S.I.C.: 6531
N.A.I.C.S.: 531210
Mark Evanoff *(Mng Dir & Principal)*
Christopher Bonbright *(Principal)*
Michael Dettling *(Principal)*
John Tronson *(Principal)*
Chris Baer *(Sr VP)*
Dan Wakumoto *(Sr VP-Real Estate Svcs)*

Avison Young (USA) Inc. - New Jersey **(2)**
1120 Headquarters Plz West Twr 4th Fl
Morristown, NJ 07960
Tel.: (973) 898-6360
Fax: (973) 898-9062
Web Site: www.avisonyoung.com
Emp.: 53
Real Estate Brokerage & Construction Management Services
S.I.C.: 6531
N.A.I.C.S.: 531210
Jeffrey L. Heller *(Principal & Mng Dir)*
Edward Sharp Walsh *(Principal & Mng Dir-Project Mgmt Svcs)*
Thomas J. Walsh *(Principal & Mng Dir-Project Mgmt Svcs)*
William E. McCaffrey *(Principal)*
Bart Oates *(Sr VP)*
Christopher K. Richter *(Sr VP-Dev)*
Thomas Semler *(Sr VP)*
Brian A. Tobiasz *(Sr VP-Ops)*

Avison Young (USA) Inc. - South Florida-Fort Lauderdale **(2)**
515 E Las Olas Blvd Ste 400
Fort Lauderdale, FL 33301
Tel.: (954) 903-1800
Fax: (954) 938-1812
Web Site: www.avisonyoung.com
Emp.: 30
Commercial Real Estate Brokerage, Property Management & Asset Solution Services
S.I.C.: 6531
N.A.I.C.S.: 531210
S. Pike Rowley *(Mng Dir & Principal)*
Scott Auker *(Principal)*
A.J. Belt, III *(Principal)*
Brian Mark *(Principal-Fin Ops)*
Greg Martin *(Principal)*
Michael Vullis *(Principal)*

Avison Young (USA) Inc. - Raleigh-Durham **(2)**
(Formerly Thomas Linderman Graham Inc.)
1511 Sunday Dr Ste 200
Raleigh, NC 27607 NC
Tel.: (919) 785-3434
Fax: (919) 785-0802
Web Site: www.tlgcre.com
Emp.: 61
Commercial Real Estate Brokerage Services
S.I.C.: 6531

Avison Young (Canada) Inc.—(Continued)

N.A.I.C.S.: 531210
John B. Linderman, Jr. *(Mng Dir & Principal)*
Gina Ide *(Principal & Sr VP-Property Mgmt)*
Virginia L. Moulton *(Principal & VP-Property Mgmt)*
William A. Allen, IV *(Principal)*
H. Lee Clyburn *(Principal)*
Bryan Everett *(Principal)*
Arnold J. Siegmund *(Principal)*
J. Rex Thomas *(Principal)*
Chester F. Allen *(Sr VP)*
Jake Jones *(Sr VP)*
Hal V. Worth, IV *(Sr VP-Capital Markets Grp)*

Lane Witherspoon & Carswell Commercial Real Estate Advisors (1)
1715 N Westhore Blvd Ste 130
Tampa, FL 33607
Tel.: (813) 288-1800
Fax: (813) 288-1866
E-Mail: klane@lwccommercial.com
Web Site: www.lwccommercial.com
Sales Range: $50-74.9 Million
Emp.: 19
Commercial Real Estate Services
S.I.C.: 6531
N.A.I.C.S.: 531390
Trey Carswell *(Mng Dir)*
Kenneth E. Lane, III *(Mng Dir)*
Clay Witherspoon *(Mng Dir)*

Division:

L & W Commercial Property Management (2)
1715 N Westshore Blvd
Tampa, FL 33607
Tel.: (813) 288-1800
Fax: (813) 288-1866
Real Estate Management & Leasing
S.I.C.: 6531
N.A.I.C.S.: 531312
Suzi Dixon *(Dir-Property Mgmt)*

AVISTA OIL AG

Bahnhofstrasse 82
31311 Uetze, Germany
Tel.: (49) 5177850
Fax: (49) 517785104
E-Mail: info@avista-oil.com
Web Site: www.avista-oil.com
Emp.: 400
Business Description:
Used Oil Recycling Services
S.I.C.: 4212
N.A.I.C.S.: 562119
Personnel:
Bernd Merle *(Chm-Mgmt Bd)*

U.S. Holding:

Universal Environmental Services, LLC (1)
411 Dividend Dr
Peachtree City, GA 30269
Tel.: (770) 486-8816
Fax: (770) 486-0616
Toll Free: (800) 988-7977
Web Site: www.universalenvironmentalservices.com
Sales Range: $10-24.9 Million
Emp.: 100
Waste Materials Recycling Services
S.I.C.: 2821
N.A.I.C.S.: 325211
Doug Berry *(CFO)*

AVITA MEDICAL LTD

Level 9 The Quadrant 1 William Street
Perth, WA, 6000, Australia
Tel.: (61) 893890700
Fax: (61) 893890733
E-Mail: investor@avitamedical.com
Web Site: www.avitamedical.com
AVH—(ASX OTC)
Rev.: $4,222,876
Assets: $13,452,084
Liabilities: $2,556,606
Net Worth: $10,895,479
Earnings: ($8,433,652)
Emp.: 21
Fiscal Year-end: 06/30/13
Business Description:
Biotechnology Company
S.I.C.: 8731
N.A.I.C.S.: 541711
Personnel:
William Ford Dolphin *(CEO & Mng Dir)*
Timothy Rooney *(CFO & COO)*
Gabriel Chiappini *(Sec)*
Board of Directors:
Dalton Gooding
Jeremy Curnock Cook
William Ford Dolphin
Ian Macpherson
Matthew McNamara
Michael S. Perry
Fiona Wood
Legal Counsel:
Clifford Chance
Level 12 London House 216 St Georges Terrace
Perth, Australia

Non-U.S. Subsidiary:

Avita Medical Europe Ltd (1)
Unit B1 Beech House Melbourn Science Park
Cambridge Road Melbourn, Royston, Herts, SG8 6HB, United Kingdom
Tel.: (44) 1763 269770
Fax: (44) 1763 269780
E-Mail: info.eu@avitamedical.com
Web Site: www.avitamedical.com
Emp.: 13
Medical Equipments Mfr & Sales
S.I.C.: 3845
N.A.I.C.S.: 334510

Subsidiary:

Visiomed Group Ltd (1)
PO Box 207
Subiaco, WA, 6008, Australia
Tel.: (61) 893890700
Fax: (61) 893890733
E-Mail: sales@visiomed.com.au
Web Site: www.visiomed.com.au
Emp.: 5
Medical Equipments Mfr & Sales
S.I.C.: 3845
N.A.I.C.S.: 334510

U.S. Subsidiary:

Avita Medical Americas LLC (1)
9221 Corbin Ave Ste 220
Northridge, CA 91324
Tel.: (781) 995-4174
Fax: (781) 955-4176
E-Mail: info.am@avitamedical.com
Emp.: 6
Respiratory Devices Mfr & Sales
S.I.C.: 3845
N.A.I.C.S.: 334510
William Marshal *(VP-Ops)*

AVIVA CORPORATION LIMITED

Level 9 BGC Centre 28 The Esplanade
Perth, WA, 6000, Australia
Tel.: (61) 893226322
Fax: (61) 893226558
E-Mail: info@avivacorp.com.au
Web Site: www.avivacorp.com.au
AVA—(ASX)
Sales Range: Less than $1 Million
Emp.: 4
Business Description:
Coal Production
S.I.C.: 1222
N.A.I.C.S.: 212112
Personnel:
Stef S. Weber *(CFO & Sec)*
Board of Directors:
Ian Middlemas
Robert E. Kirtlan
Mark Pearce
Lindsay G. Reed
Legal Counsel:
Hardy Bowen Lawyers
Level 1 28 Ord Street
West Perth, Australia

Non-U.S. Subsidiary:

DTD Ltd (1)
Rm 1505 08 & 1515 22 Asia Trade Ctr
79 Lei Muk Rd, Kwai Chung, New Territories, China (Hong Kong)
Tel.: (852) 24181881
Fax: (852) 83437555
E-Mail: jess.chan@sammart.com.hk
Apparals Mfr
S.I.C.: 2389
N.A.I.C.S.: 315280

AVIVA PLC

Saint Helen's 1 Undershaft
London, EC3P 3DQ, United Kingdom
Tel.: (44) 2072832000
Fax: (44) 2076622753
E-Mail: aviva.info@aviva.com
Web Site: www.aviva.com
Year Founded: 1998
AV—(LSE)
Rev.: $68,059,502,550
Assets: $498,564,480,810
Liabilities: $480,623,746,410
Net Worth: $17,940,734,400
Earnings: ($4,816,834,500)
Emp.: 33,122
Fiscal Year-end: 12/31/12
Business Description:
Holding Company; Insurance & Financial Services
S.I.C.: 6311
N.A.I.C.S.: 524113
Personnel:
John McFarlane *(Chm)*
Mark Andrew Wilson *(CEO)*
Phil Willcock *(Mng Dir)*
Amanda Mackenzie *(CMO & Chief Comm Officer)*
John Lister *(Chief Risk Officer & Chief Capital Officer)*
Tim Harris *(Chief Capital Officer & Deputy Grp CFO)*
Mahesh Misra *(Chief Distr Officer-Aviva Life Insurance Co India Ltd)*
Susan Penwarden *(Chief Underwriting Officer-Comml, Corp & Speciality Lines)*
Axel Schmidt *(Chief Underwriting Officer-Gen Insurance-UK & Ireland)*
Jason Windsor *(Chief Strategy & Dev Officer)*
David Barral *(CEO-United Kingdom & Ireland Life)*
David McMillan *(CEO-Europe)*
Khor Hock Seng *(CEO-Asia)*
Maurice Tulloch *(CEO-Gen Insurance-UK & Ireland)*
Kirsty Cooper *(Gen Counsel & Sec)*
Board of Directors:
John McFarlane
Glyn Barker
Patricia Anne Cross
Gay Huey Evans
Mary E. Francis
Richard Karl Goeltz
Michael John Hawker
Michael Mire
Adrian Montague
Bob Stein
Scott Wheway
Mark Andrew Wilson
Legal Counsel:
Clifford Chance LLP
200 Aldersgate St
London, EC1A 4JJ, United Kingdom
Tel.: (44) 171 600 1000
Fax: (44) 171 600 5555

Subsidiaries:

AssureWeb Limited (1)
Eagle Tower
Montpellier Dr, Cheltenham, Glos, GL50 1TA, United Kingdom
Tel.: (44) 8704584561
Fax: (44) 8704584562
E-Mail: enquiries@assureweb.co.uk
Web Site: www.assureweb.co.uk
Emp.: 100
Financial Software Services
S.I.C.: 3652
N.A.I.C.S.: 334614
Andrew Simon *(CEO)*

Aviva Annuity UK Limited (1)
2 Rougier Street
York, YO90 1UU, United Kingdom
Tel.: (44) 1904 628982
Fax: (44) 1603 688261
Insurance Management Services
S.I.C.: 6411
N.A.I.C.S.: 524298

Aviva Equity Release UK Limited (1)
37-43 Surrey Street
Norwich, NR1 3UY, United Kingdom
Tel.: (44) 1603 622 200
Fax: (44) 1904 558 727
Mortgage Brokerage Services
S.I.C.: 6163
N.A.I.C.S.: 522310

Aviva Group Holdings Limited (1)
8 Surrey Street
Norwich, NR1 3ST, United Kingdom
Tel.: (44) 16 0362 2200
Fax: (44) 16 0368 3659
Investment Management Services
S.I.C.: 6211
N.A.I.C.S.: 523999

Subsidiary:

Aviva Central Services UK Limited (2)
8 Surrey Street
Norwich, Norfolk, NR1 3ST, United Kingdom
Tel.: (44) 1603 622200
Fax: (44) 1603761355
Insurance Agency Services
S.I.C.: 6411
N.A.I.C.S.: 524210

Aviva Insurance UK Limited (1)
8 Surrey Street
Norwich, NR1 3NG, United Kingdom
Tel.: (44) 1603 684 506
Insurance Management Services
S.I.C.: 6411
N.A.I.C.S.: 524298

Aviva Investors Holdings Limited (1)
Saint Helens 1 Undershaft
London, EC3P 3DQ, United Kingdom
Tel.: (44) 20 7283 2000
Investment Management Services
S.I.C.: 6211
N.A.I.C.S.: 523999
John Misselbrook *(Interim CEO)*
Euan Munro *(CEO-Global Asset Mgmt)*

Subsidiaries:

Aviva Investors Global Services Limited (2)
Fourth Floor No 1 Poultry
London, EC2R 8EJ, United Kingdom
Tel.: (44) 20 7809 6000
Fax: (44) 20 7809 6503
Investment Management Services
S.I.C.: 6211
N.A.I.C.S.: 523999
Jean-Francois Milette *(Mng Dir-Institutional Sls-Toronto)*

Aviva Investors UK Fund Services Limited (2)
Surrey Street
Norwich, Norfolk, NR1 3GG, United Kingdom
Tel.: (44) 1603 622200
Fax: (44) 1603 683659
Investment Management Services
S.I.C.: 6211
N.A.I.C.S.: 523999

U.S. Subsidiaries:

Aviva Investors North America, Inc. (2)
215 10th St Ste 1000
Des Moines, IA 50309 IA

Tel.: (515) 657-8563
Web Site: www.avivainvestors.us
Emp.: 80
Asset Management Services
S.I.C.: 6799
N.A.I.C.S.: 523920
Patrick O'Brien *(CEO)*
Charles Preseau *(CFO)*
Lyda Iturralde *(Chief Compliance Officer)*
Ross A. Junge *(Chief Investment Officer-Fixed Income)*
Andra Purkalitis *(Chief Legal Officer)*
Timothy S. Reimer *(Sr VP-Alternative Investments)*

Aviva Life & Pensions UK Limited (1)
2 Rougier Street
York, YO90 1UU, United Kingdom UK
Tel.: (44) 1603622200 (100%)
Fax: (44) 1603683659
E-Mail: helpdesk@aviva.co.uk
Web Site: www.aviva.co.uk
Emp.: 100
Life Insurance, Annuity & Pensions
S.I.C.: 6399
N.A.I.C.S.: 524128
Mark Hodges *(CEO)*

Aviva Risk Management Solutions UK Limited (1)
1 Friars Gate Stratford Rd
Solihull, West Midlands, B90 4BN, United Kingdom
Tel.: (44) 845 3016030
Fax: (44) 800 687 288
E-Mail: risksolutions@aviva.co.uk
Emp.: 150
Business Consulting Services
S.I.C.: 8748
N.A.I.C.S.: 541618
Brian Wallace *(Mng Dir & Head)*

CGU Underwriting Limited (1)
1 Undershaft
London, EC3P 3DQ, United Kingdom
Tel.: (44) 2072837500
Web Site: www.aviva.com
Insurance Management Services
S.I.C.: 6411
N.A.I.C.S.: 524298

London and Edinburgh Insurance Company Limited (1)
The Warren Warren Road
Worthing, BN14 9QD, United Kingdom
Tel.: (44) 1903 820 820
Fax: (44) 1903 821 991
General Insurance Services
S.I.C.: 6411
N.A.I.C.S.: 524210

Non-U.S. Subsidiaries:

Aviva Canada Inc. (1)
2206 Eglinton Ave E Ste 160
Scarborough, ON, M1L 4S8, Canada ON
Tel.: (416) 288-1800 (100%)
Fax: (416) 288-9756
Toll Free: (800) 387-4518
E-Mail:
Web Site: www.avivacanada.com
Emp.: 3,100
Insurance Provider
S.I.C.: 6399
N.A.I.C.S.: 524128
Greg Somerville *(Pres & CEO)*
Jim Falle *(CFO & Exec VP)*
Robert Merizzi *(COO-Ops & Tech & Exec VP)*
Greg Dunn *(Exec VP-Claims & Customer Svcs Ops)*
Paul Fletcher *(Sr VP-Brand Mktg)*
Martin-Eric Tremblay *(Sr VP-Quebec & Atlantic Canada)*

Subsidiaries:

Aviva Insurance Company of Canada (2)
2206 Eglinton Ave E
Scarborough, ON, M1L 4S8, Canada
Tel.: (416) 288-1800
Fax: (416) 288-9756
Property & Casualty Insurance Services
S.I.C.: 6331
N.A.I.C.S.: 524126

Pilot Insurance Company (2)
191 Bloor St E Unit 11
Oshawa, ON, L1H 3M3, Canada
Tel.: (905) 723-1103
Fax: (905) 728-9095
Web Site: www.pilot.ca
Emp.: 13
Insurance Management Services
S.I.C.: 6411
N.A.I.C.S.: 524298
Glenn Davis *(Branch Mgr)*

Scottish & York Insurance Co. Limited (2)
2206 Eglinton Ave E Ste 160
Scarborough, ON, M1L 4S8, Canada
Tel.: (416) 288-1800
Fax: (416) 487-1821
Insurance Agency Services
S.I.C.: 6411
N.A.I.C.S.: 524210
Maurice Tulloch *(CEO)*

Aviva France (1)
80 Avenue de l'Europe
92770 Bois-Colombes, France FR
Tel.: (33) 176625000 (100%)
Fax: (33) 176527555
Web Site: www.aviva.fr
Emp.: 3,000
Underwriter & Broker of Life Insurance
S.I.C.: 6399
N.A.I.C.S.: 524128
Nicolas Schimel *(CEO)*

Subsidiaries:

Aviva Assurances SA (2)
13 Rue Du Moulin Bailly
Bois-Colombes, Paris, 92271, France
Tel.: (33) 233389892
Web Site: www.aviva-assurances.com
Insurance Management Services
S.I.C.: 6411
N.A.I.C.S.: 524298

Aviva Vie S.A. (2)
70 Avenue De l'Europe
92270 Bois-Colombes, France
Tel.: (33) 1 76 62 50 00
Fax: (33) 176625560
Emp.: 2,000
Insurance Management Services
S.I.C.: 6411
N.A.I.C.S.: 524298

Aviva Group Ireland plc (1)
One Park Place Hatch Street
Dublin, 2, Ireland IE
Tel.: (353) 16078000
Emp.: 177
Holding Company; Insurance Products & Services
S.I.C.: 6719
N.A.I.C.S.: 551112
Alison Burns *(CEO)*

Subsidiaries:

Aviva Insurance Europe SE (2)
One Park Place Hatch Street
Dublin, 2, Ireland IE
Tel.: (353) 18988000 (100%)
Fax: (353) 16078112
Web Site: www.aviva.ie
Emp.: 1,000
Title, Property & Casualty Insurance Products & Services
S.I.C.: 6331
N.A.I.C.S.: 524126
Gary Owens *(Mng Dir)*

Aviva Life & Pensions Ireland Ltd. (2)
One Park Place Hatch Street
Dublin, 2, Ireland IE
Tel.: (353) 18987000 (100%)
Fax: (353) 167748617
E-Mail: csc@aviva.ie
Web Site: www.aviva.ie/online/life&pensions
Emp.: 700
Life Insurance & Pension Provider
S.I.C.: 6399
N.A.I.C.S.: 524128
Kevin Moss *(Mng Dir)*

Aviva Investors Australia Limited (1)
Level 28 Freshwater Place 2 Southbank Boulevard
Southbank, VIC, 3006, Australia
Tel.: (61) 3 9220 0300
Fax: (61) 3 9220 0333
Web Site: www.investors.com.au
Emp.: 4
Investment Management Services
S.I.C.: 6211
N.A.I.C.S.: 523999
Peter Poulopoulos *(Mgr-Bus Dev-VIC,SA & TAS)*

Aviva Italia Holding S.p.A (1)
Viale Abruzzi 94
20131 Milan, Italy
Tel.: (39) 02 2775 1
Fax: (39) 02 2775204
Emp.: 24
Insurance Management Services
S.I.C.: 6411
N.A.I.C.S.: 524298

Aviva Life Insurance Company Limited (1)
Suite 1701 City Plaza One 1111 King's Road
Taikoo Shing, Hong Kong, China (Hong Kong)
Tel.: (852) 35509600
Fax: (852) 29071787
E-Mail: enquiry@aviva-asia.com
Web Site: www.aviva.com.hk
Emp.: 100
Insurance Management Services
S.I.C.: 6411
N.A.I.C.S.: 524298
Elba Tse *(Mng Dir)*

Aviva Limited (1)
4 Shenton Way 01-01 SGX Centre 2
Singapore, 068807, Singapore
Tel.: (65) 6827 9933
Fax: (65) 6827 7480
E-Mail: cs_life@aviva-asia.com
Web Site: www.aviva.com.sg
Insurance Management Services
S.I.C.: 6411
N.A.I.C.S.: 524298
Simon Newman *(CEO)*
Hock Seng Khor *(CEO-Asia)*

Aviva Powszechne Towarzystwo Emerytalne Aviva BZ WBK S.A. (1)
Ul Domaniewska 44
02-672 Warsaw, Poland
Tel.: (48) 225574050
Fax: (48) 225574039
E-Mail: bok@aviva.pl
Investment Management Services
S.I.C.: 6211
N.A.I.C.S.: 523999

Aviva Sigorta A.S. (1)
Fahrettin Kerim Gokay Caddesi No 72-74 Aviva Binas
34662 Istanbul, Turkey TR
Tel.: (90) 216 547 7575
Fax: (90) 216 326 94 52
E-Mail: avivasigorta@avivasigorta.com.tr
Web Site: www.avivasigorta.com.tr
AVIVA—(IST)
Long-Term Savings, Fund Management & General Insurance Services
S.I.C.: 6411
N.A.I.C.S.: 524298
Serkan Avci *(Head-IT)*

Aviva Towarzystwo Ubezpieczen Na Zycie SA (1)
Ul Domaniewska 44
02-672 Warsaw, Poland
Tel.: (48) 22 557 40 50
Fax: (48) 22 557 40 75
E-Mail: bok@aviva.pl
Insurance Management Services
S.I.C.: 6411
N.A.I.C.S.: 524298

Aviva Towarzystwo Ubezpieczen Ogolnych SA (1)
Ul Domaniewska 44
02-672 Warsaw, Poland
Tel.: (48) 22 557 40 50
Fax: (48) 22 557 49 22
E-Mail: bok@aviva.pl
Web Site: www.aviva.pl
Emp.: 150
General Insurance Management Services
S.I.C.: 6411
N.A.I.C.S.: 524298

Aviva zivotni pojist (1)
Londynska 41
120 21 Prague, Czech Republic
Tel.: (420) 221 416 111
Fax: (420) 221 416 101
E-Mail: info@avivazp.cz
Web Site: www.aviva-pojistovna.cz
Insurance Management Services
S.I.C.: 6411
N.A.I.C.S.: 524298

Eurovita Assicurazioni S.p.A (1)
Via dei Maroniti 12
187 Rome, Italy IT
Tel.: (39) 06 474821
Fax: (39) 06 42900089
E-Mail: assicurazioni@eurovita.it
Web Site: www.eurovita.it
Life Insurance Services
S.I.C.: 6311
N.A.I.C.S.: 524113

AVIVAGEN INC.

(Formerly Chemaphor Inc.)
100 Sussex Drive
Ottawa, ON, K1A 0R6, Canada
Tel.: (613) 949-8164
Fax: (613) 993-0796
E-Mail: g.burton@avivagen.com
Web Site: www.avivagen.com
Year Founded: 1997
VIV—(TSXV)
Rev.: $415,067
Assets: $392,729
Liabilities: $4,587,769
Net Worth: ($4,195,040)
Earnings: ($1,961,960)
Fiscal Year-end: 10/31/12

Business Description:
Organic Pharmaceuticals Mfr
S.I.C.: 2834
N.A.I.C.S.: 325412

Personnel:
Graham Burton *(Co-Founder & Dir-Commercialization Svcs)*
Janusz Daroszewski *(Co-Founder & Dir-Process Validation)*
Jacques Brault *(Chm)*
Cameron Groome *(CEO)*
Chris Boland *(CFO)*

Board of Directors:
Jacques Brault
Graham Burton
Janusz Daroszewski
Cameron Groome
David Hankinson
Amin I. Khalifa
Chandrakant J. Panchal

Transfer Agent:
Computershare Trust Company of Canada
9th Floor 100 University Avenue
Toronto, ON, Canada

AVK HOLDING A/S

Bizonvej 1
DK 8464 Skovby, Denmark
Tel.: (45) 87542100
Fax: (45) 87542120
Web Site: www.avkvalves.com
Sales Range: $550-599.9 Million
Emp.: 2,171

Business Description:
Water Supply & Valve Equipment Mfr
S.I.C.: 3491
N.A.I.C.S.: 332911

Personnel:
Niels A. Kjaer *(CEO)*
Lars Kudsk *(CFO)*

AVL LIST GMBH

Hans-List-Platz 1
8020 Graz, Austria
Tel.: (43) 316787
Fax: (43) 316707
E-Mail: info@avl.com
Web Site: www.avl.com
Year Founded: 1948
Emp.: 3,640

AVL List GmbH—(Continued)

Business Description:
Diesel Powertrain Engineering, Simulation & Powertrain Testing Systems
S.I.C.: 3714
N.A.I.C.S.: 336310

Personnel:
Helmut O. List *(Chm & CEO)*
Werner Schuster *(CFO)*
Robert Fischer *(Exec VP-Engrg & Tech-Powertrain Engrg)*
Franz X. Moser *(Exec VP-Comml Powertrain Sys)*
Friedrich Radke *(Exec VP-Instrumentation & Test Sys)*
Patrick Signargout *(Exec VP-Sls & Intl Ops-Powertrain Sys)*

U.S. Subsidiary:

AVL Michigan Holding Corporation (1)
47519 Halyard Dr
Plymouth, MI 48170-2438
Tel.: (734) 414-9600
Fax: (734) 414-9691
Web Site: www.avlna.com
Sales Range: $50-74.9 Million
Emp.: 300
Holding Company; Diesel Engine Design & Testing
S.I.C.: 3714
N.A.I.C.S.: 336310
Helmut O. List *(Chm & CEO)*
Danaod Manvell *(CEO)*
Werner Schuster *(CFO)*

Subsidiaries:

AVL North America Inc. (2)
47603 Halyard Dr
Plymouth, MI 48170-2438
Tel.: (734) 414-9600
Fax: (734) 414-9690
Toll Free: (800) 222-5283
Web Site: www.avlna.com
Emp.: 450
Powertrain & Engine Testing Services
S.I.C.: 8734
N.A.I.C.S.: 541380
Kyle Kimel *(Dir-Sls)*

AVL Powertrain Engineering, Inc. (2)
47519 Halyard Dr
Plymouth, MI 48170-2438
Tel.: (734) 414-9618
Fax: (734) 414-9690
Toll Free: (877) 285-4278
E-Mail: powertrain@avlna.com
Web Site: www.avl.com
Engine Design & Development
S.I.C.: 3714
N.A.I.C.S.: 336310
Dimitri Kazarinoff *(Pres)*

Non-U.S. Subsidiaries:

AVL AST d.o.o. (1)
Av Dubrovnik 10/II
10020 Zagreb, Croatia
Tel.: (385) 16598600
Fax: (385) 17775123
E-Mail: goran.mirkovic@avl.com
Web Site: www.avl.com
Emp.: 80
Powertrain Engine Design, Development & Testing
S.I.C.: 3519
N.A.I.C.S.: 333618
Goran Mirkovic *(Mng Dir)*

AVL Autokut Engineering Ltd. (1)
Csoka utca 7-13
1115 Budapest, Hungary
Tel.: (36) 14643950
Fax: (36) 12037624
Web Site: www.avl.com
Engine & Powertrain Development & Testing
S.I.C.: 3519
N.A.I.C.S.: 333618

AVL Cechy spol. s r.o. (1)
Tovarni 605
75301 Hranice, Czech Republic
Tel.: (420) 581 653, ext. 111
Fax: (420) 267 288 208
Web Site: www.avl.com
Engine & Powertrain Development & Testing
S.I.C.: 3519
N.A.I.C.S.: 333618
Bronislav Kasparek *(Mng Dir)*

AVL Deutschland GmbH (1)
Peter-Sander-Strasse 32
D 55252 Mainz-Kastel, Germany
Tel.: (49) 613471790
Fax: (49) 61343588
E-Mail: avl.deutschland@avl.com
Web Site: www.avl.com
Emp.: 500
Engine & Powertrain Development & Testing
S.I.C.: 3519
N.A.I.C.S.: 333618
Sabine Mueller *(Sec)*

AVL France S.A. (1)
Espace Claude Monet
2-4 rue Hans List, 78290 Croissy-sur-Seine, France
Tel.: (33) 130157500
Fax: (33) 130157531
Web Site: www.avl.com
Emp.: 60
Powertrain Engineering Sales, Marketing & Support; Instrumentation & Test Systems Sales & Marketing
S.I.C.: 3714
N.A.I.C.S.: 336310
Gilbert Lemieux *(Mng Dir)*

AVL Iberica S.A. (1)
Jaume Vicens Vives 22 Edif El Rengle nucleo
Mataro, E 08302 Barcelona, Spain
Tel.: (34) 937554848
Fax: (34) 937907717
E-Mail: avl@avl.es
Web Site: www.avl.com
Emp.: 45
Engine & Powertrain Development & Testing
S.I.C.: 3519
N.A.I.C.S.: 333618
Joan Anton Mikuel *(Mng Dir)*

AVL Italy S.r.l. (1)
Via Lanzo 181
Borgaro Torinese, 10071 Turin, Italy
Tel.: (39) 0114705111
Fax: (39) 0114704960
E-Mail: avlitaly@avl.com
Web Site: www.avl.com
Powertrain Engineering Support & Instrumentation & Test Systems Design, Development, Sales & Distribution
S.I.C.: 3519
N.A.I.C.S.: 333618

AVL List Nordiska AB (1)
Transmissionsvagen 2
PO Box 223
SE 15148 Sodertalje, Sweden
Tel.: (46) 850065600
Fax: (46) 850028328
Web Site: www.avl.com
Emp.: 20
Powertrain Engine Design, Testing & Sales
S.I.C.: 3519
N.A.I.C.S.: 333618
Gam Gasste *(Mng Dir)*

AVL United Kingdom Limited (1)
Avon House
Hartlebury Trading Estate, Hartlebury, Worcestershire, DY10 4JB, United Kingdom
Tel.: (44) 1299254600
Fax: (44) 1299253734
E-Mail: uk.sales@avl.com
Web Site: www.avl.com
Emp.: 50
Powertrain Engine Design, Development, Testing & Sales
S.I.C.: 3519
N.A.I.C.S.: 333618
Antonio Ciriello *(Mng Dir)*

AVMAX GROUP INC.

2055 Pegasus Road NE
Calgary, AB, T2E 8C3, Canada
Tel.: (403) 291-2464
Fax: (403) 735-5905
Toll Free: (888) 524-9444
E-Mail: info@avmaxgrp.ca
Web Site: www.avmax.ca
Year Founded: 1996
Rev.: $33,073,127
Emp.: 275

Business Description:
Airline Support Services & Aircraft Spares Distr
S.I.C.: 4581
N.A.I.C.S.: 488190

Personnel:
John Binder *(Pres)*
Rick Giacomuzzi *(CFO)*
Don Parkin *(Exec VP)*

U.S. Subsidiary:

Avmax Montana, Inc. (1)
1930 Airport Ct
Great Falls, MT 59404 MT
Tel.: (406) 453-2344
Fax: (406) 453-2366
Emp.: 50
Support Activities for Air Transportation
S.I.C.: 4581
N.A.I.C.S.: 488190
Marty Craig *(Dir-Sls)*

AVMOR LTEE

950 Michelin
Laval, QC, H7L 5C1, Canada
Tel.: (450) 629-8074
Fax: (450) 629-4512
Toll Free: (800) 387-8074
E-Mail: info@avmor.com
Web Site: www.avmor.com
Year Founded: 1948
Rev.: $15,561,000
Emp.: 100

Business Description:
Cleaning Chemicals & Sanitation Systems Mfr
S.I.C.: 2842
N.A.I.C.S.: 325612

Personnel:
Erik Hoffmann *(Pres)*

AVNEL GOLD MINING LIMITED

Carey Olsen Elizabeth House Les Ruettes Brayes
Saint Peter Port, GY1 4LX, Guernsey
Tel.: (44) 1481700300
Fax: (44) 1481711220
Web Site: www.avnelgold.com
AVK—(TSX)
Rev.: $16,804,000
Assets: $31,051,000
Liabilities: $7,558,000
Net Worth: $23,493,000
Earnings: $4,786,000
Fiscal Year-end: 12/31/12

Business Description:
Gold Mining & Exploration Services
S.I.C.: 1041
N.A.I.C.S.: 212221

Personnel:
Howard B. Miller *(Chm & CEO)*
Alan McFarlane *(Sec & VP-Fin)*

Board of Directors:
Howard B. Miller
Anthony M. Bousfield
Ibrahim Kantao
John Kearney
Derek Kyle
Roy Meade
Jonas U. Rydell

Legal Counsel:
Davies Ward Phillips & Vineberg LLP
1 First Canadian Place 44th Floor
Toronto, ON, Canada

Anne-Severine Le Doare
8 rue des Saussaies
Paris, France

Transfer Agent:
Computershare Investor Services Inc
100 University Avenue 8th Floor
Toronto, ON, Canada

AVOCET MINING PLC

3rd FLoor 30 Haymarket
London, SW1Y 4EX, United Kingdom
Tel.: (44) 2077667676
Fax: (44) 2077667699
E-Mail: avocet@avocetmining.com
Web Site: www.avocet.co.uk
AVM—(LSE)
Rev.: $204,110,000
Assets: $332,655,000
Liabilities: $56,850,000
Net Worth: $275,805,000
Earnings: ($102,601,000)
Emp.: 886
Fiscal Year-end: 12/31/12

Business Description:
Gold Mining Services
S.I.C.: 1041
N.A.I.C.S.: 212221

Personnel:
David Cather *(CEO)*
Jason Lee *(Legal Counsel)*
Jim Wynn *(Sec & Head-Fin)*
Hans-Arne L'orange *(Exec VP-Bus Dev & IR)*

Board of Directors:
Russell Philip Edey
David Cather
Mike J. Donoghue
A. Mike Norris
Robert A. Pilkington
Barry John William Rourke
Gordon Wylie

Legal Counsel:
Field Fisher Waterhouse
35 Vine Street
London, United Kingdom

Computershare Investor Services PLC
The Pavilions Bridgewater Road
PO Box 82
Bristol, BS13 8AE, United Kingdom
Tel.: (44) 870 702 0000
Fax: (44) 870 703 6119

Transfer Agent:
Computershare Investor Services PLC
The Pavilions Bridgewater Road
PO Box 82
Bristol, BS13 8AE, United Kingdom
Tel.: (44) 870 702 0000
Fax: (44) 870 703 6119

Subsidiary:

Avocet Gold Limited (1)
30 Haymarket 3rd Fl
SW1Y4EX London, United Kingdom (100%)
Tel.: (44) 2077667676
Fax: (44) 2077667699
E-Mail: avocet@avocetmining.com
Web Site: www.avocetmining.com
Emp.: 15
Gold Ore Mining
S.I.C.: 1041
N.A.I.C.S.: 212221
David Cather *(CEO)*

Non-U.S. Subsidiary:

Avocet Gold Ltd. (2)
Penjom Gold Mine Empang Jaleh
PO Box 49
Kuala Lipis, Pahang, 27200, Malaysia
Tel.: (60) 93227288
Fax: (60) 93227292
E-Mail: mailbox@penjom.com
Emp.: 600
Gold Ore Mining Services
S.I.C.: 1041
N.A.I.C.S.: 212221
Aldrin Alambono *(Gen Mgr)*

Non-U.S. Subsidiaries:

PT Avocet Bolaang Mongondow (1)
J1 Kol Sugiono No 24 Kotabangun
95712 Kotamobagu, Indonesia (80%)
Tel.: (62) 43421018
Fax: (62) 43423387
Sales Range: $50-74.9 Million
Emp.: 400
Holding Company: Gold Ore Mining

S.I.C.: 6719
N.A.I.C.S.: 551112
Alistair Frowde *(Gen Mgr)*

Specific Resources Sdn. Bhd. (1)
Penjom Gold Mine Empang Jalih
PO Box 49
27207 Pahang, Malaysia (100%)
Tel.: (60) 93227288
Fax: (60) 93227292
Web Site: www.avocet.com
Emp.: 600
Gold Ore Mining
S.I.C.: 1041
N.A.I.C.S.: 212221
Jesper Christan *(Gen Mgr)*

Wega Mining Mali S.A. (1)
Korofina Nord Rue 110 Porte 329
Bamako, Mali
Tel.: (223) 20245039
Fax: (223) 20245053
Emp.: 4
Gold Mining Services
S.I.C.: 1041
N.A.I.C.S.: 212221
Charles Pattrick *(Mgr)*

AVOCET RESOURCES LIMITED
(Acquired & Absorbed by Lion One Metals Limited)

AVOD KURUTULMUS GIDA VE TARIM URUNLERI SAN. TIC. A.S.
Canakkale-Izmir Asfalti No 36
Turkelli-Menemen, Izmir, Turkey
Tel.: (90) 232 835 45 24
Fax: (90) 232 835 45 33
E-Mail: a.ihsan@avod.com.tr
Web Site: www.avod.com.tr
Business Description:
Dried Vegetable Distr
S.I.C.: 5148
N.A.I.C.S.: 424480

AVON CORPORATION LTD.
15/B 2nd Floor Kamal kunj Opp Vijay Sales S V Road Irla Bridge
Andheri West, Mumbai, 400058, India
Tel.: (91) 2266804064
Fax: (91) 2226717475
E-Mail: marketing@avon.co.in
Web Site: www.avon.co.in
532995—(BOM)
Rev.: $11,378,678
Assets: $24,202,279
Liabilities: $27,513,892
Net Worth: ($3,311,613)
Earnings: ($23,406,976)
Emp.: 70
Fiscal Year-end: 03/31/13
Business Description:
Electronic Weighing Balances Mfr
S.I.C.: 3829
N.A.I.C.S.: 333997
Personnel:
Pankaj P. Saraiya *(Chm, CEO & Mng Dir)*
Board of Directors:
Pankaj P. Saraiya
Ramesh M. Joshi
Satish Mehta
Rupal Pankaj Saraiya
Shantaben P. Saraiya
Gaurav Sinha
Transfer Agent:
Datamatics Financial Services Limited
Plot No A16 & A17 MIDC Part B Cross Lane
400093 Mumbai, India

AVON LIPPIATT HOBBS (CONTRACTING) LIMITED
(d/b/a ALHCO)
114 Station Road
Westbury, Wiltshire, BA13 4TW, United Kingdom
Tel.: (44) 1373855122
Fax: (44) 1373 858455
E-Mail: enquiries@alhco.co.uk
Web Site: www.alhco.com
Year Founded: 1986
Sls.: $80,000,000
Emp.: 300
Business Description:
Utility Contractor; Pipework Installation; Heater Installation & Servicing
S.I.C.: 1711
N.A.I.C.S.: 238220
Personnel:
John H.A. Clarke *(Chm)*
David W. Reynolds *(Grp Mng Dir)*

Subsidiary:

FlowMole (1)
Unit C Edison Courtyard
Earlstrees Industrial Estate, Corby, Northamptonshire, NN17 4LS, United Kingdom UK
Tel.: (44) 1536400141 (100%)
Fax: (44) 1536400142
Emp.: 27
Underground Utility Installation & Replacement Services
S.I.C.: 1623
N.A.I.C.S.: 237120

AVON RUBBER PLC
Hampton Park West Semington Road
Melksham, Wiltshire, SN12 6NB, United Kingdom
Tel.: (44) 1225896800
Fax: (44) 1225896898
E-Mail: enquiries@avon-rubber.com
Web Site: www.avon-rubber.com
Year Founded: 1890
AVON—(LSE)
Rev.: $207,432,445
Assets: $118,588,603
Liabilities: $84,203,441
Net Worth: $34,385,162
Earnings: $15,996,344
Emp.: 747
Fiscal Year-end: 09/30/13
Business Description:
Rubber Products Mfr
S.I.C.: 3069
N.A.I.C.S.: 326299
Personnel:
Peter C. Slabbert *(CEO)*
Miles Ingrey-Counter *(Sec)*
Board of Directors:
David R. Evans
Andrew G. Lewis
Stella J. Pirie
Peter C. Slabbert
Richard K. Wood
Transfer Agent:
Capita Asset Services
The Registry 34 Beckenham Road
Beckenham, BR3 4TU, United Kingdom

Subsidiaries:

Avon Polymer Products Limited (1)
Hampton Park W
Semington Rd, Melksham, Wiltshire, SN126NB, United Kingdom (100%)
Tel.: (44) 1225896300
Fax: (44) 1225896302
E-Mail: enquiries@avon-rubber.com
Web Site: www.avonrubber.com
Emp.: 150
Rubber & Plastics Hoses & Belting Mfr
S.I.C.: 3052
N.A.I.C.S.: 326220
Peter Slabbert *(CEO)*

Avon Rubber Overseas Limited (1)
Hampton Park West
Semington Road, Melksham, Wiltshire, SN12 6NB, United Kingdom (100%)
Tel.: (44) 1225896300
Fax: (44) 1225896302
E-Mail: admin@avon-rubber.com
Emp.: 150
Rubber & Plastics Hoses & Belting Mfr
S.I.C.: 3052
N.A.I.C.S.: 326220
Peter Slabbert *(CEO)*

Avon Rubber Pension Trust Limited (1)
Unit 5 Brook Lane Trading Estate
Westbury, Wiltshire, BA13 4EP, United Kingdom
Tel.: (44) 1225 896300
Fax: (44) 1225 896301
Web Site: www.avon-rubber.com
Emp.: 150
Pension Investment Advisory Services
S.I.C.: 6371
N.A.I.C.S.: 525110
Craig Sage *(Gen Mgr)*

U.S. Subsidiaries:

Avon Engineered Fabrications, Inc (1)
1200 Martin Luther King Blvd
Picayune, MS 39466-5427
Tel.: (601) 799-1217
Fax: (601) 799-1360
E-Mail: enquiries@avon-rubber.com
Web Site: www.avon-protection.com
Rubber Products Mfr
S.I.C.: 3052
N.A.I.C.S.: 326220

Avon Hi-Life Inc. (1)
110 Lincoln St
Johnson Creek, WI 53038-0009
Tel.: (920) 699-3431
Fax: (920) 699-2344
E-Mail: enquiries@avon-rubber.com
Emp.: 140
Rubber Product & Glass Mfr
S.I.C.: 3069
N.A.I.C.S.: 326299
Dunderfon Larry *(Gen Mgr)*

Avon International Safety Instruments, Inc. (1)
922 Hurricane Shoals Rd
Lawrenceville, GA 30043-4822
Tel.: (770) 962-2552
Fax: (770) 963-2797
E-Mail: ernie@intsafety.com
Web Site: www.intsafety.com
Emp.: 63
Rubber Product & Glass Mfr
S.I.C.: 3069
N.A.I.C.S.: 326299
Mark Williamson *(Mgr-Mktg)*

Avon Milk-Rite USA Inc. (1)
110 Lincoln St
Johnson Creek, WI 53038-0009
Tel.: (920) 699-3431
Fax: (920) 699-2344
E-Mail: enquiries@avon-rubber.com
Web Site: www.avon-rubber.com
Emp.: 140
Rubber Product & Glass Mfr
S.I.C.: 3069
N.A.I.C.S.: 326299
Larry Gunderson *(Gen Mgr)*

Avon Protection Systems, Inc. (1)
503 Eighth St
Cadillac, MI 49601-9282
Tel.: (231) 779-6200
Fax: (231) 779-6202
E-Mail: customerservice@avon-protection.com
Web Site: www.avon-protection.com
Emp.: 300
Respiratory Protection Mask Mfr
S.I.C.: 3842
N.A.I.C.S.: 339113
Gary Dunn *(VP-Sls & Mktg)*

Avon Rubber & Plastics Inc. (1)
603 W 7th St
Cadillac, MI 49601 (100%)
Tel.: (231) 775-6571
Fax: (231) 775-7304
E-Mail: enquiries@avon-rubber.com
Web Site: www.avon-rubber.com
Emp.: 500
Rubber Products Mfr
Export
S.I.C.: 3089
N.A.I.C.S.: 326199
Scott Marish *(Controller)*

AVONDALE FOOD STORES LIMITED
4520 Jordan Rd
Jordan Station, Lincoln, ON, L0R 1S0, Canada
Tel.: (905) 562-4173
Fax: (905) 562-4414
E-Mail: larry.stewart@avondalestores.com
Web Site: www.avondalestores.com
Sales Range: $100-124.9 Million
Emp.: 800
Business Description:
Convenience Store
S.I.C.: 5411
N.A.I.C.S.: 445120
Personnel:
Robert G. Stewart *(Pres)*

AVONLEA MINERALS LIMITED
(Name Changed to AVZ Minerals Limited)

AVONMORE CAPITAL & MANAGEMENT SERVICES LTD.
(Formerly Almondz Capital & Management Services Ltd.)
2nd Floor 3 Scindia House
Janpath, New Delhi, 110 001, India
Tel.: (91) 11 32947374
Fax: (91) 11 41514665
Web Site: avonmorecapital.in
511589—(BOM)
Sales Range: Less than $1 Million
Business Description:
Financial Management Services
S.I.C.: 6211
N.A.I.C.S.: 523999
Personnel:
Ashok Kumar Gupta *(Mng Dir)*
Transfer Agent:
Beetal Financial & Computer Services Pvt. Ltd
Beetal House 3rd Floor 99 Madangir Behind L S C Near Dada Harsukh Dass
New Delhi, India

AVRA, INC.
Exchange Ocho Rios
Saint Ann's Bay, Jamaica
Tel.: (876) 975 5471
Year Founded: 2010
AVRN—(OTC OTCB)
Assets: $650
Liabilities: $8,106
Net Worth: ($7,456)
Earnings: ($49,465)
Fiscal Year-end: 01/31/13
Business Description:
Smart TV Boxes Marketer & Distr
S.I.C.: 5065
N.A.I.C.S.: 423690
Personnel:
David Bailey *(Pres, CEO, CFO, Treas & Sec)*
Board of Directors:
David Bailey
Transfer Agent:
Globex Transfer, LLC
780 Deltona Blvd Ste 202
Deltona, FL 32725

AVRUPA MINERALS LTD.
410-325 Howe Street
Vancouver, BC, V6C 1Z7, Canada
Tel.: (604) 687-3520
Fax: (604) 688-3392
E-Mail: info@avrupaminerals.com

Avrupa Minerals Ltd.—(Continued)

Web Site: www.avrupaminerals.com
Year Founded: 2008
AVU—(TSXV)
Rev.: $12,132
Assets: $2,967,899
Liabilities: $272,978
Net Worth: $2,694,921
Earnings: ($1,519,910)
Fiscal Year-end: 12/31/12

Business Description:
Mineral Exploration Services
S.I.C.: 1081
N.A.I.C.S.: 213114

Personnel:
Paul W. Kuhn *(Pres & CEO)*
Winnie Wong *(CFO & Sec)*

Board of Directors:
Mark Thomas Brown
Paul Dircksen
Paul W. Kuhn
Gregory Ellis McKelvey
Ross Stringer

AVT NATURAL PRODUCTS LTD.

S Vazhakulam Marampily PO
Ernakulam Dist
Aluva, 683 107, India
Tel.: (91) 4842677262
Fax: (91) 4842677512
Web Site: www.avtnatural.com
AVTNPL—(NSE)
Rev.: $49,520,529
Assets: $42,230,588
Liabilities: $16,561,092
Net Worth: $25,669,497
Earnings: $8,860,379
Fiscal Year-end: 03/31/13

Business Description:
Grinding Spices Mfr
S.I.C.: 2087
N.A.I.C.S.: 311942

Personnel:
Satheesh Kumar *(Pres & COO)*
M. S. A. Kumar *(Mng Dir)*
Alex K. Abraham *(CMO & Sr VP)*
P. Dileepraj *(Compliance Officer & Sec)*

Board of Directors:
Ajit Thomas
M. A. Alagappan
Shyam B. Ghia
Habib Hussain
M. S. A. Kumar
P. Shankar

Transfer Agent:
Cameo Corporate Services Limited
Subramanian Building No 1 Club House Road
5th Floor
Chennai, India

AVTECH SWEDEN AB

Lonnvaaen 2
S-184 43 Akersberga, Sweden
Tel.: (46) 8 54 41 04 80
Fax: (46) 8 544 104 89
E-Mail: info@avtech.aero
Web Site: avtech.aero
AVT B—(OMX)
Sales Range: $1-9.9 Million
Emp.: 13

Business Description:
Digital Air Traffic Management
S.I.C.: 4581
N.A.I.C.S.: 488190

Personnel:
Lars G. V. Lindberg *(Chm)*
David Alvord *(CEO)*
Jonas Saric *(CFO)*

Board of Directors:
Lars G. V. Lindberg
Christer Fehrling
Christer Staaf
Ingvar Zoogling

Subsidiary:

AviaQ AB (1)
Lonnvagen 2
SE-184 43 Akersberga, Sweden
Tel.: (46) 8 544 104 80
Fax: (46) 8 544 104 89
E-Mail: sales@aviaq.com
Web Site: www.aviaq.com
Air Transportation Services
S.I.C.: 4581
N.A.I.C.S.: 488190

Non-U.S. Subsidiaries:

AVTECH France SARL (1)
Aeropole 3 5 Avenue Albert Durand
31700 Blagnac, France
Tel.: (33) 561 300 400
Air Transportation Services
S.I.C.: 4581
N.A.I.C.S.: 488190

AVTECH Middle East LLC (1)
Al Garhoud 57th Street Bu Shaqar Building
Office # 301
PO Box 97332
Dubai, United Arab Emirates
Tel.: (971) 4 250 44 66
Fax: (971) 4 250 44 77
Air Transportation Services
S.I.C.: 4581
N.A.I.C.S.: 488190

AVTOTEHNA, D.D.

Litijska 259
Ljubljana, 1000, Slovenia
Tel.: (386) 15853800
Fax: (386) 12301614
E-Mail: info@avtotehna.si
Web Site: www.avtotehna.si
Year Founded: 1953
Sales Range: $350-399.9 Million
Emp.: 1,400

Business Description:
Holding Company
S.I.C.: 6719
N.A.I.C.S.: 551112

Personnel:
Jordan Kocjancic *(Chm)*
Roman Groselj *(CEO)*

Board of Directors:
Jordan Kocjancic
Roman Groselj
Vitomir Kocutar
Peter Strbenk

Subsidiaries:

Advertus d.o.o. (1)
Slovenceva ulica 24
1000 Ljubljana, Slovenia
Tel.: (386) 15853711
Fax: (386) 15414432
E-Mail: info@advertus.si
Web Site: www.advertus.si
Emp.: 15
Wholesale Trade Agents & Brokers
S.I.C.: 7389
N.A.I.C.S.: 425120
Jeraj Marjeta *(Mng Dir)*

AT Adria d.o.o. (1)
Litijska 259
1261 Ljubljana, Dobrunje, Slovenia
Tel.: (386) 15853728
Fax: (386) 12301614
E-Mail: info@atadria.com
Web Site: www.atadria.com
Wholesale Trade Agents & Brokers
S.I.C.: 7389
N.A.I.C.S.: 425120
Gregor Smolnikar *(Mgr-Sls)*

Atrik d.o.o. (1)
Litijska Cesta 261
1261 Ljubljana, Slovenia
Tel.: (386) 15208700
Fax: (386) 15208702
E-Mail: atrik@avtotehna.si
Web Site: www.atrik.si
Wholesale Trade Agents & Brokers
S.I.C.: 7389
N.A.I.C.S.: 425120

Avtera d.o.o. (1)
Smartinska 106
1000 Ljubljana, Slovenia
Tel.: (386) 15853610
Web Site: www.avtera.si
Emp.: 120
Wholesale Trade Agents & Brokers
S.I.C.: 7389
N.A.I.C.S.: 425120
Damjan Celofiga *(Mng Dir)*

Avtotehna Oprema d.o.o. (1)
Litijska cesta 259
1261 Ljubljana, Slovenia
Tel.: (386) 15853700
Fax: (386) 15853725
E-Mail: info@at-oprema.si
Web Site: www.at-oprema.si
Emp.: 10
Wholesale Trade Agents & Brokers
S.I.C.: 7389
N.A.I.C.S.: 425120
Janez Susman *(Mng Dir)*

Avtotehna VIS d.o.o. (1)
Celovska Cesta 228
1000 Ljubljana, Slovenia
Tel.: (386) 15818510
Fax: (386) 15073843
E-Mail: info@avtotehna-vis.si
Web Site: www.avtotehna-vis.si
Automobile Sales
S.I.C.: 3711
N.A.I.C.S.: 336111

Birotehna d.o.o. (1)
Smartinska 106
Ljubljana, Slovenia
Tel.: (386) 15853410
E-Mail: info@birotehna.si
Web Site: www.birotehna.si
Wholesale Trade Agents & Brokers
S.I.C.: 7389
N.A.I.C.S.: 425120
Andrej Plesnik *(Mng Dir)*

Istra Avto d.o.o. (1)
Smarska Cesta 5A
6000 Koper, Slovenia
Tel.: (386) 56682300
Fax: (386) 56682470
E-Mail: info@istra-avto.si
Web Site: www.istra-avto.si
Emp.: 30
Wholesale Trade Agents & Brokers
S.I.C.: 7389
N.A.I.C.S.: 425120
Iztok Klabjan *(Gen Mgr)*

Repro-MS 03 d.o.o. (1)
Dolenjska cesta 242 C
1000 Ljubljana, Slovenia
Tel.: (386) 15853577
E-Mail: info@reproms.si
Web Site: www.reproms.si
Emp.: 10
Wholesale Trade Agents & Brokers
S.I.C.: 7389
N.A.I.C.S.: 425120
Ivo Rojec *(CEO)*

Swaty d.d. (1)
Titova cesta 60
2000 Maribor, Slovenia (73%)
Tel.: (386) 23331600
Fax: (386) 23331790
E-Mail: info@swatycomet.com
Web Site: www.swatycomet.si
Sales Range: $25-49.9 Million
Emp.: 610
Grinding Wheels Mfr
S.I.C.: 3542
N.A.I.C.S.: 333517
Drago Brence *(Asst Gen Mgr)*

AVTOVAZ OAO

Yuzhnoye Shosse
Togliatti, 445024, Russia
Tel.: (7) 8482739295
Fax: (7) 8482738221
Web Site: www.lada-auto.ru
AVAZ—(MIC RUS)
Sls.: $6,285,317,270
Assets: $4,688,598,460
Liabilities: $2,456,175,040
Net Worth: $2,232,423,420
Earnings: $964,982,600
Emp.: 112,200
Fiscal Year-end: 12/31/12

Business Description:
Passenger Car Mfr
S.I.C.: 3711
N.A.I.C.S.: 336111

Personnel:
Carlos Ghosn *(Chm)*
Sergey Chemezov *(Deputy Chm)*
Bo Inge Andersson *(CEO)*

Board of Directors:
Carlos Ghosn
Bruno Ancelin
Vladimir Vladimirovich Artjakov
Sergey Chemezov
Vincent Cobee
Sergey Kogoghin
Joseph Peter
Sergey Skvortsov
Carlos Tavares
Dominique Thormann
Ruben Vardanyan
Serge Yoccoz
Sergey Zaitsev
Igor Zavyalov

AVVAA WORLD HEALTH CARE PRODUCTS INC.

#4 4602 31st Street
Vernon, BC, V1T 5J9, Canada
Fax: (250) 275-8522
Toll Free: (866) 864-6598
E-Mail: info@avvaa.com
Web Site: www.avvaa.com
Year Founded: 1998
AVVH—(OTC)
Sales Range: Less than $1 Million
Emp.: 2

Business Description:
Skin Care & Animal Care Pharmaceuticals Mfr & Distr
S.I.C.: 2834
N.A.I.C.S.: 325412

Personnel:
Lance Loose *(CEO)*
Ruth Brennan *(CFO)*
Roland Busch *(COO)*

Board of Directors:
Mark E. Alden
Ruth Brennan
Paul C. Ryan

Legal Counsel:
Pushor Mitchell
301, 1665 Ellis Street
Kelowna, BC, V1Y 2B3, Canada

Anslow & Jaclin LLP
195 Route 9 South, Suite 204
Manalapan, NJ 07726

Transfer Agent:
Signature Stock Transfer Company
2632 Coachlight Court
Plano, TX 75093

AVY PRECISION TECHNOLOGY, INC.

10F No 101 Fu-Hsing North Road
Taipei, Taiwan
Tel.: (886) 225472089
Fax: (886) 2 25472909
Web Site: www.avy.com.tw
Year Founded: 1975
5392—(TAI)
Sales Range: $75-99.9 Million
Emp.: 5,080

Business Description:
Professional Camera Parts Distr
S.I.C.: 5731
N.A.I.C.S.: 443142

Personnel:
Mincheng Li *(Pres)*

AVZ MINERALS LIMITED

(Formerly Avonlea Minerals Limited)

Level 1 33 Ord Street
West Perth, WA, 6005, Australia
Mailing Address:
PO Box 637
West Perth, WA, 6872, Australia
Tel.: (61) 8 9420 9300
Fax: (61) 8 9420 9399
E-Mail: admin@avonleaminerals.com.au
Web Site: www.avonleaminerals.com.au
AVZ—(ASX)
Rev.: $32,048
Assets: $2,862,483
Liabilities: $26,211
Net Worth: $2,836,272
Earnings: ($2,514,589)
Fiscal Year-end: 06/30/13
Business Description:
Gold & Base Metals Exploration & Mining Services
S.I.C.: 1041
N.A.I.C.S.: 212221
Personnel:
Roger Steinepreis *(Chm)*
Gary Steinepreis *(Sec)*
Board of Directors:
Roger Steinepreis
David Riekie
Gary Steinepreis
Legal Counsel:
Steinepreis Paganin
Level 4 The Read Buildings 16 Milligan Street
Perth, Australia

A.W. FRASER LTD.

39 Lunns Rd
PO Box 6055
Christchurch, New Zealand
Tel.: (64) 33410027
Fax: (64) 33480457
E-Mail: info@awfraser.co.nz
Web Site: www.awfraser.co.nz
Sales Range: $10-24.9 Million
Emp.: 155
Fiscal Year-end: 03/31/13
Business Description:
Aluminum Extrusions Mfr
S.I.C.: 3399
N.A.I.C.S.: 331314
Personnel:
Gordon Sutherland *(CEO)*
Paul Isitt *(CFO)*

THE AWA BANK, LTD.

24-1 Nishisemba-cho 2-chome
Tokushima, 770-8601, Japan
Tel.: (81) 886233131
Fax: (81) 886237729
Web Site: www.awabank.co.jp
Year Founded: 1896
8388—(TKS)
Sales Range: $750-799.9 Million
Emp.: 1,393
Business Description:
Banking Services
S.I.C.: 6029
N.A.I.C.S.: 522110
Personnel:
Takehiro Furukawa *(Chm)*
Yoshifumi Okada *(Pres)*

AWA LIMITED

151 Arthur St
Homebush, NSW, 2140, Australia
Tel.: (61) 297647777
Fax: (61) 2987460016
E-Mail: info@awa.com.au
Web Site: www.awa.com.au
Year Founded: 1909
Sales Range: $25-49.9 Million
Emp.: 450
Business Description:
Information & Communications Technology Services
S.I.C.: 4899
N.A.I.C.S.: 517919
Personnel:
John Dougall *(Chm)*
Board of Directors:
John Dougall
Michael Brogan
Robert Moran

AWA PAPER MFG. CO., LTD.

3-10-18 Minamiyaso-cho
Tokushima-shi, Tokushima, 770-0005, Japan
Tel.: (81) 88 631 8100
Fax: (81) 88 632 5951
Web Site: www.awapaper.co.jp
Year Founded: 1916
38960—(TKS)
Sls.: $172,964,000
Assets: $170,225,000
Liabilities: $108,416,000
Net Worth: $61,809,000
Earnings: $4,862,000
Emp.: 400
Fiscal Year-end: 03/31/13
Business Description:
Paper Products Mfr
S.I.C.: 2621
N.A.I.C.S.: 322121
Personnel:
Yasuhiro Miki *(Pres)*

AWAY RESORTS LTD.

Barmouth Bay Holiday Park Tal-Y-Bont
Gwynedd, Wales, LL43 2BJ, United Kingdom
Tel.: (44) 1341 247350
Web Site: www.awayresorts.co.uk
Year Founded: 2008
Sales Range: $10-24.9 Million
Emp.: 142
Business Description:
Hotel Management Services
S.I.C.: 7011
N.A.I.C.S.: 721110
Personnel:
Carl Castledine *(Mng Dir)*

AWC BERHAD

20-2 Subang Business Centre Jalan USJ 9/5T UEP
Subang Jaya, Selangor, 47620, Malaysia
Tel.: (60) 380244505
Fax: (60) 380259343
E-Mail: info@awc.com.my
Web Site: www.awc.com.my
AWC—(KLS)
Rev.: $47,548,400
Assets: $50,936,386
Liabilities: $19,703,719
Net Worth: $31,232,668
Earnings: $1,832,435
Emp.: 604
Fiscal Year-end: 06/30/13
Business Description:
Building Automation System Mfr
S.I.C.: 1731
N.A.I.C.S.: 238210
Personnel:
Ahmad Kabeer Mohamed Nagoor *(CEO & Co-Mng Dir)*
Adnan Mohd Salleh *(Co-Mng Dir)*
Pek Hoong Shee *(Co-Sec)*
Sor Hua Tea *(Co-Sec)*
Board of Directors:
Mod Amin Abd Majid
Nagappan Chanthiran
Hussian Junid
Ahmad Kabeer Mohamed Nagoor
Roslan Mohd Latif
Sulaiman Mohd Yusof

Subsidiaries:

Ambang Wira Sdn. Bhd. **(1)**
18-5 Subang Business Centre Jalan USJ 9/5T
47620 Subang Jaya, Selangor, Malaysia
Tel.: (60) 380244505
Fax: (60) 380246243
Emp.: 308
Industrial Engineering Services
S.I.C.: 8711
N.A.I.C.S.: 541330
Tuan Farezuddeen Ahmad Tuan Ibrahim *(Mng Dir)*

Environmental and Landscape Services Sdn. Bhd. **(1)**
18-5 Subang Business Centre Jalan USJ 9/5T UEP
47620 Subang Jaya, Selangor, Malaysia
Tel.: (60) 380244505
Fax: (60) 380246243
Landscaping Services
S.I.C.: 0783
N.A.I.C.S.: 561730

Infinite QL Sdn. Bhd. **(1)**
G 02 Block A Dataran Hamodal
No 4 Jalan 13 4, 46300 Petaling Jaya, Selangor, Malaysia (51%)
Tel.: (60) 379626688
Fax: (60) 379601992
E-Mail: inquiries@infiniteql.com
Web Site: www.infiniteql.com
Emp.: 60
Surveillance & Communication System Mfr
S.I.C.: 3663
N.A.I.C.S.: 334220
P. Deivindran *(Mng Dir)*

Subsidiaries:

Cardax Sales & Services Sdn. Bhd. **(2)**
G 02 Ground Floor Block A Dataran Hamodal
No 4 Jalan 13/4 Section 13, 46300 Petaling Jaya, Selangor Darul Ehsan, Malaysia
Tel.: (60) 379626688
Fax: (60) 379601992
E-Mail: info@cardax.com.my
Web Site: www.cardax.com.my
Emp.: 70
Industrial Electronic Systems Sales & Maintenance Services
S.I.C.: 5065
N.A.I.C.S.: 423690
Bilal Chehime *(Co-Mng Dir)*
P. Deivendren *(Mng Dir)*

Device 4U Sdn. Bhd. **(2)**
G 02 Ground Floor Block A Dataran Hamodal
4 Jalan 13 4, 46300 Petaling Jaya, Selangor, Malaysia
Tel.: (60) 379626688
Fax: (60) 379601992
E-Mail: info@infiniteql.com
Web Site: www.infiniteql.com
Emp.: 70
Surveillance & Communication System Mfr
S.I.C.: 3812
N.A.I.C.S.: 334511
P. Deivindran *(CEO)*

Meps Devices Sdn. Bhd. **(2)**
G 02 Block A Dataran Hamodal
No 4 Jalan 13 4 Section 13, 46200 Petaling Jaya, Selangor, Malaysia
Tel.: (60) 379626688
Fax: (60) 379601992
E-Mail: info@infiniteql.com
Web Site: www.infiniteql.com
Emp.: 70
Surveillance & Communication System Mfr
S.I.C.: 3812
N.A.I.C.S.: 334511
P. Deivendran *(Mng Dir)*

Vdosoft Sdn. Bhd. **(2)**
G 02 Ground Floor Block A Dataran Hamodal
No 4 Jalan13/4 Section 13, 46300 Petaling Jaya, Selangor Darul Ehsan, Malaysia
Tel.: (60) 379626688
Fax: (60) 379601992
E-Mail: sales@vdosoft.com
Web Site: www.vdosoft.com
Emp.: 70
Digital Video Technological Research & Development Services
S.I.C.: 8731
N.A.I.C.S.: 541712
Thara Devi *(Mgr-Bus Dev)*

M&C Engineering & Trading Sdn. Bhd. **(1)**
79 Jalan SS25 2
Taman Bukit Emas, 47301 Petaling Jaya, Selangor, Malaysia MY
Tel.: (60) 378039511
Fax: (60) 378039517
E-Mail: mncpj@screamyx.com
Electrical Engineering Services
S.I.C.: 8711
N.A.I.C.S.: 541330
Jeffrey Lim *(Mng Dir)*

Nexaldes Sdn. Bhd. **(1)**
11 Jalan Sungai Besi Indah 5/2
Taman Sungai Besi Indah, 43300 Seri Kembangan, Selangor, Malaysia (51%)
Tel.: (60) 389418118
Fax: (60) 389418228
E-Mail: info@nexaldes.com
Web Site: www.nexaldes.com
Automated Waste Collection System Mfr
S.I.C.: 4952
N.A.I.C.S.: 221320
Gan Geok Soon *(Gen Mgr)*

Non-U.S. Subsidiary:

Nexaldes (S) Pte. Ltd. **(2)**
Block 9002 Tampines St 93 02 38
Singapore, 528836, Singapore
Tel.: (65) 68484366
Fax: (65) 67832680
E-Mail: info@nexaldes.com
Industrial Engineering Services
S.I.C.: 8711
N.A.I.C.S.: 541330

AWE LTD.

Level 16 40 Mount Street
North Sydney, NSW, 2060, Australia
Mailing Address:
PO Box 733
North Sydney, NSW, 2059, Australia
Tel.: (61) 2 8912 8000
Fax: (61) 2 9460 0176
E-Mail: awe@awexplore.com
Web Site: www.awexplore.com
AWE—(ASX)
Rev.: $314,478,685
Assets: $1,229,219,476
Liabilities: $302,822,797
Net Worth: $926,396,679
Earnings: $20,880,558
Emp.: 157
Fiscal Year-end: 06/30/13
Business Description:
Oil & Gas Exploration & Production
S.I.C.: 1311
N.A.I.C.S.: 211111
Personnel:
Bruce F. W. Clement *(Mng Dir)*
Ayten Saridas *(CFO)*
Drew Drew *(Gen Counsel & Gen Mgr-Comml)*
Neville Kelly *(Sec & Gen Mgr-Corp)*
Board of Directors:
Bruce J. Phillips
Raymond J. Betros
Vijoleta Braach-Maksvytis
Bruce F. W. Clement
Andy J. Hogendijk
David I. McEvoy
Karen L. C. Penrose
Ken G. Williams
Legal Counsel:
Piper Alderman
Level 23 Governor Macquarie Tower 1 Farrer Place
Sydney, NSW, 2000, Australia
Subsidiaries:

ARC Energy Limited **(1)**
Level 16 40 Mount Street
North Sydney, NSW, 2060, Australia
Tel.: (61) 289128000

AWE Ltd.—(Continued)

Fax: (61) 294600176
E-Mail: arc@arcenergy.com.au
Web Site: www.arcenergy.com.au
Sales Range: $100-124.9 Million
Emp.: 67
Petroleum Production & Exploration
S.I.C.: 2999
N.A.I.C.S.: 324199
B. J. Phillips *(Chm)*

Peedamullah Petroleum Pty. Ltd. **(1)**
Level 9 60 Miller St
North Sydney, Sydney, New South Wales, 2060, Australia
Tel.: (61) 294600165
Fax: (61) 294600176
Emp.: 40
Oil & Gas Field Exploration Services
S.I.C.: 1311
N.A.I.C.S.: 211111

Non-U.S. Subsidiaries:

AWE New Zealand Pty. Limited **(1)**
8th Fl Genesis Energy House 33 Gill St
New Plymouth, 4342, New Zealand
Tel.: (64) 67592173
Fax: (64) 6 759 2175
E-Mail: awenz@awexplore.com
Web Site: www.awexplore.com
Emp.: 16
Oil & Gas Exploration Services
S.I.C.: 1381
N.A.I.C.S.: 213111
Bruce Clement *(Mng Dir)*

AWE Taranaki Limited **(1)**
Level 8 25 33 Gill St New Plymouth Cent
PO Box 8156
New Plymouth, 4342, New Zealand
Tel.: (64) 67592173
Fax: (64) 67592175
E-Mail: awez@aweexplore.com
Web Site: www.aweexplore.com
Emp.: 12
Oil & Gas Field Exploration Services
S.I.C.: 1311
N.A.I.C.S.: 211111
Bruce Philips *(Mng Dir)*

AWE PLC

Aldermaston
Reading, Berkshire, RG7 4PR, United Kingdom
Tel.: (44) 1189814111
Fax: (44) 1189815320
E-Mail: enquiries@awe.co.uk
Web Site: www.awe.co.uk
Sales Range: $550-599.9 Million
Emp.: 8,000
Business Description:
Nuclear Warhead Maintenance Services
S.I.C.: 9711
N.A.I.C.S.: 928110
Personnel:
Lindsey Appleton *(Sec)*

AWEA MECHANTRONIC CO., LTD.

629 Suezhetou Section KwanPu Rd
305 Hsinpu, Hsinchu, Taiwan
Tel.: (886) 35885191
Fax: (886) 35889896
E-Mail: service@awea.com
Web Site: www.awea.com
1530—(TAI)
Sales Range: $25-49.9 Million
Business Description:
Boring & Milling Machinery Mfr
S.I.C.: 3542
N.A.I.C.S.: 333517
Personnel:
Edward Yang *(Chm)*

Plant:

Awea Mechantronic Co., Ltd. - Taiwan Taichung Factory **(1)**
No 15 Keyuan 2nd Road Central Taiwan Science Park, Taichung, 407, Taiwan
Tel.: (886) 424629698
Fax: (886) 424628002
E-Mail: service@awea.com
Industrial Machine Tools Mfr
S.I.C.: 3541
N.A.I.C.S.: 333517

Non-U.S. Subsidiary:

Best Way Mechantronic Co. **(1)**
No 7801 Song Ze Road Qingpu Industrial Zone
Shanghai, 201700, China
Tel.: (86) 2169210588
Fax: (86) 21 69210760
Machine Tools Mfr
S.I.C.: 3541
N.A.I.C.S.: 333517

AWESOME INVESTMENTS INC.

720 West Broadway 999
Vancouver, BC, V5Z IK5, Canada
Tel.: (604) 288-5350
Fax: (604) 357-4740
E-Mail: info@awesomeinvestments.ca
Web Site: www.awesomeinvestments.ca
A2W—(DEU)
Business Description:
Investment Services; Gold & Other Metal Mining; Renewable Energy
S.I.C.: 6211
N.A.I.C.S.: 523999
Personnel:
Hans J. Bocker *(Chm-Supervisory Bd)*
Johan Goldsmith *(Member-Exec Bd)*
Philipp Muray *(Member-Exec Bd)*
Wolfgang Rensing *(Member-Exec Bd)*
Paul Richards *(Member-Exec Bd)*
David Rigoll *(Member-Exec Bd)*
David Rush *(Member-Exec Bd)*
Supervisory Board of Directors:
Hans J. Bocker
Jack Lifton
Ben Paton

AWF GROUP LIMITED

2 Walls Road
PO Box 12832
Penrose, New Zealand
Tel.: (64) 95268770
Fax: (64) 95790224
Web Site: www.awf.co.nz
Year Founded: 1988
AWF—(NZE)
Rev.: $109,209,249
Assets: $29,608,875
Liabilities: $11,523,816
Net Worth: $18,085,059
Earnings: $5,794,551
Emp.: 200
Fiscal Year-end: 03/31/13
Business Description:
Temporary Help Services
S.I.C.: 7363
N.A.I.C.S.: 561320
Personnel:
Ross Keenan *(Chm)*
Mike Huddleston *(CEO)*
Simon Hull *(Mng Dir)*
David Sutherland *(CFO)*
Board of Directors:
Ross Keenan
Mike Huddleston
Simon Hull
Eduard van Arkel
Legal Counsel:
Russell McVeagh
Vero Centre 48 Shortland Street 8
Auckland, New Zealand

Subsidiaries:

Allied Work Force Christchurch Limited **(1)**
2 Gasson Street
Sydenham, Christchurch, Canterbury, New Zealand
Tel.: (64) 33749176
Fax: (64) 33749376
Web Site: www.aws.co.nz
Emp.: 4
Labor Hiring Services
S.I.C.: 7361
N.A.I.C.S.: 561311
Mike Huddlestone *(CEO)*

Allied Work Force Dunedin Limited **(1)**
163 Hillside Road
Dunedin, Otago, 9012, New Zealand
Tel.: (64) 34555511
Fax: (64) 34555520
E-Mail: dunedin@awf.co.nz
Web Site: www.awf.co.nz
Emp.: 3
Labor Hiring Services
S.I.C.: 7361
N.A.I.C.S.: 561311
Ken Schumacher *(Branch Mgr)*

Allied Work Force Hamilton Limited **(1)**
Unit 3 27 norten road
Te Rapa, Hamilton, Waikato, New Zealand
Tel.: (64) 78508595
Fax: (64) 78508579
E-Mail: hamilton@awf.co.nz
Web Site: www.awf.co.nz
Emp.: 4
Labor Hiring Services
S.I.C.: 7361
N.A.I.C.S.: 561311
Toni Harris *(Mgr)*

Allied Work Force Limited **(1)**
7A Vega Pl
Penrose, Mairangi Bay, Auckland, New Zealand
Tel.: (64) 94756882
Fax: (64) 9 479 8011
Labor Hiring Services
S.I.C.: 7361
N.A.I.C.S.: 561311
Chris Moore *(Branch Mgr)*

Allied Work Force Nelson Limited **(1)**
101 Bolt Rd
Tahunanui, Nelson, 7011, New Zealand
Tel.: (64) 35475467
Fax: (64) 35472475
Web Site: www.awf.co.nz
Emp.: 3
Labor Hiring Services
S.I.C.: 7361
N.A.I.C.S.: 561311
Graham Pitman *(Mgr-Trade)*

Allied Work Force Palmerston North Limited **(1)**
45 Walding St
Palmerston North, 4410, New Zealand
Tel.: (64) 63558080
Fax: (64) 63552209
E-Mail: info@awf.co.nz
Web Site: www.awf.co.nz
Emp.: 3
Labor Hiring Services
S.I.C.: 7361
N.A.I.C.S.: 561311
Graham Musson *(Branch Mgr)*

Allied Work Force Tauranga Limited **(1)**
6 Marsh St
Tauranga, 3110, New Zealand
Tel.: (64) 75718575
Fax: (64) 7 577 1773
E-Mail: tauranga@0800labour.co.nz
Labor Hiring Services
S.I.C.: 7361
N.A.I.C.S.: 561311
Miles Taiaroa *(Branch Mgr)*

Allied Work Force Wellington Limited **(1)**
89 Thorndon Quay
Petone, Wellington, 6035, New Zealand
Tel.: (64) 45665171
Fax: (64) 45665172
E-Mail: wellington@awf.co.nz
Web Site: www.awf.co.nz
Emp.: 9
Labor Hiring Services
S.I.C.: 7361
N.A.I.C.S.: 561311
Mark Sorenson *(Mgr)*

Allied Work Force Whangarei Limited **(1)**
33B Commerce St
Whangarei, 0110, New Zealand
Tel.: (64) 94597273
Fax: (64) 094597271
E-Mail: Whangarei@awf.co.nz
Web Site: www.awf.co.nz
Emp.: 101
Labor Hiring Services
S.I.C.: 7361
N.A.I.C.S.: 561311
John Robins *(Mgr)*

Quin Workforce Limited **(1)**
30 Queens Drive
Lower Hutt, 5040, New Zealand
Tel.: (64) 45862761
Fax: (64) 45862762
Web Site: www.quin.co.nz
Emp.: 12
Labor Hiring Services
S.I.C.: 7361
N.A.I.C.S.: 561311

AWILCO DRILLING PLC

12 Abercrombie Court Prospect Road
Westhill, Aberdeen, AB32 6FE, United Kingdom
Tel.: (44) 1224 737900
Fax: (44) 1224 737905
Web Site: www.awilcodrilling.com
Year Founded: 2009
AWDR—(OSL OTC)
Rev.: $152,227,000
Assets: $317,107,000
Liabilities: $138,760,000
Net Worth: $178,347,000
Earnings: $39,394,000
Emp.: 215
Fiscal Year-end: 12/31/12
Business Description:
Oil & Gas Drilling Services
S.I.C.: 1381
N.A.I.C.S.: 213111
Personnel:
Jon Oliver S. Bryce *(CEO)*
Ian Wilson *(CFO)*
Roddy Smith *(Exec VP)*
Board of Directors:
Sigurd E. Thorvildsen
Jon Oliver S. Bryce
Henrik Fougner
Daniel Gold
John Simpson
Synne Syrrist

AWILCO LNG ASA

Beddingen 8 Aker Brygge
NO-0250 Oslo, Norway
Mailing Address:
PO Box 1583
Vika, NO-0118 Oslo, Norway
Tel.: (47) 2201 4200
Fax: (47) 2201 4370
E-Mail: jea@awilcolng.no
Web Site: www.awilcolng.no
ALNG—(OSL)
Business Description:
LNG Vessel Owner & Operator
S.I.C.: 4731
N.A.I.C.S.: 488510
Personnel:
Sigurd E. Thorvildsen *(Chm)*
Jon Skule Storheill *(CEO)*
Snorre Schie Krogstad *(CFO)*
Ian S. Walker *(Sr VP-Chartering)*
Board of Directors:
Sigurd E. Thorvildsen
Henrik Fougner

Annette Malm Justad
Synne Syrrist
Jon-Aksel Torgersen

Subsidiaries:

Awilco LNG 1 AS (1)
Beddingen 8
Oslo, 250, Norway
Tel.: (47) 22014200
Liquefied Natural Gas Transportation Services
S.I.C.: 4412
N.A.I.C.S.: 483111

Awilco LNG 2 AS (1)
Beddingen 8
Oslo, 250, Norway
Tel.: (47) 22014200
Fax: (47) 22014370
E-Mail: mail@awilcolng.no
Web Site: www.awilcolng.no
Emp.: 7
Liquefied Natural Gas Transportation Services
S.I.C.: 4412
N.A.I.C.S.: 483111
Jon Skule Storheill *(CEO)*

Awilco LNG 3 AS (1)
Beddingen 8
Oslo, 250, Norway
Tel.: (47) 22014200
Web Site: www.awilcolng.no
Emp.: 7
Liquefied Natural Gas Transportation Services
S.I.C.: 4412
N.A.I.C.S.: 483111
Jon Skule Storheill *(CEO)*

Awilco LNG 4 AS (1)
Beddingen 8
Oslo, 0250, Norway
Tel.: (47) 22014200
Fax: (47) 22014372
Liquefied Natural Gas Transportation Services
S.I.C.: 4412
N.A.I.C.S.: 483111

Awilco LNG 5 AS (1)
Beddingen 8
Oslo, 250, Norway
Tel.: (47) 22014200
Fax: (47) 22014372
Liquefied Natural Gas Transportation Services
S.I.C.: 4412
N.A.I.C.S.: 483111

Awilco LNG 6 AS (1)
Beddingen 8
Oslo, 250, Norway
Tel.: (47) 22014200
Fax: (47) 22014370
Web Site: www.awilcolng.no
Emp.: 7
Liquefied Natural Gas Transportation Services
S.I.C.: 4412
N.A.I.C.S.: 483111
Jon Skule Storheill *(CEO)*

Awilco LNG 7 AS (1)
Beddingen 8
Oslo, 250, Norway
Tel.: (47) 22014200
Fax: (47) 22014378
Liquefied Natural Gas Transportation Services
S.I.C.: 4412
N.A.I.C.S.: 483111

AWS ACHSLAGERWERK STASSFURT GMBH

An der Liethe 5
39418 Stassfurt, Germany
Tel.: (49) 3925960402
Fax: (49) 3925960405
E-Mail: info@aws-tec.de
Web Site: www.aws-tec.de
Rev.: $33,409,084
Emp.: 175

Business Description:
Industrial Machinery Mfr
S.I.C.: 3559
N.A.I.C.S.: 333249

Personnel:
Thomas Heb *(Mng Dir)*

AWTAD FOR DIVERSIFIED INVESTMENTS PLC

AbdulHamid Sharaf Street Building No 65
Al-Shmesani, Amman, 11180, Jordan
Tel.: (962) 6 5560909
Fax: (962) 6 5662903
Year Founded: 2005
AWTD—(AMM)
Sales Range: $1-9.9 Million
Emp.: 4

Business Description:
Financial Investment Services
S.I.C.: 6211
N.A.I.C.S.: 523999

Personnel:
Radi Ghazi Farhan Al Marji *(Gen Mgr)*

AXA S.A.

(d/b/a The AXA Group)
25 avenue Matignon
75008 Paris, France
Tel.: (33) 140755700
Fax: (33) 140755954
E-Mail: infos.web@axa.com
Web Site: www.axa.com
Year Founded: 1816
CS—(EUR OTC)
Rev.: $121,324,917,420
Liabilities: $950,167,171,100
Net Worth: $75,411,097,230
Earnings: $5,765,646,110
Emp.: 94,364
Fiscal Year-end: 12/31/12

Business Description:
Holding Company; Insurance & Financial Products, Including Reinsurance, Asset Management & Real Estate Services
S.I.C.: 6311
N.A.I.C.S.: 524113

Personnel:
Henri de Castries *(Chm & CEO)*
Norbert Dentressangle *(Vice Chm)*
Denis Pierre Marie Duverne *(Deputy CEO-Fin, Strategy & Ops)*
Gerald Harlin *(CFO)*
Veronique Weill *(COO)*
Alban de Mailly Nesle *(Grp Chief Risk Officer)*
Shubhro Mitra *(Chief HR Officer-Asia)*
Christiane Bisanzio *(Grp Chief Diversity & Inclusion Officer & Head-HR)*
Guillaume Borie *(Media Rels Officer)*
Helene Caillet *(Media Rels Officer)*
Jean-Laurent Granier *(Chm/CEO-AXA Global P&C & CEO-Mediterranean & Latin America)*
Peter Steven Kraus *(Chm/CEO-AllianceBersntein)*
Nicolas Moreau *(Chm/CEO-AXA France)*
Mark Pearson *(Pres/CEO-AXA Financial Inc)*
Jacques M. de Vaucleroy *(CEO-Northern, Central & Eastern Europe & Head-Life & Savings)*
Michael Bishop *(CEO-AXA Asia)*
Thomas Buberl *(CEO-AXA Konzern AG)*
Emmanuel de Talhouet *(CEO-AXA Belgium)*
Philippe Egger *(CEO-Insurance Activities-Switzerland)*
Paul Evans *(CEO-AXA UK)*
Jean-Louis Laurent Josi *(CEO-AXA Japan)*
George Stansfield *(Grp Gen Counsel & Head-HR)*
Mattieu Rouot *(Sr VP & Head-IR)*

Board of Directors:
Henri de Castries
Jean-Pierre Clamadieu
Ramon de Oliveira
Norbert Dentressangle
Denis Pierre Marie Duverne
Jean-Martin Folz
Paul Hermelin
Isabelle Kocher
Suet Fern Lee
Stefan Lippe
Francois Martineau
Deanna W. Oppenheimer
Doina Palici-Chehab
Dominique Reiniche
Marcus Schenck

Mazars
61 rue Henri Regnault
Courbevoie, France

Subsidiaries:

AXA Assistance S.A. (1)
6 rue Andre Gide
92328 Chatillon, France FR
Tel.: (33) 155924000 (100%)
Fax: (33) 155924050
E-Mail: info@axa-assistance.com
Web Site: www.axa-assistance.com
Emp.: 1,000
Holding Company
S.I.C.: 6719
N.A.I.C.S.: 551112
Serge Morelli *(Chm & CEO)*

Subsidiary:

AXA Assistance France (2)
6 Rue Andre Gide
92321 Chatillon, Cedex 92328, France (100%)
Tel.: (33) 155924000
Fax: (33) 155924050
E-Mail: management@axa-assistance.com
Web Site: www.axa-assistance.com
Emp.: 2,941
Insurance
S.I.C.: 6399
N.A.I.C.S.: 524128
Yves Masson *(Pres & Dir Gen)*

Subsidiaries:

Pluridis (3)
87 Rue Saint-Lazare
F-75009 Paris, France FR
Tel.: (33) 155319595 (60%)
Fax: (33) 155319940
E-Mail: info@pluridis.tm.fr
Web Site: www.pluridis.tm.fr
Rev.: $12,015
Emp.: 5
Employee Support Services
S.I.C.: 7389
N.A.I.C.S.: 561499
Pataecea Cavre *(Mng Dir)*

U.S. Unit:

AXA Assistance USA, Inc. (2)
122 S Michigan Ave Ste 1100
Chicago, IL 60603 IL
Tel.: (312) 935-3500
Fax: (312) 935-3575
E-Mail: medassist-usa@axa-assistance.us
Web Site: www.axa-assistance-usa.com
Emp.: 150
Personal Service Agents Brokers & Bureaus
S.I.C.: 7299
N.A.I.C.S.: 812990
Bernard Ferrand *(Sr VP-North America)*

Non-U.S. Subsidiaries:

AXA ASSISTANCE (BEIJING) Co., LTD. (2)
Rm 2801 Tower B Pengrun Palaza No 26
Xiao Yun Road
Chaoyang District, Beijing, 100016, China
Tel.: (86) 108468 5899
Fax: (86) 1084580295
Web Site: www.axa-assistance.com.cn
Medical Assistance Services
S.I.C.: 9441
N.A.I.C.S.: 923130

AXA Assistance Canada Inc. (2)
2001 University Street Suite 1850
Montreal, QC, H3A 2L8, Canada
Tel.: (877) 472-2623
Fax: (514) 285-9017
Toll Free: (877) 472-2623
Web Site: www.axa-assistance.ca
Roadside Medical Assistance Services
S.I.C.: 9441
N.A.I.C.S.: 923130

AXA Assistance Chile S.A (2)
Josue Smith Solar 390
Santiago, Chile
Tel.: (56) 29418900
Fax: (56) 29418951
E-Mail: comercial@axa-assistance.cl
Web Site: www.axa-assistance.cl
Emp.: 3
General Insurance Services
S.I.C.: 6411
N.A.I.C.S.: 524298
Waldo Lavados *(Dir-Comml)*

AXA Assistance Deutschland GmbH (2)
Garmischer Strasse 8-10
80339 Munich, Germany De
Tel.: (49) 8950070500
Fax: (49) 8950070250
E-Mail: info@axa-assistance.de
Web Site: www.axa-assistance.de
General Insurance Services
S.I.C.: 6411
N.A.I.C.S.: 524298
Aziza Bendzko *(Deputy Mng Dir & Dir-HR & Svcs Centre)*

AXA Assistance India Private Limited (2)
A 265 1st Floor Defence Colony
New Delhi, 110024, India
Tel.: (91) 11 4573 5555
Fax: (91) 11 4507 0617
E-Mail: enquiries@axa-assistance.in
Web Site: www.axa-assistance.in
Emp.: 35
General Assistance Services
S.I.C.: 6411
N.A.I.C.S.: 524298
Pradeep Bery *(CEO & Dir-Medical)*

AXA Assistance Japan Co., Ltd. (2)
Tower 14F 1-17-3 NBF Platinum Platinum
Minato-ku, Tokyo, 108-0072, Japan
Tel.: (81) 3 6737 5050
Fax: (81) 3 6737 5074
E-Mail: contact@axa-assistance.co.jp
Web Site: www.axa-assistance.co.jp
Emp.: 15
General Insurance Services
S.I.C.: 6411
N.A.I.C.S.: 524298
Hiromitsu Matsumoto *(Gen Mgr)*

AXA Assistance Mexico SA de CV (2)
Lago Victoria 74 Piso 6
Miguel Hidalgo, Mexico, Mexico
Tel.: (52) 5552559426
E-Mail: servicio.cliente@axa-asistance.com.mx
Web Site: www.axa-assistance.com.mx
General Insurance Services
S.I.C.: 6411
N.A.I.C.S.: 524210

AXA Assistance Ocean Indien Ltd (2)
No 8 DBM Building Industrial Zone
Coromandel
Port Louis, Mauritius
Tel.: (230) 233 0340
Fax: (230) 233 0457
E-Mail: axaaoi@axa-assistance-mauritius.com
Web Site: www.axa-assistance-mauritius.com
General Insurance Services
S.I.C.: 6411
N.A.I.C.S.: 524210

AXA Assistance Panama SA. (2)
Ave Via Espana Plaza Comercial San Fernando Local 1 y 2
Panama, Panama
Tel.: (507) 3661400
Fax: (507) 3661402
E-Mail: servicioalcliente@axa-assistance.com.pa
Web Site: www.axa-assistance.com.pa
Emp.: 6

AXA S.A.—(Continued)

General Insurance Services
S.I.C.: 6411
N.A.I.C.S.: 524298
Lena Bonilla *(Mng Dir)*

AXA Assistance (UK) Ltd (2)
The Quadrangle 106-118 Station Road
Redhill, Surrey, RH1 1PR, United Kingdom
Tel.: (44) 1737 815 023
Fax: (44) 870 609 0024
E-Mail: enquiries@axa-assistance.co.uk
Web Site: www.axa-assistance.co.uk
Emp.: 442
General Insurance Services
S.I.C.: 6411
N.A.I.C.S.: 524298
Bob Ewers *(CEO)*
Sharon Scully *(CFO & Gen Mgr-Property & Legal)*

AXA Assistance (2)
Hvezdova 1689/2a
140 62 Prague, Czech Republic
Tel.: (420) 272 101 099
Fax: (420) 272 101 009
E-Mail: office@axa-assistance.cz
Web Site: www.axa-assistance.cz
Emp.: 20
General Insurance Services
S.I.C.: 6411
N.A.I.C.S.: 524298
Haimo Primas *(Gen Mgr)*

Inter Partner Assistance S.A (2)
Ave Louise 166 B1
1050 Brussels, Belgium (100%)
Tel.: (32) 25500400
Fax: (32) 25525223
E-Mail: Direction.Brussels@ip-assistance.com
Web Site: www.ip-assistance.be
Emp.: 320
Personal insurance services
S.I.C.: 6411
N.A.I.C.S.: 524298
Theresa Deman *(Dir-HR)*

Non-U.S. Subsidiaries:

Call Us Assistance International GmbH (3)
Waschhausgasse 2
1020 Vienna, Austria
Tel.: (43) 1 316 70 0
Fax: (43) 3167070110
E-Mail: office@call-us-assistance.com
Web Site: www.call-us-assistance.com
Emp.: 30
Business Process Outsourcing Services
S.I.C.: 7389
N.A.I.C.S.: 561499
Konrad Legat *(CEO)*

Inter Partner Asistencia Servicios Espana SA (3)
Valores 1
28007 Madrid, Spain
Tel.: (34) 91 468 87 00
Fax: (34) 914682210
E-Mail: comercial@ipartner.es
Web Site: www.ip-assistance.es
General Assistance Services
S.I.C.: 7389
N.A.I.C.S.: 561990
Enrique Lamarca *(Dir Gen)*

Inter Partner Assistance Algerie Spa (3)
76 Boulevard Krim Belkacem
16 000 Algiers, Algeria
Tel.: (213) 21 98 00 00
Fax: (213) 1321980002
E-Mail: Info.Alger@ip-assistance.dz
Web Site: www.ip-assistance.dz
Emp.: 33
General Assistance Services
S.I.C.: 7389
N.A.I.C.S.: 561990
Cherifa Taif *(Mgr-Ops)*

Inter Partner Assistance Co., Ltd. (3)
41 Soi Loetpanya Si Ayutthaya Khwang Thanon
Phyathai Khet Ratcha Thewi, Bangkok, Thailand
Tel.: (66) 22065400
Fax: (66) 26427786
E-Mail: medical@ipa.co.th
Medical Assistance Services
S.I.C.: 9441
N.A.I.C.S.: 923130

Inter Partner Assistance Greece (3)
377 Syngrou Avenue
Palio Phaliro, 17564 Athens, Greece
Tel.: (30) 210 9475 900
Fax: (30) 210 948338
E-Mail: sales@inter-partner.gr
Web Site: www.inter-partner.gr
Medical Assistance Services
S.I.C.: 9441
N.A.I.C.S.: 923130
Sven V. Loison *(Gen Mgr)*

Inter Partner Assistance Hong-Kong Ltd (3)
Unit 1015-1018 10th Floor Tower 1
Millennium City 1 388 Kwun Tong Road
Kwun Tong, Kowloon, China (Hong Kong)
Tel.: (852) 2851 0620
Fax: (852) 2851 0910
E-Mail: enquiry@ipahk.com.hk
Web Site: www.ipahk.com.hk
Emp.: 30
General Assistance Services
S.I.C.: 7389
N.A.I.C.S.: 561990
Joseph Lee *(Gen Mgr)*

Inter Partner Assistance Ltd (3)
17/F-1 No 77 Sec 2 Tun Hua S Rd Rm B
Taipei, 10682, Taiwan
Tel.: (886) 2 2700 7700
Fax: (886) 2 2703 2900
E-Mail: oea@ipassistance.com.tw
Web Site: www.ipassistance.com.tw
Medical Assistance Services
S.I.C.: 9441
N.A.I.C.S.: 923130

Inter Partner Assistance Polska S.A. (3)
Ul Chlodna 51 Warsaw Trade Tower VII Pietro
00-867 Warsaw, Poland
Tel.: (48) 22 529 84 00
Fax: (48) 22 529 84 41
E-Mail: biuro@ipa.com.pl
Web Site: www.ipa.com.pl
General Assistance Services
S.I.C.: 7389
N.A.I.C.S.: 561990
Marta Kalenska-Jaskiewicz *(CEO)*

Inter Partner Assistance s/c Ltda (3)
Al Rio Negro 433 - 5 Andar Alphaville
Barueri, Sao Paulo, 06454-904, Brazil
Tel.: (55) 11 41965922
E-Mail: comercial@interpartner.com.br
Web Site: www.interpartner.com.br
General Assistance Services
S.I.C.: 7389
N.A.I.C.S.: 561990

Inter Partner Assistance S.A. (3)
Cours de Rive 2
1204 Geneva, Switzerland
Tel.: (41) 22 819 44 00
E-Mail: info.ch@axa-assistance.com
Web Site: www.inter-partner.ch
Medical Assistance Services
S.I.C.: 9441
N.A.I.C.S.: 923130
Serge Morelli *(Gen Mgr)*

Inter Partner Assistance Services BV (3)
Joop Geesinkweg 901-999
Amsterdam, 1096 AZ, Netherlands
Tel.: (31) 206640131
Fax: (31) 206731171
General Assistance Services
S.I.C.: 7389
N.A.I.C.S.: 561990

Inter Partner Assistance Turkey (3)
Kisikli Mah Bosna Bulvari No 39 Camlica
Uskudar, 34760 Istanbul, Uskudar, Turkey
Tel.: (90) 216 524 3636
Fax: (90) 216 524 3637
E-Mail: info@interpartnerassistance.com
Web Site: www.interpartnerassistance.com
General Assistance Services
S.I.C.: 7389
N.A.I.C.S.: 561990

Inter Partner Assistenza Servizi Spa (3)
Via Bernardino Alimena 111
00173 Rome, Italy
Tel.: (39) 06421181
E-Mail: servizio.comunicazione@ip-assistance.com
Web Site: www.axa-assistance.it
General Insurance Services
S.I.C.: 6411
N.A.I.C.S.: 524210

AXA Assurances (1)
26 rue Drouot
75458 Paris, Cedex 09, France (100%)
Tel.: (33) 147741001
Fax: (33) 149498540
Web Site: www.axa.fr
Emp.: 280
S.I.C.: 6399
N.A.I.C.S.: 524128
Francois Pierson *(Pres)*

AXA Banque (1)
203 Rue Carnot Cevex Cedex
Fontenay-sous-Bois, 94138, France (100%)
Mailing Address:
137 Rue Victor Hugo
92687 Levallois-Perret, Cedex, France
Tel.: (33) 155628000
Fax: (33) 155128210
E-Mail: information@axabanque.fr
Web Site: www.axabanque.com
Emp.: 500
Asset Management & Financial Services
S.I.C.: 6099
N.A.I.C.S.: 522320

AXA Cessions (1)
9 Avenue De Messine
75008 Paris, France
Tel.: (33) 156 437 800
Fax: (33) 156 437 801
Web Site: www.axa.com
Insurance Service Provider
S.I.C.: 6411
N.A.I.C.S.: 524298

AXA Conseil (1)
21 Rue De Chateaudun
75009 Paris, France (100%)
Tel.: (33) 156023000
Fax: (33) 156023232
Web Site: www.axa.fr
S.I.C.: 6399
N.A.I.C.S.: 524128

AXA Corporate Solutions Assurance S.A (1)
2 4Jules Lefebvre
92320 Paris, France
Tel.: (33) 1 56 92 80 00
Fax: (33) 1 56928001
General Insurance Services
S.I.C.: 6411
N.A.I.C.S.: 524298
Philippe Rocard *(Gen Mgr)*

AXA Corporate Solutions (1)
52 Rue Jules Lefebvre
75009 Paris, 75009, France (100%)
Tel.: (33) 156928000
Fax: (33) 0147743019
E-Mail: serge.morelli@axa.fr
Web Site: www.axa-corporatesolutions.com
Emp.: 777
S.I.C.: 6399
N.A.I.C.S.: 524128
Jean Paul Rignault *(CEO)*

AXA Credit (1)
203 rue Carnot
94138 Fontenay-sous-Bois, Cedex, France (100%)
Tel.: (33) 155628000
Fax: (33) 155629010
E-Mail: information@axabank.fr
Web Site: www.axabank.com
Emp.: 600
S.I.C.: 6399
N.A.I.C.S.: 524128
Kipierre Janin *(Gen Dir)*

AXA France Assurance SAS (1)
313 Gerrasses de l'Arche
92727 Nanterre, Cedex, France FR
Tel.: (33) 147741001 (100%)
Fax: (33) 147742822
Web Site: www.axa.fr
Emp.: 200
S.I.C.: 6399
N.A.I.C.S.: 524128
Francois Pierson *(Chm & CEO)*
Henry De Castries *(CEO)*

Subsidiaries:

AXA Epargne Entreprise (2)
313 Terrasses de l'Arche
92727 Nanterre, France
Tel.: (33) 147 741 001
Web Site: www.epargneretraiteentreprise.axa.fr
General Insurance Services
S.I.C.: 6411
N.A.I.C.S.: 524298

AXA France IARD (2)
26 rue Drouot
75009 Paris, France
Tel.: (33) 3 23 53 27 64
Reinsurance Services
S.I.C.: 6399
N.A.I.C.S.: 524130

AXA France Vie S.A (2)
313 Terrasses de l'Arche
92727 Nanterre, Cedex, France
Tel.: (33) 147741001
Fax: (33) 147742822
Web Site: www.axa.fr
Emp.: 100
General Insurance Services
S.I.C.: 6411
N.A.I.C.S.: 524210
Nicolas Moreau *(CEO)*

AXA Investment Managers S.A. (1)
100 Esplanade du General de Gaulle
92932 Paris, France FR
Tel.: (33) 144458565 (100%)
Fax: (33) 144458743
E-Mail: serviceclientsaxa-im@axa-im.com
Web Site: www.axa-im.com
Emp.: 2,500
Holding Company; Investment Advisory & Asset Management Services
S.I.C.: 6719
N.A.I.C.S.: 551112
Andrea Rossi *(CEO)*

Subsidiaries:

AXA Investment Managers Paris S.A. (2)
100 Esplanade du General De Gaulle
92932 Paris, Cedex, France FR
Tel.: (33) 144457000 (100%)
Fax: (33) 155077307
E-Mail: axa.partelaire@axa.fr
Web Site: www.axa-im.fr
Emp.: 1,000
Asset Management & Financial Services
S.I.C.: 6282
N.A.I.C.S.: 523920

AXA Real Estate Investment Managers S.A. (2)
Coeur Defense Tour B 100 Esplanade du General de Gaulle
La Defense, 92932 Paris, France FR
Tel.: (33) 1 44 45 95 00
E-Mail:
Web Site: www.axa-realestate.com
Emp.: 1,500
Real Estate Portfolio Management Services
S.I.C.: 6531
N.A.I.C.S.: 531390
Pierre Vaquier *(CEO)*

Non-U.S. Subsidiaries:

AXA Real Estate Investment Managers Italia S.r.l. (3)
Corso Di Porta Romana 68
20122 Milan, Italy IT
Tel.: (39) 02 5844 201
Real Estate Investment Services
S.I.C.: 6531
N.A.I.C.S.: 531390
Leone Colombo *(Head-Local Asset Mgmt)*

AXA Real Estate Investment Managers Japan KK (3)
1-17-3 Shirokane NBF Platinum Tower 14F
Minato-ku, 108-0072 Tokyo, Japan
Tel.: (81) 3 57 93 22 00
Fax: (81) 3 34 49 38 25
Web Site: www.axa.com
Emp.: 10
Real Estate Investment Services
S.I.C.: 6531
N.A.I.C.S.: 531390
Tetsuya Karasawa *(Sr Mgr-Bus Dev)*

AXA Real Estate Investment Managers Nederland B.V. (3)
Strawinskylaan 2701 Atrium Tower A - 14th Floor
1077 ZZ Amsterdam, Netherlands NL
Tel.: (31) 20 30 11 150
Web Site: www.axa-realestate.com
Real Estate Management Services
S.I.C.: 6531
N.A.I.C.S.: 531390
Alphons Spaninks *(Head-Asset Mgmt)*

Non-U.S. Units:

AXA Real Estate Investment Managers - Hungary (3)
Kalman Imre Utca 1 2nd Floor
1054 Budapest, Hungary
Tel.: (36) 1 288 5090
Fax: (36) 1 238 8001
Web Site: www.axa-realestate.com
Emp.: 3
Real Estate Investment Services
S.I.C.: 6531
N.A.I.C.S.: 531390
Jake Lodge *(Sr Mgr-Asset)*

AXA Real Estate Investment Managers - Spain (3)
Edificio Cadagua Paseo de la Castellana 93 6 Planta
28046 Madrid, Spain
Tel.: (34) 914067200
Real Estate Investment Services
S.I.C.: 6531
N.A.I.C.S.: 531390
Vincent Darrort *(Head-Asset Mgmt)*

AXA Real Estate Investment Managers - Switzerland (3)
42 Affolternstrasse
8050 Zurich, Switzerland
Tel.: (41) 43 299 11 99
Emp.: 10
Real Estate Investment Services
S.I.C.: 6531
N.A.I.C.S.: 531390
Jurg Burkhard *(Head-Dev)*

AXA Real Estate Investment Managers - UK (3)
155 Bishopsgate
London, EC2M 3XJ, United Kingdom
Tel.: (44) 20 7374 4100
Fax: (44) 2075758446
Emp.: 15
Real Estate Investment Services
S.I.C.: 6531
N.A.I.C.S.: 531390
Harry Badham *(Head-Local Dev)*

U.S. Subsidiary:

AXA Investment Managers, Inc. (2)
1 Fawcett Pl Ste 100
Greenwich, CT 06830 DE
Tel.: (203) 863-8900
Fax: (203) 863-8947
Web Site: www.axa.com
Asset Management Services
S.I.C.: 6799
N.A.I.C.S.: 523920
Lawrence Remstedt *(Dir-Institutional Dev & Rels)*

Non-U.S. Subsidiaries:

AXA Investment Managers Asia Limited (2)
Suite 5701-4 57/F One Island East 18 Westlands Road
Quarry Bay, China (Hong Kong) HK
Tel.: (852) 2285 2000
Fax: (852) 2285 2999
Web Site: www.axa-im.com.hk
Emp.: 5
Asset Management Services
S.I.C.: 6799
N.A.I.C.S.: 523920
Terence Lam *(Mng Dir & Head-Sls & Mktg-Asia)*

AXA Investment Managers Asia (Singapore) Ltd. (2)
1 George St 14-02/03
Singapore, 049145, Singapore
Tel.: (65) 62 36 22 88
Fax: (65) 62 36 22 77
Web Site: www.axa.com
Asset Management Services
S.I.C.: 6282
N.A.I.C.S.: 523920

AXA Investment Managers Benelux SA/NV (2)
36 Boulevard du Souverain
1170 Brussels, Belgium BE
Tel.: (32) 2679 6350
Fax: (32) 2678 9399
E-Mail: axaim.be@axa-im.com
Web Site: www.axa-im.be
Investment Management & Real Estate Investment Services
S.I.C.: 6799
N.A.I.C.S.: 523920
Stephan Deceulaer *(Head-Product Mgmt & Grp Distr)*

Non-U.S. Branches:

AXA Investment Managers Benelux SA/NV - Netherlands (3)
Atrium - Tower A 14th Floor Strawinskylaan 2701
1077 ZZ Amsterdam, Netherlands
Tel.: (31) 20 795 1900
E-Mail: axaim.nl@axa-im.com
Web Site: www.axa-im.nl
Emp.: 8
Asset Management Services
S.I.C.: 6282
N.A.I.C.S.: 523920
Hanneke Veringa *(Head-AXA IM Netherlands)*

AXA Investment Managers Deutschland GmbH (2)
Im MediaPark 8a
50823 Cologne, Germany De
Tel.: (49) 221 1615 15800
Web Site: www.axa-im.de
Emp.: 9
Investment Management & Real Estate Investment Services
S.I.C.: 6282
N.A.I.C.S.: 523920
Daniela Kolb *(Head-Local Transactions)*

Non-U.S. Branch:

AXA Investment Managers Deutschland GmbH - Austria Branch (3)
Waschhausgasse 2
1020 Vienna, Austria
Tel.: (43) 1316700
Fax: (43) 3167070100
Web Site: www.axa-im.at
Asset Management Services
S.I.C.: 6282
N.A.I.C.S.: 523920
Stephan Heitz *(CFO)*

AXA Investment Managers Italia S.p.A. (2)
68 Corso Di Porta Romana
20122 Milan, Italy IT
Tel.: (39) 02 582 9911
Fax: (39) 0228 800 0960
Web Site: www.axa-im.it
Asset Management Services
S.I.C.: 6799
N.A.I.C.S.: 523920

AXA Investment Managers Japan Ltd. (2)
NBF Platinum Tower 14F 1-17-3 Shirokane
Minato-ku, Tokyo, 108-0072, Japan
Tel.: (81) 354473100
Fax: (81) 354473200
Web Site: www.axa-im.co.jp
Asset Management Services
S.I.C.: 6282
N.A.I.C.S.: 523920

AXA Investment Managers LLC (2)
PO Box 22415
Doha, Qatar
Tel.: (974) 4496 7201
Fax: (974) 4496 7205
Emp.: 2
Investment Management Services
S.I.C.: 6211
N.A.I.C.S.: 523999
Fadi Salibi *(Head-Middle East)*

AXA Investment Managers Schweiz AG (2)
Affolternstrasse 42
Postfach 6949
8050 Zurich, Switzerland
Tel.: (41) 43 299 15 55
Fax: (41) 43 299 15 56
E-Mail: clientserviceswitzerland@axa-im.com
Web Site: www.axa-im.ch
Asset Management Services
S.I.C.: 6282
N.A.I.C.S.: 523920

AXA Investment Managers UK Limited (2)
7 Newgate Street
London, EC1A 7NX, United Kingdom UK
Tel.: (44) 2070031234 (100%)
Fax: (44) 2070032313
E-Mail: proker.services@axa-im.com
Web Site: www.axa-im.co.uk
Emp.: 500
S.I.C.: 6399
N.A.I.C.S.: 524128
Martin Hall *(CEO)*

Division:

AXA Framlington (3)
7 Newgate Street
London, EC1A 7NX, United Kingdom
Tel.: (44) 20 7003 1000
Fax: (44) 2073306649
Web Site: www.axa-framlington.com
Emp.: 150
Specialty Investment Fund Management Services
S.I.C.: 6799
N.A.I.C.S.: 523920
Mark Beveridge *(Mng Dir)*

Subsidiary:

AXA Investment Managers GS Limited (3)
7 Newgate Street
London, EC1A 7NX, United Kingdom UK
Tel.: (44) 20 7003 1000
Fax: (44) 2075758585
E-Mail:
Emp.: 50
Holding Company; Investment Management Services
S.I.C.: 6719
N.A.I.C.S.: 551112

Non-U.S. Branch:

AXA Investment Managers GS Ltd., Sucursal en Espana (4)
Paseo de la Castellana 93 6 planta
28046 Madrid, Spain
Tel.: (34) 91 406 7200
E-Mail: informacion@axa-im.com
Web Site: www.axa-im.es
Investment Management Services
S.I.C.: 6799
N.A.I.C.S.: 523920

London Luton Airport Group Limited (2)
Percival House Percival Way
London Luton Airport, Luton, Beds, LU2 9LY, United Kingdom
Tel.: (44) 1582405100
Air Transportation Management Services
S.I.C.: 4581
N.A.I.C.S.: 488190

Subsidiary:

London Luton Airport Operations Ltd (3)
Navigation House
Airport Way, Luton, Bedfordshire, LU2 9LY, United Kingdom UK
Tel.: (44) 1582405100
E-Mail: info@ltn.aero
Web Site: www.london-luton.co.uk
Airport Operation Services
S.I.C.: 4581
N.A.I.C.S.: 488119
Glyn Jones *(Mng Dir)*

AXA Liabilities Managers SAS (1)
40 rue du Colisee
75008 Paris, France
Tel.: (33) 1 58 36 75 00
Fax: (33) 1 58 36 76 49
E-Mail: axa-lm@axa-lm.com
Web Site: www.axa-lm.com
Emp.: 30
Liability Management Services
S.I.C.: 6799
N.A.I.C.S.: 523920
Cedric de Linares *(Pres & CEO)*
Sylvain Villeroy de Galhau *(CFO)*
John Byrne *(Exec VP & Head-Global Ops)*
Klaus Endres *(Exec VP & Head-Bus Dev & Acq)*

AXA Protection juridique (1)
1 Place Victorien Sardou
78166 Marly-le-Roi, France
Tel.: (33) 1 30 09 90 00
Fax: (33) 1 30 09 90 89
Web Site: www.axa.com
Insurance Management Services
S.I.C.: 6411
N.A.I.C.S.: 524298

AXA Technology Services SAS. (1)
76 Route de la Demi-Lune
Paris, 92057, France
Tel.: (33) 1 55 67 20 00
Web Site: www.axa-tech.com
Data Processing Services
S.I.C.: 7374
N.A.I.C.S.: 518210
Dirk Marzluf *(CEO)*

Direct Assurance (1)
Parc Des Fontaines 163 167 Ave Georges Clemenceau
92742 Nanterre, Cedex, France FR
Tel.: (33) 146144500
Fax: (33) 146144565
Web Site: www.directassurance.fr
Rev.: $179,795,000
Insurance
S.I.C.: 6399
N.A.I.C.S.: 524128
Yves Masson *(CEO)*

GIE AXA (1)
25 Avenue Matignon
75008 Paris, France
Tel.: (33) 1 40 75 57 00
Fax: (33) 1 40754660
General Insurance Services
S.I.C.: 6411
N.A.I.C.S.: 524210

Juridica (1)
1 Place Victorien Sardou
78160 Marly-le-Roi, Cedex, France (100%)
Tel.: (33) 130099000
Fax: (33) 130099089
E-Mail: serviceclient@axa.fr
Web Site: www.axa.fr
Emp.: 150
Insurance Services
S.I.C.: 6399
N.A.I.C.S.: 524128
Jean Sebastian Antonioti *(Mgr)*

Mutuelle Saint-Christophe (1)
277 Rue Saint Jacques
75005 Paris, Cedex, France FR
Tel.: (33) 156247600 (100%)
Fax: (33) 156247627
E-Mail: service.accueil@msc-assurance.fr
Web Site: www.msc-assurance.fr
Emp.: 120
Insurance
S.I.C.: 6399
N.A.I.C.S.: 524128
Heneri Brisehoux *(Pres)*

Joint Venture:

Maxis S.A.S. (1)
26 rue Drouot
75009 Paris, France FR
Tel.: (33) 149498265
Fax: (33) 149498250
Web Site: www.maxisnetwork.com
Sales Range: $75-99.9 Million
Employee Benefits Services; Owned (50%) by The AXA Group & (50%) by MetLife, Inc.
S.I.C.: 6411
N.A.I.C.S.: 524298

Non-U.S. Branch:

AXA Insurance (2)
Blvd Du Souverain 25
1170 Brussels, Belgium
Tel.: (32) 26786861
Fax: (32) 26789340
E-Mail: info@axa.be
Web Site: www.axa.be
Sales Range: $1-4.9 Billion
Emp.: 6,000
S.I.C.: 6399

AXA S.A.—(Continued)

N.A.I.C.S.: 524128
Noel Richardson *(Dir-Fin)*

U.S. Subsidiary:

AXA America Holdings, Inc (1)
525 Washington Blvd 23rd Fl
Jersey City, NJ 07310
Tel.: (201) 746-6029
Investment Management Services
S.I.C.: 6282
N.A.I.C.S.: 523920

Subsidiaries:

AXA Corporate Solutions (2)
17 State St Fl 37
New York, NY 10004-1501
Tel.: (212) 493-9300
Fax: (212) 859-0577
Web Site: www.axaln.com
Emp.: 65
Insurance Agents & Brokers
S.I.C.: 6411
N.A.I.C.S.: 524210
Arjun Thawani *(CFO)*

Subsidiary:

AXA Corporate Solutions Insurance (3)
17 State St 37th Fl
New York, NY 10004-1501
Tel.: (212) 493-9300
Fax: (212) 425-8778
Property & Casualty Insurance Services
S.I.C.: 6351
N.A.I.C.S.: 524126

Subsidiary:

AXA Corporate Solutions Life Reinsurance Company (4)
1290 Ave of Americas
New York, NY 10104-1501
Tel.: (212) 554-1234
Fax: (212) 859-0537
Reinsurance Services
S.I.C.: 6399
N.A.I.C.S.: 524130
Chris Conpri *(Pres)*

AXA Equitable (2)
1290 Ave of the Americas
New York, NY 10104-0101 DE
Tel.: (212) 554-1234
Fax: (212) 315-3141
Web Site: www.axa-financial.com
Rev.: $13,344,900,000
Emp.: 11,350
Insurance Services
S.I.C.: 6311
N.A.I.C.S.: 524113
Mark Pearson *(Chm & CEO)*
Mary Farrell *(Vice Chm, Exec VP Senior Vice President)*
Andrew J. McMahon *(Pres)*
Amy J. Radin *(CMO & Sr Exec VP)*
Richard V. Silver *(Chief Admin Officer, Chief Legal Officer & Sr Exec VP)*
Alvin H. Fenichel *(Sr VP & Controller)*
Stacy Braun *(Sr VP-Strategic Mktg Solutions)*
David Kahal *(Sr VP-Life Distr Mgmt)*

Subsidiaries:

The Advest Group, Inc. (3)
90 State House Sq
Hartford, CT 06103-3708 DE
Tel.: (860) 509-1000
Fax: (860) 509-5544
E-Mail: privacy@advest.com
Web Site: www.advest.com
Emp.: 1,700
Financial Services
S.I.C.: 6211
N.A.I.C.S.: 523110

Subsidiaries:

Boston Advisors LLC (4)
One Liberty Sq
Boston, MA 02110
Tel.: (617) 348-3100
Fax: (617) 348-0081
Toll Free: (800) 523-5903
E-Mail: info@bostonadvisors.com
Web Site: www.bostonadvisors.com
Emp.: 42
Registered Investment Advisors
S.I.C.: 6282
N.A.I.C.S.: 523930
Michael J. Vogelzang *(Pres & CIO)*
Richard Shea *(CFO & VP)*
Tanya A. Kerrigan *(Gen Counsel & Compliance Officer)*
Peter Anderson *(Exec VP & Dir-Distr)*
David Hanna *(Sr VP & Dir-Alternative Investments)*
Donna C. McAdam *(Sr VP & Dir-Ops)*
Francis Feger *(Sr VP & Portfolio Mgr)*
Donald C. Fox *(Sr VP & Portfolio Mgr)*
Douglas A. Riley *(Sr VP & Portfolio Mgr)*

AllianceBernstein Holding L.P. (3)
1345 Ave of the Americas
New York, NY 10105-0302 DE
Tel.: (212) 969-1000 (65.5%)
Fax: (212) 969-2229
Web Site: www.alliancebernstein.com
AB—(NYSE)
Rev.: $2,917,971,000
Assets: $7,385,851,000
Liabilities: $3,316,125,000
Net Worth: $4,069,726,000
Earnings: $527,422,000
Emp.: 3,764
Fiscal Year-end: 12/31/13
Investment Advisory Services
S.I.C.: 6722
N.A.I.C.S.: 525910
Peter Steven Kraus *(Chm & CEO)*
John C. Weisenseel *(CFO & Sr VP)*
James A. Gingrich *(COO)*
Sharon E. Fay *(Head-Equities & Chief Investment Officer-Global Value)*
Edward J. Farrell *(Chief Acctg Officer)*
Lori A. Massad *(Chief Talent Officer & Head-Human Capital)*
Robert P. van Brugge *(Chm/CEO-SCB LLC)*
Laurence E. Cranch *(Gen Counsel)*
Christine Johnson *(Sr VP & Head-Alternatives Product Mgmt)*

Subsidiaries:

AllianceBernstein L.P. (4)
1345 Ave of the Americas
New York, NY 10105
Tel.: (212) 969-1000
Fax: (212) 969-2293
Web Site: www.alliancebernstein.com
Rev.: $2,917,971,000
Assets: $7,385,851,000
Liabilities: $3,316,125,000
Net Worth: $4,069,726,000
Earnings: $527,422,000
Emp.: 3,295
Fiscal Year-end: 12/31/13
Financial Management Services
S.I.C.: 6211
N.A.I.C.S.: 523999
Peter S. Kraus *(Chm & CEO)*
John C. Weisenseel *(CFO)*
Edward J. Farrell *(Chief Acctg Officer)*
Mona Bhalla *(Sec)*

Subsidiaries:

AllianceBernstein Global Derivatives Corporation (5)
1345 Avenue of The Americas
New York, NY 10105
Tel.: (212) 969-1000
Fax: (212) 969-2293
Investment Management Services
S.I.C.: 6282
N.A.I.C.S.: 523930

AllianceBernstein Global Wealth Management (5)
1345 Avenue of the Americas
New York, NY 10105
Tel.: (212) 486-5800
Web Site: www.alliancebernstein.com
Financial Management Services
S.I.C.: 6211
N.A.I.C.S.: 523999
Thomas S. Hexner *(Pres)*

AllianceBernstein Institutional Investments (5)
1345 Avenue of the Americas
New York, NY 10105
Tel.: (212) 969-1000
Web Site: www.alliancebernstein.com
Investment Management Services
S.I.C.: 6211
N.A.I.C.S.: 523999

AllianceBernstein Investments, Inc. (5)
1345 Avenue of the Americas
New York, NY 10105
Tel.: (212) 486-5800
Investment Management Services
S.I.C.: 6282
N.A.I.C.S.: 523930
Thomas S. Hexner *(Pres)*
Daniel J. Loewy *(Co-CIO & Dir-Research)*
Sharon E. Fay *(Head-Equities & Chief Investment Officer-Global Value)*

AllianceBernstein Investor Services, Inc. (5)
8000 Inerstate Hwy 10 W
San Antonio, TX 78230
Tel.: (210) 384-6000
Investment Management Services
S.I.C.: 6282
N.A.I.C.S.: 523930

W.P. Stewart & Co., Ltd. (5)
527 Madison Ave 20th Fl
New York, NY 10022 DE
Tel.: (212) 750-8585
Fax: (212) 980-8039
Toll Free: (888) 695-4092
E-Mail: info@wpstewart.com
Web Site: www.wpstewart.com
Rev.: $22,611,210
Assets: $29,103,023
Liabilities: $6,039,869
Net Worth: $23,063,154
Earnings: $2,172,732
Emp.: 48
Fiscal Year-end: 12/31/12
Global Investment Advisor
S.I.C.: 6211
N.A.I.C.S.: 523110
William Peirce Stewart *(Chm & Portfolio Mgr)*
Mark I. Phelps *(Pres & Mng Dir-Global Investments)*
Michael Maquet *(CEO)*
James T. Tierney, Jr. *(Mng Dir & Chief Investment Officer)*
Sylvia A. Cart *(Deputy Mng Dir)*
Frederick M. Ryan *(Deputy Mng Dir-IR)*
Seth L. Pearlstein *(Gen Counsel & Sec)*
Anthony J. R. Cook *(Exec VP-New York)*
Kevin F. Crook *(Exec VP-New York)*
Joris van Hees *(Exec VP-Amsterdam)*
Thomas L. Piper, III *(Sr VP-New York)*

Subsidiaries:

W.P. Stewart Asset Management Ltd. (6)
527 Madison Ave 2oth Fl
New York, NY 10022 DE
Tel.: (212) 750-8585
Fax: (212) 980-8039
E-Mail: info@wpstewart.com
Web Site: www.wpstewart.com
Asset Management Services
S.I.C.: 6531
N.A.I.C.S.: 531390

W.P. Stewart Asset Management (NA), Inc. (6)
527 Madison Ave 20th Fl
New York, NY 10022 NY
Tel.: (212) 750-8585
Fax: (212) 980-8039
Asset Management Services
S.I.C.: 6799
N.A.I.C.S.: 523920

WPS Advisors, Inc. (6)
527 Madison Ave 20th Fl
New York, NY 10022-4362 DE
Tel.: (212) 750-8585
Fax: (212) 980-8039
Web Site: www.wpstewart.com
Investment Management Services
S.I.C.: 6211
N.A.I.C.S.: 523999
Mark I. Phelps *(CEO & Portfolio Mgr)*

Non-U.S. Subsidiaries:

W.P. Stewart & Co. (Europe), Ltd. (6)
32 Curzon St
London, W1J 7WS, United Kingdom (100%)
Tel.: (44) 2079588585
Fax: (44) 2079588888
E-Mail: info@wpstewart.com
Web Site: www.wpstewart.com
Emp.: 11
Provider of Investment Management Services
S.I.C.: 6282
N.A.I.C.S.: 523930
Mark Phelps *(CEO)*

W.P. Stewart Asset Management (Curacao) N.V. (6)
Penstraat 35
Willemstad, Curacao
Tel.: (599) 94650658
Fax: (599) 94651246
E-Mail: info@wpstewart.nl
Web Site: www.wpstewart.nl
Emp.: 3
Provides Support for Asset Management Clients & Fund Management
S.I.C.: 6282
N.A.I.C.S.: 523920
Bert Vis *(Mng Dir)*

W.P. Stewart Asset Management (Europe) N.V. (6)
WTC Schiphol Airport Schiphol Boulevaard 189
1118 BG Schiphol, Netherlands (100%)
Tel.: (31) 202014985
Fax: (31) 20 201 4988
E-Mail: info@wpstewart.nl
Web Site: www.wpstewart.nl
Emp.: 6
Asset Management Services
S.I.C.: 6282
N.A.I.C.S.: 523920

W.P. Stewart Fund Management Limited (6)
HSBC House Harcourt Ctr Harcourt St
Dublin, Ireland
Tel.: (353) 14072000
Fund Management
S.I.C.: 6282
N.A.I.C.S.: 523920

Non-U.S. Subsidiaries:

ACMBernstein GmbH (5)
Maximilianstrasse 21
80539 Munich, Germany
Tel.: (49) 89 255 40 0
Fax: (49) 8925540111
E-Mail: acm@acmbernstein.com
Emp.: 8
Financial Management Services
S.I.C.: 6211
N.A.I.C.S.: 523999

AllianceBernstein (Argentina) S.R.L (5)
Torre Bouchard Plaza Bouchard 599 20th Floor
C1106ABG Buenos Aires, Argentina
Tel.: (54) 1148501222
Investment Management Services
S.I.C.: 6211
N.A.I.C.S.: 523999
James Gingrich *(COO)*

AllianceBernstein Asset Management (Korea) Ltd. (5)
Seoul Finance Center 14th Floor 84 Taepyungro 1-Ga
Jung-gu, Seoul, 100-101, Korea (South)
Tel.: (82) 237073400
Web Site: www.alliancebernstein.com
Financial Management Services
S.I.C.: 6211
N.A.I.C.S.: 523999

AllianceBernstein Australia Limited (5)
Level 50 Rialto South Tower 525 Collins Street
Melbourne, VIC, 3000, Australia
Tel.: (61) 386302200
Financial Management Services
S.I.C.: 6211
N.A.I.C.S.: 523999
Ross Kent *(CEO)*

AllianceBernstein Canada, Inc (5)
Brookfield Place 161 Bay Street 27th Floor
Toronto, ON, M5J 2S1, Canada
Tel.: (416) 572-2534

E-Mail: canadateam@alliancebernstein.com
Web Site: www.alliancebernstein.com
Emp.: 5
Financial Management Services
S.I.C.: 6211
N.A.I.C.S.: 523999
Wendy Brodkin *(Mng Dir)*

AllianceBernstein (France) S.A.S. **(5)**
90 Avenue des Champs Elysees
75008 Paris, France
Tel.: (33) 156435046
Emp.: 2
Investment Management Services
S.I.C.: 6211
N.A.I.C.S.: 523999

AllianceBernstein Hong Kong Limited **(5)**
One International Finance Centre One Harbour View Street
Suite 3401 34th Floor, Central, China (Hong Kong)
Tel.: (852) 02918 7888
Fax: (852) 2918 0200
E-Mail: info@alliancebernstein.com
Emp.: 10
Investment Management Services
S.I.C.: 6211
N.A.I.C.S.: 523999

AllianceBernstein Investment Management Australia Limited **(5)**
Level 37 Chifley Tower 2 Chifley Square
Sydney, NSW, 2000, Australia
Tel.: (61) 2 9255 1200
Financial Investment Services
S.I.C.: 6211
N.A.I.C.S.: 523999

AllianceBernstein Investments Taiwan Limited **(5)**
Tunnan Tower 32F 99 Tunhwa South Road Sec 2
Taipei, Taiwan
Tel.: (886) 223259000
Web Site: www.alliancebernstein.com
Financial Investment Services
S.I.C.: 6211
N.A.I.C.S.: 523999

AllianceBernstein Japan Ltd **(5)**
Marunouchi Trust Tower Main 17F 1-8-3 Marunouchi
Chiyoda-ku, Tokyo, 100-0005, Japan
Tel.: (81) 359629000
Web Site: www.alliancebernstein.co.jp
Financial Investment Services
S.I.C.: 6211
N.A.I.C.S.: 523999
Ken Kobayashi *(Sr Portfolio Mgr)*

AllianceBernstein Limited **(5)**
50 Berkeley Street
London, W1J 8HA, United Kingdom
Tel.: (44) 2074700100
Web Site: www.alliancebernstein.com
Financial Management Services
S.I.C.: 6211
N.A.I.C.S.: 523999

Subsidiaries:

AllianceBernstein Holdings Limited **(6)**
50 Berkeley Street
London, United Kingdom
Tel.: (44) 2074700100
Investment Management Services
S.I.C.: 6799
N.A.I.C.S.: 523920

AllianceBernstein Preferred Limited **(6)**
50 Berkeley Street
London, W1J 8HA, United Kingdom
Tel.: (44) 20 74 700100
E-Mail: info@alliancebernstein.com
Web Site: www.alliancebernstein.com
Investment Management Services
S.I.C.: 6211
N.A.I.C.S.: 523999

Sanford C. Bernstein Limited **(6)**
50 Berkeley Street West Central
London, W1J 8HD, United Kingdom
Tel.: (44) 20 7170 5000
Web Site: www.alliancebernstein.com
Financial Investment Services
S.I.C.: 6211
N.A.I.C.S.: 523999

AllianceBernstein Limited **(5)**
Paseo del Club Deportivo Edificio 15A
Pozuelo de Alarcon
28223 Madrid, Spain ES
Tel.: (34) 91 297 97 03
Financial Management Services
S.I.C.: 6211
N.A.I.C.S.: 523999

AllianceBernstein Limited **(5)**
BMB Center 6th Floor Diplomatic Area
PO Box 10515
Manama, Bahrain
Tel.: (973) 17530510
Fax: (973) 17530520
Web Site: www.alliancebernstein.com
Emp.: 2
Financial Investment Services
S.I.C.: 6211
N.A.I.C.S.: 523999
Ehab Amiri *(Mng Dir)*

AllianceBernstein (Luxembourg) S.A. **(5)**
2-4 rue Eugene Ruppert
2453 Luxembourg, Luxembourg
Tel.: (352) 463936151
Financial Management Services
S.I.C.: 6211
N.A.I.C.S.: 523999

AllianceBernstein (Singapore) Limited **(5)**
Prudential Tower No 30 Cecil Street 28-08
Singapore, 49712, Singapore
Tel.: (65) 62304600
Fax: (65) 65356008
Emp.: 45
Investment Management Services
S.I.C.: 6211
N.A.I.C.S.: 523999
Suchet Padhye *(CEO-Strategic Initiatives-Asia & Mng Dir-Mktg-Mutual Fund)*

AllianceBernstein Taiwan Limited **(5)**
25F-7 No 3 Ziqiang 3rd Rd
Lingya Dist, Kaohsiung, Taiwan
Tel.: (886) 75668811
Web Site: www.alliancebernstein.com
Investment Management Services
S.I.C.: 6211
N.A.I.C.S.: 523999

AXA Towarzystwo Funduszy Inwestycyjnych S.A. **(5)**
ul Chlodna 51
00-867 Warsaw, Poland
Tel.: (48) 22 555 07 00
Fax: (48) 22 555 07 01
E-Mail: axa.tfi@axa-polska.pl
Web Site: www.tfi.axa.pl
Assest Management Services
S.I.C.: 6282
N.A.I.C.S.: 523920

Unit:

Sanford C. Bernstein & Co., LLP **(4)**
1345 Ave of the Americas
New York, NY 10105 NY
Tel.: (212) 756-4400 (55%)
Toll Free: (800) 611-4015
E-Mail: prospects@bernstein.com
Web Site: www.bernsteinresearch.com
Emp.: 4,000
Investment Services
S.I.C.: 6282
N.A.I.C.S.: 523930
Robert P. van Brugge *(Chm & CEO)*

Non-U.S. Subsidiaries:

ACM Bernstein GmbH **(4)**
Maximilianstrasse 21
80539 Munich, Germany
Tel.: (49) 89255400
Fax: (49) 8925540111
E-Mail: acm@acmbernstein.com
Emp.: 8
Investment Management Services
S.I.C.: 6282
N.A.I.C.S.: 523930
Martin vom Hagen *(Mng Dir)*

AllianceBernstein Services Limited **(4)**
50 Berkeley Street
London, W1J 8HA, United Kingdom
Tel.: (44) 2074700100
Investment Management Services
S.I.C.: 6282
N.A.I.C.S.: 523930

Sanford C. Bernstein (CREST Nominees) Limited **(4)**
Devonshire House 1 Mayfair Place
London, United Kingdom
Tel.: (44) 2071705019
Trade Financing Services
S.I.C.: 6159
N.A.I.C.S.: 522293

AXA Advisors, LLC **(3)**
2 Meridian Crossing Ste 450
Minneapolis, MN 55423 MN
Tel.: (612) 243-3200
Fax: (952) 938-5884
Web Site: www.axa-equitable.com
Rev.: $750,000
Emp.: 8
Mortgage Bankers & Loan Correspondence
S.I.C.: 6211
N.A.I.C.S.: 523120
Edward Balfour *(Branch Mgr)*

AXA Advisors, LLC **(3)**
1290 Avenue of the Americas 8th Fl
New York, NY 10104
Tel.: (212) 314-4600
Fax: (212) 314-2837
Toll Free: (800) 222-2144
Web Site: www.axaonline.com
Financial Planning Services
S.I.C.: 6211
N.A.I.C.S.: 523999
Andrew J. McMahon *(Chm)*
Christine Nigro *(Pres)*
Scott Newman *(Exec VP-Western Div)*
Steve Howell *(Sr VP-Western Div)*
John Parham *(Sr VP-Natl Div)*

AXA Corp. Solutions Insurance Company **(3)**
17 State St 37nd Fl
New York, NY 10004-1501
Tel.: (212) 859-0555
Fax: (212) 859-0577
Web Site: www.axainsurance.com
Emp.: 80
Provides Commercial & Aviation/Space Insurance & Reinsurance Services
S.I.C.: 6411
N.A.I.C.S.: 524210
Alex Scherer *(Gen Mgr)*

AXA Distributors, LLC. **(3)**
1290 Ave Of The Americas
New York, NY 10104-0101 CA
Tel.: (212) 314-4600
Fax: (212) 314-3583
Toll Free: (888) 517-9900
Web Site: www.axadistributors.com
Emp.: 200
Security & Commodity Exchanges
S.I.C.: 6311
N.A.I.C.S.: 524113

AXA Equitable Life Assurance Company **(3)**
1290 Avenue of the Americas 13th Fl
New York, NY 10104-0101 (100%)
Tel.: (212) 554-1234
Web Site: www.axa-equitable.com
Sales Range: $1-4.9 Billion
Emp.: 5,139
Insurance Provider
S.I.C.: 6411
N.A.I.C.S.: 524210
Tracey Gray-Walker *(Chief Diversity Officer)*
Richard V. Silver *(Gen Counsel & Exec VP)*
Mary Farrell *(Exec VP-Svc Delivery)*
Robert Jones *(Exec VP-Distr)*
Adrienne Johnson-Guider *(Sr VP & Head-Strategic Initiatives Grp)*
Connie O'Brien *(Sr VP-Internet Strategy & Dev)*

AXA Network, LLC **(3)**
4251 Crums Mill Rd
Harrisburg, PA 17112 DE
Tel.: (717) 541-8164
Fax: (800) 235-6945
Toll Free: (800) 487-6244
Web Site: www.axanetwork.com
Emp.: 180
Holding Company; Life Insurance, Annuities, Disability Income, Mutual Funds & Securities
S.I.C.: 6411
N.A.I.C.S.: 524210
Kib Condor *(Gen Mgr)*

Non-U.S. Subsidiary:

MONY Life Insurance Company of the Americas, Ltd. **(3)**
23 Palm Tree Ave Bldg 4 2nd Floor
Georgetown, Grand Cayman, KY1-1102, Cayman Islands NY
Mailing Address:
PO Box 31461
Georgetown, Grand Cayman, KY1-1206, Cayman Islands
Tel.: (345) 949 8704
Fax: (345) 949 1117
Web Site: www.axa-equitable.com
Emp.: 2
Life Insurance & Annuities
S.I.C.: 6399
N.A.I.C.S.: 524130
Victor Ugolyn *(Chm)*

AXA Financial, Inc. **(2)**
1290 Avenue of the Americas
New York, NY 10104
Tel.: (212) 554-1234
Fax: (212) 707-1746
Toll Free: (800) 777-6510
Web Site: www.axa-financial.com
Financial Management Services
S.I.C.: 6211
N.A.I.C.S.: 523999
Markus Pearson *(CEO)*

AXA Global Structured Products Inc. **(2)**
600 5th Ave 24th Fl
New York, NY 10020
Tel.: (212) 218-2000
Fax: (212) 218-2044
Life Insurance Management Services
S.I.C.: 6311
N.A.I.C.S.: 524113

AXA Insurance **(2)**
17 State St 37th Fl
New York, NY 10004 DE
Tel.: (212) 493-9300 (100%)
Fax: (212) 425-4125
Web Site: www.axa-lm.com
Emp.: 150
Reinsurance Carriers Accident & Health
S.I.C.: 6399
N.A.I.C.S.: 524130
Sylvain Villeroy De Galhau *(CFO)*
Alex Scherer *(CEO-USA)*

AXA Liabilities Managers Inc. **(2)**
125 Broad St
New York, NY 10004-1501
Tel.: (212) 493-9300
Fax: (212) 425-2914
Web Site: www.axa-liabilitiesmanagers.com
Emp.: 200
Reinsurance
S.I.C.: 6411
N.A.I.C.S.: 524210
Klaus Endres *(CEO)*

AXA Multi Manager **(2)**
600 5th Ave 24th Fl
New York, NY 10020
Tel.: (212) 218-2000
Asset Management Services
S.I.C.: 6799
N.A.I.C.S.: 523920

AXA Rosenberg Investment Management LLC **(2)**
4 Orinda Way Bldg E
Orinda, CA 94563
Tel.: (925) 254-6464
Fax: (925) 253-2288
E-Mail: contactaxarosenberg@axarosenberg.com
Web Site: www.axarosenberg.us
Emp.: 58
Investment Management Services
S.I.C.: 6211
N.A.I.C.S.: 523999
Heidi Ridley *(Global COO)*
Bruno Pradal *(CTO & Head-Ops)*
Jeremy Baskin *(Global CEO & Chief Investment Officer)*

AXA S.A.—(Continued)

Kevin Chen *(Chief Investment Officer-Pan Asia)*
Will Jump *(Chief Investment Officer)*
Gideon Smith *(Chief Investment Officer-Europe)*

AXA Space, Inc. (2)
4800 Montgomery Ln 11th Fl
Bethesda, MD 20814
Tel.: (301) 654-8585
Fax: (301) 654-7569
E-Mail: info@axaspace.com
Web Site: www.axaspace.com
Health Insurance Management Services
S.I.C.: 6324
N.A.I.C.S.: 524114

AXA Technology Services America Inc (2)
525 Washington Blvd 23rd Fl
Jersey City, NJ 07310
Tel.: (201) 746-6029
Information Technology Consulting Services
S.I.C.: 7373
N.A.I.C.S.: 541512

MATRIX RISK CONSULTANTS, INC. (2)
3130 S Tech Blvd
Miamisburg, OH 45342
Tel.: (937) 886-0000
Fax: (937) 432-2099
E-Mail: usa@axa-matrixrc.com
Web Site: www.axa-matrixrc.com
Emp.: 30
Business Management Consulting Services
S.I.C.: 8748
N.A.I.C.S.: 541618
Sheryl Hickman *(Exec VP)*

Non-U.S. Subsidiaries:

Asuransi AXA Indonesia (1)
Blok Emerald No G35
Jl M Soepeno, Jakarta, 12920, Indonesia Id
Tel.: (62) 2153664572 (80%)
Fax: (62) 2153664575
E-Mail: axaindo@axa-insurance.co.id
Web Site: www.axa-insurance.co.id
Emp.: 113
Insurance Provider
S.I.C.: 6399
N.A.I.C.S.: 524128
Jahanath Muthusamy *(CEO)*

Avanssur S.A. (1)
Street Chlodna 59
00-867 Warsaw, Poland
Tel.: (48) 22 599 90 00
Fax: (48) 22 599 90 01
E-Mail: recepcja@axadirect.pl
General Insurance Services
S.I.C.: 6411
N.A.I.C.S.: 524210

AXA-ARAG Protection juridique SA (1)
Birmensdorferstrasse 108
PO Box 9829
8036 Zurich, Switzerland
Tel.: (41) 848 11 11 00
Web Site: www.axa-winterthur.ch/en/Pages/publishing-details.aspx
Asset Management Services
S.I.C.: 6282
N.A.I.C.S.: 523920

AXA-ARAG Rechtsschutz AG. (1)
Birmensdorferstrasse 108
Postfach 9829
8036 Zurich, Switzerland
Tel.: (41) 58 855 95 13
Fax: (41) 58 855 95 99
E-Mail: info@axa-arag.ch
Web Site: www.axa-winterthur.ch
Emp.: 163
General Insurance Services
S.I.C.: 6411
N.A.I.C.S.: 524210

AXA ART Versicherung AG (1)
Thurgauerstrasse 105
Postfach 1533
Glattbrugg, 8065 Zurich, Switzerland
Tel.: (41) 44 874 84 84
Fax: (41) 44 874 84 00
E-Mail: info@axa-art.ch
Web Site: www.axa-art.ch
Art Insurance Services
S.I.C.: 6411
N.A.I.C.S.: 524298
David Saillen *(Mng Dir)*

U.S. Subsidiary:

AXA Art Insurance Corporation (2)
3 W 35th St 11th Fl
New York, NY 10001
Tel.: (212) 415-8400
E-Mail:
Web Site: www.axa-art-usa.com
Art Insurance Services
S.I.C.: 6411
N.A.I.C.S.: 524298
Christiane Fischer *(Pres & CEO)*
Anthony Osborn *(Mng Dir)*

Non-U.S. Subsidiaries:

AXA Art Canada (2)
130 King Street West Suite 2350
Toronto, ON, M5X 1C7, Canada
Tel.: (416) 928-8524
Web Site: www.axa-art.ca
Emp.: 5
Art & Collectable Insurance Services
S.I.C.: 6411
N.A.I.C.S.: 524298
Ann-Louise Seago *(VP)*

AXA ART FRANCE (2)
19 Rue d'Orleans
92200 Neuilly-sur-Seine, France
Tel.: (33) 1 46 40 85 85
Fax: (33) 1 47 38 32 14
E-Mail: contactweb@axa-art.fr
Web Site: www.axa-art.fr
Art Insurance Services
S.I.C.: 6411
N.A.I.C.S.: 524298
Christian Muller *(Mng Dir)*

AXA ART Insurance Ltd. (2)
Marlow House 1A Lloyd s Avenue
London, EC3N 3AA, United Kingdom
Tel.: (44) 20 3217 1200
Fax: (44) 20 7702 0898
E-Mail: info@axa-art.co.uk
Web Site: www.axa-art.co.uk
Emp.: 3
Art Insurance Services
S.I.C.: 6411
N.A.I.C.S.: 524298
Annabel Fell-Clark *(CEO)*

AXA ART LUXEMBOURG (2)
7 Rue De La Chapelle
1325 Luxembourg, Luxembourg
Tel.: (352) 4530204775
Fax: (352) 4530204615
E-Mail: info@axa.lu
Web Site: www.axa-art.lu
Art Insurance Services
S.I.C.: 6411
N.A.I.C.S.: 524298

AXA ART - NEDERLAND (2)
Ginnekenweg 213
4835 NA Breda, Netherlands
Tel.: (31) 76 514 85 58
Fax: (31) 76 514 86 61
E-Mail: info@axa-art.nl
Web Site: www.axa-art.nl
Art Insurance Services
S.I.C.: 6411
N.A.I.C.S.: 524298

AXA ART (2)
Via Lazzaro Palazzi 2/A
20124 Milan, Italy
Tel.: (39) 02 888 965 1
Fax: (39) 02 888 965 59
E-Mail: info@axa-art.it
Web Site: www.axa-art.it
Art Insurance Services
S.I.C.: 6411
N.A.I.C.S.: 524298

AXA ART (2)
Chlodna 51
00-867 Warsaw, Poland PL
Tel.: (48) 22 555 00 50
Fax: (48) 22 555 05 00
Art Insurance Services
S.I.C.: 6411
N.A.I.C.S.: 524298

AXA Assicurazioni (1)
Via Leopardi 15
20123 Milan, Italy (100%)
Tel.: (39) 0248084376
Fax: (39) 0248084668
Web Site: www.axa-italia.it/
Emp.: 400
Insurance
S.I.C.: 6399
N.A.I.C.S.: 524128
Frederic de Courtois *(CEO)*

AXA Assurance Maroc (1)
120 122 avenue Hassan II
20000 Casablanca, Morocco Ma
Tel.: (212) 522889292
Fax: (212) 522889189
E-Mail: communication@axa.ma
Web Site: www.axa.ma
Emp.: 514
Insurance
S.I.C.: 6399
N.A.I.C.S.: 524128

AXA Assurances Gabon (1)
BP 4047
Libreville, Gabon Ga
Tel.: (241) 762897 (99%)
Fax: (241) 760334
E-Mail: axa.gabon@inet.ga
Web Site: www.axa.com
Emp.: 118
Insurance Provider
S.I.C.: 6399
N.A.I.C.S.: 524128

AXA Assurances IARD (1)
4 F 25 Tunhua S Rd
Section 1, Taipei, ROC, 10557, Taiwan TW
Tel.: (886) 225774352 (100%)
Fax: (886) 225774157
E-Mail: axatwn@ms9.hinet.net
Web Site: www.axatwn.com.tw
Emp.: 5
Insurance Provider
S.I.C.: 6399
N.A.I.C.S.: 524128
Sophia Lin *(Mng Dir)*

AXA Assurances - Ivory Coast (1)
BP 378
Abidjan, Cote d'Ivoire
Tel.: (225) 2031 8888
Fax: (225) 2031 8800
E-Mail: contact@axa-assurances.ci
Web Site: www.axa.ci
General Insurance Services
S.I.C.: 6411
N.A.I.C.S.: 524210

AXA Assurances Luxembourg S.A. (1)
7 Rue De La Chapelle
1325 Luxembourg, Luxembourg (100%)
Tel.: (352) 4424241
Fax: (352) 4424244588
E-Mail: info@axa.lu
Web Site: www.axa.lu
Emp.: 200
Reinsurance
S.I.C.: 6399
N.A.I.C.S.: 524130
Paul Decomann *(Mng Dir)*

Subsidiary:

AXA Assurances Vie Luxembourg (2)
7 Rue De La Chapelle
1325 Luxembourg, Luxembourg (100%)
Tel.: (352) 4424241
Fax: (352) 4424244664
E-Mail: info@axa.lu
Web Site: www.axa.lu
Emp.: 180
Insurance Services
S.I.C.: 6399
N.A.I.C.S.: 524128
Paul De Cooman *(Mgr)*

AXA Assurances Senegal (1)
5 Pl De Ildependance
BP 182 Dakar, Senegal (100%)
Tel.: (221) 8491010
Fax: (221) 8234672
E-Mail: info@axa.sn
Web Site: www.axagroup.com
Emp.: 60
Insurance Services
S.I.C.: 6399
N.A.I.C.S.: 524128

AXA Bank Europe Czech Republic (1)
Uzka 8/488
602 00 Brno, Czech Republic
Tel.: (420) 494 945 240
E-Mail: info@axabank.cz
Web Site: www.axabank.cz
Commercial Banking Services
S.I.C.: 6029
N.A.I.C.S.: 522110
Ladislav Krocak *(CEO)*

AXA Bank Europe Slovakia (1)
Kolarska 6
Bratislava, 81106, Slovakia
Tel.: (421) 229292929
E-Mail: info@axabanka.sk
Web Site: www.axabanka.sk
Commercial Banking Services
S.I.C.: 6029
N.A.I.C.S.: 522110
Ladislav Krocak *(CEO)*

AXA Business Services Private Limited (1)
Sjr Plaza 29th Main Road Btm 1st Stage Ring Road
Bengaluru, 560068, India
Tel.: (91) 80 41830000
Fax: (91) 80 41834300
E-Mail: siteadmin@axa-abs.co.in
Web Site: www.axa-bs.com
Emp.: 250
Business Process Outsourcing Services
S.I.C.: 7389
N.A.I.C.S.: 561499

AXA Ceska republika s.r.o (1)
Lazarska 13/8
120 00 Prague, Czech Republic
Tel.: (420) 292 292 292
E-Mail: info@axa.cz
Web Site: www.axa.cz
General Insurance Services
S.I.C.: 6411
N.A.I.C.S.: 524210
Hani Himmat *(Mgr)*

AXA China Region Insurance Company (Bermuda) Limited (1)
Avenida Do Infante D Henrique No 43-53A
20 Andar The Macau Square
Macau, China (Macau)
Tel.: (853) 2878 1188
Web Site: www.axa.com.hk/html/AXA_PRO/eng/cs/coo/office_locations.html
Insurance Management Services
S.I.C.: 6411
N.A.I.C.S.: 524298

AXA China Region Insurance Company Limited (1)
20/F AXA Centre 151 Gloucester Road
Wanchai, China (Hong Kong)
Tel.: (852) 2519 1111
Fax: (852) 2598 7623
E-Mail: life.insurance@axa.com.hk
Web Site: www.axa.com.hk
Emp.: 100
Financial Protection & Wealth Management Services
S.I.C.: 6799
N.A.I.C.S.: 523920
Stuart Harrison *(CEO)*
Angela Chui *(CFO)*
Paul Carson *(COO)*
Andrea Wong *(Chief Mktg & Strategy Officer)*
Alger Fung *(Chief Proprietary Distr Officer)*
Isabel Lam *(Chief Corp Mgmt Officer)*
Xavier Lestrade *(Chief Distr Officer)*
Benjamin Li *(Chief Health & Employee Benefits Officer)*
Sabrina Yuan *(Cheif HR Officer)*

AXA China Region Ltd. (1)
18 F Axa Ctr 151 Gloucester Rd
Wanchai, China (Hong Kong) (100%)
Tel.: (852) 25191111
Fax: (852) 25984965
E-Mail: priscilla.law@axa.com.hk
Web Site: www.axa.com.hk
Emp.: 500
S.I.C.: 6399
N.A.I.C.S.: 524128

Andrea Wong *(CMO-AXA Hong Kong)*

Subsidiary:

AXA Wealth Management (HK) Limited (2)
AXA Centre
151 Gloucester Road, Wanchai, China (Hong Kong)
Tel.: (852) 25191111
Fax: (852) 25984965
Web Site: www.axa.com.hk
Financial Services
S.I.C.: 6211
N.A.I.C.S.: 523999
David Thompson *(Mng Dir)*

AXA Colonia Insurance Limited (1)
Wolfe Tone House Wolfe Tone Street
Dublin, 1, Ireland (100%)
Tel.: (353) 018726444
Fax: (353) 18722104
E-Mail: axacolonia@eircom.net
Web Site: www.axa.ie
Insurance Services
S.I.C.: 6399
N.A.I.C.S.: 524128

AXA Corporate Solutions Australia (1)
Level 21 Australia Square 264 George Street
GPO Box 3973
Sydney, NSW, 2000, Australia
Tel.: (61) 2 9274 3000
Fax: (61) 2 9274 3033
Web Site: www.axa-corporatesolutions.com
Emp.: 2
Property & Casualty Insurance Management Services
S.I.C.: 6411
N.A.I.C.S.: 524298
Didier Grimault *(Mng Dir)*

AXA Corporate Solutions Dubai (1)
Wafi Residential Centre Ground Floor
PO Box 290
Dubai, United Arab Emirates
Tel.: (971) 4 3150205
Fax: (971) 50 5525741
Property & Casualty Insurance Services
S.I.C.: 6351
N.A.I.C.S.: 524126
Xavier Luscan *(Mgr-Underwriting-Property & Engrg Corp Solutions)*

AXA Corporate Solutions Germany (1)
Colonia-Allee 10-20
51067 Cologne, Germany
Tel.: (49) 221 148 21180
Fax: (49) 221 148 23345
Property & Casualty Insurance Services
S.I.C.: 6351
N.A.I.C.S.: 524126
Juergen Kurth *(CEO)*

AXA Corporate Solutions Hong Kong (1)
Unit 1204-05 DCH Commercial Centre 25 Westlands Road
Quarry Bay, China (Hong Kong)
Tel.: (852) 2161 0000
Fax: (852) 2866 4688
E-Mail: hongkong@axa-cs.com
Web Site: www.axa-corporatesolutions.com
Property & Casualty Insurance Services
S.I.C.: 6351
N.A.I.C.S.: 524126
Pierre Martelly *(CEO)*

AXA Corporate Solutions Switzerland (1)
General Guisan-Strasse 40
Postfach 4600
8401 Winterthur, Switzerland
Tel.: (41) 52 261 63 00
Fax: (41) 52 261 63 30
E-Mail: info-ch@axa-cs.com
Web Site: www.axa-corporatesolutions.com
Property & Casualty Insurance Management Services
S.I.C.: 6411
N.A.I.C.S.: 524298
Hansruedi Schoch *(CEO)*

AXA Corporate Solutions UK (1)
140 Fenchurch Street
London, EC3M 6BL, United Kingdom
Tel.: (44) 2077026600
Fax: (44) 2077026676
Web Site: www.axa-corporatesolutions.com
Emp.: 5
Property & Casualty Insurance Services
S.I.C.: 6331
N.A.I.C.S.: 524126
Matthieu Caillat *(Co-CEO & Mng Dir)*
Emmanuel Nivet *(Co-CEO)*
Vlictor Mayer *(CFO)*

AXA Corporate Solutions (1)
Via Della Moscova 18
20121 Milan, Italy
Tel.: (39) 02 65538 1
Fax: (39) 02 65538 301
Property & Casualty Insurance Management Services
S.I.C.: 6411
N.A.I.C.S.: 524298

AXA Corporate Solutions (1)
143 Cecil Street 09-02 GB Building
Singapore, 069542, Singapore SG
Tel.: (65) 63 38 72 88
Property & Casualty Insurance Services
S.I.C.: 6331
N.A.I.C.S.: 524126

AXA Cote D'Ivoire (1)
BP 378
Abidjan, Cote d'Ivoire CI
Tel.: (225) 20318888 (100%)
Fax: (225) 2031 8800
E-Mail: contact@axa.ci
Web Site: www.axa.ci
Emp.: 15
Insurance Services
S.I.C.: 6399
N.A.I.C.S.: 524128
Jacques Bardoux *(Mng Dir)*

AXA Customer Services Ltd (1)
8 DBM Industrial Estate Coromandel
Port Louis, Mauritius
Tel.: (230) 206 79 00
Fax: (230) 233 04 57
E-Mail: info@axa-customerservices.com
Web Site: www.axa-customerservices.com
Emp.: 50
Business Process Outsourcing Services
S.I.C.: 7389
N.A.I.C.S.: 561499
Martin A. Weintz *(CEO)*
Rookian Toorawa *(CFO & Deputy CEO)*
Emmanuel Le Jouan *(CIO)*
Didier Leroux-Angibaud *(Chief Sls Officer)*
Diya Nababsing-Jetshan *(Chief Strategy Officer)*
Moammar Tegally *(Gen Counsel & Sec)*

AXA Czech Republic Insurance (1)
Lazarska 13/8
120 00 Prague, Czech Republic
Tel.: (420) 292 292 292
Insurance Management Services
S.I.C.: 6411
N.A.I.C.S.: 524298

AXA Czech Republic Pension Funds (1)
Uzka 8/488
602 00 Brno, Czech Republic
Tel.: (420) 292 292 292
Pension Fund Management Services
S.I.C.: 6371
N.A.I.C.S.: 525110

AXA d.d.s., a.s. (1)
Laurinska 18
811 01 Bratislava, Slovakia
Tel.: (421) 2 2929 2929
E-Mail: info.dds@axa.sk
Pension Fund Management Services
S.I.C.: 3291
N.A.I.C.S.: 327910

AXA Direct Korea (1)
395-70 Shindaebang-dong
Dongjak-gu, Seoul, 156-714, Korea (South)
Tel.: (82) 31 8002 8000
Fax: (82) 2 3479 4800
Web Site: www.axa.co.kr
Online Insurance Services
S.I.C.: 2741
N.A.I.C.S.: 519130

AXA Direct (1)
Ul Chlodna 51
00-867 Warsaw, Poland
Tel.: (48) 22 599 9522
Fax: (48) 22 599 9595
E-Mail: axa@axadirect.pl
Web Site: www.axadirect.pl
Insurance Management Services
S.I.C.: 6411
N.A.I.C.S.: 524298

AXA Fine Art China (1)
China Diamond Exchange Building 555 Pudian Rd
Pudong Xinqu, Shanghai, China
Tel.: (86) 21 61563500
Fax: (86) 21 68824600
E-Mail: axa-art@axa-ins.com.cn
Art Insurance Services
S.I.C.: 6411
N.A.I.C.S.: 524298

AXA Fine Art Hong Kong (1)
1204-05 DCH Commercial Centre 25 Westlands Road
Quarry Bay, China (Hong Kong)
Tel.: (852) 21610084
Fax: (852) 2866 4688
E-Mail: axa.art@axa-insurance.com.hk
Web Site: www.axa-insurance.com.hk
Emp.: 5
Art Insurance Services
S.I.C.: 6411
N.A.I.C.S.: 524298
Jennifer Scally *(Reg Mgr)*

AXA Fine Art Singapore (1)
8 Shenton Way 27-01 AXA Tower
Singapore, 68811, Singapore
Tel.: (65) 6880 4957
Fax: (65) 63382522
E-Mail: art@axa.com.sg
Emp.: 35
Art Insurance Services
S.I.C.: 6411
N.A.I.C.S.: 524298
Charles Liu *(Mgr-Bus Dev)*

AXA Framlington (1)
7 Newgate Street
London, EC1A 7NX, United Kingdom
Tel.: (44) 20 7003 1000
Fax: (44) 2075758585
Web Site: www.axa-im.com
Emp.: 45
Investment Management Services
S.I.C.: 6211
N.A.I.C.S.: 523999
Mark Beveridge *(CEO)*

AXA General Insurance Co., Ltd. (1)
Kairaku Building Kotobuki 2-1-13 Kotobuki
Taito-ku, Tokyo, 111-8633, Japan
Tel.: (81) 3 4335 8570
Fax: (81) 343358571
Web Site: www.axa-direct.co.jp
General Insurance Services
S.I.C.: 6411
N.A.I.C.S.: 524298

AXA General Insurance Hong Kong (1)
21/F Manhattan Pl 23 Wang Tai Road
Kowloon Bay, Kowloon, China (Hong Kong) HK
Tel.: (852) 25233061 (100%)
Fax: (852) 28100706
E-Mail: axahk@axa-insurance.com.hk
Web Site: www.axa-insurance.com.hk
Emp.: 200
Life Insurance
S.I.C.: 6311
N.A.I.C.S.: 524113
James Tang *(Reg CFO)*
Barry Yeung *(Exec VP & Dir-Tech-Greater China)*

AXA Holding Maroc S.A. (1)
120-122 Av Hassan Ii
Casablanca, Morocco
Tel.: (212) 5228892
Fax: (212) 5228891
Investment Management Services
S.I.C.: 6282
N.A.I.C.S.: 523920

AXA Holdings Belgium (1)
Boulevard du Souverain 25
1170 Brussels, Belgium BE
Tel.: (32) 26786111 (100%)
Fax: (32) 26789340
Web Site: www.axa.be
Emp.: 6,000
Holding Company
S.I.C.: 6719
N.A.I.C.S.: 551112
Emmanuel de Talhouet *(CEO)*

Subsidiaries:

AXA Bank Europe S.A. (2)
Boulevard du Souverain 25
1170 Brussels, Belgium (100%)
Tel.: (32) 26786111
Fax: (32) 26787004
E-Mail: contact@axa.be
Web Site: www.axa.be
Commercial Bank
S.I.C.: 6029
N.A.I.C.S.: 522110
Gerard Fievet *(CEO)*

Non-U.S. Subsidiary:

AXA Bank Hungary (3)
Vaci Ut 135-139
1138 Budapest, Hungary
Tel.: (36) 1 465 65 65
Fax: (36) 1 465 65 99
E-Mail: info.axa@axa.hu
Web Site: www.axabank.hu
Commercial Banking Services
S.I.C.: 6029
N.A.I.C.S.: 522110

AXA Belgium S.A. (2)
Blvd Du Souverain 25
1170 Brussels, Belgium (100%)
Tel.: (32) 3226786111
Fax: (32) 26789340
E-Mail: info@axa.be
Web Site: www.axa.be
Emp.: 6,500
Life Insurance
S.I.C.: 6311
N.A.I.C.S.: 524113
Eugene Teysen *(Gen Mgr)*

AXA Insurance (Gulf) B.S.C. (c) (1)
Safeway Building Unit 1 & 2 Ground Floor Way No 3303 Near MQ Dohat Al
PO Box 1276
Adab Street Al Khuwair, 112 Muscat, Oman
Tel.: (968) 24 400 100
Fax: (968) 24 400 120
E-Mail: Info.Muscat@axa-gulf.com
Web Site: www.axa-gulf.com
General Insurance Services
S.I.C.: 6411
N.A.I.C.S.: 524210

AXA Insurance (Gulf) B.S.C. (1)
Ground Floor Wafi Residential Centre
PO Box 290
Dubai, United Arab Emirates (100%)
Tel.: (971) 43243434
Fax: (971) 43242375
E-Mail: info.dubai@axa-gulf.com
Web Site: www.axa-gulf.com
Insurance Services
S.I.C.: 6399
N.A.I.C.S.: 524128

AXA Insurance Gulf (1)
2nd Floor Kanoo Building Abu Obeidah Avenue
PO Box 45
Manama, Bahrain
Tel.: (973) 17 210 778
Fax: (973) 17 223 857
E-Mail: Info.Bahrain@axa-gulf.com
Emp.: 5
General Insurance Services
S.I.C.: 6411
N.A.I.C.S.: 524298
Gerome Droesch *(Gen Mgr)*

AXA Insurance Gulf (1)
Kanoo Tower King Abdul Aziz Road 2nd Floor
PO Box 753
11421 Riyadh, Saudi Arabia
Tel.: (966) 1 477 6706
Fax: (966) 1 478 0418
E-Mail: Info.Riaydh@axa-gulf.com
Web Site: www.axa-cooperative.com
General Insurance Services
S.I.C.: 6411
N.A.I.C.S.: 524210

AXA Insurance Limited (1)
Unit 4 Blanchardstown Plaza Main Street
Blanchardstown, Dublin, Ireland

AXA S.A.—(Continued)

Tel.: (353) 1 8179733
Fax: (353) 1 8179736
E-Mail: axa.blanchardstown@axa.ie
Web Site: www.axa.ie
Insurance Management Services
S.I.C.: 6411
N.A.I.C.S.: 524298
Tony Higgins *(Mgr)*

AXA Insurance pcl (1)
23rd Fl Lumpini Tower 1168 67 Rama 4 Rd Sathorn
Bangkok, 10120, Thailand TH
Tel.: (66) 26797600 (100%)
Fax: (66) 22856383
E-Mail: axathai@axa-insurance.co.th
Web Site: www.axa.co.th
Emp.: 260
Retail & Commercial Insurance
S.I.C.: 6399
N.A.I.C.S.: 524128

AXA Insurance (Saudi Arabia) B.S.C. (1)
Kanoo Tower King Abdul Aziz Road 2nd Floor
PO Box 753
Riyadh, 11421, Saudi Arabia (100%)
Tel.: (966) 14776706
Fax: (966) 14780418
Web Site: www.axa-gulf.com
Emp.: 550
Insurance Provider
S.I.C.: 6399
N.A.I.C.S.: 524128
Jerome Droesch *(CEO-Gulf Reg)*

AXA Insurance Singapore Pte Ltd (1)
143 Cecil Street #01-01 GB Building
Singapore, 069542, Singapore (100%)
Tel.: (65) 63387288
Fax: (65) 63382522
E-Mail: customer.service@axa.com.sg
Web Site: www.axa.com
Emp.: 200
Life Insurance
S.I.C.: 6311
N.A.I.C.S.: 524113

AXA Insurance (1)
48 Michalakopoulou Str
115 28 Athens, Greece GR
Tel.: (30) 210 72 68 000
Fax: (30) 210 7268 408
E-Mail: info@axa-insurance.gr
Web Site: www.axa-insurance.gr
General Insurance Services
S.I.C.: 6411
N.A.I.C.S.: 524210

AXA Insurance (1)
Chemin De Primerose 11
PO Box 7753
1002 Lausanne, Switzerland CH
Tel.: (41) 21 319 53 63
Fax: (41) 21 319 53 93
General Insurance Services
S.I.C.: 6411
N.A.I.C.S.: 524210

AXA investicni spolecnost a.s. (1)
Laurinska 18
811 01 Bratislava, Slovakia
Tel.: (421) 229292929
E-Mail: info@axa.sk
Financial Investment Services
S.I.C.: 6211
N.A.I.C.S.: 523999
Lubor Vrlak *(Head-Org Section)*

Non-U.S. Branch:

AXA investicni spolecnost a.s. (3)
Lazarska 13/8
120 00 Prague, Czech Republic
Tel.: (420) 292 292 292
E-Mail: info@axa.cz
Financial Investment Services
S.I.C.: 6211
N.A.I.C.S.: 523999
Hani Himmat *(Member-Exec Bd)*
Mojmir Member-Exec Bd *(Member-Exec Bd)*
L'ubomir Vrlak *(Member-Exec Bd)*

AXA Ireland Limited (1)
Wolfe Tone House Wolfe Tone Street
Dublin, Ireland
Tel.: (353) 1 8726444
Fax: (353) 1 8729703
General Insurance Services
S.I.C.: 6411
N.A.I.C.S.: 524210

AXA Italia S.p.A. (1)
Via Leopardi 15
20123 Milan, Italy
Tel.: (39) 02 480841
Fax: (39) 02 48084331
Web Site: www.axa.it
General Insurance Services
S.I.C.: 6411
N.A.I.C.S.: 524298

Subsidiary:

AXA Interlife S.p.A. (2)
Via Leopardi 15
20123 Milan, Italy
Tel.: (39) 02 480841
Fax: (39) 02 48084331
Web Site: ww.axa.it
Life Insurance Management Services
S.I.C.: 6311
N.A.I.C.S.: 524113

AXA Japan Holding Co. (1)
NBF Platinum Tower 1-17-3 Shirokane
Minato-ku, Tokyo, 108 8020, Japan JP
Tel.: (81) 367377700 (100%)
Web Site: www.axa.co.jp
Emp.: 7,000
Insurance Holding Company
S.I.C.: 6411
N.A.I.C.S.: 524298
Jean-Louis Laurent Josi *(CEO)*

Subsidiaries:

NEXTIA Life Insurance Co., Ltd. (2)
8th Floor Kojimachi Building 3-3-4KDX Kojimachi
Chiyoda-ku, Tokyo, 102-0083, Japan
Tel.: (81) 120953831
Web Site: www.nextialife.co.jp
Life Insurance Management Services
S.I.C.: 6311
N.A.I.C.S.: 524113

AXA Konzern AG (1)
Colonia Allee 10 20
Cologne, 51067, Germany (100%)
Tel.: (49) 221148101
Fax: (49) 22114822740
E-Mail: service@axa.de
Web Site: www.axa.de
Emp.: 4,500
S.I.C.: 6399
N.A.I.C.S.: 524128

Subsidiaries:

AXA ART Versicherung AG (2)
Colonia-Allee 10-20
80339 Cologne, Germany
Tel.: (49) 89540618120
Fax: (49) 89540618149
Web Site: www.axa-art.de
Emp.: 4,500
Art Insurance Services
S.I.C.: 6411
N.A.I.C.S.: 524298
Helga Fabig *(Gen Mgr)*

AXA Bank AG. (2)
Colonia-Allee 10-20
51067 Cologne, Germany
Tel.: (49) 22114841111
Fax: (49) 22114838901
Commercial Banking Services
S.I.C.: 6029
N.A.I.C.S.: 522110

AXA Krankenversicherung AG (2)
Colonia-Allee 10-20
51067 Cologne, Germany
Tel.: (49) 221 148 125
Fax: (49) 221 148 36202
E-Mail: service@axa.de
Web Site: www.axa.com
General Insurance Services
S.I.C.: 6411
N.A.I.C.S.: 524210
Thomas Buberl *(CEO)*

AXA Liabilities Managers Belgium (1)
25 Boulevard du Souverain
1170 Brussels, Belgium
Tel.: (32) 2 678 6111
Fax: (32) 2 678 9340
Reinsurance Management Services
S.I.C.: 6399
N.A.I.C.S.: 524130

AXA Liabilities Managers UK Limited (1)
Civic Drive
Ipswich, Suffolk, IP1 2AN, United Kingdom UK
Tel.: (44) 1473 212422
Fax: (44) 1473 230900
E-Mail: axa-lm@axa-lm.com
Reinsurance Management Services
S.I.C.: 6399
N.A.I.C.S.: 524130
John Byrne *(CEO)*
Robert Howe *(Deputy CEO)*
Roger Wiegley *(Gen Counsel)*

AXA Life Europe Limited (1)
3rd Floor Guild Hse Guild Street IFSC
Dublin, 2, Ireland
Tel.: (353) 1 4711716
Fax: (353) 4711895
E-Mail: axalifeeurope@axa.ie
Web Site: www.axa-life-europe.ie
Emp.: 2
Insurance Management Services
S.I.C.: 6411
N.A.I.C.S.: 524298
Francois Robinet *(Chm)*
Pat Healy *(CEO & Exec Dir)*
Roel Voogt *(Mng Dir)*

AXA Life Insurance Company Limited (1)
NBF Platinum Tower 1-17-3 Shirokane
Minato-ku, Tokyo, 1088020, Japan (100%)
Tel.: (81) 367377777
Web Site: www.axa.co.jp
Emp.: 8,000
Life Insurance
S.I.C.: 6311
N.A.I.C.S.: 524113
Mark Pearson *(Pres & CEO)*

AXA Life Insurance Singapore Pte. Ltd. (1)
8 Shenton Way Unit 27-02 Axa Tower
068811 Singapore, Singapore SG
Tel.: (65) 68805500 (100%)
Fax: (65) 68805501
E-Mail: con.sev@axa.com.sg
Web Site: www.axalife.com.sg
Emp.: 120
S.I.C.: 6399
N.A.I.C.S.: 524128

AXA Life Ltd. (1)
General-Guisan-Strasse 40
8401 Winterthur, Switzerland
Tel.: (41) 800 809 809
Life Insurance Management Services
S.I.C.: 6311
N.A.I.C.S.: 524113

AXA Luxembourg SA (1)
1 Place de l'Etoile
1325 Luxembourg, Luxembourg
Tel.: (352) 44 24 241
E-Mail: info@axa.lu
Web Site: www.axa.lu
Health Insurance Services
S.I.C.: 6321
N.A.I.C.S.: 524114

AXA MBASK IC OJSC (1)
80/90 Azi Aslanov Str
Baku, Azerbaijan
Tel.: (994) 12 596 55 70
Fax: (994) 12 596 55 72
E-Mail: axambask@axambask.az
Web Site: www.axambask.az
Emp.: 100
Insurance Management Services
S.I.C.: 6411
N.A.I.C.S.: 524298
Selcuk Adiguzel *(Acct Mgr)*

AXA Mediterranean Holding, S.A. (1)
Camino fuente de la Mora 1
28050 Madrid, Spain (100%)
Tel.: (34) 915388200
Fax: (34) 91 555 3197
Web Site: www.axa.com
Insurance Services
S.I.C.: 6399
N.A.I.C.S.: 524128
Jean-Laurent Granier *(CEO-Latin America Reg)*

Subsidiaries:

AXA Aurora Iberica S.A. de Seguros y Reaseguros (2)
Camino fuente de la Mora 1
28050 Madrid, Spain (100%)
Tel.: (34) 915388200
Fax: (34) 915553197
Web Site: www.axa.es
Emp.: 2,500
Insurance Provider
S.I.C.: 6411
N.A.I.C.S.: 524298

AXA Aurora Vida SA de Seguros y Reaseguros (2)
Place Federico Moyua 4
Bilbao, 48009, Spain
Tel.: (34) 944 20 62 00
Fax: (34) 944 20 62 65
General Insurance Services
S.I.C.: 6411
N.A.I.C.S.: 524210

AXA Seguros Generales SA de Seguros y Reaseguros (2)
Place Federico Moyua 4
Bilbao, 48009, Spain
Tel.: (34) 944 20 62 00
Fax: (34) 944 20 62 65
General Insurance Services
S.I.C.: 6411
N.A.I.C.S.: 524298

Hilo Direct Seguros y Reaseguros S.A. (2)
Camino Fuente de la Mora 1
28050 Madrid, Spain (100%)
Tel.: (34) 902 40 40 25
Fax: (34) 87 902 92 89
E-Mail: operaciones@directseguros.es
Web Site: www.directseguros.es
Emp.: 320
Insurance Services
S.I.C.: 6399
N.A.I.C.S.: 524128

Non-U.S. Subsidiaries:

AXA Insurance A.E. (2)
48 Michalakopoulou Str
115 28 Athens, Greece
Tel.: (30) 210 72 68 000
Fax: (30) 210 72 68 810
E-Mail: info@axa-insurance.gr
Web Site: www.axa-insurance.gr
General Insurance Services
S.I.C.: 6411
N.A.I.C.S.: 524298

Seguro Directo Gere Companhia de Seguros SA (2)
Av Do Mediterraneo Lote 1 01 1 2 Parque das Nacoes
1990-156 Lisbon, Portugal
Tel.: (351) 21 310 24 36
Fax: (351) 21 423 28 19
E-Mail: apoio.cliente@segurodirecto.pt
Web Site: www.segurodirecto.pt
General Insurance Services
S.I.C.: 6411
N.A.I.C.S.: 524210

AXA Merkens Fonds Gmbh (1)
Colonia-Allee 10-20
51067 Cologne, Germany
Tel.: (49) 221 1615 15800
Pension Fund Management Services
S.I.C.: 6371
N.A.I.C.S.: 525110

AXA Middle East (1)
Jal El Dib Highway Axa Middle East Bldg
PO Box 11-550
Beirut, Lebanon
Tel.: (961) 4 716 333
Fax: (961) 4 716563
E-Mail: mail@axa-middleeast.com.lb
Web Site: www.axa-middleeast.com
General Insurance Services
S.I.C.: 6411
N.A.I.C.S.: 524298
Roger Nasnas *(Chm & CEO)*
Frederic Flejou *(Vice Chm)*

AXA Multimanager (1)
7 Newgate Street
London, EC1A 7NX, United Kingdom
Tel.: (44) 207 003 1000
Fax: (44) 207 003 2055
Web Site: www.axa.com
Asset Management Services
S.I.C.: 6282
N.A.I.C.S.: 523920

AXA Osiguranje (1)
Bulevar Mihaila Pupina 6/XIV
Belgrade, Serbia
Tel.: (381) 11 71 55 444
Fax: (381) 11 22 00 401
E-Mail: contact@axa.rs
Web Site: www.axa.rs
General Insurance Services
S.I.C.: 6411
N.A.I.C.S.: 524298
Antonio Marchitelli *(CEO)*

AXA Oyak Holding A.S. (1)
Meclisi Mebusan Cad No 15 OYAK Ishani
80040 Istanbul, Turkey
Tel.: (90) 2123342424
Fax: (90) 252122521515
E-Mail: ilisim@segota.com.tr
Web Site: www.axasegota.com.tr
Emp.: 620
Insurance Provider
S.I.C.: 6399
N.A.I.C.S.: 524128
Cemal Ererdi *(CEO)*

AXA Pension Solutions AG (1)
Gertrudstrasse 15
Postfach 300
8401 Winterthur, Switzerland
Tel.: (41) 52 261 28 38
Fax: (41) 52 212 12 01
Pension Fund Services
S.I.C.: 6371
N.A.I.C.S.: 525110

AXA Philippines (1)
Sen Gil Puyat Ave Corner Tindalo St
Makati, Philippines 1200
Tel.: (63) 2 5815 292
E-Mail: Customer.Service@axa.com.ph
Web Site: www.axa.com.ph
General Insurance Services
S.I.C.: 6411
N.A.I.C.S.: 524298
Rien Hermans *(Pres & CEO)*
Don San Jose *(CFO)*
Amor Balagtas *(CMO)*
Rahul Hora *(Chief Agency Officer)*
Marie Raymundo *(Chief Bancassurance Officer)*

AXA pojisovna a.s. (1)
Lazarska 13/8
120 00 Prague, Czech Republic
Tel.: (420) 292 292 292
E-Mail: info@axa.cz
Web Site: www.axa.cz
General Insurance Services
S.I.C.: 6411
N.A.I.C.S.: 524298

AXA Poland Pension Funds (1)
ul Chlodna 51
Warsaw, 00-867, Poland
Tel.: (48) 225550000
Pension Fund Services
S.I.C.: 6371
N.A.I.C.S.: 525110

AXA Polska S.A. (1)
ul Chlodna 51 Budynek Warsaw Trade Tower
00-867 Warsaw, Poland
Tel.: (48) 22 555 00 00
Assest Management Services
S.I.C.: 6799
N.A.I.C.S.: 523920

AXA Portugal Companhia de Seguros de Vida SA (1)
Praca Marques de Pombal n 14
1250-162 Lisbon, Portugal
Tel.: (351) 707 281 281
E-Mail: contacto@axa.pt
Web Site: www.axa.pt
Life Insurance Management Services
S.I.C.: 6311
N.A.I.C.S.: 524113

AXA Portugal - Companhia de Seguros S.A. (1)
Praca Marques De Pombal No 14 Ap 1953
1058 801 Lisbon, Portugal PT
Tel.: (351) 213506100 (100%)
Fax: (351) 213506136
E-Mail: contacto@axa-seguros.pt
Web Site: www.axa.pt
Emp.: 300
Insurance Provider
S.I.C.: 6399
N.A.I.C.S.: 524128

AXA Powszechne Towarzystwo Emerytalne S.A. (1)
ul Chlodna 51
00-867 Warsaw, Poland
Tel.: (48) 22 555 00 00
Fax: (48) 22 555 05 00
E-Mail: emerytury@axa-polska.pl
Pension Fund Services
S.I.C.: 6371
N.A.I.C.S.: 525110

AXA RE Canada (1)
Place Montreal Trust 1800 McGill College Avenue Bureau 2000
Montreal, QC, H3A 3J6, Canada
Tel.: (514) 842-9262
Fax: (514) 842-9254
Reinsurance Management Services
S.I.C.: 6399
N.A.I.C.S.: 524130

AXA Rosenberg Canada Co. (1)
5700 Yonge Street Suite 1400
North York, ON, M2M 4K2, Canada
Tel.: (416) 250-1992
Fax: (416) 250-5833
Investment Management Services
S.I.C.: 6211
N.A.I.C.S.: 523999

AXA Rosenberg Investment Management Asia Pacific Ltd. (1)
57/F One Island East 18 Westlands Road
Quarry Bay, China (Hong Kong)
Tel.: (852) 2285 2000
Fax: (852) 2285 2999
Investment Management Services
S.I.C.: 6211
N.A.I.C.S.: 523999

AXA Rosenberg Investment Management Limited (1)
8th Floor 155 Bishopsgate
London, EC2M 3XJ, United Kingdom
Tel.: (44) 20 7003 1800
Fax: (44) 20 7003 1950
Web Site: www.axa.com
Emp.: 30
Investment Management Services
S.I.C.: 6211
N.A.I.C.S.: 523999
Gideon Smith *(Chief Investment Officer-Europe)*

AXA Seguros SA de CV (1)
Av Periferico Sur 3325
San Jeronimo Aculco, 10400 Mexico, DF, Mexico
Tel.: (52) 5551692500
Web Site: www.axa.com.mx
Sales Range: $1-4.9 Billion
Emp.: 4,200
Insurance Services
S.I.C.: 6411
N.A.I.C.S.: 524210
Xavier De Bellefon *(CEO)*

AXA Seguros Uruguay SA (1)
Missiones 1549
11000 Montevideo, Uruguay (100%)
Tel.: (598) 29160850
Fax: (598) 29160847
Web Site: www.axa-seguros.com.uy
Emp.: 20
S.I.C.: 6399
N.A.I.C.S.: 524128

AXA SPDB Investment Managers Co., Ltd (1)
38/F Shanghai Central Plaza 381 Middle Huai Hai Road
Shanghai, 200020, China
Tel.: (86) 4008828999
Fax: (86) 2123212890
Web Site: www.py-axa.com
Financial Investment Services
S.I.C.: 6211
N.A.I.C.S.: 523999

AXA SR (1)
Kolarska 6
811 06 Bratislava, Slovakia
Tel.: (421) 2 2929 2929
E-Mail: info@axa.sk
Web Site: www.axa.sk
General Insurance Services
S.I.C.: 6411
N.A.I.C.S.: 524210

AXA Technologies Shared Services India Pvt. Ltd (1)
RMZ Infinity Tower B 2nd & 4th Floor 3 Old Madras Road
Bengaluru, Karnataka, 560 016, India
Tel.: (91) 80 4073 5999
Fax: (91) 8041834100
Web Site: www.axa-tech.com
Emp.: 50
Information Technology Consulting Services
S.I.C.: 7373
N.A.I.C.S.: 541512
Navin G. Shivdasani *(Deputy Gen Mgr)*

AXA Technology Services Australia (1)
Level 5 750 Collins St
Docklands, Melbourne, VIC, 3008, Australia
Tel.: (61) 3 8688 2204
Information Technology Consulting Services
S.I.C.: 7373
N.A.I.C.S.: 541512

AXA Technology Services Germany Gmbh (1)
Colonia-Allee 10-20
Cologne, 51067, Germany
Tel.: (49) 221 148105
Web Site: www.axa-tech.com
Information Technology & Telecommunication Services
S.I.C.: 7373
N.A.I.C.S.: 541512

AXA Technology Services Japan K.K (1)
NBF Platinum Tower 21F 1-17-3 Shirokane
Minato-ku, Tokyo, 108-8020, Japan
Tel.: (81) 3 6737 5284
Fax: (81) 367375927
E-Mail: axatechjapan@axa-tech.com
Web Site: www.axa-tech.com
Emp.: 10
Information Technology & Telecommunication Services
S.I.C.: 7373
N.A.I.C.S.: 541512
Norbert Juettner *(Pres)*

AXA Technology Services Portugal (1)
Praca Jose Queiros n 1 Edificio Entreposto Porta 2 3 Piso
Lisbon, 1800-237, Portugal
Tel.: (351) 21 85 47 429
Web Site: www.axa-tech.com
Information Technology Consulting Services
S.I.C.: 7373
N.A.I.C.S.: 541512

AXA Technology Services South East Asia (1)
27/F Cambridge House TaiKoo Place 979 King's Road
Quarry Bay, China (Hong Kong)
Tel.: (852) 25 19 11 11
Web Site: www.axa-tech.com
Information Technology & Telecommunication Services
S.I.C.: 7373
N.A.I.C.S.: 541512

AXA Technology Services Switzerland AG (1)
Paulstrasse 12
PO Box 357
8401 Winterthur, Switzerland
Tel.: (41) 52 261 11 11
E-Mail: info.ch@axa-winterthur.ch
Web Site: www.axa.com
Emp.: 300
Information Technology & Telecommunication Services
S.I.C.: 7373
N.A.I.C.S.: 541512
Philippe Egger *(Mng Dir)*

AXA Technology Services UK Plc (1)
Spectrum Building Bond Street
Bristol, BS1 3LG, United Kingdom
Tel.: (44) 125 685 2000
Web Site: www.axa-tech.com
Information Technology & Telecommunication Services
S.I.C.: 7373
N.A.I.C.S.: 541512

AXA Towarzystwo Ubezpieczen S.A. (1)
ul Chlodna 51
00-867 Warsaw, Poland
Tel.: (48) 22 555 00 00
Fax: (48) 22 555 00 00
E-Mail: ubezpieczenia@axa-polska.pl
Life Insurance Services
S.I.C.: 6311
N.A.I.C.S.: 524113

AXA Turkey Holding A.S. (1)
Meclis-i Mebusan Cad Oyak Yp Hany No 15 Salypazary
Istanbul, 34433, Turkey
Tel.: (90) 212 334 24 24
Fax: (90) 212 252 15 15
Investment Management Services
S.I.C.: 6282
N.A.I.C.S.: 523920

Subsidiary:

AXA Sigorta A.S. (2)
Meclis-i Mebusan Cad No 15
Salipazari, 34433 Istanbul, Turkey
Tel.: (90) 2123342424
Fax: (90) 2122521515
Web Site: www.en.axasigorta.com.tr
Emp.: 588
General Insurance Services
S.I.C.: 6411
N.A.I.C.S.: 524210

AXA Ukraine (1)
Bratska Str 14 6th Floor 3rd Entrance
Kiev, 4070, Ukraine
Tel.: (380) 44 391 1122
Fax: (380) 44 391 1121
E-Mail: office@axa-ukraine.com
Web Site: www.axa-ukraine.com
General Insurance Services
S.I.C.: 6411
N.A.I.C.S.: 524210
Philippe Wautelet *(CEO)*

AXA UK plc (1)
5 Old Broad St
London, EC2 N 1AD, United Kingdom UK
Tel.: (44) 2076451600 (100%)
Fax: (44) 2079205281
E-Mail: info@axa-uk.co.uk
Web Site: www.axa.co.uk
Rev.: $4,790,799,872
Emp.: 4,500
Holding Company; Life Insurance, Pensions, Investment
S.I.C.: 6399
N.A.I.C.S.: 524128
Ian Brimecome *(Chm)*
Bertrand Poupart-Lafarge *(CFO)*
Paul Evans *(CEO-UK & Ireland)*

Division:

AXA PPP Healthcare Group PLC (2)
Crescent Road
Tunbridge Wells, Kent, TN1 2PL, United Kingdom UK
Tel.: (44) 01892512345 (100%)
Fax: (44) 1892515143
Web Site: www.axappphealthcare.co.uk
Premiums: $700,000,000
Emp.: 2,000
Heathcare Services
S.I.C.: 6321
N.A.I.C.S.: 524114
Keith Gibbs *(CEO)*
Ed Davis *(Sr Legal Advisor)*

Subsidiaries:

AXA Insurance PLC (2)
1 Aldgate
London, EC3N 1RE, United Kingdom (100%)
Tel.: (44) 2077023109
Fax: (44) 2077021612
Web Site: www.axa.co.uk

AXA S.A.—(Continued)

Emp.: 350
Life Insurance
S.I.C.: 6311
N.A.I.C.S.: 524113
Felix Maso *(CEO)*
Mark Cliff *(Mng Dir)*

AXA Insurance UK plc (2)
5 Old Broad Street
London, EC2N 1AD, United Kingdom
Tel.: (44) 20 7920 5101
E-Mail: info@axainsurance.com
General Insurance Services
S.I.C.: 6411
N.A.I.C.S.: 524298

AXA Sun Life Plc (2)
AXA Center
Brierly Furlong Stoke Gifford, Bristol, BS34 8SW, United Kingdom (100%)
Mailing Address:
PO Box 1810
Bristol, BS99 5SN, United Kingdom
Tel.: (44) 2079205900
Web Site: www.axa.co.uk
Emp.: 3,500
Life Insurance
S.I.C.: 6399
N.A.I.C.S.: 524128
Paul J. Evans *(CEO)*

Bluefin Group Limited (2)
5 Old Broad Street
London, EC2N 1AD, United Kingdom
Tel.: (44) 207 338 0111
Fax: (44) 207 338 0112
E-Mail: bcc.marketing@bluefingroup.co.uk
Web Site: www.bluefingroup.co.uk
General Insurance Services
S.I.C.: 6411
N.A.I.C.S.: 524298

Guardian Royal Exchange plc (2)
5 Old Broad Street
London, EC2N 1AD, United Kingdom
Tel.: (44) 20 7920 5900
General Insurance Services
S.I.C.: 6411
N.A.I.C.S.: 524210
Robert C. W. Organ *(Exec Dir)*

AXA Versicherung AG (1)
An Der Trift 65
63303 Dreieich, Germany (100%)
Tel.: (49) 61039890
Fax: (49) 398939000
E-Mail: info@axa.de
Web Site: www.axa.de
Emp.: 170
S.I.C.: 6399
N.A.I.C.S.: 524128
Cialdella Martine *(Sec)*

AXA Vie Gabon (1)
BP 2137
Libreville, Gabon
Tel.: (241) 743 434
Fax: (241) 724 857
E-Mail: axa.gabon@inet.ga
Web Site: www.axa.com
Emp.: 16
Insurance Provider
S.I.C.: 6399
N.A.I.C.S.: 524128

AXA Wealth Ltd (1)
Winterthur Way
Basingstoke, Hants, RG21 6SZ, United Kingdom
Tel.: (44) 1256 470707
Fax: (44) 1256 798348
E-Mail: customerenquiriesmailbox@axawealth.co.uk
Web Site: www.axawealth.co.uk
Emp.: 850
General Insurance Services
S.I.C.: 6411
N.A.I.C.S.: 524298
Mike Kellard *(CEO)*

AXA Wealth Management Singapore Pte Ltd (1)
8 Shenton Way AXA Tower
Singapore, 68811, Singapore
Tel.: (65) 68 80 55 00
Fax: (65) 68 80 55 01
E-Mail: comsvc@axa.com.sg
Web Site: www.axalife.com.sg
Life Insurance Management Services
S.I.C.: 6311
N.A.I.C.S.: 524113
Glenn Williams *(CEO)*

AXA Winterthur (1)
General Guisan Strasse 40
PO Box 357
CH 8401 Winterthur, Zurich, Switzerland
Tel.: (41) 800809809
Fax: (41) 5222189696
E-Mail: info.ch@axa-winterthur.ch
Web Site: www.axa-winterthur.ch
Sales Range: $200-249.9 Million
Emp.: 23,000
Life & Other Insurance Services
S.I.C.: 6411
N.A.I.C.S.: 524298
Philippe Egger *(CEO)*

Subsidiaries:

Technopark Immobilien AG (2)
Technoparkstrasse 1
8005 Zurich, Switzerland
Tel.: (41) 444451000
Fax: (41) 444451001
E-Mail: info@technopark.ch
Web Site: www.technopark.ch
Emp.: 8
Technology Services
S.I.C.: 4899
N.A.I.C.S.: 517919
Pheo Schwarz *(Mgr-Facility Mgmt)*

Winterthur Insurance Co (2)
Theaterstrasse 17
8401 Winterthur, Switzerland
Tel.: (41) 522619500
Fax: (41) 522619577
Web Site: www.axa-winterthur.ch/De/Seiten/home.aspx
Emp.: 2,500
Insurance
S.I.C.: 6399
N.A.I.C.S.: 524128
Philippe Egger *(Gen Mgr)*

Winterthur Life & Pensions AG (2)
General Guisan Strasse 40
PO Box 357
8401 Winterthur, Switzerland
Tel.: (41) 522611111
Fax: (41) 522616162
E-Mail: info@winterthur-leben.ch
Web Site: www.winterthur-leben.ch
Emp.: 9,000
Insurance Provider
S.I.C.: 6399
N.A.I.C.S.: 524128

Non-U.S. Subsidiaries:

AXA Winterthur Insurance (Asia) Ltd. (2)
China Diamond Exchange Building 555 Pudian Rd
Pudong Xinqu, Shanghai, China
Tel.: (86) 21 6156 3500
Fax: (86) 21 6882 4600
E-Mail: service@axa-ins.com.cn
Web Site: www.axa-ins.com.cn
Art Insurance Services
S.I.C.: 6411
N.A.I.C.S.: 524298
Raymond Chan *(CEO & Gen Mgr)*

AXA Winterthur Pensiones (2)
Avenida Diagonal 575 2nd Floor
08029 Barcelona, Spain
Tel.: (34) 902404084
Fax: (34) 933637240
E-Mail: winterthur-salud@axa.es
Web Site: www.axa.es
Insurance
S.I.C.: 6399
N.A.I.C.S.: 524128

DBV-Winterthur Holding AG (2)
Frankfurter Str 50
D 65172 Wiesbaden, Germany
Tel.: (49) 6113630
Fax: (49) 022114821599
Web Site: www.axa.de
Emp.: 2,000
Insurance Services
S.I.C.: 6411
N.A.I.C.S.: 524210
Thomas Buberl *(Mng Dir)*

La Equitativa de Madrid (2)
Marques del Riscal 2
28010 Madrid, Spain
Tel.: (34) 913196558
Fax: (34) 91 319 91 54
E-Mail: equitativa@equitativa.com
Web Site: www.equitativa.com
Insurance Services
S.I.C.: 6399
N.A.I.C.S.: 524128

Seguros Atlas S.A. (2)
Av Periferico Sur 3325
San Jeronimo Aculco, 10400 Mexico, DF, Mexico
Tel.: (52) 55 5169 2500
Web Site: www.axa.com.mx
Emp.: 493
Insurance Services
S.I.C.: 6399
N.A.I.C.S.: 524128

Winterthur Life UK Limited (2)
Winterthur Way
Basingstoke, Hampshire, RG21 6SZ, United Kingdom UK
Tel.: (44) 1256470707
Fax: (44) 1256798605
E-Mail: enquiries@winterthur-life.co.uk
Web Site: www.winterthur-life.co.uk
Life Insurance
S.I.C.: 6311
N.A.I.C.S.: 524113
Frank Parsons *(Dir-Sls)*

AXA zivotni pojistovna a.s. (1)
Laurinska 18
811 01 Bratislava, Slovakia
Tel.: (421) 2 2929 2929
E-Mail: info.zp@axa.sk
Web Site: www.axa.sk/axa/axa-group-in-sr/axa-zivotni-pojistovna/description
General Insurance Services
S.I.C.: 6411
N.A.I.C.S.: 524210

Non-U.S. Branch:

AXA zivotni pojistovna, a.s. (2)
Lazarska 13/8
120 00 Prague, Czech Republic
Tel.: (420) 292 292 292
E-Mail: info@axa.cz
Life Insurance Management Services
S.I.C.: 6311
N.A.I.C.S.: 524113
Martin Vogl *(Chm-Exec Bd)*
Mojmir Boucnik *(Member-Exec Bd)*
Hani Himmat *(Member-Exec Bd)*
Peter Socha *(Member-Exec Bd)*
L'ubor Vrlak *(Member-Exec Bd)*

AXA Zycie Towarzystwo Ubezpieczen S.A. (1)
Ul Chlodna 51
00 867 Warsaw, Poland
Tel.: (48) 22 555 00 50
Fax: (48) 22 555 00 52
E-Mail: ubezpieczenia@axa-polska.pl
Web Site: www.axa.pl
Life Insurance
S.I.C.: 6311
N.A.I.C.S.: 524113
Maciej Szwarc *(Mng Dir)*

Bluefin Advisory Services Limited (1)
1 Aldgate 1st Floor
London, EC3N 1LP, United Kingdom
Tel.: (44) 20 7709 4500
Fax: (44) 2036324801
E-Mail: bpcmarketing@bluefingroup.co.uk
Emp.: 5
General Insurance Services
S.I.C.: 6411
N.A.I.C.S.: 524298
William F. Ruprecht *(CEO)*

DBV Deutsche Beamtenversicherung AG (1)
Frankfurter Strasse 50
65189 Wiesbaden, Germany
Tel.: (49) 22114841011
Fax: (49) 22114841908
E-Mail: service@dbv.de
Web Site: www.dbv.de
General Insurance Services
S.I.C.: 6411
N.A.I.C.S.: 524210

Subsidiary:

DBV Deutsche Beamtenversicherung Lebensversicherung AG (2)
Frankfurter Strasse 50
65189 Wiesbaden, Germany
Tel.: (49) 221 14841011
Fax: (49) 221 14841908
E-Mail: service@dbv.de
Web Site: www.dbv.de
General Insurance Services
S.I.C.: 6411
N.A.I.C.S.: 524210

ICBC - AXA Life Assurance (1)
19/F Mirae Asset Tower No 166 Lu Jia Zui Ring Road
Shanghai, Pudong, China
Tel.: (86) 21 5879 2288
Fax: (86) 21 5879 2299
Web Site: www.icbc-axa.com
Medical Insurance Services
S.I.C.: 6321
N.A.I.C.S.: 524114

Insurance Corp. of Newfoundland Limited (1)
35 Blackmarsh Rd Robert Charles Anthony Bldg
Saint John's, NL, A1B 3N9, Canada (60%)
Mailing Address:
Box 8485
Saint John's, NL, A1B 3P9, Canada
Tel.: (709) 758-5650
Fax: (709) 579-4500
E-Mail: info@axa.ca
Web Site: www.axa.ca
Emp.: 150
Insurance Agents Brokers and Service
S.I.C.: 6411
N.A.I.C.S.: 524210
David Anthony *(Pres)*

IPA SINGAPORE PTE LTD (1)
20 Maxwell Road 03-02 Maxwell House
Singapore, 069113, Singapore
Tel.: (65) 6322 2600
Fax: (65) 6221 5900
E-Mail: enquiries@axa-assistance.com.sg
Web Site: www.axa-assistance.com.sg
Emp.: 40
General Insurance Services
S.I.C.: 6411
N.A.I.C.S.: 524210
Genevieve Lau *(Head-Fin & Admin)*

Kyobo AXA General Insurance Co. Ltd. (1)
395-70 Shindaebang-Dong
Dongjak-gu, Seoul, 156-714, Korea (South)
Tel.: (82) 2 3479 4888
Fax: (82) 2 3479 4800
General Insurance Services
S.I.C.: 6411
N.A.I.C.S.: 524298

SC AXA Life Insurance S.A. (1)
Strada Pechea Nr 13 Sector 1
013982 Bucharest, Romania
Tel.: (40) 21 207 99 99
Fax: (40) 21 408 91 01
E-Mail: client@axa-asigurari.ro
Web Site: www.axa-asigurari.ro
General Insurance Services
S.I.C.: 6411
N.A.I.C.S.: 524210

U A Vie (1)
9 Ave Houdaille
PO Box 2016
Abidjan, Cote d'Ivoire CI
Tel.: (225) 20310400 (100%)
Fax: (225) 20223760
E-Mail: axabbg@africaonline.co.ci
Web Site: www.uavie.ci
Emp.: 103
Insurance Services
S.I.C.: 6399
N.A.I.C.S.: 524128

UAT (1)
169 boulevard du 13 Janvier
BP 495
Lome, Togo
Tel.: (228) 2211034
Fax: (228) 218724
Insurance Services
S.I.C.: 6399
N.A.I.C.S.: 524128

UGAR (1)
BP 179
Conakry, Papua New Guinea (40%)
Tel.: (675) 414841
Fax: (675) 411711
E-Mail: ugar@mirinet.net.gn
Web Site: www.ugarassurance.com
Emp.: 91
Insurance Services
S.I.C.: 6399
N.A.I.C.S.: 524128

Non-U.S. Joint Ventures:

ICBC-AXA-Minmetals Assurance Co., Ltd. (1)
12/F China Merchants Tower 161 Lu Jai Zui Road
Pudong New District, Shanghai, 200120, China
Tel.: (86) 2158792288
Fax: (86) 21 5879 2299
E-Mail:
Web Site: www.icbc-axa.com
Sales Range: $10-24.9 Million
Insurance Services in Life, Education, Retirement, Health & Wealth Management
S.I.C.: 6311
N.A.I.C.S.: 524113

Krungthai-AXA Life Insurance Co., Ltd. (1)
2034/116-119, 136, 138-143 ItalThai Tower Floor 27 32-33
Petchaburi Road
Bang Kapi Huay Kwang, Bangkok, 10310, Thailand TH
Tel.: (66) 27234000
Fax: (66) 27234032
Web Site: www.krungthai-axa.co.th
Sales Range: $200-249.9 Million
Emp.: 526
Life Insurance Products & Services
S.I.C.: 6311
N.A.I.C.S.: 524113
Michael George Plaxton *(CEO)*
David Korunic *(CFO)*
Surasit Ploydanai *(COO)*
Yodsak Panmanotham *(CIO)*
Saifon Sutchasila *(CMO)*
Amornratana Xuto *(Chief People Officer)*
Vithaya Charnpanich *(Chief Agency Officer)*
Roger Thomas Deacon *(Chief Distr Officer)*
Sutat Larpkiattaworn *(Chief Alternative Distr Officer)*
Poramasiri Manolamai *(Chief Bancassurance Officer)*
Uqkrit Sridaromont *(Chief Trng Officer)*

PT AXA Mandiri Financial Services (1)
Plaza Mandiri 29th Floor Jalan Jen Gatot Subroto
Kav 36-38, Jakarta, 12190, Indonesia
Tel.: (62) 215270007
Fax: (62) 215271522
Financial Services; Joint Venture Owned 51% by AXA S.A. & 49% PT Bank Mandiri (Persero) Tbk.
S.I.C.: 6211
N.A.I.C.S.: 523999

AXARA

152 rue Paris 93100
Monteuil, 93100 Paris, France
Tel.: (33) 143631313
Fax: (33) 143636000
E-Mail: retail@axara.com
Web Site: www.axara.com
Sls.: $15,700,000
Emp.: 30

Business Description:
Women's Clothing Mfr
S.I.C.: 2389
N.A.I.C.S.: 315240
Personnel:
Daniel Abergel *(Mgr)*

AXCEL A/S

Sankt Annae Plads 10
1250 Copenhagen, Denmark
Tel.: (45) 33366999
Fax: (45) 33366998
E-Mail: axcel@axcel.dk
Web Site: www.axcel.dk
Emp.: 50

Business Description:
Private Equity Firm
S.I.C.: 6211
N.A.I.C.S.: 523999
Personnel:
Bent Pedersen *(Deputy Chm)*
Christian Frigast *(Mng Partner)*
Vilhelm Sundstrom *(Mng Partner)*
Lars Thomassen *(CFO & Partner)*
Per Christensen *(Partner)*
Vilhelm Hahn-Petersen *(Partner)*
Soren Lindberg *(Partner)*
Jacob Thygesen *(Partner)*
Nikolaj Vejlsgaard *(Partner)*
Board of Directors:
Niels Bjorn Christiansen
Peter Damgaard Jensen
Lars Johansen
Jens W. Moberg
Bent Pedersen
Johannes Poulsen
Jorgen E. Tandrup
Nikolaj Vejlsgaard

Holding:

Royal Scandinavia A/S (1)
Sondre Fasanvej 9
DK 2000 Frederiksberg, Denmark
Tel.: (45) 38 14 48 48
Telex: 16248
Fax: (45) 38 14 99 00
E-Mail: royal@royalscandinavia.dk
Web Site: www.royalscandinavia.com
Holding Company
Export
S.I.C.: 6719
N.A.I.C.S.: 551112
Erik Danquard Jensen *(Chm)*
Christian Frigast *(Vice Chm)*
Poul Ravn Christensen *(CEO)*

Subsidiary:

Illums Bolighus A/S (2)
Amagertorv 8-10
DK 1160 Copenhagen, Denmark (100%)
Tel.: (45) 33141941
Fax: (45) 33669766
E-Mail: info@illumsbolighus.com
Web Site: www.illumsbolighus.com
Emp.: 200
Retail Sales of Porcelain, Silver & Glass
S.I.C.: 5719
N.A.I.C.S.: 442299
Henrik Ypkendanz *(Mng Dir)*

U.S. Subsidiaries:

Orrefors Kosta Boda, Inc. (2)
900 Liberty Pl
Sicklerville, NJ 08081 PA
Tel.: (856) 768-5400
Telex: 3767315
Fax: (856) 768-7924
E-Mail: info@okbusa.com
Web Site: www.orrefors.com
Porcelain, Silverware & Glassware Retailer
S.I.C.: 5023
N.A.I.C.S.: 423220
Robin Good *(VP-Sls-Mktg)*

Non-U.S. Subsidiaries:

EskoArtwork N.V. (1)
Kortrijksesteenweg 1095
BE 9051 Gent, Belgium BE (68%)
Tel.: (32) 92169211
Fax: (32) 92169464
E-Mail: info.eur@esko.com
Web Site: www.esko.com
Sales Range: $200-249.9 Million
Emp.: 980
Commercial Printing & Professional Publishing Services
S.I.C.: 2759
N.A.I.C.S.: 323111
Jean-Claude Deschamps *(Chm)*
Vilhelm Hahn-Petersen *(Deputy Chm)*
Guido Van der Schueren *(Vice Chm)*
Carsten Knudsen *(Pres & CEO)*
Kurt Demeuleneere *(CFO)*
Mark Quinlan *(Pres-North America)*
Nicolai Gradman *(Sr VP-Supply Chain)*
Simon James *(Sr VP-Products & Solutions Mktg)*
Arjen Maarleveld *(Sr VP-Packaging Solutions)*
Bernard Zwaenepoel *(Sr VP-Software Bus)*

Subsidiaries:

Enfocus NV (2)
Kortrijksesteenweg 1095
9051 Gent, Belgium
Tel.: (32) 92169211
Fax: (32) 92169212
E-Mail: info@enfocus.com
Web Site: www.enfocus.com
Emp.: 37
Printing Solutions
S.I.C.: 2759
N.A.I.C.S.: 323111
Fabian Prudhomme *(VP)*

Non-U.S. Subsidiaries:

Esko Graphics Imaging GmbH (2)
Heerskamp 6
25524 Itzehoe, Germany
Tel.: (49) 482177010
Fax: (49) 4821770110
Web Site: www.eskographics.com
Emp.: 55
Packaging, Commercial Printing & Professional Publishing Services
S.I.C.: 2759
N.A.I.C.S.: 323111
Juergen Andresen *(VP)*

Esko Graphics Kongsberg AS (2)
Kirkegardsveien 45
PO Box 1016
3616 Kongsberg, Norway
Tel.: (47) 32289900
Fax: (47) 32288515
Packaging, Commercial Printing & Professional Publishing Services
S.I.C.: 2759
N.A.I.C.S.: 323111

Nordic Waterproofing AB (1)
Bruksgatan
PO Box 22
SE 263 21 Hoganas, Sweden SE (100%)
Tel.: (46) 42 36 22 40
Fax: (46) 42 34 27 54
E-Mail: info@nordicwaterproofing.com
Web Site: www.nordicwaterproofing.com
Sales Range: $250-299.9 Million
Emp.: 650
Roofing
S.I.C.: 5033
N.A.I.C.S.: 423330

Subsidiary:

Trebolit AB (2)
PO Box 22
263 21 Hoganas, Sweden SE (100%)
Tel.: (46) 41048000
Fax: (46) 41010311
E-Mail: info@trebolit.se
Web Site: www.trebolit.se
Develops & Markets Waterproofing Products & Other Construction Products
S.I.C.: 5039
N.A.I.C.S.: 423390
Paul Zander *(Sls Mgr)*

Non-U.S. Subsidiary:

Makati Oy (2)
Liekokuja 6
FIN 03100 Nummela, Finland FI (100%)
Tel.: (358) 9 2242 850
Fax: (358) 9 2248 221
E-Mail: myynti@mataki.com
Web Site: web.nordicwaterproofing.com
Emp.: 20
Construction Waterproofing Materials Mfr
S.I.C.: 5039
N.A.I.C.S.: 423390
Pirttu Jauhiin *(Mng Dir)*

AXEL JOHNSON GRUPPEN AB

Box 26008
SE-100 41 Stockholm, Sweden
Tel.: (46) 87016100
Fax: (46) 8211343
Web Site: www.axeljohnsongruppe n.se
Sales Range: $5-14.9 Billion
Emp.: 15,000

Business Description:
Holding Company
S.I.C.: 6719
N.A.I.C.S.: 551112
Personnel:
Antonia Axson Johnson *(Chm)*

Subsidiaries:

Axel Johnson AB (1)
Villagatan 6
Box 26008
SE-10041 Stockholm, Sweden SE (100%)
Tel.: (46) 87016100
Fax: (46) 8213026
Web Site: www.axeljohnson.se
Sls.: $9,696,362,400
Assets: $3,272,317,200
Liabilities: $1,724,007,600
Net Worth: $1,548,309,600
Earnings: $116,254,800
Emp.: 17,780
Fiscal Year-end: 12/31/12
Holding Company; Retail Trade & Trade-Related Businesses Developer, Owner & Operator
S.I.C.: 6719
N.A.I.C.S.: 551112
Antonia Axson Johnson *(Chm)*
Caroline Berg *(Vice Chm)*
Fredrik Persson *(Pres & CEO)*
Johan Fant *(CFO)*
Paul Schrotti *(Exec VP)*

Subsidiaries:

Ahlens AB (2)
Ringvagen 100
SE 118 90 Stockholm, Sweden
Tel.: (46) 84028000
Telex: 10007 ahlen s
Fax: (46) 84028180
E-Mail: ahlensab@ahlens.se
Web Site: www.ahlens.com
Emp.: 2,900
Department Stores Operator
Import
S.I.C.: 5311
N.A.I.C.S.: 452112
Thomas Axen *(Pres)*

Axel Johnson International AB (2)
Sveawvajen 166 Floor 17
11346 Stockholm, Sweden
Tel.: (46) 84537700
Telex: 12134 axtrad s
Fax: (46) 84537791
E-Mail: axinter@axinter.se
Web Site: www.axinter.se
Emp.: 5
S.I.C.: 6211
N.A.I.C.S.: 523999
Mats R. Karlsson *(Pres & CEO)*

Divisions:

AxImage AB (3)
Sveavagen 167
PO Box 23086
SE-104 35 Stockholm, Sweden SE
Tel.: (46) 850614100
Fax: (46) 850614200
Web Site: www.axinter.se
Sales Range: $75-99.9 Million
Emp.: 110
Holding Company; Photographic Film Distr
S.I.C.: 6719
N.A.I.C.S.: 551112
Nils-Petter Tetlie *(CEO)*

Division:

FUJIFILM Sverige AB (4)
Sveavagen 167
PO Box 23086
SE-104 35 Stockholm, Sweden SE
Tel.: (46) 850614100
Telex: 19019 eklow s
Fax: (46) 850614200
E-Mail: info@fujifilm.se
Web Site: www.fujifilm.se
Sls.: $71,694,688
Emp.: 55

Axel Johnson Gruppen AB—(Continued)

Photographic Equipment & Supplies Sales & Distr
S.I.C.: 3579
N.A.I.C.S.: 333316
Nils-Petter Tetlie *(Mng Dir)*

AxIndustries AB (3)
Villagatan 6
PO Box 5174
SE-10244 Stockholm, Sweden SE
Tel.: (46) 84537700
E-Mail: axindustries@axinter.se
Web Site: www.axindustries.se
Sales Range: $150-199.9 Million
Emp.: 385
Holding Company; Automotive Bearings, Transmissions & Heavy-Duty Vehicle Components Mfr & Distr
S.I.C.: 6719
N.A.I.C.S.: 551112
Louise Ringstrom *(CFO)*

Subsidiaries:

AB Karosseritillbehor (4)
Olsgardsgatan 3
PO Box 9095
21579 Malmo, Sweden
Tel.: (46) 40220020
Telex: 33070 abkati s
Fax: (46) 40224698
E-Mail: order@abkati.se
Web Site: www.abkati.se
Emp.: 25
Consumer Goods Trading
S.I.C.: 7389
N.A.I.C.S.: 425120
Gunder Nilsson *(Mng Dir)*

Eigenbrodt AB (4)
Optimusvagen 14
PO Box 704
Upplands Vasby, 19427, Sweden SE
Tel.: (46) 859463400
Telex: 12077 dab s
Fax: (46) 859463410
E-Mail: kontakt@eigenbrodt.se
Web Site: www.eigenbrodt.se
Sls.: $13,815,000
Emp.: 40
Mfr. of Commercial Vehicle Components, Industrial Components & Tools
S.I.C.: 3714
N.A.I.C.S.: 336330
Bjorn Axberg *(Mng Dir)*

Jens S. Transmissioner AB (4)
Koppargatan 9
602 23 Norrkoping, Sweden SE
Mailing Address: (100%)
Box 903
601 19 Norrkoping, Sweden
Tel.: (46) 11198000
Fax: (46) 11198054
E-Mail: info@jens-s.se
Web Site: www.jens-s.se
Emp.: 50
Motor Vehicle Power Transmission Parts Distr
S.I.C.: 5013
N.A.I.C.S.: 423120
Erik Carlsson *(Mng Dir)*

LVD Lastvagnsdelar AB (4)
Exportgatan 33
SE-422 46 Hisings Backa, Sweden SE
Tel.: (46) 317421717
Fax: (46) 317421701
E-Mail: order.gbg@lastvagnsdelar.com
Web Site: www.lastvagnsdelar.com
Emp.: 100
New Motor Vehicle Parts Distr
S.I.C.: 5013
N.A.I.C.S.: 423120
Leif Bohlenius *(Mng Dir)*

Nomo Kullager AB (4)
Gribbylundsvagen 2
Box 510
SE-183 25 Taby, Sweden SE
Tel.: (46) 86302800 (100%)
Fax: (46) 86302850
E-Mail: nomo@nomo.se
Web Site: www.nomo.se
Sales Range: $50-74.9 Million
Emp.: 70
Ball Bearings Importer & Distr
Import
S.I.C.: 5013
N.A.I.C.S.: 423120
Lars G. Akerberg *(CEO)*
Curt Carlsson *(Mng Dir)*

Sundquist Components AB (4)
Skrittgatan 1
PO Box 50579
SE-213 77 Malmo, Sweden SE
Tel.: (46) 40180075 (100%)
Telex: 32775 nordel s
Fax: (46) 40294025
E-Mail: kundservice@sundquistcomp.se
Web Site: www.sundquistcomp.se
Polymer Material Die-Cutting & Processing Services
S.I.C.: 3089
N.A.I.C.S.: 326199
Johnny Meltzer *(Mng Dir)*

Sverull AB (4)
Fridhemsvagen 17
Box 3135
SE-550 03 Jonkoping, Sweden SE
Tel.: (46) 36312600
Fax: (46) 36162055
E-Mail: info@sverull.se
Web Site: www.sverull.se
Sales Range: $25-49.9 Million
Emp.: 120
Motor Vehicle Bearings & Power Transmission Parts Distr
S.I.C.: 5013
N.A.I.C.S.: 423120
Fredrik Gopert *(Mng Dir)*

Trailereffekter AB (4)
Skenvagen 2
Box 283
281 23 Hassleholm, Sweden SE
Tel.: (46) 45142300 (100%)
Fax: (46) 45142319
E-Mail: info@trailereffekter.se
Web Site: www.trailereffekter.se
Sales Range: $25-49.9 Million
Emp.: 40
Motor Vehicle Trailer & Trailer Components Mfr
S.I.C.: 3715
N.A.I.C.S.: 336212
Anita Lennerstad *(Mng Dir)*

Subsidiaries:

AxFlow Holding AB (3)
Sveavagen 166 14th Floor
SE-113 46 Stockholm, Sweden SE
Tel.: (46) 854547670 (100%)
Telex: 12134 axtrad s
Fax: (46) 8 545 476 89
Web Site: www.axflow.com
Sales Range: $150-199.9 Million
Emp.: 397
Holding Company; Industrial Pumps Mfr & Distr
S.I.C.: 6719
N.A.I.C.S.: 551112
Ole Weiner *(Pres & CEO)*
Petra Isaksson *(Mng Dir)*

Subsidiary:

AxFlow AB (4)
Byangsgrand 6
SE-120 40 Arsta, Sweden SE
Mailing Address: (100%)
PO Box 90162
12022 Stockholm, Sweden
Tel.: (46) 86022200
Fax: (46) 8916666
E-Mail: kundservice@axflow.se
Web Site: www.axflow.se
Emp.: 10
Industrial Pumps Distr
S.I.C.: 5084
N.A.I.C.S.: 423830
Charlotte Burmester *(Mng Dir)*

Non-U.S. Subsidiaries:

AxFlow A/S (4)
Solvang 6
3450 Allerod, Denmark
Tel.: (45) 70103550
Fax: (45) 70103555
E-Mail: axflow@axflow.dk
Web Site: www.axflow.dk
Emp.: 25
Mfr. of Pumping Equipment
S.I.C.: 3561
N.A.I.C.S.: 333911
Soeren Weihrach *(Mng Dir)*

Non-U.S. Subsidiary:

Widni Oy (5)
Sahkotie 8
FI 01510 Vantaa, Finland
Tel.: (358) 975180500
Telex: 122127 widni sf
Fax: (358) 975180550
E-Mail: info@widni.fi
Web Site: www.widni.fi
Emp.: 20
S.I.C.: 3589
N.A.I.C.S.: 333318
Johan Karlberg *(Mng Dir)*

AxFlow AS (4)
Lilleakerveien 10
PO Box 98
0283 Oslo, Norway NO
Tel.: (47) 22736700
Fax: (47) 22736780
E-Mail: axflow@axflow.no
Web Site: www.axflow.no
Emp.: 45
Provider of Pumping Equipment
S.I.C.: 3561
N.A.I.C.S.: 333911
Gunnar Oedegaard *(Mng Dir)*

AxFlow B.V. (4)
Doslderwg No 2
1332 AT Almere, Netherlands
Mailing Address:
Postbus 50110
1351 AB Almere, Netherlands
Tel.: (31) 365381211
Fax: (31) 365314004
E-Mail: axflow@axflow.nl
Web Site: www.axflow.nl
Sls.: $23,420,228
Emp.: 50
Distributor of Pumps, Measuring & Control Equipment; Provider of Engineering Services
S.I.C.: 8711
N.A.I.C.S.: 541330
Joeb Verhagen *(Mng Dir)*

AxFlow GmbH (4)
Wienerstrasse 253
A 8051 Graz, Austria
Tel.: (43) 316683509
Telex: 312388 axpro a
Fax: (43) 316683492
E-Mail: office@axflow.at
Web Site: www.axflow.at
Sls.: $2,516,186
Emp.: 15
Mfr. & Distributor of Pumps
S.I.C.: 3561
N.A.I.C.S.: 333911
Andreas Lippitsch *(Gen Mgr)*

AxFlow Lda. (4)
Ave Duarte Pacheco 2
PO Box 92
Santo Amaro De Oeiras, 2780316 Oeiras, Codex, Portugal PT
Tel.: (351) 214461590
Fax: (351) 214410368
E-Mail: jl@axflow.pt
Web Site: www.axflow.pt
Emp.: 6
Mfr. of Pumping Equipment
S.I.C.: 3561
N.A.I.C.S.: 333911
Jose Vargas *(Mng Dir)*

AxFlow Ltd. (4)
Orion Park Northfield Ave
Ealing, London, W13 9SJ, United Kingdom UK
Tel.: (44) 2085792111
Telex: 27800 meller g
Fax: (44) 2085797326
E-Mail: info@axflow.co.uk
Web Site: www.axflow.co.uk
Emp.: 25
Distr of Positive Displacement Pumps & Related Products & Services
S.I.C.: 5084
N.A.I.C.S.: 423830
Tony Peters *(Mng Dir)*

Branch:

AxFlow Ltd. (5)
Unit 3 Harlaw Centre Howe Moss Crescent
Kirkhill Industrial Estate, Aberdeen, AB21 OGN, United Kingdom
Tel.: (44) 1224729367
Telex: 73422
Fax: (44) 1224 729368
E-Mail: infoscot@axflow.co.uk
Web Site: www.axflow.co.uk
Emp.: 4
Pumps & Valves Distr
S.I.C.: 5084
N.A.I.C.S.: 423830

Division:

Meller Flow Trans Limited (5)
Millersdale Close Euroway Industrial Estate
Bradford, BD4 6RX, United Kingdom UK
Tel.: (44) 1274687687
Fax: (44) 1274687744
E-Mail: info@mellerflowtrans.co.uk
Web Site: www.mellerflowtrans.com
Emp.: 25
Provider of Transport Services for Liquids, Powders, Chemicals & Gas
S.I.C.: 4731
N.A.I.C.S.: 488510

AxFlow Oy (4)
Jokinsunkuja 3
00560 Helsinki, Finland
Tel.: (358) 97771930
Telex: 123111 ajm sf
Fax: (358) 9797550
E-Mail: axflow@axflow.fi
Web Site: www.axflow.fi
Emp.: 10
S.I.C.: 4813
N.A.I.C.S.: 517110
Harri Lindroos *(Mng Dir)*

AxFlow SA (4)
Avenida de la Industria 53
280 34 Madrid, Spain ES
Tel.: (34) 917291818
Fax: (34) 917292491
E-Mail: axflow@axflow.es
Web Site: www.axflow.es
Sales Range: $1-9.9 Million
Emp.: 29
Provider of Pumping Equipment
S.I.C.: 3561
N.A.I.C.S.: 333911
Basilio Moreno *(Mgr-Tech)*

AxFlow SAS (4)
87 rue des Poiriers
BP 72
Parc Ste Apolline, 78372 Plaisir, Cedex, France
Tel.: (33) 247458458
Telex: 270384 ajandco f
E-Mail: info@axflow.fr
Web Site: www.axflow.fr
Emp.: 23
Industrial Pumps Mfr & Distr
S.I.C.: 3594
N.A.I.C.S.: 333996

AxFlow SAS (4)
87 rue des Poiriers
BP 72
F 78372 Plaisir, Cedex, France
Tel.: (33) 247458458
Fax: (33) 130684100
E-Mail: a.noel@axflow.fr
Web Site: www.axflow.fr
Emp.: 70
Distributor of Pumps
S.I.C.: 5084
N.A.I.C.S.: 423830
Bruno Breard *(Gen Mgr)*

AxFlow SpA (4)
Via Del Commercio 15 - 15/A
20090 Buccinasco, MI, Italy
Tel.: (39) 02484801
Telex: 380 455 ITABUL
Fax: (39) 248401926
E-Mail: info@axflow.it
Web Site: www.axflow.it
Emp.: 20
Marketing, Sales & Service of Ice Equipment
S.I.C.: 5078
N.A.I.C.S.: 423740

AxFlow s.r.o. (4)
Tovaren 256 14
Prague, 10200, Czech Republic
Tel.: (420) 272101180
Fax: (420) 296365771
E-Mail: axflow@axflow.cz

Web Site: www.axflow.cz
Emp.: 13
S.I.C.: 6211
N.A.I.C.S.: 523999
Renata Borovenova *(Mng Dir)*

Forankra International AB (3)
Sveavagen 166
113 46 Stockholm, Sweden SE
Tel.: (46) 31509080
Fax: (46) 31509090
E-Mail: info@forankra.com
Web Site: www.forankra.com
Sales Range: $300-349.9 Million
Emp.: 809
Industrial Lifting & Material Handling Equipment Mfr
S.I.C.: 3537
N.A.I.C.S.: 333924

Non-U.S. Subsidiaries:

Axel Johnson International AS (3)
Lilleakerveien 10
PO Box 144
N 0216 Oslo, Norway
Tel.: (47) 22736030
Telex: 76963 ajco n
Fax: (47) 22736063
E-Mail: twelbsoto@no.no
Web Site: www.fujifilm.no
Sls.: $36,042,500
Emp.: 34
S.I.C.: 4813
N.A.I.C.S.: 517110
Rolf Erik Smith *(CEO)*

Axfood AB (2)
Hemvarnsgatan 9
171 78 Solna, Sweden SE
Tel.: (46) 855399000 (50.1%)
Fax: (46) 87302689
E-Mail: info@axfood.se
Web Site: www.axfood.se
AXFO—(OMX OTC)
Sls.: $5,620,168,800
Assets: $1,361,930,400
Liabilities: $819,820,800
Net Worth: $542,109,600
Earnings: $138,546,000
Emp.: 7,254
Fiscal Year-end: 12/31/12
Holding Company; Food Retailer & Trade Whslr
S.I.C.: 6719
N.A.I.C.S.: 551112
Fredrik Persson *(Chm)*
Marcus Storch *(Vice Chm)*
Anders Stralman *(Pres & CEO)*
Karin Hygrell-Jonsson *(CFO & Sec)*
Thomas Evertsson *(Pres-Willys AB)*
Thomas Gareskog *(Pres-Hemkop AB)*

Division:

Axfood Sverige AB (3)
Hemvarnsgatan 9
SE-171 78 Solna, Sweden SE
Tel.: (46) 855399000 (100%)
Fax: (46) 87300359
E-Mail: info@axfood.se
Web Site: www.axfood.se
Emp.: 600
Food Retailer & Trade Whslr
S.I.C.: 5411
N.A.I.C.S.: 445110
Anders Stralman *(Pres & CEO)*
Karin Hygrell-Jonsson *(CFO)*

Subsidiaries:

Dagab AB (4)
Hemvarnsgatan 9
SE-171 78 Solna, Sweden SE
Tel.: (46) 850071000 (100%)
Fax: (46) 855399097
E-Mail: info@axfood.se
Web Site: www.axfood.se
Sales Range: $350-399.9 Million
Emp.: 930
Grocery Distr
S.I.C.: 5141
N.A.I.C.S.: 424410
Anders Agerberg *(Pres)*

Hemkopskedjan AB (4)
Hemvarnsgatan 9
SE-171 78 Solna, Sweden SE
Tel.: (46) 855399900 (100%)
Fax: (46) 87303037
E-Mail: info@hemkop.se
Web Site: www.hemkop.se
Sales Range: $800-899.9 Million
Emp.: 1,740
Retail Grocery Stores Operator
S.I.C.: 5411
N.A.I.C.S.: 445110
Thomas Gareskog *(Pres)*

Subsidiaries:

Axfood IT AB (3)
Parkvagen 2A
Solna, 169 35, Sweden
Tel.: (46) 855399000
Fax: (46) 8275743
Information Technology Consulting Services
S.I.C.: 7373
N.A.I.C.S.: 541512

Axfood Narlivs AB (3)
Handelsgatan 5
70117 Orebro, Sweden SE
Mailing Address: (100%)
Box 1742
70117 Orebro, Sweden
Tel.: (46) 196030350
Fax: (46) 196030306
E-Mail: info@axfood.se
Web Site: www.narlivs.se
Sales Range: $800-899.9 Million
Emp.: 567
Grocery Distr & Convenience Stores Operator
S.I.C.: 5141
N.A.I.C.S.: 424410
Nicholas Pettersson *(Pres)*

PrisXtra AB (3)
Norra Stationsgatan 58-60
Stockholm, 113 33, Sweden
Tel.: (46) 8 441 51 60
Fax: (46) 8324330
E-Mail: info@prisxtra.se
Web Site: www.prisxtra.se
Food Store Operating Services
S.I.C.: 5499
N.A.I.C.S.: 445299

Willys AB (3)
Falkenbergsgatan 3
SE-412 86 Gothenburg, Sweden SE
Tel.: (46) 317333100 (100%)
Fax: (46) 317333180
E-Mail: info@axfood.se
Web Site: www.willys.se
Sales Range: $1-4.9 Billion
Emp.: 2,886
Discount Retail Grocery Stores Operator
S.I.C.: 5411
N.A.I.C.S.: 445110
Thomas Evertsson *(Pres)*

Division:

Willys Hemma AB (4)
Falkenbergsgatan 3 van 6
SE-412 87 Gothenburg, Sweden SE
Tel.: (46) 317333100 (100%)
Fax: (46) 317333600
E-Mail: mila.johnsson@willys.se
Web Site: www.willys.se
Emp.: 300
Small Discount Retail Grocery Stores Operator
S.I.C.: 5411
N.A.I.C.S.: 445110
Thomas Edwerffom *(Mng Dir)*

Mercator International AB (2)
Regeringsgatan 82
SE 11139 Stockholm, Sweden
Tel.: (46) 86679330
Telex: 145 33 mercat s
Fax: (46) 87141460
E-Mail: cato@algonet.se
Assisting Swedish Export Companies with Counter-Purchase & Barter Transactions
S.I.C.: 7389
N.A.I.C.S.: 561990

Novax AB (2)
Villakatan 6
PO Box 26008
SE 100 41 Stockholm, Sweden SE
Tel.: (46) 87006660
E-Mail: info@novax.se
Web Site: www.novax.se
Emp.: 4
Consumer Goods Trading
S.I.C.: 7389
N.A.I.C.S.: 425120
Anders Flettenjren *(Mng Dir)*

Non-U.S. Subsidiaries:

AKO Armaturen - Separation GmbH (2)
Adam Opel Strasse 5
Allemagne, 65468 Trebur, Astheim, Germany
Tel.: (49) 614791590
Telex: 418 2804 ako d
Fax: (49) 6147915959
E-Mail: ako@ako-armaturen.de
Web Site: www.ako-armaturen.net
Emp.: 15
Mfr. of Diaphragm Valves, Squash Valves, Collar Valves, Worm-Gear Pumps, Dosing Pumps & Silt Sieves
S.I.C.: 3491
N.A.I.C.S.: 332911
Helmut Hessinger *(Mgr-Sls)*

Axel Johnson Lab Systems A/S (2)
Bygstubben 12
Copenhagen, Vidbaek, 2950, Denmark
Tel.: (45) 35431881
Telex: 15946 succas dk
Fax: (45) 35430073
E-Mail: axlab@axlab.dk
Web Site: www.ax-lab.dk
Sales Range: $1-9.9 Million
Emp.: 6
Distribution of Scientific Equipment
S.I.C.: 5049
N.A.I.C.S.: 423490

AxPro France S.A. (2)
40 Ave Des Terroirs De France
75012 Paris, France
Tel.: (33) 144745300
Fax: (33) 1 44 74 53 21
S.I.C.: 6211
N.A.I.C.S.: 523999

Normaco Ltd. (2)
45 Conduit Street
London, SW1H 9AA, United Kingdom
Tel.: (44) 207-287-7355
Telex: 912003 Normac G
Trusts
S.I.C.: 6211
N.A.I.C.S.: 523999

S.A. Cebelor (2)
Researchpark Zone 1 Nr 10
1731 Zellik, Belgium
Tel.: (32) 24269966
Fax: (32) 24265932
E-Mail: info@cebelor.be
Web Site: www.cebelor.be
Emp.: 40
S.I.C.: 3663
N.A.I.C.S.: 334220
Vanhouteghem Lever *(Gen Mgr)*

Svenska Teknisk Byra AB (2)
ul Floriana 3 5
PL 04 664 Warsaw, Poland
Tel.: (48) 226130012
Telex: 817347 stbsw pl
Fax: (48) 228121327
Web Site: www.axflow.pl
Pumping Components
S.I.C.: 3561
N.A.I.C.S.: 333911

Weir Canada, Inc. (2)
2715 18th St Northeast
Calgary, AB, T2E 7E6, Canada
Tel.: (403) 250-9458
Telex: 37-41390 belex edm
Fax: (403) 250-2032
Web Site: www.weirminerals.com
Emp.: 60
Distribution of Industrial Instrumentation
S.I.C.: 7389
N.A.I.C.S.: 425120
Russell Mackie *(Reg Mgr)*

Weir Canada Inc. (2)
8600 Rue Street Patrick
La Salle, QC, H8N 1V1, Canada
Tel.: (514) 366-5757
Fax: (514) 366-6501
Web Site: www.weirservices.com
Emp.: 100
Distributor of Industrial Products & Instrumentations
S.I.C.: 5113
N.A.I.C.S.: 424130
Maria Bellinei *(Mgr-HR)*

AxFast AB (1)
Drottninggatan 78
PO Box 216
SE-101 24 Stockholm, Sweden SE
Tel.: (46) 87525300
Fax: (46) 87516710
E-Mail: info@axfast.se
Web Site: www.axfast.se
Sales Range: $25-49.9 Million
Emp.: 40
Commercial Property Acquisition, Development & Management Services
S.I.C.: 6519
N.A.I.C.S.: 531390
Erik Lindvall *(Pres & CEO)*
Stefan Norell *(CFO)*

U.S. Subsidiary:

Axel Johnson Inc. (1)
155 Spring St 6th Fl
New York, NY 10012 DE
Tel.: (646) 291-2445
Fax: (212) 966-9516
Web Site: www.axeljohnson.com
Managed Assets: $4,800,000,000
Emp.: 1,000
Investment Services
Export
S.I.C.: 6211
N.A.I.C.S.: 523999
Michael D. Milligan *(Pres & CEO)*
Ben J. Hennelly *(CFO & Exec VP)*
John C. Pascale *(Exec VP-Tax)*

Holdings:

Parkson Corporation (2)
1401 W Cypress Creek Rd
Fort Lauderdale, FL 33309-1721
Mailing Address:
PO Box 408399
Fort Lauderdale, FL 33340-8399
Tel.: (954) 974-6610
Telex: wa 5222557 parkson ftl
Fax: (954) 974-6182
E-Mail: technology@parkson.com
Web Site: www.parkson.com
Emp.: 150
Mfr. of Process Equipment & Instrumentation for Water & Wastewater Treatment
S.I.C.: 8741
N.A.I.C.S.: 561110
Shamus M. Hurley *(Pres & CEO)*

Non-U.S. Subsidiary:

Parkson Canada Corporation (3)
1000 St Johns Blvd Ste 205
Pointe-Claire, QC, H9R 5P1, Canada
Tel.: (514) 636-8712
Telex: 5 822611 axeljohn
Fax: (514) 636-9718
E-Mail: canada@parkson.com
Web Site: www.parkson.com
Sales Range: $1-9.9 Million
Emp.: 2
Water Treatment Services
S.I.C.: 5084
N.A.I.C.S.: 423830
Jean Grenier *(Mgr-Sls)*

Sprague Resources LP (2)
2 International Dr Ste 200
Portsmouth, NH 03801 DE
Tel.: (603) 431-1000
Fax: (603) 430-5324
Toll Free: (800) 225-1560
Web Site: www.spragueenergy.com
SRLP—(NYSE)
Sls.: $4,043,907,000
Assets: $1,054,247,000
Liabilities: $913,041,000
Net Worth: $141,206,000
Earnings: ($12,831,000)
Emp.: 400
Fiscal Year-end: 12/31/12
Holding Company; Refined Petroleum Products & Natural Gas Storage & Wholesale Distr; Material Handling Services
S.I.C.: 6719
N.A.I.C.S.: 551112
Michael D. Milligan *(Chm)*
David C. Glendon *(Pres & CEO)*

Axel Johnson Gruppen AB—(Continued)

Gary A. Rinaldi *(COO, CFO & Sr VP)*
Paul A. Scoff *(Chief Compliance Officer, Gen Counsel, Sec & VP)*
John W. Moore *(Chief Acctg Officer, VP & Controller)*
Joseph S. Smith *(Chief Risk Officer & VP-Strategic Plng)*
Kevin G. Henry *(Treas & VP)*

Subsidiary:

Sprague Operating Resources LLC (3)
2 International Dr Ste 200
Portsmouth, NH 03801-6810 DE
Tel.: (603) 431-1000
Fax: (603) 430-5324
Toll Free: (800) 225-1560
Web Site: www.spragueenergy.com
Emp.: 425
Refined Petroleum Products & Natural Gas Storage & Wholesale Distr; Material Handling Services
S.I.C.: 5171
N.A.I.C.S.: 424710
David C. Glendon *(Pres & CEO)*
Gary A. Rinaldi *(COO, CFO & Sr VP)*
Paul A. Scoff *(Chief Compliance Officer, Gen Counsel, VP & Sec)*
Joseph S. Smith *(Chief Risk Officer & Sr VP)*
John W. Moore *(Chief Acctg Officer, VP & Controller)*
Kevin G. Henry *(Treas)*

AXEL POLYMERS LIMITED

309 Village Mokshi Sankarda Savli Road
Taluka Savli, Vadodara, 391780, India
Tel.: (91) 2667 244438
Fax: (91) 2667 244396
E-Mail: info@axelindia.com
Web Site: www.axelindia.com
Year Founded: 1992
513642—(BOM)
Rev.: $1,415,548
Assets: $2,268,518
Liabilities: $1,754,046
Net Worth: $514,471
Earnings: ($73,956)
Fiscal Year-end: 03/31/13

Business Description:
Specialty Polymer Mfr
S.I.C.: 2821
N.A.I.C.S.: 325211

Personnel:
B. K. Bodhanwala *(Chm)*
A. B. Bodhanwala *(Mng Dir)*

Board of Directors:
B. K. Bodhanwala
A. B. Bodhanwala
M. A. Bodhanwala
Soham Mehta
B. B. Patel
G. M. Patel
A. G. Thakore

Transfer Agent:
Link Intime India Pvt Ltd
B-102 & B-103 Shangrila Complex First Floor Opp HDFC Bank
Near Radhakrisna Char Rasta Akota, Vadodara, Gujarat, 390 020, India
Tel.: (91) 265 2356573

AXEL SPRINGER AG

Axel Springer Strasse 65
10888 Berlin, Germany
Tel.: (49) 3025910
Telex: 184 257
Fax: (49) 30259177642
E-Mail: information@axelspringer.de
Web Site: www.axelspringer.de
Year Founded: 1946
SPR—(DEU)
Rev.: $4,456,226,551
Assets: $6,472,654,594
Liabilities: $3,439,598,967
Net Worth: $3,033,055,627
Earnings: $371,273,686
Emp.: 13,651
Fiscal Year-end: 12/31/12

Business Description:
Newspapers, Magazines, Books & Electronic Media Publisher
Import Export
S.I.C.: 2711
N.A.I.C.S.: 511110

Personnel:
Giuseppe Vita *(Chm-Supervisory Bd)*
Friede Springer *(Vice Chm-Supervisory Bd)*
Mathias Doepfner *(CEO)*
Lothar Lanz *(CFO, COO & Member-Exec Bd)*
Jan Bayer *(Pres-WELT Grp & Printing & Member-Exec Bd)*
Ralph Buchi *(Pres-Intl Div & Member-Exec Bd)*
Andreas Wiele *(Pres-BILD Grp & Magazines & Member-Exec Bd)*
Christoph Keese *(Exec VP)*
Edda Fels *(Sr VP-Corp Comm)*

Supervisory Board of Directors:
Giuseppe Vita
Gerhard Cromme
Oliver Heine
Klaus Krone
Nicola Leibinger-Kammuller
Wolf Lepenies
Michael Otto
Friede Springer

Subsidiaries:

Elmshorner Nachrichten (1)
Schulstrasse 62
D 25335 Elmshorn, Germany (100%)
Tel.: (49) 41212970
Fax: (49) 4121297112
Web Site: www.shz.de
Emp.: 32
Newspaper
S.I.C.: 2711
N.A.I.C.S.: 511110

Journalistenschule Axel Springer (1)
Axel Springer Strasse 65
D 10888 Berlin, Germany (100%)
Tel.: (49) 30259172801
Fax: (49) 30259173048
E-Mail: journalistenschule@axelspringer.de
Web Site: www.axelspringer.de
Emp.: 8
Provider of Journalism Training
S.I.C.: 7929
N.A.I.C.S.: 711510
Mathias Dopfner *(Chm, CEO & Head-Subscription Paper)*

Joint Venture:

Bild.T-Online.de AG & Co. KG (1)
Axel-Springer-Strasse 65
10888 Berlin, Germany
Tel.: (49) 30259179000
Fax: (49) 30259179006
E-Mail: info@bild.t-online.de
Web Site: www.bild.t-online.de
Online Investment Services; Owned by Axel Springer Verlag AG & Deutsche Telekom AG
S.I.C.: 7379
N.A.I.C.S.: 541519

Non-U.S. Subsidiaries:

Axel Springer Budapest GmbH (1)
Varosmajor Ut 11
H 1122 Budapest, Hungary (92.93%)
Tel.: (36) 14885766
E-Mail: info@axelspringer.hu
Web Site: www.axelspringer.hu
Emp.: 110
Publisher
S.I.C.: 2711
N.A.I.C.S.: 511110
Gabriella Udvari *(Office Mgr)*

Axel Springer Espana S.A. (1)
Santiago de composcela 94 2nd Fl
E 28046 Madrid, Spain (100%)
Tel.: (34) 915140600
Fax: (34) 915560557
E-Mail: reception.axelspringer@axelspringer.es
Web Site: www.axelspringer.es
Emp.: 180
Computer Magazines Publisher
S.I.C.: 2711
N.A.I.C.S.: 511110
Mamen Perera *(CEO)*

Axel Springer Polska Sp.z o.o. (1)
Al Jerozolimskie 181
02 222 Warsaw, Poland (100%)
Tel.: (48) 226084100
Fax: (48) 227636100
E-Mail: asp@axelspringer.pl
Web Site: www.axelspringer.pl
Emp.: 700
Publisher
S.I.C.: 2711
N.A.I.C.S.: 511110
Agnieszka Milak *(Brand Mgr)*

StepStone AS (1)
Thunes Vei 2
0274 Oslo, Norway (100%)
Tel.: (47) 22033330
Fax: (47) 22033360
Web Site: www.stepstone.com
Sales Range: $150-199.9 Million
Emp.: 450
Online Job Search Portal
S.I.C.: 2741
N.A.I.C.S.: 519130
Ralf Baumann *(CEO)*
Thorsten Otte *(CFO)*
Gauthier Andries *(CTO)*
Heiner Tent *(Gen Counsel)*

AXELL CORPORATION

Akihabara UDX SouthWing 10F 4-14-1 Sotokanda Chiyoda-ku
Tokyo, 101-8973, Japan
Tel.: (81) 352981670
Fax: (81) 352981671
E-Mail: info@axell.co.jp
Web Site: www.axell.co.jp
Year Founded: 1996
6730—(TKS)
Sls.: $183,887,000
Assets: $172,139,000
Liabilities: $27,753,000
Net Worth: $144,386,000
Earnings: $22,781,000
Emp.: 75
Fiscal Year-end: 03/31/13

Business Description:
Semiconductor, Circuit Board, Gaming, Office, Graphics & Sound Equipment & Technology Products Designer, Mfr & Sales
S.I.C.: 3674
N.A.I.C.S.: 334413

Personnel:
Yuzuru Sasaki *(Chm)*
Sumihiko Ichihara *(Vice Chm)*
Kazunori Matsuura *(Pres)*
Akihiro Saito *(Exec VP)*

Board of Directors:
Yuzuru Sasaki
Sumihiko Ichihara
Koji Kanie
Kazunori Matsuura
Akihiro Saito
Nobuhiro Sendai
Takayuki Shibata
Masao Suzuki

Transfer Agent:
Mitsubishi UFJ Trust Bank
7-10-11 Higashisuna Koutouku
Tokyo, Japan

AXG MINING LIMITED

Suite 4 16 Ord Street
West Perth, WA, 6005, Australia
Mailing Address:
PO Box 1779
West Perth, WA, 6872, Australia
Tel.: (61) 8 9429 2900
Fax: (61) 894861011
E-Mail: admin@axgmining.com.au
Web Site: www.axgmining.com.au
AXC—(ASX)
Rev.: $678,570
Assets: $529,156
Liabilities: $802,468
Net Worth: ($273,312)
Earnings: ($2,299,058)
Fiscal Year-end: 06/30/13

Business Description:
Gold Mining & Exploration
S.I.C.: 1041
N.A.I.C.S.: 212221

Personnel:
Gordon A. Sklenka *(CEO & Mng Dir)*
Roland H. Berzins *(Pub Officer & Sec)*

Board of Directors:
Guy Le Page
Roland H. Berzins
Gordon A. Sklenka

AXIA NETMEDIA CORPORATION

3300 450 1st Street SW
Calgary, AB, T2P 5H1, Canada
Tel.: (403) 538-4000
Fax: (403) 538-4100
E-Mail: info@axia.com
Web Site: www.axia.com
AXX—(TSX)
Sales Range: $50-74.9 Million
Emp.: 366

Business Description:
Communications Products
S.I.C.: 3663
N.A.I.C.S.: 334220

Personnel:
Arthur R. Price *(Chm & CEO)*
Alan Hartslief *(CFO)*
Murray Sigler *(Pres-Axia North America & Exec VP)*
Jean-Michel Soulier *(Pres-Axia Networks France)*
Nicole Springer *(Gen Counsel, Sec & VP)*

Board of Directors:
Arthur R. Price
C. Kent Jespersen
Robert Lawrence Phillips
John K. Read
William H. Smith

Legal Counsel:
McCarthy Tetrault LLP
Calgary, AB, Canada

Transfer Agent:
Computershare Trust Company of Canada
9th Floor 100 University Avenue
Toronto, ON, Canada

Subsidiary:

Axia NetMedia Corporation (1)
225 10357 109th St
Edmonton, AB, T5J 1N3, Canada (100%)
Tel.: (780) 424-0275
Fax: (780) 424-0276
E-Mail: info@axia.com
Web Site: www.axia.com
Emp.: 16
Provider of Computer-Based Training Materials
S.I.C.: 2732
N.A.I.C.S.: 323117
Arthur R. Price *(Chm & CEO)*

Non-U.S. Subsidiary:

Axia France S.A. (1)
30 avenue Edouard Belin
92500 Rueil-Malmaison, France
Tel.: (33) 147148650
Fax: (33) 147148699
E-Mail: jean-michel.soulier@axia.com
Web Site: www.axia.com
Communications Products
S.I.C.: 3663
N.A.I.C.S.: 334220
Jean-Michel Soulier *(Pres)*

AXIATA GROUP BERHAD
Level 5 Axiata Centre 9 Jalan Stesen Sentral 5 Kuala Lumpur Sentral
50470 Kuala Lumpur, Malaysia
Tel.: (60) 32263 8888
Fax: (60) 3 2263 8822
E-Mail: info@axiata.com
Web Site: www.axiata.com
Year Founded: 2001
AXIATA—(KLS)
Rev.: $5,788,318,247
Assets: $14,077,802,680
Liabilities: $6,861,194,442
Net Worth: $7,216,608,238
Earnings: $944,270,890
Emp.: 20,000
Fiscal Year-end: 12/31/12
Business Description:
Telecommunications & Internet Services
S.I.C.: 4812
N.A.I.C.S.: 517210
Personnel:
Jamaludin Ibrahim *(Pres, CEO & Mng Dir)*
James Maclaurin *(CFO)*
Mohd Khairil Abdullah *(COO & CMO)*
Norman Donald Price, IV *(CTO)*
Drake M. Sani *(Chief HR Officer)*
Mohamad Idham Nawawi *(Chief Corp Officer)*
Badrunnisa Mohd Yasin Khan *(Chief Talent Officer)*
Gim Boon Tan *(Gen Counsel)*
Suryani Hussein *(Sec)*
Donald James Rae *(Sr VP-Bus Dev & Reg Ops)*
Board of Directors:
Azman Mokhtar
Ghazzali Abdul Khalid
Bella Ann Almeida
Abdul Rahman Bin Ahmad
Jamaludin Ibrahim
Azzat Kamaludin
David Nai Pek Lau
Juan Villalonga Navarro
Kenneth Shen
Subsidiaries:

Celcom Axiata Berhad **(1)**
No 82 Jalan Raja Muda Abdul Aziz
50300 Kuala Lumpur, Malaysia
Tel.: (60) 3 2688 3939
Fax: (60) 3 3630 8889
E-Mail: feedback@celcom.com.my
Web Site: www.celcom.com.my
Telecommunication Services
S.I.C.: 4899
N.A.I.C.S.: 517919
Jamaludin Bin Ibrahim *(Chm)*
Mohammed Shazalli Ramly *(CEO)*
Chari Tvt *(CFO)*
Zalman Aefendy Zainal Abidin *(CMO)*
Mohamed Adlan Ahmad Tajudin *(Chief Corp Officer)*
Eric Chong Tiong Beng *(Comml Officer & Chief Sls)*

Subsidiary:

Celcom Transmission (M) Sdn Bhd **(2)**
Level 10 Block F 3 Two Square No 2 Jalan 19/1
Petaling Jaya, 46300, Malaysia
Tel.: (60) 372602122
Fax: (60) 372602125
Web Site: www.celcom.com.my
Emp.: 40
Telecommunication Services
S.I.C.: 4899
N.A.I.C.S.: 517919
Abdul Satar Mohamed *(Chief Network Officer)*

Celcom (Malaysia) Berhad **(1)**
Level 22 Menara Celcom
Jalan Raja Muda Abdul Aziz, 50300 Kuala Lumpur, Malaysia (100%)
Tel.: (60) 326883939
Fax: (60) 336308889
E-Mail: ccd@celcom.com.my
Web Site: www.celcom.com.my
Sales Range: $1-4.9 Billion
Emp.: 3,600
Mobile Telecommunications Services
S.I.C.: 4812
N.A.I.C.S.: 517210
Jamaludin Bin Ibrahim *(Chm)*
Mohammed Shazalli Ramly *(CEO)*
Yusof Annuar Yaacob *(Exec Dir & Grp CFO)*
Nik Hasnan Nik Abd Kadir *(Sr VP & Head-Internal Audit)*
Bassaharil Mohd Yusop *(Sr VP-IT)*

Subsidiary:

Technology Resources Industries **(2)**
Menara Celcom 82 Jalan Raja Muda Abdul Azis
Kuala Lumpur, 50300, Malaysia (20.99%)
Tel.: (60) 326883939
Fax: (60) 326810284
Web Site: www.celcom.com.my
S.I.C.: 1731
N.A.I.C.S.: 238210
Zalman Aefendy *(CMO)*

Non-U.S. Subsidiaries:

Dialog Axiata PLC **(1)**
475 Union Place
Colombo, Sri Lanka
Tel.: (94) 77 7678700
Fax: (94) 77 7081000
E-Mail: service@dialog.lk
Web Site: www.dialog.lk
Emp.: 2,000
Telecommunication Services
S.I.C.: 4899
N.A.I.C.S.: 517919
Azzat Kamaludin *(Chm)*
Shridhir Sariputta Hansa Wijayasuriya *(Grp CEO)*
Nushad Mario Jayasingha Arachchige Perera *(Grp CMO)*
Sandra Marlene de Zoysa *(Grp Chief Customer Officer)*
Upali Gajanaike *(CEO-Dialog Tele Infrastructures)*

Subsidiary:

Dialog Broadband Networks (Private) Limited **(2)**
No 221/1 Dharmapala Mawatha
Colombo, Sri Lanka
Tel.: (94) 777678700
Fax: (94) 112314596
Telecommunication Services
S.I.C.: 4899
N.A.I.C.S.: 517919

Dialog Axiata PLC **(1)**
475 Union Place
Colombo, 02, Sri Lanka (85%)
Tel.: (94) 777678700
Fax: (94) 112669701
E-Mail: dialog@dialog.lk
Web Site: www.dialog.lk
DIAL—(COL)
Rev.: $442,311,845
Assets: $711,840,198
Liabilities: $419,965,070
Net Worth: $291,875,128
Earnings: $47,336,968
Emp.: 2,993
Fiscal Year-end: 12/31/12
Telecommunications & Internet Services
S.I.C.: 4812
N.A.I.C.S.: 517210
Shridhir Sariputta Hansa Wijayasuriya *(CEO)*
Lucy Tan *(CFO)*
Wewage Viranga Supun Dep Weerasinghe *(COO)*
Nirmal Anthony Rodrigo *(CIO)*
Amali Nanayakkara *(CMO)*
Palliyaralalage Don Vincent Pradeep Kumar De Almeida *(CTO)*
Sandra Marlene De Zoysa *(Chief Customer Officer)*
Mohamed Zuraish Shayam Majeed *(Chief Comml Officer & Chief Programme Mgmt Officer)*
Kavantissa Danudra Weerawardane Ratnayaka *(Chief Corp Officer)*
Upali Gajanaike *(CEO-Tele-Infrastructure)*
Viranthi Attygalle *(Sec)*

Multinet Pakistan (Private) Limited **(1)**
1D 203 Sector 30
Korangi Industrial Area, Karachi, 74900, Pakistan (89%)
Tel.: (92) 21 3511 3626
Fax: (92) 21 3511 3645
E-Mail: ibu@multinet.com.pk
Web Site: www.multinet.com.pk
Sales Range: $1-9.9 Million
Telecommunications Services
S.I.C.: 4813
N.A.I.C.S.: 517110
Yusof Annuar bin Yaacob *(Chm)*
Adnan Asdar Ali *(CEO)*
Hamal Anuar bin Md Ali *(CFO)*
Arif Hussain *(COO)*
Rashid Shafi *(Sr Exec VP & Chief Strategy Officer)*

PT XL Axiata Tbk **(1)**
Grha XL Jl DR Ide Anak Agung Gde Agung Lot E4-7 No1
Kawasan Mega Kuningan, Jakarta, 12950, Indonesia (83.8%)
Tel.: (62) 215761881
Fax: (62) 215761880
E-Mail: corpcomm@xl.co.id
Web Site: www.xl.co.id
EXCL—(INDO OTC)
Rev.: $2,096,980,600
Assets: $3,545,570,500
Liabilities: $2,008,566,900
Net Worth: $1,537,003,600
Earnings: $276,464,700
Emp.: 1,955
Fiscal Year-end: 12/31/12
Mobile Telecommunications Services
S.I.C.: 4812
N.A.I.C.S.: 517210
Hasnul Suhaimi *(Chm & CEO)*
Mohamed Adlan Ahmad Tajudin *(CFO)*
Willem Lucas Timmermans *(COO)*
P. Nicanor V. Santiago, III *(CMO)*
Dian Siswarini *(CTO & Chief Digital Svcs Officer)*
Joy Wahyudi *(Chief Comml Officer)*
Ongki Kurniawan *(Chief Svc Mgmt Officer)*
Murni Nurdini *(Sec)*

Telekom Malaysia International (Cambodia) Co. Ltd. **(1)**
No 56 Preah Norodom Blvd Sangkat Chey Chumneah
Khan Doun Penh, Phnom Penh, 23, Cambodia (100%)
Tel.: (855) 16810001
Fax: (855) 16810004
E-Mail: casacom@hello016-gsm.com.kh
Sales Range: $50-74.9 Million
Emp.: 100
Mobile Telecommunication Services
S.I.C.: 4812
N.A.I.C.S.: 517210
Simon J. Perkins *(CEO)*

Non-U.S. Joint Venture:

Robi Axiata Limited **(1)**
BRAC Centre 9th Floor
75 Mohakhali C/A, Dhaka, 1212, Bangladesh
Tel.: (880) 29887146
Fax: (880) 29885463
E-Mail: info@aktel.com
Web Site: www.robi.com.bd
Sales Range: $200-249.9 Million
Mobile Telecommunications Services; Joint Venture of Axiata Group Berhad (70%) & NTT DoCoMo, Inc. (30%)
S.I.C.: 4812
N.A.I.C.S.: 517210
Supun Weerasinghe *(CEO)*

AXICHEM AB
Vikinagatan 39 B
216 18 Limhamn, Sweden
Tel.: (46) 46 780 06 73
Web Site: www.axichem.se
AXIC A—(OMX)
Business Description:
Biochemical Mfr
S.I.C.: 2899
N.A.I.C.S.: 325998
Personnel:
Lars Thunberg *(Chm)*
Torsten Helsing *(CEO)*
Board of Directors:
Lars Thunberg
Torsten Helsing
Goran Hogstedt
Mats Lundberg
Peter Ragnarsson

AXIOHM
1 Rue D Arcueil
92542 Montrouge, Hauts De Seine, France
Tel.: (33) 158071717
Fax: (33) 158071718
E-Mail: b.voukili@pxcom.sr
Web Site: www.axiohm.com
Sales Range: $25-49.9 Million
Emp.: 155
Business Description:
Thermal Printer Mfr
S.I.C.: 3555
N.A.I.C.S.: 333244
Personnel:
Yves Alexandre *(Pres)*

AXIOM CORP.
Enterprise Road Industrial Area
PO Box 49000-00100
Nairobi, Kenya
Tel.: (254) 736 521567
E-Mail: info@axiomstructure.com
Web Site: www.axiomstructure.com
Year Founded: 2012
AXMM—(OTC OTCB)
Assets: $829
Liabilities: $15,514
Net Worth: ($14,685)
Earnings: ($58,768)
Emp.: 1
Fiscal Year-end: 08/31/13
Business Description:
Civil Construction
S.I.C.: 1629
N.A.I.C.S.: 237990
Personnel:
Kranti Kumar Kotni *(Pres, CEO, CFO, Treas & Sec)*
Board of Directors:
Kranti Kumar Kotni
Transfer Agent:
Globex Transfer, LLC
780 Deltona Blvd Ste 202
Deltona, FL 32725

AXIOM MINING LIMITED
6/76 Doggett Street
Newstead, QLD, 4006, Australia
Tel.: (61) 7 3319 4100
Fax: (61) 7 3252 7577
E-Mail: contact@axiom-mining.com
Web Site: www.axiom-mining.com
AVQ—(ASX)
Rev.: $20,698
Assets: $27,195,941
Liabilities: $4,417,605
Net Worth: $22,778,336
Earnings: ($5,907,921)
Fiscal Year-end: 09/30/12
Business Description:
Mineral Exploration Services
S.I.C.: 1099
N.A.I.C.S.: 212299
Personnel:
Ryan Mount *(CEO & Mng Dir)*
Board of Directors:
Stephen Williams
Ryan Mount

Baker Tilly Hong Kong Limited
2nd Fl 625 Kings Road North Point
Hong Kong, China (Hong Kong)
Legal Counsel:
Kemp Strang
Level 17 175 Pitt Street
Sydney, NSW, 2000, Australia

AXIOM PROPERTIES LIMITED
Level 3 25 Leigh Street
Adelaide, SA, 5000, Australia
Tel.: (61) 8 8120 2400
Fax: (61) 8 8423 4500
Web Site: www.axiompl.com.au
AXI—(ASX)
Rev.: $7,518,752
Assets: $17,294,692
Liabilities: $1,091,079
Net Worth: $16,203,613
Earnings: $2,473,945
Emp.: 10
Fiscal Year-end: 06/30/13
Business Description:
Investment Management
S.I.C.: 6282
N.A.I.C.S.: 523920
Personnel:
Ben Laurance *(Mng Dir)*
Paul Santinon *(CFO & Sec)*
Board of Directors:
Ian James Laurance
John Sylvestor Howe
Ben Laurance
Legal Counsel:
Gilbert & Tobin
1202 Hay Street
West Perth, Australia

AXIOMTEK CO., LTD
8th Floor No 4 Lane 235
Pao Chiao Road, Taipei, 231, Taiwan
Tel.: (886) 229174550
Fax: (886) 229173200
E-Mail: info@etn.axiomtek.com.tw
Web Site: www.axiomtek.com.tw
Rev.: $53,000,000
Emp.: 570
Business Description:
Computer & Computer Peripheral Equipment & Software Whslr
S.I.C.: 5045
N.A.I.C.S.: 423430
Personnel:
Y. T. Yang *(Pres)*
Subsidiaries:

Axiomtek Display Solutions Co., Ltd. **(1)**
8F No 2 Lane 235 Pao Chin Rd
Hsintien City, Taipei, Taiwan
Tel.: (886) 2291455803
Fax: (886) 2 29145455
Electronic Display Mfr
S.I.C.: 5064
N.A.I.C.S.: 423620

Etherwan Systems Inc **(1)**
4th Floor-6 Far East Ctr
79 Hsin Taiwu Rd Sec 1, Taipei, Taiwan (100%)
Tel.: (886) 226984000
Fax: (886) 266296577
E-Mail: info@etherwan.com.tw
Web Site: www.etherwan.com.tw
Computer Systems Design Services
S.I.C.: 7373
N.A.I.C.S.: 541512

U.S. Subsidiary:

Axiom Technology Inc **(1)**
18138 Rowland St
City of Industry, CA 91748 (100%)
Tel.: (626) 581-3232
Fax: (626) 581-3552
Web Site: www.axiomtek.com
Emp.: 45
Computer & Computer Peripheral Equipment & Software Whslr
S.I.C.: 5045
N.A.I.C.S.: 423430
Matthew Lee *(Gen Mgr)*

AXIOS MOBILE ASSETS CORP.
7000 Pine Valley Drive Suite 201
Vaughan, ON, L4L 4Y8, Canada
Tel.: (416) 800-6669
Toll Free: (877) 762-9467
E-Mail: info@axiosma.com
Web Site: www.axiosma.com
AXA—(CNSX)
Rev.: $35,341
Assets: $7,196,109
Liabilities: $1,825,053
Net Worth: $5,371,057
Earnings: ($1,972,417)
Fiscal Year-end: 12/31/12
Business Description:
Software, RFID & Biomaterial Technologies
S.I.C.: 3663
N.A.I.C.S.: 334220
Personnel:
James E. Taylor *(Chm)*
Richard MacDonald *(Pres & CEO)*
Marc Topacio *(CFO & VP-Fin)*
Board of Directors:
James E. Taylor
Dennis Bausch
Richard MacDonald
Marc Topacio
David J. Wickwire
Transfer Agent:
Heritage Trust
4 King Street West Suite 1320
Toronto, ON, M5H 1B6, Canada

AXIS BANK LIMITED
Trishul 3rd Floor Opp Samartheshwar Temple Nr Law Garden Ellisbridge
Ahmedabad, 380 006, India
Tel.: (91) 7926409322
Fax: (91) 7926409321
Web Site: www.axisbank.com
Year Founded: 1994
532215—(BOM)
Rev.: $6,310,048,156
Assets: $63,139,403,439
Liabilities: $56,989,517,077
Net Worth: $6,149,886,362
Earnings: $970,525,320
Emp.: 37,901
Fiscal Year-end: 03/31/13
Business Description:
Commercial Banking
S.I.C.: 6029
N.A.I.C.S.: 522110
Personnel:
Sanjeev K. Gupta *(Co-Pres & CFO)*
Bapi Munshi *(Co-Pres & Chief Risk Officer)*
S. S. Bajaj *(Co-Pres & Chief Audit Officer)*
Shikha Sharma *(CEO & Mng Dir)*
Rajendra D. Adsul *(Pres-SME)*
Rajiv Anand *(Pres-Retail Banking)*
V. K. Bajaj *(Pres-Mid Corp & SME)*
Sharad Bhatia *(Pres-Stressed Assets)*
Lalit Chawla *(Pres-Corp Credit)*
Rajesh Kumar Dahiya *(Pres-HR)*
Vinod George *(Pres-Wholesale Banking Ops)*
A. R. Gokulakrishnan *(Pres-Wholesale Banking Ops)*
B. Gopalakrishnan *(Pres-Law)*
S. K. Mitra *(Pres-Distr)*
P. Mukherjee *(Pres-Large Corp & Intl Banking)*
Sidharth Rath *(Pres-Treasury & Bus Banking)*
Nilesh Shah *(Pres-Investment Banking)*
R. V. S. Sridhar *(Pres-IT & Retail Banking Ops)*
Jairam Sridharan *(Pres-Consumer Lending)*
M. V. Subramanian *(Pres-Rural & Inclusive Banking)*
Arun Thukral *(CEO/Mng Dir-Axis Securities)*
C. Babu Joseph *(CEO-Bank Foundation)*
Sanjeev Kapoor *(Sec)*
Board of Directors:
Sanjiv Misra
Samir Kumar Barua
Rohit Bhagat
Rabindranath N. Bhattacharyya
V. R. Kaundinya
S. B. Mathur
Prasad Raghava Menon
Som Mittal
K. N. Prithviraj
Somnath Sengupta
Shikha Sharma
V. Srinivasan
Ireena Vittal
Transfer Agent:
Karvy Computershare Private Limited
Plot No 17-24 Vittal Rao Nagar Madhapur
Hyderabad, 500 081, India
Tel.: (91) 40 2342 0818

Co-Headquarters:

Axis Bank Limited - Corporate Office **(1)**
Axis House Bombay Dyeing Mills Compound
Pandurang Budhkar Marg
Worli, Mumbai, 400 025, India
Tel.: (91) 22 2425 2525
Fax: (91) 22 4325 1800
Web Site: www.axisbank.com
Corporate Office
S.I.C.: 8741
N.A.I.C.S.: 551114
Shikha Sharma *(CEO & Mng Dir)*
Somnath Sengupta *(CFO & Exec Dir)*
S. S. Bajaj *(Chief Compliance Officer & Pres-Compliance)*
Bapi Munshi *(Chief Risk Officer & Pres-Risk)*
R. K. Bammi *(Pres/Head-Retail Banking)*
Sonu Bhasin *(Pres/Head-Retail Products & Sls Mgmt)*
S. K. Mitra *(Pres/Head-Distr)*
Rajendra D. Adsul *(Pres-SME)*
V. K. Bajaj *(Pres-Mid Corporates)*
Lalit Chawla *(Pres-Corp Credit)*
Rajesh Kumar Dahiya *(Pres-HR)*
Vinod George *(Pres-Wholesale Banking Ops)*
A. R. Gokulakrishnan *(Pres-Stressed Assets)*
B. Gopalakrishnan *(Pres-Law)*
Sanjeev K. Gupta *(Pres-IR, Fin & Accts)*
P. Mukherjee *(Pres-Treasury & Intl Banking)*
S. K. Nandi *(Pres-Internal Audit & Chief Audit Exec)*
Sidharth Rath *(Pres-Infrastructure Bus)*
Nilesh Shah *(Pres-Strategic Initiatives)*
R. V. S. Sridhar *(Pres-Treasury-Global Markets)*
M. V. Subramanian *(Pres-Bus Banking)*
S. K. Chakrabarti *(Deputy Mng Dir)*

Subsidiary:

Axis Private Equity Limited **(2)**
146 Maker Chamber VI 14th Fl
Nariman Point, 400021 Mumbai, Maharashtra, India
Tel.: (91) 2222895300
Fax: (91) 2222895399
E-Mail: ralmeida@axispe.com
Emp.: 10
Equity Investment Management Services
S.I.C.: 6211
N.A.I.C.S.: 523999
Arun Prakash Korati *(CEO)*

AXIS CAPITAL HOLDINGS LIMITED
92 Pitts Bay Rd
Pembroke, Bermuda HM 08
Tel.: (441) 496 2600
Fax: (441) 405 2640
E-Mail: neera.dunleavy@axiscapital.com
Web Site: www.axis.bm
AXS—(NYSE)
Rev.: $4,196,365,000
Assets: $19,634,784,000
Liabilities: $13,766,822,000
Net Worth: $5,867,962,000
Earnings: $727,465,000
Emp.: 1,200
Fiscal Year-end: 12/31/13
Business Description:
Holding Company; Specialty Insurance & Reinsurance Products & Services
S.I.C.: 6719
N.A.I.C.S.: 551112
Personnel:
Michael A. Butt *(Chm)*
Karl Mayr *(Vice Chm-AXIS Re)*
Albert A. Benchimol *(Pres & CEO)*
Joseph Henry *(CFO)*
Dennis B. Reding *(COO)*
Koorosh Beigian *(CIO & Exec VP)*
Darryl Catts *(CIO-AXIS Insurance)*
Dean Benner *(Chief Investment Officer & Exec VP)*
Brian W. Goshen *(Chief Admin Officer)*
James P. O'Shaughnessy *(Chief Acctg Officer, Exec VP & Controller)*
Michael Steel *(Chief Risk Officer & Exec VP)*
Eric Gesick *(Group Chief Actuary)*
Linda Ventresca *(Exec VP & Corp Dev Officer)*
Richard Strachan *(Chief Claims Officer)*
William A. Fischer *(Pres-AXIS Re-US & Chief Underwriting Officer-AXIS Re)*
Michael Rutherford *(Pres-AXIS Capital Risk Solutions Div)*
David Smith *(CEO-Australia)*
Christopher DiSipio *(CEO-Accident & Health)*
Mark Gregory *(CEO-Intl Speciality)*
Jack Gressier *(CEO-AXIS Insurance)*
Jay Nichols *(CEO-AXIS Re)*
Richard T. Gieryn, Jr. *(Gen Counsel & Sec)*
Cliff Easton *(Exec VP & Mgr-Onshore Energy)*
Richard Fricker *(Exec VP & Mgr-Offshore Energy)*
Joseph England *(Exec VP-Marine Insurance)*
Tim Hennessy *(Exec VP-Regulatory & Compliance-Intl)*
John Intondi *(Exec VP-AXIS Insurance Claims)*
Alistair Robson *(Exec VP-Global Property)*
Ben Rubin *(Exec VP-Capital Markets-AXIS Re)*
Adam Grosz *(Sr VP & Mgr-Western Reg Fin Institutions)*
Bret Kilbourn *(Sr VP)*
Jonathan Marshall *(Sr VP-Property)*
Matthew Melville *(Sr VP-Renewable Energy)*
Board of Directors:
Michael A. Butt
Geoffrey Bell
Albert A. Benchimol
Jane Boisseau
Charles Arthur Davis
Robert Laurence Friedman
Christopher V. Greetham
Maurice A. Keane
Andrew M.B. Large
Cheryl-Ann Lister
Thomas C. Ramey
Henry B. Smith
Alice Young
Wilhelm Zeller

Subsidiary:

AXIS Specialty Limited **(1)**
Axis House 92 PittsBay Road
Pembroke, HM 08, Bermuda BM
Tel.: (441) 4962600
Fax: (441) 4052600

E-Mail: neera.dunleavy@axiscapital.com
Web Site: www.axiscapital.com
Provider of General Insurance & Reinsurance Services
S.I.C.: 6411
N.A.I.C.S.: 524298
Michael A. Butt *(Chm)*

U.S. Division:

AXIS Capital Holdings Limited - AXIS Global Accident & Health Division **(1)**
1 University Sq Dr Ste 200
Princeton, NJ 08540
Tel.: (609) 375-9200
E-Mail: USInsurance.AccHealth@axiscapital.com
Web Site: www.axisaccidenthealth.com
Insurance Management Services
S.I.C.: 6411
N.A.I.C.S.: 524298
Chris DiSipio *(Pres & CEO)*
Dan Bolgar *(CEO-Accident & Health Reinsurance)*
James Hamilton *(CEO-North America)*
Alfred Drowne *(Sr VP-Bus Dev)*
Mike Pellino *(Sr VP-Underwriting, Accident & Health Reinsurance)*

U.S. Subsidiaries:

AXIS Group Services, Inc. **(1)**
11680 Great Oaks Way
Alpharetta, GA 30022-2457
Tel.: (678) 746-9000
Insurance Brokerage Services
S.I.C.: 6411
N.A.I.C.S.: 524210

AXIS Insurance Company **(1)**
303 W Madison St Ste 500
Chicago, IL 60606
Tel.: (312) 977-0700
Fax: (312) 977-0327
Web Site: www.axiscapital.com
Insurance Brokerage Services
S.I.C.: 6411
N.A.I.C.S.: 524210
Peter Wilson *(Pres)*
Jack Gressier *(CEO)*
Mike Herlihy *(Sr VP & Reg Mgr-FIS Central & Southeast)*

AXIS Reinsurance Company **(1)**
430 Park Ave 4th Fl
New York, NY 10022 NY
Tel.: (212) 500-7600
Fax: (212) 715-3555
E-Mail: info-us-re@axiscapital.com
Web Site: www.axiscapital.com
Emp.: 100
Provider of Reinsurance Services
S.I.C.: 6351
N.A.I.C.S.: 524126
Mike Morrill *(Pres)*
Jay Nichols *(CEO)*
Koorosh Beigian *(CIO & Exec VP)*
Edgar Bautista *(Sr VP & Head-New Weather & Commodity Markets Initiative)*
Sandeep Ramachandran *(Sr VP & Head-New Weather & Commodity Markets Initiative)*

AXIS Specialty Finance LLC **(1)**
11680 Great Oaks Way Ste 500
Alpharetta, GA 30022-2457
Tel.: (678) 746-9000
Fax: (678) 746-9495
Emp.: 250
Insurance Management Services
S.I.C.: 6411
N.A.I.C.S.: 524298

AXIS Specialty Insurance Co. **(1)**
9 Farm Springs Rd
Farmington, CT 06032-2569 CT
Mailing Address:
PO Box 4310
Hartford, CT 06147
Tel.: (860) 674-6600
Provider of Insurance Services
S.I.C.: 6411
N.A.I.C.S.: 524210

AXIS Surplus Insurance Company **(1)**
11680 Great Oaks Way Ste 500
Alpharetta, GA 30022
Tel.: (678) 746-9000
Fax: (678) 746-94444
E-Mail: info@axiscapital.com
Web Site: www.axiscapital.com
Emp.: 300
Provider of Property & Casualty Insurance
S.I.C.: 6411
N.A.I.C.S.: 524210

Non-U.S. Subsidiaries:

AXIS Re Limited **(1)**
34 Upper Mount St
Dublin, 2, Ireland IE
Tel.: (353) 16641654
Fax: (353) 13341862
E-Mail: info-dublin@axiscapital.com
Web Site: www.axiscapital.com
Provider of Reinsurance Services
S.I.C.: 6411
N.A.I.C.S.: 524298
Tim Hennessy *(Exec VP & Dir-Fin-Europe)*

AXIS Specialty Europe Limited **(1)**
Mount Herbert Ct 34 Uppr Mount St
Dublin, 2, Ireland IE
Tel.: (353) 16325926
Fax: (353) 16325902
E-Mail: info-dublin@axiscapital.com
Web Site: www.axiscapital.com
Emp.: 30
Provider of Non-Life Insurance Services
S.I.C.: 6411
N.A.I.C.S.: 524298
Joe England *(CEO)*

AXIS Specialty UK Holdings Limited **(1)**
60 Great Tower St
London, EC3R 5AZ, United Kingdom
Tel.: (44) 20 7877 3800
Fax: (44) 20 7877 3840
Investment Management Services
S.I.C.: 6211
N.A.I.C.S.: 523999

AXIS COMMUNICATIONS AB

Emdalavaegen 14
223 69 Lund, Sweden
Tel.: (46) 462721800
Fax: (46) 46136130
E-Mail: pressoffice@axis.com
Web Site: www.axis.com
AXIS—(OMX)
Sales Range: $500-549.9 Million
Emp.: 1,127

Business Description:
Network Video, Network Cameras, Video Servers, Accessories & Software Solutions
S.I.C.: 3651
N.A.I.C.S.: 334310

Personnel:
Martin Gren *(Co-Founder)*
Lars-Erik Nilsson *(Chm)*
Ray Mauritsson *(Pres & CEO)*
Fredrik Sjostrand *(CFO & VP)*
Jonas Hansson *(CIO)*
Johan Paulsson *(CTO)*
Malin Ruijsenaars *(Chief Personnel Officer)*

Board of Directors:
Lars-Erik Nilsson
Charlotta Falvin
Martin Gren
Olle Isberg
Goran Jansson
Roland Vejdemo

Subsidiaries:

Axis Alfa AB **(1)**
Emdalav 14
223 69 Lund, Sweden
Tel.: (46) 462721800
Fax: (46) 46136130
E-Mail: reception@axis.com
Emp.: 750
Network Video Cameras & Print Servers Mfr
S.I.C.: 3651
N.A.I.C.S.: 334310
Rune Frithiof *(Mgr-Facility)*

Axis Beta AB **(1)**
Emdalav 14
223 69 Lund, Sweden
Tel.: (46) 462721800
Fax: (46) 46136130
E-Mail: info@axis.com
Emp.: 600
Network Video Cameras & Print Servers Mfr
S.I.C.: 3651
N.A.I.C.S.: 334310
Ray Mauritsson *(Mng Dir)*

Axis Technologies AB **(1)**
Emdalavagen 14
223 69 Lund, Sweden
Tel.: (46) 462721800
Fax: (46) 46136130
E-Mail: reception@axis.com
Emp.: 13
Network Video Cameras & Print Servers Mfr
S.I.C.: 3651
N.A.I.C.S.: 334310
Rune Frithiof *(Mgr-Facility)*

Non-U.S. Subsidiaries:

AxerNet Communications SA **(1)**
Calle Yunpue No 9
Tres Cantos, ES 28760 Madrid, Spain
Tel.: (34) 918034643
Fax: (34) 918035452
E-Mail: info-es@axis.com
Web Site: www.axis.com
Emp.: 12
Network Video Solutions Mfr
S.I.C.: 3651
N.A.I.C.S.: 334310
Francisco Vidal *(Controller)*

Axis Communications BV **(1)**
Glashaven 22
3011 XA Rotterdam, Netherlands
Tel.: (31) 107504600
Fax: (31) 107504699
E-Mail: info-nl@axis.com
Web Site: www.axis.com
Emp.: 8
Network Video Solutions Mfr
S.I.C.: 3651
N.A.I.C.S.: 334310
Edwin Beerentemsel *(Mgr-Bus Dev)*

Axis Communications GmbH **(1)**
Lilienthalstr 25
85399 Hallbergmoos, Germany
Tel.: (49) 811555080
Fax: (49) 8115550869
E-Mail: info-de@axis.com
Web Site: www.axis.com
Emp.: 20
Network Video Solutions Mfr
S.I.C.: 3651
N.A.I.C.S.: 334310
Edwin Roobol *(Mgr)*

Axis Communications KK **(1)**
Shinagawa E One Tower 13 Fl 2-16-1 Konan
Minato-ku, Tokyo, 108-0075, Japan
Tel.: (81) 3 6716 7850
Fax: (81) 3 6716 7851
E-Mail: info@axiscom.co.jp
Web Site: www.axiscom.co.jp
Emp.: 15
Network Video Solutions Mfr
S.I.C.: 3651
N.A.I.C.S.: 334310
Okuda Satoshi Yoshimi *(Pres)*

Axis Communications Korea Co. Ltd. **(1)**
Rm 407 Life Combi B D 61-4 Yoido-dong
Yeongdeungpo-Ku, Seoul, Korea (South)
Tel.: (82) 27809636
Fax: (82) 2 6280 9636
E-Mail: info-kr@axis.com
Web Site: www.axis.co.kr
Network Video Solutions Mfr
S.I.C.: 3651
N.A.I.C.S.: 334310
Seoung-je Yoon *(Pres)*

Axis Communications Ltd **(1)**
8F 11 101 Fushing N Rd
105 Taipei, Taiwan
Tel.: (886) 225469668
Fax: (886) 225461911
Emp.: 5
Network Video Solutions Mfr
S.I.C.: 3651
N.A.I.C.S.: 334310
Jessica Chang *(Gen Mgr)*

Axis Communications OOO **(1)**
Leningradsky prospekt 31 3 of 405
125284 Moscow, Russia
Tel.: (7) 495 940 6682
Fax: (7) 495 940 6682
E-Mail: info-ru@axis.com
Web Site: www.axis.com
Emp.: 20
Network Video Solutions Mfr
S.I.C.: 3651
N.A.I.C.S.: 334310
Stanislav Guchia *(Dir)*

Axis Communications Pty Ltd **(1)**
Level 27 101 Collins St
Melbourne, VIC, 3000, Australia
Tel.: (61) 392216133
Web Site: www.axis.com
Emp.: 10
Network Video Solutions Mfr
S.I.C.: 3651
N.A.I.C.S.: 334310
Waiking Wong *(Gen Mgr)*

Axis Communications (S) Pte Ltd **(1)**
7 Temasek Blvd
No 11-01A Suntec Tower 1, Singapore, 038987, Singapore
Tel.: (65) 68362777
Fax: (65) 63341218
E-Mail: info-sg@axis.com
Web Site: www.axis.com
Emp.: 17
Network Video Solutions Mfr
S.I.C.: 3651
N.A.I.C.S.: 334310
Oh Tee Lee *(Reg Dir)*

Axis Communications (SA) (Pty) Ltd **(1)**
2nd Floor Microsoft Bldg Microsoft Office Park
3012 William Nicol Drive, Bryanston, Johannesburg, 2021, South Africa
Tel.: (27) 115486780
Fax: (27) 115486799
E-Mail: shereenc@axis.com
Web Site: www.axis.com
Emp.: 8
Network Video Cameras & Print Servers Mfr
S.I.C.: 3651
N.A.I.C.S.: 334310
Roy Alves *(Country Mgr)*

Axis Communications SA **(1)**
Hampton Park Atterbury House
20 Georgian Crescent, Bryanston, Johannesburg, 70939, South Africa
Tel.: (27) 115486780
Fax: (27) 115486799
E-Mail: info@axis.com
Web Site: www.axis.com
Emp.: 8
Network Video Cameras & Print Servers Mfr
S.I.C.: 3651
N.A.I.C.S.: 334310
Roy Alves *(Country Mgr)*

Axis Communications (UK) Ltd **(1)**
6-7 Ladygrove Ct Hitchwood Ln
Near Hitchin, Preston, Hertfordshire, SG4 7SA, United Kingdom
Tel.: (44) 1462427910
Fax: (44) 1462427911
Web Site: www.axis.com
Emp.: 11
Network Video Cameras & Print Servers Mfr
S.I.C.: 3651
N.A.I.C.S.: 334310
Beverley Cook *(Office Mgr)*

Shanghai Axis Communication Equipment Trading Co. Ltd **(1)**
Rm 2606 26/F Yueda889 Center 1111 Changshou Road
Shanghai, 200042, China
Tel.: (86) 2164311690
Fax: (86) 2164338264
Emp.: 30
Network Video Solutions Mfr
S.I.C.: 3651
N.A.I.C.S.: 334310
Jimmy Lee *(Dir-Sls & Mktg)*

AXIS INCORPORATION BERHAD

No 26 26A Jalan Lambak Taman Johor
81200 Johor Bahru, Johor Darul Takzim, Malaysia
Tel.: (60) 72341888
Fax: (60) 72327010
Web Site: www.axisinc.biz
AXIS—(KLS)
Sales Range: $25-49.9 Million
Emp.: 294

Business Description:
Fabrics & Garments Mfr
S.I.C.: 2389
N.A.I.C.S.: 315280

Personnel:
Yuan Meng Aw *(Vice Chm)*
Nabhesh Khanna *(CEO)*
Chee Wah Lai *(Co-Sec)*
Ming Toong Lim *(Co-Sec)*
Lai Yee Ng *(Co-Sec)*

Board of Directors:
Izham Yusof
Yuan Meng Aw
Han Boon Lee
Zairi Shaz Mohd Ismail
Aslahuddin Ja'afar T. Azlan

Subsidiary:

Chongee Enterprise Sdn. Bhd. **(1)**
No 26 & 26a Jalan Lambak Taman Johor
Johor Bahru, Johor, 81200, Malaysia
Tel.: (60) 72341888
Fax: (60) 69789570
Garment Mfr & Distr
S.I.C.: 5699
N.A.I.C.S.: 315220
Allan Yuan Meng Aw *(Mng Dir)*

AXIS INFORMATION SYSTEMS

(d/b/a AxIS)
Ground Floor Prestige House
Kigali, Gikondo, 1382, Rwanda
Tel.: (250) 788 611902
E-Mail: info@axis.rw
Web Site: www.axis.rw
Year Founded: 2006
Emp.: 20

Business Description:
Development & Implementation of Web & Mobile Applications & Solutions
S.I.C.: 7372
N.A.I.C.S.: 511210

Personnel:
Clement Uwajeneza *(CEO)*

AXIS INTERMODAL LIMITED

15 Fenlock Court Lower Road
Long Hanborough, Oxfordshire, OX29 8LN, United Kingdom
Tel.: (44) 1993 883 148
Fax: (44) 1993 883 210
E-Mail: info@axisintermodal.com
Web Site: www.axisintermodal.com
Year Founded: 2003
Sales Range: $50-74.9 Million
Emp.: 57

Business Description:
Investment Management Services
S.I.C.: 6799
N.A.I.C.S.: 523920

Personnel:
Robert J. Montague *(Chm)*
Nick Smith *(Sec & Grp Dir-Legal)*

Board of Directors:
Robert J. Montague
Stephen Ball
Heiner Mangels
David Potter
Nick Smith

AXIS IT&T LIMITED

D-30 Sector 3
Noida, 201301, India
Tel.: (91) 1204518200
Fax: (91) 1202442921
Web Site: www.axisitt.com
AXIS-IT&T—(NSE)
Rev.: $53,154,588
Assets: $32,110,972
Liabilities: $14,317,544
Net Worth: $17,793,429
Earnings: $2,711,038
Emp.: 1,229
Fiscal Year-end: 03/31/13

Business Description:
Engineering Design & Software Development Services
S.I.C.: 8711
N.A.I.C.S.: 541330

Personnel:
Ravinarayanan S. *(Chm)*
Valmeeka Nathan *(CEO)*
Shweta Agarwal *(Compliance Officer & Sec)*

Board of Directors:
Ravinarayanan S.
Rohitasava Chand
Kedar Nath Choudhury
Pradeep Dadlani
Valmeeka Nathan
P. Hemanth Polavaram
Kailash M. Rustagi

Transfer Agent:
Karvy Computershare Private Limited
46 Avenue 4 Street No 1 Banjara Hills
Hyderabad, 500 034, India
Tel.: (91) 40 23320666
Fax: (91) 40 23323058

AXLE GROUP HOLDINGS LTD.

26 32 Millbrae Rd
Langside, Glasgow, G42 9TU, United Kingdom
Tel.: (44) 1416323222

Business Description:
Holding Company
S.I.C.: 6719
N.A.I.C.S.: 551112

Personnel:
Alan Revie *(Chm)*

Holdings:

National Tyre Services Ltd. **(1)**
Regent House
Heaton Lane, Stockport, Cheshire, SK4 1BS, United Kingdom
Tel.: (44) 1614291200
Fax: (44) 1614770886
E-Mail: information@national-tyres.co.uk
Web Site: www.national.co.uk
Emp.: 85
Automotive Maintenance Services & Tire & Automotive Parts Distr
S.I.C.: 5013
N.A.I.C.S.: 441310

Stepgrades Motor Accessories Ltd. **(1)**
26 32 Millbrae Road
Langside, Glasgow, G42 9TU, United Kingdom
Tel.: (44) 1416323222
Fax: (44) 4141622904
E-Mail: info@viking.co.uk
Web Site: www.viking.co.uk
Emp.: 50
General Automotive Maintenance Services & Tire Distr
S.I.C.: 7549
N.A.I.C.S.: 811198
Kevin Peck *(Mng Dir)*

AXMIN, INC.

120 Adelaide Street West Suite 800
Toronto, ON, M5H 1T1, Canada
Tel.: (416) 368-0993
E-Mail: info@axmininc.com
Web Site: www.axmininc.com
AXM—(TSXV)
Int. Income: $8,000
Assets: $39,471,000
Liabilities: $3,301,000
Net Worth: $36,170,000
Earnings: ($6,832,000)
Fiscal Year-end: 12/31/12

Business Description:
Gold Mining Services
S.I.C.: 1041
N.A.I.C.S.: 212221

Personnel:
Lucy Yan *(Chm & Interim CEO)*
Jin Kuang *(CFO)*
Graham Hill *(COO)*
Shirley Kozel *(Sec)*

Board of Directors:
Lucy Yan
David de Jongh Weill
Alexander du Plessis
Robert Shirriff
Joe Tai

Legal Counsel:
Fasken Martineau DuMoulin LLP
333 Bay Street Suite 2400 Bay Adelaide Centre
PO Box 20
Toronto, ON, Canada

Transfer Agent:
Computershare Investor Services Inc.
100 University Ave 9th Floor
Toronto, ON, Canada

AXON ACTIVE AG

Schloessli Schoenegg
Wilhelmshoehe, CH-6003 Lucerne, Switzerland

Mailing Address:
PO Box 7760
CH-6000 Lucerne, Switzerland
Tel.: (41) 412492570
Fax: (41) 412492524
E-Mail: info@axonactive.com
Web Site: www.axonactive.com
Emp.: 150

Business Description:
Holding Company; Business Services
S.I.C.: 6719
N.A.I.C.S.: 551112

Personnel:
Peter Delfosse *(CEO)*
Roman Oberli *(Mng Dir)*

Board of Directors:
Peter Delfosse
Stefen Muff
Roman Oberli

Non-U.S. Holding:

Kompass International Neuenschwander SA **(1)**
Saint Laurent
F 73800 Cruet, France
Tel.: (33) 479652508
Fax: (33) 479841395
E-Mail: webmaster@kompass.com
Web Site: www.kompass.com
Emp.: 2,500
Business Directories Publisher Import Export
S.I.C.: 2741
N.A.I.C.S.: 511140
Jerome Cazes *(Pres)*

AXON HOLDINGS S.A.

2 Ermou St
Syntgama
10563 Athens, Greece
Tel.: (30) 2103216000
Fax: (30) 2103216006
E-Mail: info@axonholdings.gr
Web Site: www.axonholdings.gr
AXON—(ATH)
Sales Range: $350-399.9 Million
Emp.: 2,740

Business Description:
Holding Company; Healthcare & Financial Services
S.I.C.: 6719
N.A.I.C.S.: 551112

Personnel:
Apostolos D. Terzopoulos *(Chm)*
Panagiotis N. Doumanoglou *(Mng Dir)*

Board of Directors:
Apostolos D. Terzopoulos
Dimitrios Nanopoulos
Petros Nikolaidis
Paka Paraskevi

Subsidiaries:

AXON Securities S.A. **(1)**
Stadiou Str 48
10564 Athens, Greece
Tel.: (30) 2103363800
Fax: (30) 2103243903
E-Mail: analysis@axonsec.gr
Web Site: www.axonsec.gr
Emp.: 20
Securities Trading Services
S.I.C.: 6211
N.A.I.C.S.: 523110
Adamopoulou Efi *(Mgr)*

Data Design S.A. **(1)**
Messogion Ave 249
154 51 Athens, Greece
Tel.: (30) 2106537422
Fax: (30) 2106542785
E-Mail: info@datadesign.gr
Web Site: www.datadesign.gr
Emp.: 15
Medical Software Development Services
S.I.C.: 7371
N.A.I.C.S.: 541511
Marios Kaminis *(Mgr)*

Euromedica Palaiou Falirou S.A. **(1)**
Leoforos Amfitheas 107
17563 Palaion Faliron, Athens, Greece
Tel.: (30) 2109803370
Fax: (30) 2109803374
E-Mail: pfaliro@euromedica.gr
Web Site: www.euromedica.gr
Emp.: 24
Healthcare Services
S.I.C.: 8062
N.A.I.C.S.: 622110
George Stamatakis *(Mgr)*

Ippokratis Magnetic Tomography S.A. **(1)**
Saint George 88
Korydallos, 18454 Piraeus, Greece
Tel.: (30) 2104941000
Fax: (30) 2104962451
E-Mail: info@ippokratis-medical.gr
Web Site: www.ippokratis-medical.gr
Emp.: 7
Diagnostic Center Services
S.I.C.: 8071
N.A.I.C.S.: 621512
Maria Psomiadou *(Mgr)*

SONAK S.A. **(1)**
Govatsi Str
PO Box 60
Lofos Aghios Georgios, 19003 Markopoulon, Greece
Tel.: (30) 2299021000
Fax: (30) 2299041001
E-Mail: info@sonak.gr
Web Site: www.sonak.gr
Emp.: 55
Defense Software & Electronic Systems Development Services
S.I.C.: 7371
N.A.I.C.S.: 541511
George Giavroutas *(Mgr-IT)*

AXON INFOTECH LTD.

E-109 Crystal Plaza New Link Road
Andheri W
Mumbai, 400053, India
Tel.: (91) 22 61522225
Fax: (91) 22 61522234
E-Mail: axoninfotech@gmail.com
Web Site: www.axoninfotech.in
Year Founded: 1982
505506—(BOM)
Rev.: $625,330
Assets: $2,454,349
Liabilities: $5,522
Net Worth: $2,448,826

Earnings: $4,360
Fiscal Year-end: 03/31/13
Business Description:
Software Development Services
S.I.C.: 7371
N.A.I.C.S.: 541511
Personnel:
Girraj Kishor Agrawal *(Chm, CEO, Mng Dir & Compliance Officer)*
Board of Directors:
Girraj Kishor Agrawal
Tanu Giriraj Kishor Agarwal
Zubin Jasi Pardiwala
Tushar Ramchandra Rane
Transfer Agent:
Sharex Dynamic (India) Pvt. Ltd
Unit 1 Luthra Indus Premises Andheri Kurla Road Safed Pool Andheri E
Mumbai, India

AXPO HOLDING AG

Parkstrasse 23
CH 5401 Baden, Switzerland
Tel.: (41) 562003777
Fax: (41) 562003131
Web Site: www.axpo.com
Sales Range: $5-14.9 Billion
Emp.: 3,600
Business Description:
Holding Company; Electric Power Generation & Distribution Services
S.I.C.: 6719
N.A.I.C.S.: 551112
Personnel:
Robert Lombardini *(Chm)*
Heinz Karrer *(CEO & Chm-Exec Bd)*
Rolf Bosch *(Member-Exec Bd)*
Hans Schulz *(Member-Exec Bd)*
Manfred Thumann *(Member-Exec Bd)*
Andrew Walo *(Member-Exec Bd)*
Board of Directors:
Robert Lombardini
Ueli Betschart
Peter C. Beyeler
Jakob Brunnschweiler
Reto Dubach
Andreas Frank
Pankraz Freitag
Ernst Frey
Rudolf Hug
Markus Kagi
Peter Reinhard
Ernst Stocker
Hansjakob Zellweger

Subsidiaries:

Axpo Holz + Energie AG (1)
Flughofstrasse 54
CH 8152 Glattbrugg, Switzerland
Tel.: (41) 44 809 74 80
E-Mail: info.axpo-holz@axpo.ch
Web Site: www.axpo-holz.ch
Engineering & Operating Biomass Power Plants
S.I.C.: 8711
N.A.I.C.S.: 541330

Axpo Kompogas AG (1)
Flughofstrasse 54
8152 Glattbrugg, Switzerland CH
Tel.: (41) 44 809 77 77 (100%)
Fax: (41) 44 809 77 00
Web Site: www.axpo-kompogas.ch
Operation & Management of Biomass Plants
S.I.C.: 4911
N.A.I.C.S.: 221118
Bernard C. Fenner *(CEO & Head-Plant Construction)*

Axpo Tegra AG (1)
Via Innovativa 11
CH 7013 Domat/Ems, Switzerland
Tel.: (41) 81 632 33 33
Fax: (41) 81 632 33 37
E-Mail: info.axpo-holz@axpo.ch
Web Site: www.axpo.com
Biomass Power Plant
S.I.C.: 4931
N.A.I.C.S.: 221118

Axpo Trading AG (1)
Werkstrasse 10
5080 Laufenburg, Switzerland CH
Tel.: (41) 628696363 (100%)
E-Mail: info@axpo.com
Web Site: www.axpo.com
Rev.: $3,745,456,264
Assets: $6,396,913,776
Liabilities: $4,657,697,528
Net Worth: $1,739,216,248
Earnings: ($92,929,452)
Emp.: 737
Fiscal Year-end: 09/30/12
Holding Company; Energy Production, Distribution & Trading Services
S.I.C.: 6719
N.A.I.C.S.: 551112
Martin Schwab *(Chm)*
Hans Schulz *(CEO)*
Markus Brokhof *(Deputy CEO)*

Affiliate:

Kernkraftwerk Gosgen-Daniken AG (2)
Kraftwerkstrasse
4658 Daniken, Switzerland (37.5%)
Tel.: (41) 622882000
Fax: (41) 622882001
E-Mail: info@kkg.ch
Web Site: www.kkg.ch
Emp.: 500
Nuclear Power Plant Operation
S.I.C.: 4911
N.A.I.C.S.: 221113
Michael Wider *(Chm)*

Corporate Headquarters:

Axpo Trading AG - Head Office & Trading Center (2)
Lerzenstrasse 10
CH-8953 Dietikon, Switzerland
Tel.: (41) 44 749 4141
Fax: (41) 44 749 4150
E-Mail: info@axpo.com
Web Site: www.axpo.com
Emp.: 20
Corporate Office
S.I.C.: 8741
N.A.I.C.S.: 551114
Hans Schulz *(CEO)*
Markus Brokhof *(Deputy CEO)*

Subsidiaries:

Calancasca AG (3)
C/o Studio Legale E Notarile
6535 Roveredo, Switzerland
Tel.: (41) 918271385
Hydropower Plant
S.I.C.: 4911
N.A.I.C.S.: 221111

Non-U.S. Subsidiaries:

Axpo Albania Sh.a. (3)
Rruga "Reshit Petrela" Pallati Usluga 17
Tirana, Albania
Tel.: (355) 4 24 20448
Web Site: www.axpo.com
Electric Power Generation
S.I.C.: 4911
N.A.I.C.S.: 221118
Bashkim Baholli *(Gen Mgr)*

Axpo Austria GmbH (3)
Eschenbachgasse 11/8
1010 Vienna, Austria
Tel.: (43) 1 585 09 09 0
Fax: (43) 1 585 09 09 99
E-Mail: info.at@axpo.com
Emp.: 5
Electric Power Distribution
S.I.C.: 4911
N.A.I.C.S.: 221122
Roman Stutz *(Gen Mgr)*

Axpo Bulgaria EAD (3)
19 Yanko Sakazov blvd Apart 5
Oborishte Residential Area, 1504 Sofia, Bulgaria
Tel.: (359) 29461294
Fax: (359) 29434299
E-Mail: office.bg@axpo.com
Web Site: www.axpo.com
Emp.: 6
Electrical Power Trading Services
S.I.C.: 4939
N.A.I.C.S.: 221122

Miroslav Damianov *(Mng Dir)*

Axpo Deutschland GmbH (3)
Messehaus am Markt-Markt 16
04109 Leipzig, Germany
Tel.: (49) 341 2 61 79 0
Fax: (49) 341 2 61 79 22
E-Mail: info.de@axpo.com
Web Site: www.axpo.com
Emp.: 21
Electric Power Distribution
S.I.C.: 4911
N.A.I.C.S.: 221122
Carsten Munch *(Mng Dir)*

Axpo d.o.o. Beograd (3)
Milutina Milankovica 11a
11070 Belgrade, Serbia
Tel.: (381) 11 260 3767
Fax: (381) 11 260 3778
Web Site: www.axpo.com
Emp.: 2
Electric Power Distribution
S.I.C.: 4939
N.A.I.C.S.: 221122
Veljko Cvijovic *(Gen Mgr)*

Axpo Energy Romania S.A. (3)
79-81 Popa Savu Street
011432 Bucharest, Sector 1, Romania
Tel.: (40) 21 230 33 23
Fax: (40) 21 230 33 35
E-Mail: info@axpo.com
Web Site: www.axpo.com
Electric Power & Gas Distribution
S.I.C.: 4939
N.A.I.C.S.: 221122
Petre Stroe *(Mng Dir)*

Axpo Hellas S.A. (3)
Leoforos Pentelis 3
Vrilissia, 152 35 Athens, Greece
Tel.: (30) 2106924510
Fax: (30) 2106924810
E-Mail:
Web Site: www.axpo.com
Emp.: 1
Electricity Trading
S.I.C.: 4911
N.A.I.C.S.: 221122
George Petonis *(VP)*

Axpo Iberia S.L. (3)
Paseo de la Castellana 66 6 planta
28046 Madrid, Spain
Tel.: (34) 915947170
Fax: (34) 915947171
E-Mail: info.es@axpo.com
Web Site: www.axpo.com
Emp.: 30
Electric Power Generation
S.I.C.: 4911
N.A.I.C.S.: 221118
Ignacio Soneira *(Mng Dir)*

Axpo Italia S.p.A. (3)
via Enrico Albareto 21
16153 Genoa, Italy
Tel.: (39) 010291041
Fax: (39) 0102910444
E-Mail: info.it@axpo.com
Web Site: www.axpo.com
Emp.: 100
Electric Power Generation
S.I.C.: 4911
N.A.I.C.S.: 221122
Salvatore Pinto *(Chm)*

Subsidiaries:

Calenia Energia S.p.A. (4)
Via Enrico Albareto 21
16153 Genoa, Italy (85%)
Tel.: (39) 010 2910 41
Fax: (39) 010 2910 444
Web Site: www.caleniaenergia.eu
Electric Power Generation
S.I.C.: 4931
N.A.I.C.S.: 221118
Simone Demarchi *(Gen Mgr)*

Rizziconi Energia SpA (4)
Via Enrico Albareto 21
I 16153 Genoa, Italy (100%)
Tel.: (39) 010 2910 41
Fax: (39) 010 2910 444
Electricity Power Plant; Electricity Generation
S.I.C.: 4939
N.A.I.C.S.: 221118

Axpo Nordic AS (3)
Tjuvholmen Alle 3 9th Fl
NO 0252 Oslo, Norway
Tel.: (47) 22018400
Fax: (47) 22018429
E-Mail: info.no@axpo.com
Emp.: 30
Electric Power Trading
S.I.C.: 4911
N.A.I.C.S.: 221118
Hakon Rohne *(Mng Dir)*

Non-U.S. Subsidiary:

Axpo Sverige AB (4)
Stortorget 29
21134 Malmo, Sweden
Tel.: (46) 40107770
Fax: (46) 40107771
E-Mail:
Web Site: www.axpo.com
Emp.: 10
Electric Power Distribution
S.I.C.: 4939
N.A.I.C.S.: 221122
Tomas Sjoberg *(Mng Dir)*

Axpo Polska Sp.z.o.o. (3)
Al Jerozolimskie 123
02-017 Warsaw, Poland
Tel.: (48) 225297945
Fax: (48) 225297944
E-Mail: biuro.pl@axpo.com
Web Site: www.axpo.com
Emp.: 3
Electric Power Trading
S.I.C.: 4911
N.A.I.C.S.: 221122
Zbigniew Olszewski *(Mng Dir)*

Axpo UK Ltd. (3)
38 Threadneedle Street
London, EC2R 8AY, United Kingdom
Tel.: (44) 20 7448 3570
Fax: (44) 20 7374 4441
E-Mail: info.uk@axpo.com
Web Site: www.axpo.com
Electricity & Gas Distribution
S.I.C.: 4911
N.A.I.C.S.: 221122
Nick Taylor *(Mng Dir)*

Centralschweizerische Kraftwerke AG (1)
Taschmattstrasse 4
6015 Lucerne, Switzerland
Tel.: (41) 412495111
Fax: (41) 41 249 5222
E-Mail: ckw@ckw.ch
Web Site: www.ckw.ch/internet/ckw/de/home.html
CKWN—(SWX)
Electric Power Distr
S.I.C.: 4939
N.A.I.C.S.: 221122
Heinz Karrer *(Chm-Supervisory Bd)*
Andrew Walo *(Chm-Mgmt Bd & CEO)*
Beat Schlegel *(CFO)*
Heinz Beeler *(Member-Mgmt Bd)*
Felix Graf *(Member-Mgmt Bd)*

Nordostschweizerische Kraftwerke AG (1)
Parkstrasse 23
5401 Baden, Switzerland
Tel.: (41) 562003111
Fax: (41) 562003755
E-Mail: expo@nok.ch
Web Site: www.nok.com
Emp.: 25
Nuclear, Solar & Hyrdoelectric Power Generation & Distr
S.I.C.: 4939
N.A.I.C.S.: 221122
Manfred Thumann *(CEO)*
Peter Enderli *(CFO)*

Subsidiary:

Axpo Contracting AG (2)
Flughofstrasse 54
CH-8152 Glattbrugg, Switzerland (60%)
Tel.: (41) 448097444
Fax: (41) 448097400
E-Mail: contracting@axpo.ch
Web Site: www.axpo.ch
Emp.: 120
Energy Efficient Building Materials Mfr
S.I.C.: 5039

Axpo Holding AG—(Continued)

N.A.I.C.S.: 423390
Valentin Gerig *(Pres)*

AXSON TECHNOLOGIES S.A.

Rue De Lequerre
PO Box 40444
95005 Cergy, France
Tel.: (33) 134403481
Fax: (33) 134219787
E-Mail: direction@axson.com
Web Site: www.axson.com
Year Founded: 1938
Sales Range: $50-74.9 Million
Emp.: 250

Business Description:
Resin Mfr
S.I.C.: 2821
N.A.I.C.S.: 325211

Personnel:
Patrick Blosse *(VP)*

Subsidiary:

Axson France (1)
Rue De Lequerre
PO Box 444
95005 Cergy, France (100%)
Tel.: (33) 134403460
Fax: (33) 134219787
E-Mail: axson@axson.fr
Web Site: www.axson.fr
Emp.: 130
Sale & Mfr. of Epoxy & Urethane Products
S.I.C.: 2899
N.A.I.C.S.: 325998
Lionel Puget *(Pres & CEO)*

U.S. Subsidiary:

Axson North America Inc. (1)
1611 Hults Dr
Eaton Rapids, MI 48827-9500 (100%)
Tel.: (517) 663-8191
Fax: (517) 663-5035
E-Mail: info@axson-na.com
Web Site: www.axson-na.com
Emp.: 30
S.I.C.: 6141
N.A.I.C.S.: 522298
Marty Polgan *(Gen Mgr)*

Non-U.S. Subsidiaries:

Axson Iberica S.A. (1)
Ramon Turro 100 1
08005 Barcelona, Spain ES
Tel.: (34) 932251620 (100%)
Fax: (34) 932250305
E-Mail: axson@axson.es
Web Site: www.axson.es
Sales Range: $25-49.9 Million
Emp.: 12
Chemical Products Sales
S.I.C.: 5169
N.A.I.C.S.: 424690
Lina Benilosa *(Mgr-Fin)*

Axson GmbH (1)
Waldstrasse 72
63128 Dietzenbach, Germany De
Tel.: (49) 6074407110 (100%)
Fax: (49) 60744071177
E-Mail: info@axson.de
Web Site: www.axson.de
Emp.: 20
Distribution Center for Manufactured Chemicals
S.I.C.: 2899
N.A.I.C.S.: 325998
Joe Heinsch *(Gen Mgr)*

Axson Italia (1)
Via Morandi 13 15
21047 Saronno, Italy (100%)
Tel.: (39) 296702336
Fax: (39) 296702369
E-Mail: axson@axson.it
Web Site: www.axson.com
Emp.: 11
Distribution Center for Manufactured Chemicals
S.I.C.: 2899
N.A.I.C.S.: 325998

AXTEL INDUSTRIES LIMITED

Village Nurpura P O Baska
Tal Halol Dist Panchmahals, Halol, Gujarat, 389350, India
Tel.: (91) 2676 247900
Fax: (91) 2676 247125
E-Mail: factory@axtelindia.com
Web Site: www.axtelindia.com
523850—(BOM)
Sales Range: $10-24.9 Million

Business Description:
Engineering Equipment Mfr & Distr
S.I.C.: 3559
N.A.I.C.S.: 333249

Personnel:
Kirit Pathak *(Chm)*
Ajay Desai *(Compliance Officer)*

Board of Directors:
Kirit Pathak
Ajay Desai
Ajay Parikh

AXTEL, S.A.B. DE C.V.

Boulevard Diaz Ordaz Km 3.33 L1
Col Unidad San Pedro
Garza Garcia, NL, CP 66215, Mexico
Tel.: (52) 8181140000
E-Mail: contacto@axtel.com.mx
Web Site: www.axtel.mx
Year Founded: 1993
AXTELCPO—(MEX)
Rev.: $801,728,114
Assets: $1,612,966,043
Liabilities: $1,212,620,645
Net Worth: $400,345,398
Earnings: ($55,773,813)
Emp.: 6,541
Fiscal Year-end: 12/31/12

Business Description:
Local, National & International Long Distance Telecommunications & Internet Services
S.I.C.: 4813
N.A.I.C.S.: 517110

Personnel:
Alberto Santos de Hoyos *(Co-Founder)*
Lorenzo H. Zambrano Trevino *(Co-Founder)*
Tomas Milmo Santos *(Chm & CEO)*

Board of Directors:
Tomas Milmo Santos
Alberto Santos de Hoyos
Alberto Garza Santos
Fernando Angel Gonzalez Olivieri
Bernardo Guerra Trevino
Patricio Jimenez Barrera
Thomas Lorenzo Milmo Zambrano
Lorenzo H. Zambrano Trevino

Subsidiaries:

Impulsora e Inmobiliaria Regional, S.A. de C.V. (1)
Platon 307
Mexico, Mexico
Tel.: (52) 5552804206
Real Estate Agents & Brokers Offices
S.I.C.: 6531
N.A.I.C.S.: 531210

Servicios Axtel, S.A. de C.V. (1)
Blvd Diaz Ordaz Km 3 33 1er Piso
Garza Garcia, Mexico
Tel.: (52) 8181140000
Fax: (52) 8181141919
E-Mail: adelossantos@axtel.co.mx
Web Site: www.axtel.co.mx
Administrative Management & General Management Consulting Services
S.I.C.: 8742
N.A.I.C.S.: 541611
Adrian Delossantos *(Officer-IR)*

AXWAY SOFTWARE SA

26 rue des Pavillons
92807 Puteaux, Cedex, France
Tel.: (33) 1 47 17 24 24
Fax: (33) 1 47 17 22 23
Web Site: www.axway.com
Year Founded: 2001
AXW—(EUR)
Rev.: $301,972,854
Assets: $507,609,745
Liabilities: $192,671,927
Net Worth: $314,937,818
Earnings: $33,196,552
Emp.: 1,774
Fiscal Year-end: 12/31/12

Business Description:
Software Publisher
S.I.C.: 7372
N.A.I.C.S.: 511210

Personnel:
Pierre Pasquier *(Chm)*
Christophe Fabre *(CEO)*
Patrick Gouffran *(Sec & Head-IR)*
Laurent Bride *(Exec VP-R&D)*
Nick Ferrante *(Exec VP-Global Sls)*

Board of Directors:
Pierre Pasquier
Kathleen Clark Bracco
Yves De Talhouet
Herve Dechelette
Christophe Fabre
Michael Gollner
Pascal Imbert
Francois Mercadal-Delasalles
Herve Saint-Sauveur

Auditeurs & Conseils Associes
Paris, France

U.S. Subsidiary:

Axway Inc. (1)
6811 E Mayo Blvd Ste 400
Phoenix, AZ 85054
Tel.: (480) 627-1800
Fax: (480) 627-1801
E-Mail: info@us.axway.com
Web Site: www.axway.com
Emp.: 200
Collaborative Business Solutions & Services
S.I.C.: 7373
N.A.I.C.S.: 541512
Christophe Fabre *(CEO)*
Paul Shortell *(Sr VP-Pro Svcs-North America)*

Subsidiary:

Axway (2)
2600 Bridge Pkwy Ste 201
Redwood City, CA 94065 DE
Tel.: (650) 801-3100
Fax: (650) 801-3101
Toll Free: (877) 988-6253
Sales Range: $50-74.9 Million
Emp.: 120
Secure Messaging Systems Software Products for Enterprises & Government
S.I.C.: 3652
N.A.I.C.S.: 334614
Joseph Fisher *(Sr VP-Product & Solution Mktg)*

Non-U.S. Subsidiary:

Tumbleweed Communications Holding GmbH (2)
Seedammstrasse 3
Pfaffikon, 8808, Switzerland
Tel.: (41) 554174670
Business Networking Services
S.I.C.: 7389
N.A.I.C.S.: 561499

Non-U.S. Subsidiaries:

Axway Asia Pacific Pte Ltd (1)
SGX Centre 2 No 04-03 4 Shenton Way
Singapore, 068807, Singapore
Tel.: (65) 67787055
Fax: (65) 67773922
Software Development Services
S.I.C.: 7371
N.A.I.C.S.: 541511

Axway Belgium SA (1)
Blue Tower Avenue Louise Louizalaan 326 Bte 29
1050 Brussels, Belgium
Tel.: (32) 26419662
Fax: (32) 26419648
Web Site: www.axway.com
Emp.: 20
Software Publishing Services
S.I.C.: 7372
N.A.I.C.S.: 511210
Jo van Audenhove *(Gen Mgr)*

Axway Bulgaria (1)
Business Park Sofia
Mladost 4 Building 11B Floor 2, 1766 Sofia, Bulgaria
Tel.: (359) 28178300
Fax: (359) 2 817 8301
E-Mail: Ptsaneva@axway.com
Web Site: www.axway.com
Emp.: 170
Secure Messaging Systems Software Products for Enterprises & Government
S.I.C.: 7372
N.A.I.C.S.: 511210
Natasha Kumcheva *(Dir-HR)*

Axway BV (1)
Hogeweg 37 D
5301 LJ Zaltbommel, Gelderland, Netherlands
Tel.: (31) 418 576090
Fax: (31) 418 576099
E-Mail: contactnetherlands@axway.com
Web Site: www.axway.com
Emp.: 1,700
Software Development Services
S.I.C.: 7373
N.A.I.C.S.: 541512

Axway GmbH (1)
Mainzer Landstr 61
60329 Frankfurt, Germany
Tel.: (49) 692 44 50 80
Fax: (49) 69 24 45 08 21
E-Mail: contactgermany@axway.com
Emp.: 150
Software Publishing Services
S.I.C.: 7372
N.A.I.C.S.: 511210
Stephan Pleyer *(CFO)*

Axway Nordic AB (1)
Knarramasgatan 7
164 29 Kista, Sweden
Tel.: (46) 852254527
Business Networking Services
S.I.C.: 7389
N.A.I.C.S.: 561499

Axway Pte. Ltd. (1)
8 Shenton Way
31 01 Temasek Tower, Singapore, 068811, Singapore
Tel.: (65) 67787055
Fax: (65) 67773922
E-Mail: contactsingapore@axway.com
Web Site: www.axway.com
Emp.: 25
Collaborative Business Solutions & Services
S.I.C.: 7372
N.A.I.C.S.: 511210
Jean-Pierre Jay *(VP)*

Non-U.S. Subsidiaries:

Axway Limited (2)
5F 10 Pottinger Street
Hong Kong, China (Hong Kong)
Tel.: (852) 35200535
Fax: (852) 35200555
E-Mail: contacthongkong@axway.com
Web Site: www.axway.com
Emp.: 10
Collaborative Business Solutions & Services
S.I.C.: 7372
N.A.I.C.S.: 511210
Jimmy Ong *(Gen Mgr)*

Axway Software Malaysia Sdn Bhd (2)
Quill 7 27 Floor Jalan Stesen 5 Kuala Lumpur Sentral
50470 Kuala Lumpur, Malaysia
Tel.: (60) 27766800
Fax: (60) 27766999
Web Site: www.axway.com
Collaborative Business Solutions & Services
S.I.C.: 7372
N.A.I.C.S.: 511210
Jude Tan *(Reg Mgr)*

Axway Pty Ltd (1)
Level 7 100 Walker Street
North Sydney, NSW, 2060, Australia

Tel.: (61) 2 9956 4555
Web Site: www.axway.com
Emp.: 3
Software Programming Services
S.I.C.: 7371
N.A.I.C.S.: 541511

Axway Software China (1)
Room 5D Block D Central International Trade Center
Chaoyang District, Beijing, 100022, China
Tel.: (86) 1065630081
Fax: (86) 10 6567 6399
Software Publishing Services
S.I.C.: 7372
N.A.I.C.S.: 511210

Axway Software GmbH (1)
Kurfurstendamm 119
10711 Berlin, Germany
Tel.: (49) 30890100
Fax: (49) 3089010100
E-Mail: contactgermany@axway.com
Web Site: www.axway.com
Collaborative Business Solutions & Services
S.I.C.: 7372
N.A.I.C.S.: 511210
Joerg Braehmig *(VP-Sls & Ops)*

Axway Srl (1)
Strada 4
20090 Assago, Milan, Italy
Tel.: (39) 0248048901
Fax: (39) 0248028337
Web Site: www.axway.it
Software Development Services
S.I.C.: 7371
N.A.I.C.S.: 541511

Axway UK Ltd (1)
Teal House 3 Cowley Business Park
Uxbridge, Middlesex, UB8 2AD, United Kingdom
Tel.: (44) 1895202780
Fax: (44) 1895255234
Web Site: www.axway.com
Emp.: 50
Information Technology Consulting Services
S.I.C.: 7373
N.A.I.C.S.: 541512

AXXESS CAPITAL

33 Aviatorilor Blvd
011853 Bucharest, Romania
Tel.: (40) 212077100
Fax: (40) 212228503
E-Mail: office@axxesscapital.net
Web Site: www.axxesscapital.net
Emp.: 20

Business Description:
Private Equity Firm
S.I.C.: 6211
N.A.I.C.S.: 523999

Personnel:
Horia D. Manda *(Mng Partner)*

Holding:

Frigotehnica S.A. (1)
2 4 Torentului Str Sector
021806 Bucharest, Romania
Tel.: (40) 212502053
Fax: (40) 212507920
E-Mail: office@frigotehnica.ro
Web Site: www.frigotehnica.ro
Sales Range: $50-74.9 Million
Commercial & Industrial Refrigeration Equipment Mfr
S.I.C.: 3585
N.A.I.C.S.: 333415

AXXICON GROUP NV

Ekkersrijy 7501
5692 HN Eindhoven, Son, Netherlands
Tel.: (31) 499 491150
Fax: (31) 499 461361
Web Site: www.axxicon.com
Emp.: 650

Business Description:
Development, Production, Marketing & Sale of Molds & Plastic Products
S.I.C.: 3089
N.A.I.C.S.: 326199

Personnel:
Joyce Hegge-Vogels *(Mgr-Mktg & Sls)*

Subsidiaries:

Axxicon Mould Technology (1)
Ekkersrijt 7501
5692 HN Son, Netherlands (100%)
Tel.: (31) 499 494450
Fax: (31) 499 461361
E-Mail: helmond@axxicon.com
Web Site: www.axxicon.com
Emp.: 450
High-Tech Precision Injection Microfluidic Consumables Mfr
S.I.C.: 3544
N.A.I.C.S.: 333511
Joyce Hegge-Cogels *(Mgr-Mktg & Sls)*

Axxicon Moulds Eindhoven B.V. (1)
Ekkersrijt 7501
PO Box 1717
NL 5602 BS Eindhoven, Netherlands (100%)
Tel.: (31) 499494450
Fax: (31) 499461361
E-Mail: eindhoven@axxicon.com
Web Site: www.axxicon.com
Emp.: 33
S.I.C.: 3589
N.A.I.C.S.: 333318
Alfred Edvers *(Mng Dir)*

U.S. Subsidiary:

Axxicon Molds Los Angeles Inc. (1)
1100 S Coast Hwy Ste 309
Laguna Beach, CA 92651
Tel.: (949) 360-9400
Fax: (949) 715-4819
Web Site: www.axxicon.com
Development, Production, Marketing & Sale of Molds & Plastic Products
S.I.C.: 3089
N.A.I.C.S.: 326199
Jan Nietsch *(Reg Mgr-Asia)*

Non-U.S. Subsidiary:

Axxicon Moulds Hong Kong Ltd. (1)
Unit B 2/F Room 205 Hing Yip Factory Building 31 Hing Yip Street
Kwun Tong, Kowloon, China (Hong Kong)
Tel.: (852) 2424 4003
Fax: (852) 2424 0503
Web Site: www.axxicon.com
Development, Production, Marketing & Sale of Molds & Plastic Products
S.I.C.: 3089
N.A.I.C.S.: 326199
Jan Nietsch *(Reg Mgr)*

AXXIS INTERNATIONAL LTD.

Aintree Avenue
White Horse Business Park,
Trowbridge, Wiltshire, BA14 0XB, United Kingdom
Tel.: (44) 1225768491
Fax: (44) 1225716100
Web Site: www.lfbeauty-uk.com
Year Founded: 1980
Emp.: 650

Business Description:
Personal Care & Household Products Mfr
S.I.C.: 7299
N.A.I.C.S.: 812199

Personnel:
Gary Armstrong *(Mng Dir)*

Subsidiary:

Lamberts Healthcare Ltd. (1)
1 Lamberts Rd
Century Pl, Tunbridge Wells, TN2 3EH, United Kingdom (100%)
Tel.: (44) 1892552121
Fax: (44) 0892515863
E-Mail: ordering@lambertshealthcare.co.uk
Web Site: www.lambertshealthcare.co.uk
Emp.: 50
Nutritional Supplement Mfr
S.I.C.: 2099
N.A.I.C.S.: 311991
John Redman *(Mng Dir)*

AXXON WERTPAPIERHANDELSBANK AG

Hafenstrasse 54
60327 Frankfurt, Germany
Tel.: (49) 6924702880
Fax: (49) 6924702850
E-Mail: info@axxon-wphbank.de
Web Site: www.axxon-wphbank.de
Emp.: 12

Business Description:
Bank
S.I.C.: 6159
N.A.I.C.S.: 522298

AYA KITCHENS & BATHS, LTD.

1551 Caterpillar Road
Mississauga, ON, L4X 2Z6, Canada
Tel.: (905) 848-1999
Fax: (905) 848-5127
Toll Free: (866) 292-4968
E-Mail: info@ayakitchens.com
Web Site: www.ayakitchens.com
Year Founded: 2000
Rev.: $11,979,030
Emp.: 150

Business Description:
Wood Kitchen Cabinets Mfr
S.I.C.: 2434
N.A.I.C.S.: 337110

Personnel:
Dave Marcus *(Pres)*

AYALA CORPORATION

34F Tower One Ayala Triangle Ayala Avenue
Makati, 1226, Philippines
Tel.: (63) 2 848 5643
Fax: (63) 2 848 5846
E-Mail: acquery@ayala.com.ph
Web Site: www.ayala.com.ph
Year Founded: 1834
AC—(OTC PHI)
Rev.: $3,063,065,909
Assets: $11,959,082,091
Liabilities: $6,975,478,790
Net Worth: $4,983,603,301
Earnings: $459,958,715
Emp.: 112
Fiscal Year-end: 12/31/12

Business Description:
Holding Company
S.I.C.: 6719
N.A.I.C.S.: 551112

Personnel:
Jaime Augusto Zobel de Ayala, II *(Chm & CEO)*
Fernando Zobel de Ayala *(Vice Chm, Pres & COO)*
Gerardo C. Ablaza, Jr. *(Pres/CEO-Manila Water Company & Sr Mng Dir)*
Antonino T. Aquino *(Pres/CEO-Ayala Land Inc & Sr Mng Dir)*
Arthur R. Tan *(Pres/CEO-Integrated Micro Electronics Inc & Sr Mng Dir)*
Aurelio R. Montinola, III *(Sr Mng Dir)*
Delfin C. Gonzalez, Jr. *(CFO & Mng Dir)*
Solomon M. Hermosura *(Mng Dir, Compliance Officer, Gen Counsel, Sec & Head-Legal)*
Ramon G. Opulencia *(Treas & Mng Dir)*
John Eric T. Francia *(Mng Dir & Head-Corp Strategy & Dev)*
John Philip S. Orbeta *(Mng Dir & Head-Corp Resources)*
Ginaflor C. Oris *(Mng Dir & Head-Corp Fin & Asset Mgmt)*
Maria Angelica B. Rapadas *(CIO & Assoc Dir)*
Cezar Peralta Consing *(Pres/CEO-Bank of the Philippine Islands)*
Ernest Lawrence Cu *(Pres/CEO-Globe Telecomm)*
Gil B. Genio *(Pres-Innove Comm)*
Maria Lourdes Heras-de Leon *(Pres-Ayala Foundation Inc)*
Jose Teodoro K. Limcaoco *(Pres-BPI Family Savings Bank Inc)*
Jaime P. Villegas *(Pres-Ayala Aviation Corporation)*
Alfredo I. Ayala *(CEO-LiveIt Investments Ltd)*

Board of Directors:
Jaime Augusto Zobel de Ayala, II
Yoshio Amano
Ramon R. del Rosario, Jr.
Delfin Lapus Lazaro
Xavier P. Loinaz
Antonio Jose U. Periquet
Fernando Zobel de Ayala

Transfer Agent:
BPI Stock Transfer Services
Makati, Philippines

Subsidiaries:

Ayala Automotive Holdings Corporation (1)
34F Tower One
Ayala Triangle Ayala Avenue, Makati, 1226, Philippines
Tel.: (63) 28485643
Fax: (63) 28485846
Web Site: www.ayala.com.ph
Holding Company; Car Dealerships
S.I.C.: 6719
N.A.I.C.S.: 551112
Rufino Luis T. Manotok *(Chm & CEO)*
Jenara Rosanna F. Ong *(CFO)*

Subsidiaries:

Honda Cars Makati, Inc. (2)
Magallanes Commercial Center
Makati, 1232, Philippines
Tel.: (63) 9029393
Fax: (63) 28526593
Web Site: www.hondamakati.com.ph
Car Dealership
S.I.C.: 5511
N.A.I.C.S.: 441110
Ramon M. Zialcita *(Gen Mgr)*

Isuzu Automotive Dealership, Inc. (2)
Alabang-Zapote Road corner Acacia Avenue
Ayala Alabang, Muntinlupa, 1780, Philippines
Tel.: (63) 28071788
Fax: (63) 28071787
E-Mail: customer-relations@isuzualabans.com
Web Site: www.isuzuautodealer.com.ph
Emp.: 165
Car Dealership
S.I.C.: 5511
N.A.I.C.S.: 441110
Rene D. Paningbatan *(Gen Mgr)*

Ayala Aviation Corporation (1)
Ayala Hangar
Domestic Airport, Pasay, 1301, Philippines (100%)
Tel.: (63) 28323595
Fax: (63) 28537693
Emp.: 20
Aviation Services
S.I.C.: 4581
N.A.I.C.S.: 488190
Carlos Reyes *(Pres)*
Tess Paleao *(CFO)*

Ayala Foundation, Inc. (1)
10th Fl BPI Main Bldg Ayala Ave Corner Paseo and De Roxas
Makati, Metro Manila, 1226, Philippines (100%)
Tel.: (63) 27521101
Fax: (63) 28134488
E-Mail: info@ayala.org
Web Site: www.ayalafoundation.org
Emp.: 50
Charitable Grant Services
S.I.C.: 6732
N.A.I.C.S.: 813211
Maria Lourdes Heras-de Leon *(Pres)*

Ayala Corporation—(Continued)

Ayala Hotels, Inc. (1)
19 Fl Tower 1 Bldg
Ayala Ave, 1226 Makati, Philippines(76.8%)
Tel.: (63) 27517711
Fax: (63) 28105175
Web Site: www.ayalahotels.com.ph
Emp.: 6
S.I.C.: 7011
N.A.I.C.S.: 721199
Jose Emmanuel Jalandoni *(Pres)*

Ayala Land, Inc. (1)
Tower 1 & Exchange Plaza Ayala Triangle
PO Box 1902
6750 Ayala Avenue, Makati, Metro Manila, 1226, Philippines (53.5%)
Tel.: (63) 28485643
Fax: (63) 2 848 5336
Web Site: www.ayalaland.com.ph
Emp.: 25
Property Development
S.I.C.: 6531
N.A.I.C.S.: 531210
Fernando Zobel de Ayala *(Chm)*
Antonino T. Aquino *(Pres & CEO)*
Jaime E. Ysmael *(CFO & Sr VP)*

Affiliate:

Cebu Holdings Inc. (2)
7/F Cebu Holdings Center Cardinal Rosales Avenue Cebu Business Park
Cebu, 6000, Philippines (47.06%)
Tel.: (63) 322315301
Fax: (63) 322315300
E-Mail: customer_care@cebuholdings.com
Web Site: www.cebuholdings.com
CHI—(PHI)
Rev.: $39,993,003
Assets: $238,754,553
Liabilities: $109,392,348
Net Worth: $129,362,205
Earnings: $11,575,345
Emp.: 107
Fiscal Year-end: 12/31/12
Real Estate Ownership, Development, Marketing & Management
S.I.C.: 6531
N.A.I.C.S.: 531210
Antonino T. Aquino *(Chm)*
Francis O. Monera *(Pres)*
Enrique B. Manuel, Jr. *(CFO & Compliance Officer)*
Ma. Theresa M. Javier *(Treas)*
Sheila Marie U. Tan *(Sec)*

Darong Agricultural & Development Corporation (1)
33rd Fl Twr One Ayala Triangle Ave
Makati, Philippines (100%)
Tel.: (63) 8415421
Fax: (63) 7594412
E-Mail: azurin.fab@ayala.com.ph
Agricultural Production Services
S.I.C.: 0762
N.A.I.C.S.: 115116

Integrated Microelectronics, Inc. (1)
North Science Avenue Special Export Processing Zone Laguna Technopark
Binan, Laguna, 4024, Philippines (67.8%)
Tel.: (63) 27566940
Fax: (63) 495440322
E-Mail: sales@global-imi.com
Web Site: www.global-imi.com
IMI—(PHI)
Rev.: $661,849,722
Assets: $455,294,581
Liabilities: $264,180,898
Net Worth: $191,113,683
Earnings: $789,755
Emp.: 15,000
Fiscal Year-end: 12/31/12
Integrated Electronics Mfr
S.I.C.: 3679
N.A.I.C.S.: 334418
Jaime Augusto Zobel de Ayala, II *(Chm)*
Arthur R. Tan *(Pres & CEO)*
Emmanuel V. Barcelon *(COO)*
Frederick L. Blancas *(Corp Info Officer)*

Livelt Investments, Inc. (1)
33/F Tower One Ayala Triangle
Ayala Avenue, Makati, Philippines
Tel.: (63) 848 5643
Sales Range: $300-349.9 Million
Holding Company; Business Process Outsourcing Products & Services
S.I.C.: 6719
N.A.I.C.S.: 551112
Alfredo I. Ayala *(CEO)*

Subsidiary:

HRMall Inc. (2)
2nd Level Street Market
Fort Bonifacio Global City, Taguig, 1634, Philippines
Tel.: (63) 2 9760308
Fax: (63) 7297552
E-Mail: scoles@hrmall.com.ph
Web Site: www.hrmall.asia
Emp.: 30
Human Resources Business Process Outsourcing Services
S.I.C.: 7389
N.A.I.C.S.: 561499
Elisa Villanueva *(Gen Mgr)*

U.S. Subsidiary:

IQ BackOffice, Inc. (3)
2121 Rosecrans Ave Ste 3350
El Segundo, CA 90245 CA
Tel.: (310) 322-2311
E-Mail: contact@iqbackoffice.com
Web Site: www.iqbackoffice.com
Emp.: 200
Finance, Accounting & Human Resources Outsourcing Services
S.I.C.: 7389
N.A.I.C.S.: 561499
David Schnitt *(CEO)*
Gilbert Santa Maria *(COO & CFO)*
Phil Jablonski *(CTO)*

U.S. Subsidiaries:

Affinity Express, Inc. (2)
2200 Point Blvd Ste 130
Elgin, IL 60123
Tel.: (847) 930-3200
Fax: (847) 930-3299
Web Site: www.affinityexpress.com
Sales Range: $10-24.9 Million
Emp.: 1,000
Advertising, Graphic Designing & Marketing Services
S.I.C.: 7319
N.A.I.C.S.: 541890
Kenneth W. Swanson *(CEO)*

Integreon Managed Solutions, Inc. (2)
1901 Ave of the Stars Ste 1080
Los Angeles, CA 90067 NY
Tel.: (310) 788-9009
Toll Free: (866) 312-7023
E-Mail: info@integreon.com
Web Site: www.integreon.com
Sales Range: $125-149.9 Million
Emp.: 2,000
Corporate Legal, Accounting, Research & Document Preparation Services
S.I.C.: 7389
N.A.I.C.S.: 561499
Liam Brown *(Pres & CEO)*
Richard Little *(CFO & Chief Admin Officer)*
Colin Gounden *(CMO)*
John Croft *(Pres-Global Sls)*

Unit:

Electronic Evidence Labs (3)
2011 Crystal Dr Ste 200
Arlington, VA 22202
Tel.: (703) 276-1123
Toll Free: (877) 4EELABS
Web Site: www.eevidencelabs.com
Computer Forensics, Data Recovery, Password Recovery & Tape Restoration
S.I.C.: 7371
N.A.I.C.S.: 541511
Jeffery Fehrman *(Pres)*

Joint Venture:

NCSI (Philippines) Inc. (1)
9/F Corporate Center 139 Valero Street
Salcedo Village, Makati, 1227, Philippines
Tel.: (63) 27931400
Fax: (63) 28132493
E-Mail: info@ayalasystems.com
Web Site: www.ayalasystems.com
Sales Range: $1-9.9 Million
Emp.: 100
Systems Integration & Information Technology Services
S.I.C.: 7373
N.A.I.C.S.: 541512
Leila Verceles *(Pres & Mng Dir)*

Subsidiary:

GlobalBridge Resources Corporation (2)
15F Corporate Center 139 Valero St
Salcedo Village, Makati, 1227, Philippines
Tel.: (63) 2 793 1447
Fax: (63) 2 813 2493
E-Mail: sales@globalbridgeresources.com
Web Site: www.globalbridgeresources.com
Corporate Human Resource Support Services
S.I.C.: 8999
N.A.I.C.S.: 541612
Emma Martinez *(Gen Mgr)*

Non-U.S. Subsidiary:

Ayala International Pte. Ltd. (1)
Raffles City Twr 32 03A
250 Northbridge Rd, Singapore, 179101, Singapore
Tel.: (65) 63392886
Fax: (65) 63115160
Web Site: www.ayala.com
Emp.: 6
Holding Company
S.I.C.: 6719
N.A.I.C.S.: 551112
Fernando Zobel de Ayala *(Chm)*
Charles H. Cosgrove *(Pres)*
Poshwan Toh *(Sec)*

AYERS EXPLORATION INC.

6 Harston Avenue
Mosman, Sydney, NSW, 2088, Australia
Tel.: (61) 411199319
Web Site: www.ayersexploration.com
Year Founded: 2006
AYXE—(OTC)
Assets: $290
Liabilities: $18,197
Net Worth: ($17,907)
Earnings: ($31,780)
Fiscal Year-end: 12/31/12

Business Description:
Mineral Clay Exploration Services
S.I.C.: 1459
N.A.I.C.S.: 212325

Personnel:
Bruce Drury *(Pres, CEO, CFO & Treas)*

AYIMA LIMITED

2nd Floor 1 Benjamin Street
London, EC1M 5QG, United Kingdom
Tel.: (44) 207 148 5970
E-Mail: contactus@ayima.com
Web Site: www.ayima.com
Year Founded: 2002
Sales Range: $10-24.9 Million
Emp.: 30

Business Description:
Webpage Development Services
S.I.C.: 7371
N.A.I.C.S.: 541511

Personnel:
Rob Kerry *(Co-Founder)*
Mike Jacobson *(CEO & Mng Dir)*

AYLEN CAPITAL INC.

Suite 3800 Royal Bank Plaza South Tower 200 Bay Street
Toronto, ON, M5J 2Z4, Canada
Tel.: (416) 596-4926
Fax: (416) 216-3930
Web Site: www.aylencapital.com
Year Founded: 2010
AYL—(CNSX)
Rev.: $674,595
Assets: $2,352,458
Liabilities: $1,017,430
Net Worth: $1,335,028
Earnings: ($141,246)
Fiscal Year-end: 12/31/12

Business Description:
Investment Services
S.I.C.: 6211
N.A.I.C.S.: 523999

Personnel:
John Pennal *(Pres & CEO)*
Jenifer Cho *(CFO & Dir-Fin)*
Richard Sutin *(Sec)*

Board of Directors:
Douglas Babcook
Brian Hemming
John Pennal

AYLESFORD NEWSPRINT HOLDINGS LTD.

Newsprint House Bellingham Way
Aylesford, Kent, ME20 7DL, United Kingdom
Tel.: (44) 1622 796 000
Fax: (44) 1622 796 001
E-Mail: info@aylesford-newsprint.co.uk
Web Site: www.aylesford-newsprint.co.uk
Year Founded: 1993
Emp.: 380

Business Description:
Holding Company; Newsprint Mills Operator
S.I.C.: 6719
N.A.I.C.S.: 551112

Personnel:
Ian Richard Broxup *(Acting Mng Dir)*

Subsidiary:

Aylesford Newsprint Limited (1)
Newsprint House Bellingham Way
Aylesford, Kent, ME20 7DL, United Kingdom UK
Tel.: (44) 1622 796 000
Fax: (44) 1622 796 001
E-Mail: info@aylesford-newsprint.co.uk
Web Site: www.aylesford-newsprint.co.uk
Newsprint Mills
S.I.C.: 2621
N.A.I.C.S.: 322122
Ian Richard Broxup *(Acting Mng Dir)*

AYOUBCO GENERAL CONTRACTING

31a Ahmed Hishmat St
Zamalek, Cairo, 11211, Egypt
Tel.: (20) 27363900
Fax: (20) 27364721
E-Mail: ayoubco@ayoubco.com
Web Site: www.ayoubco.com
Year Founded: 1941
Emp.: 400

Business Description:
Construction Services
S.I.C.: 1611
N.A.I.C.S.: 237310

Personnel:
Ayoub Adly Ayoub *(Chm)*

AYR MOTOR EXPRESS INC.

46 Poplar Street
Woodstock, NB, E7M 4G2, Canada
Tel.: (506) 325-2205
Fax: (506) 325-2200
Toll Free: (800) 668-0099
Web Site: www.ayrmotor.com
Year Founded: 1990
Rev.: $35,613,600
Emp.: 300

Business Description:
Truck Transportation Services
S.I.C.: 4213
N.A.I.C.S.: 484122

Personnel:
Joe Keenan *(Owner & Pres)*

AYRTON DRUGS MANUFACTURING COMPANY LIMITED

PO Box 2149
Accra, Ghana

Tel.: (233) 21245090
Fax: (233) 21241804
E-Mail: info@ayrtondrugs.com
Web Site: www.ayrtondrugs.com
Year Founded: 1965
AYRTN—(GHA)
Sales Range: $10-24.9 Million
Business Description:
Pharmaceutical Mfr
S.I.C.: 2834
N.A.I.C.S.: 325412
Personnel:
Richard Adu-Poku *(Chm)*
Samuel Adjepong *(CEO)*
Opoku Amponsah *(Sec)*
Board of Directors:
Richard Adu-Poku
Frances Jane Adjepong
Samuel Adjepong
Yaw Adu-Gyamfi
Opoku Amponsah
Frank Amoako Boateng
Belinda Opoku
Linda Sangari

AZ ELECTRONIC MATERIALS S.A.

32-36 Boulevard D'azranches
L 1160 Luxembourg, Luxembourg
Tel.: (352) 2649791116
Fax: (352) 2649798888
E-Mail: company.secretary@az-em.com
Web Site: www.azem.com
AZEM—(LSE)
Rev.: $793,900,000
Assets: $1,565,800,000
Liabilities: $807,100,000
Net Worth: $758,700,000
Earnings: $82,900,000
Emp.: 1,092
Fiscal Year-end: 12/31/12
Business Description:
Electronic Materials Mfr
S.I.C.: 2899
N.A.I.C.S.: 325998
Personnel:
Geoffrey Wild *(CEO)*
Mike Powell *(CFO)*
Ralph Dammel *(CTO)*
Kenji Takeuchi *(Pres-Japan & Head-Mktg-Global)*
Michael Arnaouti *(Sec)*
Board of Directors:
John W. Whybrow
Andrew J. Allner
Adrian Auer
Gerald G. Ermentrout
Philana W. Y. Poon
Mike Powell
David J. Price
Geoffrey Wild

U.S. Subsidiary:

AZ Electronic Materials USA Corp. (1)
70 Meister Ave
Branchburg, NJ 08876-3440
Tel.: (908) 429-3500
Fax: (908) 429-3635
Toll Free: (800) 515-4164
E-Mail: az-info@az-em.com
Web Site: www.az-em.com
Emp.: 800
Electronic Materials Mfr
S.I.C.: 2899
N.A.I.C.S.: 325998
Munirathna Padmanaban *(Dir-R&D)*

Non-U.S. Subsidiaries:

AZ Electronic Materials France SAS (1)
1 rue du Flottage
BP 15
60350 Trosly-Breuil, France
Tel.: (33) 344855020
Fax: (33) 344865185
E-Mail: celine.weisz@az-em.com
Web Site: www.az-em.com
Emp.: 40
Electronic Materials Mfr
S.I.C.: 2899
N.A.I.C.S.: 325998
Emmanuel Viguier *(Gen Mgr)*

AZ Electronic Materials (Germany) GmbH (1)
Rheingaustrasse 190 196
65203 Wiesbaden, Germany
Tel.: (49) 6119628563
Fax: (49) 6119629207
Web Site: www.ac-em.com
Electronic Materials Mfr
S.I.C.: 2899
N.A.I.C.S.: 325998

AZ Electronic Materials Hong Kong Limited (1)
Ste 601 2 Li Po Chun Chambers
189 Des Voeux Rd Central, Sheung Wan, China (Hong Kong)
Tel.: (852) 31960000
Fax: (852) 25062529
E-Mail: service.hk@az-em.com
Web Site: www.az-em.com
Emp.: 20
Electronic Materials Mfr
S.I.C.: 2899
N.A.I.C.S.: 325998
Anand Nambiar *(Dir-Ops)*

AZ Electronic Materials (Japan) K.K. (1)
Bunkyo Green Court Center Office 9F 2 28 8 Honkomagome
Bunkyo ku, Tokyo, 113 0021, Japan
Tel.: (81) 359777917
Fax: (81) 359777886
Web Site: www.az-em.com
Electronic Materials Mfr
S.I.C.: 2899
N.A.I.C.S.: 325998

AZ Electronic Materials (Korea) Ltd. (1)
325 25 Boche Ri Miyang Myeon
Anseong, 456 843, Korea (South)
Tel.: (82) 316708451
Fax: (82) 316776900
E-Mail: bumyoung.choi@az-em.com
Web Site: www.az-em.com
Emp.: 100
Electronic Materials Mfr
S.I.C.: 2899
N.A.I.C.S.: 325998

AZ Electronic Materials Services Ltd. (1)
Lakeside House 1 Furzeground Way
Stockley Park, Uxbridge, Middlesex, UB11 1BD, United Kingdom
Tel.: (44) 2086223385
Fax: (44) 2086223159
Web Site: www.az-em.com
Emp.: 40
Electronic Materials Mfr
S.I.C.: 2899
N.A.I.C.S.: 325998
Majid Nazir *(Head-IR)*

AZ Electronic Materials (Shanghai) Company Limited (1)
Room 905-906 Bldg B 1289 Yi Shan Rd
Shanghai, 200233, China
Tel.: (86) 2164751700
Fax: (86) 2164753203
E-Mail: service.china@az-em.com
Web Site: www.az-em.com
Emp.: 28
Electronic Materials Mfr & Distr
S.I.C.: 2899
N.A.I.C.S.: 325998

AZ Electronic Materials (Singapore) Pte. Ltd. (1)
No 2 International Business Park 11 04 The Strategy
Singapore, 609930, Singapore
Tel.: (65) 6316 7971
Fax: (65) 6316 7621
Electronic Materials Mfr
S.I.C.: 2899
N.A.I.C.S.: 325998

AZ Electronic Materials (Suzhou) Ltd. (1)
70 Long Pu Road
Suzhou Industrial Park, Suzhou, 215 021, China
Tel.: (86) 51262836220
Fax: (86) 51262836227
E-Mail: WenBing.Kang@az-em.com
Web Site: www.az-en.com
Electronic Materials Mfr
S.I.C.: 2899
N.A.I.C.S.: 325998
Sui Yu *(Gen Mgr)*

AZ Electronic Materials Taiwan Co., Ltd. (1)
5th Floor 96 Chien Kuo North Road
Section 1, Taipei, 104, Taiwan
Tel.: (886) 2 2516 3268
Fax: (886) 2 2516 5186
Web Site: www.az-em.com
Emp.: 20
Electronic Materials Mfr
S.I.C.: 2899
N.A.I.C.S.: 325998
Mike Douglas *(Pres)*

AZABACHE ENERGY INC.

Suite 910 521 - 3rd Avenue SW
Calgary, AB, T2P 3T3, Canada
Tel.: (403) 213-2937
Fax: (403) 252-0999
E-Mail: info@azaenergy.com
Web Site: www.azaenergy.com
Year Founded: 2005
AZA—(TSXV)
Assets: $23,953,635
Liabilities: $2,771,697
Net Worth: $21,181,938
Earnings: ($8,154,189)
Fiscal Year-end: 06/30/13
Business Description:
Oil & Gas Exploration & Development Services
S.I.C.: 1311
N.A.I.C.S.: 211111
Personnel:
Glenn Van Doorne *(Chm)*
Claudio A. Larotonda *(Pres & CEO)*
Mark Hopkins *(CFO)*
Ron Panchuk *(Sec)*
Board of Directors:
Glenn Van Doorne
Claudio A. Larotonda
Luis Miguel Morelli
Bill Wheeler
Legal Counsel:
Gamboa Chalela Gamboa
Cra 9 No 70-35 Piso 7
Bogota, Colombia

Brons & Salas
Maipu 1210 Piso 5
C1006ACT Buenos Aires, Argentina
Transfer Agent:
Equity Transfer & Trust Company
200 University Avenue Ste 400
Toronto, ON, M5H 4H1, Canada
Tel.: (416) 361-0152
Fax: (416) 361-0470

Non-U.S. Subsidiaries:

Argenta Energia S.A. (1)
Florida 890 Fl 18
C1003ABV Buenos Aires, Argentina
Tel.: (54) 1148934004
Fax: (54) 1148934004
E-Mail: info@argentaenergia.com
Web Site: www.acaenergia.com
Emp.: 15
Oil & Gas Field Exploration Services
S.I.C.: 1389
N.A.I.C.S.: 213112
Tlauvio Larotonda *(Mgr)*

Argenta Oil and Gas T&T Limited (1)
81 A Bel Air Dr
P O Box 7743
La Romaine, San Fernando, Trinidad & Tobago
Tel.: (868) 6521786
Fax: (868) 6521848
Oil & Gas Field Exploration Services
S.I.C.: 1389
N.A.I.C.S.: 213112
Jorge Graterol *(Gen Mgr)*

AZARBAIJAN INVESTMENT DEVELOPMENT COMPANY

No3 6th 10m st Next to Talaiyeh
Complex Parvin Etesami st
Manzariyeh, Tabriz, Iran
Tel.: (98) 411 4784057
Fax: (98) 411 4784058
E-Mail: info@azarbayjanid.com
Web Site: www.azarbayjanid.com
Year Founded: 1996
TAZB—(THE)
Business Description:
Investment Services
S.I.C.: 6211
N.A.I.C.S.: 523999
Personnel:
Mohammad-Hossein Aghasi Javid *(Chm)*
Khalil Gholipour Khalili *(Mng Dir)*
Board of Directors:
Mohammad-Hossein Aghasi Javid
B. Omid Ali
Djavadzadeh Asl
Ali Bakhshayesh
Khalil Gholipour Khalili
A. Mehdizadeh Mortazavi
Davoud Nadim

Subsidiary:

Coolack Shargh Company (P.J.S) (1)
KM24 Tehran Road
54951-18657 Tabriz, Iran
Tel.: (98) 411 6306434
Fax: (98) 411 6306803
E-Mail: info@coolackshargh.com
Web Site: www.coolackshargh.com
Soft Drink Mfr
S.I.C.: 2086
N.A.I.C.S.: 312111
Seyed Mohammad Majdoleslami, *(Mng Dir)*

AZARIT COMPANY

9 Unit - 3rd Floor - 17 No - Toward
To Shariati St Taleghani St
Postal Code 15636-74843
Tehran, Iran
Tel.: (98) 21 77536836
Fax: (98) 21 77533049
E-Mail: info@azaritco.com
Web Site: www.azaritco.com
Year Founded: 1974
AZRT—(THE)
Business Description:
Fiber Cement Product Mfr
S.I.C.: 3241
N.A.I.C.S.: 327310
Personnel:
V. Akhlaghi Fard *(Chm)*
Saeid Safdari *(Deputy Chm)*
Board of Directors:
V. Akhlaghi Fard
Abd Alreza Esmaeli Danesh
Javad SaatSaz Maghrebi
Saeid Safdari
Ali Tadayoun

AZBIL CORPORATION

19F Tokyo Building 2-7-3 Marunouchi
Chiyoda-ku, Tokyo, 100-6419, Japan
Tel.: (81) 368101000
Fax: (81) 352207270
Web Site: www.azbil.com
Year Founded: 1906
6845—(TKS)
Sls.: $2,503,435,000
Assets: $2,677,609,000
Liabilities: $1,124,442,000
Net Worth: $1,553,167,000
Earnings: $91,399,000

Azbil Corporation—(Continued)

Emp.: 5,335
Fiscal Year-end: 03/31/13

Business Description:
Holding Company
S.I.C.: 6719
N.A.I.C.S.: 551112

Personnel:
Seiji Onoki *(Chm)*
Hirozumi Sone *(Pres & CEO)*
Hiroshi Arai *(Exec Officer)*
Kazuyasu Hamada *(Exec Officer)*
Seiichiro Hayashi *(Exec Officer)*
Kenji Hidaka *(Mng Exec Officer)*
Yoshimitsu Hojo *(Exec Officer)*
Hirohiko Kazato *(Exec Officer)*
Ichio Kunii *(Mng Exec Officer)*
Mitsuharu Miyazawa *(Mng Exec Officer)*
Norio Murase *(Exec Officer)*
Kenji Okumura *(Exec Officer)*
Hiroshi Shimizu *(Exec Officer)*
Nobuo Shimizu *(Exec Officer)*
Yoshihide Sugino *(Mng Exec Officer)*
Yoshifumi Suzuki *(Exec Officer)*
Haruo Tamura *(Exec Officer)*
Michihiro Tomonaga *(Exec Officer)*

Board of Directors:
Seiji Onoki
Keiichi Fuwa
Masato Iwasaki
Makoto Kawai
Eugene H. Lee
Tadayuki Sasaki
Hirozumi Sone
Katsuhiko Tanabe
Makoto Yasuda

Transfer Agent:
Mizuho Trust & Banking Co., Ltd
1-17-7 Saga Koto-ku
Tokyo, Japan

Subsidiaries:

Azbil Care & Support Co., Ltd. (1)
1-3-5 Sanno
Ota-ku, Tokyo, 143-0023, Japan JP
Tel.: (81) 3 5718 9226
Fax: (81) 3 5718 9210
Web Site: www.acs.azbil.com
Homage & Health Care Services
S.I.C.: 8082
N.A.I.C.S.: 621610

Azbil Kimmon Co., Ltd. (1)
1-14-3 Kitaotsuka
Toshima-ku, Tokyo, 170-0004, Japan JP
Tel.: (81) 359803730
Fax: (81) 359803754
Web Site: www.ak.azbil.com
Emp.: 1,300
Meters & Electrical Equipments Mfr
S.I.C.: 3823
N.A.I.C.S.: 334513
Masaaki Iwai *(Pres)*

Azbil Kyoto Co., Ltd. (1)
1-3 Ichinodani Kamadanishimo Kyotanbacho
Funai-gun, Kyoto, 622-0442, Japan JP
Tel.: (81) 771870560
Fax: (81) 771870570
Web Site: www.akt.azbil.com
Emp.: 54
Flow Measurement Instruments Mfr & Flowmeter Calibration Facility
S.I.C.: 3824
N.A.I.C.S.: 334514

Azbil RoyalControls Co., Ltd. (1)
1-14-3 Kitaotsuka
Toshima-ku, Tokyo, 170-0004, Japan JP
Tel.: (81) 3 3576 6951
Fax: (81) 3 3576 6958
Web Site: www.arc.azbil.com
Emp.: 129
Automation & Control Equipment Whslr
S.I.C.: 5084
N.A.I.C.S.: 423830
Susumu Taniyama *(Pres)*

Azbil Trading Co., Ltd. (1)
1-14-3 Kitaotsuka
Toshima-ku, Tokyo, 170-0004, Japan JP
Tel.: (81) 3 5961 2140
Fax: (81) 3 5961 2181
Web Site: www.as.azbil.com
Emp.: 209
Automation & Control Equipment Distr
S.I.C.: 5084
N.A.I.C.S.: 423830
Kouichi Kamisawa *(Pres)*

TACO Co., Ltd. (1)
9-27-9 Takashimadaira
Itabashi-ku, Tokyo, 175-0082, Japan JP
Tel.: (81) 3 3936 2311 (100%)
Fax: (81) 3 3935 9121
E-Mail: intl@taco-ltd.com
Web Site: www.taco-ltd.com
Fluid Control Equipment Designer & Mfr
S.I.C.: 3594
N.A.I.C.S.: 333996
Tokiaki Ogawa *(Pres)*

Joint Venture:

Japan Facility Solutions, Inc. (1)
1-18 Agebacho
Tokyo, Shinjuku-ku, 162-0824, Japan
Tel.: (81) 352292911
Fax: (81) 352292912
E-Mail: info@j-facility.com
Web Site: www.j-facility.com
Emp.: 70
Facilities Environmental Management Consulting Services
S.I.C.: 8999
N.A.I.C.S.: 541620
Hideki Oka *(Pres & CEO)*

U.S. Subsidiary:

Azbil North America, Inc. (1)
3323 Kifer Rd
Santa Clara, CA 95051
Tel.: (602) 216-8199
Fax: (602) 216-8213
Web Site: www.us.azbil.com
Emp.: 20
Sensor Instruments Mfr
S.I.C.: 3829
N.A.I.C.S.: 334519
Gary Johnson *(Pres)*

Subsidiary:

Vortek Instruments, LLC (2)
8475 W I25 Frontage Rd 300
Longmont, CO 80504
Tel.: (303) 682-9999
Fax: (303) 682-4368
E-Mail: sales@vortekinst.com
Web Site: www.vortekinst.com
Sales Range: $10-24.9 Million
Emp.: 6
Precision Multivariable Flowmeters Mfr
S.I.C.: 3829
N.A.I.C.S.: 334514
Jim Storer *(Owner)*

Non-U.S. Subsidiaries:

Azbil Control Instruments (Dalian) Co., Ltd. (1)
No 18 Dong Bei Second St
Dalian Econ Tech Dev, Dalian, Liaoning, China
Tel.: (86) 41187623555
Fax: (86) 41187623560
Industrial & Airconditioning Valves & Switches Mfr
S.I.C.: 3491
N.A.I.C.S.: 332911

Azbil Control Solutions (Shanghai) Co., Ltd. (1)
Rm 1802 Qiang Sheng Bldg No 145 Pujian Rd
Pudong, Shanghai, 200127, China
Tel.: (86) 2150906661
Fax: (86) 2150908958
Web Site: www.china.azbil.com
Emp.: 300
Building Automation & Industrial Automation System Installation & Maintenance Services
S.I.C.: 1731
N.A.I.C.S.: 238210

Azbil Europe NV (1)
Bosdellestraat 120 2 B
1933 Zaventem, Belgium
Tel.: (32) 27850710
Fax: (32) 27850711
E-Mail: customerservice@eu.azbil.com
Web Site: www.yamatake-europe.com
Emp.: 10
Building Automation System Mfr
S.I.C.: 1796
N.A.I.C.S.: 238290
Masami Nishida *(Mng Dir)*

Azbil Information Technology Center (Dalian) Co., Ltd. (1)
No 18 Dong Bei Second St
Dalian Econ Tech Dev, Dalian, China
Tel.: (86) 41187188007
Fax: (86) 41187188707
Web Site: acni.cn.azbil.com
Emp.: 30
Data Processing Services
S.I.C.: 7374
N.A.I.C.S.: 518210
Konami Texogetur *(Gen Mgr)*

Azbil Korea Co., Ltd. (1)
Rm No1601 The Teachers Pension Fund Bldg 27-2 Youido-Dong
Yongdungpo-Gu, Seoul, 150-742, Korea (South)
Tel.: (82) 27850280
Fax: (82) 27823481
E-Mail: webmaster@yamatake.co.kr
Web Site: www.kr.azbil.com
Emp.: 80
Building Automation Industrial Automation System Mfr
S.I.C.: 7389
N.A.I.C.S.: 541350
Akio Nagashima *(Mgr)*

Azbil Malaysia Sdn. Bhd. (1)
Ste 11 02 Level 11 The Gardens S Tower
Lingkaran Syed Putra, 59200 Kuala Lumpur, Malaysia
Tel.: (60) 322877036
Fax: (60) 322877039
E-Mail: admin@my.azbil.com
Web Site: www.my.azbil.com
Emp.: 60
Building Automation & Industrial Automation Systems Mfr
S.I.C.: 7389
N.A.I.C.S.: 541350

Azbil Philippines Corporation (1)
3rd fl Pilgrim Bldg 111 Aguirre St
Legaspi Vlg, 1229 Makati, Philippines
Tel.: (63) 28110916
Fax: (63) 28110458
E-Mail: azbil@ph.azbil.com
Web Site: www.azbil.com
Emp.: 50
Building Automation & Industrial Automation Systems Mfr
S.I.C.: 1731
N.A.I.C.S.: 238210
Takaaki Kawamura *(Pres)*

Azbil Singapore Pte. Ltd. (1)
Blk 26 Ayer Rajah Crescent No 01-06/07/08
Ayer Rajah Indus Estate, Singapore, Singapore
Tel.: (65) 67785966
Fax: (65) 67780012
E-Mail: azbil@sg.azbil.com
Web Site: www.azbil.com.sg
Emp.: 43
Building Automation & Industrial Automation Systems Mfr
S.I.C.: 1731
N.A.I.C.S.: 238210
Yusuke Oshida *(Mng Dir)*

Azbil Telstar, S.A. (1)
Av Font i Sague 55 Parc Cientific i Tecnologic
Orbital 40, 08227 Terrassa, Spain ES
Tel.: (34) 937 361 600 (80%)
Fax: (34) 937 861 380
E-Mail:
Web Site: www.etelstar.com
Sales Range: $125-149.9 Million
Emp.: 900
Life Science & Industrial Pumps, Equipment & Instrument Designer & Mfr
S.I.C.: 3563
N.A.I.C.S.: 333912
Ton Capella *(Pres & CEO)*

Division:

Telstar Life Science Solutions (2)
Av Font i Sague 55 Parc Cientific i Tecnologic
Orbital 40, 08227 Terrassa, Spain
Tel.: (34) 937 361 600
Fax: (34) 937 859 342
Web Site: www.telstar-lifesciences.com
Medical, Pharmaceutical & Laboratory Pumps & Equipment Mfr
S.I.C.: 3845
N.A.I.C.S.: 334510

Non-U.S. Subsidiary:

Luwa B.V. (3)
Tolweg 10
PO Box 207
3740 AE Baarn, Netherlands
Tel.: (31) 355415551
Fax: (31) 355417112
E-Mail: info@telstarmc.nl
Web Site: www.telstarmc.nl
Emp.: 35
Hospital Operating Room Equipment Mfr
S.I.C.: 3564
N.A.I.C.S.: 333413
Jos Lans *(Mng Dir)*

Subsidiaries:

Telstar Industrial, S.L. (2)
Josep Tapiolas 120
08226 Terrassa, Spain ES
Tel.: (34) 937 361 600
Fax: (34) 937 859 342
Web Site: www.telstar-vacuum.com
Industrial Pumps & Equipment Designer & Mfr
S.I.C.: 3563
N.A.I.C.S.: 333912

Telstar Instrumat, S.L. (2)
Av Font i Sague 55 Parc Cientific i Tecnologic
Orbital 40, 08227 Terrassa, Spain ES
Tel.: (34) 935 442 320
Fax: (34) 935 442 911
Web Site: www.telstar-instrumat.com
Industrial & Scientific Instrument Mfr
S.I.C.: 3826
N.A.I.C.S.: 334516

Azbil (Thailand) Co., Ltd. (1)
209 1 K Tower 20th Fl Sukhumvit 21 Rd
Klongtoey-Nua
Wattana, Bangkok, 10110, Thailand
Tel.: (66) 026641900
Fax: (66) 026641911
E-Mail: info@th.azbil.com
Web Site: www.th.azbil.com
Emp.: 100
Building & Industrial Automation System Mfr
S.I.C.: 7389
N.A.I.C.S.: 541350
Srinakoin Nontha *(Mgr)*

P.T. Azbil Berca Indonesia (1)
Gedung CCM 5th Fl Jl Cikini Raya No 95
Jakarta, 10330, Indonesia
Tel.: (62) 212305538
Fax: (62) 212305539
E-Mail: s.mombang.3a@id.azbil.com
Web Site: www.azbil.com
Emp.: 100
Building Automation & Industrial Automation Services
S.I.C.: 1731
N.A.I.C.S.: 238210
Shigeru Kusumoto *(Pres)*

Yamatake Automation Products (Shanghai) Co., Ltd. (1)
Rm 1806 Qiang Sheng Bldg No 145 Pujian Rd
Pudong Dist, Shanghai, 200127, China
Tel.: (86) 2150907206
Fax: (86) 2038785453
Web Site: www.yas-yamatake.com
Automobile & Industrial Control Products Whslr
S.I.C.: 5063
N.A.I.C.S.: 423610

Yamatake Environmental Control Technology (Beijing) Co., Ltd. (1)
Rm No 706 Liangziyinzuo Bldg 23 Zhichun Rd
Haidian Dist, Beijing, 100191, China
Tel.: (86) 1082358248
Fax: (86) 1082350478
E-Mail: jd@yeco-yamatake.com
Web Site: www.yeco-yamatake.com
Emp.: 10

Building Automation Industrial Automation System Mfr
S.I.C.: 1731
N.A.I.C.S.: 238210
Guohai Xu *(Mgr)*

Non-U.S. Joint Venture:

Shanghai Azbil Automation Co., Ltd. **(1)**
Rm 2702 Qiang Sheng Bldg No 145 Pujian Rd
Pudong Dist, Shanghai, 200127, China
Tel.: (86) 2168732581
Fax: (86) 02168735966
Web Site: sacn.cn.azbil.com
Building Automation & Industrial Automation System Designing & Maintenance Services
S.I.C.: 1731
N.A.I.C.S.: 238210

AZEARTH CORPORATION

4-13-7 Kuramae Taito-ku
Tokyo, 111-8623, Japan
Tel.: (81) 338651311
Web Site: www.azearth.co.jp
Year Founded: 1947
3161—(JAS TKS)
Sales Range: $100-124.9 Million
Emp.: 110
Business Description:
Textile & Piece Goods Products Wholesale Trader
S.I.C.: 5199
N.A.I.C.S.: 424310
Personnel:
Hiroo Suzuki *(Pres)*

AZENN SA

9 rue du Grand Dome
91951 Villebon-sur-Yvette, France
Tel.: (33) 169293510
Fax: (33) 169293511
E-Mail: jean-pierre.jeanne@azenn.com
Web Site: www.azenn.com
Rev.: $30,100,000
Emp.: 48
Business Description:
Cables & Networking Products Mfr & Distr
S.I.C.: 3357
N.A.I.C.S.: 335921
Personnel:
Jean-Pierre Jeanne *(Dir Gen)*

AZEUS SYSTEMS HOLDINGS LTD.

22/F Olympia Plaza 255 Kings Road
North Point, China (Hong Kong)
Tel.: (852) 28933673
Fax: (852) 25744952
E-Mail: info@azeus.com
Web Site: www.azeus.com
A69—(SES)
Sls.: $15,053,365
Assets: $21,229,167
Liabilities: $3,500,090
Net Worth: $17,729,078
Earnings: $4,013,698
Fiscal Year-end: 03/31/13
Business Description:
Software Programming Services
S.I.C.: 7372
N.A.I.C.S.: 511210
Personnel:
Wan Lik Lee *(Founder & Mng Dir)*
Rene Toling Lindio *(CTO)*
Mary Rose T. Tan *(Pres-Philippines)*
Min-tze Lean *(Co-Sec)*
Wai Ming Yap *(Co-Sec)*
Board of Directors:
Ching Chuen Chan
Pui Wan Lam
Wan Lik Lee
Koji Miura
Michael Kiam Siew Yap

Legal Counsel:
Stamford Law Corporation
10 Collyer Quay 27-00 Ocean Financial Centre
Singapore, Singapore
Transfer Agents:
Boardroom Corporate & Advisory Services Pte. Ltd.
50 Raffles Place 32-01 Singapore Land Tower
Singapore, Singapore
Appleby Management (Bermuda) Ltd.
Canon's Court 22 Victoria Street
HM 12 Hamilton, Bermuda

AZEVEDO & TRAVASSOS S.A.

Rua Vicente Antonio de Oliveira 1 050
Pirituba, 02955-080 Sao Paulo, SP, Brazil
Tel.: (55) 11 3973 7787
Fax: (55) 11 3973 7766
E-Mail: diretoria@azevedotravassos.com.br
Web Site: www.azevedotravassos.com.br
Year Founded: 1922
AZEV3—(BRAZ)
Business Description:
Civil Engineering Services
S.I.C.: 8711
N.A.I.C.S.: 541330
Personnel:
Abelardo Gomes Parente, Jr. *(Dir-IR)*

AZGARD NINE LIMITED

Ismail Aiwan-e-Science Shahrah-e-Roomi
Lahore, 54600, Pakistan
Tel.: (92) 42111786645
Fax: (92) 35761791
Web Site: www.azgard9.com
ANL—(KAR)
Sls.: $146,268,950
Assets: $212,254,033
Liabilities: $167,548,306
Net Worth: $44,705,727
Earnings: ($23,759,436)
Emp.: 7,914
Fiscal Year-end: 06/30/13
Business Description:
Denim & Yarn Mfr
S.I.C.: 2299
N.A.I.C.S.: 313110
Personnel:
Aehsun M. H. Shaikh *(Chm)*
Ahmed H. Shaikh *(CEO)*
Zahid Rafiq *(CFO)*
Muhammad Ijaz Haider *(Sec)*
Board of Directors:
Aehsun M. H. Shaikh
Munir Alam
Nasir Ali Khan Bhatti
Yasir Habib Hashmi
Naseer Miyan
Usman Rasheed
Ahmed H. Shaikh

Subsidiary:

Hazara Phosphate Fertilizers (Private) Limited **(1)**
Hattar Rd
Haripur, Islamabad, 22620, Pakistan
Tel.: (92) 995616124
Emp.: 100
Phosphate Mfr
S.I.C.: 2874
N.A.I.C.S.: 325312
Fahim Uddin *(Mgr-Mining Support)*

Non-U.S. Subsidiary:

Montebello SRL **(1)**
Martiri Delle Foibe No 9
Montebello Vicentino, Lonigo, VI 36045, Italy
Tel.: (39) 0444449422
Fax: (39) 0444449822
E-Mail: montebello@montebellodenim.com
Web Site: www.montebellodenim.com
Emp.: 30
Textile & Apparel Products & Accessories Mfr
S.I.C.: 2299
N.A.I.C.S.: 313310
Naseer Miyan *(Dir-Sls & Mktg)*

AZIANA LIMITED

Level 3 123 Adelaide Tce
Perth, WA, 6004, Australia
Mailing Address:
GPO Box 2606
Perth, WA, 6001, Australia
Tel.: (61) 8 9220 5650
Fax: (61) 8 9220 5757
E-Mail: admin@aziana.com.au
Web Site: www.aziana.com.au
Year Founded: 2006
AZK—(ASX)
Business Description:
Gold & Bauxite Mining
S.I.C.: 1041
N.A.I.C.S.: 212221
Personnel:
Peter Gerard Cook *(Chm)*
Antony Page *(CEO)*
Fiona Jayne Van Maanen *(Sec)*
Board of Directors:
Peter Gerard Cook
Warren Shaye Hallam
Phillip George Laskaris
John Roger Andrew Morris
Antony Page

Non-U.S. Subsidiary:

Tanety Zina SARL **(1)**
Lot A 12 Ter A
Antananarivo, 101, Madagascar
Tel.: (261) 32 0238689
Emp.: 90
Gold Mining Services
S.I.C.: 1041
N.A.I.C.S.: 212221
Rija Raherimandimby *(Mng Dir)*

AZIMUT EXPLORATION INC.

110 De La Barre Street Suite 214
Longueuil, QC, J4K 1A3, Canada
Tel.: (450) 646-3015
Fax: (450) 646-3045
E-Mail: info@azimut-exploration.com
Web Site: www.azimut-exploration.com
AZM—(TSXV)
Int. Income: $31,888
Assets: $10,106,793
Liabilities: $561,996
Net Worth: $9,544,797
Earnings: ($2,979,181)
Emp.: 6
Fiscal Year-end: 08/31/13
Business Description:
Mineral Exploration Services
S.I.C.: 1481
N.A.I.C.S.: 213115
Personnel:
Dennis Wood *(Chm)*
Jean-Marc Lulin *(Pres & CEO)*
Moniroth Lim *(Treas & Sec)*
Board of Directors:
Dennis Wood
Jean-Marc Lulin
Jean-Charles Potvin
Louis P. Salley
Jacques Simoneau
Legal Counsel:
Miller Thomson Pouliot SENCRL / LLP
Montreal, QC, Canada
Transfer Agent:
CST Trust Company
PO Box 4202 Postal Station A
Toronto, ON, M5W 0E4, Canada

AZIMUT HOLDING SPA

Via Cusani 4
20121 Milan, Italy
Tel.: (39) 02 88981
E-Mail: sales@azfund.com
Web Site: www.azimutholding.com
Year Founded: 1989
HDB—(DEU ITA)
Rev.: $243,252,919
Assets: $3,284,924,034
Liabilities: $2,489,606,798
Net Worth: $795,317,236
Earnings: $216,194,902
Emp.: 173
Fiscal Year-end: 12/31/12
Business Description:
Asset Management Services
S.I.C.: 6799
N.A.I.C.S.: 523920
Personnel:
Pietro Giuliani *(Chm & Co-CEO)*
Marco Malcontenti *(Co-CEO)*
Board of Directors:
Pietro Giuliani
Alessandro Baldin
Pietro Belotti
Attilio Boldori
Guido Casella
Marco Malcontenti
Aldo Milanese
Stefano Missora
Paola Mungo
Franco Novelli
Romano Stievano

AZIMUTH RESOURCES LIMITED

(Acquired & Absorbed by Troy Resources Limited)

AZINCOURT RESOURCES INC.

789 West Pender Street Suite 800
Vancouver, BC, V6C 1H2, Canada
Tel.: (604) 638-8063
Fax: (604) 648-8105
Year Founded: 2011
AAZ—(TSXV)
Business Description:
Metal Mining
S.I.C.: 1099
N.A.I.C.S.: 212299
Personnel:
Darren P. Devine *(Pres, CEO & Sec)*
Latika D. Prasad *(CFO)*
Board of Directors:
Ian M. Burns
Darren P. Devine
Latika D. Prasad
Paul Reynolds
Transfer Agent:
Equity Financial Trust Company
1185 West Georgia Street Suite 1620
Vancouver, BC, Canada

AZKOYEN, S.A.

San Silvestre S N
31350, 31350 Peralta, Navarra, Spain
Tel.: (34) 948 709 709
Fax: (34) 948 709 720
Web Site: www.azkoyen.com
Year Founded: 1976
AZK—(MAD)
Sales Range: $150-199.9 Million
Emp.: 925
Business Description:
Automatic Vending Machine Mfr
S.I.C.: 3589
N.A.I.C.S.: 333318
Personnel:
Juan Miguel Sucunza Nicasio *(Chm)*
Francisco Jose Bauza More *(Sec)*
Board of Directors:
Juan Miguel Sucunza Nicasio
Marco Adriani
Rafael Mir Andreu
Arturo Leyte Coello

AZKOYEN, S.A.—(Continued)

Jacobo Llanza Figueroa
Javier Tomas Forester
Ignacio Suarez-Zuloaga Galdiz
Pedro Ibarrondo

Subsidiaries:

Azkoyen Industrial, S.A. (1)
San Silvestre S N
31350 Peralta, Navvara, Spain
Tel.: (34) 948709709
Fax: (34) 948709720
E-Mail: salesservice@azkoyen.com
Web Site: industrial.azkoyen.com
Emp.: 150
Vending Machines Mfr
S.I.C.: 3589
N.A.I.C.S.: 333318
Francisco Vera *(Dir-Fin)*

Azkoyen Medios de Pago, S.A. (1)
Av San Silvestre S N
31350 Peralta, Navarra, Spain
Tel.: (34) 948709709
Fax: (34) 948709785
E-Mail: sales@azkoyen.com
Web Site: www.azkoyenmediosdepago.com
Emp.: 108
Electronic Devices Mfr
S.I.C.: 3679
N.A.I.C.S.: 334419
Miguel Angel Maiza *(Mng Dir)*

Subsidiary:

Coges Espana Medios de Pago, S.L. (2)
C La Granja 15 Bloque B 2a Planta B 3
28108 Alcobendas, Madrid, Spain
Tel.: (34) 914901311
Fax: (34) 91 662 72 57
E-Mail: coges.es@coges.eu
Web Site: www.coges.es/jsp/es/home/index.jsp
Vending Machines Mfr
S.I.C.: 3589
N.A.I.C.S.: 333318
Marco Adriani *(Pres)*

Non-U.S. Subsidiary:

Coges S.p.A. (2)
Via Luigi Dalla Via 10
36015 Schio, Vicenza, Italy
Tel.: (39) 0445502811
Fax: (39) 0445502999
E-Mail: coges@coges.eu
Web Site: www.coges.eu
Emp.: 75
Electronic Payment Systems & Vending Machines Mfr
S.I.C.: 3589
N.A.I.C.S.: 333318
Dario Brunello *(Mng Dir)*

Impulsa Soluciones Tecnologicas, S.L. (1)
C La Granja No 15 Bloque B 2a Planta B 3
28108 Alcobendas, Madrid, Spain
Tel.: (34) 914901311
Fax: (34) 91 662 7257
Vending Machines Mfr
S.I.C.: 3589
N.A.I.C.S.: 333318

Non-U.S. Subsidiaries:

Azkoyen Comercial Deutschland GmbH (1)
Am Turm 15
Siegburg, Nordrhein-Westfalen, 53721, Germany
Tel.: (49) 224159570
Fax: (49) 2241595790
Emp.: 4
Vending Machines Mfr
S.I.C.: 3589
N.A.I.C.S.: 333318

Coges France, S.A.S. (1)
3 Avenue De La Foire Aux Vins Lot No 2
68000 Colmar, France
Tel.: (33) 389277007
Fax: (33) 3 89 27 50 30
E-Mail: accueil@cogesfrance.com
Cash Machines Mfr
S.I.C.: 3569
N.A.I.C.S.: 333999

Marco Adriani *(Pres)*
Rene Panetta *(Mng Dir)*

primion Technology AG (1)
Steinbeisstrasse 2-5
72510 Stetten am kalten Markt, Germany (88.5%)
Tel.: (49) 75739520
Fax: (49) 757392034
E-Mail: info@primion.de
Web Site: www.primion.de
P4T—(DEU)
Sales Range: $50-74.9 Million
Emp.: 250
Security, Time Recording & Access Control Systems & Services
S.I.C.: 7382
N.A.I.C.S.: 561621
Heinz Roth *(CEO)*
Thomas Becker *(CFO)*
Thomas Bredehorn *(COO)*

AZO GMBH & CO. KG

Rosenberger Strasse 28
74706 Osterburken, Germany
Tel.: (49) 6291920
Fax: (49) 62929500
E-Mail: info@azo.de
Web Site: www.azo.de
Sales Range: $125-149.9 Million
Emp.: 700
Fiscal Year-end: 12/31/12

Business Description:
Industrial Machinery Mfr
S.I.C.: 3589
N.A.I.C.S.: 333318

Personnel:
Robert Zimmermann *(Founder & Pres)*

U.S. Subsidiary:

AZO, Inc. (1)
4445 Malone Rd
Memphis, TN 38118-1070
Tel.: (901) 794-9480
Fax: (901) 794-9934
E-Mail: info@azo.com
Web Site: www.azo.com
Emp.: 30
Materials Handling Machinery Mfr
S.I.C.: 5084
N.A.I.C.S.: 423830
Chuck Kerwin *(Controller)*

Subsidiary:

HSH-Systeme Fur Prozess-IT GmbH (1)
Heiner-Fleischmann-Str 7
74172 Neckarsulm, Germany
Tel.: (49) 713293420
Fax: (49) 7132934293
E-Mail: info@hsh-systeme.com
Web Site: www.hsh-systeme.com
Emp.: 130
Measuring Displaying & Controlling & Industrial Process & Variables Instruments & Related Products Mfr
S.I.C.: 3823
N.A.I.C.S.: 334513
Hendrick Langer *(Mgr-Sls)*

Non-U.S. Subsidiaries:

AZO EURL (1)
9 rue de la Fontaine Grillee
La Haye-Fouassiere, 44690 Nantes, France
Tel.: (33) 49629192445
Fax: (33) 228210828
E-Mail: contact@azo.fr
Web Site: www.azo.fr
Emp.: 20
Industrial Machinery Mfr
S.I.C.: 3559
N.A.I.C.S.: 333249
Frederec Loiseau *(Dir-Comml)*

AZO Ltd. (1)
410 137 Soi Ratchrada 22
Ratchradapisek Road
Samsennok Huay Kwang, 10310 Bangkok, Thailand
Tel.: (66) 25415192
Fax: (66) 25415198
E-Mail: info@azo.de
Web Site: www.azo.com
Inorganic Dye & Pigment Mfr
S.I.C.: 2816
N.A.I.C.S.: 325130
Jan Wilko Helms *(Gen Mgr)*

AZO N.V. (1)
Katwilgweg 15
2050 Antwerp, Belgium
Tel.: (32) 32501600
Fax: (32) 003232529002
E-Mail: info@azo.be
Web Site: www.azo.be
Emp.: 72
Industrial Machinery Mfr
S.I.C.: 3559
N.A.I.C.S.: 333249
Frank Opdebeeck *(Mng Dir)*

AZPECT PHOTONICS AB

Aminogatan 34
Molndal, 431 53, Sweden
Tel.: (46) 855442480
Fax: (46) 8 55 44 24 99
E-Mail: info@azpect.com
Web Site: www.azpect.com
Year Founded: 1994
Sales Range: $10-24.9 Million
Emp.: 13

Business Description:
Measurement Instrument Mfr
S.I.C.: 3826
N.A.I.C.S.: 334516

AZRIELI GROUP LTD.

Azrieli Center 1
Tel Aviv, 67021, Israel
Tel.: (972) 36081300
Fax: (972) 36094518
Web Site: www.azrieli.com
Year Founded: 1983
AZRG—(TAE)
Sales Range: $1-4.9 Billion

Business Description:
Holding Company; Real Estate Development
S.I.C.: 6719
N.A.I.C.S.: 551112

Personnel:
David Azrieli *(Chm)*
Danna Azrieli *(Vice Chm)*
Menachem Einan *(Pres & CEO)*
Pe'er Nadir *(Pres-Malls Grp)*

Board of Directors:
Danna Azrieli

Holding:

Granite Hacarmel Investments Ltd. (1)
Hagavish St Industrial Area Kiryat Sapir
PO Box 8401
Netanya, 42507, Israel (60%)
Tel.: (972) 98637700
Fax: (972) 98852524
E-Mail: efratf@granitehacarmel.co.il
Web Site: www.granitehacarmel.co.il
GRNT—(TAE)
Sales Range: $1-4.9 Billion
Emp.: 15
Investment Holding Company
S.I.C.: 6719
N.A.I.C.S.: 551112
Joseph Singer *(CEO)*
Ehud Amir *(Deputy CEO)*
Dganit Palti *(CFO & VP)*
Yael Siekierski *(Sec)*

Subsidiaries:

Global Environmental Solutions Ltd. (2)
Akko Industrial Area
Acre, 24123, Israel (100%)
Tel.: (972) 49876107
Fax: (972) 4 9876133
Web Site: www.ges.co.il
Emp.: 400
Environmental Solution
S.I.C.: 4971
N.A.I.C.S.: 221310
Zoli Bihari *(Mgr-Engrg & Ops)*

Sonol Israel, Ltd. (2)
6 Hagavish St
PO Box 8401
Industrial Zone Kiryat Sefer, Netanya, 42507, Israel (100%)
Tel.: (972) 98637777
Fax: (972) 98859733
Web Site: www.sonol.co.il
Gas Station & Convenience Store Operator
S.I.C.: 5541
N.A.I.C.S.: 447110
Tamir Polikar *(CEO)*

Supergas Israel Gas Distribution Co. Ltd (2)
36 Yad Harutzim Street
South IZ, Netanya, Israel (100%)
Tel.: (972) 98308101
Fax: (972) 98308181
Web Site: www.supergas.co.il/
Emp.: 80
Liquefied Petroleum Gas Distr
S.I.C.: 4924
N.A.I.C.S.: 221210
Eyal Hankin *(Gen Mgr)*

Tambour Limited (2)
Haagavish 6 St Industrial Area
PO Box 8488
Kiryat Sapir, Netanya, 42504, Israel (85%)
Tel.: (972) 98925555
Telex: 46293 PAINT IL
Fax: (972) 9895593
E-Mail: export@tambour.co.il
Web Site: www.tambourpaints.com
TMBU—(TAE)
Sales Range: $125-149.9 Million
Emp.: 530
Paint & Varnish Mfr & Distr
S.I.C.: 2851
N.A.I.C.S.: 325510
Michael Dayan *(CEO)*
Yifat Cherpack *(Gen Counsel & CEO Asst)*

Subsidiaries:

Serafon (3)
Southern Industrial Zone
Ashkelon, 78289, Israel
Tel.: (972) 86710486
Fax: (972) 86710492
Web Site: www.serafon.com
Polymers & Adhesives Mfr & Marketer
S.I.C.: 2891
N.A.I.C.S.: 325520

Tzah-Serafon Ltd. (3)
Beer Tuvia Industrial Area
PO Box 1132
Kiryat Malachi, 83112, Israel
Tel.: (972) 88507755
Fax: (972) 88506946
E-Mail: tzahink@tambour.co.il
Web Site: www.tzah-serafon.co.il
Emp.: 40
Printing Ink Mfr & Marketer
S.I.C.: 2893
N.A.I.C.S.: 325910
Ronen Cohen *(Mng Dir)*

AZTECH GROUP LTD.

31 Ubi Road 1 09-01 Aztech Building
Singapore, 408694, Singapore
Tel.: (65) 65942288
Fax: (65) 67491198
E-Mail: sales@aztech.com
Web Site: www.aztech-group.com
Year Founded: 1986
560—(SES)
Rev.: $181,048,496
Assets: $119,376,790
Liabilities: $56,959,369
Net Worth: $62,417,422
Earnings: $186,226
Emp.: 1,600
Fiscal Year-end: 12/31/12

Business Description:
Multimedia Products & Computer Peripherals Mfr
S.I.C.: 3679
N.A.I.C.S.: 334419

Personnel:
Michael Hong Yew Mun *(Chm & CEO)*

Pavani Nagarajah *(Co-Sec & Sr VP-Legal & Corp Affairs)*
Pradeep Kumar Singh *(Co-Sec)*
Martin Heok Miin Chia *(Sr VP)*
Michael Thiam Seong Lee *(Sr VP-Strategic Alliance)*
Jeremy Weng Hung Mun *(Sr VP)*
Jason Chwee Meng Saw *(Sr VP-R&D)*
Herman Kam Hung So *(Sr VP-Fin)*
Board of Directors:
Michael Hong Yew Mun
Martin Heok Miin Chia
Ho Tong Khoo
Jeremy Weng Hung Mun
Colin Teck Sim Ng
Philip Tee Yong Tan

Subsidiaries:

Azfin Semiconductors Pte Ltd (1)
31 Ubi Rd 1 Aztech Bldg
408694 Singapore, Singapore (82%)
Tel.: (65) 67479855
Fax: (65) 67479655
Semiconductor & Related Device Mfr
S.I.C.: 3674
N.A.I.C.S.: 334413
Michael Mun *(CEO)*

Shiro Corporation Pte Ltd (1)
31 Ubi Road 1
#08-00 Aztech Building, 408694 Singapore, Singapore (100%)
Tel.: (65) 65942233
Fax: (65) 67493083
E-Mail: enquiries@shirocorp.com
Web Site: www.shirocorp.com
Emp.: 7
Computer & Computer Peripheral Equipment & Software Whslr
S.I.C.: 5045
N.A.I.C.S.: 423430
Michael Mun *(CEO)*

Non-U.S. Subsidiary:

AZ-Technology Sdn Bhd (1)
Unit 901 9th Floor Block B
Kelana Business Centre Selango, 47301
Petaling Jaya, Malaysia (100%)
Tel.: (60) 378048450
Fax: (60) 378048457
E-Mail: allen.pan@aztech.com
Web Site: rc.aztech.com
Emp.: 10
Telephone Apparatus Mfr
S.I.C.: 3661
N.A.I.C.S.: 334210
Michael Mun *(CEO)*

U.S. Subsidiary:

Aztech Labs Inc. (1)
4005 Clipper Ct
Fremont, CA 94538 (100%)
Tel.: (510) 683-9800
Fax: (510) 683-9803
Web Site: www.aztech.com
Emp.: 50
Other Computer Peripheral Equipment Mfr
S.I.C.: 3577
N.A.I.C.S.: 334118

AZUL S.A.

Edificio Jatoba 8th Floor Castelo Branco Office Park
Avenida Marcos Penteado de Ulhoa Rodrigues 939
Tambore Barueri, Sao Paulo, 06460-040, Brazil
Tel.: (55) 11 4831 2880
Web Site: www.voeazul.com.br
Year Founded: 2008
Rev.: $1,336,639,751
Assets: $2,337,355,524
Liabilities: $2,164,686,885
Net Worth: $172,668,639
Earnings: ($84,035,471)
Emp.: 8,914
Fiscal Year-end: 12/31/12
Business Description:
Air Transportation Services
S.I.C.: 4512
N.A.I.C.S.: 481111
Personnel:
David Neeleman *(Chm)*
John Rodgerson *(CFO & Chief IR Officer)*
Jose Mario Caprioli dos Santos *(COO)*
Maximilian Urbahn *(Chief Revenue Officer)*
Board of Directors:
David Neeleman
Jose Mario Caprioli dos Santos
Decio Luiz Chieppe
Renan Chieppe
Henrique de Campos Meirelles
Pedro Barcellos Janot Marinho
Michael Lazarus
Carolyn Luther Trabuco
Gelson Pizzirani
Sergio Eraldo Salles Pinto

AZUL VENTURES INC.

330 Bay Street Suite 820
Toronto, ON, M5H 2S8, Canada
Tel.: (604) 907-7363
Fax: (416) 907-7363
E-Mail: info@azul-ventures.com
Web Site: www.azul-ventures.com
Year Founded: 2007
AZL—(TSXV)
Int. Income: $89
Assets: $3,299,320
Liabilities: $1,228,882
Net Worth: $2,070,438
Earnings: ($1,245,414)
Fiscal Year-end: 12/31/12
Business Description:
Investment Services
S.I.C.: 6211
N.A.I.C.S.: 523999
Personnel:
Tony Wonnacott *(Chm)*
David O'Connor *(Pres & CEO)*
Brad Boland *(CFO & Sec)*
Board of Directors:
Tony Wonnacott
Mike Hoffman
David O'Connor

Transfer Agent:
Computershare Trust Company of Canada
510 Burrard St 2nd Fl
Vancouver, BC, Canada

AZUMA HOUSE CO., LTD.

1-2-17 Kuroda
Wakayama, 640-8341, Japan
Tel.: (81) 73 475 1018
Web Site: www.azumahouse.com
3293—(JAS)
Rev.: $110,149,314
Emp.: 165
Fiscal Year-end: 03/31/13
Business Description:
Real Estate Services
S.I.C.: 6531
N.A.I.C.S.: 531390
Personnel:
Yukio Azuma *(Chm)*
Katsuhiko Sowa *(Pres)*

AZUMAH RESOURCES LIMITED

Suite 2 11 Ventnor Avenue
West Perth, WA, 6005, Australia
Tel.: (61) 894867911
Fax: (61) 894814417
E-Mail: info@azumahresources.com.au
Web Site: www.azumahresources.com.au
AZM—(ASX)
Rev.: $229,390
Assets: $7,289,568
Liabilities: $765,582
Net Worth: $6,523,986
Earnings: ($19,934,320)
Emp.: 2
Fiscal Year-end: 06/30/13
Business Description:
Gold Mining
S.I.C.: 1041
N.A.I.C.S.: 212221
Personnel:
Stephen Stone *(Mng Dir)*
Dennis William Wilkins *(Sec)*
Board of Directors:
Michael Atkins
Geoff M. Jones
William LeClair
Stephen Stone

Legal Counsel:
Gilbert & Tobin
1202 Hay Street
West Perth, Australia

AZUR INDUSTRIES

Z I La Feuillane 42 Zi La Feuillane
13270 Fos-sur-Mer, Bouches Du Rhone, France
Tel.: (33) 442051228
Fax: (33) 442052430
E-Mail: contact@azurindustries.com
Web Site: www.azurindustries.com
Sls.: $14,400,000
Emp.: 100
Business Description:
Fabricated Structural Metal Mfr
S.I.C.: 3441
N.A.I.C.S.: 332312
Personnel:
Philip Grattarola *(Mng Dir)*
Board of Directors:
Philip Grattarola
Patrick Chatelier

AZURE HEALTHCARE LIMITED

Level 18 60 Albert Road
South Melbourne, VIC, 3205, Australia
Tel.: (61) 3 9209 9688
Fax: (61) 3 9209 9699
Web Site: www.azurehealthcare.com.au
AZV—(ASX)
Rev.: $23,451,418
Assets: $17,428,080
Liabilities: $6,345,347
Net Worth: $11,082,734
Earnings: $1,083,784
Emp.: 115
Fiscal Year-end: 06/30/13
Business Description:
Nursecall Systems & Clinical Workflow Solutions
S.I.C.: 7389
N.A.I.C.S.: 561499
Personnel:
Robert Edward Grey *(Chm & CEO)*
Jason D'Arcy *(CFO & Sec)*
Board of Directors:
Robert Edward Grey
William Brooks
Michael Howard

Subsidiaries:

Austco Communications Systems Pty. Ltd. (1)
40 O'Malley St
Osborne Park, Western Australia, 6017, Australia
Tel.: (61) 892444499
Fax: (61) 892444727
E-Mail: info@austco.com
Web Site: www.austco.ca
Emp.: 15
Electronic Communication Systems Mfr
S.I.C.: 3669
N.A.I.C.S.: 334290
Robert Grey *(Mng Dir-TSV)*

Calltec Pty. Ltd. (1)
Unit 21 35 Dunlop Rd
Mulgrave, Victoria, 3170, Australia
Tel.: (61) 385627575
Fax: (61) 385627550
E-Mail: info@tsvaustralia.com.au
Web Site: www.tsvaustralia.com.au
Electronic Communication Solutions & Services
S.I.C.: 4899
N.A.I.C.S.: 517919

Tecsound (QLD) Pty. Ltd. (1)
Unit 11 Northport Bus Park
441 Nudgee Rd, Hendra, QLD, 4011, Australia
Tel.: (61) 738684900
Fax: (61) 738683344
E-Mail: info@tecsound.com.au
Web Site: www.tecsound.com.au
Audio System Design & Integrated Services
S.I.C.: 7389
N.A.I.C.S.: 541490

Tecsound (VIC) Pty. Ltd. (1)
Unit 21 35 Dunlop Rd
PO Box 5083
Mulgrave, Victoria, 3170, Australia
Tel.: (61) 385627575
Fax: (61) 385627577
E-Mail: info@tecsound.com.au
Web Site: www.tecsound.com.au
Emp.: 55
Audio System Design & Integration Services
S.I.C.: 7389
N.A.I.C.S.: 541490

Tecsound (West Australia) Pty. Ltd. (1)
78B Collingwood St
Osborne Park, Western Australia, 6017, Australia
Tel.: (61) 894458844
Fax: (61) 894458866
E-Mail: info@tecsound.com.au
Web Site: www.tecsound.com.au
Emp.: 15
Audio Systems Design & Integration Services
S.I.C.: 7389
N.A.I.C.S.: 541490
Ron Anderson *(Mgr-Sls)*

U.S. Subsidiary:

Austco Marketing & Service (USA) Ltd. (1)
8706 N Royal Ln
Irving, TX 75063
Tel.: (972) 929-0974
Fax: (972) 929-0976
E-Mail: info@austco.us
Web Site: www.austco.us
Emp.: 5
Electronic Communication Systems Mfr
S.I.C.: 3669
N.A.I.C.S.: 334290
Judy Whitehead *(Office Mgr)*

Non-U.S. Subsidiaries:

Austco Marketing & Service (Asia) Pte. Ltd. (1)
Blk 5014 Ang Mo Kio Ave 5
No 05-07/08 Tech Pl II, 569881 Singapore, Singapore
Tel.: (65) 64818400
Fax: (65) 64819400
E-Mail: info@austco.com.sg
Web Site: www.austco.com.sg
Emp.: 10
Electronic Communication Systems Mfr
S.I.C.: 3669
N.A.I.C.S.: 334290
Michael Chia *(Mng Dir)*

Austco Marketing & Service (Canada) Ltd. (1)
60 Granton Dr Unit 6
Richmond Hill, ON, L4B 2N6, Canada
Tel.: (416) 932-2080
Fax: (416) 932-2955
Toll Free: (888) 670-9997
E-Mail: info@austco.ca
Web Site: www.austco.ca
Electronic Communication Systems Mfr
S.I.C.: 3669
N.A.I.C.S.: 334290

Azure Healthcare Limited—(Continued)

Clayton Astles *(VP)*

Austco Marketing & Service (UK) Ltd. (1)
13 The Courtyard Buntsford Gate Buntsford Hill
Stoke Pound, Bromsgrove, Worcestershire, B60 3DJ, United Kingdom
Tel.: (44) 1527877778
Fax: (44) 1527836872
E-Mail: info.uk@austco.com
Web Site: www.austco.com
Emp.: 7
Electronic Communication Systems Mfr
S.I.C.: 3669
N.A.I.C.S.: 334290
Allen Jones *(Mng Dir)*

AZURE MINERALS LIMITED

Level 1 30 Richardson Street
West Perth, WA, 6005, Australia
Tel.: (61) 894812555
Fax: (61) 894851290
E-Mail: admin@azureminerals.com.au
Web Site: www.azureminerals.com.au
AZS—(ASX)
Rev.: $48,658
Assets: $5,599,896
Liabilities: $765,107
Net Worth: $4,834,790
Earnings: ($4,055,970)
Emp.: 10
Fiscal Year-end: 06/30/13
Business Description:
Minerals Exploration
S.I.C.: 1481
N.A.I.C.S.: 213115
Personnel:
Anthony Paul Rovira *(Mng Dir)*
Brett Douglas Dickson *(CFO & Sec)*
Board of Directors:
Peter Anthony John Ingram
Wolf Gerhard Martinick
Anthony Paul Rovira
Legal Counsel:
Middletons
Level 32 St Martins Tower 44 St Georges Terrace
Perth, WA, 6000, Australia

Non-U.S. Subsidiary:

Minera Piedra Azul, S.A. de C.V. (1)
Ave Javier De Leon 707 Col Pitic
Hermosillo, Sonora, Mexico
Tel.: (52) 6622855350
Fax: (52) 6622144708
Web Site: www.azureminerals.com
Mineral Exploration Services
S.I.C.: 1481
N.A.I.C.S.: 213115
Alejandro Fuentes *(Mgr-Admin)*

AZURE RESOURCES CORPORATION

Suite 502 815 Hornby Street
Vancouver, BC, V6Z 2E6, Canada
Tel.: (604) 684-2401
Fax: (604) 684-2407
Toll Free: (888) 273-3671
E-Mail: azu@azure-res.com
Web Site: www.azure-res.com
Year Founded: 1984
AZU—(TSXV)
Assets: $4,256,289
Liabilities: $4,320,722
Net Worth: ($64,432)
Earnings: ($963,044)
Emp.: 8
Fiscal Year-end: 06/30/13
Business Description:
Diamond, Copper & Gold Exploration, Development & Production Services
S.I.C.: 1429
N.A.I.C.S.: 212319
Personnel:
Lutfur Rahman Khan *(Chm)*
Waseem Rahman *(Pres & CEO)*
Omair Choudhry *(CFO & VP)*
Board of Directors:
Lutfur Rahman Khan
Mahmood Arshad
Timothy S. Hoar
Afzal Mahmood
Waseem Rahman
Legal Counsel:
ProVenture Law LLP
Suite 2 Mount Royal Village 880 16th Avenue SW
Calgary, AB, Canada
Transfer Agent:
Computershare
510 Burrard St 2nd Floor
Vancouver, BC, Canada

AZUREWAVE TECHNOLOGIES, INC.

8F 94 Baozhong Road
Xindian, Taipei, 231, Taiwan
Tel.: (886) 2 55995599
Fax: (886) 2 66289666
E-Mail: sales@azurewave.com
Web Site: www.azurewave.com
3694—(TAI)
Sales Range: $200-249.9 Million
Business Description:
Wireless Communication Products
S.I.C.: 3663
N.A.I.C.S.: 334220
Personnel:
Shih-chang Hsu *(Chm)*
Tseng-chieh Lee *(CEO & Gen Mgr)*

AZZALIN SRL

Strada Marziana 9
27020 Parona, PV, Italy
Tel.: (39) 0384 253136
Fax: (39) 0384 253574
E-Mail: info@azzalinsrl.it
Web Site: www.azzalinsrl.it
Sales Range: $1-9.9 Million
Emp.: 16
Business Description:
Industrial Valves, Gears, Actuators & Tools Mfr & Distr
S.I.C.: 3491
N.A.I.C.S.: 332911
Personnel:
Luciano Azzalin *(CEO)*

Non-U.S. Subsidiary:

Valvesource Ltd (1)
31 Hampstead Ave
Mildenhall, Suffolk, IP28 7AS, United Kingdom
Tel.: (44) 1638 711 500
Fax: (44) 1638 711 521
E-Mail: sales@valvesource.co.uk
Web Site: www.valvesource.co.uk
Emp.: 11
Supplier of Industrial Valves to Oil, Gas, Petrochemical & Other Related Industries
S.I.C.: 5084
N.A.I.C.S.: 423830

AZZEDINE ALAIA S.A.S.

7 Rue De Moussy
75004 Paris, France
Tel.: (33) 142721919
E-Mail: presse@alaia.fr
Sls.: $13,000,000
Emp.: 45
S.I.C.: 5137
N.A.I.C.S.: 424330
Personnel:
Azzedine Alaia *(Pres)*

B & A PACKAGING INDIA LIMITED

113 Park Street 9th Floor
Kolkata, 700 016, India
Tel.: (91) 33 2226 9582
Fax: (91) 33 2227 7538
E-Mail: contact@bampl.com
Web Site: www.bampl.com
Year Founded: 1915
523186—(BOM)
Rev.: $5,794,959
Assets: $6,573,837
Liabilities: $4,746,466
Net Worth: $1,827,371
Earnings: $2,710
Emp.: 80
Fiscal Year-end: 03/31/13
Business Description:
Paper Sack Mfr
S.I.C.: 2672
N.A.I.C.S.: 322220
Personnel:
Ranudurjoy Roy Choudhury *(Mng Dir)*
Gunjan Kumar Chaurasia *(Sec)*
Board of Directors:
Gargi Barooah
Somnath Chatterjee
Anjan Ghosh
Transfer Agent:
MCS Limited
77/2A Hazra Road
Kolkata, India

B&B INVESTMENT PARTNERS LLP

Third Floor 55 Blandford Street
London, W1U 7HW, United Kingdom
Business Description:
Private Equity Firm
S.I.C.: 6211
N.A.I.C.S.: 523999
Personnel:
Chris Britton *(Principal)*

Holding:

Aromatherapy Associates Ltd. (1)
6 Great W Trading Estate
Brentford, Middlesex, TW8 9DN, United Kingdom
Tel.: (44) 2085697030
Fax: (44) 2085697090
E-Mail: info@aromatherapyassociates.com
Web Site: www.aromatherapyassociates.com
Emp.: 35
Aromatherapy Products
S.I.C.: 2844
N.A.I.C.S.: 325620
Geraldine Howard *(Pres)*

B&B TOOLS AB

Linnegatan 18
PO Box 10024
SE-100 55 Stockholm, Sweden
Tel.: (46) 104547700
Fax: (46) 104547701
E-Mail: info@bbtools.com
Web Site: www.bb.se
Year Founded: 1906
BBTO-B—(OMX)
Rev.: $1,225,861,200
Assets: $809,139,600
Liabilities: $482,821,200
Net Worth: $326,318,400
Earnings: $34,365,600
Emp.: 2,780
Fiscal Year-end: 03/31/13
Business Description:
Industrial & Construction Tools Distr Import
S.I.C.: 5084
N.A.I.C.S.: 423830
Personnel:
Anders Borjesson *(Chm)*
Tom Hedelius *(Vice Chm)*
Ulf Lilius *(Pres & CEO)*
Eva Hemb *(CFO)*
Pontus Boman *(CEO-ESSVE Produkter AB & Mgr-Fastening Elements)*
Torbjorn Eriksson *(CEO-TOOLS Sverige AB & Mgr-Sweden)*
Jens Henriksen *(CEO-TOOLS AS & Mgr-Norway)*
Stefan Lind *(CEO-Luna Verktyg & Maskin AB & Mgr-Tools & Machinery)*
Mikael Malmgren *(CEO-Skydda Protecting People Europe AB & Mgr-Personal Protective)*
Olof Nyberg *(CEO-Gigant Arbetsplats AB & Grunda AB & Mgr-Work Environment)*
Jimmy Norlinder *(CEO-TOOLS Momentum AB)*
Carl Johan Lundberg *(Exec VP, Head-Bus Infrastructure Unit & Mgr-Finland)*
Board of Directors:
Anders Borjesson
Per Axelsson
Roger Bergqvist
Charlotte Hansson
Tom Hedelius
Joakim Rubin
Lillemor Svensson
Anette Swanemar

Subsidiaries:

B&B TOOLS Corporate Development AB (1)
Linnegatan 87D
11459 Stockholm, Sweden
Tel.: (46) 86662800
Fax: (46) 8 450 26 71
Industrial Tools Mfr
S.I.C.: 3542
N.A.I.C.S.: 333517

B&B TOOLS Fastigheter AB (1)
Box 10024
100 55 Stockholm, Sweden
Tel.: (46) 8 660 10 30
Industrial Tools Mfr
S.I.C.: 3542
N.A.I.C.S.: 333517

B&B TOOLS Services AB (1)
Linnegatan 87 D
PO Box 24053
104 50 Stockholm, Sweden
Tel.: (46) 84502670
Fax: (46) 8 450 26 71
E-Mail: info@bbinfotrans.com
Industrial Tools Distr
S.I.C.: 5085
N.A.I.C.S.: 423840

B&B TOOLS Solutions AB (1)
Sandbergsvagen 3
441 39 Alingsas, Vastra Gotaland, Sweden
Tel.: (46) 322606700
Fax: (46) 322606104
Web Site: www.bbtools.com
Emp.: 3,000
Industrial Tools Mfr
S.I.C.: 3542
N.A.I.C.S.: 333517

Bergman & Beving Tools AB (1)
Sidensvansvagen 10
PO Box 770
SE 191 27 Sollentuna, Sweden (100%)
Tel.: (46) 86236190
Fax: (46) 86231708
E-Mail: info@effve.se
Web Site: www.effve.se
Emp.: 200
S.I.C.: 3663
N.A.I.C.S.: 334220
Bentt Marg *(Mgr)*

Essve Produkter AB (1)
Sidensvansvagen 10
PO Box 770
191 27 Sollentuna, Stockholm, Sweden
Tel.: (46) 86236100
Fax: (46) 86926865
E-Mail: info@essve.se
Web Site: www.essve.com
Emp.: 52
Industrial Tools & Fire Seals Distr
S.I.C.: 5085
N.A.I.C.S.: 423840
Lennart Nystrom *(COO)*

Gigant Arbetsplats AB (1)
Sandbergsvagen 3
441 80 Alingsas, Vastra Gotaland, Sweden
Tel.: (46) 322606800
Fax: (46) 322606840
E-Mail: gigant@gigant.se
Web Site: www.gigant.se
Emp.: 30
Industrial Equipments Distr
S.I.C.: 5084
N.A.I.C.S.: 423830
Olof Nyberg *(Mng Dir)*

Grunda AB (1)
Karlsnas Industriomrade
523 85 Ulricehamn, Vastra Gotaland, Sweden
Tel.: (46) 321677600
Fax: (46) 321677405
E-Mail: grunda@grunda.se
Web Site: www.grunda.se
Emp.: 50
Industrial Tools Distr
S.I.C.: 5085
N.A.I.C.S.: 423840
Olof Nyberg *(Gen Mgr)*

Luna AB (1)
Sandbergsvagen 3
441 80 Alingsas, Vastra Gotaland, Sweden
Tel.: (46) 322606000
Fax: (46) 322606470
E-Mail: info@luna.se
Web Site: www.luna.se
Emp.: 250
Industrial Tools Mfr
S.I.C.: 3541
N.A.I.C.S.: 333517

Skydda Protecting People Europe AB (1)
Karlsnas Industriomrade
523 85 Ulricehamn, Vastergotland, Sweden
Tel.: (46) 321677300
Fax: (46) 321 67 71 29
E-Mail: info@skydda.com
Web Site: www.skydda.com
Emp.: 100
Personal Protection Products Distr
S.I.C.: 5999
N.A.I.C.S.: 446199
Leif Reinholdsson *(Pres)*

TOOLS Momentum AB (1)
Von Utfallsgatan 16 B
415 05 Gothenburg, Vastergotland, Sweden
Tel.: (46) 313409900
Fax: (46) 313409920
E-Mail: mail@toolsmomentum.com
Web Site: www.toolsmomentum.com
Emp.: 250
Industrial Equipment Resellers
S.I.C.: 5084
N.A.I.C.S.: 423830
Ola Jonsson *(Mgr-Fin)*

TOOLS Sydost AB (1)
Nydalavagen 1
331 40 Varnamo, Jonkoping, Sweden
Tel.: (46) 370300300
Fax: (46) 370300390
E-Mail: order.varnamo.sydost@tools.se
Web Site: www.tools.se
Industrial Equipments & Tools Distr
S.I.C.: 5084
N.A.I.C.S.: 423830
Arvidsson Lars-Olof *(Mgr-Fin)*

Holding:

Mercus Yrkesklader Group AB (1)
Kampevagen 31
554 02 Jonkoping, Sweden
Tel.: (46) 36100120
E-Mail: mercus@mercus.se
Web Site: www.mercus.se
Sls.: $12,870,900
Emp.: 39
Clothing Mfr & Distr
S.I.C.: 2329
N.A.I.C.S.: 315220

Non-U.S. Subsidiaries:

ACTE Inc A/S (1)
Vallensbaekvej 41
2605 Brondby, Denmark (100%)
Tel.: (45) 46900400
Fax: (45) 46900500
E-Mail: info@acte.dk
Web Site: www.acte.dk
Emp.: 60
S.I.C.: 3663
N.A.I.C.S.: 334220
Peter Bjornskov *(CEO)*

B&B TOOLS Services AS (1)
Bergshagan 3
1401 Ski, Akershus, Norway
Tel.: (47) 91 57 90 00
Fax: (47) 85 03 22 07
Industrial Tools Mfr
S.I.C.: 3541
N.A.I.C.S.: 333517
Ellen Langseth *(Mng Dir)*

Gigant Tyopisteet Oy (1)
Opistokatu 11
65100 Vaasa, Ostrobothnia, Finland
Tel.: (358) 207570500
Fax: (358) 207570510
Web Site: www.gigant.fi
Emp.: 7
Industrial Components Mfr
S.I.C.: 3999
N.A.I.C.S.: 339999
Steven Pham *(Mgr)*

B&B TRADE DISTRIBUTION CENTRE

675 York St
London, ON, N5W 2S6, Canada
Tel.: (519) 679-1770
Fax: (519) 679-6010
Toll Free: (800) 265-0382
E-Mail: sales@bandbtrade.com
Web Site: www.bandbtrade.com
Rev.: $15,389,256
Emp.: 70

Business Description:
Heating Ventilation Air conditioning Refrigeration Whslr
S.I.C.: 1711
N.A.I.C.S.: 238220

Personnel:
Tom Boutette *(Pres)*

B&C SPEAKERS SPA

Via Poggiomoro 1 - Vallina
50012 Florence, Italy
Tel.: (39) 3905565721
Fax: (39) 390556572312
E-Mail: mail@bcspeakers.com
Web Site: www.bcspeakers.com
Year Founded: 1944
BEC—(ITA)
Sales Range: Less than $1 Million
Emp.: 85

Business Description:
Audio Equipment Mfr & Distr
S.I.C.: 3651
N.A.I.C.S.: 334310

Personnel:
Roberto Coppini *(Founder & Chm)*
Lorenzo Coppini *(CEO & Dir-Mktg & Sls)*
Simone Pratesi *(CFO & Dir-IR)*
Alessandro Pancani *(CTO)*

Board of Directors:
Roberto Coppini
Marco Biagioni
Lorenzo Coppini
Alessandro Pancani
Roberta Pecci
Simone Pratesi

B & R ECKEL'S TRANSPORT LTD.

5114 B 50th Ave
Bonnyville, AB, T9N 2K8, Canada
Tel.: (780) 826-3889
Fax: (780) 826-4301
Toll Free: (800) 661-3290
E-Mail: hrdept@breckels.com
Web Site: www.breckels.com
Year Founded: 1965
Sales Range: $50-74.9 Million
Emp.: 310

Business Description:
Oil & Gas Transportation Services
S.I.C.: 1389
N.A.I.C.S.: 213112

Personnel:
Victor Ringuette *(Owner)*

B&S MEDIA CO., LTD.

703 JNK Digital Tower 111 Didtalro 26gil Guro-dong
Guro-gu, Seoul, Korea (South)
Tel.: (82) 2 588 3323
Fax: (82) 2 588 3659
E-Mail: info@bsmedia.co.kr
Web Site: www.bnsmedia.com
Year Founded: 2002
156170—(KRS)
Emp.: 50

Business Description:
Educational Hardware & Software Products
S.I.C.: 3575
N.A.I.C.S.: 334118

Personnel:
Yun-Gi Baik *(Pres)*

B&T EXACT GMBH

Gewerbestrasse 31
52825 Gevelsberg, Germany
Tel.: (49) 233275530
Fax: (49) 2332755315
E-Mail: info@but-exact.de
Web Site: www.but-exact.de
Year Founded: 1997
Rev.: $15,175,995
Emp.: 67

Business Description:
Vehicle Repair & Spare Parts Services
S.I.C.: 7549
N.A.I.C.S.: 811198

Personnel:
Jorg-Peter Tepel *(Mng Partner)*

B & W INSTRUMENTATION & ELECTRICAL LIMITED

42 Fourth Avenue
Alberton, 1456, South Africa
Mailing Address:
PO Box 956
Alberton, 1450, South Africa
Tel.: (27) 11 907 1663
Fax: (27) 11 907 1957
E-Mail: bwie@bwie.co.za
Web Site: www.bwie.co.za
Year Founded: 1973
BWI—(JSE)
Rev.: $36,519,214
Assets: $26,298,017
Liabilities: $13,719,593
Net Worth: $12,578,424
Earnings: ($3,266,143)
Emp.: 77
Fiscal Year-end: 08/31/13

Business Description:
Electrical & Instrumentation Engineering Services
S.I.C.: 8711
N.A.I.C.S.: 541330

Personnel:
Brian Harley *(CEO)*

Board of Directors:
Leonard John Barrow
Danie Evert
Brian Harley
Unati Mabandla
Dean Stuart Nevay
Roger Pitt
George Robertson
Gary William Roberts Swanepoel
Wolf Wassermeier

Legal Counsel:
Fluxmans Incorporated
11 Bierman Avenue Rosebank
Johannesburg, South Africa

Transfer Agent:
Computershare Investor Services (Proprietary) Limited
Ground Floor 70 Marshall St
Johannesburg, South Africa

B. BRAUN MELSUNGEN AG

(d/b/a B. Braun Medical Group)
Carl-Braun-Strasse 1
34212 Melsungen, Germany
Mailing Address:
PO Box 1120
34209 Melsungen, Germany
Tel.: (49) 5661710
Fax: (49) 5661754567
E-Mail: info@bbraun.com
Web Site: www.bbraun.com
Year Founded: 1839
Sls.: $6,795,258,850
Assets: $7,381,746,080
Liabilities: $4,340,511,124
Net Worth: $3,041,234,956
Earnings: $388,558,509
Emp.: 46,559
Fiscal Year-end: 12/31/12

Business Description:
Holding Company; Medical Instruments & Supplies Mfr & Distr
S.I.C.: 6719
N.A.I.C.S.: 551112

Personnel:
Heinz-Walter Grosse *(Chm-Mgmt Bd & Chief HR Officer)*
Annette Beller *(CFO & Member-Mgmt Bd)*
Hanns-Peter Knaebel *(Member-Mgmt Bd-Aesculap Div)*
Meinrad Lugan *(Member-Mgmt Bd-Hospital Care & OPM Div)*
Caroll H. Neubauer *(Member-Mgmt Bd-North America)*
Otto Philipp Braun *(Member-Mgmt Bd-Iberian Peninsula & Latin America)*
Markus Strotmann *(Deputy Member-Mgmt Bd-Avitum Div)*

Division:

Aesculap AG & Co. KG (1)
Am Aesculap Platz
D 8532 Tuttlingen, Germany
Tel.: (49) 7461950
Fax: (49) 7461952600
E-Mail: information@aesculap.de
Web Site: www.aesculap.com
Sls.: $586,000,000
Emp.: 3,000
Mfr. of Cable Clippers, Electric Surgery Apparatus & Equipment, Medical Instruments, Dental Instruments, Veterinary Instruments, Electric Hair Clippers
S.I.C.: 3999
N.A.I.C.S.: 335210
Hanns Peter Knaebel *(Chm)*
Harald Stallforth *(CEO)*

U.S. Subsidiary:

Aesculap, Inc. (2)
3773 Corporate Pkwy
Center Valley, PA 18034-8217
Tel.: (610) 797-9300
Fax: (610) 791-6880
Toll Free: (800) 258-1946
E-Mail: info@aesculap-usa.com
Web Site: www.aesculap-usa.com
Emp.: 350
Surgical Instrumentation, Power Systems, Neurosurgical Instruments & Implants, Disposables, Cardiovascular Instruments & Sterile Processing Containers Whslr & Distr Import Export
S.I.C.: 5047
N.A.I.C.S.: 423450
Chuck DiNardo *(Pres)*

U.S. Subsidiaries:

B. Braun Medical, Inc. (1)
824 12th Ave
Bethlehem, PA 18018

B. Braun Melsungen AG—(Continued)

Tel.: (610) 691-5400
Fax: (610) 691-2202
Web Site: www.bbraunusa.com
Emp.: 3,500
Medical Instruments & Supplies Mfr & Distr
S.I.C.: 5047
N.A.I.C.S.: 423450
Caroll H. Neubauer *(CEO)*
Bob Comer *(Pres-B. Braun of Canada, Ltd.)*

Division:

B. Braun Interventional Systems Inc. (2)
824 12th Ave
Bethlehem, PA 18018 DE
Tel.: (610) 691-5400
Fax: (610) 266-3928
Toll Free: (877) 836-2228
Web Site: www.bisusa.org
Medical Instruments & Supplies Mfr & Distr
S.I.C.: 3841
N.A.I.C.S.: 339112
Paul O'Connell *(Pres)*

Central Admixture Pharmacy Services, Inc. (1)
18012 Cowan Ste 250
Irvine, CA 92614
Tel.: (949) 660-2000
Fax: (949) 660-2730
Web Site: www.capspharmacy.com
Outsourced Admixture Pharmacy Services
S.I.C.: 2834
N.A.I.C.S.: 325412
Mike Koch *(VP-Sls & Support Svcs)*

Non-U.S. Subsidiaries:

Ahlcon Parenterals (India) Ltd. (1)
Unit no-201-205 Second Floor of ND Mall-1 Plot No 2-4 Wazirpur District, New Delhi, 110 034, India
Tel.: (91) 1142344234
Fax: (91) 114234221
E-Mail: info@ahlconindia.com
Web Site: www.ahlconindia.com
524448—(BOM DES JAI)
Rev.: $21,916,170
Assets: $17,558,343
Liabilities: $7,364,098
Net Worth: $10,194,245
Earnings: $2,386,035
Fiscal Year-end: 03/31/13
Pharmaceutical Products Mfr
S.I.C.: 2834
N.A.I.C.S.: 325412
Arun Mudgal *(CEO & Mng Dir)*
Rajeev Kumar Walia *(CFO)*
Ranjan Kumar Sahu *(Compliance Officer, Sec & Sr Mgr-Legal)*

B. Braun Medical AG (1)
Seesatz 17
CH-6204 Sempach, Switzerland CH
Tel.: (41) 58 258 5000
Fax: (41) 58 258 6000
E-Mail: info.bbmch@bbraun.com
Web Site: www.bbraun.ch
Medical Instruments & Supplies Distr
S.I.C.: 5047
N.A.I.C.S.: 423450
Roland Marti *(Mng Dir)*

B. Braun Medical (India) Pvt. Ltd. (1)
Unit No 1 5th Flr East Quadrant The IL&FS Financial Centre
Bandra-Kurla Complex
Bandra East, Mumbai, 400051, India In
Tel.: (91) 22 6668 2222
Fax: (91) 22 6668 2121
Web Site: www.bbraun.co.in
Emp.: 540
Medical Instruments & Supplies Mfr & Distr
S.I.C.: 5047
N.A.I.C.S.: 423450
Anand Apte *(Mng Dir & Country Head-India)*

B. Braun Medical Ltd. (1)
Thorncliffe Park
Sheffield, S35 2PW, United Kingdom UK
Tel.: (44) 114 225 9000
Fax: (44) 114 225 9111
E-Mail: info.bbmuk@bbraun.com
Web Site: www.bbraun.co.uk
Emp.: 350
Medical Instruments & Supplies Mfr & Distr
S.I.C.: 5047
N.A.I.C.S.: 423450
Hans Hux *(Mng Dir)*

B. Braun Medical SAS (1)
204 Avenue du Marechal Juin
F-92660 Boulogne-Billancourt, Cedex, France FR
Tel.: (33) 1 4110 5300
Fax: (33) 1 4110 5399
E-Mail: infofrance@bbraun.com
Web Site: www.bbraun.fr
Emp.: 1,360
Medical Instruments & Supplies Mfr & Distr
S.I.C.: 5047
N.A.I.C.S.: 423450
Christof Hennigfeld *(CEO)*

B. Braun Singapore Pte. Ltd. (1)
600 North Bridge Road #15-05 Parkview Square
Singapore, 188778, Singapore SG (100%)
Tel.: (65) 6213 0933
Fax: (65) 6213 0930
E-Mail: bbraun.sg@bbraun.com
Web Site: www.bbraun.com.sg
Emp.: 35
Medical Instruments & Supplies Distr
S.I.C.: 5047
N.A.I.C.S.: 423450
Chee Hong Lam *(Mng Dir)*

B C HOUSING MANAGEMENT COMMISSION

4555 Kingsway Ste 1701
Burnaby, BC, V5H 4V8, Canada
Tel.: (604) 433-1711
Fax: (604) 439-4722
E-Mail: webeditor@bchousing.org
Web Site: www.bchousing.org
Sales Range: $200-249.9 Million
Emp.: 550

Business Description:
Subsidized Housing & Housing Assistance Services
S.I.C.: 8322
N.A.I.C.S.: 624229

Personnel:
Shayne Ramsay *(CEO)*
Dan Maxwell *(CFO & VP-Corp Svcs)*

B. GRIMM GROUP

Dr Gerhard Link Bldg 88 9th Fl
Krungthepkreetha Rd Huamark
Bangkapi
Bangkok, 10240, Thailand
Tel.: (66) 27103000
Fax: (66) 23794224
Web Site: www.bgrimmgroup.com
Year Founded: 1878
Sales Range: $100-124.9 Million
Emp.: 1,500

Business Description:
Mfr. of Air Conditioners, Aluminum Curtain Walls, Medical Equipment, Engineering Systems & Rail Road Signaling Equipment
S.I.C.: 3585
N.A.I.C.S.: 333415

Personnel:
Harald Link *(CEO)*

Subsidiaries:

Amata Power Ltd. (1)
15th 16th Fl Dr Gerhard Link Bldg
88 Krungthepkreetha Rd Huamark,
Bangkok, 10240, Thailand (56%)
Tel.: (66) 27103000
Fax: (66) 23794245
Web Site: www.amatapower.com
Emp.: 50
Distribution & Generation of Power
S.I.C.: 3612
N.A.I.C.S.: 335311

B. Grimm & Co. R.O.P. (1)
88 Krungtsepkreecha Huamark, 10240
Bangkok, Bangkapi, Thailand (100%)
Tel.: (66) 27103000
Fax: (66) 23794224
E-Mail: info@bgrimmgroup.com
Web Site: www.brimmgroup.com
Emp.: 200
High Tech Medical Equipment Distributor
S.I.C.: 3841
N.A.I.C.S.: 339112
Oranee Thongyai *(Sec)*

B. Grimm Trading Company (1)
Fl 17 Dr Gerhard Link Bldg 88
Krungthepkreetha Road
Huamark, 10240 Bangkok, Bangkapi, Thailand (100%)
Tel.: (66) 27103000
Fax: (66) 2379447
Web Site: www.bgrimmgroup.com
Emp.: 50
Construction & Energy Services
S.I.C.: 1442
N.A.I.C.S.: 212321

B. Grimm Group (1)
Fl 9 Dr Gerhard Link Bldg 88 Soi Lertnava
Krungthepkreetha Rd Huamark, 10240
Bangkok, Bangkapi, Thailand (100%)
Tel.: (66) 27103470
Fax: (66) 27103473
E-Mail: atchada@bgrimm.co.th
Web Site: www.brimmgroup.com
Distributor of Equipment for Energy Technology, Pulp & Paper Technology
S.I.C.: 5084
N.A.I.C.S.: 423830

B. Grimm Healthcare Co., Ltd. (1)
Fl 6 Dr Gerhard Link Bldg 88
Krungthepkreetha Rd Huamark, Bangkok, Bangkapi, 10240, Thailand (100%)
Tel.: (66) 27103032
Fax: (66) 23794469
E-Mail: bghc@mozart.inet.co.th
Web Site: www.brimmhealthcare.com
Emp.: 100
Mfr. of Medical Equipment
S.I.C.: 3841
N.A.I.C.S.: 339112

B. Grimm Holding Co., Ltd. (1)
88 Krungthepkreetha Rd Huamark
9th Fl Dr Gerhard Link Bldg, 10240
Bangkok, Bangkapi, Thailand (100%)
Tel.: (66) 27103000
Fax: (66) 23794224
E-Mail: oranee.bghd@bgrimmgroup.com
Web Site: www.bgrimmgroup.com
Emp.: 100
Holding Company
S.I.C.: 6719
N.A.I.C.S.: 551112

B. Grimm International Service Co., Ltd. (1)
Ground Fl Dr Gerhard Link Bldg 88
Krungthepkreetha Rd Huamark, Bangkok, 10240, Thailand (100%)
Tel.: (66) 27103311
Fax: (66) 23794262
E-Mail: haraldlink@bgrimmgroup.com
Web Site: www.bgrimmgroup.com
Emp.: 200
Provider of Real Estate Services
S.I.C.: 6531
N.A.I.C.S.: 531210
Harald Link *(Chm)*

B. Grimm MBM Metalworks Limited (1)
59 Moo 14 Suwinthawong Rd
Nongchok, Bangkok, 10530, Thailand (100%)
Tel.: (66) 2988237086
Fax: (66) 29882387
E-Mail: brgimm@bgrimm.co.th
Web Site: www.bgrimm.co.th
Emp.: 30
Mfr of Curtain Walls & Facades
S.I.C.: 3449
N.A.I.C.S.: 332323
Frank Moller *(Mng Dir)*

B. Grimm Power Engineering Co., Ltd. (1)
Fl 17 Dr Gerhard Link Bldg 33 Soi Lertnava
Krungthepkreetha Rd Huamark, 10240
Bangkok, Bangkapi, Thailand (100%)
Tel.: (66) 27103000
Fax: (66) 23794450
E-Mail: btep@brimmgroup.com
Web Site: www.brimmgroup.com
Emp.: 50
Distributor of Mechanical & Electrical Products
S.I.C.: 5064
N.A.I.C.S.: 423620

B. Grimm Transport Ltd. (1)
Fl 8 Dr Gerhard Link Bldg 88
Krungthepkreetha Rd Huamark, Bangkok, Bangkapi, 10240, Thailand (100%)
Tel.: (66) 27103270
Fax: (66) 23794430
E-Mail: bgrimmtl@ksc.th.com
Web Site: www.bgrimmgroup.com
Emp.: 25
Provider of Transportation Services
S.I.C.: 4789
N.A.I.C.S.: 488210

SMT World Travel Co., Ltd. (1)
Ground Fl Dr Gerhard Link Bldg
33 Soi Lertnava
Krungthepkreetha Rd Huamark, Bangkapi
Bangkok, 10240, Thailand
Tel.: (66) 37941803
Fax: (66) 3794179
E-Mail: bgrim@cscoms.com
Web Site: www.bgrimmgroup.com
Provider of Travel Agency Services
S.I.C.: 4724
N.A.I.C.S.: 561510

B L KASHYAP & SONS LIMITED

409 4th Floor DLF Tower - A Jasola
New Delhi, 110 025, India
Tel.: (91) 1140500300
Fax: (91) 1140500333
E-Mail: info@blkashyap.com
Web Site: www.blkashyap.com
BLKASHYAP—(NSE)
Rev.: $289,956,963
Assets: $374,284,543
Liabilities: $272,604,783
Net Worth: $101,679,760
Earnings: $1,558,789
Fiscal Year-end: 03/31/13

Business Description:
Construction Engineering Services
S.I.C.: 8711
N.A.I.C.S.: 541330

Personnel:
Vinod Kashyap *(Chm)*
K. Gopal *(CEO & CFO)*
Vikram Kashyap *(Co-Mng Dir)*
Vineet Kashyap *(Co-Mng Dir)*
Pushpak Kumar *(Sec)*

Board of Directors:
Vinod Kashyap
Vikram Kashyap
Vineet Kashyap
C. K. Mahajan
H. N. Nanani
P. S. Shenoy

Transfer Agent:
Link InTime India Private Limited
44 Community Center Phase-I Near PVR
Naryana Industrial Area
New Delhi, India

Subsidiary:

Soul Space Projects Limited (1)
B-1 Extn/ E23 Mohan Co-operative Industrial Estate Mathura Road
New Delhi, 110044, India
Tel.: (91) 11 40500300
Fax: (91) 11 40500333
E-Mail: info@soulspace.co.in
Web Site: www.soulspace.co.in
Emp.: 150
Real Estate Development Services
S.I.C.: 6531
N.A.I.C.S.: 531390
Stuart Sneyd *(Mgr-Mktg)*

B-MAVEN, INC.

428 Katingdig Avenue
Quezon City, Metro Manila, Philippines
Tel.: (63) 914 215 6799
Year Founded: 2011

BMAV—(OTC OTCB)
Rev.: $57,393
Assets: $212
Liabilities: $19,414
Net Worth: ($19,202)
Earnings: $20,562
Fiscal Year-end: 06/30/13
Business Description:
Skin Care Products Mfr
S.I.C.: 2844
N.A.I.C.S.: 325620
Personnel:
Restituto S. Cenia, Jr. *(Chm, Pres, CEO, CFO, Chief Acctg Officer, Sec & Treas)*
Board of Directors:
Restituto S. Cenia, Jr.
Transfer Agent:
Pacific Stock Transfer
4045 S Spencer St Ste 403
Las Vegas, NV 89044

B. METZLER SEEL. SOHN & CO. HOLDING AG

Grosse Gallusstrasse 18
D-60311 Frankfurt am Main, Germany
Tel.: (49) 6921040
Fax: (49) 69281429
E-Mail: metzler@metzler.com
Web Site: www.metzler.com
Emp.: 750
Business Description:
Asset Management, Investment Advisory & Private Banking Services
S.I.C.: 6282
N.A.I.C.S.: 523920
Personnel:
Friedrich von Metzler *(Partner & Chm-Mgmt Bd)*
Emmerich Muller *(Partner & Member-Mgmt Bd)*
Karl-Emil Fuhrmann *(Partner)*
Michael Klaus *(Partner)*
Frank-Peter Martin *(Partner)*
Hartmut Petersmann *(Partner)*
Johannes Reich *(Partner)*
Gerhard Wieshau *(Partner)*
Non-U.S. Joint Venture:

LeasePlan Corporation N.V. (1)
PJ Oudweg 41
1314 CJ Almere, Netherlands NL
Tel.: (31) 365393911
Fax: (31) 365393912
E-Mail: info@leaseplan.com
Web Site: www.leaseplan.com
Emp.: 6,200
Holding Company; Motor Vehicle Leasing & Fleet Management Services
S.I.C.: 6719
N.A.I.C.S.: 551112
F. Witter *(Chm-Supervisory Bd)*
V. Daemi *(Chm-Mgmt Bd & CEO)*
A. B. Stoelinga *(CFO & Member-Mgmt Bd)*
S. T. Huster *(COO & Member-Mgmt Bd)*
Flora Hennekes *(Sec)*
Tricia Desnos *(Sr VP-HR Mgmt)*

Subsidiary:

LeasePlan Nederland N.V. (2)
PJ Oudweg 41
1314 CH Almere, Netherlands NL
Mailing Address:
PO Box 3001
1300 EB Almere, Netherlands
Tel.: (31) 365272700
Fax: (31) 365272710
E-Mail: info@leaseplan.nl
Web Site: www.leaseplan.nl
Emp.: 600
Motor Vehicle Leasing & Fleet Management Services
S.I.C.: 7515
N.A.I.C.S.: 532112

Non-U.S. Subsidiaries:

LeasePlan Italia S.p.A. (2)
Viale Alessandro Marchetti 105
00148 Rome, Italy IT
Tel.: (39) 06 96707 1
Fax: (39) 06 96707 400
Web Site: www.leaseplan.it
Passenger Car Leasing & Fleet Management Services
S.I.C.: 7515
N.A.I.C.S.: 532112

Subsidiaries:

Nolauto Genova Systems-N.G.S. S.R.L. (3)
Via De Marini 1 Torre WTC
Genoa, Italy
Tel.: (39) 010461091
Web Site: www.e-ngs.it/guidautilizzo/furto.html
Motor Vehicle Rental Services
S.I.C.: 7513
N.A.I.C.S.: 532120

Unirent Comercio e Algue de Bens de Equipamento e Consumo S.A. (2)
Praca Avalade 6 8
1700-036 Lisbon, Portugal
Tel.: (351) 217944400
Car Rental Services
S.I.C.: 7514
N.A.I.C.S.: 532111

B-N GROUP LIMITED

Bembridge Airport
Bembridge, Isle of Wight, PO35 5PR, United Kingdom
Tel.: (44) 2033714000
Telex: 86277 PBNBEM G
Fax: (44) 2033714001
E-Mail: reception@britten-norman.com
Web Site: www.britten-norman.com
Year Founded: 1955
Sales Range: $10-24.9 Million
Emp.: 200
Business Description:
Aircraft Mfr
S.I.C.: 3721
N.A.I.C.S.: 336411
Personnel:
Alawi Zawawi *(Chm)*
William Hynett *(CEO)*
Subsidiary:

Fly BN Limited (1)
Hangar 3 Bembridge Airport
Bembridge, Isle of Wight, PO35 5PR, United Kingdom UK
Tel.: (44) 2033714980
Fax: (44) 2033714001
E-Mail: info@flybn.com
Web Site: www.flybn.com
Emp.: 10
Aircraft Maintenance Services
S.I.C.: 7629
N.A.I.C.S.: 811219
Peter Dalby *(Mgr)*

B N RATHI SECURITIES LTD.

6-3-652 4th Floor Kautilya Amrutha Estates Somajiguda
Hyderabad, 500 082, India
Tel.: (91) 40 3052 7777
Fax: (91) 40 30526283
E-Mail: support@bnrsecurities.com
Web Site: www.bnrsecurities.com
523019—(BOM)
Sales Range: $1-9.9 Million
Business Description:
Financial Security Services
S.I.C.: 6211
N.A.I.C.S.: 523120
Personnel:
Laxminivas Sharma *(Chm)*
Hari Narayan Laxminivas *(Mng Dir)*
M. V. Rao *(Compliance Officer)*
Board of Directors:
Laxminivas Sharma
Hari Narayan Laxminivas
K. Harish Chandra Prasad
Badri Narayan Rathi
Transfer Agent:
Karvy Computershare Private Limited
Plot No 17 to 24 Vittalrao Nagar Madhapur
Hyderabad, India
Subsidiary:

B N Rathi Comtrade Private Limited (1)
6-3-652 4th Floor Kautilya Amrutha Estates Somajiguda, Hyderabad, 500 082, India
Tel.: (91) 40 3052 7777
Fax: (91) 40 30526283
E-Mail: support@bnrsecurities.com
Emp.: 30
Commodity Trading Services
S.I.C.: 6231
N.A.I.C.S.: 523210
H. N. Rathi, *(Mng Dir)*

B. PACORINI S.P.A.

Via Caboto 19 2
34147 Trieste, Italy
Tel.: (39) 403899111
Fax: (39) 040828783
E-Mail: info@pacorini.com
Web Site: www.pacorini.it
Year Founded: 1933
Sls.: $85,705,285
Emp.: 300
Business Description:
Supplies Services for Loading & Unloading, Materials, Fulfilment, Storage, Customs Clearance, Land & Sea Transportation
S.I.C.: 4789
N.A.I.C.S.: 488210
Personnel:
Roberto Pacorini *(Pres & Mng Dir)*
Daniela Gregoratti *(CFO)*
Subsidiaries:

Interporto di Vado I.O.S.C.p.A. (1)
Via Trieste 25
17047 Vado Ligure, Italy
Tel.: (39) 0197750211
Fax: (39) 0197750205
E-Mail: info@interportovado.it
Emp.: 7
General Warehousing & Storage
S.I.C.: 4225
N.A.I.C.S.: 493110
Alessandro Piccardo *(Mng Dir)*

Pacorini Forwarding S.p.A. (1)
Via Pietro Chiesa 9
Torri Piane 12 piano, 16149 Genoa, Italy
Tel.: (39) 0104698111
Fax: (39) 0104698169
E-Mail: infoge@fwd.pacorini.com
Web Site: www.pacorini.it/itcompanies/storyeng$num=5
Emp.: 43
Freight Transportation Arrangement
S.I.C.: 4731
N.A.I.C.S.: 488510
Claudia Bassi *(Mng Dir)*

Pacorini Metals Italia S.r.l (1)
Via Caboto 19 2
34147 Trieste, Italy
Tel.: (39) 0403899604
Fax: (39) 0403899649
E-Mail: metalsts@pacorini.com
Web Site: www.pacorini.it/itstorieseng/story$num=16
Emp.: 100
Local Freight Trucking
S.I.C.: 4212
N.A.I.C.S.: 484110
Sergio Garbin *(Mng Dir)*

Pacorini Silocaf S.r.l. (1)
Via Caboto 19-2
34147 Trieste, Italy
Tel.: (39) 0403899111
Fax: (39) 040828783
E-Mail: info@pacorini.silocaf.it
Web Site: www.pacorini.com.it
Emp.: 100
General Warehousing & Storage
S.I.C.: 4225
N.A.I.C.S.: 493110
Enrico Pacorini *(Gen Mgr)*

Santandrea Terminali Specializzati S.r.l. (1)
19/2 Via Caboto Giovanni E Sebastiano
34147 Trieste, Italy
Tel.: (39) 0403183111
Fax: (39) 040317916
E-Mail: info@santandrea.pacorini.com
Web Site: www.pacorini.com
Emp.: 25
Freight Transportation Arrangement
S.I.C.: 4731
N.A.I.C.S.: 488510
Michela Fonda *(Mng Dir)*

U.S. Subsidiaries:

Pacorini Customs & Forwarding LLC (1)
1Coffee Plz 5240 Coffee Dr
New Orleans, LA 70115-7755
Tel.: (504) 896-4343
Fax: (504) 896-4344
Freight Transportation Arrangement
S.I.C.: 4731
N.A.I.C.S.: 488510

Pacorini Global Services LLC (1)
1 Alabo St Wharf
New Orleans, LA 70117
Tel.: (904) 786-8038
Fax: (504) 270-0125
Web Site: www.pacoriniglobal.com
Freight Transportation Arrangement
S.I.C.: 4731
N.A.I.C.S.: 488510
Richard Sharp *(VP)*

Pacorini Metals USA LLC (1)
1657C S Highland Ave
Baltimore, MD 21224
Tel.: (410) 327-2931
Fax: (410) 327-2655
E-Mail: info.metals@pacorinimetals.com
Web Site: www.pacorini.it/itcompanies/storyeng$num=28
Emp.: 70
Freight Transportation Arrangement
S.I.C.: 4731
N.A.I.C.S.: 488510
Paolo Pacorini *(CEO)*

Pacorini U.S.A. Inc. (1)
1 Alabo St
New Orleans, LA 70117 DE
Tel.: (504) 270-0100 (100%)
Fax: (504) 270-0125
E-Mail: pacorini@pacoriniusa.com
Emp.: 250
Stevedoring
S.I.C.: 4491
N.A.I.C.S.: 488310
Mark Gier *(CFO)*

Silocaf of New Orleans Inc. (1)
1Coffee Plz 5240 Coffee Dr
New Orleans, LA 70115-7755
Tel.: (504) 896-7800
Fax: (504) 896-7834
E-Mail: info@silocaf.com
Web Site: www.silocaf.com
Coffee & Tea Mfr
S.I.C.: 2095
N.A.I.C.S.: 311920
Maurizio Zaves *(Mng Dir)*

Non-U.S. Subsidiaries:

Pacorini Beo d.o.o. (1)
Kralja Milutina 21
11000 Belgrade, Serbia
Tel.: (381) 113232157
Fax: (381) 113235436
E-Mail: info@pacorini.rs
Emp.: 5
Refrigerated Warehousing & Storage
S.I.C.: 4222
N.A.I.C.S.: 493120
Aleksandar Adamovic *(Mng Dir)*

Pacorini DMCC (1)
306 Al Khaleej Ctr
PO Box 35593
Al-Mankhool Rd, Dubai, United Arab Emirates
Tel.: (971) 43518903
Fax: (971) 43556806
E-Mail: sqazi@pacorinidmcc.ae
Web Site: www.pacorini.it/itcompanies/storyeng$num=13
Freight Transportation Arrangement

B. Pacorini S.p.A.—(Continued)

S.I.C.: 4731
N.A.I.C.S.: 488510
Shamin Anwer *(Gen Mgr)*

Pacorini Iberica SAU (1)
Muntaner No 322 1st Floor
08021 Barcelona, Spain
Tel.: (34) 932896425
Fax: (34) 932896497
E-Mail: pacorini.iberica@pacorini.com
Web Site: www.pacorini.com
Emp.: 8
Process Physical Distribution & Logistics Consulting Services
S.I.C.: 4731
N.A.I.C.S.: 541614
Daniel Saez *(Mng Dir)*

Pacorini Koper d.o.o (1)
Verdijseva 1
6000 Koper, Slovenia
Tel.: (386) 56104000
Fax: (386) 56271904
E-Mail: info@pacorini.si
Web Site: www.pacorini.it/itcompanies/storyeng$num=31
Emp.: 40
General Warehousing & Storage
S.I.C.: 4225
N.A.I.C.S.: 493110
Clelia Vidic *(Mng Dir)*

Pacorini Montenegro d.o.o. (1)
Jovana Tomasevica 6-E5
Bar, 85000 Podgorica, Montenegro
Tel.: (382) 85317254
Fax: (382) 85317252
E-Mail: info@pacorini.cg.yu
Refrigerated Warehousing & Storage
S.I.C.: 4222
N.A.I.C.S.: 493120
Aleksandar Adamovic *(Mng Dir)*

Pacorini Rotterdam B.V. (1)
Shannonweg 76-78
3197 LH Rotterdam, Netherlands
Tel.: (31) 108200800
Fax: (31) 108200801
E-Mail: sales@pacorini.nl
Web Site: www.pacorini.nl
Emp.: 15
Refrigerated Warehousing & Storage
S.I.C.: 4222
N.A.I.C.S.: 493120
Simon Yntema *(Mng Dir)*

Pacorini Toll Pte. Ltd. (1)
3 Clementi Loop 3rd Floor
129815 Singapore, Singapore
Tel.: (65) 68737123
Fax: (65) 68737023
E-Mail:
Freight Transportation Arrangement
S.I.C.: 4731
N.A.I.C.S.: 488510
Michael Goh *(Gen Mgr)*

Pacorini Vietnam Ltd (1)
Office Suite 1621 Level 16 Gemadept Tower 6
Le Thanh Ton St
District 1, Ho Chi Minh City, Vietnam
Tel.: (84) 6503744180
Fax: (84) 6503744182
E-Mail: jose.serzedelo@pacoviet.com
Web Site: www.pacorini.it/itcompanies/storyeng$num=15
General Warehousing & Storage
S.I.C.: 4225
N.A.I.C.S.: 493110
Jose Serzedelo *(Mng Dir)*

Pacorini Vlissingen B.V. (1)
Engelandweg 25
4389PC Vlissingen, Netherlands
Tel.: (31) 118493350
Fax: (31) 118493351
E-Mail: sales@pacorini.nl
Web Site: www.pacorini.nl
Emp.: 30
Marine Cargo Handling
S.I.C.: 4491
N.A.I.C.S.: 488320
Simon Yntema *(Mng Dir)*

Non-U.S. Divisions:

Cafeco Armazens Gerais Ltda (1)
Rodovia ES 010 Km 02 S-N
Jardim Limoeiro, 29164-140 Serra, ES, Brazil
Tel.: (55) 2733280008
Fax: (55) 2733280008
Web Site: www.cafeco.com.br
Emp.: 50
General Warehousing & Storage Facilities to the Coffee Industry
S.I.C.: 4225
N.A.I.C.S.: 493110
Victor Garcez *(CEO)*

Pacorini Toll (Shanghai) Warehousing Limited (1)
D1 31st Fl E Bldg Shanghai Hi-Tech King World 668
Beijing Rd E, 200001 Shanghai, China
Tel.: (86) 2163403458
Fax: (86) 2163403468
E-Mail: info@cn.pacorinitoll.com
Web Site: www.pacorinitoll.com
Emp.: 40
Freight Transportation Arrangement
S.I.C.: 4731
N.A.I.C.S.: 488510
Michael Goh *(Mng Dir)*

B+F DORSTEN GMBH

Barbarastrasse 50
46282 Dorsten, Germany
Tel.: (49) 23629260
Fax: (49) 2362926152
E-Mail: info@bf-dorsten.de
Web Site: www.bf-dorsten.eu
Rev.: $45,492,612
Emp.: 120

Business Description:
Prefabricated Construction Services
S.I.C.: 3448
N.A.I.C.S.: 332311

Personnel:
Hans-Robert Nollen *(Head-Technical Office)*

B+H OCEAN CARRIERS LTD.

3rd Floor Par La Ville Place 14 Par La Ville Road
Hamilton, HM 08, Bermuda
Tel.: (441) 295 6875
Fax: (441) 295 6796
E-Mail: info@bhcousa.com
Web Site: www.bhocean.com
Year Founded: 1988
Sales Range: $50-74.9 Million
Emp.: 175

Business Description:
Operates & Sells Vessels for Dry Bulk & Liquid Cargo
S.I.C.: 4412
N.A.I.C.S.: 483111

Personnel:
Michael S. Hudner *(Chm, Pres & CEO)*
R. Anthony Dalzell *(CFO & Treas)*

Board of Directors:
Michael S. Hudner
Charles L. Brock
R. Anthony Dalzell
Per Ditlev Simonsen
Hope F. Hudner
John M. LeFrere
O. Michael Lewis
Trevor J. Williams

Subsidiaries:

B+H Management Ltd. (1)
3rd Floor Par La Ville Pl
14 Par La Ville Rd, Hamilton, HM08, Bermuda
Tel.: (441) 2956875
Fax: (441) 2956876
E-Mail: kptak@bhcousa.com
Web Site: www.bhocean.com
Holding Company
S.I.C.: 6719
N.A.I.C.S.: 551112
Michael Hutner *(Mng Dir)*

Equimar Shipholdings, Ltd. (1)
3rd Floor ParLaVille Place 14 Par-La-Ville Road
Hamilton, HM JX, Bermuda (100%)
Mailing Address:
PO Box HM2257
Hamilton, HM JX, Bermuda
Tel.: (441) 2956875
Fax: (441) 2956796
Operates & Sells Vessels for Dry Bulk & Liquid Cargo
S.I.C.: 7389
N.A.I.C.S.: 561990

U.S. Subsidiaries:

B+H Potier LLC (1)
516 15th Ave Ste 306
New York, NY 10036
Tel.: (212) 840-5582
Fax: (212) 840-5782
Web Site: www.bhocean.com
Marine Cargo Handling
S.I.C.: 4491
N.A.I.C.S.: 488320

Product Transport (US) Inc (1)
19 Burnside St
Bristol, RI 02809
Tel.: (401) 410-1140
Fax: (401) 410-1145
E-Mail: chartering@producttransport.com
Freight Transportation Arrangement
S.I.C.: 4731
N.A.I.C.S.: 488510
Michael S. Hudner *(Pres)*

Non-U.S. Subsidiaries:

B+H Equimar (Norway) AS (1)
Bryggegaten 7
0250 Oslo, Norway
Tel.: (47) 22862910
Fax: (47) 22839830
Web Site: www.bhocean.com
Management Consulting Services
S.I.C.: 8748
N.A.I.C.S.: 541618

B+H Equimar Singapore Pte. Ltd. (1)
78 Shenton Way # 20-02
079120 Singapore, Singapore
Tel.: (65) 63235253
Fax: (65) 63235248
Web Site: www.bhocean.com
Emp.: 20
Inland Water Freight Transportation
S.I.C.: 4449
N.A.I.C.S.: 483211
Mercin Wolasiewicz *(Gen Mgr)*

Product Transport (S) Pte. Ltd (1)
78 Shenton Way No 20-02
079120 Singapore, Singapore
Tel.: (65) 63237330
Fax: (65) 63234814
Web Site: www.bhocean.com
Emp.: 20
Marine Cargo Handling
S.I.C.: 4491
N.A.I.C.S.: 488320
Haraod Svensen *(Mng Dir)*

B+S BANKSYSTEME AG

Ruedesheimer Strasse 7
80686 Munich, Germany
Tel.: (49) 89741190
Fax: (49) 8974119599
E-Mail: office@bs-ag.com
Web Site: www.bs-ag.com
Year Founded: 1992
DTD2—(DEU)
Emp.: 22

Business Description:
Electronic Banking Software & Other Applications for Secure Internet Banking
S.I.C.: 7373
N.A.I.C.S.: 541512

Personnel:
Herbert Kofler *(Chm-Supervisory Bd)*
Heinz Schier *(Chm-Exec Bd)*
Manfred Seyfried *(Deputy Chm-Supervisory Bd)*
Peter Bauch *(Member-Exec Bd)*
Wilhelm Berger *(Member-Exec Bd)*

Supervisory Board of Directors:
Herbert Kofler
Manfred Seyfried
Werner Steinwender

Subsidiaries:

B+S Banksysteme Aktiengesellschaft (1)
Rudesheimer St 7
80686 Munich, Germany
Tel.: (49) 89741190
Fax: (49) 8974119599
E-Mail: office@bs-ag.com
Web Site: www.bs-ag.com
Emp.: 20
Banking Software Solutions Provider
S.I.C.: 7371
N.A.I.C.S.: 541511
Peter Paul *(Mng Dir)*

B+S Banksysteme Deutschland GmbH (1)
Rudesheimer St 7
80686 Munich, Germany
Tel.: (49) 89741190
Fax: (49) 8974119599
E-Mail: office@bs-ag.com
Emp.: 20
Banking Software Solutions Provider
S.I.C.: 7371
N.A.I.C.S.: 541511
Peter Bauch *(CEO)*

Non-U.S. Subsidiaries:

B+S Banksysteme Aktiengesellschaft (1)
Bichl Feld St 11
5020 Salzburg, Austria
Tel.: (43) 6624305910
Fax: (43) 662434059
E-Mail: office@bs-ag.com
Emp.: 50
Banking Software Solutions Provider
S.I.C.: 7371
N.A.I.C.S.: 541511
Bernd Maerzluft *(Mgr-Sls)*

B+S Banksysteme Schweiz AG (1)
Frutigen St 2
3600 Thun, Switzerland
Tel.: (41) 332230444
Fax: (41) 33 223 04 43
Banking Software Solutions Provider
S.I.C.: 7371
N.A.I.C.S.: 541511

B2B SOFTWARE TECHNOLOGIES LIMITED

6-3-1112 3rd and 4th Floor AVR Towers Behind Westside Show Room
Near Somajiguda Circle Begumpet, Hyderabad, Andhra Pradesh, 500 016, India
Tel.: (91) 40 2337 2522
Fax: (91) 40 2332 2385
E-Mail: info@b2bsoftech.com
Web Site: www.b2bsoftech.com
531268—(BOM)
Rev.: $1,172,579
Assets: $942,773
Liabilities: $238,958
Net Worth: $703,815
Earnings: $49,278
Fiscal Year-end: 03/31/13

Business Description:
Software Development Services
S.I.C.: 7371
N.A.I.C.S.: 541511

Personnel:
V. V. Nagendra *(CEO & Mng Dir)*
N. Bala Raju *(Compliance Officer & Mgr-Admin & Comml)*

Board of Directors:
Ram Nemani
Murthy Mutyala
V. V. Nagendra
A. Rambabu
M. Rambabu
Y. Satyanarayana
Ch Suresh

Transfer Agent:
Cil Securities Limited
214 Raghava Ratna Towers Chirag Ali Lane
Hyderabad, 500 001, India

Tel.: (91) 40 23202465
Fax: (91) 40 23203028

B2GOLD CORP.

Suite 3100 595 Burrard St
PO Box 49143
Vancouver, BC, V7X 1J1, Canada
Tel.: (604) 681-8371
Fax: (604) 681-6209
Toll Free: (800) 316-8855
E-Mail: investor@b2gold.com
Web Site: www.b2gold.com
Year Founded: 2006
BTG—(NAM NYSEMKT TSX)
Rev.: $259,051,000
Assets: $676,465,000
Liabilities: $110,146,000
Net Worth: $566,319,000
Earnings: $51,907,000
Emp.: 1,393
Fiscal Year-end: 12/31/12
Business Description:
Gold Ore Mining Services
S.I.C.: 1041
N.A.I.C.S.: 212221
Personnel:
Robert Melvin Douglas Cross *(Chm)*
Clive T. Johnson *(Pres & CEO)*
Mark Anthony Corra *(CFO & Sr VP-Fin)*
Roger Richer *(Gen Counsel, Sec & Exec VP)*
Thomas A. Garagan *(Sr VP-Exploration)*
George Johnson *(Sr VP-Ops)*
Dennis Stansbury *(Sr VP-Production & Dev)*
Board of Directors:
Robert Melvin Douglas Cross
Michael Joseph Carrick
Robert J. Gayton
John William Ivany
Clive T. Johnson
Jerry Korpan
Bongani Mtshisi
Barry Donald Maurice Rayment
Transfer Agent:
Computershare Investor Services Inc.
3rd Floor 510 Burrard Street
Vancouver, BC, Canada
Non-U.S. Subsidiaries:

Mocoa Ventures Ltd. **(1)**
Carrera 43 A 1 50
Medellin, Antioquia, Colombia
Tel.: (57) 43115333
E-Mail: rgomzalev@b2gold.com
Emp.: 10
Gold Ore Mining Services
S.I.C.: 1041
N.A.I.C.S.: 212221

BA CONSULTING GROUP LTD.

45 St Clair Avenue West Suite 300
Toronto, ON, M4V 1K9, Canada
Tel.: (416) 961-7110
Fax: (416) 961-9807
E-Mail: bagroup@bagroup.com
Web Site: www.bagroup.com
Rev.: $18,600,000
Emp.: 40
Business Description:
Transportation Planning & Engineering Services
S.I.C.: 8711
N.A.I.C.S.: 541330
Personnel:
Robert McBride *(Pres)*
Ralph Bond *(Sr VP)*

BA RIA - VUNG TAU HOUSE DEVELOPMENT JOINT STOCK COMPANY

3F Hodeco Plaza 36 Nguyen Thai Hoc Ward 7
Vung Tau, Vietnam
Tel.: (84) 64 3856 274
Fax: (84) 64 3856 205
E-Mail: info@hodeco.vn
Web Site: hodeco.vn
HDC—(HOSE)
Business Description:
Real Estate Services
S.I.C.: 6531
N.A.I.C.S.: 531390
Personnel:
Huu Thuan Doan *(Chm & Gen Dir)*
Phan Van Minh *(Vice Chm & Mgr-Sls)*
Board of Directors:
Huu Thuan Doan
Phan Van Minh

BAADER BANK AG

Weihenstephaner Strasse 4
85716 Unterschleissheim, Germany
Tel.: (49) 8951500
Fax: (49) 8951501111
E-Mail: info@baaderbank.de
Web Site: www.baaderbank.de
BWB—(DEU)
Int. Income: $20,415,800
Assets: $694,808,027
Liabilities: $544,542,962
Net Worth: $150,265,065
Earnings: $12,496,907
Emp.: 430
Fiscal Year-end: 12/31/12
Business Description:
Brokerage & Investment Banking Services
S.I.C.: 6211
N.A.I.C.S.: 523999
Personnel:
Horst Schiessl *(Chm-Supervisory Bd)*
Uto Baader *(Chm-Mgmt Bd)*
Christoph Niemann *(Deputy Chm-Supervisory Bd)*
Nico Baader *(Member-Mgmt Bd-Customers, Products, Capital Market Svcs & Comm)*
Dieter Brichmann *(Member-Mgmt Bd-Fin)*
Dieter Silmen *(Member-Mgmt Bd-Trading & Institutional Brokerage Ops)*
Supervisory Board of Directors:
Horst Schiessl
Karl-Ludwig Kamprath
Christoph Niemann
Helmut Schreyer
Jan Vrbsky
Theresia Weber
Subsidiaries:

Baader & Heins Capital Management AG **(1)**
Weihenstephaner Str 4
85716 Unterschleissheim, Germany
Tel.: (49) 89 23 18 000
Fax: (49) 89 23 18 00 10
E-Mail: info@baaderheins.de
Web Site: www.baaderheins.de
Emp.: 14
Financial Support Services
S.I.C.: 6211
N.A.I.C.S.: 523999
Andree Heins *(Chm-Mgmt Bd)*
Markus Britzl *(Member-Mgmt Bd)*
Rudiger Seemann *(Member-Mgmt Bd)*

Baader Bank Aktiengesellschaft **(1)**
Weihenstephaner Strasse 4
85716 Unterschleissheim, Germany
Tel.: (49) 8951500
Fax: (49) 8951501111
Web Site: www.baaderbank.de
Emp.: 400
Financial Management Consulting Services
S.I.C.: 8742
N.A.I.C.S.: 541611

Baader Heins & Seitz Capital Management AG **(1)**
Freisinger Str 9
85716 Unterschleissheim, Germany (70%)
Tel.: (49) 892318000
Fax: (49) 8923180010
E-Mail: info@baaderheinsseitz.de
Web Site: www.baaderheinsseitz.de
Emp.: 15
Investment Management Services
S.I.C.: 6211
N.A.I.C.S.: 523999
Markus Britzl *(Mng Dir)*
Andree Heins *(Mng Dir)*
Rudiger Seeman *(Mng Dir)*

Baader Service Bank GmbH **(1)**
Weihnstephaner Str 4
85716 Unterschleissheim, Germany (100%)
Tel.: (49) 8951501910
Fax: (49) 8951502442
E-Mail: info@baaderbank.de
Web Site: www.baaderservicebank.de
Emp.: 400
Brokerage & Investment Banking Services
S.I.C.: 6211
N.A.I.C.S.: 523999
Nico Baader *(Mng Dir)*

Conservative Concept Portfolio Management AG **(1)**
Schoene Aussicht 6
61348 Bad Homburg, Germany (49.96%)
Tel.: (49) 6172673000
Fax: (49) 6172673011
E-Mail: info@ccpm.de
Web Site: www.ccpm.de
Emp.: 15
Portfolio Management
S.I.C.: 6282
N.A.I.C.S.: 523920
Martin Hess *(Dir-Sls)*

direcct AG **(1)**
Schillerstrasse 30-40
60313 Frankfurt am Main, Germany (75%)
Tel.: (49) 6913881180
Fax: (49) 6913881189
E-Mail: info@direcctag.de
Web Site: www.direcctag.de
Emp.: 3
Investment Management Services
S.I.C.: 6211
N.A.I.C.S.: 523999
Hubertus Neuhaus *(CEO)*

KA.DE.GE KG **(1)**
Weihenstephaner Strasse 4
85716 Unterschleissheim, Germany
Tel.: (49) 89 216300
Fax: (49) 89 21630111
E-Mail: info@kadege.de
Web Site: www.kadege.de
Financial Management Consulting Services
S.I.C.: 8742
N.A.I.C.S.: 541611

KDG Abwicklungsgesellschaft mbh **(1)**
Freisinger Str 9
85716 Unterschleissheim, Germany
Tel.: (49) 89 216300
Fax: (49) 89 21630111
Web Site: www.kdg.de
Emp.: 9
Financial Management Consulting Services
S.I.C.: 8742
N.A.I.C.S.: 541611
Helfreid Gast *(Mng Dir)*

N.M. Fleischhacker AG **(1)**
Goetheplatz 4
603011 Frankfurt, Germany
Tel.: (49) 699218930
Fax: (49) 6992 18 935555
E-Mail: general@fleischhacker.de
Web Site: www.fleischhacker.de
Investment Management Services
S.I.C.: 6211
N.A.I.C.S.: 523999
Michael Wilhelm *(CEO)*
Frank-Andreas Schmidt *(Mng Dir)*
Torsten Kuck *(Mng Dir)*

Non-U.S. Subsidiary:

Conservative Concept AG **(1)**
Lussiweg 37
6300 Zug, Switzerland (100%)
Tel.: (41) 417267552
Fax: (41) 417267594
E-Mail: info@ccag.ch
Web Site: www.ccag.com
Emp.: 8
Real Estate Agents & Brokers Offices
S.I.C.: 6531
N.A.I.C.S.: 531210
Mitzler Hins *(Gen Mgr)*

BAAN ROCK GARDEN PUBLIC COMPANY LIMITED

601 Ramkhamheang 39 Pracha-Uthit Road
Wangthonglang, Bangkok, 10310, Thailand
Tel.: (66) 29347000
Fax: (66) 29347186
E-Mail: info@rockgarden.co.th
Web Site: www.rockgarden.co.th
Year Founded: 1990
BROCK—(THA)
Rev.: $4,096,622
Assets: $41,803,058
Liabilities: $913,067
Net Worth: $40,889,992
Earnings: $1,015,877
Fiscal Year-end: 12/31/12
Business Description:
Real Estate Development Services
S.I.C.: 6531
N.A.I.C.S.: 531390
Personnel:
Virat Chinprapinporn *(Chm)*
Naowanit Silaprarat *(Mng Dir)*
Board of Directors:
Virat Chinprapinporn
Preecha Janethanavijit
Wanchai Mekasut
Surapol Satimanont
Naowanit Silaprarat
Naowarat Suthamjariya

BABA ARTS LTD.

3-A Valecha Chambers New Link Road
Andheri West, Mumbai, Maharashtra, 400 053, India
Tel.: (91) 22 2673 3131
Fax: (91) 22 2673 3375
Web Site: www.babaartslimited.com
532380—(BOM)
Rev.: $1,562,922
Assets: $6,730,020
Liabilities: $304,056
Net Worth: $6,425,964
Earnings: $155,736
Fiscal Year-end: 03/31/13
Business Description:
Film Production Services
S.I.C.: 7812
N.A.I.C.S.: 512110
Personnel:
Gordhan P. Tanwani *(Chm & Mng Dir)*
N. H. Mankad *(Compliance Officer & Sec)*
Transfer Agent:
Universal Capital Securities Pvt. Ltd
21 Shakil Niwas Mahakali Caves Road Andheri East
Mumbai, India

BABCOCK INTERNATIONAL GROUP PLC

33 Wigmore Street
London, W1U 1QX, United Kingdom
Tel.: (44) 2073555300
Fax: (44) 2073555360
E-Mail: info@babcock.co.uk
Web Site: www.babcock.co.uk
Year Founded: 1989
BAB—(LSE)
Rev.: $5,122,427,115
Assets: $4,744,503,018
Liabilities: $3,214,328,937
Net Worth: $1,530,174,081
Earnings: $286,009,419
Emp.: 26,155
Fiscal Year-end: 03/31/13

Babcock International Group PLC—(Continued)

Business Description:
Defense Systems, Materials Handling, Marine & Rail Refurbishing & Engineering Services
Import Export
S.I.C.: 8711
N.A.I.C.S.: 541330

Personnel:
Michael John Turner *(Chm)*
Peter Rogers *(CEO)*
Archie Bethel *(CEO-Marine & Tech Div)*
John Davies *(CEO-Defence & Security Div)*
Kevin Thomas *(CEO-Support Svcs Div)*
Albert Dungate *(Gen Counsel & Sec)*

Board of Directors:
Michael John Turner
Archie Bethel
Justin Crookenden
John Davies
Ian Duncan
David Omand
Peter Rogers
Anna Stewart
Kate Swann
Bill Tame
Kevin Thomas

Legal Counsel:
Hammond Suddards
2 Park Lane
Leeds, LS3 1ES, United Kingdom

Divisions:

Babcock Airports (1)
Cambridge Rd
Whetstone, Leics, LE8 6LH, United Kingdom
Tel.: (44) 1162750750
Fax: (44) 1162750954
E-Mail: ged.conway@babcock.co.uk
Web Site: www.babcock.co.uk
Emp.: 150
Airport Baggage Handling Systems Developer & Mfr
S.I.C.: 4581
N.A.I.C.S.: 488119
Stephen Haines *(Deputy Gen Mgr)*

Babcock Defence & Security Services (1)
Pembroke House Herald Way Pegasus Business Park
Castle Donington, Derby, DE74 2TZ, United Kingdom
Tel.: (44) 1509676869
Fax: (44) 1509676866
Web Site: www.babcock.co.uk
Emp.: 50
Aircraft Flight Training & Maintenance Services
S.I.C.: 8249
N.A.I.C.S.: 611512
John Davies *(CEO)*

Babcock Marine (1)
33 Wigmore St
London, W1U 1QX, United Kingdom
Tel.: (44) 2073555300
Fax: (44) 1383417774
E-Mail: archie.bethel@babcock.co.uk
Web Site: www.babcock.co.uk
Emp.: 300
Naval Base Management Services, Submarine & Warship Systems Developer & Marine Equipment Mfr
S.I.C.: 3731
N.A.I.C.S.: 336611
Archie Bethel *(CEO)*

Subsidiaries:

Babcock Engineering Services Ltd. (2)
Rosyth Dockyards
Rosyth, Dunfermline, Fife, KY11 2YD, United Kingdom UK
Tel.: (44) 1383412131 (100%)
Fax: (44) 1383417774
Web Site: www.babcock.co.uk
Emp.: 2,000
Repair, Refitting & Servicing of Military & Civilian Ships; Small Boat Construction & Outfitting & Rail Rolling Stock Refurbishment
S.I.C.: 3731
N.A.I.C.S.: 336611
Ken Munro *(Gen Mgr)*

Devonport Management Limited (2)
Devonport Royal Dockyard
Plymouth, PL1 4SG, United Kingdom
Tel.: (44) 1752605665
Fax: (44) 1752323587
Web Site: www.devonport.co.uk
Rev.: $736,400,000
Emp.: 4,800
Ship & Boat Design, Construction & Support Services
S.I.C.: 3732
N.A.I.C.S.: 336612

Babcock Rail (1)
Kintail House 3 Lister Way Hamilton International Technology Park
Glasgow, G72 0FT, United Kingdom
Tel.: (44) 1698203005
Fax: (44) 1698203006
Web Site: www.babcock.co.uk
Emp.: 250
Railway Engineering, Systems Design & Maintenance Services
S.I.C.: 8711
N.A.I.C.S.: 541330
Andy Pearson *(CEO)*

BNS Nuclear (1)
Cambridge Road
Whetstone, Leicester, LE8 6LH, United Kingdom
Tel.: (44) 1162750750
Fax: (44) 1162750787
Web Site: www.babcock.co.uk
Emp.: 900
Nuclear Power Systems Engineering, Management & Maintenance Services
S.I.C.: 8711
N.A.I.C.S.: 541330
Chris Carter *(Gen Mgr)*

Subsidiaries:

Appledore Shipbuilders (2004) Limited (1)
H M Dockyard
Plymouth, Devonshire, PL1 4SG, United Kingdom
Tel.: (44) 1752 605665
Fax: (44) 1752552887
Ship Building Services
S.I.C.: 3731
N.A.I.C.S.: 336611

Babcock Design & Technology Limited (1)
Building 1020 Rosyth Royal Dockyard
Dunfermline, Fife, KY11 2YL, United Kingdom
Tel.: (44) 1383 412131
Fax: (44) 1383 417771
Engineering Support Services
S.I.C.: 8711
N.A.I.C.S.: 541330
Ian Lindsay *(Mng Dir-Design & Tech)*

Babcock Education & Skills Limited (1)
33 Wigmore Street
London, W1U 1QX, United Kingdom
Tel.: (44) 1372834444
Fax: (44) 2392326809
Educational Support Services
S.I.C.: 8299
N.A.I.C.S.: 611710

Babcock Integrated Technology Limited (1)
Ashton House Ashton Vale Road
Bristol, Avon, BS3 2HQ, United Kingdom
Tel.: (44) 1179 664677
Engineering Support Services
S.I.C.: 8711
N.A.I.C.S.: 541330

Babcock International Limited (1)
223-224 Newfields Rd Walton Summit Bamber Bridge
Preston, Lancashire, PR5 8AL, United Kingdom
Tel.: (44) 1772404400
Fax: (44) 1772404405
Emp.: 300
Engineering Support Services
S.I.C.: 8711
N.A.I.C.S.: 541330

Babcock International Support Services Limited (1)
1000 Lakeside North Harbour Western Road
Portsmouth, Hampshire, PO6 3EN, United Kingdom
Tel.: (44) 2392316244
Fax: (44) 23 9231 6270
Web Site: www.babcockinternational.com
Emp.: 10
Business Support Services
S.I.C.: 7389
N.A.I.C.S.: 561499
Fiona Stilwell *(Mgr-Ops)*

Babcock Land Limited (1)
Bournemouth International Airport
Christchurch, BH2 36BS, United Kingdom
Tel.: (44) 1202 365200
Fax: (44) 1202 573692
Emp.: 140
Real Estate Management Services
S.I.C.: 6531
N.A.I.C.S.: 531390
Nic Anderson *(Dir-Land & Sea)*

Babcock Marine (Clyde) Limited (1)
Rosyth Dockyard
Dunfermline, KY112YD, United Kingdom
Tel.: (44) 1383 412131
Fax: (44) 1383417774
Marine Engineering Services
S.I.C.: 8711
N.A.I.C.S.: 541330

Babcock Training Limited (1)
31a Pinchbeck Road
Spalding, Lincolnshire, PE11 1QD, United Kingdom
Tel.: (44) 1775 723523
Emp.: 600
Commercial Training Services
S.I.C.: 8299
N.A.I.C.S.: 611430

Babcock West Sussex Careers Limited (1)
1 The Chambers Chapel St
Chichester, West Sussex, PO19 1DL, United Kingdom
Tel.: (44) 1243771666
Fax: (44) 1243533111
Web Site: www.vtplc.com
Emp.: 20
Human Resource Consulting Services
S.I.C.: 8999
N.A.I.C.S.: 541612
Stewart Farrar *(Mgr-Ops)*

BNS Nuclear Services Limited (1)
Cambridge Road Whetstone
Leicester, Leicestershire, LE8 6LH, United Kingdom
Tel.: (44) 1162 750750
Fax: (44) 1162 750787
Engineering Services
S.I.C.: 8711
N.A.I.C.S.: 541330

Devonport Royal Dockyard Limited (1)
Devonport Royal Dockyard
Plymouth, PL1 4SG, United Kingdom
Tel.: (44) 1752 323 652
Fax: (44) 1752 324 756
Ship Repair & Maintenance Services
S.I.C.: 3731
N.A.I.C.S.: 336611

Dounreay Site Restoration Limited (1)
Dounreay
Thurso, Caithness, KW14 7TZ, United Kingdom
Tel.: (44) 1847 802121
Fax: (44) 1847 804615
E-Mail: info@dounreay.com
Web Site: www.dounreay.com
Rev.: $244,671,000
Emp.: 900
Engineering Support Services
S.I.C.: 8711
N.A.I.C.S.: 541330
Stephen White *(Chm)*
Tony Wratten *(Deputy Mng Dir)*
Philip Colville *(Sec & Dir-Fin)*

Frazer-Nash Consultancy Ltd. (1)
Styonebridge House Dorking Business Park
Dorking, Surrey, RH4 1HJ, United Kingdom
Tel.: (44) 1306885050
Fax: (44) 1306886464
E-Mail: info@fnc.co.uk
Web Site: www.fnc.co.uk
Sales Range: $25-49.9 Million
Emp.: 350
Engineering & Technical Services for Defense, Aerospace, Power & Transportation Industries
S.I.C.: 8711
N.A.I.C.S.: 541330
Andy Milton *(Chm)*

Liquid Gas Equipment Limited (1)
Young House 42 Discovery Ter Heriot Watt University Research Park
Edinburgh, Scotland, EH14 4AP, United Kingdom UK
Tel.: (44) 131 317 8787
Fax: (44) 131 452 3333
Emp.: 75
Engineering Design & System Integration Services
S.I.C.: 8711
N.A.I.C.S.: 541330
Gary Robinson *(Dir-Fin)*

LSC Group Limited (1)
Lincoln House Wellington Crescent
Lichfield, Staffordshire, WS138RZ, United Kingdom
Tel.: (44) 1543 446 800
Fax: (44) 1543 446 900
E-Mail: group@lsc.co.uk
Web Site: www.lsc.co.uk
Emp.: 130
Business Management Consulting Services
S.I.C.: 8742
N.A.I.C.S.: 541611
George Webb *(Mng Dir)*

Research Sites Restoration Limited (1)
Harwell Oxford
Didcot, OX11 0DF, United Kingdom
Tel.: (44) 1235 820220
E-Mail: news@research-sites.com
Web Site: www.research-sites.com
Engineering Support Services
S.I.C.: 8711
N.A.I.C.S.: 541330
Stephen White *(Chm)*
Alan Neal *(Mng Dir)*

Rosyth Royal Dockyard Limited (1)
Rosyth Royal Dockyard
Dunfermline, Fife, KY11 2Yd, United Kingdom
Tel.: (44) 1383 412131
Fax: (44) 1383417774
Ship Repair & Maintenance Services
S.I.C.: 3731
N.A.I.C.S.: 336611
Archie Bethel *(Gen Mgr)*

U.S. Subsidiaries:

Babcock Eagleton Inc. (1)
2900 N Loop W Ste 1000
Houston, TX 77092
Tel.: (713) 871-8787
Fax: (713) 871-1914
E-Mail: eagleton@eagletoninc.com
Web Site: www.eagletoninc.com
Emp.: 150
Oil & Gas Pipeline Engineering & Support Services
S.I.C.: 1389
N.A.I.C.S.: 213112
Duain Cagle *(Pres)*
Mark Meis *(CFO & VP)*

VT Griffin Services, Inc. (1)
72919 Carter St
Fort Huachuca, AZ 85670
Tel.: (520) 533-1722
Fax: (520) 533-5391
Emp.: 8
Facilities Management Services
S.I.C.: 8744
N.A.I.C.S.: 561210
Karl Greenman *(Bus Mgr)*

VT Group, U.S. (1)
10745 Westside Way Ste 300
Alpharetta, GA 30009
Tel.: (770) 952-1479

Fax: (770) 859-0410
Web Site: www.vt-group.com
Emp.: 2,500
Facilities Management & Technical Support Services
S.I.C.: 7389
N.A.I.C.S.: 561990
Terry Ryan *(CEO)*
Allan Garner *(CFO)*
Chris Taylor *(Pres-Technical Svcs)*
Walt Yourstone *(Pres-Integrated Solutions)*
Susan Springer *(Exec VP-Bus Svcs)*

Non-U.S. Division:

Babcock Africa (Pty) Ltd **(1)**
1 Osborne Lane
Bedfordview, 2007, South Africa (100%)
Mailing Address:
PO Box 4561
Johannesburg, 2000, South Africa
Tel.: (27) 0116011000, ext. 116011000
Fax: (27) 116011052
E-Mail: requestinfoact@babcock.co.za
Web Site: www.babcock.co.za
Emp.: 100
Industrial & Civil Engineering Equipment Mfr
S.I.C.: 8711
N.A.I.C.S.: 541330
Roger O'Callaghan *(CEO)*

Non-U.S. Subsidiaries:

Babcock Africa Services (Pty) Limited **(1)**
49 Great North Road
Benoni, Gauteng, 1501, South Africa
Tel.: (27) 1 000 12561
Fax: (27) 100012569
Engineering Support Services
S.I.C.: 8711
N.A.I.C.S.: 541330

Babcock International Holdings BV **(1)**
Bezuidenhoutseweg 1 S
Hague, 2594 AB, Netherlands
Tel.: (31) 703814411
Fax: (31) 703473471
Investment Management Services
S.I.C.: 6211
N.A.I.C.S.: 523999

Babcock Ntuthuko Engineering (Pty) Limited **(1)**
5 6 Bickley Rd
Nigel, Gauteng, 1491, South Africa
Tel.: (27) 117398200
Fax: (27) 117398201
E-Mail: enquiries@babcock.co.za
Web Site: www.babcock.co.za
Emp.: 16
Engineering Services
S.I.C.: 8711
N.A.I.C.S.: 541330
Madhu Kumar *(Gen Mgr)*

Babcock (NZ) Ltd **(1)**
HMNZ Dockyard Queens Parade
Devonport, Auckland, 744, New Zealand
Tel.: (64) 9 4461999
Fax: (64) 9 4461740
E-Mail: enquiries@babcocknz.co.nz
Web Site: www.babcocknz.co.nz
Emp.: 20
Marine Engineering Services
S.I.C.: 8711
N.A.I.C.S.: 541330
Ivo Bols *(Office Mgr)*

Strachan & Henshaw Australia (PTY) Limited **(1)**
689-695 Mersey Road
Osborne, SA, 5017, Australia
Tel.: (61) 883468921
Fax: (61) 884401401
Emp.: 7
Industrial Truck Mfr
S.I.C.: 3537
N.A.I.C.S.: 333924
Patrick Donovan *(Mng Dir)*

BABIS VOVOS INTERNATIONAL CONSTRUCTION S.A.

340 Kifissias Ave
15451 Neo Psichico, Greece
Tel.: (30) 2106726036
Fax: (30) 2106725866
E-Mail: info@babisvovos.gr
Web Site: www.babisvovos.gr
VOVOS—(ATH)
Sales Range: $50-74.9 Million
Emp.: 349
Business Description:
Real Estate Property Development & Construction Services
S.I.C.: 6531
N.A.I.C.S.: 531312
Personnel:
Charalampos Vovos *(Chm)*
Thaleia Vovos *(Vice Chm)*
Armodios Vovos *(CEO)*
Hatziavraam Stavros *(CFO)*
Board of Directors:
Charalampos Vovos
Asimakopoulos Evangelia
Corina Sylira
Nicolaas J. M. Van Ommen
Armodios Vovos
Thaleia Vovos
Triada Vovos

BABYLON BANK S.A.

Babylon Bank Bldg Sadoon St
Baghdad, Iraq
Tel.: (964) 7176089
Fax: (964) 7191014
E-Mail: info@babylonbank-iq.com
Web Site: www.babylonbank-iq.com
BBAY—(IRAQ)
Sales Range: $10-24.9 Million
Business Description:
Commercial Banking Services
S.I.C.: 6029
N.A.I.C.S.: 522110
Personnel:
Abdul-Razzak Mansour *(Chm)*
Tariq Abdul-Baki Al-Ani *(Gen Dir)*
Board of Directors:
Abdul-Razzak Mansour
Faiq Saleem Rasheed Al-Ani
Tariq Abdul-Baki Al-Ani
Haider Kadhim Al-Ebadi
Ahmad Hussain Abid Al-Izairjawi
Jaafar Raffi Sheikl Ali
Mazen Abdul-Razzak Mansour

BABYLON LTD.

10 Hataasiya Street
60212 Or Yehud, Israel
Tel.: (972) 3 5382111
Web Site: www.babylon.com
Year Founded: 1997
BBYL—(TAE)
Sales Range: $50-74.9 Million
Emp.: 165
Business Description:
Translation Software
S.I.C.: 7372
N.A.I.C.S.: 511210
Personnel:
Noam Lanir *(Chm)*
Nadav Shemesh *(Deputy CEO & CIO)*
Shanit Pe'er Tsfoni *(CFO)*
Shlomi Zaig *(CTO)*
Board of Directors:
Noam Lanir
Rami Entin
Gil Rozen
Efrat Tolkowsky

BAC KAN MINERAL JOINT STOCK CORPORATION

Duc Xuan Ward
Bac Kan District, Hanoi, Bac Kan, Vietnam
Tel.: (84) 2813871779
Fax: (84) 2813871837
E-Mail: info@backanco.com
Web Site: www.backanco.com
Year Founded: 2000
BKC—(HNX)
Rev.: $2,433,540
Assets: $7,058,445
Liabilities: $3,213,432
Net Worth: $3,845,014
Earnings: ($848,771)
Emp.: 1,008
Fiscal Year-end: 12/31/12
Business Description:
Metal & Mineral Products Mfr & Distr
S.I.C.: 3499
N.A.I.C.S.: 332999
Personnel:
Mai Van Ban *(Chm)*
Board of Directors:
Mai Van Ban
Nguyen Thi Xuan Huong
Nguyen Ngoc Son
Hoang Ngoc Thai

BAC LIEU FISHERIES JOINT STOCK COMPANY

72 Le Loi Street Floor 01
District 1, Ho Chi Minh City, Vietnam
Tel.: (84) 8 38247201
Fax: (84) 8 38246747
E-Mail: dam@baclieufis.vn
Web Site: www.baclieufis.vn
BLF—(HNX)
Business Description:
Processed Seafood Distr
S.I.C.: 5421
N.A.I.C.S.: 445220
Personnel:
Thanh Dam Nguyen *(Gen Mgr)*

BAC NINH AGRICULTURAL PRODUCTS JOINT-STOCKS COMPANY

Ly Thai To street
Bac Ninh, Vietnam
Tel.: (84) 241 820712
Fax: (84) 241 821377
Web Site: www.dabaco.com.vn
DBC—(HNX)
Sales Range: $125-149.9 Million
Business Description:
Animal Feed Mfr
S.I.C.: 2048
N.A.I.C.S.: 311119
Personnel:
Nhu So Nguyen *(Chm & Gen Mgr)*

BACANORA MINERALS LTD.

1800 510 5 ST SW
Calgary, AB, T2P 3S2, Canada
Tel.: (403) 237-6122
Fax: (403) 237-6144
E-Mail: info@bacanoraminerals.com
Web Site: www.bacanoraminerals.com
Year Founded: 2008
BCN.P—(TSXV)
Int. Income: $10,852
Assets: $12,308,160
Liabilities: $1,049,095
Net Worth: $11,259,066
Earnings: ($810,885)
Fiscal Year-end: 06/30/13
Business Description:
Investment Services
S.I.C.: 6211
N.A.I.C.S.: 523999
Personnel:
Paul Conroy *(Founder & VP-Special Projects)*
Martin Fernando Vidal Torres *(Pres)*
Shane W. Shircliff *(CEO)*
Derek Batorowski *(CFO)*
Paul Bolger *(Sec)*
Board of Directors:
Derek Batorowski
Paul Conroy
James Leahy
Colin Orr-Ewing
Martin Fernando Vidal Torres
Guy Walker
Transfer Agent:
Alliance Trust Company
450 407 2nd St SW
Calgary, AB, Canada

BACARDI LIMITED

65 Pitts Bay Rd
Pembroke, HM 08, Bermuda
Mailing Address:
PO Box HM 720
Hamilton, HM CX, Bermuda
Tel.: (441) 2954345
Fax: (441) 2920562
E-Mail: webmaster@bacardi.com
Web Site: www.bacardilimited.com
Year Founded: 1862
Emp.: 6,000
Business Description:
Holding Company: Distilleries Import Export
S.I.C.: 2085
N.A.I.C.S.: 312140
Personnel:
Facundo L. Bacardi *(Chm)*
Edward D. Shirley *(Pres & CEO)*
Rich Andrews *(Mng Dir)*
Joseph J. Schena *(CFO & Sr VP)*
Caroline Basyn *(CIO)*
Ron Anderson *(Chief Comml Officer, Sr VP & Head-Global Travel Retail)*
Eric A. Kraus *(Chief Comm & Corp Affairs Officer & Sr VP)*
Jon Grey *(Reg Pres-MEA & Sr VP-Global Ops)*
Robert Furniss-Roe *(Pres-North America)*
Eduardo B. Sanchez *(Gen Counsel & Sr VP)*
Scott M. Northcutt *(Sr VP-HR)*
Board of Directors:
Facundo L. Bacardi
Victor R. Arellano, Jr.
Jamie Bergel
Francisco V. Carrera-Justiz
Robert J. Corti
Adolfo L. Danguillecourt
Paul M. de Hechavarria
Ignacio De La Rocha
Michael J. Dolan
John S. Galantic
Georgia Garinois-Melenikiotou
Barry E. Kabalkin
Patrice Louvet
Roman Martinez, IV
Philip Shearer
Edward D. Shirley
Theodore C. Walker

Subsidiaries:

Bacardi Capital Limited **(1)**
65 Pitts Bay Road
Pembroke, HM 08, Bermuda
Mailing Address:
PO Box HM 1495
Hamilton, HM FX, Bermuda
Tel.: (441) 2954345
Fax: (441) 2923007
Web Site: www.bacardi.com
Emp.: 70
S.I.C.: 2084
N.A.I.C.S.: 312130

Bacardi International Limited **(1)**
65 Pitts Bay Road
Pembroke, HM 08, Bermuda
Mailing Address:
PO Box HM 720
Hamilton, HM CX, Bermuda
Tel.: (441) 2954345
Fax: (441) 2920562
Web Site: www.onebacardi.com
Emp.: 65
S.I.C.: 2084
N.A.I.C.S.: 312130

Bacardi Limited—(Continued)

Ed Shirley *(Pres & CEO)*

U.S. Subsidiaries:

Bacardi Corporation **(1)**
PO Box 363549
San Juan, PR 00936-3549 DE
Tel.: (787) 788-1500
Fax: (787) 788-0340
E-Mail: info@barcardi.com
Web Site: www.barcardi.com
Emp.: 300
Distillation, Aging, Bottling & Wholesale Distributor of Rum; Marketing of Home Appliances; Refreshment Bottlers; Environmental Testing; Distribution of Liquors & Food Stuffs
Import Export
S.I.C.: 2085
N.A.I.C.S.: 312140
Joaquin Bacardi *(Pres & CEO)*

Subsidiaries:

Bacardi Bottling Corporation **(2)**
12200 N Main St
Jacksonville, FL 32218-3819 FL
Mailing Address: (100%)
PO Box 26368
Jacksonville, FL 32226-6368
Tel.: (904) 757-1290
Fax: (904) 751-1397
Web Site: www.ashgrove.com
Emp.: 300
Rectifies & Bottles Rum
S.I.C.: 5181
N.A.I.C.S.: 424810
Laurent Dijon *(Mgr-Engrg & Maintenance)*

Bacardi Corporation **(2)**
200 Rd 165 Kil 26
San Juan, PR 00962-3127 DE
Tel.: (787) 788-1500 (100%)
Fax: (787) 275-3902
E-Mail: info@bacardi.com
Emp.: 350
Distributor of Rum & Foodstuffs
S.I.C.: 5182
N.A.I.C.S.: 424820
Jose Melendez *(Dir-Fin)*

Non-U.S. Holding:

Bacardi Centroamerica, S.A. **(2)**
Calle 50 y Aquilino de la Guardia Edifico American International
Piso 5 Officina 1, Panama, Panama (100%)
Mailing Address:
PO Box 0819
05470 Panama, Panama
Tel.: (507) 2697002
Fax: (507) 2691124
E-Mail: i.velballe@bacardi.com
Emp.: 12
Distilled & Blended Liquors
Import Export
S.I.C.: 2084
N.A.I.C.S.: 312130
Ignacio Velyalle *(Mgr)*

Bacardi Global Brands Inc. **(1)**
866 Ponce De Leon Blvd Fl 2
Coral Gables, FL 33134-3039 FL
Tel.: (305) 446-9050
Fax: (305) 446-2137
Web Site: www.knight-sec.com
Emp.: 20
Distilled & Blended Liquors
S.I.C.: 5182
N.A.I.C.S.: 424820
Gianpaolo Perego *(Pres-Latin America)*

Bacardi USA, Inc. **(1)**
2701 Le Jeu Rd
Coral Gables, FL 33134-5014 DE
Tel.: (305) 573-8511
Telex: 305-573-1235
Fax: (305) 573-7507
E-Mail: info@bacardi.com
Web Site: www.bacardi.com
Sales Range: $1-4.9 Billion
Emp.: 400
Wholesale Spirits & Liquor
Import
S.I.C.: 5182
N.A.I.C.S.: 424820
Michael Misiorski *(CFO & Sr VP)*
Robert Furniss-Roe *(Pres-North America)*

Non-U.S. Subsidiaries:

Bacardi & Company Limited **(1)**
1000 Bacardi Road
PO Box N-4880
Nassau, Bahamas
Tel.: (242) 3623100
Fax: (242) 3621718
Distilled & blended Liquors
S.I.C.: 2085
N.A.I.C.S.: 312140
Felix Mateo *(Plant Dir)*

Bacardi Canada, Inc. **(1)**
1000 Steeles Ave E
Brampton, ON, L6T 1A1, Canada (100%)
Mailing Address:
PO Box 368
Brampton, ON, L6V 2L3, Canada
Tel.: (905) 451-6100
Fax: (905) 451-6753
Web Site: www.bacardi.ca
Emp.: 150
Distilled & Blended Liquors
S.I.C.: 2085
N.A.I.C.S.: 312140
Craig Bradshaw *(VP-HR)*

Bacardi Espana S.A. **(1)**
Calle Facundo Bacardi 14
Mollet Del Valles, 08100 Barcelona, Spain (100%)
Tel.: (34) 935657100
Fax: (34) 935939855
Web Site: www.bacardi.com
Emp.: 400
Distilled & Blended Liquors
S.I.C.: 2085
N.A.I.C.S.: 312140

Bacardi France S.A.S. **(1)**
19 Ave Michelet
F 93400 Saint-Ouen, France (100%)
Mailing Address:
BP 50
F-93401 Saint-Ouen, Cedex, France
Tel.: (33) 49454800
Fax: (33) 149454903
E-Mail: lbach@bacardi.com
Emp.: 250
Distilled & Blended Liquors
S.I.C.: 2085
N.A.I.C.S.: 312140

Bacardi Global Brands Limited **(1)**
205 Brooklands Rd
Weybridge, Surrey, KT13 0BG, United Kingdom (100%)
Tel.: (44) 1932826400
Fax: (44) 1932826500
E-Mail: info@bacardi.co.uk
Web Site: www.bacardi.co.uk
Emp.: 40
Distilled & Blended Liquors
S.I.C.: 2085
N.A.I.C.S.: 312140
Andy J. Gibson *(Pres & CMO)*

Bacardi GmbH **(1)**
Hindenburg Strasse 49
D 22297 Hamburg, Germany (100%)
Mailing Address:
Postfach 10 31 40
D-20021 Hamburg, Germany
Tel.: (49) 40339500
Fax: (49) 4033950214
E-Mail: info@bacardi.com
Web Site: www.bacardi-deutschland.de
Emp.: 300
Distilled & Blended Liquors
S.I.C.: 2085
N.A.I.C.S.: 312140
Michael Volke *(CEO)*
Joerg Hansch *(CFO & Dir-Fin)*

Bacardi-Martini Asia-Pacific Limited **(1)**
Fl 18 Bank Of E Asia Harbour View Center
56 Gloucester Rd, Wanchai, China (Hong Kong) (100%)
Tel.: (852) 25280009
Fax: (852) 28042879
Web Site: www.bacardiltd.com
Emp.: 25
Distilled & Blended Liquors
S.I.C.: 2085
N.A.I.C.S.: 312140
Siddik Tetik *(Pres)*

Bacardi-Martini Belgium NV **(1)**
Rue Vanden Boogaerde 108
B-1080 Brussels, Belgium
Tel.: (32) 24234811
Fax: (32) 24277960
Web Site: www.bacardi-martini.be
Sales Range: $75-99.9 Million
Emp.: 75
Wines, Brandy & Brandy Spirits; Distilled & Blended Liquors
Import Export
S.I.C.: 2084
N.A.I.C.S.: 312130
Francis Debeuckelaere *(Gen Mgr)*

Bacardi-Martini BV **(1)**
PO Box 914
NL 2800 AX Gouda, Netherlands (100%)
Tel.: (31) 182390000
Fax (31) 182390099
E-Mail: bmbz@bacardi.com
Web Site: www.bacardinederland.nl
Emp.: 20
Distilled & Blended Liquors
S.I.C.: 2085
N.A.I.C.S.: 312140

Bacardi-Martini Chile S.A. **(1)**
595 Ureta Cox
San Miguel, Santiago, Chile (99%)
Tel.: (56) 25522194
Fax: (56) 25522163
E-Mail: bacardi@netline.cl
Emp.: 16
Distilled & Blended Liquors
S.I.C.: 2085
N.A.I.C.S.: 312140

Bacardi-Martini Danmark A/S **(1)**
Baltorpbakken 1
DK 2750 Ballerup, Denmark (100%)
Tel.: (45) 44866644
Fax: (45) 44663722
E-Mail: danmark@bacardi.com
Web Site: www.bacardi.dk
Emp.: 20
Distilled & Blended Liquors
S.I.C.: 2085
N.A.I.C.S.: 312140
Anne Marie Eberhardt *(Mgr-Mktg)*

Non-U.S. Subsidiary:

Bacardi-Martini Finland **(2)**
Punavuorenkatu 17
00150 Helsinki, Finland (100%)
Tel.: (358) 96980610
Web Site: www.bacardi.fi
Emp.: 4
Distilled & Blended Liquors Sales & Marketing
S.I.C.: 5182
N.A.I.C.S.: 424820
Timo Laurila *(Acct Mgr)*

Bacardi-Martini France **(1)**
19 Ave Michelet
93400 Saint-Ouen, France (100%)
Tel.: (33) 149454800
Fax: (33) 149454903
Web Site: www.bacardi-martini.fr
Emp.: 200
Distilled & Blended Liquors
S.I.C.: 2085
N.A.I.C.S.: 312140
Sylvie Henon *(CEO)*

Bacardi-Martini GmbH **(1)**
Handelskai
94296, A 1200 Vienna, Austria (100%)
Tel.: (43) 610310
Fax: (43) 61031230
E-Mail: info@bacardi.at
Web Site: www.bacardi.at
Emp.: 35
Distilled & Blended Liquors
S.I.C.: 2085
N.A.I.C.S.: 312140
Dietir Angermair *(Mgr)*

Bacardi-Martini Hungary Kft. **(1)**
Retkoz Utca 5
H 1118 Budapest, Hungary (80%)
Tel.: (36) 12464283
Fax: (36) 12464288
Web Site: www.bacardi.hu
Emp.: 50
Provider of Distilled & Blended Liquors
S.I.C.: 2085
N.A.I.C.S.: 312140

Bacardi-Martini India Limited **(1)**
227 Ground Fl Okhla Industrial Estate Phase III
New Delhi, 110020, India (100%)
Tel.: (91) 11 6310422
Fax: (91) 11 6315610
E-Mail: info@bacardi.com
Web Site: www.bacardilimited.com
Emp.: 35
Distilled & Blended Liquors
S.I.C.: 2085
N.A.I.C.S.: 312140
Mahesh Madhvan *(Mng Dir)*

Bacardi-Martini Pacific Pty. Ltd. **(1)**
Level 8 Kent St 201
Sydney, NSW, 2000, Australia (100%)
Tel.: (61) 296901911
Fax: (61) 296900529
E-Mail: harrys@Bacardi-Martini.com.au
Web Site: www.bacardilion.com.au/
Emp.: 40
Distilled & Blended Liquors
S.I.C.: 2085
N.A.I.C.S.: 312140

Bacardi-Martini Russia **(1)**
Riverside Towers Kosmodamianskaya Nabereznhaya 22 4
Moscow, 115054, Russia (100%)
Tel.: (7) 0957559785
Fax: (7) 4957559787
E-Mail: info@bacardi.com
Emp.: 100
Distilled & Blended Liquors
S.I.C.: 2085
N.A.I.C.S.: 312140
Robert Furniss Roe *(Gen Mgr)*

Bacardi-Martini (Suisse) S.a.r.L. **(1)**
267 Rte De Meyrin
Case Postale 105, CH 1217 Meyrin, Switzerland (100%)
Tel.: (41) 227193500
Fax: (41) 227193499
E-Mail: info@bacardi-martini.com
Web Site: www.bacardi-martini.com
Emp.: 218
Distilled & Blended Liquors
S.I.C.: 2085
N.A.I.C.S.: 312140
John Grey *(Gen Mgr)*

Bacardi-Martini UK Limited **(1)**
W Bay Rd
Western Docks, Southampton, SO15 1DT, United Kingdom (100%)
Tel.: (44) 2380318000
Fax: (44) 2380226147
Web Site: www.bacardi.co.uk
Emp.: 600
Distilled & Blended Liquors
S.I.C.: 2085
N.A.I.C.S.: 312140
John Beard *(Mng Dir)*
Maurice Doyle *(Mng Dir-Global Travel & Retail)*
Stella David *(CMO-Global)*

Bacardi-Martini Uruguay S.A. **(1)**
Eduardo Pondal 782
Montevideo, 12090, Uruguay (100%)
Tel.: (598) 23091416
Telex: 22118
Fax: (598) 23093216
E-Mail: adas@bacardi.com
Emp.: 50
Wines, Brandy & Brandy Spirits
Import
S.I.C.: 2084
N.A.I.C.S.: 312130
Selvena Deresa *(CFO)*

Bacardi Nederland N.V. **(1)**
Groningenweg 8
2803 PV Gouda, Netherlands (100%)
Tel.: (31) 182569999
Fax: (31) 182569900
E-Mail: bacardinl@bacardi.com
Web Site: www.bacardi.nl
Emp.: 75
Distilled & Blended Liquors
S.I.C.: 2085
N.A.I.C.S.: 312140
Francis Debeuckelaere *(Gen Mgr)*

Bacardi Shanghai Limited **(1)**
19F Peregrine Plaza 1 Baoquing Rd
Shanghai, Xuhui, 200031, China (100%)
Tel.: (86) 2164660299
Fax: (86) 216466298
Web Site: www.bacardilimited.com
Emp.: 50
Distilled & Blended Liquors

S.I.C.: 2085
N.A.I.C.S.: 312140
Carol Cheng *(Portfolio Mgr-Luxury Brands)*

Bacardi Venezuela C.A. (1)
Ave Venezuela Clement
El Rosal, Caracas, Miranda, 1060, Venezuela
Tel.: (58) 2129515987
Fax: (58) 2129514701
Emp.: 20
Distilled & Blended Liquors
S.I.C.: 2085
N.A.I.C.S.: 312140

Bacardi y Compania, S.A. de C.V. (1)
Autopista Mexico Queretaro No 4431
54900 Tultitlan, Mexico (100%)
Mailing Address:
Apartado 8304
CP 06000 Mexico, D.F., Mexico
Tel.: (52) 5558990900
Fax: (52) 5558990999
Emp.: 700
Distilled & Blended Liquors
S.I.C.: 2085
N.A.I.C.S.: 312140

BACH DANG TMC CONSTRUCTION INVESTMENT JSC

24 22 Trung Kinh
Trung Hoa
Cau Giay, Hanoi, Vietnam
Tel.: (84) 437834070
Fax: (84) 437834071
E-Mail: bachdangtmc@gmail.com
Web Site: www.bachdangtmc.com
BHT—(HNX)
Emp.: 110
Business Description:
Construction Services
S.I.C.: 1542
N.A.I.C.S.: 236220
Personnel:
Thuong Van Nguyen *(Chm-Mgmt Bd)*

BACHEM HOLDING AG

Hauptstrasse 144
4416 Bubendorf, Switzerland
Tel.: (41) 619352333
Fax: (41) 619352325
E-Mail: sales.ch@bachem.com
Web Site: www.bachem.com
Year Founded: 1971
BANB—(SWX)
Sls.: $169,774,877
Assets: $491,424,110
Liabilities: $138,677,510
Net Worth: $352,746,600
Earnings: $16,513,596
Emp.: 645
Fiscal Year-end: 12/31/12
Business Description:
Holding Company; Biochemicals & Pharmaceutical Compounds Mfr
S.I.C.: 6719
N.A.I.C.S.: 551112
Personnel:
Kuno Sommer *(Chm)*
Thomas Fruh *(CEO)*
Stephan Schindler *(CFO)*
Jose de Chastonay *(CMO)*
Daniel Erne *(CTO)*
Alex Fassler *(Pres/COO-Bachem Americas)*
Damir Vidovic *(Pres/COO-Peninsula Laboratories LLC)*
Fritz Dick *(COO/Exec VP-Bachem AG)*
Thomas Burckhardt *(Sec)*
Board of Directors:
Kuno Sommer
Jurgen Brokatzky-Geiger
Thomas Burckhardt
Hans Hengartner
Nicole Grogg Hotzer
Rolf Nyfeler

Subsidiaries:

Bachem AG (1)
Hauptstrasse 144
4416 Bubendorf, Switzerland (100%)
Tel.: (41) 619352323
Fax: (41) 619352325
E-Mail: empfang@bachem.com
Web Site: www.bachem.com
Emp.: 400
Mfr. of Technical Equipment for Solid Phase Synthesis & Purification of Peptides
S.I.C.: 3559
N.A.I.C.S.: 333249
Thomas Fruh *(COO-Switzerland & Exec VP)*

Sochinaz SA (1)
Rte Du Samtlon 22
Vionnaz, CH 1895, Switzerland CH (100%)
Tel.: (41) 244824444
Fax: (41) 244824445
E-Mail: info@sochinaz.ch
Web Site: www.sochinaz.ch
Emp.: 100
Mfr. of Organic Intermediates & Active Pharmaceutical Ingredients
S.I.C.: 2834
N.A.I.C.S.: 325412
Frederic Besancon *(COO)*

Joint Venture:

Pevion Biotech AG (1)
Worblentalstrasse 32
Ittigen, CH 3063 Bern, Switzerland
Tel.: (41) 315504444
Fax: (41) 315504445
E-Mail: info@pevion.com
Web Site: www.pevion.com
Emp.: 24
Biopharmaceutical Research, Development & Mfr
S.I.C.: 2834
N.A.I.C.S.: 325412
Didier Hoch *(Chm)*
Evert Kueppers *(CEO)*

U.S. Subsidiaries:

Bachem Americas, Inc. (1)
3132 Kashiwa St
Torrance, CA 90505
Tel.: (310) 539-4171
Fax: (310) 539-9428
Emp.: 32
Active Pharmaceutical Ingredient Sales & Distribution Services
S.I.C.: 5169
N.A.I.C.S.: 424690
Alex Fassler *(Pres & COO)*

Bachem Bioscience. Inc. (1)
3700 Horizon Dr
King of Prussia, PA 19406
Tel.: (610) 239-0300
Fax: (610) 239-0800
Web Site: www.bachem.com
Emp.: 5
Research, Development & Manufacturer of Amino Acids, Peptides & Solid Phase Synthesis
S.I.C.: 2836
N.A.I.C.S.: 325414
Denise Wynn-Southerland *(Dir-Logistics)*

Bachem, Inc. (1)
3132 Kashiwa St
Torrance, CA 90505
Tel.: (310) 784-4440
Fax: (310) 530-2426
E-Mail: customerservice@usbachem.com
Web Site: www.bachem.com
Emp.: 90
Mfr of Active Pharmaceutical Ingredients, Peptides & Organic Molecules Mfr
S.I.C.: 2834
N.A.I.C.S.: 325412
Alex Fassler *(Pres & COO)*

Peninsula Laboratories LLC (1)
305 Old County Rd
San Carlos, CA 94070-6241
Tel.: (650) 801-6090
Fax: (650) 595-4071
Emp.: 8
Mfr. of Biochemicals
S.I.C.: 2833
N.A.I.C.S.: 325411
Damir Vidovic *(Pres & COO)*

Non-U.S. Subsidiaries:

Bachem Distribution Services GmbH (1)
Hegenheimer Strasse 5
79576 Weil am Rhein, Germany De (100%)
Tel.: (49) 41619352323
Fax: (49) 41619352325
Web Site: www.bachem.com
Emp.: 5
Mfr of Peptide Active Pharmaceutical Ingredients
S.I.C.: 2899
N.A.I.C.S.: 325998
Rolf Nyfeler *(CEO)*

Bachem (UK) Ltd. (1)
Delph Court Sullivans Way
Saint Helens, Merseyside, WA9 5GL, United Kingdom UK (100%)
Tel.: (44) 1744612108
Fax: (44) 1744730064
E-Mail: uk.inequiries@bachem.com
Web Site: www.bachem.com
Emp.: 19
Mfr. & Reseach of Peptides & Solid Phase Synthesis
S.I.C.: 2899
N.A.I.C.S.: 325998
Stanley Moore *(COO)*

BACIL PHARMA LIMITED

71 Laxmi Building Sir P M Road
Fort, Mumbai, 400001, India
Tel.: (91) 22 22661541
E-Mail: info@bacilpharma.com
Web Site: www.bacilpharma.com
524516—(BOM)
Rev.: $199,222
Assets: $1,285,709
Liabilities: $60,958
Net Worth: $1,224,751
Earnings: ($4,350)
Fiscal Year-end: 03/31/13
Business Description:
Agro Product Whslr
S.I.C.: 5153
N.A.I.C.S.: 424510
Personnel:
Prakash Shah *(Compliance Officer)*
Board of Directors:
Lalit Jain
Prakash Shah
Shirish Shetye
Transfer Agent:
Bigshare Services Pvt. Ltd.
E-2/3 Ansa Industrial Estate Sakivihar Road
Saki Naka Andheri E
Mumbai, India

BACKERHAUS VEIT LTD

70 Whitmore Road
Woodbridge, ON, L4L 7Z4, Canada
Tel.: (905) 850-9229
Fax: (905) 850-9292
E-Mail: info@backerhausveit.com
Web Site: www.backerhausveit.com
Year Founded: 1986
Rev.: $20,000,000
Emp.: 100
Business Description:
Bakery Products Mfr & Distr
S.I.C.: 2053
N.A.I.C.S.: 311813
Personnel:
Sabine Veit *(Pres & CEO)*

BACKWEB TECHNOLOGIES LTD.

10 Ha'amal Street
Park Afek, 48092 Rosh Ha'Ayin, Israel
Tel.: (972) 39002700
Fax: (972) 39002702
E-Mail: bwebf@backweb.com
Web Site: www.backweb.com
Year Founded: 1995
BWEBF—(OTC)
Sales Range: $1-9.9 Million
Business Description:
Offline Web Infrastructure Software Developer
S.I.C.: 3652
N.A.I.C.S.: 334614
Personnel:
Tomer Assis *(VP-Fin)*
Board of Directors:
Kara Andersen Reiter
Uday Bellary
Yael Resnik Cramer
Amir Makleff
Transfer Agent:
American Stock Transfer & Trust Company
59 Maiden Ln Plz Level
New York, NY 10038
Tel.: (212) 936-5100
Toll Free: (800) 937-5449

BACTECH ENVIRONMENTAL CORPORATION

50 Richmond Street East Suite 300
Toronto, ON, M5C 1N7, Canada
Tel.: (416) 813-0303
Fax: (416) 596-9840
E-Mail: info@bactechgreen.com
Web Site: www.bactechgreen.com
Year Founded: 2010
BAC—(CNSX OTC)
Assets: $1,317,396
Liabilities: $936,434
Net Worth: $380,961
Earnings: ($1,369,159)
Fiscal Year-end: 12/31/12
Business Description:
Biotechnology Researcher & Developer
S.I.C.: 8731
N.A.I.C.S.: 541711
Personnel:
John C. Gingerich *(Chm)*
M. Ross Orr *(Pres & CEO)*
Louis Robert Nagy *(CFO & Sec)*
David J. Salari *(COO)*
Board of Directors:
John C. Gingerich
W. Walter Cimowsky
Elena Gerasimovskaya
Jay L. Naster
M. Ross Orr
Donald A. Whalen
Legal Counsel:
Borden Ladner Gervais LLP
2400 Scotia Plaza 40 King Street West
Toronto, ON, M5H 3C2, Canada
Transfer Agent:
Computershare Investor Services Inc.
100 University Ave 9th Floor
Toronto, ON, Canada

BACVIET STEEL JSC

53 Duc Giang
Long Bien District, Hanoi, Vietnam
Tel.: (84) 436559257
Fax: (84) 438773648
Web Site: www.bacvietgroup.com
BVG—(HNX)
Emp.: 330
Business Description:
Steel Product Mfr
S.I.C.: 3312
N.A.I.C.S.: 331110
Personnel:
Vuong Anh Tran *(Chm)*

BAD BOY FURNITURE WAREHOUSE LIMITED

500 Fenmar Drive
Weston, ON, M9L 2V5, Canada
Tel.: (416) 667-7546

Bad Boy Furniture Warehouse Limited—(Continued)

Fax: (416) 736-8090
Web Site: www.badboy.ca
Year Founded: 1991
Rev.: $36,062,400
Emp.: 200
Business Description:
Furniture & Appliance Supplier
S.I.C.: 5712
N.A.I.C.S.: 442110
Personnel:
Blayne Lastman *(Chm & CEO)*

BAD RULMENTI SA

111 Zizinului street
Brasov, Romania
Tel.: (40) 268 331 984
Fax: (40) 268 330 941
E-Mail: office@rulmenti-badr.ro
Web Site: www.rulmenti-badr.ro
Year Founded: 1949
BARU—(BUC)
Rev.: $2,507,757
Assets: $12,502,189
Liabilities: $5,713,861
Net Worth: $6,788,328
Earnings: $5,617
Emp.: 57
Fiscal Year-end: 12/31/12
Business Description:
Bearing Mfr
S.I.C.: 3562
N.A.I.C.S.: 332991
Personnel:
Constantin Cartana *(Pres)*
Board of Directors:
Constantin Cartana
Constanta Gaman

BADANAI MOTORS LTD

399 Memorial Ave
Thunder Bay, ON, P7B 3Y4, Canada
Tel.: (807) 683-4900
Fax: (807) 345-8005
Toll Free: (800) 465-3915
Web Site: www.badanaimotors.gm.ca
Rev.: $29,039,613
Emp.: 60
Business Description:
New & Used Car Dealers
S.I.C.: 5511
N.A.I.C.S.: 441110
Personnel:
George Badanai *(Owner)*

BADEL 1862 D.D.

Vlaska 116
10000 Zagreb, Croatia
Tel.: (385) 14609555
Fax: (385) 14609106
E-Mail: jadranka.koprivnjak@badel1862.hr
Web Site: www.badel1862.hr
Year Founded: 1862
BD62-R-A—(ZAG)
Sales Range: $50-74.9 Million
Emp.: 500
Business Description:
Wine & Spirits Mfr & Distr
S.I.C.: 2084
N.A.I.C.S.: 312130
Personnel:
Ana Mandac *(Chm-Supervisory Bd)*
Tomislav Vujic *(Deputy Chm-Supervisory Bd)*
Srdan Oreb *(Gen Mgr & Member-Mgmt Bd)*
Supervisory Board of Directors:
Ana Mandac
Zdenko Ljevak
Ante Vrancic
Tomislav Vujic

Non-U.S. Subsidiaries:

Badel 1862 d.o.o (1)
Bulevar Mihajla Pupina 121
Novi, 10070 Belgrade, Serbia
Tel.: (381) 112137832
Fax: (381) 112132588
E-Mail: officebg@badel1862.co.rs
Emp.: 10
Wine & Spirits Mfr
S.I.C.: 2084
N.A.I.C.S.: 312130
Mirko Babic *(Gen Mgr)*

Badel d.o.o.e.l. (1)
Kolektorska bb
91000 Skopje, Macedonia
Tel.: (389) 23175114
Fax: (389) 23173838
E-Mail: badel@mt.net.mk
Emp.: 10
Wine & Spirits Mfr
S.I.C.: 2084
N.A.I.C.S.: 312130
Lobco Bavlovske *(Mng Dir)*

Badel Sarajevo d.o.o. (1)
Fetaha Beirbegovica 45
71000 Sarajevo, Bosnia & Herzegovina
Tel.: (387) 33712470
Fax: (387) 33712472
E-Mail: badel1862@badel1862.ba
Emp.: 15
Wine & Spirits Mfr
S.I.C.: 2084
N.A.I.C.S.: 312130
Jasminka Sahinovic *(Mgr)*

BADGER DAYLIGHTING LTD.

1000 635 8th Avenue SW
Calgary, AB, T2P 3M3, Canada
Tel.: (403) 264-8500
Fax: (403) 228-9773
Toll Free: (800) 465-4273
E-Mail: corporate@badgerinc.com
Web Site: www.badgerinc.com
Year Founded: 1992
BAD—(TSX)
Rev.: $237,798,113
Assets: $224,233,425
Liabilities: $85,361,106
Net Worth: $138,872,320
Earnings: $27,882,021
Emp.: 1,085
Fiscal Year-end: 12/31/12
Business Description:
Excavating Services
S.I.C.: 1381
N.A.I.C.S.: 213111
Personnel:
Tor Wilson *(Pres & CEO)*
Greg Kelly *(CFO & VP)*
David Calnan *(Sec)*
John G. Kelly *(Exec VP-US)*
Board of Directors:
David Calnan
J. Richard Couillard
Garry Paul Mihaichuk
Glen D. Roane
George William Watson
Tor Wilson
Transfer Agent:
Computershare Trust Company of Canada
Calgary, AB, Canada

U.S. Subsidiary:

Badger Daylighting (1)
777 Orchard
Bayfield, CO 81122
Tel.: (970) 884-7380
Web Site: www.badgerinc.com
Emp.: 12
Excavation Work
S.I.C.: 1799
N.A.I.C.S.: 238910
Richard Couillard *(Pres & CEO)*
Corey Gosney *(Pres)*

BAE SYSTEMS PLC

6 Carlton Gardens
London, SW1Y 5AD, United Kingdom
Tel.: (44) 1252373232
Telex: 919221
Fax: (44) 1252383991
E-Mail: baesystems.hr@hr.xchanging.com
Web Site: www.baesystems.com
Year Founded: 1977
BA—(LSE)
Sls.: $28,165,057,860
Assets: $35,177,105,460
Liabilities: $29,216,865,000
Net Worth: $5,960,240,460
Earnings: $1,704,053,910
Emp.: 88,200
Fiscal Year-end: 12/31/12
Business Description:
Holding Company; Military Equipment & Technologies Developer & Mfr Export
S.I.C.: 6719
N.A.I.C.S.: 551112
Personnel:
Richard Olver *(Chm)*
Ian G. King *(CEO)*
Ben Bridge *(Mng Dir-Middle East & Africa)*
DeEtte Gray *(Pres-Intelligence & Security)*
Erin Moseley *(Pres-Support Solutions Sector)*
Frank Pope *(Pres-Enterprise Shared Svcs)*
Ian T. Graham *(Gen Counsel & Sr VP-BAE Systems Inc)*
Philip Bramwell *(Gen Counsel)*
David Parkes *(Sec)*
Curt Gray *(Sr VP-HR & Admin & Acting VP-Internal Audit-BAE Systems Inc)*
Douglas Belair *(Sr VP-Strategy & Plng-BAE Systems Inc)*
D. Michael Bennett *(Sr VP-Info Mgmt-BAE Systems Inc)*
Brad Jacobs *(Sr VP-Fin-BAE Systems Inc)*
Board of Directors:
Richard Olver
Paul M. Anderson
Jerry DeMuro
Keryn Harriet Green
Chris Grigg
Ian G. King
Peter J. Lynas
Paula G. Rosput Reynolds
Nicholas C. Rose
Carl Symon
Ian P. Tyler

Subsidiaries:

BAE Systems Detica (1)
Waterside House 170 Priestley Road
Surrey Research Park
Guildford, Surrey, GU2 7RQ, United Kingdom
Tel.: (44) 1483 816000
Fax: (44) 1483 816144
E-Mail: marketing@baesystemsdetica.com
Web Site: www.baesystemsdetica.com
Information Technology Consulting Services
S.I.C.: 7373
N.A.I.C.S.: 541512
Dave Brown *(Mng Dir)*
Martin Sutherland *(Mng Dir)*
Neil Medley *(COO)*
Morag Lucey *(CMO)*
David Garfield *(CTO & Mng Dir-Cyber Security)*

Non-U.S. Subsidiary:

BAE Systems Detica GCS A/S (2)
Bouet Moellevej 3-5
PO Box 132
9400 Sundby, Denmark
Tel.: (45) 38 10 62 00
Fax: (45) 38 16 00 16
E-Mail: europe@eticonnect.net
Web Site: www.eticonnect.net
Emp.: 230
Communication Services
S.I.C.: 4899
N.A.I.C.S.: 517919

BAE Systems Electronics Limited (1)
6 Carlton Gardens
London, SW1Y 5AD, United Kingdom
Tel.: (44) 1252 373 232
Fax: (44) 1252 383 000
Electronic Component Mfr
S.I.C.: 3679
N.A.I.C.S.: 334419

BAE Systems Enterprises Limited (1)
Chester House
Farnborough, Hampshire, GU14 6TQ, United Kingdom
Tel.: (44) 1252 373232
Fax: (44) 1252 383000
Electronic Security Equipment Mfr
S.I.C.: 3669
N.A.I.C.S.: 334290

Subsidiary:

BAE Systems (Operations) Limited (2)
Warton Aerodrome
Preston, Lancashire, PR4 1AX, United Kingdom
Tel.: (44) 1772 633333
Fax: (44) 1772 855262
Emp.: 8,000
Aerospace Software Development Services
S.I.C.: 7371
N.A.I.C.S.: 541511
Christopher George Boardman *(Mng Dir)*

BAE Systems Integrated System Technologies (1)
Victory Point Lyon Way
Frimley, Surrey, GU16 7EX, United Kingdom UK
Tel.: (44) 1252373232 (100%)
Fax: (44) 1276603001
E-Mail: insyte@baesystems.com
Web Site: www.baesystems.com
Emp.: 500
Aircraft Sensor & Electronic Systems Mfr
S.I.C.: 3812
N.A.I.C.S.: 334511
Rory Fisher *(Mng Dir)*

BAE Systems (Overseas Holdings) Limited (1)
Warwick Ho
Farnborough, Hampshire, GU14 6YU, United Kingdom
Tel.: (44) 1252 373232
Fax: (44) 1252 383000
Investment Management Services
S.I.C.: 6282
N.A.I.C.S.: 523920

BAE Systems Regional Aircraft (1)
Prestwick International Airport
Prestwick, Ayrshire, KA9 2RW, United Kingdom
Tel.: (44) 1292 675000
Fax: (44) 1292 675700
Web Site: www.baesystems.com
Aircraft Repair & Maintenance Services
S.I.C.: 4581
N.A.I.C.S.: 488190

BAE Systems Surface Ships (Holdings) Limited (1)
Warwick House
Farnborough, GU14 6TQ, United Kingdom
Tel.: (44) 1252 373232
Fax: (44) 1252 383000
Investment Management Services
S.I.C.: 6211
N.A.I.C.S.: 523999

BAE Systems Surface Ships Ltd. (1)
Daring Building 2-166
Portsmouth Naval Base, Portsmouth, PO1 3NJ, United Kingdom (100%)
Tel.: (44) 2392857200
Telex: 779996 YARROW G
Fax: (44) 2392857400
Web Site: www.baesystems.co
Emp.: 3,842
Naval Surface Ship Building & Support Services
S.I.C.: 3731

N.A.I.C.S.: 336611
Alan Johnston *(Mng Dir)*

Detica Group Limited (1)
Surrey Research Park
Guildford, Surrey, GU2 7YP, United Kingdom UK
Tel.: (44) 1483816000
Fax: (44) 1483816144
E-Mail: hrqueries@baebaesystemsdetica.com
Web Site: www.baesystemsdetica.com
Sales Range: $300-349.9 Million
Emp.: 1,464
Business & Information Technology Consulting Services
S.I.C.: 8999
N.A.I.C.S.: 541690
Martin Sutherland *(Mng Dir)*
Neil Medley *(COO)*
Kevin Wilson *(Chief Legal Officer)*

Subsidiaries:

Detica Limited (2)
Surrey Research Park
Guildford, Surrey, GU25YP, United Kingdom UK
Tel.: (44) 1483442000
Fax: (44) 1483816144
E-Mail: hrqueries@baesystemsdetica.com
Web Site: www.baesystemsdetica.com
Emp.: 3,000
Management Consulting Services
S.I.C.: 8748
N.A.I.C.S.: 541618
Martin Sutherland *(CEO)*

Divisions:

Detica-StreamShield (3)
St Marys Court The Broadway
Amersham, Bucks, HP7 0UT, United Kingdom
Tel.: (44) 8701149465
Fax: (44) 8701149467
Web Site: www.baesystemsdetica.com
Emp.: 65
Data Processing Services
S.I.C.: 7374
N.A.I.C.S.: 518210
Jon Curnyn *(CTO)*

Detica System Integration Limited (3)
Surrey Research Park
Guildford, Surrey, GU25YP, United Kingdom UK
Tel.: (44) 1483442000
Fax: (44) 1483816144
Management Consulting Services
S.I.C.: 8748
N.A.I.C.S.: 541618
Thomas Black *(CEO)*

U.S. Subsidiaries:

Detica Consulting LLC (2)
260 Madison Ave Ste 8057
New York, NY 10016 NY
Tel.: (646) 216-2143
Web Site: www.baesystemsdetica.com
Emp.: 50
Technical Consulting Services
S.I.C.: 8999
N.A.I.C.S.: 541690

Detica Solutions, Inc. (2)
265 Franklin St Ste 5
Boston, MA 02110 DE
Tel.: (617) 737-4170
Fax: (617) 737-4190
Web Site: www.baesystemsdetica.com
Developer of Fraud Detection & Compliance Software
S.I.C.: 7372
N.A.I.C.S.: 511210
Joe Friscia *(Exec VP & Gen Mgr)*

Non-U.S. Subsidiary:

Detica Group Holdings (Ireland) Limited (2)
5th Floor Chapel House
21-26 Parnell Street, Dublin, 1, Ireland IE
Tel.: (353) 18739600
Fax: (353) 18739601
E-Mail: admin.dublin@baesystemsdetica.com
Web Site: www.baesystemsdetica.com
Sales Range: $50-74.9 Million
Emp.: 301
Holding Company; Fraud Detection & Compliance Software Developer
S.I.C.: 6719
N.A.I.C.S.: 551112
Paul Kerley *(CEO)*
Liam Davis *(CFO & Sec)*
Cecil Hayes *(COO)*
Kilian Colleran *(CTO)*
Liam Griffin *(Chief Comml Officer)*

Unit:

BAE Systems Advanced Technology Centre (1)
New Filton House
PO Box 5
Filton, Bristol, BS34 7QW, United Kingdom (100%)
Tel.: (44) 1173028000
Fax: (44) 1173028007
E-Mail: info@baesystems.com
Emp.: 1,000
Technology & Systems Research
S.I.C.: 8731
N.A.I.C.S.: 541712
James Baker *(Gen Mgr)*

Plants:

BAE Systems (1)
Warton Aerodrome
Preston, PR4 1AX, United Kingdom (100%)
Tel.: (44) 1772633333
Fax: (44) 1772634724
Web Site: www.baesystems.com
Emp.: 7,000
Aircraft Mfr
S.I.C.: 3721
N.A.I.C.S.: 336411
Chris Boardman *(Grp Mng Dir)*

BAE Systems (1)
Prestwick International Airport
Prestwick, KA9 2RW, United Kingdom (100%)
Tel.: (44) 1292675000
Fax: (44) 1292675700
Emp.: 450
Aircraft Design, Research & Development, Build Testing, Manufacture & Sales Services
S.I.C.: 3721
N.A.I.C.S.: 336411
Neil McManus *(Mng Dir & VP)*

U.S. Subsidiary:

BAE Systems, Inc. (1)
1601 Research Blvd
Rockville, MD 20850-3173 DE
Tel.: (301) 838-6000 (100%)
Fax: (301) 838-6925
Web Site: www.baesystems.com
Emp.: 52,000
Developer of Military Electronics, Radar Systems, Artillery, Ballistic Missiles, Airplanes & Armored Vehicles
S.I.C.: 3728
N.A.I.C.S.: 336413
Michael Chertoff *(Chm & Sec)*
Jerry DeMuro *(Pres & CEO)*
Tom Arseneault *(COO)*
Dan Gobel *(Pres-Electronic Sys Sector)*
DeEtte Gray *(Pres-Intelligence & Security Sector)*
Ian T. Graham *(Gen Counsel, Sec & Sr VP)*
Doug Belair *(Sr VP-Plng & Strategy)*
Kristie Cunningham *(Sr VP-Comm)*
John Suttle *(Sr VP-Intl Bus Dev)*

Groups:

BAE Systems Customer Solutions (2)
4075 Wilson Blvd
Arlington, VA 22203
Tel.: (703) 387-2200
Fax: (703) 387-4947
Web Site: www.baesystems.com
Emp.: 14,000
Developer of Radar Communication Equipment & Information Technology Services & Operator of Non-Nuclear Ship Repair Facilities
S.I.C.: 3812
N.A.I.C.S.: 334511
Mike Heffron *(Pres)*

Divisions:

BAE Systems Information Technology (3)
8201 Greensboro Dr Ste 1200
McLean, VA 22102-3846 (100%)
Tel.: (703) 847-5820
Fax: (703) 847-5880
Web Site: www.bae.com
Emp.: 330
Systems Engineering, Technical Assistance, Software Development, Communications Engineering, Training to the U.S. Defense & Intelligence Community
S.I.C.: 8742
N.A.I.C.S.: 541611

Branch:

BAE Systems Information Technology (4)
2525 Network Pl
Herndon, VA 20171-3514 DE
Tel.: (703) 563-7500 (100%)
Fax: (703) 563-7516
Toll Free: (888) 873-7522
Web Site: www.digitalnet.com
Network Infrastructure & Information Assurance Solutions Developer
S.I.C.: 7371
N.A.I.C.S.: 541511

BAE Systems Ship Repair (3)
750 W Berkley Ave
Norfolk, VA 23523-1032 DE
Mailing Address:
PO Box 2100
Norfolk, VA 23501-2100
Tel.: (757) 494-4000
Fax: (757) 494-4184
E-Mail: al.krekich@baesystems.com
Emp.: 2,200
Non-Nuclear Ship Repair, Modernization, Overhaul & Conversion Services
Import Export
S.I.C.: 3731
N.A.I.C.S.: 336611

Subsidiaries:

BAE Systems Hawaii Shipyards (4)
Cushing St Drydock No 4
Pearl Harbor, HI 96810
Mailing Address:
PO Box 30989
Honolulu, HI 96820
Tel.: (808) 423-8888
Fax: (808) 423-8399
Web Site: www.baesystems-hawaiishipyards.com
Emp.: 200
Ship Repair Services
S.I.C.: 3731
N.A.I.C.S.: 336611
Ken Fukuji *(VP-Fin)*

BAE Systems Norfolk Ship Repair (4)
750 W Berkley Ave
Norfolk, VA 23523-1032 VA
Mailing Address:
PO Box 2100
Norfolk, VA 23501-2100
Tel.: (757) 494-4000
Fax: (757) 494-4030
Web Site: www.baesystems.com
Emp.: 1,000
Ship Building, Conversion & Repair Services
S.I.C.: 3731
N.A.I.C.S.: 336611
Bill Clifford *(Pres & Gen Mgr)*

BAE Systems San Diego Ship Repair (4)
2205 E Belt
San Diego, CA 92113 CA
Mailing Address:
PO Box 13308
San Diego, CA 92170-3308
Tel.: (619) 238-1000
Fax: (619) 239-1751
Web Site: www.baesystems.com
Emp.: 1,000
Ship Building & Repairing Services
S.I.C.: 3731
N.A.I.C.S.: 336611
Robert Kilpatrick *(Pres & Gen Mgr)*

BAE Systems Southeast Shipyards AMHC Inc. (4)
8500 Heckscher Dr
Jacksonville, FL 32226-2434 FL
Tel.: (904) 251-1790
Fax: (904) 251-3500
Web Site: www.baesystemsssyi.com
Sales Range: $300-349.9 Million
Emp.: 1,200
Maintenance, Repair, Overhaul & Conversion Services for Commercial & Military Vessels
Import Export
S.I.C.: 3731
N.A.I.C.S.: 336611
Craig Honour *(CIO)*

Subsidiaries:

BAE Systems Southeast Shipyards Alabama, LLC (5)
Main Gate Dunlap Dr
Mobile, AL 36652
Tel.: (251) 690-7100
Fax: (251) 690-7107
Web Site: www.baesystemsssyi.com
Emp.: 600
Ship Building & Repair Services
Import Export
S.I.C.: 3731
N.A.I.C.S.: 336611
Greg Guarisco *(VP-Sls & Mktg)*

BAE Systems Southeast Shipyards Jacksonville, LLC (5)
8500 Heckscher Dr
Jacksonville, FL 32226-2434
Tel.: (904) 251-1545
Fax: (904) 251-3500
Web Site: www.baesystemsssyi.com
Emp.: 650
Ship Building & Repair Services
Import Export
S.I.C.: 3731
N.A.I.C.S.: 336611
Chuck Nugent *(VP-Marine Fabrication & Dir-Plng & Engrg)*

BAE Systems (4)
Foot of 20th St
San Francisco, CA 94107 CA
Tel.: (415) 861-7447
Fax: (415) 558-8466
Web Site: www.sfdrydock.com
Emp.: 400
Ship Building and Repairing
S.I.C.: 3731
N.A.I.C.S.: 336611
Bret Carter *(Mgr-Sys & Software Quality Assurance)*

BAE Systems-Technology Solutions & Services Sector (3)
1601 Research Blvd
Rockville, MD 20850-3173 (100%)
Tel.: (301) 838-6000
Web Site: www.tss.na.baesystems.com
Emp.: 600
Systems Engineering, Technical & Analytical Services
S.I.C.: 7373
N.A.I.C.S.: 541512
Mark D. Baker *(Gen Counsel & VP)*
Brad Jacobs *(Sr VP-Fin)*

Divisions:

BAE Systems-Analytical & Ordinance Solutions (4)
308 Voyager Way
Huntsville, AL 35806-3560 DE
Tel.: (256) 890-8000
Fax: (256) 890-0000
E-Mail:
Emp.: 250
Engineering Services
Import Export
S.I.C.: 8731
N.A.I.C.S.: 541712

Plant:

BAE Systems-Ordnance Systems (5)
4509 W Stone Dr
Kingsport, TN 37660-1048 (100%)
Tel.: (423) 578-8010
Fax: (423) 247-2261
E-Mail: info@baesystems.com

BAE Systems plc—(Continued)

Web Site: www.na.baesystems.com
Emp.: 500
Ordnance Systems
S.I.C.: 8742
N.A.I.C.S.: 541611
Jerry Hammonds *(Gen Mgr & VP)*

BAE Systems-Applied Technologies (4)
4545A Viewridge Ave
San Diego, CA 92123 (100%)
Tel.: (858) 569-1886
Fax: (858) 569-0387
Web Site: www.bae-systemsmarine.co.uk
Emp.: 60
Aircraft Mfr
S.I.C.: 8711
N.A.I.C.S.: 541330
Marshall Banker *(Pres)*

BAE Systems-Applied Technologies (4)
16541 Commerce Dr
King George, VA 22485-5806 (100%)
Tel.: (540) 663-6300
Fax: (540) 663-6382
Aircraft Mfr
S.I.C.: 1799
N.A.I.C.S.: 238990

BAE Systems-Applied Technologies (4)
1844 Poulsbo Ave
Keyport, WA 98345 DE
Tel.: (360) 598-8800 (100%)
Fax: (360) 598-8888
Web Site: www.na.baesystems.com
Aircraft Systems Mfr
S.I.C.: 3728
N.A.I.C.S.: 336413

BAE Systems-Integrated Electronic Solutions (4)
23481 Cottonwood Pkwy
California, MD 20619-2038 (100%)
Tel.: (301) 863-0888
Web Site: www.baesystems.com
Developer & Mfr of Naval Radio Communications Systems
S.I.C.: 3663
N.A.I.C.S.: 334220

BAE Systems-Integrated O & M Solutions (4)
Industrial Park 557 Mary Esther Cut Off
Fort Walton Beach, FL 32548-4090 (100%)
Tel.: (850) 244-7711
Fax: (850) 664-6070
E-Mail: info@integrated-om-solutions.com
Web Site: www.integrated-om-solutions.com
Emp.: 55
Engineering Services
S.I.C.: 8744
N.A.I.C.S.: 561210

BAE Systems Performance Based Solutions (4)
520 Gaither Rd
Rockville, MD 20850
Tel.: (301) 738-4000
Web Site: www.tss.na.baesystems.com
Emp.: 50
Designer of Submarine Based Ballistic Missile Technology
S.I.C.: 3761
N.A.I.C.S.: 336414

Subsidiaries:

Advanced Concepts, Inc. (4)
9861 Broken Land Pkwy Ste 150
Columbia, MD 21046 MD
Tel.: (410) 381-3780
Fax: (410) 381-9275
Web Site: www.baesystems.com
Sales Range: $75-99.9 Million
Emp.: 300
Information Technology, Network Security Solutions & Systems Engineering & Development Services for US Intelligence & Military
S.I.C.: 7371
N.A.I.C.S.: 541511

BAE Systems Information Solutions Inc. (4)
2525 Network Pl
Herndon, VA 20190-5228
Tel.: (703) 563-7704
Fax: (703) 563-7702
Aerospace Software Development Services
S.I.C.: 7371
N.A.I.C.S.: 541511

McClendon, LLC (4)
14900 Bogle Dr Ste 300
Chantilly, VA 20151 VA
Tel.: (703) 263-0490
Fax: (703) 263-0495
Web Site: www.baesystems.com
Sales Range: $50-74.9 Million
Technical & Professional Services to Intelligence & Military Communities
S.I.C.: 8999
N.A.I.C.S.: 541690

SpecTal, LLC (4)
1875 Campus Commons Dr Ste 100
Reston, VA 20191 VA
Tel.: (703) 860-6180
Fax: (703) 860-6186
Toll Free: (866) 773-2825
E-Mail: info@spectal.com
Web Site: www.baesystems.com
Sales Range: $650-699.9 Million
Security & Intelligence Solutions, Specializing in Government Consulting, Training & Technology Development
S.I.C.: 8999
N.A.I.C.S.: 541690
Ann Holcomb *(Pres)*

BAE Systems-Electronics & Integrated Solutions (2)
65 Spit Brook Rd
Nashua, NH 03060 (100%)
Tel.: (603) 885-4321
Web Site: www.eis.na.baesystems.com
Emp.: 15,000
Mfr of Electronic Systems & Subsystems for Military & Commercial Applications
S.I.C.: 3812
N.A.I.C.S.: 334511
Michael A. Heffron *(Pres)*
Mark Haley *(Gen Counsel & VP-Legal)*
Bradley W. Jacobs *(Sr VP-Fin)*

Divisions:

BAE Systems-ADR (3)
124 Gaither Dr Ste 100
Mount Laurel, NJ 08054
Tel.: (856) 866-9700
Fax: (856) 486-7778
Toll Free: (800) 257-7960
E-Mail: rsutton@adrinc.com
Web Site: www.adr.na.baesystems.com
Emp.: 100
Digital Mapping & Surveying Services
S.I.C.: 8713
N.A.I.C.S.: 541360

BAE Systems-Communications, Navigation, Identification & Reconnaissance (3)
164 Totowa Rd
Wayne, NJ 07474 (100%)
Tel.: (973) 633-6000
Fax: (973) 663-6431
E-Mail: info@eis.na.baesystems.com
Web Site: www.eis.na.baesystems.com
Emp.: 1,300
Providing Technological Support for Aerospace Engineering
Import Export
S.I.C.: 3812
N.A.I.C.S.: 334511
Philip Bramwell *(Gen Counsel)*

Branches:

BAE Systems-Communication, Navigation, Identification & Reconnaissance (4)
450 Pulaski Rd
Greenlawn, NY 11740-1606 DE
Tel.: (631) 261-7000 (100%)
Fax: (631) 262-8020
Web Site: www.eis.na.baesystems.com
Emp.: 600
Avionics, Navigation & Military Communication Services
S.I.C.: 3812
N.A.I.C.S.: 334511
Paul Markwatt *(VP)*

BAE Systems-Information Warfare (3)
144 Daniel Webster Hwy N
Merrimack, NH 03054 MA
Mailing Address: (100%)
PO Box 868
Nashua, NH 03061-0868
Tel.: (603) 885-4321
Fax: (603) 885-3655
Web Site: www.baesystems.com
Emp.: 4,500
Developer of Signal Management & Electronic Attack Systems
S.I.C.: 3812
N.A.I.C.S.: 334511
Michael A. Heffron *(Pres)*
Kevin M. Perkins *(Gen Counsel & VP)*

Branch:

BAE Systems (4)
4075 Wilson Blvd Ste 900
Arlington, VA 22203 PA
Tel.: (703) 387-2200 (100%)
Fax: (703) 387-4947
Web Site: www.eis.na.baesystems.com
Emp.: 450
Aircraft System Mfr
Import Export
S.I.C.: 3812
N.A.I.C.S.: 334511
Fergio Perez *(CEO)*

BAE Systems-Platform Solutions (3)
600 Main St
Johnson City, NY 13790-1806 (100%)
Tel.: (607) 770-2000
Fax: (607) 770-3524
E-Mail: platformsolutions@baesystems.com
Web Site: www.eis.na.baesystems.com
Emp.: 1,500
Mfr of Aircraft & Vehicle Control & Guidance Systems
S.I.C.: 3728
N.A.I.C.S.: 336413
Maryann Johnson *(VP-HR)*
Greg J. White *(Pres)*

BAE Systems (3)
10920 Technology Pl
San Diego, CA 92127 (100%)
Tel.: (858) 675-2600
Fax: (858) 675-1966
Web Site: www.baesystems.com
Emp.: 2,000
Developer of Information Technology Systems & Geospatial Exploitation Software
S.I.C.: 7379
N.A.I.C.S.: 518210
Jeff Rice *(Dir-Engrg-Advanced Res)*

BAE Systems (3)
95 Canal St
Nashua, NH 03061
Tel.: (603) 885-4321
Web Site: www.baesystems.com
Developer of Aircraft Radar & Electronic Countermeasure Systems
S.I.C.: 3812
N.A.I.C.S.: 334511
Mark Drake *(Mgr-Bus Dev)*

Branches:

BAE Systems-Flight Systems (4)
116880 Flight Systems Dr
Mojave, CA 93501
Tel.: (661) 824-6438
E-Mail: fs.marketing@baesystems.com
Web Site: www.eis.na.baesystems.com
Emp.: 170
Commercial & Military Aircraft Modification Services
S.I.C.: 3721
N.A.I.C.S.: 336411

BAE Systems (4)
6500 Tracor Ln
Austin, TX 78725-2151 (100%)
Tel.: (512) 926-2800
Fax: (512) 929-2312
E-Mail: idsmarketing@baesystems.com
Web Site: www.baesystems.com
Emp.: 550
Developer of Situational Awareness Sensor Systems
S.I.C.: 3812
N.A.I.C.S.: 334511
Lisa Aucoin *(Dir-Integrated Vision Solutions)*

BAE Systems Land & Armaments Holdings Inc. (2)
1300 N 17th St Ste 1400
Arlington, VA 22209-2293 DE
Tel.: (703) 907-8200 (100%)
Web Site: www.baesystems.com
Emp.: 7,700
Holding Company; Armored Combat Vehicles, Artillery Systems & Intelligent Munitions Developer & Mfr
S.I.C.: 6719
N.A.I.C.S.: 551112
Erwin W. Bieber *(Pres)*

Subsidiaries:

BAE Systems Land & Armaments Inc. (3)
1300 N 17th St Ste 1400
Arlington, VA 22209 DE
Tel.: (703) 907-8200
Web Site: www.baesystems.com
Landing Craft & Armored Vehicles Mfr
S.I.C.: 3795
N.A.I.C.S.: 336992
Erwin W. Bieber *(Pres)*

Divisions:

BAE Systems Armament Systems Division (4)
4800 E River Rd
Minneapolis, MN 55421-1498
Tel.: (763) 571-9201
Telex: 17031
Fax: (763) 572-9826
E-Mail: jeff.van.keuren@udlp.com
Web Site: www.uniteddefense.com
Emp.: 2,000
Designer & Mfr of Artillery & Missile Launching Systems
S.I.C.: 3764
N.A.I.C.S.: 336415
Mark Signorelli *(VP-Army Programs)*

BAE Systems Ground Systems Division (4)
1100 Bairs Rd
York, PA 17408
Tel.: (717) 225-8000
Fax: (717) 225-8003
Web Site: www.uniteddefense.com
Emp.: 2,500
Designer & Mfr of Manned Armored Combat Vehicles & Unmanned Robotic Weapons Systems
S.I.C.: 3795
N.A.I.C.S.: 336992

BAE Systems Steel Products Division (4)
2101 W 10th St
Anniston, AL 36201-4223
Mailing Address:
PO Box 1030
Anniston, AL 36202-1030
Tel.: (256) 237-2841
Telex: 6714-994
Fax: (256) 235-9691
Emp.: 550
Mfr of Steel Components & Suspension Equipment for Tracked Combat Vehicles
S.I.C.: 3795
N.A.I.C.S.: 336992
Fred Crenshaw *(Mgr-Comml Products)*

BAE Systems (4)
1205 Coleman Ave
Santa Clara, CA 95050
Mailing Address:
PO Box 58123
Santa Clara, CA 95052-8123
Tel.: (408) 289-0111
Telex: 0346-462
Research & Development of Military Weaponry
S.I.C.: 8731
N.A.I.C.S.: 541712
Gary Layton *(Gen Mgr)*

BAE Systems Products Group (2)
13386 International Pkwy
Jacksonville, FL 32218 DE
Tel.: (904) 741-5400
Fax: (904) 741-5403
Toll Free: (800) 654-9943
Web Site: www.baesystems.com
Sales Range: $1-4.9 Billion
Emp.: 8,150
Security & Business Intelligence Solutions

Export
S.I.C.: 3841
N.A.I.C.S.: 339113

Divisions:

BAE Systems Mobility & Protection Systems (3)
7822 S 46th St
Phoenix, AZ 85044
Tel.: (602) 643-7603
Fax: (602) 643-7699
Toll Free: (866) 390-1944
E-Mail: info@baesystems.com
Web Site: www.bae.com
Emp.: 400
Advanced Survivability Systems Mfr for the Ground Vehicle, Individual Equipment & Aerospace Markets
S.I.C.: 3795
N.A.I.C.S.: 336992

Subsidiary:

Stewart & Stevenson Services, Inc. (4)
1000 Louisiana Ste 5900
Houston, TX 77002-1051 TX
Mailing Address:
PO Box 1637
Houston, TX 77251-1637
Tel.: (713) 751-2600
Telex: 794221
Web Site: www.ssss.com
Sales Range: $900-999.9 Million
Emp.: 1,200
Diesel Engines, Diesel Generators, Irrigation Equipment, Pumps, Aircraft Ground Support Equipment & Oil Field Equipment Mfr
S.I.C.: 3519
N.A.I.C.S.: 333618
Frank C. Carlucci *(Vice Chm)*
Gary W. Stratulate *(Pres & COO)*
Robert L. Hargrave *(CEO)*
Jeff Merecka *(CFO, Sec & VP)*

Subsidiaries:

Stewart & Stevenson Tactical Vehicle Systems, LP (5)
5000 I-10 W
Sealy, TX 77474
Tel.: (979) 885-2977
Fax: (979) 885-7910
Toll Free: (800) 221-3688
Web Site: www.ssss.com
Emp.: 2,500
Tactical Vehicles Designer & Mfr
S.I.C.: 3795
N.A.I.C.S.: 336992

Subsidiaries:

BAE Systems Mobility & Protection Systems (3)
7822 S 46th St
Phoenix, AZ 85044 AZ
Tel.: (602) 643-7603
Fax: (602) 643-7699
Toll Free: (866) 390-1944
Web Site: www.baesystems.com
Emp.: 800
Energy Absorbing Seating & Systems
S.I.C.: 5049
N.A.I.C.S.: 423490

BAE Systems Survivability Systems LLC (3)
9113 Le Saint Dr
Fairfield, OH 45014-5453 DE
Tel.: (513) 881-9800
Fax: (513) 881-1840
Toll Free: (800) 697-0307
Web Site: www.baesystems.com
Emp.: 700
Armored Vehicles; Personal, Industrial, Corporate & Government Security
S.I.C.: 7381
N.A.I.C.S.: 561613
Gary Allen *(VP)*

Bianchi International Inc. (3)
3120 E. Mission Blvd
Ontario, CA 91761
Tel.: (904) 741-5400
Fax: (904) 741-5407
Toll Free: (800) 347-1200
Web Site: www.bianchi-intl.com
Emp.: 280
Leather Goods Mfr & Sales
Import Export
S.I.C.: 2393
N.A.I.C.S.: 314910
Mike Shire *(VP-Sls-Mktg)*

Break-Free (3)
13386 International Pkwy
Jacksonville, FL 32218-2383
Tel.: (904) 741-5400
Fax: (904) 741-5403
Toll Free: (800) 433-2909
E-Mail: info@break-free.com
Web Site: www.break-free.com
Emp.: 50
Gun Cleaning Lubricants & Preservatives
S.I.C.: 2992
N.A.I.C.S.: 324191

Monadnock Lifetime Products, Inc. (3)
126 NH Route 12 N
Fitzwilliam, NH 03447
Tel.: (603) 585-6810
Fax: (603) 585-9575
Web Site: www.batons.com
Develops, Manufactures & Sells Police Equipment, Primarily Police Batons
S.I.C.: 5049
N.A.I.C.S.: 423490

PROTECH Armored Products (3)
13386 International Pkwy
Jacksonville, FL 32218
Tel.: (904) 741-5400
Fax: (904) 741-5406
Web Site: www.protecharmored.com
Hard Armor Products Including Ballistic Shields, Bullet Resistant Vests, Visors, & Accessories; Mfrs. Protective Armor Products for Helicopters, Automobiles, & Riot Control Vehicles
S.I.C.: 5049
N.A.I.C.S.: 423490

Subsidiaries:

BAE Systems Imaging Solutions (2)
1801 McCarthy Blvd
Milpitas, CA 95035
Tel.: (408) 433-2500
Fax: (408) 435-7352
Toll Free: (800) 325-6975
E-Mail: sales@fcimg.com
Web Site: www.fairchildimaging.com
Emp.: 160
Electronic Imaging Components & Systems Mfr & Developer
S.I.C.: 3674
N.A.I.C.S.: 334413
Jack Mills *(Mgr-Sls)*

BAE Systems Information and Electronic Systems Integration Inc. (2)
65 Spit Brook Rd
Nashua, NH 03060-6909
Tel.: (603) 885-4321
Fax: (603) 885-2772
Electronic Equipment Mfr
S.I.C.: 3679
N.A.I.C.S.: 334419

BAE Systems TVS Inc. (2)
5000 Interstate 10
Sealy, TX 77474-9506
Tel.: (979) 885-2977
Fax: (979) 885-7910
Automobile Parts Mfr
S.I.C.: 3714
N.A.I.C.S.: 336390

Non-U.S. Subsidiaries:

BAE Systems Australia Limited (1)
78 Northbourne Ave
Canberra, Australian Capital T, 2612, Australia AU
Tel.: (61) 262291600 (100%)
Telex: 88342
Fax: (61) 262304345
E-Mail: info@baesystems.com.au
Web Site: www.baesystems.com.au
Emp.: 65
Electronic Systems Mfr
S.I.C.: 3812
N.A.I.C.S.: 334511

BAE Systems India (Services) Pvt. Ltd (1)
2nd Floor Hotel Le-Meridien Commercial Tower Raisina Road
New Delhi, 110 001, India
Tel.: (91) 11 4341 2345
Web Site: www.baesystems.com
Aviation & Defense Security Device Mfr
S.I.C.: 3812
N.A.I.C.S.: 334511
John Brosnan *(Mng Dir)*

BAE SYSTEMS OMC (1)
12 Barnsley Road Industrial Sites
Benoni, Gauteng, 1501, South Africa
Tel.: (27) 11 747 3300
Fax: (27) 11 749 8277
Armored Vehicle Mfr
S.I.C.: 3795
N.A.I.C.S.: 336992

BAE Systems Saudi Arabia (1)
Po Box 1732
Riyadh, 11441, Saudi Arabia
Tel.: (966) 1445 9100
Fax: (966) 1445 9101
Electronic Equipment Mfr
S.I.C.: 3679
N.A.I.C.S.: 334419
Andy Carr *(CEO & Mng Dir)*

Heckler & Koch GmbH (1)
PO Box 1329
78722 Oberndorf, Germany (100%)
Tel.: (49) 7423790
Fax: (49) 7423 792497
Web Site: www.heckler-koch.de
Small Arms Mfr
S.I.C.: 3484
N.A.I.C.S.: 332994

U.S. Subsidiary:

Heckler & Koch Inc. (2)
19980 Highland Vista Dr Ste 190
Ashburn, VA 20147 VA
Tel.: (703) 450-1900
Fax: (703) 450-8160
E-Mail: info@hecklerkoch-usa.com
Web Site: www.hecklerkoch-usa.com
Emp.: 13
Distributors of Military & Federal Law Enforcement Sporting Firearms
S.I.C.: 5091
N.A.I.C.S.: 423910
Steven Galloway *(Mgr-Creative Svcs)*

Non-U.S. Joint Ventures:

Eurofighter GmbH (1)
Am Soldnermoos 17
D-85399 Hallbergmoos, Germany (100%)
Tel.: (49) 0811800
Fax: (49) 09811801557
E-Mail: info@eurofighter.com
Web Site: www.eurofighter.com
Emp.: 100
Fighter-Aircraft Mfr; Joint Venture of EADS Deutschland GmbH (33%), BAE Systems Plc (33%), Alenia Aeronautica SpA (21%) & EADS Construcciones Aeronauticas SA (13%)
S.I.C.: 3721
N.A.I.C.S.: 336411
Enzo Casolini *(Chm & CEO)*

MBDA Holdings S.A.S. (1)
37 Boulevard de Montmorency
75016 Paris, France FR
Tel.: (33) 142242424
Fax: (33) 145245414
Web Site: www.mbda-systems.com
Holding Company; Guided Missiles & Missle Systems Mfr
S.I.C.: 6719
N.A.I.C.S.: 551112
Antoine Bouvier *(CEO)*
Peter Bols *(CFO)*
Antonio Perfetti *(COO)*

Subsidiary:

MBDA France SAS (2)
1 Ave Reaumer
92358 Le Plessis-Robinson, Cedex, France FR
Tel.: (33) 171541000
Telex: AISPA X 250 881 F
Fax: (33) 171540190
Web Site: www.mbda.fr
Emp.: 100
Missiles & Missile Systems
S.I.C.: 3724
N.A.I.C.S.: 336412

Joint Ventures:

EUROSAM (3)
Centre d'affaires de la Boursidiere Batiment Kerguelen
92357 Le Plessis-Robinson, France FR
Tel.: (33) 1 4187 1416
Fax: (33) 1 4187 1442
Web Site: www.eurosam.com
Emp.: 100
Missile Defense Systems Mfr
Import
S.I.C.: 3761
N.A.I.C.S.: 336414

ROXEL S.A.S. (3)
La Boursidi Immeuble Jura
92357 Le Plessis-Robinson, France
Tel.: (33) 141 07 82 95
Fax: (33) 146 30 22 37
Web Site: www.roxelgroup.com
Propulsion System Mfr
S.I.C.: 3764
N.A.I.C.S.: 336415
David Quancard *(CEO)*

Subsidiary:

ROXEL France (4)
Route D Ardon
45240 La Ferte-Saint-Aubin, France FR
Tel.: (33) 238516666
Fax: (33) 238516633
Emp.: 300
Rocket Propulsion Systems Mfr
S.I.C.: 3621
N.A.I.C.S.: 335312

Non-U.S. Subsidiaries:

MBDA Deutschland GmbH (2)
Hagenauer Forst 27
Schrobenhausen, Germany
Tel.: (49) 8252 99 0
Fax: (49) 8252 99 6120
Aircraft Machinery Mfr
S.I.C.: 3728
N.A.I.C.S.: 336413
Thomas Homberg *(Mng Dir)*

Subsidiaries:

Bayern-Chemie Gesellschaft fur Flugchemische Antriebe mbH (3)
Liebigstr 17
PO Box 11
D 84544 Aschau, Germany
Tel.: (49) 86386010
Fax: (49) 8638601399
E-Mail: info-de@mbda-systems.de
Web Site: www.bayernchemie.de
Rev.: $71,900,000
Emp.: 160
Rocket Propulsion Systems Mfr
S.I.C.: 3764
N.A.I.C.S.: 336415
Stoerchlee Ulrich *(CEO)*

TDW-Gesellschaft fur verteidigungstechnische Wirksysteme GmbH (3)
Hagenauer Forst 27
86529 Schrobenhausen, Germany
Tel.: (49) 8252 99 0
Fax: (49) 8252 99 6120
E-Mail: empfang-sob@mbda-systems.com
Web Site: www.eads.com
Emp.: 1,000
Aircraft Parts Mfr
S.I.C.: 3728
N.A.I.C.S.: 336413
Thomas Homberg *(Gen Mgr)*

MBDA Italia SpA (2)
Via Carciano 4-50/60-70
00131 Rome, Italy
Tel.: (39) 06 87711
Web Site: www.mbda-systems.com
Missile Systems Developer & Mfr
S.I.C.: 3761
N.A.I.C.S.: 336414

MBDA UK Ltd. (2)
Six Hills Way
Stevenage, SG1 2DA, United Kingdom UK

BAE Systems plc—(Continued)

Tel.: (44) 1438312422
Fax: (44) 1438753377
Web Site: www.mbda.co.uk
Emp.: 2,000
Missile Mfr
S.I.C.: 3761
N.A.I.C.S.: 336414
Steve Wadey *(Mng Dir)*

Branch:

MBDA UK **(3)**
11 Strand
London, WC2N 5HR, United Kingdom
Tel.: (44) 1714516000
Fax: (44) 1714516001
Web Site: www.mbda.co.uk
Missile Mfr
S.I.C.: 3761
N.A.I.C.S.: 336414

Panavia Aircraft GmbH **(1)**
Am Soeldnermoos 17
85399 Hallbergmoos, Germany De
Tel.: (49) 811800
Telex: 529 825
Fax: (49) 801427
E-Mail: info@panavia.de
Web Site: www.panavia.de
Emp.: 100
Military Aircraft Designer & Mfr
S.I.C.: 3721
N.A.I.C.S.: 336411

BAEKKWANG MINERAL PRODUCTS CO., LTD.

Songwon B/D 6F 652-12 Dungchon-Dong
Gangseo-Gu, Seoul, Korea (South)
Tel.: (82) 2 3661 2993
Fax: (82) 2 3661 1338
Web Site: www.bkmp.co.kr
Year Founded: 1980
014580—(KRS)
Sales Range: $100-124.9 Million

Business Description:
Lime Product Mfr
S.I.C.: 3274
N.A.I.C.S.: 327410
Personnel:
Gyu Nam Cho *(Pres & CEO)*

BAFFIN INC

346 Arvin Ave
Stoney Creek, ON, L8E 2M4, Canada
Tel.: (905) 664-3930
Fax: (905) 664-0824
E-Mail: info@baffin.com
Web Site: www.baffin.com
Sales Range: $125-149.9 Million
Emp.: 250

Business Description:
Work Boot & Arctic Footwear Mfr
S.I.C.: 2389
N.A.I.C.S.: 316210
Personnel:
Marvin Mimms *(VP)*

BAFNA PHARMACEUTICALS LIMITED

Bafna Towers 299 Thambu Chetty Street
Chennai, 600 001, India
Tel.: (91) 4425267517
Fax: (91) 4425231264
E-Mail: info@bafnapharma.com
Web Site: www.bafnapharma.com
532989—(BOM)
Rev.: $33,151,122
Assets: $48,312,510
Liabilities: $35,648,990
Net Worth: $12,663,519
Earnings: $734,681
Emp.: 572
Fiscal Year-end: 03/31/13

Business Description:
Pharmaceutical Mfr
S.I.C.: 2834
N.A.I.C.S.: 325412
Personnel:
Bafna Mahaveer Chand *(Chm & Mng Dir)*
Shyam Sundar Bharti *(CEO)*
K. Premnatha *(Sec)*
Board of Directors:
Bafna Mahaveer Chand
Paras Bafna
U. Sunil Bafna
R. Dwarakanathan
V. Rajamani
A. Sahasranaman

Transfer Agent:
Cameo Corporate Services Limited
No 1 Club House Road
Chennai, India

BAGATELLE

150 Montee de Liesse
Montreal, QC, H4T 1N6, Canada
Tel.: (514) 344-5270
Fax: (514) 342-0248
Toll Free: (800) 616-0209
Web Site: www.bagatelle.ca
Sales Range: $10-24.9 Million
Emp.: 15
Fiscal Year-end: 12/31/12

Business Description:
Leather Apparel Mfr
S.I.C.: 2389
N.A.I.C.S.: 315280
Personnel:
Michael Litvack *(Pres)*
Harris Snyder *(Pres-USA)*

BAGESHWARI DEVELOPMENT BANK LIMITED

PO Box 46
Nepalgunj, Banke, Nepal
Tel.: (977) 81 526246
Fax: (977) 81 526346
E-Mail: office@bdbl.com.np
Web Site: www.bdbl.com.np
Year Founded: 2004
BBBLN—(NEP)
Emp.: 1,300

Business Description:
Banking Services
S.I.C.: 6029
N.A.I.C.S.: 522110
Personnel:
Achyut Prasai *(Chm)*
Rajendra Prasad Poudel *(CEO)*
Jayandra Bahadur Khadka *(Sec)*
Board of Directors:
Achyut Prasai
Chudamani Dhakal
Banubhakta Kandel
Ujjwal Satyal
Madhusudhan Sharma
Rajesh Kumar Shrestha

BAGO GROUP

Bernardo de Irigoyen 248
Capital Federal, C1072AAF Buenos Aires, Argentina
Tel.: (54) 11 4344 2000
Fax: (54) 11 4334 5813
Web Site: www.bago.com.ar
Emp.: 3,850

Business Description:
Holding Company: Pharmaceuticals, Animal Husbandry & Farming
S.I.C.: 6719
N.A.I.C.S.: 551112

Subsidiary:

Laboratorios Bago S.A. **(1)**
Bernardo de Irigoyen 248
Autonoma de Buenos Aires, Buenos Aires, C 1072 AAF Cdad, Argentina
Tel.: (54) 1143442000
Fax: (54) 1143442169
E-Mail: siorio@bago.com.ar
Web Site: www.bago.com.ar
Emp.: 1,050
Mfr. of Pharmaceutical Products
S.I.C.: 2834
N.A.I.C.S.: 325412
Sebastian Bago *(Pres)*

Joint Venture:

Nutricia Bago S.A. **(2)**
Marcelo T de Alvear 590 Piso 1
C 1058 AAF Buenos Aires, Argentina Ar
Tel.: (54) 1153545400
Fax: (54) 1153545401
E-Mail: customerservices@nutricia.com
Web Site: www.nutricia-bago.com.ar
Emp.: 40
Newly Developed Baby & Clinical Nutrition Products Marketer; Owned 51% by Danone Baby & Medical Nutrition B.V. & 49% by Laboratorios Bago S.A.
S.I.C.: 8742
N.A.I.C.S.: 541613
Juan Carlos Bago *(Pres)*

BAHAMAS INTERNATIONAL SECURITIES EXCHANGE

Ste 201 Fort Nassau Centre British Colonial Hilton Bay St
PO Box EE-15672
Nassau, Bahamas
Mailing Address:
PO Box EE-15672
Nassau, Bahamas
Tel.: (242) 323 2330
Fax: (242) 323 2320
E-Mail: info@bisxbahamas.com
Web Site: www.bisxbahamas.com

Business Description:
Stock Exchange Operator
S.I.C.: 6231
N.A.I.C.S.: 523210
Personnel:
Ian Fair *(Chm)*
Keith Davies *(CEO)*

BAHAMAS PETROLEUM COMPANY PLC

IOMA House Hope Street
Douglas, Isle of Man IM1 1AP
Tel.: (44) 1624 647883
Fax: (44) 1624 665121
E-Mail: info@bpcplc.com
Web Site: www.bpcplc.com
Year Founded: 2005
BPC—(AIM OTC)
Rev.: $44,272
Assets: $68,413,789
Liabilities: $1,278,152
Net Worth: $67,135,637
Earnings: ($6,299,686)
Emp.: 5
Fiscal Year-end: 12/31/12

Business Description:
Oil & Gas Exploration Services
S.I.C.: 1389
N.A.I.C.S.: 213112
Personnel:
Simon Craig Potter *(CEO)*
Paul Gucwa *(COO)*
Benjamin Proffitt *(Sec)*
Board of Directors:
Adrian John Reginald Collins
Ross McDonald
Simon Craig Potter
Edward Shallcross
Steven A. Weyel

Legal Counsel:
Laurence Keenan Advocates & Solicitors
Victoria Chambers 47 Victoria Street
Douglas, Isle of Man IM1 2LD

Graham Thompson & Co
Sassoon House Shirley Street & Victoria Avenue
PO Box N-272
Nassau, Bahamas

BAHAMASAIR HOLDINGS LIMITED

Windsor Field
N-4881
Nassau, Bahamas
Tel.: (242) 3778451
Fax: (242) 3777409
Web Site: www.bahamasair.com
Year Founded: 1970
Emp.: 700

Business Description:
Air Transportation Services
S.I.C.: 4512
N.A.I.C.S.: 481111
Personnel:
Barry Farrington *(Chm)*

BAHEMA S.A.

R Estados Unidos 1342
1427001 Sao Paulo, Brazil
Tel.: (55) 11 3085 1522
Fax: (55) 11 3081 7142
Web Site: www.bahema.com.br
Year Founded: 1960
BAHI3—(BRAZ)

Business Description:
Investment Management Services
S.I.C.: 6282
N.A.I.C.S.: 523920
Personnel:
Guilherme Affonso Ferreira *(Dir-IR)*

BAHLSEN GMBH & CO. KG

Podbielskistr 11
30163 Hannover, Germany
Tel.: (49) 5119600
E-Mail: info@Bahlsen.com
Web Site: www.bahlsen.de
Sales Range: $700-749.9 Million
Emp.: 3,652

Business Description:
Cookie & Candy Mfr
S.I.C.: 2052
N.A.I.C.S.: 311821
Personnel:
Werner Michael Bahlsen *(CEO)*
Supervisory Board of Directors:
David B. Burritt
Walter J. Galvin
Mary L. Howell
John A. Luker Jr
Gracia C. Martore
Robert J. O'Toole
David Pulman
Elisabeth M. Struckell
James C. Thyen
Alfer J. Verrecchia

BAHRAIN BOURSE

PO Box 3203
Manama, Bahrain
Tel.: (973) 17261260
Fax: (973) 17256 362
E-Mail: info@bahrainbourse.com.bh
Web Site: www.bahrainbourse.com.bh
Year Founded: 1989
Sales Range: $1-9.9 Million
Emp.: 54

Business Description:
Stock Exchange
S.I.C.: 6231
N.A.I.C.S.: 523210
Personnel:
Rasheed Mohammed Al Meraj *(Chm)*
Anwar Khalifa Al Sadah *(Vice Chm)*
Board of Directors:
Rasheed Mohammed Al Meraj
Anwar Khalifa Al Sadah
Mohammed Bin Isa Al-Khalifa
Majeed A. Salam Breish
Mohammed A. Shafi El Labban
Esam Abdulla Fakhroo
Hassan Ali Juma

Khalid Mohammed Kanoo
Ali Salman Thamer

BAHRAIN CINEMA COMPANY B.S.C.

PO Box 26573
Manama, Bahrain
Tel.: (973) 17 25 89 00
Fax: (973) 17 27 36 80
E-Mail: cineco@cineco.net
Web Site: www.bahraincinema.com
Year Founded: 1967
CINEMA—(BAH)
Rev.: $33,020,411
Assets: $95,070,774
Liabilities: $7,440,346
Net Worth: $87,630,428
Earnings: $11,500,300
Emp.: 345
Fiscal Year-end: 12/31/12
Business Description:
Movie Screening Services
S.I.C.: 7832
N.A.I.C.S.: 512131
Personnel:
Esam Abdulla Fakhro *(Chm)*
Ali Yousif Ubaydli *(Vice Chm)*
Ahmed A. Rahman Rashed *(CEO)*
Yugandhar Karnam *(CFO)*
Karima Farhad *(Chief Admin Officer)*
Sardar Khan *(Chief Programmation Officer)*
Board of Directors:
Esam Abdulla Fakhro
Fareed Yousif Almoayed
Jehad Yousif Amin
Shawqi Ali Fakhro
Jalal Mohamed Jalal
Mohammed Ebrahim Kanoo
Ahmed A. Rahman Rashed
Ali Yousif Ubaydli

BAHRAIN COMMERCIAL FACILITIES COMPANY BSC

PO Box 1175
Manama, Bahrain
Tel.: (973) 17 78 60 00
Fax: (973) 17 786 010
E-Mail: bcredit@bahraincredit.com.bh
Web Site: www.bahraincredit.com.bh
Year Founded: 1983
BCFC—(BAH)
Int. Income: $48,330,935
Assets: $501,893,784
Liabilities: $280,440,710
Net Worth: $221,453,075
Earnings: $31,910,494
Emp.: 628
Fiscal Year-end: 12/31/12
Business Description:
Financial Services
S.I.C.: 6211
N.A.I.C.S.: 523999
Personnel:
Abdulrahman Yusif Fakhro *(Chm)*
Abdulkareem Ahmed Bucheery *(Vice Chm)*
Adel Hubail *(CEO)*
Soad Radhi *(Complaints Officer & Mgr-Relationship)*
Fadhel Al Mahoozi *(Sr VP-Credit & Mktg)*
Rajiv Mittal *(Sr VP-Fin & Ops)*
Board of Directors:
Abdulrahman Yusif Fakhro
Ali Abdulla Ahmedi
Abdulaziz Abdulla A. Aziz Al-Ahmed
Jamal Abdulla Al-Mutawa
Abdulrahman Yousif Al-Qasim
Khalid Mohammed Ali Mattar
Abdulkareem Ahmed Bucheery
Ebrahim Abdulla Buhindi
Jamal Mohammed Jassim Hejres
Abdulghani Hamza Qarooni

BAHRAIN DUTY FREE SHOP COMPLEX BSC

Building 261 Al Shabab Avenue
Manama, Bahrain
Tel.: (973) 17723100
Fax: (973) 17725511
E-Mail: info@bdutyfree.com
Web Site: www.bdutyfree.com
Year Founded: 1990
DUTYF—(BAH)
Rev.: $71,313,669
Assets: $115,779,008
Liabilities: $18,328,164
Net Worth: $97,450,844
Earnings: $16,572,649
Emp.: 38,948
Fiscal Year-end: 12/31/12
Business Description:
Operator of Duty Free Shopping in Bahrain International Airport
S.I.C.: 7389
N.A.I.C.S.: 561499
Personnel:
Abdulla Buhindi *(Mng Dir)*
Abdul Wahid Noor *(Sec)*
Board of Directors:
Farouk Yousuf Almoayyed
Mazen Abdulkarim
Jawad Al Hawaj
Mohammed Al Khan
Ghassan Al Sabbagh
Jassim Mohammed Al Shaikh
Nabil Al Zain
Mohammed Ali Mohammed Al Khalifa
Abdulla Buhindi
Jalal Mohammed Jalal

BAHRAIN FAMILY LEISURE COMPANY BSC

PO Box 11612
Manama, Bahrain
Tel.: (973) 17292973
Fax: (973) 17294676
E-Mail: info@bflc.com.bh
Web Site: www.bflc.com.bh
Year Founded: 1994
FAMILY—(BAH)
Sales Range: $1-9.9 Million
Business Description:
Restaurant Operating Services
S.I.C.: 5812
N.A.I.C.S.: 722511
Personnel:
Abdul Latif Khalid Al Aujan *(Chm)*
Aqeel Raees *(Vice Chm)*
Board of Directors:
Abdul Latif Khalid Al Aujan
Sharif Mohammed Ahmadi
Bashar Mohammed Ali Al Hassan
Mohammed Jassim Al Zayani
Shawki Ali Yousif Fakhroo
Garfield Jones
Adel Salman Kanoo
Aqeel Raees

BAHRAIN ISLAMIC BANK

PO Box 5240
Manama, Bahrain
Tel.: (973) 17 51 51 51
Fax: (973) 17535808
E-Mail: info@bisb.com
Web Site: www.bisb.com
Year Founded: 1979
BISB—(BAH)
Rev.: $79,463,946
Assets: $2,158,303,174
Liabilities: $263,776,657
Net Worth: $1,894,526,517
Earnings: ($93,803,324)
Emp.: 175
Fiscal Year-end: 12/31/12
Business Description:
Banking Services
S.I.C.: 6029
N.A.I.C.S.: 522110
Personnel:
Abdul Razak Al Qassim *(Chm)*
Khalid Mohammed Al Mannai *(Vice Chm)*
Mohammed Ebrahim Mohammed *(CEO)*
Khalid Mohd. Al Dossari *(CFO & Head-Fin Control)*
Board of Directors:
Abdul Razak Al Qassim
Ebrahim Hussain Ebrahim Abdul Rahman
Mohammed Ahmed Abdulla Ali
Fatima Abdulla Budhaish
Khalid Mohammed Al Mannai
Talal Ali Al Zain
Othman Ebrahim Naser Al Askar
Khalil Ebrahim Nooruddin
Mohammed Al Zarrouq Rajab
Subsidiary:

Abaad Real Estate Company B.S.C. (1)
PO Box 20714
20714 Manama, Bahrain
Tel.: (973) 17511999
Fax: (973) 17511997
E-Mail: info@abaadrealestate.com
Web Site: www.abaadrealestate.com
Emp.: 8
Real Estate Management Services
S.I.C.: 6531
N.A.I.C.S.: 531390
Ahmed Ahmed Abdulla *(CEO)*

BAHRAIN MIDDLE EAST BANK BSC

BMB Centre
PO Box 797
Manama, Bahrain
Tel.: (973) 17528183
Fax: (973) 17530526
E-Mail: requests@bmb.com.bh
Web Site: www.bmb.com.bh
BMB—(BAH)
Rev.: $10,159,000
Assets: $55,265,000
Liabilities: $24,820,000
Net Worth: $30,445,000
Earnings: $2,188,000
Emp.: 30
Fiscal Year-end: 12/31/12
Business Description:
Investment Banking Services
S.I.C.: 6211
N.A.I.C.S.: 523110
Personnel:
Wilson S. Benjamin *(Chm)*
Abdulla Ali K. Al Sabah *(Vice Chm)*
Ritchie Skelding *(CEO)*
Thaer Ali Rabea *(Complaints Officer & Head-Compliance & MLRO)*
Board of Directors:
Wilson S. Benjamin
Abdulla Ali K. Al Sabah
Awadh Kh. Al-Enezi
Ebrahim A. S. Bu Hendi
Karunaker Nampalli
Subsidiary:

BMB Property Services (1)
Block 317 Building 135 Road 1702
Diplomatic Area
135 Manama, Bahrain
Tel.: (973) 1752 8127
Fax: (973) 1753 5492
Construction Engineering Services
S.I.C.: 8711
N.A.I.C.S.: 541330

Non-U.S. Subsidiary:

Universal Merchant Holdings NV (1)
Claude Debussylaan 24-10
1082MD Amsterdam, Netherlands
Tel.: (31) 20 5222555
Investment Management Services
S.I.C.: 6282
N.A.I.C.S.: 523920

BAHRAIN NATIONAL HOLDING COMPANY BSC

BNH Tower Seef Business District
PO Box 843
Manama, Bahrain
Tel.: (973) 17 587 300
Fax: (973) 17 583 099
E-Mail: bnh@bnhgroup.com
Web Site: www.bnhgroup.com
BNH—(BAH)
Premiums: $60,405,246
Assets: $198,874,968
Liabilities: $87,790,789
Net Worth: $111,084,179
Earnings: $6,025,493
Emp.: 200
Fiscal Year-end: 12/31/12
Business Description:
Insurance & Risk Management Services
S.I.C.: 6411
N.A.I.C.S.: 524298
Personnel:
Farouk Yousif Almoayyed *(Chm)*
Abdulhussain Khalil Dawani *(Vice Chm)*
Mahmood Al Soufi *(CEO)*
Anand Subramaniam *(CFO)*
Board of Directors:
Farouk Yousif Almoayyed
Jassim Hasan Abdulaal
Ayad Saad Khalifa Algosaibi
Jehad Yousif Amin
Abdulhussain Khalil Dawani
Ghassan Qassim Mohd Fakhroo
Abdul-Rahman Mohamed Juma
Talal Fuad Kanoo
Ali Hasan Mahmood
Sami Mohammed Sharif Zainal

Subsidiaries:

Bahrain National Insurance Company B.S.C. (1)
2491 Road 2832 Block 428
Seef Area, Manama, Bahrain
Tel.: (973) 17 587 444
Fax: (973) 17 583 477
E-Mail: e-support@bnhgroup.com
Web Site: www.bnidirect.com
Emp.: 110
General Insurance Services
S.I.C.: 6411
N.A.I.C.S.: 524210
Abdulhussain Khalil Dawani *(Chm)*
Ghassan Qassim Fakhro *(Vice Chm)*

Bahrain National Life Assurance Company B.S.C. (1)
BNH Tower 2491 Road 2832
PO Box 843
Seef Business District, 428 Manama, Bahrain
Tel.: (973) 17587333
Fax: (973) 17583277
E-Mail: bnlhealthcare@bnhgroup.com
Web Site: www.bnl4life.com
Emp.: 31
General Insurance Services
S.I.C.: 6411
N.A.I.C.S.: 524210
Abdulrahman Mohammed Juma *(Chm)*
Abdulla Ahmed Al-Thani *(Vice Chm)*

BAHRAIN SHIP REPAIR AND ENGINEERING COMPANY

PO Box 568
Manama, Bahrain
Tel.: (973) 17 727129
E-Mail: mainoffice@basrec.com
Web Site: www.basrec.com
BASREC—(BAH)
Rev.: $14,103,868
Assets: $62,215,519
Liabilities: $6,748,254
Net Worth: $55,467,265
Earnings: $3,699,103

Bahrain Ship Repair and Engineering Company—(Continued)

Fiscal Year-end: 12/31/12
Business Description:
Ship Repair & Engineering Services
S.I.C.: 3731
N.A.I.C.S.: 336611
Personnel:
Mubarak Jasim Kanoo *(Chm)*
Khalid Mohamed Kanoo *(Deputy Chm)*
Board of Directors:
Mubarak Jasim Kanoo
Abdulla Yousuf Akbar Ali Reza
Fawzi Ahmed Kanoo
Khalid Mohamed Kanoo
Khalid Yousuf Abdul Rahman
Habib Mahmood Shehab

BAHRAIN TELECOMMUNICATIONS COMPANY BSC

(d/b/a BATELCO)
PO Box 14
Manama, Bahrain
Tel.: (973) 17881881
Fax: (973) 17611898
E-Mail: investor@batelcogroup.com
Web Site: www.batelco.com.bh
Year Founded: 1981
BATELCO—(BAH)
Rev.: $789,689,483
Assets: $1,786,573,002
Liabilities: $438,466,721
Net Worth: $1,348,106,281
Earnings: $169,343,572
Emp.: 2,428
Fiscal Year-end: 12/31/12
Business Description:
Telecommunications Services
S.I.C.: 4813
N.A.I.C.S.: 517110
Personnel:
Hamad Abdulla Al-Khalifa *(Chm)*
Murad Ali Murad *(Deputy Chm)*
Sameer Altaf *(CFO)*
Hamid Husain *(CIO)*
John Ford *(CTO)*
Rashid Abdulla *(CEO-Bahrain)*
Peter Kaliaropoulos *(CEO-Strategic Assignments)*
Bernadette Baynie *(Gen Counsel)*
Board of Directors:
Hamad Abdulla Al-Khalifa
Waleed Ahmed Al Khaja
Khalid Mohammed Al Mannaei
Adel Hussain Al Maskati
Abdul Razak Abdulla Al Qassim
Nedhal Saleh Al-Aujan
Ali Yusif Engineer
Abdulrahman Yusuf Fakhro
Zakaria Ahmed Hejres
Murad Ali Murad
Subsidiaries:

Batelco Middle East Company SPC (1)
PO BOX 14
Manama, kingdom of Bahrain, Bahrain
Tel.: (973) 17884424
Fax: (973) 17884339
Telecommunication Services
S.I.C.: 4812
N.A.I.C.S.: 517210

Non-U.S. Subsidiaries:

Dhivehi Raajjeyge Gulhun Plc (1)
19 Medhuziyaaraiy
PO Box 2082
Magu, Male, Maldives (52%)
Tel.: (960) 3322802
Fax: (960) 3322800
E-Mail: 123@dhiraagu.com.mv
Web Site: www.dhiraagu.com.mv
Emp.: 500
Telecommunication Services
S.I.C.: 4813
N.A.I.C.S.: 517110
Ismail Rasheed *(CEO)*
Avnish Jindal *(CFO)*

Monaco Telecom SAM (1)
25 blvd de Suisse
98008 Monaco, Monaco (55%)
Tel.: (377) 99666300
Fax: (377) 99663333
E-Mail: serviceclient@monaco-telecom.mc
Web Site: www.monaco-telecom.mc
Emp.: 438
Cable & Wireless Telecommunications Services
S.I.C.: 4812
N.A.I.C.S.: 517210
M. Etienne Franzi *(Chm)*
Martin Peronnet *(Dir Gen)*
Markus Lackermaier *(CFO)*
Thierry Berthouloux *(CTO)*
Laurent Lafarge *(Sr VP)*

Umniah Mobile Company PSC (1)
Queen Noor Street Shmeisani Area
Amman, Jordan
Tel.: (962) 65005000
Fax: (962) 65622772
Web Site: www.umniah.com
Wired & Wireless Telecommunication Services
S.I.C.: 4812
N.A.I.C.S.: 517210
Ihab Hinnawi *(CEO)*
Klaus Solling Rimmen *(CFO)*

BAHRAIN TOURISM COMPANY BSC

PO Box 5831
Manama, Bahrain
Tel.: (973) 17 530530
Fax: (973) 17 530867
E-Mail: btc@alseyaha.com
Web Site: www.alseyaha.com
Year Founded: 1974
BTC—(BAH)
Rev.: $13,666,143
Assets: $85,083,689
Liabilities: $5,948,211
Net Worth: $79,135,477
Earnings: $3,260,033
Fiscal Year-end: 12/31/12
Business Description:
Hotel Management & Tour Operating Services
S.I.C.: 7011
N.A.I.C.S.: 721110
Personnel:
Qassim Mohammed Yousif Fakhroo *(Chm)*
Waleed Ahmed Al Khajah *(Vice Chm)*
Abdulnabi Mohammed Daylami *(CEO)*
Board of Directors:
Qassim Mohammed Yousif Fakhroo
Waleed Ahmed Al Khajah
Abdulla Mohammed Turki Al Mahmood
Adel Hussain Al Maskati
Thabia Jasim Abdulla Almanaea
Abdulnabi Mohammed Daylami
Anwar Abdulla Ghuloom
Jalal Mohamed Jalal
Hala Ali Hussain Yateem

BAIADA POULTRY PTY LIMITED

642 Great Western Highway
Pendle Hill, NSW, 2145, Australia
Tel.: (61) 2 9842 1000
Fax: (61) 2 9688 4818
Web Site: www.baiada.com.au
Emp.: 2,200
Business Description:
Poultry Producer
S.I.C.: 2015
N.A.I.C.S.: 311615
Personnel:
John Camilleri *(Mng Dir)*

BAIDU, INC.

No 10 Shangdi 10th Street
Haidian District, Beijing, 100085, China
Tel.: (86) 10 5992 8888
Fax: (86) 10 5992 0000
Web Site: www.baidu.com
BIDU—(NASDAQ)
Rev.: $3,543,312,230
Assets: $7,254,503,177
Liabilities: $3,095,517,575
Net Worth: $4,158,985,602
Earnings: $1,650,654,510
Emp.: 20,877
Fiscal Year-end: 12/31/12
Business Description:
Holding Company; Chinese Language Internet Search Engine
S.I.C.: 2741
N.A.I.C.S.: 519130
Personnel:
Robin Yanhong Li *(Founder, Chm & CEO)*
Jennifer Li *(CFO)*
Board of Directors:
Robin Yanhong Li
William Decker
Liu Dejian
Jian Ding
Nobuyuki Idei
Gregory Boyd Penner
Subsidiaries:

Baidu (China) Co., Ltd. (1)
7-8/F Building B Guangzhou Information Port No 16 Keyun Rd
Guangzhou, China
Tel.: (86) 2085658800
Internet Service Provider
S.I.C.: 4899
N.A.I.C.S.: 517919

Baidu International Technology (Shenzhen) Co., Ltd. (1)
Fuhong road Futian district Huaqiang Garden 9E
Futian Dist, Shenzhen, Guangdong, 51800, China
Tel.: (86) 75582567896
E-Mail: owenchen@gmail.com
Web Site: www.baidu.en.alibaba.com
Emp.: 2
Online Marketing Services
S.I.C.: 8742
N.A.I.C.S.: 541613
Owen Chen *(Mgr)*

Baidu.com Times Technology (Beijing) Co., Ltd. (1)
Baidu Campus No 10 Shangdi No 10 Street
Haidian Dist, Beijing, China
Tel.: (86) 1059928888
Internet Search Portal Operator
S.I.C.: 2741
N.A.I.C.S.: 519130

Non-U.S. Subsidiaries:

Baidu Holdings Limited (1)
PO Box 957
Road Town, Virgin Islands (British) VG
Tel.: (284) 494 8184 (100%)
Fax: (284) 494 5132
Holding Company
S.I.C.: 6719
N.A.I.C.S.: 551112
Robin Li *(CEO)*

Non-U.S. Subsidiary:

Baidu Online Network Technology (Beijing) Co. Ltd. (2)
12/F Ideal International Plaza
No 58 West-North 4th Ring, Beijing, 100080, China CN
Tel.: (86) 1082621188 (100%)
Web Site: ir.baidu.com
Chinese Language Internet Search Engine
S.I.C.: 2741
N.A.I.C.S.: 519130
Robin Li *(CEO)*

Baidu Japan Inc. (1)
6-10-1 Roppongi Roppongi Hills Mori Tower 34f
Minato-Ku, Tokyo, 106-0032, Japan
Tel.: (81) 368112080
Search Engine Optimization Services
S.I.C.: 7373
N.A.I.C.S.: 541512

BAIKAL FOREST CORP.

300-1055 West Hastings Street
Vancouver, BC, V6E 2E9, Canada
Tel.: (604) 669-2246
Fax: (888) 289-4360
E-Mail: info@baikalforest.com
Web Site: www.baikalforest.com
Year Founded: 2007
BFC—(TSXV)
Rev.: $24,818,865
Assets: $17,374,933
Liabilities: $3,917,193
Net Worth: $13,457,740
Earnings: $46,653
Fiscal Year-end: 04/30/13
Business Description:
Wood Product Mfr & Sales
S.I.C.: 5031
N.A.I.C.S.: 423310
Personnel:
Zhenyan Ding *(Chm & CEO)*
Hongmei Ding *(CFO)*
Michael Woods *(Legal Counsel)*
Board of Directors:
Zhenyan Ding
Jingwei Liu
Gang Yan
Transfer Agent:
Computershare Investor Services Inc
Suite 200 - 510 Burrard Street
Vancouver, BC, Canada

BAIKSAN OPC CO., LTD.

45-10 Yongsomal-gil Deoksan-myeon
Jincheon, Chungcheongbuk-do, Korea (South)
Tel.: (82) 43 536 7561
Fax: (82) 43 536 7565
Web Site: www.baiksanopc.com
Year Founded: 1994
066110—(KRS)
Business Description:
Digital Output Device Part Mfr
S.I.C.: 3679
N.A.I.C.S.: 334419
Personnel:
Sang-hwa Kim *(CEO)*

BAILEY METAL PRODUCTS LIMITED

One Caldari Rd
Concord, ON, L4K 3Z9, Canada
Tel.: (905) 738-6738
Fax: (905) 738-5712
Toll Free: (800) 668-2154
E-Mail: sales@bmp-group.com
Web Site: www.bmp-group.com
Sales Range: $25-49.9 Million
Emp.: 300
Business Description:
Steel Products Mfr
S.I.C.: 3325
N.A.I.C.S.: 331513
Personnel:
David Hunt *(Chm & CEO)*
Angelo Sarracini *(Exec VP)*
Subsidiary:

Bailey Metal Products Limited (1)
5710 Roper Rd Suite 101
Edmonton, AB, T6B 3G7, Canada AB
Tel.: (780) 462-5757
Fax: (780) 450-3378
Toll Free: (800) 563-1751
E-Mail: sales@bmp-group.com
Web Site: www.bmp-group.com
Sales Range: $10-24.9 Million
Emp.: 25
Mfr. of Fabricated Structural Metal
S.I.C.: 3441
N.A.I.C.S.: 332312

BAILIAN GROUP CO., LTD.
13 Zhongshan South Road 100
Union Bldg 315
Shanghai, Huangpu, 200010, China
Tel.: (86) 21 633 23636
Fax: (86) 21 633 22323
E-Mail: bljt@bailiangroup.com
Web Site: www.bailiangroup.cn
Year Founded: 2003
Business Description:
Holding Company: Supermarkets, Department Stores, Pharmacies & Convenience Stores Owner & Operator
S.I.C.: 6719
N.A.I.C.S.: 551112
Personnel:
Xin-Sheng Ma *(Chm)*

Affiliate:

Shanghai Friendship Group Incorporated Company (1)
Level 10 518 Shangcheng Road
Pudong, Shanghai, 200120, China CN
Tel.: (86) 21 63223344
Fax: (86) 21 63517447
Web Site: www.shfriendship.com.cn
600827—(SHG)
Sales Range: $1-4.9 Billion
Emp.: 54,599
Commodities Retailing; Commercial Real Estate Developer
S.I.C.: 5411
N.A.I.C.S.: 445110
Xinsheng Ma *(Chm)*
Tao He *(Vice Chm)*
Xiaochun Dong *(CFO)*

Holdings:

Lianhua Supermarket Holdings Co., Ltd. (2)
7th Floor No 1258 Zhen Guang Road
Shanghai, 200333, China CN
Tel.: (86) 2152629922 (34.03%)
Fax: (86) 2152797976
Web Site: www.lhok.com.cn
0980—(HKG OTC)
Sls.: $4,604,671,523
Assets: $3,304,744,946
Liabilities: $2,706,090,128
Net Worth: $598,654,818
Earnings: $71,824,345
Emp.: 59,224
Fiscal Year-end: 12/31/12
Supermarket Services
S.I.C.: 5411
N.A.I.C.S.: 445110
Jian-jun Chen *(Chm-Supervisory Bd)*
Zhong-qi Zhou *(CFO)*

Orient Shopping Centre Ltd. (2)
No 8 North Caoxi Road
Shanghai, 200030, China CN
Tel.: (86) 2164870000
Fax: (86) 2164870888
Web Site: www.bldfqj.com
Emp.: 600
Shopping Mall Facility Leasing & Property Management Services
S.I.C.: 6512
N.A.I.C.S.: 531120
Xun Qiu Ming *(Gen Mgr)*

Units:

Orient Shopping Centre - Huaihai (3)
No 755 Middle Huaihai Road
Luwan District, Shanghai, China
Tel.: (86) 21 6445 8000
Fax: (86) 21 6445 5000
Web Site: www.bldfhh.com
Shopping Mall Facility Leasing & Property Management Services
S.I.C.: 6512
N.A.I.C.S.: 531120

Orient Shopping Centre - Jiading (3)
No 66 Shanghai Road
Shanghai, 201800, China
Tel.: (86) 2160941688
Fax: (86) 2160941666
Web Site: www.bldfjd.com
Shopping Mall Facility Leasing & Property Management Services
S.I.C.: 6512
N.A.I.C.S.: 531120

Orient Shopping Centre - Nandong (3)
No 800 East Nanjing Road
Huangpu District, Shanghai, 200001, China
Tel.: (86) 21 6322 3344 (Switchboard)
Fax: (86) 21 6361 4684
Web Site: www.bldfnd.com
Shopping Mall Facility Leasing & Property Management Services
S.I.C.: 6512
N.A.I.C.S.: 531120

Orient Shopping Centre - Ningbo (3)
No 151 E Zhongshan Rd
Haishu District, Ningbo, Zhejiang, 315000, China
Tel.: (86) 57487255700
Fax: (86) 57487253776
Web Site: www.blnbdf.com
Shopping Mall Facility Leasing & Property Management Services
S.I.C.: 6512
N.A.I.C.S.: 531120

Orient Shopping Centre - Yangpu (3)
No 2500 Siping Road
Yangpudian District, Shanghai, 200433, China
Tel.: (86) 2155053888
Fax: (86) 21 5505290
Web Site: www.bldfyp.com
Shopping Mall Facility Leasing & Property Management Services
S.I.C.: 6512
N.A.I.C.S.: 531120

Shanghai No. 1 Yaohan Co., Ltd. (2)
No 501 Zhangyang Rd
Pudong New Area, Shanghai, 200120, China CN
Tel.: (86) 2158360000 (64%)
Web Site: www.bldybbb.com
Commercial & Shopping Facility Leasing & Property Management Services
S.I.C.: 6512
N.A.I.C.S.: 531120

Units:

Bailian Linyi Shopping Mall (2)
No 140 Linyi Road
Pudong New Area, Shanghai, China
Tel.: (86) 2158732556
Web Site: blgfjt.blemall.com
Shopping Mall Facility Leasing & Property Management Services
S.I.C.: 6512
N.A.I.C.S.: 531120

Bailian Nanqiao Shopping Mall (2)
No 588 Baiqi Road
Fengxian District, Shanghai, China
Tel.: (86) 2133610000
Web Site: www.blnqmall.com
Shopping Mall Facility Leasing & Property Management Services
S.I.C.: 6512
N.A.I.C.S.: 531120

Bailian Outlets Plaza (2)
No 2888 Hu-Qing-Ping Highway
Qingpu District, Shanghai, 201703, China
Tel.: (86) 2159756655
Fax: (86) 2159756598
E-Mail: shanghaioutlets@126.com
Web Site: www.bloqp.com
Brand Outlet Shopping Plaza Leasing & Property Management Services
S.I.C.: 6512
N.A.I.C.S.: 531120

Bailian Shenyang Shopping Mall (2)
No 55 Qingnian Street
Shenhe District, Shenyang, Liaoning, China
Tel.: (86) 24 8297 0181
Web Site: www.blsymall.com
Shopping Mall Facility Leasing & Property Management Services
S.I.C.: 6512
N.A.I.C.S.: 531120

Bailian Youyicheng Shopping Mall (2)
No 8 Songhu Road
Shanghai, China
Tel.: (86) 2155529900
Web Site: www.blyycmall.com
Shopping Mall Leasing & Property Management Services
S.I.C.: 6512
N.A.I.C.S.: 531120

Shanghai Fashion Store (2)
No 650-690 East Nanjing Road
Huangpu District, Shanghai, 200001, China
Tel.: (86) 2163225445
Fax: (86) 2163517889
Web Site: www.blszsd.com
Department Store Facility Leasing & Property Management Services
S.I.C.: 6512
N.A.I.C.S.: 531120

Shanghai Hualian Commercial Building - Huangpu (2)
No 340 East Nanjing Road
Huangpu District, Shanghai, 200001, China
Tel.: (86) 2163515300
Web Site: www.blhlss.com
Commercial Facility Leasing & Property Management Services
S.I.C.: 6512
N.A.I.C.S.: 531120

Shanghai Hualian Commercial Building - Putuo (2)
No 788 Jinshajiang Road
Putuo District, Shanghai, 200062, China
Tel.: (86) 21 6265 2222
Fax: (86) 21 5250 0202
Web Site: www.blhlpt.com
Commercial Facility Leasing & Property Management Services
S.I.C.: 6512
N.A.I.C.S.: 531120

Shanghai Lady Fashion Department Store (2)
No 447-449 Middle Huahai Road
Luwan District, Shanghai, China
Tel.: (86) 21 5386 8686
Web Site: www.blfnsd.com
Department Store Facility Leasing & Property Management Services
S.I.C.: 6512
N.A.I.C.S.: 531120

Shanghai No. 1 Department Store - Huangpu (2)
No 830 East Nanjing Road
Huangpu District, Shanghai, China
Tel.: (86) 2163223344
Fax: (86) 2163616608
Web Site: www.bldybh.com
Department Store Facility Leasing & Property Management Services
S.I.C.: 6512
N.A.I.C.S.: 531120

Shanghai No. 1 Department Store - Songjiang (2)
No 98-116 Zhongshan Road
Songjiang District, Shanghai, China
Tel.: (86) 2157713090
Web Site: www.bldysj.com
Department Store Facility Leasing & Property Management Services
S.I.C.: 6512
N.A.I.C.S.: 531120

Yong'an Department Store (2)
No 365 East Nanjing Road
Huangpu District, Shanghai, 200001, China
Tel.: (86) 2163224466
Fax: (86) 21 6351 7122
Web Site: www.blyabh.com
Department Store Facility Leasing & Property Management Services
S.I.C.: 6512
N.A.I.C.S.: 531120

BAILLIE GIFFORD & CO.
Calton Sq 1 Greenside Row
Edinburgh, Scotland, EH1 3AN, United Kingdom
Tel.: (44) 1312752000
Fax: (44) 1312753999
E-Mail: trustenquiries@bailliegifford.com
Web Site: www.bailliegifford.com
Year Founded: 1908
Emp.: 670
Business Description:
Manager of Pension Funds & Investment Trusts & Provider of Retail Financial Products
S.I.C.: 6371
N.A.I.C.S.: 524292
Personnel:
Andrew Telfer *(CEO)*
James Anderson *(Partner & Chief Investment Officer)*
Mick Brewis *(Partner, Head-North America & Mgr-Investment)*
Peter Hollis *(Head-Investment-Europe & Partner)*
Sarah Whitley *(Partner & Head-Japan)*
Elaine Morrison *(Partner & Sr Mgr-Investment)*
Charles Plowden *(Joint Sr Partner)*
Gerald Smith *(Deputy Chief Investment Officer)*

Joint Venture:

Guardian Baillie Gifford Ltd. (1)
Calton Sq 1 Greenside Row
Edinburgh, Scotland, EH1 3AN, United Kingdom
Tel.: (44) 1312752000
Fax: (44) 1312753999
E-Mail: info@bailliegifford.com
Web Site: www.bailliegifford.com
Sales Range: $300-349.9 Million
Emp.: 650
Provider of Insurance & Annuities; Joint Venture of The Guardian Life Insurance Company of America & Baillie Gifford & Co.
S.I.C.: 6399
N.A.I.C.S.: 524128

BAILLIE GIFFORD SHIN NIPPON PLC
Calton Sq 1 Greenside Row
Edinburgh, EH1 3AN, United Kingdom
Tel.: (44) 1312752000
Fax: (44) 1312753999
Web Site: www.bailliegifford.com
BGS—(LSE)
Sales Range: $10-24.9 Million
Emp.: 670
Business Description:
Investment Services
S.I.C.: 6211
N.A.I.C.S.: 523999
Personnel:
Barry M. Rose *(Chm)*
Board of Directors:
Barry M. Rose
Francis Charig
Iain A. McLaren
Simon C. N. Somerville

BAINE JOHNSTON CORPORATION
410 East White Hills
Saint John's, NL, A1A 5J7, Canada
Tel.: (709) 576-1780
Fax: (709) 576-1273
Web Site: www.bainejohnston.com
Year Founded: 1780
Rev.: $18,904,585
Emp.: 150
Business Description:
Fishing Industry
S.I.C.: 0919
N.A.I.C.S.: 114119
Personnel:
Chris Collingwood *(Chm & CEO)*
Gregory W. Dickie *(Sr VP-Ops)*

BAINULTRA INC.
956 chemin Olivier
Saint-Nicolas, QC, G7A 2N1, Canada
Tel.: (418) 831-7701
Fax: (418) 831-6623
Toll Free: (800) 463-2187

BainUltra Inc.—(Continued)

E-Mail: info@bainultra.com
Web Site: www.bainultra.com
Year Founded: 1977
Rev.: $27,926,240
Emp.: 100
Business Description:
Bathroom Furniture & Products Mfr
S.I.C.: 3269
N.A.I.C.S.: 327110
Personnel:
Henry Brunelle *(Pres)*

BAIRAHA FARMS PLC

2nd Floor No 407 Galle Road
Colombo, 00300, Sri Lanka
Tel.: (94) 112575255
Fax: (94) 112575256
E-Mail: corporateoffice@bairahalk.com
Web Site: www.bairaha.com
BFL—(COL)
Rev.: $22,902,577
Assets: $18,466,542
Liabilities: $4,999,323
Net Worth: $13,467,220
Earnings: $1,267,630
Fiscal Year-end: 03/31/13
Business Description:
Poultry Services
S.I.C.: 0254
N.A.I.C.S.: 112340
Personnel:
Yakooth Naleem *(CEO & Mng Dir)*
Ahamed Zahiri *(CFO)*
Board of Directors:
M. T. A. Furkhan
Charitha P. de Silva
Nowfel Sally Jabir
Ilyas Naleem
Kamil Naleem
Mubarak Naleem
Yakooth Naleem
Riyal Yakoob

BAIRD MACGREGOR INSURANCE BROKERS LP

825 Queen Street East
Toronto, ON, M4M 1H8, Canada
Tel.: (416) 778-8000
Fax: (416) 778-4492
Toll Free: (800) 268-1424
Year Founded: 1979
Rev.: $23,413,936
Emp.: 70
Business Description:
Insurance Brokerage Services
S.I.C.: 6411
N.A.I.C.S.: 524210
Personnel:
Philomena Comerford *(Pres & CEO)*
Corrie DaPrato *(CFO)*

BAIYANG AQUATIC GROUP CO., LTD.

16 Chuangxin West Road
Nanning, 530004, China
Tel.: (86) 771 3210585
Fax: (86) 771 3219992
Web Site: www.baiyang.com
002696—(SSE)
Emp.: 1,640
Business Description:
Fish Production & Distribution
S.I.C.: 0921
N.A.I.C.S.: 112511
Personnel:
Zhongyi Sun *(Chm)*

BAIYIN NONFERROUS METAL (GROUP) CO., LTD.

96 Youhao Road
Baiyin, Gansu, 730900, China
Tel.: (86) 94 3881 1954
Fax: (86) 94 3822 3120
Web Site: www.bynmc.com
Year Founded: 1954
Business Description:
Holding Company; Nonferrous Metal Products Mfr
S.I.C.: 6719
N.A.I.C.S.: 551112
Non-U.S. Joint Venture:

Gold One International Limited (1)
Level 3 100 Mount Street
Sydney, NSW, 2060, Australia AU
Mailing Address:
PO Box 1244
Sydney, NSW, 2059, Australia
Tel.: (61) 2 9963 6400
Fax: (61) 2 9963 6499
E-Mail:
Web Site: www.gold1.co.za
Rev.: $397,699,749
Assets: $834,971,162
Liabilities: $453,524,004
Net Worth: $381,447,158
Earnings: $31,421,399
Emp.: 6,420
Fiscal Year-end: 12/31/12
Holding Company; Gold Ore Exploration, Development & Mining
S.I.C.: 6719
N.A.I.C.S.: 551112
Christopher Damon Chadwick *(Acting CEO & CFO)*
Hartley Dikgale *(Legal Counsel & Sr VP)*
Pierre B. Kruger *(Sec & Sr VP)*
Izak J. Marais *(Exec VP-Ops-Modder East)*
Wayne Robinson *(Exec VP-Ops-South Africa)*
Richard Stewart *(Exec VP-Technical Svcs)*
Michael Li *(Sr VP-Asia)*
Dick Plaistowe *(Sr VP-Surface Ops)*

Subsidiary:

Twin Hills Operations Pty Limited (2)
Level 7 145 Eagle Street
Brisbane, QLD, 4000, Australia
Tel.: (61) 749835499
Gold Ore Mining Services
S.I.C.: 1041
N.A.I.C.S.: 212221

Non-U.S. Subsidiary:

Gold One Africa Limited (2)
45 Empire Road
Parktown, Gauteng, 2193, South Africa ZA
Mailing Address:
Private Bag X17
Weltevreden Park, Johannesburg, 1715, South Africa
Tel.: (27) 117261047
Fax: (27) 117261087
Web Site: www.gold1.co.za
Gold Resource Exploration, Development & Mining
S.I.C.: 1041
N.A.I.C.S.: 212221
Neal J. Froneman *(CEO & Mng Dir)*
Christopher Damon Chadwick *(CFO)*
Pierre B. Kruger *(Gen Counsel, Sec & VP)*
Izak J. Marais *(Sr VP)*

Subsidiaries:

Goliath Gold Mining Limited (3)
45 Empire Road First Floor
Parktown, 2193 Gauteng, South Africa ZA
Tel.: (27) 11 726 1047
Fax: (27) 11 726 1087
Web Site: www.goliathgold.com
GGM—(JSE)
Sales Range: Less than $1 Million
Emp.: 3
Gold Mining
S.I.C.: 1041
N.A.I.C.S.: 212221
Neal Froneman *(CEO)*
Christopher Chadwick *(CFO)*
Pierre Kruger *(Sec)*

New Kleinfontein Mining Company Limited (3)
Postnet Suite 115
Private Bag X17
Weltevreden Park, Johannesburg, 1715, South Africa ZA
Tel.: (27) 11 726 1047
Fax: (27) 11 726 1087
Holding Company; Gold Ore Exploration & Mining Services
S.I.C.: 6719
N.A.I.C.S.: 551112

Subsidiary:

New Kleinfontein Goldmine (Proprietary) Limited (4)
Postnet Suite 115
Private Bag X17
Weltevreden Park, Johannesburg, 1715, South Africa ZA
Tel.: (27) 10 591 5200
Gold Ore Mining Services
S.I.C.: 1041
N.A.I.C.S.: 212221

BAJA MINING CORP.

1430 - 800 West Pender Street
Vancouver, BC, V6C 2V6, Canada
Tel.: (604) 685-2323
Fax: (604) 629-5228
E-Mail: info@bajamining.com
Web Site: www.bajamining.com
Year Founded: 1985
BAJ—(OTC TSXV)
Rev.: $457,000
Assets: $54,376,000
Liabilities: $11,795,000
Net Worth: $42,581,000
Earnings: ($321,269,000)
Emp.: 6
Fiscal Year-end: 12/31/12
Business Description:
Copper, Zinc, Cobalt & Other Metal Mining & Processing Services
S.I.C.: 1021
N.A.I.C.S.: 212234
Personnel:
Charles Thomas Ogryzlo *(Chm & Interim CEO)*
Nigel Kirkwood *(CFO & Sec)*
Board of Directors:
Charles Thomas Ogryzlo
Peter M. Clausi
Ross Glanville
Wolf Seidler
Transfer Agent:
Computershare Investor Services inc
3rd Fl 510 Burrard Street
Vancouver, BC, Canada
Non-U.S. Subsidiary:

Baja International S.a r.l. (1)
121 Avenue de la Faiencerie
1511 Luxembourg, Luxembourg
Tel.: (352) 26 20 04 33
Mineral Exploration Services
S.I.C.: 1481
N.A.I.C.S.: 213115

BAJAJ AUTO LTD.

(d/b/a Bajaj Group of Companies)
Akurdi
Pune, 411035, India
Tel.: (91) 20 27472851
Fax: (91) 20 27476151
E-Mail: customerservice@bajajauto.co.in
Web Site: www.bajajauto.com
Year Founded: 1926
532977—(BOM)
Rev.: $3,863,572,848
Assets: $2,350,080,342
Liabilities: $854,773,722
Net Worth: $1,495,306,620
Earnings: $580,800,726
Emp.: 8,036
Fiscal Year-end: 03/31/13
Business Description:
Motorcycle & Three-Wheeled Vehicles & Parts Mfr
S.I.C.: 3751
N.A.I.C.S.: 336991
Personnel:
Rahul Bajaj *(Chm)*
Madhur Bajaj *(Vice Chm)*
Rajiv Bajaj *(Mng Dir)*
Pradeep Shrivastava *(COO)*
Abraham Joseph *(CTO)*
J. Sridhar *(Compliance Officer & Sec)*
Kevin P. D'Sa *(Pres-Fin)*
R. C. Maheshwari *(Pres-Comml Vehicle Bus)*
Rakesh Sharma *(Pres-Intl Bus)*
K. Srinivas *(Pres-Motorcycle Bus)*
Eric Vas *(Pres-Retail Fin)*
S. Ravikumar *(Sr VP-Bus Dev & Assurance)*
Board of Directors:
Rahul Bajaj
Madhur Bajaj
Niraj Bajaj
Rajiv Bajaj
Sanjiv Bajaj
Shekhar Bajaj
Naresh Chandra
J. N. Godrej
Manish Kejriwal
S. H. Khan
Suman Kirloskar
D. S. Mehta
P. Murari
Nanoo Pamnani
Kantikumar R. Podar
D. J. Balaji Rao
Transfer Agent:
Karvy Computershare Private Limited
Plot 17 to 24 Near Image Hospital Vittalrao Nagar Madhapur
Hyderabad, India
Subsidiaries:

Bajaj Finance Ltd. (1)
Akurdi
Pune, 411035, India
Tel.: (91) 2030405060
Fax: (91) 2030405020
Web Site: www.bajajfinservlending.in
500034—(BOM NSE)
Rev.: $576,847,998
Assets: $3,304,044,918
Liabilities: $2,679,795,702
Net Worth: $624,249,216
Earnings: $109,628,874
Emp.: 3,086
Fiscal Year-end: 03/31/13
Financial Services
S.I.C.: 6726
N.A.I.C.S.: 525990
Rajeev Jain *(CEO)*
Pankaj Thadani *(CFO)*
Rakesh Bhatt *(COO)*
Diwakar Chief C *(Chief Credit Officer)*
K. Rajesh *(Chief Risk Officer)*
Anant H. Damle *(Compliance Officer & Sec)*
Atul Jain *(Chief Collections Officer)*
Devang Mody *(Pres-Consumer Bus)*
M. M. Muralidharan *(Treas)*

Bajaj Electricals Limited (1)
51 Mahatma Gandhi Road Fort
Mumbai, 400023, India
Tel.: (91) 22043780
Fax: (91) 22828250
Web Site: www.bajajelectricals.com
BAJAJELEC—(NSE)
Sls.: $631,498,412
Assets: $399,964,477
Liabilities: $264,874,825
Net Worth: $135,089,652
Earnings: $9,494,019
Emp.: 745
Fiscal Year-end: 03/31/13
Consumer Electronic Appliances Mfr & Distr
S.I.C.: 3699
N.A.I.C.S.: 335999
Shekhar Bajaj *(Chm & Mng Dir)*
Pratap Gharge *(Pres & CIO)*
Anant Bajaj *(Mng Dir)*
Anant M. Purandare *(CFO & VP)*
Mangesh Patil *(Compliance Officer, Sec & VP-Legal)*
C. G. S. Mani *(Pres-Bus Unit-Lighting)*
Rakesh Ashok Markhedkar *(Pres-Bus Unit-Engrg & Projects)*
A. S. Radhakrishna *(Pres-Bus Unit-Fans)*

Vivek Sharma *(Pres-Bus Unit-Morphy Richards)*
R. Sundararajan *(Pres-Bus Unit-Luminaires)*
Aloke Kumar Dube *(Exec VP-Special Projects)*
Siddhartha Kanodia *(Exec VP-Corp Svcs)*
Atul Sharma *(Exec VP-HR & Admin)*
Sandeep Sharma *(Exec VP-Export & Import)*

Bajaj Finserv Limited (1)
6th Floor Survey No 208/1B Behind Weikfield IT Park
Off Pune Nagar Road, Pune, 411014, India
Tel.: (91) 2027472851
Fax: (91) 2030405700
Web Site: www.bajajfinserv.in
532978—(BOM)
Rev.: $940,884,606
Assets: $12,121,244,352
Liabilities: $10,105,119,468
Net Worth: $2,016,124,884
Earnings: $291,752,856
Fiscal Year-end: 03/31/13
Financial Services & Life Insurance Company
S.I.C.: 6411
N.A.I.C.S.: 524210
Sanjiv Bajaj *(Mng Dir)*
Sonal R. Tiwari *(Compliance Officer & Sec)*
Kevin P. D'sa *(Pres/CFO-Bus Dev)*
Ranjit Gupta *(Pres-Insurance)*
V. Rajagopalan *(Pres-Legal)*
S. Sreenivasan *(Pres-Fin)*
Tapan Singhel *(CEO/Mng Dir-Bajaj Allianz General Insurance)*
Arpit Agarwal *(CEO-Bajaj Financial Solutions Ltd)*
Anand Gore *(CEO-Infrastructure Fin)*
Rajeev Jain *(CEO-Bajaj Finance Limited)*
V. Philip *(CEO-Bajaj Allianz life Insurance Company Limited)*

Hercules Hoists Limited (1)
Bajaj Bhawan 2nd Floor Jamnalal Bajaj Marg Nariman Point
Mumbai, 400 021, India
Tel.: (91) 2222023626
Fax: (91) 2222025160
E-Mail: indef@indef.com
Web Site: www.indef.com
HERCULES—(NSE)
Rev.: $25,044,090
Assets: $35,018,807
Liabilities: $5,381,684
Net Worth: $29,637,123
Earnings: $5,289,654
Emp.: 116
Fiscal Year-end: 03/31/13
Material Handling Equipment Mfr
S.I.C.: 3999
N.A.I.C.S.: 339999
Prakash Subramaniam *(Pres & CEO)*
Vijay Singh *(Compliance Officer & Gen Mgr-Fin & Accts)*
Sandeep Sahasrabudhe *(Risk Officer & Mgr-Internal Audit & Control)*

Mukand Engineers Ltd (1)
Bajaj Bhavan 226 Jamanalal Bajaj Marg Nariman Point
400021 Mumbai, Maharashtra, India
Tel.: (91) 2222021060
Fax: (91) 2222021174
Web Site: www.mukand.com
MUKANDEN—(BOM)
Sales Range: $350-399.9 Million
Alloy & Stainless Steel Mfr
S.I.C.: 3325
N.A.I.C.S.: 331513
Niraj R. Bajaj *(Chm)*

Mukand Ltd (1)
Bajaj Bhawan 3rd Floor 226 Nariman Point
Mumbai, 400021, India
Tel.: (91) 22 6121 6666
Fax: (91) 22 2202 1174
E-Mail: kjmallya@mukand.com
Web Site: www.mukand.com
500460—(BOM)
Rev.: $437,412,366
Assets: $964,543,500
Liabilities: $612,450,360
Net Worth: $352,093,140
Earnings: ($41,533,308)
Emp.: 1,970
Fiscal Year-end: 03/31/13
Alloy & Stainless Steel Mfr
S.I.C.: 3312
N.A.I.C.S.: 331110
Niraj R. Bajaj *(Co-Chm & Mng Dir)*
Rajesh V. Shah *(Co-Chm & Mng Dir)*
Suketu V. Shah *(Mng Dir)*
S. B. Jhaveri *(CFO)*
K. J. Mallya *(Compliance Officer & Sec)*
R. Jagannathan *(CEO-Indus Machinery Div)*
A. M. Kulkarni *(CEO-Steel Plant-Thane)*
R. Sampath Kumar *(CEO-Steel Plant-Ginigera)*

Joint Venture:

Bajaj Allianz General Insurance Co. Ltd. (1)
1st Floor GE Plaza Airport Road
Yerwada, Pune, Maharashtra, 411006, India
Tel.: (91) 2056026666
Fax: (91) 2056026667
E-Mail: info@bajajallianz.co.in
Web Site: www.bajajallianz.co.in
Sales Range: $250-299.9 Million
Emp.: 1,371
Insurance Services; Owned by Allianz AG & by Bajaj Auto Limited
S.I.C.: 6411
N.A.I.C.S.: 524298

Subsidiary:

Bajaj Allianz Life Insurance Co. Ltd. (2)
Ground Floor GE Plaza Airport Road
Yerwada, Pune, Maharashtra, 411006, India
Tel.: (91) 2066026666
Fax: (91) 2066026667
E-Mail: life@bajajallianz.co.in
Web Site: www.bajajallianz.com
Emp.: 2,000
Life Insurance Services
S.I.C.: 6311
N.A.I.C.S.: 524113
Manoj Agrawal *(Mgr)*

Plants:

Bajaj Auto Ltd. - Akurdi Plant (1)
Mumbai Pune Rd
Akurdi, Pune, Maharashtra, 411035, India
Tel.: (91) 2027472851
Fax: (91) 2027473398
E-Mail: bajaj@bajajauto.co.in
Emp.: 11,576
Mfr of Scooters, M80 Motorcycles & Front Engine Three-Wheelers
S.I.C.: 3751
N.A.I.C.S.: 336991
Rajiv Bajaj *(Mng Dir)*

Bajaj Auto Ltd. - Waluj Plant (1)
Waluj Industrial Area
Aurangabad, Maharashtra, India
Web Site: www.bajajauto.com
Emp.: 9,523
Mfr. of Scooters, Motorcycles, Scooterettes, Rear Engine Three-Wheelers
S.I.C.: 3751
N.A.I.C.S.: 336991

BAJAJ HINDUSTHAN LTD.

(d/b/a Bajaj Group)
Bajaj Bhavan 2nd Floor Jamnalal Bajaj Marg
226 Nariman Point, Mumbai, Maharashtra, 400021, India
Tel.: (91) 2222023626
Fax: (91) 2222022238
E-Mail: shares@bajajhindusthan.com
Web Site: www.bajajhindusthan.com
Year Founded: 1931
BAJAJHIND—(NSE)
Rev.: $881,357,400
Assets: $2,853,675,000
Liabilities: $2,018,988,180
Net Worth: $834,686,820
Earnings: ($54,780,660)
Emp.: 7,259
Fiscal Year-end: 09/30/12
Business Description:
Sugar & Ethanol Mfr
S.I.C.: 2869
N.A.I.C.S.: 325193
Personnel:
Shishir Bajaj *(Chm & Mng Dir)*
Kushagra Nayan Bajaj *(Vice Chm & Mng Dir)*
Anand Kumar Kanodia *(CFO)*
Manoj Maheshwari *(Grp CFO)*
Pradeep Parakh *(Pres-GRC & Sec)*
Board of Directors:
Shishir Bajaj
Alok Krishna Agarwal
M. L. Apte
Kushagra Nayan Bajaj
Ashok Kumar Gupta
Sanjeev Kumar
Manoj Maheshwari
D. S. Mehta
Ravindrakumar V. Ruia
D. K. Shukla
Transfer Agent:
Sharepro Services (India) Private Limited
13 AB Samhita Warehousing Complex II Floor
Sakinaka Telephone Lane
Off Andheri Kurla Rd Sakinaka, Mumbai, India

Subsidiary:

Bajaj Corp Ltd. (1)
221 Solitaire Corporate Park 151 M Vasanji Marg Opp Apple Heritage
Chakala Andheri East, Mumbai, 400 093, India
Tel.: (91) 2266919477 In (84.75%)
Fax: (91) 2266919476
E-Mail: consumer@bajajcorp.com
Web Site: www.bajajcorp.com
BAJAJCORP—(BOM NSE)
Rev.: $119,911,121
Assets: $102,925,403
Liabilities: $13,457,037
Net Worth: $89,468,367
Earnings: $30,805,786
Emp.: 362
Fiscal Year-end: 03/31/13
Hair Care Products Mfr
S.I.C.: 2844
N.A.I.C.S.: 325620
Sumit Malhotra *(Mng Dir)*
V. C. Nagori *(CFO)*
Sujoy Sircar *(Compliance Officer & Sec)*

BAJAJ STEEL INDUSTRIES LTD.

Imambada Road
Nagpur, Maharashtra, India 440018
Tel.: (91) 712 2720071
Fax: (91) 712 2723068
E-Mail: bsi@bajajngp.com
Web Site: www.bajajsteel.net
507944—(BOM)
Rev.: $53,525,312
Assets: $35,559,238
Liabilities: $24,331,999
Net Worth: $11,227,239
Earnings: $697,385
Fiscal Year-end: 03/31/13
Business Description:
Cotton Ginning Machinery Mfr
S.I.C.: 3523
N.A.I.C.S.: 333111
Personnel:
Rohit Bajaj *(Chm & Mng Dir)*
Manish Sharma *(CFO)*
Jagdish Shirke *(Compliance Officer & Sec)*
Board of Directors:
Rohit Bajaj
Mohan Agrawal
Sunil Bajaj
Vinod Kumar Bajaj
Deepak Batra
Alok Goenka
Kamal Kishore Kela
Rajkumar Lohia
Rajiv Ranka
Transfer Agent:
Adroit Corporate Services Private Limited
1st Floor 19/20 Jaferbhoy Industrial Estate
Makwana Road Marol Naka
Mumbai, India 400 059

BAKER & PROVAN PTY. LTD.

Level 9 11 Power Street
Saint Marys, NSW, 2760, Australia
Tel.: (61) 288019000
Fax: (61) 296734025
E-Mail: info@bakerprovan.com.au
Web Site: www.bakerprovan.com.au
Sales Range: $25-49.9 Million
Emp.: 51
Business Description:
Mechanical Engineering Services
S.I.C.: 8711
N.A.I.C.S.: 541330
Personnel:
Peter Allan Baker *(Chm & Mng Dir)*

BAKER PERKINS GROUP LTD.

Manor Dr
Paston Pkwy, Peterborough, PE4 7AP, United Kingdom
Tel.: (44) 1733283000
Telex: 32809
Fax: (44) 1733283001
Web Site: www.bakerperkinsgroup.com
Emp.: 350
Business Description:
Food Machinery Mfr
S.I.C.: 3556
N.A.I.C.S.: 333241
Personnel:
Brian Taylor *(Chm)*
John Cowx *(Mng Dir)*

U.S. Subsidiary:

Baker Perkins Inc. (1)
3223 Kraft Ave SE
Grand Rapids, MI 49512
Tel.: (616) 784-3111
Telex: 22-6428
Fax: (616) 784-0973
Web Site: www.apvbaker.com
Sales Range: $10-24.9 Million
Emp.: 50
Food Industry Machinery Mfr.
S.I.C.: 3556
N.A.I.C.S.: 333241
Dwight Wagaman *(VP-Sls & Mktg)*

BAKER TECHNOLOGY LIMITED

6 Pioneer Sector 1
Singapore, 628418, Singapore
Tel.: (65) 62621380
Fax: (65) 62622108
E-Mail: enquiry@bakertech.com.sg
Web Site: www.bakertech.com.sg
Year Founded: 1981
568—(SES)
Rev.: $79,546,293
Assets: $236,819,436
Liabilities: $19,709,499
Net Worth: $217,109,938
Earnings: $66,062,729
Emp.: 145
Fiscal Year-end: 12/31/12
Business Description:
Truck & Trailer Components Mfr & Distr
S.I.C.: 3714
N.A.I.C.S.: 336390
Personnel:
Ho Seng Lim *(Chm)*
Benety Chang *(CEO)*
Anthony Sabastian Aurol *(COO)*
Ko Nie Nga *(Sec)*
Alvin Keng Tiong Tan *(Sr VP-Bus Dev)*
Board of Directors:
Ho Seng Lim
Anthony Sabastian Aurol
Benety Chang
Yang Guan Tan
Meng Yeng Wong
Robert Kwan Seng Wong

Baker Technology Limited—(Continued)

Subsidiary:

Sea Deep Shipyard Pte. Ltd (1)
No 6 Pioneer Sector One
Singapore, 628418, Singapore
Tel.: (65) 68613255
Fax: (65) 68612516
E-Mail: marketing@seadeep.com.sg
Web Site: www.seadeep.com.sg
Emp.: 100
Crane Design & Mfr
S.I.C.: 3536
N.A.I.C.S.: 333923
Albert Thian Whee Ong *(Mng Dir)*

Subsidiary:

Interseas Shipping (Private) Limited (2)
No 6 Pioneer Sector One
Singapore, 628418, Singapore
Tel.: (65) 68613255
Fax: (65) 68612516
E-Mail: marketing@interseas.com.sg
Web Site: www.seadeep.com.sg
Emp.: 10
Crane Design & Mfr
S.I.C.: 3536
N.A.I.C.S.: 333923
Albert Ong *(Mng Dir)*

BAKER TILLY INTERNATIONAL LIMITED

2 Bloomsbury Street
London, WC1B 3ST, United Kingdom
Tel.: (44) 2073146875
Fax: (44) 2073146876
E-Mail: info@bakertillyinternational.com
Web Site: www.bakertillyinternational.com
Sales Range: $1-4.9 Billion
Emp.: 26,000
Business Description:
Accountancy & Business Network Services Organization
S.I.C.: 8621
N.A.I.C.S.: 813920
Personnel:
Geoff Barnes *(Pres & CEO)*

BAKER TILLY UK HOLDINGS LIMITED

6th Floor 25 Farringdon Street
London, EC4A 4AB, United Kingdom
Tel.: (44) 20 3201 8000
Fax: (44) 20 3201 8001
Web Site: www.bakertilly.co.uk
Year Founded: 2006
Sales Range: $250-299.9 Million
Emp.: 1,600
Business Description:
Holding Company; Accounting & Business Advisory Services
S.I.C.: 6719
N.A.I.C.S.: 551112
Personnel:
Martin Rodgers *(Chm)*
Laurence Longe *(Mng Partner-Natl)*
David Gwilliam *(Mng Partner-London Reg)*
Elfred Jarvis *(Mng Partner-Southern Reg)*
Kevin O'Connor *(Mng Partner-Northern Reg)*
Jon Randall *(COO)*

Subsidiaries:

Baker Tilly UK Audit LLP (1)
25 Farringdon Street
London, EC4A 4AB, United Kingdom UK
Tel.: (44) 20 3201 8000
Fax: (44) 20 3201 8001
E-Mail: info@bakertilly.co.uk
Web Site: www.bakertilly.co.uk
Accounting & Business Advisory Services
S.I.C.: 8721
N.A.I.C.S.: 541211
Martin Rodgers, *(Chm)*
Laurence Longe *(Mng Partner-Natl)*
David Gwilliam *(Mng Partner-London Reg)*
Elfred Jarvis *(Mng Partner-Southern Reg)*
Kevin O'Connor *(Mng Partner-Reg)*
Jon Randall *(COO)*

RSM Tenon Investment Solutions Limited (1)
(Formerly Lemontree Wealth Limited)
66 Chiltern Street
London, W1U 4JT, United Kingdom UK
Tel.: (44) 2075351400 (100%)
Fax: (44) 2075351401
E-Mail: chilternstreet@rsmtenon.com
Emp.: 400
Financial Management Services
S.I.C.: 6799
N.A.I.C.S.: 523920

BAKKAVOR GROUP HF

Tjarnargata 35
101 Reykjavik, Iceland
Tel.: (354) 5509700
Fax: (354) 5509701
E-Mail: investor.relations@bakkavor.com
Web Site: www.bakkavor.com
Year Founded: 1986
Sales Range: $1-4.9 Billion
Emp.: 18,121
Business Description:
Prepared Food Mfr
S.I.C.: 2099
N.A.I.C.S.: 311991
Personnel:
Agust Gudmundsson *(CEO)*
Chris Thomas *(Mng Dir)*
Brian Walton *(Mng Dir)*
Peter Gates *(CFO)*
John Gorman *(Pres-Bakkavor USA Inc.)*
Gordon Pates *(CEO-UK & Europe)*
Board of Directors:
Lydur Gudmundsson
Bjarni Pordur Bjarnason
Agust Gudmundsson
Halldor B. Ludviksson
Asgeir Thoroddsen

Non-U.S. Subsidiary:

Bakkavor Limited (1)
W Marsh Rd
Spalding, Lincs, PE11 2BB, United Kingdom UK
Tel.: (44) 1775761111
Fax: (44) 1775768206
E-Mail: becky.fathers@bakkavor.co.uk
Web Site: www.bakkavor.com
Emp.: 2,000
Food Products Distr
S.I.C.: 5141
N.A.I.C.S.: 424410

Subsidiaries:

Alresford Salads Ltd. (2)
The Nythe
Alresford, Hampshire, SO24 9DZ, United Kingdom
Tel.: (44) 1962734084
Fax: (44) 1962734212
E-Mail: carey.routley@bakkavor.co.uk
Web Site: www.bakkavor.co.uk
Emp.: 100
Watercress, Leafy Salads & Herbs Producer
S.I.C.: 5499
N.A.I.C.S.: 445299
Steven Turner *(Mng Dir)*

International Produce Ltd. (2)
Spade Lane Cold Store
Sittingbourne, Kent, ME9 7TT, United Kingdom (76%)
Tel.: (44) 1634371371
Fax: (44) 1634269269
E-Mail: anita.wilson@internationalproduce.com
Web Site: www.internationalproduce.com
Emp.: 300
Fruit & Vegetable Importer, Exporter & Whslr
S.I.C.: 5499
N.A.I.C.S.: 445299

Units:

Bourne Prepared Produce (2)
Spalding Road
Bourne, Lincolnshire, PE10 0AT, United Kingdom
Tel.: (44) 1778 393222
Fax: (44) 1778 393001
E-Mail:
Web Site: www.bakkavor.com
Emp.: 1,000
Salad Production Services: Leafy Salads, Prepared Fruit, Stir Fry & Prepared Vegetables
S.I.C.: 2099
N.A.I.C.S.: 311999
Tracey Brightey *(Mgr-HR)*

Bourne Stir Fry (2)
Tunnel Bank
Cherry Holt Road, Bourne, Lincolnshire, PE10 0DJ, United Kingdom
Tel.: (44) 778571211
Fax: (44) 778394990
E-Mail: ian.siunders@geest.co.uk
Web Site: www.geest.co.uk
Emp.: 250
Beansprouts Mfr
S.I.C.: 2099
N.A.I.C.S.: 311999

Caledonian Produce (2)
Carriden Indus Estate
Bo'ness, West Lothian, EH51 9SJ, United Kingdom
Tel.: (44) 1506823491
Fax: (44) 1506821100
Web Site: www.bakkavor.co.uk
Emp.: 500
Vegetables & Potatoes Retailer
S.I.C.: 5149
N.A.I.C.S.: 424490

Katie's (2)
Forward Dr
Christchurch Ave, Harrow, Middlesex, HA3 8NT, United Kingdom
Tel.: (44) 2084242666
Fax: (44) 2084200606
Web Site: www.geest.co.uk
Emp.: 1,000
Pre-Prepared Pizzas Mfr
S.I.C.: 2099
N.A.I.C.S.: 311999

The Pizzeria (2)
Sluice Road
Holbeach Saint Marks, Spalding, Lincolnshire, PE12 8HF, United Kingdom
Tel.: (44) 1406703000
Fax: (44) 1406701143
E-Mail: caron.varney@bakkavor.co.uk
Emp.: 350
Pre-Prepared Pizza Mfr
S.I.C.: 2099
N.A.I.C.S.: 311999

Wingland Foods (2)
Wingland Enterprise Park Millennium Way
Sutton Bridge, Spalding, Lincs, PE12 9TD, United Kingdom
Tel.: (44) 1406352500
Fax: (44) 1406352501
E-Mail: katherine.rowney@bakkavor.co.uk
Web Site: www.bakkavor.co.uk
Emp.: 400
Pre-Prepared Leafy Salads Mfr
S.I.C.: 2099
N.A.I.C.S.: 311999
Katherine Rowney *(Mgr-HR)*

Non-U.S. Holdings:

Vaco Olen (1)
Lammerdries Zuid 16F
2250 Olen, Belgium
Tel.: (32) 14564110
Fax: (32) 14564135
E-Mail: jover.steppen@bakkavor.eu
Web Site: www.bakkavor.eu
Emp.: 350
Ready Meals, Dips, Dressings & Soups Mfr
S.I.C.: 2099
N.A.I.C.S.: 311999
Jover Steppen *(Mng Dir)*

BAKU STOCK EXCHANGE

19 Bul-Bul Ave
AZ1000 Baku, Azerbaijan
Tel.: (994) 4989820
Fax: (994) 4937793
E-Mail: info@bse.az
Web Site: www.bse.az
Year Founded: 2000
Business Description:
Stock Exchange Services
S.I.C.: 6231
N.A.I.C.S.: 523210
Personnel:
Akhundov Anar *(Chm)*

BAKUER S.P.A.

Via Degli Stagnacci 7A
50010 Badia a Settimo, Florence, Italy
Tel.: (39) 0557310141
Telex: 570490
Fax: (39) 0557310145
E-Mail: info@bakuer.it
Web Site: www.bakuer.it
Year Founded: 1940
Emp.: 70
Business Description:
Mfr. of Tooling Systems for CNC Machine Tools & FMS; Traditional Machine Tools & Fixture Systems Import Export
S.I.C.: 3542
N.A.I.C.S.: 333517
Personnel:
Laura Pierozzi *(Controller)*

U.S. Subsidiary:

Bakuer American Co. (1)
c/o Teledyne Firth Stering 1 Teledyne Place
La Vergne, TN 37086 (100%)
Mailing Address:
PO Box 72
Morton Grove, IL 60053
Sls.: $8,000,000
Emp.: 80
Machine Tool Parts
S.I.C.: 7389
N.A.I.C.S.: 425120

BAL PHARMA LTD

21&22 Bommasandra Industrial Area
Hosur Road
Bengaluru, Karnataka, 560 099, India
Tel.: (91) 80 22354057
Fax: (91) 80 22354058
E-Mail: info@balpharma.com
Web Site: www.balpharma.com
524824—(BOM)
Rev.: $27,855,744
Assets: $27,779,892
Liabilities: $19,507,645
Net Worth: $8,272,247
Earnings: $794,164
Fiscal Year-end: 03/31/13
Business Description:
Pharmaceutical Company
S.I.C.: 2834
N.A.I.C.S.: 325412
Personnel:
Shailesh Siroya *(Mng Dir)*
V. Murali *(Compliance Officer, Sec & Gen Mgr-Fin)*
Board of Directors:
Ajit Kumar
S. Prasanna
G. S. R. Subba Rao
Pramod Kumar S.
Shailesh Siroya
Shrenik Siroya
Transfer Agent:
TSR Darashaw Limited
6 10 Haji Moosa Patrawala Ind 20 Dr E Moses Road Mahalaxmi
Near Famous Studio, Mumbai, 400 011, India

BALA TECHNO GLOBAL LTD.

P-22 CIT Road Scheme - 55
Kolkata, West Bengal, 700014, India
Tel.: (91) 33 22658157

Fax: (91) 33 22652863
E-Mail: balatechnoglobal@gmail.com
Web Site: www.balatechnoglobal.com
511395—(BOM)
Sales Range: $10-24.9 Million
Business Description:
Cotton Yarn Distr
S.I.C.: 2299
N.A.I.C.S.: 313110
Personnel:
Tapas Kar *(Compliance Officer)*
Board of Directors:
Ashok Mehra
C. P. Mehra
Kapil Ashok Mehra
Siddharth Mehra
Anil Kumar Saha
Transfer Agent:
Niche Technologies Private Limited
D-511 Bagree Market 71 B. R. B. Basu Road
Kolkata, India

BALA TECHNO INDUSTRIES LTD.

P-22 C I T Road Scheme - 55
Kolkata, West Bengal, 700014, India
Tel.: (91) 33 2265 2431
Fax: (91) 33 2265 2863
E-Mail: balatechnoindustries@gmail.com
Web Site: www.balatechnoindustries.com
514199—(BOM)
Business Description:
Narrow Woven Fabric Mfr
S.I.C.: 2397
N.A.I.C.S.: 313220
Personnel:
Tarun Kumar Das *(Sec)*

BALAJI AMINES LIMITED

Balaji Tower No 9/1A/1 Hotgi Road
Asara Chowk
Sholapur, Maharashtra, 413001, India
Tel.: (91) 2172451500
Fax: (91) 2172451521
E-Mail: info@balajiamines.com
Web Site: www.balajiamines.com
BALAMINES—(NSE)
Sls.: $103,144,251
Assets: $96,287,281
Liabilities: $64,513,559
Net Worth: $31,773,722
Earnings: $5,778,696
Fiscal Year-end: 03/31/13
Business Description:
Speciality Chemicals Mfr
S.I.C.: 2819
N.A.I.C.S.: 325180
Personnel:
A. Prathap Reddy *(Chm & Co-Mng Dir)*
D. Ram Reddy *(Co-Mng Dir)*
N. Rajeshwar Reddy *(Co-Mng Dir)*
Arati S. Dudhawale *(Compliance Officer & Sec)*
Board of Directors:
A. Prathap Reddy
T. Naveena Chandra
Kashinath R. Dhole
C. S. N. Murthy
S. V. Pattabhiraman
A. Srinivas Reddy
D. Ram Reddy
G. Hemanth Reddy
M. Amarender Reddy
N. Rajeshwar Reddy
Transfer Agent:
Venture Capital & Corporate Investments Private Limited
12-10-167 Bharat Nagar
500018 Hyderabad, India

BALAJI TELEFILMS LTD.

C 13 Balaji House Dalia Industrial Estate Opposite Laxmi Industries
New Link Road Andheri West,
Mumbai, 400 053, India
Tel.: (91) 2240698000
Fax: (91) 2240698181
E-Mail: balaji@balajitelefilms.com
Web Site: www.balajitelefilms.com
532382—(BOM)
Rev.: $37,887,528
Assets: $83,272,280
Liabilities: $8,570,226
Net Worth: $74,702,054
Earnings: $2,703,466
Emp.: 110
Fiscal Year-end: 03/31/13
Business Description:
Television Software Producer
S.I.C.: 7372
N.A.I.C.S.: 511210
Personnel:
Jeetendra Kapoor *(Chm)*
Ekta Kapoor *(Mng Dir)*
Shobha Kapoor *(Mng Dir)*
Sanjay Dwivedi *(CFO)*
Simmi Singh Bisht *(Sec & Compliance Officer)*
Board of Directors:
Jeetendra Kapoor
Akshay Chudasama
Ekta Kapoor
Shobha Kapoor
Tusshar Kapoor
Ashutosh Khanna
D. G. Rajan
Pradeep Kumar Sarda

Deloitte Haskins & Sells
Mumbai, India
Transfer Agent:
Karvy Computershare Private Limited
Plot 17 to 24 Near Image Hospital Vittalrao Nagar Madhapur
Hyderabad, India
Subsidiary:

Balaji Motion Pictures Ltd (1)
C-13 Balaji House Dalia Indus Estate Opposite Laxmi Indus Estate
New Link Rd Andheri W, Mumbai, 400 053, India
Tel.: (91) 2240698200
Fax: (91) 2240698183
E-Mail: balaji@balajimotionpictures.com
Web Site: www.balajimotionpictures.com
Television Programming Services
S.I.C.: 7812
N.A.I.C.S.: 512110
Tanuj Garg *(CEO)*
Kanika Saxena *(CMO)*

BALAMORA RESOURCES LIMITED

Level 1 350 Hay Street
Subiaco, WA, 6008, Australia
Mailing Address:
PO Box 222
Subiaco, WA, 6904, Australia
Tel.: (61) 8 6365 4519
Fax: (61) 8 9388 6040
E-Mail: enquiries@balamara.com.au
Web Site: www.balamara.com.au
BMB—(ASX DEU)
Rev.: $47,769
Assets: $7,767,344
Liabilities: $2,039,870
Net Worth: $5,727,474
Earnings: ($7,326,238)
Fiscal Year-end: 06/30/13
Business Description:
Zinc Exploration Services
S.I.C.: 1031
N.A.I.C.S.: 212231
Personnel:
Derek Lenartowicz *(Chm)*
Mike Ralston *(Mng Dir)*
Daniel Kendall *(Sec & Controller-Fin)*
Board of Directors:
Derek Lenartowicz
Milos Bosnjakovic
Michael Hale
Mike Ralston

BALASORE ALLOYS LIMITED

Balgopalpur
Baleshwar, Orissa, India
Tel.: (91) 6782 2757 81
Fax: (91) 6782 2757 24
E-Mail: mail@balasorealloys.com
Web Site: www.balasorealloys.com
Year Founded: 1984
513142—(BOM)
Rev.: $132,619,549
Assets: $277,217,125
Liabilities: $104,759,399
Net Worth: $172,457,727
Earnings: $5,323,075
Emp.: 696
Fiscal Year-end: 03/31/13
Business Description:
Ferro Alloys Production Services
S.I.C.: 3999
N.A.I.C.S.: 339999
Personnel:
Pramod Kumar Mittal *(Chm)*
Anil Sureka *(Mng Dir)*
R. K. Parakh *(CFO & Dir-Fin)*
Trilochan Sharma *(Compliance Officer, Sec & Sr Gen Mgr)*
Board of Directors:
Pramod Kumar Mittal
A. K. Bhattacharyya
K. P. Khandelwal
S. K. Majumdar
Vartika Mittal
S. Mohapatra
S. K. Pal
R. K. Parakh
Anil Sureka
Mahesh Trivedi
Transfer Agent:
MCS Limited
77/2A Hazra Road
Kolkata, India

BALATON POWER INC.

Suite 206 20257 54th Avenue
Langley, BC, V3A 3W2, Canada
Tel.: (604) 533-5075
Fax: (604) 533-5065
E-Mail: boxbal@shaw.ca
BPWRF—(OTC OTCB)
Business Description:
Metal Mining
S.I.C.: 1099
N.A.I.C.S.: 212299
Personnel:
Michael Rosa *(Pres & CEO)*
Paul E. Preston *(CFO)*
Board of Directors:
Nicole Bouthillier
Paul E. Preston
Michael Rosa

BALDA AG

Bergkirchener Str 228
32549 Bad Oeynhausen, Germany
Tel.: (49) 57349220
Fax: (49) 57349222604
E-Mail: info@balda.de
Web Site: www.balda.de
BAF—(DEU)
Sales Range: $75-99.9 Million
Emp.: 3,358
Business Description:
Communication & Entertainment Electronics Mfr; Plastics Systems for Medical Appliances
S.I.C.: 3089
N.A.I.C.S.: 326199
Personnel:
Dominik Muser *(CEO)*
James Lim *(COO)*
Supervisory Board of Directors:
Klaus Rueth
Thomas van Aubel
Frauke Vogler
Legal Counsel:
Axel Baue
Dresden, Germany
Subsidiaries:

Aimtec GmbH (1)
Werster Str 17
32584 Lohne, Germany (50%)
Tel.: (49) 57318693100
Fax: (49) 57 34 661 1601
E-Mail: info@aimtec.de
Web Site: www.aimtec.de
Custom Computer Programming Services
S.I.C.: 7371
N.A.I.C.S.: 541511

Balda Grundstucks-Vermietungs GmbH & Co. KG (1)
Bergkirchener Str 228
32549 Bad Oeynhausen, Germany (100%)
Tel.: (49) 57349220
Fax: (49) 57349222747
E-Mail: info@balda.de
Web Site: www.balda.de/kontakt/00109_en.php
Investment Advice
S.I.C.: 6282
N.A.I.C.S.: 523930
Rainer Mohr *(CEO & CFO)*

Balda Grundstucks-Verwaltungs GmbH (1)
Bergkirchener Str 228
32549 Bad Oeynhausen, Germany (100%)
Tel.: (49) 57349220
Fax: (49) 57349222747
E-Mail: info@balda.de
Web Site: www.balda.de/contact/adresses.php
Telecommunications Resellers
S.I.C.: 4812
N.A.I.C.S.: 517911
Rainir Mohr *(CEO)*

Balda Lumberg Deutschland GmbH & Co. KG (1)
Bergkirchener Str 228
32549 Bad Oeynhausen, Germany
Tel.: (49) 57349220
Fax: (49) 57349222747
E-Mail: info@balda.de
Investment Advice Services
S.I.C.: 6282
N.A.I.C.S.: 523930
Joachim Gut *(Chm)*
Dirk Eichelberger *(CFO)*

Balda Lumberg Verwaltungsgesellschaft mbH (1)
Bergkirchener Str 228
32549 Bad Oeynhausen, Germany (100%)
Tel.: (49) 57349220
Fax: (49) 57349222747
E-Mail: info@balda.de
Web Site: www.balda.de/kontakt/00109_en.php
Investment Advice
S.I.C.: 6282
N.A.I.C.S.: 523930
Dino Kitzinger *(Chm)*
Raine Mohr *(CFO)*

Balda Medical GmbH & Co. KG (1)
Bergkirchener Str 228
32549 Bad Oeynhausen, Germany (100%)
Tel.: (49) 57345130
Fax: (49) 57349222747
E-Mail: info@balda-medical.de
Web Site: www.balda-medical.de
Emp.: 30
Purchased Glass Product Mfr
S.I.C.: 3231
N.A.I.C.S.: 327215

Balda Medical Verwaltungsgesellschaft mbH (1)
Bergkirchener Str 228
32549 Bad Oeynhausen, Germany (100%)
Tel.: (49) 57349220
Fax: (49) 57349222747

Balda AG—(Continued)

E-Mail: info@balda.de
Web Site: www.balda.de/kontakt/00109_en.php
Purchased Glass Product Mfr
S.I.C.: 3231
N.A.I.C.S.: 327215

Balda Solutions Deutschland GmbH (1)
Bergkirchener Str 228
32549 Bad Oeynhausen, Germany (100%)
Tel.: (49) 57349220
Fax: (49) 57349222747
E-Mail: info@balda-solutions.de
Web Site: www.balda-solutions.de
Special Die & Tool Die Set Jig & Fixture Mfr
S.I.C.: 3544
N.A.I.C.S.: 333514
Michael Sienkiewicz *(CEO)*

Balda Werkzeug- und Vorrichtungsbau GmbH (1)
Bergkirchener Str 228
32549 Bad Oeynhausen, Germany (100%)
Tel.: (49) 57349220
Fax: (49) 57349222604
E-Mail: info@balda.de
Web Site: www.balda.de
Hand & Edge Tool Mfr
S.I.C.: 3425
N.A.I.C.S.: 332216
Joachim Gut *(Chm)*
Dirk Eichelberger *(CFO)*

Balda (1)
Eupenerstrasse 35 Ste 2051
32045 Herford, Germany (100%)
Tel.: (49) 52211860
Fax: (49) 5221186111
E-Mail: info@heinzekunstst.de
Web Site: www.balda.de
Emp.: 320
Plastics
S.I.C.: 3084
N.A.I.C.S.: 326199

U.S. Subsidiary:

Balda Solutions USA, Inc. (1)
2803 Slater Rd
Morrisville, NC 27560-8463 (100%)
Tel.: (919) 459-1660
Fax: (919) 459-1661
Web Site: www.balda.com
Emp.: 11
Business Services
S.I.C.: 7389
N.A.I.C.S.: 561499
Stefan Stalgren *(Gen Mgr)*

Non-U.S. Subsidiaries:

Balda Ltd. (1)
Suzhou Singapore Industrial Park
5 Hong Feng Rd, Suzhou, 215006, China
Tel.: (86) 51267020102
Fax: (86) 5127616312
Web Site: www.balda.com
Emp.: 40
Machinery
S.I.C.: 3589
N.A.I.C.S.: 333318
Ken Cheng *(Mng Dir)*

Balda Solutions (Beijing) Ltd. (1)
No 1 South Road Jinma Development Zone
Shunyi Geist, Beijing, China (100%)
Tel.: (86) 1069490633
Fax: (86) 1069491977
E-Mail: info@baldabelgium.com
Web Site: www.baldabelgium.com
Emp.: 2,000
Plastics Product Mfr
S.I.C.: 3089
N.A.I.C.S.: 326199

Balda Solutions Hungaria Kft (1)
Videoton Ipari P Alsoerdo Ut 1
Veszprem, Hungary (73.47%)
Tel.: (36) 34542995
Communications Equipment Mfr
S.I.C.: 3669
N.A.I.C.S.: 334290

Balda Solutions Malaysia Sdn. Bhd. (1)
No 3 Jalan Zarib 6 Kawasan Perindustrian Zarib
Lahat Ipoh, 31500 Perak, Malaysia MY
Tel.: (60) 6053222028
Fax: (60) 6053222029
E-Mail: admin@balda.com.my
Web Site: www.balda.com.my
Emp.: 800
Electronics & Telecommunications Mfr
S.I.C.: 4812
N.A.I.C.S.: 517210
Foo Wan Seng *(Gen Mgr)*

Balda Solutions (Suzhou) Ltd. (1)
No 3 Yangqing Rd Suzhou Park Zone
Suzhou, China (100%)
Tel.: (86) 51267016916
Fax: (86) 51267020119
Plastics Product Mfr
S.I.C.: 3089
N.A.I.C.S.: 326199

BALDERTON CAPITAL

20 Balderton St
London, W1K 6TL, United Kingdom
Tel.: (44) 2070166800
Fax: (44) 2070166810
E-Mail: information@balderton.com
Web Site: www.balderton.com
Managed Assets: $1,900,000,000
Emp.: 35

Business Description:
Private Equity Firm
S.I.C.: 6211
N.A.I.C.S.: 523999

Personnel:
Suranga Chandratillake *(Gen Partner)*
Bernard Liautaud *(Gen Partner)*
Daniel Waterhouse *(Gen Partner)*
Roberto Bonanzinga *(Partner)*
Tim Bunting *(Partner)*
Mark Evans *(Partner)*
Barry Maloney *(Partner)*
Jerome Misso *(Partner)*
Dharmash Mistry *(Partner)*

BALFOUR BEATTY PLC

130 Wilton Road
London, SW1V 1LQ, United Kingdom
Tel.: (44) 2072166800
Fax: (44) 2072166950
E-Mail: info@balfourbeatty.com
Web Site: www.balfourbeatty.com
Year Founded: 1909
BBY—(LSE OTC)
Rev.: $17,207,943,840
Assets: $9,147,247,680
Liabilities: $7,079,957,070
Net Worth: $2,067,290,610
Earnings: $69,488,760
Emp.: 50,174
Fiscal Year-end: 12/31/12

Business Description:
International Engineering & Construction Services; Specializing in Rail, Road & Power Systems, Buildings & Complex Structures
Export
S.I.C.: 8711
N.A.I.C.S.: 541330

Personnel:
Andrew J. McNaughton *(CEO)*
Jim Moynihan *(Grp Mng Dir)*
Duncan J. Magrath *(CFO)*
Chris Vaughan *(Chief Corp Officer & Sec)*
Mark W. Layman *(Chm/CEO-Construction Svcs-US)*
Kevin Craven *(CEO-Support Svcs)*
John Moore *(CEO-Rail)*
Mike Peasland *(CEO-Construction Svcs-UK)*
George Pierson *(CEO-Pro Svcs)*
Ian K. Rylatt *(CEO-Infrastructure Investments)*

Board of Directors:
Steven Marshall
Robert M. Amen
Maureen Kempston Darkes
Iain Ferguson
Hubertus Krossa
Duncan J. Magrath
Andrew J. McNaughton
Belinda Richards
Peter John Louis Zinkin

Legal Counsel:
Mayer Brown Rowe & Maw
1675 Broadway
New York, NY 10019

Linklaters
1 Silk Street
London, EC2Y 8HQ, United Kingdom

Transfer Agent:
Computershare Investor Services PLC
Owen House 8 Bankhead Crossway North
P.O. Box 435
Edinburgh, EH11 4BR, United Kingdom
Tel.: (44) 870 702 0139

Subsidiary:

Balfour Beatty Group Ltd (1)
130 Wilton Road
London, SW1V 1LQ, United Kingdom
Tel.: (44) 20 7216 6800
Fax: (44) 20 7216 6950
Civil Engineering Services
S.I.C.: 1629
N.A.I.C.S.: 237990

Subsidiaries:

Balfour Beatty Building Management & Services (2)
130 Wilton Road
London, SW1V 1LQ, United Kingdom
Tel.: (44) 2072166800
Fax: (44) 2072166950
E-Mail: info@balfourbeatty.com
Web Site: www.balfourbeatty.com
Emp.: 200
Building Management & Services
S.I.C.: 7349
N.A.I.C.S.: 561790
Peter John Louis Zinkin *(Dir-Plng & Dev)*

Subsidiary:

Mansell Plc (3)
Roman House Grant Road
CR96BU Croydon, Surrey, United Kingdom
Tel.: (44) 2086548191
Fax: (44) 2086551578
E-Mail: mailbox@mansell.plc.uk
Web Site: www.mansell.plc.uk
Emp.: 200
Building Services
S.I.C.: 7349
N.A.I.C.S.: 561790
Steve Waite *(Mng Dir)*

Subsidiary:

Mansell Construction Services Ltd. (4)
Roman House Grant Rd
Croydon, CR9 6BU, United Kingdom
Tel.: (44) 2086548191
Fax: (44) 2086551286
E-Mail: mailbox@mansell.plc.uk
Web Site: www.mansell.plc.uk
Emp.: 200
Construction Services
S.I.C.: 1542
N.A.I.C.S.: 236220

Subsidiaries:

Mansell Build Limited (5)
4 Station Rd Alexander House
Cheadle Hulme, Cheshire, SK8 5AE, United Kingdom UK
Tel.: (44) 1614861156
Fax: (44) 1614853145
Web Site: www.mansell.plc.uk
Emp.: 100
Building Construction
S.I.C.: 1542
N.A.I.C.S.: 236220
Peter Commins *(Reg Mng Dir)*

U.S. Subsidiary:

Heery International, Inc. (3)
999 Peachtree St NE
Atlanta, GA 30309-3953 GA
Tel.: (404) 881-9880 (100%)
Fax: (404) 875-1283
E-Mail: corporate@heery.com
Web Site: www.heery.com
Sales Range: $250-299.9 Million
Emp.: 250
Construction Management & Design Services
S.I.C.: 8712
N.A.I.C.S.: 541310
Theodore E. Sak *(CFO & Exec VP)*
Richard Nikonovich-Kahn *(Gen Counsel & Sr VP)*
Lin Redden *(Sr VP & Dir-Construction Mgmt)*
Greg Peirce *(Sr VP)*

Subsidiaries:

Charter Builders, LTD (4)
1505 LBJ Fwy Ste 700
Dallas, TX 75234-4332
Tel.: (972) 484-4888
Fax: (972) 484-4373
E-Mail: info@balfourbeatty.com
Web Site: www.charterbuilders.com
Emp.: 20
Commercial Construction
S.I.C.: 1542
N.A.I.C.S.: 236220
Bruce D. Helm *(Exec VP)*

Heery-HLM Design (4)
820 16th St Mall
Denver, CO 80202 DE
Tel.: (720) 946-0276
Fax: (720) 946-0277
Web Site: www.hlmdesign.com
Emp.: 434
Architectural Design, Engineering & Construction Services
S.I.C.: 8712
N.A.I.C.S.: 541310
Mark Johnson *(VP)*

Heery International (4)
444 S Flower St Ste 700
Los Angeles, CA 90071 CA
Tel.: (323) 651-1998
Fax: (323) 606-4248
Web Site: www.heery.com
Emp.: 100
Construction Management Services
S.I.C.: 8748
N.A.I.C.S.: 541618
Jim Isaf *(Reg Mgr)*

Balfour Beatty Capital Ltd (2)
350 Euston Road Regent's Place
London, NW1 3AX, United Kingdom
Tel.: (44) 20 7121 3700
Fax: (44) 20 7121 3701
E-Mail: marketing@bbcap.co.uk
Web Site: www.bbcap.co.uk
Emp.: 10
Financial Management Services
S.I.C.: 6211
N.A.I.C.S.: 523999
Maureen Omrod *(Dir-Corp Comm-Balfour Beatty Capital Group, Inc)*

Balfour Beatty Civil Engineering Ltd (2)
86 Station Road
Redhill, Surrey, RH1 1PQ, United Kingdom
Tel.: (44) 1737785000
Fax: (44) 1737785100
E-Mail: enquiries@bbcel.co.uk
Web Site: www.bbcel.co.uk
Civil Engineering & Project Management
S.I.C.: 8711
N.A.I.C.S.: 541330
Ian Barr *(Mng Dir-Northern Div)*
Murray Easton *(Mng Dir-Southern Div)*
Stephen Tarr *(Mng Dir)*
Marshall Scott *(Mng Dir)*
Philip Morris *(Sec)*

Division:

Balfour Beatty Civil Engineering Limited Metro (3)
86 Station Rd
Redhill, Surrey, RH1 1PQ, United Kingdom
Tel.: (44) 1737785000
Fax: (44) 1737785100
Web Site: www.bbcel.co.uk
Emp.: 300
Management of London's Underground Rail System

S.I.C.: 4111
N.A.I.C.S.: 485112
Brian Walker *(Gen Mgr)*

Subsidiaries:

Balvac, Ltd. (4)
Sherwood House
Gadbrook Business Centre
Rudheath, Northwich, CW9 7UQ, United Kingdom
Tel.: (44) 1606333036
Fax: (44) 160645093
E-Mail: enquiries@bbcel.co.uk
Web Site: www.balvac.co.uk
Civil Enginering & Building Refurbishment Contractor
S.I.C.: 1629
N.A.I.C.S.: 237990
Richard Bailey *(Mng Dir)*

Birse Metro Limited (4)
Lyon House
160-166 Borough High Street, London, SE1 1LB, United Kingdom
Tel.: (44) 2071735250
Fax: (44) 2071735249
E-Mail: enquiries@birsemetro.com
Web Site: www.birsemetro.co.uk
Emp.: 50
Construction Services for London Underground Network
S.I.C.: 1629
N.A.I.C.S.: 237990
Jim Purves *(Mng Dir)*
Mark Hearne *(Mng Dir)*

Connect Roads South Tyneside Ltd (4)
Unit 14 Brooklands Way Bolden Business Park
Boldon Colliery, Tyne and Wear, NE35 9LZ, United Kingdom
Tel.: (44) 191 519 6070
Fax: (44) 191 519 6080
Web Site: www.bbcap.co.uk/contact
Emp.: 30
Road Construction Engineering Services
S.I.C.: 1611
N.A.I.C.S.: 237310
Philip Jordan *(Gen Mgr)*

Connect Roads Sunderland Ltd (4)
13 Tiley Road Crowther Industrial Estate
Washington, Tyne & Wear, NE38 0AE, United Kingdom
Tel.: (44) 191 418 3100
Fax: (44) 191 418 3115
Web Site: www.bbcap.co.uk/contact/
Emp.: 22
Road Construction Engineering Services
S.I.C.: 1622
N.A.I.C.S.: 237310
Ronnie Barnett *(Mgr-Contractor)*

Subsidiaries:

Birse Civils Limited (3)
3 Grimston Grimston Sherburn Rd
Tadcaster, North Yorkshire, LS24 9BX, United Kingdom
Tel.: (44) 1937830091
Fax: (44) 1937830093
E-Mail: enquiries@birsecl.co.uk
Web Site: www.birsecl.co.uk
Sls.: $351,631,008
Emp.: 433
Civil Engineering Project Development, Construction & Maintenance
S.I.C.: 1629
N.A.I.C.S.: 237990
Robert Adams *(Mng Dir)*

Birse Group (3)
Humber Road
Barton-upon-Humber, United Kingdom
Tel.: (44) 1652633222
Fax: (44) 1652633360
Web Site: www.birse.co.uk
Sls.: $591,866,432
Emp.: 60
Building, Civil & Process Engineering Services; Plant Hire Services & Equipment Rental Services
S.I.C.: 8711
N.A.I.C.S.: 541330
Len Storrow *(Mgr-Mktg)*

Divisions:

Birse Group Services (4)
Humber Rd
Barton-upon-Humber, DN18 5BW, United Kingdom
Tel.: (44) 1652633222
Fax: (44) 1652633360
Web Site: www.birse.co.uk
Emp.: 75
Business Services
S.I.C.: 7389
N.A.I.C.S.: 561499
Christine Jaeckel *(Mng Dir)*

Birse Process Engineering Limited (3)
Alexander House 4 Station Road
Cheadle Hulme, Cheshire, SK8 5AE, United Kingdom
Tel.: (44) 1619624880
Fax: (44) 1614884686
E-Mail: bpe@birse.co.uk
Web Site: www.birse.co.uk
Emp.: 20
Engineering & Construction for the Process, Energy & Environmental Sectors
S.I.C.: 8711
N.A.I.C.S.: 541330

Birse Rail Ltd. (3)
15th Fl Lyndon House 58-62 Hagley Rd
Birmingham, Edgbaston, B16 8PE, United Kingdom
Tel.: (44) 1214564200
Fax: (44) 1214563880
E-Mail: enqurie@birserail.co.uk
Web Site: www.birserail.co.uk
Emp.: 100
Railway Engineering & Construction
S.I.C.: 1629
N.A.I.C.S.: 237990
Martin White *(Mng Dir)*

BPH Equipment Limited (3)
Humber Rd
Barton-upon-Humber, North Lincolnshire, DN18 5XD, United Kingdom
Tel.: (44) 01652633340
Fax: (44) 01652635920
E-Mail: info@bphequipment.co.uk
Web Site: www.bphequipment.co.uk
Emp.: 15
Crane, Plant & Machinery Equipment Rental
S.I.C.: 7359
N.A.I.C.S.: 532490
Graham Booth *(Mng Dir)*

Non-U.S. Joint Venture:

Gammon Construction Ltd. (3)
28th Fl Devon House TaiKoo Pl 979 Kings Rd
Quarry Bay, China (Hong Kong)
Tel.: (852) 25168823
Fax: (852) 25166260
E-Mail: hongkong@gammonconstruction.com
Web Site: www.gammonconstruction.com
Sales Range: $1-4.9 Billion
Emp.: 5,000
Construction Services
S.I.C.: 1542
N.A.I.C.S.: 236220
Thomas Ho *(CEO)*
Philco Wong *(COO)*

Balfour Beatty Construction Limited (2)
Dean House
24 Ravelston Terrace, Edinburgh, EH4 3TP, United Kingdom UK
Tel.: (44) 1313329411
Fax: (44) 1313325937
E-Mail: headoffice@bbcl.co.uk
Web Site: www.balfourbeattyconstruction.co.uk
Sales Range: $1-4.9 Billion
Emp.: 150
Construction Services
S.I.C.: 1542
N.A.I.C.S.: 236220
Nicholas Pollard *(CEO)*
Robert Clark *(Mng Dir)*

Subsidiaries:

Balfour Beatty Construction Northern Limited (3)
Cavendish House
Cross Street, Sale, M33 7BU, United Kingdom UK
Tel.: (44) 1619727501
Web Site: www.balfoubeattyconstruction.co.uk/
Emp.: 80
Construction Services
S.I.C.: 1542
N.A.I.C.S.: 236220
Dave Donaldson *(Mng Dir)*

Balfour Beatty Construction Scottish & Southern Limited (3)
Dean House
24 Ravelston Terrace, Edinburgh, EH4 3TP, United Kingdom
Tel.: (44) 1313329411
Fax: (44) 1313325937
Web Site: www.bbrl.co.uk/
Construction Services
S.I.C.: 1542
N.A.I.C.S.: 236220
Bob Clark *(Mng Dir)*

Cowlin Group Ltd. (3)
Stratton House Cater Road
Bishopsworth, Bristol, BS13 7UH, United Kingdom
Tel.: (44) 1179832000
Fax: (44) 1179877758
E-Mail: bristol@cowlin.co.uk
Web Site: www.cowlin.co.uk
Sales Range: $250-299.9 Million
Emp.: 350
Commercial Building Contractor
S.I.C.: 1542
N.A.I.C.S.: 236220
Bob Clark *(Mng Dir)*

Subsidiaries:

Cowlin Timber Frame (4)
Duffryn Bach Terrace
Church Village, Pontypridd, United Kingdom
Tel.: (44) 3209953
E-Mail: timberframe@cowlin.co.uk
Timber Frame Mfr
S.I.C.: 1542
N.A.I.C.S.: 236220

U.S. Subsidiary:

Balfour Beatty Construction Group Inc (3)
3100 McKinnon St 10th Fl
Dallas, TX 75201
Tel.: (214) 451-1000
Fax: (214) 451-1097
Web Site: www.balfourbeattyus.com
Construction Engineering Services
S.I.C.: 8711
N.A.I.C.S.: 541330
Mark W. Layman *(Chm & CEO)*
Robert Van Cleave *(Chm & CEO)*
Kasey Bevans *(CIO & VP)*
Glenn Burns *(Chief Legal Officer & Sr VP)*
John L. Parolisi *(Sr VP-Strategic Plng & Mktg)*

Subsidiaries:

Balfour Beatty Construction LLC (4)
3100 McKinnon St 10th Fl
Dallas, TX 75201-1593 NV
Tel.: (214) 451-1000
Fax: (214) 981-5600
E-Mail: info@balfourbeattyus.com
Web Site: www.balfourbeattyus.com
Emp.: 1,496
Commercial & Industrial Building Construction
S.I.C.: 1629
N.A.I.C.S.: 236210
Mark W. Layman *(Chm & CEO)*
John Tarpey *(COO)*
Kasey Bevans *(CIO & VP)*
Glenn S. Burns *(Chief Legal Officer & Exec VP)*
Douglas H. Jones *(Pres/CEO-Dallas, Fort Worth & Nashville)*
Leon Blondin *(Pres-Washington)*
Steve Olson *(Pres-North)*
Frank Spears *(Pres-Georgia)*
John F. Woodcock *(Pres-Carolinas Div)*
Eric Stenman *(CEO-Southwest Reg)*
Bill McIntosh *(Sr VP-Bus Acq)*
John L. Parolisi *(Sr VP-Strategic Plng & Mktg)*
Steve Smithgall *(Corp Sr VP-Safety, Health & Environment)*

Subsidiary:

Balfour Beatty Construction LLC (5)
7901 SW 6th Ct
Plantation, FL 33324-3282
Tel.: (954) 585-4000
Fax: (954) 585-4501
Web Site: www.balfourbeattyus.com
Emp.: 90
General Construction Services
S.I.C.: 1542
N.A.I.C.S.: 236220
Al Petrangeli *(CEO-Southeast Reg)*
Steve Holt *(Gen Counsel)*
Kent Long *(Sr VP)*
Louyse Poirier *(Sr VP-HR)*
Scott Skidelsky *(Sr VP-Bus Acq-Orlando)*

Howard S. Wright Construction Co. (4)
425 NW 10th Ave Ste 200
Portland, OR 97209 WA
Tel.: (503) 220-0895
Fax: (503) 220-0892
E-Mail: resume@hswcc.com
Web Site: www.howardswright.com
Sales Range: $600-649.9 Million
Commercial & Institutional Building Construction Services
S.I.C.: 1542
N.A.I.C.S.: 236220
Dale Pellow *(Pres)*
Brad Nydahl *(CEO)*
Gordon Childress *(Pres-Oregon Div)*
Jim Constance *(Pres-Washington Div)*
Mitchell Hornecker *(Exec VP)*
John Bullwinkel *(Sr VP-Strategic Bus Dev)*

SpawMaxwell Company, LLC (4)
4321 Directors Row Ste 200
Houston, TX 77092 TX
Tel.: (713) 222-0900
Fax: (713) 222-1414
Web Site: www.spawmaxwell.com
Sales Range: $350-399.9 Million
Emp.: 252
Commercial & Office Building Construction
S.I.C.: 1542
N.A.I.C.S.: 236220
Steve Mechler *(Pres)*
David Spaw *(CEO)*
Steve Keffeler *(Sr VP-Ops)*

Balfour Beatty Engineering Services Ltd (2)
Lumina Building 40 Ainslie Road
Hillington Park, Glasgow, G52 4RU, United Kingdom
Tel.: (44) 141 880 2000
Fax: (44) 141 880 2201
E-Mail: enquiry@bbesl.com
Web Site: www.bbesl.com
Emp.: 200
Mechanical Engineering Services
S.I.C.: 8711
N.A.I.C.S.: 541330
Bill Merry *(Dir-Bus Dev)*

Balfour Beatty Ground Engineering Ltd (2)
Pavilion C2 Ashwood Park Ashwood Way
Basingstoke, Hampshire, RG23 8BG, United Kingdom
Tel.: (44) 1256 365200
Fax: (44) 1256 365201
E-Mail: info@bbge.com
Web Site: www.bbge.com
Emp.: 7
Ground Engineering Services
S.I.C.: 8711
N.A.I.C.S.: 541330
Chris Wilson *(Mgr-Factory)*

Balfour Beatty Infrastructure Investments Ltd (2)
130 Wilton Road
London, SW1V 1LQ, United Kingdom
Tel.: (44) 20 7216 6800
Real Estate Development Services
S.I.C.: 6531
N.A.I.C.S.: 531390

Balfour Beatty plc—(Continued)

Balfour Beatty Investment Holdings Ltd (2)
130 Wilton Rd
London, SW1V 1LQ, United Kingdom
Tel.: (44) 2072166800
Fax: (44) 2072166950
E-Mail: info@balfourbeatty.com
Web Site: www.balfourbeatty.com
Emp.: 100
Investment Management Services
S.I.C.: 6211
N.A.I.C.S.: 523999
Daniel Hardcastle *(Mng Dir)*

Balfour Beatty Rail Ltd (2)
86 Station Road
Redhill, Surrey, United Kingdom
Tel.: (44) 1737 785000
Fax: (44) 1737 785001
E-Mail: Info@bbrail.com
Web Site: www.bbrail.co.uk
Railway Infrastructure Services
S.I.C.: 4789
N.A.I.C.S.: 488210
Peter Anderson *(Mng Dir)*

Non-U.S. Subsidiaries:

Balfour Beatty Rail GmbH (3)
Garmischer Strasse 35
81373 Munich, Germany
Tel.: (49) 89419990
Fax: (49) 8941999270
E-Mail: info.de@bbrail.de
Web Site: www.bbrail.de
Railway Electrification & Power Supply System Whslr
S.I.C.: 5063
N.A.I.C.S.: 423610
Manfred Lerch *(Mng Dir)*

Balfour Beatty Rail SpA (3)
Via Lampedusa 13/F
20141 Milan, Italy
Tel.: (39) 02 89536 1
Fax: (39) 02 89536 901
E-Mail: info.it@bbrail.com
Web Site: www.bbrail.it
Railway Engineering Services
S.I.C.: 8711
N.A.I.C.S.: 541330

Balfour Beatty Utility Solutions Ltd (2)
Park Square Newton Chambers Road
Thorncliffe Park
Chapeltown, Sheffield, S35 2PH, United Kingdom
Tel.: (44) 114 232 9700
Fax: (44) 114 232 9701
E-Mail: info@bbusl.com
Web Site: www.bbusl.com
Emp.: 300
Engineering Services
S.I.C.: 8711
N.A.I.C.S.: 541330
Mike Sparrow *(Mng Dir)*

Joint Ventures:

Scotland TranServ (1)
Broxden House
Broxden Business Park, Perth, PH1 1RA, United Kingdom
Tel.: (44) 1738455300
Fax: (44) 1738455301
E-Mail: info@scotland.transerv.co.uk
Web Site: www.scotlandtranserv.co.uk
Emp.: 70
Highway Maintenance, Street Lighting & Other Transportation Infrastructure Support Services
S.I.C.: 4789
N.A.I.C.S.: 488490
Norrie Westbrooke *(Gen Mgr)*

Westminster TranServ (1)
City Hall 2nd Fl 64 Victoria St
London, SW1E 6QP, United Kingdom
Tel.: (44) 2078116999
Fax: (44) 2078116998
Web Site: www.mouchel.com
Highway Maintenance, Street Lighting & Other Transportation Infrastructure Support Services
S.I.C.: 4789
N.A.I.C.S.: 488490
Adrian Croot *(Mgr-Contracts)*

U.S. Subsidiaries:

Balfour Beatty Capital Group Inc (1)
10 Campus Blvd
Newtown Square, PA 19073
Tel.: (610) 355-8100
Fax: (610) 325-2032
Toll Free: (888) 622-2477
Web Site: www.bbcgrp.com
Asset Management Services
S.I.C.: 6799
N.A.I.C.S.: 523920
Denise Hubley *(CFO & Exec VP)*
Marina Dikos *(Chief Acctg Officer & Sr VP)*
Leslie Cohn *(Gen Counsel & Sr VP)*
Richard Taylor *(Exec VP)*
Christopher Williams *(Exec VP)*
Tabitha Crawford *(Sr VP-Sustainability & Innovation)*
Louis DeRogatis *(Sr VP-Fin)*
Kathleen Grim *(Sr VP-Mktg & Comm)*
Rosemary Phillips *(Sr VP-HR)*

Subsidiary:

Balfour Beatty Communities LLC (2)
10 Campus Blvd
Newtown Square, PA 19073
Tel.: (610) 355-8100
Fax: (610) 325-2032
Web Site: www.balfourbeattycommunities.com
Real Estate Development Services
S.I.C.: 6531
N.A.I.C.S.: 531390
Christopher Williams *(Pres)*
Denise Hubley *(CFO)*
Marina Dikos *(Chief Acctg Officer & Sr VP)*
Leslie Cohn *(Gen Counsel & Sr VP)*
Richard Taylor *(Exec VP)*
Louis DeRogatis *(Sr VP-Fin)*
Theresa Edelman *(Sr VP-Community Mgmt)*
Mark Lavin *(Sr VP-Project Mgmt)*
Ron Nestor *(Sr VP-Project Mgmt)*
Rosemary Phillips *(Sr VP-HR)*

Parsons Brinckerhoff Inc. (1)
1 Penn Plz Ste 200
New York, NY 10119-0002 DE
Tel.: (212) 465-5000
Telex: RCA 232 117
Fax: (212) 465-5096
E-Mail: pbinfo@pbworld.com
Web Site: www.pbworld.com
Sales Range: $1-4.9 Billion
Emp.: 14,000
Engineering Services
S.I.C.: 8711
N.A.I.C.S.: 541330
George J. Pierson *(Pres & CEO)*
John Murphy *(CFO)*
Gregory A. Kelly *(Global COO)*
Keith Zecchini *(CIO)*
Guy Templeton *(Pres/COO-Sydney)*
Clifford Eby *(Pres-Transportation-Americas)*
Roger Blair *(Pres-US Power)*
Scott Ney *(Principal-Engr & Sr Project Mgr)*
Kenneth Hopson *(Treas-Global & Sr VP-Fin)*
Juan Murillo *(Sr VP & Dir-Tech-Bridges)*
John Porcari *(Sr VP & Natl Dir-Strategic Consulting-Washington)*
Jeff Morales *(Sr VP)*

Branches:

Mile High Toll Services (2)
22470 E 6th Pkwy Ste 130
Aurora, CO 80018-2428 CO
Tel.: (303) 537-3400
Fax: (303) 537-3402
Rev.: $8,200,000
Emp.: 200
Toll Road Operation Services
S.I.C.: 4789
N.A.I.C.S.: 488490
Thomas O Neill *(CEO)*

Subsidiaries:

Parsons Brinckerhoff Power, Inc. (2)
1 Penn Plz
New York, NY 10119-0002 DE
Tel.: (212) 465-5000 (100%)
Fax: (212) 465-5096
Web Site: www.pbworld.com
Emp.: 9,000
Detailed Planning, Engineering, Construction Management & Inspection Services
S.I.C.: 7349
N.A.I.C.S.: 561720

Parsons Brinckerhoff Quade & Douglas, Inc. (2)
1 Penn Plz Fl 2
New York, NY 10119-0299 NY
Tel.: (212) 465-5000 (100%)
Fax: (212) 465-5096
Web Site: www.pbworld.com
Emp.: 900
Engineering Consultanting Services
S.I.C.: 8711
N.A.I.C.S.: 541330

Divisions:

Parsons Brinckerhoff Michigan (3)
500 Griswold St Ste 2900
Detroit, MI 48226-3679 MI
Tel.: (313) 963-5760
Fax: (313) 963-6910
Web Site: www.pbworld.com
Sales Range: Less than $1 Million
Emp.: 60
Consulting Engineering Services
S.I.C.: 8711
N.A.I.C.S.: 541330
Barbara Arens *(VP)*

Parsons Brinckerhoff Ohio (3)
2545 Farmers Dr St 350
Columbus, OH 43235 OH
Tel.: (614) 793-0191
Fax: (614) 793-0199
Web Site: www.pbworld.com
Sales Range: $1-9.9 Million
Emp.: 20
Management Engineering Consultants Transportation Planning Services
S.I.C.: 8742
N.A.I.C.S.: 541611

PB Transit & Rail Systems Inc. (3)
2 Gateway Ctr
Newark, NJ 07102-5003 NJ
Tel.: (973) 645-1400
Fax: (973) 648-0888
Web Site: www.pbworld.com
Emp.: 30
Engineering Services
S.I.C.: 8711
N.A.I.C.S.: 541330
Sal Matina *(Co-Chm)*
Bruce Pohlot *(Sr VP)*

PB Americas Inc (2)
1 Penn Plz Fl 2
New York, NY 10119
Tel.: (212) 465-5000
Fax: (212) 465-5096
Toll Free: (800) 877-7754
E-Mail: info@pbworld.com
Web Site: www.pbworld.com
Emp.: 800
Construction Engineering Services
S.I.C.: 8711
N.A.I.C.S.: 541330
George J. Pierson *(CEO)*

PB Telecommunications, Inc. (2)
1 Penn Plz
New York, NY 10119-0002 DE
Tel.: (212) 465-5000 (100%)
Fax: (212) 465-5096
Web Site: www.pbworld.com
Emp.: 500
Core Telecommunication Services, Including Infrastructure & Facilities Engineering, Business & Policy Planning, Design, Building, Operations & Maintainence Services & Program & Project Management
S.I.C.: 8742
N.A.I.C.S.: 541611
George Pierson *(CEO)*

Non-U.S. Subsidiaries:

Parsons Brinckerhoff Asia Ltd. (2)
7th Fl 1 Wangyuen St
Kowloon Bay, North Point, China (Hong Kong) (100%)
Tel.: (852) 25798899
Fax: (852) 28569902
E-Mail: info.hk@pbworld.com
Web Site: www.pbworld.com
Sales Range: $25-49.9 Million
Emp.: 500
Engineering Consulting Services
S.I.C.: 8711
N.A.I.C.S.: 541330
Vincent Tse *(Mng Dir)*

Parsons Brinckerhoff Ltd. (2)
Westbrook Mills
Godalming, Surrey, GU7 2AZ, United Kingdom (100%)
Tel.: (44) 1483528400
Fax: (44) 1483528989
Web Site: www.pbworld.com
Emp.: 300
Engineering Services
S.I.C.: 8711
N.A.I.C.S.: 541330

BALHOUSIE HOLDINGS LIMITED

(d/b/a Balhousie Care Group)
Earn House Broxden Business Park
Lamberkine Drive, Perth, PH1 1RA, United Kingdom
Tel.: (44) 1738 254 254
Web Site: www.balhousiecare.co.uk
Sales Range: $10-24.9 Million
Emp.: 850

Business Description:
Holding Company; Nursing Care Facilities Owner & Operator
S.I.C.: 6719
N.A.I.C.S.: 551112

Personnel:
Tony Banks *(Chm)*
Graham Ogilvie *(Mng Dir)*

Board of Directors:
Tony Banks
David Brooks
Russell Hogan
Graham Ogilvie
Ross Smith

Units:

Alastrean Care Home Aboyne (1)
Tarland
Aboyne, Aberdeenshire, AB34 4TA, United Kingdom
Tel.: (44) 1339 881235
Fax: (44) 1339 267804
Nursing Care Facility
S.I.C.: 8051
N.A.I.C.S.: 623110

Antiquary Care Home Arbroath (1)
Westway
Arbroath, Scotland, DD11 2BW, United Kingdom
Tel.: (44) 1241 434969
Fax: (44) 1241 434959
Nursing Care Facility
S.I.C.: 8051
N.A.I.C.S.: 623110
Sylvia Nicoll *(Mgr-Care Home)*

Auchterarder Care Home (1)
Abbey Road
Auchterarder, Scotland, PH3 1DN, United Kingdom
Tel.: (44) 1764 664192
Fax: (44) 1764 661811
Nursing Care Facility
S.I.C.: 8051
N.A.I.C.S.: 623110
Fiona Lucraft *(Mgr-Perthshire)*

Clement Park Care Home Dundee (1)
4 Clement Park Place
Dundee, DD2 3JN, United Kingdom
Tel.: (44) 1382 610960
Fax: (44) 1382 000702
Nursing Care Facility
S.I.C.: 8051
N.A.I.C.S.: 623110
Shone Blair *(Mgr-Care Home)*

Coupar Angus Care Home (1)
Meadowside Close
Coupar Angus, Perth & Kinross, PH13 9FB, United Kingdom
Tel.: (44) 1828 424930
Fax: (44) 1828 838200
Web Site: www.balhousiecare.co.uk/view-care-home-coupar-angus-care-home
Nursing Care Facility
S.I.C.: 8051

N.A.I.C.S.: 623110

Crieff Care Home (1)
Comrie Road
Crieff, Perth and Kinross, PH7 4BJ, United Kingdom
Tel.: (44) 1764 655231
Fax: (44) 1764 653374
Nursing Care Facility
S.I.C.: 8051
N.A.I.C.S.: 623110
Nisha Soman *(Mgr-Care Home)*

The Dalguise Centre Care Home Perth (1)
Balbeggie
Perth, PH2 6AT, United Kingdom
Tel.: (44) 1821 650591
Fax: (44) 1821 650592
Nursing Care Facility
S.I.C.: 8051
N.A.I.C.S.: 623110
Sara Murphy *(Mgr-Care Home)*

Forthview Care Home (1)
6 Sea Road
Methil, Fife, KY8 3DE, United Kingdom
Tel.: (44) 1592 716500
Fax: (44) 1592 719257
Nursing Care Facility
S.I.C.: 8051
N.A.I.C.S.: 623110
Maria Hutchinson *(Mgr-Care Home)*

Glens Care Home Brechin (1)
18-20 Church Street
Edzell, Brechin, Dundee and Angus, DD9 7TQ, United Kingdom
Tel.: (44) 1356 648888
Fax: (44) 1356 648671
Nursing Care Facility
S.I.C.: 8051
N.A.I.C.S.: 623110
Jacqueline Donley *(Mgr-Care Home)*

The Grange Care Home Perth (1)
Balbeggie
Perth, PH2 6AT, United Kingdom
Tel.: (44) 1821 650690
Fax: (44) 1821 650640
Emp.: 21
Nursing Care Facility
S.I.C.: 8051
N.A.I.C.S.: 623110
Karen Austin *(Mgr-Care Home)*

Lisden Care Home Kirriemuir (1)
63 Brechin Road
Kirriemuir, Angus, DD8 4DE, United Kingdom
Tel.: (44) 1575 574499
Fax: (44) 1575 574422
Nursing Care Facility
S.I.C.: 8051
N.A.I.C.S.: 623110
Alison Miller *(Mgr-Care Home)*

Luncarty Care Home (1)
Scarth Road
Luncarty, Perth and Kinross, PH1 3HE, United Kingdom
Tel.: (44) 1738 828163
Fax: (44) 1738 828703
Nursing Care Facility
S.I.C.: 8051
N.A.I.C.S.: 623110
Tracy McEwan *(Mgr-Care Home)*

Methven Care Home Perth (1)
31 Lynedoch Road
Methven, Perth, PH1 3PH, United Kingdom
Tel.: (44) 1738 840644
Fax: (44) 1738 842870
Emp.: 2
Nursing Care Facility
S.I.C.: 8051
N.A.I.C.S.: 623110
Lars Arne Hoff *(Mgr)*

Monkbarns Care Home Arbroath (1)
14 Monkbarns Drive
Arbroath, DD11 2DS, United Kingdom
Tel.: (44) 1241 871713
Nursing Care Facility
S.I.C.: 8051
N.A.I.C.S.: 623110
Joyce Chalmers *(Mgr-Care Home)*

Moyness Care Home Dundee (1)
76 Grove Road
Broughty Ferry, Dundee, Dundee and Angus, DD5 1JP, United Kingdom
Tel.: (44) 1382 480899
Fax: (44) 1382 774166
Nursing Care Facility
S.I.C.: 8051
N.A.I.C.S.: 623110
Terry Banks *(Mgr-Care Home)*

North Grove Care Home Perth (1)
101 Hay Street
Perth, Perth and Kinross, PH1 5HS, United Kingdom
Tel.: (44) 1738 628771
Fax: (44) 1738 643516
Nursing Care Facility
S.I.C.: 8051
N.A.I.C.S.: 623110
Diane Halley *(Mgr-Care Home)*

North Inch Care Home Perth (1)
99 Hay Street
Perth, Perth and Kinross, PH1 5HS, United Kingdom
Tel.: (44) 1738 632233
Fax: (44) 1738 632288
Nursing Care Facility
S.I.C.: 8051
N.A.I.C.S.: 623110
Diane Halley *(Mgr-Care Home)*

Pitlochry Care Home (1)
Burnside Road
Pitlochry, PH16 5BP, United Kingdom
Tel.: (44) 1796 473280
Fax: (44) 1796 474330
Nursing Care Facility
S.I.C.: 8051
N.A.I.C.S.: 623110
Keith Porter *(Mgr-Care Home)*

Rigifa Care Home Perth (1)
College Road
Perth, PH1 3PB, United Kingdom
Tel.: (44) 1738 840747
Fax: (44) 1738 840115
Nursing Care Facility
S.I.C.: 8051
N.A.I.C.S.: 623110
Tracy McEwan *(Mgr-Care Home)*

Rumbling Bridge Care Home Kinross (1)
Rumbling Bridge
Crook of Devon, Kinross, KY13 0PX, United Kingdom
Tel.: (44) 1577 840478
Fax: (44) 1577 840002
Nursing Care Facility
S.I.C.: 8051
N.A.I.C.S.: 623110

Stormont Care Home Blairgowrie (1)
Kirk Wynd
Blairgowrie, Perth and Kinross, PH10 6HN, United Kingdom
Tel.: (44) 1250 872853
Fax: (44) 1250 875888
Nursing Care Facility
S.I.C.: 8051
N.A.I.C.S.: 623110
Helen Norrie *(Mgr-Care Home)*

Wheatlands Care Home Bonnybridge (1)
Larbert Road
Bonnybridge, Stirlingshire, FK4 1ED, United Kingdom
Tel.: (44) 1324 814561
Fax: (44) 1324 815280
Web Site: www.balhousie.co.uk
Emp.: 4
Nursing Care Facility
S.I.C.: 8051
N.A.I.C.S.: 623110
Grace Sloan *(Mgr-Care Home)*

Willowbank Care Home Carnoustie (1)
56 Maule Street
Carnoustie, Dundee and Angus, DD7 6AB, United Kingdom
Tel.: (44) 1241 852160
Fax: (44) 1241 851151
Nursing Care Facility
S.I.C.: 8051
N.A.I.C.S.: 623110
Terry Banks *(Mgr-Care Home)*

BALIUS CORP.

38 Sea View Park Cliffoney
Sligo, Ireland
Tel.: (353) 851997078
E-Mail: Baliuscorp@gmail.com
Year Founded: 2012
BALI—(OTC OTCB)
Rev.: $3,587
Assets: $8,776
Liabilities: $2,424
Net Worth: $6,352
Earnings: ($28,850)
Emp.: 1
Fiscal Year-end: 12/31/13

Business Description:
Horse Training & Reselling
S.I.C.: 0272
N.A.I.C.S.: 112920

Personnel:
Vitaliy Gladky *(Pres, Treas & Sec)*

Board of Directors:
Vitaliy Gladky

BALKAN INVESTMENT BANK AD BANJA LUKA

61 Aleja Svetog Save
78000 Banja Luka, Bosnia & Herzegovina
Tel.: (387) 51 245 142
Fax: (387) 51 245 069
E-Mail: contact@bib.ba
Web Site: www.bib.ba
Year Founded: 2000
BLKB—(BANJ)
Emp.: 18,500

Business Description:
Banking Services
S.I.C.: 6029
N.A.I.C.S.: 522110

Personnel:
Edvinas Navickas *(Chm)*
Angele Dementaviciute *(Chm-Supervisory Bd)*

Supervisory Board of Directors:
Angele Dementaviciute
Laura Baroniene
Sergejus Fedotovas
Laura Ivaskeviciute
Mindaugas Valancius

BALKANCAR ZARYA PLC

1 Tosho Kutev Str
Pavlikeni, 5200, Bulgaria
Tel.: (359) 610 53061
Fax: (359) 610 52603
E-Mail: info@balkancarzarya.com
Web Site: www.balkancarzarya.com
4BUA—(BUL)

Business Description:
Steel Wheels & Rims Mfr
S.I.C.: 3312
N.A.I.C.S.: 331221

Personnel:
P. Penchev *(Dir-IR)*

BALKRISHNA INDUSTRIES LIMITED

BKT House C/15 Trade World
Kamala Mills Compound
Senapati Bapat Lower Parel,
Mumbai, 400 013, India
Tel.: (91) 2266663800
Fax: (91) 2266663898
Web Site: www.bkt-tires.com
BALKRISIND—(NSE)
Rev.: $630,070,296
Assets: $769,545,236
Liabilities: $502,012,174
Net Worth: $267,533,062
Earnings: $64,871,867
Fiscal Year-end: 03/31/13

Business Description:
Pneumatic Tire Mfr
S.I.C.: 3011
N.A.I.C.S.: 326211

Personnel:
Arvind Poddar *(Chm & Mng Dir)*
Rajiv Poddar *(Mng Dir)*
Vipul Shah *(Compliance Officer & Sec)*

Board of Directors:
Arvind Poddar
Sanjay Asher
Sachin Nath Chaturvedi
Khurshed Doongaji
Subhash Chand Mantri
Laxmidas Merchant
Rajiv Poddar
Rameshkumar Poddar
Vijaylaxmi A. Poddar
Ashok Saraf
Vipul Shah

Transfer Agent:
Sharepro Services (India) Pvt. Ltd
13AB Samhita Warehousing Complex 2nd Floor Near
Mumbai, India

BALLARD POWER SYSTEMS, INC.

9000 Glenlyon Parkway
Burnaby, BC, V5J 5J8, Canada
Tel.: (604) 454-0900
Fax: (604) 412-4700
E-Mail: investors@ballard.com
Web Site: www.ballard.com
Year Founded: 1979
BLDP—(NASDAQ TSX)
Rev.: $61,251,000
Assets: $120,214,000
Liabilities: $49,960,000
Net Worth: $70,254,000
Earnings: ($21,700,000)
Emp.: 335
Fiscal Year-end: 12/31/13

Business Description:
Fuel Cell & Fuel Cell Systems Mfr
S.I.C.: 3699
N.A.I.C.S.: 335999

Personnel:
Ian A. Bourne *(Chm)*
John William Sheridan *(Pres & CEO)*
Tony Guglielmin *(CFO & VP)*
Christopher Guzy *(CTO & VP)*
William Foulds *(Pres-Matl Products)*

Board of Directors:
Ian A. Bourne
Douglas P. Hayhurst
Edwin J. Kilroy
John William Sheridan
David J. Smith
Carol M. Stephenson
David B. Sutcliffe
Douglas W. G. Whitehead

Transfer Agent:
Computershare Trust Company of Canada
9th Floor 100 University Avenue
Toronto, ON, Canada

Subsidiary:

Ballard Power Systems Corporation (1)
9000 Glenlyon Pkwy
Burnaby, BC, V5J 5J8, Canada (100%)
Tel.: (604) 454-0900
Fax: (604) 412-4700
Web Site: www.ballard.com
Emp.: 400
Physical Engineering & Life Sciences Research & Development
S.I.C.: 8731
N.A.I.C.S.: 541712
John William Sheridan *(CEO)*

U.S. Subsidiaries:

Ballard Material Products Inc. (1)
2 Industrial Ave
Lowell, MA 01851-5107 (100%)
Tel.: (978) 934-7522
Fax: (978) 934-7590
Web Site: www.ballard.com
Emp.: 50
Broadwoven Fabric Mills

Ballard Power Systems, Inc.—(Continued)

S.I.C.: 2299
N.A.I.C.S.: 313210
William Foulds *(Pres)*

BALLARPUR INDUSTRIES LIMITED

First India Place Tower C Mehrauli Gurgaon Road
Gurgaon, Haryana, 122 002, India
Tel.: (91) 124 2804 242
Fax: (91) 124 2804 260
E-Mail: corpcom@bilt.com
Web Site: www.bilt.com
Year Founded: 1945
500102—(BOM)
Sls.: $947,299,446
Assets: $2,188,294,740
Liabilities: $1,396,227,006
Net Worth: $792,067,734
Earnings: $17,344,170
Emp.: 2,097
Fiscal Year-end: 06/30/13

Business Description:
Paper Mfr
Export
S.I.C.: 2621
N.A.I.C.S.: 322122

Personnel:
R. R. Vederah *(Vice Chm & Mng Dir)*
Vivek Kumar Goyal *(CFO)*
Akhil Mahajan *(Sec)*

Board of Directors:
Gautam Thapar
P. V. Bhide
A. S. Dulat
Ashish Guha
B. Hariharan
Sanjay Labroo
A. P. Singh
R. R. Vederah
Jane Fields Wicker-Miurin

Transfer Agent:
RCMC Share Registry Pvt. Ltd.
B-106 Sector-2
Noida, India

BALLAST NEDAM N.V.

Ringwade 71
3439 LM Nieuwegein, Netherlands
Tel.: (31) 302853333
Telex: 12880 bals ned
Fax: (31) 0302854875
E-Mail: infodesk@ballast-nedam.nl
Web Site: www.ballast-nedam.nl
Year Founded: 1877
BALNE—(EUR)
Rev.: $1,744,636,320
Assets: $1,192,706,620
Liabilities: $1,016,358,350
Net Worth: $176,348,270
Earnings: ($55,192,970)
Emp.: 3,859
Fiscal Year-end: 12/31/12

Business Description:
Civil Engineering & General Building Contracts; Marine Dredging & Land Reclamation; General & Industrial Building, Housing & Roads
S.I.C.: 1629
N.A.I.C.S.: 237990

Personnel:
A. N. A. M. Smits *(Chm-Supervisory Bd)*
Theo A. C. M. Bruijninckx *(Chm-Mgmt Bd & CEO)*
J. C. Huis In'T Veld *(Vice Chm-Supervisory Bd)*
Peter van Zwieten *(CFO & Member-Mgmt Bd)*
Sylvie C. Bleker-van Eyk *(Chief Compliance Officer & Chief Risk Officer)*
O. P. Padberg *(Sec)*

Supervisory Board of Directors:
A. N. A. M. Smits
J. Bout
J. C. Huis In'T Veld
C. M. Insinger
L. W. A. M. van Donne

Subsidiaries:

Ballast Nedam Bouw en Ontwikkeling Holding B.V. **(1)**
Ringwade 71
Nieuwegein, 3439 LM, Netherlands
Tel.: (31) 302854250
Fax: (31) 302854865
Investment Management Services
S.I.C.: 6211
N.A.I.C.S.: 523999

Subsidiaries:

Ballast Nedam Bouw & Ontwikkeling B.V. **(2)**
Vaalmuiden 1
Amsterdam, 1046 BV, Netherlands
Tel.: (31) 204804040
Fax: (31) 204804088
Civil Engineering Construction Services
S.I.C.: 1629
N.A.I.C.S.: 237990

Subsidiary:

Bouwcombinatie Kohnstammlocatie v.o.f. **(3)**
Vaalmuiden 1
Amsterdam, North Holland, 1046 BV, Netherlands
Tel.: (31) 204804000
Fax: (31) 204804088
Emp.: 10
Industrial Building Construction Services
S.I.C.: 1541
N.A.I.C.S.: 236210

Ballast Nedam Ontwikkelingsmaatschappij B.V. **(2)**
Ringwade 71
3439 LM Nieuwegein, Netherlands
Tel.: (31) 30 285 44 00
Fax: (31) 30 285 48 81
E-Mail: info.bno@ballast-nedam.nl
Web Site: www.ballast-nedam.nl
Emp.: 20
Real Estate Development Services
S.I.C.: 6531
N.A.I.C.S.: 531390
Ruud Jacobs *(Mng Dir)*

Subsidiary:

Ballast Nedam Langedijk B.V. **(3)**
Ringwade 71
Nieuwegein, 3430 LM, Netherlands
Tel.: (31) 302854400
Fax: (31) 302854865
E-Mail: info@ballast-nedam.nl
Web Site: www.ballast-nedam.nl
Emp.: 200
Property Management Services
S.I.C.: 6531
N.A.I.C.S.: 531311

B.V. Aannemingsbedrijf F.W. Onrust **(2)**
Rijshoutweg 1
1505 HL Zaandam, Netherlands
Tel.: (31) 75 615 69 55
Fax: (31) 75 670 07 91
E-Mail: info@fwonrust.nl
Household Goods Repair & Maintenance Services
S.I.C.: 7699
N.A.I.C.S.: 811490
Rana Vonk *(Gen Mgr)*

Ballast Nedam Infra B.V. **(1)**
Ringwade 71
PO Box 1505
3439LM Nieuwegein, Utrecht, Netherlands NL
Tel.: (31) 302853030 (100%)
Fax: (31) 302854800
E-Mail: info.infra@ballast-nedam.nl
Web Site: www.bnb.ballast-nedam.nl
Emp.: 150
Provider of Infrastructure, Civil Engineering, Dry Earth Moving, Roads, Railways, Sand Supply & Environmental Technology Services
S.I.C.: 1629
N.A.I.C.S.: 237990
Peter Begl *(Mng Dir)*
Romeo Rmalizia *(Mng Dir)*

Subsidiaries:

Ballast Nedam Asfalt B.V. **(2)**
Amersfoortsestraat 124d
3769 AN Soesterberg, Netherlands
Tel.: (31) 334602285
Fax: (31) 334610802
E-Mail: asfalt@ballast-nedam.nl
Civil Engineering Construction Services
S.I.C.: 1629
N.A.I.C.S.: 237990

Ballast Nedam Asset Management B.V. **(2)**
Ringwade 71
Nieuwegein, 3439 LM, Netherlands
Tel.: (31) 302853333
Fax: (31) 302854902
Asset Management Services
S.I.C.: 6282
N.A.I.C.S.: 523920

Ballast Nedam Engineering B.V. **(2)**
Ringwade 51
3439 LM Nieuwegein, Netherlands
Tel.: (31) 30 285 40 00
Fax: (31) 30 285 40 40
E-Mail: info.BNE@Ballast-Nedam.nl
Web Site: www.bne.ballast-nedam.nl
Civil Engineering Construction Services
S.I.C.: 1629
N.A.I.C.S.: 237990
W. J. van Niekerk *(Mng Dir)*
Mascha Knoester *(Co-Sec)*
Anka van Rooden *(Co-Sec)*

Ballast Nedam Funderingstechnieken B.V. **(2)**
Straatweg 29-a
3439 LM Maarssen, Netherlands
Mailing Address:
PO Box 2
Maarssen, 3600AA, Netherlands
Tel.: (31) 346249100
E-Mail: bnf@ballast-nedam.nl
Web Site: www.bnft.nl
Emp.: 52
Offshore Engineering Services
S.I.C.: 8711
N.A.I.C.S.: 541330
Leen van Vliet *(Head-Equipment Dept)*

Ballast Nedam Gebiedsontwikkeling B.V. **(2)**
Limburglaan 24
Eindhoven, 5652 AA, Netherlands
Tel.: (31) 402661320
Fax: (31) 402661330
Web Site: www.ballast-nedam.nl
Emp.: 7
Construction Engineering Services
S.I.C.: 8711
N.A.I.C.S.: 541330

Ballast Nedam Geluidwering **(2)**
Sluispolderweg
Postbus 195
1500 EG Zaandam, Netherlands (100%)
Tel.: (31) 756557700
Fax: (31) 756557701
E-Mail: infodesk@ballastnedam.nl
Emp.: 200
Acoustic Baffles
S.I.C.: 3443
N.A.I.C.S.: 332313

Ballast Nedam Huis Zaandam **(2)**
Sluispolderweg 67
1505 HJ Zaandam, Netherlands (100%)
Tel.: (31) 75 655 77 00
Fax: (31) 756557751
E-Mail: info-desk@ballastnedam.nl
Web Site: www.ballast-nedam.nl
Emp.: 15
Supplier of Primary & Secondary Building Materials
S.I.C.: 5039
N.A.I.C.S.: 423390

Ballast Nedam ICT B.V. **(2)**
Ringwade 71
Nieuwegein, 3439 LM, Netherlands
Tel.: (31) 302853500
Fax: (31) 302854875
Real Estate Management Services
S.I.C.: 6531
N.A.I.C.S.: 531390

Ballast Nedam Infra B V **(2)**
Ringwade 71
PO Box 1505
3430 BM Nieuwegein, Netherlands (100%)
Tel.: (31) 302853060
Fax: (31) 302854800
Web Site: www.ballast-nedam.com
Sls.: $631,243,584
Emp.: 4,000
Special Projects in the Fields of Earth Moving & Road Construction
S.I.C.: 1622
N.A.I.C.S.: 237310
Dayle Bruijnincks *(CEO)*

Subsidiary:

Ballast Nedam B.V. Specialistisch Grondverzet **(3)**
Koningsweg 30
3762 EC Soest, Netherlands (100%)
Tel.: (31) 356098888
Fax: (31) 356098800
E-Mail: roelfremak@bngw.ballast-nedam.com
Web Site: www.ballast-nedam.nl/page_3038.asp
Emp.: 30
Specialized Earthmoving
S.I.C.: 1799
N.A.I.C.S.: 238910
Roelf Remak *(Gen Mgr)*

Ballast Nedam Infra Business Development B.V. **(2)**
Ringwade 71
Nieuwegein, 3439 LM, Netherlands
Tel.: (31) 302853185
Fax: (31) 302897084
Commercial Building Construction Services
S.I.C.: 1542
N.A.I.C.S.: 236220

Subsidiary:

Libella Nederland B.V. **(3)**
Ringwade 71
3439 LM Nieuwegein, Netherlands
Tel.: (31) 30 2853750
Civil Engineering Construction Services
S.I.C.: 1629
N.A.I.C.S.: 237990
Nanne Ravenhorst *(Gen Mgr)*

Ballast Nedam Infra Materieel v.o.f. **(2)**
Straatweg 29a
Maarssen, 3603 CV, Netherlands
Tel.: (31) 346 581790
Fax: (31) 346 581796
Civil Engineering Construction Services
S.I.C.: 1629
N.A.I.C.S.: 237990

Ballast Nedam Infra Midden Zuid B.V. **(2)**
Meander 551
Arnhem, 6825 MD, Netherlands
Tel.: (31) 263682600
Fax: (31) 262682634
Emp.: 40
Civil Engineering Construction Services
S.I.C.: 1629
N.A.I.C.S.: 237990

Ballast Nedam Infra Noord West B.V. **(2)**
Sluispolderweg 67
Zaandam, 1505 HJ, Netherlands
Tel.: (31) 756557700
Fax: (31) 756701454
Web Site: www.infranw.ballast-nedam.nl
Emp.: 15
Civil Engineering Construction Services
S.I.C.: 1629
N.A.I.C.S.: 237990
F. Louter *(Gen Mgr)*

Ballast Nedam Infra Participatie B.V. **(2)**
Ringwade 71
3439 LM Nieuwegein, Utrecht, Netherlands
Tel.: (31) 302853030
Fax: (31) 302854900
Commercial Building Construction Services
S.I.C.: 1542

N.A.I.C.S.: 236220

Ballast Nedam Infra Specialiteiten B.V. (2)
Nijverheidstraat 12 PO Box 236
PO Box 280
4140 AE Leerdam, Netherlands (100%)
Tel.: (31) 345639200
Fax: (31) 345619107
Web Site: www.bni.ballast-nedam.com
Emp.: 130
Special Projects & Technologies for the Dry Earth Moving & Road Construction Sector
S.I.C.: 1622
N.A.I.C.S.: 237310
A. van der Zijden *(Mng Dir)*

Ballast Nedam Infra Zuid West B.V. (2)
Fascinatio Boulevard 582
Capelle aan den IJssel, 2909 VA, Netherlands
Tel.: (31) 102350111
Fax: (31) 102350110
Emp.: 10
Civil Engineering Construction Services
S.I.C.: 1629
N.A.I.C.S.: 237990
Ronald Franken *(Mgr)*

Ballast Nedam International Product Management B.V. (2)
Nijverheidstraat 12
Leerdam, 4143 HM, Netherlands
Tel.: (31) 345639250
Fax: (31) 345639207
Emp.: 40
Civil Engineering Construction Services
S.I.C.: 1629
N.A.I.C.S.: 237990

Ballast Nedam Milieutechniek B.V. (2)
Sluispolderweg 67
PO Box 195
1500 EB Zaandam, Netherlands (100%)
Tel.: (31) 756557750
Fax: (31) 756557701
E-Mail: infodesk@ballast-nedam.nl
Emp.: 30
Provider of Environmental Services
S.I.C.: 3822
N.A.I.C.S.: 334512
J. Folkarts *(Mng Dir)*

Ballast Nedam Offshore B.V. (2)
Ringwade 71
3439 LM Nieuwegein, Netherlands
Tel.: (31) 30 285 37 27
Fax: (31) 30 285 48 41
E-Mail: offshore@ballast-nedam.nl
Web Site: www.bn-offshore.com
Offshore Wind Energy Construction Services
S.I.C.: 1629
N.A.I.C.S.: 237130
Jurjan Blokland *(Mgr-Ops)*

Ballast Nedam Zuiveringe (2)
Limburglaan 36
PO Box 8708
5605 LS Eindhoven, Netherlands (100%)
Tel.: (31) 402661320
Fax: (31) 402661330
E-Mail: t.meegens@ballast-nedam.nl
Emp.: 60
Water & Sewage Treatment Installations
S.I.C.: 1629
N.A.I.C.S.: 237110
A. D. Stoop *(Mng Dir)*

Dibec B.V. (2)
Meander 551
PO Box 5470
6802 EL Arnhem, 6825 MD, Netherlands (100%)
Tel.: (31) 263682625
Fax: (31) 263682657
E-Mail: info@dibec.nl
Web Site: www.dibec.nl
Sls.: $1,258,093
Emp.: 15
Provider of Environmental Technology Consulting
S.I.C.: 8742
N.A.I.C.S.: 541611
P. G. Ballast *(Mng Dir)*

Gebr. Van Leeuwen Harmelen B.V. (2)
Energieweg 16
3481 MC Harmelen, Netherlands
Tel.: (31) 348 441499
Fax: (31) 348 44 37 54
Web Site: www.gebr-vanleeuwen.nl
Emp.: 85
Hydraulic Engineering Services
S.I.C.: 8711
N.A.I.C.S.: 541330
Frits Swinkels *(Project Mgr)*

Ingenieursbureau voor Systemen en Octrooien Spanstaal B.V. (2)
Koningsweg 28
3762 EC Soest, Netherlands
Tel.: (31) 35 603 80 50
Fax: (31) 35 603 29 02
E-Mail: spanstaal@spanstaal.nl
Civil Engineering Construction Services
S.I.C.: 1629
N.A.I.C.S.: 237990

International Products Management (2)
Nijverheidstraat 12
Leerdam, 4143 HM, Netherlands (100%)
Tel.: (31) 345639239
Fax: (31) 345639207
E-Mail: info@ballast-nedam.com
Emp.: 70
Cable & Pipeline Construction
S.I.C.: 1623
N.A.I.C.S.: 237120
R Vhmhlpan *(Mng Dir)*

Recycling Maatschappij Feniks B.V. (2)
Sluispolderweg 67
PO Box 485
1505 HA Zaandam, Netherlands (100%)
Tel.: (31) 756557680
Fax: (31) 756557699
E-Mail: info@feniksrecycling.nl
Web Site: www.feniksrecycling.nl
Emp.: 25
Recycling of Waste Products in New Raw Materials
S.I.C.: 9511
N.A.I.C.S.: 924110
Goshen Beurden *(Mng Dir)*

Van Drooge Transport en Handelmaatschappij (2)
Industrieweg 4
PO Box 4
8860 AA Harlingen, Netherlands (100%)
Tel.: (31) 517432032
Fax: (31) 517415226
Provider of Construction Services
S.I.C.: 7699
N.A.I.C.S.: 811310

Non-U.S. Subsidiary:

Ballast Phoenix Ltd. (2)
Victoria Stables South Road
Bourne, PE10 9JZ, United Kingdom UK (100%)
Tel.: (44) 1778423345
Fax: (44) 1778423354
E-Mail: info@ballastphoenix.co.uk
Web Site: www.ballastphoenix.co.uk
Sales Range: $1-9.9 Million
Emp.: 4
Supplier of Primary & Secondary Building Materials; Recycling & Industrial Residuals
S.I.C.: 5039
N.A.I.C.S.: 423390
George Overfield *(Mgr-Comml)*

Ballast Nedam International Project B.V. (1)
Ringwade 71
Nieuwegein, Utrecht, 3439LM, Netherlands NL
Mailing Address: (100%)
PO Box 1289
3430 BG Nieuwegein, Netherlands
Tel.: (31) 302853600
Fax: (31) 302854875
E-Mail: infodesk@ballast-nedam.nl
Emp.: 300
Civil Engineering & General Building Projects Outside of the Home Market
S.I.C.: 8711
N.A.I.C.S.: 541330
Rude Jacobs *(Mng Dir)*
A. Kok *(Mng Dir)*

Subsidiaries:

Ballast Nedam Africa B.V. (2)
Ringwade 71
Nieuwegein, 3439 LM, Netherlands
Tel.: (31) 302853727
Civil Engineering Construction Services
S.I.C.: 1629
N.A.I.C.S.: 237990

Ballast Nedam Ghana B.V. (2)
Ringwade 71
Nieuwegein, 3439 LM, Netherlands
Tel.: (31) 302853727
Fax: (31) 302854875
Commercial Building Construction Services
S.I.C.: 1542
N.A.I.C.S.: 236220

Ballast Nedam Infra Suriname B.V. (2)
Ringwade 71
Nieuwegein, 3439 LM, Netherlands
Tel.: (31) 302853727
Fax: (31) 302897084
Construction Engineering Services
S.I.C.: 8711
N.A.I.C.S.: 541330

Ballast Nedam IPM B.V. (2)
Nijverheidstraat 12
PO Box 280
4140AG Leerdam, South Holland, Netherlands (100%)
Mailing Address:
PO Box 280
4140 AG Leerdam, Netherlands
Tel.: (31) 345639250
Fax: (31) 345639207
E-Mail: gh.de.vries@ballast-nedam.nl
Web Site: www.bnipm.nedam.nl
Rev.: $50,323,720
Emp.: 120
Construction & Renovation of Petrol Stations
S.I.C.: 1623
N.A.I.C.S.: 237120
M.A.M. Alphen *(Gen Mgr)*

Ballast Nedam Telecom Infrastructures B.V. (2)
Nyverheidstraat 12
PO Box 280
4140 AG Leerdam, Netherlands NL
Tel.: (31) 345639250 (100%)
Fax: (31) 345639207
E-Mail: info@bni.ballast-nedam.nl
Web Site: www.bni.ballast-nedam.nl
Emp.: 20
Engineering, Construction, Installation & Implementation of Infrastructure for Telecommunications Projects
S.I.C.: 8711
N.A.I.C.S.: 541330

U.S. Subsidiary:

Ballast Nedam Construction Inc. (2)
639 S Olive Ave
West Palm Beach, FL 33401 DE
Tel.: (561) 651-7226 (100%)
Fax: (561) 671-9969
Web Site: www.ballast-nedam.com
Emp.: 1
General Building Construction
S.I.C.: 1521
N.A.I.C.S.: 236115

Non-U.S. Subsidiaries:

Ballast Nedam Caribbean N.V. (2)
E Commerce Park
PO Box 4092
Willemstad, Curacao AN
Tel.: (599) 94338844 (100%)
Fax: (599) 94338843
Web Site: www.bni.ballast-nedam.nl
Civil Engineering, General Building & Housing Projects
S.I.C.: 8711
N.A.I.C.S.: 541330

Ballast Nedam Equipment Services Pte. Ltd. (2)
20 Harbour Dr Fl 7 Unit 4 PSA Vista
Singapore, 117612, Singapore (100%)
Tel.: (65) 67745066
Fax: (65) 67742647
Web Site: www.ballastnedam.com
Emp.: 1
S.I.C.: 1629
N.A.I.C.S.: 237110

Ballast Nedam Ghana B.V. (2)
Branch Ofc Ghana 149 Achimoto Rd
PO Box 2827
233 Accra, Ghana (100%)
Tel.: (233) 21760622
Fax: (233) 21760624
E-Mail:
Emp.: 35
Civil Engineering & General Building Services
S.I.C.: 1629
N.A.I.C.S.: 237990
Jeff Ginkney *(Mng Dir & Project Mgr)*

Ballast Nedam International B.V. (2)
Vietnam City Ofc E Town Bldg Ste 9 1B
364 Cong Hoa St
Tan Binh District, Ho Chi Minh City, Vietnam (100%)
Tel.: (84) 838109863
Fax: (84) 838109866
E-Mail: bnivietnam@saijonnet.vn
Emp.: 10
S.I.C.: 1629
N.A.I.C.S.: 237110

P.T. Worldwide Equipments (2)
Jalan Brigjen Katumso Km 6
Tanju Nguncang, Batam, 29422, Indonesia Id
Tel.: (62) 778391167 (100%)
Fax: (62) 778391168
Web Site: www.worldwidebatam.com
Emp.: 100
Technology Equipment Services
S.I.C.: 7699
N.A.I.C.S.: 811310

Non-U.S. Affiliate:

P.T. Ballast Indonesia Construction (2)
Jalan T B Sima Tu Pang
No 41 Blty Office Pk
Building C, 12550 Jakarta, Indonesia ID
Tel.: (62) 217800940 (47.5%)
Fax: (62) 217892151
E-Mail: info@teamworx.com.id
Web Site: www.teamworx.com.id
Emp.: 60
Civil Engineering, General & Industrial Building
S.I.C.: 8711
N.A.I.C.S.: 541330
Bude Hartono *(Mgr-Fin)*

Ballast Nedam Special Ground Work B.V. (1)
Koningsweg 30
PO Box 447
3760 AK Soest, Netherlands (100%)
Tel.: (31) 356098888
Fax: (31) 356098800
E-Mail: info@ballast-nedam.nl
Emp.: 35
Provide Materials & Services to the Construction Industry Including Sand, Gravel, Precast Concrete, Wood Fiber Concrete & Products for the Sewage Industry
S.I.C.: 1542
N.A.I.C.S.: 236220
Koos Roelssema *(Mng Dir)*

Subsidiaries:

Haitsma Beton B.V. (2)
Pinksterblomstrjittle 2
Postbus 7
Kootstertille, 9288 ZG Amsterdam, Friesland, Netherlands (100%)
Tel.: (31) 512335678
Fax: (31) 512335666
E-Mail: info@haitsma.nl
Web Site: www.haitsma.nl
Emp.: 100
Fabrication, Supply & Installation of Prefabricated Concrete Elements
S.I.C.: 3272
N.A.I.C.S.: 327390
Jaap Edel *(Head-Production)*

Hoco Beton B.V. (2)
Trancheeweg 16 18
PO Box 168
600 AD Weert, Netherlands (100%)
Tel.: (31) 495579679
Fax: (31) 495579600
E-Mail: info@hoco-beton.nl
Web Site: www.hoco-beton.nl
Emp.: 80
Mfr. of Prefabricated Concrete Elements
S.I.C.: 3272

Ballast Nedam N.V.—(Continued)

N.A.I.C.S.: 327390
Jos Holtackers *(Mng Dir)*

Rademakers Gieterij B.V. **(2)**
Langestraat 12
PO Box 2
7890 AA Klazienaveen, Netherlands (100%)
Tel.: (31) 591312433
Fax: (31) 591547001
E-Mail: info@rademakersgieterij.com
Web Site: www.rademakersgieterij.com
Sls.: $25,161,860
Emp.: 140
Mfr. & Supplier of Products & Components for Sewage & Water Transport Systems
S.I.C.: 1623
N.A.I.C.S.: 237110
Woolden Dorp *(Mng Dir)*

Spanstaal B.V. **(2)**
Koningsweg 28
PO Box 386
3760 AK Soest, Netherlands (100%)
Tel.: (31) 356038050
Fax: (31) 356032902
E-Mail: spanstaal@spanstaal.nl
Web Site: www.spanstaal.nl
Emp.: 40
Pre-Stressing Technology
S.I.C.: 1629
N.A.I.C.S.: 237110
Willem Smit *(Mng Dir)*

TBS Soest **(2)**
Koningsweg 30
PO Box 34
3760 AA Soest, Utracht, Netherlands (100%)
Tel.: (31) 356095611
Fax: (31) 356017359
E-Mail: tbs@tbs.nl
Web Site: www.tbs.nl
Emp.: 100
Mfr. & Supplier of Products & Components for Sewage & Water Transport Systems
S.I.C.: 1629
N.A.I.C.S.: 237110
Nonald Jkokoosten *(Mgr-Sls)*

Waco Lingen Beton NV **(2)**
Lelyweg 23
4612 PS Bergen-op-Zoom, Netherlands
Tel.: (31) 164274200
Fax: (31) 164234364
E-Mail: info@wacolingen.nl
Web Site: www.wacolingen.nl
Emp.: 20
Precast Concrete Products Developer & Mfr
S.I.C.: 3272
N.A.I.C.S.: 327390
Ron van Boven *(Acct Mgr)*

Affiliates:

Ballast Nedam Bulkgrindstoffen v.o.f. **(2)**
Koningsweg 30
PO Box 447
3762 EC Soest, Netherlands
Tel.: (31) 356098810
Fax: (31) 356098800
E-Mail: info@bnit.nl
Web Site: www.ballastnedam.nl
Emp.: 16
Supplier of Bulk Raw Materials
S.I.C.: 5159
N.A.I.C.S.: 424590
P. Van Vugt *(Mng Dir)*

Grind en Zandhandel Verkaik B.V. **(2)**
Koningsweg 30
3762 EC Soest, Utrecht, Netherlands
Mailing Address:
PO Box 423
3760AK Soest, Netherlands
Tel.: (31) 356030000
Emp.: 7
Gravel & Sand Trade
S.I.C.: 1442
N.A.I.C.S.: 212321
H. M. Bronder *(Gen Mgr)*

Vibouw Van Happen V.o.F. **(2)**
Churchilllaan 204 a
5705 BK Helmond, Netherlands
Tel.: (31) 492505350
Fax: (31) 492537324
Web Site: www.vibouw.nl
Emp.: 18
Gravel & Sand Trade
S.I.C.: 1442
N.A.I.C.S.: 212321

Non-U.S. Subsidiaries:

Ballast Nedam Ipm N.V. **(2)**
Krijnlaan 11
Kapellen, 2950, Belgium BE
Mailing Address: (100%)
Savelkouls Beton
Grote Baan 201
B-2380 Ravels, Belgium
Tel.: (32) 82612045
Fax: (32) 82612046
Supplier of Raw Materials
S.I.C.: 5159
N.A.I.C.S.: 424590
Hans P. van der Meer *(Mng Dir)*

N.V. Immobilien en Grindexploitatlemaatschappij Bichterweerd **(2)**
Maasdijk Z N
Dilsen, B 3650 Stokkem, Belgium BE
Tel.: (32) 89755771 (100%)
Fax: (32) 89790931
E-Mail: administrator@bichterweerd.be
Web Site: www.bichterweerd.be
Emp.: 3
Supplier of Aggregates, Gravel & Raw Materials
S.I.C.: 3531
N.A.I.C.S.: 333120
Hans P. van der Meer *(Mng Dir)*

Subsidiary:

N.V. Algri **(3)**
Maasdijk Z/N
Dilsen, 3650, Belgium
Tel.: (32) 89790930
Fax: (32) 89790931
Construction Sand Mining Services
S.I.C.: 1442
N.A.I.C.S.: 212321

Ballast Nedam Vleuterweide B.V. **(1)**
Ringwade 61
Nieuwegein, 3439 LM, Netherlands
Tel.: (31) 302854400
Fax: (31) 302854875
Property Leasing Services
S.I.C.: 6519
N.A.I.C.S.: 531190

Bouwborg Noordwest **(1)**
Canalmuiden 1
Amsterdam, 58089, Netherlands (100%)
Tel.: (31) 204804040
Fax: (31) 201804088
E-Mail: bouwborg-noordwest@ballast-nedam.nl
Web Site: www.ballastnedam.nl
Rev.: $7,000,000
Emp.: 80
Industrial Building Construction
S.I.C.: 1629
N.A.I.C.S.: 236210
P Briccign *(Dir Gen)*

Bouwborg Oost **(1)**
Meander 551
PO Box 5450
6825 MD Arnhem, Netherlands (100%)
Tel.: (31) 263682700
Fax: (31) 263682724
E-Mail: bnb.bouwborgoost@ballastnedam.nl
Web Site: www.ballastnedam.nl
Rev.: $6,919,512
Emp.: 20
Industrial Building Construction
S.I.C.: 1541
N.A.I.C.S.: 236210
Ed Celthuis *(Gen Mgr)*

Hollestelle Vastgoed Ontwikkeling B.V. **(1)**
Postbus 3015
9701 DA Groningen, Netherlands
Tel.: (31) 505494121
Fax: (31) 505494113
E-Mail: info@hollestelle-vastgoed.nl
Web Site: www.hollestelle-vastgoed.nl
Emp.: 25
Construction Engineering Services
S.I.C.: 8711
N.A.I.C.S.: 541330
J. Roewen *(Gen Mgr)*

Infra Consult + Engineering **(1)**
Ringwade 71
3439 LM Nieuwegein, Netherlands (100%)
Mailing Address:
Postbus 1555
3430 BH Nieuwegein, Netherlands
Tel.: (31) 302854000
Fax: (31) 302854040
E-Mail: info@icpluse.nl
Web Site: www.icpluse.nl
Emp.: 90
Design & Engineering of Civil & General Building Projects
S.I.C.: 8711
N.A.I.C.S.: 541330
William J. van Niekerk *(Mng Dir)*

IQ Woning B.V. **(1)**
Trancheeweg 16-18
Weert, 6002 ST, Netherlands
Tel.: (31) 495579679
Commercial Building Construction Services
S.I.C.: 1542
N.A.I.C.S.: 236220

Laudy Bouw en Ontwikkeling B.V. **(1)**
Irenelaan 8
6133 BG Sittard, Netherlands
Tel.: (31) 46 451 69 33
Fax: (31) 46 452 06 31
E-Mail: laudy@laudybouw.nl
Commercial Building Construction Services
S.I.C.: 1542
N.A.I.C.S.: 236220

Omnia Plaatvloer B.V. **(1)**
Monierweg 14-16
Postbus 4
7740 AA Coevorden, Netherlands
Tel.: (31) 524 51 58 51
Fax: (31) 524 51 45 61
E-Mail: info@omniaplaatvloer.nl
Web Site: www.omniaplaatvloer.nl
Emp.: 7
Floor Insulation Materials Mfr
S.I.C.: 3272
N.A.I.C.S.: 327390
Carlos Lima *(Gen Mgr)*

Zomers Bouwbedrijf B.V. **(1)**
Hoofdweg 43
7871 TC Klijndijk, Netherlands
Tel.: (31) 591 512 386
Fax: (31) 591 513 538
E-Mail: info@zomersbouwbedrijf.nl
Construction Engineering Services
S.I.C.: 8711
N.A.I.C.S.: 541330

Affiliate:

Van Oord nv **(1)**
Watermenweg 64
PO Box 8574
3067GG Rotterdam, Zuid Holland, Netherlands
Mailing Address:
PO Box 149
3700 AC Zeist, Netherlands
Tel.: (31) 104478444
Fax: (31) 104478100
E-Mail: info@vanoord.com
Web Site: www.vanoord.com
Emp.: 4,500
Dredging & Reclamation Services
S.I.C.: 1629
N.A.I.C.S.: 237990
B. Groothuizen *(Mgr-Mktg & PR)*

U.S. Affiliate:

Natco Limited Partnership **(2)**
2122 York Rd
Oak Brook, IL 60523-1930 DE
Tel.: (630) 574-3008 (25%)
Fax: (630) 574-2980
Dredging & Reclamation
S.I.C.: 1541
N.A.I.C.S.: 236210

Non-U.S. Subsidiaries:

Van Oord Dredging and Marine Contractors bv **(2)**
20 Harbour Drive PSA Vista 07-02
Singapore, 117612, Singapore (100%)
Tel.: (65) 67736643
Fax: (65) 67734332
E-Mail: off-sin@vanoord.com
Web Site: www.vanoord.com
Emp.: 15
Dredging & Land Reclamation Services
S.I.C.: 8711
N.A.I.C.S.: 541330

Non-U.S. Subsidiaries:

Ballast Nedam International (Malaysia) Sdn. Bhd. **(1)**
Lot 1303 13Fl Plaza OSK Jalan Ampang
PO Box 12035
Jalan Ampang, 50450 Kuala Lumpur, Malaysia (100%)
Tel.: (60) 321660855
Fax: (60) 321668929
E-Mail: j.rolfe@ballast-nedam.com
Web Site: www.bni.ballast-nedam.com
Emp.: 1
Industrial Building Construction
S.I.C.: 1541
N.A.I.C.S.: 236210
J. Rolfe *(Mgr)*

Ballast Nedam IPM Luxembourg S.A.R.L. **(1)**
P a VGD Luxembourg
11B Boulevard Joseph II, L 1840 Luxembourg, Luxembourg
Tel.: (352) 26259450
Fax: (352) 26259454
Web Site: www.bni.ballast-nedam.com
Emp.: 2
S.I.C.: 3993
N.A.I.C.S.: 339950

Ballast Nedam Wabau GmbH **(1)**
Lubecker Str 53-63
Magdeburg, 39124, Germany
Tel.: (49) 3917265630
Fax: (49) 3917265631
E-Mail: info.md@ballast-nedam.nl
Web Site: www.ballast-nedam.de
Emp.: 2
Civil Engineering Construction Services
S.I.C.: 1629
N.A.I.C.S.: 237990
Thomas Herrmann *(Gen Mgr)*

Ballast Plc, Central Services **(1)**
Manor Ct High St
Harmondsworth, Mddx, UB7 0AQ, United Kingdom (100%)
Tel.: (44) 2087593331
Fax: (44) 2087591821
Web Site: www.ballast.co.uk
Emp.: 30
Industrial Building Construction
S.I.C.: 1629
N.A.I.C.S.: 236210

Ballast plc **(1)**
Manor Ct High St
Harmondsworth, Mddx, UB7 0AQ, United Kingdom UK
Tel.: (44) 2087591821 (100%)
E-Mail: nigel.burke@ballast.co.uk
Emp.: 30
General Building & Civil Engineering Projects
S.I.C.: 8711
N.A.I.C.S.: 541330

Divisions:

Ballast Wiltshier Plc-Airport Services Div. **(2)**
The Gatehouse 360 Cranford Lane
Hayes, Middlesex, UB3 5HD, United Kingdom UK
Tel.: (44) 2087594359 (100%)
Fax: (44) 208 759 4364
Construction Projects for Airports in the United Kingdom
S.I.C.: 1611
N.A.I.C.S.: 237310

Rok Ltd. **(2)**
Dockyard Rd
Ellesmere Port, South Wirral, CH85 4EF, United Kingdom UK
Tel.: (44) 1513557262 (100%)
Fax: (44) 1513571740
Web Site: www.rok.com.uk
Emp.: 20
General Building & Civil Engineering Projects
S.I.C.: 8711

N.A.I.C.S.: 541330

Wiltshier Interiors (Brunei) Sdn. Bhd. (1)
6 Bloxi Latissudin Complex
Kampong Pentkalan Gadong, BE 4119
Negara, Brunei Darussalam
Tel.: (673) 2444578
Fax: (673) 2444581
Web Site: www.bni.ballast-nedam.com
Emp.: 20
Industrial Building Construction
S.I.C.: 1629
N.A.I.C.S.: 236210

BALLERINA-KUCHEN H.-E. ELLERSIEK GMBH

Bruchstrasse 49-51
D-32289 Roding, Germany
Tel.: (49) 52265990
Fax: (49) 5226599211
E-Mail: info@ballerina.de
Web Site: www.ballerina.de
Year Founded: 1978
Rev.: $55,176,000
Emp.: 250

Business Description:
Kitchenware Mfr
S.I.C.: 2434
N.A.I.C.S.: 337110

Personnel:
Heidrun Brinkmeyer *(Mng Dir)*
Heiko Ellersiek *(Mng Dir)*
Heinz Erwin Ellersiek *(Mng Dir)*

BALLI GROUP PLC

33 Cavendish Square
London, W1G 0PW, United Kingdom
Tel.: (44) 2073062000
Fax: (44) 2074919000
E-Mail: info@balli.co.uk
Web Site: www.balli.co.uk
Year Founded: 1991
Sales Range: $1-4.9 Billion
Emp.: 2,000

Business Description:
Steel, Aluminum, Chemicals & Other Commodity Trader & Distr
S.I.C.: 7389
N.A.I.C.S.: 425120

Personnel:
Hassan Alaghband *(Owner)*
Vahid Alaghband *(Chm)*
Derek Dalby *(Vice Chm)*
Hossein Adle *(Co-CEO)*
Nasser Alaghband *(Co-CEO)*

Board of Directors:
Vahid Alaghband
Hossein Adle
Hassan Alaghband
Nasser Alaghband
Donald Chilvers
Derek Dalby
Lord Lamont of Lerwick
David Spriddell

U.S. Subsidiaries:

Balli Steel Inc (1)
1100 Louisiana St Ste 5300
Houston, TX 77002-5215
Tel.: (713) 627-7310
Fax: (713) 627-2923
Web Site: www.balli.co.uk/Contact_us/Address_book.asp?AddressByCountry=13
Metal Service Centers & Metal Merchant Whslr
S.I.C.: 5051
N.A.I.C.S.: 423510
James Cooper *(VP)*

Balli Steel Pipe LLC (1)
1100 Louisiana St Ste 5300
Houston, TX 77002-5215
Tel.: (713) 627-7310
Fax: (713) 627-2923
Web Site: www.balli.co.uk/Contact_us/Address_book.asp?AddressByCountry=13
Purchased Steel & Iron & Steel Pipe & Tube Mfr
S.I.C.: 3317
N.A.I.C.S.: 331210
Jake Monreal *(Gen Mgr)*

WeBco International LLC (1)
210 3rd Springs Dr Ste 2
Weirton, WV 26062
Tel.: (304) 723-6101
Fax: (304) 723-6104
E-Mail: bill@webcosteel.com
Sheet Metal Work Mfr
S.I.C.: 3444
N.A.I.C.S.: 332322
Marcia Wodnicki *(Gen Mgr)*

Non-U.S. Subsidiaries:

Balli Klockner GmbH (1)
Schifferestrasse 200
47059 Duisburg, Germany
Tel.: (49) 2032896000
Fax: (49) 2032896060
E-Mail: trading@ballikloeckner.de
Web Site: www.balli-germany.de
Emp.: 10
Metal Service Centers & Metal Merchant Whslr
S.I.C.: 5051
N.A.I.C.S.: 423510
Axel Kopp *(Mng Dir)*

Balli Klockner Middle East FZE (1)
Jebel Ali Free Zone
PO Box 16936
Dubai, United Arab Emirates
Tel.: (971) 48816549
Fax: (971) 48816446
E-Mail: klockme@emirates.net.ae
Web Site: www.balli.co.uk/Contact_us/Address_book.asp?AddressByName=6
Iron & Steel Mills
S.I.C.: 3312
N.A.I.C.S.: 331110
Clara Bastian *(Mgr)*

Balli West Africa Limited (1)
57 Ring Rd Central
PO Box AN 5144
Accra, Ghana
Tel.: (233) 21270167
Fax: (233) 21270167
E-Mail: sunilb@balli.co.uk
Web Site: www.balli.co.uk/Contact_us/Address_book.asp?AddressByCountry=30
Emp.: 7
Metal Service Centers & Metal Merchant Whslr
S.I.C.: 5051
N.A.I.C.S.: 423510
G. Phillip *(Gen Mgr)*

Balmin Kommerz AG (1)
Industriestrasse 16
6300 Zug, Switzerland
Tel.: (41) 41 720 3000
Fax: (41) 41 720 3001
E-Mail: ballizurich@bluwin.ch
Web Site: www.balli.co.uk/Contact_us/Address_book.asp?AddressByCountry=9
Emp.: 4
Industrial Supplies Whslr
S.I.C.: 5085
N.A.I.C.S.: 423840

Klockner Demir ve Celik Sanayi ve Ticaret Limited Sirketi A.S. (1)
Buyukdere Caddesi Harman Sokak
4 Kat 10 Levent, 34330 Istanbul, Turkey
Tel.: (90) 2123252324
Fax: (90) 2123253233
E-Mail: info@bkturkey.com
Web Site: www.balli.co.uk/Contact_us/Address_book.asp?AddressByCountry=10
Emp.: 8
Iron & Steel Forging
S.I.C.: 3462
N.A.I.C.S.: 332111
Aylin Asral *(Mgr)*

BALLIN, INC.

2825 Brabant-Marineau
Montreal, QC, H4S 1R8, Canada
Tel.: (514) 333-5501
Fax: (514) 333-0016
E-Mail: General@Ballin.com
Web Site: www.ballin.com
Rev.: $23,334,211
Emp.: 351

Business Description:
Men's Dress Slacks Marketer & Mfr
S.I.C.: 5699
N.A.I.C.S.: 315220

Personnel:
Joseph Balinsky *(Pres)*

BALLY WULFF AUTOMATEN GMBH

Maybachufer 48-51
12045 Berlin, Germany
Tel.: (49) 30620020
Fax: (49) 3062002200
E-Mail: managemant@bally-wulff.de
Web Site: www.ballywulff.de
Year Founded: 1950
Emp.: 325

Business Description:
Wall & Touch-Screen Game Machines Mfr & Distr
S.I.C.: 3589
N.A.I.C.S.: 333318

Personnel:
Sascha Blodau *(CEO)*

BALLYVESEY HOLDINGS LIMITED

607 Antrim Road
Newtownabbey, BT36 4RF, United Kingdom
Tel.: (44) 2890 849321
Fax: (44) 2890 849406
Web Site: www.ballyveseyholdings.com
Year Founded: 1970
Sales Range: $550-599.9 Million
Emp.: 1,857

Business Description:
Investment Management Services
S.I.C.: 6799
N.A.I.C.S.: 523920

Personnel:
Paul Jones *(Gen Mgr-Truck & Plant)*

BALMAIN CORP.

Level 14 60 Castlereagh Street
Sydney, NSW, 2000, Australia
Tel.: (61) 292328888
Fax: (61) 292328588
E-Mail: info@balmainfirst.com.au
Web Site: www.balmainfirst.com.au
Emp.: 130

Business Description:
Commercial Lending Services
S.I.C.: 6163
N.A.I.C.S.: 522310

Personnel:
Michael Holm *(Chm)*
Andrew Griffin *(CEO)*

Subsidiary:

Scottish Pacific Business Finance Pty. Limited (1)
L 2 50 Carrington St
2000 Sydney, NSW, Australia
Tel.: (61) 293729999
Web Site: www.spbf.com.au
Factoring & Business Finance Services
S.I.C.: 6159
N.A.I.C.S.: 522220
Peter Lingham *(Mng Dir)*

BALMER LAWRIE & CO. LTD.

21 Netaji Subash Road
Kolkata, 700 001, India
Tel.: (91) 3322225218
Fax: (91) 3322225292
E-Mail: ghosh.amit@balmerlawrie.com
Web Site: www.balmerlawrie.com
Year Founded: 1867
523319—(BOM)
Rev.: $502,629,115
Assets: $242,268,910
Liabilities: $104,595,987
Net Worth: $137,672,923
Earnings: $29,778,522
Emp.: 1,465
Fiscal Year-end: 03/31/13

Business Description:
Diversified Products Manufacturing & Trading Including Greases, Lubricants, Leather, Functional Chemicals, Packaging, Turnkey Projects, Tea Exports, Travel, Tourism, Cargo & Logistics
S.I.C.: 3999
N.A.I.C.S.: 339999

Personnel:
Virendra Sinha *(Chm & Mng Dir)*
Amit Ghosh *(Compliance Officer & Sec)*
Biswarup Chakraborti *(Sr VP-Project-IP)*
Sanjiban Dhar *(Sr VP-Asset Rationalisation & New Initiatives)*
Manoj Lakhanpal *(Sr VP-Fin)*
G. N. Mattoo *(Sr VP-HR)*
Amrit Mukhopadhyay *(Sr VP-Technical)*
Manash Mukhopadhyay *(Sr VP-IT)*

Board of Directors:
Virendra Sinha
Prabal Basu
Partha S. Das
Anand Dayal
Niraj Gupta
V. L. V. S. S. Subba Rao
Prem Prakash Sahoo

Transfer Agent:
Link Intime India Pvt. Ltd.
59-C Chowringhee Road 3rd Floor
Kolkata, 700 020, India
Tel.: (91) 33 2289 0540
Fax: (91) 33 2289 0539

BALMER LAWRIE INVESTMENTS LTD.

21 Netaji Subhas Road
Kolkata, 700001, India
Tel.: (91) 33 22225292
Fax: (91) 33 22225678
Web Site: www.blinv.com
532485—(BOM)
Rev.: $6,122,965
Assets: $17,203,730
Liabilities: $4,728,497
Net Worth: $12,475,232
Earnings: $5,769,333
Fiscal Year-end: 03/31/13

Business Description:
Investment Management Services
S.I.C.: 6211
N.A.I.C.S.: 523999

Personnel:
P. Kalyanasundaram *(Chm)*
Proadyot Kumar Ghosh *(Compliance & Pub Info Officer & Sec)*

Board of Directors:
P. Kalyanasundaram
Prabal Basu
Sukhvir Singh

Transfer Agent:
C. B. Management Services (P) Ltd
P-22 Bondel Road
700019 Kolkata, India

BALMORAL GROUP LTD.

Balmoral Park
Loirston, Aberdeen, AB12 3GY, United Kingdom
Tel.: (44) 1224859000
Fax: (44) 01224859123
E-Mail: group@balmoral-group.com
Web Site: www.balmoral-group.com
Year Founded: 1980
Sales Range: $50-74.9 Million
Emp.: 350

Balmoral Group Ltd.—(Continued)

Business Description:
Lightweight Plastic Composites Mfr; Liquid Storage & Treatment Products Designer & Mfr; Marine Equipment Supplier
S.I.C.: 3089
N.A.I.C.S.: 326199
Personnel:
James S. Milne *(Chm & Mng Dir)*

Subsidiaries:

Balmoral Advanced Composites Limited (1)
Balmoral Park Loirston
Loriston, Aberdeen, AB12 3GY, United Kingdom UK
Tel.: (44) 1224859000
Fax: (44) 1224859059
E-Mail: balmoralac@balmoral.co.uk
Emp.: 400
Lightweight Plastic Composites Mfr
S.I.C.: 3089
N.A.I.C.S.: 326199
James S. Milne *(Chm & Mng Dir)*

Balmoral Marine Ltd. (1)
Balmoral Park
Loriston, Aberdeen, AB12 3GY, United Kingdom
Tel.: (44) 1224859000
Fax: (44) 1224859059
E-Mail: offshore@balmoral.co.uk
Web Site: www.balmoral-group.com
Marine Equipment Supplier
S.I.C.: 4491
N.A.I.C.S.: 488320

Balmoral Tanks Limited (1)
Unit 2 Coomber Way Industrial Estate
Croydon, Surrey, CR0 4TQ, United Kingdom UK
Tel.: (44) 2086654100
Fax: (44) 2086650200
E-Mail: tanks@balmoral.co.uk
Web Site: www.balmoratanks.com
Emp.: 10
Liquid Storage & Treatment Tanks & Other Related Products
S.I.C.: 3443
N.A.I.C.S.: 332420
Norman Ross *(Dir-Sls)*

Balmoral Wellbeing Ltd. (1)
Longdon Manor
Shipston-on-Stour, Warwickshire, CV36 4PW, United Kingdom
Tel.: (44) 1608 682888
Fax: (44) 1608 6822998
E-Mail: info@the-egg.co.uk
Web Site: www.the-egg.co.uk
Relaxation Chamber
S.I.C.: 3089
N.A.I.C.S.: 326199

BALMORAL INTERNATIONAL LAND HOLDINGS PLC

29 North Anne Street
Dublin, 7, Ireland
Tel.: (353) 1 887 2788
Fax: (353) 1 887 2789
E-Mail: info@bilplc.com
Web Site: www.bilplc.com
Year Founded: 2011
Business Description:
Holding Company
S.I.C.: 6719
N.A.I.C.S.: 551112
Personnel:
Robert Knox *(CEO)*
Philip Halpenny *(COO & Fin Dir)*
Niall Quigley *(Sec)*
Board of Directors:
Carl McCann
Philip Halpenny
Andrew Kelliher
Robert Knox
Declan McCourt
Tom Neasy
Alan D. White
Legal Counsel:
Arthur Cox
Earlsfort Terrace
Dublin, 2, Ireland

Holding:

Balmoral International Land Limited (1)
29 North Anne Street
Dublin, 7, Ireland (100%)
Tel.: (353) 18872788
Fax: (353) 18872789
E-Mail: info@bilplc.com
Web Site: www.bilplc.com
Sales Range: $10-24.9 Million
Emp.: 9
Real Estate Development Services
S.I.C.: 6531
N.A.I.C.S.: 531390
Robert Knox *(CEO)*
Catherine Ghose *(COO & Dir-Fin)*
Niall Quigley *(Sec)*

Subsidiaries:

Balmoral Land Naul Ltd (2)
29 North Anne Street
Dublin, 7, Ireland
Tel.: (353) 18872788
Real Estate Property Development Services
S.I.C.: 6531
N.A.I.C.S.: 531210

Non-U.S. Subsidiary:

Balmoral International Land UK Ltd (2)
Fairbourne Drive
Atterbury Lakes, Milton Keynes, Buckinghamshire, MK10 9RG, United Kingdom
Tel.: (44) 1908488627
Fax: (44) 1908487501
E-Mail: info@bilplc.com
Web Site: www.bilplc.com
Emp.: 3
Real Estate Property Management Services
S.I.C.: 6531
N.A.I.C.S.: 531311

BALMORAL RESOURCES LTD.

2300 - 1177 West Hastings Street
Vancouver, BC, V6E 2K3, Canada
Tel.: (604) 638-3664
Fax: (604) 648-8809
Toll Free: (877) 838-3664
E-Mail: info@balmoralresources.com
Web Site: www.balmoralresources.com
Year Founded: 2010
BAR—(OTC TSX)
Int. Income: $83,082
Assets: $39,040,512
Liabilities: $2,439,422
Net Worth: $36,601,090
Earnings: ($911,116)
Emp.: 7
Fiscal Year-end: 12/31/12
Business Description:
Gold Exploration Services
S.I.C.: 1041
N.A.I.C.S.: 212221
Personnel:
Darin W. Wagner *(Pres & CEO)*
Ross McDonald *(CFO)*
Sue Chipperfield *(Sec)*
Board of Directors:
Graeme Currie
Daniel MacInnis
Gordon Neal
Lawrence W. Talbot
Darin W. Wagner
Legal Counsel:
Gowling Lafleur Henderson LLP
Suite 2300-550 Burrard Street
Vancouver, BC, Canada
Transfer Agent:
Computershare Investor Services
3rd Floor, 510 Burrard Street
Vancouver, BC, Canada

BALOCCO S.P.A.

Santa Lucia 51
Fossano, 12045 Cuneo, Italy
Tel.: (39) 0172 653411
Fax: (39) 0172 653470
Web Site: www.balocco.it
Year Founded: 1927
Sales Range: $150-199.9 Million
Emp.: 323
Business Description:
Bakery Product Mfr
S.I.C.: 2052
N.A.I.C.S.: 311821
Personnel:
Silvia Caffetti *(Mgr-Export)*

BALOCHISTAN PARTICLE BOARD LIMITED

3rd Floor Imperial Court Dr Ziauddin Ahmed Road
Karachi, 75530, Pakistan
Tel.: (92) 2135680036
Fax: (92) 2135684086
Web Site: www.bpbl.net
BPBL—(LAH)
Rev.: $35,668
Assets: $115,219
Liabilities: $190,393
Net Worth: ($75,175)
Earnings: $19,500
Emp.: 1
Fiscal Year-end: 06/30/13
Business Description:
Particle Board, Formaldehyde & Formaldehyde Based Resins Mfr
S.I.C.: 2821
N.A.I.C.S.: 325211
Personnel:
Muslim R. Habib *(Chm & CEO)*
Amir Bashir Ahmed *(Sec)*
Board of Directors:
Muslim R. Habib
Iqbal Ahmed
Ali Niaz Akhter
Muhammad Salman Husain Chawala
Murtaza H. Habib
Ghulam Abbas Karjatwala
Ali A. Rahim

BALOG AUCTION SERVICES INC.

PO Box 786
Lethbridge, AB, T1J 3Z6, Canada
Tel.: (403) 320-1980
Fax: (403) 320-2660
Toll Free: (877) 320-1988
Web Site: www.balogauction.com
Rev.: $27,300,714
Emp.: 40
Business Description:
Hosts Livestock & Machinery Auction Services
S.I.C.: 5961
N.A.I.C.S.: 454112
Personnel:
Darwin G. Balog *(Co-Owner)*
Robert C. Balog *(Co-Owner)*

BALOISE HOLDING AG

(d/b/a Baloise Group)
Aeschengraben 21
4002 Basel, Switzerland
Tel.: (41) 582858585
Fax: (41) 582857070
E-Mail: info@baloise.com
Web Site: www.baloise.com
Year Founded: 1863
BALN—(OTC SWX)
Rev.: $10,155,321,880
Assets: $79,359,377,504
Liabilities: $74,100,067,008
Net Worth: $5,259,310,496
Earnings: $477,491,168
Emp.: 8,795
Fiscal Year-end: 12/31/12
Business Description:
Holding Company; Insurance & Pension Products & Services
S.I.C.: 6719
N.A.I.C.S.: 551112
Personnel:
Andreas Burckhardt *(Chm)*
Georg F. Krayer *(Vice Chm)*
Martin Strobel *(CEO & Head-Intl)*
German Egloff *(CFO & Head-Fin)*
Jan De Meulder *(CEO-Basler-Germany)*
Michael Muller *(CEO-Basler-Switzerland)*
Markus von Escher *(Sec)*
Board of Directors:
Andreas Burckhardt
Michael Becker
Andreas Beerli
Georges-Antoine de Boccard
Karin Keller-Sutter
Georg F. Krayer
Werner Kummer
Thomas Pleines
Eveline Saupper

Subsidiaries:

Baloise Asset Management International AG (1)
Aeschengraben 21
4051 Basel, Switzerland
Tel.: (41) 58 285 85 85
Fax: (41) 58 285 90 19
Asset Management Services
S.I.C.: 6282
N.A.I.C.S.: 523920

Baloise Asset Management Schweiz AG (1)
Lautengartenstrasse 6
4002 Basel Basel, Switzerland
Tel.: (41) 612858585
Fax: (41) 612857070
E-Mail: media.relations@baloise.com
Web Site: www.baloise.com
Asset Management Services
S.I.C.: 6282
N.A.I.C.S.: 523920

Baloise Bank SoBa (1)
Amtshausplatz 4
4502 Solothurn, Switzerland
Tel.: (41) 326260202
Fax: (41) 582850333
E-Mail: bank@baloise.ch
Web Site: www.baloise.ch
Emp.: 220
Banking & Financial Support Services
S.I.C.: 6029
N.A.I.C.S.: 522110

Baloise Fund Invest (1)
Lautengartenstrasse 6
PO Box 2275
4002 Basel, Switzerland
Tel.: (41) 612857032
Fax: (41) 612859147
E-Mail: bfi.info@baloise.ch
Web Site: www.baloise.ch
Financial Investment Services
S.I.C.: 6211
N.A.I.C.S.: 523999

Basler Versicherungs-Gesellschaft (1)
Aeschengraben 21
Basel, 4002, Switzerland (100%)
Tel.: (41) 612858585
Fax: (41) 61200857070
E-Mail: insurance@baloise.ch
Web Site: www.baloise.ch
Sales Range: $1-4.9 Billion
Emp.: 3,300
Non-Life Insurance Services
S.I.C.: 6411
N.A.I.C.S.: 524298
Rolf Schaeuble *(Mng Dir)*

Haakon AG (1)
Pfeffingerstrasse 41
4053 Basel, Switzerland
Tel.: (41) 61 366 91 91
Fax: (41) 61 366 91 81

E-Mail: hakch@haakon.ch
Web Site: www.haakon.ch
Reinsurance Services
S.I.C.: 6399
N.A.I.C.S.: 524130
Guenther Boerlin *(Chm)*
Thomas Meier *(Co-CEO)*
Paul Oeschger *(Co-CEO)*
Jacques Aigeldinger *(Exec VP)*
Eric Mueller *(Exec VP)*
Alexandra Deiss *(Sec-Corp Svcs)*

Non-U.S. Subsidiary:

HAAKON (ASIA) LTD **(2)**
Suite 17 5 Level 17 Menara IMC 8 Jalan Sultan Ismail
50250 Kuala Lumpur, Malaysia
Tel.: (60) 3 2031 82 08
Fax: (60) 3 2031 63 23
E-Mail: asia@haakon.com.my
Emp.: 4
Reinsurance Services
S.I.C.: 6399
N.A.I.C.S.: 524130
Paul Oeschger *(CEO)*

Non-U.S. Subsidiaries:

Amazon Insurance nv **(1)**
City Link
Posthofbrug 14
2600 Antwerp, Belgium
Tel.: (32) 32 47 23 80
Fax: (32) 32 47 23 99
E-Mail: info@amazon.be
Web Site: www.amazon.be
General Insurance Services
S.I.C.: 6411
N.A.I.C.S.: 524210

Avetas Versicherungs-Aktiengesellschaft **(1)**
Postfach 11 53
61281 Bad Homburg, Germany
Tel.: (49) 180 3 18 18 51
Fax: (49) 180 3 18 18 52
E-Mail: info@avetas.de
Automotive & Accidental Insurance Services
S.I.C.: 6311
N.A.I.C.S.: 524113

Baloise Assurances IARD S.A. **(1)**
Boite Postale 28
2010 Luxembourg, Luxembourg
Tel.: (352) 290 190 530
Fax: (352) 290 190 531
Web Site: www.baloise.lu
Emp.: 270
Insurance Management Services
S.I.C.: 6411
N.A.I.C.S.: 524298
Andre Bredimus *(Gen Mgr)*

Baloise Assurances Luxembourg S.A. **(1)**
23 Rue du Puits Romain
L2010 Bertrange, Luxembourg (100%)
Mailing Address:
Boite Postale 28
2010 Luxembourg, Luxembourg
Tel.: (352) 2901901
Fax: (352) 2901902999
E-Mail: info@baloise.lu
Web Site: www.baloise.lu
Sales Range: $650-699.9 Million
Emp.: 250
Insurance & Pension Services
S.I.C.: 6399
N.A.I.C.S.: 524128
Romain Braas *(Mng Dir)*

Baloise Delta Holding S.a.r.l. **(1)**
Rue Du Puits Romain 23
8070 Strassen, Luxembourg
Tel.: (352) 2901901
Fax: (352) 290592
Investment Management Services
S.I.C.: 6211
N.A.I.C.S.: 523999

Baloise Europe Vie SA **(1)**
"23, rue du Roman Wells "
L 8070 Bertrange, Bourmicht, Luxembourg
Tel.: (352) 2901901
Fax: (352) 290190462
E-Mail: info@baloise.lu
Web Site: www.baloise.lu
Emp.: 210
Life Insurance Services
S.I.C.: 6399
N.A.I.C.S.: 524128

Baloise Fund Invest Advico **(1)**
Rue Emile Bian 1
Luxembourg, 1235, Luxembourg
Tel.: (352) 2901901
Fax: (352) 290591
Investment Management Services
S.I.C.: 6211
N.A.I.C.S.: 523999

Baloise Insurance Company (I.O.M.) Ltd. **(1)**
3 Fl IOMA House
Hope St, Douglas, IM1 1AP, Isle of Man (100%)
Emp.: 10
Reinsurance
S.I.C.: 6399
N.A.I.C.S.: 524130

Baloise Life (Liechtenstein) AG **(1)**
Alte Landstrasse 6
94 96 Balzers, Liechtenstein
Tel.: (423) 3889000
Fax: (423) 3889021
E-Mail: information@baloise-life.com
Web Site: www.baloise-life.com
Emp.: 25
Insurance Services
S.I.C.: 6411
N.A.I.C.S.: 524298
Roger Matthes *(CEO)*

Baloise (Luxembourg) Holding S.A. **(1)**
Rue Du Puits Romanian 23
8070 Bertrange, Luxembourg
Tel.: (352) 2901901
Fax: (352) 290592
Investment Management Services
S.I.C.: 6211
N.A.I.C.S.: 523999
Romain Braas *(Mng Dir)*

Baloise Vie Luxembourg S.A **(1)**
23 Rue du Puits Romain Bourmicht
Boite Postale 28
2010 Bertrange, Luxembourg
Tel.: (352) 290 190 1
Fax: (352) 291 968
E-Mail: info@baloise.lu
General Insurance Services
S.I.C.: 6411
N.A.I.C.S.: 524210

Basler Lebens-Versicherungs Gesellschaft-AG **(1)**
Basler Strasse 4
61345 Bad Homburg, Germany (100%)
Tel.: (49) 6172130
Fax: (49) 6172125456
E-Mail: info@basler.de
Web Site: www.basler.de
Emp.: 500
Life Insurance
S.I.C.: 6311
N.A.I.C.S.: 524113

Basler Securitas Versicherungs-Aktiengesellschaft **(1)**
Basler Strasse 4
Bad Homburg, 61352, Germany
Tel.: (49) 6172 13202
Fax: (49) 617213 5499
E-Mail: balcert.service@basler.de
Nonlife Insurance Services
S.I.C.: 6411
N.A.I.C.S.: 524298

Basler Versicherungs-Aktienges **(1)**
Brigittenauer Lande 50 54
Vienna, 1203, Austria (100%)
Tel.: (43) 1331600
Fax: (43) 133160200
E-Mail: office@basler.co.at
Web Site: www.basler.co.at
Sales Range: $125-149.9 Million
Emp.: 100
Insurance, Pension & Asset Management Services
S.I.C.: 6311
N.A.I.C.S.: 524113
Otmar Bodner *(CEO)*

Basler Versicherungs-Gesellschaft **(1)**
Basler Strasse 4
61345 Bad Homburg, Germany (100%)
Mailing Address:
POB 1145
61345 Bad Homburg, Germany
Tel.: (49) 6172130
Fax: (49) 6172125456
E-Mail: info@basler.de
Web Site: www.basler.de
Sales Range: $800-899.9 Million
Emp.: 1,300
Life Insurance
S.I.C.: 6311
N.A.I.C.S.: 524113
Frank Gaund *(Mng Dir)*

Deutscher Ring Beteiligungsholding GmbH **(1)**
Ludwig Erhard Strasse 22
20459 Hamburg, Germany
Tel.: (49) 40 35990
Fax: (49) 40 35993636
E-Mail: kunde@basler.de
Web Site: www.basler.de
Investment Management Services
S.I.C.: 6211
N.A.I.C.S.: 523999
Frank Grund *(Gen Mgr)*

Deutscher Ring Financial Services GmbH **(1)**
Ludwig-Erhard-Strasse 22
20459 Hamburg, Germany
Tel.: (49) 40 3599 3020
Fax: (49) 40 3599 3062
E-Mail: Fonds@DeutscherRing-FS.de
Financial Management Services
S.I.C.: 6211
N.A.I.C.S.: 523999

Deutscher Ring Lebensversicherungs-AG **(1)**
Ludwig Erhard Strasse 22
Hamburg, 22459, Germany (97%)
Tel.: (49) 4035997711
Fax: (49) 4035993636
E-Mail: kunde@basler.de
Web Site: www.basler.de
Sales Range: $1-4.9 Billion
Emp.: 1,900
Life Insurance & Pension Products & Services
S.I.C.: 6311
N.A.I.C.S.: 524113
Jan De Meulder *(Mng Dir)*

Subsidiaries:

Deutscher Ring Bausparkasse Aktiengesellschaft **(2)**
Ludwig Erhard Strasse 22
20459 Hamburg, Germany
Tel.: (49) 40 3599 50
Fax: (49) 40 3599 5128
E-Mail: Bausparservice@DeutscherRing-Bausparen.de
Commercial Banking Services
S.I.C.: 6029
N.A.I.C.S.: 522110

MoneyMaxx Lebensversicherungs-AG **(2)**
Emanuel Leutze Strasse 11
40547 Dusseldorf, Germany
Tel.: (49) 18025757
Fax: (49) 18025656
E-Mail: info@moneymaxx.de
Web Site: www.moneymaxx.de
Emp.: 60
Life Insurance Services
S.I.C.: 6311
N.A.I.C.S.: 524113

Deutscher Ring Sachversicherungs-AG **(1)**
Ludwig Erhard Strasse 22
D 20459 Hamburg, Germany (100%)
Tel.: (49) 4035990
Fax: (49) 4035993636
E-Mail: service@deutscherring.de
Web Site: www.deutscherring.de
Emp.: 1,600
Property Insurance Products & Services
S.I.C.: 6351
N.A.I.C.S.: 524126
Wolfgang Fautdr *(Dir)*

Euromex N.V. **(1)**
Prins Boidewijnlaan 45
2650 Edegem, Antwerp, Belgium (100%)
Tel.: (32) 34514400
Fax: (32) 34514499
E-Mail: info@euromex.be
Web Site: www.euromex.be
Premiums: $23,800,552
Emp.: 90
Non-Life Insurance
S.I.C.: 6399
N.A.I.C.S.: 524128
Rob Vromen *(Mng Dir)*

GROCON Erste Grundstucksgesellschaft mbH **(1)**
Ludwig Erhard Strasse 22
20459 Hamburg, Germany
Tel.: (49) 40 35992874
Property Management Services
S.I.C.: 6531
N.A.I.C.S.: 531312

Jurpartner Rechtsschutz-Versicherung AG **(1)**
Eumeniusstrase 15-17
50679 Cologne, Germany
Tel.: (49) 221 80264 0
Fax: (49) 221 80264 44
E-Mail: service@jurpartner.de
General Insurance Services
S.I.C.: 6411
N.A.I.C.S.: 524210

Mercator Verzekeringen N.V. **(1)**
Desguinlei 100
2018 Antwerp, Belgium (96%)
Tel.: (32) 32472111
Fax: (32) 32475400
E-Mail: info@mercator.be
Web Site: www.mercator.be
Sales Range: $700-749.9 Million
Emp.: 600
General Insurance & Pension Services
S.I.C.: 6311
N.A.I.C.S.: 524113
Jan De Meulder *(CEO)*
Luc Verhaert *(Vice CEO)*
Patrick Van De Sype *(Sec Gen)*

Subsidiary:

Mercator Bank **(2)**
Posthofbrug 16
B 2600 Antwerp, Belgium (100%)
Tel.: (32) 32472111
Fax: (32) 32472777
E-Mail: info@mercator.be
Web Site: www.mercator.be
Emp.: 50
Banking Services
S.I.C.: 6029
N.A.I.C.S.: 522110

ROLAND Assistance GmbH **(1)**
Deutz-Kalker Strasse 46
50679 Cologne, Germany
Tel.: (49) 221 8277 8277
Fax: (49) 221 8277 6009
E-Mail: service@roland-assistance.de
Roadway Repair Services
S.I.C.: 7389
N.A.I.C.S.: 561990

ROLAND ProzessFinanz AG **(1)**
Deutz-Kalker Strasse 46
50679 Cologne, Germany
Tel.: (49) 221 8277 3001
Fax: (49) 221 8277 3009
E-Mail: service@roland-prozessfinanz.de
Web Site: www.roland-prozessfinanz.de
Emp.: 7
Legal Support Services
S.I.C.: 7389
N.A.I.C.S.: 541199
Arndt Eversberg *(Gen Mgr)*

Roland Rechtsschutz Beteiligungs GmbH **(1)**
Deutz-Kalker Strasse 46
50679 Cologne, Germany
Tel.: (49) 221 8277 500
Fax: (49) 221 8277 460
Legal Support Services
S.I.C.: 7389
N.A.I.C.S.: 541199

Non-U.S. Subsidiaries:

ROLAND Rechtsschutz-Versicherungs-AG **(2)**
Mariannengasse 14
1090 Vienna, Austria
Tel.: (43) 1 7 18 77 33 0

Baloise Holding AG—(Continued)

Fax: (43) 1 7 18 77 33 30
E-Mail: roland.info@roland-rechtsschutz.at
Emp.: 13
Legal Support Services
S.I.C.: 7389
N.A.I.C.S.: 541199

ROLAND Rechtsschutz-Versicherungs-AG (2)
Herengracht 141
1015 BH Amsterdam, Netherlands
Tel.: (31) 205538 000
Fax: (31) 205537 100
E-Mail: info@roland-rechtsbijstand.nl
General Insurance Services
S.I.C.: 6411
N.A.I.C.S.: 524210
Claudia van de Kuil *(Mgr-Sls)*

ROLAND Schutzbrief-Versicherung AG (1)
Deutz-Kalker Strasse 46
50679 Cologne, Germany
Tel.: (49) 221 8277 500
Fax: (49) 221 8277 460
E-Mail: service@roland-schutzbrief.de
Accidental Insurance Services
S.I.C.: 6311
N.A.I.C.S.: 524113

BALRAMPUR CHINI MILLS LIMITED

FMC Fortuna 234/3A AJC Bose Road
Kolkata, 700 020, India
Tel.: (91) 3322874749
Fax: (91) 3322873083
E-Mail: bcml@bcml.in
Web Site: www.chini.com
Year Founded: 1965
BALRAMCHIN—(BOM NSE)
Sls.: $627,399,218
Assets: $782,992,664
Liabilities: $538,994,583
Net Worth: $243,998,080
Earnings: $29,905,187
Emp.: 5,924
Fiscal Year-end: 03/31/13
Business Description:
Sugar, Molasses, Alcohol, Bagasse, Power & Organic Manure Mfr
S.I.C.: 2061
N.A.I.C.S.: 311314
Personnel:
Meenakshi Saraogi *(Co-Mng Dir)*
Vivek Saraogi *(Co-Mng Dir)*
Kishor Shah *(CFO)*
S. K. Agrawala *(Compliance Officer & Sec)*
K. P. Singh *(Pres-Haidergarh & Head & Sr Gen Mgr-Maizapur)*
N. K. Agarwal *(Pres-Gularia)*
N. K. Khetan *(Pres-Balrampur)*
S. N. Misra *(Pres-Akbarpur)*
Board of Directors:
Naresh Chandra
Ram Kishore Choudhury
R. N. Das
Krishnava Dutt
Mittal D. K.
Meenakshi Saraogi
Vivek Saraogi
Arvind Krishna Saxena
Kishor Shah
Rangarajan Vasudevan
Legal Counsel:
Khaitan Co & LLP
1B Old Post Office Street
Kolkata, India
Subsidiary:

Balrampur Overseas Pvt. Ltd. (1)
FMC Fortuna 234 3A
A J C Bose Rd, 700 020 Kolkata, India
Tel.: (91) 3322874749
Fax: (91) 3322873083
E-Mail: bcml@bcml.in
Web Site: www.chini.in
Emp.: 100
Sugar Mfr
S.I.C.: 2063
N.A.I.C.S.: 311313
Vivek I Saraog *(Mng Dir)*
Kishor Shah *(CFO)*

BALS CORPORATION

5-53-67 Jingumae
Shibuya-ku, Tokyo, 1500001, Japan
Tel.: (81) 354597500
Web Site: www.bals.co.jp
Sales Range: $350-399.9 Million
Emp.: 588
Business Description:
Interior Design
S.I.C.: 7389
N.A.I.C.S.: 541410
Personnel:
Fumio Takashima *(Pres & CEO)*
Nobukuni Taneya *(Sr Mng Dir)*
Hiroshi Nakiri *(Exec VP)*
Board of Directors:
Minoru Ihara
Satoshi Kimura
Seiichi Mizuno
Yasumichi Morita
Kazuyuki Sano
Fumio Takashima
Nobukuni Taneya
Isao Yamakage
Kiyomi Yokohari
Subsidiary:

REALFLEET Co., Ltd. (1)
Cosmos Aoyama B1F 5-53-67 Jingumae
Shibuya-ku, Tokyo, 150-0001, Japan
Tel.: (81) 357740641
Fax: (81) 354670431
E-Mail: info@realfleet.co.jp
Web Site: www.realfleet.co.jp
Home & Electrical Appliances Whslr
S.I.C.: 5064
N.A.I.C.S.: 423620
Hiroshi Kumamoto *(Pres)*
Hayakawa Taro *(Mng Dir)*
Non-U.S. Subsidiary:

BALS Hong Kong Limited (1)
Shop 1032 Elements 1 Austin Rd W
Kowloon, China (Hong Kong)
Tel.: (852) 23021961
Fax: (852) 23021962
E-Mail: pt_elements@bals.com.hk
Web Site: www.balseokyo.com
Emp.: 20
Interior Goods Mfr
S.I.C.: 2541
N.A.I.C.S.: 337212
Dennis Tham *(Mgr)*

BALTEC MASCHINENBAU AG

Obermattstrasse 65
8330 Pfaffikon, Switzerland
Tel.: (41) 44 953 13 33
Fax: (41) 44 953 13 44
E-Mail: baltec@baltec.com
Web Site: www.baltec.com
Sales Range: $10-24.9 Million
Emp.: 50
Business Description:
Riveting Machines Mfr & Distr
S.I.C.: 3542
N.A.I.C.S.: 333517
Personnel:
Walter Graenicher *(Chm)*
U.S. Subsidiary:

BalTec Corporation (1)
121 Hillpointe Dr Ste 900
Canonsburg, PA 15317-9563 (100%)
Tel.: (724) 873-5757
Fax: (724) 873-5858
E-Mail: crupprecht@baltecusa.com
Web Site: www.baltecorporation.com
Emp.: 24
Riveting Machine Distr
S.I.C.: 5084
N.A.I.C.S.: 423830
Chuck Rupprecht *(Exec VP)*
Non-U.S. Subsidiaries:

BalTec (UK) Ltd. (1)
Baltec House Danehill
Lower Earley, Reading, RG6 4UT, United Kingdom (100%)
Tel.: (44) 118 9311191
Fax: (44) 118 9311103
E-Mail: sales@baltecuk.com
Web Site: www.baltec.co.uk
Emp.: 7
Riveting Machines Distr
S.I.C.: 5084
N.A.I.C.S.: 423830

BALTI UUDISTETALITUSE AS

(d/b/a Baltic News Service Ltd.)
Toompuiestee 35
EE-15043 Tallinn, Estonia
Tel.: (372) 6108800
Fax: (372) 6108811
E-Mail: bns@bns.ee
Web Site: news.bns.ee
Year Founded: 1990
Emp.: 50
Business Description:
Holding Company; News Syndicate
S.I.C.: 6719
N.A.I.C.S.: 551112
Personnel:
Markus Nisula *(Mng Dir)*
Subsidiary:

BNS Eesti OU (1)
Toompuiestee 35
EE-15043 Tallinn, Estonia EE
Tel.: (372) 6108800 (100%)
Fax: (372) 6108811
E-Mail: bns@bns.ee
Web Site: www.news.bns.ee
News Syndicate
S.I.C.: 7383
N.A.I.C.S.: 519110
Anvar Samost *(Mng Dir & Editor-In-Chief)*
Non-U.S. Subsidiaries:

BNS Latvija SIA (1)
Berga Bazars Marijas iela 13 korpuss 1
LV-1050 Riga, Latvia LV
Tel.: (371) 67088600 (99.99%)
Fax: (371) 67088601
E-Mail: bns@bns.lv
Web Site: www.bns.lv
Emp.: 30
News Syndicate
S.I.C.: 7383
N.A.I.C.S.: 519110
Sigita Kirilka *(Chm, Mng Dir & Editor-in-Chief)*

Subsidiary:

Mediju Monitorings SIA (2)
Marijas Iela 13-2
Riga, 1050, Latvia
Tel.: (371) 67 088 600
Fax: (371) 67 088 601
E-Mail: monitorings@monitorings.lv
Web Site: www.monitorings.lv
Emp.: 18
Media Monitoring & Analysis Services
S.I.C.: 7313
N.A.I.C.S.: 541840

BNS UAB (1)
Jogailos g 9/1
LT-01116 Vilnius, Lithuania LT
Tel.: (370) 852058501 (99.95%)
Fax: (370) 852058504
E-Mail: bns@bns.lt
Web Site: www.bns.lt
Emp.: 45
News Syndicate
S.I.C.: 7383
N.A.I.C.S.: 519110
Arthur Racas *(Mng Dir & Editor-in-Chief)*

THE BALTIC EXCHANGE LTD.

38 St Mary Axe
London, EC3A 8BH, United Kingdom
Tel.: (44) 2072839300
Fax: (44) 2073691622
E-Mail: enquiries@balticexchange.com
Web Site: www.balticexchange.com
Rev.: $8,602,601
Assets: $43,475,700
Liabilities: $2,745,112
Net Worth: $40,730,587
Earnings: $1,890,146
Emp.: 28
Fiscal Year-end: 03/31/13
Business Description:
Shipping Exchange Services
S.I.C.: 4412
N.A.I.C.S.: 483111
Personnel:
Quentin B. Soanes *(Chm)*
Guy M. Campbell *(Vice Chm)*
Jeremy Penn *(CEO)*
Duncan W. T. Bain *(Sec & Head-Fin)*
Board of Directors:
Quentin B. Soanes
S. Albertijn
S. C. Baldey
Guy M. Campbell
A. C. Carroll
D. C. Dragazis
D. L. Dunn
H. J. Fafalios
C. A. Fowle
A. J. Francis
C. J. Nolan
W. M. Robson
L. C. Varnavides
A. J. Westbrook
A. R. Wooldridge

BALTIC OIL TERMINALS PLC

(Name Changed to Pan European Terminals PLC)

BALURGHAT TECHNOLOGIES LTD.

170 / 2 C Acharya Jagadish Chandra Bose Road
Kolkata, 700014, India
Tel.: (91) 33 22840612
Fax: (91) 33 22842084
Web Site: www.balurghat.net
520127—(BOM)
Business Description:
Transportation Services
S.I.C.: 4789
N.A.I.C.S.: 488999
Personnel:
Pawan Kumar Sethia *(Mng Dir)*
Board of Directors:
Madanlal Agarwal
Mahavir Prasad Goenka
Arun Kumar Sethia
Hansraj Sethia
Pawan Kumar Sethia

BALVER ZINN JOSEF JOST GMBH & CO. KG

Blintroper Weg 11
58802 Balve, Germany
Tel.: (49) 23759150
Fax: (49) 2375915114
E-Mail: cia@balverzinn.com
Web Site: www.balverzinn.com
Year Founded: 1976
Rev.: $26,132,956
Emp.: 51
Business Description:
Electronic Components Mfr
S.I.C.: 3679
N.A.I.C.S.: 334419
Personnel:
Marshal Jusmal *(Gen Mgr-South East Asia)*

BALZAC CARAVANES

Ratarieux Rn 82
42580 L'Etrat, Loire, France

Tel.: (33) 477740424
Web Site: www.balzac-caravanes.com
Sls.: $10,500,000
Emp.: 14
S.I.C.: 5941
N.A.I.C.S.: 451110
Personnel:
Gilbert Goubatian *(Pres)*

BALZER'S CANADA INC.

North Service Road Emerald Park
Regina, SK, S4L 1B6, Canada
Tel.: (306) 781-2400
Fax: (306) 781-2240
E-Mail: bci@balzerscanada.com
Web Site: www.balzerscanada.com
Year Founded: 1937
Rev.: $59,700,000
Emp.: 350
Business Description:
Industrial & commercial Building ConstructionWaste Water & Themal Power Plant Construction
S.I.C.: 1541
N.A.I.C.S.: 236210
Personnel:
C. H. Balzer *(Founder)*

BAM INVESTMENTS CORP.

(Name Changed to Partners Value Fund, Inc.)

BAM SPLIT CORP.

181 Bay Street Brookfield Place Suite 300
Toronto, ON, M5J 2T3, Canada
Tel.: (416) 363-9491
Fax: (416) 365-9642
E-Mail: ir@brookfield.com
Web Site: www.bamsplit.com
Year Founded: 2001
BNA—(TSX)
Sales Range: $25-49.9 Million
Business Description:
Investment Services
S.I.C.: 6211
N.A.I.C.S.: 523999
Personnel:
Frank N. C. Lochan *(Chm)*
Ed C. Kress *(Pres)*
Derek E. Gorgi *(CFO)*
Loretta M. Corso *(Sec)*
Board of Directors:
Frank N. C. Lochan
John P. Barratt
Derek E. Gorgi
James L. R. Kelly
Ed C. Kress
Brian D. Lawson
R. Frank Lewarne
Transfer Agent:
CIBC Mellon Trust Company
PO Box 700 Station B
Montreal, QC, Canada

BAMA GOLD CORP.

Suite 1450 - 701 West Georgia Street
Vancouver, BC, V6C 1T4, Canada
Tel.: (604) 689-7422
Fax: (604) 689-7442
Web Site: www.bamagoldcorp.com
Year Founded: 2008
BMA—(TSXV)
Int. Income: $5,874
Assets: $408,265
Liabilities: $657,011
Net Worth: ($248,747)
Earnings: ($1,049,002)
Fiscal Year-end: 06/30/13
Business Description:
Mineral Exploration Services
S.I.C.: 1099
N.A.I.C.S.: 212299
Personnel:
Karl Kottmeier *(CEO)*
Douglas E. Ford *(CFO)*
Board of Directors:
Douglas E. Ford
Karl Kottmeier

BAMBERGER KALIKO GMBH

Kronacher Strasse 59
Bamberg, 96052, Germany
Tel.: (49) 95140990
Fax: (49) 9514099176
E-Mail: info@bamberger-kaliko.de
Web Site: www.bamberger-kaliko.com
Year Founded: 1963
Emp.: 175
Business Description:
Mfr of Industrial Textile Products
S.I.C.: 2299
N.A.I.C.S.: 313210
Personnel:
Peter Klenner *(Mng Dir)*

BAMBI-BANAT AD

Bulevar Mihaila Pupina 115/g New
11070 Belgrade, Serbia
Tel.: (381) 2222 555
Fax: (381) 11 2222 559
E-Mail: office@bambi.rs
Web Site: ukusnidani.bambi.rs
Year Founded: 1967
BMBI—(BEL)
Emp.: 1,013
Business Description:
Snack Food Mfr
S.I.C.: 2096
N.A.I.C.S.: 311919
Personnel:
Miroslav Miletic *(CEO)*

BAMBINO AGRO INDUSTRIES LIMITED

4E Surya Towers Sardar Patel Road
Secunderabad, Andhra Pradesh, 500 003, India
Tel.: (91) 40 44363322
Fax: (91) 40 27816615
E-Mail: feedback@bambinoagro.com
Web Site: www.bambinofood.com
Year Founded: 1982
519295—(BOM)
Rev.: $38,027,140
Assets: $22,214,779
Liabilities: $16,807,216
Net Worth: $5,407,563
Earnings: $611,752
Fiscal Year-end: 09/30/13
Business Description:
Food Product Mfr
S.I.C.: 2099
N.A.I.C.S.: 311999
Personnel:
M. Kishan Rao *(Chm & Mng Dir)*
C. Durga Prasad *(Compliance Officer, Sec & VP)*
Board of Directors:
M. Kishan Rao
P. Easwara Das
Mansoor Yar Khan
M. Raghuveer
S. Nageswara Rao
M. Subramanyam
S. Venkataraman
Transfer Agent:
Karvy Computershare Private Limited
Plot No 17-24 Vittal Rao Nagar Madhapur
Hyderabad, 500 081, India
Tel.: (91) 40 2342 0818

BAMESA ACEROS

Angli 92
08017 Barcelona, Spain
Tel.: (34) 932541950
Fax: (34) 932126910
E-Mail: angli@bamesa.com
Web Site: www.bamesa.com
Emp.: 500
Business Description:
Steel Services
S.I.C.: 3312
N.A.I.C.S.: 331221
Personnel:
Jorge Arasa Masclans *(Founder & Pres)*
Jorge Arasa Figueras *(CEO & Mng Dir)*
Alejandro Quintanilla *(Mng Dir)*

Non-U.S. Subsidiary:

Cofrafer S.A. (1)
8-10 route de Stains
F-94381 Bonneuil-Matours, Cedex, France
Tel.: (33) 145134420
Fax: (33) 149804872
E-Mail: cofrafer@bamesa.com
Emp.: 85
Steel Services
S.I.C.: 5051
N.A.I.C.S.: 423510
J. Raquani *(Dir)*

BAN CORP HOLDINGS PLC

Level 11 191 Queen Street
Auckland, 1010, New Zealand
Tel.: (64) 9 309 8270
Fax: (64) 9 309 8367
E-Mail: admin@bancorp.co.nz
Web Site: www.bancorp.org.nz
4BN—(DEU)
Business Description:
Banking Services
S.I.C.: 6029
N.A.I.C.S.: 522110
Personnel:
Craig Browne *(Mng Dir)*

Non-U.S. Subsidiary:

East & Partners Pty Ltd. (1)
Level 39 2 Park Street
Sydney, NSW, 2000, Australia
Tel.: (61) 2 9004 7848
Fax: (61) 2 9004 7070
E-Mail: info@east.com
Web Site: www.east.com.au
Emp.: 3
Banking Research & Advisory Services
S.I.C.: 6211
N.A.I.C.S.: 523110

BAN JOO & COMPANY LIMITED

26A Circular Road
Singapore, 049381, Singapore
Tel.: (65) 65338338
Fax: (65) 65332596
E-Mail: enq@banjoo.com.sg
Web Site: www.banjoo.com.sg
Year Founded: 1953
B07—(SES)
Sales Range: $10-24.9 Million
Emp.: 815
Business Description:
Textiles & Household Fabrics Mfr & Distr
S.I.C.: 2391
N.A.I.C.S.: 314120
Personnel:
Lee G. Lam *(Chm)*
Hady Hartanto *(Deputy Chm)*
Board of Directors:
Lee G. Lam
Michael Tai Jooi Boon
Tao Yeoh Chi
Pang Joo Chin
Chin Chit
Joseph Sim Soo Chye
Hady Hartanto
Ah Seng Lam
Ivan Pang Joo Lam

BAN LEONG TECHNOLOGIES LIMITED

150 Ubi Avenue 4 Ubi Biz-Hub 04-01
Singapore, 408825, Singapore
Tel.: (65) 65129221
Fax: (65) 67419295
E-Mail: sales@banleong.com.sg
Web Site: www.banleong.com.sg
B26—(SES)
Rev.: $105,911,840
Assets: $46,412,019
Liabilities: $27,036,189
Net Worth: $19,375,830
Earnings: $1,153,567
Emp.: 27
Fiscal Year-end: 03/31/13
Business Description:
Computer Peripheral Distr
S.I.C.: 5045
N.A.I.C.S.: 423430
Personnel:
Ronald Woo Boon Teng *(Mng Dir)*
You Hong Tan *(Deputy Mng Dir)*
Wei Hsiung Lee *(Co-Sec)*
Mi Keay Pan *(Co-Sec)*
Board of Directors:
Hock Huat Chng
Yih Loh
Gim Kiong Neo
Eng Bock Tan
Ronald Woo Boon Teng
Transfer Agent:
M & C Services Private Limited
112 Robinson Road 05-01
Singapore, 068902, Singapore

Subsidiary:

Digital Hub Pte Ltd (1)
No 150 Ubi Avenue 4 Level 4
Singapore, 408825, Singapore
Tel.: (65) 6512 9206
Fax: (65) 6512 9205
E-Mail: sales@digitalhub.com.sg
Web Site: www.digitalhub.com.sg
Multimedia Equipment & Accessories Distr
S.I.C.: 5045
N.A.I.C.S.: 423430

Non-U.S. Subsidiaries:

AUDION INNOVISION PTY LTD (1)
20 Callister Street
Shepparton, VIC, 3630, Australia
Tel.: (61) 358318833
Fax: (61) 358318844
E-Mail: sales@audion-mm.com
Web Site: www.audion-mm.com
Rev.: $50,512,000
Emp.: 30
Multimedia Equipment & Accessories Distr
S.I.C.: 5099
N.A.I.C.S.: 423990

Ban Leong Technologies Sdn Bhd (1)
3 02 Level 3 Wisma Academy 4A Jalan 19/1
46300 Petaling Jaya, Selangor, Malaysia
Tel.: (60) 3 79566300
Fax: (60) 3 79565911
E-Mail: sales@banleong.com.my
Web Site: www.banleong.com.my/desktop/my/index.aspx
Computer Peripheral Equipment Distr
S.I.C.: 5045
N.A.I.C.S.: 423430

BANARAS BEADS LIMITED

A-1 Industrial Estate
Varanasi, 221106, India
Tel.: (91) 542 2370161
Fax: (91) 542 2370165
E-Mail: info@banarasbead.com
Web Site: www.banarasbead.com
Year Founded: 1940
526849—(BOM)
Rev.: $5,445,439
Assets: $8,563,113
Liabilities: $1,506,352
Net Worth: $7,056,761

BANARAS BEADS LIMITED—(Continued)

Earnings: $613,219
Emp.: 284
Fiscal Year-end: 03/31/13

Business Description:
Glass Beads Mfr & Distr
S.I.C.: 3911
N.A.I.C.S.: 339910

Personnel:
Ashok Kumar Gupta *(Chm, CEO & Mng Dir)*
R. K. Singh *(Compliance Officer & Sec)*

Board of Directors:
Ashok Kumar Gupta
Tanmay Deva
Siddharth Gupta
Ashok Kumar Kapoor
Praveen Singh

Transfer Agent:
MAS Services Limited
T-34 2nd Floor Okhla Industrial Area Phase - II
New Delhi, India

BANC METAL INDUSTRIES LTD.

61 Estates Road
Dartmouth, NS, B2Y 4K3, Canada
Tel.: (902) 830-0908
Fax: (902) 482-6501
E-Mail: info@bancmetals.com
Web Site: www.bancmetals.com
Year Founded: 1983
Emp.: 300

Business Description:
Custom Steel & Alloy Products Mfr
S.I.C.: 3462
N.A.I.C.S.: 332111

Personnel:
Besim Halef *(Pres)*

BANCA CARIGE S.P.A.

(d/b/a Gruppo Carige)
Via Cassa Di Risparmio 15
Genoa, Italy
Tel.: (39) 0105791
Fax: (39) 0105794000
E-Mail: carige@carige.it
Web Site: www.carige.it
CRG—(ITA)
Rev.: $1,914,774,708
Assets: $66,400,956,610
Liabilities: $55,098,100,015
Net Worth: $11,302,856,594
Earnings: ($84,155,818)
Emp.: 5,914
Fiscal Year-end: 12/31/12

Business Description:
Banking & Insurance Services
S.I.C.: 6029
N.A.I.C.S.: 522110

Personnel:
Cesare Castelbarco Albani *(Chm)*
Alessandro Scajola *(Deputy Chm)*
Piero Luigi Montani *(CEO)*

Board of Directors:
Cesare Castelbarco Albani
Piergiorgio Alberti
Luca Bonsignore
Remo Angelo Checconi
Ivo De Michelis
Philippe Marie Michel Garsuault
Giovanni Marongiu
Piero Luigi Montani
Paolo Cesare Odone
Guido Pescione
Alessandro Repetto
Lorenzo Roffinella
Alessandro Scajola
Philippe Wattecamps

BANCA CENTRALE DELLA REPUBBLICA DI SAN MARINO

Via del Voltone 120
San Marino, 47890, San Marino
Tel.: (378) 0549 882 325
Fax: (378) 0549 882 328
Web Site: www.bcsm.sm
Emp.: 59

Business Description:
Central Bank
S.I.C.: 6011
N.A.I.C.S.: 521110

Personnel:
Renato Clarizia *(Chm)*
Orietta Berardi *(Vice Chm)*
Daniel Bernardi *(Vice Dir Gen)*
Mario Giannini *(Dir Gen)*

Board of Directors:
Renato Clarizia
Orietta Berardi
Stefano Bizzocchi
Giorgio Lombardi
Marco Mularoni
Aldo Simoncini

BANCA FINNAT EURAMERICA S.P.A.

(d/b/a Gruppo Banca Finnat)
Palazzo Altieri Piazza del Gesu 49
00186 Rome, Italy
Tel.: (39) 06699331
Fax: (39) 066791984
E-Mail: banca@finnat.it
Web Site: www.finnat.it
BFE—(ITA)
Sales Range: $10-24.9 Million
Emp.: 125

Business Description:
Investment, Insurance & Banking Services
S.I.C.: 6712
N.A.I.C.S.: 551111

Personnel:
Giampietro Nattino *(Chm)*
Tommaso Gozzetti *(Vice Chm)*
Angelo Nattino *(Vice Chm)*
Arturo Nattino *(Vice Chm)*

Board of Directors:
Giampietro Nattino
Ermanno Boffa
Leonardo Buonvino
Francesco Caltagirone
Carlo Carlevaris
Tommaso Gozzetti
Enrico Laghi
Angelo Nattino
Arturo Nattino
Ettore Quadrani
Lupo Rattazzi

Subsidiaries:

Calipso SpA (1)
Via Meravigli 3
20123 Milan, Italy (80.3%)
Tel.: (39) 02876836
Fax: (39) 02876821
E-Mail: info@calipso-gbf.it
Web Site: www.calipso-gbf.it
Emp.: 7
Corporate Asset & Liability Solutions
S.I.C.: 6411
N.A.I.C.S.: 524298
Arturo Nattino *(Pres)*
Paolo Chiaia *(CEO)*

Finnat Fiduciaria SpA (1)
Piazza del Gesu 49
00186 Rome, Italy (95%)
Tel.: (39) 066783956
Fax: (39) 0039066796081
Web Site: www.finnat.it
Fiduciary Services
S.I.C.: 6099
N.A.I.C.S.: 523991

Finnat Investments SpA (1)
Piazza Del Gesu 49
00186 Rome, Italy (100%)
Tel.: (39) 0669940038
Fax: (39) 066791984
Web Site: www.finnat.it
Investment Services
S.I.C.: 6211
N.A.I.C.S.: 523110

Finnat Servizi Assicurativi S.r.l. (1)
Viale Liegi 10
00198 Rome, Italy IT
Tel.: (39) 685304484
Fax: (39) 0685304476
E-Mail: info@finnatinsurance.it
Insurance Services
S.I.C.: 6411
N.A.I.C.S.: 524298

Investire Immobiliare SGR S.p.A. (1)
Palazzo Altieri Piazza del Gesu n 49
00186 Rome, Italy IT
Tel.: (39) 06 699 331
Fax: (39) 06 678 4950
E-Mail: info@investireimmobiliare.it
Web Site: www.investireimmobiliaresgr.com
Real Estate Fund Management Services
S.I.C.: 6531
N.A.I.C.S.: 531390

BANCA IFIS S.P.A.

Via Terraglio 63
Mestre, 30174 Venice, Italy
Tel.: (39) 0415027511
Fax: (39) 0415027555
E-Mail: ifis@bancaifis.it
Web Site: www.bancaifis.it
Year Founded: 1983
IF—(ITA)
Rev.: $345,186,258
Assets: $10,936,460,082
Liabilities: $10,518,385,450
Net Worth: $418,074,632
Earnings: $105,103,569
Emp.: 457
Fiscal Year-end: 12/31/12

Business Description:
Financial Services
S.I.C.: 6211
N.A.I.C.S.: 523999

Personnel:
Sebastien Egon Von Furstenberg *(Chm)*
Alessandro Csillaghy *(Deputy Chm)*
Giovanni Bossi *(CEO)*
Carlo Sirombo *(Corp Acctg Reporting Officer)*

Board of Directors:
Sebastien Egon Von Furstenberg
Giovanni Bossi
Leopoldo Conti
Alessandro Csillaghy
Francesca Maderna
Andrea Martin
Riccardo Preve
Marina Salamon

BANCA MONTE DEI PASCHI DI SIENA S.P.A.

(d/b/a GruppoMontePaschi)
Piazza Salimbeni 3
53100 Siena, Italy
Tel.: (39) 0577294111
Telex: 570080
Fax: (39) 055 215 824
E-Mail: info@mps.it
Web Site: www.mps.it
Year Founded: 1472
BMPS—(ITA)
Rev.: $9,034,164,639
Assets: $294,652,610,495
Liabilities: $285,963,606,610
Net Worth: $8,689,003,885
Earnings: ($4,296,865,385)
Emp.: 30,265
Fiscal Year-end: 12/31/12

Business Description:
International Banking, Asset Management, Investment & Insurance Services
S.I.C.: 6029
N.A.I.C.S.: 522110

Personnel:
Alessandro Profumo *(Chm)*
Pietro Giovanni Corsa *(Deputy Chm)*
Marco Turchi *(Deputy Chm)*
Fabrizio Viola *(CEO & Gen Mgr)*
Fabrizio Rossi *(Sr Deputy CEO, Interim COO & Head-HR & Org Dev)*
B. Mingrone *(CFO)*
Antonio Montalbano *(COO)*
Marco Massacesi *(Gen Counsel & Head-Compliance)*

Board of Directors:
Alessandro Profumo
Alberto Giovanni Aleotti
Pietro Giovanni Corsa
Frederic Marie de Courtois d'Arcollieres
Paola Demartini
Angelo Dringoli
Lorenzo Gorgoni
Tania Groppi
Marco Turchi
Fabrizio Viola

Subsidiaries:

Banca Antonveneta S.p.A. (1)
Piazzeta Turati 2
35131 Padua, Italy IT
Tel.: (39) 0496991111
Fax: (39) 0496991800
E-Mail: press@antonveneta.it
Web Site: www.antonveneta.it
Sales Range: $1-4.9 Billion
Emp.: 10,767
Commercial Banking, Asset Management & Insurance Services
S.I.C.: 6029
N.A.I.C.S.: 522110
Daniele Pirondini *(Vice Dir Gen)*
Gilberto Muraro *(Chm-Foundation)*

BANCA NATIONALA A MOLDOVEI

7 Renasterii Avenue
2006 Chisinau, Moldova
Tel.: (373) 22221679
Web Site: www.bnm.org

Business Description:
Banking Services
S.I.C.: 6011
N.A.I.C.S.: 521110

Personnel:
Dorin Draqutanu *(Governor & Chm)*
Marin Molosag *(First Deputy Governor & Deputy Chm)*
Galina Balanov *(Comptroller & Gen Dir-Audit)*

Board of Directors:
Dorin Draqutanu
Marin Molosag
Emma Tabirta

BANCA POPOLARE DELL'EMILIA ROMAGNA

Via San Carlo 20
41121 Modena, Italy
Tel.: (39) 0592021111
Fax: (39) 0592022033
E-Mail: bpergroup@bper.it
Web Site: www.bper.it
BPE—(ITA)
Rev.: $2,956,793,750
Assets: $82,974,900,687
Liabilities: $76,563,022,976
Net Worth: $6,411,877,711
Earnings: ($43,882,450)
Emp.: 11,834
Fiscal Year-end: 12/31/12

Business Description:
Banking Services
S.I.C.: 6712
N.A.I.C.S.: 551111

Personnel:
Ettore Caselli *(Chm)*
Giosue Boldrini *(Vice Chm)*
Piero Ferrari *(Vice Chm)*
Alberto Marri *(Vice Chm)*
Luigi Odorici *(CEO & Mng Dir)*
Gian Enrico Venturini *(Sec Gen)*

Board of Directors:
Ettore Caselli
Antonio Angelo Arru
Giosue Boldrini
Giulio Cicognani
Piero Ferrari
Pietro Ferrari
Elisabetta Gualandri
Manfredi Luongo
Giuseppe Lusignani
Alberto Marri
Valeriana Maria Masperi
Giuseppina Mengano
Fioravante Montanari
Luigi Odorici
Daniela Petitto
Deanna Rossi
Erminio Spallanzani
Angelo Tantazzi

Subsidiaries:

Banca C.R.V.-Cassa di Risparmio di Vignola S.p.A. (1)
Viale Mazzini 1
41058 Vignola, Italy (100%)
Tel.: (39) 059777111
Fax: (39) 059760855
E-Mail: marketing@bancacrv.it
Web Site: www.bancacrv.it
Emp.: 300
Business Services
S.I.C.: 7389
N.A.I.C.S.: 561499
Franco Rabitti *(Pres)*
Franco Crotali *(Gen Dir)*

Banca del Monte di Foggia S.p.A. (1)
Corso Garibaldi 72
Foggia, 71100 Naples, Italy
Tel.: (39) 0881710111
Fax: (39) 0881710399
E-Mail: info@bancacampania.it
Web Site: www.bancacampania.it
Financial Investment Services
S.I.C.: 6211
N.A.I.C.S.: 523999
Francesco Fornaro *(Gen Dir)*

Banca della Campania S.p.A. (1)
Localita Collina Liguorini Centro Direzionale
83100 Avellino, Italy
Tel.: (39) 0825651111
Fax: (39) 0825656273
E-Mail: info@bancacampania.it
Web Site: www.bancacampania.it
Emp.: 1,000
Commercial Banking
S.I.C.: 6029
N.A.I.C.S.: 522110
Francesco Fornaro *(Gen Dir)*

Banca di Sassari S.p.A. (1)
Viale Mancini 2
07100 Sassari, Italy
Tel.: (39) 079221511
Web Site: www.bancasassari.it
Emp.: 71
Commercial Banking
S.I.C.: 6029
N.A.I.C.S.: 522110
Giorgio Mario Ledda *(Pres)*
Fabrizio Togni *(Gen Dir)*

Banca Popolare di Aprilia S.p.A. (1)
Piazza Roma
04011 Aprilia, Italy
Tel.: (39) 069286251
Fax: (39) 069275940
E-Mail: contattaci@popaprilia.it
Web Site: www.popaprilia.it
Emp.: 200
Savings Institutions
S.I.C.: 6036
N.A.I.C.S.: 522120
Emilio Vescovi *(Pres)*

Banca Popolare di Crotone S.p.A. (1)
Via Panella
Crotone, 88074 Calabria, Italy
Tel.: (39) 0962933111
E-Mail: infobpc@bpcbank.it
Web Site: www.bpcbank.it
Commercial Banking
S.I.C.: 6029
N.A.I.C.S.: 522110
Francesco Antonio Lucifero *(Pres)*
Franco Corigliano *(Gen Dir)*
Andrea Molinaro *(Gen Dir)*

Banca Popolare di Lanciano e Sulmona S.p.A. (1)
Viale Cappuccini 76
Lanciano, Chieti, 66034, Italy
Tel.: (39) 08 727041
Fax: (39) 0872 70 42 46
E-Mail: info@bpls.it
Commercial Banking Services
S.I.C.: 6029
N.A.I.C.S.: 522110

Banca Popolare di Ravenna S.p.A. (1)
Via Arnaldo Guerrini 14
Ravenna, Italy (75%)
Tel.: (39) 0544540111
E-Mail: bpr@bpr.it
Web Site: www.bpr.it
Emp.: 400
Commercial Banking
S.I.C.: 6029
N.A.I.C.S.: 522110
Piergiorgio Giuliani *(Gen Dir)*
Roberto Vitti *(Gen Dir)*

Banco di Sardegna S.p.A. (1)
Viale Umberto 36
07100 Sassari, Italy IT
Tel.: (39) 079226000 (51%)
Fax: (39) 079226015
Web Site: www.bancosardegna.it
BNDS—(ITA)
Sales Range: $550-599.9 Million
Emp.: 3,739
Banking Services
S.I.C.: 6029
N.A.I.C.S.: 522110
Franco Antonio Farina *(Pres)*

Subsidiaries:

NUMERA Sistemi e Informatica S.p.A. (2)
Predda Niedda Nord - Strada 6
7100 Sassari, Italy
Tel.: (39) 079 223194
Fax: (39) 079 237967
E-Mail: info@numera.it
Information Technology Consulting Services
S.I.C.: 7373
N.A.I.C.S.: 541512

Sardaleasing S.p.A. (2)
Via IV Novembre 27Sassari
Sassari, 7100, Italy
Tel.: (39) 079 289000
Fax: (39) 079 289011
E-Mail: commerciale@sardaleasing.it
Financial Services
S.I.C.: 6211
N.A.I.C.S.: 523999

BPER Services S.C.p.A. (1)
16 Via Sorrentino Andrea
84013 Cava de Tirreni, Italy
Tel.: (39) 0894 689 711
Fax: (39) 089444 252
Information Technology Consulting Services
S.I.C.: 7373
N.A.I.C.S.: 541512

Cassa di Risparmio della Provincia dell Aquila S.p.A. (1)
Corso Vittorio Emanuele II 48
67100 L'Aquila, Italy
Tel.: (39) 08626491
Fax: (39) 0862649250
E-Mail: infocarispaq@carispaq.it
Web Site: www.carispaq.it
Emp.: 48
Savings Institutions
S.I.C.: 6035
N.A.I.C.S.: 522120
Antonio Battaglia *(Pres)*
Rinaldo Tordera *(Gen Dir)*

EMIL-RO LEASING S.p.A. (1)
Strada Maggiore 29
Bologna, Italy
Tel.: (39) 0516482111
Fax: (39) 0516482199
E-Mail: leasing@emilro.it
Financial Leasing Services
S.I.C.: 6159
N.A.I.C.S.: 522220

EMILIA ROMAGNA FACTOR S.p.A. (1)
Strada Maggiore 29
40125 Bologna, Italy
Tel.: (39) 05 16 48 21 11
Fax: (39) 051 26 75 57
E-Mail: commerciale@emilro.it
Web Site: www.emilro.it
Emp.: 30
Factoring Services
S.I.C.: 6159
N.A.I.C.S.: 522298
Paolo Licciardello *(Gen Mgr)*

Em.Ro. popolare S.p.A. (1)
Via San Carlo 8/20
Modena, 41100, Italy
Tel.: (39) 0592021111
Fax: (39) 0592022033
Commercial Banking Services
S.I.C.: 6029
N.A.I.C.S.: 522110
Guido Leoni *(Mng Dir)*

Subsidiary:

Forum Guido Monzani s.r.l. (2)
Via Aristotele 33
41126 Modena, Italy
Tel.: (39) 059 2021093
Fax: (39) 059 2021094
E-Mail: info@forumguidomonzani.it
Telecommunication Equipment Distr
S.I.C.: 5065
N.A.I.C.S.: 423690

Meliorbanca SpA (1)
Via Gaetano Negri No 10
20123 Milan, Italy IT
Tel.: (39) 02290228
Fax: (39) 0229022529
E-Mail:
Web Site: www.bper.it
Sales Range: $150-199.9 Million
Emp.: 475
Banking Services
S.I.C.: 6029
N.A.I.C.S.: 522110
Giovanni Ascari *(Chm)*
Enrico Maria Fagioli Marzocchi *(Deputy Chm)*

Subsidiaries:

Gallo & C SpA (2)
Via Borromei 5
20123 Milan, Italy
Tel.: (39) 02290221
Fax: (39) 0229022561
Investment Banking
S.I.C.: 6211
N.A.I.C.S.: 523110

MeliorConsulting SpA (2)
Via Bissolati 54
00187 Rome, Italy
Tel.: (39) 06 68488380
Fax: (39) 06 68488315
Consulting Services
S.I.C.: 8748
N.A.I.C.S.: 541618

Meliorfactor SpA (2)
Via Gaetano Negri 10
20123 Milan, Italy
Tel.: (39) 02290228
Fax: (39) 0229022560
Web Site: www.meliorbanca.it
Banking & Asset Management Services
S.I.C.: 6211
N.A.I.C.S.: 523110

Sistemi Parabancari SpA (2)
Via Anton Cechov 50/2
20151 Milan, Italy
Tel.: (39) 02 3001101
Fax: (39) 02 300110244
Web Site: www.sistemiparabancari.it/pagine/contatti.htm
Banking Services
S.I.C.: 6029
N.A.I.C.S.: 522110

Affiliates:

Banca della Nuova Terra (2)
via Cechov 50/2
Milan, 20151, Italy
Tel.: (39) 023035251
Fax: (39) 02 30352573
E-Mail: infobanca@bancanuovaterra.it
Web Site: www.bancanuovaterra.it
Financial Services
S.I.C.: 6029
N.A.I.C.S.: 522110

Melior Trust SpA (2)
iale Bruno Buozzi 98
Rome, 00197, Italy
Tel.: (39) 06 3211945
Fax: (39) 06 3211945
Fiduciary Trust Services
S.I.C.: 6091
N.A.I.C.S.: 523991

Modena Terminal S.r.l. (1)
Piazzale Delle Nazioni 14
41011 Campogalliano, Modena, Italy
Tel.: (39) 059 52 55 54
Fax: (39) 059 52 77 07
E-Mail: info@modenaterminal.it
Material Handling & Storage Services
S.I.C.: 4225
N.A.I.C.S.: 493110

Nadia S.p.A. (1)
140 Via Danimarca
41122 Modena, Italy
Tel.: (39) 0593 162 011
Commercial Banking Services
S.I.C.: 6029
N.A.I.C.S.: 522110

Optima SGR S.p.A. (1)
Via Camperio 8
Milan, 20123, Italy
Tel.: (39) 02 72265237
Fax: (39) 02 72265230
E-Mail: segreteria@optimasgr.it
Asset Management Services
S.I.C.: 6282
N.A.I.C.S.: 523920

Presticinque S.p.A. (1)
Viale Shakespeare 47
144 Rome, Italy
Tel.: (39) 06 54 52 51 20
Fax: (39) 06 54 52 51 33
E-Mail: info@presticinque.it
Investment Management Services
S.I.C.: 6211
N.A.I.C.S.: 523999

Non-U.S. Subsidiaries:

Banca Popolare dell'Emilia Romagna (Europe) International S.A. (1)
Sede Sociale 30 Blvd Royal
2012 Luxembourg, Luxembourg (99%)
Tel.: (352) 2224301
Fax: (352) 474887
E-Mail: bperlux@pt.lu
Web Site: www.pt.lu
Emp.: 10
Financial Transactions Processing Reserve & Clearinghouse Services
S.I.C.: 6099
N.A.I.C.S.: 522320
Enrico Gorla *(Mng Dir)*

EMRO Finance Ireland Limited (1)
AIB International Centre IFSC
Dublin, Ireland
Tel.: (353) 1 6700895
Fax: (353) 1 6700896
E-Mail: info@emrofinance.ie
Web Site: www.emrofinance.ie
Emp.: 10
Financial Management Services
S.I.C.: 6211
N.A.I.C.S.: 523999
Paolo Zanni *(Gen Mgr)*

BANCA POPOLARE DELL'ETRURIA E DEL LAZIO S.C.

Via Calamandrei 255
52100 Arezzo, Italy
Tel.: (39) 05753371
Fax: (39) 57526829
E-Mail: investor.relation@bancaetruria.it
Web Site: www.bancaetruria.it
Year Founded: 1882
PEL—(ITA)

Banca Popolare dell'Etruria e del Lazio S.C.—(Continued)

Rev.: $623,263,248
Assets: $19,785,694,349
Liabilities: $17,732,475,480
Net Worth: $2,053,218,869
Earnings: ($273,872,902)
Emp.: 1,743
Fiscal Year-end: 12/31/12

Business Description:
Banking Services
S.I.C.: 6029
N.A.I.C.S.: 522110

Personnel:
Giuseppe Fornasari *(Chm)*
Giovanni Inghirami *(Sr Deputy Chm)*
Lorenzo Rosi *(Vice Chm)*

Board of Directors:
Giuseppe Fornasari
Alfredo Berni
Alberto Bonaiti
Luigi Bonollo
Pier Luigi Boschi
Claudia Bugno
Giovan Battista Cirianni
Giampaolo Crenca
Enrico Fazzini
Giovanni Inghirami
Luciano Nataloni
Andrea Orlandi
Lorenzo Rosi
Felice Emilio Santonastaso

Subsidiaries:

Banca Popolare Lecchese SpA **(1)**
Piazza Manzoni angolo Via Azzone Visconti
23900 Lecco, Italy
Tel.: (39) 0341 357511
Fax: (39) 341282478
E-Mail: segreteria.generale@bppl.it
Web Site: www.bppl.it
Emp.: 41
Commercial Banking Services
S.I.C.: 6029
N.A.I.C.S.: 522110
Alberto Bonaiti *(Mgr)*

Etruria Informatica Srl **(1)**
Via Calamandrei 255
52100 Arezzo, Italy
Tel.: (39) 0575 398255
Fax: (39) 0575 398280
Software Development Services
S.I.C.: 7371
N.A.I.C.S.: 541511

BANCA POPOLARE DI MILANO S.P.A.

Piazza Filippo Meda 4
20121 Milan, Italy
Tel.: (39) 0277001
Telex: 333043/333053 Popban I
Fax: (39) 02 7700 2993
Web Site: www.bpm.it
Year Founded: 1865
PMI—(ITA LUX OTC)
Rev.: $2,086,178,495
Assets: $70,640,277,481
Liabilities: $64,656,847,988
Net Worth: $5,983,429,493
Earnings: ($578,441,172)
Emp.: 8,467
Fiscal Year-end: 12/31/12

Business Description:
Domestic & International Banking, Real Estate & Corporate Financial Services
S.I.C.: 6029
N.A.I.C.S.: 522110

Personnel:
Andrea C. Bonomi *(Chm)*
Piero Luigi Montani *(CEO)*
Giovanni Sordello *(COO)*
Iacapo De Francisco *(Chief Comml Officer)*
Paolo Testi *(Chief Lending Officer)*
Carlo Gagliardi *(Gen Counsel)*

Board of Directors:
Andrea C. Bonomi
Davide Croff
Alessandro Foti
Piero Luigi Montani
Dante Razzano

Subsidiaries:

Banca di Legnano S.p.A. **(1)**
Largo Franco Tosi 9
20025 Legnano, MI, Italy
Tel.: (39) 331521111
Fax: (39) 0331521310
E-Mail: info@bancadilegnano.it
Web Site: www.bancadilegnano.it
Banking Services
S.I.C.: 6099
N.A.I.C.S.: 522320

Bipiemme Fiduciaria Spa **(1)**
Galleria De Cristoforis 1
20121 Milan, Italy (100%)
Tel.: (39) 277005106
Fax: (39) 277005107
Fiduciary Services
S.I.C.: 6091
N.A.I.C.S.: 523991

Affiliates:

SelmaBipiemme Leasing S.p.A. **(1)**
Via Luisa Battistotti Sassi 11 A
20133 Milan, Italy (38.35%)
Tel.: (39) 02748221
Telex: 340579
Fax: (39) 0270005136
E-Mail: info@selmabipiemme.it
Web Site: www.selmabipiemme.it
Emp.: 80
Leasing Services
S.I.C.: 7359
N.A.I.C.S.: 532490

BANCA POPOLARE DI SONDRIO

Piazza Garibaldi 16
23100 Sondrio, Italy
Tel.: (39) 0342528111
Fax: (39) 0342528204
E-Mail: info@popso.it
Web Site: www.popso.it
Year Founded: 1871
BPSO—(ITA)
Rev.: $1,362,906,932
Assets: $43,547,422,947
Liabilities: $40,935,803,339
Net Worth: $2,611,619,608
Earnings: $54,093,149
Emp.: 2,569
Fiscal Year-end: 12/31/12

Business Description:
Banking & Financial Services
S.I.C.: 6029
N.A.I.C.S.: 522110

Personnel:
Piero Melazzini *(Chm)*
Miles Emilio Negri *(Deputy Chm)*
Francesco Venosta *(Deputy Chm)*
Mario Alberto Pedranzini *(Mng Dir & Gen Mgr)*
Maurizio Bertoletti *(Fin Reporting Officer)*

Board of Directors:
Piero Melazzini
Claudio Benedetti
Paolo Biglioli
Nicolo Melzi di Cusana
Federico Falck
Attilio Piero Ferrari
Giuseppe Fontana
Mario Galbusera
Miles Emilio Negri
Mario Alberto Pedranzini
Adriano Propersi
Renato Sozzani
Lino Enrico Stoppani
Domenico Triacca
Francesco Venosta

Subsidiary:

Factorit S.p.A. **(1)**
Via cino del duca 12
IT-20122 Milan, Italy IT
Tel.: (39) 02581501 (100%)
Fax: (39) 0258150205
E-Mail: info@factorit.it
Web Site: www.factorit.it
Emp.: 20
Corporate Loan Services
S.I.C.: 6159
N.A.I.C.S.: 522298
Antonio De Martini *(Chm)*

Non-U.S. Subsidiary:

Banca Popolare di Sondrio (SUISSE) S.A. **(1)**
Via Maggio 1
6900 Lugano, Switzerland
Tel.: (41) 588553100
Fax: (41) 588553115
E-Mail: contact@bps-suisse.ch
Web Site: www.bps-suisse.ch
Emp.: 150
Banking Service
S.I.C.: 6211
N.A.I.C.S.: 523110
Piero Melazzini *(Pres)*

BANCA POPOLARE DI SPOLETO S.P.A.

Piazza Luigi Pianciani 5
06049 Spoleto, Italy
Tel.: (39) 07432151
Fax: (39) 0743215390
E-Mail: dir_investor_relator@bpspoleto.it
Web Site: www.bpspoleto.it
SPO—(ITA)
Sales Range: $200-249.9 Million
Emp.: 686

Business Description:
Banking Services
S.I.C.: 6029
N.A.I.C.S.: 522110

Personnel:
Giovannino Antonini *(Chm)*

Board of Directors:
Giovannino Antonini
Aldo Amoni
Paolo Arcelli
Claudio Bernardini
Marco Carbonari
Gabriele Chiocci
Valentino Conti
Nazzareno D'Atanasio
Francesco Di Bello
Mario Fagotti
Michele Logi
Claudio Umbrico

Subsidiary:

Spoleto Credito E Servizi **(1)**
Via Porta Fuga 4
Perugia, Spoleto, 06049, Italy (53.11%)
Tel.: (39) 074349817
Fax: (39) 074349623
E-Mail: info@grupposcs.it
Web Site: www.grupposcs.it
Financial Services
S.I.C.: 6099
N.A.I.C.S.: 522320

BANCA PRIVADA D'ANDORRA, SA

Av Carlemany 119
AD700 Escaldes-Engordany, Andorra
Tel.: (376) 873500
Fax: (376) 376873515
E-Mail: bpa@bpa.ad
Web Site: www.bpa.ad
Year Founded: 1958
Rev.: $18,000,000
Emp.: 149

Business Description:
Banking Services
S.I.C.: 6029
N.A.I.C.S.: 522110

Personnel:
Higini Cierco Noguer *(Chm)*

Board of Directors:
Higini Cierco Noguer
Roser Noguer Enriquez
Julia Bonet Fite
Luis-Cesar Jayme Garcia-Salcedo
Joan Pau Miguel Prats
Ramon Cierco Noguer
Bonaventura Riberaygua Sasplugas

Subsidiaries:

BPA Assegurances, SA **(1)**
Calle de la Unio 3 1r
AD700 Escaldes-Engordany, Andorra (100%)
Tel.: (376) 873555
Fax: (376) 873 557
Web Site: www.bpa.ad
Insurance Services
S.I.C.: 6411
N.A.I.C.S.: 524298

BPA Fons, SA **(1)**
Aravina Cafef Unio 3
AD 500 Andorra La Vella, Andorra (100%)
Tel.: (376) 808696
Fax: (376) 873525
E-Mail: bpa@bpa.ad
Web Site: www.bpa.ib
Emp.: 50
Fund Management Services
S.I.C.: 6722
N.A.I.C.S.: 525910
Ramon Cierco Noguer *(Pres)*

BPA Gestio, SA **(1)**
Calle de la Unio 3 5a
AD700 Escaldes-Engordany, Andorra (100%)
Tel.: (376) 873500
Fax: (376) 873515
Financial Services
S.I.C.: 6211
N.A.I.C.S.: 523999
Ramon Cierco Noguer *(Chm)*

BPA Serveis, SA **(1)**
119 Carlamin Ave
AD700 Escaldes-Engordany, Andorra (100%)
Tel.: (376) 876359
Fax: (376) 876435
E-Mail: bpa@bpa.ad
Web Site: www.bpa.ad
Emp.: 200
Business Services
S.I.C.: 7389
N.A.I.C.S.: 561499
Ramon Cierco Noguer *(Pres)*

BANCA PROFILO S.P.A.

Corso Italia 49
20122 Milan, Italy
Tel.: (39) 02584081
Fax: (39) 0258301590
E-Mail: comunicazione@bancaprofilo.it
Web Site: www.bancaprofilo.it
Year Founded: 1992
PRO—(ITA LSE)
Sales Range: $10-24.9 Million
Emp.: 202

Business Description:
Retail & Investment Banking Services
Export
S.I.C.: 6211
N.A.I.C.S.: 523110

Personnel:
Matteo Arpe *(Pres)*
Fabio Candeli *(Mng Dir)*

Board of Directors:
Matteo Arpe
Guido Bastianini
Fabio Candeli
Giorgio Di Giorgio
Giacomo Garbuglia
Ramzi Hijazi
Carlo Felice Maggi
Umberto Paolucci
Carlo Puri Negri

Luigi Spaventa
Renzo Torchiani

BANCA TRANSILVANIA S.A.
8 G Baritiu Str
400027 Cluj-Napoca, Romania
Tel.: (40) 264407150
Fax: (40) 264407179
E-Mail: piatacapital@bancatransilvania.ro
Web Site: www.bancatransilvania.ro
TLV—(BUC)
Int. Income: $632,154,713
Assets: $9,141,540,785
Liabilities: $8,275,418,201
Net Worth: $866,122,584
Earnings: $106,597,582
Emp.: 6,780
Fiscal Year-end: 12/31/12
Business Description:
Banking & Financial Services
S.I.C.: 6211
N.A.I.C.S.: 523110
Personnel:
Horia Ciorcila *(Chm)*
Roberto Marzanati *(Vice Chm)*
Nicolae Tarcea *(Deputy CEO)*
Board of Directors:
Horia Ciorcila
Costel Ceocea
Peter Franklin
Roberto Marzanati
Radu Palagheanu
Carmen Retegan
Subsidiaries:

BT Finop Leasing S.A. (1)
43 Sos Bucuresti-Ploiesti
013685 Bucharest, Romania
Tel.: (40) 213088008
Fax: (40) 212692100
E-Mail: finop@bt-finopleasing.ro
Web Site: www.bt-finopleasing.ro
Emp.: 15
Operational Leasing Services
S.I.C.: 6141
N.A.I.C.S.: 522220

BT Investments S.R.L. (1)
B-Dul Eroilor 36
Cluj-Napoca, Cluj, Romania
Tel.: (40) 264407150
Fax: (40) 264407179
Financial Investment Services
S.I.C.: 6282
N.A.I.C.S.: 523930

BT Leasing Transilvania IFN S.A. (1)
G Baritiu 1 etaj 1
Cluj-Napoca, Cluj, Romania
Tel.: (40) 264438816
Fax: (40) 264444150
E-Mail: office@btleasing.ro
Web Site: www.btleasing.ro
Emp.: 100
Vehicles Financial Leasing Services
S.I.C.: 6726
N.A.I.C.S.: 525990
Titus-Liviu Nicoara *(Mng Dir)*
Simona Sopon *(Mng Dir)*

BT Securities S.A. (1)
Maestro Business Center 104 21 Decembrie
1989 Blvd 1st Floor, Cluj-Napoca, Cluj, Romania
Tel.: (40) 26 443 0564
Fax: (40) 26 443 1718
E-Mail: office@btsecurities.ro
Web Site: www.btsecurities.ro
Emp.: 60
Financial Investment Services
S.I.C.: 6282
N.A.I.C.S.: 523930
Ionut Octavian Patrahau *(Chm)*

Rent-a-Med S.R.L. (1)
Bucharest Ploiesti 43
Bucharest, 013685, Romania
Tel.: (40) 212226508
Fax: (40) 212226504
E-Mail: office@btml.co.ro
Emp.: 10
Financial Investment Services
S.I.C.: 6282
N.A.I.C.S.: 523930
Iona Misculcu *(Gen Mgr)*

Non-U.S. Subsidiary:

BT Leasing MD SRL (1)
Chisinau Republica Moldova Str
A Puskin nr 60/2, Chisinau, MD-2005, Moldova
Tel.: (373) 22260780
Fax: (373) 22260791
E-Mail: contact@btleasing.md
Web Site: www.btleasing.md
Emp.: 11
Consumer Lending Services
S.I.C.: 6141
N.A.I.C.S.: 522291
Vasile Tomita *(Dir-Admin)*

BANCO ALFA DE INVESTIMENTO SA
Al Santos 466
Cerqueira Cesar, Sao Paulo, 01418-000, Brazil
Tel.: (55) 11 4004 3344
Fax: (55) 11 3175 5026
E-Mail: alfanet@alfanet.com.br
Web Site: www.alfanet.com.br
Year Founded: 1925
BRIV3—(BRAZ)
Sales Range: $100-124.9 Million
Business Description:
Banking Services
S.I.C.: 6029
N.A.I.C.S.: 522110
Personnel:
Adilson Herrero *(Dir-IR)*

BANCO ALIADO, S.A.
Urbanizacion Obarrio 50th & 56th Streets
PO Box 0831-02109
Panama, Panama
Tel.: (507) 302 1555
Fax: (507) 302 1556
E-Mail: bkaliado@bancoaliado.com
Web Site: www.bancoaliado.com
Year Founded: 1992
BALI—(PAN)
Emp.: 122
Business Description:
Banking Services
S.I.C.: 6029
N.A.I.C.S.: 522110
Personnel:
L. Alexis A. Arjona *(Sr VP & Gen Mgr)*
R. Maria del Rosario Fabrega *(Sr VP & Deputy Gen Mgr)*
H. Gabriel E. Diaz *(Sr VP-Fin)*
Subsidiaries:

Aliado Factoring, S.A. (1)
Calle 50 y 56 Obarrio Edificio Banco Aliado 1er Piso
Apartado Postal 0831-02109
Panama, Panama
Tel.: (507) 302 1600
Fax: (507) 214 7124
Web Site: www.bancoaliado.com
AFAC—(PAN)
Emp.: 10
Financial Services
S.I.C.: 6211
N.A.I.C.S.: 523999
Moises Chreim Sasson *(Pres)*

Aliado Leasing, S.A. (1)
Edifico Banco Aliado 1er Piso Calle 50 y 56 Obarrio
Apartado Postal 0831-02109
Panama, Panama
Tel.: (507) 302 1600
Fax: (507) 214 7124
Web Site: www.bancoaliado.com
ALBR—(PAN)
Emp.: 7
Financial Services
S.I.C.: 6211
N.A.I.C.S.: 523999
Moises Chreim Sasson *(Pres)*

Financiera Davivienda, S.A. (1)
Edificio 37-20 Calle 37 Perejil y Avenida Peru
Apartado Postal 0832-2671
Panama, Panama
Tel.: (507) 209 2460
Fax: (507) 209 2489
Web Site: www.bancoaliado.com
FDAV—(PAN)
Emp.: 15
Financial Services
S.I.C.: 6211
N.A.I.C.S.: 523999
Moises Chreim Sasson *(Pres)*

BANCO BIC PORTUGUES S.A.
Av Antonio Augusto Aguiar no 132 6 piso
1250050 Lisbon, Portugal
Tel.: (351) 210 944 497
Web Site: www.bancobic.pt
Year Founded: 2008
Business Description:
Corporate & Investment Banking
S.I.C.: 6211
N.A.I.C.S.: 523110
Personnel:
Fernando Teles *(Chm)*
Board of Directors:
Fernando Teles
Luis Mira Amaral
Americo Amorim
Diogo Barrote
Isabel dos Santos
Artur Marques
Jaime Pereira
Carlos Traguelho

BANCO BILBAO VIZCAYA ARGENTARIA, S.A.
(d/b/a BBVA)
Plaza de San Nicolas 4
48005 Bilbao, Spain
Tel.: (34) 94 487 6000
Fax: (34) 94 374 7730
E-Mail: comunica@grupobbva.com
Web Site: www.bbva.com
Year Founded: 1999
BBVA—(LSE MAD NYSE)
Int. Income: $35,353,116,540
Assets: $858,567,033,450
Liabilities: $799,602,095,110
Net Worth: $58,964,938,340
Earnings: $3,132,537,590
Emp.: 115,852
Fiscal Year-end: 12/31/12
Business Description:
International Financial & Banking Services
S.I.C.: 6029
N.A.I.C.S.: 522110
Personnel:
Francisco Gonzalez Rodriguez *(Chm & CEO)*
Angel Cano Fernandez *(Pres & COO)*
Manuel Gonzalez Cid *(CFO)*
Domingo Armengol *(Sec)*
Board of Directors:
Francisco Gonzalez Rodriguez
Tomas Alfaro Drake
Juan Carlos Alvarez Mezquiriz
Ramon Bustamante y de la Mora
Jose Antonio Fernandez Rivero
Angel Cano Fernandez
Jose Luis Palao Garcia-Suelto
Belen Garijo Lopez
Jose Manuel Gonzalez-Paramo Martinez-Murillo
Ignacio Ferrero Jordi
Carlos Loring Martinez de Irujo
Enrique Medina Fernandez
Juan Pi Llorens
Susana Rodriguez Vidarte
Subsidiaries:

Anida Desarrollos Inmobilarios, S.L. (1)
Calle Julian Camarillo 4
Madrid, 28037, Spain ES
Tel.: (34) 913746742
Fax: (34) 913744001
Real Estate Development Services
S.I.C.: 6531
N.A.I.C.S.: 531390
Sainz Rubio Francisco Javier *(Gen Mgr)*

Banco Depositario BBVA, S.A. (1)
Calle Clara Del Rey 26 Paseo De Lasacastell Ana No 8
Madrid, 28002, Spain ES
Tel.: (34) 915377000
Fax: (34) 915564010
Commercial Banking Services
S.I.C.: 6029
N.A.I.C.S.: 522110

BBV America, S.L. (1)
Paseo Castellana 81
Madrid, 28046, Spain ES
Tel.: (34) 915377000
Investment Management Services
S.I.C.: 6211
N.A.I.C.S.: 523999

BBVA Servicios, S.A. (1)
Monforte De Lemos
Madrid, 28029, Spain ES
Tel.: (34) 913746417
Fax: (34) 913744339
Emp.: 3
Consumer Goods Distr
S.I.C.: 5199
N.A.I.C.S.: 424990
Fernando de la Rica *(CEO)*

El Milanillo, S.A. (1)
Cl Factor 5
Madrid, 28013, Spain ES
Tel.: (34) 918 900 459
Real Estate Development Services
S.I.C.: 6531
N.A.I.C.S.: 531390

Europea de Titulizacion, S.A., S.G.F.T. (1)
Sociedad Gestora de Fondos de Titulizacion Lagasca 120 1
28006 Madrid, Spain
Tel.: (34) 914 118 467
Fax: (34) 914 118 468
E-Mail: info@eurotitulizacion.com
Web Site: www.edt-sg.com
Fund Management Services
S.I.C.: 6799
N.A.I.C.S.: 523920
Sergio Fernandez-Pacheco Ruiz-Villar *(Chm)*
Pedro Maria Urresti Laca *(Vice Chm)*
Belen Rico Arevalo *(Sec)*

Finanzia AutoRenting, S.A. (1)
Almogavers St No 183 185 2nd Fl
Barcelona, 08010, Spain ES
Tel.: (34) 902117300
Fax: (34) 902200434
Automotive Financial Leasing Services
S.I.C.: 6141
N.A.I.C.S.: 522220

Inverahorro, S.L. (1)
Paseo Castellana 81
Madrid, 28046, Spain ES
Tel.: (34) 915377000
Investment Management Services
S.I.C.: 6211
N.A.I.C.S.: 523999

Sport Club 18, S.A. (1)
Paseo Castellana 81
Madrid, 28046, Spain ES
Tel.: (34) 915377000
Real Estate Development Services
S.I.C.: 6531
N.A.I.C.S.: 531390

Affiliates:

Banca Catalana (1)
Avda Diagonal 662 664
08034 Barcelona, Spain (100%)
Tel.: (34) 934014232

Banco Bilbao Vizcaya Argentaria, S.A.—(Continued)

Fax: (34) 934014100
Web Site: www.bbva.com
Investment Banking Services
S.I.C.: 6211
N.A.I.C.S.: 523110

BBV Privanza (1)
Padilla 17
28006 Madrid, Spain (100%)
Tel.: (34) 913748700
Fax: (34) 915768394
Web Site: www.bbva.es
Emp.: 100
Investment Banking Services
S.I.C.: 6211
N.A.I.C.S.: 523110

Units:

BBV Bilbao (1)
Gran Via 1
48001 Bilbao, Spain (100%)
Tel.: (34) 944876000
Fax: (34) 944876161
E-Mail: info@grupobbva.com
Web Site: www.bbva.com
Emp.: 1,000
Investment Banking Services
S.I.C.: 6211
N.A.I.C.S.: 523110
Francisco Gonzalez *(Pres)*

BBV Interactivos (1)
Clara Del Rey 26
Madrid, 28002, Spain (100%)
Tel.: (34) 913748515, ext. 913747368
Fax: (34) 915379726
Web Site: www.bbva.com
Emp.: 1,000
Investment Banking Services
S.I.C.: 6211
N.A.I.C.S.: 523110

BBV Madrid (1)
Paseo De La Castellana 81
28046 Madrid, Spain (100%)
Tel.: (34) 913746000
Fax: (34) 913746202
Web Site: www.bbva.com
Emp.: 100
Investment Banking Services
S.I.C.: 6211
N.A.I.C.S.: 523110
Francisco G. Rodriguez *(Pres)*

U.S. Subsidiaries:

BBVA Compass Bancshares, Inc. (1)
15 20th St S Ste 100
Birmingham, AL 35233 AL
Tel.: (205) 933-3000
Web Site: www.bbvacompass.com
Bank Holding Company
S.I.C.: 6712
N.A.I.C.S.: 551111
Manolo Sanchez *(Chm)*
William C. Helms *(Vice Chm)*
Gabriel Sanchez Iniesta *(CIO-BBVA Compass)*
Peggy Holt *(Exec VP)*
Jeffrey Hauser *(Sr VP & Mgr-Relationship-Large Middle Market)*

Subsidiaries:

Compass Bank (2)
15 S 20th St
Birmingham, AL 35233-2000 AL
Mailing Address:
PO Box 10566
Birmingham, AL 35296-0002
Tel.: (205) 297-3000
Fax: (205) 297-7836
Toll Free: (800) 239-2265
E-Mail: feedback@compassweb.com
Web Site: www.bbvacompass.com
Savings, Loans, Commercial & Investment Banking Services
S.I.C.: 6029
N.A.I.C.S.: 522110
Manolo Sanchez *(Pres & CEO)*
William C. Helms *(Sr Exec VP-Wealth Mgmt)*

Subsidiaries:

Compass Insurance Agency, Inc. (3)
24 Greenway Plz Ste 1600
Houston, TX 77046
Tel.: (713) 968-8254
Fax: (713) 968-8297
Toll Free: (866) 616-3981
E-Mail: info@compassinsurance.com
Web Site: www.compassinsurance.com
Emp.: 100
Insurance Services
S.I.C.: 6411
N.A.I.C.S.: 524210
Harold Shults *(Pres)*
Joyce Pankonien *(COO)*

Compass Mortgage Financing, Inc. (3)
701 32nd St S
Birmingham, AL 35233
Tel.: (205) 933-3000
Fax: (205) 558-5076
Financial Management Services
S.I.C.: 6211
N.A.I.C.S.: 523999

BBVA USA Bancshares, Inc. (1)
2001 Kirby Dr 661
Houston, TX 77019
Tel.: (713) 831-5525
Bank Holding Company
S.I.C.: 6712
N.A.I.C.S.: 551111

BBVA Wealth Solutions, Inc. (1)
1300 Post Oak Blvd Ste 1500
Houston, TX 77056
Tel.: (713) 552-9277
Fax: (713) 552-0906
Toll Free: (800) 538-8152
E-Mail: contact_us@BBVAWealthSolutions.com
Web Site: www.bbvawealthsolutions.com
Financial Advisory Services
S.I.C.: 6211
N.A.I.C.S.: 523999

Capital Investment Counsel, Inc. (1)
210 University Blvd Ste 550
Denver, CO 80206
Tel.: (303) 329-9000
Fax: (303) 329-9666
Toll Free: (800) 756-9008
E-Mail: info@cicinvestments.com
Web Site: www.cicinvestments.com
Emp.: 20
Investment Advisory & Management Services
S.I.C.: 6282
N.A.I.C.S.: 523930
Stephen Dreiling *(Pres)*
Chris Johnson *(CEO)*
Tom Hackett *(Sr VP)*
Clark Johnson *(Sr VP)*

CB Transport, Inc. (1)
8506 Cedarhome Dr NW
Stanwood, WA 98292
Tel.: (360) 629-4542
Fax: (360) 629-6518
General Freight Trucking Services
S.I.C.: 4212
N.A.I.C.S.: 484110

River Oaks Bank Building, Inc. (1)
2001 Kirby Dr
Houston, TX 77019
Tel.: (713) 526-6211
Financial Services
S.I.C.: 6211
N.A.I.C.S.: 523999

Non-U.S. Subsidiaries:

Aplica Soluciones Tecnologicas Chile Limitada (1)
Moneda 1096 Piso 5 Santiago Centro
Santiago, Chile CL
Tel.: (56) 23516800
Financial Management Services
S.I.C.: 6211
N.A.I.C.S.: 523999

Banco Bilbao Vizcaya Argentaria, Chile S.A. (1)
Huerfanos 1234
Santiago, Chile
Tel.: (56) 2 679 1026
Fax: (56) 2 679 41350
Web Site: www.bbva.cl
BBVACL—(SGO)
Sales Range: $150-199.9 Million
Emp.: 1,771
Banking Services
S.I.C.: 6029
N.A.I.C.S.: 522110
Ignacio Lacasta Casado *(CEO)*

Subsidiaries:

BBVA Seguros de Vida, S.A. (2)
Bandera 76 Piso 6 Oficina 602
Santiago, Chile CL
Tel.: (56) 2 640 16 60
Fax: (56) 2 640 1670
Life Insurance Products & Services
S.I.C.: 6311
N.A.I.C.S.: 524113

ECASA, S.A. (2)
Isidora Goyenechea 3365
Santiago, Chile CL
Tel.: (56) 51 543024
Financial Services
S.I.C.: 6211
N.A.I.C.S.: 523999

Forum Servicios Financieros, S.A. (2)
Avenida Isidora Goyenechea No 3365 Level 4
Las Condes, Santiago, Chile CL
Tel.: (56) 2 369 3000
Fax: (56) 2 369 3100
Emp.: 500
Automotive Financial Leasing Services
S.I.C.: 6159
N.A.I.C.S.: 522220
Raul Aronsohn *(Gen Mgr)*

Banco Bilbao Vizcaya Argentaria (Portugal), S.A. (1)
Avenida da Liberdade 222
Lisbon, 1250-148, Portugal PT
Tel.: (351) 213117200
Fax: (351) 213117500
Commercial Banking Services
S.I.C.: 6029
N.A.I.C.S.: 522110

Banco Provincial Overseas N.V. (1)
Sta Rosaweg 51-53-55
Willemstad, Curacao CW
Tel.: (599) 9 737 6010
Fax: (599) 9 737 6346
Commercial Banking Services
S.I.C.: 6029
N.A.I.C.S.: 522110

BBVA Banco Frances S.A. (1)
Reconquista 199
C1003ABB Buenos Aires, Argentina Ar (76%)
Tel.: (54) 1143464286
Fax: (54) 11 4346 4320
Web Site: www.bancofrances.com
BFR—(BUE MAD NYSE)
Rev.: $1,150,527,896
Assets: $9,016,031,444
Liabilities: $7,959,118,154
Net Worth: $1,056,913,290
Earnings: $254,403,856
Emp.: 5,146
Fiscal Year-end: 12/31/12
Provider of Commercial Banking Services
S.I.C.: 6029
N.A.I.C.S.: 522110
Jorge Carlos Bledel *(Chm)*
Jose Manuel Tamayo Perez *(Vice Chm)*
Ignacio Sanz y Arcelus *(CFO & Dir-Plng & Fin Area)*

BBVA Banco Provincial, S.A. (1)
Avda Este Oeste San Bernardino
Provincial Financial Center, 1011 Caracas, Venezuela (55.14%)
Tel.: (58) 2125044300
Fax: (58) 2125046075
Web Site: www.provincial.com
BPV—(CAR)
Sales Range: $450-499.9 Million
Emp.: 5,544
Commercial Banking Services
S.I.C.: 6029
N.A.I.C.S.: 522110
Leon Henrique Cottin *(Pres)*
Rene Toro Cisneros *(Gen Counsel)*
Aura Marina Kolster *(Sec)*

BBVA Colombia S.A. (1)
Carrera 9 No 72-21 Piso 11
53851 Bogota, Colombia (73.7%)
Tel.: (57) 13471600
Fax: (57) 12359829
E-Mail: claudia.restrepo@bbva.com.co
Web Site: www.bbva.com.co
Provider of Commercial Banking Services
S.I.C.: 6029
N.A.I.C.S.: 522110
Oscar Cabrera *(Mng Dir)*

BBVA Instituicao Financeira de Credito, S.A. (1)
Av D Joao II Lote 1 16 05 - 2 Piso Edificio Infante
1990-083 Lisbon, Portugal
Tel.: (351) 217 985 800
Fax: (351) 217 614 394
E-Mail: bbva.fz@bbvafinanziamento.com
Financial Management Services
S.I.C.: 6211
N.A.I.C.S.: 523999

BBVA Ireland plc (1)
1 Guild Street IFSC
Dublin, 1, Ireland IE
Tel.: (353) 16702847
Fax: (353) 16702848
Emp.: 5
Financial Management Services
S.I.C.: 6211
N.A.I.C.S.: 523999
Pablo Vallejo *(Mng Dir)*

BBVA Luxinvest, S.A. (1)
76 Avenue de la Liberte
1930 Luxembourg, Luxembourg LU
Tel.: (352) 48 30 71 1
Fax: (352) 48 30 71 50
Emp.: 3
Investment Management Services
S.I.C.: 6211
N.A.I.C.S.: 523999

BBVA (Suiza) S.A. (1)
Zeltweg 63
PO Box 3930
8021CH Zurich, Switzerland (100%)
Tel.: (41) 442659511
Fax: (41) 442659891
E-Mail: info@bbvasuiza.ch
Web Site: www.bbva.ch
Emp.: 110
S.I.C.: 6159
N.A.I.C.S.: 522298
Javier Marin *(Gen Mgr)*

Continental S.A. Sociedad Administradora de Fondos (1)
Primer Piso 3055 Av Republica De Panama
San Isidro, Lima, Peru
Tel.: (51) 1 211 1970
Fax: (51) 1 211 1974
E-Mail:
Insurance & Pension Fund Services
S.I.C.: 6411
N.A.I.C.S.: 524298
Marco Shiva *(Gen Mgr)*

Continental Sociedad Titulizadora, S.A. (1)
Av Republica De Panama No 3055
San Isidro, Lima, Peru PE
Tel.: (51) 1 211 2076
Fax: (51) 1 211 2464
Financial Management Services
S.I.C.: 6211
N.A.I.C.S.: 523999

Copromed S.A. de C.V. (1)
Bosque de Duraznos 61 Piso 11 A
Bosques de las Lomas, Mexico, Mexico 11700 MX
Tel.: (52) 55 5245 2760
Financial Services
S.I.C.: 6211
N.A.I.C.S.: 523999

Facileasing S.A. de C.V. (1)
61 Bosque de Duraznos 11th Floor
Bosques de las Lomas, Mexico, 11700, Mexico MX
Tel.: (52) 55 52 45 27 60
E-Mail: fernanda.gonzalez@bbva.com
Web Site: www.facileasing.com.mx
Motor Vehicle Leasing Services
S.I.C.: 7513
N.A.I.C.S.: 532120
Fernanda Gonzalez *(Mgr-HR)*

Subsidiary:

Facileasing Equipment, S.A. de C.V. (2)
Av Universidad No 1200 Xoco Benito Juarez
Mexico, 03339, Mexico MX

Tel.: (52) 5552012000
Fax: (52) 5556212765
Financial Services
S.I.C.: 6211
N.A.I.C.S.: 523999
Ignacio Deschamps *(Gen Mgr)*

Financiera Ayudamos S.A. de C.V., SOFOMER (1)
Av Canal De Miramontes No 2600 Avante Coyoacan
Mexico, 00460, Mexico
Tel.: (52) 5555991543
Financial Services
S.I.C.: 6211
N.A.I.C.S.: 523999

Grupo Financiero BBVA-Bancomer, S.A. (1)
Avenida Universidad 1200 N1 CNCE M At'n Al Publico
Col Xco, 03339 Mexico, DF, Mexico
Tel.: (52) 5556 210399
Telex: 1775781
Web Site: www.bancomer.com.mx
GFBBO—(MEX)
Emp.: 29,000
Retail & Commercial Banking; Other Financial Services
S.I.C.: 6029
N.A.I.C.S.: 522110
Ignacio Deschamps Gonzalez *(Chm)*
Augusto Larrondo Arcaute *(Pres-Queretaro)*
Vito Alessio Aguirre Chavez *(Pres-Pachuca)*
Eduardo Avila Zaragoza *(Gen Dir-Fin & Comptroller)*
Juan Pablo Avila *(Gen Dir-Retail Banking)*
Sergio Salvador Sanchez *(Gen Dir-Sys & Ops)*

Divisions:

Banca Hipotecaria (2)
Montes Urales 424 2o Piso
Col Lomas de Chapultepec
Deleg Miguel Hidalgo, Mexico, DF, CP 11000, Mexico
Tel.: (52) 55 9178 4600
E-Mail: hipotecariabancomer@mailbancomer.com
Web Site: www.hipnal.com.mx
S.I.C.: 6159
N.A.I.C.S.: 522298

BBVA Bancomer Afore (2)
Montes Urales 424 1er Piso Col Lomas de Chapultepec
CP 11000 Mexico, D.F., Mexico
Tel.: (52) 91 71 40 00
Web Site: www.bancomer.com
Banking & Financial Services
S.I.C.: 6029
N.A.I.C.S.: 522110

Casa de Cambio Bancomer (2)
Av Manuel L Barragan
860 Mexico, D.F., Mexico
Tel.: (52) 53760399
Fax: (52) 52387715
S.I.C.: 6159
N.A.I.C.S.: 522298

Factoraje Bancomer (2)
J. Balmes 11 Torre C Mezzanine
Piso 3 Col Los Morales
Polanco, 11510 Mexico, D.F., Mexico
Tel.: (52) 5 283 3000
Fax: (52) 5 283 3182
S.I.C.: 6159
N.A.I.C.S.: 522298

Sistema de Ahorro para el Retiro (2)
Ave Universidad 1200 Col Xoco
03339 Mexico, D.F., Mexico
Branches & Agencies of Foreign Bank
S.I.C.: 6029
N.A.I.C.S.: 522110

U.S. Subsidiary:

Bancomer Transfer Services, Inc. (2)
16825 Northchase Dr Ste 1525
Houston, TX 77060
Tel.: (281) 765-1525
Fax: (281) 877-9622
Emp.: 55
Financial Transfer Services
S.I.C.: 6099
N.A.I.C.S.: 522320

Jaimes Moises *(CEO)*

Leasemart Holding B.V. (1)
Bellsingel 26
1119 NL Schiphol-Rijk, Netherlands NL
Tel.: (31) 204064444
Investment Management Services
S.I.C.: 6211
N.A.I.C.S.: 523999

Societe Inmobiliere BBV D (1)
29 Rue DeE Masure
64100 Bayonne, France
Tel.: (33) 5 59 58 22 44
Real Estate Management Services
S.I.C.: 6531
N.A.I.C.S.: 531390

Non-U.S. Affiliate:

AFP Horizonte SA (1)
Avda Republica de Panama
San Isidro
3055 Lima, Peru PE
Tel.: (51) 12154082 (24.85%)
Fax: (51) 12212381
Web Site: www.afphorizonte.com.pe
Pension Fund Management Services
S.I.C.: 6371
N.A.I.C.S.: 524292

BANCO BPI, S.A.

Rua Tenente Valadim 284
4100-476 Porto, Portugal
Tel.: (351) 226073337
Fax: (351) 226004738
E-Mail: investor.relations@bancobpi.pt
Web Site: www.bancobpi.pt
BPI—(EUR OTC)
Rev.: $2,530,389,018
Assets: $59,991,502,005
Liabilities: $57,217,524,871
Net Worth: $2,773,977,133
Earnings: $335,378,063
Emp.: 8,680
Fiscal Year-end: 12/31/12

Business Description:
Banking Services
S.I.C.: 6029
N.A.I.C.S.: 522110

Personnel:
Artur Eduardo Brochado Dos Santos Silva *(Chm)*
Abel Antonio Pinto dos Reis *(Chm-Supervisory Bd)*
Fernando Maria da Costa Duarte Ulrich *(Deputy Chm)*
Joao Avides Moreira *(Sec)*

Board of Directors:
Artur Eduardo Brochado Dos Santos Silva
Ignacio Alvarez-Rendueles
Edgar Alves Ferreira
Marcelino Armenter Vidal
Pedro Barreto
Antonio Domingues
Klaus Duhrkop
Isidro Faine Casas
Antonio Farinha Morais
Manuel Ferreira da Silva
Maria Celeste Hagatong
Tomaz Jervell
Mario Leite da Silva
Armando Leite de Pinho
Antonio Bernardo Aranha da Gama Lobo Xavier
Carlos Moreira da Silva
Juan Maria Nin Genova
Jose Pena do Amaral
Alfredo Rezende de Almeida
Fernando Maria da Costa Duarte Ulrich
Herbert Walter

Supervisory Board of Directors:
Abel Antonio Pinto dos Reis
Miguel Artiaga Barbosa
Jorge de Figueiredo Dias
Jose Neves Adelino

Subsidiaries:

Banco Portugues de Investimento, S.A. (1)
Rua Tenente Valadim 284
4100-476 Porto, Portugal PT
Tel.: (351) 226073100 (100%)
Fax: (351) 226098787
E-Mail: bancobpi@mail.bancobpt.pt
Web Site: www.bancobpi.pt
Emp.: 150
Banking Services
S.I.C.: 6029
N.A.I.C.S.: 522110
Fernando Ulrich *(Chm)*

BPI Gestao de Activos - Gestao de Fundos de Investimento Mobiliarios, S.A. (1)
Rua Braamcamp 11 4th Fl
1250-049 Lisbon, Portugal
Tel.: (351) 213111025
Fax: (351) 213111189
E-Mail: bpigestaoactivos@bancobpi.pt
Web Site: www.bancobpi.pt/pagina.asp?s=6&a=176&f=2712&e=539&opt=e
Investment Funds Management Services
S.I.C.: 6211
N.A.I.C.S.: 523999
Fernando Ulrich *(Pres)*

BPI Locacao de Equipamentos, Lda. (1)
Rua Fanqueiros Nr 12 3
Lisbon, 1149-090, Portugal
Tel.: (351) 217241700
Fax: (351) 213181616
E-Mail: bpi@bancobpi.pt
Web Site: www.bpi.bancobpi.pt
Emp.: 200
Securities Brokerage Services
S.I.C.: 6211
N.A.I.C.S.: 523120

BPI Vida - Companhia de Seguros de Vida, S.A. (1)
Rua Braamcamp 11-5
1250-049 Lisbon, Portugal
Tel.: (351) 213111020
Fax: (351) 213111082
E-Mail: bpipensoes_planocd@bancobpi.pt
Web Site: www.bancobpi.pt/pagina.asp?s=6&a=176&f=2712&e=540&opt=e
Emp.: 25
Insurance Brokerage Services
S.I.C.: 6411
N.A.I.C.S.: 524210
Carla Siopi *(Sec)*

Inter-Risco - Sociedade de Capital de Risco, S.A. (1)
Rua Tenente Valadim 284
4100-476 Porto, Norte, Portugal
Tel.: (351) 22 607 43 19
Fax: (351) 22 607 43 72
Emp.: 8
Venture Capital Fund Providers
S.I.C.: 6722
N.A.I.C.S.: 525910
Asonso Barros *(Mng Dir)*

U.S. Subsidiary:

BPI, Inc. (1)
278 Warren Ave
East Providence, RI 02914
Tel.: (401) 438-0602
Fax: (401) 434-3395
E-Mail: er.rhode-island@BancoBPI.pt
Web Site: www.bpi.bp.com
Emp.: 4
Foreign Money Remittance Services
S.I.C.: 7389
N.A.I.C.S.: 561990

Non-U.S. Subsidiaries:

Banco de Fomento Angola (1)
58 Rua Amilcar Cabral
Maianga, Luanda, Angola (100%)
Tel.: (244) 222638900
Fax: (244) 222638925
Web Site: www.bfa.ao
Emp.: 100
Commercial Banking
S.I.C.: 6029
N.A.I.C.S.: 522110
Emildio Pinheiro *(Chm)*

BPI (Suisse) S.A. (1)
Rue Etienne-Dumont 1-1er
1204 Geneva, Switzerland
Tel.: (41) 223183760
Fax: (41) 228104410
E-Mail: bpisuisse@bpisuisse.ch
Emp.: 20
Portfolio Management Services
S.I.C.: 6282
N.A.I.C.S.: 523920
Thomas Krayenbuhl *(Chm)*

BANCO BRADESCO S.A.

Cidade de Deus S/N Vila Yara
06029 900 Osasco, SP, Brazil
Tel.: (55) 1136843311
Telex: 11 36460 BBDE BR
Fax: (55) 1136844570
Web Site: www.bradesco.com.br
Year Founded: 1943
BBD—(BRAZ MAD NYSE RIO)
Rev.: $40,892,643,563
Assets: $394,095,725,371
Liabilities: $359,001,149,594
Net Worth: $35,094,575,777
Earnings: $5,583,784,762
Emp.: 103,385
Fiscal Year-end: 12/31/12

Business Description:
Banking Services
S.I.C.: 6029
N.A.I.C.S.: 522110

Personnel:
Lazaro de Mello Brandao *(Chm)*
Antonio Bornia *(Vice Chm)*
Luiz Carlos Trabuco Cappi *(CEO)*
Mauricio Machado de Minas *(Mng Dir)*
Candido Leonelli *(Mng Dir)*
Antonio Jose da Barbara *(Dept Officer & Gen Secretariat)*
Claudio Borges Cassemiro *(Officer & Deputy VP)*
Carlos Alberto Alastico *(Reg Officer)*
Alex Silva Braga *(Reg Officer)*
Andre Bernardino da Cruz Filho *(Dept Officer)*
Antonio de Jesus Mendes *(Officer-Acctg Dept)*
Altair Antonio De Souza *(Deputy Officer)*
Antonio Gualberto Diniz *(Reg Officer)*
Antonio Carlos Melhado *(Officer-Centralized Svcs Dept)*
Antonio Chinellato Neto *(Officer-Intl Ops)*
Amilton Nieto *(Officer-Tech Svcs Dept)*
Antonio Piovesan *(Reg Officer)*
Almir Rocha *(Reg Officer)*
Adineu Santesso *(Officer-Retail Dept)*
Luiz Carlos Angelotti *(Member-Exec Bd)*
Andre Rodriques Cano *(Member-Exec Bd)*
Alexandre da Silva Gluher *(Member-Exec Bd)*
Andre Marcelo da Silva Prado *(Member-Exec Bd)*
Marcelo de Araujo Noronha *(Member-Exec Bd)*
Octavio de Lazari, Jr. *(Member-Exec Bd)*
Alfredo Antonio Lima de Menezes *(Member-Exec Bd)*
Moacir Nachbar, Jr. *(Member-Exec Bd)*
Nilton Pelegrino Nogueira *(Member-Exec Bd)*
Josue Augusto Pancini *(Member-Exec Bd)*
Denise Pauli Pavarina de Moura *(Member-Exec Bd)*
Luiz Fernando Peres *(Member-Exec Bd)*

Banco Bradesco S.A.—(Continued)

Julio de Siqueira Carvalho de Araujo *(Exec VP)*
Domingos Figueiredo de Abreu *(Exec VP)*

Board of Directors:
Lazaro de Mello Brandao
Joao Aguiar Alvarez
Denise Aquiar Alvarez Valente
Antonio Bornia
Mario da Silveira Teixeira, Jr.
Ricardo Espirito Santo Silva Salgado
Milton Matsumoto
Carlos Alberto Rodrigues Guilherme
Joao Sabino
Luiz Carlos Trabuco Cappi

Subsidiaries:

Agora Corretora de Titulos e Valores Mobiliarios S.A. **(1)**
Praia De Botafogo 300 Salas 601 301
Parte e Loja 101
Rio de Janeiro, 02225-040, Brazil
Tel.: (55) 21 2529 0800
Fax: (55) 21 2529 0822
E-Mail: contato@agorainvest.com.br
Web Site: www.agorainvest.com.br
Securities Brokerage Services
S.I.C.: 6211
N.A.I.C.S.: 523120

Banco Boavista S.A. **(1)**
Rua Min Edgard Costa 68 Centro
Nova Iguacu, Rio de Janeiro, 22430-190, Brazil
Tel.: (55) 21 2668 2720
Commercial & Retail Banking Services
S.I.C.: 6029
N.A.I.C.S.: 522110

Banco Bradesco Financiamentos S.A. **(1)**
Cidade De Deus S/N - Vila Yara Osasco
Sao Paulo, 06029-900, Brazil
Tel.: (55) 11 4004 4433
Web Site: www.bradescofinanciamentos.com.br
Commercial Banking Services
S.I.C.: 6029
N.A.I.C.S.: 522110

Bradesco Auto/RE Companhia de Seguros **(1)**
Rua Barao de Itapagipe N 186 225 - Parte
Rio Comprido, Rio de Janeiro, 20261-901, Brazil
Tel.: (55) 21 2503 1199
Web Site: www.bradescoautore.com.br
General Insurance Services
S.I.C.: 6411
N.A.I.C.S.: 524298

Subsidiary:

Atlantica Companhia de Seguros S.A. **(2)**
Rua Barao de Itapagipe no 225 - parte
Rio Comprido, Rio de Janeiro, 20261-901, Brazil
Tel.: (55) 21 2503 1199
Fax: (55) 21 2503 1042
General Insurance Services
S.I.C.: 6411
N.A.I.C.S.: 524298

Bradesco Capitalizacao S.A. **(1)**
Avenida Paulista 1415
Bela Vista, Sao Paulo, 01311-200, Brazil
Tel.: (55) 11 3265 5433
Web Site: www.bradescocapitalizacao.com.br
Life Insurance Services
S.I.C.: 6411
N.A.I.C.S.: 524298

Bradesco Corretora T.V.M. **(1)**
Av Paulista 1450 7th Floor
01310-917 Sao Paulo, Brazil
Tel.: (55) 11 2178 5757
Fax: (55) 11 2178 5409
E-Mail: 5900.faq@bradesco.com.br
Web Site: www.bradescocorretora.com.br
Commercial Banking Services
S.I.C.: 6029
N.A.I.C.S.: 522110

Bradesco Leasing S.A. Arrendamento Mercantil **(1)**
Av Alphaville 1500-Piso 2
Barueri, 06480-900, Brazil
Tel.: (55) 11 4197 2906
Fax: (55) 11 4197 2801
Web Site: www.bradescoleasing.com.br
Financial Management Services
S.I.C.: 6211
N.A.I.C.S.: 523999
Antonio Bornia *(Vice Chm)*

Bradesco Saude S.A. **(1)**
Rua Barao de Itapagipe 225
Rio Comprido, Rio de Janeiro, 20261-901, Brazil
Tel.: (55) 21 2503 1101
Fax: (55) 21 2293 9489
E-Mail: imprensa@bradescoseguros.com.br
Web Site: www.bradescosaude.com.br
Health Insurance Services
S.I.C.: 6321
N.A.I.C.S.: 524114

Bradesco Vida E Previdencia S.A. **(1)**
Cidade de Deus s/n - Vila lara
Osasco, 06029-900, Brazil
Tel.: (55) 11 3684 5760
Fax: (55) 11 3684 7011
Web Site: www.bradescoprevidencia.com.br
Life Insurance Services
S.I.C.: 6411
N.A.I.C.S.: 524298

Companhia Brasileira de Solucoes e Servicos S.A. **(1)**
Alameda Rio Negro 161 17th Fl
Barueri, 06454, Brazil
Tel.: (55) 11 2188 1845
Emp.: 300
Credit Card Processing Services
S.I.C.: 6099
N.A.I.C.S.: 522320
Osvaldo Cervi *(Pres)*

Subsidiary:

IBI promotora de vendas ltda **(2)**
Estr do Portela 77 - Madureira
21351-050 Rio de Janeiro, Brazil
Tel.: (55) 21 2106 0008
Commercial Banking Services
S.I.C.: 6029
N.A.I.C.S.: 522110

Elo Participacoes S.A. **(1)**
Alameda Rio Negro No 585 Padauiri
Building 1st floor side B
Barueri, 06454-000, Brazil
Tel.: (55) 1148316802
Financial Management Services
S.I.C.: 6211
N.A.I.C.S.: 523999

Scopus Tecnologia Ltda **(1)**
Avenida Mutinga 4 105 Jd Santo Elias - Pirituba
Sao Paulo, 05110-000, Brazil
Tel.: (55) 11 3909 3400
Fax: (55) 11 3904 1094
E-Mail: solucoes@scopus.com.br
Web Site: www.scopus.com.br
Emp.: 3,000
Information Technology Consulting Services
S.I.C.: 7373
N.A.I.C.S.: 541512

Uniao Participacoes Ltda **(1)**
Rua Araujo Porto Alegre 36 - Castelo
Rio de Janeiro, 20030-013, Brazil
Tel.: (55) 11 5504 6500
Fax: (55) 21 2220 9237
Commercial Banking Services
S.I.C.: 6029
N.A.I.C.S.: 522110

U.S. Division:

Banco Bradesco New York **(1)**
450 Park Ave 32nd Fl
New York, NY 10022 (100%)
Tel.: (212) 688-9855
Telex: 661955 BRADESCO
Fax: (212) 754-4032
E-Mail: newyork@bradesco.com.br
Web Site: www.bradesco.com
Emp.: 26
International Banking
S.I.C.: 6159
N.A.I.C.S.: 522298
Bruno Boetger *(Gen Mgr)*

U.S. Subsidiary:

Bradesco Securities, Inc., **(1)**
126 E 56th St Rm 9r
New York, NY 10022-3084
Tel.: (212) 888-9141
Web Site: www.bradescori.b.br/site/conteudo/interna/default.aspx?secaold=662&idiomald=2
Securities Brokerage Services
S.I.C.: 6211
N.A.I.C.S.: 523120
Marcelo Cabral *(CEO)*

Non-U.S. Subsidiaries:

Banco Bradesco Argentina S.A. **(1)**
25 De Mayo 555 7th Fl
1002 Buenos Aires, Argentina (100%)
Tel.: (54) 1141146111
Fax: (54) 1141146199
E-Mail: bradesco@arnet.com.ar
Web Site: www.bradesco.com
Emp.: 15
S.I.C.: 6159
N.A.I.C.S.: 522298
Lucas Luciana de Martin *(Pres)*

Banco Bradesco Europa S.A. **(1)**
29 Avenue de la Porte-Neuve
2227 Luxembourg, Luxembourg
Tel.: (352) 25 41 31 1
Fax: (352) 25 41 39
E-Mail: info@bradesco.lu
Web Site: www.bradesco.lu
Emp.: 39
Commercial Banking Services
S.I.C.: 6029
N.A.I.C.S.: 522110
Lazaro de Mello Brandao *(Chm)*

Bradesco Argentina de Seguros S.A **(1)**
Paraguay 610 Piso 5 Dto B
Buenos Aires, Argentina
Tel.: (54) 11 4313 7867
Insurance Management Services
S.I.C.: 6411
N.A.I.C.S.: 524298

Columbus Holdings **(1)**
750 Shaw Boulevard
Mandaluyong, 1552, Philippines
Tel.: (63) 28183601
Fax: (63) 28159096
Investment Management Services
S.I.C.: 6282
N.A.I.C.S.: 523920

BANCO CENTRAL DE CHILE

Agustinas 1180
PO Box 967
8340454 Santiago, Chile
Tel.: (56) 26702000
Fax: (56) 6972271
E-Mail: bcch@bcentral.cl
Web Site: www.bcentral.cl
Year Founded: 1926
Sales Range: $1-4.9 Billion
Emp.: 562
Business Description:
Central Bank
S.I.C.: 6011
N.A.I.C.S.: 521110
Personnel:
Miguel Angel Nacrur Gazali *(Gen Counsel)*
Board of Directors:
Jorge Desormeaux Jimenez
Jose Manuel Marfan Lewis

BANCO CENTRAL DE CUBA

Municipio Habana Vieja La Habana
PO Box 746
Havana, 402, Cuba
Tel.: (53) 78668003
Fax: (53) 7 8666601
Web Site: www.bc.gov.cu
Year Founded: 1950
Emp.: 450
Business Description:
Banking Services
S.I.C.: 6011
N.A.I.C.S.: 521110
Personnel:
Ernesto Medina Villaveiran *(Pres)*

BANCO CENTRAL DE HONDURAS

3165 Barrio El Centro Avenida Juan Ramon Molina Primera Calle
Septima Avenida, Tegucigalpa, Honduras
Tel.: (504) 2372270
Web Site: www.bch.hn
Rev.: $214,264,277
Assets: $4,594,602,547
Liabilities: $4,511,109,355
Net Worth: $83,493,192
Earnings: ($19,652,584)
Emp.: 504
Fiscal Year-end: 12/31/12
Business Description:
Banking Services
S.I.C.: 6011
N.A.I.C.S.: 521110
Personnel:
Maria Elena Mondragon de Villar *(Pres)*
Carlos Roman Martinez *(Chief Officer-Acctg)*
Board of Directors:
Armando Aguilar Cruz
Manuel de Jesus Bautista
Renan Sagastume Fernandez
Ricardo Enrique Marichal Matuty
Sandra Midence
Maria Elena Mondragon de Villar

BANCO CENTRAL DE LA REPUBLICA ARGENTINA

Reconquista 266
C1003ABF Buenos Aires, Argentina
Tel.: (54) 1143483500
Web Site: www.bcra.gov.ar
Business Description:
Central Bank
S.I.C.: 6011
N.A.I.C.S.: 521110
Personnel:
Mercedes Marco del Pont *(Pres)*

BANCO CENTRAL DE LA REPUBLICA DOMINICA

Calle Pedro Henriquez Urena esq Leopoldo Navarro, Santo Domingo, Dominican Republic
Tel.: (809) 2219111
E-Mail: info@bancentral.gov.do
Web Site: www.bancentral.gov.do
Year Founded: 1947
Business Description:
Central Bank
S.I.C.: 6011
N.A.I.C.S.: 521110
Personnel:
Hector Valdez Albizu *(Pres & Governor)*
Consuelo Matos de Guerrero *(Sec)*
Board of Directors:
Hector Valdez Albizu
Vicente Bengoa
Rafael Camilo
Emilio De Luna Peguero
Miguel Feris Iglesias
George Manuel Hazoury
Consuelo Matos de Guerrero
Ramon Nunez Ramirez
Cesar Nicolas Penson
Hector Rizek Llabaly

BANCO CENTRAL DE RESERVA DE EL SALVADOR

Alameda Juan Pablo II entre 15 y 17 Av Norte

Apartado Postal 106
San Salvador, El Salvador
Tel.: (503) 2281 8000
Fax: (503) 2281 8011
E-Mail: julio.alvarenga@bcr.com.sv
Web Site: www.bcr.gob.sv
Sales Range: $75-99.9 Million
Business Description:
Banking Services
S.I.C.: 6011
N.A.I.C.S.: 521110
Personnel:
Carlos Acevedo *(Pres)*
Juan Alberto Hernandez *(Treas)*
Board of Directors:
Carlos Acevedo
Luis Adalberto Aquino
Ricardo Salvador Calvo Munoz
Marta Evelyn de Rivera
Ricardo Antonio Morales Estupinian
Guillermo Alejandro Ruiz Maida

BANCO CENTRAL DE RESERVA DEL PERU
Jr Antonio Miro Quesada 441-445
Lima, 1, Peru
Tel.: (51) 16132000
Fax: (51) 5116132502
E-Mail: webmaster@bcrp.gob.pe
Web Site: www.bcrp.gob.pe
Emp.: 150
Business Description:
Banking Services
S.I.C.: 6011
N.A.I.C.S.: 521110
Personnel:
Julio Velarde Flores *(Chm)*
Board of Directors:
Julio Velarde Flores
Beatriz Boza Dibos
Alfonso Lopez Chau
Jose Chlimper Ackerman
Martha Rodriguez
Abel Salinas Izaguirre
Jose Valderrama Leon

BANCO CENTRAL DE VENEZUELA
Av Urdaneta esq Las Carmelitas
1010 Caracas, Venezuela
Tel.: (58) 2128015111
Fax: (58) 2128611649
E-Mail: info@bcv.org.ve
Web Site: www.bcv.org.ve
Emp.: 2,000
Business Description:
Central Bank
S.I.C.: 6011
N.A.I.C.S.: 521110
Personnel:
Eudomar Tovar *(Pres)*
Board of Directors:
Jose Felix Rivas Alvarado
Rafael J. Crazut
Jose Salamat Khan Fernandez
Bernardo Ferran
Jorge A. Giordani C
Armando Leon Rojas

BANCO CENTRAL DEL ECUADOR
Avenue Amazonas N34-451 y
Avenue Atahualpa
Quito, Ecuador
Tel.: (593) 2 2255777
Fax: (593) 2 2264529
E-Mail: pweb@bce.ec
Web Site: www.bce.fin.ec
Emp.: 780
Business Description:
Banking Services
S.I.C.: 6029
N.A.I.C.S.: 522110
Personnel:
Eduardo Cabezas Molina *(Chm)*

BANCO CENTRAL DEL PARAGUAY
Federacion Rusa y Cabo 1 Marecos
Santo Domingo, Asuncion, Paraguay
Tel.: (595) 21608011
Fax: (595) 216192637
E-Mail: info@bcp.gov.py
Web Site: www.bcp.gov.py
Emp.: 900
Business Description:
Central Bank
S.I.C.: 6011
N.A.I.C.S.: 521110
Personnel:
Carlos Gustavo Fernandez Valdovinos *(Pres)*
Board of Directors:
Santiago Pena Palacios
Carlos Gustavo Fernandez Valdovinos
Rafael Lara Valenzuela
Roland Holst Wenninger
Rolando Arrellaga Yaluk

BANCO CENTRAL DEL URUGUAY
Diagonal Fabini 777
Montevideo, Uruguay
Tel.: (598) 219671658
Fax: (598) 219671693
E-Mail: info@bcu.gub.uy
Web Site: www.bcu.gub.uy
Business Description:
Central Bank
S.I.C.: 6011
N.A.I.C.S.: 521110
Personnel:
Walter Cancela *(Pres)*
Aureliano Berro *(Gen Sec)*

BANCO CENTRAL DO BRASIL
Setor Bancario Sul SBS Quadra 3
Bloco B Ed
Caixa Postal 08670
70074-900 Brasilia, Brazil
Tel.: (55) 6134143980
Fax: (55) 6134143749
Web Site: www.bcb.gov.br
Sales Range: $1-4.9 Billion
Business Description:
Banking Services
S.I.C.: 6011
N.A.I.C.S.: 521110
Personnel:
Henrique de Campos Meirelles *(Governor)*
Mario Magalhaes Carvalho Mesquita *(Deputy Governor)*
Rodrigo Telles da Rocha Azevedo *(Deputy Governor)*
Antonio Gustavo Matos do Vale *(Deputy Governor)*
Alexandre Antonio Tombini *(Deputy Governor)*

BANCO COMAFI S.A.
Av Roque Saenz Pena 660
CP 1035 AAO Buenos Aires, Argentina
Tel.: (54) 43470400
Web Site: www.comafi.com.ar
Year Founded: 1984
Sales Range: $125-149.9 Million
Business Description:
Retail, Commercial & Investment Banking, Brokerage & Trust Services
S.I.C.: 6029
N.A.I.C.S.: 522110
Personnel:
Guillermo Alejandro Cervino *(Pres)*

BANCO COMERCIAL PORTUGUES, S.A.
(d/b/a Millennium bcp)
Praca D Joao I 28
4000-295 Porto, Portugal
Tel.: (351) 210030880
Fax: (351) 210 066 858
E-Mail: investors@millenniumbcp.pt
Web Site: www.millenniumbcp.pt
Year Founded: 1985
BCP—(EUR OTC)
Int. Income: $4,436,361,120
Assets: $115,215,801,419
Liabilities: $110,147,246,559
Net Worth: $5,068,554,860
Earnings: ($1,996,857,424)
Emp.: 20,365
Fiscal Year-end: 12/31/12
Business Description:
Commercial, Investment & Personal Banking, Insurance & Asset Management
S.I.C.: 6029
N.A.I.C.S.: 522110
Personnel:
Antonio Vitor Martins Monteiro *(Chm)*
Nuno Manuel da Silva Amado *(Vice Chm & CEO)*
Carlos Jose da Silva *(Vice Chm)*
Pedro Maria Calainho Teixeira Duarte *(Vice Chm)*
Ana Isabel dos Santos de Pina Cabral *(Sec)*
Board of Directors:
Antonio Vitor Martins Monteiro
Nuno Manuel da Silva Amado
Rui Manuel da Silva Teixeira
Carlos Jose da Silva
Jose Guilherme Xavier de Basto
Miguel de Campos Pereira de Braganca
Luis Maria Franca de Castro Pereira Coutinho
Jose Rodrigues de Jesus
Jaime de Macedo Santos Bastos
Joao Manuel de Matos Loureiro
Maria da Conceicao Mota Soares de Oliveira Calle Lucas
Alvaro Roque de Pinho Bissaia Barreto
Antonio Henriques de Pinho Cardao
Bernardo de Sa Braamcamp Sobral Sottomayor
Antonio Manuel Costeira Faustino
Andre Magalhaes Luiz Gomes
Antonio Luis Guerra Nunes Mexia
Cesar Paxi Manuel Joao Pedro
Miguel Maya Dias Pinheiro
Joao Bernardo Bastos Mendes Resende
Jose Jacinto Iglesias Soares
Pedro Maria Calainho Teixeira Duarte

Subsidiary:

Millennium bcp Gestao de Activos - Sociedade Gestora de Fundos de Investimento, S.A. **(1)**
Av Professor Doutor Cavaco Silva Tagus Park Edif 3 Piso 1 Ala A
2744-002 Porto Salvo, Portugal
Tel.: (351) 211132000
Fax: (351) 211101113
E-Mail: fundos@millenniumbcp.pt
Web Site: www.fundos.millenniumbcp.pt
Asset Management Services
S.I.C.: 8748
N.A.I.C.S.: 541618

Non-U.S. Subsidiaries:

Bank Millennium S.A. **(1)**
Ul Stanislawa Zaryna 2A
02-593 Warsaw, Poland (50%)
Tel.: (48) 22 598 4040
Fax: (48) 22 598 2563
Web Site: www.bankmillennium.pl
MIL—(WAR)
Int. Income: $989,567,695
Assets: $16,726,228,708
Liabilities: $15,196,339,676
Net Worth: $1,529,889,032
Earnings: $149,742,761
Emp.: 4,000
Fiscal Year-end: 12/31/12
Banking Services
S.I.C.: 6029
N.A.I.C.S.: 522110
Maciej Bednarkiewicz *(Chm-Supervisory Bd)*
Boguslaw Kott *(Chm-Mgmt Bd)*
Nuno Manuel da Silva Amado *(Deputy Chm-Supervisory Bd)*
Joao Bras Jorge *(First Deputy Chm-Mgmt Bd)*
Fernando Bicho *(Deputy Chm-Mgmt Bd)*
Artur Klimczak *(Deputy Chm-Mgmt Bd)*
Julianna Boniuk-Gorzelanczyk *(Member-Mgmt Bd)*
Maria Jose Campos *(Member-Mgmt Bd)*
Andrzej Glinski *(Member-Mgmt Bd)*
Wojciech Haase *(Member-Mgmt Bd)*

Bitalpart B.V. **(1)**
Claude Debussylam 24
1082 MD Amsterdam, Noord-Holland, Netherlands
Tel.: (31) 205222555
Fax: (31) 205222500
Investment Management Services
S.I.C.: 6282
N.A.I.C.S.: 523920
Petrus Hendrik Bosse *(Principal)*

BANCO CRUZEIRO DO SUL SA
(d/b/a BCSul)
Rua Funchal 418 7-9 andares Ed E-Tower
Vila Olimpia, CEP-04551-060 Sao Paulo, SP, Brazil
Tel.: (55) 11 3848 1800
Fax: (55) 11 3848 1842
E-Mail: luisfelippe@bcsul.com.br
Web Site: www.bcsul.com.br
CZRS4—(BRAZ)
Sales Range: $750-799.9 Million
Emp.: 600
Business Description:
Banking Services
S.I.C.: 6029
N.A.I.C.S.: 522110
Personnel:
Luis Octavio A. L. Indio da Costa *(Chm & Officer-IR)*
Charles Alexander Forbes *(Vice Chm)*
Sergio Marra Pereira Capella *(Member-Exec Bd)*
Roberto Vieira da Silva de Oliveira Costa *(Member-Exec Bd)*
Jose Carlos Lima de Abreu *(Member-Exec Bd)*
Maria Luisa Garcia de Mendonca *(Member-Exec Bd)*
Fabio Caramuru Correa Meyer *(Member-Exec Bd)*
Renato Alves Rabello *(Member-Exec Bd)*
Board of Directors:
Luis Octavio A. L. Indio da Costa
Fabio Rocha do Amaral
Charles Alexander Forbes
Horacio Martinho Lima
Progreso Vano Puerto
Flavio Nunes Ferreira Rietmann

BANCO DA AMAZONIA S/A
Av Presidente Vargas 800 9th floor
Belem, 66017-901, Brazil
Tel.: (55) 9140083526
Fax: (55) 9140083405
Web Site: www.bancoamazonia.com.br
BAZA3—(BRAZ)
Sales Range: $450-499.9 Million
Business Description:
Financial Banking Services

Banco da Amazonia S/A—(Continued)

S.I.C.: 6029
N.A.I.C.S.: 522110
Personnel:
Luiz Fernando Pires Augusto *(Chm)*
Abidias Jose de Sousa, Jr. *(Pres & CEO)*
Board of Directors:
Luiz Fernando Pires Augusto
Jose Helder Silveira da Almeida
Eliomar Wesley Ayres da Foseca Rios
Fabricio da Soller
Abidias Jose de Sousa, Jr.
Marcos Jose Pereira Damasceno

BANCO DAYCOVAL S.A.

Av Paulista 1793
01311 200 Bela Vista, Sao Paulo, Brazil
Tel.: (55) 1131380500
Fax: (55) 1131380752
E-Mail: ri@daycoval.com.br
Web Site: www.daycoval.com.br
Year Founded: 1968
DAYC4—(BRAZ)
Sales Range: $750-799.9 Million
Business Description:
Banking Services
S.I.C.: 6029
N.A.I.C.S.: 522110
Personnel:
Sasson Dayan *(Chm & CEO)*
Nilo Cavarzan *(Officer)*
Carlos Moche Dayan *(Exec Officer)*
Morris Dayan *(Officer-IR)*
Salim Dayan *(Exec Officer)*
R. M. Nogueira *(Officer)*
Albert Rouben *(Officer)*
Board of Directors:
Sasson Dayan
Rony Dayan
Gustavo Henrique de Barroso Franco
Peter M. Yu

BANCO DE ESPANA

C Alcala 48
28014 Madrid, Spain
Tel.: (34) 913385000
Fax: (34) 913386488
Web Site: www.bde.es
Int. Income: $11,070,686,693
Assets: $739,966,831,419
Liabilities: $732,165,466,649
Net Worth: $7,801,364,769
Earnings: $5,176,333,269
Emp.: 2,705
Fiscal Year-end: 12/31/12
Business Description:
Banking Services
S.I.C.: 6011
N.A.I.C.S.: 521110
Personnel:
Jose Maria Roldan Alegre *(Dir Gen-Banking Regulation & Fin Stability)*
Jose Luis Malo de Molina Martin-Montalvo *(Dir Gen-Economics, Statistics & Res)*
Pilar L'Hotellerie-Fallois *(Dir Gen-Intl Affairs)*
Inigo Fernandez de Mesa *(Sec Gen-Treasury & Fin Policy)*
Francisco Javier Priego *(Gen Sec)*
Board of Directors:
Carmen Alonso
Maximino Carpio
Luis M. Linde
Angel Luis Lopez
Guillem Lopez
Jose Maria Marin
Fernando Restoy
Vicente Salas

BANCO DE GUATEMALA

7a Av 22-01 zona 1
Guatemala, Guatemala
Tel.: (502) 2429 6000
Fax: (502) 2253 4035
Web Site: www.banguat.gob.gt
Business Description:
Banking Services
S.I.C.: 6011
N.A.I.C.S.: 521110
Personnel:
Maria Antonieta Del Cid Navas de Bonilla *(Pres)*
Board of Directors:
Manuel Augusto Alonzo Araujo
Maria Antonieta Del Cid Navas de Bonilla
Lidya Antonieta Gutierrez Escobar
Julio Roberto Suarez Guerra
Leonel Hipolito Moreno Merida
Sergio Francisco Recinos Rivera
Oscar Roberto Monterroso Sazo

BANCO DE LA NACION ARGENTINA

Bartolome Mitre 346 5th Fl
5411 Buenos Aires, Argentina
Tel.: (54) 1143476000
Fax: (54) 1143478078
Web Site: www.bna.com.ar
Year Founded: 1891
Emp.: 16,000
Business Description:
Retail, Commercial & Investment Banking, Leasing & International Trade Financing Services
S.I.C.: 6029
N.A.I.C.S.: 522110
Personnel:
Juan Carlos Fabrega *(Chm)*
Esteban Alejandro Acerbo *(Vice Chm)*
Raul Duzevic *(Gen Mgr)*
Jose Antonio Caceres Monie *(Sec)*
Board of Directors:
Juan Carlos Fabrega
Esteban Alejandro Acerbo
Angel Jose De Dios
Raul Duzevic
Juan Ignacio Forlon
Silvia Gallego
Patricia Susana

U.S. Subsidiary:

Banco de la Nacion Argentina **(1)**
777 Brickell Ave Ste 802
Miami, FL 33131 FL
Tel.: (305) 371-7500
Fax: (305) 374-7805
International Trade Financing
S.I.C.: 6159
N.A.I.C.S.: 522293
Claudio R. Alemann *(Gen Mgr)*

Branch:

Banco de la Nacion Argentina - New York **(2)**
230 Park Ave Frnt B
New York, NY 10169-0017
Tel.: (212) 303-0600
Fax: (212) 303-0857
E-Mail: mgmt@bnany.com
Web Site: www.bna.com.ar
Emp.: 42
International Trade Financing
S.I.C.: 6159
N.A.I.C.S.: 522293
Miguel Angel Mandrile *(Gen Mgr)*

BANCO DE LA PROVINCIA DE BUENOS AIRES

San Martin 137
C1004AAC Buenos Aires, Argentina
Tel.: (54) 1143470000
Fax: (54) 1143319401
Web Site: www.bapro.com.ar
Year Founded: 1882
Emp.: 14,000
Business Description:
International Banking
S.I.C.: 6159
N.A.I.C.S.: 522293
Personnel:
Carlos Francisco Dellepiane *(Vice Chm)*
Rodolfo Fridgeri *(Pres)*

U.S. Subsidiary:

Banco de la Provincia de Buenos Aires **(1)**
609 5th Ave Fl 10
New York, NY 10017-1093
Tel.: (212) 220-0544
Telex: 80-3153
Fax: (212) 220-0549
Web Site: www.bapro.com.ar/
Emp.: 3
International Banking
S.I.C.: 6159
N.A.I.C.S.: 522298

BANCO DE LA REPUBLICA COLOMBIA

Carrera 7 14-78
PO Box 3551
Bogota, Colombia
Tel.: (57) 13431111
Fax: (57) 12861686
Web Site: www.banrep.gov.co
Year Founded: 1923
Sales Range: $450-499.9 Million
Business Description:
Central Bank
S.I.C.: 6011
N.A.I.C.S.: 521110
Personnel:
Jose Dario Uribe Escobar *(Gen Mgr)*
Board of Directors:
Carlos Gustavo Cano Sanz
Juan Jose Echavarria Soto
Fernando Tenjo Galarza
Jose Dario Uribe Escobar
Cesar Vallejo Mejia
Juan Pablo Zarate Perdomo
Oscar Ivan Zuluaga Escobar

BANCO DE MOCAMBIQUE

Av 25 de Setembro 1695
PO Box 423
Maputo, Mozambique
Tel.: (258) 21354600
Fax: (258) 21323247
Web Site: www.bancomoc.mz
Sales Range: $1-9.9 Million
Business Description:
Banking Services
S.I.C.: 6011
N.A.I.C.S.: 521110
Personnel:
Ernesto Gouveia Gove *(Governor)*
Board of Directors:
Joana Jacinto David
Antonio Pinto de Abreu
Waldemar de Sousa
Victor Pedro Gomes
Ernesto Gouveia Gove
Esselina Macome

BANCO DE OCCIDENTE

Piso 15
No 7-61 Carrera 4a, Cali, Colombia
Tel.: (57) 92 886 1111
Fax: (57) 92 886 1291
Web Site: www.bancodeoccidente.com.co
Sales Range: $100-124.9 Million
Business Description:
Banking & Financial Services
S.I.C.: 6029
N.A.I.C.S.: 522110

BANCO DE PORTUGAL

R do Ouro 27
1100-150 Lisbon, Portugal
Tel.: (351) 213213200
Fax: (351) 213464843
E-Mail: info@bportugal.pt
Web Site: www.bportugal.pt
Sales Range: $1-4.9 Billion
Emp.: 1,689
Business Description:
Banking Services
S.I.C.: 6011
N.A.I.C.S.: 521110
Personnel:
Carlos da Silva Costa *(Governor)*
Board of Directors:
Carlos da Silva Costa
Jose da Silveira Godinho
Jose Joaquim Berberan e Santos Ramalho
Pedro Duarte Neves
Joao Jose Amaral Tomaz

BANCO DE SABADELL, S.A.

Plaza Sant Roc 20
08201 Sabadell, Barcelona, Spain
Tel.: (34) 902 323 555
Fax: (34) 935 916 062
E-Mail: info@bancsabadell.com
Web Site: www.bancsabadell.com
Year Founded: 1881
SAB—(MAD)
Rev.: $6,374,950,922
Assets: $217,469,839,414
Liabilities: $205,003,265,971
Net Worth: $12,466,573,443
Earnings: $129,279,436
Emp.: 15,596
Fiscal Year-end: 12/31/12
Business Description:
Banking Services
S.I.C.: 6029
N.A.I.C.S.: 522110
Personnel:
Jose Oliu Creus *(Chm)*
Isak Andic Ermay *(Vice Chm)*
Javier Echenique Landiribar *(Vice Chm)*
Jose Manuel Lara Bosch *(Vice Chm)*
Jaime Guardiola Romojaro *(Mng Dir)*
Board of Directors:
Jose Oliu Creus
Joan Llonch Andreu
Hector Maria Colonques Moreno
Sol Daurella Comadran
Jose Permanyer Cuniller
Isak Andic Ermay
Joaquin Folch-Rusinol Corachan
Maria Teresa Garcia-Mila Lloveras
Javier Echenique Landiribar
Jose Manuel Lara Bosch
Jose Manuel Martinez Martinez
Jose Ramon Martinez Sufrategui
Antonio Vitor Martins Monteiro
Jose Luis Negro Rodriguez
Jaime Guardiola Romojaro

Subsidiaries:

Aurica XXI, S.C.R., S.A. **(1)**
Avenida diagonal 407 bis 11 Fl
08008 Barcelona, Spain
Tel.: (34) 934033266
Fax: (34) 934033494
E-Mail: barconsc@bancsabadell.com
Web Site: www.auricaxxi.es
Emp.: 13
Financial Investment Activities
S.I.C.: 6211
N.A.I.C.S.: 523999
Jose Oliu Creus *(Pres)*

Banco Gallego, S.A. **(1)**
Linares Rivas 30
15005 La Coruna, Spain ES
Tel.: (34) 902157800 (25%)
E-Mail: info@bancogallego.es
Web Site: www.bancogallego.es
Sales Range: $75-99.9 Million
Emp.: 594
Foreign Trade Banking Services
S.I.C.: 6099
N.A.I.C.S.: 522320
Juan Manuel Urgoiti *(Pres)*
Eduardo Medina *(Treas)*

Banco Guipuzcoano S.A. (1)
Avenida de la Libertad 21
20012 San Sebastian, Spain
Tel.: (34) 943418100
Fax: (34) 943418550
Sales Range: $500-549.9 Million
Banking Services
S.I.C.: 6029
N.A.I.C.S.: 522110
Javier Echenique Landiribar *(Chm)*
Antonio Salvador Serrats Iriarte *(Vice Chm)*

Subsidiaries:

Ederra, S.A. (2)
Camino de Portuetxe 35-A Igara
20018 San Sebastian, Guipuzcoa, Spain
Tel.: (34) 943 21 79 10
Real Estate Services
S.I.C.: 6531
N.A.I.C.S.: 531210

Grao Castalia, S.L. (2)
Haygon La Almazara SL San Vicente del Raspe
Valencia, 46004, Spain
Tel.: (34) 963528181
Real Estate Property Management Services
S.I.C.: 6531
N.A.I.C.S.: 531312

Guipuzcoano Capital, S.A. (2)
Avenida de la Libertad 2
20004 San Sebastian, Guipuzcoa, Spain
Tel.: (34) 943 418 564
Fax: (34) 943 418 271
Emp.: 200
Securities Brokerages & Banking Services
S.I.C.: 6211
N.A.I.C.S.: 523120
Jesus Maria Mijangos Ugarte *(Pres)*

Guipuzcoano Correduria de Seguros del Grupo Banco Guipuzcoano, S.A. (2)
Camino de Portuetxe 35-A Igara
20018 San Sebastian, Guipuzcoa, Spain
Tel.: (34) 943 41 85 85
Fax: (34) 943 41 84 39
Commercial Banking Services
S.I.C.: 6029
N.A.I.C.S.: 522110

Guipuzcoano Entidad Gestora de Fondos de Pensiones , S.A. (2)
Paseo De La Concha 11
San Sebastian, Guipuzcoa, 20007, Spain
Tel.: (34) 943418692
Fax: (34) 943418705
E-Mail: mamgurrutx@bancogui.com
Emp.: 3
Pension Fund Management Services
S.I.C.: 6282
N.A.I.C.S.: 523920
Marina Gurruchaga Aizpuru *(Gen Mgr)*

Haygon La Almazara, S.L. (2)
Avenida Haygon 16
03690 San Vicente del Raspeig, Alicante, Spain
Tel.: (34) 965661033
Real Estate Property Management Services
S.I.C.: 6531
N.A.I.C.S.: 531312

Banco Urquijo S.A. (1)
Serrano 71
28006 Madrid, Spain ES
Tel.: (34) 913372000
Fax: (34) 914366959
E-Mail: burrhh@bancourquijo.com
Web Site: www.bancourquijo.com
Emp.: 200
Banking Services
S.I.C.: 6029
N.A.I.C.S.: 522110
Ismail Picon *(Gen Mgr)*

BanSabadell Correduria de Seguros SA (1)
Calle Del Sena Pg Ind Can Sant Joan
Barcelona, Spain
Tel.: (34) 937289459
Emp.: 100
Insurance Agencies & Brokerages
S.I.C.: 6411
N.A.I.C.S.: 524210

Bansabadell Factura, S.L. (1)
C Del Sena Pq Actividades Economicas Cant San 12
8174 Sant Cugat del Valles, Barcelona, Spain
Tel.: (34) 937289289
Fax: (34) 935916061
Commercial Banking Services
S.I.C.: 6029
N.A.I.C.S.: 522110

BanSabadell Fincom, E.F.C., S.A. (1)
Sant Cugat Of Valles
08190 Barcelona, Spain
Tel.: (34) 935916300
Fax: (34) 935916305
E-Mail: bsincon@bansabadellfinom.com
Web Site: www.bansabadellfincom.com
Emp.: 100
Financial Investment Activities
S.I.C.: 6211
N.A.I.C.S.: 523999
Jose Gomez *(Gen Mgr)*

BanSabadell Holding, S.L. (1)
C Del Seine Pq AE Can Sant Joan 12
08174 Sant Cugat del Valles, Spain
Tel.: (34) 937289289
Investment Management Services
S.I.C.: 6211
N.A.I.C.S.: 523999

BanSabadell Inversion, S.A., S.G.I.I.C. (1)
Calle Del Sena Pq Activ Economicas Can San Joa
Sant Cugat Del Valles, Barcelona, Spain
Tel.: (34) 937289289
Web Site: www.bsinversion.com
Nondepository Credit Intermediation
S.I.C.: 6159
N.A.I.C.S.: 522298
Tomas Varela Muina *(Chm)*

Easo Bolsa, S.A. (1)
Portuetxe Street 35
20018 San Sebastian, Spain
Tel.: (34) 943418564
Fax: (34) 943217929
Financial Management Services
S.I.C.: 6211
N.A.I.C.S.: 523999

Emte Renovables, S.L. (1)
Avenida Roma 25
Barcelona, 8029, Spain
Tel.: (34) 932282120
Electric Power Generation Services
S.I.C.: 4931
N.A.I.C.S.: 221118

Espais SL (1)
Ave Diagonal 67 6th floor
8019 Barcelona, Spain
Tel.: (34) 932920000
Fax: (34) 932177033
E-Mail: info@espais.es
Web Site: www.espais.es
Emp.: 14
Real Estate Agents & Brokers
S.I.C.: 6531
N.A.I.C.S.: 531210
Consejero Delegado *(Pres)*

Landscape Parcsud SL (1)
Calle Sant Vicenc 51
Sabadell, Spain
Tel.: (34) 932473957
Land Subdivision
S.I.C.: 6552
N.A.I.C.S.: 237210

Sabadell Corporate Finance, S.L. (1)
Principe de Vergara 125
Madrid, 28002, Spain
Tel.: (34) 913 19 88 07
Fax: (34) 913 19 32 04
E-Mail: contactar@sabadellcorporatefinance.com
Web Site: www.sabadellcorporatefinance.com
Emp.: 10
Investment Banking & Financial Advisory Services
S.I.C.: 6211
N.A.I.C.S.: 523110
Pablo Rocamora *(Mng Dir-Merger & Acq)*

SabadellCAM (1)
San Fernando 40
03001 Alicante, Spain ES
Tel.: (34) 902100112
E-Mail: cam@cam.es
Web Site: www.cam.es
Banking Services
S.I.C.: 6029
N.A.I.C.S.: 522110
Jose Oliu Creus *(Chm & CEO)*

Subsidiaries:

CAM Capital, S.A.U. (2)
Avenida Oscar Espla 37
03007 Alicante, Spain
Tel.: (34) 965143791
Fax: (34) 965200252
Banking Services
S.I.C.: 6029
N.A.I.C.S.: 522110

Mediterraneo Vida S.A. (2)
Avda de Elche N 178 Edificio Centro Administrativo
03008 Alicante, Spain
Tel.: (34) 965905344
Fax: (34) 965 905 354
General Insurance Services
S.I.C.: 6411
N.A.I.C.S.: 524210

Meserco, S.L. (2)
Pasaje Mercader 7-21
Barcelona, 08022, Spain
Tel.: (34) 934342210
Fax: (34) 934187002
Business Management Consulting Services
S.I.C.: 8742
N.A.I.C.S.: 541611

Tabimed Gestion de Proyectos, S.L (2)
Avenida General Marva 8
03004 Alicante, Spain
Tel.: (34) 965901400
Web Site: www.tabimed.es
Engineering Consulting Services
S.I.C.: 8711
N.A.I.C.S.: 541330

Servicios Reunidos, S.A. (1)
Avenida Pena De Francia
La Alberca, 37624, Spain
Tel.: (34) 923415093
Fax: (34) 923415093
Insurance Management Sercives
S.I.C.: 6411
N.A.I.C.S.: 524298

Spanish Power, S.L. (1)
Calle Antonio Maura 8
28014 Madrid, Spain
Tel.: (34) 915313907
Fax: (34) 915320360
E-Mail: power@fusgar.com
Emp.: 15
Automotive Mechanical & Electrical Repair & Maintenance
S.I.C.: 7539
N.A.I.C.S.: 811118
Don Ricardo Fuster *(Mgr)*

Tecnocredit, S.A. (1)
Plz Catalunya 1
Sabadell, Spain
Tel.: (34) 934194440
Web Site: www.tecnocredit.com
Management Consulting Services
S.I.C.: 8748
N.A.I.C.S.: 541618
Joan Ribo Casaus *(Pres)*

U.S. Subsidiaries:

Geysers International Inc. (1)
4811 Beach Blvd Ste 401
Jacksonville, FL 32207-4867
Tel.: (904) 356-1100
Fax: (904) 356-1150
Web Site: www.geysers.net
Software Publishers
S.I.C.: 7372
N.A.I.C.S.: 511210

Sabadell United Bank, N.A. (1)
1111 Brickell Ave Ste 2910
Miami, FL 33131
Tel.: (305) 441-5310
Fax: (305) 444-0939
Web Site: www.sabadellunited.com
Emp.: 533
Banking Services
S.I.C.: 6029
N.A.I.C.S.: 522110
Mario Trueba *(Pres & CEO)*
Louis-Albert H. Jolivert *(Sr VP)*

Transatlantic Bank Inc. (1)
48 E Flagler St
Miami, FL 33131 FL
Tel.: (305) 377-0200 (100%)
Fax: (305) 577-8238
E-Mail: customerservice@transatlanticbank.com
Web Site: www.transatlanticbank.com
Sales Range: $25-49.9 Million
Emp.: 79
Commercial Banking Services
S.I.C.: 6029
N.A.I.C.S.: 522110
Fernando Perez-Hickman *(Chm)*
Miriam Lopez *(CEO)*
Jordi Torras *(CFO)*

Non-U.S. Subsidiaries:

BancSabadell d'Andorra, S.A. (1)
Av del Fener 7
AG500 Escaldes-Engordany, Andorra
Tel.: (376) 735600
Fax: (376) 735650
E-Mail: info@bsandorra.com
Web Site: www.bsandorra.com
Emp.: 100
Commercial Banking
S.I.C.: 6029
N.A.I.C.S.: 522110
Miquel Alabern *(Gen Mgr)*

BanSabadell Finanziaria SpA. (1)
Corso Venezia 5
20121 Milan, Italy
Tel.: (39) 0276007552
Fax: (39) 0276015009
E-Mail: bsfinanz@tin.it
Web Site: www.grupobancosabadell.com
Commercial Banking
S.I.C.: 6029
N.A.I.C.S.: 522110
Paolo Provera *(Mgr)*

Financiera Iberoamericana, S.A. (1)
5th Ave 78-80 St Miramar Trade Center
Edificio Barcelona office 314
Playa La Habana, Havana, Cuba
Tel.: (53) 72043196
Fax: (53) 72043198
Financial Investment Activities
S.I.C.: 6211
N.A.I.C.S.: 523999
Jose Julio Rodriguez *(Pres)*

BANCO DEL CARIBE, C.A. BANCO UNIVERSAL

Dr Paul a Salvador del Leon Edif
Banco del Caribe
Piso 10, 101A Caracas, Venezuela
Tel.: (58) 2125055511
Fax: (58) 212 505 5370
E-Mail: secret@bancaribe.com.ve
Web Site: www.bancaribe.com.ve
ABC.A—(CAR)
Sales Range: $50-74.9 Million
Emp.: 2,000

Business Description:
Banking Services
S.I.C.: 6029
N.A.I.C.S.: 522110

Personnel:
Miguel Ignacio Purroi *(Chm)*
Juan Carlos Dao *(Pres)*
Rosa Maria Salas de Argotte *(Sec)*

BANCO DI CARIBE NV

Schottegatweg Oost 205
Willemstad, Curacao
Tel.: (599) 9 432 3000
Fax: (599) 6 461 5220
E-Mail: management@bancodicaribe.com
Web Site: www.bancodicaribe.com
Sales Range: $800-899.9 Million
Emp.: 275

Business Description:
Commercial Banking
S.I.C.: 6029
N.A.I.C.S.: 522110

Banco di Caribe NV—(Continued)

Personnel:
Percival N. Virginia *(CEO)*

Subsidiary:

Ennia Caribe Holding NV (1)
JB Gorsiraweg 6
PO Box 585
Willemstad, Curacao (100%)
Tel.: (599) 94343800
Fax: (599) 94343890
E-Mail: mail@ennia.com
Web Site: www.ennia.com
Emp.: 180
Holding Company; Life Insurance Products & Services
S.I.C.: 6719
N.A.I.C.S.: 551112
Brown Anna *(Pres)*

BANCO DI DESIO E DELLA BRIANZA S.P.A.

Rovagnati 1
20033 Desio, Italy
Tel.: (39) 03626131
Fax: (39) 03626139204
E-Mail: segreteriag@bancodesio.it
Web Site: www.bancodesio.it
Year Founded: 1909
BDB—(ITA)
Sales Range: $300-349.9 Million
Emp.: 1,397

Business Description:
Banking Services
S.I.C.: 6029
N.A.I.C.S.: 522110

Personnel:
Agostino Gavazzi *(Chm)*
Stefano Melchiorre Lado *(Deputy Chm)*
Guido Pozzoli *(Deputy Chm)*
Nereo Dacci *(Mng Dir)*
Alberto Mocchi *(Gen Dir)*

Board of Directors:
Agostino Gavazzi
Francesco Cesarini
Pier Antonio Cutelle
Nereo Dacci
Egidio Gavazzi
Luigi Gavazzi
Paolo Gavazzi
Luigi Guatri
Stefano Melchiorre Lado
Gerolamo Pellicano
Guido Pozzoli

Subsidiaries:

Banco Desio Lazio S P A (1)
Via Po 6 8
00198 Rome, Italy
Tel.: (39) 06852571
Fax: (39) 0685304119
E-Mail: segreteriabdl@bancodesio.it
Web Site: www.bancodesiolazio.it
Commercial Banking Services
S.I.C.: 6029
N.A.I.C.S.: 522110
Nereo Dacci *(CEO)*

Banco Desio Toscana S P A (1)
Via de Tornabuoni 9
50123 Florence, Italy
Tel.: (39) 055267791
Fax: (39) 055 2677960
E-Mail: diroperbdt@bancodesio.it
Web Site: www.bancodesiotoscana.it
Commercial Banking Services
S.I.C.: 6029
N.A.I.C.S.: 522110
Angelo Antoniazzi *(Gen Mgr)*

Banco Desio Veneto S P A (1)
Piazza Castello 27
36100 Vicenza, Italy
Tel.: (39) 0444391290
Fax: (39) 0444330929
E-Mail: diroperbdv@bancodesio.it
Web Site: www.bancodesioveneto.it
Commercial Banking Services
S.I.C.: 6029
N.A.I.C.S.: 522110
Mauro Boscolo *(CEO)*

Chiara Assicurazioni S P A (1)
Via Galileo Galilei 7
Milan, 20124, Italy
Tel.: (39) 026328811
Fax: (39) 0263288145
E-Mail: chiaraassicurazion@chiaraassicurazioni.it
Web Site: www.chiaraassicurazioni.it
Emp.: 42
Non-Life Insurance Services
S.I.C.: 6399
N.A.I.C.S.: 524128
Graniari Rosalba *(Gen Mgr)*

Non-U.S. Subsidiary:

Brianfid-Lux S A (1)
6 placedenacy
L-1840 Luxembourg, Luxembourg
Tel.: (352) 2602881
Fax: (352) 26459977
E-Mail: info@brianfid.lu
Emp.: 10
Commercial Banking Services
S.I.C.: 6029
N.A.I.C.S.: 522110
Alberto Cavadini *(Gen Mgr)*

BANCO DO BRASIL S.A.

SBS Qd 01 Bloco C Edificio Sede III 13th Fl
70073-901 Brasilia, DF, Brazil
Tel.: (55) 6131020000
Telex: 61 730-0120
Fax: (55) 6133102444
E-Mail: ri@bb.com.br
Web Site: www.bb.com.br
Year Founded: 1808
BBAS3—(BRAZ)
Rev.: $51,039,426,726
Assets: $565,912,651,507
Liabilities: $533,413,496,423
Net Worth: $32,499,155,084
Earnings: $6,003,576,477
Emp.: 114,182
Fiscal Year-end: 12/31/12

Business Description:
International Banking Services
S.I.C.: 6159
N.A.I.C.S.: 522293

Personnel:
Aldemir Bendine *(Chm-Exec Bd)*
Alexandre Correa Abreu *(Member-Exec Bd & VP-Retail Svcs)*
Benito da Gama Santos *(Member-Exec Bd & VP-Govt Affairs)*
Ivan de Souza Monteiro *(Member-Exec Bd & VP-Fin Mgmt & IR)*
Geraldo Afonso Dezena da Silva *(Member-Exec Bd & VP-Tech)*
Osmar Fernandes Dias *(Member-Exec Bd & VP-Agribus & Small Medium Enterprises)*
Paulo Roberto Lopes Ricci *(Member-Exec Bd & VP-Retail Svc, Distr & Ops Svcs)*
Walter Malieni, Jr. *(Member-Exec Bd & VP-Internal Controls & Risk Mgmt)*
Robson Rocha *(Member-Exec Bd & VP-HR & Sustainable Dev)*
Paulo Rogerio Caffarelli *(Member-Exec Bd & VP-Wholesale, Intl Bus & Private Banking)*
Gustavo Henrique Santos de Sousa *(Member-Exec Bd & Head-IR Unit)*
Rodrigo Santos Nogueira *(Member-Exec Bd & Gen Mgr-Sustainable Dev Unit)*
Daniel Oliveira da Silva *(Member-Exec Bd & Gen Mgr-Ops-IT Solutions Unit)*
Rogerio Fernando Lot *(Member-Exec Bd & Gen Mgr-Private Bank Unit)*
Wagner Aparecido Mardegan *(Member-Exec Bd & Gen Mgr-Pension Plan Unit)*
Anderson Freire Nobre *(Member-Exec Bd & Gen Mgr-Construction-IT Solutions Unit)*
Carlos Alberto Araujo Netto *(Member-Exec Bd & Dir-HR)*
Marco Antonio Ascoli Mastroeni *(Member-Exec Bd & Dir-Strategy & Org)*
Edmar Jose Casalatina *(Member-Exec Bd & Dir-Consumer Lending & Fin)*
Jose Mauricio Pereira Coelho *(Member-Exec Bd & Dir-Fin)*
Hayton Jurema da Rocha *(Member-Exec Bd & Dir-Mktg & Comm)*
Antonio Pedro da Silva Machado *(Member-Exec Bd & Dir-Legal)*
Jose Carlos Reis da Silva *(Member-Exec Bd & Dir-Distr)*
Adilson do Nascimento Anisio *(Member-Exec Bd & Dir-Micro & Small Bus)*
Marcio Hamilton Ferreira *(Member-Exec Bd & Dir-Credit)*
Sandro Jose Franco *(Member-Exec Bd & Dir-Bus Support & Ops)*
Ives Cezar Fulber *(Member-Exec Bd & Dir-Risk Mgmt)*
Admilson Monteiro Garcia *(Member-Exec Bd & Dir-Intl Bus & Affairs)*
Gueitiro Matsuo Genso *(Member-Exec Bd & Dir-Mortgage)*
Luiz Henrique Guimaraes de Freitas *(Member-Exec Bd & Dir-Tech)*
Carlos Eduardo Leal Neri *(Member-Exec Bd & Dir-Employee Rels & Sponsored Entities)*
Janio Carlos Endo Macedo *(Member-Exec Bd & Dir-Govt Affairs)*
Sandro Kohler Marcondes *(Member-Exec Bd & Dir-Controlling)*
Antonio Mauricio Maurano *(Member-Exec Bd & Dir-Comml)*
Nilson Martiniano Moreira *(Member-Exec Bd & Dir-Internal Controls)*
Raul Francisco Moreira *(Member-Exec Bd & Dir-Credit & Debt Cards)*
Sergio Peres *(Member-Exec Bd & Dir-Distr-Sao Paulo)*
Adriano Meira Ricci *(Member-Exec Bd & Dir-Restructuring-Ops Asset)*
Clenio Severio Teribele *(Member-Exec Bd & Dir-Agribus)*
Claudemir Andreo Alledo *(Member-Exec Bd-Partners Channel Unit)*
Edson Rogerio da Costa *(Member-Exec Bd-Governance-Related Companies Unit)*
Gustavo de Souza Fosse *(Member-Exec Bd-Structuring-IT Solutions Unit)*
Antonio Carlos Bizzo Lima *(Member-Exec Bd-Acq & Strategic Partnerships Unit)*
Eduardo Cesar Pasa *(Member-Exec Bd-Acctg Unit)*
Luiz Claudio Ligabue *(Sec)*

Board of Directors:
Sergio Eduardo Arbulu Mendonca
Aldemir Bendine
Adriana Queiroz De Carvalho
Elvio Lima Gaspar
Bernardo Goutheir Macedo
Henrique Jager

Subsidiaries:

BB Administradora de Cartoes de Credito S.A. (1)
SBS Quadra 1 Bloco A Lote 25 Ed Sede I Fl 9
70073-900 Brasilia, Brazil (100%)
Tel.: (55) 6133101300
Fax: (55) 6133101888
E-Mail: bbcartoes@bb.com.br
Emp.: 100
S.I.C.: 6159
N.A.I.C.S.: 522298
Douglas MacEdo *(Gen Mgr)*

BB Banco de Investimento S.A. (1)
Rua Senador Dantas 105 36th Floor
Rio de Janeiro, Brazil
Tel.: (55) 21 3808 6340
Investment Banking Services
S.I.C.: 6211
N.A.I.C.S.: 523110

BB Leasing-Arrandemento Mercantil (1)
Setor Bancario Sul Quadra 4 Bloco C Ed Sede III
7 Andar, 70089 900 Brasilia, DF, Brazil (100%)
Tel.: (55) 6133103253
Fax: (55) 6133102871
E-Mail: dicom@bb.com.br
Emp.: 25
S.I.C.: 6159
N.A.I.C.S.: 522298
Allan Simoes Toledo *(Mgr)*

BBBI Banco de Investimento (1)
R Senador Dantas Fl 37
105 36 Andar, 20031-201 Rio de Janeiro, RJ, Brazil (100%)
Tel.: (55) 2138083625
Fax: (55) 2138083191
Emp.: 300
S.I.C.: 6159
N.A.I.C.S.: 522298
Leonardo Loyola *(Mgr)*

Brasilprev Seguros e Previdencia S.A. (1)
Rua Alexandre Dumas 1671
Sao Paulo, 04717-004, Brazil
Tel.: (55) 11 2162 6600
Fax: (55) 11 2162 6304
Web Site: www.brasilprev.com.br
Pension Fund Management Services
S.I.C.: 6282
N.A.I.C.S.: 523920
Miguel Terra Lima *(Office Mgr)*

Cobra Technologia S.A. (1)
Estrada Dos Bandeirantes 7966 Curicica
Jacarepagua, 22783 110 Rio de Janeiro, Brazil BR
Tel.: (55) 2124428800 (100%)
Fax: (55) 4411762
E-Mail: info@cobra.com.br
Web Site: www.cobra.com.br
Sales Range: $300-349.9 Million
Emp.: 450
Computer Industry
S.I.C.: 7374
N.A.I.C.S.: 518210
George Wilson *(Pres)*

U.S. Branch:

Banco do Brasil S.A.-New York (1)
600 5th Ave Fl 3
New York, NY 10020-2302 (100%)
Tel.: (212) 626-7000
Fax: (212) 626-7045
E-Mail: newyark@bbs.com.br
Web Site: www.bancobrasil-us.com
Emp.: 100
International Banking
S.I.C.: 6029
N.A.I.C.S.: 522110
Daniel Costa *(Gen Mgr)*

Non-U.S. Subsidiaries:

Banco do Brasil AG Austria (1)
Praterstrasse
A 1020 Vienna, Austria (100%)
Tel.: (43) 151266630
Fax: (43) 15121042
E-Mail: vienna@bb.com.br
Web Site: www.bb.com.br
Rev.: $3,410,690
Emp.: 20
Banking Activities
S.I.C.: 6159
N.A.I.C.S.: 522298
Nestor Joung *(Mng Dir)*

U.S. Subsidiary:

BB Money Transfers, Inc (2)
709 Westchester Ave
White Plains, NY 10604
Tel.: (866) 832-2201
Fax: (407) 608-1890

Web Site: www.bbmt.com
Emp.: 50
Money Transfer Services
S.I.C.: 6099
N.A.I.C.S.: 522320
Adriano Trad *(Gen Mgr)*

Banco Patagonia Sudameris S.A. **(1)**
Teneiente General J d peron 500 - 3 piso
Buenos Aires, Argentina
Tel.: (54) 11 4323 5000
Fax: (54) 11 4131 5760
E-Mail: investors@bancopatagonia.com.ar
Web Site: www.bancopatagonia.com.ar
BPAT33—(BRAZ)
Sales Range: $450-499.9 Million
Emp.: 2,240
Commercial Banking Services
S.I.C.: 6029
N.A.I.C.S.: 522110
Carlos Barbosa Mello, *(Dir-IR)*

Brasilian American Merchant Bank **(1)**
Elizabethan Sq Phase 3 Bldg 4th Fl
PO Box 1360 GT
Shedden Rd, Georgetown, Grand Cayman, Cayman Islands (100%)
Tel.: (345) 9495907
Fax: (345) 9498872
Emp.: 12
Merchant Banking Activities
S.I.C.: 6159
N.A.I.C.S.: 522298
Idel Albereto Blajseder *(Branch Mgr)*

Non-U.S. Subsidiary:

BB Securities Ltd. **(2)**
16 St Martins Le Trand Fl 7
EC1A 4NA London, United Kingdom (100%)
Tel.: (44) 2073675800
Fax: (44) 2077960863
E-Mail: bbsecs@bloomberg.net
Emp.: 16
Securities House
S.I.C.: 6211
N.A.I.C.S.: 523999

BANCO DO ESTADO DO RIO GRANDE DO SUL SA
(d/b/a Banrisul)
Rua Capitao Montanha 177 4th Floor
Porto Alegre, Brazil 90010-040
Tel.: (55) 51 3215 3232
Fax: (55) 51 3215 3200
E-Mail: ri@banrisul-ri.com.br
Web Site: www.banrisul.com.br
BRSR3—(BRAZ)
Rev.: $2,938,540,530
Assets: $23,311,985,365
Liabilities: $20,802,685,265
Net Worth: $2,509,300,100
Earnings: $410,093,120
Emp.: 10,225
Fiscal Year-end: 12/31/12
Business Description:
Banking Services
S.I.C.: 6029
N.A.I.C.S.: 522110
Personnel:
Odir Alberto Pinheiro Tonollier *(Chm)*
Tulio Luiz Zamin *(Vice Chm & CEO)*
Joao Emilio Gazzana *(CFO & IR Officer)*
Ivandre de Jesus Medeiros *(COO & Chief Customer Svc Officer)*
Joel dos Santos Raymundo *(CIO)*
Luiz Carlos Morlin *(Chief Compliance Officer & Chief Risk Officer)*
Guilherme Cassel *(Chief Credit Officer)*
Jone Luiz Hermes Pfeiff *(Chief Comml Officer)*
Julimar Roberto Rota *(Asset Mgmt Officer)*
Jorge Irani da Silva *(Sec Gen)*
Board of Directors:
Odir Alberto Pinheiro Tonollier
Aldo Pinto da Silva
Marcelo Tuerlinckx Daneris
Olivio de Oliveira Dutra
Francisco Carlos Braganca de Souza
Flavio Luiz Lammel
Dilio Sergio Penedo
Erineu Clovis Xavier
Tulio Luiz Zamin

BANCO FIBRA S.A.
Avenida Presidente Juscelino Kubitschek 360
4th to 9th Floors, 04543-000 Sao Paulo, Brazil
Tel.: (55) 1138476640
Fax: (55) 1138114788
E-Mail: ir@bancofibra.com.br
Web Site: www.bancofibra.com.br
Sales Range: $550-599.9 Million
Emp.: 1,051
Business Description:
Credit Operations & Banking Services
S.I.C.: 6141
N.A.I.C.S.: 522210
Personnel:
Ricardo Steinbruch *(Chm)*

BANCO FINANCIERO Y DE AHORROS, S.A.U.
(d/b/a Grupo BFA)
Paseo de la Castellana 189
28046 Madrid, Spain
Tel.: (34) 902 460 460
Web Site: www.bancofinancieroydeahorros.com
Year Founded: 2010
Int. Income: $10,905,966,639
Assets: $416,218,597,640
Liabilities: $412,026,699,646
Net Worth: $4,191,897,994
Earnings: ($28,590,596,545)
Fiscal Year-end: 12/31/12
Business Description:
Bank Holding Company
S.I.C.: 6712
N.A.I.C.S.: 551111
Personnel:
Jose Ignacio Goirigolzarri Tellaeche *(Chm)*
Miguel Crespo Rodriguez *(Sec)*
Board of Directors:
Jose Ignacio Goirigolzarri Tellaeche
Fernando Fernandez Mendez of Andes
Antonio Ortega Parra
Joaquim Saurina Maspoch
Jose Sevilla Alvarez

Affiliate:

Bankia, S.A.U. **(1)**
Calle Pintor Sorolla 8
46002 Valencia, Spain ES
Tel.: (34) 917877575 (48.05%)
Fax: (34) 917911600
E-Mail: accionista@bankia.com
Web Site: www.bankia.com
BKIA—(BAR MAD OTC)
Rev.: $9,773,522,665
Assets: $375,908,572,195
Liabilities: $384,238,427,152
Net Worth: ($8,329,854,957)
Earnings: ($24,643,584,373)
Emp.: 18,554
Fiscal Year-end: 12/31/12
Commercial Banking Services
S.I.C.: 6029
N.A.I.C.S.: 522110
Jose Ignacio Goirigolzarri Tellaeche *(Chm)*
Jose Sevilla Alvarez *(Gen Dir-Chm Office)*
Amalia Blanco Lucas *(Asst Gen Dir-Comm & External Rels)*
Antonio Ortega Parra *(Gen Dir-People, Resources & Tech)*
Antonio Zafra Jimenez *(Vice Sec)*
Miguel Crespo Rodriguez *(Gen Sec)*

Subsidiaries:

Altae Banco S.A. **(2)**
Calle Monte Esquinta 48
28010 Madrid, Spain (100%)
Tel.: (34) 913915380
Fax: (34) 913915410
Web Site: www.altae.es
Emp.: 80
Banking
S.I.C.: 6159
N.A.I.C.S.: 522298
Jose Manuel Wdabriow *(Mng Dir)*

Aseguradora Valenciana SA de Seguros y Reaseguros **(2)**
Plaza de la Legion Espanola 8
Entresuelo, 46010 Valencia, Spain ES
Tel.: (34) 963 87 5900
Fax: (34) 963 87 5944
Insurance Brokerage Services
S.I.C.: 6411
N.A.I.C.S.: 524298

Atenea Comunicacion Y Mecenazgo, S.A. **(2)**
Calle Santander 3 Segunda Planta
28003 Madrid, Spain (80%)
Tel.: (34) 915989820
Fax: (34) 915541422
E-Mail: info@ateneacm.es
Web Site: www.ateneacm.es
Emp.: 20
Provider of Research Services
S.I.C.: 8732
N.A.I.C.S.: 541910
Carlos Sanchez Oloya *(Chm)*

Bankia Pensiones, S.A.U., E.G.F.P. **(2)**
Paseo de la Castellana 189
28046 Madrid, Spain ES
Tel.: (34) 914239494 (100%)
Fax: (34) 914239326
Web Site: www.bankiapensiones.es
Sales Range: $1-9.9 Million
Emp.: 35
Pension Fund Management
S.I.C.: 6371
N.A.I.C.S.: 524292

Caja de Madrid de Seguros Generales, S.A. de Seguros y Reaseguros **(2)**
Paseo Recoletos 23
ES 28004 Madrid, Spain (100%)
Tel.: (34) 902136524
Fax: (34) 915812447
General Insurance
S.I.C.: 6311
N.A.I.C.S.: 524113

Corporacion Financiera Caja de Madrid, S.A. **(2)**
Gabriel Garcia Marquez 1
Madrid, 28230, Spain (100%)
Tel.: (34) 902246810
Fax: (34) 914 239 807
Web Site: www.cajamadrid.es/CajaMadrid/Home/puente?pagina=907
Corporate Management
S.I.C.: 8741
N.A.I.C.S.: 551114

Madrid Vida, S.A. de Seguros y Reaseguros **(2)**
Avenida General Peron 49
ES 28020 Madrid, Spain (100%)
Tel.: (34) 902136524
Life Insurance
S.I.C.: 6311
N.A.I.C.S.: 524113

Sociedad de Participacion y Promocion Empresarial Caja de Madrid **(2)**
Eloy Gonzalo 10
Madrid, Spain (100%)
Web Site: www.cajamadrid.es/CajaMadrid/Home/puente?pagina=907
Venture Capital; Financial Company
S.I.C.: 6799
N.A.I.C.S.: 523910

Affiliates:

Auseco, S.A. **(2)**
San Bernardo 123
Madrid, Spain (20%)
Provider of Debt Collection Services
S.I.C.: 7322
N.A.I.C.S.: 561440

Cresan, S.A. **(2)**
Hierro 33
28045 Madrid, Spain (20%)
Tel.: (34) 915062193
Fax: (34) 914277526
Web Site: www.cresan.es
Data Files
S.I.C.: 7374
N.A.I.C.S.: 518210

Registro de Prestaciones Informaticas, S.A. **(2)**
Capitan Haya 51
Madrid, Spain (20%)
Web Site: www.registro-sa.com
Savings Institutions, Federally Chartered
S.I.C.: 6036
N.A.I.C.S.: 522120

S.L. de Gestion Mobiliaria **(2)**
Avenida Diagonal 530
Barcelona, Spain (50%)
Portfolio Management
S.I.C.: 6799
N.A.I.C.S.: 523920

U.S. Subsidiary:

City National Bank of Florida **(2)**
25 W Flagler St
Miami, FL 33130-1712
Tel.: (305) 577-7333
Fax: (305) 577-7451
Toll Free: (800) 435-8839
E-Mail: info@citynational.com
Web Site: www.citynational.com
Sales Range: $125-149.9 Million
Emp.: 434
Retail & Commercial Banking
S.I.C.: 6029
N.A.I.C.S.: 522110
Jorge Gonzalez *(Pres & CEO)*
Daniel Kushner *(CFO)*
Lloyd B. DeVaux *(COO)*
Javier Sanchez *(Chief Dev Officer)*

BANCO GALLEGO SA
(Acquired by Banco de Sabadell, S.A.)

BANCO GENERAL, S.A.
Ave Aquilino De La Guardia y Ave 5ta B Sur Torre Banco General
Apartado Postal 0816-00843
Panama, Panama
Tel.: (507) 205 1750
Fax: (507) 301 8587
Web Site: www.bgeneral.com
Year Founded: 1955
BGEN—(PAN)
Emp.: 2,617
Business Description:
Banking Services
S.I.C.: 6029
N.A.I.C.S.: 522110
Personnel:
Federico Humbert *(Chm & Pres)*
Stanley A. Motta *(Treas)*
Z. Raul Aleman *(Sec, Exec VP & Gen Mgr)*
Federico Albert *(Exec VP-Intl Banking)*
Luis Garcia de Paredes *(Exec VP-Support & Ops)*
Juan Raul Humbert *(Exec VP-Bus)*
Francisco Sierra *(Exec VP-Fin)*
Board of Directors:
Federico Humbert
Z. Raul Aleman
Ricardo M. Arango
A. Ricardo A. Arias
Tatiana Fabrega de Varela
Juan Raul Humbert
C. Alberto Motta
Felipe Motta
Stanley A. Motta
Osvaldo Mouynes
J. Emanuel Gonzalez Revilla
L. Emanuel Gonzalez Revilla
Jaime Rivera
Francisco Salerno

BANCO GUIPUZCOANO S.A.
(Acquired by Banco de Sabadell, S.A.)

BANCO INDUSTRIAL E COMERCIAL S.A
(d/b/a BICBANCO)
Avenida Paulista 1048 7th Floor
CEP 01310-100 Sao Paulo, SP, Brazil
Tel.: (55) 1121739010
Fax: (55) 1132668951
E-Mail: investor.relations@bicbanco.com.br
Web Site: www.bicbanco.com.br
Year Founded: 1938
BICB4—(BRAZ)
Rev.: $1,304,071,222
Assets: $8,982,896,656
Liabilities: $8,013,185,693
Net Worth: $969,710,962
Earnings: $54,369,094
Emp.: 920
Fiscal Year-end: 12/31/12
Business Description:
Banking Services
S.I.C.: 6029
N.A.I.C.S.: 522110
Personnel:
Jose Adauto Bezerra *(Chm)*
Jose Bezerra de Menezes *(CEO & Member-Exec Bd)*
Milto Bardini *(Deputy CEO, IR Officer, Member-Exec Bd & Exec VP-Ops)*
Paulo Celso Del Ciampo *(Deputy CEO, Member-Exec Bd & Dir-Intl)*
Jose Adauto Bezerra, Jr. *(Deputy CEO & Member-Exec Bd)*
Francisco Edenio Barbosa Nobre *(Exec Officer & Member-Exec Bd)*
Sergio da Silva Bezerra de Menezes *(Exec Officer & Member-Exec Bd)*
Carlos Jose Roque *(Exec Officer & Member-Exec Bd)*
Board of Directors:
Jose Adauto Bezerra
Francisco Humberto Bezerra
Heraldo Gilberto de Oliveira
Daniel Joseph McQuoid
Jose Bezerra de Menezes

BANCO INDUSVAL S.A.
Rua Iguatemi 151 - 6th Floor
Sao Paulo, 01451-011, Brazil
Tel.: (55) 1133156821
Fax: (55) 1133150136
E-Mail: shatarta@indusval.com.br
Web Site: www.indusval.com.br
Year Founded: 1967
IDVL4—(BRAZ)
Rev.: $312,731,365
Assets: $1,978,372,726
Liabilities: $1,689,534,426
Net Worth: $288,838,300
Earnings: $7,011,400
Emp.: 436
Fiscal Year-end: 12/31/12
Business Description:
Banking Services
S.I.C.: 6211
N.A.I.C.S.: 523110
Personnel:
Manoel Felix Cintra Neto *(Chm)*
Carlos Ciampolini *(Vice Chm)*
Jair Ribeiro da Silva Neto *(Co-CEO)*
Luiz Masagao Ribeiro *(Co-CEO)*
Ziro Murata *(CFO)*
Gilberto Barshad Faiwichow *(IR Officer & VP)*
Claudio Roberto Cusin *(Exec Officer)*
Jair da Costa Balma *(Exec Officer)*
Gilmar Melo de Azevedo *(Comml Officer)*
Roberto Carlos de Carvalho Almeida *(Comml Officer)*
Gilberto Luiz dos Santos Lima Filho *(Treasury Officer)*
Katia Aparecida Rocha Moroni *(Intl Dept Officer)*
Board of Directors:
Manoel Felix Cintra Neto
Alain Juan Pablo Belda
Carlos Ciampolini
Antonio Geraldo da Rocha
Jair Ribeiro da Silva Neto
Alfredo de Goeye, Jr.
Guilherme Affonso Ferreira
Walter Iorio
Luiz Masagao Ribeiro

Units:

Banco Indusval Multistock - Maringa Unit **(1)**
Av Duque de Caxias 882 - Sala 303
87020-025 Maringa, Parana, Brazil
Tel.: (55) 4433024000
Fax: (55) 44 3303 4016
Commercial Banking Services
S.I.C.: 6029
N.A.I.C.S.: 522110

Banco Indusval Multistock - Porto Alegre Unit **(1)**
Rua Furriel Luiz Antonio Vargas 250 - sala 802
90470-130 Porto Alegre, Rio Grande do Sul, Brazil
Tel.: (55) 5134069100
Fax: (55) 5134069116
Commercial Banking Services
S.I.C.: 6029
N.A.I.C.S.: 522110

Banco Indusval Multistock - Recife Unit **(1)**
Av Engenheiro Domingos Ferreira 2589 - sala 204
51020-031 Recife, Pernambuco, Brazil
Tel.: (55) 81 3092 2150
Fax: (55) 81 3092 2166
Commercial Banking Services
S.I.C.: 6029
N.A.I.C.S.: 522110

Banco Indusval Multistock - Rio de Janeiro Unit **(1)**
Rua Lauro Muller 116 - sala 3501
22290-160 Rio de Janeiro, Brazil
Tel.: (55) 2135783200
Fax: (55) 2135783202
E-Mail:
Emp.: 10
Commercial Banking Services
S.I.C.: 6029
N.A.I.C.S.: 522110
Andres Pedrera *(Gen Mgr)*

BANCO INTERNACIONAL DE COSTA RICA, S.A.
Calle Manuel Maria Icaza No 25
Apartado 0816-07810
Panama, Panama
Tel.: (507) 208 9500
Fax: (507) 208 9581
E-Mail: servicioalcliente@bicsa.com
Web Site: www.bicsapan.com
Year Founded: 1976
BICSA—(PAN)
Sales Range: $50-74.9 Million
Emp.: 170
Business Description:
Banking Services
S.I.C.: 6029
N.A.I.C.S.: 522110
Personnel:
S. Daniel Gonzalez *(Deputy CEO & Country Mgr-Panama)*
David Rincon *(CFO)*
Fabio Arciniegas *(Chief Credit Officer)*
Alexis Angulo *(Bus Officer)*
Noris Esther Ferrin *(Bus Officer-Leasing)*
Mariluz Garrido *(Bus Officer)*
Erasmo Espino *(Treas)*

BANCO LATINOAMERICANO DE COMERCIO EXTERIOR, S.A.
(d/b/a Bladex)
Torre V Business Park Avenida La Rotonda Urb Costa del Este
PO Box 0819-08730
Panama, Panama
Tel.: (507) 2108500
Fax: (507) 2696333
E-Mail: webmaster@blx.com
Web Site: www.blx.com
Year Founded: 1979
BLX—(NYSE)
Int. Income: $192,437,000
Assets: $6,756,396,000
Liabilities: $5,929,921,000
Net Worth: $826,475,000
Earnings: $93,325,000
Emp.: 201
Fiscal Year-end: 12/31/12
Business Description:
International Banking Services
S.I.C.: 6159
N.A.I.C.S.: 522293
Personnel:
Gonzalo Menendez Duque *(Chm)*
Rubens V. Amaral, Jr. *(CEO)*
Christopher Schech *(CFO & Exec VP)*
Miguel Moreno *(COO & Exec VP)*
Ulysses Marciano *(Chief Comml Officer & Exec VP)*
Daniel Otero *(Chief Risk Officer & Exec VP)*
Ricardo Manuel Arango *(Sec)*
Gregory D. Testerman *(Chief Strategy & Products Officer & Exec VP)*
Julio C. Aguirre *(Sr VP & Head-Compliance)*
Board of Directors:
Gonzalo Menendez Duque
Esteban Alejandro Acerbo
Herminio A. Blanco
Mario Covo
Maria da Graca Franca
Joao Carlos de Nobrega Pecego
Guillermo Guemez Garcia
William Dick Hayes

U.S. Subsidiary:

Bladex Asset Management, Inc **(1)**
370 Lexington Ave 5th Fl
New York, NY 10017
Tel.: (212) 271-1900
Fax: (212) 308-7613
E-Mail: infofunds@bladex.com
Web Site: www.bladexassetmanagement.com
Emp.: 6
Investment Advisory Services
S.I.C.: 6282
N.A.I.C.S.: 523930
Manuel E. Mejia-Aoun *(Chief Investment Officer)*

Non-U.S. Subsidiary:

Bladex Representacao Ltda. **(1)**
R Leopoldo Couto de Magalhaes Junior 110 1 Fl
Sao Paulo, 04542-000, Brazil
Tel.: (55) 1121989602
Commercial Banking Services
S.I.C.: 6029
N.A.I.C.S.: 522110

BANCO MACRO S.A.
Sarmiento 447
Buenos Aires, Argentina
Tel.: (54) 11 5222 6730
Fax: (54) 11 5222 7826 (IR)
Web Site: www.macro.com.ar
BMA—(BUE NYSE)
Rev.: $1,389,987,768
Assets: $9,739,659,273
Liabilities: $8,491,657,468
Net Worth: $1,248,001,805
Earnings: $300,695,176
Emp.: 8,534
Fiscal Year-end: 12/31/12
Business Description:
Banking Services
S.I.C.: 6029
N.A.I.C.S.: 522110
Personnel:
Jorge Horacio Brito *(Chm)*
Delfin Jorge Ezequiel Carballo *(Vice Chm)*
Board of Directors:
Jorge Horacio Brito
Emmanuel Antonio Alvarez Agis
Juan Pablo Brito Devoto
Constanza Brito
Jorge Pablo Brito
Marcos Brito
Luis Carlos Cerolini
Delfin Jorge Ezequiel Carballo
Roberto Jose Feletti
Alejandro Macfarlane
Guillermo Eduardo Stanley
Carlos Enrique Videla
Legal Counsel:
Simpson Thacher & Bartlett LLP
425 Lexington Ave
New York, NY 10017
Shearman & Sterling LLP
599 Lexington Ave
New York, NY 10022

Subsidiaries:

Argentina Clearing S.A. **(1)**
Paraguay 777 15th Floor
Rosario, Argentina
Tel.: (54) 3414113666
Fax: (54) 3415302976
E-Mail: nbaross@argentinaclearing.com.ar
Web Site: www.argentinaclearing.com.ar
Emp.: 10
Investment Advice
S.I.C.: 6282
N.A.I.C.S.: 523930
Nicolas Barossi *(CEO)*
Nacio Miles *(Mng Dir)*

Banco del Tucuman S.A. **(1)**
San Martin 721
San Miguel de Tucuman, 4000, Argentina
Tel.: (54) 38 1450 3303
Fax: (54) 38 1450 3300
Web Site: www.bancodeltucuman.com.ar
Emp.: 800
Commercial Banking Services
S.I.C.: 6029
N.A.I.C.S.: 522110
Claudio Cerezo *(Gen Mgr)*

Banelco S.A. **(1)**
Mexico 444
Buenos Aires, Argentina
Tel.: (54) 1143455678
Fax: (54) 1143319911
Web Site: www.banelco.com.ar
Scientific & Technical Consulting Services
S.I.C.: 8999
N.A.I.C.S.: 541690

Garantizar S.G.R. **(1)**
Sarmiento 663 Piso 6
C1041AAM Buenos Aires, Argentina
Tel.: (54) 1143252898
Fax: (54) 1143252898
E-Mail: contactosdesdeweb@garantizar.com.ar
Web Site: www.garantizar.com.ar
Scientific & Technical Consulting Services
S.I.C.: 8999
N.A.I.C.S.: 541690
Norberco Schor *(Mng Dir)*

Macro Fondos S.G.F.C.I.S.A. **(1)**
Sarmiento 447 - piso 8
C1041AAI Buenos Aires, Argentina
Tel.: (54) 1152226696
Fax: (54) 1152226845
Web Site: www.MacroFondos.com.ar
Emp.: 8
Commercial Banking
S.I.C.: 6029
N.A.I.C.S.: 522110
Marcelo Agustin Devoto *(Pres)*

Macro Securities S.A. **(1)**
Sarmiento St 447 8th Fl
C1041AAI Buenos Aires, Argentina
Tel.: (54) 1152228970
Fax: (54) 1152228969
E-Mail: macrosecurities@macrosecurities.com.ar

Web Site: www.macrosecurities.com.ar
Emp.: 30
Commercial Banking
S.I.C.: 6029
N.A.I.C.S.: 522110
Andres Ronchietto *(CEO)*

Nuevo Banco Suquia S.A. (1)
25 de Mayo 160
Cordoba, Argentina
Tel.: (54) 3514200200
Fax: (54) 3514200443
Web Site: www.bancosuquia.com.ar
Commercial Banking
S.I.C.: 6029
N.A.I.C.S.: 522110
Jose P. Porta *(Pres)*

Visa Argentina S.A. (1)
Avenida Corrientes 1437
Buenos Aires, Argentina
Tel.: (54) 1143793300
Fax: (54) 1143793262
Web Site: www.visa.com.ar
Retail Electronic Payment Operator
S.I.C.: 6159
N.A.I.C.S.: 522298

Non-U.S. Subsidiaries:

Macro Bank Ltd (1)
PO Box N-4444
Nassau, Bahamas
Tel.: (242) 3236418
Fax: (242) 3236427
Trusts Estates & Agency Accounts
S.I.C.: 6733
N.A.I.C.S.: 525920
Alejandro Maciel *(Mng Dir)*

Proin S.A. (1)
Apartado Postal 319 6150
Santa Ana, San Jose, Costa Rica
Tel.: (506) 22395271
Fax: (506) 25890280
E-Mail: info@proincr.com
Web Site: www.proincr.com
Real Estate Property Lessors
S.I.C.: 6519
N.A.I.C.S.: 531190
Alejandrina Gutierrez *(Dir-Ops)*

BANCO MERCANTIL DO BRASIL S.A.

Rua Rio de Janeiro 654
30160 912 Belo Horizonte, Minas Gerais, Brazil
Tel.: (55) 3130576701
Fax: (55) 3130576298
E-Mail: christino.pinheiro@mercantil.com.br
Web Site: www.mercantildobrasil.com.br
Sales Range: $800-899.9 Million
Emp.: 2,644

Business Description:
Banking Services
S.I.C.: 6211
N.A.I.C.S.: 523110
Personnel:
Milton de Araujo *(Chm & Pres)*

Subsidiaries:

Banco Mercantil de Investimentos S.A. (1)
R Rio de Janeiro 654 - 6 Floor
30160912 Belo Horizonte, MG, Brazil
Tel.: (55) 31 3057 6336
Fax: (55) 31 3057 6778
BMIN3—(BRAZ)
Sales Range: $1-9.9 Million
Financial Services
S.I.C.: 6211
N.A.I.C.S.: 523999
Athaide Vieira Dos Santos, *(Dir-IR)*

Mercantil do Brasil Financeira S.A. (1)
R Rio de Janeiro 654 - 6 Floor
30160912 Belo Horizonte, MG, Brazil
Tel.: (55) 31 3057 6336
Fax: (55) 31 3057 6778
MERC3—(BRAZ)
Sales Range: $10-24.9 Million
Consumer Financial Services
S.I.C.: 6141
N.A.I.C.S.: 522291
Athaide Vieira Dos Santos, *(Dir-IR)*

BANCO MODAL S.A.

Praia de Botafogo 501 6 andar Torre Pao de Acucar
Rio de Janeiro, 22250-040, Brazil
Tel.: (55) 21 3223 7700
Fax: (55) 21 3223 7738
E-Mail: ouvidoria@modal.com.br
Web Site: www.modal.com.br
Emp.: 232

Business Description:
Banking Services
S.I.C.: 6029
N.A.I.C.S.: 522110
Personnel:
Diniz Ferreira Baptista *(CEO)*

Subsidiary:

Modal Administradora de Recursos S.A. (1)
Praia de Botafogo 501 6 andar Torre Pao de Acucar
Rio de Janeiro, 22250-040, Brazil
Tel.: (55) 21 3223 7700
Fax: (55) 21 3223 7738
Private Equity Firm
S.I.C.: 6211
N.A.I.C.S.: 523999
John Michael Streithorst *(PArtner & Mng Dir)*

BANCO OCCIDENTAL DE DESCUENTO BANCO UNIVERSAL

Avenida 5 de Julio Calle 77
Caracas, Venezuela
Tel.: (58) 261 721 2990
Fax: (58) 261 721 3758
Web Site: www.bodinternet.com
BOU—(CAR)

Business Description:
Commercial Banking Services
S.I.C.: 6029
N.A.I.C.S.: 522110
Personnel:
Victor J. Vargas Irausquin *(Chm)*
Tomas Niembro Concha *(Pres)*
Board of Directors:
Victor J. Vargas Irausquin
Guillermo Belloso Conde
Fernando Chumaceiro Chiarelli
Carlos Enrique d'Empaire Belloso
Jose Manuel Egui Medina
Jose Luis Feaugas
Eduardo Gallegos Garcia
Ivan Gonzalez Rubio
Vicente Lozano Rivas
Jose Vicente Matos San Juan
Carmelo Antonio Moscuela Carnabucci
Tomas Niembro Concha
Candido Rodriguez Losada
Enrique Soto Belloso

BANCO OPPORTUNITY S/A

Av Presidente Wilson n 231 28 andar
20030-021 Rio de Janeiro, Brazil
Tel.: (55) 2138043434
Fax: (55) 213803450
E-Mail: opportunity@opportunity.com.br
Web Site: www.opportunity.com.br
Emp.: 100

Business Description:
Investment Services
S.I.C.: 6211
N.A.I.C.S.: 523999
Personnel:
Dorio Ferman *(Chm & CEO)*

BANCO PANAMERICANO S.A.

Av Paulista 1374 - 12 Floor
01310-100 Sao Paulo, SP, Brazil
Tel.: (55) 11 3264 5343
Fax: (55) 11 3264 5275
E-Mail: ri@panamericano.com.br
Web Site: www.bancopan.com.br
BPNM3—(BRAZ)
Sales Range: $1-4.9 Billion
Emp.: 8,107

Business Description:
Commercial Banking Services
S.I.C.: 6029
N.A.I.C.S.: 522110
Personnel:
Jorge Fontes Hereda *(Chm)*
Andre Santos Esteves *(Vice Chm)*
Jose Luiz Acar Pedro *(CEO)*
Jose Carlos Macedo *(Insurance Officer)*
Fabio Nogueira *(BFRE Officer)*
Board of Directors:
Jorge Fontes Hereda
Mateus Affonso Bandeira
Marcos Antonio Macedo Cintra
Fabio de Barros
Joao Cesar de Queiroz Tourinho
Andre Santos Esteves
Antonio Carlos Porto Filho
Otto Steiner Junior
Fabio Lenza
Roy Martelanc
Jose Luiz Acar Pedro
Marcio Percival Alves Pinto
Roberto Balls Sallouti
Marcos Roberto Vanconcelos

BANCO PINE S.A.

Edificio Eldorado Business Tower
Avenida das Nacoes Unidas 8 501 3 and
Pinheiros, Sao Paulo, Brazil
Tel.: (55) 1133725200
Fax: (55) 1133725404
E-Mail: ri@pine.com
Web Site: www.pine.com
PINE4—(BRAZ)
Rev.: $617,817,775
Assets: $5,118,436,162
Liabilities: $4,518,356,924
Net Worth: $600,079,238
Earnings: $92,206,256
Emp.: 424
Fiscal Year-end: 12/31/12

Business Description:
Banking, Financial & Investment Services
S.I.C.: 6029
N.A.I.C.S.: 522110
Personnel:
Noberto Nogueira Pinheiro *(Chm)*
Noberto Nogueira Pinheiro, Jr. *(Vice Chm & CEO)*
Harumi Susana Ueta Waldeck *(CFO IR Officer)*
Norberto Zaiet, Jr. *(COO)*
Ulisses Marcio Alcantarilla *(Chief Admin Officer)*
Gabriela Redona Chiste *(Chief Risk Officer)*
Jefferson Dias Miceli *(Legal Officer)*
Rodrigo Esteves Pinheiro *(Corp Banking Officer)*
Gustavo Gierum *(Corp Banking Officer)*
Luiz Eduardo Marinho *(Corp Banking Officer)*
Sergio Luis Patricio *(Asset Mgmt Officer)*
Board of Directors:
Noberto Nogueira Pinheiro
Gustavo Diniz Junqueira
Mailson Ferreira da Nobrega
Maurizio Mauro
Noberto Nogueira Pinheiro, Jr.

BANCO POPOLARE SOCIETA COOPERATIVA

(d/b/a Gruppo Bancario - Banco Popolare)
Piazza Nogara 2
37121 Verona, Italy
Tel.: (39) 0458675111
Fax: (39) 0458675131
Web Site: www.bancopopolare.it
BP—(ITA OTC)
Rev.: $5,459,850,133
Assets: $177,588,609,499
Liabilities: $165,498,785,962
Net Worth: $12,089,823,538
Earnings: ($1,278,318,993)
Emp.: 18,693
Fiscal Year-end: 12/31/12

Business Description:
Bank Holding Company
S.I.C.: 6712
N.A.I.C.S.: 551111
Personnel:
Carlo Fratta Pasini *(Chm)*
Guido Duccio Castellotti *(Vice Chm)*
Maurizio Comoli *(Vice Chm)*
Pier Francesco Saviotti *(CEO)*
Board of Directors:
Carlo Fratta Pasini
Alberto Bauli
Angelo Benelli
Pietro Buzzi
Guido Duccio Castellotti
Aldo Civaschi
Vittorio Coda
Maurizio Comoli
Giovanni Francesco Curioni
Domenico De Angelis
Maurizio Di Maio
Maurizio Faroni
Gianni Filippa
Andrea Guidi
Valter Lazzari
Claudio Rangoni Machiavelli
Maurizio Marino
Enrico Perotti
Gian Luca Rana
Fabio Ravanelli
Pier Francesco Saviotti
Sandro Veronesi
Tommaso Zanini
Cristina Zucchetti

Subsidiaries:

Arena Broker S.r.l. (1)
Via Pancaldo 70
37138 Verona, Italy
Tel.: (39) 045 8185 411
Fax: (39) 045 8185 911
E-Mail: info@arenabroker.it
Web Site: www.arenabroker.it
Insurance Brokerage Services
S.I.C.: 6411
N.A.I.C.S.: 524210

Banca Aletti & C. S.p.A. (1)
Via Roncaglia 12
IT-20146 Milan, Italy
Tel.: (39) 02433581
Fax: (39) 0243358090
E-Mail: info@alettibank.it
Web Site: www.alettibank.it
Sales Range: $125-149.9 Million
Private & Investment Banking
S.I.C.: 6211
N.A.I.C.S.: 523110
Urbano Aletti *(Pres)*

Subsidiaries:

Alletti Gestielle SGR S.p.A. (2)
Via Roncaglia 12
20146 Milan, Italy
Tel.: (39) 0249967340
Fax: (39) 0249967914
E-Mail: segreteria@gestielle.it
Web Site: www.gestielle.it
Emp.: 70
Asset Management
S.I.C.: 6726
N.A.I.C.S.: 525990

Banco Popolare Societa Cooperativa—(Continued)

Mario Tomasi *(Gen Mgr)*

Banca Italease S.p.A. **(1)**
Via Sile 18
IT-20139 Milan, Italy IT
Tel.: (39) 0277651 (100%)
Fax: (39) 02 7765 2261
E-Mail: info@italease.it
Web Site: www.bancaitalease.it
Sales Range: $1-4.9 Billion
Emp.: 1,120
Bank Holding Company
S.I.C.: 6712
N.A.I.C.S.: 551111
Massimo Mazzega *(CEO & Interim CFO)*

Subsidiaries:

Italease Finance S.p.A. **(2)**
Via Sile 18
IT-20139 Milan, Italy IT
Tel.: (39) 0277651 (70%)
Fax: (39) 02 7765 2261
Lease Financing Services
S.I.C.: 6726
N.A.I.C.S.: 525990

Italease Gestione Beni S.p.A. **(2)**
Via Sile 18
IT-20139 Milan, Italy IT
Tel.: (39) 0277651 (100%)
Fax: (39) 02 7602 1766
E-Mail: info@italeasegestionebeni.it
Web Site: www.italeasegestionebeni.it
Holding Company; Evaluation, Management & Sale of Formerly Leased Assets
S.I.C.: 6719
N.A.I.C.S.: 551112
Marco Cappelletto *(Chm)*
Carlo Boselli *(CEO)*

Branch:

Italease Gestione Beni - Operational Headquarters **(3)**
Via Milano 110
IT-26025 Pandino, CR, Italy
Tel.: (39) 0373975411
Fax: (39) 0373975466
Web Site: www.italeasegestionebeni.it
Evaluation, Management & Sale of Formerly Leased Assets
S.I.C.: 7389
N.A.I.C.S.: 561499
Carlo Boselli *(CEO)*

Subsidiaries:

Essegibi Finanziaria S.p.A. **(3)**
Via Sile 18
IT-20139 Milan, MI, Italy IT
Tel.: (39) 02 7765 1 (Switchboard) (100%)
Fax: (39) 02 76398267
Web Site: www.essegibi.it
Secondary Market Financing Services
S.I.C.: 6159
N.A.I.C.S.: 522294
Carlo Boselli *(CEO)*

Essegibi Promozioni Immobiliari S.r.l. **(3)**
Via Sile 18
IT-20139 Milan, Italy IT
Tel.: (39) 02 7765 1 (Switchboard) (100%)
Fax: (39) 02 7765 261
Web Site: www.essegibi.it
Real Estate Intermediation Services
S.I.C.: 6159
N.A.I.C.S.: 522292

Joint Venture:

Renting Italease S.r.l. **(3)**
Via Tortona 7
IT-20144 Milan, Italy IT
Tel.: (39) 0277653361
Fax: (39) 02 7765 3371
Web Site: www.rentingitalease.it
Long-Term Car Leasing Services; Owned 50% by Banca Italease S.p.A. & 50% by General Electric Capital Services, Inc.
S.I.C.: 7515
N.A.I.C.S.: 532112
Carla Acitelli *(Pres)*

Italease Network S.p.A. **(2)**
Piazza Monsignor G Almici 15
IT-25124 Brescia, Italy IT
Tel.: (39) 030 22851 (100%)
Fax: (39) 030 2422 841
E-Mail: info@italeasenetwork.it
Corporate Lending Services
S.I.C.: 6159
N.A.I.C.S.: 522298
Mario Lugli *(Chm)*

Mercantile Leasing S.p.A. **(2)**
Viale Don Minzoni 1
IT-50129 Florence, Italy IT
Tel.: (39) 05556701 (100%)
Fax: (39) 055 5670250
E-Mail: info@mercantileleasing.it
Web Site: www.mleas.it
Emp.: 220
Real Estate, Vehicle & Capital Goods Leasing Services
S.I.C.: 6519
N.A.I.C.S.: 531190
Carlo Audino *(Chm)*

Release S.p.A. **(2)**
Via Sile 18
Milan, 20139, Italy
Tel.: (39) 02 367031
Fax: (39) 02 36703317
Financial Management Services
S.I.C.: 6211
N.A.I.C.S.: 523999
Murcelini Diunpuolo *(Gen Mgr)*

Banca Popolare di Cremona S.p.A. **(1)**
Via Cesare Battisti
Cremona, Italy
Tel.: (39) 0372 404 1
Investment Banking Services
S.I.C.: 6211
N.A.I.C.S.: 523110

Banca Popolare di Lodi S.p.A. **(1)**
Via Polenghi Lombardo 13
Bipielle City, 26900 Lodi, Italy IT
Tel.: (39) 0371580111
Fax: (39) 0371580829
E-Mail: investor.relations@bipielle.it
Web Site: www.bancobolare.it
Sales Range: $1-4.9 Billion
Emp.: 8,579
Retail & Commercial Loans & Deposit Products, Credit Cards, Insurance & Online Brokerage Services
S.I.C.: 6211
N.A.I.C.S.: 523110
Vittorio Coda *(Deputy Chm)*
Franceso Saviotti *(CEO)*

Banca Popolare di Novara S.p.A. **(1)**
Via Negroni 11
IT-26100 Novara, Italy
Tel.: (39) 0321337111
Fax: (39) 0321337348
Web Site: www.bpn.it
Commercial Banking
S.I.C.: 6029
N.A.I.C.S.: 522110

Banca Popolare di Verona - S. Geminiano e S. Prospero S.p.A. **(1)**
Piazza Nogara 2
IT-37121 Verona, Italy IT
Tel.: (39) 0458675111
Fax: (39) 0458675412
Web Site: www.bpv.it
Emp.: 14,000
Banking Services
S.I.C.: 6029
N.A.I.C.S.: 522110
Alberto Bauli *(Chm)*
Fratta Pasini Carlo *(Pres)*
Franco Baronio *(CEO)*

Credito Bergamasco S.p.A. **(1)**
Largo Porta Nuova 2
IT-24122 Bergamo, Italy IT
Tel.: (39) 035393111
Fax: (39) 035393211
E-Mail: segreteria.generale@creberg.it
Web Site: www.creberg.it
Sales Range: $1-4.9 Billion
Commercial & Merchant Banking & Asset Management Services
S.I.C.: 6029
N.A.I.C.S.: 522110
Giorgio Papa *(Dir Gen)*
Maurizio Castelli *(Deputy Dir Gen)*
Angelo Piazzoli *(Sec)*

Tecmarket Servizi S.p.A. **(1)**
Via Antonio Meucci 5
Verona, 37135, Italy
Tel.: (39) 0458274790
Fax: (39) 0458274609
Marketing Consulting Services
S.I.C.: 8742
N.A.I.C.S.: 541613

U.S. Subsidiary:

Bormioli Rocco Glass Co. Inc. **(1)**
41 Madison Ave 17th Fl Ofc Showroom
New York, NY 10010
Tel.: (212) 719-0606
Fax: (212) 719-3605
Web Site: www.bormioliroccousa.com
Glass Products Mfr
S.I.C.: 3229
N.A.I.C.S.: 327212

Non-U.S. Subsidiaries:

Auto Trading Leasing IFN s.a. **(1)**
Sector 2 Str C A Rosetti Nr 17 Parterul Si Supanta Cladirii
Mezanin, Bucharest, Romania
Tel.: (40) 21 312 70 52
Fax: (40) 21 312 70 54
E-Mail: office@atleasing.ro
Emp.: 25
Automotive Leasing Services
S.I.C.: 6159
N.A.I.C.S.: 522220
Gabriela Mateescu *(Gen Mgr)*

Banco Popolare Luxembourg S.A. **(1)**
26 Bd Royal
BP 555
2449 Luxembourg, Luxembourg
Tel.: (352) 46 57 57 1
Fax: (352) 47 01 70
E-Mail: Direction@BancoPopolare.lu
Investment Banking Services
S.I.C.: 6211
N.A.I.C.S.: 523110

Glass Italy B.V. **(1)**
Keizersgracht 638
Amsterdam, 1017 ES, Netherlands
Tel.: (31) 20 421 1110
Glass Products Mfr
S.I.C.: 3229
N.A.I.C.S.: 327212

Non-U.S. Subsidiary:

Partecipazioni Italiane S.p.A. **(2)**
Via Chiaravalle 2
20122 Milan, Italy
Tel.: (39) 02 58328609
Fax: (39) 02 58323091
E-Mail: info@p-ita.it
Investment Banking Services
S.I.C.: 6211
N.A.I.C.S.: 523110

BANCO POPULAR ESPANOL, S.A.

Velazquez 34
28001 Madrid, Spain
Tel.: (34) 902301000
Fax: (34) 915779826
E-Mail: info@bancopopular.es
Web Site: www.bancopopular.es
Year Founded: 1926
POP—(MAD OTC)
Rev.: $7,399,106,288
Assets: $212,180,781,908
Liabilities: $198,779,092,820
Net Worth: $13,401,689,088
Earnings: ($3,312,847,638)
Emp.: 16,501
Fiscal Year-end: 12/31/12

Business Description:
Commercial & Retail Banking Services
S.I.C.: 6029
N.A.I.C.S.: 522110

Personnel:
Angel Carlos Ron Guimil *(Chm)*
Luis Herrando Prat de la Riba *(Vice Chm)*
Roberto Higuera Montejo *(Vice Chm)*
Jose Maria Arias Mosquera *(Vice Chm)*
Francisco Gomez Martin *(CEO)*
Rafael S. de Mena *(CFO)*
Fernando Rodriguez Baquero *(COO & Dir-Technical Resources)*
Jose Maria Sagardoy *(Chief Risk Officer)*
Jesus Arellano Escobar *(Chief Control Officer & Chief Audit Officer)*
Miguel Angel Moral *(Gen Sec)*

Board of Directors:
Angel Carlos Ron Guimil
Francisco Aparicio Valls
Jose Gracia Barba
Vicente Tardio Barutel
Jan Ricard Carendi
Americo Ferreira de Amorim
Luis Herrando Prat de la Riba
Miguel Angel de Solis Martinez-Campos
Helena Revoredo Delveccio
Alain Fradin
Jose Ramon Rodriguez Garcia
Ana Jose Varela Gonzalez
Ana Maria Molins Lopez-Rodo
Roberto Higuera Montejo
Jose Maria Arias Mosquera
Jorge Oroviogoicoechea Ortega
Vicente Jose Perez Jaime

Subsidiaries:

Aliseda S.A. **(1)**
Calle Jose Ortega Y Gasset 29
C-Arenal 21, 28013 Madrid, Spain (49%)
Tel.: (34) 915765921
Fax: (34) 915592904
E-Mail: info@aliseda.com
Web Site: www.aliseda.com
Land Subdivision
S.I.C.: 6552
N.A.I.C.S.: 237210
Angel Ron *(Mng Dir)*

Aula 2000 S.A. **(1)**
Calle Jose Ortega Y Gasset 29
Madrid, Spain (100%)
Tel.: (34) 915765921
Business Support Services
S.I.C.: 7389
N.A.I.C.S.: 561499
Angel Ron *(Mng Dir)*

Banco de Castilla **(1)**
34 Velazquez Street
28010 Madrid, Spain ES
Tel.: (34) 913199604
Fax: (34) 913100666
E-Mail: 00755785@bancocastilla.es
Web Site: www.bancocastilla.es
CAS—(MAD)
Sales Range: $100-124.9 Million
Banking Services
S.I.C.: 6011
N.A.I.C.S.: 521110
Francisco Aparicio *(Sec)*

Banco de Credito Balear S.A. **(1)**
Plz de Espana 1
Palma de Mallorca, Spain (95.18%)
Tel.: (34) 971170118
Fax: (34) 971170167
E-Mail: bancopopular@bancopopular.es
Web Site: www.escredit.es
Emp.: 376
Commercial Banking
S.I.C.: 6029
N.A.I.C.S.: 522110
Berenguer Gilan *(Gen Mgr)*

Banco de Galicia S.A. **(1)**
C-o Policarpo Sanz 23
36202 Vigo, Pontevedra, Spain (93.14%)
Tel.: (34) 986822100
Fax: (34) 986822139
Web Site: www.bancogalicia.es
Emp.: 22
Savings Institutions
S.I.C.: 6035
N.A.I.C.S.: 522120

Banco de Vasconia S.A. **(1)**
Plz del Castillo 39
31001 Pamplona, Navarra, Spain (96.86%)
Tel.: (34) 915207900
Fax: (34) 948211625

Web Site: www.bancovasconia.es
Emp.: 503
Commercial Banking
S.I.C.: 6029
N.A.I.C.S.: 522110
Jose Ramon Rodriguez *(Pres)*
Francisco Aparicio *(CEO)*

Banco Pastor, S.A. (1)
Canton Pequeno 1
15003 La Coruna, Spain
Tel.: (34) 98 112 76 00
Fax: (34) 98 112 7568
E-Mail:
Web Site: www.bancopastor.es
Sales Range: $600-649.9 Million
Emp.: 4,542
Commercial Banking, Mortgage Lending & Leasing Services
S.I.C.: 6029
N.A.I.C.S.: 522110
Jos Manuel Fernandez Hevia *(CEO)*
Juan Babio Fernandez *(CFO)*

Joint Venture:

Construcciones Costa Coruna, S.L. (2)
Calle Menendez Y Pelayo 8 A Coruna
15005 La Coruna, Spain
Tel.: (34) 981126786
Fax: (34) 981126787
E-Mail: cccteresa@mundo.com
Web Site: www.mundo.com
Emp.: 7
Land Subdivision
S.I.C.: 6552
N.A.I.C.S.: 237210
C. O. Lolen *(Mng Dir)*

BPE Financiaciones S.A. (1)
Calle Jose Ortega Y Gasset 29
Madrid, 28006, Spain (100%)
Tel.: (34) 915207265
Web Site: www.bancopopular.es
Real Estate Credit
S.I.C.: 6159
N.A.I.C.S.: 522292
Angel Ron *(Mng Dir)*

Desarrollo Aplicaciones Especiales S.A. (1)
Calle Juan De Olias 1
Madrid, Spain (50.67%)
Tel.: (34) 915672510
Fax: (34) 915702454
Web Site: www.daesa.es
Emp.: 300
Computer Related Services
S.I.C.: 7379
N.A.I.C.S.: 541519

Eurocorredores S.A. (1)
Maria Molena No 34
28006 Madrid, Spain (100%)
Tel.: (34) 914360300
Fax: (34) 914320069
Computer Related Services
S.I.C.: 7379
N.A.I.C.S.: 541519

Finespa S.A. (1)
Calle Jose Ortega Y Gasset 29
Madrid, Spain (100%)
Tel.: (34) 915765921
Real Estate Agents & Brokers
S.I.C.: 6531
N.A.I.C.S.: 531210
Angel Ron *(Mng Dir)*

Gestora Popular S.A. (1)
Calle Jose Ortega Y Gasset 29
Madrid, Spain (100%)
Tel.: (34) 915765921
Real Estate Agents & Brokers
S.I.C.: 6531
N.A.I.C.S.: 531210

IM Banco Popular FTPYME 1, FTA (1)
Plaza Pablo Ruiz Picasso Torre Picasso 1 - Planta 23
Madrid, 28020, Spain
Tel.: (34) 914326488
Fax: (34) 915971105
Web Site: www.imtitulisacion.com
Fund Management Services
S.I.C.: 6282
N.A.I.C.S.: 523920

Inmobiliaria Viagracia S.A. (1)
Calle Jose Ortega Y Gasset 29
Madrid, Spain (100%)
Tel.: (34) 915765921
Real Estate Agents & Brokers
S.I.C.: 6531
N.A.I.C.S.: 531210
Angel Ron *(Mng Dir)*

Inmobiliaria Vivesa S.A. (1)
Calle Jose Ortega Y Gasset 29
Madrid, Spain (100%)
Tel.: (34) 915765921
Real Estate Agents & Brokers
S.I.C.: 6531
N.A.I.C.S.: 531210
Angel Ron *(Mng Dir)*

Intermediacion y Servicios Tecnologicos, S.A. (1)
Calle Torneros Pg Ind Los Angeles 9
Getafe, 28906, Spain
Tel.: (34) 914365024
Fax: (34) 914365064
Information Technology Consulting Services
S.I.C.: 7373
N.A.I.C.S.: 541512

Popular Banca Privada S.A. (1)
Calle Jose Ortega y Gasset 29-3o
3rd Floor, E-28006 Madrid, Spain ES
Tel.: (34) 914189340 (100%)
Fax: (34) 914189350
E-Mail: contacto@popularbancaprivada.es
Web Site: www.popularbancaprivada.es
Emp.: 200
Banking Services
S.I.C.: 6029
N.A.I.C.S.: 522110
Smejuel Angel Luna *(CEO)*

Popular Bolsa S.A. (1)
Calle Labastida 11
28034 Madrid, Spain (100%)
Tel.: (34) 915208070
Fax: (34) 915206934
E-Mail: popularbolsa@bancopopular.es
Emp.: 12
Real Estate Credit
S.I.C.: 6159
N.A.I.C.S.: 522292
Amadld Gonzalez *(Chm)*

Popular Capital S.A. (1)
Calle Jose Ortega Y Gasset 29
Madrid, Spain (100%)
Tel.: (34) 915765921
Securities Brokerage
S.I.C.: 6211
N.A.I.C.S.: 523120
Angel Ron *(Mng Dir)*

Popular de Comunicaciones S.A. (1)
Calle Jose Ortega Y Gasset 29
Madrid, Spain (100%)
Tel.: (34) 915765921
Telecommunications
S.I.C.: 4899
N.A.I.C.S.: 517919
Angel Ron *(Mng Dir)*

Popular de Informatica S.A. (1)
Calle Jose Ortega Y Gasset 29
Madrid, Spain (100%)
Tel.: (34) 915765921
Computer Related Services
S.I.C.: 7379
N.A.I.C.S.: 541519
Angel Ron *(Mng Dir)*

Popular de Mediacion, S.A. (1)
Calle Jose Ortega Y Gasset 29
Madrid, 28006, Spain
Tel.: (34) 91 436 03 00
Fax: (34) 91 576 64 34
Commercial Banking Services
S.I.C.: 6029
N.A.I.C.S.: 522110

Popular de Renting S.A. (1)
Calle Labastida 11 9
Madrid, Spain (100%)
Tel.: (34) 917812350
Fax: (34) 917812354
Consumer Goods Rental
S.I.C.: 7359
N.A.I.C.S.: 532299

Popular Gestion Privada S.A. (1)
C Jose Ortega y Gasset 29 3
Calle Juan Ignacio Luca De Ten, 28006
Madrid, Spain (60%)
Tel.: (34) 914189300
Fax: (34) 914189350
Web Site: www.popularbancaprivada.es
Emp.: 50
Real Estate Credit
S.I.C.: 6159
N.A.I.C.S.: 522292
Jordi Padilla *(Mng Dir)*

Joint Ventures:

Popular de Factoring S.A. (1)
labastiba No 11 2 Floor
28034 Madrid, Spain
Tel.: (34) 915903676
Fax: (34) 915903685
E-Mail: populardefactoring@bancopopular.es
Web Site: www.populardefactoring.es
Emp.: 30
Sales Financing
S.I.C.: 6141
N.A.I.C.S.: 522220
Francisco Rubio *(Gen Mgr)*

Sociedad Conjunta para la Emision y Gestion de Medios de Pago S.A. (1)
Calle Jose Ortega Y Gasset 22
Madrid, Spain
Tel.: (34) 915765921
Financial Transactions Processing Reserve & Clearinghouse Activities
S.I.C.: 6099
N.A.I.C.S.: 522320
Angel Ron *(Mng Dir)*

U.S. Subsidiary:

TotalBank Corp. (1)
2720 Coral Way
Miami, FL 33145
Tel.: (305) 448-6500
Fax: (305) 448-8201
E-Mail: contactus@totalbank.com
Web Site: www.totalbank.com
Sales Range: $75-99.9 Million
Emp.: 396
Commercial Banking Services
Import Export
S.I.C.: 6029
N.A.I.C.S.: 522110
Jorge Rossell *(Chm)*
Luis de la Aguilera *(Pres & CEO)*
Raul Alvarez *(Mng Dir & VP)*
Janessa Cabo *(Mng Dir & VP)*
Robert Revilla *(Mng Dir & Mgr-Market)*
Jose Marina *(CFO & Exec VP)*
Lyan Fernandez *(COO & Exec VP)*
Benigno Pazos *(Chief Credit Officer)*
Francisco Garcia-Nieto *(Exec VP & Dir-Intl Personal Banking & Project Mgmt)*
Thomas Baschoff *(Exec VP-Insurance Premium Fin)*
Lourdes Rey-Wilson *(Exec VP-HR)*
Martin Rivas *(Sr VP & Controller)*
Andres Collazo *(Sr VP & Mgr-Bank Ops)*
Axel Lacau *(Sr VP & Mgr-Market)*
Fabricio Gomez *(Sr VP-Debt Restructure Div)*
David Hitt *(Sr VP)*
Maritza Jaime *(Sr VP-Credit Admin)*
Mark Leider *(Sr VP)*
Omar Ojeda *(Sr VP)*
Alex Pascual *(Sr VP-Lending Div)*
Eduardo Quiros *(Sr VP)*
Elsa Soler *(Sr VP)*
Juan F. Sotolongo *(Sr VP)*
William Turner *(Sr VP-Credits)*

Subsidiary:

Totalbank Leasing Corp. (2)
2720 Coral Way
Miami, FL 33145-3202
Tel.: (305) 448-6500
Fax: (305) 448-8201
E-Mail: contactus@totalbank.com
Web Site: www.totalbank.com
Emp.: 8
Commercial Leasing & Lending Services
Import Export
S.I.C.: 6029
N.A.I.C.S.: 522110
Enrique Flores *(VP & Branch Relationship Mgr)*

Non-U.S. Subsidiaries:

Banco Popular Portugal S.A. (1)
Rua Ramalho Ortigao 51
1099-090 Lisbon, Portugal (100%)
Tel.: (351) 210071000
Fax: (351) 210071966
E-Mail: sca@bancopopular.pt
Web Site: www.bancopopular.pt
Emp.: 1,000
Commercial Banking
S.I.C.: 6029
N.A.I.C.S.: 522110
Rui Semedo *(Pres)*

Banco Popular S.A. (1)
Rua Ramalho OrtigAo 51
Lisbon, 1099-090, Portugal (100%)
Tel.: (351) 210071352
Fax: (351) 210071961
E-Mail: 00460997@bancopopular.pt
Web Site: www.bancopopular.pt
Emp.: 1,500
Real Estate Agents & Brokers
S.I.C.: 6531
N.A.I.C.S.: 531210
Rui Semedo *(Pres)*

Eurovida, S.A. (1)
Rua Ramalho Ortigao 51
Lisbon, 1099-090, Portugal
Tel.: (351) 217924700
Fax: (351) 217924701
E-Mail: seguros@eurovida.pt
General Insurance Services
S.I.C.: 6411
N.A.I.C.S.: 524210
Jose Antonio Coutinho *(Gen Mgr)*

Popular Capital Europe B.V. (1)
Strawinskylaan 3105-7e Etage
1077ZX Amsterdam, Netherlands (100%)
Tel.: (31) 204064444
Financial Investment Activities
S.I.C.: 6211
N.A.I.C.S.: 523999

Popular Espanol Asia Trade Ltd. (1)
Tity Plaza 4 12 Tarkoo Wen Road
Tai Koo Shing, Quarry Bay, China (Hong Kong) (100%)
Tel.: (852) 28785746
Fax: (852) 28452673
Emp.: 20
Durable Goods Merchant Whslr
S.I.C.: 5099
N.A.I.C.S.: 423990

Popular Factoring, S.A. (1)
Rua Ramalho Ortigao 51
1099-090 Lisbon, Portugal
Tel.: (351) 21 007 17 70
Fax: (351) 21 007 17 79
E-Mail: popular@popularfactoring.pt
Web Site: www.popularfactoring.pt
Factoring Accounts Receivable Services
S.I.C.: 6159
N.A.I.C.S.: 522298
Rui Manuel Morganho Semedo *(Chm)*
Francisco Javier Lleo Fernandez *(Sec)*

Popular Gestao de Activos - Sociedade Gestora de Fundos de Investimento, S.A. (1)
Rua Ramalho Ortigao 51
Lisbon, 1099-090, Portugal
Tel.: (351) 210071352
E-Mail: 00460585@bancopopular.pt
Securities Brokerage Services
S.I.C.: 6211
N.A.I.C.S.: 523120

Populargest Gestao de Imoveis, S.L. (1)
Rua Ramalho Ortigao 51
Lisbon, 1099-090, Portugal
Tel.: (351) 210071000
Fax: (351) 210071961
Web Site: www.bancopopular.pt
Real Estate Management Services
S.I.C.: 6531
N.A.I.C.S.: 531390

Predifundos S.A. (1)
Rua Ramalho OrtigAo 51
1099-090 Lisbon, Portugal (100%)
Tel.: (351) 210071352
Real Estate Credit
S.I.C.: 6159
N.A.I.C.S.: 522292
Rui Semedo *(Gen Mgr)*

BANCO PRODUCTS (I) LTD.
Bil Near Bhaili Railway Station Padra Road
Baroda, Gujarat, 391 410, India

Banco Products (I) Ltd.—(Continued)

Tel.: (91) 2652680220
Fax: (91) 2652680433
E-Mail: mail@bancoindia.com
Web Site: www.bancoindia.com
BANCOINDIA—(NSE)
Rev.: $199,203,586
Assets: $159,029,390
Liabilities: $71,420,085
Net Worth: $87,609,305
Earnings: $11,365,391
Fiscal Year-end: 03/31/13

Business Description:
Gaskets & Radiators Mfr
S.I.C.: 3053
N.A.I.C.S.: 339991

Personnel:
Vimal K. Patel *(Chm)*
Mehul K. Patel *(Vice Chm & Mng Dir)*
Shailesh A. Thakker *(CFO)*
Upendra Joshi *(Compliance Officer)*
Dinesh Kavthekar *(Sec)*

Board of Directors:
Vimal K. Patel
Ram Devidayal
S. K. Duggal
M. G. Patel
Mehul K. Patel
Mukesh D. Patel
Samir K. Patel
Kiran Shetty
Atul G. Shroff
Shailesh A. Thakker

Transfer Agent:
Link Intime India Pvt. Ltd
B-102 & 103 Shangrila Complex I Fl Opp HDFC Bank Nr. Radhakrishna Char
Vadodara, India

Non-U.S. Subsidiaries:

Nederlandse Radiateuren Fabriek BV (1)
Langenboomseweg 64
5451 JM Mill en Sint Hubert, Netherlands
Tel.: (31) 485 476 476
Fax: (31) 485 476 403
E-Mail: info@nrf.eu
Web Site: www.nrf.eu
Emp.: 20
Radiator & Air Conditioning Equipment Mfr
S.I.C.: 3433
N.A.I.C.S.: 333414
Paul Allinson *(Mgr)*

Non-U.S. Subsidiary:

NRF Espana S.A. (2)
Poligono Industrial Asegra Avenida Asegra 22 Apartado 46
18210 Peligros, Granada, Spain
Tel.: (34) 958 405 030
Fax: (34) 958 405 330
E-Mail: spain@nrf.eu
Automotive Air Conditioning System & Radiator Distr
S.I.C.: 5013
N.A.I.C.S.: 423120

NRF BVBA (1)
Boomsesteenweg 2
2627 Schelle, Belgium
Tel.: (32) 3 8877 676
Fax: (32) 3 8871 101
E-Mail: belgium@nrf.eu
Web Site: www.nrf.eu/en_US/branches-1
Automobile Radiator Mfr
S.I.C.: 3714
N.A.I.C.S.: 336390

NRF Deutschland GmbH (1)
Werner-Heisenberg-Strasse 22
46446 Emmerich am Rhein, Germany
Tel.: (49) 2 82296 740
Fax: (49) 2 82296 7420
E-Mail: germany@nrf.eu
Emp.: 11
Heat Exchanger Mfr
S.I.C.: 3443
N.A.I.C.S.: 332410
Alok Gupta *(Gen Mgr)*

NRF France SAS (1)
Zone Industrielle N 2 Rue Elsa Triolet - Batterie 500
59309 Valenciennes, France
Tel.: (33) 327 211 717
Fax: (33) 327 210 550
E-Mail: france@nrf.eu
Automobile Radiator Mfr
S.I.C.: 3714
N.A.I.C.S.: 336390

NRF Handelsges. GmbH (1)
Breitenleerstrasse 101/Halle 3
1220 Vienna, Austria
Tel.: (43) 1259 335 5
Fax: (43) 1259 335 520
E-Mail: austria@nrf.eu
Web Site: www.nrf.eu/en_US/branches-1
Automotive Air Conditioning System Mfr
S.I.C.: 3714
N.A.I.C.S.: 336390

NRF Poland Spolka. Z.O.O (1)
Ul Sucha 20
80-531 Gdansk, Poland
Tel.: (48) 5 834 314 77
Fax: (48) 5 834 214 33
E-Mail: poland@nrf.eu
Radiator & Air Conditioning Component Mfr
S.I.C.: 3433
N.A.I.C.S.: 333414
Sylwia Rutkowska *(Mgr)*

NRF Switzerland AG (1)
Postfach 407
8902 Urdorf, Switzerland
Tel.: (41) 4 477 722 92
Fax: (41) 4 477 722 94
E-Mail: switzerland@nrf.eu
Emp.: 15
Radiator Mfr
S.I.C.: 3714
N.A.I.C.S.: 336390
Marian Boom *(Mgr-Sls)*

NRF United Kingdom Ltd (1)
Lamport Drive Heartlands Business Park
Daventry, Northamptonshire, NN11 8YH, United Kingdom
Tel.: (44) 1327 300 242
Fax: (44) 1327 300 225
E-Mail: uk@nrf.eu
Emp.: 3
Automotive Radiator & Air Conditioning System Distr
S.I.C.: 5013
N.A.I.C.S.: 423120

Skopimex BV (1)
Langenboomseweg 64
5451 JM Cuijk, Netherlands
Tel.: (31) 485 476476
Fax: (31) 484 476400
E-Mail: info@nrf.eu
Web Site: www.nrf.eu
Emp.: 20
Air Conditioning Component Mfr
S.I.C.: 3585
N.A.I.C.S.: 333415
Paul Allinson *(Mng Dir)*

BANCO SAFRA S.A.

(d/b/a Grupo Safra / Safra Group)
Avenida Paulista 2100 8 Andar
Sao Paulo, Brazil 01310 930
Tel.: (55) 11 3175 7575
Web Site: www.safta.com.br
Rev.: $4,736,550,474
Assets: $54,822,279,225
Liabilities: $51,257,670,449
Net Worth: $3,564,608,776
Earnings: $630,099,777
Emp.: 5,605
Fiscal Year-end: 12/31/12

Business Description:
Commercial Banking
S.I.C.: 6029
N.A.I.C.S.: 522110

Personnel:
Carlos Alberto Vieira *(Pres)*
Rossano Maranhao Pinto *(CEO)*
Silvio Aparecido de Carvalho *(Member-Mgmt Bd)*
Joao Inacio Puga *(Member-Mgmt Bd)*
Alberto Joseph Safra *(Member-Mgmt Bd)*
David Joseph Safra *(Member-Mgmt Bd)*

Board of Directors:
Sergio Luiz Ambrosi
Marcio Appel
Paulo Sergio Cavalheiro
Alberto Corsetti
Sidney da Silva Mano
Joao Eduardo de Assis Pacheco Dacache
Walton Magalhaes de Campos Filho
Silvio Aparecido de Carvalho
Eduardo Pinto de Oliveira
Agostinho Stefanelli Filho
Eduardo Sosa Filho
Murilo Roboton Filho
Hiromiti Mizusaki
Rossano Maranhao Pinto
Helio Albert Sarfaty
Luiz Carlos Zambaldi

Non-U.S. Subsidiary:

Bank Sarasin & Cie AG (1)
Elisabethenstrasse 62
CH-4002 Basel, Switzerland CH
Tel.: (41) 61 277 77 77
Fax: (41) 61 272 02 05
E-Mail: pbbs@sarasin.ch
Web Site: www.sarasin.ch
Sales Range: $200-249.9 Million
Emp.: 1,100
Banking & Investment Services
S.I.C.: 6029
N.A.I.C.S.: 522110
Joachim H. Straehle *(CEO)*
Thomas A. Mueller *(CFO & Head-Corp Center Div)*
Burkhard P. Varnholt *(Chief Investment Officer & Head-Asset Mgmt, Products & Sls Div)*

Non-U.S. Subsidiaries:

Bank Sarasin & Co. Ltd. (2)
1st Fl Frances House Sir William Place
PO Box 348
Saint Peter Port, GY1 3UY, Guernsey
Tel.: (44) 1481725147
Fax: (44) 1481725157
Web Site: www.sarasin.ch
Emp.: 6
Banking & Investment Services
S.I.C.: 6029
N.A.I.C.S.: 522110
Nicola Tanguy *(Mng Dir)*

BANCO SANTANDER, S.A.

Ciudad Grupo Santander 28660
Boadilla del Monte
Madrid, Spain
Tel.: (34) 912893280
Fax: (34) 91 257 12 82
E-Mail: investor@gruposantander.com
Web Site: www.gruposantander.com
Year Founded: 1857
SAN—(MAD NYSE)
Int. Income: $79,456,338,080
Net Worth: $113,517,131,420
Earnings: $3,994,086,390
Emp.: 186,763
Fiscal Year-end: 12/31/12

Business Description:
Bank Holding Company
S.I.C.: 6712
N.A.I.C.S.: 551111

Personnel:
Emilio Botin-Sanz *(Chm)*
Fernando de Asua Alvarez *(First Vice Chm)*
Matias Rodriguez Inciarte *(Third Vice Chm)*
Manuel Soto Serrano *(Fourth Vice Chm)*
Javier Marin Romano *(CEO)*
Ignacio Benjumea Cabeza de Vaca *(Sec)*
Jose Antonio Alvarez Alvarez *(Exec VP-Fin & IR)*
Juan Manuel Cendoya *(Sr VP-Comm, Corp Mktg & Res)*

Board of Directors:
Emilio Botin-Sanz
Sheila C. Bair
Francisco Javier Botin-Sanz
Vittorio Corbo Lioi
Fernando de Asua Alvarez
Angel Jado Becerro de Bengoa
Guillermo de la Dejesa Romero
Ana Patricia Botin Sanz De Sautuola y O'Shea
Rodrigo Echenique Gordillo
Esther Gimenez-Salinas i Colomer
Abel Matutes
Juan Rodriguez Inciarte
Matias Rodriguez Inciarte
Javier Marin Romano
Manuel Soto Serrano
Isabel Tocino Biscarolasaga

Branch:

Banco Santander (1)
Pasco De Pereda 9 12
39004 Santander, Spain
Tel.: (34) 942206100
Banking Services
S.I.C.: 6029
N.A.I.C.S.: 522110
Carlos Hazas *(Mng Dir)*

Subsidiaries:

Allfunds Bank, S.A. (1)
Espasetra 6 Building 3
28109 Madrid, Spain (100%)
Tel.: (34) 912709500
Fax: (34) 912746466
E-Mail: rarazueque@allfundsbank.com
Web Site: www.allfundsbank.com
Emp.: 200
Banking Services
S.I.C.: 6029
N.A.I.C.S.: 522110
Stephen Mohan *(Mng Dir-Operational Svcs-Cofunds)*

Aviacion Intercontinental, A.I.E. (1)
Avenida Cantabria Ed Amazonia S/N-Piso 2
Boadilla del Monte, 28660, Spain
Tel.: (34) 912894714
Fax: (34) 915189193
Emp.: 200
Airline Transportation Services
S.I.C.: 4581
N.A.I.C.S.: 488190
Aneen Catalan *(Gen Mgr)*

Aviacion Regional Cantabra, A.I.E. (1)
Avenida De Cantabria S/N-Ed Amazonia
Boadilla del Monte, 28660, Spain
Tel.: (34) 912894714
Fax: (34) 91 5189193
Industrial Machinery & Equipment Whslr
S.I.C.: 5084
N.A.I.C.S.: 423830

Banco Banif, S.A. (1)
Paseo de La Castellana 53
28046 Madrid, Spain (100%)
Tel.: (34) 917224422
Fax: (34) 915208535
Web Site: www.banif.es
Emp.: 200
Financial Services
S.I.C.: 6211
N.A.I.C.S.: 523120

Banco Espanol de Credito, S.A. (1)
Avenida Gran Via de Hortaleza No 3
28043 Madrid, Spain ES
Tel.: (34) 913381500
Fax: (34) 91 338 1701
E-Mail: correo@banesto.es
Web Site: www.banesto.es
Emp.: 9,800
Banking Services
S.I.C.: 6029
N.A.I.C.S.: 522110
Victor Manuel Menendez Millan *(Vice Chm)*
Jose Garcia Cantera *(CEO)*
Juan Delibes Liniers *(Exec VP-Fin Plng & Control)*

Iberica de Compras Corporativas, S.L. **(1)**
Avenida De Cantabria Lg Ciudad Grupo Santander S/N
Boadilla Del Monte, Madrid, 28660, Spain
Tel.: (34) 912895314
Fax: (34) 912571514
Emp.: 80
Financial Management Services
S.I.C.: 6211
N.A.I.C.S.: 523999
Andres Franco *(Gen Mgr)*

Ingenieria de Software Bancario, S.L. **(1)**
Avenida Cantabria 3 S/N
Boadilla del Monte, 28660, Spain
Tel.: (34) 914704001
Fax: (34) 914704002
E-Mail: rrhhisban@isban.es
Web Site: www.isban.es
Emp.: 300
Software Development Services
S.I.C.: 7371
N.A.I.C.S.: 541511

Laparanza, S.A. **(1)**
Carretera De Colmenar Viejo 21
Tres Cantos, 28760, Spain
Tel.: (34) 916521233
Fax: (34) 918049635
Agricultural Farming Services
S.I.C.: 0711
N.A.I.C.S.: 115112

Luri 4, S.A. **(1)**
Plaza Independencia 8
Madrid, 28001, Spain
Tel.: (34) 915315405
Fax: (34) 915313415
Web Site: www.lurisa.com
Emp.: 1
Real Estate Administration
S.I.C.: 6029
N.A.I.C.S.: 522110

Naviera Trans Gas, A.I.E. **(1)**
Calle Goya Tafira Alta 7 Las Palmas De Gran Canari
Las Palmas, 35017, Spain
Tel.: (34) 928472515
Natural Gas Transportation Services
S.I.C.: 4923
N.A.I.C.S.: 486210

Open Bank, S.A. **(1)**
Avenida Cantabria s/n Ciudad Gr Santander
Boadilla del Monte, Madrid, 28660, Spain
Tel.: (34) 913 42 10 00
Fax: (34) 913 42 10 20
Web Site: www.bancoonline.openbank.es
Commercial Banking Services
S.I.C.: 6029
N.A.I.C.S.: 522110

Patagon Bank, S.A. **(1)**
Plaza Manuel Gomez Moreno 2
28020 Madrid, Spain (100%)
Tel.: (34) 913421000
Fax: (34) 913421020
Web Site: www.openbank.es
Banking Services
S.I.C.: 6029
N.A.I.C.S.: 522110

Santander Consumer, EFC, S.A. **(1)**
Avenida De Cantabria S/N-Ciudad Grupo Santander Ed Dehesa
Boadilla del Monte, 28660, Spain
Tel.: (34) 912892547
Fax: (34) 915665555
Web Site: www.santanderconsumer.es
Financial Management Services
S.I.C.: 6211
N.A.I.C.S.: 523999

Santander Consumer Finance, S.A. **(1)**
Costa Brava 10-12
E-28034 Madrid, Spain
Tel.: (34) 915665500
Fax: (34) 915665555
E-Mail: info@hispamer.es
Web Site: www.hispamer.es
Emp.: 1,126
Banking Services
S.I.C.: 6029
N.A.I.C.S.: 522110
Antonio Escamez Torres *(Chm)*
Juan Rodriguez Inciarte *(CEO)*

U.S. Subsidiary:

Santander Consumer USA Holdings Inc. **(2)**
8585 N Stemmons Frwy Ste 1100-N
Dallas, TX 75247 DE
Tel.: (214) 634-1110
Web Site: www.santanderconsumerusa.com
SC—(NYSE)
Rev.: $3,934,021,000
Assets: $26,401,896,000
Liabilities: $23,715,064,000
Net Worth: $2,686,832,000
Earnings: $695,670,000
Emp.: 4,100
Fiscal Year-end: 12/31/13
Bank Holding Company; Consumer Lending
S.I.C.: 6712
N.A.I.C.S.: 551111
Thomas G. Dundon *(Chm & CEO)*
Alberto Sanchez *(Vice Chm)*
Jason A. Kulas *(Pres & CFO)*
Jason W. Grubb *(COO)*
James W. Fugitt *(CIO)*
R. Michele Rodgers *(Chief Compliance Officer & Chief Risk Officer)*
Eldridge A. Burns, Jr. *(Chief Legal Officer & Gen Counsel)*
Nathan Staples *(Chief Credit Officer)*
Jennifer Popp *(Chief Acctg Officer)*
Michelle L. Whatley *(Chief HR Officer)*
Hugo R. Dooner *(Exec VP-Consumer Lending)*
Brad Martin *(Exec VP-Bus Ops)*
Richard Morrin *(Exec VP-New Bus)*

Subsidiary:

Santander Consumer USA Inc. **(3)**
PO Box 961245
Fort Worth, TX 76161-0244
Tel.: (214) 634-1110
Fax: (214) 630-0828
Toll Free: (877) 374-8305
Web Site: www.drivefinancial.com
Emp.: 820
Purchasing, Securitization & Servicing of Automobile Retail Installment Contracts for Non-Prime Consumers
S.I.C.: 6141
N.A.I.C.S.: 522291
Thomas G. Dundon *(CEO)*
Jason Kulas *(CFO)*

Santander Consumer Renting, S.L. **(1)**
C/Santa Barbara 1
Torrelaguna, Madrid, Spain
Tel.: (34) 902151601
Fax: (34) 902020425
Vehicle Rental & Automotive Services
S.I.C.: 7514
N.A.I.C.S.: 532111

Santander Global Property, S.L. **(1)**
Paseo Castellana 93-PLT 13
Madrid, 28046, Spain
Tel.: (34) 911773780
Fax: (34) 917703123
Emp.: 2
Real Estate Management Services
S.I.C.: 6531
N.A.I.C.S.: 531390
Juan Antonio Guitart *(Gen Mgr)*

Sistema 4B, S.A. **(1)**
C/Francisco Sancha 12
Madrid, 28034, Spain
Tel.: (34) 91 362 63 00
Fax: (34) 91 362 63 40
Financial Management Services
S.I.C.: 6211
N.A.I.C.S.: 523999

Vista Desarrollo, S.A. SCR de Regimen Simplificado **(1)**
Calle Serrano 67
Madrid, 28006, Spain
Tel.: (34) 914360781
Fax: (34) 915782915
Investment Management Services
S.I.C.: 6211
N.A.I.C.S.: 523999
Rafael Garabito *(Mgr)*

Affiliates:

Cableuropa, S.A.U. **(1)**
Calle Basauri 7-9
Urbanizacion la Florida
Aravaca, 28023 Madrid, Spain (19%)
Tel.: (34) 911809300
Fax: (34) 912025019
Web Site: www.ono.es
Rev.: $537,189,504
Emp.: 500
Internet & Cable Services
S.I.C.: 7373
N.A.I.C.S.: 541512
Enrique Iglesias *(Dir-Sls)*

Grupo Taper, S.A. **(1)**
Ave Avenida De La Industria No 49 Bldg Egifizio Fresno 1st Fl
28108 Alcobendas, Madrid, Spain (27.77%)
Tel.: (34) 914841960
Fax: (34) 916596520
E-Mail: information@grupotaper.com
Web Site: www.grupotaper.com
Emp.: 70
Medical Equipment Distr
S.I.C.: 5499
N.A.I.C.S.: 446191
Fernando Gumuzio Iniguez de Onzono *(Chm)*

La Union Resinera Espanola, S.A. **(1)**
Plaza de la Independencia 8 2nd Flr
28001 Madrid, Spain
Tel.: (34) 915315405
Fax: (34) 915313415
E-Mail: corparete@luresa.com
Web Site: www.luresa.com
Emp.: 25
Resin Products
S.I.C.: 2899
N.A.I.C.S.: 325998
Jose Maria Carballo *(Chm)*

U.S. Branch:

Banco Santander International **(1)**
1401 Brickell Ave Ste 1500
Miami, FL 33131-3506
Tel.: (305) 530-2900
Fax: (305) 530-2992
E-Mail: info@pbsantander.com
Web Site: www.pbsantander.com
Emp.: 500
Banking Services
S.I.C.: 6029
N.A.I.C.S.: 522110
Luis H. Navas *(Sr VP & Dir-Comml-Central America & Caribbean)*
Jose Luis Marroquin *(Sr VP)*
Borja Martinez-Pardo *(Sr VP)*
Rafael Moreno *(Sr VP)*

U.S. Subsidiaries:

Banco Santander Puerto Rico **(1)**
207 Ponce De Leon Ave
San Juan, PR 00917-1818
Tel.: (787) 274-7200
Toll Free: (800) 726-8263
Commercial Banking Services
S.I.C.: 6029
N.A.I.C.S.: 522110
Marlene Hernandez *(Product Mgr)*

BST International Bank, Inc. **(1)**
221 Ponce de Leon Ave Ste 1001
San Juan, PR 00917
Tel.: (787) 641-8996
Fax: (787) 250-3911
E-Mail:
Web Site: www.bstipr.com
Emp.: 4
Commercial Banking Services
S.I.C.: 6029
N.A.I.C.S.: 522110
Sandra Collazo *(Gen Mgr)*

Santander BanCorp **(1)**
B7 Tabonuco St 18th Fl San Patricio
Guaynabo, PR 00968-3028 (91%)
Tel.: (787) 281-2000
Web Site: www.santander.pr
SBP—(MAD NYSE)
Sales Range: $600-649.9 Million
Emp.: 1,764
Bank Holding Company
S.I.C.: 6712
N.A.I.C.S.: 551111
Gonzalo de Las Heras *(Chm)*
Juan S. Moreno Blanco *(Pres & CEO)*

Subsidiaries:

Island Finance, Inc. **(2)**
Verizon Bldg Rd 1 Km 15.1
Rio Piedras, PR 00926 DE
Mailing Address:
PO Box 71504
San Juan, PR 00936-8604
Tel.: (787) 759-7044
Fax: (787) 773-7583
Rev.: $93,700,000
Emp.: 100
Consumer Lending Services
S.I.C.: 6141
N.A.I.C.S.: 522291

Santander Securities Corporation **(2)**
B7 Calle Tabonuco Ste 1800
Guaynabo, PR 00968 (88.63%)
Tel.: (787) 759-5330
Fax: (787) 759-5366
Toll Free: (888) 756-0003
Web Site: www.santandersecurities.com
Emp.: 150
Investment Banking & Asset Management
S.I.C.: 6211
N.A.I.C.S.: 523120
Rosalie Torres *(Sr VP-Compliance)*

Santander Investment Securities Inc. **(1)**
45 E 53rd St
New York, NY 10022-4604 DE
Tel.: (212) 350-3500
Fax: (212) 350-3535
Web Site: www.santander.us
Emp.: 200
International Banking
S.I.C.: 6029
N.A.I.C.S.: 522110
Juan Andres Yanes *(Pres)*

Services and Promotions Miami LLC **(1)**
1401 Brickell Ave 810
Miami, FL 33131-3506
Tel.: (305) 358-1401
Scientific & Technical Consulting Services
S.I.C.: 8999
N.A.I.C.S.: 541690

Synergy Abstract, LP **(1)**
25 W Moreland Ave
Hatboro, PA 19040
Tel.: (215) 441-5177
Fax: (215) 441-0694
Web Site: www.beaconabstract.com
Insurance Agencies
S.I.C.: 6411
N.A.I.C.S.: 524210

Totta & Acores Inc. **(1)**
71 Ferry St A
Newark, NJ 07105-1830
Tel.: (973) 578-8633
Credit Intermediation Services
S.I.C.: 6099
N.A.I.C.S.: 522390

U.S. Holding:

SANTANDER HOLDINGS USA, INC. **(1)**
75 State St
Boston, MA 02109 VA
Tel.: (617) 346-7200
Toll Free: (877) 768-2265
Web Site: www.santanderconsumerusa.com
SOV—(NYSE)
Rev.: $3,383,974,000
Assets: $77,144,021,000
Liabilities: $63,599,038,000
Net Worth: $13,544,983,000
Earnings: $628,103,000
Emp.: 8,250
Fiscal Year-end: 12/31/13
Bank Holding Company
S.I.C.: 6712
N.A.I.C.S.: 551111
Jerry A. Grundhofer *(Chm)*
Roman Suarez Blanco *(CEO)*
Juan Guillermo Sabater *(CFO & Sr Exec VP)*
Donna Howe *(Chief Risk Officer & Sr Exec VP)*
Francisco J. Simon *(Chief HR Officer & Sr Exec VP)*
Carlos M. Garcia *(Chief Corp Affairs & Comm Officer)*
Juan Andres Yanes *(Chief Compliance & Internal Controls Officer)*
Richard A. Toomey *(Gen Counsel)*
Juan Carlos Alvarez *(Treas & Exec VP)*
Nuno G. Matos *(Mng Dir-Retail Bus Dev & Sr Exec VP)*

BANCO SANTANDER, S.A.—(Continued)

Edvaldo Morata *(Sr Exec VP & Mng Dir-Corp Banking)*
Juan Davila *(Chief Risk Mgmt Officer & Sr Exec VP)*
David Miree *(Mng Dir-Retail Network & Exec VP)*

Subsidiaries:

Capital Street Delaware LP (2)
900 N Michigan Ave
Chicago, IL 60611-1542
Tel.: (312) 915-2400
Investment Management Services
S.I.C.: 6282
N.A.I.C.S.: 523930

Independence Community Commercial Reinvestment Corp. (2)
103 Foulk Rd
Wilmington, DE 19803
Tel.: (302) 691-6408
Investment Management Services
S.I.C.: 6282
N.A.I.C.S.: 523930

Meridian Capital Group, LLC (2)
1 Battery Park Plz
New York, NY 10004
Tel.: (212) 972-3600
Fax: (212) 612-0100
E-Mail: sales@meridiancapital.com
Web Site: www.meridiancapital.com
Commercial Mortgage Brokerage Services
S.I.C.: 6163
N.A.I.C.S.: 522310
Ralph Herzka *(Founder, Chm & CEO)*
Aaron Birnbaum *(Co-Founder & Exec VP)*
Jeff Weinberg *(Co-Founder & Exec VP)*
Avi Weinstock *(Exec VP)*

PBE Companies, LLC (2)
2711 Centerville Rd
Wilmington, DE 19808-1660
Tel.: (617) 346-7459
Investment Management Services
S.I.C.: 6282
N.A.I.C.S.: 523930
Scott Dow, *(Pres)*

Santander Insurance Agency, U.S., LLC (2)
75 State St
Boston, MA 02109
Tel.: (770) 248-3546
Fax: (678) 966-6103
Insurance Brokerage Services
S.I.C.: 6411
N.A.I.C.S.: 524210

Sovereign Delaware Investment Corporation (2)
103 Foulk Rd
Wilmington, DE 19803
Tel.: (302) 691-6123
Investment Management Services
S.I.C.: 6282
N.A.I.C.S.: 523930

Sovereign Real Estate Investment Trust (2)
103 Foulk Rd Ste 200
Wilmington, DE 19803
Tel.: (302) 654-7584
Real Estate Investment Services
S.I.C.: 6531
N.A.I.C.S.: 531390

Sovereign REIT Holdings, Inc. (2)
103 Foulk Rd Ste 236
Wilmington, DE 19803-3742
Tel.: (302) 421-9003
Investment Management Services
S.I.C.: 6719
N.A.I.C.S.: 551112

Sovereign Securities Corporation, LLC (2)
1500 Market St
Philadelphia, PA 19102-2106
Tel.: (267) 256-2818
Fax: (610) 320-8448
Security Brokerage Services
S.I.C.: 6211
N.A.I.C.S.: 523120

Waypoint Insurance Group, Inc. (2)
1805 Loucks Rd Ste 400
York, PA 17408
Tel.: (717) 767-9006
Insurance Brokerage Services
S.I.C.: 6411
N.A.I.C.S.: 524210

Holdings:

Sovereign Bank (2)
1130 Berkshire Blvd
Wyomissing, PA 19610
Mailing Address:
PO Box 12646
Reading, PA 19612
Tel.: (610) 320-8400
Fax: (610) 320-8448
E-Mail: info@esovbank.com
Web Site: www.sovereignbank.com
Emp.: 100
Savings, Loans, Commercial & Investment Banking Services
S.I.C.: 6035
N.A.I.C.S.: 522120
Jerry A. Grundhofer *(Chm)*
Roman Suarez Blanco *(CEO)*
Andrew P. Gully *(Sr VP & Mng Dir-Corp Affairs)*

Subsidiaries:

Nantucket Bank (3)
104 Pleasant St
Nantucket, MA 02554-4004
Tel.: (508) 228-0580
Fax: (508) 228-1322
Toll Free: (800) 533-9313
E-Mail: bank@nantucket.com
Web Site: www.nantucketbank.com
Emp.: 60
Commercial Banking Services
S.I.C.: 6029
N.A.I.C.S.: 522110
William P. Hourihan, Jr. *(Pres & CEO)*
Zona V. Butler *(Sr VP-Ops & Info Svcs)*
Quint Waters *(Sr VP-Lending)*

Non-U.S. Subsidiaries:

Abbey National Financial Investments 4 B.V. (1)
Fred Roeskestraat 123
Amsterdam, 1076 EE, Netherlands
Tel.: (31) 206422415
Financial Management Services
S.I.C.: 6211
N.A.I.C.S.: 523999

Abbey National Treasury Investments Ltd (1)
2-3 Triton Square
London, NW1 3AN, United Kingdom
Tel.: (44) 870 607 6000
Treasury Investment Management Services
S.I.C.: 9311
N.A.I.C.S.: 921130

Banco de Asuncion (1)
Calle Palma Esquina 14 de Mayo
Asuncion, Paraguay
Tel.: (595) 21493191
Fax: (595) 21493190
E-Mail: bancoasuncion@basa.com.py
Emp.: 64
International Banking
S.I.C.: 6211
N.A.I.C.S.: 523110

Banco de Venezuela, S.A. (1)
Piso 18 Torre Banco De Venezuela
Avenida Universidad
esquina Sociedad a Traposos, Caracas, 1010A, Venezuela
Tel.: (58) 2125013333
Fax: (58) 2125012546
Web Site: www.bancodevenezuela.com
Emp.: 5,189
Banking Services
S.I.C.: 6029
N.A.I.C.S.: 522110

Banco Madesant - Sociedade Unipessoal, S.A. (1)
2nd Floor Avenida Arriaga 73 2 Sala 211
Funchal, 9000-060, Portugal
Tel.: (351) 291203110
Fax: (351) 291203128
Financial Management Services
S.I.C.: 6211
N.A.I.C.S.: 523999

Banco Rio de la Plata S.A. (1)
Bartolome Mitre 480
1036 Buenos Aires, Argentina
Tel.: (54) 1143411000
Fax: (54) 1143411074
Web Site: www.bancorio.com.ar
Emp.: 4,640
Commercial & Investment Banking Services
S.I.C.: 6029
N.A.I.C.S.: 522110

Banco Santa Cruz, S.A. (1)
Calle Junin 154
PO Box 865
Santa Cruz, Bolivia
Tel.: (591) 33369911
Fax: (591) 33358259
E-Mail: bancruz@mail.bsc.com.bo
Web Site: www.bsc.com.bo
Banking Services
S.I.C.: 6029
N.A.I.C.S.: 522110
Benigno Rodriguez *(Pres)*

Banco Santander Central Hispano (Guernsey), Ltd. (1)
Dorey Court Atmiral Park Elizabeth Avenue
PO Box 191
Saint Peter Port, GY1 4HW, Guernsey (99.98%)
Tel.: (44) 1481715424
Fax: (44) 1481746499
E-Mail: info@confiance.gg
Web Site: www.confiance.gg
Emp.: 24
Banking Services
S.I.C.: 6029
N.A.I.C.S.: 522110
Roger T. Knights *(CEO)*

Banco Santander-Chile (1)
Bandera 140
Santiago, Chile CL
Tel.: (56) 2 320 2000 (83.94%)
Fax: (56) 2 320 8877
Web Site: www.santandersantiago.cl
BSAC—(BRAZ NYSE SGO)
Int. Income: $4,008,820,360
Assets: $52,490,962,560
Liabilities: $47,832,510,600
Net Worth: $4,658,451,960
Earnings: $765,570,160
Emp.: 11,713
Fiscal Year-end: 12/31/12
Banking Services
S.I.C.: 6099
N.A.I.C.S.: 522320
Mauricio Larrain Garces *(Chm)*
Oscar Von Chrismar Carvajal *(Vice Chm)*
Jesus Ma Zabalza Lotina *(Vice Chm)*
Claudio Melandri *(CEO)*
Miguel Mata *(CFO)*
Jose Manuel Manzano Tagle *(Chief Risk Officer)*
Jose Pedro Santa Maria *(Gen Counsel)*

Banco Santander de Negocios Portugal, S.A. (1)
Avenida Eng Duarte Pacheco
Amoreiras Torre 1 Piso 6
P-1099 024 Lisbon, Portugal (99.35%)
Tel.: (351) 213801500
Fax: (351) 213859133
E-Mail: info@santander.pt
Web Site: www.santander.pt
Emp.: 100
Banking Services
S.I.C.: 6029
N.A.I.C.S.: 522110
Nuno Amadl *(Pres)*
Eurico da Silva Teixeira de Melo *(Pres)*

Banco Santander (Panama), S.A. (1)
Piso 7 Edificio PH Torre ADR Local 700B
Avenida Samuel Lewis y C 58
Santo Domingo Obarrio, Panama, Panama (100%)
Tel.: (507) 2636577
Fax: (507) 2636865
Web Site: www.bancosantander.com.pa/
Emp.: 5
Banking Services
S.I.C.: 6029
N.A.I.C.S.: 522110

Banco Santander Portugal, S.A. (1)
Praca Marqes de Pombal No 2
Lisbon, P-1250 161, Portugal
Tel.: (351) 707212424
E-Mail: superlinha@santander.pt
Web Site: www.santander.pt
Emp.: 1,287
Banking Services
S.I.C.: 6029
N.A.I.C.S.: 522110

Banco Santander Rio S.A. (1)
Bartolome Mitre 480
1036 Buenos Aires, Argentina
Tel.: (54) 11 4341 1000
Fax: (54) 11 4341 1296
Web Site: www.santanderrio.com.ar
BRIO—(BUE)
Sales Range: $1-4.9 Billion
Emp.: 6,281
Banking Services
S.I.C.: 6029
N.A.I.C.S.: 522110
Jose Luis Enrique Cristofani *(Chm & CEO)*
Guillermo Ruben Tempesta *(Vice Chm)*
Gabriel Juan Ribisich *(CFO)*

Banco Santander (Suisse), S.A. (1)
Rue Ami-Levrier 5-7
PO Box 1256
1211 Geneva, 1, Switzerland (99.96%)
Tel.: (41) 229092222
Fax: (41) 227386728
E-Mail: receptiondl@bpe-gruposantander.com
Web Site: www.bsch.es
Emp.: 150
Banking Services
S.I.C.: 6029
N.A.I.C.S.: 522110
Antonio Costa *(Gen Mgr)*

Bank Zachodni WBK S.A. (1)
Rynek 9/11
50-950 Wroclaw, Poland PL
Tel.: (48) 713701000 (76.5%)
E-Mail: contact@bzwbk.pl
Web Site: www.bzwbk.pl
BZW—(WAR)
Int. Income: $1,226,495,518
Assets: $19,033,881,602
Liabilities: $16,186,779,161
Net Worth: $2,847,102,441
Earnings: $463,845,438
Emp.: 8,835
Fiscal Year-end: 12/31/12
Bank Holding Company
S.I.C.: 6712
N.A.I.C.S.: 551111
Gerry Byrne *(Chm-Supervisory Bd)*
Mateusz Morawiecki *(Chm-Mgmt Bd)*
Jose Manuel Varela *(Deputy Chm-Supervisory Bd)*
Andrzej Burliga *(Member-Mgmt Bd-Risk Mgmt Div)*
Eamonn Crowley *(Member-Mgmt Bd-Fin Div)*
Juan de Porras Aguirre *(Member-Mgmt Bd-Global Banking & Markets Div)*
Michael McCarthy *(Member-Mgmt Bd-Bus & Corp Banking Div)*
Piotr Partyga *(Member-Mgmt Bd-HR Mgmt Div)*
Marcin Prell *(Member-Mgmt Bd-Legal & Compliance Div)*
Marco Antonio Silva Rojas *(Member-Mgmt Bd)*
Miroslaw Skiba *(Member-Mgmt Bd-Retail Banking Div)*
Feliks Szyszkowiak *(Member-Mgmt Bd-Bus Support Div)*

Subsidiaries:

Brytyjsko-Polskie Towarzystwo Finansowe WBK-CU Sp. z o.o. (2)
Jasielska 16
60-476 Poznan, Poland
Tel.: (48) 618528133
Fax: (48) 618476430
E-Mail: wbkcu@polbox.com
Insurance & Financial Products
S.I.C.: 6411
N.A.I.C.S.: 524298

BZ WBK AIB Asset Management S.A. (2)
Plac Wolnosci 16
61739 Poznan, Poland
Tel.: (48) 618519268
Fax: (48) 618533387
E-Mail: am@bzwbk.pl
Web Site: www.am.bzwbk.pl
Emp.: 100
Advisory Services in the Area of Public Trading in Securities

S.I.C.: 6282
N.A.I.C.S.: 523930

BZ WBK Finanse & Leasing S.A. (2)
Poznanskie Centrum Finansowe Placa Andersa 5
61 894 Poznan, Poland (100%)
Tel.: (48) 618503500
Fax: (48) 618503590
E-Mail: wbkfl@home.pl
Web Site: www.leasing24.pl
Emp.: 100
Lease & Rental of Fixed Assets & Selling Goods on Instalments
S.I.C.: 6514
N.A.I.C.S.: 531110

WBK Nieruchomosci S.A. (2)
Palac W Zakrzewie
Zakrzewo, 62 270 Poznan, Klecko, Poland (100%)
Tel.: (48) 614270203
Fax: (48) 614249001
E-Mail: zakrzewo@wbk.com.pl
Web Site: www.zakrzewo.bzwbk.pl
Emp.: 20
Investment Banking
S.I.C.: 6211
N.A.I.C.S.: 523110
Diana Matlosz *(Gen Mgr)*

CC-Bank Aktiengesellschaft (1)
Kaiserstrasse 74
D-41061 Monchengladbach, Germany (100%)
Tel.: (49) 21616900
Fax: (49) 21616905370
E-Mail: kontakt@santander.de
Web Site: www.santander.de
Emp.: 2,080
Banking Services
S.I.C.: 6159
N.A.I.C.S.: 522298
Gerd Schumeckers *(Chm)*
Andreas Finkenberg *(Vice Chm)*
Ulrich Leuschner *(Mng Dir-Retail Banking & Consumer Fin Svcs)*

CCB Finance, s.r.o. (1)
Safrankova 1
155 00 Prague, Czech Republic (100%)
Tel.: (420) 225285111
E-Mail:
Emp.: 301
Leasing Services
S.I.C.: 7334
N.A.I.C.S.: 561499

Companhia Geral de Credito Predial Portugues, S.A. (1)
Rua Augusta 237 Apartado 2002
Lisbon, P-1101-802, Portugal (99.36%)
Tel.: (351) 213263273
Web Site: www.cpp.pt
Banking Services
S.I.C.: 6029
N.A.I.C.S.: 522110

Dom Maklerski BZ WBK S.A. (1)
Pl Wolnosci 15
Poznan, 60-967, Poland
Tel.: (48) 618564880
Fax: (48) 618564770
E-Mail: dm.inwestor@bzwbk.pl
Online Brokerage Services
S.I.C.: 6211
N.A.I.C.S.: 523120

Optimal Investment Services S.A. (1)
Beccolat 8
1201 Geneva, Switzerland
Tel.: (41) 22 909 74 74
Fax: (41) 22 909 62 22
Web Site: www.optimal.biz
Emp.: 10
Financial Management Services
S.I.C.: 6211
N.A.I.C.S.: 523999
Javier Echave *(CIO)*

Santander Asset Management S.A. (1)
Bombero Ossa 1068 Piso 8
Santiago, Chile
Tel.: (56) 2 550 0357
Asset Management Services
S.I.C.: 6282
N.A.I.C.S.: 523920

Santander Banespa Grupo (1)
Praca Antonio Prado 6
Centro, Sao Paulo, SP, 01602-900, Brazil
Tel.: (55) 112499338
Fax: (55) 112497858
Holding Company
S.I.C.: 6712
N.A.I.C.S.: 551111

Subsidiaries:

Banco Santander (Brasil) S.A. (2)
Avenida Presidente Juscelino Kubitschek 2041 & 2235 Bloco Vila Olimpia, Sao Paulo, 04543-011, Brazil (95.93%)
Tel.: (55) 1131748589
Fax: (55) 115538660
E-Mail: fundingtradefinance@santander.com.br
Web Site: www.santander.com.br
BSBR—(NYSE)
Rev.: $19,093,787,097
Assets: $207,127,482,450
Liabilities: $167,005,928,110
Net Worth: $40,121,554,340
Earnings: $2,685,364,255
Emp.: 53,992
Fiscal Year-end: 12/31/12
Banking Services
S.I.C.: 6029
N.A.I.C.S.: 522110
Celso Clemente Giacometti *(Vice Chm)*
Jesus Maria Lotina Zabalza *(CEO)*
Conrado Engel *(Member-Exec Bd & Sr VP-Retail)*
Fernando Byington Egydio Martins *(Exec VP)*
Lilian Guimaraes *(Exec VP)*
Jose de Paiva Ferreira *(Sr VP)*

Santander Bank and Trust (Bahamas), Ltd. (1)
Goodmans Bay Corporate Center
PO Box 1682
Nassau, Bahamas (100%)
Tel.: (242) 3223588
Fax: (242) 3223585
Banking Services
S.I.C.: 6159
N.A.I.C.S.: 522298
Michael Richard *(Sr VP & Head-Seafood Indus Banking)*

Santander Bank & Trust, Ltd. (1)
Goodmans Bay Corporate Centre Sea View Dr 3rd Fl W Bay St
Nassau, N1682, Bahamas (100%)
Tel.: (242) 322 3588
Fax: (242) 322 3585
Earnings: $12,731,200
Investment & Banking Services
S.I.C.: 6211
N.A.I.C.S.: 523110

Santander Benelux SA/NV (1)
Avenue Des Larciviens 85
1040 Brussels, Belgium BE
Tel.: (32) 22865411
Fax: (32) 2305232
E-Mail: eusobrussels@santanderbenelux.be
Emp.: 20
Banking Services
S.I.C.: 6029
N.A.I.C.S.: 522110
Guillermo Sanz Murat *(Mng Dir)*

Santander Consumer Bank AG (1)
Santander-Platz 1
Monchengladbach, 41061, Germany
Tel.: (49) 21616900
Fax: (49) 1619065598
E-Mail: service@santander.de
Emp.: 200
Financial Services
S.I.C.: 6211
N.A.I.C.S.: 523999
Ulrich Andrews *(Gen Mgr)*

Santander Consumer Bank AS (1)
Strandvn 18
PO Box 177
1325 Lysaker, Norway
Tel.: (47) 21 08 30 00
Fax: (47) 21 08 33 68
Web Site: www.santander.no
Emp.: 300
Commercial Banking Services
S.I.C.: 6029
N.A.I.C.S.: 522110
Michael Hvidsten *(CEO)*

Santander Consumer Bank GmbH (1)
Donau-City Strasse 6
Vienna, 1220, Austria
Tel.: (43) 50203
Fax: (43) 50203 9325
E-Mail: infoservice@santanderconsumer.at
Web Site: www.santanderconsumer.at
Emp.: 43
Automobile Financial Management Services
S.I.C.: 6726
N.A.I.C.S.: 525990
Georg Gfrerer *(Gen Mgr)*

Santander Consumer Credit Services Limited (1)
Malvern House Hatters Lane
Watford, Herts, WD18 8YF, United Kingdom
Tel.: (44) 1923 426426
Credit Management Services
S.I.C.: 6159
N.A.I.C.S.: 522298

Santander Consumer Finance Benelux B.V. (1)
Winthontlaan 171
Utrecht, 3526 KV, Netherlands
Tel.: (31) 30 638 8100
Fax: (31) 30 638 8960
Financial Management Services
S.I.C.: 6211
N.A.I.C.S.: 523999

Santander Consumer Holding GmbH (1)
Nordrhein-Westfalen
Monchengladbach, 41061, Germany
Tel.: (49) 2161 6900
Fax: (49) 2161 690370
Emp.: 500
Investment Management Services
S.I.C.: 6211
N.A.I.C.S.: 523999
Ulrich Leuschner *(Mng Dir)*

Santander Consumer Leasing GmbH (1)
Santander-Platz 1
Monchengladbach, 41061, Germany
Tel.: (49) 21616907808
Fax: (49) 01805556490
E-Mail: satander@santander-leasing.de
Emp.: 2
Leasing Services
S.I.C.: 7515
N.A.I.C.S.: 532112

Santander Consumer Leasing s.r.o. (1)
Safrankova 1 Praha 5
Prague, 190 00, Czech Republic
Tel.: (420) 2 8301 9550
Fax: (420) 2 2528 5500
Automobile Leasing Services
S.I.C.: 7515
N.A.I.C.S.: 532112

Santander Financial Products, Ltd. (1)
Block 8 Harcourt Centre
Dublin, 2, Ireland (100%)
Tel.: (353) 14757850
Fax: (353) 14757855
E-Mail: sspdublin@gruposantander.com
Emp.: 6
Financial Services
S.I.C.: 7389
N.A.I.C.S.: 561499
Michael McInerney *(Mng Dir)*

Santander Insurance Services UK Limited (1)
2 Triton Square Regents Place
London, NW1 3AN, United Kingdom
Tel.: (44) 8706076000
Insurance Management Services
S.I.C.: 6411
N.A.I.C.S.: 524298

Santander UK plc (1)
2 Triton Square Regent's Place
London, NW1 3AN, United Kingdom UK (100%)
Tel.: (44) 8706076000
Fax: (44) 2077565628
Web Site: www.santander.co.uk
SANB—(LSE)
Rev.: $11,912,524,800
Assets: $449,095,539,200
Liabilities: $428,294,310,400
Net Worth: $20,801,228,800
Earnings: $1,516,894,720
Emp.: 20,064
Fiscal Year-end: 12/31/13
Bank Holding Company
S.I.C.: 6712
N.A.I.C.S.: 551111
Terence Burns *(Chm)*
Ana Patricia Botin Sanz De Sautuola y O'Shea *(CEO)*
Stephen Jones *(CFO)*
Nathan Bostock *(Chief Risk Officer)*

Subsidiaries:

Abbey National General Insurance Services Ltd. (2)
2 Triton Square
Regent's Place, London, NW1 3AN, United Kingdom (100%)
Tel.: (44) 8706076000
Web Site: www.santander.co.uk
Emp.: 1,000
Insurance & Pension Services
S.I.C.: 6399
N.A.I.C.S.: 524128
Ana Botin *(CEO)*

Abbey National Treasury Services plc (2)
2 Triton Square Regents Place
London, NW1 3AN, United Kingdom
Tel.: (44) 8706076000
Fax: (44) 84 5600 3048
Web Site: www.ants.co.uk
Rev.: $4,480,903,680
Assets: $347,784,250,880
Liabilities: $342,520,808,960
Net Worth: $5,263,441,920
Earnings: $272,476,160
Emp.: 764
Fiscal Year-end: 12/31/13
Financial Treasury Management Services
S.I.C.: 9311
N.A.I.C.S.: 921130
Ana Botin *(Mng Dir)*

Cater Allen Limited (2)
Santander House 9 Nelson Street
Bradford, BD15AN, United Kingdom
Tel.: (44) 2077564500
Fax: (44) 08702406263
Web Site: www.caterallen.co.uk
Commercial Banking Services
S.I.C.: 6029
N.A.I.C.S.: 522110
Siobhan O'Shea *(Sr Mgr-Media Rels)*

Santander Cards UK Ltd. (2)
6 Agar Street
London, WC2N 4HR, United Kingdom UK
Tel.: (44) 113 280 7080 (Switchboard)
Web Site: www.santandercards.com
Sales Range: $1-4.9 Billion
Emp.: 3,000
Credit Card Services
S.I.C.: 6153
N.A.I.C.S.: 522210
Nigel Sparrow *(Chief Risk Officer)*

Santander UK plc (2)
Carlton Park
Narborough, Leicester, LE19 0AL, United Kingdom UK
Tel.: (44) 1162011000
Fax: (44) 1162004040
E-Mail: ir@santander.co.uk
Web Site: www.santander.com
Sales Range: $5-14.9 Billion
Emp.: 7,279
Retail & Commercial Banking Services
S.I.C.: 6029
N.A.I.C.S.: 522110
Ana Patricia Botin Sanz De Sautuola y O'Shea *(CEO)*

Subsidiaries:

Alliance & Leicester Independent Financial Advisors Ltd. (3)
Carlton Pk
Narborough, Leicester, LE19 OAL, United Kingdom
Tel.: (44) 1162011000
Fax: (44) 1162004040
Web Site: www.alliance-leicestergroup.co.uk
Emp.: 2,000
Financial Advisors
S.I.C.: 6282

BANCO SANTANDER, S.A.—(Continued)

N.A.I.C.S.: 523930

Alliance & Leicester Personal Finance Ltd. (3)
Heritage House 61 Southgates
Leicester, LE1 5RR, United Kingdom
Tel.: (44) 620 11 000
Web Site: www.alliance-leicester.co.uk/loans/loan-repayment-insurance-policy-summary.aspx?theme=print&ct=printpagerhn
Personal Financing
S.I.C.: 6141
N.A.I.C.S.: 522291

Non-U.S. Subsidiaries:

Alliance & Leicester International Limited (2)
19/21 Prospect Hill
PO Box 226
British Isles, Douglas, IM99 1RY, Isle of Man
Tel.: (44) 1624 641 888
Fax: (44) 1624 663 577
E-Mail: customer.services@alil.co.im
Web Site: www.alliance-leicester.co.im
Commercial Banking Services
S.I.C.: 6029
N.A.I.C.S.: 522110
Chris Tunley *(Chm)*
Tania Sobey *(CEO)*
John Pearson *(Mng Dir)*

Totta (Ireland), PLC (1)
AIB International Cntr IFSC 1 Co
Dublin, Ireland
Tel.: (353) 1 8291208
Fax: (353) 1 8291210
Financial Management Services
S.I.C.: 6211
N.A.I.C.S.: 523999

Non-U.S. Holding:

Grupo Financiero Santander Mexico, S.A.B. de C.V. (1)
(Formerly Grupo Financiero Santander S.A.B. de C.V.)
Avenida Prolongacion Paseo De La Reforma 500
Colonia Lomas de Santa Fe, 01219 Mexico, DF, Mexico MX
Tel.: (52) 5552578000
Fax: (52) 5552617562
E-Mail: investor@santander.com.mx
Web Site: www.santander.com.mx
BSMX—(MEX NYSE)
Rev.: $4,368,392,280
Assets: $62,382,854,240
Liabilities: $54,467,174,160
Net Worth: $7,915,680,080
Earnings: $1,370,212,200
Emp.: 13,385
Fiscal Year-end: 12/31/12
Bank Holding Company
S.I.C.: 6719
N.A.I.C.S.: 551112
Carlos Gomez y Gomez *(Chm)*
Marcos Alejandro Martinez Gavica *(Pres & CEO)*
Eduardo Fernandez Garcia-Travesi *(Gen Counsel)*
Alfredo Acevedo Rivas *(Sec)*

Subsidiaries:

Banca Serfin, S.A. (2)
Prolongacion Paseo de la Reforma Mod 409 Nivel 4
Colonia Lomas de Santa Fe, CP 01219 Mexico, Mexico (100%)
Tel.: (52) 5552598860
Fax: (52) 5552578387
Web Site: www.serfin.com.mx
Banking Services
S.I.C.: 6029
N.A.I.C.S.: 522110

Casa de Bolsa Santander Serfin, S.A. de C.V. (2)
Prolongacion Paseo de la Reforma 500 Modulo 206
Colonia Lomas de Santa Fe, 01210 Mexico, DF, Mexico (73.95%)
Tel.: (52) 55 5261 5435
Fax: (52) 55 5592 6988
Emp.: 1,200
Investment Services
S.I.C.: 6221
N.A.I.C.S.: 523130

Non-U.S. Affiliate:

Attijariwafa Bank (1)
2 boulevard Moulay Youssef
BP 11141
20000 Casablanca, Morocco
Tel.: (212) 5 22 22 41 69
Fax: (212) 22 29 41 25
E-Mail: contact@attijariwafa.com
Web Site: www.attijariwafabank.com
BCMA—(CAS EUR)
Sales Range: $1-4.9 Billion
Emp.: 2,525
Banking Services
S.I.C.: 6029
N.A.I.C.S.: 522110
Mohamed El Kettani *(Chm)*
Wafaa Guessous *(Sec)*

BANCO SOFISA S.A.

Alameda Santos 1496 10 andar
1418 100 Sao Paulo, Brazil
Tel.: (55) 1131765990
Fax: (55) 1131765880
E-Mail: ri@sofisa.com.br
Web Site: www.sofisadireto.com.br
SFSA4—(BRAZ)
Int. Income: $272,250,785
Assets: $1,931,046,513
Liabilities: $1,541,066,284
Net Worth: $389,980,230
Earnings: $11,449,724
Emp.: 502
Fiscal Year-end: 12/31/12
Business Description:
Banking Services
S.I.C.: 6029
N.A.I.C.S.: 522110
Personnel:
Alexandre Burmaian *(Chm)*
Andre Jafferian Neto *(Vice Chm)*
Gilberto Maktas Meiches *(CEO)*
Marcelo Balan *(Exec Officer & VP)*
Pepe Diaz Alencar de Melo *(Exec Officer)*
Ricardo Simone Pereira *(Exec Officer)*
Bazili Rossi Swioklo *(Exec Officer)*
Board of Directors:
Alexandre Burmaian
Antenor Araken Caldas Farias
Antonio Carlos Feitosa
Andre Jafferian Neto
Gilberto Maktas Meiches

BANCO UNIVERSAL S.A.

Calle J Sosa y Ave 1 Este
Apartado postal 426-564
David, Chiriqui, Panama
Tel.: (507) 775 4394
Fax: (507) 777 4271
E-Mail: buniversal@bancouniversal.com
Web Site: www.bancouniversal.com
Year Founded: 1994
BUNI—(PAN)
Emp.: 110
Business Description:
Banking Services
S.I.C.: 6029
N.A.I.C.S.: 522110
Personnel:
Jose Isaac Virzi Lopez *(Chm)*
Alberto Jose Paredes Villegas *(Vice Chm)*
Elvira Maria Virzi Vallarino *(Treas)*
Ofelia Mercedes Mendez Moreno *(Sec)*
Board of Directors:
Jose Isaac Virzi Lopez
Gabriel Enrique Barletta de la Guardia
Diego Alonzo de la Guardia Porras
Ofelia Mercedes Mendez Moreno
Manuel Antonio Morales Diez
Alberto Jose Paredes Henriquez
Alberto Jose Paredes Villegas
Jose Guillermo Virzi Saint Malo
Elvira Maria Virzi Vallarino

BANCOLOMBIA S.A.

(d/b/a Grupo Bancolombia)
Carrera 48 26-45 Avenida Los Industriales
Medellin, Colombia
Tel.: (57) 4404 1837
Fax: (57) 44041838
E-Mail: Investorrelations@bancolombia.com
Web Site: www.grupobancolombia.com
Year Founded: 1998
CIB—(COLO NYSE)
Int. Income: $4,290,654,480
Assets: $54,833,172,800
Liabilities: $48,333,278,000
Net Worth: $6,499,894,800
Earnings: $953,145,760
Emp.: 24,820
Fiscal Year-end: 12/31/12
Business Description:
Banking Services
S.I.C.: 6029
N.A.I.C.S.: 522110
Personnel:
Carlos Raul Yepes Jimenez *(CEO)*
Jaime Alberto Velasquez Botero *(CFO & Chief Strategy Officer)*
Mauricio Rosillo Rojas *(Chief Legal Officer)*
Luis Arturo Penagos Londono *(Chief HR Officer)*
Rodrigo Prieto Uribe *(Chief Risk Officer)*
Gonzalo Toro Bridge *(Chief Banking Officer)*
Sergio Restrepo Isaza *(Exec VP)*
Board of Directors:
David Emilio Bojanini Garcia
Hernando Jose Gomez Restrepo
Rafael Martinez Villegas
Gonzalo Alberto Perez Rojas
Carlos Enrique Piedrahita Arocha
Ricardo Sierra Moreno
Jose Alberto Velez Cadavid

U.S. Subsidiary:

Bancolombia Puerto Rico Internacional Inc (1)
270 Muoz Rivera Ave
San Juan, PR 00918
Tel.: (787) 756-5511
Fax: (787) 756-8180
E-Mail: sohernandez@bancolombiapuertorico.com
Web Site: www.bancolombiapuertorico.com
Emp.: 12
Commercial Banking Services
S.I.C.: 6029
N.A.I.C.S.: 522110

Non-U.S. Subsidiary:

Banistmo S.A. (1)
(Formerly HSBC Bank (Panama) S.A.)
47 Avenida Aquilino de la Guardia
Panama, Panama Pa
Tel.: (507) 205 4751
Fax: (507) 206 6300
E-Mail: panama_contacto@banistmo.com
Web Site: www.banistmo.com
Rev.: $425,314,990
Assets: $9,432,066,826
Liabilities: $8,529,239,544
Net Worth: $902,827,282
Earnings: $57,003,423
Fiscal Year-end: 12/31/12
Commercial & Investment Banking
S.I.C.: 6029
N.A.I.C.S.: 522110
Aimee Sentmat de Grimaldo *(Pres)*

BANCROFT MOTORS LTD

29668 Hwy 62 N
PO Box 1420
Bancroft, ON, K0L 1C0, Canada
Tel.: (613) 332-2438
Fax: (613) 332-0529
Toll Free: (800) 361-2438
Web Site: www.bancroftmotors.ca
Rev.: $11,221,695
Emp.: 25
Business Description:
New & Used Car Dealers
S.I.C.: 5511
N.A.I.C.S.: 441110
Personnel:
Doug Edwards *(Mgr-Svc)*

BANDANNA ENERGY LIMITED

Level 4 260 Queen Street
Brisbane, QLD, 4000, Australia
Tel.: (61) 730414400
Fax: (61) 730414444
E-Mail: info@bandannaenergy.com.au
Web Site: www.bandannaenergy.com.au
BND—(ASX)
Rev.: $12,630,482
Assets: $212,429,978
Liabilities: $3,096,547
Net Worth: $209,333,431
Earnings: ($7,909,861)
Emp.: 16
Fiscal Year-end: 06/30/13
Business Description:
Oil & Gas Exploration
S.I.C.: 1311
N.A.I.C.S.: 211111
Personnel:
Michael John Gray *(Mng Dir)*
Matthew Scott *(CFO)*
Stuart Clarke *(Chief Dev Officer)*
Tess Lye *(Gen Counsel & Sec)*
Board of Directors:
John Harry Pegler
Michael John Gray
Gil Yong Ha
Robert Karlo Johansen
Terry O'Reilly
Gordon Saul

BANDAR RAYA DEVELOPMENTS BERHAD

Level 11 Menara BRDB 285 Jalan Maarof
Bukit Bandaraya, 59000 Kuala Lumpur, Malaysia
Tel.: (60) 3 26882888
Fax: (60) 3 22877515
E-Mail: info@brdb.com.my
Web Site: www.brdb.com.my
Sales Range: $200-249.9 Million
Business Description:
Residential & Commercial Properties Development Services
S.I.C.: 1521
N.A.I.C.S.: 236115
Personnel:
Mohamed Moiz *(Chm)*
Jaganath Sabapathy *(CEO)*
Kim Seng Low *(CFO)*
C. C. Pan *(COO)*
K. C. Chong *(CMO)*
Swee Ling Ho *(Sec)*
Subsidiaries:

Capital Square Sdn. Bhd. (1)
Ge-6 Cape Square E-Centre 8 Persiaran Cape Square Capital Square
50100 Kuala Lumpur, Federal Territory, Malaysia
Tel.: (60) 326981288
Fax: (60) 326915825
Emp.: 12

Real Estate Management & Development Services
S.I.C.: 6531
N.A.I.C.S.: 531210
Jaganath Steven Sabapathy *(CEO)*

Midwest Profits Sdn. Bhd. (1)
B Capsquare Centre Psn Capsquare
50100 Kuala Lumpur, Malaysia
Tel.: (60) 3 2698 0128
Fax: (60) 3 2698 0243
Emp.: 50
Gourmet Delicatessen & Supermarkets Operation Services
S.I.C.: 5411
N.A.I.C.S.: 445110
Kueh Hui Ming *(Mgr)*

Permas Jaya Sdn. Bhd. (1)
G 33 Blok A Permas Mall No 3 Jalan Permas Utara
Bandar Baru Permas Jaya, 81750 Johor Bahru, Johor, Malaysia
Tel.: (60) 73871333
Fax: (60) 73872333
E-Mail: permasjaya@brdb.com.my
Emp.: 15
Property Management Services
S.I.C.: 6531
N.A.I.C.S.: 531311
Teh Ku Yong *(Gen Mgr)*

BANDERA GOLD LTD.

9320 49th St
Edmonton, AB, T6B 2L7, Canada
Tel.: (780) 465-4129
Fax: (780) 469-8407
E-Mail: info@banderagold.com
Web Site: www.banderagold.com
Year Founded: 1993
BGL—(TSXV)
Assets: $15,376,161
Liabilities: $2,117,190
Net Worth: $13,258,971
Earnings: ($541,789)
Fiscal Year-end: 11/30/12

Business Description:
Mineral Exploration Services
S.I.C.: 1081
N.A.I.C.S.: 213114

Personnel:
Stephen Roehrig *(Pres & CEO)*
Donald R. Bossert *(CFO)*

Board of Directors:
Donald R. Bossert
Peter Gommerud
Robert Morrison
Russel J. Renneberg
Stephen Roehrig

Non-U.S. Subsidiary:

Nueva California S.A. (1)
Calle 12 30 356
Medellin, Colombia
Tel.: (57) 44482950
Gold Mining Services
S.I.C.: 1041
N.A.I.C.S.: 212221

BANDO CHEMICAL INDUSTRIES, LTD.

6-6 Minatojima Minamimachi 4-chome Chuo-ku
Kobe, 650-0047, Japan
Tel.: (81) 78 304 2923
Telex: J78711
Fax: (81) 78 304 2983
E-Mail: int.business@bando.co.jp
Web Site: www.bando.co.jp
Year Founded: 1906
5195—(TKS)
Sls.: $943,481,000
Assets: $904,277,000
Liabilities: $428,791,000
Net Worth: $475,486,000
Earnings: $27,610,000
Emp.: 3,592
Fiscal Year-end: 03/31/13

Business Description:
Mfr of Transmission Belts & V-Belts
S.I.C.: 3052
N.A.I.C.S.: 326220

Personnel:
Akio Ogura *(Chm)*
Kazuyoshi Tani *(Vice Chm)*
Mitsutaka Yoshii *(Pres)*
Katsuhiko Hata *(Exec Officer)*
Keiji Iwai *(Sr Exec Officer)*
Shinji Kashiwada *(Exec Officer)*
Masayuki Kitabayashi *(Sr Exec Officer)*
Joseph David Laudadio *(Exec Officer)*
Kyosuke Nakamura *(Exec Officer)*
Masao Ohara *(Sr Exec Officer)*
Yoshitaka Oshima *(Exec Officer)*
Hisashi Samejima *(Sr Exec Officer)*
Yoshihisa Tamagaki *(Sr Exec Officer)*
Katsuya Yamaguchi *(Exec Officer)*

Board of Directors:
Akio Ogura
Shinji Kashiwada
Yutaka Kato
Masao Ohara
Kazuyoshi Tani
Mitsutaka Yoshii

Plants:

Bando Chemical Industries, Ltd. - Ashikaga Plant (1)
188-6 Arakane-cho
Ashikaga, Tochigi, 326-0832, Japan
Tel.: (81) 284 72 4121
Fax: (81) 284 72 4426
Web Site: www.bando.co.jp/english-1/en-nt2-3-4.html
Industrial Rubber Belt Mfr
S.I.C.: 3052
N.A.I.C.S.: 326220

Bando Chemical Industries, Ltd. - Kakogawa Plant (1)
648 Komoikenouchi Tsuchiyama-aza Hiraoka-cho
Kakogawa, Hyogo, 675-0198, Japan
Tel.: (81) 78 942 3232
Fax: (81) 78 942 3389
Industrial Rubber Belt Mfr
S.I.C.: 3052
N.A.I.C.S.: 326220

Bando Chemical Industries, Ltd. - Nankai Plant (1)
20-1 Onosato 5-chome
Sennan, Osaka, 590-0526, Japan
Tel.: (81) 72 482 7711
Fax: (81) 72 482 1173
Web Site: www.bando.co.jp/english-1/en-nt2-3-4.html
Industrial Rubber Belt Mfr
S.I.C.: 3052
N.A.I.C.S.: 326220

Bando Chemical Industries, Ltd. - Wakayama Plant (1)
1242-5 Mogami Momoyama-cho
Kinokawa, Wakayama, 649-6111, Japan
Tel.: (81) 736 66 0999
Fax: (81) 736 66 2152
Web Site: www.bando.co.jp/english-1/en-nt2-3-4.html
Industrial Rubber Belt Mfr
S.I.C.: 3052
N.A.I.C.S.: 326220

U.S. Subsidiary:

Bando USA, Inc. (1)
1149 W Bryn Mawr Ave
Itasca, IL 60143-1508 (100%)
Tel.: (630) 773-6600
Fax: (630) 773-6912
Web Site: www.bandousa.com
Emp.: 45
Distribution of Automotive & Industrial V-Belts
S.I.C.: 3052
N.A.I.C.S.: 326220
Joseph Laudadio *(Pres & CEO)*

Division:

Bando USA, Inc . (2)
2720 Pioneer Dr
Bowling Green, KY 42101 (90%)
Tel.: (270) 842-4110
Fax: (270) 842-6139
Web Site: www.bandousa.com
Emp.: 135
Mfr. of Fan Belts
S.I.C.: 3052
N.A.I.C.S.: 326220
Joe Laudadio *(Pres & CEO)*

Non-U.S. Subsidiaries:

Bando Europe GmbH (1)
Krefelder Str 671
41066 Monchengladbach, Germany
Tel.: (49) 2161 90104 0
Fax: (49) 2126 90104 50
E-Mail: info@bando.de
Web Site: www.bando.de
Emp.: 20
Industrial Rubber Belt Mfr
S.I.C.: 3052
N.A.I.C.S.: 326220
Koichi Miyabayashi *(Mng Dir)*

Bando Iberica S.A. (1)
Francesc Layret 12 14 Naves 4 5 Poligono Industrial Sant Ermengol 2, 08630 Abrera, Barcelona, Spain
Tel.: (34) 937778740
Fax: (34) 937778741
E-Mail: bandoiberica@bandoiberica.es
Web Site: www.bandoiberica.es
Emp.: 100
S.I.C.: 3714
N.A.I.C.S.: 336340

Bando (India) Pvt. Ltd. (1)
Plot No 255 Sector-7 IMT Manesar
Gurgaon, Haryana, 122050, India
Tel.: (91) 124 4305600
Fax: (91) 124 4368954
Emp.: 10
Plastic & Rubber Belt Mfr
S.I.C.: 3052
N.A.I.C.S.: 326220
Hiroshi Yamada *(Mng Dir)*

Bando Jung Kong, Ltd. (1)
4Ba 705 Shihwa Indus Zone Mechatronics Complex
Songgok Dong Assan City, Kyongki, Korea (South)
Tel.: (82) 314329800
Fax: (82) 314328198
Web Site: www.bando.co.jp/english-1/en-nt2-3-1.html
Power Belts & Systems Mfr
S.I.C.: 3714
N.A.I.C.S.: 336340

Bando Manufacturing (Dongguan) Co., Ltd. (1)
Building ZF8 Zhen An Industrial Park Zhen An Road
Changan Town, Dongguan, GuangDong, China
Tel.: (86) 769 8564 5075
Fax: (86) 769 8564 5081
E-Mail: marketing@bando.com.cn
Web Site: www.bando.com.sg/worldwide.htm
Rubber & Plastic Belt Mfr
S.I.C.: 3052
N.A.I.C.S.: 326220

Bando Manufacturing (Thailand) Ltd. (1)
47 7 Moo 4 Soi Wat Bangpla Tamol Bankao Amphr Muang
Samutsakorn, Bangkok, 74000, Thailand
Tel.: (66) 34831209
Fax: (66) 34468415
Web Site: www.bando.co.jp
S.I.C.: 3714
N.A.I.C.S.: 336340

Bando Sakata, Ltd. (1)
Ste 5B 154 Tower 6
Central, China (Hong Kong) (100%)
Tel.: (852) 24944815
Fax: (852) 24810444
E-Mail: mini@bandosiixc.com.hk
Emp.: 56
S.I.C.: 3714
N.A.I.C.S.: 336340
Hayakawa Makio *(Mng Dir)*

Bando Siix Ltd. (1)
Room 2210 Shun Tak Centre West Tower
200 Connaught Road
Central, Hong Kong, China (Hong Kong)
Tel.: (852) 2494 4815
Fax: (852) 2481 0444
Web Site: www.bando.com.sg/worldwide.htm
Rubber Belt Mfr
S.I.C.: 3052
N.A.I.C.S.: 326220

Bando (Singapore) Pte. Ltd. (1)
3 C Toh Guan Rd E Unit 05 01
Singapore, 608832, Singapore (100%)
Tel.: (65) 64752233
Fax: (65) 64796261
E-Mail: belt@bando.com.sg
Web Site: www.bando.com.sg
Emp.: 25
S.I.C.: 3714
N.A.I.C.S.: 336340

Dongil-Bando Co., Ltd. (1)
869 1 Eogok Dong Yang San City
Gyung Sang Nam Do, Yangsan, 626-220, Korea (South) (100%)
Tel.: (82) 553719200
Fax: (82) 553719350
E-Mail: mran@bandakorea.co.kr
Emp.: 100
Chemical Mfr
S.I.C.: 2819
N.A.I.C.S.: 325180

Kee Fatt Industries, Sdn. Bhd. (1)
22 M S Jalan Air Hitam
81000 Kulai, Johor, Malaysia (39%)
Tel.: (60) 76639663
Fax: (60) 76639664
E-Mail: kfi@keefatt.com
Web Site: www.keefatt.com
Sales Range: $1-9.9 Million
Emp.: 300
S.I.C.: 3714
N.A.I.C.S.: 336340
Tay Keng Meng *(Gen Mgr)*

Pengeluaran Getah Bando (Malaysia) Sdn. Bhd. (1)
No 2 Jalan Sengkang Batu 22
81000 Kulai, Johor, Malaysia (100%)
Tel.: (60) 76635021
Fax: (60) 76635023
E-Mail: pgbandon@pd.jaring.my
Web Site: www.bando.co.jp/english-1/en-nt2-3-1.html
Emp.: 180
S.I.C.: 3714
N.A.I.C.S.: 336340
Toshiharu Taniguchi *(Mng Dir)*

Philippine Belt Mfg. Corp. (1)
2 Fl Siemkang Bldg
PO Box 205
280 282 Dasmarinas St Binondo, Manila, 1099, Philippines
Tel.: (63) 22410794
Fax: (63) 22413279
Web Site: www.philbelt.com
Emp.: 30
S.I.C.: 3714
N.A.I.C.S.: 336340
Vicente H. Chim *(Pres)*

Sanwu Bando Inc. (1)
11th Fl 2 No 51 Sec 1 Min Sheng E Rd
Taipei, 886, Taiwan (50%)
Tel.: (886) 225678255
Fax: (886) 225117653
Web Site: www.sanban.com.tw
Emp.: 8
S.I.C.: 3714
N.A.I.C.S.: 336340
Seiken Ho *(Mgr-Mktg)*

Non-U.S. Joint Venture:

P.T. Bando Indonesia (1)
Jln Gajah Tunggal St Km 7 Tangerang Kel Pasir Jaya
Kotamadya, Tangerang, 15135, Indonesia
Tel.: (62) 215903921
Fax: (62) 215901274
E-Mail: bandojkt@dentrin.net.id
Web Site: www.bandoindonesia.com
Power Transmission Belt Mfr
S.I.C.: 3714
N.A.I.C.S.: 336350
Hartonod Jojo *(Mng Dir)*

BANDSTRA TRANSPORTATION SYSTEMS LTD.

3394 Hwy 16 E
PO Box 95
Smithers, BC, V0J 2N0, Canada
Tel.: (250) 847-2057
Fax: (250) 847-5042
Toll Free: (800) 571-2057
E-Mail: info@bandstra.com
Web Site: www.bandstra.com
Year Founded: 1955
Rev.: $15,482,000
Emp.: 160
Business Description:
Household Goods Carrier Services
S.I.C.: 4214
N.A.I.C.S.: 484210
Personnel:
John Bandstra, Jr. *(Pres)*

BANDVULC TYRES LTD.

Gillard Way Lee Mill Industrial Estate
Ivybridge
Devon, PL21 9LN, United Kingdom
Tel.: (44) 1752 893559
Fax: (44) 1752 690794
Web Site: www.bandvulc.com
Year Founded: 1971
Sales Range: $75-99.9 Million
Emp.: 320
Business Description:
Tire Rebuilding Services
S.I.C.: 7534
N.A.I.C.S.: 326212
Personnel:
Patrick O'Connell *(Mng Dir)*

BANENG HOLDINGS BHD.

Lot 4979 2 1/2 Miles Jalan Tanjong Laboh
83000 Batu Pahat, Johor Darul Takzim, Malaysia
Tel.: (60) 74355700
Fax: (60) 74318322
Web Site: www.bhb.net.my
BANENG—(KLS)
Sales Range: $25-49.9 Million
Business Description:
Fabrics & Garments Mfr
S.I.C.: 2389
N.A.I.C.S.: 315280
Personnel:
Choon Hiok Lim *(Mng Dir)*
Siew Chuan Chua *(Co-Sec)*
Seng Wee Pan *(Co-Sec)*
Board of Directors:
Sulaiman Shah Almarhum Sultan Salahuddin Abdul Aziz Shah
Hon Chow Choong
Choon Hiok Lim
Kwee Seng Lim
Meng Seng Lim

Subsidiary:

Maxlin Garments Sdn. Bhd. **(1)**
Lot 4979 2 1/2 Miles Km 4 Jalan Tanjung Labuh
83000 Batu Pahat, Johor, Malaysia
Tel.: (60) 74355701
Fax: (60) 074318322
Emp.: 400
Apparels Mfr & Distr
S.I.C.: 2259
N.A.I.C.S.: 315190
Betty Choon Hiok Lim *(Mng Dir)*

Non-U.S. Subsidiary:

Chenille International Pte. Ltd. **(1)**
120 Lower Delta Road 07-11 Cendex Centre
Singapore, 169208, Singapore
Tel.: (65) 67352511
Fax: (65) 67359259
Clothing Apparels Mfr & Distr
S.I.C.: 2329
N.A.I.C.S.: 315220

BANESCO BANCO UNIVERSAL C.A.

Principal de Bello Monte Avenue
Lincoln St & Sorbona St
Banesco City Bldg, Caracas, Venezuela
Tel.: (58) 212 5017111
E-Mail: atclient@banesco.com
Web Site: www.banesco.com
BBC—(CAR)
Sales Range: $1-4.9 Billion
Business Description:
Banking Services
S.I.C.: 6029
N.A.I.C.S.: 522110
Personnel:
Juan Carlos Rodriguez Escotet *(Chm)*
Board of Directors:
Juan Carlos Rodriguez Escotet
Nelson Becerra Orlando Mendez
Gonzalo Jose Clemente Corner
Josefina Daisy Eulate Veliz
Cores Salvador Eduardo Gonzalez
Luis Xavier Lujan Puigbo
Miguel Angel Marcano Cartea
Jose Rafael Padron Salazar
Maria Josefina Rodriguez Fernandez Marono

BANESTES S.A. BANCO DO ESTADO DO ESPIRITO SANTO

Av Princesa Isabel 574 Bloco B 9 Andar
Centro, 29010-931 Vitoria, ES, Brazil
Tel.: (55) 27 3383 1083
Fax: (55) 27 3383 1090
E-Mail: ri@banestes.com.br
Web Site: www.banestes.com.br
Year Founded: 1937
BEES3—(BRAZ)
Business Description:
Commercial Banking Services
S.I.C.: 6029
N.A.I.C.S.: 522110
Personnel:
Mauricio Cezar Duque *(Co-CEO)*
Bruno Pessanha Negris *(Co-CEO)*
Ranieri Feres Doelinger *(CFO & IR Officer)*
Bruno Curty Vivas *(Chief Legal & Admin Officer)*
Pedro Paulo Braga Bolzani *(CTO)*
Monica Campos Torres *(Chief Risk & Control Officer)*
Jose Antonio Bof Buffon *(Chief Comml Officer)*
Anderson Ferrari Junior *(Chief Asset Mgmt Officer)*
Board of Directors:
Jose Eduardo Faria de Azevedo
Mauricio Cezar Duque
Vitor Marcio Nunes Feitosa
Jovenal Gera
Bruno Pessanha Negris
Wellington Tesch Sabaini
Estanislau Kostka Stein
Jussara Goncalves Vieira

BANEXI VENTURES PARTNERS SA

13-15 rue Taitbout
75009 Paris, France
Tel.: (33) 1 73 02 89 69
Fax: (33) 173028970
E-Mail: contact@banexiventures.com
Web Site: www.banexiventures.com
Business Description:
Private Equity Firm
S.I.C.: 6722
N.A.I.C.S.: 525910
Personnel:
Michel Dahan *(Chm & Gen Partner)*
Philippe Mere *(Gen Partner-Electronics)*
Sophie Pierrin-Lepinard *(Gen Partner-Healthcare)*
Philippe Herbert *(Partner-Internet)*
Jacqueline Renard *(Sec Gen)*

Joint Venture:

Vexim SA **(1)**
75 rue Saint Jean
31130 Balma, France FR
Tel.: (33) 5 61 48 86 63
Fax: (33) 5 61 48 95 19
E-Mail: vexim@vexim.com
Web Site: www.vexim.fr
ALVXM—(EUR)
Rev.: $3,660,236
Assets: $15,642,495
Liabilities: $3,106,960
Net Worth: $12,535,535
Earnings: ($9,110,879)
Emp.: 45
Fiscal Year-end: 12/31/12
Spine Pain Medical Device Mfr; Owned 59% by Truffle Capital & 31% by Banexi Venture Partners
S.I.C.: 3841
N.A.I.C.S.: 339112
Bruce de la Grange *(Chm)*
Vincent Gardes *(CEO)*
Jerome Marzinski *(Deputy CEO)*
Yves-Alain Ratron *(CTO)*

BANG & OLUFSEN A/S

Peter Bangs Vej 15
7600 Struer, Denmark
Tel.: (45) 96841122
Fax: (45) 96845033
E-Mail: investors@bang-olufsen.com
Web Site: www.bang-olufsen.com
Year Founded: 1925
BO—(OMX)
Rev.: $507,533,040
Earnings: ($28,857,600)
Emp.: 2,106
Fiscal Year-end: 05/31/13
Business Description:
Televisions, Radios, Audio/Visual Recorders, Gramophones, Compact Disc Players, Complete Music Systems, Digital Switching Systems, Telephones & Shop-Profiling Solutions Mfr
S.I.C.: 3651
N.A.I.C.S.: 334310
Personnel:
Ole Gjesso Andersen *(Chm)*
Jim Hagemann Snabe *(Deputy Chm)*
Tue Mantoni *(Pres & CEO)*
Henning Bejer Beck *(CFO & Exec VP)*
Board of Directors:
Ole Gjesso Andersen
Rolf Eriksen
Per Ostergaard Frederiksen
Andre Loesekrug-Pietri
Jesper Olesen
Knud Olesen
Majken Schultz
Jim Hagemann Snabe

Subsidiaries:

Bang & Olufsen Danmark a/s **(1)**
Peter Bangs Vej 15
7600 Struer, Denmark (100%)
Tel.: (45) 96841122
Fax: (45) 97851888
E-Mail: info@bang-olufsen.com
Emp.: 2,000
Audio & Video Equipment Mfr
S.I.C.: 3651
N.A.I.C.S.: 334310
Kalle Hytt Nielsen *(Pres)*

Bang & Olufsen Finance A/S **(1)**
Peter Bangs Vej 15
7600 Struer, Denmark (100%)
Tel.: (45) 96841122
Fax: (45) 96845033
E-Mail: info@bang-olufsen.dk
Web Site: www.bang-olufsen.dk
Emp.: 2,000
Promotes & Supports the Distribution of Company Products
S.I.C.: 5734
N.A.I.C.S.: 443142
Tue Mantoni *(Mng Dir)*

Bang & Olufsen Operations a/s **(1)**
Peter Bangs Vej 15
7600 Struer, Denmark
Tel.: (45) 96 84 11 22
Fax: (45) 96 84 11 44
Web Site: www.bang-olufsen.com
Emp.: 200
Logistics Consulting Services
S.I.C.: 4731
N.A.I.C.S.: 541614
Tue Mantoni *(Gen Mgr)*

Subsidiaries:

Bang & Olufsen Expansion a/s **(2)**
Peter Bangs Vej 15
7600 Struer, Denmark
Tel.: (45) 96841122
Fax: (45) 97865959
E-Mail: expansion@bang-olufsen.dk
Web Site: www.bang-olufsen.com
Emp.: 100
Audio Equipment Mfr
S.I.C.: 3651
N.A.I.C.S.: 334310
Tue Mantoni *(Gen Mgr)*

Bang & Olufsen Svenska AB **(2)**
Gl Lundtoftevej 1B
2800 Lyngby, Denmark
Tel.: (45) 9684 1122
Fax: (45) 9684 5899
E-Mail: beoinfo1@bang-olufsen.dk
Emp.: 100
Audio Product Mfr
S.I.C.: 3651
N.A.I.C.S.: 334310
Yasuyuki Tanaka *(Pres & CEO)*

Bang & Olufsen Telecom a/s **(1)**
Peter Bangs Vej 15
7600 Struer, Denmark DK
Tel.: (45) 96841122 (100%)
Fax: (45) 97854540
E-Mail: info@bang-olufsen.dk
Web Site: www.telecom.bang-olufsen.com
Emp.: 2,000
Develops, Produces & Markets Telecommunications Products & Accessories
S.I.C.: 4899
N.A.I.C.S.: 517919

U.S. Subsidiary:

Bang & Olufsen America, Inc. **(1)**
780 W Dundee Rd
Arlington Heights, IL 60004-1562 IL
Tel.: (847) 590-4900 (100%)
Fax: (847) 255-9053
Web Site: www.bang-olufsen.com
Emp.: 35
Consumer Electronics; Audio, Video & Multimedia Products
S.I.C.: 5064
N.A.I.C.S.: 423620
Kathy Thornton-Bias *(Pres-North America)*

Non-U.S. Subsidiaries:

Bang & Olufsen A/S **(1)**
PO Box 645
Skoyen, N 0214 Oslo, Norway (100%)
Tel.: (47) 80010532
Fax: (47) 23283001
Web Site: www.bang-olufsen.com
Emp.: 8
Sale of Electrical Products
S.I.C.: 5064
N.A.I.C.S.: 423620

Bang & Olufsen AG **(1)**
Grindelstrasse 15
CH 8303 Bassersdorf, Switzerland (100%)
Tel.: (41) 844727272
Fax: (41) 844757575
E-Mail: info@bangolufsen.dk
Web Site: www.bangolufsen.com
Emp.: 8

Markets Telecommunications Products & Accessories
S.I.C.: 5064
N.A.I.C.S.: 423620
Heinz Muller *(Mng Dir)*

Bang & Olufsen Deutschland GmbH (1)
Dr Carl von Linde-Strasse 2
82049 Pullach, Germany
Tel.: (49) 89 75905 0
Fax: (49) 89 75905 280
E-Mail: ce-product-support@bang-olufsen.de
Audio & Video Equipment Mfr
S.I.C.: 3651
N.A.I.C.S.: 334310

Bang & Olufsen Espana S.A. (1)
Avenida Europa 2
Parque Empresarial La Moraleja, 28108
Alcobendas, Madrid, Spain (100%)
Tel.: (34) 916616575
Fax: (34) 916616576
E-Mail: bac@bang-olufsen.dk
Web Site: www.bang-olufsen.com
Emp.: 28
S.I.C.: 3651
N.A.I.C.S.: 334310
Jakob Odgaard *(Mng Dir)*

Bang & Olufsen France S.A. (1)
141 Rue Jules Guesde
92304 Levallois-Perret, France (100%)
Tel.: (33) 55212155
Fax: (33) 149460064
Web Site: www.bang-olufsen.com
Emp.: 30
S.I.C.: 3651
N.A.I.C.S.: 334310

Bang & Olufsen GPS Taiwan (1)
9F 1 No 413 Rueiguang Rd
Neihu, Taipei, 11492, Taiwan
Tel.: (886) 2 27183400
Fax: (886) 2 27183420
Audio Product Mfr
S.I.C.: 3651
N.A.I.C.S.: 334310

Non-U.S. Subsidiary:

Bang & Olufsen ICEpower a/s (2)
Gl Lundtoftevej 1b
2800 Lyngby, Denmark
Tel.: (45) 96 84 11 22
Fax: (45) 96 84 57 99
E-Mail: ICEpowerinfo@bang-olufsen.dk
Web Site: www.icepower.bang-olufsen.com
Emp.: 3
Audio Power Conversion Equipment Mfr
S.I.C.: 3651
N.A.I.C.S.: 334310
Martin Bruun Helms *(Acct Mgr)*

Bang & Olufsen Italia S.p.A. (1)
Via Meravigli 2
20123 Milan, Italy (100%)
Tel.: (39) 0027259141
Fax: (39) 0272591444
Web Site: www.bang-olufsen.com
Emp.: 20
Electrical Appliances, Television & Radio
S.I.C.: 5722
N.A.I.C.S.: 443141

Bang & Olufsen s.r.o (1)
Prumyslovy Park 305
742 21 Koprivnice, Czech Republic
Tel.: (420) 556880700
Audio Equipment Mfr
S.I.C.: 3651
N.A.I.C.S.: 334310

Bang & Olufsen United Kingdom Ltd. (1)
630 Wharfdale Rd
Winnersh Triangle, Wokingham, Berks, RG41 5TP, United Kingdom (100%)
Tel.: (44) 1189692288
Fax: (44) 1189693388
Emp.: 30
Sales of Electrical Products
S.I.C.: 5064
N.A.I.C.S.: 423620
Derek Mottershead *(Mng Dir)*

Bang & Olufsen Wholesale Pty Ltd. (1)
579 Church St
Hawthorn, Richmond, VIC, 3121, Australia
Tel.: (61) 3 9835 7700
Fax: (61) 398357799
Emp.: 5
Audio Equipment Distr
S.I.C.: 5064
N.A.I.C.S.: 423620
Julian Kipping *(Gen Mgr)*

Bang & Olufsen (1)
Het Arsenaal Kooljesbuurt 1
Naarden, 1411 RZ, Netherlands (100%)
Tel.: (31) 356947763
Fax: (31) 356782366
E-Mail: info@robscrepper.nl
Web Site: www.bang-olufsen.com
Emp.: 12
Sale of Electrical Products
S.I.C.: 5064
N.A.I.C.S.: 423620
Stefen Rostrestraad *(Gen Mgr)*

Division:

Bang & Olufsen Expansion Markets (2)
Heide 9
B-1980 Wemmel, Belgium (100%)
Tel.: (32) 24560811
Web Site: www.bang-olfusen.com
S.I.C.: 3651
N.A.I.C.S.: 334310

Non-U.S. Subsidiaries:

Bang & Olufsen Asia Pte. Ltd. (3)
10 -12 Scotts Rd 01 05 Grand Hyatt
Singapore, 228211, Singapore (100%)
Tel.: (65) 67377500
Fax: (65) 67492519
E-Mail: hyatt.singapore@beostoies.com
Emp.: 4
S.I.C.: 3651
N.A.I.C.S.: 334310
Kalle Hvidt Nielsen *(Pres & CEO)*

Bang & Olufsen Japan K.K. (3)
Shiba Boat Bldg 9th Fl 3 1 15 Shipa
Minato Ku, Tokyo, 1050014, Japan (100%)
Tel.: (81) 354401844
Fax: (81) 354401845
Web Site: www.bang-olufsen.com
Emp.: 45
S.I.C.: 3651
N.A.I.C.S.: 334310

OU BO-Soft (1)
Parnu Mnt 139
Tallinn, 11317, Estonia
Tel.: (372) 6283614
Audio Equipment Mfr
S.I.C.: 3651
N.A.I.C.S.: 334310

BANG OVERSEAS LTD.

405-406 Kewal Industrial Estate
Senapati Bapat Marg
Lower Parel West, Mumbai, 400013, India
Tel.: (91) 2266607965
Fax: (91) 2266607970
E-Mail: bol@banggroup.com
Web Site: www.banggroup.com
532946—(BOM)
Rev.: $51,205,552
Assets: $33,169,940
Liabilities: $16,606,062
Net Worth: $16,563,878
Earnings: $242,603
Emp.: 1,028
Fiscal Year-end: 03/31/13

Business Description:
Men's Clothing Mfr & Exporter
S.I.C.: 2329
N.A.I.C.S.: 315220

Personnel:
Brijgopal Bang *(Chm & Mng Dir)*
Jaydas Dighe *(CFO)*
Nishi Vijay Vargiya *(Compliance Officer & Sec)*

Board of Directors:
Brijgopal Bang
Vijay D. Ajgaonkar
Purshottam Bang
Raghvendra Bang
Subrata Kumar Dey
Mithilesh Kumar Sinha

Transfer Agent:
Karvy Computershare Private Limited
Plot No 17-24 Vittal Rao Nagar Madhapur
Hyderabad, 500 081, India
Tel.: (91) 40 2342 0818

Subsidiary:

Vedanta Creations Limited (1)
No 50 Kewal Indl Estate Ground Fl Lowr Parel W
Mumbai, Maharashtra, 400013, India
Tel.: (91) 2230402212
Fax: (91) 2266607970
Readymade Garments Whslr
S.I.C.: 2389
N.A.I.C.S.: 315210

BANGALORE STOCK EXCHANGE LIMITED

51 Stock Exchange Towers
1st Cross JC Road, Bengaluru, 560 027, India
Tel.: (91) 8041575235
Fax: (91) 8041575232
Web Site: www.bgse.co.in
Year Founded: 1963

Business Description:
Stock Exchange Services
S.I.C.: 6231
N.A.I.C.S.: 523210

Board of Directors:
Cheriyan Abraham
I. N. Ashok
K. K. Belliappa
V.C. Davey Davey
Kannan Doss
Anil H. Lad
Appa Rao Mallavarapu
A. Murali
G. Pavan
V. H. Prasad

THE BANGCHAK PETROLEUM PUBLIC COMPANY LIMITED

555/1 Energy Complex Building A
10th Floor Vibhavadi Rangsit Road
Chatuchak, Bangkok, 10900, Thailand
Tel.: (66) 2140 8999
Fax: (66) 2140 8900
E-Mail: info@bangchak.co.th
Web Site: www.bangchak.co.th
BCP—(THA)
Rev.: $5,474,597,773
Assets: $2,347,374,563
Liabilities: $1,276,506,597
Net Worth: $1,070,867,966
Earnings: $142,544,581
Emp.: 1,027
Fiscal Year-end: 12/31/12

Business Description:
Petroleum Products
S.I.C.: 1311
N.A.I.C.S.: 211111

Personnel:
Pichai Chunhavajira *(Chm)*
Chai-Anan Samudavanija *(Vice Chm)*
Vichien Usanachote *(Pres)*
Pakawadee Junrayapes *(Sec & VP)*
Surachai Kositsareewong *(Sr Exec VP-Acctg & Fin)*
Wattana Opanon-Amata *(First Sr Exec VP-Refinery Bus)*
Bundit Sapianchai *(Sr Exec VP-Bus Dev & Strategy)*
Yodphot Wongrukmit *(Sr Exec VP-Mktg Bus)*
Pongchai Chaichirawiwat *(Exec VP-Renewable Energy Bus)*
Kiatchai Maitriwong *(Exec VP-Corp Admin & IT)*
Somchai Tejavanija *(Exec VP-Mktg Bus)*
Chalermchai Udomrenu *(Exec VP-Refinery Bus)*
Chokchai Atsawarangsalit *(Sr VP-Bus Dev & Corp Dev)*
Kitti Nivatvongs *(Sr VP-Refinery Technique & Refinery Bus)*
Pichit Wongrujiravanich *(Sr VP-Internal Control Office)*

Board of Directors:
Pichai Chunhavajira
Nattachart Charuchinda
Surin Chiravisit
Vikrom Koompirochana
Chaiwat Kovavisarach
Sarakorn Kulatham
Arunporn Limskul
Krairit Nilkuha
Prasong Poontaneat
Dapong Ratanasuwan
Chai-Anan Samudavanija
Anusorn Tamajai
Vichien Usanachote
Suthep Wongvorazathe

Subsidiaries:

The Bangchak Biofuel Co., Ltd. (1)
28 Moo 9 T Banggason A Bang Pa-in Pranakornsri
Ayutthaya, 13160, Thailand
Tel.: (66) 35276500
Fax: (66) 35 276 549
Web Site: www.bangchakbiofuel.co.th
Biodiesel Mfr
S.I.C.: 2911
N.A.I.C.S.: 324110
Pongchai Chaichirawiwat *(Mng Dir)*

The Bangchak Green Net Co. Ltd (1)
210 Moo 1 Sukhumvit 64 Road
Phra Khanong, Bangkok, Thailand (100%)
Tel.: (66) 23354999
Fax: (66) 23316395
Emp.: 1,000
Fuel Dealers
S.I.C.: 5989
N.A.I.C.S.: 454310
Tawat Ked-Unkoon *(Chm)*

BANGKO SENTRAL NG PILIPINAS

A Mabini St cor P Ocampo St
Manila, 1004, Philippines
Tel.: (63) 27087701
Fax: (63) 5246696
E-Mail: bpsmail@bsp.gov.ph
Web Site: www.bsp.gov.ph
Rev.: $1,178,654,720
Assets: $96,978,260,554
Liabilities: $95,559,857,452
Net Worth: $1,418,403,102
Earnings: ($2,113,609,450)
Emp.: 5,234
Fiscal Year-end: 11/30/12

Business Description:
Banking Services
S.I.C.: 6011
N.A.I.C.S.: 521110

Personnel:
Amando M. Tetangco, Jr. *(Chm)*
Alphew T. Cheng *(Chief Reserve Mgmt Officer-Treasury Dept)*
Juan D. De Zuniga, Jr. *(Gen Counsel)*

Board of Directors:
Amando M. Tetangco, Jr.
Alfredo C. Antonio
Ignacio R. Bunye
Peter B. Favila
Felipe M. Medalla
Cesar V. Purisima
Armando L. Suratos

BANGKOK AIRWAYS CO., LTD.

99 Mu 14 Vibhavadirangsit Rd Chom Phon Chatuchak
Bangkok, 10900, Thailand

Bangkok Airways Co., Ltd.—(Continued)

Tel.: (66) 22655678
Fax: (66) 22655500
Web Site: www.bangkokair.com
Emp.: 1,300
Business Description:
Air Transportation Services
S.I.C.: 4512
N.A.I.C.S.: 481111
Personnel:
Prasert Prasartthongosot *(CEO)*

BANGKOK AVIATION FUEL SERVICES PUBLIC COMPANY LIMITED

171/2 Kamphaeng Phet 6 Rd Don Mueang Khet Don Mueang
Bangkok, 10210, Thailand
Tel.: (66) 28348900
Fax: (66) 2834 8999
Web Site: www.bafsthai.com
BAFS—(BAK THA)
Rev.: $88,486,800
Assets: $244,853,740
Liabilities: $102,799,152
Net Worth: $142,054,588
Earnings: $27,599,675
Emp.: 402
Fiscal Year-end: 12/31/12
Business Description:
Aviation Fuel Services
S.I.C.: 5989
N.A.I.C.S.: 454310
Personnel:
Palakorn Suwanrath *(Chm)*
M. R. Supadis Diskul *(Mng Dir)*
Mayuree Nalinwong *(Exec-Internal Audit)*
Pugdee Manaves *(Deputy Mng Dir-Admin)*
Board of Directors:
Palakorn Suwanrath
Soopachai Dhadagittisarn
M. R. Supadis Diskul
Ath Hemvijitraphan
Montree Jumrieng
Aswin Kongsiri
Navee Lertphanichkul
Visut Montriwat
Alongot Pullsuk
Pipat Purnananda
Trintr Subakarn
Sumon Surathin
Wasukarn Visansawatdi
Pachara Yutidhammadamrong
Subsidiary:

Thai Aviation Refuelling Company Limited **(1)**
99 Moo 10 Srisa Jorakhanol
Bang Sao Thong, Bangkok, 10540, Thailand
Tel.: (66) 213440216
Fax: (66) 21344020
E-Mail: pariwat@tarco.co.th
Web Site: www.tarco.co.th
Emp.: 18
Pipeline Network Operating Services
S.I.C.: 4619
N.A.I.C.S.: 486990
Vattanasup Pariwat *(Gen Mgr)*

BANGKOK BANK PUBLIC COMPANY LIMITED

333 Silom Road
Bangrak, Bangkok, 10500, Thailand
Mailing Address:
PO Box 95
BMC, Bangkok, 10000, Thailand
Tel.: (66) 26455555
Telex: 82638 BK BANK TH
Web Site: www.bangkokbank.com
Year Founded: 1944
BBL—(THA)
Assets: $80,136,111,256
Liabilities: $71,071,275,129
Net Worth: $9,064,836,127
Earnings: $1,096,252,418
Emp.: 21,229
Fiscal Year-end: 12/31/12
Business Description:
Commercial Banking Services
S.I.C.: 6029
N.A.I.C.S.: 522110
Personnel:
Chatri Sophonpanich *(Chm)*
Kosit Panpiemras *(Chm-Exec Bd)*
Deja Tulananda *(Vice Chm-Exec Bd)*
Chartsiri Sophonpanich *(Pres)*
Amorn Chandarasomboon *(Member-Exec Bd)*
Singh Tangtatswas *(Member-Exec Bd)*
Suvarn Thansathit *(Member-Exec Bd)*
Apichart Ramyarupa *(Sec)*
Virasak Sutanthavibul *(Sr Exec VP & Head-Metropolitan Comml Banking)*
Boonsong Bunyasaranand *(Sr Exec VP & Mgr-Treasury Div)*
Chansak Fuangfu *(Sr Exec VP)*
Suteera Sripaibulya *(Sr Exec VP-Tech Div)*
Chong Toh *(Sr Exec VP-Intl Banking Grp)*
Siridej Aungudomsin *(Exec VP & Head-Provincial Bus Banking)*
Chaiyong Ratanacharoensiri *(Exec VP & Head-Provincial Corp Banking)*
Than Siripokee *(Exec VP & Head-Metropolitan Bus Banking)*
Thawat Treewannakul *(Exec VP & Head-Special Asset/Credit Mgmt)*
Kraisorn Barameeauychai *(Exec VP & Mgr-Legal Dept)*
Panit Dunnvatanachit *(Exec VP-Construction, Property Dev, Telecom & Mgr-Telecom/Banking)*
Pornnit Dunnvatanachit *(Exec VP & Mgr-Shared Ops & Securities & Trade Svcs)*
Wallapa Klinpratoom *(Exec VP-Correspondence Banking Dept)*
Yaowadee Nakhata *(Exec VP & Mgr-Metropolitan Corp Banking)*
Ruchanee Nopmuang *(Exec VP & Mgr-HR)*
Narin Opamuratawongse *(Exec VP & Mgr-Merchants Banking Div)*
Bussakorn Pao-In *(Exec VP & Mgr-Banking)*
Kenneth See *(Exec VP & Mgr)*
Ian Guy Gillard *(Exec VP)*
Pornthep Kitsanayothin *(Exec VP-Audit)*
Lin Cheng Leo Kung *(Exec VP-Reg Bus Expansion)*
Songkram Sakulphramana *(Exec VP-Loan Recovery & Legal)*
Saowanee Siripat *(Exec VP-HR Div)*
Kulathida Sivayathorn *(Exec VP)*
Piyada Sucharitkul *(Exec VP)*
Kajornvut Tayanukorn *(Exec VP-Tech Div)*
Sa-Ard Theerarojanawong *(Exec VP-Foreign Exchange Trading & Treasury Div)*
Rushda Theeratharathorn *(Exec VP-Credit Mgmt)*
Bhakorn Vanuptikul *(Exec VP-Property Mgmt Dept)*
Board of Directors:
Chatri Sophonpanich
Amorn Chandarasomboon
Chansak Fuangfu
Kanung Luchai
Kosit Panpiemras
Phornthep Phornprapha
Kovit Poshyananda
Thaweelap Rittapirom
Prachet Siridej
Piti Sithi-Amnuai
Charn Sophonpanich
Chartsiri Sophonpanich
Singh Tangtatswas
Suvarn Thansathit
Deja Tulananda
Gasinee Witoonchart
Mongkolchaleam Yugala
Subsidiaries:

Bualuang Securities Public Company Limited **(1)**
29th Floor Silom Complex Office Building
Bang Rak 191 Silom Road
Bangkok, 10500, Thailand TH
Tel.: (66) 22313777 (99.7%)
Fax: (66) 22313797
E-Mail: info@bualuang.co.th
Web Site: www.bualuang.co.th
Emp.: 200
Securities Brokerage Services
S.I.C.: 6211
N.A.I.C.S.: 523120
Pichet Siphiamuanuai *(Pres)*

Sinnsuptawee Asset Management Co., Ltd. **(1)**
323 United Center Building Unit No 3001
30th Floor Silmon Road
Bangkok, 10500, Thailand
Tel.: (66) 2635 5001
Fax: (66) 2635 5004
Web Site: www.stamc.com
Emp.: 9
Asset Management Services
S.I.C.: 6794
N.A.I.C.S.: 533110
Kulathida Sivaya Thorn *(Mng Dir)*

Non-U.S. Subsidiaries:

Bangkok Bank Berhad **(1)**
105 Jalan Tun HS Lee
5000 Kuala Lumpur, Malaysia MY
Tel.: (60) 3 2173 7200 (100%)
Fax: (60) 3 2173 7300
E-Mail: bbb@bangkokbank.com
Web Site: www.bangkokbank.com.my
Emp.: 75
Commercial Bank
S.I.C.: 6029
N.A.I.C.S.: 522110
Robert Loke Tan Cheng *(CEO)*

Bangkok Bank (China) Co., Ltd. **(1)**
No 7 Zhongshan East-1 Road
Shanghai, 200002, China
Tel.: (86) 2123290100
Fax: (86) 2123290101
Emp.: 130
Commercial Banking Services
S.I.C.: 6029
N.A.I.C.S.: 522110
Suwatchai Songwanich *(CEO)*

BANGKOK BUSINESS EQUIPMENT AUTOMATION CO., LTD.

(d/b/a Bangkok Busiquipt Group)
199/82-84 Vipawadee Rangsit Road
Samsennai Phayathai, Bangkok, 10400, Thailand
Tel.: (66) 22710213
Fax: (66) 22714991
E-Mail: bbea@bbe-group.com
Web Site: www.bbe-group.com
Year Founded: 1970
Emp.: 250
Business Description:
Office & Other Professional Equipment Distr
S.I.C.: 5044
N.A.I.C.S.: 423420
Personnel:
Dej Churdsuwanrak *(Mng Dir-Security Sys)*
Subsidiary:

Bangkok OA Coms Co., Ltd. **(1)**
199-82-84 Vipavadee Rangsit Highway
Bangkok, 10400, Thailand (100%)
Tel.: (66) 22710213
Fax: (66) 22714991
E-Mail: oacoms@bbe-group.com
Web Site: www.bbe-group.com
Security Equipment Distr
S.I.C.: 5063
N.A.I.C.S.: 423610
Dej Churdsuwanrak *(Mng Dir)*

BANGKOK DEC-CON PUBLIC COMPANY LIMITED

52/3 Moo 8 Bangbuathong-Supanburi Rd Lahan
Bangbuathong, Nonthaburi, 11110, Thailand
Tel.: (66) 2925 5777
Fax: (66) 2925 5778
E-Mail: admin@bangkokdeccon.com
Web Site: www.bangkokdeccon.com
Year Founded: 1992
BKD—(THA)
Rev.: $32,095,350
Assets: $21,040,200
Liabilities: $7,010,308
Net Worth: $14,029,892
Earnings: $5,373,023
Emp.: 180
Fiscal Year-end: 12/31/12
Business Description:
Hotel & Commercial Furniture Mfr
S.I.C.: 2599
N.A.I.C.S.: 337127
Personnel:
Tawee Butsuntorn *(Chm)*
Nuchanart Ratanasuwanachart *(Mng Dir)*
Board of Directors:
Tawee Butsuntorn
Kanokart Ratanasuwanachart
Nuchanart Ratanasuwanachart
Theeramate Ratanasuwanachart
Thananan Sato
Yasuhiko Sato
Akekasith Thipakkarayod
Napassorn Thipakkarayod

BANGKOK DUSIT MEDICAL SERVICES PUBLIC COMPANY LIMITED

2 Soi Soonvijai 7 New Petchaburi Road Bangkapi
Huay Khwang, Bangkok, 10320, Thailand
Tel.: (66) 2310 3000
Fax: (66) 2310 3252
Web Site: www.bangkokhospital.com
Year Founded: 1969
BGH—(OTC THA)
Rev.: $1,585,673,330
Assets: $2,268,112,298
Liabilities: $981,771,308
Net Worth: $1,286,340,990
Earnings: $273,396,505
Fiscal Year-end: 12/31/12
Business Description:
Holding Company; Hospitals Owner & Operator
S.I.C.: 6719
N.A.I.C.S.: 551112
Personnel:
Arun Pausawasdi *(Chm)*
Wichai Thongtang *(Second Vice Chm)*
Chuladej Yossundharakul *(First Vice Chm)*
Prasert Prasarttong-Osoth *(Pres & CEO)*
Kessara Wongsekate *(Sec & Asst VP)*
Board of Directors:
Arun Pausawasdi
Chatree Duangnet
Thongchai Jira-Alongkorn
Kanoknuj Lekvichit
Prasert Prasarttong-Osoth
Sripop Sarasas

Chawalit Setmeteekul
Santasiri Sornmani
Chirotchana Suchato
Somchai Sujjapongse
Thavatvong Thanasumitra
Pradit Theekakul
Wichai Thongtang
Pongsak Viddyakorn
Chuladej Yossundharakul

Thailand Securities Depository Co., Ltd.
The Stock Exchange of Thailand Building 4th Floor 62 Rachdapisek Road
Klongtoey Sub-district, Bangkok, Thailand

Subsidiaries:

Bangkok Hospital Hat Yai Co., Ltd. (1)
54/113 Moo 3 Klongrean 1 Road
Kohong Subdistrict, Hat Yai, Songkhla, 90110, Thailand TH
Tel.: (66) 7427 2800 (98.78%)
Fax: (66) 7436 5790
E-Mail: admin@bangkokhatyai.com
Web Site: www.bangkokhatyai.com
Hospital Operator
S.I.C.: 8062
N.A.I.C.S.: 622110

Bangkok Hospital Pattaya Co., Ltd. (1)
301 Moo 6 Sukhumvit Road Km 143
Muang, Pattaya, Chonburi, 20150, Thailand TH
Tel.: (66) 3825 9999 (97.22%)
Fax: (66) 3872 7307
E-Mail: inquiry@bph.co.th
Web Site: www.bangkokpattayahospital.com
Hospital Operator
S.I.C.: 8062
N.A.I.C.S.: 622110
Chirotchana Suchato *(Chm)*

Bangkok Hospital Phuket Co., Ltd. (1)
2/1 Hongyok Utis Road
Muang, Phuket, 83000, Thailand TH
Tel.: (66) 7625 4421 (-9) (99.67%)
Fax: (66) 7625 4430
E-Mail: info@phukethospital.com
Web Site: www.phukethospital.com
Hospital Operator
S.I.C.: 8062
N.A.I.C.S.: 622110
Pongsak Viddayakorn *(Chm)*

Bangkok Hospital Prapadaeng Co., Ltd. (1)
288 Moo 1 Suksawat Road Km 18
Prasamutjadee District, Samut Prakan, 10290, Thailand TH
Tel.: (66) 2818 9000 (79%)
Fax: (66) 2425 9859
Web Site: www.bpdhospital.com
Hospital Operator
S.I.C.: 8062
N.A.I.C.S.: 622110
Chuladej Yossundharakul *(Chm)*

Bangkok Hospital Ratchasima Co., Ltd. (1)
1308/9 Mitrapap Road Tambon Nai Muang
Amphur Muang, Nakhon Ratchasima, 30000, Thailand TH
Tel.: (66) 4426 2000 (89.53%)
Fax: (66) 4425 6421
E-Mail: contact@bangkokratchasima.com
Web Site: www.bangkokratchasima.com
Hospital Operator
S.I.C.: 8062
N.A.I.C.S.: 622110
Pongsak Viddayakorn *(Chm)*

Bangkok Hospital Trat Co., Ltd. (1)
376 Moo 2 Sukhumvit Road
Wangkhrajae Muang, Trat, 23000, Thailand TH
Tel.: (66) 3953 2735 (99.76%)
Fax: (66) 3952 2567
E-Mail: bthmkt@bgh.co.th
Web Site: www.bangkoktrathospital.com
Hospital Operator
S.I.C.: 8062
N.A.I.C.S.: 622110

Sammakorn Public Company Limited (1)
Head Office 195 Phayathai Road Pathumwan
Bangkok, 10330, Thailand
Tel.: (66) 2255 5740
Fax: (66) 2255 2806
E-Mail: marketing@sammakorn.co.th
Web Site: www.sammakorn.co.th
SAMCO—(THA)
Rev.: $31,216,080
Assets: $104,287,939
Liabilities: $44,397,182
Net Worth: $59,890,758
Earnings: $1,475,279
Fiscal Year-end: 12/31/12
Real Estate Development Services
S.I.C.: 6531
N.A.I.C.S.: 531390
Luang Usni Pramoj *(Chm)*
Kittipol Pramoj Na Ayudhya *(Mng Dir)*
Teeravat Pipatdhitakul *(Deputy Mng Dir)*
Yuwadee Nuchtavorn *(Sec & Mgr-Admin)*

Unit:

Bangkok Hospital Medical Center (1)
2 Soi Soonvijai 7 New Petchaburi Road
Bangkapi Huay Khwang, Bangkok, 10310, Thailand
Tel.: (66) 2310 3000
Fax: (66) 2310 3327
E-Mail: info@bangkokhospital.com
Web Site: www.bangkokhospital.com
Hospital Operator
S.I.C.: 8062
N.A.I.C.S.: 622110
Chatree Duangnet *(CEO)*

BANGKOK FIRST INVESTMENT & TRUST PUBLIC COMPANY LIMITED

23rd Floor Bangkok Insurance Building 25 Sathon Tai Road
Thung Mahamek Sathon, Bangkok, 10120, Thailand
Tel.: (66) 26774300
Fax: (66) 26774301
E-Mail: kingthien@bfit.co.th
Web Site: www.bfit.co.th
BFIT—(THA TSXV)
Sales Range: $10-24.9 Million
Emp.: 335

Business Description:
Investment Banking Services
S.I.C.: 6211
N.A.I.C.S.: 523110

Personnel:
Wissanu Krea-ngam *(Chm)*
Sakorn Suksriwong *(Vice Chm & CEO)*
Kingthien Bang-or *(Mng Dir)*
Manop Himakorn *(Asst Mng Dir)*

Board of Directors:
Wissanu Krea-ngam
Kingthien Bang-or
Siriwut Buranapin
Tida Chonlavorn
Vorakit Srangsriwang
Sakorn Suksriwong
Thira Wipuchanin

BANGKOK INSURANCE PUBLIC COMPANY LTD.

Bangkok Insurance Building 25 Sathon Tai Road Khwaeng Thung Maha Mek
Khet Sathon, Bangkok, 10120, Thailand
Tel.: (66) 2285 8888
Fax: (66) 2610 2100
E-Mail: ir@bangkokinsurance.com
Web Site: www.bangkokinsurance.com
Year Founded: 1947
BKI—(THA)
Rev.: $301,512,850
Assets: $1,838,974,872
Liabilities: $1,097,044,656
Net Worth: $741,930,216
Earnings: $20,731,594
Emp.: 1,278
Fiscal Year-end: 12/31/12

Business Description:
Insurance Services
S.I.C.: 6411
N.A.I.C.S.: 524298

Personnel:
Chai Sophonpanich *(Chm & CEO)*
Panus Thiravanitkul *(Pres)*
Voravit Rojrapitada *(Sec)*
Apisit Anantanatarat *(Exec VP)*
Anon Vangvasu *(Exec VP)*
Suphat Yookongbandhu *(Exec VP)*
Sontaya Chaichomlert *(Sr VP-Internal Audit)*
Jakkrit Chewanuntapornchai *(Sr VP-Comml Lines Bus Unit)*
Suchart Chirayuwat *(Sr VP-Branch Network & Ventures)*
Satit Liptasiri *(Sr VP-Agent Bus Unit)*
Pimjai Luemrung *(Sr VP-HR)*
Srichittra Pramojaney *(Sr VP-Acctg & Treasury)*
Aree Vanairlor *(Sr VP-Fin Institutional Bus Unit)*

Board of Directors:
Chai Sophonpanich
Chor Nun Petpaisit
Plengsakdi Prakaspesat
Voravit Rojrapitada
Nintira Sophonpanich
Virasak Sutanthavibul
Makoto Suzuki
Singh Tangtaswas
Potjanee Thanavaranit
Suvarn Thansathit
Panus Thiravanitkul
Thira Wongjirachai

Legal Counsel:
Manukit Law Office
59/6 Suapa Road
Bangkok, Thailand

BANGKOK LAND PUBLIC COMPANY LIMITED

47/569-576 Moo 3 10th Floor New Geneva Industry Condominium Popular 3
Road Tambol Bannmai Amphur Pak, Nonthaburi, 11120, Thailand
Tel.: (66) 2 5044949
Fax: (66) 2 5044986
Web Site: www.bangkokland.co.th
Year Founded: 1973
BLAND—(THA)
Rev.: $123,483,461
Assets: $1,683,078,007
Liabilities: $343,558,130
Net Worth: $1,339,519,877
Earnings: $83,910,524
Fiscal Year-end: 03/31/13

Business Description:
Property Development Services
S.I.C.: 6531
N.A.I.C.S.: 531390

Personnel:
Anant Kanjanapas *(Chm & CEO)*
Peter Kanjanapas *(Co-Mng Dir)*
Sui Hung Kanjanapas *(Co-Mng Dir)*
Pravate Earmsamuth *(Sec & Mgr-Legal)*

Board of Directors:
Anant Kanjanapas
Tawin Boonruangkhao
Panya Boonyapiwat
Thumrong Chientachakul
Sakorn Kanjanapas
Shui Pang Kanjanapas
Sui Hung Kanjanapas
Siriwat Likitnuruk
Supavat Saicheua
Wattanasak Sanitwongse
Burin Wongsanguan

Legal Counsel:
Siam Premier International Law Office Limited
26th Floor The Offices at Central World 999/9 Rama I Road Pathumwan
Bangkok, 10330, Thailand

Non-U.S. Subsidiary:

Bangkok Land (Cayman Islands) Limited (1)
G/F Caledonian House Mary Street
PO Box 1043
Georgetown, Cayman Islands KY1-1102
Tel.: (345) 9490050
Financing Services
S.I.C.: 6159
N.A.I.C.S.: 522294

Subsidiaries:

Bangkok Land Agency Limited (1)
47/217-222 9/F Kimpo Building
Chaengwattana Road
Pakkred, Nonthaburi, 11120, Thailand
Tel.: (66) 25035040
Fax: (66) 25035064
Property Rental Services
S.I.C.: 6531
N.A.I.C.S.: 531210

Impact Exhibition Management Company Limited (1)
99 Popular Road Banmai Subdistrict
Pakkred, Nonthaburi, 11120, Thailand
Tel.: (66) 2833 4455
Fax: (66) 2833 4456
E-Mail: info@impact.co.th
Web Site: www.impact.co.th
Property Rental Services
S.I.C.: 6512
N.A.I.C.S.: 531120
Anant Kanjanapas, *(Chm)*
Paul Kanjanapas *(Mng Dir)*

THE BANGKOK NYLON PUBLIC COMPANY LIMITED

4th Floor Boonmitr Building 138 Silom Road
Bangrak, Bangkok, 10500, Thailand
Tel.: (66) 2234 1472
Fax: (66) 2 634 4324
E-Mail: info@bncsocks.com
Web Site: www.bncsocks.com
Year Founded: 1964
BNC—(THA)
Rev.: $11,353,982
Assets: $9,935,687
Liabilities: $6,976,515
Net Worth: $2,959,172
Earnings: ($1,864,556)
Fiscal Year-end: 12/31/12

Business Description:
Sock Mfr
S.I.C.: 2252
N.A.I.C.S.: 315110

Personnel:
Supoj Srirojanant *(Chm)*
Pulvith Dhanasubsombul *(Mng Dir & Office Mgr)*

Board of Directors:
Supoj Srirojanant
Pulvith Dhanasubsombul
Sommas Koonanantawanich
Supavith Ngamrassameewongse
Prasit Nimmarnsamai
Manus Ongsaranakom
Boonchai Wanchaijiraboon

BANGKOK RANCH PUBLIC COMPANY LIMITED

18/1 Moo 12 Lang Wat
Bangplee Yai Nai Road
Bangplee, Samut Prakan, 10540, Thailand
Tel.: (66) 23373280
Fax: (66) 23373295
E-Mail: info@bangkokranch.co.th
Web Site: www.bangkokranch.co.th
Year Founded: 1984
RANCH—(THA)

Bangkok Ranch Public Company Limited—(Continued)

Sales Range: $150-199.9 Million
Emp.: 1,722
Business Description:
Duck Producer & Processor
S.I.C.: 0259
N.A.I.C.S.: 112390
Personnel:
Timothy Alan Mckinlay *(Chm)*
Joseph Suchaovanich *(CEO)*
Penhurai Chaichatchaval *(CFO)*
Rosanna Suchaovanich *(COO)*
Wutinai Ulit *(CIO)*
Board of Directors:
Timothy Alan Mckinlay
Ronald De Haan
Richard Elletson Foyston
David Martin Ireland
Jaithip Kanjanapoo
Marcel C.A. Kannekens
Niels Henri Kok
Joseph Suchaovanich
Vudhiphol Suriyabhivadh
Gertjan Tomassen
Legal Counsel:
Allen & Overy (Thailand) Co., Ltd.
22nd Fl Sidhorn Tower III
130 132 Wireless Road
Lumpini Pathumwan, Bangkok, Thailand

Non-U.S. Subsidiary:

Tomassen Bangkok Ranch BV **(1)**
Fokko Kortlanglaan 116
3853 KH Ermelo, Netherlands
Tel.: (31) 341553675
Fax: (31) 341562358
E-Mail: info@br-tomassen.com
Web Site: www.tomassen.com
Emp.: 90
Poultry Farming Services
S.I.C.: 0254
N.A.I.C.S.: 112340
Gertjan Tomas *(Gen Mgr)*

BANGKOK RUBBER PUBLIC CO., LTD.

(d/b/a Pan-Group)
611/40 Soi Watchan Nai Rajuthit 2
Bangkhlo Bangkholaem, Bangkok, 10140, Thailand
Tel.: (66) 26899500
Fax: (66) 22911353
E-Mail: panglobal@pan-group.in.th
Web Site: www.pan-group.in.th
Year Founded: 1976
BRC—(THA)
Rev.: $176,265,183
Assets: $72,900,577
Liabilities: $186,771,700
Net Worth: ($113,871,123)
Earnings: $8,539,589
Emp.: 2,800
Fiscal Year-end: 12/31/12
Business Description:
Sports Shoes & Other Footwear Mfr
S.I.C.: 2389
N.A.I.C.S.: 316210
Personnel:
Chernchai Pinijsutapoch *(Chm)*
Prasert Chulthira *(Vice Chm)*
Prateep Bumroongvityapan *(Sr VP)*
Board of Directors:
Chernchai Pinijsutapoch
Prateep Bumroongvityapan
Prasert Chulthira
Thamrongrat Keokarn
Kittinun Panichakrai
Pramothya Pavarolarvidya
Phanom Sompagdee
Ravadee Tangwongcharioen
Nuchanart Thammanomai
Thamrong Tritiprasert
Watana Yuckpan

Subsidiaries:

Bangkok Athletic Co., Ltd. **(1)**
611/210-213 Soi Watchannai Rajuthit 2
Bangklo Bangkholeam, Bangkok, 10120, Thailand TH
Tel.: (66) 2689834559 (99.9%)
Telex: 72119 BRC TH
Fax: (66) 22912563
E-Mail: pingpong@chaiyo.com
Web Site: www.pan-sportswear.com
Int. Income: $7,000,000
Emp.: 450
Sporting Goods Mfr
S.I.C.: 3949
N.A.I.C.S.: 339920
Kittinun Piachanichkai *(Gen Mgr)*

Innovation Footwear Co., Ltd. **(1)**
82 Mu9 Samkok-Sena Road Bangnomko Sena
Ayutthaya, 13110, Thailand
Fax: (66) 3 520 1535
Footwear Mfr
S.I.C.: 2389
N.A.I.C.S.: 316210

BANGKOK STEEL INDUSTRY PUBLIC COMPANY LIMITED

205 United Flour Mill Building 7th Floor
Samphantawongse Rajawongse Rd, Bangkok, 10100, Thailand
Tel.: (66) 26868282
Fax: (66) 26868281
E-Mail: info@bangkoksteel.co.th
Web Site: www.bangkoksteel.co.th
Year Founded: 1964
Sales Range: $300-349.9 Million
Emp.: 1,345
Business Description:
Steel Bar & Galvanized Steel Sheet Mfr
S.I.C.: 3399
N.A.I.C.S.: 331110
Personnel:
Jaray Bhumichitra *(CEO)*

BANGLADESH BANK

PO Box 325
Dhaka, Bangladesh
Tel.: (880) 27122566
Fax: (880) 29566212
Web Site: www.bangladesh-bank.org.bd
Sales Range: $400-449.9 Million
Emp.: 3,848
Business Description:
Banking Services
S.I.C.: 6011
N.A.I.C.S.: 521110
Personnel:
Atiur Rahman *(Chm)*
Jahangir Alam *(Sec)*
Board of Directors:
Atiur Rahman
Nasiruddin Ahmed
Sadiq Ahmed
Hannana Begum
Mustafa Kamal Mujeri
Shafiqur Rahman Patwary
Abul Quasem
Bishnu Pada Saha
Sanat Kumar Saha
Mohammad Tareque
ACNABIN
Dhaka, Bangladesh

BANGLADESH FINANCE & INVESTMENT COMPANY LTD.

Baitul Hossain Building 2nd Floor
27 Dilkusha C/A, Dhaka, 1000, Bangladesh
Tel.: (880) 27114489
Fax: (880) 2 9566493
E-Mail: info@bangladeshfinance.net
Web Site: www.bdfinance.net
Year Founded: 2000
BDFINANCE—(CHT DHA)
Sales Range: $1-9.9 Million
Business Description:
Financial & Investment Services
S.I.C.: 6141
N.A.I.C.S.: 522291
Personnel:
Anwar Hossain *(Chm)*
Khaled Hossain *(Vice Chm)*
G. M. Salehuddin Ahmed *(CEO & Mng Dir)*
Luthful Karim *(Deputy Mng Dir)*
Ranjit Kumar Chakraborty *(Sec & Sr VP)*
Atiqul Islam Chowdhury *(Sr VP)*
Abdul Mabud *(Sr VP)*
Board of Directors:
Anwar Hossain
Geasuddin Ahmed
Hossain Akhtar
S. M. Didarul Alam
Khaled Hossain
Md Imtiyaj
Hossain Mehmud
Chowdhury Erteza Ahmed Siddiqui
Haji M.A. Taher
Haji Md Yousuf

BANGLADESH GENERAL INSURANCE COMPANY LIMITED

42 Dilkusha C/A Motijheel
Dhaka, Bangladesh
Tel.: (880) 2 9555073
Fax: (880) 2 9564212
E-Mail: info@bgicinsure.com
Web Site: www.bgicinsure.com
Year Founded: 1985
BGIC—(DHA)
Business Description:
Insurance Services
S.I.C.: 6411
N.A.I.C.S.: 524298
Personnel:
Towhid Samad *(Chm)*
Salim Bhuiyan *(Vice Chm)*
Ahmed Saifuddin Chowdhury *(Mng Dir & CEO)*
Chowdhury Mohammad Abdul Sayead *(CFO & Deputy Mng Dir)*
Rashida Banu *(Deputy Mng Dir-Claims & Re-Insurance)*
Mohammad Imran Rouf *(Deputy Mng Dir-Underwriting)*
Board of Directors:
Towhid Samad
Mustafa Zaman Abbasi
S. Ahmed
Aftab Alam
Salim Bhuiyan
Ahmed Saifuddin Chowdhury
Sohail Humayun

BANGLADESH INDUSTRIAL FINANCE COMPANY LIMITED

63 Dilkusha Commercial Area 1st Floor
Dhaka, 1000, Bangladesh
Tel.: (880) 29558039
Fax: (880) 29562636
E-Mail: bifc@bol-online.com
Web Site: www.bifcol.com
BIFC—(DHA)
Int. Income: $15,665,755
Assets: $108,104,981
Liabilities: $93,402,604
Net Worth: $14,702,376
Earnings: $121,076
Emp.: 75
Fiscal Year-end: 12/31/12
Business Description:
Lease Finance & Loan Services
S.I.C.: 6141
N.A.I.C.S.: 522291
Personnel:
Umme Kulsum Mannan *(Chm)*
Inamur Rahman *(Mng Dir)*
Ahsanul Bari *(CFO & Exec VP)*
Ahamed Karim Chowdhury *(Sec, Head-Corp Fin Unit-1 & Sr Asst VP)*
Fakhre Faisal *(Sr VP & Head-Bus)*
Board of Directors:
Umme Kulsum Mannan
Abbas Uddin Ahmed
A. N. M. Jahangir Alam
Sze Hung Chan
Khaled A. Karim
Tajrina Mannan
Tanzila Mannan
Arshad Ullah
Jaroslav M. Vyskovsky
Legal Counsel:
Hassan & Associates
DCC Building 6th Floor 65-Motijheel C/A
Dhaka, Bangladesh

BANGLADESH LAMPS LIMITED

Sadar Road Mohakhali
Dhaka, 1206, Bangladesh
Tel.: (880) 25537180
Fax: (880) 28810055
Web Site: www.bll.com.bd
Year Founded: 1960
BDLAMPS—(DHA)
Sls.: $11,804,662
Assets: $16,646,234
Liabilities: $9,037,675
Net Worth: $7,608,559
Earnings: ($616,486)
Emp.: 248
Fiscal Year-end: 12/31/12
Business Description:
Electric Bulbs Mfr
S.I.C.: 3641
N.A.I.C.S.: 335110
Personnel:
Shahnaz Rahman *(Chm)*
Latifur Rahman *(CEO & Mng Dir)*
Mohammad Habibur Rahman Mollah *(CFO & COO)*
Abdullah Ismail *(Sec)*
Board of Directors:
Shahnaz Rahman
Ahmed Shafi Choudhury
Simeen Hossain
Shahzreh Huq
Obaidur Rahman Khan
Arshad Waliur Rahman
Atiqur Rahman
Latifur Rahman
Rokia A. Rahman
Saifur Rahman
Shamsur Rahman

BANGLADESH SERVICES LIMITED

1 Minto Road
Dhaka, 1000, Bangladesh
Tel.: (880) 2 9342955
Fax: (880) 2 8330142
Web Site: www.bsl.gov.bd
Year Founded: 1973
BDSERVICE—(DHA)
Business Description:
Hotel Management Services
S.I.C.: 7011
N.A.I.C.S.: 721110
Personnel:
Lutfur Rahman *(Mng Dir)*
Imtiaz Hossain Chowdhury *(Sec)*
Board of Directors:
Khurshidul Hasan
Mohammad Enayet Hossain
Marshal Mahmud Hussain
Asif Ibrahim
Mohammad Atharul Islam
Syed Monjurul Islam
A. S. M. Ismail

Sardar Abul Kalam
Sayed Rana Moostofee
Lutfur Rahman

BANGLADESH THAI ALUMINIUM LIMITED

BTA Tower 29 Kemal Ataturk Avenue
Banani C/A Road No 17
Dhaka, 1213, Bangladesh
Tel.: (880) 2 9882111
Fax: (880) 2 9881713
E-Mail: bta@btaalul.com
Web Site: www.btaalu.com
Year Founded: 1979
BDTHAI—(DHA)
Emp.: 411

Business Description:
Aluminium Mfr
S.I.C.: 3334
N.A.I.C.S.: 331313

Personnel:
Zahid Maleque *(Chm)*
Rubina Hamid *(Vice Chm)*
Mohammad Shah Newaz *(Mng Dir)*
Mohammad Jahidul Alam *(Sec)*

Board of Directors:
Zahid Maleque
Kazi Aktar Hamid
Rubina Hamid
Fouzia Maleque
Shabana Maleque
Rafiq Mujtaba

BANGO PLC

5 Westbrook Centre Milton Road
Cambridge, CB4 1YG, United Kingdom
Tel.: (44) 1223472777
Fax: (44) 1223472778
Web Site: www.bango.com
BGO—(LSE)
Sales Range: $10-24.9 Million
Emp.: 51

Business Description:
Business Services
S.I.C.: 7371
N.A.I.C.S.: 541511

Personnel:
Ray Anderson *(Co-Founder & CEO)*
Anil Malhotra *(Co-Founder, CMO & Sr VP-Mktg & Alliances)*
Gerald Louis Tucker *(CFO)*
David Keeling *(COO)*
Glenn Walker *(CTO)*
Tim Moss *(Chief Data Officer)*
Henry Goldstein *(Sec)*
Martin Harris *(Sr VP-Strategic Accts)*

Board of Directors:
David Sear
Ray Anderson
Rudy Burger
Anil Malhotra
Martin Rigby
Gerald Louis Tucker

Legal Counsel:
Mills & Reeve
Francis House 112 Hills Road
Cambridge, CB2 1PH, United Kingdom

Subsidiary:

Bango.net Limited (1)
5 Westbrook Centre
Cambridge, Cambridgeshire, CB4 1YG, United Kingdom
Tel.: (44) 1223 472 777
Fax: (44) 1223 472 778
E-Mail: support@bango.com
Web Site: web.bango.net
Emp.: 40
Mobile Payment Solutions
S.I.C.: 6099
N.A.I.C.S.: 522320
Ray Anderson *(Founder & CEO)*

Non-U.S. Subsidiary:

Bango GmbH (1)
Stadlauerstrasse 6
1220 Vienna, Austria
Tel.: (43) 1285 3431
Fax: (43) 1285 3454
Mobile Payment Services
S.I.C.: 6099
N.A.I.C.S.: 522320

BANGPAKONG TERMINAL PUBLIC COMPANY LIMITED

8/1 Mu8 Sukhumvit Road Tahkarm
Bangpakong, Chachoengsao, Thailand
Tel.: (66) 38 828421
Fax: (66) 38 828420
E-Mail: sales@btc.th.com
Web Site: www.btc.th.com
BTC—(THA)
Sales Range: $1-9.9 Million

Business Description:
Marine & Cargo Handling services
S.I.C.: 4491
N.A.I.C.S.: 488320

Personnel:
Seng Lim Shu *(Chm)*

Board of Directors:
Seng Lim Shu
Thananya Chumponkulwong
Li Kuang Ling
Lim Sukanya

BANIF BANCO INTERNACIONAL DO FUNCHAL SA

(d/b/a Banif Financial Group)
Rua de Jao Tavira 30
9004-509 Funchal, Portugal
Tel.: (351) 217 211 200
Fax: (351) 217 211 201
E-Mail: info@banif.pt
Web Site: www.banif.pt
BANIF—(EUR)
Rev.: $1,069,802,645
Assets: $18,836,005,068
Liabilities: $18,329,635,145
Net Worth: $506,369,923
Earnings: ($776,114,121)
Emp.: 2,669
Fiscal Year-end: 12/31/12

Business Description:
Banking Services
S.I.C.: 6029
N.A.I.C.S.: 522110

Personnel:
Luis Filipe Marques Amado *(Chm)*
Maria Teresa Henriques da Silva Moura Roque dal Fabbro *(Vice Chm)*
Jorge Humberto Correia Tome *(Vice Chm)*
Bruno Miguel dos Santos de Jesus *(Sec)*

Board of Directors:
Luis Filipe Marques Amado
Goncalo Vaz Gago da Camara de Medeiros Botelho
Maria Teresa Henriques da Silva Moura Roque dal Fabbro
Diogo Antonio Rodrigues da Silveira
Joao Paulo Pereira Marques de Almeida
Manuel Carlos de Carvalho Fernandes
Antonio Carlos Custodio de Morais Varela
Joao Jose Goncalves de Sousa
Jose Antonio Vinhas Mouquinho
Vitor Manuel Farinha Nunes
Carlos Eduardo Pais e Jorge
Nuno Jose Roquette Teixeira
Jorge Humberto Correia Tome

Subsidiaries:

Banif Banco de Investimento, S.A (1)
Sede Social Rua Tierno Galvan
1070 Lisbon, Portugal (100%)
Tel.: (351) 213816200
Fax: (351) 213816201
E-Mail: banifinvestimento@banifiaab.pt
Web Site: www.banifinvestimento.pt
Emp.: 150
Miscellaneous Financial Investment Activities
S.I.C.: 6211
N.A.I.C.S.: 523999
Artur Fernandez *(Mng Dir)*

Banif Capital - Sociedade De Capital De Risco, S A (1)
Rua Tierno Galvan Tower 3 15th Fl
Lisbon, Portugal
Tel.: (351) 213816200
Fax: (351) 213816201
E-Mail: banif.investment@banifib.com
Web Site: www.banifib.com
Emp.: 115
Open-End Investment Funds
S.I.C.: 6722
N.A.I.C.S.: 525910
Artur Fernandas *(Pres)*

Banif Gestao de Activos - Sociedade Gestora de Fundos de Investimento Mobiliario, S.A. (1)
Rua Tierno Galvan Torre 3 12 14 Fl
1070274 Lisbon, Portugal
Tel.: (351) 213816200
Fax: (351) 213816201
E-Mail: investimento@banifib.pt
Web Site: www.banifib.pt
Emp.: 115
Open-End Investment Funds
S.I.C.: 6722
N.A.I.C.S.: 525910
Ahtuf Fernandes *(Pres)*

Banifserv - Empresa de Servicos Sistemas e Tecnologias de Informacao A C E (1)
Coronel Bento Roma 4
Lisbon, 1700, Portugal (100%)
Tel.: (351) 213843200
Fax: (351) 213843298
E-Mail: fCardofo@banif.pt
Web Site: www.banif.pt
Emp.: 100
Other Computer Related Services
S.I.C.: 7379
N.A.I.C.S.: 541519
Filip Cardofo *(Mng Dir)*

Companhia de Seguros Asoreana, SA (1)
Largo da Matriz 45-52
9501-922 Ponta Delgada, Portugal (100%)
Tel.: (351) 296201400
Fax: (351) 296201800
E-Mail: acoreana@csanet.pt
Web Site: www.acoreanaseguros.pt
Emp.: 600
Miscellaneous Financial Investment Activities
S.I.C.: 6211
N.A.I.C.S.: 523999
Diamantino Marcous *(Mng Dir)*

InvestaCor - Sociedade Gestora de Participacoes Sociais, S A (1)
Rue lisboa Roalt Garden Hotel
Ponta Delgada, 9500216, Portugal
Tel.: (351) 296307300
Fax: (351) 296307307
E-Mail: recervansst@hotel.investacor.com
Web Site: www.investacor.com
Emp.: 65
Hotels (except Casino Hotels) & Motels
S.I.C.: 7011
N.A.I.C.S.: 721110
Jose M. Matos de Sousa *(Gen Mgr)*

Metalsines - Companhia de Vagoes de Sines, S A (1)
Herdade Da Brejeira
Quinta Dos Pegos Apartado 18, 7520-901 Sines, Portugal (100%)
Tel.: (351) 269870110
Fax: (351) 269870113
E-Mail: geral@metalsines.com
Web Site: www.metalsines.com
Emp.: 60
Railroad Rolling Stock Mfr
S.I.C.: 3743
N.A.I.C.S.: 336510
Juan Mashado *(Mng Dir)*

Non-U.S. Subsidiaries:

Banif-Banco Internacional do Funchal (Brasil), SA (1)
Av Juscelino Kubitscheck 1 700
Sao Paulo, Brazil
Tel.: (55) 1131652000
Fax: (55) 31673960
Web Site: www.bancobanif.com.br/exec_bc/BCRedir?navegmapa=agencia_SP
Commercial Banks
S.I.C.: 6029
N.A.I.C.S.: 522110
Angalo Rica Scotilo *(Mng Dir)*

Banif Corretora de Valores e Cambio S.A. (1)
Rua Minas da Prata 30 Ave JK 3rd Fl
04542-000 Sao Paulo, Brazil (100%)
Tel.: (55) 1130748000
Fax: (55) 1130748140
Web Site: www.banifcorretora.com
Emp.: 100
Offices of Real Estate Agents and Brokers
S.I.C.: 6531
N.A.I.C.S.: 531210
Fabio Seola *(Mng Dir)*

Banif Nitor Asset Management (1)
Rua Minas da Prata 30 Ave JK 3rd Fl
04542-000 Sao Paulo, Brazil (51%)
Tel.: (55) 1130748000
Fax: (55) 1130748144
E-Mail: banifnitor@banifnitor.com.br
Web Site: www.banifnitor.com.br
Emp.: 100
Investment Banking & Securities Dealing
S.I.C.: 6211
N.A.I.C.S.: 523110
Fabio Seola *(Mng Dir)*

BANIF SGPS SA

(See Under Banif Banco Internacional do Funchal SA)

BANIJAY HOLDING SAS

(d/b/a Banijay Group)
5 rue Francois 1er
75008 Paris, France
Tel.: (33) 1 4318 9191
E-Mail: contact@banijay.com
Web Site: www.banijay.com

Business Description:
Holding Company; Television & Digital Entertainment Content Production Services
S.I.C.: 6719
N.A.I.C.S.: 551112

Personnel:
Stephane Courbit *(Pres)*
Sophie Kurinckx *(CFO)*
Francois de Brugada *(COO)*
Frederique Sauvage *(Gen Counsel)*
Pascale Amiel *(Exec VP-Fin & Bus Dev)*

Subsidiary:

Banijay Entertainment SAS (1)
5 rue Francois 1er
75008 Paris, France FR
Tel.: (33) 1 4318 9191
Web Site: www.banijay.com
Television & Digital Entertainment Content Production Services
S.I.C.: 4841
N.A.I.C.S.: 515210
Francois de Brugada *(Co-Founder & Exec VP-Creative & Comml Affairs)*
Stephane Courbit *(Co-Founder)*
Marco Bassetti *(CEO)*
Pascale Amiel *(Exec VP-Fin & Bus Dev)*

Subsidiary:

H2O Productions SAS (2)
5 rue Francois 1er
75008 Paris, France FR
Tel.: (33) 1 43 18 91 91
Video Production Services
S.I.C.: 7812
N.A.I.C.S.: 512110

BANJA LAKTASI A.D.

Karadordeva 44
Laktasi, Bosnia & Herzegovina

Banja Laktasi a.d.—(Continued)

Tel.: (387) 51 532 256
Fax: (387) 51 530 392
E-Mail: info@banja-laktasi.info
Web Site: www.banja-laktasi.info
BLAK—(BANJ)
Emp.: 45
Business Description:
Hotel Management Services
S.I.C.: 7011
N.A.I.C.S.: 721110
Personnel:
Dragan Jevtovic *(Chm-Mgmt Bd)*
Milkica Radeljic *(Deputy Chm-Mgmt Bd)*
Branko Cvijic *(Member-Mgmt Bd)*

BANJA LUKA CONSTRUCTION INSTITUTE, INC.

Marije Bursac 4
78000 Banja Luka, Bosnia & Herzegovina
Tel.: (387) 51 225 900
Fax: (387) 51 216 651
Web Site: www.zibl.org
ZIBL—(BANJ)
Emp.: 113
Business Description:
Architectural & Construction Services
S.I.C.: 8712
N.A.I.C.S.: 541310
Personnel:
Budimir Balaban *(Chm-Mgmt Bd)*
Branka Savic *(Deputy Chm-Mgmt Bd)*
Dragomir Dukic *(Member-Mgmt Bd)*
Verica Kunic *(Member-Mgmt Bd)*
Darko Tadic *(Member-Mgmt Bd)*

BANJALUCKA PIVARA AD BANJA LUKA

(See Under Altima Partners LLP)

BANK AL-MAGHRIB

277 Avenue Mohammed V Boite postale 445
Rabat, Morocco
Tel.: (212) 37702626
Fax: (212) 37706667
E-Mail: webmaster@bkam.ma
Web Site: www.bkam.ma
Sales Range: $400-449.9 Million
Business Description:
Banking Services
S.I.C.: 6011
N.A.I.C.S.: 521110
Personnel:
Abdellatif Jouahri *(Governor & Chm)*
Board of Directors:
Abdellatif Jouahri
Abdellatif Belmadani
Mohamed Benamour
Meriem Bensaleh Chaqroun
Abdellatif Faouzi
Bassim Jai-Hokimi
Mustapha Moussaoui
Fouzia Zaaboul

BANK ALBILAD

Al Malaz Steen Street
PO Box 140
Riyadh, 11411, Saudi Arabia
Tel.: (966) 14798888
Fax: (966) 14798898
E-Mail: info@bankalbilad.com.sa
Web Site: www.bankalbilad.com.sa
1140—(SAU)
Rev.: $462,664,294
Assets: $7,929,748,516
Liabilities: $6,765,800,215
Net Worth: $1,163,948,301
Earnings: $250,802,405
Emp.: 2,840
Fiscal Year-end: 12/31/12
Business Description:
Retail & Investment Banking Services
S.I.C.: 6211
N.A.I.C.S.: 523110
Personnel:
Abdulrhman Ibrahim Al-Humaid *(Chm)*
Nasser Mohammad Al-Subeaei *(Vice Chm)*
Board of Directors:
Abdulrhman Ibrahim Al-Humaid
Khalid Abdulaziz Al-Mukairin
Ahmad Abdulaziz Alohali
Khalid Abdullah Al Subeaei
Fahad Abdullah Bindekhayel
Abdulmohsen Abdullatif Alissa
Ahmed Abdulrahman Alhossan
Ibrahim Abdulrhman Al-Barrak
Khaled Abdulrahman Al-Rajhi
Nasser Mohammad Al-Subeaei
Abdulrhman Mohammed Ramzi Addas

Deloitte & Touche Bakr Abulkhair & Co.
PO Box 213
Riyadh, 11411, Saudi Arabia
Tel.: (966) 1463 0018
Fax: (966) 96614630865

BANK ALJAZIRA

King Abdulaziz Road
PO Box 6277
Jeddah, 21442, Saudi Arabia
Tel.: (966) 26098888
Fax: (966) 26098881
E-Mail: info@baj.com.sa
Web Site: www.baj.com.sa
Year Founded: 1975
1020—(SAU)
Rev.: $426,334,316
Assets: $13,569,721,809
Liabilities: $12,188,797,061
Net Worth: $1,380,924,747
Earnings: $133,319,633
Emp.: 1,574
Fiscal Year-end: 12/31/12
Business Description:
Banking Services
S.I.C.: 6029
N.A.I.C.S.: 522110
Personnel:
Taha Abdulla Al-Kuwaiz *(Chm)*
Nabil Al-Hoshan *(CEO & Mng Dir)*
Shahid Amin *(CFO & Sr VP)*
Robert Hadley *(COO & Sr VP)*
Charles Brodie *(Chief Risk Officer & Sr VP)*
Ziad T. Aba Al-Khail *(CEO-Aljazira Capital)*
Sager Nedershah *(CEO-Aljazira Takaful Ta'awuni)*
Yasser Al Hedaithy *(Treas & Sr VP)*
Fahed Al Akeel *(Sr VP & Head-Strategy & Bus Transformation Grp)*
Mohammed Al Ghamdi *(Sr VP & Grp Head-Shariah)*
Khalid Al Othman *(Sr VP & Head-Retail Banking Grp)*
Tarek A. Al Shubaily *(Sr VP & Head-Human Capital Grp)*
Hamad Abdulaziz Al-Ajaji *(Sr VP & Head-Private Banking)*
Ibrahim Al-Hurabi *(Sr VP & Head-Internal Audit)*
Khalid Omar Abdullah Al-Mogrin *(Sr VP & Head-Legal)*
Abdullah Al-Shmassi *(Sr VP & Head-Corp & Institutional Banking Grp)*
Board of Directors:
Taha Abdulla Al-Kuwaiz
Khalid Omar Al-Baltan
Mohammed A. Al-Hagbani
Majed Al-Hogail
Tarek Osman Al-Kasabi
Khalifa Abdullateef Al-Mulhem
Abdulmajeed Ibrahim Al-Sultan
Abdullah S. Kamel

Deloitte & Touche Bakr Abulkhair & Co.
PO Box 442
Jeddah, 21411, Saudi Arabia
Tel.: (966) 2 6572725
Fax: (966) 2 65722722

BANK ASIA LIMITED

Rangs Tower 2nd to 6th Floor 68
Purana Paltan
Dhaka, 1000, Bangladesh
Tel.: (880) 27110042
Fax: (880) 27175524
E-Mail: bankasia@bankasia.com.bd
Web Site: www.bankasia-bd.com
BANKASIA—(DHA)
Int. Income: $171,943,356
Assets: $1,748,493,903
Liabilities: $1,586,140,542
Net Worth: $162,353,361
Earnings: $10,522,274
Emp.: 1,485
Fiscal Year-end: 12/31/12
Business Description:
Banking Services
S.I.C.: 6036
N.A.I.C.S.: 522120
Personnel:
A. Rouf Chowdhury *(Chm)*
A. M. Nurul Islam *(Vice Chm)*
Mohammed Lakiotullah *(Vice Chm)*
Md. Mehmood Husain *(Pres & Mng Dir)*
Imran Ahmed *(CFO & Sr VP)*
S. M. Khorshed Alam *(Deputy Mng Dir)*
Md. Arfan Ali *(Deputy Mng Dir)*
Humaira Azam *(Deputy Mng Dir)*
Aminul Islam *(Deputy Mng Dir)*
Mohammed Roshangir *(Deputy Mng Dir)*
Nasirul Hossain *(Sr Exec VP)*
Md. Touhidul Alam Khan *(Sr Exec VP)*
Syed Nazimuddin *(Sr Exec VP)*
Ashfaque Hasan Jamilur Rahman *(Sr Exec VP)*
A. K. M. Shahnawaj *(Exec VP)*
Md. Ashrafuddin Ahmed *(Sr VP)*
Md. Zia Arfin *(Sr VP)*
Asif Ainul Hoque *(Sr VP)*
Md. Abdul Qaium Khan *(Sr VP)*
Md. Abu Bakar Laskar *(Sr VP)*
Nandan Kumer Saha *(Sr VP)*
Board of Directors:
A. Rouf Chowdhury
Shah Md. Nurul Alam
Mohd. Safwan Choudhury
Farhana Haq Chowdhury
Rumee A. Hossain
Md. Mehmood Husain
A. M. Nurul Islam
Nafees Khundker
Mohammed Lakiotullah
Hosneara Sinha
Naheed Akhter Sinha
Legal Counsel:
Shameem Aziz & Associates
Paramount Heights Suit no 5D2 5th Floor
Purana Paltan
Dhaka, Bangladesh

Hasan & Associates
Dhaka Chamber of Commerce Building 65 66
Motijheel C/A
Dhaka, Bangladesh

BANK AUDI SAL

(d/b/a Audi Saradar Group)
Bank Audi Plaza - Bab Idriss
Beirut, 2021 8102, Lebanon
Mailing Address:
PO Box 11 2560
Beirut, Lebanon
Tel.: (961) 1994000
Telex: DIRODI 42291
Fax: (961) 1990555
E-Mail: contactus@banqueaudi.com
Web Site: www.banqueaudi.com
Year Founded: 1962
AUDI—(BEY)
Rev.: $1,435,530,850
Assets: $30,671,854,850
Liabilities: $28,048,330,050
Net Worth: $2,623,524,800
Earnings: $375,887,850
Emp.: 5,070
Fiscal Year-end: 12/31/12
Business Description:
Retail, Commercial, Investment Banking & Wealth Management Services
S.I.C.: 6029
N.A.I.C.S.: 522110
Personnel:
Raymond W. Audi *(Chm & Gen Mgr)*
Marwan M. Ghandour *(Vice Chm)*
Samir N. Hanna *(CEO & Gen Mgr)*
Freddie C. Baz *(CFO, Gen Mgr & Dir-Strategy)*
Tamer M. Ghazaleh *(Asst CFO & Asst Gen Mgr)*
Danny N. Dagher *(Acting CIO & Asst Gen Mgr)*
Chahdan E. Jebeyli *(Chief Legal Officer, Chief Compliance Officer & Gen Mgr)*
Elia S. Samaha *(Chief Credit Officer & Gen Mgr)*
Adel N. Satel *(Chief Risk Officer & Gen Mgr)*
Farid F. Lahoud *(Sec)*
Board of Directors:
Raymond W. Audi
Abdullah I. Al Hobayb
Suad H. Al-Homaizi
Mariam N. Al-Sabbah
Marc J. Audi
Freddie C. Baz
Khalil M. Bitar
Marwan M. Ghandour
Samir N. Hanna
Imad I. Itani

BDO Semaan Gholam & Co
Gholam Building Sioufi Street
Beirut, Lebanon

Subsidiaries:

Audi Saradar Investment Bank sal **(1)**
Bank Audi Plaza Block D France Street
Bab Idriss, Beirut, 2021-8102, Lebanon LB
Mailing Address: (99.99%)
PO Box 16-5110
Beirut, Lebanon
Tel.: (961) 1994000
Fax: (961) 1 999 406
E-Mail: contactus@asib.com
Web Site: www.asib.com
Emp.: 4,000
Investment Banking & Securities Dealing
S.I.C.: 6211
N.A.I.C.S.: 523110
Marwan M. Ghandour *(Chm & Gen Mgr)*
Ramzi Z. Saliba *(Gen Mgr & Sec)*

Subsidiary:

Infi Gamma Holding sal **(2)**
Clover Building Charles Malik Avenue Mar Nicolas Sector
Beirut, Lebanon
Tel.: (961) 1 977488
Investment Management Services
S.I.C.: 6211
N.A.I.C.S.: 523999

Audi Saradar Private Bank sal **(1)**
Clover Bldg Charles Malek Ave
PO Box 11-1121
Riad El-Solh, 1107-2805 Beirut, Lebanon LB
Tel.: (961) 1205400 (99.99%)
Fax: (961) 1205480

E-Mail: contactus@audisaradarpb.com
Web Site: www.audisaradarpb.com
Sales Range: $75-99.9 Million
Emp.: 500
Wealth Management & Investment Banking Services
S.I.C.: 6091
N.A.I.C.S.: 523991
Fady Georges Amatoury *(Chm & Gen Mgr)*

Subsidiaries:

Agence Saradar d'Assurances sal (2)
Clover Bldg Charles Malek Avenue Ashrafieh
PO Box 11-1121
Beirut, 1107-2805, Lebanon LB
Tel.: (961) 1338676 (100%)
Fax: (961) 1338685
E-Mail: courrier@asa.com.lb
Emp.: 12
Insurance Agency
S.I.C.: 6411
N.A.I.C.S.: 524210
Khalil Tawil *(Mng Dir)*

Societe Libanaise de Factoring sal (2)
Zen Building
Beirut, Lebanon (91%)
Tel.: (961) 1209200
Fax: (961) 1209205
E-Mail: solifac@solifac.com
Web Site: www.solifac.com
Emp.: 18
Factoring & Credit Intermediation Services
S.I.C.: 6159
N.A.I.C.S.: 522298
Pierre Najjear *(Chm & Gen Mgr)*

Non-U.S. Subsidiaries:

Audi Capital (KSA) cjsc (1)
Centria Bldg 3rd Floor Prince Mohammad Bin Abdul Aziz Road
PO Box 250744
Riyadh, 11391, Saudi Arabia SA
Tel.: (966) 12199300 (99.99%)
Fax: (966) 1 462 7942
E-Mail: contactus@audicapital.com
Web Site: www.audicapital.com
Investment Banking & Wealth Management Services
S.I.C.: 6211
N.A.I.C.S.: 523110
Samir N. Hanna *(CEO)*
Abdallah I. Saade *(Deputy CEO & Exec Dir-Investment Banking)*

Bank Audi LLC (1)
Qatar Financial Centre Office 1801 18th Floor Qatar Financial Centre
Tower Diplomatic Area, Doha, Qatar QA
Mailing Address: (100%)
PO Box 23270
Doha, Qatar
Tel.: (974) 4967365
Fax: (974) 4967373
E-Mail: contactus.qatar@banqueaudi.com
Emp.: 25
Retail, Commercial & Private Banking Services
S.I.C.: 6029
N.A.I.C.S.: 522110
Saad A. El Zein *(Deputy Gen Mgr)*

Bank Audi sae (1)
Pyramids Heights Office Park Cairo-Alexandria Desert Road Km 22
Cairo, Egypt EG
Tel.: (20) 235343300 (100%)
Fax: (20) 235362120
E-Mail: contactus.egypt@banqueaudi.com
Web Site: www.banqueaudi.com
Retail & Commercial Banking
S.I.C.: 6029
N.A.I.C.S.: 522110
Hatem A. Sadek *(Chm & Mng Dir)*
Mohamed M. Bedier *(CFO & Gen Mgr)*
Yehia K. Youssef *(Sr Gen Mgr & COO)*
Ahmed F. Ibrahim *(Sec)*

Bank Audi S.A.M. (1)
24 Boulevard des Moulins
BP 23
98001 Monaco, Monaco
Tel.: (377) 97701701
Fax: (377) 97701741
Web Site: www.bankaudimonaco.com
Emp.: 19
Investment Services
S.I.C.: 6211
N.A.I.C.S.: 523999
Falk Fischer *(Chm)*
Joachim Strautmann *(Mng Dir)*

Bank Audi Saradar France sa (1)
73 Ave des Champs-Elysees
75008 Paris, France FR
Tel.: (33) 153835000 (99.99%)
Fax: (33) 142560974
E-Mail: contactus.france@banqueaudi.com
Emp.: 100
Retail, Commercial & Investment Banking
S.I.C.: 6029
N.A.I.C.S.: 522110
Freddie C. Baz *(Chm)*
Luc H. Debieuvre *(Gen Mgr)*
Sherine R. Audi *(Deputy Gen Mgr)*

Banque Audi (Suisse) sa (1)
3841211
Geneva, Switzerland CH
Tel.: (41) 227041111 (100%)
Fax: (41) 227041100
E-Mail: contactus@bankaudi.ch
Web Site: www.bankaudi.ch
Emp.: 80
Investment Banking & Trust Services
S.I.C.: 6211
N.A.I.C.S.: 523110
Philippe Sednaoui *(CEO)*
Fouad Hakim *(Mng Dir)*

National Bank of Sudan (1)
National Bank of Sudan Bldg Block 1
Kasr Avenue, Khartoum, Sudan Sd
Mailing Address: (76.56%)
PO Box 1183
Khartoum, Sudan
Tel.: (249) 183797993
Fax: (249) 183779545
E-Mail: contactus@nbs.com.sd
Retail & Commercial Banking
S.I.C.: 6029
N.A.I.C.S.: 522110
Imad I. Itani *(Chm)*
Moawia A. Mohamad Ali *(Deputy Gen Mgr & Sec)*

Non-U.S. Affiliate:

Bank Audi Syria sa (1)
Mohafaza Bldg Youssef Al-Azmeh Square
PO Box 6228
Damascus, Syria SY
Tel.: (963) 1123888000 (47%)
Fax: (963) 112248510
E-Mail: contactus.syria@banqueaudi.com
Retail & Commercial Banking
S.I.C.: 6029
N.A.I.C.S.: 522110
Bassel S. Hamwi *(Deputy Chm & Gen Mgr)*
Mahmoud A. Al-Kurdy *(Asst Gen Mgr & CFO)*

Subsidiary:

Audi Capital (Syria) LLC (2)
Tanzeem kafarsouseh - Cham City Center - plaza 86 Bldg 2nd Floor
PO Box 6228
Damascus, Syria
Tel.: (963) 11 23888630
Fax: (963) 11 2110959
Web Site: www.audicapitalsyria.com
Emp.: 7
Security Brokerage Services
S.I.C.: 6211
N.A.I.C.S.: 523120
Basel Hamwi *(Mng Dir)*

Non-U.S. Unit:

Bank Audi sal - Jordan Branches (1)
Le Royal Hotel Complex Zahran Street 3rd Circle 4th Fl
Jabal Amman, Amman, Jordan
Mailing Address:
PO Box 840006
Amman, 11184, Jordan
Tel.: (962) 64604000
Fax: (962) 64680015
E-Mail: contactus.jordan@banqueaudi.com
Emp.: 60
Retail & Commercial Banking Services
S.I.C.: 6029
N.A.I.C.S.: 522110
Samer I. Al Aloul *(Deputy Mgr & Head-Corp Dept)*

BANK CENTERCREDIT JSC

98 Panfilov St
Almaty, 050000, Kazakhstan
Tel.: (7) 7273443000
Fax: (7) 7272598622
E-Mail: info@bcc.kz
Web Site: www.bcc.kz
CCBN—(KAZ)
Int. Income: $482,283,050
Assets: $7,125,201,350
Liabilities: $6,554,578,450
Net Worth: $570,622,900
Earnings: $2,292,500
Emp.: 2,830
Fiscal Year-end: 12/31/12

Business Description:
Banking Services
S.I.C.: 6029
N.A.I.C.S.: 522110

Personnel:
Bakhytbeck Baiseitov *(Chm)*
Vladislav S. Lee *(Chm-Mgmt Bd)*
Bulan A. Adilkhanov *(Mng Dir & Member-Mgmt Bd)*
Maksat K. Alzhanov *(Mng Dir & Member-Mgmt Bd)*
Nam Kyu Lee *(Mng Dir & Member-Mgmt Bd)*
Ki Hong Oh *(Mng Dir & Member-Mgmt Bd)*
Moo Gil Shim *(Mng Dir & Member-Mgmt Bd)*

Board of Directors:
Bakhytbeck Baiseitov
Jumageldy R. Amankulov
Werner Claes
Oh-Ki Kwon
Vladislav S. Lee
Ki Youl Suh

Subsidiary:

BCC Invest JSC (1)
100 Shevchenko St
Almaty, 050020, Kazakhstan (100%)
Tel.: (7) 7272443230
Fax: (7) 7272443231
E-Mail: info@bcc-invest.kz
Web Site: www.bcc-invest.kz
Emp.: 60
Investment Banking & Securities Dealing
S.I.C.: 6211
N.A.I.C.S.: 523110
Burambaye Asan *(Gen Mgr)*

BANK CENTRALI TA' MALTA

Pjazza Kastilja
Valletta, VLT 1060, Malta
Tel.: (356) 25500000
Fax: (356) 25502500
E-Mail: info@centralbankmalta.org
Web Site: www.centralbankmalta.org
Int. Income: $115,895,814
Assets: $4,850,362,242
Liabilities: $4,374,835,767
Net Worth: $475,526,475
Earnings: $89,960,503
Emp.: 321
Fiscal Year-end: 12/31/12

Business Description:
Central Bank
S.I.C.: 6011
N.A.I.C.S.: 521110

Personnel:
Josef Bonnici *(Chm & Governor)*
Rene G. Saliba *(Dir Gen-Fin Policy & Special Projects)*

Board of Directors:
Josef Bonnici
Peter J. Baldacchino
Victor Busuttil
Alfred DeMarco
Philomena Meli

BANK COOP AG

Aesenplatz 3
4002 Basel, Switzerland
Tel.: (41) 612862121
Fax: (41) 612862650
E-Mail: info@bankcoop.ch
Web Site: www.bankcoop.ch
Year Founded: 1927
BC—(SWX)
Sales Range: $200-249.9 Million
Emp.: 700

Business Description:
Banking Services
S.I.C.: 6029
N.A.I.C.S.: 522110

Personnel:
Andreas Waespi *(Chm-Mgmt Bd & CEO)*
Irene Kaufmann *(Vice Chm)*
Andreas C. Albrecht *(Member-Mgmt Bd)*

Board of Directors:
Irene Kaufmann
Erwin Klaey

BANK DHOFAR SAOG

PO Box 1507
112 Ruwi, Oman
Tel.: (968) 24 790 466
E-Mail: care@bankdhofar.com
Web Site: www.bankdhofar.com
Year Founded: 1990
BKDB—(MUS)
Int. Income: $242,471,952
Assets: $5,547,631,768
Liabilities: $4,870,932,637
Net Worth: $676,699,131
Earnings: $97,673,491
Emp.: 1,266
Fiscal Year-end: 12/31/12

Business Description:
Banking Services
S.I.C.: 6029
N.A.I.C.S.: 522110

Personnel:
Abdul Hafidh Salim Rajab Al Aujaili *(Chm)*
Hamoud Mustahail Ahmed Al Mashani *(Vice Chm)*
Abdul Hakeem Omar Al Ojaili *(Acting CEO)*
Shankar Sharma *(CFO & Deputy Gen Mgr)*
Tariq Saleh Taha *(CIO, Chief Transformation Officer & Asst Gen Mgr)*

Board of Directors:
Abdul Hafidh Salim Rajab Al Aujaili
Saleh Nasser Juma Al Araimi
Tarik Abdul Hafidh Salim Al Aujaili
Majid Said Sulaiman Al Bahri
Mohammed Yousuf Alawi Al Ibrahim
Ahmed Mohammed Al Mahrezi
Hamoud Mustahail Ahmed Al Mashani
Qais Mustahail Ahmed Al Mashani
Abdul Sattar Mohammed Abdullah Al Murshidi

BANK FOR INTERNATIONAL SETTLEMENTS

Centralbahnplatz 2
CH-4002 Basel, Switzerland
Tel.: (41) 612808080
Fax: (41) 612809100
E-Mail: email@bis.org
Web Site: www.bis.org
Year Founded: 1930
Int. Income: $2,324,855,280
Assets: $228,764,464,368
Liabilities: $208,272,710,712
Net Worth: $20,491,753,656
Earnings: $969,445,224
Emp.: 576
Fiscal Year-end: 03/31/13

Bank for International Settlements—(Continued)

Business Description:
International Monetary & Financial Cooperation Promoter Between Central Banks & International Organisations
S.I.C.: 6099
N.A.I.C.S.: 522320

Personnel:
Christian Noyer *(Chm)*
Josef Tosovsky *(Chm-Fin Stability Institute)*
Diego Devos *(Gen Counsel)*
Jim Etherington *(Deputy Sec Gen)*

Board of Directors:
Christian Noyer
Ben S. Bernanke
Mark Carney
Agustin Carstens
Luc Coene
Andreas Dombret
Mario Draghi
William C. Dudley
Stefan Ingves
Thomas Jordan
Klaas Knot
Haruhiko Kuroda
Fabio Panetta
Stephen S. Poloz
Guy Quaden
Paul Tucker
Ignazio Visco
Jens Weidmann
Zhou Xiaochuan

Subsidiary:

Financial Stability Institute (1)
Centralbahnplatz 2
CH 4002 Basel, Switzerland (100%)
Tel.: (41) 612808080
Fax: (41) 612809100
E-Mail: fsi@bis.org
Web Site: www.bis.org
Emp.: 600
Promoter of Financial Stability
S.I.C.: 7999
N.A.I.C.S.: 711310
Josef Tosovsky *(Chm)*

BANK FUR TIROL UND VORARLBERG AG

Stadtforum
PO Box 573
6020 Innsbruck, Austria
Tel.: (43) 5053330
Fax: (43) 5053331180
E-Mail: btv@btv.at
Web Site: www.btv.at
Sales Range: $200-249.9 Million
Emp.: 807

Business Description:
Banking Services
S.I.C.: 6029
N.A.I.C.S.: 522110

Personnel:
Heinrich Treichl *(Chm)*

Subsidiaries:

BKS Bank AG (1)
St Veiter Ring 43
9020 Klagenfurt, Austria
Tel.: (43) 46358580
Fax: (43) 463585123
E-Mail: bks@bks.at
Web Site: www.bks.at
BKS—(VIE)
Sales Range: $250-299.9 Million
Emp.: 744
Banking Services
S.I.C.: 6029
N.A.I.C.S.: 522110
Hermann Bell *(Chm-Supervisory Bd)*
Franz Gasselsberger *(Vice Chm-Supervisory Bd)*
Peter Gaugg *(Vice Chm-Supervisory Bd)*
Heimo Johannes Penker *(CEO)*
Dieter Krasnitzer *(Member-Mgmt Bd)*
Herta Stockbauer *(Member-Mgmt Bd)*

Subsidiaries:

BKS Immobilien-Service Gesellschaft mbH (2)
St Veiter Ring 43
9020 Klagenfurt, Austria (100%)
Tel.: (43) 46358580
Fax: (43) 4635858897
E-Mail: office@bks.at
Web Site: www.bks.at
Emp.: 100
Nonresidential Buildings Lessors
S.I.C.: 6512
N.A.I.C.S.: 531120
Josef Hebein *(Mng Dir)*

BKS-Immobilienleasing Gesellschaft mbH (2)
St. Veiter Ring 43
9020 Klagenfurt, Austria (100%)
Tel.: (43) 4635858790
All Other Nondepository Credit Intermediation
S.I.C.: 6159
N.A.I.C.S.: 522298
Josef Hebein *(Mng Dir)*

BKS-Leasing Gesellschaft mbH (2)
St Veiter Ring 43
9020 Klagenfurt, Austria (100%)
Tel.: (43) 4635858795
Fax: (43) 4635858688
E-Mail: klagenfurt.leasing@bks.at
Web Site: www.bks.at
All Other Nondepository Credit Intermediation
S.I.C.: 6159
N.A.I.C.S.: 522298
Heimo Hebein *(Mng Dir)*

BKS Zentrale-Errichtungs- u. Vermietungsgesellschaft mbH (2)
St Veiter Ring 43
9020 Klagenfurt, Austria (50%)
Tel.: (43) 46358580
Fax: (43) 4635858903
E-Mail: bks@bks.at
Web Site: www.bks.at
Emp.: 200
Nonresidential Buildings Lessors
S.I.C.: 6512
N.A.I.C.S.: 531120
Herta Stockbauer *(Mng Dir)*

BTV Anlagenleasing 1 GmbH (1)
Stadtsorun 1
6020 Innsbruck, Austria (100%)
Tel.: (43) 51253330
Fax: (43) 51253332029
E-Mail: info@btv-leasing.com
Web Site: www.btv-leasing.com
Emp.: 20
Other Activities Related to Credit Intermediation
S.I.C.: 6099
N.A.I.C.S.: 522390
Gerd Schwab *(CEO)*

BTV Anlagenleasing 2 GmbH (1)
Stadtsorun 1
6020 Innsbruck, Austria (100%)
Tel.: (43) 505333
Fax: (43) 5053332031
Web Site: www.btv.at
Emp.: 400
Other Activities Related to Credit Intermediation
S.I.C.: 6099
N.A.I.C.S.: 522390

BTV Anlagenleasing 3 GmbH (1)
Stadtsorun 1
6020 Innsbruck, Austria (100%)
Tel.: (43) 5125333
Fax: (43) 51253332031
E-Mail: info@btv-leasing.com
Web Site: www.btv-leasing.com
Other Activities Related to Credit Intermediation
S.I.C.: 6099
N.A.I.C.S.: 522390

BTV Leasing GmbH (1)
Stadtsorun 1
6020 Innsbruck, Austria (100%)
Tel.: (43) 51253330
Fax: (43) 51253330809
E-Mail: info@btv-leasing.com
Web Site: www.btv-leasing.com
Emp.: 28
Commercial Banking
S.I.C.: 6029
N.A.I.C.S.: 522110
Geere Schvab *(Gen Mgr)*

BTV Mobilien Leasing GmbH (1)
Stadtsorun 1
6020 Innsbruck, Austria (100%)
Tel.: (43) 505333
Fax: (43) 5053331408
E-Mail: btv@btv.at
Emp.: 400
Other Activities Related to Credit Intermediation
S.I.C.: 6099
N.A.I.C.S.: 522390

BTV Real-Leasing GmbH (1)
Stadtsorun 1
6020 Innsbruck, Austria (100%)
Tel.: (43) 1534817780
Fax: (43) 153338869
E-Mail: info@btv-leasing.com
Web Site: www.btv-leasing.com
Emp.: 15
Real Estate Agents & Brokers Offices
S.I.C.: 6531
N.A.I.C.S.: 531210

BTV Real-Leasing I GmbH (1)
Stadtsorun 1
6020 Innsbruck, Austria (100%)
Tel.: (43) 51253330
Fax: (43) 51253332031
E-Mail: info@btv-leasing.com
Web Site: www.btv-leasing.com
All Other Miscellaneous Mfr
S.I.C.: 3999
N.A.I.C.S.: 339999

BTV Real-Leasing II GmbH (1)
Stadtsorun 1
6020 Innsbruck, Austria (100%)
Tel.: (43) 5053332028
Fax: (43) 5053332031
E-Mail: info@btv-leasing.com
Web Site: www.btv-leasing.com
Emp.: 15
Office Machinery & Equipment Rental & Leasing
S.I.C.: 7359
N.A.I.C.S.: 532420
Gere Sehae *(Gen Mgr)*

BTV Real-Leasing III Nachfolge GmbH And Co KG (1)
Stadtsorun 1
6020 Innsbruck, Austria (100%)
Tel.: (43) 505333
Fax: (43) 5053331408
E-Mail: btv@btv.at
Web Site: www.btv-leasing.com
All Other Nondepository Credit Intermediation
S.I.C.: 6159
N.A.I.C.S.: 522298

Drei-Banken-Versicherungs AG (1)
Wiener Strasse 32
4020 Linz, Austria (20%)
Tel.: (43) 73265445550
Fax: (43) 73265445570
E-Mail: office@dbvag.at
Web Site: www.dbv.at
Emp.: 50
Direct Life Insurance Carriers
S.I.C.: 6311
N.A.I.C.S.: 524113
Alexander Errammersaor *(Mng Dir)*

Oberbank AG (1)
Lower banks of the Danube 28
A-4010 Linz, Austria
Tel.: (43) 73278020
Fax: (43) 73278022140
E-Mail: office@oberbank.at
Web Site: www.oberbank.at
OBS—(VIE)
Rev.: $759,460,652
Assets: $23,793,653,020
Liabilities: $21,986,495,181
Net Worth: $1,807,157,839
Earnings: $146,208,870
Emp.: 2,020
Fiscal Year-end: 12/31/12
Banking Services
S.I.C.: 6029
N.A.I.C.S.: 522110
Hermann Bell *(Chm-Supervisory Bd)*
Franz Gasselsberger *(Chm-Mgmt Bd & CEO)*
Peter Gaugg *(Vice Chm-Supervisory Bd)*
Heimo Johannes Penker *(Vice Chm-Supervisory Bd)*
Florian Hagenauer *(Member-Mgmt Bd)*
Josef Weissl *(Member-Mgmt Bd)*

Non-U.S. Subsidiaries:

Oberbank Geschaftsbereich Tschechien spol S.r.o. (2)
I P Pavlova 5
120 00 Prague, Czech Republic
Tel.: (420) 224190100
Fax: (420) 224190150
E-Mail: praha@oberbank.cz
Web Site: www.oberbank.cz
Emp.: 250
Commercial Banking
S.I.C.: 6029
N.A.I.C.S.: 522110

Oberbank Leasing spol S.r.o. (2)
Namesti I P Pavlova 1789-5
12000 Prague, Czech Republic
Tel.: (420) 224190160
Fax: (420) 224190170
E-Mail: office@oberbankleasing.cz
Web Site: www.oberbankleasing.cz
Emp.: 30
Commercial Banking
S.I.C.: 6029
N.A.I.C.S.: 522110
Ludek Knypl *(Mng Dir)*

Oberbank Leasing S.r.o. (2)
Galvaniho 7-B
82104 Bratislava, Slovakia
Tel.: (421) 248214320
Fax: (421) 248214339
Web Site: www.oberbank.sl
Emp.: 22
Commercial Banking
S.I.C.: 6029
N.A.I.C.S.: 522110

Non-U.S. Subsidiary:

BTV Leasing Deutschland GmbH (1)
Buxacher Rd 1
87700 Memmingen, Germany (100%)
Tel.: (49) 821599807172
Fax: (49) 833192777044
Web Site: www.btv-leasing.com
Emp.: 50
Investment Banking & Securities Dealing
S.I.C.: 6211
N.A.I.C.S.: 523110
Gehart Schwab *(Mng Dir)*

BANK HAPOALIM B.M.

(d/b/a Bank Hapoalim Group)
104 Hayarkon Street
Tel Aviv, 63432, Israel
Mailing Address:
PO Box 27
Tel Aviv, 61000, Israel
Tel.: (972) 35200777
Telex: 342342 PHEAD IL
Fax: (972) 35200771
E-Mail: international@bnhp.co.il
Web Site: www.bankhapoalim.com
Year Founded: 1921
POLI—(TAE)
Rev.: $5,326,043,640
Assets: $101,127,927,840
Liabilities: $93,858,253,080
Net Worth: $7,269,674,760
Earnings: $690,776,280
Emp.: 13,629
Fiscal Year-end: 12/31/12

Business Description:
Retail, Commercial & Investment Banking
S.I.C.: 6029
N.A.I.C.S.: 522110

Personnel:
Yair Seroussi *(Chm)*
Zion Kenan *(Pres & CEO)*
Ran Oz *(CFO)*
Tzahi Cohen *(Chief Risk Officer)*
Yoram Weissbrem *(Sec)*

Board of Directors:
Yair Seroussi
Mali Baron
Ammon Dick
Irit Izakson
Moshe Koren
Yacov Peer
Efrat Peled
Nehama Ronen
Dafna Schwartz
Ido Stern
Yair Tauman
Imri Tov
Meir Wietchner
Yosef Yarom
Nir Zichlinsky

Somekh Chaikin
Tel Aviv, Israel

Subsidiaries:

Aminit Ltd. (1)
40 Hamasger
Tel Aviv, 67211, Israel
Tel.: (972) 36895327
Fax: (972) 6364204
Emp.: 100
Credit Card Services
S.I.C.: 6141
N.A.I.C.S.: 522210
Dov Kotler *(Mng Dir)*

Bank Yahav for Government Employees Ltd. (1)
PO Box 36333
80 Yirmiyahu Street
Jerusalem, 91363, Israel (50.1%)
Tel.: (972) 25009666
Fax: (972) 2538 5869
Emp.: 500
Banking Services
S.I.C.: 6029
N.A.I.C.S.: 522110
David Ben David *(Chm)*
Shaul Gelbard *(Gen Mgr)*

Isracard Ltd. (1)
40 Hamasger St
PO Box 62030
Tel Aviv, 61620, Israel
Tel.: (972) 3636 4636
Web Site: www.isracard.co.il
Credit Card Services
S.I.C.: 6141
N.A.I.C.S.: 522210
Haim Krupsky *(Gen Mgr)*

Units:

Europay (Eurocard) Israel Ltd. (2)
40 Hamasger St
PO Box 62030
Tel Aviv, 61620, Israel
Tel.: (972) 36364636
Fax: (972) 36895538
Credit Card Services
S.I.C.: 6141
N.A.I.C.S.: 522210
Ami Alpan *(Dir)*

Poalim American Express Ltd. (2)
40 Hamasger Street
PO Box 62030
61620 Tel Aviv, 61620, Israel
Tel.: (972) 36364455
Fax: (972) 36895538
Web Site: www.isracard.co.il
Emp.: 20
Credit Card Services
S.I.C.: 6141
N.A.I.C.S.: 522210
Dove Kolter *(CEO)*

Peilim-Portfolio Management Company Ltd. (1)
11 Begin St FL 28
Ramat Gan, 52681, Israel
Tel.: (972) 36360755
Fax: (972) 35377006
Emp.: 70
Investment Management Services
S.I.C.: 6282
N.A.I.C.S.: 523920
Rebecca Algrisi *(CEO)*

Poalim Capital Markets (1)
46 Rothschild Boulevard Alrov Tower
66883 Tel Aviv, Israel
Tel.: (972) 35675333
Fax: (972) 35675760
E-Mail: ohaimx@poalimcm.com
Web Site: www.poalimcm.com
Emp.: 25
Investment Banking
S.I.C.: 6211
N.A.I.C.S.: 523999
Yair Seroussi *(Chm)*
Amir Aviv *(Pres & CEO)*
Hannah Feuer *(CFO)*

Units:

Lahak-Mutual Funds Management Ltd. (2)
52 Menachem Begin Street
13th Floor Sonol Tower, Tel Aviv, 67137, Israel
Tel.: (972) 37813400
Fax: (972) 37913405
E-Mail: lahak@bnhp.co.il
Web Site: www.lahak.co.il
Investment Management Services
S.I.C.: 6211
N.A.I.C.S.: 523999
Amnon Perelman *(Chm)*

Poalim I.B.I. Managing & Underwriting Ltd. (2)
9 Ahad Ha'am Street Shalom Tower 26th Floor
65251 Tel Aviv, Israel
Tel.: (972) 35193444
Fax: (972) 35175411
E-Mail: ibi@ibi.co.il
Web Site: www.ibi.co.il
Emp.: 13
Financial Services
S.I.C.: 7389
N.A.I.C.S.: 561499
Emanuel Kook *(Chm)*

Poalim Trust Services Ltd. (2)
23 Menahem Begin Rd Levinstein Tower 13th Fl
PO Box 27
Tel Aviv, 61000, Israel
Tel.: (972) 35673723
Fax: (972) 35674220
E-Mail: bhtrust@poalimtrust.co.il
Web Site: www.bankhapoalim.com
Emp.: 10
Investment Management Services
S.I.C.: 6211
N.A.I.C.S.: 523999
Ran Oz *(CFO)*

Poalim Sahar Ltd. (1)
23 Menachem Begin Rd Levinseion Tower Fl 22
Tel Aviv, 66184, Israel
Tel.: (972) 37104555
Fax: (972) 037104576
E-Mail: info@sahar.co.il
Web Site: www.sahar.co.il
Emp.: 60
Investment Services
S.I.C.: 6211
N.A.I.C.S.: 523999
Nachum Kaplan *(CEO)*
Ehud Chitiat *(CFO)*
Yehuda Schwartzappel *(COO)*
Shalom Benisty *(CIO)*
Lucy Rabin *(Treas)*

U.S. Subsidiary:

Hapoalim U.S.A. Holding Company, Inc. (1)
1177 Ave Of The Americas 14th Fl
New York, NY 10036-2714 NY
Tel.: (212) 782-2000 (100%)
Telex: 66619 BHRM NYK
Fax: (212) 782-2054
E-Mail: info@bankhapoalim.com
Web Site: www.hapoalimusa.com
Emp.: 200
Bank Holding Company; Private & Corporate Banking
S.I.C.: 6712
N.A.I.C.S.: 551111
Yair Talmor *(Gen Mgr-New York Branches)*

Subsidiaries:

Hapoalim Securities USA, Inc. (2)
1 Battery Park Plz 2nd Fl
New York, NY 10004-1405 DE
Tel.: (212) 898-6200
Fax: (212) 898-6255
Web Site: www.hapoalimsec.com
Security Brokers and Dealers
S.I.C.: 6211
N.A.I.C.S.: 523120
Dennis Loudon *(CEO)*
Michael Felix *(Mng Dir & Head-Fin Institutions Grp)*
Raymond D. Potter *(Mng Dir & Head-Emerging Markets Desk)*
John W. Young *(Mng Dir & Head-Agency Trading)*
Steven J. Paraggio *(CFO)*
Joshua M. Brenner *(Sr VP-Structured Product, Brokered CD Underwriting & Distr)*
Rick Cabanes *(Sr VP-Structured Product, Brokered CD Underwriting & Distr)*
Oren Monhite Yahav *(Sr VP-Private Equity & Alternative Investments)*
John J. Murabito *(Sr VP-Structured Product, Brokered CD Underwriting & Distr)*

Non-U.S. Subsidiaries:

Bank Hapoalim (Cayman) Ltd. (1)
PO Box 1043
Georgetown, Grand Cayman, Cayman Islands
Telex: 6812043 6812044 HAPOALIM; MIAB
Provider of International Banking Services
S.I.C.: 6159
N.A.I.C.S.: 522293

Bank Hapoalim (Luxembourg) S.A. (1)
18 Blvd Royal
PO Box 703
L 2017 Luxembourg, Luxembourg LU
Tel.: (352) 4752561 (100%)
Fax: (352) 475256400
Web Site: www.bankhapoalim.com
Int. Income: $8,500,000
Emp.: 35
International Banking
S.I.C.: 6159
N.A.I.C.S.: 522293
Allouche Nosche *(Mng Dir)*

Bank Hapoalim (Switzerland) Ltd. (1)
Stockerstrasse 33
PO Box 870
8027 Zurich, Switzerland (100%)
Tel.: (41) 442838181
Telex: 813762 POAL CH
Fax: (41) 442027740
E-Mail: info@hapoalim.ch
Web Site: www.bhibank.com
Emp.: 80
International Banking
S.I.C.: 6159
N.A.I.C.S.: 522293
Micheal Warsvaski *(CEO)*

Non-U.S. Subsidiary:

BHI Investment Advisors (Asia) Limited (2)
701 Ruttonjee House 11 Duddell Street
Central, Hong Kong, China (Hong Kong)
Tel.: (852) 3423 0828
Fax: (852) 2840 0678
Emp.: 6
Investment Advisory Services
S.I.C.: 6282
N.A.I.C.S.: 523930
Eli Bitan *(CEO)*

BankPozitif Kredi ve Kalkinma Bankasi A.S. (1)
Beybi Giz Plaza Kat 7 Meydan Sok 28
Maslak, Istanbul, 34398, Turkey
Tel.: (90) 2124444365
Fax: (90) 2122903212, ext. 2165384247
Web Site: www.bankpozitif.com.tr
Banking Services
S.I.C.: 6029
N.A.I.C.S.: 522110
Ismail Hasan Ackakayalioglu *(CEO)*

Non-U.S. Subsidiary:

JSC Bank Pozitiv (2)
Tole bi Street 83
Almaty, 050012, Kazakhstan
Tel.: (7) 727 244 92 44
Fax: (7) 727 244 92 35
Web Site: www.bankpozitiv.kz
Commercial Banking Services
S.I.C.: 6029
N.A.I.C.S.: 522110
Ismail Hasan Akcakayalioglu *(Chm)*
Madina Auykhanova *(CFO & Assoc Gen Mgr)*
Kadir Cevik *(Gen Mgr)*
Sener Durak *(Assoc Gen Mgr-Corp Mktg)*
Jainar Joumakanov *(Assoc Gen Mgr-Treasury & Fin Instituation)*
Burulkan Moldobekova *(Assoc Gen Mgr-Ops & Admin)*

BankPozitiv Kazakhstan (1)
83 Tole bi Street
Almaty, Kazakhstan
Tel.: (7) 7272449243
Fax: (7) 7272449235
E-Mail: demirbank@demirbank.kz
Web Site: www.bankpozitiv.kz
Int. Income: $6,343,570
Assets: $109,104,103
Liabilities: $35,423,101
Net Worth: $73,681,002
Earnings: $1,244,349
Emp.: 82
Fiscal Year-end: 12/31/12
Banking Services
S.I.C.: 6029
N.A.I.C.S.: 522110
Ismail Hasan Akcakayalioglu *(Chm)*
Yusuf Ziya Aslan *(Chm-Mgmt Bd & Gen Mgr)*
Sener Durak *(Member-Mgmt Bd & Assoc Gen Mgr-Mktg)*
Jainar Joumakanov *(Member-Mgmt Bd & Assoc Gen Mgr-Treasury & Fin Institutions)*
Burulkan Moldobekova *(Member-Mgmt Bd & Assoc Gen Mgr-Regulatory Issues & Rels)*
Mehmet Sengun *(Member-Mgmt Bd & Assoc Gen Mgr-Retail Banking)*

Hapoalim Fiduciioy Services (1)
1 Fl Intl House 41 Tarate
PO Box 484
Saint Helier, JE4 5SS, Jersey (100%)
Tel.: (44) 1534500982
Fax: (44) 1534500901
E-Mail: info@bhimail.je
Web Site: www.bhibank.com
Emp.: 30
Trust Services
S.I.C.: 6091
N.A.I.C.S.: 523991

Hapoalim (Latin America) S.A. (1)
World Trade Ctr Av Luis Alberto De Herrera 1248 Torre B Piso 6
11300 Montevideo, Uruguay (100%)
Tel.: (598) 26230303
Telex: 31290
Fax: (598) 26235867
E-Mail: hapoalim@hapoalim.com.uy
Web Site: www.bankhapoalim.com
Emp.: 25
International Banking
S.I.C.: 6159
N.A.I.C.S.: 522293
Victor Waynbuch *(Gen Mgr)*

BANK INDONESIA

Jl MH Thamrin 2
Jakarta, 10350, Indonesia
Tel.: (62) 213817317
Fax: (62) 3864884
E-Mail: humasbi@bi.go.id
Web Site: www.bi.go.id
Emp.: 6,000

Business Description:
Banking Services
S.I.C.: 6011
N.A.I.C.S.: 521110

Personnel:
Hartadi A. Sarwono *(Deputy Governor)*

BANK KERJASAMA RAKYAT MALAYSIA BERHAD

(d/b/a Bank Rakyat)
Bangunan Bank Rakyat Jalan Tangsi
50732 Kuala Lumpur, Malaysia
Tel.: (60) 3 26129600

Bank Kerjasama Rakyat Malaysia Berhad—(Continued)

Fax: (60) 3 26129636
Web Site: www.bankrakyat.com.my
Year Founded: 1954
Rev.: $1,920,952,081
Assets: $26,030,535,540
Liabilities: $22,560,977,324
Net Worth: $3,469,558,216
Earnings: $406,670,972
Fiscal Year-end: 12/31/12
Business Description:
Banking Services
S.I.C.: 6029
N.A.I.C.S.: 522110
Personnel:
Sabbaruddin Chik *(Chm)*
Mustafha Abd Razak *(Mng Dir)*
Muzamir Omar *(Sec & Head-Strategic Plng)*
Board of Directors:
Sabbaruddin Chik
Abdul Mutalib Alias
Zuraidah Atan
Saripuddin Kasim
Mat Noor Nawi
Mustafha Abd Razak
Mangsor Saad

BANK LEUMI LE-ISRAEL B.M.

34 Yehuda Halevi Street
Tel Aviv, 65546, Israel
Tel.: (972) 35148111
Telex: 33586
Fax: (972) 35148656
E-Mail: pniot@bll.co.il
Web Site: www.bankleumi.com
Year Founded: 1902
LUMI—(TAE)
Rev.: $4,911,739,080
Assets: $101,066,668,800
Liabilities: $94,288,409,760
Net Worth: $6,778,259,040
Earnings: $278,083,800
Emp.: 6,853
Fiscal Year-end: 12/31/12
Business Description:
International Banking Services
S.I.C.: 6029
N.A.I.C.S.: 522110
Personnel:
David Brodet *(Chm)*
Rakefet Russak-Aminoach *(Pres & CEO)*
Daniel Tsiddon *(Deputy CEO & Head-Capital Markets Div)*
Shlomo Goldfarb *(Chief Acctg Officer, Exec VP & Head-Acctg Div)*
Yael Rudnicki *(Sec)*
Gideon Altman *(First Exec VP & Head-Comml Banking Div)*
Itai Ben-Zeev *(Exec VP-Head-Capital Markets Div)*
Hedva Ber *(Exec VP & Head-Risk Mgmt Div)*
Ron Fainaro *(Exec VP & Head-Economics & Fin Div)*
Yaacov Haber *(First Exec VP & Head-Corp Div)*
Meira Karni *(Exec VP & Head-Compliance & Enforcement Dept)*
Yoel Mintz *(Exec VP & Head-Structured Fin & Real Estate)*
Sasson Mordechay *(Exec VP & Head-Internal Audit Div)*
Naomi Sandhaus *(Exec VP & Head-Legal Div)*
Tamar Yassur *(Exec VP & Head-Banking Div)*
Dan Yerushalmi *(Exec VP & Head-Ops & Info Sys Div)*
Board of Directors:
David Brodet
David Avner
Doron Cohen
Moshe Dovrat
Yehuda Drori
Arieh Gans
Rami Avraham Guzman
Miriyam Katz
Yoav Nardi
Efraim Sadka
Haim Samet
Zipora Samet-Shalmon
Amos Sapir
Gabriela Shalev
Yedidia Stern

Kost Forer Gabbay & Kasierer
3 Aminadav Street
Tel Aviv, 67067, Israel
Tel.: (972) 3 623 2525
Fax: (972) 3 562 2555

Subsidiaries:

Bank Leumi Le-Israel Trust Co. Ltd. **(1)**
8 Rothschild Blvd
Tel Aviv, 66881, Israel (100%)
Tel.: (972) 35170777
Fax: (972) 35170770
Web Site: www.trust.co.il
Emp.: 20
Financial Services
S.I.C.: 6282
N.A.I.C.S.: 523930

Leumi & Co. Investment House Ltd. **(1)**
25 Kalisher St
Tel Aviv, 65156, Israel (100%)
Tel.: (972) 35141222
Fax: (972) 35141215
E-Mail: invest@leumico.co.il
Web Site: www.leumico.co.il/e/econtact.html
Emp.: 40
S.I.C.: 6159
N.A.I.C.S.: 522298

Leumi Finance Co., Ltd. **(1)**
35 Yehuda Halevi St
Tel Aviv, 65136, Israel (100%)
Tel.: (972) 35149908
Fax: (972) 35149920
E-Mail: leasing@bankleumi.co.il
Web Site: www.leumi.com
Emp.: 10
S.I.C.: 6159
N.A.I.C.S.: 522298
Davidovitch Bezalel *(Gen Mgr)*

Leumi Industrial Development Ltd. **(1)**
13 Ahad Haam St
Tel Aviv, 65136, Israel (100%)
Tel.: (972) 35149951
Fax: (972) 35149897
Web Site: www.leumi.co.il
Emp.: 5
S.I.C.: 6159
N.A.I.C.S.: 522298
Bezalel Davidovich *(Gen Mgr)*

Leumi Leasing and Investments Ltd. **(1)**
13 Ahad Haam
Tel Aviv, 65151, Israel
Tel.: (972) 35149908
Fax: (972) 35148560
Investment Management Services
S.I.C.: 6211
N.A.I.C.S.: 523999

Leumi Leasing Ltd. **(1)**
13 Ehad Haam St
Tel Aviv, 65546, Israel (100%)
Tel.: (972) 35148111
Fax: (972) 35148560
E-Mail: info@leumi.co.il
Web Site: www.leumi.co.il
Emp.: 35
S.I.C.: 6159
N.A.I.C.S.: 522298
Shaul Sharoni *(Sec)*

Leumi Mortgage Bank Ltd. **(1)**
43 Alenby St
Tel Aviv, Israel (100%)
Tel.: (972) 3 514 7676
Fax: (972) 3 579 3605
Emp.: 20
S.I.C.: 6159
N.A.I.C.S.: 522298

Leumi-PIA Trust Management Co., Ltd. **(1)**
Dizengoff 55 Fl 17
Tel Aviv, 64332, Israel (100%)
Tel.: (972) 36217333
Fax: (972) 36217355
Web Site: www.leumi.co.il
S.I.C.: 6159
N.A.I.C.S.: 522298

U.S. Subsidiaries:

Bank Leumi USA **(1)**
19495 Biscayne Blvd Ste 500
Miami, FL 33180-2320
Tel.: (305) 702-3500
Fax: (305) 377-6540
Web Site: www.leumicard.com
Emp.: 20
Banking Services
S.I.C.: 6029
N.A.I.C.S.: 522110
Akiva Segal *(VP)*

Bank Leumi USA **(1)**
579 5th Ave
New York, NY 10017-1917 IL
Tel.: (917) 542-2343 (99.8%)
Fax: (917) 542-2254
Toll Free: (800) 892-5430
Web Site: www.bankleumiusa.com
Sales Range: $150-199.9 Million
Emp.: 447
International Banking
S.I.C.: 6029
N.A.I.C.S.: 522110
David Brodet *(Chm)*
Avner Mendelson *(Pres & CEO)*
John P. McGann *(Chief Compliance Officer-Branch Banking, Exec VP & Dir-HR)*
Raymond P. Cooney *(Chief Risk Officer & Sr VP)*
Chaim Fromowitz *(Exec VP & Dir-Banking-Intl Svcs)*
Joseph A. Sciarillo *(Sr VP)*

Non-U.S. Subsidiaries:

Bank Leumi Le-Israel (Switzerland) **(1)**
Diana Strasse 5
CH 8022 Zurich, Switzerland (69.2%)
Tel.: (41) 582079111
Fax: (41) 582079100
E-Mail: info@leumi.ch
Web Site: www.leumi.ch
Emp.: 120
International Banking
S.I.C.: 6159
N.A.I.C.S.: 522293
Amnon Zaidenberg *(Co-Chm)*

Bank Leumi (Luxembourg) S.A. **(1)**
6 D route de Treves
L 2633 Senningerberg, Luxembourg (100%)
Tel.: (352) 346390
Fax: (352) 346396
E-Mail: bleulux@pt.lu
Web Site: www.pt.lu
Emp.: 30
International Banking
S.I.C.: 6159
N.A.I.C.S.: 522293
Uri Rom *(Chm)*

Bank Leumi (UK) plc **(1)**
20 Stratford Place
London, W1C 1BG, United Kingdom (78.4%)
Tel.: (44) 2079078000
Telex: 888738
Fax: (44) 2079078001
Web Site: www.leumi.co.uk
Emp.: 130
International Banking
S.I.C.: 6159
N.A.I.C.S.: 522293
Larry Weiss *(CEO)*

Non-U.S. Subsidiary:

Bank Leumi (Jersey) Ltd. **(2)**
2 Hill St
PO Box 510
Saint Helier, JE4 5TR, Jersey (100%)
Tel.: (44) 1534702525
Fax: (44) 1534167446
E-Mail: info@leumijersey.com
Web Site: www.leumijersey.com
Emp.: 20
Banking Services
S.I.C.: 6029
N.A.I.C.S.: 522110
David Cooper *(Mng Dir)*

Leumi (Latin America) **(1)**
Luis A de Herrera 1248
Torre A Piso 10, 11000 Montevideo, Uruguay (100%)
Mailing Address:
PO Box 89
11000 Montevideo, Uruguay
Tel.: (598) 26285838
Fax: (598) 26229033
E-Mail: leumont@montevideo.com.uy
Web Site: www.leumi.com.uy
Emp.: 18
International Banking
S.I.C.: 6159
N.A.I.C.S.: 522293

Leumi Overseas Trust Corporation Ltd **(1)**
2 Hill St
PO Box 510
Saint Helier, JE4 5TR, Jersey (100%)
Tel.: (44) 1534702525
Fax: (44) 1534702570
E-Mail: info@leumijersey.com
Web Site: www.leumijersey.com
Emp.: 40
Trust & Fiduciary Services
S.I.C.: 6091
N.A.I.C.S.: 523991
Robert Guillaume *(Mng Dir)*

BANK MELLAT

327 Taleghani Ave
15817 Tehran, Iran
Tel.: (98) 21 82961
Fax: (98) 21 82962702
E-Mail: info@bankmellat.ir
Web Site: en.bankmellat.ir
Sales Range: $1-4.9 Billion
Emp.: 24,737
Business Description:
Banking Services
S.I.C.: 6029
N.A.I.C.S.: 522110
Personnel:
Ali Divandari *(Chm & Mng Dir)*
Board of Directors:
Ali Divandari
Mohsen Fadavi
Abdolkarim Ghavamifar
Younes Hormozi
Mohammad Reza Saroukhani

Non-U.S. Subsidiary:

Persia International Bank PLC London **(1)**
6 Lothbury
London, EC2R 7HH, United Kingdom
Tel.: (44) 2076068521
Fax: (44) 2076062020
E-Mail: info@persiabank.co.uk
Web Site: www.persiabank.co.uk
Emp.: 20
Banking Services
S.I.C.: 6029
N.A.I.C.S.: 522110
M. R. Meskarian *(CEO)*
A. Akhondi *(CFO)*

BANK MUSCAT SAOG

PO Box 134
Ruwi, 112, Oman
Tel.: (968) 24795555
Fax: (968) 24767242
E-Mail: customerservice@bankmuscat.com
Web Site: www.bankmuscat.com
Year Founded: 1993
BKMB—(MUS)
Int. Income: $829,281,453
Assets: $20,478,359,545
Liabilities: $17,702,716,731
Net Worth: $2,775,642,814
Earnings: $360,226,150
Emp.: 3,210

Fiscal Year-end: 12/31/12
Business Description:
Banking Services
S.I.C.: 6029
N.A.I.C.S.: 522110
Personnel:
Khalid Mustahail Al Mashani *(Chm)*
Sulaiman Mohamed Hamed Al Yahyai *(Vice Chm)*
AbdulRazak Ali Issa *(CEO)*
T. Ganesh *(CFO)*
Ahmed M. Al Abri *(COO)*
Leen Kumar *(Chief Risk Officer)*
Ahmed Faqir Al Bulushi *(CEO-Riyadh & Asst Gen Mgr)*
Abdul Wahid Mohammed Al Murshidi *(CEO-Muscat Capital LLC & Asst Gen Mgr)*
Osamah Abdullatif *(CEO-Kuwait Branch)*
Board of Directors:
Khalid Mustahail Al Mashani
Said Mohamed Ahmed Al Harthy
Nasser Mohammed Salim Al Harthy
Abdullatif Abdulla Ahmed AlMulla
Sulaiman Mohamed Hamed Al Yahyai
Hamoud Ibrahim Soomar Al Zadjali
Farida Khambata
Saud Mustahail Al Mashani
K. K. Abdul Razak
Non-U.S. Subsidiary:

Muscat Security House LLC (1)
Opposite Al Faisaliya Foundation King Fahad Road
PO Box No 54488
Riyadh, 11514, Saudi Arabia
Tel.: (966) 12799888
Fax: (966) 1279 9898
Securities Trading & Custodial Services
S.I.C.: 6211
N.A.I.C.S.: 523110

BANK NEGARA MALAYSIA
Jalan Dato Onn
PO Box 10922
50929 Kuala Lumpur, Malaysia
Tel.: (60) 326988044
Fax: (60) 326942990
E-Mail: info@bnm.gov.my
Web Site: www.bnm.gov.my
Year Founded: 1959
Rev.: $2,266,705,014
Assets: $156,198,467,678
Liabilities: $146,874,130,388
Net Worth: $9,324,337,291
Earnings: $1,836,459,223
Emp.: 2,838
Fiscal Year-end: 12/31/12
Business Description:
Central Bank
S.I.C.: 6011
N.A.I.C.S.: 521110
Personnel:
Zeti Akhtar Aziz *(Chm & Governor)*
Board of Directors:
Zeti Akhtar Aziz
Mohd Irwan Serigar Abdullah
Kwai Yoong Chin
Muhammad Ibrahim
Sulaiman Mahbob
Mohd Hassan Marican
Nor Shamsiah Mohd Yunus
Amar Bujang Mohd. Nor
Siew Nam Oh
N. Sadasivan
Sukhdave Singh

BANK OCHRONY SRODOWISKA S.A.
(d/b/a BOS Bank)
Al Jana Pawla II 12
00-950 Warsaw, Poland
Tel.: (48) 225433434
Fax: (48) 228508891
E-Mail: bos@bosbank.pl
Web Site: www.bosbank.pl
BOS—(WAR)
Rev.: $285,474,083
Assets: $5,352,120,556
Liabilities: $4,891,951,924
Net Worth: $460,168,632
Earnings: $11,890,472
Emp.: 1,763
Fiscal Year-end: 12/31/12
Business Description:
Banking Services
S.I.C.: 6036
N.A.I.C.S.: 522120
Personnel:
Marcin Likierski *(Chm-Supervisory Bd)*
Mariusz Klimczak *(Chm-Mgmt Bd)*
Stanislaw Kolasinski *(Vice Chm-Mgmt Bd)*
Jacek Maciej Bajorek *(Deputy Chm-Supervisory Bd)*
Przemyslaw Lech Figarski *(Vice Chm-Mgmt Bd)*
Adam Zbigniew Grzebieluch *(Vice Chm-Mgmt Bd)*
Krzysztof Wojciech Telega *(Vice Chm-Mgmt Bd)*
Supervisory Board of Directors:
Marcin Likierski
Jacek Maciej Bajorek
Jozef Koziol
Andrzej Kazimierz Kraszewski
Michal Juliusz Machlejd
Ryszard Ochwat
Krzysztof Wladyslaw Rogala
Adam Grzegorz Wasiak
Adam Aleksander Wojtas

BANK OF ALBANIA
Sheshi Skenderbej 1
Tirana, Albania
Tel.: (355) 4222152
E-Mail: public@bankofalbania.org
Web Site: www.bankofalbania.org
Sales Range: $50-74.9 Million
Emp.: 427
Business Description:
Banking Services
S.I.C.: 6011
N.A.I.C.S.: 521110
Personnel:
Ardian Fullani *(Chm-Supervisory Bd & CEO)*
Fatos Ibrahimi *(Vice Chm-Supervisory Bd & First Deputy Governor)*
Genc Mamani *(Chief Officer)*
Teuta Baleta *(Inspector Gen)*
Supervisory Board of Directors:
Ardian Fullani
Adrian Civici
Tefta Cuci
Elisabeta Gjoni
Fatos Ibrahimi
Arjan Kadareja
Ksenofon Krisafi
Limos Malaj
Halit Xhafa

BANK OF ASIA NEPAL LIMITED
(Merged with Nepal Industrial & Commercial Bank Ltd. to Form NIC Asia Bank Limited)

BANK OF AYUDHYA PUBLIC COMPANY LIMITED
(Acquired by Mitsubishi UFJ Financial Group, Inc.)

BANK OF BARODA
Suraj Plaza-1 Sayaji Ganji
Baroda, 390005, India
Tel.: (91) 2652361852
Fax: (91) 2652362395
Web Site: www.bankofbaroda.com
Year Founded: 1908
532134—(BOM)
Rev.: $7,592,626,965
Assets: $103,710,596,734
Liabilities: $97,519,752,583
Net Worth: $6,190,844,151
Earnings: $895,300,327
Emp.: 43,108
Fiscal Year-end: 03/31/13
Business Description:
Banking Services
S.I.C.: 6029
N.A.I.C.S.: 522110
Personnel:
S. S. Mundra *(Chm & Mng Dir)*
M. L. Jain *(Compliance Officer & Sec)*
Raju Gupta *(Chief Vigilance Officer)*
Board of Directors:
S. S. Mundra
Surendra Singh Bhandari
Ranjan Dhawan
Bhuwanchandra B. Joshi
Rajib Sekhar Sahoo
Vinil Kumar Saxena
Sudarshan Sen
P. Srinivas
Maulin Arvind Vaishnav

Ray & Ray
Mumbai, India

N. B. S. & Co
Mumbai, India

Laxminiwas Neeth & Co
Mumbai, India

KASG & Co
Mumbai, India

Brahmayya & Co
Mumbai, India

Transfer Agent:
Karvy Computershare Private Limited
Plot No 17-24 Vittal Rao Nagar Madhapur
Hyderabad, 500 081, India
Tel.: (91) 40 2342 0818

Subsidiaries:

BOB Capital Markets Ltd. (1)
Meher Chambers Dr SB Marg Off R Kamani Marg
Ground & 1st Floor
Ballard Estate, Mumbai, 400 038, India (100%)
Tel.: (91) 2266372302
Fax: (91) 2266372312
E-Mail: bobcaps@vsnl.com
Web Site: www.bobcapitalmarkets.com
Emp.: 25
Investment Banking
S.I.C.: 6211
N.A.I.C.S.: 523110
T. R. Prasanth Kumar *(Mng Dir)*

Bobcards Ltd. (1)
Esperanca Ground Floor
Colaba, Mumbai, 400001, India (100%)
Tel.: (91) 22 2202 0969
Fax: (91) 22 2281 3088
E-Mail: colaba@bobcards.com
Web Site: www.bobcards.com
Credit Card Issuing
S.I.C.: 6153
N.A.I.C.S.: 522210
D. K. Garg *(Mng Dir)*
Dilip Bhuta *(Mng Dir)*
M. K. Duggal *(Exec VP)*
S. K. Gupta *(Exec VP)*
Deepak Jain *(Sr VP-Recovery, Legal & Vigilance)*

Affiliate:

The Nainital Bank Ltd. (1)
Naini Bank House 7 Oaks
Kolkata, 263001, India
Tel.: (91) 5942235823
Fax: (91) 236120
E-Mail: nainitalbank@yahoo.co.in
Web Site: www.nainitalbank.co.in
Emp.: 800
Commercial Banking
S.I.C.: 6029
N.A.I.C.S.: 522110
H. S. Sharma *(Deputy Gen Mgr)*

Non-U.S. Subsidiaries:

Bank of Baroda (Botswana) Ltd. (1)
Plot No 1108
PO Box 21559
Queens Road The Main Mall, Gaborone, Botswana
Tel.: (267) 3933775
Fax: (267) 3188879
E-Mail: botswana@barodabank.co.bw
Web Site: www.bankofbaroda.com
Emp.: 35
Banking Services
S.I.C.: 6029
N.A.I.C.S.: 522110
B. Nandha Gopal *(Mng Dir-Botswana)*

Bank of Baroda (Ghana) Ltd. (1)
Kwame Nkrumah Avenue Next to Melcom
Post Mail Bag No 298 AN
Adabraka, Accra, Ghana
Tel.: (233) 21250072
Fax: (233) 21250067
E-Mail: md.ghana@bankofbaroda.com
Web Site: www.bankofbaroda.com
Emp.: 20
Banking Services
S.I.C.: 6029
N.A.I.C.S.: 522110
Arvind Kumar *(Mng Dir)*

Bank of Baroda (Guyana) Inc. (1)
10 Avenue of the Republic
PO Box 10768
Regent Street, Georgetown, Guyana
Tel.: (592) 2266423
Fax: (592) 2251691
E-Mail: bobinc@networksgy.com
Web Site: www.bankofbaroda.com
Emp.: 17
Banking Services
S.I.C.: 6029
N.A.I.C.S.: 522110
Pradeep Kumar Kala *(Mng Dir)*

Bank of Baroda (Kenya) Ltd. (1)
Baroda House
PO Box 30033
29 Koinage St, 00100 Nairobi, Kenya
Tel.: (254) 202248402
Fax: (254) 20316070
E-Mail: ho.kenya@bankofbaroda.com
Web Site: www.bankofbaroda.com
Emp.: 70
Banking Services
S.I.C.: 6029
N.A.I.C.S.: 522110
Vindhya Vittal Ramesh *(Gen Mgr)*

Bank of Baroda (New Zealand) Ltd. (1)
114 Dominion Road
PO Box 56580
Auckland, 1446, New Zealand
Tel.: (64) 96321020
Fax: (64) 96385082
E-Mail: aucknz@bankofbaroda.com
Web Site: www.barodanzltd.co.nz
Emp.: 11
Commercial Banking Services
S.I.C.: 6029
N.A.I.C.S.: 522110
Navin Chandra Upreti *(Co-Mng Dir)*

Bank of Baroda (Tanzania) Ltd. (1)
Plot No 149/32
PO Box 5356
Ohio/Sokoine Drive, Dar es Salaam, Tanzania
Tel.: (255) 222124456
Fax: (255) 222124457
E-Mail: md.tanzania@bankofbaroda.com
Web Site: www.bankofbaroda.com
Banking Services
S.I.C.: 6029
N.A.I.C.S.: 522110
D. P. Gayen *(Mng Dir)*

Bank of Baroda (Trinidad & Tobago) Ltd. (1)
Furness House
90 Independence Square, Port of Spain, Trinidad & Tobago
Tel.: (868) 6253964
Fax: (868) 6254215

Bank of Baroda—(Continued)

E-Mail: md.tt@bankofbaroda.com
Web Site: www.bankofbaroda.com
Emp.: 12
Banking Services
S.I.C.: 6029
N.A.I.C.S.: 522110
Yashpal Chhabra *(CEO)*
Kishor P. Kharat *(Mng Dir)*

Bank of Baroda (Uganda) Ltd. (1)
PB No 7197 18
Kampala Road, Kampala, Uganda
Tel.: (256) 414232783
Fax: (256) 414230781
E-Mail: md.uganda@bankofbaroda.com
Web Site: www.bankofbaroda.com
Emp.: 200
Banking Services
S.I.C.: 6029
N.A.I.C.S.: 522110
Ashok Garg *(Mng Dir)*

Non-U.S. Joint Venture:

Indo Zambia Bank Ltd. (1)
Plot No 6907 Cairo Road
PO Box 35411
Lusaka, Zambia
Tel.: (260) 211225080
Fax: (260) 1225090
E-Mail: izb@izb.co.zm
Web Site: www.izb.co.zm
Banking Services
S.I.C.: 6029
N.A.I.C.S.: 522110
S. R. Shukla *(Mng Dir)*

BANK OF BEIJING CO., LTD.

BOB Building No 17C Financial Ave
XiCheng District, Beijing, 100033, China
Tel.: (86) 10 6622 3826
Fax: (86) 10 6622 3833
Web Site: www.bankofbeijing.com.cn
601169—(SHG)
Sales Range: $1-9.9 Million
Emp.: 6,455

Business Description:
Banking Services
S.I.C.: 6029
N.A.I.C.S.: 522110

Personnel:
Bingzhu Yan *(Chm)*
Xiaoyan Yan *(Vice Chm & Pres)*
Zhihong Du *(CFO)*
Deyao Jiang *(COO & Deputy Head-Bank)*
Huizhen Zhang *(Chief Risk Officer)*
Shujian Yang *(Sec)*

Board of Directors:
Bingzhu Yan
Michael Knight Ipson
Baoren Li
Zhiqiang Ren
Bachar Samra
Xiaoqiu Wu
Xiaoyan Yan
Ning Yu
Dongning Zhang
Huizhen Zhang
Jie Zhang
Zhengyu Zhang
Xinli Zheng

Subsidiary:

Bank of Xian Co., Ltd . (1)
No 239 Changan Middle Road
Beilin District, Xi'an, Shaanxi, 710061, China
Tel.: (86) 2985248060
Fax: (86) 2985214245
Commercial Banking Services
S.I.C.: 6029
N.A.I.C.S.: 522110

BANK OF BEIRUT S.A.L.

Bank of Beirut SAL Building Foch Street
Beirut, Lebanon
Tel.: (961) 1972972
Telex: 23640 LE
Fax: (961) 1970236
E-Mail: contactus@bankofbeirut.com
Web Site: www.bankofbeirut.com.lb
Year Founded: 1973
BOB—(BEY)
Int. Income: $496,782,127
Assets: $11,079,008,718
Liabilities: $9,962,867,557
Net Worth: $1,116,141,161
Earnings: $114,715,875
Emp.: 1,529
Fiscal Year-end: 12/31/12

Business Description:
Banking Services
S.I.C.: 6029
N.A.I.C.S.: 522110

Personnel:
Salim G. Sfeir *(Chm & Gen Mgr)*
Adib S. Millet *(Vice Chm)*

Board of Directors:
Salim G. Sfeir
Rashid Al-Rashid
Anwar El Khalil
Khaled Kalban
Antoine A. Abdel Massih
Adib S. Millet
Fawaz H. Naboulsi
Krikor Sadikian
Antoine Wakim

Deloitte & Touche
Arabia House 131 Phoenicia Street
PO Box 961
Beirut, Lebanon

Non-U.S. Subsidiary:

Bank of Beirut (UK) Ltd (1)
17 A Curzon St
London, United Kingdom (100%)
Tel.: (44) 2074938342
Fax: (44) 2074080053
E-Mail: mail@bankofbeirut.co.uk
Web Site: www.bankofbeirut.co.uk
Emp.: 25
Commercial Banking
S.I.C.: 6029
N.A.I.C.S.: 522110
Bob Dziengeleski *(CEO & Mng Dir)*

BANK OF BOTSWANA

Khama Crescent
Private Bag 154
Gaborone, Botswana
Tel.: (267) 3606000
Fax: (267) 3974859
Web Site: www.bankofbotswana.bw
Emp.: 500

Business Description:
Banking Services
S.I.C.: 6011
N.A.I.C.S.: 521110

Personnel:
L.K. Mohohlo *(Governor)*
O.A. Motshidisi *(Deputy Governor)*

Board of Directors:
B. Bolele
C. S. Botlhole-Mmopi
U. Corea
G.K. Cunliffe
B. Moeletsi
L.K. Mohohlo
B. Molosiwa
H. Siphambe
S.S.G. Tumelo

BANK OF CEYLON

1 BOC Square Bank of Ceylon Mawatha
Colombo, 01, Sri Lanka
Tel.: (94) 11 2446790
Fax: (94) 11 2321160
E-Mail: boc@boc.lk
Web Site: www.boc.lk
Year Founded: 1939
Rev.: $906,888,214
Assets: $8,472,922,761
Liabilities: $8,012,577,857
Net Worth: $460,344,905
Earnings: $114,672,753
Emp.: 8,115
Fiscal Year-end: 12/31/12

Business Description:
Banking Services
S.I.C.: 6029
N.A.I.C.S.: 522110

Personnel:
Razik Zarook *(Chm)*
W. A. A. Rupasinghe *(CFO)*
Indunil Liyanage *(CMO)*
S. H. Ranawaka *(Chief Legal Officer)*
Lalith J. Fernando *(Chief Risk Officer)*
J. S. Siriwardane *(Sec)*

Board of Directors:
Razik Zarook
Nalini Abeywardene
Chandrasiri de Silva
K. M. Mahinda Siriwardana
Raju Sivaraman
Lalith Withana

Subsidiaries:

BOC Property Development & Management (Pvt) Ltd (1)
19th Fl BOC Head Ofc Bldg
No 4 Bank of Ceylon Mw, Colombo, Sri Lanka
Tel.: (94) 112388229
Fax: (94) 112544329
Web Site: www.boc.lk/bochome/subsi/subpdlman.jsp
Residential Property Managers
S.I.C.: 6531
N.A.I.C.S.: 531311
Gamini Rajapakse *(CEO)*

Ceybank Holiday Homes (Pvt) Ltd (1)
12th Floor BOC Head Ofc Bldg
No 4 Bank of Ceylon Mw, Colombo, Sri Lanka (100%)
Tel.: (94) 112447845
Fax: (94) 112447845
E-Mail: Ceybankhh@gmail.com
Web Site: www.boc.lk/bochome/subsi/subceybankhol.jsp
Emp.: 8
Travel Arrangement & Reservation Services
S.I.C.: 4729
N.A.I.C.S.: 561599
K. Dharmasiri *(Gen Mgr)*

Merchant Bank of Sri Lanka Ltd (1)
18th Floor 28 St Michaels Rd
BoC Merchant Tower, Colombo, 3, Sri Lanka
Tel.: (94) 114711711
Fax: (94) 114711716
E-Mail: mbslbank@mbslbank.com
Web Site: www.mbslbank.com
Emp.: 120
Securities Brokerage
S.I.C.: 6211
N.A.I.C.S.: 523120
T. Mutugala *(CEO)*

Merchant Credit of Sri Lanka Ltd (1)
11th Floor 28 St Michaels Rd
BoC Merchant Tower, Colombo, Sri Lanka (87.76%)
Tel.: (94) 112301501
Fax: (94) 4627850
E-Mail: mcsl@mbslbank.com
Web Site: www.mcsl.lk
Emp.: 100
Real Estate Credit
S.I.C.: 6159
N.A.I.C.S.: 522292
Janaka Ratnayake *(Chm)*

Property Development Ltd (1)
19th Floor BOC Head Office Building
No 4 Bank of Ceylon Mw, Colombo, Sri Lanka
Tel.: (94) 112448549
Fax: (94) 112544329
Administrative Management & General Management Consulting Services
S.I.C.: 8742
N.A.I.C.S.: 541611

Joint Venture:

Lanka Securities Pvt. Ltd. (1)
228/2 Galle Road
Colombo, 4, Sri Lanka
Tel.: (94) 114706757
Fax: (94) 114706767
E-Mail: lankasec@sltnet.lk
Web Site: www.lsl.lk
Emp.: 60
Securities Trading & Brokerage Services; Owned by First Capital Securities Corporation & Bank of Ceylon
S.I.C.: 6211
N.A.I.C.S.: 523120
Kosala Gamage *(CEO-Trading Div)*

BANK OF CHINA, LTD.

1 Fuxingmen Nei Dajie
Beijing, 100818, China
Tel.: (86) 1066596688
Telex: 22254 BCHO CN 22289 BCHO
Fax: (86) 1066593777
E-Mail: gwic@boci.com.cn
Web Site: www.boc.cn
Year Founded: 1912
3988—(HKG)
Int. Income: $80,461,972,800
Net Worth: $136,855,946,700
Earnings: $23,116,169,700
Emp.: 302,016
Fiscal Year-end: 12/31/12

Business Description:
International Banking Services
S.I.C.: 6159
N.A.I.C.S.: 522293

Personnel:
Jun Li *(Chm-Supervisory Bd)*
Lihui Li *(Vice Chm & Pres)*
Wai Kin Chim *(Chief Credit Officer)*
Yanfen Liu *(Chief Audit Officer)*
Cheung Ying Yeung *(Sec)*
Siqing Chen *(Exec VP)*
Yongli Wang *(Exec VP)*
Yi Yue *(Exec VP)*
Li Zaohang *(Exec VP)*
Shumin Zhu *(Exec VP)*

Board of Directors:
Paul Man Yiu Chow
Danhan Huang
Yansong Jiang
Lihui Li
Lina Liu
Anthony Francis Neoh
Zhijun Sun
Yongli Wang
Arnout Henricus Elisabeth Maria Wellink
Li Zaohang
Qi Zhang
Xiangdong Zhang

Supervisory Board of Directors:
Jun Li
Guoming Bao
Zhiying Deng
Wanming Liu
Xiaozhong Liu
Xingbao Mei
Xueqiang Wang
Xi Xiang

PricewaterhouseCoopers
22nd Floor Prince's Building
Central, China (Hong Kong)
Tel.: (852) 2 826 2111

U.S. Branch:

Bank of China-New York (1)
410 Madison Ave
New York, NY 10017-1118
Tel.: (212) 935-3101
Telex: 42635 BKCHI UI
Fax: (212) 593-1831
E-Mail: service_us@bankofchina.com
Web Site: www.bocusa.com
Emp.: 200
International Banking

S.I.C.: 6159
N.A.I.C.S.: 522293
Shiqianj Wu *(Gen Mgr)*

Non-U.S. Branch:

Bank of China-Singapore (1)
4 Battery Rd
Singapore, 049908, Singapore
Tel.: (65) 65352411
Telex: RS 23046 BKCHINA
Fax: (65) 65343401
E-Mail: bocsg@bank-of-china.com
Web Site: www.bank-of-china.com
Emp.: 500
S.I.C.: 6159
N.A.I.C.S.: 522298
Liu Yanfen *(Gen Mgr)*

Subsidiaries:

Bank of China-Katong Branch (2)
188 192 E Coast Rd
Singapore, 428898, Singapore (100%)
Tel.: (65) 64402440
Fax: (65) 64440737
E-Mail: bocsg@bank-of-china.com
Web Site: www.bank-of-china.com
Emp.: 12
S.I.C.: 6159
N.A.I.C.S.: 522298
Chai Hong Ng *(Mgr)*

Bank of China-Singapore South Branch (2)
01 - 01 Maxwell House 20 Maxwell Rd
Singapore, 69113, Singapore (100%)
Tel.: (65) 62233466
Fax: (65) 62236601
Emp.: 10
S.I.C.: 6159
N.A.I.C.S.: 522298

Bank of China-Singapore (2)
133 Middle Rd BOC Plz
Singapore, 188974, Singapore (100%)
Tel.: (65) 68328108
Fax: (65) 63339281
Emp.: 15
S.I.C.: 6159
N.A.I.C.S.: 522298

Non-U.S. Subsidiaries:

Bank of China Group Investment Limited (1)
23/F Bank of China Tower 1 Garden Road
Central, China (Hong Kong) HK
Tel.: (852) 2200 7500
Fax: (852) 2877 2629
E-Mail: bocginv_bgi@bocgroup.com
Web Site: www.bocgi.com
Investment Management Services
S.I.C.: 6799
N.A.I.C.S.: 523920
Xiao Jing Li *(Chm)*
Jianzhong Gong *(CEO)*

BOC Aviation (1)
8 Shenton Way 18-01
Singapore, 068811, Singapore (100%)
Tel.: (65) 63235559
Fax: (65) 63236962
E-Mail: information@bocaviation.com
Web Site: www.bocaviation.com
Sales Range: $250-299.9 Million
Aircraft & Fleet Leasing Services
S.I.C.: 7359
N.A.I.C.S.: 532411
Siqing Chen *(Chm)*
Wang Genshan *(Vice Chm & Deputy Mng Dir)*
Robert Martin *(CEO & Mng Dir)*
Phang Thim Fatt *(Deputy Mng Dir & CFO)*
Steven Townend *(Deputy Mng Dir & Chief Comml Officer)*
Nick Seah *(Sr VP-Airline Leasing & Sls-Asia Pacific)*

BOC Hong Kong (Holdings) Limited (1)
52/F Bank of China Tower 1 Garden Road
Hong Kong, China (Hong Kong) HK
Tel.: (852) 28462700 (66.06%)
Fax: (852) 28105830
Web Site: www.bochk.com
2388—(HKG OTC SHG)
Int. Income: $4,566,506,350
Assets: $236,076,888,850
Liabilities: $216,080,096,550
Net Worth: $19,996,792,300
Earnings: $2,778,485,650
Emp.: 14,638
Fiscal Year-end: 12/31/12
Bank Holding Company
S.I.C.: 6712
N.A.I.C.S.: 551111
Tian Guoli *(Chm)*
Guangbei He *(Vice Chm & CEO)*
Lihui Li *(Vice Chm)*
Yanlai Zhu *(Asst CEO)*
Yingxin Gao *(Deputy CEO)*
Hong Huang *(Deputy CEO-Fin Markets)*
Jason Chi Wai Yeung *(Deputy CEO)*
Chengwen Zhuo *(CFO)*
Alex Wing Kwai Lee *(COO)*
Jiuzhong Li *(Chief Risk Officer)*
Chun Ying Chan *(Sec)*

Subsidiaries:

Bank of China (Hong Kong) Limited (2)
9th Floor Bank of China Tower 1 Garden Road
Hong Kong, China (Hong Kong)
Tel.: (852) 28266888
Fax: (852) 34062326
Web Site: www.bochk.com
Emp.: 90
Commercial Banking
S.I.C.: 6029
N.A.I.C.S.: 522110
Tian Guoli *(Chm)*
He Guangbei *(Vice Chm & CEO)*
Wong David See Hong *(Deputy CEO)*

Chiyu Banking Corporation Limited (2)
78 Des Voeux Road
Central, China (Hong Kong) HK
Tel.: (852) 28430111
Fax: (852) 28104207
E-Mail: chiyu@chiyubank.com
Web Site: www.chiyubank.com
Int. Income: $158,612,369
Assets: $6,205,831,323
Liabilities: $5,422,145,951
Net Worth: $783,685,372
Earnings: $99,357,136
Emp.: 115
Fiscal Year-end: 12/31/12
Commercial Banking
S.I.C.: 6029
N.A.I.C.S.: 522110
Siu Ling Tse *(CEO)*

BOC International Holdings Limited (1)
26/F Bank of China Tower 1 Garden Road
Hong Kong, China (Hong Kong) HK
Tel.: (852) 3988 6000
Fax: (852) 2147 9065
E-Mail: info@bocigroup.com
Web Site: www.bocigroup.com
Investment Banking
S.I.C.: 6211
N.A.I.C.S.: 523110
Tong Li *(CEO)*

Kiu Kwong Investment Co. Ltd. (1)
8/F Chiao Shang Building
92 104 Queen's Road, Central, China (Hong Kong)
Tel.: (852) 25 22 7339
Fax: (852) 28 45 2613
Provider of Investment Services
S.I.C.: 6282
N.A.I.C.S.: 523930

Joint Venture:

Crown Beverage Cans HK Ltd. (2)
Ste 1315 Tower 1 Grand Central Plz
Sha Tin, China (Hong Kong)
Tel.: (852) 26656312
Fax: (852) 26643837
E-Mail: elizabeth.wong@crowncork.com.sg
Web Site: www.crown.com
Emp.: 10
Mfr. of Packaging Products for Consumer Goods; Joint Venture of Crown Cork & Seal Co., Inc. (51%), Swire Pacific Limited (40%) & Kiu Kwong Investment Co. Ltd. (9%)
S.I.C.: 3411
N.A.I.C.S.: 332431
Robert Bourque *(Pres)*

Non-U.S. Joint Ventures:

Foshan Crown Can Co. Ltd. (2)
20 Qinggong San Rd
Foshan, 528000, China
Tel.: (86) 75783376948
Fax: (86) 757 8221 3295
Sales Range: $50-74.9 Million
Emp.: 190
Mfr. of Packaging Products for Consumer Goods; Joint Venture of Crown Cork & Seal Co., Inc., Swire Pacific Limited & Kiu Kwong Investment Co. Ltd.
S.I.C.: 3089
N.A.I.C.S.: 326199

Foshan Easy-Opening End Company Ltd. (2)
20 Qinggong San Rd
Foshan, 528000, China
Tel.: (86) 75782219400
Fax: (86) 75782213295
E-Mail: yong-keng.huang@crowncork.com.sg
Emp.: 150
Mfr. of Packaging Products for Consumer Goods; Joint Venture of Crown Cork & Seal Co., Inc., Swire Pacific Limited & Kiu Kwong Investment Co. Ltd.
S.I.C.: 3082
N.A.I.C.S.: 326199
Gilbert Kung *(Gen Mgr)*

BANK OF CHONGQING CO., LTD.

153 Zourong Road
Yuzhong District, Chongqing, 400010, China
Tel.: (86) 23 63836229
Fax: (86) 23 63824699
E-Mail: syyh@cqcbank.com.cn
Web Site: www.cqcbank.com
1963—(HKG)
Emp.: 3,000

Business Description:
Banking Services
S.I.C.: 6029
N.A.I.C.S.: 522110

Personnel:
Weimin Gan *(Chm)*
Qianzhen Ma *(Chm-Supervisory Bd)*
Hailing Ran *(Pres)*
Guohua Zhou *(COO)*
Xiaobo Zuo *(CIO)*
Wanghua Zhan *(Chief Risk Officer)*
Jianhua Liu *(Chief Officer-Retail Bus)*
Shiyin Yang *(Chief Officer-Co Bus)*

BANK OF COMMUNICATIONS CO., LTD.

188 Yin Cheng Zhong Road
Shanghai, 200120, China
Tel.: (86) 2158766688
Fax: (86) 2158798398
E-Mail: investor@bankcomm.com
Web Site: www.bankcomm.com
3328—(HKG)
Int. Income: $38,218,674,600
Assets: $837,676,254,150
Liabilities: $777,083,398,200
Net Worth: $60,592,855,950
Earnings: $9,288,912,600
Emp.: 96,259
Fiscal Year-end: 12/31/12

Business Description:
Banking Services
S.I.C.: 6029
N.A.I.C.S.: 522110

Personnel:
Qingshan Hua *(Chm-Supervisory Bd)*
Ximing Niu *(Vice Chm & Pres)*
Yali Yu *(CFO & Exec VP)*
Weidong Hou *(CIO & Exec VP)*
Dongping Yang *(Chief Risk Officer)*
Meisheng Shou *(Pres-Labour Union & Exec VP)*
Hexin Zhu *(Pres-Admin Dept & Gen Mgr-Beijing)*
Jianglong Du *(Sec)*
Benxian Lv *(Exec VP-Admin Dept-Beijing, Gen Mgr-Corp Bus Dept & Dir-Corp Dev)*
Wenhui Qian *(Exec VP)*

Board of Directors:
Zhiwu Chen
Yiu Kwan Choi
Yuemei Du
Anita Yuen Mei Fung
Mingchao Gu
Huating Hu
Jun Lei
Eric Ka Cheung Li
Qiang Ma
Ximing Niu
Peter Hugh Nolan
Wenhui Qian
Weiqiang Wang
Peter Tung Shun Wong
Yali Yu
Jixiang Zhang

Supervisory Board of Directors:
Qingshan Hua
Qing Chen
Hongjun Chu
Yarong Du
Huizhong Gu
Yu Guo
Yunbao Jiang
Zuqi Jiang
Jin Li
Sha Liu
Shi Shuai
Hong Yan
Fajia Yang

China Securities Depository & Clearing Corporation Limited
3/F China Insurance Building No 166 Lujiazui Dong Road
Shanghai, China

Transfer Agents:
Computershare Hong Kong Investor Services Limited
Room 1712-1716 17th Floor Hopewell Centre
183 Queen's Road East
Hong Kong, China (Hong Kong)

China Securities Depository & Clearing Corporation Limited
3/F China Insurance Building No 166 Lujiazui Dong Road
Shanghai, China

Subsidiaries:

Bank of Communications Trustee Limited (1)
1st Fl Far E Consortium Bldg
121 Des Voeux, Central, China (Hong Kong) (100%)
Tel.: (852) 22699699
Fax: (852) 28540880
E-Mail: bocomtrustee@bankcomm.com.hk
Web Site: www.bocomtrust.com.hk
Bank Holding Company
S.I.C.: 6712
N.A.I.C.S.: 551111

BOCOM International Holdings Co., Ltd. (1)
Rm 201-202 Far E Consortium Bldg
121 Des Voeux, Central, China (Hong Kong) (100%)
Tel.: (852) 22979888
Fax: (852) 28519876
E-Mail: enquiry@bocomgroup.com
Web Site: www.bocomgroup.com
Investment Banking & Securities Dealing
S.I.C.: 6211
N.A.I.C.S.: 523110

China BOCOM Insurance Co., Ltd. (1)
16th Floor Bank Of Communications Twr
Wanchai, China (Hong Kong) (100%)
Tel.: (852) 25912938
Fax: (852) 28319192
Web Site: www.cbic.hk
Insurance Agencies & Brokerages
S.I.C.: 6411
N.A.I.C.S.: 524210

BANK OF CYPRUS LTD.
51 Stassinos Street Ayia Paraskevi Strovolos
PO Box 24884
CY-1398 Nicosia, Cyprus
Mailing Address:
PO Box 21472
CY-1599 Nicosia, Cyprus
Tel.: (357) 22122100
Fax: (357) 22336258
E-Mail: info@bankofcyprus.com
Web Site: www.bankofcyprus.com
Year Founded: 1899
BOCY—(ATH CYP)
Sales Range: $1-4.9 Billion
Emp.: 11,326
Business Description:
Banking Services
S.I.C.: 6029
N.A.I.C.S.: 522110
Personnel:
Andreas Artemis *(Chm)*
Evdokimos Xenophontos *(Vice Chm)*
John Patrick Hourican *(Grp CEO)*
Board of Directors:
Andreas Artemis
Stavros J. Constantinides
Anna Diogenous
George M. Georgiades
Costas Hadjipapas
Irene Karamanou
Symeon Matsis
Christos Mouskis
Elias Neocleous
Vassilis G. Rologis
Costas Z. Severis
Nikolas P. Tsakos
Evdokimos Xenophontos

Subsidiaries:

The Cyprus Investment and Securities Corporation Ltd (1)
4 Evros St Eurolife House
Strovolos, Nicosia, 2003, Cyprus
Tel.: (357) 22121700
Fax: (357) 22338488
E-Mail: info@cisco.bankofcyprus.com
Web Site: www.cisco-online.com.cy
Emp.: 36
Financial Investment Activities
S.I.C.: 6211
N.A.I.C.S.: 523999
Anna Sofroniou Vafeades *(Gen Mgr)*

EuroLife Ltd (1)
4 Evrou St Strovolos
PO Box 21655
Nicosia, 2003, Cyprus
Tel.: (357) 22474000
Fax: (357) 22341090
E-Mail: info@eurolife.bankofcyprus.com
Web Site: www.eurolife.com.cy
Emp.: 100
Direct Life Insurance Carriers
S.I.C.: 6311
N.A.I.C.S.: 524113
Artemis Pantelidou *(Gen Mgr)*

General Insurance of Cyprus Ltd (1)
101 Arch Makarios III Avenue
Nicosia, 1071, Cyprus
Mailing Address:
PO Box 21312
Nicosia, 1506, Cyprus
Tel.: (357) 22505000
Fax: (357) 22676682
E-Mail: nicosia@cgi.com.cy
Web Site: www.cgi.com.cy
Direct Life Insurance Carriers
S.I.C.: 6311
N.A.I.C.S.: 524113
Andreas Artemis *(Chm)*

JCC Payment Systems Ltd (1)
Stadiou 1
PO Box 21043
1500 Nicosia, Cyprus
Tel.: (357) 22868150
Fax: (357) 22868591
Web Site: www.jcc.com.cy
Credit Card Issuing
S.I.C.: 6141
N.A.I.C.S.: 522210
Neophytos Karamanos *(Gen Mgr)*

Kermia Hotels Ltd (1)
PO Box 30110
5340 Ayia Napa, Cyprus
Tel.: (357) 23721401
Fax: (357) 23721429
E-Mail: welcome@kermiabeach.com
Web Site: www.kermiabeach.com.cy
Emp.: 70
Hotels & Motels
S.I.C.: 7011
N.A.I.C.S.: 721110
Charalampous Papakyriacou *(Mgr-Ops)*

Kermia Ltd (1)
4 Diagorou Street
Kermia Bldg 8th Floor, 1097 Nicosia, Cyprus
Tel.: (357) 22663692
Fax: (357) 22660938
E-Mail: info@kermia.bankofcyprus.com
Emp.: 150
Commercial Banking
S.I.C.: 6029
N.A.I.C.S.: 522110
Stavros Stavrinides *(Gen Mgr)*

Kermia Properties & Investments Ltd (1)
155 Makariou Avenue Proteas House Office 104 1Floor
Limassol, 3602, Cyprus
Tel.: (357) 25 343658
Fax: (357) 25 343716
E-Mail: info@properties.bankofcyprus.com
Web Site: www.kermia.com.cy
Emp.: 2
Real Estate Investment Services
S.I.C.: 6531
N.A.I.C.S.: 531390
Stavros Stavrinides *(Gen Mgr)*

U.S. Subsidiary:

Limestone Properties Ltd (1)
115 Cave Springs Dr
Hunt, TX 78024
Tel.: (830) 238-3232
Fax: (830) 238-3239
E-Mail: info@limestoneproperties.us
Web Site: www.limestoneproperties.us
Real Estate Management Services
S.I.C.: 6531
N.A.I.C.S.: 531390

Non-U.S. Subsidiaries:

Bank of Cyprus (Channel Islands) Ltd (1)
Canada Court
PO Box 558
Upland Road, Saint Peter Port, GY1 6JF, Guernsey
Tel.: (44) 1481716026
Fax: (44) 1481716020
Commercial Banking
S.I.C.: 6029
N.A.I.C.S.: 522110
Andreas Artemis *(Vice Chm)*

Bank of Cyprus Romania Ltd (1)
Calea Dorobantilor 187B
Sector 1, Bucharest, Romania
Tel.: (40) 214099100
Fax: (40) 2144099106
E-Mail: info@ro.bankofcyprus.com
Web Site: www.bankofcyprus.ro
Emp.: 100
Commercial Banking
S.I.C.: 6029
N.A.I.C.S.: 522110
George Christoforou *(Gen Mgr)*

Bank of Cyprus United Kingdom Ltd (1)
27-31 Charlotte St
London, W1T1RP, United Kingdom
Tel.: (44) 2073045800
Fax: (44) 2088866462
Web Site: www.bankofcyprus.co.uk
Emp.: 400
Commercial Banking
S.I.C.: 6029
N.A.I.C.S.: 522110
Iacovos Koumi *(Gen Mgr)*

Battersee Real Estate SRL (1)
Spl Independentei 52
Bucharest, 50085, Romania
Tel.: (40) 21409919
Fax: (40) 123156102
Real Estate Management Services
S.I.C.: 6531
N.A.I.C.S.: 531390

Blindingqueen Properties SRL (1)
Spl Independentei nr 52
Bucharest, Romania
Tel.: (40) 756085649
Real Estate Property Management Services
S.I.C.: 6531
N.A.I.C.S.: 531390

Cobhan Properties Ltd (1)
5 Woodend Park
Cobham, Surrey, KT11 3BX, United Kingdom
Tel.: (44) 1932 576444
Property Management Services
S.I.C.: 6531
N.A.I.C.S.: 531312

Cyprus Leasing Romania IFN SA (1)
Calea Dorobantilor nr 187
Bucharest, 10565, Romania
Tel.: (40) 214099258
Fax: (40) 214099202
Web Site: www.bankofcyprus.ro
Emp.: 9
Real Estate & Vehicle Leasing Services
S.I.C.: 6531
N.A.I.C.S.: 531390
Anca Petcu *(Gen Mgr)*

Drysdale Properties Ltd (1)
3385 Senkler Rd
Belcarra, BC, V3H 4S3, Canada
Tel.: (604) 936-1000
Fax: (604) 936-1014
Real Estate Management Services
S.I.C.: 6531
N.A.I.C.S.: 531390

Green Hills Properties SRL (1)
Spl Independentei 52 5th District
50085 Bucharest, Romania
Tel.: (40) 213156100
Real Estate Property Management Services
S.I.C.: 6531
N.A.I.C.S.: 531390

Kyprou Finance (NL) B.V. (1)
Teleportboulevard
Amsterdam, 1043 EJ, Netherlands
Tel.: (31) 20 5405800
Fax: (31) 206447011
Financial Management Services
S.I.C.: 6211
N.A.I.C.S.: 523999

Kyprou Insurance Services Ltd (1)
170 Alexandras Ave
11521 Athens, Greece
Tel.: (30) 2106418012
Fax: (30) 2106418041
Web Site: www.bankofcyprus.gr/locations.asp?lCity=161&lCountry=0
Emp.: 25
Insurance Related Activities
S.I.C.: 6411
N.A.I.C.S.: 524298
Eliaves Andreas *(Gen Mgr)*

Kyprou Leasing SA (1)
Sinopsis 27 Ampelokipi
11521 Athens, Greece
Tel.: (30) 210 6477030
Fax: (30) 2107760890
E-Mail: leasing@bankofcyprus.gr
Emp.: 45
Real Estate Property & Automotive Leasing Services
S.I.C.: 6519
N.A.I.C.S.: 531190
Korakianitis Nikolaos *(Gen Mgr)*

Kyprou Mutual Fund Management Company S.A. (1)
170 Alexandras Ave
11527 Athens, Greece
Tel.: (30) 2106418888
Fax: (30) 2106477309
Web Site: www.bankofcyprus.gr
Emp.: 15
Management Consulting Services
S.I.C.: 8748
N.A.I.C.S.: 541618
N. Strapatsakis *(Pres)*

Kyprou Securities SA (1)
Fidippidou St 26
11527 Athens, Greece
Tel.: (30) 2108701000
Fax: (30) 2108701049
E-Mail: infosec@kyprousecurities.gr
Web Site: www.kyprousecurities.gr
Emp.: 22
Investment Banking & Securities Dealing
S.I.C.: 6211
N.A.I.C.S.: 523110
Nicolas Strobolas *(Gen Mgr)*

Thames Properties Ltd (1)
6 Forge Lane Petersham Road
Richmond, Surrey, TW10 7BF, United Kingdom
Tel.: (44) 2089487982
Real Estate Management Services
S.I.C.: 6531
N.A.I.C.S.: 531390

THE BANK OF EAST ASIA, LIMITED
10 Des Voeux Road
Central, China (Hong Kong)
Tel.: (852) 36083608
Telex: HX73017
Fax: (852) 36086000
E-Mail: info@hkbea.com
Web Site: www.hkbea.com
Year Founded: 1918
BKEAY—(HKG OTCB)
Int. Income: $2,918,783,250
Assets: $89,248,100,300
Liabilities: $81,299,751,250
Net Worth: $7,948,349,050
Earnings: $793,558,300
Emp.: 12,441
Fiscal Year-end: 12/31/12
Business Description:
Banking Services
S.I.C.: 6029
N.A.I.C.S.: 522110
Personnel:
David Kwok-po Li *(Chm & CEO)*
Arthur Kwok-cheung Li *(Deputy Chm)*
Allan Chi Yun Wong *(Deputy Chm)*
Hon-shing Tong *(Deputy CEO & COO)*
Samson Kai-cheong Li *(Deputy CEO & Chief Investment Officer)*
Adrian David Man-kiu Li *(Deputy CEO)*
Brian David Man-bun Li *(Deputy CEO)*
Alson Chun-tak Law *(Sec)*
Board of Directors:
David Kwok-po Li
Valiant Kin-piu Cheung
William Wai Hoi Doo
Kay-peng Khoo
Khoon Ean Kuok
Thomas Ping-kwong Kwok
Shau-kee Lee
Arthur Kwok-cheung Li
Aubrey Kwok-sing Li
Eric Fook-chuen Li
Richard Tzar-kai Li
Stephen Charles Kwok-sze Li
Kenneth Chin-ming Lo
Winston Yau-lai Lo
Allan Chi Yun Wong
Chung-hin Wong

Subsidiaries:

Blue Cross (Asia-Pacific) Insurance Limited (1)
29F BEA Towe Millennium City 5
418 Kwun Tong Road
Kwun Tong, Hong Kong, Kowloon, China (Hong Kong) HK (100%)
Tel.: (852) 36082888
Fax: (852) 36082989
E-Mail: cs@bluecross.com.hk
Web Site: www.bluecross.com.hk
Emp.: 200
Healthcare, General & Life Insurance Services

S.I.C.: 6311
N.A.I.C.S.: 524113
Manlo Cheung *(Mng Dir)*

Credit Gain Finance Company Limited (1)
33/F Millennium City 5 Bea Tower 418 Kwun Tong Road
Kwun Tong, China (Hong Kong)
Tel.: (852) 36081904
Fax: (852) 36086203
Web Site: www.creditgain.com.hk
Commercial Banking Services
S.I.C.: 6029
N.A.I.C.S.: 522110

East Asia Property Agency Co., Ltd. (1)
35th floor PEA Tower Millennium City 5 418 Kwun Kong Road
Nathan Rd Mongkoa, Kowloon, China (Hong Kong) HK (100%)
Tel.: (852) 36083228
Fax: (852) 36086233
Property Sale & Leasing Services
S.I.C.: 6531
N.A.I.C.S.: 531210

East Asia Securities Company Limited (1)
9th Fl The Bank of East Asia Bldg
10 Des Voeux Rd, Central, China (Hong Kong) (100%)
Tel.: (852) 36088077
Fax: (852) 36086128
E-Mail: info@easecurities.com.hk
Web Site: www.easecurities.com.hk
Emp.: 80
Brokerage Services
S.I.C.: 6211
N.A.I.C.S.: 523120
Joseph Pang Yuk-wing *(Pres)*
Samson Li Kai-Cheong *(Mng Dir)*

East Asia Strategic Holdings Limited (1)
11/F 8 Queens Road C
Central, China (Hong Kong)
Tel.: (852) 22838000
Fax: (852) 28662715
Commercial Banking Services
S.I.C.: 6029
N.A.I.C.S.: 522110

Tricor Services Limited (1)
Level 28 3 Pacific Place 1 Queen's Road East
Hong Kong, China (Hong Kong) (100%)
Tel.: (852) 29801888
Fax: (852) 28610285
E-Mail: info@hk.tricorglobal.com
Web Site: www.tricor.com.hk
Emp.: 200
Integrated Business, Corporate & Investor Services
S.I.C.: 7389
N.A.I.C.S.: 561499
Johnny Ng *(CEO & Mng Dir)*
Julian Chow *(Mng Dir)*

Subsidiary:

Tricor Japan Limited (2)
Level 28 Three Pacific Place 1 Queens Road East
Hong Kong, China (Hong Kong)
Tel.: (852) 3485 5120
Fax: (852) 3485 5121
E-Mail: info@jp.tricorglobal.com
Web Site: www.jp.tricorglobal.com
Emp.: 25
Business Management Consulting Services
S.I.C.: 8742
N.A.I.C.S.: 541611
Suen Moon *(Gen Mgr)*

Non-U.S. Subsidiaries:

PT Amalgamated Tricor (2)
Penthouse 01B Wisma GKBI 28 Jl Jend Sudirman
Jakarta, 10210, Indonesia
Tel.: (62) 21 574 1177
Fax: (62) 21 574 1188
E-Mail: info@id.tricorglobal.com
Web Site: www.id.tricorglobal.com
Business Management Consulting Services
S.I.C.: 8742
N.A.I.C.S.: 541611

Tricor - ATC Europe LLP (Tricor Europe) (2)
7th Floor 52/54 Gracechurch Street
London, EC3V 0EH, United Kingdom
Tel.: (44) 2076488960
Fax: (44) 2032162002
E-Mail: info@uk.tricorglobal.com
Web Site: www.uk.tricorglobal.com
Emp.: 20
Business Management Consulting Services
S.I.C.: 8742
N.A.I.C.S.: 541611
Richard Tozer *(Mng Dir)*

Tricor (B) Sdn Bhd (2)
Room 308B 3rd Floor Wisma Jaya
Jalan Pemancha, Bandar Seri Begawan, BS8811, Brunei Darussalam
Tel.: (673) 2232780
Fax: (673) 2232783
E-Mail: info@bn.tricorglobal.com
Web Site: www.bn.tricorglobal.com
Business Management Consulting Services
S.I.C.: 8742
N.A.I.C.S.: 541611
Cecilia Wong *(COO)*

Tricor Caribbean Limited (2)
Worthing Corporate Centre
PO Box 169W
Worthing, Christ Church, BB15008, Barbados
Tel.: (246) 430 8400
Fax: (246) 429 6446
E-Mail: info@bb.tricorglobal.com
Web Site: www.bb.tricorglobal.com
Emp.: 15
Business Management Consulting Services
S.I.C.: 8742
N.A.I.C.S.: 541611
Connie Smith *(Co-Mng Dir)*
Jennifer Smith *(Co-Mng Dir)*

Tricor Consultancy (Beijing) Limited (2)
Suite 1803 18/F Tower 1 Prosper Center No 5 Guanghua Road
Chaoyang District, Beijing, 100020, China
Tel.: (86) 1085876818
Fax: (86) 10 8587 6811
E-Mail: info@cn.tricorglobal.com
Web Site: www.cn.tricorglobal.com
Business Support Services
S.I.C.: 7389
N.A.I.C.S.: 561499

Tricor K.K. (2)
Oak Minami Azabu Building 2F 3-19-23 Minami Azabu
Minato-Ku, Tokyo, Japan
Tel.: (81) 3 4580 2700
Fax: (81) 3 4580 2701
E-Mail: info@jp.tricorglobal.com
Web Site: www.jp.tricorglobal.com
Business Management Consulting Services
S.I.C.: 8742
N.A.I.C.S.: 541611
Yasunori Homma *(Co-Mng Dir)*
Naoto Kira *(Co-Mng Dir)*

Tricor Praesidium Limited (2)
Office 4 Level 1 Currency House
PO Box 506676
Dubai, United Arab Emirates
Tel.: (971) 43587715
Fax: (971) 4 358 7315
E-Mail: info@ae.tricorglobal.com
Web Site: www.tricor.com.hk
Emp.: 8
Business Management Consulting Services
S.I.C.: 8742
N.A.I.C.S.: 541611
Hari Bhambra *(Gen Mgr)*

Tricor Services (Macau) Limited (2)
17 Andar East No 417-429 Avenue Da Praia Grande
Praia Grande Commercial Centre, Macau, China (Macau)
Tel.: (853) 2878 8022
Fax: (853) 2878 8021
E-Mail: tricor@macau.ctm.net
Web Site: www.cn.tricorglobal.com
Business Management Consulting Services
S.I.C.: 8742
N.A.I.C.S.: 541611

Tricor Services (Malaysia) Sdn. Bhd (2)
Level 18 The Gardens N Tower Mid Valley City
Lingkaran Syed Putra, 59200 Kuala Lumpur, Malaysia
Tel.: (60) 322648888
Fax: (60) 322822733
E-Mail: info@my.tricorglobal.com
Web Site: www.my.tricorglobal.com
Business Management Consulting Services
S.I.C.: 8742
N.A.I.C.S.: 541611
Yeap Kok Leong *(CEO & Mng Dir)*

Tricor Singapore Pte Ltd (2)
80 Robinson Road Unit 02-00
Singapore, 068898, Singapore
Tel.: (65) 62363333
Fax: (65) 6236 4399
E-Mail: info@sg.tricorglobal.com
Web Site: www.sg.tricorglobal.com
Business Management Consulting Services
S.I.C.: 8742
N.A.I.C.S.: 541611

Tricor Trustco (Labuan) Ltd (2)
Level 15 A2 Main Office Tower
Financial Park Labuan, 87000 Labuan, Malaysia
Tel.: (60) 87443118
Fax: (60) 087451288
E-Mail: info@my.tricorglobal.com
Web Site: www.tricor.com.hk/HK/locations.asp
Emp.: 13
Business Management Consulting Services
S.I.C.: 8742
N.A.I.C.S.: 541611

Non-U.S. Subsidiaries:

The Bank of East Asia (BVI) Limited (1)
East Asia Chambers
PO Box 901
Road Town, Tortola, Virgin Islands (British)
Tel.: (284) 4955588
Fax: (284) 4955088
E-Mail: patrick-nicholas@cricorbviglobal.com
Web Site: www.hkbea.com
Banking Services
S.I.C.: 6029
N.A.I.C.S.: 522110
Patrick Andrew Nicholas *(Mng Dir)*

The Bank of East Asia (China) Limited (1)
29/F BEA Finance Tower 66 Hua Yuan Shi Qiao Road
Pudong New Area, Shanghai, 200120, China CN (100%)
Tel.: (86) 2138663866
Fax: (86) 21 3866 3966
Web Site: eng.hkbea.com.cn
Banking Services
S.I.C.: 6029
N.A.I.C.S.: 522110
Tat-Cheong Kwan *(CEO)*

BEA Wealth Management Services (Taiwan) Limited (1)
8F 2 Tun Hua South Road Sec 1
Taipei, 10506, Taiwan
Tel.: (886) 281615000
Fax: (886) 287738565
Commercial Banking Services
S.I.C.: 6029
N.A.I.C.S.: 522110

Tricor Holdings Pte. Ltd. (1)
PWC Building 11-00 8 Cross St
Singapore, 048424, Singapore
Tel.: (65) 62363333
Fax: (65) 62364399
Commercial Banking Services
S.I.C.: 6029
N.A.I.C.S.: 522110
Holon Gee *(Mng Dir)*

BANK OF ENGLAND

Threadneedle Street
London, EC2R 8AH, United Kingdom
Tel.: (44) 2076014444
Fax: (44) 2076014771
E-Mail: enquiries@bankofengland.co.uk
Web Site: www.bankofengland.co.uk
Year Founded: 1694
Emp.: 1,613

Business Description:
Banking Services
S.I.C.: 6011
N.A.I.C.S.: 521110

Personnel:
Charlotte Hogg *(COO)*
Don Randall *(Chief Info Security Officer)*
John Footman *(Sec & Exec Dir-Central Svcs)*

Board of Directors:
Brendan Paul Barber
Roger Carr
Michael Cohrs
Nicholas E. T. Prettejohn
Susan Rice
John Stewart
Mark Tucker
Paul Tucker
Adair Turner
Harrison Young

BANK OF GEORGIA HOLDINGS PLC

84 Brook Street
London, W1K 5EH, United Kingdom
Tel.: (44) 203 178 4052
Fax: (44) 203 178 4053
E-Mail: ir@bog.ge
Web Site: www.bogh.co.uk
Year Founded: 2011
6BG—(DEU)
Int. Income: $342,010,459
Assets: $3,406,591,092
Liabilities: $2,768,404,634
Net Worth: $638,186,458
Earnings: $108,151,352
Emp.: 3,734
Fiscal Year-end: 12/31/12

Business Description:
Commercial Banking Services
S.I.C.: 6029
N.A.I.C.S.: 522110

Personnel:
Neil Janin *(Chm)*
Irakli Gilauri *(CEO)*
Irakli Burdiladze *(Deputy CEO-Affordable Housing)*
Archil Gachechiladze *(Deputy CEO-Asset & Wealth Mgmt)*
Nikoloz Gamkrelidze *(Deputy CEO-Fin)*
Mikheil Gomarteli *(Deputy CEO-Retail Banking)*
Sulkhan Gvalia *(Deputy CEO-Corp Banking)*
Avto Namicheishvili *(Deputy CEO-Legal)*
George Sharia *(CIO)*
Murtaz Kikoria *(CEO-Aldagi BCI)*

Board of Directors:
Neil Janin
Kim Bradley
Alasdair Breach
Bozidar Djelic
Tamaz Georgadze
Irakli Gilauri
Kakhaber Kiknavelidze
David Morrison

Non-U.S. Holding:

JSC Bank of Georgia (1)
29a Gagarin Str
Tbilisi, 0160, Georgia GE
Tel.: (995) 32 2444256
E-Mail: ir@bog.ge
Web Site: www.bog.ge/ir
Sales Range: $25-49.9 Million
Emp.: 800
Banking Services
S.I.C.: 6029
N.A.I.C.S.: 522110
Neil Janin *(Chm-Supervisory Bd)*
David Morrison *(Vice Chm-Supervisory Bd)*

Bank of Georgia Holdings PLC—(Continued)

Irakli Gilauri *(CEO)*
Irakli Burdiladze *(Member-Mgmt Bd & Deputy CEO-Affordable Housing)*
Archil Gachechiladze *(Member-Mgmt Bd & Deputy CEO-Asset & Wealth Mgmt)*
Nikoloz Gamkrelidze *(Member-Mgmt Bd & Deputy CEO-Fin)*
Mikheil Gomarteli *(Member-Mgmt Bd & Deputy CEO-Retail Banking)*
Sulkhan Gvalia *(Member-Mgmt Bd & Deputy CEO-Corp Banking)*
Avto Namicheishvili *(Member-Mgmt Bd & Deputy CEO-Legal Affairs)*
George Chiladze *(Chief Risk Officer)*

Subsidiary:

BG Capital **(2)**
23 Chavchavadze Avenue
Tbilisi, 0179, Georgia GE
Tel.: (995) 32235800 (100%)
Fax: (995) 32235804
E-Mail: info@bgcap.ge
Web Site: bgcapital.ge/en/contacts/
Brokerage & Asset Management Services
S.I.C.: 6211
N.A.I.C.S.: 523120
Giorgi Shengelia *(Gen Mgr)*

Affiliate:

JSC Georgian Card **(2)**
221 Nutcubidze Str
Tbilisi, 0168, Georgia GE
Tel.: (995) 32317040 (55.4%)
Fax: (995) 32315765
Web Site: www.gc.com.ge
Credit Card Services
S.I.C.: 6141
N.A.I.C.S.: 522210
Nana Kaburia *(CEO)*
George Keshelashvili *(CEO)*

BANK OF GHANA

One Thorpe Road
PO Box 2674
Accra, Ghana
Tel.: (233) 26661746
Fax: (233) 2662996
E-Mail: bogsecretary@bog.gov.gh
Web Site: www.bog.gov.gh
Year Founded: 1957
Sales Range: $125-149.9 Million
Emp.: 500
Business Description:
Banking Services
S.I.C.: 6029
N.A.I.C.S.: 522110
Personnel:
Paul A. Acquah *(Chm)*
L. Van Lare Dosoo *(Deputy Chm)*
Board of Directors:
Paul A. Acquah
Togbe Afeda
Sam Appah
W. Kwadwo Asenso-Okyere
George Gyan Baffour
Kwabena Darko
Joshua Hamidu
Gloria Nikoi
Sam Okudzeto
L. Van Lare Dosoo

Non-U.S. Subsidiary:

Ghana International Bank plc **(1)**
67 Cheapside 1st Fl
London, EC2V 6AZ, United Kingdom (51%)
Tel.: (44) 2076530350
Fax: (44) 2072482929
E-Mail: customer.services@ghanabank.co.uk
Web Site: www.ghanabank.co.uk
Emp.: 46
Banking Services
S.I.C.: 6029
N.A.I.C.S.: 522110
Festus Mensah *(Head-Fin)*

BANK OF GREECE S.A.

21 E Venizelos Avenue
102 50 Athens, Greece
Tel.: (30) 210 320 1111
Fax: (30) 210 323 2239
Web Site: www.bankofgreece.gr
Year Founded: 1927
TELL—(ATH)
Int. Income: $5,152,141,072
Assets: $215,088,673,109
Liabilities: $213,990,879,427
Net Worth: $1,097,793,682
Earnings: $428,955,998
Fiscal Year-end: 12/31/12
Business Description:
Banking Services
S.I.C.: 6029
N.A.I.C.S.: 522110
Personnel:
Helen Hadjidaki *(Chief Risk Officer)*

BANK OF GUYANA

1 Church Street & Avenue of the Republic
PO Box 1003
Georgetown, Guyana
Tel.: (592) 2263250
Fax: (592) 2272965
E-Mail: communications@bankofguyana.org.gy
Web Site: www.bankofguyana.org.gy
Sales Range: $10-24.9 Million
Emp.: 260
Business Description:
Banking Services
S.I.C.: 6011
N.A.I.C.S.: 521110
Personnel:
Lawrence T. Williams *(Chm)*
G. Ganga *(Deputy Chm)*
Board of Directors:
Lawrence T. Williams
P. Bhim
G. Ganga
V. Persaud
C. Solomon

BANK OF INDIA

Star House C-5 G Block Bandra Kurla Complex Bandra East
Mumbai, 400 051, India
Tel.: (91) 22 66684444
Fax: (91) 2566668431
E-Mail: HeadOffice.CSD@bankofindia.co.in
Web Site: www.bankofindia.com
Year Founded: 1906
532149—(BOM)
Rev.: $6,652,231,722
Assets: $84,617,820,720
Liabilities: $80,067,281,544
Net Worth: $4,550,539,176
Earnings: $522,809,460
Emp.: 39,676
Fiscal Year-end: 03/31/13
Business Description:
Banking Services
S.I.C.: 6029
N.A.I.C.S.: 522110
Personnel:
Vijayalakshmi R. Iyer *(Chm & Mng Dir)*
Krishnakumar K. Nair *(CFO)*
Rajeev Bhatia *(Sec)*
Board of Directors:
Vijayalakshmi R. Iyer
Pramod Bhasin
Neeraj Bhatia
Umesh Kumar Khaitan
R. Koteeswaran
Kuttappan K. Nair
Antonio Maximiano Pereira
P. R. Ravimohan
B. P. Sharma
Arun Shrivastava
Harvinder Singh
P. M. Sirajuddin
Anup Wadhawan

Sankaran & Krishnan
Mumbai, India

L.B. Jha & Co.
Mumbai, India

Karnavat & Co.
Mumbai, India

Isaac & Suresh
Mumbai, India

Chaturvedi & Shah
Mumbai, India

Transfer Agent:
Sharepro Services (I) Private Limited
13 AB Samhita Warehousing Complex Off AndheriKurla Road Sakinaka
Telephone Exchange Lane, Mumbai, India

Subsidiary:

BOI Shareholding Limited **(1)**
Stock Exchange Rotunda Bldg
Versova Andheri W, 400053 Mumbai, MH, India
Tel.: (91) 2256684444
Web Site: www.boislindia.com
Investment Advice
S.I.C.: 6282
N.A.I.C.S.: 523930

Non-U.S. Subsidiary:

PT Bank Swadesi Tbk **(1)**
Jalan KH Samanhudi 37
Jakarta, 10710, Indonesia (76%)
Tel.: (62) 213500007
Fax: (62) 213808178
E-Mail: corporate@bankswadesi.co.id
Web Site: www.bankswadesi.co.id
Emp.: 370
Banking Services
S.I.C.: 6029
N.A.I.C.S.: 522110
Ningsih Suciati *(Mng Dir)*

Non-U.S. Joint Venture:

Indo-Zambia Bank Ltd. **(1)**
Cairo Rd route no 6907
PO Box 35411
Lusaka, Zambia (20%)
Tel.: (260) 01224653
Fax: (260) 01225090
Web Site: www.izb.co.zm
Emp.: 300
Commercial Banking
S.I.C.: 6029
N.A.I.C.S.: 522110
Satish Shukla *(Mng Dir)*

THE BANK OF ISRAEL

PO Box 780
91007 Jerusalem, Israel
Tel.: (972) 26552211
Fax: (972) 26528805
Web Site: www.bankisrael.gov.il
Sales Range: $1-4.9 Billion
Business Description:
Banking Services
S.I.C.: 6011
N.A.I.C.S.: 521110
Personnel:
Stanley Fischer *(Governor)*
Svi Eckstein *(Deputy Governor)*

THE BANK OF IWATE, LTD.

2-3 Chuodori 1-chome
Morioka, Iwate, 020-8688, Japan
Tel.: (81) 19 623 1111
Fax: (81) 19 651 9868
E-Mail: ir-gpd@iwatebank.co.jp
Web Site: www.iwatebank.co.jp
Year Founded: 1932
8345—(TKS)
Sales Range: $550-599.9 Million
Emp.: 1,526
Business Description:
Commercial Banking Services
S.I.C.: 6029
N.A.I.C.S.: 522110
Personnel:
Masahiro Takahashi *(Pres)*
Susumu Kanno *(Sr Mng Dir)*
Masahiro Saito *(Sr Mng Dir)*
Kazuhiko Kudo *(Mng Dir)*
Osamu Sakamoto *(Mng Dir)*
Sachio Taguchi *(Mng Dir)*
Yuichi Kato *(Exec Officer)*
Yuto Takasawa *(Exec Officer)*
Board of Directors:
Keiji Iwata
Susumu Kanno
Kazuhiko Kudo
Hiroshi Miura
Masahiro Saito
Osamu Sakamoto
Katsuya Sato
Sachio Taguchi
Atsushi Takahashi
Masahiro Takahashi
Zenji Yasuda

Subsidiary:

Iwagin Business Service Co., Ltd. **(1)**
2-3 Chuodori 1-chome
Morioka, Iwate, 020-6866, Japan (100%)
Tel.: (81) 196291111
Emp.: 125
Cash Management Services
S.I.C.: 7389
N.A.I.C.S.: 561499
Keiichi Sasaki *(Pres)*

BANK OF JAMAICA

Nethersole Place
PO Box 621
Kingston, Jamaica
Tel.: (876) 9220750
Fax: (876) 9220854
E-Mail: info@boj.org.jm
Web Site: www.boj.org.jm
Sales Range: $350-399.9 Million
Emp.: 490
Business Description:
Banking Services
S.I.C.: 6011
N.A.I.C.S.: 521110
Personnel:
Derick Latibeaudiere *(Chm)*
Livingstone Morrison *(Deputy Governor-Fin, Tech, Payment Sys, Investment & Risk Mgmt)*
Board of Directors:
Derick Latibeaudiere
Colin Bullock
Carlton Davis
Rosalea Hamilton
Jeffrey Pyne
Shirley Tyndall

BANK OF JAPAN

2-1-1 Nihonbashi-Hongokucho Chuo-ku
Tokyo, 103-8660, Japan
Tel.: (81) 3 3279 1111
Web Site: www.boj.or.jp
8301—(JAS)
Sales Range: $700-749.9 Million
Business Description:
Banking Services
S.I.C.: 6029
N.A.I.C.S.: 522110
Personnel:
Hiroshi Nakaso *(Asst Governor)*

BANK OF JORDAN PLC

Al-Shmeisani
PO Box 2140
Amman, 11181, Jordan
Tel.: (962) 65696277
Fax: (962) 65696291
E-Mail: boj@bankofjordan.com.jo
Web Site: www.bankofjordan.com
BOJX—(AMM AMMAN)

Sales Range: $125-149.9 Million
Business Description:
Banking Services
S.I.C.: 6029
N.A.I.C.S.: 522110
Personnel:
Shaker Tawfiq Fakhouri *(Chm & Gen Mgr)*
Abdel Rahman Touqan *(Vice Chm)*
Board of Directors:
Shaker Tawfiq Fakhouri
Omar Mahmoud Abu Namous
Mazen Mohammad Al-Basheir
Yahiya Al-Kadamani
Haitham Abu-Al-Naser Al-Mufti
Haitham Mohmad Barakat
Walid Tawfiq Shaker Fakhouri
Shadi Ramzi A. Majali
Yanal Maouloud Naghouj
Jan J. Shamoun
Abdel Rahman Touqan

BANK OF KAOHSIUNG CO., LTD.

168 Po Ai 2nd Road
Tsoying District, Kaohsiung, Taiwan
Tel.: (886) 75570535
Fax: (886) 75590549
E-Mail: chun@mail.bok.com.tw
Web Site: www.bok.com.tw
2836—(TAI)
Int. Income: $135,447,214
Assets: $7,486,382,189
Liabilities: $7,116,989,703
Net Worth: $369,392,486
Earnings: $13,080,662
Emp.: 942
Fiscal Year-end: 12/31/12
Business Description:
Financial Banking Services
S.I.C.: 6099
N.A.I.C.S.: 522320
Personnel:
Toong-Min Chen *(Chm)*
Moan-Sheug Huang *(Pres)*
Li-Ming Hsu *(Mng Dir)*
Ruey-Tsang Lee *(Mng Dir)*
Wen-Yuan Lin *(Mng Dir)*
Tsui-Mei Hsu *(Sec)*
Chun-Ching Ko *(Exec VP)*
Yi-Jong Liou *(Exec VP)*
Board of Directors:
Toong-Min Chen
Lai-Chuan Chang
Chien-Tsai Chao
Jueifang P. Chen
Yuan-Pei Chou
Mei-Yueh Ho
Li-Ming Hsu
Richard Lee
Ruey-Tsang Lee
Wen-Yuan Lin
Tzen-Ping Su
Wen-Ching Yang
Supervisory Board of Directors:
Shan-Hui Chang
Yu-Hui Su
Yung-Yu Tsai
Transfer Agent:
Yuanta Securities Co Ltd
B1 B2 210 Sec 3 Chengde Road
Datong District, Taipei, Taiwan
Tel.: (886) 225865859

BANK OF KATHMANDU LIMITED

Kamal Pokhari
PO Box 9044
Kathmandu, Nepal
Tel.: (977) 14414541
Fax: (977) 14418990
E-Mail: info@bok.com.np
Web Site: www.bok.com.np
BOK—(NEP)
Emp.: 452
Business Description:
Banking Services
S.I.C.: 6029
N.A.I.C.S.: 522110
Personnel:
Satya Narayan Manandhar *(Chm)*
Ajay Shrestha *(CEO)*
Prabin Prakash Chhetri *(COO)*
Anju Nakarmi *(HR Dev Officer)*
Manish Kumar Singh *(Sec & Head-Integrated Risk Mgmt & Compliance)*
Board of Directors:
Satya Narayan Manandhar
Ramesh Nath Dhungel
Balaram Neupane
Govinda Prasad Sharma
Chop Narayan Shrestha
Hem Raj Subedi
Santa Bar Singh Thapa

THE BANK OF KOREA

110 3-Ga Namdaemunno Jung-Gu
Seoul, 100-794, Korea (South)
Tel.: (82) 27594114
Fax: (82) 27594060
E-Mail: info@bok.or.kr
Web Site: www.bok.or.kr
Rev.: $16,206,421,947
Assets: $415,236,678,012
Liabilities: $404,468,879,944
Net Worth: $10,767,798,068
Earnings: $3,613,418,205
Emp.: 2,198
Fiscal Year-end: 12/31/12
Business Description:
Banking Services
S.I.C.: 6011
N.A.I.C.S.: 521110
Personnel:
Jae Sung Hur *(Deputy Governor)*

THE BANK OF KYOTO, LTD.

700 Yakushimae-cho Karasuma-dori
Matsubara-Agaru Shimogyo-ku
Kyoto, 600-8652, Japan
Tel.: (81) 75 361 2211
Fax: (81) 75 3431276
Web Site: www.kyotobank.co.jp
Year Founded: 1941
8369—(TKS)
Rev.: $1,268,267,000
Assets: $83,895,548,000
Liabilities: $78,801,734,000
Net Worth: $5,093,814,000
Earnings: $193,314,000
Emp.: 3,360
Fiscal Year-end: 03/31/13
Business Description:
Banking Services
S.I.C.: 6029
N.A.I.C.S.: 522110
Personnel:
Yasuo Kashihara *(Chm)*
Hideo Takasaki *(Pres)*
Issei Daido *(Sr Mng Dir)*
Nobuhiro Doi *(Co-Mng Dir)*
Junji Inoguchi *(Co-Mng Dir)*
Masayuki Kobayashi *(Co-Mng Dir)*
Hisayoshi Nakamura *(Co-Mng Dir)*
Yoshio Nishi *(Co-Mng Dir)*
Katsuyuki Toyobe *(Co-Mng Dir)*
Satoru Kitagawa *(Exec Officer)*
Hideya Naka *(Mng Exec Officer)*
Ko Nishizawa *(Mng Exec Officer)*
Hiroshi Okuno *(Mng Exec Officer)*
Hirokazu Tagano *(Exec Officer)*
Shinichi Takenaka *(Mng Exec Officer)*
Keizo Tokomoto *(Exec Officer)*
Hiroyuki Yamamoto *(Exec Officer)*
Board of Directors:
Yasuo Kashihara
Masaya Anami
Issei Daido
Nobuhiro Doi
Hiroshi Hitomi
Junji Inoguchi
Masayuki Kobayashi
Takayuki Matsumura
Masahiko Naka
Hisayoshi Nakamura
Yoshio Nishi
Hideo Takasaki
Katsuyuki Toyobe
Division:

The Bank of Kyoto, Ltd. - Treasury & Investment Division (1)
2-3-14 Yaesu
Chuo-ku, Tokyo, 104-0028, Japan
Tel.: (81) 3 3281 1212
Fax: (81) 3 3281 8026
Commercial Banking Services
S.I.C.: 6029
N.A.I.C.S.: 522110

Subsidiaries:

Karasuma Shoji Co., Ltd. (1)
9 Umetadacho
Sanjodori-Karasumahigashiiru N, Kyoto, Japan
Tel.: (81) 752550114
Web Site: www.karasumashoji.co.jp
Nonresidential Buildings Lessors
S.I.C.: 6512
N.A.I.C.S.: 531120

Kyogin Business Service Co., Ltd. (1)
25 Minamitonomotocho
Kamitoba Minami-Ku, Kyoto, Japan
Tel.: (81) 756825403
Fax: (81) 0756826103
Emp.: 200
Business Support Services
S.I.C.: 7389
N.A.I.C.S.: 561499
Takamoto Tetsutaro *(Mgr)*

Kyogin Card Service Co., Ltd. (1)
731 Higashishiokojicho
600-8216 Kyoto, Japan
Tel.: (81) 753442211
Fax: (81) 753442545
Web Site: www.kyotojcb.jp
Emp.: 25
Nondepository Credit Intermediation
S.I.C.: 6159
N.A.I.C.S.: 522298
Satoshi Umehara *(Mgr-Gen Affairs)*

Kyogin Lease & Capital Co., Ltd. (1)
731 Higashishiokojicho
Karasumadori nanajyo sagaru Sh, Kyoto, Japan
Tel.: (81) 753613232
Machinery & Equipment Rental & Leasing
S.I.C.: 7359
N.A.I.C.S.: 532420
Hideaki Shirota *(Pres)*

Kyoto Credit Service Co., Ltd. (1)
731 Higashishiokojicho Karasumadori
Nanajyo Sagaru Shimogyo-ku
Kyoto-shi Shimogyo-ku Karasum, Kyoto, 600-8216, Japan
Tel.: (81) 753415500
Fax: (81) 753714321
Web Site: www.kyotodc.co.jp
Emp.: 30
Nondepository Credit Intermediation
S.I.C.: 6159
N.A.I.C.S.: 522298
Takasi Otuki *(Pres)*

Kyoto Guaranty Service Co., Ltd. (1)
700 Yakushimaecho
Karasumadori-Matsubaraagaru Sh, Kyoto, Japan
Tel.: (81) 752110400
Nondepository Credit Intermediation
S.I.C.: 6159
N.A.I.C.S.: 522298

Kyoto Research Institute, Inc. (1)
700 Yakushimaecho
Karasumadori-Matsubaraagaru Sh, Kyoto, Japan
Tel.: (81) 753612377
Fax: (81) 753617590
General Economic Programs Administration
S.I.C.: 9611
N.A.I.C.S.: 926110
Toshihiko Ueda *(Pres)*

BANK OF MALDIVES PLC

11 Boduthakurufaanu Magu
Male, 20094, Maldives
Tel.: (960) 332 2948
Fax: (960) 332 8233
E-Mail: info@bml.com.mv
Web Site: www.bankofmaldives.com.mv
Year Founded: 1982
Sales Range: $10-24.9 Million
Emp.: 190
Business Description:
Banking Services
S.I.C.: 6029
N.A.I.C.S.: 522110
Personnel:
Shiham Abdullah Hassan *(Chm & Exec Dir)*
Lucian Jayakody *(Chief Internal Auditor & Chief Compliance Officer)*
Board of Directors:
Shiham Abdullah Hassan
Aminath Ali Maniku
Aishath Noordeen

BANK OF MAURITIUS

Sir William Newton Street
Port Louis, Mauritius
Tel.: (230) 2023800
Fax: (230) 2089204
E-Mail: info@bom.mu
Web Site: www.bom.mu
Rev.: $38,594,693
Assets: $3,589,315,822
Liabilities: $2,915,663,542
Net Worth: $673,652,280
Earnings: ($58,093,993)
Emp.: 213
Fiscal Year-end: 06/30/13
Business Description:
Banking Services
S.I.C.: 6011
N.A.I.C.S.: 521110
Personnel:
Rundheersing Bheenick *(Chm & Governor)*
Hemlata Sadhna Sewraj-Gopal *(Sec)*
Board of Directors:
Rundheersing Bheenick
Yandraduth Googoolye
Shyam Razkumar Seebun
Issa Mohamad Soormally
Jacques Miow Li Wan Po Tin
Gooroonaden Vydelingum

THE BANK OF MONGOLIA

Baga Toiruu 9
Ulaanbaatar, 46, Mongolia
Tel.: (976) 11310413
Fax: (976) 11322471
Web Site: www.mongolbank.mn
Sales Range: $150-199.9 Million
Emp.: 321
Business Description:
Banking Services
S.I.C.: 6011
N.A.I.C.S.: 521110
Personnel:
B. Enkhhuyag *(First Deputy Governor)*
Board of Directors:
M. Amgalan
N. Batsaikhan
D. Boldbaatar
B. Enkhhuyag
D. Enkhjargal
G. Erdenebayar
J. Ganbaatar
C. Hashchuluun
G. Purevbaatar
G. Togtokhbaatar

BANK OF MONTREAL
(d/b/a BMO Financial Group)
100 King Street West 1 First Canadian Place
Toronto, ON, M5X 1A1, Canada
Tel.: (416) 867-6785
Fax: (416) 867-6793
E-Mail: feedback@bmo.com
Web Site: www.bmo.com
Year Founded: 1817
BMO—(NYSE TSX)
Rev.: $16,165,747,260
Assets: $534,085,951,980
Liabilities: $502,793,208,360
Net Worth: $31,292,743,620
Earnings: $4,222,596,960
Emp.: 45,500
Fiscal Year-end: 10/31/13

Business Description:
Commercial Banking & Investment Services
S.I.C.: 6029
N.A.I.C.S.: 522110

Personnel:
J. Robert S. Prichard *(Chm)*
Kevin G. Lynch *(Vice Chm)*
Eric C. Tripp *(Pres-BMO Capital Markets)*
Thomas E. Flynn *(CFO)*
Jean-Michel R. Ares *(Co-COO & CTO)*
Franklin J. Techar *(Co-COO)*
Joanna Rotenberg *(CMO & Head-Strategy)*
Surjit S. Rajpal *(Chief Risk Officer)*
Richard D. Rudderham *(Chief HR Officer)*
L. Jacques Menard *(Chm-BMO Nesbitt Burns & Pres-Quebec)*
Christopher B. Begy *(CEO-BMO Financial Corp & Head-US)*
Mark F. Furlong *(CEO-BMO Harris NA & Head-P&C Banking-US)*
Albert Yu *(CEO-Asia)*
Simon A. Fish *(Gen Counsel)*
Russel C. Robertson *(Exec VP & Head-Anti-Money Laundering)*

Board of Directors:
J. Robert S. Prichard
Robert M. Astley
Janice M. Babiak
Sophie Brochu
George A. Cope
William A. Downe
Christine A. Edwards
Ronald H. Farmer
Eric R. La Fleche
Kevin G. Lynch
Bruce H. Mitchell
Philip S. Orsino
Martha C. Piper
Donald M. Wilson, III

Computershare Trust Company, N.A.
Golden, CO 80401

Computershare Investor Services PLC
London, United Kingdom

Transfer Agents:
Computershare Trust Company of Canada
Toronto, ON, Canada

Computershare Trust Company, N.A.
Golden, CO 80401

Computershare Investor Services PLC
London, United Kingdom

Division:

BMO Capital Markets **(1)**
100 King St W 1 First Canadian Pl
Toronto, ON, M5X 1H3, Canada
Tel.: (416) 867-5000
Web Site: www.bmocm.com
Risk Management & Investment Banking Services
S.I.C.: 6211
N.A.I.C.S.: 523110
Luc Bachand *(Vice Chm & Head-Quebec)*
Chuck Adair *(Vice Chm)*
Brian Tobin *(Vice Chm)*
Ken Tuchman *(Vice Chm)*
Eric C. Tripp *(Pres)*
Thomas V. Milroy *(CEO)*
David L. Sawyer *(Mng Dir & Head-Restructuring Div)*
Mathieu L. L'Allier *(Mng Dir & Head-Investment & Corp Banking-Quebec)*
Miles Redfield *(Mng Dir & Head-Acq & Divestitures-US)*
Richard Vieira *(Mng Dir & Head-Tech)*
Debbie Rechter *(Mng Dir & Mgr-Sls-US)*
Ed Solari *(Mng Dir & Mgr-Sls-New York Reg)*

Subsidiary:

BMO Nesbitt Burns Inc. **(2)**
1 First Canadian Place
Toronto, ON, M5X 1H3, Canada ON (100%)
Tel.: (416) 359-4000
Fax: (416) 359-7499
Web Site: www.bmonesbittburns.com
Emp.: 2,500
Provider of Banking Services
S.I.C.: 6099
N.A.I.C.S.: 522320
Luc Bachand *(Vice Chm-Investment Banking Group)*
Darryl White *(Mng Dir)*
David C. Ferguson *(CFO)*

Subsidiaries:

Bank of Montreal Finance Ltd. **(1)**
100 King Street West 21st Floor First Canadian Place
Toronto, ON, M5X 1A1, Canada
Tel.: (416) 867-4711
Commercial Banking Services
S.I.C.: 6029
N.A.I.C.S.: 522110

BMO Capital Trust **(1)**
100 King St W First Canadian Pl
Toronto, ON, M5X 1A1, Canada ON
Tel.: (416) 867-5000
Fax: (416) 867-6793
Web Site: www.bankofmontreal.com
Rev.: $4,833,749
Nondeposit Trust Facilities
S.I.C.: 6091
N.A.I.C.S.: 523991
Paul A. Hawkinson *(Mng Dir & Head-Indus)*

BMO Group Retirement Services Inc. **(1)**
181 Bay St Suite 2820
Toronto, ON, Canada
Tel.: (877) 446-8347
Fax: (866) 362-2659
E-Mail: bmogrs.helpdesk@bmo.com
Web Site: www.bmo.com
Administrative Services
S.I.C.: 8741
N.A.I.C.S.: 561110
Kurt Mueller *(Mgr-Relationship)*

BMO Investments, Inc. **(1)**
77 King St W Ste 4200
Toronto, ON, M5K 1J5, Canada ON
Tel.: (416) 867-7755
Fax: (416) 867-6250
E-Mail:
Emp.: 100
Mutual Fund Firm
S.I.C.: 6722
N.A.I.C.S.: 525910
Ross Kappele *(Co-Pres)*
Linda Knight *(Co-Pres)*
Hugh Mc Kee *(Co-Pres)*

BMO Investorline, Inc. **(1)**
1st Canadian Pl 100 King St W B1 Fl
Toronto, ON, M5X 1H3, Canada ON (100%)
Tel.: (416) 867-4000
Fax: (416) 359-5607
E-Mail: info@bmoinvestorline.com
Web Site: www.bmoinvestorline.com
Sales Range: $1-9.9 Million
Emp.: 120
Investment Management & Brokerage Services
S.I.C.: 6211
N.A.I.C.S.: 523110

BMO Life Assurance Company **(1)**
60 Yonge Street
Toronto, ON, M5E 1H5, Canada
Tel.: (416) 596-3900
Fax: (416) 596-4143
Toll Free: (800) 387-4483
E-Mail: insurance.clientservices@bmo.com
Web Site: www.bmolifeinsurance.com
Emp.: 30
Life Insurance Services
S.I.C.: 6411
N.A.I.C.S.: 524298
Peter Mccarthy *(CEO & Pres)*

BMO Life Insurance Company **(1)**
60 Yonge St
Toronto, ON, M5E 1H5, Canada ON
Tel.: (416) 596-3900
Fax: (416) 596-4143
Web Site: www.bmo.com
Rev.: $14,323,020
Emp.: 250
Insurance Agents Brokers & Service
S.I.C.: 6411
N.A.I.C.S.: 524298
Peter McCarthy *(Pres & CEO)*

BMO Private Equity (Canada) Inc. **(1)**
100 King St W Fl 50
Toronto, ON, M5X 1H3, Canada
Tel.: (416) 359-4000
Investment Banking Services
S.I.C.: 6211
N.A.I.C.S.: 523110

BMO Trust Company **(1)**
1 1st Canadian Pl 41 Fl
Toronto, ON, M5X 1A1, Canada (100%)
Tel.: (416) 359-5901
Fax: (416) 359-8515
Toll Free: (866) 501-5056
Web Site: bmoharris.com
Emp.: 70
Trust & Fiduciary Services
S.I.C.: 6733
N.A.I.C.S.: 523991
Sara Plant *(VP-Personal Web Svcs)*

Affiliate:

Guardian Group of Funds Ltd. **(1)**
Commerce Ct W Ste 4100
Toronto, ON, M5L 1G6, Canada ON (100%)
Mailing Address:
PO Box 577
Toronto, ON, M5L 1G6, Canada
Tel.: (416) 947-4011
Fax: (416) 364-9169
E-Mail: info@ggof.com
Web Site: www.ggof.com
Emp.: 110
Mutual Funds
S.I.C.: 6722
N.A.I.C.S.: 525910
Debbie Stansens *(VP-Mktg Svcs)*

Joint Venture:

Moneris Solutions Corporation **(1)**
3300 Bloor St W 10th Fl
Toronto, ON, M8X 2X2, Canada
Tel.: (416) 734-1000
Fax: (416) 734-1009
Toll Free: (866) 319-7450
E-Mail: info@moneris.com
Web Site: www.moneris.com
Emp.: 1,500
Payment Processing Services; Owned by RBC Financial Group & Bank of Montreal
S.I.C.: 6099
N.A.I.C.S.: 522320
Angela Brown *(Pres & CEO)*
Samir Zabaneh *(CFO)*
Fern Glowinsky *(COO)*
Rob Cameron *(Chief Product & Mktg Officer)*
Amer Matar *(Sr VP-Product & Tech)*
Joan Mitchell *(Sr VP-HR)*
Brian Prentice *(Sr VP-Credit & Risk Mgmt-North America)*

Division:

Ernex **(2)**
4259 Canada Way Ste 225
Burnaby, BC, V5G 1H1, Canada
Tel.: (604) 415-1500
Fax: (604) 415-1591
E-Mail: info@ernex.com
Web Site: www.ernex.com
Sales Range: $1-9.9 Million
Emp.: 65
Electronic Marketing Services
S.I.C.: 7373
N.A.I.C.S.: 541512
James Baumgartner *(Pres)*

Subsidiary:

MSC Moneris Services Corp. **(2)**
7350 Rue Transcanadienne
Saint Laurent, QC, H4T 1A3, Canada
Tel.: (514) 733-5403
Web Site: www.msposcorp.com
Emp.: 300
Payment Processing Services
S.I.C.: 6099
N.A.I.C.S.: 522320
Wayne Griffiths *(Gen Mgr)*

U.S. Subsidiary:

Moneris Solutions, Inc. **(2)**
Woodfield Corp Ctr 150 N Martingale Rd Ste 900
Schaumburg, IL 60173
Tel.: (847) 240-7553
Fax: (847) 240-6583
Toll Free: (800) 471-0511
Web Site: www.monerisusa.com
Payment Processing Services
S.I.C.: 6099
N.A.I.C.S.: 522320

U.S. Subsidiaries:

BMO Financial Corp. **(1)**
111 W Monroe St
Chicago, IL 60603-4096
Tel.: (312) 461-2121
Fax: (312) 461-2347
Web Site: www.harrisbank.com
Emp.: 6,638
Bank Holding Company
S.I.C.: 6712
N.A.I.C.S.: 551111
Ellen Costello *(Pres)*
Pamela C. Piarowski *(CFO & Sr VP-Fin)*
John Benevides *(Pres-Family Office Svcs)*
Anthony Lopez *(Pres-South Reg-Chicago Metro)*
David Mika *(Pres-Northwest Indiana Reg)*
Albert Yu *(CEO-Asia)*
Judy Rice *(Sr VP & Head-Community Affairs & Economic Dev)*
Darrell Hackett *(Sr VP-Small-Bus Banking)*

Subsidiaries:

BMO Asset Management Corp. **(2)**
190 S LaSalle St 4th Fl
Chicago, IL 60603
Tel.: (312) 461-7699
Fax: (312) 461-7096
Mutual Fund Management Services
S.I.C.: 6282
N.A.I.C.S.: 523920
Mike Robinson *(Head-Intermediary Distr)*

BMO Capital Markets Corp. **(2)**
3 Times Sq
New York, NY 10036-6564
Tel.: (212) 702-1900
Web Site: www.bmocm.com
Investment Banking & Financial Advisory Services
S.I.C.: 6211
N.A.I.C.S.: 523110
Tod Benton *(Vice Chm)*
Mark Decker, Sr. *(Vice Chm)*
Eric C. Tripp *(Pres)*
Thomas V. Milroy *(CEO)*
Jim Gallagher *(Mng Dir & Head-Equity Sector Trading)*

BMO Capital Markets Equity Group (U.S.), Inc. **(2)**
115 S La Salle St 1200
Chicago, IL 60603-3801
Tel.: (312) 845-4019
Commercial Banking Services
S.I.C.: 6029
N.A.I.C.S.: 522110

BMO Harris Bank N.A. **(2)**
111 W Monroe St
Chicago, IL 60603-4096 DE
Mailing Address:
PO Box 755
Chicago, IL 60690-0755
Tel.: (312) 461-2121
Fax: (312) 293-4780
Toll Free: (888) 340BANK

E-Mail: webinfo@harrisbank.com
Web Site: www.harrisbank.com
Sales Range: $650-699.9 Million
Emp.: 6,850
Commercial Banking Services
S.I.C.: 6029
N.A.I.C.S.: 522110
Peter B. McNitt *(Vice Chm)*
Mark F. Furlong *(CEO & Head-P&C Banking-US)*
Jennifer Muench *(Mng Dir & VP-Private Banking-British Columbia)*
Ghram Debes *(Mng Dir & Head-Dealership Fin)*
Pam C. Piarowski *(CFO & Sr VP)*
Todd Senger *(Pres-Minnesota, Mng Dir-Comml Banking & Mgr-Minnesota & Kansas)*
Michael Colclough *(Pres-Duluth Superior)*
Matt Crowell *(Pres-Ashland)*
Dave Mika *(Pres-Lakeshore Market)*
Steven Zandpour *(Pres-Market-North Shore)*
Justine Fedak *(Sr VP & Head-Mktg & Customer Strategies)*
Jim Gallimore *(Sr VP & Dir-Comml Banking)*
Ivy Bennett *(Sr VP-Mktg & Customer Strategies)*
Deirdre Drake *(Sr VP-HR)*
Christy Horn *(Sr VP-Retail Lending)*
Margie Lawless *(Sr VP-Small Bus Banking)*

BMO Harris Equipment Finance Company **(2)**
250 E Wisconsin Ave Ste 1400
Milwaukee, WI 53202-4219 WI
Tel.: (414) 272-2374 (100%)
Web Site: www4.harrisbank.com
Sales Range: $10-24.9 Million
Emp.: 60
Lease Financing of Business Equipment & Machinery to Commercial, Industrial & Institutional Customers
S.I.C.: 7359
N.A.I.C.S.: 532490
Jud Snyder *(Pres)*
Brad Hansen *(Exec VP)*
Bruce Homan *(Sr VP)*

BMO Harris Financial Advisors, Inc. **(2)**
111 W Monroe St
Chicago, IL 60603
Tel.: (312) 461-2121
Web Site: www4.harrisbank.com
Investment Advice & Securities Brokerage Services
S.I.C.: 6282
N.A.I.C.S.: 523930
David R. Casper *(Exec VP & Head-Comml Banking)*

BMO Harris Financing, Inc. **(2)**
111 W Monroe St
Chicago, IL 60603
Tel.: (312) 461-2121
Fax: (312) 461-7869
Toll Free: (888) 340-2265
Web Site: www.bmoharris.com
Emp.: 2,000
Commercial Banking Services
S.I.C.: 6029
N.A.I.C.S.: 522110
Bill Downe *(Pres)*

Harris myCFO, Inc. **(2)**
1080 Mars Rd Ste 100
Menlo Park, CA 94025
Tel.: (312) 461-3754
Fax: (312) 765-8375
Toll Free: (877) 692-3611
E-Mail: clientinfo@harrismycfo.com
Web Site: www.mycfo.com
Emp.: 100
Financial Management Services
S.I.C.: 6282
N.A.I.C.S.: 523930
Thomas Meilinger *(Mng Dir)*

Subsidiary:

CTC Consulting LLC **(3)**
4380 SW Macadam Ave Ste 490
Portland, OR 97239
Tel.: (503) 228-4300
Fax: (503) 220-4576
E-Mail: vince.gimarelli@ctcconsulting.com
Web Site: www.ctcconsultinginc.com
Managed Assets: $23,000,000,000
Emp.: 60
Financial Investment Consulting Services
S.I.C.: 6282
N.A.I.C.S.: 523930
Garbis P. Mechigian *(Mng Partner, Chm & CEO)*
Kristi Hanson *(Pres & Dir-Investment Res)*
Michael D. Finan *(Mng Partner)*
Karen M. Harding *(Mng Partner)*
David Upson *(Mng Dir, Partner & Dir-Hedge Fund Res)*
Claude R. Perrier *(Mng Dir & Partner)*
Kathy Kamerer *(Chief Admin Officer, Partner & Chief Compliance Officer)*
John Banker *(Partner & Dir-Traditional Res)*
Kristi Combs *(Partner & Dir-Mktg)*
Robert T. Elsasser *(Partner & Dir-Fixed Income Res)*
J. B. Hayes *(Partner & Dir-Private Markets Res)*
Rex T. Kim *(Partner & Dir-Hedge Fund Res)*
Rod Larson *(Partner & Dir-Private Markets Res)*
Mark Thomas *(Partner & Dir-Community Res)*
Jeannette Armitage *(Partner)*
Isabelle K. Campbell *(Partner)*
Stacey Flier *(Partner)*
Heather Gilroy *(Partner)*
Cheryl L. Holland *(Partner)*
Jennifer Martin *(Partner)*
Patrick M. Parisi *(Partner)*
Robert Gray *(COO)*
Curt Fintel *(Sr VP & Chief Investment Strategist)*

Harris RIA Holdings, Inc. **(2)**
111 W Monroe St Ste 1200
Chicago, IL 60603-4014
Tel.: (312) 461-2121
Investment Management Services
S.I.C.: 6211
N.A.I.C.S.: 523999

M&I Servicing Corp. **(2)**
3993 Howard Hughes Pkwy Ste 100
Las Vegas, NV 89109-0961
Tel.: (702) 735-1832
Sales Range: $10-24.9 Million
Emp.: 2
Management Investment Services
S.I.C.: 6722
N.A.I.C.S.: 525910
Monica Louie *(COO)*

Stoker Ostler Wealth Advisors, Inc. **(2)**
4900 N Scottsdale Rd Ste 2600
Scottsdale, AZ 85251-7658
Tel.: (480) 890-8088
Fax: (480) 890-8770
Wealth Management Services
S.I.C.: 6799
N.A.I.C.S.: 523920

Non-U.S. Subsidiaries:

Bank of Montreal Assessoria e Servicos Ltda. **(1)**
Av Rio Branco 143 1801
Rio de Janeiro, 20040-006, Brazil
Tel.: (55) 21 3852 6407
Fax: (55) 21 2507 1589
Emp.: 5
Commercial Banking Services
S.I.C.: 6029
N.A.I.C.S.: 522110

Bank of Montreal Capital Markets (Holdings) Limited **(1)**
95 Queen Victoria St
London, EC4V 4HG, United Kingdom
Tel.: (44) 20 7236 1010
Fax: (44) 20 7248 3647
Web Site: www.bmo.com
Emp.: 20
Investment Management Services
S.I.C.: 6211
N.A.I.C.S.: 523999
William Smith *(Mng Dir)*

Subsidiaries:

BMO Capital Markets Limited **(2)**
95 Queen Victoria Street 2nd Floor
London, EC4V 4HG, United Kingdom
Tel.: (44) 20 7236 1010
Web Site: www.bmocm.com
Investment Banking Services
S.I.C.: 6211
N.A.I.C.S.: 523110

Pyrford International Limited **(2)**
79 Grosvenor Street
London, W1K 3JU, United Kingdom
Tel.: (44) 20 7495 4641
Fax: (44) 20 7399 2204
E-Mail: information@pyrford.co.uk
Web Site: www.pyrford.co.uk
Emp.: 25
Asset Management Services
S.I.C.: 6799
N.A.I.C.S.: 523920
Tony Cousins *(CEO & Chief Investment Officer)*
Drew Newman *(COO)*
Victor Williams *(Chief Compliance Officer)*
Bruce Campbell *(Chm-Investment)*

Bank of Montreal (China) Co. Ltd. **(1)**
Unit 01 27th Floor Tower 3 China Central Place No 77 Jianguo Road
Chaoyang District, Beijing, 100025, China
Tel.: (86) 10 8588 1688
Fax: (86) 10 8518 8169
E-Mail: enquiry.bj@bmo.com
Commercial Banking Services
S.I.C.: 6029
N.A.I.C.S.: 522110

Bank of Montreal Ireland plc **(1)**
6th Floor 2 Harbourmaster Place
Dublin, Ireland
Tel.: (353) 1 6629300
Fax: (353) 1 6147819
Web Site: www.bmo.com
Emp.: 19
Banking Services
S.I.C.: 6029
N.A.I.C.S.: 522110
Neil Ward *(Gen Mgr)*

BMO Finance Company I, S.A R.L. **(1)**
9 Rue Gabriel Lippmann
5365 Munsbach, Luxembourg
Tel.: (352) 27 69 35
Fax: (352) 35227 6921
Commercial Banking Services
S.I.C.: 6029
N.A.I.C.S.: 522110

Lloyd George Management (Hong Kong) Limited **(1)**
Suite 3808 1 Exchange Square
Central, China (Hong Kong)
Tel.: (852) 28454433
Fax: (852) 28453911
E-Mail: info@lloydgeorge.com
Web Site: www.lloydgeorge.com
Emp.: 80
Asset Management & Investment Banking Services
S.I.C.: 6211
N.A.I.C.S.: 523110
Robert Lloyd George *(Founder & Chm-Investment)*
Tony Cousins *(CEO)*
Susanna Ng *(COO)*
Thomas Vester *(Chief Investment Officer)*

Non-U.S. Subsidiaries:

Lloyd George Management (Europe) Limited **(2)**
78 Brook Street
London, W1K 5EF, United Kingdom
Tel.: (44) 207 408 7688
Fax: (44) 207 495 8651
E-Mail: info@uk.lloydgeorge.com
Web Site: www.lloydgeorge.com
Emp.: 2
Portfolio Management Services
S.I.C.: 6282
N.A.I.C.S.: 523920
Irina Hunter *(Sr Portfolio Mgr)*

Lloyd George Management (Singapore) Pte Ltd. **(2)**
11a Stanley St
Downtown, Singapore, 68730, Singapore
Tel.: (65) 62223877
Fax: (65) 62223878
Emp.: 2
Asset Management Services
S.I.C.: 6282
N.A.I.C.S.: 523920
How Teng Chiou *(Gen Mgr)*

THE BANK OF NAGOYA, LTD.

19 17 Nishiki 3 chome
Naka ku, Nagoya, 460-0003, Japan
Tel.: (81) 529629520
Fax: (81) 529626043
Web Site: www.meigin.com
Year Founded: 1949
8522—(NGO TKS)
Sales Range: $800-899.9 Million
Emp.: 2,036

Business Description:
Banking Services
S.I.C.: 6029
N.A.I.C.S.: 522110

Personnel:
Kazumaro Kato *(Chm)*
Yukio Yanase *(Pres)*
Toshiro Goto *(Sr Mng Dir)*
Katsuhiro Sota *(Sr Mng Dir)*
Ichiro Fujiwara *(Mng Dir)*
Yoji Kasahara *(Mng Dir)*
Chiharu Kozakai *(Exec Officer)*
Ikuo Yamada *(Exec Officer)*

Subsidiary:

Nagoya Lease Co., Ltd. **(1)**
2-chome Kamimaedu District 5 Bill Kamimaedu Silver Guest
4th Fl No 3, Nagoya, 460 0013, Japan
Tel.: (81) 523227531
Fax: (81) 52 322 7541
E-Mail: info@nagoyalease.co.jp
Web Site: www.nagoyalease.co.jp
Bank Leasing Services
S.I.C.: 7359
N.A.I.C.S.: 532490

BANK OF NAMIBIA

71 Robert Mugabe Ave
Windhoek, 2882, Namibia
Mailing Address:
PO Box 2882
Windhoek, Namibia
Tel.: (264) 612835111
Fax: (264) 612835067
Web Site: www.bon.com.na
Year Founded: 1990
Rev.: $50,053,987
Assets: $1,703,360,647
Liabilities: $1,468,592,678
Net Worth: $234,767,969
Earnings: $35,798,710
Emp.: 306
Fiscal Year-end: 12/31/12

Business Description:
Banking Services
S.I.C.: 6029
N.A.I.C.S.: 522110

Personnel:
Ipumbu W. Shiimi *(Chm & Governor)*
Michael Mukete *(Asst Governor & Head-Fin Stability)*

Board of Directors:
Ipumbu W. Shiimi
Omu Kakujaha-Matundu
Faniel G. Kisting
Ericah B. Shafudah
Nashilongo Shivute
Ebson Uanguta
Adv Charmaine van der Westhuizen

BANK OF NANJING CO., LTD.

50 Huaihai Road
Bai Xia District, Nanjing, 210005, China
Tel.: (86) 25 84551009
Fax: (86) 25 84553505
E-Mail: webmaster@njcb.com.cn
Web Site: www.njcb.com.cn
601009—(SHG)
Int. Income: $2,659,335,013
Assets: $49,845,883,663
Liabilities: $45,935,262,419
Net Worth: $3,910,621,244
Earnings: $642,472,955
Emp.: 2,700

Bank of Nanjing Co., Ltd.—(Continued)

Fiscal Year-end: 12/31/12
Business Description:
Banking Services
S.I.C.: 6029
N.A.I.C.S.: 522110
Personnel:
Fu Lin *(Chm)*
Zhiqiang Yu *(Chm-Supervisory Bd)*
Ping Xia *(Pres)*
Enqi Liu *(CFO)*
Zhexin Tang *(Sec)*
Board of Directors:
Fu Lin
Philippe Aguignier
Conglai Fan
Qingwu Fan
Zhenggui Hong
Haitao Wang
Ping Xia
Yimin Xu
Yan Yan
Zhonghua Yan
Weinian Zhang
Yuanchao Zhang
Xiaoqi Zhou
Zengjin Zhu
Supervisory Board of Directors:
Zhiqiang Yu
Wenzhang Ji
Huirong Wang
Xinping Yu
Lan Zhao
Feng Zhu

THE BANK OF NEVIS LTD.

Main Street
PO Box 450
Charlestown, Saint Kitts & Nevis
Tel.: (869) 469 5564
Fax: (869) 469 5798
E-Mail: bon@caribsurf.com
Web Site: www.thebankofnevis.com
BON—(ECA)
Sales Range: $1-9.9 Million
Emp.: 60
Business Description:
Banking Services
S.I.C.: 6029
N.A.I.C.S.: 522110
Personnel:
Rawlinson Isaac *(Chm)*
Lisa O. Herbert *(CFO)*
Aiandra E. Knights *(Gen Counsel & Sec)*
Board of Directors:
Rawlinson Isaac
Kishu Chandiramani
Janice Daniel-Hodge
Telbert R. Glasgow
Desmond Herbert
Richard Lupinacci
Chris Morton
Sonya L.E. Parry
Vernel Powell
Subsidiary:

The International Bank of Nevis (1)
Main Street
PO Box 450
Charlestown, Saint Kitts & Nevis
Tel.: (869) 469 0800
Fax: (869) 469 5798
Web Site: www.thebankofnevis.com
International Banking Services
S.I.C.: 6029
N.A.I.C.S.: 522110

BANK OF NINGBO CO., LTD.

No 700 Ningnan South Road
Ningbo, Zhejiang, China 315100
Tel.: (86) 57487050028
Fax: (86) 57487050027
E-Mail: dsh@nbcb.com.cn
Web Site: www.nbcb.com.cn
Year Founded: 1997
002142—(SSE)
Int. Income: $2,833,844,605
Assets: $59,336,287,163
Liabilities: $55,823,008,067
Net Worth: $3,513,279,096
Earnings: $646,223,562
Emp.: 5,329
Fiscal Year-end: 12/31/12
Business Description:
Commercial Banking
S.I.C.: 6029
N.A.I.C.S.: 522110
Personnel:
Huayu Lu *(Chm)*
Hui Zhang *(Chm-Supervisory Bd)*
Fengying Yu *(Vice Chm)*
Mengbo Luo *(Pres)*
Board of Directors:
Huayu Lu
Laixing Cai
Guanghua Chen
Yongming Chen
Zhiyong Dai
Lifeng Hong
Rucheng Li
Yunqi Li
Mengbo Luo
Lizhong Shi
Hanping Song
Zequn Sun
Sining Tang
Qingjian Xie
Wanmao Xu
Xiaoping Yang
Fengying Yu
Jiandi Zhu
Supervisory Board of Directors:
Hui Zhang
Zhongjing Chen
Suying Liu
Dong Shen
Liming Xu
Ningning Yu
Yingfang Zhang

THE BANK OF NOVA SCOTIA

(d/b/a Scotiabank)
44 King St West Scotia Plaza 8th Floor
Toronto, ON, M5H 1H1, Canada
Tel.: (416) 866-3672
Telex: WUI 6719400
Fax: (416) 866-3750
E-Mail: email@scotiabank.com
Web Site: www.scotiabank.com
Year Founded: 1832
BNS—(NYSE TSX)
Rev.: $21,215,368,860
Assets: $739,340,147,760
Liabilities: $693,067,522,740
Net Worth: $46,272,625,020
Earnings: $6,656,951,940
Emp.: 83,874
Fiscal Year-end: 10/31/13
Business Description:
International Banking Services
S.I.C.: 6029
N.A.I.C.S.: 522110
Personnel:
John Thomas Mayberry *(Chm)*
Richard Earl Waugh *(Deputy Chm)*
Sarabjit S. Marwah *(Vice Chm & COO)*
Brian J. Porter *(Pres & CEO)*
Mike Durland *(Grp Head & Co-CEO-Global Banking & Markets)*
Stephen D. McDonald *(Grp Head & Co-CEO-Global Banking & Markets)*
Sean McGuckin *(CFO & Exec VP)*
John W. Doig *(CMO)*
Terry K. Fryett *(Chief Credit Officer & Exec VP)*
Marianne Hasold-Schilter *(Chief Admin Officer-Intl Banking & Exec VP)*
Anne Marie O'Donovan *(Chief Admin Officer & Exec VP-Global Banking & Markets)*
Stephen Hart *(Chief Risk Officer)*
Barbara Mason *(Chief HR Officer)*
Troy T. K. Wright *(Pres/CEO-Grupo Financiero Scotiabank-Mexico & Exec VP)*
Deborah M. Alexander *(Gen Counsel, Sec & Exec VP)*
Jeffrey C. Heath *(Treas & Exec VP)*
Alberta G. Cefis *(Exec VP & Head-Global Transaction Banking)*
Wendy Hannam *(Exec VP-Latin America)*
Robin S. Hibberd *(Exec VP-Retail Products & Svcs-Canadian Banking)*
Kim B. McKenzie *(Exec VP-IT & Solutions)*
James Ian McPhedran *(Exec VP-Retail Distr-Canadian Banking)*
James O'Sullivan *(Exec VP-Global Asset Mgmt)*
Sue Graham Parker *(Exec VP-HR & Comm)*
Board of Directors:
John Thomas Mayberry
Ronald Alvin Brenneman
Choong Joong Chen
Charles Dallara
David Allison Dodge
N. Ashleigh Everett
John C. Kerr
Thomas Charles O'Neill
Brian J. Porter
Aaron W. Regent
Indira V. Samarasekera
Susan L. Segal
Paul David Sobey
Barbara S. Thomas
Richard Earl Waugh

Computershare Trust Company, N.A.
250 Royall St
Canton, MA 02021
Tel.: (781) 575-2724

Transfer Agents:
Computershare Trust Company of Canada
100 University Avenue 8th Floor
Toronto, ON, M5J 2Y1, Canada

Computershare Trust Company, N.A.
250 Royall St
Canton, MA 02021
Tel.: (781) 575-2724

Division:

ScotiaMcLeod Direct Investing (1)
40 King St W Ste 1500
Box 402
Toronto, ON, M5H 3Y2, Canada (100%)
Tel.: (416) 863-7272
Fax: (416) 862-3869
E-Mail:
Emp.: 120
Securities Trading Services
S.I.C.: 6211
N.A.I.C.S.: 523120
Shane Jones *(Chief Investment Officer)*

Subsidiaries:

TradeFreedom Securities Inc. (2)
Scotia Twr 1002 Sherbrooke St St W
Montreal, QC, H3A 3L6, Canada
Tel.: (514) 344-5111
Fax: (514) 344-5160
Toll Free: (866) 837-3336
E-Mail: support@tradefreedom.com
Web Site: www.tradefreedom.com
Online Securities Trading Service
S.I.C.: 6211
N.A.I.C.S.: 523120
Franklin Wolf *(Branch Mgr)*

Subsidiaries:

The Bank of Nova Scotia Properties Inc. (1)
Scotia Plz 44 King St W
Toronto, ON, M5H 1H1, Canada (100%)
Tel.: (416) 866-7872
Fax: (416) 866-4304
Emp.: 100
Real Estate Management Services
S.I.C.: 6531
N.A.I.C.S.: 531210
Andrew B. Lennox *(Sr VP-Real Estate Dept)*

Subsidiaries:

Scotia Properties Quebec Inc. (2)
Scotia Plz 44 King St W
Toronto, ON, M5H 1H1, Canada
Tel.: (416) 866-7872
Fax: (416) 866-4092
E-Mail: andrew.lennox@scotiabank.com
Emp.: 100
Real Estate Services
S.I.C.: 6531
N.A.I.C.S.: 531210
Andrew B. Lennox *(Sr VP-Real Estate)*

Scotia Realty Limited (2)
Scotia Plaza 44 King Street West
Woodgate Bus Park
Toronto, ON, M5H 1H1, Canada
Tel.: (416) 866-7872
Fax: (416) 866-4304
Web Site: www.scotiabank.com
Emp.: 150
Real Estate Services
S.I.C.: 6531
N.A.I.C.S.: 531210
Troy T. K. Wright *(Exec VP-Retail Distr-Banking)*
Andrew B. Lennox *(Sr VP)*

BNS Investments Inc. (1)
Scotia Plz 44 King St W
Toronto, ON, M5H 1H1, Canada
Tel.: (416) 866-6161
Fax: (416) 866-6430
E-Mail: email@scotiabank.com
Web Site: www.scotia.com
Emp.: 1,000
Holding Company
S.I.C.: 6719
N.A.I.C.S.: 551112
Richard Waugh *(CEO)*

Subsidiaries:

MontroServices Corporation (2)
2 Scotia Bldg 1002 Sherbrooke W Fl 4
1002 Sherbrooke St W, Montreal, QC, H3A 3M3, Canada
Tel.: (514) 846-8017
Fax: (514) 846-7992
Web Site: scotiabank.com
Banking Services
S.I.C.: 6159
N.A.I.C.S.: 522298

DundeeWealth Inc. (1)
1 Adelaide Street East 28th Floor
Toronto, ON, M5C 2V9, Canada (100%)
Tel.: (416) 350-3250
Toll Free: (888) 292-3847
E-Mail: inquiries@dundeewealth.com
Web Site: www.dundeewealth.com
Sales Range: $750-799.9 Million
Emp.: 800
Investment Management, Securities Brokerage, Financial Planning & Investment Advisory Services
S.I.C.: 6282
N.A.I.C.S.: 523999
David J. Goodman *(Pres & CEO)*
John Pereira *(CFO & Exec VP)*
David Whyte *(COO)*
Robert Pattillo *(Exec VP-Comm & Mktg)*
Jean-Francois Thibault *(Exec VP)*

Subsidiaries:

Dundee Insurance Agency Ltd (2)
1 Adelaide St E 27th Fl
Toronto, ON, M5C 2V9, Canada (100%)
Tel.: (416) 350-3250
E-Mail: inquirics@dundeewealth.com
Web Site: www.dundeewealth.com
Emp.: 1,500
Insurance Agencies & Brokerages

S.I.C.: 6411
N.A.I.C.S.: 524210
David J. Goodman *(CEO)*

Dundee Mortgage Services Inc. (2)
1 Adelaide St E 27th Fl
Toronto, ON, M5C 2V9, Canada (100%)
Tel.: (416) 350-3250
Fax: (416) 365-5459
Toll Free: (888) 332-2661
E-Mail: inquiries@dundeemortgage.com
Web Site: www.dundeewealth.com
Emp.: 1,500
Mortgage Loan Brokers
S.I.C.: 6163
N.A.I.C.S.: 522310
David J. Goodman *(Pres & CEO)*

ING Bank of Canada (1)
111 Gordon Baker Rd Ste 110
Toronto, ON, M2H 3R1, Canada ON
Tel.: (416) 756-2424 (100%)
Fax: (416) 756-2422
E-Mail: clientservices@ingdirect.ca
Web Site: www.ingdirect.ca
Emp.: 1,100
Commercial Banking, Mortgages & Financial Services
S.I.C.: 6029
N.A.I.C.S.: 522110
Peter R. Aceto *(Pres & CEO)*
Charaka Kithulegoda *(CIO)*
Andrew Zimakas *(CMO)*

Roynat Inc. (1)
Scotia Plz 40 King St W 26th Fl
Toronto, ON, M5H 1H1, Canada (100%)
Tel.: (416) 933-2730
Fax: (416) 933-2783
E-Mail: info@roynat.com
Web Site: www.roynat.com
Emp.: 45
Holding Company; Equity Investment, Asset & Lease Finance Services
S.I.C.: 6719
N.A.I.C.S.: 551112
Rania Llewellyn *(Pres/CEO-Roynat Capital)*

Division:

Roynat Capital Inc. (2)
Scotia Plaza 40 King Street West 26th Floor
Toronto, ON, M5H 1H1, Canada (100%)
Tel.: (416) 933-2730
Fax: (416) 933-2783
E-Mail: info@roynat.com
Web Site: www.roynat.ca
Private Equity Firm
S.I.C.: 6211
N.A.I.C.S.: 523999
Rania Llewellyn *(Pres & CEO)*
Richard Kanemy *(Sr VP & Head-Ops-Canada)*
Jeff Chernin *(Sr VP-Risk Mgmt)*

Joint Venture:

Pineridge Foods Inc. (3)
91 Delta Park Blvd Unit 2
L6T 5E7 Brampton, ON, Canada
Tel.: (905) 458-8696
Web Site: www.pineridgefoods.com
Prepared Frozen Dessert Mfr
S.I.C.: 2038
N.A.I.C.S.: 311412
Roger M. Dickhout *(Pres & CEO)*
Dan C. Swander *(Partner)*

Subsidiary:

Gourmet Baker, Inc. (4)
502 4190 Lougheed Hwy
Burnaby, BC, V5C 6A8, Canada ON
Tel.: (604) 298-2652
Fax: (604) 296-1001
Toll Free: (800) 663-1972
Web Site: www.gourmetbaker.com
Sales Range: $10-24.9 Million
Emp.: 15
Frozen Bakery Products
S.I.C.: 2053
N.A.I.C.S.: 311813

Scotia Capital Inc. (1)
Scotia Plaza 40 King Street West
PO Box 4085
Toronto, ON, M5W 2X6, Canada (100%)
Tel.: (416) 863-7411
Fax: (416) 862-3052
Web Site: www.scotiacapital.com
Sales Range: $10-24.9 Million
Emp.: 1,900
Banking & Financial Services
S.I.C.: 6159
N.A.I.C.S.: 522298
Michael Durland *(Co-Chm & Co-CEO)*
Kevin Ray *(Vice Chm & Head-Mergers & Acq)*
John L. Sherrington *(Vice Chm & Head-Private Equity-North America)*
Barry Wainstein *(Vice Chm & Deputy Head-Global Capital Markets)*
John Madden *(Vice Chm-Capital Markets Grp)*
Stephen McDonald *(Co-CEO)*
Philip Smith *(Mng Dir & Head-Investment Banking)*
Robert Finlay *(Mng Dir)*
Mike Jackson *(Mng Dir)*
Anne Marie O'Donovan *(Chief Admin Officer & Exec VP)*

Divisions:

Scotia Waterous (2)
Ste 1800 Scotia Centre 700 2nd Street SW
Calgary, AB, T2P 2W1, Canada
Tel.: (403) 265-8077
Fax: (403) 269-8355
E-Mail: calgary@scotiawaterous.com
Web Site: www.scotiawaterous.com
Emp.: 60
Investments in Oil & Gas
S.I.C.: 6211
N.A.I.C.S.: 523999

U.S. Division:

Scotia Waterous USA Inc. (3)
Pennzoil Pl South Tower 711 Louisiana Ste 1400
Houston, TX 77002-2716
Tel.: (713) 222-0546
Fax: (713) 222-0572
E-Mail: houston@scotiawaterous.com
Web Site: www.scotiawaterous.com
Investments in Oil & Gas
S.I.C.: 6211
N.A.I.C.S.: 523999
Randy Crath *(Mng Dir)*

Holding:

Summit Gas Resources, Inc. (4)
1 E Alger St
Sheridan, WY 82801 DE
Tel.: (307) 673-9710
Fax: (307) 673-9711
Web Site: www.summitgas.com
Sales Range: $10-24.9 Million
Emp.: 38
Gas & Oil Exploration Services
S.I.C.: 1311
N.A.I.C.S.: 211111
Peter G. Schoonmaker *(Pres & CEO)*
Ronald T. Barnes *(CFO, Sec & Sr VP)*

Subsidiaries:

Scotia Asset Management L.P. (2)
40 King St W
Toronto, ON, M5H 1H1, Canada
Tel.: (416) 866-6430
Fax: (416) 933-2375
Asset Management Services
S.I.C.: 6799
N.A.I.C.S.: 523920
Jane Jayarajah *(Mgr)*

Scotia Managed Companies Administration Inc. (2)
Scotia Plaza 26th Floor 40 King Street West
PO Box 4085
Station A, Toronto, ON, M5W 2X6, Canada
Tel.: (416) 945-4800
Fax: (416) 863-7425
Web Site: www.scotiamanagedcompanies.com
Investment Fund Administration Services
S.I.C.: 6282
N.A.I.C.S.: 523920

Affiliates:

Advantaged Canadian High Yield Bond Fund (3)
40 King Street West 26th Floor Scotia Plaza Station A
P O Box 4085
Toronto, ON, M5W 2X6, Canada ON
Tel.: (416) 945-5353
Fax: (416) 863-7425
AHY.UN—(TSX)
Sales Range: Less than $1 Million
Closed-End Investment Fund
S.I.C.: 6726
N.A.I.C.S.: 525990
Brian D. McChesney *(Pres & CEO)*
Stephen D. Pearce *(CFO)*
Farooq N. P. Moosa *(Sec)*

Allbanc Split Corp. II (3)
40 King Street West Scotia Plaza 26th Floor
PO Box 4085
Toronto, ON, M5W 2X6, Canada
Tel.: (416) 863-7711
Fax: (416) 863-7425
ALB—(TSX)
Rev.: $3,079,477
Assets: $60,458,209
Liabilities: $25,944,178
Net Worth: $34,514,031
Earnings: $1,258,186
Fiscal Year-end: 02/28/13
Closed-End Investment Fund
S.I.C.: 6726
N.A.I.C.S.: 525990
D. Anthony Ross *(Chm)*
Brian D. McChesney *(Pres & CEO)*
Stephen D. Pearce *(CFO & Sec)*

Allbanc Split Corp. (3)
40 King Street Scotia Plaza 26th Floor
PO Box 4085
Station A, Toronto, ON, M5W 2X6, Canada Ca
Tel.: (416) 945-4171
Fax: (416) 863-7425
E-Mail: mc.allbanc@scotiabank.com
Web Site: www.scotiamanagedcompanies.com
ABK—(TSX)
Sales Range: $1-9.9 Million
Emp.: 80
Closed-End Investment Fund
S.I.C.: 6726
N.A.I.C.S.: 525990
E. Stuart Griffith *(Chm)*
Brian D. McChesney *(Pres & CEO)*
Stephen D. Pearce *(CFO & Sec)*

BNS Split Corp. (3)
40 King Street West
Scotia Plaza 26th Floor, Toronto, ON, M5W 2X6, Canada
Tel.: (416) 862-3191
Fax: (416) 863-7425
Web Site: www.scotiamanagedcompanies.com
Closed-End Investment Fund
S.I.C.: 6726
N.A.I.C.S.: 525990

Moneda LatAm Corporate Bond Fund (3)
40 King Street West 26th Floor
PO Box 4085
Station A, Toronto, ON, M5W 2X6, Canada ON
Tel.: (416) 945-4262
E-Mail: mc.monedabondfund@scotiabank.com
Web Site: www.scotiamanagedcompanies.com
MLD.UN—(TSX)
Closed-End Investment Fund
S.I.C.: 6726
N.A.I.C.S.: 525990
Brian D. McChesney *(Pres & CEO)*
Stephen D. Pearce *(CFO)*
Farooq N.P. Moosa *(Sec)*

Moneda LatAm Fixed Income Fund (3)
40 King Street West 26th Floor
PO Box 4085
Station A, Toronto, ON, M5W 2X6, Canada ON
Tel.: (416) 945-4994
E-Mail: mc.monedafixedincomefund@scotiabank.com
Web Site: www.scotiamanagedcompanies.com
MLF.UN—(TSX)
Closed-End Investment Fund
S.I.C.: 6726
N.A.I.C.S.: 525990
Brian D. McChesney *(Pres & CEO)*
Stephen D. Pearce *(CFO)*
Farooq N.P. Moosa *(Sec)*

NewGrowth Corp. (3)
Scotia Plaza 26th Floor
40 King Street West
Station A, Toronto, ON, M5W 2X6, Canada ON
Tel.: (416) 862-3931
Fax: (416) 863-7425
E-Mail: mc_newgrowth@scotiacapital.com
Web Site: www.scotiamanagedcompanies.com
NEW.A—(TSX)
Emp.: 8
Closed-End Investment Fund
S.I.C.: 6726
N.A.I.C.S.: 525990
Donald W. Paterson *(Chm)*
Robert C. Williams *(Pres & CEO)*

SCITI ROCS Trust (3)
Scotia Plaza 26th Floor 40 King Street West
Toronto, ON, M5W 2X6, Canada
Tel.: (416) 863-7251
Fax: (416) 863-7425
SCI.UN—(TSX)
Rev.: $7,385
Assets: $53,482,598
Liabilities: $460,953
Net Worth: $53,021,645
Earnings: ($245,969)
Fiscal Year-end: 12/31/12
Closed-End Investment Fund
S.I.C.: 6726
N.A.I.C.S.: 525990
Brian D. McChesney *(CEO)*

SCITI Trust (3)
Scotia Plaza 26th Floor 40 King Street West
Toronto, ON, M5W 2X6, Canada
Tel.: (416) 945-4394
Fax: (416) 863-7425
SIN.UN—(TSX)
Rev.: $19,906,428
Assets: $324,965,775
Liabilities: $64,693,059
Net Worth: $260,272,716
Earnings: $17,389,529
Fiscal Year-end: 12/31/12
Closed-End Investment Fund
S.I.C.: 6726
N.A.I.C.S.: 525990
Brian D. McChesney *(CEO)*

Top 20 Dividend Trust (3)
40 King Street West Scotia Plaza 26th Fl
PO Box 4085
Station A, Toronto, ON, M5W 2X6, Canada ON
Tel.: (416) 862-3734
Fax: (416) 862-7425
TTY.UN—(TSX)
Closed-End Investment Fund
S.I.C.: 6726
N.A.I.C.S.: 525990
Thomas A. Pippy *(Chm)*
Brian D. McChesney *(Pres & CEO)*
Stephen D. Pearce *(CFO)*

Top 20 Europe Dividend Trust (3)
40 King Street West 26th Floor
PO Box 4085
Station A, Toronto, ON, M5W 2X6, Canada ON
Tel.: (416) 945-4160
E-Mail: stephen_pearce@scotiacapital.com
TTE.UN—(TSX)
Closed-End Investment Fund
S.I.C.: 6726
N.A.I.C.S.: 525990
Thomas C. Dawson *(Chm)*
Brian D. McChesney *(Pres & CEO)*
Stephen D. Pearce *(CFO)*
Farooq N.P. Moosa *(Sec)*

Top 20 U.S. Dividend Trust (3)
40 King Street West 26th Floor
PO Box 4085
Station A, Toronto, ON, M5W 2X6, Canada ON
Tel.: (416) 945-4160
E-Mail: stephen_pearce@scotiacapital.com
TUT.UN—(TSX)
Closed-End Investment Fund
S.I.C.: 6726

The Bank of Nova Scotia—(Continued)

N.A.I.C.S.: 525990
Thomas A. Pippy *(Chm)*
Brian D. McChesney *(Pres & CEO)*
Stephen D. Pearce *(CFO)*
Farooq N.P. Moosa *(Sec)*

Utility Corp. (3)
26th Fl Scotia Plz 40 King St W
Toronto, ON, M5W 2X6, Canada
Tel.: (416) 863-7893
Fax: (416) 863-7425
E-Mail: mc_utlity@scotiacapital.com
Web Site: www.scotiamanagedcompanies.com
UTC—(TSX)
Sales Range: $1-9.9 Million
Emp.: 100
Closed-End Investment Fund
S.I.C.: 6726
N.A.I.C.S.: 525990
Donald W. Paterson *(Chm)*
Robert C. Williams *(Vice Chm)*
Michael K. Warman *(CFO & Sec)*

U.S. Subsidiary:

Scotia Capital (USA) Inc. (2)
1 Liberty Plz Fl 26
New York, NY 10006 NY
Tel.: (212) 225-5000 (100%)
Fax: (212) 225-5090
Web Site: www.scotiacapital.com
Emp.: 350
Commodity Trading Services
S.I.C.: 6211
N.A.I.C.S.: 523110
Kevin R. Ray *(Vice Chm-US Corp Origination)*
Steve McDonald *(Co-CEO)*
Tim Dinneny *(Mng Dir)*
Kathryn Kiplinger *(Mng Dir & Head-Risk Assessment)*
James R. Trimble *(Mng Dir & Head-Power Indus Grp)*
Barry C. Delman *(Mng Dir)*
Brian Allen *(Mng Dir)*
Robert Donaldson *(Mng Dir)*

Branches:

Scotia Capital (USA) Inc. - Houston (3)
711 Louisiana St Ste 1400
Houston, TX 77002-5216
Tel.: (713) 752-0900
Fax: (713) 752-2425
E-Mail: info@scotiacapital.com
Web Site: www.scotiacapital.com
Emp.: 16
Corporate & Investment Banking Services
S.I.C.: 6159
N.A.I.C.S.: 522298
Mark Ammerman *(Mng Dir)*

Scotia Capital (USA) Inc. - San Francisco (3)
580 California St Ste 2100
San Francisco, CA 94104-1042
Tel.: (415) 986-1100
Fax: (415) 397-0791
Web Site: www.scotiacapital.com
Emp.: 30
Corporate & Investment Banking Services
S.I.C.: 6091
N.A.I.C.S.: 523991
Christopher P. Johnson *(Mng Dir)*

Scotia Cassels Investment Counsel Limited (1)
Suite 1200 1 Queen Street East
Toronto, ON, M5C 2W5, Canada (100%)
Tel.: (416) 814-4000
Fax: (416) 933-2400
Toll Free: (800) 263-2385
Web Site: www.scotiacassels.com
Emp.: 75
Investment Services
S.I.C.: 6159
N.A.I.C.S.: 522298

Scotia Dealer Advantage Inc. (1)
4190 Lougheed Highway Suite 300
Burnaby, BC, V5C6A8, Canada
Tel.: (877) 375-2771
Fax: (877) 473-3816
Emp.: 300
Automotive Financial Leasing Services
S.I.C.: 6153
N.A.I.C.S.: 522220
Joe Oviatt *(VP)*

Scotia Life Insurance Company (1)
Ste 400 100 Yonge St
Toronto, ON, M5H 1H1, Canada (100%)
Tel.: (416) 866-7075
Fax: (416) 866-7773
Web Site: www.scotiabank.com
Emp.: 70
Life Insurance Services
S.I.C.: 6399
N.A.I.C.S.: 524128
Mark Cummings *(Pres & CEO)*

Subsidiaries:

The Mortgage Insurance Company of Canada (2)
100 Yonge St Ste 1210
Toronto, ON, M5C 2W1, Canada
Tel.: (416) 933-1039
Fax: (416) 933-1034
Emp.: 1
Mortgage Insurance Services
S.I.C.: 6411
N.A.I.C.S.: 524298
Oscar Zimmerman *(Pres)*

Scotia General Insurance Company (2)
Ste 400 100 Yonge St
Toronto, ON, M5H 1H1, Canada
Tel.: (416) 866-7075
Fax: (416) 866-7773
Emp.: 70
Insurance Services
S.I.C.: 6411
N.A.I.C.S.: 524298
Mark Cummings *(Pres)*

Scotia Merchant Capital Corporation (1)
Scotia Plaza 40 King St West Ste 3800
Toronto, ON, M5W 2X6, Canada ON
Tel.: (416) 863-7411 (100%)
Fax: (416) 862-3052
E-Mail: smc@scotiacapital.com
Web Site: www.gbm.scotiabank.com
Emp.: 10
Investment Services
S.I.C.: 6282
N.A.I.C.S.: 523930
Michael Durland *(Grp Head & Co-CEO)*
Rick Waugh *(Co-CEO)*

Scotia Mortgage Corporation (1)
Ste 200 2206 Eglinton Ave E
Scarborough, ON, M1L 4S7, Canada
Tel.: (416) 933-1973
Fax: (416) 288-4904
E-Mail: smc@scotiabank.ca
Emp.: 47
Mortgage Services
S.I.C.: 6099
N.A.I.C.S.: 522390

Scotia Securities, Inc. (1)
40 King St W Scotia Plz
Toronto, ON, M5H 1H1, Canada ON
Tel.: (416) 866-6161
Fax: (416) 866-2018
Rev.: $818,640
Security Broker & Dealer
S.I.C.: 6211
N.A.I.C.S.: 523120
Wendy Hannam *(Exec VP-Sls & Bus Dev)*

Tour Scotia (1)
1002 Sherbrooke St W
Montreal, QC, H3A 3L6, Canada QC
Tel.: (514) 288-1002
Fax: (514) 499-5504
E-Mail: info@scotia.com
Web Site: www.scotia.com
Emp.: 10
Nonresidential Building Operator
S.I.C.: 6512
N.A.I.C.S.: 531120
Berdj Meguerian *(Gen Mgr)*

Units:

The Bank of Nova Scotia - Atlantic Region (1)
1709 Hollis St 6th Fl
Halifax, NS, B3J 1W1, Canada
Mailing Address:
PO Box 2146
Halifax, NS, B3J 3B7, Canada
Tel.: (902) 420-3600
Fax: (877) 841-9920
E-Mail:
Web Site: www.scotiabank.com
Emp.: 100
Banking Services
S.I.C.: 6029
N.A.I.C.S.: 522110
Steve Groves *(Branch Mgr)*

The Bank of Nova Scotia - British Columbia & Yukon Region (1)
650 W Georgia St 34th Fl
Vancouver, BC, V6B 4P6, Canada
Tel.: (604) 668-2094
Fax: (604) 668-2861
Web Site: www.scotiabank.com
Banking Services
S.I.C.: 6029
N.A.I.C.S.: 522110
David Poole *(Sr VP)*

The Bank of Nova Scotia - Manitoba Region (1)
200 Portage Ave at Main
PO Box 845
Winnipeg, MB, R3C 2R7, Canada
Tel.: (204) 985-3030
Fax: (204) 985-3079
Web Site: www.scotiabank.com
Emp.: 45
Banking Services
S.I.C.: 6029
N.A.I.C.S.: 522110
Brock Alexander *(VP)*

The Bank of Nova Scotia - Ontario Region (1)
44 King Street West 22nd Floor
Toronto, ON, M5H 1H1, Canada
Tel.: (416) 866-6318
Fax: (416) 866-7010
E-Mail: info@scotiabank.com
Web Site: www.scotiabank.com
Banking Services
S.I.C.: 6029
N.A.I.C.S.: 522110

The Bank of Nova Scotia - Prairie Region (1)
700 2nd St SW Ste 4000
Calgary, AB, T2P 2N7, Canada
Tel.: (403) 221-6477
Fax: (403) 221-6511
Web Site: www.scotiabank.com
Emp.: 10
Banking Services
S.I.C.: 6029
N.A.I.C.S.: 522110
George Marlatte *(Sr VP)*

The Bank of Nova Scotia - Quebec & Eastern Ontario Region (1)
1002 Sherbrooke St W Ste 430
Montreal, QC, H3A 3L6, Canada
Tel.: (514) 499-5404
Fax: (514) 499-5550
Web Site: www.scotiabank.com
Banking Services
S.I.C.: 6029
N.A.I.C.S.: 522110
Diane Giard *(Sr VP)*

The Bank of Nova Scotia - Toronto Region (1)
40 King Street
Toronto, ON, M5C 2W1, Canada
Tel.: (416) 866-3840
Fax: (416) 933-2440
Web Site: www.scotiabank.com
Banking Services
S.I.C.: 6029
N.A.I.C.S.: 522110
Joe Brandt *(Sr VP)*

U.S. Subsidiary:

Scotia Holdings (US) Inc. (1)
600 Peachtree St NE Ste 2700
Atlanta, GA 30308-2223 (100%)
Tel.: (404) 877-1500
Fax: (404) 888-8898
Emp.: 60
Holding Company
S.I.C.: 6159
N.A.I.C.S.: 522293

Subsidiaries:

The Bank of Nova Scotia Trust Company of New York (2)
1 Liberty Plz 23rd Fl
New York, NY 10006 NY
Tel.: (212) 225-5470 (100%)
Fax: (212) 225-5436
Web Site: www.scotiabank.com
Emp.: 400
Investment & Corporate Banking Services
S.I.C.: 6733
N.A.I.C.S.: 523991
Warren Goshine *(VP)*

Howard Weil, Inc. (2)
1100 Poydras St Ste 3500
New Orleans, LA 70163
Tel.: (504) 582-2500
Fax: (504) 582-2451
Toll Free: (800) 322-3005
E-Mail: howardweil@howardweil.com
Web Site: www.howardweil.com
Sales Range: $150-199.9 Million
Emp.: 55
Securities, Futures & Commodities Dealers
S.I.C.: 6211
N.A.I.C.S.: 523110
Paul E. Pursley *(Pres)*

Branch:

Howard Weil, Inc. (3)
3200 Southwest Fwy Ste 1490
Houston, TX 77027-7557 LA
Tel.: (713) 393-4500
Toll Free: (800) 326-7557
E-Mail: howardweil@howardweil.com
Web Site: www.howardweil.com
Brokers Security
S.I.C.: 6211
N.A.I.C.S.: 523120
Gordon B. Gsell, Jr. *(Mgr-Equity Sls)*

Scotiabanc Inc. (2)
711 Louisiana St Ste 1400
Houston, TX 77002-2847
Tel.: (832) 426-6001
Fax: (832) 426-6000
International Trade Financing Services
S.I.C.: 6159
N.A.I.C.S.: 522293

ScotiaMocatta Depository Corporation (2)
230 59 International Airport Central Blvd
Bldg C Ste 120
Jamaica, NY 11413
Tel.: (212) 912-8531
Fax: (212) 912-8533
Emp.: 100
Banking Services
S.I.C.: 6029
N.A.I.C.S.: 522110

U.S. Units:

The Bank of Nova Scotia (1)
214 C Altone
Saint Thomas, VI 00802
Tel.: (340) 774-0037
Fax: (340) 693-5994
E-Mail: info@scotiabank.com
Web Site: www.scotiabank.com
Emp.: 120
Banking Services
S.I.C.: 6159
N.A.I.C.S.: 522298
Lawrence Aqui *(VP)*

Scotiabank de Puerto Rico (1)
Carr 3 Km 82 Rio Abajo
Humacao, PR 00936-2649 (100%)
Tel.: (787) 766-7900
Fax: (787) 766-7879
Web Site: www.scotiabankpr.com
Banking Services
S.I.C.: 6029
N.A.I.C.S.: 522110
Jorge Sierra *(First VP-Consumer Banking)*

Non-U.S. Branches:

The Bank of Nova Scotia (1)
3 Ibn Arhab Street
PO Box 656
Giza, Cairo, 11511, Egypt
Tel.: (20) 237479800
Fax: (20) 237479807
E-Mail: bns.cairo@scotiabank.com

Web Site: www.scotiabank.com
Emp.: 29
Banking Services
S.I.C.: 6159
N.A.I.C.S.: 522298
Mohamed Jahangir *(Country Mgr)*

The Bank of Nova Scotia (1)
16th Floor Dong-A Media Centre 139
Sejongno Jongno-gu
Seoul, 110-715, Korea (South)
Tel.: (82) 220202340
Fax: (82) 220202344
E-Mail: bns.seoul@scotiabank.com
Web Site: www.scotiabank.com
Emp.: 23
Banking Services
S.I.C.: 6159
N.A.I.C.S.: 522298
Y.K. Rim *(VP)*

The Bank of Nova Scotia (1)
Toranomon Waiko Building 6th Floor 12-1
Toranomon 5-Chome Minato-ku
Tokyo, 105-0001, Japan
Tel.: (81) 354080900
Fax: (81) 354080937
E-Mail: bns.tokyo@scotiabank.com
Web Site: www.scotiabank.com
Emp.: 20
Banking Services
S.I.C.: 6159
N.A.I.C.S.: 522298
Hiroshi Fujita *(VP)*

The Bank of Nova Scotia (1)
Ave Federico Boyd Y Esquina Calle 51
PO Box 0833
Panama, 083300174, Panama
Tel.: (507) 2087700
Fax: (507) 2087702
E-Mail: bns.panama@scotiabank.com
Web Site: www.scotiabank.com
Emp.: 90
Banking Services
S.I.C.: 6159
N.A.I.C.S.: 522298
Stephen Dagnarol *(VP & Gen Mgr)*

The Bank of Nova Scotia (1)
28 Hillsborough Street
PO Box 520
Roseau, Dominica
Tel.: (767) 4485800
Fax: (767) 4485805
E-Mail: bns.dominica@scotiabank.com
Web Site: www.scotiabank.com
Emp.: 42
Banking Services
S.I.C.: 6159
N.A.I.C.S.: 522298
Jim Alston *(Country Mgr)*

The Bank of Nova Scotia (1)
1-2 Floor Ploenchit Tower
898 Ploenchit Road, Bangkok, 10330, Thailand
Tel.: (66) 22630303
Fax: (66) 22630150
E-Mail: bbangkok@scotiabank.com
Web Site: www.scotiabank.com
Banking Services
S.I.C.: 6159
N.A.I.C.S.: 522298

The Bank of Nova Scotia (1)
6 William Peter Boulevard
Castries, Saint Lucia
Tel.: (758) 4562100
Fax: (758) 4562130
E-Mail: bns.stlucia@scotiabank.com
Web Site: www.scotiabank.com
Banking Services
S.I.C.: 6159
N.A.I.C.S.: 522298
Chester Hinkson *(Gen Mgr)*

The Bank of Nova Scotia (1)
Halifax Street
PO Box 237
Kingstown, Saint Vincent & Grenadines
Tel.: (784) 4571601
Fax: (784) 457 2623
E-Mail: bns.stvincent@scotiabank.com
Web Site: www.scotiabank.com
Emp.: 40
Banking Services
S.I.C.: 6159
N.A.I.C.S.: 522298
Leslie Bowman *(Asst Mgr-Personal Banking)*

The Bank of Nova Scotia (1)
14th Floor Dr Gopal Das Bhavan
28 Barakhamba Road, New Delhi, 110-001, India
Tel.: (91) 1123351522
Fax: (91) 1123312847
E-Mail: bns.newdelhi@scotiabank.com
Web Site: www.scotiabank.com
Banking Services
S.I.C.: 6159
N.A.I.C.S.: 522298
Rajan Gupta *(Gen Mgr)*

The Bank of Nova Scotia (1)
Box 433
Basseterre, Saint Kitts & Nevis
Tel.: (869) 4654141
Fax: (869) 4658600
E-Mail: bns.stkitts@scotiabank.com
Web Site: www.scotiabank.com
Banking Services
S.I.C.: 6159
N.A.I.C.S.: 522298

The Bank of Nova Scotia (1)
104 Carmichael St
PO Box 10631
Georgetown, Guyana
Tel.: (592) 2259222
Fax: (592) 2259309
E-Mail: bns.guyana@scotiabank.com
Web Site: www.scotiabank.com
Emp.: 186
Banking Services
S.I.C.: 6159
N.A.I.C.S.: 522298
Adele Farier *(Mgr-Acctg)*

The Bank of Nova Scotia (1)
Box 342
Saint John's, Antigua & Barbuda
Tel.: (268) 4801500
Fax: (268) 4801554
E-Mail: bns.antigua@scotiabank.com
Web Site: www.scotiabank.com
Emp.: 60
Banking Services
S.I.C.: 6159
N.A.I.C.S.: 522298

The Bank of Nova Scotia (1)
Apartado 1494 John F Kennedy & Lope de Vega Av, Santo Domingo, Dominican Republic
Tel.: (809) 5458000
Fax: (809) 5675732
E-Mail: drinfo@scotiabank.com
Web Site: www.scotiabank.com
Banking Services
S.I.C.: 6159
N.A.I.C.S.: 522298
John Meek *(Sr VP & Gen Mgr)*

The Bank of Nova Scotia (1)
360 Blvd JJ Dessalines
Port-au-Prince, Haiti
Tel.: (509) 2993000
Fax: (509) 2993024
E-Mail: bnshaiti@scotiabank.com
Web Site: www.scotiabank.com
Emp.: 82
Banking Services
S.I.C.: 6159
N.A.I.C.S.: 522298

The Bank of Nova Scotia (1)
Box 194
Saint George's, Grenada
Tel.: (473) 440 3274
Fax: (473) 440 4173
E-Mail: bns.grenada@scotiabank.com
Web Site: www.scotiabank.com
Banking Services
S.I.C.: 6159
N.A.I.C.S.: 522298

Non-U.S. Subsidiaries:

The Bank of Nova Scotia Berhad (1)
Menara Boustead 69 Jalan Raja Chulan
50200 Kuala Lumpur, Malaysia MY (100%)
Tel.: (60) 321410766
Fax: (60) 321412160
E-Mail: bns.kualalumpur@scotiabank.com
Web Site: www.scotiabank.my
Sales Range: $25-49.9 Million
Emp.: 120
International Banking
S.I.C.: 6159
N.A.I.C.S.: 522293
Lodewijk Govaerts *(Mng Dir)*

The Bank of Nova Scotia International Limited (1)
Scotiabank Building Rawson Square
PO Box N-7518
Nassau, Bahamas
Tel.: (242) 3561518
Fax: (242) 3288473
Web Site: scotiabank.com
Banking Services
S.I.C.: 6159
N.A.I.C.S.: 522298

Subsidiaries:

The Bank of Nova Scotia Trust Company (Bahamas) Limited (2)
Scotia House 404 East Bay Street
PO Box N3016
Nassau, Bahamas (100%)
Tel.: (242) 3561400
Fax: (242) 3935344
Web Site: www.scotiabank.com
Emp.: 80
International Banking
S.I.C.: 6159
N.A.I.C.S.: 522293
Ravi Jesubatham *(Deputy Mng Dir & VP)*

Non-U.S. Subsidiary:

Scotiabank & Trust (Cayman) Limited (3)
Scotia Centre 6 Cardinal Avenue
PO Box 689 GT
Georgetown, Grand Cayman, Cayman Islands (100%)
Tel.: (345) 9497666
Fax: (345) 949 0200
E-Mail: scotiaci@candw.ky
Web Site: www.scotiabank.com
Trust, Fiduciary & Private Banking Services
S.I.C.: 6099
N.A.I.C.S.: 522320
Farried Sulliman *(Mng Dir)*

Scotiabank (Bahamas) Ltd. (2)
Scotiabank Building Rawson Square
PO Box N-7518
Nassau, Bahamas (100%)
Tel.: (242) 356 1697
Fax: (242) 356-1689
E-Mail: scotiacb@batelnet.bs
Web Site: www.scotiabank.com
Emp.: 130
Banking Services
S.I.C.: 6719
N.A.I.C.S.: 551112
Anthony C. Allen *(Mng Dir)*

Scotiabank Caribbean Treasury Limited (2)
One Bay Street
PO Box N-7518
Nassau, Bahamas
Tel.: (242) 3022950
Fax: (242) 3287432
Emp.: 10
Investment Banking Services
S.I.C.: 6211
N.A.I.C.S.: 523110
Brodie Townley *(Mng Dir)*

Non-U.S. Subsidiaries:

The Bank of Nova Scotia Asia Limited (2)
10 Collyer Quay
15-01 Ocean Building, Singapore, 049315, Singapore (100%)
Tel.: (65) 6535 8688
Fax: (65) 6532 7554
E-Mail: bns_sgc@scotiacapital.com
Web Site: www.scotiabank.com
International Banking Services
S.I.C.: 6159
N.A.I.C.S.: 522293
Kevin Cumbers *(Mng Dir)*
Claude D. Morin *(Mng Dir)*

Grupo BNS de Costa Rica, S.A. (2)
Fte A La Esq Nor-Este De
San Jose, Costa Rica
Tel.: (506) 22104000
Commercial Banking Services
S.I.C.: 6029
N.A.I.C.S.: 522110

Scotiabank (British Virgin Islands) Limited (2)
Box 434
Wickham's Cay 1 Road Town, Tortola, Virgin Islands (British)
Tel.: (284) 494 2526
Fax: (284) 494 4657
E-Mail: bns.bvi@scotiabank.com
Web Site: scotiabank.com
Banking Services
S.I.C.: 6159
N.A.I.C.S.: 522298

Scotiabank (Hong Kong) Limited (2)
25/F United Ctr 95 Queensway Admiralty
Hong Kong, China (Hong Kong)
Tel.: (852) 25295511
Commercial Banking Services
S.I.C.: 6029
N.A.I.C.S.: 522110

Scotiatrust (Hong Kong) Limited (2)
25th Floor United Center 95 Queensway
Hong Kong, China (Hong Kong) (100%)
Tel.: (852) 25295511
Fax: (852) 28611471
E-Mail: scotiabank.hongkong@scotiabank.com
Web Site: www.scotiabank.com
Emp.: 100
International Banking Services
S.I.C.: 6159
N.A.I.C.S.: 522293
Kitty Iu *(Mng Dir)*

Grupo Financiero Scotiabank Inverlat, S.A. de C.V. (1)
Blvd Manuel Avila Camacho 1 Piso 19
Mexico, DF, CP-11009, Mexico (97%)
Tel.: (52) 5552292310
Fax: (52) 5522292447
E-Mail: callcenter@scotiabankinverlat.com
Web Site: www.scotiabank.com.mx
Sales Range: $200-249.9 Million
Emp.: 6,700
Banking Services
S.I.C.: 6029
N.A.I.C.S.: 522110
Peter C. Cardinal *(Pres)*

Division:

Scotia Inverlat Casa de Bolsa (2)
Bosque de Ciruelos 120
Col Bosque de las Lomas, CP 11700
Mexico, Mexico
Tel.: (52) 5553253000
Fax: (52) 5553253699
Web Site: www.scotiabankinverlat.com
Banking Services
S.I.C.: 6159
N.A.I.C.S.: 522298

Nuevo Banco Comercial S.A. (1)
Misiones 1399
Montevideo, 11000, Uruguay
Tel.: (598) 2 140
Fax: (598) 2 915 35 69
E-Mail: GerenciaCasaCentral@nbc.com.uy
Commercial Banking Services
S.I.C.: 6029
N.A.I.C.S.: 522110

Scotia Capital (Europe) Limited (1)
201 Bishopsgate
EC2M 3NS London, United Kingdom
Tel.: (44) 2076385644
Fax: (44) 2076388488
Web Site: www.scotiabank.com
Emp.: 250
Banking Services
S.I.C.: 6159
N.A.I.C.S.: 522298
Cesare Roselli *(Mng Dir & Head-Sovereign, Supranational & Agency Origination)*

Scotia El Salvador, S.A. (1)
25 Avenida Norte y 23 Calle Poniente
San Salvador, El Salvador
Tel.: (503) 22344577
Fax: (503) 22343434
E-Mail: apencion@cniente.com.sv
Web Site: www.scotiabank.com.sv
Banking Services
S.I.C.: 6159
N.A.I.C.S.: 522298
Robert A. Williams *(Dir-Comml)*

Scotia Group Jamaica Ltd. (1)
Scotiabank Centre Corner Duke & Port Royal Streets

The Bank of Nova Scotia—(Continued)

PO Box 709
Kingston, Jamaica (70%)
Tel.: (876) 9221000
Fax: (876) 9226548
E-Mail: customercare-jam@scotiabank.com
Web Site: www.scotiabank.com.jm/
SGJ—(JAM)
Int. Income: $317,559,719
Assets: $3,800,601,957
Liabilities: $3,084,267,722
Net Worth: $716,334,235
Earnings: $112,201,716
Emp.: 2,315
Fiscal Year-end: 10/31/12
Banking Services
S.I.C.: 6159
N.A.I.C.S.: 522293
Sylvia D. Chrominska *(Chm)*
Jacqueline T. Sharp *(Pres & CEO)*
Hug Reid *(Pres-Scotia Jamaica Life Insurance Company Ltd & Sr VP)*
Lissant Mitchell *(CEO-Scotia Investments & Sr VP-Scotia Wealth Management)*
Julie Thompson-James *(Sr Legal Counsel, Sec & VP)*
Rosemarie A. Pilliner *(Exec VP-Shared Svcs-Caribbean North)*
H. Wayne Powell *(Exec VP-Retail Banking)*
Anya Schnoor *(Exec VP-Wealth Mgmt & Insurance)*
Monique French *(Sr VP-Credit Risk Mgmt)*
Heather Goldson *(Sr VP-Mktg & Products)*
Maya Johnston *(Sr VP-Non-Branch Sls & Svc)*
Michael D. Jones *(Sr VP-HR)*
Suzette A.M. McLeod *(Sr VP-Bus Support)*

Subsidiaries:

Scotia Investments Jamaica Limited (2)
7 Holborn Road
Kingston, 10, Jamaica
Tel.: (876) 9606699
Fax: (876) 9606705
Web Site: www.scotiainvestmentsjm.com
SIJL—(JAM)
Rev.: $43,793,645
Assets: $783,775,501
Liabilities: $663,096,735
Net Worth: $120,678,766
Earnings: $20,407,051
Emp.: 200
Fiscal Year-end: 10/31/12
Investment Banking Services
S.I.C.: 6211
N.A.I.C.S.: 523110
Bruce F. Bowen *(Chm)*
Lissant Mitchell *(CEO)*
Yvonne Pandohie *(CFO & VP)*
Hugh Miller *(COO)*
Julie Thompson-James *(Sec)*
Berisford Grey *(Sr VP-Origination & Capital Markets)*

Scotia Jamaica Building Society (2)
95 Harbour Street
PO Box 8463
Kingston, Jamaica (100%)
Tel.: (876) 9223600
Fax: (876) 9223253
E-Mail: sjbsgen@scotiabank.com
Web Site: www.scotiabank.com.jm
Emp.: 25
International Banking
S.I.C.: 6159
N.A.I.C.S.: 522293
J.A. Dixon *(Chm)*

Scotia Jamaica Financial Services Limited (2)
Scotiabank Centre Duke & Port Streets
PO Box 709
Kingston, Jamaica
Tel.: (876) 922 1000
Fax: (876) 967 4104
Web Site: www.scotiabank.com.jm
International Banking
S.I.C.: 6159
N.A.I.C.S.: 522293

Scotia Jamaica General Insurance Brokers Limited (2)
5th Floor Scotiabank Centre Duke & Port Royal Streets
PO Box 709
Kingston, Jamaica (100%)
Tel.: (876) 9484447
Fax: (876) 9484185
Web Site: www.scotiabank.com.jm
Insurance Services
S.I.C.: 6159
N.A.I.C.S.: 522293

Scotia Jamaica Investment Management Limited (2)
4th Floor Scotiabank Centre Duke Street & Port Royal Street
PO Box 627
Kingston, Jamaica (100%)
Tel.: (876) 922 1000
Fax: (876) 922 3378
Web Site: www.scotiabank.com.jm
Investment Banking Services
S.I.C.: 6159
N.A.I.C.S.: 522293

Scotia Jamaica Life Insurance Company Limited (2)
5th Fl Scotiabank Ctr
Corner Duke & Port Royal Sts, Kingston, Jamaica
Tel.: (876) 948 4453
Fax: (876) 922 8675
Web Site: www.scotiajamaicainsurance.scotiabank.com
Life Insurance Services
S.I.C.: 6399
N.A.I.C.S.: 524128

Scotia International Limited (1)
Rawson Square
PO Box N-7518
Nassau, Bahamas
Tel.: (242) 3561400
Fax: (242) 3263149
Commercial Banking Services
S.I.C.: 6029
N.A.I.C.S.: 522110

Scotiabank (Belize) Ltd. (1)
4 A Albert Street
PO Box 708
Belize, Belize
Tel.: (501) 2210135
Fax: (501) 2277416
E-Mail: sbl.mdo@scotiabank.com
Web Site: www.scotiabank.com
Emp.: 75
Banking Services
S.I.C.: 6159
N.A.I.C.S.: 522298
Patrick Andrews *(Mng Dir)*

Scotiabank Brasil S.A. Banco Multiplo (1)
Av Brig Faria Lima 2277 7 Andar
Sao Paulo, 01452-000, Brazil
Tel.: (55) 1122028100
Fax: (55) 1122028200
Web Site: www.br.scotiabank.com
Corporate & Investment Banking Services
S.I.C.: 6211
N.A.I.C.S.: 523110

Scotiabank Europe plc (1)
201 Bishopsgate
London, EC2M 3NS, United Kingdom
Tel.: (44) 2076385644
Fax: (44) 2076388488
E-Mail: enquries@scotiabank.com
Web Site: www.scotiabank.com
Emp.: 200
Banking Services
S.I.C.: 6159
N.A.I.C.S.: 522298
Rod M. Reynolds *(Exec Mng Dir)*
Karen Pollard *(Mng Dir-Foreign Exchange)*
Simon Last *(Mng Dir & Head-Fixed Income)*

Subsidiary:

ScotiaMocatta Limited (2)
201 Bishopsgate 6th Fl
London, EC2M 3NS, United Kingdom (100%)
Tel.: (44) 2078265655
Telex: 887419
Fax: (44) 2078265874
Web Site: www.scotiamocatta.com
Emp.: 100
Commodity Trading Services
S.I.C.: 3339
N.A.I.C.S.: 331410
Steven Lowe *(Mng Dir)*

Scotiabank International Limited (1)
Broad Street
PO Box 202
Bridgetown, Barbados
Tel.: (246) 426 7000
Fax: (246) 228 8574
Bank Holding Company
S.I.C.: 6712
N.A.I.C.S.: 551111

Subsidiaries:

The Bank of Nova Scotia Trust Company (Caribbean) Limited (2)
Broad Street
PO Box 202
Bridgetown, Barbados (100%)
Tel.: (246) 431 3100
Fax: (246) 426 0969
Web Site: www.scotiabank.com
International Banking
S.I.C.: 6159
N.A.I.C.S.: 522293

BNS International (Barbados) Limited (2)
Broad Street
Bridgetown, Barbados (100%)
Tel.: (246) 426-7000
Fax: (246) 228-8574
E-Mail: scotians@caribsurf.com
Web Site: www.scotiabank.com
Emp.: 20
Investment & Corporate Banking
S.I.C.: 6211
N.A.I.C.S.: 523110
Richard Tucker *(Mng Dir)*

Scotia Insurance (Barbados) Limited (2)
3rd Floor International Trading Centre
Warrens, Saint Michael, 22026, Barbados
Tel.: (246) 4252164
Fax: (246) 4252165
Emp.: 10
Insurance Services
S.I.C.: 6371
N.A.I.C.S.: 524298
Gordon Macrae *(Gen Mgr)*

Non-U.S. Subsidiaries:

Corporacion Mercaban de Costa Rica, S.A. (2)
Ave Primera Calle 0-2
PO Box 5395-1000
San Jose, Costa Rica
Tel.: (506) 22104000
E-Mail: servicioalcliente@scotiabank.com
Web Site: www.scotiabankcr.com
Banking Services
S.I.C.: 6159
N.A.I.C.S.: 522298

Scotiabank Anguilla Limited (2)
Box 250
The Valley, Anguilla, Anguilla
Tel.: (264) 497 3333
Fax: (264) 497 3344
E-Mail: bns.anguilla@scotiabank.com
Web Site: www.scotiabank.com
Banking Services
S.I.C.: 6159
N.A.I.C.S.: 522298

Scotiabank Peru S.A. (1)
Dionisio Derteano 102 Esquina con Miguel Seminario
PO Box 1235
Lima, Peru (98%)
Tel.: (51) 12116000
Fax: (51) 14407945
Web Site: www.scotiabank.com.pe
Emp.: 2,700
Banking Services
S.I.C.: 6029
N.A.I.C.S.: 522110
Carlos Gonzalez Taboada *(CEO)*

Scotiabank Sud Americano, S.A. (1)
Morande 226 Casilla 90-D
Santiago, 1, Chile (98%)
Tel.: (56) 26926000
Fax: (56) 26926001
E-Mail: scotiabank@scotiabank.cl
Web Site: www.scotiabank.cl
Sales Range: $125-149.9 Million
Banking Services
S.I.C.: 6159
N.A.I.C.S.: 522298
James Callahan *(Pres & CEO)*

Scotiabank Turks & Caicos Limited (1)
PO Box 15
Providenciales, Turks & Caicos Islands
Tel.: (649) 9464750
Fax: (649) 9464755
E-Mail: bns.turks.caicos@scotiabank.com
Web Site: www.scotiabank.com
Emp.: 130
Banking Services
S.I.C.: 6159
N.A.I.C.S.: 522298
David Tait *(Mng Dir)*

Non-U.S. Affiliate:

Scotiabank Trinidad & Tobago Limited (1)
Scotiabank Centre 56-58 Richmond St
Port of Spain, Trinidad & Tobago (48%)
Tel.: (868) 6253566
Fax: (868) 6242179
E-Mail: scotiamain.tt@scotiabank.com
Web Site: www.scotiabanktt.com
Sales Range: $75-99.9 Million
International Banking Services
S.I.C.: 6029
N.A.I.C.S.: 522110
Richard P. Young *(Mng Dir)*

Subsidiary:

Scotiatrust & Merchant Bank Trinidad & Tobago Limited (2)
Scotia Centre 56-58 Richmond Street
Port of Spain, Trinidad & Tobago
Tel.: (868) 6253566
Fax: (868) 625 4405
Web Site: www.scotiabanktt.com
Merchant Banking Services
S.I.C.: 6159
N.A.I.C.S.: 522298

THE BANK OF N.T. BUTTERFIELD & SON LIMITED

(d/b/a Butterfield Group)
65 Front Street
Hamilton, HM 12, Bermuda
Mailing Address:
PO Box HM 195
Hamilton, HM AX, Bermuda
Tel.: (441) 2993826
Fax: (441) 2924365
E-Mail: info@butterfieldgroup.com
Web Site: www.butterfieldgroup.com
Year Founded: 1758
NTB.BH—(BERM CAY)
Rev.: $373,350,000
Assets: $8,942,030,000
Liabilities: $8,084,856,000
Net Worth: $857,174,000
Earnings: $25,581,000
Emp.: 1,210
Fiscal Year-end: 12/31/12
Business Description:
Banking Services
S.I.C.: 6099
N.A.I.C.S.: 522320
Personnel:
Brendan McDonagh *(Chm & CEO)*
E. Barclay Simmons *(Vice Chm)*
Bradley Rowse *(CFO & Exec VP)*
Wilton Dolloff *(CIO & Exec VP)*
Shaun Morris *(Chief Legal Officer & Gen Counsel)*
Curtis Ballantyne *(Chief Credit Officer & Sr VP-Credit Risk Mgmt)*
Daniel Fumkin *(Chief Risk Officer & Exec VP)*
Michael W. Collins *(Sr Exec VP-Bermuda)*
Conor J. O'Dea *(Sr Exec VP-Intl Banking)*
M. Sean Lee *(Exec VP & Head Retail Banking-Bermuda)*
Robert S. Moore *(Exec VP & Head-Grp Trust)*

Curtis L. Dickinson *(Exec VP-Grp Capital Markets & Treasury)*
Donna E. Harvey-Maybury *(Exec VP-HR)*
Michael Neff *(Exec VP-Asset Mgmt)*
Bob W. Wilson *(Exec VP-Corp Banking)*
G. John Maragliano *(Sr VP & Head-Fin)*
James McPherson *(Sr VP & Head-Audit)*
Aaron M. Spencer *(Sr VP-Investment Svcs)*
Board of Directors:
Brendan McDonagh
Alastair Barbour
Victor Dodig
Pauline D. E. Richards
Olivier Sarkozy
Wolf Schoellkopf
E. Barclay Simmons
Richard Venn
John R. Wright
Transfer Agent:
Butterfield Fulcrum Group (Bermuda) Limited
Rosebank Centre 11 Bermudiana Road
Pembroke, Bermuda
Subsidiaries:

Butterfield Trust (FE) Limited (1)
65 Front Street
Hamilton, HM 12, Bermuda
Tel.: (441) 298 4691
Web Site: www.ch.butterfieldgroup.com
Emp.: 5
Investment Trust Management Services
S.I.C.: 6211
N.A.I.C.S.: 523999
Bradford Kopp *(CEO)*

Grosvenor Trust Company Limited (1)
2nd Floor Butterfield Bank 65 Front Street
Hamilton, HM 12, Bermuda
Tel.: (441) 292 7474
Fax: (441) 292 2668
Investment Trust Management Services
S.I.C.: 6211
N.A.I.C.S.: 523999
Pearline McIntosh *(VP)*

Non-U.S. Subsidiaries:

Butterfield Bank (Cayman) Limited (1)
Butterfield House 68 Fort Street
Georgetown, Grand Cayman, Cayman Islands
Tel.: (345) 949 7055
Fax: (345) 949 7004
E-Mail:
Web Site: www.ky.butterfieldgroup.com
Banking & Securities Services
S.I.C.: 6029
N.A.I.C.S.: 522110
Conor J. O'Dea *(Mng Dir)*
Erwin Dikau *(CFO)*
Michael McWatt *(Exec VP-Banking & Deputy Mng Dir)*

Bank of Butterfield (UK) PLC (1)
St Helens 1 Undershaft
BC2VNJ London, United Kingdom (100%)
Tel.: (44) 2078168300
Fax: (44) 2078168306
E-Mail: info@bankofbutterfield.co.uk
Web Site: www.bankofbutterfield.co.uk
Emp.: 34
Institutional & Commercial Bank
S.I.C.: 6029
N.A.I.C.S.: 522110

Butterfield Bank (Bahamas) Limited (1)
3rd Floor Montague Sterling Centre
PO Box 3242
Nassau, Bahamas
Tel.: (242) 393 8622
Fax: (242) 393 3772
E-Mail: info@bs.butterfieldgroup.com
Web Site: www.bs.butterfieldgroup.com
Commercial Banking Services
S.I.C.: 6029
N.A.I.C.S.: 522110
Timothy J. Colclough *(VP & Head-Trust & Fiduciary Svcs)*

Butterfield Bank International (Guernsey) Ltd. (1)
Regency Court Glategny Esplanade
PO Box 25
Saint Peter Port, TY1 3AP, Guernsey (100%)
Tel.: (44) 1481711521
Fax: (44) 481714533
E-Mail: info@butterfield.gg
Web Site: www.butterfieldbank.gg
Emp.: 250
Merchant Bank
S.I.C.: 6159
N.A.I.C.S.: 522298
Robert Moore *(Mng Dir)*

Subsidiary:

Butterfield Bank Fund Manager Ltd. (2)
Regency Court Glategny Esplanade
Saint Peter Port, GY1 3NQ, Guernsey (100%)
Tel.: (44) 1481720321
Fax: (44) 1481716117
Web Site: www.butterfieldbank.gg
Emp.: 60
S.I.C.: 6726
N.A.I.C.S.: 525990

Butterfield Bank (UK) Limited (1)
99 Gresham Street
London, EC2V 7NG, United Kingdom
Tel.: (44) 2077766700
Fax: (44) 2077766701
E-Mail: info@uk.butterfieldgroup.com
Web Site: www.uk.butterfieldgroup.com
Emp.: 100
Banking Services
S.I.C.: 6211
N.A.I.C.S.: 523110

Butterfield International Private Office Limited (1)
26 Upper Brook Street
London, W1K 7QE, United Kingdom
Tel.: (44) 2077766795
Fax: (44) 20 7776 6739
Emp.: 2
Banking Services
S.I.C.: 6029
N.A.I.C.S.: 522110

Butterfield Trust (Guernsey) Limited (1)
Regency Court Glategny Esplanade
PO Box 25
Saint Peter Port, GY1 3AP, Guernsey
Tel.: (44) 1481 711521
Fax: (44) 1481 714533
E-Mail: guernsey@butterfieldgroup.com
Emp.: 20
Banking & Financial Services
S.I.C.: 6029
N.A.I.C.S.: 522110
Robert Moore *(Mng Dir)*

Butterfield Trust (Malta) Limited (1)
Level 7 Portomaso Business Tower St Julians
Valletta, STJ4011, Malta
Tel.: (356) 21378828
Fax: (356) 21378383
E-Mail: malta@bentleyreid.com.mt
Web Site: www.bentleyreid.com
Emp.: 15
Banking Services
S.I.C.: 6211
N.A.I.C.S.: 523110
Malcolm Becker *(CEO)*

Butterfield Trust (Switzerland) Limited (1)
Boulevard des Tranchees 16
1206 Geneva, Switzerland
Tel.: (41) 22 839 0000
Fax: (41) 22 839 0099
Web Site: www.ch.butterfieldgroup.com
Emp.: 6
Banking Services
S.I.C.: 6211
N.A.I.C.S.: 523110
Jim Parker *(Head-Country)*

THE BANK OF OKINAWA, LTD.

3-10-1 Kumoji
Naha, Okinawa, 900 8651, Japan
Tel.: (81) 988672141
Fax: (81) 988638186
E-Mail: bank@okinawa-bank.co.jp
Web Site: www.okinawa-bank.co.jp
Year Founded: 1956
8397—(TKS)
Rev.: $546,700,000
Assets: $21,550,914,000
Liabilities: $20,132,552,000
Net Worth: $1,418,362,000
Earnings: $65,483,000
Emp.: 1,107
Fiscal Year-end: 03/31/13
Business Description:
Banking Services
S.I.C.: 6029
N.A.I.C.S.: 522110
Personnel:
Yoshiaki Tamaki *(Pres)*
Takao Kakinohana *(Sr Mng Dir)*
Shin Benoki *(Mng Dir)*
Yoshinori Matsugawa *(Mng Dir)*
Isamu Nerome *(Mng Dir)*
Board of Directors:
Shin Benoki
Takao Kakinohana
Tadashi Kinjo
Yoshinori Matsugawa
Isamu Nerome
Noriaki Nishikira
Yoshiaki Tamaki
Subsidiaries:

Okigin Business Service Co., Ltd. (1)
1-21-13 Izumizaki
Naha, Okinawa, 900-0021, Japan
Tel.: (81) 988628057
Fax: (81) 988628051
Emp.: 1,986
Clerical Services
S.I.C.: 8741
N.A.I.C.S.: 561110

Okigin General Lease Co., Ltd. (1)
2-21-1 Maejima
Naha, Okinawa, 900-0016, Japan
Tel.: (81) 988673141
Fax: (81) 988623966
Web Site: www.okigin-lease.co.jp
Emp.: 60
Commercial Banking
S.I.C.: 6029
N.A.I.C.S.: 522110
Kunioa Sato *(Gen Mgr)*

Okigin JCB Co., Ltd. (1)
2-12-21 Kumoji
Naha, Okinawa, 900-0015, Japan
Tel.: (81) 988623201
Web Site: www.okigin-jcb.co.jp
Credit Card Services
S.I.C.: 6153
N.A.I.C.S.: 522210

Okigin SPO Co., Ltd. (1)
5-5-8 Makiminato
Urasoe, Okinawa, 901-2131, Japan
Tel.: (81) 988780096
Fax: (81) 988794749
Data Processing Services
S.I.C.: 7374
N.A.I.C.S.: 518210

BANK OF PAPUA NEW GUINEA

Douglas St
PO Box 121
Port Moresby, 121, Papua New Guinea
Tel.: (675) 3227200
Fax: (675) 3211617
E-Mail: info@bankpng.gov.pg
Web Site: www.bankpng.gov.pg
Sales Range: $100-124.9 Million
Emp.: 300
Business Description:
Banking Services
S.I.C.: 6011
N.A.I.C.S.: 521110
Personnel:
Loi M. Bakani *(Chm)*
Board of Directors:
Loi M. Bakani
Simon Foo
John Leahy
Samson Lowa
Michael Malabag
Ken Ngangan
Betty Palaso
Benny Popoitai
James Tjeong

BANK OF QUEENSLAND LIMITED

Level 17 BOQ Centre 259 Queen Street
Brisbane, QLD, 4000, Australia
Mailing Address:
GPO Box 898
Brisbane, QLD, 4001, Australia
Tel.: (61) 732123333
Fax: (61) 732123399
E-Mail: reception@boq.com.au
Web Site: www.boq.com.au
Year Founded: 1874
BOQ—(ASX OTC)
Int. Income: $2,394,120,540
Assets: $44,318,741,430
Liabilities: $41,382,312,050
Net Worth: $2,936,429,380
Earnings: $193,622,180
Emp.: 1,448
Fiscal Year-end: 08/31/13
Business Description:
Banking Services
S.I.C.: 6099
N.A.I.C.S.: 522320
Personnel:
Stuart Grimshaw *(CEO & Mng Dir)*
Anthony Rose *(CFO)*
Jon Sutton *(COO)*
Julie Bale *(CIO)*
Peter Deans *(Chief Risk Officer)*
Matt Baxby *(Grp Exec-Retail & Online Banking)*
Karyn Munsie *(Grp Exec-Corp Affairs, IR & Govt Rels)*
Brendan White *(Grp Exec-Bus Banking, Agribus & Fin Markets)*
Brian Bissaker *(CEO-Virgin Money-Australia)*
Melissa Grundy *(Sec)*
Board of Directors:
Roger Andrew Davis
Neil A. Berkett
Steve Crane
Carmel Gray
Stuart Grimshaw
Richard George Andrew Haire
Margaret L. Seale
Michelle Tredenick
David Willis
Subsidiary:

BOQ Equipment Finance Limited (1)
Level 17 259 Queens St
Brisbane, QLD, 4000, Australia
Tel.: (61) 733362420
Web Site: www.boq.com.au
Emp.: 38
Banking
S.I.C.: 6141
N.A.I.C.S.: 522210
David Liddy *(Mng Dir)*

THE BANK OF SAGA LTD.

7-20 Tojin 2-chome
Saga, 840-0813, Japan
Tel.: (81) 952245111
Web Site: www.sagabank.co.jp
Year Founded: 1955
8395—(FKA TKS)
Rev.: $468,303,000
Assets: $23,368,620,000
Liabilities: $22,244,805,000

The Bank of Saga Ltd.—(Continued)

Net Worth: $1,123,815,000
Earnings: $24,398,000
Emp.: 1,441
Fiscal Year-end: 03/31/13
Business Description:
Banking Services
S.I.C.: 6029
N.A.I.C.S.: 522110
Personnel:
Yoshihiro Jinnouchi *(Pres)*
Kunihiko Akiba *(Co-Mng Dir)*
Mitsunori Furukawa *(Co-Mng Dir)*
Akihisa Ueno *(Co-Mng Dir)*
Board of Directors:
Kunihiko Akiba
Mitsunori Furukawa
Hirohisa Furuzono
Sunao Imaizumi
Yoshihiro Jinnouchi
Tsutomu Kimura
Toshio Muraki
Hideaki Sakai
Akira Tashiro
Akihisa Ueno

BANK OF SHANGHAI

168 Yincheng Middle Rd
Shanghai, 200120, China
Tel.: (86) 2168475888
Fax: (86) 2168476111
E-Mail: webmaster@bankofshanghai.com
Web Site: www.bankofshanghai.com
Emp.: 4,900
Business Description:
Banking Services
S.I.C.: 6029
N.A.I.C.S.: 522110
Personnel:
Liming Ning *(Chm)*

BANK OF SHARJAH P.S.C.

Al Hosn Avenue
PO Box 1394
Sharjah, United Arab Emirates
Tel.: (971) 6 5694411
Fax: (971) 6 5694422
E-Mail: enquire@bankofsharjah.com
Web Site: www.bankofsharjah.com
Year Founded: 1973
BOS—(EMI)
Int. Income: $274,173,174
Assets: $6,214,601,020
Liabilities: $5,076,330,923
Net Worth: $1,138,270,097
Earnings: $75,424,616
Fiscal Year-end: 12/31/12
Business Description:
Banking Services
S.I.C.: 6029
N.A.I.C.S.: 522110
Personnel:
Ahmed Abdalla Ali Alnoman *(Chm)*
Mohammed Saud Sultan S. Alqasimi *(Vice Chm)*
Board of Directors:
Ahmed Abdalla Ali Alnoman
Saif Mohamed Butti Al Hamed
Saud A.K. Albesharah
Abdulaziz M.A.S. Alhasawi
Abdelaziz Hassan Abdulrahman Almidfa
Humaid Nasser Alowais
Mohammed Saud Sultan S. Alqasimi
Abdulrahman Mohd Bukhatir
Francois Dauge
Varoujan Nerguizian
Jean-Jacques Santini

BANK OF SIERRA LEONE

Siaka Stevens Street
Freetown, Western Area, Sierra Leone
Tel.: (232) 22 226501
Fax: (232) 22 224764
E-Mail: info@bsl.gov.sl
Web Site: www.bsl.gov.sl
Sales Range: $10-24.9 Million
Emp.: 572
Business Description:
Banking Services
S.I.C.: 6011
N.A.I.C.S.: 521110
Personnel:
James D. Rogers *(Chm & Governor)*
Board of Directors:
James D. Rogers
Maigore Kallon
Mariatu Mahdi
Morie Komba Manyeh
I.B. Peters
Momodu Bah Yilla

BANK OF ST. VINCENT & THE GRENADINES

Bedford Street
PO Box 880
Kingstown, Saint Vincent & Grenadines
Tel.: (784) 4571844
Fax: (784) 4562612
E-Mail: info@bosvg.com
Web Site: www.svgncb.com
Sales Range: $10-24.9 Million
Emp.: 182
Business Description:
Banking Services
S.I.C.: 6029
N.A.I.C.S.: 522110
Personnel:
Desmond Morgan *(Chm)*
Phillip H. Hernandez *(CEO)*
Derry T. Williams *(Deputy CEO)*
Michele Samuel *(CFO)*
Nandi Williams *(Sec)*
Board of Directors:
Desmond Morgan
Erroll Allen
Liley Cato
Godwin Daniel
Edmond Jackson
Evelyn Jackson
Richard MacLeish
Leopold Stoddard
Winston Venner

BANK OF THAILAND

273 Samsen Road Watsamphraya, Phra Nakhon District
Bangkok, 10200, Thailand
Tel.: (66) 22835353
Fax: (66) 22800449
E-Mail: viyada@bot.or.th
Web Site: www.bot.or.th
Year Founded: 1942
Sales Range: $1-4.9 Billion
Emp.: 3,461
Business Description:
Banking Services
S.I.C.: 6011
N.A.I.C.S.: 521110
Personnel:
Virabongsa Ramangkura *(Chm)*
Prasarn Trairatvorakul *(Deputy Chm)*
Chirarat Tankurat *(Sr Chief Legal Officer)*
Chanchai Boonritchaisri *(Sec)*
Board of Directors:
Virabongsa Ramangkura
Siri Ganjarerndee
Suchada Kirakul
Ampon Kittiampon
Nontaphon Nimsomboon
Kanit Sangsubhan
Sorasit Soontornkes
Somchai Sujjapongse
Arkhom Termpittayapaisith
Prasarn Trairatvorakul
Borwornsak Uwanno
Krirk Vanikkul

BANK OF THE PHILIPPINE ISLANDS

6768 Ayala Avenue
Makati, 0720, Philippines
Tel.: (63) 28185541
Fax: (63) 28188801
E-Mail: investorrelations@bpi.com.ph
Web Site: www.bpiexpressonline.com
Year Founded: 1851
BPI—(OTC PHI)
Rev.: $1,470,355,110
Assets: $24,124,339,810
Liabilities: $21,711,536,030
Net Worth: $2,412,803,780
Earnings: $402,640,090
Emp.: 12,406
Fiscal Year-end: 12/31/12
Business Description:
Bank Holding Company
S.I.C.: 6712
N.A.I.C.S.: 551111
Personnel:
Jaime Augusto Zobel de Ayala, II *(Chm)*
Cezar Peralta Consing *(Pres & CEO)*
Michael Angelo D. Oyson *(CEO/Mng Dir-Investment Banking Grp)*
Antonio V. Paner *(Treas, Exec VP & Head-Global Banking Grp)*
Carlos B. Aqunio *(Sec)*
Natividad N. Alejo *(Exec VP-Consumer Banking Grp)*
Fidelina A. Corcuera *(Sr VP-HR Mgmt)*
Raul D. Dimayuga *(Sr VP-Overseas Banking Grp)*
Paul Joseph M. Garcia *(Sr VP-Asset Mgmt & Trust Grp)*
Ma. Cristina L. Go *(Sr VP-Card Banking Grp)*
Ma. Corazon G. Guzman *(Sr VP-Pres Office)*
Maria Theresa M. Javier *(Sr VP-Asset Mgmt & Trust Grp)*
Florendo G. Maranan *(Sr VP-COO Office)*
Pilar Bernadette C. Marquez *(Sr VP-Info Sys Grp)*
Eugenio P. Mercado *(Sr VP-Asset Mgmt & Trust Grp)*
Mario T. Miranda *(Sr VP-Asset Mgmt & Trust Grp)*
Gertie K. Sinio *(Sr VP-Pres Office)*
Manuel C. Tagaza *(Sr VP-Electronic Channels Grp)*
Cecilia L. Tan *(Sr VP-Investment Banking Grp)*
Roland Gerard R. Veloso, Jr. *(Sr VP-Pres Office)*
Heidi P. Ver *(Sr VP-Integrated Mktg Office)*
Board of Directors:
Jaime Augusto Zobel de Ayala, II
Romeo L. Bernardo
Sok Hui Chng
Cezar Peralta Consing
Octavio V. Espiritu
Rebecca G. Fernando
Solomon M. Hermosura
Teng Cheong Khoo
Xavier P. Loinaz
Aurelio R. Montinola, III
Mercedita S. Nolledo
Artemio V. Panganiban
Antonio Jose U. Periquet
Oscar S. Reyes
Fernando Zobel de Ayala

Subsidiaries:

BPI Capital Corporation **(1)**
8/F BPI Building 6768 Ayala Avenue
Makati, 1226, Philippines (100%)
Tel.: (63) 28455008
Fax: (63) 2 818 7809
Web Site: www.bpiexpressonline.com
Emp.: 20
Investment Banking & Securities Dealing
S.I.C.: 6211
N.A.I.C.S.: 523110
Cecilia Tan *(Pres)*

Subsidiaries:

BPI Asset Management **(2)**
17/F BPI Building 6768 Ayala Avenue
Makati, 1226, Philippines (45%)
Tel.: (63) 28455295
Fax: (63) 28169118
Web Site: www.bpiexpressonline.com
Sales Range: $10-24.9 Million
Emp.: 100
Investment & Asset Management Services
S.I.C.: 6799
N.A.I.C.S.: 523920
Fernando J. Sison, III *(Pres)*

BPI Securities Corporation **(2)**
8/F BPI Building 6768 Ayala Avenue
Makati, 1226, Philippines (100%)
Tel.: (63) 2 816 9190
Fax: (63) 2 816 9191
Web Site: www.bpitrade.com
Emp.: 20
Securities Brokerage Services
S.I.C.: 6211
N.A.I.C.S.: 523120
Spencer T. Yap *(Pres)*

BPI Card Corporation **(1)**
8753 Paseo de Roxas 8th Fl BPI Card Center
Makati, Metro Manila, 1226, Philippines
Tel.: (63) 28169562
Fax: (63) 28169494
E-Mail: bpidirect@bpi.com.ph
Web Site: www.bpiexpressonline.com
Credit Card Services
S.I.C.: 6153
N.A.I.C.S.: 522210

BPI Computer Systems Corp **(1)**
BPI Card Center Building Ayala Ave And Paseo De Roxas
Makati, 1226, Philippines
Tel.: (63) 28169578
Fax: (63) 2 818 9059
Commercial Banking Services
S.I.C.: 6029
N.A.I.C.S.: 522110

BPI Direct Savings Bank **(1)**
8/F BPI Card Center
8753 Paseo de Roxas, Makati, 1226, Philippines (100%)
Tel.: (63) 2 816 9562
Fax: (63) 2 816 9424
E-Mail: bpidirect@bpi.com.ph
Web Site: www.bpidirect.com
Int. Income: $400,000
Emp.: 20
Internet & Mobile Banking Services
S.I.C.: 6035
N.A.I.C.S.: 522120
Raul D. Dimayuga *(Pres)*

BPI Family Savings Bank, Inc. **(1)**
BPI Family Savings Bank Center
Paseo de Roxas
corner Dela Rosa Street, Makati, 1200, Philippines (100%)
Tel.: (63) 2 818 5541
Fax: (63) 28456992
Web Site: www.bpiexpressonline.com
Emp.: 15
Savings & Loan Services
S.I.C.: 6035
N.A.I.C.S.: 522120
Alfonso L. Salcedo, Jr. *(Pres)*
Yvonne C. Lih *(Sr VP)*
David G. Sarmiento, Jr. *(Sr VP)*

BPI Forex Corporation **(1)**
6Fl Ayala Wing BPI Head Office Bldg
Ayala Ave cor Paseo de Roxas, Makati, Metro Manila, 1201, Philippines
Tel.: (63) 28169476
Fax: (63) 28455191
E-Mail: info@bpi.com.ph
Web Site: www.bpiexpressonline.com
Emp.: 20
Currency Exchange Services
S.I.C.: 7389

N.A.I.C.S.: 561499
Manuel C. Sanchez *(Pres)*

BPI Foundation, Inc. (1)
16/F BPI Building Ayala Avenue
Makati, 1226, Philippines (100%)
Tel.: (63) 28169288
Fax: (63) 28169749
Web Site: www.bpiexpressonline.com
Emp.: 5
Charitable Grant Services
S.I.C.: 6732
N.A.I.C.S.: 813211
Florendo Merenen *(Exec Dir)*

BPI Leasing Corporation (1)
8/F BPI Building 6768 Ayala Avenue
Makati, 1226, Philippines (100%)
Tel.: (63) 2 816 9124
Fax: (63) 2 891 6605
Web Site: www.bpiexpressonline.com
Emp.: 30
Lease Financing Services
S.I.C.: 6153
N.A.I.C.S.: 522220
Georgiana A. Gamboa *(Pres)*

BPI Operations Management Corporation (1)
5/F BPI Intramuros Operations Center
Muralla Street
Solana Street Intramuros, Manila, Philippines (100%)
Tel.: (63) 25286988
Fax: (63) 25286833
Sales Range: Less than $1 Million
Emp.: 450
Management Consulting Services
S.I.C.: 8742
N.A.I.C.S.: 541611
Rafael Pertierra *(Gen Mgr)*

BPI PHILAM LIFE ASSURANCE CORPORATION (1)
12th 14th 15th Floor Ayala Life-FGU Center
6811 Ayala Avenue
Makati, 1226, Philippines
Tel.: (63) 28885433
Fax: (63) 28882949
E-Mail: customerservice@ayalalife.com.ph
Web Site: www.ayalalife.com.ph
General Insurance Services
S.I.C.: 6411
N.A.I.C.S.: 524210
Ariel G. Cantos *(Pres & CEO)*

Joint Ventures:

Ayala Life Assurance Inc. (1)
12-15/F Ayala Life-FGU Center Building
6811 Ayala Avenue, Makati, 1226, Philippines
Tel.: (63) 2 888 5433
Fax: (63) 2 888 2949
E-Mail: customer_service@ayalalife.com.ph
Web Site: www.ayalalife.com.ph
Emp.: 1,500
Life Insurance Products & Services; Owned 51% by The Philippine American Life & General Insurance Company & 49% by Bank of the Philippine Islands
S.I.C.: 6311
N.A.I.C.S.: 524113
Xavier P. Loinaz *(Chm)*

BPI/MS Insurance Corporation (1)
11-14 16/F Ayala Life-FGU Center Building
6811 Ayala Avenue, Makati, 1226, Philippines
Tel.: (63) 28409000
Fax: (63) 28409099
Toll Free: 8001000-BPIMS
E-Mail: insure@bpims.com
Web Site: www.bpims.com
Emp.: 300
Non-Life Insurance Products & Services; Owned by Bank of the Philippine Islands & by Mitsui Sumitomo Insurance Co., Ltd.
S.I.C.: 6331
N.A.I.C.S.: 524126
Takaaki Ueda *(Pres)*

U.S. Subsidiaries:

BPI Express Remittance Corp. (1)
875 3rd Ave
New York, NY 10022
Tel.: (212) 644-6700
Fax: (212) 752-5969
Web Site: www.bpi.com
Emp.: 4
Commercial Banking Services
S.I.C.: 6029
N.A.I.C.S.: 522110
Margaret Fortuno *(Branch Mgr)*

Prudential Investments, Inc (1)
100 Mulberry St Gateway Ctr 3 14th Fl
Newark, NJ 07102
Tel.: (973) 802-2991
Fax: (973) 367-8663
Investment Management Services
S.I.C.: 6211
N.A.I.C.S.: 523999

Speed International, Inc (1)
1460 Military Rd
Kenmore, NY 14217-1308
Tel.: (716) 876-2235
Commercial Banking Services
S.I.C.: 6029
N.A.I.C.S.: 522110

Non-U.S. Subsidiaries:

Bank of the Philippine Islands (Europe) Plc (1)
26 And 27 A Earl s Court Gardens
London, SW5 0SZ, United Kingdom
Tel.: (44) 207 835 0088
Fax: (44) 2073731848
E-Mail: bpinoy@bpieuropeplc.com
Web Site: www.bpieuropeplc.com
Emp.: 21
Commercial Banking Services
S.I.C.: 6029
N.A.I.C.S.: 522110
Alex Tan *(Mng Dir)*

BPI Express Remittance Spain S.A (1)
Calle Joaquin Costa 50
08001 Barcelona, Spain
Tel.: (34) 933011537
Fax: (34) 933173280
E-Mail: bpispain@yahoo.com
Emp.: 7
Commercial Banking Services
S.I.C.: 6029
N.A.I.C.S.: 522110
Roderick Lucido *(Gen Mgr)*

BPI International Finance Limited (1)
Rm 1202 12f Lippo Ctr Twr 1 89 Queensway
Central, China (Hong Kong)
Tel.: (852) 25211155
Fax: (852) 2 84 59170
E-Mail: bpi_ifl@bpi.com.ph
Emp.: 12
Commercial Banking Services
S.I.C.: 6029
N.A.I.C.S.: 522110
Bless Tan *(Sr Mgr)*

BANK OF THE RYUKYUS, LTD.

1-11-1 Kumoji
Naha, 900-0015, Japan
Tel.: (81) 988661212
Fax: (81) 988638504
Web Site: www.ryugin.co.jp
Year Founded: 1948
8399—(FKA TKS)
Rev.: $433,048,000
Assets: $21,100,255,000
Liabilities: $20,110,156,000
Net Worth: $990,099,000
Earnings: $30,536,000
Emp.: 1,219
Fiscal Year-end: 03/31/13

Business Description:
Banking Services
S.I.C.: 6029
N.A.I.C.S.: 522110

Personnel:
Tokei Kinjo *(Pres)*
Ikuo Yasuda *(Sr Mng Dir)*
Tooru Ikehata *(Mng Dir)*
Morihisa Inoha *(Corp Officer)*
Yasushi Kawakami *(Corp Officer)*
Ryota Nakamura *(Corp Officer)*

Board of Directors:
Hidehiro Hayashi
Tooru Ikehata
Shinichi Ishikawa
Tokei Kinjo
Tomoyuki Matsubara
Taketora Miyagi
Hajime Miyazato
Komei Takara
Ikuo Yasuda

Subsidiaries:

Ryugin Business Service Co., Ltd. (1)
19-17 Kumoji Naha
900-0015 Naha, Japan
Tel.: (81) 988634572
Fax: (81) 988630130
Web Site: www.ryugin.co.jp/english/annual/2001new/corporate_data.htm
Emp.: 100
All Other Business Support Services
S.I.C.: 7389
N.A.I.C.S.: 561499
Shuji Sakibara *(Mgr)*

Ryugin DC Co., Ltd. (1)
7-1 Kumoji 1-chome
Naha, 900-0015, Japan
Tel.: (81) 988621525
Fax: (81) 8628787
E-Mail: letter@ryugindc.co.jp
Web Site: www.ryugindc.co.jp
Emp.: 35
Credit Card Issuing
S.I.C.: 6153
N.A.I.C.S.: 522210

Ryugin Hosho Co., Ltd. (1)
1-9 Tsubokawa 1-chome
900-0015 Naha, Okinawa, Japan
Tel.: (81) 988321200
Fax: (81) 988321201
Web Site: www.ryugin.co.jp
Emp.: 50
Housing Loans, Debt Guaranty & Insurance Services
S.I.C.: 6411
N.A.I.C.S.: 524210
Tooru Ikehata *(Mng Dir)*

Ryugin Office Service Co., Ltd. (1)
4-1-1 Uchima Urasoe
Urasoe, Okinawa, 901-2121, Japan
Tel.: (81) 988767130
Emp.: 100
Clerical Services
S.I.C.: 8741
N.A.I.C.S.: 561110

Ryugin Research Institute., Ltd. (1)
1-9 Tsubokawa 1-chome
Naha, Okinawa, 900-0025, Japan
Tel.: (81) 988354650
Fax: (81) 988333732
E-Mail: ryugin@ryugin.co.jp
Emp.: 10
Suryveying & Research Consulting Services
S.I.C.: 8742
N.A.I.C.S.: 541611
Minoru Sakima *(Chm)*

Ryugin Sougo Kenkyusho., Ltd. (1)
1/1-9 Tsubokawa 1-chome
Naha, Japan
Tel.: (81) 988354650
Fax: (81) 988333732
E-Mail: chosabu@ryugin.co.jp
Web Site: www.ryugin-ri.co.jp
Emp.: 9
All Other Information Services
S.I.C.: 7389
N.A.I.C.S.: 519190
Yutaka Kutaka *(Gen Mgr)*

Ryukyu Leasing Co., Ltd. (1)
7-1 Kumoji 1-chome
Naha, 900-8550, Japan
Tel.: (81) 988665500
Fax: (81) 8630381
E-Mail: tadahiro@rlease.co.jp
Web Site: www.rlease.co.jp
Emp.: 64
Equipment Rental & Leasing
S.I.C.: 7359
N.A.I.C.S.: 532420
Tomomatsu Higa *(Pres)*

BANK OF UGANDA

37-43 Kampala Rd
PO Box 7120
710 Kampala, Uganda
Tel.: (256) 41258441
Fax: (256) 41230878
E-Mail: info@bou.or.ug
Web Site: www.bou.or.ug
Year Founded: 1966
Sales Range: $50-74.9 Million
Emp.: 957

Business Description:
Banking Services
S.I.C.: 6029
N.A.I.C.S.: 522110

Personnel:
Emmanuel Tumusiime Mutebile *(Chm)*

Board of Directors:
Emmanuel Tumusiime Mutebile
Juma Wasswa Balunywa
Benigna Mukiibi
Rweyemamu Rweikiza
Manzi Tumubweinee

BANK OF VALLETTA P.L.C.

(d/b/a BOV Group)
BOV Centre Cannon Road
Santa Venera, SVR 9030, Malta
Tel.: (356) 21312020
Fax: (356) 22753711
E-Mail: customercare@bov.com
Web Site: www.bov.com
BOV—(MAL)
Int. Income: $195,343,726
Assets: $9,309,226,906
Liabilities: $8,620,782,716
Net Worth: $688,444,190
Earnings: $98,147,564
Emp.: 1,522
Fiscal Year-end: 09/30/12

Business Description:
Banking Services
S.I.C.: 6029
N.A.I.C.S.: 522110

Personnel:
Frederick Mifsud Bonnici *(Chm)*
Charles Borg *(CEO)*
Elvia George *(CFO)*
Michael Borg Costanzi *(Chief Legal Officer & Chief Compliance Officer)*
Albert Frendo *(Chief Credit Ops Officer)*
Joseph M. Camilleri *(Chief HR Officer)*
Romeo Cutajar *(Chief Fin Markets & Investments Officer)*
Victor Denaro *(Chief IT & Info Officer)*
Kenneth Farrugia *(Chief Fund Svcs Officer)*
Michael Galea *(Chief Ops & Multi-Channel Banking Officer)*
Mario Mallia *(Chief Risk Mgmt Officer)*
Peter Perotti *(Chief Personal Banking Officer)*
Anthony Scicluna *(Chief Internal Audit Officer)*

Board of Directors:
Frederick Mifsud Bonnici
Joseph Borg
Roberto Cassata
Gordon Cordina
Ann Fenech
George Portanier
Paul Testaferrata Moroni Vani
George Wells
Franco Xuereb

Deloitte Audit Ltd
Deloitte Place Mriehel Bypass
Mriehel, Malta

Bank of Valletta p.l.c.—(Continued)

Subsidiaries:

Valletta Fund Management Limited (1)
Complex 2 Level 3 Brewery St
Mriehel, VLT 16, Malta
Tel.: (356) 21227311
Fax: (356) 21234565
E-Mail: infovfm@vfm.com.mt
Web Site: www.vfm.com.mt
Emp.: 6
Fund Management Services
S.I.C.: 6733
N.A.I.C.S.: 525190

Valletta Fund Services Limited (1)
TG Complex, Ste 2, Level 3, Brewery St
Mriehel, BKR 3000, Malta
Tel.: (356) 21227311
Fax: (356) 21234565
E-Mail: infovfs@bov.com
Web Site: www.vfs.com.mt
Emp.: 45
Fund Administration Services
S.I.C.: 6371
N.A.I.C.S.: 524292
Kenneth Farrugia *(Gen Mgr)*

THE BANK OF YOKOHAMA, LTD.

1 1 Minatomirai 3 Chome
Nishi Ku, Yokohama, Kanagawa, 220 8611, Japan
Tel.: (81) 452251111
Telex: J24945 HAMABK
Fax: (81) 452251160
E-Mail: iroffice@hamagin.co.jp
Web Site: www.boy.co.jp
Year Founded: 1920
8332—(TKS)
Sales Range: $1-4.9 Billion
Emp.: 4,637
Business Description:
Regional Banking Services
S.I.C.: 6211
N.A.I.C.S.: 523110
Personnel:
Tadashi Ogawa *(Chm)*
Tatsumaro Terazawa *(Pres)*
Chiyuki Okubo *(Deputy Pres)*
Yasutaka Nozawa *(Dir-Sls Plng)*
Yoshiyuki Hiranuma *(Exec Officer)*
Osamu Ishida *(Exec Officer)*
Tomonori Ito *(Exec Officer)*
Kenichi Kawamura *(Exec Officer)*
Shunji Komatsu *(Mng Exec Officer)*
Susumu Koshida *(Exec Officer)*
Shizumi Maesako *(Mng Exec Officer)*
Atsushi Mochizuki *(Exec Officer)*
Soh Okada *(Exec Officer)*
Hironobu Onishi *(Exec Officer)*
Yasuyoshi Oya *(Exec Officer)*
Yasuhiro Shibuya *(Exec Officer)*
Yuji Shirai *(Exec Officer)*
Kengo Takano *(Exec Officer)*
Shinya Yamada *(Exec Officer)*
Seiichi Yoneda *(Mng Exec Officer)*
Board of Directors:
Tadashi Ogawa
Shoji Hanawa
Yoshiyuki Hiranuma
Osamu Ishida
Tomonori Ito
Kenichi Kawamura
Shunji Komatsu
Susumu Koshida
Shizumi Maesako
Atsushi Mochizuki
Yasutaka Nozawa
Soh Okada
Chiyuki Okubo
Hironobu Onishi
Yasuyoshi Oya
Harumi Sakamoto
Yasuhiro Shibuya
Yuji Shirai
Kengo Takano
Tatsumaro Terazawa
Shinya Yamada
Seiichi Yoneda

Subsidiaries:

Hamagin Finance Co., Ltd. (1)
Minato Mirai 3-1-1
Nishi-ku, Yokohama, Kanagawa, 220 8613, Japan
Tel.: (81) 452252321
Leasing & Factoring Services
S.I.C.: 6141
N.A.I.C.S.: 522220

Hamagin Research Institute Ltd (1)
3-1-1 Minatomirai
Nishi ku, Yokohama, Kanagawa, 220 8616, Japan
Tel.: (81) 452252371
Fax: (81) 452252198
Web Site: www.yokohama-ri.co.jp
Emp.: 80
Business Mangement Consulting Services
S.I.C.: 8742
N.A.I.C.S.: 541611
Yoshio Ota *(Mng Dir)*

Hamagin Tokai Tokyo Securities Co., Ltd. (1)
3-1-1 Minatomirai
Nishi-ku, Yokohama, Kanagawa, 220 0012, Japan
Tel.: (81) 452251133
Fax: (81) 452252091
Web Site: www.hamagintt.co.jp
Emp.: 200
Securities Brokerage Services
S.I.C.: 6211
N.A.I.C.S.: 523120
Tetsunobu Ikeda *(Pres)*

Yokohama Capital Co., Ltd. (1)
3-1-1 Minatomirai
Nishi ku, Yokohama, Kanagawa, 220-0012, Japan
Tel.: (81) 452252331
Fax: (81) 452252330
Investments & Financing Services to Small & Medium-Sized Enterprises
S.I.C.: 6282
N.A.I.C.S.: 523930

BANK OF ZAMBIA

Bank Square Cairo Road
PO Box 30080
Lusaka, Zambia
Tel.: (260) 1228888
Fax: (260) 1221722
E-Mail: pr@boz.zm
Web Site: www.boz.zm
Business Description:
Banking Services
S.I.C.: 6011
N.A.I.C.S.: 521110
Personnel:
Caleb M. Fundanga *(Chm & Governor)*
Tukiya Kankasa-Mabula *(Deputy Governor-Administration)*
Mathew Chisunka *(Sec-Bank)*
Likolo Ndalamei *(Sec-Treasury)*
Board of Directors:
Caleb M. Fundanga
Imwiko Anang'anga
Dennis Chiwele
Judith C.N. Lungu
Mwene Mwinga
Likolo Ndalamei

BANK PASARGAD

No 430 Mirdamad Blvd
Tehran, 1969774511, Iran
Tel.: (98) 21 82890
E-Mail: info@bankpasargad.com
Web Site: bpi.ir
BPAS—(THE)
Sales Range: $1-4.9 Billion
Business Description:
Financial & Banking Services
S.I.C.: 6029
N.A.I.C.S.: 522110
Personnel:
Seyyed Kazem Mirvalad *(Chm)*
Majid Ghasemi *(Vice Chm & CEO)*
Board of Directors:
Seyyed Kazem Mirvalad
Mostafa Beheshtirouy
Kamran Ekhtiar
Majid Ghasemi
Zabiallah Khazayee
Davood Mojtahed
Ahmad Vadidar

BANK SADERAT OF IRAN

Panzdah Khordad Ave
Tehran, Iran
Tel.: (98) 33907224
Fax: (98) 33907815
Web Site: in.bsi.ir
Year Founded: 1961
BSDR—(THE)
Sales Range: $1-4.9 Billion
Business Description:
Banking Services
S.I.C.: 6029
N.A.I.C.S.: 522110
Personnel:
Mohammadreza Pishro *(Chm)*
Ali Mobini Dehkordi *(Deputy CEO & Head-Res)*
Board of Directors:
Mohammadreza Pishro
Mohammadreza Erfani
Mohammadhosein Fathalizadeh
Rohollah Khodarahmi
Mohammad Rabizade

BANK SADERAT PLC

5 Lothbury
London, EC2R 7HD, United Kingdom
Tel.: (44) 2076000133
Fax: (44) 2077963216
E-Mail: enquiries@saderat-plc.com
Web Site: www.saderat-plc.com
Year Founded: 1973
Int. Income: $10,433,998
Assets: $320,045,872
Liabilities: $91,874,847
Net Worth: $228,171,025
Earnings: $1,442,105
Emp.: 29
Fiscal Year-end: 12/31/12
Business Description:
Banking & International Trade Financing Services
S.I.C.: 6029
N.A.I.C.S.: 522110
Personnel:
M. R. Pishrow *(Chm)*
H. Borhani *(Mng Dir)*
C. R. Wakefield *(Asst Mng Dir)*
R. G. Wetton *(Sec & Controller-Fin)*
Board of Directors:
M. R. Pishrow
H. Borhani
D. J. Reid
R. J. Speedy

BANK SOHAR SAOG

Bank Sohar Building
PO Box 44
Muscat, PC 114, Oman
Tel.: (968) 24730000
Fax: (968) 24730010
E-Mail: info@banksohar.net
Web Site: www.banksohar.net
BKSB—(MUS)
Int. Income: $186,944,656
Assets: $4,624,685,202
Liabilities: $4,249,776,328
Net Worth: $374,908,874
Earnings: $59,546,025
Emp.: 573
Fiscal Year-end: 12/31/12
Business Description:
Banking Services
S.I.C.: 6029
N.A.I.C.S.: 522110
Personnel:
Abdullah Humaid Said Al Mamary *(Chm)*
Mohammed Abdullah Mohammed Al Khunji *(Deputy Chm)*
Mohamed Abdulaziz Kalmoor *(CEO)*
Rashad Ali Al Musafir *(CFO)*
Board of Directors:
Abdullah Humaid Said Al Mamary
Ghazi Nasser Salim Al Alawi
Mohammed Abdullah Mohammed Al Khunji
Salim Mohamed Al Mashaiky
Hassan Ahmed Al Nabhani
Omar Ahmed Abdullah Al Shaikh
Shabir M. Al Yousef

BANK SOUTH PACIFIC LIMITED

Cnr Douglas Street & Musgrave Street
PO Box 78
Port Moresby, Papua New Guinea
Tel.: (675) 320 1212
Fax: (675) 3211954
E-Mail: servicebsp@bsp.com.pg
Web Site: www.bsp.com.pg
BSP—(POM)
Int. Income: $350,394,772
Assets: $6,287,090,917
Liabilities: $5,595,863,732
Net Worth: $691,227,185
Earnings: $192,267,606
Emp.: 3,890
Fiscal Year-end: 12/31/12
Business Description:
Banking Services
S.I.C.: 6029
N.A.I.C.S.: 522110
Personnel:
Robin Fleming *(CEO)*
Johnson Kalo *(Deputy CEO & CFO)*
Roberto Loggia *(COO)*
Haroon Ali *(Grp Chief Risk Officer)*
Mary Johns *(Sec)*
Board of Directors:
Kostas Constantinou
Gerea Aopi
Nagora Bogan
Tom Fox
John Jeffery
Lyle Procter
Geoffrey J. Robb
Freda Talao
Ila Temu

BANK TEJARAT

182 in front of Asia Insurance Co
Between Nejatollahi and Gharani St
PO Box 14157
Taleghani Ave, Tehran, Iran
Tel.: (98) 88895102
Fax: (98) 88900280
Web Site: www.tejaratbank.ir
BTEJ—(THE)
Business Description:
Banking Services
S.I.C.: 6029
N.A.I.C.S.: 522110
Personnel:
M. R. Davari *(Chm)*
M. R. Ranjbar Fallah *(Mng Dir)*
Board of Directors:
M. R. Davari
R. Akrami
S. Dolati
M. R. Ranjbar Fallah

BANK VAN DE NEDERLANDSE ANTILLEN

Simon Bolivar Plein 1
Willemstad, Curacao

Tel.: (599) 94345500
Fax: (599) 94615004
E-Mail: info@centralbank.an
Web Site: www.centralbank.an
Emp.: 200
Business Description:
Central Bank
S.I.C.: 6011
N.A.I.C.S.: 521110
Personnel:
R. Palm *(Chm-Supervisory Bd)*
E. D. Tromp *(Pres)*
Brian Mezas *(Gen Counsel)*
S. Sinlae-Elhage *(Treas)*
Supervisory Board of Directors:
R. Palm
N. Chaclin
O. F. Cuales
R. P. Koeijers
C.J. Roemer

BANK WESTLB VOSTOK (ZAO)

ul Povarskaya 23
Bldg 4, 121069 Moscow, Russia
Tel.: (7) 4952586102
Fax: (7) 4952586105
Web Site:
Emp.: 75
Business Description:
Central Bank
S.I.C.: 6011
N.A.I.C.S.: 521110
Personnel:
Igor V. Kim *(Owner)*

BANKA SLOVENIJE

Slovenska 35
1505 Ljubljana, Slovenia
Tel.: (386) 14719000
Fax: (386) 12515516
Web Site: www.bsi.si
Sales Range: $300-349.9 Million
Emp.: 200
Business Description:
Banking Services
S.I.C.: 6011
N.A.I.C.S.: 521110
Personnel:
Marko Kranjec *(Chm)*
Darko Bohnec *(Vice Chm)*
Stanislava Zadravec Caprirolo *(Vice Chm)*
Janez Fabijan *(Vice Chm)*
Mejra Festic *(Vice Chm)*
Board of Directors:
Marko Kranjec
Darko Bohnec
Stanislava Zadravec Caprirolo
Ernest Ermenc
Janez Fabijan
Mejra Festic
Tomaz Kosak
Damjan Kozamernik
Matjaz Noc
Ivan Ribnikar

BANKERS PETROLEUM LTD

Bow Valley Square III Suite 1700 255 5 Avenue SW
Calgary, AB, T2P 3G6, Canada
Tel.: (403) 513-2699
Fax: (403) 228-9506
Toll Free: (888) 797-7170
E-Mail: corporate@bankerspetroleum.com
Web Site: www.bankerspetroleum.com
Year Founded: 2004
BNK—(AIM OTC TSX)
Rev.: $432,138,000
Assets: $825,816,000
Liabilities: $342,784,000
Net Worth: $483,032,000
Earnings: $34,413,000
Emp.: 480
Fiscal Year-end: 12/31/12
Business Description:
Oil & Gas Exploration Services
S.I.C.: 1389
N.A.I.C.S.: 213112
Personnel:
Abdel F. Z. Badwi *(Vice Chm)*
David Lawrence French *(Pres & CEO)*
Douglas C. Urch *(CFO & Exec VP-Fin)*
Suneel Gupta *(COO & Exec VP)*
Leonidha Cobo *(Gen Dir & VP)*
Richard Walter Pawluk *(Sec)*
Board of Directors:
Robert Melvin Douglas Cross
Abdel F. Z. Badwi
Eric M. Brown
Wesley K. Clark, Sr.
Jonathan Harris
Phillip Raymond Knoll
Ian B. McMurtrie
John B. Zaozirny
Legal Counsel:
McCarthy Tetrault LLP
Calgary, AB, Canada
Transfer Agent:
Alliance Trust Company
450 407 2nd St SW
Calgary, AB, Canada

BANKHAUS WOLBERN AG & CO. KG

Am Sandtorkai 54
20457 Hamburg, Germany
Tel.: (49) 40376080
Fax: (49) 4037608101
E-Mail: info@woelbern.de
Web Site: www.woelbern.de
Emp.: 90
Business Description:
Banking Services
S.I.C.: 6029
N.A.I.C.S.: 522110
Personnel:
Hans Detlef Boesel *(Chm)*

BANKIA S.A.

(See Under Banco Financiero y de Ahorros, S.A.U.)

BANKINTER, S.A.

Paseo de la Castellana 29
28046 Madrid, Spain
Tel.: (34) 913397500
Fax: (34) 913398323
E-Mail: buzon@bankinter.es
Web Site: www.bankinter.es
Year Founded: 1965
BKT—(MAD)
Rev.: $14,414,379,124
Assets: $78,301,176,141
Liabilities: $73,951,570,293
Net Worth: $4,349,605,848
Earnings: $167,805,475
Emp.: 4,068
Fiscal Year-end: 12/31/12
Business Description:
Commercial Banking Services
S.I.C.: 6029
N.A.I.C.S.: 522110
Personnel:
Pedro Guerrero Guerrero *(Chm)*
Maria Dolores Dancausa Trevino *(CEO)*
Inigo War *(CEO-Investment Banking)*
Monica Lopez-Monis *(Gen Sec)*
Board of Directors:
Pedro Guerrero Guerrero
Gonzalo de la Hoz Lizcano
Rafael Mateu de Ros Cerezo
Alfonso Botin-Sanz de Sautuola y Naveda
Marcelino Botin-Sanz de Sautuola y Naveda
John de Zulueta Greenebaum
Pedro Gonzalez Grau
Fernando Masaveu Herrero
Jaime Terceiro Lomba
Maria Dolores Dancausa Trevino

Subsidiaries:

Bankinter Consultoria, Asesoramiento y Atencion Telefonica, S.A. (1)
Avenida de Bruselas No 12
28108 Alcobendas, Madrid, Spain
Tel.: (34) 916234322
Fax: (34) 916578606
Web Site: www.bankinter.es
Emp.: 25
Telebanking Services
S.I.C.: 4899
N.A.I.C.S.: 517919
Javier Bollain *(Mng Dir)*

Bankinter Consumer Finance, EFC, S.A. (1)
Avenida De Bruselas Arroyo Vega 7
28108 Alcobendas, Madrid, Spain
Tel.: (34) 916578729
Commercial Banking Services
S.I.C.: 6029
N.A.I.C.S.: 522110
Hermosa Burgos Yolanda *(Sec)*

Bankinter Emisiones, S.A. (1)
Paseo Castellana 29
Madrid, 28046, Spain
Tel.: (34) 913397500
Fax: (34) 913398325
Web Site: www.bankinter.com
Banking Services
S.I.C.: 6029
N.A.I.C.S.: 522110
Mariaane Leijte *(Sec)*

Bankinter Seguros de Vida, de Seguros y Reaseguros SA (1)
Pico de San Pedro 2
Tres Cantos, 28760 Madrid, Spain
Tel.: (34) 913398424
Fax: (34) 913398518
Insurance Related Activities
S.I.C.: 6411
N.A.I.C.S.: 524298

BANKISLAMI PAKISTAN LIMITED

11th Floor Executive Tower Dolmen City Marine Drive
Block-4 Clifton, 74000 Karachi, Pakistan
Tel.: (92) 213589906
Fax: (92) 2135378373
E-Mail: info@bankislami.com.pk
Web Site: www.bankislami.com.pk
BIPL—(KAR)
Int. Income: $60,545,673
Assets: $750,960,999
Liabilities: $694,508,059
Net Worth: $56,452,940
Earnings: $4,210,626
Emp.: 1,414
Fiscal Year-end: 12/31/12
Business Description:
Financial & Banking Services
S.I.C.: 6211
N.A.I.C.S.: 523110
Personnel:
Mahboob Ahmed *(Chm)*
Hasan A. Bilgrami *(CEO)*
Khawaja Ehrar ul Hassan *(Acting Sec, Head-Compliance & Legal & Acting Head-Fin)*
Board of Directors:
Mahboob Ahmed
Fawad Anwar
Hasan A. Bilgrami
Abdul Hakim Binherz
Ali Hussain
Shabir Ahmed Randeree
Abdulla Abdulkarim Showaiter
Ali Raza Siddiqui

BANKMECU LTD.

222 High Street
Kew, VIC, 3121, Australia
Mailing Address:
Private Bag 12
Kew, VIC, 3101, Australia
Tel.: (61) 3 9854 4666
Fax: (61) 3 9853 9294
E-Mail: mail@bankmecu.com.au
Web Site: www.bankmecu.com.au
Rev.: $159,992,571
Assets: $3,169,292,878
Liabilities: $2,812,142,281
Net Worth: $357,150,596
Earnings: $26,466,214
Emp.: 304
Fiscal Year-end: 06/30/13
Business Description:
Banking & Financial Services
S.I.C.: 6029
N.A.I.C.S.: 522110
Personnel:
John W. Baistow *(Chm)*
Helen M. Clarke *(Deputy Chm)*
Damien G. Walsh *(Mng Dir)*
John P. Yardley *(COO)*
Christopher H. Newey *(Sec & Gen Mgr-Corp Svcs)*
Board of Directors:
John W. Baistow
Melissa Bastian
Greg Camm
Helen M. Clarke
Judith Downes
Peter J. Ford
Peter J. Taylor
Damien G. Walsh

BANKS HOLDINGS LTD.

PO Box 507 C
Saint Michael, Barbados
Tel.: (246) 2276700
Fax: (246) 4270772
E-Mail: bhl@banksholdings.com.bb
Web Site: www.thebhlgroup.com
BNKS—(BARB)
Sales Range: $75-99.9 Million
Emp.: 500
Business Description:
Food & Beverage Holding Company
S.I.C.: 6719
N.A.I.C.S.: 551112
Personnel:
Allan C. Fields *(Chm)*
Richard Cozier *(CEO & Mng Dir)*
Natalie Brace *(Sec)*
Board of Directors:
Allan C. Fields
Natalie Brace
Richard Cozier
Ruall Harris
Azam A. Khan
Anthony King
Robert Ramchand
Elvin Sealy
Dan B. Stoute
Gervase Warner
Peter Weatherhead

Subsidiaries:

B&B Distribution Ltd. (1)
Newton
PO Box 955
Christchurch, Barbados
Tel.: (246) 4208881
Fax: (246) 420-6975
Web Site: www.thebhlgroup.com
Bottled Beverage Distribution
S.I.C.: 2086
N.A.I.C.S.: 312111
Jeremy Whitelaw *(Gen Mgr)*

Banks (Barbados) Breweries Limited (1)
PO Box 507 C
Saint Michael, Barbados

Banks Holdings Ltd.—(Continued)

Tel.: (246) 429 2113
Fax: (246) 428 1769
E-Mail: brewery@banksholdings.com.bb
Web Site: www.banksbeer.com
Bottled Beverage Mfr
S.I.C.: 5182
N.A.I.C.S.: 424820
Akash Ragbir *(Gen Mgr)*

Barbados Bottling Co. Limited (1)
Newton Industrial Park
Christchurch, Barbados
Tel.: (246) 428 8920
Fax: (246) 428 4095
Soft Drink & Beverage Mfr & Bottler
S.I.C.: 2086
N.A.I.C.S.: 312111
William Haslett *(Gen Mgr)*

Barbados Dairy Industries Ltd. (1)
PO Box 56B
Saint Michael, Barbados BB
Tel.: (246) 4304100
Telex: 2592
Fax: (246) 4293514
Web Site: www.banksholdings.com.bb/showsubsidiary.cfm?p=pinehilldairyinbrief
Sales Range: $25-49.9 Million
Emp.: 200
Dry, Condensed & Evaporated Dairy Products
S.I.C.: 2023
N.A.I.C.S.: 311514
Allan C. Fields *(Chm)*
William Haflett *(Mng Dir)*
A. R.S. Marshall *(Sec)*

Plastic Containers Limited (1)
Thornbury Hill
Christchurch, Barbados
Tel.: (246) 428 7780
Fax: (246) 428 7112
E-Mail: gale.containerplus@yahoo.com
Emp.: 21
Plastic Bottle Mfr
S.I.C.: 3085
N.A.I.C.S.: 326160
Richard Taurel *(Plant Mgr)*

BANKS ISLAND GOLD LTD.

300 1055 W Hastings St
Vancouver, BC, V6E 2E9, Canada
Tel.: (604) 245-0066
E-Mail: info@banksislandgold.com
Web Site: www.banksislandgold.com
Year Founded: 2011
BOZ—(TSXV)

Business Description:
Gold Mining
S.I.C.: 1041
N.A.I.C.S.: 212221

Personnel:
Wolfgang Nickel *(Chm)*
Benjamin Mossman *(Pres & CEO)*
Sharon Muzzin *(CFO)*

Board of Directors:
Wolfgang Nickel
Saurabh Handa
Benjamin Mossman
Jason Nickel
Frederick J. Sveinson

Transfer Agent:
Computershare Investor Services Inc.
3rd Floor 510 Burrard St
V6C 3B9 Vancouver, BC, Canada

BANNARI AMMAN SPINNING MILLS LTD.

252 Mettupalayam Road
Coimbatore, 641 043, India
Tel.: (91) 422 2435555
Fax: (91) 422 2434446
E-Mail: sales@bannarimills.com
Web Site: www.bannarimills.com
532674—(BOM)
Rev.: $103,973,703
Assets: $128,654,031
Liabilities: $88,796,944
Net Worth: $39,857,086
Earnings: $5,064,780
Fiscal Year-end: 03/31/13

Business Description:
Textile Products Mfr
S.I.C.: 2299
N.A.I.C.S.: 314999

Personnel:
S. V. Arumugam *(Chm & Mng Dir)*
A. Senthil *(CEO)*
N. Krishnaraj *(Compliance Officer & Sec)*

Board of Directors:
S. V. Arumugam
S. Palaniswami
C. S. K. Prabhu
K. N. V. Ramani
K. Sadhasivam
K. R. Thillainathan

Transfer Agent:
Link Intime India Private Limited
Surya 35 May Flower Avenue Behind Senthil
Nagar Souripalayam Road
Coimbatore, India

BANNARI AMMAN SUGARS LTD

1212 Trichy Road
Coimbatore, 641018, India
Tel.: (91) 4222302277
Fax: (91) 4222305599
E-Mail: bascbe@bannari.com
Web Site: www.bannari.com
BANARISUG—(NSE)
Rev.: $253,646,927
Assets: $317,913,908
Liabilities: $143,268,072
Net Worth: $174,645,836
Earnings: $26,417,164
Emp.: 1,851
Fiscal Year-end: 03/31/13

Business Description:
Sugar & Alcohol Mfr
S.I.C.: 2084
N.A.I.C.S.: 312130

Personnel:
S. V. Balasubramaniam *(Chm)*
B. Saravanan *(Mng Dir)*
C. Palaniswamy *(Compliance Officer & Sec)*

Board of Directors:
S. V. Balasubramaniam
S. V. Alagappan
S. V. Arumugam
T. Gundan
E. P. Muthukumar
A. K. Perumalsamy
V. Venkata Reddy
B. Saravanan
M. P. Vijayakumar

Transfer Agent:
Cameo Corporate Services Limited
Subramanian Building No 1 Club House Road
5th Floor
Chennai, India

BANNER CHEMICALS LIMITED

(d/b/a Banner Chemicals Group UK)
Hampton Court Tudor Road
Manor Park, Runcorn, WA71TU, United Kingdom
Tel.: (44) 1928597000
Fax: (44) 1928597001
E-Mail: info@bannerchemicals.com
Web Site: www.bannerchemicals.com
Year Founded: 1860
Sales Range: $100-124.9 Million
Emp.: 170

Business Description:
Chemical Mfr & Distr
S.I.C.: 2899
N.A.I.C.S.: 325998

Personnel:
Mordechai Kessler *(Chm & CEO)*

Units:

Banner Chemicals-Pharmaceutical Products (1)
Hampton Court Manor Park
Runcorn, Cheshires, WA7 1TU, United Kingdom
Tel.: (44) 1928597020
Fax: (44) 1928597002
E-Mail: pharma@bannerchemicals.com
Web Site: www.bannerchemicals.com
Emp.: 25
Pharmaceutical Preparations
S.I.C.: 2834
N.A.I.C.S.: 325412
Chris Hall *(Dir-Sls & Mktg)*

Banner Chemicals-Biocides (1)
Hampton Court, Tudor Road Manor Park
Runcorn, Cheshire, WA7 1TU, United Kingdom
Tel.: (44) 1928597000
Fax: (44) 1928597001
E-Mail: info@bannerchemicals.com
Web Site: www.bannerchemicals.com
Emp.: 20
Chemicals Manufacturing
S.I.C.: 2899
N.A.I.C.S.: 325998
Graham Cauchois *(Dir-Ops)*

Banner Chemicals-BlueCat-AdBlue Solutions (1)
Hampton Court Manor Park
Runcorn, Cheshire, WA7 1TU, United Kingdom
Tel.: (44) 1928597010
Fax: (44) 1928597001
E-Mail: bluecat@bannerchemicals.com
Emp.: 30
Chemicals Distribution
S.I.C.: 5169
N.A.I.C.S.: 424690
Collin Boyle *(Dir-Fin)*

Banner Chemicals-Cosmetics & Personal Care (1)
Hampton Ct Tudor Rd Manor Pk
Runcorn, Cheshire, WA7 1TU, United Kingdom
Tel.: (44) 1928597025
Fax: (44) 1928597001
E-Mail: spec@bannerchemicals.com
Web Site: www.bannerchemicals.com
Emp.: 59
Chemicals Manufacturing
S.I.C.: 2899
N.A.I.C.S.: 325998
Graham Cauchois *(Dir-Speciality Bus)*

Banner Chemicals-Hydrocarbon Solvents (1)
Hampton Court Manor Park
Runcorn, Cheshire, WA7 1TU, United Kingdom
Tel.: (44) 1928597020
Fax: (44) 1928597001
E-Mail: info@bannerchemicals.com
Web Site: www.bannerchemicals.com
Emp.: 50
Chemical Manufacturing
S.I.C.: 2899
N.A.I.C.S.: 325998
Mottie Kessler *(Mng Dir)*

Banner Chemicals-Oil Field Applications (1)
Hampton Ct Manor Pk
Runcorn, Cheshire, WA7 1TU, United Kingdom
Tel.: (44) 1928597024
Fax: (44) 1928597001
E-Mail: oil@bannerchemicals.com
Web Site: www.bannerchemicals.com
Emp.: 80
Chemical Manufacturing
S.I.C.: 5169
N.A.I.C.S.: 424690
Rachel Hankin *(Coord-Sls & Mktg)*

Banner Chemicals-Oxygenated Solvents & Intermediates (1)
Hampton Court Manor Park
Runcorn, Cheshire, WA7 1TU, United Kingdom
Tel.: (44) 1928597020
Fax: (44) 1928597002
E-Mail: solvents@bannerchemicals.com
Web Site: www.bannerchemicals.com
Emp.: 92
Pharmaceutical, Food & Personal Care Solvents
S.I.C.: 2869
N.A.I.C.S.: 325199
Chris Hall *(Bus Dir)*

Banner Chemicals-Precision & Electronics Cleaning (1)
Hampton Court Tudor Road Manor Park
Runcorn, Cheshire, WA7 1TU, United Kingdom
Tel.: (44) 1928597030
Fax: (44) 1928597001
E-Mail: PEC@bannerchemicals.com
Web Site: www.bannerchemicals.com
Emp.: 80
Cleaning & Degreasing Solvents
S.I.C.: 2899
N.A.I.C.S.: 325998
Motti Kessler *(Dir-Ops)*

Banner Chemicals-Specialty Chemicals (1)
Hampton Court Tudor Road Manor Park
Runcorn, Cheshire, WA7 1TU, United Kingdom
Tel.: (44) 1928597000
Fax: (44) 01928597001
E-Mail: inquiries@bannerchemicals.com
Web Site: www.bannerchemicals.com
Emp.: 80
Specialty Chemicals
S.I.C.: 5169
N.A.I.C.S.: 424690
Graham Cauchois *(Bus Dir)*

Banner Chemicals-Surface Coatings & Industrial (1)
Hampton Ct, Tudor Rd Manor Pk
WA7 1TU Runcorn, Cheshire, United Kingdom
Tel.: (44) 1928597025
Fax: (44) 1928597002
E-Mail: coatings@bannerchemicals.com
Web Site: www.bannerchemicals.com
Emp.: 40
Coatings & Industrial Chemicals
S.I.C.: 2899
N.A.I.C.S.: 325998
Graham Cauchois *(Dir-Ops)*

MP Storage & Blending (1)
Dockside Rd
Middlesbrough, Cleveland, TS3 8AS, United Kingdom
Tel.: (44) 1642244125
Fax: (44) 1642231780
E-Mail: storage@bannerchemicals.com
Web Site: www.mpstorage.com
Emp.: 25
Chemical Storage & Blending
S.I.C.: 4226
N.A.I.C.S.: 493190
Mike Goodwin *(Mgr-Bus Dev)*

Prism Chemicals (1)
59-61 Sandhills Lane
Liverpool, L59 XE, United Kingdom
Tel.: (44) 151 922 7871
Fax: (44) 151 944 1517
E-Mail: info@prismchemicals.co.uk
Web Site: www.bannerchemicals.com
Emp.: 7
Pigment Formulations
S.I.C.: 2816
N.A.I.C.S.: 325130

Samuel Banner & Co. (1)
Hampton Court Manor Park
Runcorn, Cheshire, WA7 1TU, United Kingdom
Tel.: (44) 1928597021
Fax: (44) 1928597003
E-Mail: info@bannerchemicals.com
Web Site: www.bannerchemicals.com
Emp.: 75
Chemicals Transportation
S.I.C.: 5169
N.A.I.C.S.: 424690
Mark Johnson *(Mgr-Supply Chain)*

BANNERMAN RESOURCES LIMITED

Suite 18 Level 1 513 Hay Street
Subiaco, WA, 6008, Australia
Tel.: (61) 893811436
Fax: (61) 893811068

E-Mail: admin@bannermanresources.com.au
Web Site: www.bannermanresources.com.au
BMN—(ASX OTC)
Rev.: $200,083
Assets: $67,410,323
Liabilities: $8,338,884
Net Worth: $59,071,439
Earnings: ($5,927,465)
Emp.: 14
Fiscal Year-end: 06/30/13
Business Description:
Exploration & Pre-Feasibility Stage Mining
S.I.C.: 1099
N.A.I.C.S.: 212299
Personnel:
Leonard Stanley Jubber *(CEO & Mng Dir)*
Leigh-Ayn Absolom *(Sec & Controller-Fin)*
Board of Directors:
Ronnie Beevor
Ian Burvill
Clive Jones
Leonard Stanley Jubber
David C. Tucker
Legal Counsel:
Blake, Cassels & Graydon LLP
10 Lloyd's Avenue 7th Floor
London, United Kingdom EC3N 3AX
Tel.: (44) 20 7680 4600
Fax: (44) 20 7680 4646

Computershare Investor Services Inc.
510 Burrard St 2nd Floor
Vancouver, BC, V6C 3B9, Canada
Tel.: (604) 661-9400

Non-U.S. Subsidiary:

Bannerman Mining Resources (Namibia) (Pty.) Ltd. **(1)**
45 Mandume Ya Ndemufayo St
Swakopmund, Erongo, Namibia
Tel.: (264) 64416200
Fax: (264) 64416240
E-Mail: admin@bannermanresources-na.com
Web Site: www.bannermanresources.com
Emp.: 25
Mineral Exploration Services
S.I.C.: 1499
N.A.I.C.S.: 212399
Werner Ewald *(Gen Mgr)*

BANNON LIMITED

Level 1 6 Thelma Street
West Perth, WA, 6005, Australia
Mailing Address:
PO Box 136
Subiaco, WA, 6904, Australia
Tel.: (61) 8 9486 8237
Fax: (61) 8 9323 2033
Web Site: www.bannonlimited.com.au
BNX—(ASX)
Business Description:
Gold & Other Metal Mining
S.I.C.: 1041
N.A.I.C.S.: 212221
Personnel:
Gino D'Anna *(Sec)*

BANNU WOOLLEN MILLS LIMITED

M/s Janana De Malucho Textile Mills Limited
Habibabad, Kohat, Pakistan
Tel.: (92) 922 510063
Fax: (92) 922 510474
E-Mail: janana_textile@hotmail.com
Web Site: www.bwm.com.pk
Year Founded: 1953
BNWM—(ISL)
Sls.: $8,182,254
Assets: $18,190,228
Liabilities: $4,303,629
Net Worth: $13,886,599
Earnings: $1,463,349
Emp.: 482
Fiscal Year-end: 06/30/13
Business Description:
Woollen Products Mfr
S.I.C.: 2399
N.A.I.C.S.: 314999
Personnel:
Shahnaz Sajjad Ahmad *(CEO)*
A. R. Tahir *(CFO)*
Amin-Ur Rasheed *(Sec & Sr Gen Mgr-Corp Affairs)*
Board of Directors:
Raza Kuli Khan Khattak
Shahnaz Sajjad Ahmad
Mushtaq Ahmad Khan
Shaheen Kuli Khan
Sher Ali Khan
Zeb Gohar Ayub Khan
Ahmad Kuli Khan Khattak
Ali Kuli Khan Khattak
Manzoor Ahmad Sheikh
Legal Counsel:
Hassan & Hassan Advocates
PAAF Building 1D Kashmir/Egerton Road
Lahore, Pakistan
Transfer Agent:
Management & Registration Services (Pvt.) Ltd.
Business Executive Centre F/17/3 Block-8
Clifton, Karachi, Pakistan

BANPU PUBLIC COMPANY LIMITED

26th-28th Floor Thanapoom Tower
1550 New Petchburi Road Makkasan
Ratchathewi, Bangkok, 10400, Thailand
Tel.: (66) 2694 6600
Fax: (66) 2207 0695
Web Site: www.banpu.com
BANPU—(OTC THA)
Sls.: $3,887,380,376
Assets: $7,356,408,032
Liabilities: $4,420,942,703
Net Worth: $2,935,465,329
Earnings: $473,751,446
Emp.: 6,000
Fiscal Year-end: 12/31/12
Business Description:
Coal Mining & Coal-Fired Power Generation Services
S.I.C.: 1222
N.A.I.C.S.: 212112
Personnel:
Krirk-Krai Jirapaet *(Chm)*
Vitoon Vongkusolkit *(Vice Chm)*
Chanin Vongkusolkit *(CEO)*
Somyot Ruchirawat *(Deputy CEO)*
Voravudhi Linananda *(COO)*
Metee Auapinyakul *(Exec Officer)*
Ongart Auapinyakul *(Exec Officer)*
Somruedee Chaimongkol *(Asst CEO-Fin)*
Akaraphong Dayananda *(Asst CEO-Strategy & Bus Dev)*
Sathidpong Wattananuchit *(Asst CEO-Corp Svcs)*
Udomlux Olarn *(Sr VP-Corp Affairs)*
Board of Directors:
Krirk-Krai Jirapaet
Metee Auapinyakul
Ongart Auapinyakul
Teerana Bhongmakapat
Somkiat Chareonkul
Rawi Corsiri
Montri Mongkolswat
Rutt Phanijphand
Anothai Techamontrikul
Chanin Vongkusolkit
Verajet Vongkusolkit
Vitoon Vongkusolkit

Subsidiaries:

Banpu Coal Power Ltd. **(1)**
26-28th Floor Thanapoom Tower 1550 New Petchburi Road
Makasan National TV, 10400 Bangkok, Thailand (100%)
Tel.: (66) 26946600
Fax: (66) 022070697
Web Site: www.banpu.co.th
Emp.: 250
Other Electric Power Generation
S.I.C.: 4911
N.A.I.C.S.: 221118
Direk Sang *(Mgr-Mktg)*

Banpu International Ltd. **(1)**
26-28th Floor Thanapoom Tower
1550 New Petchburi Road, 10400 Bangkok, Thailand (99.99%)
Tel.: (66) 26946600
Fax: (66) 22070697
E-Mail: somchai_c@banpu.co.th
Web Site: www.banpu.co.th
Emp.: 200
Support Activities for Coal Mining
S.I.C.: 1241
N.A.I.C.S.: 213113

Banpu Minerals Co., Ltd. **(1)**
1150 Thanatoom Tower 1550 New Petchburi Rd Makkasan
Ratchathewi, Bangkok, 10400, Thailand (99.99%)
Tel.: (66) 26946600
Fax: (66) 22070697
Web Site: www.banpu.co.th
Emp.: 300
Support Activities for Coal Mining
S.I.C.: 1241
N.A.I.C.S.: 213113
Csamin Vonckusortit *(CEO)*

Non-U.S. Subsidiary:

Banpu Australia Co., Pty Ltd. **(2)**
Level 12 31 Queen Street
Melbourne, VIC, 3000, Australia
Tel.: (61) 3 8613 8888
Coal Mining Services
S.I.C.: 1241
N.A.I.C.S.: 213113

Power Generation Services Co., Ltd. **(1)**
9 i-8 Rd
Map Ta Phut Industrial Estate, Rayong, Thailand (40%)
Tel.: (66) 38925140
Fax: (66) 38925109
Web Site: www.blcp.co.th
Other Electric Power Generation
S.I.C.: 4939
N.A.I.C.S.: 221118

Non-U.S. Subsidiaries:

Banpu Power International Ltd. **(1)**
One Cathedral Square
Level 11, Port Louis, Mauritius (100%)
Tel.: (230) 2104000
Fax: (230) 2117549
E-Mail: info@mitco.mu
Web Site: www.mitco.mu
Emp.: 75
Other Electric Power Generation
S.I.C.: 4939
N.A.I.C.S.: 221118
K. C. Li *(Chm)*

Banpu Power Investment (China) Ltd. **(1)**
9A 9th Floor Tower B Gateway Plaza No 18 Xia Guang Li North Road
East Third Ring, 100027 Beijing, Chaoyang, China (100%)
Tel.: (86) 10 57580388
Fax: (86) 10 57580390
Web Site: www.banpupower.com.cn
Electric Power Generation Services
S.I.C.: 4939
N.A.I.C.S.: 221118

Non-U.S. Subsidiary:

Peak Pacific Investment Company (L) BHD **(2)**
Level 15 A2 Main Office Tower Financial Park
87000 Labuan, Malaysia
Tel.: (60) 87 443 118
Fax: (60) 87441288
Investment Management Services
S.I.C.: 6211
N.A.I.C.S.: 523999
Jesslyn Lam *(Assoc Dir)*

Centennial Coal Company Limited **(1)**
Level 18 BT Tower 1 Mkt St
Sydney, NSW, 2000, Australia AU
Tel.: (61) 292662700
Fax: (61) 292615533
E-Mail: cey1@centennialcoal.com.au
Web Site: www.centennialcoal.com.au
Sales Range: $700-749.9 Million
Emp.: 1,700
Coal Mining Services
S.I.C.: 1222
N.A.I.C.S.: 212112
Robert G. Cameron *(CEO & Mng Dir)*
Robert Dougall *(CFO)*
David Moult *(COO)*
John Hempenstall *(Chief Risk Officer)*
Louise Baldwin *(Gen Counsel)*
Tony Macko *(Sec & Gen Mgr-Corp Affairs)*

Subsidiaries:

Berrima Coal Pty Limited **(2)**
Medway Road
Medway, Sydney, NSW, Australia (100%)
Tel.: (61) 248771304
Fax: (61) 248771373
Emp.: 22
Coal Mining Services
S.I.C.: 1241
N.A.I.C.S.: 213113

Centennial Airly Pty Limited **(2)**
Level 18 BT Tower 1 Market Street
Sydney, NSW, 2000, Australia
Tel.: (61) 2 9266 2700
Coal Mining Services
S.I.C.: 1241
N.A.I.C.S.: 213113

Centennial Angus Place Pty Limited **(2)**
Level 18 BT Tower
1 Market Street, Sydney, NSW, 2000, Australia
Tel.: (61) 263548700
Coal Mining Services
S.I.C.: 1222
N.A.I.C.S.: 212112
Jacques Leroux *(Mgr-Mine)*

Centennial Clarence Pty Limited **(2)**
Level 18 BT Tower 1 Market Street
Sydney, NSW, 2000, Australia
Tel.: (61) 2 9266 2700
Fax: (61) 92615533
Web Site: www.centennialcoal.com.au
Coal Mining Services
S.I.C.: 1241
N.A.I.C.S.: 213113

Centennial Mandalong Pty Limited **(2)**
177 Mandalong Rd
Hunter Valley, Mandalong, NSW, 2264, Australia
Tel.: (61) 2 4973 090
Fax: (61) 2 4973 099
Coal Mining Services
S.I.C.: 1241
N.A.I.C.S.: 213113

Centennial Mannering Pty Limited **(2)**
Rutleys Road
Doyalson, NSW, Australia
Tel.: (61) 2 4358 0580
Fax: (61) 2 4358 1892
Coal Mining Services
S.I.C.: 1241
N.A.I.C.S.: 213113

Centennial Munmorah Pty Limited **(2)**
Level 18 BT Tower 1 Market St
Sydney, NSW, 2000, Australia
Tel.: (61) 292662700
Fax: (61) 292615533
E-Mail: cey1@centennialcoal.com.au
Emp.: 28
Coal Mining Services
S.I.C.: 1241

Banpu Public Company Limited—(Continued)

N.A.I.C.S.: 213113
Robert Cameron *(CEO & Mng Dir)*

Centennial Myuna Pty Limited (2)
Level 18 BT Tower 1 Market Street
Sydney, NSW, 2000, Australia
Tel.: (61) 249752044
Fax: (61) 292615533
E-Mail: cey1@centennialcoal.com.au
Emp.: 28
Coal Mining Services
S.I.C.: 1241
N.A.I.C.S.: 213113
Robert Cameron *(Mng Dir)*

Centennial Newstan Pty Limited (2)
Level 18 BT Tower 1 Market St
Sydney, NSW, 2000, Australia
Tel.: (61) 292662700
Fax: (61) 292615533
E-Mail: cey1@centennialcoal.com.au
Web Site: www.centennialcoal.com.au
Emp.: 28
Coal Mining Services
S.I.C.: 1241
N.A.I.C.S.: 213113
Robert Cameron *(Mng Dir)*

Charbon Coal Pty Limited (2)
PO Box 84
2848 Kandos, NSW, Australia
Tel.: (61) 292662700
Fax: (61) 292615533
E-Mail: cey1@centennialcoal.com.au
Emp.: 30
Coal Mining Services
S.I.C.: 1241
N.A.I.C.S.: 213113
Robert Cameron *(CEO & Mng Dir)*

Clarence Coal Pty Limited (2)
Level 18 BT Tower 1 Market Street
Sydney, NSW, 2000, Australia
Tel.: (61) 292662700
Fax: (61) 292615533
E-Mail: info@centennialcoal.com.au
Web Site: www.centennialcoal.com.au
Emp.: 28
Coal Mining Services
S.I.C.: 1241
N.A.I.C.S.: 213113

Clarence Colliery Pty Limited (2)
Level 18 BT Tower 1 Market Street
2000 Sydney, NSW, Australia
Tel.: (61) 263552656
Fax: (61) 292615533
E-Mail: cey1@centennialcoal.com.au
Web Site: www.centennialcoal.com.au
Emp.: 28
Coal Mining Services
S.I.C.: 1241
N.A.I.C.S.: 213113
Robert Cameron *(Mng Dir)*

Coalex Pty Limited (2)
Level 18 BT Tower 1 Market St
2000 Sydney, NSW, Australia
Tel.: (61) 292662700
Fax: (61) 292615533
E-Mail: cey1@centennialcoal.com.au
Emp.: 28
Coal Mining Services
S.I.C.: 1241
N.A.I.C.S.: 213113
Robert Cameron *(CEO & Mng Dir)*

Ivanhoe Coal Pty Limited (2)
Level 18 BT Tower 1 Market St
Sydney, NSW, 2000, Australia
Tel.: (61) 292662700
Fax: (61) 292615533
E-Mail: info@centennialcoal.com.au
Web Site: www.centennialcoal.com.au
Emp.: 28
Coal Mining Services
S.I.C.: 1241
N.A.I.C.S.: 213113
David Moult *(CEO & Mng Dir)*

Powercoal Pty Limited (2)
Level 18 BT Tower 1 Market St
2000 Sydney, NSW, Australia
Tel.: (61) 292662700
Fax: (61) 292615533
E-Mail: cey1@centennialcoal.com.au
Web Site: www.centennialcoal.com.au
Emp.: 30
Coal Mining Services
S.I.C.: 1241
N.A.I.C.S.: 213113
Robert Cameron *(CEO & Mng Dir)*

Springvale Coal Pty Limited (2)
Castlereagh Hwy
Lidsdale, NSW, 2790, Australia
Tel.: (61) 2 6350 1600
Coal Mining Services
S.I.C.: 1241
N.A.I.C.S.: 213113

Hunnu Coal Limited (1)
Level 1 33 Richardson Street
West Perth, WA, 6005, Australia AU
Tel.: (61) 892004267
Fax: (61) 892004469
E-Mail: info@hunnucoal.com
Web Site: www.hunnucoal.com
Sales Range: Less than $1 Million
Coal Mining Services
S.I.C.: 1222
N.A.I.C.S.: 212112
Chanin Vongkusolkit *(Chm)*
George Lkhagvadorj Tumur *(Mng Dir)*
Batjargal Tsog *(COO)*

Shijiazhuang Chengfeng Cogen Co., Ltd. (1)
East of Jingshen Express Way Zhengding County
Shijiazhuang, 050800 Shijiazhuang, Hebei, China (100%)
Tel.: (86) 311 88789288
Fax: (86) 311 85178553
Web Site: www.banpupower.com.cn
Emp.: 250
Other Electric Power Generation
S.I.C.: 4911
N.A.I.C.S.: 221118

Zouping Peak CHP Co., Ltd. (1)
Xiwang Industrial Region Handian Town
Zouping County, 256209 Zouping, Shandong, China (70%)
Tel.: (86) 5434615655
Web Site: www.banpupower.com.cn/frm_cntct_sb02.html
Other Electric Power Generation
S.I.C.: 4911
N.A.I.C.S.: 221118

Zouping Peak Pte. Ltd. (1)
8 Marina Boulevard 05-02 Marina Bay Financial Centre
Singapore, 018981, Singapore
Tel.: (65) 6338 1888
Electric Power Generation Services
S.I.C.: 4911
N.A.I.C.S.: 221118

BANQUE BEMO S.A.L.

BEMO Building Sassine Square
Elias Sarkis Ave
Ashrafieh, Beirut, 1100-2120, Lebanon
Mailing Address:
PO Box 16-6353
Beirut, Lebanon
Tel.: (961) 1992600
Telex: 44881 LE
Fax: (961) 1330780
E-Mail: bemosal@dm.net.lb
Web Site: www.bemobank.com
Year Founded: 1964
BEMO—(BEY)
Sales Range: $900-999.9 Million
Emp.: 150
Business Description:
Banking Services
S.I.C.: 6029
N.A.I.C.S.: 522110
Personnel:
Henry Yordan Obegi *(Chm & Gen Mgr)*
Board of Directors:
Henry Yordan Obegi
Karim Samir Abilamaa
Emir Karim Samir Abullama
Ara O. Hrechdakian
Hasan Kabbani
Georges B. Obegi
Riad B. Obegi

Subsidiary:

BSEC S.A. (1)
3rd Fl Block A Two Park Ave Bldg Minet El Hosn Central District
Park Ave Beirut, Beirut, Lebanon
Tel.: (961) 1997998
Fax: (961) 1994801
E-Mail: contact@bsec-sa.com
Web Site: www.bsec-sa.com
Emp.: 15
Financial Services
S.I.C.: 6211
N.A.I.C.S.: 523999

BANQUE CANTONALE DE GENEVE S.A.

(d/b/a BCGE Group)
Quai de l'Ile 17
PO Box 2251
CH-1211 Geneva, 2, Switzerland
Tel.: (41) 58 211 21 00
Fax: (41))58 211 21 99
E-Mail: info@bcge.ch
Web Site: www.bcge.ch
Year Founded: 1816
BCGE—(SWX)
Rev.: $320,465,218
Assets: $17,779,260,598
Liabilities: $16,607,386,749
Net Worth: $1,171,873,849
Earnings: $72,323,075
Emp.: 723
Fiscal Year-end: 12/31/12
Business Description:
Financial & Real Estate Development Services
S.I.C.: 6211
N.A.I.C.S.: 523999
Personnel:
Jean-Pierre Roth *(Chm)*
Blaise Goetschin *(Chm-Exec Bd & CEO)*
Bernard Clerc *(Deputy Chm)*
Eric Bourgeaux *(CFO, Member-Exec Bd & Head-Fin & Risk Control Div)*
Claude Bagnoud *(Member-Exec Bd & Head-Swiss Corp & Institutional Clients Div)*
Pierre-Olivier Fragniere *(Member-Exec Bd & Head-Intl Corp & Private Banking Div)*
Jean-Marc Joris *(Member-Exec Bd & Head-Org & IT Div)*
Jerome Monnier *(Member-Exec Bd & Head-Geneva Private Clients & Family Bus Div)*
Board of Directors:
Jean-Pierre Roth
Bernard Clerc
Angela de Wolff
Asma Hovagemyan
Fabienne Knapp
Josef Kuttel
Patrick Mage
Jean-Marc Mermoud
Ton Schurink
John Tracey

Subsidiaries:

Anker Bank SA (1)
Avenue de la Gare
PO Box 159
1001 Lausanne, Switzerland (100%)
Tel.: (41) 213210707
Fax: (41) 213210798
E-Mail: welcome@bcge.ch
Web Site: www.bcge.ch
Emp.: 800
Banking Services
S.I.C.: 6029
N.A.I.C.S.: 522110
Nicolas Gerber *(Branch Mgr)*

Synchrony Asset Management SA (1)
7 Rue du Mont-Blanc
PO Box 2196
1211 Geneva, 1, Switzerland (100%)
Tel.: (41) 229097575
Fax: (41) 229097500
E-Mail: info@synchrony.ch
Web Site: www.synchrony.ch
Emp.: 15
Asset Management Services
S.I.C.: 6211
N.A.I.C.S.: 523999
Constantino Cancela *(Investment Mgr)*

Non-U.S. Subsidiary:

Banque Cantonale de Geneve (France) SA (1)
20 Pl Louis Pradel
69001 Lyon, France (100%)
Tel.: (33) 472073150
Fax: (33) 472073160
E-Mail: lyon@bcgef.fr
Web Site: www.bcgef.fr
Emp.: 29
Banking Services
S.I.C.: 6029
N.A.I.C.S.: 522110
Alain Bochet *(Pres)*

BANQUE CANTONALE VAUDOISE

(d/b/a BCV)
Place St-Francois 14
1003 Lausanne, Switzerland
Mailing Address:
Case Postale 300
1001 Lausanne, Switzerland
Tel.: (41) 212121000
Telex: 454 304 A BCVL CH
Fax: (41) 212121222
E-Mail: info@bcv.ch
Web Site: www.bcv.ch
Year Founded: 1845
BCV—(SWX)
Rev.: $768,799,636
Assets: $42,956,936,000
Liabilities: $39,378,990,200
Net Worth: $3,577,945,800
Earnings: $335,776,452
Emp.: 1,931
Fiscal Year-end: 12/31/12
Business Description:
Banking Services
Export
S.I.C.: 6159
N.A.I.C.S.: 522298
Personnel:
Olivier Steimer *(Chm)*
Stephan A. J. Bachmann *(Vice Chm)*
Pascal Kiener *(CEO & Member-Exec Bd)*
Thomas W. Paulsen *(CFO, Member-Exec Bd & Head-Fin & Risks Div)*
Bertrand Sager *(Chief Credit Officer, Member-Exec Bd & Head-Credit Mgmt Div)*
Aime Achard *(Member-Exec Bd & Head-Bus Support Div)*
Stefan Bischel *(Member-Exec Bd & Head-Asset Mgmt & Trading Div)*
Markus Gygax *(Member-Exec Bd & Head-Retail Banking Div)*
Gerard Haeberli *(Member-Exec Bd & Head-Private Banking Div)*
Jean-Francois Schwarz *(Member-Exec Bd & Head-Corp Banking Div)*
Board of Directors:
Olivier Steimer
Stephan A. J. Bachmann
Reto Donatsch
Beth Krasna
Pierre Lamuniere
Luc Recordon
Paul-Andre Sanglard

Subsidiaries:

Banque Piguet Galland & Cie SA (1)
1 rue Rodolphe Toepffer
PO Box 3254
CH 1211 Geneva, Switzerland (75%)
Tel.: (41) 583104000
Fax: (41) 583104450

Web Site: www.banque-piguet.ch
Managed Assets: $1,000,000,000
Emp.: 200
Private Banking
S.I.C.: 6211
N.A.I.C.S.: 523110
Calloud Olivier *(CEO)*

Gerifonds S.A. (1)
Rue du Maupas 2 Case postale 6249
Lausanne, 1002, Switzerland (100%)
Tel.: (41) 213213200
Fax: (41) 213213228
Web Site: www.gerifonds.ch
Emp.: 30
Investment Management
S.I.C.: 6282
N.A.I.C.S.: 523930
Christian Carron *(CIO & CEO)*
Bertrand Jillabert *(CFO)*

Groupe Baumgartner Holding SA (1)
Rue de la Vernie 12
Crissier, Lausanne, Switzerland
Tel.: (41) 448866181
Fax: (41) 448866188
E-Mail: manuela.dennler@cellpack.com
Web Site: www.baumgartnerholding.ch/
Holding Company
S.I.C.: 6719
N.A.I.C.S.: 551112
Jacques Baumgartner *(Chm & CEO)*
Francois Burnand *(CFO)*

Office Vaudois de Cautionnement SA (1)
Ave Des Jordils 1
Lausanne, Switzerland
Tel.: (41) 216142433
Credit Intermediation
S.I.C.: 6159
N.A.I.C.S.: 522298

Societe Pour la Gestion de Placements Collectifs GEP SA (1)
Rue Du Maupas 2
1004 Lausanne, Switzerland (100%)
Tel.: (41) 213187272
E-Mail: info@fir.ch
Open-End Investment Funds
S.I.C.: 6722
N.A.I.C.S.: 525910

Joint Venture:

Finarbit SA (1)
Kohlrainstrasse 10
8700 Kusnacht, Switzerland
Tel.: (41) 449138100
Fax: (41) 449138010
E-Mail: info@finarbit.ch
Web Site: www.finarbit.ch
Emp.: 20
Securities & Commodity Exchanges
S.I.C.: 6231
N.A.I.C.S.: 523210
Jean-Jack Badet *(COO)*

Non-U.S. Subsidiaries:

Asesores y Gestores Financieros SA (1)
Calle Balbina Valverde 15
Madrid, Spain (50%)
Tel.: (34) 915902121
Web Site: www.ayg.es
Emp.: 65
Credit Intermediation Services
S.I.C.: 6099
N.A.I.C.S.: 522390
Alberto Fraile Rodriguez *(Pres)*

BCV Italia Srl (1)
Viale Spagna 88
20093 Cologno Monzese, Italy (100%)
Tel.: (39) 22544055
Fax: (39) 226700774
E-Mail: info@bcv-vacuum.com
Web Site: www.bcv-vacuum.com
Credit Intermediation
S.I.C.: 6159
N.A.I.C.S.: 522298
Vaghi Sesano *(Mng Dir)*

BANQUE CENTRALE DES COMORES
Place de France
BP 405
Moroni, Comoros
Tel.: (269) 7731814
Fax: (269) 730349
Web Site: www.banque.comoros.org
Emp.: 50
Business Description:
Banking Services
S.I.C.: 6029
N.A.I.C.S.: 522110

BANQUE CENTRALE DES ETATS DE L'AFRIQUE DE L'OUEST
(d/b/a Central Bank of West African States)
Avenue Abdoulaye Fadiga
Dakar, Senegal
Tel.: (221) 338390500
Fax: (221) 338239335
E-Mail: webmaster@bceao.int
Web Site: www.bceao.int
Sales Range: $200-249.9 Million
Business Description:
Central Bank
S.I.C.: 6011
N.A.I.C.S.: 521110
Personnel:
Tiemoko Meyliet Kone *(Governor)*

BANQUE CENTRALE DU LUXEMBOURG
Boulevard Royal 2
2983 Luxembourg, Luxembourg
Tel.: (352) 477441
Fax: (352) 47744910
E-Mail: info@bcl.lu
Web Site: www.bcl.lu/
Business Description:
Central Bank
S.I.C.: 6011
N.A.I.C.S.: 521110
Personnel:
Yves Mersch *(Pres)*

BANQUE CENTRALE POPULAIRE S.A.
101 blvd Zerktouni
BP 10 622
21 100 Casablanca, Morocco
Tel.: (212) 522 46 91 00
Fax: (212) 522 48 06 23
Web Site: www.gbp.ma
Year Founded: 1926
BCP—(CAS)
Rev.: $1,485,567,960
Earnings: $375,653,162
Emp.: 2,448
Fiscal Year-end: 12/31/12
Business Description:
Banking Services
S.I.C.: 6029
N.A.I.C.S.: 522110
Personnel:
Mohamed Benchaaboun *(Chm-Exec Bd & Mng Dir)*
Mohamed Karim Mounir *(Sec & Gen Mgr)*

BANQUE COMMERCIALE DU CONGO S.A.R.L.
Boulevard du 30 juin
BP 2798
Kinshasa, 1, Congo, Democratic Republic of
Tel.: (243) 815181768
Fax: (243) 99631048
E-Mail: bweb@bcdc.cd
Web Site: www.bcdc.cd
Year Founded: 1909
Sales Range: $50-74.9 Million
Emp.: 400
Business Description:
Commercial Banking Services
S.I.C.: 6029
N.A.I.C.S.: 522110
Personnel:
Yves Cuypers *(Chm & Mng Dir)*

BANQUE D'ALGERIE
Immeuble Joly 38 Avenue Franklin Roosevelt
Algiers, Algeria
Tel.: (213) 21 230023
Fax: (213) 21 230371
Web Site: www.bank-of-algeria.dz
Business Description:
Banking Services
S.I.C.: 6011
N.A.I.C.S.: 521110
Personnel:
Mohammed Laksaci *(Pres)*
Said Dib *(Sec Gen)*

BANQUE DE KIGALI S.A.
63 Avenue du Commerce
BP 175
Kigali, Rwanda
Tel.: (250) 252593100
Fax: (250) 57346
E-Mail: bk@bk.rw
Web Site: www.bk.rw
Year Founded: 1966
Sales Range: $25-49.9 Million
Business Description:
Commercial Banking & Lending Services
S.I.C.: 6029
N.A.I.C.S.: 522110
Personnel:
Lado Gurgenidze *(Chm)*
James Gatera *(Mng Dir)*
Lawson Naibo *(COO)*
Shivon Byamukama *(Sec & Id-Corp Affairs)*
Board of Directors:
Lado Gurgenidze
Marc Holtzman
Liliane Igihozo
Angelique Kantengwa
Julien Kavaruganda
Sudadi S. Kayitana
Alphonsine Niyigena
Apollo Mugisha Nkunda
Caleb Rwamuganza

BANQUE DE LA REPUBLIQUE D'HAITI
Angle rues Pavee et du Qai
BP 1570
Port-au-Prince, Haiti
Tel.: (509) 2991200
Fax: (509) 2991045
E-Mail: webmaster@brh.net
Web Site: www.brh.net
Business Description:
Banking Services
S.I.C.: 6011
N.A.I.C.S.: 521110
Personnel:
Raymond Magloire *(Governor)*
Philippe Lahens *(Governor Adjoint)*
Charles Castel *(Dir Gen)*
Board of Directors:
Charles Castel
Georges Henry
Philippe Lahens
Raymond Magloire
Remy Montas

BANQUE DE TUNISIE ET DES EMIRATS
5bis rue Mohamed Badra
1002 Tunis, Tunisia
Tel.: (216) 71 783 600
Fax: (216) 71 783 756
Web Site: www.bte.com.tn
Year Founded: 1982
BTE—(BVT)
Business Description:
Banking Services
S.I.C.: 6029
N.A.I.C.S.: 522110
Personnel:
Salem Rached El Mohannadi *(Chm)*
Board of Directors:
Salem Rached El Mohannadi
Obaid Murad Al Swaidi
Jabr Zaal Albuflassa
Khaleefa Ali Alqamzi
Hedi Bejaoui
Abdellatif Chaabene
Mohamed El Agrebi
Saqr Salem El Amri
Nasser Shotait El Ketbi
Abdelhamid Elghanemi
Mohamed Taieb Elyousfi
Golsom Jaziri

BANQUE DEGROOF S.A.
Rue de l'Industrie 44
1040 Brussels, Belgium
Tel.: (32) 22879111
Fax: (32) 22306700
E-Mail: contact@degroof.be
Web Site: www.degroof.be
Year Founded: 1871
Int. Income: $131,586,771
Assets: $7,184,517,367
Liabilities: $6,355,699,344
Net Worth: $828,818,023
Earnings: $74,108,005
Emp.: 1,081
Fiscal Year-end: 09/30/12
Business Description:
Bank Holding Company
S.I.C.: 6712
N.A.I.C.S.: 551111
Personnel:
Alain Philippson *(Chm)*
Etienne de Callatay *(Mng Dir)*
Gautier Bataille de Longprey *(Mng Dir)*
Pierre Paul De Schrevel *(Mng Dir)*
Regnier Haegelsteen *(Mng Dir)*
Patrick Keusters *(Mng Dir)*
Jan Longeval *(Mng Dir)*
Alain Schockert *(Mng Dir)*
Board of Directors:
Alain Philippson
Damien Bachelot
Jean-Pierre de Buck van Overstraeten
Etienne de Callatay
Gautier Bataille de Longprey
Pierre Paul De Schrevel
Regnier Haegelsteen
Christian Jacobs
Jean-Marie Laurent Josi
Patrick Keusters
Jan Longeval
Theo Maes
Luc Missorten
Jacques-Martin Philippson
Alain Schockert
Frank van Bellingen
Gaetan Waucquez

Subsidiary:

Bearbull (Belgium) S.A. (1)
Chee de Waterloo 880
1000 Brussels, Belgium (100%)
Tel.: (32) 23730020
Fax: (32) 23747641
Web Site: www.degroof.be/sites/degroof/en-us/contact/Pages/Contact.aspx
Emp.: 9
All Other Insurance Related Activities
S.I.C.: 6411
N.A.I.C.S.: 524298
Lionel Giot *(Gen Mgr)*

Non-U.S. Subsidiaries:

Banque Degroof Luxembourg S.A. (1)
2 Rue Eugene Ruppert
Zone d'activite La Cloche d'or, L-2453
Luxembourg, Luxembourg (100%)

Banque Degroof S.A.—(Continued)

Tel.: (352) 4535451
Fax: (352) 250721
Web Site: www.degroof.be/sites/degroof/en-us/presence-internationale/Pages/default.aspx
Emp.: 300
Commercial Banking
S.I.C.: 6029
N.A.I.C.S.: 522110
Geert de Bruyne *(Mng Dir)*

Bearbull International Ltd (1)
Charlotte House 2nd Floor
Charlotte Street New Providenc, 2453
Nassau, Bahamas (100%)
Tel.: (242) 3237376
Fax: (242) 3265625
Emp.: 5
Miscellaneous Financial Investment Activities
S.I.C.: 6211
N.A.I.C.S.: 523999
Nicole Dupey *(CEO)*

Philippe Patrimoine S.A. (1)
1 Rond-Point des Champs-Elysees
75008 Paris, France (99.92%)
Tel.: (33) 145615555
Fax: (33) 145619625
E-Mail: philip@degroofphilip.com
Web Site: www.degroofphilip.com
Emp.: 30
Open-End Investment Funds
S.I.C.: 6722
N.A.I.C.S.: 525910
Laura Philips *(Gen Dir)*

Subsidiary:

Philippe Gestion S.A. (2)
1 Rond-Point des Champs-Elysees
75008 Paris, France (49.91%)
Tel.: (33) 145615555
Fax: (33) 145619625
Emp.: 4
Open-End Investment Funds
S.I.C.: 6722
N.A.I.C.S.: 525910

BANQUE DU LIBAN

Masraf Lubnan Street
PO Box 11-5544
Beirut, Lebanon
Tel.: (961) 1750000
Web Site: www.bdl.gov.lb
Emp.: 1,500
Business Description:
Central Bank
S.I.C.: 6011
N.A.I.C.S.: 521110
Personnel:
Riad T. Salameh *(Governor)*
Saad Andary *(Second Vice Governor)*
Board of Directors:
Alain Biffani
Fadi Makkeh
Riad T. Salameh

BANQUE FEDERALE DES BANQUES POPULAIRES

(d/b/a Groupe Banque Populaire)
Le Ponant de Paris 5 rue Leblanc
75511 Paris, Cedex 15, France
Tel.: (33) 140396000
Fax: (33) 140396001
Sales Range: $25-49.9 Billion
Emp.: 40,500
Business Description:
Bank Holding Company
S.I.C.: 6712
N.A.I.C.S.: 551111
Personnel:
Philippe Dupont *(Chm & CEO)*
Yvan de La Porte du Theil *(Vice Chm)*
Steve Gentili *(Vice Chm)*
Jean-Louis Tourret *(Vice Chm)*
Michel Goudard *(Deputy CEO)*
Bruno Mettling *(Deputy CEO)*
Bernard Jeannin *(Sec)*
Francois Credot *(Sr Exec VP-Legal Affairs & Compliance)*
Alain David *(Sr Exec VP-Fin)*
Chantal Fournel *(Sr Exec VP-Logistics & Org)*
Bernard Gouraud *(Sr Exec VP-Tech)*
Josiane Lancelle *(Sr Exec VP-Strategy)*
Martine Lefebvre *(Sr Exec VP-Grp Internal Audit)*
Pascal Marchetti *(Sr Exec VP-Bus Dev)*
Isabelle Maury *(Sr Exec VP-Grp Risk)*
Board of Directors:
Philippe Dupont
Jean Clochet
Yvan de La Porte du Theil
Pierre Delourmel
Pierre Desvergnes
Jean-Claude Detilleux
Michel Dolige
Christian du Payrat
Bernard Fleury
Steve Gentili
Yves Gevin
Jacques Hausler
Marc Jardin
Francois Moutte
Jean-Louis Tourret

Subsidiaries:

Banque Populaire Atlantique (1)
1 rue Francoise Sagan
Saint-Herblain, F-44919 Nantes, Cedex 9, France
Tel.: (33) 2 40 46 08 08
Fax: (33) 2 40 46 46 61
Web Site: www.atlantique.banquepopulaire.fr
Sales Range: $350-399.9 Million
Emp.: 1,908
Banking Services
S.I.C.: 6029
N.A.I.C.S.: 522110
Yves Gevin *(Co-CEO)*
Stephane Paix *(Co-CEO)*

Banque Populaire Bourgogne Franche-Comte (1)
14 boulevard de la Tremouille
BP 310
F-21008 Dijon, Cedex, France
Tel.: (33) 380337500
Fax: (33) 380710310
Web Site: www.bpbfc.banquepopulaire.fr
Sales Range: $450-499.9 Million
Emp.: 1,8
Banking Services
S.I.C.: 6029
N.A.I.C.S.: 522110
Jean-Philippe Girard *(Chm)*
Bernard Jeannin *(Mng Dir)*

Banque Populaire Centre Atlantique (1)
32 boulevard Carnot
BP 10416
87011 Limoges, Cedex 1, France
Tel.: (33) 5 33 63 99 98
Web Site: www.centreatlantique.banquepopulaire.fr
Sales Range: $200-249.9 Million
Emp.: 1,004
Banking Services
S.I.C.: 6029
N.A.I.C.S.: 522110
Jacques Raynaud *(Chm)*
Gonzague de Villele *(CEO)*

Banque Populaire Cote d'Azur (1)
457 promenade des Anglais
BP 241
F-06292 Nice, Cedex 3, France
Tel.: (33) 493215200
Fax: (33) 493215445
Web Site: www.cotedazur.banquepopulaire.fr
Sales Range: $200-249.9 Million
Emp.: 1,148
Banking Services
S.I.C.: 6029
N.A.I.C.S.: 522110

Bernard Fleury *(Chm)*
Jean-Francois Comas *(CEO)*

Banque Populaire d'Alsace (1)
Immeuble Le Concorde 4 quai Kleber
BP 10401
F-67001 Strasbourg, Cedex, France
Tel.: (33) 389625525
Web Site: www.alsace.banquepopulaire.fr
Sales Range: $250-299.9 Million
Emp.: 1,354
Banking Services
S.I.C.: 6029
N.A.I.C.S.: 522110
Thierry Cahn *(Chm)*
Dominique Didon *(CEO)*

Banque Populaire de l'Ouest (1)
1 place de la Trinite
CS 434
F-35064 Rennes, Cedex, France
Tel.: (33) 299297979
Fax: (33) 299297885
E-Mail: ouest@banquepopulaire.fr
Web Site: www.ouest.banquepopulaire.fr
Sales Range: $350-399.9 Million
Emp.: 1,807
Banking Services
S.I.C.: 6029
N.A.I.C.S.: 522110
Pierre Delourmel *(Chm)*
Yves Breu *(CEO)*

Banque Populaire des Alpes (1)
30 avenue Charles de Gaulle
BP 17
F-74800 La Roche-sur-Foron, France
Tel.: (33) 820870870
Fax: (33) 476888420
E-Mail: contact@alpes.banquepopulaire.fr
Web Site: www.alpes.banquepopulaire.fr
Sales Range: $350-399.9 Million
Emp.: 1,54
Banking Services
S.I.C.: 6029
N.A.I.C.S.: 522110
Pascal Marchetti *(CEO)*

Banque Populaire du Massif Central (1)
18 Blvd Jean Moulin
BP 53
63002 Clermont-Ferrand, Cedex 1, France
Tel.: (33) 473234623
Web Site: www.massifcentral.banquepopulaire.fr
Sales Range: $150-199.9 Million
Emp.: 911
Banking Services
S.I.C.: 6029
N.A.I.C.S.: 522110
Dominique Martinie *(Chm)*

Banque Populaire du Nord (1)
847 Avenue de la Republique
F-59700 Marcq-en-Baroeul, France
Tel.: (33) 66 333000
Fax: (33) 66 333010
Web Site: www.nord.banquepopulaire.fr
Sales Range: $200-249.9 Million
Emp.: 1,128
Banking Services
S.I.C.: 6029
N.A.I.C.S.: 522110
Jacques Beauguerlange *(Chm)*
Gils Berrous *(CEO)*

Banque Populaire du Sud-Ouest (1)
10 Quai des Queyries
Cedex, F-33 072 Bordeaux, France
Tel.: (33) 5 57 776809
Web Site: www.sudouest.banquepopulaire.fr
Sales Range: $250-299.9 Million
Emp.: 1,124
Banking Services
S.I.C.: 6029
N.A.I.C.S.: 522110
Francois de la Giroday *(Chm)*
Francis Thibaud *(CEO)*

Banque Populaire du Sud (1)
38 boulevard Clemenceau
F-66966 Perpignan, Cedex 09, France
Tel.: (33) 468382200
Fax: (33) 4 6838 4803
Web Site: www.sud.banquepopulaire.fr
Sales Range: $450-499.9 Million
Emp.: 1,911
Banking Services
S.I.C.: 6029

N.A.I.C.S.: 522110
Claude Cordel *(Chm)*
Francois Moutte *(CEO)*

Banque Populaire Loire et Lyonnais (1)
141 rue Garibaldi
BP 3152
F-69211 Lyon, Cedex 3, France
Tel.: (33) 478955555
Fax: (33) 478710399
E-Mail: contact@bdl2l.banquepopulaire.fr
Web Site: www.loirelyonnais.banquepopulaire.fr
Sales Range: $250-299.9 Million
Emp.: 1,252
Banking Services
S.I.C.: 6029
N.A.I.C.S.: 522110
Herve Genty *(Chm)*
Olivier de Marignan *(CEO)*

Banque Populaire Lorraine Champagne (1)
3 rue Francois de Curel
BP 40124
57021 Metz, Cedex 1, France
Tel.: (33) 890 90 90 90
E-Mail: bplc@bplc.fr
Web Site: www.bplc.fr
Sales Range: $400-449.9 Million
Emp.: 1,655
Banking Services
S.I.C.: 6029
N.A.I.C.S.: 522110
Raymond Oliger *(Chm)*
Jacques Hausler *(CEO)*

Banque Populaire Occitane (1)
33-43 avenue Georges Pompidou
F-31135 Balma, Cedex, France
Tel.: (33) 5 65 23 66 50
Fax: (33) 5 65 23 66 88
E-Mail: agencedirecte@occitane.banquepopulaire.fr
Web Site: www.occitane.banquepopulaire.fr
Sales Range: $550-599.9 Million
Emp.: 2,315
Banking Services
S.I.C.: 6029
N.A.I.C.S.: 522110
Michel Dolige *(Chm)*

Banque Populaire Provencale et Corse (1)
245 Boulevard Michelet
F-13009 Marseilles, France
Tel.: (33) 49 2430
Fax: (33) 49 0937
E-Mail: contact@bppc.fr
Web Site: www.provencecorse.banquepopulaire.fr
Sales Range: $150-199.9 Million
Emp.: 806
Banking Services
S.I.C.: 6029
N.A.I.C.S.: 522110
Jean-Louis Tourret *(Chm)*
Francois-Xavier de Fornel *(CEO)*

Banque Populaire Rives de Paris (1)
76-78 avenue de France
F-75204 Paris, Cedex 13, France
Tel.: (33) 141862440
Web Site: www.rivesparis.banquepopulaire.fr
Sales Range: $700-749.9 Million
Emp.: 2,852
Banking Services
S.I.C.: 6029
N.A.I.C.S.: 522110
Marc Jardin *(Chm)*
Jean Criton *(CEO)*

Banque Populaire Val de France (1)
9 avenue Newton
F-78180 Montigny-le-Bretonneux, France
Mailing Address:
9 avenue Newton
F-78183 Saint-Quentin-en-Yvelines, Cedex, France
Tel.: (33) 1 30 14 66 00
Fax: (33) 1 3014 6602
E-Mail: contact@bpvf.banquepopulaire.fr
Web Site: www.bpvf.banquepopulaire.fr
Sales Range: $500-549.9 Million
Emp.: 2,345
Banking Services
S.I.C.: 6029

N.A.I.C.S.: 522110
Gerard Bellemon *(Chm)*
Gonzague de Villele *(Dir Gen)*

BRED Banque Populaire (1)
18 quai de la Rapee
75604 Creteil, Cedex 12, France
Tel.: (33) 148986000
Web Site: www.bred.banquepopulaire.fr
Rev.: $1,358,832,075
Assets: $62,282,123,338
Liabilities: $58,184,682,054
Net Worth: $4,097,441,284
Earnings: $245,568,331
Emp.: 5,000
Fiscal Year-end: 12/31/12
Banking Services
S.I.C.: 6029
N.A.I.C.S.: 522110
Steve Gentili *(Chm)*
Francois Martineau *(Vice Chm)*
Georges Tissie *(Vice Chm)*
Olivier Klein *(CEO)*
Yves Jacquot *(Deputy CEO)*
Olivier Lendrevie *(CFO)*
Gabriel Devilder *(Gen Sec)*

Casden Banque Populaire (1)
91 cours des roches Noisiel
F-77424 Marne-la-Vallee, Cedex 2, France
Tel.: (33) 164807000
Fax: (33) 116480337
Web Site: www.casden.banquepopulaire.fr
Sales Range: $250-299.9 Million
Emp.: 454
Banking Services
S.I.C.: 6029
N.A.I.C.S.: 522110
Pierre Desvergnes *(Chm & CEO)*

Credit Cooperatif (1)
2 Boulevard de Pesaro
BP 211
F-92002 Nanterre, France
Tel.: (33) 147248500
E-Mail: com@credit-cooperatif.coop
Web Site: www.credit-cooperatif.coop
Sales Range: $450-499.9 Million
Emp.: 1,702
Commercial Banking Services
S.I.C.: 6029
N.A.I.C.S.: 522110
Hugues Sibille *(COO)*

Joint Venture:

BPCE S.A. (1)
50 Avenue Pierre Mendes France
75013 Paris, France FR
Tel.: (33) 158404142
Fax: (33) 158404800
E-Mail: investor.relations@bpce.fr
Web Site: www.bpce.fr
Emp.: 127,000
Bank Holding Company
S.I.C.: 6712
N.A.I.C.S.: 551111
Philippe Dupont *(Chm-Supervisory Bd)*
Francois Perol *(Chm-Mgmt Bd)*
Yves Toublanc *(Vice Chm-Supervisory Bd)*
Nicolas Duhamel *(CFO & Member-Mgmt Bd)*
Olivier Klein *(Member-Mgmt Bd & CEO-Comml Banking)*
Philippe Queuille *(Member-Mgmt Bd & CEO-Ops & Organization)*
Jean-Luc Vergne *(Member-Mgmt Bd & CEO-HR)*

Subsidiaries:

Credit Foncier de France (2)
19 rue des Capucines
BP 65
75050 Paris, Cedex 1, France
Tel.: (33) 142448000
Fax: (33) 142448699
E-Mail: admin@creditfoncier.fr
Web Site: www.creditfoncier.fr
Sales Range: $1-4.9 Billion
Real Estate Banking Services
S.I.C.: 6159
N.A.I.C.S.: 522292

Subsidiary:

Compagnie de Financement Foncier (3)
4 quai de Bercy
94224 Charenton-le-Pont, France
Tel.: (33) 1 57 44 72 27
Fax: (33) 1 57 44 92 88
E-Mail: ir@creditfoncier.fr
Web Site: www.foncier.fr
CFF—(ASX)
Rev.: $6,864,736,030
Assets: $135,670,093,983
Liabilities: $133,160,353,866
Net Worth: $2,509,740,117
Earnings: $178,476,565
Fiscal Year-end: 12/31/12
Financial Management Services
S.I.C.: 6211
N.A.I.C.S.: 523999
Thierry Dufour *(Chm & CEO)*
Sandrine Guerin *(Deputy CEO)*

Mancelle d'Habitation SA (2)
11 rue du Donjon
72055 Le Mans, France
Tel.: (33) 2 43 74 45 45
Fax: (33) 2 43 74 45 40
E-Mail: contact@mancelle-habitation.fr
Web Site: www.mancelle-habitation.fr
Banking Services
S.I.C.: 6029
N.A.I.C.S.: 522110

Subsidiary:

Manceliere Logement Soc Economie Mixte (3)
10 rue Hippolyte Lecornue
72015 Le Mans, Cedex 2, France
Tel.: (33) 2 43 43 74 33
Fax: (33) 2 43 43 74 36
Web Site: www.manceliere-logement.fr
Sales Range: $10-24.9 Million
Emp.: 16
Real Estate Management Services
S.I.C.: 6513
N.A.I.C.S.: 531110
Annick Vignez *(VP)*

Natixis, S.A. (2)
30 avenue Pierre Mendes
75013 Paris, France FR
Mailing Address:
BP 4
F-75060 Paris, Cedex 02, France
Tel.: (33) 158323000
Fax: (33) 158199393
E-Mail: relinvest@natixis.fr
Web Site: www.natixis.com
KN—(EUR)
Rev.: $8,717,796,920
Assets: $711,275,842,900
Liabilities: $658,104,820,240
Net Worth: $53,171,022,660
Earnings: $1,274,822,990
Emp.: 20,198
Fiscal Year-end: 12/31/12
Bank Holding Company; Investment & Commercial Banking, Private Equity, Insurance & Asset Management Services
S.I.C.: 6712
N.A.I.C.S.: 551111
Francois Perol *(Chm)*
Laurent Mignon *(CEO & Member-Mgmt Bd)*
Jacques Sudre *(Chief Compliance Officer)*
Christian Le Hir *(Chief Legal Officer)*
Andre-Jean Olivier *(Member-Mgmt Bd & Sec)*
Luc-Emmanuel Auberger *(Member-Mgmt Bd-Ops & IS)*
Aline Bec *(Member-Mgmt Bd-Info Sys Pur Logistics)*
Alain Delouis *(Member-Mgmt Bd-HR)*
De Doan Tran *(Member-Mgmt Bd-Corp & Investment Banking)*
Olivier Perquel *(Member-Mgmt Bd-Wholesale Banking-Fin & Global Markets)*
Pierre Servant *(Member-Mgmt Bd-Investment Solutions)*

Divisions:

Natixis - Corporate & Investment Banking (3)
47 quai d'Austerlitz
F-75648 Paris, Cedex 13, France
Tel.: (33) 158551515
Fax: (33) 158552002
Web Site: www.natixis.com
Sales Range: $5-14.9 Billion
Corporate & Investment Banking Services
S.I.C.: 6211
N.A.I.C.S.: 523110
Jean-Marc Moriani *(CEO)*
Christophe Lanne *(COO)*

Subsidiaries:

Natixis Finance (4)
30 Avenue Pierre Mendes
75013 Paris, France
Tel.: (33) 158192400
Fax: (33) 158198549
Web Site: www.natixis.com
Emp.: 400
Commercial Banking Services to Agribusiness; Foreign Exchange; Credit & Cash Management Services
S.I.C.: 6159
N.A.I.C.S.: 522298
Daniel Giroux *(CEO)*

Natixis Lease (4)
4 place de la Coupole
F-94676 Charenton-le-Pont, Cedex, France
Tel.: (33) 158328080
Fax: (33) 158328081
E-Mail: contact@lease.natexis.fr
Web Site: www.lease.natixis.fr
Emp.: 50
Mobile & Property Lease Financing Services
S.I.C.: 6159
N.A.I.C.S.: 522294
Francois Brabander *(CEO)*
Henri Doumerc *(Mng Dir)*

U.S. Subsidiaries:

Natixis Bleichroeder Inc. (4)
1345 Ave of the Americas
New York, NY 10105-4300 NY
Tel.: (212) 698-3000
Fax: (212) 299-4444
Web Site: www.natexisblr.us/en/index.html
Emp.: 50
Investment Banking & Securities Brokerage Services
S.I.C.: 6211
N.A.I.C.S.: 523120

Natixis North America Inc. (4)
9 W 57th St 36th Fl
New York, NY 10019 DE
Tel.: (212) 891-6100
Web Site: www.cm.natixis.com
Holding Company
S.I.C.: 6719
N.A.I.C.S.: 551112
Philippe Becret *(CIO)*

Holding:

Natixis Capital Markets Inc. (5)
9 W 57th St 36th Fl
New York, NY 10019
Tel.: (212) 891-6100
Fax: (212) 891-6295
Web Site: www.cm.natixis.com
Corporate Investment Banking & Risk Management Services
S.I.C.: 6211
N.A.I.C.S.: 523110
Mitch Karig *(VP-Mktg Comm)*

Subsidiaries:

Natixis Real Estate Capital Inc. (6)
9 West 57th St 36th Fl
New York, NY 10019
Tel.: (212) 891-5700
Fax: (212) 891-5777
E-Mail: realestate@cm.natixis.com
Web Site: www.re.natixis.com
Emp.: 25
Commercial Real Estate Financing Services
S.I.C.: 6163
N.A.I.C.S.: 522310
Greg Murphy *(Head-Fin & Real Estate)*

Natixis Securities North America Inc. (6)
9 W 57th St 35th Fl
New York, NY 10019 NY
Tel.: (212) 891-6100
Fax: (212) 891-6260
Web Site: www.sp.natixis.com
Securities Broker & Dealer
S.I.C.: 6211
N.A.I.C.S.: 523120

Non-U.S. Branches:

Natixis - Bogota (4)
Carrera 15 n 91-30- of 601
Bogota, Colombia
Tel.: (57) 16231631
Fax: (57) 16234190
E-Mail: servicioalcliente@coface.com.co
Web Site: www.coface.com.co
Emp.: 30
Commercial Banking Services
S.I.C.: 6029
N.A.I.C.S.: 522110

Natixis - Buenos Aires (4)
Cerrito 1294 6th Fl
C1010AAZ Buenos Aires, Argentina
Tel.: (54) 1148160388
Fax: (54) 1148160427
E-Mail: sandra.smimmo@ar.natixis.com
Web Site: www.natixis.com
Emp.: 45
Commercial Banking Services
S.I.C.: 6029
N.A.I.C.S.: 522110

Natixis - Cairo (4)
50 rue Abdel Khalek Sarwat
Cairo, Egypt
Tel.: (20) 223904667
Fax: (20) 223915705
Web Site: www.natixis.com
Emp.: 2
Commercial Banking Services
S.I.C.: 6029
N.A.I.C.S.: 522110

Natixis Corporate Solutions Asia (4)
9 Raffles Place #60-01 Republic Plaza
Singapore, 048619, Singapore
Tel.: (65) 68231188
Telex: 28277 BFCE SG
Fax: (65) 68231199
Web Site: www.natixis.com
Emp.: 20
Commercial & Corporate Banking Services
S.I.C.: 6029
N.A.I.C.S.: 522110
Jenny Ong *(Mng Dir)*

Natixis - Hanoi (4)
Prime Center 53 Quang Trung
Room 16-02 16th Floor, Hanoi, Vietnam
Tel.: (84) 49433667
Telex: 805 811563
Fax: (84) 4 9433 665
Web Site: www.natixis.com
Commercial Banking Services
S.I.C.: 6029
N.A.I.C.S.: 522110

Natixis - Ho Chi Minh (4)
173 Vo Thi Sau
3e arrondissement, Ho Chi Minh City, Vietnam
Tel.: (84) 89320827
Fax: (84) 89320844
Web Site: www.natixis.com
Commercial Banking Services
S.I.C.: 6029
N.A.I.C.S.: 522110

Natixis - Hong Kong (4)
Level 23 Two Pacific Place
88 Queensway, Hong Kong, China (Hong Kong)
Tel.: (852) 28280999
Telex: 80186 BFCEX HX
Fax: (852) 25839801
E-Mail: hongkong.info@ap.natixis.com
Web Site: www.natixis.com
Rev.: $128,210
Emp.: 50
Commercial Banking Services
S.I.C.: 6029
N.A.I.C.S.: 522110

Natixis - Kuala Lumpur (4)
Marketing Office Suite 16-5 Level 16th
Menara Weld 76
Jalan Raja Chulan, MY 50200 Kuala Lumpur, Malaysia
Tel.: (60) 60320263900
Fax: (60) 60320263901
E-Mail: rizal.abdullah@ap.natixis.com
Web Site: www.natixis.com
Emp.: 7
Commercial Banking Services
S.I.C.: 6029
N.A.I.C.S.: 522110

Natixis - Labuan (4)
Unit Level 9 Main Office Tower
Financial Park Labuan Complex
Jalan Merdeka, 87000 Labuan, Malaysia

Banque Federale des Banques Populaires—(Continued)

Tel.: (60) 87582009
Fax: (60) 87583009
Web Site: www.natixis.com
Commercial Banking Services
S.I.C.: 6029
N.A.I.C.S.: 522110

Natixis - London (4)
Cannon Bridge House
25 Dowgate Hill, London, EC4R 2YA, United Kingdom
Tel.: (44) 2032169000
Fax: (44) 2032169201
Web Site: www.natixis.com
Emp.: 200
Commercial Banking Services
S.I.C.: 6029
N.A.I.C.S.: 522110
Olivier Allard *(Head-Capital Markets)*

Non-U.S. Subsidiaries:

Natixis Algerie Sp.A. (4)
62 chemin Mohamed Drareni
Hydra, 16035, Algeria
Tel.: (213) 2154 9015 (-9020)
Fax: (213) 2154 9193
E-Mail: Nasr-Eddine.Bouharaoua@algerie.natixis.com
Web Site: www.natixis.com
Commercial Banking Services
S.I.C.: 6029
N.A.I.C.S.: 522110

Natixis Luxembourg S.A. (4)
51 avenue JF Kennedy
L-1855 Luxembourg, Luxembourg LU
Tel.: (352) 253418315
Fax: (352) 253418342
E-Mail: luxembourgnatixis@luxembourgnatixis.lu
Web Site: www.natixis.com
Emp.: 9
Bank Holding Company; Investment & Commercial Banking Services
S.I.C.: 6712
N.A.I.C.S.: 551111

Natixis Global Asset Management S.A. (3)
21 quai d'Austerlitz
F-75634 Paris, Cedex 13, France
Tel.: (33) 178409000
Fax: (33) 178406500
E-Mail: christian.silianoff@globalam.natixis.com
Web Site: www.globalam.natixis.com
Emp.: 2,800
Financial & Real Estate Asset Management Services
S.I.C.: 6719
N.A.I.C.S.: 551112
Laurent Mignon *(Chm)*
Pierre Servant *(Global CEO)*
Jamal Saab *(Mng Dir & Head-MENA)*
Geoffroy Sartorius *(CFO & Exec VP)*
Pascal Delaunay *(Chief Compliance Officer)*
Herve Guinament *(Pres/CEO-Intl Distr)*
John T. Hailer *(Pres/CEO-Americas & Asia)*
Pascal Voisin *(CEO-Natixis Asset Mgmt)*
Jeffrey D. Plunkett *(Gen Counsel & Exec VP)*
Beverly M. Bearden *(Exec VP-HR)*
Caren Leedom *(Exec VP-Global Comm)*

Division:

Natixis Global Asset Management (France) (4)
21 quai d'Austerlitz
F-75634 Paris, Cedex 13, France
Tel.: (33) 178409000
Fax: (33) 178406500
Web Site: www.globalam.natixis.com
Sales Range: $400-449.9 Billion
Holding Company; Financial & Real Estate Asset Management Services
S.I.C.: 6719
N.A.I.C.S.: 551112
Pascal Voisin *(CEO)*

Subsidiaries:

AEW Europe (5)
21 quai d''Austerlitz
F-75634 Paris, France
Tel.: (33) 178409200
Fax: (33) 178406601
Web Site: www.aeweurope.com
Managed Assets: $22,463,630,000
Emp.: 270
Real Estate Investment Management Services
S.I.C.: 6726
N.A.I.C.S.: 525990
Mireille Chetioui *(CFO & Sec)*
Rob Wilkinson *(Chief Investment Officer)*
Coralie Auguet *(Gen Counsel)*

Subsidiary:

NAMI-AEW Europe (6)
1-1 rue des Italiens
F-75009 Paris, France
Tel.: (33) 178403300
Web Site: www.namiaeweurope.com
Real Estate Fund Management Services
S.I.C.: 6531
N.A.I.C.S.: 531390
Alain Pivert *(Dir Gen)*
Philippe Agenis-Nevers *(Deputy Dir Gen)*

Non-U.S. Subsidiary:

AEW Europe-London (6)
33 Jermyn Street
London, SW1Y 6DN, United Kingdom UK
Tel.: (44) 2070164800
Fax: (44) 470164842
E-Mail: enquiries@curzonglobal.com
Emp.: 80
Real Estate Investment Management Services
S.I.C.: 6726
N.A.I.C.S.: 525990
Ric Lewis *(CEO & Chief Investment Officer-AEW Europe)*

Natixis Asset Management S.A. (5)
21 quai d'Austerlitz
F-75634 Paris, Cedex 13, France
Tel.: (33) 178408000
Fax: (33) 178406000
Web Site: www.am.natixis.com
Asset Management Services
S.I.C.: 6799
N.A.I.C.S.: 523920
Pascal Voisin *(CEO)*
Dominique Sabassier *(Deputy Mng Dir)*

Subsidiary:

Natixis Multimanager (6)
21 quai d'Austerlitz
75634 Paris, Cedex, 13, France
Tel.: (33) 178403200
Fax: (33) 178403299
E-Mail: rh@am.natixis.com
Web Site: www.multimanager.natixis.com
Mutual Fund & Other Asset Multimanagement Services
S.I.C.: 6722
N.A.I.C.S.: 525910
Dominique Mourocq *(CEO & CIO)*
Brigitte Minard *(CFO)*

U.S. Division:

Natixis Global Asset Management, L.P. (4)
399 Boylston St 13th Fl
Boston, MA 02116-3305 DE
Tel.: (617) 449-2100
Fax: (617) 247-1447
Web Site: www.globalam.natixis.com
Sales Range: $250-299.9 Billion
Emp.: 1,400
Holding Company; Financial & Real Estate Asset Management Services
S.I.C.: 6719
N.A.I.C.S.: 551112
John T. Hailer *(Pres & CEO)*
Faith Yando *(Sr VP)*

Subsidiaries:

AEW Capital Management, L.P. (5)
World Trade Center E 2 Seaport Ln
Boston, MA 02210-2021
Tel.: (617) 261-9000
Fax: (617) 261-9555
Web Site: www.aew.com
Managed Assets: $26,000,000,000
Emp.: 150
Real Estate Investment Management Services
S.I.C.: 6726
N.A.I.C.S.: 525990
Jeffrey Davis Furber *(CEO & Mng Dir)*
James J. Finnegan *(Mng Dir, Gen Counsel & Chief Compliance Officer)*
Pamela J. Herbst *(Mng Dir & Head-Direct Investment Grp)*
Michael J. Acton *(Mng Dir & Dir-Res)*
Robert J. Plumb *(Mng Dir & Dir-Acq)*
Marc L. Davidson *(Mng Dir & Portfolio Mgr-Partners Funds)*
Matthew A. Troxell *(Mng Dir & Sr Portfolio Mgr-Construction & Mgmt-Real Estate)*

AlphaSimplex Group, LLC (5)
One Cambridge Ctr 7th Fl
Cambridge, MA 02142 DE
Tel.: (617) 475-7100
Fax: (617) 588-1925
Web Site: www.alphasimplex.com
Emp.: 25
Investment Management Services
S.I.C.: 6722
N.A.I.C.S.: 525910
Andrew W. Lo *(Founder, Chm & Chief Scientific Officer)*
Arnout M. Eikeboom *(Chief Compliance Officer)*

Capital Growth Management, L.P. (5)
1 International Pl 45th Fl
Boston, MA 02110
Mailing Address:
PO Box 8511
Boston, MA 02266-8511
Tel.: (617) 737-3225
Fax: (617) 261-0572
Toll Free: (800) 345-4048
E-Mail: staff@cgmfunds.com
Web Site: www.cgmfunds.com
Sales Range: $75-99.9 Million
Emp.: 20
Mutual Funds & Advisory Accounts Management Services
S.I.C.: 6722
N.A.I.C.S.: 525910
Robert L. Kemp *(Co-Founder & Pres)*
G. Kenneth Heebner *(Co-Founder & VP/Portfolio Mgr)*
David C. Fietze *(Chief Compliance Officer)*
Jem A. Hudgins *(Treas)*
Leslie A. Lake *(Sec & VP-Admin)*

Gateway Investment Advisers, L.P. (5)
312 Walnut St Fl 35
Cincinnati, OH 45202-9834 DE
Tel.: (513) 719-1100
Fax: (513) 719-1199
Web Site: www.gia.com
Sales Range: $5-14.9 Billion
Emp.: 25
Investment & Portfolio Management Services
S.I.C.: 6722
N.A.I.C.S.: 525910
J. Patrick Rogers *(Pres, CEO & Portfolio Mgr)*
Paul R. Stewart *(CIO, Sr VP & Portfolio Mgr)*
Geoffrey Keenan *(Exec VP)*

Hansberger Global Investors, Inc. (5)
401 E Las Olas Blvd Ste 1700
Fort Lauderdale, FL 33301
Tel.: (954) 522-5150
Fax: (954) 713-2525
Web Site: www.hansberger.com
Managed Assets: $7,400,000,000
Emp.: 60
Investment Management Services
S.I.C.: 6211
N.A.I.C.S.: 523110
Ron Holt *(CEO & Co-Chief Investment Officer-Value Team)*
David Lemanski *(Chief Admin Officer)*
Susan Moore-Wester *(Chief Compliance Officer)*
Andrew Powers *(Sr VP & Mng Dir-IT)*
Mary Foglia *(Sr VP & Dir-Trading)*
Moira McLachlan *(Sr VP-Res-Fort Lauderdale)*
Evelyn Orley *(Sr VP-Mktg-Western US)*
Sharon Pelletier *(Sr VP-Investment Ops & Acct Admin)*

Non-U.S. Branch:

Hansberger Global Investors (6)
5500 N Service Rd 11th Fl
Burlington, ON, L7L 6W6, Canada
Tel.: (905) 331-5770
Fax: (905) 331-5776
Web Site: www.hansberger.com
Emp.: 10
Investment Management Services
S.I.C.: 6211
N.A.I.C.S.: 523110
Thomas R.H. Tibbles *(Mng Dir & Chief Investment Officer-Growth Team)*
Barry A. Lockhart *(Deputy Mng Dir-Canada)*
Trevor Graham *(Sr VP-Res)*
Patrick Tan *(Sr VP-Res)*

Harris Associates, L.P. (5)
2 N La Salle St Ste 500
Chicago, IL 60602-3790
Tel.: (312) 621-0600
Fax: (312) 621-9929
Web Site: www.harrisassoc.com
Sales Range: $50-74.9 Billion
Emp.: 190
Investment & Portfolio Management Services
S.I.C.: 6211
N.A.I.C.S.: 523110
Robert M. Levy *(Chm, Chief Investment Officer & Partner)*
David G. Herro *(Chief Investment Officer-Intl Equity & Partner)*
Janet L. Reali *(Partner & Gen Counsel)*
Michael J. Neary *(Partner & Mng Dir-Mktg & Client Rels)*
Robert A. Taylor *(Partner & Dir-Intl Res & Portfolio Mgr)*
Henry R. Berghoef *(Partner, Mgr-Portfolio & Dir-Res)*
Edward S. Loeb *(Partner & Portfolio Mgr)*
Michael J. Mangan *(Partner & Portfolio Mgr)*
Clyde S. McGregor *(Partner & Portfolio Mgr)*
William C. Nygren *(Partner & Portfolio Mgr)*
Edward A. Studzinski *(Partner & Portfolio Mgr)*
Judson H. Brooks *(Partner)*
Anthony P. Coniaris *(Partner)*
M. Colin Hudson *(Partner)*
John R. Raitt *(Partner)*
Thomas E. Herman *(CFO)*
John N. Desmond *(COO)*
Dermot Putnam *(CIO)*
Richard J. Gorman *(Chief Compliance Officer)*
Colin P. McFarland *(Chief Compliance Officer)*

Loomis, Sayles & Company, L.P. (5)
1 Financial Ctr
Boston, MA 02111-2621
Tel.: (617) 482-2450
Fax: (617) 482-1985
Toll Free: (800) 343-2029
Web Site: www.loomissayles.com
Sales Range: $100-149.9 Billion
Emp.: 200
Securities Investment & Fund Management Services
S.I.C.: 6211
N.A.I.C.S.: 523110
Dan Fuss *(Vice Chm)*
Robert J. Blanding *(CEO)*
Kevin Charleston *(CFO)*
Mark Baribeau *(CIO & VP)*
Lauriann Kloppenburg *(Chief Strategy Officer)*
Jae Park *(Chief Investment Officer)*
David Waldman *(Deputy Chief Investment Officer)*
Jean Loewenberg *(Gen Counsel)*

Natixis Global Associates, LLC (5)
399 Bolston St
Boston, MA 02116
Tel.: (617) 449-2600
Fax: (617) 449-2688
Web Site: www.ga.natixis.com
Emp.: 500
Holding Company; Financial Investment Advisory & Distribution Services
S.I.C.: 6719
N.A.I.C.S.: 551112
David Giunta *(Pres & CEO)*
Matthew Coldren *(Exec VP-Global Relationships & Retirement Strategy Grp)*

Subsidiaries:

Natixis Asset Management Advisors, L.P. (6)
399 Bolston St
Boston, MA 02116
Tel.: (617) 449-2600
Fax: (617) 449-2688
Web Site: www.ga.natixis.com
Investment Advisory Services
S.I.C.: 6282
N.A.I.C.S.: 523930
David Giunta *(Pres & CEO)*
Coleen Downs Dinneen *(Gen Counsel, Sec & Exec VP)*

Natixis Distributors, L.P. (6)
399 Bolston St
Boston, MA 02116
Tel.: (617) 449-2600
Fax: (617) 449-2688
Toll Free: (800) 283-1155
Web Site: www.ga.natixis.com
Managed Assets: $10,000,000,000
Financial Distribution Services
Import Export
S.I.C.: 6371
N.A.I.C.S.: 524292
David Giunta *(Pres & CEO-U.S.)*
Sharon Wratchford *(Exec VP-Admin & Ops-Global Distr)*
Faith Yando *(Sr VP-PR)*

Non-U.S. Branch:

Natixis Global Associates International (6)
21 Quai d'Austerlitz
F-75013 Paris, Cedex 13, France
Tel.: (33) 178409600
Fax: (33) 178406000
Web Site: www.ga.natixis.com
Investment Advisory & Distribution Services
S.I.C.: 6282
N.A.I.C.S.: 523930
Herve Guinamant *(Pres & CEO)*
Fabrice Chemouny *(Exec VP & Head-Intl Mktg & Strategy)*

Reich & Tang Asset Management, LLC (5)
1411 Broadway Ste 28
New York, NY 10018-3496
Tel.: (617) 449-2100
Web Site: www.reichandtang.com
Emp.: 200
Portfolio Management Services
Import Export
S.I.C.: 6282
N.A.I.C.S.: 523920
Michael Lydon *(Pres)*
Richard De Sanctis *(CFO & Exec VP)*

Divisions:

Reich & Tang Capital Management (6)
1411 Broadway
New York, NY 10018
Tel.: (212) 830-5200
Fax: (212) 830-5468
Toll Free: (800) 676-6779
E-Mail: cminfo@rnt.com
Web Site: www.reichandtang.com
Emp.: 100
Asset Management & Investment Services
S.I.C.: 6799
N.A.I.C.S.: 523920
Naomi Friedland-Wechsler *(Gen Counsel & Exec VP)*
Sandra Arcaro *(Sr VP-Portfolio Admin)*

Divisions:

Global Investment Advisors (7)
12 E 49th St # 36
New York, NY 10017-1028
Tel.: (212) 830-5460
Fax: (212) 974-2057
Web Site: www.reichandtang.com
Fixed Income Assets Management Services
S.I.C.: 6799
N.A.I.C.S.: 523920
Christopher Brancazio *(Chief Compliance Officer)*

Reich & Tang Funds (6)
1411 Broadway Rm 2800
New York, NY 10018-3450
Tel.: (212) 830-5200
Fax: (212) 330-5477
Web Site: www.reichandtang.com
Emp.: 80
Short-Term Money Market Funds Management Services
S.I.C.: 6722
N.A.I.C.S.: 525910
Michael P. Lydon *(Pres & CEO)*

Snyder Capital Management, L.P. (5)
1 Market Plz Steuart Tower Ste 1200
San Francisco, CA 94105
Tel.: (415) 392-3900
Fax: (415) 391-9437
Emp.: 13
Small & Mid-Cap Equities Investment Management
S.I.C.: 6722
N.A.I.C.S.: 525910
Peter Eisele *(Pres)*
Walter Niemasik, Jr. *(CEO)*
Sonja L. Commer *(Chief Compliance Officer)*

Vaughan Nelson Investment Management, L.P. (5)
600 Travis St Ste 6300
Houston, TX 77002-3071
Tel.: (713) 224-2545
Fax: (713) 228-4292
Web Site: www.vaughannelson.com
Emp.: 50
Investment Management Services
S.I.C.: 6799
N.A.I.C.S.: 523920
Eugene H. Vaughan *(Chm)*
Lee Alan Lahourcade *(Pres & CEO)*
Jay Wagner *(CIO)*
Richard B. Faig *(Dir-Fin, Admin & Chief Compliance Officer)*

Subsidiary:

Vaughan Nelson Trust Company (6)
600 Travis St Ste 6300
Houston, TX 77002
Tel.: (713) 224-2545
Fax: (713) 247-9534
E-Mail: info@vaughannelson.com
Web Site: www.vaughannelson.com
Emp.: 50
Financial Trust Services
S.I.C.: 6733
N.A.I.C.S.: 523991
Richard Faig *(Pres)*
Mark E. Farrell *(Sr VP)*

Westpeak Global Advisors, L.P. (5)
1470 Walnut St Ste 101
Boulder, CO 80302-5114
Tel.: (303) 786-7700
Fax: (303) 786-7411
Web Site: www.westpeak.com
Emp.: 7
Equity Investment & Management Services
S.I.C.: 6211
N.A.I.C.S.: 523110
Khalid Ghayur *(CEO & Chief Investment Officer)*
Deborah A. Gamel *(CFO & Chief Compliance Officer)*
Eric D. Krawetz *(Chief Admin Officer)*
Ronan G. Heaney *(Sr VP & Dir-Res)*
Stephen C. Platt *(Sr VP & Dir-Portfolio Mgmt)*

Natixis - Private Equity & Private Banking (3)
5-7 rue de Monttessuy
F-75007 Paris, France
Tel.: (33) 158323000
Fax: (33) 158324248
Web Site: www.privatebanking.natixis.com
Emp.: 3,000
Private Equity & Private Banking Services
S.I.C.: 6211
N.A.I.C.S.: 523999
Nicolas Homassel *(CEO)*

Subsidiaries:

Banque Privee Saint Dominique (4)
12-14 Rond Point des Champs Elysees
F-75382 Paris, Cedex 08, France
Tel.: (33) 156888000
Fax: (33) 156888199
E-Mail: alexandra.ellert@banque-bpsd.fr
Web Site: www.bpsd.fr
Emp.: 125
Private Banking & Wealth Management Services
S.I.C.: 6282
N.A.I.C.S.: 523920
Jacques-Antoine Allain *(COO)*

Natixis Private Equity (4)
5-7 rue de Monttessuy
F-75340 Paris, Cedex 07, France
Tel.: (33) 158192000
Fax: (33) 158192010
Web Site: www.natixis-pe.com
Emp.: 250
Private Equity Firm
S.I.C.: 6211
N.A.I.C.S.: 523999
Jean-Louis Delvaux *(Deputy CEO & Chm-Intl)*
Jean Duhau de Berenx *(CEO)*
Francois Baubeau *(COO)*

Division:

Natixis Private Equity International (5)
5-7 rue de Monttessuy
F-75340 Paris, Cedex 07, France
Tel.: (33) 158192350
E-Mail: Jeanfrancois.helfer@npeim.com
Web Site: www natixis-pe.com
Emp.: 7
Private Equity Firm
S.I.C.: 6211
N.A.I.C.S.: 523999
Jean-Louis Delvaux *(Chm)*
Jean-Francois Helfer *(Chm-Mgmt Bd)*
Jean de Severac *(Mng Dir)*
Francois Feige *(Member-Mgmt Bd)*

Subsidiaries:

Initiative & Finance (5)
96 avenue d'Lena
F-75783 Paris, Cedex 16, France
Tel.: (33) 156899700
Fax: (33) 147208690
E-Mail: info@initiative-finance.com
Web Site: www.initiative-finance.com
Emp.: 20
Equity Investment Firm
S.I.C.: 6211
N.A.I.C.S.: 523999
Jean-Bernard Meurisse *(Pres)*
Valerie Bouillier *(Partner)*
Matthieu Douchet *(Partner)*
Thierry Giron *(Partner)*
Jean-Michel Laveu *(Partner)*

iXEN S.A. (5)
5-7 rue de Monttessuy
F-75340 Paris, Cedex 07, France
Tel.: (33) 1 5819 2000
Fax: (33) 1 5819 2010
Emp.: 10
Private Equity Firm
S.I.C.: 6211
N.A.I.C.S.: 523999
Caroline Remus *(Chm-Mgmt Bd)*
Yves Roucaud *(CEO)*
Veronique Bernard *(CFO)*

Natixis Investissement Partners (5)
5-7 rue de Monttessuy
F-75340 Paris, Cedex 07, France
Tel.: (33) 158192100
Fax: (33) 1 5819 2110
E-Mail: contact@ni-partners.com
Web Site: www.ni-partners.com
Emp.: 15
Private Equity Firm
S.I.C.: 6211
N.A.I.C.S.: 523999
Jean-Paul Bernardini *(Chm-Mgmt Bd)*
Philippe Taranto *(Assoc Dir)*
Vincent Lardoux *(Member-Mgmt Bd)*
Jean-Pierre Magagnin *(Sec)*

Naxicap Partners SA (5)
5-7 rue de Monttessuy
F-75340 Paris, Cedex 07, France
Tel.: (33) 158192220
Fax. (33) 158192230
E-Mail: contact@naxicap.fr
Web Site: www.naxicap.fr
Emp.: 50
Equity Investment Firm
S.I.C.: 6211
N.A.I.C.S.: 523999
Eric Aveillan *(Mng Dir)*

nempartners (5)
5-7 rue de Monttessuy
F-75340 Paris, Cedex 07, France
Tel.: (33) 158192130
Fax: (33) 158192140
E-Mail: info@nem-partners.com
Web Site: www.nem-partners.com
Emp.: 15
Equity Investment Firm
S.I.C.: 6211
N.A.I.C.S.: 523999
Eric Girardin *(Dir-Publ)*

Seventure Partners (5)
5-7 Rue de Monttessuy
F-75340 Paris, Cedex 07, France
Tel.: (33) 158192270
Fax: (33) 158192280
E-Mail: contact@seventure.fr
Web Site: www.seventure.fr
Managed Assets: $584,044,800
Emp.: 19
Equity Investment Firm
S.I.C.: 6211
N.A.I.C.S.: 523999
Jean-Patrick Demonsang *(Chm-Mgmt Bd)*
Isabelle de Cremoux *(Partner & Dir-Life Sciences Dept)*
Emmanuel Fiessinger *(Partner)*
Didier Piccino *(Partner)*
Bruno Rivet *(Partner)*
Ioana Simionescu *(Partner)*
Thi Than Vu *(CFO)*
Sylvie Padrazzi *(Sec)*

Spef LBO (5)
5-7 rue de Monttessuy
F-75340 Paris, Cedex, France
Tel.: (33) 158192250
Fax: (33) 158192260
E-Mail: contact@spef-lbo.fr
Web Site: www.spef-lbo.fr
Emp.: 10
Equity Investment Firm
S.I.C.: 6211
N.A.I.C.S.: 523999
Jacques Vachelard *(Chm-Mgmt Bd)*
Laurent Allegot *(Mng Dir)*
Arnaud Leclercq *(Member-Mgmt Bd)*

Ventech (5)
5-7 rue de Monttessuy
F-75007 Paris, Cedex 07, France
Tel.: (33) 158192150
Fax: (33) 158192160
E-Mail: contact@ventech.fr
Web Site: www.ventech.fr
Managed Assets: $474,536,400
Emp.: 16
Equity Investment Firm
S.I.C.: 6211
N.A.I.C.S.: 523999
Alain Caffi *(Chm & Gen Partner)*
Jean Bourcereau *(Gen Partner)*
Alain Cassi *(Gen Partner)*
Mounia Chaoui *(Gen Partner)*
Eric Huet *(Gen Partner)*

Affiliate:

EPF Partners (5)
11/13 avenue de Friedland
F-75008 Paris, France
Tel.: (33) 156436520
Fax: (33) 156436530
E-Mail: contact@epf-partners.com
Web Site: www.epf-partners.com
Managed Assets: $438,033,600
Emp.: 12
Private Equity Firm
S.I.C.: 6211
N.A.I.C.S.: 523999
Christian d'Argoubet *(Gen Mgr)*

Non-U.S. Subsidiaries:

Finatem Beteiligungsgesellschaft (5)
feldbergstrasse 5
D-60323 Frankfurt am Main, Germany
Tel.: (49) 695095640
Fax: (49) 6950956430
E-Mail: info@finatem.de
Web Site: www.finatem.de
Emp.: 11
Private Equity Firm
S.I.C.: 6211
N.A.I.C.S.: 523999

Banque Federale des Banques Populaires—(Continued)

Christophe Hemmerle *(Founder, Mng Dir & Partner)*
Robert Hennigs *(Mng Dir & Partner)*
Eric Jungblut *(Partner & Dir-Investment)*
Irmgard Schade *(Partner & Dir-Investment)*

MCH Private Equity Asesores, S.L. (5)
Plaza de Colon 2 Torre I Planta 15
28046 Madrid, Spain ES
Tel.: (34) 914264444
Fax: (34) 914264440
E-Mail: mch@mch.es
Web Site: www.mch.es
Emp.: 20
Private Equity Firm
S.I.C.: 6211
N.A.I.C.S.: 523999
Jose Maria Munoz *(Co-Founder & Mng Partner)*
Jaime Hernandez Soto *(Co-Founder & Mng Partner)*
Andres Pelaez Collado *(Mng Partner)*
Andres Pelaez *(Mng Dir)*
Idoya Aguirre *(Gen Counsel)*

Non-U.S. Affiliate:

Axxon Group (5)
Ladeira de Nossa Senhora 311
Gloria, 22211-100 Rio de Janeiro, RJ, Brazil
Tel.: (55) 2132350770
Fax: (55) 2132350772
E-Mail: axxon@axxongroup.com.br
Web Site: www.axxongroup.com.br
Managed Assets: $150,000,000
Emp.: 20
Private Equity Firm
S.I.C.: 6211
N.A.I.C.S.: 523999
Nicolas Wollak *(Founder & Partner)*
Jose Augusto de Carvalho *(Partner)*

Non-U.S. Joint Ventures:

Cape-Natixis S.G.R. S.p.A. (5)
Monte Rosa No 88
I-20149 Milan, Italy
Tel.: (39) 027636131
Fax: (39) 0277331617
E-Mail: info@cape.it
Web Site: www.cape.it
Emp.: 25
Private Equity Funds Management Services
S.I.C.: 6211
N.A.I.C.S.: 523999
Simone Cimino *(Founder, Chm & Mng Partner)*
Marco Visarma *(CEO & Mng Partner)*
Guido De Vecchi *(Mng Partner)*
Annamaria Petrillo *(Partner)*
Emanuela Trezzi *(Partner)*
Maddalena De Liso *(CFO)*

Krokus Private Equity Sp. z o.o. (5)
Al Jana Pawla II 25
00-854 Warsaw, Poland PL
Tel.: (48) 226534700
Fax: (48) 226534707
E-Mail: biuro@krokuspe.pl
Web Site: www.krokuspe.pl
Emp.: 10
Private Equity Firm
S.I.C.: 6211
N.A.I.C.S.: 523999
Witold Radwanski *(CEO & Partner)*
Marzena Tomecka *(CFO & Partner)*
Robert Bozyk *(Partner)*
Piotr Oskroba *(Partner)*

Natixis - Receivables Management (3)
30 Ave Tierr Menges France
F-75013 Paris, France
Tel.: (33) 158323000
Web Site: www.natixis.fr
Receivables Management, Credit Insurance, Factoring & Collections Services
S.I.C.: 6099
N.A.I.C.S.: 522390
Jerome Cazes *(CEO)*

Subsidiaries:

Coface S.A. (4)
12 cours Michelet
La Defense 10, F-92800 Puteaux, France FR
Tel.: (33) 149022000
Fax: (33) 1 4902 2741
E-Mail: info@coface.com
Web Site: www.coface.com
Sales Range: $1-4.9 Billion
Emp.: 7,000
Credit Insurance & Credit Management Services
S.I.C.: 6159
N.A.I.C.S.: 522298
Jean-Marc Pillu *(CEO)*
Daniel Garcia *(CIO)*
Carole Lytton *(Officer-Legal & Compliance)*
Thierry Coldefy *(Sec & Head-HR & Fin)*

Subsidiary:

Coface Services (5)
1 rue de l'Union
92843 Rueil-Malmaison, France
Tel.: (33) 147524360
Fax: (33) 147524361
Web Site: www.cofaceservices.fr
Emp.: 800
Business Intelligence & Receivables Management Services
S.I.C.: 6099
N.A.I.C.S.: 522390
Jerome Cazes *(Chm)*
Jacques Romand *(Deputy Mng Dir & Dir-HR/Admin)*

U.S. Subsidiary:

Coface North America Holding Company (5)
1350 Broadway Ste 2000
New York, NY 10018
Tel.: (212) 389-6500
Fax: (917) 322-0433
E-Mail: cofaceusa@coface.com
Web Site: www.coface-usa.com
Sales Range: $100-124.9 Million
Emp.: 360
Holding Company; Credit Insurance & Credit Management Services
S.I.C.: 6719
N.A.I.C.S.: 551112
Michael Ferrante *(Chm & CEO)*

Subsidiary:

Coface North America, Inc. (6)
Windsor Corp Park Bldg 100 Ste 350 50 Millstone Rd
East Windsor, NJ 08520
Tel.: (609) 469-0400
E-Mail: cofaceusa@coface.com
Web Site: www.coface-usa.com
Credit Insurance & Credit Management Services
S.I.C.: 6159
N.A.I.C.S.: 522298
Mike Ferrante *(Chm & CEO)*
Val Goldstein *(Exec VP-Credit Mgmt Div)*

Divisions:

Coface Credit Management North America, Inc. (7)
50 Millstone Rd Windsor Corp Park Bldg 100 Ste 360
East Windsor, NJ 08520
Tel.: (609) 469-0400
Fax: (609) 490-1580
Web Site: www.coface-usa.com
Credit Management Services
S.I.C.: 6159
N.A.I.C.S.: 522298
Val Goldstein *(Exec VP)*

Coface North America Insurance Company, Inc. (7)
50 Millstone Rd Windsor Corp Park Bldg 100 Ste 360
East Windsor, NJ 08520
Tel.: (609) 469-0400
Fax: (609) 490-1581
E-Mail: insurance@coface-usa.com
Web Site: www.coface-usa.com
Corporate Credit & Political Risk Insurance Services
S.I.C.: 6399
N.A.I.C.S.: 524130
Cristina Lane *(VP-Comml-Political Risk Insurance)*

Unit:

Coface North America Political Risk (8)
1350 Broadway Ste 2000
New York, NY 10018
Tel.: (212) 389-6470
Fax: (212) 322-0430
E-Mail: political_risk@coface-usa.com
Web Site: www.coface-usa.com
Political Risk Insurance Services
S.I.C.: 6733
N.A.I.C.S.: 525190
Cristina Lane *(VP-Comml)*

Subsidiary:

Coface Collections North America, Inc. (7)
2400 Veterans Blvd Ste 300
Kenner, LA 70062
Tel.: (504) 469-9545
Fax: (504) 471-0948
Toll Free: (800) 509-6060
Web Site: www.coface-usa.com
Sales Range: $10-24.9 Million
Emp.: 107
Commercial Debt Collection Services
S.I.C.: 7322
N.A.I.C.S.: 561440
Thomas E. Brenan *(Pres)*
Cliff Sanders *(Exec VP-Bus Dev)*
Don Beetcher *(Sr VP)*
James McDermott *(Sr VP)*

Non-U.S. Subsidiaries:

Coface Central Europe Holding AG (5)
Stubenring 24
1010 Vienna, Austria AT
Tel.: (43) 1515540
Fax: (43) 15124415
Web Site: www.cofacecentraleurope.com
Sales Range: $200-249.9 Million
Emp.: 640
Holding Company; Credit Insurance & Credit Management Services
S.I.C.: 6159
N.A.I.C.S.: 522298
Martina Dobringer *(Chm-Supervisory Bd & CEO)*
Christian Berger *(Member-Mgmt Bd)*

Coface Holding AG (5)
Isaac-Fulda-Allee 1
55124 Mainz, Germany De
Mailing Address:
Postfach 1209
55002 Mainz, Germany
Tel.: (49) 61313230
Fax: (49) 6131372766
E-Mail:
Web Site: www.coface.de
Sales Range: $400-449.9 Million
Emp.: 700
Holding Company; Credit Insurance & Credit Management Services
S.I.C.: 6719
N.A.I.C.S.: 551112
Norbert Langenbach *(Member-Mgmt Bd)*
Anna Saylor *(Sec)*

Subsidiary:

Coface Kreditversicherung AG (6)
Isaac-Fulda-Allee 1
D-55124 Mainz, Germany De
Mailing Address:
Postfach 1209
D-55002 Mainz, Germany
Tel.: (49) 61313230
Fax: (49) 6131372766
E-Mail: info@coface.de
Web Site: www.coface.de
Emp.: 6,000
Credit Insurance Services
S.I.C.: 6399
N.A.I.C.S.: 524130
Stefan Brauel *(Member-Mgmt Bd)*
Norbert Langenbach *(Member-Mgmt Bd)*

Non-U.S. Branch:

Coface Danmark (6)
Bulowsevej 3
1870 Frederiksberg, Denmark
Tel.: (45) 33862500
Fax: (45) 33862505
E-Mail: info@coface.dk
Web Site: www.coface.dk
Emp.: 8
Credit Insurance & Credit Management Services
S.I.C.: 6159
N.A.I.C.S.: 522298
Vagn Thorsager *(Gen Mgr)*

Non-U.S. Holding:

Coface Austria Holding AG (6)
Stubenring 24
1010 Vienna, Austria AT
Tel.: (43) 1515540
Fax: (43) 15124415
E-Mail: office@coface.at
Web Site: www.coface.at
Sales Range: $75-99.9 Million
Emp.: 115
Holding Company; Credit Insurance & Credit Management Services
S.I.C.: 6719
N.A.I.C.S.: 551112
K. R. Martina Dobringer *(Chm)*
Benoit Claire *(Chm-Supervisory Bd)*
Susanne Krones *(Mng Dir)*
Christian Berger *(Member-Mgmt Bd)*

Subsidiaries:

Coface Austria Bank AG (7)
Stubenring 24
1010 Vienna, Austria AT
Tel.: (43) 1515540
Fax: (43) 15124415
E-Mail: info@coface.at
Web Site: www.coface.at
Emp.: 130
Factoring Services
S.I.C.: 6099
N.A.I.C.S.: 522390
Gabriele Duker *(Member-Mgmt Bd)*
Rudolf Kandioler *(Member-Mgmt Bd)*

Coface Austria Kreditversicherung AG (7)
Stubenring 24
1010 Vienna, Austria AT
Tel.: (43) 1515540
Fax: (43) 151554221
Web Site: www.coface.at
Credit Insurance & Credit Management Services
S.I.C.: 6159
N.A.I.C.S.: 522298
Martina Dobringer *(Chm)*
Christian Berger *(Member-Mgmt Bd)*
Gabriele Duker *(Member-Mgmt Bd)*

Coface Italia S.p.A. (5)
Via Giovanni Spadolini 4
I-20141 Milan, Italy IT
Tel.: (39) 0248335111
Fax: (39) 0248335404
E-Mail: info@coface.it
Web Site: www.coface.it
Sales Range: $200-249.9 Million
Emp.: 180
Holding Company; Credit Insurance & Credit Management Services
S.I.C.: 6719
N.A.I.C.S.: 551112
Riccardo Carradori *(Mng Dir)*

Subsidiary:

Coface Assicurazioni S.p.A. (6)
Via Giovanni Spadolini 4
I 20141 Milan, Italy IT
Tel.: (39) 0248335111
Fax: (39) 0248335404
E-Mail: info@coface.it
Web Site: www.coface.it
Emp.: 100
Credit Insurance Services
S.I.C.: 6399
N.A.I.C.S.: 524130
Massimo Coletti *(Deputy Mng Dir)*
Ernesto De Martinis *(Deputy Mng Dir)*

Coface UK Holding Ltd. (5)
15 Appold St
London, EC2A 2DL, United Kingdom UK
Tel.: (44) 2073257500
Fax: (44) 1923478101
E-Mail: enquiries@cofaceuk.com
Web Site: www.cofaceuk.com
Sales Range: $75-99.9 Million
Emp.: 180
Holding Company; Credit Management Services
S.I.C.: 6719
N.A.I.C.S.: 551112
Xavier Denecker *(Mng Dir)*

Subsidiaries:

Coface Receivables Finance Limited (6)
Egale 1 80 St Albans Rd
Watford, Herts, WD17 1RP, United Kingdom UK
Tel.: (44) 1923478100
Fax: (44) 1923659091
Emp.: 100
Receivables Management Services
S.I.C.: 6099
N.A.I.C.S.: 522390
Frederic Bourgeois *(Mng Dir)*

Coface UK Services Limited (6)
15 Appold Street
London, EC2A 2DL, United Kingdom UK
Tel.: (44) 2073257500
Fax: (44) 2073257699
E-Mail: enquiries@cofaceuk.com
Web Site: www.cofaceuk.com
Emp.: 30
Credit Intermediation Services
S.I.C.: 6159
N.A.I.C.S.: 522298
Xavier Denecker *(Mng Dir)*

Natixis Factor S.A. (4)
10-12 Avenue Winston Churchill
F-94676 Charenton-le-Pont, Cedex, France
Tel.: (33) 158328000
Fax: (33) 158328100
Web Site: www.factor.natixis.com
Emp.: 475
Factoring & Credit Insurance Services
S.I.C.: 6022
N.A.I.C.S.: 522190
Gils Berrous *(Chm)*
Philippe Petiot *(CEO)*

Subsidiaries:

Natixis Assurances S.A. (3)
115 rue Reaumur CS 40230
75086 Paris, Cedex 02, France FR
Tel.: (33) 158199000
Fax: (33) 158199140
E-Mail: service.clients@assurances.natixis.fr
Web Site: www.assurances.natixis.fr
Sales Range: $1-4.9 Billion
Emp.: 310
Holding Company; Life, Personal Risk & Other Insurance Carrier
S.I.C.: 6719
N.A.I.C.S.: 551112
Nathalie Broutele *(Dir Gen)*
Laurent Doubrovine *(Mng Dir)*
Jean Marches *(CEO-Life Insurance Div)*
Veronique Necker *(Sec General-Quality/ Gen Svcs Dept)*
Bernard Paris *(Exec VP-Legal & Tax)*

Subsidiary:

Vitalia Vie (4)
115 rue Reaumur CS 40230 75086
F-75606 Paris, Cedex 02, France
Tel.: (33) 158199381
Fax: (33) 158199220
Life Insurance Carrier
S.I.C.: 6311
N.A.I.C.S.: 524113

Natixis Interepargne S.A. (3)
5 Ave Ge la liberge
BP 4 75060
F-94220 Paris, Cedex, France
Tel.: (33) 158194300
Fax: (33) 158324001
Web Site: www.interepargne.natixis.fr
Employee Savings Plans Management Services
S.I.C.: 6726
N.A.I.C.S.: 525990
Didier Trupin *(CEO & Mng Dir)*

SLIB S.A. (3)
22 28 Rue Joubert
75012 Paris, France
Tel.: (33) 170369700
Fax: (33) 170369701
Web Site: www.slib.fr
Emp.: 100
Investment Banking Software Publisher & Information Technologies Management
S.I.C.: 7372
N.A.I.C.S.: 511210
Philippe Cognet *(CEO)*

Societe de Banque Francaise et Internationale (3)
30 Ave Pierre Mendes
F-75013 Paris, France
Tel.: (33) 158323000
Fax: (33) 178406000
Web Site: www.natixis.com
Emp.: 2,000
Commercial Bank
S.I.C.: 6029
N.A.I.C.S.: 522110
Laurent Mignon *(Mng Dir)*

Thermocompact SA (3)
route de Sarves
BP 21
Zone Industrielle Metz-Tessy, 74371 Pringy, France
Tel.: (33) 4 50 27 20 02
Fax: (33) 4 50 27 17 37
E-Mail: thermo@thermocompact.com
Web Site: www.thermocompact.com
Sls.: $29,300,000
Emp.: 247
Metal Heat Treating
S.I.C.: 3398
N.A.I.C.S.: 332811
Jean-Claude Cornier *(Chm)*
Gilles Mollard *(CEO)*
Philippe Descaillot *(Mng Dir)*

Non-U.S. Joint Venture:

CIFG Holding, Ltd. (1)
44 Church Street
Hamilton, HM 12, Bermuda BM
Tel.: (441) 294 8730
Fax: (441) 294 8729
Web Site: www.cifg.com
Sales Range: $200-249.9 Million
Emp.: 120
Holding Company; Reinsurance Carriers
S.I.C.: 6719
N.A.I.C.S.: 551112
John Salvatore Pizzarelli *(CEO)*
Michael Stuart Knopf *(Gen Counsel & Mng Dir)*
James Joseph O'Keefe, III *(CFO)*

Holding:

CIFG Guaranty, Ltd. (2)
44 Church Street
Hamilton, HM 12, Bermuda
Tel.: (441) 294 8730
Fax: (441) 294 8729
Web Site: www.cifg.com
Reinsurance Carrier
S.I.C.: 6399
N.A.I.C.S.: 524130
Gabriel Topor *(Chief Underwriting Officer)*

U.S. Subsidiary:

CIFG Assurance North America, Inc. (3)
850 3rd Ave 10th Fl
New York, NY 10022
Tel.: (212) 909-3939
Fax: (212) 909-3958
Web Site: www.cifg.com
Premiums: $40,986,384
Assets: $757,899,775
Liabilities: $380,844,775
Net Worth: $377,055,000
Earnings: ($212,191,154)
Emp.: 70
Fiscal Year-end: 12/31/12
Primary Financial Guaranty Reinsurance Carrier
S.I.C.: 6399
N.A.I.C.S.: 524130
David A. Buzen *(Pres, CFO & COO)*
Lawrence P. English *(CEO)*
Jessica Stern *(Mng Dir & Head-Global HR & Facilities)*
Maurice Toledano *(Deputy CFO-Europe)*
Michael Stuart Knopf *(Gen Counsel)*

Non-U.S. Subsidiary:

CIFG Europe S.A. (3)
19 boulevard Malesherbes
75008 Paris, France FR
Tel.: (33) 155273748
Fax: (33) 155273756
E-Mail: c.bertrand@cifg.com
Web Site: www.cifg.com
Rev.: $2,917,150
Assets: $106,152,235
Liabilities: $57,108,570
Net Worth: $49,043,665
Earnings: ($1,766,175)
Emp.: 3
Fiscal Year-end: 12/31/12
Primary Financial Guaranty Reinsurance Carrier
S.I.C.: 6399
N.A.I.C.S.: 524130
Maurice Toledano *(Deputy CFO)*

BANQUE INTERNATIONALE A LUXEMBOURG S.A.

69 Rte D'Esch
L 2953 Luxembourg, Luxembourg
Tel.: (352) 45901
Telex: 3626 bil lu
Fax: (352) 45902010
E-Mail: contact@bil.com
Web Site: www.bil.com
Year Founded: 1856
Emp.: 2,100

Business Description:
Domestic & International Banking Services
S.I.C.: 6159
N.A.I.C.S.: 522293

Personnel:
Francois Pauly *(Gen Mgr)*

Subsidiaries:

BIL Lease S.A. (1)
136 Rute D Arlon
1150 Luxembourg, Luxembourg (100%)
Tel.: (352) 2277331
Fax: (352) 227744
E-Mail: info@dexia-bil.com
Web Site: www.dexia-bil.com
Emp.: 9
Equipment Rental & Leasing Services
S.I.C.: 7359
N.A.I.C.S.: 532490

Non-U.S. Subsidiaries:

Banque Internationale a Luxembourg (Suisse) SA (1)
(Formerly Dexia Private Bank (Switzerland))
Rue de Jargonnant 2
1207 Geneva, Switzerland
Tel.: (41) 58 810 88 58
Emp.: 80
Pension, Health & Welfare Funds
S.I.C.: 6371
N.A.I.C.S.: 524292

BIL Finance SA (1)
(Formerly Dexia Banque Privee France)
23-25 rue de Berri
75008 Paris, France (100%)
Tel.: (33) 1 58 56 96 40
E-Mail: contact-france@bil.com
Emp.: 400
Federal Reserve Bank
S.I.C.: 6011
N.A.I.C.S.: 521110

BANQUE INTERNATIONALE ARABE DE TUNISIE

70-72 Avenue Habib Bourguiba BP 520
Tunis, 1001, Tunisia
Tel.: (216) 71340733
Fax: (216) 71340680
Web Site: www.biat.com.tn
Year Founded: 1976
BIAT—(LSE)

Business Description:
Investment Banking Services
S.I.C.: 6211
N.A.I.C.S.: 523110

Personnel:
Ismail Mabrouk *(Chm)*

Board of Directors:
Ismail Mabrouk
M'hamed Driss
Michel Farrugia
Mohsen Hachicha
Slaheddine Ladjimi
Jean Messinesi
Aziz Miled
Guido Ottolenghi
Tahar Sioud

Subsidiaries:

Assurances BIAT (1)
les Jardins du Lac-Lac II
Les Berges du Lac, 1053 Tunis, Tunisia
Tel.: (216) 71 197 820
Fax: (216) 71 197 810
E-Mail: general@assurancesbiat.com
Web Site: www.assurancesbiat.com
Emp.: 92
General Insurance Services
S.I.C.: 6411
N.A.I.C.S.: 524298
Hedi Saadaoui *(CEO)*

Compagnie Internationale Arabe de Recouvrement (1)
7 Rue Alain Savary
1002 Tunis, Tunisia
Tel.: (216) 71783712
Fax: (216) 71785652
Commercial Banking Services
S.I.C.: 6029
N.A.I.C.S.: 522110

Societe de pole de competitivite de Monastir - El Fejja (1)
Mfcpole Grand Boulevard du Lac Immeuble BIAT 2eme etage
Les Berges du Lac, Tunis, Tunisia
Tel.: (216) 71 138 543
Fax: (216) 71 862 068
Commercial Banking Services
S.I.C.: 6029
N.A.I.C.S.: 522110

BANQUE INTERNATIONALE POUR LAFRIQUE AU TOGO SA

(d/b/a/ B.I.A. Togo)
13 Rue du Commerce
BP 346
Lome, Togo
Tel.: (228) 221 3286
Fax: (228) 221 1019
E-Mail: bia-togo@cafe.tg
Web Site: www.biat.tg
Sales Range: $10-24.9 Million

Business Description:
Retail & Commercial Banking
S.I.C.: 6029
N.A.I.C.S.: 522110

Personnel:
Jean-Paul Le Calm *(Dir Gen)*

BANQUE LIBANO-FRANCAISE S.A.L.

Beirut Liberty Plz Bldg
PO Box 808
Rue De Rome Hamra, Beirut, 1808, Lebanon
Tel.: (961) 1791332
Telex: 21078 LIFREX
Fax: (961) 1340355
E-Mail: eblf@eblf.com
Web Site: www.eblf.com
Emp.: 700

Business Description:
International Banking
S.I.C.: 6159
N.A.I.C.S.: 522293

Personnel:
Farid Raphael *(Chm, Pres & Gen Mgr)*
Albert Letayf *(CEO)*

Board of Directors:
Farid Raphael
M. Robert Benoit
Zafer Chaoui
Jean-Frederic De Leusse
Sleiman El Zein
Ali Janoudi
Habib Letayf
Philippe Lette

Banque Libano-Francaise S.A.L.—(Continued)

Jamal Mansour
Elie Nahas
Moussa Raphael
Walid Raphael
Wafic Said
M. Emmanuel Vercoustre
M. Bernard Vernhes

Non-U.S. Subsidiary:

BANQUE SBA S.A. (1)
68 Champs Elysees Avenue
75008 Paris, France
Tel.: (33) 1 53 93 25 00
Fax: (33) 1 56 88 51 00
Web Site: www.banque-sba.com
Emp.: 66
Financial Management Services
S.I.C.: 6211
N.A.I.C.S.: 523999
Bernard Vernhes *(Chm & CEO)*
Walid Raphael *(Vice Chm & Deputy CEO)*
Marc Demeulenaere *(Deputy CEO)*
Nagi Letayf *(Deputy CEO)*
Caroline de la Vauzelle *(Sec)*

Non-U.S. Subsidiary:

LF FINANCE (SUISSE) S.A. (2)
86 Rhone Street
1211 Geneva, Switzerland
Tel.: (41) 22 319 72 00
Fax: (41) 22 319 72 27
E-Mail: contact@lffinance.com
Web Site: www.lffinance.com
Emp.: 8
Financial Management Services
S.I.C.: 6211
N.A.I.C.S.: 523999
Dory Hage, *(Mgr)*

BANQUE MAROCAINE DU COMMERCE EXTERIEUR SA

(d/b/a BMCE Bank Group)
140 Avenue Hassan II
20000 Casablanca, Morocco
Tel.: (212) 22200472
Fax: (212) 522200512
E-Mail: communicationfinanciere@bmcebank.co.ma
Web Site: www.bmcebank.ma
Year Founded: 1959
BCE—(CAS)
Rev.: $1,267,014,191
Assets: $27,030,232,126
Liabilities: $24,874,560,286
Net Worth: $2,155,671,840
Earnings: $184,907,499
Emp.: 5,000
Fiscal Year-end: 12/31/12

Business Description:
Retail, Commercial & Investment Banking, International Trade Financing, Financial Advisory & Asset Management Services
S.I.C.: 6029
N.A.I.C.S.: 522110

Personnel:
Othman Benjelloun *(Chm & CEO)*

Board of Directors:
Othman Benjelloun
Mamoun Belghiti
Brahim Benjelloun-Touimi
Mohamed Bennani
Mario Zouheir Bensaid
Amine Bouabid
Adil Douiri
Mario Azeddine Guessous
Michel Jean Francis Lucas
Mario Mosqueira do Amaral
David Suratgar

Ernst & Young
37 Bd Abdellatif Ben Kaddour
20060 Casablanca, Morocco

Subsidiaries:

BMCE Capital (1)
Tour BMCE Rond Point Hassan II
20 000 Casablanca, Morocco Ma
Tel.: (212) 522498978 (100%)
Fax: (212) 522481377
E-Mail: info@bmcecapital.com
Web Site: www.bmcecapital.com
Emp.: 700
Investment Banking, Securities Brokerage, Advisory & Asset Management Services
S.I.C.: 6211
N.A.I.C.S.: 523110
Khalid Nasr *(Chm-Mgmt Bd)*

Divisions:

BMCE Capital Bourse (2)
Tour BMCE Rond Point Hassan II
20 000 Casablanca, Morocco Ma
Tel.: (212) 522481001 (100%)
Fax: (212) 522481015
E-Mail: bkb@bmcek.co.ma
Web Site: www.bmcecapitalbourse.com
Emp.: 20
Brokerage Services
S.I.C.: 6211
N.A.I.C.S.: 523120
Anas Mikou *(CEO)*

BMCE Capital Gestion (2)
140 Tour BMCE Rond Point Hassan II
20 000 Casablanca, Morocco Ma
Tel.: (212) 522470847 (100%)
Fax: (212) 522471097
E-Mail: bkg@bmcek.co.ma
Emp.: 25
Asset Management Services
S.I.C.: 6282
N.A.I.C.S.: 523920
Amine Amor *(Gen Mgr)*

Unit:

BMCE Capital Conseil (2)
30 Boulevard Moulay Youssef
20 000 Casablanca, Morocco
Tel.: (212) 522429100
Fax: (212) 522430021
E-Mail: bkc@bmcek.co.ma
Web Site: www.bmcecapital.com
Emp.: 36
Investment Advisory Services
S.I.C.: 6282
N.A.I.C.S.: 523930
Mehdi Drafate *(Gen Mgr)*

Maroc Factoring (1)
243 Boulevard Mohamed V
20000 Casablanca, Morocco Ma
Tel.: (212) 522302008 (100%)
Fax: (212) 522306277
E-Mail: n.azzouzi@maroc_factoring.co.ma
Web Site: www.maroc-factoring.co.ma
Emp.: 14
Factoring Services
S.I.C.: 6159
N.A.I.C.S.: 522298
Hicham Daouk *(Gen Mgr)*

Non-U.S. Subsidiary:

MediCapital Bank Plc (1)
Juxon House 2nd Floor 100 St Pauls Churchyard
London, EC4M 8BU, United Kingdom
Tel.: (44) 207 429 5500
Fax: (44) 207 248 8595
E-Mail: Info@bmce-intl.co.uk
Web Site: www.medicapitalbank.com
Emp.: 30
Commercial Banking Services
S.I.C.: 6029
N.A.I.C.S.: 522110
David Suratgar *(Chm)*
Jaloul Ayed *(Vice Chm & CEO)*
Ramz Hamzaoui *(Mng Dir & Head-Corp Banking)*
Mohammed Bircharef *(CFO)*

Non-U.S. Unit:

BMCE International, S.A.U. (1)
Calle Serrano 59
28006 Madrid, Spain ES
Tel.: (34) 915756800
Fax: (34) 914316310
E-Mail: bmce_bank@bmce-intl.com
Web Site: www.bmce-intl.com
Retail & Commercial Banking
S.I.C.: 6029
N.A.I.C.S.: 522110

BANQUE MAURITANIENNE POUR LE COMMERCE INTERNATIONAL

(d/b/a BMCI)
Avenue Gamal abdel Nasser
BP 628
Nouakchott, Mauritania
Tel.: (222) 5252826
Fax: (222) 5252045
E-Mail: info@bmci.mr
Web Site: www.bmci.mr
Sales Range: $1-9.9 Million
Emp.: 260

Business Description:
Banking Services
S.I.C.: 6029
N.A.I.C.S.: 522110

BANQUE MISR

151 Mohamed Farid Street
Cairo, Egypt
Tel.: (20) 223912106
E-Mail: info@banquemisr.com.eg
Web Site: www.banquemisr.com.eg
Year Founded: 1920
Sales Range: $650-699.9 Million
Emp.: 13,000

Business Description:
Commercial Bank
S.I.C.: 6029
N.A.I.C.S.: 522110

Personnel:
Mohamed Kamal El-Din Barakat *(Chm)*
Mohamed Abbas Hassan Fayed *(Vice Chm)*

Board of Directors:
Mohamed Kamal El-Din Barakat
Ali Fahmy Al Saiedi
Mohamed El Hamamsy
Mohamed Abbas Hassan Fayed

BANQUE NATIONALE DE BELGIQUE S.A.

Boulevard de Berlaimont 14
1000 Brussels, Belgium
Tel.: (32) 22212111
Telex: 21355 bknle b; 21105 bnbsg b
Fax: (32) 22213100
E-Mail: info@nbb.be
Web Site: www.nbb.be
Year Founded: 1850
Int. Income: $2,638,786,665
Assets: $147,746,365,627
Liabilities: $141,942,134,247
Net Worth: $5,804,231,381
Earnings: $1,800,060,831
Emp.: 2,000
Fiscal Year-end: 12/31/12

Business Description:
Banking Services
S.I.C.: 6029
N.A.I.C.S.: 522110

Personnel:
Jean Hilgers *(Treas)*
Luc Dufresne *(Sec)*

Board of Directors:
Luc Coene
Norbert De Batselier
Marcia De Wachter
Mathias Dewatripont
Jean Hilgers
Francoise Masai
Jan Smets
Pierre Wunsch

BANQUE NATIONALE DU RWANDA

PO Box 531
Kigali, Rwanda
Tel.: (250) 574282
Fax: (250) 572551
E-Mail: webmaster@bnr.rw
Web Site: www.bnr.rw
Emp.: 500

Business Description:
Banking Services
S.I.C.: 6011
N.A.I.C.S.: 521110

Personnel:
Kanimba Francois *(Mgr)*

BANQUE PROFIL DE GESTION SA

Cours de Rive 11
PO Box 3668
1211 Geneva, Switzerland
Tel.: (41) 228183131
Fax: (41) 228183100
E-Mail: info@bpdg.ch
Web Site: www.bpdg.ch
BPDG—(SWX)
Rev.: $2,031,860
Assets: $210,990,043
Liabilities: $147,403,256
Net Worth: $63,586,788
Earnings: $140,636
Emp.: 24
Fiscal Year-end: 12/31/12

Business Description:
Banking Services
S.I.C.: 6029
N.A.I.C.S.: 522110

Personnel:
Eric Alves de Souza *(Chm)*
Fabio Candeli *(Vice Chm)*
Silvana Cavanna *(CEO)*

Board of Directors:
Eric Alves de Souza
Nicolo Angileri
Fabio Candeli
Ivan Mazuranic

BANQUE PUBLIQUE D'INVESTISSEMENT

27-31 Avenue du General Leclerc
94710 Maisons-Alfort, France
Tel.: (33) 1 41 79 80 00
Web Site: www.bpifrance.fr

Business Description:
Financial Services
S.I.C.: 6211
N.A.I.C.S.: 523999

Personnel:
Jean-Pierre Jouyet *(Pres)*

Joint Venture:

Nexeya SA (1)
Centrale Parc 2 avenue Sully prud hommes
92290 Chatenay-Malabry, France
Tel.: (33) 1 41 87 30 00
Fax: (33) 1 41 87 30 08
Web Site: www.nexeya.com
ALNEX—(EUR)
Emp.: 1,200
Industrial Engineering Services
S.I.C.: 8711
N.A.I.C.S.: 541330
Philippe Gautier *(Co-Chm & Mng Dir)*
Jean-Yves Riviere *(Co-Chm & Mgr-HR)*
Benoit de La Motte *(CFO)*

BANQUE SAUDI FRANSI

Maather Rd
PO Box 56006
Riyadh, 11554, Saudi Arabia
Tel.: (966) 12899999
Fax: (966) 14042311
Web Site: www.alfransi.com.sa
Year Founded: 1977
1050—(SAU)
Rev.: $1,083,649,264
Assets: $42,016,095,523
Liabilities: $35,974,595,889
Net Worth: $6,041,499,633
Earnings: $802,930,717
Emp.: 2,677
Fiscal Year-end: 12/31/12

Business Description:
International Banking Services
S.I.C.: 6159
N.A.I.C.S.: 522293

Personnel:
Saleh A. Al Omair *(Chm)*
Patrice Couvegnes *(Mng Dir)*
Jullien Peri Maze *(CFO)*
Philippe Enjalbal *(COO & Sr Exec Dir)*
Abdulaziz Omar Osman *(Chief Compliance Officer)*
Jean-Michel Castelnau *(Chief Risk Officer)*
Abdulrahman A. Jawa *(Deputy Mng Dir)*
Board of Directors:
Saleh A. Al Omair
Abdulaziz H. Al-Habdan
Ibrahim Al-Issa
Mousa Omran Al-Omran
Abdulrahman Rashed All-Rashed
Patrice Couvegnes
Abdulrahman A. Jawa
Khalid H. Mutabagani
Marc Oppenheim
Thierry Paul Michel Marie Simon

KPMG Al Fozan & Al Sadhan
PO Box 92876
Riyadh, Saudi Arabia

BANRO CORPORATION
1 First Canadian Place 100 King Street West
Suite 7070, Toronto, ON, M5X 1E3, Canada
Tel.: (416) 366-2221
Fax: (416) 366-7722
Toll Free: (800) 714-7938
E-Mail: info@banro.com
Web Site: www.banro.com
BAA—(NYSEMKT TSX)
Rev.: $42,631,000
Assets: $635,787,000
Liabilities: $212,502,000
Net Worth: $423,285,000
Earnings: ($4,561,000)
Emp.: 1,221
Fiscal Year-end: 12/31/12
Business Description:
Gold Mining, Exploration & Development Services
S.I.C.: 1041
N.A.I.C.S.: 212221
Personnel:
Arnold T. Kondrat *(Founder & Exec VP)*
Bernard R. van Rooyen *(Chm)*
John U. Clarke *(Pres & CEO)*
Donat K. Madilo *(CFO)*
Johan Botha *(Exec VP-Ops)*
Board of Directors:
Bernard R. van Rooyen
Richard W. Brissenden
Maurice John Colson
Peter Nigel Cowley
Peter V. Gundy
Arnold T. Kondrat
Richard J. Lachcik
Derrick H. Weyrauch
Transfer Agents:
Registrar & Transfer Company
Cranford, NJ 07016

Equity Financial Trust Company
Toronto, ON, Canada

BANSARD INTERNATIONAL
7-19 Rue des 15 Arpents
Zone Senia 501, 94577 Orly, Cedex, France
Tel.: (33) 141731060
Fax: (33) 146870929
E-Mail: info@bansard.com
Web Site: www.bansard.com
Sales Range: $100-124.9 Million
Emp.: 110
Business Description:
Freight Transportation Services
S.I.C.: 4731
N.A.I.C.S.: 488510
Personnel:
Simon Pinto *(Pres)*

BANSWARA SYNTEX LIMITED
Industrial Area Dohad Road
Banswara, Rajasthan, 327 001, India
Tel.: (91) 2962257676
Fax: (91) 2962240692
E-Mail: info@banswarafabrics.com
Web Site: www.banswarasyntex.com
BANSWRAS—(NSE)
Rev.: $209,583,817
Assets: $197,975,867
Liabilities: $162,999,453
Net Worth: $34,976,415
Earnings: $2,236,962
Fiscal Year-end: 03/31/13
Business Description:
Yarn & Fabric Mfr
S.I.C.: 2299
N.A.I.C.S.: 313110
Personnel:
R. L. Toshniwal *(Chm)*
Rakesh Mehra *(Vice Chm)*
S. S. Sajal *(Pres)*
Ravindra Kumar Toshniwal *(Co-Mng Dir)*
Shaleen Toshniwal *(Co-Mng Dir)*
J. K. Rathi *(Pres-Comml)*
J. K. Jain *(Sec & Sr VP-Fin & Comm)*
S. N. Gupta *(Sr VP-Tech)*
Kavita Soni *(Sr VP-HR & CSR)*
Board of Directors:
R. L. Toshniwal
S. B. Agarwal
Vijay Kumar Agarwal
P. K. Bhandari
D. P. Garg
A. N. Jariwala
Kamal Kishore Kacholia
Parduman Kumar
Rakesh Mehra
Vijay Mehta
C. P. Ravindranath Menon
Ravindra Kumar Toshniwal
Shaleen Toshniwal
Transfer Agent:
Computech Sharecap Limited
147 Mahatma Gandhi Road Opp Jehangir Art Gallery Fort
Mumbai, 400 023, India

Subsidiary:

Banswara Fabrics Limited (1)
Dohad Road Industrial Area
Banswara, 327 001, India
Tel.: (91) 29 6225 7676
Fax: (91) 29 6224 0692
E-Mail: info@banswarasyntex.com
Web Site: www.banswarasyntex.com
Emp.: 1,000
Fabric Yarn Mfr
S.I.C.: 2299
N.A.I.C.S.: 313110
Shyam Sunder Sajal *(Pres)*

BANTREL CO.
Bantrel Tower 700 6th Ave SW
Calgary, AB, T2P 0T8, Canada
Tel.: (403) 290-5000
Fax: (403) 290-5050
E-Mail: mailbox@bantrel.com
Web Site: www.bantrel.com
Year Founded: 1983
Emp.: 1,400
Business Description:
Design, Engineering, Procurement & Construction Management Services for the Energy Sector
S.I.C.: 8711
N.A.I.C.S.: 541330
Personnel:
Ken Baron *(CFO & VP)*
Roger Mapp *(Sr VP)*

Subsidiaries:

Bantrel Constructors Co. (1)
2010 700 6 Avenue SW
Calgary, AB, T2P 0T8, Canada
Tel.: (403) 515-8800
Emp.: 4,500
Industrial Building Construction Services
S.I.C.: 1541
N.A.I.C.S.: 236210
Mark Timler *(Pres)*

Bantrel Management Services Co. (1)
400 700 6 Avenue SW
Calgary, AB, T2P 0T8, Canada
Tel.: (403) 290-2750
Construction Engineering Services
S.I.C.: 8711
N.A.I.C.S.: 541330
Mike Gordon, *(Pres)*

Bemac Construction Corp. (1)
500 800 5 Avenue SW
Calgary, AB, T2P 3T2, Canada
Tel.: (587) 233-6000
Industrial Building Construction Services
S.I.C.: 1629
N.A.I.C.S.: 236210
Sig Ruud, *(Pres)*

BANYAN COAST CAPITAL CORP.
166 Cougarstone Crescent SW
Calgary, AB, T3H 4Z5, Canada
Tel.: (403) 450-8450
Fax: (403) 450-8450
E-Mail: drutt.calgary@gmail.com
Year Founded: 2010
BYN.P—(TSXV)
Int. Income: $2,483
Assets: $235,443
Liabilities: $51,115
Net Worth: $184,328
Earnings: ($77,624)
Fiscal Year-end: 09/30/12
Business Description:
Investment Services
S.I.C.: 6211
N.A.I.C.S.: 523999
Personnel:
Richmond Graham *(Pres & CEO)*
David M. Rutt *(CFO & Sec)*
Board of Directors:
Mark Ayranto
Richmond Graham
John Hilland
David M. Rutt
Transfer Agent:
Valiant Trust Company
606 4th Street SW Suite 310
Calgary, AB, T2P 1T1, Canada
Tel.: (403) 233-2801
Fax: (403) 233-2857

BANYAN TREE HOLDINGS LTD.
211 Upper Bukit Timah Road
Singapore, 588182, Singapore
Tel.: (65) 68495888
Fax: (65) 64622463
E-Mail: corporate@banyantree.com
Web Site: www.banyantree.com
B58—(OTC SES)
Rev.: $292,529,287
Assets: $1,126,708,585
Liabilities: $549,894,982
Net Worth: $576,813,603
Earnings: $12,431,827
Emp.: 4,617
Fiscal Year-end: 12/31/12
Business Description:
Holding Company; Hotels & Resorts
S.I.C.: 6719
N.A.I.C.S.: 551112
Personnel:
Kwon Ping Ho *(Chm)*
Surapon Supratya *(Deputy Chm-Laguna Resorts & Hotels)*
Ariel P. Vera *(Mng Dir)*
Eddy Hock Lye See *(CFO & Sr VP)*
Michael Lee *(CIO & VP)*
Abid Butt *(CEO-Banyan Tree Hotels & Resorts)*
Paul Chong *(Co-Sec & VP-Bus Dev & Legal)*
Jane Teah *(Co-Sec & Asst VP)*
Shankar Chandran *(Mng Dir-Spa Ops & Sr VP)*
Claire See Ngoh Chiang *(Mng Dir-Retail Ops & Sr VP)*
Dharmali Kusumadi *(Mng Dir-Design Svcs & Sr VP)*
Kwon Cjan Ho *(Sr VP)*
Board of Directors:
Kwon Ping Ho
Heng Wing Chan
Timothy Chee Ming Chia
Ai Lian Fang
Elizabeth Nee Wee Kim Choo Sam
Kui Seng Tham
Ariel P. Vera

Non-U.S. Subsidiary:

LAGUNA RESORTS & HOTELS PUBLIC COMPANY LIMITED (1)
Thai Wah Tower I 6th & 22nd floor South Sathorn Road
Tungmahamek Sathorn, Bangkok, 10120, Thailand
Tel.: (66) 2677 4455
Fax: (66) 2285 0733
E-Mail: ir@lagunaresorts.com
Web Site: www.lagunaresorts.com
LRH—(THA)
Rev.: $142,435,128
Assets: $642,885,133
Liabilities: $156,719,065
Net Worth: $486,166,068
Earnings: $1,940,024
Emp.: 110
Fiscal Year-end: 12/31/12
Hotel Management Services
S.I.C.: 7011
N.A.I.C.S.: 721110
Ho KwonPing *(Chm & CEO)*
Surapon Supratya *(Deputy Chm)*
Mahmud Ziya Birkan *(Deputy Mng Dir)*
Stuart David Reading *(Deputy Mng Dir)*
Nanchalee Kecharananta *(Sec)*
Kuan Chiet *(Sr Asst VP-Grp Asst Mgmt, Dev & Special Projects)*
Niphon Kitisook *(Sr Asst VP-Resort & Property Dev)*
Cindy Ho Soo Hooi *(Sr Asst VP-Internal Audit)*
Niyom Tassaneetipagorn *(Sr Asst VP-Corp Affairs & Community Rels)*

BAO MINH INSURANCE CORPORATION
26 Ton That Dam Ward Nguyen Thai Binh District 1
Ho Chi Minh City, Vietnam
Tel.: (84) 8 3829 4180
Fax: (84) 8 3829 4185
E-Mail: baominh@baominh.com.vn
Web Site: www.baominh.com.vn
Year Founded: 1995
BMI—(HOSE)
Sales Range: $75-99.9 Million
Business Description:
Insurance Services
S.I.C.: 6411
N.A.I.C.S.: 524298
Personnel:
Vinh Duc Tran *(Chm)*
Viet Thanh Le *(Chm-Supervisory Bd)*
Costa Jean - Luc Francois *(Vice Chm)*
Van Thanh Le *(CEO)*
Sinh Tien Nguyen *(Vice CEO)*
The Nang Nguyen *(Vice CEO)*
Xuan Phong Pham *(Vice CEO)*
Board of Directors:
Vinh Duc Tran
Costa Jean - Luc Francois
Song Lai Le

Bao Minh Insurance Corporation—(Continued)
Van Thanh Le
Huu Tho Mai
The Nang Nguyen
Prasanna Rajashekhar Patil
Supervisory Board of Directors:
Viet Thanh Le
Minh Dung Nguyen
Nhu Khoa Nguyen
Claude Pierre Seigne
Duc Hiep Tran

BAO VIET HOLDINGS

8 Le Thai To Str Hoan Kiem Dist
Hanoi, Vietnam
Tel.: (84) 4 3928 9898
Fax: (84) 4 3928 9609
E-Mail: service@baoviet.com.vn
Web Site: www.baoviet.com.vn
Year Founded: 1964
BVH—(HOSE)
Premiums: $542,504,398
Assets: $2,403,299,232
Liabilities: $1,685,058,231
Net Worth: $718,241,001
Earnings: $58,534,252
Emp.: 5,500
Fiscal Year-end: 12/31/12
Business Description:
Financial Services
S.I.C.: 6211
N.A.I.C.S.: 523999
Personnel:
Quang Binh Le *(Chm)*
Kim Bang Phan *(Chm-Supervisory Bd)*
Ngoc Anh Nguyen *(Vice Chm)*
Hai Phong Le *(CFO & Chief Real Estate Officer)*
Viet Ha Hoang *(COO)*
Duc Chuyen Duong *(Chief Investment Officer)*
Tien Nguyen Phan *(Chief HR Officer)*
Alan Royal *(Chief IT Officer)*
Board of Directors:
Quang Binh Le
Duc Chuyen Duong
Charles Bernard Gregory
Hai Phong Le
Duc Tuan Nguyen
Ngoc Anh Nguyen
Quoc Huy Nguyen
Trong Phuc Tran
Supervisory Board of Directors:
Kim Bang Phan
Thai Quy Dang
Danny Ho Yin Lui
Ngoc Thuy Nguyen
Tien Hung Ong
Subsidiaries:

Bao Viet Commercial Joint Stock Bank **(1)**
8 Le Thai To Hoan Kiem District
Hoan Kiem District, Hanoi, Vietnam
Tel.: (84) 4 3928 9898
Fax: (84) 4 3928 9609
Web Site: www.baoviet.co.vn
Banking Services
S.I.C.: 6029
N.A.I.C.S.: 522110

Bao Viet Fund Management Company **(1)**
8 Le Thai To
Hoan Kiem District, Hanoi, Vietnam
Tel.: (84) 4 3928 9898
Fax: (84) 4 3928 9609
Investment Services
S.I.C.: 6211
N.A.I.C.S.: 523999

Bao Viet Securities Joint Stock Company **(1)**
8 Le Thai To
Hoan Kiem District, Hanoi, Vietnam
Tel.: (84) 4 3928 9898
Fax: (84) 4 3928 9609
Brokerage Services
S.I.C.: 6211
N.A.I.C.S.: 523120

Joint Venture:

Baoviet Tokio Marine Insurance Joint Venture Company **(1)**
Room 601 6th Floor Sun Red River Building
23 Phan Chu Trinh
Hoan Kiem District, Hanoi, Vietnam
Tel.: (84) 439330704
Fax: (84) 439330706
E-Mail: info@baoviettokiomarine.com
Web Site: www.baoviettokiomarine.com
Sales Range: $1-9.9 Million
Emp.: 50
Non-Life Insurance Products & Services
S.I.C.: 6399
N.A.I.C.S.: 524128
Hidaki Mishima *(Gen Mgr)*

BAO YUAN HOLDINGS LTD.

(Name Changed to China Household Holdings Limited)

BAOBAB RESOURCES PLC

27/28 Eastcastle Street
London, W1W 8DHN, United Kingdom
Tel.: (44) 7813 498 098
E-Mail: info@baobabresources.com
Web Site: www.baobabresources.com
BAO—(AIM)
Rev.: $243,967
Assets: $3,678,350
Liabilities: $739,394
Net Worth: $2,938,956
Earnings: ($12,594,847)
Emp.: 63
Fiscal Year-end: 06/30/13
Business Description:
Iron Mining Services
S.I.C.: 1011
N.A.I.C.S.: 212210
Personnel:
Jeremy Dowler *(Chm)*
Ben James *(Mng Dir)*
Francis John Eagar *(CFO & Mgr-New Bus)*
Graham Douglas Anderson *(Sec)*
Board of Directors:
Jeremy Dowler
Carlo Baravalle
Jonathan Beardsworth
Ben James
Mohan Kaul
David Twist
Legal Counsel:
Watson, Farley & Williams LLP
15 Appold Street
London, United Kingdom

Steinepreis Paganin
Level 4 Next Building 16 Milligan St
Perth, Australia

H. Gamito, Couto, Goncalves Perreira, Castelo Branco & Associados
Avenida Kim Il Sung n 961
Maputo, Mozambique

Non-U.S. Subsidiary:

Baobab Mining Services Pty Ltd. **(1)**
Ste 25 S Ter Piazza 26-30
Fremantle, WA, 6160, Australia
Tel.: (61) 894307151
Fax: (61) 894307664
E-Mail: info@baobabresources.com
Web Site: www.baobabresources.com
Mining Services
S.I.C.: 1499
N.A.I.C.S.: 212399

BAOBAG

2 Boulevard De Vintimille
13015 Marseilles, Bouches Du Rhone, France
Tel.: (33) 491627719
Fax: (33) 557778490
E-Mail: contact@baobag.eu
Web Site:
Sales Range: $10-24.9 Million
Emp.: 45
Fiscal Year-end: 12/31/12
S.I.C.: 5099
N.A.I.C.S.: 423990
Personnel:
Alain Cavalier *(Pres)*

BAODING HEAVY INDUSTRY CO., LTD.

Industrial Park
Tangqi Town, Hangzhou, 311106, China
Tel.: (86) 571 86380888
Fax: (86) 571 86380688
E-Mail: info@bd-zg.com
Web Site: www.bd-zg.com
002552—(SSE)
Emp.: 480
Business Description:
Iron & Steel Products Mfr & Engineering Services
S.I.C.: 3462
N.A.I.C.S.: 332111
Personnel:
Baosong Zhu *(Chm)*

BAOFENG MODERN INTERNATIONAL HOLDINGS COMPANY LIMITED

Huoju Industrial Zone Jiangnan Town
Licheng District
Quanzhou, Fujian, China 362300
Tel.: (86) 59522467169
Fax: (86) 59522486889
Web Site: www.chinabaofeng.com
1121—(HKG)
Rev.: $214,692,764
Assets: $226,853,844
Liabilities: $59,012,457
Net Worth: $167,841,387
Earnings: $24,452,098
Emp.: 2,704
Fiscal Year-end: 12/31/12
Business Description:
Slippers & Other Footwear Mfr
S.I.C.: 2389
N.A.I.C.S.: 316210
Personnel:
Jingdong Zheng *(Chm & CEO)*
Aiguo Zhang *(Vice Chm)*
Wai Ming Wong *(CFO)*
Wai Keung Au *(Sec)*
Board of Directors:
Jingdong Zheng
Na An
Changhong Bai
Miu Cheung
Keung Lee
Ching Bor Sze
Aiguo Zhang

Royal Bank of Canada Trust Company (Cayman) Limited
4th Floor Royal Bank House 24 Shedden Road
Georgetown, Cayman Islands
Transfer Agent:
Royal Bank of Canada Trust Company (Cayman) Limited
4th Floor Royal Bank House 24 Shedden Road
Georgetown, Cayman Islands

BAOLINGBAO BIOLOGY CO., LTD.

1 Dongwaihuan Road Hi-tech Development Zone
Yucheng, Shandong, 251200, China
Tel.: (86) 5342126096
Fax: (86) 5342126097
E-Mail: jiawc@blb-cn.com
Web Site: en.blb-cn.com
002286—(SSE)
Emp.: 560
Business Description:
Oligosaccharide, High Fructose Syrup & Tetrahydroxy Butane Mfr & Sales
S.I.C.: 2836
N.A.I.C.S.: 325414
Personnel:
Zongli Liu *(Chm)*

BAOSHENG SCIENCE & TECHNOLOGY INNOVATION CO., LTD

No 1 Middle Baosheng Road
225800 Yangzhou, Jiangsu, China
Tel.: (86) 51488238888
Fax: (86) 51488248888
E-Mail: baosheng@baoshenggroup.com
Web Site: www.baoshengcable.com
Year Founded: 2000
600973—(SHG)
Sales Range: $800-899.9 Million
Emp.: 2,000
Business Description:
Electric Cables & Wires Mfr
S.I.C.: 3357
N.A.I.C.S.: 335929
Personnel:
Zhenhua Sun *(Chm)*
Chongjian Tang *(Pres)*

BAOSHIDA HOLDING GROUP CO., LTD.

Baoshida Hi-Tech Industrial Park 8 Kaiyuan Road
Gong Ye Bei Road, Jinan, Shandong, 250101, China
Tel.: (86) 531 8888 6788
Fax: (86) 531 8888 6999
E-Mail: baoshida@vip.163.com
Web Site: www.baoshida.cn
Business Description:
Holding Company; Investment, Real Estate, Trade & Industrial Services
S.I.C.: 6719
N.A.I.C.S.: 551112
Personnel:
Xingjun Shang *(Pres)*
Subsidiary:

Shandong Baoshida Cable Co., Ltd. **(1)**
Baoshida Scientific Industrial Park
Gongye North Road Licheng District, Jinan, Shandong, China
Tel.: (86) 531 8868 1868
Fax: (86) 531 8868 6368
E-Mail: sales@baoshidacable.com
Web Site: en.baoshidacable.com
Cable Mfr
S.I.C.: 3315
N.A.I.C.S.: 331222

Non-U.S. Subsidiary:

Baoshida Swissmetal Ltd. **(1)**
(Formerly Swissmetal Holding AG)
Weidenstrasse 50
4143 Dornach, 1, Switzerland CH
Tel.: (41) 61 705 3212
Fax: (41) 61 705 3451
E-Mail: contact@swissmetal.com
Web Site: www.baoshida-swissmetal.net
Emp.: 10
Holding Company; Copper Wire, Rods, Extruded Strips & Copper Alloy Products Mfr
S.I.C.: 6719
N.A.I.C.S.: 551112
Martin Hellweg *(Chm)*

U.S. Subsidiary:

Avins USA, Inc. **(2)**
242 Old New Brunswick Road
Piscataway, NJ 08854
Tel.: (732) 469-8800
Fax: (732) 469-8801

E-Mail: info@avins.com
Web Site: www.avins.com
Emp.: 9
Precious Metal Products Mfr
S.I.C.: 3339
N.A.I.C.S.: 331410
Joe Rudden, Jr. *(Pres)*

Non-U.S. Subsidiaries:

Swissmetal East Asia Ltd. (2)
One Peking Unit 1202 Level 12
1 Peking Road Tsim Sha Tsue, Kowloon, China (Hong Kong)
Tel.: (852) 3980 9286
Fax: (852) 3980 9334
E-Mail: saleshongkong@swissmetal.com
Metal Products Mfr
S.I.C.: 3499
N.A.I.C.S.: 332999

BAOSHINN CORPORATION

A-B 8/F Hart Avenue Tsimshatsui
Kowloon, China (Hong Kong)
Tel.: (852) 28151355
Fax: (852) 27224008
E-Mail: info@baoshinn.com.hk
Web Site: www.baoshinncorporation.com
BHNN—(OTC)
Sls.: $39,090,912
Assets: $4,950,369
Liabilities: $4,148,903
Net Worth: $801,466
Earnings: ($143,521)
Emp.: 30
Fiscal Year-end: 12/31/12

Business Description:
Extended Wholesale & Corporate Travel Services
S.I.C.: 4729
N.A.I.C.S.: 561599

Personnel:
Sean L. Webster *(Pres)*
Benny Kan *(CEO)*
Bernard Leung *(COO)*
Ritesh Jha *(CTO)*

Board of Directors:
Akimasa Fujita
Benny Kan
Chiu Wan Kee
Ka Yeung Lee
Sean L. Webster

Transfer Agent:
Madison Stock Transfer Inc.
PO Box 145
Brooklyn, NY 11229-0145

Subsidiary:

BaoShinn International Express Limited (BSIE) (1)
Flat A-B 8F No 8 Hart Avenue
Kowloon, China (Hong Kong) HK
Tel.: (852) 28151355
Fax: (852) 27224008
E-Mail: info@baoshinn.com.hk
Web Site: www.baoshinn.com.hk
Bulk Ticketing & Travel Related Services
S.I.C.: 4729
N.A.I.C.S.: 561599
Aries Cheng *(Mgr-Sls & Mktg)*

Non-U.S. Affiliates:

Chung Tai Travel and Tour Co., Ltd. (1)
13F No 131 Song Jiang Road
Taipei, 104, Taiwan
Tel.: (886) 22509 1588
Fax: (886) 22509 6988
Web Site: www.baoshinn.com.hk
Travel & Tour Services
S.I.C.: 4729
N.A.I.C.S.: 561599

Grand Power Express Tourism Co., Ltd. (1)
11 Andar B-C Macau Finance Centre
No 244-246 Rua de Pequim, Macau, China (Macau)
Tel.: (853) 701777
Fax: (853) 701565
Web Site: www.grandpowerexpress.com
Travel Services
S.I.C.: 4724
N.A.I.C.S.: 561510

Affiliates:

Bao Shinn Express Co., Ltd. (1)
Flat E-F 8F No 8 Hart Avenue
Kowloon, Tsim Sha Tsui, China (Hong Kong)
Tel.: (852) 23668818
Fax: (852) 23678678
E-Mail: roh@roh.com.hk
Web Site: www.roh.com.hk
Emp.: 50
Sales Agents for Thai Airways
S.I.C.: 4724
N.A.I.C.S.: 561510
Isaac Yau *(Gen Mgr)*

Bao Shinn Holidays Limited (1)
Room 208 Takshing House
20 Des Voeux Road, Hong Kong, China (Hong Kong)
Tel.: (852) 21118868
Fax: (852) 21118863
E-Mail: info@bsholidays.com
Web Site: www.baoshinn.com.hk/about_network_eng.html
Emp.: 20
Travel Services
S.I.C.: 4724
N.A.I.C.S.: 561510
Bonnie Chan *(Mgr-Ops)*

HK Airlines Holiday Travel Company Limited (1)
Flat C 8/F No.8 Hart Avenue
20 Des Voeux Road Central, Hong Kong, Tsim Sha Tsui, China (Hong Kong)
Tel.: (852) 23698888
Fax: (852) 35685698
E-Mail: book@hkairlinesholidays.com
Web Site: www.hkairlinesholidays.com
Emp.: 10
Hong Kong Airlines Services
S.I.C.: 4724
N.A.I.C.S.: 561510
Eric Yeung *(Gen Mgr)*

Patterson Travel Service (1)
Flat F 8/F 8 Hart Ave
Tsim Sha Tsui, Hong Kong, China (Hong Kong)
Tel.: (852) 31022382
Fax: (852) 31022380
E-Mail: kevin.law@pattersontravel.com.hk
Web Site: www.pattersontravel.com.hk
Sales Agents for MAS Golden Holidays & Malaysia Airlines
S.I.C.: 4724
N.A.I.C.S.: 561510
Kevin Law *(Mgr-Ops)*

Patterson Travel Services (1)
No 8 Hart Ave, Tsim Sha Tsui
Kowloon, Kowloon, China (Hong Kong)
Tel.: (852) 31022371
Fax: (852) 28684213
E-Mail: kevin.law@pattersontravel.com.hk
Web Site: www.pattersontravel.com.hk
Emp.: 20
Travel Services
S.I.C.: 4724
N.A.I.C.S.: 561510
Kevin Law *(Mgr-Ops)*

BAOSTEEL GROUP CORPORATION

Baosteel Tower Pu Dian Road 370
Pudong New District, Shanghai, China
Tel.: (86) 2158350000
Fax: (86) 2168404832
E-Mail: webman@baosteel.com
Web Site: www.baosteel.com
Year Founded: 1978
Sales Range: $25-49.9 Billion
Emp.: 127,000

Business Description:
Iron & Steel Production, Metallurgical Equipment Mfr, Finished Steel Processing, Non-Hazardous Chemical Mfr, Transportation Information, Building & Finance
S.I.C.: 3399
N.A.I.C.S.: 331110

Personnel:
Lejiang Xu *(Chm)*
Guosheng Liu *(Vice Chm & Sec)*
Wenbo He *(Pres)*

Board of Directors:
Lejiang Xu
Victor Kwok King Fung
Yong Gan
Wenbo He
Tianliang Jing
Stephen Ching Yen Lee
Guosheng Liu
Jinde Wang
Yaowen Wu
Dawei Xia
Xianzu Yang

Subsidiaries:

Baoshan Iron & Steel Co., Ltd. (1)
Guoyuan Fujin Road
Baoshan District, Shanghai, 201900, China
Tel.: (86) 2126647000
Fax: (86) 2126646999
Web Site: www.baosteel.com
600019—(SHG)
Sales Range: $25-49.9 Billion
Emp.: 43,800
Iron & Steel Mfr
S.I.C.: 3399
N.A.I.C.S.: 331110
Wenbo He *(Chm)*

Shanghai Baosight Software Co., Ltd. (1)
515 Guoshoujing Road Zhangjiang Hi-Tech Park
Shanghai, Pudong, 201203, China
Tel.: (86) 21 50801155
Fax: (86) 21 50800701
E-Mail: investor@baosight.com
Web Site: www.baosight.com
Software Development
S.I.C.: 7372
N.A.I.C.S.: 511210

Shanghai Baosteel Chemical Co., Ltd. (1)
1800 Tongji Road
Baoshan District, Shanghai, 201900, China (100%)
Tel.: (86) 2126648409
Fax: (86) 66789201
Web Site: www.baosteel.com
Emp.: 1,500
Chemicals Mfr
S.I.C.: 2899
N.A.I.C.S.: 325998
Qian Kian Xint *(Pres)*

U.S. Subsidiary:

Baosteel America Inc. (1)
Continental Plz Ste 1 401 Hackensack Ave
Hackensack, NJ 07601-6404 (100%)
Tel.: (201) 457-1144
Fax: (201) 457-0909
E-Mail: info@baosteelusa.com
Web Site: www.baosteelusa.com
Emp.: 16
Steel Importer Exporter & Whslr
S.I.C.: 3399
N.A.I.C.S.: 331110
Jing Wang *(Pres)*

Non-U.S. Subsidiaries:

Bao Island Enterprises Limited (1)
Add: 29/F Harbour Centre
25 Harbour Road, Hong Kong, China (Hong Kong)
Tel.: (852) 28333223
Fax: (852) 28270001
Steel Importer Exporter & Whslr
S.I.C.: 3312
N.A.I.C.S.: 331110

Bao-Trans Enterprises Ltd. (1)
50F Flat L Office Tower Convention Plaza 1 Harbour Road
Hong Kong, China (Hong Kong)
Tel.: (852) 25285766
Fax: (852) 25295117
E-Mail: shipping@baotrans.com.hk
Web Site: www.baotrans.com.hk
Steel Importer Exporter & Whslr
S.I.C.: 3291
N.A.I.C.S.: 327910

Baosteel Do Brasil Ltda (1)
Rua Lauro Muller116
Sala 3103, 22299-900 Rio de Janeiro, Brazil
Tel.: (55) 2125311363
Fax: (55) 2125310298
E-Mail: joyce@baosteel.usa.com
Web Site: www.baosteel.com
Emp.: 4
Steel Importer Exporter & Whslr
S.I.C.: 3312
N.A.I.C.S.: 331110
Yonghong Zhao *(Gen Mgr)*

Baosteel Europe GmbH (1)
Nonnenstieg 1
20149 Hamburg, Germany
Tel.: (49) 40419940
Fax: (49) 4041994120
E-Mail: info@baosteel.eu
Web Site: www.baosteel.eu
Emp.: 30
Steel Importer Exporter & Whslr
S.I.C.: 3399
N.A.I.C.S.: 331110
Chang Zheng Zou *(Gen Mgr)*

Baosteel Italia Distribution Center S.p.A. (1)
Via XII Ottobre 214
Genoa, 16121, Italy
Tel.: (39) 0105308872
Fax: (39) 0105308895
Web Site: www.baosteel.com
Steel Distr
S.I.C.: 3399
N.A.I.C.S.: 331110

Baosteel Singapore Pte. Ltd. (1)
7 Temasek Blvd
Suntec Tower 1 40 02/03, Singapore, 038987, Singapore
Tel.: (65) 63336818
Fax: (65) 63336819
Web Site: www.baosteel.sg
Emp.: 20
Steel Importer Exporter & Whslr
S.I.C.: 3312
N.A.I.C.S.: 331110
Xie Weidong *(Gen Mgr)*

Baosteel Trading Europe GmbH (1)
Nonnensteig 1 20149
Hamburg, Germany
Tel.: (49) 40 41994101
Fax: (49) 40 41994120
Steel Importer Exporter & Whslr
S.I.C.: 3399
N.A.I.C.S.: 331110

Baovale Mineracao S.A. (1)
Rua Lauro Muller116 Sala 3103
22299-900 Rio de Janeiro, Brazil
Tel.: (55) 21 25311363
Fax: (55) 21 25310298
Steel Importer Exporter & Whslr
S.I.C.: 3312
N.A.I.C.S.: 331110

BAOTOU BEIFANG CHUANGYE CO., LTD.

PO Box No 2
Baotou, Inner Mongolia, China 014032
Tel.: (86) 472 3116810
Fax: (86) 472 3118057
Web Site: www.bfcy.cc
600967—(SHG)

Business Description:
Railway Freight Vehicle Mfr
S.I.C.: 3743
N.A.I.C.S.: 336510

Personnel:
Fu Sen Gao *(Project Mgr)*

BAOTOU DONGBAO BIO-TECH CO., LTD.

46 Yellow River Street Baotou Rare Earth High-tech Development Zone
Baotou, 014030, China
Tel.: (86) 4725319855

Baotou Dongbao Bio-tech Co., Ltd.—(Continued)

Fax: (86) 4725319866
Web Site: www.dongbaoshengwu.com
Year Founded: 1997
300239—(CHIN)
Sales Range: $25-49.9 Million
Emp.: 300

Business Description:
Gelatin & Collagen Products Mfr
S.I.C.: 2899
N.A.I.C.S.: 325998

Personnel:
Jun Wang *(Chm)*

BAOTOU IRON & STEEL (GROUP) COMPANY LIMITED

Hexi Industrial Zone
Kun District, Baotou, Inner Mongolia, 014010, China
Tel.: (86) 4722183163
Fax: (86) 4725155484
E-Mail: shigh@public.hh.nm.cn
Web Site: www.btsteel.com
Year Founded: 1954
Sales Range: $5-14.9 Billion
Emp.: 80,000

Business Description:
Iron & Steel Mfr
S.I.C.: 3462
N.A.I.C.S.: 332111

Personnel:
Bingli Zhou *(Chm)*

Subsidiaries:

Inner Mongolia Baotou Steel Rare-Earth Group Hi-Tech Company Limited **(1)**
No 83 Yellow River Road Rare Earth Hi-tech Ind Zone
Baotou, 014030, China
Tel.: (86) 472 2207 799
Fax: (86) 472 2207 788
Web Site: www.reht.com
600111—(SHG)
Rare Earth Mineral Mining
S.I.C.: 1099
N.A.I.C.S.: 212299
Zhong Zhang *(Gen Mgr)*

Inner Mongolia Baotou Steel Union Company Limited **(1)**
Xinxi Building East Bldg Kun Dist Hexi Factory Dist
Baotou, China
Tel.: (86) 472 2189528
Fax: (86) 472 2189530
600010—(SHG)
Iron & Steel Mfr
S.I.C.: 3462
N.A.I.C.S.: 332111
Bingli Zhou *(Chm)*

BAOYE GROUP COMPANY LIMITED

No 501 Shanyin West Road
Keqiao, Shaoxing, Zhejiang, China 312030
Tel.: (86) 575 84135897
Fax: (86) 575 84882587
E-Mail: iirbaoye@baoyegroup.com
Web Site: www.baoyegroup.com
Year Founded: 1974
2355—(HKG)
Rev.: $2,744,276,556
Assets: $2,181,497,852
Liabilities: $1,372,980,422
Net Worth: $808,517,430
Earnings: $120,182,574
Emp.: 3,532
Fiscal Year-end: 12/31/12

Business Description:
Construction Services
S.I.C.: 1542
N.A.I.C.S.: 236220

Personnel:
Baogen Pang *(Founder, Chm & CEO)*
Esther Lin Chun Ngan *(Sec)*

Board of Directors:
Baogen Pang
Dennis Yin Ming Chan
Simon Ching Fung
Jiming Gao
Jun Gao
Lin Gao
Jixiang Jin
Youqing Wang
Rulong Zhao

PricewaterhouseCoopers
22/F Prince's Building
Central, China (Hong Kong)

Legal Counsel:
King & Wood Mallesons
9/F Hutchison House 10 Harcourt Road
Central, China (Hong Kong)

Fenxun Partners
Suite 1008 China World Tower 2 China World Trade Centre
No 1 Jianguomenwai Avenue, Beijing, China 100004

BAQUS GROUP PLC

2/3 North Mews
London, WC1N 2JP, United Kingdom
Tel.: (44) 2078311283
Fax: (44) 2072429512
E-Mail: enquiries@baqus.co.uk
Web Site: www.baqus.co.uk
Rev.: $9,952,686
Assets: $17,575,918
Liabilities: $1,250,798
Net Worth: $16,325,121
Earnings: $164,246
Emp.: 86
Fiscal Year-end: 03/31/13

Business Description:
Professional & Management Services
S.I.C.: 4731
N.A.I.C.S.: 541614

Personnel:
Clive Sayer *(CEO)*
Patrick Lineen *(Sec & Dir-Fin)*

Board of Directors:
Patrick Lineen
Robert McNeill
Clive Sayer
Graham Williams

Legal Counsel:
Neil Myerson LLP
The Cottages Regent Road
Altrincham, Cheshire, United Kingdom

Subsidiaries:

Fletcher McNeill & Partners Limited **(1)**
Quantum House 23 Roscoe St
Liverpool, Merseyside, L1 2SX, United Kingdom
Tel.: (44) 1517085896
Fax: (44) 1517096763
Web Site: www.baqus.co.uk
Emp.: 11
Quantity Surveying Services
S.I.C.: 7389
N.A.I.C.S.: 541990
Robert McNeill *(Exec Dir)*

Sworn King & Partners **(1)**
31 W Way Botley
Oxford, Oxfordshire, OX2 OJE, United Kingdom
Tel.: (44) 1865241159
Fax: (44) 1865790595
E-Mail: qs@skp.co.uk
Web Site: www.skp.co.uk
Emp.: 10
Chartered Quantity Surveying & Construction Cost Consultant Services
S.I.C.: 7389
N.A.I.C.S.: 541990

BAR 2 LIMITED

Unit 4 Century Ct
Moor Pk Industrial Centre, London, WD18 9RS, United Kingdom
Tel.: (44) 8458381641
Fax: (44) 8458381642
E-Mail: agency@bar2.co.uk
Web Site: www.bar2.co.uk
Sales Range: $1-9.9 Million
Emp.: 13
Fiscal Year-end: 12/31/12

Business Description:
Temporary Help Services
S.I.C.: 7363
N.A.I.C.S.: 561320

Personnel:
Jison Hiogreiven *(Gen Mgr)*

BARAK VALLEY CEMENTS LIMITED

202 Royal View BK Kakoti Road
Ulubari
Guwahati, Assam, 781007, India
Tel.: (91) 3612464670
Fax: (91) 3612464672
E-Mail: guwahati@barakcement.com
Web Site: www.barakcement.com
BVCL—(NSE)
Rev.: $24,971,962
Assets: $41,789,362
Liabilities: $24,514,338
Net Worth: $17,275,024
Earnings: ($830,565)
Emp.: 245
Fiscal Year-end: 03/31/13

Business Description:
Cement Mfr
S.I.C.: 3241
N.A.I.C.S.: 327310

Personnel:
Bijay Kumar Garodia *(Chm)*
Kamakhya Chamaria *(Vice Chm, CEO & Mng Dir)*
Sushil Kumar Kothari *(CFO)*
Bhavna Jangid *(Compliance Officer & Sec)*

Board of Directors:
Bijay Kumar Garodia
Dhanpat Ram Agarwal
Mahendra Kumar Agarwal
Ramesh Chandra Bajaj
Santosh Kumar Bajaj
Brahm Prakash Bakshi
Kamakhya Chamaria
Prahlad Rai Chamaria
Renu Kejriwal
Vishal More

Transfer Agent:
MCS Limited
F-65 1st Floor Okhla Industrial Area Phase-I
New Delhi, India

Subsidiary:

Valley Strong Cements (Assam) Limited **(1)**
281 Deepali Pitampura
New Delhi, 110034, India
Tel.: (91) 11 2703 3407
Fax: (91) 11 2703 3830
E-Mail: delhi@barakcement.com
Web Site: www.barakcement.com
Emp.: 6
Cement Mfr
S.I.C.: 3241
N.A.I.C.S.: 327310

BARAKA ENERGY & RESOURCES LIMITED

Shop 12 South Shore Piazza 85 The Esplanade
South Perth, WA, 6151, Australia
Mailing Address:
PO Box 255
South Perth, WA, 6951, Australia
Tel.: (61) 8 6436 2350
Fax: (61) 8 9367 2450
E-Mail: info@barakaenergy.com.au
Web Site: www.barakaenergy.com.au
BKP—(ASX DEU)
Rev.: $207,468
Assets: $5,195,832
Liabilities: $88,715
Net Worth: $5,107,117
Earnings: ($386,928)
Fiscal Year-end: 06/30/13

Business Description:
Energy & Resource Exploration Services
S.I.C.: 1311
N.A.I.C.S.: 211111

Personnel:
Collin Vost *(Chm & Mng Dir)*
Patrick J. O'Neill *(Sec)*

Board of Directors:
Collin Vost
Ray Chang
Justin Vost

Legal Counsel:
Steinepreis Paganin
GPO Box 2799
Perth, Australia

BARAKAH OFFSHORE PETROLEUM BERHAD

No 28 Jln PJU 5/4 Dataran Sunway
Petaling Jaya, Kota Damansara, Malaysia
Tel.: (60) 3 6141 8820
Fax: (60) 3 6141 8826
E-Mail: info@barakah.my
Web Site: www.barakahpetroleum.com

Business Description:
Offshore Petroleum Transport
S.I.C.: 4613
N.A.I.C.S.: 486910

Personnel:
Syed Abdul Rahim bin Syed Jaafar *(Pres & CEO)*
Firdauz Edmin bin Moktar *(CFO & VP)*

Subsidiary:

Vastalux Energy Berhad **(1)**
Unit 621 6th Floor Block A Kelana Centre Point
No 3 Jalan SS7/19 Kelana Jaya, 47301
Petaling Jaya, Selangor Darul Ehsan, Malaysia
Tel.: (60) 3 7880 9699
Fax: (60) 3 7880 8699
Web Site: www.vastalux.com.my
VASTALX—(KLS)
Rev.: $203,047
Assets: $1,242,233
Liabilities: $1,970,477
Net Worth: ($728,244)
Earnings: ($1,407)
Fiscal Year-end: 12/31/12
Offshore Manpower, Equipment, Materials & Fabrication Work
S.I.C.: 1389
N.A.I.C.S.: 213112
Mohamad Hasif Mohd Nahar *(Mng Dir)*
Mei Ling Chew *(Co-Sec)*
Cynthia Gloria Louis *(Co-Sec)*

BARAKATULLAH ELECTRO DYNAMICS LIMITED

Khairun Bhaban 6th Floor Mirboxtola
Sylhet, 3100, Bangladesh
Tel.: (880) 821 711815
Fax: (880) 821 2830282
E-Mail: info@bedlbd.com
Web Site: www.bedlbd.com
Year Founded: 2007
BEDL—(DHA)
Rev.: $8,361,338
Assets: $67,780,285
Liabilities: $28,009,915
Net Worth: $39,770,371
Earnings: $2,281,157
Fiscal Year-end: 06/30/13

Business Description:
Electric Power Generation Services
S.I.C.: 4911

N.A.I.C.S.: 221118
Personnel:
Faisal Ahmed Chowdhury *(Chm & Head-Plng & Bus Dev)*
Md. Ahsanul Kabir *(Vice Chm & Head-Admin)*
Abdul Bari *(Vice Chm)*
Gulam Rabbani Chowdhury *(Mng Dir)*
Mohammed Monirul Islam *(CFO & Sec)*
Board of Directors:
Faisal Ahmed Chowdhury
Tofayel Ahmed
Abdul Bari
Robin Choudhury
Gulam Rabbani Chowdhury
Md. Ahsanul Kabir
Md. Khizir Khan
Nanu Kazi Mohammed Miah
Legal Counsel:
P&H Associates
123 New Kakrail Road Shantinagar 2nd Floor Suit-1
Dhaka, Bangladesh
Law Concept
Room 802 7th Floor 27 Dilkusha C/A
Dhaka, Bangladesh

BARAN GROUP LTD.

Baran House 8 Omarim St Industrial Park
Omer, Israel 84965
Tel.: (972) 86200200
Fax: (972) 86200201
E-Mail: barang@barangroup.com
Web Site: www.barangroup.com
Year Founded: 1979
BRANF—(TAE)
Rev.: $346,350,014
Assets: $187,041,313
Liabilities: $119,437,664
Net Worth: $67,603,650
Earnings: $4,343,212
Emp.: 1,330
Fiscal Year-end: 12/31/12
Business Description:
Provides Engineering, Construction, Projects Management & Consulting Services Worldwide
S.I.C.: 8711
N.A.I.C.S.: 541330
Personnel:
Meir Dor *(Co-Founder & Chm)*
Issac Friedman *(Co-Founder & Gen Mgr-Infrastructure & Construction)*
Israel Scop *(Co-Founder & Gen Mgr-Baran Engrg-South)*
Israel Gotman *(Co-Founder)*
Nahman Tsabar *(CEO)*
Sasson Shilo *(CFO & VP)*
Steven Senter *(CEO-Intl)*
Dan Shenbach *(CEO-Israel)*
Haim Assael *(Gen Legal Counsel)*
Saar Bracha *(Sr VP-Telecomm Div)*
Ron Raviv *(Sr VP-Asia)*
Alon Yegnes *(Sr VP-America)*
Sharon Zaid *(Sr VP-Israel Div)*
Board of Directors:
Meir Dor
Avraham Dotan
Israel Gotman
Mordechai Levin
Zvi Lieber
Ester Luzzatto
Giora Shlomo Meyuhas
Ehud Rieger
Zvi Waldman
Subsidiaries:

Baran Construction and Infrastructure Ltd. (1)
5 Begin Menachem Boulevard
Bet Dagan, 50200, Israel
Tel.: (972) 39775110
Fax: (972) 39775120
Construction Engineering Services
S.I.C.: 8711
N.A.I.C.S.: 541330
Nahman Tsabar *(Gen Mgr)*

Baran Industries (91) Ltd. (1)
Menachem Begin 5 Baran Building
Bet Dagan, 50200, Israel
Tel.: (972) 39775000
Fax: (972) 39775001
Construction Engineering Services
S.I.C.: 8711
N.A.I.C.S.: 541330
Nahman Tsabar *(CEO)*

Baran-Oil & Petrochemical (1987) Projects Ltd. (1)
9 Hashalom Avenue
Nesher, 36651, Israel
Tel.: (972) 48304888
Fax: (972) 48468889
Web Site: www.barangroup.com
Emp.: 80
Engineering & Construction Services
S.I.C.: 8711
N.A.I.C.S.: 541330
Zvika Achrai *(Mng Dir)*

U.S. Subsidiary:

Baran Telecom, Inc. (1)
2355 Industrial Park Blvd
Cumming, GA 30041-6463 GA
Tel.: (678) 455-1181
Fax: (678) 455-1153
Web Site: www.barantelecom.com
Emp.: 475
Network Wireless Telecommunications Services
S.I.C.: 1629
N.A.I.C.S.: 237130
Sasson Shilo *(CFO)*
Saar Bracha *(Sr VP)*

BARARELAGET KRANCENTER AB

Mosaregatan 15
254 66 Helsingborg, Sweden
Tel.: (46) 42162030
Fax: (46) 42157031
E-Mail: c.jakobsson@bararelaget.se
Web Site: www.bararelaget.se
Emp.: 36
Business Description:
Trucking, Transportation & Heavy Lifting Services
S.I.C.: 4789
N.A.I.C.S.: 488210
Personnel:
Erik Jakobsson *(Mgr-Fin)*
Subsidiary:

Ralling AB (1)
Hammarvagen 5
23237 Malmo, Sweden (100%)
Tel.: (46) 40158050
Fax: (46) 40158055
E-Mail: info@ralling.se
Web Site: www.ralling.se
Emp.: 40
Rental of Mobil Cranes, Forklifts & Trucks; Contracting Work in the Heavy Lifting Field
S.I.C.: 7359
N.A.I.C.S.: 532412

BARBADOS SHIPPING & TRADING CO. LTD.

1st Floor The AutoDome
Warrens, Saint Michael, Barbados
Tel.: (246) 4175110
Fax: (246) 4175116
E-Mail: info@bsandtco.com
Web Site: www.bsandtco.com
BST—(BARB)
Sales Range: $350-399.9 Million
Emp.: 2,032
Business Description:
Diversified Holding Company
S.I.C.: 6719
N.A.I.C.S.: 551112
Personnel:
Gervase Warner *(Chm)*
G. Anthony King *(CEO)*
Natalie Brace *(Sec)*
Board of Directors:
Gervase Warner
Earl Boodsingh
Frere F. C. Delmas
G. Anthony King
Paula Rajkumarsingh
Ralph W. Taylor
Joseph E. Teixeira
Subsidiaries:

Agro Chemicals Inc (1)
41 Warrens Industrial Park
Saint Michael, Barbados
Tel.: (246) 4253939
Fax: (246) 4253943
E-Mail: info@agro-chemicals.com
Web Site: www.agro-chemicals.com
Emp.: 30
Chemicals & Agricultural Products Distr
S.I.C.: 2879
N.A.I.C.S.: 325320
Lisa G. Mustor *(Gen Mgr)*

BCB Communications (1)
First Fl The Auto Dome Warrens
Saint Michael, Barbados
Tel.: (246) 417 5010
Fax: (246) 417 5033
E-Mail: trevor@bcbcom.com
Emp.: 13
Marketing & Advertising Services
S.I.C.: 8732
N.A.I.C.S.: 541910
C A Clarke *(Mng Dir)*

Booth Steamship Company (Barbados) Ltd. (1)
Prescod Blvd
Bridgetown, Barbados
Tel.: (246) 4366094
Fax: (246) 4260484
E-Mail: info@boothsteamship.com
Web Site: www.boothsteamship.com
Emp.: 15
Shipping Services
S.I.C.: 4412
N.A.I.C.S.: 483111

DaCosta Mannings Inc. (1)
The Auto Dome Warrens
Saint Michael, Barbados
Tel.: (246) 4318700
Fax: (246) 228 8590
Web Site: www.dacostamannings.com
Household Appliances Retailer
S.I.C.: 5064
N.A.I.C.S.: 423620
T. A. Mahon *(Mng Dir)*

Knights Limited (1)
Prescod Blvd
Saint Michael, Barbados
Tel.: (246) 4297700
Fax: (246) 4295144
E-Mail: info@knight.bb
Paper Products Mfr & Distr
S.I.C.: 2679
N.A.I.C.S.: 322299
Andrew Wiles *(Mgr)*

Peronne Manufacturing Company Ltd (1)
Peronne Complex Worthing
Christchurch, Barbados
Tel.: (246) 4356921
Fax: (246) 4352065
E-Mail: orders@peronne.bb
Emp.: 20
Food Products Mfr
S.I.C.: 2099
N.A.I.C.S.: 311991
Kathyann Ollivierre *(Gen Mgr)*

Roberts Manufacturing Company Ltd (1)
Lower Estate
1275 Saint Michael, Barbados
Tel.: (246) 4292131
Fax: (246) 4265604
E-Mail: roberts@rmco.com
Web Site: www.rmco.com
Emp.: 160
Animal Feeds Mfr
S.I.C.: 2047
N.A.I.C.S.: 311111
D. Foster *(Mng Dir)*

S.P. Musson Son & Company (1)
Saint George St
Bridgetown, Barbados
Tel.: (246) 4295686
Fax: (246) 4293237
E-Mail: info@mussonrealty.com
Web Site: www.mussonrealty.com
Emp.: 30
Land & Property Management Services
S.I.C.: 6531
N.A.I.C.S.: 531311
Walter Short *(Mng Dir)*

Super Centre Limited (1)
Super Ctr Corp Off Sargeant's Village
JB Complex, Christchurch, 15098, Barbados
Tel.: (246) 2282020
Fax: (246) 4369820
E-Mail: info@supercentre.com
Web Site: www.supercentre.com
Emp.: 50
Food Products & Pharmaceutical Retailer
S.I.C.: 5122
N.A.I.C.S.: 424210
Frere Delmas *(Chm)*
Neville Brewster *(Mng Dir)*

United Insurance Company (1)
Lower Broad St
United Insurance Bldg, Bridgetown, Barbados
Tel.: (246) 4301900
Fax: (246) 4367573
E-Mail: mail@unitedinsure.com
Web Site: www.unitedinsure.com
Emp.: 80
General Non-Life Insurance Services
S.I.C.: 6411
N.A.I.C.S.: 524210
Howard Hall *(Pres)*

Warrens Motors Inc. (1)
The Auto Dome Warrens
Saint Michael, Barbados
Tel.: (246) 4175000
Fax: (246) 4175150
E-Mail: info@warrensmotors.com
Web Site: www.warrensmotors.com
Emp.: 50
Motor Industrial Services
S.I.C.: 3566
N.A.I.C.S.: 333612

U.S. Subsidiary:

BS&T International Development, LC (1)
13100 NW 113 Ave Rd
Miami, FL 33178
Tel.: (305) 477-9809
Fax: (305) 477-9819
Web Site: www.bsandtco.com
Emp.: 8
Marketing Services
S.I.C.: 8742
N.A.I.C.S.: 541613
Ryan Fields *(Gen Mgr)*

BARBADOS STOCK EXCHANGE INC.

1st Floor Carlisle House Hincks Street
Bridgetown, Saint Michel, Barbados
Tel.: (246) 4369871
Fax: (246) 4298942
Web Site: www.bse.com.bb
Emp.: 25
Business Description:
Stock Exchange Services
S.I.C.: 6231
N.A.I.C.S.: 523210
Personnel:
Andrew St. John *(Chm)*
Kerry Greene *(Sec)*
Board of Directors:
Andrew St. John
Marlon Yarde

BARBARA BUI SA

Route De Vannes Zi Du Pigeon Blanc
Locmine, 56500 Lorient, France
Tel.: (33) 153018805
Web Site: www.barbarabui.fr
Sls.: $24,800,000
Emp.: 121

Barbara Bui Sa—(Continued)

Business Description:
Womens & Misses Suits & Coats
S.I.C.: 2389
N.A.I.C.S.: 315240
Personnel:
William Halimi *(Pres & Dir Gen)*
Board of Directors:
William Halimi
Jerome Cherki

BARBARA PERSONNEL INC.

200 Montcalm St
Gatineau, QC, J8Y 3B5, Canada
Tel.: (613) 236-9689
Fax: (613) 236-7524
E-Mail: order@barbarapersonnel.com
Web Site: www.barbarapersonnel.com
Year Founded: 1973
Rev.: $35,607,965
Emp.: 300
Business Description:
Employment Agencies
S.I.C.: 7361
N.A.I.C.S.: 561311
Personnel:
Barbara Cloutier *(Pres)*

BARBER GLASS RETAIL

167 Suffolk St W
Guelph, ON, N1H 2J7, Canada
Tel.: (519) 824-0310
Fax: (519) 824-8820
Web Site: www.barberglassretail.ca
Year Founded: 1883
Rev.: $15,202,452
Emp.: 12
Business Description:
Fabricated Glass Products Mfr
S.I.C.: 5211
N.A.I.C.S.: 444190
Personnel:
Susan Barber *(Pres)*

BARBICAN GROUP HOLDINGS LTD.

Rue du Pre North Town Mills Suite 4
Saint Peter Port, Guernsey
Tel.: (44) 1481 750400
Web Site: www.barbicaninsurance.com
Business Description:
Insurance Holding Company
S.I.C.: 6719
N.A.I.C.S.: 551112
Personnel:
David Reeves *(CEO)*
Jon Godfray *(COO)*
Mark Harrington *(Chief Underwriting Officer)*

Subsidiary:

Barbican Reinsurance Company Limited (1)
Suite 4 North Town Mills
Rue du Pre, Saint Peter Port, GY1 1LT, Guernsey
Tel.: (44) 1481 750400
Web Site: www.barbicanre.gg
Reinsurance
S.I.C.: 6399
N.A.I.C.S.: 524130
David Reeves *(CEO)*

BARCELO CORPORACION EMPRESARIAL S.A.

(d/b/a Barcelo Hotels & Resorts)
Jose Rover Motta 27
07006 Palma de Mallorca, Baleares, Spain
Tel.: (34) 971771700
Fax: (34) 971469581
E-Mail: comunicacion@barcelo.com
Web Site: www.barcelo.com
Sales Range: $5-14.9 Billion
Emp.: 28,000
Business Description:
Hotels & Resorts Operator
S.I.C.: 7011
N.A.I.C.S.: 721110
Personnel:
Simon Pedro Barcelo Vadell *(Chm)*
Simon Barcelo Tous *(Chm)*
Raul Gonzalez *(CEO-EMEA)*
Board of Directors:
Simon Pedro Barcelo Vadell
Simon Barcelo Tous

BARCLAY TECHNOLOGIES HOLDING AG

Baarerstrasse 45
CH-6300 Zug, Switzerland
Tel.: (41) 44 712 0146
Fax: (41) 44 712 0148
E-Mail: info@bthag.com
Web Site: www.bthag.com
Year Founded: 2008
BT9—(BER)
Sales Range: Less than $1 Million
Business Description:
Holding Company; Software Developer
S.I.C.: 6719
N.A.I.C.S.: 551112
Personnel:
Claudio Mohr *(Chm)*
Alexandros Siapis *(CEO)*
Marcus Wohlrab *(CFO)*
Board of Directors:
Claudio Mohr
Thomas Egolf
Emil Inderkummen
Marcus Wohlrab
Freddy Zahner

Subsidiary:

Barclay Technologies (Schweiz) AG (1)
Grossmattstrasse 9
CH-8902 Urdorf, Switzerland CH
Tel.: (41) 448473131 (100%)
Fax: (41) 448473139
E-Mail: info@barclaytechnologies.ch
Web Site: www.barclaytechnologies.ch
Emp.: 8
Data Security Software Developer & Distr
S.I.C.: 7372
N.A.I.C.S.: 511210
Alexandros Siapis *(CEO)*
Sven Knotig *(COO)*

BARCLAYS PLC

1 Churchill Place
London, E14 5HP, United Kingdom
Tel.: (44) 20 7116 2901
E-Mail: irsec@barclays.com
Web Site: www.barclays.com
BCS—(LSE NYSE)
Int. Income: $30,429,273,600
Net Worth: $106,247,426,560
Earnings: $2,154,887,680
Emp.: 139,600
Fiscal Year-end: 12/31/13
Business Description:
Financial Holding Company
S.I.C.: 6712
N.A.I.C.S.: 551111
Personnel:
David Walker *(Grp Chm)*
Richard Broadbent *(Deputy Chm)*
Michael Rake *(Deputy Chm)*
Eric Bommensath *(Co-CEO-Corp & Investment Banking & Head-Markets)*
Peter Horrell *(Interim CEO-Wealth & Investment Mgmt)*
Antony Jenkins *(Grp CEO)*
Thomas King *(Co-CEO-Corp & Investment Banking)*
Maria Ramos *(Grp CEO-Absa & Barclays Africa)*
Mark Brown *(Mng Dir & Head-Barclays Natural Resource Investments)*
Maurice Cleaves *(Mng Dir, Global Head-Cash Mgmt & Product)*
Robert Le Blanc *(Chief Risk Officer)*
Valerie Soranno Keating *(CEO-Barclaycard)*
Hugh E. McGee *(CEO-America)*
Ashok Vaswani *(CEO-Retail & Bus Banking)*
John F. Vitalo *(CEO-Middle East & North Africa)*
Robert Hoyt *(Grp Gen Counsel)*
Board of Directors:
David Walker
Michael Ashley
David Booth
Timothy James Breedon
Richard Broadbent
Fulvio Conti
Diane de Saint Victor
Simon Fraser
Reuben Jeffery, III
Antony Jenkins
Andrew Likierman
Wendy Elizabeth Lucas-Bull
Dambisa F. Moyo
Michael Rake
John Michael Sunderland
Stephen G. Thieke

Subsidiaries:

54 Lombard Street Investments Limited (1)
1 Churchill Place
London, E14 5HP, United Kingdom
Tel.: (44) 2076261567
Investment Management Services
S.I.C.: 6211
N.A.I.C.S.: 523999

B D & B Investments Limited (1)
1 Church Place
London, E14 5HP, United Kingdom
Tel.: (44) 2076261567
Investment Management Services
S.I.C.: 6211
N.A.I.C.S.: 523999

Barafor Limited (1)
1 Churchill Place
London, E14 5HP, United Kingdom
Tel.: (44) 20 7116 1000
Investment Management Services
S.I.C.: 6211
N.A.I.C.S.: 523999

Barclay Leasing Limited (1)
Churchill Plaza Churchill Way
Basingstoke, Hampshire, RG21 7GP, United Kingdom
Tel.: (44) 1256791245
Financial Leasing Services
S.I.C.: 6159
N.A.I.C.S.: 522220

Barclaycard Funding PLC (1)
54 Lombard Street
London, EC3P 4AH, United Kingdom
Tel.: (44) 20 7699 5000
Fax: (44) 20 7699 2721
Fund Management Services
S.I.C.: 6799
N.A.I.C.S.: 523920

Barclays Aldersgate Investments Limited (1)
1 Churchill Place
London, E14 5HP, United Kingdom
Tel.: (44) 2071161000
Investment Management Services
S.I.C.: 6211
N.A.I.C.S.: 523999

Barclays Alma Mater General Partner Limited (1)
1 Churchill Place
London, E14 5HP, United Kingdom
Tel.: (44) 2071161000
Asset Management Services
S.I.C.: 6282
N.A.I.C.S.: 523920

Barclays Bank PLC (1)
1 Churchill Place Canary Wharf
London, E14 5HP, United Kingdom UK
Tel.: (44) 2071161000 (100%)
Telex: 884970
Web Site: bank.barclays.co.uk
Rev.: $39,701,771,310
Net Worth: $75,340,029,450
Earnings: ($606,447,360)
Emp.: 121,000
Fiscal Year-end: 12/31/12
Retail & Commercial Banking, Loans, Insurance & Credit Card Services
S.I.C.: 6029
N.A.I.C.S.: 522110
David Walker *(Chm)*
Michael Rake *(Deputy Chm)*
Antony Jenkins *(CEO)*
Robert Le Blanc *(Chief Risk Officer)*
Thomas L. Kalaris *(CEO-Wealth & Investment Mgmt)*
Valerie Soranno Keating *(CEO-Barclaycard)*
Maria Ramos *(CEO-Absa Grp & Africa)*
Rich Ricci *(CEO-Corp & Investment Banking)*
Ashok Vaswani *(CEO-Retail & Bus Banking)*
Lawrence Dickinson *(Sec)*

Division:

Barclays Bank PLC - Wealth & Investment Management Division (2)
International Banking Centre 38 Hans Crescent
PO Box 391
Knightsbridge, London, SW1X 0LZ, United Kingdom
Tel.: (44) 1624 684 316
E-Mail: ukcommunity@barclays.com
Investment Management Services
S.I.C.: 6799
N.A.I.C.S.: 523920
Vivian Chan *(Head-North Asia)*

Subsidiaries:

Barclays Bank Trust Co. Ltd. (2)
PO Box 15
Northwich, CW9 7UR, United Kingdom (100%)
Tel.: (44) 8457660936
Fax: (44) 1606313005
E-Mail: eandtclone@barclays.co.uk
Web Site: www.wills.barclays.com
Emp.: 200
Trust & Fiduciary Services
S.I.C.: 6159
N.A.I.C.S.: 522298
Gary Colins *(Sr Mgr)*

Barclays Capital Securities Limited (2)
5 The North Colonnade
Canary Wharf, London, E14 4BB, United Kingdom UK
Tel.: (44) 2076232323 (100%)
Web Site: www.barcap.com
Investment Banking & Securities Dealing Services
S.I.C.: 6211
N.A.I.C.S.: 523110
Patrick Clackson *(CFO & Mng Dir)*
Benoit de Vitry *(Mng Dir & Head-Commodities & Emerging Mkts/Global Trading-Europe)*
Patrick McMullan *(Mng Dir & Co-Head-Global Healthcare Grp-Investment Banking Div)*
Guglielmo Sartori di Borgoricco *(Mng Dir & Head-Distr)*
Stefano Marsaglia *(Chm-Global Fin Institutions Grp-Investment Banking Div)*

Barclays Funds Ltd. (2)
54 Lombard St
London, EC3P 3AH, United Kingdom (100%)
Tel.: (44) 8457660936
Telex: 23366
Fax: (44) 01606313005
E-Mail: attention@stockbrokers.barclays.com
Web Site: www.barclays.co.uk
Emp.: 500
Unit Trust Management
S.I.C.: 6733

N.A.I.C.S.: 523991
Robert Barley *(Mng Dir)*

Barclays Global Investors Limited (2)
Murray House 1 Royal Mint Court
London, EC3N 4HH, United Kingdom
Tel.: (44) 2076688000
Fax: (44) 2076688001
Web Site: www.barclaysglobal.com
Assets Management
S.I.C.: 6211
N.A.I.C.S.: 523999
Karen Prooth *(Mng Dir & COO-iShares, Global Index & Markets Grp-Europe)*
David Semaya *(CEO-Europe & Asia)*
Rory Tobin *(CEO-iShares, Global Index & Markets Grp-Europe)*

Barclays Insurance Services Co. Ltd. (2)
8 Bedford Park
Croydon, CR9 2XX, United Kingdom (100%)
Tel.: (44) 2082533000
Fax: (44) 206415458
Emp.: 100
Insurance Brokers
S.I.C.: 6411
N.A.I.C.S.: 524210

Barclays Stockbrokers Ltd. (2)
Tay House 300 Bath Street
Glasgow, Strathclyde, G2 4LN, United Kingdom (100%)
Tel.: (44) 8456089000
Fax: (44) 8456052143
E-Mail: stockbrokers@barclays.co.uk
Web Site: www.stockbrokers.barclays.co.uk
Emp.: 800
Stockbroking Services
S.I.C.: 6799
N.A.I.C.S.: 523910
Nathan Dawes *(Head-Mktg Comm)*

Barclays Venture Nominees Limited (2)
7th Floor United Kingdom House 180
Oxford Street, London, W1D 1EA, United Kingdom UK
Tel.: (44) 20 7441 4213
Web Site: www.business.barclays.co.uk
Emp.: 50
Venture Capital Firm
S.I.C.: 6211
N.A.I.C.S.: 523999
Kip Kapur *(Mng Dir)*

Holdings:

The Cornhill Partnership (3)
Second Floor 17 Dominion Street
London, EC2M 2EF, United Kingdom
Tel.: (44) 2034405202
Web Site: www.cornhillpartnership.com
Executive Search & Interim Management Services
S.I.C.: 8999
N.A.I.C.S.: 541612
Robert Walker *(CEO)*

Subsidiaries:

Archer Mathieson Ltd. (4)
St Leonards House 126 130
St Leonards Road, Windsor, Berks, SL4 3DG, United Kingdom
Tel.: (44) 1753754333
Fax: (44) 1753754334
E-Mail: info@biegroupltd.com
Web Site: www.biegroupltd.com
Emp.: 24
Executive Search & Interim Management Services
S.I.C.: 8999
N.A.I.C.S.: 541612
Rob Walker *(CEO)*

BIE Interim Executive Ltd. (4)
2nd Floor 17 Dominion Street
London, EC2M 2EF, United Kingdom
Tel.: (44) 2034405250
E-Mail: info@bieinterim.com
Web Site: www.bieinterim.co.uk
Interim Management Services
S.I.C.: 8748
N.A.I.C.S.: 541618
Robert Walker *(CEO)*

Euromedica Ltd. (4)
17 Dominion St
London, EC2 M2EF, United Kingdom UK
Tel.: (44) 2075367950
Fax: (44) 2075388362
E-Mail: london@euromedica.com
Web Site: www.euromedica.com
Emp.: 20
Healthcare & Life Sciences Industry Executive Search & Management Consultancy Services
S.I.C.: 8999
N.A.I.C.S.: 541612

Non-U.S. Subsidiaries:

Euromedica Executive Search GmbH (5)
Lessingstrasse 5
D-60325 Frankfurt am Main, Germany De
Tel.: (49) 69271030
E-Mail: frankfurt@euromedica.com
Web Site: www.euromedica.com
Healthcare & Life Sciences Industry Executive Search & Management Consultancy Services
S.I.C.: 8999
N.A.I.C.S.: 541612
Michael Ade *(Mgr)*

Euromedica International Ltd. (5)
Pegasuslaan 5
BE-1831 Diegem, Belgium
Tel.: (32) 27092950
Fax: (32) 27092222
E-Mail: brussels@euromedica.com
Web Site: www.euromedica.com
Emp.: 7
Healthcare & Life Sciences Industry Executive Search & Management Consultancy Services
S.I.C.: 8999
N.A.I.C.S.: 541612
Frank Lippens *(Mng Dir-Benelux)*

Euromedica SARL (5)
18 rue de Marignan
F-75008 Paris, France
Tel.: (33) 149530511
Fax: (33) 149530544
E-Mail: paris@euromedica.com
Web Site: www.euromedica.com
Emp.: 50
Healthcare & Life Sciences Industry Executive Search & Management Consultancy Services
S.I.C.: 8999
N.A.I.C.S.: 541612
Jennifer Chase *(Mng Dir)*

FIRSTPLUS Financial Group PLC (2)
The Avenue Business Park
Pentwyn, Cardiff, CF23 8FF, United Kingdom
Tel.: (44) 29 2030 3020
E-Mail: customercare@firstplus.co.uk
Web Site: www.firstplus.co.uk
Financial Investment Services
S.I.C.: 6211
N.A.I.C.S.: 523999

Standard Life Bank Limited (2)
Standard Life House
30 Lothian Road, Edinburgh, EH1 2DH, United Kingdom UK
Tel.: (44) 1312252552
Fax: (44) 1312220761
Web Site: www.standardlife.co.uk
Sales Range: $1-4.9 Billion
Emp.: 300
Banking Services
S.I.C.: 6029
N.A.I.C.S.: 522110

Joint Venture:

MRBL Limited (2)
Export House Cawsey Way
Woking, Surrey, GU21 6QX, United Kingdom UK
Tel.: (44) 1483 731 000
Fax: (44) 1483 731 001
Web Site: www.mouchel.com
Holding Company; Engineering Services
S.I.C.: 6719
N.A.I.C.S.: 551112
Grant Rumbles *(CEO)*

Subsidiaries:

Mouchel Business Services Limited (3)
Northgate House 3rd Floor
Upper Borough Walls, Bath, BA1 1RG, United Kingdom
Tel.: (44) 1225477255
Fax: (44) 1225 477267
Business Consulting Services
S.I.C.: 7389
N.A.I.C.S.: 561499
Craig Apsey *(Mng Dir)*

Mouchel Ewan Limited (3)
Canterbury House Stephensons Way
Derby, Derbs, DE21 6LY, United Kingdom
Tel.: (44) 1332 680066
Fax: (44) 1332 680080
Engineering Services
S.I.C.: 8711
N.A.I.C.S.: 541330

Mouchel Limited (3)
Export House Cawsey Way
Woking, Surrey, GU21 6QX, United Kingdom
Tel.: (44) 1483 731 000
Fax: (44) 1483 731 001
Web Site: www.mouchel.com
Engineering Services
S.I.C.: 8711
N.A.I.C.S.: 541330

Mouchel Management Consulting Limited (3)
4 Matthew Parker Street
London, SW1H 9NP, United Kingdom
Tel.: (44) 20 7227 6800
Fax: (44) 20 7227 6801
E-Mail: consult@mouchel.com
Web Site: www.mouchel.com
Business Consulting Services
S.I.C.: 8748
N.A.I.C.S.: 541618

Joint Ventures:

2020 Liverpool Limited (3)
Station House Mercury Court Tithebarn Street
Liverpool, L2 2QP, United Kingdom UK
Tel.: (44) 1512372020
Fax: (44) 1512374000
E-Mail: enquiries@2020liverpool.co.uk
Web Site: www.2020liverpool.co.uk
Emp.: 320
Property Valuation, Surveying, Engineering & Transportation Infrastructure Services
S.I.C.: 0781
N.A.I.C.S.: 531390
Chris Lavery *(Mng Dir)*

The Impact Partnership (Rochdale Borough) Limited (3)
Floor 11 Municipal Offices Smith Street
PO Box 516
Rochdale, Lancs, OL16 9BS, United Kingdom UK
Tel.: (44) 1706647474
Fax: (44) 1706924626
E-Mail: info@theimpactpartnership.com
Web Site: www.theimpactpartnership.com
Engineering Services
S.I.C.: 8711
N.A.I.C.S.: 541330

Scotland TranServ (3)
Broxden House
Broxden Business Park, Perth, PH1 1RA, United Kingdom
Tel.: (44) 1738455300
Fax: (44) 1738455301
E-Mail: info@scotland.transerv.co.uk
Web Site: www.scotlandtranserv.co.uk
Emp.: 70
Highway Maintenance, Street Lighting & Other Transportation Infrastructure Support Services
S.I.C.: 4789
N.A.I.C.S.: 488490
Norrie Westbrooke *(Gen Mgr)*

Westminster TranServ (3)
City Hall 2nd Fl 64 Victoria St
London, SW1E 6QP, United Kingdom
Tel.: (44) 2078116999
Fax: (44) 2078116998
Web Site: www.mouchel.com
Highway Maintenance, Street Lighting & Other Transportation Infrastructure Support Services
S.I.C.: 4789
N.A.I.C.S.: 488490
Adrian Croot *(Mgr-Contracts)*

Units:

Barclays Asset Finance (2)
Churchill Plaza Churchill Way
Basingstoke, RG21 7GL, United Kingdom (100%)
Tel.: (44) 256797000
Telex: 859202
Fax: (44) 256810273
E-Mail: premier.support@barclays.co.uk
Web Site: www.barclays.co.uk
Emp.: 1,005
Finance House Providing Leasing & Other Financial Facilities to Business Customers
S.I.C.: 6159
N.A.I.C.S.: 522298
Ian Stuart *(Mng Dir)*

Barclays Group Property Services (2)
Northwest House 119 - 127 Marylebone
London, NW15 PX, United Kingdom
Tel.: (44) 2077237668
Emp.: 60
Manager of Barclays' Property Portfolio
S.I.C.: 6512
N.A.I.C.S.: 531120

Barclays Home Finance (2)
Meridian House Anchor Boulevard
Crossways, Dartford, DA2 6QH, United Kingdom
Tel.: (44) 1322426426
Fax: (44) 1322425024
Web Site: www.barclays.co.uk
Sales Range: $300-349.9 Million
Emp.: 400
Loan Processing Services; Owned 20% by Barclays PLC
S.I.C.: 6531
N.A.I.C.S.: 531390

U.S. Branch:

Barclays Bank (2)
1111 Brickell Ave
Miami, FL 33131-3112
Tel.: (305) 533-3333
Fax: (305) 533-3124
Web Site: www.barcap.com
Retail & Corporate Banking Services
S.I.C.: 6029
N.A.I.C.S.: 522110
Ros Stephenson *(Global Chm-Banking)*

U.S. Subsidiaries:

Barclays Capital Inc. (2)
200 Park Ave
New York, NY 10166 CT (100%)
Tel.: (212) 412-4000
Fax: (212) 412-7300
Toll Free: (800) 227-2529
E-Mail: info@barcap.com
Web Site: www.barcap.com
Emp.: 1,600
Investment Banking & Securities Dealing Services
S.I.C.: 6211
N.A.I.C.S.: 523110
Roger Jenkins *(Chm)*
Gregg Chow *(Mng Dir & Head-North American FX Sls)*
Gerald A. Donini *(Mng Dir & Head-Equities & Trading)*
Hans Olsen *(Mng Dir & Head-Investment Strategy-Americas)*
Jeffrey Pio *(Mng Dir & Head-FX Sls)*
Huang Yiping *(Mng Dir)*
Hugh E. McGee, III *(CEO-Americas)*

Joint Venture:

Crescent Real Estate Holdings LLC (3)
777 Main St Ste 2000
Fort Worth, TX 76102
Tel.: (817) 321-2100
Fax: (817) 321-2000
Web Site: www.crescent.com
Holding Company
S.I.C.: 6719
N.A.I.C.S.: 551112
John C. Goff *(Chm & CEO)*

Subsidiary:

Crescent Real Estate Equities LP (4)
777 Main St Ste 2000
Fort Worth, TX 76102 TX

Barclays PLC—(Continued)

Tel.: (817) 321-1566
Fax: (817) 321-2090
E-Mail: jsuitt@crescent.com
Web Site: www.crescent.com
Sales Range: $900-999.9 Million
Emp.: 748
Real Estate Investment & Management Services; Owned by Goff Capital Partners, L.P. & Barclays Capital
S.I.C.: 6726
N.A.I.C.S.: 525990
John C. Goff *(Chm & CEO)*
Suzanne M. Stevens *(CFO & Mng Dir)*
Robert H. Boykin, Jr. *(Mng Dir)*
James H. Wilson *(Mng Dir)*
John L. Zogg, Jr. *(Mng Dir)*
Jason E. Anderson *(COO)*
Jason Phinney *(Sr VP & Controller)*
Joseph Pitchford *(Sr VP-Dev)*

Barclays Investments Inc. (2)
693 5th Ave Fl 18
New York, NY 10022
Tel.: (212) 421-8901
Fax: (609) 587-1930
Web Site: www.emtecinc.com
Rev.: $27,960,270
Emp.: 10
Stock Brokers & Dealers
S.I.C.: 6211
N.A.I.C.S.: 523120

Non-U.S. Subsidiaries:

Absa Group Limited (2)
7th Floor Absa Towers West 15 Troye Street
PO Box 7735
Johannesburg, 2001, South Africa ZA
Tel.: (27) 113504000 (58.8%)
Fax: (27) 113504928
E-Mail: groupsec@absa.co.za
Web Site: www.absa.co.za
ASA—(JSE)
Rev.: $5,670,562,200
Assets: $90,246,786,300
Liabilities: $82,115,696,500
Net Worth: $8,131,089,800
Earnings: $976,369,700
Emp.: 33,717
Fiscal Year-end: 12/31/12
Bank Holding Company
Export
S.I.C.: 6712
N.A.I.C.S.: 551111
Maria Ramos *(CEO)*
V. Alfie Naidoo *(COO)*
Jan Lubbe *(Chief Risk Officer)*
David A. Skillen *(COO-Africa & Chief Integration Officer)*
Kennedy G. Bungane *(CEO-Barclays Africa & Head-Strategy)*
Craig L. Bond *(CEO-Barclays Africa & Absa RBB)*
Willie T. Lategan *(CEO-Absa Fin Svcs)*
Nomkhita Nqweni *(CEO-Absa Wealth)*
Stephen van Coller *(CEO-Absa Capital & Wealth)*
Charles S. Wheeler *(Gen Counsel-Africa)*
N. R. Drutman *(Sec)*

Subsidiaries:

Absa Asset Management (Proprietary) Limited (3)
Block A First Floor 65 Empire Road
Parktown, 2193, South Africa (100%)
Mailing Address:
PO Box 44952
Claremont, 7735, South Africa
Tel.: (27) 114805146
Fax: (27) 114805351
E-Mail: info@abam.co.za
Web Site: www.abam.co.za
Asset Management Services
S.I.C.: 6211
N.A.I.C.S.: 523999
Alan Miller *(CEO)*
Errol Shear *(Chief Investment Officer)*

Absa Bank Limited (3)
3rd Fl Absa Towers E 170 Main St
170 Main St, Johannesburg, South Africa
Tel.: (27) 3504000
Fax: (27) 3504928
E-Mail: groupsec@absa.co.za
Web Site: www.absa.co.za
Banking, Mortgage & Credit Card Services
S.I.C.: 6029
N.A.I.C.S.: 522110
Steve Booysen *(CEO)*

Non-U.S. Branch:

Absa Bank (Asia) Limited (4)
13th Fl Dah Sing Financial Ctr
108 Gloucester Rd, Wanchai, Hong Kong, China (Hong Kong) (100%)
Tel.: (852) 25319388
Fax: (852) 28021908
E-Mail: absahk@absaasia.com
Web Site: www.absaasia.com
Emp.: 39
Banking Services
S.I.C.: 6029
N.A.I.C.S.: 522110

Non-U.S. Subsidiary:

Absa Namibia Proprietary Limited (4)
1st Floor Ausspann Plaza Unit 6 Dr Agostinho Neto Road
Ausspannplatz, Namibia
Tel.: (264) 61 289 3000
Fax: (264) 61 289 3008
E-Mail: absanamibia@absa.co.za
Web Site: www.absanamibia.com.na
Emp.: 10
Financial Management Services
S.I.C.: 6211
N.A.I.C.S.: 523999
Marius Alberts *(Mng Dir)*

Absa Capital Private Equity (Pty) Limited (3)
8th Rivonia Rd Illovo
2146 Sandton, Gauteng, South Africa
Tel.: (27) 118956896
Fax: (27) 102454881
E-Mail: gareth.druce@absacapital.com
Web Site: www.absacapitalprivateequity.com
Emp.: 8
Private Equity Investment
S.I.C.: 6211
N.A.I.C.S.: 523999
Tony Brewitt *(Principal)*
Andrew Dewar *(Principal)*
Gareth Druce *(Principal)*
Ekow Duker *(Principal)*
Marlene Jennings *(Principal)*
Peter van den Heever *(Principal)*
Gert van der Merwe *(Principal)*

Subsidiaries:

EnviroServ Holdings Limited (4)
Brickfield Road
Germiston, South Africa
Mailing Address:
PO Box 1547
Bedforview, 2008 Johannesburg, South Africa
Tel.: (27) 114565660
Fax: (27) 114566016
E-Mail: info.ho@enviroserv.co.za
Web Site: www.enviroserv.co.za
Sales Range: $100-124.9 Million
Emp.: 1,533
Holding Company; Waste Management Services
S.I.C.: 4959
N.A.I.C.S.: 562998
Alistair McLean *(Chm)*
Des Gordon *(CEO)*

Safripol (Pty) Ltd (4)
Eden Gardens Building Dimension Data Campus
Main Road
Bryanston, Sandton, 2191, South Africa (49%)
Mailing Address:
Private Bag X52
Bryanston, 2021, South Africa
Tel.: (27) 11 575 4549
Fax: (27) 11 576 4549
E-Mail: info@safripol.com
Web Site: www.safripol.com
Sales Range: $75-99.9 Million
Emp.: 300
Plastics Mfr
S.I.C.: 2821
N.A.I.C.S.: 325211
Joaquin Schoch *(CEO)*
Frans van Dyk *(CFO)*
Geoff Gaywood *(COO)*

Absa Finance Company (Proprietary) Limited (3)
3rd Fl Absa Towers East 170 Main St
Johannesburg, 2001, South Africa
Mailing Address:
PO Box 11055
Johannesburg, 2000, South Africa
Tel.: (27) 113504000
Fax: (27) 112217569
E-Mail: ceo@absa.co.za
Web Site: www.absa.co.za
Emp.: 43
Factoring & Invoice Discounting Services
S.I.C.: 6091
N.A.I.C.S.: 523991
Maria Ramos *(CEO)*

Absa Financial Services Limited (3)
Absa Towers E 170 Main St
2001 Johannesburg, South Africa
Mailing Address:
PO Box 7735
Johannesburg, 2000, South Africa
Tel.: (27) 113504000
Fax: (27) 113503946
E-Mail: info@absa.co.za
Web Site: www.absa.co.za
Emp.: 10,000
Finance & Insurance Services
S.I.C.: 6211
N.A.I.C.S.: 523999
John F. Vitalo *(CEO)*
Maria Ramos *(Deputy CEO)*

Subsidiaries:

Absa Investment Management Services Proprietary Limited (4)
65 Empire Road
Parktown, Johannesburg, 2128, South Africa
Tel.: (27) 11 480 5000
Fax: (27) 11 480 5278
Investment Management Services
S.I.C.: 6211
N.A.I.C.S.: 523999

Absa Life Limited (4)
21 Kruis Street
Johannesburg, 2001, South Africa
Tel.: (27) 113504000
Fax: (27) 113504009
General Insurance Services
S.I.C.: 6411
N.A.I.C.S.: 524298
Willie T. Lategan *(CEO)*

Absa Stockbrokers (Proprietary) Limited (3)
Absa Investment Campusrk Block A 65 Empire Rd
Parktown, 2193, South Africa
Mailing Address:
PO Box 61320
Marshalltown, 2107, South Africa
Tel.: (27) 116470892
Fax: (27) 116470877
E-Mail: info@absa.co.za
Web Site: www.absastockbrokers.co.za
Emp.: 24
Stock Management & Investment Services
S.I.C.: 6211
N.A.I.C.S.: 523999
Alan Miller *(Mng Dir)*

Barclays Bank of South Africa Limited (3)
3rd Floor Absa Towers East 170 Main St
2001 Johannesburg, South Africa
Tel.: (27) 117727000
Web Site: www.barclays.com
Emp.: 50
Commercial, Retail & Corporate Banking Services
S.I.C.: 6029
N.A.I.C.S.: 522110
Mark Springett *(Dir-Complaince)*

Non-U.S. Subsidiaries:

Barclays Bank Mocambique SA (3)
Av 25 De Setembro
Caixa Postal 757
Maputo, 1184, Mozambique
Tel.: (258) 21351700
Fax: (258) 21 323470
Web Site: www.barclays.co.mz
Commercial Banking Services
S.I.C.: 6029
N.A.I.C.S.: 522110

Commercial Bank of Zimbabwe Limited (3)
60 Kwame Nkrumah Avenue
PO Box 3313
Harare, Zimbabwe
Tel.: (263) 4749714
Fax: (263) 4758077
E-Mail: info@cbz.co.zw
Web Site: www.cbz.co.zw
Emp.: 900
Full Banking Services
S.I.C.: 6029
N.A.I.C.S.: 522110

National Bank of Commerce Limited (3)
Sokoine Drive & Azikiwe Street
PO Box 1863
Dar es Salaam, Tanzania (55%)
Tel.: (255) 22 2199793
Fax: (255) 222112887
E-Mail: contact.centre@nbctz.com
Web Site: www.nbctz.com
Rev.: $74,826,870
Assets: $925,840,920
Liabilities: $842,921,790
Net Worth: $82,919,130
Earnings: $1,373,720
Emp.: 1,331
Fiscal Year-end: 12/31/12
Banking Services
S.I.C.: 6029
N.A.I.C.S.: 522110
Pius Tibazarwa *(Acting Mng Dir)*
Maharage Chande *(COO)*
Clara Rubambe *(Sec)*

Barclays Bank Ireland PLC (2)
Two Park Place Hatch St
Dublin, 2, Ireland (100%)
Tel.: (353) 16182626
Telex: 30427 BARD E1
E-Mail: dublinclientservices@barclays.com
Web Site: www.business.barclays.co.uk
Emp.: 75
Retail & Corporate Banking Services
S.I.C.: 6159
N.A.I.C.S.: 522298
Donal Roche *(Chm)*
Andrew Hastings *(CEO)*

Barclays Bank Mexico, S.A. (2)
Paseo De La Reforma 505 Piso 41 Col Cuauhtemoc, 06500, Mexico
Tel.: (52) 55 5241 3200
Commercial Banking Services
S.I.C.: 6029
N.A.I.C.S.: 522110
Raul Martinez-Ostos *(Country Mgr)*

Barclays Bank of Botswana Ltd. (2)
Barclays House Khama Crescent
PO Box 478
Gaborone, Botswana BW
Tel.: (267) 2673905575
Fax: (267) 2673180060
E-Mail: keith.segolodi@barclays.com
Web Site: www.barclays.com
Sales Range: $100-124.9 Million
Emp.: 947
Banking Services
S.I.C.: 6029
N.A.I.C.S.: 522110

Barclays Bank of Ghana Ltd. (2)
High St
PO Box 2949
Accra, Ghana GH
Tel.: (233) 216649014 (100%)
Telex: 2722 BBGACC GH
Fax: (233) 21669254
E-Mail: barclays.ghana@barclays.com
Web Site: www.barclays.com
Emp.: 100
Banking Services
S.I.C.: 6029
N.A.I.C.S.: 522110

Barclays Bank of Kenya Ltd. (2)
Barclays Plaza
PO Box 30120
Loita Street, Nairobi, Kenya (68.5%)
Tel.: (254) 2213915
Telex: 22210 Barcladom ke
Fax: (254) 202241270
E-Mail: barclays.kenya@barclays.com
Banking Services

S.I.C.: 6029
N.A.I.C.S.: 522110

Barclays Bank of Uganda Ltd. (2)
16 Kampala Rd
PO Box 2971
Kampala, Uganda
Tel.: (256) 412309726
Telex: 61014 BARCLADOM UG
Fax: (256) 41259467
E-Mail: barclays.uganda@barclays.com
Web Site: www.barclays.com
Emp.: 150
Retail & Corporate Banking Services
S.I.C.: 6159
N.A.I.C.S.: 522298
Charles Ongwae *(Dir-Fin & Plng)*

Barclays Bank of Zambia Ltd. (2)
PO Box 31936
Cairo Rd, Lusaka, Zambia
Tel.: (260) 211228858
Telex: 41570 BARKA ZA
Fax: (260) 211222510
Web Site: www.barclays.com
Emp.: 750
Retail & Corporate Banking Services
S.I.C.: 6159
N.A.I.C.S.: 522298

Barclays Bank of Zimbabwe Ltd. (2)
Barclay House
PO Box 1279
Corner 1st St & Jason Moyo Ave, Harare, Zimbabwe ZW
Tel.: (263) 4758281 (67.8%)
Fax: (263) 4752913
E-Mail: barclays.zimbabwe@barclays.com
Emp.: 1,000
Banking Services
S.I.C.: 6029
N.A.I.C.S.: 522110
George Gugamatnga *(Mng Dir)*

Barclays Bank PLC-Mauritius (2)
PO Box 284
Port Louis, Mauritius (100%)
Tel.: (230) 402 1000
Fax: (230) 467 0618
E-Mail: barclays.mauritius@barclays.com
Web Site: www.barclays.com
Sales Range: $50-74.9 Million
Emp.: 300
Retail & Corporate Banking Services
S.I.C.: 6159
N.A.I.C.S.: 522298

Barclays Bank SA (2)
Plz De Colon 1
28046 Madrid, Spain ES
Tel.: (34) 913361260 (99.7%)
Fax: (34) 913361104
E-Mail: prensa.es@barclays.com
Web Site: www.barclays.es
Emp.: 30
Retail & Corporate Banking Services
S.I.C.: 6029
N.A.I.C.S.: 522110
Claudio Corradini *(CEO-Retail & Bus Banking-Iberia)*

Barclays Bank (Seychelles) Ltd. (2)
Independence Ave
PO Box 167
Victoria Mahe, Seychelles
Tel.: (248) 383838
Fax: (248) 226191
E-Mail: guyliane.joubert@barclays.com
Web Site: www.barclays.com
Emp.: 249
Retail & Corporate Banking Services
S.I.C.: 6159
N.A.I.C.S.: 522298
Frank Hoarau *(Mng Dir)*

Barclays Bank (South East Asia) Nominees Private Limited (2)
23 Church Street 13-08 Capital Square
Singapore, 049481, Singapore
Tel.: (65) 63953388
Commercial Banking Services
S.I.C.: 6029
N.A.I.C.S.: 522110

Barclays Bank Tanzania Ltd. (2)
TDFL Building
PO Box 5137
Ohio St, Dar es Salaam, Tanzania
Tel.: (255) 222129381
Fax: (255) 222129750
E-Mail: karl.stumke@barclays.com
Web Site: www.barclays.com
Retail & Corporate Banking Services
S.I.C.: 6159
N.A.I.C.S.: 522298
Rished Vade *(Mng Dir)*
Kihara Maina *(Mng Dir)*

Barclays Bank (2)
Via Della Moscova 18
20121 Milan, Italy (100%)
Mailing Address:
P.O. Box 1069
20100 Milan, Italy
Tel.: (39) 263721
Fax: (39) 263722045
Web Site: www.barclays.it
Emp.: 60
Retail & Corporate Banking Services
S.I.C.: 6159
N.A.I.C.S.: 522298

Barclays Bank (2)
183 Ave Daumesnil
75012 Paris, France (100%)
Mailing Address:
P.O. Box 30409
75428 Paris, Cedex, 09, France
Tel.: (33) 55787878
Telex: 210015 Barse f
Fax: (33) 55787000
E-Mail: contact.fr@barclays.co.fr
Web Site: www.barclays.fr
Emp.: 96
Retail & Corporate Banking Services
S.I.C.: 6159
N.A.I.C.S.: 522298
Pascal Roche *(Mng Dir & Mgr-Country)*

Barclays Bank (2)
24/F Ferrum Tower 66 Suha-dong Jung-gu
Seoul, 100-210, Korea (South) (100%)
Tel.: (82) 221262600
Telex: 24480 BARINT K
Fax: (82) 221262601
Web Site: www.barclaysbank.com
Emp.: 50
Retail & Corporate Banking Services
S.I.C.: 6159
N.A.I.C.S.: 522298
John Chang *(Head-Equities & Country Mgr)*

Barclays Bank (2)
Av Barbosa du Bocage 54 D
1000-072 Lisbon, Portugal
Tel.: (351) 707505050
Telex: 42838 BARLIS P
E-Mail: comunicacao.pt@barclays.co.uk
Web Site: www.barclays.pt
Retail & Corporate Banking Services
S.I.C.: 6159
N.A.I.C.S.: 522298

Barclays Bank (2)
601/603 Ceejay House Shivsagar Estate Dr Annie Besant Road
Mumbai, Worli, 400018, India (100%)
Tel.: (91) 2267196000
Telex: 11 82073 BBIL IN; 11 84481 BBIN IN
Fax: (91) 2267196100
Web Site: www.barclays.in
Emp.: 75
Retail & Corporate Banking Services
S.I.C.: 6159
N.A.I.C.S.: 522298
Mani Subramanian *(CEO)*

Barclays Bank (2)
Rm 1211 Scitech Tower
22 Jianquomenwai Dajie, Beijing, 100004, China
Tel.: (86) 1065150006
Telex: 22589 BARPK CN
Fax: (86) 1065127889
Retail & Corporate Banking Services
S.I.C.: 6159
N.A.I.C.S.: 522298

Barclays Bank (2)
Regal House
PO Box 187
Gibraltar, Gibraltar
Tel.: (350) 52378
Telex: 2231 GK BARINT
Fax: (350) 79987
E-Mail: gibraltar@barclays.com
Web Site: www.barclays.com
Retail & Corporate Banking Services
S.I.C.: 6159
N.A.I.C.S.: 522298

Barclays Bank (2)
23 Church St 13 08 Capital Sq
Singapore, 049481, Singapore (100%)
Tel.: (65) 63953000
Telex: 26877 Barint RS
Fax: (65) 63083139
E-Mail: info@barclays.com.sg
Web Site: www.barclays.com.sg
Retail & Corporate Banking Services
S.I.C.: 6159
N.A.I.C.S.: 522298
Rafael Carrillo *(Mng Dir & Head-Fin Institutions Grp-South East Asia)*
Anand Ramachandran *(Mng Dir & Head-Equity Res-ASEAN)*
Adrian McGowan *(Mng Dir & Foreign Exchange Trading-Asia Pacific)*

Barclays Bank (2)
Level 8 Castrol House
36 Customhouse Quay, Wellington, 6000, New Zealand (100%)
Tel.: (64) 44730050
Telex: NZ30097 BARNZ
Fax: (64) 44730051
Web Site: www.barclay.com
Emp.: 10
Retail & Corporate Banking Services
S.I.C.: 6159
N.A.I.C.S.: 522298

Barclays Capital Canada Inc (2)
333 Bay Street Suite 4910
Toronto, ON, M5H 2R2, Canada
Tel.: (416) 863-8900
Fax: (416) 863-8925
Commercial Banking Services
S.I.C.: 6029
N.A.I.C.S.: 522110

Barclays Capital Japan Limited (2)
31F Roppongi Hills Mori Tower 6-10-1 Roppongi Minato-ku
Tokyo, 106-6131, Japan JP
Tel.: (81) 345301100 (100%)
Telex: 24968 BARGROUP J
Fax: (81) 345301110
Web Site: www.barclayscapital.com
Emp.: 1,000
Corporate & Retail Banking Services
S.I.C.: 6159
N.A.I.C.S.: 522298
Tetsuya Kawano *(Vice Chm & Head-IBD)*
Eiji Nakai *(Pres & CEO)*
Akihiko Asami *(Mng Dir & Head-Corp Fin & Investment Banking)*

Barclays Capital (2)
7 Rue des Alpes
CH 1201 Geneva, Switzerland (100%)
Tel.: (41) 227150240
Telex: 423247
Fax: (41) 227150249
Web Site: www.barcap.com
Emp.: 200
Investment Banking Services
S.I.C.: 6211
N.A.I.C.S.: 523110
Kuno Kennel *(Head-Distr)*

Barclays Capital (2)
World Trade Centre Tower C 14th Floor
Strawinskylaan 1453, NL-1077 XX
Amsterdam, Netherlands (100%)
Mailing Address:
P.O. Box 160
1000 AD Amsterdam, Netherlands
Tel.: (31) 205707840
Fax: (31) 205707848
Web Site: www.barcap.nl
Investment Banking
S.I.C.: 6211
N.A.I.C.S.: 523110

Barclays Global Investors Canada Ltd. (2)
161 Bay Street Suite 2500
PO Box 614
Toronto, ON, M5J 2S1, Canada (100%)
Tel.: (416) 643-4000
Telex: 6-22160
Fax: (416) 643-4049
E-Mail: info@barclaysglobal.com
Web Site: www.barclaysglobal.com
Emp.: 50
Investment Advice & Products
S.I.C.: 6722
N.A.I.C.S.: 525910
Michael Wilson *(Chm)*

Barclays Investments & Loans (India) Limited (2)
Ganesh Chs Sector 1 Vashi
Mumbai, 400703, India
Tel.: (91) 22 65977313
E-Mail: barclaysfinance.customerservice@barclays.com
Web Site: www.barclaysfinance.in
Financial Management Services
S.I.C.: 6211
N.A.I.C.S.: 523999

Barclays Private Bank & Trust Company (2)
39-41 Broad St
Saint Helier, JE4 8PU, Jersey
Tel.: (44) 1534873741
Fax: (44) 1534872737
E-Mail:
Web Site: www.barclayswells.co.uk
Emp.: 300
Investment & Corporate Banking Services
S.I.C.: 6211
N.A.I.C.S.: 523110

Barclays Private Bank & Trust Ltd. (2)
Le Marchant House Le Truchot
PO Box 41
Saint Peter Port, GY1 3BE, Guernsey
Tel.: (44) 1481724500
Telex: 4191629
Fax: (44) 1481715260
E-Mail: correspondence@barclayswealth.com
Web Site: www.barclays.com
Private Banking, Trust & Fiduciary Services
S.I.C.: 6029
N.A.I.C.S.: 522110

Barclays Securities (India) Private Limited (2)
Units 1305 & 1306 12th Floor Prestige Meridian II M G Road
Bengaluru, 560001, India
Tel.: (91) 80 6648 5200
Fax: (91) 80 6648 5265
Web Site: www.barclayswealth.com
Emp.: 10
Investment & Security Services
S.I.C.: 6211
N.A.I.C.S.: 523110

Barclays Shared Services Private Limited (2)
Unitech Infospace Park Tower A 5th to 10th floor B-2
Sector-62, Noida, 201307, India
Tel.: (91) 120 3895000
Web Site: www.barclayssharedservices.com
Operational Support Services
S.I.C.: 7389
N.A.I.C.S.: 561499

Cairo Barclays Bank SAE (2)
12 Midan El Sheikh Youssef Garden City
Cairo, Egypt
Tel.: (20) 23662600
Telex: 93734, 92343
Fax: (20) 23662810
E-Mail: Mona.Zin.El.Din@barclayscorporate.com
Web Site: www.barclays.com
Emp.: 275
Retail & Corporate Banking Services
S.I.C.: 6159
N.A.I.C.S.: 522298
Amr El Shafei *(Dir-Corp Banking)*

Barclays Capital Asia Holdings Limited (1)
1 Churchill Place
London, E14 5HP, United Kingdom
Tel.: (44) 20 7116 1000
Investment Management Services
S.I.C.: 6211
N.A.I.C.S.: 523999

Barclays Capital Finance Limited (1)
5 The North Colonnade
Canary Wharf, London, E14 4BB, United Kingdom
Tel.: (44) 20 7623 2323
Fax: (44) 20 7516 7742
Web Site: www.barcap.com
Financial Investment Services
S.I.C.: 6211
N.A.I.C.S.: 523999

Barclays PLC—(Continued)

Barclays Capital Japan Securities Holdings Limited (1)
1 Churchill Place
London, E14 5HP, United Kingdom
Tel.: (44) 2071161000
Investment Management Services
S.I.C.: 6211
N.A.I.C.S.: 523999

Barclays Capital Margin Financing Limited (1)
1 Churchill Place
London, E14 5HP, United Kingdom
Tel.: (44) 2071161000
Venture Capital Services
S.I.C.: 6211
N.A.I.C.S.: 523999

Barclays Capital Nominees Limited (1)
1 Churchill Place
London, E14 5HP, United Kingdom
Tel.: (44) 2071161000
Securities Brokerage Services
S.I.C.: 6211
N.A.I.C.S.: 523120

Barclays Capital Nominees (No.2) Limited (1)
1 Churchill Place
London, E14 5HP, United Kingdom
Tel.: (44) 2071161000
Financial Management Services
S.I.C.: 6211
N.A.I.C.S.: 523999

Barclays Capital Nominees (No.3) Limited (1)
1 Churchill Place
London, E14 5HP, United Kingdom
Tel.: (44) 2071161000
Financial Management Services
S.I.C.: 6211
N.A.I.C.S.: 523999

Barclays Capital Overseas Limited (1)
1 Churchill Place
London, E14 5HP, United Kingdom
Tel.: (44) 2071161000
Investment Management Services
S.I.C.: 6211
N.A.I.C.S.: 523999

Barclays Capital Principal Investments Limited (1)
1 Churchill Place
London, E14 5HP, United Kingdom
Tel.: (44) 20 7116 1000
Investment Management Services
S.I.C.: 6211
N.A.I.C.S.: 523999

Barclays Capital Services Limited (1)
5 The North Colonnade Canary Wharf
London, E14 4BB, United Kingdom
Tel.: (44) 20 7623 2323
Fax: (44) 20 7773 7104
Investment Banking Services
S.I.C.: 6211
N.A.I.C.S.: 523110

Barclays Capital Strategic Advisers Limited (1)
1 Churchill Place
London, E14 5HP, United Kingdom
Tel.: (44) 2071161000
Investment Management Services
S.I.C.: 6211
N.A.I.C.S.: 523999

Barclays CCP Funding LLP (1)
1 Churchill Place
London, E14 5HP, United Kingdom
Tel.: (44) 20 7116 5695
Fund Management Services
S.I.C.: 6282
N.A.I.C.S.: 523920

Barclays Converted Investments Limited (1)
1 Churchill Place
London, E14 5HP, United Kingdom
Tel.: (44) 2071161000
Investment Management Services
S.I.C.: 6211
N.A.I.C.S.: 523999

Barclays Converted Investments (No.2) Limited (1)
1 Churchill Place
London, E14 5HP, United Kingdom
Tel.: (44) 2071161000
Investment Management Services
S.I.C.: 6211
N.A.I.C.S.: 523999

Barclays Covered Bond Funding LLP (1)
1 Churchill Place
London, E14 5HP, United Kingdom
Tel.: (44) 2071165695
Fund Management Services
S.I.C.: 6282
N.A.I.C.S.: 523920

Barclays Covered Bonds Limited Liability Partnership (1)
1 Churchill Place
London, E14 5HP, United Kingdom
Tel.: (44) 2071165695
Asset Management Services
S.I.C.: 6799
N.A.I.C.S.: 523920

Barclays Darnay Euro Investments Limited (1)
1 Churchill Place
London, E14 5HP, United Kingdom
Tel.: (44) 2071161000
Investment Management Services
S.I.C.: 6211
N.A.I.C.S.: 523999

Barclays Directors Limited (1)
1 Churchill Place
London, E14 5HP, United Kingdom
Tel.: (44) 2071161000
Investment Management Services
S.I.C.: 6211
N.A.I.C.S.: 523999

Barclays European Infrastructure II Limited (1)
1 Churchill Place
London, E14 5HP, United Kingdom
Tel.: (44) 2071161000
Real Estate Management Services
S.I.C.: 6531
N.A.I.C.S.: 531390

Barclays European Infrastructure Limited (1)
1 Churchill Place
London, E14 5HP, United Kingdom
Tel.: (44) 20 7116 1000
Real Estate Management Services
S.I.C.: 6531
N.A.I.C.S.: 531390

Barclays Executive Schemes Trustees Limited (1)
1 Churchill Place
London, E14 5HP, United Kingdom
Tel.: (44) 2071161000
Employee Benefit Services
S.I.C.: 6371
N.A.I.C.S.: 524292

Barclays Fiduciary Services (UK) Limited (1)
Osborne Court Gadbrook Park
Northwich, CW9 7UE, United Kingdom
Tel.: (44) 84 5766 0936
Fax: (44) 16 0631 3421
Fiduciary Services
S.I.C.: 6091
N.A.I.C.S.: 523991

Barclays Finance Europe Limited (1)
1 Churchill Place
London, E14 5HP, United Kingdom
Tel.: (44) 20 7116 1000
Fax: (44) 20 7116 7665
Financial Management Services
S.I.C.: 6211
N.A.I.C.S.: 523999

Barclays Financial Planning Ltd (1)
30 Tower View
West Malling, Kent, ME19 4WA, United Kingdom
Tel.: (44) 1732849748
Financial Management Services
S.I.C.: 6211
N.A.I.C.S.: 523999

Barclays Financial Planning Nominee Company Limited (1)
1 Churchill Place
London, E14 5HP, United Kingdom
Tel.: (44) 2071161000
Financial Management Services
S.I.C.: 6211
N.A.I.C.S.: 523999

Barclays Funds Investments Limited (1)
1 Churchill Place
London, E14 5HP, United Kingdom
Tel.: (44) 2071161000
Fax: (44) 2071167665
Investment Management Services
S.I.C.: 6211
N.A.I.C.S.: 523999

Barclays GBP Funding Limited (1)
1 Churchill Place
London, E14 5HP, United Kingdom
Tel.: (44) 20 7116 1000
Fax: (44) 20 7116 7665
Fund Management Services
S.I.C.: 6799
N.A.I.C.S.: 523920

Barclays Group Holdings Limited (1)
1 Churchill Place
London, E14 5HP, United Kingdom
Tel.: (44) 2071161000
Fax: (44) 20 7116 7665
Investment Management Services
S.I.C.: 6211
N.A.I.C.S.: 523999

Barclays Leasing (No.9) Limited (1)
Churchill Plaza
Basingstoke, Hampshire, RG21 7GP, United Kingdom
Tel.: (44) 1256791245
Financial Leasing Services
S.I.C.: 6141
N.A.I.C.S.: 522220

Barclays Long Island Limited (1)
1 Churchill Place
London, E14 5HP, United Kingdom
Tel.: (44) 2071165695
Investment Management Services
S.I.C.: 6211
N.A.I.C.S.: 523999

Barclays Marlist Limited (1)
Churchill Plaza Churchill Way
Basingstoke, Hampshire, RG21 7GP, United Kingdom
Tel.: (44) 1256817777
Financial Management Services
S.I.C.: 6211
N.A.I.C.S.: 523999

Barclays Mercantile Business Finance Limited (1)
Churchill Plaza Churchill Way 5th Floor
Basingstoke, Hampshire, RG21 7GP, United Kingdom
Tel.: (44) 1256 817 777
Fax: (44) 1256 810 273
Investment Management Services
S.I.C.: 6211
N.A.I.C.S.: 523999

Barclays Mercantile Limited (1)
Churchill Way
Basingstoke, Hampshire, RG21 7GP, United Kingdom
Tel.: (44) 1256 817777
Fax: (44) 1256 791122
Investment Management Services
S.I.C.: 6211
N.A.I.C.S.: 523999

Barclays Metals Limited (1)
1 Churchill Place
London, E14 5HP, United Kingdom
Tel.: (44) 2071161000
Investment Management Services
S.I.C.: 6211
N.A.I.C.S.: 523999

Barclays Nominees (Branches) Limited (1)
Presthaven Sands Holiday Park
Prestatyn, LL19 9TT, United Kingdom
Tel.: (44) 1745 853343
Investment Management Services
S.I.C.: 6211
N.A.I.C.S.: 523999

Barclays Nominees (George Yard) Limited (1)
1 Churchill Place
London, E14 5HP, United Kingdom
Tel.: (44) 2071161000
Commercial Banking Services
S.I.C.: 6029
N.A.I.C.S.: 522110

Barclays Nominees (K.W.S.) Limited (1)
1 Churchill Place
London, E14 5HP, United Kingdom
Tel.: (44) 2071161000
Investment Management Services
S.I.C.: 6211
N.A.I.C.S.: 523999

Barclays Nominees (Monument) Limited (1)
1 Churchill Place
London, E14 5HP, United Kingdom
Tel.: (44) 2071161000
Securities Brokerage Services
S.I.C.: 6211
N.A.I.C.S.: 523120

Barclays Nominees (Provincial) Limited (1)
1 Churchill Place
London, E14 5HP, United Kingdom
Tel.: (44) 2071161000
Business Management Consulting Services
S.I.C.: 8742
N.A.I.C.S.: 541611

Barclays Nominees (United Nations For UNJSPF) Limited (1)
1 Churchill Place
London, E14 5HP, United Kingdom
Tel.: (44) 2071161000
Business Management Consulting Services
S.I.C.: 8742
N.A.I.C.S.: 541611

Barclays Pension Funds Trustees Limited (1)
Level 8 1 Churchill Place
London, E14 5HP, United Kingdom
Tel.: (44) 2071161000
Pension Fund Management Services
S.I.C.: 6371
N.A.I.C.S.: 525110

Barclays Physical Trading Limited (1)
1 Churchill Place
London, E14 5HP, United Kingdom
Tel.: (44) 2071161000
Financial Management Services
S.I.C.: 6211
N.A.I.C.S.: 523999

Barclays Private Bank Ltd (1)
43 Brook Street
London, W1K 4HJ, United Kingdom
Tel.: (44) 20 7487 2000
Commercial Banking Services
S.I.C.: 6029
N.A.I.C.S.: 522110

Barclays Private Banking Services Limited (1)
56 Grosvenor Street West Central
London, W1K 3HZ, United Kingdom
Tel.: (44) 20 7487 2000
Commercial Banking Services
S.I.C.: 6029
N.A.I.C.S.: 522110

Barclays Private Trust Limited (1)
1 Churchill Place
London, E14 5HP, United Kingdom UK
Tel.: (44) 2071161000
Investment Trust Management Services
S.I.C.: 6799
N.A.I.C.S.: 523920

Barclays Secured Funding (LM) Limited (1)
1 Churchill Place
London, E14 5HP, United Kingdom
Tel.: (44) 2071161000
Fund Management Services
S.I.C.: 6282
N.A.I.C.S.: 523920

Barclays Secured Notes Finance LLP (1)
1 Churchill Place
London, E14 5HP, United Kingdom

Tel.: (44) 2071161000
Financial Management Services
S.I.C.: 6211
N.A.I.C.S.: 523999

Barclays (Security Realisation) Limited (1)
1 Churchill Place
London, E14 5HP, United Kingdom
Tel.: (44) 2071161000
Securities Brokerage Services
S.I.C.: 6211
N.A.I.C.S.: 523120

Barclays Services (Japan) Limited (1)
1 Churchill Place
London, E14 5HP, United Kingdom
Tel.: (44) 2071161000
Commercial Banking Services
S.I.C.: 6029
N.A.I.C.S.: 522110

Barclays Sharedealing Limited (1)
1 Churchill Place
London, E14 5HP, United Kingdom
Tel.: (44) 2071161000
Securities Brokerage Services
S.I.C.: 6211
N.A.I.C.S.: 523120

Barclays Shea Limited (1)
1 Churchill Place
London, E14 5HP, United Kingdom
Tel.: (44) 2071165695
Commercial Banking Services
S.I.C.: 6029
N.A.I.C.S.: 522110

Barclays SLCSM (No.1) Limited (1)
Standard Life House 30 Lothian Road
Edinburgh, United Kingdom
Tel.: (44) 131 225 2552
Fax: (44) 131 246 0761
Commercial Banking Services
S.I.C.: 6029
N.A.I.C.S.: 522110

Barclays Stockbrokers (Holdings) Limited (1)
1 Churchill Place
London, E14 5HP, United Kingdom
Tel.: (44) 2071161000
Investment Management Services
S.I.C.: 6211
N.A.I.C.S.: 523999

Barclays Stockbrokers (Nominees) Limited (1)
1 Church Place Poplar
London, E14 5HP, United Kingdom
Tel.: (44) 20 7116 1000
Investment Management Services
S.I.C.: 6211
N.A.I.C.S.: 523999

Barclays Unquoted Investments Limited (1)
1 Churchill Place
London, E14 5HP, United Kingdom
Tel.: (44) 2071161000
Investment Management Services
S.I.C.: 6211
N.A.I.C.S.: 523999

Barclays Unquoted Property Investments Limited (1)
1 Churchill Place
London, E14 5HP, United Kingdom
Tel.: (44) 2071161000
Real Estate Management Services
S.I.C.: 6531
N.A.I.C.S.: 531390

Barclays Wealth Nominees Limited (1)
1 Churchill Place
London, E14 5HP, United Kingdom
Tel.: (44) 2071161000
Asset Management Services
S.I.C.: 6282
N.A.I.C.S.: 523920

Barclayshare Nominees Limited (1)
1 Churchill Place
London, E14 5HP, United Kingdom
Tel.: (44) 2071161000
Investment Management Services
S.I.C.: 6211
N.A.I.C.S.: 523999

Barmac (Construction) Limited (1)
Churchill Plaza Churchill Way
Basingstoke, Hampshire, RG21 7GP, United Kingdom
Tel.: (44) 1256 817777
Construction Engineering Services
S.I.C.: 8711
N.A.I.C.S.: 541330

BEIF Management Limited (1)
High Street
Hoddesdon, Hertford, EN11 8HD, United Kingdom
Tel.: (44) 8456 000200
Investment Management Services
S.I.C.: 6211
N.A.I.C.S.: 523999

Bevan Nominees Limited (1)
Kings Orchard 1 Queen Street
Bristol, BS2 0HQ, United Kingdom
Tel.: (44) 8701941000
Fax: (44) 8701941001
Investment Management Services
S.I.C.: 6211
N.A.I.C.S.: 523999

BMBF (No.12) Limited (1)
Churchill Plaza Churchill Way
Basingstoke, RG21 7GP, United Kingdom
Tel.: (44) 1256 817 777
Fax: (44) 1256 791 950
Financial Management Services
S.I.C.: 6211
N.A.I.C.S.: 523999

BMBF (No.18) Limited (1)
Churchill Plaza Churchill Way
Basingstoke, RG21 7GP, United Kingdom
Tel.: (44) 1256 817777
Fax: (44) 1256 810283
Financial Management Services
S.I.C.: 6211
N.A.I.C.S.: 523999

BMBF (No.3) Limited (1)
Churchill Plaza Churchill Way
Basingstoke, RG21 7GP, United Kingdom
Tel.: (44) 1256 817777
Fax: (44) 1256 810273
Financial Management Services
S.I.C.: 6211
N.A.I.C.S.: 523999

BMI Marine Limited (1)
Churchill Plaza Churchill Way
Basingstoke, Hampshire, RG21 1GP, United Kingdom
Tel.: (44) 23 80329100
Fax: (44) 23 80329204
Financial Leasing Services
S.I.C.: 6141
N.A.I.C.S.: 522220

BMI (No.9) Limited (1)
Churchill Plaza Churchill Way
Basingstoke, RG21 7GL, United Kingdom
Tel.: (44) 1256817777
Fax: (44) 1256791950
Financial Management Services
S.I.C.: 6211
N.A.I.C.S.: 523999

B.P.B. (Holdings) Limited (1)
54 Lombard Street
London, EC3P 3AH, United Kingdom
Tel.: (44) 8714 333 000
Investment Management Services
S.I.C.: 6211
N.A.I.C.S.: 523999

Chapelcrest Investments Limited (1)
1 Churchill Place
London, E14 5HP, United Kingdom
Tel.: (44) 2076261567
Investment Management Services
S.I.C.: 6211
N.A.I.C.S.: 523999

Clearlybusiness.com Limited (1)
1 Churchill Place
London, E14 5HP, United Kingdom
Tel.: (44) 845 601 5962
E-Mail: businessdevelopment@clearlybusiness.com
Web Site: www.clearlybusiness.com
Software Development Services
S.I.C.: 7371
N.A.I.C.S.: 541511

Cobalt Investments Limited (1)
1 Churchill Place
London, E14 5HP, United Kingdom
Tel.: (44) 2076261567
Investment Management Services
S.I.C.: 6211
N.A.I.C.S.: 523999

CP Propco 1 Limited (1)
Unit 1 Craven Court Willie Snaith Road
Newmarket, Suffolk, CB8 7FA, United Kingdom
Tel.: (44) 1638 606 300
Fax: (44) 1638 606 301
Investment Management Services
S.I.C.: 6211
N.A.I.C.S.: 523999

CP Propco 2 Limited (1)
Redbourne House Redbourne Park
Redbourne
Gainsborough, Lincolnshire, DN21 4JG, United Kingdom
Tel.: (44) 1652 649 008
Investment Management Services
S.I.C.: 6211
N.A.I.C.S.: 523999

Denham Investments Limited (1)
1 Churchill Place
London, E14 5HP, United Kingdom
Tel.: (44) 2076261567
Investment Management Services
S.I.C.: 6211
N.A.I.C.S.: 523999

Ebbgate Investments Limited (1)
1 Churchill Place
London, E14 5HP, United Kingdom
Tel.: (44) 2076261567
Investment Management Services
S.I.C.: 6211
N.A.I.C.S.: 523999

Eldfell Investments Limited (1)
1 Churchill Place
London, E14 5HP, United Kingdom
Tel.: (44) 2076261567
Investment Management Services
S.I.C.: 6211
N.A.I.C.S.: 523999

Equity Value Investments No.1 Limited (1)
1 Churchill Place
London, E14 5HP, United Kingdom
Tel.: (44) 2076261567
Investment Management Services
S.I.C.: 6211
N.A.I.C.S.: 523999

Gerrard Financial Planning Limited (1)
1a-1b Greenfield Crescent
B15 3BE Birmingham, United Kingdom
Tel.: (44) 800 5875800
Financial Management Services
S.I.C.: 6211
N.A.I.C.S.: 523999

Gerrard Investment Management Limited (1)
1 Churchill Place
London, E14 5HP, United Kingdom
Tel.: (44) 20 7114 1000
Fax: (44) 20 7977 3576
Web Site: www.gerrard.com
Investment Management Services
S.I.C.: 6211
N.A.I.C.S.: 523999

Gerrard Management Services Limited (1)
1 Churchill Place
London, E14 5HP, United Kingdom
Tel.: (44) 2031342000
Investment Management Services
S.I.C.: 6211
N.A.I.C.S.: 523999

Greig Middleton Holdings Limited (1)
Old Mutual Place 2 Lambeth Hill
London, EC4V 4GG, United Kingdom
Tel.: (44) 904 049 8229
Investment Management Services
S.I.C.: 6211
N.A.I.C.S.: 523999

Hoardburst Limited (1)
54 Lombard Street
London, EC3P 3AH, United Kingdom
Tel.: (44) 904 049 8229
Financial Management Services
S.I.C.: 6211
N.A.I.C.S.: 523999

Iveco Capital Limited (1)
Iveco House Station Road
Watford, Hertfordshire, WD17 1SR, United Kingdom
Tel.: (44) 19 2325 9777
Fax: (44) 19 2325 9707
Web Site: web.iveco.com
Investment Management Services
S.I.C.: 6211
N.A.I.C.S.: 523999

Iveco Finance Holdings Limited (1)
Iveco House Station Road
Watford, WD17 1ZS, United Kingdom
Tel.: (44) 1923 259777
Fax: (44) 1923 259707
Investment Management Services
S.I.C.: 6211
N.A.I.C.S.: 523999

Maloney Investments Limited (1)
1 Churchill Place
London, E14 5HP, United Kingdom
Tel.: (44) 2076261567
Investment Management Services
S.I.C.: 6211
N.A.I.C.S.: 523999

MCC Leasing (No.24) Limited (1)
Churchill Plaza Churchill Way
Basingstoke, RG21 7QU, United Kingdom
Tel.: (44) 904 049 8229
Financial Leasing Services
S.I.C.: 6159
N.A.I.C.S.: 522220

Mercantile Credit Company Limited (1)
Churchill Plaza Churchill Way
Basingstoke, Hampshire, RG21 7GP, United Kingdom
Tel.: (44) 1256817777
Financial Leasing Services
S.I.C.: 6141
N.A.I.C.S.: 522220

Mercantile Industrial Leasing Limited (1)
Churchill Plaza Churchill Way
Basingstoke, Hampshire, RG21 7GP, United Kingdom
Tel.: (44) 1256817777
Financial Leasing Services
S.I.C.: 6153
N.A.I.C.S.: 522220

Mercantile Leasing Company (No.132) Limited (1)
Churchill Plaza Churchill Way
Basingstoke, Hampshire, RG21 7GP, United Kingdom
Tel.: (44) 1256817777
Financial Leasing Services
S.I.C.: 6153
N.A.I.C.S.: 522220

Mercantile Leasing Company (No.144) Limited (1)
Churchill Plaza Churchill Way
Basingstoke, Hampshire, RG21 7GP, United Kingdom
Tel.: (44) 1256817777
Financial Leasing Services
S.I.C.: 6141
N.A.I.C.S.: 522220

Murray House Investments Limited (1)
1 Churchill Place
London, E14 5HP, United Kingdom
Tel.: (44) 2076261567
Investment Management Services
S.I.C.: 6211
N.A.I.C.S.: 523999

Myers Grove Investments Limited (1)
1 Churchill Place
London, E14 5HP, United Kingdom
Tel.: (44) 2076261567
Investment Management Services
S.I.C.: 6211
N.A.I.C.S.: 523999

Red House Management Company (Norfolk) Limited (1)
9 Sewell Cottages Redhouse Buxton
Norwich, Norfolk, NR10 5PF, United Kingdom

Barclays PLC—(Continued)

Tel.: (44) 904 049 8229
Property Management Services
S.I.C.: 6531
N.A.I.C.S.: 531311

Relative Value Investments UK Limited Liability Partnership (1)
1 Churchill Place
London, E14 5HP, United Kingdom
Tel.: (44) 2076261567
Investment Management Services
S.I.C.: 6211
N.A.I.C.S.: 523999

Ruthenium Investments Limited (1)
1 Churchill Place
London, E14 5HP, United Kingdom
Tel.: (44) 2076261567
Investment Management Services
S.I.C.: 6211
N.A.I.C.S.: 523999

Scotlife Home Loans (No.3) Limited (1)
2-6 Express House Baches Street
London, N1 6DL, United Kingdom
Tel.: (44) 8456035000
Mortgage Loan Brokerage Services
S.I.C.: 6163
N.A.I.C.S.: 522310

Westferry Investments Limited (1)
1 Churchill Place
London, E14 5HP, United Kingdom
Tel.: (44) 2076261567
Investment Management Services
S.I.C.: 6211
N.A.I.C.S.: 523999

Woolwich Homes Limited (1)
54 Lombard Street
London, EC3P 3AH, United Kingdom
Tel.: (44) 904 049 8229
Real Estate Management Services
S.I.C.: 6531
N.A.I.C.S.: 531390

Woolwich Surveying Services Limited (1)
Drake House Anchor Boulevard Crossways
Dartford, DA2 6QH, United Kingdom
Tel.: (44) 845 605 1111
Surveying & Mapping Services
S.I.C.: 8713
N.A.I.C.S.: 541360

Zeban Nominees Limited (1)
54 Lombard Street
London, EC3P 3AH, United Kingdom
Tel.: (44) 904 049 8229
Financial Management Services
S.I.C.: 6211
N.A.I.C.S.: 523999

U.S. Subsidiaries:

16th & K Hotel Sublessee LP (1)
712 5th Ave
New York, NY 10019
Tel.: (202) 638-2626
Fax: (202) 638-4231
Hotel Management Services
S.I.C.: 7011
N.A.I.C.S.: 721110

475 Fifth 09 LLC (1)
Corporation Trust Ctr 1209 Orange St
Wilmington, DE 19801
Tel.: (302) 658-7581
Financial Management Services
S.I.C.: 6211
N.A.I.C.S.: 523999

Appalachian NPI, LLC (1)
1 Oxford Ctr 301 Grant St
Pittsburgh, PA 15219
Tel.: (412) 553-5700
Fax: (412) 553-5757
Commercial Banking Services
S.I.C.: 6029
N.A.I.C.S.: 522110

Barclays Asset Management Group LLC (1)
1620 26th St Ste 2000N
Santa Monica, CA 90404-4045
Tel.: (310) 907-0510
Fax: (310) 828-5747
Asset Management Services
S.I.C.: 6799
N.A.I.C.S.: 523920

Barclays Capital Energy Inc. (1)
200 Park Ave
New York, NY 10166
Tel.: (212) 412-1000
Investment Management Services
S.I.C.: 6211
N.A.I.C.S.: 523999

Barclays Commercial Mortgage Securities LLC (1)
745 7th Ave
New York, NY 10019
Tel.: (212) 412-4000
Mortgage Loan Brokerage Services
S.I.C.: 6163
N.A.I.C.S.: 522310

Barclays Services LLC (1)
822 Broadway
New York, NY 10003-4804
Tel.: (212) 412-4000
Financial Management Services
S.I.C.: 6211
N.A.I.C.S.: 523999

BCAP LLC (1)
200 Park Ave
New York, NY 10166
Tel.: (212) 412-4000
Asset Management Services
S.I.C.: 6799
N.A.I.C.S.: 523920

CPIA Acquisition No.1 LLC (1)
Corporation Trust Center 1209 Orange St
Wilmington, DE 19801
Tel.: (302) 658-7581
Investment Management Services
S.I.C.: 6211
N.A.I.C.S.: 523999

Crescent Crown Nine Greenway SPV LLC (1)
9 Greenway Plz Ste 650
Houston, TX 77046
Tel.: (713) 966-3900
Fax: (713) 966-3981
Real Estate Development Services
S.I.C.: 6531
N.A.I.C.S.: 531390

Crescent Crown Seven Greenway SPV LLC (1)
777 Main St Ste 2100
Fort Worth, TX 76102-5366
Tel.: (713) 965-2994
Hotel Management Services
S.I.C.: 7011
N.A.I.C.S.: 721110

Crescent Peakview Tower, LLC (1)
6465 S Greenwood Plaza Blvd
Centennial, CO 80111
Tel.: (303) 295-6200
Fax: (303) 295-0660
Hotel Management Services
S.I.C.: 7011
N.A.I.C.S.: 721110

Crescent Tower Residences, L.P. (1)
777 Main St Ste 2100
Dallas, TX 75206
Tel.: (817) 321-2100
Fax: (817) 321-2907
Real Estate Management Services
S.I.C.: 6531
N.A.I.C.S.: 531390

Desert Mountain Associates, Inc. (1)
37700 N Desert Mountain Pkwy
Scottsdale, AZ 85262
Tel.: (480) 488-2998
Real Estate Management Services
S.I.C.: 6531
N.A.I.C.S.: 531390

Desert Mountain Development Corporation (1)
74765 Del Coronado Dr
Palm Desert, CA 92260
Tel.: (760) 832-5773
Real Estate Development Services
S.I.C.: 6531
N.A.I.C.S.: 531390

Fulton Investments LLC (1)
17380 Nadora St
Southfield, MI 48076-7704
Tel.: (248) 787-1445
Investment Management Services
S.I.C.: 6211
N.A.I.C.S.: 523999

Mira Vista Development Corp. (1)
502 S 1040 E
American Fork, UT 84003
Tel.: (801) 756-5464
Financial Management Services
S.I.C.: 6211
N.A.I.C.S.: 523999

Mira Vista Golf Club, L.C. (1)
6600 Mira Vista Blvd
Fort Worth, TX 76132
Tel.: (817) 294-6600
Fax: (817) 294-6622
E-Mail: info@miravistacountryclub.com
Web Site: www.miravista.clubhouseonline-e3.com
Golf Course & Country Club Operator
S.I.C.: 7999
N.A.I.C.S.: 713910
Courtney Connell *(Head-Golf Pro)*

Obsidian Holdings LLC (1)
9709 178th Pl NE Unit 2
Redmond, WA 98052-6972
Tel.: (425) 299-3031
Investment Management Services
S.I.C.: 6211
N.A.I.C.S.: 523999

The Park at One Riverfront, LLC (1)
1690 Little Raven St
Denver, CO 80202
Tel.: (303) 988-4200
Commercial Building Construction Services
S.I.C.: 1542
N.A.I.C.S.: 236220

Parkside Townhomes, LLC (1)
1122 Millview Dr
Arlington, TX 76012
Tel.: (817) 422-0118
Web Site: www.parksidearlington.com
Residential Construction Services
S.I.C.: 1521
N.A.I.C.S.: 236115

Rhode Investments LLC (1)
7110 E Continental Dr Ste 103
Scottsdale, AZ 85257
Tel.: (480) 656-7814
Fax: (480) 656-7216
Investment Management Services
S.I.C.: 6211
N.A.I.C.S.: 523999

Riverfront Park Retail, LLC (1)
1610 Little Raven St Ste 115
Denver, CO 80202-6187
Tel.: (303) 623-1500
Property Management Services
S.I.C.: 6531
N.A.I.C.S.: 531311

SMI Operating Company, LLC (1)
18140 Hwy 12
Sonoma, CA 95476-3630
Tel.: (707) 938-9000
Fax: (707) 938-4250
Investment Management Services
S.I.C.: 6211
N.A.I.C.S.: 523999

SMI Real Estate, LLC (1)
777 Main St 2100
Fort Worth, TX 76102-5366
Tel.: (817) 321-1415
Real Estate Management Services
S.I.C.: 6531
N.A.I.C.S.: 531390
Sam Mark, *(Pres)*

Sonoma Golf Club, LLC (1)
17700 Arnold Dr
Sonoma, CA 95476
Tel.: (707) 939-4100
Fax: (707) 996-8464
E-Mail: reservation@SonomaGolfClub.com
Web Site: www.sonomagolfclub.com
Golf Course & Country Club Operator
S.I.C.: 7999
N.A.I.C.S.: 713910

Taurus Investments LLC (1)
185 Village Sq
Baltimore, MD 21204
Tel.: (410) 532-9501
Investment Management Services
S.I.C.: 6211
N.A.I.C.S.: 523999

Townhomes at Riverfront Park, LLC (1)
1400 Little Raven St
Denver, CO 80202
Tel.: (303) 988-4200
Commercial Building Construction Services
S.I.C.: 1542
N.A.I.C.S.: 236220

Triangle Fund LLC (1)
80 E Market St Ste 202
Corning, NY 14830
Tel.: (607) 962-0189
Fax: (607) 962-0269
Web Site: www.trianglefund.org
Fund Management Services
S.I.C.: 6371
N.A.I.C.S.: 524292

Non-U.S. Subsidiaries:

Absa Capital Representative Office Nigeria Limited (1)
Southgate House Udi Street
Lagos, Nigeria
Tel.: (234) 12210000
Business Management Consulting Services
S.I.C.: 8748
N.A.I.C.S.: 541618

Absa Financial Services Africa Holdings Proprietary Limited (1)
H/V President & Grosstra
Kroonstad, 9499, South Africa
Tel.: (27) 562167300
Fax: (27) 5621216230
Emp.: 32
Financial Management Services
S.I.C.: 6211
N.A.I.C.S.: 523999
Louis du Plessis *(Gen Mgr)*

Absa Fleet Services Limited (1)
151 Katherine St
Johannesburg, Gauteng, 2010, South Africa
Tel.: (27) 123170255
Fax: (27) 123173784
Fleet Management Services
S.I.C.: 7515
N.A.I.C.S.: 532112

Absa Fund Managers Limited (1)
65 Empire Road
Parktown, Johannesburg, Gauteng, 2000, South Africa
Tel.: (27) 11 480 5000
Fax: (27) 11 480 5440
E-Mail: invest@absa.co.za
Web Site: www.absainvestments.co.za
Fund Management Services
S.I.C.: 6282
N.A.I.C.S.: 523920

Absa Health Care Consultants Proprietary Limited (1)
2nd Floor Absa Building 1263 Heuwel Avenue
Centurion, Pretoria, 0157, South Africa
Tel.: (27) 12 674 8800
Fax: (27) 12 663 8673
Health Care Consulting Services
S.I.C.: 8099
N.A.I.C.S.: 621999

Absa idirect Limited (1)
3rd Floor Absa Towers East 170 Main Street
Johannesburg, Gauteng, 2001, South Africa
Tel.: (27) 113504000
Fax: (27) 113504769
E-Mail: idirect@absa.co.za
General Insurance Services
S.I.C.: 6411
N.A.I.C.S.: 524210

Absa Insurance and Financial Advisers Proprietary Limited (1)
Absa Towers 3rd Flr 130 Main Street
Johannesburg, Gauteng, 2000, South Africa
Tel.: (27) 113504000
Fax: (27) 113504009
General Insurance & Financial Advice Services
S.I.C.: 6411
N.A.I.C.S.: 524210

Absa Insurance Company Limited (1)
21 Kruis Street
Johannesburg, 2001, South Africa
Tel.: (27) 11 330 2111
Fax: (27) 11 331 7414
General Insurance Services
S.I.C.: 6411
N.A.I.C.S.: 524210

Absa Manx Insurance Company Limited (1)
3rd Floor Saint Georges Court Upper Church Street
Douglas, IMI 1EE, Isle of Man
Tel.: (44) 16 2469 2411
Insurance Underwriting Services
S.I.C.: 6311
N.A.I.C.S.: 524113

Absa Portfolio Managers Proprietary Limited (1)
Absa Investment Campus Block C 65 Empire Road
Parktown, Johannesburg, 2193, South Africa
Tel.: (27) 11 480 5000
Fax: (27) 11 480 5351
Asset Management Services
S.I.C.: 6799
N.A.I.C.S.: 523920

Absa Secretarial Services Proprietary Limited (1)
7 Murati Ave
Lyttelton, Centurion, South Africa
Tel.: (27) 12 664 3914
Fax: (27) 12 664 3919
Secretarial Services
S.I.C.: 7389
N.A.I.C.S.: 561410

Absa Trading & Investment Solutions Holdings Limited (1)
Absa Building 15 Alice Lane Sandown
Sandown, Sandton, 2196, South Africa
Tel.: (27) 11 895 6000
Fax: (27) 11 895 7802
Investment Management Services
S.I.C.: 6211
N.A.I.C.S.: 523999

Absa Trust Limited (1)
56 Eloff Street
Johannesburg, 11 244 9000, South Africa
Tel.: (27) 11 244 9000
Fax: (27) 11 467 8442
Financial Management Services
S.I.C.: 6211
N.A.I.C.S.: 523999

Absa Vehicle Management Proprietary Limited (1)
22 Louis Trichardt St
Nelspruit, Mpumalanga, 1201, South Africa
Tel.: (27) 113504000
Fleet Management Services
S.I.C.: 7515
N.A.I.C.S.: 532112

Absa Vehicle Management Solutions Proprietary Limited (1)
Block A 151 Katherine Street
Johannesburg, South Africa
Tel.: (27) 11 685 9500
Fax: (27) 11 685 9800
Fleet Management Services
S.I.C.: 7515
N.A.I.C.S.: 532112

Aros Mineral AB (1)
Observatoriegatan 23
PO Box 70426
107 25 Stockholm, Sweden
Tel.: (46) 854542630
Mineral Mining Services
S.I.C.: 1481
N.A.I.C.S.: 213115

Banco Barclays S.A. (1)
Av Faria Lima 4440 - 12th Floor Itaim Bibi
Sao Paulo, 04552-040, Brazil
Tel.: (55) 11 3757 7000
Fax: (55) 11 3757 7343
Web Site: www.barcap.com
Commercial Banking Services
S.I.C.: 6029
N.A.I.C.S.: 522110

Bankfil Limited (1)
170 Main Street
Johannesburg, Gauteng, 2001, South Africa
Tel.: (27) 113504000
Investment Management Services
S.I.C.: 6211
N.A.I.C.S.: 523999

Barclays Asia Limited (1)
41/F Cheung Kong Center 2 Queen's Road
Central, China (Hong Kong)
Tel.: (852) 2903 2938
Fax: (852) 2903 2999
Commercial Banking Services
S.I.C.: 6029
N.A.I.C.S.: 522110
Ester Li *(Mng Dir & Head-Generalist Equities Sls)*
Paul Louie *(Mng Dir & Head-Property Sector-Equity Res-Asia)*
Robert Morrice *(Chm/CEO-Asia Pacific)*

Barclays Capital Asia Limited (1)
41/F Cheung Kong Ctr 2 Queen's Road
Central, China (Hong Kong)
Tel.: (852) 2903 2938
Fax: (852) 2903 2999
Investment Management Services
S.I.C.: 6211
N.A.I.C.S.: 523999

Barclays Capital Charitable Trust (1)
19-21 Broad St
Saint Helier, Jersey
Tel.: (44) 1534 602901
Charitable Trust Management Services
S.I.C.: 6732
N.A.I.C.S.: 813211

Barclays Capital Global Services Singapore Pte. Limited (1)
60B Orchard Rd 10-00 Atrium Orchard
Singapore, 238891, Singapore
Tel.: (65) 6828 5000
Fax: (65) 6828 5923
Investment Management Services
S.I.C.: 6211
N.A.I.C.S.: 523999

Barclays Capital Luxembourg S.a r.l. (1)
9 Allee Scheffer
2520 Luxembourg, Luxembourg
Tel.: (352) 26 63 5100
Fax: (352) 26 63 5013
Asset Management Services
S.I.C.: 6282
N.A.I.C.S.: 523920

Barclays Capital Markets Malaysia Sdn Bhd. (1)
70th Floor Petronas Twin Tower 2 Jln Ampang
50888 Kuala Lumpur, Malaysia
Tel.: (60) 3 2170 0000
Fax: (60) 3 2170 0101
Financial Management Services
S.I.C.: 6211
N.A.I.C.S.: 523999

Barclays Diversification SA. (1)
183 Avenue Daumesnil
Paris, 75012, France
Tel.: (33) 1 55 78 78 78
Financial Management Services
S.I.C.: 6211
N.A.I.C.S.: 523999
Tony Blanco *(Gen Mgr)*

Barclays Family S.p.A (1)
Via Costanza Arconati 1
Milan, 20135, Italy
Tel.: (39) 025 4151
Credit Management Services
S.I.C.: 6099
N.A.I.C.S.: 522390

Barclays Financial Services Italia S.p.A. (1)
Via Della Moscova 18
Milan, Italy
Tel.: (39) 0263721
Fax: (39) 0263722044
Financial Management Services
S.I.C.: 6211
N.A.I.C.S.: 523999

Barclays Financial Services Limited (1)
Barclays Plaza M6 Loita Street
Nairobi, 00100, Kenya
Tel.: (254) 20310843
Financial Management Services
S.I.C.: 6211
N.A.I.C.S.: 523999

Barclays France SA (1)
32 Avenue George V
Paris, 75008, France
Tel.: (33) 1 55 78 78 78
Fax: (33) 1 55 78 70 00
Web Site: www.barclays.fr
Investment Banking Services
S.I.C.: 6211
N.A.I.C.S.: 523110

Barclays Holdings (Isle of Man) Limited (1)
4th Floor Queen Victoria House 41 Victoria St
Douglas, IM1 2LF, Isle of Man
Tel.: (44) 1624 683828
Investment Management Services
S.I.C.: 6211
N.A.I.C.S.: 523999
Simon Scott *(Mng Dir)*

Barclays International Fund Managers Limited (1)
28-30 The Parade
JE4 8RA Saint Helier, Jersey
Tel.: (44) 1534 812700
Fund Management Services
S.I.C.: 6282
N.A.I.C.S.: 523920

Barclays Patrimoine S.C.S. (1)
2 Boulevard De Strasbourg
Toulouse, Haute-Garonne, 31000, France
Tel.: (33) 562737373
Emp.: 24
Investment Management Services
S.I.C.: 6799
N.A.I.C.S.: 523920
Christen Varley *(Mng Dir)*

Barclays Private Bank & Trust (Isle of Man) Limited (1)
Floor 4 Queen Victoria House 41 Victoria Street
Douglas, IM1 2LF, Isle of Man
Tel.: (44) 1624 682 828
Fax: (44) 1624 620 905
Commercial Banking Services
S.I.C.: 6029
N.A.I.C.S.: 522110

Barclays Private Equity S.p.A. (1)
Via Della Moscova 18
20121 Milan, Italy IT
Tel.: (39) 02 63721
Fax: (39) 02 6372 2045
Private Equity Firm
S.I.C.: 6211
N.A.I.C.S.: 523999

Barclays Vie SA (1)
183 Avenue Daumesnil
Paris, 75012, France
Tel.: (33) 1 55 78 77 00
Fax: (33) 1 55 78 77 11
General Insurance Services
S.I.C.: 6411
N.A.I.C.S.: 524210

Barclays Wealth Asset Management (Monaco) S.A.M (1)
31 Avenue de la Costa
98000 Monte Carlo, Monaco
Tel.: (377) 93 10 51 51
Fax: (377) 93 25 15 68
E-Mail: monacobw@barclayswealth.com
Asset Management Services
S.I.C.: 6282
N.A.I.C.S.: 523920

Barclays Wealth Corporate Services (Guernsey) Limited (1)
Level 1 Regency Court Glategny Esplanade
Saint Peter Port
Saint Peter Port, GY1 3ST, Guernsey
Tel.: (44) 1534 711 111
Fax: (44) 1481 710147
Investment Management Services
S.I.C.: 6211
N.A.I.C.S.: 523999

Barclays Wealth Fund Managers (Guernsey) Limited (1)
Level 1 Regency Court Glategny Esplanade
Saint Peter Port, GY1 3ST, Guernsey
Tel.: (44) 1481 747474
Fax: (44) 1481 710147
Asset Management Services
S.I.C.: 6282
N.A.I.C.S.: 523920

Barclays Wealth Fund Managers (Isle of Man) Limited (1)
Finch Hill House Bucks Road
PO Box 58
Douglas, Isle of Man
Tel.: (44) 1624 689300
Fax: (44) 1624 689399
Asset Management Services
S.I.C.: 6799
N.A.I.C.S.: 523920

Barclays Wealth Managers France SA (1)
183 Avenue Daumesnil
Paris, 75012, France
Tel.: (33) 1 55 78 78 78
Asset Management Services
S.I.C.: 6799
N.A.I.C.S.: 523920

Barclays Wealth Nominees (Jersey) Limited (1)
66-68 Esplanade
Saint Helier, JE4 5PS, Jersey
Tel.: (44) 15347 111 11
Financial Management Services
S.I.C.: 6211
N.A.I.C.S.: 523999

Barclays Wealth Trustees (Guernsey) Limited (1)
Level 1 Regency Court Glategny Esplanade
Saint Peter Port, GY1 3ST, Guernsey
Tel.: (44) 1534 711 111
Fax: (44) 1481 710147
Fund Management Services
S.I.C.: 6799
N.A.I.C.S.: 523920

Barclays Wealth Trustees (Hong Kong) Limited (1)
42/F Citibank Tower 3 Garden Road
Central, China (Hong Kong)
Tel.: (852) 2903 4692
Fax: (852) 2903 4680
Fund Management Services
S.I.C.: 6282
N.A.I.C.S.: 523920

Barclays Wealth Trustees (India) Private Limited (1)
Titanium 2nd Floor Western Express Highway Plot No 201
Goregaon East, Mumbai, 400063, India
Tel.: (91) 22 6731 5000
Fax: (91) 22 6731 5099
Fund Management Services
S.I.C.: 6799
N.A.I.C.S.: 523920

Barclays Zimbabwe Nominees (Pvt) Limited (1)
Floor 2 Three Anchor Hse Jason Moyo Ave
PO Box 1279
Harare, Zimbabwe
Tel.: (263) 4 75 8281
Fax: (263) 4 75 2913
E-Mail: barclays.zimbabwe@barclays.com
Investment Management Services
S.I.C.: 6211
N.A.I.C.S.: 523999

Barclaytrust Channel Islands Limited (1)
39-41 Broad St
Saint Helier, JE2 3RR, Jersey
Tel.: (44) 1534873741
Fax: (44) 1534872737
Financial Management Services
S.I.C.: 6211
N.A.I.C.S.: 523999

Barclaytrust International (Jersey) Limited (1)
39-41 Broad Street
Saint Helier, JE4 8PU, Jersey
Tel.: (44) 1534 873741
Fax: (44) 1534 872737
Financial Management Services
S.I.C.: 6211
N.A.I.C.S.: 523999

Barclaytrust (Suisse) SA (1)
Chemin De Grange-Canal 18-20
1224 Chene-Bougeries, Switzerland

Barclays PLC—(Continued)

Tel.: (41) 22 819 59 00
Fax: (41) 22 819 59 99
Commercial Banking Services
S.I.C.: 6029
N.A.I.C.S.: 522110

BauBeCon Assets GmbH (1)
Erik-Blumenfeld-Platz 27b
Hamburg, 22587, Germany
Tel.: (49) 51184000
Asset Management Services
S.I.C.: 6799
N.A.I.C.S.: 523920

BauBeCon BIO GmbH (1)
Schuetzenallee 3
Hannover, 30519, Germany
Tel.: (49) 51184000
Real Estate Rental Services
S.I.C.: 6514
N.A.I.C.S.: 531110

Baubecon Holding 1 GmbH (1)
Schuetzenallee 3
Hannover, 30519, Germany
Tel.: (49) 511 84000
Fax: (49) 511 8400327
Investment Management Services
S.I.C.: 6211
N.A.I.C.S.: 523999

BauBeCon Immobilien GmbH (1)
Schutzenallee 3
Hannover, 30519, Germany
Tel.: (49) 51184000
Fax: (49) 5118400327
Real Estate Development Services
S.I.C.: 6531
N.A.I.C.S.: 531390

BauBeCon Wohnwert GmbH (1)
Erik-Blumenfeld-Platz 27B
Hamburg, 22587, Germany
Tel.: (49) 511988350
Investment Management Services
S.I.C.: 6211
N.A.I.C.S.: 523999

BBSA Servicos e Participacoes Limitada (1)
Praca Prf Jose Lannes 40
Sao Paulo, 04571-100, Brazil
Tel.: (55) 9 3270
Investment Management Services
S.I.C.: 6211
N.A.I.C.S.: 523999

BPB Holdings S.A. (1)
Rue D'Italie 8-10
1204 Geneva, Switzerland
Tel.: (41) 22819 51 11
Fax: (41) 22310 64 60
Investment Management Services
S.I.C.: 6211
N.A.I.C.S.: 523999

Capital Property Fund Nominees Proprietary Limited (1)
4th Floor Rivonia Village Rivonia Boulevard
Rivonia
PO Box 2555
Johannesburg, Gauteng, 2128, South Africa
Tel.: (27) 11 612 6870
Fax: (27) 11 612 6899
Real Estate Management Services
S.I.C.: 6531
N.A.I.C.S.: 531390

Chewdef GP GmbH (1)
Eysseneckstr 4
Frankfurt am Main, Germany
Tel.: (49) 8969381680
Investment Management Services
S.I.C.: 6211
N.A.I.C.S.: 523999

Crescendo Investment Holdings Limited (1)
Tropic Isle
PO Box 438
Road Town, Virgin Islands (British)
Tel.: (284) 4942616
Investment Management Services
S.I.C.: 6211
N.A.I.C.S.: 523999

Gordon Holdings (Netherlands) B.V. (1)
Fred Roeskestraat 123-1
Amsterdam, Noord-Holland, 1076 EE, Netherlands
Tel.: (31) 20 577 1177
Investment Management Services
S.I.C.: 6211
N.A.I.C.S.: 523999

Grupo Financiero Barclays Mexico, S.A. de C.V. (1)
Eje 3 Sur Av Morelos 41 Artes Graficas
Cuauhteemoc
Mexico, Mexico
Tel.: (52) 1 55 5241 3200
Fax: (52) 1 55 5241 3271
Securities Brokerage Services
S.I.C.: 6211
N.A.I.C.S.: 523120

Hamnes Investments BV (1)
Dam 7F-6e Etage
1012 JS Amsterdam, Netherlands
Tel.: (31) 204867646
Financial Management Services
S.I.C.: 6211
N.A.I.C.S.: 523999

ISB CANARIAS SA (1)
Calle Albareda 5
Las Palmas, 35007, Spain
Tel.: (34) 913 362 055
Commercial Banking Services
S.I.C.: 6029
N.A.I.C.S.: 522110

Iveco Finance AG (1)
Oberfeldstrasse 20
8302 Kloten, Switzerland
Tel.: (41) 44804 30 00
Fax: (41) 44804 30 01
Financial Leasing Services
S.I.C.: 6141
N.A.I.C.S.: 522220

Iveco Finance GmbH (1)
Salzstrasse 185
74076 Heilbronn, Germany
Tel.: (49) 71 31 27 88 0
Fax: (49) 71 31 27 88 800
E-Mail: info@ivecofinance.de
Web Site: www.ivecocapital.de
Financial Management Services
S.I.C.: 6211
N.A.I.C.S.: 523999

Iveco Finanziaria S.p.A. (1)
Lungo Stura Lazio 49
10156 Turin, Italy
Tel.: (39) 0110078078
Fax: (39) 0110076786
E-Mail: ivecocapital_contact@iveco.com
Financial Management Services
S.I.C.: 6211
N.A.I.C.S.: 523999

Kafue House Limited (1)
Cairo Rd
PO Box 31936
Lusaka, Zambia
Tel.: (260) 211 366100
Fax: (260) 211 222519
Commercial Banking Services
S.I.C.: 6029
N.A.I.C.S.: 522110

Lantern Financial Services Proprietary Limited (1)
6 Albert St
Peddie, South Africa
Tel.: (27) 40 6733031
Financial Management Services
S.I.C.: 6211
N.A.I.C.S.: 523999

Limited Liability Company Barclays Capital (1)
125047 G Moskva Ul Tverskaya-Yamskaya 1-Ya d 21
Moscow, Russia
Tel.: (7) 495 786 84 00
Fax: (7) 495 786 84 02
Web Site: www.barcap.com
Investment Banking Services
S.I.C.: 6211
N.A.I.C.S.: 523110

MB Acquired Operations Limited (1)
Meeg Bank Bldg
Mthatha, 5100, South Africa
Tel.: (27) 475026200
Fax: (27) 475026302
Real Estate Management Services
S.I.C.: 6531
N.A.I.C.S.: 531390

Mercurio Mortgage Finance S.r.l. (1)
Foro Buonaparte 70
20121 Milan, Italy
Tel.: (39) 02861914
Fax: (39) 02862495
Mortgage Loan Brokerage Services
S.I.C.: 6163
N.A.I.C.S.: 522310
Andrea Dicola *(Gen Mgr)*

Merque Financial Services Proprietary Limited (1)
104 Park St
Klerksdorp, North West, 2571, South Africa
Tel.: (27) 437014200
Fax: (27) 437270134
Financial Management Services
S.I.C.: 6211
N.A.I.C.S.: 523999

Nabucco RE BV (1)
Dam 7f 6e Etage
Amsterdam, Noord-Holland, 1012 JS, Netherlands
Tel.: (31) 204867646
Real Estate Management Services
S.I.C.: 6531
N.A.I.C.S.: 531390

Newfunds Proprietary Limited (1)
PO Box 5438
Johannesburg, South Africa 2000
Tel.: (27) 11 895 5517
Fax: (27) 11 895 7832
Fund Management Services
S.I.C.: 6282
N.A.I.C.S.: 523920

Ou Skip Beleggings Proprietary Limited (1)
401 Parkgebou Durbanweg 49
Bellville, Western Cape, 7530, South Africa
Tel.: (27) 113504000
Investment Management Services
S.I.C.: 6211
N.A.I.C.S.: 523999

Patus 216 GmbH (1)
Erik-Blumfeld-Platz 27b
Hamburg, 22587, Germany
Tel.: (49) 511 84000
Fax: (49) 511 8400327
Financial Management Services
S.I.C.: 6211
N.A.I.C.S.: 523999

Ruval SA (1)
Plaza Colon 1
Madrid, 28046, Spain
Tel.: (34) 913361000
Fax: (34) 913361406
Building Maintenance Services
S.I.C.: 1522
N.A.I.C.S.: 236118

Societe Francaise de Gestion et de Construction (SFGC) SA (1)
183 Av Daumesnil
Paris, France 75012
Tel.: (33) 1 42 47 82 47
Fax: (33) 1 44 79 77 21
Property Management Services
S.I.C.: 6531
N.A.I.C.S.: 531311

Somerset West Autopark Proprietary Limited (1)
75 Hartshorne Street
Benoni, South Africa
Tel.: (27) 115109900
Property Management Services
S.I.C.: 6531
N.A.I.C.S.: 531311

Svenska Kaolin AB (1)
Drottningg 92-94
111 36 Stockholm, Sweden
Tel.: (46) 8 545426 30
E-Mail: info@svenskakaolin.se
Web Site: www.svenskakaolin.se
Clay Mining Services
S.I.C.: 1455
N.A.I.C.S.: 212324

UB Group Limited (1)
33 Sloane Dr
Johannesburg, 2191, South Africa
Tel.: (27) 113507071
Investment Management Services
S.I.C.: 6211
N.A.I.C.S.: 523999

Unifer Holdings Limited (1)
27 Impala Road Hurston Place
Sandton, Johannesburg, 2196, South Africa
Tel.: (27) 11 783 0100
Fax: (27) 11 784 9761
Investment Management Services
S.I.C.: 6211
N.A.I.C.S.: 523999

BARCO MATERIALS HANDLING LTD.

24 Kerr Crescent Keer Industrial Park
Guelph, ON, N1H 6H9, Canada
Tel.: (519) 763-1037
Fax: (519) 763-7353
Web Site: www.barco.ca
Rev.: $31,944,472
Emp.: 146

Business Description:
Pallet & Box Mfr
S.I.C.: 2448
N.A.I.C.S.: 321920

Personnel:
Bob Baranski *(Pres)*

BARCO N.V.

President Kennedypark 35
8500 Kortrijk, Belgium
Tel.: (32) 56233211
Fax: (32) 56262262
E-Mail: webmaster@barco.com
Web Site: www.barco.com
Year Founded: 1934
BAR—(EUR)
Sls.: $1,556,150,981
Assets: $1,241,005,853
Liabilities: $516,699,085
Net Worth: $724,306,769
Earnings: $126,864,407
Emp.: 3,727
Fiscal Year-end: 12/31/12

Business Description:
Display Monitor, Projector, Lighting Solutions & Visual System Control Software Mfr
S.I.C.: 3648
N.A.I.C.S.: 335129

Personnel:
Herman Daems *(Chm)*
Eric Van Zele *(Pres & CEO)*
Carl Peeters *(CFO & Sr VP)*
Filip Pintelon *(COO & Sr VP)*
Jacques Bertrand *(Chief Sls Officer & Sr VP)*
Jan Van Acoleyen *(Chief HR Officer & Sr VP)*
Stephan Paridaen *(Pres-Media & Entertainment)*
Kurt Verheggen *(Gen Counsel & Sec)*
Wim Buyens *(Sr VP & Gen Mgr-Projection)*
Piet Candeel *(Sr VP & Gen Mgr-Healthcare)*
Steve Leyland *(Sr VP & Gen Mgr-Advanced Visualization)*
Dave Scott *(Sr VP & Gen Mgr-Defense & Aerospace)*
Luc Vandenbroucke *(Sr VP-Wholly Owned Ventures)*

Board of Directors:
Herman Daems
Antoon De Proft
Bruno Holthof
Ashok K. Jain
Luc Missorten
Jan Pieter Oosterveld
Eric Van Zele
Christina von Wackerbarth

Subsidiaries:

Barco Coordination Center NV (1)
President Kennedy Park 35
Kortrijk, 8500, Belgium

Tel.: (32) 56233211
Fax: (32) 56233279
Emp.: 100
Software Development Services
S.I.C.: 7371
N.A.I.C.S.: 541511
Eric Van Zele *(CEO)*

Barco Silex N.V. (1)
Scientific Park
Rue du Bosquet 7, 1348 Louvain-la-Neuve, Belgium (99%)
Tel.: (32) 10454904
Fax: (32) 10454636
E-Mail: barco-silex@barco.com
Web Site: www.barco.com
Sales Range: $1-9.9 Million
Emp.: 20
S.I.C.: 7374
N.A.I.C.S.: 518210
Watteyn Thierru *(Mng Dir)*

BarcoView Avionics (1)
President Kennedy Park 35
8500 Kortrijk, Belgium (79.99%)
Tel.: (32) 56233579
Fax: (32) 56368116
Web Site: www.barcoaerospace.com
Emp.: 2,000
S.I.C.: 7374
N.A.I.C.S.: 518210
Koen Helsen *(Mgr-Mktg)*

Innovative Designs (1)
Akkerstraat 1
8020 Waardamme, Belgium BE
Tel.: (32) 50217042 (100%)
Fax: (32) 50 22 18 29
E-Mail: info@id-be.com
Web Site: www.id-be.com
Emp.: 15
Video Technology Mfr
S.I.C.: 7812
N.A.I.C.S.: 512110

U.S. Subsidiaries:

Barco Federal Systems LLC (1)
3059 Premiere Pkwy
Duluth, GA 30097
Tel.: (678) 475-8000
Fax: (678) 475-8100
Search & Navigation System Mfr
S.I.C.: 3812
N.A.I.C.S.: 334511

Barco, Inc. (1)
3059 Premiere Pkwy Ste 400
Duluth, GA 30097
Tel.: (678) 475-8000
Fax: (678) 475-8100
Web Site: www.barco.com
Emp.: 250
Communication & Visualization Equipment Mfr
S.I.C.: 3669
N.A.I.C.S.: 334290
Andries Van Duffel *(Mgr-Tech Support & Escalation)*

Barco Simulations (1)
600 Bellbrook Ave
Xenia, OH 45385-4053 (100%)
Tel.: (937) 372-7579
Fax: (937) 372-8645
E-Mail: info@barcosimulations.com
Web Site: www.barcosimulations.com
Emp.: 110
Mfr. & Distributor of Calligraphic Projectors for Flight Simulation
S.I.C.: 3663
N.A.I.C.S.: 334220
Greg Packet *(VP-Ops)*

Barco Visual Solutions (1)
3059 Premiere Pkwy
Duluth, GA 30097-4905
Tel.: (770) 218-3200
Fax: (770) 218-3250
Distributor of Large Screen Projectors
S.I.C.: 7371
N.A.I.C.S.: 541511

High End Systems, Inc. (1)
2105 Gracy Farms Ln
Austin, TX 78758-4031
Tel.: (512) 836-2242
Fax: (512) 837-5290
Toll Free: (800) 890-8989
E-Mail: info@barco.com
Web Site: www.highend.com
Sales Range: $25-49.9 Million
Emp.: 156
Stage Lighting & Control Systems Mfr
S.I.C.: 3648
N.A.I.C.S.: 335129
Richard Belliveau *(Co-Founder & CTO)*
Lowell Fowler *(Co-Founder)*
Merritt Belisle *(Chm)*
Bill Morris *(CEO)*

Non-U.S. Subsidiaries:

Barco Co., Ltd. (1)
5 1 1 Heiwajima Otaku
Tokyo, 143006, Japan (100%)
Tel.: (81) 357628720
Fax: (81) 357628738
E-Mail: info@barco.co.jp
Web Site: www.barco.co.jp
Emp.: 55
S.I.C.: 7374
N.A.I.C.S.: 518210
Mark Poot *(CEO)*

Barco Control Rooms (1)
An Der Rossweid 5
Karlsruhe, 76229, Germany (100%)
Tel.: (49) 72162010
Fax: (49) 7216201190
E-Mail: info.de.bcd@barco.com
Web Site: www.barco.com
Emp.: 150
S.I.C.: 7374
N.A.I.C.S.: 518210
Carl Peetrs *(CFO)*

Barco Electronic Systems Ltd. (1)
103 Balarama Bandra Kurla Complex
Bandra East, Mumbai, 400051, India (100%)
Tel.: (91) 2230685995
Fax: (91) 2230685996
E-Mail: info@baro.com
Web Site: www.barco.com
Emp.: 500
S.I.C.: 7374
N.A.I.C.S.: 518210

Barco Electronic Systems Ltd. (1)
53 Etzel St
Rishon le Zion, 75706, Israel (100%)
Tel.: (972) 35628090
Fax: (972) 35626010
E-Mail: itzik@barco.co.al
Web Site: www.barco.com
Emp.: 7
S.I.C.: 7374
N.A.I.C.S.: 518210
Itzik Shapira *(Mgr-Mktg)*

Barco Electronic Systems S.A. (1)
Travessera De Les Corts 371
Barcelona, 8029, Spain (100%)
Tel.: (34) 934442103
Fax: (34) 934442125
Web Site: www.barco.com
Emp.: 20
S.I.C.: 7379
N.A.I.C.S.: 518210

Barco GmbH (1)
Anberdrossweid No 5
Karlsruhe, 76229, Germany (100%)
Tel.: (49) 72162010
Fax: (49) 7216201190
E-Mail: info.de.bcd@barco.com
Emp.: 180
S.I.C.: 7374
N.A.I.C.S.: 518210
Klause Kartuasser *(Gen Mgr)*

Barco GmbH (1)
Greschbachtrasse 2-4
77971 Kippenheim, Germany (75%)
Tel.: (49) 72162010
Fax: (49) 7216201610
E-Mail: kippenheim@barco.com
Web Site: www.barco.de
Emp.: 34
S.I.C.: 7374
N.A.I.C.S.: 518210

Barco Ltda. (1)
Av Dr Cardoso De Melo 1855 8 Andar CJ 81
Vila Olimpia, Sao Paulo, 04548005, Brazil (100%)
Tel.: (55) 01138421656
Fax: (55) 1130451160
E-Mail: danilo.binheiro@barco.com
Web Site: www.barco.com.br
Sales Range: Less than $1 Million
Emp.: 12
S.I.C.: 7379
N.A.I.C.S.: 518210
Louiz Anthones *(Mgr-Sls)*

Barco Ltd. (1)
165 2 Samsong Pong Gangnangu
Kangnam Ku, Seoul, 135-090, Korea (South) (99%)
Tel.: (82) 234458900
Fax: (82) 234458907
E-Mail: jangsung.park@parko.com
Sales Range: $1-9.9 Million
Emp.: 20
S.I.C.: 7374
N.A.I.C.S.: 518210

Barco Ltd. (1)
11F No 102 Guangfu S Rd Daan Dist
Taipei, Hsien, 10694, Taiwan (94%)
Tel.: (886) 287710699
Fax: (886) 287710606
E-Mail: sales.gc@barco.com
Web Site: www.barco.com
Emp.: 14
Designs & Develops Visualization Solutions for Professional Markets
S.I.C.: 7374
N.A.I.C.S.: 518210
Marc Toot *(Mng Dir)*

Barco Ltd. (1)
65 42 Tower 19th Fl Rm 1902 Sukhumvit 42 Rd
Prakanong Klongtoey, Bangkok, 10110, Thailand (100%)
Tel.: (66) 27122533
Fax: (66) 27122538
E-Mail: info@barco.com
Emp.: 2
S.I.C.: 7374
N.A.I.C.S.: 518210

Barco Ltd. (1)
Rm 2801 28th Fl Central Plz
18 Harbour Rd, Wanchai, China (Hong Kong) (100%)
Tel.: (852) 21725625
Fax: (852) 23971903
Web Site: www.barco.com
Emp.: 20
S.I.C.: 7379
N.A.I.C.S.: 518210

Barco Ltd. (1)
Farley Haoo London Rd Binsield
RG424EU Bracknell, RG61AZ, United Kingdom (100%)
Tel.: (44) 1189664611
Fax: (44) 1189267716
E-Mail: info@barco.com
Web Site: www.barco.com
Emp.: 23
S.I.C.: 7374
N.A.I.C.S.: 518210

Barco Manufacturing s.r.o. (1)
Billundska 2756
Kladno, 272 01, Czech Republic
Tel.: (420) 312 818 411
Emp.: 100
Electronic Component Mfr
S.I.C.: 3679
N.A.I.C.S.: 334419

Barco Orthogon GmbH (1)
Hastedter Osterdeich 222
Bremen, 28207, Germany
Tel.: (49) 421 20 12 20
Fax: (49) 421 20 12 2999
Web Site: www.orthogon.com
Emp.: 55
Air Traffic Control System Software Development Services
S.I.C.: 7371
N.A.I.C.S.: 541511
Frank Koehne *(Gen Mgr)*

Barco Pte. Ltd. (1)
No 10 Changi South Lane
#04-01 Ossia Building, Singapore, 486162, Singapore (100%)
Tel.: (65) 62437610
Fax: (65) 65434322
E-Mail: info@barco.com
Web Site: www.barco.com
Emp.: 20
S.I.C.: 7379
N.A.I.C.S.: 518210

Barco S.A. (1)
6 Blvd De La Liberation ZA Urbaparc 1
93200 Saint Denis, France (100%)
Tel.: (33) 148135900
Fax: (33) 148200326
Web Site: www.barco.com
Sales Range: $25-49.9 Million
Emp.: 30
S.I.C.: 7374
N.A.I.C.S.: 518210

Barco SAS (1)
Immeuble Le Plein Ouest 177 Avenue Georges Clemenceau
Nanterre, 920001, France
Tel.: (33) 155691020
Electronic Component Mfr
S.I.C.: 3679
N.A.I.C.S.: 334419

Barco Sdn Bhd (1)
Block D1 Jalan Pju 1 41 Dataran Prima
Selangor Darul, 47301 Petaling Jaya, Malaysia (100%)
Tel.: (60) 378803362
Fax: (60) 378802362
Web Site: www.barco.com
Emp.: 7
S.I.C.: 7374
N.A.I.C.S.: 518210
M. Soo *(Mng Dir)*

Barco Silex SAS (1)
Zone Industrielle Rousset Immeuble CCE 6 Route De Trets
13790 Peynier, France
Tel.: (33) 4 42 16 41 06
Fax: (33) 4 42 16 41 38
Electronic Engineering Services
S.I.C.: 8711
N.A.I.C.S.: 541330

Barco Sp. Z o.o. (1)
Ul Marywilska 16
3428 Warsaw, Poland (100%)
Tel.: (48) 228142791
Fax: (48) 228143276
E-Mail: info@barco.pl
Web Site: www.barco.pl
Sls.: $183,474
Emp.: 10
S.I.C.: 7379
N.A.I.C.S.: 518210
Joanna Skopczynska *(Office Mgr)*

Barco S.r.L. (1)
Via Monferrato 7
I 20094 Corsico, MI, Italy (100%)
Tel.: (39) 24587981
Fax: (39) 245879831
Web Site: www.barco.com
Emp.: 20
Developer of Imaging Technologies
S.I.C.: 7379
N.A.I.C.S.: 518210

Barco Sverige AB (1)
Kyrkvagen 1
Sollentuna, 192 72, Sweden
Tel.: (46) 86268905
Computer Peripheral Equipment Mfr
S.I.C.: 3575
N.A.I.C.S.: 334118

Barco Systems Pty Ltd. (1)
Unit 6 11 Lord St
Botany, NSW, 2019, Australia (100%)
Tel.: (61) 296951146
Fax: (61) 296951139
E-Mail: sales@barco.com.au
Emp.: 4
S.I.C.: 7379
N.A.I.C.S.: 518210
George Hoiuros *(Product Mgr)*

Barco Trading (Shanghai) Co., Ltd. (1)
7F Fen Yang Road 138
Shanghai, 200031, China (100%)
Tel.: (86) 2160912222
Fax: (86) 2154655502
E-Mail: china.hr@barco.com
Emp.: 30
S.I.C.: 7379
N.A.I.C.S.: 518210
Diana Lu *(Gen Mgr)*

Barco N.V.—(Continued)

Barco Visual (Beijing) Electronics Co., Ltd. (1)
No 16 Changsheng Rd Changping Technology Park
Changping Dist, Beijing, 102200, China
Tel.: (86) 1080101166
Fax: (86) 1080105852
Projector Mfr
S.I.C.: 3575
N.A.I.C.S.: 334118

Barco Visual (Beijing) Trading Co., Ltd. (1)
12F Citychamp Building No 12 Tai Yang Gong Zhong Lu
Chao Yang District, 100028 Beijing, China
Tel.: (86) 10 5650 2288
E-Mail: sales.gc@barco.com
Electronic Component Mfr
S.I.C.: 3679
N.A.I.C.S.: 334419

Barco Visual Solutions, Inc. (1)
5925 Airport Rd Suite 200
Mississauga, ON, L4V 1W1, Canada
Tel.: (905) 405-6225
Fax: (905) 672-8630
Microfilm Equipment Whslr
S.I.C.: 5065
N.A.I.C.S.: 423690

Barco Visual Solutions S.A. de C.V. (1)
Av Presidente Masaryk No 111 Piso 1
11560 Mexico, Mexico
Tel.: (52) 55 33005920
Web Site: www.barco.com
Digital Cinema Projector Mfr
S.I.C.: 3679
N.A.I.C.S.: 334419

BarcoView Texen SAS (1)
Parc Techn Basso Cambo 7 Rue Roger Camboulives
Toulouse, 31100, France
Tel.: (33) 534637000
Computer Peripheral Equipment Mfr & Distr
S.I.C.: 3575
N.A.I.C.S.: 334118

FIMI S.r.l. (1)
Via Saul Banfi 1
Saronno, Varese, 21047, Italy
Tel.: (39) 02 961751
Fax: (39) 0296 17 53 05
Emp.: 9
Medical Device Mfr
S.I.C.: 3845
N.A.I.C.S.: 334510
Ian Yates *(Gen Mgr)*

Tulsarr Industrial Research B.V. (1)
Marinus Van Meelweg 20
5657EN Eindhoven, Noord Brabanc, Netherlands (100%)
Tel.: (31) 402922622
Fax: (31) 402922633
E-Mail: info@bestsorting.com
Web Site: www.bestsorting.com
Emp.: 45
S.I.C.: 7374
N.A.I.C.S.: 518210
Edy Tereys *(Mgr)*

BARD VENTURES LTD.

Suite 615 800 West Pender Street
Vancouver, BC, V6C 2V6, Canada
Tel.: (604) 687-2038
Fax: (604) 687-3141
Web Site: www.bardventures.com
Year Founded: 2005
CBS—(TSXV)
Int. Income: $372
Assets: $164,762
Liabilities: $139,751
Net Worth: $25,011
Earnings: ($443,414)
Fiscal Year-end: 09/30/13

Business Description:
Mineral Exploration Services
S.I.C.: 1081
N.A.I.C.S.: 213114

Personnel:
Eugene Beukman *(Pres & CEO)*

Board of Directors:
Eugene Beukman
John B. Malysa
Emmet McGrath
Jim Miller-Tait
Robert Pryde

Legal Counsel:
Boughton Law Corporation
1000- 595 Burrard Street
Vancouver, BC, Canada

Transfer Agent:
Valiant Trust Company
Suite 600 750 Cambie Street
Vancouver, BC, Canada

BARDELLA S.A. INDUSTRIAS MECANICAS

Av Antonio Bardella 525
Guarulhos, SP, Brazil 07220-020
Tel.: (55) 11 2487 1000
E-Mail: comunicacao@bardella.com.br
Web Site: www.bardella.com.br
Year Founded: 1911
BDLL3—(BRAZ)

Business Description:
Industrial Equipment Mfr & Whslr
S.I.C.: 3569
N.A.I.C.S.: 333999

Personnel:
Claudio Bardella *(Pres)*
Jose Roberto Mendes Da Silva *(CEO)*

Board of Directors:
Claudio Bardella
Jose Eduardo Carvalho De Almeida Machado
Alfredo Camargo Penteado Neto
Sheila Periard Henrique Silva

BARDIS

Avenue Du General Leclerc
10200 Bar-sur-Aube, Aube, France
Tel.: (33) 325923792
Sales Range: $10-24.9 Million
Emp.: 75

Business Description:
Supermarkets & Grocery Stores
S.I.C.: 5411
N.A.I.C.S.: 445110

Personnel:
Jean-Jacques Maltoni *(Pres)*

BARENBRUG HOLDING B.V.

Stationsstraat 40
PO Box 4
NL 6678 ZG Oosterhout, Netherlands
Tel.: (31) 243488100
Fax: (31) 243488109
E-Mail: info@barenbrug.nl
Web Site: www.barenbrug.com
Year Founded: 1904
Sales Range: $150-199.9 Million
Emp.: 500

Business Description:
Plant Breeding, Seed Production & Seed Trade
Import Export
S.I.C.: 0119
N.A.I.C.S.: 111199

Personnel:
Simone Jeurissen *(Sec)*

Board of Directors:
Bastiaan J. Barenbrug
Frank Barenbrug
Rob A. DeVries

Subsidiaries:

Barenbrug Holland B.V. (1)
Stationsstraat 40
6515 AB Nijmegen, Netherlands UK
Mailing Address: (100%)
Postbus 4
NL-6678 ZG Oosterhout, Netherlands
Tel.: (31) 243488100
Fax: (31) 243488139
E-Mail: info@barenbrug.com
Web Site: www.barenbrug.nl
Emp.: 100
Plant Breeding, Seed Production & Seed Trade
S.I.C.: 0119
N.A.I.C.S.: 111199
Bas Barenbrug *(Mng Dir)*
Wei Fu *(CFO)*

Barenbrug Research Wolfheze (1)
Duitsekampweg 60
NL 6874 BX Wolfheze, Netherlands (100%)
Tel.: (31) 264835100
Fax: (31) 264821812
E-Mail: info@barenbrug.nl
Web Site: www.barenbrug.nl
Emp.: 13
Plant Breeding
S.I.C.: 0181
N.A.I.C.S.: 111422
P. Arts *(Gen Mgr)*

U.S. Subsidiaries:

Barenbrug Research USA (1)
33477 Hwy 99 E
Tangent, OR 97389-0239 (100%)
Tel.: (541) 926-5801
Fax: (541) 926-9435
Toll Free: (800) 547-4101
E-Mail: info@barusa.com
Web Site: www.barusa.com
Emp.: 100
Provider of Plant Breeding & Seed Production
S.I.C.: 5191
N.A.I.C.S.: 424910
John Thyssen *(Pres & CEO)*

Barenbrug USA (1)
33477 Hwy 99 E
Tangent, OR 97389-0239 (100%)
Tel.: (541) 926-5801
Fax: (541) 926-9435
Toll Free: (800) 547-4101
E-Mail: info@barusa.com
Web Site: www.barusa.com
Emp.: 100
Plant Breeding, Seed Production & Seed Trade
S.I.C.: 5191
N.A.I.C.S.: 424910
John Tison *(CEO)*
John H. Thyssen *(Pres-Ops)*

Non-U.S. Subsidiaries:

Barenbrug Belgium NV/SA (1)
Hogenakkerhoekstraat 19
9150 Kruibeke, Belgium BE (100%)
Tel.: (32) 32191947
Fax: (32) 32193927
E-Mail: sales@barenbrug.be
Web Site: www.barenbrug.be
Emp.: 6
Plant Breeding, Seed Production & Seed Trade
S.I.C.: 0119
N.A.I.C.S.: 111199
Bastiaan J. Barenbrug *(Mng Dir)*

Barenbrug China R.O. (1)
16F City Plaza 2 Shilipu
Chaoyang Dist, Beijing, 100025, China (100%)
Tel.: (86) 1065561872
Fax: (86) 1065561876
E-Mail: general@barenbrug.com.cn
Web Site: www.barenbrug.com.cn
Emp.: 10
Plant Breeding, Seed Production & Seed Trade
S.I.C.: 0119
N.A.I.C.S.: 111199

Barenbrug France S.A. (1)
Parc D Activites ZAC Les Portes De La Foret
77615 Marne-la-Vallee, Cedex, France FR (100%)
Tel.: (33) 0160068100
Fax: (33) 160068119
E-Mail: info@barenbrug.fr
Web Site: www.barenbrug.fr
Emp.: 25
Plant Breeding, Seed Production & Seed Trade
S.I.C.: 0119
N.A.I.C.S.: 111199
Benoit Petitjean *(Dir-Mktg)*

Barenbrug Luxembourg S.A. (1)
Industriezone Ingeldorf Strae Diekirch
PO Box 12
Ettelbruck, L 9201 Diekirch, Luxembourg (100%)
Tel.: (352) 808484
Fax: (352) 802283
Web Site: www.barenbrug.lu
Emp.: 15
Plant Breeding, Seed Production & Seed Trade
S.I.C.: 0119
N.A.I.C.S.: 111199
Patrick Holper *(Gen Mgr)*

Barenbrug Polska Sp. z.o.o. (1)
Ul Sowia 15
62 080 Poznan, Poland (100%)
Tel.: (48) 618164133
Fax: (48) 618146305
E-Mail: info@barenbrug.pl
Web Site: www.barenbrug.pl
Emp.: 4
Plant Breeding, Seed Production & Seed Trade
S.I.C.: 0119
N.A.I.C.S.: 111199
Eliza Kosmidr *(Office Mgr)*

Barenbrug Tourneur Recherches SA (1)
Negadis Rte De Bourret
82600 Mas-Grenier, France (100%)
Tel.: (33) 563271200
Fax: (33) 563271201
E-Mail: info@barenbrug-recherches.fr
Web Site: www.barenbrug-recherches.fr
Emp.: 16
Plant Breeding
S.I.C.: 0181
N.A.I.C.S.: 111422
Jean Saulue *(Mgr)*

Barenbrug U.K. Ltd. (1)
Rougham Industrial Estate
Bury Saint Edmunds, Suffolk, ID30 9ND, United Kingdom UK (100%)
Tel.: (44) 1359272000
Fax: (44) 1359272001
E-Mail: info@baruk.co.uk
Web Site: www.barenbrug.co.uk
Emp.: 20
Plant Breeding, Seed Production & Seed Trade
S.I.C.: 0119
N.A.I.C.S.: 111199
Paul R. Johnson *(Mng Dir)*

Heritage Seeds Pty. Ltd. (1)
7-9 McDonalds Lane
PO Box 4020
Mulgrave, VIC, 3170, Australia (92%)
Tel.: (61) 395017000
Fax: (61) 395619333
E-Mail: heritage@heritageseeds.com.au
Web Site: www.heritageseeds.com.au
Emp.: 20
Plant Breeding, Seed Production & Seed Trade
S.I.C.: 0119
N.A.I.C.S.: 111199
Peter J. England *(Mng Dir)*

New Zealand Agriseeds Ltd. (1)
2547 Old West Coast Road
RD 1 Christchurch, 7671, New Zealand NZ (100%)
Tel.: (64) 33188514
Fax: (64) 33188549
E-Mail: mail@agriseeds.co.nz
Web Site: www.agriseeds.co.nz
Emp.: 45
Plant Breeding, Seed Production & Seed Trade
S.I.C.: 0119
N.A.I.C.S.: 111199
Murray J. Willocks *(CEO)*

Palaversich Y Cia S.A. (1)
Alvarez Condarco 612
2700 Pergamino, Argentina (100%)
Tel.: (54) 2477433230
Fax: (54) 24774332330
E-Mail: palasem@arovateudrt.com.ar
Web Site: www.barenbrug.com.ar
Emp.: 50
Plant Breeding, Seed Production & Seed Trade

S.I.C.: 0119
N.A.I.C.S.: 111199
Eduardo Bayley *(Gen Mgr)*

THE BARGAIN! SHOP HOLDINGS INC.
6877 Goreway Dr Ste 3
Mississauga, ON, L4V 1L9, Canada
Tel.: (905) 293-9700
Fax: (905) 949-5233
Web Site: www.tbsstores.com
Year Founded: 1999
Emp.: 1,000
Business Description:
Discount Department Store Owner & Operator
Import
S.I.C.: 5311
N.A.I.C.S.: 452112
Personnel:
Eric Claus *(Chm)*

BARGETTE DISTRIBUTION
1030 Avenue Guillibert De La Lauziere
13794 Aix-en-Provence, Bouches Du Rhone, France
Tel.: (33) 477798809
Rev.: $22,300,000
Emp.: 300
Business Description:
Miscellaneous General Merchandise Stores
S.I.C.: 5211
N.A.I.C.S.: 444190
Personnel:
Bernard Barday *(Pres)*

BARIBUNMA HOLDINGS LIMITED
2/56 Hewlett Street
Bronte, NSW, 2024, Australia
Tel.: (61) 2 9089 8693
Fax: (61) 2 8021 9624
Web Site: www.baribunma.com.au
Year Founded: 2001
Business Description:
Electric Wheelchair Mfr
S.I.C.: 3699
N.A.I.C.S.: 335999
Personnel:
Harold Victor Holden *(Chm)*
Peter John Bancroft *(Mng Dir)*
Board of Directors:
Harold Victor Holden
Peter John Bancroft
Robert John Pringle
Legal Counsel:
Hagan & Company
Level 3 2 Bligh Street
Sydney, NSW, 2000, Australia

BARILLA HOLDING S.P.A.
Via Mantova 166
43100 Parma, Italy
Tel.: (39) 52126321
Fax: (39) 0521262083
Web Site: www.barillagroup.it
Year Founded: 1877
Sales Range: $5-14.9 Billion
Business Description:
Pasta
S.I.C.: 2034
N.A.I.C.S.: 311423
Personnel:
Guido M. Barilla *(Chm & Pres)*

U.S. Subsidiary:

Barilla America, Inc. **(1)**
1200 Lakeside Dr
Bannockburn, IL 60015 (100%)
Tel.: (847) 405-7500
Fax: (847) 405-7511
E-Mail: consumer.relations@barilla-usa.com
Web Site: www.barillaus.com
Emp.: 140
Pasta Mfr
S.I.C.: 2045
N.A.I.C.S.: 311824
Giannella Alvarez *(Pres)*

BARING EMERGING EUROPE PLC
155 Bishopsgate
London, EC2M 3XY, United Kingdom
Tel.: (44) 2076286000
Fax: (44) 2076387928
E-Mail: uk.sales@barings.com
Web Site: www.barings.com
Year Founded: 2002
BEE—(LSE)
Sales Range: $10-24.9 Million
Business Description:
Investment Services
S.I.C.: 6211
N.A.I.C.S.: 523999
Personnel:
Steven Andrew Ralph Bates *(Chm)*
M. J. Nokes *(Sec)*
Board of Directors:
Steven Andrew Ralph Bates
Ivo Coulson
Josephine Dixon
Saul Estrin
Jonathan Woollett
Transfer Agent:
Capita Registrars
The Registry 34 Beckenham Road
Beckenham, United Kingdom

BARING PRIVATE EQUITY ASIA LIMITED
Two International Finance Centre
8 Finance Street Ste 3801, Central, China (Hong Kong)
Tel.: (852) 28439300
Fax: (852) 28439372
E-Mail: hongkong@bpeasia.com
Web Site: www.bpeasia.com
Managed Assets: $5,000,000,000
Business Description:
Private Equity Firm
S.I.C.: 6211
N.A.I.C.S.: 523999
Personnel:
Jean Eric Salata *(CEO)*

Non-U.S. Holding:

Courts Singapore Limited **(1)**
50 Tampines North Drive 2
Singapore, Singapore SG
Tel.: (65) 63097888
Fax: (65) 67848071
E-Mail: ecourts@courts.com.sg
Web Site: www.courts.com.sg
Sales Range: $150-199.9 Million
Emp.: 877
Household Products Retailer; Owned by Baring Private Equity Asia & The International Investor Company K.S.C.
S.I.C.: 5999
N.A.I.C.S.: 453998
Terence D. O'Connor *(CEO)*

BARING VOSTOK CAPITAL PARTNERS
7 Gasheka Street Building 1 Ducat Place II Suite 750
Moscow, 123056, Russia
Tel.: (7) 4959671307
Fax: (7) 4959671308
E-Mail: info@bvcp.ru
Web Site: www.newweb.bvcp.ru
Emp.: 50
Business Description:
Private Equity Firm
S.I.C.: 6211
N.A.I.C.S.: 523999
Personnel:
Gabbas Kazhimuratov *(Partner & CFO)*
Andrey Costyashkin *(Partner & COO)*
Mikhail Ivanov *(Partner & Dir-Oil & Gas Projects)*
Vagan Abgaryan *(Partner)*
Michael Calvey *(Sr Partner)*
Elena Ivashentseva *(Sr Partner-Investments)*
Alexei Kalinin *(Sr Partner)*
Anatoly Karyakin *(Partner)*
Michael Lomtadze *(Partner)*

Non-U.S. Holding:

Kaspi Bank JSC **(1)**
90 Adi Sharipov Street
050012 Almaty, Kazakhstan (51%)
Tel.: (7) 727 2501720
Fax: (7) 727 2509596
E-Mail: office@kaspibank.kz
Web Site: www.kaspibank.kz
CSBN—(KAZ)
Sales Range: $400-449.9 Million
Emp.: 3,600
Banking Services
S.I.C.: 6029
N.A.I.C.S.: 522110
Vyacheslav Kim *(Chm)*
Mikheil Lomtadze *(Chm-Mgmt Bd)*
Gulmira Dzhumadillayeva *(Deputy Chm-Mgmt Bd)*
Iurii Didenko *(Member-Mgmt Bd)*
Mamuka Kirvalidze *(Member-Mgmt Bd)*

Non-U.S. Subsidiary:

Caspian Capital B.V. **(2)**
Schouwburgplein 30-34
Rotterdam, Zuid-Holland, 3012 CL, Netherlands
Tel.: (31) 102245333
Fax: (31) 104117894
Financial Services
S.I.C.: 8742
N.A.I.C.S.: 541611
Tim Ruoff *(Gen Mgr)*

BARISAN GOLD CORPORATION
Suite 1588-609 Granville Street
Vancouver, BC, V7Y 1G5, Canada
Tel.: (604) 684-8676
Fax: (604) 357-1987
Toll Free: (888) 371-5832
E-Mail: info@barisangold.com
Web Site: www.barisangold.com
Year Founded: 2011
BG—(TSXV)
Int. Income: $51,998
Assets: $19,665,870
Liabilities: $451,687
Net Worth: $19,214,183
Earnings: ($2,457,264)
Emp.: 19
Fiscal Year-end: 08/31/13
Business Description:
Gold & Copper Mining
S.I.C.: 1041
N.A.I.C.S.: 212221
Personnel:
Alex Granger *(CEO)*
Michael Nayyar *(CFO)*
Karen Dyczkowski *(Sec)*
Board of Directors:
Peter C. Akerley
Alex Granger
J. T. Lionel Martin
Legal Counsel:
Fang & Associates Barristers & Solicitors
Suite 300 576 Seymour Street
Vancouver, BC, V6B 3K1, Canada
Transfer Agent:
Computershare
510 Burrard Street
Vancouver, BC, Canada

Non-U.S. Subsidiary:

PT East Asia Minerals Indonesia **(1)**
Wisma 46 Kota BNI 11th Floor Suite 11 01
Jl Jend Sudirman Kav 1, Jakarta, Indonesia
Tel.: (62) 21 5749118
Fax: (62) 21 5749131
Gold & Copper Exploration Services
S.I.C.: 1041
N.A.I.C.S.: 212221

BARKAWI HOLDING GMBH
Baierbrunner Str 35
81379 Munich, Germany
Tel.: (49) 89 74 98 26 0
Fax: (49) 89 74 98 26 709
E-Mail: info@barkawi.com
Web Site: www.barkawigroup.com
Emp.: 300
Business Description:
Holding Company
S.I.C.: 6719
N.A.I.C.S.: 551112
Personnel:
Karim Barkawi *(Founder & CEO)*

Subsidiary:

B2X Care Solutions GmbH **(1)**
Baierbrunner Str 35
81379 Munich, Germany
Tel.: (49) 89 45 23 53 0
E-Mail: info@b2xcare.com
Web Site: www.b2xcare.com
Emp.: 200
After-Sales Solutions
S.I.C.: 7372
N.A.I.C.S.: 511210
Karim Barkawi *(Founder)*
Thomas Berlemann *(CEO)*
Tilo Brandis *(COO)*

BARKER MINERALS LTD.
8384 Toombs Drive
Prince George, BC, V2K 5A3, Canada
Tel.: (250) 563-8752
Fax: (250) 563-8751
E-Mail: barker@telus.net
Web Site: www.barkerminerals.com
Year Founded: 1993
BML—(TSXV)
Int. Income: $505
Assets: $11,151,768
Liabilities: $944,249
Net Worth: $10,207,519
Earnings: ($666,004)
Fiscal Year-end: 11/30/12
Business Description:
Mineral Exploration Services
S.I.C.: 1081
N.A.I.C.S.: 213114
Personnel:
Louis E. Doyle *(Pres & CEO)*
Robert H. Kuhl *(CFO)*
Gil A. Malfair *(Sec)*
Board of Directors:
Louis E. Doyle
Peter Hardychuk
James A. Kasten
Jerry A. Kristian
Jerry J. Kristian
Robert H. Kuhl
Harold Oxley
Legal Counsel:
McMillan
1500 Royal Centre 1055 Georgia Street
Vancouver, BC, Canada
Transfer Agent:
Computershare Trust Company of Canada
510 Burrard St 2nd Fl
Vancouver, BC, Canada

BARKERVILLE GOLD MINES LTD.
15th Floor 675 West Hastings Street
Vancouver, BC, V6B 1N2, Canada
Tel.: (604) 669-6463
Fax: (604) 669-3041
Toll Free: (800) 663-9688
E-Mail: info@barkervillegold.com
Web Site: www.barkervillegold.com

Barkerville Gold Mines Ltd.—(Continued)

Year Founded: 1970
BGM—(OTC TSXV)
Rev.: $1,493,582
Assets: $36,464,693
Liabilities: $15,303,493
Net Worth: $21,161,201
Earnings: ($12,463,810)
Emp.: 10
Fiscal Year-end: 02/28/13

Business Description:
Gold Mining & Exploration Services
S.I.C.: 1041
N.A.I.C.S.: 212221

Personnel:
Norman Anderson *(Chm)*
James Francis Gerard Callaghan *(Pres & CEO)*
Minaz Dhanani *(CFO)*
Lorraine Pike *(Sec)*

Board of Directors:
Norman Anderson
James Francis Gerard Callaghan
Elena Clarici
Minaz Dhanani
John Joseph Kutkevicius
David McMillan
Andrew Hutchinson Rees
Michael Steele

Legal Counsel:
McMillan LLP
Royal Centre 1055 West Georgia Street Suite 1500 PO Box 11117
Vancouver, BC, Canada

Transfer Agent:
Computershare Investor Services Inc.
510 Burrard St 2nd Floor
Vancouver, BC, V6C 3B9, Canada
Tel.: (604) 661-9400

BARKING APPLICATIONS CORPORATION

5114 Lakeshore Road
Burlington, ON, L7L 1B9, Canada
Tel.: (905) 464-5493
E-Mail: info@barkingapplications.com
Web Site: www.barkingapplications.com
Year Founded: 2011

Business Description:
Mobile Device Software Developer
S.I.C.: 7372
N.A.I.C.S.: 511210

Personnel:
Raymond Kitzul *(Pres, CEO & CFO)*

Board of Directors:
Raymond Kitzul

BARKMAN CONCRETE LTD.

152 Brandt Street
Steinbach, MB, R5G 0R2, Canada
Tel.: (204) 326-3445
Fax: (204) 326-5915
Toll Free: (800) 461-2278
E-Mail: steinbach@barkmanconcrete.com
Web Site: www.barkmanconcrete.com
Year Founded: 1948
Rev.: $17,427,632
Emp.: 85

Business Description:
Concrete Products Mfr
S.I.C.: 3271
N.A.I.C.S.: 327331

Personnel:
Brian Pries *(Gen Mgr)*

BARLAGE GMBH

Am Gleis 5
49740 Haselunne, Germany
Tel.: (49) 59629390
Fax: (49) 5962939256
E-Mail: info@barlage.com
Web Site: www.barlage.com
Year Founded: 1980
Rev.: $29,902,130
Emp.: 900

Business Description:
Welded Structures Mfr
S.I.C.: 3499
N.A.I.C.S.: 332999

Personnel:
Dieter Barlage *(Gen Mgr)*

BARLINEK S.A.

Al Solidarnosci 36
25-323 Kielce, Poland
Tel.: (48) 413331111
Fax: (48) 413330000
E-Mail: biuro@barlinek.com.pl
BRK—(WAR)
Sales Range: $150-199.9 Million
Emp.: 3,321

Business Description:
Wooden Flooring Mfr
S.I.C.: 2421
N.A.I.C.S.: 321918

Personnel:
Mariusz Gromek *(Chm-Supervisory Bd)*
Pawel Wrona *(Pres & Chm-Mgmt Bd)*
Krzysztof Kwapisz *(Vice Chm-Supervisory Bd)*
Wioleta Bartosz *(Member-Mgmt Bd)*
Marek Janke *(Member-Mgmt Bd)*
Ryszard Pyrek *(Member-Mgmt Bd)*

Supervisory Board of Directors:
Mariusz Gromek
Krzysztof Kwapisz
Grzegorz Mironski
Robert Oskard
Mariusz Waniolka

BARLOWORLD LTD.

180 Katherine Street
PO Box 782248
Sandton, 2146, South Africa
Mailing Address:
PO Box 782248
2146 Sandton, South Africa
Tel.: (27) 114451000
Fax: (27) 114443643
E-Mail: jaceydg@barloworld.com
Web Site: www.barloworld.com
Year Founded: 1902
BAW—(JSE LSE)
Rev.: $7,500,181,860
Assets: $4,586,902,900
Liabilities: $2,900,341,870
Net Worth: $1,686,561,030
Earnings: $209,427,150
Emp.: 19,238
Fiscal Year-end: 09/30/12

Business Description:
Integrated Holding Company; Earthmoving & Power Systems Equipment; Automotive; Materials Handling & Logistics Management
S.I.C.: 4731
N.A.I.C.S.: 541614

Personnel:
Clive Bradney Thomson *(CEO)*
Peter John Blackbeard *(CEO-Handling)*
Peter John Bulterman *(CEO-Equipment-Sourthern Africa & Russia)*
Richard Forrest *(CEO-Supply Chain Software)*
Martin Laubscher *(CEO-Automotive & Logistics)*
Viktor Salzmann *(CEO-Iberia & Global Power)*
Bethuel Ngwenya *(Sec)*
Steve Christensen *(Sr VP-Supply Chain Software-Americas)*

Board of Directors:
Dumisa Buhle Ntsebeza
Thembalihle Hixonia Nyasulu
Peter John Blackbeard
Peter John Bulterman
Gonzalo Rodriquez de Castro Garcia de los Rios
Neo Phakama Dongwana
Alexander Gordon Kelso Hamilton
Martin Laubscher
Sibongile Susan Mkhabela
Babalwa Ngonyama
Sango Siviwe Ntsaluba
Steven Bernard Pfeiffer
Oupa Isaac Shongwe
Clive Bradney Thomson
Donald Gret Wilson

Transfer Agents:
Transfer Secretaries (Proprietary) Limited
Shop 8 Kaiser Krone Centre Post Street Mall 2401
Windhoek, Namibia

Link Market Services South Africa (Pty) Limited
13th Floor Rennie House 19 Ameshoff Street
Braamfontein, South Africa

Subsidiaries:

Avis Southern Africa Ltd. (1)
3 Brabazon Road
1600 Isando, South Africa
Tel.: (27) 119233735
Fax: (27) 119233726
E-Mail: ibrandao@avis.co.za
Web Site: www.avis.co.za
Emp.: 1,600
Passenger Car Rental
S.I.C.: 7514
N.A.I.C.S.: 532111
Keith Rankin *(Mng Dir)*

Barloworld Automotive (Pty) Limited (1)
6 Anvil Road
Johannesburg, Isando, South Africa ZA
Mailing Address: (100%)
Private Bag 2028
1600 Isando, South Africa
Tel.: (27) 861 225529
E-Mail: customercare@barloworldmotor.com
Web Site: www.barloworldmotor.co.za
Emp.: 2,000
Other Motor Vehicle Electrical & Electronic Equipment Manufacturing
Import Export
S.I.C.: 3711
N.A.I.C.S.: 336111
Clive Thomson *(CEO)*

Barloworld Equipment - Southern Africa (1)
Electron Ave
Isando, Gauteng, 1600, South Africa ZA
Tel.: (27) 119290000 (100%)
Fax: (27) 119290044
E-Mail: barcat@barloworld-equipment.com
Web Site: www.barloworld-equipment.com
Emp.: 2,000
Dealers in Earthmoving Equipment
S.I.C.: 5084
N.A.I.C.S.: 423830
Lester S. Day *(CEO)*

Barloworld Equipment (Pty) Limited (1)
180 Katherine Street
PO Box 781291
2146 Sandton, South Africa
Tel.: (27) 113014000
Fax: (27) 113014130
E-Mail: info@barloworld-equipment.com
Web Site: www.barloworld-equipment.com
Emp.: 60
Industrial Machinery & Equipment Merchant Whslrs
Export
S.I.C.: 3559
N.A.I.C.S.: 333249
Peter Bulterman *(CEO)*

Barloworld Logistics (Pty) Limited (1)
PO Box 652753
Benmore, 2010, South Africa ZA
Tel.: (27) 114451600 (75%)
Fax: (27) 114451113
E-Mail: info@barloworld-logistics.com
Web Site: www.barloworld-logistics.com
Emp.: 250
Process, Physical Distr & Logistics Consulting Services
Import Export
S.I.C.: 4731
N.A.I.C.S.: 541614
Sainath Natarajan *(Dir-Sls Div-Middle East)*

Barloworld Logistics (1)
180 Katherine St
Sandton, Johannesburg, 2146, South Africa
Tel.: (27) 114451600
Fax: (27) 114451113
E-Mail: logzaafricacorporateoffice@bwlog.com
Web Site: www.barloworld-logistics.com
Emp.: 250
Information Systems Services
S.I.C.: 7389
N.A.I.C.S.: 561499
Steve Ford *(CEO)*

Barloworld Plascon (Pty) Ltd. (1)
180 Katherine St
Sandton, Johannesburg, 2000, South Africa ZA
Tel.: (27) 113014600 (100%)
Fax: (27) 113014684
Web Site: www.plascon.co.za
Emp.: 60
Mfr. of Paints & Protective Coatings, Surface Preparations, Printing Inks & Industrial Soaps
S.I.C.: 2851
N.A.I.C.S.: 325510

Barloworld South Africa (Pty) Limited (1)
6 Anvil Road
Isando, Gauteng, 1600, South Africa
Tel.: (27) 11 552 9000
Web Site: www.barloworldmotor.com
Motor Vehicle Parts Distr
S.I.C.: 5013
N.A.I.C.S.: 423120
Alma Heustis *(Gen Mgr)*

NMI Durban South Motors (Pty) Ltd. (1)
PO Box 1290
3600 Pinetown, South Africa ZA
Tel.: (27) 317171333
Fax: (27) 317171302
E-Mail: seelan.pillay@barloworldmotor.com
Web Site: www.nmidsm.co.za
Sales Range: $250-299.9 Million
Emp.: 650
Other Motor Vehicle Electrical & Electronic Equipment Manufacturing
Import Export
S.I.C.: 3711
N.A.I.C.S.: 336111
Yunus Akoo *(Mng Dir)*

Pretoria Portland Cement Co. Ltd. (1)
180 Katherine St
PO Box 787416
Park Extension Soudton, Johannesburg, 2146, South Africa ZA
Tel.: (27) 113869000 (60%)
Fax: (27) 113869001
E-Mail: webmaster@ppc.co.za
Web Site: www.ppc.co.za
Emp.: 300
Mfr. of Cement, Lime & Related Building Products
S.I.C.: 3241
N.A.I.C.S.: 327310
R.H. Dent *(Dir-Strategic Projects)*

Robor Industrial (Pty) Limited (1)
8 Barbara Road Elandsfontein
PO Box 1229
Isando, 1600, South Africa (100%)
Tel.: (27) 19711600
Fax: (27) 113922351
Web Site: www.robor.co.za
Emp.: 3,000
Mfr. of Steel Tubing; Metals Merchant & International Shipping/Trading
S.I.C.: 3317
N.A.I.C.S.: 331210
Michael D. Coward *(CEO)*
Stuart Neethling *(Mng Dir)*
Eddie Collins *(Mng Dir)*

Zeda Car Leasing (Pty) Limited (1)
6 Anvil Road Cnr Industrial Road
Isando, 1600, South Africa
Tel.: (27) 115529000
Web Site: www.barloworld.co.za
Passenger Car Leasing Services
S.I.C.: 7515
N.A.I.C.S.: 532112

U.S. Subsidiaries:

Barloworld Industrial Distribution Limited (1)
440 E Westinghouse Blvd
Charlotte, NC 28273
Tel.: (704) 587-1003
Fax: (704) 587-9269
Web Site: www.handling.barloworld.com
Emp.: 1,100
Industrial Machinery & Equipment Merchant Whslrs
Export
S.I.C.: 3559
N.A.I.C.S.: 333249

Non-U.S. Subsidiaries:

Barloworld Australia (Pty) Limited (1)
972 Nepean Highway
Moorabbin, 3189, Australia
Tel.: (61) 3 8506 6700
Fax: (61) 3 9553 1095
Web Site: www.barloworld.com.au
New Car Dealers
S.I.C.: 5511
N.A.I.C.S.: 441110
Sue Goldman *(Mng Dir)*

Barloworld Botswana (Pty) Limited (1)
Barlow House Building Lithuli Road
Gaborone, Botswana
Tel.: (267) 3973917
Fax: (267) 3974004
Fleet Management Services
S.I.C.: 7515
N.A.I.C.S.: 532112
Sean Walsh *(Gen Mgr)*

Barloworld Equipment Martex (1)
Plot 1226 Haile Selassie Rd
Old Industrial Area, Gaborone, Botswana (100%)
Tel.: (267) 3973917
Fax: (267) 3974004
Web Site: www.barloworld-equipment.com
Emp.: 521
Distributor Earthmoving Equipment, Materials Handling Equipment, Motor Vehicles, Paint, Building Materials, Office Automation Products, Household Appliances
S.I.C.: 2851
N.A.I.C.S.: 325510
Ian Duthie *(Gen Mgr)*

Barloworld Equipment UK Limited (1)
Ground Fl Statesman House Stefeton Way
Maidenhead, Bershire, SL6 1AB, United Kingdom (100%)
Tel.: (44) 1628592900
Fax: (44) 1628672692
Web Site: www.barloworld.co.uk
Emp.: 20
Purchasing Agent for Earthmoving & Allied Capital Equipment
S.I.C.: 3531
N.A.I.C.S.: 333120
Andrew Bannisper *(Dir-Fin)*

Barloworld Finanzauto (Spain) (1)
Av de la Madrid 43
Arganda del Rey, 28500, Spain
Tel.: (34) 918 71 26 12
Fax: (34) 918 70 16 79
E-Mail: info@mytractor.com
Web Site: www.finanzauto.es
Emp.: 20
Industrial Machinery Whslr
S.I.C.: 5084
N.A.I.C.S.: 423830
Sergio Touris *(Gen Mgr)*

Barloworld Holdings PLC (1)
Ground Floor Statesman House Stafferton Way
Slough, Berkshire, SL1 1JU, United Kingdom
Tel.: (44) 800 137449
Investment Management Services
S.I.C.: 6211
N.A.I.C.S.: 523999

Barloworld Mera SA (1)
Avenida De Madrid 43
Arganda del Rey, 28500, Spain
Tel.: (34) 918740000
Fax: (34) 918720522
E-Mail: barloworldfinancezauto@aroundbarloworldekuitmant.com
Web Site: www.mera-cat.com
Emp.: 20
Industrial Equipment Distr
S.I.C.: 5084
N.A.I.C.S.: 423830
Salzmann Victor *(Office Mgr)*

Barloworld Netherlands (1)
De Witboom 1
Vianen, 4131 PL, Netherlands
Tel.: (31) 347349400
Fax: (31) 347349490
Web Site: www.barloworld.nl
Emp.: 160
Fleet Management Services
S.I.C.: 7515
N.A.I.C.S.: 532112
Lex Knol *(Mgr)*

Finanzauto, S.A. (1)
Avenida de Madrid 43
28500 Madrid, Arganda del Rey, Spain (100%)
Tel.: (34) 901130013
Fax: (34) 18720522
E-Mail: barloworld.sa@fenarzaoto.es
Web Site: www.finanzauto.es
Emp.: 1,200
Seller of Fully Warranted Used Machinery
Export
S.I.C.: 3523
N.A.I.C.S.: 333111
Rodriguez DeCaspro *(Pres)*

Sociedade Technica De Equipamentos e Tractores SA (1)
Rua da Guine Apartado 3050
Prior Velho, 2686-401, Portugal
Tel.: (351) 21 940 9300
Fax: (351) 21 940 9447
Ground Moving & Extraction Machinery Distr
S.I.C.: 5046
N.A.I.C.S.: 423440
Vasque Santos *(Gen Mgr)*

Sonnex Investments (Pty.) Ltd. (1)
P.O. Box 215
Windhoek, Namibia NA
Tel.: (264) 61 26 2161 (100%)
Emp.: 275
Distr of Household Appliances, Paint, Earthmoving Equipment, Cement Products & Office Automation Products
S.I.C.: 3639
N.A.I.C.S.: 335228

BARMINCO LTD.

390 Stirling Crescent
Midland, WA, 6055, Australia
Tel.: (61) 894161000
Fax: (61) 894161099
E-Mail: info@barminco.com.au
Web Site: www.barminco.com.au
Year Founded: 1989
Emp.: 2,000

Business Description:
Underground Mining Services
S.I.C.: 1081
N.A.I.C.S.: 213114

Personnel:
Jock Muir *(CEO)*
Stuart Tonkin *(COO)*

Board of Directors:
Peter Bartlett
Roger Casey
Sarah Farrell
Peter Hatfull
Mark Rimmer

BARNIER ET FILS

Le Bas Chirat Rue De La Loire
42160 Saint Etienne, France
Tel.: (33) 477550164
Sls.: $10,300,000
Emp.: 46
S.I.C.: 3568
N.A.I.C.S.: 333613

Personnel:
Patrick Robert *(Pres)*

BARODA EXTRUSION LIMITED

At & Po Garadiya Jarod Samalaya Road
Tal Savli, Vadodara, Gujarat, India
Tel.: (91) 2667 251630
Fax: (91) 2667 251784
E-Mail: info@barodaextrusion.com
Web Site: www.barodaextrusion.com
Year Founded: 1993
513502—(BOM)
Sls.: $10,622,971
Assets: $9,540,176
Liabilities: $10,224,407
Net Worth: ($684,230)
Earnings: ($2,520,223)
Fiscal Year-end: 03/31/13

Business Description:
Copper Product Mfr
S.I.C.: 3339
N.A.I.C.S.: 331410

Personnel:
Parasmal B. Kanugo *(Chm & Mng Dir)*

Board of Directors:
Parasmal B. Kanugo
Rina G. Patel
Kesrichand Shah

Transfer Agent:
Purva Sharegistry (India) Pvt. Ltd.
Unit No 9 Shiv Shakti Ind Estt J R Boricha marg
Opp Kasturba Hospital Lane Lower Parel (E), Mumbai, 400 011, India

BARON DE LEY, S.A.

Carretera Mendavia a Lodosa km 55
Mendavia
31897 Navarra, Spain
Tel.: (34) 948694303
Fax: (34) 948 69 43 04
E-Mail: info@barondeley.com
Web Site: www.barondeley.com
Year Founded: 1985
BDL—(MAD)
Sales Range: $100-124.9 Million
Emp.: 190

Business Description:
Wineries; Wine, Other Alcoholic & Non-Alcoholic Beverages Sales & Distr
S.I.C.: 2084
N.A.I.C.S.: 312130

Personnel:
Eduardo Santos-Ruiz Diaz *(Chm & Mng Dir)*

Board of Directors:
Eduardo Santos-Ruiz Diaz
Francisco de Asis Royo-Villanova Paya
Jose Maria Garcia-Hoz Rosales
Joaquin Diez Martin
Julio Noain Sainz

Subsidiaries:

Dehesa Baron de Ley S.A. (1)
Carretera de Mendavia a Navarra, Spain
Tel.: (34) 948694303
Fax: (34) 948694304
E-Mail: info@barondeley.com
Emp.: 35
Wines Mfr
S.I.C.: 2084
N.A.I.C.S.: 312130
Julio Noain *(Gen Mgr)*

El Coto de Rioja S.A. (1)
Camino Viejo de Oyon 26
Oyon-Oion, 01320 Alava, Spain
Tel.: (34) 945622216
Fax: (34) 945622315
E-Mail: cotorioja@elcoto.com
Web Site: www.elcoto.com
Emp.: 100
Wines Mfr
S.I.C.: 2084
N.A.I.C.S.: 312130
Julio Noain *(Gen Mgr)*

Finca Museum S.L. (1)
Camino Viejo De Logrono 26
Oyon Euskad Pais Vasco Cigales, 01320 Valladolid, Valladolid, Spain
Tel.: (34) 983581029
Fax: (34) 983581030
E-Mail: fincamuseum@bodegasmuseum.com
Museum
S.I.C.: 8412
N.A.I.C.S.: 712110

BARON INFOTECH LIMITED

Off 1-8-313 4th Floor Linus Building
Chiran Fort Lane
Begumpet, Secunderabad, 500 003, India
Tel.: (91) 40 32492514
E-Mail: info@baroninfotech.com
Web Site: www.baroninfotech.com
Year Founded: 1994
532336—(BOM)
Rev.: $15,889
Assets: $587,947
Liabilities: $14,011
Net Worth: $573,936
Earnings: ($13,761)
Fiscal Year-end: 06/30/13

Business Description:
Software Development Services
S.I.C.: 7371
N.A.I.C.S.: 541511

Personnel:
N. Viswanadha Rama Raju *(Mng Dir)*
S. Nageswara Rao *(Compliance Officer & Gen Mgr-Fin)*

Board of Directors:
Surampudi Pavan Nandan
Katari Venkata Narasimha Raju
N. Viswanadha Rama Raju
Aareti Chandra Sekhar
Dutta Chandra Subash

Transfer Agent:
Venture Capital & Corporate Investments Private Limited
12-10-167 Bharat Nagar
500018 Hyderabad, India

BARON PARTNERS LIMITED

Level 32 Deutsche Bank Place 126 Phillip Street
Sydney, NSW, 2000, Australia
Tel.: (61) 292325500
Fax: (61) 292325300
E-Mail: sydney@baronpartners.com.au
Web Site: www.baronpartners.com.au
Year Founded: 1987
Emp.: 12

Business Description:
Investment Services
S.I.C.: 6211
N.A.I.C.S.: 523999

Personnel:
Stephen Chapman *(Co-Founder)*
Paul Young *(Co-Founder)*

Board of Directors:
Stephen Chapman
Paul Young

BARONSMEAD VCT 5 PLC

100 Wood Street
London, EC2V 7AN, United Kingdom
Tel.: (44) 2075065717
Fax: (44) 2075065718
E-Mail: baronsmeadvcts@isisep.com

Baronsmead VCT 5 PLC—(Continued)

Web Site: www.baronsmeadvct5.co.uk
BAV—(LSE)
Sales Range: Less than $1 Million
Business Description:
Investment Services
S.I.C.: 6211
N.A.I.C.S.: 523110
Personnel:
John Davies *(Chm)*
Board of Directors:
John Davies
David Hunter
Gillian Nott
Charles Pinney
Legal Counsel:
Norton Rose LLP
3 More London Riverside
London, SE1 2AQ, United Kingdom
Tel.: (44) 20 7283 6000
Fax: (44) 20 7283 6500
Transfer Agent:
Computershare Investor Services PLC
The Pavilions Bridgewater Road
PO Box 82
Bristol, BS13 8AE, United Kingdom
Tel.: (44) 870 702 0000
Fax: (44) 870 703 6119

BARONSMEAD VCT PLC

100 Wood St
London, EC2V 7AN, United Kingdom
Tel.: (44) 2075065717
Fax: (44) 2075065718
E-Mail: baronsmeadvcts@isisep.com
Web Site: www.baronsmeadvct.co.uk
BDV—(LSE)
Sales Range: $10-24.9 Million
Emp.: 4
Business Description:
Securities
S.I.C.: 6282
N.A.I.C.S.: 523930
Personnel:
Peter Lawrence *(Chm)*
Board of Directors:
Peter Lawrence
Godfrey Jillings
John Mackie
Valerie Marshall
Legal Counsel:
Martineau
No.1 Colmore Square Brimingham
London, United Kingdom
Transfer Agent:
Computershare Investor Services PLC
The Pavilions Bridgewater Road
PO Box 82
Bristol, BS13 8AE, United Kingdom
Tel.: (44) 870 702 0000
Fax: (44) 870 703 6119

BAROYECA GOLD & SILVER INC.

Penthouse 8 1060 Alberni St
Vancouver, BC, V6E 4K2, Canada
Tel.: (604) 669-3999
Fax: (604) 687-3581
E-Mail: doug@eacrettlaw.com
Web Site: www.baroyeca.com
Year Founded: 2006
BGS—(TSXV)
Assets: $4,310,342
Liabilities: $1,059,202
Net Worth: $3,251,140
Earnings: ($300,813)
Fiscal Year-end: 05/31/13
Business Description:
Gold & Silver Mining Services
S.I.C.: 1041
N.A.I.C.S.: 212221
Personnel:
Richard Wilson *(Pres & CEO)*
Douglas Eacrett *(CFO)*
Brooke Turner *(Sec)*
Board of Directors:
William Carr
Erik A. Ostensoe
Richard Wilson
Transfer Agent:
Valiant Trust Company
700 Cambie Street Suite 600
Vancouver, BC, V6B 0A2, Canada
Tel.: (604) 699-4880

BARR + WRAY LIMITED

1 Buccleuch Avenue
Hillington Park, Glasgow, G52 4NR, United Kingdom
Tel.: (44) 1418829991
Fax: (44) 1418823690
E-Mail: sales@barrandwray.com
Web Site: www.barrandwray.com
Year Founded: 1959
Rev.: $19,172,016
Emp.: 81
Business Description:
Water Treatment & Design Services
S.I.C.: 4941
N.A.I.C.S.: 221310
Personnel:
Alister MacDonald *(Grp Mng Dir)*

BARRA RESOURCES LIMITED

Ground Floor 6 Thelma Street
West Perth, WA, 6005, Australia
Tel.: (61) 894813911
Fax: (61) 894813283
E-Mail: admin@barraresources.com.au
Web Site: www.barraresources.com.au
BAR—(ASX)
Rev.: $546,684
Assets: $11,298,592
Liabilities: $519,029
Net Worth: $10,779,563
Earnings: ($1,407,744)
Fiscal Year-end: 06/30/13
Business Description:
Gold Nickel & Cobalt Exploration & Production
S.I.C.: 3339
N.A.I.C.S.: 331410
Personnel:
Gary John Berrell *(Chm)*
Grant Jonathan Mooney *(Sec)*
Board of Directors:
Gary John Berrell
Lindsay Franker
Grant Jonathan Mooney
Legal Counsel:
DLA Phillips Fox
44 St Georges Terr
Perth, Australia

BARRACHD LTD.

10 Lochside Place Edinburgh Park
Edinburgh, EH12 9RG, United Kingdom
Tel.: (44) 131 564 0575
Fax: (44) 131 464 4859
E-Mail: support@barrachd.com
Web Site: www.barrachd.co.uk
Year Founded: 2007
Sales Range: $10-24.9 Million
Emp.: 35
Business Description:
Software Development Services
S.I.C.: 7371
N.A.I.C.S.: 541511
Personnel:
Clark Wilson *(Mng Dir)*
Board of Directors:
David Fletcher
Clark Wilson

BARRAMUNDI LIMITED

Level 1 67-73 Hurstmere Road
Private Bag 93502
Takapuna, Auckland, 0740, New Zealand
Tel.: (64) 94897074
Fax: (64) 94897139
E-Mail: enquire@barramundi.co.nz
Web Site: www.barramundi.co.nz
BRM—(NZE)
Sales Range: $1-9.9 Million
Business Description:
Investment Services
S.I.C.: 6211
N.A.I.C.S.: 523110
Personnel:
Alistair Ryan *(Chm)*
Ben Doshi *(CFO)*
Board of Directors:
Alistair Ryan
Carol Campbell
Andy Coupe
Carmel M. Fisher
Legal Counsel:
Bell Gully
Level 21 48 Shortland Street
Auckland, 1010, New Zealand

BARRANCO RESOURCES CORP.

(Name Changed to Goldeneye Resources Corp.)

BARRATT DEVELOPMENTS PLC

Barratt House Cartwright Way Forest Business Park
Bardon Hill, Coalville, Leicestershire, LE67 1UF, United Kingdom
Tel.: (44) 1530278278
Telex: 538210 G
Fax: (44) 1530278279
Web Site: www.barrattdevelopments.co.uk
Year Founded: 1958
BDEV—(LSE)
Rev.: $4,115,945,598
Assets: $7,666,505,376
Liabilities: $2,813,031,348
Net Worth: $4,853,474,028
Earnings: $118,446,750
Emp.: 5,003
Fiscal Year-end: 06/30/13
Business Description:
Residential Building Construction
S.I.C.: 1521
N.A.I.C.S.: 236115
Personnel:
Mark Clare *(CEO)*
Steven J. Boyes *(COO)*
Tom Keevil *(Gen Counsel & Sec)*
Board of Directors:
Robert A. Lawson
Richard Akers
Tessa E. Bamford
Nina Bibby
Steven J. Boyes
Mark Clare
Mark E. Rolfe
David F. Thomas
Legal Counsel:
Slaughter & May
35 Basinghall St
London, EC2V 5DB, United Kingdom
Tel.: (44) 207 600 1200
Telex: 883486
Fax: (44) 207 726 0038

Divisions:

Barratt Central (1)
4 Brindley Rd City Park
Manchester, M16 9HQ, United Kingdom (100%)
Tel.: (44) 1618720161
Fax: (44) 1618552828
Web Site: www.barrtthomes.co.uk
Emp.: 2
House & Apartment Construction
S.I.C.: 1522
N.A.I.C.S.: 236118
Pop Lawson *(Chm)*

Branches:

Barratt Chester (2)
Oak House
Ellmport, Chester, Cheshire, CH65 9HQ, United Kingdom (100%)
Tel.: (44) 513574800
Fax: (44) 513574801
Web Site: www.barratt.com
Emp.: 50
House & Apartment Construction
S.I.C.: 1522
N.A.I.C.S.: 236118

Barratt East Midlands (2)
16 Regan Chilwell
Beeston, Nottingham, Nottinghamshire, NG9 6RZ, United Kingdom (100%)
Tel.: (44) 15900755
Rev.: $65,000,000
Emp.: 50
House & Apartment Construction
S.I.C.: 1522
N.A.I.C.S.: 236118

Barratt Manchester (2)
4 Brindley Rd
Manchester, M16 9HQ, United Kingdom (100%)
Tel.: (44) 1618720161
Fax: (44) 1618552828
E-Mail: info@barrathomes.co.uk
Web Site: www.barrathomes.co.uk
Emp.: 70
House & Apartment Construction
S.I.C.: 1522
N.A.I.C.S.: 236118
Niel Goodwin *(Mng Dir)*

Barratt Northampton (2)
Barratt House Sandy Way Grange Park
Northampton, NN4 7EJ, United Kingdom (100%)
Tel.: (44) 1604664500
Fax: (44) 1604664501
E-Mail: info@barratt.co.uk
Web Site: www.barratthomes.co.uk
Emp.: 50
House & Apartment Construction
S.I.C.: 1522
N.A.I.C.S.: 236118
Andrew Swindell *(Mng Dir)*

Barratt Sheffield (2)
Barratt House Newton Chambers Rd
Thorncliffe Park Chapeltown, Sheffield, S35 2PH, United Kingdom (100%)
Tel.: (44) 01142572500
Fax: (44) 1142572501
E-Mail: sheffield.reception@barratthomes.co.uk
House & Apartment Construction
S.I.C.: 1522
N.A.I.C.S.: 236118
Ian Pendlebury *(Mng Dir)*

Barratt West Midlands (2)
No 60 Whitehall Rd
Halesowen, West Midland, B63 3JF, United Kingdom (100%)
Tel.: (44) 1215855303
Fax: (44) 215855304
Web Site: www.barratthomes.co.uk
Emp.: 50
House & Apartment Construction
S.I.C.: 1522
N.A.I.C.S.: 236118
Adrian Farr *(Mng Dir)*

KingsOak Milton Keynes (2)
Gazeley House 26 Rockingham Dr
Linford Wood, Milton Keynes, MK14 6PD, United Kingdom
Tel.: (44) 1908541900
Fax: (44) 1908541901
Construction Building & Development
S.I.C.: 6726
N.A.I.C.S.: 525990

Barratt London & Thames Gateway Region (1)
Wallis House Great West Road
TW8 9BS Brentford, Middlesex, United

Kingdom UK
Tel.: (44) 2083267100 (100%)
Fax: (44) 2083267272
E-Mail: info@baratthomes.co.uk
Web Site: www.baratthomes.co.uk
Emp.: 100
Real Estate Developments & Investments
S.I.C.: 6726
N.A.I.C.S.: 525990
Alistar Tabard *(Pres)*

Branch:

Barratt Thames Gateway (2)
32-66 High St Central House
E15 2PF London, United Kingdom
Tel.: (44) 2085225500
Fax: (44) 02085195536
Web Site: www.barrattthames.co.uk
Emp.: 80
Residential Property Developers
S.I.C.: 6531
N.A.I.C.S.: 531311
Alastair Baird *(Mng Dir)*

Barratt Northern (1)
Barratt House City West Buisness Pk
Scottswood Road, Newcastle upon Tyne,
NE4 7DF, United Kingdom (100%)
Tel.: (44) 1912986100
Fax: (44) 1912568341
Web Site: www.barratthome.co.uk
Emp.: 50
House & Apartment Construction
S.I.C.: 1522
N.A.I.C.S.: 236118
Bernerd Rooney *(Mng Dir)*
Mike Roberts *(Mng Dir)*

Branches:

Barratt & David Wilsons (2)
Vico Court Ring Road
Lower Wortley, Leeds, Yorkshire, LS12
6AN, United Kingdom (100%)
Tel.: (44) 1132790099
Fax: (44) 1132790038
Emp.: 100
House & Apartment Construction
S.I.C.: 1522
N.A.I.C.S.: 236118

Barratt Newcastle (2)
Barratt House Airport Ind Est
Kenton, Newcastle upon Tyne, NE3 2EQ,
United Kingdom (100%)
Tel.: (44) 912869866
Fax: (44) 912715985
E-Mail: jadmoore@barratt-newcastle.fsnet.co.uk
Web Site: www.barratthomes.co.uk
Emp.: 60
House & Apartment Construction
S.I.C.: 1522
N.A.I.C.S.: 236118

Barratt Southern (1)
Alexandra House Balfour Road
Hounslow, Middlesex, TW3 1JX, United
Kingdom (100%)
Tel.: (44) 2086071900
Fax: (44) 208 577 8263
House & Apartment Construction
S.I.C.: 1522
N.A.I.C.S.: 236118

Branches:

Barratt East Anglia (2)
Barratt House 7 Mill Tye
Great Cornard, CO10 0JA Sudbury, Suffolk,
United Kingdom
Tel.: (44) 1787468950
Fax: (44) 1787468969
Residential Construction
S.I.C.: 6726
N.A.I.C.S.: 525990

Barratt East London (2)
Central House 32 66 High Street
London, E15 2PF, United Kingdom (100%)
Tel.: (44) 2085225500
Fax: (44) 2085195536
Web Site: www.barrattdevelopments.com
Emp.: 80
House & Apartment Construction
S.I.C.: 1522
N.A.I.C.S.: 236118
Alastair Baird *(Mng Dir)*

Barratt Eastern Counties (2)
7 Spring Feilds Lions Approach
Chelmsford, CM2 5EY, United
Kingdom (100%)
Tel.: (44) 245232200
Fax: (44) 245232277
Web Site: www.barratthomes.co.uk
Emp.: 70
House & Apartment Construction
S.I.C.: 1522
N.A.I.C.S.: 236118
Keith Parrett *(Mng Dir)*

Barratt Kent (2)
Weald House 88 Main Rd
Sundridge, Kent, 3N146ER, United
Kingdom (100%)
Tel.: (44) 1959 568 400
Fax: (44) 1959 569 064
Web Site: www.barrattkent.co.uk
Emp.: 50
House & Apartment Construction
S.I.C.: 1522
N.A.I.C.S.: 236118

Barratt North London (2)
Barratt House Wellstones
Watford, WD17 2AF, United
Kingdom (100%)
Tel.: (44) 1923297300
Fax: (44) 1923 297301
Web Site: www.barrathomes.co.uk
Emp.: 47
House & Apartment Construction
S.I.C.: 1522
N.A.I.C.S.: 236118
Brendan O'Neill *(Mng Dir)*

Barratt Southern Counties (2)
Barratt House
Walnut Tree Close, Guildford, Surrey, GU1
4SW, United Kingdom (100%)
Tel.: (44) 483505533
Fax: (44) 483405606
Web Site: www.barratt.com
Emp.: 60
House & Apartment Construction
S.I.C.: 1522
N.A.I.C.S.: 236118
Kristine Johnston *(Mktg Mgr)*

Barratt West London (2)
Alexandra House Balfour Road
Hounslow, Middlesex, TW3 1JX, United
Kingdom (100%)
Tel.: (44) 181 607 1900
Fax: (44) 181 577 4366
House & Apartment Construction
S.I.C.: 1522
N.A.I.C.S.: 236118

KingsOak North London (2)
3 The Orient Centre
Greycaine Road
WD24 7JT Watford, United Kingdom
Tel.: (44) 1923810870
Fax: (44) 1923810871
Residential Construction
S.I.C.: 6726
N.A.I.C.S.: 525990

KingsOak Thames Valley (2)
KingsOak House
Clivemont Rd
SL6 7BZ Maidenhead, Berkshire, United
Kingdom
Tel.: (44) 1628629922
Fax: (44) 1628629500
Residential Construction
S.I.C.: 6726
N.A.I.C.S.: 525990

Barratt West (1)
Barratt House Woodlands Almondsbury
Business Ctr
Almondsbury, Bristol, BS32 4QH, United
Kingdom (100%)
Tel.: (44) 1454202202
Fax: (44) 1454612277
Web Site: www.barratt.com
Emp.: 120
House & Apartment Construction
S.I.C.: 1522
N.A.I.C.S.: 236118
Richard Gregory *(Mng Dir)*

Branches:

Barratt Exeter (2)
Barratt House Hennock Rd Central
Exeter, EX2 8LL, United Kingdom (100%)
Tel.: (44) 392439022
Fax: (44) 392216104
E-Mail: info@barratt.co.uk
Web Site: www.barratt.co.uk
Emp.: 100
House & Apartment Construction
S.I.C.: 1522
N.A.I.C.S.: 236118
Tim Larner *(Mng Dir)*

Barratt Homes - Bristol (2)
Barratt House Almondsbury Business Ctr
Woodlands, Bristol, BS32 4QH, United
Kingdom (100%)
Tel.: (44) 1454202202
Fax: (44) 1454612277
Web Site: www.barratthomes.co.uk
Emp.: 45
House & Apartment Construction
S.I.C.: 1522
N.A.I.C.S.: 236118
Richard Gregory *(Gen Mgr)*

Barratt Homes South Wales (2)
Oak House Village Way
Tongwynlais, Cardiff, CF15 7NE, United
Kingdom (100%)
Tel.: (44) 2920544744
Fax: (44) 2920544745
Web Site: www.barrattdevelopments.co.uk
Rev.: $48,000,000
Emp.: 90
House & Apartment Construction
S.I.C.: 1522
N.A.I.C.S.: 236118
Mark Clare *(Grp CEO)*

Barratt Mercia (2)
2 Cranbrook Way Remus 2
Shirley, Solihull, B90 4GT, United
Kingdom (100%)
Tel.: (44) 121 713 7310
Fax: (44) 121 713 7311
Web Site: www.barrattmercia.co.uk
Emp.: 40
House & Apartment Construction
S.I.C.: 1522
N.A.I.C.S.: 236118
Andrew Peter *(Mng Dir)*

Barratt Southampton (2)
Barratt House Bampton Court
Hursley Road, Chandlers Ford, Hampshire,
SO53 2TA, United Kingdom (100%)
Tel.: (44) 2380275275
Fax: (44) 703269922
Web Site: www.aap-arc.co.uk/pf_barratt.html
Sls.: $72,000,000
Emp.: 50
House & Apartment Construction
S.I.C.: 1522
N.A.I.C.S.: 236118

KingsOak South West (2)
Broadway House Almondsbury Business
Centre
Woodlands, Almondsbury, Bristol, BS32
4QH, United Kingdom
Tel.: (44) 1454275800
Fax: (44) 1454275831
Residential Construction
S.I.C.: 6726
N.A.I.C.S.: 525990

KingsOak Southampton (2)
1 Eagle Close
SO53 4NF Chandlers Ford, Hampshire,
United Kingdom
Tel.: (44) 2380461000
Fax: (44) 2380461007
Residential Construction
S.I.C.: 6726
N.A.I.C.S.: 525990

Wilson Bowden Developments
Ltd. (1)
Forest Business Park
Bardon Hill, Leics, LE67 1UB, United
Kingdom UK
Tel.: (44) 1530276276 (100%)
Fax: (44) 1530814810
Web Site: www.wilsonbowden.co.uk
Sales Range: $1-4.9 Billion
Emp.: 25
Commercial Property Development Services
S.I.C.: 1542
N.A.I.C.S.: 236220
Nick Richardson *(Mng Dir)*

Subsidiaries:

Barratt Commercial Ltd. (1)
Barratt House Cartwright Way Forest
Business Park
Bardon Hill, Coalville, Leicestershire, LE67
1UF, United Kingdom (100%)
Tel.: (44) 1530 278278
Fax: (44) 1530 278279
Web Site: www.barrattdevelopments.co.uk/companies/contacts/
House & Apartment Construction
S.I.C.: 1522
N.A.I.C.S.: 236118

Barratt Construction Ltd. (1)
Golf Rd
Ellon, Aberdeenshire, AB41 9AT, United
Kingdom (100%)
Tel.: (44) 358720765
Fax: (44) 358724043
Web Site: www.barratthomes.co.uk/Find-a-Home/Plan-a-visit/?did=H2766
House & Apartment Construction
S.I.C.: 1522
N.A.I.C.S.: 236118

BDW East Scotland Limited (1)
Blairton House Old Aberdeen Road
Balmedie, Aberdeenshire, AB23 8SH,
United Kingdom
Tel.: (44) 1358 741 300
Fax: (44) 1358 743 858
Web Site: www.barrattdevelopments.co.uk/barratt/en/contact/officelocations
Property Management Services
S.I.C.: 6531
N.A.I.C.S.: 531311

KingsOak Homes Ltd. (1)
Wingrove House
Ponteland Rd, Newcastle upon Tyne, NE5
3DP, United Kingdom (100%)
Tel.: (44) 1912272000
Fax: (44) 1912712242
Web Site: www.kingsoakhomes.com
House & Apartment Construction
S.I.C.: 1522
N.A.I.C.S.: 236118

BARRATTS TRADING LIMITED

(Filed Ch 11 on 11/11/13. Duff & Phelps Appointed Administrator)
BPL House 880 Harrogate Rd
Apperley Bridge, Bradford, W
Yorkshire, BD10 0NW, United
Kingdom
Tel.: (44) 1274617761
Fax: (44) 1274616111
E-Mail: hrhelpdesk@Stylo.co.uk
Web Site: www.barratts.co.uk
Year Founded: 1907
Emp.: 1,184

Business Description:
Shoes & Leather Goods Retailer
S.I.C.: 5661
N.A.I.C.S.: 448210

Personnel:
Richard Segal *(Chm)*
Michael Stiff *(CEO)*

BARRAULT

521 Route De Limoges
79000 Niort, Deux Sevres, France
Tel.: (33) 549283311
Fax: (33) 549333774
Web Site: www.barrault.com
Sales Range: $25-49.9 Million
Emp.: 188
S.I.C.: 5013
N.A.I.C.S.: 423120

BARRDAY, INC.

75 Moorefield Street
PO Box 790
Cambridge, ON, N1T 1S2, Canada
Tel.: (519) 621-3620
Fax: (519) 621-4123
Toll Free: (800) 667-3725
E-Mail: protective@barrday.com
Web Site: www.barrday.com
Year Founded: 1958

Barrday, Inc.—(Continued)

Rev.: $12,121,041
Emp.: 100
Business Description:
Industrial Textiles, Coatings Adhesives & Sealants Mfr
S.I.C.: 2891
N.A.I.C.S.: 325520
Personnel:
Michael J. Buckstein *(Owner, Pres & CEO)*
Andrew Galbraith *(COO)*

U.S. Subsidiary:

Barrday Composite Solutions (1)
86 Providence Rd
Millbury, MA 01527
Tel.: (508) 581-2100
Fax: (508) 865-0302
Toll Free: (800) 225-7725
Web Site: www.lewcott.com
Sales Range: $10-24.9 Million
Wheels, Abrasive
S.I.C.: 3291
N.A.I.C.S.: 327910
Michael Buck *(Pres)*

BARRE LOGISTIQUE SERVICES
Rue du Val Clair
51683 Reims, Cedex 2, France
Tel.: (33) 326041313
Fax: (33) 326047878
Rev.: $20,100,000
Emp.: 56
Business Description:
Freight Transportation Arrangement
S.I.C.: 4731
N.A.I.C.S.: 488510
Personnel:
Pascal Barre *(Chm)*

BARRETT CORPORATION
300 Lockhart Mill Rd
Woodstock, NB, E7M 5C3, Canada
Tel.: (506) 328-8853
Fax: (506) 328-1207
Web Site: www.barrettcorp.com
Sales Range: $150-199.9 Million
Emp.: 800
Business Description:
Sales, Marketing, Logistical & Distribution Support Services
S.I.C.: 7389
N.A.I.C.S.: 561499
Personnel:
Bill Barrett *(Co-CEO)*
Edward Barrett *(Co-CEO)*

BARRETT STEEL LIMITED
Barrett House Cutler Heights Lane
Dudley Hill
Bradford, West Yorkshire, BD4 9HU, United Kingdom
Tel.: (44) 1274 682281
Fax: (44) 1274 651052
E-Mail: sales@barrettsteel.com
Web Site: www.barrettsteel.com
Year Founded: 1866
Sales Range: $350-399.9 Million
Emp.: 910
Business Description:
Steel Product Mfr
S.I.C.: 3399
N.A.I.C.S.: 331110
Personnel:
Roy Butcher *(Chm & CEO)*

BARRHEAD TRAVEL SERVICE LIMITED
190-194 Main Street Barrhead
Glasgow, G78 1SL, United Kingdom
Tel.: (44) 871 226 2673
Web Site: www.barrheadtravel.co.uk
Year Founded: 1975
Sales Range: $50-74.9 Million
Emp.: 800
Business Description:
Travel Agency Services
S.I.C.: 4724
N.A.I.C.S.: 561510
Personnel:
Bill Munro *(Founder)*

BARRICK GOLD CORPORATION
Brookfield Place TD Canada Trust Tower 161 Bay Street Suite 3700
PO Box 212
Toronto, ON, M5J 2S1, Canada
Mailing Address:
PO Box 212
Toronto, ON, M5J 2S1, Canada
Tel.: (416) 816-9911
Telex: 6 218626 BRC TOR
Fax: (416) 861-2492
Toll Free: (800) 720-7415
E-Mail: investors@barrick.com
Web Site: www.barrick.com
Year Founded: 1983
ABX—(NYSE TSX)
Rev.: $14,547,000,000
Assets: $47,282,000,000
Liabilities: $22,774,000,000
Net Worth: $24,508,000,000
Earnings: ($677,000,000)
Emp.: 18,400
Fiscal Year-end: 12/31/12
Business Description:
Gold & Copper Mining
S.I.C.: 1041
N.A.I.C.S.: 212221
Personnel:
Peter Munk *(Founder & Chm)*
Charles William David Birchall *(Vice Chm)*
Jamie C. Sokalsky *(Pres & CEO)*
Ammar Al-Joundi *(CFO & Exec VP)*
Igor Gonzales *(COO & Exec VP)*
Sybil E. Veenman *(General Counsel & Sr VP)*
Faith T. Teo *(Sec)*
Kelvin P. M. Dushnisky *(Sr Exec VP)*
Rob Krcmarov *(Sr VP-Global Exploration)*
Richard McCreary *(Sr VP-Corp Dev)*
Ivan Mullany *(Sr VP-Capital Projects)*
Greg Panagos *(Sr VP-IR & Comm)*
Donald D. Ritz *(Sr VP-Safety & Leadership)*
Board of Directors:
Peter Munk
Howard L. Beck
Charles William David Birchall
Gustavo A. Cisneros
J. Brett Harvey
Dambisa F. Moyo
M. Brian Mulroney
Anthony Munk
Steven J. Shapiro
Jamie C. Sokalsky
John Lawson Thornton
Legal Counsel:
Davies, Ward & Beck
1 First Canadian Place, 44th Floor
P.O. Box 63
Toronto, ON, M5X 1B1, Canada
Tel.: (416) 863-0900

American Stock Transfer & Trust Company, LLC
6201 15th Ave
Brooklyn, NY 11219
Transfer Agents:
CIBC Mellon Trust Company
PO Box 700 Station B
Montreal, QC, Canada

American Stock Transfer & Trust Company, LLC
6201 15th Ave
Brooklyn, NY 11219

Branches:

Doyon Mine (1)
PO Box 970
Rouyn-Noranda, QC, J9X 5C8, Canada (100%)
Tel.: (819) 759-3611
Fax: (819) 759-3342
Web Site: www.camdior.com
Emp.: 500
S.I.C.: 1041
N.A.I.C.S.: 212221
Bertrand Potgin *(Gen Mgr)*

Subsidiaries:

Barrick Gold Finance Company (1)
161 Bay St Suite 3700
Toronto, ON, M5J 2S1, Canada
Tel.: (416) 861-9911
Fax: (416) 861-2492
Web Site: www.barrick.com
Emp.: 40
Financial Management Services
S.I.C.: 6211
N.A.I.C.S.: 523999
Jamie C. Sokalsky *(CEO)*

Barrick Gold (1)
1055 Georgia St Ste 700
Vancouver, BC, V6E 3P3, Canada (100%)
Tel.: (604) 684-2345
Fax: (604) 684-9831
E-Mail: info@barrick.com
Web Site: www.barrick.com
Emp.: 15
Gold & Copper Mining & Exploration Services
S.I.C.: 1041
N.A.I.C.S.: 212221

U.S. Division:

Barrick Gold of North America, Inc. (1)
136 E S Temple Ste 1800
Salt Lake City, UT 84111-1163 DE
Tel.: (801) 741-4660
Fax: (801) 539-0665
Emp.: 100
Holding Company; Gold Mining
S.I.C.: 6719
N.A.I.C.S.: 551112
Lou Schack *(Dir-Comm & Community Affairs)*

Subsidiary:

Barrick Gold U.S. Inc. (2)
136 E S Temple St Ste 1800
Salt Lake City, UT 84111-1163 CA
Tel.: (801) 741-4660
Fax: (801) 539-0665
Web Site: www.barrick.com
Emp.: 50
Gold Ore Mining
S.I.C.: 1041
N.A.I.C.S.: 212221

Branches:

Ruby Hill Mine (3)
Intersection of Hwy 50 and 278
Eureka, NV 89316-0676 (100%)
Tel.: (775) 237-6060
Fax: (775) 237-5408
Web Site: www.barrick.com
Emp.: 120
Gold Mine
S.I.C.: 1041
N.A.I.C.S.: 212221
Andy Cole *(Gen Mgr)*

Subsidiaries:

Barrick Cortez Inc. (3)
8C 66 Box 1250
Crescent Valley, NV 89821
Tel.: (775) 468-4400
Fax: (775) 468-4610
Gold Ore Mining Services
S.I.C.: 1041
N.A.I.C.S.: 212221
Brian Grebenc *(Gen Mgr)*

Barrick Gold Exploration Inc. (3)
293 Spruce Rd
Elko, NV 89801
Tel.: (775) 738-2062
Web Site: www.barrickgold.com
Emp.: 100
Acquires, Invests in & Develops Gold Mining Projects
S.I.C.: 1041
N.A.I.C.S.: 212221

Barrick Goldstrike Mines, Inc. (3)
PO Box 29
Elko, NV 89803
Tel.: (775) 778-8183
Fax: (775) 778-8266
Emp.: 1,600
Gold Mining
S.I.C.: 1041
N.A.I.C.S.: 212221

Joint Venture:

Round Mountain Gold Corporation (2)
1 Smokey Valley Mine Rd
Round Mountain, NV 89045-0480
Tel.: (775) 377-2366
Fax: (775) 377-3240
Web Site: www.kinross.com
Sales Range: $75-99.9 Million
Emp.: 650
Gold Mining; Owned 50% by Barrick Gold Corporation & 50% by Kinross Gold Corporation
S.I.C.: 1041
N.A.I.C.S.: 212221

Non-U.S. Subsidiaries:

African Barrick Gold plc (1)
5th Floor No 1 Cavendish Place
London, W1G 0QF, United Kingdom
Tel.: (44) 207 129 7150
Fax: (44) 207 129 7180
Web Site: www.africanbarrickgold.com
ABG—(LSE)
Rev.: $1,087,339,000
Assets: $3,328,723,000
Liabilities: $553,742,000
Net Worth: $2,774,981,000
Earnings: $48,184,000
Emp.: 5,668
Fiscal Year-end: 12/31/12
Gold & Copper Mining Services
S.I.C.: 1041
N.A.I.C.S.: 212221
Bradley A. Gordon *(CEO)*
Andrew Wray *(CFO)*
Marco Zolezzi *(COO)*
Katrina White *(Gen Counsel & Sec)*

Barrick (Australian Pacific Holdings) Pty Ltd. (1)
Level 9 125 St Georges Terrace
Perth, WA, 6000, Australia
Tel.: (61) 8 9212 5777
Web Site: www.barrick.com
Investment Management Services
S.I.C.: 6211
N.A.I.C.S.: 523999

Barrick Chile Ltda. (1)
Ave Ricardo Lyon 222 Fl 8
Providencia, Santiago, Chile (100%)
Tel.: (56) 23402022
Fax: (56) 223402062
E-Mail: bmardones@barrick.com
Web Site: www.barricksudamirica.com
Emp.: 200
S.I.C.: 1041
N.A.I.C.S.: 212221
Igor Gonzales *(Pres)*

Barrick (Darlot) NL (1)
L 10 Quayside On Mill 2 Mill St
Perth, WA, 6000, Australia
Tel.: (61) 892125777
Gold Ore Mining Services
S.I.C.: 1041
N.A.I.C.S.: 212221
Andrew Bywater *(Gen Mgr)*

Barrick Gold Australia Limited (1)
Level 9 Brookfield Pl 125 St George Terrace
Perth, WA, 6000, Australia AU
Tel.: (61) 892125777 (100%)
Fax: (61) 893225700
Web Site: www.barrick.com
Emp.: 300
Gold, Copper & Nickel Mining & Exploration Services
S.I.C.: 1041
N.A.I.C.S.: 212221

Subsidiaries:

Barrick Australia Pacific (2)
125 St Georges Terrace
Perth, WA, 6000, Australia
Tel.: (61) 8 9212 5777
Fax: (61) 8 9322 5700
E-Mail: publicaffairsap@barrick.com
Web Site: www.barrick.com
Emp.: 300
Gold & Silver Mining
S.I.C.: 1041
N.A.I.C.S.: 212221
Michael Feehan *(Reg Pres)*

Subsidiaries:

Barrick (Cowal) Limited (3)
L 10 2 Mill St
Perth, Australia
Tel.: (61) 892125777
Fax: (61) 269744740
Web Site: www.barrick.com.au
Emp.: 35
Gold Ore Mining Services
S.I.C.: 1041
N.A.I.C.S.: 212221
Alan Fearon *(Gen Mgr)*

Granny Smith Mines Ltd. (2)
Mount Weld Rd
PO Box 33
Laverton, WA, 6440, Australia AU
Tel.: (61) 890882111
Fax: (61) 890313103
Web Site: www.placerdome.com
Emp.: 62
Miner of Gold
S.I.C.: 1041
N.A.I.C.S.: 212221

Barrick International (Barbados) Corp. (1)
1st Floor Enfield House Upper Collymore Rock
PO Box 1395
Saint Michael, 14004, Barbados
Tel.: (246) 430 8875
Fax: (246) 437 8860
Emp.: 14
Metal Mining Services
S.I.C.: 1081
N.A.I.C.S.: 213114
Stephen Galbraith *(Mng Dir)*

Barrick Mining Company (Australia) Limited (1)
Level 9 125 St George Ter
Perth, WA, 6000, Australia
Tel.: (61) 8 9212 5777
Fax: (61) 8 9322 5700
Emp.: 300
Gold Mining Services
S.I.C.: 1041
N.A.I.C.S.: 212221
John Rietveld *(Office Mgr)*

Subsidiary:

Barrick (Lawlers) NL (2)
L 10 2 Mill St
Locked Bag 12
Cloisters Square, Perth, WA, 6850, Australia
Tel.: (61) 892125777
Fax: (61) 63185555
Emp.: 500
Gold Ore Mining Services
S.I.C.: 1041
N.A.I.C.S.: 212221
Alan Fearon *(Gen Mgr)*

Barrick (Niugini) Limited (1)
2nd Fl The Lodge Bldg Brampton St
PO Box 851
Port Moresby, Papua New Guinea
Tel.: (675) 322 4800
Fax: (675) 322 4824
Web Site: www.barrick.com
Emp.: 15
Gold Mining Services
S.I.C.: 1041
N.A.I.C.S.: 212221
Jerry Agnes *(Country Mgr)*

Barrick (PD) Australia Limited (1)
Level 9 125 St Georges Terrace
Perth, WA, 6000, Australia
Tel.: (61) 8 9212 57770
Fax: (61) 8 9322 5700
Web Site: www.barrick.com
Emp.: 10
Gold Mining Services
S.I.C.: 1041
N.A.I.C.S.: 212221

Barrick (Plutonic) Limited (1)
Locked Bag 12
Perth, WA, 6850, Australia
Tel.: (61) 892125777
Fax: (61) 893225700
Gold Ore Mining Services
S.I.C.: 1041
N.A.I.C.S.: 212221

Compania Minera Casale Limitada (1)
Diego De Almagro 204
Copiapo, Chile
Tel.: (56) 52221025
Fax: (56) 52225808
Gold Ore Mining Services
S.I.C.: 1041
N.A.I.C.S.: 212221

Compania Minera Nevada Spa. (1)
Barrio Industrial coquimbo Sitio 58
Alto Penuelas, Coquimbo, Chile
Tel.: (56) 51 202 131
Web Site: www.barrick.com
Emp.: 200
Metal Mining Services
S.I.C.: 1099
N.A.I.C.S.: 212299
Michael Luciano *(Gen Mgr)*

Compania Minera Zaldivar S.A. (1)
Avenida Grecia 750
Antofagasta, Chile
Tel.: (56) 55 433 400
Fax: (56) 55 433 491
Gold Mining Services
S.I.C.: 1041
N.A.I.C.S.: 212221

Minera Barrick Misquichilca S.A. (1)
Av Manuel Olguin 375 Piso 11
Lima, Peru
Tel.: (51) 1 612 4100
Fax: (51) 1 612 4110
Gold Mining Services
S.I.C.: 1041
N.A.I.C.S.: 212221

Minera Barrick Misquithilca (1)
Pasaje Los Delfines 159 3rd Piso
Urb Las Gardenias, Lima, 33, Peru (100%)
Tel.: (51) 12750600
Fax: (51) 12753733
Emp.: 450
S.I.C.: 1041
N.A.I.C.S.: 212221

BARRIE BROWN NISSAN INC.
2700 North Island Highway
Campbell River, BC, V9W 2H5, Canada
Tel.: (250) 287-7272
Fax: (250) 287-8701
Toll Free: (866) 854-7081
E-Mail: info@bbnissan.ca
Web Site: www.barriebrownnissan.ca
Year Founded: 1975
Rev.: $11,476,733
Emp.: 25
Business Description:
New & Used Car Dealers
S.I.C.: 5511
N.A.I.C.S.: 441110
Personnel:
Barrie Brown *(Owner)*

BARRY & FITZWILLIAM LTD.
50 Dartmouth Square
Dublin, 6, Ireland
Tel.: (353) 16671755
Fax: (353) 16600479
E-Mail: info@bandf.ie
Web Site: www.bandf.ie
Emp.: 120
Business Description:
Spirits Distr
S.I.C.: 5182
N.A.I.C.S.: 424820
Personnel:
Chris Murphy *(Chm)*
Michael Barry *(Mng Dir)*

BARRY CALLEBAUT AG
Westpark Pfingstweidstrasse 60
PO Box 8021
8005 Zurich, Switzerland
Tel.: (41) 432040404
Fax: (41) 432040400
E-Mail: investorrelations@barry-callebaut.com
Web Site: www.barry-callebaut.com
Year Founded: 1996
BARN—(SWX)
Rev.: $5,271,496,019
Assets: $4,886,198,207
Liabilities: $2,980,039,217
Net Worth: $1,906,158,990
Earnings: $240,212,380
Emp.: 8,658
Fiscal Year-end: 08/31/13
Business Description:
Holding Company; Chocolate & Chocolate-Related Products Mfr & Distr
S.I.C.: 6719
N.A.I.C.S.: 551112
Personnel:
Juergen B. Steinemann *(CEO)*
Victor Balli *(CFO)*
Dirk Poelman *(COO)*
Peter Boone *(Chief Innovation Officer & Chief Quality Officer)*
David S. Johnson *(Pres/CEO-Americas)*
Massimo Garavaglia *(Pres-Western Europe)*
Steven Retzlaff *(Pres-Global Cocoa)*
Roland Maurhofer *(Gen Counsel & Sec)*
Board of Directors:
W. Andreas Jacobs
Fernando Aguirre
Jakob Baer
James L. Donald
Markus Fiechter
Nicolas Jacobs
Timothy E. Minges
Ajai Puri
Andreas Schmid

U.S. Subsidiaries:

Barry Callebaut USA LLC (1)
1500 Suckle Hwy
Pennsauken, NJ 08110-1432 (100%)
Tel.: (856) 663-2260
Fax: (856) 665-0474
Toll Free: (800) 836-2626
Web Site: www.barry-callebaut.com
Emp.: 100
Mfr. of Chocolate Products
S.I.C.: 2066
N.A.I.C.S.: 311351
Bill Hayes *(Plant Mgr)*

Barry Callebaut USA LLC (1)
400 Industrial Park Rd
Saint Albans, VT 05478-1875
Tel.: (802) 524-9711
Fax: (802) 524-5418
Toll Free: (800) 774-9131
E-Mail: barry-callebaut@barry-callebaut.com
Web Site: www.barry-callebaut.com
Emp.: 200
Mfr. of Cocoa & Chocolate Products
S.I.C.: 2066
N.A.I.C.S.: 311351
Jerry Dukas *(Plant Mgr)*

Barry Callebaut (1)
1500 Suckle Hwy
Pennsauken, NJ 08110 (100%)
Tel.: (856) 663-2260
Fax: (856) 665-0474
Web Site: www.barrycallebaut.com
Emp.: 75
Mfr. of Chocolate Products
S.I.C.: 5149
N.A.I.C.S.: 424490

Non-U.S. Subsidiaries:

Barry Callebaut France SAS (1)
5 boulevard Michelet
BP 8
Hardricourt, 78250 Meulan, France (100%)
Tel.: (33) 130228400
Fax: (33) 130228484
E-Mail: standardiste@barry-callebaut.com
Emp.: 200
Chocolate & Chocolate Related Products Mfr
S.I.C.: 2064
N.A.I.C.S.: 311352
Coulibaly Arouna *(Dir-Ops)*

Barry Callebaut-North America (1)
2950 Nelson St
Saint-Hyacinthe, QC, J2S 1Y7, Canada (100%)
Tel.: (450) 774-9131
Fax: (450) 774-8335
Web Site: www.barrycallebaut.com
Emp.: 600
Mfr. of Chocolate Products
S.I.C.: 2066
N.A.I.C.S.: 311352
Sebastian Gilbert *(Plant Mgr)*

Barry Callebaut UK Ltd. (1)
Wildmere Road Industrial Estate
Banbury, Oxfordshire, OX16 3UU, United Kingdom
Tel.: (44) 1295224700
Telex: 837382 SUNHO G
Fax: (44) 1295224780
E-Mail: gbenquiries@barry-callebaut.com
Emp.: 250
Mfr of Chocolate Confectionery & Coatings
S.I.C.: 2066
N.A.I.C.S.: 311352

Luijckx BV Chocolade (1)
Deambachten 4
PO Box 100
4881 XZ Zundert, Netherlands
Tel.: (31) 765978300
Fax: (31) 765976493
E-Mail: info@luijckx.nl
Web Site: www.luijckx-chocolade.com
Emp.: 100
S.I.C.: 2022
N.A.I.C.S.: 311513
Theo J.M. Graban *(Dir Gen)*

BARRY CULLEN CHEVROLET CADILLAC LTD
905 Woodlawn Rd West
Guelph, ON, N1K 1B7, Canada
Tel.: (519) 824-0210
Fax: (519) 824-9837
E-Mail: info@barrycullen.com
Web Site: www.barrycullen.com
Year Founded: 1950
Rev.: $34,359,600
Emp.: 70
Business Description:
New & Used Cars Dealers
S.I.C.: 5511
N.A.I.C.S.: 441110
Personnel:
Craig Cullen *(Gen Mgr-Sls)*

BARTLE & GIBSON CO. LTD.
13475 Fort Road NW
Edmonton, AB, T5A 1C6, Canada
Tel.: (780) 472-2850
Fax: (780) 476-6686
Toll Free: (800) 661-5615
Web Site: www.bartlegibson.com
Year Founded: 1944
Rev.: $65,065,500
Emp.: 300
Business Description:
Plumbing, Heating & Electrical Products Whslr
S.I.C.: 5074
N.A.I.C.S.: 423720
Personnel:
Robert Whitty *(Pres)*

BARTON STORAGE SYSTEMS LTD.
Barton Industrial Park
Mount Pleasant, Bilston, W Midlands, WV14 7NG, United Kingdom
Tel.: (44) 1902499500
Telex: 335496
Fax: (44) 1902353098
E-Mail: enquiries@barton-storage-systems.co.uk
Web Site: www.barton-storage-systems.co.uk
Year Founded: 1964
Sales Range: $1-9.9 Million
Emp.: 200
Business Description:
Shelving & Storage Systems Mfr
S.I.C.: 2599
N.A.I.C.S.: 337215
Personnel:
Keith Bibb *(Mng Dir)*

BARTRONICS INDIA LTD.
Survey Number 351 Raj Bollaram
Village Medchal Mandal
Ranga Reddy District, Bachupally, 501401, India
Tel.: (91) 40 23606316
Fax: (91) 40 23558076
E-Mail: info@bartronicsindia.com
Web Site: www.bartronicsindia.com
532694—(BOM)
Sales Range: $125-149.9 Million
Emp.: 130
Business Description:
Hardware Products Mfr
S.I.C.: 3429
N.A.I.C.S.: 332510
Personnel:
S. Tirumala Prasad *(Chm)*
Sudhir Rao *(Mng Dir)*
Board of Directors:
S. Tirumala Prasad
Jimmy Rustom Anklesaria
R. V. Panchapakesan
Sudhir Rao
Y. R. Rao
A. B. S. Reddy
M. M. Yesaw
Transfer Agent:
Bigshare Services Private Limited
E 2/3 Ansa Industrial Estate Sakivihar Road
Sakinaka Andheri(E)
Mumbai, India

BARTSCHER GMBH
Franz-Kleine-Strasse 28
D-33154 Salzkotten, Germany
Tel.: (49) 52589710
Fax: (49) 5258971120
E-Mail: info@bartscher.de
Web Site: www.bartscher.de
Year Founded: 1876
Rev.: $35,864,400
Emp.: 68
Business Description:
Catering Equipment Mfr
S.I.C.: 3421
N.A.I.C.S.: 332215
Personnel:
Siegfried Littschwager *(Head-Quality Assurance)*

BARU RESOURCES LIMITED
Suite 304 22 St Kilda Road
Saint Kilda, VIC, 3182, Australia
Tel.: (61) 3 9692 7222
Fax: (61) 3 9529 8057
E-Mail: info@baru.com.au
Web Site: www.baru.com.au
Year Founded: 2003
BAC—(ASX)
Business Description:
Coal Mining
S.I.C.: 1222
N.A.I.C.S.: 212112
Personnel:
Richard Anthon *(Chm)*
Melanie Leydin *(Sec)*
Board of Directors:
Richard Anthon
Peter Avery
Kevin Nichol

BARUNSON GAMES CORPORATION
SuDang B/D 4F 509 Bongeunsa-ro
Gangnan-gu, Seoul, Korea (South)
Tel.: (82) 70 7609 1443
Fax: (82) 2 3444 2837
E-Mail: global@barunsongames.com
Web Site: www.barunsongames.com
Year Founded: 1997
035620—(KRS)
Business Description:
Online Game Publisher
S.I.C.: 2741
N.A.I.C.S.: 519130
Personnel:
Genehong Park *(CEO)*

BARVIC
Zac De La Cerisaie 22 Rue Des Huleux
93240 Stains, Seine Saint Denis, France
Tel.: (33) 149711515
Sls.: $18,700,000
Emp.: 23
S.I.C.: 5137
N.A.I.C.S.: 424330
Personnel:
Pinhas Attias *(Gen Mgr)*

BARWA BANK GROUP
Barwa Bank Building Grand Hamad Street
PO Box 27778
Doha, Qatar
Tel.: (974) 4448 8888
Fax: (974) 4448 8889
E-Mail: info@barwabank.com
Web Site: www.barwabank.com
Business Description:
Islamic Banking Services
S.I.C.: 6029
N.A.I.C.S.: 522110
Personnel:
Mohamed Hamad Jassim al Thani *(Chm)*
Mohammad Abdel Aziz Al Saad *(Vice Chm)*
Khalid Yousef Al-Subeai *(Acting CEO)*
Keith Bradley *(COO & Gen Mgr-Intl)*
Nasser Mohamad Al-Hajiri *(Chief Admin Officer)*
Khalid Mahdi Al-Ahbabi *(Chief Bus Officer & Exec Gen Mgr)*
Board of Directors:
Mohamed Hamad Jassim al Thani
Ali Sabah Al Asseri
Khalid Mubarak Al Dulaimi
Thani Abdul Rahman Al Kuwari
Hassan Lahdan Al Mohannadi
Jamal Abdul Rahman Al Musalmani
Mohammad Abdel Aziz Al Saad
Aisha Muhammad Al-Noaimi
Ahmad Abdul Rahman Kamal
Subsidiary:

First Finance Company Q.S.C. **(1)**
Al-Salata Al-Jadeeda C Ring Road
PO Box 7258
Doha, Qatar
Tel.: (974) 4559999
Fax: (974) 4 559955
E-Mail: info@ffcqatar.com
Web Site: www.ffcqatar.com
Sales Range: $50-74.9 Million
Consumer Financial Services
S.I.C.: 6153
N.A.I.C.S.: 522220
Ghanim Bin Saad Al-Saad *(Chm)*
Eslah Assem Saad Eddine *(Acting CEO)*
Ali Ahmad Al-Zubid *(Mng Dir)*

BARWA REAL ESTATE COMPANY QSC
Barwa Al Sadd Towers Tower No 1
Suhaim bin Hamad Street C Ring Road
PO Box 27777
Doha, Qatar
Tel.: (974) 44088888
Fax: (974) 44998994
E-Mail: info@barwa.com.qa
Web Site: www.barwa.com.qa
Year Founded: 2006
BRES—(QE)
Rev.: $666,939,084
Assets: $13,418,978,730
Liabilities: $9,865,927,456
Net Worth: $3,553,051,275
Earnings: $308,957,775
Fiscal Year-end: 12/31/12
Business Description:
Land Acquisition & Related Services
S.I.C.: 6531
N.A.I.C.S.: 531390
Personnel:
Hitmi Ali Khalifa Al Hitmi *(Chm)*
Mohammed Abd Al Aziz Al Saad *(Deputy Chm)*
Abdulla Abdulaziz Al Subaie *(CEO)*
Board of Directors:
Hitmi Ali Khalifa Al Hitmi
Khalid Mubark Abd Al Aziz Al Delaimi
Yousef Ali Abd Al Rahman Al Obaidan
Mohammed Abd Al Aziz Al Saad
Abdulla Abdulaziz Al Subaie
Mohammed Ebrahim Mohammed Al Sulaiti
Subsidiary:

Barwa City Real Estate Company WLL **(1)**
PO Box 27777
Doha, Qatar
Tel.: (974) 44998888
Fax: (974) 44998887
Real Estate Management Services
S.I.C.: 6531
N.A.I.C.S.: 531390

BAS CASTINGS LIMITED
Wharf Road Industrial Estate
Alfreton, Nottinghamshire, NG16 6LE, United Kingdom
Tel.: (44) 1933677777
Fax: (44) 1773812028
E-Mail: sales@bascastings.com
Web Site: www.bascastings.co.uk
Year Founded: 1973
Rev.: $11,810,684
Emp.: 70
Business Description:
Iron Castings Mfr
S.I.C.: 3322
N.A.I.C.S.: 331511
Personnel:
Robert Radford *(Mng Dir)*

BAS LOGISTICS PLC
Thames House Portsmouth Road
Esher, KT10 9AD, United Kingdom
Tel.: (44) 701 760 2530
Fax: (44) 704 305 8573
Web Site: www.bas-logistics.co.uk
LDA—(DEU)
Business Description:
Logistics & Transportation Services
S.I.C.: 4731
N.A.I.C.S.: 541614
Personnel:
Wolfgang Hertrich *(CEO)*

BASANT AGRO TECH (INDIA) LTD.
Near S T Workshop Kaulkhed
Akola, 444 044, India
Tel.: (91) 724 2436321
E-Mail: customercare@basantagro.com
Web Site: www.krishisanjivani.com
524687—(BOM)
Rev.: $54,127,252
Assets: $49,031,014
Liabilities: $36,033,584
Net Worth: $12,997,430
Earnings: $1,930,941
Fiscal Year-end: 03/31/13
Business Description:
Agricutural Products Mfr
S.I.C.: 2879
N.A.I.C.S.: 325320
Personnel:
Shashikant C. Bhartia *(Chm & Mng Dir)*
Akshay D. Bhartia *(Pres)*
Deepak C. Bhartia *(Mng Dir)*
Narendra Pathak *(CFO)*
Prasad Todankar *(Sec)*
Board of Directors:
Shashikant C. Bhartia
B. G. Bathkal
Ashwin N. Bhartia
Deepak C. Bhartia
Sharad W. Sawant
R. S. Tayade
P. C. Baradiya & Co
208 Rewa Chambers 31 New Marine Lines
Mumbai, India
Transfer Agent:
Sharex Dynamic (India) Pvt. Ltd
Unit 1 Luthra Indus Premises Andheri Kurla Road Safed Pool Andheri E
Mumbai, India

BASCOGEL
Zone Industrielle De Jalday
64500 Saint-Jean-de-Luz, Pyrenees Atlantiques, France
Tel.: (33) 559080202
Fax: (33) 559080203
E-Mail: bascogel.uff@wanadoo.fr
Sls.: $12,900,000
Emp.: 25
S.I.C.: 5142
N.A.I.C.S.: 424420
Personnel:
Nathalie Arana *(Mgr-DP)*

BASE D'INFORMATIONS LEGALES HOLDING S.A.S.
33 Rue Sadi Carnot
78 Rambouillet, France
Tel.: (33) 134941000
Fax: (33) 134941099
Web Site: www.bil.fr
Emp.: 300
Business Description:
Holding Company
S.I.C.: 6719
N.A.I.C.S.: 551112
Personnel:
Thierry Asmar *(CEO-Altares)*
Subsidiary:

Dun & Bradstreet France SA **(1)**
55 Ave Des Champs Pierreux
92012 Nanterre, Cedex, France
Tel.: (33) 141375000
Telex: DBISFR616925F
Fax: (33) 141375001
E-Mail: info@nanterre.accueilaltaref.fr
Web Site: www.altaref.fr.com
Emp.: 100
Business Information Services
S.I.C.: 7389
N.A.I.C.S.: 519190
Thierry Asmal *(Gen Mgr)*

BASE RESOURCES LIMITED
Level 1 50 Kings Park Road
West Perth, WA, 6005, Australia
Mailing Address:
PO Box 928
West Perth, BC, 6872, Australia
Tel.: (61) 8 9413 7400
Fax: (61) 8 9322 8912
E-Mail: info@baseresources.com.au
Web Site: www.baseresources.com.au
BSE—(AIM ASX)
Rev.: $15,372
Assets: $441,653,122
Liabilities: $214,344,921
Net Worth: $227,308,201
Earnings: ($6,941,600)
Emp.: 2,200
Fiscal Year-end: 06/30/13
Business Description:
Iron Ore Mining Services
S.I.C.: 1011
N.A.I.C.S.: 212210
Personnel:
Tim Carstens *(Mng Dir)*
K. Balloch *(CFO)*
Winton Willesee *(Sec)*
Board of Directors:
Andrew King
Michael Anderson
Colin Bwye
Tim Carstens
Malcolm Macpherson
Trevor Schultz
Sam Willis
Legal Counsel:
Ashurst Australia
Level 32 Exchange Plaza 2 The Esplanade
Perth, Australia

Computershare Investor Services Pty Limited
Level 2 45 St Georges Terrace
Perth, Australia

Non-U.S. Subsidiary:

Base Titanium Ltd. **(1)**
Power Factor Complex Diani Beach Road
PO Box 1214
Ukunda, 80400, Kenya
Tel.: (254) 5822733
Fax: (254) 40 320 2253
Titanium Mining Services
S.I.C.: 1099
N.A.I.C.S.: 212299
Joseph Kamuya Maitha *(Chm)*

BASELLANDSCHAFTLICHE KANTONALBANK
Rheinstrasse 7
4410 Liestal, Switzerland
Tel.: (41) 619259494
Fax: (41) 619259594
E-Mail: investoren@blkb.ch
Web Site: www.blkb.ch
BLKB—(SWX)
Sales Range: $300-349.9 Million
Emp.: 767
Business Description:
Banking Services
S.I.C.: 6029
N.A.I.C.S.: 522110
Personnel:
Elisabeth Schirmer *(Chm)*
Claude Janiak *(Deputy Chm)*
Adrian Ballmer *(Vice Chm)*
Beat Oberlin *(CEO)*
Herbert Kumbartzki *(CFO)*
Board of Directors:
Elisabeth Schirmer
Adrian Ballmer
Urs Baumann
Doris Greiner
Wilhelm Hansen
Claude Janiak
Frenk Mutschlechner
Daniel Schenk
Hans Ulrich Schudel
Andreas Spindler
Dieter Voellmin
Subsidiaries:

ATAG Asset Management AG **(1)**
Centralbahnstrasse 7
4051 Basel, Switzerland (100%)
Tel.: (41) 612781111
Fax: (41) 612781112
Web Site: www.aan.ph
Emp.: 116
Commercial Banking
S.I.C.: 6029
N.A.I.C.S.: 522110
Ralch Sauser *(Mng Dir)*

ATAG Private Client Services AG **(1)**
St Jakobs-Strasse 17
4052 Basel, Switzerland (75%)
Tel.: (41) 615646565
Fax: (41) 615646560
E-Mail: info@atag-pcs.ch
Web Site: www.atag-pcs.ch
Emp.: 25
Other Accounting Services
S.I.C.: 8721
N.A.I.C.S.: 541219
Egor Rusek *(Mng Dir)*

Graff Capital Management AG **(1)**
Fraumunsterstrasse 13
8022 Zurich, Switzerland (100%)
Tel.: (41) 442153000
Fax: (41) 442153001
E-Mail: info@graffcapital.ch
Web Site: www.graffcapital.ch
Securities & Commodity Exchanges
S.I.C.: 6231
N.A.I.C.S.: 523210
Markus Graff *(Owner)*

Affiliate:

EVA Erfindungs-Verwertungs AG **(1)**
Hochbergerstrasse 60c
4054 Basel, Switzerland (41.9%)
Tel.: (41) 612838485
Fax: (41) 612838486
E-Mail: info@eva-basel.ch
Web Site: www.eva-basel.ch
Business Services for Start-Up Companies in Life Sciences Industry
S.I.C.: 7389
N.A.I.C.S.: 561499
Fritz Wittwer *(Pres)*
Peter E. Burckhardt *(Mng Dir)*

Non-U.S. Subsidiary:

ATAG Asset Management (Luxembourg) S.A. **(1)**
Blvd Grande-Duchesse Charlotte 34a
1330 Luxembourg, Luxembourg (100%)
Tel.: (352) 2531311
Fax: (352) 252899
E-Mail: info@atag.lu
Web Site: www.aam.lu
Emp.: 16
Miscellaneous Financial Investment Activities
S.I.C.: 6211
N.A.I.C.S.: 523999

BASEPOINT BUSINESS CENTRES
61 Thames St
Windsor, Berkshire, SL4 1LQW, United Kingdom
Tel.: (44) 1753853515
Fax: (44) 1753753901
E-Mail: hq@basepoint.co.uk
Web Site: www.basepoint.co.uk
Sales Range: $10-24.9 Million
Emp.: 120
Business Description:
Office Space & Workshops for Small to Medium Sized Businesses
S.I.C.: 7389
N.A.I.C.S.: 561499
Personnel:
Brian Andrews *(Exec Dir)*

BASF SE
(d/b/a BASF Group)
Carl-Bosch-Strasse 38
67056 Ludwigshafen, Germany
Tel.: (49) 621 60 0
Telex: 46499-0 bas d
Fax: (49) 621 60 42525
E-Mail: global.info@basf.com
Web Site: www.basf.com
Year Founded: 1865
BAS—(DEU)
Sls.: $105,982,617,930
Assets: $86,595,077,590
Liabilities: $51,858,506,910
Net Worth: $34,736,570,680
Earnings: $6,567,963,430
Emp.: 113,262
Fiscal Year-end: 12/31/12
Business Description:
Holding Company; Automotive & Industrial Coatings, Chemicals, Plastics, Agricultural & Performance Products Mfr; Oil & Natural Gas Production
Import Export
S.I.C.: 6719
N.A.I.C.S.: 551112
Personnel:
Eggert Voscherau *(Chm-Supervisory Bd)*
Kurt Bock *(Chm-Exec Bd-Legal, Taxes & Insurance)*
Michael Diekmann *(Vice Chm-Supervisory Bd)*
Robert Oswald *(Vice Chm-Supervisory Bd)*
Martin Brudermuller *(Vice Chm-Exec Bd-Performance Matls)*
Hans-Ulrich Engel *(CFO & Mmber-Exec Bd-Finance & Catalysts)*
Gops Pillay *(Pres-South & East Asia, ASEAN, Australia & New Zealand)*
Andreas Kreimeyer *(Member-Exec Bd-Crop Protection & Coatings & Exec Dir-Res)*
Margret Suckale *(Member-Exec Bd-HR, Engrg & Maintenance & Dir-Indus Rels)*
Michael Heinz *(Member-Exec Bd-Care Chemicals, Nutrition & Healt)*
Harald Schwager *(Member-Exec Bd-Construction Chemicals, Procurement, Oil & Gas)*
Wayne T. Smith *(Member-Exec Bd-Intermediates, Monomers & Petrochemicals)*
Jeff Knight *(Sr VP-Dispersions & Pigments-Asia Pacific)*
Magdalena Moll *(Sr VP-IR)*
Joachim Queisser *(Sr VP-Polyamides & Precursors)*
Paul Rea *(Sr VP-Crop Protection-Asia Pacific)*
Supervisory Board of Directors:
Eggert Voscherau
Ralf-Gerd Bastian
Wolfgang Daniel
Francois Diederich
Michael Diekmann
Franz Fehrenbach
Max Dietrich Kley
Robert Oswald
Anke Schaferkordt
Denise Schellemans
Ralf Sikorski
Michael Vassiliadis

Groups:

BASF Coatings AG **(1)**
Glasuritstrasse 1
48165 Munster, Germany DE
Mailing Address: (100%)
Postfach 6123
48136 Munster, Germany
Tel.: (49) 2501140
Telex: 892 511 gtvh d
Fax: (49) 2501143373
E-Mail: info.service@basf-ag.de
Web Site: www.basf-coatings.de
Emp.: 18,000
Holding Company; Paints & Coatings Mfr
S.I.C.: 6719
N.A.I.C.S.: 551112
Stefan Marcinowski *(CEO)*
Thomas Hartmann *(Mng Dir, Dir-Indus Rels, Global Head-HR)*

Subsidiary:

BASF Coatings GmbH **(2)**
Glasuritstrasse 1
Munster, 48165, Germany De
Mailing Address:
Postfach 61 23
Munster, 48136, Germany
Tel.: (49) 2501140
Fax: (49) 2501143373
E-Mail: info-coatings@basf.com
Web Site: www.basf-coatings.de
Emp.: 2,300
Chemical Products Mfr
S.I.C.: 2899
N.A.I.C.S.: 325998
Wolfgang Kranig *(Mng Dir)*

Subsidiary:

BASF Akquisitions GmbH **(3)**
Carl-Bosch-Str 38
Ludwigshafen, Rheinland-Pfalz, 67063, Germany
Tel.: (49) 2501140
Fax: (49) 2501142077
E-Mail: glasurit@basf.com
Management Consulting Services
S.I.C.: 8748
N.A.I.C.S.: 541618
Markus Kamieth *(Gen Mgr)*

Non-U.S. Subsidiary:

BASF Coatings A.S. **(3)**
Mete Plaza Degirmenyolu Cad Huzurhoca Sok No 84 Kat 9-17
Icerenkoy-Atasehir, 34752 Istanbul, Turkey
Tel.: (90) 216 5703400
Fax: (90) 216 5703779
E-Mail: info@basf.com.tr
Web Site: www.basf.com.tr
Emp.: 800
Paint & Coating Mfr
S.I.C.: 2851
N.A.I.C.S.: 325510
Mehmet Uzel *(Mgr-Technical Sls)*

Non-U.S. Subsidiaries:

BASF Argentina S.A. **(2)**
Avda De Los Constituyentes 1758
B1667 FYF Tortuguitas, Argentina (100%)
Tel.: (54) 23 20 49151013
Fax: (54) 2320497007
Web Site: www.basf.com.ar
Emp.: 2,000
Distr of Coatings & Paints
S.I.C.: 2851
N.A.I.C.S.: 325510

BASF Coating Services (Pty) Ltd. **(2)**
F Planet Bldng 2 Ctr Pk Century City
7435 Cape Town, South Africa
Tel.: (27) 215559800
Fax: (27) 215558141
E-Mail: lauren.page@basf.com
Web Site: www.basf.com
Emp.: 340
Chemical Product Mfr
S.I.C.: 2899
N.A.I.C.S.: 325998
Org May *(Mng Dir)*

BASF Coatings Australia Pty. Ltd. **(2)**
231-233 Newton Road
Locked Bag 101
2164 Wetherill Park, NSW, Australia
Tel.: (61) 287870111
Fax: (61) 287870133
E-Mail: contact@basf-coatings.com.au
Web Site: www.glasurit.com.au
Emp.: 25
Automotive Coating Product Mfr
S.I.C.: 2851
N.A.I.C.S.: 325510
Ian Wilkinson *(Gen Mgr)*

BASF Coatings Boya Sanayi ve Ticaret A.S. **(2)**
Keyap B2 No 28 Y Dudullu Umraniye
34752 Istanbul, Turkey

BASF SE—(Continued)

Tel.: (90) 216 499 3240
Fax: (90) 216 499 3210
Web Site: www.salcomix.com
Emp.: 60
Paint & Coating Distr
S.I.C.: 5198
N.A.I.C.S.: 424950
Filippo Alesi *(Gen Mgr)*

BASF Coatings de Mexico S.A. de C.V. (2)
Planta Hermosillo Calle del Oro y Trigales No 118
Parque Industrial de Hermosill, 83290
Sonora, Mexico
Tel.: (52) 6622510083
Fax: (52) 6622510715
Web Site: www.basf.com
Chemical Products
S.I.C.: 2899
N.A.I.C.S.: 325998
Juan Carlos Ordonez *(Sr VP-North America)*

BASF Coatings de Mexico S.A. de C.V. (2)
Avenida No 9 Parque Industrial Cartagena
CP 54900 Tultitlan, DF, Mexico MX
Tel.: (52) 5558993831 (100%)
Fax: (52) 5558993885
E-Mail: louis.orozco@basf.com
Web Site: www.basf.corp.com
Emp.: 380
Mfr. of Automotive Coatings
S.I.C.: 2851
N.A.I.C.S.: 325510
Louis Orozco *(Dir-Logistics)*

BASF Coatings Holding B.V. (2)
Industrieweg 12
3606 AS Maarssen, Netherlands
Mailing Address:
Postbus 1015
3600 BA Maarssen, Netherlands
Tel.: (31) 346581004
Fax: (31) 346576344
Emp.: 2
Holding Company; Chemical Product Mfr
S.I.C.: 6719
N.A.I.C.S.: 551112

Subsidiary:

BASF Coatings Nederland B.V. (3)
Industrieweg 12
Postbus 1015
3606 AS Maarssen, Netherlands
Tel.: (31) 346573232
Fax: (31) 346568264
Web Site: www.glasarit.nl
Emp.: 80
Chemical Product Mfr
S.I.C.: 2899
N.A.I.C.S.: 325998
Deck We Browns *(Mng Dir)*

BASF Coatings, Inc. (2)
11F HHIC Building 1128 University Parkway
North Bonifacio Global City
1634 Manila, Taguig, Philippines PH
Tel.: (63) 2 811 8000 (100%)
Telex: 22020 colmas ph
Fax: (63) 2 838 1025
Web Site: www.asiapacific.basf.com
Emp.: 210
Distr of Adhesive Coatings
S.I.C.: 2891
N.A.I.C.S.: 325520
Marcelino M. Quismundo *(Pres & CEO)*

BASF Coatings India Private Ltd. (2)
Thurbe
Thane-Belapur Road, Navi Mumbai, 400 705, India IN
Tel.: (91) 22 6712 7600
Fax: (91) 22 6712 7695
Web Site: www.basf.com
Mfr. of Chemicals
S.I.C.: 2899
N.A.I.C.S.: 325998

BASF Coatings Japan Ltd. (2)
296 Shimokurata Cho Totsuka Ku
Yokohama, 244 0815, Japan JP
Tel.: (81) 458656391 (100%)
Fax: (81) 458656396
E-Mail: info@basf.com
Web Site: www.basf.de
Emp.: 400
Distributor of Automotive OEM Coatings
S.I.C.: 2891
N.A.I.C.S.: 325520
Asejandro Shimazaki *(Pres)*

BASF Coatings Limited (2)
Unit 101 10th Avenue
Deeside Industrial Park, Deeside, Flintshire, CH5 2UA, United Kingdom UK
Tel.: (44) 1244281315 (100%)
Fax: (44) 1244281316
E-Mail: coilcoatings.uk@coating.basf
Web Site: www.basf.co.uk/ecp1/Group_companies_UK_Ireland/BASF_Coatings_Ltd
Emp.: 60
Mfr. & Sales of Industrial Coatings
S.I.C.: 2851
N.A.I.C.S.: 325510

BASF Coatings Private Ltd. (2)
302 T V Industrial Estate S K Ahire Marg
400025 Mumbai, India
Tel.: (91) 2256618000
Fax: (91) 2224982690
Web Site: www.basf.com
Automotive Coating Product & Solutions Supplier
S.I.C.: 2851
N.A.I.C.S.: 325510

BASF Coatings (Pty) Ltd. (2)
Iscor Works
1911 Vanderbijlpark, South Africa
Mailing Address:
PO Box 10174
Vanderbijlpark, 1906, South Africa
Tel.: (27) 168897490
Fax: (27) 168897493
E-Mail: drian.de-la-guerre@basf.com
Web Site: www.basf.com
Emp.: 42
Chemical Product Mfr
S.I.C.: 2899
N.A.I.C.S.: 325998
Driaan De La Guerre *(Gen Mgr)*

BASF Coatings Refinish GmbH (2)
Gewerbestrasse 25
A 5301 Eugendorf, Austria AT
Tel.: (43) 622571180 (100%)
Fax: (43) 6225711820
E-Mail: info@basf.at
Web Site: www.basf.at
Emp.: 80
Mfr. of Coatings, Paints, Printing Inks, Pigments, Fiber Technology
S.I.C.: 2851
N.A.I.C.S.: 325510
Peter Valenta *(Mgr-Comm Sls Support)*

BASF Coatings S.A. (2)
Cristobal Colon s/n Poligono Industrial del Henares
19004 Guadalajara, Spain
Tel.: (34) 949 209 000
Fax: (34) 949 209 116
E-Mail: basfesa.basfagro@basf.es
Emp.: 60
Paint & Coating Mfr
S.I.C.: 2851
N.A.I.C.S.: 325510
Jan Gunzel *(Gen Mgr)*

BASF Coatings S.A.S. (2)
Zone Industrielle De Breuil Le Sec
F 60676 Clermont, France FR
Tel.: (33) 344777777 (100%)
Fax: (33) 344783010
Web Site: www.basf.fr
Emp.: 600
Mfr. of Paints & Lacquers
S.I.C.: 2851
N.A.I.C.S.: 325510
Perisse Philippe *(Mng Dir)*

Subsidiary:

BASF Coatings Services S.A.R.L. (3)
16 rue Jean-Mermoz
Zac de la Feuchere, Compans, France (100%)
Tel.: (33) 60949870
Fax: (33) 60949898
Web Site: www.basf.com
Emp.: 100
Automotive Coating Mfr
S.I.C.: 2851
N.A.I.C.S.: 325510
Guy Velport *(Gen Mgr)*

BASF Coatings Services AB (2)
Transportgatan 37
Box 23
Hisings Karra, SE-425 02 Gothenburg, Sweden SE
Tel.: (46) 31578730 (100%)
Fax: (46) 31578737
Web Site: www.glasurit.com
Coatings & Paints Distr
S.I.C.: 5198
N.A.I.C.S.: 424950
Roar Solberg *(Country Mgr-Nordics)*

BASF Coatings Services AG (2)
Postfach 63
8820 Wadenswil, Switzerland
Tel.: (41) 7819611
Fax: (41) 7819612
E-Mail: glasurit.ch@coatings.basf.org
Web Site: www.glasurit.ch
Chemical Product Mfr
S.I.C.: 2899
N.A.I.C.S.: 325998

BASF Coatings Services GmbH (2)
Gewerbestrasse 25
5301 Eugendorf, Austria
Tel.: (43) 622571180
Fax: (43) 6225711820
E-Mail: bestellung.at@basf.com
Web Site: www.basf-coatings-services.at
Emp.: 70
Automotive Coating Mfr
S.I.C.: 2851
N.A.I.C.S.: 325510
Peter Valenta *(Gen Mgr)*

BASF Coatings Services S.A./N.V. (2)
Chaussee de La Hulpa
Terhulpsesteenweg 178, Brussels, 1170, Belgium
Tel.: (32) 23732781
Fax: (32) 223732830
E-Mail: info@basf.com
Web Site: www.basf.com
Automotive Coating Product Mfr
S.I.C.: 2851
N.A.I.C.S.: 325510
Jack Delmoit *(Mgr-Departing)*

BASF Coatings Services S.A. (2)
Antonio de la Pena y Lopez 13-B Pol Ind Ctra Amarilla
Seville, 41007, Spain
Tel.: (34) 94 920 90 00
Fax: (34) 94 920 91 16
Web Site: www.basf-coatings-services.es
Paint & Coating Distr
S.I.C.: 5198
N.A.I.C.S.: 424950

BASF Coatings Services S.A. (2)
Rua 25 De Abril 1
Prior Velho, 2685-368, Portugal
Tel.: (351) 229405000
Fax: (351) 219499949
E-Mail: logisadm@basf.com
Paint & Coating Distr
S.I.C.: 5198
N.A.I.C.S.: 424950

BASF Coatings Services Sp. z o.o. (2)
Janikowo ul 19 Pilotow
62-006 Kobylnica, Poland
Tel.: (48) 616464870
Fax: (48) 616464873
E-Mail: coatings@basf.com
Web Site: www.basf.pl
Emp.: 13
Automotive Paints & Industrial Coatings Mfr
S.I.C.: 2851
N.A.I.C.S.: 325510
Anna Dennert *(Gen Mgr)*

BASF Coatings Services S.R.L. (2)
Mioveni Str Uzinei Nr 1-3 Ro-Mio-Vop P70
Arges, Romania
Tel.: (40) 21 529 90 00
Fax: (40) 24 850 41 07
E-Mail: office.romania@basf.com
Emp.: 18
Paint & Coating Distr
S.I.C.: 5198
N.A.I.C.S.: 424950
Luminita Teodorescu *(Gen Mgr)*

BASF Coatings Services s.r.o. (2)
Prievozska 2
821 09 Bratislava, Slovakia
Tel.: (421) 258266111
Fax: (421) 258266166
E-Mail: recebdia-bratislava@basf.com
Web Site: www.basf-sh.sk
Sales Range: $100-124.9 Million
Emp.: 40
Chemical Product Mfr
S.I.C.: 2899
N.A.I.C.S.: 325998
Edita Hippova *(Mgr)*

BASF Coatings S.p.A. (2)
Via Marconato 8
20811 Cesano Maderno, MB, Italy
Tel.: (39) 03625121
Fax: (39) 0396656269
Web Site: www.basf-coatings.com
Chemical Product Mfr
S.I.C.: 2899
N.A.I.C.S.: 325998

BASF Coatings, storitve za avtomobilske premaze, d.o.o. (2)
Dunajska cesta 111A
1000 Ljubljana, Slovenia
Tel.: (386) 73372144
Fax: (386) 73314875
Web Site: www.basf.com
Sales Range: $1-9.9 Million
Emp.: 25
Automotive Coatings Mfr
S.I.C.: 2851
N.A.I.C.S.: 325510
Simon Franko *(Mng Dir)*

BASF S.A. (2)
Av Dr Julio Maranhao 3219
Bairro Prazeres, 54325 620 Jaboatao, Brazil BR
Tel.: (55) 1130433663 (100%)
Fax: (55) 1130432505
Web Site: www.basf.com.br
Emp.: 250
Mfr. of Coatings & Paints
S.I.C.: 2851
N.A.I.C.S.: 325510
Gislaine Rossetti *(Dir-Comm)*

BASF Construction Chemicals GmbH (1)
Dr-Albert-Frank-Strasse 32
Chemiepark Trostberg, D-83308 Trostberg, Germany De
Tel.: (49) 86218610 (100%)
Fax: (49) 86212911
Web Site: www.construction-chemicals.basf.com
Emp.: 7,100
Holding Company; Construction Chemical Products Mfr
S.I.C.: 6719
N.A.I.C.S.: 551112
Jurgen Hambrecht *(Chm)*
Kurt Bock *(CFO)*

Subsidiaries:

PCI Augsburg GmbH (2)
Piccardstrasse 11
86159 Augsburg, Germany
Tel.: (49) 82159010
Fax: (49) 8215901372
E-Mail: pci-info@basf.com
Web Site: www.pci-augsburg.de
Sales Range: $250-299.9 Million
Emp.: 750
Mfr of Chemical Products for the Building Industry
S.I.C.: 5211
N.A.I.C.S.: 444190

Relius Coatings GmbH & Co. KG (2)
Postfach 2561
26015 Oldenburg, Germany
Tel.: (49) 4413402416
Fax: (49) 44134028223
E-Mail: relius.mail@basf.com
Web Site: www.relius.de
Emp.: 600
Mfr of Surface Coatings
S.I.C.: 3479
N.A.I.C.S.: 332812
Martin Wulle *(Mng Dir)*

Plant:

BASF Construction Chemicals GmbH - Frankfurt am Main (2)
Kennedy-Allee 93
605596 Frankfurt am Main, Germany
Tel.: (49) 69633080
Fax: (49) 6216042525
E-Mail: info@construction-chemicals.basf.com
Web Site: www.construction-chemicals.basf.com
Emp.: 7,685
Mfr of Chemicals & Products for Construction Industry
S.I.C.: 2891
N.A.I.C.S.: 325520
Bernhard Hofmann *(Mng Dir)*

U.S. Subsidiaries:

BASF Construction Chemicals, LLC (2)
23700 Chagrin Blvd
Cleveland, OH 44122 DE
Tel.: (216) 839-7500
Fax: (216) 839-8815
Web Site: www.basf.com
Sales Range: $400-449.9 Million
Emp.: 200
Mfr of Expansion Joints, Exterior Insulation & Finish Systems & Concrete Repair & Construction Products
S.I.C.: 2891
N.A.I.C.S.: 325520
Dirk Bremm *(Sr VP-Americas)*

Subsidiaries:

BASF Corp. - Building Systems (3)
889 Vly Park Dr S
Shakopee, MN 55379-1854
Tel.: (952) 496-6000
Fax: (952) 496-6062
Toll Free: (800) 433-9517
Web Site: www.buildingsystems.basf.com
Emp.: 113
Mfr of Sealants & Adhesives, Concrete Repair Products, Grouts, Performance Flooring, Traffic Deck Membranes & Preformed Expansion Joints
S.I.C.: 2891
N.A.I.C.S.: 325520
Doug MacRae *(VP-Bus Mgmt)*

BASF Wall Systems, Inc. (3)
3550 Saint Johns Bluff Rd S
Jacksonville, FL 32224-2614
Tel.: (904) 996-6000
Fax: (904) 996-6300
Toll Free: (800) 221-9255
E-Mail: senergyinfo@basf.com
Web Site: www.senergy.cc
Emp.: 30
Mfr of Exterior Insulation & Finish Systems, Stucco Systems & Architectural Finish Coatings
S.I.C.: 1799
N.A.I.C.S.: 238190

Non-U.S. Group:

BASF Construction Chemicals Asia/Pacific (2)
Room 2207 Shanghai Times Square
93 Huai Hai Zhong Road, Shanghai, 200021, China
Tel.: (86) 2151332839
Fax: (86) 2153069055
Web Site: www.ap.cc.basf.com
Emp.: 1,000
Mfr of Concrete, Pavement & Mortar Additives & Admixtures
S.I.C.: 3272
N.A.I.C.S.: 327390
Boris Gorella *(Pres)*
Christian Mombaur *(Sr VP)*

Non-U.S. Units:

BASF Construction Chemicals (Hong Kong) Limited (3)
20 F EW International Tower
120 124 Texaco Road, Tsuen Wan, NT, China (Hong Kong)
Tel.: (852) 24074291
Fax: (852) 24067391
E-Mail: daniel.sham@basf.com
Web Site: www.basf.com
Emp.: 30
Distr of Construction Materials
S.I.C.: 5211
N.A.I.C.S.: 444190
Daniel Sham *(Mgr-Sls)*

BASF Construction Chemicals Singapore Pte Ltd (3)
No 33 Tuas Ave 11
639090 Singapore, Singapore
Tel.: (65) 68616766
Fax: (65) 68613186
E-Mail: sales.sg@basf.com
Web Site: www.basf-cc.com.sg
Emp.: 60
Construction Supplies Mfr & Distr
S.I.C.: 5211
N.A.I.C.S.: 444190
Brenda Lee *(Mgr-Sls)*

Non-U.S. Subsidiaries:

BASF Construction Chemicals Australia Pty. Ltd. (4)
11 Stanton Road
Seven Hills, NSW, 2147, Australia
Tel.: (61) 288114200
Fax: (61) 288113299
E-Mail: colin.peterson@basf.com
Web Site: www.basf-cc.com.au
Emp.: 40
Distr of Construction Materials
S.I.C.: 5211
N.A.I.C.S.: 444190
Angus Peruzzo *(Mng Dir)*

BASF Construction Chemicals Malaysia Sdn Bhd (4)
Kawasan Perindustrian Bukit Raja No 8
Jalan Keluli 2
41050 Kelang, Selangor Darul Ehsan, Malaysia
Tel.: (60) 333443388
Fax: (60) 333445330
Web Site: www.basf-cc.com.my
Emp.: 40
Sales & Marketing of Construction Supplies
S.I.C.: 5211
N.A.I.C.S.: 444190
Vincent Loke *(Mng Dir)*

BASF Construction Chemicals New Zealand Ltd (4)
45 C William Pickering Dr
PO Box 302668
Auckland, New Zealand
Tel.: (64) 94147233
Fax: (64) 94145925
Web Site: www.basf-cc.com.au
Sls.: $2,484,500
Emp.: 8
Distr of Construction Supplies
S.I.C.: 5211
N.A.I.C.S.: 444190

BASF Construction Chemicals (Taiwan) Co., Ltd (3)
No 11 Chih-Li 1st Road
540, Nant'ou, 540, Taiwan
Tel.: (886) 492255138
Fax: (886) 492256022
Web Site: www.basf.net
Emp.: 100
Distr of Construction Materials
S.I.C.: 5211
N.A.I.C.S.: 444190

NMB Co., Ltd. (3)
16 26 Roppongi 3 Chome
Minatu Ku, Tokyo, 106-0032, Japan
Tel.: (81) 3 3584 7099
Fax: (81) 3 3505 5955
Web Site: www.ap.construction-chemicals.basf.com
Emp.: 400
Distr of Concrete, Pavement & Mortar Additives & Admixtures
S.I.C.: 3272
N.A.I.C.S.: 327390
Takashi Furusawa *(Mgr-Strategic Mktg)*

Non-U.S. Subsidiaries:

BASF Construction Chemicals Algeria S.A.R.L. (2)
Zone Industrielle Baba Ali District Shaoula
District 05 ilot 03 Hydra
Saoula, 16305 Algiers, Algeria
Tel.: (213) 17060875
Fax: (213) 17060867
Web Site: www.basf.com.dz
Construction Chemicals Mfr
S.I.C.: 2899
N.A.I.C.S.: 325998

BASF Construction Chemicals Austria GmbH (2)
Roseggerstrasse 101
8670 Krieglach, Austria
Tel.: (43) 385523710
Fax: (43) 3855237123
Web Site: www.basf.at
Chemical Products for the Construction Industry Distr
S.I.C.: 5211
N.A.I.C.S.: 444190

BASF Construction Chemicals Belgium NV (2)
Industrieterrien Ravenshout 3711
3945 Hamme, Belgium
Tel.: (32) 11340434
Fax: (32) 11402933
E-Mail: basf-cc-be@basf.com
Web Site: www.basf-cc.be
Emp.: 72
Distr of Chemical Products for the Construction Industry
S.I.C.: 5211
N.A.I.C.S.: 444190
Nicole Van Griekem *(Mgr-Fin)*

Non-U.S. Subsidiary:

BASF Nederland B.V., Construction Chemicals (3)
Karolusstraat 2
Postbus 132
4900 AC Oosterhout, Netherlands
Tel.: (31) 162476660
Fax: (31) 162429694
E-Mail: basf-cc-nl@basf.com
Web Site: www.basf-cc.nl
Emp.: 40
Distr of Chemical Products for the Construction Industry
S.I.C.: 5211
N.A.I.C.S.: 444190
Pieter Van Gent *(Mng Dir)*

BASF Construction Chemicals Canada Ltd. (2)
1800 Clark Blvd
Brampton, ON, L6T 4M7, Canada
Tel.: (905) 792-2012
Fax: (905) 792-0651
E-Mail: colin.hoxby@basf.com
Web Site: www.basf-admixtures.com
Emp.: 20
Mfr of Concrete, Pavement & Mortar Additives
S.I.C.: 3272
N.A.I.C.S.: 327390

Subsidiary:

BASF Construction Canada Holdings Inc. (3)
100 Milverton Dr 5th Fl
Mississauga, ON, L5R 4H1, Canada
Tel.: (289) 360-1300
Investment Management Services
S.I.C.: 6211
N.A.I.C.S.: 523999

BASF Construction Chemicals (China) Co. Ltd. (2)
Room 1801-1802 Habour Ring Plaza 18
Xizang Zhong Road
Shanghai, China
Tel.: (86) 21 2320 3844
Fax: (86) 135 0168 3662
Web Site: www.basf-cc.cn
Chemical Product Distr
S.I.C.: 5169
N.A.I.C.S.: 424690

BASF Construction Chemicals Denmark A/S (2)
Hallandsvej 1
DK 6230 Rodekro, Denmark
Tel.: (45) 74661511
Telex: 52161
Fax: (45) 74694411
E-Mail: denmark@basf.com
Web Site: www.basf-cc.dk
Emp.: 50
Production & Distribution of Chemical Products for the Building Industry
S.I.C.: 2899
N.A.I.C.S.: 325998
Hanshenrick Paulson *(Mng Dir)*

BASF Construction Chemicals Espana SA (2)
Basters 15
08184 Barcelona, Spain
Tel.: (34) 938620000
Fax: (34) 938620020
E-Mail: basf-cc@basf-cc.es
Web Site: www.basf-cc.es
Emp.: 1,000
Distr of Construction Chemicals & Materials
S.I.C.: 5039
N.A.I.C.S.: 423390
Xavier Garcia *(Product Mgr)*

BASF Construction Chemicals Europe AG (2)
Vulkanstrasse 110
8048 Zurich, Switzerland
Tel.: (41) 58 958 22 11
Fax: (41) 58 958 34 15
Web Site: www.basf-cc.ch
Construction Chemical Mfr
S.I.C.: 2899
N.A.I.C.S.: 325998

BASF Construction Chemicals France S.A.S. (2)
Z I Petite Montagne Sud
F 91017 Evry, Cedex, France
Tel.: (33) 169475000
Fax: (33) 160860632
Web Site: www.basf-cc.fr
Sales Range: $50-74.9 Million
Emp.: 150
Distr of Chemical Products for the Construction Industry
S.I.C.: 5211
N.A.I.C.S.: 444190
Faict Philippe *(Pres)*
G. Laurent *(Mng Dir)*

BASF Construction Chemicals Italia SpA (2)
Via Vicinale Delle Corti 21
31100 Treviso, Italy
Tel.: (39) 0422 304251
Fax: (39) 0422 30118
E-Mail: infomac@basf.com
Web Site: www.basf-cc.it
Chemical Additive Mfr
S.I.C.: 2899
N.A.I.C.S.: 325998

BASF Construction Chemicals Limitada (2)
Rio Palena 9665 ENEA
Pudahuel, Santiago, Chile
Tel.: (56) 2 799 4300
Fax: (56) 2 799 4340
E-Mail: bcc_chile@basf.com
Web Site: www.basf-cc.cl
Construction Chemicals Mfr
S.I.C.: 2899
N.A.I.C.S.: 325998

BASF Construction Chemicals Peru S.A. (2)
Jr Placido Jimenez No 630/790
Cercado, 01 Lima, Peru
Tel.: (51) 1 385 0109
Fax: (51) 1 385 2065
Web Site: www.la.cc.basf.com
Construction Chemical Mfr
S.I.C.: 2899
N.A.I.C.S.: 325998

BASF Construction Chemicals (Pty) Ltd (2)
11 Pullinger Street
1780 Westonaria, South Africa
Tel.: (27) 11 754 1343
Fax: (27) 11 754 1105
Web Site: www.basf.co.za
Construction Chemical Mfr & Distr
S.I.C.: 2899
N.A.I.C.S.: 325998
Warren Trew *(Dir-Bus Dev)*

BASF Construction Chemicals (Schweiz) AG (2)
Industriestrasse 26
8207 Schaffhausen, Switzerland CH
Tel.: (41) 589582525

BASF SE—(Continued)

Fax: (41) 589583525
E-Mail: infoconica@basf.com
Web Site: www.conica.basf.com
Emp.: 150
Mfr of Sports Flooring Surfaces
S.I.C.: 3089
N.A.I.C.S.: 326199
Daniel Dunki *(Gen Mgr-Sls)*

Unit:

BASF Admixture Systems Europe (3)
Vulkanstrasse 110
CH 8048 Zurich, Switzerland
Tel.: (41) 444382361
Fax: (41) 444327220
Web Site: www.basf.com
Sls.: $792,814,400
Emp.: 200
Mfr of Concrete, Mortar & Pavement Additives & Admixtures
S.I.C.: 3272
N.A.I.C.S.: 327390
Don Cronin *(Mng Dir)*

BASF Construction Chemicals Sweden AB (2)
Metalvagen 42
19572 Stockholm, Rosersberg, Sweden
Tel.: (46) 87560165
Fax: (46) 87560167
Web Site: www.construction-chemicals.basf.com
Emp.: 15
Distr of Concrete Additives & Building Supplies
S.I.C.: 5211
N.A.I.C.S.: 444190
Per Berglund *(Mng Dir)*

BASF Construction Chemicals UK (2)
Albany House Swinton Hall Rd
Manchester, M27 4DT, United Kingdom
Tel.: (44) 01617947411
Telex: 965236 AQUA G
Fax: (44) 01617278547
E-Mail: mbtfeb@mbt.com
Web Site: www.basf.com
Emp.: 70
Mfr. of Waterproofing & Roofing Products
S.I.C.: 2295
N.A.I.C.S.: 313320
Geoss McManus *(Mgr)*

BASF Construction Chemicals Venezuela, S.A. (2)
Av Libertador CC Av Libertador Torre
Caracas, Venezuela
Tel.: (58) 2127625471
Fax: (58) 2127626120
E-Mail: ceclines@ceclines.com
Web Site: www.basf-cc-la.com
Emp.: 40
Distr of Concrete Additives
S.I.C.: 5211
N.A.I.C.S.: 444190
Nelly Gil *(Mgr-Mktg-Sls)*

BASF Construction Systems (China) Co. Ltd. (2)
69 Guiquig Road Caohejing Develpment Area
200233 Shanghai, China
Tel.: (86) 21 6485 33 00
Fax: (86) 21 6485 73 10
Construction Chemicals Mfr
S.I.C.: 2899
N.A.I.C.S.: 325998

BASF Yapi Kimyasallari San A/S (2)
Mete Plaza Degirmenyolu cad Huzurhoca Sok No 84 Kat 9 17
34752 Istanbul, Kavacik, Turkey
Tel.: (90) 2165703400
Fax: (90) 2165703779
E-Mail: info@basf.com
Web Site: www.basf-yks.com.tr
Emp.: 100
Distr of Construction Chemicals
S.I.C.: 5169
N.A.I.C.S.: 424690
Cuneyt Dayicioglu *(Gen Mgr)*

BASF Crop Protection Division (1)
Speyerer Strasse 27
D-67117 Limburgerhof, Germany
Tel.: (49) 621600
Fax: (49) 6216042525
E-Mail: globalifo@basf.com
Web Site: www.agro.basf.com
Sales Range: $1-4.9 Billion
Emp.: 1,350
Holding Company; Pesticides & Other Crop Protection Chemicals Mfr
S.I.C.: 6719
N.A.I.C.S.: 551112
Markus Heldt *(Pres)*
Paul Rea *(Sr VP-Asia Pacific)*

Subsidiary:

BASF Plant Science Company GmbH (2)
Speyerer Strasse 2
D-67117 Limburgerhof, Germany De
Tel.: (49) 621600 (100%)
Fax: (49) 6216042525
Web Site: www.agro.basf.com
Emp.: 120
Holding Company; Nitrogenous Fertilizer & Other Agro-Chemical Product Developer & Mfr
S.I.C.: 6719
N.A.I.C.S.: 551112
Peter Eckes *(Pres)*

Subsidiary:

BASF Plant Science GmbH (3)
Speyerer Strasse 2
67117 Limburgerhof, Germany De
Tel.: (49) 621600 (100%)
Fax: (49) 6216092081
Web Site: www.agro.basf.com
Emp.: 120
Nitrogenous Fertilizer & Other Agro-Chemical Product Developer & Mfr
S.I.C.: 2873
N.A.I.C.S.: 325311
Reiner Emrich *(Mng Dir)*

Subsidiary:

SunGene GmbH (4)
Corrensstr 3
06466 Gatersleben, Sachsen-Anhalt, Germany
Tel.: (49) 39482 760 0
Fax: (49) 39482 760 199
E-Mail: gatersleben@sungene.de
Web Site: www.sungene.de
Emp.: 700
Biotechnology Research & Development Services
S.I.C.: 8731
N.A.I.C.S.: 541711
Christian Biesgen *(Co-Mng Dir)*
Rainer Lemke *(Co-Mng Dir)*

Non-U.S. Subsidiaries:

DNA LandMarks Inc. (4)
84 richelieu Street
Saint-Jean-sur-Richelieu, QC, J3B 6X3, Canada
Tel.: (450) 358-2621
Fax: (450) 358-1154
Web Site: www.dnalandmarks.ca
Emp.: 47
Assisted Breeding Services
S.I.C.: 0752
N.A.I.C.S.: 115210
Charles Pick *(Mgr-Bus Dev)*

Plant Science Sweden AB (4)
Herman Ehles Vag 3-4
268 31 Svalov, Sweden
Tel.: (46) 418 66 70 80
Fax: (46) 418 66 70 81
Agricultural Chemicals Mfr
S.I.C.: 2879
N.A.I.C.S.: 325320

U.S. Subsidiaries:

BASF Plant Science LP (3)
26 Davis Dr
Research Triangle Park, NC 27709 DE
Tel.: (919) 547-2000 (100%)
Fax: (919) 547-2423
Web Site: www.agproducts.basf.com
Emp.: 600
Insecticide & Other Agro-Chemical Product Developer & Mfr
S.I.C.: 2879
N.A.I.C.S.: 325320
Paul Rea *(VP-Ops)*

Plants:

BASF Agricultural Products de Puerto Rico (4)
State Rd Ste 2 KM 47 2
Manati, PR 00674
Tel.: (787) 621-1700
Fax: (787) 621-1670
Web Site: www2.basf.us/corporate/aboutbasfnaftaindex.html
Emp.: 200
Pesticides & Other Agricultural Products Mfr
S.I.C.: 2879
N.A.I.C.S.: 325320
Ricardo Morales *(Gen Mgr)*

BASF Corp. - Beaumont Agricultural Products Plant (4)
14385 W Port Arthur Rd
Beaumont, TX 77705
Tel.: (409) 981-5000
Fax: (409) 981-5299
Web Site: www2.basf.us/corporate/aboutbasfnaftaindex.html
Emp.: 165
Pesticides & Other Agricultural Products Mfr
S.I.C.: 2879
N.A.I.C.S.: 325320
John Smoter *(Plant Mgr)*

BASF Corp. - Palmyra (Hannibal) Agricultural Products Plant (4)
3150 Hwy JJ
Palmyra, MO 63461
Tel.: (573) 769-2011
Fax: (573) 769-5600
Web Site: www2.basf.us/corporate/aboutbasfnaftaindex.html
Emp.: 310
Pesticides & Other Agricultural Products Mfr
S.I.C.: 2879
N.A.I.C.S.: 325320

Becker Underwood, Inc. (3)
801 Dayton Ave
Ames, IA 50010 DE
Tel.: (515) 232-5907
Fax: (515) 232-5961
Toll Free: (800) 232-5907
E-Mail: info@beckerunderwood.com
Web Site: www.beckerunderwood.com
Sales Range: $200-249.9 Million
Emp.: 479
Colorants & Bio-Agronomics Products Mfr & Marketer
S.I.C.: 2879
N.A.I.C.S.: 325320
Peter Innes *(CEO)*

Non-U.S. Subsidiaries:

BASF Agricultural Research Foundation, Inc. (2)
103 Progress Ave Phase 1 GIZ
4037 Laguna, Philippines
Tel.: (63) 2 889 4321
Fax: (63) 49 549 1026
E-Mail: lie.chico@basf.com
Emp.: 100
Agricultural Research
S.I.C.: 8731
N.A.I.C.S.: 541712
Jessica Huanglara *(Pres)*

BASF Agro B.V. - Arnhem (NL) (2)
Wddenswil Branch Steinacherstrasse 101
Postfach 69
8820 Wadenswil, Switzerland
Tel.: (41) 7819911
Fax: (41) 7819912
Chemical Product Mfr
S.I.C.: 2899
N.A.I.C.S.: 325998

BASF Agro Hellas Industrial and Commercial S.A. (2)
449 Mesogion Avenue
15343 Athens, Agia Paraskevi, Greece
Tel.: (30) 2106860100
Fax: (30) 2106860200
E-Mail: vassilis.gounaris@basf.gr
Web Site: www.basf.com
Emp.: 80
Chemical Product Mfr
S.I.C.: 2899
N.A.I.C.S.: 325998
Vassilis Gounaris *(Mng Dir)*

BASF Agro, Ltd. (2)
Roppongi 25 Mori Bldg 23F
1 4 30 Roppongi Minato Ku, Tokyo, 106-6121, Japan JP
Tel.: (81) 335869911 (100%)
Fax: (81) 37969419
Web Site: www.basf-japan.co.jp
Emp.: 170
Mfr. of Agricultural Chemicals
S.I.C.: 2899
N.A.I.C.S.: 325998

BASF Agro SAS (2)
21 chemin de la Sauvegarde
69134 Ecully, France
Tel.: (33) 472324545
Fax: (33) 478342886
E-Mail: benjamin.pinto@basf.com
Web Site: www.agro.basf.fr
Emp.: 150
Agricultural Chemical Mfr
S.I.C.: 2879
N.A.I.C.S.: 325320

Subsidiary:

BASF Agri-Production S.A.S. (3)
Rue du Vieux Chemin de Loon
Site Industriel Leurette, 59820 Gravelines, France
Tel.: (33) 328235250
Fax: (33) 328235253
E-Mail: philippe.boudier@basf.com
Web Site: www.basf.com
Emp.: 120
Agricultural Product Mfr
S.I.C.: 2879
N.A.I.C.S.: 325320
Philippe Boudier *(Mng Dir)*

Wintershall AG (1)
Friedrich Ebert Str 160
D 34119 Kassel, Hessen, Germany (100%)
Tel.: (49) 5613010
Fax: (49) 5613011702
E-Mail: info@wintershall.com
Web Site: www.wintershall.de
Emp.: 500
Crude Oil, Natural Gas & Petroleum Products
S.I.C.: 2999
N.A.I.C.S.: 324199
Rainer Seele *(Chm)*

Subsidiaries:

Haidkopf GmbH (2)
Friedrich-Ebert-Strasse 160
34119 Kassel, Germany
Mailing Address:
Postfach 10 40 20
34112 Kassel, Germany
Tel.: (49) 5613010
Fax: (49) 5613011702
E-Mail: info@wintershall.com
Web Site: www.wintershall.com
Emp.: 1,600
Natural Gas Distr
S.I.C.: 4924
N.A.I.C.S.: 221210
Reinier Switserloot *(Chm)*

Wintershall Erdgas Beteiligungs GmbH (2)
Friedrich Ebert St 160
34119 Kassel, Hessen, Germany (100%)
Tel.: (49) 5613010
Fax: (49) 5613011702
E-Mail: info@wingas.de
Web Site: www.wingas.de
Emp.: 500
Oil & Gas Exploration & Production
S.I.C.: 1389
N.A.I.C.S.: 213112
Rainer Seele *(Chm)*

Wintershall Erdgas Handelshaus GmbH AG (2)
Dusseldorfer Strasse 38
10707 Berlin, Germany (100%)
Mailing Address:
Postfach 15 14 25
10676 Berlin, Germany
Tel.: (49) 308859230
Fax: (49) 3088592399
Web Site: www.wintershall.com
Emp.: 20
Oil & Gas Exploration & Production
S.I.C.: 1389

N.A.I.C.S.: 213112
Arthounr Chrkhdinarov *(Mgr)*

Non-U.S. Joint Venture:

Wirom Gas S.A. (3)
Str Popa Savu 77
011432 Bucharest, Romania
Tel.: (40) 212221564
Fax: (40) 212221567
E-Mail: wirom@wirom.ro
Web Site: www.wiee.ch
Emp.: 20
Chemical Product Mfr; Owned 51% by Wintershall Erdgas Handelshaus Zug AG & 49% by Distrigaz Sud S.A.
S.I.C.: 2899
N.A.I.C.S.: 325998

Wintershall Norwegen Explorations- und Produktions- GmbH (2)
Friedrich-Ebert-Str 160
34119 Kassel, Germany
Tel.: (49) 561 3010
Fax: (49) 561 3011702
E-Mail: info@wintershall.com
Web Site: www.wintershall.com
Oil & Gas Exploration Services
S.I.C.: 1389
N.A.I.C.S.: 213112

Wintershall Russia Holding GmbH (2)
Friedrich-Ebert-Str 160
Kassel, Hessen, 34119, Germany
Tel.: (49) 5613010
Fax: (49) 5611702
Investment Management Services
S.I.C.: 6211
N.A.I.C.S.: 523999

Wintershall Vermogensverwaltungsgesellschaft mbH (2)
Friedrich-Ebert-Str 160
34119 Kassel, Hessen, Germany
Tel.: (49) 561 301 0
E-Mail: info@wintershall.com
Web Site: www.wintershall.com
Oil & Gas Exploration Services
S.I.C.: 1389
N.A.I.C.S.: 213112

Wintershall Wolga Petroleum GmbH (2)
Friedrich-Ebert-Strasse 160
Kassel, Hessen, 34119, Germany
Tel.: (49) 5613010
Fax: (49) 5613011702
E-Mail: info@wintershall.com
Web Site: www.wintershall.com
Oil & Gas Exploration Services
S.I.C.: 1389
N.A.I.C.S.: 213112

Joint Venture:

WINGAS Holding GmbH (2)
Friedrich-Ebert-Strasse 160
34119 Kassel, Hessen, Germany De
Tel.: (49) 561 301 0
Fax: (49) 561 3011702
E-Mail: info@wintershall.com
Web Site: www.wintershall.com
Investment Management Services
S.I.C.: 6211
N.A.I.C.S.: 523999

Subsidiary:

WINGAS GmbH (3)
Friedrich-Ebert-Strasse 160
D-34119 Kassel, Germany
Mailing Address:
Postfach 10 40 20
D-34112 Kassel, Germany
Tel.: (49) 5613010
Fax: (49) 5613011702
E-Mail: info@wingas.de
Web Site: www.wingas.de
Rev.: $2,194,307,584
Emp.: 500
Commercial & Industrial Natural Gas Supply Services
S.I.C.: 4924
N.A.I.C.S.: 221210
Artour Chakhdinarov *(Mng Dir & Head-Procurement)*
Gerhard Konig *(Mng Dir & Head-Sls-Germany)*

Subsidiaries:

WINGAS Transport GmbH & Co. KG (4)
Baumbachstrasse 1
34119 Kassel, Germany
Tel.: (49) 5619340
Fax: (49) 5619341702
E-Mail: kontakt@wingas-transport.de
Web Site: www.wingas-transport.de
Emp.: 250
Commercial & Industrial Natural Gas Supply Services
S.I.C.: 4923
N.A.I.C.S.: 486210
Bjorn Kaiser *(Mng Dir)*
Sabine Schittek *(Sec)*

WINGAS Verwaltungs-GmbH (4)
Friedrich-Ebert-Str 160
34119 Kassel, Germany
Tel.: (49) 561 3010
Fax: (49) 561 3011702
E-Mail: info@wingas.de
Web Site: www.wingas.de
Investment Management Services
S.I.C.: 6211
N.A.I.C.S.: 523999

Non-U.S. Subsidiaries:

WINGAS Belgium s.p.r.l./b.v.b.a. (4)
Avenue des Arts Kunstlaan 21
1000 Brussels, Belgium
Tel.: (32) 22806724
Fax: (32) 2 280 6732
Web Site: www.wintershall.com
Commercial & Industrial Natural Gas Supply Services
S.I.C.: 4924
N.A.I.C.S.: 221210

WINGAS UK Ltd. (4)
Bridge House Berleith House 73-75 Sheen Rd
3 Heron Square, Richmond, Surrey, TW9 1Yj, United Kingdom UK
Tel.: (44) 2084399680
Fax: (44) 2084399696
E-Mail: info@wingas-uk.com
Web Site: www.wingas-uk.com
Emp.: 23
Commercial & Industrial Natural Gas Supply Services
S.I.C.: 4924
N.A.I.C.S.: 221210
Tobias Rob *(Mng Dir)*

Non-U.S. Subsidiaries:

Wintershall AG Doha (2)
Salam Tower 11th Fl Al Corniche St
PO Box 2541
Doha, Qatar
Tel.: (974) 4839554
Fax: (974) 4830942
Chemical Product Mfr
S.I.C.: 2899
N.A.I.C.S.: 325998

Wintershall AG Vertretung Moskau (2)
Ul Namjotkina 16
W-420 GSP 7, 117997 Moscow, Russia
Tel.: (7) 4957198689
Fax: (7) 4957186386
Web Site: www.wintershall.com
Chemical Product Mfr
S.I.C.: 2899
N.A.I.C.S.: 325998

Wintershall Chile Lda. (2)
Av Isidora Goyenechea 3120 Piso 3
Las Condes, Santiago, Chile
Tel.: (56) 24312700
Fax: (56) 24312701
Natural Gas Exploration Services
S.I.C.: 1389
N.A.I.C.S.: 213112

Wintershall Energia S.A. (2)
Della Paolera 265 14th Fl
C1006 ACI Buenos Aires, Argentina
Tel.: (54) 1155542700
Fax: (54) 1155542701
E-Mail: hr@wintershall.com
Web Site: www.wintershall.com
Sales Range: $200-249.9 Million
Emp.: 60
Chemical Product Mfr
S.I.C.: 2899
N.A.I.C.S.: 325998

Wintershall Erdgas Handelshaus Zug AG (2)
Grafenauweg 8
6300 Zug, Switzerland
Tel.: (41) 417114618
Fax: (41) 417111412
E-Mail: wiee@wiee.ch
Web Site: www.wiee.ch
Oil & Gas Exploration & Production
S.I.C.: 1389
N.A.I.C.S.: 213112

Wintershall Gas spol. s r.o. (2)
Safrankova 3
15500 Prague, 5, Czech Republic
Tel.: (420) 235 000 111
Fax: (420) 519 427 032
Web Site: www.wintershall.com
Oil & Gas Exploration & Production
S.I.C.: 1389
N.A.I.C.S.: 213112

Wintershall Libya (2)
The Commercial Centre
Tripoli, Libya
Tel.: (218) 213350140
Fax: (218) 213350136
Web Site: www.wintershall.com
Emp.: 200
Oil & Gas Production & Exploration
S.I.C.: 1389
N.A.I.C.S.: 213112

Wintershall Middle East GmbH-Abu Dhabi (2)
P.O. Box 47193
Abu Dhabi, United Arab Emirates
Tel.: (971) 26810517
Fax: (971) 26813031
E-Mail: reception@wintershall.com
Web Site: www.wintershall.com
Emp.: 2
Oil & Gas Exploration & Production
S.I.C.: 1389
N.A.I.C.S.: 213112

Wintershall Nederland B.V. (2)
Bogaaretlein 47
2284DP Rijswijk, Netherlands (100%)
Mailing Address:
Postbus 82102
2508EC Hague, Netherlands
Tel.: (31) 703583100
Fax: (31) 703583333
Web Site: www.wintershall.nl
Sales Range: $150-199.9 Million
Emp.: 250
Oil & Gas Exploration & Production
S.I.C.: 1389
N.A.I.C.S.: 213112
Gilbert Van Benbrint *(Gen Mgr)*

Subsidiaries:

Clyde Netherlands BV (3)
Stadhoudersplantsoen 2
2517 JL Hague, Netherlands
Tel.: (31) 703560085
Telex: 30962
Fax: (31) 703560085
Mfr. of Petroleum
S.I.C.: 1311
N.A.I.C.S.: 211111

Wintershall Exploration and Production International C.V. (3)
Bogaardplein 47
Rijswijk, South Holland, 2284 DP, Netherlands
Tel.: (31) 70 358 3100
Fax: (31) 70 358 3333
Oil & Gas Exploration Services
S.I.C.: 1389
N.A.I.C.S.: 213112
Gilbert Brink *(Gen Mgr)*

Wintershall Nederland Transport and Trading B.V. (3)
Bogaardplein 47
Rijswijk, South Holland, 2284 DP, Netherlands
Tel.: (31) 703583100
Fax: (31) 703583333
Oil & Gas Exploration Services
S.I.C.: 1389
N.A.I.C.S.: 213112

Wintershall Noordzee B.V. (3)
Bogaardplein 47
2284 DP Rijswijk, Netherlands
Tel.: (31) 703583100
Fax: (31) 703583333
E-Mail: Info@wintershall.com
Web Site: www.wintershall.com
Emp.: 300
Oil & Gas Exploration & Production
S.I.C.: 1389
N.A.I.C.S.: 213112
Gelbert Brink *(Gen Mgr)*

Wintershall Petroleum (E&P) B.V. (3)
Bogaardplein 47
Rijswijk, Zuid-Holland, 2284 DP, Netherlands
Tel.: (31) 70 358 3100
Fax: (31) 70 358 3333
E-Mail: info@wintershall.com
Web Site: www.wintershall.com
Oil & Gas Exploration Services
S.I.C.: 1389
N.A.I.C.S.: 213112

Wintershall Services B.V. (3)
Bogaardplein 47
Rijswijk, 2284 DP, Netherlands
Tel.: (31) 70 358 3100
Fax: (31) 70 358 3333
E-Mail: info@wintershall.com
Emp.: 300
Oil & Gas Exploration Services
S.I.C.: 1389
N.A.I.C.S.: 213112
Gilbert van den Brink *(Gen Dir)*

Wintershall Oil AG (2)
Grafenauweg 6-8
6300 Zug, Switzerland
Tel.: (41) 417108828
Fax: (41) 417110101
E-Mail: info@wintershall.com
Web Site: www.wintershall.com
Emp.: 6
Oil & Gas Exploration & Production
S.I.C.: 1389
N.A.I.C.S.: 213112
Reinhard Soelter *(Gen Mgr)*

Wintershall Petroleum Iberia S.A. (2)
Abogado Aranegui Van Ingen
Fuente Del Romero 29B, 28023 Madrid, Spain (100%)
Tel.: (34) 913572403
Fax: (34) 913572703
E-Mail: wiagspain@infonegocio.com
Web Site: www.badspaininfo.com
Emp.: 4
Oil & Gas Exploration & Production
S.I.C.: 1389
N.A.I.C.S.: 213112

Wintershall (UK North Sea) Ltd. (2)
83 Baker Street
London, W1U 6AG, United Kingdom
Tel.: (44) 20 703 47048
Oil & Gas Exploration Services
S.I.C.: 1389
N.A.I.C.S.: 213112

Non-U.S. Joint Venture:

OOO Wolgodeminoil (2)
Ul Rabotche-Krestyanskaya Street 30 A
400074 Volgograd, Russia
Tel.: (7) 8442333420
Fax: (7) 8442333459
Web Site: www.basf.com
Chemical Product Mfr; Owned 50% by Wintershall AG & 50% by OAO Lukoil
S.I.C.: 2899
N.A.I.C.S.: 325998

Subsidiaries:

baseclick GmbH (1)
Bahnhofstrasse 9-15
82327 Tutzing, Germany
Tel.: (49) 8158 903867
Fax: (49) 8158 903894
E-Mail: info@baseclick.eu
Web Site: www.baseclick.eu
Emp.: 6
Chemical Products Mfr
S.I.C.: 2899
N.A.I.C.S.: 325998
Antonio Manetto *(Head-R&D)*

BASF SE—(Continued)

BASF Agro Trademarks GmbH (1)
Carl-Bosch-Str 38
Ludwigshafen, Rheinland-Pfalz, 67063, Germany
Tel.: (49) 621600
Fax: (49) 621 6042525
Administrative Management Consulting Services
S.I.C.: 8742
N.A.I.C.S.: 541611

BASF Akquisitions- und Objektverwertungsgesellschaft mbH (1)
Carl-Bosch-Str 38
Ludwigshafen, 67063, Germany
Tel.: (49) 621600
Fax: (49) 6216042525
Business Management Consulting Services
S.I.C.: 8742
N.A.I.C.S.: 541611

BASF Battery Technology Investment GmbH & Co. KG (1)
Carl-Bosch-Str 38
Ludwigshafen, Rheinland-Pfalz, 67063, Germany
Tel.: (49) 621 60 0
Fax: (49) 621 60 42525
Investment Management Services
S.I.C.: 6211
N.A.I.C.S.: 523999

BASF Bautechnik GmbH (1)
Dr-Albert-Frank-Str 32
Trostberg, Bayern, 83308, Germany
Tel.: (49) 8621863700
Fax: (49) 8621863703
Construction Chemical Mfr
S.I.C.: 2899
N.A.I.C.S.: 325998

BASF Beteiligungsgesellschaft mbH (1)
Carl-Bosch-Str 38
Ludwigshafen, Rheinland-Pfalz, 67063, Germany
Tel.: (49) 621600
Fax: (49) 6216042525
Chemical Product Mfr
S.I.C.: 2899
N.A.I.C.S.: 325998

BASF Biorenewable Beteiligungs GmbH & Co. KG (1)
Carl-Bosch-Str 38
Ludwigshafen, Rheinland-Pfalz, 67063, Germany
Tel.: (49) 621600
Chemical Product Mfr
S.I.C.: 2899
N.A.I.C.S.: 325998

BASF Catalysts Grundbesitz GmbH (1)
Carl-Bosch-Str 38
Ludwigshafen, 67063, Germany
Tel.: (49) 1715697125
Chemical Product Mfr
S.I.C.: 2899
N.A.I.C.S.: 325998

BASF Chemikalien GmbH (1)
Carl-Bosch-Str 38
Ludwigshafen, 67063, Germany
Tel.: (49) 621600
Fax: (49) 621604040
Chemical Product Mfr
S.I.C.: 2899
N.A.I.C.S.: 325998

BASF ChemTrade GmbH (1)
Industriestr 20
91593 Burgbernheim, Bavaria, Germany DE
Tel.: (49) 0984398280 (100%)
Fax: (49) 98439828900
E-Mail: info@basf-chemtrade.com
Web Site: www.basf-chemtrade.com
Emp.: 50
Sales of Fine Chemicals
S.I.C.: 5169
N.A.I.C.S.: 424690
Elisa Hamm de Bantleon *(Mng Dir)*

BASF Color Solutions Germany GmbH (1)
Site Koeln-Muelheim Clevischer Ring 180
51063 Cologne, Germany
Tel.: (49) 221 96498 0
Fax: (49) 221 96498 391
E-Mail: info.masterbatch@basf.com
Emp.: 14
Plastic Colorant Mfr
S.I.C.: 2899
N.A.I.C.S.: 325998
Cesare Pollini *(Plant Mgr)*

Non-U.S. Subsidiary:

BASF Color Solutions France S.A.S. (2)
Zone Industrielle de Breuil le Sec
60676 Clermont, Oise, France
Tel.: (33) 3 44 77 77 77
Fax: (33) 3 44 78 30 10
Emp.: 53
Specialty Chemical Distr
S.I.C.: 5169
N.A.I.C.S.: 424690
K. K. Chan *(Gen Mgr)*

BASF Construction Chemicals Grundbesitz GmbH & Co. KG (1)
Carl-Bosch-Str 38
Ludwigshafen, Rheinland-Pfalz, 67063, Germany
Tel.: (49) 621600
Fax: (49) 621 6042525
Chemical Product Mfr
S.I.C.: 2899
N.A.I.C.S.: 325998

BASF Electronic Materials Gmbh (1)
Carl Bosch Strasse 38
67056 Ludwigshafen, Germany
Tel.: (49) 6216040228
Fax: (49) 6216091354
E-Mail: global.info@basf.com
Web Site: www.basf.com
Emp.: 30,000
Electronic & Chemicals Research, Producer & Retailer
S.I.C.: 3679
N.A.I.C.S.: 334419
Vincent Liu *(Mng Dir)*

BASF Finance Malta GmbH (1)
Carl-Bosch-Str 38
Ludwigshafen, 67063, Germany
Tel.: (49) 621600
Financial Management Services
S.I.C.: 6211
N.A.I.C.S.: 523999

BASF Future Business GmbH (1)
Bau Z 025 4 Gartenweg
67063 Ludwigshafen, Germany
Tel.: (49) 6216076811
Fax: (49) 6216076818
E-Mail: info_fb@basf.com
Web Site: www.basf-fb.de
Sales Range: $1-9.9 Million
Emp.: 20
Energy Management, Electronics & Technology System Developer
S.I.C.: 8731
N.A.I.C.S.: 541712
Thomas Webea *(Mng Dir)*

BASF Grenzach GmbH (1)
Kochlinstrasse 1
D-79630 Grenzach-Wyhlen, Germany De
Tel.: (49) 7624120 (100%)
Fax: (49) 7624122600
Web Site: www.basf.com
Chemicals Developer & Mfr
S.I.C.: 2899
N.A.I.C.S.: 325998

BASF Immobilien-Gesellschaft mbH (1)
Carl-Bosch-Str 38
67063 Ludwigshafen, Rheinland-Pfalz, Germany
Tel.: (49) 621 60 0
Fax: (49) 621 60 42525
Property Management Services
S.I.C.: 6531
N.A.I.C.S.: 531311

BASF Immobilien Pigment GmbH (1)
Carl-Bosch-Str 38
Ludwigshafen, 67063, Germany
Tel.: (49) 621600
Fax: (49) 6216042525
Chemical Product Mfr
S.I.C.: 2899
N.A.I.C.S.: 325998

BASF Innovationsfonds GmbH (1)
4 Gartenweg 7a Z 34
67063 Ludwigshafen, Germany
Tel.: (49) 6216076801
Fax: (49) 6216076819
E-Mail: michaela.kemper@basf.com
Emp.: 14
Research & Development Services
S.I.C.: 8731
N.A.I.C.S.: 541712
Dirk Nachtigal *(Mng Dir)*

BASF IT Services Holding GmbH (1)
Jaegerstrasse 1
67059 Ludwigshafen, Germany
Tel.: (49) 621 60 99550
Fax: (49) 621 60 99555
E-Mail: touchIT@basf-it-services.com
Web Site: www.information-services.basf.com
Rev.: $635,588,590
Investment Management Services
S.I.C.: 6211
N.A.I.C.S.: 523999

Subsidiary:

BASF IT Services GmbH (2)
Jaegerstrasse 1
67059 Ludwigshafen, Germany DE
Tel.: (49) 216058497 (100%)
Fax: (49) 6216058510
Web Site: www.information-services.basf.com
Emp.: 2,400
Information Technology Support Services
S.I.C.: 7376
N.A.I.C.S.: 541513
Ralf Sonnberger *(Mng Dir)*

Subsidiary:

BASF IT Services Consult GmbH (3)
Christoph-Probst-Weg 3
20251 Hamburg, Germany
Tel.: (49) 40 41000 0
Fax: (49) 40 41000 100
E-Mail: information-services@basf.com
Web Site: www.basf.com
Information Technology Consulting Services
S.I.C.: 7373
N.A.I.C.S.: 541512

Non-U.S. Subsidiaries:

BASF IT Services Holding Ltd. (3)
Cheadle Hulme Earl Road
Cheadle, SK8 6QG, United Kingdom
Tel.: (44) 161 485 6222
Fax: (44) 161 488 5220
Investment Management Services
S.I.C.: 6211
N.A.I.C.S.: 523999

BASF IT Services Ltd. (3)
Malmparken 5
2750 Ballerup, Denmark
Tel.: (45) 44730100
Fax: (45) 44730101
Web Site: www.information-services.basf.com
Emp.: 160
Information Technology Support Services
S.I.C.: 7376
N.A.I.C.S.: 541513
Preben Sorensen *(Mgr-Site)*

BASF IT Services N.V./S.A. (3)
Haven 725 Scheldelaan 600
2040 Antwerp, Belgium BE
Tel.: (32) 35613710 (100%)
Fax: (32) 003235613220
E-Mail: basf-it-services@basf.com
Web Site: www.basf.be
Emp.: 8,000
Information Technology Support Services
S.I.C.: 7376
N.A.I.C.S.: 541513
Sals Sonnderger *(Mgr)*

Non-U.S. Branch:

BASF IT Services N.V./S.A. - France (4)
49 Avenue Georges Pompidou
92593 Levallois-Perret, France (100%)
Tel.: (33) 49645164
Fax: (33) 4964 5190
Web Site: www.information-services.basf.com
Information Technology Support Services
S.I.C.: 7376
N.A.I.C.S.: 541513

BASF IT Services S.A. (3)
Crta N-340 Km 1 156
43006 Tarragona, Spain
Tel.: (34) 977 256 200
Fax: (34) 977 256 201
Information Technology Consulting Services
S.I.C.: 7373
N.A.I.C.S.: 541512

BASF IT Services S.p.A. (3)
Via Marconato 8
20031 Cesano Maderno, MI, Italy IT
Tel.: (39) 03625121 (100%)
Fax: (39) 0362512826
Web Site: www.information-services.basf.com
Information Technology Support Services
S.I.C.: 7376
N.A.I.C.S.: 541513

BASF Jobmarkt GmbH (1)
Wohlerstrasse 14
67063 Ludwigshafen, Germany
Tel.: (49) 6216048072
Fax: (49) 6216048281
Web Site: www.basf.com
Employment Placing Services
S.I.C.: 7361
N.A.I.C.S.: 561311
Fritz Krieg *(CEO)*

BASF Lampertheim GmbH (1)
Chemiestrasse 22
D-68619 Lampertheim, Germany De
Tel.: (49) 6206150 (100%)
Fax: (49) 6206151368
Web Site: www.basf.com
Emp.: 1,000
Chemicals Developer, Mfr & Whslr
S.I.C.: 2899
N.A.I.C.S.: 325998
Helmut Prestel *(Mng Dir)*

BASF Leuna GmbH (1)
Am Haupttor
06237 Leuna, Germany
Tel.: (49) 3461433872
Fax: (49) 3461433096
E-Mail: info-leuna@basf.com
Web Site: www.basf-leuna.de
Sls.: $6,864,606
Emp.: 140
Chemical Product Mfr
S.I.C.: 2899
N.A.I.C.S.: 325998
Manfred Heckmann *(Mng Dir)*

BASF Lizenz GmbH (1)
Carl-Bosch-Str 38
Ludwigshafen, 67063, Germany
Tel.: (49) 621600
Fax: (49) 6 216042525
Asset Management Services
S.I.C.: 6282
N.A.I.C.S.: 523920

BASF Ludwigshafen Grundbesitz SE & Co. KG (1)
Carl-Bosch-Str 38
67063 Ludwigshafen, Rheinland-Pfalz, Germany
Tel.: (49) 621 6048661
Fax: (49) 621 6042525
Web Site: www.basf.com
Emp.: 3,100
Management Consulting Services
S.I.C.: 8748
N.A.I.C.S.: 541618

BASF Mobilienleasing GmbH (1)
Carl-Bosch-Str 38
Ludwigshafen, 67063, Germany
Tel.: (49) 6216099911
Fax: (49) 6216042525
E-Mail: info.service@basf-ag.de
Chemical Product Mfr
S.I.C.: 2899
N.A.I.C.S.: 325998

BASF Performance Polymers GmbH (1)
Breitscheidstr 137
07407 Erfurt, Germany

Tel.: (49) 36723700
Fax: (49) 3672370309
E-Mail: info-audolfstad@basf.com
Web Site: www.basf.com
Emp.: 170
Polymer Product Mfr
S.I.C.: 3086
N.A.I.C.S.: 326140
Eckhard Kuhn *(Mng Dir)*
Heckmann Manfred *(Mng Dir)*

BASF Personal Care and Nutrition GmbH (1)
Rheinpromenade 1
40789 Monheim, Germany
Tel.: (49) 2173 4995 0
Fax: (49) 2173 4995 500
E-Mail: personal-care-eu@basf.com
Web Site: www.personal-care.basf.com
Personal Care Product Mfr
S.I.C.: 2844
N.A.I.C.S.: 325620

BASF PharmaChemikalien GmbH & Co. KG (1)
Karlstrabe 15
Karlstrasse 15-39 42 - 44, 32423 Minden, Germany
Tel.: (49) 5713910
Fax: (49) 571392408
Web Site: www.basf.com
Sales Range: $25-49.9 Million
Emp.: 500
Pharmaceutical Chemicals Mfr
S.I.C.: 2869
N.A.I.C.S.: 325199

BASF Pigment GmbH (1)
Gustav-Siegle-Strasse 19
74354 Besigheim, Germany (100%)
Tel.: (49) 71438080
Fax: (49) 7143808399
Web Site: www.basf.com
Sales Range: $1-9.9 Million
Emp.: 250
Chemical Product Mfr
S.I.C.: 2899
N.A.I.C.S.: 325998
Andreas Stor *(Mng Dir)*

BASF Polyurethanes GmbH (1)
Elastogranstrasse 60
49448 Lemforde, Germany
Tel.: (49) 5443 12 0
Fax: (49) 5443 12 2115
E-Mail: pu-eu@basf.com
Web Site: www.polyurethanes.basf.de
Polyurethane Material Mfr & Distr
S.I.C.: 3086
N.A.I.C.S.: 326150
Rene Lochtman *(VP & Mng Dir)*

Subsidiary:

BASF Polyurethane Licensing GmbH (2)
Elastogranstr 60
49448 Lemforde, Germany
Tel.: (49) 5443120
Fax: (49) 5443122201
E-Mail: pu-eu@basf.com
Web Site: www.pu.basf.de
Emp.: 1,000
Chemical Products Mfr
S.I.C.: 2899
N.A.I.C.S.: 325998
Martin Anton *(Mng Dir)*

Non-U.S. Subsidiaries:

BASF Poliuretani Italia SpA (2)
Strada Per Poirino 38
14019 Villanova d'Asti, Asti, Italy
Tel.: (39) 0141 949 111
Fax: (39) 0141 949 270
E-Mail: pu-it@basf.com
Web Site: www.polyurethanes.basf.de/pu/Italy
Chemical Products Mfr
S.I.C.: 2899
N.A.I.C.S.: 325998

BASF Poliuretanos Iberia S.A. (2)
Poligono Industrial Can Jardi Calle Compositor Vivaldi 1-7
8191 Rubi, Barcelona, Spain
Tel.: (34) 93 6806 100
Fax: (34) 93 6806 200
E-Mail: pu-es@basf.com
Web Site: www.polyurethanes.basf.de
Emp.: 75
Polyurethane Material Distr
S.I.C.: 5162
N.A.I.C.S.: 424610
Arturo Orea *(Dir Gen)*
Alexandra Forst *(Asst Mng Dir)*

BASF Poliuretany Polska Sp. z o.o. (2)
Ul Wiosenna 9
63-100 Srem, Poland
Tel.: (48) 61 636 63 66
Fax: (48) 61 636 63 99
E-Mail: pu-pl@basf.com
Emp.: 21
Polyurethane Material Mfr
S.I.C.: 3086
N.A.I.C.S.: 326150
Slawomir Gorski *(Mng Dir)*

BASF Polyurethanes Benelux B.V. (2)
Hemelrijk 11-13
5281 PS Boxtel, Netherlands
Tel.: (31) 411 615 615
Fax: (31) 411 615 616
E-Mail: pu-nl@basf.com
Web Site: www.polyurethanes.basf.eu
Emp.: 3
Chemical Products Mfr
S.I.C.: 2899
N.A.I.C.S.: 325998
Victor Coenen *(Mng Dir)*

BASF Polyurethanes (Chongqing) Co. Ltd. (2)
No 1 Huabei Second Rd Changshou Economic
Technology Development Zone, Chongqing, 401221, China
Tel.: (86) 2386626666
Fax: (86) 2386596555
Chemical Products Mfr
S.I.C.: 2899
N.A.I.C.S.: 325998
Christian Tragut *(Gen Mgr)*

BASF Polyurethanes France S.A.S. (2)
ZI Rue Decauville
77292 Mitry-Mory, France
Tel.: (33) 16021 4249
Fax: (33) 16021 4248
E-Mail: pu-fr@basf.com
Web Site: www.pu.basf.de/fr
Emp.: 55
Polyurethane Material Mfr
S.I.C.: 3086
N.A.I.C.S.: 326150
Olivier Ubrich *(Mng Dir)*

BASF Polyurethanes Nordic AB (2)
Angeredsvinkeln 5
42467 Angered, Sweden
Tel.: (46) 31 330 0050
Fax: (46) 31 330 7405
E-Mail: pu-se@basf.com
Web Site: www.elastogran.se
Emp.: 23
Chemical Product Mfr
S.I.C.: 2899
N.A.I.C.S.: 325998
Ake Lundberg *(Mng Dir)*

BASF Polyurethanes Pars (Private Joint Stock) Company (2)
Sohrevardi Shomali Avenue Kangavar Alley No 5
Tehran, 15579, Iran
Tel.: (98) 2188747571
Fax: (98) 2188748387
Polyurethane Material Mfr & Distr
S.I.C.: 3086
N.A.I.C.S.: 326150

BASF Polyurethanes South Africa (Pty.) Ltd. (2)
Evergreen Road Tunney Ext 7 Greenhills
PO Box 1449
Elandsfontein, Johannesburg, 1610, South Africa
Tel.: (27) 11 437 7600
Fax: (27) 862956582
E-Mail: enquiries-pu-za@basf.com
Emp.: 54
Polyurethane Material Distr
S.I.C.: 5162
N.A.I.C.S.: 424610

BASF Polyurethanes U.K. Ltd. (2)
Wimsey Way
Somercotes, Alfreton, Derbyshire, DE55 4NL, United Kingdom
Tel.: (44) 177360 7161
Fax: (44) 1773540 429
E-Mail: pu-uk@basf.com
Polyurethane Material Mfr & Distr
S.I.C.: 3086
N.A.I.C.S.: 326150

BASF Services Europe GmbH (1)
Rotherstrasse 11
10245 Berlin, Germany
Tel.: (49) 3020055000
Fax: (49) 3020055500
E-Mail: basf-services-europe@basf.com
Web Site: www.basf-services-europe.com
Emp.: 100
Finance & Accounting & Human Resources Services
S.I.C.: 8999
N.A.I.C.S.: 541612
Gabriela Anna Thomas *(Mng Dir)*

BASF US Verwaltung GmbH (1)
Carl-Bosch-Str 38
Ludwigshafen, Rheinland-Pfalz, 67063, Germany
Tel.: (49) 621600
Fax: (49) 6216042525
Chemical Product Distr
S.I.C.: 5169
N.A.I.C.S.: 424690

BASF Venture Capital GmbH (1)
4 Grarten Weg
67063 Ludwigshafen, Germany DE
Tel.: (49) 6216076801 (100%)
Fax: (49) 6216076819
E-Mail: info@basf-vc.de
Web Site: www.basf-vc.de
Emp.: 12
Venture Capital & Investment Services
S.I.C.: 6799
N.A.I.C.S.: 523910
Dirk Nachtigal *(Mng Dir)*

Subsidiary:

BASF VC Beteiligungs- und Managementgesellschaft (2)
Carl-Bosch-Str 38
Ludwigshafen, 67063, Germany
Tel.: (49) 621600
Investment Management Services
S.I.C.: 6211
N.A.I.C.S.: 523999

BASF watertechnologies GmbH & Co. KG (1)
Carl-Bosch-Str 38
67063 Ludwigshafen, Germany
Tel.: (49) 621 60 0
Fax: (49) 621 60 42525
Chemical Product Distr
S.I.C.: 5169
N.A.I.C.S.: 424690

Subsidiary:

BASF watertechnologies Beteiligungs GmbH (2)
Schipkauer Str 1
Schwarzheide, 01987, Germany
Tel.: (49) 3575260
Fax: (49) 3575262300
E-Mail: info@basf-schwarzheide.vom
Web Site: www.basf-schwarzheide.com
Chemical Product Mfr
S.I.C.: 2899
N.A.I.C.S.: 325998
Karl Eibel *(Mng Dir)*

BTC Europe GmbH (1)
Maarweg 163 / 165
50825 Cologne, Germany
Tel.: (49) 221 95464 0
Fax: (49) 221 95464 211
E-Mail: info@btc-europe.com
Web Site: www.btc-europe.com
Emp.: 300
Specialty Chemical Distr
S.I.C.: 5169
N.A.I.C.S.: 424690
Bettina Juchem *(Customer Svc Officer)*
Marc Nonnenmacher *(Customer Svc Officer)*

Cognis GmbH (1)
Rheinpromenade 1
D-40789 Monheim, Germany De
Mailing Address:
Postfach 100263
D-40766 Monheim, Germany
Tel.: (49) 21179400
Fax: (49) 2117984008
E-Mail: info@cognis.com
Web Site: www.cognis.com
Sales Range: $1-4.9 Billion
Emp.: 5,500
Holding Company; Specialty Chemical Mfr; Owned by Permira Advisers LLP, The Goldman Sachs Group, Inc. & SV Life Sciences
S.I.C.: 6719
N.A.I.C.S.: 551112
Michael Schulenburg *(Chm-Supervisory Bd)*
Thomas Fischer *(Vice Chm-Supervisory Bd)*
Michael Heinz *(CEO)*
Marco Panichi *(CFO)*
Helmut Heymann *(Chief Admin Officer & Exec VP)*
Paul Allen *(Exec VP-Functional Products)*

Subsidiaries:

Cognis Trust Management GmbH (2)
Henkelstr 67
Dusseldorf, Nordrhein-Westfalen, 40589, Germany
Tel.: (49) 21179400
Fax: (49) 2117984008
Business Management Consulting Services
S.I.C.: 8742
N.A.I.C.S.: 541611

Plant:

Cognis GmbH - Illertissen (2)
Robert-Hansen-Strasse 1
D-89257 Illertissen, Germany De
Tel.: (49) 7303130
Fax: (49) 703313737
Web Site: www.cognis.com
Emp.: 374
Chemicals & Resins Mfr
S.I.C.: 2821
N.A.I.C.S.: 325211
Robert Graf *(Mgr)*

Non-U.S. Subsidiaries:

Cognis Chemicals (China) Co. Ltd. (2)
15/F Xingmao Building 99 Tianzhou Road
Shanghai, 200233, China CN
Tel.: (86) 2154644666
Fax: (86) 2164858898
Emp.: 400
Chemicals & Resins Mfr
S.I.C.: 2821
N.A.I.C.S.: 325211
Manuel Zerwes *(Mng Dir)*

Cognis France S.A.S. (2)
185 Ave De Fontainebleau Saint Fargeau
77310 Ponthierry, France FR
Tel.: (33) 0160652100
Fax: (33) 160652101
Emp.: 533
Mfr of Additives
S.I.C.: 2819
N.A.I.C.S.: 325180
Stephane Baseden *(Mng Dir)*

Cognis Thai Ltd. (2)
71/1 Phyathai Road
Rajthevee, Bangkok, 10400, Thailand TH
Tel.: (66) 26547000
Fax: (66) 26547005
E-Mail: info@cognis.com
Emp.: 50
Production & Sale of Specialty Chemicals
S.I.C.: 2899
N.A.I.C.S.: 325998

P.T. Cognis Indonesia (2)
Jalan Raya Jakarta Bogor Km 31-2
Jakarta, 16953, Indonesia Id
Tel.: (62) 218711096
Fax: (62) 218710309
E-Mail: info@cognis.com
Cosmetics & Adhesives Mfr
S.I.C.: 2844
N.A.I.C.S.: 325620
Jimmy Lau *(Mng Dir)*

Construction Research & Technology GmbH (1)
Dr Albert-Frank-Str 32
Trostberg, Bayern, 83308, Germany

BASF SE—(Continued)

Tel.: (49) 8621860
Fax: (49) 8621 2911
Emp.: 500
Construction Chemical Research & Development Services
S.I.C.: 8731
N.A.I.C.S.: 541712
Raveling Hermann *(Mgr-Production)*

Dr. Wolman GmbH (1)
Dr Wolman Strasse 31 33
D 76547 Sinsheim, Germany DE
Mailing Address: (100%)
Postfach 11 60
D 76545 Sinsheim, Germany
Tel.: (49) 72218000
Telex: 781207 drwol d
Fax: (49) 7221800290
E-Mail: info@wolman.de
Web Site: www.wolman.de
Emp.: 100
Mfr. of Fire Proofing Agents, Wood Preserving Agents
S.I.C.: 2491
N.A.I.C.S.: 321114
Rolf Reinecke *(Mng Dir)*

Elastogran GmbH (1)
Elastogran Strasse 60
49448 Lemforde, Germany DE
Tel.: (49) 5443120 (100%)
Fax: (49) 5443122201
E-Mail: pu-eu@basf.com
Web Site: www.pu.basf.de
Emp.: 1,200
Polyurethane Products & Systems, Specialty Elastomers & Technical Parts Mfr
S.I.C.: 3086
N.A.I.C.S.: 326150
Uwe Hartwig *(Mng Dir)*

Subsidiaries:

BASF Schwarzheide GmbH (2)
Schipkauer Strasse 1
01986 Schwarzheide, Germany DE
Tel.: (49) 3575260 (100%)
Fax: (49) 3575262300
E-Mail: global.info@basf.com
Web Site: www.basf-Schwarzheide.de
Emp.: 2,266
Mfr. of Polyurethane Systems, Thermoplastic Polyurethane Elastomers & Polyurethane Processing Equipment & Facilities
S.I.C.: 2821
N.A.I.C.S.: 325211
Hans-Ulrich Engel *(Gen Mgr)*

Elastogran Innovationsprojekte Beteiligungsgesellschaft mbH (2)
Elastogranstr 60
49448 Lemforde, Germany
Tel.: (49) 5443122688
Chemical Products Mfr
S.I.C.: 2899
N.A.I.C.S.: 325998

Non-U.S. Subsidiaries:

BASF Poliuretan Hungaria Kft. (2)
Terstyanszky ut 89
2083 Solymar, Budapest, Hungary
Tel.: (36) 26560580
Fax: (36) 26560590
E-Mail: pu-hu@basf.com
Web Site: www.elastogran.hu
Sls.: $10,984,800
Emp.: 24
Polyurethane Mfr
S.I.C.: 3086
N.A.I.C.S.: 326140
Zoltan Demjen *(Mng Dir)*

BASF Polyurethane Industry and Trade Co., Ltd. Sti (2)
Sheikh Mah Ankara Cad No 334
34912 Istanbul, Seyhli-Pendik, Turkey
Tel.: (90) 2163786443
Fax: (90) 2163781433
E-Mail: pu-tr@basf.com
Web Site: www.polyurethanes.basf.de/pu/Turkey
Emp.: 5
Polyurethane Systems Mfr, Thermoplastic Polyurethane Elastomers & Polyurethane Processing Equipment & Facilities
S.I.C.: 2821
N.A.I.C.S.: 325211
Christain Marnnjel *(Dir)*

Elastogran France S.A.S (2)
Rue Decauville
PO Box 207
77292 Mitry-Mory, France FR
Tel.: (33) 160214249 (100%)
Fax: (33) 160212712
E-Mail: elastogran_fr@elastogran.fr
Web Site: www.elastogran.de
Emp.: 160
Mfr. of Polyurethane Systems, Thermoplastic Polyurethane Elastomers & Polyurethane Processing Equipment & Facilities
S.I.C.: 2821
N.A.I.C.S.: 325211
Jacques Delmoitiez *(Pres)*

Elastogran Italia S.p.A. (2)
Strada Per Poirino 38
I 14019 Villanova d'Asti, Italy IT
Tel.: (39) 141949111 (100%)
Fax: (39) 141949270
E-Mail: elastogran-it@elastogran.de
Web Site: www.elastogran.de
Mfr. of Polyurethane Systems, Thermoplastic Polyurethane Elastomers & Polyurethane Processing Equipment & Facilities
S.I.C.: 2821
N.A.I.C.S.: 325211

Elastogran Lagomat Nordic AB (2)
Angeredsvinkeln 5
42467 Angered, Sweden
Tel.: (46) 313300050
Fax: (46) 313307405
Web Site: www.elastogran.de
Emp.: 23
Polyurethane Products & Systems, Specialty Elastomers & Technical Parts Mfr
S.I.C.: 2821
N.A.I.C.S.: 325211
Kent Lundderg *(Gen Mgr)*

Elastogran S.A. (2)
Poligono Indus Can Jardi Calle Vivaldi 1 7
PO Box 94
E 08191 Rubi, Spain ES
Tel.: (34) 936806100 (100%)
Fax: (34) 936806200
E-Mail: elastogran@elastogran.es
Web Site: www.elastogran.es
Emp.: 80
Mfr. of Polyurethane Systems, Thermoplastic Polyurethane Elastomers & Polyurethane Processing Equipment & Facilities
S.I.C.: 2821
N.A.I.C.S.: 325211
Andre Lioninsi *(Mng Dir)*

Elastogran UK Limited (2)
Alfreton Industrial Est
Somercotes Way, Derby, Derbyshire, DE55 4NL, United Kingdom UK
Tel.: (44) 773607161 (100%)
Fax: (44) 773602089
Web Site: www.elastogran.de
Emp.: 75
Polyurethane Systems Mfr, Thermoplastic Polyurethane Elastomers & Polyurethane Processing Equipment & Facilities
S.I.C.: 2821
N.A.I.C.S.: 325211
Colin Dunn *(Mng Dir)*

OOO Elastokam (2)
Promzona PF 52
Republik Tatarstan
423574 Nizhnekamsk, 4, Russia
Tel.: (7) 8555383062
Fax: (7) 8555383063
E-Mail: elastokam@basf.com
Web Site: www.polyurethanes.basf.de
Chemical Product Mfr
S.I.C.: 2899
N.A.I.C.S.: 325998

Elfte BASF Projektentwicklungsgesellschaft mbH (1)
Carl-Bosch-Str 38
67063 Ludwigshafen, Germany
Tel.: (49) 621600
Fax: (49) 621 60 42525
E-Mail: info.service@basf-ag.de
Project Management Consulting Services
S.I.C.: 8748
N.A.I.C.S.: 541618

Funfzehnte BASF Erwerbsgesellschaft mbH (1)
Carl-Bosch-Str 38
67063 Ludwigshafen, Germany
Tel.: (49) 621 600
Fax: (49) 621 6042525
Chemical Product Whslr
S.I.C.: 5169
N.A.I.C.S.: 424690

Funfzehnte BASF Finanzbeteiligungsgesellschaft mbH (1)
Carl-Bosch-Str 38
67063 Ludwigshafen, Rheinland-Pfalz, Germany
Tel.: (49) 621 60 0
Fax: (49) 621 60 42525
Financial Manangement Services
S.I.C.: 6211
N.A.I.C.S.: 523999

Funfzehnte BASF Projektentwicklungsgesellschaft mbH (1)
Carl-Bosch-Str 38
67063 Ludwigshafen, Rheinland-Pfalz, Germany
Tel.: (49) 621 60 0
Fax: (49) 621 60 42525
E-Mail: info.service@basf-ag.de
Project Management Consulting Services
S.I.C.: 8748
N.A.I.C.S.: 541618

Gewerkschaft des konsolidierten Steinkohlenbergwerks Breitenbach GmbH (1)
Carl-Bosch-Str 38
67063 Ludwigshafen, Rheinland-Pfalz, Germany
Tel.: (49) 621 60 0
Fax: (49) 621 60 42525
E-Mail: info.service@basf-ag.de
Coal Mining Services
S.I.C.: 1241
N.A.I.C.S.: 213113

Glasurit GmbH (1)
Glasuritstrasse 1
48165 Munster, Germany
Tel.: (49) 2501 14 0
Fax: (49) 2501 14 3373
Web Site: www.basf.com
Industrial Chemical Mfr
S.I.C.: 2899
N.A.I.C.S.: 325998

Grunau Illertissen GmbH (1)
Robert-Hansen-Str 1
89257 Illertissen, Germany
Tel.: (49) 730 31 30
Fax: (49) 730 31 32 05
Chemical Product Mfr
S.I.C.: 2899
N.A.I.C.S.: 325998

Guano-Werke GmbH & Co. KG (1)
Carl-Bosch-Strasse 38
67056 Ludwigshafen, Germany
Tel.: (49) 621600
Fax: (49) 6216042525
E-Mail: global.info@basf.com
Web Site: www.basf.com
Chemical Products Mfr
S.I.C.: 2899
N.A.I.C.S.: 325998

hte Aktiengesellschaft (1)
Kurpfalzring 104
69123 Heidelberg, Germany
Tel.: (49) 62 21 74 97 0
Fax: (49) 62 21 74 97 137
E-Mail: info@hte-company.de
Web Site: www.hte-company.com
Emp.: 250
Technology Research & Development Services
S.I.C.: 8731
N.A.I.C.S.: 541712
Dirk Demuth *(Co-Founder, CEO & COO)*
Wolfram Stichert *(Co-Founder & CFO)*
Friedrich Seitz *(Chm-Supervisory Bd)*

inge GmbH (1)
Flurstrasse 27
86926 Greifenberg, Germany
Tel.: (49) 8192 997 700
Fax: (49) 8192 997 999
E-Mail: info@inge.ag
Web Site: www.inge.ag
Emp.: 13
Water Purification Membrane Mfr
S.I.C.: 3999
N.A.I.C.S.: 339999
Peter Berg *(Founder & CTO)*
Bruno Steis *(CEO)*

LUCARA Immobilienverwaltungs GmbH (1)
Rheinuferstr 65-69
67061 Ludwigshafen, Rheinland-Pfalz, Germany
Tel.: (49) 621 6049810
Real Estate Management Services
S.I.C.: 6531
N.A.I.C.S.: 531390

Lucura Ruckversicherungs AG (1)
Wohlerstr 19
67063 Ludwigshafen, Rheinland-Pfalz, Germany
Tel.: (49) 621 622181
Fax: (49) 621 626 676
General Insurance Services
S.I.C.: 6411
N.A.I.C.S.: 524210
Eberhard Faller *(CEO)*

LUWOGE GmbH (1)
Brunckstrasse 49
67063 Ludwigshafen, Germany
Mailing Address:
Postfach 21 08 20
67008 Ludwigshafen, Germany
Tel.: (49) 6216044044
Fax: (49) 6216041555
E-Mail: info@luwoge.com
Web Site: www.luwoge.com
Emp.: 100
Property Management
S.I.C.: 6531
N.A.I.C.S.: 531312
Matthias Hensel *(Mng Dir)*

Subsidiary:

LUWOGE consult GmbH (2)
Donnersbergweg 2
67059 Ludwigshafen, Germany
Tel.: (49) 621 55 90 989 0
Fax: (49) 621 55 90 989 99
E-Mail: info@luwoge-consult.de
Web Site: www.luwoge-consult.de
Real Estate Development Services
S.I.C.: 6531
N.A.I.C.S.: 531390

Units:

LUWOGE GmbH Haus Breitnau (2)
Gastehaus der BASF
Im Talgrund 11, 79874 Breitnau, Germany
Tel.: (49) 765291190
Fax: (49) 76529119444
E-Mail: gaestehaus.breitnau@luwoge.com
Web Site: www.basf.com
Emp.: 26
Property Management
S.I.C.: 6531
N.A.I.C.S.: 531312
Bernd Pollak *(Mng Dir)*

LUWOGE GmbH Haus Westerland (2)
Brunckstrasse 49
67063 Ludwigshafen, Germany
Tel.: (49) 6216095430
Fax: (49) 6216041555
E-Mail: info@luwoge.com
Web Site: www.luwoge.de
Emp.: 35
Property Management
S.I.C.: 6531
N.A.I.C.S.: 531312
Matthias Hensel *(Mng Dir)*

LUWOGE GmbH Studienhaus St. Johann (2)
Schlossstrasse 5
Schlossstrasse 5, 76857 Albstadt, Germany
Tel.: (49) 6345480
Fax: (49) 634548145
E-Mail: st-johann.studienhaus@luwoge.com
Property Management
S.I.C.: 6531
N.A.I.C.S.: 531312

Thomas Herrmann *(Gen Mgr)*

Metanomics GmbH (1)
Tegeler Weg 33
10589 Berlin, Germany
Tel.: (49) 30 34807 100
Fax: (49) 30 34807 300
E-Mail: company.info@metanomics.de
Web Site: www.metanomics.de
Emp.: 150
Biotechnology Research & Development Services
S.I.C.: 8731
N.A.I.C.S.: 541711
Arno J. Krotzky *(Co-Founder & CEO)*
Richard Trethewey *(Co-Founder & CEO)*
Thomas Ehrhardt *(CEO)*
Ralf Looser *(CEO)*
Astrid Giese *(CFO)*

Metanomics Health GmbH (1)
Tegeler Weg 33
10589 Berlin, Germany
Tel.: (49) 30 34807 400
Fax: (49) 30 34807 401
E-Mail: company.info@metanomics-health.de
Web Site: www.metanomics-health.de
Health Care Research & Drug Development Services
S.I.C.: 8099
N.A.I.C.S.: 621999
Tim P. Boelke *(Co-Mng Dir)*
Niels Moeller *(Co-Mng Dir)*

OPAL NEL TRANSPORT GmbH (1)
Emmerichstrasse 11
34119 Kassel, Germany
Tel.: (49) 561 934 0
Fax: (49) 561 934 2383
E-Mail: contact@opal-nel-transport.de
Web Site: www.opal-nel-transport.de
Natural Gas Transportation Services
S.I.C.: 4922
N.A.I.C.S.: 486210

PolyAd Services GmbH (1)
Chemiestrasse Building L 31
68623 Lampertheim, Germany
Tel.: (49) 6206 15 2301
Fax: (49) 6206 15 2309
E-Mail: europe.servicedesk@polyadservices.com
Web Site: www.polyadservices.com
Emp.: 6
Plastic Additive Mfr
S.I.C.: 2899
N.A.I.C.S.: 325998
Bernd Klingert *(Mng Dir)*

Projektentwicklungs-GmbH Friesenheimer Insel (1)
Lindenallee 55
Essen, Nordrhein-Westfalen, 45127, Germany
Tel.: (49) 201820240
Fax: (49) 2018202494
Chemical Products Distr
S.I.C.: 5169
N.A.I.C.S.: 424690

Relius Coatings Beteiligungs-GmbH (1)
Donnerschweer Str 372
Oldenburg, Niedersachsen, 26123, Germany
Tel.: (49) 44134020
Fax: (49) 4413402350
Paint & Coating Mfr
S.I.C.: 2851
N.A.I.C.S.: 325510
Andreas Fehren *(Mng Dir)*

SEWOGE Service- und Wohnungsunternehmen GmbH (1)
Am Markt 6
Postfach 13 34
01987 Schwarzheide, Germany
Tel.: (49) 3575294890
Fax: (49) 35752948955
E-Mail: sewoge@basf-sh.de
Web Site: www.basf-schwarzheide.de/pcms/basf/en/dt.jsp?setCursor=1_211599
Chemical Products
S.I.C.: 2899
N.A.I.C.S.: 325998

SGS-Schwarzheider Gastronomie und Service GmbH (1)
Schipkauer Strasse 1
Schwarzheide, 1986, Germany
Tel.: (49) 35752 62397
Fax: (49) 35752 62778
E-Mail: info@sgs-gastronomieservice.de
Web Site: www.sgs-gastronomieservice.de
Catering Services
S.I.C.: 5812
N.A.I.C.S.: 722320

Thermische Ruckstandsverwertung GmbH & Co. KG (1)
Postfach 16 16
50380 Wesseling, Germany
Tel.: (49) 2236 722581
Special Industry Machinery
S.I.C.: 3559
N.A.I.C.S.: 333249

Ultraform Verwaltungsgesellschaft mbH (1)
Carl-Bosch-Str 38
67063 Ludwigshafen, Rheinland-Pfalz, Germany
Tel.: (49) 621 60 0
Fax: (49) 621 60 42525
E-Mail: global.info@basf.com
Chemical Product Distr
S.I.C.: 5169
N.A.I.C.S.: 424690

Untertage-Speicher-Gesellschaft mbH (USG) (1)
Friedrich-Ebert-Strasse 160
34119 Kassel, Germany
Mailing Address:
Postfach 10 40 20
34112 Kassel, Germany
Tel.: (49) 5613010
Fax: (49) 5613011702
E-Mail: press@wintershall.com
Web Site: www.wintershall.com
Emp.: 120
Chemical Product Mfr
S.I.C.: 2899
N.A.I.C.S.: 325998

Wintershall Holding GmbH (1)
Friedrich-Ebert-Strasse 160
34119 Kassel, Germany
Tel.: (49) 561 301 0
Fax: (49) 561 301 1702
E-Mail: info@wintershall.com
Web Site: www.wintershall.com
Emp.: 2,000
Oil & Gas Exploration Services
S.I.C.: 1389
N.A.I.C.S.: 213112
Harald Schwager *(Chm-Supervisory Bd)*
Manfredo Ruebens *(Deputy Chm-Supervisory Bd)*
Michael Winkler *(Deputy Chm-Supervisory Bd)*

Zweite BASF Immobilien-Gesellschaft mbH (1)
Carl-Bosch-Str 38
Ludwigshafen, 67063, Germany
Tel.: (49) 621600
Fax: (49) 621 6042525
Property Management Services
S.I.C.: 6531
N.A.I.C.S.: 531311

Joint Venture:

Styrolution Group GmbH (1)
Erlenstrasse 2
60325 Frankfurt am Main, Germany De
Tel.: (49) 69 509550 1200
E-Mail: globalinfo@styrolution.com
Web Site: www.styrolution.com
Sales Range: $5-14.9 Billion
Emp.: 340
Holding Company; Styrene Products Mfr
S.I.C.: 6719
N.A.I.C.S.: 551112
Roberto Gualdoni *(Chm-Mgmt Bd & CEO)*
Christoph de la Camp *(CFO)*
Kevin McQuade *(Member-Mgmt Bd & Pres-Americas Reg)*
Hyung Tae Chang *(Pres-Asia Pacific Reg)*

Subsidiaries:

Styrolution GmbH (2)
Carl-Bosch-Strasse 38
D-67056 Ludwigshafen, Germany De
Tel.: (49) 621600
Web Site: www.styrolution.com
Styrene Products Mfr
S.I.C.: 3089
N.A.I.C.S.: 326199
Martin Pugh *(Mng Dir & Head-Europe)*

Styrolution Koln GmbH (2)
Alte Strasse 201
50769 Cologne, Germany De
Tel.: (49) 22135550
Fax: (49) 22135551
E-Mail: info@ineos-abs.com
Web Site: www.styrolution.com
Sales Range: $1-4.9 Billion
Emp.: 1,700
Thermoplastic Resin Mfr
S.I.C.: 2821
N.A.I.C.S.: 325211
Gerd Franken *(CEO)*

U.S. Subsidiary:

Styrolution America LLC (2)
25846 SW Frontage Rd
Channahon, IL 60410 DE
Tel.: (815) 423-5541
Fax: (815) 423-1224
E-Mail:
Emp.: 700
Styrene & Styrenic Polymer Mfr
S.I.C.: 3086
N.A.I.C.S.: 326140
Kevin McQuade *(Pres)*
Tom Striller *(Sr VP-Mfg)*

Plants:

Styrolution America LLC (3)
950 Worcester St
Indian Orchard, MA 01551
Tel.: (413) 781-1441
Fax: (413) 736-5140
Web Site: www.styrolution.com
Emp.: 70
Styrene & Styrenic Polymers Mfr
S.I.C.: 2821
N.A.I.C.S.: 325211
Chris Danison *(Mgr-Quality)*

Styrolution America LLC (3)
1609 Biddle Ave
Wyandotte, MI 48192
Tel.: (734) 324-5608
Web Site: www.styrolution.com
Styrenic Products Mfr
S.I.C.: 3089
N.A.I.C.S.: 326199

Non-U.S. Subsidiaries:

Styrolution ABS (India) Limited (2)
6th Floor ABS Towers Old Padra Road
Vadodara, 390 007, India In
Tel.: (91) 265 2355861
Fax: (91) 265 2341012
E-Mail: mdsec@styrolutionabsindia.com
Web Site: www.styrolutionabsindia.com
506222—(BOM NSE)
Rev.: $21,511,665
Assets: $118,243,967
Liabilities: $37,589,387
Net Worth: $80,654,581
Earnings: $11,704,321
Fiscal Year-end: 12/31/12
Thermoplastic Resin Product Mfr
S.I.C.: 2821
N.A.I.C.S.: 325211
Tae Chang Hyung *(Chm)*
Suk Chi Myung *(Mng Dir)*
Suryakant Parlikar *(CFO)*
S. M. Vaishnav *(Sec & VP-Legal)*

Subsidiary:

Styrolution India Pvt. Ltd. (3)
1st Floor VIBGYOR Tower Plot No C-62 G Block
Bandra Kurla Complex, 400 018 Mumbai, India In
Tel.: (91) 2256618000
Fax: (91) 2256604877
Web Site: www.styrolution.com
Polystyrene Mfr
S.I.C.: 3086
N.A.I.C.S.: 326140

Styrolution International S.A. (2)
Avenue De Le Gare
141700 Fribourg, Switzerland
Tel.: (41) 264265656
Fax: (41) 264265657
E-Mail:
Styrene & Styrenic Polymer Mfr
S.I.C.: 3086
N.A.I.C.S.: 326140
Matthew Rimmer *(VP-Fin-EMEA)*

Styrolution (Thailand) Co., Ltd. (2)
No 4/2 I-8 Road
Map Ta Phut A Muang, Rayong, 21150, Thailand TH
Tel.: (66) 38910700
Fax: (66) 38 910 777
Web Site: www.styrolution.com
Thermoplastic Resin Product Mfr
S.I.C.: 2821
N.A.I.C.S.: 325211
Permporn Sangsawang *(Gen Mgr)*

Units:

BASF SE - Laenderbereich Vertrieb Europe (1)
Benckiserplatz 1
67056 Ludwigshafen, Germany
Tel.: (49) 621600
Telex: 46499-0 bas d
Fax: (49) 6216042525
E-Mail: global.info@basf.com
Sales of Chemical
S.I.C.: 5169
N.A.I.C.S.: 424690

U.S. Subsidiaries:

BASF Americas Corporation (1)
100 Park Ave
Florham Park, NJ 07932-1006
Tel.: (973) 245-6000
Fax: (973) 245-5439
Web Site: www.basf.com
Chemical Products Distr
S.I.C.: 5169
N.A.I.C.S.: 424690
Frank Freiler *(VP-Key Acct Mgmt-Home & Personal Care-Americas)*

BASF Corporation (1)
100 Campus Dr
Florham Park, NJ 07932 DE
Tel.: (973) 245-6000 (100%)
Fax: (973) 895-8002
Toll Free: (800) 526-1072
Web Site: www.basf.com
Sales Range: $15-24.9 Billion
Emp.: 1,000
Holding Company; North America Regional Managing Office
Import Export
S.I.C.: 6719
N.A.I.C.S.: 551112
Kurt Bock *(Chm & CEO)*
Wayne T. Smith *(Pres)*
Fried-Walter Munstermann *(CFO & Exec VP)*
Beate Ehle *(Exec VP & Pres-Market & Bus Dev-North America)*
Matthew Lepore *(Gen Counsel & Sr VP)*
Joseph C. Breunig *(Exec VP)*

Subsidiaries:

Automotive Refinish Technologies LLC (2)
400 Galleria Ofc Ctr Ste 217
Southfield, MI 48034
Tel.: (248) 304-5569
Fax: (248) 304-4722
Automotive Paint & Coating Distr
S.I.C.: 5198
N.A.I.C.S.: 424950
Harry Dhanjal *(Bus Mgr-Canada)*

BASF California Inc. (2)
100 Campus Dr 301
Florham Park, NJ 07932-1006
Tel.: (973) 245-6000
Chemical Product Whslr
S.I.C.: 5169
N.A.I.C.S.: 424690

BASF Catalysts Holding LLC (2)
100 Campus Dr
Florham Park, NJ 07932-1020
Tel.: (973) 245-6000
Fax: (973) 245-5439
Investment Management Services
S.I.C.: 6211
N.A.I.C.S.: 523999

Subsidiary:

BASF Catalysts LLC (3)
25 Middlesex Essex Tpke
Iselin, NJ 08830-0770 DE

BASF SE—(Continued)

Mailing Address:
PO Box 770
Iselin, NJ 08830-0770
Tel.: (732) 205-5000
Fax: (732) 906-0337
Toll Free: (800) 458-9823
E-Mail: info-ec@basf.com
Web Site: www.catalysts.basf.com
Emp.: 7,100
Material Science Technology & Precious Metal Services
Import Export
S.I.C.: 5169
N.A.I.C.S.: 424690
Kenneth T. Lane *(Pres)*
Edward T. Wolynic *(CTO & VP)*
Rui-Artur Goerck *(Sr VP-Mobile Emissions)*

Subsidiaries:

BASF Catalysts Delaware LLC (4)
100 Campus Dr
Florham Park, NJ 07932-1020
Tel.: (973) 245-6000
Fax: (973) 245-6714
Chemical Product Mfr
S.I.C.: 2899
N.A.I.C.S.: 325998

BASF Catalysts Holding China LLC (4)
100 Campus Dr
Florham Park, NJ 07932-1020
Tel.: (973) 245-6000
Fax: (973) 245-6002
Investment Management Services
S.I.C.: 6211
N.A.I.C.S.: 523999

Engelhard Asia Pacific LLC (4)
101 Wood Ave S
Iselin, NJ 08830-2703
Tel.: (732) 205-5000
Fax: (732) 906-0337
Chemical Product Whslr
S.I.C.: 5169
N.A.I.C.S.: 424690

Engelhard Energy Corporation (4)
101 Wood Ave S
Iselin, NJ 08830-2703
Tel.: (732) 205-5000
Chemical Product Whslr
S.I.C.: 5169
N.A.I.C.S.: 424690

Engelhard Power Marketing Inc. (4)
101 Wood Ave
Iselin, NJ 08830
Tel.: (732) 205-7320
Fax: (732) 205-6290
Electric Power Distribution Services
S.I.C.: 4939
N.A.I.C.S.: 221122

Ovonic Battery Company, Inc. (4)
2983 Waterview Dr
Rochester Hills, MI 48309 MI
Tel.: (248) 293-7002
Fax: (248) 299-4228
Web Site: www.catalysts.basf.com
Sales Range: $25-49.9 Million
Emp.: 93
Batteries Mfr
S.I.C.: 3691
N.A.I.C.S.: 335911
Michael A. Fetcenko *(Pres)*

Units:

BASF Catalysts LLC - Appearance & Performance Technologies (4)
25 Middlesex Essex Tpke
Iselin, NJ 08830-0770
Tel.: (732) 205-5000
Fax: (732) 205-7141
Pigments, Additives, Thickeners & Absorbents for Paint, Coatings, Plastic & Allied Industries
S.I.C.: 2819
N.A.I.C.S.: 325180

BASF Catalysts LLC - Environmental Technologies (4)
25 Middlesex Essex Tpke
Iselin, NJ 08830-0770
Tel.: (732) 205-5000
Fax: (732) 321-1161
Web Site: www.basf.com
Emissions Control Technologies & Systems Mfr
S.I.C.: 3564
N.A.I.C.S.: 333413

BASF Catalysts LLC - Material Services (4)
25 Middlesex Essex Tpke
Iselin, NJ 08830-0770
Tel.: (732) 205-5000
Fax: (732) 205-7141
Web Site: www.basf.com
Purchase & Sale of Precious & Base Metals & Related Products; Related Services for Precious Metal Refining; Production of Salts & Solutions
S.I.C.: 3339
N.A.I.C.S.: 331410

BASF Catalysts LLC - Paper Pigments & Additives (4)
25 Middlesex Essex Tpke
Iselin, NJ 08830-0770
Tel.: (732) 205-5000
Fax: (732) 321-1161
Coatings, Extenders & Pigments for the Paper Industry
S.I.C.: 2851
N.A.I.C.S.: 325510
Robert Spadoni *(VP & Gen Mgr-Minerals Tech)*

BASF Catalysts LLC - Process Technologies (4)
25 Middlesex Essex Tpke
Iselin, NJ 08830-0770
Tel.: (732) 205-5000
Mfr & Marketer of Advanced Chemical & Polymerization Catalysts, Sorbents, Separation Products & Cracking & Hydroprocessing Technologies
S.I.C.: 2899
N.A.I.C.S.: 325998

BASF Catalysts LLC - Separation Systems & Ventures (4)
25 Middlesex Essex Tpke
Iselin, NJ 08830-0770
Tel.: (732) 205-5000
Fax: (732) 321-1161
Web Site: www.basf.com
Mfr of Pigments
S.I.C.: 2816
N.A.I.C.S.: 325130

Plants:

BASF Catalysts LLC - East Windsor (4)
12 Thompson Rd
East Windsor, CT 06088-9696
Tel.: (860) 623-9901
Fax: (860) 623-4657
Web Site: www.catalysts.basf.com
Sales Range: $10-24.9 Million
Emp.: 73
Thermal Spray Coatings Mfr
S.I.C.: 2851
N.A.I.C.S.: 325510
David Lamontagne *(Plant Mgr)*

BASF Catalysts LLC - Quincy (4)
1101 N Madison St
Quincy, FL 32352-0981
Tel.: (850) 627-7688
Fax: (850) 875-8279
Sales Range: $10-24.9 Million
Emp.: 176
Industrial Minerals, Fullers Earth, Attapulgite Clay
Export
S.I.C.: 2816
N.A.I.C.S.: 325130
Anthony Sedd *(Dir-Mfg-Ops)*

Non-U.S. Subsidiaries:

BASF Catalyst Canada ULC (4)
100 Milverton Dr 5th Fl
Mississauga, ON, L5R 4H1, Canada
Tel.: (289) 360-1300
Fax: (289) 360-6000
Chemical Product Mfr
S.I.C.: 2899
N.A.I.C.S.: 325998

BASF Catalysts Asia B.V. (4)
Groningensingel 1
Arnhem, 6835 EA, Netherlands
Tel.: (31) 26 371 7171
Investment Management Services
S.I.C.: 6211
N.A.I.C.S.: 523999

BASF Catalysts Canada B.V. (4)
Groningensingel 1
Arnhem, Gelderland, 6835 EA, Netherlands
Tel.: (31) 263717171
Chemical Product Mfr
S.I.C.: 2899
N.A.I.C.S.: 325998

BASF Catalysts Germany GmbH (4)
Freundallee 23
D 30173 Hannover, Germany
Tel.: (49) 511288660
Telex: 41-922755 SOLV D
Fax: (49) 5112886652
Web Site: www.basf.com
Emp.: 75
Absorbents Mfr
S.I.C.: 3841
N.A.I.C.S.: 339113

BASF Catalysts (Guilin) Co. Ltd. (4)
Sub-district No 1 Guilin Hi-Tech Development Zone
No 18 Can Luan Road, Guilin, Guangxi Zhuang, 541004, China
Tel.: (86) 773 380 5678
Fax: (86) 773 5815961
Emission Control Catalyst Mfr & Distr
S.I.C.: 3829
N.A.I.C.S.: 334519

BASF Catalysts Holding Asia B.V. (4)
Groningensingel 1
Arnhem, Gelderland, 6835 EA, Netherlands
Tel.: (31) 263717171
Investment Management Services
S.I.C.: 6211
N.A.I.C.S.: 523999

BASF Catalysts NL Finance C.V. (4)
Groningensingel 1
6835 EA Arnhem, Netherlands
Tel.: (31) 26 3717171
Fax: (31) 26 3717 246
Financial Management Services
S.I.C.: 6211
N.A.I.C.S.: 523999

BASF Catalysts (Shanghai) Co. Ltd. (4)
199 Luqiao Road
Pudong, Shanghai, 201206, China
Tel.: (86) 21 6109 1777
Fax: (86) 21 6109 1799
Chemical Product Mfr
S.I.C.: 2899
N.A.I.C.S.: 325998

BASF Catalysts UK Holdings Limited (4)
63 St Mary Axe
London, EC3A 8LE, United Kingdom
Tel.: (44) 20 7456 7300
Fax: (44) 20 74567389
Investment Management Services
S.I.C.: 6211
N.A.I.C.S.: 523999

Engelhard Metals AG (4)
Grafenauweg 6
CH 6300 Zug, Switzerland
Tel.: (41) 417108277
Fax: (41) 417108288
Web Site: www.pasf.com
Emp.: 4
Precious Metals Dealing & Management
S.I.C.: 5944
N.A.I.C.S.: 448310

Engelhard Metals Ltd. (4)
63 St Mary Ave
London, EC3A 8NH, United Kingdom
Tel.: (44) 2074567300
Fax: (44) 207 929 3994
Web Site: www.basf.pl/ecp1/Group_companies_UK_Ireland/Engelhard_Metals_Ltd.
Emp.: 45
Precious Metals Dealing & Management
S.I.C.: 5944
N.A.I.C.S.: 448310

Non-U.S. Joint Venture:

N.E. ChemCat Corporation (4)
24th Fl World Trade Center Bldg 2-4-1 Hamamatsu-cho
Minato-ku, Tokyo, 105 6124, Japan JP
Tel.: (81) 334355490
Fax: (81) 334355484
Web Site: www.ne-chemcat.co.jp/eg/index.html
Emp.: 697
Chemical Catalysts, Precious Metal Coating & Automotive Exhaust Catalysts Mfr
S.I.C.: 2899
N.A.I.C.S.: 325998
Akira Okumura *(Pres)*
Yukio Ishikawa *(Exec VP)*
Masaki Funabiki *(Sr VP & Gen Mgr-Catalysts Dev)*

BASF Fina Petrochemicals LP (2)
100 Campus Dr
Florham Park, NJ 07932-1020
Tel.: (973) 245-6000
Toll Free: (800) 526-1072
Ehylene & Propylene Mfr
S.I.C.: 2869
N.A.I.C.S.: 325110

BASF Fuel Cell Inc. (2)
39 Veronica Ave
Somerset, NJ 08873-6800
Tel.: (732) 545-5100
Fax: (732) 545-5170
Web Site: www.basf-fuelcell.com
Emp.: 31
Fuel Cell Mfr
S.I.C.: 3674
N.A.I.C.S.: 334413
Moritz Ehrenstein *(CEO & Gen Mgr)*

BASF Intertrade Corporation (2)
1111 Bagby St Ste 2630
Houston, TX 77002-2621
Tel.: (713) 759-3070
Chemical Products Distr
S.I.C.: 5169
N.A.I.C.S.: 424690

BASF Pipeline Holdings LLC (2)
100 Campus Dr
Florham Park, NJ 07932-1020
Tel.: (973) 245-6000
Fax: (973) 245-6715
Investment Management Services
S.I.C.: 6211
N.A.I.C.S.: 523999

BASF Polyurethanes North America (2)
(Formerly ITWC Inc.)
106 Main St
Malcom, IA 50157
Mailing Address:
PO Box 247
Malcom, IA 50157
Tel.: (641) 528-3000
Fax: (641) 528-4041
Toll Free: (888) 489-2462
Web Site: www.polyurethanes.basf.us
Sales Range: $50-74.9 Million
Emp.: 80
Cast Elastomer Polyurethane Systems & Polyester Polyols Mfr
S.I.C.: 2821
N.A.I.C.S.: 325211
Gerry Podesta *(Grp VP)*

BASF Venture Capital America Inc. (2)
46820 Fremont Blvd
Fremont, CA 94538
Tel.: (510) 445-6141
Investment Management Services
S.I.C.: 6211
N.A.I.C.S.: 523999
Daniela Proske *(Principal)*

Mustang Property Corporation (2)
1535 SE 17th St 107
Fort Lauderdale, FL 33316-1737
Tel.: (954) 356-5800
Property Management Services
S.I.C.: 6531
N.A.I.C.S.: 531312

Novolyte Technologies, Inc. (2)
8001 E Pleasant Valley Rd
Independence, OH 44131
Tel.: (216) 867-1040
Fax: (216) 867-1089
E-Mail:
Web Site: www.basf.com
Emp.: 20
Specialty Electrolyte Materials, High Performance Solvents, Aryl Phosphorus Derivatives & Other Custom Manufactured Products

S.I.C.: 2899
N.A.I.C.S.: 325998
Ralph Wise *(Mgr-Site)*

Oliver Warehouse Inc. (2)
260 Mutual Ave
Winchester, KY 40391
Tel.: (859) 744-7641
Commercial Storage & Warehousing Services
S.I.C.: 4226
N.A.I.C.S.: 493190

PolyAd Services Inc. (2)
4170 Shoreline Dr
Earth City, MO 63045
Tel.: (314) 506-3136
Fax: (314) 506-3200
Toll Free: (800) 223-2286
E-Mail: nafta.customerservice@polyadservices.com
Web Site: www.polyadservices.com
Plastic Additive Mfr
S.I.C.: 2899
N.A.I.C.S.: 325998

ProCat Testing LLC (2)
30844 Century Dr
Wixom, MI 48393
Tel.: (248) 926-8200
Fax: (248) 926-8300
E-Mail: contact.us@procat-testing.com
Web Site: www.procat-testing.com
Emission Testing Services
S.I.C.: 8734
N.A.I.C.S.: 541380
Ashley Barrett *(Gen Mgr)*

Tradewinds Chemicals Corporation (2)
1105 N Market St
Wilmington, DE 19801-1216
Tel.: (302) 427-0263
Chemical Products Distr
S.I.C.: 5169
N.A.I.C.S.: 424690

Verenium Corporation (2)
3550 John Hopkins Ct
San Diego, CA 92121 DE
Tel.: (858) 431-8500
E-Mail: ir@verenium.com
Web Site: www.verenium.com
Rev.: $57,171,000
Assets: $93,776,000
Liabilities: $63,123,000
Net Worth: $30,653,000
Earnings: $18,213,000
Emp.: 111
Fiscal Year-end: 12/31/12
Enzymes & Other Biologically Active Compounds Developer & Researcher
S.I.C.: 8731
N.A.I.C.S.: 541712
James Levine *(Pres & CEO)*
Jeffrey G. Black *(CFO & Sr VP)*
Janet S. Roemer *(COO & Exec VP)*
Alexander A. Fitzpatrick *(Gen Counsel, Sec & Sr VP)*
J. Chris Terajewicz *(Sr VP-Engrg & Construction)*

Unit:

Verenium Corp. - Specialty Enzymes (3)
4955 Directors Pl
San Diego, CA 92121
Tel.: (858) 526-5000
Toll Free: (800) 523-2990
E-Mail: enzymes@verenium.com
Web Site: www.verenium.com
Sales Range: $200-249.9 Million
Enzyme & Protein Production
S.I.C.: 4931
N.A.I.C.S.: 221112

Watson Bowman Acme Corp. (2)
95 Pineview Dr
Amherst, NY 14228
Tel.: (716) 691-7566
Fax: (716) 691-9239
Toll Free: (800) 677-4922
E-Mail: wabo-cs@basf.com
Web Site: www.wbacorp.com
Emp.: 100
Expansion Joint Mfr
S.I.C.: 3441
N.A.I.C.S.: 332312
Rick Patterson *(Pres)*

Units:

BASF Corp. - Charlotte (Chesapeake) Site (2)
4330 Chesapeake Dr
Charlotte, NC 28216
Tel.: (704) 392-4313
Fax: (704) 394-8336
Web Site: www2.basf.us/careers/careerscharlottencprofile.html
Emp.: 20
Chemical Testing Laboratory & Product Whslr
S.I.C.: 8734
N.A.I.C.S.: 541380
Michael Young *(Plant Mgr)*

BASF Corp. - Charlotte (Steele Creek) Technical Center (2)
11501 Steele Creek Rd
Charlotte, NC 28273
Tel.: (704) 588-5280
Fax: (704) 587-8232
Web Site: www.basf.com
Emp.: 270
Dispersions & Pigments, Paper Chemicals & Hygiene Products Whslr & Technical Services
S.I.C.: 5169
N.A.I.C.S.: 424690
Kevin M. Murphy *(Gen Mgr)*

Unit:

BASF Corp. - Superabsorbents North America (3)
11501 Steele Creek Rd
Charlotte, NC 28273
Tel.: (704) 588-5280
Fax: (704) 587-8232
Web Site: www.superabsorbents.basf.com
Superabsorbent Chemical Products Whslr & Technical Services
S.I.C.: 5169
N.A.I.C.S.: 424690
David C. Antonuccio *(Mgr-Sls & Mktg)*

BASF Corp. - Clemson Plant (2)
Hwy 93
Central, SC 29630
Tel.: (864) 639-6311
Fax: (864) 639-7144
Web Site: www2.basf.us
Chemical Product Mfr
S.I.C.: 2899
N.A.I.C.S.: 325998

BASF Corp. - Engineering Plastics NAFTA (2)
450 Clark Dr
Budd Lake, NJ 07828-1234
Tel.: (973) 426-5429
Fax: (973) 426-5440
Web Site: www2.basf.us/corporate/index.html
Emp.: 28
Engineering Plastic Materials Mfr
S.I.C.: 2821
N.A.I.C.S.: 325211

BASF Corp. - Southfield Site (2)
26701 Telegraph Rd
Southfield, MI 48033
Tel.: (248) 827-4670
Fax: (248) 827-2727
Web Site: www.basf.com
Emp.: 275
Automotive Refinishing & Coating Products Mfr & Marketer
S.I.C.: 2851
N.A.I.C.S.: 325510
Karen Cummins *(Mgr-Bus Svcs)*

BASF Corp. - Tarrytown Research Facility (2)
540 White Plains Rd
Tarrytown, NY 10591
Tel.: (914) 785-2000
Fax: (914) 785-4167
Web Site: www.basf.com
Emp.: 150
Mfr. of Additives
S.I.C.: 2819
N.A.I.C.S.: 325180

BASF Foam Enterprises (2)
13630 Water Tower Cir
Plymouth, MN 55441-3704 MN
Tel.: (763) 559-3266
Fax: (763) 559-0945
Toll Free: (800) 888-3342
E-Mail: spfinfo@basf.com
Web Site: www.basf-pfe.com
Emp.: 40
Mfr of Rigid Polyurethane Foam Products Import Export
S.I.C.: 3086
N.A.I.C.S.: 326150
Jim Anderson *(VP-Mktg)*

Plants:

BASF Corp. - Ambler - Care Chemicals (2)
300 Brookside Ave
Ambler, PA 19002-3498
Tel.: (215) 628-1000
Fax: (215) 628-1200
Web Site: www.basf.com
Emp.: 125
Cosmetics, Surfactants & Related Products Mfr
S.I.C.: 2899
N.A.I.C.S.: 325998
Dirk Buengel *(VP)*

BASF Corp. - Appleton Plant (2)
2901 N Conkey St
Appleton, WI 54911
Tel.: (920) 731-1893
Fax: (920) 731-0332
Web Site: www2.basf.us/corporate/aboutbasfnaftaindex.html
Chemical Product Mfr
S.I.C.: 2899
N.A.I.C.S.: 325998

BASF Corp. - Evans City Plant (2)
1424 Mars-Evans City Rd
Evans City, PA 16033
Tel.: (724) 538-1200
Fax: (724) 538-1260
Toll Free: (866) 426-7263
Web Site: www.basf.us/corporate/aboutbasfnaftaindex.html
Emp.: 133
Inorganic Chemical Compounds Mfr
S.I.C.: 2819
N.A.I.C.S.: 325180

BASF Corp. - Freeport Plant (2)
602 Copper Rd
Freeport, TX 77541
Tel.: (979) 415-6296
Fax: (979) 415-6710
Web Site: www.basf.us
Emp.: 1,100
Various Chemical Products Mfr
S.I.C.: 2899
N.A.I.C.S.: 325998

BASF Corp. - Geismar Plant (2)
8404 River Rd
Geismar, LA 70734
Tel.: (225) 339-7300
Fax: (225) 339-1130
Web Site: www2.basf.us
Emp.: 1,400
Various Chemical Products Mfr
S.I.C.: 2899
N.A.I.C.S.: 325998
Tom Yura *(Plant Mgr)*

BASF Corp. - Greenville Plant (2)
1175 Martin St
Greenville, OH 45331
Tel.: (937) 547-6700
Fax: (937) 547-6780
Web Site: www2.basf.com
Emp.: 104
Coating & Resin Products Mfr
S.I.C.: 2851
N.A.I.C.S.: 325510
David Wynn *(Plant Mgr)*

BASF Corp. - LaGrange - Nutrition & Health (2)
5325 S 9th St
La Grange, IL 60525-3602
Tel.: (708) 579-6150
Fax: (708) 579-6152
Emp.: 30
Chemicals & Vitamins Mfr
S.I.C.: 2819
N.A.I.C.S.: 325180
Gregory Pflum *(VP)*

BASF Corp. - Livonia Plant (2)
13000 Levan St
Livonia, MI 48150
Tel.: (734) 591-6200
Fax: (734) 591-5902
Web Site: www2.basf.us/corporate/aboutbasfnaftaindex.html
Polymers
S.I.C.: 2899
N.A.I.C.S.: 325199

BASF Corp. - Monaca Polymers Plant (2)
370 Frankfort Rd
Monaca, PA 15061
Tel.: (724) 728-6900
Fax: (724) 728-1870
Web Site: www.basf.us
Emp.: 125
Chemical Polymers Mfr
S.I.C.: 2899
N.A.I.C.S.: 325998
Ptoshia Burnett *(Dir-Site)*

BASF Corp. - Newport Plant (2)
205 S James St
Newport, DE 19804-2424
Tel.: (302) 992-5600
Toll Free: (800) 474-4731
Web Site: www.basf.com
Emp.: 250
Pigment Processing
S.I.C.: 5169
N.A.I.C.S.: 424690

BASF Corp. - Tucson - Mining Chemicals (2)
2430 N Huachuca Dr
Tucson, AZ 85745-8891
Tel.: (520) 622-8891
Fax: (520) 624-0912
Web Site: www.basf.com
Emp.: 13
Distr of Chemicals for the Mining Industry
S.I.C.: 5169
N.A.I.C.S.: 424690
Steve Olafson *(Acct Mgr)*

BASF Corp. - Washington Plant (2)
2 Pleasant View Ave
Washington, NJ 07882
Tel.: (908) 689-2500
Fax: (908) 689-7708
Web Site: www2.basf.us/corporate/aboutbasfnaftaindex.html
Chemical Product Mfr
S.I.C.: 2899
N.A.I.C.S.: 325998

BASF Corp. - West Memphis Plant (2)
100 Bridgeport Rd
West Memphis, AR 72301
Tel.: (870) 735-8750
Fax: (870) 702-5266
Web Site: www2.basf.us/corporate/aboutbasfnaftaindex.html
Emp.: 135
Specialty Industrial & Water Treatment Chemicals Mfr
S.I.C.: 2899
N.A.I.C.S.: 325998
Debbie Dalley *(Plant Mgr)*

BASF Corp. - White Stone Plant (2)
3455 Southport Rd
Spartanburg, SC 29302
Tel.: (864) 585-3411
Fax: (864) 594-5237
Web Site: www.basf.com
Chemical Product Mfr
S.I.C.: 2899
N.A.I.C.S.: 325998

BASF Corp. - Wyandotte Plant (2)
Wyandotte N Works 1609 Biddle Ave
Wyandotte, MI 48192
Tel.: (734) 324-6100
Fax: (734) 324-6533
Web Site: www.basf.com
Emp.: 1,000
Urethane, Joncryl & Specialty Plastic Products Mfr
S.I.C.: 3086
N.A.I.C.S.: 326150

Non-U.S. Subsidiaries:

BASF Canada Inc. (2)
100 Noverton Dr 5th Fl
Mississauga, ON, L5R 481, Canada Ca
Tel.: (416) 675-3611 (100%)
Fax: (289) 360-6000

BASF SE—(Continued)

E-Mail: martin.despatie@basf.com
Web Site: www.basf.ca
Emp.: 150
Chemicals
S.I.C.: 2899
N.A.I.C.S.: 325998
Carles Navarro *(Pres)*

BASF Mexicana S.A. de C.V. (2)
Insurgentes Sur 975 Deportes
Delegacion Benito Juarez, 37100 Mexico, Mexico MX
Tel.: (52) 5553252600 (100%)
E-Mail: basfmexicana@notes.basfcorp.com
Web Site: www.basf.com.mx
Sales Range: $650-699.9 Million
Emp.: 250
Plastic Products, Coatings & Dispersions Mfr
S.I.C.: 2821
N.A.I.C.S.: 325211
Claudia Georgi *(Mgr-Comm)*

Non-U.S. Subsidiaries:

Azuma Bussan Ltd. (1)
3-8-6 Saikon
Koriyama, Fukushima, 963-8862, Japan
Tel.: (81) 249240776
Chemical Products Mfr
S.I.C.: 2899
N.A.I.C.S.: 325998

BASF A/S (1)
Ved Stadsgraven 15
PO Box 4042
DK 2300 Copenhagen, Denmark DK
Tel.: (45) 32660700 (100%)
Fax: (45) 32572202
E-Mail: basfdk@nordic.basf.org
Web Site: www.basf.com
Emp.: 60
Sales of Chemicals
S.I.C.: 5169
N.A.I.C.S.: 424690

Subsidiaries:

BASF Health & Nutrition A/S (2)
Malmparken 5
2750 Ballerup, Denmark
Tel.: (45) 44730100
Fax: (45) 44730101
Web Site: www.basf.com
Emp.: 150
Health & Nutrition Services
S.I.C.: 9431
N.A.I.C.S.: 923120
Piepen Soerensen *(Chm)*

BASF AB (1)
Haraldsgatan 5
S 402 33 Gothenburg, Sweden SE
Tel.: (46) 31639800 (100%)
Fax: (46) 31639900
E-Mail: basf-se@nordic.basf.org
Web Site: www.basf.com
Emp.: 60
Sales of Chemicals
S.I.C.: 5169
N.A.I.C.S.: 424690
Torben Berlin Jensen *(Pres)*

Joint Venture:

Svaloef Weibull AB (2)
Svalov
SE-268 81 Svalov, Sweden
Tel.: (46) 418667000
Fax: (46) 418667100
E-Mail: maria.forshufvud@lantmaennen.com
Web Site: www.lantmaennen.com
Sales Range: $125-149.9 Million
Emp.: 624
Plant Breeding & Seeds Producer; Owned 60% by Svenksak Lantmaennen ek foer & 40% by BASF Aktiengesellschaft
S.I.C.: 0711
N.A.I.C.S.: 115112
Annette Olesen *(Dir-Product Dev)*

BASF Afrique de l'Ouest S.A.R.L. (1)
Bd Achalme No 3
BP 3761
Abidjan, 01, Cote d'Ivoire CI
Tel.: (225) 21261292
Telex: 43200 basf ci
Fax: (225) 21262354
E-Mail: basfao@aviso.ci
Web Site: www.basf-s-africa.co.za
Distributor & Importer of Chemicals
S.I.C.: 5169
N.A.I.C.S.: 424690

BASF Agrochemical Products B.V. (1)
Groningensingel 1
Arnhem, 6835 EA, Netherlands
Tel.: (31) 26 371 7171
Fax: (31) 263 71 72 46
Agrochemical Product Mfr
S.I.C.: 2879
N.A.I.C.S.: 325320

BASF Argentina S.A. (1)
Tucuman 1
C1049AAA Buenos Aires, Argentina AR
Tel.: (54) 11 4317 9600 (100%)
Fax: (54) 11 4317 9700
E-Mail: rrpp-ar@basf.com
Web Site: www.basf.com.ar
Emp.: 700
Distr of Styropor, Finishing Products & Crop Protection Products
S.I.C.: 0139
N.A.I.C.S.: 111998
Rosario Beltran *(Mgr)*

Subsidiary:

BASF Poliuretanos S.A. (2)
Cabo 10 Moreno 2370 Parque Industrial Burzaco
Buenos Aires, Argentina
Tel.: (54) 1142996792
Fax: (54) 1143179853
E-Mail: bpa@basf.com
Web Site: www.basf.com
Emp.: 27
Chemical Product Mfr
S.I.C.: 2899
N.A.I.C.S.: 325998

BASF AS (1)
Leangbukta 40
PO Box 233
N 1372 Asker, Norway NO
Tel.: (47) 66792100 (100%)
Fax: (47) 66904755
E-Mail: grete.mathisen@basf.com
Web Site: www.basf.com
Emp.: 12
Sales of Chemicals
S.I.C.: 5169
N.A.I.C.S.: 424690
Torben Berlin Jensen *(Sec)*

Subsidiary:

Pronova BioPharma ASA (2)
Lilleakerveien 2C
0283 Oslo, Norway (100%)
Mailing Address:
PO Box 420
1327 Lysaker, Norway
Tel.: (47) 22 53 48 50
Fax: (47) 22 53 48 51
E-Mail: pronova@pronova.com
Web Site: www.pronova.com
Emp.: 296
Omega-3 Derived Pharmaceuticals Mfr
S.I.C.: 2834
N.A.I.C.S.: 325412
Gert W. Munthe *(Chm)*
Morten Jurs *(CEO)*

Subsidiary:

Pronova BioPharma Norge AS (3)
Framnesveien 41
N-3222 Sandefjord, Norway NO
Mailing Address:
PO Box 2109
N-3202 Sandefjord, Norway
Tel.: (47) 33 44 68 00
Fax: (47) 33 44 68 01
E-Mail: henrik.fismen@pronova.com
Web Site: www.pronova.com
Emp.: 130
Mfr of Omega 3-Derived Pharmaceuticals Export
S.I.C.: 2834
N.A.I.C.S.: 325412
Henrik Fismen *(Mgr-Process Dev)*

BASF Asia Pacific (India) Pvt. Ltd. (1)
1st Floor Vibgyor Towers Plot No C-62 G Block Bandra-Kurla Complex
Mumbai, 400 051, India In
Tel.: (91) 22 6661 8000
Fax: (91) 22 6758 2753
Agricultural Chemicals Mfr
S.I.C.: 2879
N.A.I.C.S.: 325320

BASF Belgium S.A./N.V. (1)
Dreve Richelle 161
EF 1510 Waterloo, Belgium BE
Tel.: (32) 23732111 (100%)
Fax: (32) 23732850
E-Mail: reception.basfbelgium@basf.com
Web Site: www.basf.com
Emp.: 160
Sales of Chemicals
S.I.C.: 5169
N.A.I.C.S.: 424690
Geanmarie Vantriel *(Mng Dir)*

Subsidiaries:

BASF Antwerpen N.V. (2)
Haven 725 Scheldelaan 600
B 2040 Antwerp, Belgium BE
Tel.: (32) 35612111 (100%)
Fax: (32) 35613747
E-Mail: info.basf-antwerpen@basf.com
Web Site: www.basf.be
Sls.: $5,376,875,008
Emp.: 4,000
Basic Chemicals, Fine Chemicals, Fertilizers, Pre-Products for Polyurethanes, Fibers & Plastics Mfr
S.I.C.: 2899
N.A.I.C.S.: 325998
Waulter Begeest *(Mng Dir)*

BASF Polyurethanes (2)
Ave Hamoir Hamoirlaan 14
1180 Brussels, Belgium BE
Tel.: (32) 23732119 (100%)
Fax: (32) 023732150
E-Mail: info@basf.be
Web Site: www.basf.be
Emp.: 35
Sales of Polyurethane
S.I.C.: 5169
N.A.I.C.S.: 424690
Jacques Delmoitiez *(Mng Dir)*

Unit:

BASF SE - European Governmental Affairs (2)
60 Ave De Corkenbergh
B 1000 Brussels, Belgium
Tel.: (32) 27400350
Fax: (32) 27400359
Web Site: www.basf.com
Emp.: 10
Administrative Services for Chemicals
S.I.C.: 2899
N.A.I.C.S.: 325998
Wolfgang Weber *(Mng Dir)*

BASF Bolivia S.R.L. (1)
Av. San Martin No. 1800
5 Piso
Casilla, 7185 Santa Cruz, Bolivia BO
Tel.: (591) 333141080
Telex: 3278 hansa bv
Fax: (591) 33141081
Web Site: www.basf.de
Distributor of Chemicals
S.I.C.: 5169
N.A.I.C.S.: 424690

BASF Care Chemicals (Shanghai) Co. Ltd. (1)
15/F Xinmao Mansion No 99 Tianzhou Rd
Shanghai, 200233, China
Tel.: (86) 2161953666
Fax: (86) 2164858898
Chemical Product Mfr
S.I.C.: 2899
N.A.I.C.S.: 325998

BASF Chemicals Company Ltd. (1)
8 Chu Hua Road
201507 Shanghai, China
Tel.: (86) 21 3750 1228
Fax: (86) 21 6712 0559
Web Site: www.catalysts.basf.com
Industrial Chemical Mfr
S.I.C.: 2899
N.A.I.C.S.: 325998

BASF Chile S.A. (1)
Av Carrascal 3851
Quinta Normal, 7360081 Santiago, Chile CL
Mailing Address: (100%)
Casilla 3238
6501020 Santiago, Chile
Tel.: (56) 26407000
Fax: (56) 6407123
E-Mail: rpp@basfchile.com
Web Site: www.basf.com
Emp.: 500
Distributor of Chemicals
S.I.C.: 5169
N.A.I.C.S.: 424690
Aledadro Haemem *(Gen Mgr)*

Subsidiary:

Aislapol S.A. (2)
Av Carrascal 3791
7360081 Santiago, Chile
Tel.: (56) 26407070
Fax: (56) 27750936
Chemical Product
S.I.C.: 2899
N.A.I.C.S.: 325998

BASF Controls Ltd. (1)
St Michaels Industrial Estate
Widnes, Cheshire, WA8 8TJ, United Kingdom
Tel.: (44) 1514207151
Fax: (44) 1925414994
Web Site: www.basf.co.uk
Pest Control Chemical Mfr
S.I.C.: 2879
N.A.I.C.S.: 325320

BASF Coordination Center Comm.V. (1)
Haven 725 Scheldelaan 600
2040 Antwerp, Belgium
Tel.: (32) 3 561 2167
Emp.: 300
Chemical Products Mfr
S.I.C.: 2899
N.A.I.C.S.: 325998
Wouter de Geest *(Mng Dir)*

BASF Croatia d.o.o. (1)
Puskariceva 1B
10250 Zagreb, Croatia HR
Tel.: (385) 16040401 (100%)
Fax: (385) 16040403
E-Mail: zeljko.gembrih@basf.com
Web Site: www.basf.de
Emp.: 10
Sales of Chemicals
S.I.C.: 2821
N.A.I.C.S.: 325211
Zeljko Gembrih *(CFO)*

BASF (Czech) spol. s r.o. (1)
Safrankova 3
15500 Prague, Czech Republic
Tel.: (420) 235000111
E-Mail: info@basf.cz
Web Site: www.basf.com
Emp.: 70
Chemical Product Mfr
S.I.C.: 2899
N.A.I.C.S.: 325998
Etita Hippova *(Mng Dir)*

BASF de Costa Rica S.A. (1)
Edificio Los Balcones Seccion Aprimer Piso
Granadilla Norte De Curridabat, 10229
1000 San Jose, Costa Rica CR
Tel.: (506) 2011900 (100%)
Telex: 2417 basf cr
Fax: (506) 2018221
E-Mail: basfcr@racsa.co.cr
Web Site: www.basfcostarica.com
Emp.: 50
Distributor of Chemicals
S.I.C.: 5169
N.A.I.C.S.: 424690
Juan Carlos Cruz *(Gen Mgr)*

BASF de El Salvador, S.A. de C.V. (1)
Edificio World Trade Center, Torre II
Tercer Nivel, Local 313
89 Avenida Norte, Colonia Escalon San Salvador, El Salvador SV
Tel.: (503) 2640770

Telex: 20373 basf sal
Fax: (503) 2640775
E-Mail: normaespino@basf.com
Web Site: www.basf.com
Emp.: 10
Importer of Agro Chemicals
S.I.C.: 5169
N.A.I.C.S.: 424690

BASF de Guatemala, S.A. (1)
Avenida Petapa 47-31 Zona 12
Apartado Postal 850
Guatemala, Guatemala GT
Tel.: (502) 24774659 (99%)
Fax: (502) 24 774680
Web Site: www.basf.de
Emp.: 38
Mfr. of Chemicals
S.I.C.: 2899
N.A.I.C.S.: 325998

BASF de Mexico S.A. de C.V. (1)
Insurgentes Sur No 975 Ciudad De Los Deportes
Benito Juarez, Mexico, 3710, Mexico
Tel.: (52) 5553252600
Chemical Product Mfr
S.I.C.: 2899
N.A.I.C.S.: 325998

BASF Dominicana S.A. (1)
Gustavo Mejia Ricart 11
Santo Domingo, Dominican Republic DO
Tel.: (809) 3341026
Fax: (809) 3341027
E-Mail: carlos.herrera@basf.com
Web Site: www.basf-corp.com
Emp.: 30
Sales of Chemicals & Plastics
S.I.C.: 5169
N.A.I.C.S.: 424690
Carlos Herrera *(Mng Dir)*

BASF East Asia Regional Headquarters Ltd. (1)
45th Floor Jardine House
No 1 Connaught Place, Central, China (Hong Kong) HK
Tel.: (852) 27310111 (100%)
Fax: (852) 27315631
Web Site: www.basf.com
Holding Company; Regional Managing Office
S.I.C.: 6719
N.A.I.C.S.: 551112
Martin Brudermuller *(CEO-Asia Pacific Reg Div)*

Subsidiary:

BASF China Ltd. (2)
45/F Jardine House No 1 Connaught Pl
Central, China (Hong Kong) CN
Mailing Address: (100%)
PO Box 98427
Kowloon, China (Hong Kong)
Tel.: (852) 27311222
Fax: (852) 27315631
Web Site: www.basf.com.cn
Emp.: 300
Mfr. of Chemicals
S.I.C.: 2899
N.A.I.C.S.: 325998

Non-U.S. Subsidiaries:

BASF (China) Co., Ltd. (3)
20/F Harbour Ring Plaza
18 Xizang Zhong Road, Shanghai, 200001, China CN
Tel.: (86) 2123203000 (100%)
Fax: (86) 2123203088
Web Site: www.greater-china.basf.com
Emp.: 400
Mfr. of Chemicals
S.I.C.: 2899
N.A.I.C.S.: 325998
Albert Heuser *(Pres-Market & Bus Dev-Asia Pacific)*

Branches:

BASF (China) Co., Ltd. - Beijing (4)
15/F Beijing Sunflower Tower No 37
Maizidian St
Chaoyang District, Beijing, 100125, China CN
Tel.: (86) 1065876666
Fax: (86) 1065876789
Web Site: www.greater-china.basf.com
Emp.: 6,500
Mfr of Chemicals
S.I.C.: 2899
N.A.I.C.S.: 325998

BASF (China) Co., Ltd. - Guangzhou (4)
Suite 2801-06 Dongshan Plaza
69 Xian Lie Road Central, 510095
Guangzhou, Guangzou, China CN
Tel.: (86) 2087136000 (100%)
Fax: (86) 2087321894
Web Site: www.basfchina.com.cn
Emp.: 350
Mfr. of Chemicals
S.I.C.: 2899
N.A.I.C.S.: 325998

Subsidiaries:

BASF Auxiliary Chemicals Co. Ltd. (4)
300 Jiangxinsha Rd Pudong
Shanghai, 200137, China CN
Tel.: (86) 21 3865 2000 (100%)
Fax: (86) 21 3865 2588
Web Site: www.asiapacific.basf.com
Mfr of Organic Pigments, Textile Auxiliaries, Leather Auxiliaries, Acrylate Dispersion & Metal Complex Dyes
S.I.C.: 2819
N.A.I.C.S.: 325130

BASF Chemicals (Shanghai) Co., Ltd. (4)
20/F Harbour Ring Plaza
18 Xizang Zhong Road
Shanghai, 200001, China
Tel.: (86) 2123203000
Fax: (86) 2123203088
Web Site: www.basf.com
Chemical Product Mfr
S.I.C.: 2899
N.A.I.C.S.: 325998

BASF Polyurethanes (China) Co., Ltd. (4)
Suite 2801-06 Dongshan Plaza
69 Xian Lie Road Central, Guangzhou, Guangdong, 510095, China CN
Tel.: (86) 2087136000 (100%)
Fax: (86) 2087321262
Web Site: www.basfchina.com.cn
Emp.: 200
Polyurethane Systems, Thermoplastic Polyurethane Elastomers & Polyurethane Processing Equipment & Facilities
S.I.C.: 2821
N.A.I.C.S.: 325211
Dietmar Nissen *(Pres)*

BASF Shanghai Coatings Co. Ltd. (4)
521 Guanghua Rd
Shanghai, 201108, China CN
Tel.: (86) 2164895250 (60%)
Fax: (86) 2164890510
Web Site: www.basf.com
Emp.: 180
Mfr. of Coatings & Plastic Parts
S.I.C.: 2851
N.A.I.C.S.: 325510
Yal Gejun *(Mgr-Ops)*

Joint Ventures:

BASF-JCIC Neopentylglycol Co. Ltd. (4)
21 Fl Economic And Trade Ctr Bldg
Changyi District
Jilin, 132002, China CN
Tel.: (86) 4322799515 (100%)
Fax: (86) 4322799106
Web Site: www.basf.com
Emp.: 50
Mfr. of Powder Coatings, Unsaturated Polyester, Plasticers & Pharmaceuticals; Joint Venture of BASF AG (60%) & Jilin Chemical Industrial Company Limited (40%)
S.I.C.: 2834
N.A.I.C.S.: 325412
Yang Hui *(Gen Mgr)*

BASF-YPC Company Limited (4)
Luhe District
Nanjing, Jiangsu, 210048, China
Tel.: (86) 2558569999
Fax: (86) 2558569966
E-Mail: wanh@basf-ypc.com.cn
Web Site: www.basf-ypc.com.cn
Emp.: 2,000
Petrochemical Products Mfr
S.I.C.: 2869
N.A.I.C.S.: 325110
Houliang Dai *(Chm)*
Bernd Blumenberg *(Pres)*

Shanghai BASF Polyurethane Co., Ltd. (4)
No 25 Chuhua Road
Shanghai Chemical Industry Pk, Shanghai, 201507, China
Tel.: (86) 2167121199
Fax: (86) 2167121118
Web Site: www.basf.com
Polymer Product Mfr
S.I.C.: 2821
N.A.I.C.S.: 325211

Shanghai Gaoqiao BASF Dispersions Co., Ltd. (4)
No 99 Ln 1929 Pudong Bei Road
Pudong New Area, Shanghai, 200137, China CN
Tel.: (86) 2158670303
Fax: (86) 21558675050
E-Mail: sgbd@sgbd.com.cn
Web Site: www.sgbd.com.cn
Emp.: 200
Adhesive Raw Material Mfr; Owned 50% by BASF SE & 50% by China Petrochemical Corporation
S.I.C.: 2891
N.A.I.C.S.: 325520

BASF Taiwan Ltd. (3)
Empire Bldg 16th Fl No 87 Sung Chiang Rd
PO Box 3134
Taipei, 104, Taiwan (100%)
Tel.: (886) 225187600
Telex: 21649 basftwan
Fax: (886) 225061554
E-Mail: contact_us@basftaiwan.com.tw
Web Site: www.basftaiwan.com.tw
Emp.: 85
Mfr. of Chemicals
S.I.C.: 2899
N.A.I.C.S.: 325998
Kwong Yung Chu *(Gen Mgr)*

Subsidiaries:

BASF Electronic Materials Taiwan (4)
33 Chin Chien 1st Rd Kuan Yin Ind
328 Taoyuan, Taiwan
Tel.: (886) 34837701
Fax: (886) 34837700
Web Site: www.basf.com
Emp.: 100
Electronic Chemical Product Mfr
S.I.C.: 2899
N.A.I.C.S.: 325998

Non-U.S. Subsidiaries:

BASF Australia Ltd. (2)
Level 12 28 Fresh Water Place
Southbank, VIC, 3006, Australia AU
Mailing Address: (100%)
GPO Box 4705
Melbourne, Victoria, 3001, Australia
Tel.: (61) 392121500
Fax: (61) 388556511
E-Mail: info@basf.com
Web Site: www.basf.com.sg
Sales Range: $450-499.9 Million
Emp.: 500
Distributor & Importer of Chemicals
S.I.C.: 5169
N.A.I.C.S.: 424690
Ross Pilling *(Mng Dir)*

Non-U.S. Subsidiary:

BASF New Zealand Ltd. (3)
3 E Pk Dr Airports Oaks
PO Box 407
Auckland, 1140, New Zealand NZ
Mailing Address: (100%)
PO Box 407
Auckland, 1, New Zealand
Tel.: (64) 92554300
Fax: (64) 92554319
E-Mail: headofficereciptionbnz@basf.com
Web Site: www.basf.com
Emp.: 35
Distributor & Importer of Chemicals
S.I.C.: 5169
N.A.I.C.S.: 424690
Lisa Meyer *(Mgr-HR)*

BASF Company Ltd. (2)
14 16/F KCCI Building 45 Namdaemunro 4-ga
Jung-gu, Seoul, 100 743, Korea (South) Ks
Tel.: (82) 237073100 (100%)
Fax: (82) 237073122
E-Mail: parkyr@basf-korea.co.kr
Web Site: www.basf.co.kr
Sales Range: $900-999.9 Million
Emp.: 1,100
Mfr. of Plastics Materials & Basic Forms
S.I.C.: 3089
N.A.I.C.S.: 326199
Woo-sung Shin *(Chm)*
Jong Wang Kim *(CEO)*

Subsidiaries:

Daihan Swiss Chemical Corporation (3)
13th Floor Haesung 2 Building 942 10
Daechi 3 dong Gangnam gu
Seoul, 135 725, Korea (South) KS
Tel.: (82) 234517300
Telex: K25538 dhcolor
Fax: (82) 25531928
E-Mail: info@basc.com
Web Site: www.basc.com
Emp.: 200
Mfr. & Distribution of Pigments & Pigment Preparations
S.I.C.: 2816
N.A.I.C.S.: 325130
Wansoo Suh *(Mng Dir)*

BASF India Ltd. (2)
1st Floor VIBGYOR Towers Plot No C 62 G
Block Bandra-Kurla Complex
Mumbai, 400 051, India IN
Tel.: (91) 22 6661 8000 (51%)
Telex: 1171 538 basf in
Fax: (91) 22 6758 2753
Web Site: www.asiapacific.basf.com
Sales Range: $1-4.9 Billion
Emp.: 2,000
Mfr of Styropor, Colorants, Finishing Products & Crop Protection Products
S.I.C.: 2899
N.A.I.C.S.: 325998
Raman Ramachandran *(Chm & Mng Dir)*

Non-U.S. Subsidiaries:

BASF Bangladesh Limited (3)
HR Bhaban 4th Fl 26 1 Kakrail Rd
PO Box 410
Dhaka, 1000, Bangladesh BD
Tel.: (880) 29348374 (76%)
Telex: 642 653 bbl bj
Fax: (880) 8313599
E-Mail: basf.dhaka@basfbangladesh.com
Web Site: www.basf.com
Emp.: 44
Mfr. of Chemicals
S.I.C.: 2899
N.A.I.C.S.: 325998
Faria Fadique *(Chm & Mng Dir)*

Subsidiary:

BASF Bangladesh Limited (4)
Miazi Villa 1126 A E Nasirabad
PO Box 734
4000 Chittagong, Bangladesh BD
Tel.: (880) 31651256 (100%)
Fax: (880) 31653216
Emp.: 6
Distributor of Chemicals
S.I.C.: 5169
N.A.I.C.S.: 424690
Saria Saeiqut *(Mng Dir)*

BASF-Lanka (Pvt.) Ltd. (3)
186 Vauxhall Street
Colombo, 2, Sri Lanka LK
Tel.: (94) 112423388
Telex: 23147 basfsl ce
Fax: (94) 112431400
E-Mail: blpl.hr@basf.com
Web Site: www.asiapacific.basf.com
Emp.: 65
Chemicals & Dyes Mfr
S.I.C.: 2899
N.A.I.C.S.: 325998
Martin Brudermuller *(Mng Dir-Asia Pacific)*

BASF SE—(Continued)

BASF Pakistan (Private) Limited (3)
46-A Block 6 PECHS
PO Box 3171
Karachi, Karachi Sindh, 75400, Pakistan PK
Tel.: (92) 21 111550550 (51%)
Telex: 29460 basf pk
Fax: (92) 21 4547815
E-Mail: basfpak@cyber.net.pk
Web Site: www.basf.com
Emp.: 106
Mfr. & Sales of Chemicals
S.I.C.: 2899
N.A.I.C.S.: 325998
Faisal Akhtar *(Mng Dir)*

Subsidiary:

BASF Chemicals & Polymers Pakistan (Private) Limited (4)
46 A Block 6 Pechs
Karachi, 75400, Pakistan PK
Tel.: (92) 214553064 (100%)
Fax: (92) 922134546311
E-Mail: bcpplpak@cyber.net.pk
Web Site: www.basf.com
Emp.: 211
Mfr. of Chemicals
S.I.C.: 2899
N.A.I.C.S.: 325998
Saleem A. Khan *(Mng Dir)*
Faisal Akhtar *(Mng Dir)*

BASF Japan Ltd. (2)
Roppongi Hills Mori Tower 21F 6 10 1 Roppongi
Minato-ku, Tokyo, 106-6121, Japan JP
Tel.: (81) 337965111 (100%)
Fax: (81) 337964111
E-Mail: communications@basfjapan.co.jp
Web Site: www.japan.basf.com
Sales Range: $1-4.9 Billion
Emp.: 1,600
Finishing Products, Plastics, Chemicals
S.I.C.: 2899
N.A.I.C.S.: 325998
Joerg-Christian Steck *(Pres)*

Branch:

BASF Japan Ltd. - Osaka (3)
1-8-15 Azuchimachi
Chuo-ku, Osaka, 541-0052, Japan
Tel.: (81) 662666801
Fax: (81) 662666956
E-Mail: osaka@basfjapan.co.jp
Web Site: www.basfjapan.co.jp
Emp.: 50
Mfr. of Chemicals
S.I.C.: 2899
N.A.I.C.S.: 325998

Joint Ventures:

BASF Idemitsu Co., Ltd. (3)
Nanbu Building 3-3 Kioicho
Chiyoda-ku, Tokyo, Japan
Tel.: (81) 332382337
Fax: (81) 3 3238 2222
Web Site: www.basf.com
Chemical Product Mfr; Owned 50% by BASF Aktiengellschaft & 50% by Idemitsu Petrochemical Co., Ltd.
S.I.C.: 2899
N.A.I.C.S.: 325998

BASF INOAC Polyurethanes Ltd. (3)
1-196 Kawada Aza Hongudo Shinshiro-shi
441-1347 Aichi, Japan
Tel.: (81) 536235533
Fax: (81) 536232557
Web Site: www.bip-jp.com
Emp.: 100
Polyurethane Foam System Mfr; Owned 50% by BASF Asktiengesellschaft & 50% by Inoac Corporation
S.I.C.: 3086
N.A.I.C.S.: 326150
Sunio Kosaka *(Mgr-HR)*

Mitsui BASF Dyes Ltd. (3)
Osaka Tokyo Marine Insurance Bldg 13F
2-2-53 Shiromi Chuo-ku, Osaka, 540-0001, Japan JP
Tel.: (81) 669495700
Fax: (81) 669495771
Web Site: www.basf.com
Mfr. & Sales of Dyestuffs; Joint Venture of BASF AG (50%) & Mitsui & Co., Ltd. (50%)
S.I.C.: 5169
N.A.I.C.S.: 424690

NISSO BASF Agro Co., Ltd. (3)
Shinko Building 1-11-4 Kudan-Kita
Chiyoda-ku, Tokyo, 102 0073, Japan
Tel.: (81) 332370655
Fax: (81) 3 3237 0653
Web Site: www.basf.com
Herbicide Mfr
S.I.C.: 2879
N.A.I.C.S.: 325320

BASF South East Asia Pte. Ltd. (2)
7 Temasek Boulevard
35 01 Suntec Tower 1, Singapore, 38987, Singapore SG
Tel.: (65) 63370330 (100%)
Fax: (65) 63340330
Web Site: www.basfsea.com.sg
Sales Range: $1-4.9 Billion
Emp.: 1,000
Holding Company; Regional Managing Office
S.I.C.: 6719
N.A.I.C.S.: 551112
Dean Draper *(Mng Dir)*

Subsidiary:

BASF Singapore Pte. Ltd. (3)
7 Temasek Blvd
Singapore, 38987, Singapore SG
Tel.: (65) 63370330 (100%)
Fax: (65) 63340330
Web Site: www.basf.com
Sales Range: $50-74.9 Million
Emp.: 550
Marketing, Sales & Distribution of Chemicals
S.I.C.: 5169
N.A.I.C.S.: 424690

Joint Ventures:

ELLBA Eastern (Pte) Ltd. (3)
61 seraya avenue
Jurong, 627879, Singapore SG
Tel.: (65) 63370330
Fax: (65) 66618680
Emp.: 650
Styrene Monomer & Propylene Oxide Mfr; Owned 50% by BASF SE & 50% by Royal Dutch Shell plc
S.I.C.: 2899
N.A.I.C.S.: 325998

Santoku BASF Pte. Ltd. (3)
35 Tuas West Avenue
638433 Singapore, Singapore
Tel.: (65) 68631211
Fax: (65) 68631311
Emp.: 25
Chemical Products
S.I.C.: 2899
N.A.I.C.S.: 325998
Yokomizo Kunio *(Mng Dir)*

Non-U.S. Subsidiaries:

BASF (Malaysia) Sdn. Bhd. (3)
No 2 Jalan U8 87 Jelutong
40706 Shah Alam, Kuala Lumpur, Malaysia MY
Tel.: (60) 356283888 (100%)
Fax: (60) 356283777
Web Site: www.basf.com.sg
Emp.: 120
Mfr. of Chemicals
S.I.C.: 2899
N.A.I.C.S.: 325998
Daniel Loh *(Mng Dir)*
Bendy Wang *(Sec)*

Subsidiaries:

BASF Asia-Pacific Service Centre Sdn Bhd (4)
Level 25 North Wing Menara TM
Jalan Pantai Baharu, 59200 Kuala Lumpur, Malaysia MY
Tel.: (60) 322469000
Fax: (60) 322469133
Web Site: www.basf.com
Finance & Accounting, Information Technology & Human Resources Services
S.I.C.: 8742
N.A.I.C.S.: 541611

BASF PETRONAS Chemicals Sdn. Bhd. (4)
Kuantan Integrated Chemical Site Jalan Gebeng 2/1
Kawasan Perindustrian Gebeng, 26080
Kuantan, Pahang Darul Makmur, Malaysia
Tel.: (60) 95855000
Fax: (60) 27846624
Web Site: www.basf-petronas.com
Emp.: 1,500
Chemical Product Mfr
S.I.C.: 2819
N.A.I.C.S.: 325180
Stefan Beckmann *(Mng Dir)*

BASF Polyurethanes (Malaysia) Sdn. Bhd. (4)
No 2 Jln U8 87 Seksyen U8
40706 Shah Alam, Selangor, Malaysia MY
Tel.: (60) 378473196
Fax: (60) 378473192
Web Site: www.basf.com
Polyurethane Systems Mfr
S.I.C.: 3086
N.A.I.C.S.: 326140
Bendy Wang *(Sec)*

Joint Ventures:

BASF PETRONAS Chemicals Sdn. Bhd. (4)
2 Jalan U8/87 Seksyen U8 Bukit Jelutong
40706 Shah Alam, Selangor Darul Ehsan, Malaysia
Tel.: (60) 378412200
Fax: (60) 378466624
E-Mail: info@basf-petronas.com.my
Web Site: www.basf-petronas.com.my
Emp.: 48
Chemical Product Mfr; Owned 60% by BASF Aktiengesellschaft & 40% by Petroliam Nasional Berhad
S.I.C.: 2819
N.A.I.C.S.: 325180

BASF See Sen Sdn. Bhd. (4)
Lot PT 3940
Kawasan Perindustrian, 24000 Kemaman, Malaysia
Tel.: (60) 98634657
Fax: (60) 98634658
Web Site: www.basf.com
Chemical Product Mfr; Owned 70% by BASF Aktiengesellschaft & 30% by See Sen Chemical Berhad
S.I.C.: 2899
N.A.I.C.S.: 325998

BASF (Thai) Ltd. (3)
23rd Floor Emporium Tower
Klongton Kongtoey, Bangkok, 10110, Thailand TH
Tel.: (66) 26649222 (100%)
Fax: (66) 26649221
E-Mail: worlwide@basf.com
Web Site: www.basf.com
Emp.: 250
Mfr. of Chemicals
S.I.C.: 2899
N.A.I.C.S.: 325998
Pracha Chicapoin *(Mng Dir)*

BASF Ecuatoriana S.A. (1)
Srepublida 500 Sprabbra Edisio Bldg Pucsre
PO Box 17013255
Quito, Ecuador EC
Tel.: (593) 22541100 (100%)
Fax: (593) 22509194
Web Site: www.basf.de
Distributor of Chemicals
S.I.C.: 5169
N.A.I.C.S.: 424690

BASF Electronic Materials (Shanghai) Co. Ltd. (1)
No 16 Heng Er Road Qing Pu Export Processing Zone
Shanghai, 201707, China
Tel.: (86) 21 5970 5700
Fax: (86) 21 5970 5770
Electronic Component Mfr
S.I.C.: 3679
N.A.I.C.S.: 334419

BASF Engelhard Finland B.V. (1)
Groningensingel 1
Arnhem, 6835 EA, Netherlands
Tel.: (31) 263717171
Chemical Product Mfr
S.I.C.: 2899
N.A.I.C.S.: 325998

BASF Engelhard Germany B.V. (1)
Groningensingel 1
6835 EA Arnhem, Netherlands
Tel.: (31) 263717171
Chemical Product Mfr
S.I.C.: 2899
N.A.I.C.S.: 325998

BASF Engelhard Italy B.V. (1)
Groningensingel 1
Arnhem, 6835 EA, Netherlands
Tel.: (31) 263717171
Chemical Product Mfr
S.I.C.: 2899
N.A.I.C.S.: 325998

BASF Engelhard South Africa B.V. (1)
Groningensingel 1
Arnhem, Gelderland, 6835 EA, Netherlands
Tel.: (31) 263717171
Chemical Product Mfr
S.I.C.: 2899
N.A.I.C.S.: 325998

BASF Engelhard Sweden B.V. (1)
Groningensingel 1
Arnhem, 6835 EA, Netherlands
Tel.: (31) 263717171
Chemical Product Mfr
S.I.C.: 2899
N.A.I.C.S.: 325998

BASF Engelhard Switzerland B.V. (1)
Groningensingel 1
Arnhem, Gelderland, 6835 EA, Netherlands
Tel.: (31) 263717171
Chemical Product Mfr
S.I.C.: 2899
N.A.I.C.S.: 325998

BASF Engelhard UK B.V. (1)
Groningensingel 1
Arnhem, 6835 EA, Netherlands
Tel.: (31) 263717171
Industrial Chemical Mfr
S.I.C.: 2899
N.A.I.C.S.: 325998

BASF EOOD (1)
Blvd Bulgaria 118 Abacus Business Center 1st Floor
1618 Sofia, Bulgaria
Tel.: (359) 2 915 20 33
Fax: (359) 2 915 20 20
E-Mail: aleksandra.todorova@basf.com
Web Site: www.basf.bg
Chemical Product Mfr
S.I.C.: 2899
N.A.I.C.S.: 325998

BASF Espanola S.A. (1)
Canribia 35
Apartado De Correos 762, E 08008
Barcelona, Spain ES
Tel.: (34) 934964000 (100%)
Fax: (34) 934964100
Web Site: www.basf.es
Emp.: 160
Chemicals, Plastics, Finishing Products Mfr; Fertilizers & Crop Protection Products Sales
S.I.C.: 2821
N.A.I.C.S.: 325211

Subsidiaries:

BASF Espanola S.L. (2)
Ctra N 340 km 1,156
43006 Tarragona, Spain ES
Tel.: (34) 977 256200 (100%)
Fax: (34) 977 256201
Web Site: www.basf.es
Emp.: 50
Mfr of Chemical Products
S.I.C.: 2899
N.A.I.C.S.: 325998
Martin Bega *(Mng Dir)*

Non-U.S. Division:

BASF Curtex Produtos Qummicos, Lda. (3)
Rua Manuel Pinto de Azevedo 626
4100-320 Porto, Portugal
Tel.: (351) 226159600

Fax: (351) 226177510
Web Site: www.basf.com
Polymer & Chemical Product Mfr
S.I.C.: 2899
N.A.I.C.S.: 325998
Erwin Rauhe *(Mng Dir)*

BASF Naber S.A. **(2)**
Apartado de Correos 355
46460 Silla, Spain
Tel.: (34) 961219510
Fax: (34) 961213234
Web Site: www.naber.com
Emp.: 200
Chemical Product Mfr
S.I.C.: 2899
N.A.I.C.S.: 325998
Enrique Garcia *(Vice Chm)*

BASF Styrodur Iberica S.L. **(2)**
Las Labradas Vial Aragsn M-16 Apartado de Correos 79
31500 Tudela, Spain
Tel.: (34) 948402767
Fax: (34) 948402462
Web Site: www.basf.com
Emp.: 25
Polymer & Chemical Product Mfr
S.I.C.: 2899
N.A.I.C.S.: 325998
Taio Wolfschmidt *(Mng Dir)*

Joint Venture:

BASF SONATRACH PropanChem S.A. **(2)**
Carretera N-340 km 1 156
Apartado de Correos 520, 43080
Tarragona, Spain
Tel.: (34) 977256703
Fax: (34) 977256710
Web Site: www.basfsonatrachpropanchem.com
Propylene & Gasoline Producer; Owned 51% by BASF Aktiengesellschaft & 49% by SONATRACH International Holding Corporation
S.I.C.: 1389
N.A.I.C.S.: 213112

BASF Food **(1)**
W V Ivan Vasov Balscha Str 1
1408 Sofia, Bulgaria BG
Tel.: (359) 29515958
Telex: 22340 basf bg
Fax: (359) 29516579
Web Site: www.basf.de
Emp.: 17
Mfr. of Chemicals
S.I.C.: 2899
N.A.I.C.S.: 325998

BASF France S.A.S. **(1)**
49 Ave Georges Pompidou
F-92593 Levallois-Perret, Cedex, France FR
Tel.: (33) 149645000 (100%)
Telex: basfc 620445 f
Fax: (33) 149645050
E-Mail: pointinfo@basffrance.com
Web Site: www.basf.fr
Emp.: 160
Holding Company; Chemical Products Mfr & Distr
S.I.C.: 6719
N.A.I.C.S.: 551112
Philippe Krasnopolski *(Mgr-Mktg)*

Subsidiaries:

BASF Beauty Care Solutions France SAS **(2)**
49 avenue Georges Pompidou
92300 Levallois-Perret, Cedex, France FR
Tel.: (33) 149645390
Fax: (33) 149645385
E-Mail: bcs-europe@basf.com
Web Site: www.beautycaresolutions.basf.com
Emp.: 100
Cosmetic & Personal Care Biotechnology Research, Development & Materials Mfr
S.I.C.: 2869
N.A.I.C.S.: 325199

Plant:

BASF Beauty Care Solutions France SAS - Lyon **(3)**
32 Rue Saint Jean de Dieu
69366 Lyon, France
Tel.: (33) 472766000
Fax: (33) 478580971
E-Mail: pvmeurope-contact@basf.com
Web Site: www.beautycaresolutions.basf.com
Emp.: 150
Cosmetic & Personal Care Biotechnology Research, Development & Materials Mfr
S.I.C.: 2869
N.A.I.C.S.: 325199
Andreas Rathjens *(Gen Mgr)*

U.S. Subsidiary:

BASF Beauty Care Solutions LLC **(3)**
50 Health Sciences Dr
Stony Brook, NY 11790
Tel.: (631) 689-0200
Fax: (631) 689-6880
Web Site: www.beautycaresolutions.basf.com
Emp.: 100
Cosmetic & Personal Care Biotechnology Research, Development & Materials Mfr
S.I.C.: 2869
N.A.I.C.S.: 325199
Joseph D. Ceccoli *(Gen Mgr)*

BASF Health and Care Products France S.A.S. **(2)**
Usine d'Estarac
31360 Boussens, France
Tel.: (33) 5 61 98 43 60
Fax: (33) 5 61 98 43 61
Emp.: 90
Health Care Products Mfr
S.I.C.: 2834
N.A.I.C.S.: 325412
Chris Bour *(Sr Mgr-Fin)*

BASF Performance Products France SA **(2)**
24 Espace Henry Vallee Batiment 2/3 L'Artillerie
69463 Lyon, Cedex 07, France FR
Tel.: (33) 4 3751 5700 (100%)
Fax: (33) 4 3751 5701
Web Site: www.basf.fr
Inorganic Pigments Mfr & Whslr
S.I.C.: 2819
N.A.I.C.S.: 325130
Nicolas Kerfant *(Mgr-Sls)*

Plant:

BASF Performance Products France - Gron Plant **(3)**
Zone Industrielle 9 Rue des Salcys
F-89100 Gron, France
Tel.: (33) 386652525
Fax: (33) 386644805
Chemical Mfr
S.I.C.: 2899
N.A.I.C.S.: 325998

BASF Pharma (St. Vulbas) S.A.S. **(2)**
Parc Industriel de la Plaine de l'Ain
1150 Saint-Vulbas, France
Tel.: (33) 4 74 46 21 90
Fax: (33) 4 74 46 21 99
E-Mail: basfpharmafr@basf.com
Web Site: www.pharma-ingredients.basf.com
Emp.: 14
Pharmaceutical Product Mfr
S.I.C.: 2834
N.A.I.C.S.: 325412
Werner Tschersich *(Gen Mgr)*

Societe Fonciere et Industrielle S.A.S. **(2)**
Zone Industrielle de Breuil le Sec
60676 Clermont, France
Tel.: (33) 344777777
Fax: (33) 344783010
E-Mail: cazaberu.christophe@basf.com
Web Site: www.basf.com
Emp.: 500
Chemical Product Mfr
S.I.C.: 2899
N.A.I.C.S.: 325998
Cazaberu Christophe *(Mgr-HR)*

BASF FZE **(1)**
Jebel Ali Free Zone
PO Box 61309
Dubai, United Arab Emirates
Tel.: (971) 48838773
Fax: (971) 48837749
E-Mail: basf.fze@west-asia.basf.org
Web Site: www.basf.ae/contact_dubai.html
Emp.: 60
Chemical Product Mfr
S.I.C.: 2899
N.A.I.C.S.: 325998
Harald Kroll *(Gen Mgr)*

BASF Hellas Industrial and Commercial S.A. **(1)**
449 Mesogeion Ave
Agia Paraskevi, 15343 Athens, Greece
Tel.: (30) 210 6860 212
Fax: (30) 210 6860 215
Emp.: 75
Specialty Chemical Mfr
S.I.C.: 2899
N.A.I.C.S.: 325998
Hidetaka Kai *(Mgr-IT)*

BASF Hellas S.A. **(1)**
449 Mesogion Avenue
Agia Paraskevi, 15343 Athens, Greece
Tel.: (30) 210 68 60 100
Fax: (30) 210 68 60 200
Web Site: www.agro.basf.gr
Agricultural Chemicals Mfr
S.I.C.: 2879
N.A.I.C.S.: 325320

BASF Holdings South Africa (Pty.) Ltd. **(1)**
Business Center South Africa & Sub-Sahara
852 Sixteenth Road
Midrand, Johannesburg, 1685, South Africa
Tel.: (27) 11 203 2400
Fax: (27) 11 203 2430
Web Site: www.basf.co.za
Emp.: 10
Investment Management Services
S.I.C.: 6211
N.A.I.C.S.: 523999
Hardus Pretorius *(Accountant)*

BASF Hungaria Kft. **(1)**
Seregely u 1-5
1034 Budapest, Hungary HU
Tel.: (36) 2504111 (100%)
Fax: (36) 12504660
Web Site: www.basf.de
Emp.: 50
Wholesale of Chemical Products
S.I.C.: 5169
N.A.I.C.S.: 424690

BASF Industrial Metals LLC **(1)**
Kadashevskaya Nab 14/3
119017 Moscow, Russia
Tel.: (7) 495 225 6490
Fax: (7) 495 225 6496
Emp.: 1
Industrial Chemical Mfr
S.I.C.: 2899
N.A.I.C.S.: 325998
Victor Nikitin *(Gen Dir)*

BASF Interservicios S.A. de C.V. **(1)**
Av Insurgentes Sur 975 Cd de los Deportes Benito Juarez
Mexico, 3710, Mexico
Tel.: (52) 5553252600
Fax: (52) 5552252777
E-Mail: basfmexicana@basf.com
Web Site: www.basfmexicana.com
Business Management Consulting Services
S.I.C.: 8742
N.A.I.C.S.: 541611
Michael Stuntt *(Pres)*

BASF Investments Canada Inc. **(1)**
500 Railway Ave
Blackie, AB, Canada
Tel.: (403) 684-3838
Fax: (403) 684-3561
Investment Management Services
S.I.C.: 6211
N.A.I.C.S.: 523999

BASF Iran AG **(1)**
Sohrevardi Shomali Ave Kangavar Aly No 5
Tehran, 15579, Iran IR
Mailing Address: (100%)
PO Box 11365-4619
Tehran, 15579, Iran
Tel.: (98) 218768237
Telex: 212651 basf ir
Fax: (98) 218762894
E-Mail: basf_iran@mftmail.com
Web Site: www.basf.de
Distributor of Chemicals
S.I.C.: 5169
N.A.I.C.S.: 424690

BASF Ireland Limited **(1)**
Wellington Road
Little Island, Cork, Ireland IE
Tel.: (353) 21 451 7100
Telex: 75839
Fax: (353) 214353559
Web Site: www.basf.com
Emp.: 120
Production of Chemicals Used in Mining
S.I.C.: 2899
N.A.I.C.S.: 325998
Enda Quigley *(VP-Mining Chemicals)*

BASF Italia S.p.A. **(1)**
Via Marconato 8
I 20031 Cesano Maderno, Italy IT
Tel.: (39) 03625121 (100%)
Telex: 350029 basf i
Fax: (39) 362512210
E-Mail: info@basf.it
Web Site: www.basf.it
Emp.: 670
Mfr. & Sales of Dyestuffs & Finishing Products
S.I.C.: 5169
N.A.I.C.S.: 424690

Subsidiaries:

BASF Coatings Services Italy Srl **(2)**
Via del Padule 40
Scandicci, Florence, 50018, Italy
Tel.: (39) 0557 35 01 21
Fax: (39) 0557 35 05 46
Automotive Coating Distr
S.I.C.: 5198
N.A.I.C.S.: 424950

BASF Interservice Spa **(2)**
Via Marconato 8
20031 Cesano Maderno, MI, Italy
Tel.: (39) 03625121
Fax: (39) 0362512599
Web Site: www.basf.it/ecp1/Societa_del_Gruppo/BASF_IT_Services_Spa
Chemical Product Mfr
S.I.C.: 2899
N.A.I.C.S.: 325998

Units:

BASF Italia - Centro Cuoio **(2)**
Via Montorso 35
36071 Vicenza, VI, Italy
Tel.: (39) 0444485311
Fax: (39) 0444485312
Web Site: www.basf.com
Chemical Product Mfr
S.I.C.: 2899
N.A.I.C.S.: 325998

BASF Italia - Centro Ricerca e Sviluppo **(2)**
Servizio Tecnico
Via Quarantola 40, 48022 Lugo di Romagna, RA, Italy
Tel.: (39) 054524110
Fax: (39) 054523311
E-Mail: info@agroitalia.com
Web Site: www.agro.basf.it
Emp.: 12
Chemical Product Mfr
S.I.C.: 2899
N.A.I.C.S.: 325998
Mario Manaresi *(Gen Mgr)*

BASF Italia - Espansi **(2)**
Via Montesanto 46
42021 Bibbiano, Italy
Tel.: (39) 0522251011
Fax: (39) 0522881540
Web Site: www.basf.it
Chemical Product Mfr
S.I.C.: 2899
N.A.I.C.S.: 325998

BASF Italia - Nutrizione Animale **(2)**
Via Leonardo da Vinci 2
24040 Bergamo, BG, Italy
Tel.: (39) 035 45580 11
Fax: (39) 035 45580 41
Animal Nutrition Products & Services
S.I.C.: 0752
N.A.I.C.S.: 812910

BASF SE—(Continued)

BASF Kanoo Gulf FZE (1)
Jevel Ali Free Zone
PO Box 61309
Dubai, United Arab Emirates AE
Tel.: (971) 48838773 (100%)
Telex: 48479 basf em
Fax: (971) 48838779
E-Mail: basf.fze@basf.com
Web Site: www.basf.ae
Emp.: 75
Distributor of Chemicals
S.I.C.: 5169
N.A.I.C.S.: 424690
Harald Crawl *(Mng Dir)*

BASF Kaspian Yapi kimyasallari Sanayi mehud mesuliyyetli cemiyyeti (1)
H Zeynalabdin Sett
AZ1065 Sumgayit, Azerbaijan
Tel.: (994) 18 653 10 30
Fax: (994) 18 653 10 31
E-Mail: basfcaspian@basf.com
Web Site: www.basf-cc.az
Construction Material Distr
S.I.C.: 5039
N.A.I.C.S.: 423390

BASF Ltd. (1)
55 Street 18 Maadi Sarayat 5th Floor
11431 Cairo, Egypt EG
Tel.: (20) 2 378 0039 (100%)
Fax: (20) 2 378 1442
E-Mail: basf.egypt@africa.basf.org
Web Site: www.basf.com.eg
Chemical Products Distr
S.I.C.: 5169
N.A.I.C.S.: 424690

BASF Maroc S.A. (1)
7 Rue Des Orchidees
P O Box 2509
20250 Casablanca, Morocco Ma
Tel.: (212) 22354830 (100%)
Telex: 25770 basf m
Fax: (212) 22350136
E-Mail: basf.maro@basf.com
Web Site: www.basf.co.ma
Emp.: 50
Distributor of Chemicals, Plastic Products & Colorants for Industry & Agriculture
S.I.C.: 5169
N.A.I.C.S.: 424690
Aeir Gerffaillie *(Mng Dir)*

BASF Metal Forwards Limited (1)
21st Floor Heron Tower 110 Bishopsgate
London, EC2N 4AY, United Kingdom
Tel.: (44) 20 7398 2500
Fax: (44) 20 7398 2550
Emp.: 25
Commodity Contract & Brokerage Services
S.I.C.: 6221
N.A.I.C.S.: 523140
Clive Stocker *(Gen Mgr)*

BASF Metals GmbH (1)
Grafenauweg 6
6300 Zug, Switzerland
Tel.: (41) 41 710 82 77
Fax: (41) 41 710 82 88
E-Mail:
Web Site: www.basf.com
Emp.: 5
Industrial Chemical Mfr
S.I.C.: 2899
N.A.I.C.S.: 325998
Paul Conway *(Gen Mgr)*

BASF Metals Japan Ltd. (1)
World Trade Center Bldg 24F 2-4-1
Hamamatsu-cho
Minato-ku, Tokyo, 105-6124, Japan
Tel.: (81) 3 3578 6661
Fax: (81) 3 5425 7481
Emp.: 10
Industrial Chemical Mfr
S.I.C.: 2899
N.A.I.C.S.: 325998
Satoshi Souda *(Mgr-Ops)*

BASF Metals Recycling Ltd. (1)
Forest Vale Road
Cinderford, Gloucestershire, GL14 2PH, United Kingdom
Tel.: (44) 1594 827744
Fax: (44) 1594 826013
Web Site: www.basf.co.uk
Emp.: 7
Metal Scrap Recycling Services
S.I.C.: 4953
N.A.I.C.S.: 562920
Reinhard Scholz *(Gen Mgr)*

BASF Metals (Shanghai) Co. Ltd. (1)
239 Luqiao Road Jinqiao Export Processing Zone
Shanghai, 201206, China
Tel.: (86) 21 6109 1885
Fax: (86) 21 6109 1845
Metal Product Distr
S.I.C.: 5051
N.A.I.C.S.: 423510

BASF Metasheen (1)
2 Air Care Drive
PO Box 1347
K7A 5C7 Smiths Falls, ON, Canada
Tel.: (613) 283-4400
Fax: (613) 283-0377
E-Mail: colorseffectscustomercare@basf.com
Web Site: www.basf.com
Specialty Chemical Distr
S.I.C.: 5169
N.A.I.C.S.: 424690

BASF Nederland B.V. (1)
Geominuensindel 1
Arnhem, 6835 EA, Netherlands NL
Mailing Address: (100%)
Postbus 1019
6801MC Arnhem, Netherlands
Tel.: (31) 263717171
Fax: (31) 263717246
E-Mail: info@basf.nl
Web Site: www.basf.nl
Emp.: 673
Chemical Sales & Administrative Services
S.I.C.: 2899
N.A.I.C.S.: 325998

Subsidiary:

BASF Finance Europe N.V. (2)
Rijnkade 155
NL 6811 HD Arnhem, Netherlands NL
Tel.: (31) 264456856 (100%)
Telex: 45249 basfi nl
Fax: (31) 264426856
Web Site: www.basf.nl
Financial Services of Chemicals
S.I.C.: 2899
N.A.I.C.S.: 325998

Non-U.S. Subsidiary:

BASF Minerals Oy (2)
Tammasaarenkatu 3
1800 Helsinki, Finland
Tel.: (358) 9 61598 1
Fax: (358) 9 61598 250
Emp.: 15
Processed Kaolin Distr
S.I.C.: 5032
N.A.I.C.S.: 423320
Mika Laukkanen *(Mgr-Sls)*

BASF Nutrition Animale (1)
Zone Industrielle de Bellitourne-Aze
53200 Chateau-Gontier, France
Tel.: (33) 243074226
Fax: (33) 243074262
Web Site: www.basf.com
Animal Health & Nutrition Services
S.I.C.: 0752
N.A.I.C.S.: 812910

BASF Operations B.V. (1)
Groningensingel 1
Arnhem, Gelderland, 6835 EA, Netherlands
Tel.: (31) 263717171
Chemical Product Mfr
S.I.C.: 2899
N.A.I.C.S.: 325998

BASF Osterreich GmbH (1)
Millenium Tower 26th Fl
Hendelskai 94-96, 1200 Vienna, Austria AT
Tel.: (43) 1878900 (100%)
Fax: (43) 187890120
E-Mail: basf.at@basf.com
Web Site: www.basf.at
Sales Range: $25-49.9 Million
Emp.: 175
Chemical Product Mfr
S.I.C.: 2899
N.A.I.C.S.: 325998
Joachim Meier *(Mng Dir)*

BASF Oy (1)
Tannasaarenkatu 3
00180 Helsinki, Finland FI
Tel.: (358) 9615981 (100%)
Fax: (358) 961598250
E-Mail: info-finland@basf.com
Web Site: www.basf.com
Emp.: 30
Chemical Sales
S.I.C.: 5169
N.A.I.C.S.: 424690
Torben Jensen *(Mng Dir)*

Division:

BASF Oy - Wolman Division (2)
Patosillantie
Box 112
45701 Kuusankoski, Finland
Tel.: (358) 5 311 0420
Fax: (358) 5 311 0424
E-Mail: wolman.finland@basf.com
Web Site: www.basf.fi
Emp.: 1
Wood Preservative Mfr
S.I.C.: 2899
N.A.I.C.S.: 325998

Subsidiary:

Oy Mercantile Ab (2)
Graphic Dept Hakkilankaari 2
01380 Vantaa, Finland
Tel.: (358) 934501
Fax: (358) 934504279
E-Mail: info@mercantile.fi
Web Site: www.mercantile.fi
Sales Range: $10-24.9 Million
Emp.: 60
Chemical Product Mfr
S.I.C.: 2899
N.A.I.C.S.: 325998
Taipetter Purhonen *(Mng Dir)*

BASF Panama S.A. (1)
Calle 50 Torre Global Bank
Piso 12 Oficina 1204, Panama, Panama Pa
Tel.: (507) 300 1360 (100%)
Fax: (507) 300 1361
E-Mail: winston.cardenas@basf.com
Web Site: www.basf.com
Emp.: 5
Sales of Chemicals
S.I.C.: 5169
N.A.I.C.S.: 424690
Winston Cardenas *(Mgr)*

BASF Paper Chemicals (Jiangsu) Co. Ltd. (1)
No 1 Ganghan Rd Dagang New Zone
Zhenjiang, Jiangsu, 212132, China
Tel.: (86) 51183121121
Fax: (86) 51183121737
Chemical Product Mfr
S.I.C.: 2899
N.A.I.C.S.: 325998

BASF Paraguaya S.A. (1)
Independencia Nacional No 811 Esquina Fulgencio R Moreno Edificio El Productor Piso 12, 3064 Asuncion, Casilla de Correo, Paraguay PY
Tel.: (595) 21498401 (100%)
Fax: (595) 21498403
Sales Range: $10-24.9 Million
Emp.: 23
Chemical & Agricultural Products Whslr
S.I.C.: 5169
N.A.I.C.S.: 424690

BASF Performance Products GmbH (1)
Roseggerstrasse 101
8670 Krieglach, Austria
Tel.: (43) 3855 2371 42
Fax: (43) 3855 2371 23
E-Mail: office.austria@basf.com
Web Site: www.basf-cc.at
Emp.: 30
Construction Chemical Mfr & Distr
S.I.C.: 2899
N.A.I.C.S.: 325998

BASF Performance Products Ltd. (1)
18 Floor Xin An Building 1599 Tian Zhou Road
Caohejing Hi-Tech Park, Shanghai, 200233, China
Tel.: (86) 21 2403 2000
Fax: (86) 21 2403 2002
E-Mail: corporate.regionchina@cibasc.com
Chemical Products Mfr
S.I.C.: 2899
N.A.I.C.S.: 325998

BASF Peruana S.A. (1)
Av Oscar R Benavides No 5915 Callao 1
PO Box 3911
Lima, Peru PE
Tel.: (51) 15132100 (100%)
Fax: (51) 15132517
E-Mail: basfperu@basf-peru.com.pe
Web Site: www.basf.com.pe
Emp.: 160
Mfr. of Chemicals, Animal Nutrition, Dispersions for Paint & Paper
S.I.C.: 2899
N.A.I.C.S.: 325998

BASF Pharma (Callanish) Limited (1)
Studio 87 87 Ridgway
Wimbledon Village, London, SW19 4ST, United Kingdom
Tel.: (44) 20 8946 4625
Fax: (44) 20 8946 7769
Pharmaceutical Product Mfr
S.I.C.: 2834
N.A.I.C.S.: 325412
Adam Kelliher *(Mng Dir)*

BASF Pharma (Evionnaz) S.A. (1)
Route du Simplon 1 36
1902 Evionnaz, Switzerland
Tel.: (41) 27 766 12 00
Fax: (41) 27 766 14 80
E-Mail: receptionnord@basf.com
Emp.: 30
Pharmaceutical Product Mfr & Distr
S.I.C.: 2834
N.A.I.C.S.: 325412

BASF Philippines, Inc. (1)
Main Ofc & Plant ED Carmelray Industrial Pk 1
Calamba, 4028, Philippines PH
Tel.: (63) 495490001 (100%)
Telex: 29029 bas ph
Fax: (63) 495491026
Web Site: www.basf.com.sg
Emp.: 150
Distributor of Chemicals
S.I.C.: 5169
N.A.I.C.S.: 424690
Flor M. Pan *(Mng Dir)*

BASF Plastic Additives Middle East S.P.C. (1)
Building 1420 Road 1518 R 1510 Block 115 1510 Block 115, Hidd, 50993, Bahrain
Tel.: (973) 17 585 252
Fax: (973) 17002631
Web Site: www.basf.com
Emp.: 3
Plastic Additive Mfr
S.I.C.: 3089
N.A.I.C.S.: 326199

BASF Polska Sp. z o. o (1)
Aleje Jerozolimskie 154
02 326 Warsaw, Poland PL
Tel.: (48) 225709777 (100%)
Fax: (48) 225709599
E-Mail: recepcja.basfpolska@basf.pl
Web Site: www.basf.pl
Emp.: 150
Mfr. of Chemicals
S.I.C.: 2899
N.A.I.C.S.: 325998
Dirk Elvermann *(Pres)*

BASF Polyurethane Specialties (China) Co. Ltd. (1)
2333 Gang Cheng Road
Pudong, Shanghai, 200137, China
Tel.: (86) 21 3865 2000
Fax: (86) 21 3865 5516
Chemical Product Mfr
S.I.C.: 2899
N.A.I.C.S.: 325998

BASF Portuguesa, Lda. (1)
Rua 25 De Abril
PO Box 538

2689 Lisbon, Portugal PT
Mailing Address: (100%)
Apartado 3064
1012 Lisbon, Cedex, Portugal
Tel.: (351) 219499900
Fax: (351) 219499949
Web Site: www.basf-cc.pt
Emp.: 20
Chemicals Sales
S.I.C.: 5169
N.A.I.C.S.: 424690
Jose Varela *(Mng Dir)*
Anabela Sousa *(Sec)*

BASF Pozzolith Ltd. (1)
Roppongi Hills Mori Tower 21F 6-10-1
Roppongi
Minato-ku, Tokyo, 106-6121, Japan
Tel.: (81) 3 3796 9710
Fax: (81) 3 3796 9980
E-Mail: bpz-polymers@basf.com
Web Site: www.pozzolith.basf.co.jp
Construction Material Distr
S.I.C.: 5039
N.A.I.C.S.: 423390

BASF Properties Inc. (1)
345 Carlingview Dr
Etobicoke, ON, M9W 6N9, Canada
Tel.: (416) 675-3611
Property Management Services
S.I.C.: 6531
N.A.I.C.S.: 531311

BASF plc (1)
Earl Rd
PO Box 4
Cheadle, Cheshire, SK8 6QG, United Kingdom UK
Tel.: (44) 1614856222 (100%)
Fax: (44) 1614867545
Web Site: www.basf.com
Emp.: 425
Sales of Industrial Chemicals
S.I.C.: 5169
N.A.I.C.S.: 424690

Subsidiaries:

BASF Biocides Limited (2)
Mere Way Business Park Ruddington Fields
Ruddington, Nottinghamshire, NG11 6JS, United Kingdom
Tel.: (44) 1614856222
Fax: (44) 1159124592
E-Mail: info@basf.com
Web Site: www.basf.com
Emp.: 100
Chemical Product Mfr & Speciality Biocides Supplier
S.I.C.: 2899
N.A.I.C.S.: 325998

BASF Performance Products plc (2)
Charter Way
Macclesfield, Cheshire, SK10 2NX, United Kingdom UK
Tel.: (44) 1625665000 (100%)
Telex: 667336
Fax: (44) 1625619637
Web Site: www.basf.co.uk/ecp1/Group_companies_UK_Ireland/Ciba
Emp.: 200
Holding Company; Pigments, Inorganic Chemicals & Plastics Mfr & Whslr
S.I.C.: 6719
N.A.I.C.S.: 551112

Division:

BASF Performance Products plc - Pigments Division (3)
Charter Way
Macclesfield, Cheshire, SK10 2NX, United Kingdom
Tel.: (44) 1625617878
Fax: (44) 1625619637
E-Mail: enquiriesuk@cibasc.com
Emp.: 300
Inorganic Pigments Mfr
S.I.C.: 2819
N.A.I.C.S.: 325130

Plants:

BASF Performance Products plc - Bradford Plant (3)
Cleckheaton Road
PO Box 38
Low Moor, Bradford, W Yorkshire, BD12 OJZ, United Kingdom
Tel.: (44) 1274417000
Fax: (44) 1274606499
Web Site: www.basf.com
Emp.: 800
Mfr. of Specialty Water Treatment Chemicals
Import Export
S.I.C.: 2899
N.A.I.C.S.: 325998
Ulrich Kanne *(Mng Dir)*

BASF Performance Products plc - Paisley Plant (3)
Hawkhead Road
Paisley, PA2 7BG, United Kingdom
Tel.: (44) 1418871144
Telex: 777702
Fax: (44) 1418874511
Web Site: www.basf.co.uk/ecp1/Group_companies_UK_Ireland/Ciba
Sales Range: $200-249.9 Million
Emp.: 250
Mfr. of Pigments
S.I.C.: 2819
N.A.I.C.S.: 325130
Peter Wormeld *(Mng Dir)*

BASF UK Limited (2)
Earl Road
PO Box 4
Cheadle Hulme, Cheadle, Cheshire, SK8 6QG, United Kingdom
Tel.: (44) 161 485 6222
Fax: (44) 161 486 0891
E-Mail:
Care Chemical Products Sales
S.I.C.: 5169
N.A.I.C.S.: 424690

Sorex Holdings Ltd. (2)
Saint Michael's Industrial Estate
Widnes, Cheshire, WA8 8TJ, United Kingdom UK
Tel.: (44) 1514207151
Fax: (44) 1514951163
E-Mail: pestinfo@basf.com
Web Site: www.pestcontrol.basf.co.uk
Emp.: 70
Holding Company; Insecticide & Pesticide Developer & Mfr
S.I.C.: 6719
N.A.I.C.S.: 551112
David Marris *(Head-Mktg)*

Subsidiary:

Sorex Ltd. (3)
Saint Michael's Industrial Estate
Widnes, Cheshire, WA8 8TJ, United Kingdom UK
Tel.: (44) 151 420 7151 (100%)
Fax: (44) 151 420 1163
E-Mail: pestinfo@basf.com
Web Site: www.pestcontrol.basf.co.uk
Insecticide & Pesticide Mfr
S.I.C.: 2879
N.A.I.C.S.: 325320

U.S. Subsidiary:

Whitmire Micro-Gen Research Laboratories, Inc. (3)
3568 Tree Ct Industrial Blvd
Saint Louis, MO 63122-6620 DE
Tel.: (636) 225-5371
Fax: (636) 225-3739
Toll Free: (800) 777-8570
Web Site: www.pestcontrol.basf.us
Emp.: 100
Insecticides & Animal Pesticides Developer & Mfr
S.I.C.: 2879
N.A.I.C.S.: 325320
Dan Carrothers *(Bus Mgr)*

BASF Qtech Inc. (1)
100 Milverton Drive 5th Floor
Mississauga, ON, L5R 4H1, Canada
Tel.: (732) 205-7620
Fax: (732) 205-7136
Toll Free: (800) 633-3204
E-Mail: Qtech@basf.com
Web Site: www.basf-qtech.com
Catalytic Surface Coating Mfr
S.I.C.: 2851
N.A.I.C.S.: 325510

BASF Quimica Colombiana S.A. (1)
Calle 99 69 C 32
Apartado Aereo 5751 Y 7072, Bogota, DC, Colombia Co
Tel.: (57) 16322260 (100%)
Fax: (57) 16131195
E-Mail: basf@basf-col.com.co
Web Site: www.basf.com.co
Emp.: 110
Sales of Chemicals, Polyester Resins, Finishing Products, Crop Protection Products & Animal Nutrition Products
S.I.C.: 5169
N.A.I.C.S.: 424690

BASF Representation Belarus (1)
Pr Pobeditelej 5
220004 Minsk, Belarus
Tel.: (375) 17 203 9024
Fax: (375) 17 203 9013
E-Mail: basf-belarus@basf.com
Chemical Product Mfr
S.I.C.: 2899
N.A.I.C.S.: 325998

BASF S.A. (1)
Estrada Samuel Aizemberg 1707
09851-550 Sao Bernardo do Campo, SP, Brazil BR
Mailing Address: (100%)
Caixa Postal 136
09701-970 Sao Bernardo do Campo, SP, Brazil
Tel.: (55) 1143471122
Fax: (55) 1143436989
E-Mail: info@basf.com.br
Web Site: www.basf.com.br
Emp.: 3,700
Chemicals, Colorants, Finishing Products, Coatings & Paints, Crop Protection Products & Styropor Mfr & Whslr
S.I.C.: 2899
N.A.I.C.S.: 325998
Rui Artur Goerck *(VP)*

Subsidiaries:

BASF Poliuretanos Ltda. (2)
Av Papa Joao XXIII 4800
09370-904 Maua, SP, Brazil
Tel.: (55) 1145427200
Fax: (55) 1145427251
E-Mail: basfpu@basf.com
Web Site: www.basf.com.br
Emp.: 300
Chemical Product Mfr
S.I.C.: 2899
N.A.I.C.S.: 325998

BASF SA (2)
Av Angelo Demarchi 123
Caixa Postal 340
09844-900 Sao Bernardo do Campo, SP, Brazil BR
Tel.: (55) 11 4347 1122 (100%)
Fax: (55) 11 4347 6989
Web Site: www.basf.com.br
Mfr of Coatings
S.I.C.: 2851
N.A.I.C.S.: 325510

BASF (Schweiz) AG (1)
Appital
Postfach 99
CH 8820 Wadenswil, Switzerland CH
Tel.: (41) 17819111 (100%)
Fax: (41) 17819388
E-Mail: info@basf.ch
Web Site: www.basf.ch
Emp.: 40
Mfr. of Chemicals
S.I.C.: 2899
N.A.I.C.S.: 325998
Merak Odehnal *(Gen Mgr)*

Branch:

BASF (Schweiz) AG - Basel Site (2)
Klybeckstrasse 141
CH-4002 Basel, Switzerland CH
Tel.: (41) 616361111 (100%)
Fax: (41) 616362222
E-Mail: info-switzerland@basf.com
Web Site: www.cibasf.ch
Specialty Chemicals Whslr
S.I.C.: 5169
N.A.I.C.S.: 424690
Andreas Duer *(Gen Mgr)*

Subsidiaries:

BASF Fine Chemicals Switzerland SA (2)
Route Cantonale
Evionnaz, Geneva, VS, CH-1902, Switzerland (100%)
Tel.: (41) 277661620
Fax: (41) 277661660
Web Site: www.orgamol.com
Sales Range: $125-149.9 Million
Chemical & Pharmaceutical Ingredient Mfr
S.I.C.: 2899
N.A.I.C.S.: 325998
Martin Jochen Klatt *(Mng Dir)*

Non-U.S. Division:

BASF Pharma (3)
Parc industriel de la Plaine de L'Ain
01150 Saint-Vulbas, France
Tel.: (33) 4 74 46 21 90
Fax: (33) 4 74 46 21 99
E-Mail: orgamolsa@basf.com
Web Site: www.basf.fr
Emp.: 140
Fine Chemical Mfr for Pharmaceutical Industries
S.I.C.: 2899
N.A.I.C.S.: 325998
Auchatz Folkea *(CEO)*

BASF Intertrade AG (2)
Grafenauweg 8
6300 Zug, Switzerland CH
Tel.: (41) 417120123 (100%)
Telex: 862238 bit ch
Fax: (41) 417109154
E-Mail: info@basf-intertrade.ch
Web Site: www.basf-intertrade.ch
Emp.: 40
Mfr of Chemicals
S.I.C.: 2899
N.A.I.C.S.: 325998

BASF Kaisten AG (2)
Hardmatt 434
CH-5082 Kaisten, Switzerland CH
Tel.: (41) 628689111 (100%)
Fax: (41) 628689201
Web Site: www.basf.com
Chemicals Mfr
S.I.C.: 2899
N.A.I.C.S.: 325998

BASF Services (Malaysia) Sdn. Bhd. (1)
2/1 Jalan Gebeng Kawasan Perindustrian Pahang Darul Makmur
Kuantan, Pahang Darul Makmur, 26080, Malaysia
Tel.: (60) 9 585 7000
Fax: (60) 9 583 9200
Web Site: www.basf.com
Emp.: 3
Chemical Products Mfr
S.I.C.: 2899
N.A.I.C.S.: 325998
Mohamed Apandi Ali *(Gen Mgr)*

BASF Slovenija d.o.o. (1)
Dunajska Cesta 111 A
1000 Ljubljana, Slovenia SI
Tel.: (386) 15897500 (100%)
Fax: (386) 15685556
E-Mail: info@basf.com
Web Site: www.basf.com
Emp.: 17
Sales of Chemical
S.I.C.: 5169
N.A.I.C.S.: 424690
Michael Nam *(Gen Mgr)*

BASF Slovensko s.r.o. (1)
Prievozska 2
821 09 Bratislava, Slovakia Sk
Tel.: (421) 258266111 (100%)
Telex: 92250 basf sk
Fax: (421) 258266166
E-Mail: basf.slovensko@central-europe.basf.org
Web Site: www.basf.sk
Emp.: 25
Sales of Chemicals & Agricultural Chemicals & Plastics
S.I.C.: 5169
N.A.I.C.S.: 424690

BASF South Africa (Pty.) Ltd. (1)
Business Centre 852 Sixteenth Road
Midrand, 1685, South Africa ZA
Mailing Address: (100%)
PO Box 2801
Halfway House, Midrand, 1685, South Africa
Tel.: (27) 112032400
Fax: (27) 112032430

BASF SE—(Continued)

Web Site: www.basf.com
Emp.: 130
Distr & Importer of Chemicals
S.I.C.: 5169
N.A.I.C.S.: 424690
Dieter Kovar *(CEO)*

Subsidiaries:

ADVIT Animal Nutrition **(2)**
137 Terrace Road
Sebenza, 1610, South Africa
Mailing Address:
PO Box 1783
Kempton Park, Johannesburg, 1620, South Africa
Tel.: (27) 115240440
Fax: (27) 115240414
E-Mail: admin@advit.co.za
Web Site: www.advit.co.za
Emp.: 33
Animal Health, Welfare Management Products
S.I.C.: 2048
N.A.I.C.S.: 311119
Deon Elsworth *(Mng Dir)*

BASF Construction Chemicals South Africa (Pty) Ltd. **(2)**
852 16th Road
Midrand, 1685, South Africa
Tel.: (27) 11 203 2405
Fax: (27) 112032679
Web Site: www.basf-cc.co.za
Emp.: 70
Construction Chemical Distr
S.I.C.: 5169
N.A.I.C.S.: 424690
Warren Trew *(Dir-Bus Dev)*

BASF S.p.A. **(1)**
13 Rue Arezki Abri Ugra
16035 Hydra, Algeria DG
Tel.: (213) 21603493 (100%)
Telex: 67953 basfa dz
Fax: (213) 21693811
E-Mail: basf.algeria@africa.basf.org
Web Site: www.basfsafrica.co.za
Emp.: 20
Distributor of Chemicals
S.I.C.: 5169
N.A.I.C.S.: 424690

BASF spol. s.r.o. **(1)**
Crievozska 2
82109 Bratislava, Czech Republic CZ
Tel.: (420) 235000111 (100%)
Telex: 123536 basfc
Fax: (420) 258266266
E-Mail: recebcia-bratislava@basf.sk
Web Site: www.basf.sk
Emp.: 100
Chemicals Whslr
S.I.C.: 5169
N.A.I.C.S.: 424690
Joachim Meyer *(Sr VP)*

BASF Srbija d.o.o. **(1)**
Omladinskih brigada 90b
11070 Belgrade, Serbia RS
Tel.: (381) 11 309 3400 (100%)
Fax: (381) 11 309 3401
Web Site: www.basf.rs
Emp.: 24
Chemicals Whslr
S.I.C.: 5169
N.A.I.C.S.: 424690
Harald Kube *(Mng Dir)*

BASF S.r.l. **(1)**
Floreasca Business Park Calea Floreasca nr 169A Intrarea B Etaj 5, 14459 Bucharest, 1, Romania RO
Tel.: (40) 215299000
Fax: (40) 215299099
E-Mail: office.romania@basf.com
Web Site: www.basf.com
Emp.: 80
Sales of Chemicals
S.I.C.: 5169
N.A.I.C.S.: 424690

BASF Stavebni hmoty Ceska republika s.r.o. **(1)**
K Majovu 1244
537 01 Chrudim, Czech Republic
Tel.: (420) 469 607 111
Fax: (420) 469 607 112
E-Mail: info.cz@basf.com
Web Site: www.basf-cc.cz
Construction Chemical Mfr & Distr
S.I.C.: 2899
N.A.I.C.S.: 325998
Daniel Stolfa *(Head-Sls)*

BASF Taiwan B.V. **(1)**
Groningensingel 1
Arnhem, Gelderland, 6835 EA, Netherlands
Tel.: (31) 263717171
Chemical Product Mfr
S.I.C.: 2899
N.A.I.C.S.: 325998

BASF Tuerk Kimya Sanayi ve Ticaret Ltd. Sti. **(1)**
Defterdar Yokusu No 3
34421 Karakoyunlu, Istanbul, PK 424, Turkey TR
Tel.: (90) 2123343400
Telex: 24275 basf tr
Fax: (90) 2123343499
Web Site: www.basf.de
Emp.: 150
Distributor of Chemicals
S.I.C.: 5169
N.A.I.C.S.: 424690
Gurgen Barwech *(Gen Mgr)*

Subsidiary:

BASF Tuerk Kimya Sanayi ve Ticaret Ltd. Sti. **(2)**
Dilovasi Mevkii Pk 1
41455 Gebze, Dilovasi, Turkey TR
Tel.: (90) 2627547800
Telex: 34132 bstk tr
Fax: (90) 2626489299
E-Mail: ildiz.gulari@basf.com
Web Site: www.basf.com
Distributor of Chemicals
S.I.C.: 5169
N.A.I.C.S.: 424690
Iurgen Parwech *(Mng Dir)*

BASF Tunisie S.A. **(1)**
Zone Industrial De Saint Gobain
2033 Megrine, Tunisia Tn
Tel.: (216) 71427817 (100%)
Fax: (216) 71426120
E-Mail: basf.tunisie@basf-tunisie.com
Web Site: www.basf.com
Emp.: 12
Distributor of Chemicals
S.I.C.: 5169
N.A.I.C.S.: 424690

BASF UAB **(1)**
Fiausiausio 13
01114 Vilnius, Lithuania
Tel.: (370) 52107450
Fax: (370) 52107455
E-Mail: info-lithuania@basf.com
Emp.: 23
Chemical Product Mfr
S.I.C.: 2899
N.A.I.C.S.: 325998
Torban Berlin Henson *(Gen Dir)*

Non-U.S. Branch:

BASF UAB - Latvia **(2)**
Maza Novetnu iela 45/53
LV-1002 Riga, Latvia
Tel.: (371) 7 508 250
Fax: (371) 7 508 251
Web Site: www.basf.com
Chemical Product Whslr
S.I.C.: 5169
N.A.I.C.S.: 424690

BASF Uruguaya S.A. **(1)**
Camino Ariel 4620
12900 Montevideo, Uruguay UY
Mailing Address: (100%)
Casilla Correo 1925
11000 Montevideo, Uruguay
Tel.: (598) 23551414
Fax: (598) 2 355 8868
E-Mail: viscar@south-america.basf.org
Web Site: www.basf.de
Emp.: 45
Mfr. of Chemicals
S.I.C.: 2899
N.A.I.C.S.: 325998

BASF Venezolana, S.A. **(1)**
Multicentro Macaracuay Piso 10 Office 10
Avenida Principal de Macaracua, Caracas, Macaracuay, 1073, Venezuela VE
Mailing Address: (100%)
Apartado Postal 70616
Caracas, 1071 A, Venezuela
Tel.: (58) 212 256 0011
Telex: 25143 basf vc
Fax: (58) 212 256 0580
Web Site: www.basf.com.ve
Sales Range: $50-74.9 Million
Emp.: 40
Chemicals Mfr
S.I.C.: 2899
N.A.I.C.S.: 325998

BASF Vietnam Co. Ltd. **(1)**
12 Tu Do Boulevard Vietnam Singapore Industrial Park
Thuan An, Binh Duong, Vietnam
Tel.: (84) 650 3743100
Fax: (84) 650 3743200
E-Mail: compas-vn@basf.com.vn
Web Site: www.basf-cc.com.vn
Emp.: 136
Chemical Products Mfr
S.I.C.: 2899
N.A.I.C.S.: 325998
Petrus Ng *(Mng Dir)*

BASF Vitamins Company Ltd. **(1)**
No 88 Yunhai Road Shenyang Economic & Technological Development Zone
Shenyang, 110141, China
Tel.: (86) 24 2581 0788
Fax: (86) 24 2581 1236
Pharmaceutical Product Mfr
S.I.C.: 2834
N.A.I.C.S.: 325412

BNC Color Techno Co. Ltd. **(1)**
296 Shimokuratacho
Totsuka-Ku, Yokohama, Kanagawa, 244-0815, Japan
Tel.: (81) 458629225
Paint & Coating Mfr
S.I.C.: 2851
N.A.I.C.S.: 325510

BTC Speciality Chemical Distribution S.L. **(1)**
Carretera del Medio 219
08907 Barcelona, Spain (100%)
Tel.: (34) 932616100
Fax: (34) 932616196
E-Mail: informacion@btc-es.com
Web Site: www.btc-es.com
Emp.: 35
Chemical & Polymer Product Retailer & Marketer
S.I.C.: 3089
N.A.I.C.S.: 326199
Jose L. Aznar *(Mng Dir)*

Non-U.S. Subsidiaries:

BTC Speciality Chemical Distribution A/S **(2)**
Ved Stadsgraven 15
Postboks 4042
2300 Copenhagen, Denmark
Tel.: (45) 32660750
Fax: (45) 32574188
E-Mail: info@btc-nordic.com
Web Site: www.btc-nordic.com
Chemical & Polymer Product Retailer & Marketer
S.I.C.: 2899
N.A.I.C.S.: 325998
Kent-Ake Lundberg *(Mng Dir)*

BTC Speciality Chemical Distribution GmbH **(2)**
Maarweg 163
Postfach 45 12 25
50825 Cologne, Germany
Tel.: (49) 221954640
Fax: (49) 22195464211
E-Mail: info@btc-europe.com
Web Site: www.btc-de.com
Emp.: 140
Chemical & Polymer Product Retailer & Marketer
S.I.C.: 2821
N.A.I.C.S.: 325211

BTC Speciality Chemical Distribution Ltd. **(2)**
PO Box 4
Earl Road, Cheadle, Chesire, SK8 6QG, United Kingdom
Tel.: (44) 1614885223
Fax: (44) 1614860891
E-Mail: sales@btc-uk.com
Web Site: www.btc-uk.com
Emp.: 50
Chemical & Polymer Product Retailer & Marketer
S.I.C.: 2821
N.A.I.C.S.: 325211
Allan Dixon *(Acct Mgr-Plastics)*

BTC Speciality Chemical Distribution N.V./S.A. **(2)**
Terhulpsesteenweg 178
1170 Brussels, Belgium
Tel.: (32) 23732220
Fax: (32) 23732320
E-Mail: info@btc-benelux.com
Web Site: www.btc-benelux.com
Emp.: 200
Chemical & Polymer Product Retailer & Marketer
S.I.C.: 2821
N.A.I.C.S.: 325211
Hott Clement *(Mng Dir)*

BTC Speciality Chemical Distribution SAS **(2)**
49 Ave Georges Pompidou
Levallois, 92593 Perret, Cedex, France
Tel.: (33) 0149645151
Fax: (33) 0149645220
E-Mail: accueil.contact@btc-fr.com
Web Site: www.btc-fr.com
Emp.: 24
Chemical & Polymer Product Retailer & Marketer
S.I.C.: 2821
N.A.I.C.S.: 325211
Clemens Hott *(Mng Dir)*

BTC Speciality Chemical Distribution S.p.A. **(2)**
Via Marconato 8
20031 Cesano Maderno, Italy
Tel.: (39) 03625121
Fax: (39) 0362512549
E-Mail: info@btc-it.com
Web Site: www.btc-it.com
Chemical & Polymer Product Retailer & Marketer
S.I.C.: 2821
N.A.I.C.S.: 325211
Renato Chiesa *(CEO)*

BTC Speciality Chemical Distribution, Unip. Lda. **(2)**
Rua Manuel Pinto de Azevedo 626
4100-320 Porto, Portugal
Tel.: (351) 2261596
Fax: (351) 226177510
E-Mail: informacao@btc-pt.com
Web Site: www.btc-pt.com
Chemical & Polymer Product Retailer & Marketer
S.I.C.: 2821
N.A.I.C.S.: 325211
Jose Aznar *(Mng Dir)*

Chemcontrol Limited **(1)**
Suite 309 Top Floor
Cross-Crossing Centre
Cross-Crossing, San Fernando, Trinidad & Tobago
Tel.: (868) 6572000
Fax: (868) 6572555
E-Mail: support@chemcontrol.co.tt
Web Site: chemcontrol.co.tt
Chemical & Polymer Supplier
S.I.C.: 2819
N.A.I.C.S.: 325180

Cognis Australia Pty. Ltd. **(1)**
4 Saligna Dr
Tullamarine, Melbourne, VIC, 3043, Australia
Tel.: (61) 399333500
Fax: (61) 399333582
Chemical Product Mfr
S.I.C.: 2899
N.A.I.C.S.: 325998

Cognis B.V. **(1)**
Groningensingel 1
Arnhem, Gelderland, 6835 EA, Netherlands
Tel.: (31) 263717171
Chemical Product Whslr
S.I.C.: 5169
N.A.I.C.S.: 424690

Cognis S.A. (1)
Carabelas 2398
Avellaneda, B1872EQB, Argentina
Tel.: (54) 11 4001 0200
Fax: (54) 11 4205 3360
Chemical Product Mfr
S.I.C.: 2899
N.A.I.C.S.: 325998

Construction Chemicals Division in BASF A/S (1)
Hallandsvej 1
6230 Rodekro, Denmark
Tel.: (45) 74 66 15 11
Fax: (45) 74 69 44 11
E-Mail: denmark@basf.com
Web Site: www.basf-cc.dk
Emp.: 6
Construction Chemical Distr
S.I.C.: 5169
N.A.I.C.S.: 424690

Cosmetic Rheologies Ltd. (1)
Measurement House Mancunian Way
Manchester, M12 6HN, United Kingdom
Tel.: (44) 161 705 2290
Fax: (44) 161 763 9243
Cosmetic Chemicals Distr
S.I.C.: 5169
N.A.I.C.S.: 424690

CropDesign N.V. (1)
Technologiepark 21 C
9052 Zwijnaarde, Belgium
Tel.: (32) 9 242 34 00
Fax: (32) 9 242 34 89
E-Mail: info@cropdesign.com
Web Site: www.cropdesign.com
Emp.: 15
Agricultural Research & Development Services
S.I.C.: 8731
N.A.I.C.S.: 541711
Wim van Camp *(Mng Dir & Head-Strategic Mgmt)*

De Mattos & Sullivan Limited (1)
47-1 Tigne Seafront
Sliema, SLM15, Malta Mt
Tel.: (356) 021312953
Telex: 1974 dmatos mw
Fax: (356) 021342364
E-Mail: demattos@waldonet.net.mt
Emp.: 4
Chemicals, Gifts & Soft Toys Importer
S.I.C.: 2899
N.A.I.C.S.: 325998
Andrew Portelli *(Mgr-Sls)*

Dr. D.A. Delis AG (1)
Paleologou Benizelou 5
10556 Athens, Greece GR
Tel.: (30) 2103297222
Telex: 215336 deli gr
Fax: (30) 2103230550
E-Mail: info@delis.gr
Web Site: www.delis.gr
Sales Range: $25-49.9 Million
Emp.: 70
Importer of Chemicals
S.I.C.: 5169
N.A.I.C.S.: 424690
Konstantinos Marinos *(Mng Dir)*

Engelhard Arganda S.L. (1)
Doctor Fleming 3
Madrid, Spain
Tel.: (34) 914589940
Chemical Product Distr
S.I.C.: 5169
N.A.I.C.S.: 424690

Engelhard Peru S.A. (1)
Av San Borja Norte 1302
Lima, Peru
Tel.: (51) 1 2251080
Mineral Mining Services
S.I.C.: 1479
N.A.I.C.S.: 212393

Engelhard South Africa (Pty.) Ltd. (1)
Struan Way
Port Elizabeth, 6000, South Africa
Tel.: (27) 414011000
Fax: (27) 414011099
Emp.: 30
Catalytic Converter Machinery Mfr
S.I.C.: 3559
N.A.I.C.S.: 333249

Michael Tribelhorn *(Dir-Site)*

Esuco Beheer B.V. (1)
Groningensingel 1
Arnhem, Gelderland, 6835 EA, Netherlands
Tel.: (31) 263717171
Investment Management Services
S.I.C.: 6211
N.A.I.C.S.: 523999

HEMOMAK HEM Uros DOOEL (1)
Basino Selo
PO Box 11
1400 Veles, Macedonia
Tel.: (389) 43212552
Chemical Product Mfr
S.I.C.: 2899
N.A.I.C.S.: 325998

Hythe Chemicals Ltd. (1)
The Charleston Indstl Est
Southampton, Hampshire, SO45 3ZG, United Kingdom
Tel.: (44) 23 8089 4666
Fax: (44) 23 8024 3113
Chemical Product Mfr & Distr
S.I.C.: 2899
N.A.I.C.S.: 325998

Inca Bronze Powders Ltd. (1)
Springfield Road
Bolton, Lancashire, BL1 7LQ, United Kingdom
Tel.: (44) 1254 873 888
Industrial Chemicals Mfr
S.I.C.: 2899
N.A.I.C.S.: 325998

Interlates Ltd. (1)
Gladden Place
Skelmersdale, Lancashire, WN8 9SX, United Kingdom
Tel.: (44) 1695729577
Chemical Product Whslr
S.I.C.: 5169
N.A.I.C.S.: 424690

Jordanian Swiss Company for Manufacturing & Marketing Construction Chemicals Company Ltd. (1)
Al Madina Al Monawarah Street
PO Box 752
Amman, 11118, Jordan
Tel.: (962) 6 5521672
Fax: (962) 6 5523148
E-Mail: enquirycc.neareast@basf.com
Web Site: www.basf-cc.com.jo
Emp.: 9
Construction Chemical Mfr & Distr
S.I.C.: 2899
N.A.I.C.S.: 325998
Ismail Ratrout *(Gen Mgr-Sls)*

Kartal Kimya Sanayi ve Ticaret A.S. (1)
Gebze Organize Sanayi Bolgesi Cikisi
Mollafenari Yolu Uzeri, Gebze, 41490, Turkey
Tel.: (90) 2627512020
Fax: (90) 2627512023
Web Site: www.kartal.com.tr/
Chemical Products
S.I.C.: 2899
N.A.I.C.S.: 325998

Lig Ace Co. Ltd. (1)
1-24-43 Junka Sutoku Bldg
Fukui, 910-0023, Japan
Tel.: (81) 776282566
Chemical Product Mfr
S.I.C.: 2899
N.A.I.C.S.: 325998

Lipogene AB (1)
Svalof Weibull Ab
Svalov, Skane, 268 81, Sweden
Tel.: (46) 86574200
Biotechnology Research & Development Services
S.I.C.: 8731
N.A.I.C.S.: 541711

M/s. Amaravati International (1)
c/o Soaltee Hotel Limited
POB 1481
Kathmandu, Tahachal, Nepal
Tel.: (977) 14272555
Chemical Product Whslr
S.I.C.: 5169

N.A.I.C.S.: 424690
Nalin Mendiratta *(Gen Mgr)*

Magenta Master Fibers Srl (1)
Via Alessandrini 42/56
20013 Magenta, Milan, Italy
Tel.: (39) 02 9721991
Fax: (39) 02 97219936
E-Mail: info@magentamaster.com
Web Site: www.magentamaster.com
Emp.: 37
Synthetic Fiber Product Mfr
S.I.C.: 2823
N.A.I.C.S.: 325220
Andrea Lampertico *(Gen Mgr)*

MetalFX Technology Ltd. (1)
The Sidings Station Road
Guiseley, Leeds, LS20 8BX, United Kingdom
Tel.: (44) 1943 884 888
Fax: (44) 1943 870 185
Paint & Coating Mfr
S.I.C.: 2851
N.A.I.C.S.: 325510

NOF (Thailand) Ltd. (1)
11th Floor R 11-07/3 2034/52 Italthai Tower
New Phetchburi Road
Huaykwang District, Bangkok, Thailand
Tel.: (66) 27160095
Fax: (66) 2 716 0099
Web Site: www.basf.com
Chemical Product Mfr
S.I.C.: 2899
N.A.I.C.S.: 325998

OOO BASF Stroitelnye Sistemy (1)
Kadaschewskaja Nabereshnaja d 14/3
Moscow, 119017, Russia
Tel.: (7) 4952 25 64 36
Fax: (7) 4952 25 64 17
E-Mail: stroysist@basf.com
Web Site: www.stroysist.ru
Emp.: 15
Construction Chemical Distr
S.I.C.: 5169
N.A.I.C.S.: 424690
Sergey Vetlov *(Gen Dir)*

P. Papas & Co. O.E. Trading Company (1)
Paparrigopoulou 7
12132 Peristeri, Athen, Greece
Tel.: (30) 2105752944
Fax: (30) 2105754540
E-Mail: tsouris@souris.gr
Web Site: www.sourischemicals.gr
Emp.: 6
Chemical Product Mfr
S.I.C.: 2899
N.A.I.C.S.: 325998
Tena Souris *(Gen Mgr)*

PCI Bauprodukte AG (1)
Im Tiergarten 7
Postfach 13 33
8048 Zurich, Switzerland
Tel.: (41) 58 958 21 21
Fax: (41) 58 958 31 22
E-Mail: pci-ch-info@basf.com
Web Site: www.pci.ch
Emp.: 3
Construction Material Distr
S.I.C.: 5039
N.A.I.C.S.: 423390
Fred Noordam *(Area Mgr)*

P.T. BASF Care Chemicals Indonesia (1)
Jl Raya Jakarta-Bogor Km 31 2
Cimanggis, Depok, 16953, Indonesia
Tel.: (62) 21 8711096
Fax: (62) 21 8710309
Chemical Product Mfr & Distr
S.I.C.: 2899
N.A.I.C.S.: 325998

P.T. BASF Indonesia (1)
Plz GRI 10th And 11th Fl
Jakarta, 12950, Indonesia ID
Mailing Address: (100%)
PO Box 2431
Jakarta, 10024, Indonesia
Tel.: (62) 215262481
Telex: 62619 basf ia
Fax: (62) 215262493
Web Site: www.basf.com.sg
Emp.: 200
Mfr. of Chemicals

S.I.C.: 2899
N.A.I.C.S.: 325998
Danny Jozal *(Chm & CEO)*

Relius France S.A.S. (1)
10 Rue Michael Faraday
Ostwald, 67540, France
Tel.: (33) 3 88 67 45 42
Fax: (33) 3 88 67 45 43
E-Mail: relius.contact@basf.com
Web Site: www.relius.fr
Coating & Decorative Paint Mfr & Distr
S.I.C.: 2851
N.A.I.C.S.: 325510

Relius Nederland B.V. (1)
Geijzerstraat 3/9
5753 RP Deurne, Netherlands
Tel.: (31) 493 352452
Fax: (31) 493 310535
E-Mail: info@reliusnederland.nl
Web Site: www.reliushoeka.nl
Emp.: 50
Paint & Coating Mfr
S.I.C.: 2851
N.A.I.C.S.: 325510
Joost Bartels *(Mgr-Sls)*

Saudi BASF for Building Materials Co. Ltd. (1)
2nd Industrial City
Dammam, Saudi Arabia
Tel.: (966) 3 812 1140
Fax: (966) 3 812 1822
E-Mail: enquirycc.saudi@basf.com
Web Site: www.saudi-basf.com
Building Construction Material Distr
S.I.C.: 5039
N.A.I.C.S.: 423390
Mohammed Shahin *(Mng Dir)*

S.T.I.M.A. S.A.R.L. (1)
Residence Yasmine
2045 Tunis, Tunisia
Tel.: (216) 71862262
Fax: (216) 71862938
E-Mail: stima@planet.tn
Web Site: www.planet.tn
Emp.: 12
Agricultural Chemical Product Mfr
S.I.C.: 2879
N.A.I.C.S.: 325320
Kxelifi Abdelmonem *(Mng Dir)*

Styrolution Mexicana S.A. de C.V. (1)
Insurgentes No 975 Ciudad De Los Deportes Benito Ju Rez
Mexico, 03710, Mexico
Tel.: (52) 5553252600
Fax: (52) 5553252777
Chemical Product Mfr
S.I.C.: 2899
N.A.I.C.S.: 325998

Taiko Shoji Ltd. (1)
Meito Bldg 2f
Tokorozawa, Saitama, 359-0046, Japan
Tel.: (81) 429983056
Fax: (81) 429983075
Emp.: 15
Construction Material Distr
S.I.C.: 5039
N.A.I.C.S.: 423390

Tasfiye Halinde Meges Boya Sanayi ve Ticaret A.S. (1)
Sanayi Mah Hizir Reis Cad No 14
Pendik, 34912 Istanbul, Turkey
Tel.: (90) 216 378 1119
Fax: (90) 216 378 1197
E-Mail: info@meges.com
Web Site: www.meges.com.tr
Paint & Coating Whslr
S.I.C.: 5198
N.A.I.C.S.: 424950

Wilhelm Rosenstein Ltd. (1)
14 Shenkar Street 4th Floor
PO Box 12691
46733 Herzliyya, Israel
Tel.: (972) 99718802
Fax: (972) 99718850
E-Mail: wrl@wrl-ltd.com
Web Site: www.basf.com
Chemical Product Mfr
S.I.C.: 2899
N.A.I.C.S.: 325998

ZAO BASF (1)
Kadaschewskaja Nabereshnaja 14 Korp 3
119017 Moscow, Russia RU

BASF SE—(Continued)

Tel.: (7) 4952317176
Fax: (7) 4952317295
Web Site: www.basf.ru
Emp.: 150
Chemical Products Mfr & Whslr
S.I.C.: 2899
N.A.I.C.S.: 325998
Anereev Sergey *(Gen Mgr)*

Subsidiaries:

OOO BASF Wostok **(2)**
Ulitsa Pavlovskaya 26
Pavlosky Posad, 142500 Moscow, Russia
Tel.: (7) 4964351949
Fax: (7) 4964351676
Web Site: www.basf.com
Chemical Product Mfr
S.I.C.: 2899
N.A.I.C.S.: 325998

Non-U.S. Branches:

BASF - Belarus **(2)**
Business Centre Silver Tower 1st Summer Lane 20 8th Floor
220073 Minsk, Belarus (100%)
Tel.: (375) 172022471
Telex: 252604 basf by
Fax: (375) 172022470
E-Mail: basf-belarus@basf.com
Web Site: www.basf.by
Emp.: 30
Chemical Products Distr & Technical Support Services
S.I.C.: 5169
N.A.I.C.S.: 424690

BASF - Ukraine **(2)**
9 Naberezhno-Kreschatitskaya str
04070 Kiev, Ukraine (100%)
Tel.: (380) 445915595
Telex: 131278 basfu ux
Fax: (380) 445915597
E-Mail: basf.ukraine@basf.com
Emp.: 80
Chemical Products Distr & Technical Support Services
S.I.C.: 5169
N.A.I.C.S.: 424690

BASF - Uzbekistan **(2)**
75 Independence Str
100000 Tashkent, Uzbekistan (100%)
Tel.: (998) 71 120 5151
Fax: (998) 711206231
Web Site: www.basf.ru/ecp2/Group_companies_russia/BASF_Uzbekistan_Groupcompanies
Emp.: 2
Chemical Products Distr & Technical Support Services
S.I.C.: 5169
N.A.I.C.S.: 424690

Non-U.S. Subsidiary:

BASF Construction Chemicals Central Asia LLP **(2)**
211 A Raiymbek Avenue
050016 Almaty, Kazakhstan KZ (100%)
Tel.: (7) 727 279 0013
Telex: 251430 basf kz
Fax: (7) 727 233 3282
E-Mail: basfkaz@asdc.kz
Web Site: www.basf-cc.kz
Emp.: 9
Chemical Products Mfr & Distr
S.I.C.: 2899
N.A.I.C.S.: 325998

BASIC ELEMENT COMPANY

30 Rochdelskaya Street
123022 Moscow, Russia
Tel.: (7) 4957205025
Fax: (7) 4957205395
E-Mail: info@basel.ru
Web Site: www.basel.ru
Sales Range: $25-49.9 Billion

Business Description:
Investment Services
S.I.C.: 6211
N.A.I.C.S.: 523999

Personnel:
Oleg Deripaska *(CEO)*
Andrey Elinson *(Deputy CEO)*
Marina Kaldina *(Deputy CEO-Legal)*
Valery Pechenkin *(Deputy CEO-Security)*
Alexandeer Lukin *(CFO)*

BASIC ENERGY CORPORATION

7F Basic Petroleum Building 104
Carlos Palanca Jr Street
Legaspi Village, Makati, 1229, Philippines
Tel.: (63) 28178596
Fax: (63) 28170191
E-Mail: basic@basicenergy.ph
Web Site: www.basicenergy.ph
BSC—(PHI)
Rev.: $7,803,345
Assets: $21,048,055
Liabilities: $554,701
Net Worth: $20,493,354
Earnings: $6,010,477
Emp.: 20
Fiscal Year-end: 12/31/12

Business Description:
Oil Exploration Services
S.I.C.: 1389
N.A.I.C.S.: 213112

Personnel:
Oscar C. de Venecia *(Chm)*
Francis C. Chua *(Second Vice Chm)*
Ramon L. Mapa *(Vice Chm)*
Oscar L. de Venecia, Jr. *(Pres & CEO)*
Angel P. Gahol *(Compliance Officer, Asst VP & Asst Sec)*
Marietta V. Villafuerte *(Treas & VP)*
Corazon M. Bejasa *(Sec & VP)*

Board of Directors:
Oscar C. de Venecia
Ma. Florina M. Chan
Francis C. Chua
Oscar L. de Venecia, Jr.
Dennis D. Decena
Eduardo V. Manalac
Ramon L. Mapa
Jaime J. Martirez
Oscar S. Reyes
Gabriel R. Singson Jr.
Isidoro O. Tan

Subsidiary:

Basic Diversified Industrial Holdings, Inc **(1)**
7th Fl Basic Petroleum Bldg 104 C Palanca Jr St
Legaspi Village, Makati, 1229, Philippines
Tel.: (63) 28178596
Fax: (63) 28170191
Investment Holding & Management Services
S.I.C.: 6282
N.A.I.C.S.: 523920
Oscar L. De Venecia *(Pres & COO)*

BASICNET S.P.A.

Largo Maurizio Vitale 1
10152 Turin, Italy
Tel.: (39) 01126171
Fax: (39) 0112617595
E-Mail: someone@basic.net
Web Site: www.basicnet.com
Year Founded: 1983
BAN—(ITA)
Rev.: $148,113,700
Assets: $277,704,102
Liabilities: $193,121,549
Net Worth: $84,582,553
Earnings: ($23,335,857)
Emp.: 565
Fiscal Year-end: 12/31/12

Business Description:
Sportswear Mfr & Designer
S.I.C.: 5136
N.A.I.C.S.: 424320

Personnel:
Marco Daniele Boglione *(Chm)*
Franco Spalla *(CEO)*
Paola Bruschi *(COO)*
Paolo Cafasso *(Grp Fin Officer)*

Board of Directors:
Marco Daniele Boglione
Paola Bruschi
Paolo Cafasso
Giovanni Crespi
Alessandro Gabetti Davicini
Adriano Marconetto
Daniela Ovazza
Carlo Pavesio
Elisabetta Rolando
Franco Spalla

Subsidiaries:

Basic Village S.p.A. **(1)**
Largo Maurizio Vitale 1
Turin, Italy (100%)
Tel.: (39) 1126171
Fax: (39) 112617595
E-Mail: someone@basic.net
Mens Clothing Stores
S.I.C.: 5611
N.A.I.C.S.: 448110

BasicItalia S.p.A. **(1)**
Strada della Cebrosa 106
10156 Turin, Italy (90%)
Tel.: (39) 1126171
Fax: (39) 112617575
Mens & Boys Cut & Sew Other Outerwear Mfr
S.I.C.: 5699
N.A.I.C.S.: 315220
Franco Spalla *(Mng Dir)*

Non-U.S. Subsidiary:

Basic Properties B.V. **(1)**
Strawinskylaan 3111-6e Etage
1077ZX Amsterdam, Netherlands (100%)
Tel.: (31) 204420266
Fax: (31) 6446605
Trusts Estates & Agency Accounts
S.I.C.: 6733
N.A.I.C.S.: 525920
Cincent Mahieu *(Gen Mgr)*

BASICS OFFICE SUPPLY

1040 Foundation Street North
Cambridge, ON, N3E IA3, Canada
Tel.: (519) 653-8984
Fax: (519) 653-9828
E-Mail: info@basics.com
Web Site: www.basics.com
Rev.: $29,607,269
Emp.: 31

Business Description:
Office Products Whslr
S.I.C.: 5044
N.A.I.C.S.: 423420

Personnel:
Sean Macey *(Pres)*

BASIL READ HOLDINGS LIMITED

The Basil Read Campus 7 Romeo Street
Hughes, Boksburg, South Africa
Tel.: (27) 114186300
Fax: (27) 114186333
Web Site: www.basilread.co.za
BSR—(JSE)
Sales Range: $750-799.9 Million
Emp.: 5,682

Business Description:
Civil Engineering Construction & Development Services
S.I.C.: 1622
N.A.I.C.S.: 237310

Personnel:
Marius Lodewucus Heyns *(CEO & Mng Dir)*
Manuel Donnell Grota Gouveia *(Deputy CEO)*
Amanda Wightman *(Interim CFO)*
Andiswa Ndoni *(Sec)*

Board of Directors:
Sindile Lester Peteni
Paul Cambo Baloyi
Charles Peter Davies
Manuel Donnell Grota Gouveia
Marius Lodewucus Heyns
Nopasika Vuyelwa Lila
Claudia Estelle Manning
Andrew Conway Gaorekwe Molusi
Sango Siviwe Ntsaluba
Thabiso Alexander Tlelai
Amanda Wightman

Subsidiaries:

Basil Read (Pty) Limited **(1)**
7 Romeo Street Hughes Extension
Private Bag X 170
1459 Boksburg, Gauteng, South Africa
Tel.: (27) 114186300
Fax: (27) 114186333
Emp.: 200
Building Construction Services
S.I.C.: 1542
N.A.I.C.S.: 236220
Ma Heyns *(CEO)*

Blasting & Excavating (Pty) Limited **(1)**
7 Vernier Street
Witfield Extn 33, Boksburg, Gauteng, 1469, South Africa
Tel.: (27) 113234000
Fax: (27) 113234057
E-Mail: paulm@blasting.co.za
Web Site: www.blasting.co.za
Mining Support Services
S.I.C.: 1221
N.A.I.C.S.: 212111
Antonie Fourie *(Mng Dir)*

Contract Plumbing and Sanitation (Pty) Limited **(1)**
256 Vonkprop St Samcor Park Ext 1
Silverton, Gauteng, Gauteng, 0117, South Africa
Tel.: (27) 128038310
Fax: (27) 128039063
Emp.: 50
Plumbing & Sanitation Engineering Services
S.I.C.: 1711
N.A.I.C.S.: 238220
Ian Boyes *(Mgr)*

Facets Interiors (Pty) Limited **(1)**
Ground Fl Guild Hall 5 Anerley Rd
Parktown, Johannesburg, Gauteng, 2193, South Africa
Tel.: (27) 116467449
Fax: (27) 116467446
E-Mail: info@facetsinteriors.co.za
Web Site: www.facetsinteriors.co.za
Emp.: 8
Interior Designing Services
S.I.C.: 7389
N.A.I.C.S.: 541410
Sarah Brothers *(Mng Dir)*

Mvela Phanda Construction (Pty) Limited **(1)**
256 Vonkprop St Samcor Park Ext 1
Pretoria, Gauteng, 0184, South Africa
Tel.: (27) 128034099
Fax: (27) 128034105
Plumbing Services
S.I.C.: 1711
N.A.I.C.S.: 238220

Newport Construction (Pty) Limited **(1)**
448 Oldsmobile St
Port Elizabeth, Eastern Cape, 6001, South Africa
Tel.: (27) 414611488
Fax: (27) 414611355
E-Mail: info@newportconstruction.co.za
Emp.: 20
Commercial Building Construction Services
S.I.C.: 1542
N.A.I.C.S.: 236220
Paul Walker *(Mng Dir)*

P. Gerolemou Construction (Pty) Limited **(1)**
1-256 Vonkprop Samcor Park Silverton Sydafrika
Pretoria, Gauteng, 0117, South Africa

Tel.: (27) 128034100
Fax: (27) 128034105
E-Mail: admin@mpconstruction.co.za
Commercial Building Construction Services
S.I.C.: 1542
N.A.I.C.S.: 236220
Panayiotis Andreou Gerolemou *(Mng Dir)*

Portal Partnership Incorporated (1)
24 Third Ave
Parktown N, Sandton, Gauteng, 2193, South Africa
Tel.: (27) 114471307
Fax: (27) 114471308
E-Mail: global@ppinc.co.za
Building Architectural Design Services
S.I.C.: 8712
N.A.I.C.S.: 541310
Matthew Nayler *(Mgr)*

Roadcrete Africa (Pty) Limited (1)
7 Romeo st hugen ext
Boksburg, Gauteng, 1459, South Africa
Tel.: (27) 113234100
Fax: (27) 113234141
E-Mail: enquiries@roadcrete.co.za
Web Site: www.roadcrete.co.za
Civil Engineering Services
S.I.C.: 8711
N.A.I.C.S.: 541330
Bahle Sibisi *(Chm)*
Greg Badenhorst *(Mng Dir)*

Spray Pave (Pty) Limited (1)
7 Evans St Alrode
PO Box 674
S Alberton, Alberton, Gauteng, 1450, South Africa
Tel.: (27) 118685451
Fax: (27) 117001470
E-Mail: alana@spraypave.co.za
Web Site: www.spraypave.co.za
Emp.: 70
Bituminous Products Spraying & Supplier
S.I.C.: 1221
N.A.I.C.S.: 212111
Antonie Fourie *(Chm)*
Steven Single *(Mng Dir)*

TRG Trading (Pty) Limited (1)
Postnet Ste 281
Private Bag X 5091
Brits, Brits, 0250, South Africa
Tel.: (27) 12 254 0999
Stone Quarrying Services
S.I.C.: 1411
N.A.I.C.S.: 212311

BASILEA PHARMACEUTICA LTD.

Grenzacherstrasse 487
4005 Basel, Switzerland
Tel.: (41) 616061111
Fax: (41) 616061112
E-Mail: info_basilea@basilea.com
Web Site: www.basileapharma.com
BSLN—(SWX)
Rev.: $62,962,944
Assets: $405,117,045
Liabilities: $291,246,659
Net Worth: $113,870,386
Earnings: ($57,239,691)
Emp.: 200
Fiscal Year-end: 12/31/12

Business Description:
Biopharmaceutical Products Mfr
S.I.C.: 2834
N.A.I.C.S.: 325412

Personnel:
Martin Nicklasson *(Chm)*
Domenico Scala *(Vice Chm)*
Ronald Scott *(CEO)*
Donato Spota *(CFO)*
Ingrid Heinze-Krauss *(CTO)*
Achim Kaufhold *(Chief Medical Officer)*
Laurenz Kellenberger *(Chief Scientific Officer)*

Board of Directors:
Martin Nicklasson
Hans-Beat Gurtler
Daniel Lew
Thomas M. Rinderknecht
Domenico Scala
Steven D. Skolsky
Thomas Werner

Subsidiary:

Basilea Pharmaceutica International Ltd. (1)
Grenzacherstrasse 487
4005 Basel, Switzerland
Tel.: (41) 616061111
Fax: (41) 616061112
E-Mail: info@basilea.com
Web Site: www.basilea.com
Emp.: 120
Drugs Mfr
S.I.C.: 2834
N.A.I.C.S.: 325412
Ronald Scott *(CEO)*

Non-U.S. Subsidiaries:

Basilea Pharma S.A.S. (1)
121 rue d Aguesseau
92100 Boulogne-Billancourt, France
Tel.: (33) 141031515
Fax: (33) 1 41 03 15 14
E-Mail: Office.fr@basilea.com
Web Site: www.basilea.com
Pharmaceutical Products Sales
S.I.C.: 5122
N.A.I.C.S.: 424210

Basilea Pharmaceutica China Ltd (1)
No 638 Xiushan Rd E
Haimen, Nantong, Jiangsu, 226100, China
Tel.: (86) 51382198008
Fax: (86) 51382198009
E-Mail: hr@basilea.com.cn
Web Site: www.basilea.com.cn
Emp.: 100
Pharmaceutical Products Research & Development Services
S.I.C.: 8731
N.A.I.C.S.: 541711

Basilea Pharmaceutica Deutschland GmbH (1)
Kistlerhofstr 75
81379 Munich, Germany
Tel.: (49) 8978576740
Fax: (49) 897857674100
E-Mail: Office.de@basilea.com
Web Site: www.basilea.com
Emp.: 38
Pharmaceutical Products Sales
S.I.C.: 5122
N.A.I.C.S.: 424210
Thomas Trilling *(Mng Dir)*

Basilea Pharmaceutica S.R.L. (1)
Piazza Meda 3
20121 Milan, Italy
Tel.: (39) 0258215592
Fax: (39) 0258215400
E-Mail: mario.levrero@basilea.com
Web Site: www.basilea.com
Emp.: 1
Pharmaceutical Products Sales
S.I.C.: 5122
N.A.I.C.S.: 424210
Mario Levrero *(Gen Mgr)*

Basilea Pharmaceuticals A/S (1)
Blokken 15 St Tv
3460 Birkerod, Denmark
Tel.: (45) 45704704
Fax: (45) 45704705
E-Mail: office.dk@basilea.com
Web Site: www.basilea.com
Pharmaceutical Products Sales
S.I.C.: 5122
N.A.I.C.S.: 424210

Basilea Pharmaceuticals Iberia S.L. (1)
Calle Lopez de Aranda 35
28027 Madrid, Spain
Tel.: (34) 913208070
Fax: (34) 913202535
E-Mail: office.es@basilea.com
Web Site: www.basilea.com
Emp.: 5
Pharmaceutical Products Sales
S.I.C.: 5122
N.A.I.C.S.: 424210
Rls Halbach *(Gen Mgr)*

Basilea Pharmaceuticals Ltd. (1)
c/o Langwood House 63-81 High St
Rickmansworth, Hertfordshire, WD3 1EQ, United Kingdom
Tel.: (44) 203 281 7645
E-Mail: office.uk@basilea.com
Web Site: www.basilea.com
Emp.: 8
Pharmaceutical Products Sales
S.I.C.: 5122
N.A.I.C.S.: 424210

BASIN CONTRACTING LIMITED

100 Bedrock Lane
Elmsdale, NS, B2S 2B1, Canada
Tel.: (902) 883-2235
Fax: (902) 883-8881
E-Mail: info@basin-gallant.com
Web Site: www.basin-gallant.com
Year Founded: 1985
Rev.: $16,017,090
Emp.: 100

Business Description:
Paving Contract Services
S.I.C.: 2951
N.A.I.C.S.: 324121

Personnel:
Fred Benere *(Pres)*

BASLER AG

An der Strusbek 60-62
22926 Ahrensburg, Germany
Tel.: (49) 41024630
Fax: (49) 4102463109
E-Mail: info@baslerweb.com
Web Site: www.baslerweb.com
Year Founded: 1988
BSL—(DEU)
Rev.: $75,193,018
Assets: $78,719,983
Liabilities: $38,893,544
Net Worth: $39,826,439
Earnings: $5,500,451
Emp.: 290
Fiscal Year-end: 12/31/12

Business Description:
Digital Cameras, Optical Components & Inspection Systems Mfr
S.I.C.: 3827
N.A.I.C.S.: 333314

Personnel:
Norbert Basler *(Chm-Supervisory Bd)*
Eckart Kottkamp *(Deputy Chm-Supervisory Bd)*
Arndt Bake *(COO & Member-Mgmt Bd)*
John P. Jennings *(Chief Comml Officer & Member-Mgmt Bd)*
Dietmar Ley *(CEO-Bus Units, Product Dev, Fin & HR & Member-Mgmt Bd)*

Supervisory Board of Directors:
Norbert Basler
Konrad Ellegast
Eckart Kottkamp

U.S. Subsidiary:

Basler, Inc. (1)
855 Springdale Dr Ste 203
Exton, PA 19341
Tel.: (610) 280-0171
Fax: (610) 280-7608
E-Mail: info@baslerweb.com
Web Site: www.baslerweb.com
Emp.: 16
Electrical Apparatus & Equipment, Wiring Supplies, & Related Equipment Merchant Whslr
S.I.C.: 5063
N.A.I.C.S.: 423610
John Jennings *(COO)*

Non-U.S. Subsidiaries:

Basler Asia Pte Ltd. (1)
8 Boon Lay Way 03-03 Tradehub 21
Singapore, 609964, Singapore
Tel.: (65) 6425 0472
Fax: (65) 6425 0473
E-Mail: bc.sales.asia@baslerweb.com
Emp.: 7
Industrial Application Digital Camera Distr
S.I.C.: 5045
N.A.I.C.S.: 423430

Basler Vision Technologies Taiwan Inc. (1)
No 21 Sianjheng 8th St
Jhubei, Hsinchu, 30268, Taiwan
Tel.: (886) 35583955
Fax: (886) 35583956
Web Site: www.baslerweb.com
Digital Camera Mfr
S.I.C.: 3579
N.A.I.C.S.: 333316

BASLER KANTONALBANK AG

Aeschenvorstadt 41
4002 Basel, Switzerland
Tel.: (41) 612663333
Fax: (41) 612662596
E-Mail: bkb@bkb.ch
Web Site: www.bkb.ch
BSKP—(SWX)
Sales Range: $600-649.9 Million
Emp.: 1,347

Business Description:
Banking Services
S.I.C.: 6029
N.A.I.C.S.: 522110

Personnel:
Andreas C. Albrecht *(Chm-Supervisory Bd)*
Hans Jakob Bernoulli *(Vice Chm-Supervisory Bd)*
Guy Lachappelle *(CEO)*
Dominik Galliker *(Deputy CEO)*
Michael Buess *(Head-General Secretariat & Media & IR)*

Supervisory Board of Directors:
Andreas C. Albrecht
Hans Jakob Bernoulli
Sebastian Frehner
Jan Goepfert
Helmut Hersberger
Christine Keller
Markus Lehmann
Ralph Lewin
Bruno Mazotti
Felix Meier
Markus Ritter
Andreas Sturm
Richard Widmer

BASLINI S.P.A.

Piazza Baslini 1
24047 Treviglio, Bergamo, Italy
Tel.: (39) 03633191
Telex: 310534
Fax: (39) 036348866
E-Mail: info@baslini.it
Web Site: www.baslini.it
Year Founded: 1925
Emp.: 150

Business Description:
Agricultural & Industrial Accessory Materials Producer
S.I.C.: 2899
N.A.I.C.S.: 325998

Personnel:
Antonio Baslini *(Pres)*

Subsidiary:

Baslini Metalli S.p.A. (1)
Via Lodi 29
24047 Treviglio, BG, Italy
Tel.: (39) 03633101
Fax: (39) 0363303926
E-Mail: info@baslini.it
Web Site: www.baslini.it/eng/default.asp?ca p=4
Emp.: 10
Metal Producer
S.I.C.: 3499
N.A.I.C.S.: 332999
Antonia Baslini *(Pres)*

BASS METALS LIMITED
Suite 7 186 Hay Street
Subiaco, WA, 6005, Australia
Mailing Address:
PO Box 8107
Subiaco, WA, 6008, Australia
Tel.: (61) 863151300
Fax: (61) 894812846
E-Mail: admin@bassmetals.com.au
Web Site: www.bassmetals.com.au
BSM—(ASX)
Rev.: $1,639,662
Assets: $7,010,929
Liabilities: $1,085,710
Net Worth: $5,925,219
Earnings: ($12,679,285)
Emp.: 30
Fiscal Year-end: 06/30/13
Business Description:
Mineral Exploration
S.I.C.: 1481
N.A.I.C.S.: 213115
Personnel:
Mark Sykes *(Interim COO & Dir-Technical)*
Pierre Malherbe *(Sec)*
Board of Directors:
Rick Anthon
Tony Treasure
Legal Counsel:
Page Seager Lawyers
162 Macquaire Street
Hobart, TAS, 7000, Australia
Ashurst
Level 32 Exchange Plaza 1 The Esplanade
Perth, WA, 6000, Australia
Allion Legal
50 Kings Park Road
West Perth, Australia

BASS STRAIT OIL COMPANY
Level 1 99 William Street
Melbourne, VIC, 3000, Australia
Tel.: (61) 399273000
Fax: (61) 396146533
E-Mail: admin@bassoil.com.au
Web Site: www.bassoil.com.au
BAS—(ASX)
Rev.: $187,499
Assets: $7,918,879
Liabilities: $138,861
Net Worth: $7,780,018
Earnings: ($3,794,463)
Fiscal Year-end: 06/30/13
Business Description:
Oil & Gas Exploration
S.I.C.: 1311
N.A.I.C.S.: 211111
Personnel:
Steven Robert Noske *(CEO)*
Andrew P. Whittle *(Mng Dir)*
Robyn M. Hamilton *(Sec)*
Board of Directors:
John Lachlan Charles McInnes
David J. Lindh
Andrew P. Whittle

BASSARI RESOURCES LIMITED
Level 17 500 Collins Street
Melbourne, VIC, 3000, Australia
Tel.: (61) 396140600
Fax: (61) 396140550
E-Mail: admin@bassari.com.au
Web Site: www.bassari.com.au
BSR—(ASX)
Rev.: $146,936
Assets: $38,248,196
Liabilities: $1,332,846
Net Worth: $36,915,350
Earnings: ($2,159,231)
Fiscal Year-end: 12/31/12
Business Description:
Gold & Other Metal Mining & Exploration Services
S.I.C.: 1041
N.A.I.C.S.: 212221
Personnel:
Alex MacKenzie *(Chm)*
Jozsef Patarica *(CEO & Mng Dir)*
Ian D. Riley *(CFO & Sec)*
Board of Directors:
Alex MacKenzie
Philip Bruce
Jozsef Patarica
Chris H. Young
Legal Counsel:
Quinert Rodda Associates
Level 19 500 Collins Street
Melbourne, Australia

BASSETT & WALKER INTERNATIONAL, INC.
2 Berkeley Street Suite 303
Toronto, ON, M5A 4J5, Canada
Tel.: (416) 363-7070
Fax: (416) 352-1480
E-Mail: logistics@bassettwalkerinc.com
Web Site: www.bassettwalkerinc.com
Year Founded: 1992
Rev.: $36,187,609
Emp.: 21
Business Description:
Agricultural Commodities Provider
S.I.C.: 9641
N.A.I.C.S.: 926140

BASSI CONSTRUCTION LTD.
2575 Delzotto Avenue Unit A
Gloucester, ON, K1T 3V6, Canada
Tel.: (613) 822-6767
Fax: (613) 822-6777
E-Mail: office@bassi.ca
Web Site: www.bassi.ca
Year Founded: 1963
Rev.: $17,053,290
Emp.: 100
Business Description:
Construction & Remodeling Services
S.I.C.: 1522
N.A.I.C.S.: 236118
Personnel:
Mario Bassi *(Owner)*
John Bassi *(Pres)*

BASSILICHI S.P.A.
Via delle Nazioni Unite 30/32
Monteriggioni, 53035 Siena, Italy
Tel.: (39) 0577 578121
Fax: (39) 0577 578158
E-Mail: mktg@bassilichi.it
Web Site: www.bassilichi.it
Year Founded: 1957
Sales Range: $350-399.9 Million
Emp.: 1,107
Business Description:
Business Process Outsourcing Services
S.I.C.: 7389
N.A.I.C.S.: 561499
Personnel:
Marco Bassilichi *(Chm)*
Leonardo Bassilichi *(CEO)*
Attilio Serrone *(Mng Dir)*

BASSO INDUSTRY CORPORATION
No 24 36th Rd Taichung Industrial Park
Taichung, Taiwan
Tel.: (886) 423500628
Fax: (886) 423598880
Web Site: www.basso.com.tw
1527—(TAI)
Sales Range: $25-49.9 Million
Business Description:
Pneumatic Fastening Tools Mfr
S.I.C.: 3823
N.A.I.C.S.: 334513
Personnel:
Wilson Lai *(Chm)*
Plant:
Basso Industry Corporation - Plastic Injection Plant (1)
24 36th Road Taichung Industrial Road
Taichung, 40768, Taiwan
Tel.: (886) 423598877
Fax: (886) 423598860
E-Mail: sales@basso.com.tw
Emp.: 700
Injection Molded Plastic Products Mfr
S.I.C.: 3082
N.A.I.C.S.: 326121
Hsing Lai Ming *(Gen Mgr)*

BASTA FRANCE
Lieu Dit Beaulieu
58500 Clamecy, Nievre, France
Tel.: (33) 386270701
Fax: (33) 386272865
Web Site: www.bastagroup.com
Sls.: $17,300,000
Emp.: 109
Business Description:
Cycle Lighting & Immovable Locks Supplier
S.I.C.: 3714
N.A.I.C.S.: 336320
Personnel:
Allen Mrozinski *(Dir-Pur)*

BASTA HOLDINGS, CORP.
Room 2105 Sino Life Tower No 707 Zhang Yang Rd
Pudong, Shanghai, 200120, China
Tel.: (86) 18721459159
E-Mail: basta.hold.corp@gmail.com
Year Founded: 2011
BSTA—(OTCB)
Assets: $7,429
Liabilities: $14,383
Net Worth: ($6,954)
Earnings: ($31,571)
Emp.: 1
Fiscal Year-end: 10/31/13
Business Description:
Copper Pipes & Fittings Distr
S.I.C.: 5051
N.A.I.C.S.: 423510
Personnel:
Jacob Gitman *(Pres, CEO & Sec)*
Adam C. Wasserman *(CFO)*
Board of Directors:
Jacob Gitman
Adam C. Wasserman
Shufen Xue

BASTE
Route De La Schlucht
68140 Colmar, France
Tel.: (33) 389778827
Sls.: $23,600,000
Emp.: 21
Business Description:
Groceries & Related Products
S.I.C.: 5149
N.A.I.C.S.: 424490
Personnel:
Didier Chervin *(Chm)*

BASTEI LUBBE AG
Schanzenstrasse 6-20
51063 Cologne, Germany
Tel.: (49) 221 8200 0
Fax: (49) 221 8200 18 50
E-Mail: webmaster@luebbe.de
Web Site: www.luebbe.de
Year Founded: 1953
BST—(DEU)
Sls.: $132,328,511
Earnings: $10,634,743
Emp.: 242
Fiscal Year-end: 03/31/13
Business Description:
Trade Magazines Publisher
S.I.C.: 2721
N.A.I.C.S.: 511120
Personnel:
Friedrich Wehrle *(Chm-Supervisory Bd)*
Thomas Schierack *(Chm-Exec Bd)*
Klaus Kluge *(Member-Exec Bd)*
Felix Rudloff *(Member-Exec Bd)*
Supervisory Board of Directors:
Friedrich Wehrle
Gordian Hasselblatt
Michael Nelles

BASTIDE DIFFUSION
Route De Bagnols
30340 Ales, France
Tel.: (33) 466562727
Fax: (33) 0466302746
E-Mail: bastide@bastide.fr
Web Site: www.bastide.fr
Sls.: $20,100,000
Emp.: 83
Business Description:
Homefurnishings
S.I.C.: 5023
N.A.I.C.S.: 423220
Personnel:
Dominique Bastide *(Chm)*
Board of Directors:
Dominique Bastide
Olivier Fraquet

BASTIDE MANUTENTION
Centre De Gros 37 Avenue De Larrieu
31100 Toulouse, Haute Garonne, France
Tel.: (33) 561315959
Fax: (33) 561400010
E-Mail: contact@bastide-manut.fr
Sls.: $21,800,000
Emp.: 68
Business Description:
Industrial Machinery & Equipment
S.I.C.: 5084
N.A.I.C.S.: 423830
Personnel:
Lalau Gregory *(Pres)*

BASTION RESOURCES LTD.
810 675 W Hastings Street
Vancouver, BC, V6B 1N2, Canada
Tel.: (604) 802-7372
Fax: (604) 684-2349
Web Site: www.bastionresources.com
Year Founded: 2009
BSN—(CNSX)
Business Description:
Gold Mining Services
S.I.C.: 1041
N.A.I.C.S.: 212221
Personnel:
Peter Hughes *(CEO)*
Board of Directors:
Michael A. Evans
Peter Hughes
Richard Lee
Kurt Loewen
Derrick Strickland
Transfer Agent:
Computershare Trust Company of Canada
510 Burrard St 3rd Fl
Vancouver, BC, V6C 3B9, Canada

BASTOGI S.P.A.
Via GB Piranesi 10
20137 Milan, Italy
Tel.: (39) 02739831
Fax: (39) 0273983298

E-Mail: info@bastogi.com
Web Site: www.bastogi.com
Year Founded: 1862
BTGI—(ITA)
Sales Range: $25-49.9 Million
Emp.: 22

Business Description:
Holding Company; Art Education Services
S.I.C.: 6719
N.A.I.C.S.: 551112

Personnel:
Marco Cabassi *(Chm)*
Andrea Raschi *(CEO)*

Board of Directors:
Marco Cabassi
Francesco Cataluccio
Giulio Ferrari
Barbara Masella
Andrea Raschi
Maria Teresa Salerno

Subsidiaries:

Brioschi Finanziaria S.p.A. **(1)**
Via Tamburini 13
20123 Milan, Italy
Tel.: (39) 2 4856161
Web Site: www.brioschi.it/home.php?lingua=2
Real Estate Developer
S.I.C.: 6531
N.A.I.C.S.: 531210

Frigoriferi Milanesi S.p.A. **(1)**
Via G.B. Piranesi 10
Milan, Italy
Tel.: (39) 273983232
Web Site: www.frigoriferimilanesi.it/main.html
Warehouse & Cold Storage Facility
S.I.C.: 4222
N.A.I.C.S.: 493120

BASTY PERE ET FILS

1400 Avenue D Antibes
45200 Amilly, Loiret, France
Tel.: (33) 238951515
Fax: (33) 0238951502
Sls.: $35,800,000
Emp.: 86
S.I.C.: 5511
N.A.I.C.S.: 441110

Personnel:
Jacques Basty *(Pres)*

BASWARE CORPORATION

Linnoitustie 2 Building Cello
PO Box 97
FIN 02601 Espoo, Finland
Tel.: (358) 9 879 171
Fax: (358) 209 3410 244
Web Site: www.basware.com
Year Founded: 1985
BWV—(OMX)
Sls.: $145,960,485
Assets: $129,503,226
Liabilities: $34,532,778
Net Worth: $94,970,448
Earnings: $14,626,630
Emp.: 913

Business Description:
Software Publisher
S.I.C.: 7372
N.A.I.C.S.: 511210

Personnel:
Hannu Vaajoensuu *(Chm)*
Esa Tihila *(CEO)*
Mika Harjuaho *(CFO)*
Matti Copeland *(Sr VP-M&A & IR)*
Olli Hyppanen *(Sr VP-Strategy & Dev)*
Jorma Kemppainen *(Sr VP-Products)*
Pekka Lindfors *(Sr VP)*
Steve Muddiman *(Sr VP-Mktg)*
Matti Rusi *(Sr VP-Europe)*
Jukka Virkkunen *(Sr VP-Scandinavia)*

Board of Directors:
Hannu Vaajoensuu
Pentti Heikkinen
Sakari Perttunen
Eeva Sipila
Ilkka Toivola

U.S. Subsidiary:

Basware, Inc. **(1)**
60 Long Ridge Rd
Stamford, CT 06902
Tel.: (203) 487-7900
Fax: (203) 487-7950
E-Mail: Info.usa@basware.com
Emp.: 50
Software Development Services
S.I.C.: 7371
N.A.I.C.S.: 541511
Robert Cohen, *(VP)*

Non-U.S. Subsidiaries:

Basware A/S **(1)**
Generatorvej 8D 2 sal
2730 Herlev, Denmark DK
Tel.: (45) 70 22 99 55
E-Mail: Info.dk@basware.com
Web Site: www.basware.dk
Software Development Services
S.I.C.: 7371
N A I.C.S.: 541511
Jukka Virkkunen, *(Sr VP-Scandinavia)*

Basware AB **(1)**
Gustavslundsvagen 141 A
16751 Bromma, Sweden
Tel.: (46) 8 50 57 44 00
Fax: (46) 8 50 57 44 99
E-Mail: info.se@basware.com
Web Site: www.basware.se
Emp.: 35
Software Development Services
S.I.C.: 7371
N.A.I.C.S.: 541511
Jukka Virkkunen, *(Sr VP)*

Basware AS **(1)**
Drammensveien 288
PO Box 241
Lilleaker, 0216 Oslo, Norway
Tel.: (47) 23 37 03 00
Fax: (47) 23 37 03 01
Web Site: www.basware.no
Financial Software Development Services
S.I.C.: 7371
N.A.I.C.S.: 541511
Bjorn Rosten, *(Country Mgr)*

Basware Belgium NV **(1)**
Clinton Park Ninovesteenweg 196
Erembodegem, 9320 Aalst, Belgium
Tel.: (32) 53 60 11 11
Fax: (32) 53 60 11 01
E-Mail: info.benelux@basware.com
Software Development Services
S.I.C.: 7371
N.A.I.C.S.: 541511

Basware B.V. **(1)**
Joop Geesinkweg 701
Amsterdam, 1096 AZ, Netherlands
Tel.: (31) 20 850 8020
Fax: (31) 20 850 8085
Web Site: www.basware.nl
Software Development Services
S.I.C.: 7371
N.A.I.C.S.: 541511
Jorgen Hensgens, *(VP-Sls)*

Basware Corporation **(1)**
Ocean Financial Centre Level 40 10 Collyer Quay, Singapore, 049315, Singapore
Tel.: (65) 6808 6494
Fax: (65) 6334 5981
Software Development Services
S.I.C.: 7371
N.A.I.C.S.: 541511

Basware GmbH **(1)**
Rossstr 96
40476 Dusseldorf, Germany
Tel.: (49) 211 41 55 95 50
Fax: (49) 211 41 55 95 79
E-Mail: info@basware.com
Emp.: 70
Software Development Services
S.I.C.: 7371
N.A.I.C.S.: 541511
Frank Wuschech *(Mng Dir)*

Basware India Private Limited **(1)**
DLF IT Park Tower F Third Floor
Chandigarh, 160 001, India
Tel.: (91) 172 3012 020
Fax: (91) 172 3012 019
E-Mail: hrindia@Basware.com
Software Development Services
S.I.C.: 7371
N.A.I.C.S.: 541511

Basware Pty Ltd **(1)**
Level 15 67 Albert Ave
PO Box 148
Chatswood, NSW, 2067, Australia
Tel.: (61) 2 8622 5850
Fax: (61) 2 8622 5899
E-Mail: info.au@basware.com
Software Development Services
S.I.C.: 7371
N.A.I.C.S.: 541511
Jari Paananen *(Dir-Consulting)*

Basware Russia **(1)**
Helsinki House 4 Rostovsky per 1/2
Moscow, 119121, Russia
Tel.: (7) 499 248 16 73
Fax: (7) 499 248 06 58
Web Site: www.basware.ru
Software Development Services
S.I.C.: 7371
N.A.I.C.S.: 541511

Basware SAS **(1)**
7 rue du General Foy
Paris, 75008, France
Tel.: (33) 1 40 08 18 20
Fax: (33) 1 40 08 18 30
Web Site: www.basware.fr
Software Development Services
S.I.C.: 7371
N.A.I.C.S.: 541511
Matthieu Reynier, *(VP-Sls)*

Basware UK Ltd. **(1)**
1-3 Berkeley Court Borough Road
Newcastle, Staffordshire, ST5 1TT, United Kingdom
Tel.: (44) 845 6711953
Software Development Services
S.I.C.: 7371
N.A.I.C.S.: 541511
Andrew Jesse, *(VP-Sls)*

BASWELL RESOURCES BERHAD

Wisma Baswood Lot 6516 Batu 5-3/4 Jalan Kapar
42100 Kelang, Selangor Darul Ehsan, Malaysia
Tel.: (60) 332912001
Fax: (60) 332912070
E-Mail: finance@baswell.com.my
BASWELL—(KLS)
Sales Range: $1-9.9 Million
Emp.: 62

Business Description:
Wooden Furniture Mfr
S.I.C.: 2511
N.A.I.C.S.: 337122

Personnel:
Chee Chuen Lai *(CEO & Mng Dir)*
Siew Chuan Chua *(Co-Sec)*
Elaine Wei Syn Wong *(Co-Sec)*

Board of Directors:
Hashim Ab Rahman
Yong Kai Chong
Yew Kheng Khoo
Yew Nean Khoo
Chee Chuen Lai
Boon Chiang Lim
Kam Hoong Wong

Subsidiary:

Deswell Packaging (M) Sdn. Bhd. **(1)**
Lot 1261 Batu 14
Jalan Kapar, 42200 Kapar, Selangor, Malaysia
Tel.: (60) 332500126
Fax: (60) 332500135
E-Mail: deswell1991@gmail.com
Web Site: www.deswell.com.my
Paper & Printing Equipment Mfr
S.I.C.: 3555
N.A.I.C.S.: 333244
Khoo Yew Nean *(Mng Dir)*

BAT SA BASCOV

str Paisesti DN nr 5
Bascov, Arges, Romania
Tel.: (40) 248270872
Fax: (40) 248270545
E-Mail: bat.bascov@rdspt.ro
Web Site: www.batbascov.ro
Year Founded: 1958
BATV—(BUC)
Rev.: $14,160,892
Assets: $15,119,714
Liabilities: $4,143,130
Net Worth: $10,976,584
Earnings: $516,421
Emp.: 152
Fiscal Year-end: 12/31/12

Business Description:
Repairing Services
S.I.C.: 7549
N.A.I.C.S.: 811198

Personnel:
Adrian Pantea *(Gen Mgr)*

BAT S.P.A.

Via Henry Ford ZI EST
Noventa di Piave, 30020 Venice, Italy
Tel.: (39) 42165672
Fax: (39) 0421659007
E-Mail: info@batgroup.com
Web Site: www.batgroup.com
Year Founded: 1983
Sales Range: $25-49.9 Million
Emp.: 113

Business Description:
Canopies & Sun Awnings Systems & Components Designer, Mfr & Marketer
Import Export
S.I.C.: 3999
N.A.I.C.S.: 339999

Personnel:
Amorino Barbieri *(Founder & Pres)*
Simone Mazzon *(CEO)*

Subsidiary:

KE Protezioni Solari srl **(1)**
Via Calnova 160/a
Noventa di Piave, 30020 Venice, Italy
Tel.: (39) 0421307000
Fax: (39) 0421658840
E-Mail: info@keitaly.it
Web Site: www.keitaly.it
Canopies & Sun Awnings Systems & Components Designer, Mfr & Marketer
S.I.C.: 3999
N.A.I.C.S.: 339999
Amorino Barbieri *(Pres)*

U.S. Subsidiary:

Durasol Awnings, Inc. **(1)**
445 Delldale Rd
Chester, NY 10918-2049 NY
Tel.: (845) 692-1100
Fax: (845) 610-1101
Toll Free: (888) 387-2765
Web Site: www.durasol.com
Emp.: 225
Retractable Canvas Awnings Mfr
S.I.C.: 2393
N.A.I.C.S.: 314910
Vince Best *(Pres)*

Non-U.S. Subsidiaries:

BAT Iberica, S.L. **(1)**
Travesia Cuenca-3 num 2 Pol Ind Camporrosso Apartado de Correos n 22
Chinchilla de Monte-Aragon, 2520 Albacete, Spain
Tel.: (34) 967261779
Fax: (34) 967261584
E-Mail: bat.iberica@batgroup.com
Web Site: www.batgroup.com
Canopies & Sun Awnings Systems & Components Designer, Mfr & Marketer
S.I.C.: 3999

BAT S.p.A.—(Continued)

N.A.I.C.S.: 339999

Floris Obdam B.V. (1)
Poel 5
1713 GL Koggenland, North Holland, Netherlands
Tel.: (31) 226331393
Fax: (31) 226451272
E-Mail: info@floriszonwering.nl
Web Site: www.floriszonwering.nl
Canopies & Sun Awnings Systems & Components Designer, Mfr & Marketer
S.I.C.: 3999
N.A.I.C.S.: 339999
Robert V. Raaff *(CEO)*

BATA INDIA LIMITED

Bata House 418/02 M G Road Sector - 17
Gurgaon, 122 002, India
Tel.: (91) 1244120100
Fax: (91) 1244120116
Web Site: www.bata.in
Year Founded: 1931
BATAINDIA—(NSE)
Rev.: $347,163,354
Assets: $209,414,491
Liabilities: $79,812,104
Net Worth: $129,602,387
Earnings: $31,904,374
Emp.: 5,162
Fiscal Year-end: 12/31/12
Business Description:
Footwear & Accessories Mfr & Distr
S.I.C.: 2389
N.A.I.C.S.: 316210
Personnel:
Uday Khanna *(Chm)*
R. Gopalakrishnan *(Mng Dir)*
Maloy Kumar Gupta *(Compliance Officer & Sec)*
Board of Directors:
Uday Khanna
J. Carbajal
A. Chudasama
Jack G. N. Clemons
R. Gopalakrishnan
R. Mathur
A. Singh
Transfer Agent:
R&D Infotech Private Limited
1st Floor 7A Beltala Road
Kolkata, India

BATA SHOE COMPANY (BANGLADESH) LIMITED

Tongi Industrial Area Tongi
Gazipur, Dhaka, Bangladesh
Tel.: (880) 2 9800501
Fax: (880) 2 9800511
E-Mail: marketing@batabd.com
Web Site: www.batabd.com
Year Founded: 1894
BATASHOE—(DHA)
Sales Range: $50-74.9 Million
Business Description:
Leather Products Mfr
S.I.C.: 3199
N.A.I.C.S.: 316998
Personnel:
Muhammad Qayyum *(Mng Dir)*
Yee Siew Ng *(CFO)*

BATAILLE MATERIAUX

A 71 69 Rue Jules Ferry
27500 Pont Audemer, Eure, France
Tel.: (33) 232415205
Fax: (33) 232571229
Sls.: $24,300,000
Emp.: 91
Business Description:
Plumbing Fixtures, Equipment & Supplies
S.I.C.: 5074
N.A.I.C.S.: 423720
Personnel:
Philippe Bataille *(Pres)*

BATALPHA BOBACH GMBH

Raiffeisenstrasse 17 18 Langenfeld
40764 Langenfeld, Germany
Tel.: (49) 217385350
Fax: (49) 21738535113
E-Mail: info@batalpha.de
Web Site: www.batalpha.de
Emp.: 350
Business Description:
Musical, Theatre & Opera Stage Automation
S.I.C.: 3931
N.A.I.C.S.: 339992
Personnel:
Max Gunter Bobach *(CEO & Gen Mgr)*

BATEMAN LITWIN N.V.

Haaksbergweg 59
1101 BR Amsterdam, Netherlands
Tel.: (31) 205640491
Fax: (31) 205640490
E-Mail: info@bateman-litwin.com
Web Site: www.bateman-litwin.com
Sales Range: $800-899.9 Million
Emp.: 50
Business Description:
Construction Services
S.I.C.: 1623
N.A.I.C.S.: 237120
Personnel:
Eyal Hahn *(Chm & CEO)*
Moti Navon *(CFO & Gen Mgr-Admin)*
Irad Rekem *(Chief Legal Officer)*
Board of Directors:
Eyal Hahn
Gustaf Bodin
Arthur Shore

BATENBURG BEHEER N.V.

Stolwijkstraat 33
3079 DN Rotterdam, Netherlands
Tel.: (31) 102928080
Fax: (31) 104825141
E-Mail: info@batenburg.nl
Web Site: www.batenburg.nl
BATEN—(EUR)
Sales Range: $200-249.9 Million
Emp.: 947
Business Description:
Technical Installation & Trading Services
S.I.C.: 1799
N.A.I.C.S.: 238190
Personnel:
G. N. G. Wirken *(Chm-Supervisory Bd)*
P. C. van der Linden *(Chm-Exec Bd)*
Supervisory Board of Directors:
G. N. G. Wirken
P. A. Sluiter
M. C .J. van Pernis

BATH BUILDING SOCIETY

15 Queen Square
Bath, BA1 2HN, United Kingdom
Tel.: (44) 1225 423271
Fax: (44) 1225 446914
E-Mail: bsoc@bibs.co.uk
Web Site: www.bathbuildingsociety.co.uk
Sales Range: $1-9.9 Million
Emp.: 50
Business Description:
Mortgage Lending & Other Investment Services
S.I.C.: 6163
N.A.I.C.S.: 522310
Personnel:
Christopher Moorsom *(Chm)*
Terry Fussell *(Vice Chm)*
Dick Jenkins *(CEO)*
Board of Directors:
Christopher Moorsom
Ann Beresford
Terry Fussell
Tony Harris
Chris Nott

BATHURST RESOURCES LIMITED

(Formerly Bathurst Resources (New Zealand) Limited)
Level 12 1 Willeston Street
Wellington, 6011, New Zealand
Tel.: (64) 4 499 6830
Fax: (64) 4 974 5218
E-Mail: wellington@bathurstresources.co.nz
Web Site: www.bathurstresources.co.nz
BRL—(ASX NZE)
Assets: $415,499,355
Liabilities: $247,677,507
Net Worth: $167,821,848
Earnings: ($251,937)
Emp.: 130
Fiscal Year-end: 06/30/13
Business Description:
Mineral Exploration
S.I.C.: 1481
N.A.I.C.S.: 213115
Personnel:
Dave Frow *(Chm)*
Hamish Bohannan *(CEO & Mng Dir)*
Marshall Maine *(CFO & Co-Sec)*
Richard Tacon *(COO)*
Alison Brown *(Gen Counsel)*
Graham Anderson *(Co-Sec)*
Board of Directors:
Dave Frow
Hamish Bohannan
Toko Kapea
Rob Lord
Malcolm Macpherson
Legal Counsel:
Chapman Tripp
25 Albert Streeet
Auckland, 1140, New Zealand

Bell Gully
171 Featherston Street
PO Box 1291
Wellington, New Zealand

Allion Legal
Level 2 50 Kings Park Rd
Perth, Australia

Computershare Investor Services Limited
Level 2 159 Hurstmere Road Takapuna
Private Bag 92119
Auckland, New Zealand
Tel.: (64) 9 488 8700
Fax: (64) 9 488 8787

BATIGERE NORD EST

15 Rue De Paris
69170 Tarare, Rhone, France
Tel.: (33) 382395050
Rev.: $35,500,000
Emp.: 108
S.I.C.: 6514
N.A.I.C.S.: 531110
Personnel:
Claude Gerard *(Chm)*

BATIMENTS ET LOGEMENTS RESIDENTIELS

4 Rue De Chatillon
25480 Besancon, Doubs, France
Tel.: (33) 381882626
Rev.: $16,800,000
Emp.: 19
S.I.C.: 6531
N.A.I.C.S.: 531210
Personnel:
David Baudiquey *(Pres)*

BATISOL DALLAGES

Zone d'Activite Mondaults
29 avenue des Mondaults, 33270 Floirac, France
Tel.: (33) 556402335
Sls.: $20,900,000
Emp.: 41
Business Description:
Plastering, Drywall & Insulation
S.I.C.: 1742
N.A.I.C.S.: 238310
Personnel:
Fernando Francisco Marques *(Pres)*

BATISTYL PRODUCTION

Zi De La Fromentiniere
49360 Maulevrier, Maine Et Loire, France
Tel.: (33) 241494950
Web Site: www.batistyl.fr/formulaire-contact.php
Sls.: $38,600,000
Emp.: 68
S.I.C.: 5074
N.A.I.C.S.: 423720
Personnel:
Eric Legeais *(Pres)*

BATIVAL

Zone Industrielle Les Banardes
25800 Valdahon, Doubs, France
Tel.: (33) 381562711
Sales Range: $10-24.9 Million
Emp.: 108
Business Description:
Construction
S.I.C.: 1521
N.A.I.C.S.: 236115
Personnel:
Claude Pretre *(Pres)*

BATLA MINERALS SA

Immeuble le Solar 1 ZAE le Monestie
3 avenue de l'Occitanie
34760 Boujan-sur-Libron, France
Tel.: (33) 4 42 93 89 19
Fax: (33) 4 67 98 71 59
E-Mail: batlaminerals@arnaudvercruysse.fr
Web Site: www.batlaminerals.com
MLBAT—(EUR)
Sales Range: $1-9.9 Million
Business Description:
Diamond Mining Services
S.I.C.: 1499
N.A.I.C.S.: 212399
Personnel:
Patrick Morin *(Pres)*
Arnaud Vercruysse *(Mng Dir)*

BATLIBOI LTD.

Bharat House 5th Floor 104 Bombay Samachar Marg
Fort, Mumbai, 400 001, India
Tel.: (91) 22 6637 8200
Fax: (91) 22 2267 5601
E-Mail: info@batliboi.com
Web Site: www.batliboi.com
522004—(BOM)
Rev.: $50,241,935
Assets: $40,797,863
Liabilities: $29,495,953
Net Worth: $11,301,910
Earnings: $452,395
Emp.: 510
Fiscal Year-end: 03/31/13
Business Description:
Industrial Machinery Mfr
S.I.C.: 3559
N.A.I.C.S.: 333249
Personnel:
Nirmal Bhogilal *(Chm & Mng Dir)*
Prema Chandrashekhar *(CFO)*
Ashok Joshi *(Chief HR Officer)*

S. H. Joshi *(CEO-Batliboi Environmental Engineering Ltd)*
Milind Kulkarni *(CEO-Machine Tool Bus Grp)*
Pradeep Pradhan *(CEO-Batliboi International Ltd & Batliboi Impex Pvt Ltd)*
Edwyn Rodrigues *(CEO-Textile Machinery Grp)*
Board of Directors:
Nirmal Bhogilal
Subodh Bhargava
Ulrich H. Duden
Ameet Hariani
Vijay R. Kirloskar
E. A. Kshirsagar
George Verghese
Transfer Agent:
Datamatics Financial Services Ltd
Plot No A/16 & 17 MIDC Part-B Cross Lane
Marol Andheri E
Mumbai, India

BATM ADVANCED COMMUNICATIONS LTD.

Neve Ne'eman Ind Area 4 Ha'harash Street
PO Box 7318
45240 Hod Hasharon, Israel
Tel.: (972) 98662525
Fax: (972) 98662500
E-Mail: info@batm.co.il
Web Site: www.batm.com
Year Founded: 1992
BVC—(LSE)
Rev.: $107,774,000
Assets: $152,669,000
Liabilities: $42,428,000
Net Worth: $110,241,000
Earnings: $159,000
Emp.: 735
Fiscal Year-end: 12/31/12
Business Description:
Data Communications Equipment Import Export
S.I.C.: 3669
N.A.I.C.S.: 334290
Personnel:
Zvi Marom *(Founder & CEO)*
Ofer Barner *(CFO)*
Robert Resinger *(COO)*
Steven Curtis *(Sr VP-Sls & Svc-Americas)*
Board of Directors:
Peter Sheldon
Gideon Barak
Ofer Barner
Gideon Chitayat
Zvi Marom
Amos Shani
Legal Counsel:
Lipa Meir & Co.
4 Itamar Ben Avi Street
Tel Aviv, Israel
Fladgate Fielder
25 North Row
London, W1K 6DJ, United Kingdom
U.S. Subsidiaries:

Integral Access Inc. (1)
6 Omni Way
Chelmsford, MA 01824 (100%)
Tel.: (978) 367-7500
Fax: (978) 256-8077
Web Site: www.integralaccess.com
Telephone Apparatus Mfr
S.I.C.: 3661
N.A.I.C.S.: 334210

Metrobility Optical Systems Inc. (1)
25 Manchester St
Merrimack, NH 03054 (100%)
Tel.: (603) 880-1833
Fax: (603) 594-2887
Web Site: www.metrobility.com
Computer Peripheral Equipment Mfr
S.I.C.: 3575
N.A.I.C.S.: 334118
Alex Saunders *(Pres & CEO)*
Steven Curtis *(Sr VP)*

Telco Systems (1)
15 Berkshire Rd
Mansfield, MA 02048 DE
Tel.: (781) 551-0300 (100%)
Fax: (781) 255-2344
Toll Free: (800) 221-2849
E-Mail: sales@telco.com
Web Site: www.telco.com
Emp.: 75
Fiber Optic Transmission Products Mfr
S.I.C.: 3669
N.A.I.C.S.: 334290
Itzik Weinstein *(CEO)*
Bob Resinger *(COO)*
Steve Curtis *(Sr VP-Svcs)*
Francois Tournesac *(Sr VP-Sls & Support-Europe)*

Vigilant Technology Inc. (1)
15 Berkshire Rd
Mansfield, MA 02048
Tel.: (800) 708-0169
Fax: (866) 580-0160
E-Mail: sales@vglnt.com
Web Site: www.vglnt.com
Surveillance Device Mfr
S.I.C.: 3679
N.A.I.C.S.: 334419
Eran Dotan *(CEO)*
Harmesh Bhambra *(Mng Dir)*
Dany Pizen *(Exec VP-Intl Sls)*

Non-U.S. Subsidiaries:

Adaltis Srl (1)
Via Luigi Einaudi 7 Guidonia di Montecelio
00012 Rome, Italy
Tel.: (39) 07745791
Fax: (39) 0774353085
E-Mail: info@adaltis.net
Web Site: www.adaltis.net
Emp.: 60
Diagnostic Instruments Mfr & Distr
S.I.C.: 3845
N.A.I.C.S.: 334510
Daniel Spadaccioli *(Mng Dir)*

A.M.S. 2000 (1)
Ion Tuculescu Nr 37 A Sect 3
Bucharest, Romania
Tel.: (40) 21 324 70 50
Fax: (40) 21 324 76 79
E-Mail: office.ams@ams.ro
Web Site: www.ams.ro
Emp.: 45
Medical Laboratory Equipment Distr
S.I.C.: 5047
N.A.I.C.S.: 423450
Yaacov Hof *(Dir Gen)*

BATM France (1)
6 Avenue Des Bleuets
94380 Bonneuil-sur-Marne, France
Tel.: (33) 156712773
Fax: (33) 143771780
E-Mail: batm@batm.fr
Web Site: www.batm.fr
Emp.: 4
Telecommunication Services
S.I.C.: 4899
N.A.I.C.S.: 517919
Frank Boujnah *(Gen Mgr)*

B.A.T.M. Germany GmbH (1)
Hammerweg 4
52074 Aachen, Germany (100%)
Tel.: (49) 2414635490
Fax: (49) 2414635491
E-Mail: info@batm.de
Web Site: www.batm.de
Computer Peripheral Equipment Mfr
S.I.C.: 3577
N.A.I.C.S.: 334118

Critical Telecom Inc. (1)
Ste 500 340 March Rd
K2K2E4 Ottawa, ON, Canada (100%)
Tel.: (613) 271-1599
Fax: (613) 271-9593
E-Mail: info@criticaltelecom.com
Web Site: www.criticaltelecom.com
Telephone Apparatus Mfr
S.I.C.: 3661
N.A.I.C.S.: 334210
Nancy Macartney *(Pres & CEO)*
Mark Labbe *(CTO)*

Telco Systems Asia Pacific Ltd (1)
350 Orchard Rd
11-08 Shaw House, 238868 Singapore, Singapore (100%)
Tel.: (65) 67259901
Fax: (65) 67259889
E-Mail: support.apac@telco.com
Web Site: www.telco.com
Telephone Apparatus Mfr
S.I.C.: 3661
N.A.I.C.S.: 334210
Orlando Tan *(VP-Sls)*

Subsidiaries:

BATM Advanced Communications Ltd. (1)
Industrial Park
POB 203, Yokneam, 20692, Israel IL
Tel.: (972) 49096444
Web Site: www.batm.com
Emp.: 25
Telecommunications Research & Development
S.I.C.: 4899
N.A.I.C.S.: 517919

CAT Technologies Ltd (1)
Communication Center G G Israel Studio Jerusalem Ltd
Neve Ilan, Jerusalem, 90850, Israel
Tel.: (972) 25704005
Fax: (972) 25704006
E-Mail: info@cat-tc.com
Web Site: www.cat-tc.com
Medical Equipment Mfr
S.I.C.: 3845
N.A.I.C.S.: 334510

NGSoft Ltd (1)
4 Hacharash St Neve Ne'eman Building-B 1st Floor
Hod Hasharon, 45240, Israel
Tel.: (972) 72 2754500
Fax: (972) 3 5781278
E-Mail: marketing@ngsoft.com
Web Site: www.ngsoft.com
Software Development Services
S.I.C.: 7371
N.A.I.C.S.: 541511
Alex Kaplun *(CEO)*
Alon Zieve *(CFO)*
Moshe Kosher *(Sr VP-Bus Dev)*

Vigilant Technologies Ltd (1)
4 Haharsh St
Hod Hasharon, Israel 45240
Tel.: (972) 3 6491110
Fax: (972) 3 648 8849
E-Mail: sales@vglnt.com
Web Site: www.vglnt.com
Surveillance Equipment Mfr
S.I.C.: 3812
N.A.I.C.S.: 334511
Eran Dotan *(CEO)*
Harmesh Bhambra *(Mng Dir)*

BATTIKHA SECURITY INC.

168 Shorting Road
Scarborough, ON, M1S 3S7, Canada
Tel.: (416) 493-3939
Fax: (416) 493-7498
Web Site: www.battikhasecurity.ca
Year Founded: 2000
Rev.: $12,326,862
Emp.: 50
Business Description:
Commercial & Residential Security Systems Supplier
S.I.C.: 7382
N.A.I.C.S.: 561621
Personnel:
Lilian Battikha *(Owner)*

BATTISTELLA ADMINISTRACAO E PARTICIPACOES S.A.

Al Bom Pastor 3700-Sala 06
83015-140 Curitiba, PR, Brazil
Tel.: (55) 41 3250 2464
Fax: (55) 41 3250 2490
E-Mail: battistella@battistella.com.br
Web Site: www.battistella.com.br
Year Founded: 1949
BTTL3—(BRAZ)
Business Description:
Heavy Duty Truck Mfr & Forestry Services
S.I.C.: 3711
N.A.I.C.S.: 336120
Personnel:
Rildo Pinheiro *(Dir-IR)*

BAUBA PLATINUM LIMITED

Hammets Crossing Office Park
Building 816/5 First Floor
2 Selbourne Road Fourways,
Johannesburg, 2055, South Africa
Tel.: (27) 116995720
Fax: (27) 114626184
E-Mail: info@bauba.co.za
Web Site: www.bauba.co.za
Year Founded: 1986
BAU—(JSE)
Rev.: $97,402
Assets: $4,062,194
Liabilities: $90,030
Net Worth: $3,972,164
Earnings: ($1,069,304)
Emp.: 9
Fiscal Year-end: 06/30/13
Business Description:
Platinum Exploration & Mining Services
S.I.C.: 1099
N.A.I.C.S.: 212299
Personnel:
Sydney John Maurice Caddy *(CEO)*
Board of Directors:
Jonathan Best
Sydney John Maurice Caddy
Kenneth Victor Dicks
Sholto Mokgoaje Dolamo
Willem Moolman
Kholeka Winifred Mzondeki
Nakedi Mathews Phosa
Damian Stephen Smith
Legal Counsel:
Eversheds LLP
22 Fredman Drive
2146 Sandton, South Africa
Transfer Agent:
Computershare Investor Services (Pty) Limited
70 Marshall Street
PO Box 61051
2107 Marshalltown, South Africa
Subsidiary:

Diamond Quartzite Processing (Pty) Ltd (1)
Number 3 Anerley Road
Johannesburg, Gauteng, 2193, South Africa
Tel.: (27) 115487240
Mineral Exploration Services
S.I.C.: 1499
N.A.I.C.S.: 212399

BAUCH ENGINEERING GMBH & CO. KG

Lilienthalstrasse 36
85080 Gaimersheim, Germany
Tel.: (49) 845832340
Fax: (49) 8458323410
E-Mail: info@bauch-engineering.de
Web Site: www.bauch-engineering.de
Rev.: $10,690,350
Emp.: 19
Business Description:
Machines & Mechanical Components Consulting & Sales
S.I.C.: 3541
N.A.I.C.S.: 333517
Personnel:
Manfred Bauch *(Gen Mgr-Maschine Projects & Plng-Sls Dept)*

BAUDOUIN INDUSTRIES

Rue De La Sablonniere
14980 Caen, France

Baudouin Industries—(Continued)

Tel.: (33) 232841581
Sales Range: $10-24.9 Million
Emp.: 35

Business Description:
Concrete Products
S.I.C.: 3272
N.A.I.C.S.: 327390

Personnel:
Stephane Bruck *(Personnel Mgr)*

BAUDOUX CONSTRUCTION METALLIQUES

12 Route De Sissonne
02820 Saint-Erme-Outre-et-Ramecourt, Aisne, France
Tel.: (33) 323226377
Web Site: www.baudouxcm.com
Sls.: $13,900,000
Emp.: 63
S.I.C.: 3441
N.A.I.C.S.: 332312

Personnel:
Pascale Raffelet *(Mgr-Pur)*

BAUDRY AUTOMOBILES

85 Boulevard Lavoisier
85000 La Roche-sur-Yon, Vendee, France
Tel.: (33) 251477747
Sls.: $21,400,000
Emp.: 43

Business Description:
New & Used Car Dealers
S.I.C.: 5511
N.A.I.C.S.: 441110

Personnel:
Jean-Luc Sayah *(Pres)*

BAUER AKTIENGESELLSCHAFT

BAUER-Strasse 1
86529 Schrobenhausen, Germany
Tel.: (49) 8252970
Fax: (49) 8252971359
E-Mail: info@bauer.de
Web Site: www.bauer.de
B5A—(DEU)
Rev.: $1,865,605,849
Assets: $2,048,162,655
Liabilities: $1,397,861,582
Net Worth: $650,301,073
Earnings: $34,110,602
Emp.: 10,253
Fiscal Year-end: 12/31/12

Business Description:
Construction Machinery Manufacturer
S.I.C.: 1799
N.A.I.C.S.: 238910

Personnel:
Klaus Reinhardt *(Chm-Supervisory Bd)*
Thomas Bauer *(Chm-Mgmt Bd & CEO)*
Robert Feiger *(Deputy Chm-Supervisory Bd)*
Hartmut Beutler *(CFO & Member-Mgmt Bd)*
Heinz Kaltenecker *(Member-Mgmt Bd & Dir-Labour Rels)*

Supervisory Board of Directors:
Klaus Reinhardt
Regina Andel
Joannes Bauer
Norbert Ewald
Robert Feiger
Reinhard Irrenhauser
Manfred Nussbaumer
Rainer Schuster
Gerold Schwab
Walter Sigl
Elisabeth Teschemacher
Gerardus N. G. Wirken

Subsidiaries:

BAUER Maschinen GmbH. **(1)**
Pfarrer-Bauer-Strasse 1
Neuburg-Schrobenhausen Dist, 86529 Schrobenhausen, Bavaria, Germany
Tel.: (49) 8252971379
Fax: (49) 8252971896
E-Mail: info@bauer.de
Emp.: 5,000
Consturction Machinery Mfr
S.I.C.: 3531
N.A.I.C.S.: 333120
Sebastian Bauer *(Mng Dir-Techl Resource Div)*
Josef Soier *(Mng Dir-Admin Div)*
Dieter H K Stetter *(Mng Dir-Sls)*

Plants:

BAUER Maschinen GmbH - Aresing Plant **(2)**
Sonnenhamerstrasse 55
86561 Aresing, Bavaria, Germany
Tel.: (49) 8252972175
Fax: (49) 8252972810
Web Site: www.bauer.ge
Consturction Machinery Mfr
S.I.C.: 3531
N.A.I.C.S.: 333120
Rene Guyon *(Mng Dir)*

BAUER Maschinen GmbH - Edelshausen Plant **(2)**
Bauer Strasse 1
86529 Schrobenhausen, Bavaria, Germany
Tel.: (49) 8252972222
Fax: (49) 8252972102
E-Mail: info@bauer.de
Web Site: www.paeur.de
Emp.: 200
Consturction Machinery Mfr
S.I.C.: 3531
N.A.I.C.S.: 333120
Thomas Schmitz *(Gen Mgr)*

BAUER Maschinen GmbH - Schrobenhausen Plant **(2)**
Burgermeister-Gotz-Strasse 36
86529 Schrobenhausen, Bavaria, Germany
Tel.: (49) 8252970
Fax: (49) 8252972129
E-Mail: info@bauer.de
Web Site: www.bauer.de
Emp.: 400
Consturction Machinery Mfr
S.I.C.: 3553
N.A.I.C.S.: 333243
Thomas Bauer *(Pres)*

Non-U.S. Subsidiaries:

BAUER Equipment Gulf FZE. **(2)**
Dubai Airport Free Zone Bldg 4E Ofc 4A 321
PO Box 54253
Dubai, United Arab Emirates
Tel.: (971) 42997807
Fax: (971) 42997806
E-Mail: bauereqg@eim.ae
Web Site: www.bauer.ae
Foundation Equipments Sales
S.I.C.: 7353
N.A.I.C.S.: 532412
Peter F. Hammer *(Mng Dir)*

BAUER Technologies Far East Pte. Ltd. **(2)**
No 27 Senoko Rd
Singapore, Singapore
Tel.: (65) 65766633
Fax: (65) 65766636
E-Mail: btfe@bauerfe.com
Web Site: www.bauerfe.com
Emp.: 40
Drilling Rigs & Accessories Mfr
S.I.C.: 3533
N.A.I.C.S.: 333132
Klaus Schwarz *(Mng Dir)*

Subsidiary:

BAUER EQUIPMENT SOUTH ASIA PTE. LTD. **(3)**
No 27 Senoko Rd
Singapore, 758135, Singapore
Tel.: (65) 6576 6631
Fax: (65) 76 6632
E-Mail: besa@bauerfe.com
Web Site: www.bauerfe.com
Emp.: 4
Foundation Work Equipment & Supplies
S.I.C.: 7353
N.A.I.C.S.: 532412

Non-U.S. Subsidiaries:

BAUER Equipment Hong Kong Ltd. **(3)**
Unit 4A Ground Fl Jon Hanssen Ctr
Quarry Bay, China (Hong Kong)
Tel.: (852) 25449613
Fax: (852) 25454676
E-Mail: bhk@bauer.de
Emp.: 5
Drilling Rigs & Accessories Mfr
S.I.C.: 3533
N.A.I.C.S.: 333132
Richard Lan *(Gen Mgr)*

BAUER Equipment (Malayasia) SDN. BHD. **(3)**
11 Jalan Seputeh Batu 3 Jalan Kelang Lama
58000 Kuala Lumpur, Selangor, Malaysia
Tel.: (60) 379808334
Fax: (60) 79813745
E-Mail: bem@bauerfe.com
Drilling Rigs Mfr
S.I.C.: 3533
N.A.I.C.S.: 333132

BAUER Equipment (Shanghai) Co. Ltd. **(3)**
Ste 2112 Block B Intl Plz 317 Xianxia Rd
Changning Dist, Shanghai, 200051, China
Tel.: (86) 2162351133
Fax: (86) 2162192516
E-Mail: bes@bauerfe.com
Web Site: www.bauerchina.net
Emp.: 50
Drilling Rigs Mfr
S.I.C.: 3533
N.A.I.C.S.: 333132
Richard Lan *(Gen Mgr)*

BAUER Tianjin Technologies Co. Ltd. **(3)**
No 1 Kai Yuan Road Xiqing Car Industrial Park
Xiqing Development Area, Tianjin, 300380, China
Tel.: (86) 2223078833
Fax: (86) 2223078822
E-Mail: bttcl@bauerfe.com
Rotary Drilling Rigs Mfr
S.I.C.: 3533
N.A.I.C.S.: 333132

Shanghai BAUER Technologies Co. Ltd. **(3)**
No 28 Caolian Rd 4th Xietong Indus Zone Huangdu
Jiading Dist, Shanghai, 201804, China
Tel.: (86) 2139597180
Fax: (86) 2139597185
E-Mail: sbt@bauerfe.com
Web Site: www.bauerchina.net
Emp.: 86
Rotary Drilling Rigs Mfr
S.I.C.: 3533
N.A.I.C.S.: 333132

BAUER Mietpool GmbH. **(1)**
Bauer Strasse 1
86529 Schrobenhausen, Germany
Tel.: (49) 8252970
Fax: (49) 8252971359
E-Mail: info@bauer.de
Web Site: www.bauer.be
Emp.: 50
Consturction Machinery Mfr
S.I.C.: 3531
N.A.I.C.S.: 333120
Hartmut Beutler *(Mgr)*

BAUER Resources GmbH. **(1)**
Wittelsbacherstrasse 5
86529 Schrobenhausen, Germany
Tel.: (49) 8252970
Fax: (49) 8252971845
E-Mail: info@bauer.de
Emp.: 300
Management Services
S.I.C.: 8741
N.A.I.C.S.: 551114
Johann Mesch *(Mng Dir)*

Non-U.S. Subsidiary:

BAUER Foundations (IRL) Ltd. **(2)**
621 Greenogue Indus Estate
Rathcoole, Dublin, Ireland
Tel.: (353) 14018810
Fax: (353) 14018817
E-Mail: info@bauerfoundations.ie
Web Site: www.bauerfoundations.ie
Emp.: 1
Foundation Work Contract Services
S.I.C.: 1799
N.A.I.C.S.: 238910
Michael Jones *(Mng Dir)*

BAUER Spezialtiefbau GmbH. **(1)**
Bauer Strasse 1
86529 Schrobenhausen, Bavaria, Germany
Tel.: (49) 8252970
Fax: (49) 8252971359
E-Mail: bst@bauer.de
Emp.: 500
Foundation Engineering Services
S.I.C.: 1799
N.A.I.C.S.: 238910
Harald Heinzelmann *(Mng Dir)*
Alexander Hofer *(Mng Dir)*

Non-U.S. Subsidiaries:

BAUER BULGARIA EOOD. **(2)**
Blvd Samokovsko Schosse Nr 2 Europart Bus Ctr
1138 Sofia, Bulgaria
Tel.: (359) 29743537
Fax: (359) 29744426
E-Mail: office@bauer.bg
Web Site: www.bauer.bg
Emp.: 50
Foundation Work Contract Services
S.I.C.: 2491
N.A.I.C.S.: 321114

BAUER Fondations Speciales S.A.S. **(2)**
5 rue La Fayette
67100 Strasbourg, Bas-Rhin, France
Tel.: (33) 390409850
Fax: (33) 388400501
E-Mail: info@bauer-france.fr
Web Site: www.bauer-france.fr
Emp.: 2
Foundation Work Contract Services
S.I.C.: 1799
N.A.I.C.S.: 238910
Pierre Klein *(Dir Gen)*
Felix Buche *(CFO)*

BAUER FUNDACIONES PANAMA S.A. **(2)**
Edificio T 319 Corozal Oeste
PO Box 0819-03827
Ancon, Panama, Panama
Tel.: (507) 3176078
Fax: (507) 3176079
E-Mail: info@bauerpanama.com.pa
Web Site: www.bauerpanama.com.pa
Emp.: 100
Civil Engineering Services
S.I.C.: 8711
N.A.I.C.S.: 541330
Hans Schwarzweller *(Mng Dir)*

BAUER ROMANIA S.R.L. **(2)**
3B Dimitrie Racovita Str Sector 2
023991 Bucharest, Romania
Tel.: (40) 213150020
Fax: (40) 213150091
E-Mail: office@bauer.ro
Web Site: www.bauer.ro
Emp.: 50
Foundation Work Contract Services
S.I.C.: 1799
N.A.I.C.S.: 238910
Ovidiu Constantinescu *(Mng Dir)*

BAUER Spezialtiefbau Schweiz AG. **(2)**
Im Langacker 20a
Dattwil, 5405 Baden, Switzerland
Tel.: (41) 562039050
Fax: (41) 56 20390 59
E-Mail: info@bauer-schweiz.ch
Web Site: www.bauer-schweiz.ch
Emp.: 30
Civil Engineering Services
S.I.C.: 8711
N.A.I.C.S.: 541330
Gerd Donig *(Gen Mgr)*

BAUER Technologies Limited (2)
Millers Three Southmill Rd
Bishop's Stortford, Hertfordshire, CM23 3DH, United Kingdom
Tel.: (44) 1279653108
Fax: (44) 1279653481
E-Mail: info@bauertech.co.uk
Web Site: www.bauertech.co.uk
Emp.: 20
Piling Works Contract Services
S.I.C.: 1799
N.A.I.C.S.: 238910
Michael Jones *(Mng Dir)*
Paul Wilter *(Mng Dir)*

BAUER Umwelt GmbH. (1)
In der Scherau 1
86529 Schrobenhausen, Germany
Tel.: (49) 8252970
Fax: (49) 8252973111
E-Mail: env@bauer.de
Web Site: www.bauerenvironment.com
Emp.: 80
Environmental Services
S.I.C.: 8711
N.A.I.C.S.: 541330
Peter Hingott *(Mng Dir)*
Johann Mesch *(Mng Dir)*

Esau & Hueber GmbH. (1)
Kapellenweg 10
86529 Schrobenhausen, Germany
Tel.: (49) 825289850
Fax: (49) 8252898585
E-Mail: info@esau-hueber.de
Web Site: www.esau-hueber.de
Emp.: 35
Water Treatment Services
S.I.C.: 1623
N.A.I.C.S.: 237110
Helmut Kuhnl *(Mgr-Sls)*

EURODRILL GmbH. (1)
Industriestr 5
57489 Drolshagen, Germany
Tel.: (49) 2763212280
Fax: (49) 27632122822
E-Mail: info@eurodrill.de
Web Site: www.eurodrill.de
Emp.: 39
Rotary Drill Heads & Drifters Mfr
S.I.C.: 3532
N.A.I.C.S.: 333131
Rudolf Grueneberg *(Mng Dir)*
Ralf Sonnecken *(Mng Dir)*

GF-Tec GmbH. (1)
Kronberger Strasse 4
63110 Rodgau, Germany
Tel.: (49) 61062668880
Fax: (49) 61062668888
E-Mail: info@gf-tec.com
Web Site: www.gf-tec.com
Emp.: 6
Plastics & Metal Components Development & Mfr
S.I.C.: 3544
N.A.I.C.S.: 333511
Hubert Graf *(Mgr)*

GWE pumpenboese GmbH. (1)
Moorbeerenweg 1
31224 Peine, Germany
Tel.: (49) 51712940
Fax: (49) 5171294188
E-Mail: kontakt@gwe-gruppe.de
Web Site: www.gwe-gruppe.de
Emp.: 50
Well Casings & Screening Services
S.I.C.: 1389
N.A.I.C.S.: 213112
Falk Olaf Petersdorf *(Mgr)*

KLEMM Bohrtechnik GmbH. (1)
Wintersohler Str 5
57489 Drolshagen, Germany
Tel.: (49) 27617050
Fax: (49) 276170550
E-Mail: klemm-bt@klemm-mail.de
Web Site: www.klemm-bt.de
Emp.: 230
Drilling Rigs & Accessories Mfr
S.I.C.: 3533
N.A.I.C.S.: 333132
Bodo Berendt *(Dir-Sls)*

MAT Mischanlagentechnik GmbH. (1)
Illerstrasse 6
87509 Immenstadt, Germany
Tel.: (49) 832396410
Fax: (49) 83239641650
E-Mail: mat@mat-oa.de
Web Site: www.mat-oa.de
Emp.: 80
Industrial Machinery & Pumps Mfr
S.I.C.: 3559
N.A.I.C.S.: 333249
Manfred Kleimeier *(Mng Dir)*
Rainer Rossbach *(Mng Dir)*

MMG Mitteldeutsche MONTAN GmbH. (1)
Industrieweg 2a
99734 Nordhausen, Germany
Tel.: (49) 36316320
Fax: (49) 3631632584
E-Mail: mmg@mdt-montan.de
Web Site: www.mdt-montan.de
Consturction & Mining Machinery Mfr
S.I.C.: 3531
N.A.I.C.S.: 333120
Eberhard Anders *(Mng Dir)*

Olbersdorfer GuB GmbH. (1)
An Der Stadtgrenze 4
02785 Olbersdorf, Saxony, Germany
Tel.: (49) 358357620
Fax: (49) 3583576266
E-Mail: info@olbersdorfer.de
Web Site: www.olbersdorfer-guss.de
Emp.: 128
Ductile Iron Castings Mfr
S.I.C.: 3321
N.A.I.C.S.: 331511
Johannes Kunze *(Mng Dir)*

PRAKLA Bohrtechnik GmbH. (1)
Moorbeerenweg 1
31228 Peine, Germany
Tel.: (49) 517190550
Fax: (49) 51719055100
E-Mail: info@prakla.de
Web Site: www.prakla.de
Emp.: 70
Drilling Rigs Mfr
S.I.C.: 3533
N.A.I.C.S.: 333132
Alfred Widmann *(Mng Dir)*

RTG Rammtechnik GmbH. (1)
Bauer Strasse 1
86529 Schrobenhausen, Bavaria, Germany
Tel.: (49) 8252970
Fax: (49) 8252971702
E-Mail: info@rtg-gmbh.de
Web Site: www.rtg-rammtechnik.de
Emp.: 83
Pilings & Drilling Rigs Mfr & Sales
S.I.C.: 3399
N.A.I.C.S.: 331110
Bernhard Lindermair *(Mng Dir)*
Rainer Rossbach *(Mng Dir)*

SBF-Hagusta GmbH. (1)
Schwarzwaldstrasse 7
77871 Renchen, Baden-Wurttemberg, Germany
Tel.: (49) 78437020
Fax: (49) 78437924
E-Mail: diringer.mansfred@hagusta-renchen.de
Emp.: 40
Corrosion Protected Steel Processing Services
S.I.C.: 3462
N.A.I.C.S.: 332111

SCHACHTBAU NORDHAUSEN GmbH - Mechanical Engineering Division (1)
Industrieweg 2a
99734 Nordhausen, Thuringia, Germany
Tel.: (49) 3631632498
Fax: (49) 3631632592
E-Mail: maschinenbau@schachtbau.de
Web Site: www.schachtbau.de
Emp.: 300
Rotary Drilling Rigs & Pilings Mfr
S.I.C.: 3533
N.A.I.C.S.: 333132
Thoralf Wilke *(Mgr-Engrg Div)*

SCHACHTBAU NORDHAUSEN GmbH. (1)
Industrieweg 2a
99734 Nordhausen, Germany
Tel.: (49) 36316320
Fax: (49) 3631632334
E-Mail: sbn@schachtbau.de
Web Site: www.schachtbau.de
Emp.: 400
Mining Engineering Services
S.I.C.: 8711
N.A.I.C.S.: 541330
Jens Peters *(Mng Dir)*
Jurgen Stater *(Mng Dir)*

Divisions:

SCHACHTBAU NORDHAUSEN GmbH - Civil Engineering Division (2)
Industrieweg 2a
99734 Nordhausen, Germany
Tel.: (49) 3631632214
Fax: (49) 3631632585
E-Mail: ingenieurbau@schachtbau.de
Web Site: www.schachtbau.de
Emp.: 870
Civil Engineering Services
S.I.C.: 8711
N.A.I.C.S.: 541330
Jens Peters *(Mng Dir)*
Juergen Staeter *(Mng Dir)*

SCHACHTBAU NORDHAUSEN GmbH - Environmental Technology Division (2)
Industrieweg 2a
99734 Nordhausen, Germany
Tel.: (49) 3631632355
Fax: (49) 3631632578
E-Mail: umwelttechnik@schachtbau.de
Web Site: www.schachtbau.de
Emp.: 870
Water Resources Management Construction & Installation Services
S.I.C.: 1629
N.A.I.C.S.: 237110

SCHACHTBAU NORDHAUSEN GmbH - Reconstruction Division (2)
Industrieweg 2a
99734 Nordhausen, Thuringia, Germany
Tel.: (49) 3631632215
Fax: (49) 3631632503
E-Mail: rekonstruktion@schachtbau.de
Emp.: 200
Civil Engineering Services
S.I.C.: 1611
N.A.I.C.S.: 237310
Stater Stater *(CEO)*

SCHACHTBAU NORDHAUSEN GmbH - Underground Construction Division (2)
Industrieweg 2a
99734 Nordhausen, Thuringia, Germany
Tel.: (49) 3631632571
Fax: (49) 3631632584
E-Mail: untertagebau@schachtbau.de
Web Site: www.schachtbau.de
Emp.: 850
Underground Engineering & Mining Services
S.I.C.: 8711
N.A.I.C.S.: 541330
Jens Peters *(Mng Dir)*
Jurgen Stater *(Mng Dir)*

SPESA Spezialbau und Sanierung GmbH. (1)
Bauer Strasse 1
86529 Schrobenhausen, Germany
Tel.: (49) 8252971300
Fax: (49) 8252971031
E-Mail: spesa.info@spesa.de
Web Site: www.spesa.de
Emp.: 75
Civil Engineering Services
S.I.C.: 8711
N.A.I.C.S.: 541330
Bernd Schittal *(Mgr)*

U.S. Subsidiaries:

BAUER Manufacturing Inc. (1)
100 N FM 3083 Rd
Conroe, TX 77303-1866
Tel.: (936) 539-5030
Fax: (936) 539-5048
E-Mail: contactus@bauer-conroe.com
Web Site: www.bauer-conroe.com
Emp.: 52
Swaging Machines Mfr
S.I.C.: 3541
N.A.I.C.S.: 333517
Thomas L. Jarboe *(Pres & CEO)*

BAUER Foundation Corp. (1)
13203 Byrd Legg Dr
Odessa, FL 33556
Tel.: (727) 531-2577
Fax: (727) 530-1571
Toll Free: (800) 270-0313
E-Mail: info@bauerfoundations.com
Web Site: www.bauerfoundations.com
Rev.: $60,000,000
Emp.: 100
Civil Engineering Services
S.I.C.: 8711
N.A.I.C.S.: 541330
Charles Puccini *(Pres)*
Michael Germana *(CFO)*

Non-U.S. Subsidiaries:

BAUER Corporate Services Private Limited (1)
104 VIP Plz Veera Indus Estate Off Link Rd
Andheri W, Mumbai, Maharashtra, 400 053, India
Tel.: (91) 22 24910104
Fax: (91) 22 26743855
Web Site: www.bauerindia.in
Information Technology Solutions
S.I.C.: 7373
N.A.I.C.S.: 541512

BAUER EGYPT S.A.E. (1)
197 26 July St
Mohandeseen, 112 455 Giza, Egypt
Tel.: (20) 233026083
Fax: (20) 233023805
E-Mail: baueregypt@baueregypt.com
Web Site: www.baueregypt.com
Emp.: 500
Foundation Contractors
S.I.C.: 1771
N.A.I.C.S.: 238110
Mohamed Mustafa *(Gen Mgr)*

BAUER ENVIRO Kft. (1)
Aradi U 16 II 2
1062 Budapest, Hungary
Tel.: (36) 14522070
Fax: (36) 14522079
E-Mail: karmentesites@bauerenviro.hu
Web Site: www.bauerenviro.hu
Environmental Consulting Services
S.I.C.: 8999
N.A.I.C.S.: 541620

BAUER Foundations Canada Inc. (1)
5050 74th Ave SE
Calgary, AB, T2C 3C9, Canada
Tel.: (403) 723-0159
Fax: (403) 723-0169
E-Mail: info@bauerfoundations.ca
Web Site: www.bauerfoundations.ca
Emp.: 20
Civil Engineering Services
S.I.C.: 8711
N.A.I.C.S.: 541330
Ehab Endrawes *(Mng Dir)*

BAUER Foundations Philippines, Inc. (1)
Unit 405 Web-Jet Acropolis 88 Rodriguez Jr Ave
Bagumbayan, Quezon City, Philippines
Tel.: (63) 26388687
Fax: (63) 26328685
E-Mail: info@bauer.net.ph
Web Site: www.bauer.net.ph
Emp.: 20
Civil Engineering Services
S.I.C.: 8711
N.A.I.C.S.: 541330
Thomas Albrecht *(Mng Dir)*

BAUER Funderingstechniek B.V. (1)
Rendementsweg 15
3641 SK Mijdrecht, Netherlands
Tel.: (31) 297231151
Fax: (31) 297231155
E-Mail: info@bauernl.nl
Web Site: www.bauernl.nl
Emp.: 8
Foundation Work Contract Services
S.I.C.: 1799
N.A.I.C.S.: 238910
Fender Celde *(Mng Dir)*

BAUER Aktiengesellschaft—(Continued)

BAUER Hong Kong Limited (1)
Units 1604-6 16th Fl Chinachem Tsuen Wan Plaza 455-457 Castle Peak Rd
Tsuen Wan, New Territories, China (Hong Kong)
Tel.: (852) 24309928
Fax: (852) 24309768
E-Mail: info@bauer.com.hk
Web Site: www.bauer.de
Emp.: 10
Construction & Project Management Services
S.I.C.: 8711
N.A.I.C.S.: 541330
Egon Stahl *(Mgr)*

BAUER (MALAYASIA) SDN. BHD. (1)
Unit 506 Blk G Phileo Damansara 1 No 9 Jln 16 11 Off Jln Damansara
46350 Petaling Jaya, Selangor, Malaysia
Tel.: (60) 379569366
Fax: (60) 379569580
E-Mail: info@bauer.com.my
Web Site: www.bauer.com.my
Emp.: 40
Construction Machinery Mfr
S.I.C.: 3531
N.A.I.C.S.: 333120
Thomas Domanski *(Mgr)*

Non-U.S. Subsidiary:

BAUER Foundations Australia Pty Ltd. (2)
Unit 16 No 40 Blackwood St
Mitchelton, QLD, 4053, Australia
Tel.: (61) 733555466
Fax: (61) 733555477
E-Mail: info@bauerfoundationsaustralia.com.au
Web Site: www.baueraustralia.com.au
Emp.: 60
Pile Driving Equipment Mfr
S.I.C.: 3699
N.A.I.C.S.: 335999
Gerhard Zylowski *(Mgr)*

BAUER (NEW ZEALAND) LIMITED (1)
Unit 16 No 40 Blackwood St
Mitchelton, Brisbane, QLD, 4053, Australia
Tel.: (61) 733555466
Fax: (61) 733555477
E-Mail: info@baueraustralia.com.au
Web Site: www.baueraustralia.com.au
Emp.: 60
Civil Engineering Services
S.I.C.: 1629
N.A.I.C.S.: 237990
Gerhard Zylowski *(Gen Mgr)*

BAUER Resources Canada Ltd. (1)
8003 102 St NW Ste 202
Edmonton, AB, T6E 4A2, Canada
Tel.: (780) 433-3448
Fax: (780) 433-3403
Emp.: 2
Coal & Diamond Mining Services
S.I.C.: 1222
N.A.I.C.S.: 212112
Holger Itzeck *(Mgr)*

BAUER Services Singapore Pte. Ltd. (1)
51 Goldhill Plaza 08-06/07
308900 Singapore, Singapore
Tel.: (65) 62585113
Fax: (65) 62580631
E-Mail: bauersvc@starhub.net.sg
Emp.: 5
Foundation Work Contract Services
S.I.C.: 1799
N.A.I.C.S.: 238910
Panema Lim *(Mng Dir)*

BAUER SPEZIALTIEFBAU Gesellschaft m.b.H. (1)
Warneckestrasse 1-3
1110 Vienna, Austria
Tel.: (43) 1760220
Fax: (43) 17602222
E-Mail: info@bauer-spezialtiefbau.at
Web Site: www.bauer-spezialtiefbau.at
Foundation Work Contract Services
S.I.C.: 1799
N.A.I.C.S.: 238910

BAUER Technologies South Africa (PTY) Ltd. (1)
Rodium Indus Park Unit 1 Fabriek St Strijdom Park
Randburg, Gauteng, 2194, South Africa
Tel.: (27) 117932616
Fax: (27) 117932598
E-Mail: info@bauersa.co.za
Web Site: www.bauersa.co.za
Emp.: 10
Mineral Exploration & Drilling Services
S.I.C.: 1481
N.A.I.C.S.: 213115
Lars Rosbler *(Mng Dir)*

BAUER Vietnam Ltd. (1)
9 Dinh Tien Hoang St Dakao Ward
Dist 1, Ho Chi Minh City, Vietnam
Tel.: (84) 838206137
Fax: (84) 838206138
E-Mail: info@bauervietnam.com
Web Site: www.bauervietnam.com
Emp.: 20
Foundation Engineering Services
S.I.C.: 1799
N.A.I.C.S.: 238190
Joern Lohse *(Mng Dir)*
Frank Schubert *(Gen Dir)*

BRK Specialis Melyepito Kft. (1)
Koppany u 5-11
1097 Budapest, Hungary
Tel.: (36) 12163053
Fax: (36) 12163049
E-Mail: office@brk.hu
Web Site: www.brk.hu
Emp.: 50
Underground Work Contract Services
S.I.C.: 8711
N.A.I.C.S.: 541330
Cfanadi Govsif *(Mgr)*

FORALITH Equipment AG. (1)
Bionstrasse 4
9015 Saint Gallen, Switzerland
Tel.: (41) 713137050
Fax: (41) 713137060
E-Mail: info@foralith.ch
Emp.: 20
Industrial Machinery & Equipment Whslr
S.I.C.: 5084
N.A.I.C.S.: 423830
Rienhard Pingel *(Mgr)*

PESA ENGINEERING, S.A. (1)
C Laguna Dalga 12 nave A1
Pol Ind La Resina, 28021 Madrid, Spain
Tel.: (34) 917920330
Fax: (34) 914759300
E-Mail: pesaeng@pesa-gwe.es
Web Site: www.pesa-gwe.es
Water Distribution Services
S.I.C.: 4941
N.A.I.C.S.: 221310

Pol-Bud Technologia Wody Sp.z.o.o (1)
Demokratyczna 89
92-142 Lodz, Poland
Tel.: (48) 426388930
Fax: (48) 426388949
E-Mail: polbud@gwe-polbud.pl
Web Site: www.gwe-polbud.pl
Emp.: 50
Stainless Steel & Plastic Pipes & Tubes Mfr
S.I.C.: 3084
N.A.I.C.S.: 326122
Thomas Jankowski *(Mgr)*

P.T. BAUER Pratama Indonesia (1)
Cilandak Comml Estate Bldg 110 NGW
JL Cilandak KKO Raya, Jakarta, 12560, Indonesia
Tel.: (62) 217803865
Fax: (62) 217824183
E-Mail: bauerina@bauer.co.id
Web Site: www.bauer.co.id
Emp.: 25
Foundation Equipments Mfr & Contract Services
S.I.C.: 1799
N.A.I.C.S.: 238910
Anthony Setiawan *(Mgr)*

Saudi BAUER Foundation Contractors Ltd. (1)
Sharabatly Bus Ctr S6 Fl Off No 64-65
Bagdadiyah Dist, Jeddah, Makkah, 21443, Saudi Arabia
Tel.: (966) 26441727
Fax: (966) 26432782
E-Mail: saudi-bauer@saudibauer.com
Web Site: www.saudibauer.com
Emp.: 60
Foundation Works Contract Services
S.I.C.: 1799
N.A.I.C.S.: 238910
Hossam Hamdi *(Gen Mgr)*

Thai BAUER Co.Ltd. (1)
19th Fl Two Pacific Pl 142 Sukhumvit Rd
Klong Toey, Bangkok, 10110, Thailand
Tel.: (66) 26532076
Fax: (66) 26532075
E-Mail: bauer@asiaaccess.net.th
Web Site: www.thaibauer.com
Emp.: 12
Foundation Work Equipment & Supplies
S.I.C.: 1799
N.A.I.C.S.: 238910
Mike Sinkinson *(Mng Dir)*

BAUER COMP HOLDING AG

Sollner Strasse 43B
81479 Munich, Germany
Tel.: (49) 897450100
Fax: (49) 8974501018
E-Mail: holding@bauergroup.de
Web Site: www.bauergroup.de
Year Founded: 1946
Sls.: $132,804,100
Emp.: 1,000

Business Description:
Holding Company
S.I.C.: 6719
N.A.I.C.S.: 551112

Personnel:
Heinz Bauer *(Founder & CEO)*

Subsidiaries:

BAUER KOMPRESSOREN GmbH Systemwerk (1)
Drygalski-Allee 37
81477 Munich, Germany
Tel.: (49) 89780490
Fax: (49) 8978049167
E-Mail: industrie@bauer-kompressoren.de
Air Compressors Mfr
S.I.C.: 3563
N.A.I.C.S.: 333912

ROTORCOMP VERDICHTER GmbH (1)
Industriestr 9
82110 Germering, Germany
Tel.: (49) 89724090
Fax: (49) 897240938
E-Mail: info@rotorcomp.de
Web Site: www.rotorcomp.de
Air & Gas Compressor Mfr
S.I.C.: 3563
N.A.I.C.S.: 333912

UNICCOMP GmbH (1)
Bayerwaldstr. 6
82538 Geretsried, Germany
Tel.: (49) 81713440
Fax: (49) 8171344320
E-Mail: info@uniccomp.de
Web Site: www.uniccomp.de
Air & Gas Compressor Mfr
S.I.C.: 3563
N.A.I.C.S.: 333912
Heinz Bauer *(Gen Mgr)*

U.S. Subsidiary:

BAUER COMPRESSORS Inc. (1)
1328 Azalea Garden Rd
Norfolk, VA 23502
Tel.: (757) 855-6006
Fax: (757) 857-1041
E-Mail: sls@bauercomp.com
Web Site: www.bauercomp.com
Sls.: $24,380,954
Emp.: 135
Air & Gas Compressors Including Vacuum Pumps
S.I.C.: 3563
N.A.I.C.S.: 333912
Bob Straddeck *(Mgr-Sls-Parts)*

Non-U.S. Subsidiaries:

BAUER COMPRESSEURS S.A.R.L. (1)
60 Avenue Franklin D. Roosevelt
F-73100 Aix-les-Bains, France
Tel.: (33) 479882100
Fax: (33) 479882114
E-Mail: info@bauer-compresseurs.com
Web Site: www.bauer-compresseurs.com
Emp.: 800
Air & Gas Compressor Mfr
S.I.C.: 3563
N.A.I.C.S.: 333912

BAUER COMPRESSEURS S.A.R.L. (1)
60 Avenue Franklin D Roosevelt
F-73100 Aix-les-Bains, France
Tel.: (33) 479882100
Fax: (33) 479882114
E-Mail: info@bauer-compresseurs.com
Web Site: www.bauer-compresseurs.com
Emp.: 25
Air Compressors
S.I.C.: 3563
N.A.I.C.S.: 333912

BAUER COMPRESSORI s.r.l. unipersonale (1)
Via Galileo Galilei 9
36057 Vicenza, Italy
Tel.: (39) 444 653653
Fax: (39) 444 653600
Air & Gas Compressor Mfr
S.I.C.: 3563
N.A.I.C.S.: 333912

BAUER COMPRESSORS ASIA PTE LTD (1)
2 Penjuru Place
01-05 Penjuru Tech Hub, 608783
Singapore, Singapore
Tel.: (65) 62716271
Fax: (65) 62723345
E-Mail: info@bauer-kompressoren.de
Web Site: www.bauer-kompressoren.de
Air & Gas Compressor Mfr
S.I.C.: 3563
N.A.I.C.S.: 333912
Steve Kellett *(Mng Dir)*

BAUER COMPRESSORS Co. Ltd. (1)
10-36 Ryutsu-Ctr Kitakami-shi
024 0014 Iwate, Japan
Tel.: (81) 197682251
Fax: (81) 197682225
Web Site: www.bauer.co.jp
Emp.: 11
Air & Gas Compressor Mfr
S.I.C.: 3563
N.A.I.C.S.: 333912
Teruki Oitome *(Mng Dir)*

BAUER KOMPRESSOREN AUSTRALIA PTY LTD (1)
2/35 Hallstrom Place
Wetherill Park, Sydney, 2164, Australia
Tel.: (61) 297562700
Fax: (61) 297561700
E-Mail: enquiries@bauer-kompressoren.com.au
Web Site: www.bauer-kompressoren.com.au
Emp.: 14
Air & Gas Compressor Mfr
S.I.C.: 3563
N.A.I.C.S.: 333912
Neno Padjen *(Gen Mgr)*

BAUER KOMPRESSOREN China Ltd. (1)
707 Block A MP Industrial Ctr
18 Ka Yip St, Hong Kong, Chaiwan, China (Hong Kong)
Tel.: (852) 25951898
Fax: (852) 25950878
E-Mail: ptc@bauerchina.com
Web Site: www.bauerchina.com
Air & Gas Compressor Mfr
S.I.C.: 3563
N.A.I.C.S.: 333912

BAUER KOMPRESSOREN Egypt Ltd. (1)
Nasser Street
Suez, Hurghada, Egypt
Tel.: (20) 65 335 2747
Fax: (20) 65 355 2747
Air & Gas Compressor Mfr
S.I.C.: 3563
N.A.I.C.S.: 333912

BAUER KOMPRESSOREN India Pvt. Ltd. (1)
Plot No A-71 & A-72 H Block
411 018 Pune, India
Tel.: (91) 2067308100
Fax: (91) 2027487000
E-Mail: info@bauerkompressoren.com
Web Site: www.bauerkompressoren.com
Air & Gas Compressor Mfr
S.I.C.: 3563
N.A.I.C.S.: 333912
Anand Pradhan *(Gen Mgr)*

BAUER KOMPRESSOREN Middle East (1)
Jebel Ali Free Zone
Dubai, United Arab Emirates
Tel.: (971) 4 8860259
Fax: (971) 4 8860260
Air & Gas Compressor Mfr
S.I.C.: 3563
N.A.I.C.S.: 333912

BAUER KOMPRESSOREN Shanghai Ltd. (1)
878 Jianchuan Road
Minhang, Shanghai, 200240, China
Tel.: (86) 2154713598
Fax: (86) 2154713818
E-Mail: adminsh@bauerchina.com
Web Site: www.bauerchina.com
Air & Gas Compressor Mfr
S.I.C.: 3563
N.A.I.C.S.: 333912

BAUER-POSEIDON KOMPRESSOREN Ges.m.b.H. (1)
Strasse 3 Objekt 26
2355 Wiener Neudorf, Austria
Tel.: (43) 2236636250
Fax: (43) 2236 62952
Air & Gas Compressor Mfr
S.I.C.: 3563
N.A.I.C.S.: 333912

BAUER-WALSER AG

Bunsenstrasse 4-6
75210 Pforzheim, Germany
Tel.: (49) 72367040
Fax: (49) 7236704270
E-Mail: info@bauer-walser.de
Web Site: www.bauer-walser.de
Year Founded: 2004
Rev.: $86,104,129
Emp.: 124
Business Description:
Jewellery & Watches Mfr
S.I.C.: 5094
N.A.I.C.S.: 423940
Personnel:
Bernd Augenstein *(Mgr-Production-Semi-Finished Products)*

BAUHAUS INTERNATIONAL (HOLDINGS) LIMITED

Room 501 Sino Industrial Plaza No 9 Kai Cheung Road
Kowloon, China (Hong Kong)
Tel.: (852) 35131800
Fax: (852) 27967625
E-Mail: sales@bauhaus.com.hk
Web Site: www.bauhaus.com.hk
0483—(HKG)
Rev.: $166,819,649
Assets: $97,891,103
Liabilities: $20,989,578
Net Worth: $76,901,525
Earnings: $12,798,932
Emp.: 1,486
Fiscal Year-end: 03/31/13
Business Description:
Garments & Accessories Mfr
S.I.C.: 2389
N.A.I.C.S.: 315280
Personnel:
Yui Lam Wong *(Founder, Chm & CEO)*
Kin Cheong Li *(Sec & Controller-Fin)*
Board of Directors:
Yui Lam Wong
To Ki Chu
Yuk Ming Lee
Wing Kit Mak
Yun Kuen Wong
Yat Hang Yeung

Butterfield Bank (Cayman) Limited
Butterfield House, 68 Fort Street
PO Box 705
Georgetown, Grand Cayman, Cayman Islands

Transfer Agents:
Tricor Investor Services Limited
26th Floor Tesbury Centre 28 Queens Road East
Wanchai, China (Hong Kong)

Butterfield Bank (Cayman) Limited
Butterfield House, 68 Fort Street
PO Box 705
Georgetown, Grand Cayman, Cayman Islands

BAULOISE AUTOMOBILES S.A.

Route De La Baule
44350 Guerande, Loire Atlantique, France
Tel.: (33) 240111220
Fax: (33) 240119753
Web Site: www.baulautos.peugeot.fr/
Sls.: $19,500,000
Emp.: 49
S.I.C.: 5511
N.A.I.C.S.: 441110
Personnel:
Patrice Huray *(Pres)*

BAUMANN FEDERN AG

Fabrikstrasse
CH-8734 Ermenswil, Switzerland
Mailing Address:
PO Box 8630
CH-8630 Ruti, Switzerland
Tel.: (41) 552868111
Fax: (41) 552868511
E-Mail: info@baumann-springs.com
Web Site: www.baumann-springs.com
Year Founded: 1886
Sales Range: $25-49.9 Million
Emp.: 1,200
Business Description:
Mfr. of Springs, Wire Forms & Couplings
S.I.C.: 3829
N.A.I.C.S.: 334519
Personnel:
Hans Juert Hartmann *(Pres)*
Huko Hinger *(CFO)*
Subsidiaries:

Bamatec AG (1)
Fabrikstrasse
Ermenswil, 8734, Switzerland (100%)
Tel.: (41) 552868585
Fax: (41) 552868525
E-Mail: info@bamatec.ch
Web Site: www.bamatec.ch
Sls.: $23,513,164
Emp.: 300
S.I.C.: 3829
N.A.I.C.S.: 334519
Marco Sama *(Mng Dir)*

U.S. Subsidiaries:

Baumann Springs Texas Holdings LLC (1)
3075 N Great SW Pkwy 10
Grand Prairie, TX 75050
Tel.: (972) 641-7272
Fax: (972) 641-0180
E-Mail: info.us@baumann-springs.com
Web Site: www.baumann-springs.com
Emp.: 39
Spring (Light Gauge) Mfr
S.I.C.: 3495
N.A.I.C.S.: 332613
Pedro Sainz *(Pres)*

Baumann Springs Texas Ltd. (1)
3075 N Great SW Pkwy Ste 100
Grand Prairie, TX 75050-7823
Tel.: (972) 641-7272
Fax: (972) 641-0180
E-Mail: info.tx@bauman-springs.com
Web Site: www.baumann-springs.com
Emp.: 60
Mfr. of Wire Springs
S.I.C.: 3493
N.A.I.C.S.: 332613
Pedro Sainz *(Pres)*

Baumann Springs USA, Inc. (1)
3075 No Great SW Pkwy Ste 100
Grand Prairie, TX 75050 (100%)
Mailing Address:
PO Box 536089
Grand Prairie, TX 75053-6089
Tel.: (972) 641-7272
Fax: (972) 641-0180
E-Mail: info.us@baumann-springs.com
Web Site: www.baumann-springs.com
Emp.: 65
Mfr. of Springs & Retaining Rings for Wheel Covers
Import Export
S.I.C.: 3493
N.A.I.C.S.: 332613
Pedro Sainz *(Pres)*

Non-U.S. Subsidiaries:

Baumann GmbH (1)
Friedrich List Str 131
72805 Lichtenstein, Germany (100%)
Tel.: (49) 71296970
Telex: 41 729821
Fax: (49) 7129697100
E-Mail: info.bli@baumann-springs.com
Emp.: 190
Mfr of Springs, Wire Forms, Couplings & Automotive Parts
S.I.C.: 3495
N.A.I.C.S.: 332613
Klaus Schissler *(Mgr-IT)*

Baumann Muelles S.A. (1)
Poligono Industrial Gojain c/ Padurea s/n
1770 Legutiano, Alava, Spain
Tel.: (34) 945 46 55 10
Fax: (34) 945 46 55 29
E-Mail: info.es@baumann-springs.com
Web Site: www.baumann-springs.com
Emp.: 15
Mfr of Annular Springs & Torsion Springs for Automotive Industry
S.I.C.: 3495
N.A.I.C.S.: 332613
Ricardo Omaechevarria *(Mng Dir)*

Baumann Ressorts S.A. (1)
727 Rte les Tattes de Borly
BP 3
74380 Cranves Sales, France
Tel.: (33) 4 50 31 67 00
Fax: (33) 4 50 36 75 25
E-Mail: info.fr@baumann-springs.com
Emp.: 6
Compression & Torsion Springs Mfr
S.I.C.: 3496
N.A.I.C.S.: 332618
Gaime Belarve *(Mng Dir)*
S. Lomartire *(Mng Dir)*

Baumann Spring Co. (S) Pte. Ltd. (1)
33 Gul Lane
Singapore, 629427, Singapore
Tel.: (65) 6268 5222
Telex: 87 23618
Fax: (65) 6863 3708
E-Mail: info.sgp@baumann-springs.com
Web Site: www.baumann-springs.com
Emp.: 75
Mfr of Technical Springs & Stampings
S.I.C.: 3493
N.A.I.C.S.: 332613
Lilien Cheong *(Mng Dir)*

Baumann Springs & Pressings (UK) Ltd. (1)
E Mill Ln
Sherborne, Dorset, DT9 3DR, United Kingdom (100%)
Tel.: (44) 935818100
Fax: (44) 935814141
E-Mail: info.bsp@baumann-springs.com
Web Site: www.baumann-springs.com
Sales Range: $1-9.9 Million
Emp.: 50
Mfr. of Springs & Pressings
S.I.C.: 3452
N.A.I.C.S.: 332722

Baumann Springs Leon S. de R.L. Dec. V. (1)
Kappa 310 y 312
Fracc Industrial Delta, 37545 Leon, Mexico
Tel.: (52) 477 152 1400
Fax: (52) 477 715 21401
E-Mail: info.mx@baumann-springs.com
Web Site: www.baumann-springs.com
Mfr of Springs for Automotive Industry
S.I.C.: 3714
N.A.I.C.S.: 336390
L. Sanchez *(Mng Dir)*

Baumann Springs (Shanghai) Co. Ltd. (1)
No 358-2 Shen Xia Road
Forward High Tech Zone, Shanghai, 201818, China
Tel.: (86) 21 5990 0606
Fax: (86) 21 5990 0505
E-Mail: info.cn@baumann-springs.com
Emp.: 20
Springs Mfr
S.I.C.: 3495
N.A.I.C.S.: 332613
R. Tan *(Mng Dir)*

Baumann Springs s.r.o. (1)
Na Novem poli 384/6
CZ 733 01 Karvina, Czech Republic
Tel.: (420) 595 390 010
Fax: (420) 595 390 090
E-Mail: info.cz@baumann-springs.com
Web Site: www.baumann-springs.com
Springs Mfr
S.I.C.: 3493
N.A.I.C.S.: 332613
M. Vrla *(Mng Dir)*

Prodotti Baumann SpA (1)
Via Brescia 261
I 25075 Cortine di Nave, Brescia, Italy (100%)
Tel.: (39) 0302534221
Telex: 043 300196
Fax: (39) 0302532149
E-Mail: info.it@baumann-springs.com
Web Site: www.baumann-springs.com
Emp.: 70
Valve Springs & Compression Springs Mfr
S.I.C.: 3495
N.A.I.C.S.: 332613
P. Tanfoglio *(Mng Dir)*

BAUMER BOURDON-HAENNI S.A.S.

125 Rue De La Marre
BP 70214
41103 Orleans, Vendome, France
Tel.: (33) 254737475
Fax: (33) 254737442
E-Mail: info.fr@baumerprocess.com
Web Site: www.baumerprocess.com
Sls.: $22,000,000
Emp.: 278
Business Description:
Instruments To Measure Electricity
S.I.C.: 3825
N.A.I.C.S.: 334515
Personnel:
Axel Vietze *(Pres)*

BAUMER S.A.

Av Prefeito Antonio Tavares Leite 181
13830-330 Mogi Mirim, SP, Brazil
Tel.: (55) 19 3805 7660
Fax: (55) 19 3806 3282
E-Mail: baumer@baumer.com.br
Web Site: www.baumer.com.br
Year Founded: 1952
BALM3—(BRAZ)
Business Description:
Medical Equipment Mfr
S.I.C.: 3841
N.A.I.C.S.: 339112
Personnel:
Monica Salvari Baumer *(Dir-IR)*

BAUUNTERNEHMAN ECHTERHOFF GMBH & CO. KG

(d/b/a Echterhoff-Gruppe)
Industriestrasse 9
49492 Westerkappeln, Germany
Tel.: (49) 5456 81 0
Fax: (49) 5456 81 27
E-Mail: info@echterhoff.de
Web Site: www.echterhoff.de
Year Founded: 1968
Business Description:
Holding Company; Civil Engineering & Industrial Construction Services
S.I.C.: 6719
N.A.I.C.S.: 551112
Personnel:
Thomas Echterhoff *(Member-Mgmt Bd)*
Rainer Kossmann *(Member-Mgmt Bd)*
Theo Reddemann *(Member-Mgmt Bd)*

Subsidiaries:

Bauunternehmung Gebr. Echterhoff GmbH & Co. KG **(1)**
Industriestrasse 9
Westerkappeln, Germany De
Tel.: (49) 5456 81 0
E-Mail: info@echterhoff.de
Web Site: www.echterhoff.de
Civil Engineering & Industrial Construction Services
S.I.C.: 1629
N.A.I.C.S.: 237990

domoplan Baugesellschaft m.b.H. **(1)**
Langekampstrasse 36
D-44652 Herne, Germany De
Tel.: (49) 2325577200 (100%)
Fax: (49) 2325577209
E-Mail: info@domoplan.net
Web Site: www.domoplan.net
Sales Range: $25-49.9 Million
Emp.: 200
Residential Housing Concrete Structure Repair Services
S.I.C.: 1771
N.A.I.C.S.: 238110
Klaus-Dieter Schindler *(Mng Dir & Member-Mgmt Bd)*
Willi Grennigloh *(Member-Mgmt Bd)*
Gerhard Wilwerding *(Member-Mgmt Bd)*

BAUVAL INC.

210 Montarville Blvd Suite 2006
Boucherville, QC, Canada
Tel.: (514) 875-4270
Fax: (450) 655-2833
E-Mail: legroupe@bauval.com
Web Site: www.bauval.com
Year Founded: 1954
Sales Range: $25-49.9 Million
Emp.: 40
Business Description:
Building Contractors & Industrial Works Provider
S.I.C.: 1542
N.A.I.C.S.: 236220
Personnel:
Luc Lachapelle *(Pres)*

BAUXITE CORPORATION

Lukic Polje bb
75446 Milici, Bosnia & Herzegovina
Tel.: (387) 56 745 140
Fax: (387) 56 741 067
E-Mail: boksit@ad-boksit.com
Web Site: www.ad-boksit.com
Year Founded: 1959
BOKS—(BANJ)
Emp.: 605
Business Description:
Bauxite Ore Mining
S.I.C.: 1099
N.A.I.C.S.: 212299
Personnel:
Rajko Dukic *(Chm-Mgmt Bd)*
Aleksandar Dukic *(Member-Mgmt Bd)*
Dragan Kajkut *(Member-Mgmt Bd)*
Borivoje Lalovic *(Member-Mgmt Bd)*
Mladen Milic *(Member-Mgmt Bd)*
Virginius Vajega *(Member-Mgmt Bd)*
Miladin Vasiljevic *(Member-Mgmt Bd)*

BAUXITE RESOURCES LIMITED

Level 2 Building E 355 Scarborough Beach Rd
Osborne Park, WA, 6017, Australia
Mailing Address:
PO Box 1315
Osborne Park, WA, 6916, Australia
Tel.: (61) 8 9200 8200
Fax: (61) 8 9200 8299
E-Mail: admin@bauxiteresources.com.au
Web Site: www.bauxiteresources.com.au
BAU—(ASX)
Rev.: $3,363,227
Assets: $54,396,956
Liabilities: $553,267
Net Worth: $53,843,690
Earnings: ($5,526,239)
Fiscal Year-end: 06/30/13
Business Description:
Mineral Exploration
S.I.C.: 1481
N.A.I.C.S.: 213115
Personnel:
Peter Canterbury *(CEO)*
Kelvin May *(CFO)*
Robert Samuel Middlemas *(Sec)*
Board of Directors:
Robert John Nash
Luke Frederick Atkins
Peter Canterbury
Cunliang Lai
Neil Alexander Lithgow
John Sibly
Chenghai Yang
Legal Counsel:
Steinepreis Paganin
Level 4 The Read Buildings 16 Milligan Street
6000 Perth, WA, Australia

Subsidiary:

BRL Landholdings Pty Ltd. **(1)**
163 Wells Glover Rd
Bindoon, WA, 6502, Australia
Tel.: (61) 895760880
Bauxite Ore Mine Site Development Services
S.I.C.: 1099
N.A.I.C.S.: 212299

BAVARIA FILM GMBH

Bavariafilmplatz 7
Geiselgasteig, 82031 Munich, Germany
Tel.: (49) 89 64990
Fax: (49) 89 6492507
E-Mail: info@bavaria-film.de
Web Site: www.bavaria-film.de
Year Founded: 1919
Sales Range: $250-299.9 Million
Emp.: 740
Business Description:
TV & Film Production
S.I.C.: 7812
N.A.I.C.S.: 512110
Personnel:
Monika Piel *(Chm-Supervisory Bd)*
Achim Rohnke *(CEO & Mng Dir)*
Matthias Esche *(Mng Dir)*
Supervisory Board of Directors:
Monika Piel
Otto Beierl
Peter Boudgoust
Marc Jan Eumann
Karl Gerhold
Thomas Gruber
Monika Gruning
Marc Haug
Walter Holzl
Marianne Hundsoder
Verena Kulenkampff
Bernd Lenze
Gisela Losseff-Tillmanns
Ulrich Muller
Udo Reiter
Michael Schneider
Alfred Spitzer
Herbert Tisler

Subsidiaries:

Bavaria Fernsehproduktion GmbH **(1)**
Bavariafilmplatz 7
Geiselgasteig, 82031 Munich, Germany
Tel.: (49) 8964990
Fax: (49) 896492507
E-Mail: info@bavaria-film.de
Web Site: www.bavaria-fernsehproduktion.de
Emp.: 300
Motion Picture & Video Production
S.I.C.: 7812
N.A.I.C.S.: 512110
Matthias Esche *(Mng Dir)*

Bavaria Film Interactive GmbH **(1)**
Bavariafilmplatz 7
Geiselgasteig, 82031 Munich, Germany (100%)
Tel.: (49) 8964992288
Fax: (49) 8964993038
E-Mail: info@bavaria-film-interactive.de
Web Site: www.bavaria-film-interactive.de
Emp.: 30
Motion Picture & Video Industries
S.I.C.: 7819
N.A.I.C.S.: 512199
Lars Rechmann *(Mng Dir)*

Bavaria Film- und Fernsehstudios GmbH **(1)**
Bavariafilmplatz 7
Geiselgasteig, 82031 Munich, Germany
Tel.: (49) 8964993110
Fax: (49) 8964993753
E-Mail: produktionsbetreuung@bavaria-studios.de
Web Site: www.bavaria-studios.de
Emp.: 71
Television Broadcasting
S.I.C.: 4833
N.A.I.C.S.: 515120
Michael Klee *(Mng Dir)*
Martin Moll *(Mng Dir)*
Markus Vogelbacher *(Mng Dir)*

Bavaria Filmverleih- und Produktions GmbH **(1)**
Bavariafilmplatz 7
Geiselgasteig, 82031 Munich, Germany (100%)
Tel.: (49) 8964992873
Fax: (49) 8964993143
E-Mail: filmverleih@bavaria-film.de
Emp.: 3
Motion Picture & Video Production
S.I.C.: 7812
N.A.I.C.S.: 512110
Uschi Reich *(Mng Dir)*

Bavaria Media Television GmbH **(1)**
Bavariafilmplatz 7
Geiselgasteig, 82031 Munich, Germany (100%)
Tel.: (49) 89 6499 2694
Fax: (49) 89 6499 2240
E-Mail: tvinfo@bavaria-media.tv
Web Site: www.bavaria-media.tv
Emp.: 40
Television Broadcasting
S.I.C.: 4833
N.A.I.C.S.: 515120
Philipp Kreuzer *(VP-Intl & Production)*

Bavaria Pictures GmbH **(1)**
Bavariafilmplatz 7
Geiselgasteig, 82031 Munich, Germany (100%)
Tel.: (49) 8964993903
Fax: (49) 8964993788
Web Site: www.bavaria-pictures.de
Emp.: 40
Motion Picture & Video Production
S.I.C.: 7812
N.A.I.C.S.: 512110
Philipp Kreuzer *(Mng Dir)*

Bavaria Production Services GmbH **(1)**
Bavariafilmplatz 7
Geiselgasteig, 82031 Munich, Germany
Tel.: (49) 8964992500
Fax: (49) 896492507
E-Mail: iffo@bavariafilm.de
Web Site: www.bavaria.film.de
Emp.: 70
Motion Picture & Video Production
S.I.C.: 7812
N.A.I.C.S.: 512110
Martin Moll *(Mng Dir)*

Bavaria Sonor Musikverlag und Merchandising GmbH **(1)**
Bavariafilmplatz 7
Geiselgasteig, 82031 Munich, Germany (100%)
Tel.: (49) 8964992238
Fax: (49) 896499370
E-Mail: anna.michel@bavaria-film.de
Web Site: www.bavaria-sonor.de
Emp.: 13
Prerecorded Compact Disc & Tape & Record Reproducing
S.I.C.: 3652
N.A.I.C.S.: 334614
Rolf Moser *(Mng Dir)*
Anne Michel *(Sec)*

Bayerisches Filmzentrum Wirtschaftsforderungs GmbH **(1)**
Bavariafilmplatz 7
Geiselgasteig, 82031 Munich, Germany
Tel.: (49) 89649810
Fax: (49) 89649810
Web Site: www.bavaria-film.de/index.php?id=1999
Motion Picture & Video Production
S.I.C.: 7812
N.A.I.C.S.: 512110
Christiane M. Conradi *(Mng Dir)*
Klaus Schaefer *(Mng Dir)*

Bremedia Produktion GmbH **(1)**
Grobenstrabe 2
28195 Bremen, Germany
Tel.: (49) 4212464000
Fax: (49) 42124634509
E-Mail: info@bremedia-produktion.de
Web Site: www.bremedia-produktion.de
Emp.: 200
Motion Picture & Video Production
S.I.C.: 7812
N.A.I.C.S.: 512110
Bernd Bielefeld *(Mng Dir)*

Colonia Media Filmproduktions GmbH **(1)**
Moltkestrasse 131
50674 Cologne, Germany
Tel.: (49) 2219514040
Fax: (49) 2219514044
E-Mail: info@coloniamedia.de
Web Site: www.coloniamedia.de
Emp.: 20
Motion Picture & Video Production
S.I.C.: 7812
N.A.I.C.S.: 512110

Drefa Immobilien Management GmbH **(1)**
Altenburger Strasse 13
04275 Leipzig, Germany
Tel.: (49) 34135002501
Fax: (49) 34135002511
Web Site: www.drefa.de/drefa-immobilien-management.html
Administrative Management & General Management Consulting Services
S.I.C.: 8742
N.A.I.C.S.: 541611
Ulrike von Radowitz *(Mng Dir)*

Eurotape Media Services GmbH **(1)**
Buckower Chaussee 134
12277 Berlin, Germany (100%)
Tel.: (49) 30742070
Fax: (49) 3074207100
E-Mail: info@eurotape.de
Web Site: www.eurotape.de

Emp.: 70
Motion Picture & Video Distribution
S.I.C.: 7829
N.A.I.C.S.: 512120

First Entertainment GmbH (1)
Bavaria film platz 7
82031 Munich, Germany
Tel.: (49) 8964994100
Fax: (49) 8964994110
E-Mail: info@first-entertainment.de
Web Site: www.first-entertainment.de
Emp.: 50
Broadcasting Services
S.I.C.: 4833
N.A.I.C.S.: 515120
Florian Karl Otto Bahr *(Mng Dir)*
Tobias Gerlach *(Mng Dir)*

FTA Film- und Theaterausstattung GmbH (1)
Bavariafilmplatz 7
Geiselgasteig, 82031 Munich, Germany
Tel.: (49) 89649890
Fax: (49) 896498930
E-Mail: mail@fta-muenchen.de
Web Site: www.fta-muenchen.de
Motion Picture & Video Industries
S.I.C.: 7819
N.A.I.C.S.: 512199
Marc Bockenforde *(Mng Dir)*

Maran Film GmbH (1)
Lange Str 71
76530 Baden-Baden, Germany
Tel.: (49) 722130250
Fax: (49) 72213025139
E-Mail: info@maranfilm.de
Web Site: www.maranfilm.de
Emp.: 5
Motion Picture & Video Industries
S.I.C.: 7819
N.A.I.C.S.: 512199
Sabine Tettenborn *(Mng Dir)*

Media & Communication Systems (MCS) GmbH (1)
Konigsbrucker Strasse 88
01099 Dresden, Germany
Tel.: (49) 3518463508
Fax: (49) 3518463603
E-Mail: info@mcs-sachsen.de
Web Site: www.mcs-sachsen.de
Media Representatives
S.I.C.: 7313
N.A.I.C.S.: 541840
Bernhard Obenaus *(Mng Dir)*

Media City Atelier (MCA) GmbH (1)
Altenburger Strasse 13
04275 Leipzig, Germany
Tel.: (49) 341 3500 2299
Fax: (49) 34135002015
E-Mail: info@mca.de
Web Site: www.mca.de
Motion Picture & Video Production
S.I.C.: 7812
N.A.I.C.S.: 512110
Uwe Geissler *(Mng Dir)*
Hans Georg Witthohn *(Mng Dir)*

MotionWorks GmbH (1)
Mansfelder Strasse 56
Halle, 06108, Germany (100%)
Tel.: (49) 345205690
Fax: (49) 3452056922
E-Mail: office@motionworks.eu
Web Site: www.motionworks-halle.com
Emp.: 60
Motion Picture & Video Production
S.I.C.: 7812
N.A.I.C.S.: 512110
Anthony Loeser *(CEO)*

Ottonia Media GmbH (1)
Altenburger Strasse 7
04275 Leipzig, Germany
Tel.: (49) 34135002010
Fax: (49) 34135002015
E-Mail: info@ottonia.de
Web Site: www.ottonia.de
Emp.: 50
Motion Picture & Video Production
S.I.C.: 7812
N.A.I.C.S.: 512110
Frank Hofling *(Mng Dir)*

Saxonia Entertainment GmbH (1)
Altenburger Strasse 9
04275 Leipzig, Germany
Tel.: (49) 34135004100
Fax: (49) 3417660060950
Web Site: www.saxonia-entertainment.de
Emp.: 9
Amusement & Recreation Industries
S.I.C.: 7999
N.A.I.C.S.: 713990
Wolfgang Gunther *(Mng Dir)*

Saxonia Media Filmproduktions GmbH (1)
Altenburger Strasse 7
04275 Leipzig, Germany (100%)
Tel.: (49) 34135001200
Fax: (49) 34135001225
E-Mail: info@saxonia-media.de
Web Site: www.saxonia-media.de
Emp.: 20
Motion Picture & Video Production
S.I.C.: 7812
N.A.I.C.S.: 512110
Sven Sund *(Mng Dir)*

Non-U.S. Subsidiaries:

Bavaria Media Italia S.r.l. (1)
Piazza San Bernardo 108/A
00187 Rome, Italy (100%)
Tel.: (39) 0648907856
Fax: (39) 0648930161
E-Mail: info@bavariamedia.it
Web Site: www.bavariamedia.it
Emp.: 2
Motion Picture & Video Production
S.I.C.: 7812
N.A.I.C.S.: 512110
Philipp Kreuzer *(Mng Dir)*

Noon Filmtechnik Spol.S r.o. (1)
Jihlavska 610-16
14000 Prague, Czech Republic
Tel.: (420) 261262111
Fax: (420) 261262560
E-Mail: noonfilm@volny.cz
Web Site: www.noon.cz
Emp.: 6
Photography Studios Portrait
S.I.C.: 7221
N.A.I.C.S.: 541921
Jiri Ondracek *(Mgr)*

Satel Fernseh- und Filmproduktions GmbH (1)
Limzer Strasse 375
1140 Vienna, Austria
Tel.: (43) 1588720
Fax: (43) 158872106
E-Mail: office@satel.at
Web Site: www.satel.at
Sls.: $15,932,507
Emp.: 14
Film Production Company
S.I.C.: 7812
N.A.I.C.S.: 512110
Heinrich Ambrosch *(Mng Dir)*

Vienna Cine & TV Services GmbH (1)
Hetmanekgasse 1B
1230 Vienna, Austria (100%)
Tel.: (43) 14952238
Fax: (43) 1495223814
E-Mail: info@bavaria-production-services.de
Web Site: www.bavaria-production-services.de
Emp.: 5
Television Broadcasting
S.I.C.: 4833
N.A.I.C.S.: 515120
Marc Bockenforde *(Mng Dir)*

BAVARIA INDUSTRIEKAPITAL AG

Bavariaring 24
80336 Munich, Germany
Tel.: (49) 89 72989670
Fax: (49) 89 729 896710
E-Mail: info@baikap.de
Web Site: www.baikap.de
B8A—(DEU)
Sls.: $923,977,370
Assets: $480,965,063
Liabilities: $367,322,466
Net Worth: $113,642,597
Earnings: $74,922,972
Emp.: 5,106
Fiscal Year-end: 12/31/12
Business Description:
Investment Services
S.I.C.: 6211
N.A.I.C.S.: 523999
Personnel:
Oliver Schmidt *(Chm-Supervisory Bd)*
Reimar Scholz *(Chm-Exec Bd & CEO)*
Hans-Peter Lindlbauer *(Vice Chm-Supervisory Bd)*
Harald Ender *(COO & Member-Exec Bd)*
Supervisory Board of Directors:
Oliver Schmidt
Wanching Ang
Hans-Peter Lindlbauer

BAVARIAN NORDIC A/S

Hejreskovvej 10A
3490 Kvistgaard, Denmark
Tel.: (45) 33268383
Fax: (45) 33268380
E-Mail: info@bavarian-nordic.com
Web Site: www.bavarian-nordic.com
Year Founded: 1994
BAVA—(CSE OTC)
Rev.: $183,360,469
Assets: $277,606,685
Liabilities: $97,305,122
Net Worth: $180,301,563
Earnings: ($43,286,580)
Emp.: 450
Fiscal Year-end: 12/31/12
Business Description:
Novel Vaccines Mfr
S.I.C.: 2834
N.A.I.C.S.: 325412
Personnel:
Asger J. Aamund *(Chm)*
Anders Hedegaard *(Pres & CEO)*
Ole Larsen *(CFO & Exec VP)*
James B. Breitmeyer *(Pres-Cancer Vaccine Div & Exec VP)*
Paul Chaplin *(Pres-Infectious Diseases Div & Exec VP)*
Board of Directors:
Asger J. Aamund
Claus Braestrup
Erik G. Hansen
Peter Kurstein
Anders Gersel Pedersen
Gerard van Odijk
Legal Counsel:
Kromann Reumert
Sundkrogsgade 5
Copenhagen, Denmark

U.S. Subsidiaries:

Bavarian Nordic, Inc. (1)
2425 Garcia Ave
Mountain View, CA 94043
Tel.: (650) 681-4660
Fax: (650) 681-4680
E-Mail: info@bavarian-nordic.com
Emp.: 90
Vaccine Mfr
S.I.C.: 2836
N.A.I.C.S.: 325414
Erin Stonestreet *(Mgr-HR)*

Bavarian Nordic Washington DC, Inc. (1)
2900 K St NW N Tower Ste 450
Washington, DC 20007
Tel.: (202) 568-8090
Fax: (202) 595-9822
E-Mail: info@bavarian-nordic.com
Vaccine Mfr
S.I.C.: 2836
N.A.I.C.S.: 325414

Non-U.S. Subsidiary:

Bavarian Nordic GmbH (1)
Fraunhoferstrasse 13
82152 Martinsried, Germany
Tel.: (49) 89 255 446 030
Fax: (49) 89 255 446 333
E-Mail: info@bavarian-nordic.com
Emp.: 100
Vaccine Mfr
S.I.C.: 2836
N.A.I.C.S.: 325414
Paul Chaplin, *(Gen Mgr)*

BAWAG P.S.K. BANK FUR ARBEIT UND WIRTSCHAFT UND OSTERREICHISCHE POSTSPARKASSE AKTIENGESELLSCHAFT

(d/b/a BAWAG P.S.K. Group)
Georg-Coch-Platz 2
Vienna, 1018, Austria
Tel.: (43) 59905
Fax: (43) 5990522840
E-Mail: invest@bawagpsk.at
Web Site: www.bawagpsk.com
Sales Range: $1-4.9 Billion
Emp.: 6,300
Business Description:
Bank Holding Company; Retail, Commercial & Private Banking Services
S.I.C.: 6712
N.A.I.C.S.: 551111
Personnel:
Byron Haynes *(CEO & Chm-Mgmt Bd)*

Subsidiaries:

easybank AG (1)
Quellenstrasse 51-55
A-1100 Vienna, Austria AT
Mailing Address: (100%)
Postfach 1450
A-1011 Vienna, Austria
Tel.: (43) 1217110
Fax: (43) 057005590
E-Mail: easy@easybank.at
Web Site: www.easybank.at
Direct Banking Services
S.I.C.: 6029
N.A.I.C.S.: 522110
Regina Prehofer *(Chm-Supervisory Bd)*
Sonja Sarkozi *(Mng Dir)*
Jochen Bottermann *(Deputy Chm-Supervisory Bd)*
Robert Cerwinka *(Member-Mgmt Bd)*

BAWAN COMPANY

2nd Floor Hoshan Complex Al-Ahsa Street
PO Box 331
11371 Riyadh, Saudi Arabia
Tel.: (966) 112917799
Fax: (966) 112915858
E-Mail: info@bawan.com.sa
Web Site: www.bawan.com.sa
1302—(SAU)
Business Description:
Building Materials Mfr & Distr
S.I.C.: 2499
N.A.I.C.S.: 321999
Personnel:
Abdullahn Abdul Latif Al Fozan *(Chm)*
Sulaiman Ayesh Abu Lehyah *(CEO)*
Board of Directors:
Abdullahn Abdul Latif Al Fozan
Fozan Mohammed Al Fozan
Basel Mohammed Al Gadhib
Mazen Ahmad Al Jubair
Raed Ahmad Al Mazrou
Raed Ibrahim Al Mudaiheem
Essam Abdulkader Al Muhaidib
Fouad Fahad Al Saleh
Farraj Mutalq Abu Thenain

BAWANG INTERNATIONAL (GROUP) HOLDING LIMITED

6/F 181 Tangle Road Tangyong Village Xinshi Baiyun
Guangzhou, 510410, China
Tel.: (86) 20 8611 7005
Fax: (86) 20 8611 7003
E-Mail: qiong@bawang.com.cn

BaWang International (Group) Holding Limited—(Continued)

Web Site: www.bawang.com.cn
1338—(HKG)
Rev.: $88,313,452
Assets: $119,553,846
Liabilities: $54,001,375
Net Worth: $65,552,471
Earnings: ($98,100,836)
Fiscal Year-end: 12/31/12
Business Description:
Home & Personal Care Products Mfr
S.I.C.: 2844
N.A.I.C.S.: 325620
Personnel:
Qiyuan Chen *(Chm)*
Yuhua Wan *(CEO)*
Sin Yung Wong *(CFO & Sec)*
Xiaodi Shen *(Vice CEO)*
Board of Directors:
Qiyuan Chen
Kaizhi Chen
Jing Guo
Bida Li
Wai Fung Ngai
Xiaodi Shen
Yuhua Wan
Sin Yung Wong
Legal Counsel:
Herbert Smith Freehills
23rd Floor Gloucester Tower 15 Queen's Road Central, China (Hong Kong)

Codan Trust Company (Cayman) Limited
Cricket Square Hutchins Drive
PO Box 2681
Georgetown, Grand Cayman, Cayman Islands
Transfer Agents:
Computershare Hong Kong Investor Services Limited
Rooms 1712-1716 17/F Hopewell Centre 183 Queen's Road East
Wanchai, China (Hong Kong)
Tel.: (852) 2862 8628
Fax: (852) 2865 0990

Codan Trust Company (Cayman) Limited
Cricket Square Hutchins Drive
PO Box 2681
Georgetown, Grand Cayman, Cayman Islands

BAXI PARTNERSHIP LIMITED

Pitreavie Business Park
Dunfermline, KY11 8UU, United Kingdom
Tel.: (44) 845 680 6702
Fax: (44) 846 680 6703
E-Mail: support@baxipartnership.co.uk
Web Site: www.baxipartnership.co.uk
Business Description:
Business Support Services
S.I.C.: 7389
N.A.I.C.S.: 561499
Personnel:
Peter Stocks *(CEO)*
Subsidiary:

Verco Advisory Services Ltd. (1)
Overmoor Farm
Neston, SN13 9TZ Corsham, United Kingdom
Tel.: (44) 1225812102
Fax: (44) 1225812103
E-Mail: info@camcoglobal.com
Web Site: www.vercoglobal.com
Emp.: 30
Environmental Consulting Services
S.I.C.: 8999
N.A.I.C.S.: 541620
Dave Worthington *(Mng Dir)*

Subsidiary:

The Edinburgh Centre for Carbon Management Limited (2)
Tower Mains Studios
18F Liberton Brae, Edinburgh, EH16 6AE, United Kingdom UK
Tel.: (44) 1316665070
Fax: (44) 1316665070
Emp.: 10
Environmental Consulting Services
S.I.C.: 8999
N.A.I.C.S.: 541620

BAY CITY KIA

2037 Lougheed Hwy
Port Coquitlam, BC, V3B 1A7, Canada
Tel.: (604) 944-8904
Fax: (604) 944-7499
Year Founded: 1990
Rev.: $16,084,816
Emp.: 35
Business Description:
New & Used Car Dealers
S.I.C.: 5511
N.A.I.C.S.: 441110
Personnel:
Marco Abenante *(Pres)*

BAY HILL CONTRACTING LTD.

19122 21st Avenue
Surrey, BC, V3S 3M3, Canada
Tel.: (604) 533-3306
Fax: (604) 536-3376
E-Mail: bayhill@uniserve.com
Web Site: www.bayhillcontracting.com
Year Founded: 1986
Rev.: $15,000,190
Emp.: 60
Business Description:
Electrical Contractors
S.I.C.: 1731
N.A.I.C.S.: 238210
Personnel:
R. C. Burns *(Gen Mgr)*

BAY KING CHRYSLER DODGE JEEP

1655 Upper James Street
Hamilton, ON, L9B 2J1, Canada
Tel.: (905) 383-7700
Fax: (905) 383-4834
Web Site: www.bayking.ca
Year Founded: 1968
Rev.: $31,500,460
Emp.: 85
Business Description:
New Car Dealers
S.I.C.: 5511
N.A.I.C.S.: 441110
Personnel:
Hyman R. Richter *(Pres)*
Jacques Poulin *(Sec, Treas & VP)*

BAY LEASING & INVESTMENT LIMITED

Printer Building 7th Floor 5 Rajuk Avenue Motijheel C/A
Dhaka, 1000, Bangladesh
Tel.: (880) 2 9565026
Fax: (880) 2 9565027
E-Mail: info@blilbd.com
Web Site: www.blilbd.com
Year Founded: 1996
BAYLEASING—(DHA)
Business Description:
Financial Services
S.I.C.: 6211
N.A.I.C.S.: 523999
Personnel:
Maswooda Ghani *(Chm)*
Iftekhar Ali Khan *(Mng Dir)*
Sharmin Akther *(Senior Principle Officer)*
M. Maniruz Zaman Khan *(Sec, VP & Head-Fin)*
Mohammad Lutfur Rahman *(Sr VP & Head-Treasury)*
Board of Directors:
Maswooda Ghani
Hasnat Ara Begum
Jahan Ara Begum
Hamida Hossain
Zubayer Kabir
Iftekhar Ali Khan
Zakir Ahmed Khan
Fatema Zahir Majumder
A. K. M. Azizur Rahman
Tarik Sujat

BAY OF QUINTE MUTUAL INSURANCE CO.

13379 Loyalist Parkway
PO Box 6050
Picton, ON, K0K 2T0, Canada
Tel.: (613) 476-2145
Fax: (613) 476-7503
Toll Free: (800) 267-2126
E-Mail: info@bayofquintemutual.com
Web Site: www.bayofquintemutual.com
Year Founded: 1874
Rev.: $16,917,543
Emp.: 32
Business Description:
Insurance & Brokerage Services
S.I.C.: 6411
N.A.I.C.S.: 524298
Personnel:
Jeffery D. Howell *(Pres)*

BAYAN INVESTMENT COMPANY K.S.C.C.

Suad Commercial Complex 11th &12th Floors Al-Qibla
Fahad Al-Salem Street, Kuwait, 35151, Kuwait
Tel.: (965) 1840000
Fax: (965) 22431435
E-Mail: info@bayaninvest.com
Web Site: www.bayaninvest.com
BAYANINV—(KUW)
Rev.: $2,583,277
Assets: $408,395,204
Liabilities: $238,395,017
Net Worth: $170,000,187
Earnings: ($22,384,858)
Fiscal Year-end: 12/31/12
Business Description:
Investment & Portfolio Management Services
S.I.C.: 6211
N.A.I.C.S.: 523110
Personnel:
Faisal Ali Abdul Wahab Al-Mutawa *(Chm)*
Mohammad Hamad Al-Mutawa *(Vice Chm & Mng Dir)*
Wajih Wajih Noujaim *(CFO)*
Board of Directors:
Faisal Ali Abdul Wahab Al-Mutawa
Mohammad Hamed Mubarak Al Ali
Ali Faisal Al-Mutawa
Fawzi Daoud Al-Mutawa
Mohammad Hamad Al-Mutawa

Al-Waha Auditing Office
PO Box 27387
Safat, Kuwait

BAYAN SULU JSC

198 Borodin Street
110006 Kostanay, Kazakhstan
Tel.: (7) 7142562952
E-Mail: bayansulu@bayansulu.kz
Web Site: www.bayansulu.com
BSUL—(KAZ)
Sales Range: $50-74.9 Million
Emp.: 1,340
Business Description:
Confectionery Products Mfr & Sales
S.I.C.: 2064
N.A.I.C.S.: 311340
Personnel:
Vitaliy Tryber *(Pres)*

BAYARD-PRESSE S.A.

18 Rue Barbes
92128 Montrouge, Cedex, France
Tel.: (33) 174316060
Fax: (33) 174316069
E-Mail: communication@bayard-presse.com
Web Site: www.bayardpresse.com
Sales Range: $350-399.9 Million
Emp.: 1,773
Business Description:
Provider of Publishing Services
S.I.C.: 2721
N.A.I.C.S.: 511120
Personnel:
Bruno Frappat *(Pres)*
U.S. Holding:

Bayard Inc. (1)
1 Montauk Ave Ste 200
New London, CT 06320 MN
Mailing Address:
PO Box 6015
New London, CT 06320
Tel.: (860) 437-3012
Fax: (860) 437-3013
Toll Free: (800) 321-0411
Web Site: www.bayard-inc.com
Emp.: 50
Publisher of Magazines & Books
S.I.C.: 7371
N.A.I.C.S.: 541511
Daniel Connors *(Editor-in-Chief)*

BAYDONHILL PLC

(See Under Ekwienox Limited)

BAYER AKTIENGESELLSCHAFT

Kaiser-Wilhelm-Allee 1
D-51368 Leverkusen, Germany
Tel.: (49) 214301
Fax: (49) 2143066328
E-Mail: ir@bayer-ag.de
Web Site: www.bayer.com
Year Founded: 1863
BAY—(DEU)
Sls.: $53,523,719,200
Assets: $69,106,983,120
Liabilities: $44,109,952,390
Net Worth: $24,997,030,730
Earnings: $3,360,040,320
Emp.: 110,500
Fiscal Year-end: 12/31/12
Business Description:
Holding Company
Export
S.I.C.: 6719
N.A.I.C.S.: 551112
Personnel:
Werner Wenning *(Chm-Supervisory Bd)*
Marijn E. Dekkers *(Chm-Mgmt Bd)*
Thomas de Win *(Vice Chm-Supervisory Bd)*
Michael Konig *(Dir-Labor & Member-Mgmt Bd)*
Werner Baumann *(Member-Mgmt Bd-Fin)*
Wolfgang Plischke *(Member-Mgmt Bd-Tech & Innovation & Sustainability)*
Richard Pott *(Member-Mgmt Bd-Strategy & HR)*
Roland Hartwig *(Gen Counsel-Law & Patents)*
Supervisory Board of Directors:
Werner Wenning
Paul M. L. Achleitner
Clemens A. H. Boersig
Thomas de Win
Thomas Ebeling
Thomas Fischer

Peter Hausmann
Reiner Hoffmann
Yuksel Karaaslan
Klaus-Christian Kleinfeld
Petra Kronen
Helmut Gunter Wihelm Panke
Sue H. Rataj
Petra Reinbold-Knape
Michael Schmidt-Kiessling
Ekkehard D. Schulz
Klaus Sturany
Andre van Broich
Ernst-Ludwig Winnacker
Oliver Zuhlke

Groups:

Bayer CropScience AG (1)
Alfred-Nobel-Strasse 50
40789 Monheim, Germany (100%)
Tel.: (49) 2173383125
Fax: (49) 2173380
E-Mail: info@bayercropscience.com
Web Site: www.bayercropscience.com
Sales Range: $5-14.9 Billion
Emp.: 1,800
Crop Protection, Pest Control, Seeds & Biotechnology Products Mfr
S.I.C.: 2879
N.A.I.C.S.: 325320
Werner Baumann *(Chm-Supervisory Bd)*
Klaus Kuhn *(Chm-Supervisory Bd)*
Rudiger Scheitza *(Head-Global Portfolio Mgmt & Dir-Labor)*

Subsidiaries:

Bayer CropScience Deutschland GmbH (2)
Elisabeth Selbert Strasse 4A
D 40764 Langenfeld, Germany De
Tel.: (49) 217320760 (100%)
Fax: (49) 21732076450
Web Site: www.bayercropscience.de
Emp.: 300
Crop Protection & Pesticides Marketer & Whslr
S.I.C.: 5159
N.A.I.C.S.: 424590
Tobias Marchand *(Mng Dir)*

Bayer CropScience Raps GmbH (2)
Streichmuhler Str 8
24977 Grundhof, Schleswig-Holstein, Germany
Tel.: (49) 46 36 89 0
Fax: (49) 46 36 89 22
Web Site: raps.bayer.de
Oil Seed Production Services
S.I.C.: 2079
N.A.I.C.S.: 311224

Bayer CropScience Vermogensverwaltungsgesellschaft mbH (2)
Alfred-Nobel-Str 50 Ambrhein
40789 Monheim, Germany
Tel.: (49) 214 30 1
Fax: (49) 214 30 66328
Web Site: www.bayercropscience.com
Crop Protection Chemicals Mfr & Distr
S.I.C.: 2879
N.A.I.C.S.: 325320

U.S. Subsidiary:

Bayer CropScience LP (2)
2 TW Alexander Dr
Research Triangle Park, NC 27709
Tel.: (919) 549-2000
Toll Free: (866) 992-2937
Web Site: www.bayercropscienceus.com
Sls.: $130,000,000
Emp.: 400
Mfr. of Pesticides: Bifenox, Ethoprop, Merphos, Bromoxynil & Bromonxynil Octanoate
S.I.C.: 2879
N.A.I.C.S.: 325320
Mark Schneid *(CMO-Environmental Science-North America)*
Gilles Galliou *(Pres-Environmental Science-North America)*

Subsidiaries:

Bayer CropScience Holding Inc. (3)
100 Bayer Rd Bldg 4
Pittsburgh, PA 15205-9707
Tel.: (412) 777-2000
Crop Farming Services
S.I.C.: 0191
N.A.I.C.S.: 111998

US Seeds LLC (3)
2528 Alexander Dr
Jonesboro, AR 72401
Tel.: (870) 336-0111
Fax: (877) 787-1610
Agricultural Crop Farming Services
S.I.C.: 0191
N.A.I.C.S.: 111998
Jamie Boone *(Gen Mgr)*

WorldWide Soy Technologies, LLC (3)
210 Drier Rd
De Witt, AR 72042
Tel.: (870) 946-2087
Fax: (870) 946-3253
Web Site: www.soytec.us
Agricultural Chemicals Mfr
S.I.C.: 2879
N.A.I.C.S.: 325320

Units:

Bayer CropScience (3)
8400 Hawthorne Rd
Kansas City, MO 64120-2301
Tel.: (816) 242-2000
Fax: (816) 242-2830
E-Mail: gail.rothrock@bayercropscience.com
Web Site: www.bayercropscience.com
Insecticides & Herbicides Distr
S.I.C.: 2879
N.A.I.C.S.: 325320

Non-U.S. Subsidiary:

Bayer CropScience Inc. (3)
160 Quarry Park Blvd Suite 200
Calgary, AB, T2C 3G3, Canada
Tel.: (403) 723-7400
Fax: (403) 723-7488
Toll Free: (888) 283-6847
E-Mail: info@bayercropscience.ca
Web Site: www.bayercropscience.ca
Emp.: 25
Crop Farming Services
S.I.C.: 0139
N.A.I.C.S.: 111998

Subsidiary:

Bayer CropScience Holdings Inc. (4)
Suite 200 160 Quarry Park Blvd SE
Calgary, AB, T2C 3G3, Canada
Tel.: (403) 723-7400
Fax: (403) 723-7488
Emp.: 7
Crop Farming Services
S.I.C.: 0139
N.A.I.C.S.: 111998
Suman Bose *(Pres & CEO)*

Non-U.S. Subsidiaries:

Bayer CropScience Holding SA (2)
16 Rue Jean Marie Leclair
69009 Lyon, Rhone, France
Tel.: (33) 472 85 45 45
Fax: (33) 472 85 43 83
Investment Management Services
S.I.C.: 6211
N.A.I.C.S.: 523999

Bayer CropScience Ltda. (2)
Rua Domingos Jorge 1100 Predio 9504
Socorro, CEP: 04779-900 Sao Paulo, Brazil
Tel.: (55) 11 56945166
E-Mail: conversebayer@bayercropscience.com
Web Site: www.bayercropscience.com.br
Sales Range: $800-899.9 Million
Emp.: 850
Seeds Mfr & Distr
S.I.C.: 5193
N.A.I.C.S.: 424930
Fabiana Pinho *(Coord-Comm)*

Bayer CropScience Limited (2)
Olympia First Floor Central Avenue
Hiranandani Gardens Powai
Mumbai, 400 076, India In
Tel.: (91) 22 253 1234 (28.45%)
Web Site: www.bayer.co.in
506285—(BOM)
Rev.: $526,350,600
Assets: $447,741,000
Liabilities: $89,677,980
Net Worth: $358,063,020
Earnings: $215,379,180
Emp.: 1,181
Fiscal Year-end: 03/31/13
Agricultural Seed Production
S.I.C.: 0119
N.A.I.C.S.: 111199
Richard van der Merwe *(Vice Chm & Mng Dir)*
Thomas Hoffmann *(CFO)*
Rajiv Wani *(Compliance Officer, Sec & VP-Law, Patents & Compliance)*

Bayer CropScience Limited (2)
230 Cambridge Science Park Milton Road
Cambridge, CB4 0WB, United Kingdom
Tel.: (44) 1223 226500
Fax: (44) 1223 426240
E-Mail: ukinfo@bayercropscience.com
Web Site: www.bayergarden.co.uk
Chemical Products Mfr & Distr
S.I.C.: 2879
N.A.I.C.S.: 325320

Bayer CropScience Norwich Limited (2)
Sweet Briar Road
Norwich, Norfolk, NR6 5AP, United Kingdom
Tel.: (44) 1603242424
Chemical Product Mfr
S.I.C.: 2879
N.A.I.C.S.: 325320

Bayer CropScience N.V. (2)
Emiel Mommaertslaan 14
Diegem, Machelen, 1831, Belgium
Tel.: (32) 25356311
Fax: (32) 25343576
E-Mail: bcs@bayercropscience.com
Web Site: www.bayercropscience.be
Emp.: 5
Crop Protection Chemical Mfr
S.I.C.: 2899
N.A.I.C.S.: 325998
Klaus Koetting *(Mng Dir)*

Bayer CropScience (Portugal) Produtos para a Agricultura, Lda. (2)
Rua Quinta do Pinheiro
Carnaxide, 2794-003, Portugal
Tel.: (351) 21 417 2121
Fax: (351) 21 417 2064
E-Mail: contact@datacombuyer.com
Web Site: www.bayercropscience.pt
Agriculture Fertilizer Mfr
S.I.C.: 2875
N.A.I.C.S.: 325314
Nelson Ambrogio *(Mng Dir)*

Bayer CropScience S.A.S. (2)
16 rue Jean-Marie Leclair
PO Box 310
F-69009 Lyon, Cedex 09, France FR
Tel.: (33) 472854321 (100%)
Fax: (33) 472854383
E-Mail: gunnar.riemann@bayer.com
Web Site: www.bayercropscience.fr
Sales Range: $800-899.9 Million
Emp.: 700
Insecticides, Fungicides, Herbicides, Growth Regulators, Garden & Household Products, Cosmetics & Perfumes; Joint Venture of Aventis S.A. (76%) & Schering AG (24%)
S.I.C.: 2844
N.A.I.C.S.: 325620
Garnier Frank *(Dir Gen)*

Bayer CropScience, S.L. (2)
Parque Tecnologico - C/ Charles Robert Darwin 13
Paterna, Valencian, 46980, Spain
Tel.: (34) 96 196 53 00
Fax: (34) 96 196 53 45
E-Mail: info@bayercropscience.es
Web Site: www.bayercropscience.es
Emp.: 55
Crop Farming & Protection Services
S.I.C.: 0711
N.A.I.C.S.: 115112
Rolf Deege *(Dir Gen)*

Bayer CropScience S.r.l. (2)
Viale Certosa 130
Milan, 20156, Italy
Tel.: (39) 0239781
Fax: (39) 0239722896
Web Site: www.bayercropscience.it
Crop Protection Chemicals Distr
S.I.C.: 5191
N.A.I.C.S.: 424910

Bayer (South East Asia) Pte Ltd. (2)
63 Chulia St OCBC Ctr E 14th Fl
Singapore, 049514, Singapore
Tel.: (65) 6496 1888
Fax: (65) 6496 1490
Web Site: www.bayer.com
Pharmaceutical Products Distr
S.I.C.: 5122
N.A.I.C.S.: 424210

Non-U.S. Subsidiaries:

Bayer CropScience Holdings Pty Ltd. (3)
391-393 Tooronga Rd
Hawthorn East, Melbourne, VIC, 3123, Australia
Tel.: (61) 392486888
Fax: (61) 392486800
Investment Management Services
S.I.C.: 6211
N.A.I.C.S.: 523999

Bayer CropScience, Inc. (3)
Bayer House Canlubang Industrial Estate
Canlubang Calamba
Laguna, 4028, Philippines
Tel.: (63) 2 450 5400
Fax: (63) 2 450 3691
Farm Chemicals & Fertilizer Whslr
S.I.C.: 5169
N.A.I.C.S.: 424690

Bayer CropScience K.K. (3)
Marunouchi Kitaguchi Bldg 1-6-5 Marunouchi
Chiyoda-ku, Tokyo, 100-8262, Japan JP
Tel.: (81) 3 6266 7386
Fax: (81) 352199730
Web Site: www.bayercropscience.co.jp
Emp.: 100
Crop Protection Chemicals Mfr & Distr
S.I.C.: 2879
N.A.I.C.S.: 325320

Bayer CropScience Ltd. (3)
16 F Sambu Bldg 676 Yoksam-dong
Gangnam-gu, Seoul, 135-979, Korea (South)
Tel.: (82) 2 3450 1335
Fax: (82) 2 3450 1396
E-Mail: bayer@bayercropscience.co.kr
Web Site: www.bayercropscience.co.kr
Emp.: 185
Crop Protection Chemicals Mfr & Distr
S.I.C.: 2879
N.A.I.C.S.: 325320

Bayer CropScience (Private) Limited (3)
Bahria Complex II 4th Floor M T Khan Road
Karachi, Pakistan
Tel.: (92) 21 35646700
Crop Farming Services
S.I.C.: 0139
N.A.I.C.S.: 111998

Bayer CropScience Pty Limited (3)
391-393 Tooronga Rd
Hawthorn East, Melbourne, VIC, 3123, Australia
Tel.: (61) 3 9248 6888
Fax: (61) 3 9248 6802
E-Mail: enquiries.australia@bayercropscience.com
Web Site: www.bayercropscience.com.au
Crop Protection Services
S.I.C.: 0723
N.A.I.C.S.: 115114

Nunhems B.V. (2)
Voort 6
6083 AC Nunhem, Netherlands
Tel.: (31) 475 599 222
Fax: (31) 475 599 223
E-Mail: sales@nunhems.com
Web Site: www.nunhems.com
Emp.: 1,700
Vegetable Seeds Distr
S.I.C.: 5159
N.A.I.C.S.: 424590
Steffen Gunther *(CFO)*
Ron Amarel *(Mng Dir-Ops)*

Bayer Aktiengesellschaft—(Continued)

Vicente Navarro *(Mng Dir-Strategy)*
Johan Peleman *(Mng Dir-R&D)*
Ko Remijnse *(Mng Dir-Mktg & Sls)*

Subsidiary:

Nunhems Netherlands B.V. (3)
PO Box 4005
6080 AA Haelen, Netherlands
Tel.: (31) 47 559 9222
Fax: (31) 47 559 9223
E-Mail: nunhems.customerservice.nl@bayer.com
Web Site: www.nunhems.nl
Vegetable Seed Distr
S.I.C.: 5191
N.A.I.C.S.: 424910
Bob Eijmael *(Mgr-Pur)*

U.S. Subsidiary:

Nunhems USA, Inc. (3)
1200 Anderson Corner Rd
Parma, ID 83660
Tel.: (208) 674-4000
Fax: (208) 674-4090
Toll Free: (800) 733-9505
E-Mail: nunhems.customerservice.us@bayer.com
Web Site: www.nunhemsusa.com
Vegetable Seeds Distr
S.I.C.: 5159
N.A.I.C.S.: 424590

Non-U.S. Subsidiaries:

Nunhems Chile S.A. (3)
Avenida Presidente Riesco No 5335 Oficina 2101
Las Condes, Santiago, Chile
Tel.: (56) 2 620 9700
Fax: (56) 2 620 9790
Emp.: 55
Vegetable Seed Distr
S.I.C.: 5159
N.A.I.C.S.: 424590
Albert Schurte *(Gen Mgr)*

Nunhems do Brasil Comercio de Sementes Ltda. (3)
Rua Umbu 302 - Sala 01 - Terreo Alphaville Campinas Empresarial
13098-325 Campinas, Sao Paulo, Brazil
Tel.: (55) 19 3733 9500
Fax: (55) 19 3733 9505
E-Mail: tatiana.lue@bayer.com
Web Site: www.nunhems.com.br
Emp.: 16
Agriculture Seed Distr
S.I.C.: 5191
N.A.I.C.S.: 424910
Fabricio Benatti *(Gen Dir)*

Nunhems France S.A.R.L. (3)
La Rougerie
49140 Soucelles, France
Tel.: (33) 241 311 280
Fax: (33) 241 311 283
E-Mail: nunhems.fr@bayer.com
Web Site: www.nunhems.fr
Emp.: 40
Seed Mfr & Whslr
S.I.C.: 2068
N.A.I.C.S.: 311911
Daniel Kretzschmar *(Mng Dir)*

Nunhems Hungary Kft. (3)
Dobo Ul 37
5000 Szolnok, Hungary
Tel.: (36) 564 21174
Fax: (36) 564 26121
Web Site: www.nunhems.com
Emp.: 8
Crop Planting & Protection Services
S.I.C.: 0191
N.A.I.C.S.: 111998
laszlo Sarfalvi *(Gen Mgr & Country Mgr-Sls)*

Nunhems India Private Limited (3)
Opp Brahama Kumari Ashram Pataudi Road Bhora Kalan
Bilaspur, Gurgaon, Haryana, 122413, India
Tel.: (91) 124 305 1300
Fax: (91) 124 305 1400
E-Mail: nunhems.gurgaon@bayer.com
Web Site: www.nunhems.com
Emp.: 6
Vegetable Seeds Mfr & Distr
S.I.C.: 2037
N.A.I.C.S.: 311411
Sushil Kaushik *(Head-Fin & Accounts)*

Nunhems Italy S.r.l. (3)
Via Ghiarone 2
40019 Sant'Agata Bolognese, Bologna, Italy
Tel.: (39) 051 68107411
Fax: (39) 051 681 7400
E-Mail: nunhems@nunhems.it
Web Site: www.nunhems.it
Vegetable Seeds Distr
S.I.C.: 5159
N.A.I.C.S.: 424590

Nunhems Mexico S.A. de C.V. (3)
Blvd Campestre 2502 1er Piso 101 El Refugio Campestre
37156 Leon, Guanajuato, Mexico
Tel.: (52) 477 772 7960
Fax: (52) 477 772 7967
Web Site: www.nunhems.mx
Emp.: 42
Vegetable Seed Distr
S.I.C.: 5191
N.A.I.C.S.: 424910
Ricardo Ramos Perez *(Mgr-Crop Sls)*

Nunhems Poland Sp. z o.o. (3)
Ul Grochowska 7A
60277 Poznan, Poland
Tel.: (48) 61 6621 427
Fax: (48) 61 6621 429
Web Site: www.nunhems.com
Emp.: 7
Vegetable Seed Distr
S.I.C.: 5159
N.A.I.C.S.: 424590
Alexandra Dolata *(Gen Mgr)*

Nunhems Spain, S.A. (3)
Camino De Los Huertos s/n
Picana, 46210 Valencia, Spain
Tel.: (34) 96 159 4210
Fax: (34) 96 159 1720
E-Mail: nunhems.customerservice.es@bayer.com
Web Site: www.nunhems.es
Vegetable Seed Distr
S.I.C.: 5159
N.A.I.C.S.: 424590

Nunhems Tohumculuk Limited Sirketi (3)
Abdurrahmanlar Yolu Uzeri 3 Km
Serik, Antalya, 7510, Turkey
Tel.: (90) 242 710 22 44
Fax: (90) 242 710 22 55
E-Mail: Suleuman.Kenar@bayer.com
Emp.: 68
Vegetable Seed Distr
S.I.C.: 5159
N.A.I.C.S.: 424590
Suleyman Kenar *(Gen Mgr)*

Bayer HealthCare AG (1)
Chemiepark Gebaude Q30
Kaiser-Wilhelm-Allee, 51368 Leverkusen, Germany (100%)
Tel.: (49) 2143061380
Fax: (49) 2143055563
Web Site: www.bayerhealthcare.com
Sales Range: $15-24.9 Billion
Emp.: 55,700
Mfr. of Healthcare Products
S.I.C.: 2834
N.A.I.C.S.: 325412
Olivier Brandicourt *(Chm-Mgmt Bd)*
Johannes Schubmehl *(CIO)*
Kemal Malik *(Chief Medical Officer & Head-Global Dev-Schering Pharma)*
Werner Baumann *(Pres-Bus Dev & Licensing & Member-Mgmt Bd)*
Gary S. Balkema *(Pres-Consumer Care Div-Worldwide)*
Sandra E. Peterson *(Pres-Diabetes Care Div)*

Subsidiaries:

Bayer Animal Health GmbH (2)
Global Communications New Media Management Building 6210
51368 Leverkusen, Germany De
Tel.: (49) 2173 38 2177
Fax: (49) 2173 38 5518
Web Site: www.animalhealth.bayerhealthcare.com
Rev.: $132,139,000
Pest Control Products Research & Development Services
S.I.C.: 8731
N.A.I.C.S.: 541711
Marijn E. Dekkers *(Chm)*
Dirk Ehle *(Mng Dir)*

Plant:

Bayer Animal Health GmbH - Monheim (3)
Mittelstrasse 11 - 13
40789 Monheim, Germany
Tel.: (49) 2173380
Fax: (49) 2173383414
E-Mail:
Web Site: www.animalhealth.bayer.com
Sales Range: $1-4.9 Billion
Emp.: 100
Animal Health Products & Services
S.I.C.: 0742
N.A.I.C.S.: 541940

U.S. Unit:

Bayer Animal Health - USA (3)
12707 Shawnee Mission Pkwy
Shawnee Mission, KS 66216
Mailing Address:
PO Box 390
Shawnee Mission, KS 66201
Tel.: (913) 268-2000
Fax: (913) 268-2803
Toll Free: (800) 633-3796
Web Site: www.bayer.com
Emp.: 400
Animal Health Products & Services
S.I.C.: 2834
N.A.I.C.S.: 325412
Cary Christensen *(Sr Dir-FAP)*

Plant:

Bayer Animal Health (4)
(Formerly Teva Animal Health, Inc.)
3915 S 48th Street Ter
Saint Joseph, MO 64503 FL
Mailing Address:
PO Box 8039
Saint Joseph, MO 64508
Tel.: (816) 364-3777
Fax: (816) 676-6871
Toll Free: (800) 759-3664
E-Mail:
Sales Range: $50-74.9 Million
Emp.: 300
Veterinary Pharmaceutical Preparations
S.I.C.: 2834
N.A.I.C.S.: 325412
Valerie Welter *(Dir-Quality Mgmt)*

Bayer BioScience GmbH (2)
Alfred-Nobel-Str 50
Monheim am Rhein, 40789, Germany
Tel.: (49) 2173380
Fax: (49) 2173383454
E-Mail: email@bayer.com
Web Site: www.bayer.com
Crop Farming Services
S.I.C.: 0191
N.A.I.C.S.: 111998

Non-U.S. Subsidiary:

Bayer BioScience Pvt. Ltd. (3)
8-1-39 Qutub Shahi Tombs Road Tolichowki
Hyderabad, 500008, India
Tel.: (91) 40 2358 5200
Fax: (91) 40 2356 3029
Hybrid Seed Mfr & Whslr
S.I.C.: 2879
N.A.I.C.S.: 325320

Bayer Gastronomie GmbH (2)
Kaiser-Wilhelm-Allee 3
51373 Leverkusen, Germany
Tel.: (49) 2143056141
Fax: (49) 2143071094
E-Mail: info.leverkusen@bayer-gastronomie.de
Web Site: www.bayer-gastronomie.de
Hotel Management Services
S.I.C.: 7011
N.A.I.C.S.: 721110
Thomas Bernhorster *(Head-Comm)*

Bayer Pharma AG (2)
Mullerstrasse 178
13353 Berlin, Germany De
Tel.: (49) 30 468 1111
Fax: (49) 30 468 1530 5
Web Site: www.bayerpharma.com
Pharmaceutical Products Mfr & Distr
S.I.C.: 2834
N.A.I.C.S.: 325412
Hartmut Klusik *(Chm-Mgmt Bd)*
Andreas Fibig *(CEO)*
Manfred Vehreschild *(Member-Mgmt Bd)*

Subsidiary:

Bayer Schering Pharma AG (3)
Mullerstrasse 178
D-13353 Berlin, Germany DE
Tel.: (49) 304681111
Telex: 18 203 0 sch d
Fax: (49) 3046815305
Web Site: www.bayerhealthcare.com
Sales Range: $15-24.9 Billion
Emp.: 15,726
Pharmaceuticals Researcher, Mfr & Distr
S.I.C.: 2834
N.A.I.C.S.: 325412
Richard Pott *(Chm-Supervisory Bd)*
Hubertus Erlen *(Vice Chm-Supervisory Bd)*
Heinz-Georg Webers *(Vice Chm-Supervisory Bd)*
Andreas Fibig *(CEO)*
Ulrich Kostlin *(Member-Mgmt Bd)*
Kemal Malik *(Member-Mgmt Bd)*
Christine Howarth *(Sec)*

Subsidiaries:

Jenapharm GmbH & Co. KG (4)
Otto Schott Strasse 15
07745 Jena, Germany DE
Tel.: (49) 3641645
Fax: (49) 36416085
E-Mail: astrid.lindorfer@jenapharm.de
Web Site: www.jenapharm.de
Emp.: 80
Developer & Manufacturer of Fertility Control & Hormone Replacement Products
S.I.C.: 2834
N.A.I.C.S.: 325412
Frietrech Walter *(Mng Dir-Clinical Res)*

Subsidiaries:

EnTec Gesellschaft fur Endokrinologische Technologie GmbH (5)
Adolf Reichwein Strasse 22
D 07745 Jena, Germany DE
Tel.: (49) 3641658430
Fax: (49) 3641658436
E-Mail: anke.hundack@jenapharm.de
Emp.: 18
Endocrine Therapy Reseach
S.I.C.: 2833
N.A.I.C.S.: 325411

EnTec Gesellschaft fur Endokrinologische Technologie mbH (5)
Grandweg 64
D 22529 Hamburg, Germany DE
Tel.: (49) 3641658430
Fax: (49) 3641 658 436
E-Mail: hedden@ihf.de
Web Site: www.schering.de
Endocrine Therapy Research
S.I.C.: 2833
N.A.I.C.S.: 325411

Schering GmbH & Co. Produktions KG (5)
Dobereinerstrasse 20
99427 Weimar, Thuringia, Germany DE
Tel.: (49) 36434330
Fax: (49) 3643433350
E-Mail: information@scheringpg.de
Web Site: www.bayer.de
Emp.: 500
Mfr. of Pharmaceuticals
S.I.C.: 2834
N.A.I.C.S.: 325412
Alfred Merz *(Gen Mgr)*

Marotrast GmbH (4)
Otto-Schott-Strasse 15
7745 Jena, Germany
Tel.: (49) 3641 64 69 12
Fax: (49) 3641 64 69 11
E-Mail: info@marotrast.de
Web Site: www.marotrast.de
Pharmaceutical Products Distr
S.I.C.: 5122
N.A.I.C.S.: 424210

Joint Venture:

ALK-Scherax Arzneimittel GmbH (4)
PO Box 22876
Wedel, Germany DE
Tel.: (49) 408707070
Fax: (49) 4103701788
E-Mail: info@alk-scherax.de
Web Site: www.alkscherax.de
Emp.: 83
Allergy Treatment Sales
S.I.C.: 5122
N.A.I.C.S.: 424210
Eckhard Puchert *(Mng Dir)*

Non-U.S. Subsidiaries:

Bayer HealthCare Pharma (4)
92 Je 2 Gongdan 1 Miyang-myun Ansung-si Kyunggi-do
Anseong, Gyeonggi-do, 456 843, Korea (South)
Tel.: (82) 31 670 8700
Fax: (82) 31 677 5819
Web Site: www.bayer.co.kr
Emp.: 260
Pharmaceuticals Mfr
S.I.C.: 2834
N.A.I.C.S.: 325412

Bayer HealthCare Pharmaceuticals Canada (4)
334 Ave Avro
Pointe-Claire, QC, H9R 5W5, Canada
Tel.: (514) 631-7400
Fax: (514) 636-9177
Web Site: www.bayerhealth.com
Emp.: 200
Mfr. of Pharmaceuticals
S.I.C.: 2834
N.A.I.C.S.: 325412
Roland Turck *(Pres)*

Bayer Oy (4)
Pansiontie 47
PO Box 415
20101 Turku, Finland FR
Tel.: (358) 2078521
Fax: (358) 207852020
E-Mail: internet.avoimet@bayer.com
Web Site: www.bayer.fi
Sales Range: $300-349.9 Million
Emp.: 712
Pharmaceutical Products Mfr
S.I.C.: 2834
N.A.I.C.S.: 325412

Bayer Schering Pharma (4)
Bayer House
Strawberry Hill, Newbury, Berkshire, RG14 1JA, United Kingdom UK
Tel.: (44) 1635563000
Fax: (44) 1635563513
E-Mail: bsp-communications@bayerhealthcare.com
Web Site: www.bayerscheringpharma.co.uk
Sales Range: $200-249.9 Million
Emp.: 330
Pharmaceuticals Research, Development & Distr
S.I.C.: 2834
N.A.I.C.S.: 325412
P. S. Woodward *(Mng Dir)*
M. Tybus *(CFO)*

Bayer S.p.A. (4)
Viale Certosa 130
20156 Milan, Italy
Tel.: (39) 0239781
Web Site: www.bayer.it
Emp.: 40
Pharmaceutical Products Mfr
S.I.C.: 2834
N.A.I.C.S.: 325412
Sergio Libaratore *(Pres & CEO)*

Bayer s.r.o. (4)
Safarikova 17
120 00 Prague, 2, Czech Republic
Tel.: (420) 271730661
Fax: (420) 271730957
E-Mail: info@bayer.com
Web Site: www.schering.cz
Emp.: 100
Pharmaceutical Products Mfr
S.I.C.: 2834
N.A.I.C.S.: 325412
Jens Becker *(Mgr-Ops)*

Bayer Thai Company Limited (4)
130-1 North Sathon Road
Silom Bangrak, 10500 Bangkok, Thailand
Tel.: (66) 22327000
Fax: (66) 2236 7738
E-Mail: vicharn.aramvareekul@bayer.co.th
Web Site: www.bayer.co.th
Pharmaceutical Mfr & Distr
S.I.C.: 2834
N.A.I.C.S.: 325412

BayerHealth Care (4)
33 Rue De L Industries
74240 Gaillard, France
Tel.: (33) 450877070
Fax: (33) 450877077
Web Site: www.bayer.com
Emp.: 200
Mfr. & Sales of Pharmaceuticals (OTC)
S.I.C.: 2834
N.A.I.C.S.: 325412
Dirk Ossenberg-Engels *(Pres)*

Berlimed-Productos Quimicos Farmaceuticos e Biologicos Ltda. (4)
Rua Cancioneiro De Evora 255
CEP 04708 010 Sao Paulo, Brazil
Tel.: (55) 1151863000
Fax: (55) 51834576
E-Mail: info@schering.com.br
Web Site: www.schering.com.br
Mfr. of Electroplating Equipment & Processes
S.I.C.: 3559
N.A.I.C.S.: 333249

Berlimed, S.A. (4)
Poligono Santa Rosa Francisco Alonso No7
28806 Alcala de Henares, Spain ES
Tel.: (34) 918871400
Fax: (34) 918871401
E-Mail: carmen.pinilla@bayer.com
Web Site: www.Bayer.es
Emp.: 280
Pharmaceutical Products Mfr
S.I.C.: 2834
N.A.I.C.S.: 325412
Carmen Pinilla *(Sec)*

Nihon Schering KK (4)
Breeze Tower 2 4 9 Umeda Kita ku
Osaka, 530 0001, Japan
Tel.: (81) 661337000
Web Site: www.bayer.co.jp
Pharmaceutical Products
S.I.C.: 2834
N.A.I.C.S.: 325412
Jean-Luc Lowinski *(Pres)*

N.V. Schering S.A. (4)
PO Box 8
B 1831 Mechelen, Belgium BE
Tel.: (32) 27128500
Telex: 25176 sherph b
Fax: (32) 27203305
Web Site: www.schering.be
Emp.: 100
Sales of Pharmaceuticals
S.I.C.: 5122
N.A.I.C.S.: 424210

PT Schering Indonesia (4)
Jl TB Simatupang
Pasar Rebo, Jakarta, 13760, Indonesia
Tel.: (62) 2130014200
Fax: (62) 2130014381
Web Site: www.schering.com
Sales Range: $50-74.9 Million
Emp.: 350
Provider of Pharmaceuticals
S.I.C.: 2834
N.A.I.C.S.: 325412
Parulian Simanjuntak *(Mng Dir)*
Siegfried Wagner *(Chief Security Officer)*

Schering A/S (4)
Herstedostervej 27 29
Postboks 69
2620 Albertslund, Denmark
Tel.: (45) 43290999
Telex: 19775 sch dk
Fax: (45) 43290998
Web Site: www.schering.dk
Sales Range: $1-9.9 Million
Emp.: 14
Pharmaceuticals Sales
S.I.C.: 5122
N.A.I.C.S.: 424210

Schering AG Regional Scientific Office, Malaysia (4)
P O Box 13 4
46200 Petaling Jaya, Malaysia
Tel.: (60) 379551366
Fax: (60) 379551724
Web Site: www.schering.de/eng/index.html
Emp.: 100
Provider of Pharmaceutical Products
S.I.C.: 2834
N.A.I.C.S.: 325412

Schering China Limited (4)
24 Cosco Tower
Grand Millennium Plaza
Bayer Health Care Ltd 801 808, Central, China (Hong Kong)
Tel.: (852) 25293078
Fax: (852) 28734245
Web Site: www.bayer.com.cn
Management Services
S.I.C.: 8742
N.A.I.C.S.: 541611

Schering de Chile S.A. (4)
General Del Canto No 421 Piso 6
Casilla Postal 3926
Santiago, Chile CL
Tel.: (56) 25208200
Fax: (56) 26360660
E-Mail: info@schering.cl
Web Site: www.schering.cl
Pharmaceutical Products Mfr
S.I.C.: 2834
N.A.I.C.S.: 325412
Raener Grause *(Mgr)*

Schering do Brasil Ltda. (4)
Rua Cancioneiro de Evora 255
Caixa Postal 21457
CEP 04602-970 Sao Paulo, Brazil
Mailing Address:
Caixa Postal 21.457
CEP 04602-970 Sao Paulo, Brazil
Tel.: (55) 1151863000
Fax: (55) 11 5181 9939
Web Site: www.schering.com.br
Sales Range: $150-199.9 Million
Emp.: 753
Mfr. of Pharmaceuticals
S.I.C.: 2834
N.A.I.C.S.: 325412
Theo van der Loo *(Pres)*
Rainer Manfred Juengke *(CEO)*

Schering Norge A/S (4)
Ringsveien 3
PO Box 1 83
N 1321 Stabekk, Norway NO
Mailing Address:
PO Box 331
N-1326 Lysaker, Norway
Tel.: (47) 67592000
Fax: (47) 67592001
E-Mail: info.scand@schering.de
Web Site: www.schering.no
Sales Range: $1-9.9 Million
Emp.: 19
Pharmaceutical Products Mfr
S.I.C.: 2834
N.A.I.C.S.: 325412

Schering Pharmaceutical Limited (4)
Youyi Economic And Tech Dist
103 Youyi Rd, 510730 Guangzhou, China
Tel.: (86) 82214680
Fax: (86) 2082214681
E-Mail: matthias.hartisch@schering.de
Web Site: www.schering.com.cn
Emp.: 130
Pharmaceutical Products Mfr
S.I.C.: 2834
N.A.I.C.S.: 325412

Schering Predstavnistvo u Jugoslavijii (4)
Omlaeskahvragea 88 B
11 070 Belgrade, Serbia
Tel.: (381) 113020523
Fax: (381) 112070277
E-Mail: officescg@Bayerhealthcare.com
Web Site: www.schering.com
Pharmaceutical Products Mfr
S.I.C.: 2834
N.A.I.C.S.: 325412
Miroslae Kourinsky *(Pres)*

Schering (Schweiz) AG (4)
Grubenstrasse 6
CH 8045 Zurich, Switzerland
Tel.: (41) 444658111
Telex: 45-82 92 41 sch ch
Fax: (41) 444620754
E-Mail: info@bayer.ch
Web Site: www.bayer.ch
Emp.: 180
Pharmaceutical Products Mfr
S.I.C.: 2834
N.A.I.C.S.: 325412

Schering Taiwan Ltd. (4)
Min Sheng E Rd
PO Box 17-183
Min Sheng E Rd, Taipei, 105, Taiwan
Tel.: (886) 2 8712 5282
Fax: (886) 2 8712 5259
E-Mail: service@schering.com.tw
Web Site: www.schering.com.tw
Emp.: 67
Pharmaceutical Products Mfr
S.I.C.: 2834
N.A.I.C.S.: 325412

Non-U.S. Affiliate:

Schering AG (4)
Parnu Rd 139 E
Eesti Filiaal, EE 11317 Tallinn, Estonia
Tel.: (372) 6558565
Fax: (372) 6 558566
Web Site: www.schering.co.kr/scripts/en/00_meta/contact/addresses.php
Pharmaceutical Products Mfr
S.I.C.: 2834
N.A.I.C.S.: 325412
Katri-Nele Ilves *(Country Mgr)*

Plant:

Bayer Pharma AG - Wuppertal (3)
Friedrich-Ebert-Strasse 217
42117 Wuppertal, Germany
Tel.: (49) 214301
Fax: (49) 2143066328
Web Site: www.healthcare.bayer.com
Pharmaceutical Services
S.I.C.: 2834
N.A.I.C.S.: 325412
Gunnar Riemann *(Pres & Gen Mgr)*

U.S. Subsidiaries:

Bayer HealthCare Pharmaceuticals Inc. (3)
340 Changebridge Rd
Pine Brook, NJ 07058 DE
Mailing Address:
PO Box 1000
Montville, NJ 07045
Tel.: (973) 487-2000
Fax: (973) 487-2300
Web Site: www.pharma.bayer.com
Emp.: 2,400
Pharmaceutical Services
S.I.C.: 2834
N.A.I.C.S.: 325412
Reinhart Franzen *(Pres & CEO)*

Subsidiaries:

MEDRAD, Inc. (4)
100 Global View Dr
Warrendale, PA 15086 PA
Tel.: (412) 767-2400
Fax: (412) 767-4120
Toll Free: (800) 633-7231
Web Site: www.medrad.com
Sales Range: $600-649.9 Million
Emp.: 1,700
Diagnostic Imaging & Therapeutic Medical Device Mfr
Export
S.I.C.: 3841
N.A.I.C.S.: 339112
Joseph Havrilla *(CTO & Sr VP-Corp Dev & Innovations)*
Gary Bucciarelli *(Chief Admin Officer)*
Jeff Owoc *(Sr VP-Ops)*
Julio Rivera *(Sr VP-Corp Compliance)*

Subsidiary:

MEDRAD Interventional/Possis (5)
9055 Evergreen Blvd NW
Minneapolis, MN 55433-5833 MN
Tel.: (763) 780-4555
Fax: (763) 783-8463
Toll Free: (888) 848-7677
E-Mail: market@possis.com
Web Site: www.possis.com
Sales Range: $50-74.9 Million
Emp.: 30
Catheter Systems & Other Medical Devices Mfr

Bayer Aktiengesellschaft—(Continued)

Export
S.I.C.: 3841
N.A.I.C.S.: 339112
James D. Gustafson *(Sr VP-R & D & Engrg & Clinical Evaluation & Chief Quality Officer)*

Non-U.S. Subsidiaries:

Imaxeon Pty. Ltd. **(5)**
Rydalmere Metro Ctr Unit 1 38-46 S St
Rydalmere, Sydney, NSW, 2116, Australia
Tel.: (61) 2 8845 4999
Fax: (61) 2 8845 4998
E-Mail: info@imaxeon.com
Web Site: www.imaxeon.com
Medical Device Mfr
S.I.C.: 3841
N.A.I.C.S.: 339112

Medrad Asia Pte. Ltd. **(5)**
Blk 5000 Ang Mo Kio Ave 05-08 Techplace II
Singapore, 569870, Singapore
Tel.: (65) 67525318
Fax: (65) 67525807
Web Site: www.bayer.com
Emp.: 4
Medical Equipment Whslr
S.I.C.: 5049
N.A.I.C.S.: 423490
Francis Han *(Head-Medrad Asia)*

Medrad Denmark ApS **(5)**
Arne Jacobsens Alle 13
2300 Copenhagen, Denmark
Tel.: (45) 38 16 16 16
Fax: (45) 38 16 16 46
Emp.: 2
Medical Equipment Whslr
S.I.C.: 5049
N.A.I.C.S.: 423490
Frederik R. Jakobsen *(Mgr-Scandinavia)*

Medrad do Brasil Ltda. **(5)**
Av Nove de Julho 5109-11o andar Jardim Paulista
01407-200 Sao Paulo, Brazil
Tel.: (55) 11 3702 6000
Fax: (55) 11 3078 4026
Medical Equipment Distr
S.I.C.: 5047
N.A.I.C.S.: 423450

Medrad Europe B.V. **(5)**
Horsterweg 24
6199 AC Maastricht, Netherlands
Tel.: (31) 433585600
Fax: (31) 433656598
E-Mail: medrad-nederland@medrad.com
Web Site: www.medrad.com
Emp.: 50
Diagnostic Imaging & Therapeutic Medical Device Mfr
S.I.C.: 3841
N.A.I.C.S.: 339112
Peter Cleber *(Reg Dir)*

Medrad France S.A.R.L. **(5)**
32-34 rue du Jura P A Silic
BP 70514
94623 Rungis, France
Tel.: (33) 1 46 86 98 84
Fax: (33) 1 46 86 98 83
E-Mail: medrad-france@medrad.com
Pharmaceutical Goods Whslr
S.I.C.: 5122
N.A.I.C.S.: 424210
Valerie Cournot *(Office Mgr)*

Medrad Italia S.r.l. **(5)**
Via Togliatti 111
27051 Cava Manara, Pavia, Italy
Tel.: (39) 0382 552882
Fax: (39) 0382 552876
E-Mail: medrad-italia@medrad.com
Emp.: 4
Medical Equipment Mfr
S.I.C.: 3845
N.A.I.C.S.: 334510
Enrico Liberali *(Country Mgr)*

Medrad Medical Equipment Trading Company **(5)**
Air China Plz Xiao Yun Lu 36 401-402
Chao Yang District, Beijing, 100027, China
Tel.: (86) 10 84475288
Fax: (86) 10 184475292
Web Site: www.medrad.com
Medical Equipment Distr
S.I.C.: 5047
N.A.I.C.S.: 423450
Da Bo *(Gen Mgr)*

Medrad Medizinische Systeme GmbH **(5)**
Kaiser Wilhelm Allee 70
97332 Leverkusen, Germany
Tel.: (49) 9381 803680
Fax: (49) 214308223
E-Mail: medrad-kundunservice@bayer.com
Web Site: www.medrad.com
Medical Equipment Mfr & Distr
S.I.C.: 3845
N.A.I.C.S.: 334510
Bernd Rehbein *(Mgr-Sls)*

Medrad Mexicana S. de R.L. de CV **(5)**
Calzada Mexico Xochimilco 77 Col San Lorenzo Huipulco Delegacion
Tlalpan, 14370 Mexico, Mexico
Tel.: (52) 5552506575
Fax: (52) 5552509762
Medical Instrument Mfr
S.I.C.: 3841
N.A.I.C.S.: 339112
Rodolfo Diaz *(Mgr-Central America Reg)*

Medrad Sweden AB **(5)**
Neongatan 4B
431 53 Molndal, Sweden
Tel.: (46) 31 748 28 80
Fax: (46) 31 748 28 81
Web Site: www.medrad.com
Emp.: 3
Medical Products Whslr
S.I.C.: 5047
N.A.I.C.S.: 423450
Christian Stromberg *(Country Mgr-Scandinavia)*

Medrad UK Limited **(5)**
Strawberry Hill
Newbury, Berkshire, RG14 1JA, United Kingdom
Tel.: (44) 1635 563999
Fax: (44) 1635 563998
E-Mail: ukcustomersupport@bayer.com
Medical & Hospital Equipment Distr
S.I.C.: 5047
N.A.I.C.S.: 423450
Peter Matthews *(Office Mgr)*

Nihon Medrad K.K. **(5)**
Breeze Tower 2-4-9 Umeda
Kita-ku, Osaka, 530-0001, Japan
Tel.: (81) 661336250
Fax: (81) 663442395
E-Mail: NMKK-CS@Medrad.com
Web Site: www.medrad.com
Medical Equipment Distr
S.I.C.: 5047
N.A.I.C.S.: 423450
Michael Bobrove *(Pres & Dir-Sls-Asia Pacific Reg)*

Units:

Bayer HealthCare Pharmaceuticals Inc. - Wayne **(4)**
6 W Belt Rd
Wayne, NJ 07470-6806
Tel.: (973) 694-4100
Telex: 136 354
Fax: (973) 942-1610
Web Site: www.pharma.bayer.com
Sales Range: $1-4.9 Billion
Emp.: 2,400
Diagnostic & Therapeutic Pharmaceuticals Distr & Mfr
S.I.C.: 2834
N.A.I.C.S.: 325412
Richard Nieman *(Head-Medical Affairs & VP)*

Bayer Vital GmbH **(2)**
Bldg D 162
D 51368 Leverkusen, Germany DE
Tel.: (49) 214301 (100%)
Fax: (49) 2143051458
Web Site: www.bayervital.de
Emp.: 5,000
Pharmaceutical & Healthcare Products Distr
S.I.C.: 2834
N.A.I.C.S.: 325412
Werner Baumann *(Mng Dir)*
Hans Joachim Rothe *(Mng Dir)*

Drugofa GmbH **(2)**
Welserstr 5-7
Cologne, 51149, Germany
Tel.: (49) 22035680
Fax: (49) 2203568350
Transportation Services
S.I.C.: 4789
N.A.I.C.S.: 488999

Generics Holding GmbH **(2)**
Kaiser-Wilhelm-Allee 10
51373 Leverkusen, Germany
Tel.: (49) 214301
Fax: (49) 2143056524
Investment Management Services
S.I.C.: 6211
N.A.I.C.S.: 523999

GP Grenzach Produktions GmbH **(2)**
Emil-Barell-Str 7
79639 Grenzach-Wyhlen, Germany
Tel.: (49) 7624 907 0
Fax: (49) 7624 907 34 20
E-Mail: gp-grenzach@bayerhealthcare.com
Web Site: www.gp-grenzach.de
Emp.: 47
Pharmaceutical Products Mfr
S.I.C.: 2834
N.A.I.C.S.: 325412
Christian Baumann *(CEO)*

KVP Pharma+Veterinar Produkte GmbH **(2)**
Projensdorfer Strasse 324
24106 Kiel, Germany
Tel.: (49) 431 3820 0
Fax: (49) 431 3820 150
E-Mail: info@kvp-kiel.de
Web Site: www.kiel.bayer.com
Emp.: 50
Pharmaceutical Products Mfr
S.I.C.: 2834
N.A.I.C.S.: 325412
Olaf Assenheimer *(Mng Dir)*

Pharma-Verlagsbuchhandlung GmbH **(2)**
Mullerstr 170-178
13353 Berlin, Germany
Tel.: (49) 30 46812601
Fax: (49) 30 46918050
Pharmaceutical Products Mfr
S.I.C.: 2834
N.A.I.C.S.: 325412

Unit:

Bayer HealthCare AG - Dermatology Unit **(2)**
Max-Dohrn-Strasse 10
Berlin, 10589, Germany
Tel.: (49) 30 520 075 650
E-Mail: info.dermatology@bayer.com
Web Site: www.dermatology.bayer.com
Sls.: $417,559,240
Emp.: 12
Pharmaceutical Products Mfr & Distr
S.I.C.: 2834
N.A.I.C.S.: 325412
Marc Lafeuille *(Pres & CEO)*

U.S. Subsidiary:

Conceptus, Inc. **(2)**
331 E Evelyn
Mountain View, CA 94041 DE
Tel.: (650) 962-4000
Fax: (650) 962-5000
E-Mail: webservices@conceptus.com
Web Site: www.conceptus.com
Sls.: $140,731,000
Assets: $243,300,000
Liabilities: $68,928,000
Net Worth: $174,372,000
Earnings: $5,377,000
Emp.: 286
Fiscal Year-end: 12/31/12
Minimally Invasive Devices for Reproductive Medical Applications
S.I.C.: 3841
N.A.I.C.S.: 339112
Lori Ciano *(Exec VP-HR)*
Joseph G. Sharpe *(Exec VP-Ops)*

Non-U.S. Subsidiaries:

Conceptus Medical Limited **(3)**
Sloane House 2 Littleworth Avenue
Esher, Surrey, KT10 9PB, United Kingdom UK
Tel.: (44) 1372849762
Fax: (44) 1372849832
E-Mail: ukinfo@conceptus.com
Web Site: www.essure.co.uk
Emp.: 4
Health Care Services
S.I.C.: 8082
N.A.I.C.S.: 621610
Justin Hall *(Mng Dir)*

Conceptus, SAS **(3)**
50 Ave de St Cloud
78000 Versailles, France
Tel.: (33) 130847515
Fax: (33) 130211925
E-Mail: info@conceptus.com
Web Site: www.conceptus.com
Sales Range: $10-24.9 Million
Emp.: 15
Contraceptive Device Mfr
S.I.C.: 2834
N.A.I.C.S.: 325412

N. Stenning & Co. Pty Ltd. **(3)**
174 Parramatta Road
Camperdown, NSW, 2050, Australia
Tel.: (61) 285949100
Fax: (61) 285949188
E-Mail: nstenning@nstenning.com.au
Web Site: www.nstenning.com.au
Sales Range: $10-24.9 Million
Emp.: 30
Contraceptive Device Mfr
S.I.C.: 2834
N.A.I.C.S.: 325412
Gordon Stenning *(Gen Mgr)*

Provincial Medical Supplies Ltd. **(3)**
51 Pippy Place
Saint John's, NL, A1B 4H8, Canada
Tel.: (709) 754-3033
Fax: (709) 754-3014
Toll Free: (800) 563-8755
Web Site: www.pmscanada.com
Sales Range: $10-24.9 Million
Emp.: 15
Contraceptive Device Mfr
S.I.C.: 2834
N.A.I.C.S.: 325412

U.S. Units:

Bayer HealthCare Biological Products **(2)**
800 Dwight Way
Berkeley, CA 94710-2428
Mailing Address:
PO Box 1986
Berkeley, CA 94701-1986
Tel.: (510) 705-5000
Fax: (510) 705-5542
Web Site: www.livingwithhemophilia.com
Emp.: 1,500
Research Development & Products Facility for Pharmaceutical Drugs
S.I.C.: 2834
N.A.I.C.S.: 325412

Bayer HealthCare Consumer Care **(2)**
36 Columbia Rd
Morristown, NJ 07962-1910
Mailing Address:
PO Box 1910
Morristown, NJ 07962
Tel.: (973) 254-5000
Fax: (973) 408-8126
Toll Free: (800) 348-2240
Web Site: www.bayercare.com
Emp.: 500
Over-the-Counter Consumer Healthcare Products Research, Development, Mfr & Marketing
S.I.C.: 5122
N.A.I.C.S.: 424210
Jay Kolpon *(VP-Strategic Bus Unit-Global)*

Non-U.S. Subsidiaries:

Bayer HealthCare Co. Ltd. **(2)**
Bldg A Jiaming Center No 27 North Dongshanhuan Rd
Chaoyang, Beijing, 100020, China
Tel.: (86) 105 921 8282
Fax: (86) 105 921 8181
Web Site: www.bayerhealthcare.com.cn
Pharmaceutical Products Mfr & Distr
S.I.C.: 2834
N.A.I.C.S.: 325412

Bayer HealthCare Manufacturing S.r.l. (2)
Via Delle Groane 126
Garbagnate Milanese, Milan, 20024, Italy
Tel.: (39) 0239781
Fax: (39) 0239788392
Pharmaceutical Products Mfr
S.I.C.: 2834
N.A.I.C.S.: 325412

Bayer Healthcare S.r.l. (2)
Viale Certosa 130
Milan, 20156, Italy
Tel.: (39) 0239781
Fax: (39) 0239782430
Web Site: www.bayerhealthcare.it
Pharmaceutical Products Distr
S.I.C.: 5122
N.A.I.C.S.: 424210

Quimica Farmaceutica Bayer, S.A. (2)
Ave Baix Llobregat 3-5
08970 Barcelona, Spain (100%)
Tel.: (34) 932284000
Fax: (34) 932174149
E-Mail: healthcare@bayer.es
Web Site: www.bayer.es
Emp.: 1,200
Mfr. of Pharmaceuticals
S.I.C.: 2834
N.A.I.C.S.: 325412
Theo Van Der Loo *(Mng Dir)*

Bayer MaterialScience AG (1)
Chemiepark Gebaude K12
Kaiser-Wilhelm-Allee, D-51368 Leverkusen, Germany De
Tel.: (49) 214 30 1
Fax: (49) 66328
Web Site: www.bayermaterialscience.de
Sales Range: $5-14.9 Billion
Emp.: 14,900
Polymer & Plastic Materials Mfr
S.I.C.: 3089
N.A.I.C.S.: 326199
Patrick Thomas *(CEO)*
Axel Steiger-Bagel *(Chief Admin Officer)*

Subsidiaries:

Bayer MaterialScience GmbH (2)
Otto-Hesse-Strasse 19/T9
64293 Darmstadt, Germany
Tel.: (49) 6151 1303 0
Fax: (49) 6151 1303 500
E-Mail: sales@bayersheeteurope.com
Web Site: www.bayersheeteurope.com
Plastic Product Mfr & Whslr
S.I.C.: 3089
N.A.I.C.S.: 326199

Bayer MaterialScience Oldenburg Verwaltungs-GmbH (2)
Mittelkamp 112
26125 Oldenburg, Germany
Tel.: (49) 4419317257
Fax: (49) 4419317500
E-Mail: info@pu-systems.bayermaterialscience.de
Emp.: 90
Plastic Products Mfr
S.I.C.: 3089
N.A.I.C.S.: 326199

Epurex Films GmbH & Co.KG (2)
Bayershofer Weg 21
Postfach 1652
29699 Walsrode, Germany
Tel.: (49) 5161443393
Fax: (49) 51614433
E-Mail: info@epurex.de
Web Site: www.epurex.de
Polyurethane Products Mfr
S.I.C.: 3083
N.A.I.C.S.: 326130

U.S. Subsidiaries:

Bayer Automotive Products Center (2)
2401 Walton Blvd
Auburn Hills, MI 48326-1957
Tel.: (248) 475-7700
Fax: (248) 475-7701
E-Mail: info@bayermaterialsciencenafta.com
Web Site: www.bayermaterialsciencenafta.com
Emp.: 20
Sales Office of Raw Materials For Plastics
S.I.C.: 3089
N.A.I.C.S.: 326199

Bayer MaterialScience LLC (2)
100 Bayer Rd
Pittsburgh, PA 15205-9741
Tel.: (412) 777-2000
Web Site: www.bayerus.com
Plastics & Polymer Products Mfr
S.I.C.: 3089
N.A.I.C.S.: 326199
John Lemmex *(CFO)*
Jerry MacCleary *(Pres-NAFTA Reg)*
Scott G. Brown *(Gen Counsel, Sec & VP)*
Gerald F. MacCleary *(Sr VP & Head-Mktg & Dev-Polyurethanes)*
Volker Mirgel *(Sr VP-Coatings, Adhesives & Specialties-NAFTA)*

Division:

Bayer MaterialScience LLC (3)
119 Salisbury Rd
Sheffield, MA 01257
Tel.: (413) 229-8711
Fax: (413) 229-8717
Toll Free: (800) 628-5084
E-Mail:
Web Site: www.materialscience.bayer.com
Emp.: 160
Plastic Products Mfr
Import Export
S.I.C.: 3081
N.A.I.C.S.: 326113
Dennis Duff *(Mng Dir)*

Deerfield Urethane, Inc. (2)
8 Fairview Way
Whatley, MA 01093 (100%)
Mailing Address:
8 Fairview Way
South Deerfield, MA 01373-9674
Tel.: (413) 665-7016
Fax: (413) 665-6000
Toll Free: (800) 644-0116
E-Mail: deerfieldurethane@bayerpolymers.com
Web Site: www.deerfieldurethane.com
Emp.: 72
Mfr of Thermoplastic Polyurethane Film
S.I.C.: 3081
N.A.I.C.S.: 326113

Non-U.S. Subsidiaries:

Bayer Antwerpen N.V. (2)
Haven 507 Scheldelaan 420
2040 Antwerp, Belgium BE
Tel.: (32) 35403011 (100%)
Fax: (32) 35416936
E-Mail: info@bayer.be
Web Site: www.bayer.be
Sales Range: $1-4.9 Billion
Emp.: 900
Polymer & Plastic Materials Mfr
S.I.C.: 3089
N.A.I.C.S.: 326199
Uwe Arndt *(Mng Dir)*
Volker Weintritt *(Mng Dir)*

Bayer Hellas AG (2)
Sorou 18-20 Maroussi
Maroussi, 15125 Athens, Greece
Tel.: (30) 210 6187 500
Fax: (30) 210 6187 575
E-Mail:
Sls.: $248,421,320
Emp.: 400
Agrochemicals Distr
S.I.C.: 5169
N.A.I.C.S.: 424690
Aristae Mavrona *(Sec)*

Bayer International S.A. (2)
Route De Beaumont 10
Fribourg, 1700, Switzerland
Tel.: (41) 26 422 81 11
Fax: (41) 26 422 81 76
Emp.: 10
Pharmaceutical Products Distr
S.I.C.: 5122
N.A.I.C.S.: 424210
Nicolas Barras *(Head-Credit & Risk Mgmt)*

Bayer Malibu Polymers Private Limited (2)
Navdeep House 2nd Floor Ashram Road
Ahmedabad, 380 014, India
Tel.: (91) 79 2754 2266
Fax: (91) 79 2754 4400
E-Mail: inquiry@bayermalibu.com
Web Site: www.bayermalibu.com
Polycarbonate Sheet Mfr
S.I.C.: 2821
N.A.I.C.S.: 325211

Bayer MaterialScience A/S (2)
Kronborgvej 24
5450 Otterup, Denmark
Tel.: (45) 63939393
Fax: (45) 70230399
E-Mail: bms.dk@bayer.com
Emp.: 12
Chemical Products Mfr & Whslr
S.I.C.: 2869
N.A.I.C.S.: 325199
Niels Bomholt *(Project Mgr)*

Bayer MaterialScience B.V. (2)
Korte Groningerweg 1a
9607 PS Foxhol, Netherlands
Tel.: (31) 297 280 426
Web Site: www.materialscience.bayer.com
Emp.: 4
Polyurethane Plastic Products Mfr
S.I.C.: 2821
N.A.I.C.S.: 325211

Bayer MaterialScience (China) Company Limited (2)
18th Fl Citigroup Tower No 33 Huayuan Shiqiao Rd
Shanghai, 200120, China
Tel.: (86) 21 6146 8802
Fax: (86) 21 6146 8585
Emp.: 600
Chemical Products Mfr
S.I.C.: 2899
N.A.I.C.S.: 325998
Wolfgang Miebach *(Pres)*
Patrick Sion *(CEO)*

Bayer MaterialScience Ltd. (2)
1-6-5 Marunouchi
Chiyoda-ku, Tokyo, 100-8261, Japan
Tel.: (81) 3 6266 7260
Fax: (81) 3 5219 9706
E-Mail: info@bayerbms.com
Polymer Plastic Materials Mfr
S.I.C.: 2821
N.A.I.C.S.: 325211
Ken Yonemaru *(Pres)*

Bayer MaterialScience Ltd. (2)
Howell center 44 floor
99 Queens Road, Wanchai, China (Hong Kong)
Tel.: (852) 28947256
Fax: (852) 35264718
Web Site: www.bayermaterialscience.com
Emp.: 100
Polymer & Plastic Materials Mfr
S.I.C.: 3089
N.A.I.C.S.: 326199
Berthold Alfes *(Reg Mgr)*

Bayer MaterialScience N.V. (2)
Industriepark Zuid Wakkensesteenweg 47
8700 Tielt, Belgium
Tel.: (32) 51 42 62 00
Fax: (32) 51 42 62 02
Web Site: www.materialscience.bayer.com
Emp.: 13
Plastic Products Mfr & Distr
S.I.C.: 3089
N.A.I.C.S.: 326199
Frank van Butsele *(Mgr-Engrg & Maintenance)*

Bayer MaterialScience Private Limited (2)
Building No C 195 Kolshet Road
Thane, Maharashtra, 400607, India
Tel.: (91) 22 25311234
Fax: (91) 22 25455069
Web Site: www.bayergroupindia.com
Plastic Products Mfr
S.I.C.: 3089
N.A.I.C.S.: 326199

Bayer MaterialScience (Shanghai) Management Company Limited (2)
No 82 Muhua Road Sganghai Chemical Industry Park
Shanghai, China
Tel.: (86) 21 37491000
Plastic Product Mfr
S.I.C.: 3089
N.A.I.C.S.: 326199

Bayer MaterialScience, S.L. (2)
Ctra Vilaseca-La Pineda s/n
Tarragona, 43006, Spain
Tel.: (34) 977 35 83 42
Fax: (34) 977 35 82 20
Emp.: 200
Pharmaceutical Products Mfr
S.I.C.: 2834
N.A.I.C.S.: 325412
Juan Carlos Nebot *(Head-Pur)*

Bayer MaterialScience s.r.o. (2)
Siemensova 2717/4
155 80 Prague, Czech Republic
Tel.: (420) 266 101 111
Fax: (420) 266 101 199
E-Mail: info.cz@bayer.com
Web Site: www.bayer.cz
Emp.: 16
Foam Products Mfr & Distr
S.I.C.: 3086
N.A.I.C.S.: 326140
Antonio Payano *(Mng Dir)*

Bayer MaterialScience Trading (Shanghai) Co. Ltd. (2)
18F Citigroup Tower No 33 Huayuan-Shiqiao Road
Pudong, Shanghai, 200120, China
Tel.: (86) 2161468282
Web Site: www.bayermaterialscience.de/internet/global_portal_cms.nsf/id/AsiaPacificAP_EN
Polymer & Plastic Materials Mfr
S.I.C.: 3089
N.A.I.C.S.: 326199

Bayer SA (2)
Rua Domingos Jorge
Bairro do Socorro, CEP 04799-900 Sao Paulo, Brazil
Tel.: (55) 1156942574
Fax: (55) 1156945585
E-Mail: silvana.miron@bayer.com
Web Site: www.bayer.com
Emp.: 2,000
Polymer & Plastic Materials Mfr
S.I.C.: 3089
N.A.I.C.S.: 326199
Ive Ferreira *(Head-Comm)*

Subsidiaries:

Bayer 04 Immobilien GmbH (1)
Bismarckstrasse 122-124
Leverkusen, 122-124, Germany
Tel.: (49) 214 8660 500
Fax: (49) 214 8660 509
E-Mail: info@bayer04.de
Real Estate Development Services
S.I.C.: 6531
N.A.I.C.S.: 531390

Bayer 04 Leverkusen Fussball GmbH (1)
BayArena Bismarckstr 122 - 124
51373 Leverkusen, Germany
Tel.: (49) 1805040404
Fax: (49) 2148660512
E-Mail: info@bayer04.de
Web Site: www.bayer04.de
Football Club Services
S.I.C.: 7941
N.A.I.C.S.: 711211

Bayer 04 Marketing GmbH (1)
Bismarckstrasse 122-124
Leverkusen, 51373, Germany
Tel.: (49) 214 8660 394
Fax: (49) 214 8660 267
E-Mail: marketing@bio04.de
Web Site: www.bio04.de
Emp.: 2
Sports & Recreation Facilities Operation Services
S.I.C.: 5091
N.A.I.C.S.: 423910
Martin Kowalewske *(Mng Dir)*

Bayer Beteiligungsverwaltung Goslar GmbH (1)
Lilienthalstr 4
Schonefeld, Brandenburg, 12529, Germany
Tel.: (49) 214301
Fax: (49) 2143066328
Investment Management Services
S.I.C.: 6799
N.A.I.C.S.: 523920

Bayer Aktiengesellschaft—(Continued)

Bayer Bitterfeld GmbH (1)
Salegaster Chaussee 1
Bitterfeld, Saxony-Anhalt, 06749, Germany
Tel.: (49) 3493355
Fax: (49) 3493356006
E-Mail: bitterfeld@bayer-ag.de
Web Site: www.bitterfeld.bayer.de
Logistics Consulting Services
S.I.C.: 4731
N.A.I.C.S.: 541614

Bayer Business Services GmbH (1)
Bldg No151 Parkplatz Otto-Bayer-Strasse C
D-51368 Leverkusen, Germany De
Tel.: (49) 214301 (100%)
Fax: (49) 2143066328
E-Mail: info@bayerbbs.com
Web Site: www.bayerbbs.com
Sales Range: $1-4.9 Billion
Emp.: 4,555
Information Technology & Business Management Services
S.I.C.: 8742
N.A.I.C.S.: 541611
Daniel Hartert *(Chm)*
Andreas Resch *(CEO)*

Subsidiary:

Bayer Direct Services GmbH (2)
Kaiser-Wilhelm-Allee 50
51373 Leverkusen, Germany
Tel.: (49) 214 3066 222
Fax: (49) 214 3052 110
Business Support Services
S.I.C.: 7389
N.A.I.C.S.: 561499

Bayer Chemicals AG (1)
Chemiepark Leverkusen Gebaude K10
51369 Leverkusen, Germany
Tel.: (49) 214301
Fax: (49) 214 3051444
Chemical Mfr & Whslr
S.I.C.: 2899
N.A.I.C.S.: 325998

Bayer-Handelsgesellschaft mit beschrankter Haftung (1)
Kaiser-Wilhelm-Allee 20
51373 Leverkusen, Germany
Tel.: (49) 214 30 81949
Fax: (49) 1430267886
Web Site: www.bayer.com
Chemical Product Distr
S.I.C.: 5169
N.A.I.C.S.: 424690
Armin Buchmeier *(Gen Mgr)*

Bayer Industry Services GmbH & Co. OHG (1)
Chemiepark Gebaude Q26
Kaiser-Wilhelm-Allee, D-51368 Leverkusen, Germany De
Tel.: (49) 214301
Fax: (49) 2143021257
Web Site: www.bayerindustry.com
Emp.: 5,500
Chemical Industry Utility Supply, Waste Management, Infrastructure, Safety, Security & Technical Services; Owned 60% by Bayer Aktiengesellschaft & 40% by LANXESS AG
S.I.C.: 8744
N.A.I.C.S.: 561210
Klaus Schafer *(Chm & CEO)*

Bayer Intellectual Property GmbH (1)
Alfred-Nobel-Str 10
Monheim am Rhein, 40789, Germany
Tel.: (49) 2143010
Property Rights Services
S.I.C.: 8399
N.A.I.C.S.: 813311

Bayer MaterialScience Oldenburg GmbH & Co. KG (1)
Mittelkamp 112
26125 Oldenburg, Germany
Tel.: (49) 4419317257
Fax: (49) 4419317500
Web Site: www.materialscience.bayer.com
Pharmaceutical Products Mfr
S.I.C.: 2834
N.A.I.C.S.: 325412

Bayer Real Estate GmbH (1)
Hauptstr 119 Bldg 4809
51373 Leverkusen, Germany
Tel.: (49) 214 30 57673
E-Mail: immoservice@bayer.com
Web Site: www.bayer-realestate.com
Real Estate Management Services
S.I.C.: 6531
N.A.I.C.S.: 531390
Michael Muller *(Mng Dir)*

Bayer Technology Services GmbH (1)
Chemiepark Gebaude K9
Kaiser-Wilhelm-Allee, D-51368 Leverkusen, Germany De
Tel.: (49) 214301 (100%)
Fax: (49) 00492143066328
E-Mail: info@bayertechnology.com
Web Site: www.bayertechnology.com
Emp.: 2,200
Plant Engineering, Technical Process Development & Optimization Services
S.I.C.: 8999
N.A.I.C.S.: 541690
Norbert Kuschnerus *(Head-Process Mgmt Tech)*

Subsidiary:

Ehrfeld Mikrotechnik BTS GmbH (2)
Mikroforum Ring 1
55234 Wendelsheim, Germany
Tel.: (49) 6734 919300
Fax: (49) 6734 919305
E-Mail: info@ehrfeld.com
Web Site: www.ehrfeld.com
Micro Technology Products Research & Development Services
S.I.C.: 8731
N.A.I.C.S.: 541712
Joachim Heck *(Mng Dir)*

U.S. Branch:

Bayer Technology Services Americas (2)
8500 W Bay Rd
Baytown, TX 77523 (100%)
Tel.: (281) 383-6000
Fax: (281) 383-6910
Toll Free: (877) 229-3787
E-Mail: btsamericas@bayer.com
Web Site: www.btsamericas.com
Emp.: 495
Plant Engineering, Technical Process Development & Optimization Services
S.I.C.: 8999
N.A.I.C.S.: 541690

Bayer-Unterstutzungskasse GmbH (1)
Chemiepark Leverkusen Q 26
51368 Leverkusen, Germany
Tel.: (49) 214 3061354
Fax: (49) 214 3066373
Business Management Services
S.I.C.: 7389
N.A.I.C.S.: 561499

Bayer Weimar GmbH & Co. KG (1)
Dobereinerstr 20
99427 Weimar, Germany
Tel.: (49) 3643 433 0
Fax: (49) 3643 433 13 50
E-Mail: Kontakt@bayer-weimar.de
Web Site: www.bayer-weimar.de
Pharmaceutical Products Mfr
S.I.C.: 2834
N.A.I.C.S.: 325412

CleanTech NRW GmbH (1)
Chempark Geb K12
51368 Leverkusen, Germany
Tel.: (49) 214 30 44006
E-Mail: info@cleantechnrw.de
Web Site: www.cleantechnrw.de
Emp.: 20
Cluster Management Services
S.I.C.: 8748
N.A.I.C.S.: 541618
Tony Van Osselaer *(Chm-Exec Bd)*
Ingo Gaida *(Mng Dir & Mgr-Cluster)*

Currenta Geschaftsfuhrungs-GmbH (1)
Kaiser-Wilhelm-Allee 20
51368 Leverkusen, Germany
Tel.: (49) 214 30 1
Fax: (49) 214 30 66328
Financial Management Services
S.I.C.: 6211
N.A.I.C.S.: 523999

Non-U.S. Branch:

Bayer Technology & Engineering (Shanghai) Co., Ltd. (2)
Shanghai Chemical Industrial Park
Lot F3 Muhua Rd, 201507 Shanghai, PR, China CN
Tel.: (86) 2161465100 (100%)
Fax: (86) 2167120393
E-Mail: btsasia_info@bayertechnology.com
Web Site: www.bayertechnology.cn
Emp.: 700
Plant Engineering, Technical Process Development & Optimization Services
S.I.C.: 8999
N.A.I.C.S.: 541690

Epurex Films Geschaftsfuhrungs-GmbH (1)
Bayershofer Weg 21
29699 Bomlitz, Lower Saxony, Germany
Tel.: (49) 5161443301
Fax: (49) 5161443314
Administrative Management Services
S.I.C.: 8742
N.A.I.C.S.: 541611

Erste K-W-A Beteiligungsgesellschaft mbH (1)
Kaiser-Wilhelm-Allee 20
Leverkusen, 51373, Germany
Tel.: (49) 214301
Financial Advisory Services
S.I.C.: 6282
N.A.I.C.S.: 523930

Euroservices Bayer GmbH (1)
Building E47
Leverkusen, 51368, Germany
Tel.: (49) 214301
Fax: (49) 2143062983
Accounting Services
S.I.C.: 8721
N.A.I.C.S.: 541219

Hild Samen GmbH (1)
Kirchenweinbergstr 115
71672 Marbach am Neckar, Germany
Tel.: (49) 7144 8473 11
Fax: (49) 7144 8473 99
E-Mail: hild@bayer.com
Web Site: www.hildsamen.de
Food Products Mfr & Distr
S.I.C.: 2099
N.A.I.C.S.: 311991
Paul Rubitschek *(Gen Mgr)*

Pallas Versicherung AG (1)
Chempark Gebaude Q 26
51368 Leverkusen, Germany
Tel.: (49) 214 30 61398
Fax: (49) 214 30 71289
E-Mail: pallas.privat.pp@bayer.com
Web Site: www.pallas-versicherung.de
General Insurance Services
S.I.C.: 6411
N.A.I.C.S.: 524210

TecArena+ GmbH (1)
Bismarck Strasse 122-124
Leverkusen, 51373, Germany
Tel.: (49) 214 8660 500
Fax: (49) 214 8660 509
Management Consulting Services
S.I.C.: 8748
N.A.I.C.S.: 541618

TECTRION GmbH (1)
Vertreten Durch Den Geschaftsfuhrer Matthias Kuball
51368 Leverkusen, Germany
Tel.: (49) 2133 51 22100
Fax: (49) 2133 51 22164
E-Mail: tec-kundencenter@tectrion.de
Web Site: www.tectrion.de
Pharmaceutical Products Mfr
S.I.C.: 2834
N.A.I.C.S.: 325412

TravelBoard GmbH (1)
Kaiser-Wilhelm-Allee K17
51368 Leverkusen, Germany
Tel.: (49) 214 30 62633
Fax: (49) 214 30 55335
E-Mail: touristik@travelboard.de
Web Site: www.travelboard.de
Emp.: 60
Travel Arrangement Services
S.I.C.: 4729
N.A.I.C.S.: 561599
Patricia Schwarz *(Gen Mgr)*

Zweite K-W-A Beteiligungsgesellschaft mbH (1)
Kaiser-Wilhelm-Allee 20
Leverkusen, 51373, Germany
Tel.: (49) 2141301
Business Management Consulting Services
S.I.C.: 8748
N.A.I.C.S.: 541618

U.S. Division:

Bayer Corporation (1)
100 Bayer Rd
Pittsburgh, PA 15205-9707 IN
Tel.: (412) 777-2000 (100%)
Fax: (412) 777-2034
Toll Free: (800) 422-9374 (Sci Ed Prog)
Web Site: www.bayerus.com
Sales Range: $5-14.9 Billion
Emp.: 22,300
Science & Technology Product Mfr Import Export
S.I.C.: 8731
N.A.I.C.S.: 541712
Philip Blake *(CEO)*
Berry Bier *(CFO)*
Ray Kerins *(Sr VP & Head-Comm & Pub Affairs)*

Divisions:

Bayer Corporation/Coatings & Colorants Division (2)
100 Bayer Rd
Pittsburgh, PA 15205-9741 (100%)
Tel.: (412) 777-2000
Fax: (412) 778-4431
Toll Free: (800) 662-2927
Web Site: www.bayerus.com
Emp.: 2,000
Mfr of Industrial Chemicals Colorants
S.I.C.: 2899
N.A.I.C.S.: 325998

Bayer Corporation/Polyurethanes Division (2)
100 Bayer Rd
Pittsburgh, PA 15205-9707
Tel.: (412) 777-2000
Fax: (412) 778-4431
Web Site: www.bayerus.com
Emp.: 2,000
Polyurethane & Plastic Products for Industrial & Consumer Use
S.I.C.: 2821
N.A.I.C.S.: 325211

Subsidiaries:

Bayer Puerto Rico, Inc. (2)
Lote 6 St 1 Km 25.2 Quebraba Arena
Rio Piedras, PR 00922-1848 PR
Tel.: (787) 622-2937
Fax: (787) 622-2901
Emp.: 20
Drugs, Proprietaries & Sundries
S.I.C.: 5122
N.A.I.C.S.: 424210
Mari T. Musignac *(Mgr-Credit)*

BAYPO Limited Partnership (2)
Hc 2 Box N
New Martinsville, WV 26155
Tel.: (304) 455-3688
Healthcare Consulting Services
S.I.C.: 8999
N.A.I.C.S.: 541690

Subsidiaries:

Baypo I LLC (3)
164 Fairview Dr
New Martinsville, WV 26155-2806
Tel.: (304) 455-3122
Chemical Product Mfr
S.I.C.: 2899
N.A.I.C.S.: 325998

Baypo II LLC (3)
103 Foulk Rd
Wilmington, DE 19803-3742
Tel.: (302) 571-8909
Medical Laboratory Testing Services
S.I.C.: 8734
N.A.I.C.S.: 541380

Co-Ex Corp. (2)
5 Alexander Dr
Wallingford, CT 06492-2429 (100%)
Tel.: (203) 679-0500
Fax: (203) 679-0600
Toll Free: (800) 888-5364
E-Mail: info@co-excorp.com
Web Site: www.co-excorp.com
Emp.: 9
Plastics Sheets & Rods Mfr
S.I.C.: 5162
N.A.I.C.S.: 424610
Erik K. Verhoeff *(Mng Dir)*
Cynthia Siniscalco *(CFO)*
Cosimo Conterno *(Exec VP)*

U.S. Subsidiaries:

Bayer Business and Technology Services LLC (1)
100 Bayer Rd
Pittsburgh, PA 15205-9741
Tel.: (412) 777-2000
Business Support Services
S.I.C.: 7389
N.A.I.C.S.: 561499
Andrew J. Diana *(Pres)*

Bayer International Trade Services Corporation (1)
100 Bayer Rd Bldg 4
Pittsburgh, PA 15205-9707
Tel.: (412) 777-2000
Plastics Material Mfr
S.I.C.: 2821
N.A.I.C.S.: 325211

NippoNex Holdings LLC (1)
100 Bayer Rd Bldg 4
Pittsburgh, PA 15205-9707
Tel.: (412) 777-2000
Investment Management Services
S.I.C.: 6799
N.A.I.C.S.: 523920

NippoNex Inc. (1)
100 Bayer Rd Bldg 4
Pittsburgh, PA 15205-9707
Tel.: (412) 777-2000
Plastic Material Mfr
S.I.C.: 2821
N.A.I.C.S.: 325211

NOR-AM Agro LLC (1)
100 Bayer Rd Bldg 4
Pittsburgh, PA 15205-9707
Tel.: (412) 777-2000
Plastic Material Mfr
S.I.C.: 2821
N.A.I.C.S.: 325211

NOR-AM Land Company (1)
100 Bayer Rd Bldg 4
Pittsburgh, PA 15205-9707
Tel.: (412) 777-2000
Plastic Material Mfr
S.I.C.: 2821
N.A.I.C.S.: 325211

SB Capital Corporation (1)
6701 Beryl Dr
Arlington, TX 76002-5468
Tel.: (817) 707-7305
Business Support Services
S.I.C.: 7389
N.A.I.C.S.: 561499

Schering Berlin Inc. (1)
340 Changebridge Rd
Pine Brook, NJ 07058
Tel.: (973) 487-2000
Fax: (973) 487-2005
Pharmaceutical Product Mfr
S.I.C.: 2899
N.A.I.C.S.: 325998

The SDI Divestiture Corporation (1)
100 Bayer Rd Bldg 4
Pittsburgh, PA 15205-9707
Tel.: (412) 777-2000
Plastic Resin Mfr
S.I.C.: 2821
N.A.I.C.S.: 325211

STWB Inc. (1)
100 Bayer Rd Bldg 4
Pittsburgh, PA 15205-9707
Tel.: (412) 777-2000
Pharmaceutical Product Mfr & Whslr
S.I.C.: 2834
N.A.I.C.S.: 325412

Viterion Telehealthcare LLC (1)
555 White Plains Rd
Tarrytown, NY 10591
Tel.: (914) 333-6600
Fax: (914) 931-5540
Toll Free: (800) 866-0133
E-Mail: info@viterion.com
Web Site: www.viterion.com
Emp.: 30
Healthcare Technology Services
S.I.C.: 8099
N.A.I.C.S.: 621999

Non-U.S. Subsidiaries:

Alimtec S.A. (1)
Carlos Fernandez 260 San Joaquin
Santiago, Chile
Tel.: (56) 25208200
Fax: (56) 25542996
E-Mail: info@alimtec.com
Web Site: www.alimtec.com
Bioactive Ingredients Mfr
S.I.C.: 2836
N.A.I.C.S.: 325414

Bayer A/S (1)
Arne Jacobsens Alle 13
2800 Copenhagen, Denmark
Tel.: (45) 235000
Fax: (45) 235250
Web Site: www.bayers.com
Emp.: 120
Chemical & Pharmaceutical Products Mfr
S.I.C.: 2834
N.A.I.C.S.: 325412
Burkhard Leidemann *(Head-HealthCare)*

Bayer AB (1)
Gustav 3 Blvd 56
PO Box 606
16974 Solna, Stockholm, 16926, Sweden SE
Tel.: (46) 31839800 (100%)
Fax: (46) 858022301
E-Mail: info@bayer.se
Web Site: www.bayer.se
Sls.: $169,200,000
Emp.: 120
Pharmaceutical & Chemical Products
S.I.C.: 2834
N.A.I.C.S.: 325412
Christoph Paschke *(Head-Scandinavia Country Div)*

Bayer AGCO Limited (1)
230 Cambridge Science Park Milton Road
Cambridge, CB4 0WB, United Kingdom
Tel.: (44) 1223 226 500
Fax: (44) 1923 211 580
Emp.: 10
Crop Protection Chemicals Mfr
S.I.C.: 2879
N.A.I.C.S.: 325320

Bayer Agriculture Limited (1)
230 Cambridge Science Park
CB4 0WB Cambridge, United Kingdom
Tel.: (44) 12 23 22 65 00
Fax: (44) 12 23 42 62 40
Emp.: 150
Agricultural Chemicals Mfr
S.I.C.: 2879
N.A.I.C.S.: 325320

Bayer Argentina S.A. (1)
Ricardo Gutierrez 3652
B1605EHD Buenos Aires, Argentina AR
Tel.: (54) 1147627000 (99.9%)
Fax: (54) 1147627100
E-Mail: info@bayer.com.ar
Web Site: www.bayer.com.ar
Sales Range: $700-749.9 Million
Emp.: 1,200
Pharmaceuticals, Organic & Inorganic Chemicals, Dyes, Synthetic Fibers, Agrichemicals, Veterinary Products & Toiletries Mfr
S.I.C.: 2834
N.A.I.C.S.: 325412
Richard Van der Merwe *(Pres & CEO)*

Bayer AS (1)
Drammensveien 147 B
PO Box 14
0212 Oslo, Norway
Tel.: (47) 24111800
Fax: (47) 24111990
Web Site: www.bayernorden.com
Chemical & Pharmaceutical Products Mfr
S.I.C.: 2834
N.A.I.C.S.: 325412
Tone Jahren-Herud *(Mgr-HR)*

Subsidiary:

Algeta ASA (2)
Kjelsasveien 172 A
PO Box 54
Kjelsas, 0411 Oslo, Norway NO
Tel.: (47) 23 00 79 90
Fax: (47) 23 00 79 91
E-Mail: post@algeta.com
Web Site: www.algeta.com
Rev.: $113,550,773
Assets: $194,483,347
Liabilities: $49,874,147
Net Worth: $144,609,200
Earnings: $42,600,340
Fiscal Year-end: 12/31/12
Pharmaceutical Preparation Mfr
S.I.C.: 2834
N.A.I.C.S.: 325412
Oliver Rittgen *(Chm)*
Thomas Ramdahl *(Mng Dir)*
Oystein Soug *(CFO)*
Roger Harrison *(Chief Bus Officer)*
Andreas Menrad *(Chief Scientific Officer)*
Gillies O'Bryan-Tear *(Chief Medical Officer)*
Mike Booth *(Sr VP-Comm & Corp Affairs)*
Alan Cuthbertson *(Sr VP-R&D)*
Kari Gronas Dyvik *(Sr VP-Ops)*
Ragnhild M. Loberg *(Sr VP-Quality & Regulatory Affairs)*

Bayer Australia Limited (1)
875 Pacific Highway
PO Box 903
Pymble, NSW, 2073, Australia AU
Tel.: (61) 293916000 (100%)
Fax: (61) 299883311
Web Site: www.bayer.com
Sales Range: $450-499.9 Million
Emp.: 980
Mfr. of Pharmaceuticals, Over-the-Counter Medicines, Diagnostic Products & Dyes
S.I.C.: 2834
N.A.I.C.S.: 325412
Jacqueline Applegate *(Mng Dir)*

Divisions:

Bayer CropScience Australia Pty. Ltd. (2)
391-393 Tooronga Rd
Hawthorn East, VIC, 3123, Australia
Tel.: (61) 392486888
Fax: (61) 392486800
E-Mail: australia@bayercropscience.com.au
Web Site: www.bayercropscience.com.au
Emp.: 200
Crop Protection Products Mfr
S.I.C.: 2879
N.A.I.C.S.: 325320
Joerg Ellmanns *(Mng Dir)*

Bayer HealthCare Australia (2)
391-393 Tooronga Road
Hawthorn East, VIC, 3123, Australia
Tel.: (61) 392486888
Fax: (61) 392486800
Emp.: 100
Health Care Products Mfr
S.I.C.: 2834
N.A.I.C.S.: 325412
George Ellmanns *(Chm & Mng Dir)*

Bayer MaterialScience Australia (2)
391-393 Tooronga Road
Hawthorn East, VIC, 3123, Australia
Tel.: (61) 95819888
Fax: (61) 392486800
Web Site: www.bayer.com.au
Chemicals & Compounds Mfr
S.I.C.: 2899
N.A.I.C.S.: 325998
Andrew Windsor *(Mng Dir)*

Subsidiary:

Bayer MaterialScience Pty. Ltd. (3)
17-19 Wangara Road
Cheltenham, VIC, 3192, Australia
Tel.: (61) 3 9581 9888
Fax: (61) 3 9583 9003
E-Mail: laserlite@laserlite.com.au
Web Site: www.bayermaterialscience.com.au
Polycarbonate Building Material Mfr
S.I.C.: 3089
N.A.I.C.S.: 326199
Rod King *(Mng Dir)*

Bayer Austria GmbH. (1)
Herdstrasse 6-10
1160 Vienna, Austria AT
Tel.: (43) 171146220 (100%)
Fax: (43) 17114614
E-Mail: office@bayer.at
Web Site: www.bayer.at
Emp.: 241
Sales of Pharmaceutical & Chemical Products
S.I.C.: 5169
N.A.I.C.S.: 424690
Martin Hagenlocher *(Mng Dir)*

Bayer Bulgaria EOOD (1)
Poduyane Distr 5 Rezbarska
Sofia, 1510, Bulgaria
Tel.: (359) 28140111
Fax: (359) 28140111
E-Mail: office@bayer.com
Web Site: www.bayer.bg
Emp.: 15
Pharmaceutical Products Mfr
S.I.C.: 2834
N.A.I.C.S.: 325412
Martin Gerganov *(Mgr-Bus Unit)*

Bayer B.V. (1)
Energieweg 1
PO Box 80
3641 RT Mijdrecht, Netherlands NL
Tel.: (31) 297280666 (92%)
Telex: 16541
Fax: (31) 297284165
E-Mail: info@bayer.nl
Web Site: www.bayer.nl
Sales Range: $500-549.9 Million
Emp.: 300
Pharmaceuticals & Chemicals Mfr Import
S.I.C.: 5169
N.A.I.C.S.: 424690
A. Koersvelt *(CFO)*

Bayer Canadian Holdings Inc. (1)
77 Belfield Road
Etobicoke, ON, M9W 1G6, Canada
Tel.: (416) 248-0771
Fax: (416) 248-1780
Investment Management Services
S.I.C.: 6211
N.A.I.C.S.: 523999

Bayer Capital Corporation B.V. (1)
PO Box 80
Mijdrecht, 3640 AB, Netherlands
Tel.: (31) 29 728 0340
Security Brokerage Services
S.I.C.: 6211
N.A.I.C.S.: 523120

Bayer (China) Limited (1)
34/F Jing Guang Center Hu Jia Lou
Choayang District, Beijing, 100020, China CN
Tel.: (86) 1065973181
Fax: (86) 1065973292
Web Site: www.bayerchina.com.cn
Emp.: 50
Executive Offices
S.I.C.: 9111
N.A.I.C.S.: 921110
Jurgen Dahmer *(Pres-Greater China Grp)*

Bayer Co. (Malaysia) Sdn. Bhd. (1)
T1-14 Jaya 33 No 3 Jalan Semangat Seksyen 13
Petaling Jaya, Selangor, 46200, Malaysia
Tel.: (60) 3 6209 3088
Fax: (60) 3 7960 5718
E-Mail: bayer.malaysia@bayer.com
Pharmaceutical Products Distr
S.I.C.: 5122
N.A.I.C.S.: 424210

Bayer de Mexico, S.A. de C.V. (1)
Blvd Miguel De Cervantes Saavedra 259
Mexico, 11520, Mexico MX
Tel.: (52) 5557283001 (100%)
Fax: (52) 5557283000
E-Mail: info@bayercropscience.com.mx
Web Site: www.bayer.com.mx
Sales Range: $600-649.9 Million
Emp.: 3,400
Mfr. & Marketer of Chemical Products, Pharmaceuticals, Consumer Products, Animal Health Products & Agrichemicals

Bayer Aktiengesellschaft—(Continued)

S.I.C.: 2834
N.A.I.C.S.: 325412
Ralph Guenter Kaiser *(CFO)*

Bayer d.o.o. Sarajevo (1)
Trg Solidarnosti Broj 2a
71000 Sarajevo, Bosnia & Herzegovina
Tel.: (387) 33 941 600
Fax: (387) 33 941 620
Chemical Products Mfr
S.I.C.: 2879
N.A.I.C.S.: 325320

Bayer d.o.o. (1)
Radnicka Cesta 80
Zagreb, 10000, Croatia
Tel.: (385) 16599900
Fax: (385) 16599984
Web Site: www.bayer.hr
Pharmaceutical Product Mfr & Distr
S.I.C.: 2834
N.A.I.C.S.: 325412
Markus Heldt *(Gen Dir)*

Bayer d.o.o. (1)
Airport City Beograd Omladinskih brigada 88b
11070 Belgrade, Serbia
Tel.: (381) 11 2070 270
Fax: (381) 11 2070 236
E-Mail: office@bayer.co.rs
Web Site: www.bayer.co.rs
Chemical Products Mfr & Whslr
S.I.C.: 2899
N.A.I.C.S.: 325199

Bayer d.o.o. (1)
Bravnicarjeva 13
PO Box 2354
1000 Ljubljana, Slovenia
Tel.: (386) 1 5814400
Fax: (386) 1 5814403
Web Site: www.bayer.si
Pharmaceutical Product Whslr
S.I.C.: 5122
N.A.I.C.S.: 424210

Bayer Finance Ltda. (1)
Av Isidora Goyenechea 2800 Oficina 1702
Las Condes
Las Condes, Santiago, Chile
Tel.: (56) 25208417
Emp.: 1
Financial Management Services
S.I.C.: 6211
N.A.I.C.S.: 523999
Claudio Alvarez *(Gen Mgr)*

Bayer Global Investments B.V. (1)
Energieweg 1
Mijdrecht, Utrecht, 3641 RT, Netherlands
Tel.: (31) 297280340
Investment Management Services
S.I.C.: 6211
N.A.I.C.S.: 523999

Bayer Hispania SL (1)
Ave Baex Llobregat 3 5 San Juan Besbib
08970 Barcelona, Spain ES
Tel.: (34) 932284000 (100%)
Fax: (34) 932284423
E-Mail: communication@bayer.com
Web Site: www.bayer.es
Sls.: $433,269,088
Emp.: 500
Mfr. of Pharmaceutical, Chemical & Agricultural Products
S.I.C.: 2834
N.A.I.C.S.: 325412
Reiner Krauser *(VP)*

Bayer Holding Ltd. (1)
1-6-5 Marunouchi
Chiyoda-ku, Tokyo, 100-8268, Japan
Tel.: (81) 3 6266 7010
Fax: (81) 3 5219 9703
Web Site: www.bayer.co.jp
Sls.: $3,091,992,940
Emp.: 339
Investment Management Services
S.I.C.: 6211
N.A.I.C.S.: 523999
Hans-Dieter Hausner *(Pres)*
Hans Cremers *(Sr Mng Dir)*

Bayer Hungaria Kft. (1)
Alkotas u 50
1123 Budapest, Hungary
Tel.: (36) 1 487 4100
Fax: (36) 1 212 1517
E-Mail: info.bayhun@bayer-ag.de
Web Site: www.bayerhungaria.hu
Emp.: 200
Pharmaceutical Products Distr
S.I.C.: 5122
N.A.I.C.S.: 424210
Kokavecz Pal *(Head-Fin & Admin)*

Bayer Inc. (1)
77 Belfield Rd
Toronto, ON, M9W 1G6, Canada (100%)
Tel.: (416) 248-0771
Fax: (416) 248-6762
Web Site: www.bayer.ca
Emp.: 1,000
Pharmaceutical Preparations
S.I.C.: 2834
N.A.I.C.S.: 325412
Philip Blake *(Pres & CEO)*

Bayer Israel Ltd. (1)
36 Hacharash St
Hod Hasharon, 45240, Israel
Tel.: (972) 9 7626700
Fax: (972) 9 7626730
E-Mail: info.bil@bayerhealthcare.com
Pharmaceutical Products Mfr & Distr
S.I.C.: 2834
N.A.I.C.S.: 325412
Tomer Feffer *(Mng Dir)*

Bayer Jinling Polyurethane Co., Ltd. (1)
No 46 Taixin Road
Qixia District, Nanjing, 210038, China
Tel.: (86) 2585311682
Fax: (86) 2585306682
Organic Chemical Mfr
S.I.C.: 2869
N.A.I.C.S.: 325199

Bayer Korea Ltd. (1)
Samsung Boramae Omni Tower 395-62
Sindaebang-dong
Dongjak-Ku, Seoul, 156-712, Korea (South)
Tel.: (82) 2 829 6600
Fax: (82) 2 836 7985
E-Mail: bayer@bayer.co.kr
Web Site: www.bayer.co.kr
Emp.: 600
Crop Protection Chemicals Distr
S.I.C.: 5191
N.A.I.C.S.: 424910
Niels Hessmann *(CEO)*

Bayer Ltd. (1)
4-b Verkhiny Val Str
04071 Kiev, Ukraine
Tel.: (380) 44 220 3300
Fax: (380) 44 220 3301
Web Site: www.bayer.ua
Crop Protection Chemicals Distr
S.I.C.: 5191
N.A.I.C.S.: 424910
Olena Boiko *(Mgr-Quality & Medicinal)*

Bayer Limited (1)
The Atrium Blackthorn Road
Dublin, Ireland
Tel.: (353) 1 2999313
Fax: (353) 2061456
E-Mail: info.ireland@bayerhealthcare.com
Web Site: www.bayer.ie
Pharmaceutical Products Distr
S.I.C.: 5122
N.A.I.C.S.: 424210

Bayer (Malaysia) Sdn. Bhd. (1)
T1-14 Jaya 33 No 3 Jalan Semangat
Seksyen 13
46200 Petaling Jaya, Selangor, Malaysia
Tel.: (60) 3 6209 3088
Fax: (60) 3 7960 5718
E-Mail: bayer.malaysia@bayer.com
Pharmaceutical Products Distr
S.I.C.: 5122
N.A.I.C.S.: 424210

Bayer MaterialScience (Beijing) Company Limited (1)
20 Hong Da Beilu Beijing Development Area Yi Zhuang
Daxing County, Beijing, 100176, China
Tel.: (86) 10 67 88 33 31
Fax: (86) 10 67 88 28 63
Web Site: www.bayersheetchina.com
Emp.: 18
Polycarbonate Sheet Mfr
S.I.C.: 3081
N.A.I.C.S.: 326113
Chin Yih See *(Mgr-Customer Svc)*

Bayer Middle East FZE (1)
PO Box 262369
Jebel Ali, Dubai, United Arab Emirates
Tel.: (971) 48817774
Fax: (971) 48814323
E-Mail: bme_info@bayer-ag.de
Sales Range: $125-149.9 Million
Emp.: 700
Plastic Product Mfr
S.I.C.: 3089
N.A.I.C.S.: 326199

Bayer New Zealand Limited (1)
3 Argus Place
PO Box 2825
Glenfield, Auckland, New Zealand
Tel.: (64) 9 443 3093
Fax: (64) 9 443 3094
Web Site: www.bayer.co.nz
Rev.: $891,611,280
Pharmaceutical Products Mfr
S.I.C.: 2834
N.A.I.C.S.: 325412
Joerg Ellmanns *(Chm & Mng Dir)*

Bayer OU (1)
Lootsa 2
Tallinn, 11415, Estonia
Tel.: (372) 6558565
Fax: (372) 6558565
Medical Equipment Mfr
S.I.C.: 3841
N.A.I.C.S.: 339112

Bayer Oy (1)
Keilaranta 12
PO Box 73
02150 Espoo, Finland
Tel.: (358) 9887887
Fax: (358) 0207858200
E-Mail: markku.eloranta@bayer.fi
Web Site: www.bayer.fi
Chemical & Pharmaceutical Products Mfr
S.I.C.: 2834
N.A.I.C.S.: 325412
Markku Eloranta *(Mgr-HR)*

Bayer Pakistan (Private) Limited (1)
Bahria Complex II 4th Floor M T Khan Road
Karachi, 74000, Pakistan
Tel.: (92) 21 35646700
Fax: (92) 5611694
Emp.: 116
Pharmaceutical Products Mfr
S.I.C.: 2834
N.A.I.C.S.: 325412
Muneeb Ur Rehman *(Mng Dir)*

Bayer Parsian AG (1)
No 264 Dr Fatemi Ave
14186 43914 Tehran, Iran
Tel.: (98) 21 669457 26
Fax: (98) 21 669457 28
E-Mail: bayer.parsian@bayer.com
Web Site: www.bayer.com
Pharmaceutical Products Mfr
S.I.C.: 2834
N.A.I.C.S.: 325412

Bayer Pharma d.o.o. (1)
Bravnicarjeva 13
PO Box 2354
1000 Ljubljana, Slovenia
Tel.: (386) 1 5814400
Fax: (386) 1 5814403
E-Mail: info@bayer.com
Web Site: www.bayer.si
Emp.: 95
Pharmaceutical Products Mfr & Distr
S.I.C.: 2834
N.A.I.C.S.: 325412
Paul Watts *(Gen Mgr)*

Bayer Philippines, Inc. (1)
Canlubang Industrial Estate
Bayer House
Canlubang, 4028 Calamba, Philippines (100%)
Tel.: (63) 495624507200
Fax: (63) 495625493064
Web Site: www.bayer.com
Emp.: 100
Mfr. of Pharmaceuticals & Chemicals
S.I.C.: 2834
N.A.I.C.S.: 325412
Dieter Lonisher *(Gen Mgr)*

Bayer Polyols S.N.C. (1)
49-51 Quai de Dion Bouton
92815 Puteaux, France
Tel.: (33) 1 49 06 56 00
Fax: (33) 1 49 06 52 19
Chemical Product Mfr & Distr
S.I.C.: 2879
N.A.I.C.S.: 325320

Bayer Polyurethanes B.V. (1)
Energieweg 1
Mijdrecht, 3641 RT, Netherlands
Tel.: (31) 297280340
Fax: (31) 297280231
Commercial Banking Services
S.I.C.: 6029
N.A.I.C.S.: 522110

Bayer Portugal S.A. (1)
Rua Qinta do Pinheiro 5
PO Box 666
2794-003 Carnaxide, Portugal PT
Tel.: (351) 214172121 (89%)
Fax: (351) 214172064
E-Mail: contacto@bayer.pt
Web Site: www.bayer.pt
Rev.: $31,400,000
Emp.: 180
Mfr. of Pharmaceuticals & Chemicals
S.I.C.: 2834
N.A.I.C.S.: 325412
Joao Barroco *(Gen Mgr)*

Bayer (Proprietary) Limited (1)
27 Wrench Road
PO Box 143
1600 Isando, South Africa
Tel.: (27) 11 921 5911
Fax: (27) 11 921 5766
E-Mail: zacommunications@bayer.com
Web Site: www.bayer.co.za
Pharmaceutical Products Mfr
S.I.C.: 2834
N.A.I.C.S.: 325412
Hans-Peter Diederichs *(Chm)*
Bjoern Skogum *(CEO)*

Bayer plc (1)
Bayer House Strawberry Hill
Newbury, Berkshire, RG14 1JA, United Kingdom UK
Tel.: (44) 1635563000 (100%)
Fax: (44) 1635563393
E-Mail: communications.ukireland@bayer.com
Web Site: www.bayer.co.uk
Emp.: 500
Mfr. of Healthcare, Crop Science, Polymer & Chemical Products
S.I.C.: 7359
N.A.I.C.S.: 532210

Bayer SA-NV (1)
J.E.Mommaertslaan 14
1831 Diegem, Belgium BE
Tel.: (32) 25356301
Fax: (32) 25391750
E-Mail: info@bayer.com
Web Site: www.bayer.be
Sls.: $101,600,000
Emp.: 350
Chemicals Mfr
S.I.C.: 2899
N.A.I.C.S.: 325998
Markus Arnold *(Mng Dir)*

Bayer SA (1)
Ave Paseo De La Republica 3074
Lima, 27, Peru PE
Tel.: (51) 14219601 (60%)
Fax: (51) 14213381
E-Mail: javier.mogollon.jm@bayer-ag.de
Web Site: www.bayerandina.com
Sls.: $20,819,720
Emp.: 300
Plastic Compounds Mfr
S.I.C.: 2823
N.A.I.C.S.: 325220
Carlos Cornazo *(Gen Mgr)*

Bayer S.A. (1)
Ave Tamanaco Torre Bayer
El Rosal, Caracas, Venezuela VE
Tel.: (58) 2129052111 (100%)
Fax: (58) 2129052164
Web Site: www.bayerandina.com
Emp.: 480
Mfr of Pharmaceuticals & Chemicals
S.I.C.: 2834
N.A.I.C.S.: 325412

Roland Bindovar *(Pres)*

Bayer S.A. (1)
Domingos Jorge 1100
Sao Paulo, 04779 900, Brazil BR
Tel.: (55) 1156945030 (100%)
Telex: 11 54101 BAYE
Fax: (55) 115698156
E-Mail: comuaca@bayer.com
Web Site: www.bayer.com.br
Sales Range: $1-9.9 Million
Emp.: 100
Mfr. & Marketer of Chemical Products, Pharmaceuticals, Consumer Products, Animal Health Products & Agrichemicals
S.I.C.: 2834
N.A.I.C.S.: 325412
Theo Vanderloo *(Pres)*

Non-U.S. Subsidiaries:

Bayer S.A. (2)
Av Americas No 57-52
Bogota, Colombia
Tel.: (57) 1 4142277
Fax: (57) 1 4234070
E-Mail: contacto.bayerandina@bayer.com
Web Site: www.bayerandina.com
Corp Farming Services
S.I.C.: 0139
N.A.I.C.S.: 111998

Bayer S.A. (2)
Eurocenter II Quinto Piso Barreal De Heredia
San Jose, Costa Rica
Tel.: (506) 25898600
Fax: (506) 25898900
Web Site: www.bayer-ca.com
Pharmaceutical Products Distr
S.I.C.: 5122
N.A.I.C.S.: 424210

Bayer S.A. (2)
Km 14 5 Carretera Roosevelt Zona 3 de Mexico
Apartado Postal 1573
01901 Guatemala, Guatemala
Tel.: (502) 2436 9090
Fax: (502) 2436 9700
Pharmaceutical Products Mfr
S.I.C.: 2834
N.A.I.C.S.: 325412

Bayer S.A. (2)
Carlos Fernandez 260
San Joaquin, Santiago, Chile
Tel.: (56) 2 5208200
Fax: (56) 2 5562407
Web Site: www.bayer.cl
Pharmaceutical Products Distr
S.I.C.: 5122
N.A.I.C.S.: 424210

Bayer S.A. (2)
Casilla De Correo 84 Ricardo Gutierrez 3652 1605 Munro Pcia
Buenos Aires, Argentina
Tel.: (54) 11 47627000
Fax: (54) 11 47627100
Web Site: www.bayer.com.ar
Emp.: 1,200
Pharmaceutical Products Mfr
S.I.C.: 2834
N.A.I.C.S.: 325412
Richard van der Merwe *(Pres & CEO)*

Bayer Sante Familiale SAS (1)
33 Rue De L'Industrie
74240 Gaillard, Haute-Savoie, France
Tel.: (33) 4 50 87 70 70
Fax: (33) 4 50 87 70 77
E-Mail: info-bsf@bayer.com
Web Site: www.bayer.com
Emp.: 350
Pharmaceutical Products Mfr & Distr
S.I.C.: 2834
N.A.I.C.S.: 325412
Dirk Ossenberg-Engels *(Mgr-Mktg & Sls)*

Bayer Sante SAS (1)
Parc Eurasante 220 Ave de la Recherche
BP 60 114
59373 Loos, France
Tel.: (33) 3 28 16 34 00
Fax: (33) 3 28 16 39 00
Pharmaceutical Products Mfr & Distr
S.I.C.: 2834
N.A.I.C.S.: 325412

Bayer S.A.S. (1)
13 Rue Jean Jaures
92815 Puteaux, France FR
Tel.: (33) 0149065000 (100%)
Fax: (33) 149065219
Web Site: www.bayer.fr
Emp.: 160
Mfr. of Pharmaceutical, Chemical & Agricultural Products
S.I.C.: 2834
N.A.I.C.S.: 325412
Frank Garnier *(Pres)*

Bayer (SCHWEIZ) AG (1)
Grubenstrasse 6
8045 Zurich, Switzerland (100%)
Tel.: (41) 14658111
Fax: (41) 4414620754
E-Mail: homepage@bayer.ch
Web Site: www.bayer.ch
Rev.: $458,500,000
Emp.: 250
Corporate Business Services
S.I.C.: 7389
N.A.I.C.S.: 561499

Subsidiary:

Berlis AG (2)
Grubenstrasse 6
Zurich, 8045, Switzerland
Tel.: (41) 44 465 84 44
Fax: (41) 44 461 22 64
E-Mail: info@berlis.ch
Web Site: www.berlis.ch
Emp.: 2
Pharmaceutical Drugs Mfr & Whslr
S.I.C.: 2834
N.A.I.C.S.: 325412

Bayer (Sichuan) Animal Health Co., Ltd. (1)
No 189 Section 1 Changcheng Road Xinan Airport Economic
Chengdu, Sichuan, 610225, China
Tel.: (86) 2885860334
Biological Product Mfr
S.I.C.: 2836
N.A.I.C.S.: 325414

Bayer South Africa (Pty.) Ltd. (1)
27 Wrench Rd
PO Box 143
1600 Isando, Gauteng, South Africa (100%)
Tel.: (27) 119215911
Fax: (27) 119215766
E-Mail: contact@bayer.co.za
Web Site: www.bayer.co.za
Sales Range: $700-749.9 Million
Emp.: 600
Mfr. of Pharmaceutical, Diagnostic, Agricultural & Chemical Products
S.I.C.: 2834
N.A.I.C.S.: 325412
Richard van der Merwe *(Co-CEO)*
Bjoern Skogum *(Co-CEO)*

Bayer Sp. z o.o. (1)
Al Jerozolimskie 158
02-326 Warsaw, Poland
Tel.: (48) 22 5723500
Fax: (48) 22 5723555
E-Mail: dsiciomspoland@bayer.com
Web Site: www.bayer.com.pl
Emp.: 300
Pharmaceutical Products Mfr
S.I.C.: 2834
N.A.I.C.S.: 325412
Marcin Rogoz *(Reg Mgr-Sls)*

Bayer S.p.A. (1)
Viale Certosa 130
20156 Milan, Italy IT
Tel.: (39) 0239781 (100%)
Fax: (39) 0239782896
Web Site: www.bayer.it
Sales Range: $1-4.9 Billion
Emp.: 2,322
Mfr. & Marketer of Chemicals, Pharmaceuticals & Agricultural Chemicals, Dyestuffs & Fibers
S.I.C.: 2899
N.A.I.C.S.: 325998
Daniele Rosa *(Mgr-Comm)*

Bayer, spol. s.r.o. (1)
Digital Park II Einsteinova 25
851 01 Bratislava, Slovakia
Tel.: (421) 2 5921 31 11
Fax: (421) 2 5921 33 33
E-Mail: bayer@bayer.sk
Web Site: www.bayer.sk
Emp.: 100
Pharmaceutical Products Distr
S.I.C.: 5122
N.A.I.C.S.: 424210
Antonio Payano *(Gen Mgr)*

Bayer Taiwan Co., Ltd. (1)
54F Xinyi Rd
101 Taipei, Taiwan TW
Tel.: (886) 287221273 (100%)
Fax: (886) 287221189
E-Mail: bayertaiwan@bayerbbs.com
Web Site: www.bayer.com.tw
Emp.: 300
Provider of Pharmaceutical & Chemical Products
S.I.C.: 2834
N.A.I.C.S.: 325412
Steffan Huber *(Mng Dir)*
Bickie Loin *(Coord-Admin)*

Bayer TPU (Shenzhen) Co. Ltd. (1)
No 1 Nan 2nd road Datianyang Songgang street
Bao'an District, Shenzhen, Guangdong, 518105, China
Tel.: (86) 75527068308
Fax: (86) 75527068921
Plastic Material Distr
S.I.C.: 5162
N.A.I.C.S.: 424610

Bayer Turk Kimya Sanayi Limited Sirketi (1)
Fatih Sultan Mehmet Mah Balkan Cad No 53
Umraniye, 34770 Istanbul, Turkey
Tel.: (90) 216 5283600
Fax: (90) 216 5283702
E-Mail:
Web Site: www.bayer.com
Emp.: 200
Chemical Products Mfr
S.I.C.: 2879
N.A.I.C.S.: 325320
Axel Hamann *(CEO)*

Bayer UK Limited (1)
Bayer House Strawberry Hill
Newbury, Berkshire, United Kingdom RG14 1JA
Tel.: (44) 1635 563000
Fax: (44) 1635 563513
E-Mail: communications.ukireland@bayer.co.uk
Web Site: www.bayer.co.uk
Pharmaceutical Products Distr
S.I.C.: 5122
N.A.I.C.S.: 424210

Bayer Uretech Ltd. (1)
8 Chang-Pin E 6th Rd Chang Hwa Changping Industrial Park
Hsien-Hsi Hsiang, Chang-Hua, Taiwan
Tel.: (886) 4791 0099
Fax: (886) 4791 0088
Web Site: www.bayer.com.tw/tc/bayer-uretech.asp
Emp.: 150
Thermoplastic Polyurethane Mfr
S.I.C.: 2821
N.A.I.C.S.: 325211

Bayer Yakuhin, Ltd. (1)
2-4-9 Umeda Kitaku
Kita-ku, Osaka, 530 0001, Japan JP
Tel.: (81) 661337000 (100%)
Fax: (81) 66344 2359
Web Site: www.bayer.co.jp
Sales Range: $800-899.9 Million
Emp.: 1,650
Development, Import, Manufacture & Sales of Pharmaceuticals, Medical Devices & Animal Products
S.I.C.: 2834
N.A.I.C.S.: 325412
Norikazu Eiki *(Pres)*

Bayhealth Comercializacao de Produtos Farmaceuticos Unipessoal Lda. (1)
Rua Quinta Do Pinheiro 5
2794-003 Carnaxide, Portugal
Tel.: (351) 214164200
Fax: (351) 214172068
E-Mail: contact@bayer.com
Pharmaceutical Products Distr
S.I.C.: 5122
N.A.I.C.S.: 424210

Bayhealth, S.L. (1)
Avenida Baix Llobregat 3 - 5
Sant Joan Despi, Barcelona, 8970, Spain
Tel.: (34) 932284331
Fax: (34) 932284408
Web Site: www.bayerhealthcare.es
Pharmaceutical Products Mfr
S.I.C.: 2834
N.A.I.C.S.: 325412
Rainer Kruse *(Gen Mgr)*

Berlimed - Especialidades Farmaceuticas Lda. (1)
Rua Quinta Do Pinheiro 5
Carnaxide, Oeiras, 2794-003, Portugal
Tel.: (351) 214172121
Fax: (351) 214172064
E-Mail: contact@bayer.com
Web Site: www.bayer.com
Pharmaceutical Products Whslr
S.I.C.: 5122
N.A.I.C.S.: 424210

Corporacion Bonima S.A. de C.V. (1)
Carretera Panamericana Km 11 1/2 Ilopango
San Salvador, El Salvador
Tel.: (503) 22950577
Fax: (503) 22961240
Pharmaceutical Products Mfr
S.I.C.: 2834
N.A.I.C.S.: 325412

Euroservices Bayer S.L. (1)
Avda Baix Llobregat 3 - 5
Sant Joan Despi, Barcelona, 8970, Spain
Tel.: (34) 932284000
Fax: (34) 934757222
Business Support Services
S.I.C.: 7389
N.A.I.C.S.: 561499

Intendis Derma, S.L. (1)
Avenida Baix Llobregat 3 - 5
Sant Joan Despi, Barcelona, 08970, Spain
Tel.: (34) 932284331
Fax: (34) 932284408
Pharmaceutical Products Mfr & Distr
S.I.C.: 2834
N.A.I.C.S.: 325412
Rainer Erich Krause *(Mng Dir & Gen Mgr)*

Intendis Manufacturing S.p.A. (1)
Ring Via She 21
20090 Segrate, Milan, Italy
Tel.: (39) 0221651
Fax: (39) 022165820
Pharmaceutical Products Whslr
S.I.C.: 5122
N.A.I.C.S.: 424210

Intendis S.p.A. (1)
Via E Schering 21
Segrate, Milan, 20090, Italy
Tel.: (39) 02 39781
Fax: (39) 02 782740
Web Site: www.intendis.it
Health Care Services
S.I.C.: 8099
N.A.I.C.S.: 621999

Mediterranean Seeds Ltd. (1)
Kibbutz Einat
Einat, 4880500, Israel
Tel.: (972) 3 902 7008
Fax: (972) 3 902 7233
Web Site: www.nunhems.com
Emp.: 15
Vegetable Seed Distr
S.I.C.: 5191
N.A.I.C.S.: 424910
Alexandre Reibel *(Gen Mgr)*

Mediwest Norway AS (1)
Drammensveien 147B
0212 Oslo, Norway
Tel.: (47) 22065710
Fax: (47) 22065715
E-Mail: NorwayCustomerSupport@medrad.com
Web Site: www.medrad.com
Pharmaceutical Products Distr
S.I.C.: 5122
N.A.I.C.S.: 424210

Pandias Re AG (1)
Rue de Neudorf 534
2220 Luxembourg, Luxembourg

Bayer Aktiengesellschaft—(Continued)

Tel.: (352) 267547
General Insurance Services
S.I.C.: 6411
N.A.I.C.S.: 524298

PGS International N.V. **(1)**
Energieweg 1
Mijdrecht, 3641 RT, Netherlands
Tel.: (31) 297280340
Stock Broking Services
S.I.C.: 6211
N.A.I.C.S.: 523120

Productos Quimicos Naturales, S.A. de C.V. **(1)**
Domicilio Conocido S/N Col Ojo De Agua
94450 Veracruz, Mexico
Tel.: (52) 272 728 1100
Fax: (52) 272 728 1329
Chemical Products Mfr
S.I.C.: 2899
N.A.I.C.S.: 325998

P.T. Bayer Indonesia **(1)**
MidPlz 1 11th - 15 Fl Jl Jend Sudirman Kav 10-11
Jakarta, 10220, Indonesia
Tel.: (62) 21 570 3661
Fax: (62) 21 570 3660
Web Site: www.bayer.co.id/eng/coverview.php
Pharmaceutical Products Mfr & Whslr
S.I.C.: 2834
N.A.I.C.S.: 325412
Thomas-Peter Hausner *(Chm)*

PT. Bayer MaterialScience Indonesia **(1)**
MidPlaza 1 11th - 15 Fl Jl Jend Sudirman Kav 10-11
Jakarta, 10220, Indonesia
Tel.: (62) 21 570 3661
Fax: (62) 21 560 40860
Web Site: www.bayer.co.id/eng/coverview.php
Polyether Chemicals Mfr & Whslr
S.I.C.: 2899
N.A.I.C.S.: 325998
Thomas-Peter Hausner *(Chm)*

SIA Bayer **(1)**
Skanstes Iela 50
1013 Riga, Latvia
Tel.: (371) 67845563
Fax: (371) 67895841
Web Site: www.bayer.lv
Emp.: 20
Agricultural Chemicals Mfr
S.I.C.: 2879
N.A.I.C.S.: 325320

Sumika Bayer Urethane Co., Ltd. **(1)**
2-4-9 Umeda
Kita-ku, Osaka, 530-0001, Japan
Tel.: (81) 6 6133 6112
Fax: (81) 6 6344 2464
Plastics Materials Mfr
S.I.C.: 2821
N.A.I.C.S.: 325211

UAB Bayer **(1)**
Zirmunu St 68A
09124 Vilnius, Lithuania
Tel.: (370) 5 233 68 68
Fax: (370) 5 233 68 33
Web Site: www.nordic.bayer.com
Pharmaceutical Products Mfr
S.I.C.: 2834
N.A.I.C.S.: 325412

ZAO Bayer **(1)**
3rd Rybinskaya St 18 build 2
107113 Moscow, Russia
Tel.: (7) 495 234 20 00
Fax: (7) 495 234 20 01
Web Site: www.bayer.com
Emp.: 500
Polycarbonate Products Distr
S.I.C.: 5162
N.A.I.C.S.: 424610
Irina Yasina *(Mgr-Logistics)*

BAYERISCHE BORSE AG

(d/b/a Borse Munchen (Munich Stock Exchange))
Karolinenplatz 6
80333 Munich, Germany
Tel.: (49) 895490450
Fax: (49) 8954904531
E-Mail: info@bayerische-boerse.de
Web Site: www.bayerische-boerse.de
Emp.: 30

Business Description:
Stock Securities Exchange
S.I.C.: 6231
N.A.I.C.S.: 523210

Personnel:
Christine Bortenlanger *(Co-CEO & Member-Mgmt Bd)*
Andreas Schmidt *(Co-CEO & Member-Mgmt Bd)*
Uto Baader *(Co-CEO)*
Hans-Peter Schmid *(Co-CEO)*

Supervisory Board of Directors:
Joe Kaeser
Karl-Hermann Lowe
Thomas Posovatz
Theodor Weimer

BAYERISCHE MASINDUSTRIE A. KELLER GMBH

Rosengasse 12
91217 Hersbruck, Germany
Tel.: (49) 915173010
Fax: (49) 9151730144
E-Mail: info@bmi.de
Web Site: www.bmi.de
Year Founded: 1993
Rev.: $21,802,935
Emp.: 150

Business Description:
Measuring Equipment Mfr
S.I.C.: 3829
N.A.I.C.S.: 334519

Personnel:
Hans Keller *(Mng Partner)*
Herbert Dengler *(Mng Dir)*

BAYERISCHE MOTOREN WERKE AKTIENGESELLSCHAFT

(d/b/a BMW Group)
Petuelring 130
80788 Munich, Germany
Tel.: (49) 893820
Telex: 5 286-9 bmw d
Fax: (49) 8938224418
E-Mail: bmwgroup.customerservice@bmwgroup.com
Web Site: www.bmwgroup.com
Year Founded: 1916
BMW—(DEU EUR)
Rev.: $103,450,472,160
Assets: $177,492,514,500
Liabilities: $136,566,254,160
Net Worth: $40,926,260,340
Earnings: $6,895,082,740
Emp.: 105,876
Fiscal Year-end: 12/31/12

Business Description:
Cars & Motorbikes Mfr & Whslr
S.I.C.: 3711
N.A.I.C.S.: 336111

Personnel:
Joachim Milberg *(Chm-Supervisory Bd)*
Norbert Reithofer *(Chm-Mgmt Bd)*
Karl-Ludwig Kley *(Deputy Chm-Supervisory Bd)*
Stefan Quandt *(Deputy Chm-Supervisory Bd)*
Stefan Schmid *(Deputy Chm-Supervisory Bd)*
Manfred Schoch *(Deputy Chm-Supervisory Bd)*
Milagros Caina Carreiro-Andree *(Member-Mgmt Bd-HR)*
Herbert Diess *(Member-Mgmt Bd-Dev)*
Klaus Draeger *(Member-Mgmt Bd-Pur & Supplier Network)*
Friedrich Eichiner *(Member-Mgmt Bd-Fin)*
Harald Kruger *(Member-Mgmt Bd-Production)*
Ian Robertson *(Member-Mgmt Bd-Sls & Mktg)*
Peter Schwarzenbauer *(Member-Mgmt Bd-Mini, Motorrad, Rolls-Royce & After Sls B)*
Dieter Lochelt *(Gen Counsel)*

Supervisory Board of Directors:
Joachim Milberg
Bertin Eichler
Franz Markus Haniel
Reinhard F. Huttl
Henning Kagermann
Susanne Klatten
Karl-Ludwig Kley
Renate Kocher
Robert W. Lane
Horst Lischka
Willibald Low
Wolfgang Mayrhuber
Dominique Mohabeer
Stefan Quandt
Stefan Schmid
Maria Schmidt
Manfred Schoch
Jurgen Wechsler
Werner Zierer

Subsidiaries:

Alphabet Fuhrparkmanagement GmbH **(1)**
Georg-Brauchle-Ring 50
80788 Munich, Germany
Tel.: (49) 89 99822 0
E-Mail: a-z@alphabet.de
Web Site: www.alphabet.de
Passenger Car Leasing & Rental
S.I.C.: 7515
N.A.I.C.S.: 532112
Marco Lessacher *(CEO)*
Eberhard Schrempf *(Mng Dir)*

Non-U.S. Subsidiaries:

Alphabet Belgium Long Term Rental N.V. **(2)**
Ingberthoeveweg 6
B 2630 Aartselaar, Belgium (100%)
Tel.: (32) 34501818
Fax: (32) 34574131
E-Mail: info@alphabetcarlease.be
Web Site: www.alphabet.be
Emp.: 130
Passenger Car Rental
S.I.C.: 7514
N.A.I.C.S.: 532111
Vim Vatans *(Mgr-Fin)*

Branch:

Alphabet Belgium N.V./S.A. **(3)**
Leuvensesteenweg 400
1930 Zaventem, Belgium
Tel.: (32) 27259090
Fax: (32) 27259191
E-Mail: str@alphabetcarlease.be
Web Site: www.alphabet.be
Passenger Car Rental
S.I.C.: 7514
N.A.I.C.S.: 532111

Alphabet Nederland B.V. **(2)**
Takkebijsters 59
4817 BL Breda, Netherlands (100%)
Mailing Address:
PO Box 6890
Breda, NL-4802 HW, Netherlands
Tel.: (31) 765793200
Fax: (31) 765780030
E-Mail: info@alphabetcarlease.nl
Web Site: www.alphabetcarlease.nl
Emp.: 500
Passenger Car Rental
S.I.C.: 7514
N.A.I.C.S.: 532111
John Spies *(Mng Dir)*

Bavaria Wirtschaftsagentur GmbH **(1)**
Knorrstrasse 147
80788 Munich, Germany (100%)
Tel.: (49) 8938226041
Insurance Broker Firm
S.I.C.: 6411
N.A.I.C.S.: 524298

Subsidiary:

Bavaria Lloyd Reisebuero GmbH **(2)**
Heidemanstrasse 164
80788 Munich, Germany (51%)
Tel.: (49) 89143275
Fax: (49) 8935406139
Web Site: www.bmw.com
Emp.: 25
Travel Agency
S.I.C.: 4724
N.A.I.C.S.: 561510
Raymond Freymann *(Mng Dir)*

BMW Bank GmbH **(1)**
Heidemannstrasse 164
80787 Munich, Germany
Tel.: (49) 893 184 2020
Fax: (49) 893 184 3900
E-Mail: bmw.bank@bmw.de
Web Site: www.bmwbank.de
Automotive Financial Leasing Services
S.I.C.: 6159
N.A.I.C.S.: 522220

BMW Fahrzeugtechnik GmbH **(1)**
Stedtfelder Strasse 2
99819 Krauthausen, Germany
Tel.: (49) 3691 680 0
Fax: (49) 3691 680 204
E-Mail: werkeisenach@bmw.de
Web Site: www.bmw-werk-eisenach.de
Automotive Component Mfr
S.I.C.: 3714
N.A.I.C.S.: 336390

BMW Financial Services GmbH **(1)**
Heidemannstrasse 164
80787 Munich, Germany DE
Tel.: (49) 89318403 (100%)
Fax: (49) 8931844040
E-Mail: bmwbank@bmw.tes
Web Site: www.schering.com
Emp.: 1,500
Provider of Financial Services
S.I.C.: 6099
N.A.I.C.S.: 522320

BMW Finanz Verwaltungs GmbH **(1)**
Petuelring 130
Munich, Bavaria, Germany
Tel.: (49) 893820
Fax: (49) 8938255155
Web Site: www.bmw.de
Financial Management Services
S.I.C.: 6211
N.A.I.C.S.: 523999
Norbert Reithofer *(Gen Mgr)*

BMW Hams Hall Motoren GmbH **(1)**
Petuelring 130
Munich, Bavaria, 80788, Germany
Tel.: (49) 893820
Fax: (49) 893895389
Automotive Engine Mfr
S.I.C.: 3714
N.A.I.C.S.: 336310

BMW Ingenieur Zentrum GmbH & Co. **(1)**
P.O. Box 40 02 40
D-8000 Munich, 40, Germany (100%)
Real Estate Management Company
S.I.C.: 6531
N.A.I.C.S.: 531210

BMW INTEC Beteiligungs GmbH **(1)**
Petuelring 130
Munich, 80809, Germany
Tel.: (49) 893820
Fax: (49) 893895289
Investment Management Services
S.I.C.: 6211
N.A.I.C.S.: 523999

BMW Kundenbetreuung **(1)**
Kundenbetreuung
80788 Munich, Germany (100%)
Tel.: (49) 1802324252, ext. 893820
Fax: (49) 1802123484
E-Mail: kundenbetreuung@bmw.de
Web Site: www.bmw.com
Emp.: 550
Automobile Mfr & Distr
S.I.C.: 3711

N.A.I.C.S.: 336111
Peter Walker *(Gen Mgr-Mktg)*

BMW Leasing GmbH (1)
Heidemannstr 164
Munich, 80787, Germany
Tel.: (49) 89 3184 2137
Fax: (49) 89 3184 4461
E-Mail: bmw.bank@bmw.de
Web Site: www.bmw.de
Emp.: 700
Automotive Financial Leasing Services
S.I.C.: 6153
N.A.I.C.S.: 522220
Hans-Juergen Cohrs *(Gen Mgr)*

BMW M GmbH Gesellschaft fur individuelle Automobile (1)
Preussenstrasse 45
80809 Munich, Germany
Tel.: (49) 89 329030
Fax: (49) 89 32903782
Automobile Distr
S.I.C.: 5012
N.A.I.C.S.: 423110

BMW Maschinenfabrik Spandau GmbH (1)
Am Juliusstrum 14
13599 Berlin, Germany (100%)
Tel.: (49) 33962250
Fax: (49) 3033964038
Web Site: www.bmw.ag
Mfr. of BMW Automobiles
S.I.C.: 3711
N.A.I.C.S.: 336111

Joint Venture:

SGL Automotive Carbon Fibers GmbH & Co. KG (1)
Anton-Ditt-Bogen 5
80939 Munich, Germany
Tel.: (49) 89 316 0568 0
E-Mail: info@sglacf.de
Web Site: www.sgl-acf.com
Mfr of Non-Crimp Carbon Fiber Fabrics; Joint Venture of SGL Carbon AG & BMW Group
S.I.C.: 3624
N.A.I.C.S.: 335991
Jorg Pohlman *(Mng Dir)*
Andreas Wullner *(Mng Dir)*

Plants:

Bayerische Motoren Werke Aktiengesellschaft - Berlin Plant (1)
Am Juliusturm 14-38
13599 Berlin, Germany
Tel.: (49) 30 33 96 20 20
Fax: (49) 30 33 96 26 56
E-Mail: info-werk-berlin@bmw.de
Automobile Mfr
S.I.C.: 3711
N.A.I.C.S.: 336111

Bayerische Motoren Werke Aktiengesellschaft - Leipzig Plant (1)
BMW Allee 1
04349 Leipzig, Germany
Tel.: (49) 341 445 0
Fax: (49) 341 445 50010
E-Mail: info.werk-leipzig@bmw.de
Web Site: www.bmw-plant-leipzig.com
Automobile Mfr
S.I.C.: 3711
N.A.I.C.S.: 336111

Bayerische Motoren Werke Aktiengesellschaft - Munich Plant (1)
Petuelring 130
80788 Munich, Germany
Tel.: (49) 89 12 501 6001
E-Mail: info@monocom.com
Web Site: www.bmw-werk-muenchen.de
Automobile Mfr
S.I.C.: 3711
N.A.I.C.S.: 336111

Bayerische Motoren Werke Aktiengesellschaft - Wackersdorf Plant (1)
Oskar-von-Miller-Strasse 21
92442 Wackersdorf, Germany
Tel.: (49) 94316307806
Fax: (49) 94316307815
Automobile Mfr
S.I.C.: 3711
N.A.I.C.S.: 336111

U.S. Subsidiaries:

BMW Manufacturing Co., LLC (1)
1400 Hwy 101 S
Greer, SC 29651-6731 SC
Mailing Address: (100%)
PO Box 11000
Spartanburg, SC 29304-4100
Tel.: (864) 989-6000
Web Site: www.bmwusfactory.com
Sls.: $348,700,000
Emp.: 5,000
Automobile Assembly Including Specialty Automobiles
S.I.C.: 3711
N.A.I.C.S.: 336111
Helmut Leube *(Pres)*

BMW of North America, LLC (1)
300 Chestnut Ridge Rd
Woodcliff Lake, NJ 07675 (100%)
Mailing Address:
PO Box 1227
Westwood, NJ 07675-1227
Tel.: (201) 307-4000
Fax: (201) 307-4095
Toll Free: (800) 831-1117
Web Site: www.bmwgroupna.com
Emp.: 900
BMW Automobiles, Motorcycles, Parts & Accessories Mfr & Sales Import
S.I.C.: 5012
N.A.I.C.S.: 423110
Peter Miles *(Exec VP-Ops)*

Subsidiaries:

BMW Bank of North America Inc. (2)
2735 E Parleys Way Ste 301
Salt Lake City, UT 84109 UT
Tel.: (801) 461-6500
Fax: (801) 461-6594
Toll Free: (877) 269-3655
Web Site: www.bmwusa.com
Emp.: 35
Financial Services
S.I.C.: 6159
N.A.I.C.S.: 522298
Jim O'Donnell *(Pres)*
Mike Kobayashi *(CFO)*

BMW Financial Services NA, LLC (2)
300 Chestnut Rdg Rd
Woodcliff Lake, NJ 07677-7739 NJ
Mailing Address:
PO Box 1227
Westwood, NJ 07675-1227
Tel.: (201) 307-4000
Fax: (201) 307-4095
Web Site: www.bmwusa.com
Rev.: $83,000,000
Emp.: 400
Automobile Finance Leasing
S.I.C.: 6153
N.A.I.C.S.: 522220
Jim Gonnell *(Pres)*

BMW Leasing Corp. (2)
PO Box 3608
Dublin, OH 43016-3606 (100%)
Toll Free: (800) 578-5000
Web Site: www.fs.bmwusa.com
Finance Leasing of Automobiles
S.I.C.: 7515
N.A.I.C.S.: 532112

BMW US Capital, LLC (1)
300 Chestnut Ridge Rd
Woodcliff Lake, NJ 07677-1227
Tel.: (201) 307-4000
Fax: (201) 307-0264
Financial Management Services
S.I.C.: 6211
N.A.I.C.S.: 523999

BMW (US) Holding Corporation (1)
1100 N Market St Ste 780
Wilmington, DE 19801-1297
Tel.: (201) 307-4000
Holding Company
S.I.C.: 3589
N.A.I.C.S.: 333318
Tom Purves *(Chm & CEO)*

Subsidiaries:

BMW of Manhattan Inc. (2)
555 W 57th St
New York, NY 10019-2925 NY
Tel.: (212) 586-2269
Fax: (212) 262-8722
Web Site: www.bmwnyc.com
Rev.: $25,700,000
Emp.: 170
Automobiles New & Used
S.I.C.: 5511
N.A.I.C.S.: 441110
Jeff Falk *(CFO)*

Westchester BMW Inc. (2)
525 Tarrytown Rd
White Plains, NY 10607-1315 NY
Tel.: (914) 761-5555 (100%)
Fax: (914) 761-7297
Web Site: www.westchesterbmw.com
Rev.: $63,000,000
Emp.: 121
Car Dealership
S.I.C.: 5511
N.A.I.C.S.: 441110
Andre Accurso *(Mgr-Sls)*

Designworks USA (1)
2201 Corporate Ctr Dr
Newbury Park, CA 91320-1421 CA
Tel.: (805) 499-9590
Fax: (805) 499-9650
E-Mail: contact@designworksusa.com
Web Site: www.designworksusa.com
Emp.: 115
Designing Services For Ship Boat Machine and Product
S.I.C.: 8711
N.A.I.C.S.: 541330
Laurenz Schaffer *(Pres)*

Non-U.S. Subsidiaries:

BMW China Automotive Trading Ltd (1)
28/f Suite B Jiacheng Plaza No 18 Xiaguangli
Beijing, 100027, China
Tel.: (86) 1084558000
Web Site: www.bmw.com.cn
Motor Vehicle Whslr
S.I.C.: 5012
N.A.I.C.S.: 423110

BMW de Mexico, S. A. de C. V. (1)
Paseo De Los Tamarindos No 100-501
Colonia Bosques De Las Lomas
05120 Mexico, Mexico
Tel.: (52) 55 9140 8700
E-Mail: crm@bmw.com.mx
Web Site: www.bmw.com.mx
Automobile Whslr
S.I.C.: 5012
N.A.I.C.S.: 423110

BMW Financial Services (GB) Ltd (1)
Europa House Bartley Way
Hook, RG27 9UF, United Kingdom
Tel.: (44) 87 0505 0120
Fax: (44) 1256749010
E-Mail: customersevices@bmwfin.com
Emp.: 400
Personal Financial Services
S.I.C.: 6211
N.A.I.C.S.: 523999

BMW France S.A. (1)
3 Ave Ampere
78180 Montigny-le-Bretonneux, France (100%)
Tel.: (33) 130439300
Fax: (33) 1304333571
Web Site: www.bmw.fr
Emp.: 200
Sales of BMW Products
S.I.C.: 5012
N.A.I.C.S.: 423110

BMW Group Australia Ltd. (1)
783 Springvale Rd
PO Box 745
Mulgrave, VIC, 3170, Australia (100%)
Tel.: (61) 392644000
Fax: (61) 395620274
E-Mail: info@bmw.com.au
Web Site: www.bmw.com.au
Emp.: 300
Marketing of BMW Products
S.I.C.: 5012
N.A.I.C.S.: 423110
Stipros Yallojis *(Mng Dir)*
Phil Horton *(Mng Dir)*
Guenther Seemann *(Mng Dir)*

BMW Group Belgium (1)
Lodderstrasse 16 Industriepark De Vliet
2880 Bornem, Belgium (100%)
Tel.: (32) 38909711
Fax: (32) 38909811
E-Mail: bmw.financialservices@bmw.be
Web Site: www.bmw.be
Emp.: 250
Automobile Manufacturing
S.I.C.: 3711
N.A.I.C.S.: 336111
Philipp Vonsahr *(Mng Dir)*

BMW Group Canada (1)
50 Ultimate Drive Richmond Hill, Ontario L4S 0C8.
Whitby, ON, L1N 6K9, Canada (100%)
Tel.: (905) 683-1200
Fax: (905) 428-5091
E-Mail: bmwfinance@bmw.ca
Web Site: www.bmw.ca
Emp.: 250
Marketing of BMW Products
S.I.C.: 5012
N.A.I.C.S.: 423110
Eduardo Dilladerde *(Pres)*

BMW Holding B.V. (1)
Einsteinlaan 5
PO Box 5808
NL 2289 CC Rijswijk, Zuidhood, Netherlands (100%)
Tel.: (31) 704133222
Fax: (31) 0703907771
E-Mail: bmw-kis@bmw.nl
Web Site: www.bmw.nl
Emp.: 200
Holding Company
S.I.C.: 6719
N.A.I.C.S.: 551112
Arjende Jong *(Mng Dir)*

BMW Iberica S.A. (1)
Avda de Burgos 118
28050 Madrid, Spain (100%)
Tel.: (34) 913350505
Web Site: www.bmw.es
Emp.: 100
Marketing of BMW Products
S.I.C.: 5012
N.A.I.C.S.: 423110
Hendrik von Kuenheim *(Pres)*
Edoaldo villaverde *(Mng Dir)*

BMW Italia S.p.A. (1)
1 Via Dell Unione Europea
20097 San Donato Milanese, Italy (100%)
Tel.: (39) 02 51610111
Fax: (39) 02 516100187
E-Mail: bmw@bmw.it
Web Site: www.bmw.it
Emp.: 250
BMW Products Marketing
S.I.C.: 5012
N.A.I.C.S.: 423110

BMW Japan Corp. (1)
1 -10 -2 Nakafe
Mihama Ku, Chiba, 261-0023, Japan (100%)
Tel.: (81) 432977070
Fax: (81) 432977077
Web Site: www.bmw.co.jp
Rev.: $4,000,000
BMW Products Whslr
S.I.C.: 5012
N.A.I.C.S.: 423110
Yuichiro Suzuki *(Dir-Comm)*

BMW Lease (Malaysia) Sdn. Bhd. (1)
3501 Jalan Teknokrats
63000 Cyberjaya, Selangor, Malaysia MY
Tel.: (60) 327 307 888
Fax: (60) 3 26913775
Web Site: www.bmwgroup.com
Leasing & Closed-End Leasing Services
S.I.C.: 6159
N.A.I.C.S.: 522298
Sarah Tan *(Mgr-HR)*

Subsidiary:

BMW Credit (Malaysia) Sdn Bhd (2)
Suite 7-7 Level 7 Wisma UOA Damansara II No 6 Jalan Changkat Semantan
Damansara Heights, 50490 Kuala Lumpur, Malaysia
Tel.: (60) 327307888
Fax: (60) 327307899

Bayerische Motoren Werke Aktiengesellschaft—(Continued)

E-Mail: bmwvoice@bmw.com.my
Financing Services
S.I.C.: 6099
N.A.I.C.S.: 522390
Joe Hall *(Mng Dir)*

BMW Motoren Ges.m.b.H. (1)
Hinterbergerstrasse 2
4400 Steyr, Austria (100%)
Tel.: (43) 72528880
Fax: (43) 7252888700
Web Site: www.bmw.co.at
Rev.: $2,713,184,768
Emp.: 4,400
Development, Production & Marketing of Engines
S.I.C.: 3711
N.A.I.C.S.: 336111
Gerhard Woelfel *(CEO)*

Subsidiary:

BMW Austria Gesellschaft m.b.H. (2)
Siegfried Marcus Strasse 24
5020 Salzburg, Austria (100%)
Tel.: (43) 66283830
Fax: (43) 6628383295
Web Site: www.bmw.at
Emp.: 300
Marketing of BMW Products
S.I.C.: 5012
N.A.I.C.S.: 423110

BMW Nederland B.V. (1)
Einsteinlaan 5
PO Box 5808
2289 CC Rijswijk, Zuidhood, Netherlands (100%)
Tel.: (31) 704133222
Fax: (31) 703907771
E-Mail: info@bmw.nl
Web Site: www.bmw.nl
Sales Range: $800-899.9 Million
Emp.: 140
Marketing of BMW Products
S.I.C.: 5012
N.A.I.C.S.: 423110
Janchristiaan Koenders *(Mng Dir)*

BMW New Zealand Ltd. (1)
7 Pacific Rise
PO Box 9510
1149 Auckland, Mount Wellington, 1060, New Zealand (100%)
Tel.: (64) 95736999
Fax: (64) 95736280
E-Mail: info@bmw.co.nz
Web Site: www.bmw.co.nz
Sls.: $18,210
Emp.: 55
Marketing of BMW Products
S.I.C.: 5012
N.A.I.C.S.: 423110
Nina Englert *(Mng Dir)*

BMW Overseas Enterprises N. V. (1)
Einsteinlaan 5
Rijswijk, South Holland, 2289 CC, Netherlands
Tel.: (31) 704133222
Financial Management Services
S.I.C.: 6211
N.A.I.C.S.: 523999

BMW Portugal Lda (1)
Lagoas Park Ed 11 - 2 Piso
2740-244 Porto Salvo, Portugal
Tel.: (351) 214873000
Fax: (351) 214873220
E-Mail: info@bmw.pt
Web Site: www.bmw.pt
Automobile Mfr
S.I.C.: 3711
N.A.I.C.S.: 336111

BMW (Schweiz) AG (1)
Industriestrasse 20
8157 Dielsdorf, Switzerland
Tel.: (41) 58 269 11 11
Fax: (41) 58 269 14 52
E-Mail: info@bmw.ch
Web Site: www.bmw.ch
Emp.: 200
Automobile Mfr & Distr
S.I.C.: 3711
N.A.I.C.S.: 336111
Philippe Dehennin *(CEO)*

BMW (South Africa) Pty. Ltd. (1)
1 Bavaria Ave Randjes Park Ext 17
1685 Midrand, Gauteng, South Africa (100%)
Tel.: (27) 125223000
E-Mail: bmwhelpdesk@bmw.co.za
Web Site: www.bmw.co.za
Emp.: 4,000
Production & Marketing of BMW Products
S.I.C.: 3711
N.A.I.C.S.: 336111
Bodo Donauer *(Mng Dir)*

BMW Sverige AB (1)
Gardsvagen 9 M
PO Box 1525
17129 Solna, Sweden (100%)
Tel.: (46) 84706000
Fax: (46) 84706090
E-Mail: marknad@bmw.se
Web Site: www.bmw.se
Sls.: $431,105
Emp.: 100
S.I.C.: 3711
N.A.I.C.S.: 336111
Christer Stahl *(Mng Dir)*

BMW (UK) Capital Plc (1)
Ellesfield Avenue
Bracknell, RG12 8TA, United Kingdom
Tel.: (44) 13 4442 6565
Financial Management Services
S.I.C.: 6211
N.A.I.C.S.: 523999

BMW (UK) Ltd (1)
Ellesfield Ave
Bracknell, RG12 8TA, United Kingdom (100%)
Tel.: (44) 1344426565
Telex: 849158
Fax: (44) 13444480203
Web Site: www.bmw.co.uk
Emp.: 450
Marketing of BMW Products
S.I.C.: 5012
N.A.I.C.S.: 423110
Richard Hudson *(Dir-Sls)*

Non-U.S. Plants:

Bayerische Motoren Werke Aktiengesellschaft - Hams Hall Plant (1)
Canton Lane Hams Hall
Coleshill, North Warwickshire, B46 1GB, United Kingdom
Tel.: (44) 16 75 4 60742
Fax: (44) 16 75 4 60403
E-Mail: communications.hamshall@bmwgroup.com
Automotive Engine Mfr
S.I.C.: 3714
N.A.I.C.S.: 336310

Bayerische Motoren Werke Aktiengesellschaft - Rosslyn Plant (1)
6 Frans Du Troit Street
Rosslyn, Pretoria, South Africa
Tel.: (27) 12 5 22 22 04
Fax: (27) 12 5 22 44 36
Automobile Mfr
S.I.C.: 3711
N.A.I.C.S.: 336111

BAYERISCHE STADTE- UND WOHNUNGSBAU GMBH & CO. KG

Lilienthalallee 25
80939 Munich, Germany
Tel.: (49) 8932358555
Fax: (49) 8932358502
E-Mail: info@bayerische-staedtebau.de
Web Site: www.bayerische-staedtebau.de
Emp.: 100
Business Description:
Investors
S.I.C.: 6221
N.A.I.C.S.: 523130
Personnel:
Alfons Doblinger *(Mng Dir)*
Guenther Kamm *(Mng Dir)*
Subsidiary:

Monachia AG (1)
Nymphenburger Strasse 48
80335 Munich, Germany
Tel.: (49) 89126910
Fax: (49) 8912691114
E-Mail: info@monachia.de
Web Site: www.monachia.de
Management & Trading of Real Estate Property & Capital Assets
S.I.C.: 6531
N.A.I.C.S.: 531311

BAYERNGAS GMBH

Poccistr 9
80336 Munich, Germany
Tel.: (49) 8972000
Fax: (49) 897200422
E-Mail: info@bayerngas.de
Web Site: www.bayerngas.de
Emp.: 154
Business Description:
Natural Gas Purchasing & Distribution Services
S.I.C.: 4924
N.A.I.C.S.: 221210
Personnel:
Claus Gebhardt *(Chm-Supervisory Bd)*
Marc Hall *(Mng Dir)*
Supervisory Board of Directors:
Claus Gebhardt
Oliver Belik
Matthias Berz
Klaus Blum
Norbert Breidenbach
Kurt Gribl
Philipp Hiltpolt
Alfred Lehmann
Kurt Muhlhauser
Hans Podiuk
Andreas Springer
Non-U.S. Subsidiary:

Bayerngas Norge AS (1)
Lilleakerveien 8
0283 Oslo, Norway
Tel.: (47) 22529900
Fax: (47) 22529901
E-Mail: info@bayerngas.com
Web Site: www.bayerngas.com
Emp.: 76
Natural Gas Purchasing & Distribution Services
S.I.C.: 4924
N.A.I.C.S.: 221210
R. Westeng *(Mgr)*

BAYERNLAND EG

Platenstrasse 31
90441 Nuremberg, Germany
Mailing Address:
PO Box 31 60
90015 Nuremberg, Germany
Tel.: (49) 91141400
Fax: (49) 9114140377
E-Mail: info@bayernland.de
Web Site: www.bayernland.de
Year Founded: 1972
Sales Range: $550-599.9 Million
Emp.: 419
Business Description:
Dairy Product Distr; Butter & Cheese Mfr
Import Export
S.I.C.: 5143
N.A.I.C.S.: 424430
Personnel:
Herbert Sachs *(Chm-Supervisory Bd)*
Albert Dess *(Chm-Mgmt Bd)*
Heinz Lipp *(Deputy Chm-Supervisory Bd)*
Gerhard M. Meier *(CEO)*
Johann Engl *(Member-Mgmt Bd)*
Markus Gotz *(Member-Mgmt Bd)*
Max Hartmannsgruber *(Member-Mgmt Bd)*
Johann Jordan *(Member-Mgmt Bd)*
Franz Kustner *(Member-Mgmt Bd)*
Supervisory Board of Directors:
Herbert Sachs
Arthur Auernhammer
Josef Bauer
Johann Daschner
Reinfried Geithner
Gerhard Gradl
Thomas Graf
Hans Haller
Franz Hummel
Heinz Lipp
Hermann Meyer
Ludwig Moller
Georg Schmausser
Gerhard Walter
Hans Wehr
Ludwig Weiss
Holding:

Bergland GmbH (1)
Hauptstrasse 71
88161 Lindenberg im Allgau, Germany De (50%)
Tel.: (49) 83815050
Fax: (49) 8381505296
Emp.: 150
Cheese Mfr
S.I.C.: 2022
N.A.I.C.S.: 311513
Klaus-Dieter Reiter *(Mng Dir)*

BAYERNLB HOLDING AG

Brienner Strasse 18
D-80333 Munich, Germany
Tel.: (49) 89217101
Telex: 52 8620 gzm d
Fax: (49) 89217123578
E-Mail: info@bayernlb.de
Web Site: www.bayernlb.de
Year Founded: 1972
Sales Range: $15-24.9 Billion
Emp.: 11,800
Business Description:
Financial Management & Investment Banking Services
S.I.C.: 6211
N.A.I.C.S.: 523999
Personnel:
Georg Fahrenschon *(Chm-Supervisory Bd)*
Alexander Mettenheimer *(First Deputy Chm-Supervisory Bd)*
Walter Strohmaier *(Second Deputy Chm-Supervisory Bd)*
Gerd Haeusler *(CEO)*
Edgar Zoller *(Deputy CEO)*
Jan-Christian Dreesen *(Member-Mgmt Bd)*
Marcus Kramer *(Member-Mgmt Bd)*
Nils Niermann *(Member-Mgmt Bd)*
Stephan Winkelmeier *(Member-Mgmt Bd)*
Supervisory Board of Directors:
Georg Fahrenschon
Michael Bauer
Georg Crezelius
Axel Diekmann
Joachim Herrmann
Diethard Irrgang
Alexander Mettenheimer
Hans Schaidinger
Walter Strohmaier
Klaus von Lindeiner-Wildau
Martin Zeil
Holding:

BayernLB (1)
Brienner Strasse 18
D 80333 Munich, Germany
Tel.: (49) 89217101
Fax: (49) 89217123578

Web Site: www.bayernlb.de/internet/en/meta/Ueber_uns/Ueber_uns.html
Emp.: 5,000
Financial Management & Investment Banking Services
S.I.C.: 6211
N.A.I.C.S.: 523999
Gerd Hausler *(CEO)*

Subsidiaries:

Bayerische Landesbodenkreditanstalt **(2)**
Prienner Str 22
80333 Munich, Germany (100%)
Tel.: (49) 89217128003
Fax: (49) 89217128015
E-Mail: bayernlabo@bayern.de
Web Site: www.labobayern.de
Emp.: 210
S.I.C.: 6159
N.A.I.C.S.: 522298

Deutsche Kreditbank AG **(2)**
Taubenstrasse 7-9
D 10117 Berlin, Germany (100%)
Tel.: (49) 3033023444
Fax: (49) 30 52 13 51 99
E-Mail: info@dkb.de
Web Site: www.dkb.de
Emp.: 1,200
Banking Services
S.I.C.: 6211
N.A.I.C.S.: 523110
Guenther Troppmann *(Mng Dir)*

LBS Bayerische Landesbausparkasse **(2)**
Arnulfstrasse 50
80335 Munich, Germany (100%)
Tel.: (49) 1803114477
Fax: (49) 89217147000
E-Mail: info@lbs-bayern.de
Emp.: 700
S.I.C.: 6159
N.A.I.C.S.: 522298

Non-U.S. Branch:

Bayerische Landesbank Girozentrale **(2)**
Bavaria House
13/14 Appold St, London, EC2A 2NB, United Kingdom
Tel.: (44) 1712470056
Telex: 886437 BAYLON G
Fax: (44) 1719555173
Web Site: www.bayernlb.de/internet/en/meta/BayernLB/corpstruc/weltweit.html
Emp.: 140
International Banking
S.I.C.: 6159
N.A.I.C.S.: 522293

Non-U.S. Subsidiary:

Bayerische Landesbank International S.A. **(2)**
3 Rue Jean Monnet
L 2180 Luxembourg, Luxembourg (100%)
Tel.: (352) 2000424341
Telex: 1229 bayer lu
Fax: (352) 424345099
E-Mail: privatebanking@lblux.lu
Web Site: www.bayernlux.lu
Emp.: 200
International Banking; Securities Trading
S.I.C.: 6159
N.A.I.C.S.: 522293

Non-U.S. Joint Ventures:

LB (Swiss) Investment AG **(2)**
Fraumunsterstrasse 25
CH-8001 Zurich, Switzerland
Tel.: (41) 442253790
Fax: (41) 442253791
E-Mail: investement@lbswiss.ch
Web Site: www.lbswiss.ch
Emp.: 11
Investment Banking Services
S.I.C.: 6211
N.A.I.C.S.: 523110

Frankfurter Bankgesellschaft (Switzerland) Ltd. **(2)**
Borsenstrasse 16
CH-8022 Zurich, Switzerland
Tel.: (41) 442654444
Fax: (41) 44 2654411
E-Mail: medien@frankfurter-bankgesellschaft.ch
Web Site: www.lbswiss.ch
Sales Range: $10-24.9 Million
Emp.: 90
Investment Banking Services; Owned by Bayern LB & Helaba Landesbank Hessen-Thuringen Girozentrale
S.I.C.: 6211
N.A.I.C.S.: 523110
Holger Mai *(Mgr)*

BAYFIELD VENTURES CORP.

Suite 2230 885 West Georgia Street
Vancouver, BC, V6C 3E8, Canada
Tel.: (604) 687-3376
Fax: (604) 687-3119
Toll Free: (800) 567-8181
E-Mail: info@bayfieldventures.com
Web Site: www.bayfieldventures.com
BYV—(OTC TSXV)
Int. Income: $38,695
Assets: $18,666,971
Liabilities: $1,498,845
Net Worth: $17,168,126
Earnings: ($1,849,560)
Fiscal Year-end: 10/31/12
Business Description:
Gold & Silver Exploration Services
S.I.C.: 1041
N.A.I.C.S.: 212221
Personnel:
James G. Pettit *(Chm & CEO)*
Donald C. Huston *(Pres)*
Nancy Ackerfeldt *(Sec)*
Board of Directors:
James G. Pettit
Amanda Chow
Donald C. Huston
Donald G. Myers
Transfer Agent:
Computershare Trust Company of Canada
9th Floor 100 University Avenue
Toronto, ON, Canada

BAYLIN TECHNOLOGIES INC.

Suite 3800 200 Bay Street Royal Bank Plaza South Tower
Toronto, ON, M5J 2Z4, Canada
Tel.: (416) 815-0700
Fax: (416) 222-7809
E-Mail: info@baylintech.com
Web Site: www.baylintech.com
Year Founded: 2013
BYL—(TSX)
Business Description:
Antenna Mfr
S.I.C.: 3663
N.A.I.C.S.: 334220
Personnel:
Jeffrey C. Boyer *(Chm)*
Randy L. Dewey *(Vice Chm)*
Ephraim Ulmer *(Pres & CEO)*
Yuval Katzir *(Interim CFO)*
Matti Martiskainen *(CTO)*
Benjamin Bar *(Exec VP-Sls & Mktg)*
Board of Directors:
Jeffrey C. Boyer
Stockwell Day
Randy L. Dewey
Douglas A. Jones
Barry J. Reiter
Don Simmonds
Harold M. Wolkin

BAYLIS MEDICAL CO. INC.

5959 Trans Canada Highway
Montreal, QC, H4T 1A1, Canada
Tel.: (514) 488-9801
Fax: (514) 488-7209
E-Mail: info@baylismedical.com
Web Site: www.baylismedical.com
Year Founded: 1986
Emp.: 130
Business Description:
Cardiology, Pain Management & Radiology Products Mfr & Distr
S.I.C.: 3842
N.A.I.C.S.: 339113
Personnel:
Frank Baylis *(Pres)*
Subsidiary:

Fralex Therapeutics Inc. **(1)**
190 Attwell Drive Suite 580
Toronto, ON, M9W 6H8, Canada
Tel.: (416) 213-8118
Fax: (416) 213-8668
E-Mail: info@fralex.com
Web Site: www.fralex.com
Pharmaceutical Mfr
S.I.C.: 2834
N.A.I.C.S.: 325412
Donald Wright *(Chm)*
Leslie Auld *(CFO)*
Sesh M. Chari *(COO)*

BAYO

Aerodrome d'Auxerre- Branches
89380 Appoigny, France
Tel.: (33) 386482022
Fax: (33) 386481948
Web Site: www.bayo.fr/
Sls.: $21,500,000
Emp.: 42
S.I.C.: 5084
N.A.I.C.S.: 423830
Personnel:
Richard Le Francois Des Courtis *(Mng Partner)*

BAYOU HOLZWERKSTOFFE GMBH

Siemensstrasse 2
97855 Lengfurt, Germany
Tel.: (49) 939587770
Fax: (49) 9395877720
E-Mail: info@bayou-holz.de
Web Site: www.bayou-holz.com
Rev.: $16,782,562
Emp.: 14
Business Description:
Plywood Distr
S.I.C.: 5031
N.A.I.C.S.: 423310
Personnel:
Simon Klee *(Co-CEO)*
Bekir Nakic *(Co-CEO)*
Gunter Zimmermann *(Co-CEO)*

BAYSHORE PETROLEUM CORP.

Suite 303 602-11 Ave SW
Calgary, AB, T2R 1J8, Canada
Tel.: (403) 265-8820
Fax: (403) 290-6565
E-Mail: corporate@bayshorepetroleum.com
Web Site: www.bayshorepetroleum.com
Year Founded: 2003
BSH—(TSXV)
Rev.: $59,108
Assets: $266,743
Liabilities: $1,148,385
Net Worth: ($881,642)
Earnings: ($2,703,049)
Fiscal Year-end: 12/31/12
Business Description:
Oil & Gas Exploration Services
S.I.C.: 1311
N.A.I.C.S.: 211111
Personnel:
Peter Ho *(Pres & CEO)*
Anna Lentz *(CFO)*
Board of Directors:
C. F. Cheng
Raymond Go
Peter Ho

BAYSWATER URANIUM CORPORATION

Suite 1100 1111 Melville Street
Vancouver, BC, V6E 3V6, Canada
Tel.: (604) 687-2153
Fax: (604) 669-8336
E-Mail: info@bayswateruranium.com
Web Site: www.bayswateruranium.com
BYU—(TSXV)
Int. Income: $20,477
Assets: $8,446,111
Liabilities: $2,079,418
Net Worth: $6,366,693
Earnings: ($3,015,371)
Fiscal Year-end: 02/28/13
Business Description:
Uranium Mining & Exploration Services
S.I.C.: 1094
N.A.I.C.S.: 212291
Personnel:
Victor Tanaka *(Pres & CEO)*
Mark Gelmon *(CFO)*
Marion McGrath *(Sec)*
Board of Directors:
Ken Armstrong
George M. Leary
James Stewart
Victor Tanaka
Praveen K. Varshney
Transfer Agent:
Pacific Corporate Trust Company
2nd Floor 510 Burrard Street
Vancouver, BC, V6V 3B9, Canada

BAYTEX ENERGY CORP.

Centennial Place East Tower 520 3rd Avenue SW Suite 2800
Calgary, AB, T2P 0R3, Canada
Tel.: (587) 952-3000
Fax: (587) 952-3029
Toll Free: (800) 524-5521
E-Mail: investor@baytex.ab.ca
Web Site: www.baytex.ab.ca
BTE—(NYSE TSX)
Rev.: $1,018,819,805
Assets: $2,522,899,300
Liabilities: $1,231,257,783
Net Worth: $1,291,641,516
Earnings: $257,084,387
Emp.: 219
Fiscal Year-end: 12/31/12
Business Description:
Oil & Natural Gas Exploration & Production
S.I.C.: 1311
N.A.I.C.S.: 211111
Personnel:
Raymond T. Chan *(Chm)*
James L. Bowzer *(Pres & CEO)*
W. Derek Aylesworth *(CFO)*
Marty L. Proctor *(COO)*
Murray J. Desrosiers *(Gen Counsel, Sec & VP)*
Board of Directors:
Raymond T. Chan
James L. Bowzer
John A. Brussa
Edward Chwyl
Naveen Dargan
Rusty E. T. Goepel
Gregory K. Melchin
Mary Ellen Peters
Dale O. Shwed
Legal Counsel:
Burnet, Duckworth & Palmer LLP
Suite 1400 350 7th Avenue Southwest
Calgary, AB, T2P 3N9, Canada
Tel.: (403) 263-3050
Valiant Trust Company
550 6th Avenue Southwest Suite 510
Calgary, AB, T2P 0S2, Canada

Baytex Energy Corp.—(Continued)

Transfer Agent:
Valiant Trust Company
Suite 310 606 4th Street S.W.
Calgary, AB, Canada

BAYVIEW CHRYSLER DODGE LTD.

255 South Indian Road
Sarnia, ON, N7T3W5, Canada
Tel.: (519) 337-7561
Fax: (519) 337-5618
Toll Free: (888) 229-4512
E-Mail: sales@bayview.ca
Web Site: www.bayview.fivestardealers.ca
Sales Range: $25-49.9 Million
Emp.: 58
Business Description:
New & Used Car Dealers
S.I.C.: 5511
N.A.I.C.S.: 441110
Personnel:
Dave Orr *(Pres)*

BAYWA AG

(d/b/a BayWa Group)
Arabellastrasse 4
D-81925 Munich, Germany
Tel.: (49) 8992220
Fax: (49) 8992223448
E-Mail: investorrelations@baywa.de
Web Site: www.baywa.com
Year Founded: 1966
BYW6—(EUR)
Rev.: $14,176,676,464
Assets: $6,000,354,888
Liabilities: $4,539,574,667
Net Worth: $1,460,780,221
Earnings: $158,837,291
Emp.: 16,559
Fiscal Year-end: 12/31/12
Business Description:
Building Materials, Farm Supplies, Farm & Garden Machinery, Fuel & Agricultural Products Whslr
S.I.C.: 5039
N.A.I.C.S.: 423390
Personnel:
Manfred Nussel *(Chm-Supervisory Bd)*
Klaus Josef Lutz *(CEO & Member-Mgmt Bd)*
Andreas Helber *(Member-Mgmt Bd-Fin, Controlling, IR, Legal Dept & Credit Mgmt)*
Josef Krapf *(Member-Mgmt Bd-Agriculture & Fruit)*
Roland Schuler *(Member-Mgmt Bd-Agricultural Equipment & Energy)*
Supervisory Board of Directors:
Manfred Nussel
Theo Bergmann
Klaus Buchleitner
Renate Glashauser
Stephan Gotzl
Monika Hohlmeier
Wolfgang Kruger
Michael Kuffner
Johann Lang
Albrecht Merz
Gunnar Metz
Joachim Rukwied
Gregor Scheller
Josef Schraut
Manuela Schraut
Werner Waschbichler

Subsidiaries:

Bayerische Futtersaatbau GmbH (1)
Max Von Eyth Str 2-4
85737 Ismaning, Germany De
Tel.: (49) 899624350
Fax: (49) 89 962435 11
E-Mail: info@bsv-saaten.de
Web Site: www.bsv-saaten.de
Emp.: 100
Agriculture Products Whslr
S.I.C.: 5191
N.A.I.C.S.: 424910
George Johann Brand *(Mng Dir)*

BayWa Assekuranz-Vermittlung GmbH (1)
Arabellastr 4
Munich, 81925, Germany
Tel.: (49) 8992220
Fax: (49) 899223736
Web Site: www.baywa.de
Emp.: 800
Insurance Brokerage Services
S.I.C.: 6411
N.A.I.C.S.: 524210
Klaus Josef Lutz *(Gen Mgr)*

BayWa Handels-Systeme-Service GmbH (1)
Arabellastr 4
Munich, Bayern, 81925, Germany
Tel.: (49) 8992220
Fax: (49) 8992223576
Agricultural Equipment Whslr
S.I.C.: 5083
N.A.I.C.S.: 423820
Klaus Josef Lutz *(Gen Mgr)*

BayWa InterOil Mineralolhandelsgesellschaft mbH (1)
Arabellastr 4
Munich, Bayern, 81925, Germany
Tel.: (49) 8992220
Fax: (49) 8992123217
Oil & Gas Exploration Services
S.I.C.: 1389
N.A.I.C.S.: 213112

BayWa-Lager und Umschlags GmbH (1)
Arabellastr 4
Munich, Bayern, 81925, Germany
Tel.: (49) 8992223762
Fax: (49) 8992223476
Agricultural Equipment Whslr
S.I.C.: 5083
N.A.I.C.S.: 423820

BayWa r.e GmbH (1)
Arabellastr 4
Munich, Bayern, 81925, Germany
Tel.: (49) 8992220
Agricultural Equipment Whslr
S.I.C.: 5083
N.A.I.C.S.: 423820

BayWa-Tankstellen-GmbH (1)
Arabellastr 4
Munich, Bayern, 81925, Germany
Tel.: (49) 8992220
Agricultural Equipment Whslr
S.I.C.: 5083
N.A.I.C.S.: 423820

Brands + Schnitzler Tiefbau-Fachhandel GmbH & Co. KG (1)
Folradstr 11
Monchengladbach, 41065, Germany
Tel.: (49) 2161496900
Fax: (49) 216695960
Agricultural Equipment Whslr
S.I.C.: 5083
N.A.I.C.S.: 423820

bs Baufachhandel Brands & Schnitzler GmbH & Co. KG (1)
Folradstr 11
Monchengladbach, 41065, Germany
Tel.: (49) 2161496900
Fax: (49) 21614969013
Web Site: www.brandsschnitzler.de
Construction Engineering Services
S.I.C.: 8711
N.A.I.C.S.: 541330
Dieter Jaschinski *(Gen Mgr)*

Subsidiary:

bs Baufachhandel Brands & Schnitzler Verwaltungs-GmbH (2)
Folradstr 11
Monchengladbach, Nordrhein-Westfalen, 41065, Germany
Tel.: (49) 2161496900
Fax: (49) 21614969013
Agricultural Equipment Whslr
S.I.C.: 5083
N.A.I.C.S.: 423820
Peter Jasinski *(Mng Dir)*

CLAAS Nordostbayern GmbH & Co. KG (1)
Bahnhofstrasse 18
92507 Nabburg, Germany
Tel.: (49) 94336055
Fax: (49) 8992124446
Web Site: www.nordostbayern.claas-partner.de
Agricultural Equipment Whslr
S.I.C.: 5083
N.A.I.C.S.: 423820

Claas Sudostbayern GmbH (1)
Franz Marc Str 12
84513 Toging am Inn, Germany
Tel.: (49) 8631167560
Fax: (49) 86311675672
Web Site: www.claas-suedostbayern.de
Agricultural Equipment Mfr
S.I.C.: 3523
N.A.I.C.S.: 333111
Noiey Maya *(Mng Dir)*

DTL Donau-Tanklagergesellschaft mbH & Co. KG (1)
Wallnerlande 34
94469 Deggendorf, Bayern, Germany
Tel.: (49) 99130073
Fax: (49) 991 30075
Agricultural Equipment Whslr
S.I.C.: 5083
N.A.I.C.S.: 423820

EUROGREEN GmbH (1)
Industriestrasse 83-85
57518 Betzdorf, Germany
Tel.: (49) 27 41 281 555
Fax: (49) 27 41 281 344
E-Mail: info@eurogreen.de
Web Site: www.eurogreen.de
Agriculture Products Whslr
S.I.C.: 5191
N.A.I.C.S.: 424910
Thomas Peters *(Mng Dir)*

Frucom Fruitimport GmbH (1)
Brooktorkai 20
Hamburg, 20457, Germany
Tel.: (49) 4.0320826885e+011
Fax: (49) 403208268859
E-Mail: info@frucom.de
Agricultural Products Whslr
S.I.C.: 5191
N.A.I.C.S.: 424910

Karl Theis GmbH (1)
Industriestr 15
57076 Siegen, Germany
Tel.: (49) 271 7 72 85 0
Fax: (49) 271 7 72 85 99
E-Mail: info@theis-tubes.com
Web Site: www.theis-tubes.com
Metal Pipes Mfr
S.I.C.: 3498
N.A.I.C.S.: 332996

MHH Solartechnik GmbH (1)
Eisenbahnstrasse 150
72072 Tubingen, Germany
Tel.: (49) 7071989870
Fax: (49) 70719898710
E-Mail: solarsysteme@baywa-re.de
Web Site: www.baywa-re.com
Emp.: 15
Photovoltaic System Distr
S.I.C.: 5065
N.A.I.C.S.: 423690
Gunter Haug *(Mng Dir)*

r.e Biomethan GmbH (1)
Blumenstr 16
Regensburg, 93055, Germany
Tel.: (49) 8931605790
Web Site: www.rebiomethan.de
Biomethane Distr
S.I.C.: 5191
N.A.I.C.S.: 424910

RENERCO GEM 2 GmbH (1)
Herzog Heinrich Strasse 9
80336 Munich, Germany
Tel.: (49) 893839320
Fax: (49) 8938393211
E-Mail: inof@renerco.com
Web Site: www.renerco.com
Emp.: 170
Agricultural Products Whslr
S.I.C.: 5191
N.A.I.C.S.: 424910
Matthias Taft *(Gen Mgr)*

Renerco Renewable Energy Concepts AG (1)
Herzog Heinrich Str 9
Munich, 80336, Germany
Tel.: (49) 893839320
Fax: (49) 8938393232
Web Site: www.renerco.de
Electric Power Generation Services
S.I.C.: 4931
N.A.I.C.S.: 221118

RI-Solution GmbH Gesellschaft fur Retail-Informationssysteme, Services und Losungen mbH (1)
Arabellastr 4
Munich, 81925, Germany
Tel.: (49) 8992220
Fax: (49) 8992123022
Information Technology Consulting Services
S.I.C.: 7373
N.A.I.C.S.: 541512

RI-Solution Service GmbH (1)
Kaiserstr 17
Auerbach, 08209, Germany
Tel.: (49) 374483480
Fax: (49) 3744834833
Web Site: www.ri-solution.com
Information Technology Consulting Services
S.I.C.: 7373
N.A.I.C.S.: 541512

Schradenbiogas GmbH & Co. KG (1)
Groden-nord 2
Groden, 04932, Germany
Tel.: (49) 35343786310
Fax: (49) 35343786311
E-Mail: info@schradenbiogas.de
Web Site: www.schradenbiogas.de
Biogas Mfr
S.I.C.: 2999
N.A.I.C.S.: 324199

TechnikCenter Grimma GmbH (1)
Oststrasse 6
04688 Mutzschen, Germany
Tel.: (49) 3 43 85 5 09 0
Fax: (49) 3 43 85 5 09 19
E-Mail: info@tc-grimma.de
Web Site: www.tc-grimma.de
Agricultural Equipment Whslr
S.I.C.: 5083
N.A.I.C.S.: 423820

Voss GmbH & Co. KG (1)
Rotbuchenstrasse 1
81547 Munich, Germany
Tel.: (49) 895421510
Fax: (49) 89 54 21 51 26
E-Mail: info@immobilien-voss.de
Web Site: www.immobilien-voss.de
Real Estate Management Services
S.I.C.: 6531
N.A.I.C.S.: 531390

Wind am Speckberg GmbH (1)
Herzog Heinrich Str 9
80336 Munich, Germany
Tel.: (49) 893839320
Agricultural Equipment Mfr
S.I.C.: 3523
N.A.I.C.S.: 333111

Wingenfeld Energie GmbH (1)
Zum Wolfsgraben 1
36088 Hunfeld, Germany
Tel.: (49) 66523033
Fax: (49) 665272229
E-Mail: info@wingenfeldenergie.de
Web Site: www.wingenfeldenergie.de
Emp.: 25
Agricultural Equipment Whslr
S.I.C.: 5083
N.A.I.C.S.: 423820
Joseph Pfanner *(Mng Dir)*

Non-U.S. Subsidiaries:

AFS Franchise-Systeme GmbH (1)
Wienerbergstrasse 3
Vienna, Austria
Tel.: (43) 1605150
Fax: (43) 1605154149

E-Mail: afs@afs-gmbh.at
Agricultural Equipment Whslr
S.I.C.: 5083
N.A.I.C.S.: 423820
Christian Appel *(Gen Mgr)*

Agrarproduktenhandel GmbH (1)
Sudring 240
Klagenfurt, Carinthia, 9020, Austria
Tel.: (43) 463382540
Fax: (43) 4633865500
Agricultural Products Whslr
S.I.C.: 5191
N.A.I.C.S.: 424910

AgroMed Austria GmbH (1)
Bad Hallerstr 23
4550 Kremsmunster, Austria
Tel.: (43) 75835105
Fax: (43) 7583 5105 40
E-Mail: info@agromed.at
Web Site: www.agromed.at
Emp.: 8
Animal Feeds Mfr
S.I.C.: 2048
N.A.I.C.S.: 311119
Helmut Grabherr *(Mng Dir)*

Agrosaat d.o.o (1)
Devova 5
1000 Ljubljana, Slovenia
Tel.: (386) 15140070
Fax: (386) 15140073
Web Site: www.agrosaat.si
Agriculture Products Mfr
S.I.C.: 5191
N.A.I.C.S.: 424910

BayWa Bulgaria EOOD (1)
Evlogi-Georgiev-Str 137
1504 Sofia, Bulgaria
Tel.: (359) 2448324
Fax: (359) 2448224
Farm Supplies-Wholesale
S.I.C.: 5191
N.A.I.C.S.: 424910

BayWa CR Spol. s.r.o. (1)
Brnenska 311
CZ66482 Ricany, Czech Republic (100%)
Tel.: (420) 546427341
Web Site: www.baywa.cz
Farm supplier
S.I.C.: 5191
N.A.I.C.S.: 424910

BayWa Vorarlberg HandelsGmbH (1)
Scheibenstrasse 2
6923 Lauterach, Austria AT
Tel.: (43) 5574700600 (51%)
Fax: (43) 5574700604
E-Mail: baywa.vlbg@baywa.at
Web Site: www.baywa.at
S.I.C.: 5261
N.A.I.C.S.: 444220

BOR s.r.o. (1)
Na Bile 1231
56514 Chocen, Czech Republic CZ
Tel.: (420) 465461751 (92.8%)
Fax: (420) 465461771
E-Mail: chocen@bor-sro.cz
Web Site: www.bor-sro.cz
Emp.: 45
Farm Supplies Whslr
S.I.C.: 5191
N.A.I.C.S.: 424910
Jaroslav Plodek *(Mng Dir)*

Danufert Handelsgesellschaft mbH (1)
Karl Mierka Strasse 7-9
Krems an der Donau, 3500, Austria
Tel.: (43) 273273571
Fax: (43) 2732735710
E-Mail: office@mierka.com
Web Site: www.mierka.com
Emp.: 70
Agricultural Products Whslr
S.I.C.: 5191
N.A.I.C.S.: 424910
Hubert Mierka *(Mng Dir)*

EUROGREEN CZ s.r.o., (1)
Namesti Jiriho 2 Jiretin Pod Jedlovou
Decin, 40756, Czech Republic
Tel.: (420) 412375333
Fax: (420) 412379115
E-Mail: info@eurogreen.cz
Web Site: www.eurogreen.cz
Emp.: 30
Agricultural Equipment Whslr
S.I.C.: 5083
N.A.I.C.S.: 423820
Rudolf Synek *(Mng Dir)*

F. Url & Co. Gesellschaft m.b.H (1)
Seering 7
Unterpremstatten, 8141, Austria
Tel.: (43) 313590070
Fax: (43) 31359007170
E-Mail: office@f-url.at
Web Site: www.en.f-url.at
Agricultural Products Whslr
S.I.C.: 5191
N.A.I.C.S.: 424910
Andreas Hartbauer *(Mgr-Product)*

Garant-Tiernahrung Gesellschaft m.b.H (1)
Raiffeisenstrasse 3
Pochlarn, 3380, Austria
Tel.: (43) 275722810
E-Mail: office@garant.co.at
Web Site: www.garant.co.at
Emp.: 170
Animal Food Mfr
S.I.C.: 2048
N.A.I.C.S.: 311119

Graninger & Mayr Gesellschaft m.b.H (1)
Alberner Hafenzufahrtsstrasse 17
Vienna, Austria
Tel.: (43) 1 728 91 80
E-Mail: office@gmreifen.at
Web Site: www.gmreifen.at
Tire Repair & Maintenance Services
S.I.C.: 7539
N.A.I.C.S.: 811198
Johann Oberger *(Gen Mgr)*

MHH France S.A.S (1)
24 Ave Marcel Dassault
31500 Toulouse, France
Tel.: (33) 562577488
Fax: (33) 562577480
E-Mail: info@mhh-france.fr
Web Site: www.mhh-france.fr
Emp.: 8
Photovoltaics Distr
S.I.C.: 5074
N.A.I.C.S.: 423720

Raiffeisen Agro d.o.o (1)
Bulevar Zorana Djindjica 67/17
11070 Belgrade, Serbia
Tel.: (381) 112123035
Fax: (381) 112123036
E-Mail: dmezulic@raiffeisenagro.rs
Emp.: 7
Agricultural Products Whslr
S.I.C.: 5191
N.A.I.C.S.: 424910
Dusan Mezulic *(Gen Mgr)*

Raiffeisen Agro Magyarorszag Kft. (1)
Takarodo ut 2
H-8000 Szekesfehervar, Hungary HU
Tel.: (36) 22534401 (100%)
Fax: (36) 22534409
E-Mail: info@raiffeisen-agro.hu
Web Site: www.raiffeisen-agro.hu
Farm & Garden Supplies Whslr
S.I.C.: 5191
N.A.I.C.S.: 424910
Laszlo Bene *(CEO)*

Raiffeisen-Lagerhaus GmbH (1)
Lagerhausstrasse 3
Bruck an der Leitha, 2460, Austria
Tel.: (43) 2162210
Fax: (43) 216221040
Agricultural Products Whslr
S.I.C.: 5191
N.A.I.C.S.: 424910

Raiffeisen-Lagerhaus Investitionsholding GmbH (1)
Wienerbergstrasse 3
Vienna, 1100, Austria
Tel.: (43) 1605156390
Fax: (43) 1605156389
Agricultural Equipment Whslr
S.I.C.: 5083
N.A.I.C.S.: 423820

Ri-Solution Data GmbH (1)
Wienerbergstrasse 3
Vienna, 1100, Austria
Tel.: (43) 1605150
Fax: (43) 1605152159
Web Site: www.ri-solutions.com
Emp.: 400
Agricultural Equipment Whslr
S.I.C.: 5083
N.A.I.C.S.: 423820
Gunter Bauer *(Mng Dir)*

RWA RAIFFEISEN AGRO d.o.o (1)
Buzetkki Trilaz 10
Zagreb, 10010, Croatia
Tel.: (385) 12022650
Fax: (385) 12022659
E-Mail: rwa@rwagratska.hr
Web Site: www.rwa.hr
Emp.: 21
Agricultural Products Whslr
S.I.C.: 5191
N.A.I.C.S.: 424910

Sempol spol. s r.o (1)
Pri Trati 15
Bratislava, 820 14, Slovakia
Tel.: (421) 2 4020 1111
Fax: (421) 2 4020 1122
E-Mail: sempol@sempol.sk
Web Site: www.sempol.sk
Agriculture Products Whslr
S.I.C.: 5191
N.A.I.C.S.: 424910

Turners & Growers Limited (1)
Markets Complex 2 Monahan Road
Mt Wellington, Auckland, 1140, New Zealand NZ
Tel.: (64) 9 573 8700 (73.1%)
Fax: (64) 9 573 8901
E-Mail: info@turnersandgrowers.com
Web Site: www.turnersandgrowers.com
TUR—(NZE)
Sls.: $560,067,669
Assets: $383,927,715
Liabilities: $149,961,105
Net Worth: $233,966,610
Earnings: ($11,113,686)
Emp.: 1,400
Fiscal Year-end: 12/31/12
Fresh Fruits & Vegetables Marketer, Distr & Exporter
Export
S.I.C.: 5148
N.A.I.C.S.: 424480
Klaus Josef Lutz *(Chm)*
John A. Anderson *(Deputy Chm)*
Alastair Hulbert *(CEO)*
Harald R. Hamster-Egerer *(CFO)*
Philipp Wahl *(COO)*
Doug Bygrave *(Sec)*

Subsidiaries:

ENZAFOODS New Zealand Limited (2)
1305 Tomoana Rd
Hastings, Hawkes Bay, 4120, New Zealand
Tel.: (64) 68781460
Fax: (64) 68760391
E-Mail: sales@enzafoods.co.nz
Web Site: www.enzafoods.co.nz
Emp.: 150
Fruits & Vegetable Juice Mfr
S.I.C.: 2037
N.A.I.C.S.: 311411
Jon Marks *(Mng Dir)*

ENZAFRUIT Marketing Limited (2)
8 Groome Place Whakatu
PO Box 279
Hastings, Hawkes Bay, 4172, New Zealand
Tel.: (64) 68781898
Fax: (64) 68715601
Web Site: www.enza.co.nz
Emp.: 40
Pipfruit Distr
S.I.C.: 5148
N.A.I.C.S.: 424480

Status Produce Limited (2)
42 Favona Road
Mangere, Auckland, 2151, New Zealand
Tel.: (64) 92751819
Fax: (64) 92758459
E-Mail: statusmail@turnersandgrowers.com
Web Site: www.statusproduce.co.nz
Emp.: 250
Tomato Farming & Distr
S.I.C.: 0182
N.A.I.C.S.: 111419
Colin Lyfoid *(Gen Mgr)*

Non-U.S. Subsidiaries:

ENZACOR Pty Limited (2)
Unit 7 9 Compark Circuit
Mulgrave, VIC, 3170, Australia
Tel.: (61) 385613188
Fax: (61) 395601177
E-Mail: melbourne@fruitmark.com.au
Web Site: www.fruitmark.com.au
Emp.: 11
Frozen & Processed Fruits & Vegetables Whslr
S.I.C.: 5142
N.A.I.C.S.: 424420
Michael James *(Gen Mgr)*

ENZAFRUIT New Zealand (Continent) NV (2)
Tongersesteenweg 135
3800 Saint Truiden, Limburg, Belgium
Tel.: (32) 11689941
Fax: (32) 11688109
E-Mail: continent.info@enza.co.nz
Web Site: www.enzafruit.be
Emp.: 12
Fresh Fruits Distr
S.I.C.: 5148
N.A.I.C.S.: 424480
Tony Fissette *(Mng Dir)*

Unser Lagerhaus Warenhandelsgesellschaft m.b.H. (1)
Sudring 242
9020 Klagenfurt, Austria AT
Tel.: (43) 46338650 (51.1%)
Fax: (43) 4633865419
E-Mail: office@unser-lagerhaus.at
Web Site: www.unserlagerhaus.at
Sales Range: $650-699.9 Million
Emp.: 1,100
Farm Supplies, Building Materials, Fuel & Garden Products Whslr & Retailer
S.I.C.: 4225
N.A.I.C.S.: 493110
Peter Messner *(Co-CEO & Member-Mgmt Bd)*
Arthur Schifferl *(Co-CEO & Member-Mgmt Bd)*
Klaus Josef Lutz *(Co-CEO)*
Georg Messner *(Co-CEO)*

Holding:

RWA Raiffeisen Ware Austria Aktiengesellschaft (2)
Wienerbergstrasse 3
A-1100 Vienna, Austria AT
Tel.: (43) 1605150 (50%)
Fax: (43) 01605155099
E-Mail: office@rwa.at
Web Site: www.rwa.at
Sales Range: $1-4.9 Billion
Emp.: 2,045
Farm Supplies, Building Materials, Fuel & Garden Products Whslr & Warehousing Services
S.I.C.: 4225
N.A.I.C.S.: 493110
Johann Lang *(Chm-Supervisory Bd)*
Klaus Buchleitner *(Chm-Mgmt Bd & CEO)*
Stefan Mayerhofer *(Member-Mgmt Bd-Tech)*
Reinhard Wolf *(Member-Mgmt Bd-Resources)*

Subsidiaries:

GENOL Gesellschaft m.b.H. & Co. KG (3)
Wienerbergstrasse 3
1100 Vienna, Austria AT
Tel.: (43) 1605150 (100%)
Fax: (43) 7719
E-Mail: genol@rwa.at
Web Site: www.genol.at
Emp.: 100
Petroleum Products Whslr
S.I.C.: 5172
N.A.I.C.S.: 424720
Philipp Koerbler Mag *(Gen Mgr)*

RWA International Holding GmbH (3)
Wienerbergstrasse 3 Business Park
Vienna, 1100, Austria
Tel.: (43) 1605150
Fax: (43) 1605156139

BayWa AG—(Continued)

Web Site: www.rwa.at
Agricultural Products Whslr
S.I.C.: 5191
N.A.I.C.S.: 424910

Saatzucht Gleisdorf Gesellschaft m.b.H (3)
Am Tieberhof 33
Gleisdorf, 8200, Austria
Tel.: (43) 311221050
Fax: (43) 311221055
Web Site: www.saatzuchtgleisdorf.at
Emp.: 12
Agricultural Equipment Whslr
S.I.C.: 5083
N.A.I.C.S.: 423820
Johann Posch *(Gen Mgr)*

Joint Venture:

AUSTRIA JUICE GmbH (3)
(Formerly YBBSTALER AGRANA JUICE GmbH)
Kroellendorf 45
A- 3365 Allhartsberg, Austria
Tel.: (43) 7448 2304 0
Fax: (43) 7448 2304 312
E-Mail: sales@austriajuice.com
Web Site: www.austriajuice.com
Emp.: 900
Juice Concentrate Mfr
S.I.C.: 2033
N.A.I.C.S.: 311421
Stephan Buttner *(CEO)*

Subsidiary:

Ybbstaler Fruit Austria GmbH (4)
Kroellendorf 45
3365 Allhartsberg, Austria
Tel.: (43) 744823040
Fax: (43) 74482304900
E-Mail: info@ybbstaler.at
Web Site: www.ybbstaler.at
Emp.: 60
Beverage Compounds Mfr & Whslr
S.I.C.: 2086
N.A.I.C.S.: 312111
Stephan Buttner *(Mng Dir)*

Non-U.S. Subsidiaries:

Lukta Polska Sp. z o.o (4)
ul Plantowa 231
96-230 Biala Rawska, Poland
Tel.: (48) 814 60 25
Fruit Juices Mfr & Whslr
S.I.C.: 2037
N.A.I.C.S.: 311411

Ybbstaler Fruit Polska Sp. z o.o (4)
Ul Plantowa 231
Biala Rawska, Poland
Tel.: (48) 825622150
Fax: (48) 825622112
Web Site: www.ybbstaler.pl
Fruit Juices Whslr
S.I.C.: 5149
N.A.I.C.S.: 424490
Helmut Stoger *(Gen Mgr)*

BB MINAQUA AD

Ruzin gaj 1/a
21000 Novi Sad, Serbia
Tel.: (381) 21 402 611
Fax: (381) 21 402 495
Web Site: www.bbminaqua.com
BBMN—(BEL)

Business Description:
Mineral Water Mfr
S.I.C.: 2086
N.A.I.C.S.: 312112

Personnel:
Sanja Bjelica *(Gen Mgr)*

BBA AVIATION PLC

105 Wigmore Street
London, W1U 1QY, United Kingdom
Tel.: (44) 2075143999
Telex: 51106
Fax: (44) 2074082318
E-Mail: info@bbaaviation.com
Web Site: www.bbaaviation.com
Year Founded: 1897
BBA—(LSE)
Rev.: $2,178,900,000
Assets: $2,386,200,000
Liabilities: $1,364,800,000
Net Worth: $1,021,400,000
Earnings: $115,500,000
Emp.: 11,430
Fiscal Year-end: 12/31/12

Business Description:
Holding Company; Aircraft Parts Mfr, Repair, Maintenance & Flight Support Services
S.I.C.: 6719
N.A.I.C.S.: 551112

Personnel:
Simon Pryce *(CEO)*
Peg Billson *(Pres/CEO-Aftermarket Svcs)*
Michael Scheeringa *(Pres/CEO-Flight Support)*
Hugh E. McElroy *(Pres-Bus Dev)*
Keith P. Ryan *(Pres-ASIG)*
Iain Simm *(Gen Counsel & Sec)*

Board of Directors:
Michael Harper
Wayne Edmunds
Mark Harper
Mark Hoad
Susan Saltzbart Kilsby
Nick Land
Simon Pryce
Peter G. Ratcliffe
Hansel E. Tookes, II

Subsidiary:

Balderton Aviation Holdings Limited (1)
20 Balderton Street
London, W1K 6TL, United Kingdom
Tel.: (44) 20 7016 6800
Fax: (44) 2070166810
E-Mail: reception.uk@balderton.com
Web Site: www.baldertoncapital.com
Emp.: 23
Investment Management Services
S.I.C.: 6211
N.A.I.C.S.: 523999

U.S. Groups:

Aircraft Service International Group, Inc. (1)
201 S Orange Ave Ste 100-A
Orlando, FL 32801 DE
Tel.: (407) 648-7373
Fax: (407) 206-5391
E-Mail: info@asig.com
Web Site: www.asig.com
Holding Company; Commercial Airline Ground Support Services
S.I.C.: 6719
N.A.I.C.S.: 551112
Tony Lefebvre *(Pres & COO)*
Tim Ramsey *(Sr VP-Sls & Mktg)*

Subsidiary:

Aircraft Service International, Inc. (2)
201 S Orange Ave Ste 1100-A
Orlando, FL 32801 DE
Tel.: (407) 648-7373 (100%)
Fax: (407) 206-5391
Toll Free: (800) 557-2744
E-Mail: info@asig.com
Web Site: www.asig.com
Emp.: 100
Commercial Airline Ground Support Services
S.I.C.: 4581
N.A.I.C.S.: 488190
Keith Ryan *(Pres)*

Unit:

Aircraft Service International - ONT (3)
1049 S Vineyard Ave
Ontario, CA 91761
Mailing Address:
PO Box 4178
Ontario, CA 91761
Tel.: (909) 937-3998
Fax: (909) 937-7158
Web Site: www.asig.com
Emp.: 80
Commercial Airline Ground Support Services
S.I.C.: 4581
N.A.I.C.S.: 488190
Robert J. Libby *(Gen Mgr-Fuel)*

Non-U.S. Subsidiary:

ASIG Limited (2)
1st Floor Crown House 137-139 High Street
Egham, Surrey, TW20 9HL, United Kingdom UK
Tel.: (44) 1784497400
Fax: (44) 1784 497 401
E-Mail: seniormgmt@asig.co.uk
Web Site: www.asig.com
Commercial Airline Ground Support Services
S.I.C.: 4581
N.A.I.C.S.: 488190
Pat Pearse *(Mng Dir-Europe)*

BBA Aviation Engine Repair & Overhaul Group (1)
900 Nolen Dr Ste 100
Grapevine, TX 76051-8641
Tel.: (214) 956-3000
Fax: (214) 956-2825
Toll Free: (800) 527-5003
E-Mail: turbines@bbaaviationero.com
Web Site: www.bbaaviationero.com
Emp.: 220
Subsidiary Managing Office; Aircraft Engine Repair & Overhaul Services
S.I.C.: 8741
N.A.I.C.S.: 551114
Hugh E. McElroy, Jr. *(Pres)*
Nandakumar Madireddi *(Sr VP-Bus Ops)*

Subsidiary:

Dallas Airmotive, Inc. (2)
900 Nolen Dr Ste 100
Grapevine, TX 76051-8641 TX
Tel.: (214) 956-3001 (100%)
Fax: (214) 956-2825
Toll Free: (800) 527-5003
E-Mail: turbines@bbaaviationero.com
Web Site: www.bbaaviationero.com
Sls.: $42,750,769
Emp.: 80
Aircraft Engine Repair & Overhaul Services
S.I.C.: 3724
N.A.I.C.S.: 336412
Doug Meador *(Pres)*
Hugh McElroy *(CEO)*

Units:

Dallas Airmotive, Inc. - Dallas Facility (3)
6114 Forest Park Rd
Dallas, TX 75235-6498 (100%)
Tel.: (214) 956-3000
Fax: (214) 956-3007
E-Mail: info@dallasairmotive.com
Web Site: www.dallasairmotive.com
Emp.: 100
Aircraft Engine Repair & Overhaul Services
S.I.C.: 3724
N.A.I.C.S.: 336412
Willy Harmon *(VP-Sls)*

Dallas Airmotive, Inc. - Millville Facility (3)
Millville Municipal Airport 101 Bogden Blvd
Millville, NJ 08332-4814 (100%)
Tel.: (856) 825-6000
Fax: (856) 327-8224
Emp.: 510
Aircraft Engine Repair & Overhaul Services
S.I.C.: 3724
N.A.I.C.S.: 336412

Non-U.S. Subsidiary:

H+S Aviation Limited (2)
Airport Service Road
Portsmouth, Hants, PO3 5PJ, United Kingdom UK
Tel.: (44) 2392304000 (100%)
Fax: (44) 23 9230 4020
E-Mail: post@hsaviation.co.uk
Aircraft Engine Repair & Overhaul Services
S.I.C.: 3724
N.A.I.C.S.: 336412
Mark Taylor *(Mng Dir)*

BBA Aviation Legacy Support Group (1)
20400 Plummer St
Chatsworth, CA 91311
Mailing Address:
PO Box 2424
Chatsworth, CA 91313-2424
Tel.: (818) 678-6555 (Switchboard)
Fax: (818) 678-6618
Web Site: www.bbaaviation.com
Subsidiary Managing Office; Legacy Aircraft Parts Mfr & Whslr
S.I.C.: 8741
N.A.I.C.S.: 551114
Peg Billson *(Pres)*

Subsidiaries:

International Governor Services, LLC (2)
7290 W 118th Pl
Broomfield, CO 80020 DE
Tel.: (303) 464-0043
Fax: (303) 464-0044
Toll Free: (888) 808-5297
E-Mail: sales@internationalgovernor.com
Web Site: www.internationalgovernor.com
Small Aircraft Turbine Engine Controls Repair & Overhaul Services
S.I.C.: 3625
N.A.I.C.S.: 335314
Steve Yates *(Plant Mgr)*

Ontic Engineering & Manufacturing, Inc. (2)
20400 Plummer St
Chatsworth, CA 91311 CA
Tel.: (818) 678-6555
Fax: (818) 678-6618
E-Mail: info@ontic.com
Web Site: www.ontic.com
Sales Range: $10-24.9 Million
Emp.: 250
Legacy Aircraft Parts Mfr & Whslr
S.I.C.: 5088
N.A.I.C.S.: 423860
Gareth Hall *(Pres & Mng Dir)*

Subsidiary:

APPH Houston, Inc. (3)
4150 N Sam Houston E Pkwy
Houston, TX 77032 TX
Tel.: (281) 590-1431
Fax: (281) 590-4945
Toll Free: (800) 451-1431
E-Mail: houstonsales@ontic.com
Web Site: www.ontic.com
Sales Range: $1-9.9 Million
Emp.: 34
Aircraft Parts Whslr & Repair Services
S.I.C.: 5088
N.A.I.C.S.: 423860
Nicholas Stander *(Gen Mgr)*

Non-U.S. Subsidiary:

Ontic Engineering & Manufacturing UK Limited (3)
122 Malton Avenue
Slough Trading Estate, Slough, Berks, SL1 4DE, United Kingdom UK
Tel.: (44) 1753560600
Fax: (44) 1753823191
Web Site: www.ontic.com
Metal Tank & Gauge Mfr & Whslr
S.I.C.: 3443
N.A.I.C.S.: 332420

Signature Flight Support Corp. (1)
201 S Orange Ave Ste 1100-S
Orlando, FL 32801 DE
Tel.: (407) 648-7200 (100%)
Fax: (407) 206-8428
E-Mail: marketing@signatureflight.com
Web Site: www.signatureflight.com
Emp.: 1,300
Private Aircraft Ground Support Services
S.I.C.: 4581
N.A.I.C.S.: 488119
Maria A. Sastre *(Pres)*
Sami T. Teittinen *(CFO)*
David Best *(Chief Comml Officer)*
Geoff Heck *(Sr VP-Sls & Mktg)*

Units:

Signature Flight Support - BED (2)
180 Hanscom Dr
Bedford, MA 01730

Tel.: (781) 274-0012
Rev.: $1,900,000
Emp.: 25
Air Transportation Support Services
S.I.C.: 4581
N.A.I.C.S.: 488190
Rick Blaze *(Gen Mgr)*

Signature Flight Support - MKE (2)
923 E Layton Ave Mitchell Field
Milwaukee, WI 53207
Tel.: (414) 747-5100
Fax: (414) 747-4588
E-Mail: mke@signatureflight.com
Web Site: www.signatureflight.com
Emp.: 33
Private Aircraft Ground Support Services
S.I.C.: 4581
N.A.I.C.S.: 488119
Doug Drescher *(Gen Mgr)*

Signature Flight Support - MMU (2)
1 Airport Rd
Morristown, NJ 07960
Tel.: (973) 292-1300
Fax: (973) 292-2331
E-Mail: mmu@signatureflight.com
Web Site: www.signatureflight.com
Sls.: $3,600,000
Emp.: 44
Private Aircraft Ground Support Services
S.I.C.: 4581
N.A.I.C.S.: 488119
Marilyn Vela *(Gen Mgr)*

Signature Flight Support - PIE (2)
14525 Airport Pkwy
Clearwater, FL 33762
Tel.: (727) 531-1441
Fax: (727) 536-6567
E-Mail: pie@signatureflight.com
Web Site: www.signatureflight.com
Emp.: 120
Private Aircraft Ground Support Services
S.I.C.: 4581
N.A.I.C.S.: 488119
Scott Nixon *(Gen Mgr)*

Signature Flight Support - PWK (2)
1100 S Milwaukee Ave
Wheeling, IL 60090-6309
Tel.: (847) 537-1200
Fax: (847) 537-2738
E-Mail: pwk@signatureflight.com
Web Site: www.signatureflight.com
Emp.: 13
Private Aircraft Ground Support Services
S.I.C.: 4581
N.A.I.C.S.: 488119
Mark Costa *(Gen Mgr)*

Signature Flight Support - STL (2)
5995 J S McDonnell Blvd
Saint Louis, MO 63134
Tel.: (314) 731-7111
Fax: (314) 731-1915
E-Mail: stl@signatureflight.com
Web Site: www.signatureflight.com
Emp.: 30
Private Aircraft Ground Support Services
S.I.C.: 4581
N.A.I.C.S.: 488119
Bobby Courtney *(Dir-Ops)*

U.S. Subsidiaries:

Barrett Turbine Engine Company (1)
1626 Tobacco Rd
Augusta, GA 30906
Tel.: (706) 790-1977
Fax: (706) 790-1664
Toll Free: (800) 891-1977
E-Mail: info@barrettturbineengine.com
Web Site: www.barrettturbineengine.com
Aircraft Engine Mfr
S.I.C.: 3724
N.A.I.C.S.: 336412
William H. Barrett *(Founder)*

Non-U.S. Subsidiary:

Signature Flight Support Paris SA (1)
1241 Avenue de l Europe
Le Bourget, 93352, France
Tel.: (33) 141691000
Fax: (33) 149927505
E-Mail: lbgt1@signatureflight.fr
Web Site: www.signatureflight.com
Emp.: 25
Air Transportation Services
S.I.C.: 4581
N.A.I.C.S.: 488190
Andriot Nathalie *(Gen Mgr)*

BBK B.S.C.

43 Government Avenue
PO Box 597
Manama, Bahrain
Tel.: (973) 17223388
Fax: (973) 17229822
E-Mail: bbkrbd@batelco.com.bh
Web Site: www.bbkonline.com
BBK—(BAH)
Rev.: $270,732,539
Assets: $8,053,586,163
Liabilities: $7,302,882,269
Net Worth: $750,703,894
Earnings: $110,166,749
Emp.: 1,092
Fiscal Year-end: 12/31/12

Business Description:
Banking Services
S.I.C.: 6029
N.A.I.C.S.: 522110

Personnel:
AbdulKarim Ahmed Bucheery *(CEO)*
Reyadh Yousif Sater *(Deputy CEO-Bus Grp)*
Amit Kumar *(Chief Risk Officer & Head-Credit & Risk Mgmt)*

Board of Directors:
Murad Ali Murad
Abdulmohsen Medej Mohammed Al Medej
Mutlaq Mubarak Al Sanei
Zakareya Sultan Al-Abbasi
Jassem Hasan Ali Zainal
Khalifa Duaj Al Khalifa
Elham Ebrahim Hasan
Mohammed Abdulrahman Hussain
Yusuf Saleh Khalaf
Abdulla Khalifa Salman Al Khalifa
Aref Saleh Khamis
Hassan Mohammed Mahmood

Subsidiaries:

CrediMax B.S.C. (1)
Building 858 Road 3618 Block 436
PO Box 5350
Seef, Manama, Bahrain
Tel.: (973) 17117117
Fax: (973) 17 117 116
E-Mail: credimax@credimax.com.bh
Web Site: www.credimax.com.bh
Credit Card Issuing Services
S.I.C.: 6141
N.A.I.C.S.: 522210

Global Payment Services W.L.L. (1)
383 Road
PO Box 2110
Manama, Bahrain
Tel.: (973) 17 201 666
Fax: (973) 17 201 677
E-Mail: info@gps.com.bh
Web Site: www.gpsbah.com
Emp.: 24
Credit Card Issuing Services
S.I.C.: 6141
N.A.I.C.S.: 522210
Mohammed Malik *(Acting Chm)*

Invita B.S.C. (1)
Suite 107 Bahrain Car Park Commercial Centre
Manama, Bahrain
Tel.: (973) 17 50 6000
Fax: (973) 17917711
E-Mail: info@invita.com.bh
Web Site: www.invita.com.bh
Business Process Outsourcing Services
S.I.C.: 7389
N.A.I.C.S.: 561499

BBKO CONSULTING S.A.

Calc Dos Cravos 98
06453-000 Barueri, SP, Brazil
Tel.: (55) 1135284080
Web Site: www.bbko.com.br
Sales Range: $10-24.9 Million
Emp.: 400

Business Description:
Computer Consulting Services
S.I.C.: 8999
N.A.I.C.S.: 541690

Personnel:
Jose Eduardo F. Nascimento *(CEO)*

BBMG CORPORATION

129 Xuanwumen West Street
Xicheng District, Beijing, 100031, China
Tel.: (86) 1066416688
Fax: (86) 1066412086
E-Mail: webmaster@bbmg.com.cn
Web Site: www.bbmg.com.cn
Year Founded: 2005
2009—(HKG)
Rev.: $5,409,493,150
Assets: $13,210,252,507
Liabilities: $9,235,080,639
Net Worth: $3,975,171,867
Earnings: $500,414,126
Emp.: 28,753
Fiscal Year-end: 12/31/12

Business Description:
Building Materials Mfr
S.I.C.: 3291
N.A.I.C.S.: 327910

Personnel:
Weiping Jiang *(Chm)*
Yi Liu *(Chm-Supervisory Bd)*
Deyi Jiang *(Pres)*
Hongjun Wang *(CFO)*
Lawrence Fai Lau *(Sec)*

Board of Directors:
Weiping Jiang
Zhaoguang Hu
Deyi Jiang
Xijun Shi
Hongjun Wang
Shizhong Wang
Yongmo Xu
Wai Ming Yip
Shiliang Yu
Feng Zang
Chengfu Zhang

Supervisory Board of Directors:
Yi Liu
Jingshan Hu
Bichi Li
Xiaoqiang Qian
Xin Wang
Dengfeng Zhang
Yifeng Zhang

China Securities Depository & Clearing Corporation Limited
36/F China Insurance Building No 166 Lujiazui Dong Road
Pudong New Area, Shanghai, China

Subsidiaries:

Beijing Building Materials Import and Export Co., Ltd (1)
Rm B302 Jin Yu Mansion No 129 Jia Xuan Wu Men Xi Da Jie
Xicheng, Beijing, 100031, China
Tel.: (86) 1066414599
Fax: (86) 1066412134
E-Mail: bbmiec@bbmiec.com
Web Site: www.bbmiec.com
Building Materials Suppliers
S.I.C.: 5211
N.A.I.C.S.: 444190

Beijing Liulihe Cement Co., Ltd (1)
15 Chezhan Jie Liulihe Xiang
Fangshan, 102403 Beijing, China
Tel.: (86) 1089382980
Fax: (86) 1089381602
Cement Mfr
S.I.C.: 3241
N.A.I.C.S.: 327310

Beijing Sanchong Mirrors Co., Ltd (1)
No 2 W Rd Xisanqi Bldg Material City Haiding
Beijing, 100096, China
Tel.: (86) 1082910836
Fax: (86) 1082915970
Web Site: www.bjsanchong.com.cn
Emp.: 100
Optical Glass Mfr
S.I.C.: 3231
N.A.I.C.S.: 327215

Beijing Star Building Materials Co., Ltd (1)
No 2 Gaojin Chaoyang
Beijing, China
Tel.: (86) 1085767806
Fax: (86) 1085760213
E-Mail: star@bsbm.cc
Web Site: www.bsbm.cc
Mineral Wool Mfr
S.I.C.: 3296
N.A.I.C.S.: 327993

Beijing Woodworking Factory Co., Ltd (1)
4 Dahongmen W Rd Yongwai Ave Fengtai
Beijing, 100075, China
Tel.: (86) 1067248319
Fax: (86) 1067248319
Building Materials Mfr
S.I.C.: 7349
N.A.I.C.S.: 561790

Luquan Dongfang Dingxin Cement Co., Ltd (1)
Tongge Indust Zone
Luquan, Shijiazhuang, Hebei, China
Tel.: (86) 31182213023
Fax: (86) 31182213000
Cement Mfr
S.I.C.: 3241
N.A.I.C.S.: 327310

BBR HOLDING (S) LTD.

BBR Building 50 Changi South St 1
Singapore, 486126, Singapore
Tel.: (65) 65462280
Fax: (65) 65462268
E-Mail: enquiry@bbr.com.sg
Web Site: www.bbr.com.sg
Year Founded: 1944
KJ5—(LUX SES WAR)
Rev.: $222,042,595
Assets: $206,771,220
Liabilities: $118,325,016
Net Worth: $88,446,204
Earnings: $10,855,380
Fiscal Year-end: 12/31/12

Business Description:
Holding Company; Structural Engineering Design & Services
S.I.C.: 6719
N.A.I.C.S.: 551112

Personnel:
Andrew Kheng Hwee Tan *(CEO)*
Maria Siew Joo Low *(CFO)*
Chai Foong Chiang *(Sec)*

Board of Directors:
Kwet Yew Yong
Peter Michael Ekberg
Carrie Ka Lai Luk
Gim Teik Soh
Andrew Kheng Hwee Tan
Bruno Sergio Valsangiacomo

Subsidiaries:

BBR Construction Systems Pte Ltd (1)
50 Changi S St 1 BBR Bldg
Singapore, 486126, Singapore
Tel.: (65) 65462280
Fax: (65) 65462268
E-Mail: enquiry@bbr.com.sg
Web Site: www.bbr.com.sg
Emp.: 70
Engineering Services
S.I.C.: 8711
N.A.I.C.S.: 541330
John Mo Kuan Sheng *(Mng Dir)*

BBR Piling Pte Ltd. (1)
BBR Building 50 Changi South Street 1
Singapore, 486126, Singapore
Tel.: (65) 6546 2280
Fax: (65) 6546 2268
E-Mail: hr@bbr.com.sg

BBR Holding (S) Ltd.—(Continued)

Web Site: www.bbr.com.sg
Piling & Foundation Systems
S.I.C.: 1629
N.A.I.C.S.: 237990

Singapore Piling & Civil Engineering Private Limited (1)
50 Changi S St 1 BBR Bldg
Singapore, 486126, Singapore
Tel.: (65) 62355088
Fax: (65) 65462268
E-Mail: general@sporepiling.com.sg
Web Site: www.singaporepiling.com.sg
Emp.: 2
Piling & Civil Engineering Services
S.I.C.: 8711
N.A.I.C.S.: 541330
Lee Layna *(Gen Mgr)*

Subsidiary:

Singa Development Pte Ltd (2)
50 Changi S St 1
Singapore, 486126, Singapore
Tel.: (65) 65465257
Fax: (65) 67372711
E-Mail: enquiry@bbr.com.sg
Web Site: www.singdev.com
Emp.: 35
Civil Engineering Services
S.I.C.: 8711
N.A.I.C.S.: 541330

Non-U.S. Subsidiary:

BBR Construction Systems (M) Sdn. Bhd. (1)
17 Jalan PJS 11/2 Bandar Sunway
Petaling Jaya, Selangor, 46150, Malaysia
Tel.: (60) 356363270
Fax: (60) 356363285
E-Mail: bbrm@bbr.com.my
Web Site: www.bbr.com.my
Emp.: 40
Engineering Services
S.I.C.: 8711
N.A.I.C.S.: 541330
Yok Lin Voon *(Mng Dir)*

BBX MINERALS LIMITED

Suite 1 Level 1 35 Havelock Street
West Perth, WA, 6005, Australia
Tel.: (61) 8 6555 2955
Fax: (61) 2 6210 1153
E-Mail: psuriano@aphillip.com.au
Web Site: www.bbxminerals.com.au
BBX—(ASX)
Int. Income: $13,841
Assets: $1,570,234
Liabilities: $345,697
Net Worth: $1,224,537
Earnings: ($1,473,594)
Emp.: 60
Fiscal Year-end: 06/30/13
Business Description:
Mineral Exploration Services
S.I.C.: 1481
N.A.I.C.S.: 213115
Personnel:
Simon Robertson *(Sec)*
Board of Directors:
Michael Leon Schmulian
William Dix
Michael John Hogg
Legal Counsel:
Kings Park Corporate Lawyers
Suite 8 8 Clive Street
West Perth, Australia

Subsidiaries:

BBX MANAGEMENT PTY. LTD (1)
916 Pacific Hwy
Gordon, NSW, 2072, Australia
Tel.: (61) 294991100
Fax: (61) 294991199
E-Mail: headoffice@ebbx.com
Emp.: 20
Barter Business Providers
S.I.C.: 7389
N.A.I.C.S.: 561990
Timothy Creasy *(Sec)*

BBX Money Pty Ltd (1)
916 Pacific Hwy
Gordon, NSW, 2072, Australia
Tel.: (61) 416525233
Fax: (61) 0294991199
Emp.: 20
Financial Support Services
S.I.C.: 6282
N.A.I.C.S.: 523930
Rick Powell *(Natl Mktg Mgr)*

BBX Property Investment Fund Limited (1)
916 Pacific Highway
Gordon, NSW, 2072, Australia
Tel.: (61) 2 9499 1100
Fax: (61) 2 9499 1199
E-Mail: propertyfund@ebbx.com
Web Site: www.bbxpropertyfund.com.au
BPI—(NSXA)
Real Estate Investment Fund Services
S.I.C.: 6211
N.A.I.C.S.: 523999
Caroline MacDonald *(Sec)*

Non-U.S. Subsidiaries:

BBX Centroamerica La Uruca (1)
De la plz 200 mts Norte
PO Box 1298-1000
San Jose, Costa Rica
Tel.: (506) 22332839
Fax: (506) 22332736
E-Mail: info@ebbx.co.cr
Web Site: www.ebbx.co.cr
Emp.: 5
Barter Business Providers
S.I.C.: 7389
N.A.I.C.S.: 561990
Mariamalia Jacobo *(Mgr)*

BBX CHINA CO., LTD (1)
Zhaolin Mansion No 15 Ronghua Middle Rd BDA
Beijing, 100176, China
Tel.: (86) 1051078888
Fax: (86) 1068391623
E-Mail: cdz840810@yahoo.com.cn
Barter Business Providers
S.I.C.: 7389
N.A.I.C.S.: 561499

BBX India Pvt. Limited (1)
E-8 2nd Fl Kalkaji
New Delhi, 110019, India
Tel.: (91) 11 4058 7777
Fax: (91) 11 4058 7788
E-Mail: info@ebbx.in
Web Site: www.ebbx.in
Barter Business Providers
S.I.C.: 7389
N.A.I.C.S.: 561990

BBX Management Ltd (1)
1/11 Homersham Pl Burnside
Christchurch, Canterbury, 8053, New Zealand
Tel.: (64) 33721562
Fax: (64) 33721563
E-Mail:
Web Site: www.ebbx.co.nz
Emp.: 3
Business Exchange Services
S.I.C.: 7389
N.A.I.C.S.: 561990
Joyce Chen *(Mgr-South Island)*

B.C. HYDRO

333 Dunsmuir St 16th Fl
Vancouver, BC, V6B 5R3, Canada
Tel.: (604) 528-1600
Fax: (604) 623-3937
Toll Free: (800) 224-9376
Web Site: www.bchydro.com
Year Founded: 1945
Emp.: 4,406
Business Description:
Electric Utility Services
S.I.C.: 9631
N.A.I.C.S.: 926130
Personnel:
Dan Doyle *(Chm)*
Bev van Ruyven *(Deputy CEO & Exec VP)*
Charles Reid *(CFO & Exec VP-Fin)*
Don Stuckert *(CIO)*
Debbie Nagle *(Chief HR Officer & Sr VP)*
Lisa Seppala *(Chief Safety, Health & Environment Officer)*
Raymond A. Aldeguer *(Gen Counsel & Sr VP)*
Chris O'Riley *(Exec VP-Generation)*
Susan Yurkovich *(Exec VP-Site C Clean Energy Project)*
Michele Morgan *(Sr VP-Smart Metering Infrastructure Project)*
Leigh Ann Shoji-Lee *(Sr VP-Field Ops)*
Board of Directors:
Dan Doyle
Chief Kim Baird
James M. Brown
Peter Busby
Wanda C. Costuros
Jonathan Drance
Tracey L. McVicar
Nancy D. Olewiler
Peter J. Powell

Subsidiaries:

Powerex Corp. (1)
1300 666 Burrard St
Vancouver, BC, V6C 2X8, Canada (100%)
Tel.: (604) 891-5000
Fax: (604) 891-6060
E-Mail: reception@powerex.com
Web Site: www.powerex.com
Emp.: 118
Marketer of Wholesale Energy Products & Services in Western Canada & the Western United States
S.I.C.: 4911
N.A.I.C.S.: 221122
Teresa Conway *(Pres & CEO)*

Powertech Labs, Inc. (1)
12388 88th Ave
Surrey, BC, V3W 7R7, Canada
Tel.: (604) 590-7500
Fax: (604) 590-6611
E-Mail:
Web Site: www.powertechlabs.com
Emp.: 150
Provider of Testing, Consulting & Research Services to the Electric & Natural Gas Industries
S.I.C.: 8734
N.A.I.C.S.: 541380
Livio Gambone *(Mgr-Vehicle Programs-Gas Sys)*

BC INSTITUTE D.D. ZAGREB

Rugvica Dugoselska 7
10370 Dugo Selo, Croatia
Tel.: (385) 12781510
Fax: (385) 14854076
E-Mail: bc-uprava@bc-institut.hr
Web Site: www.bc-institut.hr
BCIN-R-A—(ZAG)
Sales Range: $10-24.9 Million
Business Description:
Seed Producer
S.I.C.: 0139
N.A.I.C.S.: 111211
Personnel:
Boris Varga *(Chm-Supervisory Bd)*
Dragomir Parlov *(Deputy Chm-Supervisory Bd)*
Daniel Skoro *(Member-Mgmt Bd & Mng Dir)*
Supervisory Board of Directors:
Tomislav Ledic
Dragomir Parlov
Boris Varga

BC IRON LIMITED

Level 1 15 Rheola Street
West Perth, WA, 6005, Australia
Tel.: (61) 8 6311 3400
Fax: (61) 8 6311 3449
E-Mail: info@bciron.com.au
Web Site: www.bciron.com.au
BCI—(ASX)
Rev.: $339,001,002
Assets: $439,331,937
Liabilities: $213,099,123
Net Worth: $226,232,814
Earnings: $50,854,838
Emp.: 63
Fiscal Year-end: 06/30/13
Business Description:
Mineral Exploration
S.I.C.: 1011
N.A.I.C.S.: 212210
Personnel:
Morgan Scott Ball *(Mng Dir)*
Chris Hunt *(CFO)*
Blair Duncan *(COO)*
Linda Edge *(Co-Sec & Controller-Fin)*
Anthea Bird *(Co-Sec & Gen Mgr-Fin)*
Board of Directors:
Anthony William Kiernan
Morgan Scott Ball
Andrew Malcolm Haslam
Malcolm John McComas
Terrence William Ransted
Peter John Wilshaw
Michael Charles Young

BC PARTNERS LIMITED

40 Portman Square
London, W1H 6DA, United Kingdom
Tel.: (44) 2070094800
Fax: (44) 2070094899
E-Mail: london@bcpartners.com
Web Site: www.bcpartners.com
Year Founded: 1986
Managed Assets: $14,973,700,000
Emp.: 60
Business Description:
Private Equity Firm
S.I.C.: 6211
N.A.I.C.S.: 523999
Personnel:
Francesco Loredan *(Co-Chm, Mng Partner & Head-Geneva Office)*
Raymond Svider *(Co-Chm & Mng Partner)*
Stefano Quadrio Curzio *(Mng Partner)*
Nikos Stathopoulos *(Mng Partner)*
Joe Cronly *(Sr Partner)*
Stefano Ferraresi *(Partner)*
Mark Philip Hersee *(Partner)*
Jonathan Hosgood *(Partner)*
Torsten Mack *(Partner)*
Joachim Ogland *(Partner)*
Jamie Rivers *(Partner)*
Moritz von Hauenschild *(Partner)*

Holding:

Phones 4u Ltd. (1)
Phones 4u House Ore Close
Lymedale Business Park, Newcastle-under-Lyme, Staffordshire, ST5 9QD, United Kingdom
Tel.: (44) 844 871 2231
E-Mail: enquiry@phones4u.co.uk
Web Site: www.phones4u.co.uk
Sales Range: $1-4.9 Billion
Emp.: 6,000
Retailer of Mobile Telecommunications Products & Services
S.I.C.: 4812
N.A.I.C.S.: 517210
David Kassler *(CEO)*
Tim Whiting *(Interim Grp CEO)*

U.S. Subsidiary:

BC Partners, Inc. (1)
667 Madison Ave
New York, NY 10065 DE
Tel.: (212) 891-2880
Fax: (212) 891-2899
E-Mail: newyork@bcpartners.com
Web Site: www.bcpartners.com
Emp.: 25
Private Equity Firm
S.I.C.: 6211
N.A.I.C.S.: 523999

Raymond Svider *(Co-Chm & Mng Partner)*
Justin Bateman *(Sr Partner)*
Hans Haderer *(Partner)*
Michael Chang *(Principal)*

Holdings:

ATI Enterprises, Inc. (2)
6331 Blvd 26 Ste 275
North Richland Hills, TX 76180 TX
Tel.: (855) 203-1599
Web Site: www.aticareertraining.edu
Sales Range: $200-249.9 Million
Technical & Trade Career Training Schools
S.I.C.: 8299
N.A.I.C.S.: 611519
Phung Burns *(CFO)*
Paul Eppen *(CMO)*
Sue Edwards *(Chief Compliance Officer)*

MultiPlan Inc. (2)
115 5th Ave Fl 7
New York, NY 10003
Tel.: (212) 780-2000
Fax: (212) 780-0420
E-Mail: info@multiplan.com
Web Site: www.multiplan.com
Emp.: 800
Medical Cost Management Services
S.I.C.: 6371
N.A.I.C.S.: 524292
Mark Tabak *(CEO)*
David Redmond *(CFO & Exec VP)*
Marcy Feller *(Gen Counsel & Exec VP)*
Michael Ferrante *(Exec VP-Ops)*
Dale White *(Exec VP-Sls & Acct Mgmt)*

Subsidiaries:

MultiPlan, Inc. (3)
1100 Winter St
Waltham, MA 02451-1440 MA
Tel.: (781) 895-7500
Fax: (781) 895-3458
Toll Free: (800) 253-4417
E-Mail: info@multiplan.com
Web Site: www.multiplan.com
Sales Range: $125-149.9 Million
Emp.: 1,100
Healthcare Management Services
S.I.C.: 6324
N.A.I.C.S.: 524114
Mark Tabak *(CEO)*

Joint Ventures:

Cequel Communications, LLC (2)
12444 Powerscourt Dr
Saint Louis, MO 63131 DE
Tel.: (314) 965-2020
Fax: (314) 965-0050
Toll Free: (800) 999-6845
Web Site: www.suddenlink.com
Sales Range: $1-4.9 Billion
Emp.: 6,100
Digital Cable TV, High-Speed Internet & Home Security Services
S.I.C.: 4841
N.A.I.C.S.: 515210
Jerald L. Kent *(Chm & CEO)*
Mary E. Meduski *(CFO & Exec VP)*
Thomas P. McMillin *(COO & Exec VP)*
Robert L. Putnam *(CIO & Sr VP)*
Jerry Dow *(CMO & Chief Sls Officer)*
Terry M. Cordova *(CTO & Sr VP)*
James B. Fox *(Chief Acctg Officer & Sr VP)*
Katherine Payne *(Chief Programming Officer & Sr VP)*
Kevin A. Stephens *(Pres-Comml & Adv Ops)*
Craig L. Rosenthal *(Gen Counsel & Sr VP)*
Ralph G. Kelly *(Treas & Sr VP)*
Wendy Knudsen *(Sec & Exec VP)*
Peter M. Abel *(Sr VP-Corp Comm)*
John E. Fuhler *(Sr VP-Fiscal Ops)*
Gregg Graff *(Sr VP-Sls)*
Gibbs Jones *(Sr VP-Customer Experience)*
Patricia L. McCaskill *(Sr VP-Programming & Chief Programming Officer)*
Mary R. Meier *(Sr VP-Mktg)*
Douglas G. Wiley *(Sr VP-HR)*

Subsidiary:

Perimeter Technology Center, Inc. (3)
4100 Perimeter Ctr Dr Ste 300
Oklahoma City, OK 73112
Tel.: (405) 917-3700
Toll Free: (888) 782-2656
E-Mail: sales@perimetercenter.com
Web Site: www.perimetercenter.com
Sales Range: $1-9.9 Million
Emp.: 20
Commercial Data Center Services, Monitored & Managed Network Services & Professional Engineering Services
S.I.C.: 7374
N.A.I.C.S.: 518210
R. Todd Currie *(Founder, Treas & VP-Ops)*
John W. Parsons *(CEO)*
Brad Thomas *(Sec & VP-Tech)*

Neodyne Industries (2)
1 Hamilton Rd
Windsor Locks, CT 06095
Tel.: (860) 654-6000
Sales Range: $1-4.9 Billion
Holding Company; Industrial Pumps & Compressors Mfr
S.I.C.: 6719
N.A.I.C.S.: 551112
John J. Doucette *(Pres & CEO)*

Subsidiaries:

Milton Roy, LLC (3)
201 Ivyland Rd
Ivyland, PA 18974-1706 PA
Tel.: (215) 441-0800
Telex: 47-61138
Fax: (215) 441-8620
E-Mail: info@miltonroy.com
Web Site: www.miltonroy.com
Sales Range: $75-99.9 Million
Emp.: 150
Controlled Volume (Metering) Pumps & Related Equipment Mfr
Import Export
S.I.C.: 3561
N.A.I.C.S.: 333911
Jean Claude Pharamond *(Pres)*
Bruno Dirringer *(CFO)*

Division:

Milton Roy - Hartell Division (4)
201 Ivyland Rd
Ivyland, PA 18974
Tel.: (215) 322-0730
Fax: (800) 322-5519
E-Mail: info@hartell.com
Web Site: www.hartell.com
Sales Range: $50-74.9 Million
Emp.: 150
Pumps Mfr
S.I.C.: 3561
N.A.I.C.S.: 333911
Steve Wolfe *(Product Mgr)*

Subsidiaries:

Milton Roy Liquid Metronics Incorporated (4)
8th Post Office Sq
Acton, MA 01720-3948 MA
Tel.: (978) 635-4999
Fax: (978) 635-4992
Web Site: www.lmipumps.com
Sales Range: $25-49.9 Million
Emp.: 75
Measuring & Dispensing Pumps
S.I.C.: 3586
N.A.I.C.S.: 333913
Jean-Claude Pharamond *(Pres)*

Pressure Products Industries Inc. (4)
900 Louis Dr
Warminster, PA 18974-2841
Tel.: (215) 675-1600
Fax: (215) 443-8341
E-Mail: info@pressureproductsindustries.com
Web Site: www.pressureproductsindustries.com
Sales Range: $25-49.9 Million
Emp.: 75
Fluid Handling Equipment Mfr
S.I.C.: 3563
N.A.I.C.S.: 333912

Williams Instrument Company (4)
201 Ivyland Rd
Warminster, PA 18974-1706 PA
Tel.: (215) 293-0415
Fax: (215) 293-0498
E-Mail: info@williamspumps.com
Web Site: www.williamspumps.com
Sales Range: $1-9.9 Million
Emp.: 150
Pneumatic Metering Pumps & Chemical Injection Systems Mfr
S.I.C.: 3561
N.A.I.C.S.: 333911
Coogan Cameron *(Product Mgr)*

Y-Z Systems Inc. (4)
2408 Timberloch Pl Ste B-10
The Woodlands, TX 77380 TX
Tel.: (281) 362-6500
Fax: (281) 362-6513
Toll Free: (800) 344-5399
E-Mail: sales@yzhq.com
Web Site: www.yzsystems.com
Sales Range: $25-49.9 Million
Emp.: 100
Odorization Systems Mfr
S.I.C.: 3826
N.A.I.C.S.: 334516
Kris Kimmel *(Product Mgr & Sls Mgr)*

Non-U.S. Subsidiary:

Milton Roy Europe (4)
10 Grande Rue
27360 Pont-Saint-Pierre, France
Tel.: (33) 232683000
Fax: (33) 232683093
E-Mail: contact@miltonroy-europe.com
Web Site: www.miltonroy-europe.com
Sales Range: $100-124.9 Million
Emp.: 300
Pumps & Compressors Mfr
S.I.C.: 3561
N.A.I.C.S.: 333911

Sullair, LLC (3)
3700 E Michigan Blvd
Michigan City, IN 46360-6527 IN
Tel.: (219) 879-5451
Fax: (219) 874-1273
Toll Free: (800) 785-5247
E-Mail: sullairsolutions@sullair.com
Web Site: www.sullair.com
Sales Range: $150-199.9 Million
Emp.: 520
Air & Gas Compressors Mfr
S.I.C.: 3563
N.A.I.C.S.: 333912
Kathy Hamilton *(Dir-Fin)*

Non-U.S. Holdings:

Sullair Argentina S.A. (4)
Goncalves Dias 1145
Buenos Aires, C1276ACQ, Argentina
Tel.: (54) 11 5941 4444
Fax: (54) 1159414540
E-Mail: contacto@sullair.com.ar
Web Site: www.sullairargentina.com
Sales Range: $125-149.9 Million
Emp.: 300
Compressors Mfr
S.I.C.: 3563
N.A.I.C.S.: 333912
Luis Vado *(Mng Dir)*

Sullair Asia Ltd. (4)
74 Joo Koon Cir Jurong
Singapore, 629093, Singapore
Tel.: (65) 6861 1211
Fax: (65) 6861 2967
E-Mail: info@sullair.com
Web Site: www.sullair.com.sg
Sales Range: $25-49.9 Million
Emp.: 10
Compressors Mfr
S.I.C.: 3563
N.A.I.C.S.: 333912
Christopher Loo *(Reg Mgr)*

Sullair Australia Pty Ltd (4)
324-332 Frankston-Dandenong Rd
Dandenong, VIC, 3175, Australia
Tel.: (61) 3 9703 9000
Fax: (61) 3 9703 9053
Compressors Sales & Service
S.I.C.: 5084
N.A.I.C.S.: 423830

Sullair Taiwan Ltd. (4)
3F 1 No 248 Chung Shan Rd Lin Kou Hsiang
Taipei, 244, Taiwan
Tel.: (886) 226013500
Fax: (886) 226013032
E-Mail: rosestw@ms24.hinet.net
Web Site: www.sullair.com
Sales Range: $10-24.9 Million
Emp.: 5
Compressors Mfr
S.I.C.: 3563
N.A.I.C.S.: 333912
Louis Wang *(Mng Dir)*

Sundyne, LLC (3)
14845 W 64th Ave
Arvada, CO 80007-7523
Tel.: (303) 425-0800
Fax: (303) 940-3141
E-Mail: pumps@sundyne.com
Web Site: www.sundyne.com
Sales Range: $125-149.9 Million
Emp.: 400
Pumps & Pumping Equipment Mfr
S.I.C.: 3561
N.A.I.C.S.: 333911
Jeffrey Wiemelt *(Pres)*

Non-U.S. Holdings:

Aenova Holding GmbH (1)
Gut Kerschlach 1
82396 Pahl, Germany
Tel.: (49) 88 08 9243 111
E-Mail: info@aenova.de
Web Site: www.aenova.de
Sales Range: $650-699.9 Million
Emp.: 2,500
Vitamins & Pharmaceuticals Mfr
S.I.C.: 2834
N.A.I.C.S.: 325412
Heiner Hoppmann *(CEO)*
Frank Elsen *(CFO)*

Subsidiaries:

Dragenopharm Apotheker Puschl GmbH & Co. KG (2)
Gollstr 1
84549 Munich, Germany
Tel.: (49) 86838950
Fax: (49) 8683895100
E-Mail: info@dragenopharm.de
Web Site: www.dragenopharm.de
Emp.: 600
Mfr of Generic Pharmaceutical Products
S.I.C.: 2834
N.A.I.C.S.: 325412

Temmler Pharma GmbH & Co. KG (2)
TemmlerstraSSe 2
35039 Marburg, Germany
Tel.: (49) 64214940
Fax: (49) 6421494200
E-Mail: info@temmler.eu
Web Site: www.temmler.de
Sales Range: $200-249.9 Million
Emp.: 750
Pharmaceuticals Mfr
S.I.C.: 2834
N.A.I.C.S.: 325412
Werner Schneider *(Mng Dir)*

Subsidiaries:

C.P.M. ContractPharma GmbH & Co. KG (3)
Gutenbergstrasse 1
D 83052 Bruckmuhl, Germany
Tel.: (49) 80629048 25
Fax: (49) 80629048 32
Web Site: www.cpm-contractpharma.com
Emp.: 150
Pharmaceuticals Mfr
S.I.C.: 2834
N.A.I.C.S.: 325412
Stefan Fasching *(Mng Dir)*
Uwe Reimers *(Mng Dir)*

Temmler Werke GmbH (3)
Weihenstephaner Strasse 28
81673 Munich, Germany DE
Tel.: (49) 8942729901
Fax: (49) 894272991000
Web Site: www.temmler.eu
Emp.: 200
Pharmaceuticals Mfr
S.I.C.: 2834
N.A.I.C.S.: 325412
Bernd Hubar *(Gen Mgr)*

Non-U.S. Subsidiaries:

SwissCo Services AG (3)
Bahnhofstr 14
CH 4334 Sisseln, Switzerland
Tel.: (41) 628664141
Fax: (41) 628664140
E-Mail: sisseln@swissco.ch

BC Partners Limited—(Continued)

Web Site: www.temmler.eu
Emp.: 160
Pharmaceuticals Mfr
S.I.C.: 2834
N.A.I.C.S.: 325412
Reto Stahl *(Mng Dir)*

Temmler Ireland Ltd. **(3)**
Banshagh
Killorglin, Co Kerry, Ireland IE
Tel.: (353) 6697926 00
Fax: (353) 6697926 06
Web Site: www.temmler.de/wps/tp/home/en/address_killorglin/
Emp.: 65
Pharmaceuticals Mfr
S.I.C.: 2834
N.A.I.C.S.: 325412
Peter Quane *(Mng Dir)*

Temmler Italia S.r.l. **(3)**
Via delle Industrie 2
20061 Carugate, MI, Italy IT
Tel.: (39) 029250341
Fax: (39) 0292151827
Web Site: www.temmler.de/wps/tp/home/en/address_carugate/
Pharmaceuticals Mfr
S.I.C.: 2834
N.A.I.C.S.: 325412
Aldo Castelli *(Mng Dir)*
Massimiliano Del Frate *(Mng Dir)*

Non-U.S. Subsidiary:

SWISS CAPS AG **(2)**
Husenstrasse 35
9533 Kirchberg, Switzerland
Tel.: (41) 71 93 26 262
Fax: (41) 719314191
E-Mail: info.ch@aenova-group.com
Emp.: 285
Vitamins & Pharmaceuticals Mfr
S.I.C.: 2834
N.A.I.C.S.: 325412

U.S. Subsidiary:

SWISS CAPS USA, Inc. **(3)**
14193 SW 119th Ave
Miami, FL 33186 FL
Tel.: (305) 234-0102
Fax: (305) 234-0105
Web Site: www.swisscaps.com
Emp.: 54
Vitamins & Pharmaceuticals Mfr
S.I.C.: 2834
N.A.I.C.S.: 325412
Hans Engels *(CEO)*

Allflex Europe SA **(1)**
35 Rue des Eaux
35500 Vitre, France
Tel.: (33) 2 99 75 77 00
Web Site: www.allflex-europe.com
Emp.: 1,200
Animal Identification Tag Mfr
S.I.C.: 3089
N.A.I.C.S.: 326199
Jacques Martin *(COO)*

U.S. Subsidiary:

Allflex USA, Inc. **(2)**
2805 E 14th St DFW Airport
Irving, TX 75261
Tel.: (972) 456-3686
Fax: (972) 456-3882
Toll Free: (800) 989-8247
Web Site: www.allflexusa.com
Sales Range: $250-299.9 Million
Emp.: 70
Animal Identification Tag Mfr
S.I.C.: 3089
N.A.I.C.S.: 326199
Brian Bolton *(Pres & CEO)*
Glenn Fischer *(Sr VP-Mktg)*

FutureLAB Holding GmbH **(1)**
Gymnasiumstrasse 39
1180 Vienna, Austria
Tel.: (43) 14799297
Fax: (43) 1479929720
E-Mail: office@futurebiolab.at
Web Site: www.futurebiolab.at
Sales Range: $150-199.9 Million
Emp.: 2,200
Medical-Diagnostic Laboratory Services
S.I.C.: 8071
N.A.I.C.S.: 621511
Bartl Wimmer *(CEO)*
Bernhard Auer *(CFO)*
Mathias M. Muller *(Chief Medical Officer)*

Gruppo Coin S.p.A. **(1)**
Via Terraglio 17
30174 Mestre, Venice, Italy IT
Tel.: (39) 041 2398000
Fax: (39) 041 982722
E-Mail: infogruppo@gruppocoin.it
Web Site: www.gruppocoin.it
GCN—(ITA)
Sales Range: $1-4.9 Billion
Emp.: 9,498
Operator & Franchiser of Apparel, Accessories & Home Furnishing Stores
S.I.C.: 2389
N.A.I.C.S.: 315990
Stefano Beraldo *(CEO)*

Migros Ticaret A.S. **(1)**
Turgut Ozal Caddesi 12 Atasehir
34758 Istanbul, Turkey (50.8%)
Tel.: (90) 2165793000
Fax: (90) 2164565905
E-Mail: investor_relations@migros.com.tr
Web Site: www.migros.com.tr
MGROS—(IST)
Sales Range: $1-4.9 Billion
Supermarket Chain Operator
S.I.C.: 5411
N.A.I.C.S.: 445110
Fevzi Bulend Ozaydinli *(Chm)*
Omer Ozgur Tort *(Gen Mgr)*

Non-U.S. Joint Venture:

Intelsat S.A. **(1)**
(Formerly Intelsat Global Holdings S.A.)
4 rue Albert Borschette
L-1246 Luxembourg, Luxembourg LU
Tel.: (352) 27841600
Fax: (352) 27841690
Web Site: www.intelsat.com
I—(NYSE)
Rev.: $2,603,623,000
Assets: $16,589,670,000
Liabilities: $17,524,337,000
Net Worth: ($934,667,000)
Earnings: ($251,993,000)
Emp.: 1,079
Fiscal Year-end: 12/31/13
Satellite Telecommunications
S.I.C.: 4899
N.A.I.C.S.: 517410
David McGlade *(Chm & CEO)*
Stephen Spengler *(Pres & Chief Comml Officer)*
Michael McDonnell *(CFO & Exec VP)*
Michelle Bryan *(Chief Admin Officer, Gen Counsel & Exec VP)*
Thierry Guillemin *(CTO & Exec VP)*
Kurt Riegelman *(Sr VP-Global Sls)*

BC POWER CONTROLS LTD.

7A/39 WEA Channa Market
Karol Bagh, New Delhi, 110005, India
Tel.: (91) 11 47532795
Fax: (91) 11 47532798
Web Site: www.bcpowercontrols.com
Year Founded: 2008
Emp.: 40
Business Description:
Wire & Cable Mfr
S.I.C.: 3357
N.A.I.C.S.: 335929
Personnel:
Arun K. Jain *(Mng Dir)*

B.C. TREE FRUITS LTD.

1473 Water St
Kelowna, BC, V1Y 1J6, Canada
Tel.: (250) 470-4200
Fax: (250) 762-5571
E-Mail: info@bctree.com
Web Site: www.bctree.com
Year Founded: 1936
Sales Range: $1-9.9 Million
Emp.: 43
Business Description:
Fruit & Vegetable Broker
Export
S.I.C.: 5431
N.A.I.C.S.: 445230
Personnel:
Rick Austin *(Dir-Sls & Mktg)*

BCB BERHAD

No 4B 2nd & 3rd Floor Jalan Sentol
South Wing-Kluang Parade
86000 Keluang, Johor, Malaysia
Tel.: (60) 77760089
Fax: (60) 77720089
E-Mail: info@bcbbhd.com.my
Web Site: www.bcbbhd.com.my
BCB—(KLS)
Rev.: $53,968,701
Assets: $256,715,859
Liabilities: $138,341,801
Net Worth: $118,374,059
Earnings: $5,280,016
Fiscal Year-end: 06/30/13
Business Description:
Property Development & Hotel Operations
S.I.C.: 1622
N.A.I.C.S.: 237310
Personnel:
Seng Leong Tan *(Grp Mng Dir)*
Bee Hwee Tan *(Co-Sec)*
Kok Leong Yeap *(Co-Sec)*
Board of Directors:
Ismail Yusof
Ash'ari Ayub
M. Arif Kataman
Kok Yung Low
Lay Hiang Tan
Lindy Tan
Seng Leong Tan
Vin Sern Tan
Vin Shyan Tan

Subsidiaries:

BCB Management Sdn. Bhd. **(1)**
Pejabat Tapak BCB Management
81110 Kangkar Pulai, Johor, Malaysia
Tel.: (60) 75213128
Fax: (60) 75212129
Property Development Services
S.I.C.: 6531
N.A.I.C.S.: 531390

BCB Resources Sdn. Bhd. **(1)**
4B 2nd and 3rd Fl Jalan Sentol S Wing Kluang Parade, 86000 Keluang, Johor, Malaysia
Tel.: (60) 77760089
Fax: (60) 77720089
E-Mail: mandytan@bcbbhd.com.my
Property Development Services
S.I.C.: 1522
N.A.I.C.S.: 236116
Yung Kuk Low *(Controller-Fin)*

Johbase Development Sdn. Bhd. **(1)**
7th Floor Plaza BCB 20 Jalan Bakawali
86000 Keluang, Johor, Malaysia
Tel.: (60) 77722567
Fax: (60) 77722108
Property Development Services
S.I.C.: 6531
N.A.I.C.S.: 531390

BCB FINANCE LTD

1204 PJ Towers Dalal Street
Fort, Mumbai, 400001, India
Tel.: (91) 22 2272 2414
E-Mail: manish@bcbfinance.com
Web Site: www.bcbfinance.com
534109—(BOM)
Sales Range: $1-9.9 Million
Business Description:
Financial Services
S.I.C.: 6726
N.A.I.C.S.: 525990
Personnel:
Bharat Bagri *(Chm)*
Manish Kumar Mourya *(Compliance Officer & Sec)*
Board of Directors:
Bharat Bagri
V.D. Ajgaonkar
Sarla Bagri
Uttam Bagri
Kalpesh Ranka

BCB HOLDINGS LIMITED

60 Market Square
PO Box 1764
Belize, Belize
Tel.: (501) 2277132
Fax: (501) 2232389
E-Mail: info@bcbholdings.com
Web Site: www.bcbholdings.com
Year Founded: 1999
BCB—(LSE)
Rev.: $53,500,000
Assets: $690,600,000
Liabilities: $604,600,000
Net Worth: $86,000,000
Earnings: ($21,600,000)
Emp.: 6,082
Fiscal Year-end: 03/31/13
Business Description:
Bank Holding Company
S.I.C.: 6712
N.A.I.C.S.: 551111
Personnel:
Lyndon Guiseppi *(CEO)*
Peter M. R. Gaze *(CFO)*
Philip T. Osborne *(Sec)*
Board of Directors:
Euric Allan Bobb
Peter M. R. Gaze
Lyndon Guiseppi
Cheryl C. Jones
Philip T. Osborne
Philip Priestley
John M. Searle
Legal Counsel:
Allen & Overy
One Bishops Square
London, United Kingdom

The Belize Bank Limited
60 Market Square PO Box 364
Belize, Belize
Transfer Agent:
Capita IRG (Offshore) Limited
Victoria Chambers Liberation Square 1/3 The Esplanade
Saint Helier, Jersey

Subsidiary:

The Belize Bank Limited **(1)**
60 Market Square
Belize, Belize
Tel.: (501) 2277132
Fax: (501) 2272712
E-Mail: bblbz@belizebank.com
Web Site: www.belizebank.com
Commercial Banking
S.I.C.: 6029
N.A.I.C.S.: 522110
Philip C. Johnson *(Pres)*

BCC FUBA INDIA LTD.

C-136 Defence Colony
New Delhi, 110 024, India
Tel.: (91) 11 29553257
Fax: (91) 11 29553259
E-Mail: bccfuba@vsnl.com
Web Site: www.bccfuba.com
517246—(BOM)
Sales Range: $1-9.9 Million
Business Description:
Industrial Machinery Mfr
S.I.C.: 3559
N.A.I.C.S.: 333249
Personnel:
V. S. Bhagat *(Chm & Mng Dir)*
Board of Directors:
V. S. Bhagat
H. R. Ansari
Renu Bhagat
A. P. Mathur
R. M. Mehta
Veenu Pasricha

Transfer Agent:
Link Intime India Private Limited
A-40 2nd Floor Naraina Industrial Area Phase-II
New Delhi, India

BCD HOLDINGS N.V.

Utrechtseweg 67
3704 HB Zeist, Netherlands
Tel.: (31) 306976140
Fax: (31) 306976142
E-Mail: bcd@bcd-nv.com
Web Site: www.bcd-nv.com
Year Founded: 1975
Sales Range: $100-124.9 Million
Emp.: 15
Business Description:
Holding Company; Financial & Travel Services
S.I.C.: 6719
N.A.I.C.S.: 551112
Personnel:
J. A. Fentener Van Vlissingen *(Founder & Chm)*
Joop G. Dreschel *(CEO)*

U.S. Holdings:

Park 'N Fly, Inc. (1)
2060 Mount Paran Rd NW Ste 207
Atlanta, GA 30327-2935 GA
Tel.: (404) 264-1000
Fax: (404) 264-1115
E-Mail: info@pnf.com
Web Site: www.pnf.com
Emp.: 1,000
Real Estate Agents & Managers
Import Export
S.I.C.: 7521
N.A.I.C.S.: 812930
Tony Paalz *(Pres & CEO)*

BCD Travel (1)
6 Concourse Pkwy Ste 2400
Atlanta, GA 30328-6003
Tel.: (678) 441-5200
E-Mail: inquiries@bcdtravel.com
Web Site: www.bcdtravel.com
Emp.: 150
Travel Agencies
Import Export
S.I.C.: 4724
N.A.I.C.S.: 561510
John A. Fentener van Vlissingen *(Founder)*
Danny Hood *(Pres)*

Subsidiary:

BCD Travel (2)
Ste 220 7 Parkway Ctr
Pittsburgh, PA 15220-3704 DE
Tel.: (412) 928-7500
Fax: (412) 402-7675
Web Site: www.bcdtravel.us
Emp.: 90
Travel Services
Import Export
S.I.C.: 4724
N.A.I.C.S.: 561510
Kiley Ottaviani *(Gen Mgr)*

BCD RESOURCES NL

1 Rifle Range Road
Perth, TAS, 7270, Australia
Tel.: (61) 3 6383 6500
Fax: (61) 3 6383 6590
E-Mail: enquiries@bcdresources.com.au
Web Site: www.bcdresources.com.au
BCD—(ASX)
Rev.: $13,223,207
Assets: $12,386,401
Liabilities: $4,440,388
Net Worth: $7,946,013
Earnings: ($8,979,776)
Fiscal Year-end: 06/30/13
Business Description:
Gold, Copper & Other Metal Mining Services
S.I.C.: 1041
N.A.I.C.S.: 212221
Personnel:
Richelle A. Greenwood *(COO)*
Brian David Coulter *(Sec)*
Board of Directors:
Clive S. Carroll
David F. Groves
Nigel Barry Webb
Legal Counsel:
Mills Oakley Lawyers
Level 6 530 Collins Street
Melbourne, Australia

BCE INC.

(d/b/a Bell Canada Enterprises)
1 Carrefour Alexander-Graham-Bell
Building A 8th Floor
Verdun, QC, H3E 3B3, Canada
Tel.: (514) 870-8777
Fax: (514) 766-5735
Toll Free: (888) 932-6666
E-Mail: investor.relations@bce.ca
Web Site: www.bce.ca
Year Founded: 1880
BCE—(NYSE TSX)
Rev.: $18,346,740,000
Assets: $40,816,100,400
Liabilities: $26,201,662,900
Net Worth: $14,614,437,500
Earnings: $2,147,647,800
Emp.: 55,830
Fiscal Year-end: 12/31/13
Business Description:
Holding Company;
Telecommunication & Broadcast Media Services
Export
S.I.C.: 6719
N.A.I.C.S.: 551112
Personnel:
Thomas Charles O'Neill *(Chm)*
Martine Turcotte *(Vice Chm-Quebec)*
George A. Cope *(Pres & CEO)*
Siim A. Vanaselja *(CFO & Exec VP)*
Michael Cole *(CIO & Exec VP)*
Mirko Bibic *(Chief Legal Officer & Chief Regulatory Officer & Exec VP)*
Stephen Howe *(CTO & Exec VP)*
Charles Brown *(Pres-The Source)*
Kevin W. Crull *(Pres-Bell Media)*
Tom Little *(Pres-Bell Bus Markets)*
Bernard le Duc *(Exec VP-Corp Svcs)*
Mary Anne Turcke *(Exec VP-Field Ops)*
John Watson *(Exec VP-Customer Ops)*
Board of Directors:
Thomas Charles O'Neill
Barry K. Allen
Andre Berard
Ronald Alvin Brenneman
Sophie Brochu
Robert Ellis Brown
George A. Cope
David F. Denison
Anthony S. Fell
Ian Greenberg
Edward C. Lumley
James Prentice
Robert C. Simmonds
Carole S. Taylor
Paul R. Weiss
American Stock Transfer & Trust Company, LLC
Brooklyn, NY 11210
Transfer Agents:
CST Trust Company
Vancouver, BC, Canada
American Stock Transfer & Trust Company, LLC
Brooklyn, NY 11210
Subsidiaries:

Bell Canada (1)
1 Carrefour Alexander Graham Bell Building A 4th Fl
Verdun, QC, H3E 3B3, Canada (100%)
Tel.: (514) 870-8777
Fax: (514) 766-5735
Toll Free: (888) 932-6666
E-Mail: bcecomms@bce.ca
Web Site: www.bce.ca/en/contact/
Telecommunications Services; Voice, Data & Image Transmissions
S.I.C.: 4813
N.A.I.C.S.: 517110
Thomas C. O'Neill *(Chm)*
George A. Cope *(Pres & CEO)*
Siim A. Vanaselja *(CFO & Exec VP)*
Wade Oosterman *(Chief Brand Officer)*
Patricia A. Olah *(Sec & Lead Governance Counsel)*
Martine Turcotte *(Chief Legal & Regulatory Officer & Exec VP)*
David Wells *(Exec VP-Corp Svcs)*
Karyn A. Brooks *(Sr VP & Controller)*

Subsidiaries:

NorthwesTel Inc. (2)
301 Lambert St
PO Box 2727
Whitehorse, YT, Y1A 4Y4, Canada (100%)
Tel.: (867) 668-5300
Fax: (867) 668-7079
E-Mail: info@nwtel.ca
Web Site: www.nwtel.ca
Sales Range: $100-124.9 Million
Emp.: 650
Telephone, Telecommunications, Mobile Communications & Cable Television Services
S.I.C.: 4813
N.A.I.C.S.: 517110
Charles Brown *(Chm)*
Paul Flaherty *(Pres & CEO)*

The Source (Bell) Electronics Inc. (2)
279 Bayview Drive
Barrie, ON, L4M 4W5, Canada
Tel.: (705) 728-2262
Fax: (705) 728-1369
Toll Free: (866) 384-3422
Web Site: www.thesource.ca
Emp.: 50
Online Marketing Services
S.I.C.: 8742
N.A.I.C.S.: 541613
Charles Brown *(Pres)*

Bell ExpressVu, L.P. (1)
100 Wynford Dr Ste 300
Toronto, ON, M3C 4B4, Canada (100%)
Tel.: (416) 446-2600
Fax: (416) 383-6136
Toll Free: (800) 339-6908
Web Site: www.expressvu.com
Emp.: 100
S.I.C.: 4812
N.A.I.C.S.: 517210
Gary Smith *(Pres)*

Branch:

Bell ExpressVu (2)
100 Wynford Dr
North York, ON, M3C 4B4, Canada (100%)
Tel.: (416) 383-6600
Fax: (416) 383-6692
Toll Free: (888) 759-3474
Web Site: www.bell.ca
Emp.: 250
S.I.C.: 4812
N.A.I.C.S.: 517210
George Cope *(CEO & Pres)*

Bell Media Inc. (1)
299 Queen Street West
Toronto, ON, M5V 2Z5, Canada
Tel.: (416) 384-8000
E-Mail: bellmediacommunications@bellmedia.ca
Web Site: www.bellmedia.ca
Emp.: 3,000
Multi-Media Holding Company
S.I.C.: 6719
N.A.I.C.S.: 551112
Kevin W. Crull *(Pres)*
Steven Bickley *(CMO & Head-Bus Dev)*
Mirko Bibic *(Chief Legal Officer, Chief Regulatory Officer & Exec VP)*
Michel Houle *(Chm-Harold Greenberg Fund & Pres-French Language Program)*
Charles Benoit *(Pres-Television & Radio)*
Rick Brace *(Pres-Specialty Channels & CTV Production)*
Wendy Freeman *(Pres-CTV News)*
Chris Gordon *(Pres-Bell Media Radio)*
Phil King *(Pres-CTV Sports & Entertainment)*
Luc Sabbatini *(Pres-Sls)*
Andre Serero *(Sec & Exec VP-Bus & Pub Affairs)*
Dominic Vivolo *(Exec Vp-Content Sls & Distribution Mktg)*
Bart Yabsley *(Exec VP-Content Sls & Distr)*
Adam Ashton *(Sr VP-Bus Ops)*
Bonnie Brownlee *(Sr VP-Corp Comm)*
Corrie Coe *(Sr VP-Independent Production)*
Patrick Jutras *(Sr VP-Sls-Quebec)*
Nikki Moffat *(Sr VP-Fin)*

Division:

Bell Media Radio (2)
299 Queen Street West
Toronto, ON, M5V 2Z5, Canada
Tel.: (416) 384-8000
Web Site: www.bellmedia.ca
Radio Broadcasting Stations Operator
S.I.C.: 4832
N.A.I.C.S.: 515112
Chris Gordon *(Pres)*

Subsidiaries:

Bell Media Inc. (2)
(Formerly Astral Media Inc.)
1800 Avenue McGill College Bureau 2700
Montreal, QC, H3A 3J6, Canada Ca
Tel.: (514) 939-5000
Fax: (514) 939-1515
E-Mail: bellmediacommunications@bellmedia.ca
Web Site: www.bellmedia.ca
Emp.: 2,713
Specialty & Pay-Per-View Television Services; Broadcasting, Video Mfr & Marketing & Technical Services
S.I.C.: 7812
N.A.I.C.S.: 512110
Charles Benoit *(Pres-Television & Radio-Quebec)*

Subsidiaries:

Artech Digital Entertainments, Inc. (3)
6 Hamilton Ave N
Ottawa, ON, K1Y 4R1, Canada (51%)
Tel.: (613) 728-4880
Fax: (613) 728-4523
Emp.: 50
Develops Media Games & Software Mfr
S.I.C.: 3652
N.A.I.C.S.: 334614

Astral Out-of-Home (3)
1800 McGill College Ave Ste 1600
Montreal, QC, H3A 3J6, Canada
Tel.: (514) 529-6664
Fax: (514) 529-1489
E-Mail: outofhome@astral.com
Web Site: www.astralmediaaffichage.com
Emp.: 500
Outdoor Advertising Services
S.I.C.: 7312
N.A.I.C.S.: 541850
Luc Quetel *(Pres)*

MusiquePlus Inc. (3)
355 Rue Sainte-Catherine West
Montreal, QC, H3B 1A5, Canada
Tel.: (514) 284-7587
Fax: (514) 284-1889
Web Site: www.musiqueplus.com
Emp.: 200
Television Broadcasting Services
S.I.C.: 4833
N.A.I.C.S.: 515120
Luc Doyon *(Pres)*

Viewers Choice Canada Inc. (3)
Brookfield Pl 181 Bay St Ste 100
PO Box 787
Toronto, ON, M5J 2T3, Canada
Tel.: (416) 956-8584
Fax: (416) 956-5415
Toll Free: (800) 565-6684
E-Mail: customercare@viewerschoice.ca
Web Site: www.viewerschoice.ca
Television Broadcasting Services
S.I.C.: 4833
N.A.I.C.S.: 515120
Lee Mattina *(Mgr-Ops)*

BCE INC.—(Continued)

CTV Inc. (2)
9 Channel 9 Ct
Toronto, ON, M1S 4B5, Canada (51%)
Mailing Address:
PO Box 9
Station O, Toronto, ON, M4A 2M9, Canada
Tel.: (416) 332-5000
Fax: (416) 384-4533
E-Mail: info@ctv.ca
Web Site: www.ctv.ca
Emp.: 2,600
Holding Company; Television Broadcasting Stations Operator
S.I.C.: 6719
N.A.I.C.S.: 551112
Wendy Freeman *(Pres-News)*
Phil King *(Pres-Programming & Sports)*

Subsidiaries:

Agincourt Productions, Inc. (3)
9 Channel Nine Ct
Scarborough, ON, M1S 4B5, Canada DE
Tel.: (416) 299-2000 (20%)
Fax: (416) 299-2067
Sales Range: $150-199.9 Million
Emp.: 1,053
Production & Television Programming
S.I.C.: 4833
N.A.I.C.S.: 515120
Ivan Fecan *(CEO)*

The Comedy Network (3)
299 Queenstreet W
Toronto, ON, M5V 2ZY, Canada (65.1%)
Tel.: (416) 332-5000
Fax: (416) 384-5301
E-Mail: info@ctv.ca
Web Site: www.ctv.ca
Emp.: 34
S.I.C.: 4812
N.A.I.C.S.: 517210
Nikki Moffat *(Sr VP-Fin)*

CTV Newsnet (3)
9 Channel 9 Ct
Toronto, ON, M1S 4B5, Canada (100%)
Tel.: (416) 332-5000
Fax: (416) 291-5337
Web Site: www.ctvnews.ca/newschannel
Emp.: 2,500
Cable Television Services
S.I.C.: 4841
N.A.I.C.S.: 515210
Wendy Freeman *(Pres)*

The Discovery Channel (3)
9 Channel 9 Ct
Scarborough, ON, M1S 4B5, Canada (51%)
Tel.: (416) 332-5000
Fax: (416) 332-4230
Web Site: www.discoverychannel.ca
Emp.: 5,000
Television Station
S.I.C.: 4833
N.A.I.C.S.: 515120
Clark Bunting *(Pres & Gen Mgr-Discovery Channel)*
Andrea Golstein *(Mng Dir)*
Wonya Y. Lucas *(COO & Exec VP)*
Steve McGowan *(Sr VP-Res)*

TSN Communications (3)
9 Channel 9 Ct
Toronto, ON, M1S 4B5, Canada (51%)
Tel.: (416) 332-5000
Fax: (416) 332-7659
Web Site: www.tsn.ca
Emp.: 2,500
Television Broadcasting Company
S.I.C.: 4833
N.A.I.C.S.: 515120
Stewart Johnston *(Pres)*
Mark Milliere *(Sr VP-Production)*

Units:

CTV Atlantic, Halifax (3)
2885 Robie St
Halifax, NS, B3K 5Z4, Canada
Tel.: (902) 453-4000
Fax: (902) 454-3302
E-Mail: atlanticnews@ctv.ca
Web Site: www.ctv.ca
Emp.: 200
Television Broadcasting Station
S.I.C.: 4833
N.A.I.C.S.: 515120
Mike Elgie *(VP & Gen Mgr)*

CTV Atlantic, Moncton (3)
191 Halifax Street
E1C 9R7 Moncton, NB, Canada
Tel.: (506) 857-2600
Fax: (506) 857-2617
E-Mail: ctvatlantic@ctv.ca
Web Site: www.ctv.ca
Emp.: 15
Television Broadcasting Station
S.I.C.: 4833
N.A.I.C.S.: 515120
C. Lewis *(Mgr)*

CTV Atlantic, Saint John (3)
12 Smythe Street Suite 126
Saint John, NB, E2L 5G5, Canada
Tel.: (506) 658-1010
Fax: (506) 658-1208
E-Mail: atlanticnews@ctv.ca
Web Site: www.ctv.ca
Sales Range: $1-9.9 Million
Emp.: 3
Television Broadcasting Station
S.I.C.: 4833
N.A.I.C.S.: 515120

CTV Atlantic, Sydney (3)
1283 George St
Sydney, NS, B1P 1N7, Canada
Tel.: (902) 562-5511
Fax: (902) 562-9714
E-Mail: cjcbtv@ctv.ca
Web Site: www.ctv.ca
Emp.: 10
Television Broadcasting Station
S.I.C.: 4833
N.A.I.C.S.: 515120

CTV British Columbia (3)
750 Burrard St Ste 300
Vancouver, BC, V6Z 1X5, Canada
Tel.: (604) 608-2868
Fax: (604) 608-2698
Web Site: www.ctvbc.ctv.ca
Emp.: 250
Television Broadcasting Station
S.I.C.: 4833
N.A.I.C.S.: 515120
Tom Haberstroh *(VP)*

CTV Calgary (3)
80 Patina Rise SW
Calgary, AB, T3H 2W4, Canada (100%)
Tel.: (403) 240-5600
Fax: (403) 240-5759
E-Mail: cfcnnews@ctv.ca
Web Site: www.calgary.ctv.ca
Emp.: 150
Television Broadcasting Station
S.I.C.: 4833
N.A.I.C.S.: 515120
Len Perry *(VP & Gen Mgr)*

CTV Edmonton (3)
18520 Stony Plain Rd
Edmonton, AB, T5S 1A8, Canada (100%)
Tel.: (780) 483-3311
Fax: (780) 489-5883
E-Mail: edmonton@ctv.ca
Web Site: www.edmonton.ctv.ca
Emp.: 130
Television Broadcasting Station
S.I.C.: 4833
N.A.I.C.S.: 515120
Lloyd Lewis *(VP & Gen Mgr)*

CTV Lethbridge (3)
640 13th St N
Lethbridge, AB, T1H 2S8, Canada
Tel.: (403) 329-3644
Fax: (403) 317-2420
E-Mail: info@ctv.ca
Web Site: www.ctv.ca
Emp.: 15
Television Broadcasting Station
S.I.C.: 4833
N.A.I.C.S.: 515120
Dave Lelek *(Gen Mgr & Mgr-Sls)*

CTV Montreal (3)
1205 Papineau Ave
Montreal, QC, H2K 4R2, Canada
Tel.: (514) 273-6311
Fax: (514) 276-9399
E-Mail: contact12@ctv.ca
Web Site: www.montreal.ctv.ca/
Emp.: 130
Television Broadcasting Station
S.I.C.: 4833
N.A.I.C.S.: 515120

CTV Northern Ontario, North Bay (3)
245 Oak St E
North Bay, ON, P1B 8P8, Canada
Tel.: (705) 476-3111
Fax: (705) 495-4474
E-Mail: northbaynews@ctv.ca
Web Site: www.c-tv.ca
Emp.: 12
Television Broadcasting Station
S.I.C.: 4833
N.A.I.C.S.: 515120
Scott Lund *(VP & Gen Mgr)*

CTV Northern Ontario, Sault Saint Marie (3)
119 E St
Sault Sainte Marie, ON, P6A 3C7, Canada
Tel.: (705) 759-7788
Fax: (705) 759-7783
Web Site: www.ctv.ca
Emp.: 13
Television Broadcasting Station
S.I.C.: 4833
N.A.I.C.S.: 515120
Scott Lund *(Mgr)*

CTV Northern Ontario, Sudbury (3)
699 Frood Rd
Sudbury, ON, P3C 5A3, Canada
Tel.: (705) 674-8301
Fax: (705) 673-0730
E-Mail: newsforthenorth@ctv.ca
Web Site: www.ctv.ca
Sales Range: $10-24.9 Million
Emp.: 60
Television Broadcasting Station
S.I.C.: 4833
N.A.I.C.S.: 515120
Scott Lund *(VP & Gen Mgr)*

CTV Northern Ontario, Timmins (3)
681 Pine St N
PO Box 620
Timmins, ON, P4N 7G3, Canada
Tel.: (705) 264-4211
Fax: (705) 264-3266
Web Site: www.ctv.ca
Emp.: 11
Television Broadcasting Station
S.I.C.: 4833
N.A.I.C.S.: 515120

CTV Ottawa (3)
87 George St
Ottawa, ON, K1N 9H7, Canada
Mailing Address:
PO Box 5813
Merivale Depot, Ottawa, ON, K2C 3G6, Canada
Tel.: (613) 224-1313
Fax: (888) 770-2190
Web Site: www.ctv.ca
Emp.: 100
Television Broadcasting Station
S.I.C.: 4833
N.A.I.C.S.: 515120
Louis Douville *(Gen Mgr)*

CTV Prince Albert (3)
22 10th St W
Prince Albert, SK, S6V 3A5, Canada
Tel.: (306) 922-6066
Fax: (306) 763-3041
E-Mail: cipa@ctv.ca
Web Site: www.ctv.ca
Emp.: 15
Television Broadcasting Station
S.I.C.: 4833
N.A.I.C.S.: 515120
Wade Moffat *(Gen Mgr)*

CTV Regina (3)
1 Hwy E
PO Box 2000
Regina, SK, S4P 3E5, Canada (100%)
Tel.: (306) 569-2000
Fax: (306) 522-0090
E-Mail: ckcknews@ctv.ca
Web Site: www.ctv.ca
Emp.: 55
Television Broadcasting Station
S.I.C.: 4833
N.A.I.C.S.: 515120
Wade Moffit *(VP)*

CTV Saskatoon (3)
216 1st Ave N
Saskatoon, SK, S7K 3W3, Canada (100%)
Tel.: (306) 665-8600
Fax: (306) 665-0450
E-Mail: cfqcnews@bellmedia.ca
Web Site: www.ctv.ca
Emp.: 80
Television Broadcasting Station
S.I.C.: 4833
N.A.I.C.S.: 515120
Wade Moffatt *(Gen Mgr)*

CTV Southwestern Ontario (3)
864 King St W STN C
PO Box 91026
Kitchener, ON, N2G 4E9, Canada
Tel.: (519) 578-1313
Fax: (519) 743-8857
E-Mail: news@ctv.ca
Web Site: www.kitchener.ctvnews.ca
Emp.: 110
Television Broadcasting Station
S.I.C.: 4833
N.A.I.C.S.: 515120
Don Mumford *(Gen Mgr)*

CTV Winnipeg (3)
400 345 Graham Ave
Winnipeg, MB, R3C 5S6, Canada (100%)
Tel.: (204) 788-3300
Fax: (204) 788-3399
Web Site: www.ctv.ca
Sales Range: $10-24.9 Million
Emp.: 100
Television Broadcasting Station
S.I.C.: 4833
N.A.I.C.S.: 515120
Scott Williams *(Controller)*

CTV Yorkton (3)
95 E Broadway
Yorkton, SK, S3N 0L1, Canada (100%)
Tel.: (306) 786-8400
Fax: (306) 782-7212
E-Mail: ciccnews@ctv.ca
Web Site: www.ctv.ca
Emp.: 8
Television Broadcasting Station
S.I.C.: 4833
N.A.I.C.S.: 515120
Bob Maloney *(Dir-News)*

Unit:

Sympatico (2)
207 Queens St W
Toronto, ON, M5J 1A7, Canada
Tel.: (416) 353-0123
Fax: (416) 703-8040
Web Site: www.sympatico.ca
Emp.: 40
Internet Portal
S.I.C.: 4899
N.A.I.C.S.: 517919

Bell Mobility Inc. (1)
5099 Creekbank Rd
Mississauga, ON, L4W 5N2, Canada (100%)
Tel.: (905) 282-2000
Fax: (800) 818-7449
Web Site: www.bell.ca/Mobility
Emp.: 4,000
Mobile Telecommunications Products & Services
S.I.C.: 4812
N.A.I.C.S.: 517210
Wade Oosterman *(Pres)*

Unit:

Virgin Mobile Canada (2)
720 King St W
Suite 905
M5V2T3 Toronto, ON, Canada
Tel.: (888) 999-2321
Fax: (888) 999-9470
Web Site: www.virginmobile.ca
Mobile Telecommunications
S.I.C.: 4812
N.A.I.C.S.: 517210
Joseph Ottorino *(Mng Dir)*

Affiliate:

Bell Aliant Inc. (1)
1505 Barrington Street
Halifax, NS, B3J 2W3, Canada ON
Tel.: (709) 739-2320 (44.7%)

Fax: (709) 739-2046
Toll Free: (877) 248-3113
E-Mail: investors@bellaliant.ca
Web Site: www.bellaliant.ca
BA—(TSX)
Rev.: $328,026,600
Assets: $3,218,934,966
Liabilities: $10,834,818
Net Worth: $3,208,100,148
Earnings: $326,734,374
Emp.: 10,500
Fiscal Year-end: 12/31/12
Telephone, Wireless, Internet, Data & Information Technology Services
Import Export
S.I.C.: 4813
N.A.I.C.S.: 517110
George Cope *(Chm)*
Karen H. Sheriff *(Pres & CEO)*
Glen LeBlanc *(CFO & Exec VP)*
Fred Crooks *(Chief Legal Officer & Exec VP-Corp Svcs)*
Zeda Redden *(VP-IR & Assoc Treas)*
Chuck Hartlen *(Sr VP-Customer Experience)*
Dan McKeen *(Sr VP-Customer Solutions)*

Branches:

Bell Aliant (2)
69 Belevedere Avenue
Charlottetown, PE, C1A 9K5, Canada
Fax: (902) 429-8755
Toll Free: (800) 565-4737
Web Site: www.aliant.ca
Telecommunications Services
S.I.C.: 4813
N.A.I.C.S.: 517110

Subsidiaries:

Bell Aliant Preferred Equity Inc. (2)
4 South Maritime Centre 1505 Barrington Street
Halifax, NS, B3J 3K5, Canada
Tel.: (902) 487-3166
Fax: (902) 420-3166
BAF—(TSX)
Investment Management Services
S.I.C.: 6282
N.A.I.C.S.: 523920
Glen LeBlanc, *(CFO & Exec VP)*

Bell Nordiq Group Inc. (2)
7151 Jean Talon E 7th Fl
Anjou, QC, H1M 3N8, Canada Ca
Tel.: (514) 493-5531 (63.4%)
Fax: (514) 493-5516
E-Mail: press@bellnordiq.ca
Web Site: www.bellnordiq.ca
Sales Range: $1-9.9 Million
Emp.: 800
Telecommunications
S.I.C.: 4813
N.A.I.C.S.: 517110
Roch L. Dube *(Pres & CEO)*

Subsidiaries:

NorthernTel Limited Partnership (3)
PO Box 1110
Timmins, ON, P4N 7J4, Canada (63.4%)
Tel.: (705) 360-8555
Fax: (705) 647-3580
Toll Free: (800) 360-8555
Web Site: www.northerntel.ca
Emp.: 50
Wired & Wireless Telecommunications & Internet Services
S.I.C.: 4813
N.A.I.C.S.: 517110

Telebec Limited Partnership (3)
7151 Jean Talon E
Anjou, QC, H1M 3N8, Canada (63.4%)
Tel.: (514) 493-5335
Fax: (514) 493-5389
Toll Free: (888) 835-3232
E-Mail: telebec@telebec.com
Web Site: www.telebec.com
Emp.: 800
Telecommunications & Internet Services
S.I.C.: 4813
N.A.I.C.S.: 517110
Roch Dube *(Pres)*

Innovatia Inc. (2)
One St Germain
PO Box 6081
Saint John, NB, E2L 4V1, Canada
Tel.: (506) 640-4000
Fax: (506) 642-1938
E-Mail: innovatia@innovatia.net
Web Site: www.innovatia.net
Emp.: 150
Employee Performance & Operational Efficiency Services & Products
S.I.C.: 8742
N.A.I.C.S.: 541611
Roxanne Fairweather *(Pres & CEO)*

Unit:

Xwave (2)
1 Brunswick Sq
Saint John, NB, E2L 1Z4, Canada
Tel.: (506) 694-4102
Fax: (506) 693-2331
Toll Free: (877) 449-9283
E-Mail: solutions@xwave.com
Web Site: www.xwave.com
Sales Range: $300-349.9 Million
Emp.: 1,500
Information Technology, Website & Network Management Services
S.I.C.: 7373
N.A.I.C.S.: 541512
Peter Cornick *(Mng Dir-Delivery Mngmt)*
Jules Fauteux *(Mng Dir-Consultant Svcs)*
Ray Miller *(Mng Dir-Managed Svcs)*
Paul Kent *(COO)*

Joint Ventures:

Maple Leaf Sports & Entertainment Ltd. (1)
50 Bay St Ste 400
Toronto, ON, M5J 2L2, Canada ON
Tel.: (416) 815-5400
Fax: (416) 359-9205
Web Site: www.mlse.com
Sales Range: $500-549.9 Million
Emp.: 900
Holding Company; Professional Sports Teams, Broadcast Media Licensing, Internet Publishing, Sports & Entertainment Venues Owner & Operator
S.I.C.: 6719
N.A.I.C.S.: 551112
Larry Tanenbaum *(Chm)*
Tim Leiweke *(Pres & CEO)*
Ian Clarke *(CFO & Exec VP-Bus Dev)*
David Hopkinson *(Chief Comml Officer)*
Robert Hunter *(Chief Facilities & Live Entertainment Officer)*
Peter Miller *(Chief Legal & Dev Officer)*
Kevin Nonomura *(Sr VP-Fin)*

Subsidiaries:

Toronto Maple Leafs Hockey Club Inc. (2)
50 Bay Street Suite 500
Toronto, ON, M5J 2X2, Canada ON
Tel.: (416) 815-5700
Web Site: www.mapleleafs.com
Professional Hockey Club
S.I.C.: 7941
N.A.I.C.S.: 711211
David Nonis *(Sr VP-Hockey Ops & Gen Mgr)*

Toronto Raptors Basketball Club Inc. (2)
40 Bay St Ste 400
Toronto, ON, M5J 2X2, Canada ON
Tel.: (416) 815-5500
Fax: (416) 359-9332
Web Site: www.raptors.com
Professional Basketball Team
S.I.C.: 7941
N.A.I.C.S.: 711211
Jeff Weltman *(Exec VP-Basketball Ops)*

Unit:

The Air Canada Centre (2)
50 Bay Street Ste 500
Toronto, ON, M5J 2L2, Canada
Tel.: (416) 815-5500
Web Site: www.theaircanadacentre.com
Sports & Entertainment Facility Operator
S.I.C.: 7999
N.A.I.C.S.: 711310
Robert Hunter *(Exec VP-Venues & Entertainment)*
Beth Robertson *(Sr VP-Ticket Sls & Svc)*

Q9 Networks Inc. (1)
Suite 4400 77 King Street West
PO Box 235
Toronto, ON, M5K 1J3, Canada ON
Tel.: (416) 362-7000
Fax: (416) 362-7001
Toll Free: (888) 696-2266
E-Mail: info@q9.com
Web Site: www.q9.com
Sales Range: $50-74.9 Million
Outsourced Information Technology Infrastructure Design, Installation & Management Services
S.I.C.: 7389
N.A.I.C.S.: 541519
Paul Sharpe *(Pres & COO)*
Osama Arafat *(CEO)*
Robert McQuade *(CFO & Sr VP-Fin)*
Victoria Coombs *(Gen Counsel)*
Kareem Arafat *(Sr VP-Software Engrg)*
Warren Bridle *(Sr VP-Svc Delivery)*
David Chaloner *(Sr VP-Mktg)*
Richard Morton *(Sr VP-Product Engrg)*
David Ralston *(Sr VP-Sls)*

BCGOLD CORP.

Suite 520 - 800 West Pender St
Vancouver, BC, V6C 2V6, Canada
Tel.: (604) 681-2626
Fax: (604) 646-8088
E-Mail: bcgir@bcgoldcorp.com
Web Site: www.bcgoldcorp.com
Year Founded: 2006
BCG—(TSXV)
Rev.: $1,031
Assets: $1,953,724
Liabilities: $121,982
Net Worth: $1,831,742
Earnings: ($1,545,528)
Fiscal Year-end: 02/28/13

Business Description:
Mineral Mining Exploration Services
S.I.C.: 1081
N.A.I.C.S.: 213114

Personnel:
Brian P. Fowler *(Pres & CEO)*
Larry Minoru Okada *(CFO)*
Jacqueline Collins *(Sec)*

Board of Directors:
Brian P. Fowler
Peter Kendrick
John Kowalchuck

Legal Counsel:
DuMoulin Black LLP
10th Floor 595 Howe St
Vancouver, BC, Canada

Transfer Agent:
Computershare Investor Services Inc.
2nd Fl 510 Burrard St
Vancouver, BC, Canada

BCL INDUSTRIES & INFRASTRUCTURE LIMITED

Hazi Rattan Link Road
Bathinda, Punjab, 151005, India
Tel.: (91) 1642240163
Fax: (91) 1642240424
E-Mail: bcl@connectzone.in
Web Site: www.bcl.ind.in
524332—(BOM)
Rev.: $106,386,729
Assets: $60,511,853
Liabilities: $46,766,946
Net Worth: $13,744,907
Earnings: ($619,941)
Fiscal Year-end: 03/31/13

Business Description:
Real Estate Development Services
S.I.C.: 6531
N.A.I.C.S.: 531390

Personnel:
Rajinder Mittal *(Chm & Mng Dir)*
Nikita Sheth *(Sec)*

BCM RESOURCES CORP.

Suite 480 - 1040 West Georgia Street
Vancouver, BC, V6E 4H1, Canada
Tel.: (604) 646-0144
Fax: (604) 646-0142
Toll Free: (888) 646-0144
E-Mail: info@bcmresources.com
Web Site: www.bcmresources.com
Year Founded: 2005
B—(TSXV)
Int. Income: $90
Assets: $5,488,403
Liabilities: $187,444
Net Worth: $5,300,959
Earnings: ($164,525)
Fiscal Year-end: 08/31/13

Business Description:
Mineral Exploration Services
S.I.C.: 1081
N.A.I.C.S.: 213114

Personnel:
Dale McClanaghan *(Pres & CEO)*
Deborah L. Goldbloom *(CFO & Sec)*

Board of Directors:
Rene David
Deborah L. Goldbloom
Dale McClanaghan
Craig Dalton Thomas

Transfer Agent:
Computershare Investor Services
2nd Floor 510 Burrard Street
Vancouver, BC, Canada

BD AGRO AD

Lole Ribara b b Dobanovci
11272 Belgrade, Serbia
Tel.: (381) 11 8465 400
Fax: (381) 11 8465 270
E-Mail: office@bdagro.com
Web Site: www.bdagro.com
Year Founded: 1947
AGRD—(BEL)
Emp.: 299

Business Description:
Milk Production
S.I.C.: 0241
N.A.I.C.S.: 112120

Personnel:
Ljubisa Jovanovic *(CEO)*

BD DIESEL PERFORMANCE

33541 MacLure Rd
Abbotsford, BC, Canada
Tel.: (604) 853-6096
Fax: (604) 853-6089
Toll Free: (800) 887-5030
E-Mail: sales@dieselperformance.com
Web Site: www.dieselperformance.com
Year Founded: 1971
Rev.: $15,472,337
Emp.: 70

Business Description:
Diesel Parts Mfr
S.I.C.: 3714
N.A.I.C.S.: 336390

Personnel:
Brian Roth *(Pres)*

BD MULTIMEDIA SA

16 Cite Joly
75011 Paris, France
Tel.: (33) 1 53 36 24 24
Fax: (33) 1 48 06 49 46
Web Site: www.bdmultimedia.fr
Year Founded: 1986
ALBDM—(EUR)
Sales Range: $10-24.9 Million
Emp.: 94

Business Description:
Telecommunications & Internet Services
S.I.C.: 4899
N.A.I.C.S.: 517919

Personnel:
Daniel Dorra *(Pres)*

BDCOM ONLINE LIMITED

Rangs Nilu Square 5th Floor
Satmosjid Road House 75 Road 5A
Dhanmondi RA, Dhaka, 1209,
Bangladesh

BDCOM Online Limited—(Continued)

Tel.: (880) 9666333666
Fax: (880) 28122789
E-Mail: office@bdcom.com
Web Site: www.bdcom.com
BDCOM—(DHA)
Rev.: $3,151,858
Assets: $6,438,884
Liabilities: $490,773
Net Worth: $5,948,111
Earnings: $577,875
Emp.: 230
Fiscal Year-end: 06/30/13
Business Description:
Internet Service Providers
S.I.C.: 4812
N.A.I.C.S.: 517210
Personnel:
Wahidul Haque Siddiqui *(Chm)*
S. M. Golam Faruk Alamgir *(Mng Dir)*
A. K. M. Kutub Uddin *(Sec)*
Board of Directors:
Wahidul Haque Siddiqui
S. M. Golam Faruk Alamgir
Das Deba Prashad
Quarratul Ann Siddiqui

BDH INDUSTRIES LTD.

Nair Baug Akurli Road Kandivali East
Mumbai, 400 101, India
Tel.: (91) 22 61551234
Fax: (91) 22 2886 8349
E-Mail: info@bdhind.com
Web Site: www.bdhind.com
Year Founded: 1935
524828—(BOM)
Rev.: $7,735,982
Assets: $7,727,806
Liabilities: $3,676,779
Net Worth: $4,051,027
Earnings: $310,100
Fiscal Year-end: 03/31/13
Business Description:
Pharmaceutical Preparation Mfr
S.I.C.: 2834
N.A.I.C.S.: 325412
Personnel:
Jayashree Nair *(Chm & Mng Dir)*
Nikita Phatak *(Compliance Officer & Sec)*
Board of Directors:
Jayashree Nair
S. C. Kachhara
A. V. Menon
Karthika Nair
Bhagirath Singh Sihag
Dinesh Variar
Transfer Agent:
TSR Darashaw Limited
6-10 Haji Moosa Patrawala Industrial Estate 20
Dr. E Moses Road
Near Famous Studio Mahalaxmi, Mumbai, India

BDI - BIOENERGY INTERNATIONAL AG

Parkring 18
8074 Grambach, Austria
Tel.: (43) 316 4009 100
Fax: (43) 316 4009 110
E-Mail: bdi@bdi-bioenergy.com
Web Site: www.bdi-bioenergy.com
D7I—(DEU)
Sls.: $40,084,904
Assets: $100,939,865
Liabilities: $32,750,970
Net Worth: $68,188,895
Earnings: ($5,943,341)
Emp.: 132
Fiscal Year-end: 12/31/12
Business Description:
Fuel Exploration Services
S.I.C.: 1389
N.A.I.C.S.: 213112
Personnel:
Gunter Griss *(Chm-Supervisory Bd)*
Werner Schuster *(Deputy Chm-Supervisory Bd)*
Dagmar Heiden-Gasteiner *(CFO & Member-Mgmt Bd)*
Markus Dielacher *(CTO & Member-Mgmt Bd)*
Edgar Ahn *(Chief Scientific Officer & Member-Mgmt Bd)*
Supervisory Board of Directors:
Gunter Griss
Michael Koncar
Werner Schuster
Hubert Zankel

Subsidiary:

Enbasys Gmbh **(1)**
Parkring 18
Grambach, 8074 Graz, Austria
Tel.: (43) 316 4009 5600
Fax: (43) 316 4009 5605
E-Mail: office@enbasys.com
Web Site: www.enbasys.com
Waste Water Treatment Services
S.I.C.: 4959
N.A.I.C.S.: 562998

Non-U.S. Subsidiary:

UIC Gmbh **(1)**
Am Neuen Berg 4
Horstein, 63755 Alzenau, Germany
Tel.: (49) 6023 950 0
Fax: (49) 6023 950 0
E-Mail: info@uic-gmbh.de
Web Site: www.uic-gmbh.de
Emp.: 35
Vacuum Distilling Equipment Mfr
S.I.C.: 3559
N.A.I.C.S.: 333249
Manfred van Treel *(Mng Dir)*

BDL HOTEL GROUP

40 Brund St
Glasgow, G51 1DG, United Kingdom
Tel.: (44) 1414194567
Fax: (44) 1414194560
E-Mail: info@bdlhotels.co.uk
Web Site: www.bdlhotels.co.uk
Year Founded: 1997
Sales Range: $10-24.9 Million
Emp.: 5,000
Business Description:
Hotel Operator
S.I.C.: 7011
N.A.I.C.S.: 721110
Personnel:
Louis Woodcock *(CEO)*
Stewart Campbell *(Mng Dir)*
Board of Directors:
Stuart McCaffer
David G.F. Thompson
Louis Woodcock

BDO AG WIRTSCHAFTSPRUFUNGS GESELLSCHAFT

Fuhlentwiete 12
20355 Hamburg, Germany
Tel.: (49) 40 30293 0
Fax: (49) 40 337691
E-Mail: hamburg@bdo.de
Web Site: www.bdo.de
Sales Range: $250-299.9 Million
Emp.: 1,896
Business Description:
Accounting, Tax, Financial Advisory & Consulting Services
S.I.C.: 8721
N.A.I.C.S.: 541211
Personnel:
Johann C. Lindenberg *(Chm-Supervisory Bd)*
Holger Otte *(Chm-Exec Bd)*
Hans Michael Gaul *(Deputy Chm-Supervisory Bd)*
Werner Jacob *(Vice Chm-Exec Bd)*
Frank Biermann *(Member-Exec Bd)*
Christian Dyckerhoff *(Member-Exec Bd)*
Klaus Eckmann *(Member-Exec Bd)*
Christian Gorny *(Member-Exec Bd)*
Arno Probst *(Member-Exec Bd)*
Manuel Rauchfuss *(Member-Exec Bd)*
Kai Niclas Rauscher *(Member-Exec Bd)*
Roland Schulz *(Member-Exec Bd)*
Supervisory Board of Directors:
Johann C. Lindenberg
Hans Michael Gaul
Ira Hubecker-Kleusch
Erhard Schipporeit
Gunnar Uldall
Dagmar von Glan-Witte

Subsidiaries:

BDO Dr. Lauter & Fischer GmbH Wirtschaftsprufungs-gesellschaft **(1)**
Im Zollhafen 22
50678 Cologne, Germany (100%)
Tel.: (49) 221973570
Fax: (49) 2217390395
E-Mail: guido.siepert@bdo.de
Web Site: www.bdo.com
Emp.: 120
Other Accounting Services
S.I.C.: 8721
N.A.I.C.S.: 541219
Guido Siepert *(Gen Mgr)*

BDO Schleswig-Holsteinische Treuhandgesellschaft mbH Wirtschaftsprufungsgesellschaft Steuerberatungsgesellschaft **(1)**
Dahlmannstr 1-3
24103 Kiel, Germany (100%)
Tel.: (49) 431519600
Fax: (49) 4315196040
E-Mail: kial@bdo.de
Web Site: www.bdo.de/Kiel.276.0.html
Emp.: 40
Tax Preparation Services
S.I.C.: 7291
N.A.I.C.S.: 541213
Ettard Hes *(Mng Dir)*

BDO Schurmann & Glashoff Steuerberatungsgesellschaft mbH **(1)**
Gruneburgweg 102
60323 Frankfurt, Germany (100%)
Tel.: (49) 6995941356
Fax: (49) 6995941361
E-Mail: klaus.frieh@bdo.de
Web Site: www.bdo.de/MaRisk-Tagung-der-BDO.1111.0.html
Emp.: 150
Other Accounting Services
S.I.C.: 8721
N.A.I.C.S.: 541219

BDO Westfalen-Revision GmbH Wirtschaftsprufungsgesellschaft **(1)**
Markische Str 216-218
41414 Dortmund, Germany (74.9%)
Tel.: (49) 231419040
Fax: (49) 231419048
E-Mail: info@bdo.de
Web Site: www.westfalen-revision.com
Emp.: 50
Other Accounting Services
S.I.C.: 8721
N.A.I.C.S.: 541219

BDO DEUTSCHE WARENTREUHAND AG

(See Under BDO AG Wirtschaftsprufungsgesellschaft)

BDO DUNWOODY LLP

36 Toronto St Ste 600
Toronto, ON, M5C 2C5, Canada
Tel.: (416) 865-0111
Fax: (416) 367-3912
E-Mail: national@bdo.ca
Web Site: www.bdo.ca
Sales Range: $100-124.9 Million
Emp.: 1,941
Business Description:
Accounting & Consulting Services
S.I.C.: 8742
N.A.I.C.S.: 541611
Personnel:
Keith Farlinger *(CEO)*
Randy Berry *(COO)*

BDO KENDALLS

Level 8 85 Macquarie Street
Hobart, TAS, 7000, Australia
Tel.: (61) 362342499
Fax: (61) 362342392
E-Mail: info.hobart@bdo.com.au
Web Site: www.bdo.com.au
Sales Range: $25-49.9 Million
Emp.: 35
Business Description:
Public Accounting Firm
S.I.C.: 8721
N.A.I.C.S.: 541219
Personnel:
Craig Stevens *(Mng Dir)*

BDO UNIBANK, INC.

7899 Makati Avenue
Makati, 0726, Philippines
Tel.: (63) 2 8407000
Fax: (63) 2 6340477
E-Mail: investor-relations@bdo.com.ph
Web Site: www.bdo.com.ph
BDO—(OTC PHI)
Int. Income: $1,322,802,860
Assets: $30,475,551,920
Liabilities: $26,624,450,440
Net Worth: $3,851,101,480
Earnings: $351,235,580
Emp.: 21,746
Fiscal Year-end: 12/31/12
Business Description:
Commercial & Investment Banking Services
S.I.C.: 6029
N.A.I.C.S.: 522110
Personnel:
Teresita T. Sy-Coson *(Chm)*
Jesus Albert Jacinto, Jr. *(Vice Chm)*
Nestor V. Tan *(Pres)*
Rebecca S. Torres *(Chief Compliance Officer)*
Evelyn L. Villanueva *(Chief Risk Officer, Exec VP & Head-Risk Mgmt Grp)*
Elmer B. Serrano *(Corp Info Officer)*
Pedro M. Florescio, III *(Treas)*
Edmundo L. Tan *(Sec)*
Antonio N. Cotoco *(Sr Exec VP)*
Walter C. Wassmer *(Sr Exec VP)*
Jaime C. Yu *(Sr Exec VP)*
Ador A. Abrogena *(Exec VP & Head-Trust & Investments Grp)*
Rolando C. Tanchanco *(Exec VP & Head-Consumer Lending)*
Stella L. Cabalatungan *(Exec VP)*
Julie Y. Chua *(Exec VP)*
Lucy C. Dy *(Exec VP)*
Eduardo V. Francisco *(Exec VP)*
Bienvenido M. Juat, Jr. *(Exec VP)*
Ricardo V. Martin *(Exec VP)*
Edmundo S. Soriano *(Exec VP)*
Dennis B. Velasquez *(Exec VP-Central Ops)*
Ursula A. Alano *(Sr VP)*
Noel L. Andrada *(Sr VP)*
Victor C. Arboleda *(Sr VP)*
Melanie S. Belen *(Sr VP)*
Gamalielh Ariel O. Benavides *(Sr VP)*
Rafael G. Besa *(Sr VP)*
Marilou L. Cesario *(Sr VP)*
Arthur Vincent D. Chung *(Sr VP)*
Jonathan T. Cua *(Sr VP)*
Ramon S. David *(Sr VP)*
Arthur L. Tan *(Sr VP)*
Edel Mary D. Vegamora *(Sr VP)*

Board of Directors:
Teresita T. Sy-Coson
Jose F. Buenaventura
Jones M. Castro, Jr.
Chai Hong Cheo
Jesus Albert Jacinto, Jr.
Antonio C. Pacis
Henry T. Sy, Jr.
Josefina N. Tan
Nestor V. Tan
Jimmy T. Tang
Transfer Agent:
Stock Transfer Service Inc
34/F Unit D Rufino Pacific Tower 6784 Ayala Avenue
Makati, Philippines
Subsidiaries:

Armstrong Securities, Inc. (1)
20th Floor South BDO Corporate Center
7899 Makati Avenue
Makati, Philippines
Tel.: (63) 2 878 4552
Investment Services
S.I.C.: 6211
N.A.I.C.S.: 523999
Tony O. King *(Chm)*
Elinor M. Hilado *(Pres)*
Ricardo V. Martin *(Treas)*
Antonio C. Pacis *(Sec)*

BDO Capital & Investment Corporation (1)
20th Floor South Tower
BDO Corporate Center
7899 Makati Avenue, Makati, Philippines
Tel.: (63) 2 878 4155
Investment Banking Services
S.I.C.: 6211
N.A.I.C.S.: 523999
Teresita T. Sy *(Chm)*
Nestor V. Tan *(Vice Chm)*
Eduardo V. Francisco *(Pres)*
Erlaster C. Sotto *(COO & Sr VP)*
Lazaro Jerome C. Guevarra *(Sr VP & Treas)*
Elmer B. Serrano *(Sec)*
Eleanor M. Hilado *(Sr VP)*
Gabriel U. Lim *(Sr VP)*

BDO Insurance Brokers, Inc. (1)
8th Floor JMT Condominium 27 ADB Avenue
Ortigas Center, Pasig, Philippines
Tel.: (63) 2 688 1288
Insurance Services
S.I.C.: 6411
N.A.I.C.S.: 524210
Jesus Albert Jacinto, Jr. *(Chm & Pres)*
Larry G. Ong *(Treas)*
Elmer B. Serrano *(Sec)*
Francisco P. Ramos *(Sr VP)*
Maria Theresa L. Tan *(Sr VP)*

BDO Leasing & Finance, Inc. (1)
BDO Leasing Centre Corinthian Gardens
Ortigas Avenue, 1100 Quezon City, Philippines
Tel.: (63) 26356416
Fax: (63) 26355811
Web Site: www.bdo.com.ph
BLFI—(PHI)
Rev.: $43,139,135
Assets: $507,812,395
Liabilities: $394,318,388
Net Worth: $113,494,007
Earnings: $9,852,327
Emp.: 200
Fiscal Year-end: 12/31/12
Leasing & Financial Services
S.I.C.: 6153
N.A.I.C.S.: 522220
Teresita T. Sy *(Chm)*
Robert E. Lapid *(Vice Chm)*
Georgiana A. Gamboa *(Pres)*
Rodolfo M. Carlos, Jr. *(Chief Risk Officer, Chief Compliance Officer & VP)*
Sergio M. Ceniza *(Compliance Officer & Asst VP)*
Elmer B. Serrano *(Corp Info Officer)*
Renato G. Onate *(Treas & First VP)*
Jason Joseph M. Natividad *(Sec)*

BDO Private Bank, Inc. (1)
27th Floor Ayala Tower 1
Ayala Triangle Ayala Avenue
Makati, Philippines
Tel.: (63) 2 848 6300
Banking Services
S.I.C.: 6029
N.A.I.C.S.: 522110
Teresita T. Sy *(Chm)*
Nestor V. Tan *(Vice Chm)*
Josefina N. Tan *(Pres)*
Bienvenido M. Juat, Jr. *(Exec VP & Treas)*
Roderico V. Puno *(Sec)*
Stella L. Cabalatungan *(Exec VP)*

BDO Rental, Inc. (1)
BDO Leasing Centre Corinthian Gardens
Ortigas Avenue, Quezon City, Philippines
Tel.: (63) 2 635 6416
Rental & Leasing Services
S.I.C.: 7359
N.A.I.C.S.: 532490
Antonio N. Cotoco *(Chm)*
Roberto E. Lapid *(Pres & COO)*
Renato G. Onate *(Treas)*
Florecita R. Gonzales *(Sec)*

BDO Securities Corporation (1)
20th Floor South Tower BDO Corporate Center
7899 Makati Avenue, Makati, Philippines
Tel.: (63) 2 878 4155
Investment Services
S.I.C.: 6211
N.A.I.C.S.: 523999
Violeta O. Luym *(Chm)*
Erlaster C. Sotto *(Pres)*
Eduardo V. Francisco *(Treas)*
Roderico V. Puno *(Sec)*

BDO Strategic Holdings, Inc. (1)
BDO Building Paseo de Roxas corner Sen Gil Puyat Avenue
Makati, Philippines
Tel.: (63) 2 840 7897
Holding Company
S.I.C.: 6712
N.A.I.C.S.: 551111
Nestor V. Tan *(Chm)*
Ricardo V. Martin *(Pres)*
Lucy C. Dy *(Treas)*
Mario D. Rabanal *(Sec)*

Equimark-NFC Development Corporation (1)
Room 603 EBC Building 262 Juan Luna Street
Binondo, Manila, Philippines
Tel.: (63) 2 840 7897
Financial Services
S.I.C.: 7389
N.A.I.C.S.: 561499
Du Bin *(Chm)*
Horacio C. Rodriguez, Jr. *(Pres)*
Jonathan C.B. Go *(Treas)*
Lazaro Jerome C. Guevarra *(Sec)*

BDO Elite Savings Bank, Inc. (1)
10th & 11th Floors Net Cube Bldg 30th St crnr 3rd Ave Crescent Park W
Bonifacio Global City, Taguig, Philippines PH
Tel.: (63) 8 777 8600 (99%)
Commercial Banking & Lending Services
S.I.C.: 6029
N.A.I.C.S.: 522110
Walter C. Wassmer *(Chm)*
Alan David L. Matutina *(CEO)*
Ione Fay S. Canto *(Sec & Sr VP)*
Nerissa Gloria C. Berba *(Sr VP)*
Salvador R. Serrano *(Sr VP)*

PCIB Securities, Inc. (1)
20th Floor South Tower BDO Corporate Center
7899 Makati Avenue, Makati, Philippines
Tel.: (63) 2 878 4564
Investment Services
S.I.C.: 6211
N.A.I.C.S.: 523110

U.S. Subsidiary:

BDO Remittance (USA) Inc. (1)
1559 E Amar Rd Ste U
West Covina, CA 91792
Tel.: (626) 363-9800
Fax: (626) 363-9811
Toll Free: (800) 472-3252
Web Site: www.bdo.com.ph
Money Transfer Services
S.I.C.: 6099
N.A.I.C.S.: 522320
Alex Dulay *(Gen Mgr)*

BDR THERMEA GROUP B.V.

Marchantstraat 55
7332 AZ Apeldoorn, Netherlands
Tel.: (31) 555496969
Web Site: www.bdrthermea.com
Sales Range: $1-4.9 Billion
Emp.: 6,300
Business Description:
Heating & Hot Water System Mfr
S.I.C.: 3559
N.A.I.C.S.: 332410
Personnel:
Rob van Banning *(CEO)*
Hubert Schwein *(CFO)*
Martyn Coffey *(Member-Mgmt Bd)*
Adrian Darling *(Member-Mgmt Bd)*

Subsidiary:

De Dietrich Remeha Group (1)
Marchantstraat 55
7332 AZ Apeldoorn, Netherlands (100%)
Tel.: (31) 555496969
Fax: (31) 555496496
E-Mail: remeha@remeha.com
Web Site: www.dedietrichremeha.com
Sales Range: $750-799.9 Million
Emp.: 2,200
Heating & Hot Water Equipment Mfr
S.I.C.: 3433
N.A.I.C.S.: 333414
Rob van Banning *(CEO)*

Non-U.S. Subsidiary:

Baxi Group Ltd. (1)
Brooks House
Coventry Road, Warwick, CV34 4LL, United Kingdom UK
Tel.: (44) 844 8711525 (100%)
E-Mail: info@baxi.co.uk
Web Site: www.baxi.co.uk
Sales Range: $1-4.9 Billion
Emp.: 5,500
Boiler, Heater, Shower & Related Appliance Mfr
Import Export
S.I.C.: 3433
N.A.I.C.S.: 333414
David Pinder *(Mng Dir)*

Subsidiaries:

Baxi Potterton Ltd. (2)
Brooks House Coventry Road
Warwick, CV34 4LL, United Kingdom
Tel.: (44) 8448711560
Fax: (44) 01926410006
E-Mail: info@potterton.co.uk
Web Site: www.potterton.co.uk
Emp.: 400
Boilers & Water Heaters Mfr
S.I.C.: 3433
N.A.I.C.S.: 333414
Paul Moss *(Dir-Fin)*

Heatrae Saidia Heating Ltd. (2)
Hurricane Way
Norwich, Norfolk, NR6 6EA, United Kingdom (100%)
Tel.: (44) 1603420100
Fax: (44) 1603420149
Web Site: www.heatraesadia.com
Emp.: 250
Electric Water Heater Mfr
S.I.C.: 3433
N.A.I.C.S.: 333414
Jon Cockburn *(Head-Mktg)*

Non-U.S. Subsidiaries:

August Brotje GmbH (2)
August Brotje Str 17
26180 Rastede, Germany De
Tel.: (49) 4402800 (100%)
Fax: (49) 440280583
E-Mail: webmaster@broetje.de
Web Site: www.broetje.de
Commercial Boilers & Burners
S.I.C.: 3433
N.A.I.C.S.: 333414
Sten Daugaard-Hansen *(Mng Dir)*

Baxi A/S (2)
Smedevej
6880 Tarm, Denmark (100%)
Tel.: (45) 97371511
Fax: (45) 97372434
E-Mail: baxi@baxi.dk
Web Site: www.baxi.dk
Sales Range: $1-9.9 Million
Emp.: 160
Boiler & Heater Mfr & Distr
S.I.C.: 3433
N.A.I.C.S.: 333414

Baxi France (2)
157 Ave Charles Floquet
93158 Le Blanc-Mesnil, France (100%)
Tel.: (33) 145915600
Fax: (33) 145915990
Web Site: www.baxifrance.com
Emp.: 100
Mfr. of Plumbing Products
S.I.C.: 3089
N.A.I.C.S.: 326199
Francois Hiriart *(Gen Mgr)*

Baxi S.p.A. (2)
Via Trozzetti 20
Bassano Del Grappa, 36061 Vicenza, Italy (80%)
Tel.: (39) 0424517111
Fax: (39) 042438089
E-Mail: info@baxi.it
Web Site: www.baxi.it
Emp.: 800
Boiler & Heater Mfr & Distr
S.I.C.: 3433
N.A.I.C.S.: 333414

THE BDRC GROUP

Kingsbourne House 229 231 High Holborn
London, WC1V 7DA, United Kingdom
Tel.: (44) 2074001000
Fax: (44) 2074054778
Web Site: www.bdrc-continental.com
Sales Range: $25-49.9 Million
Emp.: 80
Business Description:
Market Research Services
S.I.C.: 8732
N.A.I.C.S.: 541910
Personnel:
Crispian Tarrant *(CEO)*

Subsidiary:

Continental Research Ltd. (1)
Laser House, 132-140 Goswell Rd
London, EC1V 7DY, United Kingdom
Tel.: (44) 74905944
Fax: (44) 2074901174
E-Mail: mail@continentalresearch.com
Web Site: www.continentalresearch.com
Sales Range: $10-24.9 Million
Emp.: 40
Market Research Services
S.I.C.: 8732
N.A.I.C.S.: 541910

BE RESOURCES INC.

360 Bay Street Ste 500
Toronto, ON, M5H 2V6, Canada
Tel.: (416) 200-7200
Fax: (416) 361-0923
Web Site: www.beresources.ca
Year Founded: 2007
BER—(TSXV)
Assets: $387,281
Liabilities: $423,010
Net Worth: ($35,729)
Earnings: ($369,425)
Fiscal Year-end: 12/31/12
Business Description:
Beryllium Exploration & Mining Services
S.I.C.: 1099
N.A.I.C.S.: 212299
Personnel:
Edward Godin *(Chm)*
Jon Pereira *(CEO)*
Carmelo Marrelli *(CFO)*
Board of Directors:
Edward Godin
Robert Lufkin
Jon Pereira

BE RESOURCES INC.—(Continued)

David Q. Tognoni
Mani M. Verma
Transfer Agent:
Equity Financial Trust Company
200 University Avenue Suite 400
Toronto, ON, Canada

BE SEMICONDUCTOR INDUSTRIES N.V.

Ratio 6
6921 Duiven, Netherlands
Mailing Address:
PO Box 90
6920 Duiven, Netherlands
Tel.: (31) 263194500
Fax: (31) 263194550
E-Mail: info@besi.com
Web Site: www.besi.com
BESI—(EUR OTC)
Rev.: $368,473,652
Assets: $489,200,870
Liabilities: $132,531,783
Net Worth: $356,669,088
Earnings: $21,253,332
Emp.: 1,539
Fiscal Year-end: 12/31/12
Business Description:
Semiconductor Packaging, Plating & Die Handling Equipment Mfr
S.I.C.: 3559
N.A.I.C.S.: 333242
Personnel:
Tom de Waard *(Chm-Supervisory Bd)*
Douglas J. Dunn *(Vice Chm-Supervisory Bd)*
Richard W. Blickman *(Pres & CEO)*
Henk-Jan Jonge Poerink *(Mng Dir-Besi APac Sdn Bhd & Sr VP-Global Ops)*
Berthold Butzmann *(COO-Malaysia)*
Michael Auer *(Sr VP-Sls & Customer Support)*
Johan Hamelink *(Sr VP-Plating)*
J. K. Park *(Sr VP-Sls & Customer Support-Besi APac Sdn Bhd)*
Guido Slump *(Sr VP-Packaging)*
Patrick Stoessel *(Sr VP-Wire Bonding)*
J. Cor te Hennepe *(Sr VP-Fin & Legal)*
Peter Wiedner *(Sr VP-Die Attach-Switzerland)*
Hans Wunderl *(Sr VP-Strategic Dev)*
Supervisory Board of Directors:
Tom de Waard
Douglas J. Dunn
Mona ElNaggar
Dirk Lindenbergh
Jan Vaandrager
Legal Counsel:
Freshfields Bruckhaus Deringer
Amsterdam, Netherlands
Transfer Agent:
ABN AMRO Bank N.V.
Amsterdam, Netherlands
Subsidiaries:

Fico B.V. (1)
Ratio 6
6921 Duiven, Netherlands (100%)
Tel.: (31) 263193600
Fax: (31) 2631096200
E-Mail: sales@fico.nl
Web Site: www.fico.nl
Emp.: 150
Industrial Mold Mfr
S.I.C.: 3544
N.A.I.C.S.: 333511
Richard Blickman *(Mng Dir)*

Subsidiaries:

Fico Singulation B.V. (2)
Ratio 6
6921 Duiven, Netherlands
Tel.: (31) 263196100
Fax: (31) 263196200
E-Mail: info@besi.com
Web Site: www.ficosingulation.com
Emp.: 300
Internet Publishing & Broadcasting
S.I.C.: 2741
N.A.I.C.S.: 519130
Richard Plickman *(Gen Mgr)*

Non-U.S. Subsidiaries:

Fico Asia Sdn. Bhd. (2)
3 Jalan 26-7
Shah Alam, Malaysia (100%)
Tel.: (60) 351911799
Fax: (60) 351919632
Web Site: www.ficosingulation.com
Emp.: 200
All Other Industrial Machinery Mfr
S.I.C.: 3559
N.A.I.C.S.: 333249
Sink Jan *(Mng Dir)*

Fico Tooling Leshan Company Ltd. (2)
Electronic Park
Leshan High Tech Zone, Leshan, Sichuan, 614012, China (87%)
Tel.: (86) 8332596385
Fax: (86) 8332596385
Web Site: www.pesi.com
Emp.: 100
Semiconductor & Related Device Mfr
S.I.C.: 3674
N.A.I.C.S.: 334413
Peter Gregoor *(Mng Dir)*

Fico International B.V. (1)
Ratio 6
6921 RW Duiven, Netherlands
Tel.: (31) 26 3196100
Fax: (31) 26 3196200
Emp.: 20
Semiconductor Device Mfr
S.I.C.: 3674
N.A.I.C.S.: 334413
Richard Blickman *(Gen Mgr)*

Meco Equipment Engineers B.V (1)
Marconilaan 2
5151DR Drunen, Netherlands (100%)
Tel.: (31) 416384384
Fax: (31) 416384300
E-Mail: meco.sales@besi.com
Web Site: www.meco.nl
Emp.: 30
Plate Work Mfr
S.I.C.: 3443
N.A.I.C.S.: 332313
Johan Hamelink *(Mng Dir)*

U.S. Subsidiaries:

BE Semiconductor Industries USA, Inc. (1)
14 Keewaydin Dr
Salem, NH 03079
Tel.: (603) 626-4700
Fax: (603) 626-4242
Web Site: www.besi.com
Emp.: 30
Semiconductor Equipment Distr
S.I.C.: 5065
N.A.I.C.S.: 423690
David Peacock *(Gen Mgr)*

Besi North America, Inc. (1)
14 Keewaydin Dr
Salem, NH 03079 (100%)
Tel.: (603) 626-4700
Fax: (603) 626-4242
Web Site: www.laurierinc.com
Emp.: 30
Microelectronic Assembly Equipment Mfr
S.I.C.: 3559
N.A.I.C.S.: 333242
David Peacock *(VP)*

Besi USA, Inc. (1)
10 Tinker Ave
Londonderry, NH 03053
Tel.: (603) 626-4700
Fax: (603) 626-4242
Semiconductor Device Distr
S.I.C.: 5065
N.A.I.C.S.: 423690

Non-U.S. Subsidiaries:

Besi Japan Co. Ltd. (1)
Nakamura Building 6th Floor
31-7 Shinbashi 4-chome Minato, 105-0004 Tokyo, Japan (100%)
Tel.: (81) 334341251
Fax: (81) 334341252
E-Mail: customer@bcbsi.co.jp
Web Site: www.besi.com
Emp.: 9
Industrial Machinery & Equipment Whslr
S.I.C.: 5084
N.A.I.C.S.: 423830
Sugito Shinithi *(Mng Dir)*

Besi Korea Ltd. (1)
1204 Downtown Building 22 3 Sunae Dong Bundang gu
Sungnam si, 463 825 Seoul, Gyeonggi do, Korea (South) (100%)
Tel.: (82) 317189002
Fax: (82) 317189003
Web Site: www.besi.com
Space Research & Technology
S.I.C.: 9661
N.A.I.C.S.: 927110

Besi Singapore Pte. Ltd. (1)
40 Ubi Crescent
#01-07 Ubi Techpark, 408567 Singapore, Singapore (100%)
Tel.: (65) 67430600
Fax: (65) 67430660
Web Site: www.datacon.at/index.php?sp=/english/about/dctechnologyag/asia.htm&
Emp.: 10
Semiconductor Machinery Mfr
S.I.C.: 3559
N.A.I.C.S.: 333242

Datacon Technology GmbH (1)
Innstr 16
A 6240 Radfeld, Austria
Tel.: (43) 53376000
Fax: (43) 5337600660
E-Mail: info.dceu@datacon.at
Web Site: www.dceu.com
Emp.: 290
Microchip Assembly Equipment Mfr
S.I.C.: 3559
N.A.I.C.S.: 333242
Peter Weidner *(Gen Mgr)*

U.S. Subsidiary:

Datacon North America, Inc. (2)
3150 Tremont Ave
Trevose, PA 19053 (100%)
Tel.: (215) 791-7070
Fax: (215) 791-7074
E-Mail: info.dcna@datacon.at
Web Site: www.datacon.at/index.php?sp=/english/sales/amerika.htm&
Emp.: 15
Marketing Consulting Services
S.I.C.: 8742
N.A.I.C.S.: 541613

Non-U.S. Subsidiary:

Datacon Hungary Termelo Kft. (2)
Juharfa Utca 24
Gyor, Hungary (100%)
Tel.: (36) 96510400
Fax: (36) 696510401
E-Mail: info@datacon.at
Web Site: www.datacon.at
Emp.: 20
Electronic Capacitor Mfr
S.I.C.: 3675
N.A.I.C.S.: 334416
Freadl Muhlagaggar *(Mng Dir)*

Esec AG (1)
Hinterbergstrasse 32
6330 Cham, Switzerland
Tel.: (41) 417495111
Fax: (41) 417416484
E-Mail: info.esec@besi.com
Web Site: www.esec.com
Emp.: 200
Chip Assembly Equipment Mfr
S.I.C.: 3559
N.A.I.C.S.: 333242
Peter Wiedner *(Gen Mgr)*

Esec (Singapore) Pte. Ltd. (1)
1 Science Park Road Singapore Science Park 2 04-12
Capricorn Building, Singapore, 117528, Singapore
Tel.: (65) 6303 7000
Fax: (65) 6873 1133
E-Mail: sales@besi.com
Emp.: 7
Semiconductor Device Mfr
S.I.C.: 3674
N.A.I.C.S.: 334413
Soh Kianloo *(Gen Mgr)*

BEACH ENERGY LIMITED

25 Conyngham Street
Glenside, SA, 5065, Australia
Tel.: (61) 883382833
Fax: (61) 883382336
E-Mail: info@beachenergy.com.au
Web Site: www.beachenergy.com.au
BPT—(ASX OTC)
Sls.: $727,605,683
Assets: $2,506,029,575
Liabilities: $648,480,072
Net Worth: $1,857,549,503
Earnings: $160,118,665
Emp.: 180
Fiscal Year-end: 06/30/13
Business Description:
Petroleum Exploration Services
S.I.C.: 1311
N.A.I.C.S.: 211111
Personnel:
Reginald George Nelson *(Mng Dir)*
Kathryn Anne Presser *(CFO & Co-Sec)*
Neil M. Gibbins *(COO)*
Steve B. Masters *(Chief Comml Officer)*
Rodney A. Rayner *(Exec-Strategic Bus & External Affairs)*
Catherine Louise Oster *(Gen Counsel & Co-Sec)*
Board of Directors:
Glenn Stuart Davis
Fiona Rosalyn Vivienne Bennett
John Charles Butler
Franco Giacomo Moretti
Reginald George Nelson
Belinda Robinson
Douglas Arthur Schwebel
Subsidiaries:

Delhi Petroleum Pty. Ltd. (1)
25 Conyngham St
Glenside, SA, 5065, Australia
Tel.: (61) 883382833
Fax: (61) 883382336
Oil & Gas Exploration Services
S.I.C.: 1381
N.A.I.C.S.: 213111

Impress Energy Pty Limited (1)
83 Havelock St
6005 West Perth, Western Australia, Australia
Tel.: (61) 892142500
Fax: (61) 892142511
Sales Range: $1-9.9 Million
Emp.: 3
Exploration Of Oil & Gas
S.I.C.: 1389
N.A.I.C.S.: 213112
Eddie Smith *(Chm)*
Greg Smith *(Acting CEO)*
Ernie Myers *(Sec)*

BEACHCOMBER HOT TUBS

13245 Comber Way
Surrey, BC, V3W 5V8, Canada
Tel.: (604) 591-8611
Fax: (604) 597-2853
Toll Free: (800) 663-3779
E-Mail: contact@beachcomberhottubs.com
Web Site: www.beachcomberhottubs.com
Year Founded: 1978
Rev.: $33,718,135
Emp.: 350
Business Description:
Spas & Hot Tub Accessories Mfr
S.I.C.: 2652
N.A.I.C.S.: 322219
Personnel:
Keith Scott *(Co-Owner & Pres)*
Judy Scott *(Co-Owner)*

BEACON HILL RESOURCES PLC
Regus Building Ground Floor
Lakeview Building
1277 Mike Crawford Street,
Centurion, South Africa
Tel.: (27) 12 688 3884
E-Mail: info@bhrplc.com
Web Site: www.bhrplc.com
BHR—(AIM)
Rev.: $1,067,006
Assets: $104,069,511
Liabilities: $48,032,474
Net Worth: $56,037,037
Earnings: ($44,392,951)
Emp.: 240
Fiscal Year-end: 12/31/12
Business Description:
Magnesium & Other Metal Minerals Mining Services
S.I.C.: 1099
N.A.I.C.S.: 212299
Personnel:
Rowan Aubrey Karstel *(CEO)*
Stefanie Cronje *(CFO)*
John Daly *(COO)*
Timothy Jones *(Sec)*
Board of Directors:
Justin S. Farr-Jones
Murray d'Almeida
Rowan Aubrey Karstel
David Premraj
Cristian Ramirez
Nicholas von Bruemmer
Legal Counsel:
Sal & Caldeira
Avenida Julius Nyerere, 3412
Maputo, Mozambique
Rockwell Bates
Level 2 189 Flinders Lane
Melbourne, United Kingdom
Memery Crystal LLP
44 Southampton Buildings
London, United Kingdom
Boardroom Pty Limited
Level 7 207 Kent Street
Sydney, Australia
Non-U.S. Subsidiary:
Carnegie Services Australia Pty. Limited (1)
Level 6 22 William St
Melbourne, Western Australia, 3000, Australia
Tel.: (61) 396299505
Fax: (61) 3 9629 9503
Web Site: www.carnegiemens.com.au
Emp.: 2
Mining Services
S.I.C.: 1081
N.A.I.C.S.: 213114

BEACON INTERNATIONAL SPECIALIST CENTRE SDN. BHD.
(d/b/a Beacon Hospital)
No 1 Jalan 215 Section 51 Off Jalan Templer
46050 Petaling Jaya, Selangor, Malaysia
Tel.: (60) 3 76207979
Fax: (60) 3 76207929
E-Mail: info@beaconhospital.com.my
Web Site: www.beaconhospital.com.my
Year Founded: 2005
Emp.: 150
Business Description:
Hospital & Medical Diagnostic Services
S.I.C.: 8062
N.A.I.C.S.: 622110
Personnel:
Joen Chua *(Mgr)*

BEACON MINERALS LTD
1/115 Cambridge St
PO Box 1305
West Leederville, Perth, WA, 6007, Australia
Tel.: (61) 8 9322 6600
Fax: (61) 8 9322 6610
E-Mail: admin@beaconminerals.com.au
Web Site: www.beaconminerals.com
BCN—(ASX)
Rev.: $45,126
Assets: $7,762,289
Liabilities: $192,176
Net Worth: $7,570,113
Earnings: ($1,337,534)
Fiscal Year-end: 06/30/13
Business Description:
Copper-Goldmolybdenum Mineralization
S.I.C.: 1021
N.A.I.C.S.: 212234
Personnel:
Geoff Greenhill *(Chm)*
Graham McGarry *(Mng Dir)*
Sarah Shipway *(Sec)*
Board of Directors:
Geoff Greenhill
Graham McGarry
Marcus Michael
Legal Counsel:
Steinepreis Paganin
Level 4 The Read Buildings 16 Milligan Street
Perth, Australia

BEACON PHARMACEUTICALS LTD.
153-154 Tejgaon I/A
Dhaka, 1208, Bangladesh
Tel.: (880) 29888176
Fax: (880) 28829314
E-Mail: beacon@beacon-pharma.com
Web Site: www.beacon-pharma.com
Emp.: 1,264
Business Description:
Pharmaceutical Mfr
S.I.C.: 2834
N.A.I.C.S.: 325412
Personnel:
Mohammad Ebadul Karim *(Mng Dir)*
Nitai Chandra Das *(Exec VP-Factory Ops)*
Sheikh Enayet Karim *(Exec VP-HR & Admin)*

BEACON RESOURCES INC.
246 Stewart Green SW Suite 1614
Calgary, AB, T3H 3C8, Canada
Tel.: (403) 618-8989
E-Mail: enquiries.beaconresources@gmail.com
Web Site:
TAL—(TSXV)
Business Description:
Gold Mining Services
S.I.C.: 1041
N.A.I.C.S.: 212221
Personnel:
Troy Mochoruk *(Pres & CEO)*
Bill Thompson *(CFO)*

BEACONSFIELD FOOTWEAR LIMITED
2 Peel Road West Pimbo
Skelmersdale, Lancashire, WN8 9PT, United Kingdom
Tel.: (44) 1695 712 720
Fax: (44) 1695 712 715
E-Mail: generalinfo@hotter.com
Web Site: www.hottershoes.com
Year Founded: 1959
Sales Range: $100-124.9 Million
Emp.: 588
Business Description:
Footwear Mfr
S.I.C.: 2389
N.A.I.C.S.: 316210
Personnel:
Stewart Houlgrave *(Founder)*

BEADELL RESOURCES LIMITED
2nd Fl 16 Ord St
6005 West Perth, Western Australia, Australia
Tel.: (61) 894290800
Fax: (61) 894813176
E-Mail: paul.tan@beadellresources.com.au
Web Site: www.beadellresources.com.au
BDR—(ASX)
Sales Range: $1-9.9 Million
Emp.: 10
Business Description:
Gold Exploration
S.I.C.: 1041
N.A.I.C.S.: 212221
Personnel:
Craig Readhead *(Chm)*
Peter Bowler *(Mng Dir)*
Gregory Barrett *(CFO & Sec)*
Boyd Timler *(COO)*
Board of Directors:
Craig Readhead
Peter Bowler
Mike Donaldson
Jim Jewell
Ross Kestel
Robert Watkins

BEALE PLC
The Granville Chambers 21
Richmond Hill
Bournemouth, BH2 6BJ, United Kingdom
Tel.: (44) 1202552022
Fax: (44) 1202317286
Web Site: www.beales.co.uk
BAE—(LSE)
Sls.: $214,071,180
Assets: $77,532,084
Liabilities: $62,476,712
Net Worth: $15,055,372
Earnings: ($9,174,096)
Emp.: 625
Fiscal Year-end: 11/03/12
Business Description:
Department Store Operator
S.I.C.: 5311
N.A.I.C.S.: 452111
Personnel:
Michael Hitchcock *(CEO)*
Christopher R. Varley *(Sec)*
Board of Directors:
Keith Edelman
John Chillcott
Michael Hitchcock
Simon Peters
Anthony Richards
William Tuffy
Legal Counsel:
Blake Lapthorn
Southampton, United Kingdom

BEAR CREEK MINING CORPORATION
1050 - 625 Howe Street
Vancouver, BC, V6C 2T6, Canada
Tel.: (604) 685-6269
Fax: (604) 685-6268
E-Mail: info@bearcreekmining.com
Web Site: www.bearcreekmining.com
Year Founded: 1999
BCM—(TSXV)
Rev.: $323,000
Assets: $145,040,000
Liabilities: $3,685,000
Net Worth: $141,355,000
Earnings: ($31,012,000)
Emp.: 88
Fiscal Year-end: 12/31/12
Business Description:
Mineral Exploration Services
S.I.C.: 1081
N.A.I.C.S.: 213114
Personnel:
Catherine McLeod-Seltzer *(Chm)*
Andrew T. Swarthout *(Pres & CEO)*
Steven Krause *(CFO)*
Elsiario Antunez de Mayolo *(COO)*
Alvaro Diaz *(VP-Legal & Gen Counsel)*
Board of Directors:
Catherine McLeod-Seltzer
David E. De Witt
Miguel Grau
Kevin R. Morano
Andrew T. Swarthout
Frank R. Tweddle
Nolan A. Watson
Transfer Agent:
Computershare Investor Services Inc.
510 Burrard Street 2nd Floor
Vancouver, BC, V6C 3B9, Canada
U.S. Subsidiaries:
Bear Creek Exploration Company Ltd (1)
1815 E Winsett St
Tucson, AZ 85719-6547
Tel.: (520) 624-4153
Metal Mining Services
S.I.C.: 1081
N.A.I.C.S.: 213114
Bear Creek Mining Inc. (1)
7761 Shaffer Pkwy
Littleton, CO 80127-3728
Tel.: (303) 390-0071
Coal Surface Mining Services
S.I.C.: 1221
N.A.I.C.S.: 212111
Non-U.S. Subsidiaries:
Bear Creek Mining Company Sucursal del Peru. (1)
Calle Teruel No 186
Miraflores, Peru
Tel.: (51) 12220854
Nonmetallic Mineral Mining Services
S.I.C.: 1499
N.A.I.C.S.: 212399
Bear Creek Mining S.A.C. (1)
Av Republica De Panama No 3505 Dpto 601 Urb Corpac
San Isidro, Lima, Peru
Tel.: (51) 12223361
Fax: (51) 12220854
Metal Mining Services
S.I.C.: 1081
N.A.I.C.S.: 213114

BEAR LAKE GOLD LTD.
1111 St-Charles West West Tower Suite 101
Longueuil, QC, J4K 5G4, Canada
Tel.: (450) 677-1009
Fax: (450) 677-2601
Toll Free: (855) 677-4826
E-Mail: info@bearlakegold.com
Web Site: www.bearlakegold.com
BLG—(TSXV)
Rev.: $17,522
Assets: $8,556,440
Liabilities: $233,201
Net Worth: $8,323,239
Earnings: ($746,353)
Fiscal Year-end: 09/30/13
Business Description:
Gold Mining Services
S.I.C.: 1041
N.A.I.C.S.: 212221
Personnel:
David A. Fennell *(Chm & Interim CEO)*

Bear Lake Gold Ltd.—(Continued)

Thomas G. Larsen *(Vice Chm)*
Alain Krushnisky *(CFO)*
Carole Plante *(Gen Counsel & Sec)*
Board of Directors:
David A. Fennell
Elaine Bennett
Alex S. Horvath
Thomas G. Larsen
Francois Viens
John Wakeford
Transfer Agent:
Equity Financial Trust Company
200 University Avenue Suite 400
Toronto, ON, Canada

BEARCLAW CAPITAL CORP.

214-3540 West 41st Street
Vancouver, BC, V6N 3E6, Canada
Tel.: (604) 682-2201
Fax: (604) 682-0318
Year Founded: 1999
BRL—(TSXV)
Rev.: $28,218
Assets: $2,154,647
Liabilities: $62,675
Net Worth: $2,091,972
Earnings: ($70,028)
Fiscal Year-end: 12/31/12
Business Description:
Mineral Exploration Services
S.I.C.: 1099
N.A.I.C.S.: 212299
Personnel:
Scott M. Ross *(Pres & CEO)*
Arthur W. Lilly *(CFO)*
Robert B. MacGillivray *(Sec)*
Board of Directors:
William R. Gilmour
Arthur W. Lilly
Robert B. MacGillivray
Scott M. Ross
Mohan Vulimiri

BEARDSELL LIMITED

47 Greams Road
Chennai, 600 006, India
Tel.: (91) 4428293296
Fax: (91) 4428290391
E-Mail: ho@beardsell.co.in
Web Site: www.beardsell.co.in
BEARDSELL—(NSE)
Rev.: $18,826,202
Assets: $12,998,264
Liabilities: $6,970,984
Net Worth: $6,027,280
Earnings: $545,169
Fiscal Year-end: 03/31/13
Business Description:
Storage & Packaging Services
S.I.C.: 4225
N.A.I.C.S.: 493110
Personnel:
Bharat Anumolu *(Mng Dir)*
Y. Mukthar Basha *(CFO)*
K. Murali *(Sec)*
Board of Directors:
Amrith Anumolu
Bharat Anumolu
S. V. Narasimha Rao
V. Thirumal Rao
M. Uttam Reddi
R. Gowri Shankar
V. J. Singh
Transfer Agent:
Cameo Corporate Services Limited
Subramanian Building No 1 Club House Road
5th Floor
Chennai, India

BEARING RESOURCES LTD.

Suite 1280 625 Howe Street
Vancouver, BC, V6C 2T6, Canada
Tel.: (604) 682-5546
Fax: (604) 682-5542
E-Mail: gchater@bearingresources.ca
Web Site: www.bearingresources.ca
Year Founded: 2011
BRZ—(TSXV)
Assets: $2,954,794
Liabilities: $120,308
Net Worth: $2,834,486
Earnings: ($3,698,425)
Fiscal Year-end: 10/31/12
Business Description:
Metal Mining Services
S.I.C.: 1099
N.A.I.C.S.: 212299
Personnel:
Geoffrey Chater *(Chm)*
Robert Cameron *(Pres & CEO)*
Damian Towns *(CFO & Sec)*
Board of Directors:
Geoffrey Chater
Brian Eric Bayley
Robert Cameron
Ian Howat
Alan Stephens
Damian Towns
David Harold Watkins
Legal Counsel:
Blake, Cassels & Graydon LLP
Vancouver, BC, Canada
Transfer Agent:
Computershare Investor Services Inc.
510 Burrard Street 2nd Floor
Vancouver, BC, V6C 3B9, Canada

BEARINGPOINT HOLDINGS EUROPE B.V.

ITO Tower 8th Floor
Gustav Mahlerplein 62, 1082 MA
Amsterdam, Netherlands
Tel.: (31) 205049000
Fax: (31) 204420199
Web Site: www.bearingpointconsulting.com
Sales Range: $700-749.9 Million
Emp.: 3,250
Business Description:
Holding Company; Management & Technology Consulting Services
S.I.C.: 6719
N.A.I.C.S.: 551112
Personnel:
Peter Mockler *(Chm-Mgmt Bd & CEO)*

Co-Headquarters

BearingPoint GmbH **(1)**
Speicherstrasse 1
D 60327 Frankfurt, Germany De
Tel.: (49) 69130220
Fax: (49) 69130221013
E-Mail: contact.germany@bearingpointconsulting.com
Web Site: www.bearingpoint.de
Emp.: 600
Management & Technology Consulting Services
S.I.C.: 8742
N.A.I.C.S.: 541611
Peter Mockler *(Chm-Mgmt Bd & CEO)*
Werner Kreutzmann *(Member-Mgmt Bd)*
Hans-Werner Wurzel *(Member-Mgmt Bd)*

Non-U.S. Subsidiaries:

BearingPoint Denmark AS **(2)**
Islands Brygge 43
2300 Copenhagen, S, Denmark DK
Tel.: (45) 32888888
Fax: (45) 32888800
E-Mail: nordics@bearingpointconsulting.com
Web Site: www.bearingpoint.dk
Emp.: 30
Management & Technology Consulting Services
S.I.C.: 8742
N.A.I.C.S.: 541611
Soren Ohm *(Pres)*

BearingPoint Finland Oy **(2)**
Kluuvikatu 3
00100 Helsinki, Finland FI
Tel.: (358) 10802288
Fax: (358) 93214621
E-Mail: finland@bearingpoint.com
Web Site: www.bearingpoint.com
Emp.: 60
Management & Technology Consulting Services
S.I.C.: 8742
N.A.I.C.S.: 541611
Riku Sanpala *(Mng Dir)*

BearingPoint France SAS **(2)**
Tour EDF
20 Pl De La Defense, 92050 Paris, La Defense Cedex, France FR
Tel.: (33) 158863000
Fax: (33) 158865000
E-Mail: contact.france@bearingpoint.com
Web Site: www.bearingpoint.fr/
Emp.: 700
Management & Technology Consulting Services
S.I.C.: 8742
N.A.I.C.S.: 541611

BearingPoint GmbH **(2)**
Schwartzenbergplatz 16
A 1010 Vienna, Austria AT
Tel.: (43) 1506320
Fax: (43) 150632600
Web Site: www.bearingpoint.at
Emp.: 40
Management & Technology Consulting Services
S.I.C.: 8742
N.A.I.C.S.: 541611
Peter Linzner *(Mng Dir)*

BearingPoint INFONOVA GmbH **(2)**
Seering 6 Block D
8141 Graz, Austria AT
Tel.: (43) 31680030
Fax: (43) 31680031080
E-Mail: infonova@infonova.com
Emp.: 200
Management & Technology Consulting Services
S.I.C.: 8742
N.A.I.C.S.: 541611
Gerhard Greiner *(Mng Dir)*

BearingPoint Ireland Limited **(2)**
Montague House
Adelaide Rd, Dublin, 2, Ireland IE
Tel.: (353) 14181111
Fax: (353) 14181500
E-Mail: Info.ie@bearingpoint.com
Web Site: www.bearingpoint.com
Emp.: 120
Management & Technology Consulting Services
S.I.C.: 8742
N.A.I.C.S.: 541611
Peter Minogue *(Mng Dir)*

BearingPoint Norway A/S **(2)**
Tjuvholmen Alle 1
0252 Oslo, Norway NO
Tel.: (47) 24069000
Fax: (47) 24069001
E-Mail: nordics@bearingpointconsulting.com
Web Site: www.bearingpoint.no/
Emp.: 100
Management & Technology Consulting Services
S.I.C.: 8742
N.A.I.C.S.: 541611

BearingPoint Sweden AB **(2)**
Sveavagen 21
PO Box 3033
103 61 Stockholm, Sweden SE
Tel.: (46) 841011600
Fax: (46) 841011699
E-Mail: nordics@bearingpoint.com
Web Site: www.bearingpoint.se
Emp.: 68
Management & Technology Consulting Services
S.I.C.: 8742
N.A.I.C.S.: 541611
Patrick Talmgren *(Mng Dir)*

BearingPoint Switzerland AG **(2)**
West-Park
Pfingstweidstrasse 60, CH-8005 Zurich, Switzerland CH
Tel.: (41) 432996464
Fax: (41) 432996465
E-Mail: switzerland@bearingpointconsulting.com
Web Site: www.bearingpoint.ch
Emp.: 120
Management & Technology Consulting Services
S.I.C.: 8742
N.A.I.C.S.: 541611
Ronald Frey *(Partner-Banking)*
Vahan Gurmann *(Partner-Fin Transformation)*
Patrick Mader *(Partner-Insurance)*
Sven Muller *(Partner-Tech)*
Birgitta Oltersdorf *(Partner-Bus Transformation)*
Dieter Weber *(Partner-Pub & Infrastructure Svcs)*
Josef Wicki *(Partner-Reporting Solutions)*

BearingPoint Limited **(2)**
3 More London Riverside
London, 2RE UK, United Kingdom UK
Tel.: (44) 207 939 6100
Fax: (44) 207 407 7136
Web Site: www.bearingpoint.co.uk
Emp.: 100
Management & Technology Consulting Services
S.I.C.: 8742
N.A.I.C.S.: 541611
Nick Dussuyer *(Partner)*

BEARSKIN LAKE AIR SERVICE LTD.

(d/b/a Bearskin Airlines)
PO Box 1447
Sioux Lookout, ON, P8T 1C1, Canada
Tel.: (807) 737-3474
Fax: (807) 737-3093
E-Mail: administration@bearskinairlines.com
Web Site: www.bearskinairlines.com
Year Founded: 1963
Emp.: 200
Business Description:
Air Transportation Services
S.I.C.: 4512
N.A.I.C.S.: 481111
Personnel:
Harvey Friesen *(Pres)*
Cliff Friesen *(Exec VP)*

BEATE UHSE AG

Gutenbergstrasse 12
24941 Flensburg, Germany
Tel.: (49) 46199660
Fax: (49) 4619966466
E-Mail: partner@bu-newmedia.de
Web Site: www.beate-uhse.ag
USE—(DEU)
Sls.: $194,252,331
Assets: $118,866,811
Liabilities: $84,808,710
Net Worth: $34,058,101
Earnings: ($1,480,787)
Emp.: 704
Fiscal Year-end: 12/31/12
Business Description:
All Other Miscellaneous Store Retailers
S.I.C.: 5999
N.A.I.C.S.: 453998
Personnel:
Gerard Philippus Cok *(Chm-Supervisory Bd)*
Serge van der Hooft *(Chm-Mgmt Bd & CEO)*
Erwin Cok *(COO-Comml & Consumer Div & Member-Mgmt Bd)*
Supervisory Board of Directors:
Gerard Philippus Cok
Andreas Bartmann
Udo Bensing
Kerstin Klippert
B. H. Ruzette

BEATRIX VENTURES INC.
(Name Changed to Emerge Resources Corp.)

BEATTIE DODGE CHRYSLER LTD.
8 Chase Street
PO Box 550
Brockville, ON, K6V 5V7, Canada
Tel.: (613) 342-4404
Fax: (613) 342-1312
Toll Free: (877) 469-1165
E-Mail: sales@beattiedodge.com
Web Site: www.beattiedodge.com
Rev.: $11,051,669
Emp.: 25
Business Description:
New & Used Cars Dealers
S.I.C.: 5511
N.A.I.C.S.: 441110
Personnel:
Douglas Beattie *(Pres)*

BEATTIE HOMES LTD
3165 114th Ave SE
Calgary, AB, T2Z 3X2, Canada
Tel.: (403) 252-0995
Fax: (403) 253-2883
E-Mail: info@beattiehomes.com
Web Site: www.beattiehomes.com
Sales Range: $75-99.9 Million
Emp.: 77
Business Description:
Construction Services
S.I.C.: 1521
N.A.I.C.S.: 236115
Personnel:
Dean Anderson *(Mgr-Sls-SkyView Ranch)*

BEATTIES BASICS
399 Vansickle Road
Saint Catharines, ON, L2S 3T4, Canada
Tel.: (905) 688-4040
Fax: (905) 688-6840
E-Mail: vansickle@beatties.com
Web Site: www.beatties.com
Year Founded: 1900
Sales Range: $10-24.9 Million
Emp.: 130
Business Description:
Office Furniture Distr
S.I.C.: 2522
N.A.I.C.S.: 337214
Personnel:
Edward Hoxie *(Pres)*
Subsidiary:

Beatties Basics Office Products **(1)**
399 Vansickle Road
ON Saint Catharines, ON, L2R5G3, Canada
Tel.: (905) 688-4040
Fax: (905) 688-6840
Toll Free: (866) 406-5556
E-Mail: beatties@beatties.com
Web Site: www.beatties.com
Rev.: $20,002,830
Office Furniture Distr
S.I.C.: 2522
N.A.I.C.S.: 337214
Edward Hoxie *(Pres)*

BEATTY FLOORS LIMITED
1840 Pandora Street
Vancouver, BC, V5L1M7, Canada
Tel.: (604) 254-9571
Fax: (604) 254-5446
Web Site: www.beattyfloors.com
Year Founded: 1929
Rev.: $13,650,357
Emp.: 85
Business Description:
Floor Coverings & Installation Carpet & Rug Dealers
S.I.C.: 5713
N.A.I.C.S.: 442210
Personnel:
Howard Obrand *(Pres)*

BEAUFIELD RESOURCES INC.
950 - 1801 McGill College Avenue
Montreal, QC, H3A 2N4, Canada
Tel.: (514) 842-3443
Fax: (514) 842-3306
E-Mail: info@beaufield.com
Web Site: www.beaufield.com
BFD—(TSXV)
Assets: $19,636,322
Liabilities: $1,008,679
Net Worth: $18,627,644
Earnings: ($2,181,881)
Fiscal Year-end: 08/31/13
Business Description:
Gold & Base Metals Mining Services
S.I.C.: 1041
N.A.I.C.S.: 212221
Personnel:
Jens E. Hansen *(Pres & CEO)*
Vatche Tchakmakian *(CFO & Sec)*
Board of Directors:
John Budden
Peter W. Dunsford
James C. Gervais
Jens E. Hansen
John MacLatchy
Legal Counsel:
Gregory T. Chu
Ste 650 1188 W Georgia St
Vancouver, BC, Canada
Transfer Agent:
Computershare Trust Company of Canada
9th Floor 100 University Avenue
Toronto, ON, Canada

BEAUFORT CAPITAL GMBH
Alsterarkaden 20
20354 Hamburg, Germany
Tel.: (49) 40 34 99 99 6
Fax: (49) 40 34 99 99 77
E-Mail: info@bo4.de
Web Site: www.bo4.de
Business Description:
Private Equity Firm
S.I.C.: 6211
N.A.I.C.S.: 523999
Personnel:
Stefan Friese *(Partner)*
Patrick Hennings-Huep *(Partner)*
Johann David Herstatt *(Partner)*
Anja Moje *(Partner)*

BEAULIEU INTERNATIONAL GROUP NV
Holstraat 59
8790 Waregem, Belgium
Tel.: (32) 5 662 59 00
Web Site: www.bintg.com
Year Founded: 2005
Sales Range: $1-4.9 Billion
Emp.: 3,300
Business Description:
Holding Company; Mfr of Floor Coverings & Fabrics & Production of Raw Materials, Semi-Finished & Finished Products
S.I.C.: 6719
N.A.I.C.S.: 551112
Non-U.S. Subsidiary:

Juteks d.d. **(1)**
Loznica 53a
3310 Zalec, Slovenia SI
Tel.: (386) 3 71 20 700 (52.42%)
Fax: (386) 3 71 20 755
E-Mail: info@juteks.si
Web Site: www.juteks.si
Sales Range: $50-74.9 Million
Emp.: 290
PVC Floor Coverings Mfr
S.I.C.: 3089
N.A.I.C.S.: 326199
Dusan Stiherl *(Pres)*
Jure Zupin *(CEO)*
Jozica Potrc *(Sec)*

BEAUMONT AUTOMOBILES
Bd Fernand Darchicourt
62110 Henin-Beaumont, Pas De Calais, France
Tel.: (33) 321132050
Sls.: $18,000,000
Emp.: 33
S.I.C.: 5511
N.A.I.C.S.: 441110
Personnel:
Philippe Wantiez *(Pres)*

BEAUMONT SELECT CORPORATIONS INC.
915 42nd Avenue SE
Calgary, AB, T2G 1Z1, Canada
Tel.: (403) 250-8757
Fax: (403) 250-8709
E-Mail: investor_relations@bsci.ca
Web Site: www.bsci.ca
BMN.A—(TSXV)
Rev.: $14,547,430
Assets: $48,285,194
Liabilities: $23,855,353
Net Worth: $24,429,842
Earnings: $171,762
Fiscal Year-end: 06/30/13
Business Description:
Holding Company
S.I.C.: 6719
N.A.I.C.S.: 551112
Personnel:
Winston Ho Fatt *(Chm, CEO & Chief Investment Officer)*
Philip Gaiser *(CFO)*
Gina Palmer *(Sec)*
Board of Directors:
Winston Ho Fatt
Andrew Hyslop
Terry Kent
Martin Pelletier
Legal Counsel:
Borden Ladner Gervais LLP
1900 520 Third Avenue SW
Calgary, AB, Canada
Transfer Agent:
Computershare Trust Company of Canada
100 University Avenue 9th Floor
Toronto, ON, M5J 2Y1, Canada
Tel.: (416) 663-9097
Fax: (416) 263-9694
Subsidiary:

Naleway Foods Ltd. **(1)**
233 Hutchings Street
Winnipeg, MB, R2X 2R4, Canada
Tel.: (204) 633-6535
Fax: (204) 694-4310
Toll Free: (800) 665-7448
E-Mail: qc@naleway.com
Web Site: www.naleway.com
Emp.: 100
Frozen Food Mfr
S.I.C.: 2038
N.A.I.C.S.: 311412
Richard Lyles *(Gen Mgr)*

BEAUTY COMMUNITY PUBLIC COMPANY LIMITED
10/915 Nuanchan 34
Nuanchan
Bangkum, Bangkok, Thailand
Tel.: (66) 29460700
Fax: (66) 29461571
Web Site: www.beautycommunity.co.th
BEAUTY—(THA)
Business Description:
Cosmetics & Beauty Products Retailer
S.I.C.: 5122
N.A.I.C.S.: 446120
Personnel:
Padet Charuchindra *(Chm)*

BEAUTY GARAGE INC.
1-34-25 Sakura-Shinmachi Setagaya
Tokyo, 154-0015, Japan
Tel.: (81) 3 5752 3887
Fax: (81) 3 3702 0231
E-Mail: overseas@beautygarage.jp
Web Site: www.beautygarage.co.jp
Year Founded: 2003
3180—(TKS)
Sls.: $58,168,000
Assets: $22,913,000
Liabilities: $10,637,000
Net Worth: $12,276,000
Earnings: $2,090,000
Emp.: 150
Fiscal Year-end: 04/30/13
Business Description:
Hair & Nail Salon Owner
S.I.C.: 7231
N.A.I.C.S.: 812112
Personnel:
Hideki Nomura *(CEO)*
Shuichi Tomoda *(COO)*
Masayuki Ito *(Operating Officer)*
Kiyoshi Kato *(Operating Officer)*
Hideto Yoshizawa *(Operating Officer)*
Board of Directors:
Yoshiaki Kabashima
Hideki Nomura
Takahisa Nomura
Shuichi Tomoda

BEAUTY HEALTH GROUP LIMITED
Level 2 230 Church Street
Richmond, VIC, 3121, Australia
Tel.: (61) 394292888
Fax: (61) 398458373
BHG—(ASX)
Sales Range: Less than $1 Million
Business Description:
Beauty & Healthcare Services
S.I.C.: 7299
N.A.I.C.S.: 812199
Personnel:
Con Scrinis *(Chm & Sec)*
Board of Directors:
Con Scrinis
Cary Stynes
Gregory Wood

BEAUTY KADAN CO., LTD.
2-16-2 Nishishinbashi
Minato-ku, Tokyo, 105-0003, Japan
Tel.: (81) 357765850
Fax: (81) 357765851
Web Site: www.beauty-kadan.com
Year Founded: 1997
3041—(TKS)
Emp.: 270
Business Description:
Flower Whslr
S.I.C.: 5193
N.A.I.C.S.: 424930
Personnel:
Misao Mishima *(Chm)*
Keishi Oda *(Pres)*
Osamu Babasaki *(Mng Dir)*
Koji Takayama *(Chief Admin Officer)*
Kazunari Watanabe *(Exec Officer)*
Board of Directors:
Shoichi Masuda
Misao Mishima
Keishi Oda

Beauty Kadan Co., Ltd.—(Continued)

Subsidiary:

CROWN Gardenex Co., Ltd. (1)
7-11-52 Chikami
Kumamoto, 861-4101, Japan JP
Tel.: (81) 962238783 (100%)
Fax: (81) 962238788
Web Site: www.crown-g.co.jp
Bridal Bouquet Whslr
S.I.C.: 5193
N.A.I.C.S.: 424930
Taguiti Kinuko *(CEO)*

BEAVER ELECTRICAL MACHINERY LTD.

7440 Lowland Drive
Burnaby, BC, V5J 5A4, Canada
Tel.: (604) 431-5000
Fax: (604) 431-5066
Toll Free: (800) 663-6505
E-Mail: info@beaverelectrical.com
Web Site: www.beaverelectrical.com
Year Founded: 1955
Rev.: $10,684,764
Emp.: 65
Business Description:
Electrical Products Sales & Services
S.I.C.: 1731
N.A.I.C.S.: 238210
Personnel:
Serg Nosella *(Chm & CEO)*
Dave Flumerfelt *(Pres)*

BEAVER MACHINE CORPORATION

1341 Kerrisdale Boulevard
Newmarket, ON, Canada
Tel.: (905) 836-4700
Fax: (905) 836-4737
E-Mail: sales@beavervending.com
Web Site: www.beavervending.com
Year Founded: 1963
Rev.: $17,002,568
Emp.: 37
Business Description:
Automatic Vending Machine Mfr
S.I.C.: 3589
N.A.I.C.S.: 333318
Personnel:
Josef Schwarzli *(Founder)*
Bernie Schwarzli *(Pres)*

BEAZLEY GROUP PLC

(See Under Beazley plc)

BEAZLEY PLC

(Formerly Beazley Group plc)
Plantation Place South 60 Great Tower Street
London, EC3R 5AD, United Kingdom
Tel.: (44) 2076670623
Fax: (44) 2076747100
E-Mail: info@beazley.com
Web Site: www.beazley.com
Year Founded: 1986
BEZ—(LSE)
Premiums: $1,895,900,000
Assets: $6,455,400,000
Liabilities: $5,243,700,000
Net Worth: $1,211,700,000
Earnings: $214,600,000
Emp.: 847
Fiscal Year-end: 12/31/12
Business Description:
Insurance Services
S.I.C.: 6411
N.A.I.C.S.: 524298
Personnel:
Dennis Holt *(Chm)*
Andrew Horton *(CEO)*
Ian Fantozzi *(COO)*
Andrew Pryde *(Chief Risk Officer)*
Neil Maidment *(Chief Underwriting Officer)*
Sian Coope *(Sec & Head-Compliance)*
Board of Directors:
Dennis Holt
George Blunden
Martin Bride
Adrian Cox
Angela Crawford-Ingle
Andrew Horton
Neil Maidment
Padraic O'Connor
Vincent Sheridan
Ken Sroka
Rolf Tolle
Clive Washbourn

Subsidiaries:

Beazley Dedicated Ltd. (1)
60 Great Tower Street
London, EC3R 5AD, United Kingdom
Tel.: (44) 2076670623
Insurance Underwriting Services
S.I.C.: 6411
N.A.I.C.S.: 524298

Beazley Dedicated No.2 Limited (1)
One Aldgate
London, EC3N 1AA, United Kingdom
Tel.: (44) 2076670623
Fax: (44) 2076670624
Insurance Underwriting Services
S.I.C.: 6411
N.A.I.C.S.: 524298

Beazley Furlonge Holdings Limited (1)
Plantation Place South 60 Great Tower Street
London, EC3R 5AD, United Kingdom
Tel.: (44) 2076670623
Fax: (44) 2076747100
E-Mail: marketing@beazley.com
Web Site: www.beazley.com
Emp.: 600
Insurance Underwriting Services
S.I.C.: 6411
N.A.I.C.S.: 524298

Beazley Furlonge Limited (1)
Plantation Place South
60 Great Tower Street, London, EC3R 5AD, United Kingdom
Tel.: (44) 2076670623
Fax: (44) 2076747100
Emp.: 300
Insurance Services
S.I.C.: 6411
N.A.I.C.S.: 524298
Andrew Horton *(CEO)*

Beazley Group Limited (1)
Plantation Place South 60 Great Tower Street
London, EC3R 5AD, United Kingdom
Tel.: (44) 2076670623
Fax: (44) 2076747100
E-Mail: info@beazley.com
Emp.: 400
Underwriting Services
S.I.C.: 6211
N.A.I.C.S.: 523110

Beazley Investments Limited (1)
Plantation Pl S 60 Great Tower St
London, EC3R 5AD, United Kingdom
Tel.: (44) 2076670623
Fax: (44) 2076670624
Emp.: 600
Investment Management Services
S.I.C.: 6211
N.A.I.C.S.: 523999
Andrew Horton *(CEO)*

Beazley Underwriting Services Ltd. (1)
37-39 Lime Street
London, EC3M 7AY, United Kingdom
Tel.: (44) 2073983250
Fax: (44) 2073983260
Insurance Underwriting Services
S.I.C.: 6411
N.A.I.C.S.: 524298

U.S. Subsidiaries:

Beazley Holdings, Inc. (1)
30 Batterson Park Rd
Farmington, CT 06032-2579
Tel.: (860) 677-0400
Emp.: 120
Insurance Brokerage Services
S.I.C.: 6411
N.A.I.C.S.: 524210

Beazley USA Services, Inc. (1)
30 Patterson Park Rd
Farmington, CT 06032
Tel.: (860) 677-3700
Fax: (860) 679-0247
Web Site: www.beazley.com
Emp.: 130
Management Services
S.I.C.: 8742
N.A.I.C.S.: 541611

Non-U.S. Subsidiaries:

Beazley Limited (1)
Suite 1703 Central Plaza 18 Harbour Road
Wanchai, China (Hong Kong)
Tel.: (852) 25225033
Fax: (852) 28100699
E-Mail: hongkong.office@beazley.com
Web Site: www.beazley.com
General Insurance Services
S.I.C.: 6411
N.A.I.C.S.: 524210

Beazley Pte. Limited (1)
8 Marina View 14 Fl 01 Asia Sq Tower 1
Singapore, 018960, Singapore
Tel.: (65) 65365433
Fax: (65) 66361216
E-Mail: singapore.office@beazley.com
Emp.: 7
General Insurance Services
S.I.C.: 6411
N.A.I.C.S.: 524210
Byran Guan Leong Lee *(Gen Mgr)*

Beazley Underwriting Pty Ltd (1)
Level 22 215 Adelaide Street
Brisbane, QLD, 4000, Australia
Tel.: (61) 7 3228 1600
Fax: (61) 7 3210 0760
E-Mail: info@beazley.ie
Web Site: www.beazley.com
Emp.: 14
General Insurance Services
S.I.C.: 6411
N.A.I.C.S.: 524210

BEBRA BIOGAS HOLDING AG

Kanalstr 25
44147 Dortmund, Germany
Tel.: (49) 231 9982 700
Fax: (49) 231 9982 799
E-Mail: info@bebra-biogas.com
Web Site: www.bebra-biogas.com
EBG—(DEU)
Business Description:
Gas Processing & Agricultural Equipment Mfr
S.I.C.: 3533
N.A.I.C.S.: 333132
Personnel:
Benno Brachthauser *(Member-Mgmt Bd)*

BEC WORLD PUBLIC COMPANY LIMITED

3199 Maleenont Tower Floors 2 3 8
30-34 Rama 4 Rd Klongton
Klongtoey, Bangkok, 10110, Thailand
Tel.: (66) 2 204 3333
Fax: (66) 2 204 1384
E-Mail: ir@becworld.com
Web Site: www.becworld.com
BEC—(OTC THA)
Rev.: $500,428,094
Assets: $356,939,922
Liabilities: $81,719,122
Net Worth: $275,220,800
Earnings: $163,567,404
Emp.: 1,966
Fiscal Year-end: 12/31/12
Business Description:
Television & Radio Broadcasting Services
S.I.C.: 4833
N.A.I.C.S.: 515120
Personnel:
Vichai Maleenont *(Chm)*
Prasan Maleenont *(Vice Chm, Pres & COO)*
Chalaiporn Itthithavorn *(Sec)*
Pravit Maleenont *(Sr Exec VP & Exec Dir-Television Bus)*
Prachum Maleenont *(Sr Exec VP & Dir-New Media Bus)*
Board of Directors:
Vichai Maleenont
Somchai Boonnumsiri
Manit Boonprakob
Chansak Fuangfu
Matthew Kichodhan
Amphorn Maleenont
Nipa Maleenont
Prachum Maleenont
Prasan Maleenont
Pravit Maleenont
Ratana Maleenont
Arun Ngamdee
Ratchanee Nipatakusol
Prathan Rangsimaporn
Legal Counsel:
P&P Law Firm
3199 Maleenont Tower Building 22nd Fl Rama IV Rd
Klongton Klongtoey, Bangkok, Thailand

Subsidiaries:

The Bangkok Entertainment Co., Ltd. (1)
2nd Floor Maleenont Tower
3199 Rama IV Rd Klongton Klong, 10110
Bangkok, Thailand (100%)
Tel.: (66) 22623333
Fax: (66) 22041384
E-Mail: ir@becworld.com
Web Site: www.becworld.com
Emp.: 100
Television Broadcasting
S.I.C.: 4833
N.A.I.C.S.: 515120
Vichai Maleenont *(Chm)*
Prasan Maleenont *(Vice Chm & Mng Dir)*
Pravit Maleenont *(Mng Dir)*

Bangkok Satellites & Telecommunication Co., Ltd. (1)
2nd Fl Maleenont Tower
3199 Rama IV Rd Klongton Klong, 10110
Bangkok, Thailand (100%)
Tel.: (66) 22623333
Fax: (66) 22041384
E-Mail: ir@becworld.com
Web Site: www.becworld.com
Satellite Telecommunications
S.I.C.: 4899
N.A.I.C.S.: 517410
Vichai Maleenont *(Chm)*

BEC Asset Co., Ltd. (1)
3rd Floor Maleenont Tower
3199 Rama IV Rd Klongton Klong, 10110
Bangkok, Thailand (100%)
Tel.: (66) 22623333
Fax: (66) 22041384
E-Mail: ir@becworld.com
Web Site: www.thaitv3.com
Emp.: 2,000
Holding Company
S.I.C.: 6719
N.A.I.C.S.: 551112
Vichai Maleenont *(Chm)*

BEC Broadcasting Center Co., Ltd. (1)
2nd Floor Maleenont Tower
3199 Rama IV Rd Klongton Klong, 10110
Bangkok, Thailand (100%)
Tel.: (66) 22623333
Fax: (66) 22041384
E-Mail: ir@becworld.com
Web Site: www.becworld.com
Emp.: 1,000
Satellite Telecommunications
S.I.C.: 4899

N.A.I.C.S.: 517410
Vichai Maleenont *(Chm)*

BEC IT Solution Co., Ltd. (1)
3rd Floor Maleenont Tower
3199 Rama IV Rd Klongton Klong, 10110
Bangkok, Thailand (100%)
Tel.: (66) 22623333
Fax: (66) 22623780
E-Mail: ir@becworld.com
Web Site: www.itv3.com
Emp.: 1,000
Television Broadcasting
S.I.C.: 4833
N.A.I.C.S.: 515120
Vichai Maleenont *(Chm)*

BEC Multimedia Co., Ltd. (1)
4th Floor Maleenont Tower
3199 Rama IV Rd Klongton Klong, 10110
Bangkok, Thailand (100%)
Tel.: (66) 22623333
Fax: (66) 22041384
E-Mail: ir@becworld.com
Web Site: www.thaitv3.com
Emp.: 2,000
Financial Investment Activities
S.I.C.: 6211
N.A.I.C.S.: 523999
Vichai Maleenont *(Chm)*

BEC News Bureau Co., Ltd. (1)
2nd Fl Maleenont Tower
3199 Rama IV Rd Klongton Klong, 10110
Bangkok, Thailand (100%)
Tel.: (66) 22623333
Fax: (66) 22041384
E-Mail: ir@becworld.com
Web Site: www.becnews.com
Emp.: 100
Television Broadcasting
S.I.C.: 4833
N.A.I.C.S.: 515120
Vichai Maleenont *(Chm)*

BEC Studio Co., Ltd. (1)
2nd Floor Maleenont Tower
3199 Rama IV Rd Klongton Klong, 10110
Bangkok, Thailand (100%)
Tel.: (66) 22623333
Fax: (66) 22041384
E-Mail: ir@becworld.com
Web Site: www.thaitv3.com
Emp.: 100
Radio Television & Electronics Stores
S.I.C.: 5734
N.A.I.C.S.: 443142
Vichai Maleenont *(Chm)*

BECi Corporation Co., Ltd. (1)
4th Floor Maleenont Tower
3199 Rama IV Rd Klongton Klong, 10110
Bangkok, Thailand (100%)
Tel.: (66) 22623333
Fax: (66) 026835080
E-Mail: ir@becworld.com
Web Site: www.becicorp.com
Emp.: 30
Financial Investment Services
S.I.C.: 6211
N.A.I.C.S.: 523999
Vichai Maleenont *(Chm)*

Subsidiaries:

Digital Factory Co., Ltd. (2)
4th Floor Maleenont Tower
3199 Rama IV Rd Klongton Klong, 10110
Bangkok, Thailand (51%)
Tel.: (66) 22623333
Fax: (66) 22041384
E-Mail: ir@becworld.com
Satellite Telecommunications
S.I.C.: 4899
N.A.I.C.S.: 517410
Vichai Maleenont *(Chm)*

Mobi (Thai) Co., Ltd. (2)
3199 Maleenont Tower Floors 2, 3,8,9,30-34
Rama 4 Rd Klongton Klongtoey, 10110
Bangkok, Thailand (60%)
Tel.: (66) 22623333
Fax: (66) 22041384
E-Mail: ir@becworld.com
Web Site: www.becworld.com
Satellite Telecommunications
S.I.C.: 4899
N.A.I.C.S.: 517410
Vichai Maleenont *(Chm)*

New World Production Co, Ltd. (1)
2nd Floor Maleenont Tower
3199 Rama IV Rd Klongton Klong, 10110
Bangkok, Thailand (100%)
Tel.: (66) 22623333
Fax: (66) 22041384
E-Mail: ir@becworld.com
Web Site: www.becworld.com
Emp.: 500
Television Broadcasting
S.I.C.: 4833
N.A.I.C.S.: 515120
Vichai Maleenont *(Pres)*

Rungsirojvanit Co., Ltd. (1)
2nd Floor Maleenont Tower
3199 Rama IV Rd Klongton Klong, 10110
Bangkok, Thailand
Tel.: (66) 22623333
Fax: (66) 22621356
E-Mail: yuwabee@tv3.com
Web Site: www.tv3.com
Emp.: 1,200
Television Broadcasting
S.I.C.: 4833
N.A.I.C.S.: 515120
Vichai Maleenont *(Chm)*

Satellites TV Broadcasting Co., Ltd. (1)
2nd Floor Maleenont Tower
3199 Rama IV Rd Klongton Klong, 10110
Bangkok, Thailand (100%)
Tel.: (66) 22623333
Fax: (66) 22041384
E-Mail: ir@becworld.com
Web Site: www.becworld.com
Emp.: 1,000
Satellite Telecommunications
S.I.C.: 4899
N.A.I.C.S.: 517410
Vichai Maleenont *(Chm)*
Prasan Maleenont *(Vice Chm-Exec Bd & COO)*

TVB 3 Network Co., Ltd. (1)
9th Floor Maleenont Tower
3199 Rama IV Rd Klongton Klong, 10110
Bangkok, Thailand (60%)
Tel.: (66) 22623333
Fax: (66) 22041384
E-Mail: ir@becworld.com
Television Broadcasting
S.I.C.: 4833
N.A.I.C.S.: 515120
Vichai Maleenont *(Chm)*

You & I Corporation Company Limited (1)
2nd Fl Maleenont Tower 3199 Rama IV Road Klongton Klongtoey
10110 Bangkok, Thailand (100%)
Tel.: (66) 2262 3274
Fax: (66) 2262 3665
E-Mail: ir@becworld.com
Web Site: www.becworld.com
Emp.: 20
Television & Radio Broadcasting & Production
S.I.C.: 4833
N.A.I.C.S.: 515120
Vichai Maleenont *(Chm)*
Prasan Maleenont *(Vice Chm)*

Joint Ventures:

BEC Tero Entertainment Co., Ltd. (1)
22nd Floor Maleenont Twr
3199 Rama IV Rd Klongton Klong, 10110
Bangkok, Thailand
Tel.: (66) 22623333
Fax: (66) 22041384
Web Site: www.bectero.com
Audio & Video Equipment Mfr
S.I.C.: 3651
N.A.I.C.S.: 334310
Prasan Maleenont *(Chm)*

BEC-Tero Entertainment Public Company Limited (1)
25th-28th Fl Maleenont Twr
3199 Rama IV Rd Klongton Klong, 10110
Bangkok, Thailand (60%)
Tel.: (66) 22623800
Fax: (66) 22623801
E-Mail: info@bectero.com
Web Site: www.bectero.com
Television Broadcasting
S.I.C.: 4899
N.A.I.C.S.: 517410
Atita Ducci *(Mgr-PR)*

Subsidiaries:

BEC-Tero Arsenal Co., Ltd. (2)
26th Floor Maleenont Twr
3199 Rama IV Rd Klongton Klong, 10110
Bangkok, Thailand (100%)
Tel.: (66) 22623333
Fax: (66) 22041384
E-Mail: ir@becworld.com
Sports Teams & Clubs
S.I.C.: 7941
N.A.I.C.S.: 711211
Sunny Pattiyawongse *(Brand Mgr)*

BEC-TERO Sasana Co., Ltd. (2)
199 Maleenont Tower 26th Floor Rama IV Road Klongton
Klongtoey, Bangkok, 10110, Thailand
Tel.: (66) 2 262 3919
Fax: (66) 2 262 3921
E-Mail: bubet@bectero.com
Web Site: www.becterosasana.in.th
Sports Club Operating Services
S.I.C.: 7941
N.A.I.C.S.: 711211
Worawi Makudi *(Founder)*
Brian L. Marcar *(Pres)*

Thai Ticket Major Co., Ltd. (2)
27th Floor Maleenont Twr
3199 Rama IV Rd Klongton Klong, 10110
Bangkok, Thailand
Tel.: (66) 22623333
Fax: (66) 22041384
E-Mail: ir@becworld.com
Web Site: www.thaiticketmajor.com
Television Broadcasting
S.I.C.: 4833
N.A.I.C.S.: 515120

Joint Ventures:

BEC-Tero Exhibitions Co., Ltd. (2)
27th Floor Maleenont Twr
3199 Rama IV Rd Klongton Klong, 10110
Bangkok, Thailand (60%)
Tel.: (66) 22623333
Fax: (66) 22041384
E-Mail: ir@becworld.com
Convention & Trade Show Organizers
S.I.C.: 7389
N.A.I.C.S.: 561920

SMBT Publishing (Thailand) Co., Ltd. (2)
22nd Floor Maleenont Twr
3199 Rama IV Rd Klongton Klong, 10110
Bangkok, Thailand (40%)
Tel.: (66) 22623333
Fax: (66) 22041384
E-Mail: ir@becworld.com
Web Site: www.becworld.com
Audio & Video Equipment Mfr
S.I.C.: 3651
N.A.I.C.S.: 334310
Vichai Maleenont *(Chm)*

Virgin BEC-Tero Radio (Thailand) Co., Ltd. (2)
24th Floor Maleenont Twr
3199 Rama IV Rd Klongton Klong, 10110
Bangkok, Thailand (49%)
Tel.: (66) 22623333
Fax: (66) 22041384
E-Mail: ir@becworld.com
Web Site: www.becworld.com
Radio Stations
S.I.C.: 4832
N.A.I.C.S.: 515112

BECA GROUP LIMITED

132 Vincent St
PO Box 6345
Auckland, 1141, New Zealand
Tel.: (64) 93009000
Fax: (64) 3009300
E-Mail: busdev@beca.com
Web Site: www.beca.com
Emp.: 2,459
Business Description:
Provider of Engineering & Management Services
S.I.C.: 8711
N.A.I.C.S.: 541330
Personnel:
Richard Aitken *(Chm)*
Keith Reynolds *(CEO)*
Chye Heng *(CFO & Head-Legal)*

Non-U.S. Subsidiary:

Beca Pty. Ltd. (1)
Level 4 5 Queens Rd
Melbourne, VIC, 3004, Australia AU
Tel.: (61) 392721400 (100%)
Fax: (61) 392721440
Web Site: www.beca.com.au
Emp.: 300
Provider of Engineering Design & Project Management Services
S.I.C.: 8711
N.A.I.C.S.: 541330
Grag Lowa *(CEO)*

BECHTLE AG

Bechtle Platz 1
74172 Neckarsulm, Germany
Tel.: (49) 4971329810
Fax: (49) 49713298180
E-Mail: info@bechtle.com
Web Site: www.bechtle.com
BC8—(DEU)
Rev.: $2,822,696,372
Assets: $1,138,108,657
Liabilities: $521,033,752
Net Worth: $617,074,905
Earnings: $76,140,721
Emp.: 5,970
Fiscal Year-end: 12/31/12
Business Description:
Computer Peripheral Equipment & Software Merchant Wholesalers
S.I.C.: 5045
N.A.I.C.S.: 423430
Personnel:
Klaus Winkler *(Chm-Supervisory Bd)*
Thomas Olemotz *(Chm-Exec Bd)*
Uli Drautz *(Deputy Chm-Supervisory Bd)*
Jochen Wolf *(Second Deputy Chm-Supervisory Bd)*
Michael Guschlbauer *(Member-Mgmt Bd-IT Sys House & Managed Svcs Segment)*
Jurgen Schafer *(Member-Mgmt Bd-IT e-Commerce)*
Supervisory Board of Directors:
Klaus Winkler
Kurt Dobitsch
Uli Drautz
Daniela Elberle
Barbara Greyer
Thomas Hess
Walter Jaeger
Martin Meyer
Karin Schick
Volker Strohfeld
Michael Unser
Jochen Wolf

Subsidiaries:

ARP GmbH (1)
Lise-Meitner-Strasse 1
63128 Dietzenbach, Germany
Tel.: (49) 6074 491 100
Fax: (49) 6074 491 111
E-Mail: verkauf@arp.de
Web Site: www.arpoffice.de
Information Technology Consulting Services
S.I.C.: 7373
N.A.I.C.S.: 541512

Bechtle direct GmbH (1)
Bechtle Platz 1
74172 Neckarsulm, Germany
Tel.: (49) 7132 981 1600
Fax: (49) 7132 981 1110
E-Mail: vertrieb@bechtle.de
Web Site: www.bechtle.de
Information Technology Consulting Services
S.I.C.: 7373
N.A.I.C.S.: 541512

Bechtle AG—(Continued)

Bechtle Finanz- & Marketingservices GmbH (1)
Kanzleistr 17
74405 Gaildorf, Germany
Tel.: (49) 7971 95020
Fax: (49) 7971 950210
E-Mail: gaildorf@bechtle.com
Information Technology Consulting Services
S.I.C.: 7373
N.A.I.C.S.: 541512

Bechtle GmbH & Co. KG (1)
Industriestrasse 33
33689 Bielefeld, Germany
Tel.: (49) 5205 99887 0
Fax: (49) 5205 99887 15
E-Mail: bielefeld@bechtle.com
Information Technology Consulting Services
S.I.C.: 7373
N.A.I.C.S.: 541512
Michael Tappe, *(Mng Dir)*

Bechtle GmbH (1)
Kaiserin-Augusta-Allee 14
10553 Berlin, Germany
Tel.: (49) 30 364068 0
Fax: (49) 30 364068 10
E-Mail: berlin@bechtle.com
Information Technology Consulting Services
S.I.C.: 7373
N.A.I.C.S.: 541512

Bechtle IT-Systemhaus GmbH & Co. KG (1)
Usinger Strasse 114
61239 Obermorlen, Germany
Tel.: (49) 6002 9131 00
Fax: (49) 6002 9131 09
E-Mail: obermoerlen@bechtle.com
Information Technology Consulting Services
S.I.C.: 7373
N.A.I.C.S.: 541512
Christian Brengel *(Mng Dir)*

Bechtle IT-Systemhaus GmbH (1)
Parkstrasse 2-8
47829 Krefeld, Germany
Tel.: (49) 2151 455 0
Fax: (49) 2151 455 810
E-Mail: duesseldorf@bechtle.com
Information Technology Consulting Services
S.I.C.: 7373
N.A.I.C.S.: 541512

Bechtle Remarketing GmbH (1)
Am Schornacker 18 a
46485 Wesel, Germany
Tel.: (49) 281 206750 0
Fax: (49) 281 206750 15
Web Site: remarketing.bechtle.com
Information Technology Consulting Services
S.I.C.: 7373
N.A.I.C.S.: 541512
Andreas Lenzing, *(Mng Dir)*

HanseVision GmbH (1)
Barmbeker Strasse 10
22303 Hamburg, Germany
Tel.: (49) 40 2880 7590 0
Fax: (49) 40 2880 7590 9
E-Mail: info@hansevision.de
Web Site: www.hansevision.com
Information Technology Consulting Services
S.I.C.: 7373
N.A.I.C.S.: 541512
Ralph-Rene Thomas *(Mgr-Bus Dev)*

HCV Data Management GmbH (1)
Am Eichelgarten 1
65396 Walluf, Germany
Tel.: (49) 6123 9950 310
Fax: (49) 6123 9950 161
E-Mail: info@hcv.de
Web Site: www.hcv.de
Information Technology Consulting Services
S.I.C.: 7373
N.A.I.C.S.: 541512
Theodor F. Huber, *(Mng Dir)*

ITZ Informationstechnologie GmbH (1)
Heinrich-Held-Strasse 16
45133 Essen, Germany
Tel.: (49) 201 24714 0
Fax: (49) 201 24714 30
E-Mail: info@itz-essen.de
Web Site: www.itz24.biz
Emp.: 111
Information Technology Consulting Services
S.I.C.: 7373
N.A.I.C.S.: 541512
Peter Heinrichs, *(Co-Mng Dir)*
Thomas Stachorra *(Co-Mng Dir)*

PP 2000 Business Integration AG (1)
Schwieberdinger Strasse 60
70435 Stuttgart, Germany
Tel.: (49) 711 820 56 0
Fax: (49) 711 820 56 199
E-Mail: info@pp2000.com
Web Site: www.pp2000.com
Information Technology Consulting Services
S.I.C.: 7373
N.A.I.C.S.: 541512
Klaus-Dieter Helmhagen, *(Mng Dir)*

PSB GmbH (1)
Daimlerstrasse 1
63303 Dreieich, Germany
Tel.: (49) 6103 8097 0
Fax: (49) 6103 8097 27
Information Technology Consulting Services
S.I.C.: 7373
N.A.I.C.S.: 541512

Redmond Integrators GmbH (1)
Lise-Meitner-Allee 10
44801 Bochum, Germany
Tel.: (49) 234 54182 00
Fax: (49) 234 54182 11
E-Mail: info@redmondintegrators.com
Web Site: www.redmondintegrators.com
Emp.: 10
Information Technology Consulting Services
S.I.C.: 7373
N.A.I.C.S.: 541512
Mirco Kappe, *(Mng Dir)*

SolidPro Informationssysteme GmbH (1)
Benzstr 15
89129 Langenau, Germany
Tel.: (49) 7345 9617 0
Fax: (49) 7345 9617 99
E-Mail: info@solidpro.de
Web Site: www.solidpro.de
Information Technology Consulting Services
S.I.C.: 7373
N.A.I.C.S.: 541512
Werner Meiser, *(Mng Dir)*

Non-U.S. Subsidiaries:

ARP Nederland B.V. (1)
Withuisveld 30
6226 NV Maastricht, Netherlands
Mailing Address:
Postbus 1241
6201 BE Maastricht, Netherlands
Tel.: (31) 43 604 99 98
Fax: (31) 43 604 99 61
E-Mail: verkoop.nl@arp.com
Web Site: www.arpnederland.nl
Information Technology Consulting Services
S.I.C.: 7373
N.A.I.C.S.: 541512
Koos Bunnik *(Mgr-Sls & Solutions)*

ARP SAS (1)
3 Avenue du Quebec
91951 Villebon-sur-Yvette, France
Tel.: (33) 1 60 92 30 90
Fax: (33) 1 60 92 30 99
Information Technology Consulting Services
S.I.C.: 7373
N.A.I.C.S.: 541512

ARP Schweiz AG (1)
Birkenstrasse 43b
6343 Rotkreuz, Switzerland
Tel.: (41) 41 79909 09
Fax: (41) 41 79909 99
E-Mail: verkauf@arp.com
Information Technology Consulting Services
S.I.C.: 7373
N.A.I.C.S.: 541512

Bechtle Brussels NV (1)
Avenue Louise 475
1050 Brussels, Belgium
Tel.: (32) 2 613 1632
Fax: (32) 2 613 1699
E-Mail: info.brussels@bechtle.com
Information Technology Consulting Services
S.I.C.: 7373
N.A.I.C.S.: 541512
Gerhard Marz, *(Co-Mng Dir)*
Gozard Polak *(Co-Mng Dir)*

Bechtle direct AG (1)
Route des Avouillons 30
1196 Gland, Switzerland
Tel.: (41) 848 810 410
Fax: (41) 848 810 411
E-Mail: info.direct@bechtle.ch
Web Site: www.bechtle-direct.ch
Information Technology Consulting Services
S.I.C.: 7373
N.A.I.C.S.: 541512
Thierry Knecht, *(Mng Dir)*

Bechtle direct B.V. (1)
Meerenakkerplein 18
5652 BJ Eindhoven, Netherlands
Tel.: (31) 40 250 9000
Fax: (31) 40 250 9099
E-Mail: direct@bechtle.nl
Web Site: www.bechtle.nl
Information Technology Consulting Services
S.I.C.: 7373
N.A.I.C.S.: 541512
Jean-Paul Bierens, *(Dir-Comml)*

Bechtle direct Kft. (1)
Varosmajor utca 35
1122 Budapest, Hungary
Tel.: (36) 1 88273 91
Fax: (36) 1 88273 90
E-Mail: sales@bechtle.hu
Web Site: www.bechtle.hu
Information Technology Consulting Services
S.I.C.: 7373
N.A.I.C.S.: 541512
Orban Barnabas *(Mng Dir)*

Bechtle direct Limited (1)
Unit 4 C Dundrum Business Park
DundrumDublin, Dublin, Ireland
Tel.: (353) 1 296 2984
Fax: (353) 1 215 7169
E-Mail: sales@bechtle.ie
Web Site: www.bechtle.ie
Information Technology Consulting Services
S.I.C.: 7373
N.A.I.C.S.: 541512
John Malone, *(Mng Dir)*

Bechtle direct Ltd. (1)
Turnpike House Methuen Park
Chippenham, Wiltshire, United Kingdom
Tel.: (44) 1249 467900
Fax: (44) 1249 467933
E-Mail: sales@bechtle.co.uk
Web Site: www.bechtle.co.uk
Information Technology Consulting Services
S.I.C.: 7373
N.A.I.C.S.: 541512
James Napp *(Mng Dir)*

Bechtle direct Polska Sp.z.oo. (1)
ul Krakowska 119
50-428 Wroclaw, Poland
Tel.: (48) 71 33726 44
Fax: (48) 71 33726 39
E-Mail: sales@bechtle.pl
Web Site: www.bechtle.pl
Information Technology Consulting Services
S.I.C.: 7373
N.A.I.C.S.: 541512
Karolina Romanczuk, *(Mng Dir)*

Bechtle direct Portugal Unipessoal Lda (1)
Avenida Dr Lourenco Peixinho 18 Edificio Delta 2 D
3800-164 Aveiro, Portugal
Tel.: (351) 234 100 640
Fax: (351) 234 100 648
E-Mail: sales@bechtle.pt
Web Site: www.bechtle.pt
Information Technology Consulting Services
S.I.C.: 7373
N.A.I.C.S.: 541512
Paulo Carta *(Mgr-Bus Dev)*

Bechtle direct SAS (1)
Le Xenium - CS 11028
67129 Molsheim, Cedex, France
Tel.: (33) 821 74 4545
Fax: (33) 821 74 1910
E-Mail: direct@bechtle.fr
Web Site: www.bechtle.fr
Information Technology Consulting Services
S.I.C.: 7373
N.A.I.C.S.: 541512

Bechtle direct S.L. (1)
Paseo Imperial 10-12 Planta 4 B
28005 Madrid, Spain
Tel.: (34) 902 18 16 14
Fax: (34) 91 366 74 45
E-Mail: bechtle@bechtle.es
Web Site: www.bechtle.es
Information Technology Consulting Services
S.I.C.: 7373
N.A.I.C.S.: 541512

Bechtle direct Srl-GmbH (1)
Via del Vigneto 35 Weinbergweg
Bozen, 39100 Bolzano, Italy
Tel.: (39) 0471 548 548
Fax: (39) 0471 548 520
E-Mail: direct@bechtle.it
Web Site: www.bechtle.it
Information Technology Consulting Services
S.I.C.: 7373
N.A.I.C.S.: 541512
Davide Mamma *(Mng Dir)*

Bechtle direct s.r.o. (1)
U Pergamenky 1522/2a
Holesovice, 17000 Prague, Czech Republic
Tel.: (420) 2 34602 500
Fax: (420) 2 34602 502
E-Mail: sales@bechtle.cz
Web Site: www.bechtle.cz
Information Technology Consulting Services
S.I.C.: 7373
N.A.I.C.S.: 541512
Petr Polak, *(Mng Dir)*

Bechtle GmbH (1)
Rautenweg 15
1220 Vienna, Austria
Tel.: (43) 5 7004 0
Fax: (43) 5 7004 6199
E-Mail: office.at@bechtle.com
Web Site: www.at.bechtle.com
Information Technology Consulting Services
S.I.C.: 7373
N.A.I.C.S.: 541512
Christian Moser *(Key Acct Mgr)*

Bechtle Printing Solutions AG (1)
Ringstrasse 15a
8600 Dubendorf, Switzerland
Tel.: (41) 44 956 66 99
Fax: (41) 44 956 66 98
E-Mail: printing@bechtle.ch
Information Technology Consulting Services
S.I.C.: 7373
N.A.I.C.S.: 541512
Daniel Schlumpf, *(Mng Dir)*

Bechtle Regensdorf AG (1)
Bahnstrasse 58/60
8105 Regensdorf, Switzerland
Tel.: (41) 43 388 72 00
Fax: (41) 43 388 72 01
Emp.: 60
Information Technology Consulting Services
S.I.C.: 7373
N.A.I.C.S.: 541512
Albert Muller, *(Mng Dir)*

Bechtle St. Gallen AG (1)
Gaiserwaldstrasse 6
9015 Saint Gallen, Switzerland
Tel.: (41) 71272 6262
Fax: (41) 71272 6226
E-Mail: stgallen@bechtle.ch
Information Technology Consulting Services
S.I.C.: 7373
N.A.I.C.S.: 541512
Valentino Osta, *(Mng Dir)*

Buyitdirect.com N.V. (1)
Kruisweg 661-665
2132 NC Hoofddorp, Netherlands
Tel.: (31) 23 567 08 14
Fax: (31) 23 567 08 15
E-Mail: sales@buyitdirect.com
Web Site: www.buyitdirect.com
Online Electronic Retailer
S.I.C.: 5961
N.A.I.C.S.: 454111

Coma Services AG (1)
Oberebenstrasse 45
5620 Bremgarten, Switzerland
Tel.: (41) 56 6488181
Fax: (41) 56 6488180
E-Mail: verkauf@coma-services.ch
Web Site: www.coma-services.ch
Emp.: 70
Information Technology Consulting Services
S.I.C.: 7373
N.A.I.C.S.: 541512
Peter Siegel, *(Mng Dir)*

Comsoft direct B.V (1)
Flamingoweg 36
1118 EE Schiphol, Netherlands
Tel.: (31) 20 2065390
Fax: (31) 20 2065391
E-Mail: info@comsoft.nl
Web Site: www.comsoft-direct.nl
Information Technology Consulting Services
S.I.C.: 7373
N.A.I.C.S.: 541512
Victor Tiller, *(Gen Mgr)*

Comsoft direct GmbH (1)
Triester Strasse 14
2355 Wiener Neudorf, Austria
Tel.: (43) 0205293 10
Fax: (43) 0205293 20
Web Site: www.comsoft-direct.at
Information Technology Consulting Services
S.I.C.: 7373
N.A.I.C.S.: 541512
Serkan Gunes, *(Acct Mgr)*

Comsoft direct NV (1)
Heerstraat 73
3910 Neerpelt, Belgium
Tel.: (32) 3 206 86 30
Fax: (32) 3 206 86 39
E-Mail: info@comsoft-direct.be
Web Site: www.comsoft-direct.be
Software Licensing & Asset Management Services
S.I.C.: 7379
N.A.I.C.S.: 541519
Juliaan Lauwereins, *(Acct Mgr)*

Comsoft direct S.L.U. (1)
Paseo Imperial 8
28005 Madrid, Spain
Tel.: (34) 913644327
Fax: (34) 913640831
E-Mail: info@comsoft-direct.es
Web Site: www.comsoft-direct.es
Information Technology Consulting Services
S.I.C.: 7373
N.A.I.C.S.: 541512

Comsoft direct S.r.l (1)
Corso Italia 1
20122 Milan, Italy
Tel.: (39) 0245476802
Fax: (39) 0298982266
E-Mail: info.licensing@comsoft-direct.it
Web Site: www.comsoft-direct.it
Information Technology Consulting Services
S.I.C.: 7373
N.A.I.C.S.: 541512
Laura Baratella *(Acct Mgr)*

Comsoft SOS Developers SAS (1)
120 Route des Macarons
BP 265
06905 Valbonne, Cedex, France
Tel.: (33) 825 07 06 07
Fax: (33) 825 07 06 08
E-Mail: infos@comsoft.fr
Web Site: www.comsoft-direct.fr
Information Technology Consulting Services
S.I.C.: 7373
N.A.I.C.S.: 541512
Alphonse Dupierre *(Mgr-Sls)*

Gate Informatic AG (1)
Route de la Pierre 22
1024 Ecublens, Switzerland
Tel.: (41) 21 695 21 21
Fax: (41) 21 695 21 30
Web Site: www.gate.ch
Information Technology Consulting Services
S.I.C.: 7373
N.A.I.C.S.: 541512
Michel Roethlisberger, *(CEO)*

Solid Solutions AG (1)
Hohlstrasse 534
8048 Zurich, Switzerland
Tel.: (41) 44 434 21 21
Fax: (41) 44 434 21 00
E-Mail: info@solidsolutions.ch
Web Site: www.solidsolutions.ch
Information Technology Consulting Services
S.I.C.: 7373
N.A.I.C.S.: 541512
Hans Peter Lampert, *(Mng Dir)*

THE BECKER MILK COMPANY LIMITED

393 Eglinton Avenue East 2nd Floor
Toronto, ON, M4P1M6, Canada
Tel.: (416) 606-2984
Year Founded: 1988
BEK.B—(TSX)
Rev.: $4,064,583
Assets: $34,952,246
Liabilities: $4,073,283
Net Worth: $30,878,963
Earnings: $985,860
Fiscal Year-end: 04/30/13

Business Description:
Real Estate Management Services
S.I.C.: 6531
N.A.I.C.S.: 531390

Personnel:
Robert Bazos *(Vice Chm)*
G. W. J. Pottow *(Pres & CEO)*
Brian Rattenbury *(CFO)*

Board of Directors:
Robert Bazos
Stephens Lowden
George S. Panos
G. W. J. Pottow
E. Duff Scott

Transfer Agent:
Canadian Stock Transfer Company
Toronto, ON, Canada

BECKONS INDUSTRIES LTD.

D-118 Phase - VII Industrial Area
Mohali, Chandigarh, 160055, India
Tel.: (91) 172 4379900
Fax: (91) 172 5091758
E-Mail: info@beckons.org
Web Site: www.beckons.org
531937—(BOM)
Sales Range: $1-9.9 Million

Business Description:
Computer Paper Mfr & Whslr
S.I.C.: 2678
N.A.I.C.S.: 322230

Personnel:
Gurmeet Singh *(Mng Dir)*

Board of Directors:
H. S. Anand
Amrit Pal Singh Malhotra
Chandra Prakash
Gurmeet Singh
I. S. Sukhija

Transfer Agent:
Skyline Financial Services Pvt. Ltd.
246 1st Floor Sant Nagar East of Kailash
New Delhi, India

BECO BERMULLER & CO. GMBH

Rotterdamer Strasse 7
90451 Nuremberg, Germany
Tel.: (49) 911642000
Fax: (49) 9116420090
E-Mail: info@beco-bermueller.de
Web Site: www.beco-bermueller.de
Year Founded: 1960
Rev.: $13,202,030
Emp.: 30

Business Description:
Construction Materials Supplier
S.I.C.: 5039
N.A.I.C.S.: 423390

Personnel:
Rudolf Bermuller *(Co-Mng Dir)*
Stefan Bermuller *(Co-Mng Dir)*

BECRYPT LIMITED

90 Long Acre
Covent Garden, London, WC2E 9RA, United Kingdom
Tel.: (44) 8458382050
Fax: (44) 845 838 2060
E-Mail: sales@becyrpt.com
Web Site: www.becrypt.com
Year Founded: 2001
Sales Range: $10-24.9 Million
Emp.: 75

Business Description:
Data Security & Protection Solutions
S.I.C.: 7372
N.A.I.C.S.: 511210

Personnel:
Steve Bellamy *(Chm)*
Bernard Parsons *(CEO)*
Gary Thomas *(COO)*
Marc Hocking *(CTO)*
Nigel Lee *(Chief Res Officer)*

Board of Directors:
Steve Bellamy
Marc Hocking
Nigel Lee
Bernard Parsons
Gary Thomas

BEDFORD CAPITAL LTD.

130 Adelaide Street West Suite 2900
Toronto, ON, M5H 3P5, Canada
Tel.: (416) 947-1492
Fax: (416) 947-9673
Web Site: www.bedfordcapital.ca
Year Founded: 1982

Business Description:
Private Investment Firm
S.I.C.: 6211
N.A.I.C.S.: 523999

Personnel:
David Hass *(Partner)*
Tim Bowman *(Mng Dir)*
Elliott Knox *(Mng Dir)*
Sheila Murray-Tateishi *(CFO & Sr VP)*

BEDFORD FURNITURE INDUSTRIES, INC.

3035 Weston Road North York
Toronto, ON, M9M 2T1, Canada
Tel.: (416) 746-4111
Fax: (416) 746-6804
Year Founded: 1960
Rev.: $28,952,668
Emp.: 200

Business Description:
Sleeping Mattresses Mfr & Distr
S.I.C.: 2515
N.A.I.C.S.: 337910

Personnel:
Allan Erlick *(Pres)*

BEDMUTHA INDUSTRIES LIMITED

A-32 STICE Sinnar
Nasik, Maharashtra, 422 103, India
Tel.: (91) 2551 240481
Fax: (91) 2551 240482
Web Site: www.bedmutha.com
BEDMUTHA—(BOM NSE)
Sales Range: $25-49.9 Million
Emp.: 210

Business Description:
Steel Products Mfr & Distr
S.I.C.: 3312
N.A.I.C.S.: 331110

Personnel:
Kachardas R. Bedmutha *(Chm)*
Ajay K. Vedmutha *(Mng Dir)*
Vijay K. Vedmutha *(Mng Dir)*
Aditi Gajanan Bhavsar *(Sec)*

Board of Directors:
Kachardas R. Bedmutha
A. Balasubramanian
Narayan Marotrao Kadu
Shital Nahar
Ajay K. Vedmutha
Vijay K. Vedmutha

B.E.E. TEAM S.P.A.

Via dell'Esperanto 71
00144 Rome, Italy
Tel.: (39) 0654248624
Fax: (39) 0698230404
E-Mail: info@beeteam.it
Web Site: www.beeteam.it
Year Founded: 1987
BET—(ITA)
Sales Range: $75-99.9 Million
Emp.: 1,000

Business Description:
Global Outsourcing Solutions & Outsourcing of Back-Office Administration & Management
S.I.C.: 7389
N.A.I.C.S.: 561499

Personnel:
Rocco Sabelli *(Chm & Pres)*
Adriano Seymandi *(Mng Dir)*

Board of Directors:
Rocco Sabelli
Luciano Acciari
Claudio Barretti
Andrea Faragalli
Enzo Mei
Guiseppe Sammartino
Adriano Seymandi

BEECHCROFT DEVELOPMENTS LTD.

1 Church Ln
Wallingford, Oxon, OX10 0DX, United Kingdom
Tel.: (44) 1491834975
Fax: (44) 1491825433
E-Mail: info@beechcroft.co.uk
Web Site: www.beachcroft.co.uk
Emp.: 25

Business Description:
Retirement Homes
S.I.C.: 8322
N.A.I.C.S.: 624229

Personnel:
Christopher R. Thompson *(Mng Dir)*

BEEHIVE COILS LTD

Studlands Park Avenue
Newmarket, Suffolk, CB8 7AU, United Kingdom
Tel.: (44) 1638664134
Fax: (44) 1638561542
E-Mail: info@beehivecoils.co.uk
Web Site: www.beehivecoils.co.uk
Year Founded: 1968
Rev.: $18,251,677
Emp.: 87

Business Description:
Coil Mfr
S.I.C.: 3675
N.A.I.C.S.: 334416

Personnel:
Frederick J. Bartram *(Founder & Chm)*

BEFAR GROUP CO., LTD.

560 Yellow River 5th Road
Binzhou, 256619, China
Tel.: (86) 543 2118000
Fax: (86) 543 2118888
E-Mail: befar@befar.com
Web Site: www.befar.com.cn
601678—(SHG)
Sales Range: $200-249.9 Million
Emp.: 2,600

Business Description:
Chemical Products Mfr & Distr
S.I.C.: 2899
N.A.I.C.S.: 325998

Personnel:
Zhongzheng Zhang *(Chm)*

BEFIMMO SCA

Parc Goemaere Chaussee de Wavre 1945
B-1160 Brussels, Belgium
Tel.: (32) 26793860
Fax: (32) 26793866
E-Mail: contact@befimmo.be
Web Site: www.befimmo.be

Befimmo SCA—(Continued)

BEFB—(EUR)
Rev.: $174,077,281
Assets: $2,729,020,440
Liabilities: $1,385,221,046
Net Worth: $1,343,799,395
Earnings: $14,051,322
Emp.: 48
Fiscal Year-end: 12/31/12

Business Description:
Property Asset Management Services
S.I.C.: 6531
N.A.I.C.S.: 531390

Personnel:
Benoit De Blieck *(CEO & Mng Dir)*
Laurent Carlier *(CFO)*
Martine Rorif *(COO)*
Cdric Biquet *(Chief Investment Officer)*
Rikkert Leeman *(CTO)*
Marc Geens *(Chief Comml Officer)*
Caroline Kerremans *(IR Comm Officer)*
Caroline Maddens *(Legal Officer)*
Aminata Kake *(Gen Counsel & Sec)*

Board of Directors:
Alain Devos
Benoit De Blieck
Hugues Delpire
Etienne Dewulf
Benoit Godts
Jacques Rousseaux
Andre Sougne
Marcus Van Heddeghem

Subsidiary:

Fedimmo S.A. **(1)**
1945 Chaussee de Wavre
Waversesteenweg
Brussels, 1160, Belgium
Tel.: (32) 26793860
Fax: (32) 26793866
E-Mail: info@befimmo.be
Web Site: www.fedimmo.com
Emp.: 15
Real Estate Agencies
S.I.C.: 6531
N.A.I.C.S.: 531210
Benoit Deblieck *(Mgr)*

BEFUT INTERNATIONAL CO., LTD.

27th Floor Liangjiu International Tower
5 Heyi Street Xigang District, Dalian, Liaoning, 116011, China
Tel.: (86) 411 83678755
Fax: (86) 411 83670955
E-Mail: befut@126.com
Web Site: www.befut.com
BFTID—(OTC)
Sales Range: $50-74.9 Million
Emp.: 291

Business Description:
Cable & Wire Mfr & Distr
S.I.C.: 3357
N.A.I.C.S.: 335921

Personnel:
Hongbo Cao *(Chm, Pres & CEO)*
Mei Yu *(CFO & Treas)*
Haiyang Lu *(Sec)*

Board of Directors:
Hongbo Cao
Mei Yu

Legal Counsel:
Pryor Cashman LLP
7 Times Sq
New York, NY 10036
Tel.: (212) 421-4100

Transfer Agent:
Corporate Stock Transfer, Inc.
3200 Cherry Creek Dr S Ste 430
Denver, CO 80209
Tel.: (303) 282-4800
Fax: (303) 282-5800

BEGA CHEESE LTD.

23-45 Ridge Street
Bega, NSW, 2550, Australia
Mailing Address:
PO Box 123
Bega, NSW, 2550, Australia
Tel.: (61) 264917777
Fax: (61) 264917700
E-Mail: bega.admin@begacheese.com.au
Web Site: www.begacheese.com.au
BGA—(ASX)
Rev.: $1,052,610,621
Assets: $574,688,971
Liabilities: $301,708,792
Net Worth: $272,980,179
Earnings: $26,516,235
Emp.: 1,629
Fiscal Year-end: 06/30/13

Business Description:
Cheese Mfr
S.I.C.: 2022
N.A.I.C.S.: 311513

Personnel:
Barry Irvin *(Chm)*
Aidan Coleman *(CEO)*
Colin Griffin *(CFO & Co-Sec)*
Brett Kelly *(Co-Sec)*

Board of Directors:
Barry Irvin
Rick Cross
Joy Linton
Peter Margin
Jeff Odgers
Richard Parbery
Richard Platts
Max Roberts

Legal Counsel:
Addisons
Level 12, 60 Carrington Street
Sydney, Australia

Subsidiary:

Tatura Milk Industries Limited **(1)**
236 Hogan St
Tatura, VIC, 3616, Australia AU
Tel.: (61) 613582462 (70%)
E-Mail: admin@tatmilk.com.au
Web Site: www.tatmilk.com.au
Emp.: 361
Dairy Product Mfr
S.I.C.: 2021
N.A.I.C.S.: 311512
Barry Irvin *(Chm)*
Ian E. Bertram *(Deputy Chm)*
Paul van Heerwaarden *(CFO)*

Joint Venture:

Capitol Chilled Foods (Australia) Pty. Limited **(1)**
2 8 Mildura St
Griffith, ACT, 2603, Australia
Tel.: (61) 262609111
Fax: (61) 262952873
E-Mail: enquiries@ccfa.com.au
Web Site: www.ccfa.com.au
Emp.: 80
Dairy Product Whslr; Joint Venture of Australian Co-Operative Foods Limited & Bega Cheese Ltd.
S.I.C.: 5143
N.A.I.C.S.: 424430
Garry Sykes *(Mng Dir)*

BEGA ELECTROMOTOR SA

Republicii Bv no 21
Timisoara, Timis, 300159, Romania
Tel.: (40) 256 492004
Fax: (40) 256 492003
E-Mail: emt@electromotor.ro
Web Site: www.electromotor.ro
Year Founded: 1900
ELTR—(BUC)
Rev.: $2,840,637
Assets: $5,862,731
Liabilities: $2,257,258
Net Worth: $3,605,473
Earnings: ($45,350)
Emp.: 100
Fiscal Year-end: 12/31/12

Business Description:
Electric Motor Mfr
S.I.C.: 3594
N.A.I.C.S.: 333996

Personnel:
Valeriu Riscuta *(Pres & Gen Mgr)*

BEGA TURISM SA TIMISOARA

Str Marasesti nr 1-3
300086 Timisoara, Timis, Romania
Tel.: (40) 256 498 852
Fax: (40) 256 499 450
E-Mail: office@hoteltimisoara.ro
Web Site: www.hoteltimisoara.ro
SCDE—(BUC)
Sales Range: $1-9.9 Million
Emp.: 115

Business Description:
Hotel & Motel Services
S.I.C.: 7011
N.A.I.C.S.: 721110

Personnel:
Aurelian Nicolae Bibu *(Pres)*

Board of Directors:
Aurelian Nicolae Bibu
Ioan Stefan Szatmari

BEGBIES TRAYNOR GROUP PLC

340 Deansgate
Manchester, M3 4LY, United Kingdom
Tel.: (44) 1618371700
Fax: (44) 1618371701
E-Mail: enquiries@begbies-traynorgroup.com
Web Site: www.begbies-traynorgroup.com
BEG—(LSE)
Rev.: $80,689,085
Assets: $154,448,245
Liabilities: $63,331,108
Net Worth: $91,117,137
Earnings: $2,239,433
Emp.: 532
Fiscal Year-end: 04/30/13

Business Description:
Holding Company; Corporate Finance, Investigation, Forensic Accounting & Security Risk Consulting Services
S.I.C.: 6719
N.A.I.C.S.: 551112

Personnel:
Ric W. Traynor *(Chm)*
John A. Humphrey *(Sec)*

Board of Directors:
Ric W. Traynor
Mark R. Fry
John M. May
R. Graham McInnes
E. Nick Taylor

Legal Counsel:
Brabners LLP
55 King Street
Manchester, M2 4LQ, United Kingdom

Subsidiaries:

BTG Intelligence Limited **(1)**
340 Deansgate
Manchester, Lancashire, M3 4LY, United Kingdom
Tel.: (44) 8456782905
Fax: (44) 16118371701
E-Mail: manchester@begbies-traynor.com
Web Site: www.begbies-traynorgroup.com
Emp.: 5
Financial Investigation & Advisory Services
S.I.C.: 6211
N.A.I.C.S.: 523999
Darren Shelmerdine *(Reg Dir)*

BEGHELLI S.P.A.

(d/b/a Gruppo Beghelli)
Via Mozzeghine 13 15
Monteveglio, 40050 Bologna, Italy
Tel.: (39) 0519660411
Fax: (39) 0519660444
E-Mail: assarei.jenerali@beghelli.it
Web Site: www.beghelli.it
BE—(ITA)
Sales Range: $150-199.9 Million
Emp.: 1,908

Business Description:
Home Security Systems, Lamps & Other Various Lighting Systems Mfr
S.I.C.: 7382
N.A.I.C.S.: 561621

Personnel:
Gian Pietro Beghelli *(Chm & CEO)*
Graziano Beghelli *(Mng Dir)*
Luca Beghelli *(Mng Dir)*

Subsidiaries:

Becar Srl **(1)**
1 Via Della Pace
40050 Bologna, Bologna, Italy
Tel.: (39) 0516702242
Fax: (39) 0516702186
Other Electronic Component Mfr
S.I.C.: 3679
N.A.I.C.S.: 334419

Elettronica Cimone Srl **(1)**
1 Via Comunale Per Casoni
41027 Pievepelago, Modena, Italy (100%)
Tel.: (39) 53671108
Fax: (39) 53772712
E-Mail: monica.sgarbi@beghelli.it
Emp.: 150
Electric Lamp Bulb & Part Mfr
S.I.C.: 3641
N.A.I.C.S.: 335110
Achille Minghelli *(CEO)*

U.S. Subsidiary:

Beghelli Inc. **(1)**
3250 Corporateway
Miramar, FL 33025 (90%)
Tel.: (954) 442-6600
Fax: (954) 442-6677
E-Mail: beghelli@beghelliusa.com
Web Site: www.beghelliusa.com
Emp.: 50
All Other Miscellaneous Electrical Equipment & Component Mfr
S.I.C.: 3699
N.A.I.C.S.: 335999
Dania Laspada *(CEO)*
Derek Schimming *(Mng Dir)*

Non-U.S. Subsidiaries:

Beghelli Asia Pacific Ltd. **(1)**
2605 S Twr Concordia Plz Museum Rd
Kowloon, China (Hong Kong) (60%)
Tel.: (852) 26205522
Fax: (852) 26206677
E-Mail: ssku@beghelliasia.com
Web Site: www.beghelliasia.com
Emp.: 10
Other Electronic Parts & Equipment Whslr
S.I.C.: 5065
N.A.I.C.S.: 423690
Spes Stanley Wai-Nam Ku *(Gen Mgr)*

Beghelli Canada Inc. **(1)**
3900 14th Ave
Markham, ON, L3R AR3, Canada (75%)
Tel.: (905) 948-9500
Fax: (905) 948-8673
Toll Free: (877) 358-9638
E-Mail: bruno.ardito@beghellicanada.com
Web Site: www.beghellicanada.com
Emp.: 100
Electric Lamp Bulb & Part Mfr
S.I.C.: 3641
N.A.I.C.S.: 335110
Bruno Ardito *(Gen Mgr)*

Beghelli Elplast A.S. **(1)**
Porici 3a
60316 Brno, Czech Republic (92.19%)
Tel.: (420) 531014111
Fax: (420) 531014210
E-Mail: beghelli@beghelli.cz
Web Site: www.beghelli.cz
Commercial Industrial & Institutional Electric Lighting Fixture Mfr

S.I.C.: 3646
N.A.I.C.S.: 335122
Ugo Rainone *(CEO)*

BEGLES DISTRIBUTION SA

4 Rue Maurice Martin
33130 Begles, Gironde, France
Tel.: (33) 556851055
Fax: (33) 0556493901
E-Mail: christoper-baisois@scaso.fr
Sls.: $18,600,000
Emp.: 15
S.I.C.: 5411
N.A.I.C.S.: 445110
Personnel:
Francois Mortel *(Pres)*

BEHAVIOR TECH COMPUTER CORPORATION

20F-B 98 Sec 1 Sintai 5th Road
Oriental Technopolises Bldg
Taipei, 221, Taiwan
Tel.: (886) 226961888
Fax: (886) 226961899
E-Mail: sales@btc.com.tw
Web Site: www.btc.com.tw
Year Founded: 1982
Sales Range: $50-74.9 Million
Emp.: 300
Business Description:
Computer Keyboards, CD-Rom Drives & Sound Cards Mfr
S.I.C.: 3577
N.A.I.C.S.: 334118
Personnel:
Kegang Su *(Chm & CEO)*

U.S. Subsidiary:

Behavior Tech Computer (US) Corporation (1)
412 Emerson St
Fremont, CA 94539-5224
Tel.: (510) 657-3956
Fax: (510) 657-3965
E-Mail: sales@btcusa.com
Web Site: www.btcusa.com
Emp.: 20
Mfr. & Sales of Personal Computer Peripherals, Keyboards, Optical Devices & Sound Cards
Export
S.I.C.: 5045
N.A.I.C.S.: 423430

Non-U.S. Subsidiaries:

Behavior Tech Computer Corporation (1)
10 Rue Marcel Sallnave
94200 Ivry-sur-Seine, France (100%)
Tel.: (33) 241438757
Fax: (33) 146701897
E-Mail: ti.testi@btceurope.com
Sales Range: $75-99.9 Million
Emp.: 12
S.I.C.: 3575
N.A.I.C.S.: 334118
Tiziana Testi *(Country Mgr)*

BEHN MEYER (D) HOLDING AG & CO.

Ballindamm 1
20095 Hamburg, Germany
Tel.: (49) 40302990
Fax: (49) 4030299319
E-Mail: contact@behnmeyer.de
Web Site: www.behnmeyer.com
Year Founded: 1857
Emp.: 800
Business Description:
Holding Company; Manufacturer of Specialty Chemicals
S.I.C.: 6719
N.A.I.C.S.: 551112
Personnel:
Jens Kellinghusen *(Mng Dir)*
Board of Directors:
Prasonk Aramwittaya
Jens Kellinghusen
Hoh Sooi Kim
Torsten Lindhauer
Oliver Meyer
Peter-Joachim Schoenberg
Khoo Su Chin

Non-U.S. Subsidiary:

Behn Meyer Group Singapore (1)
2 Boon Leat Terrace #06-01 Harbour Side Industrial Bldg 2
Singapore, 119844, Singapore SG
Tel.: (65) 6511 6666 (100%)
Telex: bmeyer rs21390
Fax: (65) 6511 6617
Web Site: www.behnmeyer.com
Chemicals Distr
S.I.C.: 5169
N.A.I.C.S.: 424690
A. M. Todd *(Principal-SEA Region)*

BEHR GMBH & CO. KG

Mauserstrasse 3
70469 Stuttgart, Germany
Tel.: (49) 7118962057
Fax: (49) 71189022057
E-Mail: info@behrgroup.com
Web Site: www.behrgroup.com
Year Founded: 1905
Sls.: $5,018,387,143
Assets: $2,590,973,399
Liabilities: $1,941,177,140
Net Worth: $649,796,259
Earnings: ($65,962,330)
Emp.: 17,285
Fiscal Year-end: 12/31/12
Business Description:
Air Conditioning & Engine Cooling Products Mfr
S.I.C.: 3585
N.A.I.C.S.: 333415
Personnel:
Horst Geidel *(Chm-Supervisory Bd)*
Heinz K. Junker *(Deputy Chm-Supervisory Bd)*
Peter Grunow *(CEO & Member-Mgmt Bd)*
Michael Frick *(CFO & Member-Mgmt Bd)*
Colin Carter *(Member-Mgmt Bd)*
Klemens Schmiederer *(Member-Mgmt Bd-Production, Dev & QM)*
Jorg Stratmann *(Member-Mgmt Bd-Sls & Customer Centers)*
Supervisory Board of Directors:
Horst Geidel
Wolfgang Elkart
Heinz K. Junker
Armin Schuler
Martin H. Sorg
Bernhard Volkmann

Subsidiaries:

Behr Gmbh & Co. (1)
Lienzinger Strasse 82
D 75417 Muhlacker, Germany (100%)
Tel.: (49) 70419800
Fax: (49) 70419801520
E-Mail: info@behrgroup.com
Emp.: 1,200
Mfr. of Air Conditioning & Engine Cooling Products
S.I.C.: 3585
N.A.I.C.S.: 333415

Behr GmbH & Co. (1)
Eutinger Strasse 158
75175 Pforzheim, Germany (100%)
Tel.: (49) 723158070
Fax: (49) 58051725
E-Mail: gonuel.goeetuelja@notes.behrgroup.com
Web Site: www.behrgroup.com
Emp.: 200
Mfr. of Air Conditioning & Engine Cooling Products
S.I.C.: 3585
N.A.I.C.S.: 333415
Daniel Bentele *(Mng Dir)*

Behr GmbH & Co. (1)
Stuttgarter Str 105
71665 Vaihingen, Germany (100%)
Tel.: (49) 70421060
Fax: (49) 70421061850
E-Mail: info@behrgroup.com
Web Site: www.behrgroup.com
Emp.: 260
Mfr. of Air Conditioning & Engine Cooling Products
S.I.C.: 3585
N.A.I.C.S.: 333415
Hoaehim Wolf *(Plant Mgr)*

Behr GmbH & Co. (1)
Raffineriestrasse 99
D 93333 Neustadt, Germany (100%)
Tel.: (49) 94459680
Fax: (49) 7118964000
E-Mail: info@behrgroup.com
Web Site: www.behrgroup.com
Emp.: 500
Mfr. of Air Conditioning & Engine Cooling Products
S.I.C.: 3585
N.A.I.C.S.: 333415
Rudolf Vutzlhofer *(Mng Dir)*

Behr Industrietechnik Gmbh & Co KG (1)
Heilbronner Strasse 380
D 70469 Stuttgart, Germany (100%)
Tel.: (49) 7118960
Fax: (49) 711818195
E-Mail: info@behrgroup.com
Emp.: 600
Mfr. of Air Conditioning & Engine Cooling Products
S.I.C.: 3585
N.A.I.C.S.: 333415

Behr Kirchberg GmbH (1)
Bahnofstrasse 26
D 08107 Kirchheim, Saxonea, Germany (100%)
Tel.: (49) 37602680
Fax: (49) 3760268211
E-Mail: info@behrgroup.com
Web Site: www.behrgroup.com
Emp.: 300
Mfr. of Air Conditioning & Engine Cooling Products
S.I.C.: 3585
N.A.I.C.S.: 333415
Clause Woessner *(Gen Mgr)*

Behr Service GmbH (1)
Dr Manfred Behr Str 1
74523 Schwabisch Hall, Germany (100%)
Tel.: (49) 79078750
Fax: (49) 9079463779
E-Mail: info@behrgroup.com
Web Site: www.behrgroup.com
Emp.: 140
Mfr. of Air Conditioning & Engine Cooling Products
S.I.C.: 3585
N.A.I.C.S.: 333415
Juergen Laucher *(Mng Dir)*

Behr Thermot Tronik GmbH & Co. (1)
Enzstrasse 25 35
D 70806 Kornwestheim, Germany (100%)
Tel.: (49) 71541330
Fax: (49) 7154133224
E-Mail: info@behrgroup.com
Web Site: www.behrgroup.com
Sls.: $957,396,992
Emp.: 370
Mfr. of Air Conditioning & Engine Cooling Products
S.I.C.: 3585
N.A.I.C.S.: 333415
Markus Flik *(CEO)*

U.S. Subsidiary:

Behr America, Inc. (1)
2700 Daley Dr
Troy, MI 48083
Tel.: (248) 743-3700
Fax: (248) 743-3701
Web Site: www.behrgroup.com
Emp.: 260
Mfr. of Air Conditioning & Engine Cooling Products
S.I.C.: 3714
N.A.I.C.S.: 336390
Markus Flik *(Chm)*
Wilm Uhlenbecker *(Pres & CEO)*

Subsidiaries:

Behr Climate Systems, Inc. (2)
5020 Augusta Dr
Fort Worth, TX 76106
Tel.: (817) 624-7273
Fax: (817) 624-3328
Web Site: www.behrgroup.com
Mfr. of Automobile Climate Control Systems
S.I.C.: 3714
N.A.I.C.S.: 336390

Behr Dayton Thermal Products Div. (2)
1600 Webster St
Dayton, OH 45404-1144
Tel.: (937) 369-2000
Fax: (937) 224-2915
Web Site: www.behrgroup.com
Emp.: 1,200
Automotive Heaters & Air Conditioning Units, Air Conditioning Compressors, Radiators, Heat Exchangers, Oil Coolers & Condensers Mfr
S.I.C.: 3519
N.A.I.C.S.: 333618

Behr Heat Transfer Systems, Inc. (2)
4500 Leeds Ave
Charleston, SC 29405
Tel.: (843) 745-1233
Fax: (843) 745-1285
Mfr. of Air Conditioning & Engine Cooling Products
S.I.C.: 3714
N.A.I.C.S.: 336390
James Wojdyla *(Mgr-Process Plng)*

Non-U.S. Subsidiaries:

Behr France S.A.R.L. (1)
5 Ave De La Gare BP 49
F 68250 Rouffach, France (100%)
Tel.: (33) 389735800
Fax: (33) 389497418
E-Mail: info@bihrjrout.com
Web Site: www.bihrjrout.com
Emp.: 1,400
Mfr. of Air Conditioning & Engine Cooling Products
S.I.C.: 3585
N.A.I.C.S.: 333415
Henry Baunert *(Pres)*

Behr Japan K.K. (1)
1-22-1 Gotonda an Building 2 Fl
Tokyo, 141 0022, Japan (100%)
Tel.: (81) 354477388
Fax: (81) 354477390
E-Mail: japan.contact@behrgroup.co.jp
Web Site: www.behrgroup.com
Emp.: 40
Mfr. of Air Conditioning & Engine Cooling Products
S.I.C.: 3585
N.A.I.C.S.: 333415

Behr Lorraine S.A.R.L. (1)
Zone Europole De Sarreguemines
F 57912 Hambach, France (100%)
Tel.: (33) 387283400
Fax: (33) 387283401
Web Site: www.behrgroup.com
Rev.: $2,189,164
Emp.: 450
Mfr. of Air Conditioning & Engine Cooling Products
S.I.C.: 3585
N.A.I.C.S.: 333415
Jopp Pierre *(Gen Mgr)*

Frape Behr S.A. (1)
Poligono Industrial Zona Franca
Sector C Calle D 33 35, E 08040
Barcelona, Spain (100%)
Tel.: (34) 932617800
Fax: (34) 932630995
E-Mail: gisela.garcia@frape.behrgroup.com
Web Site: www.behr.com
Emp.: 1,632
Mfr. of Air Conditioning & Engine Cooling Products
S.I.C.: 3585
N.A.I.C.S.: 333415
Derik Heers *(Mng Dir)*

BEHRINGER GMBH

Industriestrasse 23
74912 Heilbronn, Germany
Tel.: (49) 72662070
Fax: (49) 7266207500
E-Mail: info@behringer.net
Web Site: www.behringer.net
Year Founded: 1919
Rev.: $51,036,310
Emp.: 383
Business Description:
Bandsaw Machines Mfr
S.I.C.: 3553
N.A.I.C.S.: 333243
Personnel:
Christian Behringer *(Co-Mng Dir)*
Rolf Behringer *(Co-Mng Dir)*

BEHSHAHR INDUSTRIAL DEVELOPMENT CORP.

No 8 24th Street Ghaem Magham Avenue
Hafte Tir Square, Tehran, Iran
Tel.: (98) 21 8830 4584
Fax: (98) 21 8830 4588
E-Mail: info@bidc.ir
Web Site: www.bidc.ir/en
TSBE1—(THE)
Sls.: $1,633,434,240
Assets: $1,494,490,000
Liabilities: $952,186,000
Net Worth: $542,304,000
Earnings: $149,266,000
Fiscal Year-end: 12/29/12
Business Description:
Investment Services
S.I.C.: 6282
N.A.I.C.S.: 523920
Personnel:
Mahmoodreza Khavari *(Chm)*
Irandokht Attarian *(Vice Chm)*
M. Dadash *(Mng Dir)*
Board of Directors:
Mahmoodreza Khavari
Irandokht Attarian
M. Dadash
R. Esmaeili Dana
G. H. Delshadi
I. Nadimi
M. Sami

Subsidiaries:

Behpak Industrial Company Limited **(1)**
1st Floor Behshahr Group No 28/1 Crossing 7th Street
Ahmad Ghasir Avenue, Tehran, 1513736611, Iran
Tel.: (98) 2188706429
Fax: (98) 2188722122
E-Mail: info@behpak.com
Web Site: www.behpak.com
Oil Extraction Services
S.I.C.: 2092
N.A.I.C.S.: 311710

Paxan Yeravan Co. **(1)**
8th Km Fath Highway
Tehran, Iran
Tel.: (98) 2164562395
Fax: (98) 662670676
E-Mail: info@bidcim.com
Web Site: www.paxando.com
Toiletries Products Mfr & Distr
S.I.C.: 2844
N.A.I.C.S.: 325620

BEIJER ALMA AB

Dragarbrunnsgatan 45
Forumgallerian
PO Box 1747
75147 Uppsala, Sweden
Tel.: (46) 18157160
Fax: (46) 18158987
E-Mail: info@beijer-alma.se
Web Site: www.beijer-alma.se
BEIA—(OMX)
Rev.: $430,302,204
Assets: $370,703,275
Liabilities: $135,080,647
Net Worth: $235,622,628
Earnings: $41,563,800
Emp.: 1,831
Fiscal Year-end: 12/31/12
Business Description:
Industrial Product & Component Producer
S.I.C.: 3559
N.A.I.C.S.: 333249
Personnel:
Anders Wall *(Chm)*
Johan Wall *(Deputy Chm)*
Bertil Persson *(Pres & CEO)*
Jan Blomen *(CFO)*
Board of Directors:
Anders Wall
Carina Andersson
Marianne Brismar
Anders G. Carlberg
Peter Nilsson
Bertil Persson
Anders Ullberg
Johan Wall

Subsidiaries:

AB Tebeco **(1)**
Box 40
301 02 Halmstad, Sweden
Tel.: (46) 35 15 32 00
Fax: (46) 35 15 32 29
E-Mail: info@tebeco.se
Core Adhesive Mfr
S.I.C.: 2891
N.A.I.C.S.: 325520

Alma Uppsala AB **(1)**
PO Box 1747
75147 Uppsala, Sweden
Tel.: (46) 18157160
Industrial Spring Mfr
S.I.C.: 3493
N.A.I.C.S.: 332613
Jan Blomen *(Gen Mgr)*

Beijer Industri AB **(1)**
Jagershillgatan 16
213 75 Malmo, Sweden
Tel.: (46) 40 358300
Fax: (46) 40 930650
E-Mail: info@beijerind.se
Web Site: www.beijerind.com
Emp.: 35
Industrial Machinery Distr
S.I.C.: 5084
N.A.I.C.S.: 423830
Bengt Hammarlund *(Mgr-Support, Logistics, Quality & Environment)*

Beijer Tech AB **(1)**
Jagershillgatan 16
211 34 Malmo, Sweden
Tel.: (46) 40 358380
E-Mail: info@beijertech.se
Web Site: www.beijertech.com
Industrial Rubber Products Mfr
S.I.C.: 3069
N.A.I.C.S.: 326299
Peter Kollert *(Mng Dir)*

Habia Cable AB **(1)**
Kanalvagen 18
Upplands Vasby, Sweden
Tel.: (46) 86307440
Fax: (46) 86307481
Web Site: www.habia.com
Emp.: 100
Other Holding Companies Offices of Holding Companies
S.I.C.: 6719
N.A.I.C.S.: 551112
Carl Modigh *(Pres)*
Johan Vinberg *(Mng Dir)*

Subsidiaries:

Habia Cable CS Technology AB **(2)**
Dalenum 27
SE-181 70 Lidingo, Sweden
Tel.: (46) 854481340
Fax: (46) 854481349
E-Mail: info@habia.com
Web Site: www.habia.com
Emp.: 7
Fiber Optic Cable Mfr
S.I.C.: 3357
N.A.I.C.S.: 335921
Adfam Morrison *(Gen Mgr)*

Habia Cable Nordic AB **(2)**
Element Vagen 8
81504 Soderfors, Sweden (100%)
Tel.: (46) 86307480
Fax: (46) 29322097
E-Mail: info.se@habia.com
Web Site: www.habia.com
Emp.: 15
Fiber Optic Cable Mfr
S.I.C.: 3357
N.A.I.C.S.: 335921
Henrik Ollandt *(VP)*

Habia Cable Production AB **(2)**
Box 8
S-81504 Soderfors, Sweden (100%)
Tel.: (46) 29322000
Fax: (46) 29330751
E-Mail: info.se@habia.com
Web Site: www.habia.com
Emp.: 200
Fiber Optic Cable Mfr
S.I.C.: 3357
N.A.I.C.S.: 335921
Henrik Ollandt *(VP-Radio Frequency & Comm)*

Non-U.S. Subsidiaries:

Habia Benelux BV **(2)**
Voorerf 33
4824 Breda, Netherlands (100%)
Tel.: (31) 765416400
Fax: (31) 765418289
E-Mail: info.nl@habia.com
Web Site: www.habia.com
Emp.: 7
Electrical Apparatus & Equipment Wiring Supplies & Construction Material Whslr
S.I.C.: 5063
N.A.I.C.S.: 423610
John Scheepens *(Mng Dir)*

Habia Cable AB **(2)**
Jukolansuora 3 C5
FI-043 40 Tuusula, Finland
Tel.: (358) 201552530
Fax: (358) 201552539
Fiber Optic Cable Mfr
S.I.C.: 3357
N.A.I.C.S.: 335921

Habia Cable Asia Ltd **(2)**
Flat 1109 11th Floor Fast Industrial Building
658 Castle Peak Rd Lai Chi Kok, Kowloon, China (Hong Kong) (100%)
Tel.: (852) 25911375
Fax: (852) 28380229
E-Mail: info.hk@habia.com
Web Site: www.habia.com
Emp.: 4
Fiber Optic Cable Mfr
S.I.C.: 3357
N.A.I.C.S.: 335921
Albin Arexis *(Mng Dir)*

Habia Cable China Ltd **(2)**
No 16 Changjiang Middle Road
213022 Changzhou, Jiangsu, China (100%)
Tel.: (86) 51985118010
Fax: (86) 5195102998
E-Mail: info.cn@habia.com
Web Site: www.habia.com
Emp.: 70
Fiber Optic Cable Mfr
S.I.C.: 5063
N.A.I.C.S.: 423610

Habia Cable India Ltd **(2)**
1st Fl RV Rd 1/1 Sai Towers
560 004 Bengaluru, India
Tel.: (91) 8041204207
Fax: (91) 8041214707
E-Mail:
Web Site: www.habia.com
Emp.: 1
Fiber Optic Cable Mfr
S.I.C.: 3357
N.A.I.C.S.: 335921
Nagaraj Aithal *(Country Mgr)*

Habia Cable Ltd **(2)**
Short Way Thornbury
Bristol, United Kingdom (100%)
Tel.: (44) 1454412522
Fax: (44) 1454416121
E-Mail: info.uk@habia.com
Web Site: www.habia.com
Emp.: 10
Electrical Apparatus & Equipment Wiring Supplies & Construction Material Whslr
S.I.C.: 5063
N.A.I.C.S.: 423610

Habia Cable SA **(2)**
13 Rue Bernard Palissy
45800 Saint Jean de Braye, France (100%)
Tel.: (33) 238221570
Fax: (33) 238221579
E-Mail: info.fr@habia.se
Web Site: www.habia.com
Emp.: 5
Structural Steel Erection Contractors
S.I.C.: 1791
N.A.I.C.S.: 238120
Benoig Debergt *(Mng Dir)*

Habia Cable SP.Z.O.O **(2)**
Lubieszyn 8
72-002 Szczecin, Poland
Tel.: (48) 913115650
Fax: (48) 913118887
E-Mail: info.pl@habia.com
Web Site: www.habia.com
Emp.: 38
Fiber Optic Cable Mfr
S.I.C.: 3357
N.A.I.C.S.: 335921

Habia Kabel GmbH **(2)**
Oststrasse 91
D-22844 Norderstedt, Germany (100%)
Tel.: (49) 4053535012
Fax: (49) 4053535035
Web Site: www.habia.com
Current-Carrying Wiring Device Mfr
S.I.C.: 3643
N.A.I.C.S.: 335931
Lutz Eisel *(VP)*

Habia Kabel Produktions GmbH & Co.KG **(2)**
Oststrasse 91
DE-22844 Norderstedt, Germany (100%)
Tel.: (49) 405353500
Fax: (49) 4053535046
E-Mail: info.de@habia.com
Web Site: www.habia.com
Emp.: 50
Current-Carrying Wiring Device Mfr
S.I.C.: 3643
N.A.I.C.S.: 335931
Lutz Eisel *(VP)*

Lesjofors AB **(1)**
Kopmannagatan 2
Karlstad, Sweden (100%)
Tel.: (46) 54137750
Fax: (46) 54210810
E-Mail: info@lesjoforsab.com
Web Site: www.lesjoforsab.com
Emp.: 10
Other Holding Companies Offices of Holding Companies
S.I.C.: 6719
N.A.I.C.S.: 551112
Kjell-Arne Lindback *(CEO)*

Subsidiaries:

Lesjofors Automotive AB **(2)**
Radjursvagen 8
SE-35245 Vaxjo, Sweden (100%)
Tel.: (46) 470707280
Fax: (46) 470707299
E-Mail: info.auto@lesjoforsab.com
Web Site: www.lesjoforsab.com
Emp.: 30
Spring (Heavy Gauge) Mfg
S.I.C.: 3493
N.A.I.C.S.: 332613
Hakan Moller *(Mng Dir)*

Lesjofors Banddetaljer AB **(2)**
Expovagen 7
SE-33142 Varnamo, Sweden (100%)
Tel.: (46) 370694500
Fax: (46) 370694599
E-Mail: info.vmo@lesjoforsab.com
Web Site: www.lesjoforsab.com
Emp.: 45
Engineering Services
S.I.C.: 8711
N.A.I.C.S.: 541330

Jakob Lindquist *(Mng Dir)*

Lesjofors Fjadrar AB (2)
Kanalvagen 3
SE-68096 Lesjofors, Sweden (100%)
Tel.: (46) 590608100
Fax: (46) 59031031
E-Mail: info.lfs@lesjoforsab.com
Web Site: www.lesjoforsab.com
Emp.: 85
Other Fabricated Wire Product Mfr
S.I.C.: 3496
N.A.I.C.S.: 332618
Bjorn Persson *(Mng Dir)*

Lesjofors Industrifjadrar AB (2)
Hudene
52492 Herrljunga, Sweden (100%)
Tel.: (46) 51322000
Fax: (46) 51323021
E-Mail: info.hja@lesjoforsab.com
Web Site: www.lesjoforsab.com
Emp.: 60
Bolt Nut Screw Rivet & Washer Mfg
S.I.C.: 3452
N.A.I.C.S.: 332722
Lars Blidberg *(Mng Dir)*

Lesjofors Stockholms Fjader AB (2)
Jamtlandsgatan 62
16212 Vallingby, Sweden (100%)
Tel.: (46) 8870250
Fax: (46) 8876350
E-Mail: info.vby@lesjoforsab.com
Web Site: www.lesjoforsab.com
Emp.: 40
Bolt Nut Screw Rivet & Washer Mfg
S.I.C.: 3452
N.A.I.C.S.: 332722
Marten Glas *(Mgr)*

Non-U.S. Subsidiaries:

European Springs & Pressings Ltd. (2)
Chaffinch Business Park Croydon Road
Beckenham, Kent, BR3 4DW, United Kingdom (100%)
Tel.: (44) 2086 631800
Fax: (44) 2086 631900
E-Mail: info.bec@harris-springs.com
Web Site: www.harris-springs.com
Emp.: 90
Heavy Gauge Spring Mfr
S.I.C.: 3493
N.A.I.C.S.: 332613

Lesjofors A/S (2)
Ringager 9-11
2605 Brondby, Denmark (100%)
Tel.: (45) 46956100
Fax: (45) 46956195
E-Mail: info.bby@lesjoforsab.com
Web Site: www.lesjoforsab.com
Emp.: 50
Structural Steel Erection Contractors
S.I.C.: 1791
N.A.I.C.S.: 238120
Tue Jensen *(Mng Dir)*

Lesjofors Automotive Ltd (2)
Lowfields Way Lowfields Business Park
HX5 9DA Elland, United Kingdom (100%)
Tel.: (44) 1422370770
Fax: (44) 1422377233
E-Mail: info@lesjofors.com
Web Site: www.lesjofors.com
Emp.: 30
All Other Motor Vehicle Parts Mfr
S.I.C.: 3714
N.A.I.C.S.: 336390
Robert Glynn *(Mng Dir)*

Lesjofors China Ltd (2)
No 22 TianShan Rd
New district of Changzhou, 213032
Changzhou, China (100%)
Tel.: (86) 5195118010
Fax: (86) 5195118670
E-Mail: info.czx@lesjoforsab.com
Web Site: www.lesjoforsab.com
Radio & Television Broadcasting & Wireless Communication Equipment Mfr
S.I.C.: 3663
N.A.I.C.S.: 334220

Lesjofors Springs GmbH (2)
Spannstift Str 2
58119 Hagen, Germany (100%)
Tel.: (49) 233450170
Fax: (49) 2334501717
E-Mail: info.hag@lesjoforsab.com
Web Site: www.lesjoforsab.com
Emp.: 17
Spring (Heavy Gauge) Mfr
S.I.C.: 3495
N.A.I.C.S.: 332613
Richard Kupper *(Mng Dir)*

Lesjofors Springs Ltd (2)
Lowfields Way Lowfields Business Park
Elland, United Kingdom (100%)
Tel.: (44) 1422377335
Fax: (44) 1422377233
E-Mail: enquries@lesjofors.com
Web Site: www.lesjofors.com
Emp.: 3
Bolt Nut Screw Rivet & Washer Mfg
S.I.C.: 3452
N.A.I.C.S.: 332722
Robert Glynn *(Mng Dir)*

Lesjofors Springs LV (2)
Kapsedes Str 2 b
LV-3414 Liepaja, Latvia (100%)
Tel.: (371) 3401840
Fax: (371) 3401850
E-Mail: info.lep@lesjoforsab.com
Web Site: www.lesjoforsab.com
Emp.: 25
Spring (Heavy Gauge) Mfr
S.I.C.: 3495
N.A.I.C.S.: 332613
Gerts Ancevskis *(Mng Dir)*

Lesjofors Springs Oy (2)
Hallimestarinkatu 7
20780 Kaarina, Finland (100%)
Tel.: (358) 22761400
Fax: (358) 22355689
E-Mail: info.abo@lesjoforsab.com
Web Site: www.lesjoforsab.com
Emp.: 7
Spring (Heavy Gauge) Mfg
S.I.C.: 3495
N.A.I.C.S.: 332613
Bertel Ridderj *(Mng Dir)*

Oy Lesjofors AB (2)
Valsverksvagen 115
10410 Aminnefors, Finland (100%)
Tel.: (358) 192766200
Fax: (358) 192766230
E-Mail: info.ami@lesjforsab.com
Web Site: www.lesjforsab.com
Emp.: 20
Spring (Heavy Gauge) Mfg
S.I.C.: 3495
N.A.I.C.S.: 332613
Dan Manninen *(Mng Dir)*

Lundgrens Sverige AB (1)
PO Box 9114
400 93 Gothenburg, Sweden
Tel.: (46) 31 84 03 90
Fax: (46) 31 25 77 08
E-Mail: lmg@lundgrenssverige.se
Plastic Pipe Mfr & Distr
S.I.C.: 3089
N.A.I.C.S.: 326122

Stece Fjadrar AB (1)
Lillgatan
Box 75
383 25 Monsteras, Sweden
Tel.: (46) 499 160 00
Fax: (46) 499 137 10
E-Mail: info@stecefjadrar.com
Web Site: www.stecefjadrar.com
Industrial Spring Mfr
S.I.C.: 3493
N.A.I.C.S.: 332613
Magnus Johansson *(Acct Mgr)*

Non-U.S. Subsidiaries:

Beijer AS (1)
Lerpeveien 25
3036 Drammen, Norway
Tel.: (47) 32 20 24 00
Fax: (47) 32 20 24 01
E-Mail: firmapost@glbeijer.no
Aluminum Treatment Services
S.I.C.: 3399
N.A.I.C.S.: 331314

Beijer OY (1)
Ellannontie 5
1510 Vantaa, Finland
Tel.: (358) 9 615 20 550
Fax: (358) 9 615 20 555
E-Mail: info@beijers.fi
Web Site: www.beijers.fi
Emp.: 1
Industrial Supplies Distr
S.I.C.: 5085
N.A.I.C.S.: 423840

European Springs & Pressings Ltd (1)
Chaffinch Business Park Croydon Road
Beckenham, BR3 4DW, United Kingdom
Tel.: (44) 2086 631 800
Fax: (44) 2086 631 900
E-Mail: info.bec@lesjoforsab.com
Web Site: www.europeansprings.com
Emp.: 10
Industrial Spring Mfr
S.I.C.: 3493
N.A.I.C.S.: 332613
Stuart McSheehy *(Mng Dir)*

Lesjofors A/S (1)
Professor Birkelandsvei 24A
1081 Oslo, Norway
Tel.: (47) 22 90 57 00
Fax: (47) 22 90 560 90
E-Mail: info.ske@lesjoforsab.com
Spring Mfr
S.I.C.: 3495
N.A.I.C.S.: 332613

Lesjofors Gas Springs LV (1)
Kapsedes Iela 2b
3402 Liepaja, Latvia
Tel.: (371) 63401 840
Fax: (371) 63401 850
E-Mail: info.lep@lesjoforsab.com
Web Site: www.lesjoforsab.com
Emp.: 10
Industrial Spring Mfr
S.I.C.: 3495
N.A.I.C.S.: 332613
Ingars Jaunzem *(Gen Mgr)*

Preben Z. Jensen A/S (1)
Guldalderen 11
2640 Hedehusene, Denmark
Tel.: (45) 46 56 36 66
Fax: (45) 46 59 05 15
E-Mail: post@prebenz.dk
Deburring Grinding & Polishing Equipment Distr
S.I.C.: 5085
N.A.I.C.S.: 423840

BEIJING AEROSPACE CHANGFENG CO., LTD.

Aerospace Building No 51-A
Yongding Rd
Haidian District, Beijing, China
Tel.: (86) 10 68385288
Fax: (86) 10 68281182
Web Site: www.ascf.com.cn
600855—(SHG)

Business Description:
Security System Mfr
S.I.C.: 3679
N.A.I.C.S.: 334419

Personnel:
Chunlai Quan *(Chm)*

BEIJING AUTOMOTIVE INDUSTRY HOLDING CO., LTD.

25 E. Third Ring Rd S
Beijing, 100021, China
Web Site: www.baihc.com
Sales Range: $25-49.9 Billion
Emp.: 83,000

Business Description:
Automobile Mfr
S.I.C.: 3711
N.A.I.C.S.: 336111

Personnel:
Heyi Xu *(Chm)*

Subsidiary:

BAIC Motor Co., Ltd. (1)
No.10 Huaweili Dongsanhuan S
Beijing, 100026, China
Tel.: (86) 10 6044 4660
Fax: (86) 10 6044 4611
Web Site: www.baicmotor.com
Passenger Automobile Mfr
S.I.C.: 3711
N.A.I.C.S.: 336111
Heyi Xu, *(cHM)*

BEIJING BEIDA JADE BIRD UNIVERSAL SCI-TECH LIMITED

3rd Floor Beida Jade Bird Building
207 Chengfu Road
Beijing, 100871, China
Tel.: (86) 10 82615888
Fax: (86) 10 62758434
Web Site: www.jbu.com.cn
8095—(HKG)
Sls.: $85,422,064
Assets: $229,236,753
Liabilities: $48,680,536
Net Worth: $180,556,217
Earnings: $14,104,133
Emp.: 1,292
Fiscal Year-end: 12/31/12

Business Description:
Embedded System Products Including Network Security, Wireless Fire Alarm Systems & Related Products Developer, Marketer & Mfr
S.I.C.: 7373
N.A.I.C.S.: 541512

Personnel:
Zhendong Xu *(Chm)*
Yongli Zhang *(Chm-Supervisory Bd)*
Zhixiang Xu *(Vice Chm)*
Wanzhong Zhang *(Pres & Compliance Officer)*
Chi Hung Chan *(Sec & Controller-Fin)*

Board of Directors:
Zhendong Xu
Chuanbing Cai
Weimin Cai
Zongbing Chen
Juncai Li
Yan Lin
Jiulin Shao
Zhixiang Xu
Wanzhong Zhang
Zhong Zheng

Supervisory Board of Directors:
Yongli Zhang
Yimin Fan
Chonghua Li
Jinguan Yang
Min Zhou

Transfer Agent:
Hong Kong Registrars Limited
Rooms 1806-7 18th Floor Hopewell Centre 183 Queens Road East
Wanchai, China (Hong Kong)

BEIJING BOHUI INNOVATION TECHNOLOGY CO., LTD.

Tower G 25A Jingxin Park
Beiwucun Road
Haidian District, Beijing, 100195, China
Tel.: (86) 10 88850168
Fax: (86) 10 88856244
Web Site: www.bohui-tech.com
300318—(CHIN)
Sales Range: $10-24.9 Million
Emp.: 185

Business Description:
Medical Testing Equipment Mfr
S.I.C.: 3841
N.A.I.C.S.: 339112

Personnel:
Jiangtao Du *(Chm)*

BEIJING CAPITAL CO., LTD.

Floor 7 Jingan Center 8 East Road
North 3rd Circle
Chaoyang District, Beijing, 100028, China
Tel.: (86) 1084552266

Beijing Capital Co., Ltd.—(Continued)

E-Mail: securities@capitalwater.cn
Web Site: www.capitalwater.cn
600008—(SHG)
Sales Range: $450-499.9 Million
Emp.: 5,514
Business Description:
Waste Water Treatment Services
S.I.C.: 4953
N.A.I.C.S.: 562211
Personnel:
Xiaoguang Liu *(Chm)*
Guijie Cao *(Deputy Chm)*
Chunqin Feng *(Deputy Chm)*
Li Yu *(CFO)*
Board of Directors:
Xiaoguang Liu
Guijie Cao
Chunqin Feng
Wentang Pan
Yulu Yang
Zhenyu Yuan
Jianping Zhang
Kang Zhao

BEIJING CAPITAL GROUP CO., LTD.

15/F Capital Group Plaza
No.6 Chaoyangmen North Street,
Dongcheng Beijing, China
Tel.: (86) 10 58385566
Fax: (86) 1058383050
Web Site: www.capitalgroup.com.cn
Business Description:
Financial Services
S.I.C.: 6211
N.A.I.C.S.: 523999
Personnel:
Xiaoguang Liu *(Chm)*
Hao Wang *(Vice Chm & Gen Mgr)*
Yongzheng Liu *(Gen Counsel)*
Board of Directors:
Xiaoguang Liu
Songping Li
Jianping Shen
Fengjing Song
Hao Wang

BEIJING CAPITAL INTERNATIONAL AIRPORT COMPANY LIMITED

(d/b/a BCIA)
Capital Airport
Beijing, 100621, China
Tel.: (86) 1064541100
E-Mail: service@bcia.com.cn
Web Site: www.bcia.com.cn
694—(HKG OTC)
Rev.: $1,090,133,541
Assets: $5,309,198,437
Liabilities: $2,881,528,675
Net Worth: $2,427,669,762
Earnings: $186,264,810
Emp.: 1,664
Fiscal Year-end: 12/31/12
Business Description:
Airport
S.I.C.: 4581
N.A.I.C.S.: 488119
Personnel:
Zhiyi Dong *(Chm)*
Yong Shu *(Sec)*
Board of Directors:
Zhiyi Dong
Guoxing Chen
Shiqing Gao
Ruiming Jiang
Eng Boon Lau
Japhet Sebastian Law
Guibin Liu
Xiaolong Wang
Yabo Yao
Guanghui Zhang
Musheng Zhang
Supervisory Board of Directors:
Dong Ansheng
Youjun Cui
Xiaomei Li
Yanbin Liu
Hua Tang
Jinglu Zhao

BEIJING CAPITAL LAND LTD.

Floor 15 Red Goldage No 2
GuangNingBo Street
Xicheng District, Beijing, 100033, China
Tel.: (86) 66523000
Fax: (86) 66523131
E-Mail: info@bjcapitalland.com
Web Site: www.bjcapitalland.com
2868—(HKG)
Rev.: $1,450,944,478
Assets: $7,551,171,119
Liabilities: $5,962,192,821
Net Worth: $1,588,978,297
Earnings: $21,232,368
Emp.: 1,345
Fiscal Year-end: 12/31/12
Business Description:
Property Development
S.I.C.: 6351
N.A.I.C.S.: 524126
Personnel:
Xiaoguang Liu *(Chm)*
Jun Tang *(Pres)*
Simon Sing Yeung Lee *(Sec)*
Board of Directors:
Xiaoguang Liu
Guijie Cao
Chunqin Feng
Zhaojie Li
Yuk Keung Ng
Jun Tang
Hong Wang
Juxing Zhang
Shengli Zhang
Supervisory Board of Directors:
Shubin Fan
Hebin Jiang
Yongzheng Liu

BEIJING CENTURY TECHNOLOGY CO., LTD.

(d/b/a iReal)
9F & 10F Block B Shangdi
Technology Comprehensive Bldg
Haidian District, Beijing, Shangdi, 100085, China
Tel.: (86) 10 62961155
Fax: (86) 10 62962298
E-Mail: liuchunjie@c-real.com.cn
Web Site: www.c-real.com.cn
300150—(CHIN)
Business Description:
Software Publisher
S.I.C.: 7372
N.A.I.C.S.: 511210
Personnel:
Qi Ma *(Chm)*

BEIJING COMENS NEW MATERIALS CO., LTD.

8 Yanshan Industrial Zone
Fangshan District, Beijing, 102502, China
Tel.: (86) 10 69342270
Web Site: www.co-mens.com
Year Founded: 1999
300200—(CHIN)
Sales Range: $50-74.9 Million
Emp.: 340
Business Description:
Adhesive Mfr
S.I.C.: 2891
N.A.I.C.S.: 325520
Personnel:
Ziping Wang *(Chm & Pres)*

BEIJING CONSTRUCTION ENGINEERING (GROUP) CO., LTD.

16th Floor No 1 Guanglian Road
Xuanwu District
Beijing, China
Tel.: (86) 10 63927209
Fax: (86) 10 63928500
Web Site: www.bcegc.com
Emp.: 20,000
Business Description:
Construction Services
S.I.C.: 1629
N.A.I.C.S.: 237990
Personnel:
Weilin Sun *(Pres)*

Subsidiary:

Beijing Chang Cheng Bilfinger Berger Construction Engineering Corp. Ltd. **(1)**
16th Fl Golden Tower 1 Xibahe S Rd
Chaoyang Dt, Beijing, 100028, China
Tel.: (86) 1064402721
Fax: (86) 1064402720
E-Mail: hoffice@bcbb.com.cn
Web Site: www.bcbb.com.cn
Transportation Infrastructure Engineering & Construction Services
S.I.C.: 1622
N.A.I.C.S.: 237310

BEIJING CREATIVE DISTRIBUTION AUTOMATION CO., LTD.

(d/b/a Creative Distribution Automation)
4th Floor Building 3 8 Chuangye Road
Shangdi
Haidian, Beijing, 100085, China
Tel.: (86) 10 62981321
Fax: (86) 10 62981320
E-Mail: creatda@creat-da.com.cn
Web Site: www.creat-da.com.cn
002350—(SSE)
Business Description:
Power Distribution & Control Equipment Mfr
S.I.C.: 3612
N.A.I.C.S.: 335311
Personnel:
Xinyu Zhang *(Chm)*

BEIJING DABEINONG TECHNOLOGY GROUP CO., LTD.

14F Zhongguancun Mansion 27
Zhongguancun Avenue
Haidian District, Beijing, China
Tel.: (86) 10 82856450
Web Site: www.dbn.com.cn
002385—(SSE)
Sales Range: $75-99.9 Million
Business Description:
Feed & Seed Products
S.I.C.: 0119
N.A.I.C.S.: 111191
Personnel:
Genhuo Shao *(Chm)*

BEIJING DYNAMIC POWER CO., LTD.

No 8 Xinghuo Road Science City
Fengtai District, Beijing, China 100070
Tel.: (86) 10 63704818
Fax: (86) 10 63783051
E-Mail: hwyx@dpc.com.cn
Web Site: www.dpc.com.cn
Year Founded: 1995
600405—(SHG)
Business Description:
Power Supply Equipment Mfr & Whslr
S.I.C.: 3699
N.A.I.C.S.: 335999
Personnel:
Zhenya He *(Chm & Gen Mgr)*

BEIJING E-HUALU INFO TECHNOLOGY CO., LTD.

(d/b/a E-Hualu)
China Hualu Building 165 Fushi Road
Shijingshan District, Beijing, 100043, China
Tel.: (86) 10 52281111
Fax: (86) 10 52281188
Web Site: www.ehualu.com
Year Founded: 2001
300212—(CHIN)
Sales Range: $25-49.9 Million
Emp.: 300
Business Description:
Traffic Management Systems & Software
S.I.C.: 3799
N.A.I.C.S.: 336999
Personnel:
Yandong Li *(Pres)*

BEIJING E-TOWN INTERNATIONAL INVESTMENT & DEVELOPMENT CO., LTD.

Beijing E-Town Economic Development Area
Beijing, China
Tel.: (86) 1067886732
Web Site: www.bdainvest.com
Business Description:
Financial Investments
S.I.C.: 6211
N.A.I.C.S.: 523999
Personnel:
Zhao Guangyi *(Chm & Gen Mgr)*

Joint Venture:

Pacific Century Motors **(1)**
Beijing E-Town Economic Development Area
Beijing, China CN
Tel.: (86) 1067886732
Auto Parts & Components Mfr & Distr; Joint Venture Owned by Beijing E-Town International Investment & Development Co., Ltd. & Tempo International Group Ltd.
S.I.C.: 3714
N.A.I.C.S.: 336390
Tianbao Zhou *(Pres)*

U.S. Subsidiary:

Nexteer Automotive Group Ltd **(2)**
3900 E Holland Rd
Saginaw, MI 48601-9494
Tel.: (989) 757-5000
Fax: (248) 655-0700
E-Mail: investors@nexteer.com
Web Site: www.nexteer.com
1316—(HKG)
Sales Range: $1-4.9 Billion
Emp.: 6,200
Motor Vehicle Steering & Driveline System Mfr
Import Export
S.I.C.: 3714
N.A.I.C.S.: 336330
Guibin Zhao *(Chm & CEO)*
Laurent Bresson *(Pres & Global COO)*
Joe Perkins *(CFO & Sr VP)*
Doug Owenby *(COO & VP)*
Mike Richardson *(CTO, Chief Strategy Officer & Sr VP)*
Matthew Paroly *(Chief Legal Officer, Gen Counsel & Sr VP)*
Mark Decker *(Chief HR Officer & Sr VP)*
Illeana Simplicean *(Gen Counsel & Sr VP)*
Yi Fan *(Co-Sec)*
Ming Wai Mok *(Co-Sec)*

BEIJING EASPRING MATERIAL TECHNOLOGY CO., LTD.

(d/b/a Easpring)

1 Wenxing Street
Beijing, 100044, China
Tel.: (86) 10 68317290
Fax: (86) 10 68342289
E-Mail: office@easpring.com.cn
Web Site: www.easpring.com.cn
300073—(CHIN)
Sales Range: $75-99.9 Million
Business Description:
Lithium Batteries & Power Supply Products Mfr
S.I.C.: 3691
N.A.I.C.S.: 335911
Personnel:
Jian Liang Zhang *(CEO)*

BEIJING EGOVA CO., LTD.
(d/b/a eGOVA)
8F Tower A Jieneng Mansion 42 Xizhimen North Avenue
Haidian District, Beijing, 100082, China
Tel.: (86) 10 62212336
E-Mail: egova@egova.com.cn
Web Site: www.egova.com.cn
300075—(CHIN)
Sales Range: $10-24.9 Million
Business Description:
Electronic Data Management Products Mfr
S.I.C.: 3572
N.A.I.C.S.: 334112
Personnel:
Qianghua Wu *(Chm)*

BEIJING ENLIGHT MEDIA CO., LTD.
Beijing Peace East Street 11 Building 3 Level 3
Dongcheng District, Beijing, 100013, China
Tel.: (86) 10 64516000
Fax: (86) 10 84222188
Web Site: www.ewang.com
300251—(CHIN)
Sales Range: $50-74.9 Million
Emp.: 460
Business Description:
Television Program Production
S.I.C.: 7812
N.A.I.C.S.: 512110
Personnel:
Changtian Wang *(Chm & CEO)*

BEIJING ENTERPRISES HOLDINGS LIMITED
66th Floor Central Plaza 18 Harbour Road
Wanchai, China (Hong Kong)
Tel.: (852) 29152898
Fax: (852) 28575084
E-Mail: mailbox@behl.com.hk
Web Site: www.behl.com.hk
Year Founded: 1997
0392—(HKG)
Rev.: $4,586,706,239
Assets: $11,542,050,281
Liabilities: $5,398,912,772
Net Worth: $6,143,137,510
Earnings: $468,471,224
Emp.: 49,000
Fiscal Year-end: 12/31/12
Business Description:
Holding Company
S.I.C.: 6719
N.A.I.C.S.: 551112
Personnel:
Dong Wang *(Chm)*
Si Zhou *(Vice Chm & CEO)*
Fucheng Li *(Vice Chm)*
Honghai Zhang *(Vice Chm)*
Jimmy Chun Fai Tam *(CFO & Sec)*
E. Meng *(Exec VP)*
Board of Directors:
Dong Wang
Tingmei Fu
Pujin Guo
Zibo Hou
Xinhao Jiang
Hoi Ham Lam
Zhengang Lei
Fucheng Li
Kai Liu
E. Meng
Hanmin Shi
Chi Ching Sze
Jimmy Chun Fai Tam
Robert A. Theleen
Jiesi Wu
Honghai Zhang
Si Zhou
Legal Counsel:
Mayer Brown JSM
17th Floor Prince's Building 10 Chater Road
Hong Kong, China (Hong Kong)
Tel.: (852) 28432211
Subsidiary:

Beijing Development (Hong Kong) Limited **(1)**
66 F Central Plaza 18 Harbour Road
Wanchai, China (Hong Kong)
Tel.: (852) 28611880
Fax: (852) 25293725
E-Mail: general@bdhk.com.hk
Web Site: www.bdhk.com.hk
154—(HKG)
Rev.: $26,871,504
Assets: $124,504,836
Liabilities: $32,282,246
Net Worth: $92,222,590
Earnings: ($3,436,518)
Emp.: 330
Fiscal Year-end: 12/31/12
Network Infrastructure Facility Construction, Network System Integration & Internet Support Services
S.I.C.: 4899
N.A.I.C.S.: 517919
E. Meng *(Chm)*
Yong Wang *(Pres)*
Robin Kwok Wai Wong *(Sec & Controller-Fin)*

BEIJING ENTERPRISES WATER GROUP LIMITED
66th Floor Central Plaza 18 Harbour Road
Wanchai, China (Hong Kong)
Tel.: (852) 2796 9963
Fax: (852) 2796 9972
E-Mail: mailbox@bewg.com.hk
Web Site: www.bewg.com.hk
371—(HKG)
Rev.: $480,645,522
Assets: $4,034,830,026
Liabilities: $2,651,004,004
Net Worth: $1,383,826,022
Earnings: $111,818,993
Emp.: 3,005
Fiscal Year-end: 12/31/12
Business Description:
Water Treatment Services
S.I.C.: 4971
N.A.I.C.S.: 221310
Personnel:
Honghai Zhang *(Chm)*
E. Meng *(Vice Chm)*
Xiaoyong Hu *(CEO)*
Eric Woon Cheung Tung *(CFO & Sec)*
Min Zhou *(Exec VP)*
Board of Directors:
Honghai Zhang
Rui Guo
Shijun Hang
Feng Hou
Xiaoyong Hu
Xinhao Jiang
Jian Ke
Haifeng Li
E. Meng
Xiaohong Qi
Chun Lok Shea
Eric Woon Cheung Tung
Kaijun Wang
Ning Yu
Gaobo Zhang
Tiefu Zhang
Min Zhou
Butterfield Fulcrum Group (Bermuda) Limited
26 Burnaby Street
Hamilton, HM 11, Bermuda
Transfer Agents:
Tricor Tengis Limited
26/F Tesbury Centre, 28 Queens Road East
Hong Kong, China (Hong Kong)
Butterfield Fulcrum Group (Bermuda) Limited
26 Burnaby Street
Hamilton, HM 11, Bermuda

BEIJING FUXING XIAOCHENG ELECTRONIC TECHNOLOGY STOCK CO., LTD.
Room 503 Block D IFEC blog No 87 Xisanhuan Beilu
Haidian District, Beijing, 100089, China
Tel.: (86) 1068459012, ext. 8020
Fax: (86) 1068466652
E-Mail: internationalmarket@xiaocheng.com
Web Site: www.xiaocheng.com
Year Founded: 2000
300139—(CHIN)
Sales Range: $25-49.9 Million
Emp.: 307
Business Description:
Integrated Circuit Mfr
S.I.C.: 3679
N.A.I.C.S.: 334419
Personnel:
Han Zhang Luo *(CEO)*

BEIJING GALLOPING HORSE FILM & TV PRODUCTION CO., LTD.
11/F Easyhome Tower No 3A Dongzhimen South Street
Dongcheng District, Beijing, 100007, China
Tel.: (86) 10 84990264
Emp.: 300
Business Description:
Motion Picture & Television Program Production Services
S.I.C.: 7812
N.A.I.C.S.: 512110
Personnel:
Ivy Zhong *(Vice Chm & Mng Dir)*
U.S. Joint Ventures:

Instant Karma Films, LLC **(1)**
212 Marine St
Santa Monica, CA 90405
Tel.: (310) 526-7703
Fax: (310) 526-7076
Web Site: www.instantkarmafilms.tv
Motion Picture & Video Production Services
S.I.C.: 7812
N.A.I.C.S.: 512110
Tanya Farkas *(Pres)*

BEIJING HAOHUA ENERGY RESOURCE CO., LTD.
2 Xingqiao Street
Beijing, 102300, China
Tel.: (86) 10 69842461
Web Site: www.bjhhny.com
601101—(SHG)
Emp.: 12,400
Business Description:
Coal Mining Services
S.I.C.: 1222
N.A.I.C.S.: 212112
Personnel:
Geng Yang Mou *(CEO)*

BEIJING HIGHLANDER DIGITAL TECHNOLOGY CO., LTD.
A605-606 SP Tower Tsinghua Science Park Building
Beijing, 100084, China
Tel.: (86) 10 82150082
Fax: (86) 10 82150083
E-Mail: market@highlander.com.cn
Web Site: www.highlander.com.cn
Year Founded: 2001
300065—(CHIN)
Emp.: 150
Business Description:
Marine Electronic Technology Products Mfr
S.I.C.: 3812
N.A.I.C.S.: 334511
Personnel:
Wanqiu Shen *(Chm)*

BEIJING HUALUBAINA FILM & TV CO., LTD.
13F 1 Building 165 Y Fushi Road
Shijingshan District, Beijing, 100043, China
Tel.: (86) 10 52281866
Fax: (86) 10 52281853
Web Site: www.hlbn-ent.com
300291—(CHIN)
Emp.: 40
Business Description:
Television & Film Production & Distribution
S.I.C.: 7812
N.A.I.C.S.: 512110
Personnel:
Runsheng Chen *(Chm)*

BEIJING IRTOUCH SYSTEMS CO., LTD.
4th Floor M8 Building 1 Jiuxianqiao East Road
Chaoyang District, Beijing, 100015, China
Tel.: (86) 10 84573471
Fax: (86) 10 84573469
Web Site: www.irtouch.com
Year Founded: 2003
300282—(CHIN)
Emp.: 320
Business Description:
Touchscreen Mfr
S.I.C.: 3674
N.A.I.C.S.: 334413
Personnel:
Xinbin Liu *(Chm)*

BEIJING JANGHO CURTAIN WALL CO., LTD.
No 5 Niuhui North 5th Street
Shunyi District, Beijing, 101300, China
Tel.: (86) 10 60411166
E-Mail: jangho@janghogroup.com
Web Site: www.janghogroup.com
601886—(SHG)
Rev.: $1,427,934,420
Assets: $1,976,427,585
Liabilities: $1,257,250,095
Net Worth: $719,177,490
Earnings: $76,009,725
Emp.: 4,848
Fiscal Year-end: 12/31/12
Business Description:
Structural Curtain Wall Products Mfr
S.I.C.: 3441
N.A.I.C.S.: 332312

Beijing Jangho Curtain Wall Co., Ltd.—(Continued)

Personnel:
Zaiwang Liu *(Chm)*
Hongwei Qi *(Pres)*
Zhongyue Liu *(VP & Sec)*

Non-U.S. Subsidiary:

Jangho Curtain Wall Hongkong Ltd **(1)**
Room 2405B Nanyang Plaza
57 Hung To Road Kwun Tong, Kowloon, China (Hong Kong)
Tel.: (852) 34991615
Fax: (852) 34991647
Structural Curtain Wall Products Mfr
S.I.C.: 3441
N.A.I.C.S.: 332312

BEIJING JETSEN TECHNOLOGY CO., LTD.

(d/b/a Jetsen)
7/F Xueyuan International Tower 1
Zhichun Road
Haidian District, Beijing, 100083, China
Tel.: (86) 10 82330868
Fax: (86) 10 82330880
E-Mail: jetsen@jetsen.cn
Web Site: www.jetsen.com.cn
300182—(CHIN)
Emp.: 480
Business Description:
Audio & Video Equipment Mfr
S.I.C.: 3651
N.A.I.C.S.: 334310
Personnel:
Ziquan Xu *(Chm)*
Qiang Zheng *(Vice Chm)*

BEIJING JIAXUN FEIHONG ELECTRICAL CO., LTD.

Building 1 5 Dijin Avenue
Zhongguancun Environmental Protection Technology Demonstration Park
Haidian District, Beijing, 100095, China
Tel.: (86) 10 62460088
Fax: (86) 10 62492088
E-Mail: liuxm@jiaxun.com
Web Site: www.jiaxun.com
Year Founded: 1995
300213—(CHIN)
Emp.: 290
Business Description:
Dispatching & Other Traffic Equipment Mfr
S.I.C.: 3799
N.A.I.C.S.: 336999
Personnel:
Jing Lin *(Chm)*

BEIJING JIAYU DOOR, WINDOW AND CURTAIN WALL JOINT-STOCK CO., LTD.

(d/b/a Jiayu Group)
1 Niufu Road
Niulanshan Town
Shunyi District, Beijing, 101301, China
Tel.: (86) 10 69414790
Fax: (86) 10 69416588
E-Mail: jiayu@jiayu.com.cn
Web Site: www.jiayu.com.cn
Year Founded: 1987
300117—(CHIN)
Emp.: 1,170
Business Description:
Energy-Saving Doors, Windows & Curtain Walls Mfr & Installation Services
S.I.C.: 3442
N.A.I.C.S.: 332321

Personnel:
Tian Jiayu *(Chm)*

BEIJING JINGCHENG MACHINERY ELECTRIC HOLDING CO., LTD.

(d/b/a Jingcheng Holding)
59 Dongsanhuan Zhonglu
Chaoyang District, Beijing, 100022, China
Tel.: (86) 1067702828
Fax: (86) 1067757096
Web Site: www.jcmeh.com
Sales Range: $1-4.9 Billion
Emp.: 20,000
Business Description:
Holding Company; Industrial Machinery Mfr
S.I.C.: 6719
N.A.I.C.S.: 551112
Personnel:
Ren Ya Guang *(CEO)*

Subsidiaries:

Beijing BEIZHONG Steam Turbine Generator Co., Ltd. **(1)**
No 57 Wujiacun
Shijingshan District, Beijing, 100040, China CN
Tel.: (86) 10 5179 2211
Fax: (86) 10 6863 9675
Web Site: www.bzd.com.cn
Emp.: 2,200
Steam Turbine Mfr
S.I.C.: 3511
N.A.I.C.S.: 333611
Janbo Qi *(Mng Dir)*

Subsidiary:

Beijing Jingcheng New Energy Co., Ltd. **(2)**
No 57 Wujiacun
Shijingshan District, Beijing, 100040, China CN
Tel.: (86) 10 5179 2570
Fax: (86) 10 5179 2812
Web Site: www.jcnewenergy.com
Wind Power Generation Equipment Mfr
S.I.C.: 3511
N.A.I.C.S.: 333611

Beijing B.J. Electric Motor Co., Ltd. **(1)**
7 Jiuxianqiaobeilu
Chaoyang District, Beijing, 100015, China CN
Tel.: (86) 10 6436 2131
Fax: (86) 10 6438 2311
E-Mail: bjem@chinabjem.com
Web Site: www.chinabjem.com
Electric Motor Mfr
S.I.C.: 3621
N.A.I.C.S.: 335312
Xiaokun Hou *(Chm)*

Beijing Huade Hydraulic Industrial Group Co., Ltd. **(1)**
No 5 Tongji North Road Economic And Technological Development Zone
Beijing E&T Development Zone, Beijing, 100176, China CN
Tel.: (86) 10 6787 2595
Fax: (86) 10 6787 2591
E-Mail: hdft@huade-hyd.net
Web Site: www.huade-hyd.com.cn
Hydraulic Components Mfr
Export
S.I.C.: 3594
N.A.I.C.S.: 333996
Xiansheng Liao *(Gen Mgr)*

Beijing Jingcheng Environmental Protection Development Co., Ltd. **(1)**
No 1 Guangming East Road
Chongwen District, Beijing, 100061, China CN
Tel.: (86) 10 6711 8725
Fax: (86) 10 6714 2237
E-Mail: jcep@jcep.com.cn
Web Site: www.jcep.com.cn
Emp.: 275
Industrial Compressor Mfr
S.I.C.: 3563
N.A.I.C.S.: 333912

Beijing Jingcheng Heavy Industry Co., Ltd. **(1)**
Xinghu Industrial Garden
Tongzhou District, Beijing, China CN
Tel.: (86) 10 6153 9210 (Sales)
Fax: (86) 61539200
E-Mail: sales@jchic.com
Web Site: www.jchic.com
Emp.: 700
Crane & Hoist Machinery Mfr
S.I.C.: 3536
N.A.I.C.S.: 333923
Su Jie *(CEO)*

Beijing No. 1 Machine Tool Plant **(1)**
No 16 Shuanghe Street Linhe Industrial Development Dist
Beijing, ShunYi, 101300, China
Tel.: (86) 105869024
Fax: (86) 1058693594
E-Mail: byjcie@byjc.cc
Web Site: www.byjc.com.cn
Sales Range: $50-74.9 Million
Machine Tool Mfr
S.I.C.: 3542
N.A.I.C.S.: 333517

Non-U.S. Subsidiary:

Waldrich Coburg Werkzeugmaschinenfabrik GmbH **(2)**
Hahnweg 116
96450 Coburg, Germany
Tel.: (49) 9561650
Telex: 663225
Fax: (49) 956160500
E-Mail: waco@waldrich-coburg.de
Web Site: www.waldrich-coburg.de
Emp.: 650
Machine Tool Mfr
S.I.C.: 3542
N.A.I.C.S.: 333517
Hubert Becker *(CEO)*

Beiren Group Corporation **(1)**
No 48 Dongsanhuan Nanlu
Chaoyang District, Beijing, 100022, China CN
Tel.: (86) 10 6771 4036 (100%)
Fax: (86) 10 6775 0734
E-Mail: international@beiren.com
Web Site: www.beiren.com
Holding Company; Printing Machinery Mfr & Distr
S.I.C.: 6719
N.A.I.C.S.: 551112
Shenggao Li *(CFO)*
Li Wei *(Deputy Gen Mgr)*

Subsidiaries:

Beijing Beiren Fuji Printing Machinery Co., Ltd. **(2)**
Fatou
Chaoyang District, Beijing, 100023, China CN
Tel.: (86) 10 6736 5831 (70%)
Fax: (86) 10 6736 5830
Printing Machinery Mfr
S.I.C.: 3555
N.A.I.C.S.: 333244

Beijing Yanlong Import & Export Co., Ltd. **(2)**
44 Dong San Huan Nan Lu
Chaoyang District, Beijing, 100022, China CN
Tel.: (86) 10 6771 8827
E-Mail: bjyl@public3.bta.net.cn
Printing Machinery Wholesale Trade Broker Import Export
S.I.C.: 7389
N.A.I.C.S.: 425120

Shaanxi Beiren Printing Machinery Co., Ltd. **(2)**
West Dongfeng Street
Gaoxin District, Weinan, Shaanxi, 714000, China CN
Tel.: (86) 91 3218 8615 (86.24%)
Fax: (86) 91 3211 8613
E-Mail: xs@shaanxibeiren.com
Web Site: www.shaanxibeiren.com
Soft Packaging Printing Machinery Mfr & Distr
S.I.C.: 3555
N.A.I.C.S.: 333244

Shenzhen Beiren Printing Co., Ltd. **(2)**
Building 702 Liantang Pengji Industry Zone
Luohu, Shenzhen, 51800, China CN
Tel.: (86) 75 5570 8272
Fax: (86) 75 5570 8173
E-Mail: szbeiren@szbeiren.com
Emp.: 60
Offset Press Printing Machinery Mfr
S.I.C.: 3555
N.A.I.C.S.: 333244

Holding:

Beiren Printing Machinery Holdings Limited **(1)**
No 6 Rong Chang Dongjie BDA
Beijing, 100176, China CN
Tel.: (86) 1067802109. (47.78%)
Fax: (86) 1067803010
E-Mail: beirengf@beirengf.com
Web Site: www.beirengf.com
600860—(HKG SHG)
Rev.: $118,860,213
Assets: $234,309,905
Liabilities: $138,595,371
Net Worth: $95,714,534
Earnings: ($27,345,397)
Emp.: 3,043
Fiscal Year-end: 12/31/12
Holding Company; Printing Machinery Mfr & Distr
S.I.C.: 6719
N.A.I.C.S.: 551112
Peiwu Zhang *(Chm)*
Liansheng Wang *(Chm-Supervisory Bd)*

BEIJING JINGKELONG COMPANY LIMITED

20th Floor Alexandra House 18
Chater Road
Central, China (Hong Kong)
Tel.: (852) 10 64688248
Fax: (852) 10 64611370
E-Mail: yg@jkl.com.cn
Web Site: www.jkl.com.cn
0814—(HKG)
Rev.: $1,458,866,010
Assets: $1,034,829,755
Liabilities: $717,122,130
Net Worth: $317,707,625
Earnings: $27,291,065
Emp.: 8,386
Fiscal Year-end: 12/31/12
Business Description:
General Merchandise Retailer & Wholesale Distr
S.I.C.: 5399
N.A.I.C.S.: 452990
Personnel:
Tingzhan Wei *(Chm)*
Wenyu Liu *(Chm-Supervisory Bd)*
Chunyan Li *(CFO & Deputy Gen Mgr)*
Bo Li *(Sec)*
Board of Directors:
Tingzhan Wei
Liping Chen
Onward Choi
Hanlin Gu
Chunyan Li
Jianwen Li
Shunxiang Li
Yuejin Liu
Liping Wang
Supervisory Board of Directors:
Wenyu Liu
Zhong Chen
Xianghong Cheng
Hong Wang
Baoqun Yang
Jie Yao
Transfer Agent:
Computershare Hong Kong Investor Services Limited
17th Floor, Hopewell Centre 183 Queens Road East
Hong Kong, China (Hong Kong)

Non-U.S. Subsidiary:

Beijing Xinyang Tongli Commercial Facilities Company Limited (1)
Beijing Liu-fang S Ln A on the 1st
Beijing, China
Tel.: (86) 1064672168
Web Site: www.xytl2002.com
Plastic Packing Materials & Commercial Equipments Mfr
S.I.C.: 2671
N.A.I.C.S.: 326112

BEIJING JINGNENG CLEAN ENERGY CO., LTD.

6 Xibahe Road
Chaoyang District, Beijing, China
Tel.: (86) 10 64469988
Web Site: www.jncec.com
579—(HKG)
Emp.: 120
Business Description:
Electric Power
S.I.C.: 4911
N.A.I.C.S.: 221122
Personnel:
Wentao Meng *(Gen Mgr)*

BEIJING KANGDE XIN COMPOSITE MATERIAL CO., LTD.

(d/b/a KDX)
26 Zhengxing road
Changping District, Beijing, 102200, China
Tel.: (86) 1089710777
E-Mail: sales@kangdexin.com
Web Site: www.kangdexin.com
002450—(SSE)
Business Description:
Laminated Film Mfr
S.I.C.: 2672
N.A.I.C.S.: 322220
Personnel:
Yu Zhong *(Chm & CEO)*
Shu Xu *(Pres)*

BEIJING LEADMAN BIOCHEMISTRY CO., LTD.

5 Hongda South Road
Beijing, 100176, China
Tel.: (86) 10 67855500
Fax: (86) 10 67856540
E-Mail: leadman@leadmanbio.com
Web Site: www.leadmanbio.com
Year Founded: 1997
300289—(CHIN)
Sales Range: $25-49.9 Million
Emp.: 270
Business Description:
In-Vitro Diagnosis Products & Biochemical Raw Materials Mfr, Developer & Researcher
S.I.C.: 2835
N.A.I.C.S.: 325413
Personnel:
Guangqian Shen *(Chm)*

BEIJING LIER HIGH-TEMPERATURE MATERIALS CO., LTD.

Industrial Park Changping District
Beijing, 102211, China
Tel.: (86) 1061712828
Fax: (86) 1061712828
Web Site: www.bjlirr.com.cn
002392—(SSE)
Business Description:
Fireproof Materials Mfr & Distr
S.I.C.: 3999
N.A.I.C.S.: 339999
Personnel:
Jizeng Zhao *(Chm & Pres)*

BEIJING MEDIA CORPORATION LIMITED

7/F Hong Kong Trade Center 161-167 Des Voeux Road
Central, China (Hong Kong)
Tel.: (852) 106590263
Fax: (852) 106590263
Web Site: www.bjmedia.com.cn
1000—(HKG)
Rev.: $109,650,343
Assets: $267,793,301
Liabilities: $52,006,060
Net Worth: $215,787,241
Earnings: $10,080,462
Emp.: 302
Fiscal Year-end: 12/31/12
Business Description:
Advertising Space Providers & Newspapers Producers
S.I.C.: 5192
N.A.I.C.S.: 424920
Personnel:
Yanping Zhang *(Chm)*
Kewu Tian *(Chm-Supervisory Bd)*
Haibo Yu *(Vice Chm)*
Sun Wei *(Pres)*
Liang Peng *(CFO)*
Da Shang *(Co-Sec & VP)*
Leung Fai Yu *(Co-Sec)*
Min Du *(Exec VP)*
Pingping He *(Exec VP)*
Xiaona He *(Exec VP)*
Board of Directors:
Yanping Zhang
Ji Chen
Baoguo Cui
Enqing Cui
Xiaona He
Shiheng Li
Xiaobing Li
Yigeng Li
Han Liu
Jianwu Song
Sun Wei
Peihua Wu
Tak Lung Wu
Xun Xu
Haibo Yu
Supervisory Board of Directors:
Daguang He
Kewu Tian
Mengmeng Yan
Chuanshui Zhang
Fumin Zhou
Legal Counsel:
DLA Piper
17 F Edinburgh Tower The Landmark 15 Queen's Road
Central, China (Hong Kong)

BEIJING METENO COMMUNICATION TECHNOLOGY COMPANY LIMITED

(d/b/a Meteno)
South 3F Main Bldg Putian Deshen
28 Xinjiekouwai Avenue
Xicheng District, Beijing, 100088, China
Tel.: (86) 10 8205 5588
Fax: (86) 10 8205 5731
Web Site: www.meteno.com.cn
300038—(CHIN)
Sales Range: $25-49.9 Million
Emp.: 160
Business Description:
Communication Tower Mfr
S.I.C.: 1623
N.A.I.C.S.: 237130
Personnel:
Zhiyong Zhang *(Chm)*

BEIJING NORTH STAR COMPANY LIMITED

No 8 Bei Chen Dong Road
Chao Yang District, Beijing, China 100101
Tel.: (86) 1064991284
Fax: (86) 1084976797
Web Site: www.beijingnorthstar.com
601588—(SHG)
Rev.: $911,148,350
Assets: $5,680,866,771
Liabilities: $3,313,187,188
Net Worth: $2,367,679,583
Earnings: $150,301,328
Emp.: 4,951
Fiscal Year-end: 12/31/12
Business Description:
Property Investment & Development Services
S.I.C.: 6282
N.A.I.C.S.: 523920
Personnel:
Jiang-Chuan He *(Chm)*
Yi Liu *(Chm-Supervisory Bd)*
Chang-Li Li *(Vice Chm)*
Guo Chuan *(Co-Sec)*
Carmelo Ka-Sze Lee *(Co-Sec)*
Board of Directors:
Jiang-Chuan He
Pei Zhong Gan
Chang-Li Li
Jian-Ping Liu
Tao Long
Yik Chung Wong
Jin Zeng
Hui Zhi Zhao
Supervisory Board of Directors:
Yi Liu
Guo-Rui Li
Yao-Zhong Liu
Jian-Ming Xue
Wei-Yan Zhang

PricewaterhouseCoopers
22nd Floor Prince's Building
Central, China (Hong Kong)
Legal Counsel:
Woo, Kwan, Lee & Lo
26th Floor Jardine House 1 Connaught Place
Central, China (Hong Kong)

Beijing Da Cheng Solicitors Office
12-15/F Guohua Plaza 3 Dongzhimennan Avenue Dongcheng
Beijing, China
Transfer Agent:
Hong Kong Registrars Limited
Rooms 1712-1716 17th Floor Hopewell Centre
183 Queen's Road East
Wanchai, China (Hong Kong)

BEIJING ORIENT NATIONAL COMMUNICATION SCIENCE & TECHNOLOGY CO., LTD.

D 11 Ye Building Block 9 Wangjing North Road
Chaoyang District, Beijing, 100102, China
Tel.: (86) 10 64398920
Fax: (86) 10 64398921
E-Mail: ivm@bonc.com.cn
Web Site: www.bonc.com.cn
300166—(CHIN)
Business Description:
Computer Programming Services
S.I.C.: 7371
N.A.I.C.S.: 541511
Personnel:
Lianping Guan *(Chm)*

BEIJING ORIENTAL YUHONG WATERPROOF TECHNOLOGY CO., LTD.

Shunping South Road Zengzhuang Yang Town
Shunyi District, Beijing, 10139, China
Tel.: (86) 1085762629
Fax: (86) 1085785519
Web Site: www.yuhong.com.cn
002271—(SSE)
Emp.: 1,120
Business Description:
Waterproofing Material Supplier
S.I.C.: 2851
N.A.I.C.S.: 325510
Personnel:
Weiguo Li *(Chm)*

BEIJING ORIGIN WATER TECHNOLOGY CO., LTD.

(d/b/a Origin Water)
2/F JiYou Building 2 Changximen Road
Haidan District, Beijing, 100097, China
Tel.: (86) 10 51660883
Fax: (86) 10 88434847
E-Mail: originwater.contact@gmail.com
Web Site: www.originwater-int.com
300070—(CHIN)
Business Description:
Industrial Sewage Treatment & Water Recycling Services
S.I.C.: 4952
N.A.I.C.S.: 221320
Personnel:
Jianping Wen *(Chm)*

BEIJING OUTSELL HEALTH PRODUCT DEVELOPMENT CO., LTD.

No 9 West Road Beisihuan
Beijing, China
Tel.: (86) 1062800800
Fax: (86) 1062800855
E-Mail: bsy@outsell.com.cn
Web Site: www.outsell.com.cn
Year Founded: 1998
Sales Range: $25-49.9 Million
Business Description:
Tea Producer
S.I.C.: 2095
N.A.I.C.S.: 311920
Personnel:
Yihong Zhao *(CEO)*

BEIJING PHILISENSE TECHNOLOGY CO., LTD.

3078 3F Jin Tang Hotel 2 Zhixincu
Beijing, 100191, China
Tel.: (86) 1062058123
Fax: (86) 1062041496
Web Site: www.philisense.com
Year Founded: 1997
300287—(CHIN)
Emp.: 340
Business Description:
Electronic & Communications Products Mfr
S.I.C.: 3679
N.A.I.C.S.: 334419
Personnel:
Xinjun Cao *(Chm)*

BEIJING PROPERTIES (HOLDINGS) LIMITED

66th Floor Central Plaza 18 Harbour Road
Wanchai, China (Hong Kong)
Tel.: (852) 2511 6016
Fax: (852) 2598 6905
Web Site: www.bphl.net.cn
925—(HKG)
Rev.: $1,419,353
Assets: $398,748,088
Liabilities: $251,563,011
Net Worth: $147,185,077
Earnings: ($13,972,119)
Emp.: 108

Beijing Properties (Holdings) Limited—(Continued)

Fiscal Year-end: 12/31/12
Business Description:
Investment Management Services
S.I.C.: 6282
N.A.I.C.S.: 523920
Personnel:
Si Zhou *(Chm)*
Li Yu *(Vice Chm)*
Xu Qian *(CEO)*
Kin Wai Siu *(CFO & Sec)*
Board of Directors:
Si Zhou
Renyi Ang
James Chan
Gen Cheung Goh
Xinhao Jiang
Xueheng Liu
Andrew Chiu Cheung Ma
Fang Meng
Ernesto Tang Fai Ng
Xu Qian
Kin Wai Siu
Taiyan Xu
Li Yu
Luning Yu
Wuxiang Zhu

HSBC Securities Services (Bermuda) Limited
6 Front Street
Hamilton, Bermuda
Transfer Agents:
Tricor Tengis Limited
26th Floor Tesbury Centre 28 Queen's Road East
Wanchai, China (Hong Kong)
Tel.: (852) 29801333
Fax: (852) 28108185

HSBC Securities Services (Bermuda) Limited
6 Front Street
Hamilton, Bermuda

BEIJING SANJU ENVIRONMENTAL PROTECTION AND NEW MATERIAL CO., LTD.

9/F Dahang Jiye Building 33 North RenDa Road
Haidian District, Beijing, 100080, China
Tel.: (86) 10 8268 4990
Fax: (86) 10 68436755
E-Mail: sanju@sanju.cn
Web Site: www.sanju.cn
300072—(CHIN)
Sales Range: $25-49.9 Million
Emp.: 180
Business Description:
Chemical Mfr & Distr
S.I.C.: 2899
N.A.I.C.S.: 325998
Personnel:
Lei Liu *(CEO)*

BEIJING SDL TECHNOLOGY CO., LTD.

3 Hi-Tech 3rd Street
Beijing, 102200, China
Tel.: (86) 10 80735600
Fax: (86) 10 80735777
Web Site: www.sdl-industry.com
002658—(SSE)
Emp.: 500
Business Description:
Analysis Instruments, Environmental Monitoring, Industrial Process Analysis Systems Mfr
S.I.C.: 3823
N.A.I.C.S.: 334513
Personnel:
Xiaoqiang Ao *(Chm)*

BEIJING SEVENSTAR ELECTRONICS CO., LTD.

1 Jiuxianqiao East Road
Chao Yang District, Beijing, 100016, China
Tel.: (86) 10 64361831
Fax: (86) 10 84566380
E-Mail: info@sevenstar.com.cn
Web Site: www.sevenstar.com.cn
Year Founded: 2001
002371—(SSE)
Sales Range: $75-99.9 Million
Emp.: 2,000
Business Description:
Electronic Equipment & Component Mfr
S.I.C.: 3679
N.A.I.C.S.: 334419
Personnel:
Wenliang Yang *(Chm)*

BEIJING SHENGTONG PRINTING CO., LTD.

11 Xingsheng Street
Beijing, 100176, China
Tel.: (86) 1067871609
Fax: (86) 1067892277
E-Mail: info@shengtongprint.com
Web Site: www.shengtongprint.com
Year Founded: 2000
002599—(SSE)
Sales Range: $25-49.9 Million
Emp.: 1,000
Business Description:
Printing Services
S.I.C.: 2759
N.A.I.C.S.: 323111
Personnel:
Chunlin Jia *(Chm)*

BEIJING SHOUHANG RESOURCES SAVING CO., LTD.

Building 20 Fengtai Technology Park
Beijing, 100072, China
Tel.: (86) 10 52255555
Fax: (86) 10 52256633
Web Site: www.sh-ihw.com
002665—(SSE)
Sales Range: $100-124.9 Million
Emp.: 700
Business Description:
Air Cooling Systems Mfr
S.I.C.: 3585
N.A.I.C.S.: 333415
Personnel:
Wenjia Huang *(Chm)*

BEIJING SPC ENVIRONMENT PROTECTION TECH CO., LTD.

10F People's Political Consul 69 West Balizhuang Road, Beijing, 100142, China
Tel.: (86) 1088146320
Web Site: www.qingxin.com.cn
002573—(SSE)
Sales Range: $25-49.9 Million
Emp.: 240
Business Description:
Gas Equipment Mfr
S.I.C.: 3533
N.A.I.C.S.: 333132
Personnel:
Kaiyuan Zhang *(Chm)*

BEIJING SWT COMMUNICATIONS CO., LTD.

Yanjiao Economic & Technical Development Zone
Yingbinbei Road Heibei, Beijing, 065201, China
Tel.: (86) 1061597788
Fax: (86) 10615977882015
E-Mail: baidongliang@swt-oc.com
Web Site: www.swt-oc.com
Sales Range: $50-74.9 Million
Emp.: 300
Business Description:
Holding Company; Optoelectronic Products Mfr
S.I.C.: 6719
N.A.I.C.S.: 551112
Personnel:
Wang Gong *(Gen Mgr)*

Joint Venture:

Beijing SWT Optical Communications Technologies, Co., Ltd. **(1)**
10th Floor Tower C2 Oriental Plaza No1 East Chang An Avenue
Dong Cheng District, Beijing, 100738, China
Tel.: (86) 1085180588
Fax: (86) 10 85185617
E-Mail: swt@swt-oc.com
Web Site: www.swt-oc.com
Sales Range: $1-9.9 Million
Optoelectronic Products Mfr; Owned 50% by Beijing SWT Communications Co., Ltd. & 50% by Polaray Optoelectronics Co., Ltd.
S.I.C.: 3674
N.A.I.C.S.: 334413

BEIJING TAIKONG PANEL INDUSTRY CORP.

5F North Road 1 Zhonghe Road
Qiaonan Fengtai District, Beijing, 100070, China
Tel.: (86) 10 63784254
Fax: (86) 10 83681107
E-Mail: qiguan@taikong.cn
Web Site: www.taikong.cn
300344—(CHIN)
Sales Range: $25-49.9 Million
Emp.: 160
Business Description:
Foam Cement Composites Mfr
S.I.C.: 3241
N.A.I.C.S.: 327310
Personnel:
Li Fan *(Chm)*

BEIJING TEAMSUN TECHNOLOGY CO., LTD.

(d/b/a Teamsun Group)
Floor 10th 11th Science Fortune Center
100085 Beijing, China
Tel.: (86) 1082733988
Fax: (86) 10 82733999
Web Site: www.teamsun.com.cn
600410—(SHG)
Sales Range: $800-899.9 Million
Emp.: 3,400
Business Description:
Computer System Integration Services; Software Products
S.I.C.: 7373
N.A.I.C.S.: 541512
Personnel:
Liankui Hu *(Chm)*
Weihang Wang *(Vice Chm & Pres)*
Board of Directors:
Liankui Hu
Xianchen Guo
Boxiong Lan
Jianzhu Liu
Yanjing Liu
Gang Su
Weihang Wang
Furong Ye
Wuxiang Zhu

Non-U.S. Subsidiary:

Automated Systems Holdings Limited **(1)**
15/F Topsail Plaza 11 On Sum Street
Sha Tin, China (Hong Kong) BM
Tel.: (852) 2601 6998 (68.43%)
Fax: (852) 2601 6936
E-Mail: asl_info@asl.com.hk
Web Site: www.asl.com.hk
0771—(HKG)
Rev.: $215,769,327
Assets: $134,651,911
Liabilities: $60,634,353
Net Worth: $74,017,558
Earnings: $5,311,966
Emp.: 1,779
Fiscal Year-end: 12/31/12
Computer Services; Communications Systems Engineering; Facilities Management; Business Data Processing Services; Systems Integration
S.I.C.: 7379
N.A.I.C.S.: 518210
Ready Yam Ting Lai *(Vice Chm)*
Henry Wing Choy Hui *(CEO)*
Yueou Wang *(CFO)*
Joan Chung Lei Chan *(Sec)*

Subsidiary:

ELM Computer Technologies Limited **(2)**
16/F Topsail Plaza 11 On Sum Street
Sha Tin, China (Hong Kong) HK
Tel.: (852) 25419900 (100%)
Fax: (852) 25411338
E-Mail: enquiry@elm.com.hk
Web Site: www.elm.com.hk
Emp.: 60
Computer Services; Communications Systems Engineering; Facilities Management; Business Data Processing Services; Systems Integration
S.I.C.: 7379
N.A.I.C.S.: 518210
John Li *(Mgr)*

Non-U.S. Subsidiaries:

ASL Automated (Thailand) Ltd. **(2)**
283 42 Home Place Office Building Unit 0901 9th Fl Soi Sukhumvit 55
Thonglor 13 Sukhumvit Rd, Bangkok, 10110, Thailand TH
Tel.: (66) 21853206 (100%)
Web Site: www.aslth.co.th
Computer Services; Communications Systems Engineering; Facilities Management; Business Data Processing Services; Systems Integration
S.I.C.: 7374
N.A.I.C.S.: 518210

Guangzhou Automated Systems Limited **(2)**
Room 2001-2003 Block 4 Dong Jun Plaza
836 Dong Feng Road East
Guangzhou, China
Tel.: (86) 2087605518
Fax: (86) 20 8767 5383
Web Site: www2.asl.com.hk/eng/aboutasl/locations.php
Computer Services; Communications Systems Engineering; Facilities Management; Business Data Processing Services; Systems Integration
S.I.C.: 7374
N.A.I.C.S.: 518210

Taiwan Automated Systems Ltd. **(2)**
3F No 18 Sec 6 Ming-Chuen E Rd
114 Nei-Hu Dist, Taipei, Taiwan
Tel.: (886) 287928598
Fax: (886) 287928569
Web Site: asl.com.hk
Computer Services; Communications Systems Engineering; Facilities Management; Business Data Processing Services; Systems Integration
S.I.C.: 7379
N.A.I.C.S.: 518210

BEIJING THUNISOFT CORPORATION LIMITED

East Road Building Tsinghua Science Park 25th Floor Block C
Haidian District, Beijing, 100084, China
Tel.: (86) 10 82622288
Fax: (86) 10 82150616
E-Mail: service@thunisoft.com
Web Site: www.thunisoft.com
300271—(CHIN)
Emp.: 880

Business Description:
Software Publisher
S.I.C.: 7372
N.A.I.C.S.: 511210
Personnel:
Xue Shao *(Chm)*

BEIJING TONG REN TANG CHINESE MEDICINE COMPANY LIMITED
3 Dai King Street Tai Po Industrial Estate
Tai Po, China (Hong Kong)
Tel.: (852) 28817989
Fax: (852) 28810839
E-Mail: info@tongrentangcm.com
Web Site: www.tongrentangcm.com
8138—(HKG)
Business Description:
Chinese Medicine Retailer, Distr & Mfr
S.I.C.: 5912
N.A.I.C.S.: 446110
Personnel:
Yong Ling Ding *(Mng Dir)*

BEIJING TRS INFORMATION TECHNOLOGY CO., LTD.
16th Floor Block B Datun Lu Feng Lin Xiao
Chaoyang District, Beijing, 100101, China
Tel.: (86) 10 64848899
Fax: (86) 10 64879084
E-Mail: trs@trs.com.cn
Web Site: www.trs.com.cn
Year Founded: 1993
300229—(CHIN)
Emp.: 430
Business Description:
Software Publisher; Search, Content Management & Text Mining Services
S.I.C.: 7372
N.A.I.C.S.: 511210
Personnel:
Yuqin Li *(Chm)*

BEIJING UNISTRONG SCIENCE & TECHNOLOGY CO., LTD.
6F East A2 Building 9 Jiuxianqiao East Road
Chaoyang District, Beijing, 100016, China
Tel.: (86) 10 5827 5050
Fax: (86) 10 5827 5100
E-Mail: overseas@unistrong.com
Web Site: www.unistrong.com
Year Founded: 1994
002383—(SSE)
Sales Range: $25-49.9 Million
Business Description:
GPS, Receivers, Multi-System Navigation, Surveying, GNSS Data Post-Processing & System Integration Products Mfr
S.I.C.: 3812
N.A.I.C.S.: 334511
Personnel:
Xinping Guo *(Pres)*
U.S. Subsidiary:

Hemisphere GNSS (USA) Inc. **(1)**
8444 N 90th St Ste 120
Scottsdale, AZ 85258 DE
Tel.: (480) 348-6380
Toll Free: (855) 203-1770
E-Mail: precision@hemispheregnss.com
Web Site: www.hemispheregnss.com
Positioning, Guidance & Machine Control Products & Software Developer & Mfr
S.I.C.: 3812
N.A.I.C.S.: 334511
Jonathan W. Ladd *(Chm)*
Philip W. Gabriel *(Pres)*
Michael Whitehead *(CTO & VP)*
Rodger Conner *(Sec)*

Non-U.S. Subsidiary:

UniStrong Technology (S) Pte. Ltd. **(1)**
51 Ubi Ave 1 Unit 01-22 Paya Ubi Industrial Park
Singapore, Singapore
Tel.: (65) 62968238
Fax: (65) 62950996
E-Mail: sales@unistrong.sg
Global Positioning System Devices Mfr
S.I.C.: 3663
N.A.I.C.S.: 334220
Edward Teo *(Gen Mgr)*

BEIJING VANTONE REAL ESTATE CO., LTD.
D-4F Vantone Center Jia No 6 Chaowai Street
Chaoyang District, Beijing, China 100020
Tel.: (86) 10 59070710
Fax: (86) 10 59071150
E-Mail: vantone@vantone.com
Web Site: www.vantone.com
Year Founded: 1998
600246—(SHG)
Rev.: $646,603,070
Assets: $1,707,003,204
Liabilities: $1,067,576,081
Net Worth: $639,427,123
Earnings: $75,581,948
Emp.: 583
Fiscal Year-end: 12/31/12
Business Description:
Property Development Services
S.I.C.: 6531
N.A.I.C.S.: 531311
Personnel:
Li Xu *(Chm)*
Peng Yao *(Deputy Chm)*
Dajun Yun *(CEO)*
Xiaoyang Xu *(CFO)*
Board of Directors:
Li Xu
Peng Yao

BEIJING VENUSTECH INC.
Building 21 ZhongGuanCun Software Park No 8 Dongbeiwang West Road
Haidian District, Beijing, China 100193
Tel.: (86) 1082779088
Fax: (86) 1082779000
E-Mail: venus@venustech.com.cn
Web Site: www.venustech.com.cn
Year Founded: 1996
002439—(SSE)
Sales Range: $50-74.9 Million
Emp.: 947
Business Description:
Network Security Management Services
S.I.C.: 7382
N.A.I.C.S.: 561621
Personnel:
Jia Wang *(CEO)*

BEIJING VRV SOFTWARE CORPORATION LIMITED
C-1602 Zhongguancun Sci Dev 34 South Street
Haidian District, Beijing, 100081, China
Tel.: (86) 10 6214 0485
Fax: (86) 10 6214 7259
Web Site: www.vrv.com.cn
300352—(CHIN)
Sales Range: $25-49.9 Million
Emp.: 630
Business Description:
Security Software Publisher
S.I.C.: 7372
N.A.I.C.S.: 511210
Personnel:
Hao Lin *(Chm)*

BEIJING WANDONG MEDICAL EQUIPMENT CO., LTD.
A3 Block 9 Jiu-Xian-Qiao-Dong Road
Chaoyang, Beijing, 100016, China
Tel.: (86) 10 8457 5792
Fax: (86) 10 8457 5794
E-Mail: office@wandong.com.cn
Web Site: www.wandong.com.cn
Year Founded: 1997
600055—(SHG)
Sales Range: $75-99.9 Million
Emp.: 930
Business Description:
Medical Equipment Mfr
S.I.C.: 3841
N.A.I.C.S.: 339112
Personnel:
Xuan He *(Chm)*

BEIJING WATER BUSINESS DOCTOR CO., LTD.
Room 9311 Jingshi Mansion 19 Xinjiekouwai Avenue
Haidian District, Beijing, 100875, China
Tel.: (86) 10 58800231
Fax: (86) 10 58800018
E-Mail: waterbd@waterbd.cn
Web Site: www.waterbd.cn
300055—(CHIN)
Sales Range: $50-74.9 Million
Emp.: 300
Business Description:
Water Treatment Systems Mfr
S.I.C.: 4953
N.A.I.C.S.: 562211
Personnel:
Piaoyang Wang *(Chm)*

BEIJING WATERTEK INFORMATION TECHNOLOGY CO., LTD.
1006 229 Haitai Mansion North Sihuan Middle Road
Haidian District, Beijing, 100083, China
Tel.: (86) 10 82883933
Fax: (86) 10 82883858
Web Site: www.watertek.com
300324—(CHIN)
Sales Range: $25-49.9 Million
Emp.: 300
Business Description:
Computer Related Services
S.I.C.: 7379
N.A.I.C.S.: 541519
Personnel:
Jiangtao Chen *(Chm)*

BEIQI FOTON MOTOR COMPANY LTD.
Shayang Road
Shahe Town Changping District, Beijing, 102206, China
Tel.: (86) 10 8072 0170
Fax: (86) 10 8071 6402
E-Mail: jckgs@foton.com.cn
Web Site: www.foton.com.cn
Year Founded: 1996
600166—(SHG)
Sales Range: $1-4.9 Billion
Emp.: 21,600
Business Description:
Motor Vehicles & Trucks Mfr
S.I.C.: 3524
N.A.I.C.S.: 336111
Personnel:
Heyi Xu *(Chm)*
Jinyu Wang *(Pres & CEO)*

BEJO ZADEN B.V.
Trambaan 1
PO Box 50
1749 ZH Warmenhuizen, Netherlands
Tel.: (31) 226396162
Fax: (31) 226393504
E-Mail: info@bejo.com
Web Site: www.bejo.com
Year Founded: 1963
Sales Range: $25-49.9 Million
Emp.: 600
Business Description:
Vegetable Seeds Breeding, Production, Processing & Sales
S.I.C.: 0139
N.A.I.C.S.: 111998
Personnel:
Ger Beemsterboer *(Pres)*
U.S. Subsidiary:

Bejo Seeds Inc. **(1)**
1972 Silver Spur Pl
Oceano, CA 93445
Tel.: (805) 473-2199
Fax: (805) 473-0897
E-Mail: info@bejoseeds.com
Web Site: www.bejoseeds.com
Sales Range: $10-24.9 Million
Emp.: 36
Wholesale Vegetable Seeds
S.I.C.: 5191
N.A.I.C.S.: 424910
Mark Overduin *(Pres)*

BEKB-BCBE
(See Under Berner Kantonalbank AG)

BEKO HOLDING AG
Karl-Farkas-Gasse 22/7 Stock
A-1030 Vienna, Austria
Tel.: (43) 171337330
Fax: (43) 17133120746
E-Mail: investor.relations@beko.at
Web Site: www.beko.eu
BEO—(BER DEU MUN)
Sales Range: $250-299.9 Million
Emp.: 1,809
Business Description:
Holding Company; IT Services & Solutions
S.I.C.: 6719
N.A.I.C.S.: 551112
Personnel:
Josef Blazicek *(Chm-Supervisory Bd)*
Hubert Gmeinbauer *(Vice Chm-Supervisory Bd)*
Peter Kotauczek *(CEO)*
Peter Fritsch *(Deputy CEO)*
Supervisory Board of Directors:
Josef Blazicek
Hubert Gmeinbauer
Rudolf Knuenz
Manfred Pauer
Stefan Pierer
Friedrich Roithner

BEKUPLAST GMBH
Industriestrasse 1
49824 Ringe, Germany
Tel.: (49) 594493330
Fax: (49) 5944933350
E-Mail: info@bekuplast.com
Web Site: www.bekuplast.com
Rev.: $22,011,880
Emp.: 160
Business Description:
Transport & Storage Container Mfr
S.I.C.: 3499
N.A.I.C.S.: 332439

bekuplast GmbH—(Continued)

Personnel:
Josef Dworok *(Co-Mng Dir)*
Wilhelm Roelofs *(Co-Mng Dir)*

BEKY A.S.
Podrybnicka
PO Box 29
069 01 Snina, Slovakia
Tel.: (421) 577682621
Fax: (421) 577682297
E-Mail: beky@beky.sk
Web Site: www.beky.sk
Year Founded: 1992
Emp.: 450
Business Description:
Flooring Mills
S.I.C.: 2421
N.A.I.C.S.: 321912

BEL AIR INDUSTRIES
15 Rue De Paris
69170 Tarare, Rhone, France
Tel.: (33) 474053060
Fax: (33) 474050601
E-Mail: cjacquenod@belairindustries.fr
Web Site: www.belairindustries.com
Sls.: $39,200,000
Emp.: 40
S.I.C.: 2299
N.A.I.C.S.: 313110
Personnel:
Tokcan Cahit *(Gen Mgr)*
Board of Directors:
Philippe Gonzalvez
Olgun Zorlu

BEL GLOBAL RESOURCES HOLDINGS LIMITED
10th Floor Haleson Building 1 Jubilee Street
Central, China (Hong Kong)
Tel.: (852) 3618 5100
Fax: (852) 3590 5115
E-Mail: general@belglobal.com
Web Site: www.belglobal.com
Sales Range: $25-49.9 Million
Emp.: 350
Business Description:
Coal & Nickel Mining Services;
Apparel Mfr
S.I.C.: 1241
N.A.I.C.S.: 213113
Personnel:
Wing Tak Li *(Sec & Dir-Fin)*
Board of Directors:
Dubing Cai
Soo-Kong Chang
Paul Wai Chi Ho
Wing Tak Li
Stephen Chin Mong Sy
Pat Shan Shan Sze
Lok Wong
Legal Counsel:
Conyers, Dill & Pearman
2901 One Exchange Square
8 Connaught Place, Central, China (Hong Kong)
Chiu & Partners
40th Fl Jardine House 1 Connaught Place
Central, China (Hong Kong)
Subsidiary:

Bel Nickel Resources Limited (1)
10 F Haleson Bldg 1 Jubilee Stch
Central, China (Hong Kong)
Tel.: (852) 36185100
Fax: (852) 35905115
E-Mail: general@belglobal.com
Emp.: 20
Minerals Whslr
S.I.C.: 5052
N.A.I.C.S.: 423520

BELANGER RV
1472 Youville Dr
Orleans, ON, K1C 2X8, Canada
Tel.: (613) 824-1599
Fax: (613) 837-9284
Toll Free: (866) 948-1917
E-Mail: belangerrv@belangerrv.ca
Web Site: orleansrv.ca
Rev.: $60,300,000
Emp.: 100
Business Description:
New & Used Car Dealers
S.I.C.: 5511
N.A.I.C.S.: 441110
Personnel:
Marc Belanger *(Gen Mgr)*

BELAPART S.A.
Av Presidente Wilson 231 - 28 Floor/parte
20030021 Rio de Janeiro, Brazil
Tel.: (55) 21 3804 3700
Fax: (55) 21 3804 3480
Web Site: www.belapart.com.br
Year Founded: 1997
PBEL3B—(BRAZ)
Business Description:
Investment Management Services
S.I.C.: 6799
N.A.I.C.S.: 523920
Personnel:
Maria Amalia Delfim de Melo Coutrim *(Dir-IR)*

BELAVIA NATSIONALYNAYA VIAKOMPANIYA R.U.P.
14 Nemiga Str
220004 Minsk, Belarus
Tel.: (375) 1722025555
Fax: (375) 172292383
E-Mail: info@belavia.by
Web Site: www.belavia.by
Year Founded: 1996
Emp.: 1,500
Business Description:
Airline Services
S.I.C.: 4512
N.A.I.C.S.: 481111
Personnel:
Anatoly Nikolayevich Gusarov *(Dir Gen)*

BELC CO., LTD.
5456 Yodo Yorii-Machi Ohsato-Gun
Saitama, 369-1298, Japan
Tel.: (81) 485791111
Fax: (81) 485791112
Web Site: www.belc.co.jp
9974—(TKS)
Sales Range: $1-4.9 Billion
Emp.: 740
Business Description:
Food Supermarkets, Grocery Stores & Restaurants Owner & Operator
S.I.C.: 5411
N.A.I.C.S.: 445110
Personnel:
Isao Harashima *(Pres)*

BELFE S.P.A.
Via Roma 28
I 36063 Marostica, VI, Italy
Tel.: (39) 0424488348
Fax: (39) 0424488560
E-Mail: info@belfe.it
Web Site: www.belfe.it
Year Founded: 1920
Emp.: 250
Business Description:
Clothing Mfr
Import Export
S.I.C.: 2399
N.A.I.C.S.: 315210

BELFIUS BANK SA/NV
Pachecolaan 44
1000 Brussels, Belgium
Tel.: (32) 22221111
Fax: (32) 22221122
E-Mail: info@dexia.com
Web Site: www.dexia.be
Emp.: 7,600
Business Description:
Banking Services
S.I.C.: 6029
N.A.I.C.S.: 522110
Personnel:
Jos Clijsters *(Pres)*
Johan Vankelecom *(CFO)*
Luc Van Thielen *(COO)*
Eric Hermann *(Chief Risk Officer)*
Ann De Roeck *(Sec & Head-Compliance, Tax & Legal Dept)*
Board of Directors:
Alfred Bouckaert
Ann De Roeck
Marie-Gemma Dequae
Wouter Devriendt
Martine Durez
Pierre Francotte
Dirk Gyselinck
Roger Leyssens
Guy Quaden
Chris Sunt
Lutgart Van den Berghe
Luc Van Thielen
Rudi Vander Vennet
Serge Wibaut

Subsidiaries:

Belfius Commercial Finance (1)
Dexia Tower Rogierplein 11
Brussels, B 1210, Belgium (100%)
Tel.: (32) 22852611
Fax: (32) 22852699
E-Mail:
Sls.: $3,648,470
Emp.: 41
Short-Term Business Credit Institution
S.I.C.: 6159
N.A.I.C.S.: 522298
Ivan DeCoen *(Mng Dir)*

Belfius Insurance (1)
Ave Livingstone 6
B 1000 Brussels, Belgium (100%)
Tel.: (32) 22866111
Fax: (32) 22867040
E-Mail:
Sales Range: $250-299.9 Million
Emp.: 1,000
Insurance Services
S.I.C.: 6411
N.A.I.C.S.: 524298
Guieo Roelendt *(Mgr)*

Belfius Lease (1)
Boulevard Pacheco 44
B 1000 Brussels, Belgium (100%)
Tel.: (32) 22223708
Fax: (32) 22223713
Web Site: www.dexia.be
Emp.: 40
Business Credit Services
S.I.C.: 6159
N.A.I.C.S.: 522298

Units:

Belfius Auto Lease SA/NV (2)
RogierTower Rogierplein 11
1210 Brussels, Belgium (99%)
Tel.: (32) 2 285 35 94
Fax: (32) 2 285 35 45
E-Mail: autolease@belfius.be
Web Site: www.belfius-autolease.be
Sls.: $34,345,940
Emp.: 30
Vehicle Leasing Services
S.I.C.: 7515
N.A.I.C.S.: 532112

Belfius Lease Services SA/NV (2)
Avenue Livingstone Rueeas 6 place Rogaer
B 1210 Brussels, Belgium (100%)
Tel.: (32) 22223836
Fax: (32) 22223713
Emp.: 60
S.I.C.: 6141
N.A.I.C.S.: 522210
Jean-Mitchel Baetsles *(Gen Mgr)*

Non-U.S. Subsidiaries:

Belfius Ireland (1)
(Formerly Dexia Investments Ireland)
6 Georges Dock IFSC
Dublin, 1, Ireland (100%)
Tel.: (353) 16455000
Fax: (353) 18291577
E-Mail:
Emp.: 50
Investment Services
S.I.C.: 6282
N.A.I.C.S.: 523930
Eamonn Tuohy *(Mng Dir)*

Colin Buchanan & Partners Ltd. (1)
20 Eastbourne Ter
W2 6LG London, United Kingdom UK
Tel.: (44) 2070531300 (100%)
Fax: (44) 2070531301
E-Mail: cbp@cbuchanan.co.uk
Web Site: www.cbuchanan.co.uk
Rev.: $26,016,690
Emp.: 150
S.I.C.: 6153
N.A.I.C.S.: 522210
Chris Pyatt *(Mng Dir)*

Eurco Ltd. (1)
6 Georges Dock IFSC
Dublin, 1, Ireland (100%)
Tel.: (353) 18515200
Fax: (353) 18290433
E-Mail: eurco@eurco.ie
Web Site: www.dexia.com
Premiums: $30,004,224
Emp.: 9
S.I.C.: 6153
N.A.I.C.S.: 522210
Carmel O'Brien *(Mng Dir)*

Eurco Re Ltd. (1)
6 Georges Dock
Dublin, IFSC, 1, Ireland (100%)
Tel.: (353) 018515200
Fax: (353) 18290433
E-Mail: eurco@eurco.ie
Premiums: $266,715,712
Emp.: 9
Insurance Agents, Brokers & Service
S.I.C.: 6411
N.A.I.C.S.: 524298
Carmel O'Brien *(Mgr)*

Eurco Ruck AG (1)
Beethovenstrasse 49
Zurich, 8022, Switzerland (100%)
Tel.: (41) 433443355
Fax: (41) 433443366
Sales Range: $50-74.9 Million
Emp.: 7
Business Services
S.I.C.: 7389
N.A.I.C.S.: 561499

Eurco SA (1)
2 Rue Nicolas Bove
L 1253 Luxembourg, Luxembourg (100%)
Tel.: (352) 227343
Fax: (352) 227347
E-Mail: eurco@eurco.lu
Web Site: www.dexia.com
Emp.: 9
Insurance Agents, Brokers & Service
S.I.C.: 6411
N.A.I.C.S.: 524298
Paridaens Rudy *(Mng Dir)*

IWI International Wealth Insurer S.A. (1)
2 Rue Nicolas Bove 2nd Fl
L 1253 Luxembourg, Luxembourg (100%)
Tel.: (352) 2625441
Fax: (352) 2625445480
E-Mail:
Web Site: www.iwi.lu
Emp.: 80
Life Insurance Services
S.I.C.: 6311
N.A.I.C.S.: 524113

Parfipar SA (1)
Boulevard Royal 10A
Luxembourg, L-2093, Luxembourg (100%)
Provider of Financial Services

S.I.C.: 6099
N.A.I.C.S.: 522320

Reagra SA (1)
Rue de la gare 65
Luxembourg, Luxembourg (33%)
Personal Credit Institution
S.I.C.: 6141
N.A.I.C.S.: 522210

Securenta Conseil (1)
10 A Boulevard Royal
Luxembourg, L-2449, Luxembourg (100%)
Personal Credit Institutions
S.I.C.: 6141
N.A.I.C.S.: 522210

Securifund NV (1)
Polarisweg 35
PB 767
Willemstad, Curacao (100%)
Personal Credit Institutions
S.I.C.: 6153
N.A.I.C.S.: 522210

BELGACOM S.A.

Boulevard du Roi Albert II 27
1030 Brussels, Belgium
Tel.: (32) 22024111
Fax: (32) 22036593
E-Mail: press@belgacom.be
Web Site: www.belgacom.com
Year Founded: 1994
BELG—(EUR)
Rev.: $8,698,950,540
Assets: $11,053,401,870
Liabilities: $6,707,965,110
Net Worth: $4,345,436,760
Earnings: $981,357,930
Emp.: 15,859
Fiscal Year-end: 12/31/12

Business Description:
Telecommunications Services
S.I.C.: 4813
N.A.I.C.S.: 517110

Personnel:
Stefaan De Clerck *(Chm)*
Dominique Leroy *(CEO)*
Ray Stewart *(CFO & Exec VP-Fin)*
Michel Georgis *(Exec VP-HR)*
Dirk Lybaert *(Exec VP-Corp Affairs)*
Geert Standaert *(Exec VP-Svc Delivery Engine & Wholesale)*
Bart Van Den Meersche *(Exec VP-Enterprise Bus Unit)*
Phillip Vandervoort *(Exec VP-Consumer Bus Unit)*

Board of Directors:
Stefaan De Clerck
Jo Cornu
Pierre Demuelenaere
Guido J. M. Demuynck
Theo Dilissen
Carine Doutrelepont
Martine Durez
Mimi Lamote
Michel Moll
Michele Sioen
Agnes Touraine
Paul Van de Perre
Lutgart Van den Berghe
Catherine Vandenborre

Subsidiaries:

Belgacom Group International Services SA (1)
Koning Albert II laan 27
1030 Brussels, Belgium
Tel.: (32) 22026040
Fax: (32) 22036192
Web Site: www.Belgacom.be
Integrated Telecom Services
S.I.C.: 8748
N.A.I.C.S.: 541618
Gilbert Kerremans *(CEO)*

Belgacom Mobile S.A (1)
Rue Du Progres 55
1210 Brussels, Belgium
Tel.: (32) 22054000
Fax: (32) 22054041
E-Mail: public.relation@belgacom.be
Web Site: www.proximus.be
Rev.: $6,608,066,560
Emp.: 2,100
Mobile Telecommunications Services
S.I.C.: 4812
N.A.I.C.S.: 517210
Michelle Georgys *(CEO)*

Connectimmo SA (1)
Rue Lebeau 2
1000 Brussels, Belgium
Tel.: (32) 22040856
Fax: (32) 22032776
E-Mail: info@connectimmo.be
Web Site: www.connectimmo.be
Emp.: 50
Real Estate Management Services
S.I.C.: 6531
N.A.I.C.S.: 531210
Steven Van Casteren *(CEO)*

Telindus Group NV (1)
Geldenaaksebaan 335
3001 Heverlee, Belgium
Tel.: (32) 16382011
Fax: (32) 16400102
Web Site: www.telindus.com
Emp.: 800
Information Technology Services
S.I.C.: 7373
N.A.I.C.S.: 541512
Marek Lowther *(Mng Dir)*

Subsidiary:

Telindus NV (2)
Geldenaaksebaan 335
Heverlee, 3001 Leuven, Flemish Brabant, Belgium
Tel.: (32) 16382011
Fax: (32) 16400102
Web Site: www.belgacom.be
Emp.: 1,000
Internet Software Development Services
S.I.C.: 7371
N.A.I.C.S.: 541511
Bart van den Meersche *(Gen Mgr)*

Non-U.S. Subsidiaries:

Groupe Telindus France SA (2)
12, avenue de l Oceanie Z.A. Courtaboeuf
3 LES ULIS
91940 Villebon-sur-Yvette, Essonne, France
Tel.: (33) 169183232
Fax: (33) 169356310
E-Mail: accueil@telindus.fr
Web Site: www.telindus.fr
Emp.: 300
Information Technology Consulting Services
S.I.C.: 7373
N.A.I.C.S.: 541512
Rhenry Juin *(Mng Dir)*

ISit BV (2)
Krommewetering 7
3543 AP Utrecht, Netherlands
Tel.: (31) 302477711
Fax: (31) 302477506
E-Mail: info@telindus-isit.nl
Web Site: www.isit.nl
Emp.: 200
Computer Software Consulting Services
S.I.C.: 7373
N.A.I.C.S.: 541512

ISit Education & Support BV (2)
Krommewetering
Utrecht, 3543AP, Netherlands
Tel.: (31) 302477711
Fax: (31) 302477737
Emp.: 200
Computer Software Consulting Services
S.I.C.: 7373
N.A.I.C.S.: 541512

ISit ICT Services BV (2)
Krommewetering 7
Utrecht, 3543 AP, Netherlands
Tel.: (31) 302477711
Fax: (31) 302477506
E-Mail: info@telindus-isit.nl
Web Site: www.telindus.nl
Telecommunication Services
S.I.C.: 4813
N.A.I.C.S.: 517110

Telectronics SA (2)
2 Rue des Mines
4244 Esch-sur-Alzette, Luxembourg
Tel.: (352) 508373
Fax: (352) 450911
E-Mail: reception@telindus.lu
Web Site: www.telindus.lu
Emp.: 330
Telecommunications Equipment Distr
S.I.C.: 5065
N.A.I.C.S.: 423690
Hoffman Gerard *(Gen Mgr)*

Telindus BV (2)
Krommewetering 7
3543 AP Utrecht, Netherlands
Tel.: (31) 302477711
Fax: (31) 302477569
E-Mail: telindus@esit.nl
Web Site: www.telindus.nl
Information Technology Consulting Services
S.I.C.: 8999
N.A.I.C.S.: 541690

Telindus France SA (2)
10 Ave de Norvege
91140 Villebon-sur-Yvette, Essonne, France
Tel.: (33) 169183232
Fax: (33) 169285501
E-Mail: infos@telindus.fr
Web Site: www.telindus.fr
Emp.: 2,700
Information Technology Consulting Services
S.I.C.: 7373
N.A.I.C.S.: 541512
Henri Juin *(Mng Dir)*

Telindus International BV (2)
Krommewetering 7
3543 AP Utrecht, Netherlands
Tel.: (31) 302477711
Fax: (31) 302477737
Information Technology Consulting Services
S.I.C.: 8999
N.A.I.C.S.: 541690

Telindus Kft. (2)
Petzval Jozsef u 52
1119 Budapest, Hungary
Tel.: (36) 14658040
Fax: (36) 13502761
E-Mail: info@ictshungary.hu
Web Site: www.ictshungary.hu/en
Emp.: 6
Information Technology Services
S.I.C.: 7373
N.A.I.C.S.: 541512
Tebor Tiss *(Mng Dir)*

Telindus Limited (2)
Unit No 1106 11th Fl Prosperity Ctr
Kowloon, China (Hong Kong)
Tel.: (852) 28022126
Fax: (852) 28023809
E-Mail: info@telindus.com
Web Site: www.telindus.com
Emp.: 100
Information Technology Services
S.I.C.: 7373
N.A.I.C.S.: 541512

Non-U.S. Subsidiary:

Yunnan Telindus Technology Co. Ltd. (3)
Room C22-23 Innovation Park No 3 Jinkai Road
Kunming Econ & Tech Devel Zone, Kunming, Yunnan, China
Tel.: (86) 8717270668
Fax: (86) 8716118560
Information Technology Services
S.I.C.: 7373
N.A.I.C.S.: 541512

Telindus SA (2)
Route d'Arlon 81-83
8009 Strassen, Luxembourg
Tel.: (352) 4509151
Fax: (352) 450911
E-Mail: calldesk@telindus.lu
Web Site: www.telindus.lu
Emp.: 100
Internet Software Development Services
S.I.C.: 7371
N.A.I.C.S.: 541511
Meyers Armand *(Mng Dir)*

Telindus SAU (2)
Plaza Ciudad de Viena 6 2a Planta
28040 Madrid, Spain
Tel.: (34) 914560008
Fax: (34) 915361074
E-Mail: info@telindus.es
Web Site: www.telindus.es
Emp.: 300
Information Technology Consulting Services
S.I.C.: 8999
N.A.I.C.S.: 541690

Non-U.S. Subsidiaries:

Carib - online NV (1)
Fokkerweg 26
Willemstad, Curacao
Tel.: (599) 94616063
Fax: (599) 94618301
E-Mail: info@carib-online.net
Web Site: www.carib-online.com
Internet Service Provider
S.I.C.: 4899
N.A.I.C.S.: 517919

Scarlet NV (1)
Carlistraat 2
1140 Evere, Belgium BE
Mailing Address:
Postbus 10008
3570 Alken, Belgium
Tel.: (32) 2275 3311
Web Site: www.scarlet.be
Holding Company; Telecommunications Services
S.I.C.: 4813
N.A.I.C.S.: 551112
Matthijs Kamp *(Gen Dir)*

Subsidiary:

Scarlet Belgium NV (2)
Belgicastraat 5
1930 Zaventem, Flemish Brabant, Belgium
Tel.: (32) 22753311
Fax: (32) 22753333
E-Mail: info@scarlet.be
Web Site: www.scarlet.be
Integrated Telecommunication Services
S.I.C.: 4899
N.A.I.C.S.: 517919

Subsidiaries:

Scarlet Business NV (3)
Belgicastraat 5
1930 Zaventem, Flemish Brabant, Belgium
Tel.: (32) 22753311
Fax: (32) 22753671
E-Mail: netcenter@belgacom.be
Web Site: www.scarletbusiness.be
Emp.: 550
Integrated Telecom Services
S.I.C.: 8748
N.A.I.C.S.: 541618

Scarlet Extended NV (3)
Carlistraat 2
1140 Evere, Belgium
Tel.: (32) 22753311
Fax: (32) 22754001
Web Site: www.scarlet.be
Emp.: 120
Internet & Telecommunication Services
S.I.C.: 4813
N.A.I.C.S.: 517110
Pierre Evrard *(Gen Mgr)*

Scarlet Telecom BVBA (3)
Belgicastraat 5
1930 Zaventem, Flemish Brabant, Belgium
Tel.: (32) 80084111
Fax: (32) 32 029 4460
Integrated Telecom Services
S.I.C.: 8748
N.A.I.C.S.: 541618

Non-U.S. Subsidiaries:

Scarlet B.V. (2)
Fokkerweg 26 Suite 106 Ground Floor
Willemstad, Curacao CW
Tel.: (599) 94616063
Fax: (599) 8663456242
Toll Free: 8663456242
E-Mail: info@scarlet.an
Web Site: www.scarlet.an
Internet Service Provider
S.I.C.: 4899
N.A.I.C.S.: 517919

Tango Services SA (1)
Rue de Luxembourg 177
8077 Bertrange, Luxembourg
Tel.: (352) 691700777
Fax: (352) 27777222

Belgacom S.A.—(Continued)

E-Mail: info@tango.lu
Web Site: www.tango.lu
Emp.: 100
Telecommunication Services
S.I.C.: 4812
N.A.I.C.S.: 517210
Didier Rouma *(Gen Mgr)*

Subsidiaries:

Tango Mobile SA (2)
Rue de Luxembourg 177
8077 Bertrange, Luxembourg
Tel.: (352) 27777101
Fax: (352) 27777312
E-Mail: tangoit@tango.lu
Web Site: www.tango.lu
Emp.: 100
Integrated Telecom Services
S.I.C.: 8748
N.A.I.C.S.: 541618
Didier Rouma *(Gen Mgr)*

Tango SA (2)
Rue de Luxembourg 177
8077 Bertrange, Luxembourg
Tel.: (352) 27777101
Fax: (352) 27777209
E-Mail: info@tango.lu
Web Site: www.tango.lu
Sales Range: $125-149.9 Million
Emp.: 100
Integrated Telecom Services
S.I.C.: 8748
N.A.I.C.S.: 541618
Didier Rouma *(CEO)*

Telindus PSF SA (1)
Rue des Mines 2
4244 Esch-sur-Alzette, Luxembourg
Tel.: (352) 5328201
Fax: (352) 4509151
Internet Software Development Services
S.I.C.: 7371
N.A.I.C.S.: 541511

BELGRAVIUM TECHNOLOGIES PLC

Campus Road Listerhills Science Park
Bradford, West Yorkshire, BD7 1HR, United Kingdom
Tel.: (44) 1274 741 860
Fax: (44) 1274 718 801
E-Mail: investor@belgravium.com
Web Site: www.belgravium-technologies.com
BVM—(AIM)
Rev.: $13,690,865
Assets: $23,439,822
Liabilities: $5,860,745
Net Worth: $17,579,077
Earnings: $530,641
Emp.: 74
Fiscal Year-end: 12/31/12

Business Description:
Enterprise Mobile Computing Solutions
S.I.C.: 7372
N.A.I.C.S.: 511210

Personnel:
John Kembery *(Chm)*
Mark Hardy *(Mng Dir)*
Chris Phillips *(Sec)*

Board of Directors:
John Kembery
Mark Hardy
Chris Phillips
Mike Unwin

Legal Counsel:
Harrison Clark
5 Deansway
Worcester, United Kingdom

Subsidiaries:

Belgravium Ltd. (1)
Campus Rd
Listerhills Sci Park, Bradford, West Yorkshire, BD7 1HR, United Kingdom
Tel.: (44) 1274741860
Fax: (44) 1274741862
E-Mail: sales@belgravium.com
Web Site: www.belgravium.com
Emp.: 3
Data Capture Systems Services
S.I.C.: 7374
N.A.I.C.S.: 518210
Mike Turner *(Mgr-Mktg)*

Novo IVC Ltd. (1)
7 Clarendon Place
Leamington Spa, Warks, CV32 5QL, United Kingdom
Tel.: (44) 1926831173
Fax: (44) 1926330311
E-Mail: mail@novoivc.com
Web Site: www.novoivc.com
Emp.: 12
Mobile Phones Services
S.I.C.: 4812
N.A.I.C.S.: 517210
Rowan Welch *(Mgr-Comml)*

Touchstar Technologies Ltd. (1)
7 Com Way Trafford Park
Manchester, M17 1HW, United Kingdom
Tel.: (44) 1618745050
Fax: (44) 1618745088
Web Site: www.touchpc.com
Emp.: 40
Mobile Computing Services
S.I.C.: 7389
N.A.I.C.S.: 561990

BELHASA GROUP OF COMPANIES

(d/b/a Belhasa International LLC)
El Ettehad St
PO Box 1286
Dubai, United Arab Emirates
Tel.: (971) 42662319
Fax: (971) 42663809
E-Mail: bhi@belhasa.ae
Web Site: www.belhasa.com
Emp.: 4,600

Business Description:
Holding Company
S.I.C.: 6719
N.A.I.C.S.: 551112

Personnel:
Ahmed Saif Belhasa *(Chm)*
Amar Ahammed Belhasa *(Vice Chm)*

Board of Directors:
Ahmed Saif Belhasa
Amar Ahammed Belhasa

Subsidiaries:

Belhasa Actioncrete International (1)
PO Box 1286
Dubai, United Arab Emirates
Tel.: (971) 42662319
Fax: (971) 42663809
E-Mail: dhi@belhasa.ae
Web Site: www.belhasa.com
Provider of Maintenance & Repair Services
S.I.C.: 7699
N.A.I.C.S.: 811412

Belhasa Anthony Pools Contracting (1)
PO Box 5120
Dubai, United Arab Emirates
Tel.: (971) 42 668440
Fax: (971) 42 692774
Mfr. of Swimming Pools; Provider of Landscaping Services
S.I.C.: 0781
N.A.I.C.S.: 541320

Belhasa Automotive Service Center & Spare Parts (1)
Alquoz 4 Interchange Shakih Rd
PO Box 61627
Dubai, United Arab Emirates (100%)
Tel.: (971) 43472050
Fax: (971) 43474078
E-Mail: autobh@emirates.net.ae
Web Site: www.belhasamotors.com
Emp.: 100
Provider of Automotive Maintenance & Repair
S.I.C.: 7539
N.A.I.C.S.: 811198
Amar Ahmed Belhasa *(Mng Dir)*

Belhasa Engineering & Contracting Company (1)
Belhasa Bldg Hor Al Anz Area Mezzanine Fl
PO Box 5450
Dubai, United Arab Emirates
Tel.: (971) 42663925
Fax: (971) 42660585
E-Mail: dhecco@belhasa.ae
Emp.: 4,000
Provider of Engineering & Construction Services
S.I.C.: 8711
N.A.I.C.S.: 541330

Belhasa International Company (1)
Dubai Sharjah Rd Belhasa Bldg M Fl
PO Box 1286
Dubai, United Arab Emirates
Tel.: (971) 42662319
Fax: (971) 42623809
E-Mail: bhi@belhasa.ae
Web Site: www.belhasa.com
Emp.: 100
Designer of Interior Decorations
S.I.C.: 7389
N.A.I.C.S.: 541410
Ahmed Sais Belhasa *(Chm)*

Belhasa Joinery & Decoration Company LLC (1)
PO Box 84918
Dubai, United Arab Emirates
Tel.: (971) 42677252
Fax: (971) 42677253
E-Mail: info@belhasajoinery.com
Web Site: www.belhasajoinery.com
Emp.: 200
Interior Design & Decoration Services
S.I.C.: 7389
N.A.I.C.S.: 541410
Mohammed Asif *(Gen Mgr)*

Belhasa Motors Company (1)
Alquoz 4 Interchange Shakih Rd
PO Box 61627
Dubai, United Arab Emirates
Tel.: (971) 43472050
Fax: (971) 43474078
E-Mail: autobh@emirates.net.ae
Web Site: www.belhasamotors.com
Importer, Promoter, Marketer & Sales of Automotive Parts & Equipment
S.I.C.: 3714
N.A.I.C.S.: 336340

Belhasa Real Estate (1)
PO Box 1286
Dubai, United Arab Emirates
Tel.: (971) 42662319
Fax: (971) 42680830
E-Mail: realestate@belhasa.ae
Provider of Real Estate Investment Services
S.I.C.: 6726
N.A.I.C.S.: 525990

Belhasa Real Estate (1)
PO Box 1286
Dubai, United Arab Emirates
Tel.: (971) 42683144
Fax: (971) 42680830
Provider of Investment & Securities Services
S.I.C.: 6282
N.A.I.C.S.: 523930

Belhasa Six Construction Company (1)
PO Box 13055
Dubai, United Arab Emirates
Tel.: (971) 43472777
Fax: (971) 43473512
E-Mail: sixco@sixco.ae
Web Site: www.bsix.com
Emp.: 15,000
Provider of Construction Services
S.I.C.: 1542
N.A.I.C.S.: 236220
Patrick Daens *(Gen Mgr)*

Belhasa Tourism, Travel & Cargo Company (1)
Deira Clock Tower
PO Box 20968
Dubai, United Arab Emirates (100%)
Tel.: (971) 42957474
Fax: (971) 42957272
E-Mail: admin@belhasatravel.com
Web Site: www.belhasatravel.com
Emp.: 50
Travel, Tourism & Transportation Services
S.I.C.: 4789
N.A.I.C.S.: 488210
Narous Sarkies *(Gen Mgr)*

Belhasa Trading & Development Company (1)
Belhasa Compound Al Quoz Industrial 3
PO Box 61627
Dubai, United Arab Emirates
Tel.: (971) 43472050
Fax: (971) 43474078
E-Mail: autobh@emirates.net.ae
Web Site: www.belhasamotors.com
Bus, Truck & Automobile Marketing, Sales & Maintenence
S.I.C.: 5012
N.A.I.C.S.: 423110
Shrikumar Nair *(Gen Mgr)*

Emirates Driving Institute (1)
Behind Al Bustan Ctr
PO Box 20948
Qusais, Dubai, United Arab Emirates
Tel.: (971) 42631100
Fax: (971) 42631268
E-Mail: edi@emirates.net.ae
Web Site: www.edi-uae.com
Emp.: 600
Provider of Driver Training Services
S.I.C.: 8299
N.A.I.C.S.: 611710
Amer Ahmed Belhasa *(Mng Dir)*

Silver Seas Shipping LLC (1)
PO Box 29242
Dubai, United Arab Emirates
Tel.: (971) 4 696923
Fax: (971) 4 692286
Developer of Port & Shipping Infrastructures
S.I.C.: 3999
N.A.I.C.S.: 339999

Union Trading Company (1)
PO Box 85983
Dubai, United Arab Emirates
Tel.: (971) 42662319
Fax: (971) 42625129
E-Mail: uniontrading@belhasa.com
Web Site: www.belhasa.com
Emp.: 40
Constructor of Power Generation Plants
S.I.C.: 3612
N.A.I.C.S.: 335311
Haidham Belhasa *(Mng Dir)*

Joint Venture:

Emirates Voltas L.L.C. (1)
PO Box 1286
Dubai, United Arab Emirates
Tel.: (971) 4698797
Fax: (971) 4 680557
Provider of Electro Mechanical Services; Joint Venture of Belhasa Group of Companies & Voltas International
S.I.C.: 1731
N.A.I.C.S.: 238210

BELIMO HOLDING AG

Brunnenbachstrasse 1
8340 Hinwil, Switzerland
Tel.: (41) 438436111
Fax: (41) 438436268
E-Mail: info@belimo.ch
Web Site: www.belimo.com
BEAN—(SWX)
Sls.: $479,890,496
Assets: $370,962,284
Liabilities: $88,884,161
Net Worth: $282,078,123
Earnings: $66,298,310
Emp.: 1,227
Fiscal Year-end: 12/31/12

Business Description:
Heating Ventilation & Air Conditioning Mfr
S.I.C.: 3585
N.A.I.C.S.: 333415

Personnel:
Jacques Sanche *(CEO)*
Beat Trutmann *(CFO)*

Board of Directors:
Hans Peter Wehrli
Martin Hess

Walter Linsi
Martin Zwyssig

Subsidiary:

BELIMO Automation AG (1)
Brunnenbachstrasse 1
8340 Hinwil, Switzerland
Tel.: (41) 438436111
Fax: (41) 438436268
E-Mail: info@belimo.ch
Web Site: www.belimo-fls.ch
Emp.: 600
Actuators & Valves Distr
S.I.C.: 5063
N.A.I.C.S.: 423610
Alfred Freitag *(Mgr-Sls)*

U.S. Subsidiaries:

BELIMO Customization (USA), Inc. (1)
43 Old Ridgebury Rd
Danbury, CT 06810-5113
Tel.: (203) 791-9915
Fax: (203) 792-2967
Actuators & Valves Mfr
S.I.C.: 3593
N.A.I.C.S.: 333995

BELIMO Technology (USA), Inc. (1)
43 Old Ridgebury Rd
Danbury, CT 06813
Tel.: (203) 791-9915
Fax: (800) 228-8283
Heating & Cooling System Controls Mfr
S.I.C.: 3585
N.A.I.C.S.: 333415
Lex van der Weerd *(Pres)*

Non-U.S. Subsidiaries:

BELIMO A/S (1)
Thomas Helstedsvej 7A
8660 Skanderborg, Denmark
Tel.: (45) 86524400
Fax: (45) 86524488
E-Mail: info@belimo.dk
Web Site: www.belimo.dk
Emp.: 10
Motors & Valves Sales
S.I.C.: 5063
N.A.I.C.S.: 423610
Ole Fornill *(Mng Dir)*

BELIMO Actuators (India) Pvt Ltd. (1)
204 Jaisingh Bus Ctr Parsiwada 104 Sahar Rd
Andheri E, Mumbai, Maharashtra, 400099, India
Tel.: (91) 22 2822 2559
Fax: (91) 22 2822 2643
E-Mail: info.india@belimo.ch
Emp.: 20
Actuators & Valves Distr
S.I.C.: 5063
N.A.I.C.S.: 423610
Sunit Tanavade *(Mng Dir)*

BELIMO Actuators Ltd. (1)
7th Fl Honjo-Azumabashi DJ Bldg 4-19-3 Honjo
Sumida-ku, Tokyo, 130-0004, Japan
Tel.: (81) 368236961
Fax: (81) 336263911
E-Mail: info.japan@belimo.ch
Emp.: 4
Actuators & Valves Distr
S.I.C.: 5063
N.A.I.C.S.: 423610
Harumi Miyaoka *(Reg Mgr)*

BELIMO Actuators Ltd. (1)
7F 343 Jhonghe Rd
Yonghe, Taipei, 234, Taiwan
Tel.: (886) 229228805
Fax: (886) 229228806
E-Mail: info.taiwan@belimo.ch
Emp.: 2
Actuators & Valves Distr
S.I.C.: 5063
N.A.I.C.S.: 423610

BELIMO Actuators Ltd. (1)
90 2 Pensiri Pl Soi Phaholyothin 32
Phaholyothin Rd Chandrakasem
Jatujak, Bangkok, 10900, Thailand
Tel.: (66) 29415582
Fax: (66) 29415584
E-Mail: info.thailand@belimo.ch
Emp.: 2
Actuators & Valves Distr
S.I.C.: 5063
N.A.I.C.S.: 423610
Songyot Smoewong *(Mgr)*

BELIMO Actuators Ltd. (1)
Rm 207 2 F New Commerce Ctr 19 On Sum St
Sha Tin, Sha Tin, China (Hong Kong)
Tel.: (852) 2687 17 16
Fax: (852) 2687 17 95
E-Mail: info.hongkong@belimo.ch
Emp.: 20
Actuators & Valves Distr
S.I.C.: 5063
N.A.I.C.S.: 423610
Mei Cheung *(Gen Mgr)*

BELIMO Actuators Limited (1)
1 Tannery Rd 08-04
Singapore, 347719, Singapore
Tel.: (65) 68421626
Fax: (65) 68421630
Emp.: 3
Actuators & Valves Distr
S.I.C.: 5063
N.A.I.C.S.: 423610
Sebastian Goh *(Mng Dir)*

BELIMO Actuators Ltd. (1)
12-1 Jalan PJS 10 2 Subang Indah
46000 Petaling Jaya, Selangor, Malaysia
Tel.: (60) 356312188
Fax: (60) 356382189
E-Mail: info.malaysia@belimo.ch
Web Site: www.belimo.com
Emp.: 3
Actuators & Valves Distr
S.I.C.: 5063
N.A.I.C.S.: 423610

BELIMO Actuators Pty. Ltd. (1)
12 Enterprise Ct Mulgrave Bus Park
Mulgrave, VIC, 3170, Australia
Tel.: (61) 395450844
Fax: (61) 395450855
E-Mail: info.australia@belimo.ch
Web Site: www.belimo.ch
Emp.: 17
Actuators & Valves Distr
S.I.C.: 5063
N.A.I.C.S.: 423610
Carrol Whitaker *(Office Mgr)*

BELIMO Actuators (Shanghai) Trading Ltd. (1)
No 479 Chun Dong Rd Bldg C-2 Xin Zhuang Indus Park
Shanghai, 201108, China
Tel.: (86) 2154832929
Fax: (86) 2154832930
E-Mail: info.shanghai@belimo.ch
Actuators & Valves Distr
S.I.C.: 5063
N.A.I.C.S.: 423610
John Tsang *(Gen Mgr)*

BELIMO Aircontrols (CAN), Inc. (1)
5845 Kennedy Rd
Mississauga, ON, L4Z 2G3, Canada
Tel.: (905) 712-3118
Fax: (905) 712-3124
Toll Free: (866) 805-7089
E-Mail: orders.ca@ca.belimo.com
Web Site: www.belimo.ca
Emp.: 12
Actuators & Valves Distr
S.I.C.: 5085
N.A.I.C.S.: 423840
Michael Leblang *(Gen Mgr)*

BELIMO Automation FZE (1)
Warehouse No K17 Al Quds St
PO Box 293644
Dubai Airport Free Zone, Dubai, United Arab Emirates
Tel.: (971) 42998050
Fax: (971) 42998051
E-Mail: info@belimo.ae
Emp.: 15
Actuators & Valves Distr
S.I.C.: 5063
N.A.I.C.S.: 423610
David Stevenson *(Mng Dir)*

BELIMO Automation Handelsgesellschaft m.b.H. (1)
Geiselbergstrasse 26-32
1110 Vienna, Austria
Tel.: (43) 174903610
Fax: (43) 1749036199
E-Mail: info@belimo.at
Web Site: www.belimo.at
Emp.: 15
Actuators & Valves Distr
S.I.C.: 5085
N.A.I.C.S.: 423840
Guantar Bartel *(Mgr)*

BELIMO Automation Norge A / S (1)
Konowsgt 5
0192 Oslo, Norway
Tel.: (47) 22707171
Fax: (47) 22707170
E-Mail: info@belimo.no
Web Site: www.belimo.no
Emp.: 6
Heating & Cooling System Controls Distr
S.I.C.: 5075
N.A.I.C.S.: 423730
Johan Brevek *(Mng Dir)*

BELIMO Automation UK Ltd. (1)
Shepperton Bus Park Govett Ave
Shepperton, Middlesex, TW17 8BA, United Kingdom
Tel.: (44) 1932260460
Fax: (44) 1932269222
E-Mail: sales@belimo.co.uk
Web Site: www.belimo.co.uk
Emp.: 15
Actuators & Valves Distr
S.I.C.: 5063
N.A.I.C.S.: 423610
Andrew Bartlett *(Mng Dir)*

BELIMO Brasil Comercio de Automacao Ltda. (1)
Rua Barbalha 251 Alto da Lapa
251 Sao Paulo, 05083-020, Brazil
Tel.: (55) 1136435656
Fax: (55) 1136435657
E-Mail: customerservice@br.belimo.com
Web Site: www.belimo.com.br
Emp.: 10
Actuators & Valves Distr
S.I.C.: 5063
N.A.I.C.S.: 423610
Pedro Medeiros *(Mgr-Sls)*

BELIMO Bulgaria Ltd. (1)
J K Lagera 6 Balchik Str
1612 Sofia, Bulgaria
Tel.: (359) 2 9523470
Fax: (359) 2 9515240
E-Mail: belimo@mbox.contact.bg
Web Site: www.belimo-bg.com
Electric Actuators & Valves Distr
S.I.C.: 5063
N.A.I.C.S.: 423610

BELIMO CZ spol. s r.o. (1)
Charkovska 16 399
10100 Prague, Czech Republic
Tel.: (420) 271740311
Fax: (420) 271743057
E-Mail: info@belimo.cz
Web Site: www.belimo.cz
Emp.: 10
Actuators & Valves Distr
S.I.C.: 5063
N.A.I.C.S.: 423610

BELIMO Iberica de Servomotores S.A. (1)
Calle de San Romualdo 12-14
28037 Madrid, Spain
Tel.: (34) 913041111
Fax: (34) 913272539
E-Mail: info@belimo.es
Web Site: www.belimo.es
Emp.: 10
Actuators & Valves Distr
S.I.C.: 5063
N.A.I.C.S.: 423610
Jean Donnars *(Mgr)*

BELIMO Servomotoren BV (1)
Radeweg 25
8171 MD Vaassen, Netherlands
Tel.: (31) 578576836
Fax: (31) 578576915
E-Mail: info@belimo.nl
Web Site: www.belimo.nl
Emp.: 10
Heating & Cooling System Controls Distr
S.I.C.: 5075
N.A.I.C.S.: 423730

BELIMO Servomotori S.r.l. (1)
Via Stezzano 5
24050 Zanica, Bergamo, Italy
Tel.: (39) 035672682
Fax: (39) 035 67 02 00
E-Mail: info@belimo.it
Web Site: www.belimo.it
Actuators & Valves Distr
S.I.C.: 5063
N.A.I.C.S.: 423610

BELIMO Silowniki S.A. (1)
Ul Zagadki 21
02-227 Warsaw, Poland
Tel.: (48) 228865305
Fax: (48) 228865308
E-Mail: info@belimo.pl
Web Site: www.belimo.pl
Actuators & Valves Distr
S.I.C.: 5063
N.A.I.C.S.: 423610

BELIMO S.R.L. (1)
Olazabal 5584
1431 Buenos Aires, Argentina
Tel.: (54) 1145239267
Fax: (54) 1145221504
E-Mail: raul.rebora@belimo.com.ar
Web Site: www.belimo.com.ar
Emp.: 15
Actuators & Valves Distr
S.I.C.: 5063
N.A.I.C.S.: 423610
Leonardo Conde *(Gen Mgr)*

BELIMO Stellantriebe Vertriebs GmbH (1)
Welfenstrasse 27
70599 Stuttgart, Baden-Wurttemberg, Germany
Tel.: (49) 711167830
Fax: (49) 7111678373
E-Mail: info@belimo.de
Web Site: www.belimo.de
Emp.: 36
Heating & Cooling System Controls Distr
S.I.C.: 5075
N.A.I.C.S.: 423730
Jurgen Metzler *(Gen Mgr)*

ENYE Ltd. Corporation (1)
131-A Sct Limbaga St Sacred Heart
Diliman, Quezon City, Philippines 1103
Tel.: (63) 2 794 5478
Fax: (63) 2 794 5479
E-Mail: enye@enye.com.ph
Web Site: www.enye.com.ph
Industrial Controls Distr
S.I.C.: 5063
N.A.I.C.S.: 423610

Hanmo Corporation (1)
1116 Kolon Digital Tower Billant Guro-3dong Guro-gu 222-7
Seoul, Korea (South)
Tel.: (82) 221035901
Fax: (82) 221035919
E-Mail: hanmo@hanmo.co.kr
Web Site: www.hanmo.co.kr
Emp.: 21
Actuators & Valves Distr
S.I.C.: 5063
N.A.I.C.S.: 423610
Jae Jun Jun *(CEO)*

Nosters (Pvt) Ltd. (1)
No 5 Park Circus Rd
Colombo, Western Province, 5, Sri Lanka
Tel.: (94) 11 420 9152
Fax: (94) 11 420 9153
E-Mail:
Web Site: www.nostersworld.com
Emp.: 25
Automated Controllers & Valves Distr
S.I.C.: 5063
N.A.I.C.S.: 423610
Sudath Joseph *(Dir-Engrg)*

Overseas Enterprises (1)
44-A Liaquat Market MA Jinnah Rd
Karachi, Sindh, 74000, Pakistan
Tel.: (92) 212412243
Fax: (92) 212420329
E-Mail: info@oe.com.pk
Web Site: www.oe.com.pk
Actuators & Valves Distr
S.I.C.: 5063
N.A.I.C.S.: 423610

Piping System Indonesia Pt. (1)
Jl Jembatan Dua Raya No 16-06
Jakarta, 14450, Indonesia

BELIMO Holding AG—(Continued)

Tel.: (62) 216618888
Fax: (62) 21 6670785
E-Mail: info@pipingsystem.com
Web Site: www.pipingsystem.com
Pipes, Fittings & Valves Distr
S.I.C.: 5074
N.A.I.C.S.: 423720

Rite Products Incorporated (1)
Rm 702 Jocfer Bldg Commonwealth Ave
Capitol Dist, Quezon City, Metro Manila, Philippines
Tel.: (63) 29327944
Fax: (63) 29327935
E-Mail: sales@riteproducts.com.ph
Web Site: www.riteproducts.com.ph
Emp.: 12
Actuators & Valves Distr
S.I.C.: 5063
N.A.I.C.S.: 423610
Virgilio Del Rosario *(Pres)*

BELIZE TELECOMMUNICATIONS LIMITED

Esquivel Telecom Ctr St Thomas St
PO Box 603
Belize, Belize
Tel.: (501) 2232868
Fax: (501) 2231800
E-Mail: prdept@btl.net
Web Site: www.belizetelemedia.net
Year Founded: 1987
Sales Range: $50-74.9 Million
Emp.: 480

Business Description:
Telecommunication Services Supplier
S.I.C.: 4813
N.A.I.C.S.: 517110

Personnel:
Nestor Vasquez *(Chm)*
Karen Bevans *(COO)*

Board of Directors:
Ediberto Tesucum
Philip Zuniga

BELKORP INDUSTRIES, INC.

1508 W Broadway Ste 900
Vancouver, BC, V6J 1W8, Canada
Tel.: (604) 688-8533
Fax: (604) 688-3569
E-Mail: dinac@belkorp.com
Web Site: www.belkorp.com
Emp.: 20

Business Description:
Provider of Management Services; Environmental, Real Estate, Pulp & Paper, Merchant Banking
S.I.C.: 8741
N.A.I.C.S.: 561110

Personnel:
Stuart Belkin *(Chm & CEO)*
Tomas Lindsay *(Pres & COO)*
Michael Heskin *(CFO & VP-Fin)*
Randolph Smith *(Sec)*
Ted Rattray *(Sr VP)*

Subsidiaries:

Big Sky Golf and Country Club (1)
1690 Airport Rd
Pemberton, BC, V0N 2L3, Canada (100%)
Tel.: (604) 894-6106
Fax: (604) 894-5545
E-Mail: info@bigskygolf.com
Web Site: www.bigskygolf.com
Emp.: 40
Owner of Golf Club
S.I.C.: 7999
N.A.I.C.S.: 713910
Chris Wallace *(Gen Mgr)*

Wastech Services Ltd. (1)
1200 United Blvd
Coquitlam, BC, V3K 6T4, Canada (50%)
Tel.: (604) 521-1715
Fax: (604) 521-0763
Web Site: www.wastech.ca
Emp.: 120
Provider of Waste & Recycling Management Services
S.I.C.: 4959
N.A.I.C.S.: 562998

BELL COPPER CORPORATION

Suite 1780 - 400 Burrard Street
Vancouver, BC, V6C 3A6, Canada
Tel.: (604) 669-1484
Fax: (604) 669-1464
E-Mail: info@bellcopper.net
Web Site: www.bellcopper.net
Year Founded: 2005
BCU—(TSXV)
Int. Income: $4,253
Assets: $3,615,977
Liabilities: $11,075,475
Net Worth: ($7,459,498)
Earnings: ($43,322,994)
Emp.: 14
Fiscal Year-end: 12/31/12

Business Description:
Copper Exploration & Development Services
S.I.C.: 1021
N.A.I.C.S.: 212234

Personnel:
Timothy Marsh *(Pres & CEO)*
Annie Storey *(CFO)*

Board of Directors:
Timothy Marsh
Geoffrey Snow
Annie Storey
Glen Zinn

BELL EQUIPMENT LIMITED

13-19 Carbonode Cell Road Alton
Richards Bay, 3900, South Africa

Mailing Address:
Private Bag X20046
Empangeni, 3880, South Africa
Tel.: (27) 359079111
Fax: (27) 357974336
E-Mail: web@bell.co.za
Web Site: www.bellequipment.com
Year Founded: 1954
BEL—(JSE)
Rev.: $633,360,000
Assets: $389,757,826
Liabilities: $158,141,286
Net Worth: $231,616,540
Earnings: $27,133,941
Emp.: 3,242
Fiscal Year-end: 12/31/12

Business Description:
Heavy Duty Equipment & Articulated Vehicle Supplier
S.I.C.: 5084
N.A.I.C.S.: 423830

Personnel:
Gary Bell *(CEO)*
Rino D'Alessandro *(Exec-Info Sys)*
Paul Bell *(Exec-Comm & Adv)*
Peter Bell *(Exec-Engrg)*
Ryan Bland *(Exec-Technical Svcs)*
Dominic Chinnapen *(Exec-Sls & Ops Plng)*
Avishkar Goordeen *(Exec-Grp Risk)*
Lucas Maloka *(Exec-HR)*
Bruce Ndlela *(Exec-Bus & Pub Sector Dev)*
Pieter van der Sandt *(Sec)*

Board of Directors:
Michael Mun-Gavin
John Barton
Gary Bell
Leon Goosen
Bharti Harie
Tiisetso Tsukudu
Karen van Haght
Danie Vlok

Transfer Agent:
Link Market Services SA (Pty) Limited
Rennie House 13th Floor 19 Ameshoff Street
Braamfontein
4844
Johannesburg, South Africa

Subsidiaries:

Bell Equipment Company SA (Pty) Limited (1)
12 Hendrick Van Eck Street Kimdustria
PO Box 2927
Kimberley, 8300, South Africa
Tel.: (27) 53 841 0710
Fax: (27) 53 841 1940
E-Mail: bellrsa@bell.co.za
Construction Machinery Mfr
S.I.C.: 3531
N.A.I.C.S.: 333120

Bell Equipment Sales South Africa Limited (1)
Gruiffiths Road
Boksburg, Gauteng, 1469, South Africa
Tel.: (27) 119289700
Fax: (27) 119289730
Web Site: www.bellequipment.com
Construction Equipment Distr
S.I.C.: 5082
N.A.I.C.S.: 423810
Bookie Coertze *(Mng Dir)*

Non-U.S. Subsidiaries:

Bell Equipment Co Swaziland (Proprietary) Limited (2)
Tambankulu Street Plot 686
PO Box 1754
Matsapha, Swaziland
Mailing Address:
PO Box 1754
Matsapha, Swaziland
Tel.: (268) 251 874 96
Fax: (268) 251 874 98
Emp.: 12
Construction Machinery Mfr
S.I.C.: 3531
N.A.I.C.S.: 333120
Charlie Boucher *(Gen Mgr)*

IA Bell Equipment Co Namibia (Proprietary) Limited (2)
37 Lazaret Street Southern Industrial
Windhoek, Namibia
Tel.: (264) 61 22 60 21
Fax: (264) 61 22 83 30
Web Site: www.bellequipment.com
Construction Machinery Mfr
S.I.C.: 3531
N.A.I.C.S.: 333120

Non-U.S. Subsidiaries:

Bell Equipment Australia (Pty) Limited (1)
4 Karrith St
Welshpool, WA, 6106, Australia (100%)
Mailing Address:
P.O. Box 34
Welshpool, WA, 6986, Australia
Tel.: (61) 893561033
Fax: (61) 893561233
E-Mail: owen@bell.net.au
Web Site: www.bellequipment.com
Emp.: 3
Heavy Duty Equipment & Articulated Vehicle Supplier
S.I.C.: 5063
N.A.I.C.S.: 423610

Bell Equipment (Deutschland) GmbH (1)
Willi-Brandt Strasse 4-6
Alsfeld, D-36304, Germany (100%)
Tel.: (49) 663191130
Fax: (49) 6631911313
E-Mail: center@de.bellequipment.de
Web Site: www.bellequipment.de
Emp.: 90
Heavy Duty Equipment & Articulated Vehicle Supplier
S.I.C.: 5082
N.A.I.C.S.: 423810
Andre Krings *(Mng Dir)*

Bell Equipment Mozambique Limitada (1)
Avenida Samora Machel No 238
Matola, Maputo, Mozambique
Tel.: (258) 21 722 031
Fax: (258) 21 724 559
Construction Machinery Mfr
S.I.C.: 3531
N.A.I.C.S.: 333120
John Ferguson *(Reg Gen Mgr)*

Bell Equipment (SEA) PTE Limited (1)
10 Anson Road
14-12 International Plaza, Singapore, 079903, Singapore (100%)
Tel.: (65) 62208004
Fax: (65) 622 03 004
E-Mail: bellequipment@singnet.com.sg
Web Site: www.bellequipment.com
Heavy Duty Equipment & Articulated Vehicle Supplier
S.I.C.: 5063
N.A.I.C.S.: 423610

Bell Equipment Switzerland SA (1)
Rue de Vevey 178
Bulle, 1630, Switzerland
Tel.: (41) 26 402 00 00
Fax: (41) 26 913 00 19
Construction Machinery Mfr
S.I.C.: 3531
N.A.I.C.S.: 333120

Bell Equipment UK Limited (1)
Unit 6C Graycar Business Park Barton Turns
Barton Under Needwood, Burton-on-Trent, Staffs, DE13 8EN, United Kingdom UK
Tel.: (44) 1283 712 862 (100%)
Fax: (44) 1283 712 687
E-Mail: general@uk.bellequipment.com
Web Site: www.bellequipment.co.uk
Emp.: 30
Heavy Duty Equipment & Articulated Vehicle Supplier
S.I.C.: 5082
N.A.I.C.S.: 423810

Bell Equipment (Zambia) Limited (1)
Kalulushi Business Park
Kalulushi, Zambia
Tel.: (260) 977770678
Fax: (260) 212731555
Emp.: 100
Construction Machinery Distr
S.I.C.: 5082
N.A.I.C.S.: 423810
Bruce Paterson *(Mgr-Sls)*

Bell France SARL (1)
75 Rroute Berry
23800 Dunkirk, France (100%)
Tel.: (33) 555892356
Fax: (33) 555892324
E-Mail: info@sr.bellequipment.com
Web Site: www.bellequipment.com
Emp.: 20
Heavy Duty Equipment & Articulated Vehicle Supplier
S.I.C.: 5082
N.A.I.C.S.: 423810
Claude Boulet *(Mng Dir)*

BELL FINANCIAL GROUP LIMITED

Level 29 101 Collins Street
Melbourne, VIC, 3000, Australia
Tel.: (61) 392568700
Fax: (61) 392568787
E-Mail: info@bellfg.com.au
Web Site: www.bellfg.com.au
BFG—(ASX)
Rev.: $137,900,051
Assets: $458,182,191
Liabilities: $281,560,831
Net Worth: $176,621,361
Earnings: ($2,873,070)
Emp.: 590
Fiscal Year-end: 12/31/12

Business Description:
Financial Advisory Services
S.I.C.: 6282
N.A.I.C.S.: 523930

Personnel:
Colin Bell *(Chm)*
Alastair Provan *(Mng Dir)*
Dean Davenport *(CFO & COO)*
A. Paul M. Vine *(Gen Counsel & Sec)*

Board of Directors:
Colin Bell

Charlie Aitken
Craig Coleman
Graham Cubbin
Alastair Provan
Brenda Shanahan
Brian Wilson

Subsidiary:

Bell Potter Capital Limited (1)
Level 12 182 Victoria Square
Adelaide, SA, 5000, Australia
Tel.: (61) 8 8224 2722
Fax: (61) 8 8224 2799
Web Site: www.bellpotter.com.au
Investment Advisory Services
S.I.C.: 6282
N.A.I.C.S.: 523930

BELL IXL INVESTMENTS LIMITED

Level 2 651-653 Doncaster Road
Doncaster, VIC, 3108, Australia
Tel.: (61) 3 9840 8788
Fax: (61) 3 9840 0088
E-Mail: info@bellixl.com
Web Site: www.bellixl.com
Year Founded: 2005
Sales Range: $1-9.9 Million

Business Description:
Investment Services
S.I.C.: 6211
N.A.I.C.S.: 523999

Personnel:
Massimo Livio Cellante *(Chm & Mng Dir)*
Ramon Jimenez *(Sec)*

Board of Directors:
Massimo Livio Cellante
Romano Livio Cellante
Ramon Jimenez

Legal Counsel:
Pointon Partners
Level 2 640 Bourke Street
Melbourne, VIC, 3000, Australia

BELL-PARK CO., LTD.

6 7 8th Floor Sanshin Hirakawa-cho Building 1-4-12 Hirakawa-cho
Chiyoda-ku, Tokyo, Japan
Tel.: (81) 332885211
Fax: (81) 332885288
Web Site: www.bellpark.co.jp
Year Founded: 1993
9441—(JAS)
Sls.: $819,157,537
Assets: $238,125,569
Liabilities: $100,596,716
Net Worth: $137,528,853
Earnings: $19,618,445
Emp.: 651
Fiscal Year-end: 12/31/12

Business Description:
Mobile Communications Equipment & Services
S.I.C.: 3663
N.A.I.C.S.: 334220

Personnel:
Takeru Nishikawa *(Pres & CEO)*

Board of Directors:
Yoshiki Akita
John Durkin
Hitoshi Furukawa
Hiroshi Ishikawa
Takeru Nishikawa
Takeo Takasu
Oleg Zuravljov

Transfer Agent:
Mitsubishi UFJ Trust & Banking Corporation
10-11 Higashisuna 1-chome Koto-ku
Tokyo, Japan

Subsidiaries:

Japan Pro Staff Co., Ltd (1)
Urban Shinjuku Building 10th Floor
Shinjuku-Ku, Tokyo, Japan
Tel.: (81) 353608545
Web Site: www.j-pro-staff.co.jp
Help Supply Services
S.I.C.: 7363
N.A.I.C.S.: 561320

Nikka Co., Ltd. (1)
1-1-47 Kozaika
Wakayama, 641-0001, Japan
Tel.: (81) 734223111
Fax: (81) 734247330
E-Mail: yamada@nikka-c.co.jp
Web Site: www.nikka-c.co.jp
Emp.: 80
Other Chemical & Allied Products Merchant Whslr
S.I.C.: 5169
N.A.I.C.S.: 424690
Koji Yamada *(Gen Mgr)*

BELLA COOLA FISHERIES LTD.

9829 River Road
Delta, BC, Canada
Tel.: (604) 583-3474
Fax: (604) 583-4940
E-Mail: info@belcofish.com
Web Site: www.belcofish.com
Year Founded: 1977
Rev.: $21,513,360
Emp.: 154

Business Description:
Seafood Products Distr
S.I.C.: 5146
N.A.I.C.S.: 424460

Personnel:
Jack Groven *(Mgr-Production)*

BELLA RESOURCES INC.

6012 85th Avenue
Edmonton, AB, T6B 0J5, Canada
Tel.: (780) 466-6006
Fax: (780) 440-1377
BP.H—(TSXV)
Assets: $2,094
Liabilities: $685,824
Net Worth: ($683,730)
Earnings: ($140,058)
Emp.: 2
Fiscal Year-end: 12/31/12

Business Description:
Oil & Gas Exploration Services
S.I.C.: 1389
N.A.I.C.S.: 213112

Personnel:
Ken Ralfs *(Pres, CEO, CFO & Sec)*

Board of Directors:
Carol MacDonald
Glen MacDonald
Ken Ralfs

Transfer Agent:
Equity Financial Trust Company
200 University Avenue Suite 400
Toronto, ON, M5H 4H1, Canada
Tel.: (416) 361-0152
Fax: (416) 361-0470
Toll Free: (866) 393-4891

BELLAIR VENTURES INC.

10 Bellair Street Suite 509
Toronto, ON, M5R 3T8, Canada
Tel.: (416) 840-5002
Year Founded: 2008
BVI—(TSXV)

Business Description:
Venture Capital Firm
S.I.C.: 6211
N.A.I.C.S.: 523999

Personnel:
Emlyn J. David *(Pres, CEO, CFO & Sec)*

Board of Directors:
Emlyn J. David
Michael Galloro
Daniel Hay
Rajiv R. Rai

Subsidiary:

Clean Energy Developments Corp. (1)
254 Attwell Drive
Toronto, ON, M9W 5B2, Canada
Tel.: (905) 603-4340
Fax: (866) 381-1714
Toll Free: (866) 607-8162
E-Mail: info@cleanenergydevelopments.com
Web Site: www.cleanenergy.ca
Thermal Energy Solutions
S.I.C.: 1799
N.A.I.C.S.: 238990

BELLATRIX EXPLORATION LTD.

Suite 2300 530 - 8th Ave SW
Calgary, AB, T2P 3S8, Canada
Tel.: (403) 266-8670
Fax: (403) 264-8163
E-Mail: reception@bellatrixexp.com
Web Site: www.bellatrixexploration.com
BXE—(NYSEMKT TSX)
Sls.: $215,839,515
Assets: $677,346,102
Liabilities: $298,519,116
Net Worth: $378,826,986
Earnings: $27,604,929
Emp.: 82
Fiscal Year-end: 12/31/12

Business Description:
Oil & Gas Explorer
S.I.C.: 1389
N.A.I.C.S.: 213112

Personnel:
William Carmichael Dunn *(Chm)*
Raymond G. Smith *(Pres & CEO)*
Edward J. Brown *(CFO & VP-Fin)*
Ving Y. Woo *(COO & VP-Engrg)*
John H. Cuthbertson *(Sec)*

Board of Directors:
William Carmichael Dunn
Douglas N. Baker
Murray L. Cobbe
John H. Cuthbertson
Melvin M. Hawkrigg
Robert Anthony Johnson
Keith Elliott Macdonald
Raymond G. Smith
Murray B. Todd
Keith S. Turnbull

Computershare Trust Company of Canada
Calgary, AB, Canada

Computershare Investor Services
Golden, CO 80401

Transfer Agents:
Computershare Trust Company of Canada
Toronto, ON, Canada

Computershare Trust Company of Canada
Calgary, AB, Canada

Computershare Investor Services
Golden, CO 80401

BELLE CORPORATION

5/F Tower A Two E-com Center
Palm Coast Avenue Mall of Asia Complex, CPB-1A Pasay, Philippines
Tel.: (63) 26353016
Fax: (63) 26353025
Web Site: www.bellecorp.com
BEL—(PHI)
Rev.: $17,473,884
Assets: $623,534,968
Liabilities: $216,546,580
Net Worth: $406,988,387
Earnings: $15,343,352
Emp.: 150
Fiscal Year-end: 12/31/12

Business Description:
Property Development Services
S.I.C.: 6531
N.A.I.C.S.: 531311

Personnel:
Benito Tan Guat *(Chm)*
Willy N. Ocier *(Vice Chm)*
Elizabeth Anne C. Uychaco *(Vice Chm)*
Frederic C. Dybuncio *(Pres & CEO)*
Manuel A. Gana *(CFO & Exec VP)*
A. Bayani K. Tan *(Sec)*
Armin B. Raquel Santos *(Exec VP-Integrated Resorts)*

Board of Directors:
Benito Tan Guat
Emilio S. de Quiros, Jr.
Frederic C. Dybuncio
Gregorio U. Kilayko
Jacinto C. Ng Jr.
Willy N. Ocier
Jose T. Sio
Washington Z. SyCip
Elizabeth Anne C. Uychaco
Cesar E. A. Virata
Virginia A. Yap

Legal Counsel:
Tan Venturanza Valdez Law Offices
2704 East Tower Philippine Stock Exchange Centre Exchanging Road
Pasig, Philippines

Tan Acut Lopez & Pison
2303 A East Tower Philippine Stock Exchange Centre
Exchange Road Ortigas Center, Pasig, Philippines

Herrera Teehankee & Cabrera
5/F SGV II Building 6758 Ayala Avenue
Makati, Philippines

Cayetano Sebastian Ata Dado & Cruz
12/F NDC Building 116 Tordesillas Street
Salcedo Village
Makati, Philippines

Transfer Agents:
Professional Stock Transfer Inc
1003 10/F City & Land Mega Plaza ADB Avenue cor Garnet Road
Pasig, Philippines

Banco de Oro Trust & Investments Group
15th Floor South Tower BDO Corporate Center
7899 Makati Avenue
Makati, Philippines

Subsidiaries:

Tagaytay Highlands, Inc. (1)
60 Km from Manila
Tagaytay, Cavite, Philippines
Tel.: (63) 464830829
Fax: (63) 464830830
E-Mail: eo@tagaytayhighlands.com
Web Site: www.tagaytayhighlands.com
Golf Club Management Services
S.I.C.: 7999
N.A.I.C.S.: 713910
Yasmin Cadungog *(Dir-Sls)*

Tagaytay Highlands International Golf Club, Inc. (1)
Barrio Calabuso
Tagaytay, Cavite, 4120, Philippines
Tel.: (63) 464830888
Fax: (63) 464830830
E-Mail: eo@tagaytayhighlands.com
Web Site: www.tagaytayhighlands.com
Golf Club Management Services
S.I.C.: 7999
N.A.I.C.S.: 713910
Juancho Baltazar *(Dir-HR)*

Tagaytay Midlands Golf Club, Inc. (1)
Talisay
6115 Batangas, Philippines
Tel.: (63) 464833808
Fax: (63) 464830810
E-Mail: eo@tagaytayhighlands.com
Web Site: www.tagaytayhighlands.com
Golf Club Management Services
S.I.C.: 7999
N.A.I.C.S.: 713910
Claire Kremer *(Gen Mgr)*

BELLE INTERNATIONAL HOLDINGS LIMITED

12/F Excellence Mansion No 98
Fuhua 1st Road
Futian District, Shanghai, China
Tel.: (86) 755 8287 7388
E-Mail: trade@belle.com.cn
Web Site: www.belleintl.com
1880—(HKG OTC)
Rev.: $5,219,652,150
Assets: $4,543,554,780
Liabilities: $959,358,690
Net Worth: $3,584,196,090
Earnings: $687,042,135
Emp.: 116,263
Fiscal Year-end: 12/31/12

Business Description:
Footwear Mfr & Sales
S.I.C.: 2389
N.A.I.C.S.: 316210

Personnel:
Yiu Tang *(Founder)*
Baijiao Sheng *(CEO)*
Kam Kwan Leung *(Sec & Mgr-Fin)*
Fang Sheng *(Sr VP)*
King Loy Tang *(Sr VP)*

Board of Directors:
Yiu Tang
Yu Ling Chan
Yu Gao
Kwok Wah Ho
Xiaoling Hu
Baijiao Sheng
Fang Sheng
King Loy Tang
Qiuzhi Xue

Legal Counsel:
Cleary Gottlieb Steen & Hamilton
39/F Bank of China Tower 1 Garden Road
Central, China (Hong Kong)

Computershare Hong Kong Investor Services Limited
17M Floor Hopewell Centre 183 Queen's Road East
Wanchai, China (Hong Kong)

Subsidiaries:

Belle Worldwide Limited **(1)**
9 F Belle Twr 918 Cheung Sha Wan Rd
Cheung Sha Wan, Kowloon, China (Hong Kong)
Tel.: (852) 27414760
Fax: (852) 22123668
Footwear Poducts Mfr & Whslr
S.I.C.: 2389
N.A.I.C.S.: 316210

Lai Wah Footwear Trading Limited **(1)**
9 F Belle Tower 918 Cheung Sha Wan Rd
Cheung Sha Wan, Kowloon, China (Hong Kong)
Tel.: (852) 27414760
Fax: (852) 27340338
Leather Footwear Whslr
S.I.C.: 5139
N.A.I.C.S.: 424340

Millie's Company Limited **(1)**
9/F Belle Tower 918 Cheung Sha Wan Road
Cheung Sha Wan, Kowloon, China (Hong Kong)
Tel.: (852) 24221268
Fax: (852) 24804670
Womens Clothing & Footwear Whslr
S.I.C.: 5139
N.A.I.C.S.: 424340

Mirabell International Holdings Limited **(1)**
9th Fl Belle Tower 918 Cheung Sha Wan Rd
Kowloon, China (Hong Kong)
Tel.: (852) 24898131
Fax: (852) 2489 8029
E-Mail: mirabell@mirabell.com.hk
Web Site: www.mirabell.com.hk
Footwear Mfr & Whslr
S.I.C.: 2389
N.A.I.C.S.: 316210
Keung Lam Tang *(Co-Founder)*
Wai Lam Tang *(Co-Founder)*
Man Kit Ng *(Deputy Mng Dir & Exec Dir)*
Yiu Fai Leung *(Sec)*

Subsidiary:

Mirabell Footwear Limited **(2)**
9 F Belle Tower 918 Cheung Sha Wan Rd
Kowloon, China (Hong Kong)
Tel.: (852) 24898131
Fax: (852) 24898029
Footwear Whslr
S.I.C.: 5139
N.A.I.C.S.: 424340

Senses Marketing International Limited **(1)**
10 F Belle Tower 918 Cheung Sha Wan Rd
Cheung Sha Wan, Kowloon, China (Hong Kong)
Tel.: (852) 28861208
Fax: (852) 25671682
Footwear Whslr
S.I.C.: 5139
N.A.I.C.S.: 424340

Staccato Footwear Company Limited **(1)**
20 F Railway Plz 39 Chatham Rd S
Tsim Tsa Tsui, Kowloon, China (Hong Kong)
Tel.: (852) 27414760
Fax: (852) 27859157
Footwear Products Whslr
S.I.C.: 5139
N.A.I.C.S.: 424340

Non-U.S. Subsidiary:

Guangzhou Taobo Sports Development Company Limited **(1)**
No 81 Xihu Rd
Yuexiu Dist, Guangzhou, Guangdong, 510030, China
Tel.: (86) 2061273333
Fax: (86) 2061273900
Sportswear Mfr
S.I.C.: 2389
N.A.I.C.S.: 315210

BELLEEK POTTERY LTD.

Main St
Belleek, Fermanagh, BT93 3FY, United Kingdom
Tel.: (44) 2868658501
Fax: (44) 2868658625
E-Mail: info@belleek.ie
Web Site: www.belleek.ie
Year Founded: 1849
Emp.: 214

Business Description:
Parian China Giftware Mfr
S.I.C.: 3999
N.A.I.C.S.: 327110

Personnel:
George Moore *(Chm)*
John Maguire *(Mng Dir)*
Martin Sharkey *(Dir-Fin)*

BELLEVUE GROUP AG

Seestrasse 16
8700 Kusnacht, Switzerland
Tel.: (41) 442676777
Fax: (41) 442676778
E-Mail: info@bellevue.ch
Web Site: www.bellevue.ch
BBN—(SWX)
Rev.: $49,142,519
Assets: $524,149,092
Liabilities: $350,147,598
Net Worth: $174,001,494
Earnings: $7,045,801
Emp.: 82
Fiscal Year-end: 12/31/12

Business Description:
Investment Banking & Asset Management Services
S.I.C.: 6211
N.A.I.C.S.: 523110

Personnel:
Walter Knabenhans *(Chm)*
Urs Baumann *(CEO & Member-Exec Bd)*
Daniel Koller *(CFO & Member-Exec Bd)*
Serge Monnerat *(CEO-Bank am Bellevue & Member-Exec Bd)*
Andre Ruegg *(CEO-Bellevue Asset Mgmt & Member-Exec Bd)*

Board of Directors:
Walter Knabenhans
Daniel H. Sigg
Thomas von Planta

Subsidiaries:

Bank am Bellevue AG **(1)**
Seestrasse 16
8700 Kusnacht, Switzerland
Tel.: (41) 442676767
Fax: (41) 442676750
E-Mail: info@bellevue.ch
Web Site: www.bellevue.ch/de/bellevuegroup/topnavigation-bellevue/kontakt/
Emp.: 50
Commercial Banking
S.I.C.: 6029
N.A.I.C.S.: 522110
Serge Monnerat *(CEO)*

Bellevue Asset Management AG **(1)**
Seestrasse 16
8700 Kusnacht, Switzerland
Tel.: (41) 442676700
Fax: (41) 442676701
E-Mail: info@bellevue.ch
Emp.: 80
Holding & Investments
S.I.C.: 6722
N.A.I.C.S.: 525910
Andre Ruegg *(CEO)*

Subsidiary:

BB Biotech AG **(2)**
Seestrasse 16
8700 Kusnacht, Switzerland CH
Tel.: (41) 442676700
Fax: (41) 442676701
E-Mail: info@bellevue.ch
Web Site: www.bbbiotech.ch
BIO—(DEU ITA SWX)
Rev.: $423,081,567
Assets: $1,482,929,555
Liabilities: $151,043,279
Net Worth: $1,331,886,277
Earnings: $397,010,593
Emp.: 100
Fiscal Year-end: 12/31/12
Investment Holding Company
S.I.C.: 6211
N.A.I.C.S.: 523999
Erich Hunziker *(Chm)*
Clive A. Meanwell *(Vice Chm)*
Daniel Koller *(Member-Mgmt Bd & Head-Mgmt Team)*
Tazio Storni *(Member-Mgmt Bd & Mgr-Portfolio)*
Lydia Banziger *(Member-Mgmt Bd)*
Jan Bootsma *(Member-Mgmt Bd)*
Felicia Flanigan *(Member-Mgmt Bd)*
Nathalie Isidora-Kwidama *(Member-Mgmt Bd)*
Hugo van Neutegem *(Member-Mgmt Bd)*
Dallas Webb *(Member-Mgmt Bd)*

BELLHAVEN COPPER & GOLD INC.

408 - 837 W Hasting St
Vancouver, BC, V6C 3N6, Canada
Tel.: (604) 684-6264
Fax: (604) 684-6242
E-Mail: Info@bellhavencg.com
Web Site: www.bellhavencg.com
BHV—(OTC TSXV)
Rev.: $45,548
Assets: $24,204,902
Liabilities: $277,871
Net Worth: $23,927,031
Earnings: ($4,646,139)
Fiscal Year-end: 04/30/13

Business Description:
Copper & Gold Mining
S.I.C.: 1021
N.A.I.C.S.: 212234

Personnel:
Julio C. Benedetti *(Co-Founder, Chm & CEO)*
Alfredo Burgos *(Co-Founder)*
Maria Milagros Paredes *(Pres, Interim CFO & COO)*

Board of Directors:
Julio C. Benedetti
Patrick M. Abraham
Alfredo Burgos
Cyrus H. Driver
Maria Milagros Paredes
Robert Steve Wasylyshyn

Legal Counsel:
McMillan Law Partners
Vancouver, BC, Canada

Transfer Agent:
Computershare Trust Company of Canada
9th Floor 100 University Avenue
Toronto, ON, Canada

Non-U.S. Subsidiary:

Aurum Exploration, Inc. **(1)**
Calle 64 No 62 San Francisco
Panama, Panama
Tel.: (507) 226 3967
Fax: (507) 226 1091
Copper & Gold Mining Services
S.I.C.: 1041
N.A.I.C.S.: 212221

BELLIARD MATERIAUX

Route Du Fief Sauvin 18 Rue Des Cedres
49600 Nantes, France
Tel.: (33) 241630888
Sls.: $11,400,000
Emp.: 15
S.I.C.: 5074
N.A.I.C.S.: 423720

Personnel:
Philippe Belliard *(Mng Partner)*

BELLUNA CO. LTD.

4 2 Miyamoto cho
Ageo, Saitama, 3628688, Japan
Tel.: (81) 487717753
Web Site: www.belluna.co.jp
9997—(TKS)
Sales Range: $1-4.9 Billion
Emp.: 969

Business Description:
Property, Finance,Catalog & Mail Order Business
S.I.C.: 5399
N.A.I.C.S.: 452990

Personnel:
Kiyoshi Yasuno *(Pres & CEO)*
Yasutaka Nomura *(Exec Officer)*
Masakazu Oikawa *(Exec Officer)*
Takeo Shimano *(Exec Officer)*
Junko Shishido *(Exec Officer)*
Toshio Takahashi *(Exec Officer)*
Yuichiro Yasuno *(Exec Officer)*

Board of Directors:
Yasutaka Nomura
Masakazu Oikawa
Takeo Shimano
Junko Shishido
Toshio Takahashi
Kiyoshi Yasuno
Yuichiro Yasuno

Transfer Agent:
Mitsubishi UFJ Trust & Banking Corporation
1-4-5 Marunouchi Chiyoda-ku
Tokyo, Japan

Subsidiaries:

Ozio Co., Ltd. **(1)**
4-2 Miyamoto-cho
Ageo, Saitama, 362-8688, Japan
Tel.: (81) 487405070
Fax: (81) 487748624
E-Mail: info@ozio.jp

Web Site: www.ozio.jp
Emp.: 200
Personal Care Products Mfr
S.I.C.: 2841
N.A.I.C.S.: 325611
Akiko Yasuno *(Pres)*

Refre Co., Ltd. (1)
1-7-28 Nakacho Annex Bldg Ageo-shi
Nakamachi, Saitama, Japan
Tel.: (81) 487744011
Fax: (81) 487792522
E-Mail: order@hc-refre.jp
Web Site: www.hc-refre.jp
Health Foods Whslr
S.I.C.: 5148
N.A.I.C.S.: 424480
Kathuta Toru *(Pres)*

Sunstage Co., Ltd. (1)
1-7-11 Naka-cho 2 Anekkusubiru
Ageo, Saitama, 362-0035, Japan
Tel.: (81) 487792411
Fax: (81) 487797219
Personal Finance Services
S.I.C.: 9311
N.A.I.C.S.: 921130

BELLUS HEALTH INC.

275 Armand Frappier Blvd
Laval, QC, H7V 4A7, Canada
Tel.: (450) 680-4500
Fax: (450) 680-4501
Toll Free: (877) 680-4500
E-Mail: ir@bellushealth.com
Web Site: www.bellushealth.com
Year Founded: 1993
BLU—(OTC TSX)
Rev.: $2,284,258
Assets: $26,935,954
Liabilities: $15,926,188
Net Worth: $11,009,766
Earnings: ($13,175,735)
Emp.: 8
Fiscal Year-end: 12/31/12

Business Description:
Biopharmaceutical Drugs for Central Nervous System Disorders
S.I.C.: 2834
N.A.I.C.S.: 325412

Personnel:
Francesco Bellini *(Chm)*
Charles G. Cavell *(Deputy Chm)*
Roberto Bellini *(Pres & CEO)*
Denis Garceau *(Sr VP-Drug Dev)*

Board of Directors:
Francesco Bellini
Roberto Bellini
Franklin M. Berger
Charles G. Cavell
Helene Fortin
Pierre Larochelle
Donald Olds
Joseph Rus
Martin Tolar

Legal Counsel:
Davies Ward Phillips & Vineberg LLP
1501 McGill College Ave Suite 2600
Montreal, QC, Canada

Transfer Agent:
Computershare Investor Services
100 University Avenue 9th Floor
Toronto, ON, Canada

BELLWAY PLC

Seaton Burn House Dudley Lane
Seaton Burn
Newcastle upon Tyne, NE13 6BE, United Kingdom
Tel.: (44) 1912170717
Fax: (44) 1912366230
E-Mail: info@bellway.co.uk
Web Site: www.bellway.co.uk
Year Founded: 1946
BWY—(LSE OTC)
Rev.: $1,754,079,500
Assets: $2,608,442,225
Liabilities: $683,543,560
Net Worth: $1,924,898,665
Earnings: $171,466,674
Emp.: 1,733
Fiscal Year-end: 07/31/13

Business Description:
House Builder & Property Developer
S.I.C.: 1531
N.A.I.C.S.: 236117

Personnel:
Edward F. Ayres *(CEO)*
Kevin G. Wrightson *(Sec)*

Board of Directors:
John K. Watson
Keith D. Adey
Edward F. Ayres
John A. Cuthbert
Denise N. Jagger
Peter M. Johnson
Paul N. Hampden Smith
Mike R. Toms

Transfer Agent:
Capita Asset Services
The Registry 34 Beckenham Road
Beckenham, BR3 4TU, United Kingdom

Branches:

Bellway Homes Limited East Midlands (1)
Romulus Ct
Meridian E, Leicester, Leicestershire, LE19 1YG, United Kingdom (100%)
Tel.: (44) 1162820400
Fax: (44) 1162820401
E-Mail: eastmids-sales@bellway.co.uk
Web Site: www.bellway.co.uk/BottomNav/ContactUs/tabid/63/Default.aspx
Emp.: 35
House Builder
S.I.C.: 1531
N.A.I.C.S.: 236117
Gary Mills *(Mng Dir)*

Bellway Homes Limited Essex (1)
Bellway House
1 Rainsford Rd, Chelmsford, Essex, CM1 2PZ, United Kingdom (100%)
Tel.: (44) 1245259989
E-Mail: essex-sales@bellway.co.uk
Emp.: 40
House Builder
S.I.C.: 1531
N.A.I.C.S.: 236117

Bellway Homes Limited Manchester (1)
Bellway House The Beacons Warrington Rd
Birchwood, Warrington, Cheshire, WA3 6GQ, United Kingdom (100%)
Tel.: (44) 925430100
Fax: (44) 925430120
Emp.: 50
House Builder
S.I.C.: 1531
N.A.I.C.S.: 236117

Bellway Homes Limited North East (1)
Bellway House Kings Park Kingsway North
Gateshead, NE11 0JH, United Kingdom (100%)
Tel.: (44) 1914828800
Fax: (44) 1914914536
Web Site: www.bellway.co.uk/BottomNav/ContactUs/tabid/63/Default.aspx
Emp.: 50
House Builder
S.I.C.: 1531
N.A.I.C.S.: 236117
Michael Drummond *(Dir-Fin)*

Bellway Homes Limited North London (1)
Breakspear House Bury St
Ruislip, HA4 7SD, United Kingdom (100%)
Tel.: (44) 1895671100
Fax: (44) 1895671111
Web Site: www.bellway.co.uk/BottomNav/ContactUs/tabid/63/Default.aspx
Emp.: 35
House Builder
S.I.C.: 1531
N.A.I.C.S.: 236117
Stuart Wallace *(Mng Dir)*

Bellway Homes Limited North West (1)
2 Alderman Rd
Liverpool, Merseyside, L24 9LR, United Kingdom (100%)
Tel.: (44) 1514862900
E-Mail: westlancs-sales@bellway.co.uk
Web Site: www.bellway.co.uk
Emp.: 50
House Builder
S.I.C.: 1531
N.A.I.C.S.: 236117
David Williams *(Mng Dir)*

Bellway Homes Limited Northern Home Counties (1)
Woodlands Business Park Breckland
Linford Wood West
Linford Wood, Milton Keynes, Buckinghamshire, MK14 6EY, United Kingdom (100%)
Tel.: (44) 1908328800
Fax: (44) 1908328801
E-Mail: john.keoo@bellway.co.uk
Emp.: 30
House Builder
S.I.C.: 1531
N.A.I.C.S.: 236117
John Keoo *(Mng Dir)*

Bellway Homes Limited Scotland (1)
Bothwell House Hamilton Business Park
Caird St, Hamilton, ML3 0QA, United Kingdom (100%)
Tel.: (44) 1698477440
Fax: (44) 1698477441
E-Mail: scotland-sales@bellway.co.uk
Web Site: www.belway.co.uk
Emp.: 70
House Builder
S.I.C.: 1531
N.A.I.C.S.: 236117
John Watson *(CEO)*

Bellway Homes Limited South East (1)
Bellway House London Rd
Merstham, RH1 3YU, United Kingdom (100%)
Tel.: (44) 1737644911
Fax: (44) 1737646319
Web Site: www.bellway.co.uk/BottomNav/ContactUs/tabid/63/Default.aspx
Emp.: 50
House Builder
S.I.C.: 1531
N.A.I.C.S.: 236117
Jason Green *(Mng Dir)*

Bellway Homes Limited Thames Gateway (1)
Osprey House 1st Floor Crayfields Business Park
New Mill Road, Orpington, Kent, BR5 3QJ, United Kingdom (100%)
Tel.: (44) 1689886400
Fax: (44) 1689886410
E-Mail: thamesgate-sales@bellway.co.uk
Web Site: www.bellway.co.uk/BottomNav/ContactUs/tabid/63/Default.aspx
Emp.: 40
House Builder
S.I.C.: 1531
N.A.I.C.S.: 236117

Bellway Homes Limited Wales (1)
Alexander House Excelsior Rd
Western Ave, Cardiff, CF14 3AT, United Kingdom (100%)
Tel.: (44) 2920544700
Fax: (44) 2920544701
Emp.: 40
House Builder
S.I.C.: 1531
N.A.I.C.S.: 236117
Paul Minnis *(Mng Dir)*

Bellway Homes Limited Wessex (1)
Bellway House Embankment Way
Castleman Bus Centre, Ringwood, Hampshire, BH24 1EU, United Kingdom (100%)
Tel.: (44) 1425477666
Fax: (44) 1425476774
E-Mail: wessex-sales@bellway.co.uk
Web Site: www.bellway.co.uk/BottomNav/ContactUs/tabid/63/Default.aspx
Emp.: 40
House Builder
S.I.C.: 1531
N.A.I.C.S.: 236117
Steven Brown *(Mng Dir)*

Bellway Homes Limited West Midlands (1)
Bellway House Relay Point
Relay Drive, Tamworth, Staffordshire, B77 5PA, United Kingdom (100%)
Tel.: (44) 1827255755
Fax: (44) 1827255766
E-Mail: wmid-sales@bellway.co.uk
Web Site: www.bellway.co.uk
Emp.: 45
House Builder
S.I.C.: 1531
N.A.I.C.S.: 236117
David Campbell-Kelly *(Mng Dir)*

Bellway Homes Limited Yorkshire (1)
2 Deighton Close
Wetherby, Yorkshire, LS22 7GZ, United Kingdom (100%)
Tel.: (44) 1937583533
Fax: (44) 1937586147
E-Mail: yorkshire.reception@bellway.co.uk
Web Site: www.bellway.co.uk/BottomNav/ContactUs/tabid/63/Default.aspx
Emp.: 30
House Builder
S.I.C.: 1531
N.A.I.C.S.: 236117
Paul Miool *(Mng Dir)*

Division:

Bellway Financial Services Limited (1)
Seaton Burn House Dudley Ln Seaton Burn
Newcastle, Newcastle Tyne Wear, NE13 6BE, United Kingdom (100%)
Tel.: (44) 1912172111
Fax: (44) 1912366230
E-Mail: financialservices@bellway.co.uk
Emp.: 2
S.I.C.: 1522
N.A.I.C.S.: 236118
Evan Hall *(Dir-Fin Svcs)*

Subsidiaries:

Bellway Housing Trust Limited (1)
Seaton Burn House Dudley Lane
Newcastle upon Tyne, NE13 6BE, United Kingdom
Tel.: (44) 191 217 0717
Fax: (44) 191 236 6230
Web Site: www.bellwayhousingtrust.bellway.co.uk
New Housing Agency Services
S.I.C.: 8322
N.A.I.C.S.: 624229
John Watson *(CEO)*

Bellway (Services) Limited (1)
Seaton Burn House Dudley La
Newcastle upon Tyne, NE13 6BE, United Kingdom
Tel.: (44) 191 217 0717
Property Management Services
S.I.C.: 6531
N.A.I.C.S.: 531311

BELLZONE MINING PLC

Level 2 88 Colin Street
West Perth, WA, 6005, Australia
Tel.: (61) 894208900
Fax: (61) 894208999
E-Mail: bellzone@bellzone.com.au
Web Site: www.bellzone.com.au
BZM—(AIM)
Rev.: $1,276,000
Assets: $184,665,000
Liabilities: $3,889,000
Net Worth: $180,776,000
Earnings: ($54,625,000)
Emp.: 17
Fiscal Year-end: 12/31/12

Business Description:
Iron Ore Mining Services
S.I.C.: 1011
N.A.I.C.S.: 212210

Personnel:
Michael Farrow *(Chm)*

Bellzone Mining plc—(Continued)

Glenn Baldwin *(CEO)*
Terry Larkan *(CFO)*
Graham Fyfe *(COO)*
Board of Directors:
Michael Farrow
Glenn Baldwin
Antony Gardner-Hillman
Terry Larkan
Legal Counsel:
Steinepreis Paganin
Level 4 The Read Building 16 Milligan Street
Perth, WA, 6000, Australia
Tel.: (61) 8 9321 4000
Fax: (61) 8 9321 4333

Lee & Lee
50 Raffles Place 06-00 Singapore Land Tower
Singapore, Singapore

Chadbourne & Parke (London) LLP
45 King William Street
London, EC4R 9AN, United Kingdom

Carey Olsen
47 Esplande
Saint Helier, Jersey

Cabinet D'Avocats Bao & Fils
Immeuble ALIMA
3a Etage - Quartier Boulbinet Commune de Kaloum
1926 Conakry, Papua New Guinea

Allen & Overy
Level 27 Exchange Plaza 2 The Esplanade
Perth, Australia

BELMONT MEAT PRODUCTS LTD.

230 Signet Drive
Toronto, ON, M9L 1V2, Canada
Tel.: (416) 749-7250
Fax: (416) 749-0604
Toll Free: (888) 267-6328
E-Mail: info@belmontmeats.com
Web Site: www.belmontmeats.com
Year Founded: 1966
Rev.: $19,552,953
Emp.: 120
Business Description:
Meat Products Supplier
S.I.C.: 5147
N.A.I.C.S.: 424470
Personnel:
Mike Mcalary *(CEO)*

BELMONT RESOURCES INC.

Suite 600-625 Howe Street
Vancouver, BC, V6C 2T6, Canada
Tel.: (604) 683-6648
Fax: (604) 683-1350
E-Mail: belmontr@telus.net
Web Site: www.belmontresources.com
Year Founded: 1978
BEA—(TSXV)
Assets: $1,372,511
Liabilities: $26,599
Net Worth: $1,345,912
Earnings: ($626,232)
Fiscal Year-end: 01/31/13
Business Description:
Mineral Exploration Services
S.I.C.: 1081
N.A.I.C.S.: 213114
Personnel:
Vojtech Agyagos *(Pres & CEO)*
Gary Musil *(CFO & Sec)*
Board of Directors:
Roger Agyagos
Vojtech Agyagos
Jake Bottay
Vadim Degen
Gary Musil
Joseph P. Ringwald
Legal Counsel:
Fang & Associates
3rd Floor, 576 Seymour Street
Vancouver, BC, Canada
Transfer Agent:
Canadian Stock Transfer Company Inc
Suite 1600 - 1066 W Hastings Street
Vancouver, BC, Canada

BELO SUN MINING CORP.

65 Queen Street West Suite 815
PO Box 75
Toronto, ON, M5H 2M5, Canada
Tel.: (416) 309-2137
Fax: (416) 861-8165
Web Site: www.belosun.com
BSX—(TSX)
Int. Income: $1,131,121
Assets: $53,459,677
Liabilities: $4,846,961
Net Worth: $48,612,716
Earnings: ($48,118,156)
Emp.: 15
Fiscal Year-end: 12/31/12
Business Description:
Mineral Exploration Services
S.I.C.: 1081
N.A.I.C.S.: 213114
Personnel:
Peter Tagliamonte *(Chm)*
Mark P. Eaton *(Pres & CEO)*
Ryan Ptolemy *(CFO)*
Ian Pritchard *(COO)*
Pat Gleeson *(Sec)*
Board of Directors:
Peter Tagliamonte
Stan Bharti
Helio Diniz
Mark P. Eaton
C. Jay Hodgson
Clay Livingston Hoes
Rui Botica Santos
Catherine Stretch
Transfer Agent:
Equity Financial Trust Company
Toronto, ON, Canada
Non-U.S. Subsidiaries:

Belo Sun Mining (Barbados) Corp (1)
Braemar Crt Deighton Rd
Saint Michael, BB14017, Barbados
Tel.: (246) 4676674
Fax: (246) 4676678
E-Mail: ryanp@forbesmanhattan.com
Mineral Mining Services
S.I.C.: 1499
N.A.I.C.S.: 212399
Ceri Sue *(Mgr)*

Intergemas Mineracao e Industrializacao Ltda (1)
SCS Q 1 Bl I S/N S 206
Brasilia, 70304-900, Brazil
Tel.: (55) 61 3322 3682
Mineral Mining Services
S.I.C.: 1499
N.A.I.C.S.: 212399

BELOVO PAPER MILL S.A.

1A Dabravsko shosse Str
Belovo, 4470, Bulgaria
Tel.: (359) 3581 2105
Fax: (359) 3581 2110
E-Mail: office@belana.bg
Web Site: www.belana.bg
58B—(BUL)
Business Description:
Tissue Household Products Mfr
S.I.C.: 3999
N.A.I.C.S.: 339999
Personnel:
Vilma Iordanova Vasileva *(Dir-IR)*

BELPHAR LTD.

333 Waterfront Drive
PO Box 3175
Road Town, Tortola, Virgin Islands (British)
Tel.: (284) 203 131 0046
E-Mail: info@belphar.com
Web Site: www.belphar.com
Business Description:
Investment Holding Company
S.I.C.: 6719
N.A.I.C.S.: 551112
Personnel:
Khofiz Shakhidi *(Founder)*

BELVEDERE RESOURCES LTD.

Suite 404 Vancouver World Trade Centre 999 Canada Place
Vancouver, BC, V6C 3E2, Canada
Tel.: (604) 844-2838
Web Site: www.belvedere-resources.com
Year Founded: 1997
BEL—(TSXV)
Rev.: $37,507,139
Assets: $32,415,691
Liabilities: $17,359,251
Net Worth: $15,056,440
Earnings: $1,747,175
Fiscal Year-end: 12/31/12
Business Description:
Mineral Exploration Services
S.I.C.: 1081
N.A.I.C.S.: 213114
Personnel:
David Pym *(Pres & CEO)*
Steven R. Cuthill *(CFO & Sec)*
Toby Strauss *(COO)*
Board of Directors:
Harry Dobson
Roger Clough
Steven R. Cuthill
M. Isohanni
David Pym
Toby Strauss
J. S. Thomson
Legal Counsel:
Edwards Kenny & Bray
Vancouver, BC, Canada
Transfer Agent:
Computer Share Trust Company
Vancouver, BC, Canada
Non-U.S. Subsidiary:

Belvedere Mining Oy (1)
Kummuntie 8
85560 Ainastalo, Finland
Tel.: (358) 8 44991
Fax: (358) 8 4499230
Web Site: www.belmining.com
Emp.: 12
Mineral Mining Services
S.I.C.: 1499
N.A.I.C.S.: 212399
Jukka Nieminen *(Mng Dir)*

BELVEDERE S.A.

(d/b/a Belvedere Group)
10 avenue Charles Jaffelin
F-21200 Beaune, France
Tel.: (33) 380229383
Fax: (33) 380229384
E-Mail: info@belvedere.fr
Web Site: www.belvedere.fr
BVD—(EUR)
Sales Range: $800-899.9 Million
Emp.: 3,729
Business Description:
Wines & Distilled Spirits Mfr & Distr
S.I.C.: 2084
N.A.I.C.S.: 312130
Personnel:
Jacques Rouvroy *(Chm & Dir Gen)*
Krzysztof Trylinski *(Dir Gen)*
Board of Directors:
Jacques Rouvroy
Luc Demarre
Xavier Paper
Alain-Dominique Perrin
Waldemar Rudnik
Erick Antony Skora
Krzysztof Trylinski
Subsidiaries:

Marie Brizard & Roger International SAS (1)
130-142 rue Fondaudege
BP 557
33002 Bordeaux, France FR
Tel.: (33) 556018585 (100%)
Fax: (33) 556018599
E-Mail: kcazaux@mabriaz.com
Web Site: www.mariebrizard.com
Sales Range: $100-124.9 Million
Emp.: 750
Holding Company; Wines & Distilled Spirits Mfr & Distr
S.I.C.: 6719
N.A.I.C.S.: 551112
Jerome Matteoli *(Deputy Dir Gen-Legal Affairs, HR & IT)*
Daniel Gainza *(Gen Dir-Spain)*
Erick Antony Skora *(Gen Dir)*

Subsidiaries:

COGNAC GAUTIER SA (2)
28 rue des Ponts
Aigre, 16140 Charenta, Angouleme, France
Tel.: (33) 545211002
Fax: (33) 545212437
E-Mail: gautier@mabriz.com
Web Site: www.cognac-gautier.com
Emp.: 32
Alcoholic Beverages Whslr
S.I.C.: 5182
N.A.I.C.S.: 424820
Olivier Bernazeau *(Mgr-Fin)*

Moncigale S.A.S. (2)
6 Quai de la Paix
Beaucaire, Gard, France
Tel.: (33) 466597400
Fax: (33) 466597403
Alcoholic Beverage Whslr
S.I.C.: 5182
N.A.I.C.S.: 424820

Non-U.S. Subsidiary:

Marie Brizard Espana S.A. (2)
Capitan Haya 56 Bajo
ES-28020 Madrid, Spain ES
Tel.: (34) 915714289 (100%)
Fax: (34) 915792380
Web Site: www.mariebrizard.com
Emp.: 15
Wine & Distilled Spirits Distr
S.I.C.: 5182
N.A.I.C.S.: 424820
Carlos Espana *(Gen Dir)*

Sobieski Sarl (1)
10 Avenue Charles Jaffelin
Beaune, Cote D Or, France
Tel.: (33) 380229383
Fax: (33) 380229384
E-Mail: info@belvedere.fr
Emp.: 8
Alcoholic Beverages Whslr
S.I.C.: 5182
N.A.I.C.S.: 424820
Christophe Trylinski *(Gen Mgr)*

William Pitters International S.A.S (1)
1 Rue Banlin
BP 6
Lormont, 33305 Bordeaux, France
Tel.: (33) 557809999
Fax: (33) 55 640 5005
Emp.: 50
Alcoholic Beverages Whslr
S.I.C.: 5182
N.A.I.C.S.: 424820
P. J. Deleu *(Mgr)*

U.S. Subsidiary:

Imperial Brands, Inc. (1)
11505 Fairchild Gardens Ave Ste 204
Palm Beach Gardens, FL 33410 FL
Tel.: (561) 624-5662 (100%)
Fax: (561) 624-5778
E-Mail: information@ibrandsinc.com
Web Site: www.ibrandsinc.com
Emp.: 18
Wines & Spirits Importer & Marketer Import

S.I.C.: 5182
N.A.I.C.S.: 424820
Chester Brandes *(Pres & CEO)*
James R. Quick *(Treas & VP)*

Non-U.S. Subsidiaries:

Augustowianka Sp. z o.o. (1)
Turystyczna 18 Street
16-300 Augustow, Podlaskie, Poland
Tel.: (48) 876443132
Fax: (48) 876443682
E-Mail: augustowianka@augustowianka.com.pl
Web Site: www.augustowianka.com.pl
Bottled Mineral Water Whslr
S.I.C.: 5149
N.A.I.C.S.: 424490

Belvedere Scandinavia A/S (1)
Generatorvej 6a 3 Sal
2730 Herlev, Denmark
Tel.: (45) 36983000
Fax: (45) 44 41 41 21
Web Site: www.belvedere.dk
Emp.: 50
Alcoholic Beverages Whslr
S.I.C.: 5182
N.A.I.C.S.: 424820
Henriette Holmgreen Thorsen *(Gen Mgr)*

Belvedere Slovensko, s. r. o. (1)
Liptovska 2 Ruzinov
Bratislava, Slovakia
Tel.: (421) 253419996
Fax: (421) 25 341 9996
Web Site: www.belvedere.sk
Emp.: 2
Alcoholic Beverages Whslr
S.I.C.: 5182
N.A.I.C.S.: 424820
Mecial Alag *(Gen Mgr)*

BOISSON ELITE, OOO (1)
Ul B Hmelnitskogo 55
18015 Cherkassy, Ukraine
Tel.: (380) 472339340
Fax: (380) 472 33 93 46
Alcoholic Beverages Whslr
S.I.C.: 5182
N.A.I.C.S.: 424820

CENTRUM TMT Sp. z o.o. (1)
ul Kilnskiego 15
58-200 Dzierzoniow, Lower Silesian, Poland
Tel.: (48) 748323901
E-Mail: biuro@centrumtmt.com
Web Site: www.centrumtmt.com
Alcoholic Beverages Whslr
S.I.C.: 5181
N.A.I.C.S.: 424810

Destylernia Polmos Krakowie SA (1)
ul Fabryczna 13
31 553 Krakow, Poland
Tel.: (48) 12 411 4843
Fax: (48) 12 412 1433
E-Mail: polmos@polmos.krakow.pl
Web Site: www.polmos.krakow.pl
Alcoholic Beverages Mfr & Distr
S.I.C.: 2082
N.A.I.C.S.: 312120
Leszek Wojtan *(Chm)*

Domain Menada Sp. z.o.o. (1)
Al Krakowska 110/114
00-971 Warsaw, Masovian, Poland
Tel.: (48) 226097295
Fax: (48) 226097297
E-Mail: domainmenada@belvedere.pl
Web Site: www.domainmenada.pl
Emp.: 80
Alcoholic Beverages Mfr & Whslr
S.I.C.: 2084
N.A.I.C.S.: 312130
Bednarz Katarzyna *(Mgr-Mktg)*

Dubar Industria E Comercio De Bebidas Ltda (1)
Bento Pires 24
Jundiai, Sao Paulo, 13202-661, Brazil
Tel.: (55) 11 4526 1140
Fax: (55) 11 4526 2281
Web Site: www.dubar.com.br
Alcoholic Beverages Whslr
S.I.C.: 5182
N.A.I.C.S.: 424820

Galerie Alkoholi Sp. z.o.o. (1)
ul Dabrowskiego 249
93-231 Lodz, Poland
Tel.: (48) 426772922
Fax: (48) 42 677 2923
E-Mail: sekretariat@galeriealkoholi.pl
Web Site: www.galeriealkoholi.pl
Alcoholic Beverages Whslr
S.I.C.: 5182
N.A.I.C.S.: 424820

Hasis Sp. z.o.o. (1)
ul Techniczna 4
05-500 Piaseczno, Masovian, Poland
Tel.: (48) 22 756 8083
Fax: (48) 22 750 2229
E-Mail: hasis@hasis.pl
Alcoholic Beverages Whslr
S.I.C.: 5182
N.A.I.C.S.: 424820

Ivan Kalita OOO. (1)
5 Korp 2 Ul Vishnyakovoi
Krasnodar, 350001, Russia
Tel.: (7) 8612682854
Fax: (7) 86 1268 2854
Alcoholic Beverages Whslr
S.I.C.: 5182
N.A.I.C.S.: 424820

Jimbo Sp. z o.o. (1)
Wojska Polskiogo 38
06-100 Pultusk, Masovian, Poland
Tel.: (48) 23 692 0745
Fax: (48) 23 692 5564
Alcoholic Beverages Whslr
S.I.C.: 5182
N.A.I.C.S.: 424820

Multihurt. Sp. z o.o. (1)
ul Chopina 5
Sztum, Pomeranian, Poland
Tel.: (48) 552772278
Fax: (48) 55 277 2278
Spirits Whslr
S.I.C.: 5182
N.A.I.C.S.: 424820

Polmos Lancut S.A. (1)
ul Kolejowa 1
37-100 Lancut, Subcarpathian, Poland
Tel.: (48) 172254261
Fax: (48) 17 225 4015
E-Mail: distillery@polmoslancut.com.pl
Web Site: www.polmoslancut.com.pl
Emp.: 300
Liquors Mfr
S.I.C.: 2084
N.A.I.C.S.: 312130
Richard Bilski *(Chm)*

Redo Sp.z.o.o. (1)
ul Tytoniowa 10
16-300 Augustow, Podlaskie, Poland
Tel.: (48) 876432362
Fax: (48) 876432362
E-Mail: redo@redo.pl
Web Site: www.redo.pl
Emp.: 50
Alcoholic Beverages Distr
S.I.C.: 5182
N.A.I.C.S.: 424820
Wojciech Wojtulewicz *(Dir-Admin)*

Rokicki sp z.o.o. (1)
ul Mszczonowska 155
Skierniewice, Lodz, Poland
Tel.: (48) 468336276
Fax: (48) 46 833 6276
Alcoholic Beverages Whslr
S.I.C.: 5182
N.A.I.C.S.: 424820

Sobieski International Sp. z o.o (1)
Bellottiego 1
01-022 Warsaw, Masovian, Poland
Tel.: (48) 22 838 9518
Fax: (48) 22 838 8285
Alcoholic Beverages Whslr
S.I.C.: 5182
N.A.I.C.S.: 424820

Sobieski Sp. z.o.o. (1)
ul Bellottiego 1
01-022 Warsaw, Masovian, Poland
Tel.: (48) 228683798
Fax: (48) 22 868 3798
Web Site: www.belvedere.pl
Alcoholic Beverages Whslr
S.I.C.: 5182
N.A.I.C.S.: 424820

Subsidiary:

Destylernia Sobieski SA (2)
ul Skarszewska 1
83-200 Starogard Gdanski, Pomeranian, Poland
Tel.: (48) 585339400
Fax: (48) 58 5339 406
E-Mail: sales@wodki.gda.pl
Web Site: www.wodki.gda.pl
Alcoholic Beverages Mfr
S.I.C.: 2084
N.A.I.C.S.: 312130
Ryszard Bilski *(Pres)*

Sobieski Trade Sp. z.o.o. (1)
Kolaczkowo 9
62-230 Witkowo, Greater Poland, Poland
Tel.: (48) 614778212
Fax: (48) 614778901
E-Mail: sobieskitrade@sobieskitrade.com.pl
Web Site: www.sobieskitrade.com.pl
Alcoholic Beverages Mfr
S.I.C.: 2082
N.A.I.C.S.: 312120

TRITEX Sp. z o.o. (1)
ul Bytomska 60
41-940 Piekary Slaskie, Silesian, Poland
Tel.: (48) 323919030
Fax: (48) 32 391 9031
E-Mail: sekretariat@tritex.com.pl
Web Site: www.tritex.com.pl
Alcoholic Beverages Whslr
S.I.C.: 5182
N.A.I.C.S.: 424820

BELVOIR LETTINGS PLC

The Old Court House 60A London Road
Grantham, Lincolnshire, NG31 6HR, United Kingdom
Tel.: (44) 1476 542100
Fax: (44) 1476 584902
E-Mail: customerservices@belvoirlettings.com
Web Site: www.belvoirlettings.com
BLV—(AIM)

Business Description:
Real Estate Services
S.I.C.: 6531
N.A.I.C.S.: 531390

Personnel:
Mike Goddard *(Chm)*
Dorian Gonsalves *(CEO)*
Carl Chadwick *(CFO)*

Board of Directors:
Mike Goddard
Nicholas John Leeming

Subsidiary:

Belvoir Property Management (UK) Limited (1)
The Old Court House 60A London Road
Grantham, NG31 6HR, United Kingdom
Tel.: (44) 84 5331 2741
Fax: (44) 1476 584 902
Emp.: 40
Real Estate Management Services
S.I.C.: 6531
N.A.I.C.S.: 531390
Dorian Gonsalves, *(Mng Dir)*

BEMATECH S.A.

Av Rui Barbosa 2529 - Modulos 07 E 08
83055-320 Sao Jose dos Pinhais, PR, Brazil
Tel.: (55) 41 3299 5800
Fax: (55) 41 3351 2800
E-Mail: ri@bematech.com.br
Web Site: www.bematech.com.br
BEMA3—(BRAZ)
Rev.: $161,531,757
Assets: $234,797,789
Liabilities: $50,484,147
Net Worth: $184,313,642
Earnings: $15,992,820
Fiscal Year-end: 12/31/12

Business Description:
Computer Hardware Mfr & Whslr
S.I.C.: 3571
N.A.I.C.S.: 334111

Personnel:
Paulo Sergio Caputo *(Chm)*
Wolney Edirley Goncalves Betiol *(Vice Chm)*
Cleber Pereira de Morais *(CEO)*
Marcos Andreetto Perillo *(Admin, Fin & IR Officer)*

Board of Directors:
Paulo Sergio Caputo
Henrique Teixeira Alvares
Wolney Edirley Goncalves Betiol
Virgilio Moreira Filho
Marcel Martins Malczewski

BEMCO HYDRAULICS LTD

Udyambag
Belgaum, Karnataka, 590 008, India
Tel.: (91) 831 4219000
Fax: (91) 831 2441263
E-Mail: info@bemcohydraulics.net
Web Site: www.bemcohydraulics.net
522650—(BOM)
Rev.: $7,852,366
Assets: $9,411,796
Liabilities: $7,665,798
Net Worth: $1,745,998
Earnings: $103,996
Fiscal Year-end: 03/31/13

Business Description:
Hydraulic Equipment Mfr
S.I.C.: 3569
N.A.I.C.S.: 333999

Personnel:
Madan Mohan Mohta *(Chm & Co-Mng Dir)*
Anirudh Mohta *(Co-Mng Dir)*
R. B. Patil *(Compliance Officer & Gen Mgr-Fin)*

Board of Directors:
Madan Mohan Mohta
Dilip Chandak
N. K. Daga
Anirudh Mohta
Urmila Devi Mohta
R. M. Shah

Transfer Agent:
Adroit Corporate Services Private Limited
19 Jaferbhoy Industrial Estate Makwana Road
Marol Naka Andheri E
Mumbai, India

BEML LIMITED

BEML SOUDHA 23/1 4th Main SR Nagar
Bengaluru, Karnataka, 560 027, India
Tel.: (91) 8022963240
Fax: (91) 8022963278
E-Mail: office@pr.beml.co.in
Web Site: www.bemlindia.com
BEML—(NSE)
Rev.: $554,394,575
Assets: $968,161,729
Liabilities: $582,524,983
Net Worth: $385,636,746
Earnings: ($15,441,892)
Emp.: 11,005
Fiscal Year-end: 03/31/13

Business Description:
Rail Coaches Mfr
S.I.C.: 1629
N.A.I.C.S.: 237990

Personnel:
P. Dawarakanath *(Chm & Mng Dir)*
M. E. V. Selvamm *(Compliance Officer & Sec)*
Kavitha Kestur *(Chief Vigilance Officer)*

Board of Directors:
P. Dawarakanath
C. Balakrishnan
Rekha Bhargava
Ramesh Bhat
Suhas Anand Bhat

BEML Limited—(Continued)

C. N. Durgesh
N. P. Gupta
Deepak Kumar Hota
Rajnish Kumar
P. K. Mishra
P. R. Naik
Kanwal Nath
S. Sadagopan
Pradeep Swaminathan
Noble Thamburaj

Legal Counsel:
Sundaraswamy & Ramdas
Bengaluru, India

Just Law
Bengaluru, India

Transfer Agent:
Karvy Computershare Private Limited
17-24 Vittal Rao Nagar Madhapur
Hyderabad, India

Divisions:

BEML Limited - Aerospace Manufacturing Division (1)
4th Fl Unity Bldg JC Rd
Bengaluru, Karnataka, 560 002, India
Tel.: (91) 8022963554
Fax: (91) 08022963520
E-Mail: edd@beml.co.in
Web Site: www.bemlindia.nic.in
Emp.: 40
Aerospace Engineering Services
S.I.C.: 8711
N.A.I.C.S.: 541330
Umesh Chandra *(Exec Dir)*

BEML Limited - Bangalore Complex (1)
New Thippasandra Post
Bengaluru, Karnataka, 560 075, India
Tel.: (91) 8025242414
Fax: (91) 8025245545
E-Mail: office@dr.beml.co.in
Rail Coaches Mfr
S.I.C.: 8711
N.A.I.C.S.: 541330

BEML Limited - Earth Moving Division (1)
Marketing Division-Service BEML Nagar
Kolar Gold Fields
Bengaluru, Karnataka, 563 115, India
Tel.: (91) 8153 269085
Fax: (91) 8153 263128
E-Mail: se@em.beml.co.in
Rail Coaches & Spare Parts Mfr
S.I.C.: 3743
N.A.I.C.S.: 336510

BEML Limited - Engine Division (1)
Engine Division-Service Belavadi Post
Mysore, Karnataka, 570 018, India
Tel.: (91) 821 2402696
Fax: (91) 821 2402429
E-Mail: sz@engine.beml.co.in
Web Site: www.bemlindia.com
Rail Coaches & Spare Parts Mfr
S.I.C.: 3743
N.A.I.C.S.: 336510

BEML Limited - Hydraulics & Powerline (H&P) Division (1)
KGF Complex BEML Nagar
Kolar Gold Fields, 563 115 Bengaluru, Karnataka, India
Tel.: (91) 8153263192
Fax: (91) 8153262610
E-Mail: bemlhpd@beml.co.in
Web Site: www.beml.com
Transmission Equipments Mfr
S.I.C.: 3714
N.A.I.C.S.: 336350

BEML Limited - International Business Division (1)
BEML Soudha 23 1 4th Main SR Nagar
Bengaluru, Karnataka, 560 027, India
Tel.: (91) 8022222730
Fax: (91) 8022224874
E-Mail: bemlexp@vsnl.com
Emp.: 22
Rail Coaches Mfr
S.I.C.: 4789
N.A.I.C.S.: 488210
P R Naik *(Exec Dir)*

BEML Limited - Technology Division (1)
BEML Soudha 23 1 4th Main SR Nagar
Bengaluru, Karnataka, 560027, India
Tel.: (91) 8022963100
Fax: (91) 80 22963101
E-Mail: office@ctd.beml.co.in
Web Site: www.bemltech.com
Engineering Services
S.I.C.: 8711
N.A.I.C.S.: 541330
Rajeev Srivastava *(Head-Technology Division)*

BEML Limited - Trading Division (1)
4th Fl Unity Bldg JC Rd
Bengaluru, Karnataka, India
Tel.: (91) 8022963522
Fax: (91) 8022963523
E-Mail: office@trading.beml.co.in
Emp.: 7
Steel Billets & Steam Coal Distr
S.I.C.: 3312
N.A.I.C.S.: 331110
V. R. S. Natarajan *(Mng Dir)*

BEML Limited - Truck Division (1)
Belavadi Post
Mysore, Karnataka, 570 018, India
Tel.: (91) 821 2402422
Fax: (91) 821 2402434
E-Mail: bemlmys@bsnl.in
Engineering Services
S.I.C.: 8711
N.A.I.C.S.: 541330

Subsidiary:

Vignyan Industries Limited (1)
B H Rd
PO Box 4
Chikmagalur, Tarikere, Karnataka, 577228, India
Tel.: (91) 8261222313
Fax: (91) 8261222236
E-Mail: vignyantarikere@sify.com
Web Site: www.vignyan.com
Emp.: 175
Steel Castings Mfr
S.I.C.: 3325
N.A.I.C.S.: 331513

Non-U.S. Subsidiaries:

BEML Brasil Industrial Ltda (1)
Sala 1201 Ed Vitoria Center 629 Avenue Princesa Isabela Centro
Vitoria, Espirito Santo, Brazil
Tel.: (55) 27 3025 2559
E-Mail: brazil@beml.co.in
Web Site: www.bemlindia.com
Rail Coaches & Spare Parts Mfr
S.I.C.: 3714
N.A.I.C.S.: 336350
Milan Das *(Gen Mgr)*

BEML (Malaysia) Sdn.Bhd. (1)
Jalan Tanjung Pelepas Warehouse No 81560
Johor Bahru, Johor, Malaysia
Tel.: (60) 127011393
Fax: (60) 60322760084
E-Mail: office@malaysia.beml.co.in
Web Site: www.bemlindia.nic.in
Emp.: 5
Rail Coaches Mfr
S.I.C.: 8711
N.A.I.C.S.: 541330
Naveen Kumar *(Dir-Technical & Engrg)*

BEN BURGESS & COMPANY

Windmill Hill Exning
Newmarket, Suffolk, CB8 7NP, United Kingdom
Tel.: (44) 1638577877
Fax: (44) 1638577977
E-Mail: enquiries@benburgess.co.uk
Web Site: www.benburgess.co.uk
Sales Range: $50-74.9 Million
Emp.: 27

Business Description:
Horticultural Machines Supplier
S.I.C.: 5083
N.A.I.C.S.: 423820

Personnel:
John F. Rupp *(Dir-Branch)*

BEN THANH SERVICE JSC

45 / 4 Nguyen Thai Hoc Street
Cau Ong Lanh Ward
District 1, Ho Chi Minh City, Vietnam
Tel.: (84) 839208792
Fax: (84) 839208794
E-Mail: benthanh1@btsc.com.vn
Web Site: www.btsc.com.vn
BSC—(HNX)

Business Description:
Holding Company; Motorcycle Distr; Logistics & Warehousing Services; Restaurant & Hotel Owner & Operator; Real Estate Rental Services
S.I.C.: 6719
N.A.I.C.S.: 551112

Personnel:
Quoc Phu Pham *(Chm)*

BEN TRE BUILDING MATERIAL JOINT STOCK COMPANY

207D Nguyen Dinh Chieu Street
Phu Hung Commune, Ben Tre, Vietnam
Tel.: (84) 753822315
Fax: (84) 753822319
E-Mail: vlxdbentre@yahoo.com.vn
Web Site: www.vlxdbentre.com
VXB—(HNX)

Business Description:
Building Materials Mfr; Sand Mining
S.I.C.: 3271
N.A.I.C.S.: 327331

Personnel:
Tai Huu Ngo *(Chm & Dir-Fin)*
Thong Quoc Phan *(Deputy Chm)*

Board of Directors:
Tai Huu Ngo
Nhien Dinh Le
Tai Trong Phan
Thong Quoc Phan
Thinh Van Le

BENALEC HOLDINGS BERHAD

(d/b/a Benalec Group)
Level 18 The Gardens North Tower
Mid Valley City Lingkaran Syed Putra
59200 Kuala Lumpur, Malaysia
Tel.: (60) 3 2264 8888
Fax: (60) 3 2282 2733
E-Mail: enquiry@benalec.com.my
Web Site: www.benalec.com.my
Year Founded: 2005
BENALEC—(KLS)
Rev.: $87,172,575
Assets: $316,541,812
Liabilities: $133,908,535
Net Worth: $182,633,276
Earnings: $18,580,466
Emp.: 380
Fiscal Year-end: 06/30/13

Business Description:
Marine & Civil Engineering Services
S.I.C.: 1629
N.A.I.C.S.: 237990

Personnel:
Seng Hai Leaw *(Mng Dir)*
Wai Foong Wong *(Sec)*

Board of Directors:
Aznam Mansor
Hoong Kwan Koo
Ah Chye Leaw
Seng Hai Leaw
Tua Choon Leaw
Yoke Nyen Wong

Subsidiaries:

Benalec Sdn Bhd (1)
38 Jalan Pengacara U1/48 Temasya Industrial Park
Glenmarie, Shah Alam, Selangor, 40150, Malaysia
Tel.: (60) 3 5569 7366
Fax: (60) 3 5569 0366
E-Mail: enquiry@benalec.com.my
Web Site: www.benalec.com.my
Emp.: 50
Marine Engineering Services
S.I.C.: 8711
N.A.I.C.S.: 541330
Brian Mak *(Mgr-Bus Dev)*

Ocaenline (Labuan) Ltd. (1)
Lot A020 Level 1 Podium Level Financial Park Labuan
Jalan Merdeka, Labuan, Federal Territory, 87000, Malaysia
Tel.: (60) 87427745
Fax: (60) 87428845
E-Mail: sue@hansworldwide.com
Web Site: www.hansworldwide.com
Marine Construction Engineering Services
S.I.C.: 1629
N.A.I.C.S.: 237990

BENCHMARK HOLDINGS PLC

Benchmark House 8 Smithy Wood Dr
Sheffield, S35 1QN, United Kingdom
Tel.: (44) 114 240 9939
E-Mail: info@benchmarkplc.com
Web Site: www.benchmarkplc.com
BMK—(AIM)

Business Description:
Animal Health Products Mfr; Technical Publishing
S.I.C.: 2834
N.A.I.C.S.: 325412

Personnel:
Alex Hambro *(Chm)*
Malcolm Pye *(CEO)*
Mark Pamplin *(CFO)*
Roland Bonney *(COO)*

Board of Directors:
Alex Hambro
Roland Bonney
Basil Brookes
Mark Pamplin
Malcolm Pye
Susan Searle

BENCIS CAPITAL PARTNERS B.V.

WTC Tower Zuidplein 76
1077 XV Amsterdam, Netherlands
Tel.: (31) 205400940
Fax: (31) 205400941
E-Mail: info@bencis.com
Web Site: www.bencis.com
Sales Range: $25-49.9 Million
Emp.: 15

Business Description:
Private Equity Firm
S.I.C.: 6211
N.A.I.C.S.: 523999

Personnel:
Zoran van Gessel *(Mng Partner)*
Eric-Joost Ernst *(Partner)*
Benoit Graulich *(Partner)*
Lesley Van Zutphen *(PArtner)*

Holdings:

Desso Group B.V. (1)
Taxandriaweg 15
5142 PA Waalwijk, Netherlands NL
Mailing Address:
Postbus 169
NL-5140 AD Waalwijk, Netherlands
Tel.: (31) 416684100
Fax: (31) 416335955
E-Mail: info@desso.com
Web Site: www.desso.com
Sales Range: $250-299.9 Million
Emp.: 300
Carpet Mfr & Distr
S.I.C.: 2273

N.A.I.C.S.: 314110
Stef Kranendijk *(CEO)*
Tom Francken *(CFO)*
Pierre van Trimpont *(COO)*
Alexander Collot d'Escury *(Chief Comml Officer)*

U.S. Subsidiary:

Desso USA Inc. **(2)**
10 Corbin Dr Fl 2
Darien, CT 06820-5403 PA
Tel.: (203) 202-7650
Fax: (203) 202-7647
Toll Free: (888) 337-7687
E-Mail: service-us@desso.com
Web Site: www.desso.com
Sales Range: $1-9.9 Million
Emp.: 10
Woven Carpet Distr
S.I.C.: 2273
N.A.I.C.S.: 314110
John Reader *(Mng Dir)*

Stork Prints B.V. **(1)**
Raamstraat 1 3
5831 AT Boxmeer, Netherlands (60%)
Mailing Address:
PO Box 67
5830 AB Boxmeer, Netherlands
Tel.: (31) 485599555
Fax: (31) 485599556
E-Mail: info@spgprints.com
Web Site: www.storkprints.com
Sales Range: $250-299.9 Million
Emp.: 1,400
Printing Machinery & Equipment Mfr
S.I.C.: 3555
N.A.I.C.S.: 333244
Dick Joustra *(CEO)*

Subsidiaries:

Stork Digital Imaging B.V. **(2)**
Raamstraat 1-3
5831 AT Boxmeer, Netherlands
Tel.: (31) 485584911
E-Mail: info.sdi@stork.com
Web Site: www.storkprints.com
Emp.: 1,400
Textile Printing Systems
S.I.C.: 2759
N.A.I.C.S.: 323111
Stephan Haagh *(Mng Dir)*

Stork Veco B.V. **(2)**
PO Box 10
6960 AA Eerbeek, Netherlands
Tel.: (31) 313672911
Fax: (31) 313672900
E-Mail: info.veco@stork.com
Web Site: www.storkveco.com
Emp.: 135
Metal Precision Product Mfr
S.I.C.: 3451
N.A.I.C.S.: 332721
Stephan Haagh *(Gen Mgr)*

U.S. Subsidiary:

Stork Prints America, Inc. **(2)**
3201 N Interstate 85
Charlotte, NC 28221
Tel.: (704) 598-7171
Fax: (704) 598-0858
E-Mail: info.veco@spgprints.com
Web Site: www.spgprints.com
Emp.: 70
Printing Machinery & Equipment Mfr
S.I.C.: 3555
N.A.I.C.S.: 333244
Varsha Adhikari *(Sec)*

Non-U.S. Subsidiaries:

P.T. Stork Prints Indonesia **(2)**
Cikarang Industrial Estate Jl Jababeka Raya
Block C No 1, Bekasi, Jawa Barat, 17550, Indonesia
Tel.: (62) 218934136
Web Site: www.storkprints.com.br/english/localizacao.html
Emp.: 22
Graphic Design Services
S.I.C.: 7336
N.A.I.C.S.: 541430

Stork Prints Austria GmbH **(2)**
Kufsteinastrasse 4
6330 Langkampfen, Austria
Tel.: (43) 537269930
Fax: (43) 5372699354
E-Mail: austria@spgprints.com
Web Site: www.spgprints.com
Emp.: 100
Rotary Screens & Systems
S.I.C.: 3559
N.A.I.C.S.: 333249
Arno Bowvmeester *(Gen Mgr)*

Stork Prints Brasil Ltda. **(2)**
Ave Comendador Leopoldo Dedini 150
Distrito Industrial Unileste, 13422-210
Piracicaba, Brazil
Tel.: (55) 1934371300
Fax: (55) 1934371310
E-Mail: brasil@stgprints.com
Web Site: www.stgprints.com
Emp.: 90
Textile Printing Equipment & Consumables
S.I.C.: 3559
N.A.I.C.S.: 333249
Jose Junior *(Mng Dir)*

Stork Prints Japan K.K. **(2)**
Daimel Bldg 7F 3-20-10 Toyosaki
Kita Ku, Osaka, 531 0072, Japan
Tel.: (81) 663598865
Fax: (81) 663598873
E-Mail: spj@spjprints.co.in
Web Site: www.spjprints.co.jp/
Emp.: 5
Printing Products Mfr
S.I.C.: 2759
N.A.I.C.S.: 323111
Tada Masahiro *(Mng Dir)*

Stork Prints Pakistan (Pvt) Ltd. **(2)**
11, Bangalore Town Cooperative Housing Society
Karachi, Shahrah-e-Faisal, 75350, Pakistan
Tel.: (92) 21 455 8334
Fax: (92) 21 455 8277
Web Site: www.storkprints.com
Emp.: 30
Graphic Design Services
S.I.C.: 7336
N.A.I.C.S.: 541430

Stovec Industries Ltd. **(2)**
NIDC Near Lambha Village
Narol Post, Ahmedabad, Gujarat State, 382 405, India
Tel.: (91) 7925710407
Fax: (91) 7925710406
E-Mail: admin@stovec.com
Web Site: www.spgprint.com
Emp.: 125
Label Printing Nickel Screens, Pre-Sensitized Plates & Antilox Rollers; Rotary Screen Heads
S.I.C.: 3399
N.A.I.C.S.: 331221

BENDIGO & ADELAIDE BANK LTD.

The Bendigo Centre
PO Box 480
Bendigo, VIC, 3552, Australia
Tel.: (61) 300 361 911
Fax: (61) 3 5485 7668
E-Mail: oncall@bendigobank.com.au
Web Site: www.bendigobank.com.au
Year Founded: 1858
BEN—(ASX OTC)
Int. Income: $3,203,102,770
Assets: $62,820,080,620
Liabilities: $58,199,409,220
Net Worth: $4,620,671,400
Earnings: $367,131,830
Emp.: 5,195
Fiscal Year-end: 06/30/13

Business Description:
Investment Banking Services
S.I.C.: 6029
N.A.I.C.S.: 522110

Personnel:
Michael John Hirst *(CEO & Mng Dir)*
Richard Fennell *(CFO & Exec-Fin & Treasury)*
Marnie A. Baker *(Exec-Customer Voice)*
Dennis Bice *(Exec-Retail)*
Robert Musgrove *(Exec-Community Engagement)*
Tim Piper *(Exec-Risk)*
Alexandra Tullio *(Exec-Margin Lending)*
Andrew Watts *(Exec-Change)*
William Conlan *(Sec)*

Board of Directors:
Robert N. Johanson
Jenny L. Dawson
James T. Hazel
Jacqueline Hey
Michael John Hirst
Robert Hubbard
David Matthews
Deborah L. Radford
Antony David Robinson

Subsidiaries:

Adelaide Bank Limited **(1)**
169 Pirie Street
Adelaide, SA, 5000, Australia
Mailing Address:
GPO Box 1048
Adelaide, SA, 5001, Australia
Tel.: (61) 883006000
Fax: (61) 883006720
E-Mail: ablsite@adelaidebank.com.au
Web Site: www.adelaidebank.com.au
Sales Range: $1-4.9 Billion
Emp.: 1,185
Commercial Banking Services
S.I.C.: 6099
N.A.I.C.S.: 522320
Richard Fennell *(CFO & COO)*
Philip Riquier *(Chief Credit Officer)*
Andrew Kamm *(Gen Counsel & Gen Mgr-Risk Mgmt)*
David Hughes *(Sec)*

Subsidiaries:

Leveraged Equities Limited **(2)**
Level 3 24 York Street
Sydney, NSW, 2000, Australia
Tel.: (61) 1300307807
Fax: (61) 282828383
E-Mail: info@leveraged.com.au
Web Site: www.leveraged.com.au
Emp.: 70
Financial Management Services
S.I.C.: 6282
N.A.I.C.S.: 523930
Lilly Elliot *(Mng Dir)*

Pirie Street Custodian Ltd. **(2)**
GPO Box 5388
Sydney, NSW, 2001, Australia
Tel.: (61) 282828282
Fax: (61) 282828383
E-Mail: info@leveraged.com.au
Web Site: www.leveraged.com.au
Emp.: 100
Nondepository Credit Intermediation
S.I.C.: 6159
N.A.I.C.S.: 522298

Bank of Cyprus Australia Pty Ltd **(1)**
Rialto Towers Level 41
525 Collins Street, Melbourne, VIC, 3000, Australia
Tel.: (61) 386272727
Fax: (61) 386272777
E-Mail: service@bankofcyprus.com.au
Web Site: www.bankofcyprus.com.au
Emp.: 50
Commercial Banking
S.I.C.: 6029
N.A.I.C.S.: 522110
George Tacticos *(Mng Dir)*

Bendigo Financial Planning Limited **(1)**
L 5 120 Harbour Esplanade
Docklands, Melbourne, VIC, 3008, Australia
Tel.: (61) 384147982
Fax: (61) 384147982
Financial Management Services
S.I.C.: 6211
N.A.I.C.S.: 523999

Bendigo Investment Services Limited **(1)**
Level 5 120 Harbour Esplanade
Docklands, Melbourne, VIC, 3008, Australia
Tel.: (61) 384147982
Fax: (61) 384147242
Web Site: www.bendigobank.com.au/public/personal/investment/financial_planning_contact.asp
Financial Investment Services
S.I.C.: 6282
N.A.I.C.S.: 523930

Community Energy Australia Pty Ltd **(1)**
PO Box 480
Bendigo, VIC, 3552, Australia
Tel.: (61) 1300304543
Fax: (61) 1300 304 542
E-Mail: communityenergy@bendigobank.com.au
Financial Management Services
S.I.C.: 6211
N.A.I.C.S.: 523999

National Mortgage Market Corporation Pty Ltd **(1)**
Level 3 120 Harbour Esplanade
Docklands, Melbourne, VIC, 3008, Australia
Tel.: (61) 384147982
Fax: (61) 384147252
E-Mail: info@nmmc.com.au
Web Site: www.nmmc.com.au
Mortgage Origination, Management & Securitisation
S.I.C.: 6163
N.A.I.C.S.: 522310

Sandhurst Trustees Limited **(1)**
18 View Street
Bendigo, VIC, 3550, Australia
Tel.: (61) 354339800
Fax: (61) 354339802
Web Site: www.sandhursttrustees.com.au
Rev.: $29,304,470
Emp.: 50
Funds Management & Financial Services
S.I.C.: 6211
N.A.I.C.S.: 523999
Robert Johanson *(Co-Chm)*
Ian G. Mansbridge *(Co-Chm)*

Tasmanian Banking Services Limited **(1)**
45 Murray Street
Hobart, TAS, 7018, Australia
Tel.: (61) 362113700
Fax: (61) 3 6211 3701
Web Site: www.tasmanianbankingservices.com.au
Commercial Banking Services
S.I.C.: 6029
N.A.I.C.S.: 522110

Victorian Securities **(1)**
6 Chancery Lane
Ballarat, VIC, 3350, Australia
Tel.: (61) 353044444
Fax: (61) 353044455
E-Mail: info@vsc.com.au
Web Site: www.vsc.com.au
Emp.: 20
Financial Products & Services
S.I.C.: 6211
N.A.I.C.S.: 523999
Michael John Hirst *(Chm)*

Joint Venture:

Rural Bank Limited **(1)**
27 Currie St
5000 Adelaide, Australia, Australia (100%)
Tel.: (61) 884254000
Fax: (61) 882311910
E-Mail: service@elders.com.au
Web Site: www.ruralbank.com.au
Emp.: 800
Banking Services
S.I.C.: 6029
N.A.I.C.S.: 522110
Paul Hutchinson *(CEO)*

BENE AG

Schwarzwiesenstrasse 3
3340 Waidhofen, Austria
Tel.: (43) 7442 500 0
E-Mail: office@bene.com
Web Site: www.bene.com
BENE—(VIE)
Sales Range: $200-249.9 Million
Emp.: 1,271

Bene AG—(Continued)

Business Description:
Office Furniture Mfr
S.I.C.: 2522
N.A.I.C.S.: 337214

Personnel:
Manfred Bene *(Chm-Supervisory Bd)*
Reinhold Sussenbacher *(Deputy Chm-Supervisory Bd)*

Supervisory Board of Directors:
Manfred Bene
Andrea Gaal
Reinhard Gleiss
August Hager
Martin Honickl
Karl Sevelda
Reinhold Sussenbacher
Richard Wolf

Non-U.S. Subsidiaries:

Bene Belgium BVBA (1)
Corporate Village Da Vincilaan 2 Bus 7
Business Centre-1
1935 Zaventem, Flemish Brabant, Belgium
Tel.: (32) 24214180
Fax: (32) 24214185
E-Mail: office@bene.com
Web Site: www.bene-belgium.be
Emp.: 6
Office Furniture Whslr
S.I.C.: 5021
N.A.I.C.S.: 423210
Elke Exelmans *(Office Mgr)*

Bene Bratislava spol.s.r.o, (1)
Zilinska 7-9
811 05 Bratislava, Slovakia
Tel.: (421) 257104311
Fax: (421) 257104319
E-Mail: bratislava@bene.com
Web Site: www.bene.sk
Emp.: 6
Office Furniture Sales
S.I.C.: 5021
N.A.I.C.S.: 423210
Vojtech Varga *(Mgr)*

Bene Budapest Kft., (1)
Aliz utca 2
1072 Budapest, Hungary
Tel.: (36) 14113411
Fax: (36) 14113419
E-Mail: budapest@bene.com
Web Site: www.bene.hu
Emp.: 7
Office Furniture Sales
S.I.C.: 5021
N.A.I.C.S.: 423210
Richard Wolf *(Country Mgr)*

Bene Deutschland GmbH (1)
Wasserweg 8-10
60594 Frankfurt am Main, Hesse, Germany
Tel.: (49) 697104040
Fax: (49) 697104046094
E-Mail: frankfurt@bene.com
Web Site: www.bene.com
Office Furniture Sales
S.I.C.: 5021
N.A.I.C.S.: 423210

Bene GmbH (1)
Magnolienweg 12
63741 Aschaffenburg, Bavaria, Germany
Tel.: (49) 602184090
Fax: (49) 6021840950
E-Mail: aschaffenburg@bene.com
Web Site: www.bene-buero.de
Emp.: 14
Office Furniture Sales
S.I.C.: 5021
N.A.I.C.S.: 423210
Richard Kampfmann *(Mng Dir)*

Bene Kyiv TOV (1)
BC Elias 8 Illinska Street 1st Floor
Podol District, 04070 Kiev, Ukraine
Tel.: (380) 44 49 940 51
Fax: (380) 44 49 940 52
E-Mail: office@bene.com
Web Site: www.bene.ua
Office Furniture Sales
S.I.C.: 5021
N.A.I.C.S.: 423210

Bene Ljubljana d.o.o., (1)
Dunajska cesta 151
1000 Ljubljana, Slovenia
Tel.: (386) 15680970
Fax: (386) 15680980
E-Mail: office@bene.com
Web Site: www.bene-slovenija.si
Emp.: 3
Office Furniture Sales
S.I.C.: 5021
N.A.I.C.S.: 423210
Ales Katic *(Mgr-Sls)*

Bene Office Furniture Ireland Ltd. (1)
50 City Quay
Dublin, 2, Ireland
Tel.: (353) 17079110
Fax: (353) 17079100
E-Mail: office@bene.com
Web Site: www.bene-ireland.ie
Emp.: 4
Office Furniture Sales
S.I.C.: 5021
N.A.I.C.S.: 423210
Gerhard Grabner *(Mgr)*

Bene Praha spol.s.r.o, (1)
The Park-Building 2 V Parku 2294/4
Chodov, 14800 Prague, Czech Republic
Tel.: (420) 221507511
Fax: (420) 221507593
E-Mail: praha@bene.com
Web Site: www.bene.com.cz
Office Furniture Sales
S.I.C.: 5021
N.A.I.C.S.: 423210

Bene PLC (1)
47-53 Saint John St
London, EC1M 4AN, United Kingdom
Tel.: (44) 2076891234
Fax: (44) 2076891250
E-Mail: office@bene.com
Web Site: www.bene.co.uk
Emp.: 40
Office Furniture Sales
S.I.C.: 5021
N.A.I.C.S.: 423210
Carolyn Knight *(Mgr-Mktg)*

Bene Romania S.R.L. (1)
Str Tipografilor No 11-15 S-Park Aripa A 1-2
Parter Sector 1, 013714 Bucharest, Romania
Tel.: (40) 312253200
Fax: (40) 312253229
E-Mail: office@bene.com
Web Site: www.bene.com.ro
Emp.: 4
Office Furniture Sales
S.I.C.: 5021
N.A.I.C.S.: 423210

Bene Rus OOO (1)
16 Strastnoy Blvd
107031 Moscow, Russia
Tel.: (7) 4957923200
Fax: (7) 4957923202
E-Mail: moscow@bene.com
Web Site: www.bene.ru
Emp.: 60
Office Furniture Retailer
S.I.C.: 5021
N.A.I.C.S.: 423210
Tatyana Nikolaevna Kobrova *(Dir Gen)*

Bene Warszawa Sp. z o.o. (1)
ul Al Armii Ludowej nr 26
00-609 Warsaw, Poland
Tel.: (48) 225793480
Fax: (48) 225793488
E-Mail: office@bene.com
Web Site: www.bene.com
Office Furniture Sales
S.I.C.: 5021
N.A.I.C.S.: 423210

BENEFIT SYSTEMS SA

ul Fredro 6
00-097 Warsaw, Poland
Tel.: (48) 22 5313000
Fax: (48) 22 8317920
E-Mail: info@benefitsystems.pl
Web Site: www.benefitsystems.pl
Year Founded: 2000
BFT—(WAR)
Sales Range: $50-74.9 Million
Emp.: 250

Business Description:
Benefit Systems
S.I.C.: 7372
N.A.I.C.S.: 511210

Personnel:
Przemyslaw Gacek *(Chm-Supervisory Bd)*
James Van Bergh *(Chm-Mgmt Bd & CEO)*
Marcin Marczuk *(Vice Chm-Supervisory Bd)*

Supervisory Board of Directors:
Przemyslaw Gacek
Miloslawa Kuznicka
Marcin Marczuk
Michael Sanderson
Agnieszka Szpara

BENESSE HOLDINGS, INC.

3-7-17 Minamigata Kita-ku Okayama-shi
Okayama, 700-0807, Japan
Tel.: (81) 862251100
Fax: (81) 423567301
E-Mail: tokyoir@mail.benesse.co.jp
Web Site: www.benesse-hd.co.jp/en
Year Founded: 1955
9783—(OTC TKS)
Sls.: $4,952,002,000
Assets: $5,062,849,000
Liabilities: $2,780,580,000
Net Worth: $2,282,269,000
Earnings: $232,617,000
Emp.: 19,739
Fiscal Year-end: 03/31/13

Business Description:
Holding Company
S.I.C.: 6719
N.A.I.C.S.: 551112

Personnel:
Soichiro Fukutake *(Chm)*
Tamotsu Fukushima *(Pres)*
Kenichi Fukuhara *(Exec VP)*

Board of Directors:
Soichiro Fukutake
Tamotsu Adachi
Eiji Aketa
Kenichi Fukuhara
Tamotsu Fukushima
Eikoh Harada
Mark W. Harris
Daisuke Iwase
Hitoshi Kobayashi
Hiroyuki Mitani

Transfer Agent:
Mitsubishi UFJ Trust & Banking Corporation
Tokyo, Japan

Subsidiaries:

Benesse Corporation (1)
3-7-17 Minamigata
Kita-ku, Okayama, 700-0807, Japan JP
Tel.: (81) 862251100 (100%)
Web Site: www.benesse.co.jp
Emp.: 1,000
Educational Materials Publisher & Support Services
S.I.C.: 2741
N.A.I.C.S.: 511199
Eiji Aketa *(Pres)*

Co-Headquarters:

Benesse Corporation - Tokyo Head Office (2)
1-34 Ochiai
Tama, Tokyo, 206-8686, Japan
Tel.: (81) 42 356 1100
Web Site: www.benesse.co.jp
Administrative & Executive Office
S.I.C.: 8741
N.A.I.C.S.: 561110

Subsidiaries:

Benesse Music Publishing Co. (2)
1-34 Ochiai
Tama, Tokyo, 206 8686, Japan (100%)
Tel.: (81) 42 356 7134
Fax: (81) 42 356 7120
Sales Range: Less than $1 Million
Emp.: 25
Music Publication Rights Management Services
S.I.C.: 6794
N.A.I.C.S.: 533110

Benesse Style Care Co., Ltd. (2)
Shionogi Shibuya Bldg 9F 2-22-3 Shibuya
Shibuya-ku, Tokyo, 150-0002, Japan JP
Tel.: (81) 3 5766 9805
Fax: (81) 3 5766 9816
Web Site: www.benesse-style-care.co.jp
Sales Range: $800-899.9 Million
Emp.: 12,105
Senior Citizen Welfare Services
S.I.C.: 8322
N.A.I.C.S.: 624120
Shinya Takiyama *(Pres)*

Tokyo Individualized Educational Institute, Inc. (2)
2F Pier West Square 1-11-8 Tuskuda
Chuo-ku, Tokyo, 104-0051, Japan JP
Tel.: (81) 3 5560 1471 (61.91%)
Fax: (81) 3 5560 1475
E-Mail: ir@tkg-jp.com
Web Site: www.tkg.jp
4745—(TKS)
Sls.: $143,187,000
Assets: $90,376,000
Liabilities: $18,348,000
Net Worth: $72,028,000
Earnings: $3,938,000
Emp.: 396
Fiscal Year-end: 02/28/13
Preparatory School Operator
S.I.C.: 8299
N.A.I.C.S.: 611699
Kazunari Matoba *(Pres)*

Naoshima Benesse (1)
Gotanji Naoshima-cho
Kagawa-gun, Kagawa, 761 3110, Japan (100%)
Tel.: (81) 878922030
Fax: (81) 878922259
E-Mail: naoshima@mail.benesse.co.jp
Web Site: www.benesse-artsite.jp/en/contact/hotel.html
Sales Range: $1-9.9 Million
Emp.: 50
Hotel & Campsite Operation & Management
S.I.C.: 7011
N.A.I.C.S.: 721110
Soichiro Fukutake *(Pres)*

Plandit Co., Ltd. (1)
Peperi Bldg 1 32 1 Ochiai
Tama Shi, Tokyo, 206 0033, Japan (100%)
Tel.: (81) 423573211
Fax: (81) 423571560
E-Mail: p-info@ns.plandit.co.jp
Web Site: www.benesse.co.jp
Sales Range: $1-9.9 Million
Emp.: 60
Developer of Published Study Materials
S.I.C.: 2731
N.A.I.C.S.: 511130
Tamotsu Fukushima *(Pres)*
Masahiro Kotani *(Pres)*

Shinken-AD Co., Ltd. (1)
Shinfujita Building 2-4-27 Dojima
Kita-ku
Osaka, 530-0003, Japan (76.35%)
Tel.: (81) 6 6345 7221
Fax: (81) 6 6345 7121
Web Site: www.shinken-ad.co.jp
Sales Range: $75-99.9 Million
Emp.: 200
Advertising Services
S.I.C.: 7311
N.A.I.C.S.: 541810
Toshiya Kawame *(Pres)*

Simul International, Inc. (1)
1-12-6 Tsukiji
Chuo-ku, Tokyo, 104 0045, Japan (100%)
Tel.: (81) 335243100
Fax: (81) 335243195
E-Mail: info@simul.co.jp
Web Site: www.simul.co.jp
Sales Range: $25-49.9 Million
Emp.: 120
Interpretation, Language Instruction & Translation Services
S.I.C.: 8299
N.A.I.C.S.: 611630

Nobutaka Fukuyama *(Pres)*

Sympres Co., Ltd. (1)
10 1 Takayanagi Higashi Cho
Okayana Shi, Okayama, 700 0034, Japan (11.8%)
Tel.: (81) 862556660
Web Site: www.benesse.com
Emp.: 50
Provider of Prepress Operations
S.I.C.: 7389
N.A.I.C.S.: 323120
Soichiro Fukutake *(Chm, Pres & CEO)*

Synform Co., Ltd. (1)
10 1 Takayanagi Higashi Cho
Okayama, 700 0034, Japan (100%)
Tel.: (81) 862560202
Fax: (81) 862566051
E-Mail: info@synform.co.jp
Web Site: www.synform.co.jp
Sales Range: $150-199.9 Million
Emp.: 400
Machine Tooling Equipment Mfr
S.I.C.: 3559
N.A.I.C.S.: 333249
Takashi Koyama *(Pres)*

Telemarketing Japan, Inc. (1)
Sumitomo Realty & Development Bldg
7-20-1 Nishi Shinjuku
Shinjuku-ku, Tokyo, 160 0023, Japan (100%)
Tel.: (81) 367582028
Fax: (81) 353210807
Web Site: www.tmj.jp
Emp.: 110
Telemarketing
S.I.C.: 7389
N.A.I.C.S.: 561422

Affiliates:

Zip Co., Ltd. (1)
301 11 Osafune Cho
Setouchi, Okayama, 714271, Japan (67%)
Tel.: (81) 869264770
Fax: (81) 869265261
E-Mail: soumu@zip-inc.co.jp
Web Site: www.zip-inc.co.jp
Emp.: 600
Provider of Distribution Services
S.I.C.: 7319
N.A.I.C.S.: 541870

U.S. Subsidiaries:

Berlitz Corporation (1)
400 Alexander Park
Princeton, NJ 08540-6306 NY
Tel.: (609) 514-9650
Fax: (609) 514-9648
Toll Free: (800) 257-9449
Web Site: www.berlitz.com
Sales Range: $450-499.9 Million
Emp.: 140
Holding Company; Language Schools Operator & Franchisor; Translation Services; Language Educational Materials Publisher
S.I.C.: 6719
N.A.I.C.S.: 551112
Mark W. Harris *(Chm, Pres & CEO)*
Mike Kashani *(Dir & Sr VP-Emerging Markets)*

Subsidiaries:

Berlitz Languages, Inc. (2)
400 Alexander Park
Princeton, NJ 08540-6306 NY
Tel.: (609) 514-9650
Fax: (609) 514-9648
Web Site: www.berlitz.us
Language Schools Operator & Franchisor
S.I.C.: 8299
N.A.I.C.S.: 611630
Mark W. Harris *(Chm, Pres & CEO)*

ELS Educational Services, Inc. (2)
400 Alexander Park
Princeton, NJ 08540-6306 NJ
Tel.: (609) 750-3500 (100%)
Fax: (609) 750-3590
E-Mail: info@els.edu
Web Site: www.els.edu
Sales Range: $10-24.9 Million
Emp.: 200
Tutoring School
S.I.C.: 8299
N.A.I.C.S.: 611691
Mark W. Harris *(Pres & CEO)*

Non-U.S. Subsidiaries:

Berlitz Japan, Inc. (2)
Aoyama Twin Tower East 16F 1-1-1
Minami-Aoyama
Minato-ku, Tokyo, 107-0062, Japan JP
Tel.: (81) 120 510 923
E-Mail:
Web Site: www.berlitz.co.jp
Emp.: 1,800
Language Schools Operator
S.I.C.: 8299
N.A.I.C.S.: 611630
Mahmoud S. Kashani *(Pres)*

Berlitz (U.K.) Ltd. (2)
Lincoln House 296-302 High Holborn
London, WC1 7JH, United Kingdom UK
Tel.: (44) 20 7611 9640
Fax: (44) 20 7611 9656
E-Mail: reception@berlitz.co.uk
Web Site: www.berlitz.co.uk
Emp.: 40
Language Schools Operator
S.I.C.: 8299
N.A.I.C.S.: 611630
Robert Worms *(Controller-Fin)*

Subsidiary:

Berlitz Publishing Company Limited (3)
58 Borough High Street
London, SE1 1XF, United Kingdom UK
Tel.: (44) 20 7403 0284
Fax: (44) 20 7403 0290
Web Site: www.berlitzbooks.com
Language Educational Materials Publisher
S.I.C.: 2731
N.A.I.C.S.: 511130

Non-U.S. Subsidiary:

Fukutake Consulting Co., Ltd. (1)
10th Fl
No 49 Guanchian Rd, Taipei, NT, 100, Taiwan (100%)
Tel.: (886) 223122419
Fax: (886) 223701001
Web Site: www.benesse.co.jp/IR/english/profile/02_01.htm
Emp.: 25
Management Consulting
S.I.C.: 8742
N.A.I.C.S.: 541611

BENETEAU S.A

Les Embruns 16 boulevard de la Mer
85800 Saint-Gilles-Croix-de-Vie, France
Tel.: (33) 251268850
Fax: (33) 251268864
Web Site: www.beneteau-group.com
Year Founded: 1884
BEN—(EUR)
Sales Range: $1-4.9 Billion
Emp.: 5,283

Business Description:
Recreational Boat Building & Sales
S.I.C.: 3732
N.A.I.C.S.: 336612

Personnel:
Yves Lyon-Caen *(Chm-Supervisory Bd)*
Annette Roux *(Vice Chm-Supervisory Bd)*
Bruno Cathelinais *(Pres)*
Aymeric Duthoit *(Member-Mgmt Bd)*
Dieter Gust *(Member-Mgmt Bd)*

Supervisory Board of Directors:
Yves Lyon-Caen
Yvon Beneteau
Jean-Louis Caussin
Christian De Labriffe
Eric Delannoy
Luc Dupe
Yves Gonnord
Patrick Mahe
Annette Roux

Subsidiaries:

Construction Navale Bordeaux SA (1)
162 quai de Brazza
33100 Bordeaux, France
Tel.: (33) 557 80 85 50
Fax: (33) 557 80 85 51
E-Mail: cnb@cnb.fr
Web Site: www.cnb.fr
Emp.: 50
Sailing Yacht Construction Services
S.I.C.: 3732
N.A.I.C.S.: 336612
Paul Hills *(Gen Mgr)*

Fonderie Vrignaud SA (1)
124 rue du Moulin des Oranges ZI La Ribotiere
85170 Le Poire-sur-Vie, France
Tel.: (33) 2 51 34 13 64
Cast Iron Mfr
S.I.C.: 3321
N.A.I.C.S.: 331511

O'Hara Vacances SAS (1)
Parc D Activits Soleil Levant BP 656
85806 Saint-Gilles-Croix-de-Vie, France
Tel.: (33) 2 51 26 20 28
Fax: (33) 2 51 26 20 27
Mobile Home Mfr
S.I.C.: 2451
N.A.I.C.S.: 321991

U.S. Subsidiaries:

Beneteau USA Inc. (1)
1313 W Hwy 76
Marion, SC 29571
Tel.: (843) 629-5300
Web Site: www.beneteauusa.com
Boat Building
S.I.C.: 3732
N.A.I.C.S.: 336612
Wayne Burdick *(Pres)*

Jeanneau America Inc (1)
105 Eastern Ave Ste 202
Annapolis, MD 21403
Tel.: (410) 280-9400
Fax: (410) 280-9401
Sailing & Power Boats Whslr
S.I.C.: 5091
N.A.I.C.S.: 423910
Catherine Guiader *(Mgr-Sls)*

Non-U.S. Subsidiary:

Ostroda Yacht Sp. z o.o. (1)
ul Spokojna 1
14-100 Ostroda, Poland
Tel.: (48) 896 46 12 81
Fax: (48) 896 46 14 31
E-Mail: info@ostroda-yacht.com.pl
Web Site: www.dobrejachty.pl
Recreational Boat Construction Services
S.I.C.: 3732
N.A.I.C.S.: 336612

BENEV CAPITAL INC.

1540 Cornwall Rd Suite 208
Oakville, ON, L6J 7W5, Canada
Tel.: (905) 339-1540
Fax: (905) 339-0016
Toll Free: (800) 386-1388
E-Mail: info@bennettenv.com
Web Site: www.bennettenv.com
BEV—(TSX)
Rev.: $28,129,360
Assets: $73,532,214
Liabilities: $2,997,061
Net Worth: $70,535,153
Earnings: $9,244,582
Emp.: 23
Fiscal Year-end: 12/31/12

Business Description:
Investment Services
S.I.C.: 6211
N.A.I.C.S.: 523999

Personnel:
Lawrence Haber *(Chm)*
Sean Morrison *(Pres & CEO)*
Fred Cranston *(CFO)*

Board of Directors:
Lawrence Haber
Jamie Farrar
Mitchell Gropper
Livia Mahler

Legal Counsel:
Cassels, Brock & Blackwell LLP
2100 Scotia Plaza 40 King St W
Toronto, ON, M5H 3C2, Canada
Tel.: (416) 869-5300
Telex: 6-23415
Fax: (416) 360-8877

Transfer Agent:
Computershare
100 University Avenue 8th Floor
Toronto, ON, Canada

BENFIELD MOTOR GROUP

Asama Ct
Newcastle Business Park, Newcastle, NE4 7YD, United Kingdom
Tel.: (44) 1912261700
Fax: (44) 1912724855
Web Site: www.benfieldmotorgroup.com
Year Founded: 1957
Emp.: 1,200

Business Description:
Car Dealership Owner & Operator
S.I.C.: 5511
N.A.I.C.S.: 441110

Personnel:
Mark Squires *(CEO)*

Subsidiary:

Benfield Toyota (1)
Silkwood Pk
Wakefield, Yorkshire, WF59TJ, United Kingdom (100%)
Tel.: (44) 1924825882
Fax: (44) 1924870134
Web Site: www.benfieldmotor.com
Vehicle Motor Retailing
S.I.C.: 5511
N.A.I.C.S.: 441110

BENG KUANG MARINE LIMITED

55 Shipyard Road
Singapore, 628141, Singapore
Tel.: (65) 62660010
Fax: (65) 62640010
E-Mail: bkm@bkmgroup.com.sg
Web Site: www.bkmgroup.com.sg
Year Founded: 1990
5MC—(SES)
Rev.: $76,572,278
Assets: $152,619,094
Liabilities: $89,403,959
Net Worth: $63,215,135
Earnings: ($4,544,036)
Emp.: 709
Fiscal Year-end: 12/31/12

Business Description:
Ship Maintenance & Supplies Services
S.I.C.: 3731
N.A.I.C.S.: 336611

Personnel:
Beng Kuang Chua *(Chm)*
Meng Hua Chua *(Mng Dir)*
William Lee *(CFO)*
Beng Hock Chua *(Deputy COO)*
Beng Yong Chua *(COO)*
Hock Heng Lee *(Co-Sec)*
Woon Hong Wee *(Co-Sec)*

Board of Directors:
Beng Kuang Chua
Hock Wee Cheong
Meng Hua Chua
Chee Wee Goh
Chiang Yin Wong
Alan Thiam Fook Yong

Transfer Agent:
M & C Services Private Limited
112 Robinson Road 05-01
Singapore, Singapore

Beng Kuang Marine Limited—(Continued)

Subsidiaries:

Asian Sealand Engineering Pte Ltd **(1)**
55 Shipyard Rd
Singapore, 628141, Singapore
Tel.: (65) 62660010
Fax: (65) 62640010
E-Mail: bkm@bkmgroup.com.sg
Web Site: www.bkmgroup.com.sg
Emp.: 50
Marine Engineering Services
S.I.C.: 3291
N.A.I.C.S.: 327910
Kelvin Chua *(Gen Mgr)*

B & J Marine Pte. Ltd. **(1)**
55 Shipyard Road
Singapore, 628141, Singapore
Tel.: (65) 62660010
Fax: (65) 62640010
Marine Tank Cleaning Services
S.I.C.: 4499
N.A.I.C.S.: 488390

Beng Kuang Marine (B&Y) Pte. Ltd. **(1)**
55 Shipyard Rd
Singapore, 628141, Singapore
Tel.: (65) 62660010
Fax: (65) 62640010
E-Mail: bkm@bkmgroup.com.sg
Emp.: 20
Corrosion Prevention Services
S.I.C.: 1629
N.A.I.C.S.: 237120
Lee Choon Hwee *(Gen Mgr)*

Nexus Sealand Trading Pte. Ltd. **(1)**
38 Tuas View Sq
637770 Singapore, Singapore
Tel.: (65) 68982345
Fax: (65) 68982712
E-Mail: sales@bkmgroup.com
Web Site: www.sg.bkmgroup.com
Emp.: 100
Marine Freight Forwarding Services
S.I.C.: 4731
N.A.I.C.S.: 488510
Lee Choon Hwee *(Asst Gen Mgr)*

Subsidiary:

BT Asia Marketing & Engineering Pte Ltd **(2)**
35 Tuas Ave
Singapore, 638997, Singapore
Tel.: (65) 98982345
Fax: (65) 68982712
Marine Engineering Services
S.I.C.: 8711
N.A.I.C.S.: 541330

Pureflow Pte. Ltd. **(1)**
167 Jalan Bukit Merah No 01-10
Connection One Tower 5, Singapore, 150167, Singapore
Tel.: (65) 62719476
Fax: (65) 62719475
E-Mail: enquiries@pureflow.com.sg
Web Site: www.pureflow.com.sg
Emp.: 9
Waste Management Services
S.I.C.: 9511
N.A.I.C.S.: 924110
Chua Meng Hua *(Mng Dir)*

Venture Automation & Engineering Pte. Ltd. **(1)**
55 Shipyard Rd
Singapore, 628141, Singapore
Tel.: (65) 62660010
Fax: (65) 62640010
E-Mail: bkm@bkmgroup.com.sg
Emp.: 20
Marine Automation Systems Mfr & Related Services
S.I.C.: 8711
N.A.I.C.S.: 541330
Lee Choon Hwee *(Gen Mgr)*

Non-U.S. Subsidiaries:

PT Berger Batam **(1)**
Jl R E Martadinata Komplek Shangri-La Gardens Blok A
No 6 Sekupang, Batam, Indonesia
Tel.: (62) 778 322603
Fax: (62) 778 322107
E-Mail: slpang@bergerbatam.com
Web Site: www.bergerbatam.com
Emp.: 75
Corrosion Prevention Services
S.I.C.: 1623
N.A.I.C.S.: 237120
S L Pang *(Gen Mgr)*

PT Master Indonesia **(1)**
Kawasan Bintang Industri II Lot D No 56
Tanjung Uncang
Batam, 29422, Indonesia
Tel.: (62) 778 392 899
Fax: (62) 778 392 811
Marine Engineering Services
S.I.C.: 8711
N.A.I.C.S.: 541330

BENGAL & ASSAM COMPANY LTD.

Link House 3 Bahadur Shah Zafar Marg
New Delhi, 110002, India
Tel.: (91) 11 30179888
Fax: (91) 11 23739475
Web Site: www.bengalassam.com
Year Founded: 1947
533095—(BOM)
Rev.: $210,700,463
Assets: $230,061,970
Liabilities: $135,155,580
Net Worth: $94,906,390
Earnings: $6,470,182
Fiscal Year-end: 03/31/13
Business Description:
Financial Investment Services
S.I.C.: 6211
N.A.I.C.S.: 523999
Personnel:
Dillip Swain *(Compliance Officer & Sec)*
A. N. Ravichandran *(Pres-Fenner India Ltd)*
Board of Directors:
Bharat Hari Singhania
J. R. C. Bhandari
O. P. Khaitan
A. K. Kinra
L. R. Puri
Raghupati Singhania
Vinita Singhania
Shailendra Swarup
Transfer Agent:
Alankit Assignments Ltd
Alankit House 2E/21, Jhandewalan Extension
New Delhi, India

Subsidiary:

Modern Cotton Yarn Spinners Ltd. **(1)**
Manavasi Post Krishnarayapuram Taluk
Karur, 639 108, India
Tel.: (91) 4323 243363
Fax: (91) 4323 243364
E-Mail: mcysl@yahoo.co.in
Emp.: 250
Cotton Yarn Mfr
S.I.C.: 2299
N.A.I.C.S.: 313110

BENGAL ENERGY LTD.

Suite 1810 801 6th Ave SW
Calgary, AB, T2P 3W2, Canada
Tel.: (403) 205-2526
Fax: (403) 263-3168
E-Mail: info@averyresources.com
Web Site: www.bengalenergy.ca
BNG—(OTC TSX)
Rev.: $5,849,808
Assets: $48,849,125
Liabilities: $8,330,882
Net Worth: $40,518,243
Earnings: ($1,788,242)
Emp.: 8
Fiscal Year-end: 03/31/13
Business Description:
Oil & Gas Exploration Services
S.I.C.: 1381
N.A.I.C.S.: 213111
Personnel:
Ian J. Towers *(Chm)*
Chayan Chakrabarty *(Pres & CEO)*
Jerrad James Blanchard *(CFO)*
Bruce Allford *(Sec)*
Richard N. Edgar *(Exec VP)*
Board of Directors:
Ian J. Towers
Chayan Chakrabarty
Peter Gaffney
James B. Howe
Stephen N. Inbusch
Brian J. Moss
Robert D. Steele
Bill Wheeler
Legal Counsel:
Johnson Winter Slattery
Brisbane, Australia
Burnet, Duckworth & Palmer LLP
Calgary, AB, Canada
Transfer Agent:
Valiant Trust Company
Calgary, AB, Canada

BENGAL GROUP

Bengal House 75 Gulshan Ave
Dhaka, 1212, Bangladesh
Tel.: (880) 29888248
Fax: (880) 28827507
E-Mail: info@bengal.com.bd
Web Site: www.bengalgroup.com
Emp.: 1,500
Business Description:
Holding & Trading Company; Plastics, Adhesives, Metal, Paper, Real Estate, Agriculture, Food, Banking, Insurance & Energy Products & Services
S.I.C.: 6719
N.A.I.C.S.: 551112
Personnel:
Md Jashim Uddin *(Vice Chm)*
Morshed Alam *(Mng Dir)*
Board of Directors:
Firoz Alam
Morshed Alam
Saiful Alam
Shamsul Alam
Humayun Kabir
Bilkis Nahar
Md Jashim Uddin

BENGAL TEA & FABRICS LTD

Century Towers 4th Floor 45
Shakespeare Sarani
Kolkata, West Bengal, 700017, India
Tel.: (91) 3322836416
Fax: (91) 3322836416
E-Mail: mail@bengaltea.com
Web Site: www.bengaltea.com
532230—(BOM)
Rev.: $41,640,840
Assets: $30,222,054
Liabilities: $19,787,742
Net Worth: $10,434,312
Earnings: $2,124,684
Emp.: 2,038
Fiscal Year-end: 03/31/13
Business Description:
Tea & Fabrics
S.I.C.: 2095
N.A.I.C.S.: 311920
Personnel:
Adarsh Kanoria *(Chm & Mng Dir)*
Dhanpat Singh Pagaria *(CFO)*
Sunita Shah *(Compliance Officer & Sec)*
Kailash Prasad Khandelwal *(CEO-Comml)*
Board of Directors:
Adarsh Kanoria
Abhijit Datta
Dhirendra Kumar
Samveg A. Lalbhai
Golam Momen
Radhe Shyam Saraogi
Transfer Agent:
C. B. Management Services (P) Ltd
P-22 Bondel Road
700019 Kolkata, India

BENGANG STEEL PLATES COMPANY LTD.

16 Renmin Road
Pingshan District, 117000 Benxi, Liaoning, China
Tel.: (86) 4147827344
Fax: (86) 4147824158
E-Mail: bgbctwg@mail.bxptt.ln.cn
Year Founded: 1997
200761—(SSE)
Sales Range: $5-14.9 Billion
Emp.: 26,000
Business Description:
Metal Smelting & Mfr
S.I.C.: 3339
N.A.I.C.S.: 331410
Personnel:
Xiaofang Zhang *(Chm)*

BENGUET CORPORATION

6th & 7th Floors Universal Re Building 106 Paseo de Roxas
1226 Makati, Philippines
Tel.: (63) 28121380
Fax: (63) 27520717
E-Mail: admin@benguetcorp.com
Web Site: www.benguetcorp.com
Year Founded: 1903
BC—(PHI)
Rev.: $44,360,451
Assets: $161,794,850
Liabilities: $84,718,037
Net Worth: $77,076,814
Earnings: $15,611,665
Emp.: 1,501
Fiscal Year-end: 12/31/12
Business Description:
Gold, Chromite, Copper & Natural Resource Exploration, Mining, Development & Marketing Services Import Export
S.I.C.: 1041
N.A.I.C.S.: 212221
Personnel:
Daniel Andrew G. Romualdez *(Chm)*
Benjamin Philip G. Romualdez *(Vice Chm, Pres & CEO)*
Renato A. Claravall *(CFO & Sr VP)*
Bienvenido M. Araw, II *(Project & Org Dev Officer & Sr VP)*
Lina G. Fernandez *(Risk Mgmt Officer & VP-Corp Plng)*
Hermogene H. Real *(Sec)*
Reynaldo P. Mendoza *(Sr VP-Legal Svcs & Asst Sec)*
Marcelo A. Bolano *(Sr VP-Engrg & Res)*
Board of Directors:
Daniel Andrew G. Romualdez
Alberto C. Agra
Isidro C. Alcantara, Jr.
Dennis R. Belmonte
Andres G. Gatmaitan
Maria Remedios R. Pompidou
Benjamin Philip G. Romualdez
Rogelio C. Salazar
Bernardo M. Villegas
Luis Juan L. Virata
Legal Counsel:
SyCip Salazar Hernandez & Gatmaitan
105 Paseo de Roxas
Makati, Philippines
Lewis D'Amato Brisbois & Bisgaard
Suite 1400 650 Town Center Drive Center Tower Building
Costa Mesa, CA 92626

Transfer Agent:
Stock Transfer Service Inc
34th Floor Rufino Plaza Avenue
Makati, Philippines

Subsidiaries:

Benguet Management Corporation (1)
Universal Re Bldg, 106 Paseo de Roxas
Makati, Philippines (100%)
Tel.: (63) 28121359
Fax: (63) 028121359
Sls.: $17,325,000
Emp.: 2
Mfrs. Castings, Production of Mango Fruits, Real Estate Development
S.I.C.: 0179
N.A.I.C.S.: 111339
Lina Fernandez *(Treas)*

Subsidiaries:

Agua de Oro Ventures Corporation (2)
Bago Antamok
Itogon, Benguet, 2604, Philippines
Tel.: (63) 28121380
Water Purification Services
S.I.C.: 4941
N.A.I.C.S.: 221310

Arrow Freight Corporation (2)
368 F San Diego Street Veinte Reales
Malanday
Valenzuela, Metro Manila, 1444, Philippines
Tel.: (63) 22929149
Fax: (63) 22929149
Logistics Services
S.I.C.: 4731
N.A.I.C.S.: 541614

Benguetrade, Inc (2)
106 Paseo De Roxas
Makati, Metro Manila, 1226, Philippines
Tel.: (63) 28121380
Fax: (63) 28121359
Gold & Copper Products Distr
S.I.C.: 5052
N.A.I.C.S.: 423520

Joint Venture:

Benguet Ebara Real Estate Corp. (2)
Canlubang Industrial Estate Diezmo
Cabuyao
Cebuyao, Laguna, 4025, Philippines
Tel.: (63) 495491914
Fax: (63) 495491915
Web Site: www.ebaraphilippines.com
Sales Range: Less than $1 Million
Emp.: 1
Real Estate; Joint Venture of Benguet Corporation (60%) & Ebara Corporation (40%)
S.I.C.: 6531
N.A.I.C.S.: 531210
Valentino Niocena *(Pres)*

Benguetcorp Nickel Mines, Inc. (1)
Monsalud Building Lipay
Santa Cruz, Zambales, 2213, Philippines
Tel.: (63) 28121380
Fax: (63) 27520717
Web Site: www.benguetcorp.com
Nickel Mining Services
S.I.C.: 1021
N.A.I.C.S.: 212234
Romeo Flores *(Gen Mgr)*

BEREC Land Resources Inc. (1)
7th Floor Universal Re Building 106 Paseo De Roxas
Makati, 1226, Philippines
Tel.: (63) 28121380
Fax: (63) 27520717
Mineral Exploration Services
S.I.C.: 1481
N.A.I.C.S.: 213115
Benjamin Romualdez *(Pres)*

Joint Venture:

Ebara-Benguet, Inc. (1)
Terelay Phase Canlubang Industrial Est
4025 Cabugao, Laguna, Philippines
Tel.: (63) 495491806
Fax: (63) 495491915
E-Mail: ebisales@ebaraphilippines.com
Web Site: www.ebaraphilippines.com
Sales Range: $1-9.9 Million
Emp.: 100
Castings Mfr
S.I.C.: 3364
N.A.I.C.S.: 331523
Valentino Niocena *(Pres)*

BENIN TELECOMS SA

01 BP 5959
Cotonou, Benin
Tel.: (229) 21312045
Fax: (229) 21313843
E-Mail: sp.dgbttelecoms@intnet.bj
Web Site: www.benintelecoms.bj
Emp.: 1,500
Business Description:
Telecommunications Services
S.I.C.: 4813
N.A.I.C.S.: 517110

BENITEC BIOPHARMA LIMITED

Level 16 356 Collins Street
Melbourne, VIC, 3000, Australia
Tel.: (61) 2 9555 6986
Fax: (61) 2 9818 2238
E-Mail: info@benitec.com
Web Site: www.benitec.com
BLT—(ASX OTC)
Rev.: $1,525,824
Assets: $1,824,415
Liabilities: $1,157,117
Net Worth: $667,298
Earnings: ($3,634,803)
Emp.: 7
Fiscal Year-end: 06/30/13
Business Description:
Biotechnology Research & Development Services
S.I.C.: 8731
N.A.I.C.S.: 541712
Personnel:
Peter William French *(CEO & Mng Dir)*
Michael Graham *(Chief Scientific Officer)*
Carl Stubbings *(Chief Bus Officer)*
Gregory West *(Sec)*
David Suhy *(Sr VP-R&D)*
Board of Directors:
Peter Francis
Melvyn John Bridges
J. Kevin Buchi
John C. Chiplin
Peter William French
Iain G. Ross

BENIX & CO INC.

98 Orfus Road
Toronto, ON, M6A 1L9, Canada
Tel.: (416) 784-0732
Fax: (416) 784-5257
E-Mail: Customerservice@Benix.ca
Web Site: www.benix.ca
Year Founded: 1991
Rev.: $50,912,400
Emp.: 500
Business Description:
House Ware Retail Stores
S.I.C.: 5719
N.A.I.C.S.: 442299
Personnel:
Fred Benitah *(Pres)*

BENJAMIN TOYS LTD.

Unit 2 The Bridge Business Centre
Bridge Rd
Southall, Middlesex, UB2 4AY, United Kingdom
Tel.: (44) 208 843 0578
Fax: (44) 208 917 9174
E-Mail: sales@benjamintoys.co.uk
Web Site:
Sales Range: $1-9.9 Million
Emp.: 9
Business Description:
Mfr., Designer, Developer & Marketer of Electronic Learning Aids, Electronic Games, Activity Books, Science & Nature Products, Board Games & Other Products for Use in Both Schools & Homes
S.I.C.: 3942
N.A.I.C.S.: 339930
Personnel:
Raj Samarani *(CEO)*

BENJI INVEST KFT.

Kossuth L ut 12
Magyarorszag, H 2251 Tapioszecso, Hungary
Tel.: (36) 309491195
Fax: (36) 57 405 933
Business Description:
Real Estate Management Services
S.I.C.: 6531
N.A.I.C.S.: 531390
Personnel:
Attila Juhasz *(Owner)*

Subsidiary:

FCI Composite Insulator Ltd. (1)
Kesmark Str 28A
1158 Budapest, Hungary
Tel.: (36) 1 4196620
Fax: (36) 1 4196627
E-Mail: euroins@fcifurukawa.hu
Web Site: www.fcifurukawa.hu
Emp.: 60
Silicon Insulator Mfr
S.I.C.: 3357
N.A.I.C.S.: 335929
Attila Juhasz *(Mng Dir)*

BENNET DISTRIBUTORS

Metal Str 2b
02190 Vilnius, Lithuania
Tel.: (370) 52131611
Fax: (370) 52339184
E-Mail: bennet-vilnius@spi-group.com
Web Site: www.bennet.lt
Year Founded: 1991
Sls.: $65,194,740
Emp.: 300
Business Description:
Alcoholic Drinks & Tobacco Products Importer & Distr
S.I.C.: 5181
N.A.I.C.S.: 424810
Personnel:
Marek Kukois *(Gen Mgr)*

BENNETT CHEVROLET OLDSMOBILE CADILLAC LTD

445 Hespeler Road
Cambridge, ON, N1R 6J2, Canada
Tel.: (519) 621-1250
Fax: (519) 740-6363
Toll Free: (866) 892-8483
Web Site: www.bennettchevroletcadillac.com
Year Founded: 1931
Rev.: $34,000,000
Emp.: 60
Business Description:
New & Used Car Dealers
S.I.C.: 5511
N.A.I.C.S.: 441110
Personnel:
David Bennett *(Principal)*

BENNETT, COLEMAN & CO. LTD.

Times of India 7 Bahadur Shah Zafar Marg
New Delhi, 110103, India
Tel.: (91) 1123302000
Fax: (91) 1123323346
Web Site: www.timesgroup.com
Year Founded: 1838
Sales Range: $700-749.9 Million
Emp.: 7,000
Fiscal Year-end: 03/31/13
Business Description:
Holding Company
S.I.C.: 6719
N.A.I.C.S.: 551112
Personnel:
Ravindra Dhariwal *(CEO)*
Vineet Jain *(Mng Dir)*

Subsidiaries:

Entertainment Network (India) Limited (1)
Trade Gardens Ground Floor Kamala Mills Compound Senapati Bapat Marg
Lower Parel West, Mumbai, 400 013, India
Tel.: (91) 2267536983
Fax: (91) 2267536800
Web Site: www.enil.co.in
ENIL—(NSE)
Rev.: $66,182,979
Assets: $109,088,348
Liabilities: $15,977,837
Net Worth: $93,110,511
Earnings: $12,666,821
Emp.: 733
Fiscal Year-end: 03/31/13
Radio Broadcasting Services
S.I.C.: 4832
N.A.I.C.S.: 515111
Prashant Panday *(CEO)*
N. Subramanian *(CFO)*
Hitesh Sharma *(COO)*
Mahesh Shetty *(Chief Strategy Officer)*
Mehul Shah *(Compliance Officer, Sec & Sr VP)*
Tapas Sen *(Chief Programming Officer)*
Sujata Bhatt *(Exec VP & Chief-Mktg & HR)*
Yatish Mehrishi *(Exec VP & Dir-West & Central)*

TIMES GUARANTY LTD. (1)
Trade House 1st Floor Kamala Mills Compound
Senapati Bapat Marg, Mumbai, Maharashtra, 400013, India
Tel.: (91) 22 22731386
Fax: (91) 22 22731587
E-Mail: info@timesguarantylimited.com
Web Site: www.timesguarantylimited.com
511559—(BOM)
Rev.: $441,938
Assets: $4,381,873
Liabilities: $137,344
Net Worth: $4,244,529
Earnings: $359,046
Fiscal Year-end: 03/31/13
Financial Advisory Services
S.I.C.: 6282
N.A.I.C.S.: 523930
Vijay S. Devadiga *(Sec)*

Holding:

The Times of India (1)
1 World Tower DLF City Phase V Opp DLF Golf Course
Gurgaon, Haryana, 122002, India
Tel.: (91) 1123302000
Web Site: in.indiatimes.com
Newspaper Publisher
S.I.C.: 2711
N.A.I.C.S.: 511110
Rajesh Kunnath *(CFO-Times Internet Limited)*

Non-U.S. Holding:

TIML Radio Ltd. (2)
1 Golden Square
London, W1F 9DJ, United Kingdom
Tel.: (44) 2074341215
Fax: (44) 2074341127
Web Site: www.absoluteradio.co.uk
Emp.: 100
Holding Company
S.I.C.: 6719
N.A.I.C.S.: 551112
Richard Huntingford *(Chm)*

BENNETT DUNLOP FORD

770 Broad St
Regina, SK, S4P 3N4, Canada

Bennett Dunlop Ford—(Continued)

Tel.: (306) 522-6612
Fax: (306) 566-8238
Toll Free: (877) 524-2817
Web Site: www.bennettdunlopford.com
Rev.: $46,775,260
Emp.: 95

Business Description:
New & Used Car Dealers
S.I.C.: 5511
N.A.I.C.S.: 441110

Personnel:
Dave Kohonick *(Gen Mgr-Sls)*

BENNETT ENVIRONMENTAL, INC.

(See Under BENEV Capital Inc.)

BENNINGER AG

Fabrikstrasse
9240 Uzwil, Switzerland
Tel.: (41) 719558585
Fax: (41) 719558747
E-Mail: info@benningergroup.com
Web Site: www.benningergroup.com
Year Founded: 1859
Sales Range: $200-249.9 Million
Emp.: 250

Business Description:
Textile Finishing & Cord Production Range Mfr
S.I.C.: 3559
N.A.I.C.S.: 333249

Personnel:
Carmen Hayoz *(CFO)*
Gerhard Huber *(COO)*

Non-U.S. Subsidiaries:

Benninger AG (1)
Leningradsky PR-T 72
Bld 4 Office 802, 125315 Moscow, Russia
Tel.: (7) 4957211899
Fax: (7) 4957213084
E-Mail: benrussia@benningergroup.com
Emp.: 2
Textile Finishing & Cord Production Range Mfr
S.I.C.: 3559
N.A.I.C.S.: 333249

Benninger India Ltd. (1)
415 Sunshine Plaza
Naigaon Cross Road Near Avon, 400 014 Mumbai, India
Tel.: (91) 2224175361
Fax: (91) 2224175362
E-Mail: benindia@benningergroup.com
Web Site: www.benningergroup.com
Emp.: 35
Textile Finishing & Cord Production Range Mfr
S.I.C.: 3559
N.A.I.C.S.: 333249
C. N. Guruprasad *(Gen Mgr)*

Benninger Zell GmbH (1)
Schopfheimerstrasse 89
79669 Zell, Germany
Tel.: (49) 76251310
Fax: (49) 7625131298
E-Mail: beninfo@benningergroup.com
Web Site: www.benningergroup.com
Emp.: 100
Textile Finishing & Cord Production Range Mfr
S.I.C.: 3559
N.A.I.C.S.: 333249
Kuercen Zaeh *(Gen Mgr)*

Kusters Far East LtdBenninger Trading (Shanghai) Co. Ltd. (1)
Room 904 Tower A
100 Zun Yi Road, 200051 Shanghai, China
Tel.: (86) 21 6237 1908
Fax: (86) 21 6237 1909
Web Site: www.benningergroup.com
Industrial Machinery & Equipment Whslr
S.I.C.: 5084
N.A.I.C.S.: 423830

Kusters Textile GmbH (1)
Gerhart-Hauptmann-Strasse 15
Zittau, 02763 Dresden, Germany
Tel.: (49) 3583830
Fax: (49) 358383303
E-Mail: KT@kuesters-textile.com
Web Site: www.kuesters-textile.com
Textile Product Mills
S.I.C.: 2299
N.A.I.C.S.: 314999

BENOIT OILFIELD CONSTRUCTION (1997) LTD.

PO Box 277
Chauvin, AB, T0B 0V0, Canada
Tel.: (780) 858-3794
Fax: (780) 858-3795
Toll Free: (877) 858-3794
E-Mail: admin@benoitoilfield.ca
Web Site: www.benoitoilfield.ca
Year Founded: 1976
Rev.: $16,519,541
Emp.: 100

Business Description:
Oil & Natural Gas Distr
S.I.C.: 4924
N.A.I.C.S.: 221210

Personnel:
Calvin Winterholt *(Pres)*

BENQ CORPORATION

16 Jihu Road
Neihu, Taipei, 114, Taiwan
Tel.: (886) 227278899
Fax: (886) 227979288
E-Mail: investor@benq.com
Web Site: www.benq.com
Year Founded: 1884
Sales Range: $1-4.9 Billion
Emp.: 19,000

Business Description:
Color CRT/LCD Monitors, Digital Projectors, CD-ROM Drives, CD-ReWrite, DVD-ROM Drives, Scanners, Photo Printers & GSM/CDMA Mobile Phones
S.I.C.: 3577
N.A.I.C.S.: 334118

Personnel:
Kuen-Yao Lee *(Chm)*
Jerry Wang *(Vice Chm)*
Conway Lee *(Pres & CEO)*
Giorgio Bignoli *(Pres-Europe)*
Adrian Chang *(Pres-Asia Pacific)*
Ben Chu *(Pres-America)*
Hank Horng *(Pres-China)*
Peter Tan *(Pres-Latin America)*
Peter Chen *(Exec VP & Gen Mgr-Tech Product Center)*

Subsidiary:

Darfon Electronics Corporation (1)
167 Shan-Ying Rd Gueishan
Taoyuan, 33341, Taiwan (58.3%)
Tel.: (886) 33294141
Fax: (886) 33208899
Web Site: www.darfon.com.tw
8163—(TAI)
Sales Range: $800-899.9 Million
Emp.: 20,000
Mfr. & Design of Keyboards, Fly Back Transformers, Chip Transformers, Motors & Ceramic
S.I.C.: 3577
N.A.I.C.S.: 334118
N. D. Su *(Pres)*

U.S. Subsidiary:

BenQ America Corp. (1)
15375 Barranca Pkwy Ste A205
Irvine, CA 92618
Tel.: (949) 255-9500
Fax: (949) 255-9600
Web Site: www.benq.us
Emp.: 50
Marketing & Sales of Brand Peripheral Products
S.I.C.: 5045
N.A.I.C.S.: 423430
Lars Yoder *(Pres)*

Non-U.S. Subsidiaries:

BenQ Benelux (1)
Ekkersryt 4130
5692 DC Son, Netherlands
Tel.: (31) 499750500
Fax: (31) 499750599
E-Mail: info@benq-eu.com
Web Site: www.benq.com
Emp.: 25
Marketer & Retailer of Brand Peripheral Products
S.I.C.: 5045
N.A.I.C.S.: 423430
Giorgio Bignoli *(Pres-Europe)*

BenQ Japan, Inc. (1)
5th Fl Akimoto Unyu 3 A 3-30-1
Kaigan, Tokyo, Minato-Ku, 108 0022, Japan (100%)
Tel.: (81) 354445901
Fax: (81) 354445903
Web Site: www.benq.co.jp
Emp.: 50
Computer Peripheral Product Retailer
S.I.C.: 5045
N.A.I.C.S.: 423430

THE BENRIACH DISTILLERY CO. LTD.

Queen Anne Drive
Lochend Industrial Estate,
Newbridge, EH28 8LN, United Kingdom
Tel.: (44) 1343 862888
Fax: (44) 1343 862999
E-Mail: info@benriachdistillery.co.uk
Web Site: www.benriachdistillery.co.uk

Business Description:
Whiskey Distillery
S.I.C.: 2082
N.A.I.C.S.: 312120

Personnel:
Trisha Savage *(Gen Mgr)*

Subsidiary:

Glenglassaugh Distillery Co., Ltd. (1)
6 Glenglassaugh Distillery Cottages
Portsoy, Banff, AB45 2SQ, United Kingdom UK
Tel.: (44) 1261 842367
Fax: (44) 1261 842421
E-Mail: info@glenglassaugh.com
Web Site: www.glenglassaugh.com
Emp.: 20
Distilled & Blended Liquors
S.I.C.: 2085
N.A.I.C.S.: 312140
Stuart Nickerson *(Mng Dir)*

BENSON STEEL LIMITED

72 Commercial Road
Bolton, ON, L7E 1K4, Canada
Tel.: (905) 857-0684
Fax: (905) 857-4005
E-Mail: info@bensonsteel.com
Web Site: www.bensonsteel.com
Year Founded: 1980
Rev.: $13,355,955
Emp.: 35

Business Description:
Steel Industry
S.I.C.: 3325
N.A.I.C.S.: 331513

Personnel:
Stephen Benson *(Pres & CEO)*
Bob Benson *(Exec VP)*

BENTLEY CAPITAL LTD.

Suite 202 Angela House 30-36 Bay Street
Double Bay, NSW, 2028, Australia
Tel.: (61) 293635088
Fax: (61) 293635488
E-Mail: info@bel.com.au
Web Site: www.bel.com.au
BEL—(ASX)
Rev.: $981,881
Assets: $19,368,931
Liabilities: $331,728
Net Worth: $19,037,204
Earnings: ($350,888)
Fiscal Year-end: 06/30/13

Business Description:
Investment Management Services
S.I.C.: 6211
N.A.I.C.S.: 523110

Personnel:
Farooq Khan *(Chm)*
Victor P. H. Ho *(Sec)*

Board of Directors:
Farooq Khan
William M. Johnson
Christopher B. Ryan

Subsidiary:

Scarborough Equities Pty. Limited (1)
Suite 202 Angela House 30-36 Bay Street
Double Bay, NSW, 2028, Australia
Tel.: (61) 293635088
Fax: (61) 293635488
E-Mail: info@scarboroughequities.com.au
Web Site: www.scarboroughequities.com.au
Emp.: 5
Investment Fund Management Services
S.I.C.: 6722
N.A.I.C.S.: 525910
Farooq Khan *(Chm)*

BENTLEY COMMERCIAL ENTERPRISES LIMITED

Bhansali House A-5 Veera Desai Road
Andheri West, Mumbai, 400 053, India
Tel.: (91) 22 26731779
Fax: (91) 22 26731796
E-Mail: bentleycomplaints@gmail.com
Web Site: www.bentleycommercialent.net
Year Founded: 1985
512195—(BOM)
Rev.: $16,740
Assets: $259,100
Liabilities: $2,342
Net Worth: $256,758
Earnings: $14,378
Fiscal Year-end: 03/31/13

Business Description:
Financial Services
S.I.C.: 6211
N.A.I.C.S.: 523999

Personnel:
Charmi Thakkar *(Compliance Officer)*

Board of Directors:
B. M. Bhansali
Jayesh B. Bhansali
L. M. Bhansali

Transfer Agent:
Link Intime India Pvt. Ltd
C-13 Pannalal Silk Mills Compound LBS Marg
Bhandup (West)
Mumbai, India

BENTLEY FAIRVIEW RESOURCES CO. LTD.

1 London Place 255 Queens Ave
Suite 1000
London, N6A 5R8, United Kingdom
E-Mail: info@bentleyfairview.com
Web Site: www.bentleyfairview.com
B06—(DEU)

Business Description:
Copper Mining Services
S.I.C.: 1021
N.A.I.C.S.: 212234

Personnel:
James Jimenez *(Pres & CEO)*
Robert Lorilla *(COO & VP)*

BENTLEY GROUP
3700 Griffith St Ste 200
Ville Saint Laurent, QC, H4T 2B3, Canada
Tel.: (514) 341-9333
Fax: (514) 341-5619
Web Site: www.onlinebags.com
Year Founded: 1987
Sales Range: $50-74.9 Million
Emp.: 5,000
Business Description:
Retailer of Handbags & Luggage
S.I.C.: 5948
N.A.I.C.S.: 448320
Personnel:
Muriel Kunzli *(Controller)*

BENTON RESOURCES INC.
3250 Hwy 130
Thunder Bay, ON, P7K 0B1, Canada
Tel.: (807) 475-7474
Fax: (807) 475-7200
E-Mail: admin@bentonresources.ca
Web Site: www.bentonresources.ca
Year Founded: 2003
BEX—(TSXV)
Sales Range: $10-24.9 Million
Business Description:
Mineral Exploration Services
S.I.C.: 1081
N.A.I.C.S.: 213114
Personnel:
Stephen Stares *(Pres & CEO)*
Evan Asselstine *(CFO)*
Gordon Fretwell *(Sec)*
Board of Directors:
Clinton Barr
Gordon Fretwell
Raphael R.W. Gerstel
William S. Harper
Michael Stares
Stephen Stares
John Sullivan

BENTRE AQUAPRODUCT IMPORT & EXPORT JOINT STOCK COMPANY
103 Myhoang Quarter Phumyhung
Nguyenbinh street Tanphong ward
District 7, Ho Chi Minh City, Vietnam
Tel.: (84) 8 54121760
Fax: (84) 8 54121760
E-Mail: abt@aquatexbentre.com
Web Site: www.aquatexbentre.com
Year Founded: 1977
ABT—(HOSE)
Rev.: $31,817,933
Assets: $25,806,661
Liabilities: $6,581,439
Net Worth: $19,225,222
Earnings: $3,955,644
Emp.: 1,200
Fiscal Year-end: 12/31/12
Business Description:
Fisheries Product Sales & Services
S.I.C.: 5099
N.A.I.C.S.: 423990
Personnel:
Dang Kiet Tuong *(Chm)*

BENXI IRON & STEEL GROUP CO. LTD.
16 Renmin Road Pingshan Area
Benxi, Liaoning, 117000, China
Tel.: (86) 414 2843 889
Fax: (86) 414 2842 074
Business Description:
Steel Producer
S.I.C.: 3325
N.A.I.C.S.: 331513
Personnel:
Tianchen Yu *(Chm)*

BENZ CAPITAL CORP.
Suite 900 570 Granville Street
Vancouver, BC, V6C 3P1, Canada
Tel.: (604) 682-3701
Fax: (604) 682-3600
E-Mail: mgvicent@telusplanet.net
Year Founded: 2011
BZ.P—(TSXV)
Business Description:
Investment Services
S.I.C.: 6211
N.A.I.C.S.: 523999
Personnel:
Miloje Vicentijevic *(Pres, CEO & Sec)*
Carlos Javier Escribano *(CFO)*
Board of Directors:
Gordon Bub
Kevin C. Drover
Carlos Javier Escribano
Transfer Agent:
Olympia Trust Company
Suite 1003 750 West Pender Street
Vancouver, BC, V6C 2T8, Canada

BEP INTERNATIONAL HOLDINGS LIMITED
Suite 1005 10th Floor Great Eagle Centre 23 Harbour Road
Wanchai, China (Hong Kong)
Tel.: (852) 39199988
Fax: (852) 39199966
E-Mail: info@bepgroup.com.hk
Web Site: www.bepgroup.com.hk
2326—(HKG)
Sls.: $19,425,673
Assets: $22,743,814
Liabilities: $2,511,559
Net Worth: $20,232,255
Earnings: $963,128
Emp.: 170
Fiscal Year-end: 03/31/13
Business Description:
Holding Company; Electronic Components Whslr
S.I.C.: 5064
N.A.I.C.S.: 423620
Personnel:
Paul Cho Hung Suen *(Chm)*
Ka Lok Sue *(CEO)*
Yee Ling Hui *(Sec & Controller-Fin)*
Board of Directors:
Paul Cho Hung Suen
George Kwong Fat Chan
Hiu Ming Li
Alick Hi Lam Siu
Ka Lok Sue
Edmond Yan Ming To
HSBC Securities Services (Bermuda) Limited
6 Front Street
Hamilton, Bermuda
Transfer Agents:
Tricor Secretaries Limited
26th Floor Tesbury Centre 28 Queens Rd E
Hong Kong, China (Hong Kong)
HSBC Securities Services (Bermuda) Limited
6 Front Street
Hamilton, Bermuda

BERENDSEN FLUID POWER PTY LIMITED
31 Powers Road
Seven Hills, NSW, 2147, Australia
Tel.: (61) 298385800
Fax: (61) 298385815
E-Mail: personnel@berendsen.com.au
Web Site: www.berendsen.com.au
Year Founded: 1993
Emp.: 300
Business Description:
Hydraulic Services
S.I.C.: 4911
N.A.I.C.S.: 221111

Personnel:
Brian Hadley Anderson *(Chm)*

BERENDSEN PLC
4 Grosvenor Place
London, SW1X 7DL, United Kingdom
Tel.: (44) 2072596663
Fax: (44) 2072596948
E-Mail: lawler@berendsen.eu
Web Site: www.berendsen.com
Year Founded: 1980
BRSN—(LSE)
Rev.: $1,555,758,579
Assets: $2,147,044,755
Liabilities: $1,367,033,424
Net Worth: $780,011,331
Earnings: $115,130,241
Emp.: 14,988
Fiscal Year-end: 12/31/12
Business Description:
Textile Maintenance Services
S.I.C.: 7219
N.A.I.C.S.: 812320
Personnel:
Peter Ventress *(CEO)*
Kevin Quinn *(CFO)*
David A. Lawler *(Sec)*
Board of Directors:
Iain Ferguson
Lucy Dimes
David Lowden
Kevin Quinn
Peter Ventress
Andrew Wood
Legal Counsel:
Slaughter & May
One Bunhill Row
London, EC1Y 8YY, United Kingdom
Tel.: (44) 20 7600 1200
Fax: (44) 20 7600 0289

Subsidiary:

The Sunlight Service Group Ltd. **(1)**
Intec 3 Wade Road
Intec Business Park, Basingstoke, Hants, RG24 8NE, United Kingdom UK
Tel.: (44) 1256471311
Fax: (44) 1256339299
E-Mail: info@sunlight.co.uk
Web Site: www.sunlight.co.uk
Emp.: 80
Linen Hire & Laundry Services to Hotels, Hospitals & Restaurants; Uniform Rental
S.I.C.: 7213
N.A.I.C.S.: 812331
D. Embleton *(CFO)*

U.S. Subsidiary:

RENTX Industries Inc. **(1)**
6000 E Evans Ave
Denver, CO 80222 DE
Tel.: (303) 512-2000
Fax: (303) 256-2243
Web Site: www.hssrentx.com
Emp.: 647
Rental & Leasing Services
S.I.C.: 7359
N.A.I.C.S.: 532299

Non-U.S. Subsidiary:

Sophus Berendsen A/S **(1)**
Edward Thomshon Bej 10 Fl 4
DK-2300 Copenhagen, Denmark DK
Tel.: (45) 39538500
Fax: (45) 39538787
E-Mail: info@berendsen.dk
Web Site: www.berendsen.dk
Sales Range: $350-399.9 Million
Emp.: 7,000
Textile Services & Solutions & Protective Gear
Export
S.I.C.: 3594
N.A.I.C.S.: 333996
Peter Haeeus *(Pres)*
Brian Christiansen *(CFO)*

Non-U.S. Subsidiaries:

Berendsen GmbH & Gluckstadler Gruppe **(2)**
Stadtstrasse 3 7
25348 Gluckstadt, Germany DE
Tel.: (49) 41249140
Fax: (49) 4124914123
E-Mail: info@berendsen.de
Web Site: www.berendsen.de
Emp.: 3,000
Laundry & Textile Service
S.I.C.: 7218
N.A.I.C.S.: 812332
Niels Peter Hansen *(Gen Mgr)*

Berendsen Tekstil Service A/S **(2)**
Hjalmar Brantingsvei 8
N 0581 Oslo, Norway NO
Tel.: (47) 22884800
Fax: (47) 22884850
E-Mail: firmapost@berendsen.no
Web Site: www.berendsen.no
Emp.: 250
Laundry & Textile Service
S.I.C.: 7219
N.A.I.C.S.: 812320
Espen Eldal *(Gen Mgr)*

Berendsen Textiel Service B.V. **(2)**
Pieter Calandweg 2
PO Box 5004
NL 6827 BK Arnhem, Netherlands
Tel.: (31) 263848140
Fax: (31) 263848147
E-Mail: info@berendsen.nl
Web Site: www.berendsen.nl
Emp.: 40
Garments, Industrial Wipers, Roller Towel Cabinets, Mats & Personal Safety Equipment Mfr
S.I.C.: 5064
N.A.I.C.S.: 423620
Eric Verstappan *(Mng Dir)*

Berendsen Textil Service AB **(2)**
Staohannes no 2
21146 Malmo, Sweden SE
Tel.: (46) 40368000
Fax: (46) 40368060
E-Mail: lena.lagheden@berendsen.se
Web Site: www.berendsen.se
Sales Range: $25-49.9 Million
Emp.: 11,000
Textile Handling Equipment for Hotels, Hospitals & Industry
S.I.C.: 7359
N.A.I.C.S.: 532490
Per Satterstrom *(Mng Dir)*

Berendsen Textile Service Sp.z.o.o. **(2)**
Ul Dunska 1
83330 Zukowo, Poland PL
Tel.: (48) 586818496
Fax: (48) 586818497
E-Mail: info@berendson.pl
Web Site: www.berendson.pl
Sales Range: $1-9.9 Million
Emp.: 200
Laundry & Textile Service
S.I.C.: 7218
N.A.I.C.S.: 812332

BERESFORD BOX COMPANY INC.
607 Kumpf Drive
Waterloo, ON, N2V 1K8, Canada
Tel.: (519) 885-4580
Fax: (519) 747-9171
Web Site: www.beresfordbox.com
Year Founded: 1964
Rev.: $31,387,127
Emp.: 200
Business Description:
Carton & Packaging Products Mfr
S.I.C.: 2657
N.A.I.C.S.: 322212
Personnel:
Dennis Boehmer *(Pres)*

BERG EARTH CO., LTD.
88-1 Kitanadako Tsushima-cho
Uwajima, Ehime, 798-3361, Japan
Tel.: (81) 895208231
E-Mail: info-berg@bergearth.co.jp
Web Site: www.bergearth.co.jp
Year Founded: 2001
1383—(JAS)
Sales Range: $25-49.9 Million

Berg Earth Co., Ltd.—(Continued)

Emp.: 160
Business Description:
Grafted Nursery Plants Production & Sales
S.I.C.: 0831
N.A.I.C.S.: 113210
Personnel:
Kazuhiko Yamaguchi *(CEO)*

BERGBAHNEN ENGELBERG-TRUBSEE-TITLIS AG

Poststrasse 3
6390 Engelberg, Switzerland
Tel.: (41) 416395050
Fax: (41) 416395060
E-Mail: titlis@titlis.ch
Web Site: www.titlis.ch/index.php?lang=en
TIBN—(SWX)
Business Description:
Tourism Services
S.I.C.: 7389
N.A.I.C.S.: 561499
Personnel:
Norbert Patt *(CEO)*
Esther Schneider *(CFO)*

BERGE Y CIA SA

Calle Barroeta Aldamar 2
48001 Bilbao, Spain
Tel.: (34) 91 420 02 28
Web Site: www.bergeycia.es
Business Description:
Holding Company
S.I.C.: 6719
N.A.I.C.S.: 551112
Personnel:
Jorge Navea *(Mng Dir)*

Subsidiary:

MMC Automoviles Espana, S.A. **(1)**
Calle Francisco Gervas 4
28108 Alcobendas, Spain ES
Tel.: (34) 91 387 74 43 (76%)
Fax: (34) 91 387 74 33
Web Site: www.mitsubishi-motors.es
Automobiles Distr & Retailer
S.I.C.: 5012
N.A.I.C.S.: 423110
Jose Carmona *(Gen Mgr)*

BERGEN GROUP ASA

Thormohlensgate 53c
5006 Bergen, Norway
Tel.: (47) 55542500
Fax: (47) 55542501
E-Mail: post@bergengroup.no
Web Site: www.bergen-group.no
BERGEN—(OSL)
Rev.: $627,963,266
Assets: $621,790,421
Liabilities: $483,176,877
Net Worth: $138,613,544
Earnings: ($136,038,238)
Emp.: 1,600
Fiscal Year-end: 12/31/12
Business Description:
Holding Company; Ship Building, Offshore Engineering & Maritime Services
S.I.C.: 6719
N.A.I.C.S.: 551112
Personnel:
Magnus Stangeland *(Chm)*
Asle Solheim *(CEO)*
Henning Nordgulen *(CFO)*
Sebjorn Madsen *(Exec VP-Svcs)*
Board of Directors:
Magnus Stangeland
Brian Chang
Ingunn Flytor
Ove Iversen
Bjorn Erik Klepsvik
Linn Cecilie Moholt
Arne Vindenes
Eva von Hirsch

Subsidiaries:

Bergen Group Hanoytangen AS **(1)**
Hanoytangen 128
5310 Hauglandshella, Hordaland, Norway
Tel.: (47) 56150000
Fax: (47) 56157219
E-Mail: hanoytangen@bergengroup.no
Emp.: 40
Drydocks Operation Services
S.I.C.: 4499
N.A.I.C.S.: 488390
Tor Eiken *(Head-Mktg & Dev)*

Bergen Group Kimek AS **(1)**
Storgata 4
9900 Kirkenes, Norway
Mailing Address:
Boks 34
9915 Kirkenes, Norway
Tel.: (47) 78977100
Fax: (47) 78977270
E-Mail: kimek@bergengroup.no
Emp.: 75
Ship Repair & Maintenance Services
S.I.C.: 3731
N.A.I.C.S.: 336611
Greger Mannsverk *(Dir-Admin)*

Bergen Group Kimek Offshore AS **(1)**
Storgata 4
9900 Kirkenes, Norway
Mailing Address:
Boks 34
9915 Kirkenes, Norway
Tel.: (47) 78977260
Fax: (47) 78977269
E-Mail: kimek-offshore@bergengroup.no
Emp.: 90
Ship Building & Repair Services
S.I.C.: 3731
N.A.I.C.S.: 336611
Greger Mannsverk *(CEO)*
Monica Hauan *(Sec)*

Bergen Group Laksevag AS **(1)**
Damsgardsv 229
5163 Laksevag, Hordaland, Norway
Tel.: (47) 55 54 24 00
Fax: (47) 55 54 24 01
E-Mail: post@bergengroup.no
Ship Repair & Maintenance Services
S.I.C.: 3731
N.A.I.C.S.: 336611
Trygve Aarland *(Dir- Bus Dev)*

Bergen Group Risnes AS **(1)**
Sunde industriomrade 3
5450 Sunde, Hordaland, Norway NO
Tel.: (47) 53477070
Fax: (47) 53477071
E-Mail: ole.risnes@bergengroup.no
Web Site: www.bergen-group.no/?page=391
Boat & Ship Building Services
S.I.C.: 3731
N.A.I.C.S.: 336611
Egil Eide *(Dir-IT)*

Bergen Group Services AS **(1)**
Damsgardsv 119
5162 Laksevag, Norway NO
Tel.: (47) 55948200
Fax: (47) 55948229
E-Mail: bergengroupservices@bergengroup.no
Emp.: 35
Maritime & Industrial Services
S.I.C.: 8711
N.A.I.C.S.: 541330
Frode Johansson *(Gen Mgr)*

Divisions:

Bergen Group Services AS - Industrial Service **(2)**
Ulsmagv 42
Nesttun, 5224 Bergen, Norway
Tel.: (47) 5592 5140
Fax: (47) 5592 5150
E-Mail:
Industrial Engineering Services
S.I.C.: 8711
N.A.I.C.S.: 541330
Frode Johansson *(Gen Mgr)*

Bergen Group Services AS - Maritime Service **(2)**
Damsgardsv 229
5163 Laksevag, Norway
Tel.: (47) 5594 8200
E-Mail:
Marine Engineering Services
S.I.C.: 8711
N.A.I.C.S.: 541330

Bergen Group Shared Services AS **(1)**
Damsgardsv 229
5163 Laksevag, Hordaland, Norway
Tel.: (47) 55542500
E-Mail: post@bergengroup.no
Web Site: www.bergen-group.no/?page=386&show=461
Shipbuilding Services
S.I.C.: 3731
N.A.I.C.S.: 336611

Bergen Group Shipbuilding AS **(1)**
Thormohlensg 53 C
1201 Bergen, Hordaland, Norway
Tel.: (47) 55542500
Fax: (47) 55542501
Holding Company; Ship Building & Repair Services
S.I.C.: 6719
N.A.I.C.S.: 551112

Subsidiaries:

Bergen Group BMV AS **(2)**
Damsgardsveien 229
5163 Laksevag, Hordaland, Norway
Tel.: (47) 55 54 24 00
Fax: (47) 55 54 24 01
E-Mail: post@bergengroup.no
Ship Building & Repair Services
S.I.C.: 3731
N.A.I.C.S.: 336611
Terje Sjumarken *(Mng Dir)*

Bergen Group Fosen Holding AS **(2)**
c/o Lyng Gruppen AS
7100 Rissa, Sor-Trondelag, Norway
Tel.: (47) 33314572
Fax: (47) 73858700
Management Services
S.I.C.: 8741
N.A.I.C.S.: 551114

Subsidiary:

Bergen Group Fosen AS **(3)**
Kvithyll
7100 Rissa, Sor-Trondelag, Norway NO
Tel.: (47) 73858600
Fax: (47) 73858700
E-Mail: fosen@fmv.st.no
Emp.: 250
Ship Building & Repair Services
S.I.C.: 3731
N.A.I.C.S.: 336611
Arnar Utseth *(CEO)*
Tom Benestad *(CFO)*

Bergen Group Shipdesign AS **(2)**
PIR-Senteret III Havnegt 9
Ressr, 7010 Trondheim, Sor-Trondelag, Norway
Tel.: (47) 73858600
Fax: (47) 97511790
E-Mail: post@bergengroup.no
Web Site: www.bergen-group.no/?page=1075
Ship Designing Services
S.I.C.: 3731
N.A.I.C.S.: 336611

Bergen Group Skarveland AS **(1)**
Sunde industriomrade 3
Sunde, Hordaland, Norway
Tel.: (47) 53477070
Fax: (47) 53477071
E-Mail: skarveland@bergengroup.no
Emp.: 110
Ship & Industrial Pipes Distr
S.I.C.: 5051
N.A.I.C.S.: 423510
Thorkildsen Tore *(Mng Dir)*

Non-U.S. Subsidiary:

BG Amia Sp. z o.o. **(1)**
Batorego 23
81-365 Gdynia, Pomeranian, Poland PL
Tel.: (48) 583500200
Fax: (48) 583500201
E-Mail: amia@bergengroup.no
Web Site: www.bergen-group.no/?page=1138
Emp.: 10
Shipbuilding Industry Staff Hiring Services
S.I.C.: 7361
N.A.I.C.S.: 561311
Maciej Nowakowski *(Gen Mgr)*

BERGER HOLDING GMBH

Aussere Spitalhofstrasse 19
D-94036 Passau, Germany
Tel.: (49) 8518060
Fax: (49) 8518061104
E-Mail: info@bergerholding.eu
Web Site: www.bergerholding.eu/
Sales Range: $300-349.9 Million
Emp.: 2,000
Business Description:
Holding Company; Concrete & Cement Products Mfr & Construction Services
S.I.C.: 6719
N.A.I.C.S.: 551112
Personnel:
Hans Berger *(Chm-Mgmt Bd)*
Hermann Bock *(Member-Mgmt Bd)*
Erwin Gessl *(Member-Mgmt Bd)*
Karl Gessl *(Member-Mgmt Bd)*
Franz Wallner *(Member-Mgmt Bd)*

Subsidiaries:

BERGER BAU GmbH **(1)**
Aussere Spitalhofstrasse 19
D-94036 Passau, Germany De
Tel.: (49) 8518060 (100%)
Fax: (49) 8518061104
E-Mail: info@bergerbau.eu
Web Site: www.bergerbau.eu
Commercial, Industrial & Civil Engineering Construction Services
S.I.C.: 1542
N.A.I.C.S.: 236220
Hans Berger *(Chm-Mgmt Bd)*
Hermann Bock *(Member-Mgmt Bd)*
Karl Gessl *(Member-Mgmt Bd)*

BERGER BETON GmbH **(1)**
Aussere Spitalhofstrasse 19
D-94036 Passau, Germany De
Tel.: (49) 8518060 (100%)
Fax: (49) 8518061242
E-Mail: info@bergerbeton.eu
Web Site: www.bergerbeton.eu
Emp.: 500
Ready-Mix Concrete, Asphalt, Mortar, Cement & Other Related Products Mfr & Contractor Services
S.I.C.: 3273
N.A.I.C.S.: 327320
Hans Berger *(Chm-Mgmt Bd)*
Erwin Gessl *(Member-Mgmt Bd)*

BERGER KAROSSERIE- UND FAHRZEUGBAU GMBH

Schmidtstrasse 49
60326 Frankfurt, Germany
Tel.: (49) 69759030
Fax: (49) 697590398
E-Mail: info@berger-frankfurt.de
Web Site: www.berger-fahrzeugbau.de
Rev.: $13,750,559
Emp.: 112
Business Description:
Vehicle Bodies Mfr
S.I.C.: 3714
N.A.I.C.S.: 336390
Personnel:
Hans Karl Berger *(Mng Dir)*

BERGER PAINTS BANGLADESH LIMITED

Berger House House 8 Road 2
Sector 3
Uttara Model Town, Dhaka, 1230, Bangladesh
Tel.: (880) 2 8953665

Fax: (880) 2 8951350
E-Mail: info@bergerbd.com
Web Site: www.bergerbd.com
Year Founded: 1973
BERGERPBL—(DHA)
Sls.: $96,510,181
Earnings: $9,545,377
Fiscal Year-end: 12/31/12

Business Description:
Paints Mfr
S.I.C.: 2851
N.A.I.C.S.: 325510

Personnel:
Gerald K. Adams *(Chm)*
Rupali Chowdhury *(Mng Dir)*
Abdul Khalek *(Sec & Dir-Fin)*

Board of Directors:
Gerald K. Adams
Anil Bhalla
Subir Bose
Rupali Chowdhury
K. R. Das
Abdul Khalek
Jean-Claude Loutreuil

BERGER PAINTS INDIA LIMITED

Berger House 129 Park Street
Kolkata, 700017, India
Tel.: (91) 33 2229 9724
Fax: (91) 33 2249 9009
Toll Free: 8003458800
E-Mail: consumerfeedback@bergerindia.com
Web Site: www.bergerpaints.com
Year Founded: 1760
509480—(BOM)
Rev.: $679,142,448
Assets: $405,508,734
Liabilities: $228,792,870
Net Worth: $176,715,864
Earnings: $40,491,360
Emp.: 2,464
Fiscal Year-end: 03/31/13

Business Description:
Paints Mfr & Marketer
S.I.C.: 2851
N.A.I.C.S.: 325510

Personnel:
Abhijit Roy *(COO & Mng Dir)*
Srijit Dasgupta *(CFO)*
Aniruddha Sen *(Compliance Officer, Sec & Sr VP)*
Rajib De *(Deputy Sec)*
Bhabesh Bera *(Sr VP-R&D)*
Sandip Mitra *(Sr VP-Sls & Mktg-Protective Coatings Div)*
Ashok Sharma *(Sr VP-Sls & Mktg-Automotive, GI & Powder Coatings Div)*

Board of Directors:
Kuldip Singh Dhingra
Gerald Kenneth Adams
Anil Bhalla
Subir Bose
Gurcharan Das
Kamal Ranjan Das
Srijit Dasgupta
Gurbachan Singh Dhingra
Pulak Chandan Prasad
Abhijit Roy

Transfer Agent:
C. B. Management Services (P) Ltd
P-22 Bondel Road
700019 Kolkata, India

Non-U.S. Subsidiary:

Bolix S.A. (1)
ul Stolarska 8
Zywiec, 34-300, Poland
Tel.: (48) 334750646
Fax: (48) 334750647
E-Mail: export@bolix.pl
Web Site: www.bolix.pl
Emp.: 250
Paint Mfr
S.I.C.: 2851
N.A.I.C.S.: 325510
Maciej Korbasiewicz *(CEO)*

BERGER PAINTS PAKISTAN LIMITED

X/3 SITE Manghopir Road
Karachi, Pakistan
Tel.: (92) 21111237437
Web Site: www.berger.com.pk
BERG—(KAR)
Sls.: $42,652,942
Assets: $31,209,892
Liabilities: $24,291,669
Net Worth: $6,918,223
Earnings: $662,634
Emp.: 462
Fiscal Year-end: 06/30/13

Business Description:
Paint Mfr
S.I.C.: 3579
N.A.I.C.S.: 339940

Personnel:
Mahmood Ahmed *(CEO)*
Abdul Wahid Qureshi *(CFO & Sec)*

Board of Directors:
Maqbool H. H. Rahimtoola
Mahmood Ahmed
Shahzad M. Husain
Muhammad Naseem
Zafar Aziz Osmani
Hamid Masood Sohail

BERGS TIMBER AB

Bergs vag 12
Morlunda, 570 84 Hultsfred, Sweden
Tel.: (46) 10 1998 500
Fax: (46) 49549250
E-Mail: info@bergstimber.se
Web Site: www.bergstimber.se
Year Founded: 1948
BRG-B—(OMX)
Sales Range: $125-149.9 Million

Business Description:
Wood Products Whslr
S.I.C.: 2499
N.A.I.C.S.: 321999

Personnel:
Jonas Campanello *(Chm)*
Ake Bergh *(Pres & CEO)*
Johan Ekelund *(CFO)*
Henrik Egnell *(CEO-Bitus AB)*
Rolf Lindstrom *(CEO-Bergs Skog AB)*

Board of Directors:
Jonas Campanello
Ake Bergh
Peter Friberg
Lars Jarnland
Anders Karlsson
Kay Nilsson
Lars Petersson
Gunvor Munck Svensson
Reino Thapper

Subsidiaries:

Bergs Skog AB (1)
Bergs vag 13
Morlunda, 570 84 Hultsfred, Smaland, Sweden
Tel.: (46) 495245550
Fax: (46) 49549250
E-Mail: skog@bergstimber.se
Web Site: www.bergstimber.se
Emp.: 10
Timber Mfr
S.I.C.: 0811
N.A.I.C.S.: 113110
Rolf Lindstrom *(CEO)*

Bergs Timber Morlunda AB (1)
Bergs Vag 13
Morlunda, 570 84 Hultsfred, Smaland, Sweden
Tel.: (46) 495245500
Fax: (46) 49523129
E-Mail: morlunda@bergstimber.se
Web Site: www.bergstimber.se
Emp.: 120
Timber Mfr
S.I.C.: 0811
N.A.I.C.S.: 113110

Bergs Timber Orrefors AB (1)
Bratemalavagen 3
Orrefors, 380 40 Nybro, Smaland, Sweden
Tel.: (46) 48134340
Fax: (46) 48130810
E-Mail: orrefors@bergstimber.se
Timber Mfr
S.I.C.: 0811
N.A.I.C.S.: 113110
Peter Nilsson *(Mng Dir)*

Bitus AB (1)
Orreforsvagen 49
382 94 Nybro, Smaland, Sweden
Tel.: (46) 48142700
Fax: (46) 48112333
E-Mail: bitus@bergstimber.se
Web Site: www.bergstimber.se
Emp.: 25
Timber Mfr
S.I.C.: 0811
N.A.I.C.S.: 113110
Henrik Egnell *(Mgr)*

BERICAP GMBH & CO. KG

Kirchstrasse 5
55257 Budenheim, Germany
Tel.: (49) 6139 2902 0
Fax: (49) 6139 2902 181
E-Mail: info.germany@bericap.com
Web Site: www.bericap.com
Sales Range: $800-899.9 Million
Emp.: 2,950

Business Description:
Plastic Bottle Cap & Other Closure Mfr & Distr
S.I.C.: 3089
N.A.I.C.S.: 326199

Personnel:
Jorg Thiels *(CEO)*

Non-U.S. Joint Venture:

BERICAP North America, Inc. (1)
835 Syscon Court
Burlington, ON, L7L 6C5, Canada ON
Tel.: (905) 634-2248
Fax: (905) 634-7780
E-Mail: info.na@bericap.com
Web Site: www.bericap.com
Emp.: 140
Plastic Bottle Cap & Other Packaging Enclosure Products Mfr & Distr
S.I.C.: 3089
N.A.I.C.S.: 326199
David Anderson *(Pres)*

U.S. Subsidiary:

BERICAP, LLC (2)
1671 Champagne Ave Ste B
Ontario, CA 91761-3650 CA
Tel.: (909) 390-5518
Fax: (909) 390-5597
E-Mail: info.usa@bericap.com
Web Site: www.bericap.com
Plastic Bottle Cap & Other Packaging Enclosure Products Mfr & Distr
S.I.C.: 3089
N.A.I.C.S.: 326199

BERJAYA ASSETS BERHAD

Lot 08-16 Level 8 Berjaya Times Square No 1 Jalan Imbi
PO Box 08-23
55100 Kuala Lumpur, Malaysia
Tel.: (60) 321491999
Fax: (60) 321440935
E-Mail: property@berjaya.com.my
Web Site: www.berjaya.com
BJASSET—(KLS)
Rev.: $118,592,596
Assets: $986,907,704
Liabilities: $260,908,236
Net Worth: $725,999,468
Earnings: $17,342,705
Fiscal Year-end: 06/30/13

Business Description:
Lottery Consultancy & Forecasting Services
S.I.C.: 7999
N.A.I.C.S.: 713290

Personnel:
Swee Hong Su *(Co-Sec)*
Siew Guek Wong *(Co-Sec)*

Board of Directors:
Shahabuddin Besar Burhanuddin
Mohd Salleh Ahmad
Kien Sing Chan
Kiah Choong Heng
Meng Kwong Lim
Ek Seang Lye
Dickson Yong Loong Tan
Thiam Chai Tan
Robert Kuen Loke Yong

Subsidiaries:

Berjaya Times Square Sdn. Bhd. (1)
Lot 08-16 Level 8 Berjaya Times Sq
PO Box 08-23
No 1 Jalan Imbi, Kuala Lumpur, 55100, Malaysia
Tel.: (60) 321449821
Fax: (60) 321433055
E-Mail: general@timessquarekl.com
Web Site: www.timessquarekl.com
Emp.: 50
Shopping Center Rental Services
S.I.C.: 6512
N.A.I.C.S.: 531120
Vincent Chee Yioun Tan *(CEO)*

Subsidiary:

Cosmo's World Theme Park Sdn. Bhd. (2)
No 09 103 9th Floor Berjaya Times Square
No 1 Jalan Imbi
55100 Kuala Lumpur, Federal Territory, Malaysia
Tel.: (60) 321173118
Fax: (60) 321432380
E-Mail: coordinator@timesquarekl.com
Emp.: 91
Theme Park & Cinema Theatre Operation Services
S.I.C.: 7996
N.A.I.C.S.: 713110
Tian Keng Swee *(Gen Mgr)*

Natural Avenue Sdn. Bhd. (1)
Lot 8189 & 8190 Town East Pending Road
93450 Kuching, Malaysia
Tel.: (60) 82333666
Fax: (60) 82330188
E-Mail: lleong@cashsweep.com.my
Web Site: www.cashsweep.com.my
Emp.: 84
Lottery Operation Services
S.I.C.: 7999
N.A.I.C.S.: 713290
Jackson Lim *(Gen Mgr)*

BERJAYA AUTO BERHAD

7 Jalan Pelukis U1/46 Tamasya Industrial Park
Seksyen U1, Shah Alam, Selangor Darul Ehsan, 40150, Malaysia
Tel.: (60) 3 7627 8888
Web Site: www.bauto.com.my
5248—(KLS)
Rev.: $349,005,256
Earnings: $17,051,840
Fiscal Year-end: 04/30/13

Business Description:
Automobile Distr & Sales
S.I.C.: 5012
N.A.I.C.S.: 423110

Personnel:
Ariff Fadzilla Awalluddin *(Chm)*
Choon San Yeoh *(CEO)*

Board of Directors:
Ariff Fadzilla Awalluddin
Kok Chuan Lee
Chen Peng Loh
Abdul Manap Abd Wahab
Choon San Yeoh

BERJAYA CORPORATION BERHAD

Level 12 East Wing Berjaya Times Square No 1 Jalan Imbi
55100 Kuala Lumpur, Malaysia

Berjaya Corporation Berhad—(Continued)

Tel.: (60) 3 2149 1999
Fax: (60) 3 2144 0935
E-Mail: padma@berjaya.com.my
Web Site: www.berjaya.com
Year Founded: 1967
BRYAF—(OTC)
Rev.: $2,418,753,332
Assets: $6,286,013,580
Liabilities: $2,748,580,515
Net Worth: $3,537,433,065
Earnings: $106,843,550
Emp.: 16,000
Fiscal Year-end: 04/30/13

Business Description:
Property Development, Entertainment Management & Financial Services
S.I.C.: 7011
N.A.I.C.S.: 721110

Personnel:
Robin Yeong Ching Tan *(Chm & CEO)*
Swee Peng Gan *(Co-Sec)*
Swee Hong Su *(Co-Sec)*

Board of Directors:
Robin Yeong Ching Tan
Mohd Zain Ahmad
Azlan Meah Ahmed Meah
Kien Sing Chan
Vivienne Chi Fan Cheng
Abdul Rahim Din
Mohd Yusoff Jaafar
Zurainah Musa
Jayanthi Naidu
Freddie Hock Cheng Pang
Dickson Yong Loong Tan
Rayvin Yeong Sheik Tan
Robert Kuen Loke Yong

Subsidiaries:

Absolute Prestige Sdn Bhd (1)
101 Jalan Bukit Bintang
55100 Kuala Lumpur, Wilayah Persekutuan, Malaysia
Tel.: (60) 3 2303 8000
Fax: (60) 3 2303 8008
E-Mail: reservations@thepiccolohotel.com
Web Site: www.thepiccolohotel.com
Hotel Management Services
S.I.C.: 7011
N.A.I.C.S.: 721110

Academy of Nursing (M) Sdn Bhd (1)
10th Floor Berjaya Times Square Jln Imbi
55100 Kuala Lumpur, Wilayah Persekutuan, Malaysia
Tel.: (60) 3 2148 8068
Fax: (60) 3 2141 3251
Nursing Educational Services
S.I.C.: 8299
N.A.I.C.S.: 611710
Norashikin Cheong Abdullah *(CEO)*

Berjaya 2nd Homes (MM2H) Sdn Bhd (1)
02-20 Level 2 West Wing Berjaya Times Square No1 Jln Imbi
Kuala Lumpur, 55100, Malaysia
Tel.: (60) 321428028
Fax: (60) 321451921
E-Mail: property@berjaya.com.my
Emp.: 1
Property Development Services
S.I.C.: 6531
N.A.I.C.S.: 531390
Mah Siew Wan *(Sr Gen Mgr)*

Berjaya Brilliance Auto Sdn Bhd (1)
Lot 3 Jalan 225 Section 51A
46100 Petaling Jaya, Selangor Darul Ehsan, Malaysia
Tel.: (60) 3 7954 1188
Fax: (60) 3 79551189
E-Mail: customerservice@brilliance-auto.com.my
Web Site: www.brilliance-auto.com.my
Automobile Distr
S.I.C.: 5012
N.A.I.C.S.: 423110
Mahamud Mohd Nor *(Branch Mgr)*

Berjaya Capital Berhad (1)
Berjaya Times Square
1 Jalan Imbi, Kuala Lumpur, 55100, Malaysia
Tel.: (60) 321491999
Fax: (60) 321431685
Web Site: www.berjaya.com
Sales Range: $50-74.9 Million
Emp.: 700
Investment Holding Company
S.I.C.: 6719
N.A.I.C.S.: 551112
Bhupatrai Mansukhlal Premji *(Deputy Chm)*
Kien Sing Chan *(CEO)*
Su Swee Hong *(Sec)*
Gan Hui Hui *(Sec)*

Subsidiary:

Inter-Pacific Capital Sdn Bhd (2)
West Wing Level 13 Berjaya Times Square
No 1 Jalan Imbi
Kuala Lumpur, 55100, Malaysia
Tel.: (60) 3 2117 1888
Fax: (60) 3 2144 1686
Emp.: 10
Online Trading Services
S.I.C.: 8742
N.A.I.C.S.: 541613
Tan Mun Choy *(Sr Gen Mgr)*

Subsidiaries:

Inter-Pacific Research Sdn Bhd (3)
West Wing Level 13 Berjaya Times Square
No 1 Jalan Imbi
Kuala Lumpur, 55100, Malaysia
Tel.: (60) 3 2117 1888
Fax: (60) 3 2142 7678
Marketing Research Services
S.I.C.: 8732
N.A.I.C.S.: 541910

Inter-Pacific Securities Sdn Bhd (3)
West Wing Level 13 Berjaya Times Square
No 1 Jalan Imbi
55100 Kuala Lumpur, Malaysia
Tel.: (60) 3 2117 1888
Fax: (60) 3 2144 1686
E-Mail: paconline@interpac.com.my
Web Site: www.paconline.com.my
Securities Brokerage Services
S.I.C.: 6211
N.A.I.C.S.: 523120
Kuok Wee Kiat *(Exec Dir)*

Subsidiary:

Inter-Pacific Asset Management Sdn Bhd (4)
West Wing Level 13 Berjaya Times Square
No1 Jalan Imbi
Kuala Lumpur, 55100, Malaysia
Tel.: (60) 3 2117 1888
Fax: (60) 3 2142 6029
Asset Management Services
S.I.C.: 6282
N.A.I.C.S.: 523920
Tan Mun Choy *(Mng Dir)*

Berjaya Food Berhad (1)
Lot 13-01A Level 13 East Wing Berjaya Times Square
No 1 Jalan Imbi, 55100 Kuala Lumpur, Malaysia MY
Tel.: (60) 3 21491999
Fax: (60) 3 21440935
Web Site: www.berjaya.com
BJFOOD—(KLS)
Rev.: $39,978,367
Assets: $54,783,955
Liabilities: $7,619,221
Net Worth: $47,164,734
Earnings: $5,667,441
Emp.: 1,373
Fiscal Year-end: 04/30/13
Holding Company; Fast Food Restaurants Operator
S.I.C.: 6719
N.A.I.C.S.: 551112
Robin Yeong Ching Tan *(Chm)*
Kok Chuan Lee *(CEO)*
Swee Peng Gan *(Co-Sec)*
Swee Hong Su *(Co-Sec)*

Berjaya Group Berhad (1)
Lot 13-01a Level 13 East Wing Berjaya Times Square No 1 Jalan Imbi
Kuala Lumpur, 55100, Malaysia
Tel.: (60) 3 2149 1999
Fax: (60) 3 2143 1685
Web Site: www.berjaya.com.my
Emp.: 700
Investment Management Services
S.I.C.: 6211
N.A.I.C.S.: 523999
Dato Robin Tan *(Chm)*

Subsidiaries:

Inter-Pacific Trading Sdn Bhd (2)
Lot 1-35A 1st Floor Podium Block Plaza
Berjaya 12 Jalan Imbi
Kuala Lumpur, 55100, Malaysia
Tel.: (60) 3 21444507
Fax: (60) 3 21449855
Emp.: 6
Commodity Trading Services
S.I.C.: 6221
N.A.I.C.S.: 523130
Tan Chin Bock *(Gen Mgr)*

VRS (Malaysia) Sdn Bhd (2)
Directorate 2 Level 12 Berjaya Times Square No 1
Jalan Imbi, 55100 Kuala Lumpur, Malaysia
Tel.: (60) 3 21491527
Fax: (60) 3 21489781
Property Development Services
S.I.C.: 6531
N.A.I.C.S.: 531390
Francis N. G. *(Gen Mgr)*

Berjaya Higher Education Sdn Bhd (1)
Level 11 West Berjaya Times Square No1
Jalan Imbi
Kuala Lumpur, 55100, Malaysia
Tel.: (60) 3 2687 7000
Fax: (60) 3 2687 7001
Educational Support Services
S.I.C.: 8299
N.A.I.C.S.: 611710

Berjaya Hills Berhad (1)
KM48 Persimpangan Bertingkat Lebuhraya Karak
Bukit Tinggi, 28750 Bentung, Pahang, Malaysia
Tel.: (60) 9 288 8888
Fax: (60) 92213667
E-Mail: sales@colmartropicale.com.my
Hotel Management Services
S.I.C.: 7011
N.A.I.C.S.: 721110

Berjaya Land Berhad (1)
Level 12 East Wing Berjaya Times Square
No 1 Jalan Imbi
55100 Kuala Lumpur, Malaysia
Tel.: (60) 321491999
Fax: (60) 321440935
Web Site: www.berjaya.com
BJLAND—(KLS)
Rev.: $1,392,549,335
Assets: $4,022,542,173
Liabilities: $1,272,029,225
Net Worth: $2,750,512,948
Earnings: $89,521,176
Emp.: 5,849
Fiscal Year-end: 04/30/13
Resort, Hotel & Casino Management Services
S.I.C.: 7011
N.A.I.C.S.: 721110
Sooi Lin Ng *(CEO)*
Swee Hong Su *(Co-Sec)*
Michelle Lai Heng Tham *(Co-Sec)*

Subsidiaries:

Amat Muhibah Sdn Bhd (2)
Taman Danau Desa Waterpark
58100 Kuala Lumpur, Wilayah Persekutuan, Malaysia
Tel.: (60) 3 7118 8338
Fax: (60) 3 7118 8383
Theme Park Operating Services
S.I.C.: 7996
N.A.I.C.S.: 713110
Gunaseelan Manickam *(Mgr)*

Berjaya Air Sdn Bhd (2)
Berjaya Hanger Sultan Abdul Aziz Shah Airport
47200 Subang Jaya, Selangor Darul Ehsan, Malaysia
Tel.: (60) 3 7847 3550
Fax: (60) 3 7847 6330
E-Mail: reservations@berjaya-air.com
Web Site: www.berjaya-air.com
Airline Reservation Services
S.I.C.: 4729
N.A.I.C.S.: 561599
Adelie Lee *(Gen Mgr)*

Berjaya Hotels & Resorts Vietnam Sdn Bhd (2)
12B-West Wing Level 12 Berjaya Times Square 1 Jalan Imbi
Kuala Lumpur, 55100, Malaysia
Tel.: (60) 3 2142 9611
Fax: (60) 3 2144 2527
Restaurant Operating Services
S.I.C.: 5812
N.A.I.C.S.: 722511

Berjaya Land Development Sdn Bhd (2)
Berjaya Times Sqaure level 12 Jalan Imbi
Kuala Lumpur, Malaysia
Tel.: (60) 3 21491999
Property Development Services
S.I.C.: 6531
N.A.I.C.S.: 531390

Subsidiaries:

Indra Ehsan Sdn Bhd (3)
Level 12 East Wing Berjaya Times Square No 1
Jalan Imbi, 55100 Kuala Lumpur, Malaysia
Tel.: (60) 3 2142 8028
Fax: (60) 3 2145 2126
Real Estate Development Services
S.I.C.: 6531
N.A.I.C.S.: 531390

Sri Panglima Sdn Bhd (3)
Level 12 East Wing Berjaya Times Square No 1
Jalan Imbi, 55100 Kuala Lumpur, Malaysia
Tel.: (60) 3 2142 8028
Fax: (60) 3 2145 2126
Real Estate Development Services
S.I.C.: 6531
N.A.I.C.S.: 531390

Berjaya Vacation Club Berhad (2)
Lot 5-04 Level 5 Fahrenheit 88 179 Jalan Bukit Bintang
55100 Kuala Lumpur, Malaysia
Tel.: (60) 3 2116 9999
Fax: (60) 3 2141 9288
E-Mail: bvcenquiry@berjaya.com.my
Web Site: www.berjayavacation.com.my
Vacation Club Operating Services
S.I.C.: 7032
N.A.I.C.S.: 721214

Subsidiaries:

Berjaya Golf Resort Berhad (3)
Jalan Jalil Perkasa 3
Bukit Jalil, 57000 Kuala Lumpur, Malaysia
Tel.: (60) 3 8994 1600
Fax: (60) 3 8994 1542
E-Mail: jalil@berjayaclubs.com
Web Site: www.berjayaclubs.com
Emp.: 280
Golf Club Operating Services
S.I.C.: 7999
N.A.I.C.S.: 713910
Faiezal Kamal *(Mgr-Club)*

Berjaya Hospitality Services Sdn Bhd (3)
14th Floor Times Square Blok B 1 Jln Imbi
Kuala Lumpur, 55100, Malaysia
Tel.: (60) 326877000
Fax: (60) 326877001
Hospitality Services
S.I.C.: 8062
N.A.I.C.S.: 622110
Seok Khen Ho Mae *(COO)*

Berjaya Langkawi Beach Resort Sdn Bhd (3)
Karung Berkunci 200 Burau Bay
7000 Kuah, Kedah, Malaysia
Tel.: (60) 4 959 1888
Fax: (60) 4 959 1886
E-Mail: langkawi.rsvn@berjayahotel.com
Emp.: 66
Resort Operating Services
S.I.C.: 7011
N.A.I.C.S.: 721110
Noel Vendawall *(Gen Mgr)*

Berjaya Penang Hotel Sdn Bhd. (3)
1-Stop Midlands Park Burmah Road
10350 George Town, Penang, Malaysia
Tel.: (60) 4 227 7111
Fax: (60) 4 226 7111
E-Mail: penang.bph@berjayahotel.com
Hotel Management Services
S.I.C.: 7011
N.A.I.C.S.: 721110
Cheah Hooi Theng *(Gen Mgr)*

Berjaya Resort Management Services Sdn Bhd (3)
Lot 8 88 East Wing Level 8 Berjaya Times Square 1 Jalan Imbi
Kuala Lumpur, 55100, Malaysia
Tel.: (60) 321429611
Fax: (60) 321442527
Resort Operating Services
S.I.C.: 7011
N.A.I.C.S.: 721110

Bukit Kiara Resort Berhad (3)
Jalan Bukit Kiara Off Jalan Damansara
60000 Kuala Lumpur, Malaysia
Tel.: (60) 320931222
Fax: (60) 320962825
E-Mail: kiara@berjayaclubs.com
Horse Riding Club Operating Services
S.I.C.: 7999
N.A.I.C.S.: 713910
Hisham Razali *(Sr Mgr-Ops)*

Budi Impian Sdn Bhd (2)
LG Berjaya Times Square Jln Imbi
55100 Kuala Lumpur, Wilayah Persekutuan, Malaysia
Tel.: (60) 3 2141 7601
Fax: (60) 3 2141 8351
Restaurant Operating Services
S.I.C.: 5812
N.A.I.C.S.: 722511

Cerah Bakti Sdn Bhd (2)
18th Floor Blok 488A One Stop Centre Jln Burma
10350 George Town, Pulau Pinang, Malaysia
Tel.: (60) 4 227 4188
Fax: (60) 4 227 6868
Property Development Services
S.I.C.: 6531
N.A.I.C.S.: 531390

Kota Raya Development Sdn Bhd (2)
Lot 307A 3rd Floor Kompleks Kotaraya Jln Cheng Lock
50000 Kuala Lumpur, Wilayah Persekutuan, Malaysia
Tel.: (60) 3 2072 2562
Fax: (60) 3 2078 2216
E-Mail: kotaraya@Berjaya.com.my
Web Site: www.Berjaya.com.my
Emp.: 13
Real Estate Development Services
S.I.C.: 6531
N.A.I.C.S.: 531390
Gunasegaran G. *(Gen Mgr)*

Nural Enterprise Sdn Bhd (2)
Lot 2 05 Second Floor Podium Block Plaza Berjaya 12 Jalan Imbi
Kuala Lumpur, 55100, Malaysia
Tel.: (60) 3 21412818
Fax: (60) 3 21447097
Emp.: 20
Financial Management Services
S.I.C.: 6211
N.A.I.C.S.: 523999
Thavidu Rajah *(Mgr-Maintenance)*

Pakar Angsana Sdn Bhd (2)
Level 12 East Wing Berjaya Times Square No 1
Jalan Imbi, 55100 Kuala Lumpur, Malaysia
Tel.: (60) 3 2142 8028
Fax: (60) 3 2145 2126
Property Management Services
S.I.C.: 6531
N.A.I.C.S.: 531311

Securiservices Sdn Bhd (2)
Level 12 East Wing Berjaya Times Square No1
Jalan Imbi, Kuala Lumpur, 55100, Malaysia
Tel.: (60) 321428028
Fax: (60) 321452126
Web Site: www.berjayaproperties.com
Emp.: 30
Property Management Services
S.I.C.: 6531
N.A.I.C.S.: 531311
Mah Siew Wan *(Gen Mgr)*

Selat Makmur Sdn Bhd (2)
Level 12 East Wing Berjaya Times Square No 1
Jalan Imbi, Kuala Lumpur, 55100, Malaysia
Tel.: (60) 3 2142 8028
Fax: (60) 3 2145 2126
Real Estate Development Services
S.I.C.: 6531
N.A.I.C.S.: 531390

Semangat Cergas Sdn Bhd (2)
Level 12 East Wing Berjaya Times Square No 1
Jalan Imbi, 55100 Kuala Lumpur, Malaysia
Tel.: (60) 3 2142 8028
Fax: (60) 3 2145 2126
Property Development Services
S.I.C.: 6531
N.A.I.C.S.: 531390

Tioman Island Resort Berhad (2)
PO Box 4
Mersing, 86807, Malaysia
Tel.: (60) 9 419 1000
Fax: (60) 9 419 1718
Resort Operating Services
S.I.C.: 7011
N.A.I.C.S.: 721110

Tiram Jaya Sdn Bhd (2)
Level 12 East Wing Berjaya Times Square No 1
Jalan Imbi, 55100 Kuala Lumpur, Malaysia
Tel.: (60) 3 2142 8028
Fax: (60) 3 2145 2126
Property Management Services
S.I.C.: 6531
N.A.I.C.S.: 531311

Berjaya Pizza Company Sdn Bhd (1)
Lot 09-23 9th Floor Berjaya Times Square No1 Jalan Imbi
55100 Kuala Lumpur, Malaysia
Tel.: (60) 3 2119 7272
Fax: (60) 3 2119 7200
E-Mail: enquiry@papajohns.com.my
Web Site: www.papajohns.com.my
Pizza Restaurant Operating Services
S.I.C.: 5812
N.A.I.C.S.: 722513
Marry Goh *(Gen Mgr)*

Berjaya Sports Toto Berhad (1)
Lot 13-01A Level 13 East Wing Berjaya Times Square No 1 Jalan Imbi
55100 Kuala Lumpur, Malaysia
Tel.: (60) 321491999
Fax: (60) 321440935
E-Mail: cosec@berjaya.com.my
Web Site: www.berjaya.com
BJTOTO—(KLS)
Rev.: $1,189,812,467
Assets: $506,003,514
Liabilities: $304,918,380
Net Worth: $201,085,135
Earnings: $132,317,688
Emp.: 932
Fiscal Year-end: 04/30/13
Gaming Services
S.I.C.: 7999
N.A.I.C.S.: 713290
Robin Yeong Ching Tan *(CEO)*
Swee Hong Su *(Co-Sec)*
Michelle Lai Heng Tham *(Co-Sec)*

Non-U.S. Subsidiaries:

Berjaya Lottery Management (HK) Ltd. (2)
Unit1701 Austin Plaza 83 Austin Rd Jordan
Kowloon, China (Hong Kong) (100%)
Tel.: (852) 28776616
Fax: (852) 28046943
Web Site: www.berjaya.com
Emp.: 50
Operator of Gambling Establishments & Casinos
S.I.C.: 7011
N.A.I.C.S.: 721120

U.S. Subsidiary:

International Lottery & Totalizator Systems, Inc. (3)
2310 Cousteau Ct
Vista, CA 92081-8346 CA (71.3%)
Tel.: (760) 598-1655
Fax: (760) 598-0219
E-Mail: mktg@ilts.com
Web Site: www.ilts.com
ITSI—(OTCB)
Rev.: $10,571,000
Assets: $16,834,000
Liabilities: $8,394,000
Net Worth: $8,440,000
Earnings: $3,099,000
Emp.: 35
Fiscal Year-end: 04/30/13
Computer-Based Ticket Processing Systems & Terminals for Pari-Mutual Wagering & On-Line Lotteries
S.I.C.: 3589
N.A.I.C.S.: 333318
Theodore A. Johnson *(Chm)*
Jeffrey M. Johnson *(Pres & Acting CFO)*

Subsidiary:

Unisyn Voting Solutions, Inc. (4)
2310 Cousteau Ct
Vista, CA 92081
Tel.: (760) 734-3233
Fax: (760) 598-0219
E-Mail: mktg@unisynvoting.com
Web Site: www.unisynvoting.com
Voting Machinery Mfr
S.I.C.: 3589
N.A.I.C.S.: 333318

Non-U.S. Subsidiary:

Berjaya Philippines, Inc. (3)
9/F Rufino Pacific Tower 6784 Ayala Avenue Corner VA Rufino Street
Legaspi Village, Makati, 1200, Philippines (68%)
Tel.: (63) 2 811 0668
Fax: (63) 2 811 0538
Web Site: www.pgpi.com.ph
BCOR—(PHI)
Rev.: $51,913,899
Assets: $122,207,985
Liabilities: $4,692,897
Net Worth: $117,515,088
Earnings: $27,025,811
Emp.: 199
Fiscal Year-end: 04/30/13
Amusement & Recreation Gaming Services
S.I.C.: 7999
N.A.I.C.S.: 713290
Ibrahim Saad *(Chm)*
Meng Kwong Lim *(Pres)*
Eng Hwa Tan *(Treas)*
Jose A. Bernas *(Sec)*

Subsidiary:

Philippine Gaming Management Corporation. (4)
9th Floor Rufino Pacific Tower 6784 Ayala Avenue
Cor VA Rufino Street, Makati, Philippines
Tel.: (63) 2 811 0668
Fax: (63) 2 811 0538
Lottery Equipment Leasing Services
S.I.C.: 7359
N.A.I.C.S.: 532490

H.R. Owen plc (2)
Melton Court Old Brompton Road
London, SW7 3TD, United Kingdom
Tel.: (44) 20 7245 1122
Fax: (44) 2072451123
E-Mail: info@hrowen.co.uk
Web Site: www.hrowen.co.uk
HRO—(LSE)
Rev.: $384,582,384
Assets: $109,422,687
Liabilities: $89,528,371
Net Worth: $19,894,316
Earnings: $2,733,751
Emp.: 352
Fiscal Year-end: 12/31/12
Automobile Sales
S.I.C.: 5511
N.A.I.C.S.: 441110
Joe Doyle *(CEO)*
James Adams *(Sec)*

Subsidiaries:

Heathrow Limited (3)
Berry Heathrow Stone Close
West Drayton, Middlesex, UB7 8JU, United Kingdom
Tel.: (44) 1895433999
Fax: (44) 1895431519
Emp.: 65
Used Car Dealers
S.I.C.: 5521
N.A.I.C.S.: 441120
Steve Kerbey *(Mgr)*

Holland Park Limited (3)
5-9 School norch Actom NW 10
London, 6TD, United Kingdom (100%)
Tel.: (44) 2089684444
Fax: (44) 20889638380
Web Site: www.bmw-net.co.uk
Emp.: 60
Motor Vehicle Dealers
S.I.C.: 5571
N.A.I.C.S.: 441228

H.R. Owen Dealerships Limited (3)
75 Kinnerton Street
SW1X8ED London, United Kingdom(100%)
Tel.: (44) 2072451122
Fax: (44) 2072451123
E-Mail: info@hrowen.co.uk
Web Site: www.hrowen.co.uk/
Emp.: 100
Car Dealers
S.I.C.: 5511
N.A.I.C.S.: 441110

Jack Barclay Limited (3)
18 Berkeley Square
W1J 6AE London, United Kingdom (100%)
Tel.: (44) 2076297444
Fax: (44) 02076298258
E-Mail: enquiries@jackbarclay.co.uk
Web Site: www.jackbarclay.co.uk
Emp.: 30
Motor Vehicle Dealers
S.I.C.: 5599
N.A.I.C.S.: 441228
John Walden *(CEO)*

Malaya Dealerships Limited (3)
75 Kinnerton Street
London, SW1X 8ED, United Kingdom (100%)
Tel.: (44) 2072451122
Emp.: 50
Car Dealers
S.I.C.: 5511
N.A.I.C.S.: 441110
Joe Doyle *(Gen Mgr)*

Bermaz Motor Sdn Bhd (1)
Lot 5 Jalan Pelukis U1/46 Temasysa Industrial Park U1
40150 Shah Alam, Selangor Darul Ehsan, Malaysia
Tel.: (60) 3 76278888
Fax: (60) 3 55692891
E-Mail: sales@mazda.com.my
Web Site: www.mazda.com.my
Emp.: 30
New Car Dealers
S.I.C.: 5511
N.A.I.C.S.: 441110
Ben Yeoh *(Mng Dir)*

BLoyalty Sdn Bhd (1)
Level 12 West Berjaya Times Square No 1 Jalan Imbi
55100 Kuala Lumpur, Malaysia
Tel.: (60) 3 2119 2999
Fax: (60) 3 2119 2988
E-Mail: enquiry@bcard.com.my
Web Site: www.bcard.com.my
Loyalty Program Operation Services
S.I.C.: 8748
N.A.I.C.S.: 541618

Changan Berjaya Auto Sdn Bhd (1)
Lot 3 Jalan 225 Section 51A
46100 Petaling Jaya, Selangor Darul Ehsan, Malaysia
Tel.: (60) 3 7954 1188
Fax: (60) 3 7955 1189
Web Site: www.changan.com.my
Automobile Distr
S.I.C.: 5012
N.A.I.C.S.: 423110

Cosway Corporation Berhad (1)
Berjaya Times Square
1 Jalan Imbi, Kuala Lumpur, 55100, Malaysia
Tel.: (60) 321491999
Fax: (60) 321431685
Sales Range: $250-299.9 Million
Emp.: 3,100
Mfg & Commercial Retail Services

Berjaya Corporation Berhad—(Continued)

S.I.C.: 5999
N.A.I.C.S.: 453998
Kanagalingam Veluppillai *(Deputy Chm)*
Canesri Dato Vincent *(Chm)*
Al Chuah Choong Heong *(CEO)*
Su Swee Hong *(Co-Sec)*
Gan Hui Hui *(Co-Sec)*

Cosway (M) Sdn Bhd (1)
2nd Floor Wisma Cosway Jalan Raja Chulan
50200 Kuala Lumpur, Malaysia
Tel.: (60) 3 2030 1000
Fax: (60) 3 2070 4754
E-Mail: info@cosway.com.my
Web Site: www.cosway.com.my
Health Care Products Distr
S.I.C.: 5122
N.A.I.C.S.: 424210
Al Chuah *(Mng Dir)*

Dunham-Bush (Malaysia) Berhad (1)
Berjaya Times Square
1 Jalan Imbi, Kuala Lumpur, 55100, Malaysia
Tel.: (60) 321491999
Fax: (60) 321431685
E-Mail: dbm@dunham-bush.com.my
Web Site: www.dunham-bush.com.my
Sales Range: $100-124.9 Million
Refrigeration & Air Conditioning Mfg & Retail Services
S.I.C.: 3585
N.A.I.C.S.: 333415

U.S. Subsidiaries:

Dunham-Bush, Inc. (2)
175 South St
West Hartford, CT 06110
Tel.: (860) 956-8500
Fax: (860) 953-3300
E-Mail: dbcustsvc@dunham-bush.com
Web Site: www.dunham-bush.com
Refrigeration & Air Conditioning Services
S.I.C.: 3585
N.A.I.C.S.: 333415

Hartford Compressors Inc. (2)
179 South St
West Hartford, CT 06110
Tel.: (860) 249-8671
Fax: (860) 548-1705
E-Mail: cserv@hartfordcompressors.com
Web Site: www.hartfordcompressors.com
Refrigeration Components Mfr
S.I.C.: 3585
N.A.I.C.S.: 333415

Graphic Press Group Sdn Bhd (1)
No 3 Jalan PJS 3/2 Jalan Medan 3 Taman Medan PJS 3
Petaling Jaya, 46000, Malaysia
Tel.: (60) 3 7783 9988
Fax: (60) 3 7785 3633
Printing & Packaging Services
S.I.C.: 2759
N.A.I.C.S.: 323111

Indah Corporation Berhad (1)
1 Persiaran Gemilang Bandar Banang Jaya
83000 Batu Pahat, Johor Darul Takzim, Malaysia
Tel.: (60) 7 428 6001
Fax: (60) 7 428 5267
E-Mail: banang@berjayaclubs.com
Golf Club Operating Services
S.I.C.: 7999
N.A.I.C.S.: 713910
Steven Seo *(Mgr-Ops)*

KDE Recreation Berhad (1)
Taman Tun Abdul Razak Jalan Kerja Air Lama
Ampang Jaya, 68000 Ampang, Selangor Darul Ehsan, Malaysia
Tel.: (60) 3 4257 2333
Fax: (60) 3 4257 2335
Emp.: 20
Golf Club Operating Services
S.I.C.: 7999
N.A.I.C.S.: 713910
Siva Kangasu *(Asst Gen Mgr)*

Kimia Suchi Marketing Sdn Bhd (1)
21 Jalan Tudm Kampung Baru Subang
Shah Alam, Selangor, 40000, Malaysia
Tel.: (60) 3 7847 6268
Personal Care Products Distr
S.I.C.: 5122
N.A.I.C.S.: 424210

Securexpress Services Sdn Bhd (1)
No 16 Jln Kecapi 33/2
40400 Shah Alam, Selangor, Malaysia
Tel.: (60) 3 5566 1999
Courier Services
S.I.C.: 4513
N.A.I.C.S.: 492110

Stephens Properties Sdn Bhd (1)
9 07 9th Floor Wisma Cosway Jln Raja Culan
50200 Kuala Lumpur, Malaysia
Tel.: (60) 3 21482722
Fax: (60) 3 21421991
Property Management Services
S.I.C.: 6531
N.A.I.C.S.: 531311

Wangsa Tegap Sdn Bhd (1)
Level 12 East Wing Berjaya Times Square No 1
Jalan Imbi, 55100 Kuala Lumpur, Malaysia
Tel.: (60) 3 2142 8028
Fax: (60) 3 2145 2126
Web Site: www.berjayaproperties.com
Property Management Services
S.I.C.: 6531
N.A.I.C.S.: 531311

Non-U.S. Subsidiaries:

Berjaya (China) Great Mall Co. Ltd (1)
38 Xing Gong West Street Yanjiao Development Zone
065201 Sanhe, China
Tel.: (86) 316 332 0309
Fax: (86) 316 332 0310
Real Estate Development Services
S.I.C.: 6531
N.A.I.C.S.: 531390

Berjaya Corporation (S) Pte Ltd (1)
67 Tanjong Pagar Road
Singapore, 088488, Singapore
Tel.: (65) 62277378
Fax: (65) 62254066
Emp.: 20
Real Estate Development Services
S.I.C.: 6531
N.A.I.C.S.: 531390
Jennifer Lin *(Head-Ops)*

Berjaya Holdings (HK) Limited (1)
2301 Wing On House 71 Des Voeux Road Central, China (Hong Kong) (100%)
Tel.: (852) 28776616
Fax: (852) 2877 8077
E-Mail: info@berjaya.com
Web Site: www.berjaya.com
Emp.: 100
Investor in Real Estate
S.I.C.: 6221
N.A.I.C.S.: 523130

Berjaya Hotels & Resorts (Singapore) Pte Ltd (1)
67 Tanjong Pagar Road
Singapore, 088488, Singapore
Tel.: (65) 6227 3688
Fax: (65) 6225 4966
E-Mail: sso.rsvn1@berjayahotel.com
Web Site: www.berjayahotel.com
Emp.: 18
Hotels Management Services
S.I.C.: 7011
N.A.I.C.S.: 721110
Jocelyn Gwee *(Dir-Sls)*

Berjaya Mount Royal Beach Hotel Limited (1)
36 College Avenue
Mount Lavinia, Sri Lanka
Tel.: (94) 11 2739610
Fax: (94) 11 2733030
E-Mail: berjaya@slt.lk
Web Site: www.berjayahotel.com
Restaurant Operating Services
S.I.C.: 5812
N.A.I.C.S.: 722511
Keerthi Wickramasinghe *(Gen Mgr)*

CarLovers Carwash Limited (1)
Unit 3/8 Tollis Place
Seven Hills, NSW, 2147, Australia (96%)
Mailing Address:
PO Box 665
Seven Hills, NSW, 1730, Australia
Tel.: (61) 296744888
Fax: (61) 296207644
E-Mail: info@carlovers.com.au
Web Site: www.carlovers.com.au
Emp.: 6
S.I.C.: 8299
N.A.I.C.S.: 611620
Robbie Fong *(Mgr)*

Cosway (China) Co. Ltd (1)
Huaqiang North
Shenzhen, China
Tel.: (86) 755 28153049
Fax: (86) 755 28153049
Web Site: www.ecosway.com.cn
Cosmetic Products Distr
S.I.C.: 5122
N.A.I.C.S.: 424210

Country Farm Organics Mart Pte Ltd (1)
49 Jalan Pemimpin 04-09 APS Building
Singapore, 577203, Singapore
Tel.: (65) 6474 6887
Fax: (65) 6475 6477
Web Site: www.countryfarmorganics.com
Food Products Distr
S.I.C.: 5142
N.A.I.C.S.: 424420
Richard Kang *(Country Mgr)*

eCosway Korea, Inc. (1)
PMK Building 3rd Floor 746 Yeoksam Dong
Gangnam-Gu, Seoul, 135925, Korea (South)
Tel.: (82) 2568 9575
Fax: (82) 2568 9576
E-Mail: marketing@ecosway.co.kr
Web Site: www.ecosway.co.kr
Personal Care Products Distr
S.I.C.: 5122
N.A.I.C.S.: 424210

Mahameru Consultancy d.o.o. (1)
Zanatski Centar-carsijska BB
Visoko, Bosnia & Herzegovina
Tel.: (387) 61 792 186
Real Estate Management Services
S.I.C.: 6531
N.A.I.C.S.: 531390

South Pacific Textiles Industries (Singapore) Pte Ltd (1)
20 Peck Seah Street 02-00
Singapore, 79312, Singapore
Tel.: (65) 62259393
Fax: (65) 62259292
Textile Products Mfr & Distr
S.I.C.: 2399
N.A.I.C.S.: 314999
Howe Seng *(Sr Mgr-Sls)*

Taiga Building Products Ltd. (1)
800-4710 Kingsway
Burnaby, BC, V5H 4M2, Canada BC
Mailing Address: (100%)
BC, V5H 3X6, Canada
Tel.: (604) 438-1471
Fax: (604) 439-4242
Toll Free: (800) 663-1470
E-Mail: invest@taigabuilding.com
Web Site: www.taigabuilding.com
TBL—(TSX)
Sls.: $1,125,969,197
Assets: $344,374,253
Liabilities: $404,453,816
Net Worth: ($60,079,563)
Earnings: $10,371,605
Emp.: 484
Fiscal Year-end: 03/31/13
Lumber, Panel Products & Related Building Products Distr
S.I.C.: 2499
N.A.I.C.S.: 321999
Ong Tong Kooi *(Chm)*
Cam White *(Pres & CEO)*
Mark Schneidereit-Hsu *(CFO, VP-Fin & Admin)*
Trent Balog *(COO & Exec VP-Sls & Ops)*
Grant Sali *(Exec VP-Supply Mgmt)*

BERKELEY COFFEE & TEA, INC.

(Name Changed to DTS8 Coffee Company, Ltd.)

THE BERKELEY GROUP HOLDINGS PLC

Berkeley House 19 Portsmouth Road
Cobham, Surrey, KT11 1JG, United Kingdom
Tel.: (44) 1932868555
Fax: (44) 1932868667
E-Mail: marketing@berkeleygroup.co.uk
Web Site: www.berkeleygroup.co.uk
Year Founded: 1976
BKG—(LSE)
Rev.: $2,167,733,454
Assets: $3,943,329,201
Liabilities: $1,854,876,105
Net Worth: $2,088,453,096
Earnings: $331,177,113
Emp.: 1,326
Fiscal Year-end: 04/30/13

Business Description:
Real Estate Development Services
S.I.C.: 6531
N.A.I.C.S.: 531390

Personnel:
Anthony W. Pidgley *(Chm)*
Rob C. Perrins *(Mng Dir)*
Sophie Harrison *(Exec-Mktg & Events)*
Rupal Parmar *(Exec-Mktg & Events)*
A. M. Bradshaw *(Sec)*

Board of Directors:
Anthony W. Pidgley
John Armitt
Glyn Barker
Sean Ellis
Greg J. Fry
David Howell
Adrian Li
Alison Nimmo
Rob C. Perrins
Nick G. Simpkin
Veronica Wadley
Karl Whiteman

Legal Counsel:
Ashurst LLP
Broadwalk House 5 Appold Street
London, EC2A 2HA, United Kingdom

Subsidiaries:

Berkeley Commercial Developments Ltd. (1)
Berkeley House
19 Portsmouth Road, Cobham, KT111JG, United Kingdom (100%)
Tel.: (44) 1932584555
Fax: (44) 1932868667
E-Mail: alison.cowsett@berkeleyhouse.co.uk
Web Site: www.berkeleygroup.co.uk/index.cfm?articleid=6
Activities Related to Real Estate
S.I.C.: 6531
N.A.I.C.S.: 531390
Alison Cowsett *(Mng Dir)*

Berkeley First Limited (1)
Berkeley House
19 Portsmouth Road, Cobham, KT11 1JG, United Kingdom (100%)
Tel.: (44) 1932584555
Fax: (44) 1932584550
E-Mail: info@berkeleygroup.co.uk
Web Site: www.berkeleyfirst.co.uk
Emp.: 85
Activities Related to Real Estate
S.I.C.: 6531
N.A.I.C.S.: 531390
Anthony Pidgley *(Mng Dir)*

The Berkeley Group plc (1)
Berkeley House
19 Portsmouth Road, Cobham, KT111JG, United Kingdom (100%)
Tel.: (44) 1932584555
Fax: (44) 1932868667
Web Site: www.berkeleygroup.co.uk/index.cfm?articleid=6
Emp.: 120
Activities Related to Real Estate
S.I.C.: 6531
N.A.I.C.S.: 531390

Rob Perrins *(Mng Dir)*

Berkeley Homes (Capital) Plc (1)
Berkeley House 7 Oakhill Road
Sevenoaks, Kent, TN13 1NQ, United Kingdom
Tel.: (44) 1732 227 500
Web Site: www.berkeleyhomes.co.uk
Emp.: 10
Property Development Services
S.I.C.: 6531
N.A.I.C.S.: 531390
Sitaram Parthasarathy *(Mng Dir)*

Berkeley Homes (Central London) Limited (1)
380 Queenstown Road
London, SW8 4PE, United Kingdom
Tel.: (44) 2077202600
Fax: (44) 2075012550
Property Development Services
S.I.C.: 6531
N.A.I.C.S.: 531390

Berkeley Homes (East Thames) Limited (1)
19 Berkeley House Portsmouth Road
Cobham, Surrey, KT11 1JG, United Kingdom
Tel.: (44) 20 7720 2600
Fax: (44) 20 7501 2550
Property Management Services
S.I.C.: 6531
N.A.I.C.S.: 531311

Berkeley Homes (Eastern Counties) Limited (1)
Berkeley House 7 Oakhill Road
Sevenoaks, TN13 1NQ, United Kingdom
Tel.: (44) 1732 227500
Web Site: www.berkeleyhomes.co.uk
Emp.: 12
Residential Property Management Services
S.I.C.: 6531
N.A.I.C.S.: 531311
Peter Gershon *(Mng Dir)*

Berkeley Homes (Eastern) Limited (1)
3 Arsenal Way
Woolwich, London, SE18 6TF, United Kingdom
Tel.: (44) 20 7720 2600
Fax: (44) 1732 227 501
Web Site: www.berkeleygroup.co.uk
Emp.: 7
Residential Property Management Services
S.I.C.: 6531
N.A.I.C.S.: 531311
Volker Christmann *(Mng Dir)*

Berkeley Homes (Hampshire) Limited (1)
1 Residence Weevil Lane Royal Clarence Yard
Gosport, Hampshire, PO12 1AX, United Kingdom
Tel.: (44) 2392525582
Property Development Services
S.I.C.: 6531
N.A.I.C.S.: 531390

Berkeley Homes (Kent) Limited (1)
Berkeley House
19 Portsmouth Road, Cobham, KT11 1JG, United Kingdom (100%)
Tel.: (44) 1932584555
Fax: (44) 1932868667
Web Site: www.berkeleygroup.co.uk/index.cfm?articleid=14
Activities Related to Real Estate
S.I.C.: 6531
N.A.I.C.S.: 531390
Anthony Pidgley *(Mng Dir)*

Berkeley Homes (Oxford & Chiltern) Limited (1)
Berkeley House Farnham Lane
Farnham Royal, SL2 3RQ, United Kingdom
Tel.: (44) 1235 559 111
Fax: (44) 753646855
Emp.: 8
Residential Property Development Services
S.I.C.: 6531
N.A.I.C.S.: 531390
Rameen Firoozan *(Mng Dir)*

Berkeley Homes plc (1)
Berkeley House
19 Portsmouth Road, Cobham, KT111JG, United Kingdom (100%)
Tel.: (44) 1932584555
Fax: (44) 1932868667
E-Mail: debbie.murphy@berkeleygroup.co.uk
Web Site: www.berkeleygroup.co.uk/index.cfm?articleid=14
Emp.: 110
Activities Related to Real Estate
S.I.C.: 6531
N.A.I.C.S.: 531390
Rob Perrins *(Mng Dir)*

Berkeley Homes (South East London) Limited (1)
Berkeley House 7 Oakhill Rd 19 Portsmouth Road
Sevenoaks, Kent, TN13 1NQ, United Kingdom (100%)
Tel.: (44) 114417322
Web Site: www.berkeleyhomes.co.uk
Emp.: 100
Activities Related to Real Estate
S.I.C.: 6531
N.A.I.C.S.: 531390
Justin Tidaldi *(Mng Dir-Div)*

Berkeley Homes (Southern) Limited (1)
Berkeley House Summers Place Stane Street
Billingshurst, West Sussex, RH14 9GN, United Kingdom
Tel.: (44) 1403 279 000
Emp.: 85
Residential Property Development Services
S.I.C.: 6531
N.A.I.C.S.: 531390
Gary Hodges *(Mng Dir)*
Andy Peters *(Mng Dir)*

Berkeley Homes (Urban Renaissance) Limited (1)
380 Queenstown Road
London, SW8 4PE, United Kingdom
Tel.: (44) 20 7720 2600
Web Site: www.berkeleygroup.co.uk
Emp.: 20
Residential Property Management Services
S.I.C.: 6531
N.A.I.C.S.: 531311
Paul Vallone *(Gen Mgr)*

Berkeley Homes (West London) Limited (1)
Bromyard Avenue
London, W3 7XH, United Kingdom
Tel.: (44) 2088112336
Fax: (44) 2087467062
E-Mail: sales.west3@berkeleyhomes.co.uk
Web Site: www.berkeleyhomes.co.uk
Emp.: 3
New Single-Family Housing Construction
S.I.C.: 1521
N.A.I.C.S.: 236115
Karl Whiteman *(Exec Dir)*

Berkeley Partnership Homes Limited (1)
Berkeley House 7 Oakhill Road
Sevenoaks, Kent, TN13 1NQ, United Kingdom
Tel.: (44) 1732 227500
Property Management Services
S.I.C.: 6531
N.A.I.C.S.: 531311

Berkeley Strategic Land Limited (1)
Berkeley House
19 Portsmouth Rd, Cobham, KT111JG, United Kingdom (100%)
Tel.: (44) 193258459
Fax: (44) 1932584548
E-Mail: enquiries@berkeleygroup.co.uk
Web Site: www.berkeleygroup.co.uk/index.cfm?articleid=6
Activities Related to Real Estate
S.I.C.: 6531
N.A.I.C.S.: 531390
Matthew Biddle *(Mng Dir)*
Adrian Brown *(Mng Dir)*

Berkeley Urban Renaissance Limited (1)
Sopwith Way
London, SW84NS, United Kingdom
Tel.: (44) 2075012555
E-Mail: sales.west3@berkeleyhomes.co.uk
Web Site: www.berkeleygroup.co.uk/index.cfm?articleid=14
Emp.: 60
Real Estate Property Lessors
S.I.C.: 6519
N.A.I.C.S.: 531190
Paul Vallone *(Mng Dir)*

St George Central London Limited (1)
St George House
7 Imperial Road Fulham, London, SW6 2AN, United Kingdom (100%)
Tel.: (44) 2074714444
Fax: (44) 2074714440
E-Mail: marketing@stgeorgecl.com
Web Site: www.stgeorgecl.com
Emp.: 40
Real Estate Property Lessors
S.I.C.: 6519
N.A.I.C.S.: 531190

St George PLC (1)
St George House
76 Crown Road, Twickenham, TW13EU, United Kingdom (100%)
Tel.: (44) 2089174000
Fax: (44) 2089174111
E-Mail: reception@stgeorgewl.com
Web Site: www.stgeorgeplc.com
Emp.: 50
Real Estate Property Lessors
S.I.C.: 6519
N.A.I.C.S.: 531190

St George South London Limited (1)
16 Boulevard Imperial Wharf
17-19 Imperial Road Fulham, London, SW6 2UB, United Kingdom (100%)
Tel.: (44) 2074714444
E-Mail: sales@stgeorgesl.com
Emp.: 50
Real Estate Property Lessors
S.I.C.: 6519
N.A.I.C.S.: 531190

St George West London Limited (1)
St George House
76 Crown Road, Twickenham, TW13 EU, United Kingdom (100%)
Tel.: (44) 2089174000
Fax: (44) 2089174111
E-Mail: sales@stgeorgewl.com
Web Site: www.stgeorgeplc.com
Emp.: 60
Real Estate Property Lessors
S.I.C.: 6519
N.A.I.C.S.: 531190
Ian Dobie *(Mng Dir)*

St. James Group Limited (1)
26 Bridge Street
Leatherhead, KT22 8BZ, United Kingdom (100%)
Tel.: (44) 1372364500
Fax: (44) 1372364501
E-Mail: info@stjameshomes.co.uk
Web Site: www.stjameshomes.co.uk
Emp.: 115
Real Estate Property Lessors
S.I.C.: 6519
N.A.I.C.S.: 531190
Chris Gilbert *(Dir-Ops)*

Joint Venture:

Saad Berkeley Limited (1)
Berkeley House St George
19 Portsmouth Road, London, SW82LE, United Kingdom
Tel.: (44) 1932584555
Fax: (44) 1932868667
Emp.: 18
Real Estate
S.I.C.: 6531
N.A.I.C.S.: 531390
Mathew Biddel *(Mng Dir)*

BERKELEY RESOURCES LTD

Level 9 BGC Centre 28 The Esplanade
Perth, WA, 6000, Australia
Tel.: (61) 8 9322 6322
Fax: (61) 8 9322 6558
E-Mail: info@berkeleyresources.com.au
Web Site: www.berkeleyresources.com.au
BKY—(AIM ASX)
Rev.: $2,341,506
Assets: $46,539,015
Liabilities: $2,628,464
Net Worth: $43,910,551
Earnings: ($11,660,137)
Emp.: 30
Fiscal Year-end: 06/30/13

Business Description:
Mineral Exploration & Development
S.I.C.: 1094
N.A.I.C.S.: 212291

Personnel:
Clint McGhie *(CFO & Sec)*
Javier Colilla Peletero *(Sr VP)*

Board of Directors:
Ian Peter Middlemas
Robert Arthur Behets
James Ross

Legal Counsel:
Herbert Smith Freehills Spain LLP
Paseo De La Castellana 66
Madrid, Spain

Hardy Bowen
Level 1 28 Ord Street
West West Perth, WA, 6005, Australia

Non-U.S. Subsidiaries:

Berkeley Minera Espana, S.A. (1)
Carretera de Madrid 13-1a Santa Marta de Tormes
37900 Salamanca, Spain
Tel.: (34) 923193903
Fax: (34) 923191684
E-Mail: bme@berkeley.es
Uranium Mining Services
S.I.C.: 1094
N.A.I.C.S.: 212291
Clint McGhie *(CFO)*

Minera de Rio Alagon, S.L. (1)
Ctra de Madrid 13-1a Santa Marta de Tormes
37900 Salamanca, Spain
Tel.: (34) 923193903
Fax: (34) 923191684
E-Mail: minera@rioalagon.es
Uranium Exploration & Development Services
S.I.C.: 1094
N.A.I.C.S.: 212291
Ian Middleman *(Gen Mgr)*

BERKIM CONSTRUCTION INC.

120 Willowdale Ave
Toronto, ON, M2N 4Y2, Canada
Tel.: (416) 224-2550
Fax: (416) 224-2675
E-Mail: berkim@berkim.com
Web Site: www.berkim.com
Year Founded: 1966
Rev.: $27,108,683
Emp.: 30

Business Description:
Construction Services
S.I.C.: 1542
N.A.I.C.S.: 236220

Personnel:
David Kimmerle *(Pres)*
Walter Kimmerle *(CEO)*

BERKLEE LIMITED

265 285 Learmonth Road Wendouree
Wendouree, Victoria, Australia
Tel.: (61) 353381110
Fax: (61) 353381111
E-Mail: headoffice@berklee.com.au
Web Site: www.berklee.com.au
BER—(ASX)
Rev.: $5,289,769
Assets: $7,056,750
Liabilities: $719,915
Net Worth: $6,336,835
Earnings: ($3,067,169)
Emp.: 29
Fiscal Year-end: 06/30/13

Business Description:
Manufacture Of Automotive products
S.I.C.: 3714

Berklee Limited—(Continued)

N.A.I.C.S.: 336310
Personnel:
Brett Andrew Jones *(Mng Dir & Sec)*
Board of Directors:
Alan Ian Beckett
Grantly Martin Anderson
Brett Andrew Jones
Legal Counsel:
Madgwicks
Level 33 140 William Street
Melbourne, Australia

Subsidiaries:

Undacar Parts (NSW) Pty Ltd. **(1)**
44-46 Gibson Ave
PO Box 210
Padstow, NSW, 2211, Australia
Tel.: (61) 297073644
Fax: (61) 297963140
E-Mail: undansw@berklee.com.au
Emp.: 80
Automobile Parts Whslr
S.I.C.: 5013
N.A.I.C.S.: 423120
Reg Wales *(Mgr)*

Undacar Parts (QLD) Pty Ltd. **(1)**
24 Container St
Brisbane, QLD, 4173, Australia
Tel.: (61) 738903900
Fax: (61) 738903395
E-Mail: undaqld@berklee.com.au
Emp.: 4
Automobile Parts Whslr
S.I.C.: 5531
N.A.I.C.S.: 441310
Lyndal Schloss *(Mgr)*

Undacar Parts (TAS) Pty Ltd. **(1)**
107 Grove Rd
Glenorchy, TAS, 7010, Australia
Tel.: (61) 362731033
Fax: (61) 362735283
E-Mail: undatas@berklee.com.au
Emp.: 3
Automobile Parts Whslr
S.I.C.: 5013
N.A.I.C.S.: 423120
Mark Jessop *(Mgr)*

Undacar Parts (VIC) Pty Ltd. **(1)**
10 Comml Pl
E Keilor, Melbourne, VIC, 3033, Australia
Tel.: (61) 393362400
Fax: (61) 393362500
E-Mail: undavic@berklee.com.au
Emp.: 2
Automobile Parts Whslr
S.I.C.: 5531
N.A.I.C.S.: 441310
Sam Vella *(Mgr-Sls)*

Undacar Parts (WA) Pty Ltd. **(1)**
62 Division St
Welshpool, WA, 6106, Australia
Tel.: (61) 894516511
Fax: (61) 894584461
E-Mail: undawa@berklee.com.au
Emp.: 4
Automobile Parts Whslr
S.I.C.: 5013
N.A.I.C.S.: 441310
Jim Lloyd *(Mgr)*

BERKLEY RENEWABLES INC.

570 Granville Street Suite 900
Vancouver, BC, V6C 3P1, Canada
Tel.: (604) 682-3701
Fax: (604) 682-3600
E-Mail: info@berkleyrenewables.com
Web Site: www.berkleyresources.com
BKS—(CNSX OTC)
Sls.: $37,523
Assets: $1,845,213
Liabilities: $353,566
Net Worth: $1,491,647
Earnings: ($783,687)
Emp.: 25
Fiscal Year-end: 12/31/12
Business Description:
Oil & Gas Resource Development
S.I.C.: 1311
N.A.I.C.S.: 211111
Personnel:
Matt Wayrynen *(Pres & CEO)*
Pamela Saulnier *(CFO)*
Board of Directors:
Ronald Andrews
Tyrone Docherty
Lindsay Edward Gorrill
Jim O'Byrne
Matt Wayrynen
David Wolfin
Legal Counsel:
Borden Ladner Gervais
1200 Waterfront Centre 200 Burrard Street
PO Box 48600
Vancouver, BC, V7X 1T2, Canada
Bacchus Law Corporation
Suite 1820 Cathedral Place 925 West Georgia Street
Vancouver, BC, Canada
Transfer Agent:
Computershare
3rd Floor 510 Burrard Street
Vancouver, BC, Canada

BERKWOOD RESOURCES LTD.

6th Floor - 890 West Pender St
Vancouver, BC, V6C 1J9, Canada
Tel.: (604) 662-7455
Fax: (604) 683-1055
E-Mail: info@berkwoodresources.com
Web Site: www.berkwoodresources.com
BKR—(TSXV)
Assets: $6,977,661
Liabilities: $317,207
Net Worth: $6,660,454
Earnings: ($547,958)
Fiscal Year-end: 02/28/13
Business Description:
Mineral Exploration Services
S.I.C.: 1081
N.A.I.C.S.: 213114
Personnel:
Robert Brian Buchanan *(Pres & CEO)*
Shiraz Hussein *(CFO & Sec)*
Board of Directors:
Robert Brian Buchanan
George A. Gorzynski
Brian V. Hall
Shiraz Hussein
Legal Counsel:
Beadle Raven Business and Securities Lawyers
1090 West Georgia St Suite 600
Vancouver, BC, V6E 3V7, Canada
Transfer Agent:
Computershare
3rd Floor 510 Burrard Street
Vancouver, BC, Canada

BERLI JUCKER PUBLIC CO. LTD.

99 Soi Rubia Sukhumvit 42 Road
Klongtoey Prakanong, Bangkok, 10110, Thailand
Tel.: (66) 23671111
Fax: (66) 23671000
E-Mail: bjc@berlijucker.co.th
Web Site: www.bjc.co.th
BJC—(OTC THA)
Sales Range: $350-399.9 Million
Emp.: 600
Business Description:
Manufactures, Imports, Distributes & Markets Industrial, Glass, Engineering, Hospital, Photographic, Pharmaceutical, Consumer & Confectionary Products
S.I.C.: 3229
N.A.I.C.S.: 327212
Personnel:
Charoen Sirivadhanabhakdi *(Chm)*
Khunying Wanna Sirivadhanabhakdi *(Vice Chm)*
Prasert Maekwatana *(Mng Dir)*
Aswin Techajareonvikul *(CFO & Exec Dir)*
Lance George Stanford *(CIO & Pres-TCC Technology Company Ltd)*
Suvarn Valaisathien *(Member-Exec Bd)*
Santichai Dumpprasertkul *(Sec)*
Phornchai Athikhomkulchai *(Exec VP-Pkg Prods)*
Karn Chitaravimol *(Exec VP-Consumer Products)*
Peter E. Romhild *(Exec VP-Tech, Indus Products, Construction & Engrg Grp)*
Board of Directors:
Charoen Sirivadhanabhakdi
Sithichai Chaikriangkrai
Weerawong Chittmittrapap
Santichai Dumpprasertkul
Staporn Kavitanon
Thirasakdi Nathikanchanalab
Chaiyut Pilun-Owad
Atinant Sirivadhanabhakdi
Khunying Wanna Sirivadhanabhakdi
Panote Sirivadhanabhakdi
Thapana Sirivadhanabhakdi
Thapanee Sirivadhanabhakdi
Suvarn Valaisathien

Subsidiaries:

Berli Jucker Cellox Limited **(1)**
99 Berli Jucker Ho 10th Floor
Soi Rubia Sukhumvit 42 Rd, 10110
Bangkok, Thailand (100%)
Tel.: (66) 23671111
Fax: (66) 23671000
Web Site: www.bjc.co.th
Emp.: 100
Paper Mills
S.I.C.: 2621
N.A.I.C.S.: 322121
Khunvat Rojanagatanyoo *(Mng Dir)*

Berli Jucker Foods Limited **(1)**
99 Berli Jucker Ho 10th Floor
Soi Rubia Sukhumvit 42 Road, Bangkok, 10110, Thailand (100%)
Tel.: (66) 23671111
Fax: (66) 23671000
E-Mail: info@bjc.co.th
Web Site: www.bjc.co.th
Emp.: 1,000
Food Service Contractors
S.I.C.: 5812
N.A.I.C.S.: 722310
Pattaphong Iamsuro *(Mng Dir)*

Berli Jucker Logistics Limited **(1)**
99 Berli Jucker Ho 10th Floor
Soi Rubia Sukhumvit 42 Road, 10110
Bangkok, Thailand (100%)
Tel.: (66) 23671111
Fax: (66) 27122273
E-Mail: chamaips@bjclogistics.co.th
Web Site: www.bjclogistics.co.th
Emp.: 200
Engineering Services
S.I.C.: 8711
N.A.I.C.S.: 541330
Wichian Csonpatsi Om Sakor *(Pres)*

Berli Jucker Specialties Limited **(1)**
99 Berli Jucker Ho 10th Floor
Soi Rubia Sukhumvit 42 Road, 10110
Bangkok, Thailand (100%)
Tel.: (66) 23671111
Fax: (66) 023671000
Web Site: www.bjc.co.th
Emp.: 20
Basic Organic Chemical Mfr
S.I.C.: 2869
N.A.I.C.S.: 325199

BJC Engineering Company Limited **(1)**
99 Berli Jucker Ho 10th Fl
Soi Rubia Sukhumvit 42 Rd, 10110
Bangkok, Thailand (100%)
Tel.: (66) 23671111
Fax: (66) 23671000
E-Mail: sutatora@bjc.co.th
Web Site: www.bjcengineering.co.th
Emp.: 100
Engineering Services
S.I.C.: 8711
N.A.I.C.S.: 541330
Rene Oknovic *(Sr VP)*

BJC Marketing Company Limited **(1)**
99 Berli Jucker Ho 10th Floor
Soi Rubia Sukhumvit 42 Road, 10110
Bangkok, Thailand (100%)
Tel.: (66) 23671111
Fax: (66) 23671000
Web Site: www.bjchealthcare.co.th
Emp.: 100
Marketing Consulting Services
S.I.C.: 8742
N.A.I.C.S.: 541613

BJC Trading Company Limited **(1)**
99 Berli Jucker Ho 10th Floor
Soi Rubia Sukhumvit 42 Rd, 10110
Bangkok, Thailand (100%)
Tel.: (66) 23671111
Fax: (66) 23671111
Web Site: www.bjc.co.th
Emp.: 1,000
Specialty Trade Contractors
S.I.C.: 1799
N.A.I.C.S.: 238990

Rubia Industries Limited **(1)**
70 Moo 13 Poochaosamingprai Road
Bangyapraek Prapadaeng, Bangkok, Samut Prakarn, Thailand (99.7%)
Tel.: (66) 23859024
Fax: (66) 23859355
E-Mail: mantanan@bjp.co.th
Web Site: www.rubia.co.th
Emp.: 400
Soap & Detergent Mfr
S.I.C.: 2841
N.A.I.C.S.: 325611

Thai Glass Industries Ltd. **(1)**
15 Rajburana Road
Bangkok, 10140, Thailand
Tel.: (66) 24270060
Fax: (66) 24276603
Web Site: www.bjc.co.th
Emp.: 1,800
Glass Packaging; Domestic Glassware
S.I.C.: 3231
N.A.I.C.S.: 327215
Peter Emil Romhild *(Exec VP-Tech/Indus & Construction/Engrg Grp)*

Thai-Scandic Steel Company Limited **(1)**
7 I-5 Rd Maptaphut Ind Est
Amphur Muang, 21150 Rayong, Thailand
Tel.: (66) 38683070
Fax: (66) 38683065
E-Mail: info@thaiscandic.com
Web Site: www.thaiscandic.com
Emp.: 250
Steel Wire Drawing
S.I.C.: 3315
N.A.I.C.S.: 331222
Rene Okanovic *(Mng Dir)*

BERLINER SYNCHRON AG

Muhlenstrabe 52-54
12249 Berlin, Germany
Tel.: (49) 30 76787 0
Fax: (49) 30 76787 111
Web Site: www.berliner-synchron.de
B5S—(DEU)
Business Description:
Studios & Film Setting Services
S.I.C.: 7221
N.A.I.C.S.: 541921
Personnel:
Ingo Janssen *(Chm-Supervisory Bd)*
Karlheinz Lubojanski *(Chm-Exec Bd)*
Peter Stark *(Member-Exec Bd)*
Supervisory Board of Directors:
Ingo Janssen
Wolfram Ludecke

BERLINER VOLKSBANK EG

Budapester Strasse 35
10787 Berlin, Germany
Tel.: (49) 3030630
Fax: (49) 30634400

E-Mail: service@berliner-volksbank.de
Web Site: www.berliner-volksbank.de
Int. Income: $400,576,709
Assets: $13,262,728,472
Liabilities: $12,335,504,433
Net Worth: $927,224,039
Earnings: $20,936,107
Emp.: 2,089
Fiscal Year-end: 12/31/12
Business Description:
Banking Services
S.I.C.: 6029
N.A.I.C.S.: 522110
Personnel:
Stephan Schwarz *(Chm-Supervisory Bd)*
Holger Hatje *(Chm-Mgmt Bd & CEO)*
Stefan Gerdsmeier *(Member-Mgmt Bd)*
Carsten Jung *(Member-Mgmt Bd)*
Andreas Mertke *(Member-Mgmt Bd)*
Tanja Mueller-Ziegler *(Member-Mgmt Bd)*

BERLING S.A.
Al Krakowska 80a
05-552 Stefanowo, Poland
Tel.: (48) 22 727 84 97
Fax: (48) 22 736 28 99
E-Mail: berling@berling.pl
Web Site: www.berling.pl
Year Founded: 1993
BRG—(WAR)
Sales Range: $25-49.9 Million
Emp.: 30
Business Description:
Refrigeration Equipment Whslr
S.I.C.: 5078
N.A.I.C.S.: 423740
Personnel:
Hanna Berling *(Chm)*
Subsidiary:

Arkton sp. z o.o. (1)
Wilkowice ul Morkowska 36
64-100 Leszno, Poland
Tel.: (48) 65 525 28 42
Fax: (48) 65 525 28 35
E-Mail: info@arkton.pl
Web Site: www.arkton.pl
Emp.: 38
Refrigeration Equipment Mfr
S.I.C.: 3585
N.A.I.C.S.: 333415
Mark Worz *(Gen Mgr)*

BERMAX CONSTRUCTION
267 Rte De Saint Jean D Angely
16710 Saint-Yrieix-sur-Charente, Charente, France
Tel.: (33) 545951005
Web Site: www.bermax.com
Rev.: $10,400,000
Emp.: 13
Business Description:
Residential Construction Services
S.I.C.: 1521
N.A.I.C.S.: 236115
Personnel:
Damien Kohler *(Pres)*

BERMONT DEVELOPMENT SDN. BHD
Wisma 1 Alliance Unit 3A-B 4th Floor No 1
Lorong Kasawari 4B Taman Eng Ann, Kelang, 41150, Malaysia
Business Description:
Property Development Services
S.I.C.: 6519
N.A.I.C.S.: 531190
Personnel:
Wong Kiew *(Mng Dir)*
Cheok Chen Nam *(Mng Dir)*

Subsidiary:

Janavista Sdn. Bhd. (1)
Wisma Hwa Lian No 482 2nd & 3rd Floor
Jalan Zamrud 6 Taman Ko-op
70200 Seremban, Negeri Sembilan, Malaysia
Tel.: (60) 67635100
Fax: (60) 67651339
Property Development Services
S.I.C.: 6531
N.A.I.C.S.: 531390
Tan Wei Lian *(Mng Dir)*

BERMUDA MONETARY AUTHORITY
BMA House 43 Victoria Street
Hamilton, HM 12, Bermuda
Tel.: (441) 2955278
Fax: (441) 2927471
E-Mail: info@bma.bm
Web Site: www.bma.bm
Sales Range: $10-24.9 Million
Emp.: 170
Business Description:
Banking Services
S.I.C.: 6011
N.A.I.C.S.: 521110
Personnel:
Alan Cossar *(Chm)*
Darren Q. Johnston *(Deputy Chm)*
Mathew Elderfield *(CEO)*
Jeremy Cox *(Deputy CEO)*
Board of Directors:
Alan Cossar
Walter A. Bell
Charles G.R. Collis
Jeremy Cox
Anthony Joaquin
Darren Q. Johnston
Lynda Milligan-Whyte
A. Shaun Morris
E. Barclay Simmons
D. Munro Sutherland

BERMUDA NATIONAL LIMITED
(Name Changed to Somers Limited)

THE BERMUDA PRESS (HOLDINGS) LIMITED
PO Box HM 1025
HM DX Hamilton, Bermuda
Tel.: (441) 2955881
Fax: (441) 2959667
E-Mail: info@bermudapress.bm
Web Site: www.bermudapress.bm
BPH.BH—(BERM)
Sales Range: $25-49.9 Million
Business Description:
Newspaper Publishing & Commercial Printing
S.I.C.: 2711
N.A.I.C.S.: 511110
Personnel:
Christopher R. Whittle *(Pres)*
Marilyn A. Simmons *(Sec)*
Board of Directors:
Gavin R. Arton
Dudley R. Cottingham
Stephen R. Davidson
Gregory D. Haycock
H. Michael King
Carl H. Paiva
Aideen Ratteray Pryse
Muriel Richardson
Richard D. Spurling
Christopher E. Swan
Stephen W. Thomson
Christopher R. Whittle
Subsidiaries:

Bermuda Directories Limited (1)
13 Addendum Lane
Pembroke, Bermuda
Mailing Address:
PO Box HM 937
Hamilton, HM DX, Bermuda
Tel.: (441) 295 4600
Fax: (441) 295 3445
E-Mail: info@bermudadirectory.com
Web Site: www.bermudadirectory.com
Business Directory Publishing Services
S.I.C.: 2741
N.A.I.C.S.: 511140
Horst Augustinovic *(Mgr)*

The Bermuda Press Limited (1)
13 Addendum Ln Pitts Bay Rd
Hamilton, Pembroke, HM 07, Bermuda
Tel.: (441) 292 6100
Fax: (441) 2926788
E-Mail: info@bermudapress.bm
Web Site: www.bermudapress.bm
Emp.: 31
Commercial Printing Services
S.I.C.: 2759
N.A.I.C.S.: 323111
Bob Legere *(Mng Dir)*

CHAMELEON Print Express Ltd. (1)
34 Burnaby Hill
Hamilton, Pembroke, HM 11, Bermuda
Tel.: (441) 2965857
Fax: (441) 296 5860
E-Mail: info@cpx.bm
Web Site: www.cpx.bm
Emp.: 5
Commercial Printing Services
S.I.C.: 2759
N.A.I.C.S.: 323111
Jonathan Howes *(CEO)*

ENGRAVERS LIMITED (1)
13 Addendum Lane Pitts Bay Road
Pembroke, HM 07, Bermuda
Tel.: (441) 295 7118
Fax: (441) 292 9934
E-Mail: info@engravers.bm
Commercial Printing Services
S.I.C.: 2759
N.A.I.C.S.: 323111
Paget J. E. Wharton *(Mng Dir)*

Office Solutions Limited (1)
Mills Creek Industrial Park Pitts Bay Road
Pembroke, HM 08, Bermuda
Tel.: (441) 2922666
Fax: (441) 2923535
E-Mail: sales@officesolutions.bm
Web Site: www.officesolutions.bm
Emp.: 48
Office Equipments & Stationary Supplies Whslr
S.I.C.: 5044
N.A.I.C.S.: 423420
Robert G. Legere *(Gen Mgr)*

BERMUDA STOCK EXCHANGE
30 Victoria Street
PO Box HM 1369
Hamilton, HM FX, Bermuda
Tel.: (441) 292-7212
Fax: (441) 292-7619
E-Mail: info@bsx.com
Web Site: www.bsx.com
Year Founded: 1971
Emp.: 8
Business Description:
Stock Exchange Services
S.I.C.: 6231
N.A.I.C.S.: 523210
Personnel:
David A. Brown *(Chm)*
Greg Wojciechowski *(Pres & CEO)*
James McKirdy *(Chief Compliance Officer)*
Board of Directors:
David A. Brown
Leanne Golding
Tom Kloet

BERNARD ATHLETIC KNIT LTD.
2 Scarlett Road
Toronto, ON, M6N 4J6, Canada
Tel.: (416) 766-6151
Fax: (416) 766-7381
Toll Free: (888) 818-5648
E-Mail: aksales@athleticknit.com
Web Site: www.athleticknit.com
Year Founded: 1962
Rev.: $14,513,471
Emp.: 250
Business Description:
Sportswear & Accessories Mfr
S.I.C.: 3949
N.A.I.C.S.: 339920
Personnel:
Bernard Sliwin *(Pres)*

BERNARD KRIEF CONSULTANTS SA
112 Avenue Kleber
75116 Paris, France
Tel.: (33) 1 53 05 80 00
Fax: (33) 1 53 05 80 01
E-Mail: contact@bernard-krief.com
Web Site: www.krief-group.com
Business Description:
Financial Restructuring & Consulting Services
S.I.C.: 6211
N.A.I.C.S.: 523999
Personnel:
Jean-Claude Dutoit *(CEO)*
Subsidiary:

Dollfus Mieg & Cie, S.A. (1)
13 rue de Pfastatt
68200 Mulhouse, France FR
Tel.: (33) 3 89 32 4444
E-Mail: dmc@dmc.fr
Web Site: www.dmc.com
Emp.: 7,600
Mfr of Fashion Apparel Fabrics & Leisure Crafts
S.I.C.: 2299
N.A.I.C.S.: 314999
Demoulin Slancois *(Pres)*

U.S. Subsidiary:

The DMC Corporation (2)
Port Kearny Bldg 10F 77 S Hackensack Ave
Kearny, NJ 07032
Tel.: (973) 589-0606
Fax: (973) 589-3744
E-Mail: dmcusa@dmc.fr
Web Site: www.dmc-usa.com
Emp.: 25
Art Needlework, Threads, Accessories & Craft Products Import
S.I.C.: 5949
N.A.I.C.S.: 451130
Joseph McCade *(CEO)*

BERNARD LOISEAU SA
2 rue d'Argentine
Saulieu, 21210 Cote-d'Or, Burgundy, France
Tel.: (33) 380905353
Fax: (33) 380640892
E-Mail: contact@bernard-loiseau.com
Web Site: www.bernard-loiseau.com
ALDBL—(EUR)
Sales Range: $10-24.9 Million
Emp.: 110
Business Description:
Restaurant & Hotel Owner & Operator
S.I.C.: 5812
N.A.I.C.S.: 722511
Personnel:
Dominique Loiseau *(Chm & CEO)*

BERNARD MATTHEWS LTD.
Great Witchingham Hall
Norwich, Norfolk, NR9 5QD, United Kingdom
Tel.: (44) 1603872611
Fax: (44) 1603871118

Bernard Matthews Ltd.—(Continued)

E-Mail: consumer.relations@bernardmatthews.com
Web Site: www.bernardmatthews.com
Year Founded: 1950
Sales Range: $750-799.9 Million
Emp.: 6,231

Business Description:
Turkey Processor
Import Export
S.I.C.: 2015
N.A.I.C.S.: 311615

Personnel:
David J. Joll *(Chm)*
David M. Reger *(Sec)*

Legal Counsel:
Slaughter & May
35 Basinghall St
London, EC2V 5DB, United Kingdom
Tel.: (44) 207 600 1200
Telex: 883486
Fax: (44) 207 726 0038

Eversheds
Holland Court, The Close
Norwich, NR1 4DX, United Kingdom
Tel.: (44) 1603 272 727

Transfer Agent:
Independent Registrars Group Limited
Bourne House 34 Beckenham Rd
Beckenham, Kent, BR3 4TU, United Kingdom
Tel.: (44) 208 639 2000

Non-U.S. Subsidiaries:

Bernard Matthews Oldenburg GmbH (1)
Wilhelmshavener Heerstrasse 100
26125 Oldenburg, Germany
Tel.: (49) 441930950
Fax: (49) 4419309530
E-Mail: info@bernard-matthews.de
Web Site: www.bernard-matthews.de
Emp.: 150
Poultry Processor
S.I.C.: 2015
N.A.I.C.S.: 311615
Gunter Volker Wardeski *(Mng Dir)*

Saga Foods Baromfiipari Rt (1)
Soproni utca 15
H-9600 Sarvar, Hungary
Tel.: (36) 95336000
Fax: (36) 95336440
E-Mail: info@saga-foods.hu
Web Site: www.saga.hu
Emp.: 1,300
Poultry Processor
S.I.C.: 2015
N.A.I.C.S.: 311615
Henk Slagp *(Gen Mgr)*

BERNARDAUD S.A.

27 Ave Albert Thomas
87050 Limoges, France
Tel.: (33) 555105550
Fax: (33) 555105555
Web Site: www.bernardaud.fr
Year Founded: 1863

Business Description:
Porcelain Mfr
S.I.C.: 3999
N.A.I.C.S.: 327110

Personnel:
Michael Bernardaud *(Pres)*

BERNDORF AG

Leobersdorfer Str 26
Berndorf, 2560, Austria
Tel.: (43) 267282900
Fax: (43) 267283426
Web Site: www.berndorf.at
Sls.: $667,670,704
Assets: $679,755,272
Liabilities: $444,614,374
Net Worth: $235,140,899
Earnings: $31,862,498
Emp.: 2,364
Fiscal Year-end: 12/31/12

Business Description:
Tool & Equipment Mfr; Metal Processing Services
S.I.C.: 3545
N.A.I.C.S.: 333515

Personnel:
Norbert Zimmermann *(Chm-Supervisory Bd)*
Peter Pichler *(Chm-Mgmt Bd & CEO)*
Dietmar Muller *(CFO & Member-Mgmt Bd)*
Franz Viehboeck *(CTO & Member-Mgmt Bd)*
Franz Viehbock *(CTO)*

Supervisory Board of Directors:
Norbert Zimmermann
Rainer Koller
Michael Lokay
Thomas Riecker
Sonja Zimmermann

Subsidiaries:

Aichelin GmbH (1)
Fabrikgasse 3
A-2340 Modling, Austria
Tel.: (43) 2263 236 46, ext. 200
Fax: (43) 2236 222 291
Web Site: www.aichelin.at
Heat Treatment Products Mfr
S.I.C.: 3398
N.A.I.C.S.: 332811
Peter Schobesberger *(CEO)*

Berndorf Band GmbH (1)
Leobersdorfer Str 26
A-2560 Berndorf, Austria
Tel.: (43) 2672 8000
Fax: (43) 2672 84176
Web Site: www.berndorf-band.at
Process & Surface Technology
S.I.C.: 2843
N.A.I.C.S.: 325613

Subsidiary:

Berndorf Band Engineering GmbH (2)
Leobersdorfer Strasse 26
A-2560 Berndorf, Austria
Tel.: (43) 2672 800 466
Fax: (43) 2672 88760
Web Site: www.berndorf-engineering.at
Process & Surface Technology
S.I.C.: 2843
N.A.I.C.S.: 325613
Marianne Herzog *(Pres-Comml)*
Karl Morgenbesser *(Pres-Tech)*

U.S. Subsidiary:

Berndorf Belt Technology Inc. (2)
2525 Bath Rd
Elgin, IL 60124
Tel.: (847) 931-5264
Fax: (847) 931-5299
Web Site: www.berndorf-usa.com
Steel Belts & Continuous Steel Belt Conveyor Systems Mfr
S.I.C.: 3462
N.A.I.C.S.: 332111
David Brucki *(Mgr-Sls)*

Non-U.S. Subsidiary:

Beijing Berndorf Technology Development Co., Ltd. (2)
Room 215A No 9 Zhenxing Street
Changping Science & Tech Zone
Beijing, China
Tel.: (86) 10 80723902
Fax: (86) 10 80723802
E-Mail: sales@berndorf.com.cn
Web Site: www.berndorf.com.cn
Process & Surface Technology
S.I.C.: 2843
N.A.I.C.S.: 325613

Berndorf Metall- und Baderbau GmbH (1)
Leobersdorfer Str 26
A-2560 Berndorf, Austria
Tel.: (43) 2672 83640
Fax: (43) 2672 8364049
Web Site: www.berndorf-baederbau.com
Pool Construction Services
S.I.C.: 8711
N.A.I.C.S.: 541330

Non-U.S. Subsidiaries:

Berndorf Baderbau SK s.r.o. (2)
Bystrica ulica 1527
SK-966 81 Zarnovica, Slovakia
Tel.: (421) 45 6844780
Fax: (421) 45 6844781
E-Mail: adamec@berndorf.sk
Web Site: www.berndorf-baederbau.com
Stainless Steel Pool Mfr
S.I.C.: 3462
N.A.I.C.S.: 332111
Tibor Adamec *(CEO)*

Berndorf Baderbau Sp. z o.o (2)
Ul Zdrojowa 78
PL 43-384 Jaworze, Poland
Tel.: (48) 3382 89700
Fax: (48) 3382 89701
E-Mail: biuro@berndorf.pl
Web Site: www.berndorf.pl
Stainless Steel Pool Mfr
S.I.C.: 3462
N.A.I.C.S.: 332111
Marek Wrzal *(CEO)*

Berndorf Baderbau srl (2)
Str 22 Decembrie nr 28
RO-430314 Baia Mare, Romania
Tel.: (40) 268 418298
Fax: (40) 262 211471
E-Mail: vlad.dizmacsek@berndorf-baderbau.ro
Stainless Steel Pool Mfr
S.I.C.: 3462
N.A.I.C.S.: 332111
Peter-Vlad Dizmacsek *(Mgr-Sls)*

Berndorf Baderbau s.r.o. (2)
Bystrice 1312
CZ-739 95 Bystrice, Czech Republic
Tel.: (420) 558 362389
Fax: (420) 558 326387
E-Mail: r.cieslar@berndorf-bazeny.cz
Stainless Steel Pool Mfr
S.I.C.: 3462
N.A.I.C.S.: 332111
Rudolf Cieslar *(CEO)*

Berndorf Metall- und Baderbau AG (2)
Gewerbestrasse 8
CH-8212 Neuhausen, Switzerland
Tel.: (41) 52674 0570
Fax: (41) 52674 0579
E-Mail: office@berndorf-baederbaus.com
Stainless Steel Pool Mfr
S.I.C.: 3462
N.A.I.C.S.: 332111
Urs Wittwer *(Reg Mgr-Sls)*

Berndorf Metallwaren GmbH (2)
Wittestrasse 24
D-13509 Berlin, Germany
Tel.: (49) 30 432 2072
Fax: (49) 30 432 2060
E-Mail: office@berndorf-baederbau.com
Stainless Steel Products & Swimming Pools Mfr
S.I.C.: 3462
N.A.I.C.S.: 332111

Joint Ventures:

Joh. Pengg AG (1)
Nr 35
Thorl, 8621 Leoben, Austria (50%)
Tel.: (43) 38615090
Fax: (43) 38612318
E-Mail: office@wire-pengg.com
Web Site: www.wire-pengg.com
Emp.: 200
Other Communication & Energy Wire Mfr
S.I.C.: 3357
N.A.I.C.S.: 335929
Alexander Philip *(Mng Dir)*

Subsidiary:

Penng Austria GmbH (2)
A-8621
Thorl, Austria
Tel.: (43) 3861 5090
Fax: (43) 3861 2318
Steel Products Mfr
S.I.C.: 3462
N.A.I.C.S.: 332111
Claus Oresnik *(Mng Dir)*
Alexander Phillipp *(Mng Dir)*

Non-U.S. Subsidiary:

Pengg Drat s.r.o. (2)
Beethovenova 1269
43013 Chomutov, Czech Republic
Tel.: (420) 474 332 050
Fax: (420) 474 332 050
Wire Product Mfr
S.I.C.: 3496
N.A.I.C.S.: 332618

Non-U.S. Joint Venture:

Peng Usha Martin Pvt. Ltd. (2)
Tatisilwai
Ranchi, 835103, India
Tel.: (91) 651 3053900
Fax: (91) 651 3054100
Wire Products Mfr
S.I.C.: 3496
N.A.I.C.S.: 332618

Lumpi-Berndorf Draht- und Seilwerk GmbH (1)
Binderlandweg 7
A-4030 Linz, Austria
Tel.: (43) 732 381 2710
Fax: (43) 732 383 84820
E-Mail: office@lumpi-berndorf.at
Web Site: www.lumpi-berndorf.at
Wire & Cable Mfr
S.I.C.: 3496
N.A.I.C.S.: 332618
Ralf Gebeshuber *(Plant Mgr)*

PC Electric GmbH (1)
Diesseits 145
A-4973 Saint Martin, Austria
Tel.: (43) 7751 61220
Fax: (43) 7751 6969
E-Mail: office@pcelectric.at
Web Site: www.pcelectric.at
Electric Products Mfr
S.I.C.: 3699
N.A.I.C.S.: 335999

Non-U.S. Subsidiaries:

HASCO Hasenclever GmbH & Co. KG (1)
Im Wiesental 77
D-58513 Ludenscheid, Germany
Tel.: (49) 2351 9570
Fax: (49) 2351 957237
E-Mail: info@hasco.com
Web Site: www.hasco.de
Tool & Mould Mfr
S.I.C.: 3541
N.A.I.C.S.: 333517

Hueck Rheinische GmbH (1)
Helmholtzstr 9
D-41747 Viersen, Germany
Tel.: (49) 2162 946940
Fax: (49) 2162 9469451
Web Site: www.hueck-rheinische.com
Process & Surface Technology
S.I.C.: 2843
N.A.I.C.S.: 325613

Silica Verfahrenstechnik GmbH (1)
Wittestrasse 24
D-13509 Berlin, Germany
Tel.: (49) 30 435 735
Fax: (49) 30 435 73300
E-Mail: info@silica.de
Web Site: www.silica.de
Sales Range: $10-24.9 Million
Emp.: 50
Engineering Services
S.I.C.: 8711
N.A.I.C.S.: 541330

BERNECKER & RAINER INDUSTRIE-ELEKTRONIK GES.M.B.H.

B & R St 1
Eggelsberg, 5142, Austria
Tel.: (43) 774865860
Fax: (43) 7748658626
E-Mail: office@br-automation.com
Web Site: www.br-automation.com
Year Founded: 1979
Sales Range: $125-149.9 Million
Emp.: 2,700

Business Description:
Mfr. of Video Interface Products
S.I.C.: 7812
N.A.I.C.S.: 512110
Personnel:
Hans Wilmmer *(Gen Mgr)*

U.S. Subsidiary:

B&R Industrial Automation Corp. **(1)**
1250 Northmeadow Pkwy Ste 100
Roswell, GA 30076-3896 DE
Tel.: (770) 772-0400 (100%)
Fax: (770) 772-0243
E-Mail: office.us@br-automation.com
Web Site: www.br-automation.com
Sls.: $2,600,000
Emp.: 30
Sale of Programmable Controllers, Industrial Computers, Interface Products & Industrial Video Terminals
Import Export
S.I.C.: 5084
N.A.I.C.S.: 423830
Mark Osterthe *(Pres)*

BERNER KANTONALBANK AG

(d/b/a BEKB-BCBE)
Bundesplatz 8
3001 Bern, Switzerland
Tel.: (41) 316661111
Fax: (41) 316666040
E-Mail: bekb@bekb.ch
Web Site: www.bekb.ch
BEKN—(SWX)
Sales Range: $500-549.9 Million
Emp.: 1,450
Business Description:
Banking Services
S.I.C.: 6029
N.A.I.C.S.: 522110
Personnel:
Jurg Rieben *(Chm)*
Hanspeter Ruefenacht *(CEO)*
Alois Scharli *(Member-Exec Bd & CFO)*
Stefan Gerber *(Member-Exec Bd)*
Johannes Hopf *(Member-Exec Bd)*
Board of Directors:
Jurg Rieben
Kathrin Anderegg-Dietrich
Daniel Bloch
Rudolf Grunig
Thomas Rufer
Rudolf Stampfli
Rudolf Wehrli

BERNER OY

Etelaranta 4B
00130 Helsinki, Finland
Tel.: (358) 2079100
Fax: (358) 207914500
E-Mail: info@berner.fi
Web Site: www.berner.fi
Year Founded: 1883
Sls.: $44,485,559,038
Assets: $20,244,064,251
Liabilities: $5,571,912,048
Net Worth: $14,672,152,203
Earnings: $1,823,391,799
Emp.: 515
Fiscal Year-end: 12/31/12
Business Description:
Chemical Specialties, Lubricating Oils, Car Care Chemicals, Crop Protection Products & Household Chemicals Importer, Mfr & Exporter
Import Export
S.I.C.: 2992
N.A.I.C.S.: 324191
Personnel:
Peter Berner *(Chm)*
Hannes Berner *(Vice Chm)*
George Berner *(Mng Dir)*
Nicolas Berner *(CFO)*
Michael Berner *(Deputy Mng Dir)*
Marja Vanhanen *(Sec)*
Board of Directors:
Peter Berner
George Berner
Hannes Berner
Klaus Berner
Michael Berner
Antti Korpiniemi
Kirsi-Maija Koskelo
Antti Rinta-Harri

Subsidiaries:

Auto-Berner Kouvola **(1)**
Kymenlaaksontie 1
45100 Kouvola, Finland (100%)
Tel.: (358) 20791011
Fax: (358) 207914102
E-Mail: etunimi.sukunimi@berner.fi
Web Site: www.autoberner.fi
Emp.: 30
Automobile Dealer
S.I.C.: 3711
N.A.I.C.S.: 336111
Harri Salminen *(CEO)*

Auto-Berner **(1)**
Toikansuontie 11
53500 Lappeenranta, Finland (100%)
Tel.: (358) 54515215
E-Mail: info@autoberner.com
Web Site: www.autoberner.fi
Emp.: 32
Automobiles
S.I.C.: 3711
N.A.I.C.S.: 336111

Berner Ltd. Health And Research **(1)**
Sahaajankatu 24
PO Box 15
00880 Helsinki, 00131, Finland (100%)
Tel.: (358) 9134511
Fax: (358) 0207914241
Web Site: www.eng.berner.fi/contact
Emp.: 50
Wholesaler of Hospital Supplies
S.I.C.: 8062
N.A.I.C.S.: 622110
Michael Berner *(Dir-Health)*

Non-U.S. Subsidiary:

Berner Eesti Oy **(1)**
Tulika 19
10613 Tallinn, Estonia (100%)
Tel.: (372) 6505040
Fax: (372) 6505060
E-Mail: mail@berner.ee
Web Site: www.berner.ee
Emp.: 7
S.I.C.: 2992
N.A.I.C.S.: 324191
Toomas Roigas *(Mng Dir)*

BERNER SE

Bernerstrasse 6
74653 Kunzelsau, Germany
Tel.: (49) 7940 121 0
E-Mail: info@berner-group.com
Web Site: www.berner-group.com
Sales Range: $1-4.9 Billion
Emp.: 9,050
Business Description:
Holding Company
S.I.C.: 6719
N.A.I.C.S.: 551112
Personnel:
Lothar Aulich *(Member-Exec Bd)*
Christian A.W. Berner *(Member-Exec Bd)*

Subsidiaries:

Albert Berner Deutschland GmbH **(1)**
Bernerstrasse 4
D-74653 Kunzelsau, Germany
Tel.: (49) 79 40 12 10
Fax: (49) 79 40 12 13 00
E-Mail: info@berner.de
Web Site: www.berner.de
Tool Distr
S.I.C.: 5072
N.A.I.C.S.: 423710
Ulf Loesenbeck *(Mng Dir)*

BTI Befestigungstechnik GmbH & Co. KG **(1)**
Salzstrasse 51
D-74653 Ingelfingen, Germany
Tel.: (49) 79 40 14 10
Fax: (49) 79 40 14 164
E-Mail: info@bti.de
Web Site: www.bti.de
Sales Range: $250-299.9 Million
Construction Equipment Distr
S.I.C.: 5039
N.A.I.C.S.: 423390
Jurgen Dietz *(Mng Dir)*

Caramba Holding GmbH **(1)**
Bernerstrasse 6
D-74653 Kunzelsau, Germany
Tel.: (49) 79 40 12 11 66 91
Fax: (49) 79 40 12 11 16 91
E-Mail: info@caramba.eu
Web Site: www.caramba.eu
Sales Range: $150-199.9 Million
Chemical Mfr
S.I.C.: 2899
N.A.I.C.S.: 325998

Subsidiary:

Caramba Chemie GmbH & Co. KG **(2)**
Wanheimer Strasse 334-336
D-47055 Duisburg, Germany
Tel.: (49) 20 37 78 601
Fax: (49) 20 37 78 61 96
E-Mail: info@caramba.de
Web Site: www.caramba.eu
Chemical Mfr
S.I.C.: 2899
N.A.I.C.S.: 325998

Subsidiaries:

Ambratec GmbH **(3)**
Carl-Zeiss-Strasse 43
55129 Mainz, Germany
Tel.: (49) 6131583930
Fax: (49) 61315839334
E-Mail: info@ambratec.de
Web Site: www.ambratec.de
Emp.: 100
Chemical & Allied Products Merchant Whslr
S.I.C.: 5169
N.A.I.C.S.: 424690
Wolfgang Schiller *(Mng Dir)*

Matecra GmbH **(3)**
Daimlerstrasse 29
D-89564 Nattheim, Germany
Tel.: (49) 73 21 97 770
Fax: (49) 73 21 97 77 27
E-Mail: info@matecra.de
Web Site: www.matecra.de
Chemical Mfr
S.I.C.: 2899
N.A.I.C.S.: 325998
Georg Rossler, *(Mng Dir)*

Non-U.S. Subsidiary:

Automotive Cleaning Chemicals Ltd. **(3)**
Showground Road
Bridgwater, TA6 6AJ, United Kingdom
Tel.: (44) 1278431310
Fax: (44) 1278413323
E-Mail: info@acc-limited.co.uk
Web Site: www.acc-limited.co.uk
Emp.: 6
Inorganic Chemical Mfr
S.I.C.: 2819
N.A.I.C.S.: 325180
Chris Waller *(Mng Dir)*

BERNHARD SCHULTE SHIPMANAGEMENT (CYPRUS) LTD.

(Formerly Hanseatic Shipping Company Ltd.)
Hanseatic House 111 Spyrou Araouzou St
3036 Limassol, Cyprus
Mailing Address:
PO Box 50127
CY 3601 Limassol, Cyprus
Tel.: (357) 25846400
Fax: (357) 25745245
E-Mail: cy-sdc-man@bs-shipmanagement.com
Web Site: www.bh-shipmanagement.com
Year Founded: 1972
Emp.: 17,000
Business Description:
Ship Management Services
S.I.C.: 4499
N.A.I.C.S.: 488330
Personnel:
Rajaish Bajpaee *(CEO)*
Norbert Aschmann *(Deputy CEO)*
Tobias Pinker *(CFO)*
David Furnival *(COO)*

Non-U.S. Subsidiary:

Bernhard Schulte Shipmanagement (Singapore) Pte. Ltd., **(1)**
(Formerly Hanseatic Shipping Co. (Singapore) Pte Ltd)
152 Beach Rd #32-00 Gateway East
Singapore, 189721, Singapore
Tel.: (65) 62722220
Fax: (65) 62724404
E-Mail: hstore@pacific.net.sg
Web Site: www.bs-shipmanagement.com
Emp.: 29
Ship Management, Logistics & Customer Services Operations
S.I.C.: 8741
N.A.I.C.S.: 561110
Sandip Mirchandani *(Gen Mgr)*

BERNINA SCHWEIZ AG

Gubelstrasse 39
8050 Zurich, Oerlikon, Switzerland
Tel.: (41) 442861060
Fax: (41) 442861065
E-Mail: info@bernina.ch
Web Site: www.bernina.ch
Emp.: 1,000
Business Description:
Mfr of Household Sewing Machines, Quilting Machines & Embroidery Machines
Import Export
S.I.C.: 3639
N.A.I.C.S.: 335228
Personnel:
Claute Dreyer *(CEO)*
Rols Hugelshofer *(CFO)*
Esther Diener *(Sec)*

Subsidiary:

Bernina International AG **(1)**
Seestrasse 161
CH 8266 Steckborn, Switzerland (100%)
Tel.: (41) 527621111
Fax: (41) 527621475
E-Mail: info@bernina.com
Web Site: www.bernina.com
Emp.: 340
Mfr of Sewing Machines
S.I.C.: 3999
N.A.I.C.S.: 339999
Claude Dreyer *(CEO)*

U.S. Subsidiary:

Bernina of America Inc. **(1)**
3702 Prairie Lake Ct
Aurora, IL 60504 IL
Tel.: (630) 978-2500
Fax: (630) 978-8214
Web Site: www.berninausa.com
Sales Range: $100-124.9 Million
Emp.: 150
Sewing Machines & Related Items
Import
S.I.C.: 2499
N.A.I.C.S.: 321999
Paul Ashworth *(Pres)*

BERRY BROS. & RUDD LIMITED

3 St James's Street
London, SW1A 1EG, United Kingdom
Tel.: (44) 2073969666
E-Mail: bbr@bbr.com

Berry Bros. & Rudd Limited—(Continued)

Web Site: www.bbr.com
Year Founded: 1698
Sales Range: $300-349.9 Million
Emp.: 200
Business Description:
Wine & Spirits Retailer
S.I.C.: 5921
N.A.I.C.S.: 445310
Personnel:
Hugh Sturges *(Mng Dir)*

BERRY ONLY INC.
(Name Changed to DelMar Pharmaceuticals, Inc.)

BERTAM ALLIANCE BERHAD
Brem House Level 3 Crystal Crown Hotel 12 Lorong Utara A
Of Jalan Utara, 46200 Petaling Jaya, Selangor Darul Ehsan, Malaysia
Tel.: (60) 379587288
Fax: (60) 379554520
Web Site: www.bertamalliance.com
BERTAM—(KLS)
Rev.: $13,543,594
Assets: $75,170,046
Liabilities: $19,603,245
Net Worth: $55,566,801
Earnings: $3,833,852
Fiscal Year-end: 12/31/12
Business Description:
Property Development Services
S.I.C.: 6531
N.A.I.C.S.: 531311
Personnel:
Ai Tong Tan *(Mng Dir)*
Hui Fang Kuan *(Co-Sec)*
Wai Foong Wong *(Co-Sec)*
Board of Directors:
Foo Ching Loong
Hui Giok Khoo
Yew Hwa Low
Ai Tong Tan
Hamdan Yahya

Subsidiaries:

Bertam Development Sdn. Bhd. **(1)**
Brem House Level 3A Crystal Crown Hotel No 12
Lorong Utara A Off Jalan Utara, Petaling Jaya, Selangor, 46200, Malaysia
Tel.: (60) 379587288
Fax: (60) 379585033
Emp.: 15
Property Development Services
S.I.C.: 6531
N.A.I.C.S.: 531312

Subsidiary:

Antara Megah Sdn. Bhd. **(2)**
3rd Floor Brem House Crystal Crown Hotel No 12 Lorong Utara A
Off Jalan Utara, Petaling Jaya, Selangor, 46200, Malaysia
Tel.: (60) 3 79587288
Fax: (60) 3 79554520
Property Development Services
S.I.C.: 6531
N.A.I.C.S.: 531312
Tan Ai Tong *(Mng Dir)*

UH Industries & Development Sdn. Bhd. **(1)**
Brem House Level 3A Crystal Crown Hotel No 12
Lorong Utara A Off Jalan Utara, Petaling Jaya, Selangor, 46200, Malaysia
Tel.: (60) 379587288
Fax: (60) 379554520
Emp.: 30
Property Development Services
S.I.C.: 6531
N.A.I.C.S.: 531312
Tan Tai Tong *(Mng Dir)*

BERTEL O. STEEN AS
Solheimveien 7
1473 Lorenskog, Norway
Mailing Address:
Postboks 52
1471 Lorenskog, Norway
Tel.: (47) 67 92 60 00
Fax: (47) 6790 53 10
Web Site: www.bos.no
Sales Range: $1-4.9 Billion
Business Description:
Holding Company
S.I.C.: 6719
N.A.I.C.S.: 551112
Personnel:
Inge Ketil Hansen *(Chm)*

Subsidiary:

Viking Fottoy A/S **(1)**
Luhrtoppen 2
PO Box 143
N-1471 Lorenskog, Norway NO
Tel.: (47) 22072400
Fax: (47) 22072499
E-Mail: viking@vikingfootwear.com
Web Site: www.vikingfootwear.com
Sales Range: $25-49.9 Million
Outdoor Footwear Mfr
S.I.C.: 2389
N.A.I.C.S.: 316210
Leif Holst-Liaeker *(Mng Dir)*

Non-U.S. Subsidiaries:

Viking Footwear A/S **(2)**
Jernholmen 38 2 sal
DK 2650 Hvidovre, Denmark (100%)
Tel.: (45) 72118180
Fax: (45) 72118182
E-Mail: vikingdk@vikingfootwear.com
Web Site: www.vikingfootwear.com
Emp.: 6
Outdoor Footwear Mfr
S.I.C.: 2389
N.A.I.C.S.: 316210

Viking Footwear AB **(2)**
Gamla Almedalsvagen 6
412 63 Gothenburg, Sweden (100%)
Tel.: (46) 31985090
Fax: (46) 31985091
E-Mail: vikingsv@vikingfootwear.com
Web Site: www.vikingfootwear.com
Emp.: 5
Outdoor Footwear Mfr
S.I.C.: 2389
N.A.I.C.S.: 316210
Stian Strom *(Gen Mgr)*

Viking Jalkineet Oy **(2)**
Pakkalankuja 6
SF-01510 Vantaa, Finland FI (100%)
Tel.: (358) 98386180
Fax: (358) 983861820
E-Mail: vikingfi@vikingfootwear.com
Web Site: www.vikingfootwear.com
Emp.: 8
Outdoor Footwear Mfr
S.I.C.: 2389
N.A.I.C.S.: 316210
Tapio Valkonen *(Mng Dir)*

BERTELSMANN SE & CO. KGAA
Carl-Bertelsmann-Strasse 270
33311 Gutersloh, Germany
Tel.: (49) 5241800
Fax: (49) 5241809662
E-Mail: info@bertelsmann.de
Web Site: www.bertelsmann.de
Year Founded: 1835
Rev.: $21,626,221,050
Assets: $36,245,627,250
Liabilities: $28,062,259,820
Net Worth: $8,183,367,430
Earnings: $833,279,230
Emp.: 100,626
Fiscal Year-end: 12/31/12
Business Description:
Holding Company; Magazine, Book & Newspaper Publisher; Television Broadcasting; Film Production; Direct Marketing Services
S.I.C.: 6719
N.A.I.C.S.: 551112
Personnel:
Christoph Mohn *(Chm-Supervisory Bd)*
Thomas Rabe *(Chm-Exec Bd & CEO)*
Anke Schaferkordt *(Co-CEO-RTL Grp & Member-Exec Bd)*
Guillaume de Posch *(Co-CEO-RTL Grp & Member-Exec Bd)*
Judith Hartmann *(CFO & Member-Exec Bd)*
Nicolas de Tavernost *(Chm/CEO-M6 & Member-Exec Bd)*
Markus Dohle *(Chm/CEO-Random House & Member-Exec Bd)*
Dame Gail Rebuck *(Chm/CEO-Random House Grp & Member-Exec Bd)*
Achim Berg *(CEO-Arvato AG & Member-Exec Bd)*
Fernando Carro *(CEO-Club & Direct Mktg & Member-Exec Bd)*
Julia Jakel *(CEO-Gruner + Jahr AG & Member-Exec Bd)*
Annabelle Yu Long *(CEO-Bertelsmann China Corporate Center & Member-Exec Bd)*
Immanuel Hermreck *(Member-Exec Bd & Exec VP-HR)*
Karin Schlautmann *(Member-Exec Bd & Exec VP-Corp Comm)*
Roger Schweitzer *(Exec VP-Treasury & Fin)*
Henrik Pahls *(Sr VP-Fin & IR)*
Supervisory Board of Directors:
Christoph Mohn
Werner J. Bauer
Wulf H. Bernotat
Kai Brettmann
Helmut Gettkant
Ian Hudson
Horst Keil
Karl-Ludwig Kley
Joachim Milberg
Brigitte Mohn
Liz Mohn
Hartmut Ostrowski
Hans Dieter Potsch
Kasper Rorstedt
Lars Rebien Sorensen
Christiane Sussieck
Bodo Uebber

Divisions:

arvato AG **(1)**
Carl Bertelsmann Strasse 270
D 33311 Gutersloh, Germany De
Tel.: (49) 5241800
Fax: (49) 5241803315
E-Mail: info@bertelsmann.de
Web Site: www.arvato.com
Sales Range: $5-14.9 Billion
Emp.: 63,985
Media & Communications Services
S.I.C.: 7389
N.A.I.C.S.: 561499
Achim Berg *(Chm-Mgmt Bd & CEO)*
Ulrich Cordes *(Member-Exec Bd & CFO)*
Matthias Mierisch *(Chm/CEO-Intl Bus Process Outsourcing-UK & Ireland)*
Ralf Bierfischer *(Member-Exec Bd)*
Hans-Peter Hulskotter *(Member-Exec Bd-Digital Svcs)*
Herve Milcent *(Member-Exec Bd)*
Markus Schmedtmann *(Member-Exec Bd)*
Michael Weinreich *(Member-Exec Bd)*

DirectGroup Bertelsmann **(1)**
Carl-Bertelsmann-Strasse
33311 Gutersloh, Germany
Tel.: (49) 5241800
Fax: (49) 52418041840
E-Mail: info@bertelsmann.de
Web Site: www.directgroup-bertelsmann.com
Sales Range: $1-4.9 Billion
Emp.: 8,485
Direct Marketing Services
S.I.C.: 5963
N.A.I.C.S.: 454390
Gerd Buhrig *(Exec VP)*

Subsidiary:

Der Club GmbH **(2)**
Carl-Bertelsmann-Strasse
D-33300 Gutersloh, Germany De
Tel.: (49) 1805415233 (100%)
Fax: (49) 1805415700
E-Mail: service@derclub.de
Web Site: www.derclub.de
Book & Media Mail-Order Services
S.I.C.: 5961
N.A.I.C.S.: 454113
Bernd Schroder *(Mng Dir)*

Non-U.S. Subsidiaries:

Book Club Associates Ltd. **(2)**
Hargreaves Rd Groundwell Industrial Estate
Swindon, Wiltshire, SN25 5BG, United Kingdom UK
Tel.: (44) 1793723547 (100%)
Fax: (44) 2077606501
E-Mail: media@bca.co.uk
Web Site: www.bca.co.uk
Sls.: $165,200,000
Emp.: 1,000
Mail Order Book Retailer
S.I.C.: 5961
N.A.I.C.S.: 454113
Claire Rose *(Dir-Product)*

Circulo de Lectores S.A. **(2)**
Travessera De Gracia 47 49
Barcelona, Catalunya, 8021, Spain (100%)
Tel.: (34) 933660100
Fax: (34) 932002220
E-Mail: atencion-socios@circulo.es
Web Site: www.circulodelectores.com
Emp.: 500
Book Club
S.I.C.: 5961
N.A.I.C.S.: 454113
Hoquin Avars *(Mng Dir)*

Doubleday Australia Pty Ltd **(2)**
Unit F33 16 Mars Road
Lane Cove, NSW, 2066, Australia (100%)
Mailing Address:
PO Box 4040
Lane Cove, NSW, 1602, Australia
Tel.: (61) 299111400
Telex: 120901 Dubday
Fax: (61) 294276973
E-Mail: memberservice@bookandmusicclubs.com.au
Web Site: www.doubleday.com.au
Emp.: 300
Book Club Publications
S.I.C.: 2731
N.A.I.C.S.: 511130

Non-U.S. Subsidiary:

Doubleday New Zealand Ltd. **(3)**
1 Parkway Dr Mairangi Bay
Industrial Estate
Auckland, 9, New Zealand (100%)
Tel.: (64) 9 479 4846
Fax: (64) 9 479 6565
Web Site: www.doubleday.co.nz
Book Club Publishing
S.I.C.: 2731
N.A.I.C.S.: 511130

France Loisirs SAS **(2)**
123 blvd. de Grenelle
F-75015 Paris, France (50%)
Tel.: (33) 891705706
Web Site: www.franceloisirs.com
Book Club
S.I.C.: 5961
N.A.I.C.S.: 454113

Non-U.S. Joint Venture:

Mondolibri S.p.A. **(2)**
Via Lampedusa 13
20141 Milan, Italy
Tel.: (39) 02844011
Fax: (39) 0289546603
Web Site: www.mondolibri.it
Emp.: 130
Book Publisher, Marketer & Distr; Owned 50% by Bertelsmann AG & 50% by Fininvest S.p.A.
S.I.C.: 2731
N.A.I.C.S.: 511130

Gruner + Jahr AG & Co. KG (1)
Am Baumwall 11
20459 Hamburg, Germany De
Mailing Address: (74.9%)
Postfach 30 20 40
20459 Hamburg, Germany
Tel.: (49) 4037030
Telex: 21952-13
Fax: (49) 4037036000
E-Mail: unternehmenskommunikation@guj.de
Web Site: www.guj.de
Rev.: $2,986,300,451
Assets: $2,223,436,681
Liabilities: $1,751,807,368
Net Worth: $471,629,313
Earnings: ($15,256,145)
Emp.: 11,585
Fiscal Year-end: 12/31/12
Magazine Publisher
S.I.C.: 2721
N.A.I.C.S.: 511120
Thomas Rabe *(Chm-Supervisory Bd)*
Winfried Steeger *(Deputy Chm-Supervisory Bd)*
Julia Jakel *(CEO & Member-Exec Bd)*
Udo Stalleicken *(CFO)*
Oliver Radtke *(COO & Member-Exec Bd)*
Stan Sugarman *(Chief Digital Officer & Chief Sls Officer)*
Stephan Schafer *(Chief Product Officer & Member-Exec Bd)*
Susanne Hacker *(Comm Officer)*
Isabelle Haesler *(Press Officer)*
Rolf Heinz *(Pres-G+J International-Europe & CEO-Prisma Media)*

Subsidiary:

G+J Electronic Media Sales GmbH (2)
Stubbenhuk 5
20459 Hamburg, Germany
Mailing Address:
Brieffach 10
20444 Hamburg, Germany
Tel.: (49) 4037037373
Fax: (49) 4037035734
E-Mail: info@ems.guj.de
Web Site: www.ems.guj.de
Emp.: 70
Mobile Advertising Network
S.I.C.: 7319
N.A.I.C.S.: 541890
Irene Vollmer *(Head-Tech)*

U.S. Subsidiaries:

Brown Printing Company (2)
1500 Broadway Ste 505
New York, NY 10036
Tel.: (212) 782-7800
Toll Free: (866) 323-9336
E-Mail: contact.us@bpc.com
Web Site: www.bpc.com
Commercial Printing
S.I.C.: 2759
N.A.I.C.S.: 323111
Mike Amundson *(Pres & CEO)*
Gregg Black *(Exec VP-HR)*
Larry Hawkey *(Exec VP-Publications)*

Divisions:

Brown Printing Company (3)
2300 Brown Ave
Waseca, MN 56093-4533 (74.9%)
Tel.: (507) 835-2410
Fax: (507) 835-0420
Web Site: www.brownprinting.com
Sls.: $300,000,000
Emp.: 1,300
Magazine & Catalog Printing, Offset & Gravure
S.I.C.: 2721
N.A.I.C.S.: 511120
Larry Hawkey *(Sr VP-Sls & Mktg)*

Brown Printing East (3)
668 Gravel Pike
East Greenville, PA 18041-2133 (100%)
Tel.: (215) 679-4451
Fax: (215) 679-3887
Web Site: www.bpc.com
Emp.: 650
Offset Printing
S.I.C.: 2759
N.A.I.C.S.: 323111
Volker Petersen *(CEO & Pres)*

Non-U.S. Subsidiaries:

G+J Espana S.A. (2)
Albasanz 15
28037 Madrid, Spain (74.9%)
Tel.: (34) 914369800
Telex: 43419
Fax: (34) 915751392
E-Mail: cperez@gyj.es
Web Site: www.guj.es
Publishing
S.I.C.: 2731
N.A.I.C.S.: 511130
Axel Ganz *(Mng Dir)*
Markus Kley *(COO)*

Gruner + Jahr AG (Schweiz) (2)
Zeltweg 15
PO Box 1672
8032 Zurich, Switzerland (100%)
Tel.: (41) 442697070
Telex: 58844
Fax: (41) 442697071
E-Mail: guj.schweiz@guj.de
Web Site: www.guj.de
Emp.: 4
Magazine Advertising & Publishing
S.I.C.: 2721
N.A.I.C.S.: 511120

Non-U.S. Joint Venture:

Gruner + Jahr Mondadori S.p.A. (2)
Corso Monforte 54
I 20122 Milan, Italy
Tel.: (39) 02762101
Fax: (39) 0276013439
E-Mail: info@gujm.it
Emp.: 130
Magazine Publisher
S.I.C.: 2721
N.A.I.C.S.: 511120
Fabienne Schwalbe *(Gen Mgr)*

Subsidiaries:

Albrecht Knaus Verlag (1)
Neumarkter Strasse 28
81673 Munich, Germany (100%)
Tel.: (49) 8941360
Fax: (49) 8941363333
Web Site: www.bertelsmann.com
Emp.: 250
Publisher of Fiction, Memoirs, History, Art, Politics
S.I.C.: 2731
N.A.I.C.S.: 511130
Markus Weitenberd *(Editor-in-Chief)*

Bertelsmann Lexikothek Verlag GmbH (1)
Carl Bertelsmann Strasse 161
33310 Gutersloh, Germany (100%)
Tel.: (49) 5241800
Telex: 933646
Fax: (49) 5241803315
E-Mail: susanne.ftern@bertelsmann.de
Web Site: www.lexikothek.de
Encyclopedias, Dictionaries, Reference Books
S.I.C.: 2731
N.A.I.C.S.: 511130
Thomas Holz *(Mng Dir)*

Blanvalet Verlag GmbH (1)
Neumarkter Strasse 28
81673 Munich, Germany (100%)
Tel.: (49) 8941360
Telex: 523259
Fax: (49) 8941363333
E-Mail: vertrieb.verlagsgruppe@randomhouse.de
Web Site: www.randomhouse.de
Emp.: 800
Book Publisher
S.I.C.: 2731
N.A.I.C.S.: 511130
Silvia Kuttny-Walser *(Dir-Pub)*

BMG Rights Management GmbH (1)
SpreePalais Anna-Louise-Karsch-Strasse 2
D-10178 Berlin, Germany DE
Tel.: (49) 303001330
Fax: (49) 30300133328
E-Mail: info@bmg.com
Web Site: www.bmg.com
Emp.: 150
Music Intellectual Property Management Services
S.I.C.: 6794
N.A.I.C.S.: 533110
Hartwig Masuch *(Founder & CEO)*
Max Dressendorfer *(CFO)*
Steve Moran *(COO)*
Kay Krafft *(CIO)*
Fred Casimir *(Exec VP-Intl Repertoire)*
Patrick Jost *(Sr VP-Licensing & Mktg)*
Gaby Urban *(Sr VP-Rights Admin)*

U.S. Subsidiary:

BMG Rights Management (US) LLC (2)
6 E 32nd St 11th Fl
New York, NY 10016 NY
Tel.: (212) 561-3000
Sales Range: $25-49.9 Million
Emp.: 70
Music Patent Owner & Publisher
S.I.C.: 2741
N.A.I.C.S.: 512230
Milton T. Okun *(Founder)*
Laurent Hubert *(Pres-Mktg & Creative-North America)*
Philip Cialdella *(Sr VP-Admin & Licensing)*

Non-U.S. Subsidiary:

Chrysalis Group PLC (2)
33 Wigmore St
London, W1U 1QX, United Kingdom
Tel.: (44) 2072212213
Fax: (44) 2032141201
E-Mail: enquiries@chrysalis.com
Web Site: www.chrysalis.com
Sales Range: $75-99.9 Million
Emp.: 50
Music, Radio, Television & Media Products
S.I.C.: 4832
N.A.I.C.S.: 515112
Chris Wright *(Chm)*
Jeremy Lascelles *(CEO)*
Andy Mollett *(CFO, Sec & Dir-Fin)*
Peter Lassman *(CEO-Lasgo Chrysalis)*

Subsidiary:

Chrysalis Music (3)
The Chrysalis Building
13 Bramley Road, London, W10 6SP, United Kingdom
Tel.: (44) 2072212213
Fax: (44) 2074656330
E-Mail: info@chrysalismusic.co.uk
Web Site: www.chrysalismusic.co.uk
Sales Range: $125-149.9 Million
Emp.: 50
Music Publishing
S.I.C.: 2741
N.A.I.C.S.: 512230
Jeremy Lascelles *(CEO)*

Subsidiary:

Lasgo Chrysalis (4)
Units 2 & 3 Chapmans Park Industrial Estate
378 High Road Willesden, London, NW10 2DY, United Kingdom
Tel.: (44) 2084598800
Fax: (44) 2084515555
E-Mail: enquiries@lasgo.com
Web Site: www.lasgo.com
Emp.: 12
CD, DVD & Book Distr
S.I.C.: 5099
N.A.I.C.S.: 423990
Peter Lassman *(CEO)*

Prisma Verlag GmbH & Co. KG (1)
Zuelpicher Strasse 10
40549 Dusseldorf, Germany
Tel.: (49) 211507028
Fax: (49) 2115051549
E-Mail: info@prisma-verlag.de
Web Site: www.prisma-verlag.de
Emp.: 10
Publisher of Magazine Supplement
S.I.C.: 2721
N.A.I.C.S.: 511120
Amett Hanck *(Dir-Adv)*

Subsidiary:

Prisma Electronic Publishing GmbH (2)
Neumarkter Strasse 28
81673 Munich, Germany (100%)
Tel.: (49) 8941360
Telex: 931149
Fax: (49) 8941363333
E-Mail:
Web Site: www.randomhouse.de
Emp.: 200
Publisher of Reprints, Special Editions, Encyclopedias, Mail Order Series
S.I.C.: 2731
N.A.I.C.S.: 511130

Non-U.S. Subsidiary:

Prisma Presse & Cie (2)
6 Rue Daru
75008 Paris, France (100%)
Tel.: (33) 144153000
Telex: 660-403
Fax: (33) 144153368
E-Mail: communication@prisma-presse.com
Web Site: www.prisma-presse.com
Sales Range: $600-649.9 Million
Emp.: 820
Magazine Publisher
S.I.C.: 2721
N.A.I.C.S.: 511120
Fabrice Boe *(Pres & CEO)*
Jean Pierre Caffin *(Deputy CEO & Mng Dir)*

Ufa Film und Fernseh GmbH (1)
Dianastr 21
14482 Potsdam, Germany
Tel.: (49) 33170600
Fax: (49) 3317060149
E-Mail: info@ufa.de
Web Site: www.ufa.de
Emp.: 215
Motion Picture Production for Television
S.I.C.: 7812
N.A.I.C.S.: 512110
Wolf Bauer *(CEO)*
Martin Lechar *(Mng Dir)*

Wilhelm Goldmann Verlag GmbH (1)
Neumarkter Strasse 28
81673 Munich, Germany (100%)
Tel.: (49) 8941360
Fax: (49) 8941363333
Web Site: www.randomhouse.de
Emp.: 500
Book Publishing
S.I.C.: 2731
N.A.I.C.S.: 511130
Joerg Pfuhl *(CEO)*

U.S. Subsidiaries:

Bertelsmann Inc. (1)
1745 Broadway
New York, NY 10019 (100%)
Tel.: (212) 782-1000
Fax: (212) 782-1010
Web Site: www.bertelsmann.com
Emp.: 800
Publishing Holding Company
S.I.C.: 6719
N.A.I.C.S.: 551112
Markus Dohle *(Chm & CEO)*
Jacqueline Chasey *(Sec & Sr VP)*

Penguin Random House LLC (1)
1745 Broadway
New York, NY 10019 (53%)
Tel.: (212) 782-9000
E-Mail: penguinrandomhouse@penguinrandomhouse.com
Web Site: www.penguinrandomhouse.com
Emp.: 10,000
Book Publisher & Distr
S.I.C.: 2731
N.A.I.C.S.: 511130
Markus Dohle, *(CEO)*
Coram Williams *(CFO)*
Frank Steinert *(Exec VP & Chief HR Officer)*
Madeline McIntosh *(Pres/COO-US)*
Ian Hudson *(CEO-Intl)*
Tom Weldon *(CEO-UK)*

Division:

Random House LLC (2)
1745 Broadway
New York, NY 10019
Tel.: (212) 782-9000
Fax: (212) 302-7985
Toll Free: (800) 726-0600
Web Site: www.randomhouse.com
Sales Range: $1-4.9 Billion
Emp.: 5,264
Book Publisher
S.I.C.: 2731

Bertelsmann SE & Co. KGaA—(Continued)

N.A.I.C.S.: 511130
Markus Dohle *(Chm & CEO)*
Gina Centrello *(Pres & Publr)*
Madeline McIntosh *(COO)*
Sonny Mehta *(Chm-Knopf Doubleday & Editor-in-Chief)*
Peter Gethers *(Pres-Studio)*
Stuart Applebaum *(Exec VP-Comm)*
Jaci Updike *(Sr VP & Dir-Sls)*

Groups:

The Ballantine Publishing Group (3)
1745 Broadway
New York, NY 10019
Tel.: (212) 782-9000
Fax: (212) 572-4962
E-Mail: vintagepublicity@randomhouse.com
Web Site: www.randomhouse.com
Emp.: 100
Mass Market Books, Trade Paperbacks
S.I.C.: 2731
N.A.I.C.S.: 511130
Gina Centrello *(Pres & Publr)*

Bantam Dell Publishing Group (3)
1745 Broadway
New York, NY 10019 (100%)
Tel.: (212) 782-9000
Fax: (212) 782-8374
Toll Free: (800) 223-6834
E-Mail: webmaster@randomhouse.com
Web Site: www.randomhouse.com
Emp.: 200
Publisher of Hardcover, Mass Market & Trade Paperback Books, General Fiction & Non-Fiction for Adults & Young Readers
Export
S.I.C.: 2731
N.A.I.C.S.: 511130
Sanyu Dillon *(VP & Dir-Creative Mktg & Bantam Dell)*

Subsidiaries:

Arvato Digital (4)
108 Monticello Rd
Weaverville, NC 28787-9442
Tel.: (828) 658-2000
Fax: (828) 658-2014
Web Site: www.arvatodigitalservices.com
Emp.: 600
Production of VCDs & CDs
S.I.C.: 3652
N.A.I.C.S.: 334614
Richard R. Smith *(Dir-Pur)*

Berryville Graphics Inc. (4)
25 Jack Enders Blvd
Berryville, VA 22611 (100%)
Tel.: (540) 955-2750
Fax: (540) 955-9217
E-Mail: info@bvgraphics.com
Web Site: www.bvgraphics.com
Emp.: 750
Book Manufacturer-Letterpress, Web & Sheetfed Offset Printing, Binding
S.I.C.: 2732
N.A.I.C.S.: 323117

Dell Publishing (4)
1745 Broadway
New York, NY 10036-4039 (100%)
Tel.: (212) 782-9000
Telex: 238781
Fax: (212) 302-7985
Web Site: www.bdd.com
Sales Range: $1-4.9 Billion
Emp.: 800
Book Publishing Services
S.I.C.: 2731
N.A.I.C.S.: 511130

Doubleday (4)
1745 Broadway
New York, NY 10019 NY
Tel.: (212) 782-9000
Fax: (212) 302-7985
Web Site: www.doubleday.com
Emp.: 100
Book Publishers; Mail Order Book Club
S.I.C.: 2731
N.A.I.C.S.: 511130
Markus Dohle *(Pres & CEO)*

Division:

Alfred A. Knopf, Inc. (5)
1745 Broadway
New York, NY 10019
Tel.: (212) 782-9000
E-Mail: alfred@randomhouse.com
Web Site: www.knopf.knopfdoubleday.com
Emp.: 85
Publishers of Fiction, Nonfiction, Juvenile Books
Import Export
S.I.C.: 2731
N.A.I.C.S.: 511130
Gabrielle Brooks *(VP-Dir-Promo)*

Dynamic Graphics Inc. (4)
945 Horsham Rd
Horsham, PA 19044-1238
Tel.: (215) 441-8880
Fax: (215) 441-4277
Web Site: www.dgs.com
Emp.: 60
Book Cover Decorating
S.I.C.: 2759
N.A.I.C.S.: 323111
Jack O'Donnell *(Exec VP)*

Offset Paperback Mfrs., Inc. (BPMC) (4)
101 Memorial Hwy Route 309
Dallas, PA 18612
Tel.: (570) 675-5261
Fax: (570) 675-8714
Web Site: www.opm.com
Emp.: 700
Mfr. of Offset Paperbacks
S.I.C.: 2731
N.A.I.C.S.: 511130
Bob Scheifflee *(Mgr-Production)*

Non-U.S. Subsidiaries:

Bantam Dell Canada (4)
1 Toronto St Ste 300
Toronto, ON, M5C 2V6, Canada (100%)
Tel.: (416) 364-4449
Fax: (416) 364-6863
Web Site: www.randomhouse.ca
Emp.: 60
Wholesale & Direct Book Supplier
S.I.C.: 5942
N.A.I.C.S.: 451211
John Neale *(Chm)*
Brad Martin *(Pres & CEO)*
Duncan Shields *(Exec VP & Dir-Sls)*

Transworld Publishers (4)
61 63 Uxbridge Road
London, W5 5SA, United Kingdom (100%)
Tel.: (44) 2085792652
Telex: 267974
Fax: (44) 2085795479
E-Mail: info@transworld-publishers.co.uk
Web Site: www.booksattransworld.co.uk
Emp.: 200
Publishers of Fiction & Non-Fiction Books
S.I.C.: 2721
N.A.I.C.S.: 511120
Larry Snilay *(Mng Dir)*

Subsidiaries:

Bantam Books Ltd. (5)
Century House 61 63 Uxbridge Rd Ealing
London, W5 5SA, United Kingdom (100%)
Tel.: (44) 2085792652
Fax: (44) 2085795749
E-Mail: info@transworld-publishers.co.uk
Web Site: www.booksattransworld.co.uk
Emp.: 200
Book Publisher
S.I.C.: 2731
N.A.I.C.S.: 511130

Bantam Paperbacks UK (5)
Century House 61 63 Uxbridge Rd Ealing
London, W5 5SA, United Kingdom (100%)
Tel.: (44) 2085792652
Fax: (44) 2085795749
E-Mail: info@transworld-publishers.co.uk
Web Site: www.booksattransworld.co.uk
Emp.: 200
Paperback Books
S.I.C.: 2721
N.A.I.C.S.: 511120

Bantam Press UK (5)
61 63 Uxbridge Rd Ealing
London, W5 5SA, United Kingdom (100%)
Tel.: (44) 2085792652
Fax: (44) 2082316716
E-Mail: info@transworld-publishers.co.uk
Web Site: www.booksattransworld.co.uk
Emp.: 200
Fiction & Non-Fiction Book Publisher
S.I.C.: 2721
N.A.I.C.S.: 511120
Larry Finlay *(Mng Dir)*

Corgi Books Ltd. (5)
61 63 Uxbridge Rd Ealing
London, W5 5SA, United Kingdom (100%)
Tel.: (44) 2085792652
Telex: 267974
Fax: (44) 2085795749
E-Mail: info@transworld-publishers.co.uk
Web Site: www.booksattransworld.co.uk
Emp.: 250
Publisher of Mass-Market & Trade Paperbacks in all General Fiction & Non-Fiction Areas
S.I.C.: 2721
N.A.I.C.S.: 511120

The Crown Publishing Group (3)
1745 Broadway
New York, NY 10019
Tel.: (212) 782-9000
Fax: (212) 940-7381
Web Site: www.crownpublishing.com
Emp.: 400
Book Publisher
S.I.C.: 2731
N.A.I.C.S.: 511130
Annsley Rosner *(VP & Dir-Publicity-Crown Publr, Hogarth & Broadway Books Imprints)*

Random House Adult Trade Group (3)
1745 Broadway
New York, NY 10019-0002
Tel.: (212) 751-2600
Fax: (212) 572-6030
E-Mail: vintagepublicity@randomhouse.com
Web Site: www.randomhouse.com
Emp.: 1,000
Book Publisher
S.I.C.: 2731
N.A.I.C.S.: 511130
Markus Dohle *(CEO)*

Units:

Random House Trade Publishing Group (4)
1745 Broadway
New York, NY 10019
Tel.: (212) 751-2600
Fax: (212) 572-6030
Toll Free: (800) 793-9000
E-Mail: vintagepublicity@randomhouse.com
Web Site: www.randomhouse.com
Sls.: $100,000,000
Emp.: 150
Trade Paperback Book Publishers
S.I.C.: 2731
N.A.I.C.S.: 511130
Mark Dohle *(CEO)*

Villard Books (4)
1745 Broadway
New York, NY 10019
Tel.: (212) 782-9000
Web Site: www.randomhouse.com
Emp.: 100
Book Publisher
S.I.C.: 2731
N.A.I.C.S.: 511130

Subsidiaries:

Books on Tape, Inc. (3)
400 Hahn Rd
Westminster, MD 21157
Tel.: (410) 848-1900
Fax: (800) 940-7046
Toll Free: (800) 733-3000
E-Mail: csorders@randomhouse.com
Web Site: www.booksontape.com
Emp.: 500
Books on Tape Operations & Distribution Center
S.I.C.: 3652
N.A.I.C.S.: 334614
Frank Steinert *(Sr VP-HR)*

Fodor's Travel Publications, Inc. (3)
1745 Broadway
New York, NY 10019 NY
Tel.: (212) 751-2600
Fax: (212) 572-2248
Toll Free: (800) 755-7244
E-Mail: editors@fodors.com
Web Site: www.fodors.com
Emp.: 40
Travel Guides Publisher
S.I.C.: 2731
N.A.I.C.S.: 511130

Pantheon Books, Inc. (3)
1745 Broadway
New York, NY 10019
Tel.: (212) 751-2600
Telex: 126-575
Fax: (212) 572-6030
E-Mail: pantheonpublicity@randomhouse.com
Web Site: www.randomhouse.com
Emp.: 22
Book Publisher
S.I.C.: 2731
N.A.I.C.S.: 511130

Random House Children's Books (3)
1745 Broadway
New York, NY 10019
Tel.: (212) 782-9000
Fax: (212) 782-9484
Web Site: www.randomhouse.com
Children's Books Publisher
S.I.C.: 2731
N.A.I.C.S.: 511130
Barbara Marcus *(Pres & Publr)*

Schocken Books (3)
1745 Broadway
New York, NY 10019
Tel.: (212) 751-2600
Fax: (212) 572-6030
E-Mail: vintagepublicity@randomhouse.com
Web Site: www.randomhouse.com
Book Publishing Services
S.I.C.: 2731
N.A.I.C.S.: 511130

Smashing Ideas, Inc. (3)
1601 2nd Ave Ste 900
Seattle, WA 98101 WA
Tel.: (206) 378-0100
Web Site: www.smashingideas.com
Sales Range: $1-9.9 Million
Emp.: 30
Motion Picture & Video Production Services
S.I.C.: 7812
N.A.I.C.S.: 512110
Stephen Jackson *(Pres & CEO)*

Non-U.S. Subsidiaries:

Penguin Books Ltd (3)
80 Strand
London, WC2R 0LR, United Kingdom
Tel.: (44) 20 7010 3000
Fax: (44) 20 7010 6060
E-Mail: enquiries.international@pearson.com
Web Site: www.penguin.co.uk
Book Publisher
S.I.C.: 2731
N.A.I.C.S.: 511130
Peter Field *(CEO)*

Subsidiary:

Penguin Random House Ltd. (4)
(Formerly The Penguin Publishing Co. Ltd.)
80 Strand
London, WC2R 0RL, United Kingdom UK
Tel.: (44) 2084163000 (100%)
Telex: 933349
Fax: (44) 208 416 3099
Web Site: www.penguin.co.uk
Holding Company; Book Publisher
S.I.C.: 6719
N.A.I.C.S.: 551112
Gail Rebuck *(Chm)*
Tom Weldon *(CEO)*
Ian Hudson *(Deputy CEO)*
Nigel Portwood *(Exec VP-Global Ops)*

Division:

Penguin Group UK (5)
80 Strand
London, WC2R 0RL, United Kingdom UK
Tel.: (44) 2070103000 (100%)
Fax: (44) 2070106060
E-Mail: customer.service@penguin.co.uk
Web Site: www.penguin.co.uk
Emp.: 950
Book Publisher
S.I.C.: 2731
N.A.I.C.S.: 511130
Helena Peacock *(Sec & Dir-Legal)*

Subsidiaries:

Dorling Kindersley Ltd. (6)
80 Strand
London, WC2R ORL, United Kingdom (100%)
Tel.: (44) 2070103000
Telex: 8954529 Deekay G
Fax: (44) 2070106060
E-Mail: press@uk.dk.com
Web Site: www.dk.co.uk
Emp.: 4,000
Nonfiction & Reference Books Publisher
S.I.C.: 2731
N.A.I.C.S.: 511130
David Lamb *(Publr)*

Ladybird Books Ltd. (6)
80 Strand
London, WC2R 0RL, United Kingdom UK
Tel.: (44) 2070103000 (100%)
Telex: 341347
Fax: (44) 207016704
E-Mail: ladybird@uk.penguingroup.com
Web Site: www.ladybird.co.uk
Emp.: 500
Children's Books & Educational Materials Publisher
S.I.C.: 2731
N.A.I.C.S.: 511130
Sally Folyer *(Mng Dir)*

U.S. Subsidiaries:

Author Solutions, LLC (5)
1663 Liberty Dr Ste 200
Bloomington, IN 47403
Tel.: (812) 339-6000
Fax: (812) 339-6554
Toll Free: (888) 519-5121
E-Mail: info@authorhouse.com
Web Site: www.authorsolutions.com
Sales Range: $100-124.9 Million
Emp.: 1,600
Self-Publishing Service for Authors
S.I.C.: 2741
N.A.I.C.S.: 511199
Andrew Phillips *(CEO)*
Kevin G. Gregory *(COO)*
Randy Davis *(CIO)*
Scott Dillon *(Gen Counsel)*
Bill Becher *(Sr VP-Production Svcs & Output Ops)*
Keith Ogorek *(Sr VP-Mktg)*
Don Seitz *(Sr VP-Sls-Worldwide)*

Subsidiary:

iUniverse, Inc. (6)
1663 Liberty Dr Ste 200
Bloomington, IN 47403 CA
Tel.: (402) 323-7800
Fax: (812) 359-0745
Toll Free: (800) 288-4677
E-Mail: press@iuniverse.com
Web Site: www.iuniverse.com
Emp.: 390
Printed & Online Self Publishing Services
S.I.C.: 2741
N.A.I.C.S.: 511199
Andrew Phillips *(CEO)*
Kevin G. Gregory *(COO)*
Keith Ogorek *(Sr VP-Mktg)*

Penguin Group (USA) Inc. (5)
375 Hudson St
New York, NY 10014-3658 (100%)
Tel.: (212) 366-2000
Fax: (212) 414-3366
Web Site: www.us.penguingroup.com
Sales Range: $1-4.9 Billion
Emp.: 1,200
Book Publisher
Import Export
S.I.C.: 2731
N.A.I.C.S.: 511130
Susan Petersen Kennedy *(Pres)*
Jim Crofton *(CFO)*
Francesco Sedita *(Pres/Publr-Grosset & Dunlap)*
Clare Ferraro *(Pres-Viking, Plume & Studio Books Imprints)*
Don Weisberg *(Pres-Young Readers Grp)*
Doug Whiteman *(Exec VP-Bus Ops)*
James C. Clark *(Sr VP-Distr)*
Alexander Gigante *(Sr VP-Legal Affairs)*

Unit:

DK Publishing (6)
375 Hudson St
New York, NY 10014 (100%)
Tel.: (212) 366-2000
Fax: (212) 689-4828
Toll Free: (800) 631-8571
E-Mail: web@dk.com
Web Site: www.us.dk.com
Emp.: 120
Nonfiction Books, CD-ROMs & Videos Publisher
Import Export
S.I.C.: 2731
N.A.I.C.S.: 511130
Nancy Ellwood *(Dir-Editorial)*

Non-U.S. Subsidiaries:

Penguin Australia Pty Ltd (4)
707 Collins St
Melbourne, VIC, 3008, Australia
Tel.: (61) 3 9811 2400
Fax: (61) 3 9811 2620
E-Mail: sales@au.penguingroup.com
Web Site: www.penguin.com.au
Rev.: $127,800,000
Emp.: 345
Book Publisher
S.I.C.: 2731
N.A.I.C.S.: 511130
Gabrielle Coyne *(CEO-Asia Pacific)*

Penguin Books Benelux BV (4)
Herengracht 418 II
Amsterdam, 1017 BZ, Netherlands
Tel.: (31) 20 625 9566
Fax: (31) 20 625 8676
Book Publisher
S.I.C.: 2731
N.A.I.C.S.: 511130

Penguin Books Deutschland GmbH (4)
Justinianstr 4
60322 Frankfurt am Main, Germany
Tel.: (49) 69 628 081
Fax: (49) 69 629 293
E-Mail: Penguin.Germany@penguinbooks.de
Web Site: www.penguin.co.uk/static/cs/uk/0/aboutus/index.html
Book Publishing Services
S.I.C.: 2731
N.A.I.C.S.: 511130
Edith Strommen *(Mng Dir)*

Penguin Books, S.A. (4)
Glorieta de Quevedo 9-7 C
28015 Madrid, Spain
Tel.: (34) 91 593 1306
Fax: (34) 91 593 4711
E-Mail: mail@penguin.es
Web Site: www.penguinspain.com
Emp.: 7
Books Distr
S.I.C.: 5192
N.A.I.C.S.: 424920
Javier Riveira *(Mng Dir)*

Penguin Books South Africa (4)
Rosebank Office Park Block D 181 Jan Smuts Avenue
Parktown, 2193, South Africa
Mailing Address:
PO Box 9
Parklands, 2121, South Africa
Tel.: (27) 11 327 3550
Fax: (27) 11 327 3660
E-Mail: info@za.penguingroup.com
Web Site: www.penguinbooks.co.za
Emp.: 52
Book Distr
S.I.C.: 5192
N.A.I.C.S.: 424920
Stephen Johnson *(Mng Dir)*

Penguin Ireland (4)
25 St Stephen's Green
Dublin, 2, Ireland
Tel.: (353) 1 661 7695
Fax: (353) 1 661 7696
E-Mail: info@penguin.ie
Web Site: www.penguin.ie
Emp.: 5
Book Publisher
S.I.C.: 2731
N.A.I.C.S.: 511130
Michael McLoughlin *(Mng Dir)*
Patricia McVeigh *(Officer-Publicity & Editorial)*

Penguin Random House Grupo Editorial (3)
(Formerly Random House Mondadori S.A.)
Travessera de Gracia 47-49
08021 Barcelona, Spain ES
Tel.: (34) 933660300 (100%)
Fax: (34) 933660449
E-Mail: info@randomhousemondadori.es
Web Site: www.randomhousemondadori.es
Emp.: 200
Book Publisher
S.I.C.: 2731
N.A.I.C.S.: 511130
Nuria Cabuti *(CEO)*

Penguin Random House Canada (3)
(Formerly Random House of Canada Limited)
2775 Mathenson Blvd E
Mississauga, ON, L4W 4P7, Canada (100%)
Tel.: (416) 364-4449
Fax: (905) 624-6217
E-Mail: rchan@randomhouse.ca
Web Site: www.randomhouse.ca
Emp.: 90
Book Publishing
S.I.C.: 2731
N.A.I.C.S.: 511130
Brad Martin *(Pres & CEO)*

Subsidiary:

McClelland & Stewart Ltd. (4)
75 Sherbourne St 5th Fl
Toronto, ON, N5A 2P9, Canada ON
Tel.: (416) 598-1114
Fax: (416) 598-7764
E-Mail: mail@mcclelland.com
Web Site: www.mcclelland.com
Sales Range: $10-24.9 Million
Emp.: 50
Book Publishing & Printing
S.I.C.: 2731
N.A.I.C.S.: 511130
Doug Pepper *(Pres & Publr)*

Subsidiary:

Tundra Books Inc. (5)
1 Toronto Street Suite 300
Toronto, ON, M5C 2V6, Canada (100%)
Tel.: (416) 364-4449
Fax: (416) 598-7764
Toll Free: (800) 788-1074
E-Mail: tundra@mcclelland.com
Web Site: www.tundrabooks.com
Emp.: 35
Childrens Book Publisher
S.I.C.: 2731
N.A.I.C.S.: 511130
Alison Morgan *(Publr)*

Non-U.S. Division:

RTL Group S.A. (1)
45 Bd Pierre Frieden
L-1543 Luxembourg, Luxembourg LU
Tel.: (352) 24861 (75.1%)
Fax: (352) 24862760
E-Mail: info@rtlgroup.com
Web Site: www.rtlgroup.com
RTL—(EUR LSE LUX MAD OTC)
Rev.: $8,074,327,660
Assets: $10,632,050,660
Liabilities: $4,092,356,800
Net Worth: $6,539,693,860
Earnings: $928,857,300
Emp.: 9,590
Fiscal Year-end: 12/31/12
Holding Company; Radio & Television Broadcasting
S.I.C.: 6719
N.A.I.C.S.: 551112
Guillaume de Posch *(Co-CEO)*
Anke Schaferkordt *(Co-CEO)*
Lutz Glandt *(Mng Dir)*
Elmar Heggen *(CFO & Head-Corp Centre)*
Janine Neves *(Comm Officer)*
Christopher Baldelli *(Chm-Radio-France)*
Alain Berwick *(CEO-Radio & Tele Letzebuerg)*
Philippe Delusinne *(CEO-Belgium)*
Cecile Frot-Coutaz *(CEO-FremantleMedia)*
Dirk Gerkens *(CEO-Klub)*
Bert Habets *(CEO-Nederland)*
Gert Zimmer *(CEO-Radio Deutschland)*
Johannes Zull *(CEO-Televizija)*
Vincent de Dorlodot *(Gen Counsel)*
Edouard De Fierlant *(Sec)*
Jean-Marie Bourhis *(Deputy CFO & Exec VP-Fin)*
Alexander Glatz *(Exec VP-Strategy & Controlling)*
Romain Mannelli *(Exec VP-HR)*
Andreas Rudas *(Exec VP-Ops & Bus Dev-Central & Eastern Europe & Asia)*
Michael Beisheim *(Sr VP-Grp Tax)*
Andrew Buckhurst *(Sr VP-IR)*
Oliver Fahlbusch *(Sr VP-Corp Comm & Mktg)*
Francois Masquelier *(Sr VP-Treasury & Corp Fin)*
Ursula Schmidt *(Sr VP-Internal Audit)*

Subsidiaries:

European News Exchange (2)
45 Blvd Pierre Frieden
L 1543 Luxembourg, Luxembourg (100%)
Tel.: (352) 421423101
Fax: (352) 421423768
E-Mail: claudine_ries@enex.lu
Web Site: www.enex.lu
Emp.: 14
Television Broadcasting
S.I.C.: 4833
N.A.I.C.S.: 515120
Nic Jacob *(Mng Dir)*

RTL Radio Letzebuerg (2)
45 Blvd Pierre Frieden
L 3850 Luxembourg, Luxembourg (100%)
Tel.: (352) 421423405
Fax: (352) 421422737
E-Mail: radionews@rtl.lu
Web Site: www.rtlgroup.com
Emp.: 700
Radio Broadcasting
S.I.C.: 4832
N.A.I.C.S.: 515112
Alain Bierwich *(Dir-Radio & Mgr-PR)*

RTL Radio (2)
45 Blvd Pierre Frieden
L 2850 Luxembourg, Luxembourg (100%)
Tel.: (352) 421423500
Fax: (352) 424444
E-Mail: rtlradio@clt-usa.com
Web Site: www.rtlradio.lu
Emp.: 30
Radio Broadcasting
S.I.C.: 4832
N.A.I.C.S.: 515112

RTL Tele Letzebuerg (2)
45 Blvd Pierre Frieden
L 1543 Luxembourg, Luxembourg LU
Tel.: (352) 421424810 (99.6%)
Fax: (352) 421427431
E-Mail: info@rtl.lu
Web Site: www.rtl.lu
Emp.: 800
Television Services
S.I.C.: 4833
N.A.I.C.S.: 515120
Alain Berwick *(CEO)*

RTL4 Holding SA (2)
45 Blvd Pierre Frieden
L 3850 Luxembourg, Luxembourg LU
Tel.: (352) 421421 (99.7%)
Fax: (352) 421422747
E-Mail: webmaster@rtlgroup.com
Web Site: www.rtl.lu
Emp.: 700
Operator of a Broadcast Television Station
S.I.C.: 4833
N.A.I.C.S.: 515120
Zeinei Gerhard *(CEO)*

Non-U.S. Subsidiaries:

104.6 RTL (2)
Kurfurstendamm 207 208
D 10719 Berlin, Germany (100%)
Tel.: (49) 3088484940
Fax: (49) 30884841261
E-Mail: marc.ackermann@104.6rtl.com
Web Site: www.104.6rtl.com
Emp.: 30
Radio Broadcasting
S.I.C.: 4832
N.A.I.C.S.: 515112
Stephen Schmitter *(Mng Dir)*

AVE Gesellschaft fur Horfunkbeteiligungen mbH (2)
Kurfurstendamm 207 208
10719 Berlin, Germany De
Tel.: (49) 3088484130 (100%)
Fax: (49) 3088484109

Bertelsmann SE & Co. KGaA—(Continued)

E-Mail: kontakt@rtlradio.com
Web Site: www.ave-hoerfunk.de
TV & Broadcasting-Music & Art
S.I.C.: 4833
N.A.I.C.S.: 515120

Berliner Rundfunk (2)
Grunewald St 3 12165
Berlin, 13355, Germany (100%)
Tel.: (49) 30201910
Fax: (49) 20191425
E-Mail: info@berliner-rundfunk.de
Web Site: www.berliner-rundfunk.de
Emp.: 25
Radio Broadcasting
S.I.C.: 4832
N.A.I.C.S.: 515112
Detlef Noorman *(Gen Mgr)*

Channel 5 Broadcasting Ltd. (2)
22 Long Acre
London, WC2E 9LY, United Kingdom UK
Tel.: (44) 2075505555
Fax: (44) 2075505554
Web Site: www.channel5.co.uk
Emp.: 200
Operator of a Broadcast Television Station; Owned by RTL Group S.A. (64.63%) & United Business Media plc (35.37%)
S.I.C.: 4833
N.A.I.C.S.: 515120
Remy Sautter *(Chm)*
Jeff Ford *(Mng Dir-Digital Channels & Acq)*
Mark White *(Mng Dir)*

Cologne Broadcasting Center (2)
Richard Byrd Strasse 4
50829 Cologne, Germany (100%)
Tel.: (49) 22191500
Fax: (49) 219150522
E-Mail: info@cbc.de
Web Site: www.cbc.de
Emp.: 102
Provider of Television Production Services
S.I.C.: 7812
N.A.I.C.S.: 512110

FremantleMedia Ltd (2)
1 Stephen St
London, W1T 1AL, United Kingdom UK
Tel.: (44) 2076916000
Fax: (44) 2076916100
E-Mail: feedback@fremantlemedia.com
Web Site: www.fremantlemedia.com
Emp.: 1,200
Independent Producer of Television Programs
S.I.C.: 7812
N.A.I.C.S.: 512110
Cecile Frot-Coutaz *(CEO)*
Stefan De Keyser *(Co-Mng Dir-Belgium)*
Kristine Willems *(Co-Mng Dir-Belgium)*
Dave Heuten *(Co-Mng Dir-Belgium)*
Sangeeta Desai *(COO)*
Trish Kinane *(Pres-Worldwide Entertainment)*
Daniela Busoli *(CEO-Brazil)*
Nathalie Garcia *(CEO-Madrid)*
Sara Geater *(CEO-UK)*
Ian Hogg *(CEO-Asia Pacific)*
Daniela Matei *(CEO-Nordics, Eastern Europe & Balkans)*
Jens Richter *(CEO-Intl)*
Adrian Santucho *(CEO-Productions-Mexico, US Hispanic & Pan Reg)*
Lisa Honig *(Sr Exec VP-Intl)*
Amber Brown *(Exec VP-Media & Brand Licensing-Spring)*
Dominic Burns *(Sr VP-Licensing & Entertainment)*
Susan Hummel *(Sr VP-Sls & Distr-Canada)*
Pete Kalhan *(Sr VP-Home Entertainment & Archive Sls)*
Emmanuelle Namiech *(Sr VP-Content & Dev-Enterprises-EMEA & Asia Pacific)*

Subsidiary:

TalkBack Thames (3)
1 Stephen Street
London, W1T 1AL, United Kingdom UK
Tel.: (44) 20 7691 6000
Telex: 22816
Fax: (44) 2076916100
E-Mail: info@talkbackthames.tv
Web Site: www.talkbackthames.tv
Rev.: $500,000,000
Emp.: 1,400
Television Broadcasting
S.I.C.: 4833
N.A.I.C.S.: 515120
Dan Baldwin *(Mng Dir)*

U.S. Subsidiary:

FremantleMedia North America Inc. (3)
28 E 28th St
New York, NY 10016 (100%)
Tel.: (212) 541-2800
Fax: (212) 541-2810
Web Site: www.fremantlemedia.com
Emp.: 15
Production & Distribution of Motion Pictures & Television Programs; Marketing of Commercial Time to National Television Advertisers
S.I.C.: 7829
N.A.I.C.S.: 512120
Thom Beers *(CEO)*
Lee Rierson *(COO)*
David Luner *(Pres-Brand Partnerships & Franchise Mgmt)*
Keith Hindle *(CEO-Digital & Branded Entertainment)*
Rick Glankler *(Exec VP & Gen Mgr-Kids & Family Entertainment)*
Craig Cegielski *(Exec VP-Scripted Programming & Dev)*
Gayle Gilman *(Exec VP-Digital Content)*
Toby Gorman *(Exec VP-Alternative Programming)*
Stefanie Berk *(Sr VP-Scripted Programming & Dev)*
Olivier Delfosse *(Sr VP-Digital-FremantleMedia Grp-Los Angeles)*
Alex Demyanenko *(Sr VP-Non Fiction Dev & Programming)*
Katharine Lewis *(Sr VP-Strategy & Ops-Digital & Branded Entertainment)*
Christine Shaw *(Sr VP-Comm & Mktg)*

Fun Radio (2)
20 22 Rue Bayard
F 75008 Paris, France (100%)
Tel.: (33) 0140704848
Fax: (33) 140704800
E-Mail: contact@funradio.fr
Web Site: www.funradio.fr
Emp.: 80
Radio Station
S.I.C.: 4832
N.A.I.C.S.: 515112
Claude Sertorio *(Dir Gen)*

Hit Radio Veronica (2)
Laapersveld 75
NL-1213 VB Hilversum, Netherlands
Tel.: (31) 356716500
Web Site: www.veronica.nl
Radio Broadcasting
S.I.C.: 4832
N.A.I.C.S.: 515112

Inadi S.A. (2)
Avenue Jacques Georgin 2
B 1030 Brussels, Belgium (43%)
Tel.: (32) 23376911
Fax: (32) 23376912
E-Mail: belrtl@belrtl.be
Web Site: www.belrtl.be
Emp.: 500
Radio Broadcasting
S.I.C.: 4832
N.A.I.C.S.: 515112
Eric Adelbrecht *(Dir Gen)*

Klassik Radio GmbH & Co. KG (2)
Planckstrasse 15
D-22765 Hamburg, Germany
Tel.: (49) 403005050
Web Site: www.klassikradio.de
Radio Broadcasting
S.I.C.: 4832
N.A.I.C.S.: 515112

Radio City 93.7 FM (2)
Korunni 98
101 00 Prague, Czech Republic (100%)
Tel.: (420) 246046211
Fax: (420) 246046112
E-Mail: zpravy@radiocity.cz
Web Site: www.radiocity.cz
Radio Broadcasting
S.I.C.: 4832
N.A.I.C.S.: 515112

Radio Contact (2)
94 Ave Des Croix De Guerre
1120 Brussels, Belgium (100%)
Tel.: (32) 22442711
Fax: (32) 22442710
Web Site: www.radiocontact.be
Emp.: 250
Radio Broadcasting
S.I.C.: 4832
N.A.I.C.S.: 515112

Radio Hamburg GmbH & Co KG (2)
Spitalerstrasse 10
20095 Hamburg, Germany
Tel.: (49) 403397140
Fax: (49) 40339714638
E-Mail: service@radiohamburg.de
Web Site: www.radiohamburg.de
Emp.: 90
Radio Broadcasting
S.I.C.: 4832
N.A.I.C.S.: 515112
Florain Wittnann *(CEO)*

Radio NRW (2)
Essener Strasse 55
46047 Oberhausen, Germany
Tel.: (49) 20885870
Fax: (49) 208853099
E-Mail: info@radionrw.de
Web Site: www.radionrw.de
Emp.: 90
Radio Broadcasting
S.I.C.: 4832
N.A.I.C.S.: 515112
Martin Kunze *(Program Dir)*

RTL 2 (2)
22 Rue Bayard
F 75008 Paris, France (100%)
Tel.: (33) 140704000
Fax: (33) 140704326
E-Mail: juillaune.piau@rtl2.fr
Web Site: www.rtl2.fr
Emp.: 50
Radio Broadcasting
S.I.C.: 4832
N.A.I.C.S.: 515112

RTL Klub (2)
Nagytetenyi ut 29
1222 Budapest, Hungary HU
Tel.: (36) 13828282 (48.8%)
Fax: (36) 13828289
Web Site: www.rtlklub.hu
Emp.: 131
Broadcast Television Station Operations
S.I.C.: 4833
N.A.I.C.S.: 515120
Dirk Gerkens *(CEO)*
Akos Robert *(Deputy CEO)*

RTL Radio (2)
Kurfurstendamm 207-208
D-10719 Berlin, Germany
Tel.: (49) 3088484111
Fax: (49) 3088484109
E-Mail: emtfang@radiocenterberlin.com
Web Site: www.104.6rtl.com
Emp.: 120
Radio Broadcasting
S.I.C.: 4832
N.A.I.C.S.: 515112
Remy Sautter *(Chm)*
Stephan Schmitter *(Chm)*

RTL Television GmbH (2)
Picassopplatz 1
50679 Cologne, Germany De
Tel.: (49) 2214560 (99.7%)
Fax: (49) 22145671690
E-Mail: angebote@rtl.de
Web Site: www.mediengruppe-rtl.de
Emp.: 800
Operator of a Television Station
S.I.C.: 4833
N.A.I.C.S.: 515120
Anke Schaeferkordt *(Gen Mgr)*

RTL (2)
22 Rue Bayard
F 75008 Paris, France (100%)
Tel.: (33) 0140704070
Fax: (33) 140704256
E-Mail: relation.auditeur@rtl.fr
Web Site: www.rtl.fr
Emp.: 300
Radio Broadcasting
S.I.C.: 4832
N.A.I.C.S.: 515112
Christopher Baldelli *(Pres)*

TVI SA (2)
Avenue Jacques Georgin 2
B 1201 Brussels, Belgium BE
Tel.: (32) 23376811 (65.8%)
Fax: (32) 23373376812
E-Mail: internet@rtl.be
Web Site: www.rtltvi.be
Emp.: 700
Operator of a Broadcast Television Station
S.I.C.: 4833
N.A.I.C.S.: 515120
Phillippe Delusinne *(Mng Dir)*

Video Communication France S.A. (2)
48 Quai Carnot
F 92210 Saint-Claud, France (100%)
Tel.: (33) 141121212
Fax: (33) 141121200
Web Site: www.vcf.fr
Emp.: 100
S.I.C.: 3651
N.A.I.C.S.: 334310

Vox Film & Fernseh GmbH & Co. KG (2)
Richard Byrd Strasse 6
D 50829 Cologne, Germany De
Tel.: (49) 22195340 (100%)
Fax: (49) 2219534375
E-Mail: mail@vox.de
Web Site: www.vox.de
Emp.: 120
Operator of a Television Station
S.I.C.: 4833
N.A.I.C.S.: 515120
Frank Hoffman *(Pres)*

Non-U.S. Joint Venture:

RTL Disney Fernsehen GmbH & Co. KG (2)
Picassoplatz 1
50679 Cologne, Germany De
Tel.: (49) 22145650
Fax: (49) 22145651019
E-Mail: communication@superrtl.de
Web Site: www.superrtl.de
Sales Range: $25-49.9 Million
Emp.: 120
Operator of a Childrens Television Station; Joint Venture of RTL Group SA (50%) & The Walt Disney Company (50%)
S.I.C.: 4833
N.A.I.C.S.: 515120
Claude Schmit *(Mng Dir)*

Non-U.S. Subsidiary:

Buchgemeinschaft Donauland Kremayr & Scheriau KG (1)
Wahringer Strasse 76 8
A 1090 Vienna, Austria AT
Tel.: (43) 171387700 (100%)
Fax: (43) 1713877020
E-Mail: office@kremayr-scheriau.at
Web Site: www.kremayr-scheriau.at
Emp.: 8
Book Publishing, Book Clubs, Book Store
S.I.C.: 2731
N.A.I.C.S.: 511130
Martin Scheriau *(Mng Dir)*

BERTHOLD TECHNOLOGIES GMBH & CO. KG

Calmbacher Str 22
75323 Bad Wilbad, Germany
Tel.: (49) 70811770
Fax: (49) 7081177100
E-Mail: info@Berthold.com
Web Site: www.berthold.com
Year Founded: 1949
Rev.: $62,744,314
Emp.: 255

Business Description:
Detection Instruments Mfr
S.I.C.: 3823
N.A.I.C.S.: 334513

Personnel:
Fritz Berthold *(Chm)*
Hans J. Oberhofer *(Mng Dir)*

BERTRANDT AG

Birkensee 1
71139 Ehningen, Germany

Tel.: (49) 4970346560
Fax: (49) 4970346564100
E-Mail: info@bertranlt.com
Web Site: www.bertrandt.com
BDT—(DEU)
Emp.: 8,603
Business Description:
Automotive & Aviation Equipment Design & Engineering Services
S.I.C.: 8711
N.A.I.C.S.: 541330
Personnel:
Klaus P. Bleyer *(Chm-Supervisory Bd)*
Dietmar Bichler *(Chm-Mgmt Bd)*
Maximilian Woelfle *(Vice Chm-Supervisory Bd)*
Ulrich Subklew *(Member-Mgmt Bd)*
Supervisory Board of Directors:
Klaus P. Bleyer
Horst Binnig
Daniela Brei
Martin Diepold
Astrid Fleischer
Wilfried Sihn
Maximilian Woelfle

U.S. Subsidiary:

Bertrandt US Inc. (1)
1775 W Hamlin Rd
Rochester Hills, MI 48309
Tel.: (248) 598-5100
Fax: (248) 598-5106
E-Mail: detroit@us.bertrandt.com
Automotive & Aviation Equipment Design & Engineering Services
S.I.C.: 8711
N.A.I.C.S.: 541330
Ronald Grosse *(Dir-Ops)*

Non-U.S. Subsidiaries:

Bertrandt S.A.S. (1)
Burospace Bat 10 Route de Gisy
BP 35
91572 Bievres, France
Tel.: (33) 1 6935 1505
Fax: (33) 1 6935 1506
E-Mail: paris@fr.bertrandt.com
Automotive & Aviation Equipment Design & Engineering Services
S.I.C.: 8711
N.A.I.C.S.: 541330

Bertrandt UK Ltd. (1)
34 Hornsby Square Southfields Industrial Park
Basildon, SS 15 6SD, United Kingdom
Tel.: (44) 1268 564 300
Fax: (44) 1268 564 301
E-Mail: dunton@uk.bertrandt.com
Automotive & Aviation Equipment Design & Engineering Services
S.I.C.: 8711
N.A.I.C.S.: 541330
Stephan Vogt *(Mng Dir)*

BERVIN INVESTMENT & LEASING LIMITED

607 Rohit House 3 Tolstoy Marg
New Delhi, 110 001, India
Tel.: (91) 11 23353697
Fax: (91) 11 23350245
E-Mail: investor@bervin.com
Web Site: www.bervin.com
Year Founded: 1990
531340—(BOM)
Rev.: $31,907
Assets: $1,568,169
Liabilities: $822,008
Net Worth: $746,161
Earnings: $25,993
Fiscal Year-end: 03/31/13
Business Description:
Investment Services
S.I.C.: 6799
N.A.I.C.S.: 523910
Personnel:
T. S. Grover *(Sec)*
Board of Directors:
V. K. Berlia
T. S. Grover
S. K. Murgai
A. C. Rekhi
Transfer Agent:
RCMC Share Registry Pvt. Ltd.
B-106 Sector-2
Noida, India

BERYL DRUGS LTD.

43-44 2nd Floor Dawa Bazar 13-14 RNT Marg
Indore, MP, 452001, India
Tel.: (91) 731 3046367
Fax: (91) 731 3046366
E-Mail: info@beryldrugs.com
Web Site: www.beryldrugs.com
Year Founded: 1993
524606—(BOM)
Rev.: $2,789,643
Assets: $1,656,525
Liabilities: $522,002
Net Worth: $1,134,524
Earnings: $72,298
Fiscal Year-end: 03/31/13
Business Description:
Pharmaceutical Product Mfr & Distr
S.I.C.: 2834
N.A.I.C.S.: 325412
Personnel:
Sanjay Sethi *(Chm & Mng Dir)*
Devendra Sinha *(Compliance Officer)*
Board of Directors:
Sanjay Sethi
Bagachand Jain
Hemant Jain
Sunil Jain
Sudhir Sethi
Avinash Sharma
Transfer Agent:
Adroit Corporate Services Pvt. Ltd
19/20 Jaferbhoy Industrial Estate 1st Floor
Makwana Road Marol Naka
Andheri East, Mumbai, 400 059, India

BES ENGINEERING CORPORATION

6F 12 Tunghsing Rd
Taipei, Taiwan
Tel.: (886) 287876687
Fax: (886) 287876987
E-Mail: besbs0@bes.com.tw
Web Site: www.bes.com.tw
2515—(TAI)
Sales Range: $250-299.9 Million
Business Description:
Civil Engineering Services
S.I.C.: 8711
N.A.I.C.S.: 541330
Personnel:
Tsun Tai Yen *(Chm)*
Shiang-Kuo Liou *(Sr VP)*

Subsidiaries:

Core Asia Human Resources Management Co., Ltd. (1)
2F No 12 Dongxing Rd
Songshan District, Taipei, 105, Taiwan
Tel.: (886) 277061288
Fax: (886) 287876838
Web Site: www.coreasia.com.tw
Human Resource Consulting Services
S.I.C.: 8999
N.A.I.C.S.: 541612

Elite Human Resource Management Co., Ltd. (1)
No 12 Dongxing Road
Songshan District, Taipei, 105, Taiwan
Tel.: (886) 287873547
Fax: (886) 287876838
Web Site: www.ehrmc.com.tw
Emp.: 40
Human Resource Consulting Services
S.I.C.: 8999
N.A.I.C.S.: 541612
Su Ping Huang *(Gen Mgr)*

Non-U.S. Subsidiaries:

Corporacion de Inversion y Desarrollo BES, S.A. (1)
Juan Santamaria International Airport
Alajuela, 21005, Costa Rica
Tel.: (506) 24381111
Fax: (506) 2438 2222
Industrial Park Operation Services
S.I.C.: 8744
N.A.I.C.S.: 561210

Xiamen Bonded Area Airport Logistics Park Construction Co., Ltd. (1)
Room 420-2 4F Xiangyu Complex
Xiandai Logistics Park, Xiamen, Fujian, 361006, China
Tel.: (86) 592 5745718
Warehousing & Logistics Services
S.I.C.: 4225
N.A.I.C.S.: 493110

BESANA UK LIMITED

Randall Rd Rissington Business Park
Bourton on the Water, Cheltenham, Gloucestershire, GL54 2QB, United Kingdom
Tel.: (44) 1451810023
Fax: (44) 1451810024
E-Mail: info@besanauk.co.uk
Web Site: www.besanagroup.com
Sales Range: $50-74.9 Million
Emp.: 15
Business Description:
Production & Processing of Nuts & Dried Fruit
S.I.C.: 2034
N.A.I.C.S.: 311423
Personnel:
Giuseppe Calcagni *(Pres)*

BESPOKE TRICYCLES, INC.

145-147 St John Street
London, EC1V 4PW, United Kingdom
Tel.: (44) 203 086 7401
E-Mail: info@bespoketricycles.co.uk
Web Site: www.bespoketricycles.co.uk
BPSR—(OTC OTCB)
Rev.: $82,968
Assets: $32,479
Liabilities: $21,145
Net Worth: $11,334
Earnings: ($32,175)
Emp.: 1
Fiscal Year-end: 10/31/13
Business Description:
Vending Tricycles Mfr
S.I.C.: 3751
N.A.I.C.S.: 336991
Personnel:
John Goodhew *(Pres, CEO & CFO)*
Board of Directors:
John Goodhew

BESRA GOLD INC.

(Formerly Olympus Pacific Minerals Inc.)
Suite 500 - 10 King Street East
Toronto, ON, M5C 1C3, Canada
Tel.: (416) 572-2525
Fax: (416) 572-4202
Toll Free: (888) 902-5522
Web Site: www.besra.com
BEZ—(ASX OTC TSX)
Sls.: $82,772,713
Assets: $101,359,498
Liabilities: $76,667,992
Net Worth: $24,691,506
Earnings: ($25,303,029)
Emp.: 1,681
Fiscal Year-end: 06/30/13
Business Description:
Gold Mining Services
S.I.C.: 1041
N.A.I.C.S.: 212221
Personnel:
David Alexander Seton *(Chm)*
Kevin Michael Tomlinson *(Deputy Chm)*
John Andrew Gowans Seton *(CEO)*
Jane Bell *(CFO)*
Darin Lee *(COO)*
Paul Seton *(Chief Comml Officer)*
Jeffrey D. Klam *(Gen Counsel & Sec)*
Board of Directors:
David Alexander Seton
Jon Morda
Leslie Robinson
Kevin Michael Tomlinson
Legal Counsel:
Gowling Lafleur Henderson LLP
Suite 2300, 1055 Dunsmuir Street Bentall IV
P.O. Box 49122
Vancouver, BC, Canada

Claymore Partners Limited
63 Fort Street
Auckland, New Zealand

Boyle & Co. LLP
Suite 1900, 25 Adelaide Street East
Toronto, ON, Canada

Blakiston & Crabb
1202 Hay Street
West Perth, Australia

Berns & Berns
767 Third Avenue
New York, NY 10017
Transfer Agents:
Computershare Investor Services Pty Limited
Yarra Falls 452 Johnston Street
Abbotsford, VIC, 3067, Australia

Computershare Investor Services Inc.
100 University Ave 9th Floor
Toronto, ON, Canada

BEST & CROMPTON ENGG. LTD.

15 Kasturi Rangan Road Alwarpet
Chennai, 600 018, India
Tel.: (91) 4445066410
Fax: (91) 4445066436
E-Mail: info@bestcrompton.com
Web Site: www.bestcrompton.com
BECREL—(NSE)
Sales Range: $50-74.9 Million
Business Description:
Electrical Component Mfr
S.I.C.: 3699
N.A.I.C.S.: 335999
Personnel:
V. P. Thirumoorthy *(Sec)*
Board of Directors:
S. V. Venkatesan
A. Annamalai
K. Prakash
N. Srinivasan
Transfer Agent:
Integrated Enterprises (India) Limited
Kences Towers II Floor No. 1 Ramakrishna Street North Usman Road
600017 Chennai, India

BEST BRIDAL, INC.

5F & 7F & 8F Ebisu Building 3-11-10 Higashi
Shibuya-ku, Tokyo, 150-0011, Japan
Tel.: (81) 3 5464 0081
Web Site: www.bestbridal.co.jp
Year Founded: 1995
2418—(TKS)
Emp.: 1,280
Business Description:
Planning, Design & Operation of Guest Houses & Chapels; Event Planning; Travel Services; Hotels
S.I.C.: 7299
N.A.I.C.S.: 812990
Personnel:
Masayuki Tsukada *(Pres)*
Keiko Tsukada *(Sr Mng Dir & Dir-Mktg)*

Best Bridal, Inc.—(Continued)

Board of Directors:
Tomoharu Fujitani
Katsuhiko Hatanaka
Keiji Ishihara
Takashi Nishibori
Masayuki Tsukada

Subsidiary:

Best Planning, Inc. **(1)**
6-23-12 Higashikashiwagaya
Ebina, Kanagawa, Japan JP
Tel.: (81) 46 234 2206
Fax: (81) 46 234 2248
Web Site: www.b-planning.co.jp
Sales Range: $10-24.9 Million
Emp.: 4
Services, Including Food & Beverage Supply, for Wedding Receptions & Other Events
S.I.C.: 7389
N.A.I.C.S.: 561990
Mikio Takahashi *(Pres)*

Subsidiary:

Hospitality Network Corporation **(2)**
1-16-2 Kaigan
Minato-ku, Tokyo, 105-8576, Japan
Tel.: (81) 3 5404 2222
Fax: (81) 3 5404 2111
E-Mail: info@interconti-tokyo.com
Web Site: www.interconti-tokyo.com
Emp.: 287
Hotel Management Services
S.I.C.: 7011
N.A.I.C.S.: 721110
Yuji Tsutsumi *(Pres)*

BEST CAST IT LTD

Best Cast House 16 Poonamallee High Rd
Vellappan Chavadi, Chennai, 600077, India
Tel.: (91) 4426801215
Fax: (91) 4426801218
E-Mail: admin@bcil.net
Web Site: www.bcil.net
Year Founded: 1974
Sales Range: $10-24.9 Million
Emp.: 260

Business Description:
Aluminum Die-Casting Services
S.I.C.: 3364
N.A.I.C.S.: 331523

Personnel:
Manohar Kabirdass *(Dir-Tech)*

Subsidiary:

Kabirdass Motor Company Ltd **(1)**
Best Cast House 16 Poonamallee High Road
Vellappan Chavadi, Chennai, 600077, India
Tel.: (91) 4426800988
Fax: (91) 4426800988
E-Mail: ips@kabirdass.com
Web Site: www.kabirdass.com
Emp.: 40
Electric Bike Mfr
S.I.C.: 3751
N.A.I.C.S.: 336991
Murali Kabirdass *(CEO)*
B. Muthukumar *(Sec)*

THE BEST CONNECTION EMPLOYMENT GROUP

9 Birmingham Street
Halesowen, West Midlands, B63 3HN, United Kingdom
Tel.: (44) 1215 043 000
Fax: (44) 1215 043 009
Web Site: www.thebestconnection.co.uk
Year Founded: 1991
Sales Range: $250-299.9 Million
Emp.: 468

Business Description:
Human Resources Consulting Services
S.I.C.: 8999
N.A.I.C.S.: 541612

Personnel:
Andrew Sweeney *(Co-Founder & CEO)*
Martin Recci *(Co-Founder)*
Neil Yorke *(Co-Founder)*

Board of Directors:
Martin Recci
Andrew Sweeney
Neil Yorke

BEST CUT LIMITED

12 Fifth Street
PO Box 128
Empangeni, 3880, South Africa
Tel.: (27) 35 787 1960
Fax: (27) 35 787 1960
Web Site: www.bestcut.co.za
Year Founded: 1989
BCH—(JSE)

Business Description:
Meat Product Whslr
S.I.C.: 5147
N.A.I.C.S.: 424470

Personnel:
A. H. Steenkamp *(CEO)*

BEST EASTERN HOTELS LTD.

401 Chartered House 293/299 Dr C H Street Near Marine Lines Church
Mumbai, India
Tel.: (91) 22 2207 8292
Fax: (91) 22 2206 1324
Web Site: www.ushaascot.com
508664—(BOM)
Rev.: $855,505
Assets: $1,470,068
Liabilities: $681,518
Net Worth: $788,550
Earnings: $98,943
Fiscal Year-end: 03/31/13

Business Description:
Hotel Management Services
S.I.C.: 7011
N.A.I.C.S.: 721110

Personnel:
Vinaychand Kothari *(Chm & Mng Dir)*
Dilip V. Kothari *(Mng Dir)*

Board of Directors:
Vinaychand Kothari
Ramnik K. Baxi
Mangal S. Chheda
Mehernoz C. Dangore
Dilip V. Kothari
Manohar R. Tambat

Transfer Agent:
Sharex Dynamic (India) Pvt. Ltd.
Unit-1 Luthra Ind Premises Safed Pool Andheri Kurla Rd Andheri (E)
Mumbai, India

BEST FENCING GROUP B.V.

Zandstraat 15
5683 PL Best, Netherlands
Tel.: (31) 499363666
Fax: (31) 499399945
E-Mail: info@hekwerk.nl
Web Site: www.bestfencinggroup.com
Sales Range: $50-74.9 Million
Emp.: 100

Business Description:
Fencing & Security System Mfr
S.I.C.: 7382
N.A.I.C.S.: 561621

Personnel:
Arthur Van Del Graas *(CEO)*

BEST N.V.

Research Park Hassrode
Romeinse Straat 20, 3001 Leuven, Belgium
Tel.: (32) 16396396
Fax: (32) 16396390
E-Mail: info@bestnv.com
Web Site: www.bestnv.com
Year Founded: 1996
Sales Range: $100-124.9 Million
Emp.: 250

Business Description:
Sorting Equipment Mfr for Food Industry
S.I.C.: 3556
N.A.I.C.S.: 333241

Personnel:
Paul Berghmans *(Mng Dir)*
Eddy De Reys *(Mng Dir)*
Marc Ruymen *(Mng Dir)*
Bert Van der Auwera *(Mng Dir)*

Non-U.S. Subsidiary:

BEST Eindhoven BV **(1)**
J.F. Kennedylaan 3
5612 Eindhoven, Netherlands NL
Tel.: (31) 402472896 (100%)
E-Mail: eindhoven@best.eu.org
Web Site: www.besteindhoven.nl
Rev.: $45,291,348
Emp.: 40
Food Industry Sorting Equipment Mfr
S.I.C.: 3556
N.A.I.C.S.: 333241

BEST OF THE BEST PLC

2 Plato Place 72-74 St Dionis Road
London, SW6 4TU, United Kingdom
Tel.: (44) 2073718866
Fax: (44) 207 736 7936
E-Mail: info@botb.com
Web Site: www.botb.com
BEST—(LSE)
Rev.: $10,186,910
Assets: $5,627,141
Liabilities: $1,261,170
Net Worth: $4,365,971
Earnings: $121,128
Emp.: 59
Fiscal Year-end: 04/30/13

Business Description:
Travel & Leisure
S.I.C.: 7999
N.A.I.C.S.: 713290

Personnel:
William Hindmarch *(Founder & CEO)*

Board of Directors:
Michael Hindmarch
Rupert Garton
Colin Hargrave
William Hindmarch

Legal Counsel:
Pinsent Masons
CityPoint 30 Crown Place
London, United Kingdom

BEST UNION COMPANY SPA

Via A Canova 16/20
40138 Bologna, BO, Italy
Tel.: (39) 0515881511
Fax: (39) 0516014383
E-Mail: info@bestunion.it
Web Site: www.bestunion.it
BEST—(ITA)
Rev.: $43,998,220
Assets: $46,795,562
Liabilities: $33,519,633
Net Worth: $13,275,929
Earnings: ($262,503)
Emp.: 275
Fiscal Year-end: 12/31/12

Business Description:
Event Support Services Including Electronic Ticket Sale, Access Control Software, Hardware & Security Services
S.I.C.: 7999
N.A.I.C.S.: 711310

Personnel:
Luca Montebugnoli *(Chm & CEO)*
Licia Montebugnoli *(CFO)*
Giovanni Martinelli *(COO)*
Alberto Pelizzaro *(CTO)*

Board of Directors:
Luca Montebugnoli
Stefano Appoggi
Stefano Landi
Licia Montebugnoli
Gianluca Muratori
Giuseppe Camillo Pilenga
Luana Sabattini
Claudio Tinti

Subsidiaries:

AMIT Srl **(1)**
Viale Manzoni 53
Rome, 00185, Italy
Tel.: (39) 06 48 07 81
Fax: (39) 06 48 07 82 53
E-Mail: amitsrl@amitsrl.it
Web Site: www.amitsrl.com
Music & Entertainment Event Organizers
S.I.C.: 7999
N.A.I.C.S.: 711310

Charta Srl **(1)**
Via S Martino 1/a
48020 Sant'Agata sul Santerno, Ravenna, Italy
Tel.: (39) 0545 915000
Fax: (39) 0545 915008
Web Site: www.charta.it
Ticketing & Entrance Control Services
S.I.C.: 4729
N.A.I.C.S.: 561599
Alessandra Sciolotto *(Gen Mgr)*

Omniticket Network Srl **(1)**
Via Ettore Ponti 55
20143 Milan, Italy
Tel.: (39) 02 581 403 1
E-Mail: sales.it@omniticket.com
Web Site: www.omniticket.com
Automated Ticketing Services
S.I.C.: 4729
N.A.I.C.S.: 561599

Team 2015 Srl **(1)**
Via Giovanni Masera 10
20129 Milan, Italy
Tel.: (39) 02 86915332
Fax: (39) 02 8051892
Web Site: www.team2015.it
Educational Event Organizing Services
S.I.C.: 8299
N.A.I.C.S.: 611710

Non-U.S. Subsidiaries:

Omniticket Network Ltd. **(1)**
15 Borough Road Berkeley Court
Newcastle-under-Lyme, Staffordshire, ST5 1TT, United Kingdom
Tel.: (44) 1782 714300
Fax: (44) 1782714566
E-Mail: sales.uk@omniticket.com
Emp.: 8
Event Organizing Services
S.I.C.: 7999
N.A.I.C.S.: 711310
John Davies *(Gen Mgr)*

Omniticket Network Pte Ltd **(1)**
54B Pagoda Street
Singapore, 059213, Singapore
Tel.: (65) 6635 1180
Fax: (65) 6534 8112
E-Mail: sales.sg@omniticket.com
Emp.: 5
Event Organizing Services
S.I.C.: 7999
N.A.I.C.S.: 711310
Ottavio Gori *(Gen Mgr)*

BEST WESTERN VILLAGE PARK INN

1804 Crowchild Trail Northwest
Calgary, AB, T2M 3Y7, Canada
Tel.: (403) 289-0241
Fax: (403) 289-4645
Toll Free: (888) 774-7716
E-Mail: info@villageparkinn.com
Web Site: www.villageparkinn.com
Emp.: 120

Business Description:
Hotel Operations
S.I.C.: 7011
N.A.I.C.S.: 721110
Personnel:
Ryan Ocbina *(Gen Mgr)*

BEST WORLD INTERNATIONAL LTD.

26 Tai Seng Street 05 01
Singapore, 534057, Singapore
Tel.: (65) 6899 0088
Fax: (65) 6636 1531
E-Mail: info@bestworld.com.sg
Web Site: www.bestworld.com.sg
Year Founded: 1990
5ER—(SES)
Rev.: $39,041,150
Assets: $47,058,602
Liabilities: $8,551,030
Net Worth: $38,507,571
Earnings: $1,338,401
Fiscal Year-end: 12/31/12
Business Description:
Health & Wellness Products Developer & Mfr
S.I.C.: 2833
N.A.I.C.S.: 325411
Personnel:
Doreen Nee Moi Tan *(Co-Chm & Pres)*
Hoan Beng Mui Dora *(Co-Chm, CEO & Mng Dir)*
Ban Chin Huang *(COO)*
Siew Koon Ang *(Co-Sec)*
Siew Tian Low *(Co-Sec)*
Board of Directors:
Hoan Beng Mui Dora
Doreen Nee Moi Tan
Ban Chin Huang
Robson Teck Leng Lee
Sen Choon Lee
Ravindran Ramasamy
Transfer Agent:
Tricor Barbinder Share Registration Services
80 Robinson Road 02-00
Singapore, Singapore
Subsidiary:

Best World Lifestyle Pte Ltd (1)
480 Lorong 6 Toa Payoh
No 15-00 HDB Hub E Wing, Singapore, 310480, Singapore
Tel.: (65) 63420888
Fax: (65) 67487970
E-Mail: info@bestworld.com.sg
Web Site: www.bestworld.com.sg/contact_us.html
Emp.: 100
Personal Care Products & Health Care Equipments Distr
S.I.C.: 5046
N.A.I.C.S.: 423440
Foo Ceyu *(Mgr-Div)*

Non-U.S. Subsidiaries:

Best World Lifestyle (HK) Company Limited (1)
Rm 1402-03 14F Causeway Bay Plz 1
489 Hennessy Rd, Causeway Bay, China (Hong Kong)
Tel.: (852) 35831838
Fax: (852) 35830118
Personal Care Products Distr
S.I.C.: 5999
N.A.I.C.S.: 446199
Pengo Chow *(Country Mgr)*

Best World Lifestyle Sdn. Bhd. (1)
No 11 Jalan Radin Anum Bandar Baru Sri Petaling, 57000 Kuala Lumpur, Federal Territory, Malaysia
Tel.: (60) 390571133
Fax: (60) 390572158
E-Mail: katherine@bwl.com.my
Web Site: www.bwl.com.my
Emp.: 30
Personal Care Products Distr
S.I.C.: 5999
N.A.I.C.S.: 446199
Foong Kuan Cheah *(Country Mgr)*

PT Best World Indonesia (1)
Mayapada Tower 8th Fl Ste 0802A
Jalan Jendral Sudirman Kav 28, Jakarta, 12920, Indonesia
Tel.: (62) 215213566
Fax: (62) 212525147
Web Site: www.bwl.co.id
Emp.: 100
Personal Care Products Distr
S.I.C.: 5999
N.A.I.C.S.: 446199
Dora Hoan *(CEO & Mng Dir)*

BESTAR INC.

4220 Rue Villeneuve
Lac Megantic, QC, G6B 2C3, Canada
Tel.: (819) 583-1017
Fax: (819) 583-5370
Toll Free: (888) 823-7827
E-Mail: ir@bestar.ca
Web Site: www.bestar.ca
Year Founded: 1948
BES—(CNSX)
Sales Range: $1-9.9 Million
Emp.: 209
Business Description:
Ready-to-Assemble Home Office & Home Entertainment Furniture Designer & Mfr
S.I.C.: 2514
N.A.I.C.S.: 337124
Personnel:
Paulin Tardif *(Chm)*
Andre Veilleux *(Sec)*
Board of Directors:
Paulin Tardif
Gilles Genest
Andre Giroux
Rene Hetu
Gilles Pansera
Mehubert Pepin
Martin Tardif
Transfer Agent:
Computershare Investor Services
100 University Avenue 11th Floor
Toronto, ON, M5J 2Y1, Canada
Tel.: (416) 263-9200
Toll Free: (800) 564-6253

BESTEC POWER ELECTRONICS CO., LTD.

10F 10 Lane 609 Sec 5 Chung-Hsin Road
San Chung City, Taipei, Hsien, 241, Taiwan
Tel.: (886) 229990133
Fax: (886) 229996880
E-Mail: guni_ku@bestec.com.tw
Web Site: www.bestec.com.tw
Year Founded: 1988
3308—(TAI)
Sales Range: $100-124.9 Million
Emp.: 4,000
Business Description:
Power Products Mfr & Supplier
S.I.C.: 3692
N.A.I.C.S.: 335912
Personnel:
Mingzhi Chen *(Chm)*

U.S. Subsidiary:

Bestec Electronics USA (1)
18221 E Railroad St
City of Industry, CA 91748
Tel.: (626) 581-4348
Electronic Goods Mfr
S.I.C.: 3679
N.A.I.C.S.: 334419

BESTLODGE UNIVERSAL CAPITAL AD

2nd floor apt 258 1A Vitosha Blvd
Sredets region, Sofia, Bulgaria
Tel.: (359) 962 14 84
Web Site: www.bestlodge-bg.com
Year Founded: 2011
7N3—(BUL)
Business Description:
Real Estate Activities
S.I.C.: 6531
N.A.I.C.S.: 531390
Personnel:
Athanasios Christaras *(Exec Dir)*
Board of Directors:
Vasileios Petrolekas
Ioannis Skountakis

BESTODECK LTD.

331 Long Ln
Hillingdon, London, Middlesex, UB10 9JU, United Kingdom
Tel.: (44) 1895209700
Fax: (44) 1895209707
E-Mail: bestodeck@smc-cars.com
Web Site: www.smc-cars.com
Emp.: 500
Business Description:
Car Dealerships Owner & Operator
S.I.C.: 5511
N.A.I.C.S.: 441110
Personnel:
Michael Warnes *(Chm)*
Subsidiary:

SMC Rover (1)
Unit 1 Perrite St InronBridge Rd S
HP11 1LG High Wycombe, Buckshire, United Kingdom (100%)
Tel.: (44) 01494520531
Fax: (44) 1895441316
E-Mail: parts.stockley@smc-cars.com
Web Site: www.smc-cars.com
Emp.: 35
Vehicle Motor Retailing
S.I.C.: 5511
N.A.I.C.S.: 441110

BESTTECHNICA TM - RADOMIR

Industrial zone
2400 Radomir, Bulgaria
Tel.: (359) 777 82185
Fax: (359) 777 80218
E-Mail: tm_radomir@besttechnica.bg
Web Site: www.besttechnica.bg
5BE—(BUL)
Business Description:
Engineering Services
S.I.C.: 8711
N.A.I.C.S.: 541330
Personnel:
Rosen Kamenov *(Mgr-IR)*
Subsidiary:

Besttechnica EOOD (1)
168 Tzar Boris III Bul Andromeda Business Center floor 1 office 12
Sofia, Bulgaria 1000
Tel.: (359) 2 9309919
Fax: (359) 2 9801448
E-Mail: office@besttechnica.bg
Industrial Supplies Whslr
S.I.C.: 5085
N.A.I.C.S.: 423840

BESTWAY (HOLDINGS) LIMITED

Abbey Rd Pk Royal
London, NW10 7BW, United Kingdom
Tel.: (44) 2084531234
Fax: (44) 2084538219
Web Site: www.bestway.co.uk
Sales Range: $1-4.9 Billion
Business Description:
Holding Company; Cement Mfr, Banking & Real Estate Services & Product Distr
S.I.C.: 6719
N.A.I.C.S.: 551112
Personnel:
Anwar Pervez *(Chm)*
Zameer Choudrey *(Mng Dir)*
Dawood Pervez *(Sec)*
Board of Directors:
Anwar Pervez
Abdul Khalique Bhatti
Adalat Khan Chaudhary
Arshad Chaudhary
Zameer Choudrey
Dawood Pervez
Rizwan Pervez
Younus Sheikh
Non-U.S. Subsidiaries:

Bestway Cement Limited (1)
Bestway Building 19-A College Road F-7 Markaz
Islamabad, 44000, Pakistan
Tel.: (92) 512654856
Fax: (92) 512654865
E-Mail: management@bestway.com.pk
Web Site: www.bestway.com.pk
BWCL—(KAR)
Sls.: $243,870,086
Assets: $403,741,088
Liabilities: $161,076,735
Net Worth: $242,664,353
Earnings: $63,700,185
Fiscal Year-end: 06/30/13
Cement Mfr
S.I.C.: 2891
N.A.I.C.S.: 325520
Mohammed Anwar Pervez *(Founder & Chm)*
Zameer Mohammed Choudrey *(CEO)*
Muhammad Irfan A. Sheikh *(CFO & Dir-Fin)*
Kaleem Ashraf *(Sec)*

United Bank Limited (1)
13th Floor UBL Building Jinnah Avenue Blue Area
Islamabad, Pakistan
Tel.: (92) 21 111 825 111
Fax: (92) 21 241 3492
Web Site: www.ubldirect.com
UBL—(KAR)
Int. Income: $763,597,992
Assets: $9,726,931,504
Liabilities: $8,705,276,594
Net Worth: $1,021,654,910
Earnings: $195,304,212
Emp.: 13,344
Fiscal Year-end: 12/31/12
Commercial Banking Services
S.I.C.: 6029
N.A.I.C.S.: 522110
Mohammed Anwar Pervez *(Chm)*
Atif R. Bokhari *(Pres & CEO)*
Raymond Kotwal *(CFO)*
Aqeel Ahmed Nasir *(Sec)*

Subsidiary:

UBL Fund Managers Limited (2)
4th Floor STSM Building Beaumont Road Civil Lines
Karachi, Sindh, 74200, Pakistan
Tel.: (92) 21111825262
Fax: (92) 2132214930
E-Mail: info@ublfunds.com
Web Site: www.ublfunds.com
Asset Management & Investment Advisory Services
S.I.C.: 6282
N.A.I.C.S.: 523930
Tariq Kirmani *(Chm)*
Mir Muhammad Ali *(CEO)*
Hassan Abbas *(COO)*
Hasnain Raza Nensey *(Chief Investment Officer)*
Shafiq ur Rehman *(CTO)*

Non-U.S. Subsidiary:

United Bank AG (2)
Feldeggstrasse 55
PO Box 1176
8034 Zurich, Switzerland
Tel.: (41) 434991920
Fax: (41) 434991933
E-Mail: info@ubag.ch
Web Site: www.ubl.com.pk/overseas/Switzerland/
Emp.: 8
Commercial Banking Services

Bestway (Holdings) Limited—(Continued)

S.I.C.: 6029
N.A.I.C.S.: 522110
Faisal Basheer *(CEO)*

Non-U.S. Joint Venture:

United National Bank Limited (UK) **(2)**
2 Brook Street
London, W1S 1BQ, United Kingdom UK
Tel.: (44) 2072908000
Telex: 883398
Fax: (44) 2072904950
E-Mail: info@unbankltd.com
Web Site: www.unbankltd.com
Emp.: 1,500
Commercial Banking & Treasury Services; Owned 55% by United Bank Limited & 45% by National Bank of Pakistan
S.I.C.: 6029
N.A.I.C.S.: 522110
Mansoor Khan *(CEO)*

BESUNYEN HOLDINGS COMPANY LIMITED

Suites 1903-5 19/F Shui On Centre
6-8 Harbour Road
Wanchai, China (Hong Kong)
Tel.: (852) 23248000
Fax: (852) 23248200
E-Mail: ir@besunyen.com
Web Site: www.besunyen.com
0926—(HKG)
Rev.: $75,482,661
Assets: $220,302,234
Liabilities: $24,041,471
Net Worth: $196,260,764
Earnings: ($54,356,405)
Emp.: 2,085
Fiscal Year-end: 12/31/12

Business Description:
Tea Mfr
S.I.C.: 2099
N.A.I.C.S.: 311920

Personnel:
Yihong Zhao *(Co-Founder, Chm & CEO)*
Yan Gao *(Co-Founder & Vice Chm)*
Chi Keung Wong *(CFO)*
Lap Ming Au *(Sec)*

Board of Directors:
Yihong Zhao
Yan Gao
Jingsheng Huang
Arthur Wong
Fenglou Zhang
Fumin Zhuo

Legal Counsel:
O' Melveny & Myers
31/F AIA Central 1 Connaught Road
Central, China (Hong Kong)

Global Law Office
15th Floor Tower 1 China Central Place No 81
Jianguo Road
100025 Beijing, China

Computershare Hong Kong Investor Services Limited
Shops 1712-1716 17th Floor Hopewell Centre
183 Queens Road East
Wanchai, China (Hong Kong)

Transfer Agent:
MaplesFS Limited
Queensgate House
PO Box 1093
Georgetown, Cayman Islands

BET-AT-HOME.COM AG

Kronprinzenstrasse 82-84
40217 Dusseldorf, Germany
Tel.: (49) 21117934770
Fax: (49) 21117934757
E-Mail: ir@bet-at-home.com
Web Site: www.bet-at-home.ag
ACX—(DEU)
Rev.: $115,040,573
Assets: $71,956,394
Liabilities: $25,789,956
Net Worth: $46,166,438
Earnings: $2,295,449
Emp.: 230
Fiscal Year-end: 12/31/12

Business Description:
Gambling Services
S.I.C.: 7999
N.A.I.C.S.: 713210

Personnel:
Martin Arendts *(Chm-Supervisory Bd)*
Isabelle Andres *(Deputy Chm-Supervisory Bd)*
Franz Omer *(Co-CEO & Member-Mgmt Bd)*
Michael Quatember *(Co-CEO & Member-Mgmt Bd)*

Supervisory Board of Directors:
Martin Arendts
Isabelle Andres
Jean-Laurent Nabet

Non-U.S. Subsidiaries:

bet-at-home.com Entertainment GmbH **(1)**
Hafenstr 47-51
4020 Linz, Austria
Tel.: (43) 732 9015 1000
Fax: (43) 732 9015 1001
E-Mail: office@bet-at-home.com
Web Site: www.bet-at-home.com
Online Sport Betting Services
S.I.C.: 7999
N.A.I.C.S.: 713290

bet-at-home.com Entertainment Ltd. **(1)**
Portomaso Business Tower Level 12
STJ 4011 San Giljan, Malta
Tel.: (356) 21314833
Fax: (356) 25401296
E-Mail: marketing.en@bet-at-home.com
Online Sport Betting Services
S.I.C.: 7999
N.A.I.C.S.: 713290

BET365 GROUP LIMITED

Hillside Festival Way
Stoke-on-Trent, ST1 5SH, United Kingdom
Tel.: (44) 1782 684 757
Fax: (44) 1782 684 792
E-Mail: support-eng@bet365.com
Web Site: www.bet365.com
Year Founded: 1974
Sales Range: $750-799.9 Million
Emp.: 1,900

Business Description:
Online Gambling Services
S.I.C.: 7999
N.A.I.C.S.: 713290

Personnel:
Denise Coates *(Joint CEO)*
John Coates *(Joint CEO)*

BETA SA BUZAU

39 Santierului Street
120226 Buzau, Romania
Tel.: (40) 238 725 500
Fax: (40) 238 710 779
E-Mail: beta@betabuzau.ro
Web Site: www.betabuzau.ro
Year Founded: 1925
BEZA—(BUC)
Sales Range: $10-24.9 Million
Emp.: 230

Business Description:
Oil & Gas Refinery Industry Services
S.I.C.: 1389
N.A.I.C.S.: 213112

Personnel:
Angelo Gruttadauria *(Pres)*

BETA SYSTEMS SOFTWARE AG

Alt-Moabit 90d
10559 Berlin, Germany
Tel.: (49) 307261180
Fax: (49) 30726118800
E-Mail: info@betasystems.com
Web Site: ww2.betasystems.com
BSS—(DEU)
Sales Range: $50-74.9 Million
Emp.: 347

Business Description:
Infrastructure Software Publisher
S.I.C.: 7372
N.A.I.C.S.: 511210

Personnel:
Stephan Helmstadter *(Deputy Chm-Supervisory Bd)*
Gernot Sagl *(CFO)*

Supervisory Board of Directors:
Peter Becker
Carsten Brautigam
Stephan Helmstadter
Stefan Hillenbach
Herbert Werle

Subsidiaries:

DETEC Decision Technology Software GmbH. **(1)**
Bensheimer Strasse 61
65428 Russelsheim, Hesse, Germany
Tel.: (49) 614235750
Fax: (49) 6142357599
E-Mail: nfo@detec.com
Web Site: www.detec.de
Emp.: 35
Software Development Services
S.I.C.: 7371
N.A.I.C.S.: 541511
Corry Homg *(Mgr)*

SI Software Innovation GmbH. **(1)**
Europastrasse 3
67433 Neustadt, Germany
Tel.: (49) 63214991500
Fax: (49) 632149915010
E-Mail: info@si-software.de
Web Site: www.si-software.com
Emp.: 36
Application Software & Data Processing Services
S.I.C.: 7379
N.A.I.C.S.: 518210
Andreas Kroeber *(Gen Mgr)*

U.S. Subsidiary:

Beta Systems of North America, Inc. **(1)**
2201 Coop Way 3rd Fl
Herndon, VA 20171-4583
Tel.: (703) 889-1240
Fax: (703) 889-1241
E-Mail: sales-us@betasystems.com
Application Software Development & Data Processing Services
S.I.C.: 7371
N.A.I.C.S.: 541511
Guy Schroen *(VP-Sls-Americas & Gen Mgr)*

Non-U.S. Subsidiary:

Beta Systems Software of Canada, Inc. **(2)**
Ste 600 736 Eighth Ave SW
Calgary, AB, T2P 1H4, Canada
Tel.: (403) 231-9800
Fax: (403) 266-6767
E-Mail: info-can@betasystems.com
Web Site: www.betasystems.com
Documents Data Processing Services
S.I.C.: 7379
N.A.I.C.S.: 518210
Scott Diamond *(Gen Mgr & Dir-Software Engrg)*

Non-U.S. Subsidiaries:

Beta Systems EDV Software Ges.m.b.H. **(1)**
Mooslackengasse 15-17
1190 Vienna, Austria
Tel.: (43) 174040290
Fax: (43) 174040291
E-Mail: austria@betasystems.com
Web Site: www.betasystems.com
Emp.: 1
Application Software & Data Processing Services
S.I.C.: 7379
N.A.I.C.S.: 518210

Beta Systems Software Espana, S.L. **(1)**
C Somera N 7-9 Planta 2
La Florida, 28023 Madrid, Spain
Tel.: (34) 913077675
Fax: (34) 913076607
E-Mail: irene.blank@betasystems.com
Web Site: www.betasystems.com
Emp.: 4
Application Software & Data Processing Services
S.I.C.: 7379
N.A.I.C.S.: 518210
Irene Blank *(Country Mgr)*

Beta Systems Software France S.A.R.L. **(1)**
2 Rue Paul Henry Spaak
77400 Lagny-sur-Marne, Seine-et-Marne, France
Tel.: (33) 164127980
Fax: (33) 1 60 07 31 06
E-Mail: info-f@betasystems.com
Web Site: www.betasystems.com
Emp.: 8
Application Software & Data Processing Services
S.I.C.: 7379
N.A.I.C.S.: 518210
Jernop Sajl *(Mng Dir)*

Beta Systems Software Ltd. **(1)**
Unit 8 Diddenham Ct Lambwood Hill
Grazeley, Reading, Berkshire, RG7 1JQ, United Kingdom
Tel.: (44) 1189885175
Fax: (44) 1189 88 48 99
E-Mail: info-gb@betasystems.com
Web Site: www.betasystems.com
Emp.: 6
Data Processing Services
S.I.C.: 7374
N.A.I.C.S.: 518210
Gernot Sagl *(CEO)*

Beta Systems Software SPRL. **(1)**
Ctr Monnet Ave Jean Monnet 1
1348 Louvain-la-Neuve, Belgium
Tel.: (32) 10230140
Fax: (32) 10230148
E-Mail: info-b@betasystems.com
Web Site: www.betasystems.com
Emp.: 3
Application Software & Data Processing Services
S.I.C.: 7371
N.A.I.C.S.: 541511
Walter Teithert *(Mng Dir)*

BETAnn Systems AB. **(1)**
Kavallerivagen 30
17402 Sundbyberg, Sweden
Tel.: (46) 87330045
Fax: (46) 87330155
E-Mail: info-s@betasystems.com
Web Site: www.betasystems.com
Emp.: 5
Data Processing Services
S.I.C.: 7379
N.A.I.C.S.: 518210

BETAPART PARTICIPACOES S/A

Av Presidente Wilson 231 - 28 Andar/ parte
20030905 Rio de Janeiro, Brazil
Tel.: (55) 21 3804 3700
Fax: (55) 21 3804 3480
Web Site: www.betapart.com.br
Year Founded: 1998
BETP3B—(BRAZ)

Business Description:
Investment Management Services
S.I.C.: 6211
N.A.I.C.S.: 523999

Personnel:
Marcos Nascimento Ferreira *(Dir-IR)*

BETER BED HOLDING N.V.

Linie 27 7689
NL-5405 AR Uden, Netherlands

Mailing Address:
PO Box 716
NL-5400 AS Uden, Netherlands
Tel.: (31) 413338819
Fax: (31) 413338829
E-Mail: bbholding@beterbed.nl
Web Site: www.beterbedholding.com
BBED—(EUR)
Rev.: $534,817,187
Assets: $149,229,675
Liabilities: $74,070,312
Net Worth: $75,159,363
Earnings: $19,409,079
Emp.: 2,495
Fiscal Year-end: 12/31/12
Business Description:
Mattresses, Bedsprings & All Other Furniture Stores
S.I.C.: 5712
N.A.I.C.S.: 442110
Personnel:
D. R. Goeminne *(Chm-Supervisory Bd)*
A. J. L. Slippens *(Vice Chm-Supervisory Bd)*
A. H. Anbeek *(CEO & Member-Mgmt Bd)*
B. F. Koops *(CFO & Member-Mgmt Bd)*
Supervisory Board of Directors:
D. R. Goeminne
E. A. de Groot
A. J. L. Slippens
W. T. C. van der Vis
Subsidiaries:

Bedden & Matrassen B.V. (1)
Linie 27
5405 AR Uden, Netherlands
Tel.: (31) 413 338902
Mattress Retailer
S.I.C.: 5999
N.A.I.C.S.: 453998

Beter Bed B.V. (1)
Industrielaan 15
5405 AA, Uden, Netherlands
Tel.: (31) 413 33 03 36
E-Mail: info@beterbed.nl
Web Site: www.beterbed.nl
Mattress Mfr & Whslr
S.I.C.: 5021
N.A.I.C.S.: 423210
Geert Duijf *(Mgr-SAP Application)*

Beter Beheer B.V. (1)
Linie 27
5405 AR Uden, Netherlands
Tel.: (31) 413338819
Fax: (31) 413338829
E-Mail: bbholding@beterbed.nl
Mattress Retailer
S.I.C.: 5999
N.A.I.C.S.: 453998

DBC International B.V. (1)
Linie 27
Postbus 57
5400 AB Uden, Noord Brabant, Netherlands
Tel.: (31) 413 243051
Fax: (31) 413 243050
E-Mail: info@mline.nl
Web Site: www.mline.nl
Emp.: 15
Mattress Mfr & Whslr
S.I.C.: 2515
N.A.I.C.S.: 337910
Jaap Westland *(Mgr-Intl Sls)*

Dormael Slaapkamers B.V. (1)
Linie 27
5405 AR Uden, Netherlands
Tel.: (31) 413 243005
Mattress Mfr & Whslr
S.I.C.: 2515
N.A.I.C.S.: 337910

M-T-M Nederland B.V. (1)
Linie 27
5405 AR Uden, Netherlands
Tel.: (31) 413 243030
Mattress Retailer
S.I.C.: 5999
N.A.I.C.S.: 453998

Slaapgenoten (1)
Postbus 148
5400 AC Uden, Netherlands
Tel.: (31) 413 245205
E-Mail: info@slaapgenoten.nl
Web Site: www.slaapgenoten.nl
Mattress Retailer
S.I.C.: 5999
N.A.I.C.S.: 453998

Non-U.S. Subsidiaries:

DBC Deutschland GmbH (1)
Bullermannshof 15
47441 Moers, Germany
Tel.: (49) 2841 88 44 9 0
Fax: (49) 2841 88 44 9 19
E-Mail: fr@dbc-deutschland.de
Web Site: www.dbc-deutschland.de
Emp.: 3
Mattress Mfr & Whslr
S.I.C.: 5021
N.A.I.C.S.: 423210

Matratzen Concord GmbH (1)
Horbeller Str 19
50858 Cologne, Germany
Tel.: (49) 2234 96 44 100
Fax: (49) 2234 96 44 111
E-Mail: info@matratzen-concord.de
Web Site: www.matratzen-concord.de
Mattress Hetailer
S.I.C.: 5999
N.A.I.C.S.: 453998

BETFAIR GROUP PLC

Waterfront Hammersmith
Embankment Chancellors Road
London, W6 9HP, United Kingdom
Tel.: (44) 20 8834 8000
Fax: (44) 20 8834 8001
E-Mail: info@betfair.com
Web Site: corporate.betfair.com
Year Founded: 2008
BET—(LSE)
Rev.: $611,185,230
Assets: $436,357,827
Liabilities: $227,891,547
Net Worth: $208,466,280
Earnings: ($104,706,927)
Emp.: 2,066
Fiscal Year-end: 04/30/13
Business Description:
Online Betting
S.I.C.: 7999
N.A.I.C.S.: 713290
Personnel:
Gerald Corbett *(Chm)*
Breon Corcoran *(CEO)*
Alexander Gersh *(CFO)*
Michael Bischoff *(CIO)*
Phil Dixon *(CTO)*
Fiona Russell *(Sec)*
Board of Directors:
Gerald Corbett
Zillah Byng-Maddick
Breon Corcoran
Ian Dyson
Alexander Gersh
Peter Jackson
Leo Quinn
Peter Rigby
Legal Counsel:
Freshfields Bruckhaus Deringer LLP
65 Fleet Street
London, United Kingdom
Subsidiary:

Blue Square Ltd. (1)
1st Floor Park House 16 Finsbury Circus
London, EC2M 7DJ, United Kingdom UK
Tel.: (44) 20 7688 6210 (100%)
E-Mail: Content@bluesq.com
Web Site: www.bluesq.com
Sales Range: $50-74.9 Million
Emp.: 150
Interactive Betting Services
S.I.C.: 2741
N.A.I.C.S.: 519130

BETHPAGE CAPITAL CORP.

Suite 918 - 1030 West Georgia Street
Vancouver, BC, V6E 2Y3, Canada
Tel.: (604) 639-9052
Fax: (604) 647-6613
E-Mail: vsorace@nevarocapital.com
Year Founded: 2010
BET—(TSXV)
Int. Income: $1,372
Assets: $484,566
Liabilities: $11,118
Net Worth: $473,448
Earnings: ($92,547)
Fiscal Year-end: 12/31/12
Business Description:
Metal Mining
S.I.C.: 1099
N.A.I.C.S.: 212299
Personnel:
Vincenzo Marco Sorace *(Pres & CEO)*
Gavin Cooper *(CFO)*
Board of Directors:
Steve Bajic
Daniel MacNeil
Robert Meister
Vincenzo Marco Sorace
Transfer Agent:
Computershare Trust Company of Canada
100 University Avenue 9th Floor
Toronto, ON, M5J 2Y1, Canada
Tel.: (416) 663-9097
Fax: (416) 263-9694

BETI D.D.

Tovarniska cesta 2
8330 Metlika, Slovenia
Tel.: (386) 73638100
Fax: (386) 73638190
E-Mail: beti@beti.si
Web Site: www.beti.si
Year Founded: 1956
Sales Range: $25-49.9 Million
Emp.: 700
Business Description:
Apparel & Accessories
S.I.C.: 2399
N.A.I.C.S.: 315990
Personnel:
Segina Matkovic *(Gen Mgr)*
Subsidiary:

Beti Preja d.o.o. (1)
2 Tovarniska Cesta
Metlika, 8330, Slovenia
Tel.: (386) 73638100
Fax: (386) 73058377
E-Mail: beti@beti.si
Web Site: www.beti.eu/eng.htm
Emp.: 176
Textile Mill
S.I.C.: 2299
N.A.I.C.S.: 314999
Mateja Gorse *(Mng Dir)*

BETON A.D.

Jurij Gagarin 15
1000 Skopje, Macedonia
Tel.: (389) 2 30 80 888
Fax: (389) 2 30 80 207
E-Mail: beton@beton.com.mk
Web Site: www.beton.com.mk
Year Founded: 1947
BESK—(MAC)
Business Description:
Civil Engineering Construction
S.I.C.: 1542
N.A.I.C.S.: 236220
Personnel:
Jordanov Minco *(Chm)*
Board of Directors:
Jordanov Minco
Mancev Blasko
Taruta Sergej
Siljanovska Snezana
Trpevski Trajko

BETON PROVINCIAL LTEE

1825 Avenue Du Phare Oust
Matane, QC, G4W 3N1, Canada
Tel.: (418) 562-0074
Fax: (418) 562-0081
E-Mail: m.lacearra@betonprovincial.com
Web Site: www.betonprovincial.com
Year Founded: 1960
Sales Range: $25-49.9 Million
Emp.: 375
Business Description:
Concrete, Asphalt, Crushed Stone & Aggregate Mfr
S.I.C.: 3272
N.A.I.C.S.: 327390
Personnel:
Andre Belanger *(Pres)*

BETON-STIP

Vanco Prke St 119
Stip, 2000, Macedonia
Tel.: (389) 92 390466
Fax: (389) 92 384484
E-Mail: admin@beton-stip.com.mk
Web Site: www.beton-stip.com.mk
BEST—(MAC)
Emp.: 205
Business Description:
Construction Services
S.I.C.: 1611
N.A.I.C.S.: 237310
Personnel:
Ilija Bresliski *(Gen Mgr)*

BETONSTAHL LEIPZIG GMBH

Am Glaeschen 6
D 04420 Grosslehna, Germany
Tel.: (49) 34205940
Fax: (49) 3420594211
E-Mail: info@betonstahl-leipzig.de
Web Site: www.betonstahl-leipzig.de
Sales Range: $25-49.9 Million
Emp.: 80
Business Description:
Welded Steel Mfr
S.I.C.: 3462
N.A.I.C.S.: 332111
Personnel:
Manfred Beggel *(Mng Dir)*

BETONUT SZOLGALTATO ES EPITO RT.

Pannonia utca 59-61
1133 Budapest, Hungary
Tel.: (36) 14511700
Fax: (36) 14511701
E-Mail: betonut@betonut.hu
Web Site: www.betonut.hu
Year Founded: 1950
Emp.: 650
Business Description:
Highway Construction Services
S.I.C.: 1611
N.A.I.C.S.: 237310
Personnel:
Laszlo Szerencses *(CEO)*
Subsidiaries:

Kotiviep 'B Kft. (1)
Gaz Utca 1
Szolnok, Hungary
Tel.: (36) 56425142
Web Site: www.kotiviepb.hu
Building Construction Services
S.I.C.: 1541
N.A.I.C.S.: 236210

SZAM-ERT Kft. (1)
Gogol Utca 13
1133 Budapest, Hungary
Tel.: (36) 14511600
Fax: (36) 14511650
Highway & Street Construction Services
S.I.C.: 1622
N.A.I.C.S.: 237310

Non-U.S. Subsidiary:

Betonut Constructii S.R.L. (1)
Intr Domnesti 4 Bucuresti Sectorul 2
Bucharest, Romania

Betonut Szolgaltato es Epito Rt.—(Continued)

Tel.: (40) 21 2115291
Building Construction Services
S.I.C.: 1541
N.A.I.C.S.: 236210

BETSSON AB
Regeringsgatan 28
111 53 Stockholm, Sweden
Tel.: (46) 8 506 403 00
Fax: (46) 8 735 57 44
E-Mail: info@betssonab.com
Web Site: www.betssonab.com
Year Founded: 1963
V72—(DEU)
Rev.: $341,134,463
Assets: $457,688,027
Liabilities: $213,444,742
Net Worth: $244,243,285
Earnings: $84,799,595
Emp.: 748
Fiscal Year-end: 12/31/12
Business Description:
Gaming Software Development Services
S.I.C.: 7371
N.A.I.C.S.: 541511
Personnel:
Pontus Lindwall *(Chm)*
Magnus Silfverberg *(Pres & CEO)*
Fredrik Ruden *(CFO)*
Martin Thorvaldsson *(Grp Gen Counsel)*
Board of Directors:
Pontus Lindwall
Per Hamberg
Carl Lewenhaupt
Lars Linder-Aronson
Patrick Svensk
Kicki Wallje-Lund
John Wattin

BETTER BATHROOMS UK LIMITED
Horizon Park Greenfold Way
Leigh, Lancashire, WN7 3XH, United Kingdom
Tel.: (44) 844 484 7678
Web Site: www.betterbathrooms.com
Year Founded: 2003
Sales Range: $25-49.9 Million
Emp.: 77
Business Description:
Bathroom Product & Tile Whslr
S.I.C.: 5023
N.A.I.C.S.: 423220
Personnel:
Colin Stevens *(Founder)*

BETTER WORLD GREEN PUBLIC COMPANY LIMITED
2674/1 Soi Drive-in Lad Phrao Rd
Bang Kapi, Bangkok, 10240, Thailand
Tel.: (66) 2731 0080
Fax: (66) 2731 2574
E-Mail: bwg@betterworldgreen.com
Web Site: www.betterworldgreen.com
BWG—(THA)
Rev.: $35,132,709
Assets: $61,729,473
Liabilities: $19,697,442
Net Worth: $42,032,031
Earnings: $2,512,911
Fiscal Year-end: 12/31/12
Business Description:
Waste Management Services
S.I.C.: 4959
N.A.I.C.S.: 562998
Personnel:
Wichan Withyasai *(Chm)*
Suwat Leungviriya *(Vice Chm)*
Tasanee Thongdee *(Sec)*
Board of Directors:
Wichan Withyasai
Thammanoon Ananthothai
Suthat Boonya-udomsart
Akarawit Khankaew
Suwat Leungviriya
Boonbaramee Sawangwong
Nartruidee Thammawan
Woradis Thanapatra
Tasanee Thongdee

BETTY BARCLAY KLEIDERFABRIK GMBH
Heidelberger Strasse 9 11
69226 Nussloch, Germany
Tel.: (49) 62249000
Fax: (49) 6224900514
E-Mail: info@bettybarclay.de
Web Site: www.bettybarclay.com
Year Founded: 1955
Sales Range: $300-349.9 Million
Emp.: 1,000
Business Description:
Mfr. of Women's Clothing
S.I.C.: 2389
N.A.I.C.S.: 315210
Personnel:
Jurgen Winter *(Mng Partner)*

BEUTLER & LANG SCHALUNGS- UND BEHALTER-BAU GMBH
Mainleite 35
97340 Kitzingen, Germany
Tel.: (49) 933250550
Fax: (49) 9332505555
E-Mail: mail@sbb-beutler-lang.de
Web Site: www.sbb-beutler-lang.de
Year Founded: 1974
Rev.: $16,561,738
Emp.: 70
Business Description:
Engineering Services
S.I.C.: 8711
N.A.I.C.S.: 541330
Personnel:
Debora Kempe *(Sec)*
Tina Kunze *(Sec-SBBiogas)*

BEUTTER PRAZISIONS-KOMPONENTEN GMBH & CO. KG
Butzensteigleweg 4-6
72348 Rosenfeld, Germany
Tel.: (49) 74289330
Fax: (49) 7428933290
E-Mail: office@beutter.de
Web Site: www.beutter.de
Year Founded: 1909
Rev.: $12,276,660
Emp.: 124
Business Description:
Mechanical Components Supplier
S.I.C.: 5084
N.A.I.C.S.: 423830
Personnel:
W. D. Kiessling *(Mng Dir)*
Ingrid Siebert *(Sec)*

BEVERLEY BUILDING SOCIETY
57 Market Place
Beverley, East Yorkshire, HU17 8AA, United Kingdom
Tel.: (44) 1482 881510
Fax: (44) 1482 872680
E-Mail: website@beverleybs.co.uk
Web Site: www.beverleybs.co.uk
Year Founded: 1866
Rev.: $7,315,271
Assets: $283,447,811
Liabilities: $269,251,573
Net Worth: $14,196,238
Earnings: $325,334
Emp.: 6
Fiscal Year-end: 12/31/12
Business Description:
Mortgage Lending
S.I.C.: 6163
N.A.I.C.S.: 522310
Personnel:
Peter Myers *(CEO)*
Board of Directors:
Stuart L. Young
Julie Good
Mike Heenan
Richard Miles
Peter Myers
Richard Pattinson
Tony Wilmot
Brian Young
Legal Counsel:
Addleshaw Goddard & Co
Sovereign House PO Box 8 Sovereign St
Leeds, LS1 1HQ, United Kingdom

BEVO AGRO INC.
7170 Glover Rd
Milner, BC, V0X 1T0, Canada
Tel.: (604) 888-0420
Fax: (604) 888-8048
E-Mail: info@bevofarms.com
Web Site: www.bevoagro.com
Year Founded: 1985
BVO—(TSXV)
Sls.: $20,464,093
Assets: $36,244,735
Liabilities: $21,916,605
Net Worth: $14,328,129
Earnings: $183,429
Emp.: 50
Fiscal Year-end: 06/30/13
Business Description:
Plant Producer & Supplier
S.I.C.: 0139
N.A.I.C.S.: 111998
Personnel:
Jack Benne *(Pres & CEO)*
John Hoekstra *(CFO)*
Leo Benne *(Sec, VP & Gen Mgr)*
Board of Directors:
Jack Benne
Leo Benne
Donald O. Fairholm
J. Wayne Green
John Hoekstra
Transfer Agent:
Computershare Trust Company of Canada
100 University Avenue 8th Floor
Toronto, ON, M5J 2Y1, Canada

Subsidiary:

Bevo Farms Ltd (1)
7170 Glover Rd
Milner, BC, V0X 1T0, Canada
Tel.: (604) 888-0420
Fax: (604) 888-8048
E-Mail: info@bevofarms.com
Web Site: www.bevoagro.com
Emp.: 60
Farming Services
S.I.C.: 0139
N.A.I.C.S.: 111998
Leo Benne *(VP & Gen Mgr)*

BEWI PRODUKTER AS
Nringsparken
7263 Froya, Norway
Tel.: (47) 72 44 88 88
Fax: (47) 72 44 88 99
E-Mail: firmapost@bewi.com
Web Site: www.bewi.no
Business Description:
Plastics Product Mfr
S.I.C.: 3089
N.A.I.C.S.: 326199
Personnel:
Svenn Bekken *(Mng Dir)*

Subsidiary:

Bewi Norplasta AS (1)
Havnegata 20B
N-7503 Stjordal, Norway
Tel.: (47) 992 38 900
Fax: (47) 74 82 35 51
E-Mail: firmapost@norplasta.com
Web Site: www.norplasta.com
Sales Range: $10-24.9 Million
Emp.: 80
Plastics Product Mfr
S.I.C.: 3089
N.A.I.C.S.: 326199
Svenn Bekken *(CEO)*

BEWITAL GMBH & CO. KG
Industriestr 10
46354 Borken, Germany
Tel.: (49) 2862581600
Fax: (49) 286258136
E-Mail: agrar@bewital.de
Web Site: www.bewital-agrar.de
Year Founded: 1963
Rev.: $89,313,543
Emp.: 160
Business Description:
Health & Nutrition Products Distr
S.I.C.: 5122
N.A.I.C.S.: 446191
Personnel:
Jurgen Petershagen *(Mng Dir)*

BEXIMCO PHARMACEUTICALS LIMITED
19 Dhanmondi R/A Road No 7
Dhaka, 1205, Bangladesh
Tel.: (880) 28619151
Fax: (880) 28613888
E-Mail: info@bpl.net
Web Site: www.beximco-pharma.com
BXP—(AIM LSE)
Rev.: $114,999,247
Assets: $304,421,855
Liabilities: $76,528,811
Net Worth: $227,893,044
Earnings: $16,334,040
Emp.: 2,670
Fiscal Year-end: 12/31/12
Business Description:
Pharmaceuticals Mfr
S.I.C.: 2834
N.A.I.C.S.: 325412
Personnel:
Ahmed Sohail Faisur Rahman *(Chm)*
Ahmed Salman Fazlur Rahman *(Vice Chm)*
Nazmul Hassan *(Mng Dir)*
Ali Nawaz *(CFO)*
Rabbur Reza *(COO)*
Mohammad Asad Ullah *(Sec)*
Board of Directors:
Ahmed Sohail Faisur Rahman
Iqbal Ahmed
Osman Kaiser Chowdhury
Nazmul Hassan
Ahsanul Karim
Abdul Alim Khan
Mohammad Abdul Qasem
Abu Bakar Siddiqur Rahman
Ahmed Salman Fazlur Rahman
Ernst & Young
1 More London Place
London, United Kingdom
Legal Counsel:
Jones Day
21 Tudor Street
London, EC4Y 6DA, United Kingdom
Huq & Company
47/1 Purana Paltan
Dhaka, Bangladesh
Eversheds LLP
Senator House 85 Queen Victoria Street
London, EC4V 4JL, United Kingdom

BEXIMCO SYNTHETICS LIMITED
17 Dhanmondi R/A Road No 2
Dhaka, 1205, Bangladesh
Tel.: (880) 2 8618220
E-Mail: beximcochq@beximco.net
Web Site: www.beximcosynthetics.com
Year Founded: 1990
BXSYNTH—(DHA)
Sales Range: $10-24.9 Million
Emp.: 408
Business Description:
Yarn Mfr
S.I.C.: 2299
N.A.I.C.S.: 313110
Personnel:
A. S. F. Rahman *(Chm & Mng Dir)*
Salman F. Rahman *(Vice Chm)*
Board of Directors:
A. S. F. Rahman
Iqbal Ahmed
O. K. Chowdhury
Mohammad Alauddin Khan
M. A. Qasem
A. B. Siddiqur Rahman
Salman F. Rahman

BEXTEX LIMITED
17 Dhanmondi R/A Rd No 2
1205 Dhaka, Bangladesh
Tel.: (880) 28611891
Fax: (880) 29677701
E-Mail: beximchq@bextex.net
Web Site: www.bextex.net
BEXTEX—(DHA)
Sales Range: $150-199.9 Million
Emp.: 5,181
Business Description:
Yarn & Denim Fabrics Mfr
S.I.C.: 2299
N.A.I.C.S.: 313210
Personnel:
A. S. Rahman *(Chm & Mng Dir)*
Salman F. Rahman *(Vice Chm)*
Syed Naved Husain *(CEO)*
Ajay Pratap Singh *(CFO)*
Sardar Ahmed Khan *(COO)*
Md. Asad Ullah *(Sec)*
Board of Directors:
A. S. Rahman
M. A. Qasem
Salman F. Rahman

BEYAZ FILO OTO KIRALAMA A.S.
Birlik Mahallesi Sehit Kurbani Akboga Sokak No 24
Ankara, 6610, Turkey
Tel.: (90) 312 454 20 00
Fax: (90) 3124542010
E-Mail: info@beyazfilo.com
Web Site: www.beyazfilo.com
Emp.: 130
Business Description:
Passenger Car Rental
S.I.C.: 7514
N.A.I.C.S.: 532111
Personnel:
Gurkan Gencler *(Chm)*

BEYERDYNAMIC GMBH & CO KG
Theresienstrasse 8
74072 Heilbronn, Germany
Tel.: (49) 71316170
Fax: (49) 7131617224
E-Mail: info@beyerdynamic.com
Web Site: www.beyerdynamic.com
Year Founded: 1924
Rev.: $47,589,300
Emp.: 300
Business Description:
Audio Equipment Mfr
S.I.C.: 3651
N.A.I.C.S.: 334310
Personnel:
Wolfgang Luckhardt *(Gen Mgr)*

BEYOND INTERNATIONAL LIMITED
109 Reserve Road
Artarmon, NSW, 2064, Australia
Tel.: (61) 294372000
Fax: (61) 294399235
Web Site: www.beyond.com.au
BYI—(ASX)
Rev.: $107,152,890
Assets: $72,581,223
Liabilities: $28,735,908
Net Worth: $43,845,315
Earnings: $9,880,150
Emp.: 174
Fiscal Year-end: 06/30/13
Business Description:
DVD Distribution
S.I.C.: 5099
N.A.I.C.S.: 423990
Personnel:
Mikael Borglund *(CEO & Mng Dir)*
Robert Milne *(Sec & Gen Mgr-Fin)*
John Luscombe *(Exec VP & Gen Mgr-Productions)*
Sherry Fynbo *(Sr VP-Sls-USA, Canada & Latin America)*
Board of Directors:
Ian Ingram
Mikael Borglund
Anthony Hsien Pin Lee
Ian Robertson
Legal Counsel:
Holding Redlich
Level 65 MLC Centre 19 Martin Place
Sydney, Australia

Gaines Solomon Law Group LLP
1901 Avenue of the Stars Suite 1100
Los Angeles, CA 90067

Arnold Bloch Leibler
Level 24 2 Chifley Square
Sydney, NSW, 2000, Australia
Subsidiaries:

Beyond Distribution Pty Ltd (1)
109 Reserve Rd
Artarmon, NSW, 2064, Australia
Tel.: (61) 294372000
Fax: (61) 294372017
E-Mail: distribution@beyond.com.au
Emp.: 16
Television Programme Distr
S.I.C.: 4833
N.A.I.C.S.: 515120

Beyond Entertainment Pty Ltd (1)
109 Reserve Rd
Artarmon, NSW, 2064, Australia
Tel.: (61) 294372000
Fax: (61) 94372181
Emp.: 200
Movie Production & Distribution Services
S.I.C.: 7812
N.A.I.C.S.: 512110
Mikael Borglund *(Gen Mgr)*

Beyond Films Limited (1)
109 Reserve Rd
Artarmon, NSW, 2064, Australia
Tel.: (61) 294372000
Fax: (61) 294372002
Emp.: 180
Motion Picture & Video Production Services
S.I.C.: 7812
N.A.I.C.S.: 512110
Joanne Azzopardi *(VP)*

Beyond Home Entertainment Pty Ltd (1)
701 Macarthur Ave
Eagle Farm, VIC, 4009, Australia
Tel.: (61) 393211200
Fax: (61) 393298116
E-Mail: sales_bhe@beyond.com.au
Web Site: www.beyondhomeentertainment.com.au
Emp.: 15
Movie Distr
S.I.C.: 7829
N.A.I.C.S.: 512120
Subsidiaries:

Arthur & Pat Laing Entertainment Pty Ltd (2)
35 Montague St
Goulburn, NSW, 2580, Australia
Tel.: (61) 2 4821 4913
Fax: (61) 2 4822 0007
Web Site: www.laing-entertainment.com.au
Events & Concerts Organizing Services
S.I.C.: 7999
N.A.I.C.S.: 711310
Geoff Bell *(Agency Mgr & Owner)*

Magna Home Entertainment Pty Ltd (2)
701 MacArthur Ave Central
PO Box 1556
Eagle Farm, QLD, 4009, Australia
Tel.: (61) 732679888
Fax: (61) 732671116
E-Mail: info@magnahe.com.au
Web Site: www.magnahomeentertainment.com.au
Emp.: 60
Movie Digital Video Disc & Blueray Disc Sales
S.I.C.: 3652
N.A.I.C.S.: 334614
Philip Maddison *(Gen Mgr)*
Non-U.S. Subsidiary:

Magna Home Entertainment (NZ) Limited (3)
25A Triton Dr
Albany North Shore, Takapuna, Auckland, 0632, New Zealand
Tel.: (64) 94772146
Fax: (64) 94760149
E-Mail: orders@mhe.co.nz
Web Site: www.mhe.co.nz
Emp.: 7
Movie Videos Whslr
S.I.C.: 7819
N.A.I.C.S.: 512199
Alistir Ramsay *(Mgr)*

Beyond Productions Pty Ltd (1)
109 Reserve Rd
Artarmon, NSW, 2064, Australia
Tel.: (61) 294372000
Fax: (61) 294372002
E-Mail: frontdesk@beyond.com.au
Web Site: www.beyond.com.au
Emp.: 100
Motion Picture Production Services
S.I.C.: 7812
N.A.I.C.S.: 512110
John Luscombe *(Head-Production)*

Beyond Properties Pty Ltd (1)
109 Reserve Rd
Artarmon, Sydney, NSW, 2064, Australia
Tel.: (61) 294372000
Fax: (61) 294372002
E-Mail: frontdesk@beyondvision.com.au
Emp.: 150
Property Management Services
S.I.C.: 6531
N.A.I.C.S.: 531311
Tim Mcgee *(Gen Mgr-Bus & Product Dev)*
Subsidiary:

Beyond Pty Ltd (2)
109 Reserve Rd
Artarmon, NSW, 2064, Australia
Tel.: (61) 294372000
Fax: (61) 294372001
E-Mail: frontdesk@beyond.com.au
Emp.: 100
Motion Picture & Video Production Services
S.I.C.: 7812
N.A.I.C.S.: 512110
Michael Borglund *(Mgr)*

dSp Beyond Pty Ltd (1)
Level 2 18-26 Dickson Ave
Artarmon, NSW, 2064, Australia
Tel.: (61) 284252430
Fax: (61) 294379416
E-Mail: info@dspbeyond.com
Emp.: 20
Television Program Production Services
S.I.C.: 7812
N.A.I.C.S.: 512110
Denis Spencer *(Gen Mgr)*

Eurocam Australia Pty Ltd (1)
Studio 47 90 Mona Vale Rd
Mona Vale, NSW, 2103, Australia
Tel.: (61) 2 9997 8899
Fax: (61) 2 9997 8099
E-Mail: info@eurocam.com.au
Web Site: www.eurocam.com.au
Emp.: 7
Sports Program Production & Distribution Services
S.I.C.: 4813
N.A.I.C.S.: 517110
Frank Chidiac *(Gen Mgr)*
U.S. Subsidiary:

Beyond Productions Inc (1)
4455 Connecticut Ave NW Ste 250
Washington, DC 20008-2324
Tel.: (202) 587-4131
Fax: (202) 587-4165
E-Mail: lottery@beyond.com.au
Emp.: 10
Motion Picture & Video Production Services
S.I.C.: 7812
N.A.I.C.S.: 512110
John Luscombe *(Sr VP & Gen Mgr)*

BEYOND IVR HOLDINGS, INC.
505 6th Street SW Suite 2806
Calgary, AB, T2P 1X5, Canada
Tel.: (403) 237-8330
Fax: (403) 228-3013
Web Site: www.beyondivr.com
Year Founded: 2009
Emp.: 5
Business Description:
Holding Company; Integrated Voice Response Products
S.I.C.: 6719
N.A.I.C.S.: 551112
Personnel:
Francis Bok *(Chm, Pres, CEO, CFO & Chief Acctg Officer)*
Tony Wong *(Treas)*
Alan P. Chan *(Sec)*
Board of Directors:
Francis Bok
Alan P. Chan
Tony Wong

BEYONDSOFT CORPORATION
18 Xinxi Street Shangdi Innovation Building
Shangdi
Haidian District, Beijing, 100085, China
Tel.: (86) 10 6297 3608
Fax: (86) 10 6297 3708
E-Mail: info@beyondsoft.com
Web Site: www.beyondsoft.com
Year Founded: 1995
002649—(SSE)
Emp.: 4,200
Business Description:
IT Services
S.I.C.: 7379
N.A.I.C.S.: 541519
Personnel:
Ben Wang *(Pres & CEO)*
Marshall Ma *(CFO & COO)*
Li Fei *(Sec & Controller)*
Li Liang *(Exec VP-R&D Engrg-Tech & Telecom Indus)*
Aaron Liu *(Exec VP-R&D Engrg & IT Outsourcing-Global Accts)*
Roger Zhang *(Exec VP-R&D-China, US & Singapore)*
Divisions:

Beyondsoft Corporation (1)
Unit D Delphini Wuxi National Software Park
18 Zhenze Road
New District, Wuxi, 214135, China
Tel.: (86) 510 8538 2368
Fax: (86) 510 8538 3459
IT Services

Beyondsoft Corporation—(Continued)

S.I.C.: 7379
N.A.I.C.S.: 541519

Beyondsoft Corporation (1)
4th Floor Building 2 Optical Valley Software Park
Eastlake Developing Zone, Wuhan, 430073, China
Tel.: (86) 27 8758 8009
IT Services
S.I.C.: 7379
N.A.I.C.S.: 541519

Beyondsoft Corporation (1)
10F Tower H R&D Building Jin Ye 1 Road
Xi'an Software Park
Hi-tech Industrial Devel Zone, Xi'an, 710065, China
Tel.: (86) 29 68659333
Fax: (86) 29 68659329
IT Services
S.I.C.: 7379
N.A.I.C.S.: 541519

Beyondsoft Corporation (1)
3/F FiberHome Technologies Building 5-3 Shangdi East Road
Haidian District, Beijing, 100085, China
Tel.: (86) 10 6296 9858
Fax: (86) 10 6296 0387
IT Services
S.I.C.: 7379
N.A.I.C.S.: 541519

Beyondsoft Corporation (1)
Unit A Zone 3 Building 9 Zhongguancun Software Park
Haidian District, Beijing, 100193, China
Tel.: (86) 10 8282 6100
Fax: (86) 10 8282 6101
IT Services
S.I.C.: 7379
N.A.I.C.S.: 541519

Beyondsoft Corporation (1)
C-7-101 Tianfu Software Park
Gaoxin District, Chengdu, 610041, China
Tel.: (86) 28 8598 0092
Fax: (86) 28 8598 0091
IT Services
S.I.C.: 7379
N.A.I.C.S.: 541519

Beyondsoft Corporation (1)
F2 Tianda Technologies Garden 88 the 4th Street
Economic & Tech Devel Area, Tianjin, 300384, China
Tel.: (86) 22 2532 1029
IT Services
S.I.C.: 7379
N.A.I.C.S.: 541519

Beyondsoft Corporation (1)
5th Floor A3 Block Binjiang Intelligence Port 301
Binxing Road, Hangzhou, 310052, China
Tel.: (86) 571 8769 6000
Fax: (86) 571 8778 8080
IT Services
S.I.C.: 7379
N.A.I.C.S.: 541519

Beyondsoft Corporation (1)
3F 1Building 500 Lane Zhangheng Road
Zhangjiang High Tech Park
Pudong District, Shanghai, 201203, China
Tel.: (86) 21 6165 6766
Fax: (86) 21 6160 5966
IT Services
S.I.C.: 7379
N.A.I.C.S.: 541519

Beyondsoft Corporation (1)
Room B604 Wuhan University Industry-Academia-Research Building
Keyuan Nan Road Hi-tech Zone
Nanshan District, Shenzhen, 518057, China
Tel.: (86) 755 8661 5116
Fax: (86) 755 8661 5110
IT Services
S.I.C.: 7379
N.A.I.C.S.: 541519

U.S. Subsidiaries:

Beyondsoft Consulting Inc. (1)
11 Crown Plza Ste 101H
Hazlet, NJ 07730
Tel.: (732) 739-8889
Fax: (732) 203-0788
Web Site: www.beyondsoft.com
IT Consulting Services
S.I.C.: 8999
N.A.I.C.S.: 541690
Ben Wang *(CEO)*

Beyondsoft Consulting Inc. (1)
4042 148th Ave NE Ste K1A
Redmond, WA 98052
Tel.: (425) 242-5419
IT Consulting Services
S.I.C.: 8999
N.A.I.C.S.: 541690
Diane Li *(VP)*

Non-U.S. Subsidiaries:

Beyondsoft Corporation (1)
3/F Koei Bldg 29-2 Takadanobaba 1-chome
Shinjuku-ku, Tokyo, 169-0075, Japan
Tel.: (81) 3 3204 2181
IT Services
S.I.C.: 7379
N.A.I.C.S.: 541519

Beyondsoft Corporation (1)
Block 1200 Depot Road #07-14/15
Singapore, 109675, Singapore
Tel.: (65) 6272 3582
Fax: (65) 6270 8953
IT Services
S.I.C.: 7379
N.A.I.C.S.: 541519

Eastern Software Systems Pvt. Ltd. (1)
B-65 Sector 63
Noida, 201 307, India
Tel.: (91) 120 4212931
Fax: (91) 120 4212930
E-Mail: contact@essindia.com
Web Site: www.essindia.com
IT Services
S.I.C.: 7379
N.A.I.C.S.: 541519
Sanjay Agarwala *(CEO & Mng Dir)*

Divisions:

Eastern Software Systems Pvt. Ltd. (2)
301 Arvind Chambers Above Sai Service
Western Express Highway
Adheri E, Mumbai, 400 069, India
Tel.: (91) 22 66945190
Fax: (91) 22 66945192
IT Services
S.I.C.: 7379
N.A.I.C.S.: 541519

Eastern Software Systems Pvt. Ltd. (2)
AK Trade Centre
1/1 Camac Centre 3rd Floor 6, Kolkata, 700 016, India
Tel.: (91) 33 2229 8327
Fax: (91) 33 2229 9282
IT Services
S.I.C.: 7379
N.A.I.C.S.: 541519

Eastern Software Systems Pvt. Ltd. (2)
S&S Business Center #224
1st Main Road Domlur 2nd Stage
Indiranagar, Bengaluru, 560 071, India
Tel.: (91) 80 41538463
IT Services
S.I.C.: 7379
N.A.I.C.S.: 541519

Eastern Software Systems Pvt. Ltd. (2)
9-1-159/3 Gomez Building Sebastian Road
Secunderabad, 500 003, India
Tel.: (91) 40 30626992
IT Services
S.I.C.: 7379
N.A.I.C.S.: 541519

BEZEQ - THE ISRAEL TELECOMMUNICATION CORP. LIMITED

(d/b/a Bezeq Group)
Azrieli Center 2
61620 Tel Aviv, Israel
Tel.: (972) 36262600
Fax: (972) 36262609
E-Mail: dover@bezeq.co.il
Web Site: www.bezeq.co.il
Year Founded: 1984
BEZQ—(OTC TAE)
Rev.: $2,761,493,040
Assets: $4,236,008,880
Liabilities: $3,575,056,080
Net Worth: $660,952,800
Earnings: $500,819,520
Emp.: 3,187
Fiscal Year-end: 12/31/12

Business Description:
Holding Company;
Telecommunications Products & Services
S.I.C.: 6719
N.A.I.C.S.: 551112

Personnel:
Shaul Elovitch *(Chm)*
Stella Handler *(CEO)*
David Mizrahi *(Deputy CEO & CFO)*
Isaac Benbenisti *(CEO-Intl)*
Ron Eiolon *(CEO-Yes)*
Gil Sharon *(CEO-Pelephone)*

Board of Directors:
Shaul Elovitch
Eldad Ben-Moshe
Felix Cohen
Yair David
Yitzhak Edelman
Or Elovitch
Orna Elovitch-Peled
Mordechai Keret
Rami Nomkin
Yehoshua Rosenzweig
Amikam Shorer
Tali Simon

Subsidiary:

Pelephone Communications, Ltd. (1)
33 Yitzhak Rabin Street
Givatayim, 53489, Israel
Tel.: (972) 3 572 8881 (100%)
Fax: (972) 3 572 8111
Web Site: www.pelephone.co.il
Emp.: 4,200
Mobile Telecommunications Services
S.I.C.: 4812
N.A.I.C.S.: 517210
Gil Sharon *(CEO)*
Nir Sztern *(Deputy CEO & Exec VP)*
Larry Akerman *(CFO)*
Jack Dabby *(Gen Counsel & VP)*

BF&M LIMITED

BF&M Insurance Building 112 Pitts Bay Road
Pembroke, HM 08, Bermuda
Mailing Address:
PO Box HM 1007
Hamilton, HM DX, Bermuda
Tel.: (441) 2955566
Fax: (441) 2928604
E-Mail: info@ageconcern.bm
Web Site: www.bfm.bm
Year Founded: 1991
BFM—(BERM)
Premiums: $319,681,000
Assets: $1,526,540,000
Liabilities: $1,273,349,000
Net Worth: $253,191,000
Earnings: $26,308,000
Fiscal Year-end: 12/31/12

Business Description:
Insurance Services
S.I.C.: 6411
N.A.I.C.S.: 524298

Personnel:
Gavin R. Arton *(Chm)*
R. John Wight *(Pres & CEO)*
Michael G. White *(CFO)*
Susan M. Reed *(COO)*
Miguel DaPonte *(Sr VP-BF&M Investment Services Limited)*
Glen P. Gibbons *(Sr VP-BF&M General Insurance Company Limited)*
Paul Matthews *(Sr VP-BF&M Life Company)*
Patrick M. Neal *(Sr VP-Bus Dev)*

Board of Directors:
Gavin R. Arton
Nancy L. Gosling
Gregory D. Haycock
L. Anthony Joaquin
Stephen W. Kempe
Catherine S. Lord
Garry A. Madeiros
Aaron E. Smith
Richard D. Spurling
Ann B. Teixeira
C. L. F. Watchorn
R. John Wight

Non-U.S. Subsidiary:

BF&M (Canada) Limited (1)
36 Brookshire Ct Ste 5
Bedford, NS, B4A 4EP, Canada
Tel.: (902) 482-8924
Fax: (902) 832-6639
Toll Free: (877) 237-2682
Emp.: 25
Investment Management Services
S.I.C.: 8748
N.A.I.C.S.: 541618
Paul Mathews *(Gen Mgr)*

BF INVESTMENT LIMITED

Mundhwa
Pune, 411036, India
Tel.: (91) 2026822552
Fax: (91) 2026823061
E-Mail: bfinvestment@vsnl.net
Web Site: www.kalyanigroup.com
BFINVEST—(NSE)
Rev.: $7,144,053
Assets: $119,881,500
Liabilities: $388,891
Net Worth: $119,492,610
Earnings: $4,889,696
Fiscal Year-end: 03/31/13

Business Description:
Investment & Real Estate Management Services
S.I.C.: 6211
N.A.I.C.S.: 523999

Personnel:
S. R. Kshirsagar *(Compliance Officer & Sec)*

Board of Directors:
B. N. Kalyani
B. B. Hattarki
A. B. Kalyani
M. U. Takale

Transfer Agent:
Link Intime India Private Limited
202 Akshay Complex Near Ganesh Mandir
Dhole Patil Road
Pune, India

B.F. LORENZETTI & ASSOCIATES

2001 McGill College Suite 2200
Montreal, QC, H3A 1G1, Canada
Tel.: (514) 843-3632
Fax: (514) 843-3842
Web Site: www.bflcanada.ca
Year Founded: 1987
Rev.: $13,209,735
Emp.: 82

Business Description:
Commercial Insurance Brokerage Services
S.I.C.: 6411
N.A.I.C.S.: 524298

Personnel:
Barry F. Lorenzetti *(Pres)*
Frank A. Howden *(Pres-Marine Div)*
Jacques Dufresne *(Exec VP-Eastern Reg)*
Moreno Fiore *(Sr VP-Bus Dev-Eastern Canada)*

BF UTILITIES LTD.

Mundhwa
Pune, 411036, India
Tel.: (91) 20 2682 2552
Fax: (91) 20 2682 3061
E-Mail: bfutilitiesltd@vsnl.net
Web Site: www.bfutilities.com
BFUTILITIE—(NSE)
Rev.: $33,456,895
Assets: $364,096,127
Liabilities: $337,546,360
Net Worth: $26,549,767
Earnings: ($17,565,579)
Fiscal Year-end: 09/30/13

Business Description:
Electric Power Generation Services
S.I.C.: 4911
N.A.I.C.S.: 221118
Personnel:
Bhalchandra S. Mitkari *(Compliance Officer, Sec & Sr VP-Fin)*
Board of Directors:
Baba N. Kalyani
G. K. Agarwal
B. B. Hattarki
Amit B. Kalyani
S. S. Vaidya
Transfer Agent:
Link Intime India Private Limited
202 Akshay Complex Near Ganesh Mandir
Dhole Patil Road
Pune, India

BF1 MOTORSPORT HOLDINGS LTD.

(Formerly BERU Motorsport Holdings Ltd.)
Technical Centre
Owen Road, Diss, Norfolk, IP22 4ER, United Kingdom
Tel.: (44) 1379 646 200
Fax: (44) 1379 646 900
E-Mail: enquiries@bf1systems.com
Web Site: www.f1systems.com
Emp.: 76

Business Description:
Holding Company
S.I.C.: 6719
N.A.I.C.S.: 551112
Personnel:
John Bailey *(Mng Dir)*

Holding:

bf1systems Ltd. (1)
(Formerly BERU F1 Systems Ltd.)
Technical Centre
Owen Road, Diss, Norfolk, IP22 4ER, United Kingdom
Tel.: (44) 1379646200
Fax: (44) 1379646900
E-Mail: marketing@bf1systems.com
Web Site: www.bf1systems.com
Sales Range: $10-24.9 Million
Automotive Ignition, Electronics & Sensor Technology
S.I.C.: 3714
N.A.I.C.S.: 336390
John Bailey *(Owner & Mng Dir)*

BFI OPTILAS INTERNATIONAL S.A.S.

4 Alle Du Cantal
91090 Lisses, France
Tel.: (33) 160795900
Fax: (33) 01607989701
E-Mail: info@bfioptilas.com
Web Site: www.bfioptilas.com
Emp.: 310

Business Description:
Electronics & Photonics Distr
S.I.C.: 5065
N.A.I.C.S.: 423690
Personnel:
Vincent Courtney *(Pres)*

Non-U.S. Subsidiaries:

BFi OPTiLAS AB (1)
Portalgatam
PO Box 1335
S-75143 Uppsala, Sweden SE
Tel.: (46) 18565830
Fax: (46) 4618696666
E-Mail: info.se@bfioptilas.com
Web Site: www.bfioptilas.se
Emp.: 18
Electronic & Photonic Products Distr
S.I.C.: 5065
N.A.I.C.S.: 423690

BFi OPTiLAS B.V. (1)
Christiaan Huygensweg 17
2408 AJ Alphen aan den Rijn, Netherlands NL
Tel.: (31) 172446060
Fax: (31) 172443414
E-Mail: info.nl@bfioptilas.com
Web Site: www.bfioptilas.nl
Emp.: 20
Electronic & Photonic Products Distr
S.I.C.: 5065
N.A.I.C.S.: 423690
Rob Satink *(Mgr-Sls)*

BFi OPTiLAS GmbH (1)
Assar-Gabrielsson-Strasse 1
63128 Dietzenbach, Germany De
Tel.: (49) 607440980
Fax: (49) 60744098110
E-Mail: ipe.de@bfioptilas.com
Web Site: www.bfioptilas.de
Emp.: 70
Electronics & Photonics Sales & Distr
S.I.C.: 5065
N.A.I.C.S.: 423690
Hans Schmidt *(Mng Dir)*

BFi OPTiLAS Limited (1)
Unit D Mill Ct Wolverton Mill South
Milton Keynes, MK12 5EU, United Kingdom UK
Tel.: (44) 1908326326
Fax: (44) 1908221110
E-Mail: info.uk@bfioptilas.com
Web Site: www.acalbfi.co.uk
Emp.: 30
Electronics & Photonics Distr
S.I.C.: 5065
N.A.I.C.S.: 423690
Mike Hyliands *(Mgr-Sls-UK)*

BFi OPTiLAS SA (1)
C Anabel Segura 7 Planta Acceso
Alcobendas, 28108 Madrid, Spain ES
Tel.: (34) 914531160
Fax: (34) 916626837
E-Mail: info.es@bfioptilas.com
Web Site: www.bfioptilas.es
Emp.: 50
Electronics & Photonics Sales & Distr
S.I.C.: 5065
N.A.I.C.S.: 423690
Oscar Romero *(Mng Dir)*

BFi OPTiLAS S.r.l. (1)
Via Brembo 27
20139 Milan, Italy IT
Tel.: (39) 0002535831
Fax: (39) 0253583201
E-Mail: info.it@bfioptilas.com
Web Site: www.bfioptilas.it
Emp.: 15
Electronics & Photonics Sales & Distr
S.I.C.: 5065
N.A.I.C.S.: 423690

BFS ENTERTAINMENT & MULTIMEDIA LIMITED

360 Newkirk Road
Richmond Hill, ON, L4C 3G7, Canada
Tel.: (905) 884-2323
Fax: (905) 884-8292
E-Mail: info@bfsent.com
Web Site: www.bfsent.com
Year Founded: 1980
BFS—(TSXV)
Sls.: $9,850,775
Assets: $5,543,635
Liabilities: $2,114,113
Net Worth: $3,429,522
Earnings: $66,651
Fiscal Year-end: 05/04/13

Business Description:
Home Video Distr
S.I.C.: 7829
N.A.I.C.S.: 512120
Personnel:
Denis B. E. Donnelly *(Chm, Pres & CEO)*
John P. Grzybowski *(CFO)*
David E. Chapman *(Sec)*
Board of Directors:
Denis B. E. Donnelly
David E. Chapman
Michael McGee
Warren Palitz
Mark C. Shoniker
Legal Counsel:
Stikeman Elliott
Toronto, ON, Canada

Lawrence Graham
London, United Kingdom

Bresver, Grossman, Schneininger & Chapman LLP
Toronto, ON, Canada
Transfer Agent:
CIBC Mellon Trust Company
PO Box 7010
Adelaide Street Postal Station, Toronto, ON, M5C 2W9, Canada
Tel.: (416) 643-5500
Fax: (416) 643-5501
Toll Free: (800) 387-0825

Subsidiaries:

BFS Film & Television Productions Inc. (1)
360 Newkirk Road
PO Box 420
Station A, Richmond Hill, ON, L4C 4Y6, Canada
Tel.: (905) 884-2323
Fax: (905) 884-8292
Toll Free: (800) 237-0511
E-Mail: info@bfsproductions.com
Web Site: www.bfsproductions.com
Video Production Services
S.I.C.: 7812
N.A.I.C.S.: 512110

Oopsadaisy Television Productions Inc (1)
360 Newkirk Rd
Richmond Hill, ON, L4C 3G7, Canada
Tel.: (905) 884-2323
Fax: (905) 884-8292
Toll Free: (800) 387-5758
Web Site: www.adventuretraveltv.com
Video Production Services
S.I.C.: 7812
N.A.I.C.S.: 512110

U.S. Subsidiary:

BFS Entertainment Limited (1)
2535 Cambridge Dr
Antioch, CA 94509-6451
Tel.: (510) 860-5853
Home Video Production Services
S.I.C.: 7812
N.A.I.C.S.: 512110

BFW LIEGENSCHAFTEN AG

Bahnhofstrasse 92
8500 Frauenfeld, Switzerland
Tel.: (41) 848 820 410
Fax: (41) 848 820 411
E-Mail: info@bfwliegenschaften.ch
Web Site: www.bfwliegenschaften.ch
Year Founded: 2002
BLIN—(SWX)

Business Description:
Real Estate Development Services
S.I.C.: 6531
N.A.I.C.S.: 531390
Personnel:
Beat Frischknecht *(CEO)*
Reto Borner *(CFO)*
Board of Directors:
Andre Robert Spathelf
Hans Jorg Brun
Beat Frischknecht

BG AGRO JSC

12 Gen Kolev Str
9000 Varna, Bulgaria
Tel.: (359) 52 601 656
Fax: (359) 52 601 803
E-Mail: bgagro@bgagro.bg
Web Site: www.bgagro.bg
AO0—(BUL)

Business Description:
Chemical & Fertilizer Distr
S.I.C.: 5169
N.A.I.C.S.: 424690
Personnel:
Nenko Nenkov *(Chm)*
Board of Directors:
Nenko Nenkov
Zlatina Chotukova
Daniel Nenkov

BG GROUP PLC

Thames Valley Park
Reading, Berks, RG6 1PT, United Kingdom
Tel.: (44) 1189353222
Fax: (44) 1189353484
E-Mail: Box.info@bg-group.com
Web Site: www.bg-group.com
Year Founded: 1986
BG—(LSE OTC)
Rev.: $18,933,000,000
Assets: $65,247,000,000
Liabilities: $32,153,000,000
Net Worth: $33,094,000,000
Earnings: $4,613,000,000
Emp.: 6,568
Fiscal Year-end: 12/31/12

Business Description:
Natural Gas Mfr & Distr
S.I.C.: 1311
N.A.I.C.S.: 211111
Personnel:
Christopher Finlayson *(CEO)*
Den Jones *(Interim CFO)*
Sami Iskander *(COO)*
Fabio Barbosa *(Chm-South America)*
Graham Vinter *(Gen Counsel)*
Steve Allen *(Sec)*
Catherine Tanna *(Exec VP & Mng Dir-Australia & East Asia)*
Robert Booker *(Exec VP-HR)*
Malcolm Brown *(Exec VP-Exploration)*
Chris Cox *(Exec VP-Advance)*
John Grant *(Exec VP-Policy & Corp Affairs)*
Matt Schatzman *(Exec VP-Energy Mktg & Shipping)*
Board of Directors:
Andrew F. J. Gould
Peter Backhouse
Vivienne Cox
Pamela Daley
Martin Ferguson
Christopher Finlayson
Baroness Hogg
John Hood
Den Jones
Caio Koch-Weser
Haw-Kuang Lim
David Manning
Mark Seligman
Patrick W. Thomas
Legal Counsel:
Herbert Smith
Watling House 35 Cannon St.
London, EC4M 5SD, United Kingdom
Transfer Agent:
JP Morgan Chase Bank N.A.
PO Box 64504
Saint Paul, MN 55164

BG Group Plc—(Continued)

Non-U.S. Subsidiaries:

B.G. Bolivia Corporation **(1)**
Sucursal Bolivia H Cuarto Anillo
El Palmar, 6400 Santa Cruz, Bolivia (100%)
Tel.: (591) 33550000
Telex: 335-4269 TESORO BV
Fax: (591) 33551000
E-Mail: info@bg-group.com
Web Site: www.bg-group.com
Emp.: 60
Hydro Carbon Explorations
S.I.C.: 2911
N.A.I.C.S.: 324110
Orlando Baca *(Pres & Gen Mgr)*

BG Canada Exploration & Production Inc. **(1)**
Ste 500 222 3rd Ave SW
Calgary, AB, T2P 0B4, Canada AB
Tel.: (403) 538-7400 (100%)
Fax: (403) 538-7500
E-Mail: info@bggroup.com
Web Site: www.bggroup.com
Emp.: 80
Oil & Gas Exploration Services
S.I.C.: 1389
N.A.I.C.S.: 213112
Glenn McNamara *(Pres & Gen Mgr)*

BG Italia S.p.A. **(1)**
Piazza Cavour 2
20121 Milan, Italy
Tel.: (39) 02777941
Fax: (39) 0277794440
E-Mail: info@bg-group.com
Web Site: www.bg-group.com
Emp.: 40
Power Plants
S.I.C.: 4911
N.A.I.C.S.: 221122
Ganiano Ratti *(Pres)*

Subsidiary:

Serene SpA **(2)**
Viale Italia 590
20099 Sesto San Giovanni, MI, Italy (32%)
Tel.: (39) 02 224 79506
Fax: (39) 02 224 79500
E-Mail: serenespa@serene.it
Web Site: www.serene.it
Emp.: 15
Power Generation
S.I.C.: 4939
N.A.I.C.S.: 221122
Alberto Stuflesser *(Mng Dir)*

MetroGas S.A. **(1)**
Gregorio Araoz de Lamadrid 1360
1267 Buenos Aires, Argentina Ar
Tel.: (54) 11430 91010 (45%)
Fax: (54) 11 4309 1025
E-Mail: info@metrogas.com.ar
Web Site: www.metrogas.com.ar
METR—(BAR BUE)
Sls.: $243,500,365
Assets: $490,172,527
Liabilities: $414,882,471
Net Worth: $75,290,056
Earnings: ($28,749,503)
Emp.: 1,147
Fiscal Year-end: 12/31/12
Distributor of Gas
S.I.C.: 4924
N.A.I.C.S.: 221210
Andres Cordero *(CEO)*

BG T&A CO.

4 5 6F L&C Tower 1026-52 Sanbon-dong
Gunpo, Gyeonggi-do, Korea (South)
Tel.: (82) 31 488 7900
Web Site: www.bgtna.com
Year Founded: 1996
046310—(BOM)
Sls.: $98,619,060
Assets: $72,105,690
Liabilities: $40,678,200
Net Worth: $31,427,490
Earnings: ($624,030)
Emp.: 58
Fiscal Year-end: 12/31/12
Business Description:
Nautical System & Instrument Mfr
S.I.C.: 3812
N.A.I.C.S.: 334511
Personnel:
Hag-gyu Lim *(CEO)*

BGE ELEKTROTECHNIK GMBH

Auf der Aue 3
99834 Gerstungen, Germany
Tel.: (49) 369279400
Fax: (49) 3692794040
E-Mail: info@bge-et.de
Web Site: www.bge-et.de
Year Founded: 1978
Rev.: $16,714,257
Emp.: 76
Business Description:
Automotive Wiring Systems Mfr
S.I.C.: 3714
N.A.I.C.S.: 336390
Personnel:
Gerald Bicking *(Mgr-Distr)*

B.G.E. SERVICE & SUPPLY LTD.

5711 103 A Street
Edmonton, AB, Canada T6H 2J6
Tel.: (780) 436-6960
Fax: (780) 437-1097
Toll Free: (866) 436-6960
E-Mail: headoffice@thefiltershop.com
Web Site: www.thefiltershop.com
Year Founded: 1968
Rev.: $37,200,000
Emp.: 130
Business Description:
Industrial Filters Mfr
S.I.C.: 5085
N.A.I.C.S.: 423840
Personnel:
Roberta MacGillivray *(Pres)*
Darrel Sutton *(CEO)*

BGI-SHENZHEN

Beishan Industrial Zone
Yantian District, Shenzhen, 518083, China
Tel.: (86) 755 2527 3620
E-Mail: tech@genomics.cn
Web Site: www.genomics.cn/en
Year Founded: 1999
Business Description:
Genomics Research & Development
S.I.C.: 8731
N.A.I.C.S.: 541711
Personnel:
Huanming Yang *(Co-Founder & Chm)*
Jian Wang *(Co-Founder)*
Jun Wang *(CEO)*
Board of Directors:
Huanming Yang
Jian Wang
Jun Wang

U.S. Subsidiary:

BGI Americas Corporation **(1)**
1 Broadway 3rd Floor
Cambridge, MA 02142 DE
Tel.: (617) 500-2741
Fax: (617) 500-2742
Web Site: www.bgiamericas.com
Genomics Research & Development
S.I.C.: 8731
N.A.I.C.S.: 541711
Joyce Peng *(Mktg Dir)*

Subsidiary:

Complete Genomics, Inc. **(2)**
2071 Stierlin Ct
Mountain View, CA 94043 DE
Tel.: (650) 943-2800
E-Mail: info@completegenomics.com
Web Site: www.completegenomics.com
Emp.: 255
DNA Sequencing Services
S.I.C.: 8731
N.A.I.C.S.: 541711
Clifford A. Reid *(CEO)*
Radoje T. Drmanac *(Chief Scientific Officer)*
Jill Hagenkord *(Chief Medical Officer)*
Ethan Knowlden *(Gen Counsel, Sec & Sr VP)*

BGIL FILMS & TECHNOLOGIES LTD.

B-13 LGF Amar Colony Lajpat Nagar IV
New Delhi, 110024, India
Tel.: (91) 11 40765562
Fax: (91) 11 41377519
E-Mail: contact@bgilinfo.com
Web Site: www.bgilfilms.com
511664—(BOM)
Rev.: $2,664,601
Assets: $5,581,695
Liabilities: $1,392,159
Net Worth: $4,189,536
Earnings: ($5,888)
Fiscal Year-end: 03/31/13
Business Description:
Post Production Services
S.I.C.: 7819
N.A.I.C.S.: 512191
Personnel:
Rakesh Bhhatia *(Chm)*
Renu Kamra *(Compliance Officer & Sec)*
Board of Directors:
Rakesh Bhhatia
Harjit Singh Anand
Ashok Kumar Juneja
Rajiv Kumar
Jaya Misra
Vimal Kumar Srivastava
Transfer Agent:
Mass Services Limited
T 34 2nd Floor Okhla Industrial Area Phase-II
New Delhi, India

BGL GROUP LIMITED

Pegasus House Bakewell Road
Orton Southgate, Peterborough, PE2 6YS, United Kingdom
Tel.: (44) 1733374444
Fax: (44) 1733845009
Web Site: www.bglgroup.co.uk
Year Founded: 1992
Sales Range: $800-899.9 Million
Emp.: 2,270
Business Description:
Holding Company; Insurance Intermediary & Brokerage Services
S.I.C.: 6719
N.A.I.C.S.: 551112
Personnel:
Douw Steyn *(Founder & Chm)*
Matthew Donaldson *(Grp CEO)*
Ian Leech *(Deputy CEO & Dir-Fin)*
Stuart Walters *(CIO)*
Board of Directors:
Douw Steyn
Chery Clifford
Matthew Donaldson
Stephen Klinkert
Ian Leech

Subsidiary:

Budget Insurance Company Limited **(1)**
Pegasus House Bakewell Road
Orton Southgate, Peterborough, PE2 6YS, United Kingdom UK
Tel.: (44) 1733374444
Fax: (44) 1733845009
E-Mail: info@bglgroup.co.uk
Web Site: www.bglgroup.co.uk
Insurance Intermediary & Brokerage Services
S.I.C.: 6411
N.A.I.C.S.: 524210
Douw Steyn *(Founder & Chm)*
Peter Winslow *(CEO)*
Ian Leech *(Deputy CEO & Dir-Fin)*

Non-U.S. Subsidiary:

Auto & General Insurance Company Limited **(2)**
Level 6 9 Sherwood Road
Toowong, QLD, 4066, Australia AU
Tel.: (61) 733778804
Fax: (61) 733778802
E-Mail: reception.toowong@aihco.com.au
Web Site: www.agic.com.au
Sales Range: $25-49.9 Million
Emp.: 400
Insurance Services
S.I.C.: 6411
N.A.I.C.S.: 524210
Donald Campbell *(Chm)*
Stephen Klinkert *(Deputy Chm)*

BGLOBAL PLC

Arkwright House 2 Arkwright Court
Commercial Road, Darwen, Lancs, BB3 0FG, United Kingdom
Tel.: (44) 1254 819600
Fax: (44) 1254 819601
E-Mail: info@bglobalplc.com
Web Site: www.bglobalplc.com
BGBL—(AIM)
Rev.: $18,284,721
Assets: $23,431,425
Liabilities: $8,161,992
Net Worth: $15,269,433
Earnings: ($669,485)
Emp.: 175
Fiscal Year-end: 03/31/13
Business Description:
Smart Energy Software & Services
S.I.C.: 7372
N.A.I.C.S.: 511210
Personnel:
John Grant *(Chm)*
Tim Jackson-Smith *(CEO)*
Nicholas John Makinson *(Sec)*
Board of Directors:
John Grant
Steven Fawkes
Tim Jackson-Smith
James Newman
Legal Counsel:
Eversheds LLP
Bridgewater Pl Water Ln
Leeds, United Kingdom

Subsidiary:

B Global Metering Limited **(1)**
Arkwright House Arkwright Ct Comml Rd
Darwen, Lancashire, BB3 0FG, United Kingdom
Tel.: (44) 1254819600
Fax: (44) 1254 819603
E-Mail: info@bglobalmetering.com
Emp.: 150
Metering Services
S.I.C.: 7389
N.A.I.C.S.: 561990
Peter Kennedy *(CEO)*

BGR ENERGY SYSTEMS LIMITED

443 Anna Salai
Teynampet, Chennai, 600 018, India
Tel.: (91) 4424335958
Fax: (91) 4424338775
E-Mail: response@bgrenergy.com
Web Site: www.bgrcorp.com
BGRENERGY—(NSE)
Rev.: $5,794,084
Assets: $12,190,996
Liabilities: $9,755,155
Net Worth: $2,435,841
Earnings: $300,515
Emp.: 2,418
Fiscal Year-end: 03/31/13
Business Description:
Industrial Machinery Mfr
S.I.C.: 7699
N.A.I.C.S.: 811310
Personnel:
Sasikala Raghupathy *(Chm)*

P. R. Easwar Kumar *(Pres & CFO)*
Swaminathan A. *(CEO & Co-Mng Dir)*
Mahadevan V. R. *(Co-Mng Dir)*
R. Ramesh Kumar *(Pres-Corp, Compliance Officer & Sec)*
V. Balakrishnan *(Pres/CEO-Electrical Projects)*
S. Ilanchezhiyan *(Pres/CEO-Air Fin Cooler)*
H. L. Khajuria *(Pres/CEO-Environmental Engrg)*
N. Murali *(Pres/CEO-Oil & Gas Equipment)*
G. Amudhan *(Pres-Project Mgmt)*
Gurvinder Jit Singh Bindra *(Pres-Project Engrg & Mgmt)*
Pradip Kumar Das *(Pres-Project Mgmt)*
S. Venkataraman *(Pres-HR)*
Board of Directors:
Sasikala Raghupathy
Swaminathan A.
Heinrich Bohmer
S. A. Bohra
K. Chandrasekhar
M. Gopalakrishna
Swarnamugi Karthik
Mahadevan V. R.
M. S. Sundara Rajan
Gnana Rajasekaran
S. R. Tagat
Transfer Agent:
Link Intime India Pvt. Ltd
C-13 Pannalal Silk Mills Compound LBS Marg
Bhandup (West)
Mumbai, India

Divisions:

BGR Energy Systems Limited - Air Fin Cooler Division **(1)**
No 443 Anna Salai
Chennai, Tamil Nadu, 600018, India
Tel.: (91) 4424334940
Fax: (91) 4424334935
E-Mail: afc@bgrenergy.com
Air Coolers Mfr
S.I.C.: 3585
N.A.I.C.S.: 333415

BGR Energy Systems Limited - Captive Power Division **(1)**
443 Anna Salai
Teynampet, Chennai, Tamil Nadu, 600018, India
Tel.: (91) 4424334826
Fax: (91) 4424360578
E-Mail: cpd@bgrenergy.com
Web Site: www.bgrenergy.com
Power Plant Construction Services
S.I.C.: 1623
N.A.I.C.S.: 237130
G. Suresh *(Pres & CEO)*

BGR Energy Systems Limited - Electrical Projects Division **(1)**
443 Anna Salai
Teynampet, Chennai, Tamil Nadu, 600 018, India
Tel.: (91) 4424332314
Fax: (91) 4424311654
E-Mail: epd@bgrenergy.com
Emp.: 200
Electrical Contracting Services
S.I.C.: 8711
N.A.I.C.S.: 541330
V. Balakrishnan *(Pres)*
R. Swaminathan *(Sr VP)*

BGR Energy Systems Limited - Environment Engineering Division **(1)**
443 Anna Salai
Teynampet, Chennai, Tamil Nadu, 60018, India
Tel.: (91) 4424354105
Fax: (91) 4424320359
E-Mail: eed@bgrenergy.com
Web Site: www.bgrenergysystems.com
Emp.: 1,000
Water Treatment Services
S.I.C.: 4941
N.A.I.C.S.: 221310

BGR Energy Systems Limited - Infrastructure Division **(1)**
443 Anna Salai
Teynampet, Chennai, Tamil Nadu, 600018, India
Tel.: (91) 4424335958
Fax: (91) 4424343374
E-Mail: infra@bgrenergy.com
Emp.: 1,005
Civil Engineering Services
S.I.C.: 8711
N.A.I.C.S.: 541330
T. Sankaralingam *(Mng Dir)*

BGR Energy Systems Limited - Oil & Gas Equipment Division **(1)**
443 Anna Salai
Teynampet, Chennai, Tamil Nadu, 600018, India
Tel.: (91) 4424334940
Fax: (91) 4424334935
E-Mail: oged@bgrenergy.com
Web Site: www.bgrenergy.com
Emp.: 2,000
Oil & Gas Equipments Mfr
S.I.C.: 3563
N.A.I.C.S.: 333912
N. Murali *(Pres & CEO)*

BGR Energy Systems Limited - Power Projects Division **(1)**
443 Anna Salai
Teynampet, Chennai, Tamilnadu, 600018, India
Tel.: (91) 4424352436
Fax: (91) 4424315678
E-Mail: ppd@bgrenergy.com
Power Plant Construction & Engineering Services
S.I.C.: 1623
N.A.I.C.S.: 237130
Srenivas Behara *(Head-Corp Commun)*

Subsidiary:

Progen Systems and Technologies Limited **(1)**
New No 443 Old No 304-305 Guna Bldg
3rd Fl Anna Salai
Teynampet, Chennai, Tamil Nadu, 600018, India
Tel.: (91) 4424334940
Fax: (91) 4424330498
E-Mail: admin@progen.bgrenergy.com
Web Site: www.bgrenergy.com
Emp.: 2,000
Heat Exchangers Mfr
S.I.C.: 3559
N.A.I.C.S.: 332410
Sankar Lingam *(Mng Dir)*

Non-U.S. Subsidiary:

SCHMITZ Reinigungskugeln GmbH **(1)**
Bahnhofstrasse 45A
31188 Holle, Germany
Tel.: (49) 50 62 26 26
Fax: (49) 50 62 26 26
E-Mail: info@schmitz-cleaningballs.com
Web Site: www.schmitz-cleaningballs.com
Sponge Cleaning Ball Mfr
S.I.C.: 3086
N.A.I.C.S.: 326140
Brigitte Schmitz *(Mng Dir)*

BGR SAWS INC.

2341 avenue de la Rotonde
Charny, QC, G6X 2M2, Canada
Tel.: (418) 832-2918
Fax: (418) 832-2910
Toll Free: (800) 363-3523
E-Mail: bgrsaws@bgrsaws.com
Web Site: www.bgrsaws.com
Year Founded: 1968
Rev.: $17,053,290
Emp.: 160
Business Description:
Circular & Band Saws Mfr
S.I.C.: 3554
N.A.I.C.S.: 333243
Personnel:
Richard Blanchet *(Pres)*

BGRIMM MAGNETIC MATERIALS & TECHNOLOGY CO., LTD.

No 28 Caoqiao
Youwai, Beijing, China
Tel.: (86) 10 63703380
E-Mail: magmat@magmat.com
Web Site: www.magmat.com
600980—(SHG)
Business Description:
Magnetic Material Mfr
S.I.C.: 3999
N.A.I.C.S.: 327110
Personnel:
Kaixi Jiang *(Chm)*

BGS ACQUISITION CORP.

Olazbal 1150
Buenos Aires, Argentina 1428
Tel.: (54) 11 47868600
Year Founded: 2011
Emp.: 5
Business Description:
Investment Services
S.I.C.: 6211
N.A.I.C.S.: 523999
Personnel:
Julio Gutierrez *(Chm)*
Rolando Horman *(Pres)*
Cesar A. Baez *(CEO)*
Mariana Gutierrez Garcia *(CFO)*
Julian Diaz Bortolotti *(Exec VP)*
Board of Directors:
Julio Gutierrez
Cesar A. Baez
Gustavo Enrique Garrido
John Grabski
Rolando Horman
Alan B. Menkes

U.S. Subsidiary:

Transnetyx, Inc. **(1)**
8110 Cordova Rd
Cordova, TN 38016
Tel.: (901) 507-0476
Fax: (901) 507-0480
Toll Free: (888) 321-2113
E-Mail: customerservice@transnetyx.com
Web Site: www.transnetyx.com
Emp.: 30
Genetic Testing Laboratories
S.I.C.: 8734
N.A.I.C.S.: 541380
Robert Bean *(Pres)*

BGT CORPORATION PUBLIC COMPANY LIMITED

No 188 Suwinthawong Road Minburi
Bangkok, 10510, Thailand
Tel.: (66) 25402888
Fax: (66) 25401953
E-Mail: info@bodyglove.co.th
Web Site: www.bodyglove.co.th
Year Founded: 1988
BGT—(THA)
Rev.: $31,134,514
Assets: $25,551,228
Liabilities: $12,066,657
Net Worth: $13,484,571
Earnings: $1,286,907
Emp.: 619
Fiscal Year-end: 12/31/12
Business Description:
Mens Apparel Retailer
S.I.C.: 2389
N.A.I.C.S.: 315210
Personnel:
Nopdol Tumwattana *(Chm)*
Dickson Kok Cheng Goh *(Pres, CEO & Dir-Ops)*
Waristha Thapanasakulvong *(CFO)*
Dolnapa Tumwattana *(CMO)*
Nuttamon Bualah *(Chief Bus Officer)*
Board of Directors:
Nopdol Tumwattana
Nantarika Chansue
Dickson Kok Cheng Goh
Kok Beng Goh
Panu Kongtan
Mallika Leeraphant
Sereepisuth Temeeyaves
Surapone Virulrak
Legal Counsel:
Allen & Overy (Thailand) Company Limited
22nd Floor Sindhorn Building Tower III 130-132
Wireless Road Lumpini
Pathumwan, Bangkok, Thailand

Non-U.S. Subsidiary:

Body Glove(M) Sdn. Bhd. **(1)**
Lot 9233 Hala Kampung Jawa 1
Kawasan Perindustrian Bayan Lepas,
11900 Bayan Lepas, Penang, Malaysia
Tel.: (60) 4 6305929
Fax: (60) 4 6305920
E-Mail: info@bodyglove.com.my
Web Site: www.bodyglove.com.my
Apparel Retailer
S.I.C.: 5611
N.A.I.C.S.: 448110
Herbert Goh, *(CEO)*

BH CO., LTD.

422-1 Cheongcheon-dong
Bupyeong-gu, Incheon, Korea (South)
Tel.: (82) 32 510 2000
Fax: (82) 32 514 8677
Web Site: www.bhe.co.kr
Year Founded: 1999
090460—(KRS)
Business Description:
Printed Circuit Board Mfr
S.I.C.: 3672
N.A.I.C.S.: 334412
Personnel:
Gyeong-hwan Lee *(CEO)*

BH GLOBAL MARINE LIMITED

8 Penjuru Lane
Singapore, 609189, Singapore
Tel.: (65) 62914444
Fax: (65) 62915777
Web Site: www.bhglobal.com.sg
B32—(SES)
Rev.: $79,121,120
Assets: $137,874,739
Liabilities: $70,391,960
Net Worth: $67,482,780
Earnings: ($28,649,717)
Fiscal Year-end: 12/31/12
Business Description:
Marine Services
S.I.C.: 3731
N.A.I.C.S.: 336611
Personnel:
Alvin Hwee Hong Lim *(Chm)*
Vincent Hui Eng Lim *(CEO)*
Keegan Tze Wee Chua *(CFO)*
Patrick Hui Peng Lim *(COO)*
Steven Wong *(CEO-Gulf Specialty Steel Industries LLC)*
Mi Keay Pan *(Co-Sec)*
Choi Fan Toon *(Co-Sec)*
Board of Directors:
Alvin Hwee Hong Lim
David Tian Bin Chia
Winston Choon Lin Kwek
Patrick Hui Peng Lim
Vincent Hui Eng Lim
Weng Whye Loh
Transfer Agent:
Tricor Barbinder Share Registration Services
80 Robinson Road 02-00
Singapore, Singapore

BHAGERIA DYE-CHEM LIMITED

A 1/101 Virwani Indl Estate Off
Western Express Highway Goregaon East
Mumbai, 400063, India

BHAGERIA DYE-CHEM LIMITED—(Continued)

Tel.: (91) 22 40436666
Fax: (91) 22 28748389
E-Mail: info@bhageriagroup.com
Web Site: www.bhageriagroup.com
Year Founded: 1989
530803—(BOM)
Rev.: $25,747,907
Assets: $9,866,525
Liabilities: $5,593,147
Net Worth: $4,273,377
Earnings: $234,068
Emp.: 17
Fiscal Year-end: 03/31/13
Business Description:
Dye Mfr & Whslr
S.I.C.: 2819
N.A.I.C.S.: 325130
Personnel:
Suresh Bhageria *(Chm)*
Vinod Bhageria *(Mng Dir)*
Rakesh Kachhadiya *(CFO)*
Shri Nath Tiwari *(Compliance Officer & Sec)*
Board of Directors:
Suresh Bhageria
Shyam Agarwal
Vinod Bhageria
O. P. Bubna
P. S. Dalvi
Surendra Shriram Gupta
Sandeep Singh
Transfer Agent:
Sharex Dynamic (India) Pvt. Ltd
Unit 1 Luthra Indus Premises Andheri Kurla Road Safed Pool Andheri E
Mumbai, India

BHAGIRADHA CHEMICALS & INDUSTRIES LTD.

Plot No 3 Sagar Society Road No 2
Banjara Hills
Hyderabad, 500 034, India
Tel.: (91) 40 23608083
Fax: (91) 40 23540444
E-Mail: info@bhagirad.com
Web Site: www.bhagirad.com
531719—(BOM)
Rev.: $29,645,993
Assets: $23,071,987
Liabilities: $14,448,914
Net Worth: $8,623,073
Earnings: $365,556
Emp.: 275
Fiscal Year-end: 03/31/13
Business Description:
Pesticides Mfr
S.I.C.: 2879
N.A.I.C.S.: 325320
Personnel:
S. Chandrasekhar *(Mng Dir)*
K. Gopala Krishna *(Compliance Officer & Gen Mgr-Fin)*
J. R. Nagajayanthi *(Sec)*
Board of Directors:
D. Ranga Raju
S. Chandrasekhar
Sudhakar Kudva
K. S. Raju
D. Sadasivudu
Transfer Agent:
XL Softech Systems Limited
Plot No.3 Sagar Society Road No.2 Banjara Hills
Hyderabad, India

BHAGWANDAS METALS LTD.

No 54 Old61 Sembudoss Street
Chennai, 600001, India
Tel.: (91) 44 25233409
Fax: (91) 44 25223644
E-Mail: bml@vsnl.net
Web Site: www.metal-bml.com
530095—(BOM)
Business Description:
Steel Distr
S.I.C.: 5051
N.A.I.C.S.: 423510
Personnel:
Govind Prasad *(Founder & Chm)*
Transfer Agent:
Cameo Corporate Services Limited
Subramanian Building No 1 Club House Road 5th Floor
Chennai, India

BHAGWATI BANQUETS & HOTELS LTD.

(Name Changed to TGB Banquets & Hotels Limited)

BHAGYANAGAR INDIA LIMITED

5th Floor Surya Towers Sardar Patel Road
Secunderabad, Andhra Pradesh, 500 003, India
Tel.: (91) 4044665700
Fax: (91) 4027818868
E-Mail: surana@surana.com
Web Site: www.bhagyanagarindia.com
BHAGYNAGAR—(NSE)
Rev.: $39,733,943
Assets: $57,108,495
Liabilities: $17,822,294
Net Worth: $39,286,201
Earnings: $615,411
Emp.: 198
Fiscal Year-end: 03/31/13
Business Description:
Copper Mfr
S.I.C.: 1021
N.A.I.C.S.: 212234
Personnel:
Devendra Surana *(Co-Mng Dir)*
Narender Surana *(Co-Mng Dir)*
Surendra Bhutoria *(CFO)*
Biswa Ranjan Subudhi *(Compliance Officer & Sec)*
Board of Directors:
G. Mangilal Surana
Kamlesh Gandhi
Narender Munoth
N. Krupakar Reddy
O. Swaminatha Reddy
R. Surender Reddy
R. N. Sreenath
Devendra Surana
Narender Surana
D. Venkatasubbiah
Transfer Agent:
Karvy Computershare Private Limited
Plot No 17-24 Vittal Rao Nagar Madhapur
Hyderabad, 500 081, India
Tel.: (91) 40 2342 0818

BHAGYODAYA INFRASTRUCTURE DEVELOPMENT LIMITED

3rd Floor Orbit Terraces 64 NM Joshi Marg Junction of SB Marg
Lower Parel West, Mumbai, 400013, India
Tel.: (91) 22 6524 2624
Fax: (91) 22 24978602
E-Mail: info@bidlgroup.com
Web Site: www.bidlgroup.com
Year Founded: 1974
501233—(BOM)
Rev.: $1,481,076
Assets: $5,117,013
Liabilities: $3,818,358
Net Worth: $1,298,654
Earnings: ($53,287)
Emp.: 130
Fiscal Year-end: 03/31/13
Business Description:
Civil Engineering Services
S.I.C.: 1629
N.A.I.C.S.: 237990
Personnel:
Sanjiv Bansal *(CEO)*
Naman Shah *(CFO & Compliance Officer)*
Ravindra V. Joshi *(Sec)*
Board of Directors:
Sanjiv Bansal
Arvind Kiran
Abdeali Mamaji
Gaurav Mehra
Naman Shah
Transfer Agent:
Sharex Dynamic (India) Pvt Ltd
Unit No 1 Luthra Industrial Premises Andheri - Kurla Road Safed Pool
Andheri E, Mumbai, India

BHANDARI HOSIERY EXPORTS LTD.

Bhandari House Village Meharban
Rahon Road
Ludhiana, 141007, India
Tel.: (91) 161 3260742
Fax: (91) 161 2690394
E-Mail: bhandari@bhandariexport.com
Web Site: www.bhandariexport.com
512608—(BOM)
Rev.: $17,895,823
Assets: $15,715,213
Liabilities: $6,910,579
Net Worth: $8,804,634
Earnings: $533,531
Fiscal Year-end: 03/31/13
Business Description:
Textile Garments Mfr
S.I.C.: 2389
N.A.I.C.S.: 315280
Personnel:
Nitin Bhandari *(Chm & Mng Dir)*
Surinder Kumar *(CFO)*
Gurinder Makkar *(Compliance Officer & Sec)*
Board of Directors:
Nitin Bhandari
Vikas Nayyar
M. M. Sikka
R. C. Singal
Ashish Thapar
Transfer Agent:
Link Intime India Pvt Limited
A-40 2nd Floor Naraina Industrial Area Phase-II
Near Batra Banquet
New Delhi, India

BHANERO TEXTILE MILLS LIMITED

Umer House 23/1 Sector 23 S M Farooq Road Korangi Industrial Area
Karachi, Pakistan
Tel.: (92) 2135115177
Fax: (92) 2135063002
E-Mail: khioff@umergroup.com
Web Site: www.umergroup.com
BHAT—(KAR)
Sls.: $70,883,833
Assets: $44,628,958
Liabilities: $14,772,228
Net Worth: $29,856,730
Earnings: $5,946,273
Emp.: 1,394
Fiscal Year-end: 06/30/13
Business Description:
Textile Products Mfr
S.I.C.: 2299
N.A.I.C.S.: 313110
Personnel:
Khurram Salim *(CEO)*
Anwar Hussain *(CFO)*
Ashraf Ali *(Sec)*
Board of Directors:
Mohammad Shaheen
Mohammad Amin
Khurram Salim
Mohammad Salim
Adil Shakeel
Mohammad Shakeel
Bilal Sharif
Mohammad Sharif

BHANOT CONSTRUCTION & HOUSING LTD.

310-311 Bhanot Corner 1 Pamposh Enclave Greater Kailash Part-1
New Delhi, 110048, India
Tel.: (91) 11 41635473
Fax: (91) 11 26239346
E-Mail: bhanotgroup@rediffmail.com
Web Site: www.bhanotgroup.com
Year Founded: 1976
534740—(BOM)
Rev.: $11,046,837
Assets: $19,242,926
Liabilities: $13,280,777
Net Worth: $5,962,149
Earnings: $39,861
Emp.: 9
Fiscal Year-end: 03/31/13
Business Description:
Construction Engineering Services
S.I.C.: 1629
N.A.I.C.S.: 237990
Personnel:
R. D. Bhanot *(Chm & Mng Dir)*
Ravinder Kumar Sapra *(Compliance Officer & Sec)*
Board of Directors:
R. D. Bhanot
Deepak Vijay Bakshi
Rajeev Bhanot
Arun Soni
Surender Kumar Vasudeva
Transfer Agent:
Beetal Financial & Computer Services Pvt. Ltd.
Beetal House 3rd Floor 99 Madangir Behind Local Shopping Centre
Near Dada Harsukhdas Mandir, New Delhi, India

BHANSALI ENGINEERING POLYMERS LIMITED

Bhansali House A-5 Off Veera Desai Road
Andheri West, Mumbai, MAH, 400 053, India
Tel.: (91) 22 26731779
Fax: (91) 22 26731796
E-Mail: Abstron@BhansaliABS.com
Web Site: www.bhansaliabs.com
Year Founded: 1986
500052—(BOM)
Rev.: $86,724,651
Assets: $69,357,992
Liabilities: $32,143,966
Net Worth: $37,214,026
Earnings: $219,773
Emp.: 490
Fiscal Year-end: 03/31/13
Business Description:
Plastic Material Mfr
S.I.C.: 2821
N.A.I.C.S.: 325211
Personnel:
B. M. Bhansali *(Mng Dir)*
D. N. Mishra *(Sec & VP-Legal)*
Board of Directors:
M. C. Gupta
B. M. Bhansali
Jayesh B. Bhansali
P. R. Bhansali
B. S. Bhesania
Transfer Agent:
Link Intime India Pvt. Ltd
C-13 Pannalal Silk Mills Compound LBS Marg
Bhandup (West)
Mumbai, India

BHARAT BHUSHAN FINANCE & COMMODITY BROKERS LTD.

5-E Rani Jhansi Road Jhandewalan Extension
New Delhi, 110055, India
Tel.: (91) 11 23540997
Fax: (91) 11 23540996
E-Mail: nse@bharatbhushan.com
Web Site: www.bharatbhushan.com
Year Founded: 1954
511501—(BOM)
Sales Range: $1-9.9 Million

Business Description:
Financial Services
S.I.C.: 6211
N.A.I.C.S.: 523999

Personnel:
Kavita Pamnani *(Sec & Compliance Officer)*

Board of Directors:
Sant Kumari Agrawal
Jogesh C. Ahuja
Nisha Ahuja
Vijay Bhushan
Arun Garg
Kuldeep Gupta
Ravindra Singh

BHARAT BIJLEE LTD

Electric Mansion 6th Floor
Appasaheb Marathe Marg
Prabhadevi
Mumbai, 400 025, India
Tel.: (91) 2224306237
Fax: (91) 2224370624
E-Mail: bblcorporate@bharatbijlee.com
Web Site: www.bharatbijlee.com
503960—(BOM)
Rev.: $110,129,918
Assets: $109,179,594
Liabilities: $51,320,296
Net Worth: $57,859,298
Earnings: ($902,583)
Emp.: 1,362
Fiscal Year-end: 03/31/13

Business Description:
Electrical Engineering Services
S.I.C.: 8711
N.A.I.C.S.: 541330

Personnel:
Nikhil J. Dhanani *(Vice Chm & Co-Mng Dir)*
Nakul P. Mehta *(Vice Chm & Co-Mng Dir)*
Durgesh N. Nagarkar *(Compliance Officer, Sec & Sr Gen Mgr-Legal)*

Board of Directors:
Bansi S. Mehta
Anand J. Danani
Shome N. Danani
Nikhil J. Dhanani
Nakul P. Mehta
Prakash V. Mehta
Harish Chandra Mishra
Sanjiv N. Shah
Jairaj C. Thacker

Transfer Agent:
Link Intime India Pvt. Ltd
C-13 Pannalal Silk Mills Compound LBS Marg
Bhandup (West)
Mumbai, India

Division:

Bharat Bijlee Ltd - Drives Division **(1)**
Opp Airoli Railway Station
Thane Belapur Rd Airoli, Navi Mumbai, Maharastra, 400 708, India
Tel.: (91) 2227637200
Fax: (91) 2227637447
E-Mail: drivesales@bharatbijlee.com
Web Site: www.bharatbijlee.com
Emp.: 1,200
Electrical Products Mfr
S.I.C.: 3699
N.A.I.C.S.: 335999
Shankar Sathawane *(Gen Mgr)*

BHARAT ELECTRONICS LIMITED

Outer Ring Road Nagavara
Bengaluru, 560 045, India
Tel.: (91) 8025039300
Fax: (91) 8025039305
E-Mail: alfint@vsnl.com
Web Site: www.bel-india.com
500049—(BOM NSE)
Rev.: $1,278,977,005
Assets: $2,753,367,613
Liabilities: $1,520,349,562
Net Worth: $1,233,018,051
Earnings: $168,935,182
Emp.: 10,305
Fiscal Year-end: 03/31/13

Business Description:
Defense Electronics Mfr
S.I.C.: 3663
N.A.I.C.S.: 334220

Personnel:
Sunil Kumar Sharma *(Chm & Mng Dir)*
M. N. Krishnamurthy *(Chief Vigilance Officer)*

Board of Directors:
Sunil Kumar Sharma
Prabhat R. Acharya
S. M. Acharya
P. C. Jain
Ajit T. Kalghatgi
S. P. Kochhar
V. K. Mehta
Pramode Kumar Mishra
Amol Newaskar
M. L. Shanmukh
Vikram Srivastava

Transfer Agent:
Integrated Enterprises (India) Ltd
30 Ramana Residency 4th Cross Sampige Road Malleswaram
Bengaluru, India

Subsidiary:

BEL Optronic Devices Ltd. **(1)**
EL-30 J Block
Bhosari Industrial Area, 411026 Pune, India
Tel.: (91) 2027122981
Fax: (91) 2027120589
E-Mail: belopto@vsnl.net
Web Site: www.bel-india.com
Emp.: 200
Other Lighting Equipment Mfr
S.I.C.: 3648
N.A.I.C.S.: 335129
J. Y. Chaudhary *(CEO)*

BHARAT FERTILISER INDUSTRIES LTD.

12 Bharat Fertiliser House Nanabhai Lane Fort
Mumbai, 400023, India
Tel.: (91) 22 2283 5547
Fax: (91) 22 2202 2173
Web Site: www.bharatrealty.co.in
531862—(BOM)

Business Description:
Fertilizer Mfr & Whslr
S.I.C.: 2875
N.A.I.C.S.: 325314

Personnel:
Yogendra D. Patel *(Chm & Mng Dir)*
A. J. Chakote *(Compliance Officer & Sec)*

BHARAT GEARS LIMITED

Hoechst House Nariman Point
Mumbai, 400 021, India
Tel.: (91) 222883180
E-Mail: info@bglindia.com
Web Site: www.bharatgears.com
Year Founded: 1971
BHARATGEAR—(NSE)
Rev.: $79,726,264
Assets: $49,348,382
Liabilities: $35,211,149
Net Worth: $14,137,232
Earnings: $920,808
Emp.: 1,306
Fiscal Year-end: 03/31/13

Business Description:
Automotive Gear Mfr & Distr
S.I.C.: 3714
N.A.I.C.S.: 336350

Personnel:
Surinder P. Kanwar *(Chm & Mng Dir)*
Sameer Kanwar *(Mng Dir)*
Milind Pujari *(CFO)*
Prashant Khattry *(Sec & Head-Legal)*

Board of Directors:
Surinder P. Kanwar
Hiroo Suresh Advani
Shiv Gopal Awasthi
Rakesh Chopra
N. J. Kamath
Sameer Kanwar
V. K. Pargal
W. R. Schilha
Ram S. Tarneja

Transfer Agent:
Link Intime India Private Limited
44 Community Centre 2nd Floor Naraina Industrial Area Phase-I
Near PVR Naraina, New Delhi, India

BHARAT HEAVY ELECTRICALS LIMITED

BHEL House Siri Fort
New Delhi, 110049, India
Tel.: (91) 1166337000
Fax: (91) 1126493021
E-Mail: query@bhel.com
Web Site: www.bhel.com
500103—(BOM NSE)
Rev.: $9,394,744,536
Assets: $13,302,950,580
Liabilities: $7,641,311,058
Net Worth: $5,661,639,522
Earnings: $1,240,950,798
Emp.: 48,399
Fiscal Year-end: 03/31/13

Business Description:
Engineering & Manufacturing Services
S.I.C.: 1629
N.A.I.C.S.: 237990

Personnel:
B. Prasada Rao *(Chm & Mng Dir)*
Inder Pal Singh *(Compliance Officer & Sec)*

Board of Directors:
B. Prasada Rao
P. K. Bajpai
R. Krishnan
Atul Saraya
W. V. K. Krishna Shankar
Ambuj Sharma

Gandhi Minocha & Co
New Delhi, India

Transfer Agent:
Karvy Computershare Private Limited
Plot No 17-24 Vittal Rao Nagar Madhapur
Hyderabad, 500 081, India
Tel.: (91) 40 2342 0818

Subsidiary:

Bharat Heavy Plates & Vessels Limited **(1)**
BHPV Post
Visakhapatnam, 530 012, India In
Tel.: (91) 8912517171 (100%)
Fax: (91) 8916681700
E-Mail: md@bhpvl.com
Web Site: www.bhpvl.com
Emp.: 1,200
Mfr of Industrial Boilers, Process Equipment & Allied Products & Cryogenic Equipment for Petrochemical, Refinery & Fertilizer Industries
S.I.C.: 3443
N.A.I.C.S.: 332410

BHARAT PETROLEUM CORPORATION LIMITED

Bharat Bhawan 4 & 6 Currimbhoy Road
Ballard Estate, Mumbai, 400001, India
Tel.: (91) 2222713000
Fax: (91) 2222713801
E-Mail: info@bharatpetroleum.in
Web Site: www.bharatpetroleum.com
Year Founded: 1952
BPCL—(BOM MDS NSE)
Rev.: $45,183,828,438
Assets: $14,751,471,510
Liabilities: $11,641,286,394
Net Worth: $3,110,185,116
Earnings: $348,705,882
Emp.: 14,016
Fiscal Year-end: 03/31/13

Business Description:
Petroleum Products Sales
S.I.C.: 2911
N.A.I.C.S.: 324110

Personnel:
S. Varadarajan *(Chm & Mng Dir)*
Manoj Pant *(Chief Vigilance Officer)*
S. V. Kulkarni *(Sec)*

Board of Directors:
S. Varadarajan
B. Chakrabarti
B. K. Datta
S. P. Gathoo
K. K. Gupta
P. H. Kurian
Neeraj Mittal
J. R. Varma

K Varghese & Co
Mumbai, India

Transfer Agent:
Data Software Research Co. Pvt. Ltd.
22 4th Cross Street Trustpuram
Sree Sovereign Complex
Kodambakkam, Chennai, 600024, India
Tel.: (91) 44 2483 3738
Fax: (91) 44 2483 4646

Subsidiary:

Bharat Petroleum Corporation Limited - Kochi Refinery **(1)**
Ambalamugal Ernakulam District
PO Box 2
Kochi, 682 302, India
Tel.: (91) 4842722061
Fax: (91) 4842720856
Web Site: www.kochirefineries.com
Sales Range: $1-4.9 Billion
Emp.: 1,900
Petroleum Refinery
S.I.C.: 2911
N.A.I.C.S.: 324110
M. P. Govindarajan *(Gen Mgr-HR)*

Joint Ventures:

Bharat Oman Refineries Limited **(1)**
Mahul Chembur
Mumbai, Maharashtra, 400 074, India IN
Tel.: (91) 2225533888
Fax: (91) 2225542970
E-Mail: vasudevanpr@bharatpetroleum.com
Web Site: www.borl.in
Emp.: 12,000
Joint Venture of Bharat Petroleum Corporation Ltd. & Oman Oil Company Limited
S.I.C.: 2911
N.A.I.C.S.: 324110
U. N. Joshi *(Mng Dir)*

Bharat Shell Limited **(1)**
3rd Floor 1 Tower A B 37 Sector 1
Gautam Budh Nagar, Noida, 201301, India IN
Tel.: (91) 202445001
Fax: (91) 202445010
Web Site: www.shell.com
Emp.: 30

Bharat Petroleum Corporation Limited—(Continued)

Petroluem Refining; Owned 49% by Bharat Petroleum Corporation Ltd. & 51% by Shell International Petroleum Company
S.I.C.: 2911
N.A.I.C.S.: 324110

Non-U.S. Subsidiaries:

BPRL International BV (1)
Strawinskylaan 1143
1077 XX Amsterdam, North Holland, Netherlands
Tel.: (31) 205788388
Oil & Gas Exploration Services
S.I.C.: 1389
N.A.I.C.S.: 213112

BPRL Ventures BV (1)
Strawinskylaan 1143
1077 XX Amsterdam, North Holland, Netherlands
Tel.: (31) 205788388
Petroleum Products Mfr & Whslr
S.I.C.: 2911
N.A.I.C.S.: 324110

BHARAT RASAYAN LIMITED

15th Floor Vikram Tower Rajendra Place
New Delhi, 110008, India
Tel.: (91) 1143661111
Fax: (91) 1143661100
E-Mail: info@bharatgroup.co.in
Web Site: www.bharatgroup.co.in
BHARATRAS—(NSE)
Rev.: $34,885,746
Assets: $45,841,524
Liabilities: $34,248,237
Net Worth: $11,593,287
Earnings: $1,777,248
Emp.: 449
Fiscal Year-end: 03/31/13
Business Description:
Pesticides Mfr
S.I.C.: 2879
N.A.I.C.S.: 325320
Personnel:
Sat Narain Gupta *(Chm & Mng Dir)*
Deepika Bhardwaj *(Compliance Officer & Sec)*
Board of Directors:
Sat Narain Gupta
Naresh Agarwal
Ajay Gupta
Amit Gupta
Mahabir Prasad Gupta
Pankaj Gupta
Rajender Prasad Gupta
Sandesh Jain
Ram Kanwar
V. K. Sharma
Transfer Agent:
Link Intime India Private Limited
44 Community Centre 2nd Floor Naraina Industrial Area Phase-I
Near PVR Naraina, New Delhi, India

BHARAT SEATS LIMITED

Plot No 1 Maruti Udyog Joint Venture Complex Palam Gurgaon Road
Gurgaon, 122015, India
Tel.: (91) 124 2341258
Fax: (91) 124 2341188
E-Mail: info@bharatseats.com
Web Site: www.bharatseats.com
523229—(BOM)
Rev.: $126,380,764
Assets: $41,017,379
Liabilities: $33,991,353
Net Worth: $7,026,026
Earnings: $991,926
Fiscal Year-end: 03/31/13
Business Description:
Automotive Seating System Mfr
S.I.C.: 2396
N.A.I.C.S.: 336360
Personnel:
Rohit Relan *(Mng Dir)*
Sanjeev Kumar *(CFO & Gen Mgr-Fin)*
Rishab Relan *(COO)*
Ritu Bakshi *(Compliance Officer & Sec)*
Rajat Bhandari *(Sr VP-Strategic Plng)*
Board of Directors:
N. D. Relan
Ravindra Gupta
Gautam Khaitan
Yoichi Kojima
P. K. Lahiri
G. N. Mehra
Kishan N. Parikh
I. V. Rao
Ajay Relan
Rohit Relan
Transfer Agent:
Alankit Assignments Limited
2E/21 Alankit House Jhandewalan Extension
New Delhi, India

BHARATI SHIPYARD LIMITED

Oberoi Chambers-II Ground Floor
Link Road Andheri W
Near Lakshmi Industrial Estate,
Mumbai, 400053, India
Tel.: (91) 22 39506800
Fax: (91) 22 39506900
E-Mail: info@bharatishipyard.com
Web Site: www.bharatishipyard.com
532609—(BOM)
Rev.: $163,496,065
Assets: $1,390,958,958
Liabilities: $1,254,127,881
Net Worth: $136,831,077
Earnings: ($91,102,167)
Fiscal Year-end: 03/31/13
Business Description:
Ship Building & Repairing Services
S.I.C.: 3731
N.A.I.C.S.: 336611
Personnel:
P. C. Kapoor *(Co-Mng Dir)*
Vijay Kumar *(Co-Mng Dir)*
Board of Directors:
V. P. Kamath
P. C. Kapoor
Vijay Kumar
Rajiv Pal Singh
Transfer Agent:
Linkintime India Private Limited
C 13 Pannalal Silk Mills Compound LBS Marg
Bhandup West
Mumbai, 400 078, India

BHARATIYA GLOBAL INFOMEDIA LTD.

B-13 LGF Amar Colony Lajpat Nagar IV
New Delhi, 110024, India
Tel.: (91) 1140765562
Fax: (91) 1141377519
E-Mail: contact@bgilinfo.com
Web Site: www.bgil.in
BGLOBAL—(BOM NSE)
Sales Range: $10-24.9 Million
Emp.: 80
Business Description:
IT & Entertainment Services
S.I.C.: 7379
N.A.I.C.S.: 541519
Personnel:
Rakesh Bhhatia *(Chm & Mng Dir)*
Transfer Agent:
Karvy Computershare (P) Limited
Plot No 17-24 Vittal Rao Nagar Madhapur
Hyderabad, India

BHARTI ENTERPRISES LIMITED

1 Nelson Mandela Rd Bharti Crescent Vasant Kunj Phase 2
New Delhi, 110 070, India
Tel.: (91) 1146666100
Fax: (91) 1141666137
E-Mail: corporate.communication@bharti.in
Web Site: www.bharti.com
Business Description:
Holding Company; Telecom, Agri-Business, Insurance & Retail
S.I.C.: 6719
N.A.I.C.S.: 551112
Personnel:
Sunil Bharti Mittal *(Chm)*
Akhil Gupta *(Vice Chm)*
Rajan Bharti Mittal *(Vice Chm)*
Rakesh Bharti Mittal *(Vice Chm)*
Manoj Kohli *(Mng Dir)*
Vijaya R. S. Sampath *(Grp Gen Counsel & Sec)*
Board of Directors:
Sunil Bharti Mittal
Akhil Gupta
Rajan Bharti Mittal
Rakesh Bharti Mittal

Subsidiaries:

Bharti Infratel Limited (1)
901 Park Centra Sector 30 NH-8
Gurgaon, Haryana, 122001, India
Tel.: (91) 124 4132600
Fax: (91) 124 4109580
Web Site: www.bharti-infratel.com
534816—(BOM NSE)
Sales Range: $1-4.9 Billion
Emp.: 2,500
Telecom Structures
S.I.C.: 1623
N.A.I.C.S.: 237130
Akhil Gupta *(Chm)*
Devender Singh Rawat *(CEO & Mng Dir)*
Sunil Khurana *(COO)*

Bharti Resources Ltd. (1)
Neelagagan Mandi Rd
Sultanpur Mehrauli, New Delhi, 110 030, India In
Tel.: (91) 1146001100 (100%)
Fax: (91) 1146001111
E-Mail: divya.s@centum.in
Web Site: www.centumlearning.com
Emp.: 150
Learning & Development Solutions for Improved Business Performance
S.I.C.: 8299
N.A.I.C.S.: 611430
Sanjeev Duggal *(CEO)*

Bharti Retail Pvt Ltd (1)
Qutab Ambience
Mehrauli Road, New Delhi, 110 030, India In
Tel.: (91) 11 46666 100 (100%)
Fax: (91) 11 4166 6011
General Merchandise Retail
S.I.C.: 5399
N.A.I.C.S.: 452990
Vinod Sawhny *(Pres & COO)*
Raj Jain *(CEO)*
Rajan Bharti Mittal *(Mng Dir)*
Pankaj Madan *(CFO)*

Holdings:

Bharti Airtel Limited (1)
Bharti Crescent 1 Nelson Mandela Road
Vasant Kunj Phase-II
New Delhi, 110 070, India
Tel.: (91) 11 46666100
Fax: (91) 11 41666137
E-Mail: ir@bharti.in
Web Site: www.airtel.com
532454—(BOM)
Rev.: $14,889,696,480
Assets: $31,021,721,280
Liabilities: $20,934,051,660
Net Worth: $10,087,669,620
Earnings: $420,283,260
Emp.: 15,563
Fiscal Year-end: 03/31/13
Telecommunications Services
S.I.C.: 4812
N.A.I.C.S.: 517210
Sunil Bharti Mittal *(Chm & Mng Dir)*
Srikanth Balachander *(CFO)*
Amrita Gangotra *(CIO-India & South Asia)*
Ashish D. Kalay *(CIO-B2C)*
Najib Khan *(CMO)*
N. Rajaram *(CMO-B2C)*
S. Balasubramaniam *(Chief Acctg Officer)*
Mukesh Bhavnani *(Compliance Officer, Gen Counsel & Sec)*
Manoj Kohli *(Chm-Bharti Airtel International (Netherlands) BV)*
K. Srinivas *(Pres-Consumer Bus)*
Christian de Faria *(CEO-Africa & Mng Dir-Bharti Airtel International (Netherlands) BV)*
Gopal Vittal *(CEO/Mng Dir-India & South Asia)*
Anant Arora *(CEO-Market Ops-Gujarat)*
Ashok Ganapathy *(Hub CEO-Maharashtra, Goa & Gujarat)*
Shishir Kumar *(CEO-Market Ops-Punjab)*
Rohit Malhotra *(CEO-Market Ops-Karnataka)*
Ramesh Menon *(CEO-Market Ops-Maharastra)*
Segun Ogunsanya *(CEO-Nigeria)*
Neil Pollock *(CEO-Nxtra Data Limited)*
Vikas Singh *(CEO-Karnataka & Tamil Nadu)*
Harjeet Kohli *(Treas & Head-Treasury & IR)*

Non-U.S. Subsidiary:

Airtel Bangladesh Limited (2)
PO Box 3016
Dhaka, Bangladesh BD
Tel.: (880) 1678600786
E-Mail:
Web Site: www.bd.airtel.com
Emp.: 400
Fixed, Mobile & Internet Telecommunications Services
S.I.C.: 4812
N.A.I.C.S.: 517210
Muneer Farooqui *(CEO)*
Tariq Gulzar *(CFO)*

Bharti Telesoft Ltd. (1)
F-13 Okhla Pase-1
New Delhi, 110020, India In
Tel.: (91) 11 4161 1666
Fax: (91) 11 4161 1777
Web Site: www.bhartitelesoft.com
Telecommunications Software Developer & Supplier
S.I.C.: 7372
N.A.I.C.S.: 511210
Rakesh Bharti Mittal *(Chm)*
Sanjiv Mital *(Vice Chm)*
Anil Gajwani *(CTO)*

Beetel Teletech Limited (1)
1st Floor Plot No 16 Udyog Vihar Phase IV
Gurgaon, Haryana, 122 002, India
Tel.: (91) 24 4823500
Fax: (91) 24 4146130
Web Site: www.beetel.in
Mobile & Telecommunications Equipment Mfr & Whslr
Export
S.I.C.: 3661
N.A.I.C.S.: 334210
Sunil Bharti Mittal *(Chm & Grp CEO)*
Rakesh Bharti Mittal *(Vice Chm & Mng Dir)*
Suresh Gupta *(COO & Head-Ops)*
Nidhi Chauhan *(Chief Officer-HR)*

Joint Venture:

FieldFresh Foods Pvt. Ltd. (1)
Tower C2 1st Fl Plot 16 Udyog Vihar Phase 4
Gurgaon, Haryana, 122015, India
Tel.: (91) 1244109400
Fax: (91) 1244109390
Web Site: www.fieldfreshfoods.in
Emp.: 200
Fresh & Processed Fruits & Vegetables Distr; Bharti Enterprises Limited & Del Monte Foods India Pvt. Ltd. Joint Venture
S.I.C.: 5148
N.A.I.C.S.: 424480
Sanjay Nandrajog *(CEO)*

BHARTIYA INTERNATIONAL LTD.

E-52 Manglapuri Mandi Road
Mehrauli
New Delhi, 110 030, India
Tel.: (91) 11 46002100
Fax: (91) 11 26803485
E-Mail: bhartiya@bhartiya.com

Web Site: www.bhartiya.com
526666—(BOM)
Rev.: $56,772,749
Assets: $53,818,258
Liabilities: $27,129,709
Net Worth: $26,688,548
Earnings: $1,879,717
Fiscal Year-end: 03/31/13

Business Description:
Textile Apparel Mfr
S.I.C.: 2389
N.A.I.C.S.: 315280

Personnel:
Snehdeep Aggarwal *(Founder, Chm & Mng Dir)*
Ajay Malhotra *(CFO)*
Shilpa Budhia *(Sec)*

Board of Directors:
Snehdeep Aggarwal
Nikhil Aggarwal
Ramesh Bhatia
Vijay Kumar Chopra
A. K. Gadhok
C. L. Handa
A. Sahasranaman
Sandeep Seth
Jaspal Sethi

Transfer Agent:
MAS Services Limited
T-34 2nd Floor Okhla Industrial Area Phase - II
New Delhi, India

Non-U.S. Subsidiary:

Ultima Italia S.R.L. **(1)**
Via Dei Tigli 4
Casaletto Vaprio, 26010 Cremona, Italy
Tel.: (39) 0373273411
Fax: (39) 0373274148
E-Mail: info@ultimaitalia.it
Emp.: 12
Solar Power Park Development Services
S.I.C.: 1629
N.A.I.C.S.: 237130
Nikhil Aggarwal *(Mng Dir)*

BHATIA BROTHERS GROUP

PO Box 275
Dubai, United Arab Emirates
Tel.: (971) 42825222
Fax: (971) 42826041
E-Mail: bbgroup@emirates.net.ae
Web Site: www.bhatia.com
Emp.: 400

Business Description:
Diverse Holding Company; Industrial Machinery Distr; Engineering Services; Hotels & Tourism Services; Consumer Electronics Distr; IT Consulting Services
S.I.C.: 6719
N.A.I.C.S.: 551112

Personnel:
Ajay B. Bhatia *(Chm)*

Subsidiaries:

Bhatia Brothers LLC - Automotive & Industrial Chemicals **(1)**
PO Box 1275
Dubai, United Arab Emirates
Tel.: (971) 42137750
Fax: (971) 42831016
E-Mail: bbauto@bbisd.com
Web Site: www.bbisd.com
Distr of Car Care Products, including Accessories, Lubricants, Spare Parts, Batteries & Maintenance Chemicals
S.I.C.: 5531
N.A.I.C.S.: 441310

Bhatia Brothers LLC - Industrial Supplies Division **(1)**
PO Box 1275
Dubai, United Arab Emirates
Tel.: (971) 4 2137715
Fax: (971) 4 2868338
E-Mail: inquiry@bbisd.com
Web Site: www.bhatia.com
Emp.: 700
Specialized Turnkey Projects (Compressed Air Systems, Air Pollution Systems & Nitrogen Gas On-Site Generating Systems) & Engineering Services for Various Industries, including Oil & Gas, Power & Water, Marine, Cement, Food & Beverages & Petro-Chemical
S.I.C.: 8711
N.A.I.C.S.: 541330
Siddhartha Tiku *(Gen Mgr)*

Bhatia Cold Storage & Trading Co., LLC **(1)**
PO Box 322
Dubai, United Arab Emirates
Tel.: (971) 42850618
Fax: (971) 42860631
E-Mail: bhatiabb@emirates.net.ae
Frozen & Chilled Food Warehousing
S.I.C.: 4222
N.A.I.C.S.: 493120

Emirates Cold Storage Company **(1)**
PO Box 337
Abu Dhabi, United Arab Emirates
Tel.: (971) 5553455
Fax: (971) 5542709
Cold Storage
S.I.C.: 4222
N.A.I.C.S.: 493120

Super General Trading Co. LLC **(1)**
Al Owais Building Behind HSBC Bank
PO Box 322
Nasser Square Deira, Dubai, United Arab Emirates
Tel.: (971) 42219495
Fax: (971) 2214779
Web Site: www.bhatiabrothers.com
Emp.: 12
Retailer, Whslr & Exporter of Branded Consumer Electronics, Office Automation Products, Home Appliances & Internet Technology Products
S.I.C.: 5099
N.A.I.C.S.: 423990
Ajay Bagwanves Bhatia *(Chm)*

Technical Parts Company LLC **(1)**
PO Box 5071
Dubai, United Arab Emirates
Tel.: (971) 42823414
Fax: (971) 42823078
E-Mail: tpcdxb@emirates.net.ae
Web Site: www.bhatia.com
Emp.: 50
Engineering Products, Services & Solutions
S.I.C.: 8711
N.A.I.C.S.: 541330
V. K. Daga *(Gen Mgr)*

BHATIA INDUSTRIES & INFRASTRUCTURE LIMITED

BCC House 8/5 Manoramaganj
Navratan Bagh Main Road
Indore, MP, 452001, India
Tel.: (91) 731 4066101
Fax: (91) 731 4066102
E-Mail: cs@bhatiacoalindia.com
Web Site: www.bhatiacoalindia.com
531178—(BOM)
Rev.: $49,141,197
Assets: $25,179,174
Liabilities: $18,792,329
Net Worth: $6,386,845
Earnings: $1,195,459
Fiscal Year-end: 03/31/13

Business Description:
Financial Services
S.I.C.: 6211
N.A.I.C.S.: 523999

Personnel:
Surinder Singh Bhatia *(CEO)*
Samir Kumar Bahri *(Compliance Officer & Sec)*

Board of Directors:
Manjeet Singh Bhatia
Surinder Singh Bhatia
Jitendra Kumar Jain
Chitranjan Singh Kahlon

Transfer Agent:
Link Intime India Private Limited
C-13 Pannalal Silk Mills Compound L.B.S. Marg Bhandup
Mumbai, India

BHEEMA CEMENTS LTD.

No 6-3-652/C/A Flat 5a Kautilya
Amrutha Estates Somajiguda
Hyderabad, 500082, India
Tel.: (91) 40 23423270
Fax: (91) 40 23311413
E-Mail: info@bheemacements.co.in
Web Site: www.bheemacements.co.in
518017—(BOM)
Rev.: $32,101,287
Assets: $105,738,366
Liabilities: $72,466,445
Net Worth: $33,271,921
Earnings: ($3,547,054)
Fiscal Year-end: 03/31/13

Business Description:
Cement Mfr
S.I.C.: 3241
N.A.I.C.S.: 327310

Personnel:
S. Chandra Mohan *(Chm)*
S. R. B. Ramesh Chandra *(Mng Dir)*
K. A. N. Subba Rao *(Sec)*

Board of Directors:
S. Chandra Mohan
S. Kishore Chandra
S. R. B. Ramesh Chandra
K. R. Chari
Jalagam Rama Rao
S. V. Reddy

Transfer Agent:
Bigshare Services Pvt Ltd
306 Right Wing Amrutha Ville Opp Yasodha Hospital Somajiguda
Raj Bhavan Road, Hyderabad, 500 082, India

BHG S.A. - BRAZIL HOSPITALITY GROUP

Rua Ramos Batista n 444 10 andar
Vila Olimpia, Sao Paulo, 04552-020, Brazil
Tel.: (55) 11 3577 2300
E-Mail: contato@bhg.net
Web Site: www.bhg.net
BHGR3—(BRAZ OTC)
Rev.: $128,134,886
Assets: $557,286,284
Liabilities: $182,489,222
Net Worth: $374,797,061
Earnings: ($3,677,862)
Emp.: 3,303
Fiscal Year-end: 12/31/12

Business Description:
Hotel Owner & Operator
S.I.C.: 7011
N.A.I.C.S.: 721110

Personnel:
Eduardo Alcalay *(Chm)*
Eduardo de Salles Bartolomeo *(CEO & Member-Exec Bd)*
Ricardo Levy *(CFO, IR Officer & Member-Exec Bd)*
Andre Luiz Dias Lameiro *(Member-Exec Bd)*
Reginaldo Luchini Olivi *(Member-Exec Bd)*
Flavio Antonio Maia Pinto *(Member-Exec Bd)*

Board of Directors:
Eduardo Alcalay
Miguel Garcia Rugeroni Ahlers
Daniel Crestian Cunha
Rubens Mario Marques de Freitas
Francisco Ribeiro de Magalhaes Filho
Fersen Lamas Lambranho
Horacio Lafer Piva
Ricardo Abecassis Espirito Santo Silva

BHI HOLDINGS INC

22nd Floor The Pearlbank Center
146 Valero Street Salcedo Village
Makati, Philippines 1227
Tel.: (63) 28171406
Fax: (63) 28172109
Web Site: www.bhi-holdings.com
BH—(PHI)
Rev.: $201,331
Assets: $2,399,739
Liabilities: $74,996
Net Worth: $2,324,743
Earnings: $68,085
Fiscal Year-end: 12/31/12

Business Description:
Investment Services
S.I.C.: 6282
N.A.I.C.S.: 523920

Personnel:
Manuel N. Tankiansee *(Chm)*
Juanita U. Tan *(Pres & CEO)*
Rosalie A. Esteibar *(CFO & VP)*
Helen C. De Leon-Manzano *(Sec)*

Board of Directors:
Manuel N. Tankiansee
Julie C. Dela Cruz
Felisa P. Escudero
Rosalie A. Esteibar
Rudin A. Gonzales, Jr.
Emma Keng Ocampo-Tan
Miguel Ocampo-Tan
Marilou U. Pua
Jalane Christie U. Tan
Jemie U. Tan
Juanita U. Tan

BHILWARA TECHNICAL TEXTILES LIMITED

LNJ Nagar Mordi
Banswara, Rajasthan, 327 001, India
Tel.: (91) 2961231640
Fax: (91) 2961231254
Web Site: www.bttl.co.in
533108—(BOM)
Rev.: $527,267
Assets: $2,203,092
Liabilities: $8,685
Net Worth: $2,194,407
Earnings: $279,487
Emp.: 1
Fiscal Year-end: 03/31/13

Business Description:
Textile Products Mfr & Distr
S.I.C.: 2299
N.A.I.C.S.: 314999

Personnel:
Shekhar Agarwal *(Chm & Mng Dir)*
Sweta Garg *(CFO, Compliance Officer & Sec)*

Board of Directors:
Shekhar Agarwal
P. S. Dasgupta
Pawan Kumar Deora
Riju Jhunjhunwala

Transfer Agent:
Beetal Financial & Computers Services (P) Limited
Beetal House 3rd Floor 99 Madangir Behind Local Shopping Complex
New Delhi, 110062, India

BHILWARA TEX-FIN LIMITED

129 Transport Centre New Rohtak Road
Punjabi Bagh, New Delhi, 110035, India
Tel.: (91) 11 28315036
Fax: (91) 11 28315044
E-Mail: info@bhilwaratexfin.com
Web Site: www.bhilwaratexfin.com
Year Founded: 1994
530879—(BOM)
Rev.: $162,836
Assets: $2,520,430
Liabilities: $1,903,083
Net Worth: $617,347
Earnings: $9,589
Fiscal Year-end: 03/31/13

Business Description:
Textile Product Mfr & Investment Management Services

Bhilwara Tex-Fin Limited—(Continued)

S.I.C.: 2389
N.A.I.C.S.: 314999
Personnel:
Satish Kumar Sharma *(Compliance Officer)*
Board of Directors:
Sanjay Hasija
Satish Kumar Sharma
Samai Singh
Vadake Chundayil Sreenivasan
Transfer Agent:
Indus Portfolio (P) Limited
G-65 Bali Nagar
New Delhi, India

BHK RESOURCES INC.

1610 400 Burrard Street
Vancouver, BC, V6C 3A6, Canada
Tel.: (604) 802-7372
Fax: (604) 732-0284
Year Founded: 2012
BHK.P—(TSXV)
Business Description:
Investment Services
S.I.C.: 6211
N.A.I.C.S.: 523999
Personnel:
Peter Hughes *(Pre & CEO)*
Brian A. Richardson *(CFO & Sec)*
Board of Directors:
Claus Andrup
Peter Hughes
Candrawijaya Kartorahardjo
Brian A. Richardson
Transfer Agent:
Olympia Trust Company
Suite 1003 750 West Pender Street
Vancouver, BC, V6C 2T8, Canada

BHORUKA ALUMINIUM LTD.

1 KRS Rd
Metagalli, Mysore, Karanataka, 570016, India
Tel.: (91) 8214286100
Fax: (91) 8212582167
E-Mail: enquiries@bhorukaaluminium.com
Web Site: www.bhorukaaluminium.com
Year Founded: 1979
BHRKALM—(BOM)
Sales Range: $25-49.9 Million
Emp.: 300
Business Description:
Aluminum Products Mfr
S.I.C.: 3339
N.A.I.C.S.: 331410
Personnel:
M. Panduranga Kasturiranga Setty *(Chm)*
Rajkumar Aggarwal *(Mng Dir)*
Ajay Kumar Dalmia *(CFO & Mgr-Fin)*
Pranab Panigrahi *(Compliance Officer & Sec)*
Board of Directors:
M. Panduranga Kasturiranga Setty
Rajkumar Aggarwal
Bansilal L. Amla
Prabir Chakravarti
Akilesh Kumar Pandey
Transfer Agent:
Karvy Computershare Private Limited
17-244 Vittal Rao Nagar Madhapur
Hyderabad, India
Subsidiaries:

Bhoruka Fabcons Private Limited **(1)**
427E Hebbal Industrial Area
Mysore, Karnataka, 570016, India
Tel.: (91) 8212510351
Fax: (91) 8212415291
E-Mail: rg.padidar@greatbhorukafabcons.com
Web Site: www.bhorukafabcons.com
Emp.: 32
Aluminum Products Mfr
S.I.C.: 3355
N.A.I.C.S.: 331318
R. G. Padidar *(Mgr)*

Maverick Infotec **(1)**
1 K R S Rd
Metagalli, Mysore, Karnataka, 570016, India
Tel.: (91) 8212582625
Fax: (91) 8212581108
E-Mail: marketing@maverickinfotec.com
Web Site: www.maverickinfotec.com
Emp.: 30
SAP Project Management Services
S.I.C.: 8748
N.A.I.C.S.: 541618
A. Raj Kumar *(Exec Dir)*

BHP BILLITON LIMITED

170 Collins Street
Melbourne, VIC, 3000, Australia
Mailing Address:
GPO Box 86A
Melbourne, VIC, 3001, Australia
Tel.: (61) 1300 55 47 57
Fax: (61) 39609 3015
E-Mail: info@bhpbilliton.com
Web Site: www.bhpbilliton.com
Year Founded: 1885
BHP—(ASX NYSE)
Rev.: $65,968,000,000
Assets: $138,109,000,000
Liabilities: $66,074,000,000
Net Worth: $72,035,000,000
Earnings: $11,075,000,000
Emp.: 49,496
Fiscal Year-end: 06/30/13
Business Description:
Petroleum, Coal, Diamond, Ferrous & Non-Ferrous Metals Exploring, Drilling, Mining & Processing Operations
S.I.C.: 1011
N.A.I.C.S.: 212210
Personnel:
Jacques A. Nasser *(Chm)*
Graham Kerr *(CFO)*
Jane F. McAloon *(Pres-Governance & Grp Sec)*
Tony Cudmore *(Pres-Corp Affairs)*
Daniel Malchuk *(Pres-Aluminium, Manganese & Nickel)*
Dean Dalla Valle *(Pres-Coal)*
Jimmy Wilson *(Pres-Iron Ore)*
Nicole Duncan *(Sec)*
Board of Directors:
Jacques A. Nasser
Malcolm W. Broomhead
John Buchanan
Carlos A. Cordeiro
David A. Crawford
Pat Davies
Carolyn Judith Hewson
Lindsay Philip Maxsted
Wayne W. Murdy
Keith Christopher Rumble
John M. Schubert
Shriti Vadera
KPMG
Level 5 161 Collins Street
Melbourne, VIC, 3000, Australia
Citibank Shareholder Services
PO Box 43077
Providence, RI 02940-3077
Transfer Agents:
Computershare Investor Services Pty. Ltd.
Yarra Falls 452 Johnston Street
Abbotsford, VIC, 3067, Australia
Tel.: (61) 3 9415 4000
Fax: (61) 3 9473 2500
Citibank Shareholder Services
PO Box 43077
Providence, RI 02940-3077
Co-Headquarters:

BHP Billiton Plc **(1)**
Neathouse Place
London, SW1V 1BH, United Kingdom UK
Tel.: (44) 2078024000
Fax: (44) 2078024111
Web Site: www.bhpbilliton.com
BBL—(JSE LSE NYSE)
Rev.: $65,967,000,000
Assets: $138,108,000,000
Liabilities: $66,073,000,000
Net Worth: $72,034,000,000
Earnings: $11,074,000,000
Emp.: 49,495
Fiscal Year-end: 06/30/13
Petroleum, Coal, Diamond, Ferrous & Non-Ferrous Metals Exploring, Drilling, Mining & Processing Operations
S.I.C.: 1311
N.A.I.C.S.: 211111
Jacques A. Nasser *(Chm)*
Jane F. McAloon *(Sec)*

Non-U.S. Divisions:

BHP Billiton Petroleum Pty. Ltd. **(2)**
180 Lonsdale St
Melbourne, VIC, 3000, Australia AU (100%)
Tel.: (61) 396093333
Fax: (61) 396093015
Web Site: www.bhpbilliton.com
Emp.: 200
S.I.C.: 1011
N.A.I.C.S.: 212210
Marius Kloppars *(CEO)*
Alex Vanselo *(CFO)*

Subsidiaries:

BHP Petroleum Pty. Ltd. **(3)**
Level 46 152 158
St Georges Terrace, Perth, WA, 6000, Australia (100%)
Mailing Address:
GPO Box J668
Perth, WA, 6001, Australia
Tel.: (61) 892784888
Fax: (61) 892784899
Web Site: www.bhpbilliton.com
Emp.: 300
S.I.C.: 1011
N.A.I.C.S.: 212210

BHP Petroleum Pty. Ltd. **(3)**
180 Longsdale St
Melbourne, VIC, 3000, Australia (100%)
Mailing Address:
GPO Box 86A
Melbourne, VIC, 3001, Australia
Tel.: (61) 396093333
Fax: (61) 396093015
E-Mail: hrsconnect@bhpbilliton.com
Web Site: www.bhpbilliton.com
Emp.: 300
Hydrocarbons Exploration, Development & Production; Manufacturer of Petrochemicals
S.I.C.: 2869
N.A.I.C.S.: 325110
Andrew Mackenzie *(CEO)*

U.S. Subsidiary:

BHP Billiton Petroleum (Americas) Inc. **(3)**
BHP Twr 1360 Post Oak Blvd Ste 150
Houston, TX 77056 DE (100%)
Tel.: (713) 961-8500
Fax: (713) 961-8400
Web Site: www.bhpbilliton.com
Sls.: $145,941,692
Emp.: 950
Oil & Gas Exploration, Development & Production
S.I.C.: 1389
N.A.I.C.S.: 213112

Non-U.S. Subsidiaries:

BHP Billiton (Bolivia), Inc. **(3)**
Km 3 5 Antigua Carretera A Cochabamba
Casilla, 3568 Santa Cruz, Bolivia (100%)
Tel.: (591) 133546404
Fax: (591) 133546414
S.I.C.: 1011
N.A.I.C.S.: 212210

BHP Minerals **(2)**
180 Lonsdale St
Melbourne, VIC, 3000, Australia (100%)
Mailing Address:
GPO Box 86A
Melbourne, VIC, 3001, Australia
Tel.: (61) 396093333
Telex: AA30408
Fax: (61) 396093015
Emp.: 350
S.I.C.: 1011
N.A.I.C.S.: 212210
Marius Klotter *(CEO)*

Subsidiaries:

BHP Coal **(3)**
180 Lonsdale Street
Melbourne, VIC, 3000, Australia (100%)
Tel.: (61) 396093333
Fax: (61) 396093015
E-Mail: info@bhpbilliton.com
Web Site: www.bhpbilliton.com
Emp.: 650
S.I.C.: 1011
N.A.I.C.S.: 212210
Marius Klotters *(CEO)*

BHP Iron Ore **(3)**
125 St Georges Terrace
Perth, WA, 6000, Australia (100%)
Mailing Address:
Cloisters Square
PO Box 7122
Perth, WA, 6850, Australia
Tel.: (61) 862244444
Fax: (61) 893204042
Web Site: www.bhpbillinton.com
Emp.: 2,000
S.I.C.: 1011
N.A.I.C.S.: 212210
Ian Ashby *(Pres)*

BHP Manganese **(3)**
Camco Rd
Bell Bay, TAS, 7253, Australia (100%)
Mailing Address:
GPO Box 86A
Melbourne, VIC, 3001, Australia
Tel.: (61) 363820200
Fax: (61) 363820410
Web Site: www.camco-alloys.com
Emp.: 280
Iron Ore Mining
S.I.C.: 1011
N.A.I.C.S.: 212210
Greg Hinnan *(Gen Mgr)*

BHP Titanium Minerals **(3)**
180 Lonsdale St
Melbourne, VIC, 3000, Australia (100%)
Tel.: (61) 396093333
Telex: AA30408
Fax: (61) 396093071
E-Mail: adelite.hra@bhpbilliton.com
Emp.: 300
S.I.C.: 1011
N.A.I.C.S.: 212210

Delta End Australia Pty. Ltd. **(3)**
Steel River Industrial Estate Lot 16
Mcintosh Dr
PO Box 249
Mayfield, NSW, 2304, Australia (100%)
Tel.: (61) 249411500
Fax: (61) 249602075
Web Site: www.deltaplc.com
Emp.: 95
S.I.C.: 1011
N.A.I.C.S.: 212210

Groote Eylandt Mining Company **(3)**
180 Lonsdale St
3000 Melbourne, NT, Australia (100%)
Tel.: (61) 1300554757
Telex: AA 85166 MNGSE
Fax: (61) 396093015
Web Site: www.bhpbilliton.com
Manganese Ore Mining
S.I.C.: 1021
N.A.I.C.S.: 212234

Tasmania Electro Metallurgical Company Pty. Ltd. (TEMCO) **(3)**
Temco Rd
Bell Bay, TAS, 7253, Australia (100%)
Tel.: (61) 363820200
Telex: AA58873
Fax: (61) 363820410
Web Site: www.temco-alloys.com
Emp.: 270
S.I.C.: 1011
N.A.I.C.S.: 212210
Greg Hannin *(Gen Mgr)*

Worsley Alumina Pty. Ltd. **(3)**
Gastaldo Rd
PO Box 344
Collie, WA, 6225, Australia (75%)

Tel.: (61) 897348311
Fax: (61) 897348413
E-Mail: info@bhpbilliton.com
Web Site: www.wapl.com.au
Emp.: 1,200
Gold Mining Services
S.I.C.: 1041
N.A.I.C.S.: 212221
Jackie Donnan *(Mgr-HR)*

Billiton Base Metals (2)
120 Adelaide St W Ste 2600
Toronto, ON, M5H 1W5, Canada
Tel.: (416) 367-4000
Fax: (416) 365-6870
E-Mail: corpcomm@rioalgom.com
Web Site: www.rioalgom.com
Emp.: 2,774
Mining & Metals Distribution Company
S.I.C.: 3532
N.A.I.C.S.: 333131

Subsidiaries:

Metaux Billiton Canada Incorporated (3)
Les Mines Selbaie
Villebois, QC, J0Z 3V0, Canada (100%)
Tel.: (819) 756-2491
Fax: (819) 756-2684
Emp.: 125
Copper Ores Mining Company
S.I.C.: 1021
N.A.I.C.S.: 212234

Rio Algom Inc. (3)
PO Box 38
Elliot Lake, ON, PSA 256, Canada
Tel.: (705) 848-0111
Fax: (705) 848-5334
Web Site: www.rioalgom.com
Emp.: 1
Minerals Exploration
S.I.C.: 1241
N.A.I.C.S.: 213113

Non-U.S. Subsidiaries:

Compania Minera Cerro Colorado Limitada (3)
Avenida Americo Vespucio Sur No 100 Piso 10
Las Condes, 7580 154 Santiago, Chile (100%)
Tel.: (56) 23305851
Fax: (56) 23305885
Web Site: www.bhp.com
Emp.: 4
S.I.C.: 1011
N.A.I.C.S.: 212210

Non-U.S. Subsidiaries:

BHP Billiton China (2)
One Corporate Ave 222 Hubin Rd
Level 12, Shanghai, 200021, China
Tel.: (86) 2161227000
Fax: (86) 61229888
Web Site: www.bhpbilliton.com
Emp.: 70
Petroleum, Coal, Diamond, Ferrous & Non-Ferrous Metals Exploring, Drilling, Mining & Processing Marketing Operations
S.I.C.: 1011
N.A.I.C.S.: 212210
Chai Tan *(Pres)*

BHP Billiton Nickel West Pty. Ltd. (2)
BHP Billiton Centre 180 Lonsdale Street
Melbourne, VIC, 3000, Australia AU
Tel.: (61) 1300 554757 (100%)
Fax: (61) 3 96093015
Web Site: www.bhpbilliton.com
Emp.: 4,863
Nickel, Uranium Oxide, Copper & Gold Miner; Fertilizer Mfr
S.I.C.: 1021
N.A.I.C.S.: 212234
Daniel Malchuk *(Pres-Aluminium, Manganese & Nickel Ops)*

Subsidiaries:

Olympic Dam Corporation Pty Ltd. (3)
Rocksbegell S Australia 5725
PO Box 150
Melbourne, VIC, 5725, Australia
Tel.: (61) 886718888
Fax: (61) 886718811
Web Site: www.bhpbilliton.com
Emp.: 2,880
Copper, Uranium Oxide, Gold & Silver Miner
S.I.C.: 1021
N.A.I.C.S.: 212234

P.T. BHP Indonesia (2)
Midplaza Bldg 3rd Fl JL Jend Sudirman Kav 11
Jakarta, 12910, Indonesia (55%)
Tel.: (62) 215706281
Fax: (62) 215707533
Web Site: www.bhpbilliton.com
Emp.: 15
S.I.C.: 1011
N.A.I.C.S.: 212210
Rock Funsbon *(Gen Mgr)*

BHS INDUSTRIES BERHAD

802 8th Floor Block C Kelana Square
17 Jalan SS7/26
47301 Petaling Jaya, Selangor Darul Ehsan, Malaysia
Tel.: (60) 378031126
Fax: (60) 378067806
Web Site: bhs.listedcompany.com
BHS—(KLS)
Rev.: $21,341,648
Assets: $27,452,918
Liabilities: $5,911,789
Net Worth: $21,541,130
Earnings: $2,375,796
Fiscal Year-end: 06/30/13
Business Description:
Magazines & Books Printing & Publishing Services
S.I.C.: 2759
N.A.I.C.S.: 323113
Personnel:
Song Khoon Heng *(Chm & Mng Dir)*
Shew Meng Kang *(Co-Sec)*
Fei San Seow *(Co-Sec)*
Board of Directors:
Song Khoon Heng
Yuit Yoo Chew
Boon Seng Heng
Sai Ying Liew
Chew Lan Thiang

BHS TABLETOP AG

Ludwigsmuhle 1
95100 Selb, Germany
Tel.: (49) 9287 73 0
E-Mail: kontakt@bhs-tabletop.de
Web Site: www.bhs-tabletop.de
HUL—(DEU)
Sls.: $110,789,791
Assets: $113,482,131
Liabilities: $63,943,075
Net Worth: $49,539,056
Earnings: $942,319
Emp.: 1,054
Fiscal Year-end: 12/31/12
Business Description:
Porcelain Tableware Products Mfr
S.I.C.: 3999
N.A.I.C.S.: 327110
Personnel:
Norbert Loos *(Chm-Supervisory Bd)*
Ulrich Muller *(Deputy Chm-Supervisory Bd)*
Christian Strootmann *(CEO & Member-Mgmt Bd)*
Uwe Kolb *(Member-Mgmt Bd)*
Rainer Schwarzmeier *(Member-Mgmt Bd)*
Supervisory Board of Directors:
Norbert Loos
Ulrich Muller
Michael Ott
Herbert Schaffner
Hans-Volker Sprave
Ernst Zenk

BHUSHAN STEEL LTD.

F Block 1st Floor International Trade Tower Nehru Place
New Delhi, 110019, India
Tel.: (91) 1142297777
Fax: (91) 1126478750
E-Mail: bsslcorporate@bhushansteel.com
Web Site: www.bhushan-group.org
500055—(BOM NSE)
Rev.: $1,995,208,278
Assets: $8,072,294,253
Liabilities: $6,347,645,497
Net Worth: $1,724,648,756
Earnings: $167,664,210
Emp.: 5,828
Fiscal Year-end: 03/31/13
Business Description:
Steel Tube Mfr
S.I.C.: 3312
N.A.I.C.S.: 331221
Personnel:
Neeraj Singal *(Vice Chm & Mng Dir)*
O. P. Davra *(Sec)*
Board of Directors:
Brij Bhushan Singal
P. K. Agarwal
Nittin Johari
Mohan Lal
V. K. Mehrotra
Rahul Sengupta
Sunita Sharma
Neeraj Singal
M. V. Suryanarayana
B. B. Tondon
Transfer Agent:
RCMC Share Registry Pvt. Ltd.
B-106 Sector-2
Noida, India

Non-U.S. Subsidiary:

Bowen Energy Ltd. (1)
Level 7 10 Barrack Street
Sydney, NSW, 2000, Australia (77.8%)
Mailing Address:
PO Box 523
Spring Hill, 4000, Australia
Tel.: (61) 738398818
Fax: (61) 7 3839 8817
E-Mail: admin@bowenenergy.com.au
Web Site: www.bowenenergy.com.au
Coal & Uranium Exploration & Development
S.I.C.: 1222
N.A.I.C.S.: 212112
Nittin Johari *(Mng Dir)*
Glenn Merchant *(Sec)*

BHUTAN NATIONAL BANK

PO Box 439
Thimphu, Bhutan
Tel.: (975) 2322767
Fax: (975) 2328839
E-Mail: thimphu@bnb.bt
Web Site: www.bnb.bt
BNB—(BHU)
Sales Range: $25-49.9 Million
Emp.: 180
Business Description:
Banking Services
S.I.C.: 6029
N.A.I.C.S.: 522110
Personnel:
Ugyen Namgyal *(Chm)*
Kipchu Tshering *(CEO)*
Sonam Tobgay *(Deputy CEO)*
Dorji Namgyal Rinchhen *(Sec)*
Board of Directors:
Ugyen Namgyal
T.S. Bhattacharya
Eutha Karchung
Tobgay S. Namgyal
Dasho Tashi Phuntsog
Sonam Rinchen
Ugyen Wangchhuk

BHUWALKA STEEL INDUSTRIES LTD.

Bhuwalka Center No 71 Residency Road
3rd Cross, Bengaluru, 560 025, India
Tel.: (91) 80 25599797
Fax: (91) 80 25596030
E-Mail: bsil@bhuwalkagroup.com
Web Site: www.bhuwalkagroup.com
513333—(BOM)
Rev.: $118,515,652
Earnings: $642,170
Fiscal Year-end: 03/31/13
Business Description:
Rolled Steel Mfr
S.I.C.: 3312
N.A.I.C.S.: 331221
Personnel:
Suresh Kumar Bhuwalka *(Chm & Mng Dir)*
Desmond Rozario *(Compliance Officer)*
Ashish Kumar A. Parmar *(Sec)*
Board of Directors:
Suresh Kumar Bhuwalka
Ajay Kumar Bhuwalka
Ankit Bhuwalka
K. C. Kondaiah
Visalakshi Vasanthan
Transfer Agent:
Integrated Enterprises (India) Ltd.
No 30 Ramana Residency Ground Floor 4th Cross Sampige Road Malleswaram
Bengaluru, India

Subsidiaries:

Benaka Sponge Iron Pvt Ltd. (1)
No 138A 138B Tumti Road Bellagal Village
Bellary, Karnakata, India
Tel.: (91) 8392 260738
Sponge Iron Mfr
S.I.C.: 3462
N.A.I.C.S.: 332111

Nava Karntaka Steels Pvt Ltd. (1)
PB No 46 Anatpur Road Bisilahally Village
Bellary, Karnataka, 583 101, India
Tel.: (91) 8392 260738
Fax: (91) 8932 260130
Steel Products Mfr
S.I.C.: 3312
N.A.I.C.S.: 331110

BI-OPTIC VENTURES INC.

Suite 1518-1030 West Georgia Street
Vancouver, BC, V6E 2Y3, Canada
Tel.: (604) 689-2646
Year Founded: 1984
BOV—(OTCB TSXV)
Assets: $6,835
Liabilities: $341,326
Net Worth: ($334,491)
Earnings: ($173,060)
Emp.: 2
Fiscal Year-end: 02/28/13
Business Description:
Investment Services
S.I.C.: 6211
N.A.I.C.S.: 523999
Personnel:
Harry Chew *(Pres, CEO & CFO)*
Board of Directors:
Harry Chew
Sonny Chew
Terrance G. Owen
Transfer Agent:
Computershare Investor Services Inc.
100 University Ave 9th Floor
Toronto, ON, Canada

BIA OVERSEAS S.A.

Avenue Einstein 6F
B-1300 Wavre, Belgium
Tel.: (32) 10 23 45 11
Fax: (32) 10 23 45 00
Web Site: www.biagroup.com
Sales Range: $250-299.9 Million

BIA Overseas S.A.—(Continued)

Business Description:
Mining & Quarrying Equipment Distr
S.I.C.: 5082
N.A.I.C.S.: 423810
Personnel:
Vincent Bia *(CEO)*

BIAFO INDUSTRIES LIMITED

Off No 203 204 2nd Floor
Muhammad Gulistan Khan House 82 East
Fazal-ul-Haq Road Blue Area,
Islamabad, Pakistan
Tel.: (92) 512277358
Fax: (92) 512274744
E-Mail: management@biafo.com
Web Site: www.biafo.com
BIFO—(KAR)
Business Description:
Industrial & Commercial Explosives Mfr
S.I.C.: 2892
N.A.I.C.S.: 325920
Personnel:
M. Afzal Khan *(Chm)*
Khawaja Amanullah Askari *(CEO & Mng Dir)*
Khawaja Shaiq Tanveer *(Sec)*
Board of Directors:
M. Afzal Khan
Khawaja Amanullah Askari
S. Z. M. Askree
Adnan Aurangzeb
Khwaja Ahmad Hosain
M. Hamayun Khan
M. Hashim Khan
M. Zafar Khan
Salim Khan
Abdul Majid Qureshi
Shirin Safdar

BIALETTI INDUSTRIE S.P.A.

Via Fogliano 1 Coccaglio
25030 Brescia, Italy
Tel.: (39) 307720011
Fax: (39) 307722389
E-Mail: info@bialettigroup.com
Web Site: www.bialetti.it
Year Founded: 1919
BIA—(ITA)
Business Description:
Housewares Mfr & Sales
S.I.C.: 3639
N.A.I.C.S.: 335210
Personnel:
Francesco Ranzoni *(Chm & CEO)*

BIANCAMANO S.P.A.

Strada 4 Palazzo Q6
20089 Rozzano, MI, Italy
Tel.: (39) 02528682255
Fax: (39) 02528862253
E-Mail: info@aimeriambiente.it
Web Site: www.gruppobiancamano.it
Year Founded: 2004
BCM—(ITA)
Rev.: $333,976,700
Assets: $492,840,914
Liabilities: $451,287,338
Net Worth: $41,553,576
Earnings: ($13,055,157)
Emp.: 3,283
Fiscal Year-end: 12/31/12
Business Description:
Holding Company; Environmental Services
S.I.C.: 4212
N.A.I.C.S.: 562119
Personnel:
Giovanni Battista Pizzimbone *(Chm & Co-CEO)*
Pier Paolo Pizzimbone *(Vice Chm)*
Massimo Delbecchi *(Co-CEO)*
Board of Directors:
Giovanni Battista Pizzimbone
Enrico Maria Bignami
Giovanni Maria Conti
Massimo Delbecchi
Maria Luisa Mosconi
Pier Paolo Pizzimbone
Luigi Reale

Subsidiaries:

Aimeri Ambiente Srl (1)
Strada 4 - Palazzo Q6
Milanofiori, 20089 Rozzano, Italy IT
Tel.: (39) 025286821 (99.95%)
Fax: (39) 02528682250
E-Mail: aimeri@aimeriambiente.it
Web Site: www.aimeriambiente.it
Emp.: 80
Solid Waste Collection
S.I.C.: 4212
N.A.I.C.S.: 562111
Caruso Giuseppe *(Mng Dir)*

Ponticelli S.R.L. (1)
Via Don Abbo il Santo 12/15
18100 Imperia, Italy
Tel.: (39) 0183720205
Fax: (39) 0183 297271
E-Mail: info@ponticelli.it
Solid Waste Disposal Services
S.I.C.: 4953
N.A.I.C.S.: 562219

BIANOR HOLDING AD

51 Alexander Malinov Blvd Entr A
1712 Sofia, Bulgaria
Tel.: (359) 2 460 4200
Fax: (359) 2 955 5686
E-Mail: info@bianor.com
Web Site: www.bianor.com
5BI—(BUL)
Business Description:
Mobile Application Development Services
S.I.C.: 7371
N.A.I.C.S.: 541511
Personnel:
Nickolay Rashev *(Co-Founder & Chm)*
Kostadin Jordanov *(Co-Founder & CEO)*
Metodi Filipov *(Mng Dir)*
Vladimir Tankov *(CFO)*
Luca Romano *(CTO)*
Board of Directors:
Nickolay Rashev
Metodi Filipov
Kostadin Jordanov
Nedelcho Nedelchev
Sev Onyshkevych

BIAO-COTE D'IVOIRE

8-10 Avenue Joseph Anoma
BP 1274
Abidjan, 01, Cote d'Ivoire
Tel.: (225) 20200702
Fax: (225) 20200700
E-Mail: info@biao.co.ci
Web Site: www.biao.co.ci
Year Founded: 1980
Sales Range: $10-24.9 Million
Emp.: 650
Business Description:
Commercial Banking Services
S.I.C.: 6029
N.A.I.C.S.: 522110
Personnel:
Deajou Jean *(Pres)*

BIBBY LINE GROUP LIMITED

105 Duke Street
Liverpool, L1 5JQ, United Kingdom
Tel.: (44) 151 708 8000
Fax: (44) 151 794 1099
E-Mail: info@bibbylinegroup.co.uk
Web Site: www.bibbylinegroup.co.uk
Sales Range: $1-4.9 Billion
Business Description:
Holding Company; Financial, Logistics & Shipping
S.I.C.: 6719
N.A.I.C.S.: 551112
Personnel:
Michael Bibby *(CEO)*

Subsidiaries:

Bibby Distribution Limited (1)
105 Duke Street
Liverpool, L1 5JQ, United Kingdom
Tel.: (44) 151 794 1074
Fax: (44) 1517941089
E-Mail: info@bibbydist.co.uk
Web Site: www.bibbydist.co.uk
Emp.: 200
Logistics & Distr
S.I.C.: 4731
N.A.I.C.S.: 541614
Iain Speak *(CEO)*
Paul Cullingford *(CFO)*
Paul Kavanagh *(COO)*

Bibby Financial Services Limited (1)
105 Duke Street
Liverpool, L1 5JQ, United Kingdom
Tel.: (44) 151 708 8000
Financial Services
S.I.C.: 6726
N.A.I.C.S.: 525990
Leigh Lones *(CEO-Americas)*

Bibby Holdings Limited (1)
105 Duke Street
Liverpool, L1 5JQ, United Kingdom
Tel.: (44) 151 708 8000
Fax: (44) 151 794 1900
E-Mail: info@bibbyholdings.com
Web Site: www.bibbyholdings.com
Investment Holding Company
S.I.C.: 6211
N.A.I.C.S.: 523999

Bibby Line Limited (1)
105 Duke Street
Liverpool, L1 5JQ, United Kingdom
Tel.: (44) 151 708 8000
Fax: (44) 151 794 1099
Web Site: www.bibbyline.co.uk
Shipping Services
S.I.C.: 4731
N.A.I.C.S.: 488510

Division:

Bibby Line Limited (2)
The Baltic Exchange Saint Mary Axe
London, EC3A 8BH, United Kingdom
Tel.: (44) 20 7621 1567
Fax: (44) 20 7979 5666
Shipping Services
S.I.C.: 4731
N.A.I.C.S.: 488510

Bibby Maritime Limited (1)
105 Duke Street
Liverpool, L1 5JQ, United Kingdom
Tel.: (44) 151 708 8000
Fax: (44) 151 794 1000
E-Mail: enquiries@bibbymaritime.com
Web Site: www.bibbymaritime.com
Emp.: 25
Water Transportation Services
S.I.C.: 4412
N.A.I.C.S.: 483111
Jon Osbourne *(Mng Dir)*

Bibby Offshore Limited (1)
Ocean Spirit House 33 Waterloo Quay
Aberdeen, Scotland, AB11 5BS, United Kingdom
Tel.: (44) 1224 857755
Fax: (44) 1224 284444
E-Mail: info@bibbyoffshore.com
Web Site: www.bibbyoffshore.com
Emp.: 40
Subsea Construction; Offshore Operational & Maintenance Support
S.I.C.: 1629
N.A.I.C.S.: 237990
Howard Woodcock *(Chm)*
Fraser Moonie *(Mng Dir)*

Non-U.S. Divisions:

Bibby Offshore Limited (2)
Loyang Offshore Supply Base 25 Loyang Crescent
Singapore, 508988, Singapore
Tel.: (65) 66039288
E-Mail: singapore@bibbyoffshore.com
Web Site: www.bibbyoffshore.com
Emp.: 2
Subsea Construction; Offshore Operational & Maintenance Support
S.I.C.: 1629
N.A.I.C.S.: 237990
Joakim Alm *(Gen Mgr)*

Bibby Offshore Limited (2)
29 Long Circular Road St James
Port of Spain, Trinidad & Tobago
Tel.: (868) 822 6060
Fax: (868) 822 6063
Subsea Construction; Offshore Operational & Maintenance Support
S.I.C.: 1629
N.A.I.C.S.: 237990

Bibby Ship Management (Group) Limited (1)
105 Duke Street
Liverpool, L1 5JQ, United Kingdom
Tel.: (44) 151 708 8000
Fax: (44) 151 794 1000
E-Mail: enquiries@bibbyshipmanagement.com
Web Site: www.bibbyshipmanagement.com
Ship Management Services
S.I.C.: 8748
N.A.I.C.S.: 541618
Chris Stone *(COO)*

Subsidiary:

GAC TRAVEL LTD (2)
GAC House Sabatier Close
Thornaby, Stockton-on-Tees, TS17 6EW, United Kingdom
Tel.: (44) 1642 637600
E-Mail: travel.middlesbrough@gac.com
Web Site: www.gac.com
Freight Transportation Services
S.I.C.: 4412
N.A.I.C.S.: 483111

Non-U.S. Subsidiaries:

Bibby Ship Management (Eastern Europe) Limited (2)
42a Marshala Biryuzova Str
Sevastopol, Ukraine
Tel.: (380) 692 540909
Fax: (380) 692 540403
E-Mail: enquiries@ee.bibbyshipmanagement.com
Web Site: ee.bibbyshipmanagement.com
Ship Management Services
S.I.C.: 8748
N.A.I.C.S.: 541618

Bibby Ship Management (India) Pvt Limited (2)
P & G Plaza 1st Floor Cardinal Gracias Road Chakala Andheri
Andheri, Mumbai, 400 099, India
Tel.: (91) 22 4086 8000
Fax: (91) 22 4086 8001
E-Mail: enquiries@india.bibbyshipmanagement.com
Web Site: india.bibbyshipmanagement.com
Emp.: 13
Ship Management Services
S.I.C.: 8748
N.A.I.C.S.: 541618
Will Dowell *(Mng Dir)*

Bibby Ship Management (Philippines) Inc. (2)
Ground Floor RIMA Building 161 Pasig Boulevard
Pasig, Metro Manila, Philippines
Tel.: (63) 2 6715591
Fax: (63) 2 6720380
E-Mail: enquiries@ph.bibbyshipmanagement.com
Web Site: ph.bibbyshipmanagement.com
Ship Management Services
S.I.C.: 8748
N.A.I.C.S.: 541618

Bibby Ship Management (Singapore) Pvt Limited (2)
Prudential Tower 24/01-02 30 Cecil Street
Singapore, 049721, Singapore
Tel.: (65) 6603 9270
Fax: (65) 6603 9289
E-Mail: enquiries@sg.bibbyshipmanagement.com

Web Site: sg.bibbyshipmanagement.com
Ship Management Services
S.I.C.: 8748
N.A.I.C.S.: 541618

Bibby Ship Management (Western Europe) Limited (2)
Compass House Isle of Man Business Park
Cooil Road, Braddan, IM2 2QZ, Isle of Man
Tel.: (44) 1624 687200
Fax: (44) 1624 687276
E-Mail: enquiries@we.bibbyshipmanagement.com
Web Site: we.bibbyshipmanagement.com
Ship Management Services
S.I.C.: 8748
N.A.I.C.S.: 541618

Costcutter Supermarkets Group Limited (1)
Harvest Mills Common Road
Dunnington, York, YO19 5RY, United Kingdom
Tel.: (44) 1904 488663
Web Site: www.costcutter.com
Grocery Stores
S.I.C.: 5411
N.A.I.C.S.: 445110
Darcy Willson-Rymer *(CEO)*

Garic Limited (1)
Kingfisher Park Aviation Road
Pilsworth, Bury, Lancashire, BL9 8GD, United Kingdom
Tel.: (44) 161 766 8808
Fax: (44) 161 766 8809
E-Mail: sales@garic-ltd.co.uk
Web Site: www.garic.co.uk
Emp.: 15
Plant, Welfare & Servicing Equipment Mfr
S.I.C.: 3559
N.A.I.C.S.: 333249
Tamilla Askerova *(Dir-Ops)*

Woodland Burial Parks Group Ltd. (1)
105 Duke Street
Liverpool, L1 5JQ, United Kingdom
Tel.: (44) 151 708 8000
Web Site: www.woodlandburialparks.co.uk
Funeral Parks
S.I.C.: 7261
N.A.I.C.S.: 812210
Andrew Paling *(Mng Dir)*

BIBENDUM WINE LIMITED

113 Regents Park Road
London, NW1 8UR, United Kingdom
Tel.: (44) 20 7449 4120
Fax: (44) 20 7722 7354
Web Site: www.bibendum-wine.co.uk
Year Founded: 1982
Sales Range: $250-299.9 Million
Emp.: 256
Business Description:
Wine Whslr
S.I.C.: 5182
N.A.I.C.S.: 424820
Personnel:
Simon Farr *(Founder)*

BIBOJEE SERVICES PRIVATE LIMITED

(d/b/a Bibojee Group of Companies)
Ghandhara House 109 2 Clifton
Karachi, Pakistan
Tel.: (92) 21 35830251 57
Fax: (92) 21 5830258
Web Site: www.bibojee.com.pk
Business Description:
Holding Company
S.I.C.: 6719
N.A.I.C.S.: 551112
Personnel:
Raza Kuli Khan Khattak *(Chm)*

Subsidiaries:

Ghanadhara Industries Ltd. (1)
F-3 Hub Chauki Road SITE
PO Box 2706
Karachi, 75730, Pakistan
Tel.: (92) 2132560083
Fax: (92) 2132560090
E-Mail: info@gil.com.pk
Web Site: www.gil.com.pk
GHNI—(KAR)
Sls.: $28,495,265
Assets: $41,900,922
Liabilities: $21,669,640
Net Worth: $20,231,281
Earnings: $1,293,966
Emp.: 149
Fiscal Year-end: 06/30/13
Motor Vehicle Chassis & Load Bodies Mfr
S.I.C.: 3714
N.A.I.C.S.: 336390
Ahmed Kuli Khan Khattak *(CEO)*
Iftikhar Ahmed Khan *(Sec)*

Ghandhara Nissan Ltd. (1)
Ghandhara House 109/2 Clifton
PO Box 3812
Karachi, 6, Pakistan
Tel.: (92) 215830251
Fax: (92) 215830258
E-Mail: info@ghandhara.com.pk
Web Site: www.ghandharanissan.com.pk
GHNL—(ISL KAR LAH)
Rev.: $18,763,171
Assets: $25,802,174
Liabilities: $8,841,312
Net Worth: $16,960,862
Earnings: $388,840
Emp.: 223
Fiscal Year-end: 06/30/13
Automotive Mfr & Distr
S.I.C.: 5012
N.A.I.C.S.: 336111
Raza Kuli Khan Khattak *(Chm)*
Ali Kuli Khan Khattak *(Pres)*
Ahmad Kuli Khan Khattak *(CEO)*
Mohammad Saleem Baig *(CFO)*
Aqiel Amjad Ghani *(Sec)*

BIC CAMERA INC.

3-23-23 Takada
Toshima-ku, Tokyo, 171 0033, Japan
Tel.: (81) 339878785
Web Site: www.biccamera.co.jp
3048—(TKS)
Sls.: $7,860,489,280
Assets: $3,391,795,200
Liabilities: $2,496,930,080
Net Worth: $894,865,120
Earnings: $23,775,360
Emp.: 4,419
Fiscal Year-end: 08/31/13
Business Description:
Audiovisual Products, Electrical Home Appliances & Information Communications Equipment Retailer
S.I.C.: 5734
N.A.I.C.S.: 443142
Personnel:
Hiroyuki Miyajima *(Pres)*

Subsidiary:

Nippon BS Broadcasting Corporation (1)
2-5 Kandasurugadai
Chiyoda-ku, Tokyo, 101-0062, Japan
Tel.: (81) 3 3518 1800
Web Site: www.bs11.jp
Rev.: $77,171,413
Emp.: 70
Fiscal Year-end: 08/31/13
Cable Television Broadcasting Services
S.I.C.: 4833
N.A.I.C.S.: 515120
Tsuyoshi Metoki, *(Pres)*

BICICLETAS MONARK S.A.

R Francisco Lanzi Tancler 130 - Distrito Indu
13347370 Indaiatuba, SP, Brazil
Tel.: (55) 19 3935 9292
Fax: (55) 19 3935 9230
E-Mail: monark@monark.com.br
Web Site: www.monark.com.br
Year Founded: 1948
BMKS3—(BRAZ)
Sales Range: $10-24.9 Million
Emp.: 81
Business Description:
Bicycle Mfr & Whslr
S.I.C.: 3751
N.A.I.C.S.: 336991
Personnel:
Sylvio Marzagao *(Dir-IR)*

BID GROUP LTD

Unit C Elland Close
Wingates Industrial Park,
Westhoughton, BL5 3XE, United Kingdom
Tel.: (44) 870 607 5050
E-Mail: sales@bidgroup.co.uk
Web Site: bidgroup1.bpweb.net
Personnel:
John Thompson *(Mng Dir)*

Subsidiary:

Lowland Doors Limited (1)
9 Netherton Road
Wishaw, Lanarkshire, ML2 0EQ, United Kingdom
Tel.: (44) 1698376444
Fax: (44) 1698376888
E-Mail: sales@lowlandensor.co.uk
Web Site: www.lowlandensor.co.uk
Emp.: 25
Industrial Door Mfr
S.I.C.: 3442
N.A.I.C.S.: 332321
Stuart West *(Mng Dir)*

BIDCO OIL REFINERIES LIMITED

PO Box 239
01000 Thika, Kenya
Tel.: (254) 6730102
Fax: (254) 6730104
E-Mail: thika@bidco-oil.com
Web Site: www.bidco-oil.com
Emp.: 3,000
Business Description:
Vegetable Oils, Fats, Margarine, Soaps & Protein Concentrates Mfr
S.I.C.: 2079
N.A.I.C.S.: 311225
Personnel:
Vimal Shah *(CEO)*

BIDV INSURANCE CORPORATION

16th Floor Tower A Vincom City Towers 191 Ba Trieu
Hanoi, Vietnam
Tel.: (84) 422200282
Fax: (84) 422200281
E-Mail: bic@bidv.com.vn
Web Site: www.bic.vn
BIC—(HOSE)
Premiums: $33,518,836
Assets: $70,130,860
Liabilities: $32,209,494
Net Worth: $37,921,366
Earnings: $4,208,908
Emp.: 589
Fiscal Year-end: 12/31/12
Business Description:
Insurance Services
S.I.C.: 6411
N.A.I.C.S.: 524298
Personnel:
Pham Quang Tung *(Chm)*
Tran Xuan Hoang *(Vice Chm)*
Ton Lam Tung *(CEO)*
Doan Thi Thu Huyen *(COO)*
Tran Hoai An *(Co-CMO)*
Vu Minh Hai *(Co-CMO)*
Tran Trung Tinh *(Chief Underwriting Officer)*
Board of Directors:
Pham Quang Tung
Tran Xuan Hoang
Trinh Minh Tam
Nguyen Thi Thanh Van
Dang Quang Vinh
Supervisory Board of Directors:
Nguyen Thanh Cong
Nguyen Trung Kien
Cao Cu Tri

BIDV SECURITIES JOINT STOCK COMPANY

10th Floor - BIDV Tower 35 Hang Voi - HK Dist
Hanoi, Vietnam
Tel.: (84) 4 22206647
Fax: (84) 4 22200669
E-Mail: services@bsc.com.vn
Web Site: www.bsc.com.vn
Year Founded: 1999
BSI—(HOSE)
Business Description:
Investment Management Services
S.I.C.: 6211
N.A.I.C.S.: 523999
Personnel:
Huy Ha Hoang *(Chm)*
Thi Hoa Bui *(Chm-Supervisory Bd)*
Huy Hoai Do *(CEO, Vice Chm & Gen Dir)*
Board of Directors:
Huy Ha Hoang
Huy Hoai Do
Quoc Hung Nguyen
Van Thang Nguyen
Phuong Tran
Supervisory Board of Directors:
Thi Hoa Bui
Thi Huong Hoang
Minh Hai Tran

THE BIDVEST GROUP LIMITED

Bidvest House 18 Crescent Drive
Melrose Arch
Melrose, Johannesburg, 2196, South Africa
Tel.: (27) 117728700
Fax: (27) 117728970
E-Mail: info@bidvest.co.za
Web Site: www.bidvest.com
Year Founded: 1988
BVT—(JSE OTC)
Rev.: $17,135,286,224
Assets: $7,447,979,402
Liabilities: $4,370,564,090
Net Worth: $3,077,415,312
Earnings: $564,354,867
Emp.: 106,371
Fiscal Year-end: 06/30/13
Business Description:
International Services, Trading & Distribution Holding Company
S.I.C.: 6719
N.A.I.C.S.: 551112
Personnel:
Brian Joffe *(CEO)*
Bernard Larry Berson *(CEO-Bidvest Foodservice)*
Anthony William Dawe *(CEO-Bidvest Freight)*
Lindsay Peter Ralphs *(CEO-Bidvest South Africa)*
Craig A. Brighten *(Sec)*
Board of Directors:
Lorato W. C. Phalatse
Paul Cambo Baloyi
Douglas Denoon Balharrie Band
Bernard Larry Berson
David Edward Cleasby
Alfred Anthony da Costa
Anthony William Dawe
Eric Kevin Diack
Brian Joffe
Alexander Komape Maditsi
Donald Masson
Nigel George Payne
Lindsay Peter Ralphs
Tania Slabbert

The Bidvest Group Limited—(Continued)

Faith Dikeledi Pansy Tlakula

Transfer Agent:
Computershare Investor Services (Pty) Ltd
PO Box 61051
Marshalltown, South Africa

Subsidiaries:

Adcock Ingram Holdings Limited **(1)**
1 New Road
Midrand, 1682, South Africa
Tel.: (27) 116350000
Web Site: www.adcock.com
AIPJ—(JSE)
Rev.: $594,901,965
Assets: $676,608,014
Liabilities: $220,518,591
Net Worth: $456,089,423
Earnings: $92,106,445
Emp.: 2,124
Fiscal Year-end: 09/30/12
Pharmaceutical Products Mfr
S.I.C.: 2834
N.A.I.C.S.: 325412
Jonathan J. Louw *(CEO)*
Andy G. Hall *(Deputy CEO & Dir-Fin)*
Werner van Rensburg *(COO)*
Frans Cronje *(CTO)*
Kofi Amegashie *(Chief Comml Officer-Rest of Africa)*
Mahendra Chibabhai *(Officer-Mfg)*
Viral N. Desai *(Officer-Comml)*
Tobie Krige *(Officer-Logistics)*
Mohamed Mangel *(Officer-Fin)*
Dorette Neethling *(Officer-Fin-Grp)*
Siobhan O'Sullivan *(Officer-Comml)*
Ashley Pearce *(Officer-Comml-Southern Africa)*
Colin Sheen *(Officer-Comml)*
Ntando E. Simelane *(Sec)*

Subsidiaries:

Adcock Ingram Critical Care (Pty) Limited **(2)**
1 Sabax Rd
Johannesburg, Gauteng, 2013, South Africa
Tel.: (27) 118403000
Fax: (27) 114941911
Diagnostic Equipment Distr
S.I.C.: 5047
N.A.I.C.S.: 423450

Adcock Ingram Healthcare (Pty) Limited **(2)**
1 New Rd Corner and 7th Rd
Halfway House, Midrand, Gauteng, 1685, South Africa
Tel.: (27) 116350000
Fax: (27) 116350001
Pharmaceutical Products Distr
S.I.C.: 5122
N.A.I.C.S.: 424210

Adcock Ingram Limited **(2)**
1 New Road Chr 7th Street
Midrand, Gauteng, 1685, South Africa
Tel.: (27) 116350000
Fax: (27) 115140088
Web Site: www.adcock.co.za
Emp.: 600
Pharmaceutical Products Distr
S.I.C.: 5122
N.A.I.C.S.: 424210
Ilonka Macdougall *(Mgr-New Bus Dev)*

Addclin Research (Pty) Limited **(2)**
178 Watermeyer St
Meyerspark, Pretoria, Gauteng, 0184, South Africa
Tel.: (27) 128037733
Fax: (27) 128038343
Web Site: www.addclinresearch.co.za
Emp.: 7
Medical Research & Development Services
S.I.C.: 8731
N.A.I.C.S.: 541712
Sanet Aspinall *(Mng Dir)*
Mark Shardelow *(COO & Project Mgr)*
Jane Bultman *(Officer-Quality Assurance)*
Hanti Gunter *(Officer-Quality Control)*

Afcom Group Limited **(1)**
3 Fortune Street City Deep Industrial Park
Johannesburg, Gauteng, 2000, South Africa
Tel.: (27) 116277000
Fax: (27) 116137441
E-Mail: info@afcom.co.za
Web Site: www.afcom.co.za
Emp.: 350
Packaging & Fastening Products Mfr & Distr
S.I.C.: 2672
N.A.I.C.S.: 322220
Howard Greenstein *(Mng Dir)*

African Commerce Developing Company (Pty) Limited **(1)**
Unit 8 Trio Industrial Park 8 Qashana Khuzwayo Road
New Germany, Kwazulu-Natal, 3620, South Africa
Tel.: (27) 317056018
Fax: (27) 317056030
E-Mail: julieb@bidvestascom.co.za
Web Site: www.bidvestascom.co.za
Packaging Devices Mfr
S.I.C.: 3565
N.A.I.C.S.: 333993
Kevin Oliver *(Mng Dir)*

African Consultancy For Transportation Security (Pty) Limited **(1)**
No 42 Pomona Road
Kempton Park, Gauteng, 1627, South Africa
Tel.: (27) 119790696
Fax: (27) 862193560
Web Site: www.bidvest.co.za
Air Cargo Services
S.I.C.: 4512
N.A.I.C.S.: 481112
Eytan Nevo *(Mng Dir)*

Bellco Electrical (Pty) Limited **(1)**
362 Victoria Road
Cape Town, Western Cape, 7925, South Africa
Tel.: (27) 214407100
Fax: (27) 214407110
E-Mail: sales@voltex.co.za
Web Site: www.voltex.co.za
Electrical Supplies Whslr
S.I.C.: 5211
N.A.I.C.S.: 444190
Shawn Roets *(Reg Mgr)*

Berzack Brothers (Jhb) (Pty) Limited **(1)**
2 Nugget Street
Johannesburg, Gauteng, 2001, South Africa
Tel.: (27) 113347634
Fax: (27) 113346890
Web Site: www.berzacks.co.za
Emp.: 30
Industrial Machinery Whslr
S.I.C.: 5084
N.A.I.C.S.: 423830
Ernst Huisamen *(Mgr-Cape Town)*

Berzack Brothers (Pty) Limited **(1)**
11 Sydow Street Maitland
Maitland, Cape Town, Western Cape, 7405, South Africa
Tel.: (27) 215117044
Fax: (27) 215115944
E-Mail: capetown@berzacks.co.za
Web Site: www.berzacks.co.za
Emp.: 30
Household Appliances & Supplies Distr
S.I.C.: 5064
N.A.I.C.S.: 423620
Ernst Huisamen *(Branch Mgr)*

Bid Food Ingredients (Pty) Limited **(1)**
31 Nguni Drive Longmeadow West
Modderfontein, Johannesburg, Gauteng, 2065, South Africa
Tel.: (27) 112019100
Fax: (27) 112019160
E-Mail: info@bidfood.co.za
Web Site: www.bidfood.co.za
Emp.: 200
Groceries Distr
S.I.C.: 5141
N.A.I.C.S.: 424410
Gavin Fasser *(Dir-Comml)*

Subsidiary:

Bidfood Technologies (Pty) Limited **(2)**
31 Nguni Drive Long Meadow West
Edenvale, Gauteng, 2065, South Africa
Tel.: (27) 112019400
Fax: (27) 112019628
E-Mail: tech@bidfood.co.za
Web Site: www.bidfoodsolutions.co.za
Emp.: 1,000
Bakery Products Mfr
S.I.C.: 2052
N.A.I.C.S.: 311821
Klaas Havenga *(Gen Mgr)*

Bid Information Exchange (Pty) Limited **(1)**
33 Modulus Road
Johannesburg, Gauteng, 2091, South Africa
Tel.: (27) 116619555
Fax: (27) 118353216
E-Mail: info@oce.co.za
Web Site: www.oce.co.za
Emp.: 43
Printing Machinery Distr
S.I.C.: 5045
N.A.I.C.S.: 423430
Dave Clark *(Gen Mgr)*

BidAir Cargo **(1)**
11 Aero Park Building 11 Boeing Street
Walmer, Port Elizabeth, Eastern Cape, 6001, South Africa
Tel.: (27) 41 581 5280
Fax: (27) 41 581 6667
E-Mail: marketing@bidaircargo.com
Web Site: www.bidaircargo.com
Airfreight Sales & Cargo Handling Services
S.I.C.: 4512
N.A.I.C.S.: 481112
Garry Marshall *(Mng Dir)*

Bidair Services (Pty) Limited **(1)**
OR Tambo International Airport
Private Bag X21
Kempton Park, Gauteng, 1627, South Africa
Tel.: (27) 113839420
Fax: (27) 118236349
E-Mail: marketing@bidair.co.za
Web Site: www.bidair.co.za
Emp.: 3,000
Aviation Support Services
S.I.C.: 4581
N.A.I.C.S.: 488119
Kobus van Niekerk *(Mng Dir)*

Bidfreight Intermodal (Pty) Limited **(1)**
30 Breeder Road
Durban, Kwazulu-Natal, 4052, South Africa
Tel.: (27) 215104673
Fax: (27) 866131018
E-Mail: rates@bidintermodal.co.za
Web Site: www.bidintermodal.co.za
Emp.: 20
Freight Forwarding Services
S.I.C.: 4731
N.A.I.C.S.: 488510
Ash Boodram *(Mng Dir)*

Bidfreight Management Services **(1)**
Rennies House 19 Ameshoff St
PO Box 4281
Braamfontein, 2001, South Africa
Tel.: (27) 114072111
Fax: (27) 113391034
Emp.: 25
Freight Forwarding & Transport, Cargo Services, & Marine Services
S.I.C.: 4412
N.A.I.C.S.: 483111

Bidfreight Port Operations (Pty) Limited **(1)**
Newark Road Richards Bay Harbour
Richards Bay, KwaZulu-Natal, 3900, South Africa
Tel.: (27) 357976260
Fax: (27) 357979350
E-Mail: marketing@bidports.co.za
Web Site: www.bidports.co.za
Emp.: 89
Port Facility Operation Services
S.I.C.: 4491
N.A.I.C.S.: 488310
D. Roux *(Mng Dir)*

Bidfreight Terminals (Pty) Limited **(1)**
169 Maydon Wharf Road Ground Floor
Millwood House
PO Box 4536
Maydon Wharf, Durban, KwaZulu-Natal, 4000, South Africa
Tel.: (27) 312742400
Fax: (27) 312056741
Web Site: www.bidvest-divisions.co.za
Terminal Operation Services
S.I.C.: 4789
N.A.I.C.S.: 488490
Mark Steyn *(Dir-Fin)*

Bidprocure (Pty) Limited **(1)**
158 Jan Smuts Avenue 1st Floor
Rosebank, Johannesburg, Gauteng, 2196, South Africa
Tel.: (27) 117317600
Fax: (27) 865458369
E-Mail: derek@bidprocure.com
Emp.: 5
Business Consulting Services
S.I.C.: 8742
N.A.I.C.S.: 541611
Derek Kinnear *(Mng Dir)*

Bidserv Industrial Products (Pty) Limited **(1)**
Unit2B Phumelela Park Montague Drive
Montague, Cape Town, Western Cape, 7441, South Africa
Tel.: (27) 114179300
Fax: (27) 215514684
E-Mail: sales@gfox.co.za
Web Site: www.gfox.co.za
Emp.: 300
Industrial Supplies Distr
S.I.C.: 5047
N.A.I.C.S.: 423450
Savvas Xenophon *(Mng Dir)*

Bidserv (Pty) Limited **(1)**
Bldg 3 Tuscany Office Park Coombe Pl
PO Box 5514
Rivonia, Gauteng, 2128, South Africa
Tel.: (27) 115198430
Fax: (27) 112341256
E-Mail: admin@bidvestservices.co.za
Web Site: www.bidserv.co.za
Emp.: 7
Hospitality Services
S.I.C.: 8999
N.A.I.C.S.: 541690
Lindsay Peter Ralphs *(CEO)*
John Taylor *(CEO)*

Bidtravel (Pty) Limited **(1)**
Number 1 Newton Avenue BOE Nedbank building
Killarney, Gauteng, 2196, South Africa
Tel.: (27) 115328000
Fax: (27) 118803254
Web Site: www.bidvest-divisions.co.za/div_bidserv_Bidtravelintro.asp
Travel Management Services
S.I.C.: 4724
N.A.I.C.S.: 561510
Allan Lunz *(Mng Dir)*

Bidvest Bank Limited **(1)**
11th Floor Rennie House 19 Ameshoff Street
Braamfontein, 2001 Johannesburg, Gauteng, South Africa
Tel.: (27) 114073000
Fax: (27) 114073322
E-Mail: info@bidvestbank.co.za
Web Site: www.bidvestbank.co.za
Commercial Banking Services
S.I.C.: 6029
N.A.I.C.S.: 522110

Bidvest Capital (Pty) Limited **(1)**
9th Floor 19 Ameshoff Street
Braamfontein, Johannesburg, Gauteng, 2001, South Africa
Tel.: (27) 11 570 7299
Fax: (27) 11 844 8617
E-Mail: customerfeedback@bidvestcapital.co.za
Web Site: www.bidvestcapital.co.za
Automobile Leasing Services
S.I.C.: 7515
N.A.I.C.S.: 532112
Byron Corcoran *(Mng Dir)*

Bidvest Foodservice International Limited **(1)**
60 Saturn Crescent Linbro Office Park
PO Box 1344
Johannesburg, Gauteng, 2000, South Africa
Tel.: (27) 115539600
Fax: (27) 115539660
E-Mail: nicolaenglish@bidvestfoodservice.co.za
Web Site: www.bidvestfoodservice.co.za

Emp.: 2,000
Groceries Distr
S.I.C.: 5142
N.A.I.C.S.: 424420
Brent Varcoe *(Mng Dir)*

Bidvest Magnum Group (1)
16 Southway Road Carlon Falco Office Park Block A-B
Kelvin, Gauteng, 2054, South Africa
Tel.: (27) 11 555 4949
Fax: (27) 11 555 4950
Web Site: www.bidvestmagnum.co.za
Emp.: 40
Integrated Security Services
S.I.C.: 7381
N.A.I.C.S.: 561612
Madie Leonard *(Reg Dir)*

Bidvest Prestige Group (1)
22 Gerhardus Street Strijdom Park Ext 25
Randburg, 2194, South Africa
Tel.: (27) 11 796 0000
Fax: (27) 11 791 2849
E-Mail: info@presclean.co.za
Web Site: www.bidvestprestigegroup.co.za
Emp.: 103
Contract Cleaning Services
S.I.C.: 7349
N.A.I.C.S.: 561720
Johan du Toit *(Grp Mng Dir)*

Bidvest Wits University Football Club (Pty) Limited (1)
Sturrock Park Raikes Road Wits University Sports Admin West Campus
PO Box 136
Braamfontein, Johannesburg, Gauteng, 2196, South Africa
Tel.: (27) 113391112
Fax: (27) 113392328
E-Mail: info@bidvestwits.co.za
Web Site: www.bidvestwits.co.za
Emp.: 40
Football Club Management Services
S.I.C.: 7941
N.A.I.C.S.: 711211
Jose Ferreira *(CEO)*

Blesston Printing and Associates (Pty) Limited (1)
280 Granville Avenue
Roodepoort, Johannesburg, Gauteng, 1709, South Africa
Tel.: (27) 114723330
Fax: (27) 114723868
Emp.: 90
Commercial Printing Services
S.I.C.: 2759
N.A.I.C.S.: 323111
Cilla McGinley *(Mng Dir)*

Bloch & Levitan (Pty) Limited (1)
Unit No 10 City Deep Mini Park Corner Hiedelburg & Outspan Road
PO Box 1557
Johannesburg, Gauteng, 2197, South Africa
Tel.: (27) 116231941
Fax: (27) 116132527
E-Mail: jhb@blochandlevitan.com
Web Site: www.blochandlevitan.com
Emp.: 128
Plumbing & Upholstery Materials Distr
S.I.C.: 5074
N.A.I.C.S.: 423720
Johan Laurance *(Mng Dir)*

Buffalo Executape (Pty) Limited (1)
44 Forge Road Spartan
Kempton Park, Johannesburg, Gauteng, 1619, South Africa
Tel.: (27) 112812600
Fax: (27) 113948300
E-Mail: buffex@mweb.co.za
Web Site: www.buffaloexecutape.co.za
Emp.: 80
Adhesive Tapes Distr
S.I.C.: 5112
N.A.I.C.S.: 424120
Jacob Zuma *(Pres)*
Wayne Pollak *(Mng Dir & Mgr-Sls & Mktg)*

Bulk Connections (Pty) Limited (1)
Island View Oil Site Corner of Wharfside Rd & Java Rd W
PO Box 21273
Bluff, Durban, Kwazulu Natal, 4052, South Africa
Tel.: (27) 314661960
Fax: (27) 314665615
E-Mail: reception@bulkconnections.com
Web Site: www.bulkconnections.co.za
Emp.: 160
Terminal Operation Services
S.I.C.: 4789
N.A.I.C.S.: 488490
Iain Geldart *(Mng Dir)*

Catersales (Pty) Limited (1)
463 Taljaard St
Hermanstad, Pretoria, Gauteng, 0082, South Africa
Tel.: (27) 123770158
Fax: (27) 123799341
E-Mail: catersales@catersales.co.za
Web Site: www.catersales.co.za
Emp.: 84
Groceries Distr
S.I.C.: 5141
N.A.I.C.S.: 424410
Eddy Eagar *(Mng Dir)*

CCW Catering Supplies (Pty) Limited (1)
24 Winston Road Off Victoria Road Quarry Road Entrance
Pietermaritzburg, Kwazulu Natal, 3201, South Africa
Tel.: (27) 333454505
Fax: (27) 333942935
E-Mail: ccwsales@futurenet.co.za
Emp.: 65
Groceries Distr
S.I.C.: 5141
N.A.I.C.S.: 424410
Craig Murray-Rawbone *(Gen Mgr)*

Cecil Nurse (Pty) Limited (1)
Cecil Nurse Premises 101 North Reef Rd
Germiston, Gauteng, 1402, South Africa
Tel.: (27) 113451500
Fax: (27) 114556746
E-Mail: info@cnonline.co.za
Web Site: www.cecilnurse.com
Emp.: 350
Office Furniture Mfr & Distr
S.I.C.: 2522
N.A.I.C.S.: 337214
Gavin Bolton *(Mng Dir-KwaZulu Natal)*

Chipkins Bakery Supplies (Pty) Limited (1)
279 Inanda Road Spring Field Park
Durban, KwaZulu-Natal, 4000, South Africa
Tel.: (27) 315747400
Fax: (27) 315747423
E-Mail: marcw@chipbake.co.za
Web Site: www.chipbake.co.za
Emp.: 200
Bakery Products Mfr & Distr
S.I.C.: 2099
N.A.I.C.S.: 311999
Allen Smith *(Gen Mgr)*

Chipkins Catering Supplies (Pty) Limited (1)
30 Paisley Road
Jacobs, Durban, Kwazulu-Natal, 4052, South Africa
Tel.: (27) 314612222
Fax: (27) 314612211
E-Mail: sales@chipkinsdbn.co.za
Web Site: www.chipkinsdbn.co.za
Emp.: 82
Catering Supplies Distr
S.I.C.: 5046
N.A.I.C.S.: 423440
Rick Lowe *(Mng Dir)*

Commuter Handling Services (Pty) Limited (1)
ACSA Park One Tambo International Airport
Boksburg, Gauteng, 1627, South Africa
Tel.: (27) 11 397 6555
Fax: (27) 11 397 6605
Web Site: www.bidvest.com
Aviation Support Services
S.I.C.: 4581
N.A.I.C.S.: 488119

Concorde Travel (Pty) Limited (1)
Samro Place 9th Floor 20 De Korte Street
PO Box 4568
Braamfontein, Johannesburg, Gauteng, 2000, South Africa
Tel.: (27) 116282300
Fax: (27) 116282301
E-Mail: sales@carlsonwagonlit.co.za
Web Site: www.carlsonwagonlit.co.za
Emp.: 260
Travel Mangement Services
S.I.C.: 4724
N.A.I.C.S.: 561510
Sharon Burgers *(Sr Mgr-Ops)*

Contract Office Products (Pty) Limited (1)
Whartons Spencer Ofc Pk Croxley Close
Heriotdale Ext 15 Germiston
PO BOX 6426
Johannesburg, Gauteng, 2000, South Africa
Tel.: (27) 113345424
Fax: (27) 066745353
Web Site: www.bidvest.com
Emp.: 75
Stationery Products & Computer Consumables Whslr & Distr
S.I.C.: 5045
N.A.I.C.S.: 423430
Harold Magid *(Mng Dir)*

Crown National (Pty) Limited (1)
31 Nguni Drive Longmeadow West
Modderfontein, Johannesburg, Gauteng, 2065, South Africa
Tel.: (27) 112019000
Fax: (27) 112019180
E-Mail: info@crownnational.co.za
Web Site: www.crownnational.co.za
Emp.: 600
Catering Supplies Distr
S.I.C.: 5149
N.A.I.C.S.: 424490
Charles Singer *(CEO & Mng Dir)*

D & R Lowe Catering Supplies (Pty) Limited (1)
No 17 Eastern Service Rd Eastgate Ext 8
Sandton, Johannesburg, Gauteng, 2012, South Africa
Tel.: (27) 118043663
Fax: (27) 118049670
E-Mail: sales@drlowe.co.za
Web Site: www.drlowe.co.za
Groceries Distr
S.I.C.: 5141
N.A.I.C.S.: 424410
Colin McCormack *(Mng Dir)*

Ditulo Office (Pty) Limited (1)
109 Oxford Road
Rosebank, Johannesburg, Gauteng, 2093, South Africa
Tel.: (27) 115379860
Fax: (27) 11 483 6752
E-Mail: designs@ditulo.co.za
Web Site: www.ditulo.co.za
Office Furniture Retailer
S.I.C.: 5712
N.A.I.C.S.: 442110

Email Connection (Pty) Limited (1)
25 Scott Street
Waverley, Johannesburg, Gauteng, 2090, South Africa
Tel.: (27) 117863116
Fax: (27) 117864813
E-Mail: enquiries@emc.co.za
Web Site: www.emc.co.za
Emp.: 25
Bulk Email Processing Services
S.I.C.: 7389
N.A.I.C.S.: 561439
Howard Rabinowitz *(Gen Mgr)*

First Food Distributors (Pty) Limited (1)
Bahrain Drive and Borchards Quarry Road
Airport Industria, Cape Town, Western Cape, 7525, South Africa
Tel.: (27) 219279100
Fax: (27) 219279102
Web Site: www.firstfoods.co.za
Groceries Distr
S.I.C.: 5141
N.A.I.C.S.: 424410
Dawie Smit *(Gen Mgr)*

Freightbulk (Pty) Limited (1)
Rennie House
PO Box 2590
Durban, KwaZulu-Natal, 4000, South Africa
Tel.: (27) 313280404
Fax: (27) 313280427
Emp.: 50
Marine Cargo Handling Services
S.I.C.: 4491
N.A.I.C.S.: 488320
Grant Stevanson *(Mng Dir)*

Home of Living Brands Holdings Limited (1)
(Formerly Amalgamated Appliance Holdings Ltd.)
West Block Pineslopes Office Park cnr The Straight & Witkoppen Roads
Fourways, Johannesburg, 2052, South Africa ZA
Mailing Address:
PO Box 2207
Fourways, Johannesburg, 2016, South Africa
Tel.: (27) 11 267 3300
Fax: (27) 114909115
E-Mail: info@amap.co.za
Web Site: www.amap.co.za
Sales Range: $125-149.9 Million
Emp.: 356
Home Appliance Mfr & Distr
S.I.C.: 3639
N.A.I.C.S.: 335210
Alan S. Coward *(CEO)*
Murray Crow *(Mng Dir)*
Bruce Drummond *(CFO)*

Hortors Stationery (Pty) Limited (1)
Entrance 3 Pencil Park Croxley Close
Heriotdale Extension 15, Johannesburg, Gauteng, 2094, South Africa
Tel.: (27) 116204800
Fax: (27) 116204806
Web Site: www.hortors.co.za
Stationery Products Retailer
S.I.C.: 5112
N.A.I.C.S.: 453210

Island View Storage Limited (1)
142 Wharfside Road Island View
Bluff, Durban, KwaZulu-Natal, 4000, South Africa
Tel.: (27) 314669000
Fax: (27) 314669088
E-Mail: reception@ivstorage.co.za
Web Site: www.ivstorage.co.za
Emp.: 250
General Warehousing Services
S.I.C.: 4225
N.A.I.C.S.: 493110
Kobus Ehlers *(Mng Dir)*

Kolok Africa (Pty) Limited (1)
44 Forge Road
Johannesburg, Gauteng, 1620, South Africa
Tel.: (27) 116801460
Fax: (27) 119753927
E-Mail: sales@kolok.co.za
Web Site: www.kolok.co.za
Emp.: 37
Computer Peripheral Equipments Distr
S.I.C.: 5045
N.A.I.C.S.: 423430
Tino Rupping *(CEO)*

Kolok (Pty) Limited (1)
Hilton Industrial Park Unit B Corner Gruis & Exton Street
Hilton, Bloemfontein, Free State, 9324, South Africa
Tel.: (27) 514331876
Fax: (27) 514332451
E-Mail: infobfn@koloksa.co.za
Web Site: www.koloksa.co.za
Computer Peripheral Equipments Distr
S.I.C.: 5045
N.A.I.C.S.: 423430
Allan Thompson *(Mng Dir)*

Langa Lethu Risk Management (Pty) Limited (1)
248 Cowan Ntuli Street
Mpumalanga, 1055, South Africa
Tel.: (27) 132430289
Fax: (27) 132430287
E-Mail: reception@bidvestmagnum.co.za
Web Site: www.bidvestmagnum.co.za
Emp.: 8
Risk Management Services
S.I.C.: 8742
N.A.I.C.S.: 541611
Lyndon Kelly *(Branch Mgr)*

Lithotech Afric Mail Cape (Pty) Limited (1)
Sibanye Park Boston Circle
Airport Industria, Cape Town, Western Cape, 7490, South Africa

The Bidvest Group Limited—(Continued)

Tel.: (27) 219353300
Fax: (27) 219353400
Bulk Mail Processing Services
S.I.C.: 5961
N.A.I.C.S.: 454113
Hennie Mentz *(Grp Mng Dir)*

Lithotech Afric Mail JHB (Pty) Limited (1)
1350 Staal Road Stormill Extension 2
Roodepoort, Johannesburg, Gauteng, 1724, South Africa
Tel.: (27) 114741554
Fax: (27) 114746522
Emp.: 45
Bulk Mail Processing Services
S.I.C.: 5961
N.A.I.C.S.: 454113
Pieter Strydo *(Mng Dir)*

Lithotech Afric Mail Pinetown (Pty) Limited (1)
48 Gillitts Road
Pinetown, Durban, Kwazulu-Natal, 3610, South Africa
Tel.: (27) 317927000
Fax: (27) 31 792 7092
Bulk Mail Processing Services
S.I.C.: 5961
N.A.I.C.S.: 454113
Sean Cleland *(Dir-Ops)*

Lithotech Group Services (Pty) Limited (1)
Bosors Circle Epping Industria 2
Cape Town, Western Cape, 7460, South Africa
Tel.: (27) 215074100
Fax: (27) 215074104
Web Site: www.Lithotech.co.za
Emp.: 300
Business Forms Printing Services
S.I.C.: 2759
N.A.I.C.S.: 323111
Grant McWilliams *(Mng Dir)*

Lithotech Labels (Pty) Limited (1)
44 Forge Road Spartan
Kempton Park, Johannesburg, Gauteng, 1619, South Africa
Tel.: (27) 114741828
Fax: (27) 119758426
E-Mail: info@lithotech.co.za
Web Site: www.lithotech.co.za
Emp.: 162
Commercial Lithographic Printing Services
S.I.C.: 2759
N.A.I.C.S.: 323111
Wikus Maritz *(Mng Dir)*

Lithotech Manufacturing Cape (Pty) Limited (1)
Bofors Circle Epping 2
Cape Town, Western Cape, 8001, South Africa
Tel.: (27) 215074226
Fax: (27) 21 507 4246
Emp.: 300
Business Forms Printing Services
S.I.C.: 2759
N.A.I.C.S.: 323111
Grant McWilliams *(Mng Dir)*

Lithotech Manufacturing Pinetown (Pty) Limited (1)
48 Gillits Road
Pinetown, Durban, KwaZulu-Natal, 3610, South Africa
Tel.: (27) 317927000
Fax: (27) 317004746
Emp.: 250
Business Forms Printing Services
S.I.C.: 2759
N.A.I.C.S.: 323111
Bob Allan-Reynolds *(Mng Dir)*

Lithotech Print On Demand Pty. Ltd. (1)
23B Junction Road Unit 456 Dundee Park
Tygerberg Business Park, Cape Town, Western Cape, 7493, South Africa
Tel.: (27) 219511400
Fax: (27) 219511404
Web Site: www.lithotechafricmail.co.za
Emp.: 50
Commercial Printing Servics
S.I.C.: 2759
N.A.I.C.S.: 323111
Peter O'Sullivan *(Gen Mgr)*

Lithotech Sales Bloemfontein (Pty) Limited (1)
2 Maroela Street Old Industria Area
Bloemfontein, Free State, 9300, South Africa
Tel.: (27) 514477966
Fax: (27) 514477976
Web Site: www.lithotech.co.za
Emp.: 23
Commercial Printing Services
S.I.C.: 2759
N.A.I.C.S.: 323111
W. P. Wiid *(Gen Mgr)*

Lithotech Sales Cape (Pty) Limited (1)
Borcherds Quarry & Bahrain Drive
Caterplus S-Signal
Airport Industria, Cape Town, Western Cape, 7490, South Africa
Tel.: (27) 219364500
Fax: (27) 219364599
Web Site: www.lithotech.co.za
Emp.: 200
Business Forms Printing Services
S.I.C.: 2759
N.A.I.C.S.: 323111
Alastair Gordon-Forbes *(Mng Dir)*

Lithotech Sales East London (Pty) Limited (1)
Settlers Warehouse
PO Box 7386
East London, Eastern Cape, 5201, South Africa
Tel.: (27) 437311605
Fax: (27) 437311582
Web Site: www.lithotechsales.co.za
Emp.: 22
Notebooks & Paper Retailer
S.I.C.: 5112
N.A.I.C.S.: 424120
Clive Saunders *(Mng Dir)*

Lithotech Sales KwaZulu-Natal (Pty) Limited (1)
48 Gillitts Road
Pinetown, Durban, Kwazulu-Natal, 3610, South Africa
Tel.: (27) 317002577
Fax: (27) 317002615
E-Mail: ingridd@lithotech.co.za
Emp.: 40
Commercial Printing Services
S.I.C.: 2759
N.A.I.C.S.: 323111
Phil Hayes *(Mng Dir)*

Lithotech Sales Port Elizabeth (Pty) Limited (1)
76c York Road North End
Port Elizabeth, Eastern Cape, 6001, South Africa
Tel.: (27) 413733889
Fax: (27) 824535843
Web Site: www.lithotech.co.za
Emp.: 32
Commercial Printing Services
S.I.C.: 2759
N.A.I.C.S.: 323111
Brian van den Berg *(Mng Dir)*

Lithotech Sales Pretoria (Pty) Limited (1)
74 Ketjen Street
Pretoria, Gauteng, 0813, South Africa
Tel.: (27) 123273239
Fax: (27) 123277195
Web Site: www.lithotech.co.za
Emp.: 40
Business Forms Printing Services
S.I.C.: 2759
N.A.I.C.S.: 323111
Gary Hillman *(Mng Dir)*

Lithotech Solutions (Pty) Limited (1)
Bofors Circle Epping 2
Cape Town, Western Cape, 7405, South Africa
Tel.: (27) 117066751
Fax: (27) 114637115
Emp.: 10
Labeling Software Development Services
S.I.C.: 7371
N.A.I.C.S.: 541511
Oostewale Immink *(Gen Mgr)*

Lou's Wholesalers (Pty) Limited (1)
68 Whitworth Road
Heriotdale, Johannesburg, Gauteng, 2000, South Africa
Tel.: (27) 114792600
Fax: (27) 116261615
Web Site: www.lous.co.za
Groceries Distr
S.I.C.: 5141
N.A.I.C.S.: 424410
Ed Webster *(Gen Mgr)*

M & M Quality Choice (Pty) Limited (1)
376 Olympic Duel Avenue Northlands Business Park Hoogland Extension
Randburg, Johannesburg, Gauteng, 2162, South Africa
Tel.: (27) 118013144
Fax: (27) 117046221
E-Mail: sales@m-m.co.za
Web Site: www.m-m.co.za
Groceries Distr
S.I.C.: 5141
N.A.I.C.S.: 424410
Clint Lee *(Mng Dir)*

Manica Africa (Pty) Limited (1)
Pencil Park Croxley Close
Heriotdale, Johannesburg, Gauteng, 2000, South Africa
Tel.: (27) 114175500
Fax: (27) 114175553
E-Mail: info@manica-africa.com
Web Site: www.manica-africa.com
Emp.: 65
Freight Management Services
S.I.C.: 4731
N.A.I.C.S.: 488510
Mark Gunther *(CEO)*

Non-U.S. Subsidiary:

Manica Zimbabwe Limited (2)
91 Coventry Road Workington
Harare, Zimbabwe
Tel.: (263) 4 661 524
Fax: (263) 4668529
Web Site: www.bidvest-divisions.co.za/di v_bidfreight_manica_harare.asp
Emp.: 120
Freight Forwarding Services
S.I.C.: 4731
N.A.I.C.S.: 488510
Tim Boulton *(Gen Mgr)*

Master Currency (Pty) Limited (1)
No 31 Hammer Schlagway 6th Floor Flreshore
Cape Town, Western Cape, 8001, South Africa
Tel.: (27) 214317700
Fax: (27) 214317991
E-Mail: support@mastercurrency.co.za
Web Site: www.mastercurrency.co.za
Emp.: 60
Foreign Currency Exchange Services
S.I.C.: 6221
N.A.I.C.S.: 523130
Byron Corcoran *(CEO)*
Charlene D. Lamb *(Mng Dir)*

Masterguard Fabric Protection Africa (Pty) Limited (1)
12 Skietlood Street Isando Kemptonpark
Kempton park, Johannesburg, Gauteng, 1601, South Africa
Tel.: (27) 113924411
Fax: (27) 113925399
E-Mail: info@masterguardfpsa.co.za
Web Site: www.masterguardfpsa.co.za
Emp.: 9
Housekeeping Services
S.I.C.: 7349
N.A.I.C.S.: 561720
Clive Bedell *(Gen Mgr)*

McCarthy Limited (1)
203 Northridge Road
Morningside, Durban, Kwazulu-Natal, 4001, South Africa
Tel.: (27) 312689200
Fax: (27) 312090950
E-Mail: club@mccarthy.co.za
Web Site: www.mccarthy.co.za
Emp.: 90
Motor Vehicles Retailer
S.I.C.: 5012
N.A.I.C.S.: 423110
Brand Pretorius *(CEO)*

Subsidiaries:

Kunene Motor Holdings Limited (2)
Corner Or Thambo and Steenkamp Road
Witbank, Mpumalanga, 1034, South Africa
Tel.: (27) 136925010
Fax: (27) 136971491
E-Mail: wilman@mcmotor.co.za
Emp.: 200
Investment Management Services
S.I.C.: 6282
N.A.I.C.S.: 523920
M. B. Kunene *(Chm)*

McLife Assurance Company Limited (2)
2nd Floor Lincoln On The Lake No 2 The High Street Park Side
Umhlanga Ridge, Umhlanga, KwaZulu-Natal, 4139, South Africa
Tel.: (27) 312689300
Fax: (27) 315148200
Life Insurance Services
S.I.C.: 6311
N.A.I.C.S.: 524113

Mocobe Properties (Pty) Limited (1)
21 Green Street
Isithebe, 4490, South Africa
Tel.: (27) 324592279
Fax: (27) 324591622
E-Mail: gevikam@lufil.co.za
Web Site: www.lufil.co.za
Emp.: 300
Packing & Crating Services
S.I.C.: 4783
N.A.I.C.S.: 488991
Kevin Swan *(Gen Mgr)*

Mymarket.Com (Pty) Limited (1)
158 Jan Smuts Ave 1st Fl
Rosebank, Johannesburg, Gauteng, 2196, South Africa
Tel.: (27) 117317700
Fax: (27) 824588880
E-Mail: helpdesk@mymarket.com
Web Site: www.mymarket.com
Emp.: 80
Web Hosting Services
S.I.C.: 7379
N.A.I.C.S.: 518210

NCP Yeast (Pty) Limited (1)
200 Stalwart Simelane Street
Durban, Kwazulu-Natal, 4000, South Africa
Tel.: (27) 313375242
Fax: (27) 313326148
E-Mail: info@yeast.co.za
Web Site: www.yeast.co.za
Yeast Mfr & Distr
S.I.C.: 2099
N.A.I.C.S.: 311999

Nuclear Corporate Furniture (Pty) Limited (1)
Kasselsvlei Road
Bellville, Western Cape, 7530, South Africa
Tel.: (27) 219516850
Fax: (27) 219514907
E-Mail: noeraan.flint@cnonline.co.za
Emp.: 80
Office Furniture Mfr
S.I.C.: 2511
N.A.I.C.S.: 337122
Noeroon Flint *(Mgr-Fin)*

Oce South Africa (Pty.) Ltd. (1)
33 Modulus Rd
PO Box 82684
Theta Ext 5, Southdale, 2135, South Africa ZA
Tel.: (27) 116619555
Fax: (27) 118353215
E-Mail: info@oce.co.za
Web Site: www.oce.co.za
Emp.: 50
High Production Printing Solutions
S.I.C.: 2759
N.A.I.C.S.: 323111
David Clark *(Mng Dir)*

Ozalid South Africa (Pty) Limited (1)
44 Forge Road
Spartan, Johannesburg, Gauteng, 1619, South Africa
Tel.: (27) 119758141
Fax: (27) 119753927
E-Mail: johnc@ozalid.co.za

Paper Mfr
S.I.C.: 2621
N.A.I.C.S.: 322121
Cino Rutting *(Mng Dir)*

Ram Fasteners (Pty) Limited (1)
Building 3 2 Old Mutual Industrial Park Fortune Road
Johannesburg, Gauteng, 2001, South Africa
Tel.: (27) 116277180
Fax: (27) 116277170
E-Mail: ascom@ascom.co.za
Web Site: www.ascom.co.za
Fasteners Retailer
S.I.C.: 5072
N.A.I.C.S.: 423710
Vincent van der Venter *(Gen Mgr)*

Rennie Murray and Company (Pty) Limited (1)
Ground Floor Unit 28 Foregate Square Table Bay Boulevard
Cape Town, Western Cape, 8001, South Africa
Tel.: (27) 214214150
Fax: (27) 214190983
E-Mail: rennie@rmurray.co.za
Web Site: www.renniemurray.co.za
Emp.: 4
Marine & Cargo Surveying Services
S.I.C.: 7389
N.A.I.C.S.: 561990
Rainer Breckwoldt *(Mng Dir)*

Rennies Distribution Services (Pty) Limited (1)
45 Richard Carte Rd
Mobeni, Durban, KwaZulu-Natal, 4092, South Africa
Tel.: (27) 314521900
Fax: (27) 4627708
E-Mail: info@rds-sa.co.za
Web Site: www.rds-sa.co.za
Warehousing & Logistics Services
S.I.C.: 4225
N.A.I.C.S.: 493110

Rennies Ships Agency (Pty) Limited (1)
1st Floor Rennie House 1 Kingsmead Boulevard Kingsmead Office Park
Durban, Kwazulu Natal, 4001, South Africa
Tel.: (27) 313280401
Fax: (27) 315710750
E-Mail: dur@rennies.co.za
Web Site: www.rsagency.co.za
Emp.: 50
Freight Management Services
S.I.C.: 4731
N.A.I.C.S.: 488510
James Reddy *(Mng Dir)*

Rennies Travel (Pty) Limited (1)
19 Ameshoff Street Rennie House 10th Floor
Braamfontein, Johannesburg, Gauteng, 2001, South Africa
Tel.: (27) 114072508
Fax: (27) 86 538 1191
Web Site: www.renniestravel.com
Emp.: 500
Corporate Travel Management Services
S.I.C.: 4729
N.A.I.C.S.: 561599
Allan Lunz *(Chm & Mng Dir)*

RFS Catering Supplies (Pty) Limited (1)
Unit F Sanlam Business Park Racecourse Road
Montague Gardens, Cape Town, Western Cape, 7441, South Africa
Tel.: (27) 215529970
Fax: (27) 215529987
E-Mail: sales@rfs.co.za
Web Site: www.rfs.co.za
Emp.: 75
Groceries Distr
S.I.C.: 5141
N.A.I.C.S.: 424410
Ricky van Vlaanderen *(Mng Dir)*

Safcor Panalpina (Pty) Ltd. (1)
Harbour View Oakworth Drive
Humerail, Port Elizabeth, Eastern Cape, 6001, South Africa
Tel.: (27) 415013200
Fax: (27) 415013220
E-Mail: safcor@safcorpanalpina.co.za
Web Site: www.safcorpanalpina.co.za
Emp.: 80
Customs Clearing & Freight Forwarding Services
S.I.C.: 4731
N.A.I.C.S.: 488510
Eileen Kings *(Gen Mgr-Ops)*

Sanlic International (Pty) Limited (1)
16 Davies Street
Doornfontein, Johannesburg, Gauteng, 2001, South Africa
Tel.: (27) 114020251
Fax: (27) 114020527
Web Site: www.sanlic.co.za
Emp.: 15
Key & Lock & Security Systems Distr
S.I.C.: 5199
N.A.I.C.S.: 424990
Andrew Phakathi *(Mgr)*

Seating (Pty) Limited (1)
14 Bunsen Street
Industria, Johannesburg, Gauteng, 2093, South Africa
Tel.: (27) 114741393
Fax: (27) 114731892
E-Mail: info@seating.co.za
Web Site: www.seating.co.za
Emp.: 550
Office Chairs Mfr
S.I.C.: 2522
N.A.I.C.S.: 337214

Silveray Manufacturers (Pty) Limited (1)
70 Richard Carte Rd
Durban, Kwazulu-Natal, 4052, South Africa
Tel.: (27) 314622081
Fax: (27) 314525448
Web Site: www.lithotech.co.za
Emp.: 500
Stationery Products Mfr
S.I.C.: 2891
N.A.I.C.S.: 325520
Neil Speres *(Mng Dir)*

Silveray Statmark Company (Pty) Limited (1)
Entrance 6 Pencil Park Croxley Close
Heriotdale Extension 15, Johannesburg, Gauteng, 2094, South Africa
Tel.: (27) 116770000
Fax: (27) 116770016
E-Mail: sandyp@silveray.co.za
Web Site: www.statmark.co.za
Emp.: 200
Stationery Equipment & Office Supplies Distr
S.I.C.: 5112
N.A.I.C.S.: 424120
Trevor Girnum *(CEO & Mng Dir)*

South African Bulk Terminals Limited (1)
Maydon Wharf Terminal 101 Maydon Road
Maydon Wharf, Durban, KwaZulu-Natal, 4001, South Africa
Tel.: (27) 313275000
Fax: (27) 313046794
Web Site: www.bidvest.co.za
Emp.: 170
Marine Terminal Operation Services
S.I.C.: 7389
N.A.I.C.S.: 561990
Hampie Lourens *(CEO & Mng Dir)*

South African Container Depots (Pty) Limited (1)
Port Industrial park Off Nereide paarden Eisland Street
Paarden Eiland, Cape Town, Western Cape, 7405, South Africa
Tel.: (27) 218127223
Fax: (27) 218127251
E-Mail: info@sacd.co.za
Web Site: www.sacd.co.za
Emp.: 600
Freight Import & Export Management Services
S.I.C.: 4432
N.A.I.C.S.: 483113
Graham Peinke *(Mng Dir)*

South African Container Stevedores (Pty) Limited (1)
Millweed House
Durban, Kwazulu-Natal, 4001, South Africa
Tel.: (27) 312742400
Stevedoring Services
S.I.C.: 4491
N.A.I.C.S.: 488320
Jannie Roux *(Mng Dir)*

South African Diaries (Pty) Limited (1)
12 Stationery Centre Beach Road
Woodstock, 7925 Cape Town, Western Cape, South Africa
Tel.: (27) 214422340
Fax: (27) 214422341
Web Site: www.sadiaries.co.za
Emp.: 7
Diary Publishing Services
S.I.C.: 2741
N.A.I.C.S.: 511199
Peter Honeyman *(CEO)*

Steiner Hygiene Montague Gardens (Pty) Limited (1)
Unit 22 Point Business Park Merinus Street
Milnerton, Cape Town, Western Cape, 7441, South Africa
Tel.: (27) 21 552 7611
Fax: (27) 21 552 7633
Emp.: 21
Contract Cleaning & Pest Control Services
S.I.C.: 7342
N.A.I.C.S.: 561710
Andre Hepburn *(Gen Mgr)*

Steiner Hygiene (Pty) Limited (1)
110 Loper Avenue Aeroport Spartan Extension 2
Kempton Park, Gauteng, 1619, South Africa
Tel.: (27) 119239490
Fax: (27) 119239520
E-Mail: info@steiner.co.za
Web Site: www.steinerhygiene.co.za
Emp.: 60
Contract Cleaning Services
S.I.C.: 7349
N.A.I.C.S.: 561720
Alan Fainman *(Mng Dir)*

Travel Connections (Pty) Limited (1)
1st Floor 25 Fredman Drive
Sandton, Johannesburg, Gauteng, 2196, South Africa
Tel.: (27) 117223500
Fax: (27) 117844386
E-Mail: info@travelconnections.co.za
Web Site: www.travelconnections.co.za
Emp.: 45
Travel Management Services
S.I.C.: 4724
N.A.I.C.S.: 561510
Lindy Preston *(Co-CEO & Co-Mng Dir)*
Geraldine Zilk *(Co-CEO & Co-Mng Dir)*

Vericon Outsourcing (Pty) Limited (1)
2 Tonetist St
Midrand, Johannesburg, Gauteng, 1685, South Africa
Tel.: (27) 115548600
Fax: (27) 115548681
E-Mail: customerservice@vericon.co.za
Web Site: www.vericon.co.za
Stock Auditing Services
S.I.C.: 4731
N.A.I.C.S.: 541614
Gustav Gericke *(Mng Dir)*

Voltex (Pty) Limited (1)
Voltex House Block B Saint Andrews Office Park 39 Wordsworth Avenue
Senderwood, Bedfordview, Gauteng, 2007, South Africa
Tel.: (27) 118792000
Fax: (27) 114542768
E-Mail: info@voltex.co.za
Web Site: www.voltex.co.za
Electrical Materials Distr
S.I.C.: 5063
N.A.I.C.S.: 423610
Drew Donald *(CEO)*

Vulcan Catering Equipment (Pty) Ltd. (1)
15 Newclare Road
Industria, Johannesburg, Gauteng, 2093, South Africa
Tel.: (27) 112498500
Fax: (27) 112498534
E-Mail: vulcan@vulcan.co.za
Web Site: www.vulcan.co.za
Emp.: 350
Food Service Equipment Mfr & Distr
S.I.C.: 3589
N.A.I.C.S.: 333318
Margaret Crawford *(Mng Dir)*

Non-U.S. Subsidiaries:

Amosco Pte Limited (1)
232 Pandan Loop
Singapore, Singapore
Tel.: (65) 67788787
Fax: (65) 67783966
Web Site: www.amosco.com.sg
Bakery Products Mfr
S.I.C.: 2051
N.A.I.C.S.: 311812
Loke Beng Song *(Mng Dir)*

Angliss China Limited (1)
47-51 Kwai Fung Crescent
Kwai Chung, New Territories, China (Hong Kong)
Tel.: (852) 24942159
Fax: (852) 24898861
E-Mail: info@angliss.com.hk
Web Site: www.angliss.com.hk
Emp.: 100
Bakery Products Distr
S.I.C.: 5142
N.A.I.C.S.: 424420
Johnny Kang *(Mng Dir)*

Angliss Hong Kong Food Service Limited (1)
47-51 Kwai Fung Crescent
Kwai Chung, New Territories, China (Hong Kong)
Tel.: (852) 24815111
Fax: (852) 24898861
E-Mail: info@angliss.com.hk
Web Site: www.angliss.com.hk
Emp.: 300
Meat & Groceries Distr
S.I.C.: 5147
N.A.I.C.S.: 424470
Johnny Kang *(Gen Mgr)*

Non-U.S. Subsidiaries:

Angliss Guangzhou Food Service Limited (2)
Unit 701 7F Gzitic Mansion 363 Dong Feng Zhong Road
Dongfeng, Zhongshan, Guangdong, 510045, China
Tel.: (86) 2083631150
Fax: (86) 2083631261
Web Site: www.angliss.com.hk/en/branch/branch6.aspx
Emp.: 30
Convenience Foods Import & Distr
S.I.C.: 5149
N.A.I.C.S.: 424490

Angliss Shanghai Food Service Limited (2)
2nd Floor No 10 Building Xintiantian No 222 Longcao Road
Shanghai, 200235, China
Tel.: (86) 2151699798
Fax: (86) 2164834583
Web Site: www.angliss.com.cn
Emp.: 50
Frozen Foods Distr
S.I.C.: 5142
N.A.I.C.S.: 424420

Angliss Macau Food Service Limited (1)
52-58 Rua dos Pescadores Edf Industrial Ocean II Fase 4 Andar C & D
Macau, China (Macau)
Tel.: (853) 28862886
Fax: (853) 28862828
E-Mail: info@angliss.com.mo
Emp.: 20
Cold Food Storage & Distr
S.I.C.: 5142
N.A.I.C.S.: 424420
Roger Chan *(Gen Mgr)*

Angliss Singapore Pte Limited (1)
232 Pandan Loop
Singapore, Singapore
Tel.: (65) 67788787
Fax: (65) 67783966
E-Mail: enquiry@angliss.com.sg
Web Site: www.angliss.com.sg
Meat & Groceries Distr

The Bidvest Group Limited—(Continued)

S.I.C.: 5141
N.A.I.C.S.: 424410
Beng Fong Loke *(Mng Dir)*

BFS Group Limited (1)
Buckingham Court Kingsmead Business Park London Road
High Wycombe, Buckinghamshire, HP11 1JU, United Kingdom
Tel.: (44) 3703663100
Fax: (44) 3703663199
E-Mail: 3663corporate@3663.co.uk
Web Site: www.3663corporate.co.uk
Emp.: 170
Catering Supplies Distr
S.I.C.: 5023
N.A.I.C.S.: 423220
Alex Fisher *(Mng Dir)*

Bidcorp Limited (1)
3rd FL 11th Hills St
London, W1J 5IF, United Kingdom
Tel.: (44) 20 7493 4733
Fax: (44) 20 7255 7888
E-Mail: info@bidvest-uk.com
Emp.: 2
Freight Transportation Services
S.I.C.: 4412
N.A.I.C.S.: 483111

Bidvest Australia Limited (1)
Level 1 31-35 Bank Street
Pyrmont, NSW, 2009, Australia
Tel.: (61) 295718666
Fax: (61) 295186444
E-Mail: bidvest@bidvest.com.au
Web Site: www.bidvest.com.au
Catering Supplies Distr
S.I.C.: 5023
N.A.I.C.S.: 423220
Glen Convery *(Gen Mgr-Newcastle)*

Bidvest Fisheries Holdings (Pty) Limited (1)
No 1 5th Street East
PO Box 4
Walvis Bay, Namibia
Tel.: (264) 64219903
Fax: (264) 64219906
E-Mail: reception@namsov.com.na
Web Site: www.bidvest.com
Emp.: 27
Management Services
S.I.C.: 8741
N.A.I.C.S.: 551114
Jan Arnold *(Mng Dir)*

Subsidiary:

Namsov Fishing Enterprises (Pty) Limited (2)
No 1 Fifth Street East
PO Box 4
Walvis Bay, Namibia
Tel.: (264) 64219902
Fax: (264) 64219905
Web Site: www.namsov.com.na
Emp.: 30
Horse Mackerel Fishing Services
S.I.C.: 0912
N.A.I.C.S.: 114111
Jan Arnold *(Mng Dir)*

Subsidiary:

Twafika Fishing Enterprises (Pty) Limited (3)
No 1 Fifth Street East
PO Box 4
Walvis Bay, Namibia
Tel.: (264) 64 201 2111
Fax: (264) 64219905
Web Site: www.namsov.com.na
Emp.: 50
Sea Bass Fishing Services
S.I.C.: 0912
N.A.I.C.S.: 114111
Jerome Mouton *(CEO)*

Bidvest International Limited (1)
Murdock Chambers Head Road
South Quay, Douglas, IM1 5AS, Isle of Man
Tel.: (44) 1624611225
Fax: (44) 1624611226
Groceries Distr
S.I.C.: 5141
N.A.I.C.S.: 424410

Bidvest Namibia Limited (1)
4 Robert Mugabe Avenue
Windhoek, Namibia
Tel.: (264) 61 417 450
Fax: (264) 61 229 290
Web Site: www.bidvestnamibia.com.na
BVN—(JSE)
Rev.: $367,605,920
Assets: $304,446,712
Liabilities: $89,794,113
Net Worth: $214,652,599
Earnings: $46,732,176
Emp.: 3,203
Fiscal Year-end: 06/30/13
Investment Management Services
S.I.C.: 6282
N.A.I.C.S.: 523920
Sebulon Inotila Kankondi *(CEO)*
Veryan Hocutt *(Sec)*

Bidvest New Zealand Limited (1)
26 Te Waiiti Pl Raumanga
Raumanga, Whangarei, 0110, New Zealand
Tel.: (64) 94381446
Fax: (64) 94389381
Web Site: www.bidvest.co.nz
Emp.: 600
Catering Supplies Distr
S.I.C.: 5113
N.A.I.C.S.: 424130
Simon Hunt *(Mgr)*

Bidvest (N.S.W) Limited (1)
Level 1 31-35 Bank Street
Pyrmont, Sydney, NSW, 2009, Australia
Tel.: (61) 295718666
Fax: (61) 295186444
E-Mail: bidvest@bidvest.com.au
Web Site: www.bidvest.com.au
Emp.: 2,000
Groceries Distr
S.I.C.: 5141
N.A.I.C.S.: 424410
Paul Moore *(Branch Mgr)*

Bidvest (UK) Limited (1)
Second Floor 63 Curzon St
London, W1J 8PD, United Kingdom
Tel.: (44) 2074934733
Fax: (44) 2072557888
Emp.: 2
Groceries & Food Service Equipment Retailer
S.I.C.: 5046
N.A.I.C.S.: 423440

Subsidiary:

Seafood Holdings Ltd (2)
Unit 10-14 Cedar Way Industrial Estate
Camley Street, London, N1C 4PD, United Kingdom
Tel.: (44) 1206 848 433
E-Mail: sales@directseafoods.co.uk
Web Site: www.directseafoods.co.uk
Sales Range: $125-149.9 Million
Emp.: 50
Fish & Seafood Distr
S.I.C.: 5146
N.A.I.C.S.: 424460
Stephen Oswald *(CEO)*

Divisions:

Daily Fish Supplies (3)
Unit 10-14 Cedar Way Industrial Estate
Camley Street, London, N1C 4PD, United Kingdom
Tel.: (44) 20 7383 3771
Fax: (44) 20 7383 5467
E-Mail: info@dailyfishsupplies.co.uk
Web Site: www.dailyfishsupplies.co.uk
Emp.: 10
Fish Supplier
S.I.C.: 5146
N.A.I.C.S.: 424460
Steve Vella *(Mgr-Depot)*

Direct Seafoods Colchester (3)
1 Crown Court Severalls Industrial Estate
Colchester, Essex, CO4 9TZ, United Kingdom
Tel.: (44) 1206 752 075
Fax: (44) 1206 751 851
E-Mail: info@directseafoodscolchester.co.uk
Web Site: www.directseafoodscolchester.co.uk
Fish Supplier
S.I.C.: 5146
N.A.I.C.S.: 424460
Rachel Flack *(Head-Sls)*

Direct Seafoods London (3)
Unit 14-15 Bermondsey Trading Estate
Rotherhithe New Road, London, SE16 3LL, United Kingdom
Tel.: (44) 20 7358 1617
Fax: (44) 20 7635 9760
E-Mail: info@directseafoodslondon.co.uk
Web Site: www.directseafoodslondon.co.uk
Fish Supplier
S.I.C.: 5146
N.A.I.C.S.: 424460
Laky Zervudachi *(Dir-Sustainability)*

Kingfisher Brixham (3)
Unit 4/5 Torbay Business Park
Woodview Road, Paignton, Devon, TQ4 7HP, United Kingdom
Tel.: (44) 1803 553 232
Fax: (44) 1803 552 030
E-Mail: info@kingfisherbrixham.co.uk
Web Site: www.kingfisherbrixham.co.uk
Fish Supplier
S.I.C.: 5146
N.A.I.C.S.: 424460
Les Daniels *(Mgr-Pur)*

Neve Fleetwood (3)
19 Copse Road
Fleetwood, FY7 6RP, United Kingdom
Tel.: (44) 1253 774 100
Fax: (44) 1253 774 110
E-Mail: info@nevefleetwood.co.uk
Web Site: www.nevefleetwood.co.uk
Emp.: 90
Fish Supplier
S.I.C.: 5146
N.A.I.C.S.: 424460
Gary Apps *(Mgr-Depot)*

Southbank Fresh Fish (3)
Unit 26 Kent Park Industrial Estate Ruby Street
Southwark, London, SE15 1LR, United Kingdom
Tel.: (44) 20 7639 6000
Fax: (44) 20 7639 1483
E-Mail: info@southbankfreshfish.co.uk
Web Site: www.southbankfreshfish.co.uk
Fish Supplier
S.I.C.: 5146
N.A.I.C.S.: 424460
John Ewing *(Mgr-Depot)*

Taylor's of Newcastle (3)
Unit 19A Elm Road
North Shields, NE29 8SE, United Kingdom
Tel.: (44) 191 258 2957
Fax: (44) 191 296 2558
E-Mail: info@taylorsofnewcastle.co.uk
Web Site: www.taylorsofnewcastle.co.uk
Emp.: 35
Fish Supplier
S.I.C.: 5146
N.A.I.C.S.: 424460
Phil Coltherd *(Mgr-Depot)*

Bidvest (Victoria) (Pty) Limited (1)
548-572 Clayton Road
Clayton, Melbourne, VIC, 3168, Australia
Tel.: (61) 385510192
Fax: (61) 385510140
E-Mail: sales.melbourne@bidvest.com.au
Web Site: www.bidvest.com.au
Groceries Distr
S.I.C.: 5141
N.A.I.C.S.: 424410

Bidvest (WA) (Pty) Limited (1)
71 Cocos Drive
Bibra Lake, Perth, WA, 6163, Australia
Tel.: (61) 894348800
Fax: (61) 894942999
E-Mail: sales.perth@bidvest.com.au
Emp.: 200
Groceries Distr
S.I.C.: 5141
N.A.I.C.S.: 424410
Colin Miller *(Gen Mgr)*

Burleigh Marr Distributions (Pty) Limited (1)
347 Lytton Road
Morningside, Brisbane, QLD, 4170, Australia
Tel.: (61) 738991999
Fax: (61) 738992657
E-Mail: sales@bidvest.com.au
Web Site: www.findfoodfast.com.au
Groceries Distr
S.I.C.: 5141
N.A.I.C.S.: 424410
Michael West *(Gen Mgr)*

Caterplus (Botswana) (Pty) Limited (1)
Plot 20594 Block 3
Gaborone, Botswana
Tel.: (267) 3924284
Fax: (267) 3923270
E-Mail: sales@caterplus.co.bw
Web Site: www.caterplus.co.bw
Emp.: 53
Groceries Distr
S.I.C.: 5141
N.A.I.C.S.: 424410
Bonolo Champane *(Gen Mgr)*

Caterplus Namibia (Pty) Limited (1)
4-6 Newcastle Street Northern Industria
PO Box 11496
Windhoek, Namibia
Tel.: (264) 61258313
Fax: (264) 61239969
E-Mail: sales@bmi-namibia.com
Emp.: 80
Seafood Distr
S.I.C.: 5146
N.A.I.C.S.: 424460
Morne Du Toit *(Gen Mgr)*

Cecil Nurse Namibia (Pty) Limited (1)
16 Gold Street Prosperita
PO Box 11507
Windhoek, Namibia
Tel.: (264) 61227000
Fax: (264) 61231052
E-Mail: windhoek@cecilnurse.com
Emp.: 30
Office Furniture Mfr
S.I.C.: 2521
N.A.I.C.S.: 337211
Bertie Kotze *(Mng Dir)*

Deli XL Belgie NV (1)
Avenue Deli XL 1
6530 Thuin, Hainaut, Belgium
Tel.: (32) 71256811
Fax: (32) 71344337
E-Mail: info@delixl.be
Web Site: www.delixl.be
Emp.: 500
Convenience Foods Distr
S.I.C.: 5411
N.A.I.C.S.: 445110
Thierry Legat *(CEO & Mng Dir)*

Eastman Staples Limited (1)
131 Lockwood Road
Huddersfield, West Yorkshire, HD1 3QW, United Kingdom
Tel.: (44) 1484888888
Fax: (44) 1484888800
E-Mail: sales@eastman.co.uk
Web Site: www.eastman.co.uk
Emp.: 30
Clothing Supplies Distr
S.I.C.: 5949
N.A.I.C.S.: 451130
Colin Werb *(Mng Dir)*

Express Air Services (Namibia) (Pty) Limited (1)
Robert Mugabe Avenue 55 Eros
PO Box 98500
Windhoek, Namibia
Tel.: (264) 61252493
Fax: (264) 61248312
E-Mail: marcovw@bidaircargo.com
Emp.: 1
Freight Forwarding Services
S.I.C.: 4731
N.A.I.C.S.: 488510
Marco Vanwyk *(Office Mgr)*

Farutex Sp.z.o.o. (1)
ul Kniewska 2H
70-846 Szczecin, West Pomeranian, Poland
Tel.: (48) 914602019
Fax: (48) 914602003
E-Mail: serwis@farutex.pl
Web Site: www.farutex.pl
Meat & Groceries Distr
S.I.C.: 5147
N.A.I.C.S.: 424470
Iwona Maglewicz *(Head-Pur)*

Horeca Trade LLC (1)
73021 alquoz Industrial Area 3
PO Box 73021
Dubai, United Arab Emirates
Tel.: (971) 43403330
Fax: (971) 43403222
E-Mail: telesales@horecatrade.ae
Web Site: www.horecatrade.com
Emp.: 101
Catering Supplies Distr
S.I.C.: 5146
N.A.I.C.S.: 424460
Hisham Jamil *(Mng Dir)*

John Lewis Foodservice (Pty) Limited (1)
304 Boundary Road
East Geelong, Geelong, VIC, 3219, Australia
Tel.: (61) 352484005
Fax: (61) 3 5248 4178
Groceries Distr
S.I.C.: 5141
N.A.I.C.S.: 424410

Kolok (Namibia) (Pty) Limited (1)
40 Nickel Street Prosperita
PO Box 40797
Windhoek, Namibia
Tel.: (264) 61370500
Fax: (264) 61370526
E-Mail: valne@kolok.com.na
Emp.: 23
Computer Peripheral Equipments Distr
S.I.C.: 5045
N.A.I.C.S.: 423430
Wilho Eliaser *(Mgr-Warehouse)*

Macardo Lodge (Pty) Limited (1)
Dennis Todd Office Park Plot 50361 The Fairground
Gaborone, Botswana
Tel.: (267) 3903244
Fax: (267) 3903245
Web Site: www.travelwise.co.bw
Emp.: 30
Travel Management Services
S.I.C.: 4724
N.A.I.C.S.: 561510
Fred MacDonald *(Mng Dir & CEO)*

Manica Group Namibia (Pty) Limited (1)
No 2 Third Street East
PO Box 4
Walvis Bay, Namibia
Tel.: (264) 642012911
Fax: (264) 64204217
E-Mail: contact@manica.com.na
Web Site: www.manica.com.na
Emp.: 150
Logistics & Warehousing Services
S.I.C.: 4225
N.A.I.C.S.: 493110
Shalli Ben-Elungu *(Gen Mgr-Mktg)*

Subsidiary:

Manica Information Technology (Pty) Limited (2)
The Maritime Building 2 Third Street
PO Box 4
Walvis Bay, Namibia
Tel.: (264) 642012666
Fax: (264) 64207680
E-Mail: contact@mit.com.na
Web Site: www.mit.com.na
Emp.: 35
Data Processing Services
S.I.C.: 7374
N.A.I.C.S.: 518210
Hanswerner Timke *(Mng Dir)*

Manica (Zambia) Limited (1)
Plot 840 Nyerere Road
Kitwe, Copperbelt, 10101, Zambia
Tel.: (260) 211273486
Fax: (260) 211237488
Freight Transportation Services
S.I.C.: 4412
N.A.I.C.S.: 483111

Namibia Bureau de Change (Pty) Limited (1)
193 Independence Avenue
PO Box 24296
Windhoek, Namibia
Tel.: (264) 61229667
Fax: (264) 61222436
E-Mail: manager@nbdc.com.na
Web Site: www.nbdc.com.na
Emp.: 16
Foreign Currency Exchange Services
S.I.C.: 6221
N.A.I.C.S.: 523130
Susan van der Westhuizen *(Area Mgr)*

Namibian Sea Products Limited (1)
No 1 Fifth Street East
PO Box 4
Walvis Bay, 2715, Namibia
Tel.: (264) 26464 219 900
Fax: (264) 64 219 905
Web Site: www.unitedfishingenterprises.com
Seafood Processing Services
S.I.C.: 5421
N.A.I.C.S.: 445220
Richard Ahrens *(Gen Mgr)*

Nowaco Czech Republic s.r.o. (1)
V Ruzoveem udoli 553
278 01 Kralupy nad Vltavou, Czech Republic
Tel.: (420) 315706111
Fax: (420) 315706222
E-Mail: bidvest@bidvest.cz
Web Site: www.bidvest.cz
Emp.: 1,500
Frozen & Fresh Food Products Distr
S.I.C.: 5142
N.A.I.C.S.: 424420
Tajovsky Jan *(Bus Dir)*

Non-U.S. Subsidiary:

Nowaco Slovakia s.r.o. (2)
Piestanska 2321/71
915 01 Nove Mesto nad Vahom, Slovakia
Tel.: (421) 327742811
Fax: (421) 327742831
E-Mail: nowaco@nowaco.sk
Web Site: www.nowaco.sk
Frozen & Fresh Food Products Distr
S.I.C.: 5142
N.A.I.C.S.: 424420

Ontime Automotive Limited (1)
Pasadena Close
Pump Lane Industrial Estate, Hayes, Mddx, UB3 3NQ, United Kingdom UK
Tel.: (44) 870 460 7999 (100%)
E-Mail: info@ontime-auto.com
Web Site: www.ontime-auto.com
Motor Vehicle Rescue & Recovery, Fleet Assistance, Distribution & Parking Support Services
S.I.C.: 7389
N.A.I.C.S.: 561499
David Brinklow *(Grp Mng Dir)*

Pastry Global Food Service Limited (1)
Unit B, 3/F Yoo Hoo Tower 38 Kwai Fung Crescent
Kwai Chung, New Territories, China (Hong Kong)
Tel.: (852) 24941908
Fax: (852) 31450756
E-Mail: info@pastryglobal.com.hk
Web Site: www.angliss.com.hk/en/branch/branch1.aspx
Emp.: 20
Bakery Products Distr
S.I.C.: 5142
N.A.I.C.S.: 424420
Christina Wong *(Gen Mgr)*

Rennies Travel (Namibia) (Pty) Limited (1)
Ohlthaver & List 6 Peter Muller Street
PO Box 211
Windhoek, Namibia
Tel.: (264) 612890760
Fax: (264) 61 225 932
E-Mail: leisure@rennies.hrgworldwide.com
Web Site: www.renniestravelnamibia.com
Emp.: 25
Travel & Tour Operating Agencies
S.I.C.: 4724
N.A.I.C.S.: 561510
Sonja Burger *(Gen Mgr-Ops)*

Steiner Hygiene Swaziland (Pty) Limited (1)
12th Street & 1st Avenue Unit 4 Lot 483
Matsapha, M202, Swaziland
Tel.: (268) 518 4818
Fax: (268) 518 6554
Emp.: 15
Housekeeping Services
S.I.C.: 7349
N.A.I.C.S.: 561720
Debbie Hulley *(Mgr)*

Top Turf Botswana (Pty) Limited (1)
Private Bag BR105
Gaborone, Botswana
Tel.: (267) 3500413
Fax: (267) 2500414
Emp.: 15
Landscaping Services
S.I.C.: 0782
N.A.I.C.S.: 561730
Paul Kirkby *(CEO & Mng Dir)*

Top Turf Mauritius (Pty) Limited (1)
Le Coco Beach Hotel Belle Mare Coastal Road
Port Louis, Mauritius
Tel.: (230) 4155987
Fax: (230) 415 2047
Landscaping Services
S.I.C.: 0783
N.A.I.C.S.: 561730

Voltex Namibia (Pty) Limited (1)
Corner of Andimba Toivo ya Toivo & Benz Street
PO Box 11508
Southern Industrial Area, Windhoek, Namibia
Tel.: (264) 61 228 231
Fax: (264) 61 232 980
Web Site: www.bidvestnamibia.com.na/contact_us.htm
Electrical Supplies Whslr
S.I.C.: 5211
N.A.I.C.S.: 444190
Kobus Heymam *(Mng Dir)*

Waltons Stationery Company (Namibia) (Pty) Limited (1)
Corner Andimba Toivo Ya Toivo & Messum Street
PO Box 3187
Windhoek, Namibia
Tel.: (264) 612838000
Fax: (264) 61233695
E-Mail: orders@waltons-namib.com
Web Site: www.bidvest.com
Emp.: 100
Office Supplies & Furniture Retailer
S.I.C.: 5021
N.A.I.C.S.: 423210
Chris Dreyer *(Mng Dir)*

Walvis Bay Stevedoring Company (Pty) Limited (1)
1 Jeppe Street Northern Industrial Area
PO Box 4
Windhoek, Namibia
Tel.: (264) 64204641
Fax: (264) 64205798
E-Mail: contact@wbs.com.na
Web Site: www.wbs.com.na/contact.php
Emp.: 16
Stevedoring Services
S.I.C.: 4491
N.A.I.C.S.: 488320
Riaan Lottering *(Branch Mgr)*

BIEMT CO., LTD.

10-6 Sodong-ri Eumbong-myeon
336-864 Asan, South Chungcheong, Korea (South)
Tel.: (82) 415396114
Fax: (82) 415396120
Web Site: www.biemt.com
Year Founded: 1997
052900—(KRS)

Business Description:
Semiconductor Materials Mfr
S.I.C.: 3674
N.A.I.C.S.: 334413

Personnel:
Kang-Youl Lee *(CEO)*

BIERHAKE GMBH & CO. KG

Eikesberg 56
49076 Osnabruck, Germany
Tel.: (49) 541912030
Fax: (49) 541129438
E-Mail: osnabrueck@bierhake.de
Web Site: www.bierhake.de
Year Founded: 1885
Rev.: $18,194,286
Emp.: 100

Business Description:
Automotive Parts Whslr
S.I.C.: 5013
N.A.I.C.S.: 423120

Personnel:
Ulf Wichern *(Mng Dir)*

BIESSE S.P.A.

Via Della Meccanica 16
61122 Pesaro, Italy
Tel.: (39) 0721439100
Fax: (39) 0721439150
E-Mail: biesse.sales@biesse.com
Web Site: www.biesse.com
BSS—(ITA)
Rev.: $515,665,226
Assets: $470,975,075
Liabilities: $318,507,861
Net Worth: $152,467,214
Earnings: ($8,834,914)
Emp.: 2,753
Fiscal Year-end: 12/31/12

Business Description:
Mfr of Woodworking Machinery
S.I.C.: 3569
N.A.I.C.S.: 333999

Personnel:
Roberto Selci *(Chm & Co-CEO)*
Giancarlo Selci *(Co-CEO)*

Board of Directors:
Roberto Selci
Giampaolo Garattoni
Salvatore Giordano
Alessandra Parpajola
Stefano Porcellini
Giancarlo Selci
Leone Sibani
Cesare Tinti

Subsidiaries:

Cabi S.r.l. (1)
2 Perceptumbero
Porto, 63018 Rome, Italy (100%)
Tel.: (39) 0734992352
E-Mail: info@cabi.it
Web Site: www.cabi.it
Emp.: 2
Industrial Machinery & Equipment Merchant Whslr
S.I.C.: 5084
N.A.I.C.S.: 423830

HSD S.p.A. (1)
Via della Meccanica
61100 Pesaro, Italy (100%)
Tel.: (39) 0721439619
Fax: (39) 0721441688
E-Mail: fabrizio.pierini@hsd-hitec.it
Industrial Machinery & Equipment Merchant Whslr
S.I.C.: 5084
N.A.I.C.S.: 423830

Sandymac S.r.l. (1)
Via Case Nuove Snc
San Giovanni In Marignano, Rimini, Italy (80%)
Tel.: (39) 0541828511
Fax: (39) 0541828510
E-Mail: luca.amabei@biesse.it
Other Business Service Centers (including Copy Shops)
S.I.C.: 7389
N.A.I.C.S.: 561439
Gino Botteghi *(Mng Dir)*

U.S. Subsidiaries:

Biesse America, Inc. (1)
4110 Meadow Oak Dr
Charlotte, NC 28208
Tel.: (704) 357-3131
Fax: (704) 357-3130
E-Mail: sales@biesseamerica.com
Web Site: www.biesseamerica.com
Emp.: 55
Mfr of Woodworking Machinery
S.I.C.: 3569

Biesse S.p.A.—(Continued)

N.A.I.C.S.: 333999
Federico Broccoli *(Pres & CEO)*

HSD USA, Inc. (1)
3764 SW 30th Ave
Hollywood, FL 33312 (100%)
Tel.: (954) 587-1991
Fax: (954) 587-8338
E-Mail: info@hsdusa.com
Web Site: www.hsdusa.com
Emp.: 10
Industrial Machinery & Equipment Merchant Whslr
S.I.C.: 5084
N.A.I.C.S.: 423830
Giuseppe Benelli *(CEO)*

Non-U.S. Subsidiaries:

Biesse Asia Pte Ltd. (1)
5 Woodlands Ter
02-01 Zagro Global Hub, 738430
Singapore, Singapore (100%)
Tel.: (65) 63682632
Fax: (65) 63681969
E-Mail: mail@biesse-asia.com
Web Site: www.biesseasia.com
Emp.: 25
All Other Industrial Machinery Mfr
S.I.C.: 3559
N.A.I.C.S.: 333249
Maffimo Ferdinandi *(Mng Dir)*

Biesse Canada Inc. (1)
18005 Lapoimte
Mirabel, QC, J7J 0G2, Canada (100%)
Tel.: (450) 437-5534
Fax: (450) 437-2859
E-Mail: sales@biessecanada.com
Web Site: www.biessecanada.com
Emp.: 40
Industrial Machinery & Equipment Merchant Whslr
S.I.C.: 5084
N.A.I.C.S.: 423830
Sedereco Barccolle *(CEO)*

Biesse Group Australia Pty Ltd. (1)
3 Widemere Road - Wetherill Park
Wales, NSW, 2164, Australia (100%)
Tel.: (61) 296095355
Fax: (61) 296094291
E-Mail: nsw@biesseaustralia.com.au
Web Site: www.biesseaustralia.com.au
Industrial Machinery & Equipment Merchant Whslr
S.I.C.: 5084
N.A.I.C.S.: 423830

Biesse Group Deutschland GmbH (1)
Gewerbestrasse 6-A
89275 Elchingen, Germany (100%)
Tel.: (49) 730896060
Fax: (49) 7308960666
E-Mail: biesse.sued@biesse.de
Web Site: www.biesse.de
Emp.: 50
Industrial Machinery & Equipment Merchant Whslr
S.I.C.: 5084
N.A.I.C.S.: 423830

Biesse Group France Sarl (1)
4 Chemin Moninsadle
69530 Lyon, Baignais, France (100%)
Tel.: (33) 478967329
Fax: (33) 478967330
E-Mail: commercial@biessefrance.fr
Web Site: www.biessefrance.fr
Emp.: 50
Industrial Machinery & Equipment Merchant Whslr
S.I.C.: 5084
N.A.I.C.S.: 423830
Laurent Mazees *(Pres)*

Biesse Group UK Ltd. (1)
Lamport Drive
Heartlands Business Park, NN118YZ
Daventry, United Kingdom (100%)
Tel.: (44) 1327300366
Fax: (44) 1327705150
E-Mail: info@biesse.co.uk
Web Site: www.biesse.co.uk
Emp.: 30
Industrial Machinery & Equipment Merchant Whslr
S.I.C.: 5084
N.A.I.C.S.: 423830
Steve Bulmer *(CEO)*

Biesservice Scandinavia AB (1)
Betavagen 11
55652 Jonkoping, Sweden (60%)
Tel.: (46) 36150380
Fax: (46) 36150380
E-Mail: biesse.scandinavia@telia.com
Web Site: www.biesse.it
Emp.: 3
Industrial Machinery & Equipment Merchant Whslr
S.I.C.: 5084
N.A.I.C.S.: 423830
Ann-Kristine Eriksson *(Head-Spare Parts Ops)*

BIG 8 SPLIT, INC.

c/o TD Securities Inc 66 Wellington St W 9th Fl
Ernst & Young Tower, Toronto, ON, M5K 1A2, Canada
Tel.: (416) 982-2680
Fax: (416) 982-3176
E-Mail: big8split@tdsecurities.com
Web Site: www.tdsponsoredcompanies.com
BIG—(TSX)
Sales Range: $1-9.9 Million
Business Description:
Investment Services
S.I.C.: 6211
N.A.I.C.S.: 523999
Personnel:
John B. Newman *(Chm)*
Cameron Goodnough *(Pres & CEO)*
Robert Linklater *(CFO & Sec)*
Board of Directors:
John B. Newman
Clive H. Coombs
Cameron Goodnough
Robert Linklater
Louise Morwick
Legal Counsel:
Osler, Hoskin & Harcourt LLP
Toronto, ON, Canada
Transfer Agent:
Computershare Investor Services Inc
100 University Avenue
Toronto, ON, Canada

BIG BANK BIG OIL SPLIT CORP.

161 Bay Street Suite 2500
Toronto, ON, M5J 2S1, Canada
Tel.: (416) 643-4015
Fax: (416) 643-4049
Year Founded: 2006
BBO—(TSX)
Rev.: $2,317,376
Assets: $78,642,529
Liabilities: $47,888,623
Net Worth: $30,753,906
Earnings: ($7,404)
Fiscal Year-end: 12/31/12
Business Description:
Financial Investment Services
S.I.C.: 6211
N.A.I.C.S.: 523999
Personnel:
Noel Archard *(CEO)*
Eric Leveille *(Co-Mng Dir)*
Mary Anne Wiley *(Co-Mng Dir)*
Jack Gee *(CFO)*
Margaret Gunawan *(Chief Compliance Officer & Sec)*
Board of Directors:
Noel Archard
John Black
Linda Currie
Margaret Gunawan
Eric Leveille
Mary Anne Wiley
Transfer Agent:
Equity Financial Trust Company
Toronto, ON, Canada

BIG FIVE CAPITAL CORP.

1200 700 2nd Street SW
Calgary, AB, T2P 4V5, Canada
Tel.: (403) 606-7787
Fax: (403) 263-5591
E-Mail: bigfivecapitalinfo@gmail.com
Year Founded: 2011
BGF.P—(TSXV)
Business Description:
Investment Services
S.I.C.: 6211
N.A.I.C.S.: 523999
Personnel:
Mark Studer *(Pres & CEO)*
Jie Liang *(CFO & Sec)*
Board of Directors:
Gregory R. Harris
Jason Krueger
Jie Liang
Mark Studer
Jim Tanner
Transfer Agent:
Olympia Trust Company
125 9th Avenue SE Suite 2300
Calgary, AB, T2G 0P6, Canada
Tel.: (403) 261-0900

BIG FREIGHT SYSTEMS INC.

360 Hwy 12 North
Steinbach, MB, R5G 1A6, Canada
Tel.: (204) 326-3434
Fax: (204) 326-2717
Toll Free: (877) 452-2323
E-Mail: bfsinfo@bigfreight.com
Web Site: www.bigfreight.com
Year Founded: 1948
Rev.: $39,889,786
Emp.: 300
Business Description:
Freight Management & International Transport Services
S.I.C.: 4731
N.A.I.C.S.: 488510
Personnel:
Gary Thurman Coleman *(Pres)*

B.I.G. INDUSTRIES BERHAD

Lot 2225 Section 66 Jalan Dermaga
Pending Industrial Estate
93450 Kuching, Sarawak, Malaysia
Tel.: (60) 82486321
Fax: (60) 82336933
Web Site: www.bigind.com.my
BIG—(KLS)
Rev.: $32,163,092
Assets: $40,918,214
Liabilities: $26,575,267
Net Worth: $14,342,947
Earnings: ($834,541)
Fiscal Year-end: 12/31/12
Business Description:
Industrial Gases Mfr & Distr
S.I.C.: 2813
N.A.I.C.S.: 325120
Personnel:
Yoke Lin Wong *(Sec)*
Board of Directors:
Sawaludin Md Din
Ban Tin Lau
Keat Hoo Lau
Chuen Wan Lee
Kai Goh Thiang

Subsidiaries:

B.I.G. Industrial Gas Sdn. Bhd. (1)
Lot 2225 Section 66 Jalan Dermaga
Pending Industrial Estate
93450 Kuching, Sarawak, Malaysia
Tel.: (60) 82486321
Fax: (60) 82336933
E-Mail: hengcl@bigind.com.my
Emp.: 50
Industrial Gases Mfr & Distr
S.I.C.: 2813
N.A.I.C.S.: 325120

B.I.G. Marketing Sdn. Bhd. (1)
19-D 4th Floor Block 2 Worldwide Business Centre
Jalan Tinju 13/50 Section 13, Shah Alam, Selangor, 40675, Malaysia
Tel.: (60) 355129999
Fax: (60) 355129282
Emp.: 300
Industrial Gases Distr
S.I.C.: 5169
N.A.I.C.S.: 424690

Puncak Luyang Sdn. Bhd. (1)
Lot 5-6-7 2nd Fl Wisma KKM Inanam
88822 Kota Kinabalu, Sabah, Malaysia
Tel.: (60) 88382352
Fax: (60) 88437430
Web Site: www.bigind.com.my/contact.asp
Emp.: 100
Residential Condominium Management Services
S.I.C.: 6531
N.A.I.C.S.: 531311
Kenny Fung *(Gen Mgr)*

Uni-Mix Sdn. Bhd. (1)
Lot 5 Base 6 7 2nd F Wisma KKM Jalan Tuaran
88450 Kota Kinabalu, Sabah, Malaysia
Tel.: (60) 88437422
Fax: (60) 88437430
E-Mail: susan@bigind.com.my
Emp.: 150
Ready Mix Concrete Mfr
S.I.C.: 3273
N.A.I.C.S.: 327320
Kenny Fong *(Gen Mgr)*

BIG M FORD LINCOLN LTD.

1312 Trans Canada Way SE
Medicine Hat, AB, T1A 7G8, Canada
Tel.: (403) 527-4406
Fax: (403) 527-7193
E-Mail: mail@bigmford.ca
Web Site: www.bigmford.ca
Rev.: $17,215,100
Emp.: 37
Business Description:
New & Used Car Dealer
S.I.C.: 5511
N.A.I.C.S.: 441110
Personnel:
Sandy MacDonald *(Gen Mgr-Sls)*

BIG NORTH CAPITAL INC.

(Name Changed to Big North Graphite Corp.)

BIG NORTH GRAPHITE CORP.

(Formerly BIG NORTH CAPITAL INC.)
Suite 350 - 885 Dunsmuir Street
Vancouver, BC, V6C 1N5, Canada
Tel.: (604) 629-8220
Fax: (604) 688-7307
E-Mail: info@bignorthgraphite.com
Web Site: www.bignorthgraphite.com
Year Founded: 2007
NRT—(OTC TSXV)
Rev.: $67,670
Assets: $1,248,585
Liabilities: $143,160
Net Worth: $1,105,424
Earnings: ($1,243,277)
Fiscal Year-end: 10/31/13
Business Description:
Graphite Exploration Services
S.I.C.: 1499
N.A.I.C.S.: 212399
Personnel:
Daniel R. Bleak *(Chm)*
Spiro I. Kletas *(Pres & CEO)*
Bryce A. Clark *(CFO)*
Connie Norman *(Sec)*
Board of Directors:
Daniel R. Bleak
Spiro I. Kletas
Eric Ostensoe
Andrew H. Rees

Transfer Agent:
Equity Financial Trust Company
200 University Avenue Suite 400
Toronto, ON, Canada

BIG RIVER TIMBERS PTY. LTD.

Trenayr Road
Junction Hill, Grafton, NSW, 2460, Australia
Tel.: (61) 266440900
Fax: (61) 266433328
E-Mail: grafton@bigrivergroup.com.au
Web Site: www.bigrivergroup.com.au
Year Founded: 1920
Sales Range: $25-49.9 Million
Emp.: 200
Business Description:
Logging & Timber Services
S.I.C.: 2411
N.A.I.C.S.: 113310
Personnel:
Jim Pindon *(Chm & Mng Dir)*

BIG ROCK BREWERY INC.

5555 76th Ave SE
Calgary, AB, T2C 4L8, Canada
Tel.: (403) 720-3239
Fax: (403) 236-7523
Toll Free: (800) 242-3107
E-Mail: investors@bigrockbeer.com
Web Site: www.bigrockbeer.com
Year Founded: 1984
BR—(TSX)
Rev.: $45,781,579
Assets: $46,023,126
Liabilities: $14,143,911
Net Worth: $31,879,215
Earnings: $4,110,273
Emp.: 160
Fiscal Year-end: 12/31/12
Business Description:
Beer Brewer & Marketer
S.I.C.: 2082
N.A.I.C.S.: 312120
Personnel:
Edward E. McNally *(Chm)*
Robert Sartor *(Pres & CEO)*
Barbara Feit *(CFO)*
Board of Directors:
Edward E. McNally
John Hartley
James M. Jackson
Michael G. Kohut
Kathleen McNally-Leitch
J. Cameron Millikin
Robert G. Peters
Jim H. T. Riddell
Gordon G. Tallman
Transfer Agent:
Valiant Trust Company
606 4th Street SW Suite 310
Calgary, AB, T2P 1T1, Canada
Tel.: (403) 233-2801
Fax: (403) 233-2857
Subsidiary:

Pine Creek Brewing Company Ltd (1)
5555 76th Ave SE
Calgary, AB, T2C 4L8, Canada
Tel.: (403) 279-2337
Toll Free: (800) 242-3107
Beer Mfr
S.I.C.: 2082
N.A.I.C.S.: 312120

BIG ROCK RESOURCES INC.

703 938 Howe Street
Vancouver, BC, V4Z 1N4, Canada
Tel.: (604) 800-2955
Web Site: www.bigrockresources.com
Year Founded: 2005
1BR—(DEU)
Business Description:
Gold Mining Services
S.I.C.: 1041
N.A.I.C.S.: 212221
Personnel:
Ken Van Boeyen *(Pres & Sec)*
Board of Directors:
Charles Irizarry
Ken Van Boeyen

BIG TREE GROUP INC.

(Formerly TRANSAX INTERNATIONAL LIMITED)
South Part 1-101 Nanshe Area
Pennan Indus Pk North Yingbinbei Road
Waisha Town Longhu, Shantou, Guangdong, 515023, China
Tel.: (86) 754 8323888
Web Site:
Year Founded: 1987
BIGG—(OTC)
Rev.: $33,888,635
Assets: $8,650,814
Liabilities: $6,045,050
Net Worth: $2,605,764
Earnings: $1,595,039
Emp.: 150
Fiscal Year-end: 12/31/12
Business Description:
Toy Sourcing & Contract Manufacturing Services
S.I.C.: 5092
N.A.I.C.S.: 423920
Personnel:
Wei Lin *(Chm & CEO)*
Jiale Cai *(CFO)*
Board of Directors:
Wei Lin
Chaojun Lin
Chaoqun Xian
Transfer Agent:
Transfer Online, Inc.
512 SE Salmon St
Portland, OR 97214
Tel.: (503) 227-2950

BIG YELLOW GROUP PLC

2 The Deans Bridge Road
Bagshot, Surrey, GU19 5AT, United Kingdom
Tel.: (44) 1276470190
Fax: (44) 1276470191
Toll Free: 8007834949
E-Mail: info@bigyellow.co.uk
Web Site: www.bigyellow.co.uk
BYG—(LSE)
Rev.: $110,030,714
Assets: $1,328,566,657
Liabilities: $455,806,783
Net Worth: $872,759,874
Earnings: $50,341,448
Emp.: 319
Fiscal Year-end: 03/31/13
Business Description:
Self Storage Services
S.I.C.: 4225
N.A.I.C.S.: 531130
Personnel:
Nicholas Vetch *(Co-Founder & Chm)*
James Gibson *(Co-Founder & CEO)*
John Trotman *(CFO)*
Shauna Beavis *(Sec & Controller-Fin)*
Board of Directors:
Nicholas Vetch
Tim Clark
Richard Cotton
James Gibson
Georgina Harvey
Steve Johnson
Adrian Lee
Mark Richardson
John Trotman
Legal Counsel:
CMS Cameron McKenna LLP
Mitre House 160 Aldersgate Street
London, United Kingdom
Subsidiaries:

Big Yellow Self Storage Company 6 Limited (1)
2 The Deans Bridge Rd
Bagshot, Surrey, GU19 5AT, United Kingdom
Tel.: (44) 1276470190
Fax: (44) 1276470191
E-Mail: info@bigyellow.co.uk
Web Site: www.bigyellow.co.uk
Emp.: 50
Self Storage Services
S.I.C.: 4226
N.A.I.C.S.: 493190
James Gibson *(CEO)*

Big Yellow Self Storage Company 8 Limited (1)
2 The Deans Bridge Road
Bagshot, Surrey, GU19 5AT, United Kingdom
Tel.: (44) 8001300170
Self Storage Services
S.I.C.: 4226
N.A.I.C.S.: 493190

Big Yellow Self Storage Company Limited (1)
2 The Deans Bridge Road
Bagshot, Surrey, GU19 5AT, United Kingdom
Tel.: (44) 1276477818
Fax: (44) 1276850680
E-Mail: customersupport@bigyellow.co.uk
Web Site: www.bigyellow.co.uk/contactus
Emp.: 70
Self Storage Services
S.I.C.: 4226
N.A.I.C.S.: 493190
Adrian Lee *(CEO)*

Big Yellow Self Storage (GP) Limited (1)
1-2 The Deans Bridge Road
Bagshot, Surrey, GU19 5AT, United Kingdom
Tel.: (44) 1276 470190
Self Storage Services
S.I.C.: 4226
N.A.I.C.S.: 493190

BYSSCo Limited (1)
Unit 2 The Deans Bridge Road
Bagshot, GU19 5AT, United Kingdom
Tel.: (44) 12 76 47 01 90
Self Storage Services
S.I.C.: 4226
N.A.I.C.S.: 493190

BIGAIR GROUP LIMITED

Level 1 59 Buckingham Street
Surry Hills, NSW, 2010, Australia
Tel.: (61) 2 9993 1300
Fax: (61) 280808132
Web Site: www.bigair.com.au
BGL—(ASX)
Rev.: $31,171,200
Assets: $40,464,162
Liabilities: $5,955,061
Net Worth: $34,509,101
Earnings: $4,951,354
Fiscal Year-end: 06/30/13
Business Description:
Wireless Communications Services.
S.I.C.: 3661
N.A.I.C.S.: 334210
Personnel:
Jason Ashton *(CEO)*
Charles Chapman *(CFO & Sec)*
Board of Directors:
Paul Tyler
Jason Ashton
Nigel Jerries
Vivian Stewart
Subsidiary:

Anittel Communications Pty Ltd. (1)
Level 10 132 Arthur Street
Sydney, NSW, 2060, Australia
Tel.: (61) 2 1300 10 11 12
Fax: (61) 2 1300 88 67 83
E-Mail: enquiries@anittel.com.au
Web Site: www.anittel.com.au
Emp.: 200
Information Technology & Telecommunication Services
S.I.C.: 4812
N.A.I.C.S.: 517911
Mark Stead *(CEO)*
Upul Mendis *(CFO)*

BIGGART BAILLIE

(Acquired by DWF LLP)

BIJELJINA PUT AD

Ul Baje Pivljanina bb
76300 Bijeljina, Bosnia & Herzegovina
Tel.: (387) 55 247 879
Fax: (387) 55 247 884
E-Mail: bijeljinaput@zona.ba
Web Site: www.bijeljinaput.com
Year Founded: 1949
BNPT—(BANJ)
Emp.: 250
Business Description:
Construction Services
S.I.C.: 1629
N.A.I.C.S.: 236210
Personnel:
Slavisa Rakovic *(Chm-Supervisory Bd)*
Srdjan Coric *(Chm-Mgmt Bd)*

BIJOUTERIE ADLER SA

23 rue du Rone
1204 Geneva, Switzerland
Tel.: (41) 228198007
Fax: (41) 228198080
E-Mail: rhone@adler.ch
Web Site: www.adler.ch
Year Founded: 1886
Sales Range: $10-24.9 Million
Emp.: 30
Business Description:
Jewelry & Watch Mfr & Retailer
S.I.C.: 5944
N.A.I.C.S.: 448310
Personnel:
Carlo Adler *(Mng Dir)*
Franklin Adler *(Mng Dir)*

BIL CONTINENTAL LIMITED

PO Thathra GT Road Kachhawan
Varanasi, 221307, India
Tel.: (91) 542 2620221
Fax: (91) 542 2620090
E-Mail: marketing@bholanath.biz
Web Site: www.bholanath.biz
530841—(BOM)
Business Description:
Household Durable Mfr
S.I.C.: 3639
N.A.I.C.S.: 335228
Personnel:
Bholanath Baranwal *(Chm & Mng Dir)*
Dinanath Baranwal *(Mng Dir)*
Vijay Yadav *(Compliance Officer)*
Subsidiary:

Kaandla Rugs Ltd (1)
A1 EPIP Zone UPSIDC Shastripuram
Sikandra, Agra, 282 007, India
Tel.: (91) 562 2372 299
Fax: (91) 562 2372 288
Web Site: www.Kandlarugs.com
Emp.: 100
Carpet Mfr
S.I.C.: 2273
N.A.I.C.S.: 314110
Dinesh Bind *(Mgr)*

BIL ENERGY SYSTEMS LIMITED

201-204 Vikas Chamber Junction of Link & Marve Road Mith Chowky
Malad West, Mumbai, Maharashtra, 400 064, India

Bil Energy Systems Limited—(Continued)

Tel.: (91) 2240897777
Fax: (91) 22 28811225
E-Mail: info@bilenergy.com
Web Site: www.bilenergy.com
BILENERGY—(NSE)
Rev.: $18,147,341
Assets: $26,812,900
Liabilities: $19,082,443
Net Worth: $7,730,457
Earnings: ($1,096,734)
Fiscal Year-end: 03/31/13
Business Description:
Rotating Machine Stamping Mfr
S.I.C.: 2679
N.A.I.C.S.: 322299
Personnel:
Rajendra Kumar Choudhary *(Mng Dir)*
Astha Rathi *(Compliance Officer & Sec)*
Board of Directors:
Rajendra Kumar Choudhary
Suresh Kumar Choudhary
Vasudeo Kulkarni
Mrugen Shah
M. K. Sugathan
Transfer Agent:
System Support Services
209 Shivai Industrial Estate Next to Parke-Davis
89 Andheri-Kurla Rd
Mumbai, India

BILAL FIBRES LIMITED

House No 112-C Block E/1 Ghalib Road Gulberg III
Lahore, Pakistan
Tel.: (92) 42 35717701
Fax: (92) 42 35717707
E-Mail: info@bilalfibres.com
Web Site: www.bilalfibres.com
Year Founded: 1987
BILF—(ISL)
Sls.: $18,468,756
Assets: $13,667,212
Liabilities: $10,689,632
Net Worth: $2,977,580
Earnings: $625,101
Emp.: 811
Fiscal Year-end: 06/30/13
Business Description:
Yarn Mfr
S.I.C.: 2299
N.A.I.C.S.: 313110
Personnel:
Naeem Omer *(Chm & CEO)*
Muhammad Ahmad *(Sec)*
Board of Directors:
Naeem Omer
Anwar Abbas
Amjad Ali
Muhammad Asghar
Muhammad Sarwar
Abdul Sattar
Muhammad Zubair

BILCARE LIMITED

(d/b/a Bilcare Research Group)
601 ICC Trade Tower
Pune, 411 016, India
Tel.: (91) 20 3025 7700
Fax: (91) 20 3025 7701
E-Mail: mail@bilcare.com
Web Site: www.bilcare.com
Year Founded: 1995
526853—(BOM)
Rev.: $658,468,902
Assets: $815,761,724
Liabilities: $560,094,105
Net Worth: $255,667,620
Earnings: $7,340,338
Emp.: 2,000
Fiscal Year-end: 03/31/13
Business Description:
Holding Company; Pharmaceutical & Healthcare Product Research & Development, Packaging Innovation & Brand Authentication Technology Services
S.I.C.: 6719
N.A.I.C.S.: 551112
Personnel:
Mohan H. Bhandari *(Founder, Chm & CEO)*
Praful R. Naik *(Chief Scientific Officer)*
Anil Tikekar *(Compliance Officer & Sec)*
Board of Directors:
Mohan H. Bhandari
Pawan G. Chandak
R. V. Chaudhari
Volker Huelck
Praful R. Naik
Rajendra B. Tapadia
Transfer Agent:
Link Intime India Pvt. Ltd
Block No 202 2nd Floor Akshay Complex Off
Dhole Patil Rd
Near Ganesh Mandir, Pune, India

Plant:

Bilcare Ltd. **(1)**
1028 Shiroli
Rajgurunagar, Pune, 410 505, India
Tel.: (91) 2135304200
Fax: (91) 2135224068
E-Mail: direct-in@bilcare.com
Web Site: www.bilcare.com
Emp.: 200
Pharmaceutical & Healthcare Product Research & Development, Packaging Innovation & Brand Authentication Technology Services
S.I.C.: 8071
N.A.I.C.S.: 621511
Mohan H. Bhandari *(Mng Dir)*

Non-U.S. Subsidiaries:

Bilcare Research GmbH **(1)**
Schlossmattenstr 2
79268 Botzingen, Germany
Tel.: (49) 7663 630
Fax: (49) 7663 635 46
E-Mail:
Web Site: www.bilcaresolutions.com
Pharmaceutical & Healthcare Product Research & Development, Packaging Innovation & Brand Authentication Technology Services
S.I.C.: 8071
N.A.I.C.S.: 621511
Heinz Gartner *(Exec Chm)*

Bilcare Marketing America Latina Ltda. **(1)**
Alameda Campinas 834 Apto 111
Jardim Paulista, 01404-001 Sao Paulo, Brazil
Tel.: (55) 11 32669064
Pharmaceutical & Healthcare Product Research & Development, Packaging Innovation & Brand Authentication Technology Services
S.I.C.: 8071
N.A.I.C.S.: 621511

Bilcare Singapore Pte. Ltd. **(1)**
52 Changi South Street 1
Singapore, 486161, Singapore
Tel.: (65) 63954130
Fax: (65) 65424386
E-Mail: enquiries@belcare.com
Emp.: 120
Pharmaceutical & Healthcare Product Research & Development, Packaging Innovation & Brand Authentication Technology Services
S.I.C.: 8071
N.A.I.C.S.: 621511
Rahul Bharadia *(Exec Dir)*

Subsidiary:

Bilcare Technologies Singapore Pte. Ltd. **(2)**
52 Changi S St 1
Singapore, 486161, Singapore
Tel.: (65) 63954130
Fax: (65) 65451810
E-Mail: ppr@bilcare.com
Web Site: www.bilcare.com
Emp.: 130
Pharmaceutical Preparation Products Mfr
S.I.C.: 2834
N.A.I.C.S.: 325412
Srinidhi Rao *(Gen Mgr)*

Non-U.S. Subsidiary:

Bilcare Technologies Italia Srl. **(3)**
Presso Veneto Nanotech Via San Crispino 106
35129 Padua, Italy
Tel.: (39) 049 7705514
Fax: (39) 049 7705555
Pharmaceutical Products Mfr
S.I.C.: 2834
N.A.I.C.S.: 325412

BILFINGER BERGER SE

(Name Changed to Bilfinger SE)

BILFINGER SE

(Formerly Bilfinger Berger SE)
Carl-Reiss-Platz 1-5
68165 Mannheim, Germany
Tel.: (49) 6214590
Telex: 418601-0 bb d
Fax: (49) 6214592366
E-Mail: info@bilfinger.de
Web Site: www.bilfinger.com
Year Founded: 1880
GBF—(DEU STU)
Rev.: $11,454,291,296
Assets: $9,221,129,883
Liabilities: $6,479,385,444
Net Worth: $2,741,744,439
Earnings: $370,062,133
Emp.: 66,826
Fiscal Year-end: 12/31/12
Business Description:
Civil, Commercial & Industrial Construction & Engineering Services
S.I.C.: 1629
N.A.I.C.S.: 237990
Personnel:
Bernhard Walter *(Chm-Supervisory Bd)*
Roland Koch *(Chm-Exec Bd)*
Stephan Bruckner *(Deputy Chm-Supervisory Bd)*
Joachim Enenkel *(Member-Exec Bd)*
Jochen Keysberg *(Member-Exec Bd)*
Pieter Koolen *(Member-Exec Bd)*
Joachim Muller *(Member-Exec Bd)*
Thomas Topfer *(Member-Exec Bd)*
Supervisory Board of Directors:
Bernhard Walter
Herbert Bodner
Volker Bohme
Stephan Bruckner
John Feldmann
Thomas Kern
Rainer Knerler
Lone Fonss Gjorup Schroder
Udo Stark
Holger Timmer
Jens Tischendorf
Marek Wrobel

Divisions:

Bilfinger Berger AG-Civil **(1)**
Gustav-Nachtigal-Strasse 3
D-65189 Wiesbaden, Germany (100%)
Tel.: (49) 61170800
Fax: (49) 611708499
Web Site: www.civil.bilfinger.com
Emp.: 500
Civil Engineering & Construction Services
S.I.C.: 1629
N.A.I.C.S.: 237990
Joachim Enenkel *(Chm & Sec)*
Axel Bock *(Member-Exec Bd)*
Matti Jaekel *(Sec)*
Jochen Keysberg *(Sec)*

Subsidiaries:

BBV Vorspanntechnik GmbH **(2)**
Industriestrasse 98
D-67240 Bobenheim-Roxheim, Germany De
Tel.: (49) 623999810 (100%)
Fax: (49) 6239998139
E-Mail: info@bbvsystems.com
Web Site: www.bbvsystems.com
Emp.: 100
Pre-Stressed Concrete Construction & Maintenance Contracting Services
S.I.C.: 1799
N.A.I.C.S.: 238990
Guido Mertens *(Chm & Mng Dir)*

Bilfinger Berger Instandsetzung GmbH **(2)**
Zielstattstrasse 19
81379 Munich, Germany De
Tel.: (49) 8972018870 (100%)
Fax: (49) 72018870
E-Mail: instandsetzung@civil.bilfinger.com
Web Site: www.instandsetzung.bilfinger.de
Emp.: 40
Civil Engineering Repair & Maintenance Services
S.I.C.: 1629
N.A.I.C.S.: 237990
Markus Held *(Mng Dir-Tech)*
Michael Reiss *(Mng Dir-Comml)*

F+Z Baugesellschaft mbH **(2)**
Kanalstrasse 44
D-22085 Hamburg, Germany De
Tel.: (49) 402272470 (100%)
Fax: (49) 40227247240
E-Mail: info@fz-bau.de
Web Site: www.fz-bau.de
Sales Range: $25-49.9 Million
Emp.: 218
Marine & Port Engineering Contractor
S.I.C.: 1799
N.A.I.C.S.: 238990
Frank Utes *(Mng Dir & Chm-Mgmt Bd)*
Kurt Bohme *(Mng Dir)*
H. Kahle *(Member-Mgmt Bd)*

Grund- und Pfahlbau GmbH **(2)**
Goldsteinstrasse 114
D-60528 Frankfurt am Main, Germany De
Tel.: (49) 696688215
Fax: (49) 696688277
E-Mail: marco.zettler@civil.bilfingerberger.com
Web Site: www.foundation-engineering.bilfingerberger.com
Emp.: 40
Foundation Contracting Services
S.I.C.: 1799
N.A.I.C.S.: 238190
Roland Wend *(Exec Mgr)*

Non-U.S. Subsidiaries:

Bilfinger Berger Construction, LLC **(2)**
Massionan Office 2 Bldg 129 4th St
PO Box 41967
Abu Dhabi, United Arab Emirates (100%)
Tel.: (971) 26324005
Fax: (971) 26324006
E-Mail: bbag_uae@bilfingerberger.ae
Web Site: www.bilfingerberger.com
Civil Engineering & Construction Services
S.I.C.: 1629
N.A.I.C.S.: 237990

Bilfinger Berger (Thai) Construction Co., Ltd. **(2)**
587 55 Sutthisarnvinijchai Rd 10th Fl
Viriyathavorn Bldg
Binbaeng District, Bangkok, 10400, Thailand TH
Tel.: (66) 26919449 (100%)
Fax: (66) 26919149
E-Mail: bilfinger@bbthai.com
Web Site: www.bilfinger-berger.com
Emp.: 70
Civil Engineering & Construction Services
S.I.C.: 1629
N.A.I.C.S.: 237990
Uwe Neidhardt *(Mng Dir)*

Bilfinger Berger UK Limited **(2)**
7400 Daresbury Park
Daresbury, Warrington, WA4 4BS, United Kingdom UK

Tel.: (44) 1928737500
Fax: (44) 1928737699
E-Mail: civil@bilfinger.co.uk
Web Site: www.civil.bilfinger.co.uk
Emp.: 200
Civil Engineering & Construction Services
S.I.C.: 1629
N.A.I.C.S.: 237990
Richard Walker *(Mng Dir)*

Companhia de Construcao e Engenharia Kin Sun (Macau), Limitada (2)
Nos 60-64 Avenida Infante D Henrique 5 Andar
Edf Centro Comercial Central, Macau, Kin Sun, China (Macau)
Tel.: (853) 28556281
Fax: (853) 28583325
E-Mail: kinsun@macau.ctm.net
Civil Engineering & Construction Services
S.I.C.: 1629
N.A.I.C.S.: 237990
Vong Kock Kei *(Gen Mgr)*

Bilfinger Berger AG-Hochbau (1)
Herriotstrasse 1
60528 Frankfurt, Germany (100%)
Tel.: (49) 69478910
Fax: (49) 6947891140
E-Mail: info@hochbau.bilfinger.de
Web Site: www.hochbau.bilfingerberger.de
Emp.: 1,800
Commercial Construction Services
S.I.C.: 1542
N.A.I.C.S.: 236220
Matthias Jacob *(Chm-Exec Bd)*
Dominik Fabry *(Member-Exec Bd)*
Frank Gaenz *(Member-Exec Bd)*
Shervin Haghsheno *(Member-Mgmt Bd)*
Frank Jainzen *(Member-Mgmt Bd)*
Gerd Simsch *(Member-Mgmt Bd)*

Subsidiaries:

bauperformance GmbH (2)
Goldsteinstrasse 114
D-60528 Frankfurt am Main, Germany De
Tel.: (49) 696688440 (100%)
Fax: (49) 696688199
E-Mail: bauperformance@bilfinger.de
Web Site: www.bauperformance.de
Commercial Building Design & Functionality Advisory Services
S.I.C.: 8999
N.A.I.C.S.: 541690
Sascha Prein *(Mng Dir)*

Bilfinger Berger Parking GmbH (2)
Herreiot Strasse 1
D-60528 Frankfurt, Germany De
Tel.: (49) 696688170 (100%)
Fax: (49) 6947891405
E-Mail: parking@bilfinger.de
Web Site: www.parking.bilfinger.de
Multilevel Parking Facility Construction Contracting Services
S.I.C.: 1799
N.A.I.C.S.: 238190

Modernbau GmbH (2)
Eschberger Weg 59
D-66121 Saarbrucken, Germany De
Tel.: (49) 68181990 (100%)
Fax: (49) 6818199145
E-Mail: info@modernbau.de
Web Site: www.modernbau.de
Emp.: 100
Civil Engineering & Commercial Construction Services
S.I.C.: 1629
N.A.I.C.S.: 237990
Stefan Klein *(Mng Dir)*

TESCH Industrie- und Rohrleitungsbau GmbH (2)
Schnabelstrasse 1
D-45134 Essen, Germany De
Tel.: (49) 2011707500 (100%)
Fax: (49) 2011707555
E-Mail: info@tesch-bau.de
Web Site: www.tesch-bau.de
Sales Range: $10-24.9 Million
Construction Finance Services
S.I.C.: 6726
N.A.I.C.S.: 525990
Gunter Gunia *(Mng Partner)*
Andre Homann *(Mng Partner)*

Bilfinger Berger Facility Services GmbH (1)
Carl-Reiss-Platz 1-5
D-68165 Mannheim, Germany De
Tel.: (49) 6214590 (100%)
Fax: (49) 6102453409
E-Mail: info@bbfs.bilfinger.de
Web Site: www.facilityservices.bilfinger.de
Emp.: 7,612
Holding Company; Facility Support & Property Management Services
S.I.C.: 6719
N.A.I.C.S.: 551112
Harald Heibel *(Mng Dir)*
Otto Kajetan Weixler *(Mng Dir)*

Subsidiaries:

EPM Assetis GmbH (2)
Berner Strasse 35
D-60437 Frankfurt am Main, Germany De
Tel.: (49) 6939001600
Fax: (49) 6939001695
E-Mail: info@epmassetis.de
Web Site: www.epmassetis.de
Emp.: 460
Portfolio Asset & Real Estate Management Services
S.I.C.: 6519
N.A.I.C.S.: 531190
Aydin Karaduman *(Mng Dir)*

Subsidiary:

EPM Asset Management GmbH (3)
Olof-Palme-Str 17
Frankfurt am Main, Hessen, 60439, Germany
Tel.: (49) 69450010710
Fax: (49) 69450010324
E-Mail: info@epmassetis.com
Emp.: 20
Property Management Services
S.I.C.: 6531
N.A.I.C.S.: 531312
Michael Hintze *(Co-Mng Dir)*
Iris Wolke-Haupt *(Co-Mng Dir)*

HSG Zander GmbH (2)
An der Gehespitz 50
D-63263 Neu-Isenburg, Germany De
Tel.: (49) 6102453400 (100%)
Fax: (49) 6102455001
E-Mail: info@hsgzander.com
Web Site: www.hsgzander.com
Sales Range: $1-4.9 Billion
Emp.: 12,000
Facility Support & Property Management Services
S.I.C.: 8744
N.A.I.C.S.: 561210
Otto Kajetan Weixler *(CEO)*
Jorn Ettenhofer *(Member-Mgmt Bd)*
Eckhart Morre *(Member-Mgmt Bd)*
Dieter Teichmann *(Member-Mgmt Bd)*

Non-U.S. Subsidiary:

HSG Zander Ireland Limited (3)
1 Exchange Place IFSC
Dublin, Ireland
Tel.: (353) 1 670 22 42
Fax: (353) 1 670 22 52
Web Site: www.hsgzander.com
Facility Management Services
S.I.C.: 8744
N.A.I.C.S.: 561210
Jeff Smith *(CEO)*

U.S. Subsidiary:

Centennial Contractors Enterprises, Inc. (2)
11111 Sunset Hills Rd Ste 350
Reston, VA 20190
Tel.: (703) 287-0000
Fax: (703) 885-4601
Toll Free: (877) 533-8057
Web Site: www.cce-inc.com
Sales Range: $25-49.9 Million
Emp.: 40
Commercial & Institutional Facility Support Contracting Services
S.I.C.: 8744
N.A.I.C.S.: 561210
Mark Bailey *(Pres & CEO)*

Non-U.S. Subsidiaries:

HSG Zander Danmark A/S (2)
Sydhavnsgade 17
DK-2450 Copenhagen, Denmark
Tel.: (45) 70 20 05 77
Fax: (45) 70 20 05 77
Web Site: www.hsgzander.dk
Facility Management Services
S.I.C.: 8744
N.A.I.C.S.: 561210
Peter J. Bang *(Mng Dir)*

HSG Zander (Schweiz) AG (2)
Alte Winterthurerstrasse 14b
8304 Wallisellen, Switzerland
Tel.: (41) 444 567 40 01
Fax: (41) 44 567 40 01
E-Mail: info@hsgzander.ch
Web Site: www.hsgzander.ch
Facility Management Services
S.I.C.: 8744
N.A.I.C.S.: 561210
Hans-Peter Bursa *(Mng Dir)*
Michael Rohner *(CFO)*
Markus Faber *(COO)*

Bilfinger Berger Industrial Services GmbH (1)
Gneisenaustrasse 15
D-80992 Munich, Germany De
Tel.: (49) 89149980 (100%)
Fax: (49) 891499150
E-Mail: ukomm@bis.bilfinger.com
Web Site: www.bis.bilfinger.com
Sales Range: $1-4.9 Billion
Emp.: 21,000
Industrial Facility & Equipment Maintenance, Repair & Modernization Services
S.I.C.: 1629
N.A.I.C.S.: 236210
Herbert Bodner *(Chm-Supervisory Bd)*
Thomas Topfer *(CEO & Chm-Exec Bd)*
Lothar Muller *(Deputy Chm-Supervisory Bd)*
Joachim Rodiger *(CFO)*
Rudolf K. Jurcke *(Member-Exec Bd-Intl Div, Northern & Eastern Europe Div)*
Peter Romanow *(Member-Exec Bd-Western Europe Div)*
Gerhard Schmidt *(Member-Exec Bd-Central Europe Div & Plant Tech Div)*
Andreas Frey *(Sec)*
Marcus Herrmann *(Exec VP-Norway/ Poland/Sweden/Czech Republic)*
Joachim Kreysing *(Exec VP-Central Europe Div)*
Harald Stohr *(Exec VP-Romania & Hungary)*

Subsidiaries:

BIS arnholdt GmbH (2)
Engelbertstrasse 23
45892 Gelsenkirchen, Germany De
Tel.: (49) 20997650
Fax: (49) 2099765156
E-Mail: info@arnholdt.de
Web Site: www.arnholdt.de
Emp.: 630
Scaffolding Construction Services
S.I.C.: 1799
N.A.I.C.S.: 238990
Klaus-Gunter Lemke *(Chm-Exec Bd)*
Winfried Hofmann *(Member-Exec Bd)*

BIS Heinrich Scheven GmbH (2)
Max-Planck-Strasse 77
D-40699 Erkrath, Germany De
Tel.: (49) 210449050 (80%)
Fax: (49) 2104490520
E-Mail: info@scheven-industries.de
Web Site: www.scheven-industries.de
Emp.: 200
Industrial Pipeline Construction Contracting Services
S.I.C.: 3494
N.A.I.C.S.: 332919
Raymond Paschen *(Controller)*

Peters Engineering AG (2)
Karl-Rader-Str 3-5
67069 Ludwigshafen, Germany
Tel.: (49) 621 6506 0
Fax: (49) 621 6506 245
E-Mail: info@pegmbh.com
Web Site: www.pegmbh.com
Construction Engineering Services
S.I.C.: 8711
N.A.I.C.S.: 541330
Bernd Bodeit *(Mng Dir)*
Roderich Hettmann *(Mng Dir)*
Erik Vogel *(Mng Dir)*

U.S. Subsidiaries:

BIS Frucon Industrial Services Inc. (2)
15933 Clayton Rd Ste 220
Ballwin, MO 63011-2146 (100%)
Tel.: (636) 391-4500
Telex: 447 631 frucon stl
Fax: (636) 391-4594
E-Mail: info@bisfrucon.com
Web Site: www.bisfrucon.com
Sales Range: $550-599.9 Million
Industrial Construction, Maintenance & Support Services
S.I.C.: 1541
N.A.I.C.S.: 236210
H. A. Donnelli *(Pres & CEO)*
Jeff L. Koop *(CFO & Sr VP)*

Non-U.S. Subsidiary:

Fru-Con Mexico S.A. de C.V. (3)
Bondojito No 340 Col Las Americas
Deleg Alvaro Obregon, C P 01120 Mexico, D F, Mexico
Tel.: (52) 5 277 8311
Fax: (52) 5 277 8554
S.I.C.: 7389
N.A.I.C.S.: 425120

Westcon, Inc. (2)
7401 Yukone Dr
Bismarck, ND 58503 ND
Mailing Address:
PO Box 1735
Bismarck, ND 58502
Tel.: (701) 222-0076
Fax: (701) 224-8178
Web Site: www.westconindustries.com
Sales Range: $150-199.9 Million
Emp.: 1,000
Construction Contracting Services Specializing in Industrial Buildings & Warehouses
S.I.C.: 1542
N.A.I.C.S.: 236220
Mark C. Peterson *(Founder & Pres)*

Non-U.S. Subsidiaries:

BIS Chemserv GmbH (2)
Saint-Peter-Strasse 25
A-4021 Linz, Austria AT
Tel.: (43) 73269170
Telex: 21324
Fax: (43) 732691762482
E-Mail: service@chemserv.at
Web Site: www.chemserv.at
Emp.: 540
Industrial Engineering, Maintenance & Repair Services
S.I.C.: 1799
N.A.I.C.S.: 238990
Gerald Pilotto *(Mng Dir)*

BIS Czech s.r.o. (2)
Jakuba Arbesa
c p 2600
434 01 Most, Czech Republic CZ
Tel.: (420) 476 206 602 (51%)
Fax: (420) 476 206 603
E-Mail: info@bisczech.cz
Web Site: www.bisczech.cz
Industrial Facility & Equipment Maintenance, Repair & Modernization Contracting Services
S.I.C.: 7699
N.A.I.C.S.: 811310
Martin Krbec *(CEO)*

BIS Engineering s.r.o. (2)
Weilova 2
CZ-102 05 Prague, 10, Czech Republic CZ
Tel.: (420) 274861249
Fax: (420) 274865751
E-Mail: info@bise.cz
Web Site: www.bise.cz
Emp.: 10
Energy Pipeline Engineering Services
S.I.C.: 8711
N.A.I.C.S.: 541330
Stanislav Libal *(Mng Dir)*

BIS Hungary Kft. (2)
Akna u 2-4
1106 Budapest, Hungary HU
Tel.: (36) 14333666 (96.63%)
Fax: (36) 14333660
E-Mail: hungary@bis.bilfinger.hu

Bilfinger SE—(Continued)

Web Site: www.bis.bilfinger.com
Emp.: 1,000
Industrial Facility & Equipment Maintenance, Repair & Other Specialty Contracting Services
S.I.C.: 7699
N.A.I.C.S.: 811310
Ferenc Aszman *(Mng Dir)*
Csaba Csiszar *(Mng Dir)*

BIS Industrial Services Limited (2)
Axis House Tudor Road Manor Park
Runcorn, Cheshire, WA7 1BD, United Kingdom
Tel.: (44) 1928 530000
Fax: (44) 1928 571800
E-Mail: enquiries@bis-is.co.uk
Web Site: www.bis-is.co.uk
Engineering Consulting Services
S.I.C.: 8711
N.A.I.C.S.: 541330
Duncan Peel *(Gen Mgr)*

BIS Industrial Services Sweden AB (2)
Frogatan 1
65343 Karlstad, Sweden SE
Tel.: (46) 54570970 (100%)
Fax: (46) 54570979
Web Site: www.bis.bilfinger.se
Emp.: 650
Holding Company; Industrial Equipment Maintenance & Facility Support Services
S.I.C.: 6719
N.A.I.C.S.: 551112
Kenneth Dahlbom *(Mng Dir)*

Subsidiaries:

BIS Industriteknik AB (3)
Utmarksvagen 21
SE-80291 Gavle, Sweden SE
Tel.: (46) 2612 5100
Fax: (46) 2612 3490
E-Mail: industriteknik@bis.bilfinger.se
Web Site: www.bis.bilfinger.se/company/industriteknik
Industrial Electronics & Instrumentation, Automation & Mechanical Engineering Consultancy Services
S.I.C.: 8999
N.A.I.C.S.: 541690
Stefan Hedqvist *(Mng Dir)*

BIS Isenta AB (3)
Frogatan 1
SE-65343 Karlstad, Sweden SE
Tel.: (46) 54570970 (100%)
Fax: (46) 5457 0979
E-Mail: isenta@bis.bilfinger.se
Industrial Facility Heat, Cold & Acoustical Insulation Contracting Services
S.I.C.: 1742
N.A.I.C.S.: 238310
Peter Kling *(Mng Dir)*

Division:

BIS Isenta Norr AB (4)
Angermanlandsg 28 A
Postboks 259
SE-89126 Ornskoldsvik, Sweden SE
Tel.: (46) 66010850
Fax: (46) 66085160
E-Mail: kent.westerlund@isenta.se
Web Site: www.bis.bilfinger.se
Emp.: 5
Industrial Facility Heat, Cold & Acoustical Insulation Contracting Services
S.I.C.: 1742
N.A.I.C.S.: 238310
Kent Westerlund *(Mng Dir)*

BIS Mixab AB (3)
Enekasvagen 4
SE-45155 Uddevalla, Sweden SE
Tel.: (46) 522261170 (90.08%)
Fax: (46) 52210444
E-Mail: peter.kling@isenta.se
Web Site: www.bis.bilfinger.se
Emp.: 160
Scaffolding Construction Services
S.I.C.: 1799
N.A.I.C.S.: 238990
Peter Kling *(Mng Dir & VP)*

BIS Nyhammar Vast AB (3)
Slattna Basteviksholmen 601
SE-45392 Lysekil, Sweden SE
Tel.: (46) 52315505
Fax: (46) 5231 5506
E-Mail: nyhammar@bis.bilfinger.se
Web Site: www.bis.bilfinger.se/company/nyhammar
Industrial Pipelines, Steel Structures, Heating & Process Equipment Contracting Services
S.I.C.: 1711
N.A.I.C.S.: 238220
Kjell-Ake Olsson *(Mng Dir)*

BIS Industrier AS (2)
Luramyrveien 51
NO-4313 Sandnes, Norway NO
Mailing Address: (88.82%)
Postboks 1134
NO-4391 Sandnes, Norway
Tel.: (47) 51637600
Fax: (47) 51637650
E-Mail: firmapost@bis-industrier.no
Web Site: www.bis-industrier.no
Industrial Contracting Services
S.I.C.: 1799
N.A.I.C.S.: 238990
Jens Christian Terjesen *(CEO)*

BIS Izomar Sp. z o.o. (2)
Ul Augustowka 24
PL-02 981 Warsaw, Poland PL
Tel.: (48) 226516083 (100%)
Fax: (48) 6226516082
E-Mail: sekretariat@izomar.com
Web Site: www.izomar.com
Emp.: 500
Industrial Heating & Insulation Contracting Services
S.I.C.: 8711
N.A.I.C.S.: 541330

BIS Nimb S.A. (2)
Platforma SNN-CNE Invest
Constanta County, 905200 Cernavoda, Romania RO
Tel.: (40) 241238488 (95.69%)
Fax: (40) 241238890
E-Mail: office@bisnimb.ro
Web Site: www.nimbconsmetal.ro
Emp.: 100
Steel Structure Erection Contracting & Industrial Equipment Maintenance & Installation Services
S.I.C.: 1791
N.A.I.C.S.: 238120
Bucur Vasile *(Gen Mgr)*

BIS plettac Sp. z o.o. (2)
ul Kosciuszki 19
63-500 Ostrzeszow, Poland PL
Tel.: (48) 625870100 (80%)
Fax: (48) 625861700
E-Mail: office@plettac.pl
Web Site: www.plettac.pl
Sales Range: $10-24.9 Million
Emp.: 500
Scaffolding Construction Services
S.I.C.: 1799
N.A.I.C.S.: 238990
Boleslaw Janik *(Pres)*

BIS VAM Anlagentechnik GmbH (2)
Dieselstrasse 2
A-4600 Wels, Austria AT
Tel.: (43) 72424060
Fax: (43) 7242406320
E-Mail: contact@vam.at
Web Site: www.vam.at
Emp.: 900
Industrial Plant, Pipework & Vessel Engineering & Construction Services
S.I.C.: 1629
N.A.I.C.S.: 236210
August Oberndorfer *(Chm-Mgmt Bd)*
Josef Koblinger *(Member-Mgmt Bd)*
Walter Roithmair *(Member-Mgmt Bd)*

MCE Stahl- und Maschinenbau GmbH & Co. KG (2)
Lunzerstrasse 64
A-4031 Linz, Austria De
Tel.: (43) 73269875843 (100%)
Fax: (43) 73269808162
E-Mail: office@mce-smb.at
Web Site: www.mce-smb.at
Complex Steel Structure Design, Assembly & Erection Services
S.I.C.: 1799
N.A.I.C.S.: 238190
Dieter Reitz *(Mng Dir)*
Gerald Hippesroither *(Member-Mgmt Bd)*

Tebodin B.V. (2)
Laan Van Nieuw Oost Indie 25
PO Box 16029
2500 BA Hague, Netherlands (100%)
Mailing Address:
PO Box 16029
2500 BA Hague, Netherlands
Tel.: (31) 703480911
Telex: 31580 tebodin nl
Fax: (31) 703480645
E-Mail: info@tebodin.com
Web Site: www.tebodin.com
Sales Range: $200-249.9 Million
Emp.: 3,200
Engineering & Consulting Services
S.I.C.: 8711
N.A.I.C.S.: 541330
Pieter Koolen *(Chm-Mgmt Bd)*
Petr Bilek *(Member-Mgmt Bd)*
Jack Overkamp *(Member-Mgmt Bd)*
Ton van der Velden *(Member-Mgmt Bd)*

Bilfinger Power Systems GmbH (1)
(Formerly Bilfinger Berger Power Services GmbH)
Europaallee 1
D-46047 Oberhausen, Germany De
Tel.: (49) 20845759 (100%)
Fax: (49) 20824561
E-Mail: info@bilfingerbergerpowerservices.de
Web Site: www.powerservices.bilfinger.de
Sales Range: $1-4.9 Billion
Emp.: 4,000
Holding Company; Power Station & Industrial Plant Technology & Engineering Services
S.I.C.: 6719
N.A.I.C.S.: 551112
Gerd Lesser *(CEO & Chm-Exec Bd)*
Alexander Neubauer *(Mng Dir)*
Klaus J. Schmitz *(Mng Dir)*
Thomas Suckut *(Mng Dir)*

Subsidiaries:

Babcock Borsig Service GmbH (2)
Duisburger Strasse 375
D-46049 Oberhausen, Germany
Tel.: (49) 20845759
E-Mail: service@babcock-service.de
Web Site: www.babcock-borsig-service.de
Emp.: 2,946
Power Station & Industrial Plant Technology & Engineering Services
S.I.C.: 8744
N.A.I.C.S.: 561210
Gerd Lesser *(Mng Dir & Chm-Exec Bd)*
Andreas Michalke *(Mng Dir)*
Alexander Neubauer *(Mng Dir)*

BHR Hochdruck-Rohrleitungsbau GmbH (2)
Wolbeckstrasse 25
D-45329 Essen, Germany De
Tel.: (49) 20136450
Fax: (49) 2013645111
E-Mail: info@bhr.bilfinger.de
Web Site: www.bhr.bilfinger.de
Emp.: 950
Industrial Pipe Mfr & Installation Services
S.I.C.: 3498
N.A.I.C.S.: 332996
Ronald Diehl *(Chm-Mgmt Bd & CEO)*
Jurgen Weyers *(Mng Dir & CFO)*
Mario Peper *(Mng Dir)*
Gunter Rychlik *(Mng Dir)*

Non-U.S. Subsidiary:

BHR Piping Systems (Pty) Ltd. (3)
Block D Homestead Park 37 Homestead Road
Rivonia, 2191, South Africa
Tel.: (27) 11 806 3911
Fax: (27) 11 806 3203
E-Mail: info@bhr-p.bilfinger.com
Web Site: www.bhr-p.bilfinger.com
Emp.: 130
Construction Piping System Mfr
S.I.C.: 3317
N.A.I.C.S.: 331210
Heinz Ott *(Mng Dir)*

Non-U.S. Subsidiaries:

Babcock Borsig Steinmuller CZ s.r.o. (2)
Krizikova 72
Brno, 612 00, Czech Republic
Tel.: (420) 5 4510 4040
Fax: (420) 5 4510 4198
Electrical Equipment Mfr
S.I.C.: 3699
N.A.I.C.S.: 335999

Steinmuller Africa (pty) Ltd. (2)
37 Homestead Road Block D Homestead Park
PO Box 1537
Rivonia, 2128 Johannesburg, South Africa
Tel.: (27) 11 806 3000
Fax: (27) 11 806 3330
E-Mail: info@steinmuller.bilfinger.com
Web Site: www.steinmuller.bilfinger.com
Electric Power Generation Services
S.I.C.: 4939
N.A.I.C.S.: 221118
Juergen Koerner *(Mng Dir)*

Subsidiaries:

Abbakus GmbH & Co. KG (1)
Einsteinstrasse 30
85520 Ottobrunn, Munich, Germany
Tel.: (49) 89 44 49 17604
E-Mail: info@abbakus.net
Web Site: www.abbakus.net
Business Management Consulting Services
S.I.C.: 8748
N.A.I.C.S.: 541618
Armin Pilger *(Mgr)*

Achatz Service GmbH (1)
Bergiusstr 19-21
Mannheim, Baden-Wurttemberg, 68219, Germany
Tel.: (49) 621898040
Construction Engineering Services
S.I.C.: 8711
N.A.I.C.S.: 541330

ahr careclean GmbH (1)
Hagelkreuzstrasse 101
46149 Oberhausen, Germany
Tel.: (49) 208 65900
Fax: (49) 208 654314
Building Cleaning Services
S.I.C.: 7349
N.A.I.C.S.: 561720

ahr catering GmbH (1)
Hagelkreuzstrasse 101
46149 Oberhausen, Germany
Tel.: (49) 208 65900
Fax: (49) 208 654314
Catering Services
S.I.C.: 5812
N.A.I.C.S.: 722320

ahr Service GmbH (1)
Hagelkreuzstrasse 101
46149 Oberhausen, Germany
Tel.: (49) 208 65 90 0
Fax: (49) 208 65 43 14
E-Mail: info@ahr-service.com
Web Site: www.ahr-service.ahr-gruppe.com
Facility Management Services
S.I.C.: 8744
N.A.I.C.S.: 561210
Martin Burger *(Mng Dir)*

ahr servita GmbH (1)
Hagelkreuzstrasse 101
46149 Oberhausen, Nordrhein-Westfalen, Germany
Tel.: (49) 208 65900
Fax: (49) 208 654314
Transportation Services
S.I.C.: 4789
N.A.I.C.S.: 488999

ALPHA Mess-Steuer-Regeltechnik GmbH (1)
Dr Julius-Leber-Strasse 12
Neustadt, 67433, Germany
Tel.: (49) 63 21 40 05 0
Fax: (49) 63 21 40 05 55
Software Development Services
S.I.C.: 7371
N.A.I.C.S.: 541511

Babcock Borsig Service GmbH (1)
Duisburger Strasse 375
D 46049 Oberhausen, Germany
Tel.: (49) 20845759
Telex: 8 56 951 dbab d
Fax: (49) 20824561
E-Mail: service@bbs.bilfinger.de
Web Site: www.babcock-borsig-service.de

Holding Company
S.I.C.: 6719
N.A.I.C.S.: 551112
Gerd Lesser *(Mng Dir)*
Andreas Michalke *(Mng Dir)*
Alexander Neubauer *(Mng Dir)*

Subsidiaries:

STS Steinmuller Siemers GmbH Serviceleistungen **(2)**
Ermlandstr 55
28777 Bremen, Germany
Tel.: (49) 4216006062
Fax: (49) 4216006064
Emp.: 150
Building Equipment Installation Services
S.I.C.: 1799
N.A.I.C.S.: 238290
Heiko Siemers *(Mng Dir)*

Babcock Borsig Steinmuller GmbH **(1)**
Duisburger Strasse 375
46049 Oberhausen, Germany
Tel.: (49) 208 4575 9
Fax: (49) 208 24561
E-Mail: info@bbs.bilfinger.com
Web Site: www.bbs.bilfinger.com
Rev.: $330,347,500
Emp.: 1,000
Power Plant Engineering Services
S.I.C.: 8711
N.A.I.C.S.: 541330
Georg Gasteiger *(CEO)*
Bernhard Kothgasser *(Mng Dir)*
Andreas Michalke *(Mng Dir)*
Manfred Roesner *(Mng Dir)*

Subsidiary:

Babcock Kraftwerkservice GmbH **(2)**
Teichlandstrasse 1
Peitz, Brandenburg, 03185, Germany
Tel.: (49) 1942 868900
Fax: (49) 3560183300
Electric Power Generation Services
S.I.C.: 4911
N.A.I.C.S.: 221118
Thomas Keppler *(CEO)*
Andreas Michalke, *(Mng Dir)*

Babcock Rohrleitungsbau GmbH **(1)**
Edisonstr 20
24145 Kiel, Schleswig-Holstein, Germany
Tel.: (49) 431 687499
Fax: (49) 431 683021
Construction Engineering Services
S.I.C.: 8711
N.A.I.C.S.: 541330

BAR Industrieservice GmbH **(1)**
Kuferstr 5
25541 Brunsbuttel, Germany
Tel.: (49) 4852 54050
Fax: (49) 4852 540520
Air-Conditioning & Heating Equipment Mfr
S.I.C.: 3585
N.A.I.C.S.: 333415

Bau-Union Potsdam GmbH **(1)**
Walter-Kohn-Str 4A
04356 Leipzig, Germany
Tel.: (49) 341 35130
Fax: (49) 341 3513550
Construction Engineering Services
S.I.C.: 8711
N.A.I.C.S.: 541330

BB Gamma PPP-Projektgesellschaft mbH **(1)**
Herriotstr 1
60528 Frankfurt, Hessen, Germany
Tel.: (49) 69 47891 0
Fax: (49) 69 47891140
Financial Management Services
S.I.C.: 6211
N.A.I.C.S.: 523999

BB Grundbesitz GmbH **(1)**
Ludwig-Erhard-Str 30
28197 Bremen, Germany
Tel.: (49) 421549940
Fax: (49) 4215499460
Investment Management Services
S.I.C.: 6282
N.A.I.C.S.: 523920

BB Infrastructure Services GmbH **(1)**
Diffenestr 14
68169 Mannheim, Germany
Tel.: (49) 621 70014 355
Fax: (49) 621 70014 360
E-Mail: BBIS-Office@civil.bilfinger.com
Construction Engineering Services
S.I.C.: 8711
N.A.I.C.S.: 541330

BBFS Alpha Verwaltungs GmbH **(1)**
Carl-ReiB-Platz 1-5
Mannheim, 68165, Germany
Tel.: (49) 6214590
Investment Management Services
S.I.C.: 6282
N.A.I.C.S.: 523920

BBS Schalungsbau GmbH **(1)**
Industriestrasse 21
67240 Bobenheim-Roxheim, Germany
Tel.: (49) 6239 9982 0
Fax: (49) 623 9982 30
E-Mail: info@schalungsbau-gmbh.de
Construction Engineering Services
S.I.C.: 8711
N.A.I.C.S.: 541330

BBV Systems GmbH **(1)**
Industriestrasse 98
67240 Bobenheim-Roxheim, Germany
Tel.: (49) 6239 9981 0
Fax: (49) 6239 9981 39
E-Mail: info@bbv-systems.com
Web Site: www.vorspanntechnik.bilfinger.de
Engineering Consulting Services
S.I.C.: 8711
N.A.I.C.S.: 541330
Guido Mertens *(Chm-Exec Bd)*
Kaufmann Herwig Pfister *(Member-Exec Bd)*

bebit Informationstechnik GmbH **(1)**
Dynamostrasse 17
D-68165 Mannheim, Germany De
Tel.: (49) 62140010 (100%)
Fax: (49) 62140012501
E-Mail: info@bebit.de
Web Site: www.bebit.de
Sales Range: $25-49.9 Million
Emp.: 140
Enterprise Solutions, Human Resource & Information Technology Support Services
S.I.C.: 7389
N.A.I.C.S.: 561499
Wilfried Hubl *(Mng Dir-Projects & Sys Solutions)*
Christian Thum *(Mng Dir-Sls & Mktg)*

BfP Beteiligungsgesellschaft fur Projekte mbH **(1)**
Volklinger Strasse 4
40219 Dusseldorf, Germany
Tel.: (49) 211 90101 03
Investment Management Services
S.I.C.: 6282
N.A.I.C.S.: 523920

Bilfinger Berger A1 mobil GmbH **(1)**
Gustav-Stresemann-Ring 1
65189 Wiesbaden, Germany
Tel.: (49) 611 33480 0
Investment Management Services
S.I.C.: 6799
N.A.I.C.S.: 523920

Bilfinger Berger Entsorgung GmbH **(1)**
Passavant-Geiger-Str 1
Aarbergen, Hessen, 65326, Germany
Tel.: (49) 612 0280
Fax: (49) 61 202 82 119
Environmental Consulting Services
S.I.C.: 8999
N.A.I.C.S.: 541620

Bilfinger Berger Government Services GmbH **(1)**
Flickerstal 5
67657 Kaiserslautern, Germany
Tel.: (49) 631 3432 0
Fax: (49) 631 3432 328
E-Mail: contact@bbgs.bilfinger.com
Web Site: www.bilfinger.com
Construction Engineering Services
S.I.C.: 8711
N.A.I.C.S.: 541330
Dirk Schubert *(Chm-Exec Bd)*
Michael Bayer *(Member-Exec Bd)*
Martin Pierenkaemper *(Member-Exec Bd)*

Bilfinger Berger Government Services Holding GmbH **(1)**
Carl-Reiss-Platz 1-5
68165 Mannheim, Baden-Wurttemberg, Germany
Tel.: (49) 621 459 0
Fax: (49) 621 4592366
Investment Management Services
S.I.C.: 6211
N.A.I.C.S.: 523999

Bilfinger Berger Ingenieurbau GmbH **(1)**
Am Rohrenwerk 50
47259 Duisburg, Germany
Tel.: (49) 203 7586 341
Construction Engineering Services
S.I.C.: 8711
N.A.I.C.S.: 541330

Bilfinger Berger PI Corporate Services GmbH **(1)**
Gustav-Stresemann-Ring 1
Wiesbaden, Hessen, 65189, Germany
Tel.: (49) 611 33480 0
Fax: (49) 611 33480 299
Construction Engineering Services
S.I.C.: 8711
N.A.I.C.S.: 541330

Bilfinger Berger PI International Holding GmbH **(1)**
Gustav-Stresemann-Ring 1
65189 Wiesbaden, Germany
Tel.: (49) 611 334800
Investment Management Services
S.I.C.: 6211
N.A.I.C.S.: 523999
Dirk Soehngen *(Gen Mgr)*

Bilfinger Berger Real Estate GmbH & Co. KG **(1)**
Dynamostr 13
68165 Mannheim, Baden-Wurttemberg, Germany
Tel.: (49) 62140040820
Fax: (49) 62140040844
Real Estate Management Services
S.I.C.: 6531
N.A.I.C.S.: 531390

Bilfinger Berger Regiobau GmbH **(1)**
Hans-Bunte-Str 12
79108 Freiburg, Germany
Tel.: (49) 761 51049 0
Fax: (49) 761 51049 40
Web Site: www.regiobau.bilfinger.com
Construction Engineering Services
S.I.C.: 8711
N.A.I.C.S.: 541330

Bilfinger Berger Spezialtiefbau GmbH **(1)**
Goldsteinstrasse 114
60528 Frankfurt am Main, Germany
Tel.: (49) 69 6688 345
Fax: (49) 69 6688 277
Web Site: www.spezialtiefbau.bilfinger.com
Construction Engineering Services
S.I.C.: 8711
N.A.I.C.S.: 541330

Bilfinger Berger Umwelttechnik GmbH **(1)**
Passavant-Roediger-Strasse 1
D-65326 Aarbergen, Germany De
Tel.: (49) 6120280 (100%)
Fax: (49) 6120282119
E-Mail: info@passavant-roediger.de
Web Site: www.passavant-roediger.de
Sales Range: $300-349.9 Million
Emp.: 368
Holding Company; Water & Waste Management Facility Construction & Engineering Services
S.I.C.: 6719
N.A.I.C.S.: 551112
Joachim Foerderer *(Chm-Exec Bd)*

Subsidiary:

Passavant-Geiger GmbH **(2)**
Passavant-Geiger-Strasse 1
D-65326 Aarbergen, Germany De
Tel.: (49) 6120282828
Fax: (49) 6120282119
E-Mail: info@passavant-geiger.de
Web Site: www.passavant-geiger.de
Emp.: 400
Water & Sewage Treatment Plant Construction & Engineering Services
S.I.C.: 1623
N.A.I.C.S.: 237110
Joachim Foerderer *(Mng Dir)*

Subsidiary:

Roediger Vacuum GmbH **(3)**
Kinzigheimer Weg 104-106
63450 Hanau, Germany
Tel.: (49) 6181 309 274
Fax: (49) 6181 309 277
E-Mail: export@roevac.com
Web Site: www.roevac.de
Emp.: 100
Vacuum Sewer System Installation Services
S.I.C.: 1629
N.A.I.C.S.: 237110
Mark Stegmayer *(Co-Mng Dir)*
Volker Zang *(Co-Mng Dir)*

Non-U.S. Subsidiary:

DIEMME FILTRATION S.R.L. **(3)**
Via Gessi n 16
48022 Lugo, Ravenna, Italy
Tel.: (39) 054520611
Fax: (39) 054533002
E-Mail: info@diemmefiltration.com
Web Site: www.diemmefiltration.com
Filter Press Mfr
S.I.C.: 3559
N.A.I.C.S.: 333249

Bilfinger Rotring Engineering GmbH **(1)**
Rudolf-Diesel-Str 2c
21614 Buxtehude, Germany
Tel.: (49) 4161 7409 0
Fax: (49) 4161 7409 94
E-Mail: info.rotring@bilfinger.com
Web Site: www.rotring.bilfinger.com
Emp.: 40
Fuel Gas System Installation Services
S.I.C.: 1711
N.A.I.C.S.: 238220
Sven Dohse *(CEO)*
Andreas Hilpert *(CFO)*

BIS E.M.S. GmbH **(1)**
Hohe Tannen 11
49661 Cloppenburg, Germany
Tel.: (49) 4471 182 0
Fax: (49) 4471 182 128
E-Mail: info@ems-clp.de
Web Site: www.ems-clp.de
Construction Engineering Services
S.I.C.: 8711
N.A.I.C.S.: 541330

BIS EnTech GmbH **(1)**
Gneisenaustr 15
Munich, Bavaria, 80992, Germany
Tel.: (49) 20997650
Fax: (49) 8914998150
Construction Engineering Services
S.I.C.: 8711
N.A.I.C.S.: 541330

BIS Geratetechnik Deutschland GmbH **(1)**
Halleschestrasse 18
06749 Bitterfeld, Germany
Tel.: (49) 3493 6099 521
Fax: (49) 3493 6099 540
E-Mail: bitterfeld@geraete.com
Web Site: www.gtd.bis.bilfinger.com
Construction Equipment Rental Services
S.I.C.: 7353
N.A.I.C.S.: 532412
Lutz Zschoch *(Mng Dir)*

BIS Gerber GmbH **(1)**
Revierstr 3
44379 Dortmund, Germany
Tel.: (49) 231 9952 0
Fax: (49) 231 9952 111
E-Mail: info@bis-gerber.com
Web Site: www.gerber.bilfinger.com
Noise Control & Air Intake System Mfr
S.I.C.: 3829
N.A.I.C.S.: 334519
Thomas Meyer *(Gen Mgr)*

BIS IKF GmbH **(1)**
Meessen 9
22113 Oststeinbek, Germany
Tel.: (49) 40 713902 0
Fax: (49) 40 7128427

Bilfinger SE—(Continued)

E-Mail: IKF@BIS.bilfinger.com
Web Site: www.ikf.bis.bilfinger.com
Construction Engineering Services
S.I.C.: 8711
N.A.I.C.S.: 541330

BIS Isoliertechnik Nord GmbH (1)
Am Haupttor Bau 3030
06237 Leuna, Germany
Tel.: (49) 34 61 43 24 95
Fax: (49) 34 61 43 24 12
E-Mail: isonord@BIS.bilfinger.com
Web Site: www.itn.bis.bilfinger.com
Engineering Consulting Services
S.I.C.: 8711
N.A.I.C.S.: 541330
G. Pilotto *(Exec VP)*

BIS Maintenance Nord GmbH (1)
In den Leuna-Werken Gebaude 8642
06237 Leuna, Germany
Tel.: (49) 3461 43 2991
Fax: (49) 3461 43 2701
E-Mail: Mainnord@BIS.bilfinger.com
Web Site: www.mn.bis.bilfinger.com
Construction Engineering Services
S.I.C.: 8711
N.A.I.C.S.: 541330

BIS Maintenance Sudwest GmbH (1)
An der Bundesstr 3
69181 Leimen, Germany
Tel.: (49) 6224 701 701
Fax: (49) 6224 701 700
E-Mail: maintenance@BIS.bilfinger.com
Web Site: www.msw.bis.bilfinger.com
Industrial Plant Construction Services
S.I.C.: 1541
N.A.I.C.S.: 236210

BIS Prozesstechnik GmbH (1)
Industriepark Hochst Geb C619
65926 Frankfurt am Main, Germany
Tel.: (49) 69 3 05 1 37 34
Fax: (49) 69 3 05 8 17 74
E-Mail: pte@BIS.bilfinger.com
Web Site: www.pte.bis.bilfinger.com
Technical Consulting Services
S.I.C.: 8999
N.A.I.C.S.: 541690

BIS Rohrbau Grenzach GmbH (1)
Gewerbestr 5
79639 Grenzach-Wyhlen, Germany
Tel.: (49) 7624 9165 0
Fax: (49) 7624 9165 21
Pipeline Construction Engineering Services
S.I.C.: 1623
N.A.I.C.S.: 237120

BIS Rohrleitungsbau GmbH (1)
Hallesche Strasse 18
06749 Bitterfeld, Germany
Tel.: (49) 3493 6099 0
Fax: (49) 3493 6099 411
E-Mail: BIS-Rohrleitungsbau@BIS.bilfinger.com
Web Site: www.bis-rohrleitungsbau.de
Emp.: 400
Pipeline Construction Engineering Services
S.I.C.: 1623
N.A.I.C.S.: 237120
Lutz Zschoch *(Gen Mgr)*

BIS TSG Industrieservice GmbH (1)
Ludwig-Hermann-Strasse 100
86368 Gersthofen, Germany
Tel.: (49) 821 4792500
Fax: (49) 821 4792600
Industrial Machinery Repair & Maintenance Services
S.I.C.: 7699
N.A.I.C.S.: 811310

CEC Construction Engineering + Contracting GmbH (1)
Gustav-Nachtigal-Str 5
Wiesbaden, Hessen, 65189, Germany
Tel.: (49) 611708587
Fax: (49) 611708795
Construction Engineering Services
S.I.C.: 8711
N.A.I.C.S.: 541330

Djuro Djakovic Montage GmbH (1)
Max-Planck-Ring 13
46049 Oberhausen, Germany
Tel.: (49) 208 85 79 70
Fax: (49) 208 85 79 777
E-Mail: buero@ddm.bilfinger.com
Web Site: www.ddm.bilfinger.com
Construction Engineering Services
S.I.C.: 1629
N.A.I.C.S.: 237990

EPM Gewerbe & Logistik GmbH (1)
Hildebrandtstrasse 24C
40215 Dusseldorf, Germany
Tel.: (49) 21130131380
Fax: (49) 211301313890
Logistics Consulting Services
S.I.C.: 4731
N.A.I.C.S.: 541614

EPM InServ GmbH (1)
Aarstrasse 1
Wiesbaden, 65195, Germany
Tel.: (49) 89 5409 5498
Fax: (49) 221 1615 22198
Real Estate Development Services
S.I.C.: 6531
N.A.I.C.S.: 531390

Euro Property Management EPM GmbH (1)
Olof-Palme-Strasse 17
60439 Frankfurt am Main, Germany
Tel.: (49) 211 87 632 206
Fax: (49) 211 87 632 42 06
Web Site: www.epmassetis-vermietung.de/index.php/ger/kontakt/mitte/EuroProperty
Real Estate Advisory Services
S.I.C.: 6531
N.A.I.C.S.: 531390

F + Z Baugesellschaft mbH (1)
Kanalstrasse 44
22085 Hamburg, Germany
Tel.: (49) 40 22 72 47 0
Fax: (49) 40 22 72 47 240
E-Mail: KIWB@civil.bilfinger.com
Web Site: www.fz-bau.de
Construction Engineering Services
S.I.C.: 8711
N.A.I.C.S.: 541330

Fondsmanagement Berlin GmbH (1)
Friedrichstr 194-199
10117 Berlin, Germany
Tel.: (49) 30 22663076
Fax: (49) 30 22663089
Fund Management Services
S.I.C.: 6282
N.A.I.C.S.: 523920

Fondsmanagement Dusseldorf GmbH (1)
Moskauer Strasse 27
40227 Dusseldorf, Nordrhein-Westfalen, Germany
Tel.: (49) 211 38059661
Fax: (49) 211 380594661
Investment Management Services
S.I.C.: 6211
N.A.I.C.S.: 523999

Franz Kassecker GmbH (1)
Egererstrasse 36
95652 Waldsassen, Germany De (60%)
Tel.: (49) 96325010
Fax: (49) 9632501290
E-Mail: info@kassecker.de
Web Site: www.kassecker.de
Sales Range: $100-124.9 Million
Emp.: 500
Commercial, Industrial, & Civil Engineering & Construction Contracting Services
S.I.C.: 1541
N.A.I.C.S.: 237990
Kurt Luddecke *(Vice Chm-Supervisory Bd)*
Walter Arnold *(Mng Dir)*
Bernd Furbringer *(Dir-Comml)*

Friedrich Eisen-GmbH (1)
August-Borsig-Strasse 4
68199 Mannheim, Germany
Tel.: (49) 6 21 85 30 51
Fax: (49) 6 21 85 30 53
Pipeline Repair & Maintenance Services
S.I.C.: 7699
N.A.I.C.S.: 811310

Hochbau Halle-Seeben GmbH (1)
Walter-Kohn-Str 4a
Leipzig, 04356, Germany
Tel.: (49) 341 35130
Construction Engineering Services
S.I.C.: 8711
N.A.I.C.S.: 541330

HSG Zander City Light & Services GmbH (1)
Hauptstrasse 2-6
93096 Kofering, Germany
Tel.: (49) 94 06 37 70
Fax: (49) 94 06 16 90
E-Mail: citylight@hsgzander.com
Web Site: www.hsgzander.com
Street Light Installation Services
S.I.C.: 1731
N.A.I.C.S.: 238210

HSG Zander culinaress GmbH (1)
Einsteinstrasse 30
85521 Ottobrunn, Germany
Tel.: (49) 89 44 49 27968
Fax: (49) 89 44 49 22253
E-Mail: info@hsgzander-culinaress.com
Web Site: www.hsgzander-culinaress.ahr-gruppe.com
Catering Services
S.I.C.: 5812
N.A.I.C.S.: 722320
Michael Heller *(Mgr)*

HSG Zander Event Services GmbH (1)
Admiral-Rosendahl-Strasse 1
63263 Neu-Isenburg, Germany
Tel.: (49) 69 69 76 47 200
Fax: (49) 69 69 76 47 299
E-Mail: eventservices@hsgzander.com
Web Site: www.hsgzander-eventservices.com
Emp.: 20
Event Management Services
S.I.C.: 7999
N.A.I.C.S.: 711310
Jens Stoeber *(CEO)*

HSG Zander FS GmbH (1)
An Der Gehespitz 50
63263 Neu-Isenburg, Hessen, Germany
Tel.: (49) 6102453400
Fax: (49) 6102453499
Facility Management Services
S.I.C.: 8744
N.A.I.C.S.: 561210

HSG Zander Nord GmbH (1)
Am Neumarkt 30
22041 Hamburg, Germany
Tel.: (49) 40 300 602 30
Fax: (49) 40 300 603 32
E-Mail: Hamburg@hsgzander.com
Web Site: www.hsgzander.com
Real Estate Development Services
S.I.C.: 6531
N.A.I.C.S.: 531390
Hans-Peter Gross *(Gen Mgr)*

HSG Zander Nordost GmbH (1)
Oberlandstrasse 88
12099 Berlin, Germany
Tel.: (49) 30 300 91 8 0
Fax: (49) 30 300 91 8 69
Facility Management Services
S.I.C.: 8744
N.A.I.C.S.: 561210
Frank Lindner, *(Mgr)*

HSG Zander Ost GmbH (1)
Zum Frischemarkt 2 a
04158 Leipzig, Germany
Tel.: (49) 341 521 13 0
Fax: (49) 341 521 13 50
E-Mail: Leipzig@hsgzander.com
Web Site: www.hsgzander.com
Facility Management Services
S.I.C.: 8744
N.A.I.C.S.: 561210
Oliver Gaber *(Mgr)*

HSG Zander Rhein-Main GmbH (1)
Admiral-Rosendahl-Strasse 1
63263 Neu-Isenburg, Germany
Tel.: (49) 69 69 76 47 100
Fax: (49) 69 69 76 47 199
E-Mail: Frankfurt@hsgzander.com
Facility Management Services
S.I.C.: 8744
N.A.I.C.S.: 561210
Peter Panzof, *(Mgr)*

HSG Zander Security & Services GmbH (1)
Admiral-Rosendahl-Strasse 1
Zeppelinheim, 63263 Neu-Isenburg, Germany
Tel.: (49) 69 697 647 400
Fax: (49) 69 697 647 499
Web Site: www.hsgzander.com
Security System Installation Services
S.I.C.: 1731
N.A.I.C.S.: 238210
Klaus-Rolf Vogt *(Gen Mgr)*

HSG Zander Sudost GmbH (1)
Nordring 69
90409 Nuremberg, Germany
Tel.: (49) 911 360 8 0
Fax: (49) 911 360 8 31 19
E-Mail: Nuernberg@hsgzander.com
Web Site: www.hsgzander.com
Facility Management Services
S.I.C.: 8744
N.A.I.C.S.: 561210
Juergen Wohlrab *(Gen Mgr)*

HSG Zander Wurttemberg GmbH (1)
Motorstrasse 51
70499 Stuttgart, Germany
Tel.: (49) 711 88 04 29 32
Facility Management Services
S.I.C.: 8744
N.A.I.C.S.: 561210
Markus Hohn, *(Mgr)*

Huser & Co GmbH (1)
Carl-Reiss-Platz 1-5
68165 Mannheim, Baden-Wurttemberg, Germany
Tel.: (49) 621 4590
Real Estate Management Services
S.I.C.: 6531
N.A.I.C.S.: 531390

J. Wolfferts Holding GmbH (1)
Hansestrasse 1
51149 Cologne, Germany
Tel.: (49) 2203 3002 0
Fax: (49) 2203 3002 175
E-Mail: info@wolfferts.de
Web Site: www.wolfferts-gruppe.de/de/index.php?id=93&L=0
Emp.: 150
Plumbing & Heating Equipment Installation Services
S.I.C.: 1711
N.A.I.C.S.: 238220

Subsidiary:

J. Wolfferts GmbH (2)
Mallwitzstrasse 14a
53177 Bonn, Germany
Tel.: (49) 228 95708 0
Fax: (49) 228 95708 50
E-Mail: bonn@wolfferts.de
Web Site: www.wolfferts.de
Construction Engineering Services
S.I.C.: 1629
N.A.I.C.S.: 237990
Rene Reissig *(Gen Mgr)*

MCE Aschersleben GmbH (1)
Gustener Str 18
Aschersleben, Sachsen-Anhalt, 06449, Germany
Tel.: (49) 34738870
Fax: (49) 3473914636
Construction Machinery Mfr
S.I.C.: 3531
N.A.I.C.S.: 333120

MCE Berlin GmbH (1)
Landsberger Allee 366
12681 Berlin, Germany
Tel.: (49) 30 54954 200
Fax: (49) 30 54954 100
E-Mail: info@mce-b.bilfinger.com
Web Site: www.mce-b.bilfinger.com
Power Plant Construction Services
S.I.C.: 1623
N.A.I.C.S.: 237130
Gunter Lange *(Gen Mgr)*

MCE Industrieservice Deutschland GmbH (1)
Am Haupttor 8642
06237 Leuna, Germany
Tel.: (49) 3461 432991
Fax: (49) 3461 432701
Construction Engineering Services
S.I.C.: 8711
N.A.I.C.S.: 541330

PJB Beteiligungs-GmbH (1)
Gustav-Stresemann-Ring 1
65189 Wiesbaden, Germany

Tel.: (49) 611 33480 0
Fax: (49) 611 33480 299
Construction Engineering Services
S.I.C.: 8711
N.A.I.C.S.: 541330

PJB Management-GmbH (1)
Gustav-Stresemann-Ring 1
65189 Wiesbaden, Germany
Tel.: (49) 611 33480 0
Fax: (49) 611 33480 299
Real Estate Management Services
S.I.C.: 6531
N.A.I.C.S.: 531390

PPP Schloss Sonnenstein GmbH (1)
Herriotstrasse 1
60528 Frankfurt am Main, Germany
Tel.: (49) 69 47891 0
Property Development Services
S.I.C.: 6531
N.A.I.C.S.: 531312

PPP Schulen Halle GmbH (1)
Grosse Brauhausstrasse 17
06108 Halle, Germany
Tel.: (49) 341 3513 0
Fax: (49) 341 3513 550
Construction Engineering Services
S.I.C.: 8711
N.A.I.C.S.: 541330

PPP Schulen Landkreis Hof GmbH (1)
Herriotstr 1
60528 Frankfurt am Main, Hessen, Germany
Tel.: (49) 69 668800
Construction Engineering Services
S.I.C.: 8711
N.A.I.C.S.: 541330

projekt-partner-online GmbH (1)
Dynamostrasse 17
68165 Mannheim, Germany
Tel.: (49) 621 4001 0
Fax: (49) 621 4001 2501
E-Mail: info@p-p-o.de
Web Site: www.p-p-o.de
Software Development Services
S.I.C.: 7371
N.A.I.C.S.: 541511

Projekt- und Betriebsgesllschaft Justizzentrum Chemnitz GmbH (1)
An Der Gehespitz 50
63263 Neu-Isenburg, Hessen, Germany
Tel.: (49) 6102 453400
Fax: (49) 6102 453499
Construction Engineering Services
S.I.C.: 8711
N.A.I.C.S.: 541330

Projektgesellschaft Justizvollzug Burg GmbH & Co. KG (1)
Madel 100
39288 Burg, Germany
Tel.: (49) 3921 9767 0
Construction Engineering Services
S.I.C.: 8711
N.A.I.C.S.: 541330

PTZ Kiel Beteiligungs GmbH (1)
Gustav-Stresemann-Ring 1
65189 Wiesbaden, Germany
Tel.: (49) 611 33480 0
Investment Management Services
S.I.C.: 6211
N.A.I.C.S.: 523999

R&M Ausbau Berlin GmbH (1)
Oberlandstrasse 89
12099 Berlin, Germany
Tel.: (49) 30 62602 0
Fax: (49) 30 62602 212
E-Mail: ausbau.berlin@rum-ausbau.de
Web Site: www.rumausbau.bilfinger.com
Construction Engineering Services
S.I.C.: 8711
N.A.I.C.S.: 541330
Roland Koch *(Gen Mgr)*

R&M Ausbau Frankfurt GmbH (1)
Carl-Zeiss-Strasse 10/3
63322 Rodermark, Germany
Tel.: (49) 6074 9200 0
Fax: (49) 6074 9200 44
E-Mail: ausbau.frankfurt@rum-ausbau.de
Web Site: www.rumausbau.bilfinger.com
Interior Design Services
S.I.C.: 7389
N.A.I.C.S.: 541410

R&M Ausbau GmbH (1)
Gneisenaustrasse 15
80992 Munich, Germany
Tel.: (49) 89 558901 101
Fax: (49) 89 558901 115
E-Mail: ausbau@rum-ausbau.de
Web Site: www.rum-ausbau.de
Interior Design Services
S.I.C.: 7389
N.A.I.C.S.: 541410
Joachim Mosch *(Gen Mgr)*

R&M Ausbau Leipzig GmbH (1)
Walter-Kohn-Strasse 4
04365 Leipzig, Germany
Tel.: (49) 341 64969 0
Fax: (49) 341 64969 14
E-Mail: ausbau.leipzig@rum-ausbau.de
Construction Engineering Services
S.I.C.: 8711
N.A.I.C.S.: 541330

R&M Ausbau Mannheim GmbH (1)
Carl-Reuther-Strasse 1
68305 Mannheim, Germany
Tel.: (49) 621 32 39 181
Fax: (49) 621 32 39 182
E-Mail: ausbau.mannheim@rum-ausbau.de
Construction Engineering Services
S.I.C.: 8711
N.A.I.C.S.: 541330

R&M Ausbau Munchen GmbH (1)
Gneisenaustrasse 15
80992 Munich, Germany
Tel.: (49) 89 558901 0
Fax: (49) 89 558901 290
E-Mail: ausbau.muenchen@rum-ausbau.de
Web Site: www.rumausbau.bilfinger.com
Emp.: 45
Interior Design Services
S.I.C.: 7389
N.A.I.C.S.: 541410
Michael Ferchland *(Mng Dir)*

R&M Ausbau Stuttgart GmbH (1)
Siemensstrasse 6
71101 Schonaich, Germany
Tel.: (49) 7031 49196 0
Fax: (49) 7031 49196 96
E-Mail: ausbau.stuttgart@rum-ausbau.de
Web Site: www.rumausbau.bilfinger.com
Construction Engineering Services
S.I.C.: 8711
N.A.I.C.S.: 541330

R&M Baudienstleistungen GmbH (1)
Gneisenaustr 15
80992 Munich, Germany
Tel.: (49) 89 149980
Fax: (49) 89 1499848499
Construction Engineering Services
S.I.C.: 8711
N.A.I.C.S.: 541330

R&M Fassadentechnik Sudwest GmbH (1)
Gneisenaustr 15
80992 Munich, Bavaria, Germany
Tel.: (49) 89 1 49 98 121
Fax: (49) 89 1 49 98 340
Industrial Machinery Repair & Maintenance Services
S.I.C.: 7699
N.A.I.C.S.: 811310

R&M Kuhllagerbau Bielefeld GmbH (1)
Sudbrackstrasse 17
33611 Bielefeld, Germany
Tel.: (49) 521 98250 0
Fax: (49) 521 98250 50
E-Mail: klb.bielefeld@rum.de
Web Site: www.rum-kuehllagerbau.de/C1257507003558D3/CurrentBaseLink/W27MEBEM989VENSDE?open&l=yes
Construction Engineering Services
S.I.C.: 8711
N.A.I.C.S.: 541330

R&M Kuhllagerbau Holding GmbH (1)
Sudbrackstrasse 17
33611 Bielefeld, Germany
Tel.: (49) 521 98250 0
Fax: (49) 521 98250 50
E-Mail: klb.bielefeld@rum.de
Web Site: www.rum-kuehllagerbau.de
Cold Storage Plant Construction Services
S.I.C.: 1542
N.A.I.C.S.: 236220

Roediger Gebaudetechnik GmbH (1)
Kinzigheimer Weg 104-106
63450 Hanau, Germany
Tel.: (49) 618 1309 0
Fax: (49) 618 1309 100
E-Mail: info@roediger-gt.de
Web Site: www.roediger-gt.de
Heating & Plumbing Equipment Installation Services
S.I.C.: 1711
N.A.I.C.S.: 238220

Roediger Grundbesitz GmbH (1)
Kinzigheimer Weg 104-106
63450 Hanau, Hessen, Germany
Tel.: (49) 61813090
Fax: (49) 6181309135
Real Estate Management Services
S.I.C.: 6531
N.A.I.C.S.: 531390

SVA Verkehrssicherungs-Anlagen Gesellschaft mit beschrankter Haftung (1)
Kreissstr 96
66127 Saarbrucken, Germany
Tel.: (49) 6898 933 80 0
Fax: (49) 6898 933 80 29
E-Mail: info@sva-verkehr.com
Web Site: www.sva-verkehr.com
Traffic Safety Equipment Installation Services
S.I.C.: 1799
N.A.I.C.S.: 238990

TWP Ingenieurburo GmbH (1)
Friedrichstrasse 5
45525 Hattingen, Germany
Tel.: (49) 2324 90292 0
Fax: (49) 2324 90292 29
E-Mail: info@twp-ing.de
Web Site: www.twp-ing.de
Project Management Consulting Services
S.I.C.: 8748
N.A.I.C.S.: 541618
George Bachman *(Gen Mgr)*

Willich Beteiligungen GmbH (1)
Gneisenaustr 15
80992 Munich, Bavaria, Germany
Tel.: (49) 51153520
Investment Management Services
S.I.C.: 6211
N.A.I.C.S.: 523999

Wolfferts Haus- und Warmetechnik GmbH (1)
Hansestrasse 1
51149 Cologne, Nordrhein-Westfalen, Germany
Tel.: (49) 220330020
Plumbing & Heating Equipment Installation Services
S.I.C.: 1711
N.A.I.C.S.: 238220

U.S. Subsidiaries:

BIS Industrial Services Inc. (1)
15933 Clayton Rd Ste 220
Ballwin, MO 63011
Tel.: (636) 391-4500
Fax: (636) 391-4594
E-Mail: info@bisis-usa.com
Web Site: www.bisis-usa.com
Construction Engineering Services
S.I.C.: 8711
N.A.I.C.S.: 541330
David Hile *(Pres & CEO)*
Jeff Koop *(CFO & Sr VP)*

BIS Salamis Inc. (1)
510 Laflamme Rd
Broussard, LA 70518
Tel.: (337) 289-0092
Fax: (337) 837-3096
Toll Free: (800) 585-2293
E-Mail: info@bissalamis.com
Web Site: www.bissalamis.com
Industrial Machinery Maintenance Services
S.I.C.: 7699
N.A.I.C.S.: 811310
David Hebert *(Pres)*
Gordon Romero *(Sr VP)*

BIS Tepsco Inc. (1)
2909 Aaron St
Deer Park, TX 77536
Tel.: (281) 604-0309
Fax: (281) 930-0788
E-Mail: thetepscoteam@bis.tepsco.com
Web Site: www.tepsco.com
Civil Engineering Construction Services
S.I.C.: 1629
N.A.I.C.S.: 237990
Dave Lumbatis *(Office Mgr)*

FCC Corporation (1)
15933 Clayton Rd
Ballwin, MO 63011
Tel.: (636) 391-4433
Real Estate Management Services
S.I.C.: 6531
N.A.I.C.S.: 531390

Millennium Risk Management LLC (1)
2236 Cahaba Valley Dr Ste 101
Birmingham, AL 35242-2677
Tel.: (205) 451-0812
Business Management Consulting Services
S.I.C.: 8742
N.A.I.C.S.: 541611

Non-U.S. Division:

Bilfinger Berger Projects S.a.r.l. (1)
Aerogolf Center Heienhaff 1A
1736 Senningerberg, Luxembourg LU
Tel.: (352) 621273100 (100%)
Fax: (352) 26347934
E-Mail: info@pi.bilfinger.lu
Web Site: www.pi.bilfinger.lu
Emp.: 6
Public Building & Transportation Infrastructure Construction Services
S.I.C.: 1542
N.A.I.C.S.: 236220
Nick Dawson *(Mng Dir)*
Dirk Sohngen *(Mng Dir)*

Non-U.S. Subsidiaries:

Bilfinger Berger Project Investments GmbH (2)
Gustav-Stresemann-Ring 1
D-65189 Wiesbaden, Germany De
Tel.: (49) 611334800 (100%)
Fax: (49) 61133480299
E-Mail: info@pi.bilfinger.de
Web Site: www.pi.bilfinger.de
Emp.: 40
Public Building & Transportation Infrastructure Construction Services
S.I.C.: 1542
N.A.I.C.S.: 236220
Frank Chramm *(Mng Dir)*

Bilfinger Berger Project Investments Inc. (2)
675 Cochrane Drive
West Tower Suite 630, Markham, ON, L3R 0B8, Canada (100%)
Tel.: (905) 530-2114
Fax: (905) 530-2214
E-Mail: info@pi.bilfinger.ca
Web Site: www.pi.bilfinger.com
Emp.: 20
Public Building & Transportation Infrastructure Construction Services
S.I.C.: 1542
N.A.I.C.S.: 236220
Damian Joy *(Pres)*

Bilfinger Berger Project Investments Ltd. (2)
3rd Floor Braywick Gate
Braywick Road, Maidenhead, Berks, SL6 1DA, United Kingdom UK
Tel.: (44) 1628503400 (100%)
Fax: (44) 1628503401
E-Mail: info@pi.bilfinger.co.uk
Web Site: www.pi.bilfinger.co.uk
Emp.: 40
Public Building & Transportation Infrastructure Construction Services
S.I.C.: 1542
N.A.I.C.S.: 236220
Martin Pugh *(Mng Dir-UK & Ireland)*

Bilfinger SE—(Continued)

Subsidiary:

BEDFORD EDUCATION PARTNERSHIP HOLDINGS LIMITED (3)
3rd Floor Braywick Gate Braywick Road
Maidenhead, SL 6 1DA, United Kingdom
Tel.: (44) 1628 503 400
Investment Management Services
S.I.C.: 6799
N.A.I.C.S.: 523920

Non-U.S. Subsidiaries:

Actys Bedrijfsmatig Onroerend Goed B.V. (1)
Euclideslaan 135
3584 BR Utrecht, Netherlands
Tel.: (31) 302565295
Fax: (31) 20646 45 36
Web Site: www.actys.nl
Real Estate Development Services
S.I.C.: 6531
N.A.I.C.S.: 531390

Actys Gebouwdiensten B.V. (1)
Euclideslaan 135
3584 BR Utrecht, Netherlands
Tel.: (31) 30 256 51 65
Real Estate Development Services
S.I.C.: 6531
N.A.I.C.S.: 531390

Actys Retail B.V. (1)
Euclideslaan 135
3584 BR Utrecht, Netherlands
Tel.: (31) 30 2565165
Real Estate Development Services
S.I.C.: 6531
N.A.I.C.S.: 531390

ATG Power Limited (1)
Prospect House Kilbuck Lane Haydock
Saint Helens, Merseyside, WA11 9UX, United Kingdom
Tel.: (44) 1942 868900
Fax: (44) 1942 868901
Financial Management Services
S.I.C.: 6211
N.A.I.C.S.: 523999

Babcock Borsig Power Usluge d.o.o. (1)
Skadarska 15
11108 Belgrade, Serbia
Tel.: (381) 11 3033 344
Consulting Engineering Services
S.I.C.: 8711
N.A.I.C.S.: 541330

Babcock Borsig Service Arabia Ltd. (1)
Al Khodari Heavy Industries Jubail Highway
PO Box 4362
Al Khobar, 31952 Dammam, Saudi Arabia
Tel.: (966) 3 815 14 63
Fax: (966) 3 815 14 72
E-Mail: info.ksa@babcock.bilfinger.com
Web Site: www.babcock.bilfinger.com
Electric Power Generation Services
S.I.C.: 4911
N.A.I.C.S.: 221118
Joachim Wuensch *(CFO)*

BBPI seNTinel Pty Ltd (1)
Level 22 111 Pacific Highway
North Sydney, NSW, 2060, Australia
Tel.: (61) 2 9923 3300
Fax: (61) 2 9460 2210
Construction Engineering Services
S.I.C.: 8711
N.A.I.C.S.: 541330

BBV Systems Sp. z o.o. (1)
Siennicka Street 25
80-758 Gdansk, Poland
Tel.: (48) 58 30067 93
Fax: (48) 58 30067 91
E-Mail: info.pl@bbv-systems.pl
Web Site: www.bbv-systems.pl
Emp.: 30
Construction Engineering Services
S.I.C.: 1629
N.A.I.C.S.: 237990
Krzysztof Lewandowski *(Pres)*

BEDFORD EDUCATION PARTNERSHIP LIMITED (1)
3rd Floor Braywick Gate
Maidenhead, SL6 1DA, United Kingdom
Tel.: (44) 1628 503 400
Financial Management Services
S.I.C.: 6211
N.A.I.C.S.: 523999

BILFINGER BERGER AMBIENTE S.r.l. (1)
Via Fermi Enrico 13/A
37135 Verona, Italy
Tel.: (39) 045 8230715
Fax: (39) 045 8230811
Construction Engineering Services
S.I.C.: 8711
N.A.I.C.S.: 541330

Bilfinger Berger Baugesellschaft mbH (1)
Diefenbachgasse 5
A-1150 Vienna, Austria AT (100%)
Tel.: (43) 1899370
Fax: (43) 189937118
E-Mail: office@bilfingerberger.at
Web Site: www.bilfingerberger.at
Emp.: 70
Private & Public Sector Construction Services
S.I.C.: 1629
N.A.I.C.S.: 237990
Ludger Koch *(Gen Mgr-Civil Engrg)*
Rudolph Kraft *(Gen Mgr-Structural Engrg)*

Bilfinger Berger Belgium S.A. (1)
Interleuvenlaan 64
B-3001 Leuven, Belgium
Tel.: (32) 1640 0305
Fax: (32) 1640 1035
Construction Services
S.I.C.: 1629
N.A.I.C.S.: 237990

Bilfinger Berger Budownictwo S.A. (1)
ul Domaniewska 50A
02-672 Warsaw, Poland
Tel.: (48) 22 24 43 400
Fax: (48) 22 24 43 541
E-Mail: centrala@bilfinger.pl
Web Site: www.bilfinger.pl
Construction Engineering Services
S.I.C.: 8711
N.A.I.C.S.: 541330
Piotr Kledzik *(Chm)*

Bilfinger Berger Building Polska Sp. z o.o. (1)
Domaniewska 50a
02-672 Warsaw, Poland
Tel.: (48) 22 854 03 20
Fax: (48) 22 854 03 29
Construction Engineering Services
S.I.C.: 8711
N.A.I.C.S.: 541330

Bilfinger Berger (Canada) Inc. (1)
1140 Pender St W Suite 1210
Vancouver, BC, V6E 4G1, Canada
Tel.: (778) 329-4404
Fax: (778) 329-4403
Construction Management Services
S.I.C.: 1629
N.A.I.C.S.: 237990

Bilfinger Berger Civil UK LIMITED (1)
10 Station Road
Chertsey, Surrey, KT16 8BE, United Kingdom
Tel.: (44) 1932 577 200
Fax: (44) 1932 571 917
Construction Engineering Services
S.I.C.: 8711
N.A.I.C.S.: 541330

Bilfinger Berger Emirates Construction B.V. (1)
Werfplein 5
3238 BH Zwartewaal, Netherlands
Tel.: (31) 045 8230715
Building Construction Services
S.I.C.: 1629
N.A.I.C.S.: 236210

Bilfinger Berger Facility Services Holding Schweiz AG (1)
Industriestrasse 21
8304 Wallisellen, Switzerland
Tel.: (41) 661 205 22 20
Fax: (41) 61 205 22 20
Investment Management Services
S.I.C.: 6211
N.A.I.C.S.: 523999

Bilfinger Berger Government Services s.r.l. (1)
Hof Via Ludovico Lazzaro Zamen 200
Vicenza, 36100, Italy
Tel.: (39) 0444239526
Construction Engineering Services
S.I.C.: 8711
N.A.I.C.S.: 541330

Bilfinger Berger Industrial Services Spain S.A. (1)
Calle Monasterio de Suso Y Yuso n 34 - Planta 3 - Puerta 4
28049 Madrid, Spain
Tel.: (34) 915 358 760
Fax: (34) 915 358 762
E-Mail: BIS@BIS-bilfinger.es
Web Site: www.bis-bilfinger.es
Emp.: 450
Insulation Installation Services
S.I.C.: 1742
N.A.I.C.S.: 238310
Ignasi Navarro *(Reg Mgr)*

Bilfinger Berger Polska S.A. (1)
Domaniewska 50 A
PL-02 672 Warsaw, Poland PL (100%)
Tel.: (48) 222010233
Fax: (48) 222443541
E-Mail: centrala@bilfinger.pl
Web Site: www.bilfinger.pl
Sales Range: $300-349.9 Million
Emp.: 1,328
Holding Company; Civil Engineering & Facility Construction Services
S.I.C.: 6719
N.A.I.C.S.: 551112
Piotr Kledzik *(Chm-Mgmt Bd)*
Ewa Korycka *(Dir-Fin)*
Waldemar Sieminski *(Member-Mgmt Bd)*
Wojciech Szwejkowski *(Member-Mgmt Bd)*

Subsidiary:

Hydrobudowa-6 S.A. (2)
ul Domaniewska 50A
PL-02 672 Warsaw, Poland PL (100%)
Tel.: (48) 224949000
Fax: (48) 22 4949 999
E-Mail: hb6@hb6.pl
Web Site: www.hb6.pl
Emp.: 1,300
Civil Engineering & Facility Construction Services
S.I.C.: 1629
N.A.I.C.S.: 237990
Wlodzimierz Zawadzki *(Chm-Supervisory Bd)*
Piotr Kledzik *(Chm-Mgmt Bd)*
Hans Helmut Schetter *(Vice Chm-Supervisory Bd)*
Jerzy Zysk *(Member-Mgmt Bd)*

Bilfinger Berger Power Holdings (pty) Ltd. (1)
37 Homestead Road Block D Homestead Park
Rivonia, 2191, South Africa
Mailing Address:
PO Box 1537
Rivonia, 2138 Johannesburg, South Africa
Tel.: (27) 11 806 3000
Fax: (27) 86 613 1965
E-Mail: info@steinmuller.bilfinger.com
Web Site: www.powerafrica.bilfinger.com
Power Plant Construction Services
S.I.C.: 1629
N.A.I.C.S.: 237130

Bilfinger Berger stavebni Praha, s.r.o. (1)
Pekarska 603/12
CZ-155 00 Prague, Czech Republic CZ
Tel.: (420) 257013612
Fax: (420) 257013622
E-Mail: bbstapraha@cz.bilfinger.de
Construction Services
S.I.C.: 1629
N.A.I.C.S.: 237990

Bilfinger Industrial Services Schweiz AG (1)
Untere Bruhlstrasse 4
4800 Zofingen, Switzerland
Tel.: (41) 62 746 7111
Fax: (41) 62 746 7101
E-Mail: info@bis.bilfinger.ch
Web Site: www.bis.bilfinger.ch
Industrial Machinery Maintenance Services
S.I.C.: 7699
N.A.I.C.S.: 811310
Volker Osdoba *(Co-CEO & Co-Mng Dir)*
Martin Tuzzolino *(Co-CEO & Co-Mng Dir)*

Bilfinger Maschinenbau GmbH & Co KG (1)
Wahringerstrasse 34
Postfach 35
4031 Linz, Austria
Tel.: (43) 732 6987 3365
Fax: (43) 732 6980 3391
E-Mail: office@maschinenbaue.bilfinger.com
Web Site: www.maschinenbau.bilfinger.com
Sls.: $66,069,500
Emp.: 350
Turbine Mfr
S.I.C.: 3511
N.A.I.C.S.: 333611
Juergen Winkler *(Chm)*
Wolfgang Preinfalk *(Mng Dir & Head-Admin)*

BIS ATG Limited (1)
Prospect House Kilbuck Lane
Haydock, Saint Helens, WA11 9UX, United Kingdom
Tel.: (44) 1942 868 900
Fax: (44) 1942 868 901
E-Mail: enquiries@bis-atg.co.uk
Web Site: www.bis-atg.co.uk
Electrical Engineering Services
S.I.C.: 8711
N.A.I.C.S.: 541330
Duncan Hall *(Mng Dir)*

BIS Beteiligungsverwaltungs GmbH (1)
Lunzerstrasse 64
Linz, 4031, Austria
Tel.: (43) 73269879798
Fax: (43) 73269878099
Investment Management Services
S.I.C.: 6211
N.A.I.C.S.: 523999
Hans-Michael Goepfert *(CEO)*

BIS Brabant Mobiel B.V. (1)
Gooikensdam 4
Postbus 612
4900 AP Oosterhout, North Brabant, Netherlands
Tel.: (31) 162 428160
Fax: (31) 162 426478
E-Mail: info.bbm@bis-is.com
Construction Engineering Services
S.I.C.: 8711
N.A.I.C.S.: 541330

BIS Geratetechnik GmbH (1)
Boschstrasse 48
4600 Wels, Austria
Tel.: (43) 7242 78101 0
Fax: (43) 7242 78101 11
E-Mail: office@geraete.com
Web Site: www.gta.bis.bilfinger.com
Construction Machinery Rental Services
S.I.C.: 7353
N.A.I.C.S.: 532412
Iris Opl *(Sec)*
A. Oberndorfer *(Exec VP)*

BIS Industrial Services Belgie N.V. (1)
Oude Brug 10
2900 Schoten, Antwerpen, Belgium
Tel.: (32) 3 3280 010
Fax: (32) 3 3265634
E-Mail: info@bis-is.com
Insulation Installation Services
S.I.C.: 1742
N.A.I.C.S.: 238310

BIS Industrial Services Nederland B.V. (1)
Werfplein 5
3238 BH Zwartewaal, Netherlands
Tel.: (31) 181 66 73 00
Fax: (31) 181 66 39 87
E-Mail: info@bis-is.com
Construction Engineering Services
S.I.C.: 8711
N.A.I.C.S.: 541330

BIS Industrial Services Osterreich GmbH (1)
Lunzer Strasse 64
4031 Linz, Austria

Tel.: (43) 732 69874588
Fax: (43) 732 69873136
Construction Engineering Services
S.I.C.: 8711
N.A.I.C.S.: 541330

BIS Industrier Danmark A/S (1)
Flakagervej 36
4400 Kalundborg, Denmark
Tel.: (45) 25 32 46 71
Nonmetallic Mineral Mining Services
S.I.C.: 1481
N.A.I.C.S.: 213115

BIS Industrietechnik Salzburg GmbH (1)
Bergerbrauhofstrasse 31
5020 Salzburg, Austria
Tel.: (43) 662 8695 0
Fax: (43) 662 8695 995
E-Mail: office@BIS-salzburg.com
Web Site: www.bis-salzburg.com
Pipeline Construction Engineering Services
S.I.C.: 1623
N.A.I.C.S.: 237120
Tobias Eitel *(Co-Mng Dir)*
Ludwig Paradeiser *(Co-Mng Dir)*

BIS Insulation B.V. (1)
Werfplein 5
3238 BH Zwartewaal, Netherlands
Tel.: (31) 181667300
Fax: (31) 186654947
Insulation Installation Services
S.I.C.: 1742
N.A.I.C.S.: 238310

BIS International Construction and Trading N.V. (1)
Oude Brug 10
2900 Schoten, Belgium
Tel.: (32) 33 28 00 10
Fax: (32) 33 26 56 34
Industrial Building Construction Services
S.I.C.: 1541
N.A.I.C.S.: 236210
Wil de Geus *(Gen Mgr)*

BIS MainServ Sp. z o.o. (1)
Ul Augustowka 30
02-981 Warsaw, Poland
Tel.: (48) 22 587 78 93
Fax: (48) 22 587 78 77
E-Mail: office@bbis.pl
Web Site: www.bbis.pl
Construction Engineering Services
S.I.C.: 8711
N.A.I.C.S.: 541330

BIS Multiserwis Sp. z o.o. (1)
ul Prudnicka 40
47-300 Krapkowice, Poland
Tel.: (48) 77 40 09 100
Fax: (48) 77 40 09 106
E-Mail: sekretariat@bis-multiserwis.pl
Web Site: www.bis-multiserwis.pl
Emp.: 1,500
Insulation Installation Services
S.I.C.: 1742
N.A.I.C.S.: 238310
Marian Siwon *(Chm & Gen Dir)*

BIS Personalservice Osterreich GmbH (1)
Lunzerstrasse 64
4031 Linz, Austria
Tel.: (43) 732 6987 6299
Fax: (43) 732 6980 4303
E-Mail: PSO@BIS.bilfinger.com
Web Site: www.psoe.bilfinger.com
Temporary Staffing Services
S.I.C.: 7363
N.A.I.C.S.: 561320

BIS Prefal - Isolamentos Termicos Lda. (1)
Rua de Marvila N 121
1950-197 Lisbon, Portugal
Tel.: (351) 21 8610550
Fax: (351) 21 8680414
E-Mail: prefalsede@prefal-isolamentos.com
Web Site: www.prefal.com.pt
Insulation Installation Services
S.I.C.: 1742
N.A.I.C.S.: 238310

BIS Production Partner AB (1)
Gesallgatan 5
444 32 Stenungsund, Sweden
Tel.: (46) 770 110 411
E-Mail: gunnar.anderson@bis.productionpartner.com
Web Site: www.se.productionpartner.com
Emp.: 330
Industrial Machinery Sales & Maintenance Services
S.I.C.: 5084
N.A.I.C.S.: 423830
Gunnar Anderson *(CEO)*

BIS Production Partner AS (1)
Postboks 1094
3905 Porsgrunn, Norway
Tel.: (47) 3592 3000
Fax: (47) 3592 2244
Web Site: www.en.productionpartner.com
Emp.: 460
Project Management Consulting Services
S.I.C.: 8748
N.A.I.C.S.: 541618

BIS Production Partner Holding AS (1)
Heroya Industripark
3908 Porsgrunn, Norway
Tel.: (47) 35 92 2000
Fax: (47) 35 92 2244
Web Site: www.bis.bilfinger.com
Investment Management Services
S.I.C.: 6211
N.A.I.C.S.: 523999
Morten Mathisen *(Sr VP)*

BIS Production Partner IFS AS (1)
Heroya Industripark
3905 Porsgrunn, Norway
Tel.: (47) 35 92 2000
Fax: (47) 35 92 2616
Web Site: www.bis.bilfinger.com
Construction Engineering Services
S.I.C.: 1629
N.A.I.C.S.: 237990
Jens Kare Aasen *(Mgr)*

BIS Production Partner Ipec AS (1)
Sagmyra 25
4624 Kristiansand, Norway
Tel.: (47) 38 11 11 50
Fax: (47) 38 11 11 51
Engineering Consulting Services
S.I.C.: 8711
N.A.I.C.S.: 541330

BIS ROB Montagebedrijf N.V. (1)
Keetberglaan 5 - Haven 1093
9120 Beveren, Belgium
Tel.: (32) 3 575 14 14
Fax: (32) 3 575 03 22
E-Mail: info@bisrob.be
Pipeline System Installation & Maintenance Services
S.I.C.: 1629
N.A.I.C.S.: 237120

BIS ROB Zeeland B.V. (1)
Ambachtstraat 15
4538 AV Terneuzen, Netherlands
Tel.: (31) 115 648 754
Fax: (31) 115 648 753
E-Mail: robzeeland@bisrob.be
Web Site: www.bisrob.be
Industrial Machinery Maintenance Services
S.I.C.: 7699
N.A.I.C.S.: 811310

BIS Salamis International Limited (1)
4 Greenhole Place Bridge Don
Aberdeen, AB23 8EU, United Kingdom
Tel.: (44) 12 24 24 60 00
Fax: (44) 12 24 24 61 00
Emp.: 200
Industrial Coating Services
S.I.C.: 1799
N.A.I.C.S.: 238990
Steve Waugh *(CEO)*

BIS Salamis (M&I) Limited (1)
Greenhole Place Bridge Don
Aberdeen, United Kingdom AB23 8EU
Tel.: (44) 1224 246000
Fax: (44) 1224 246100
E-Mail: info@salamis.com
Web Site: www.salamis.com
Industrial Insulation & Coating Services
S.I.C.: 1742
N.A.I.C.S.: 238310
Mike McKay *(Dir-Comml)*

BIS Shared Services B.V. (1)
Werfplein 5
3238 BH Zwartewaal, Netherlands
Tel.: (31) 181667300
Fax: (31) 181663987
Human Resource Consulting Services
S.I.C.: 8999
N.A.I.C.S.: 541612

BIS Shared Services Osterreich GmbH (1)
Lunzerstrasse 64
4031 Linz, Austria
Tel.: (43) 73269870
Fax: (43) 732 69803136
Human Resource Consulting Services
S.I.C.: 8999
N.A.I.C.S.: 541612

BIS Willich GmbH (1)
Alxingergasse 31
1100 Vienna, Austria
Tel.: (43) 1 3300125 0
Fax: (43) 1 3300125 20
E-Mail: office@bis-willich.at
Construction Engineering Services
S.I.C.: 8711
N.A.I.C.S.: 541330

Bohr- und Rohrtechnik GmbH (1)
Brunner Strasse 73
1210 Vienna, Austria
Tel.: (43) 1 29103 0
Fax: (43) 1 29103 253
E-Mail: contact@bur.at
Web Site: www.bur.at
Pipeline System Installation Services
S.I.C.: 1629
N.A.I.C.S.: 237990

Clackmannanshire Schools Education Partnership (Holdings) Ltd. (1)
3rd Floor Braywick Gate Braywick Road
Maidenhead, SL6 1DA, United Kingdom
Tel.: (44) 1628 503 400
Investment Management Services
S.I.C.: 6211
N.A.I.C.S.: 523999

COVENTRY EDUCATION PARTNERSHIP HOLDINGS LIMITED (1)
3rd Floor Braywick Gate Braywick Road
Maidenhead, Berkshire, SL6 1DA, United Kingdom
Tel.: (44) 1628 503 400
Investment Management Services
S.I.C.: 6211
N.A.I.C.S.: 523999

Deutsche Babcock Middle East FZE (1)
PO Box 46698
Abu Dhabi, United Arab Emirates
Tel.: (971) 2 49959 99
Fax: (971) 2 55020 76
E-Mail: info@babcock.bilfinger.com
Web Site: www.babcock.bilfinger.com
Industrial Machinery Repair & Maintenance Services
S.I.C.: 7699
N.A.I.C.S.: 811310
Thomas Suckut *(CEO & Mng Dir)*
Peer Maluck *(Mng Dir & CFO)*
Clemens Wolters *(Mng Dir & COO)*

Duro Dakovic Montaza d.d. (1)
Dr Mile Budaka 1
Slavonski Brod, 35000, Croatia
Tel.: (385) 35 44 82 67
Fax: (385) 35 44 22 79
Construction Engineering Services
S.I.C.: 1629
N.A.I.C.S.: 237990
Darko Katic *(Mgr-Fin)*

EPM Swiss Property Management AG (1)
Industriestrasse 21
8304 Wallisellen, Switzerland
Tel.: (41) 44 878 78 78
Fax: (41) 44 878 78 77
E-Mail: info@epm-swiss.ch
Web Site: www.epm-swiss.ch
Real Estate Management Services
S.I.C.: 6531
N.A.I.C.S.: 531390
Hans Peter Egloff *(CEO)*
Martin Ruh *(CFO)*
Markus Hux *(Member-Exec Bd)*
Andreas Traechslin *(Member-Exec Bd)*

Euro Ressurs AS (1)
Luramyrveien 51
4391 Sandnes, Norway
Tel.: (47) 51 63 76 00
Fax: (47) 55 98 22 51
Textile Machinery Distr
S.I.C.: 5084
N.A.I.C.S.: 423830

Europa Support Services Ltd (1)
Rosanne House Parkway
Welwyn Garden City, Herts, AL8 6HG, United Kingdom
Tel.: (44) 1707325324
Fax: (44) 1707322325
E-Mail: Infor@europa-services.co.uk
Web Site: www.europa-services.co.uk
Sales Range: $200-249.9 Million
Emp.: 3,000
Facilities Management Services
S.I.C.: 6531
N.A.I.C.S.: 531312
Billy Allan *(Chm)*
Martin Jones *(Deputy Chm)*
Greig Brown *(CEO)*

Division:

Europa Workspace Services (2)
Unit A 1 Watt Place Hamilton International Technology Park
Blantyre, G72 0AH, United Kingdom
Tel.: (44) 1698720520
Fax: (44) 1698825735
Web Site: www.europa-services.co.uk
Sales Range: $25-49.9 Million
Emp.: 35
Interior Design Services
S.I.C.: 7389
N.A.I.C.S.: 541410
David Eastlake *(Mng Dir)*

Fire Support (SSFR) Holdings Ltd. (1)
3rd Floor Braywick Gate
Maidenhead, Berkshire, SL6 1DA, United Kingdom
Tel.: (44) 1628 503 400
Investment Management Services
S.I.C.: 6211
N.A.I.C.S.: 523999

HEATEC COMPANY LIMITED (1)
49/21 Moo 5 Laemchabang Industrial Estate EP22 Tungsukla
Sriracha, Chon Buri, 20230, Thailand
Tel.: (66) 38 491 620
Fax: (66) 38 490 629
Industrial Machinery & Equipment Maintenance Services
S.I.C.: 7699
N.A.I.C.S.: 811310

Highway Management M80 TopCo Limited (1)
Braywick Gate 3rd Floor Braywick Road
Maidenhead, Berkshire, SL6 1DA, United Kingdom
Tel.: (44) 1628 503 400
Highway Construction Services
S.I.C.: 1622
N.A.I.C.S.: 237310

HSG Zander Bulgaria EOOD (1)
Petra Str 6-8
1504 Sofia, Bulgaria
Tel.: (359) 887950504
Emp.: 30
Facility Management Services
S.I.C.: 8744
N.A.I.C.S.: 561210
Johann Kutrovats *(Mng Dir)*

HSG Zander CZ s.r.o. (1)
Za Strahovem 19
169 00 Prague, Czech Republic
Tel.: (420) 233 090 520
Fax: (420) 233 090 529
E-Mail: hsgzander@hsgzander.cz
Web Site: www.hsgzander.cz
Emp.: 170
Facility Management Services
S.I.C.: 8744
N.A.I.C.S.: 561210
Jiri Folta *(Co-Mng Dir)*
Jurgen Winkler *(Co-Mng Dir)*

HSG Zander GmbH (1)
Leonard-Bernstein-Str 10
1220 Vienna, Austria
Tel.: (43) 1 21147 43100
Fax: (43) 1 21147 43200
E-Mail: office@hsgzander.at

Bilfinger SE—(Continued)

Web Site: www.hsgzander.at
Real Estate Development Services
S.I.C.: 6531
N.A.I.C.S.: 531390
Herbert Taborsky *(Gen Mgr)*

HSG Zander Hungaria Kft. (1)
Akna u 2-4
1106 Budapest, Hungary
Tel.: (36) 1 4333 680
Fax: (36) 1 4333 688
E-Mail: info@hu.hsgzander.com
Web Site: www.hsgzander.com
Facility Management Services
S.I.C.: 8744
N.A.I.C.S.: 561210
Eniko Vanohuscar *(Gen Mgr)*

HSG Zander Ireland Facility Services Ltd. (1)
Landscape House
Dublin, Ireland
Tel.: (353) 12157000
Facility Management Services
S.I.C.: 8744
N.A.I.C.S.: 561210

HSG Zander Irish Schools Limited (1)
79 Merrion Square
Dublin, Ireland
Tel.: (353) 1 634 1000
Facility Management Services
S.I.C.: 8744
N.A.I.C.S.: 561210

HSG Zander KRK O.O.O. (1)
Zemlyanoy Val Str 9
Moscow, 105064, Russia
Tel.: (7) 495 229 95 50
Fax: (7) 495 229 95 51
Facility Management Services
S.I.C.: 8744
N.A.I.C.S.: 561210

HSG Zander Luxemburg Sarl (1)
6 Place de Nancy
2212 Luxembourg, Luxembourg
Tel.: (352) 8199 2427
Fax: (352) 8199 3004
Web Site: www.hsgzander.com
Facility Management Services
S.I.C.: 8744
N.A.I.C.S.: 561210
Johannes Schwarz *(Mng Dir)*

HSG Zander Polska Sp. z o.o. (1)
Al Armii Ludowej 26
00-609 Warsaw, Poland
Tel.: (48) 22 579 32 32
Fax: (48) 22 579 32 01
E-Mail: info@hsgzander.com.pl
Web Site: www.hsgzander.pl
Emp.: 20
Facility Management Services
S.I.C.: 8744
N.A.I.C.S.: 561210
Thorsten Bruedigam *(CEO)*
Jerzy Bogdan Szulc *(Member-Mgmt Bd)*

HSG Zander RND O.O.O. (1)
Zemlyanoy val str 9
Moscow, 105064, Russia
Tel.: (7) 495 229 95 50
Facility Management Services
S.I.C.: 8744
N.A.I.C.S.: 561210

HSG Zander RUS O.O.O. (1)
Zemlyanoy Val Str 9
Moscow, 105064, Russia
Tel.: (7) 495 229 95 50
Fax: (7) 495 229 95 51
E-Mail: info@hsgzander.ru
Web Site: www.hsgzander.ru
Emp.: 800
Facility Management Services
S.I.C.: 8744
N.A.I.C.S.: 561210
Sergey Surzhin *(CEO)*
Victor Efremov *(Dir Gen)*
Nikolay Bondarenko *(CFO)*

HSG Zander Services Limited (1)
1 Exchange Place
Dublin, Ireland
Tel.: (353) 1 670 22 42
Professional Employment Services
S.I.C.: 7361
N.A.I.C.S.: 561311

HSG Zander Slovakia s.r.o. (1)
Bajkalska 17
821 02 Bratislava, Slovakia
Tel.: (421) 2 446 400 14
Fax: (421) 2 446 400 15
E-Mail: info@sk.hsgzander.com
Web Site: www.hsgzander.sk
Emp.: 70
Facility Management Services
S.I.C.: 8744
N.A.I.C.S.: 561210
Stefan Melikant *(Gen Mgr)*

HSG Zander UKR O.O.O. (1)
24-V Moskovsky Avenue
Kiev, 04073, Ukraine
Tel.: (380) 44 503 63 29
Fax: (380) 44 503 63 29
Facility Management Services
S.I.C.: 8744
N.A.I.C.S.: 561210

HSG Zander UK Limited (1)
Gloucestershire Royal Hospital Great Western Road
Gloucester, Gloucestershire, GL1 3NN, United Kingdom
Tel.: (44) 8454 228391
Web Site: www.hsgzander.com
Facility Management Services
S.I.C.: 8744
N.A.I.C.S.: 561210
Brian Jenkinson *(Assoc Dir)*

Inselko AS (1)
Heroya Naeringspark
3908 Porsgrunn, Norway
Tel.: (47) 32 92 28 10
Fax: (47) 35 56 94 99
Electrical Engineering Services
S.I.C.: 8711
N.A.I.C.S.: 541330

iNTACT Technische Gebaudemanagement Gesellschaft m.b.H. (1)
Kremser Landstrasse 2
3100 Saint Polten, Austria
Tel.: (43) 2742 88 12 79
Fax: (43) 2742 88 12 79 85
E-Mail: office@intact.co.at
Web Site: www.intact.co.at
Facility Management Services
S.I.C.: 8744
N.A.I.C.S.: 561210

L.T.M. Industrie SAS (1)
114 rue Pasteur
69780 Toussieu, France
Tel.: (33) 4 72 04 53 54
Fax: (33) 4 78 80 25 35
E-Mail: accueil@ltm-france.com
Web Site: www.ltm-france.com
Pipeline Construction Engineering Services
S.I.C.: 1629
N.A.I.C.S.: 237120

MCE Energietechnik Beteiligungs GmbH (1)
Lunzerstr 64
4031 Linz, Austria
Tel.: (43) 732 6987 8095
Fax: (43) 732 6980 3382
Engineering Consulting Services
S.I.C.: 8711
N.A.I.C.S.: 541330
Alfred Franz *(CEO)*

MCE Energietechnik GmbH & Co. KG (1)
Lunzerstrasse 64
Linz, 4031, Austria
Tel.: (43) 161036221
Industrial Machinery Maintenance Services
S.I.C.: 7699
N.A.I.C.S.: 811310
Mantfert Simmet *(Mgr)*

MCE Industrietechnik Holding GmbH (1)
Lunzer Strasse 64
Linz, Austria
Tel.: (43) 73269870
Fax: (43) 73269873100
Investment Management Services
S.I.C.: 6211
N.A.I.C.S.: 523999

MCE Slany s.r.o. (1)
Netovicka 538
PO Box 35
274 01 Slany, Czech Republic
Tel.: (420) 312 510 111
Fax: (420) 312 510 145
E-Mail: mceslany@mceslany.cz
Fabricated Structural Metal Mfr
S.I.C.: 3441
N.A.I.C.S.: 332312

MCE Ukraine Ltd. (1)
17 23 Observatorna
Kiev, Ukraine
Tel.: (380) 444867745
Human Resource Consulting Services
S.I.C.: 8999
N.A.I.C.S.: 541612

Noggerath France EURL (1)
11 Rue Du General De Gaulle
45650 Saint-Jean-le-Blanc, France
Tel.: (33) 2 38 22 40 54
Fax: (33) 2 38 22 40 56
Waste Water Treatment Services
S.I.C.: 4971
N.A.I.C.S.: 221310

Peters Engineering France SARL (1)
53-55 bd Romain Rolland
92120 Montrouge, France
Tel.: (33) 147 35 13 80
Fax: (33) 141 48 87 11
E-Mail: info@pe-france.com
Web Site: www.pe-france.com
Construction Engineering Services
S.I.C.: 8711
N.A.I.C.S.: 541330
Gilles Maes *(Gen Mgr)*

P.T. Bilfinger Berger Indonesia (1)
Jl Tol Cakung Cilincing Km 11 725
Bintara, Bekasi, 17136, Indonesia (100%)
Tel.: (62) 218894232
Telex: 61 769 royind ia
Fax: (62) 218894235
Construction Services
S.I.C.: 1629
N.A.I.C.S.: 237990

Roediger AG (1)
Jurastrasse 10
4142 Munchenstein, Switzerland
Tel.: (41) 61416 90 50
Fax: (41) 61411 21 01
Water Treatment Equipment Sales & Installation Services
S.I.C.: 5087
N.A.I.C.S.: 423850

Scottish Borders Education Partnership Holdings Ltd. (1)
3rd Floor Braywick Gate Braywick Road
Maidenhead, Berkshire, SL6 1DA, United Kingdom
Tel.: (44) 1628 503 400
Investment Management Services
S.I.C.: 6211
N.A.I.C.S.: 523999

Scottish Borders Education Partnership Ltd. (1)
3rd Floor Braywick Gate
Maidenhead, Berkshire, SL6 1DA, United Kingdom
Tel.: (44) 1628 503 400
Educational Consulting Services611710
S.I.C.: 8299
N.A.I.C.S.: 611710

Steinmuller Engineering Services (pty) Ltd. (1)
37 Homestead Road Homestead Court Block D
Rivonia, 2128, South Africa
Tel.: (27) 11 806 3000
Fax: (27) 11 806 3330
Engineering Services
S.I.C.: 8711
N.A.I.C.S.: 541330

Steinmuller Properties Number Two (pty) Ltd. (1)
37 Homestead Road Homestead Court Block D
Rivonia, 2128, South Africa
Tel.: (27) 11 806 3000
Engineering Services
S.I.C.: 8711
N.A.I.C.S.: 541330

The Stoke On Trent & Staffordshire Safer Communities Community Interest Company (1)
3rd Floor Braywick Gate Braywick Road
Maidenhead, Berkshire, SL6 1DA, United Kingdom
Tel.: (44) 1628 503 400
Construction Engineering Services
S.I.C.: 8711
N.A.I.C.S.: 541330

Victorian Correctional Infrastructure Partnership Pty. Ltd. (1)
L 22 111 Pacific Hwy
North Sydney, NSW, 2060, Australia
Tel.: (61) 299233300
Real Estate Management Services
S.I.C.: 6531
N.A.I.C.S.: 531390

Women's College Partnership (1)
790 Bay St Suite 750
Toronto, ON, M5G 1N8, Canada
Tel.: (416) 351-2535
Investment Management Services
S.I.C.: 6211
N.A.I.C.S.: 523999

Non-U.S. Affiliate:

Julius Berger Nigeria PLC (1)
10 Shettima A. Munguno Crescent
Abuja, Nigeria 900 109 NG
Tel.: (234) 803 906 7000 (49%)
Fax: (234) 9 611 4041
E-Mail: info@julius-berger.com
Web Site: www.julius-berger.com
JBERGER—(NIGE)
Rev.: $1,267,845,586
Assets: $1,126,124,892
Liabilities: $1,030,867,999
Net Worth: $95,256,892
Earnings: $50,399,845
Emp.: 19,234
Fiscal Year-end: 12/31/12
Civil, Industrial & Commercial Engineering, Construction & Contracting Services
S.I.C.: 1541
N.A.I.C.S.: 237990
Mohammed Nuruddeen Imam *(Chm)*
Heinz Stockhausen *(Vice Chm)*
Wolfgang Goetsch *(Mng Dir)*
Cecilia Ekanem Madueke *(Sec)*

BILIA AB

Norra Langebergsgatan 3
PO Box 9300
400 91 Gothenburg, Sweden
Tel.: (46) 317095500
Fax: (46) 317095550
E-Mail: info@bilia.se
Web Site: www.bilia.com
BILI—(OMX)
Sls.: $2,734,077,600
Assets: $896,756,400
Liabilities: $625,392,000
Net Worth: $271,364,400
Earnings: $23,529,600
Emp.: 3,431
Fiscal Year-end: 12/31/12

Business Description:
Automobile Sales & Services
S.I.C.: 5571
N.A.I.C.S.: 441228

Personnel:
Mats Qviberg *(Chm)*
Jan Pettersson *(Deputy Chm)*
Per Avander *(Mng Dir & CEO)*
Gunnar Blomkvist *(CFO)*
Jennifer Tunney *(Chief Legal Counsel)*

Board of Directors:
Mats Qviberg
Per Avander
Ingrid Jonasson Blank
Anna Engebretsen
Jack Forsgren
Fredrik Grevelius
Mats Holgerson
Dragan Mitrasinovic

Patrik Nordvall
Svante Paulsson
Jan Pettersson
Jon Risfelt
Tommy Strandhall
Lennart Welin

Subsidiaries:

Bilia Fordon AB (1)
Jolengatan 15
Box 9260
Goteborg, 400 96 Gothenburg, Sweden
Tel.: (46) 317517500
Fax: (46) 317517511
E-Mail: anders.aberg@Bilia.se
Web Site: www.bilia.se
Emp.: 100
Automobile Sales & Service
S.I.C.: 5571
N.A.I.C.S.: 441228
Anders Narsson *(Mng Dir)*

Bilia Group Goteborg AB (1)
Goteborgsvagen 92
431 37 Molndal, Sweden
Tel.: (46) 317061300
Fax: (46) 31 706 13 30
E-Mail: info@biliagroup.se
Web Site: www.biliagroup.bmw.se
Emp.: 80
New Car Dealers
S.I.C.: 5511
N.A.I.C.S.: 441110
Tord Johanson *(Gen Mgr)*

Bilia Personbilar AB (1)
Norra Langebergsgatan 3
PO Box 9003
400 97 Gothenburg, Sweden
Tel.: (46) 317095500
Fax: (46) 317095550
E-Mail: info@bilia.se
Web Site: www.bilia.se
Emp.: 100
Automobile Sales & Service
S.I.C.: 5599
N.A.I.C.S.: 441228
Tommy Andersson *(Mng Dir)*

Haglund & Hellberg Bil i Haninge AB (1)
Dantorpsvagen 3
SE-136 50 Haninge, Sweden
Tel.: (46) 850410300
Fax: (46) 850410309
E-Mail: info@bilia.se
Web Site: www.bilia.se
Emp.: 50
Automobile Sales & Service
S.I.C.: 5571
N.A.I.C.S.: 441228
Per Avander *(Mng Dir)*

Motoria Bil AB (1)
Danmarksgatan 52
SE-164 40 Kista, Sweden
Tel.: (46) 850162480
Fax: (46) 87505610
Automobile Sales & Service
S.I.C.: 5599
N.A.I.C.S.: 441228

Netbil i Skandinavien AB (1)
Faktorvagen 2
SE-434 37 Kungsbacka, Sweden
Tel.: (46) 300430330
Fax: (46) 300567270
E-Mail: info@netbil.se
Web Site: www.netbil.se
Emp.: 12
Automobile Sales & Service
S.I.C.: 5599
N.A.I.C.S.: 441228
Roger Lofman *(Mng Dir)*

Non-U.S. Subsidiaries:

Bilia Personbil as (1)
Postboks 240
Okern, NO-0510 Oslo, Norway
Tel.: (47) 22882500
Fax: (47) 22646955
Web Site: www.bilia.no
Emp.: 180
Automobile Sales & Service
S.I.C.: 5599
N.A.I.C.S.: 441228
Frude Hebnes *(Mng Dir)*

Bilia Personvogne A/S (1)
Husby Alle 7-9
2630 Tastrup, Denmark
Tel.: (45) 72591700
E-Mail: info@bilia.dk
Web Site: www.bilia.dk
Emp.: 70
Automobile Sales & Service
S.I.C.: 5571
N.A.I.C.S.: 441228
Michael Brodersen *(Mng Dir)*

BILL HOUSTON FORD LTD.

5786 Main Street
Stouffville, ON, L4A 8A4, Canada
Tel.: (905) 640-4541
Fax: (905) 642-4691
E-Mail: billh@billhoustonford.com
Web Site: www.billhoustonford.com
Rev.: $11,731,772
Emp.: 26
Business Description:
New & Used Car Dealers
S.I.C.: 5511
N.A.I.C.S.: 441110
Personnel:
Russell Eagen *(Gen Mgr-Sls)*

BILL HOWICH CHRYSLER LTD.

2777 North Island Hwy
Campbell River, BC, V9W2H4, Canada
Tel.: (250) 287-9555
Fax: (250) 287-2500
Toll Free: (866) 938-0143
E-Mail: bhc@billhowichchrysler.com
Web Site: www.billhowich.fivestardealers.ca
Year Founded: 1973
Rev.: $19,127,889
Emp.: 42
Business Description:
New & Used Car Dealers
S.I.C.: 5511
N.A.I.C.S.: 441110
Personnel:
Bill Howich *(Pres)*

BILLABONG INTERNATIONAL LIMITED

1 Billabong Place
Burleigh Heads, QLD, 4220, Australia
Mailing Address:
PO Box 283
Burleigh Heads, QLD, 4220, Australia
Tel.: (61) 7 5589 9899
Fax: (61) 7 5589 9800
E-Mail: info@billabong.com.au
Web Site: www.billabongbiz.com
Year Founded: 1973
BBG—(ASX)
Rev.: $1,401,843,341
Assets: $1,055,378,438
Liabilities: $777,063,749
Net Worth: $278,314,689
Earnings: ($899,334,384)
Emp.: 6,000
Fiscal Year-end: 06/30/13
Business Description:
Surfwear, Accessories & Action Sports Apparel Mfr
S.I.C.: 5136
N.A.I.C.S.: 424320
Personnel:
Neil Fiske *(CEO & Mng Dir)*
Peter Myers *(CFO)*
Ed Leasure *(Acting Pres-Americas)*
Maria Manning *(Sec)*
Board of Directors:
Ian Pollard
Neil Fiske
Gordon Merchant
Howard Mowlem
Jason Mozingo
Colette Paull
Sally Pitkin
Matthew Wilson
Legal Counsel:
Minter Ellison
159 Varsity Parade
Varsity Lakes, QLD, 4227, Australia

Clayton Utz
71 Eagle Street
Brisbane, QLD, 4000, Australia

Allens Arthur Robinson
Level 28 Deutsche Bank Place Corner Hunter & Phillip St
Sydney, Australia

Subsidiaries:

GSM (Operations) Pty Ltd (1)
1 Billabong Place
PO Box 283
Burleigh Heads, QLD, 4220, Australia
Tel.: (61) 755899899
Fax: (61) 755899800
E-Mail:
Web Site: www.billabong.com.au
Emp.: 350
Clothing Merchants
S.I.C.: 5651
N.A.I.C.S.: 448140
Shannan North *(Gen Mgr-Asia Pacific)*

GSM Rocket Australia Pty Ltd (1)
1 Billabong Pl
Burleigh Heads, QLD, 4220, Australia
Tel.: (61) 755899899
Fax: (61) 755899800
E-Mail:
Web Site: www.billabong.com.au
Emp.: 500
Clothing Merchants
S.I.C.: 5611
N.A.I.C.S.: 448110
Shannan North *(Gen Mgr-Asia Pacific)*

Nixon Pacific Pty Ltd (1)
1 Billabong Place
Burleigh Heads, QLD, 4220, Australia
Tel.: (61) 755899949
Fax: (61) 755899800
E-Mail:
Web Site: www.nixonnow.com
Watches
S.I.C.: 5094
N.A.I.C.S.: 423940
Shannan North *(Brand Mgr)*

U.S. Subsidiaries:

Billabong Retail Inc (1)
1485 Retherford St
Tulare, CA 93274
Tel.: (559) 686-5944
Fax: (559) 686-5949
Web Site: www.billabong.com
Emp.: 6
Clothing Stores
S.I.C.: 5651
N.A.I.C.S.: 448140

Burleigh Point, Ltd (1)
117 Waterworks Way Ste 100
Irvine, CA 92618
Tel.: (949) 753-7222
Fax: (949) 753-7223
E-Mail: cs@billabong-usa.com
Web Site: www.billabong.com
Emp.: 200
Women Apparels Mfr
S.I.C.: 2389
N.A.I.C.S.: 315240
Paul Naude *(Pres)*

Element Skateboards, Inc (1)
121 Waterworks Way Ste 100
Irvine, CA 92618
Tel.: (949) 789-7890
Fax: (949) 789-7891
Toll Free: (866) 927-5283
E-Mail: info@elementskateboards.com
Web Site: www.elementskateboards.com
Emp.: 100
Skateboards Mfr
S.I.C.: 3949
N.A.I.C.S.: 339920
Johnny Schillereff *(Pres)*

GSM Investments Ltd (1)
117 Waterworks Way
Irvine, CA 92618
Tel.: (714) 557-5300
Investment Consultancy Services
S.I.C.: 6282
N.A.I.C.S.: 523930

Honolua Surf International Ltd (1)
121 Waterworks Way
Irvine, CA 92618
Tel.: (949) 265-0800
Fax: (949) 265-0819
E-Mail: info@honoluasurf.com
Web Site: www.honoluasurf.com
Emp.: 300
Men's & Women's Casual Clothing
S.I.C.: 5651
N.A.I.C.S.: 448140
Paul Naude *(Pres)*

Nixon, Inc. (1)
701 S Coast Hwy
Encinitas, CA 92024 CA (48.5%)
Tel.: (760) 944-0900
Fax: (760) 944-9376
E-Mail: info@nixonnow.com
Web Site: www.nixonnow.com
Emp.: 50
Watches & Accessories
S.I.C.: 5094
N.A.I.C.S.: 423940
Andy Laats *(Pres & CEO)*

RVCA Corp. (1)
960 W 16th St
Costa Mesa, CA 92627 CA
Tel.: (949) 548-6223
Fax: (949) 548-7722
E-Mail: info@rvca.com
Web Site: www.rvca.com
Emp.: 80
Clothing Mfr
S.I.C.: 5699
N.A.I.C.S.: 315220
Patrick Tenore *(Pres)*

VeeZee, Inc (1)
121 Waterworks Way Ste 100
Irvine, CA 92618
Tel.: (949) 753-7222
Fax: (949) 753-7223
Web Site: www.vonzipper.com
Emp.: 15
Sunglasses, Goggles, Accessories & Soft Goods Mfr
S.I.C.: 3949
N.A.I.C.S.: 339920
Paul Naude *(Pres)*

Non-U.S. Subsidiaries:

Burleigh Point Canada Inc (1)
5825 Kieran
Saint Laurent, QC, H45 OA3, Canada
Tel.: (514) 336-6382
Fax: (514) 336-1753
Web Site: www.billabong.com.au/blog-post/44/contact-billabong
Emp.: 50
Clothing Merchants
S.I.C.: 5651
N.A.I.C.S.: 448140
Alan Robert *(Gen Mgr)*

GSM Brasil Ltda (1)
Rua Natividade 139
Sao Paulo, Sao Paulo, 04513 020, Brazil
Tel.: (55) 1136188600
Fax: (55) 1136188638
Web Site: www.billabongbiz.com
Clothing Merchants
S.I.C.: 5651
N.A.I.C.S.: 448140

GSM (Central Sourcing) Pty Ltd (1)
27th Fl Langham Pl Ofc Twr
8 Argyle St, Kowloon, China (Hong Kong)
Tel.: (852) 24396676
Fax: (852) 24396007
Web Site: www.billabong.com.hk
Clothing Merchants
S.I.C.: 5136
N.A.I.C.S.: 424320

GSM (Europe) Pty Ltd (1)
100 Ave Des Sabotiers
ZA De Pedebert, 40150 Hossegor, France
Tel.: (33) 558434205
Fax: (33) 558434089
E-Mail: billabong@billabong.tm.fr
Web Site: www.billabong.com
Emp.: 300

Billabong International Limited—(Continued)

Sports Goods Mfr
S.I.C.: 3949
N.A.I.C.S.: 339920
Carian San *(Mgr-Mktg Surfing)*

GSM (Japan) Limited (1)
Otsu Grand Bldg 3 Fl
4 3 2 Bakuromachi Chuo Ku, Osaka, Osaka, 541 0059, Japan
Tel.: (81) 649636272
Fax: (81) 49636644
E-Mail: kashimoto@billabong-jp.com
Web Site: www.billabongbiz.com
Emp.: 370
Apparels & Accessories Mfr
S.I.C.: 2389
N.A.I.C.S.: 315990
Kazuo Kashimoto *(Head-Accts)*

GSM (NZ Operations) Limited (1)
44 Arrenway Dr
Albany, Auckland, 0632, New Zealand
Tel.: (64) 94145106
Fax: (64) 94145039
E-Mail: gsmnz@billabong.co.nz
Emp.: 30
Clothing Merchants
S.I.C.: 5611
N.A.I.C.S.: 448110
Jason Neely *(Gen Mgr)*

GSM Trading (Singapore) Pty Ltd (1)
8 Jalan Kilang Timor 03 05
Kewalram House, Singapore, 159305, Singapore
Tel.: (65) 62709181
Fax: (65) 62700127
Web Site: www.billabongbiz.com
Emp.: 40
Clothing Merchants
S.I.C.: 5651
N.A.I.C.S.: 448140
Trina Cleose *(Product Mgr)*

GSM Trading (South Africa) Pty Ltd (1)
2A Da Gama Rd
PO Box 134
Jeffreys Bay, Port Elizabeth, Eastern Cape, 6330, South Africa
Tel.: (27) 422002600
Fax: (27) 422932478
E-Mail: info@billabong.co.za
Web Site: www.billabong.co.za
Emp.: 200
Clothing Merchants
S.I.C.: 6221
N.A.I.C.S.: 523130
Ernest Bendeman *(Gen Mgr)*

Nixon Europe S.A.R.L. (1)
185 Ave De Vas Cou Aou
40150 Hosseger, Soorts Hossengor, France
Tel.: (33) 558435917
Fax: (33) 558434089
E-Mail: nixon@nixoneurpoe.com
Web Site: www.nixonnow.com
Emp.: 25
Watches & Parts Merchants
S.I.C.: 5094
N.A.I.C.S.: 423940
Franck Corbery *(Head-Mktg)*

West 49 Inc. (1)
5555 North Service Rd
Burlington, ON, L7L 6B2, Canada ON
Tel.: (905) 336-5454
Fax: (905) 336-3490
Toll Free: (800) 669-1258
E-Mail: info@west49.com
Web Site: www.west49.com
Sales Range: $200-249.9 Million
Emp.: 647
Snowboarding, Skateboarding, Surfing, Music-Related, Women's Fashion Clothing, Footwear, Accessories & Equipment Retailer
S.I.C.: 5699
N.A.I.C.S.: 448150
Kenneth Fowler *(Chm)*
Salvatore Baio *(Pres & CEO)*

BILLBOARD JSC

Pl Balgariya 1 NDK vh Al4
Sofia, 1463, Bulgaria
Tel.: (359) 2 9166500
Fax: (359) 2 9630606
E-Mail: office@bilbord.bg
Web Site: www.bilbord.bg
Year Founded: 2001
5BP—(BUL)

Business Description:
Digital Printing Services
S.I.C.: 2759
N.A.I.C.S.: 323111

Personnel:
Kalin Vasilev Genchev *(Chm)*
Rumen Sabev Radev *(Deputy Chm)*

Board of Directors:
Kalin Vasilev Genchev
Stefan Vasilev Genchev
Rumen Sabev Radev

BILLERUD AB

(Name Changed to BillerudKorsnas AB)

BILLERUDKORSNAS AB

(Formerly Billerud AB)
Frosundaleden 2 B
Box 703
169 27 Solna, Sweden
Tel.: (46) 855333500
Fax: (46) 855333560
E-Mail: info@billerudkorsnas.com
Web Site: www.billerud.com
BILL—(OMX)
Sls.: $1,618,279,200
Assets: $3,827,120,400
Liabilities: $2,357,758,800
Net Worth: $1,469,361,600
Earnings: $104,799,600
Emp.: 4,400
Fiscal Year-end: 12/31/12

Business Description:
Packaging Material Mfr
S.I.C.: 2653
N.A.I.C.S.: 322211

Personnel:
Hannu Ryopponen *(Chm)*
Per Lindberg *(Pres & CEO)*
Susanne Lithander *(CFO)*
Christer Simren *(Exec VP, COO & Sr VP-Consumer Board)*
Per Bjurbom *(Sr VP & Dir-Production)*
Uno Brinnen *(Sr VP-Forestry)*
Lennart Eberleh *(Sr VP-Containerboard)*
Karin Hagfeldt *(Sr VP-HR)*
Johan Nellbeck *(Sr VP-Pkg Paper)*
Per Persson *(Sr VP-Supply Chain Mgmt & IT)*
Ulrika Spals *(Sr VP-Comm & Change Mgmt)*
Mikael Westerberg *(Sr VP-Bus Support)*
Magnus Wikstrom *(Sr VP-Tech & Strategic Dev)*

Board of Directors:
Hannu Ryopponen
Mia Brunell Livfors
Helen Gustafsson
Lennart Holm
Jan Homan
Gunilla Jonsson
Michael M. F. Kaufmann
Wilhelm Klingspor
Mikael Larsson
Kurt Lindvall
Kjell Olsson
Tobias Soderholm

Subsidiaries:

Billerud Karlsborg AB (1)
Karlsborgsverken
95283 Karlskoga, Sweden (100%)
Tel.: (46) 92366000
Fax: (46) 92320484
E-Mail: birgitta.lundh@billerud.com
Web Site: www.billerud.se
Emp.: 410
Paperboard Mills
S.I.C.: 2631
N.A.I.C.S.: 322130
Annica Breskys *(Mng Dir)*

Billerud Scandinavia (1)
Frosundaleden 2 b
169 70 Solna, Stockholm, Sweden
Tel.: (46) 8 553 337 00
Fax: (46) 8 553 335 90
Web Site: www.billerudskog.se
Timber Products Whslr
S.I.C.: 5099
N.A.I.C.S.: 423990
Per Lindberg *(CEO)*

Billerud Skarblacka AB (1)
Bergslagsvagen 46
Skarblacka, Norrkoping, 617 30, Sweden (100%)
Tel.: (46) 11245300
Fax: (46) 1157502
E-Mail: info.skbl@billerud.com
Web Site: www.billerud.com
Emp.: 600
Paperboard Mills
S.I.C.: 2631
N.A.I.C.S.: 322130
Tor Lundqvist *(Mng Dir)*

Billerud Skog AB (1)
Gustav IIIs boulevard 18
Box 703
169 27 Solna, Sweden
Tel.: (46) 8 553 335 00
Fax: (46) 8 553 335 70
Web Site: www.billerudskog.se
Timber Logging Services
S.I.C.: 2411
N.A.I.C.S.: 113310
Johan Sakari *(Gen Mgr)*

Billerud Tenova Bioplastics AB (1)
Torshagshuset
616 33 Aby, Sweden
Tel.: (46) 11 10 52 75
Fax: (46) 11 10 52 85
E-Mail: info@tenova.com
Web Site: www.tenova.com
Emp.: 15
Bioplastic Materials Distr
S.I.C.: 5162
N.A.I.C.S.: 424610
Staffan Stromberg *(CEO)*

Korsnas AB (1)
E4 Industrie Pl
S 801 81 Gavle, Sweden (100%)
Tel.: (46) 26151000
Telex: 47030
Fax: (46) 26152240
E-Mail: info@korsnas.com
Web Site: www.korsnas.com
Sales Range: $1-4.9 Billion
Emp.: 1,900
Fluff Pulp, Paper, Sack & Kraft Paper, Paperboard; Timber Import Export
S.I.C.: 2631
N.A.I.C.S.: 322130
Christer Simren *(Exec VP, COO & Sr VP-Consumer Board)*
Uno Brinnen *(Sr VP-Forestry)*
Per Persson *(Sr VP-Supply Chain Mgmt & IT)*
Ulrika Spals *(Sr VP-Comm & Change Mgmt)*
Mikael Westerberg *(Sr VP-Bus Support)*

Subsidiaries:

Korsnas AB - Frovi (2)
Frovifors
SE 718 80 Frovi, Sweden
Tel.: (46) 58137000
Fax: (46) 58131067
E-Mail: info.frovi@korsnas.com
Web Site: www.korsnas.com
Sales Range: Less than $1 Million
Emp.: 685
Cartonboard
S.I.C.: 2679
N.A.I.C.S.: 322299

Korsnas Rockhammar AB (2)
Rockhammar
718 91 Frovi, Sweden
Tel.: (46) 581 370 00
Fax: (46) 581 703 40
Chemical Pulp Mfr
S.I.C.: 2899
N.A.I.C.S.: 325998

Non-U.S. Subsidiaries:

Korsnas GmbH (2)
Haubachstrasse 74
DE-22765 Hamburg, Germany (100%)
Tel.: (49) 40 85 35 26 41
Paper Products Distr
S.I.C.: 2672
N.A.I.C.S.: 322220
Jan-Ole Kristensen *(Dir-Sls)*

Korsnas Shanghai Trading Ltd. (2)
Unit 2008 20th Floor Maxdo Centre No 8 Xing Yi Road
Chang Ning District, Shanghai, China
Tel.: (86) 21 5208 0186
Fax: (86) 21 5208 0185
Packaging Material Mfr
S.I.C.: 2671
N.A.I.C.S.: 322220
Alfred Wang *(Mng Dir)*

Non-U.S. Subsidiaries:

Billerud Beetham Ltd (1)
Waterhouse Mills Beetham Milnthorpe Cumbria, Lancaster, LA7 7AR, United Kingdom (100%)
Tel.: (44) 1539565000
E-Mail: ying.sou@billerud.com
Emp.: 180
Paperboard Mills
S.I.C.: 2631
N.A.I.C.S.: 322130
Ying Sou *(Gen Mgr)*

Billerud Benelux B.V (1)
Herengracht 566
1017CH Amsterdam, Netherlands (100%)
Tel.: (31) 205207680
Fax: (31) 206267560
E-Mail: salesoffice.amsterdam@billerud.com
Emp.: 8
Printing & Writing Paper Whslr
S.I.C.: 5111
N.A.I.C.S.: 424110
L. Cerhoeff *(Mng Dir)*

Billerud France S.A (1)
16 Ave Athrenes
75009 Paris, France (100%)
Tel.: (33) 144699440
Fax: (33) 144699450
E-Mail: salesoffice.paris@billerud.com
Web Site: www.boss.billerud.com
Paper Mills
S.I.C.: 2621
N.A.I.C.S.: 322121

Billerud GmbH (1)
Stadtdeich 5
20097 Hamburg, Germany (100%)
Tel.: (49) 40320160
Fax: (49) 4032016150
E-Mail: salesoffice.hamburg@billerud.com
Web Site: www.boss.billerud.com
Paperboard Mills
S.I.C.: 2631
N.A.I.C.S.: 322130
Per Lindberg *(CEO)*

Billerud Gulf (1)
Jebel Ali Free Zone
LOB 16 Unit 128, Dubai, United Arab Emirates (100%)
Tel.: (971) 48814663
Fax: (971) 48814659
E-Mail: mohamed.nayeem@billerud.com
Web Site: www.billerud.com
Emp.: 4
Paper Sales
S.I.C.: 5113
N.A.I.C.S.: 424130
Rajeev Goyal *(Mng Dir)*

Billerud Iberica S.L (1)
Calle La Constitucio 3-Plt 5 Pta 5
Sant Just Desvern, Barcelona, 08960, Spain
Tel.: (34) 934700556
Fax: (34) 934730898
E-Mail: salesoffice.barcelona@billerud.com
Packaging Paper Products Mfr
S.I.C.: 2671
N.A.I.C.S.: 322220

Billerud Ltd (1)
11 Triangle Enterprise Way
NG 2 Business Pk, NG21AA Nottingham, United Kingdom (100%)
Tel.: (44) 1159758760
Fax: (44) 1159868589
Web Site: www.billerud.com
Emp.: 10
Paper Mills
S.I.C.: 2621
N.A.I.C.S.: 322121
David Hargreaves *(Gen Mgr)*

Billerud Sales Ltd (1)
1 Phoenix Place Phoenix Centre
NG21AE Nottingham, United Kingdom (100%)
Tel.: (44) 1159758760
Fax: (44) 1159868589
E-Mail: salesoffice.nottingham@billerud.com
Web Site: www.billerud.com
Paperboard Mills
S.I.C.: 2631
N.A.I.C.S.: 322130

Billerud S.r.l. (1)
Via Pisa 250
20099 Sesto San Giovanni, Italy
Tel.: (39) 0224839085
Fax: (39) 0224104505
E-Mail: salesoffice.milano@billerud.com
Web Site: boss.billerud.com
Emp.: 8
Paper Mills
S.I.C.: 2621
N.A.I.C.S.: 322121
Arnaldo Ferrari *(Mng Dir)*

Billerud Trading (Shanghai) Co. Ltd (1)
300 Huaihai Middle Road Unit 4109
200021 Shanghai, China
Tel.: (86) 2153510622
Fax: (86) 2153515508
Emp.: 11
Printing & Writing Paper Whslr
S.I.C.: 5111
N.A.I.C.S.: 424110
Daniel Eriksson *(Gen Mgr)*

Billerud Wood Supply SIA (1)
Jaunbumani Dreilini Stopinu Novads
2130 Riga, Latvia
Tel.: (371) 67 106 836
Emp.: 3
Timber Product Whslr
S.I.C.: 5099
N.A.I.C.S.: 423990
Didzis Zalitis *(Mng Dir)*

BILLET FINDER INC.

1894 Clarence Street
Sarnia, ON, N7X 1C8, Canada
Tel.: (519) 331-1103
Year Founded: 2010
BLTF—(OTC)

Business Description:
Online Billet Information Services
S.I.C.: 2741
N.A.I.C.S.: 519130

Personnel:
Terrence Groman *(Pres, Treas & Sec)*
Denis Vorobyev *(COO)*

Board of Directors:
Terrence Groman
Denis Vorobyev

Transfer Agent:
Island Stock Transfer
15500 Roosevelt Blvd Ste 301
Clearwater, FL 33760

BILLET SAS

Zac De Volvic
63530 Volvic, Puy De Dome, France
Tel.: (33) 473387983
Fax: (33) 473389491
E-Mail: spl@sa-billet.com
Rev.: $14,100,000
Emp.: 100
S.I.C.: 1622
N.A.I.C.S.: 237310

Personnel:
Bernard Billet *(Pres)*

BILLING SYSTEM CORP.

1-6-7 Shibakoen Minato-ku
Tokyo, 105-0011, Japan
Tel.: (81) 354058671
Fax: (81) 354058672
E-Mail: toiawase@e.billingjapan.co.jp
Web Site: www.billingjapan.co.jp
Year Founded: 2000
3623—(TKS)
Sales Range: $10-24.9 Million
Emp.: 28

Business Description:
Online Transaction Settlement Services
S.I.C.: 7379
N.A.I.C.S.: 522320

Personnel:
Toshihiko Eda *(Pres)*

BILLINGTON HOLDINGS PLC

Steel House Barnsley Road
Wombwell
Barnsley, South Yorkshire, S73 8DS, United Kingdom
Tel.: (44) 1226340666
Fax: (44) 1226755947
E-Mail: info@billington-holdings.plc.uk
Web Site: www.billington-holdings.plc.uk
Year Founded: 1970
BILN—(AIM)
Rev.: $60,283,079
Assets: $32,309,115
Liabilities: $12,885,427
Net Worth: $19,423,688
Earnings: ($655,405)
Emp.: 289
Fiscal Year-end: 12/31/12

Business Description:
Structural Steel & Engineering Services
S.I.C.: 1629
N.A.I.C.S.: 237990

Personnel:
Stephen George Thomas Fareham *(CEO)*
L. S. Holloway *(Sec)*

Board of Directors:
Peter Keith Hems
Stephen George Thomas Fareham
John Stuart Gordon
Alexander Ospelt
Trevor Micheal Taylor

Legal Counsel:
Shoosmiths
Waterfront House Waterfront Plaza 35 Station Street
Nottingham, United Kingdom

Transfer Agent:
Capita Registrars
Northern House Woodsome Park Fenay Bridge
Huddersfield, United Kingdom

Subsidiaries:

Billington Structures Limited (1)
Barnsley Road Wombwell
S738DS Barnsley, South Yorkshire, United Kingdom (100%)
Tel.: (44) 1226340666
Fax: (44) 1226755947
E-Mail: reception@billington-structures.co.uk
Web Site: www.billington-structures.co.uk
Emp.: 250
Structural Steel Erection Contractors
S.I.C.: 1791
N.A.I.C.S.: 238120
Steve Pharam *(Mng Dir)*

easi-edge Limited (1)
Ollerton Rd
Tuxford, Newark, Nottinghamshire, NG22 0PQ, United Kingdom
Tel.: (44) 1777870901
Fax: (44) 1777872047
E-Mail: enquiries@easi-edge.co.uk
Web Site: www.easi-edge.co.uk
Emp.: 50
Fabricated Metal Products Mfr
S.I.C.: 3441
N.A.I.C.S.: 332312

BILLION ELECTRIC CO., LTD.

8F No 192 Sec 2 Chung Hsing Rd
Hsin Tien, Taiwan
Tel.: (886) 229145665
Fax: (886) 229182895
Web Site: www.billion.com
3027—(TAI)
Sales Range: $25-49.9 Million

Business Description:
Network Equipment & Power Supply Products Mfr
S.I.C.: 3661
N.A.I.C.S.: 334210

Personnel:
Tim Chen *(CEO)*
Felix Cheng *(COO)*

U.S. Subsidiary:

BEC Technologies Inc. (1)
15236 Transistor Ln
Huntington Beach, CA 92649
Tel.: (714) 890-0201
Fax: (972) 422-0886
E-Mail: sales@bectechnologies.net
Web Site: www.bectechnologies.net
Internet Service Provider
S.I.C.: 4812
N.A.I.C.S.: 517210

BILLION INDUSTRIAL HOLDINGS LIMITED

Fenglin Industrial Zone
Longhu Town, Jinjiang, Fujian, 362241, China
Tel.: (86) 595 88299999
Fax: (86) 595 85239999
E-Mail: baihong@baihong.com
Web Site: www.baihong.com
2299—(HKG)
Sales Range: $650-699.9 Million
Emp.: 3,500

Business Description:
Polyester Filament Yarns Mfr
S.I.C.: 2299
N.A.I.C.S.: 313110

Personnel:
Jinen Chen *(Co-Chm)*
Tin Yau Sze *(Co-Chm)*
Jinbiao Wu *(CEO)*

Board of Directors:
Jinen Chen
Tin Yau Sze
Guoqiang Ding
Yuliang Ma
Jinbiao Wu
Mangmang Xue
Donghui Yang
Jun Yang
Chi Tat Yeung
Heping Yu
Meifang Zhu

BILLIONTON SYSTEMS INC.

No 21 Sui-Lih Rd
300 Hsinchuang, Taiwan
Tel.: (886) 35729399
Fax: (886) 35729393
E-Mail: info@billionton.com.tw
Web Site: www.billionton.com.tw
6172—(TAI)
Sales Range: $10-24.9 Million

Business Description:
Personal Digital Assistant & Data Storage Device Mfr
S.I.C.: 7379
N.A.I.C.S.: 518210

Personnel:
Toyo N.F. Liao *(Chm & Gen Mgr)*

Non-U.S. Subsidiaries:

TURANLI ELEKTRONIK LTD. (1)
Selahattin Pinar Cad 4/2
Mecidiyekoy, Istanbul, 80310, Turkey
Tel.: (90) 2122160520
Fax: (90) 2122160525
E-Mail: turanli@turanli.com.tr
Web Site: www.turanli.com.tr
Emp.: 30
Computer Accessories Distr
S.I.C.: 5045
N.A.I.C.S.: 423430
Omer Turanli *(Owner)*

BILPOWER LIMITED

201-204 Vikas Chambers
Junction of Link Marve Rd
Mith Chowky Malad (West), Mumbai, Maharashtra, 400064, India
Tel.: (91) 2228885929
Fax: (91) 2228811225
E-Mail: info@bilpower.com
Web Site: www.bilpower.com
BILPOWERQ—(BOM NSE)
Sales Range: $75-99.9 Million
Emp.: 500

Business Description:
Power Engineering Solutions
S.I.C.: 3612
N.A.I.C.S.: 335311

Personnel:
Suresh Kumar Choudhary *(Chm)*
Naresh Kumar Choudhary *(Mng Dir)*

Board of Directors:
Suresh Kumar Choudhary
Vinod Kumar Agrawal
Naresh Kumar Choudhary
Rajendra Kumar Choudhary
Narendra Kumar Jain
Rajan Menda
V.K. Pandit
Alexander Koshy Prince Vaidyan

Subsidiary:

Tarapur Transformers Limited (1)
836/837 8th Floor IJMIMA Complex Raheja Metroplex Link Road Malad W
Mumbai, Maharashtra, 400064, India
Tel.: (91) 22 4272 8080
Fax: (91) 22 4272 8090
E-Mail: info@tarapurtransformers.com
Web Site: www.tarapurtransformers.com
533203—(BOM NSE)
Rev.: $10,427,712
Assets: $20,332,206
Liabilities: $7,644,895
Net Worth: $12,687,311
Earnings: ($555,199)
Emp.: 300
Fiscal Year-end: 03/31/13
Transformer Mfr
S.I.C.: 3612
N.A.I.C.S.: 335311
Ekta Kumari Srivastava *(Compliance Officer & Sec)*

Plants:

Bilpower Ltd - Kanchad Plant (1)
Kanchad Vlg Taluka Wada
Thane, Maharastra, 421 303, India
Tel.: (91) 2526235772
Fax: (91) 2526235622
Web Site: www.bilpower.com
Emp.: 100
Transformers Lamination Mfr
S.I.C.: 3675
N.A.I.C.S.: 334416
Ganesh Kumar Chaudhari *(Mng Dir)*

Bilpower Ltd - Uttranchal Plant (1)
Unit D 10 11 Raipur Notified Area
Bhagwanpur
Haridwar, 247667 Roorkee, Uttarakhand, India
Tel.: (91) 1332235070
Web Site: www.bilpower.com
Emp.: 20
Transformers Lamination Mfr
S.I.C.: 3676
N.A.I.C.S.: 334416
Rajendra Kumar Choudhary *(Mng Dir)*

BIM BIRLESIK MAGAZALAR A.S.
Ebubekir Cad No 73 Sancaktepe
Istanbul, 34887, Turkey
Tel.: (90) 216 564 03 03
Fax: (90) 216 311 79 78
E-Mail: iletisim@bim.com.tr
Web Site: www.bim.com.tr
Year Founded: 1995
BIMAS—(IST)
Sls.: $5,598,385,183
Assets: $1,205,640,995
Liabilities: $746,186,914
Net Worth: $459,454,081
Earnings: $187,239,437
Emp.: 20,724
Fiscal Year-end: 12/31/12
Business Description:
Grocery Store Operator
S.I.C.: 5411
N.A.I.C.S.: 445110
Personnel:
Mustafa Latif Topbas *(Chm)*
Mahmud Pyirali Kassamali Merali *(Vice Chm)*
Haluk Dortluoglu *(CFO)*
Galip Aykac *(COO)*
Board of Directors:
Mustafa Latif Topbas
Mustafa Buyukabaci
Talat Icoz
Mahmud Pyirali Kassamali Merali
Jozef Wilhelmus Johannes Simons
Omer Hulusi Topbas

BIM SON PACKING JOIN STOCK COMPANY
Lam Son Ward
Bim Son, Thanh Hoa, Vietnam
Tel.: (84) 37 3825 632
Fax: (84) 37 3825 633
E-Mail: bpc@baobibimson.vn
Web Site: www.baobibimson.vn
Year Founded: 1985
BPC—(HNX)
Business Description:
Packaging Products Mfr
S.I.C.: 2621
N.A.I.C.S.: 322121
Personnel:
Nhu Khue Nguyen *(Chm)*
Board of Directors:
Nhu Khue Nguyen
Nam Khanh Doan
Viet Dung Mai
Vu Van Dai
Nguyen Van Hung

BIMAN BANGLADESH AIRLINES
BALAKA Zia International Airport
Kurmitola, Dhaka, 1229, Bangladesh
Tel.: (880) 28917400
Web Site: www.bimanair.com
Year Founded: 1972
Sales Range: $250-299.9 Million
Emp.: 5,500
Business Description:
Air Transportation Services
S.I.C.: 4512
N.A.I.C.S.: 481111
Personnel:
A. M. Mosaddique Ahmed *(Exec Dir-Fin)*
Subsidiaries:

Biman Flight Catering Centre Ltd (1)
Biman Bangladesh Airlines Balaka bhaban Baba Hotels, kurmitola, Zia, Dhaka, Bangladesh
Tel.: (880) 289147004
Fax: (880) 28913006
E-Mail: gm@bfcc-bb.com
Web Site: www.bfcc-bd.com
Emp.: 500
Caterers
S.I.C.: 5812
N.A.I.C.S.: 722320
A.D. Iliyas *(Mgr)*

Biman Poultry Complex Ltd (1)
Biman Press Bldg Compound
Ganakbari
Savar, Dhaka, Bangladesh
Tel.: (880) 2 9560151 10
E-Mail: bpc@bijoy.net
Poultry Hatcheries
S.I.C.: 0254
N.A.I.C.S.: 112340

BIMECO GARNHANDEL GMBH & CO. KG
Hemdener Weg 109
D-46399 Bocholt, Germany
Tel.: (49) 287127020
Fax: (49) 287133830
E-Mail: info@bimeco.de
Web Site: www.bimeco.de
Year Founded: 1985
Rev.: $44,830,500
Emp.: 32
Business Description:
Industrial Yarns & Spuns Supply Services
S.I.C.: 5199
N.A.I.C.S.: 424990
Personnel:
Alois Busshaus *(Mng Dir-Pur & Sls Dept)*

BIMOBJECT AB
Media Evolution City Stora
Varvsgatan 6A
211 19 Malmo, Sweden
Tel.: (46) 40 685 29 00
E-Mail: info@bimobject.com
Web Site: www.bimobject.com
BIM—(OMX)
Business Description:
Data Management
S.I.C.: 7374
N.A.I.C.S.: 518210
Personnel:
Stefan Larrson *(CEO)*

BINA DARULAMAN BERHAD
Level 9 & 10 Menara BDB 88
Lebuhraya Darulaman
05100 Alor Setar, Kedah Darul Aman, Malaysia
Tel.: (60) 47300303
Fax: (60) 47342714
E-Mail: bina_darulaman@bdb.com.my
Web Site: www.bdb.com.my
BDB—(KLS)
Rev.: $102,281,173
Assets: $239,786,388
Liabilities: $155,427,321
Net Worth: $84,359,066
Earnings: $7,109,319
Fiscal Year-end: 12/31/12
Business Description:
Property Development & General Construction Services
S.I.C.: 1522
N.A.I.C.S.: 236116
Personnel:
Jahubar Sathik Abdul Razak *(Mng Dir)*
Khalil Auni Mamat *(CFO)*
Khairulmuna Abd Ghani *(Sec & Deputy Gen Mgr-Grp Corp Svcs & Legal)*
Board of Directors:
Mohd Saad Endut
Jahubar Sathik Abdul Razak
Mohd Nasir Ahmad
Had Dhali
Abdul Rahman Ibrahim
Abdul Wahab Ismail
Zamri Yusuf
Legal Counsel:
Vazeer Akbar Majid & Co
No 10 Jalan 14/48
Petaling Jaya, Malaysia
Subsidiaries:

Darulaman Aset Sdn. Bhd. (1)
30A Level 2 Wisma PKNK Jalan Sultan Badlishah
05000 Alor Setar, Kedah Darul Aman, Malaysia
Tel.: (60) 47336676
Fax: (60) 47346676
E-Mail: habsah_zainon@yahoo.com
Web Site: www.pknk.gov.my
Emp.: 10
Property Development & General Construction Services
S.I.C.: 6531
N.A.I.C.S.: 531311
Zainuddin Atan *(CEO)*

Darulaman Golf Resort Behard (1)
Darulaman Golf & Country Club Bandar Darulaman
06007 Jitra, Kedah Darul Aman, Malaysia
Tel.: (60) 49170001
Fax: (60) 49177890
E-Mail: drgb@tm.net.my
Web Site: www.darulamangolf.com.my
Emp.: 90
Golf Club Management Services
S.I.C.: 7999
N.A.I.C.S.: 713910
Azmi Othman *(Chm)*
Mohd Tajuddin Bakar *(Chm-Golf Committee)*
Khairulmuna Abdul Ghani *(Sec)*

Darulaman Realty Sdn. Bhd. (1)
Lot 1 Bandar Darulaman
PO Box 12
Kubang Pasu, 06007 Jitra, Kedah Darul Aman, Malaysia
Tel.: (60) 49178080
Fax: (60) 49173537
E-Mail: drsb@darulamanrealty.com.my
Web Site: www.darulamanrealty.com.my
Emp.: 47
Property Development & Construction Services
S.I.C.: 1522
N.A.I.C.S.: 236116
Mohammad Rohsidi Osman *(Chm)*
Jahubar Sathik Abdul Razak *(Mng Dir)*

BINA GOODYEAR BERHAD
Unit 502 Block B Phileo Damansara 2 No 15 Jalan 16/11
Off Jalan Damansara, 46350 Petaling Jaya, Selangor Darul Ehsan, Malaysia
Tel.: (60) 37960 2388
Fax: (60) 37960 2388
E-Mail: info@binagoodyear.com
Web Site: www.binagoodyear.com
BGYEAR—(KLS)
Rev.: $28,461,811
Assets: $6,521,201
Liabilities: $38,531,621
Net Worth: ($32,010,419)
Earnings: ($41,067,441)
Fiscal Year-end: 06/30/13
Business Description:
Construction & Building Contract Service
S.I.C.: 1542
N.A.I.C.S.: 236220
Personnel:
Hean Chong Moo *(Mng Dir)*
Kwee Wah Chok *(Co-Sec)*
Kean Wai Tan *(Co-Sec)*
Board of Directors:
Md Azar Ismail
Kim Leng Eng
Mei Ling Lai
Hean Chong Moo
Choon Yong Tay

BINA PURI HOLDINGS BHD
Wisma Bina Puri 88 Jalan Bukit Idaman 8/1
Bukit Idaman, 68100 Selayang, Selangor Darul Ehsan, Malaysia
Tel.: (60) 361363333
Fax: (60) 361369999
E-Mail: corpcomm@binapuri.com.my
Web Site: www.binapuri.com
BPURI—(KLS)
Rev.: $419,757,931
Assets: $335,195,233
Liabilities: $286,203,329
Net Worth: $48,991,904
Earnings: $1,916,692
Fiscal Year-end: 12/31/12
Business Description:
Property Development & Construction Services
S.I.C.: 1611
N.A.I.C.S.: 237310
Personnel:
Tony Cheng Kiat Tan *(Founder)*
Hock Seng Tee *(Grp Mng Dir)*
Gaik Bee Toh *(Sec)*
Board of Directors:
Foon Meng Wong
Mohd Najib Abdul Aziz
Ghazali Bujang
Kwe Hee Tan
Tony Cheng Kiat Tan
Hock Lee Tay
Henry Hock Hin Tee
Hock Seng Tee
Matthew Kai Woon Tee
Wah Chin Yeow
Subsidiaries:

Bina Puri Construction Sdn Bhd (1)
88 Jalan Bukit Idaman 8/1 Taman Bukit Idaman Selayang
Batu Caves, Selangor, 68100, Malaysia
Tel.: (60) 361363333
Fax: (60) 361369999
Building Construction Services
S.I.C.: 1522
N.A.I.C.S.: 236116
Tee Hock Seng *(Mng Dir)*

Bina Puri Properties Sdn Bhd (1)
Block L Lot 104-107 Block L Lorong Plaza Permai 5 Alamesra
Sulaman Coastal Highway, 88450 Kota Kinabalu, Sabah, Malaysia (100%)
Tel.: (60) 88 485727
Fax: (60) 88 4585737
E-Mail: binapuri.kk@binapuri.com
Web Site: www.binapuri.com.my
Property Development Services
S.I.C.: 6531
N.A.I.C.S.: 531390
Tee Hock Seng *(Grp Mng Dir)*

Bina Puri Sdn Bhd (1)
14 & 15 Jalan Bukit Idaman 8/1 Bukit Idaman
68100 Selayang, Selangor Darul Ehsan, Malaysia
Tel.: (60) 361378500
Fax: (60) 361378511
Building Construction Services
S.I.C.: 1522
N.A.I.C.S.: 236116
Tony Cheng Kiat Tan *(Founder & Chm)*

Maskimi Polyol Sdn. Bhd. (1)
Lot 5815 Unit 1-8 Jalan Reko
Kajang, Selangor Darul Ehsan, 43000, Malaysia
Tel.: (60) 387332078
Fax: (60) 387332084
E-Mail: maskimi@po.jaring.my
Web Site: www.maskimi.com.my
Emp.: 21
Natural Oil Mfr & Distr
S.I.C.: 0119
N.A.I.C.S.: 111120
Tee Hock Seng *(Mng Dir)*

Sungai Long Industries Sdn Bhd (1)
Jalan Hulu Langat Batu 11 3/4
Hulu Langat, Selangor, 43100, Malaysia
Tel.: (60) 390212400

Fax: (60) 390212425
E-Mail: sales@sglong-ind.com
Web Site: www.sglong-ind.com
Rev.: $27,519,300
Emp.: 150
Granites & Bricks Mfr & Distr
S.I.C.: 1423
N.A.I.C.S.: 212313
Mohd Karim Abdullah Omar *(Chm)*
Tee Hock Seng *(Mng Dir)*

Non-U.S. Subsidiaries:

Bina Puri (B) Sdn Bhd (1)
No 2 2nd Floor Block C
Negara, BE 1518, Brunei Darussalam
Tel.: (673) 2232373
Fax: (673) 2232371
E-Mail: bpbrunei@binapuri.com
Emp.: 50
Building Construction Services
S.I.C.: 1522
N.A.I.C.S.: 236116
Datuk Ali Bin Abdullah *(Chm)*

Bina Puri Pakistan (Private) Ltd. (1)
No 84 HH Phase IV
Defence Housing Authority, Lahore, Punjab, Pakistan
Tel.: (92) 425747888
Fax: (92) 425745999
Web Site: www.binapuri.com.my
Emp.: 55
Building Construction Services
S.I.C.: 1629
N.A.I.C.S.: 236210
Ooichin Diep *(Project Coord)*

BINAR AB

Batterivagen 4
SE 46138 Trollhattan, Sweden
Tel.: (46) 520473200
Fax: (46) 520474005
E-Mail: info@binar.se
Web Site: www.binar.se
Sales Range: $25-49.9 Million
Emp.: 250
Business Description:
Industrial Electronics & Industrial Production Equipment Mfr
S.I.C.: 3559
N.A.I.C.S.: 333249
Personnel:
Ingemar Pettersson *(CEO)*

Subsidiaries:

Binar Elektronik AB (1)
PO Box 2001
SE-461 Trollhattan, Sweden
Tel.: (46) 520473200
Fax: (46) 520473210
E-Mail: info@binar.se
Web Site: www.binar.se
Emp.: 30
Electronic Components Mfr
S.I.C.: 3679
N.A.I.C.S.: 334419
Anders Wilhelmsson *(Mgr-Sls & Mktg)*

Binar Olofstrom AB (1)
Vastra Storgatan 20
293 38 Olofstrom, Sweden
Tel.: (46) 454323055
Fax: (46) 454322044
E-Mail: info@binar.se
Web Site: www.binarolofstrom.se
Emp.: 6
Press Line Automation Mfr
S.I.C.: 5084
N.A.I.C.S.: 423830
Ingemar Pettersson *(Gen Mgr)*

Binar Quick-Lift Systems AB (1)
Hedekullevagen 24
461 38 Trollhattan, Sweden
Tel.: (46) 520474000
Fax: (46) 520474005
E-Mail: info@kahlman.se
Web Site: www.kahlman.se
Emp.: 18
Portable Lifts & Cranes Mfr.
S.I.C.: 3536
N.A.I.C.S.: 333923
Johan Ahlstrom *(Mgr)*

Mabema AB (1)
Teknikringen 4C
583 30 Linkoping, Sweden
Tel.: (46) 13 15 3700
Fax: (46) 735 27 4141
E-Mail: info@mabema.se
Web Site: www.dynamis.se
Material Handling & Measurement Systems
S.I.C.: 3823
N.A.I.C.S.: 334513
Anders Reyier *(Pres)*

Titech System AB (1)
Vastra Ringvagen 4
522 31 Tidaholm, Sweden
Tel.: (46) 50219500
Fax: (46) 50271254
E-Mail: info@titech.se
Web Site: www.titech.se
Emp.: 47
Industrial Automation Mfr
S.I.C.: 3559
N.A.I.C.S.: 333249
Peter Labecker *(Gen Mgr)*

BINATONE ELECTRONICS INTERNATIONAL LTD.

Floor 23A 9 Des Voeux Road West
Hong Kong, China (Hong Kong)
Tel.: (852) 28027388
Fax: (852) 28028138
E-Mail: contactus@binatonetelecom.com.hk
Web Site: www.binatoneonline.com
Year Founded: 1958
Sales Range: $1-9.9 Million
Emp.: 30
Fiscal Year-end: 03/31/13
Business Description:
Electronics & Telecommunications Products Mfr
S.I.C.: 3663
N.A.I.C.S.: 334220
Personnel:
Dino Lalvani *(Owner & Chm)*
Lisa Castor *(Pres & CEO-Binatone North America)*

Non-U.S. Subsidiary:

Binatone Telecom Plc (1)
1 Absley Way
London, NW2 7HF, United Kingdom UK
Tel.: (44) 208955270
Fax: (44) 2089552750
E-Mail: binatoneuk@binatonetelecom.co.uk
Web Site: www.binatonetelecom.com
Emp.: 20
Electronic Product Mfr
Import Export
S.I.C.: 3639
N.A.I.C.S.: 335228
Dino Lavani *(Chm)*

BINCKBANK N.V.

310 Barbara Strozzilaan
PO Box 75047
1083 HN Amsterdam, Netherlands
Tel.: (31) 20 522 03 30
Fax: (31) 20 522 03 72
E-Mail: info@binck.nl
Web Site: www.binck.nl
Year Founded: 2000
BINCK—(EUR)
Int. Income: $57,512,421
Assets: $4,035,513,426
Liabilities: $3,422,708,572
Net Worth: $612,804,854
Earnings: $31,473,455
Emp.: 505
Fiscal Year-end: 12/31/12
Business Description:
Investment Banking Services
S.I.C.: 6211
N.A.I.C.S.: 523110
Personnel:
Kees J. M. Scholtes *(Chm-Supervisory Bd)*
Koen Beentjes *(Chm-Exec Bd & CEO)*
Evert-Jan Kooistra *(CFO)*
Pieter Aartsen *(Member-Exec Bd)*
Supervisory Board of Directors:
Kees J. M. Scholtes
Hans J. K. Brouwer
Leo Deuzeman
Fons M. van Westerloo

BINDAR TRADING & INVESTMENT CO. PLC

PO Box 1921
Amman, 1115, Jordan
Tel.: (962) 6 5518916
Fax: (962) 6 5518917
E-Mail: info@bindar-jo.com
Web Site: www.bindar-jo.com
Year Founded: 2000
BIND—(AMM)
Rev.: $5,666,885
Assets: $46,094,487
Liabilities: $14,977,028
Net Worth: $31,117,459
Earnings: $1,715,695
Emp.: 17
Fiscal Year-end: 12/31/12
Business Description:
Financial Services
S.I.C.: 6211
N.A.I.C.S.: 523999
Personnel:
Khaled Yehia *(CFO & Asst Gen Mgr)*

BINDAREE BEEF PTY. LIMITED

7307 Gwydir Highway
Inverell, NSW, 2360, Australia
Tel.: (61) 267211411
Fax: (61) 267211351
E-Mail: info@bindareebeef.com.au
Web Site: www.bindareebeef.com.au
Sales Range: $150-199.9 Million
Emp.: 600
Business Description:
Beef Slaughtering Services
S.I.C.: 2011
N.A.I.C.S.: 311611
Personnel:
John Newton *(Dir-Livestock)*

BINDER+CO AG

Grazer Strasse 19-25
A-8200 Gleisdorf, Austria
Tel.: (43) 31128000
Fax: (43) 3112800300
E-Mail: office@binder-co.at
Web Site: www.binder-co.com
Year Founded: 1894
BIND—(VIE)
Rev.: $117,337,562
Assets: $103,690,090
Liabilities: $63,450,377
Net Worth: $40,239,714
Earnings: $8,256,061
Emp.: 340
Fiscal Year-end: 12/31/12
Business Description:
Bulk Material Separation & Sorting Services
S.I.C.: 4953
N.A.I.C.S.: 562920
Personnel:
Herbert W. Liaunig *(Chm-Supervisory Bd)*
Kurt Berger *(Vice Chm-Supervisory Bd)*
Karl Grabner *(Member-Exec Bd-Fin, Gen Admin, Production & Engrg)*
Joerg Rosegger *(Member-Exec Bd-Sls)*
Supervisory Board of Directors:
Herbert W. Liaunig
Kurt Berger
Erhard F. Grossnigg
Alfred Gschweitl
Gerhard Heldmann
Alexander Liaunig
Erhard Schaschl
Johann Voit

BINEX CO., LTD.

480 2 Jangrim Dong
Saha Gu
604846 Busan, Korea (South)
Tel.: (82) 512639277
Fax: (82) 512656864
Web Site: www.bi-nex.com
053030—(KRS)
Sales Range: $150-199.9 Million
Business Description:
Pharmaceutical & Medicinal Products Mfr
S.I.C.: 2834
N.A.I.C.S.: 325412
Personnel:
Baek-Chun Lee *(CEO)*

BING POWER SYSTEMS GMBH

Dorfaeckerstrasse 16
D-90427 Nuremberg, Germany
Tel.: (49) 91132670
Fax: (49) 9113267299
E-Mail: info@bing.de
Web Site: www.bingpower.de
Rev.: $46,179,829
Emp.: 220
Business Description:
Automobiles, Motorcycles & Industrial Engines Supplier
S.I.C.: 5012
N.A.I.C.S.: 423110
Personnel:
Joachim Preissl *(Mng Dir)*

BINGGRAE CO., LTD.

34-5 Paichai JeongDong B/D
JeongDong
Jung-Gu, Seoul, 100-120, Korea (South)
Tel.: (82) 2 2022 6380
Fax: (82) 2 2022 6390
E-Mail: export@bing.co.kr
Web Site: www.bing.co.kr
Year Founded: 1967
005180—(KRS)
Sls.: $733,864,860
Assets: $504,960,240
Liabilities: $99,153,810
Net Worth: $405,806,430
Earnings: $47,201,220
Fiscal Year-end: 12/31/12
Business Description:
Dairy Product Mfr
S.I.C.: 2023
N.A.I.C.S.: 311514
Personnel:
Kun-Young Lee *(CEO)*

BINGO.COM, LTD.

Hansa Bank Building Ground Floor
Landsome Road
AI-2640 The Valley, Anguilla
Tel.: (264) 461 2646
Web Site: www.bingo.com
Year Founded: 1987
BNGOF—(OTC OTCB)
Rev.: $1,765,828
Assets: $3,362,054
Liabilities: $105,608
Net Worth: $3,256,446
Earnings: ($46,235)
Emp.: 2
Fiscal Year-end: 12/31/12
Business Description:
Online Gambling Services
S.I.C.: 7999
N.A.I.C.S.: 713290
Personnel:
Jason M. Williams *(Pres & CEO)*
Henry W. Bromley *(CFO)*

BINGO.COM, LTD.—(Continued)

Board of Directors:
Tarrnie M. Williams
Fiona Mary Curtis
C. Mark Devereux
Ebba Ljungerud
George C. Whitton
Jason M. Williams

BINH AN SEAFOOD JOINT STOCK COMPANY

Lot 2.17 Tra Noc Industrial Zone
O Mon District, Can Tho, Vietnam
Tel.: (84) 7106251403
Fax: (84) 7106251402
E-Mail: madamedieuhien@bianfishco.com
Web Site: www.bianfishco.com
Sales Range: $25-49.9 Million
Emp.: 5,000
Business Description:
Fish Producer & Distr
S.I.C.: 0921
N.A.I.C.S.: 112511
Personnel:
Hien Thi Dieu Pham *(Chm & CEO)*

BINH CHANH CONSTRUCTION INVESTMENT JOINT STOCK COMPANY

550 Kinh Duong Vuong An Lac Binh Tan
Ho Chi Minh City, Vietnam
Tel.: (84) 838753021
Fax: (84) 838753552
E-Mail: info@bcci.vn
Web Site: bcci.com.vn
BCI—(HOSE)
Sls.: $9,974,536
Assets: $178,525,393
Liabilities: $84,338,520
Net Worth: $94,186,873
Earnings: $8,607,076
Fiscal Year-end: 12/31/12
Business Description:
Real Estate Management Services
S.I.C.: 6531
N.A.I.C.S.: 531390
Personnel:
Nguyen Van Le *(Chm)*
Ngoc Tien Tran *(Chm-Supervisory Bd)*
Ngoc Henri Tran *(Deputy Chm)*
Thuy Nhan Nguyen *(Gen Dir)*
Board of Directors:
Nguyen Van Le
Dinh Thang Hoang
Hoang Thuc Nguyen
Thi Kim Thoa Nguyen
Minh Duc Pham
Be Tran
Ngoc Henri Tran
Supervisory Board of Directors:
Ngoc Tien Tran
Ngoc Thien Huong Tran
Do Van Cuong

BINH TIEN IMEX CORP. PTE. LTD.

(d/b/a Biti's)
22 Ly Chieu Hoang Street
Ward 10 District 6, Ho Chi Minh City, Vietnam
Tel.: (84) 88754513
Fax: (84) 8 8753443
E-Mail: bitis.ex@bitis-vn.com
Web Site: www.bitis-vn.com
Sales Range: $25-49.9 Million
Emp.: 7,500
Business Description:
Footwear Mfr & Distr
S.I.C.: 2389
N.A.I.C.S.: 316210

Subsidiary:

Binh Tien Dong Nai Imex Corp., Pte., Ltd **(1)**
1/1 Pham Van Thuan Street Tam Hiep Ward
Bien Hoa, Dong Nai, Vietnam
Tel.: (84) 61 3813887
Fax: (84) 61 3813786
Footwear Mfr
S.I.C.: 2389
N.A.I.C.S.: 316210

BINHAI INVESTMENT COMPANY LIMITED

Suite 3205-07 32/F Tower 2 Times Square 1 Matheson Street
Causeway Bay, Hong Kong, China (Hong Kong)
Tel.: (852) 2572 9228
Fax: (852) 2572 9283
E-Mail: prd@binhaiinv.com
Web Site: www.binhaiinv.com
2886—(DEU HKG)
Rev.: $155,550,451
Assets: $415,257,685
Liabilities: $323,572,688
Net Worth: $91,684,997
Earnings: $11,924,135
Emp.: 1,375
Fiscal Year-end: 12/31/12
Business Description:
Oil & Gas Pipeline Construction Services
S.I.C.: 1623
N.A.I.C.S.: 237120
Personnel:
Bing Jun Zhang *(Chm)*
Zhong Hai Zhang *(CFO & Deputy Gen Mgr)*
Liang Gao *(Gen Mgr & Compliance Officer)*
Fu Gang Yin *(Sec & Deputy Gen Mgr)*
Board of Directors:
Bing Jun Zhang
Yan Dai
Liang Gao
Shing Hing Ip
Kevin Siu Ki Lau
Japhet Sebastian Law
Xiao Lin Shen
Tak Yin Tse
Gang Wang
Jun Zhang
Wen Fang Zhu
Legal Counsel:
Woo, Kwan, Lee & Lo
26th Floor Jardine House 1 Connaught Place
Central, China (Hong Kong)
Butterfield Corporate Services Limited
Rosebank Centre, 11 Bermudiana Road
Pembroke, Bermuda
Transfer Agents:
Hong Kong Registrars Limited
Shops 1712-1716 17/F Hopewell Centre 183 Queen's Road East
Wanchai, China (Hong Kong)
Butterfield Corporate Services Limited
Rosebank Centre, 11 Bermudiana Road
Pembroke, Bermuda

BINTER CANARIAS, S.A.

Aeropuerto de Gran Canaria
Parcela 9 Del Zima, 35230 Las Palmas, Gran Canaria, Spain
Tel.: (34) 928579601
Fax: (34) 928579603
Web Site: www.bintercanarias.com
Year Founded: 1989
Emp.: 400
Business Description:
Air Passenger Services
S.I.C.: 4512
N.A.I.C.S.: 481111
Personnel:
Pedro Agustin del Castillo Machado *(Pres & CEO)*
Alfredo Morales Martin *(Exec Officer)*
Juan Antonio Escudero Aznar *(Gen Dir)*
Carlos Cabrera Padron *(Sec)*
Board of Directors:
Rosendo Cabrera Hernandez
Carlos Cabrera Padron
Fernando del Castillo y Benitez de Lugo
Miguel Escudero del Castillo
Gilberto Morales Martin
Rafael Planol Lacalle
Carlos Plasencia Romero
Juan Miguel Sanjuan Jover
Antonio German Suarez Dominguez

Subsidiaries:

Atlantica de Handling **(1)**
Carreterra General Del Norte C-820 Ed Star
San Cristobal de La Laguna, 38206, Spain
Tel.: (34) 922 568000
Air Freight Transportation Services
S.I.C.: 4512
N.A.I.C.S.: 481112

BinterSistemas **(1)**
Calle Canon Del Ambar SN GC-1 Salinetas
35219 Telde, Spain
Tel.: (34) 928 30 56 25
Fax: (34) 928 218 103
E-Mail: admin@BinterSistemas.com
Emp.: 30
Software Development Services
S.I.C.: 7373
N.A.I.C.S.: 541512

BInterSwift **(1)**
C Canon Del Ambar Autovia GC-1km 11 600 SN
Gran Canaria, 35200 Telde, Spain
Tel.: (34) 928 305 635
E-Mail: atencionclientes@binterswift.aero
Web Site: www.binterswift.com
Emp.: 3
Air Freight Transportation Services
S.I.C.: 4512
N.A.I.C.S.: 481112

BInterTechnic **(1)**
Aeropuerto de Gran Canaria Parcela 9 Del Zima
35230 Telde, Las Palmas, Spain
Tel.: (34) 682 776 908
Fax: (34) 928 579 605
E-Mail: commercial@bintertechnic.com
Web Site: www.bintertechnic.com
Aircraft Maintenance Services
S.I.C.: 4581
N.A.I.C.S.: 488190
Rafael Lopez, *(Dir Gen)*

Servicious Aerotecnicos Insulares SL **(1)**
41th Beneficiado Jose Estupinan Industrial Park of El Goro
Gran Canaria, 35219 Telde, Las Palmas, Spain
Tel.: (34) 928 70 13 07
Fax: (34) 928 70 13 07
E-Mail: info@satiaero.com
Web Site: www.satiaero.com
Emp.: 50
Aircraft Maintenance Services
S.I.C.: 4581
N.A.I.C.S.: 488190

BINZAGR COMPANY

PO Box 54
Jeddah, 21411, Saudi Arabia
Tel.: (966) 26470000
Telex: 600795 ASMOB SJ
Fax: (966) 26480000
E-Mail: bzho@binzagr.com.sa
Web Site: www.binzagr.com.sa
Year Founded: 1925
Sales Range: $100-124.9 Million
Emp.: 1,700
Business Description:
Holding Company; Industrial & Manufacturing Services
S.I.C.: 7299
N.A.I.C.S.: 532220
Personnel:
Mohamed O. Binzagr *(Chm & Exec Partner)*
Wahib Said Binzagr *(CEO & Exec Partner)*

Subsidiaries:

Abdullah & Said M.O. Binzagr Company **(1)**
9th floor Mahmal tower
PO Box 209
Jeddah, 21411, Saudi Arabia
Tel.: (966) 26438235
Fax: (966) 26438983
E-Mail: bbca@binzagr.com.sa
Web Site: www.binzagr.com.sa
Emp.: 40
Holding Company
S.I.C.: 6719
N.A.I.C.S.: 551112
Paul Sutcliffe *(Mgr)*

Divisions:

Binzagr Industrial Cleaning Services **(2)**
PO Box 54
Jeddah, 21411, Saudi Arabia
Tel.: (966) 26470000
Industrial Cleaning Services
S.I.C.: 7389
N.A.I.C.S.: 541420

Binzagr Factory for Insulation Materials Ltd. **(1)**
PO Box 96
Al Khobar, 31952, Saudi Arabia (100%)
Tel.: (966) 38640980
Fax: (966) 38938130
E-Mail: bfim@binzagr.com
Web Site: www.binzagar-insulation.com
Emp.: 2,500
Oil & Other Industrial Services
S.I.C.: 1389
N.A.I.C.S.: 213112
Mohamed Binsagar *(Chm)*

THE BIO AGENCY

17 Gresse Street
London, W1T 1QL, United Kingdom
Tel.: (44) 207 079 2450
E-Mail: hello@thebioagency.com
Web Site: www.thebioagency.com
Year Founded: 2006
Sales Range: $10-24.9 Million
Emp.: 95
Business Description:
Digital Advertising Services
S.I.C.: 7311
N.A.I.C.S.: 541810
Personnel:
Peter Veash *(CEO)*

BIO-AMD, INC.

3rd Floor 14 South Molton Street
London, W1K 5QP, United Kingdom
Tel.: (44) 8445861910
Fax: (44) 8450038045
Web Site: www.bioamd.com
Year Founded: 2006
BIAD—(OTC)
Int. Income: $13,308
Assets: $3,031,685
Liabilities: $40,621
Net Worth: $2,991,064
Earnings: ($892,281)
Emp.: 2
Fiscal Year-end: 12/31/12
Business Description:
Holding Company; Medical Devices
S.I.C.: 6719
N.A.I.C.S.: 551112
Personnel:
David S. Miller *(Pres)*
Thomas Barr *(CEO)*
Robert Galvin *(CFO, Treas & Sec)*
Board of Directors:
Thomas Barr
Robert Galvin
David S. Miller

BIO BEAUTY GROUP LIMITED
3301 3401-06 Office Tower
Convention Plaza
1 Harbour Road, Wanchai, China (Hong Kong)
Tel.: (852) 34206100
Fax: (852) 3102 2100
Web Site: www.biobeautygroup.com
3332—(HKG)
Emp.: 654
Business Description:
Skin Care & Cosmetics Products Mfr & Marketer
S.I.C.: 2844
N.A.I.C.S.: 325620
Personnel:
Judy Lau *(Chm)*
Connie Wong Wai Kwan *(CEO)*
Ng Yuk Yeung *(Sec)*
Board of Directors:
Judy Lau
Daniel Lee Tin Chak
Connie Wong Wai Kwan
Jim Jin-wei Lau
Grace Lui Wai Mui
Tam Pei Qiang
Xie Ming Quan

BIO BLAST PHARMA LTD.
35 Ahad Ha'am Street
6520206 Tel Aviv, Israel
Tel.: (972) 3 7326616
Web Site: www.bioblast-pharma.com
Assets: $306,000
Liabilities: $131,000
Net Worth: $175,000
Earnings: ($1,145,000)
Emp.: 3
Fiscal Year-end: 12/31/12
Business Description:
Pharmaceutical Mfr
S.I.C.: 2834
N.A.I.C.S.: 325412
Personnel:
Fredric Price *(Chm)*
Dalia Megiddo *(CEO)*
Ehud Gilboa *(CFO)*
Board of Directors:
Fredric Price
Ehud Gilboa
Marlene Haffner
Dalia Megiddo
Ran Nusbaum

BIO-GATE AG
Neumeyerstrasse 28-34
90411 Nuremberg, Germany
Tel.: (49) 911 59 72 4
Fax: (49) 911 59 72 4
Web Site: www.biogate.de
BIG—(DEU)
Sls.: $3,096,191
Assets: $4,576,978
Liabilities: $3,096,191
Net Worth: $1,480,787
Earnings: ($2,961,574)
Emp.: 26
Fiscal Year-end: 12/31/12
Business Description:
Silver Products Coatings & Mfr
S.I.C.: 3479
N.A.I.C.S.: 332812
Personnel:
Knud Klingler *(Chm)*
Karl Klamann *(Asst Chm)*
Karl Richter *(CEO & Co-Mng Dir)*
Marc Lloret-Grau *(Co-Mng Dir & CFO)*
Board of Directors:
Knud Klingler
Karl Klamann
Volker Rofalski

Subsidiary:

BioEpiderm GmbH (1)
Neumeyerstrasse 28 - 34
90411 Nuremberg, Germany
Tel.: (49) 911 2526 350
Fax: (49) 911 2526 351
E-Mail: info@bioepiderm.de
Web Site: www.bioepiderm.de
Emp.: 10
Cosmetic Product Mfr
S.I.C.: 5122
N.A.I.C.S.: 446120
Karl Richter *(Mng Dir)*

BIO GREEN PAPERS LIMITED
3-691/B Raghava Reddy Complex
New Nagole
Hyderabad, 500035, India
Tel.: (91) 40 69998603
Fax: (91) 40 66668603
E-Mail: Biogreen_Paper@Yahoo.com
Web Site: www.biogreenpapers.in
534535—(BOM)
Business Description:
Kraft Paper & Duplex Board Mfr
S.I.C.: 2621
N.A.I.C.S.: 322121
Personnel:
V. Jagdish *(Mng Dir)*
Board of Directors:
M. Balakrishnamurthy
B. Rajendra Goud
T. Rajasekhar
G. Mallikarjuna Sarma
V. Venkateshwarlu

BIO METHANOL CHEMIE NEDERLAND BV
(d/b/a BioMCN)
Oosterhorn 10 Gate 2
9936 HD Delfzijl, Netherlands
Tel.: (31) 88 6647700
Telex: 53035
Web Site: www.biomcn.eu
Sales Range: $50-74.9 Million
Emp.: 100
Business Description:
Methanol Mfr
S.I.C.: 2861
N.A.I.C.S.: 325194
Personnel:
Rob Voncken *(CEO)*

BIO OSMO BERHAD
No 1A Jalan Kampung Sungai Suloh
Mukim Minyak Beku
83000 Batu Pahat, Johor Darul Takzim, Malaysia
Tel.: (60) 74285300
Fax: (60) 74285303
E-Mail: info@bioosmobhd.com
Web Site: www.bioosmobhd.com
BIOOSMO—(KLS)
Business Description:
Drinking Water Processor
S.I.C.: 2086
N.A.I.C.S.: 312112
Personnel:
Chin Kar Yang *(Deputy CEO)*
Choong Choy Lee *(Deputy COO)*
Paramalingam Doraisamy *(Co-Sec)*
Suet Wei Siew *(Co-Sec)*
Board of Directors:
Mohd Amy Azhar Mohd Harif
Auzir Mohd Yaacob
Kok Seong Wong
Chin Kar Yang
Legal Counsel:
Mathews Hun Lachimanan
10-3 3rd Mile Square 151 3rd Mile Jalan Kelang Lama
Kuala Lumpur, Malaysia

BIO-PAPEL S.A.B. DE C.V.
Ejercito Nacional 1130
Los Morales Polanco, Mexico, 11510, Mexico
Tel.: (52) 5591266000
Web Site: www.biopappel.com
Year Founded: 1982
PAPPEL—(MEX)
Sls.: $943,514,352
Assets: $1,310,587,788
Liabilities: $567,714,911
Net Worth: $742,872,877
Earnings: $51,288,109
Emp.: 7,977
Fiscal Year-end: 12/31/12
Business Description:
Paper & Packaging Products Mfr
Import Export
S.I.C.: 2631
N.A.I.C.S.: 322130
Personnel:
Miguel Rincon *(Chm, Pres, CEO, Mng Dir & Dir Gen)*
Mayela Rincon de Velasco *(CFO)*
Martin Rincon *(Chief Sustainability Officer & Chief Competitivity Officer)*
Miguel Rincon Barraza *(CEO-Bio Pappel Packaging)*
Ignacio Rincon *(CEO-Bio Pappel International)*
Wilfrido Rincon *(CEO-Bio Pappel Printing & Kraft)*
Gabriel Villegas Salazar *(Gen Counsel)*
Board of Directors:
Miguel Rincon
Miguel Rincon Barraza
Alfonso Fernandez de Castro
Mayela Rincon de Velasco
Angel Del Palacio
Ignacio Rincon
Jesus Rincon
Jose Antonio Rincon
Martin Rincon
Wilfrido Rincon
Buenventura Gonzalez Saravia
Legal Counsel:
White & Case
First Union Financial Ctr. 200 S. Biscayne Blvd.
Miami, FL 33131-2352
Tel.: (305) 371-2700
Fax: (305) 358-5744

Subsidiaries:

Empaques de Carton TITAN (1)
Miguel Barragan 207 W
Colonia 15 Mago, 64450 Monterrey, NL, Mexico (100%)
Tel.: (52) 8183749208
Fax: (52) 8183749213
Web Site: www.estitan.com.mx
Mfg., Distribution & Sales of Corrugated Containers, Packaging Products, Boxes, Sacks & Bags & Molded Pulp Egg Cartons
S.I.C.: 2653
N.A.I.C.S.: 322211

Grupo Industrial Durango, S.A. de C.V. (1)
Potasio 150
Ciudad Industrial, 34220 Durango, Mexico MX (100%)
Tel.: (52) 6188291918
Fax: (52) 6188291901
Web Site: www.larcon.corpdgo.com.mx
Emp.: 600
Mfr., Distributor & Sales of Industrial Paper & Container Board
S.I.C.: 2631
N.A.I.C.S.: 322130
Wilfrido Rincon Arredondo *(Pres)*

BIO VIEW LTD.
3 Pakris Street
PO Box 4051
Rehovot, 70400, Israel
Tel.: (972) 89366868
Fax: (972) 89366869
E-Mail: info@bioview.co.il
Web Site: www.bioview.co.il
BIOV—(TAE)
Sales Range: $1-9.9 Million
Emp.: 25
Business Description:
Medical Laboratory Equipment Mfr
S.I.C.: 3826
N.A.I.C.S.: 334516
Personnel:
Alan Schwebel *(Pres & CEO)*
Shay Shemesh *(CFO)*
Yuval Harari *(Exec VP)*

U.S. Subsidiary:

BioView Inc. (1)
44 Manning Rd
Billerica, MA 01821
Tel.: (978) 670-4741
Fax: (978) 670-4740
Web Site: www.bioview.co.il/HTMLs/categories2.aspx?c0=12528&bsp=749&bss53=12528
Emp.: 50
Medical Laboratory Instrument Distr
S.I.C.: 8741
N.A.I.C.S.: 551114
David Kutas *(Pres & CEO)*

BIOALLIANCE PHARMA S.A.
49 Boulevard du General Martial Valin
75015 Paris, France
Tel.: (33) 145587600
Fax: (33) 145580881
E-Mail: contact@bioalliancepharma.com
Web Site: www.bioalliancepharma.com
Year Founded: 1997
BIO—(EUR)
Sls.: $5,422,540
Assets: $29,777,472
Liabilities: $13,970,220
Net Worth: $15,807,252
Earnings: ($15,545,465)
Emp.: 55
Fiscal Year-end: 12/31/12
Business Description:
Biopharmaceutical Product Mfr
S.I.C.: 2834
N.A.I.C.S.: 325412
Personnel:
Patrick Langlois *(Chm)*
Judith Greciet *(CEO)*
Nicolas Fellmann *(CFO & VP)*
Board of Directors:
Patrick Langlois
Daniele Guyot Caparros
Remi Droller
Judith Greciet
Russell Greig
Thomas Hofstaetter
David Horn Solomon
Nicolas Trebouta
Ernst & Young Audit
Tour First 1-2 place des Saisons
92400 Courbevoie, France

Non-U.S. Subsidiary:

SpeBio BV (1)
Kingsfordwg 151
1043 GR Amsterdam, Netherlands
Tel.: (31) 204919602
Fax: (31) 204919090
E-Mail: info@spepharm.com
Web Site: www.spepharm.com
Pharmaceutical Medicine Whslr
S.I.C.: 5122
N.A.I.C.S.: 424210
Karl Gerhard Seifert *(Chm-Supervisory Bd)*

BIOAMBER INC.
1250 Rene Levesque W Ste 4110
Montreal, QC, H3B 4W8, Canada
Tel.: (514) 844-8000
Fax: (514) 844-1414
Web Site: www.bio-amber.com
Year Founded: 2008
BIOAU—(NYSE)
Rev.: $2,291,367
Assets: $50,003,821
Liabilities: $12,206,246

BioAmber Inc.—(Continued)

Net Worth: $37,797,575
Earnings: ($39,538,463)
Emp.: 64
Fiscal Year-end: 12/31/12

Business Description:
Chemical Products Mfr
S.I.C.: 2869
N.A.I.C.S.: 325110

Personnel:
Raymond J. Land *(Chm)*
Jean-Francois Huc *(Pres & CEO)*
Andrew P. Ashworth *(CFO)*
James Millis *(CTO)*
Babette Pettersen *(Chief Comml Officer)*
Michael A. Hartmann *(Exec VP)*
Thomas J. Dries *(Sr VP-Ops Strategy)*

Board of Directors:
Raymond J. Land
Kurt W. Briner
Heinz Haller
Jean-Francois Huc
Taro Inaba
Denis Lucquin
Jorge Nogueira
Kenneth W. Wall

BIOASIS TECHNOLOGIES INC.

Suite 600 - 1385 West 8th Avenue
Vancouver, BC, V6H 3V9, Canada
Tel.: (778) 383-3280
Fax: (604) 215-0091
E-Mail: info@bioasis.ca
Web Site: www.bioasis.ca
Year Founded: 2006
BTI—(TSXV)
Int. Income: $26,000
Assets: $3,812,327
Liabilities: $239,752
Net Worth: $3,572,575
Earnings: ($4,931,100)
Fiscal Year-end: 02/28/13

Business Description:
Neurological Disease Therapeutics & Diagnostics Researcher, Developer & Mfr
S.I.C.: 8731
N.A.I.C.S.: 541711

Personnel:
Robin B. Hutchison *(Chm & CEO)*
David Clark *(CFO & Sec)*

Board of Directors:
Robin B. Hutchison
David Clark
Ron Erickson
Chris Fibiger
Gregory David Gubitz
Michael Hutchison
Terry W. Pearson

Legal Counsel:
Thomas Rondeau LLP
Suite 300 576 Seymour Street
Vancouver, BC, V6C 3K1, Canada

Transfer Agent:
Olympia Trust Company
Suite 1003-750 West Pender Street
Vancouver, BC, Canada

BIOCANCELL LTD.

Beck Science Center 8 Hartom St
Har Hotzvim
Jerusalem, Israel
Tel.: (972) 25486555
Fax: (972) 25486550
E-Mail: info@biocancell.com
Web Site: www.biocancell.com
Year Founded: 2004
BICL—(TAE)
Rev.: $56,154
Assets: $2,548,161
Liabilities: $1,663,935
Net Worth: $884,226
Earnings: ($6,497,488)
Emp.: 8
Fiscal Year-end: 12/31/12

Business Description:
Cancer Cell Prevention Products Mfr & Researcher
S.I.C.: 2834
N.A.I.C.S.: 325412

Personnel:
Aharon Schwartz *(Chm)*
Jonathan Burgin *(CEO & CFO)*
Ira Weinstein *(COO)*
Abraham Hochberg *(Chief Scientific Officer)*

Board of Directors:
Aharon Schwartz
Aviv Boim
Ofer Goldberg
Abraham Hochberg
Ruben Krupik
Hanoch Rappaport

Subsidiary:

BioCancell Therapeutics Israel Ltd. **(1)**
8 Hartom Har Hotzvim
Jerusalem, 97775, Israel
Tel.: (972) 25486555
Fax: (972) 25486550
E-Mail: info@biocancell.com
Web Site: www.biocancell.com
Emp.: 2
Health Care Therapeutic Services
S.I.C.: 8049
N.A.I.C.S.: 621340
Uri Danon *(CEO)*
Aris Wind *(CEO)*

BIOCON LTD.

20th KM Hosur Road Electronics City
Bengaluru, India 560 100
Tel.: (91) 8028082808
Fax: (91) 8028523423
E-Mail: contact.us@biocon.com
Web Site: www.biocon.com
BIOCON—(NSE)
Rev.: $469,173,240
Assets: $818,744,940
Liabilities: $307,059,480
Net Worth: $511,685,460
Earnings: $95,054,580
Emp.: 6,727
Fiscal Year-end: 03/31/13

Business Description:
Biopharmaceutical Research, Development & Manufacturing Services
S.I.C.: 2834
N.A.I.C.S.: 325412

Personnel:
Kiran Mazumdar-Shaw *(Chm & Mng Dir)*
John Shaw *(Vice Chm)*
M. B. Chinappa *(CFO)*
Arun Chandavarkar *(COO)*
Kiran Kumar *(Compliance Officer & Sec)*
Abhijit Barve *(Pres-R&D)*
Murali Krishnan *(Pres-Fin)*

Board of Directors:
Kiran Mazumdar-Shaw
Peter Bains
Daniel M. Bradbury
Charles L. Cooney
Mary Harney
Bala S. Manian
Ravi Mazumdar
Catherine Rosenberg
John Shaw
Suresh Talwar
Russell Walls

Transfer Agent:
Karvy Computershare Private Limited
Karvy House 46 Avenue 4 Street No.1 Banjara Hills
Hyderabad, India

Subsidiaries:

Biocon Biopharmaceuticals Private Limited **(1)**
20th KM Hosur Rd
Electronics City, Bengaluru, India
Tel.: (91) 8028082808
Fax: (91) 8028523423
E-Mail: contact.us@biocon.com
Clinical Research Services
S.I.C.: 8731
N.A.I.C.S.: 541711
Sandeep Rao *(Gen Mgr)*

Clinigene International Limited **(1)**
Clinigene House Tower 1 Semicon Park
Electronic City
Phase II Hosur Rd, Bengaluru, 560100, India
Tel.: (91) 8028082780
Fax: (91) 8028522989
E-Mail: bd@clinigeneintl.com
Web Site: www.clinigeneintl.com
Emp.: 160
Clinical Research Services
S.I.C.: 8731
N.A.I.C.S.: 541711
Abhijit Barve *(COO)*

Syngene International Limited **(1)**
Biocon Park Plot 2&3 Bommasandra
Industrial Estate Phase IV
Bommasandra Jigani Link Road, Bengaluru, 560 099, India
Tel.: (91) 80 2808 2808
Fax: (91) 80 2808 3150
E-Mail: contact.us@biocon.com
Web Site: www.syngeneintl.com
Clinical Research Services
S.I.C.: 8731
N.A.I.C.S.: 541711
Goutam Das *(COO)*

BIOCUREX, INC.

7080 River Road Suite 215
Richmond, BC, V6X 1X5, Canada
Tel.: (866) 884-8669
Toll Free: (866) 884-8669
E-Mail: info@biocurex.com
Web Site: www.biocurex.com
BOCX—(OTCB)
Sales Range: Less than $1 Million
Emp.: 6

Business Description:
Cancer Detection Products & Research Services
S.I.C.: 8731
N.A.I.C.S.: 541712

Personnel:
Denis R. Burger *(Chm)*
Paul D. Slowey *(Pres)*
Ricardo Moro-Vidal *(CEO)*

Board of Directors:
Denis R. Burger
Ricardo Moro-Vidal
Paul D. Slowey

BIODIEM LIMITED

Level 4 100 Albert Road
South Melbourne, VIC, 3205, Australia
Tel.: (61) 3 9692 7240
Fax: (61) 3 9077 9233
E-Mail: info@biodiem.com
Web Site: www.biodiem.com
Rev.: $122,919
Assets: $1,412,620
Liabilities: $300,234
Net Worth: $1,112,385
Earnings: ($2,413,670)
Emp.: 3
Fiscal Year-end: 06/30/13

Business Description:
Medical Research Services
S.I.C.: 8731
N.A.I.C.S.: 541711

Personnel:
Julie Phillips *(CEO)*
Melanie Leydin *(CFO & Sec)*

Board of Directors:
Hugh M. Morgan
Donald S. Brooks
Arthur Kwok Cheung Li
Julie Phillips
Larisa Rudenko

BIOERA S.P.A.

Via della Repubblica 82
42025 Cavriago, Italy
Tel.: (39) 0522 373177
Fax: (39) 0522 373183
E-Mail: info@bioera.it
Web Site: www.bioera.it
Year Founded: 2004
BIE—(ITA)
Sales Range: $125-149.9 Million

Business Description:
Organic Food Product, Natural Cosmetics & Nutritional Supplement Mfr & Distr
S.I.C.: 5122
N.A.I.C.S.: 446191

Personnel:
Walter Burani *(Chm & CEO)*
Francesca Cesari *(CFO)*

Board of Directors:
Walter Burani
Andrea Burani
Giuseppe Gullo
Mario Massai
Giuliano Tagliavini

Subsidiaries:

CDD SpA **(1)**
Via Bosco 99 A
42019 Scandiano, Italy
Tel.: (39) 0522915401
Fax: (39) 0522915402
E-Mail: cdd@cdd.it
Web Site: www.cdd.it
Emp.: 30
Food Retailer
S.I.C.: 5411
N.A.I.C.S.: 445120
Filippo Crovetti *(Mgr)*

ERBORISTERIE D'ITALIA Srl **(1)**
Via Sandro Pertini 8/12
Bibbona, 57020, Italy
Tel.: (39) 586679101
Fax: (39) 0586679112
Natural & Organic Products Mfr
S.I.C.: 2037
N.A.I.C.S.: 311411

KI Group S.p.A **(1)**
Strada Settimo 399 11
10156 Turin, Italy
Tel.: (39) 0117176700
Fax: (39) 0117176717
E-Mail: kigroup@kigroup.com
Web Site: www.kigroup.com
KI—(ITA)
Emp.: 50
Variety Health Food Mfr & Whslr
S.I.C.: 5149
N.A.I.C.S.: 424490
Dino Boggio *(Mng Dir)*

Subsidiary:

LA FONTE DELLA VITA Srl **(2)**
Via Monviso 18
Cuneo, Italy
Tel.: (39) 0172652003
Fax: (39) 0172652030
Diet Food Mfr & Whslr
S.I.C.: 2099
N.A.I.C.S.: 311999

Natfood S.R.L. **(1)**
Via Bosco 99 A
420019 Scandiano, Reggio Emilia, Italy
Tel.: (39) 0522330259
Fax: (39) 0522 767122
E-Mail: natfood@natfood.it
Web Site: www.natfood.it
Emp.: 30
Food & Beverage Mfr
S.I.C.: 2086
N.A.I.C.S.: 312111
Franco Lusetti *(Mng Dir)*

Subsidiaries:

Natfood Puglia Srl (2)
Via Degli Imbianchini 9
70026 Modugno, Italy
Tel.: (39) 0805367053
Fax: (39) 0805125268
E-Mail: info@natfoodpuglia.it
Web Site: www.natfoodpuglia.it
Frozen Pulps Mfr
S.I.C.: 2037
N.A.I.C.S.: 311411

NATFOOD ROMAGNA Srl (2)
Via Maranello 31
Coriano, 47853, Italy
Tel.: (39) 0541658506
Fax: (39) 0541658475
Emp.: 8
Natural & Organic Products Mfr
S.I.C.: 2037
N.A.I.C.S.: 311411

Non-U.S. Subsidiary:

Natfood Iberica S.L. (2)
Can Diners 1-11 Nave 5
08310 Argentona, Spain
Tel.: (34) 93 741 18 63
Fax: (34) 937411864
E-Mail: info@natfoodiberica.com
Web Site: www.natfoodiberica.com
Emp.: 10
Food & Beverage Mfr & Whslr
S.I.C.: 5149
N.A.I.C.S.: 424490
Silvia Marino *(Gen Mgr)*

Non-U.S. Subsidiary:

NATFOOD PORTUGAL LdA (3)
Rua Ponte Da Pedra 406 Armazem A4
Bloco A
4470-108 Maia, Portugal
Tel.: (351) 229605155
Fax: (351) 229606206
E-Mail: natfoodportugal@gmail.com
Web Site: www.natfood.pt
Emp.: 8
Food Products Mfr & Distr
S.I.C.: 2099
N.A.I.C.S.: 311999
Francisco Pereira *(Mgr)*

Organic Oils S.p.A. (1)
Str Montebuono 12 b
06132 Perugia, Italy
Tel.: (39) 075529991
Fax: (39) 0756959242
E-Mail: info@organicoils.it
Web Site: www.organicoils.it
Emp.: 20
Organic Health Foods Mfr & Whslr
S.I.C.: 2099
N.A.I.C.S.: 311999
Thomas Rossi *(Mgr-Export)*

BIOEXX SPECIALTY PROTEINS LTD.

33 Fraser Ave Suite G11
Toronto, ON, M6K 3J9, Canada
Tel.: (416) 588-4442
Fax: (416) 588-1999
Toll Free: (877) 588-4442
E-Mail: skondra@bioexx.com
Web Site: www.bioexx.com
Rev.: $644,378
Assets: $18,755,169
Liabilities: $12,174,968
Net Worth: $6,580,202
Earnings: ($62,901,441)
Emp.: 29
Fiscal Year-end: 12/31/12
Business Description:
Oilseed Processing Services
S.I.C.: 2075
N.A.I.C.S.: 311224
Personnel:
William Ollerhead *(Chm)*
John MacDonald *(Interim CEO)*
Greg Furyk *(CFO)*
Samah Garringer *(Exec VP)*
Board of Directors:
William Ollerhead
Peter Alan Lacey
John MacDonald
Richard Rumble
Markus Vettiger
Transfer Agent:
Equity Financial Trust Company
Toronto, ON, Canada

BIOFARM SA

(See Under SIF BANAT-CRISANA SA)

BIOFRONTERA AG

Hemmelrather Weg 201
51377 Leverkusen, Germany
Tel.: (49) 214 87632 0
Fax: (49) 214 87632 90
E-Mail: info@biofrontera.com
Web Site: www.biofrontera.com
B8F—(DEU)
Sls.: $4,619,179
Assets: $12,163,210
Liabilities: $17,674,449
Net Worth: ($5,511,239)
Earnings: ($5,543,659)
Emp.: 34
Fiscal Year-end: 12/31/12
Business Description:
Pharmaceutical Products Mfr
S.I.C.: 2834
N.A.I.C.S.: 325412
Personnel:
Jurgen Baumann *(Chm-Supervisory Bd)*
Bernd Wetzel *(Vice Chm-Supervisory Bd)*
Hermann Lubbert *(CEO)*
Thomas Schaffer *(CFO)*
Supervisory Board of Directors:
Jurgen Baumann
Andreas Fritsch
Ulrich Granzer
Ulrike Kluge
Alfred Neimke
Bernd Wetzel

BIOFUTURES INTERNATIONAL PLC

(Name Changed to Graphene Nanochem PLC)

BIOGAIA AB

Kungsbrotlan 3A
PO Box 3242
103 64 Stockholm, Sweden
Tel.: (46) 855529300
Fax: (46) 855529301
E-Mail: info@biogaia.se
Web Site: www.biogaia.com
BIOGB—(OMX)
Sls.: $99,885,010
Assets: $80,035,006
Liabilities: $9,323,295
Net Worth: $70,711,711
Earnings: $51,064,031
Emp.: 76
Fiscal Year-end: 12/31/12
Business Description:
Foods, Beverages & Healthcare Products
S.I.C.: 8322
N.A.I.C.S.: 624210
Personnel:
Peter Rothschild *(Co-Founder & CEO)*
Jan Annwall *(Co-Founder)*
Keitaro Nomura *(Pres-Japan)*
Margareta Hagman *(Exec VP-Acctg, Fin & IR)*
Urban Strindlov *(Exec VP-Partner Alliances & Product Dev)*
Eamonn Connolly *(Sr VP-Res)*
Bjorn Lindman *(Sr VP-Quality Assurance)*
Board of Directors:
Jan Annwall
Stefan Elving
Thomas Flinck
Inger Holmstrom
Paula Zeilon
Non-U.S. Subsidiary:

BioGaia Japan Inc. (1)
3-17 Komachi
Naka-Ku, Hiroshima, 7300041, Japan
Tel.: (81) 822445021
Fax: (81) 822445022
Web Site: www.biogaia.jp
Biotechnology Development Services
S.I.C.: 8731
N.A.I.C.S.: 541711
Anders Zachrisson *(Mgr)*

BIOGAS NORD AG

Werningshof 2-4
33719 Bielefeld, Germany
Tel.: (49) 49 52196330
Fax: (49) 49 5219633500
E-Mail: info@biogas.de
Web Site: www.biogas-nord.com
Year Founded: 2000
BG8—(DEU)
Sales Range: $100-124.9 Million
Emp.: 142
Business Description:
Engineering & Construction Services
S.I.C.: 8711
N.A.I.C.S.: 541330
Personnel:
Hermann Locarek-Junge *(Chm-Supervisory Bd)*
Prezemystaw Hewelt *(Vice Chm-Supervisory Bd)*
Aleksander Rechter *(CEO)*
Friedrich Schwenker *(COO & Mng Dir-Ops)*
Supervisory Board of Directors:
Hermann Locarek-Junge
Prezemystaw Hewelt
Boleslaw Piechucki

Subsidiaries:

Bioenergie Ahlen GmbH & Co. KG (1)
Borbeiner 28 Aussenbereich
59227 Ahlen, Germany
Tel.: (49) 521 96330
Emp.: 1
Biogas Plant Construction Services
S.I.C.: 1629
N.A.I.C.S.: 237120

BIOGAS NORD Anlagenbau GmbH (1)
Werningshof 2-4
33719 Bielefeld, Germany
Tel.: (49) 521 9633 0
Fax: (49) 521 9633 500
Biogas Plant Construction Services
S.I.C.: 1629
N.A.I.C.S.: 237120

Bio.S Biogas Verwaltungs GmbH (1)
Werningshof 2-4
33719 Bielefeld, Germany
Tel.: (49) 52 15 57 50 70
Fax: (49) 52 15 57 50 733
Biogas Plant Construction Services
S.I.C.: 1623
N.A.I.C.S.: 237120

Non-U.S. Subsidiaries:

BIOGAS NORD Espana S.L. (1)
Cale Marina Alta Dos 9
Puzol, Valencia, 46530, Spain
Tel.: (34) 961 40 50 47
Fax: (34) 961 40 50 47
Web Site: www.biogasnord.com
Biogas Plant Construction Services
S.I.C.: 1623
N.A.I.C.S.: 237120
Fernando Perez, *(Mng Dir)*

BIOGAS NORD Polska Sp.z o.o. (1)
ul Pulawska 182
Warsaw, 02-670, Poland
Tel.: (48) 22 6202921
Biogas Plant Construction Services
S.I.C.: 1623
N.A.I.C.S.: 237120

BIOGAS NORD UK Ltd. (1)
2 Temple Back East Temple Quay
Bristol, BS1 6EG, United Kingdom
Tel.: (44) 1258 475300
Fax: (44) 1258 475300
Biogas Plant Construction Services
S.I.C.: 1629
N.A.I.C.S.: 237120

BIOGASPARK NV

Kruisdonk 66
6222 PH Maastricht, Netherlands
Tel.: (31) 43 631 269
E-Mail: joachim.haedke@biogaspark.de
Web Site: www.biogaspark.de
Year Founded: 2008
BPK—(DEU)
Business Description:
Investment Services
S.I.C.: 6211
N.A.I.C.S.: 523999
Personnel:
Joachim Haedke *(Chm-Mgmt Bd)*
Supervisory Board of Directors:
Michael Hasenstab
Robert Kaess
Florian Pfingsten

BIOGEN LIMITED

Level 11 225 St Georges Terr
Perth, WA, 6000, Australia
Tel.: (61) 8 9226 4033
Fax: (61) 8 9226 0333
E-Mail: office@biogen.com.au
Web Site: www.biogen.com.au
Business Description:
Renewable Electricity Generation
S.I.C.: 4911
N.A.I.C.S.: 221118
Personnel:
William Mitchell *(Chm)*
Robert Lukin *(Mng Dir)*
Raewyn Clark *(CFO & Sec)*
Board of Directors:
William Mitchell
Edward Farrell
Robert Lukin

BIOIASIS JSC

60 Deyan Belishki Str
1404 Sofia, Bulgaria
Tel.: (359) 2 9207766
Fax: (359) 2 9207667
E-Mail: office@bioiasis.com
Web Site: www.bioiasis.com
Year Founded: 2005
4OE—(BUL)
Business Description:
Medical Devices Trading Services
S.I.C.: 5047
N.A.I.C.S.: 423450
Personnel:
George P. Kissas *(Chm)*

BIOINVENT INTERNATIONAL AB

The Gamma Building Solvegatan 41
SE-223 70 Lund, Sweden
Tel.: (46) 462868550
Fax: (46) 462110806
E-Mail: info@bioinvent.com
Web Site: www.bioinvent.com
BINV—(OMX)
Sls.: $6,648,041
Assets: $18,040,856
Liabilities: $10,668,661
Net Worth: $7,372,195
Earnings: ($29,078,406)
Emp.: 50
Fiscal Year-end: 12/31/12

BioInvent International AB—(Continued)

Business Description:
Pharmaceuticals
S.I.C.: 2834
N.A.I.C.S.: 325412
Personnel:
Bjorn O. Nilsson *(Chm)*
Cristina Glad *(Pres & CEO)*
Martin Wiles *(Sr VP-Bus Dev)*
Board of Directors:
Bjorn O. Nilsson
Lars Backsell
Dharminder S. Chahal
Lars Ingelmark
Jonas Jendi
Sidonie Karlsson
Elisabeth Lindner
Ulrika T. Mattson
Fredrik Nilsson

BIOKARPET S.A.

PO Box 1129
41110 Larissa, Greece
Tel.: (30) 2410688688
Fax: (30) 2410688620
E-Mail: info@biokarpet.gr
Web Site: www.biokarpet.gr
Year Founded: 1950
BIOKA—(ATH)
Sales Range: $100-124.9 Million
Emp.: 687
Business Description:
Holding Company; Textiles, Metallurgy & Information Technology
S.I.C.: 6719
N.A.I.C.S.: 551112
Personnel:
Asterios I. Kantonias *(Chm)*
Georgios A. Kantonias *(Vice Chm)*
Board of Directors:
Asterios I. Kantonias
Ioannis G. Chatziefthimiou
Vasilios K. Floros
Georgios A. Kantonias
Ioannis A. Kantonias
Antonios N. Mavromatis
Georgios V. Papageorgiou
Athanasios V. Tsiaras
Vasileios A. Tsiaras

Subsidiaries:

Albio Data S.A. **(1)**
8 km Larissa -Thessaloniki
41500 Larissa, Greece (80%)
Tel.: (30) 2410661168
Fax: (30) 2410660179
E-Mail: info@albiodata.gr
Web Site: www.albiodata.gr
Emp.: 15
Other Management Consulting Services
S.I.C.: 8748
N.A.I.C.S.: 541618
Barboutis Vasilios *(Mng Dir)*

Exalco S.A. **(1)**
5th Km Larissa - Athens National Rd
Po Box 1129
41110 Larissa, Greece (98.39%)
Tel.: (30) 2410688688
Fax: (30) 2410688570
E-Mail: info@exalco.gr
Web Site: www.exalco.gr
Emp.: 350
Aluminum Extruded Product Mfr
S.I.C.: 3355
N.A.I.C.S.: 331318
Georgios A. Kantonias *(Vice Chm & Mng Dir)*

Persika SA **(1)**
5 Km National Road
41110 Larissa, Athens, Greece
Tel.: (30) 2410688688
Fax: (30) 2410 688510
E-Mail: info@persika.gr
Web Site: www.persika.gr
Carpet Mfr
S.I.C.: 2273
N.A.I.C.S.: 314110
John Kantonias *(Pres)*

Non-U.S. Subsidiaries:

Biokarpet Bulgaria E.O.O.D. **(1)**
348 Botevgradsko Shose Blvd
1839 Sofia, Bulgaria (100%)
Tel.: (359) 29898894
Fax: (359) 29898896
E-Mail: info@biokarpet.bg
Web Site: www.biokarpet.bg
Carpet & Upholstery Cleaning Services
S.I.C.: 7217
N.A.I.C.S.: 561740
Sarry Cacadouos *(Gen Mgr)*

Biokarpet Romania S.R.L. **(1)**
B-Dul Unirii Nr 69 Bloc G2B
Bucharest, Romania (75%)
Tel.: (40) 213212065
Fax: (40) 213212067
E-Mail: office@biokarpet.ro
Web Site: www.biokarpet.ro
Emp.: 10
Carpet & Rug Mills
S.I.C.: 2273
N.A.I.C.S.: 314110
Elina Stoecan *(Gen Mgr)*

Exalco Bulgaria A.D. **(1)**
348 Blvd Botevgradsko Rd & Ring Rd
PO Box 10
1517 Sofia, Bulgaria (95%)
Tel.: (359) 29452233
Fax: (359) 29462255
E-Mail: exalco@exalco.bg
Web Site: www.exalco.bg
Aluminum Extruded Product Mfr
S.I.C.: 3355
N.A.I.C.S.: 331318
Aris Tseledis *(Gen Mgr)*

Exalco Romania srl **(1)**
Sos Centurii Nr 11
Bragadiru, 077025 Bucharest, Ilfov, Romania (75%)
Tel.: (40) 213693275
Fax: (40) 213693278
E-Mail: office@exalco.ro
Other Aluminum Rolling & Drawing
S.I.C.: 3354
N.A.I.C.S.: 331318
Dimitris Michailidis *(Gen Mgr)*

BIOLAND CO., LTD

59 Songjeongri 2 gil Byungchon
Cheonan, Chungnam, Korea (South)
Tel.: (82) 41 550 7700
Fax: (82) 41 550 7709
Web Site: www.biolandkorea.com
Year Founded: 1995
052260—(KRS)
Business Description:
Pharmaceutical Preparation Mfr
S.I.C.: 2834
N.A.I.C.S.: 325412
Personnel:
Chan Bok Jung *(CEO)*

BIOLIGHT ISRAELI LIFE SCIENCES INVESTMENTS LTD.

Kiryat Atidim Building 3 5th Floor
6158101 Tel Aviv, Israel
Tel.: (972) 732753400
Fax: (972) 732753401
E-Mail: biolight@bio-light.co.il
Web Site: www.bio-light.co.il
Year Founded: 2005
BOLT—(OTC TAE)
Rev.: $212,257
Assets: $11,255,274
Liabilities: $1,223,300
Net Worth: $10,031,974
Earnings: ($3,832,452)
Fiscal Year-end: 12/31/12
Business Description:
Biomedical Researcher & Developer
S.I.C.: 8731
N.A.I.C.S.: 541711
Personnel:
Israel Makov *(Chm)*
Suzana Nahum-Zilberberg *(CEO)*
Itai Bar-Natan *(CFO)*
Board of Directors:
Israel Makov
Efrat Makov
Shmuel Peretz
Eli Shohet
Ron Weissberg

BIOLINERX LTD.

19 Hartum St
PO Box 45158
Jerusalem, 9777518, Israel
Tel.: (972) 25489100
Fax: (972) 25489101
E-Mail: info@biolinerx.com
Web Site: www.biolinerx.com
Year Founded: 2003
BLRX—(NASDAQ TAE)
Rev.: $740,168
Assets: $19,776,435
Liabilities: $8,193,944
Net Worth: $11,582,490
Earnings: ($17,490,170)
Emp.: 43
Fiscal Year-end: 12/31/13
Business Description:
Pharmaceutical Developer & Mfr
S.I.C.: 2834
N.A.I.C.S.: 325412
Personnel:
Aharon Schwartz *(Chm)*
Kinneret Savitsky *(CEO)*
Philip A. Serlin *(CFO & COO)*
Board of Directors:
Aharon Schwartz
Michael J. Anghel
Nurit Benjamini
B. J. Bormann
Yakov Friedman
Raphael Hofstein
Avraham Molcho
Sandra Panem

Subsidiary:

BioLine Innovations Jerusalem **(1)**
19 Hartum St
PO Box 45158
Jerusalem, 91450, Israel
Tel.: (972) 25489100
Fax: (972) 2 548 9101
E-Mail: info@biolinerx.com
Web Site: www.biojerusalem.org.il/database_tpi.asp?ID=8
Emp.: 50
Biopharmaceutical Research & Development Services
S.I.C.: 8731
N.A.I.C.S.: 541711
Kinneret Savitsky *(CEO)*

BIOLITEC AG

Otto-Schott-Str
07745 Jena, Germany
Tel.: (49) 3641 519 530
Fax: (49) 3641 519 5333
E-Mail: info@biolitec.com
Web Site: www.biolitec.com
BIB—(DEU)
Sales Range: $25-49.9 Million
Emp.: 231
Business Description:
Photosensitizers, Lasers & Optical Fibers Mfr
S.I.C.: 3845
N.A.I.C.S.: 334510
Personnel:
Dietmar Meyersiek *(Chm-Supervisory Bd)*
Wolfgang Neuberger *(Chm-Mgmt Bd & CEO)*
Supervisory Board of Directors:
Dietmar Meyersiek
Rolf C. Landgraf
Stephan Schmidt

Subsidiary:

CeramOptec GmbH **(1)**
Siemensstrabe 44
53121 Bonn, Germany
Tel.: (49) 228979670
Fax: (49) 2289796799
E-Mail: info@ceramoptec.de
Web Site: www.ceramoptec.de
Emp.: 60
Optical Fiber & Laser Mfr
S.I.C.: 3845
N.A.I.C.S.: 334510

Non-U.S. Subsidiaries:

biolitec Italia SRL **(1)**
Viale Monza 133
20123 Milan, Italy
Tel.: (39) 228172400
Fax: (39) 245485370
E-Mail: info@biolitec.it
Emp.: 3
Medical Laser Systems Mfr
S.I.C.: 3845
N.A.I.C.S.: 334510
Sabio Colluccia *(Pres)*

biolitec (M) Sdn. Bhd. **(1)**
No. 18 Jalan PJS 7 21
Bandar Sunway, 46150 Petaling Jaya, Selangor Darul Ehsan, Malaysia
Tel.: (60) 356327128
Fax: (60) 356380128
E-Mail: info@biolitec.com.my
Web Site: www.biolitec.com
Emp.: 10
Medical Laser Systems Mfr
S.I.C.: 3845
N.A.I.C.S.: 334510

biolitec Pharma (Ireland) Ltd. **(1)**
United Drug House
Magna Dr, Dublin, Ireland
Tel.: (353) 14637415
Fax: (353) 14637411
E-Mail: general.info@biolitec.com
Web Site: www.biolitecpharma.com
Emp.: 10
Medical Laser Systems Mfr
S.I.C.: 3845
N.A.I.C.S.: 334510
Wimrich Rauschning *(Mgr)*

BIOLOGICAL E. LIMITED

18/1&3 Azamabad
Hyderabad, Andra Pradesh, 500 020, India
Tel.: (91) 40 3021 3999
Fax: (91) 40 2761 5309
E-Mail: info@biologicale.co.in
Web Site: www.biologicale.com
Year Founded: 1953
Business Description:
Biopharmaceutical Products Developer, Mfr & Whslr
S.I.C.: 2836
N.A.I.C.S.: 325414
Personnel:
Vijay Kumar Datla *(Chm & Mng Dir)*

BIOLOGIX HAIR INC.

(Formerly T&G Apothecary, Inc.)
82 Avenue Road
Toronto, ON, M5R 2H2, Canada
Tel.: (647) 344-5900
Web Site: www.biologixhair.com
Year Founded: 2011
BLGXD—(OTC)
Assets: $663,961
Liabilities: $14,881,635
Net Worth: ($14,217,674)
Earnings: ($25,367,844)
Emp.: 4
Fiscal Year-end: 12/31/12
Business Description:
Personal Care Products Mfr
S.I.C.: 2841
N.A.I.C.S.: 325611
Personnel:
Mark Gerald Maybank *(Chm)*
Ronald Holland *(Pres)*
Michael Stocker *(CEO)*
Lilia Roberts *(CFO, Treas & Sec)*
Board of Directors:
Mark Gerald Maybank
David G. Csumrik

Ronald Holland
Delon Human
Wilhelm A. Keller
Michael Stocker
Ken Zadoorian

BIOMASS SECURE POWER INC.

40218 Wellsline Road
Abbotsford, BC, V3G 2K7, Canada
Tel.: (604) 807-4957
Fax: (905) 525-2662
E-Mail: sales@biomasssecurepower.ca
Web Site: www.biomasssecurepower.ca
BMSPF—(OTC)
Emp.: 1
Business Description:
Power Distr
S.I.C.: 4911
N.A.I.C.S.: 221122
Personnel:
James Carroll *(Pres & CEO)*
Murray L. Swales *(CFO)*
George Pappas *(Sec & VP)*
Board of Directors:
Andrew H. Burns
James Carroll
Leonard J. Klassen
Slawomir Kownacki
George Pappas

BIOME TECHNOLOGIES PLC

North Road Marchwood Industrial Park Marchwood
Southampton, S040 4BL, United Kingdom
Tel.: (44) 2380867100
Fax: (44) 2380867070
E-Mail: info@biometechnologiesplc.co.uk
Web Site: www.biometechnologiesplc.com
BIOM—(AIM)
Rev.: $8,883,506
Assets: $14,666,866
Liabilities: $1,820,921
Net Worth: $12,845,945
Earnings: ($9,110,924)
Emp.: 30
Fiscal Year-end: 12/31/12
Business Description:
Bioplastics Products & Radio Frequency Technologies & Equipment Mfr
S.I.C.: 3089
N.A.I.C.S.: 326199
Personnel:
Paul R. Mines *(CEO)*
Donna R. Simpson-Strange *(Sec)*
Board of Directors:
John F. Standen
Declan L. Brown
Michael A. Kayser
Paul R. Mines
Legal Counsel:
Osborne Clarke
One London Wall
London, United Kingdom

Subsidiary:

Adept Polymers Ltd. (1)
Unit 7 Woodrow Way
Fairhills Industrial Estate
Irlam, Manchester, M44 6ZQ, United Kingdom
Tel.: (44) 161 777 4830
Fax: (44) 161 777 4846
E-Mail: info@adeptpolymers.co.uk
Web Site: www.adeptpolymers.co.uk
Biodegradable Plastics Mfr
S.I.C.: 3089
N.A.I.C.S.: 326199

BIOMEDICAL COMPUTER TECHNOLOGIES NYRT.

1031st Water Molnar utca 23
Budapest, Hungary
Tel.: (36) 28488568
E-Mail: contact@biomedicalnyrt.com
Web Site: www.biomedicalnyrt.com
Year Founded: 2010
BIOMED—(BUD)
Business Description:
Hydrogen Storage Equipment & Accumulators Mfr
S.I.C.: 3841
N.A.I.C.S.: 339112
Personnel:
Sandor Kovacs *(Chm & CEO)*
Board of Directors:
Sandor Kovacs
Zsuzsanna Ertinger
Maria Feherpataky
Viktoria Kovacsne Revesz
Erzsebet Lenard

BIOMEVA GMBH

Czernyring 22
D 69115 Heidelberg, Germany
Tel.: (49) 622190260
Fax: (49) 6221902690
E-Mail: info@biomeva.com
Web Site: www.biomeva.com
Sales Range: $10-24.9 Million
Emp.: 35
Business Description:
Testing, Development & Manufacturing Services for Biotechnology & Pharmaceutical Companies
S.I.C.: 8731
N.A.I.C.S.: 541712
Personnel:
Thomas Pultar *(CEO)*

BIOMM S. A.

Praca Carlos Chagas 49 - 8th Floor
Belo Horizonte, MG, Brazil 30170-020
Tel.: (55) 31 3292 5003
Fax: (55) 31 3291 9212
E-Mail: biomm@biomm.com
Web Site: www.biomm.com
Year Founded: 1975
BIOM3—(BRAZ)
Business Description:
Drug Mfr
S.I.C.: 2834
N.A.I.C.S.: 325412
Personnel:
Francisco Carlos Marques de Freitas *(Dir-IR)*

BIONERSIS S.A.

176 avenue Charles de Gaulle
9220 Neuilly-sur-Seine, France
Tel.: (33) 1 52029080
Fax: (33) 1 43424830
E-Mail: info@bionersis.com
Web Site: www.bionersis.com
Year Founded: 2005
ALBRS—(EUR)
Sales Range: $1-9.9 Million
Emp.: 8
Business Description:
Renewable Energy Producer
S.I.C.: 4931
N.A.I.C.S.: 221118
Personnel:
Frederic Pastre *(CEO)*
Pascal Le Melinaire *(COO)*

BIONI CS GMBH

Lessingstr 21
D-46149 Oberhausen, Germany
Tel.: (49) 208 621 75 53
Fax: (49) 208 621 75 55
E-Mail: info@bioni.de
Web Site: www.bioni.de
Business Description:
Coatings Mfr
S.I.C.: 2851
N.A.I.C.S.: 325510
Personnel:
Sven Knoll *(Mng Dir)*

BIONICHE LIFE SCIENCES INC.

231 Dundas Street East
Belleville, ON, K8N 1E2, Canada
Mailing Address:
PO Box 1570
Belleville, ON, K8N 5J2, Canada
Tel.: (613) 966-8058
Fax: (613) 966-4177
Toll Free: (800) 265-5464
E-Mail: info@Bioniche.com
Web Site: www.bioniche.com
Year Founded: 1999
BNC—(OTC TSX)
Rev.: $81,510
Assets: $61,135,212
Liabilities: $73,602,211
Net Worth: ($12,466,999)
Earnings: ($33,588,930)
Emp.: 202
Fiscal Year-end: 06/30/13
Business Description:
Research, Development & Commercialization Services for Human & Veterinary Pharmaceuticals
S.I.C.: 2834
N.A.I.C.S.: 325412
Personnel:
Graeme McRae *(Founder)*
Yvon Bastien *(Chm)*
Michael J. Berendt *(CEO)*
Brian Ford *(CFO)*
Donald Olds *(COO)*
Rick Culbert *(Pres-One Health)*
Andrew Grant *(Pres-Bioniche Animal Health)*
Mairi Phillips *(Sec & VP-Legal Svcs)*
Cindy Benning *(Sr VP-Ops, Quality & Regulatory Affairs)*
Board of Directors:
Yvon Bastien
James Rae
Michael J. Berendt
Rod Budd
Lyne Fortin
Gregory David Gubitz
Legal Counsel:
Norton Rose Fulbright Canada LLP
Toronto, ON, Canada
CIBC Mellon Trust Company
PO Box 700 Station B
Montreal, QC, Canada
Transfer Agents:
Link Market Services
Locked Bag A14
Sydney, Australia
CIBC Mellon Trust Company
PO Box 700 Station B
Montreal, QC, Canada

Subsidiary:

Bioniche Animal Health Canada Inc (1)
231 Dundas St E
PO Box 1570
Belleville, ON, K8N 5J2, Canada
Tel.: (613) 966-8058
Fax: (613) 966-4177
Toll Free: (800) 265-5464
E-Mail: animalHealthInfo@Bioniche.com
Web Site: www.bionicheanimalhealth.com
Emp.: 120
Animal Health Products Distr
S.I.C.: 5122
N.A.I.C.S.: 424210
Graeme McRae *(Gen Mgr)*

U.S. Subsidiary:

Bioniche Animal Health USA, Inc. (1)
1551 Jennings Mill Rd Ste 3200A
Bogart, GA 30622 (100%)
Tel.: (706) 549-4503
Fax: (706) 548-0659
Toll Free: (888) 549-4503
E-Mail: info@bionicheanimalhealth.com
Web Site: www.bionicheanimalhealth.com
Emp.: 20
Provider of Research, Development & Commercialization Services for Human & Veterinary Pharmaceuticals
S.I.C.: 2834
N.A.I.C.S.: 325412
Jim Phillips *(Pres)*
Graeme McRae *(CEO)*

Non-U.S. Subsidiary:

Bioniche Animal Health A/Asia Pty. Ltd. (1)
46 Seaton St
Armidale, NSW, 2350, Australia
Tel.: (61) 267720677
Fax: (61) 267720922
E-Mail: info@bionicheanimalhealth.com
Web Site: www.bionicheanimalhealth.com
Emp.: 9
Provider of Research, Development & Commercialization Services for Human & Veterinary Pharmaceuticals
S.I.C.: 2834
N.A.I.C.S.: 325412
Graham McRaa *(Pres)*
Lindon Constable *(Pres-Sls & Mktg)*

BIONIME CORPORATION

694 Renhua Rd
Dali District, Taichung, 412, Taiwan
Tel.: (886) 4 24951268
Fax: (886) 4 24952568
E-Mail: info@bionime.com
Web Site: www.bionime.com
Year Founded: 2003
4737—(TAI)
Sales Range: $25-49.9 Million
Emp.: 500
Business Description:
Self Monitoring Blood Glucose System Mfr
S.I.C.: 3841
N.A.I.C.S.: 339112
Personnel:
Roy Huang *(Chm)*
Board of Directors:
Roy Huang
T.S. Chiang
L. Z. Guo
L.R. Hu
M.S. Lin
K.J. Tsai
S.W. Yau

U.S. Subsidiary:

Bionime USA Corporation (1)
10865 Rancho Bernardo Rd Ste 100
San Diego, CA 92127
Tel.: (858) 481-8485
Fax: (858) 481-8472
Toll Free: (888) 481-8485
Web Site: www.bionimeusa.com
Blood Glucose Monitoring Systems Mfr & Distr
S.I.C.: 2835
N.A.I.C.S.: 325413

Non-U.S. Subsidiaries:

Bionime Australia Pty Limited. (1)
Level 7 60 York Street
Sydney, NSW, 2000, Australia
Tel.: (61) 2 9262 6900
Fax: (61) 2 9262 6922
Electromedical Equipments Mfr
S.I.C.: 2835
N.A.I.C.S.: 325413
Irene Wu *(Mgr)*

Bionime GmbH (1)
Tramstrasse 16
9442 Berneck, Switzerland

Bionime Corporation—(Continued)

Tel.: (41) 717229840
Fax: (41) 717229843
E-Mail: info@bionime.ch
Web Site: www.company.bionime.ch
Emp.: 4
Blood Glucose Monitoring Systems Mfr
S.I.C.: 2835
N.A.I.C.S.: 325413
Klaus Ellensohn *(Gen Mgr)*

BIONOMICS LIMITED

31 Dalgleish Street
Thebarton, SA, 5031, Australia
Tel.: (61) 8 8354 6100
Fax: (61) 8 8354 6199
E-Mail: info@bionomics.com.au
Web Site: www.bionomics.com.au
BNO—(ASX OTC)
Rev.: $12,323,829
Assets: $55,868,119
Liabilities: $12,717,902
Net Worth: $43,150,217
Earnings: ($10,422,407)
Emp.: 59
Fiscal Year-end: 06/30/13

Business Description:
Pharmaceutical Research & Development Services
S.I.C.: 2834
N.A.I.C.S.: 325412

Personnel:
Deborah Rathjen *(CEO & Mng Dir)*
Melanie Young *(CFO & Sec)*
Jose Iglesias *(Chief Medical Officer)*

Board of Directors:
Graeme Roy Kaufman
Errol B. De Souza
Jonathan Lim
Deborah Rathjen
Trevor Tappenden

Legal Counsel:
Johnson Winter & Slattery
211 Victoria Square
Adelaide, SA, Australia

U.S. Subsidiary:

Bionomics Inc (1)
PO Box 817
Kingston, TN 37763
Tel.: (865) 220-8501
Fax: (865) 220-8532
Web Site: www.bionomics-inc.com
Radioactive Waste Disposal Services
S.I.C.: 4953
N.A.I.C.S.: 562211
Karen McCormick *(Pres)*

Non-U.S. Subsidiary:

Neurofit SAS (1)
Blvd Sebastien Brant Bioparc
Parc d Innovation, 67400 Illkirch-Graffenstaden, Bas-Rhin, France
Tel.: (33) 388651606
Fax: (33) 388651622
E-Mail: neurofit@neurofit.com
Web Site: www.neurofit.com
Emp.: 9
Pre Clinical Research Services
S.I.C.: 8731
N.A.I.C.S.: 541712
Deborah Rathjen *(Pres)*

BIONOR PHARMA ASA

Sykehusveien 23
PO Box 6463
9294 Tromso, Norway
Tel.: (47) 77 64 89 00
Fax: (47) 77 64 89 01
E-Mail: info@biotec.no
Web Site: www.biotec.no
NU5—(DEU)

Business Description:
Vaccines Mfr
S.I.C.: 2836
N.A.I.C.S.: 325414

Personnel:
Lars H. Hoie *(Chm)*
Steen Kroyer *(Deputy Chm)*
Anker Lundemose *(Pres & CEO)*
Maja Sommerfelt *(Chief Scientific Officer)*
Vidar Wendel-Hansen *(Chief Medical Officer)*
Gunnar Flaten *(Sr VP-Fin & Admin)*

Board of Directors:
Lars H. Hoie
Erik Danielsen
Bjorn Fuglaas
Steen Kroyer

Subsidiary:

Nutri Pharma AS (1)
Kronprinsesse Marthas Pl 1
0160 Oslo, Norway
Tel.: (47) 23310880
Vaccine Mfr
S.I.C.: 2836
N.A.I.C.S.: 325414

BIOPAC INDIA CORPORATION LTD

301/302 Sagar Avenue S V Road
Andheri West
Mumbai, 400058, India
Tel.: (91) 2226708645
Fax: (91) 2226280556
E-Mail: info@biopacindia.com
Web Site: www.biopacindia.com
BIOPAC—(BOM)
Rev.: $8,461,590
Assets: $7,138,060
Liabilities: $3,778,147
Net Worth: $3,359,913
Earnings: $36,593
Emp.: 200
Fiscal Year-end: 03/31/13

Business Description:
Polystyrene Products Producer
S.I.C.: 3086
N.A.I.C.S.: 326140

Personnel:
Harish B. Doshi *(Chm)*
Pankaj B. Doshi *(Vice Chm, Mng Dir & Compliance Officer)*
Prashant Diwan *(Sec)*

Board of Directors:
Harish B. Doshi
Hemant Bhuta
Pankaj B. Doshi
R. S. Maker
Mehul D. Patel
Smita L. Sanghavi

Transfer Agent:
Link Intime India Private Limited
C-13 Pannalal Silk Mills Compound L.B.S. Marg Bhandup
Mumbai, India

Plant:

Biopac India Corporation Ltd - Plant (1)
Survey No 38 Khanvel Rd
Dapada Vlg, Silvassa, Dadra & Naga Haveli, 396230, India
Tel.: (91) 2606452733
Fax: (91) 2602699488
E-Mail: rajiba@biopacindia.com
Emp.: 100
Foam Polystyrene Mfr
S.I.C.: 3086
N.A.I.C.S.: 326140

BIOPAK LIMITED

7824 51 Avenue
Edmonton, AB, Canada T6E 6W2
Tel.: (780) 435-4515
Fax: (780) 461-9821
E-Mail: info@biopak.com
Web Site: www.biopak.com
Year Founded: 1995
Rev.: $14,044,800
Emp.: 80

Business Description:
Dietary Supplements Mfr
S.I.C.: 2899
N.A.I.C.S.: 325998

Personnel:
Bret Smith *(Pres-Sls & Admin)*

BIOPHAGE PHARMA INC.

6100 Royalmount
Montreal, QC, H4P 2R2, Canada
Tel.: (514) 496-1488
Fax: (514) 496-1521
Toll Free: (877) 770-7773
E-Mail: info@biophagepharma.net
Web Site: www.biophagepharma.net
Sales Range: Less than $1 Million
Emp.: 15

Business Description:
Biopharmaceutical Products Mfr, Developer & Researcher
S.I.C.: 2834
N.A.I.C.S.: 325412

Personnel:
Rosemonde Mandeville *(Chm, Pres & CEO)*

Board of Directors:
Rosemonde Mandeville
Myer Bentob
Luc Dubois
Jocelyn R. Pelchat

BIOPORTO A/S

Grusbakken 8
DK-2820 Gentofte, Denmark
Tel.: (45) 45290000
Fax: (45) 45290001
E-Mail: info@bioporto.com
Web Site: www.bioporto.com
Year Founded: 2000
BIOPOR—(CSE)
Rev.: $3,220,869
Assets: $3,278,584
Liabilities: $3,485,998
Net Worth: ($207,414)
Earnings: ($2,651,292)
Emp.: 25
Fiscal Year-end: 12/31/12

Business Description:
Pharmaceutical Products Mfr
S.I.C.: 2834
N.A.I.C.S.: 325412

Personnel:
Thomas Magnussen *(Chm)*
Frank Harder *(CFO)*

Board of Directors:
Thomas Magnussen
Claus Crone Fuglsang
Torben A. Nielsen
Roar Bjork Seeger
Laura von Kobyletzki

BIOPREMIER - INOVACAO E SERVICOS EM BIOTECNOLOGIA S.A.

Ed ICAT Campus da Fac de Ciencias da Univ de Lisboa Campo Grande
1749-016 Lisbon, Portugal
Tel.: (351) 217 500 218
Fax: (351) 217 500 432
E-Mail: email@biopremier.com
Web Site: www.biopremier.com
Year Founded: 2003
BISB—(DEU)
Sales Range: Less than $1 Million

Business Description:
Biological Products Mfr
S.I.C.: 2836
N.A.I.C.S.: 325414

Personnel:
Manuel Jose Gomes Rodrigues *(Chm)*

Board of Directors:
Manuel Jose Gomes Rodrigues
Paulo Luis Cardoso Osswald
Mario Joao Gadanho

BIOPROSPECT LIMITED

Suite 25 145 Stirling Hwy
Nedlands, WA, 6009, Australia
Tel.: (61) 8 9389 3170
Fax: (61) 8 9389 3199
E-Mail: info@bioprospect.com
Web Site: www.bioprospect.com
BPO—(ASX)
Rev.: $29,786
Assets: $5,647,047
Liabilities: $3,002,038
Net Worth: $2,645,009
Earnings: ($1,142,885)
Emp.: 4
Fiscal Year-end: 06/30/13

Business Description:
Pesticide & Agricultural Products
S.I.C.: 0721
N.A.I.C.S.: 115112

Personnel:
Peter Donald May *(CEO)*
Robert Lees *(CFO & Sec)*

Board of Directors:
Winton Willesee
Benjamin Cooper
Peter Donald May

Legal Counsel:
McCullough Robertson
66 Eagle Street
Brisbane, Australia

Fairweather Corporate Lawyers
595 Stirling Highway
Cottesloe, Australia

BIOQUANTA SA

5 rue de l'Abbe de l Epee
75005 Paris, France
Tel.: (33) 146331424
Web Site: www.bioquanta.net
MLBQA—(EUR)

Business Description:
Biotechnology Pharmaceutical Researcher, Developer & Mfr
S.I.C.: 2834
N.A.I.C.S.: 325412

Personnel:
Flavio Toma *(Chief Scientific Officer)*

BIOQUELL PLC

52 Royce Close West Portway
Andover, Hampshire, SP10 3TS, United Kingdom
Tel.: (44) 1264835900
Fax: (44) 1264835901
E-Mail: enquiries@bioquell.com
Web Site: www.bioquellplc.com
BQE—(LSE)
Rev.: $64,742,994
Assets: $67,345,663
Liabilities: $18,814,082
Net Worth: $48,531,582
Earnings: $6,307,684
Emp.: 431
Fiscal Year-end: 12/31/12

Business Description:
Bio-Decontamination & Containment Equipment, Related Products & Services
S.I.C.: 2836
N.A.I.C.S.: 325414

Personnel:
Nicholas Adams *(CEO)*
Mark Bodeker *(CFO & COO)*
Georgina Pope *(Sec)*

Board of Directors:
Nigel Keen
Nicholas Adams
Mark Bodeker
Tony Bourne
Ian Carruthers
Simon Constantine
Christopher Mills

Subsidiaries:

BIOQUELL UK Limited (1)
52 Royce Close W Port Way
Andover, Hampshire, SP10 3TS, United Kingdom

Tel.: (44) 1264835835
Fax: (44) 1264835836
E-Mail: enquiries@bioquell.com
Web Site: www.bioquell.com
Emp.: 120
Design, Manufacture & Supply of Bio-Decontamination & Containment Equipment, Related Products & Services
S.I.C.: 2836
N.A.I.C.S.: 325414
Nicholas Adams *(CEO)*

TRaC EMC & Safety Ltd (1)
100 Frobisher Business Park
Leigh Sinton Road, Malvern, Worcestershire, WR14 1BX, United Kingdom
Tel.: (44) 1684571700
Fax: (44) 1684 571701
E-Mail: info@tracglobal.com
Emp.: 15
Electromagnetic Compatibility Testing Services
S.I.C.: 8734
N.A.I.C.S.: 541380

TRaC Environmental & Analysis Ltd. (1)
Rothwell Road
Warwick, CV34 5JX, United Kingdom
Tel.: (44) 1926478478
Fax: (44) 1926478479
E-Mail: sales@tracglobal.com
Web Site: www.tracglobal.com
Emp.: 68
Environmental Testing & Analysis Laboratories
S.I.C.: 8734
N.A.I.C.S.: 541380

Subsidiaries:

TRaC Global Limited (2)
Unit E South Orbital Trading Park
Hedon Road, Hull, HU9 1NJ, United Kingdom
Tel.: (44) 1482801801
Fax: (44) 1482801806
E-Mail: info@tracglobal.com
Web Site: www.tracglobal.com
Emp.: 32
Telecoms, EMC & Safety Testing Services & Accreditation
S.I.C.: 8734
N.A.I.C.S.: 541380
Mark Heaven *(CEO)*

TRL Compliance Services Limited (2)
Long Green
Forthampton, Gloucester, GL19 4QH, United Kingdom
Tel.: (44) 1684835818
Fax: (44) 1684 835 858
Web Site: www.trlcompliance.com
EMC, Radio, Safety & Calibration Testing Services
S.I.C.: 8734
N.A.I.C.S.: 541380

TRaC Telecoms & Radio Ltd (1)
Unit E Hull N Humbers Hull
Kingston upon Hull, Yorkshire, HU11 4HT, United Kingdom
Tel.: (44) 1482801801
Emp.: 30
Medical Diagnostic Equipments Mfr
S.I.C.: 3845
N.A.I.C.S.: 334510

U.S. Subsidiary:

BIOQUELL Inc. (1)
101 Witmer Rd Ste 400
Horsham, PA 19044
Tel.: (215) 682-0225
Fax: (215) 682-0395
Web Site: www.bioquell.com
Emp.: 20
Design, Manufacture & Supply of Bio-Decontamination & Containment Equipment, Related Products & Services
S.I.C.: 8731
N.A.I.C.S.: 541712
Mike Herd *(VP)*

Non-U.S. Subsidiaries:

Bioquell Asia Pacific Pte Ltd (1)
8 Eu Tong Sen Street 14-95 The Central
Singapore, 059818, Singapore
Tel.: (65) 6592 5145
Fax: (65) 6227 5878
Web Site: www.bioquell.net
Laboratory Equipments & Supplies Distr
S.I.C.: 5047
N.A.I.C.S.: 423450

Bioquell Global Logistics (Ireland) Ltd. (1)
Unit E4 Eastway Business Park Ballysimon Road
Limerick, Munster, Ireland
Tel.: (353) 61 603622
Fax: (353) 61 603627
E-Mail: info@bioquell.ie
Web Site: www.bioquell.ie
Emp.: 5
Laboratory Equipments & Supplies Distr
S.I.C.: 5047
N.A.I.C.S.: 423450
Caroline Murphy *(Gen Mgr)*

BIOREM INC.

7496 Wellinghton Road 34 RR 3
Guelph, ON, N1H 6H9, Canada
Tel.: (519) 767-9100
Fax: (519) 767-1824
Toll Free: (800) 353-2087
E-Mail: info@biorem.biz
Web Site: www.biorem.biz
BRM—(TSXV)
Rev.: $15,326,118
Assets: $9,721,936
Liabilities: $9,667,636
Net Worth: $54,300
Earnings: ($825,029)
Emp.: 27
Fiscal Year-end: 12/31/12

Business Description:
Air Filtration & Control Mfr
S.I.C.: 3829
N.A.I.C.S.: 334519

Personnel:
Bernardo H. Llovera *(Chm)*
Peter A. Bruijns *(Pres & CEO)*
Douglas Newman *(CFO)*
Derek S. Webb *(Exec VP)*

Board of Directors:
Bernardo H. Llovera
Stephen V. Ardia
Peter A. Bruijns
Robert B. Nally
Hank J. Vander Laan

Transfer Agent:
Equity Financial Trust Company
200 University Avenue Suite 400
Toronto, ON, M5H 4H1, Canada
Tel.: (416) 361-0152
Fax: (416) 361-0470
Toll Free: (866) 393-4891

Subsidiary:

Biorem Technologies Inc., (1)
7496 Wellington Rd 34RR No 3
Guelph, ON, N1H 6H9, Canada
Tel.: (519) 767-9100
Fax: (519) 767-1824
Toll Free: (800) 353-2087
E-Mail: info@biorem.biz
Web Site: www.biorem.biz
Emp.: 42
Pollution Control Services
S.I.C.: 3822
N.A.I.C.S.: 334512
Peter Bruijns *(Pres)*

U.S. Subsidiary:

Biorem Environmental Inc (1)
100 Rawson Rd Ste 230
Victor, NY 14564
Tel.: (585) 924-2220
Fax: (585) 924-8280
Toll Free: (877) 299-2108
Web Site: www.biorem.biz
Pollution Control Services
S.I.C.: 3822
N.A.I.C.S.: 334512

BIOS S.P.A.

Via Domenico Chelini 39
Rome, 00197, Italy
Tel.: (39) 06809641
Fax: (39) 068082104
Web Site: www.gruppobios.net
Emp.: 90

Business Description:
Health Services
S.I.C.: 8099
N.A.I.C.S.: 621999

Personnel:
Maria Grazia Tambroni *(CEO)*

Subsidiaries:

FISIOBIOS S.R.L. (1)
Via Francesco Denza 27
00197 Rome, Italy
Tel.: (39) 068080514
Fax: (39) 068080514
E-Mail: fisiobios@gruppobios.net
Web Site: www.fisiobios.it/
Medical Equipment Mfr & Whslr
S.I.C.: 3845
N.A.I.C.S.: 334510

LABORATORIO ANALISI CLINICHE MEDICHE IANNACCONE S.R.L. (1)
11 Via Odescalchi
00062 Bracciano, Italy
Tel.: (39) 06 99805073
Fax: (39) 06 99888454
E-Mail: info@bios-bracciano.it
Web Site: www.bios-bracciano.it
Medical Equipment Mfr & Whslr
S.I.C.: 3845
N.A.I.C.S.: 334510

BIOSCIENCE BRANDS LIMITED

4 Brewery Street
Isando, 1609, South Africa
Mailing Address:
PO Box 195
Isando, 1600, South Africa
Tel.: (27) 87 740 1300
Fax: (27) 87 740 1309
E-Mail: info@bioscience.co.za
Web Site: www.bioscience.co.za
Year Founded: 2005
BIO—(JSE)
Sales Range: $1-9.9 Million

Business Description:
Pharmaceutical Product Mfr & Whslr
S.I.C.: 2834
N.A.I.C.S.: 325412

Personnel:
Jonathan Julius Fenster *(Chm & CEO)*

BIOSENSORS INTERNATIONAL GROUP, LTD.

Blk 10 Kaki Bukit Avenue 1 06-01/04
Singapore, 417942, Singapore
Tel.: (65) 6213 5777
Fax: (65) 6213 5737
Web Site: www.biosensors.com
B20—(OTC SES)
Rev.: $272,203,890
Assets: $1,300,645,662
Liabilities: $290,198,218
Net Worth: $1,010,447,443
Earnings: $93,418,449
Fiscal Year-end: 03/31/13

Business Description:
Medical Device Mfr
S.I.C.: 3841
N.A.I.C.S.: 339112

Personnel:
Yoh-Chie Lu *(Founder & Chm)*
Jack Jicheng Wang *(CEO)*
Ronald H. Ede *(CFO & Sec)*
John E. Schulze *(CTO)*
Jeffrey B. Jump *(Pres-Cardiovascular Bus Unit)*

Board of Directors:
Yoh-Chie Lu
Soon Beng Aw
Adrian Pengee Chan
Phyllis Yuk Ying Chan
Qiang Jiang
Vincent Ong
Jack Jicheng Wang
Bing Yuan
Huawei Zhang

Transfer Agents:
M & C Services Private Limited
112 Robinson Road 05-01
Singapore, 068902, Singapore
Codan Services Limited
Clarendon House 2 Church Street
Hamilton, Bermuda

Subsidiaries:

Biosensors International Pte Ltd (1)
21 Kallang Avenue 07-167
Singapore, 339412, Singapore (100%)
Tel.: (65) 62938066
Fax: (65) 62986242
Web Site: www.biosensors.com
Mfr, Marketer & Distr of Medical Devices for Critical Care
S.I.C.: 3841
N.A.I.C.S.: 339112
Jeffrey B. Jump *(Co-CEO)*

Non-U.S. Subsidiaries:

Biosensors B.V. (2)
Arnold St 8
2182 DZ Hillegom, Netherlands (100%)
Tel.: (31) 252517676
Fax: (31) 252526782
E-Mail: f.stim@biosensors.com
Web Site: www.biosensors.com
Emp.: 12
Medical Devices Sales & Marketing
S.I.C.: 5047
N.A.I.C.S.: 423450
Bram Raetsma *(Mgr-Sls)*

JW ICU Medical Limited (2)
328 Shichang Ave
High-Tech Industry Devel Zone, Weihai, Shandong, 264209, China (100%)
Tel.: (86) 6313651906
Fax: (86) 6313651911
E-Mail: ran.yang@jwnsprt.com
Emp.: 200
Medical Devices Mfr
S.I.C.: 3841
N.A.I.C.S.: 339112
Jack Jicheng Wang *(Chm)*

Biosensors Interventional Technologies Pte Ltd (1)
Blk 10 Kaki Bukit Avenue 1 06-01/04
Kampong Ubi Industrial Estate, Singapore, 417942, Singapore (100%)
Tel.: (65) 62135777
Fax: (65) 62135737
Medical Devices Mfr, Marketer & Distr
S.I.C.: 3841
N.A.I.C.S.: 339112

Non-U.S. Subsidiary:

Biosensors Europe SA (2)
Rue de Lausanne 29
1110 Morges, Switzerland (100%)
Tel.: (41) 218048000
Fax: (41) 218048002
E-Mail: t.leutwiler@biosensors.com
Web Site: www.biosensors.com
Emp.: 80
Medical Devices Sales & Marketing
S.I.C.: 5047
N.A.I.C.S.: 423450
Jump Jeffrey *(CEO)*

U.S. Subsidiary:

Biosensors International USA (3)
20250 Sw Acacia St Ste 200
Newport Beach, CA 92660-1737 CA
Tel.: (949) 553-8300 (100%)
Fax: (949) 553-9129
Web Site: www.biosensors.com
Emp.: 52
Medical Device Mfr
S.I.C.: 3841
N.A.I.C.S.: 339112
Ronald L. Lung *(Dir)*

Subsidiary:

Devax, Inc. (4)
13900 Alton Pkwy Ste 125
Irvine, CA 92618-1621 DE

Biosensors International Group, Ltd.—(Continued)

Tel.: (949) 334-2333
Fax: (949) 334-2330
E-Mail: INFO@DEVAX.NET
Web Site: www.devax.net
Emp.: 33
Medical Device Mfr
S.I.C.: 3841
N.A.I.C.S.: 339112
Stephen L. Wilson *(CFO & Exec VP)*
Brett A. Trauthen *(VP-Clinical Affairs & Chief Scientific Officer)*

Non-U.S. Subsidiary:

Biosensors Japan Co., Ltd. **(3)**
Bellebs Nagayama 501 1-5 Nagayama
Tama-shi, Tokyo, 260 0025, Japan (100%)
Tel.: (81) 423553311
Fax: (81) 423553312
Medical Devices Sales & Marketing
S.I.C.: 5047
N.A.I.C.S.: 423450
Junrokuro Abe *(CEO)*

BIOSEV S.A.

Av Brigadeiro Faria Lima 1355 - 11 andar
01452-919 Sao Paulo, SP, Brazil
Tel.: (55) 11 3092 5200
E-Mail: conduta@biosev.com
Web Site: www.biosev.com.br
Year Founded: 2009
BSEV3—(BRAZ)
Emp.: 18,000
Business Description:
Sugar Mfr & Distr
S.I.C.: 2061
N.A.I.C.S.: 311314
Personnel:
Marco Antonio de Modesti *(Dir-IR)*

BIOSIGN TECHNOLOGIES INC.

801-100 Allstate Parkway
Markham, ON, L3R 6H3, Canada
Tel.: (416) 218-9800
Fax: (905) 886-8996
Toll Free: (877) 712-7446
E-Mail: support@biosign.com
Web Site: www.biosign.com
Year Founded: 2006
BIO—(TSXV)
Rev.: $86,208
Assets: $2,932,227
Liabilities: $943,060
Net Worth: $1,989,167
Earnings: ($4,397,090)
Emp.: 12
Fiscal Year-end: 12/31/12
Business Description:
Health Care Monitoring Products Mfr
S.I.C.: 3841
N.A.I.C.S.: 339112
Personnel:
John Rizvi *(Chm)*
Robert Kaul *(CEO)*
Mario Laflamme *(CFO)*
Christian Sleight *(CTO)*
Eva Leca *(Chief Regulatory Officer)*
Board of Directors:
John Rizvi
Michael Gross
Robert Kaul
Sandeep Kohli
Dennis Ryqwalski
Legal Counsel:
Goodmans LLP
250 Yonge Street Suite 2400
PO Box 24
Toronto, ON, M5B 2M6, Canada
Tel.: (416) 979-2211
Fax: (416) 979-1234
Transfer Agent:
Computershare Trust Company of Canada
510 Burrard St 3rd Fl
Vancouver, BC, V6C 3B9, Canada

BIOSIS GROUP BERHAD

1572 Jalan Besar Valdor Mukim 12
Seberang Perai Selatan
14200 Sungai Bakap, Penang, Malaysia
Tel.: (60) 4582 1121
Fax: (60) 4582 9121
E-Mail: info@biosis.com.my
Web Site: www.biosis.com.my
BIOSIS—(KLS)
Rev.: $4,289,651
Assets: $23,787,950
Liabilities: $19,160,482
Net Worth: $4,627,468
Earnings: ($5,481,304)
Fiscal Year-end: 03/31/13
Business Description:
Personal & Health Care Products Mfr
S.I.C.: 2844
N.A.I.C.S.: 325620
Personnel:
Shahfie Ahmad *(Mng Dir)*
Kwee Wah Chok *(Co-Sec)*
Kean Wai Tan *(Co-Sec)*
Board of Directors:
Abd Latiff Ahmad
Shahfie Ahmad
Khairul Azwan Harun
Chee Kong Khoo
Kien Yoon Koo
Pai Lan Lai
Leong Keh Ler
Tee Kein Ong

BIOSMART CO. LTD.

133 120 299 1 2nd Street Seongu
Dong Seongdong Gu
133120 Seoul, Korea (South)
Tel.: (82) 232189000
Fax: (82) 232189050
E-Mail: sales@bio-smart.com
Web Site: www.bio-smart.com
38460—(KRS)
Sls.: $39,427,536
Assets: $64,191,111
Liabilities: $28,541,793
Net Worth: $35,649,318
Earnings: $2,657,103
Emp.: 150
Fiscal Year-end: 12/31/12
Business Description:
Credit Card Services
S.I.C.: 6153
N.A.I.C.S.: 522210
Personnel:
Hyerin Park *(CEO)*

BIOSTAR PHARMACEUTICALS, INC.

No 588 Shiji Xi Avenue
Xianyang, Shaanxi, 712046, China
Tel.: (86) 2933686638
Fax: (86) 29 33685526
E-Mail: office@biostarpharmaceuticals.com
Web Site: www.biostarpharmaceuticals.com
Year Founded: 2007
BSPM—(NASDAQ)
Sls.: $49,317,844
Assets: $70,475,300
Liabilities: $12,702,552
Net Worth: $57,772,748
Earnings: ($19,997,323)
Emp.: 439
Fiscal Year-end: 12/31/12
Business Description:
Pharmaceutical Mfr
S.I.C.: 2834
N.A.I.C.S.: 325412
Personnel:
Ronghua Wang *(Chm & CEO)*
Qinghua Liu *(Interim CFO)*
Amei Zhang *(COO)*
Shuang Gong *(Sec & Dir-Admin)*
Board of Directors:
Ronghua Wang
King-fai Leung
Qinghua Liu
Zhongyang Shang
Haipeng Wu
Transfer Agent:
Interwest Transfer Co. Inc.
1981 E Murray Holladay Rd Ste 100
Salt Lake City, UT 84101

BIOSTIME INTERNATIONAL HOLDINGS LIMITED

29th Floor Guangzhou International Finance Center 5 Zhujiang West Road
Zhujiang New Town Tianhe Dist,
Guangzhou, Guangdong, 510623, China
Tel.: (86) 20 38773336
Fax: (86) 20 38773339
E-Mail: ir@biostime.com.cn
Web Site: www.biostime.com.cn
Year Founded: 1999
1112—(HKG)
Rev.: $537,214,974
Assets: $561,279,319
Liabilities: $192,326,049
Net Worth: $368,953,270
Earnings: $118,042,388
Emp.: 1,500
Fiscal Year-end: 12/31/12
Business Description:
Pediatric Nutritional Products Mfr; Baby Care Products Mfr; Pediatric & Baby Care Information Services
S.I.C.: 2833
N.A.I.C.S.: 325411
Personnel:
Fei Luo *(Chm & CEO)*
Wenhui Cao *(CFO)*
Qingjuan Kong *(COO)*
Patrice Malard *(Chief Scientific Officer)*
Tak Yee Wong *(Co-Sec)*
Wenyun Yang *(Co-Sec)*
Board of Directors:
Fei Luo
Fufang Chen
Qingjuan Kong
Yun Luo
Wai Fung Ngai
Wee Seng Tan
Xiong Wu
Baichun Xiao
Wenhui Zhang
Legal Counsel:
Orrick, Herrington & Sutcliffe
43rd Floor Gloucester Tower The Landmark 15 Queens Road Central
Hong Kong, China (Hong Kong)
Computershare Hong Kong Investor Services Limited
Shops 1712-1716 17th Floor Hopewell Centre
183 Queens Road East
Wanchai, China (Hong Kong)
Transfer Agents:
Royal Bank of Canada Trust Company (Cayman) Limited
4th Floor Royal Bank House 24 Shedden Road
Georgetown, Cayman Islands
Computershare Hong Kong Investor Services Limited
Rooms 1712-1716 17th Floor Hopewell Centre
183 Queen's Road East
Wanchai, China (Hong Kong)

BIOSYENT INC.

170 Attwell Drive Suite 520
Toronto, ON, M9W 5Z5, Canada
Tel.: (905) 206-0013
Fax: (905) 206-1413
E-Mail: info@biosyent.com
Web Site: www.biosyent.com
Year Founded: 1947
RX—(OTC TSXV)
Rev.: $4,994,110
Assets: $3,630,926
Liabilities: $808,497
Net Worth: $2,822,429
Earnings: $1,532,100
Fiscal Year-end: 12/31/12
Business Description:
Pharmaceutical Products Mfr
S.I.C.: 2834
N.A.I.C.S.: 325412
Personnel:
Rene C. Goehrum *(Chm, Pres & CEO)*
Alfred D'Souza *(CFO, VP, Controller & Dir-Fin)*
Douglas R. Larson *(Sec)*
Board of Directors:
Rene C. Goehrum
Douglas R. Larson
Peter D. Lockhard
Paul Montador
Milton E. Wakefield
Legal Counsel:
Miller Thomson LLP
Vancouver, BC, Canada
Loopstra Nixon, LLP
Toronto, ON, Canada
Transfer Agent:
Computershare Trust Company of Canada
510 Burrard St
Vancouver, BC, Canada

U.S. Subsidiary:

Hedley Technologies (USA) Inc. **(1)**
102-202 N Ave
Grand Junction, CO 81501
Tel.: (888) 476-4473
Web Site: www.hedleytech.com
Insecticides Mfr & Distr
S.I.C.: 2879
N.A.I.C.S.: 325320

BIOSYN ARZNEIMITTEL GMBH

Schorndorfer Strasse 32
70734 Fellbach, Germany
Tel.: (49) 7115753200
Fax: (49) 7115753299
E-Mail: info@biosyn.de
Web Site: www.biosyn.de
Year Founded: 1984
Sales Range: $10-24.9 Million
Emp.: 90
Business Description:
Pharmaceutical Mfr
S.I.C.: 2834
N.A.I.C.S.: 325412
Personnel:
Ortwin Kottwitz *(Co-Founder & Mng Dir)*
Thomas Stiefel *(Co-Founder & Mng Dir)*

U.S. Subsidiary:

biosyn Corporation **(1)**
5939 Darwin Ct Ste 114
Carlsbad, CA 92008
Tel.: (760) 431-0590
Fax: (760) 431-2216
E-Mail: smuddu@biosyncorp.com
Web Site: www.biosyncorp.com
Emp.: 5
Pharmaceutical Mfr & Whslr
S.I.C.: 2834
N.A.I.C.S.: 325412
S. N. Muddukrishna *(Pres)*

BIOSYNEX SA

12 rue Ettore Bugatti
Eckbolsheim - CS28006
F-67038 Strasbourg, France
Tel.: (33) 388775701
Fax: (33) 3 88 78 76 78
E-Mail: paper@biosynex.com
Web Site: www.biosynex.com
ALBIO—(EUR)
Sales Range: Less than $1 Million

Emp.: 20
Business Description:
Diagnostic Testing Kits Mfr
S.I.C.: 2835
N.A.I.C.S.: 325413
Personnel:
Thierry Paper *(Gen Mgr)*

BIOTAGE AB

Vimpelgatan 5
Box 8
751 03 Uppsala, Sweden
Tel.: (46) 18565900
Fax: (46) 18591922
E-Mail: info@biotage.com
Web Site: www.biotage.com
BIOT—(OMX)
Sls.: $71,663,422
Assets: $101,250,655
Liabilities: $19,078,171
Net Worth: $82,172,484
Earnings: $5,934,413
Emp.: 290
Fiscal Year-end: 12/31/12
Business Description:
Medicinal Chemistry Research & Applied Genetic Analysis Solution Supplier
S.I.C.: 8731
N.A.I.C.S.: 541712
Personnel:
Ove Mattsson *(Chm)*
Torben Jorgensen *(Pres & CEO)*
Erika Soderberg Johnson *(CFO)*
Anthony Rees *(Chief Scientific Officer)*
Scott Carr *(CEO-North America & VP)*
Lei Shi *(CEO-China)*
Board of Directors:
Ove Mattsson
Love Amcoff
Nils-Olof Bjork
Peter Ehrenheim
Thomas Eklund
Nils Granlund
Karolina Lawitz
Anders Walldov

Subsidiaries:

Biotage Sweden AB (1)
Kungsgatan 76
75318 Uppsala, Sweden (100%)
Tel.: (46) 18565900
Fax: (46) 18591922
E-Mail: info@biotage.com
Web Site: www.biotage.com
Emp.: 50
Medicinal Chemistry Research & Development Services
S.I.C.: 8731
N.A.I.C.S.: 541712
Torben Jorgensen *(Pres & CEO)*

Cemu Bioteknik AB (1)
Kungsgatan 76
75318 Uppsala, Sweden (100%)
Tel.: (46) 18565900
Fax: (46) 18591922
E-Mail: info@biotage.com
Emp.: 90
Medicinal Chemistry Research & Development Services
S.I.C.: 8731
N.A.I.C.S.: 541712
Torben Jorgensen *(Pres & CEO)*

U.S. Subsidiaries:

Biotage LLC (1)
10430 Harris Oak Blvd Ste C
Charlotte, NC 28269 (100%)
Tel.: (434) 979-2319
Fax: (434) 296-8217
E-Mail: ordermailbox@biotage.com
Web Site: www.biotage.or
Emp.: 20
Medicinal Chemistry Research & Development Services
S.I.C.: 8731
N.A.I.C.S.: 541712

Non-U.S. Subsidiaries:

Biotage GB Ltd. (1)
Dyffryn Industrial Est
Ystrad Mynach Hengoed, Stafford, CF82 7GF, United Kingdom (100%)
Tel.: (44) 1443811811
Fax: (44) 1443816552
E-Mail: chris.willams@biotage.com
Web Site: www.biotage.com
Emp.: 100
Medicinal Chemistry Research & Development Services
S.I.C.: 8731
N.A.I.C.S.: 541712
Chris Williams *(Mng Dir)*

Biotage (1)
Oberer Moosweg 11
Grellingen, Basel, Switzerland (100%)
Tel.: (41) 617439015
Web Site: www.separtis.com
Chemical & Allied Products Whslr
S.I.C.: 5169
N.A.I.C.S.: 424690

Separtis Holdings AG (1)
Oberer Moosweg 11
Grellingen, 4203 Basel, Switzerland (100%)
Tel.: (41) 617439015
Management Consulting Services
S.I.C.: 8748
N.A.I.C.S.: 541618

BIOTEC PHARMACON ASA

Strandgata 3
N-9008 Tromso, Norway
Tel.: (47) 77648900
Fax: (47) 77648901
E-Mail: info@biotec.no
Web Site: www.biotec.no
B4V—(DEU)
Business Description:
Pharmaceutical Product Mfr
S.I.C.: 2834
N.A.I.C.S.: 325412
Personnel:
Svein Mathisen *(Chm)*
Erik Thorsen *(Vice Chm)*
Svein W.F. Lien *(CEO)*
Rolf Engstad *(Chief Scientific Officer)*
Board of Directors:
Svein Mathisen
Ingrid Alfheim
Kjersti Grimsurd
Olav Lanes
Gunnar Rorstad
Erik Thorsen

BIOTECH CAPITAL LIMITED

1 Edmondson Crescent
Karrinyup, Perth, WA, 6018, Australia
Tel.: (61) 8 9446 5293
Fax: (61) 893271778
E-Mail: info@bioshares.com.au
Web Site: www.biotechcapital.com.au
BTC—(ASX)
Rev.: $39,300
Assets: $3,301,902
Liabilities: $14,218
Net Worth: $3,287,684
Earnings: ($522,872)
Emp.: 1
Fiscal Year-end: 06/30/13
Business Description:
Investing Service
S.I.C.: 6799
N.A.I.C.S.: 523910
Personnel:
Baden M. Bowen *(Sec)*
Board of Directors:
Alastair John Davidson
Harry Karelis
Edward Taylor
Legal Counsel:
Dibbs Barker
Level 8 123 Pitt Street
GPO Box 983
Sydney, Australia

BIOTECHPROGRESS SCIENTIFIC RESEARCH & PRODUCTION CO. ZAO

6 Shosse Entuziastov
Kirishi, 187110, Russia
Tel.: (7) 81368 255 07
E-Mail: stc@biotechprogress.ru
Business Description:
Water Treament Services
S.I.C.: 9511
N.A.I.C.S.: 924110

Subsidiary:

Sweco Lenvodokanalproekt CJCS (1)
Ul Torzhkovskaya 5
197342 Saint Petersburg, Russia
Tel.: (7) 812 324 40 30
Fax: (7) 812 441 39 24
E-Mail: office@sweco.ru
Web Site: www.sweco.ru
Emp.: 100
Engineering Consulting Services
S.I.C.: 8711
N.A.I.C.S.: 541330
Bo Carlsson *(Pres)*

BIOTEKNO

K Bakkalkoy Mah Kaysdagi Cad
Kayaoglu Plaza No 119
34750 Atasehir, Istanbul, Turkey
Tel.: (90) 2165763848
Fax: (90) 2165726290
E-Mail: biotekno@biotekno.biz
Web Site: www.biotekno.biz
Sales Range: $50-74.9 Million
Emp.: 100
Business Description:
Mobile Business Solutions
S.I.C.: 7372
N.A.I.C.S.: 511210
Personnel:
Ahmet Ilhan Oney *(CEO)*

BIOTEQ ENVIRONMENTAL TECHNOLOGIES INC.

Suite 1100 1050 West Pender Street
Vancouver, BC, V6E 3S7, Canada
Tel.: (604) 685-1243
Fax: (604) 685-7778
E-Mail: bioteq@bioteq.ca
Web Site: www.bioteq.ca
Year Founded: 1999
BQE—(TSX)
Rev.: $9,367,822
Assets: $15,266,257
Liabilities: $2,595,872
Net Worth: $12,670,384
Earnings: ($3,346,610)
Emp.: 99
Fiscal Year-end: 12/31/12
Business Description:
Water Treatment Processing Services
S.I.C.: 9511
N.A.I.C.S.: 924110
Personnel:
George W. Poling *(Chm)*
Jonathan Wilkinson *(CEO)*
Paul Kim *(CFO & VP)*
Board of Directors:
George W. Poling
C. Bruce Burton
Chris Fleming
Peter Gleeson
Clement A. Pelletier
Ron Sifton
Jonathan Wilkinson
Legal Counsel:
McCarthy Tetrault LLP
Vancouver, BC, Canada
Transfer Agent:
Computershare Investor Services Inc.
510 Burrard Street 2nd Floor
Vancouver, BC, V6C 3B9, Canada

U.S. Subsidiary:

BioteQ Arizona, Inc. (1)
36 W Hwy 92
Bisbee, AZ 85603
Tel.: (520) 432-3863
Web Site: www.bioteqwater.com
Water Treatment Services
S.I.C.: 4971
N.A.I.C.S.: 221310
David Kratochvil *(Pres)*

BIOTER S.A.

45 Eftichidou Str
Athens, 11634, Greece
Tel.: (30) 210 7248762
Fax: (30) 210 7215657
Web Site: en.bioter.gr
Year Founded: 1962
BIOT—(ATH)
Emp.: 76
Business Description:
Civil Engineering Construction Services
S.I.C.: 1629
N.A.I.C.S.: 237990
Personnel:
Ioannis I. Konstantinopoulos *(Chm)*
Mixail K. Adamantopoulos *(Deputy Chm)*
Georgios A. Mavroskotis *(Mng Dir & Gen Mgr)*
Board of Directors:
Ioannis I. Konstantinopoulos
Mixail K. Adamantopoulos
Dimitrios V. Bersos
Grigorios G. Dedes
Fotini O. Hatzi
Georgios A. Mavroskotis
Ioannis V. Pliatskas
Anastasios G. Sakelaris
Evagelos G. Stratis
Aristotelis K. Tsagaroyannis
Aristotelis V. Tsapaliras
Georgios I. Vasilakopoulos

BIOTEST AG

Landsteinerstrasse 5
63303 Dreieich, Germany
Mailing Address:
P.O. Box 10 20 40
63266 Dreieich, Germany
Tel.: (49) 61038010
Fax: (49) 6103801150
E-Mail: mail@biotest.de
Web Site: www.biotest.de
BIO3—(DEU)
Rev.: $592,270,376
Assets: $918,555,061
Liabilities: $421,235,439
Net Worth: $497,319,622
Earnings: $44,990,348
Emp.: 1,726
Fiscal Year-end: 12/31/12
Business Description:
Pharmaceutical, Biotherapeutic & Diagnostic Products
S.I.C.: 2834
N.A.I.C.S.: 325412
Personnel:
Alessandro Banchi *(Chm-Supervisory Bd)*
Gregor Schulz *(Chm-Mgmt Bd)*
Cathrin Schleussner *(Deputy Chm-Supervisory Bd)*
Michael Ramroth *(CFO & Member-Mgmt Bd)*
Georg Floss *(COO & Member-Mgmt Bd)*
Joachim Herborg *(Member-Mgmt Bd & Exec VP-Mktg & Sls Pharma)*
Martin Reinecke *(Member-Mgmt Bd & Sr VP-Plasma Alliances & Protein Supply)*
Markus Rothenburger *(Member-Mgmt Bd & Sr VP-Medical & Regulatory Affairs)*

Biotest AG—(Continued)

Joerg Schuettrumpf *(Member-Mgmt Bd & Sr VP-Global Res)*
Christina Erb *(Member-Mgmt Bd & VP-Project Mgmt Office)*
Supervisory Board of Directors:
Alessandro Banchi
Kerstin Birkhahn
Jurgen Heilmann
Thomas Jakob
Cathrin Schleussner
Christoph Schroder

Subsidiaries:

Bio-Rad Medical Diagnostics GmbH (1)
Industriestrasse 1
63303 Dreieich, Hesse, Germany
Tel.: (49) 6103801460
Fax: (49) 6103801125
E-Mail: contact.bmd@bio-rad.com.de
Web Site: www.medizinische-diagnostik-dreieich.de
Immunology Instruments & Reagents Mfr
S.I.C.: 3826
N.A.I.C.S.: 334516
John Bussell *(Mng Dir)*
Eric Thomas *(Mng Dir)*
Rolf Vornhagen *(Mng Dir)*
Gertrud Zoller *(Mng Dir)*

Biotest Grundstucksverwaltungs GmbH (1)
Landsteiner Strasse 5
63303 Dreieich, Hesse, Germany
Tel.: (49) 61038010
Fax: (49) 6103801150
E-Mail: mail@biotest.de
Emp.: 800
Pharmaceutical Products Mfr
S.I.C.: 2834
N.A.I.C.S.: 325412
Gregor Schulz *(CEO)*

Biotest Pharma GmbH (1)
Landsteiner Strasse 5
63303 Dreieich, Hesse, Germany
Tel.: (49) 61038010
Fax: (49) 6103801150
E-Mail: mail@biotest.de
Emp.: 800
Medical Diagnostic Equipments & Supplies Distr
S.I.C.: 5047
N.A.I.C.S.: 423450
Gregor Schulz *(Mng Dir)*

Plasma Service Europe GmbH (1)
Landsteiner Strasse 5
63303 Dreieich, Hesse, Germany
Tel.: (49) 61038010
Fax: (49) 6103801150
E-Mail: mail@biotest.de
Web Site: www.plasmaservice.de
Emp.: 229
Blood Plasma Collection Services
S.I.C.: 8099
N.A.I.C.S.: 621991
Martin Reinecke *(Mng Dir)*

U.S. Subsidiaries:

Biotest Pharmaceuticals Corporation (1)
5800 Park of Commerce Blvd NW
Boca Raton, FL 33487-8222
Tel.: (561) 989-5800
Fax: (561) 989-5801
Toll Free: (800) 327-7106
E-Mail: info@biotestpharma.com
Web Site: www.biotestpharma.com
Emp.: 600
Biological Products Mfr
S.I.C.: 2836
N.A.I.C.S.: 325414
Jordan I. Siegel *(CEO)*

Non-U.S. Subsidiaries:

Biotest France SARL (1)
375 rue Morane Saulnier ZI Centre
BP 405
78534 Buc, Yvelines, France
Tel.: (33) 1 3920 2080
Fax: (33) 1 3920 2081
E-Mail: info@biotest.fr
Web Site: www.biotest.fr
Pharmaceutical Products Distr
S.I.C.: 5122
N.A.I.C.S.: 424210
Gregor Schulz *(Pres)*

Biotest Hellas M.E.P.E. (1)
25 Kiprion Agoniston St
Maroussi, Athens, Greece
Tel.: (30) 2108043437
Fax: (30) 2108034695
E-Mail: infogr@biotest.gr
Web Site: www.biotest.gr
Emp.: 20
Medical Equipment Whslr
S.I.C.: 5047
N.A.I.C.S.: 423450
Giannako Poulos *(Mng Dir)*

Biotest Hungaria Kft. (1)
Torbagy Utca 15 A
Torokbalint, Pest, 2045, Hungary
Tel.: (36) 23511311
Fax: (36) 3511310
E-Mail: biotest@biotest.hu
Web Site: www.biotest.hu
Emp.: 20
Pharmaceutical Preparations Mfr
S.I.C.: 2834
N.A.I.C.S.: 325412
Borbas Gyula *(Mgr-Comml)*

Biotest K.K. (1)
Daini Yasuda Building 2F 3-32-13 Tsuruya-cho
Kanagawa-ku, Yokohama, Kanagawa, 221-0835, Japan
Tel.: (81) 453175111
Fax: (81) 453175110
Web Site: www.biotest.co.jp
Emp.: 10
Pharmaceutical Products Distr
S.I.C.: 5122
N.A.I.C.S.: 424210
Elmar Dresch *(Pres)*

Biotest Medical, S.L.U. (1)
C/Beethoven 15 4th Floor
08021 Barcelona, Spain
Tel.: (34) 931838734
Fax: (34) 931 838 701
E-Mail: info@biotestmedical.es
Pharmaceutical Products Distr
S.I.C.: 5122
N.A.I.C.S.: 424210
Moller Martin *(Mgr)*

Biotest (Schweiz) AG (1)
Schutzenstrasse 17
5102 Rupperswil, Aargau, Switzerland
Tel.: (41) 628890000
Fax: (41) 628890001
E-Mail: mail@biotest.ch
Web Site: www.biotest.ch
Emp.: 12
Pharmaceutical Products Distr
S.I.C.: 5122
N.A.I.C.S.: 424210

Biotest (UK) Ltd. (1)
28 Monkspath Business Park Highlands Road
Solihull, West Midlands, B90 4NZ, United Kingdom
Tel.: (44) 1217333393
Fax: (44) 1217333066
E-Mail: sales@biotestuk.com
Web Site: www.biotestuk.com
Emp.: 18
Pharmaceutical Products Distr
S.I.C.: 5122
N.A.I.C.S.: 424210
Christopher Hyde *(Chm)*

Plasmadienst Tirol GmbH (1)
Innrain 6-8
6020 Innsbruck, Tyrol, Austria
Tel.: (43) 5125847230
Fax: (43) 512 584 723 14
E-Mail: office@plasma-tirol.at
Web Site: www.plasma-tirol.at
Plasmapheresis Services
S.I.C.: 8099
N.A.I.C.S.: 621991

Plazmaszolgalat Kft. (1)
Czuczor Utca 10
1093 Budapest, Hungary
Tel.: (36) 13232100
Fax: (36) 13232107
E-Mail: plazmaszolgalat@plazmaszolgalat.hu
Web Site: www.plazmaszolgalat.hu
Emp.: 25
Pharmaceutical Preparations Mfr
S.I.C.: 2834
N.A.I.C.S.: 325412

BIOTIE THERAPIES CORP.

Tykistoekatu 6
FI-20520 Turku, Finland
Tel.: (358) 22748900
Fax: (358) 22748910
E-Mail: info@biotie.com
Web Site: www.biotie.com
BTH1V—(HEL)
Rev.: $6,503,347
Assets: $154,040,887
Liabilities: $53,035,059
Net Worth: $101,005,827
Earnings: ($35,478,310)
Emp.: 37
Fiscal Year-end: 12/31/12
Business Description:
Pharmaceuticals Researcher, Developer & Mfr
S.I.C.: 2834
N.A.I.C.S.: 325412
Personnel:
Peter J. Fellner *(Chm)*
William M. Burns *(Deputy Chm)*
Timo Veromaa *(Pres & CEO)*
David Cook *(CFO)*
Ian John Massey *(COO & Pres-Ops-US)*
Merja Karhapaa *(Chief Legal Officer & Sec)*
Stephen Bandak *(Chief Medical Officer)*
Board of Directors:
Peter J. Fellner
William M. Burns
Merja Karhapaa
Bernd Kastler
Ismail Kola
Guido Magni

Subsidiary:

Biotie Therapies International Ltd (1)
Tykistokatu 6
20520 Turku, Finland
Tel.: (358) 2 2748900
Fax: (358) 2 2748910
Pharmaceutical Products Mfr
S.I.C.: 2834
N.A.I.C.S.: 325412
Timo Veromaa *(CEO)*

Non-U.S. Subsidiary:

Biotie Therapies GmbH (1)
Meissner Str 191
01445 Radebeul, Germany
Tel.: (49) 35140430
Fax: (49) 35140433216
E-Mail: info@biotie.com
Web Site: www.biotie.com
Emp.: 40
Pharmaceutical Mfr
S.I.C.: 2834
N.A.I.C.S.: 325412
Thomas Taapken *(CFO)*

BIOTIKA BOHEMIA SPOL. S R.O.

Baodaki Bohemia Pod vasnokou 1662 4
140 00 Prague, Czech Republic
Tel.: (420) 244464454
Fax: (420) 244466927
E-Mail: biotika@biotika.cz
Web Site: www.biotika.cz
Emp.: 14
Business Description:
Pharmaceuticals Mfr
S.I.C.: 2834
N.A.I.C.S.: 325412
Personnel:
Vladimir Jirout *(Mng Dir)*

BIOTON S.A.

Macierzysz ul Poznanska 12
05-850 Ozarow Mazowiecki, Poland
Tel.: (48) 227214000
Fax: (48) 227211333
E-Mail: bioinfo@bioton.pl
Web Site: www.bioton.pl
Year Founded: 1989
BIO—(WAR)
Rev.: $128,850,870
Assets: $607,406,700
Liabilities: $183,520,277
Net Worth: $423,886,423
Earnings: $11,692,583
Emp.: 980
Fiscal Year-end: 12/31/12
Business Description:
Biopharmaceutical Mfr
S.I.C.: 2834
N.A.I.C.S.: 325412
Personnel:
Ryszard Krauze *(Chm-Supervisory Bd)*
Slawomir Ziegert *(Chm-Mgmt Bd)*
Zygmunt Solorz-Zak *(Vice Chm-Supervisory Bd)*
Adam Wilczega *(Vice Chm-Mgmt Bd)*
Piotr Baszczyk *(Mng Dir & Member-Mgmt Bd)*
Adam Polonek *(Member-Mgmt Bd & Dir-Fin)*
Supervisory Board of Directors:
Ryszard Krauze
Piotr Borowicz
Leon Bushara
Tomasz Buzuk
Waldemar Dabrowski
Marcin Dukaczewski
Maciej Grelowski
Barbara Ratnicka-Kiczka
Zygmunt Solorz-Zak
Andre Spark
Dariusz Trzeciak
Wieslaw Walendziak

Non-U.S. Subsidiaries:

Fisiopharma S.r.l. (1)
Nucleo Industriale
PO Box 84020
Palomonte, Salerno, 84020, Italy
Tel.: (39) 828997491
Fax: (39) 0828997383
E-Mail: uffconta@fisiopharma.com
Web Site: www.fisiopharma.com
Drugs Mfr
S.I.C.: 5122
N.A.I.C.S.: 424210

Medipolis GMP Oy (1)
Kiviharjunlenkki 2
PO Box 90220
Oulu, Finland
Tel.: (358) 207545880
Fax: (358) 207545879
E-Mail: info@medipolisgmp.com
Web Site: www.medipolisgmp.com
Emp.: 15
Pharmaceutical Products Mfr
S.I.C.: 2834
N.A.I.C.S.: 325412
Sirkka Aho *(CTO)*

MJ BioPharm Pvt Ltd (1)
B306 Raufoss Norway
Nariman Point, Mumbai, Maharashtra, 400 021, India
Tel.: (91) 2222020644
Fax: (91) 2222048030
E-Mail: mjgroup@mj-india.com
Web Site: www.mjbiopharm.com
Emp.: 100
Pharmaceutical Products Mfr
S.I.C.: 2834
N.A.I.C.S.: 325412
H. H. Pandit *(Pres)*
Amol Shah *(Mng Dir)*

SciGen Ltd. (1)
Gateway East 152 Beach Rd 26-07/08
Singapore, 189721, Singapore (90.54%)

Tel.: (65) 67796638
Fax: (65) 67793784
E-Mail: central@scigen.com.sg
Web Site: www.scigenltd.com
SIE—(ASX)
Rev.: $18,150,000
Assets: $52,575,000
Liabilities: $105,737,000
Net Worth: ($53,162,000)
Earnings: $4,143,000
Emp.: 12
Fiscal Year-end: 12/31/12
Biopharmaceuticals Mfr
S.I.C.: 2834
N.A.I.C.S.: 325412
Slawomir Ziegert *(Chm & CEO)*
Adam Tomasz Polonek *(CFO)*
Jenny Saw Imm Low *(Co-Sec & Sr VP)*
Leng Wong Lai *(Co-Sec)*

Non-U.S. Subsidiaries:

Marvel Life Sciences Pvt Ltd (2)
Ste 1 2nd Fl Congress House
Lyon Rd, Harrow, Middlesex, HA1 2EN, United Kingdom
Tel.: (44) 2084274377
Fax: (44) 2084275595
E-Mail: mjexports@aol.com
Pharmaceutical Products Mfr
S.I.C.: 2834
N.A.I.C.S.: 325412

SciGen (Australia) Pty. Ltd. (2)
Suite 1 13B Narabang Way
Belrose, NSW, 2085, Australia
Tel.: (61) 294851800
Fax: (61) 294851888
E-Mail: scigenmail@scigen.com.au
Web Site: www.scigen.com.au
Biopharmaceuticals Mfr
S.I.C.: 2834
N.A.I.C.S.: 325412
Slawomir Ziegert *(CEO)*

SciGen Biopharma Pvt Ltd (2)
Plot 18 International Biotech Park
Hinjewadi Phase II, 411 057 Pune, Maharastra, India (50.01%)
Tel.: (91) 20 3980 3220
Fax: (91) 20 3980 3222
E-Mail: administrator@scigeninc.com
Web Site: www.scigenltd.com
Emp.: 52
Therapeutic Proteins Mfr
S.I.C.: 2833
N.A.I.C.S.: 325411

BIOTONIX (2010) INC.
(Name Changed to AtmanCo Inc.)

BIOTRON LIMITED
Level 2 66 Hunter Street
Sydney, NSW, 2000, Australia
Tel.: (61) 293003344
Fax: (61) 292216333
E-Mail: enquiries@biotron.com.au
Web Site: www.biotron.com.au
BIT—(ASX)
Rev.: $929,502
Assets: $5,071,056
Liabilities: $407,543
Net Worth: $4,663,512
Earnings: ($4,012,861)
Emp.: 7
Fiscal Year-end: 06/30/13
Business Description:
Funding & Management
S.I.C.: 9651
N.A.I.C.S.: 926150
Personnel:
Michelle Miller *(Mng Dir)*
Peter J. Nightingale *(Sec)*
Board of Directors:
Michael J. Hoy
Michelle Miller
Susan Pond
Rob Thomas
Denis N. Wade
Legal Counsel:
Minter Ellison
88 Phillip Street
Sydney, Australia

BIOTRONIK GMBH & CO.
Woermannkehre 1
D 12359 Berlin, Germany
Tel.: (49) 30689050
Fax: (49) 59306844060
E-Mail: info@biotronik.de
Web Site: www.biotronik.com
Year Founded: 1969
Sales Range: $300-349.9 Million
Emp.: 3,000
Business Description:
Implantable Cardiac Devices Mfr & Sales
S.I.C.: 3845
N.A.I.C.S.: 334510
Personnel:
Max Schaldach *(Pres)*

Subsidiaries:

Biotronik GmbH & Co. (1)
Hartmann Strasse 65
PO Box 1369
91052 Erlangen, Bavaria, Germany (100%)
Tel.: (49) 913189240
Fax: (49) 3189247950
E-Mail: info@biotronikerlangen.de
Web Site: www.biotronik.com
Emp.: 140
Mfr. & Sales of Implantable Cardiac Devices
S.I.C.: 3841
N.A.I.C.S.: 339113

Biotronik GmbH & Co. Vertriebs KG (1)
Woermannkehre 1
12359 Berlin, Germany
Tel.: (49) 30689050
Fax: (49) 306844060
E-Mail: info@biotronik.com
Web Site: www.biotronik.com
Emp.: 100
Mfr. & Sales of Implantable Cardiac Devices
S.I.C.: 3842
N.A.I.C.S.: 339113
Till Hoffmann *(Mng Dir)*

U.S. Subsidiary:

Biotronik Inc. (1)
6024 Jean Rd
Lake Oswego, OR 97035-5308 OR
Tel.: (503) 635-3594
Fax: (503) 635-9936
Toll Free: (800) 547-0394
E-Mail: schroeder@biotronik.com
Web Site: www.biotronik.com
Emp.: 400
Mfr. of Implantable Cardiac Devices
S.I.C.: 5047
N.A.I.C.S.: 423450
Jake Langer *(Pres)*

Non-U.S. Subsidiary:

Medsoll Cyprus Ltd (1)
Evagoras Ste 51 31 Evagorou Ave
CY 1066 Nicosia, Cyprus (100%)
Tel.: (357) 22671638
Fax: (357) 22671276
E-Mail: medmed@cytanet.com.cy
Web Site: www.biotronic.com
Emp.: 10
Mfr. & Sales of Implantable Cardiac Devices
S.I.C.: 3841
N.A.I.C.S.: 339113
Christos Vasiliadis *(Gen Mgr)*

BIOVENTIX PLC
7 Romans Business Park East Street
Farnham, Surrey, GU9 7SX, United Kingdom
Tel.: (44) 1252 728001
Fax: (44) 1252 728002
E-Mail: info@bioventix.com
Web Site: www.bioventix.com
Year Founded: 2003
BVXP—(ISDX)
Sls.: $4,274,247
Assets: $7,126,015
Liabilities: $485,377
Net Worth: $6,640,638
Earnings: $2,402,817
Emp.: 13
Fiscal Year-end: 06/30/13
Business Description:
Biotechnology Specializing in High-Affinity Sheep Monoclonal Antibodies
S.I.C.: 8731
N.A.I.C.S.: 541711
Personnel:
Peter Harrison *(CEO)*
Board of Directors:
Ian Nicholson
Peter Harrison
Nick McCooke
Kim Tan
Treena Turner

BIOVEST CORP. I
1100 100 Queen Street
Ottawa, ON, K1P 1J9, Canada
Tel.: (613) 787-3532
Fax: (613) 230-8842
Year Founded: 2009
BVC.P—(TSXV)
Business Description:
Investment Services
S.I.C.: 6211
N.A.I.C.S.: 523999
Personnel:
Calvin Stiller *(Chm & CEO)*
Brian Baker *(CFO)*
Tim McCunn *(Sec)*
Board of Directors:
Calvin Stiller
Santo J. Costa
Garrett Herman
Michael Mueller
Transfer Agent:
Computershare Trust Company of Canada
100 University Avenue 11th Floor
Toronto, ON, M5J 2Y1, Canada
Tel.: (416) 891-9633
Toll Free: (800) 663-9097

BIOVET JSC
3a Nikolay Haytov Str
1113 Sofia, Bulgaria
Tel.: (359) 2 868 2095
Fax: (359) 2 862 5334
Web Site: www.biovet.com
53B—(BUL)
Business Description:
Pharmaceutical Products Mfr
S.I.C.: 2834
N.A.I.C.S.: 325412
Personnel:
Spas Petkov *(Chm)*
Kiril Domuschiev *(Chm-Supervisory Bd)*

BIOWIND GROUP S.A.
58 rue Pottier
78150 Le Chesnay, France
Tel.: (33) 1 39 02 25 42
Fax: (33) 73 76 87 85
E-Mail: contact@biowindgroup.com
Web Site: www.biowindgroup.com
Year Founded: 2001
MLBWG—(EUR)
Sales Range: Less than $1 Million
Emp.: 4
Business Description:
Industrial Air, Surface Cleaning & Decontamination Equipment Mfr
S.I.C.: 3564
N.A.I.C.S.: 333413
Personnel:
Valery Bonnet *(Chm & Mng Dir)*

Plant:

Biowind Group S.A. - Manufacturing Plant (1)
58 Rue Pottier
78150 Le Chesnay, France
Tel.: (33) 1 39 02 25 42
Fax: (33) 1 73 76 87 85
Air Purification Equipment Mfr
S.I.C.: 3564
N.A.I.C.S.: 333413
Sylvain Rougeau *(Mng Dir)*

BIOX CORP.
585 Wentworth Street North
Hamilton, ON, L8L 5X5, Canada
Tel.: (905) 521-8205
Fax: (905) 522-4493
E-Mail: info@bioxcorp.com
Web Site: www.bioxcorp.com
Year Founded: 2007
BX—(TSX)
Rev.: $74,796,029
Assets: $87,123,865
Liabilities: $24,540,366
Net Worth: $62,583,499
Earnings: ($2,824,011)
Emp.: 42
Fiscal Year-end: 09/30/13
Business Description:
Biodiesel Plant Construction & Production Services
S.I.C.: 1629
N.A.I.C.S.: 237990
Personnel:
David Colcleugh *(Chm)*
Kevin W. Norton *(CEO)*
Christopher A. Clinning *(CFO, Sec & Exec VP)*
Ross Marshall *(Sr VP-Equicom Grp)*
Board of Directors:
David Colcleugh
T. Robert Beamish
William A. Lambert
Michael J. Salamon
W. James Whitaker
Legal Counsel:
Wildeboer Dellelce, LLP
Suite 800 365 Bay Street
Toronto, ON, Canada
Transfer Agent:
Computershare Investor Services Inc.
Toronto, ON, Canada

U.S. Subsidiary:

BIOX USA Limited (1)
89 Headquarters Plz N 4 Speedwell Ave
Ste 1451
Morristown, NJ 07960
Tel.: (905) 337-4983
Biodiesel Mfr
S.I.C.: 2911
N.A.I.C.S.: 324110

BIOXYNE LIMITED
Suite 1A Level 2 802 Pacific Highway
Gordon, NSW, 2072, Australia
Tel.: (61) 298445422
Fax: (61) 298445445
Web Site:
BXN—(ASX)
Sales Range: Less than $1 Million
Business Description:
Biotechnology Products Mfr
S.I.C.: 2834
N.A.I.C.S.: 325412
Personnel:
Phillip Comans *(Interim CEO)*
Ashok Kumar Jairath *(CFO & Sec)*
Board of Directors:
Tony Ho
Phillip Comans
Jeremy L. Curnock-Cook
Patrick Douglas Ford
Legal Counsel:
Spruson & Ferguson
Level 35, St Martins Tower 31 Market Street
Sydney, Australia
Dipps Barker
Level 8 123 Pitt Street
Sydney, Australia

BIP - BUSINESS INTEGRATION PARTNERS S.P.A.

Piazza San Babila 5
20122 Milan, Italy
Tel.: (39) 024541521
Fax: (39) 0245415252
E-Mail: info@mail-bip.com
Web Site: www.businessintegrationpartners.com
Year Founded: 2003
Sales Range: $50-74.9 Million
Emp.: 400

Business Description:
Management Consulting Services for Energy & Telecommunications Industries
S.I.C.: 8999
N.A.I.C.S.: 541690

Personnel:
Nino Lo Bianco *(Pres)*
Carlo Cape *(Mng Dir)*
Fabio Troiani *(Mng Dir)*

BIP INVESTMENT PARTNERS S.A.

Rue des Coquelicots 1
L-1356 Luxembourg, Luxembourg
Tel.: (352) 2600261
Fax: (352) 26002650
E-Mail: info@bip.lu
Web Site: www.bip.lu
Year Founded: 2000
BIP—(LUX)
Rev.: $16,481,294
Assets: $492,460,085
Liabilities: $2,368,375
Net Worth: $490,091,710
Earnings: $2,140,573
Emp.: 8
Fiscal Year-end: 12/31/12

Business Description:
Equity Investment Firm
S.I.C.: 6211
N.A.I.C.S.: 523999

Personnel:
Michel Wurth *(Chm)*
Claude Kremer *(Deputy Chm)*
Bruno Lambert *(CEO)*
Viviane Graffe *(CFO & Chief Admin Officer)*

Board of Directors:
Michel Wurth
Romain Bausch
Norbert Becker
Nicolas Buck
Marc Giorgetti
Pit Hentgen
Claude Kremer
Bruno Lambert
Francois Pauly
Georges Prost
Carlo Thill

Non-U.S. Joint Venture:

Utimaco Safeware AG **(1)**
Germanusstrasse 4
52080 Aachen, Germany DE
Mailing Address:
Postfach 2026
D 61441 Oberursel, Hessen, Germany
Tel.: (49) 241 1696 0
Fax: (49) 241 1696 199
E-Mail: info.de@utimaco.de
Web Site: www.utimaco.com
USA—(DEU)
Sales Range: $50-74.9 Million
Emp.: 318
Information Security & Management Software
Export
S.I.C.: 7372
N.A.I.C.S.: 511210
Peter Lammer *(Chm-Supervisory Bd)*
Malte Pollmann *(CEO & Chm-Mgmt Bd)*
Frank J. Nellissen *(CFO & Member-Mgmt Bd)*
Cynthia Curtis *(Exec VP-Mktg)*

U.S. Subsidiary:

Utimaco Safeware, Inc. **(2)**
10 Lincoln Rd
Foxboro, MA 02035 DE
Tel.: (508) 543-1008
Fax: (508) 543-1009
Emp.: 25
Information Security & Management Software
S.I.C.: 7372
N.A.I.C.S.: 511210

BIRATLAXMI BIKAS BANK LIMITED

Himalaya Road
Biratnagar, 56614, Nepal
Tel.: (977) 21 538051
Fax: (977) 21 538218
E-Mail: info@biratlaxmibank.com.np
Web Site: www.biratlaxmibank.com.np
BLDBL—(NEP)

Business Description:
Banking Services
S.I.C.: 6029
N.A.I.C.S.: 522110

Personnel:
Shaligram Dahal *(Chm)*
Hemanta Raj Neupane *(Sec)*

Board of Directors:
Shaligram Dahal
Khagendra Acharya
Madhav Prasad Koirala
Hemanta Raj Neupane
Prabhu Prasad Parajuli
Badri Prasad Pyakurel
Nawaraj Subedi
Thakur Prasad Upadhaya

BIRCH & PRESTIGE INVESTMENT GROUP LIMITED

253 Wickham Road
Moorabbin, VIC, 3189, Australia
Tel.: (61) 3 9553 3229
Fax: (61) 3 9555 6061
E-Mail: info@bandpdesign.com.au
Web Site: www.bandpdesign.com.au
BOP—(ASX)

Business Description:
Custom Made Kitchen, Bathroom, Wardrobe & Laundry Products
S.I.C.: 2434
N.A.I.C.S.: 337110

Personnel:
Lei Xu *(Sec)*

BIRCH BRANCH ACQUISITION CORP.

c/o Henan Shuncheng Group Coal Coke Co Ltd New Building
Cai Cun Road Intersection, Anyang, Henan, China 455141
Tel.: (86) 372 323 7890
Year Founded: 1989
Sales Range: $350-399.9 Million
Emp.: 1,625

Business Description:
Coke & Refined Coal Mfr
S.I.C.: 3399
N.A.I.C.S.: 331110

Personnel:
Xinshun Wang *(Chm)*
Feng Wang *(Pres, CEO & CFO)*
Dexin Li *(COO)*

Board of Directors:
Xinshun Wang
Senshan Gong
Qifa Huang
Dexin Li
Feng Wang

BIRCH HILL EQUITY PARTNERS MANAGEMENT INC.

100 Wellington Street West
CP Tower Ste 2300, Toronto, ON, M5K 1A1, Canada
Tel.: (416) 775-3800
Fax: (416) 360-1688
E-Mail: info@birchhillequity.com
Web Site: www.birchhillequity.com
Managed Assets: $1,988,040,000

Business Description:
Private Equity Firm
S.I.C.: 6211
N.A.I.C.S.: 523999

Personnel:
Stephen J. Dent *(Partner)*
Paul R. Henry *(Partner)*
Matthew B. Kunica *(Partner)*
John T. Loh *(Partner)*
John B. MacIntyre *(Partner)*
Michael R. Mazan *(Partner)*
Michael J. Salamon *(Partner)*
David G. Samuel *(Partner)*
Pierre J. Schuurmans *(Partner)*
Thecla E. Sweeney *(Partner)*
Peter Zissis *(CFO)*
Lori A. E. Evans *(Gen Counsel & Sr VP)*

Holdings:

Creation Technologies LP **(1)**
3939 North Fraser Way
Burnaby, BC, V5J 5J2, Canada (70%)
Tel.: (604) 430-4336
Fax: (604) 430-4337
E-Mail: info@creationtech.com
Web Site: www.creationtech.com
Sales Range: $300-349.9 Million
Emp.: 100
Contract Electronic Manufacturing Services Including Design Support & New Product Assembly
S.I.C.: 3679
N.A.I.C.S.: 334419
Geoff Reed *(Chm)*
Arthur Tymos *(Pres & CEO)*
Michael Walsh *(CFO)*
Douglas Besse *(CIO & Exec VP-Global Supply Chain)*

U.S. Subsidiary:

Creation Technologies Lexington **(2)**
1729 Jaggie Fox Way
Lexington, KY 40511
Tel.: (859) 253-3066
Fax: (859) 254-2870
E-Mail: info@creationtech.com
Web Site: www.creationtech.com
Emp.: 325
Electronic Circuits Mfr
S.I.C.: 3679
N.A.I.C.S.: 334419
John Zurborg *(Exec VP-Bus Dev)*

Distinction Group Inc. **(1)**
695 90th Ave
LaSalle, Montreal, QC, H8R 3A4, Canada
Tel.: (514) 368-1504
Fax: (514) 368-1691
E-Mail: distinction@distinction.ca
Web Site: www.gdiservices.ca
Sales Range: $250-299.9 Million
Emp.: 9,500
Cleaning Services
S.I.C.: 7349
N.A.I.C.S.: 561720
Claude Bigras *(Pres & CEO)*
Jocelyn Trottier *(CFO & Exec VP)*
Real Pare *(Exec VP)*
Irina Dounaevskaia *(Sr VP-Fin)*
Stewart McKinney *(Sr VP-Bus Dev-Central & Eastern Canada)*

Subsidiaries:

Distinction Services Plus Inc. **(2)**
695 90th Ave
Lasalle, Montreal, QC, H8R 3A4, Canada
Tel.: (514) 351-7744
Fax: (514) 351-5793
Janitorial Services
S.I.C.: 7349
N.A.I.C.S.: 561720

Montcalm Services Techniques Inc. **(2)**
695 90 Ave
Lasalle, Montreal, QC, H8R 3A4, Canada
Tel.: (514) 426-8188
Fax: (514) 426-8169
Web Site: www.gdiservices.ca
Emp.: 7
Janitorial Services
S.I.C.: 7349
N.A.I.C.S.: 561720
Sylvain Pilon *(VP)*

Subsidiary:

Immotik Inc. **(3)**
695 90e Ave Lasalle
Montreal, QC, H8R 3A4, Canada
Tel.: (514) 368-1507
Fax: (514) 368-1723
Web Site: www.gdiservices.ca
Emp.: 30
Janitorial & Building Maintenance Services
S.I.C.: 7349
N.A.I.C.S.: 561720
Serge Lavoie *(Pres)*

Service d'entretien Empro Inc. **(2)**
1375 Rue Frank Carrel Bureau 16
Quebec, QC, G1N 2E7, Canada
Tel.: (418) 688-1172
Fax: (418) 688-1428
E-Mail: reception.empro@gdiservices.ca
Web Site: www.gdiservices.ca
Emp.: 1,000
Janitorial Services
S.I.C.: 7349
N.A.I.C.S.: 561720

HOMEQ Corporation **(1)**
1881 Yonge St Ste 300
Toronto, ON, M4V 1K9, Canada Ca
Tel.: (416) 925-4757
Fax: (416) 925-9938
E-Mail: info@homeq.ca
Web Site: www.homeq.ca
Sales Range: $75-99.9 Million
Emp.: 90
Mortgage Administration Services
S.I.C.: 6163
N.A.I.C.S.: 522310
Steven K. Ranson *(Pres & CEO)*
Gary Krikler *(CFO, Chief Risk Officer & Sr VP)*
Celia Cuthbertson *(Chief Compliance Officer, Gen Counsel, Sec & VP)*
Wendy L. Dryden *(Chief Anti Money Laundering Officer & VP-Bus Dev)*
Greg Bandler *(Sr VP-Sls & Mktg)*

Sleep Country Canada Income Fund **(1)**
140 Wendell Ave Unit 2
Toronto, ON, M9N 3R2, Canada ON
Tel.: (416) 242-4774
Fax: (416) 242-9644
Toll Free: (888) 753-3788
E-Mail: investor@sleepcountry.ca
Web Site: www.sleepcountry.ca
Sales Range: $350-399.9 Million
Emp.: 900
Holding Company; Owned by Birch Hill Equity Partners Management Inc. & Westerkirk Capital Inc.
S.I.C.: 6719
N.A.I.C.S.: 551112
Stephen Gunn *(Chm & CEO)*
Christine A. Magee *(Pres)*
Vicki Jones *(CFO)*
Glen Antonuk *(COO-Western Canada & Exec VP)*
David Friesema *(COO-Eastern Canada & Exec VP)*

Subsidiary:

Sleep Country Canada Inc. **(2)**
140 Wendell Ave Unit 2
Toronto, ON, M9N 3R2, Canada
Tel.: (416) 242-4774
Fax: (416) 242-9644
Toll Free: (888) 753-3788
E-Mail: info@sleepcountry.ca
Web Site: www.sleepcountry.ca
Emp.: 200
Mattress Retailer
S.I.C.: 5021

N.A.I.C.S.: 423210
Christine A. Magee *(Co-Founder & Pres)*
Stephen Gunn *(Chm & CEO)*

U.S. Subsidiary:

Sleep America Inc. **(3)**
1202 N 54th Ave Ste 111
Phoenix, AZ 85043
Tel.: (602) 269-7000
Fax: (602) 669-6200
Toll Free: (888) 947-5337
E-Mail: debbie@sleepamerica.com
Web Site: www.sleepamerica.com
Sales Range: $10-24.9 Million
Emp.: 120
Mattress Retailer
S.I.C.: 5021
N.A.I.C.S.: 423210
Debbie Gaby *(Co-Founder & Pres)*

Softchoice Corporation **(1)**
173 Dufferin Street Suite 200
Toronto, ON, M6K 3H7, Canada Ca
Tel.: (416) 588-9000
Fax: (416) 588-9001
Toll Free: (800) 268-7638
E-Mail: info@softchoice.com
Web Site: www.softchoice.com
Rev.: $1,065,620,000
Assets: $445,581,000
Liabilities: $280,678,000
Net Worth: $164,903,000
Earnings: $27,656,000
Emp.: 1,172
Fiscal Year-end: 12/31/12
Information Technology Products & Services
S.I.C.: 7373
N.A.I.C.S.: 541512
David L. MacDonald *(Pres & CEO)*
David A. Long *(CFO & Sr VP-Fin)*
Kevin Wright *(CIO & Sr VP-Svcs & Tech)*
Sandy Fallon *(Sr VP-People)*
Steve Leslie *(Sr VP-Sls & Mktg)*

BIRCH HILL GOLD CORP.

(Formerly Foundation Resources Inc.)
Suite 620 650 West Georgia Street
Vancouver, BC, V6N 4A9, Canada
Tel.: (604) 681-0405
Toll Free: (800) 667-4470
E-Mail: info@birchhillgold.com
Web Site: www.birchhillgold.com
Year Founded: 2006
BHG—(TSXV)
Assets: $10,227,905
Liabilities: $1,976,188
Net Worth: $8,251,717
Earnings: ($832,116)
Fiscal Year-end: 06/30/13
Business Description:
Gold Mining Services
S.I.C.: 1041
N.A.I.C.S.: 212221
Personnel:
Paul Chung *(Chm)*
Barry Girling *(Pres & CEO)*
Jerry Bella *(CFO)*
Board of Directors:
Paul Chung
J.J. Elkin
Barry Girling
John Hiner
Ralph Edward Shearing
Legal Counsel:
Armstrong Simpson
2080-777 Hornby Street
Vancouver, BC, Canada
Transfer Agent:
Computershare Investor Services inc
3rd Fl 510 Burrard Street
Vancouver, BC, Canada

BIRCH LAKE ENERGY INC.

Suite 1580 727 7th Ave SW
Calgary, AB, T2P 0Z5, Canada
Tel.: (403) 457-1944
E-Mail: info@birchlakeenergy.com
Web Site: www.birchlakeenergy.com
Year Founded: 2007
BLK—(TSXV)
Sls.: $29,460
Assets: $7,555,644
Liabilities: $1,717,366
Net Worth: $5,838,278
Earnings: ($2,101,741)
Fiscal Year-end: 12/31/12
Business Description:
Oil & Gas Exploration & Development Services
S.I.C.: 1389
N.A.I.C.S.: 213112
Personnel:
William H. Petrie, Sr. *(Pres, CEO & Acting CFO)*
Roy Hudson *(Sec)*
Board of Directors:
Tony Boogmans
Roy Hudson
Jesse Meidl
William H. Petrie, Sr.

BIRCHCLIFF ENERGY LTD

500 630 4th Avenue SW
Calgary, AB, T2P 0J9, Canada
Tel.: (403) 261-6401
Fax: (403) 261-6424
E-Mail: info@birchcliffenergy.com
Web Site: www.birchcliffenergy.com
BIR—(OTC TSX)
Rev.: $255,667,908
Assets: $1,421,770,662
Liabilities: $592,512,460
Net Worth: $829,258,203
Earnings: $13,117,088
Emp.: 90
Fiscal Year-end: 12/31/12
Business Description:
Oil & Gas Developer & Producer
S.I.C.: 1389
N.A.I.C.S.: 213112
Personnel:
Laurence Allan Shaw *(Chm)*
A. Jeffery Tonken *(Pres & CEO)*
Bruno P. Geremia *(CFO & VP)*
Myles R. Bosman *(COO & VP-Exploration)*
Board of Directors:
Laurence Allan Shaw
Gordon W. Cameron
Kenneth N. Cullen
Werner A. Siemens
A. Jeffery Tonken
Legal Counsel:
Borden Ladner Gervais LLP
1000 Canterra Tower 400 3rd Ave SW
Calgary, AB, T2P 4H2, Canada
Transfer Agent:
Olympia Trust Company
125 9th Avenue SE Suite 2300
Calgary, AB, T2G 0P6, Canada
Tel.: (403) 261-0900

BIRCHLAND PLYWOOD-VENEER LIMITED

Hwy 17
PO Box 430
Thessalon, ON, Canada P0R1L0
Tel.: (705) 842-2430
Fax: (705) 842-2496
Toll Free: (800) 461-2226
Web Site: www.birchlandplywood.com
Year Founded: 1958
Rev.: $10,626,605
Emp.: 85
Business Description:
Hardwood Plywood Distr
S.I.C.: 5031
N.A.I.C.S.: 423310
Personnel:
Eric Morgan *(Pres)*

BIRD CONSTRUCTION COMPANY

5403 Eglinton Avenue West
Toronto, ON, M9C 5K6, Canada
Tel.: (416) 620-7122
Fax: (416) 620-1516
E-Mail: corporate.info@bird.ca
Web Site: www.bird.ca
Rev.: $381,731,657
Emp.: 200
Business Description:
Construction Services
S.I.C.: 1542
N.A.I.C.S.: 236220
Personnel:
Paul A. Charette *(Chm)*
Paul R. Raboud *(Vice Chm)*
Tim J. Talbott *(Pres & CEO)*
Stephen Entwistle *(CFO & Asst Sec)*
Ian J. Boyd *(COO & Exec VP)*
Jim J. Brennan *(Pres-H.J. O'Connell, Limited & Sr VP)*
Charmane L. Morrow *(Corp Sec)*
Board of Directors:
Paul A. Charette
J. Richard Bird
D. Greg Doyle
Bonnie D. DuPont
J. Urban Joseph
Ronald D. Munkley
Paul R. Raboud
Tim J. Talbott
Arni C. Thorsteinson

BIRD PACKAGING LIMITED

670 Southgate Dr
PO Box 1506
Guelph, ON, N1H 6N9, Canada
Tel.: (519) 836-3470
Fax: (519) 836-1208
Toll Free: (800) 265-7222
E-Mail: sales@birdpackaging.com
Web Site: www.birdpackaging.com
Year Founded: 1975
Rev.: $27,200,000
Emp.: 170
Business Description:
Packaging Materials & Corrugated Boxes Mfr
S.I.C.: 2653
N.A.I.C.S.: 322211
Personnel:
Mike Dienst *(Pres & Gen Mgr)*

BIRD RIVER RESOURCES INC.

1059 Selkirk Avenue
Winnipeg, MB, R2X 0C2, Canada
Tel.: (204) 589-2848
Fax: (204) 586-6238
E-Mail: shodine@mts.net
Web Site: www.birdrivermines.com
Year Founded: 1958
BDR—(CNSX)
Rev.: $174,708
Assets: $839,001
Liabilities: $70,791
Net Worth: $768,209
Earnings: ($80,990)
Fiscal Year-end: 07/31/13
Business Description:
Precious Metals, Base Metals & Industrial Minerals Mining & Exploration Services
S.I.C.: 1041
N.A.I.C.S.: 212221
Personnel:
Nelson Shodine *(Chm, Pres & CEO)*
Jon Bridgman *(CFO)*
Edward Thompson *(Treas & Sec)*
Board of Directors:
Nelson Shodine
Jon Bridgman
Shane Shodine
David Thom
Edward Thompson
Transfer Agent:
Computershare
Suite 600 530 8th Ave SW
Calgary, AB, Canada

BIRDSTEP TECHNOLOGY ASA

Henrik Ibsens Gate 100 8th floor
PO Box 2877
0230 Oslo, Norway
Tel.: (47) 23275166
Fax: (47) 24134701
E-Mail: info@birdstep.com
Web Site: www.birdstep.com
Year Founded: 1996
BIRD—(OSL)
Rev.: $7,987,270
Assets: $14,629,784
Liabilities: $4,019,788
Net Worth: $10,609,996
Earnings: ($7,294,440)
Emp.: 61
Fiscal Year-end: 12/31/12
Business Description:
Software Developer & Marketer
S.I.C.: 7372
N.A.I.C.S.: 511210
Personnel:
Tom Nyman *(Chm)*
Lonnie Schilling *(CEO)*
Sophie Rabenius *(CFO)*
Charlotta Malargard *(Exec VP-Mktg & Comm)*
Board of Directors:
Tom Nyman
Arne Aarnes
Anna Bernsten
Kirsten English
Massimo Migliuolo

U.S. Subsidiary:

Birdstep Technology, Inc. **(1)**
720 3rd Ave Ste 1100
Seattle, WA 98104-1851 (100%)
Tel.: (206) 748-5353
Fax: (206) 748-5200
Toll Free: (877) 462-2473
E-Mail: dbsales@birdstep.com
Web Site: www.birdsteptechnology.com
Emp.: 18
Software Developer & Database Technology Services
S.I.C.: 7372
N.A.I.C.S.: 511210

Non-U.S. Subsidiaries:

Alice Systems AB **(1)**
Smidesvagen 10-12 4th Fl
Solna, SE-171 41, Sweden (100%)
Tel.: (46) 86279140
Fax: (46) 86279142
E-Mail: hello@birdstep.com
Emp.: 80
Software Developer
S.I.C.: 7371
N.A.I.C.S.: 541511
Anders Gymnander *(Chm)*

Birdstep Technology AB **(1)**
Halsingegatan 32 7th Floor
113 43 Stockholm, Sweden
Tel.: (46) 86279140
Fax: (46) 86279142
E-Mail: info@birdstep.com
Emp.: 30
Software Products Sales & Development Services
S.I.C.: 5731
N.A.I.C.S.: 443142
Lonnie Schilling *(Gen Mgr)*

Birdstep Technology Ltd **(1)**
3rd Floor, 52 Burleigh Street
Cambridge, CB1 1DJ, United Kingdom (100%)
Tel.: (44) 1223 461 656
E-Mail: uk@birdstep.com
Software Publisher
S.I.C.: 7372
N.A.I.C.S.: 511210

Birdstep Technology Oy **(1)**
Stella Business Park Lars Sonckin Kaari 16
02600 Espoo, Uusimaa, Finland
Tel.: (358) 20 740 2555
Fax: (358) 9 3487 0099
E-Mail: safemove.sales@birdstep.com
Web Site: www.birdstep.com

Birdstep Technology ASA—(Continued)

Software Products Sales & Development Services
S.I.C.: 5946
N.A.I.C.S.: 443142

BIRIMIAN GOLD LIMITED

Suite 9 5 Centro Avenue
Subiaco, WA, 6008, Australia
Tel.: (61) 8 9286 3045
Fax: (61) 8 9226 2027
E-Mail: info@birimiangold.com
Web Site: www.birimiangold.com
BGS—(ASX)
Rev.: $56,695
Assets: $12,264,125
Liabilities: $1,085,964
Net Worth: $11,178,161
Earnings: ($1,166,189)
Emp.: 6
Fiscal Year-end: 06/30/13

Business Description:
Mineral Exploration Services
S.I.C.: 1041
N.A.I.C.S.: 212221

Personnel:
Kevin Joyce *(Mng Dir)*
Beverley Nichols *(CFO & Sec)*

Board of Directors:
Hugh Bresser
Winton Willesee
Kevin Joyce

Legal Counsel:
Hardy Bowen
Level 1 28 Ord Street
West West Perth, WA, 6005, Australia

BIRKS & MAYORS INC.

1240 Phillips Square
Montreal, QC, H3B 3H4, Canada
Tel.: (514) 397-2501
Fax: (514) 397-2455
Toll Free: (800) 758-2511
Web Site: www.birksandmayors.com
Year Founded: 1879
BMJ—(NYSEMKT)
Sls.: $292,759,000
Assets: $179,952,000
Liabilities: $163,601,000
Net Worth: $16,351,000
Earnings: $1,513,000
Emp.: 790
Fiscal Year-end: 03/30/13

Business Description:
Silverware & Jewelry Retailer & Mfr
S.I.C.: 3911
N.A.I.C.S.: 339910

Personnel:
Lorenzo Rossi di Montelera *(Chm)*
Jean-Christophe Bedos *(Pres & CEO)*
Michael Rabinovitch *(CFO & Sr VP)*
Milt Thacker *(CIO & VP-Process Innovation)*
Deborah Nicodemus *(CMO, Chief Mdsg Officer & Exec VP)*
Helene Messier *(Chief Talent Officer & VP)*
Miranda Melfi *(Sec & VP-Legal Affairs)*
Albert J. Rahm, II *(Sr VP-Retail Store Ops)*

Board of Directors:
Lorenzo Rossi di Montelera
Jean-Christophe Bedos
Emily Berlin
Shirley A. Dawe
Elizabeth M. Eveillard
Louis L. Roquet
Niccolo Rossi di Montelera
Guthrie J. Stewart

U.S. Subsidiary:

Birks & Mayors Inc. (1)
5870 N Hiatus Rd
Tamarac, FL 33321 DE
Tel.: (954) 590-9000 (100%)
Toll Free: (800) 462-9677
Web Site: www.birksandmayors.com
Sales Range: $125-149.9 Million
Emp.: 384
Fine Jewelry, Watches & Gift Items Retailer Import Export
S.I.C.: 3829
N.A.I.C.S.: 334519
Michael Rabinovitch *(CFO & Sr VP)*

BIRLA CAPITAL & FINANCIAL SERVICES LIMITED

(See Under The Yash Birla Group)

BIRLA CORPORATION LTD

Birla Building 3rd & 4th Floors 9/1 R N Mukherjee Road
Kolkata, 700 001, India
Tel.: (91) 3330573700
Fax: (91) 3322482872
Web Site: www.birlacorporation.com
500335—(BOM)
Rev.: $555,151,285
Assets: $839,738,969
Liabilities: $384,954,623
Net Worth: $454,784,346
Earnings: $50,110,227
Emp.: 9,818
Fiscal Year-end: 03/31/13

Business Description:
Cement Mfr
S.I.C.: 2891
N.A.I.C.S.: 325520

Personnel:
Harsh V. Lodha *(Chm)*
P. C. Mathur *(Pres-Durgapur Cement Works & Durga Hitech Cement)*
G. Jayaraman *(Pres)*
B. R. Nahar *(Mng Dir)*
A. Saraogi *(CFO)*
D. N. Ghosh *(Pres-New Projects & R&D)*
V. K. Hamirwasia *(Pres-Birla Cement Works & Chanderia Cement Works)*
P. S. Marwah *(Pres-Satna Cement Works & Birla Vikas Cement)*
R. V. Muchhal *(Pres-Jute Purchase)*
K. K. Sharma *(Pres-Mgmt Audit)*
G. R. Verma *(Pres-Birla Jute Mills)*
Girish Sharma *(Sec & Sr VP-Indirect Taxes)*

Board of Directors:
Harsh V. Lodha
Anand Bordia
D. N. Ghosh
Pracheta Majumdar
B. R. Nahar
Deepak Nayyar
Vikram Swarup
B. B. Tandon

Transfer Agent:
MCS Limited
77/2A Hazra Road
Kolkata, India

Divisions:

Birla Corporation Ltd. - AutoTrim Division I (1)
24 Parganas S
Birlapur, West Bengal, 743118, India
Tel.: (91) 3324209095
Fax: (91) 3324209006
E-Mail: atdbirla@vsnl.net
Automotive Interiors Mfr
S.I.C.: 2396
N.A.I.C.S.: 336360
B. K. Sharma *(Mgr)*

Birla Corporation Ltd - Jute Division (1)
9 1 R N Mukherjee Rd
Kolkata, West Bengal, 700 001, India
Tel.: (91) 33 2213 0380
Fax: (91) 33 2248 2872
E-Mail: bcljute@vsnl.com
Emp.: 250
Cement & Jute Mfr
S.I.C.: 3241
N.A.I.C.S.: 327310
B. R. Nahar *(Mng Dir)*

Subsidiaries:

Birla Ericsson Optical Ltd. (1)
Udyog Vihar
PO Chorhata
Rewa, 486006, India
Tel.: (91) 7662400580
Fax: (91) 7662400680
E-Mail: info@birlaericsson.com
Web Site: www.birlaericsson.com
BIRLAERIC—(NSE)
Rev.: $25,142,854
Assets: $26,113,071
Liabilities: $14,573,219
Net Worth: $11,539,852
Earnings: $1,054,333
Emp.: 164
Fiscal Year-end: 03/31/13
Fiber Optic Cable Mfr
S.I.C.: 3357
N.A.I.C.S.: 335921
R. Sridharan *(Pres & CEO)*
D. R. Bansal *(Mng Dir)*
Somesh Laddha *(Compliance Officer, Sec & Sr Mgr-Fin)*

Budge Budge Floorcoverings Limited (1)
9 1 R N Mukherjee Rd
Kolkata, West Bengal, 700001, India
Tel.: (91) 3322489101
Floor Coverings Mfr
S.I.C.: 1752
N.A.I.C.S.: 238330

Units:

Birla Corporation Ltd - Birla Vikas Cement (1)
PO Birla Vikas
Satna, Madhya Pradesh, 485 005, India
Tel.: (91) 7672412000
Fax: (91) 7672257456
E-Mail: admin@satnacement.com
Emp.: 1,501
Cement Mfr
S.I.C.: 3241
N.A.I.C.S.: 327310
P. S. Marwah *(Pres)*

Birla Corporation Ltd - Durgapur Cement Works (1)
9 1 R N Mukherjee Rd Birla Bldg
Kolkata, West Bengal, 700 001, India
Tel.: (91) 3436454051
Fax: (91) 2585290
E-Mail: secgen@durgapurcement.com
Emp.: 400
Cement Mfr
S.I.C.: 3241
N.A.I.C.S.: 327310
P. C. Mathur *(Co-Pres)*

Birla Corporation Ltd. - Raebareli Cement Works (1)
Plot No D 9 to D 15 UPSIDC Indus Area Phase II Amawan Rd
Rae Bareli, Uttar Pradesh, 229 001, India
Tel.: (91) 5352217114
Fax: (91) 535 221 7239
Cement Mfr
S.I.C.: 3241
N.A.I.C.S.: 327310
P. S. Marwah *(Pres)*

Birla Corporation Ltd - Satna Cement Works (1)
PO Birla Vikas
Satna, Madhya Pradesh, 485 005, India
Tel.: (91) 7672412000
Fax: (91) 7672 257456
E-Mail: admin@satnacement.com
Cement Mfr
S.I.C.: 3241
N.A.I.C.S.: 327310
P. S. Marwah *(Pres)*

Birla Corporation Ltd - Vindhyachal Steel Foundry (1)
PO Birla Vikas
Satna, Madhya Pradesh, 485 005, India
Tel.: (91) 7672412000
Fax: (91) 7672 257456
E-Mail: admin@satnacement.com
Cement Plant Castings Mfr
S.I.C.: 3322
N.A.I.C.S.: 331511
P. S. Marwah *(Pres)*

BIRMINGHAM CITY FOOTBALL CLUB PLC

St Andrews Stadium
Birmingham, Midlands, B9 4RL, United Kingdom
Tel.: (44) 8445571875
Fax: (44) 8445571975
E-Mail: reception@bcfc.com
Web Site: www.bcfc.com
Sales Range: $50-74.9 Million
Emp.: 250

Business Description:
Football Team Operations
S.I.C.: 7941
N.A.I.C.S.: 711211

Personnel:
Peter Pannu *(Vice Chm)*

BIRZEIT PHARMACEUTICAL COMPANY

Industrial Zone
PO Box 79
Ramallah, Palestine
Tel.: (970) 2 2987574
Fax: (970) 2 2967206
E-Mail: info@bpc.ps
Web Site: www.bpc.ps
Year Founded: 1974
BPC—(PAL)

Business Description:
Generic Medicine Mfr
S.I.C.: 2834
N.A.I.C.S.: 325412

Personnel:
Talal Nasereddin *(Chm)*
Mohammad Nasereddin *(Vice Chm)*

Board of Directors:
Talal Nasereddin
Maher Farah
Salim Abdul Khaizaran
Farhan Abdul Leil
Firas Nasereddin
Mohammad Nasereddin
Yahya Shawar

BISALLOY STEEL GROUP LTD

18 Resolution Drive
PO Box 1246
Unanderra, NSW, 2526, Australia
Tel.: (61) 242720444
Fax: (61) 242720400
Web Site: www.bisalloy.com.au
BIS—(ASX)
Sls.: $83,976,586
Assets: $56,734,008
Liabilities: $29,771,755
Net Worth: $26,962,253
Earnings: $3,979,780
Emp.: 70
Fiscal Year-end: 06/30/13

Business Description:
Distribution Of Metal Products
S.I.C.: 3399
N.A.I.C.S.: 331221

Personnel:
Robert Terpening *(CEO & Mng Dir)*
David MacLaughlin *(CFO & Sec)*

Board of Directors:
Phillip J. Cave
Kym Godson
Richard Grellman
Dario Pong
Robert Terpening

Subsidiary:

Bisalloy Steels Pty Limited (1)
18 Resolution Dr
PO Box 1246
Unanderra, NSW, 2526, Australia
Tel.: (61) 242720444
Fax: (61) 242720456

E-Mail: bismail@bisalloy.com.au
Web Site: www.bisalloy.com.au
Emp.: 80
Steel Plates Mfr
S.I.C.: 3312
N.A.I.C.S.: 331221
Robert Terpening *(Mng Dir)*

Non-U.S. Subsidiary:

P.T. Bima Bisalloy (2)
MM2100 Indust Town Sumbawa St Kav C7 1
Cikarang Barat, Bekasi, West Java, 1750, Indonesia
Tel.: (62) 2189981540
Fax: (62) 21 899 8 1541
E-Mail: sales@ptbima.co.id
Web Site: www.bimabisalloy.com
Emp.: 25
Steel Plates Mfr
S.I.C.: 3399
N.A.I.C.S.: 331221
Iwan Sopyan *(Mgr)*

Non-U.S. Subsidiary:

Bisalloy (Thailand) Co Limited (1)
2/89 Bangna-Drive 25
Bang Na Dist, Bangkok, 10260, Thailand
Tel.: (66) 27441913
Fax: (66) 27441928
E-Mail: info@bisalloy-thailand.com
Web Site: www.bisalloy-thailand.com
Emp.: 22
Steels & Metals Distr
S.I.C.: 5051
N.A.I.C.S.: 423510
Dick Anwar *(Mng Dir)*

BISAN LIMITED

Level 1 61 Spring Street
Melbourne, VIC, 3000, Australia
Tel.: (61) 3 9286 7500
Fax: (61) 3 9662 1472
BSN—(ASX)
Rev.: $48,367
Assets: $632,235
Liabilities: $154,529
Net Worth: $477,706
Earnings: ($545,349)
Fiscal Year-end: 06/30/13
Business Description:
Financial Investment Services
S.I.C.: 6211
N.A.I.C.S.: 523999
Personnel:
Ramon Jimenez *(Sec)*
Board of Directors:
John Ceccon
Paul Delosa
David Herszberg
Alan Kaye
James Robinson

BISCHOF & KLEIN GMBH & CO. KG

Rahestrasse 47
D-49525 Lengerich, Germany
Tel.: (49) 54819200
Fax: (49) 5481920541
E-Mail: info@bk-packaging.de
Web Site: www.bk-packaging.de
Sales Range: $500-549.9 Million
Emp.: 2,300
Business Description:
Flexible Plastic & Paper Packaging Mfr & Distr
S.I.C.: 2671
N.A.I.C.S.: 322220
Personnel:
Volker Pfennig *(Mng Dir)*
Horst Sundermann *(Mng Dir)*

U.S. Subsidiaries:

THE BOXBORO GROUP (1)
86 Davidson Rd
Boxboro, MA 01719
Tel.: (617) 970-2959
Fax: (978) 263-7333
E-Mail: john@boxborogroup.com
Web Site: www.boxborogroup.com
Protective Film Mfr
N.A.I.C.S.: 326130
John Mosher *(Pres)*

MARKET QUEST, INC. (1)
Anderson St 2
Monmouth Beach, NJ 07750
Tel.: (732) 229-8127
Fax: (732) 229-8128
E-Mail: marketquest@comcast.net
Packaging Material Distr
N.A.I.C.S.: 423840

THE OVERBY GROUP INC. (1)
13807 Village Mill Dr Ste 201
Midlothian, VA 23114
Tel.: (804) 897-0110
Fax: (804) 897-4304
E-Mail: overbandk@cavtel.net
Packaging Material Distr
N.A.I.C.S.: 423840

Non-U.S. Subsidiaries:

B+K BETEILIGUNGEN GMBH (1)
Str Rahova nr 12 ap 27 11 Florin Marginean
550340 Sibiu, Romania
Tel.: (40) 371 075385
Fax: (40) 369 816265
E-Mail: florin.marginean@bk-international.com
Packaging Material Distr
N.A.I.C.S.: 423840

BERKEMPLAST SAN. VE TIC. LTD. STI. (1)
Yenidogan Mah Akin Cad 39
Sancaktepe, 34791 Istanbul, Turkey
Tel.: (90) 216 429 99 91
Fax: (90) 216 429 99 92
E-Mail: info@berkemplast.com
Web Site: www.berkemplast.com
Protective Film Mfr
N.A.I.C.S.: 326113
Semiha Berkem *(Mgr-Import & Export)*

BISCHOF + KLEIN ASIA PTE. LTD. (1)
Henderson Road 205 02-01
159549 Singapore, Singapore
Tel.: (65) 63 777555
Fax: (65) 64 651669
E-Mail: jack.ho@bk-international.com
Packaging Material Distr
N.A.I.C.S.: 423840
Jack Ho *(Gen Mgr)*

BISCHOF + KLEIN FRANCE SAS (1)
rue des Papetiers 15
PO Box 232
27500 Pont Audemer, France
Tel.: (33) 2 32 56 79 14
Fax: (33) 2 32 56 79 11
E-Mail: info.fr@bk-international.com
Web Site: www.bk-international.com
Packaging Material Distr
N.A.I.C.S.: 423840

BISCHOF + KLEIN MIDDLE EAST CO. (1)
PO Box 1176
31952 Al Khobar, Saudi Arabia
Tel.: (966) 3 8124443
Fax: (966) 3 8123135
E-Mail: info@bk-packaging.com.sa
Packaging Material Distr
N.A.I.C.S.: 423840

BISCHOF + KLEIN (SHANGHAI) TRADING CO. LTD. (1)
XiZang Middle Road 168
25/F The Headquarters Building, 200001
Shanghai, China
Tel.: (86) 21 51798313
Fax: (86) 21 51798618
E-Mail: jackie.zhu@bk-international.com
Packaging Material Distr
N.A.I.C.S.: 423840

Bischof & Klein (U.K.) Ltd. (1)
Hortonwood 2
Telford, Shropshire, TF1 7XX, United Kingdom (100%)
Tel.: (44) 1952606848
Fax: (44) 1952606698
E-Mail: info@bk-international.co.uk
Web Site: www.bk-international.co.uk
Emp.: 150
Plastic Flexible Packaging Materials Mfr
S.I.C.: 3089
N.A.I.C.S.: 326199
Carol Harrison *(Dir-HR)*

MODCHEM LTD. AGENCIES (1)
Mobile Post
Misgav, Hararit, 20182, Israel
Tel.: (972) 4 67827 77
Fax: (972) 4 67827 70
E-Mail: sales@modchem.com
Web Site: www.modchem.com
Packaging Material Distr
N.A.I.C.S.: 423840
Nachum Paran *(Gen Mgr)*

PROSIM KIMYA SANAYI VE TICARET LTD. STI. (1)
Kaleagasi Sokak No 5B 34470 Rumelihisari
Sariyer, Istanbul, Turkey
Tel.: (90) 212 263 78 21
Fax: (90) 212 263 78 25
E-Mail: info@prosim.com.tr
Web Site: www.prosim.com.tr
Chemical Product Distr
N.A.I.C.S.: 424690
Gozde Sasmaz *(Engr-Sls)*

SOBRA D.O.O. (1)
Banatska 29
10040 Zagreb, Croatia
Tel.: (385) 1 2910060
Fax: (385) 1 2910660
E-Mail: sobra@sobra.hr
Packaging Material Distr
N.A.I.C.S.: 423840

STARMER PACKAGING PTY. LTD. (1)
Gilda Street 29
PO Box 63 25
2113 North Ryde, NSW, Australia
Tel.: (61) 2 94823986
Fax: (61) 2 88194882
E-Mail: peter@starmerpackaging.com
Packaging Material Distr
N.A.I.C.S.: 423840

TREZOS & ASSOCIATES S.A. (1)
1 Lampsa Str & 135 Kifisias Ave
11524 Athens, Greece
Tel.: (30) 210 6993700
Fax: (30) 210 6993704
E-Mail: info@trezos.com
Web Site: www.trezos.com
Packaging Machinery Mfr
N.A.I.C.S.: 333993
Maro Trezou, *(Chm & Co-Mng Dir)*
Dimitri Tsipros *(Vice Chm & Co-Mng Dir)*

BISCO MISR

(d/b/a The Egyptian Company for Foods)
32 El Sawah Street
El Amerya, Cairo, Egypt
Tel.: (20) 222866600
Fax: (20) 222844132
E-Mail: info@biscomisr.com
Web Site: www.biscomisr.com
Year Founded: 1957
BISM—(EGX)
Sales Range: $10-24.9 Million
Emp.: 3,400
Business Description:
Biscuits, Chocolates, Chewing Gum, Wafers, Cakes, Cereal & Candy Mfr
S.I.C.: 2066
N.A.I.C.S.: 311352
Personnel:
Aref Hakki *(Chm & CEO)*

BISCUITS LECLERC LTD.

91 de Rotterdam Francois-Leclerc Industrial Park
Saint-Augustin-De-Desmaures, QC, G3A 1T1, Canada
Tel.: (418) 878-2601
Fax: (418) 878-4051
E-Mail: admin@leclerc.ca
Web Site: www.leclerc.ca
Year Founded: 1905
Rev.: $163,920,000
Emp.: 650
Business Description:
Cookies Mfr
S.I.C.: 2052
N.A.I.C.S.: 311821
Personnel:
Denis Leclerc *(Pres)*
Jean-Robert Leclerc *(Pres-Admin Counsel)*

BISHWA BIKASH BANK LIMITED

Ward No 4 Chipledhunga BP Chowk
Pokhara, Nepal
Tel.: (977) 61 528001
Fax: (977) 61 528003
E-Mail: bbbank@bbbank.com.np
Web Site: www.bbbank.com.np
BSBL—(NEP)
Business Description:
Banking Services
S.I.C.: 6029
N.A.I.C.S.: 522110
Personnel:
Jagan Bdr. Gurung *(Chm)*
Board of Directors:
Jagan Bdr. Gurung
Sanjeev Baniya
Arjun Banjara
K. C. Yog Bdr
Jagan Suba Gurung
Ranju Kumari Gurung
Kishor Ojha
Anil Shrestha

BISICHI MINING PLC

24 Bruton Place
London, W1J 6NE, United Kingdom
Tel.: (44) 2074155030
Fax: (44) 2074956352
E-Mail: admin@bisichi.co.uk
Web Site: www.bisichi.co.uk
BISI—(LSE)
Rev.: $56,794,427
Assets: $58,242,636
Liabilities: $30,196,025
Net Worth: $28,046,611
Earnings: $2,432,107
Emp.: 237
Fiscal Year-end: 12/31/12
Business Description:
Coal Mining
S.I.C.: 1222
N.A.I.C.S.: 212112
Personnel:
Michael A. Heller *(Chm)*
Andrew R. Heller *(Mng Dir)*
Heather A. Curtis *(Sec)*
Board of Directors:
Michael A. Heller
Garrett Casey
Robert Grobler
Andrew R. Heller
Christopher A. Joll
John A. Sibbald
Legal Counsel:
Olswang LLP
London, United Kingdom
Memery Crystal
London, United Kingdom
Fladgate LLP
London, United Kingdom
Transfer Agent:
Capita Registrars
The Registry 34 Beckenham Road
Beckenham, United Kingdom

BISON ENERGY SERVICES PLC

9a West Halkin Street
London, SW1X 8JL, United Kingdom
Tel.: (44) 20 7135 2250
Web Site: www.bison-energy.com

Bison Energy Services Plc—(Continued)

Business Description:
Oil Exploration
S.I.C.: 1311
N.A.I.C.S.: 211111
Personnel:
Graham Dransfield *(Chm)*
Gregory Charles Smith *(CEO)*
Board of Directors:
Graham Dransfield
Charles Edward Green
Leonard Steven Haynes
Gregory Charles Smith
Marcus Elliott Sturdee Edwards-Jones

BISON GOLD RESOURCES INC.

201 - 55 York Street
Toronto, ON, M5J 1R7, Canada
Tel.: (416) 488-2590
Fax: (416) 483-1516
E-Mail: info@bisongold.com
Web Site: www.bisongold.com
Year Founded: 2005
BGE—(TSXV)
Int. Income: $13,881
Assets: $11,218,549
Liabilities: $1,960,683
Net Worth: $9,257,867
Earnings: ($1,453,352)
Emp.: 7
Fiscal Year-end: 12/31/12
Business Description:
Gold, Silver, Copper, Zinc & Nickel Mining & Exploration Services
S.I.C.: 1041
N.A.I.C.S.: 212221
Personnel:
Dale Dunlop *(Chm)*
Amir Mousavi *(CEO)*
Board of Directors:
Dale Dunlop
P. David Benson
Borys Chabursky
Amir Mousavi
Mark Robinson

BISON TRANSPORT, INC.

1001 Sherwin Rd
Winnipeg, MB, R3H 0T8, Canada
Tel.: (204) 833-0000
Fax: (204) 833-0112
Toll Free: (800) 462-4766
E-Mail: online@bisontransport.com
Web Site: www.bisontransport.com
Year Founded: 1969
Sales Range: $150-199.9 Million
Emp.: 1,650
Business Description:
Freight & Truckload Services
S.I.C.: 4213
N.A.I.C.S.: 484121
Personnel:
Duncan M Jessiman *(Chm)*
Don Streuber *(Pres & CEO)*
Rob Penner *(COO & Exec VP)*

BIT-ISLE INC.

5th Fl HarborOne Bldg 2-5-5 Higashi Shinagawa
Shinagawa-ku, Tokyo, 140 0002, Japan
Tel.: (81) 3 5782 8721
Fax: (81) 3 5782 8728
E-Mail: ir@bit-isle.co.jp
Web Site: www.bit-isle.co.jp
Year Founded: 2000
3811—(TKS)
Sls.: $183,293,000
Assets: $379,808,000
Liabilities: $246,389,000
Net Worth: $133,419,000
Earnings: $18,733,000
Fiscal Year-end: 07/31/13
Business Description:
Information Technology Infrastructure Services
S.I.C.: 7389
N.A.I.C.S.: 519190
Personnel:
Kohei Terada *(Pres & CEO)*
Nobuyuki Amano *(COO & Exec VP)*
Takuya Ando *(CTO)*
Tatsuro Kubota *(Exec Officer)*
Takeshi Narisako *(Exec Officer)*
Satoshi Yoshimoto *(Exec Officer)*
Board of Directors:
Nobuyuki Amano
Kunitake Ando
Takuya Ando
Hideo Fukai
Kohei Terada
Transfer Agent:
Mizuho Trust & Banking Co., Ltd
1-2-1 Yaesu Chuo-ku
Tokyo, Japan

Subsidiary:

AXLBIT, Inc. (1)
2-2-33 Higashishinagawa
Shinagawa-Ku, Tokyo, 140-0002, Japan
Tel.: (81) 363624947
Web Site: www.axlbit.com
Information Technology Consulting Services
S.I.C.: 7373
N.A.I.C.S.: 541512

BITAUTO HOLDINGS LIMITED

New Century Hotel Office Tower 6/F
6 South Capital Stadium Road
Beijing, 100044, China
Tel.: (86) 10 68492345
Web Site: www.bitauto.com
Year Founded: 2005
BITA—(NYSE)
Rev.: $167,889,515
Assets: $226,167,590
Liabilities: $69,254,864
Net Worth: $156,912,726
Earnings: $21,470,428
Emp.: 1,980
Fiscal Year-end: 12/31/12
Business Description:
Automotive Internet Content & Marketing Services
S.I.C.: 2741
N.A.I.C.S.: 519130
Personnel:
Bin Li *(Chm & CEO)*
Jingning Shao *(Pres)*
Xuan Zhang *(CFO)*
Weihai Qu *(Sr VP)*
Board of Directors:
Bin Li
Dallas S. Clement
Sidney Xuande Huang
Erhai Liu
Yu Long
Weihai Qu
Jingning Shao

BITBURGER BRAUGRUPPE GMBH

Roemermauer 3
D 54634 Bitburg, Germany
Tel.: (49) 6561140
Fax: (49) 6561142289
E-Mail: info@bitburger-braugruppe.de
Web Site: www.bitburger-braugruppe.de
Year Founded: 1817
Emp.: 1,000
Business Description:
Breweries Operator
Export
S.I.C.: 2082
N.A.I.C.S.: 312120
Personnel:
Alfred Muller *(Chm-Fin Admin)*
Jan Niewodniczanski *(Chm-Tech Production Parts)*
Werner Wolf *(Chm-Mktg & Sls)*

Subsidiaries:

Bitburger Bier-GmbH Koln (1)
Kirchbauwirweg 19
50996 Cologne, Germany
Tel.: (49) 223639060
Fax: (49) 223639661
E-Mail: service@bit-koeln.de
Web Site: www.bit-koeln.de
Emp.: 150
Malt Beverages
S.I.C.: 2082
N.A.I.C.S.: 312120
Thomas Nuhn *(Mng Dir)*

Bitburger Brauerei Th. Simon GmbH (1)
Romermauer 3
54634 Bitburg, Germany (100%)
Tel.: (49) 6561 140
Fax: (49) 5611482496
E-Mail: info@bitburgerinternational.com
Web Site: www.bitburgerbrauerei.com
Alcoholic Beverage Brewing Services
S.I.C.: 2082
N.A.I.C.S.: 312120

Kostritzer Schwarzbierbrauerei GmbH & Co. (1)
Hemrich Schuetz St 16
7586 Bad Kostritz, Germany (100%)
Tel.: (49) 36605830
Fax: (49) 366052222
E-Mail: brauerei@koestritzer.de
Web Site: www.koestritzer.de
Emp.: 150
Malt Beverages
S.I.C.: 2082
N.A.I.C.S.: 312120
Albrecht Pitschel *(Mng Dir)*

BITCOMPUTER

1327 33 Seocho Dong
Seocho Gu
137072 Seoul, Korea (South)
Tel.: (82) 234861234
Fax: (82) 234865555
Web Site: www.bit.co.kr
32850—(KRS)
Sales Range: $10-24.9 Million
Emp.: 200
Business Description:
Software Specializing Company
S.I.C.: 7372
N.A.I.C.S.: 511210
Personnel:
Hyun Jung Cho *(Chm-Mgmt Bd)*
Jin Ok Jeon *(CEO)*

BITDEFENDER S.R.L.

24 Delea Veche Street
Bucharest, 024102, Romania
Tel.: (40) 21 206 3470
Fax: (40) 21 264 1799
Web Site: www.officebitdefender.com
Year Founded: 2001
Emp.: 300
Business Description:
Security Software Developer
S.I.C.: 7372
N.A.I.C.S.: 511210
Personnel:
Florin Talpes *(CEO)*
Niculae Dinca *(CFO)*
Bogdan Dumitru *(CTO)*
Ion Radoslovescu *(Chief Info & Process Officer)*

U.S. Subsidiary:

BitDefender LLC (1)
6301 Nw 5th Way
Fort Lauderdale, FL 33309
Tel.: (954) 776-6262
Emp.: 18
Security Software Developer
S.I.C.: 7372
N.A.I.C.S.: 511210
Ginger Yerovsek *(Dir-Sls)*

BITEBACK PUBLISHING LTD.

3 Albert Embankment
London, SE1 7SP, United Kingdom
Tel.: (44) 20 7091 1260
E-Mail: info@bitebackpublishing.com
Web Site: www.bitebackpublishing.com
Business Description:
Publishing Services
S.I.C.: 2731
N.A.I.C.S.: 511130
Personnel:
Iain Dale *(Mng Dir)*

Subsidiary:

Holyrood Communications Ltd. (1)
14-16 Holyrood Road
Edinburgh, EH8 8AF, United Kingdom
Tel.: (44) 131 2722113
Publishing Services
S.I.C.: 2721
N.A.I.C.S.: 511120
Hamish Miller *(Head-Ops)*

BITHEADS, INC.

1309 Carling Ave
Ottawa, ON, K1Z 7L3, Canada
Tel.: (613) 722-3232
Fax: (613) 722-9435
Toll Free: (877) 248-4323
E-Mail: info@bitheads.com
Web Site: www.bitheads.com
Sales Range: $10-24.9 Million
Emp.: 80
Business Description:
Software Development Services
S.I.C.: 7373
N.A.I.C.S.: 541512
Personnel:
Scott Simpson *(Co-Founder, Pres & CEO)*
Paul Winterhalder *(Co-Founder, COO & VP)*
Rick McMullin *(Co-Founder, CTO & VP)*

BITROS HOLDING S.A.

100 Nato Ave
19300 Aspropyrgos, Attiki, Greece
Tel.: (30) 2105509450
Fax: (30) 2105596205
E-Mail: info@bitros.gr
Web Site: www.bitros.gr
Year Founded: 1945
MPITR—(ATH)
Sales Range: $150-199.9 Million
Emp.: 355
Business Description:
Steel & Real Estate Development Services
S.I.C.: 3399
N.A.I.C.S.: 331110
Personnel:
Panagiotis I. Bitros *(Chm)*
Pelagia Bitrou *(Vice Chm)*
Ioannis P. Bitros *(CEO)*
Board of Directors:
Panagiotis I. Bitros
Georgios K. Bitros
Ioannis P. Bitros
Lida P. Bitrou
Pelagia Bitrou
Konstantinos F. Kalavros
Konstantinos S. Kastrinakis

Subsidiaries:

BITROS CONSTRUCTION S.A. (1)
100 Nato Ave
193 00 Aspropyrgos, Greece
Tel.: (30) 2105509155
Fax: (30) 2105596203
E-Mail: estate@bitros.gr

Residential Building Construction Services
S.I.C.: 1542
N.A.I.C.S.: 236220

BITROS REBAR CENTER S.A. (1)
100 Nato Avenue
Aspropyrgos, 193 00 Markopoulon, Greece
Tel.: (30) 2105509450
Fax: (30) 2105596205
E-Mail: oplismos@bitros.gr
Emp.: 200
Steel Products Mfr
S.I.C.: 3312
N.A.I.C.S.: 331110
Stavros Gatopoulos *(Mgr)*

BITROS STEEL S.A. (1)
100 Nato Avenue
Aspropyrgos, 193 00 Athens, Greece
Tel.: (30) 2105509000
Fax: (30) 2105596201
E-Mail: info@bitros.gr
Steel Processing & Distr
S.I.C.: 3399
N.A.I.C.S.: 331110
Panagiotis I. Bitros *(Chm)*
Pelagia Bitrou *(Vice Chm)*
Ioannis P. Bitros *(Mng Dir)*

BITS LTD.

23-1st Floor Great Western Building
130/132 Shahid Bhagat Singh Road
Fort, Mumbai, 400023, India
Tel.: (91) 11 23243611
Fax: (91) 11 42831900
E-Mail: bitslimited@gmail.com
Web Site: www.bits.net.in
526709—(BOM)
Sales Range: $10-24.9 Million
Business Description:
Computer Education Services
S.I.C.: 8243
N.A.I.C.S.: 611420
Personnel:
Ashok Agarwal *(Chm)*
Kuldeep Bansal *(Mng Dir)*
Arup Samanta *(Compliance Officer)*
Board of Directors:
Ashok Agarwal
Akhilesh Chandra Khare
Ankit Rathi
Ram Kumar Yadav

BITS PRIVATE LIMITED

Nandadeep 1st floor 1238/5 apte road Deccan Gymkhana
Pune, 411004, India
Tel.: (91) 20 2553 0241
Fax: (91) 20 6601 3440
E-Mail: pune@bitsindia.co.in
Web Site: www.bitsindia.co.in
Emp.: 200
Business Description:
Translation Services
S.I.C.: 7389
N.A.I.C.S.: 541930
Personnel:
Sandeep Nulkar *(Chm & Mng Dir)*

BITTERROOT RESOURCES LTD.

Suite 206 B 1571 Bellevue Avenue West
Vancouver, BC, V7V 1A6, Canada
Tel.: (604) 922-1351
Fax: (604) 922-8049
E-Mail: infoman@bitterrootresources.com
Web Site: www.bitterrootresources.com
BTT—(OTC TSXV)
Int. Income: $9,035
Assets: $7,384,254
Liabilities: $104,989
Net Worth: $7,279,265
Earnings: ($4,463,312)
Fiscal Year-end: 10/31/12
Business Description:
Mineral Exploration Services
S.I.C.: 1081
N.A.I.C.S.: 213114
Personnel:
Michael S. Carr *(Pres)*
Barney Magnusson *(CFO)*
Terence S. Ortslan *(Sec)*
Board of Directors:
Michael S. Carr
Terence S. Ortslan
George Walter Sanders
Legal Counsel:
Affinity Law Group
Suite 1130 - 400 Burrard Street
Vancouver, BC, Canada
Transfer Agent:
Computershare Trust Company of Canada
100 University Avenue 9th Floor
Toronto, ON, M5J 2Y1, Canada
Tel.: (416) 663-9097
Fax: (416) 263-9694

BITZER SE

Eschenbrunnlestrasse 15
71065 Sindelfingen, Germany
Tel.: (49) 7031 932 0
Fax: (49) 7031 932 146
E-Mail: mail@bitzer.de
Web Site: www.bitzer.de
Year Founded: 1934
Sales Range: $800-899.9 Million
Emp.: 3,000
Business Description:
Holding Company; Refrigeration & Air Conditioning Compressors Mfr & Distr
S.I.C.: 6719
N.A.I.C.S.: 551112
Personnel:
Peter Schaufler *(CEO & Chm-Mgmt Bd)*
Christian Wahlers *(CFO & Member-Mgmt Bd)*
Michael Bauer *(CMO, Chief Sls Officer & Member-Mgmt Bd)*
Jurgen Kleiner *(Chief Procurement Officer & Member-Mgmt Bd)*
Christian Wehrle *(Chief Production Officer & Member-Mgmt Bd)*
Rainer Grosse-Kracht *(Member-Mgmt Bd)*
Subsidiaries:

Armaturenwerk Altenburg GmbH (1)
Am Weissen Berg 30
04600 Altenburg, Germany De
Tel.: (49) 3447 89 30
Fax: (49) 3447 81 110
E-Mail: info@awa-armaturenwerk.de
Web Site: www.awa-armaturenwerk.de
Sales Range: $25-49.9 Million
Emp.: 200
Refrigerant Systems Mfr
S.I.C.: 3585
N.A.I.C.S.: 333415
Diana Schubert *(Mng Dir)*
Gunter Schuboth *(Mng Dir)*

BITZER Kuhlmaschinenbau GmbH (1)
Eschenbrunnlestrasse 15
71065 Sindelfingen, Germany De (100%)
Tel.: (49) 7031 932 0
Fax: (49) 7031 932 147
E-Mail: bitzer@bitzer.de
Web Site: www.bitzer.de
Refrigeration & Air Conditioning Compressors Mfr & Distr
S.I.C.: 3585
N.A.I.C.S.: 333415
Peter Schaufler *(CEO)*

U.S. Subsidiary:

BITZER US, Inc. (1)
4080 Enterprise Way
Flowery Branch, GA 30542 GA
Tel.: (770) 503-9226
Fax: (770) 503-9440
E-Mail: sales@bitzerus.com
Web Site: www.bitzerus.com
Refrigeration & Air Conditioning Compressors Mfr & Distr
S.I.C.: 3585
N.A.I.C.S.: 333415
Peter Narreau *(Pres)*

BIWATER HOLDINGS LIMITED

Biwater House Station Apprach
Dorking, Surrey, RH4 1TZ, United Kingdom
Tel.: (44) 1306740740
Fax: (44) 1306885233
E-Mail: corporate.communications@biwater.com
Web Site: www.biwater.com
Year Founded: 1968
Sales Range: $400-449.9 Million
Emp.: 200
Business Description:
Water Treatment & Distribution Facilities Design, Construction & Maintenance Services
S.I.C.: 4941
N.A.I.C.S.: 221310
Personnel:
Adrian E. White *(Chm)*
Mark Studholme *(Mng Dir)*
Jorg Menningman *(Pres-Desalination & Membrane Treatment Sector)*
Martin R.A. Duffy *(Sec)*
Board of Directors:
Adrian E. White
Martin R.A. Duffy
J.J. Jones
Robert E. Kottler
Mark Studholme
C.A. White
U.S. Subsidiaries:

Biwater AEWT, Inc. (1)
136 E Lemon Ave
Monrovia, CA 91016
Tel.: (626) 358-7707
Fax: (626) 358-7737
E-Mail: biwater.aewt@biwater.com
Web Site: www.biwater-aewt.com
Emp.: 15
Water Treatment Equipment Mfr
S.I.C.: 4941
N.A.I.C.S.: 221310

Biwater USA Inc. (1)
4000 Hollywood Blvd
Hollywood, FL 33021
Tel.: (954) 987-6676
Web Site: www.biwater.com
Emp.: 8
Engineering Services
S.I.C.: 8711
N.A.I.C.S.: 541330
Richard P. Smith *(VP-HR & IT)*

Non-U.S. Subsidiaries:

Biwater International Limited (Panama) (1)
C C Camino de Cruces Nivel 4
Boulevard El Dorado, Panama, El Dorado, Panama Pa (100%)
Tel.: (507) 3602160
Fax: (507) 3602164
Web Site: www.biwater.com
Emp.: 60
Water Treatment & Distribution Facilities
S.I.C.: 4941
N.A.I.C.S.: 221310
Geoffrey Thorpe *(Gen Mgr)*

Biwater (Pty) Limited (1)
Fourways North
PO Box 59
Johannesburg, 2086, South Africa
Tel.: (27) 11 510 0360
Fax: (27) 11 510 0001
Water Treatment & Distribution Facilities Design, Construction & Maintenance Services
S.I.C.: 4971
N.A.I.C.S.: 221310

Biwater S.A. (1)
15 Rue des Draperies Batiment A
69450 Saint-Cyr-au-Mont-D'or, France
Tel.: (33) 4 78 43 86 96
Fax: (33) 478432554
E-Mail: corporate.communications@biwater.com
Web Site: www.biwater.com
Emp.: 2
Water Treatment & Distribution Facilities Design, Construction & Maintenance Services
S.I.C.: 4971
N.A.I.C.S.: 221310
Matt Colclough *(Gen Mgr)*

BIXOLON CO LTD

980 3 Youngtong Dong
Youngtong Gu
443702 Suwon, Gyeonggi Do, Korea (South)
Tel.: (82) 82312185500
Fax: (82) 82312185589
Web Site: www.bixolon.com
93190—(KRS)
Sales Range: $25-49.9 Million
Emp.: 230
Business Description:
Printer Mfr
S.I.C.: 3861
N.A.I.C.S.: 325992
Personnel:
Js Oh *(CEO)*
U.S. Subsidiary:

BIXOLON America Inc. (1)
3171 Fujita St
Torrance, CA 90505
Tel.: (858) 764-4580
Fax: (310) 522-9319
E-Mail: sales@bixolonusa.com
Web Site: www.bixolonusa.com
Emp.: 10
Computer Printers Mfr
S.I.C.: 3575
N.A.I.C.S.: 334118
David Roberts *(VP-Sls & Mktg)*

Non-U.S. Subsidiaries:

BIXOLON ELECTRONICS (DONGGUAN) CO., LTD. (1)
C3A No 11 Luyi 2 Rd
Tangxia Town, Dongguan, Guangdong, 503 175, China
Tel.: (86) 76982620704
Fax: (86) 76982620703
E-Mail: sales@bixolon.com
Web Site: www.bixolon.com
Emp.: 100
Computer Printer Whslr
S.I.C.: 5045
N.A.I.C.S.: 423430
Kim Changwoon *(Mng Dir)*

BIXOLON Europe GmbH (1)
Tiefenbroicher Weg 35
40472 Dusseldorf, Germany
Tel.: (49) 2116878540
Fax: (49) 21168785420
E-Mail: sales@bixolon.de
Web Site: www.bixolon.de
Emp.: 11
Computer Printers Whslr
S.I.C.: 5045
N.A.I.C.S.: 423430
David Kim *(Gen Mgr)*

BIZERBA CANADA INC.

2810 Argentia Road Unit 9
Mississauga, ON, L5N 8L2, Canada
Tel.: (905) 816-0498
Fax: (905) 816-0497
Toll Free: (888) 240-3722
Web Site: www.bizerba.ca
Rev.: $12,636,000
Emp.: 35
Business Description:
Weight Scale Equipment Mfr
S.I.C.: 5087
N.A.I.C.S.: 423850
Personnel:
Robert Slykhuis *(Pres)*

BIZLINK HOLDING INC.
6F-1 2 Jian 8th Rd
Zhonghe District, Taipei, 23511, Taiwan
Tel.: (886) 2 82261000
Fax: (886) 2 82262583
E-Mail: ir@bizlinktech.com
Web Site: www.bizlinktech.com
3665—(TAI)
Sales Range: $150-199.9 Million
Business Description:
Wires, Connectors & Optical Components Mfr
S.I.C.: 3496
N.A.I.C.S.: 332618
Personnel:
Hwa-Tse Liang *(Chm)*
Chien-Hua Teng *(CEO & Gen Mgr)*
U.S. Subsidiary:

OptiWork, Inc. (1)
3400 Gateway Blvd
Fremont, CA 94538
Tel.: (510) 438-4560
Fax: (510) 438-4470
E-Mail: sales@optiworks.com
Web Site: www.optiworks.com
Fiber Optic Component Mfr
S.I.C.: 3357
N.A.I.C.S.: 335921
Roger Ling *(Owner)*

BIZNET CORPORATION
6-14 Sanbancho Chiyoda-Ku
Tokyo, 102-0075, Japan
Tel.: (81) 3 5860 1000
Fax: (81) 3 3512 8550
Web Site: www.biznet.co.jp
Year Founded: 2000
3381—(JAS)
Business Description:
Repair & Maintenance Services
S.I.C.: 7549
N.A.I.C.S.: 811198
Personnel:
Shuji Ogawa *(Pres)*

BJB CAREER EDUCATION COMPANY, LIMITED
Beida Jade Bird Building 3/F 207
Chengfu Road
Haidian District, Beijing, 100871, China
Tel.: (86) 1062760088
Fax: (86) 1082667065
E-Mail: yanqun.cui@jb-aptech.com.cn
Web Site: www.jbit.cn
Sales Range: $25-49.9 Million
Emp.: 1,160
Business Description:
Vocational IT Education Services
S.I.C.: 8299
N.A.I.C.S.: 611710
Personnel:
Yongli Zhang *(Chm)*
Ming Yang *(CEO)*
Xiaosong Zhang *(CFO)*
Chengxi Tang *(COO)*
Ping Yu *(Sec)*
Jun Liang *(Sr VP)*
Board of Directors:
Yongli Zhang
David M. Hand
Ninad Karpe
Li Xue
Ming Yang

BJB GMBH & CO. KG
Werler Str 1
59755 Arnsberg, Germany
Tel.: (49) 29329820
Fax: (49) 29329828201
E-Mail: info@bjb.com
Web Site: www.bjb.com
Year Founded: 1867
Rev.: $120,518,178
Emp.: 660
Business Description:
Lamp Components Mfr
S.I.C.: 3641
N.A.I.C.S.: 335110
Personnel:
Dieter Henrici *(Co-Mng Dir)*
Philipp Henrici *(Co-Mng Dir)*

BJC HEAVY INDUSTRIES PUBLIC COMPANY LIMITED
694 Moo 4 Makhamkoo
Nikompattana
Rayong, 21180, Thailand
Tel.: (66) 38 893 709
Fax: (66) 38 893 711
Web Site: www.bjc1994.com
Year Founded: 1994
BJCHI—(THA)
Rev.: $121,009,975
Assets: $62,307,591
Liabilities: $19,338,975
Net Worth: $42,968,616
Earnings: $26,226,371
Emp.: 4,080
Fiscal Year-end: 12/31/12
Business Description:
Heavy Construction
S.I.C.: 1629
N.A.I.C.S.: 237990
Personnel:
Pakavalee Jearsawatvattana *(Chm)*
Young Lee Kyu *(Pres)*
Jun Lee Young *(Mng Dir)*
Board of Directors:
Pakavalee Jearsawatvattana
Ekachidd Chungcharoen
Noppadol Dheerabutrvongkul
Boonchuay Korkitrotjana
Young Lee Kyu
Jin Lee Seong
Woo Lee Seong
Chanchira Smakthai
Jun Lee Young

BJL GROUP LIMITED
Sunlight House Quay Street
Manchester, M3 3JZ, United Kingdom
Tel.: (44) 161 831 7141
Fax: (44) 161 832 1289
E-Mail: info@bjl.co.uk
Web Site: www.bjl.co.uk
Year Founded: 1987
Emp.: 80
Business Description:
Advertising Services
S.I.C.: 7311
N.A.I.C.S.: 541810
Personnel:
Nicky Unsworth *(CEO)*
Jackie Holt *(Mng Partner)*
Division:

Mere PR @BJL (1)
(Formerly Mere PR Ltd.)
Sunlight House Quay Street
Manchester, M3 3JZ, United Kingdom
Tel.: (44) 161 831 7141
Fax: (44) 161 832 1289
E-Mail:
Web Site: www.bjl.co.uk
Public Relations Services
S.I.C.: 8743
N.A.I.C.S.: 541820
Gemma Carey *(Acct Dir)*

BJORN BORG AB
Tulegatan 11
SE-113 53 Stockholm, Sweden
Tel.: (46) 850633700
Fax: (46) 850633701
E-Mail: info@bjornborg.com
Web Site: www.bjornborg.com
BORG—(OMX)
Sls.: $85,361,674
Assets: $107,491,417
Liabilities: $54,206,780
Net Worth: $53,284,637
Earnings: $7,310,740
Emp.: 139
Fiscal Year-end: 12/31/12
Business Description:
Apparel, Footwear, Handbags, Eyewear & Fragrances Mfr & Sales
S.I.C.: 2389
N.A.I.C.S.: 315280
Personnel:
Fredrik Lovstedt *(Chm)*
Arthur Engel *(CEO)*
Magnus Teeling *(CFO & Mgr-Fin)*
Board of Directors:
Fredrik Lovstedt
Isabelle Ducellier
Kerstin Hessius
Mats H. Nilsson
Vilhelm Schotennius
Michael Storakers
Subsidiaries:

Bjorn Borg Brands AB (1)
Tulegatan 11
113 53 Stockholm, Sweden
Tel.: (46) 850633700
Fax: (46) 850633701
E-Mail: info@bjornborg.com
Web Site: www.bjornborg.com
Emp.: 65
Apparel & Accessories Mfr & Whslr
S.I.C.: 2399
N.A.I.C.S.: 315990
Arthur Engel *(CEO)*

Subsidiaries:

Anteros Lagerhantering AB (2)
Alvsjo Angsvag 6
Alvsjo, 12530 Stockholm, Sweden
Tel.: (46) 86471860
Fax: (46) 86413741
Warehouse Storage Services
S.I.C.: 5411
N.A.I.C.S.: 452910
Antero Manninen *(Mng Dir)*

Bjorn Borg Clothing AB (2)
Gotgatan 78
118 30 Stockholm, Sweden
Tel.: (46) 850633700
Fax: (46) 850633701
E-Mail: info@bjornborg.com
Web Site: www.bjornborg.net
Emp.: 70
Apparels & Accessories Mfr & Whslr
S.I.C.: 2399
N.A.I.C.S.: 315990
Arthur Engel *(Mng Dir)*

Bjorn Borg Retail AB (2)
Gotgatan 78
118 30 Stockholm, Sweden
Tel.: (46) 850633700
Fax: (46) 850633701
E-Mail: info@bjornborg.com
Emp.: 50
Apparels & Accessories Mfr & Retailer
S.I.C.: 2389
N.A.I.C.S.: 315990
Arthur Engel *(Gen Mgr)*

Bjorn Borg Sweden AB (2)
Tulegatan 11
113 53 Stockholm, Sweden
Tel.: (46) 850633700
Fax: (46) 850633701
E-Mail: info@bjornborg.com
Web Site: www.cms.bjornborg.com
Emp.: 70
Apparels & Accessories Whslr
S.I.C.: 2389
N.A.I.C.S.: 315210
Arthur Engel *(Mng Dir)*

Bjorn Borg Footwear AB (1)
Backgatan 36
PO Box 223
43225 Varberg, Sweden
Tel.: (46) 340646530
Fax: (46) 340646549
E-Mail: info@bjornborgfootwear.se
Web Site: www.bjornborgfootwear.se
Emp.: 9
Footwear Design & Mfr
S.I.C.: 2389
N.A.I.C.S.: 316210
Christian Engstrom *(Mng Dir)*

BJORNSEN BERATENDE INGENIEURE GMBH
Maria Trost 3
D-56070 Koblenz, Germany
Tel.: (49) 26188510
Fax: (49) 261805725
E-Mail: info@bjoernsen.de
Web Site: www.bjoernsen.de
Rev.: $19,989,750
Emp.: 146
Business Description:
Engineering Consulting Services
S.I.C.: 8999
N.A.I.C.S.: 541690
Personnel:
Gerhard Bjornsen *(Mng Dir)*
Ulrich Krath *(Mng Dir)*
Christoph Schopfer *(Mng Dir)*

BK ONE LIMITED
12th Floor 2 Long Street
Cape Town, 8001, South Africa
Mailing Address:
PO Box 6223
Roggebaai, 8012, South Africa
Tel.: (27) 21 402 0341
E-Mail: info@bkone.co.za
Web Site: www.bkone.co.za
BK1P—(JSE)
Rev.: $1,233,092
Assets: $18,504,195
Liabilities: $22,816,138
Net Worth: ($4,311,943)
Earnings: ($7,518,812)
Fiscal Year-end: 02/28/13
Business Description:
Financial Investment Services
S.I.C.: 6211
N.A.I.C.S.: 523999
Personnel:
Dean Paul Richards *(Exec Dir)*
Board of Directors:
Pinkie Kedibone Veronica Ncetzo
Peter Gordon Gaylard
Dean Paul Richards
Henricus Petrus van Noort
Legal Counsel:
Cliffe Dekker Hofmeyr Inc.
11 Buitengracht Street
Cape Town, 8001, South Africa
Transfer Agent:
Computershare Investor Services (Proprietary) Limited
Ground Floor 70 Marshall St
Johannesburg, South Africa

BKI INVESTMENT COMPANY LIMITED
Level 2 160 Pitt Street Mall
Sydney, NSW, 2000, Australia
Mailing Address:
GPO Box 5015
Sydney, NSW, 2001, Australia
Tel.: (61) 2 9210 7000
Fax: (61) 2 9210 7099
E-Mail: info@bkilimited.com.au
Web Site: www.bkilimited.com.au
BKI—(ASX)
Rev.: $33,316,979
Assets: $710,418,328
Liabilities: $51,777,781
Net Worth: $658,640,547
Earnings: $31,186,927
Emp.: 1
Fiscal Year-end: 06/30/13
Business Description:
Investment Services
S.I.C.: 6211

N.A.I.C.S.: 523999
Personnel:
Thomas L. Millner *(CEO)*
Jaime Perry Pinto *(Sec)*
Board of Directors:
Robert Dobson Millner
David Capp Hall
Ian Thomas Huntley
Alexander James Payne

Subsidiaries:

Pacific Strategic Investments Pty Limited (1)
Level 2 160 Pitt St
Sydney, NSW, 2000, Australia
Tel.: (61) 292107000
Fax: (61) 292107099
E-Mail: reception@pcap.com.au
Emp.: 15
Securities Brokerage Services
S.I.C.: 6211
N.A.I.C.S.: 523120
Tom Millner *(CEO)*

BKM MANAGEMENT LIMITED

Suite 1 1233 High Street
PO Box 8694
Armadale, VIC, 3143, Australia
Tel.: (61) 3 9824 5254
Fax: (61) 3 9822 7735
E-Mail: info@bkmmanagement.com
Web Site: www.bkmmanagement.com
BKM—(ASX)
Rev.: $1,414,232
Assets: $892,123
Liabilities: $1,014,328
Net Worth: ($122,205)
Earnings: ($519,668)
Emp.: 13
Fiscal Year-end: 06/30/13
Business Description:
International Model Management
Export
S.I.C.: 8742
N.A.I.C.S.: 541611
Personnel:
Phillip Hains *(Sec)*
Board of Directors:
Alvin Tan
Phillip Hains
Evan McGregor
Legal Counsel:
Pointon Partners
14/565 Bourke Street
Melbourne, Australia

Units:

Scene Model Management Pty Ltd. (1)
Level 1 872-876 Hay St
Perth, WA, 6000, Australia AU
Mailing Address: (100%)
Box 7515
Cloisters Square, Perth, WA, 6850, Australia
Tel.: (61) 894869994
E-Mail: bookings@scenemodels.com
Web Site: www.scenemodels.com
Emp.: 7
Model Management Agency
Export
S.I.C.: 7389
N.A.I.C.S.: 711410
Anthony Harden *(Gen Mgr)*

Scene Model Management Pty Ltd. (1)
Level 2 181 Riley St
Darlinghurst, NSW 2010 Sydney, Australia AU
Mailing Address: (100%)
Locked Bag 1000
Paddington, Sydney, NSW 2021, Australia
Tel.: (61) 283357293
Fax: (61) 283357299
E-Mail: sydney@scenemodels.com
Web Site: www.scenemodels.com
Modeling Agency Management
Export
S.I.C.: 7389
N.A.I.C.S.: 711410
Vicki Graham *(Gen Mgr)*

Scene Model Management Pty Ltd. (1)
Level 1 5 Cubitt St Richmond
PO Box 6072
South Yarra, 3121 Melbourne, VIC, 3141, Australia AU
Tel.: (61) 398265233 (100%)
Fax: (61) 394215473
E-Mail: melbourne@scenemodels.com
Web Site: www.scenemodels.com
Emp.: 2
Modeling Agency
Export
S.I.C.: 7389
N.A.I.C.S.: 711410
Mel Lockman *(Gen Mgr)*

BKN BIOSTROM AG

Graf von Galen Strasse 17
D-49377 Vechta, Germany
Tel.: (49) 4441909660
Fax: (49) 44419096610
E-Mail: info@bkn-biostorm.de
Web Site: www.bkn-biostorm.de
Year Founded: 2006
B9K—(DEU)
Emp.: 30
Business Description:
Holding Company; Biogas Plant Operations & Renewable Energy Resource Research
S.I.C.: 6719
N.A.I.C.S.: 551112
Personnel:
Emmerich G. Kretzenbacher *(Chm-Supervisory Bd)*
Gunter Schlotmann *(COO & Chm-Exec Bd)*
Gunnar Dresen *(CFO)*
Peter Westerhoff *(Member-Mgmt Bd)*
Supervisory Board of Directors:
Gerd-Jurgen Pohl
Wolff Lange
Emmerich G. Kretzenbacher

BKN INTERNATIONAL AG

Richmodstrasse 6
50667 Cologne, Germany
Tel.: (49) 22192042175
Fax: (49) 22192042200
E-Mail: info@bknkids.com
BKQ—(DEU LSE)
Sales Range: $10-24.9 Million
Emp.: 36
Business Description:
Animated Children's Television Production & Distribution
S.I.C.: 7812
N.A.I.C.S.: 512110
Personnel:
Sascha Ziemann *(Chm & CEO)*
Karl Benetz *(Chm-Supervisory Bd)*
Supervisory Board of Directors:
Michael J. Kugler
Robert Paff
Karl Benetz

Non-U.S. Subsidiaries:

BKN Home Entertainment Ltd (1)
77 Kingsway
London, WC2B 6SR, United Kingdom
Tel.: (44) 2072698680
Fax: (44) 2072428335
E-Mail: denise.morales@bknkies.com
Creation, Development, Production, Distribution & Marketing of Animated Television Series & Films
S.I.C.: 7812
N.A.I.C.S.: 512110
Matthew Graham-Clare *(Mng Dir)*

BKN New Media SL (1)
Ave Diagonal 403 3-4
8008 Barcelona, Spain
Tel.: (34) 933680524
Fax: (34) 933680486
E-Mail: info@bknkids.com
Web Site: www.bknkids.com
Emp.: 75
Animation Production & Distribution
S.I.C.: 4833
N.A.I.C.S.: 515120

BKN New Media Ltd (1)
77 Kingsway
London, WC2B 6SR, United Kingdom
Tel.: (44) 2072698680
Fax: (44) 2072428335
Animation Production & Distribution
S.I.C.: 4833
N.A.I.C.S.: 515120

BKN New Media Pte. Ltd (1)
6 Battery Road 11-01
Singapore, 049909, Singapore
Tel.: (65) 6820 2120
Fax: (65) 6820 2115
Animation Production & Distribution
S.I.C.: 4833
N.A.I.C.S.: 515120

U.S. Subsidiary:

BKN New Media, Inc. (1)
22 Elm Place
Rye, NY 10580
Tel.: (914) 921-6666
Fax: (914) 921-4499
Animation Production & Distribution
S.I.C.: 4833
N.A.I.C.S.: 515120

BLACK & MCDONALD LIMITED

2 Bloor St E Ste 2100
Toronto, ON, M4W 1A8, Canada
Tel.: (416) 920-5100
Fax: (416) 922-8768
E-Mail: info@blackandmcdonald.com
Web Site: www.blackandmcdonald.com
Year Founded: 1920
Sales Range: $600-649.9 Million
Emp.: 3,000
Business Description:
Electrical Contractors
S.I.C.: 1731
N.A.I.C.S.: 238210
Personnel:
J. Bruce McDonald *(Co-Pres & Co-CEO)*
W. Ian McDonald *(Co-Pres & Co-CEO)*

BLACK BIRCH CAPITAL ACQUISITION II CORP.

10 Pauline Avenue
Brooklin, ON, L1M 2H5, Canada
Tel.: (416) 318-6501
Fax: (416) 915-4265
E-Mail: phaber@blackbirchcap.com
Year Founded: 2009
BBT.P—(TSXV)
Int. Income: $1,225
Assets: $424,096
Liabilities: $19,016
Net Worth: $405,080
Earnings: ($39,031)
Fiscal Year-end: 12/31/12
Business Description:
Investment Services
S.I.C.: 6211
N.A.I.C.S.: 523999
Personnel:
Paul Haber *(Chm, Pres, CEO, CFO & Sec)*
Board of Directors:
Paul Haber
Dong Sheng Li
Yuxin Xiang
Transfer Agent:
Olympia Transfer Services Inc
750 West Pender Street Suite 1003
Vancouver, BC, V6C 2T8, Canada

BLACK BIRCH CAPITAL ACQUISITION III CORP.

10 Pauline Avenue
Brooklin, ON, L1M 2H5, Canada
Tel.: (416) 318-6501
Fax: (416) 915-4265
E-Mail: phaber@blackbirchcap.com
Year Founded: 2012
BBC.P—(TSXV)
Business Description:
Investment Services
S.I.C.: 6211
N.A.I.C.S.: 523999
Personnel:
Paul Haber *(CEO, CFO & Sec)*
Board of Directors:
Paul Haber
Kin-Man Lee
Anthony Pizarro
Tanya Rowntree
Transfer Agent:
Equity Financial Trust Company
200 University Avenue Suite 400
Toronto, ON, M5H 4H1, Canada
Tel.: (416) 361-0152
Fax: (416) 361-0470
Toll Free: (866) 393-4891

BLACK BULL RESOURCES INC.

157 Water Street
PO Box 698
Shelburne, NS, B0T 1W0, Canada
Tel.: (902) 875-1510
Fax: (902) 875-1617
Toll Free: (877) 878-2789
E-Mail: admin@blackbullresources.com
Web Site: www.blackbullresources.com
BBS—(TSXV)
Sales Range: Less than $1 Million
Emp.: 12
Business Description:
Industrial Minerals Integrated Miner, Processor & Marketer
S.I.C.: 1429
N.A.I.C.S.: 212319
Personnel:
David L. Wood *(Founder)*
Richard J. Shearer *(Chm)*
Joseph MacDonald *(Pres & CEO)*
Martin MacKinnon *(CFO)*
Board of Directors:
Richard J. Shearer
James W. Gogan
Joseph MacDonald
David L. Wood
Transfer Agent:
CIBC Mellon Trust Company
Ste 600 333 7th Ave SW
Calgary, AB, T2P 2Z1, Canada
Tel.: (403) 232-2400
Fax: (403) 264-2100
Toll Free: (800) 387-0825

BLACK CAT BLADES LTD.

5604 59 Street
Edmonton, AB, T6B 3C3, Canada
Tel.: (780) 465-6666
Fax: (780) 465-9595
Toll Free: (800) 661-6666
E-Mail: sales@blackcatblades.com
Web Site: www.blackcatblades.com
Year Founded: 1968
Rev.: $58,079,227
Emp.: 350
Business Description:
Construction Machinery Parts Mfr
S.I.C.: 3531
N.A.I.C.S.: 333120
Personnel:
Richard Buxton *(Pres)*

BLACK DIAMOND GROUP LIMITED

2000 715 5th Avenue SW
Calgary, AB, T2P 2X6, Canada
Tel.: (403) 206-4747
Fax: (403) 264-9281
Web Site: www.blackdiamondlimited.com
Year Founded: 2009
BDI—(TSX)
Rev.: $262,693,641
Assets: $553,863,968
Liabilities: $194,942,232
Net Worth: $358,921,736
Earnings: $50,849,093
Emp.: 293
Fiscal Year-end: 12/31/12

Business Description:
Holding Company; Commercial Modular Building Construction, Logistics & Energy Support Services
S.I.C.: 6719
N.A.I.C.S.: 551112

Personnel:
David Butler *(Chm)*
Trevor Haynes *(Pres & CEO)*
Marshall McRae *(Interim CFO & Interim Exec VP)*
Steve Stein *(COO & Exec VP)*
Mark Lewis *(Gen Counsel)*
Neil Runions *(Treas & VP-Black Diamond Capital Ltd)*
Fred D. Davidson *(Sec)*
Harry Klukas *(Exec VP-Intl)*
Dave Brown *(Sr VP-Energy Svcs)*
Glen Clark *(Sr VP-Comml Dev)*
Troy Cleland *(Sr VP-Structures Bus Unit)*
Paul de Rosenroll *(Sr VP-Facilitation, Integration & Trng/HSE)*

Board of Directors:
David Butler
Robert G. Brawn
Trevor Haynes
Robert Herdman
Minaz Kassam
David Olsson
Steve Stein
Robert Wagemakers

Transfer Agent:
Olympia Trust Company
Calgary, AB, Canada

Subsidiaries:

Black Diamond Energy Services Inc. **(1)**
Suite 2000 715 5th Avenue SW
Calgary, AB, T2P 2X6, Canada Ca
Tel.: (403) 206-4747
Fax: (403) 264-9281
Toll Free: (888) 569-4880
Web Site: www.blackdiamondenergyservices.com
Energy Equipment Leasing & Support Services
S.I.C.: 7359
N.A.I.C.S.: 532412
Trevor Haynes *(Pres & CEO)*
Steven Stein *(COO & Exec VP)*
Dave Brown *(Sr VP)*

Black Diamond Limited Partnership **(1)**
Suite 2000 715 5th Avenue SW
Calgary, AB, T2P 2X6, Canada Ca
Tel.: (403) 206-4747
Fax: (403) 264-9281
Toll Free: (888) 569-4880
Web Site: www.blackdiamondlimited.com
Commercial Modular Building Construction
S.I.C.: 1521
N.A.I.C.S.: 236115
Trevor Haynes *(Pres & CEO)*
Steven Stein *(COO & Exec VP)*

BOXX Modular Inc. **(1)**
Suite 2000 715 5th Avenue SW
Calgary, AB, T2P 2X6, Canada Ca
Tel.: (403) 206-4747
Fax: (403) 264-9281
Toll Free: (888) 569-4880
Web Site: www.boxxmodular.com
Commercial Modular Building Construction
S.I.C.: 1521
N.A.I.C.S.: 236115
Trevor Haynes *(Pres & CEO)*
Steven Stein *(COO & Exec VP)*

U.S. Branch:

BOXX Modular Inc. - Denver Office **(2)**
1675 Larimer St Ste 740
Denver, CO 80202
Tel.: (303) 623-0324
Fax: (303) 623-1245
Web Site: www.blackdiamondus.com
Regional Managing Office; Commercial Modular Building Construction & Leasing Services
S.I.C.: 8741
N.A.I.C.S.: 551114
Keith Swenson *(VP & Gen Mgr)*

BLACK EARTH FARMING LTD

8 Church Street
PO Box 781
JE4 0SG Saint Helier, Jersey
E-Mail: info@blackearthfarming.com
Web Site: www.blackearthfarming.com
Year Founded: 2005
BEFSDB—(OMX)
Rev.: $147,441,140
Assets: $424,039,017
Liabilities: $129,546,930
Net Worth: $294,492,087
Earnings: $7,193,552
Emp.: 2,067
Fiscal Year-end: 12/31/12

Business Description:
Agricultural Services
S.I.C.: 9641
N.A.I.C.S.: 926140

Personnel:
Vigo Carlund *(Chm)*
Richard Warburton *(CEO)*
Erik Danemar *(CFO)*
Fraser Scott *(COO)*

Board of Directors:
Vigo Carlund
Per Brilioth
Anders Kronborg
Camilla Oberg
Poul Schroder
Magnus Unger
Richard Warburton

Deloitte AB
Stockholm, Sweden

Non-U.S. Subsidiaries:

OOO Belgorodka Agro-Invest **(1)**
62 Ul Privokzalnaya
Gorshechnoye, 306800, Russia
Tel.: (7) 4713322389
Fax: (7) 4713321045
Vegetable Farming Services
S.I.C.: 0161
N.A.I.C.S.: 111219

OOO Chelnovaya Agro-Invest **(1)**
67 Ul Kolkhoznaya
Sosnovka, 393840, Russia
Tel.: (7) 4753227302
Fax: (7) 4752583522
Agricultural Farming Services
S.I.C.: 0139
N.A.I.C.S.: 111998

OOO Morshansk Agro-Invest **(1)**
1 Ul Solnechnaya
Morshansk, 393956, Russia
Tel.: (7) 4753323172
Vegetable Farming Services
S.I.C.: 0161
N.A.I.C.S.: 111219

OOO Sosnovka Agro-Invest **(1)**
67 Ul Kolkhoznaya
Sosnovka, 393840, Russia
Tel.: (7) 4753227302
Fax: (7) 4753226552
Vegetable Farming Services
S.I.C.: 0161
N.A.I.C.S.: 111219

ZAO Agro-Invest Kshen **(1)**
1 Ul Kurskaya
Kshenskiy, 306600, Russia
Tel.: (7) 4715822733
Fax: (7) 4715822405
Farm Supplies Distr
S.I.C.: 5191
N.A.I.C.S.: 424910

ZAO Dmitriev Agro-Invest **(1)**
84 Ul Lenina
Dmitriyev-L'govskiy, 307500, Russia
Tel.: (7) 4715021634
Fax: (7) 4712580018
Farm Products Distr
S.I.C.: 5191
N.A.I.C.S.: 424910

BLACK FIRE MINERALS LIMITED

Level 2 9 Colin Street
West Perth, WA, 6005, Australia
Mailing Address:
PO Box 821
West Perth, WA, 6872, Australia
Tel.: (61) 892161030
Fax: (61) 894817939
E-Mail: info@blackfireminerals.com.au
Web Site: www.blackfireminerals.com.au
BFE—(ASX)
Rev.: $40,420
Assets: $4,248,682
Liabilities: $175,504
Net Worth: $4,073,178
Earnings: ($2,863,160)
Emp.: 4
Fiscal Year-end: 06/30/13

Business Description:
Mineral Exploration Services
S.I.C.: 1041
N.A.I.C.S.: 212221

Personnel:
Graeme Purcell *(COO)*
Sonu Cheema *(Sec)*

Board of Directors:
Mick Billing
Martin Green
Matthew Sheldrick

BLACK IRON INC.

65 Queen St West Suite 800
Toronto, ON, M5H 2M5, Canada
Tel.: (416) 861-5932
Fax: (416) 861-8165
E-Mail: info@blackiron.com
Web Site: www.blackiron.com
Year Founded: 2010
BKI—(TSX)

Business Description:
Iron Ore Mining Services
S.I.C.: 1011
N.A.I.C.S.: 212210

Personnel:
Bruce Humphrey *(Chm)*
Matthew Simpson *(Pres & CEO)*
Paul Sandor Bozoki *(CFO)*
Christine Gallo *(Sec)*

Board of Directors:
Bruce Humphrey
John Detmold
Pierre S. Pettigrew
David Porter
Matthew Simpson
Christopher Westdal

Transfer Agent:
Equity Financial Trust Company
200 University Avenue Suite 400
Toronto, ON, Canada

BLACK ISLE RESOURCES CORP.

837 West Hastings Street Suite 202
Vancouver, BC, V6C 3N6, Canada
Tel.: (604) 684-6264
Fax: (604) 684-6242
Year Founded: 1987
BIT—(TSXV)
Assets: $113,225
Liabilities: $277,164
Net Worth: ($163,939)
Earnings: ($151,385)
Fiscal Year-end: 12/31/12

Business Description:
Mineral Exploration Services
S.I.C.: 1099
N.A.I.C.S.: 212299

Personnel:
Donald L. MacDonald *(Pres & CEO)*

Board of Directors:
William McLucas
Donald L. MacDonald
Marion McGrath
David Trueman

BLACK MOUNTAIN RESOURCES LIMITED

Ground Floor 1 Havelock Street
West Perth, WA, 6005, Australia
Tel.: (61) 8 9488 5220
Fax: (61) 8 9324 2400
E-Mail: info@blackmountainresources.com.au
Web Site: www.blackmountainresources.com.au
Year Founded: 2010
BMZ—(AIM ASX)
Int. Income: $27,291
Assets: $20,839,522
Liabilities: $3,309,107
Net Worth: $17,530,415
Earnings: ($3,022,367)
Fiscal Year-end: 06/30/13

Business Description:
Metal Mining Services
S.I.C.: 1099
N.A.I.C.S.: 212299

Personnel:
Peter Neil Landau *(Chm)*
John Ryan *(CEO)*
Terry Tew *(COO)*
Shannon Robinson *(Co-Sec)*
Rebecca Sandford *(Co-Sec)*

Board of Directors:
Peter Neil Landau
Jason Brewer
Shannon Robinson
John Ryan

Legal Counsel:
Steinepreis Paganin
Level 4 The Read Buildings 16 Milligan Street
Perth, Australia

Computershare Investor Services Pty Limited
Level 2 45 St Georges Terrace
Perth, Australia

BLACK PANTHER MINING CORP.

2489 Bellevue Avenue
Vancouver, BC, V7V 1E1, Canada
Tel.: (604) 922-2030
Fax: (604) 922-2037
E-Mail: info@waterfrontgroup.com
Web Site: www.blackpanthermining.com
BPC—(TSXV)
Int. Income: $223
Assets: $1,404,245
Liabilities: $168,231
Net Worth: $1,236,014
Earnings: ($937,375)
Fiscal Year-end: 10/31/12

Business Description:
Mineral Exploration Services
S.I.C.: 1081
N.A.I.C.S.: 213114

Personnel:
Douglas L. Mason *(Chm & CEO)*

Ronald A. Coombes *(Pres & COO)*
Sead Hamzagic *(CFO)*
Board of Directors:
Douglas L. Mason
Benjamin Ainsworth
Ronald A. Coombes
Sead Hamzagic
Andrzej Kowalski
Bruce E. Morley
Legal Counsel:
McCullough OConnor
Suite 2610 Oceanic Plaza 1066 West Hastings St
Vancouver, BC, Canada
Transfer Agent:
Computershare Trust Company of Canada
510 Burrard St 3rd Fl
Vancouver, BC, V6C 3B9, Canada

BLACK PRESS GROUP LTD.

5460 - 152 St #309
Victoria, BC, V3S 5J9, Canada
Tel.: (604) 575-2744
Fax: (250) 386-2624
E-Mail: blepine@blackpress.ca
Web Site: www.blackpress.ca
Emp.: 3,500
Business Description:
Newspaper Publishers
S.I.C.: 2711
N.A.I.C.S.: 511110
Personnel:
David Black *(Owner & Chm)*
Rick O'Connor *(Pres & CEO)*
John Walker *(CFO)*
Rick O'Conner *(COO)*
Frank Classen *(CIO)*
Subsidiary:

Cranbrook Daily Townsman (1)
822 Cranbrook St N
Cranbrook, BC, V1C3R9, Canada BC
Tel.: (250) 426-5201
Fax: (250) 426-5003
E-Mail: accounting@dailytownsman.com
Web Site: www.dailytownsman.com
Emp.: 40
Newspaper Publishing
S.I.C.: 2711
N.A.I.C.S.: 511110
Karen Johnston *(Publr)*

Unit:

Grand Forks Gazette (1)
7255 Riverside Drive
Grand Forks, BC, V0H 1H0, Canada
Mailing Address:
PO Box 700
Grand Forks, BC, V0H 1H0, Canada
Tel.: (250) 442-2191
Fax: (250) 442-3336
E-Mail: publisher@grandforksgazette.ca
Web Site: www.grandforksgazette.ca
Emp.: 6
Newspaper Publisher
S.I.C.: 2711
N.A.I.C.S.: 511110
Jackie Metcalfe *(Publr)*

U.S. Subsidiaries:

The Beacon Journal Publishing Company (1)
44 E Exchange St
Akron, OH 44309 OH
Tel.: (330) 996-3000
Fax: (330) 996-3033
Web Site: www.ohio.com
Emp.: 624
Newspaper Publisher
S.I.C.: 2711
N.A.I.C.S.: 511110
Black David *(Pres)*

Unit:

Akron Beacon Journal (2)
44 E Exchange St
Akron, OH 44308
Tel.: (330) 996-3487
Fax: (330) 996-3071
E-Mail: info@ohio.com
Web Site: www.ohio.com
Emp.: 500
Newspaper
S.I.C.: 2711
N.A.I.C.S.: 511110
Mark Cohen *(Publr)*

Oahu Publications Inc. (1)
500 Ala Moana Blvd Ste 7 500
Honolulu, HI 96813
Tel.: (808) 529-4700
Web Site: www.oahupublications.com
Newspaper & Magazine Publisher
S.I.C.: 2711
N.A.I.C.S.: 511110
Dennis Francis *(Pres)*
J. David Kennedy *(Sr VP-Mktg)*
Glenn Zuehls *(Sr VP-Adv)*

Unit:

Honolulu Star-Advertiser (2)
500 Ala Moana Blvd 7 210
Honolulu, HI 96813
Tel.: (808) 529-4747
Web Site: www.staradvertiser.com
Newspaper Publisher
S.I.C.: 2711
N.A.I.C.S.: 511110
Dennis Francis *(Publr)*
J. David Kennedy *(Sr VP-Mktg)*
Glenn Zuehls *(Sr VP-Adv)*

Sound Publishing, Inc. (1)
19351 8th Ave NE Ste 106
Poulsbo, WA 98370 WA
Tel.: (360) 394-5800
Fax: (360) 394-5841
E-Mail: classified@soundpublishing.com
Web Site: www.soundpublishing.com
Sales Range: $10-24.9 Million
Emp.: 50
Newspaper Publishers
S.I.C.: 2711
N.A.I.C.S.: 511110
David Theobald *(Controller)*

Subsidiary:

The Daily Herald Company (2)
1213 California St
Everett, WA 98201 WA
Mailing Address: (100%)
PO Box 930
Everett, WA 98206
Tel.: (425) 339-3000
Fax: (425) 339-3435
E-Mail: webfeedback@heraldnet.com
Web Site: www.heraldnet.com
Sales Range: $25-49.9 Million
Emp.: 300
Newspaper Publisher
S.I.C.: 2711
N.A.I.C.S.: 511110
Josh O'Connor *(Publr)*

Unit:

The Tukwila Reporter (2)
19426 68th Ave S Ste A
Kent, WA 98032
Tel.: (253) 872-6600
Web Site: www.pnwlocalnews.com
Sls.: $28,800,000
Emp.: 400
Newspaper Publishers
S.I.C.: 2711
N.A.I.C.S.: 511110
Polly Shepherd *(Reg Mgr-S Div)*

BLACK RANGE MINERALS LIMITED

Suite 9 5 Centre Ave
Subiaco, WA, 6008, Australia
Mailing Address:
PO Box 457
West Perth, WA, 6872, Australia
Tel.: (61) 894814920
Fax: (61) 892262027
E-Mail: info@blackrangeminerals.com
Web Site: www.blackrangeminerals.com
BLR—(ASX OTC)
Rev.: $40,225
Assets: $27,594,482
Liabilities: $722,423
Net Worth: $26,872,059
Earnings: ($1,933,970)
Emp.: 3
Fiscal Year-end: 06/30/13
Business Description:
Base Metal, Uranium & Coal Mining & Exploration Services
Export
S.I.C.: 1099
N.A.I.C.S.: 212299
Personnel:
Michael John Alexander Haynes *(Mng Dir & CEO)*
Beverly Nichols *(CFO)*
Ian John Cunningham *(Sec)*
Board of Directors:
Alan Scott
Joseph L. Havlin
Michael John Alexander Haynes
Benjamin Vallerine

BLACK RED WHITE SA

ul Krzeszowska 63
Bilgoraj, 23-400 Lublin, Poland
Tel.: (48) 846850202
Fax: (48) 846850290
E-Mail: brw@brw.com.pl
Web Site: www.brw.com.pl
Sales Range: $400-449.9 Million
Emp.: 890
Business Description:
Household Furniture Mfr
S.I.C.: 2511
N.A.I.C.S.: 337122
Personnel:
Stanislaw Bosak *(Pres)*

BLACK RIDGE MINING NL

Level 1 47 Ord Street
West Perth, WA, 6005, Australia
Tel.: (61) 893227822
Fax: (61) 893816060
E-Mail: admin@blackridgemining.com
Web Site: www.blackridgemining.com
BRD—(ASX)
Rev.: $110,113
Assets: $2,013,388
Liabilities: $2,095,915
Net Worth: ($82,527)
Earnings: ($970,476)
Fiscal Year-end: 06/30/13
Business Description:
Mineral Exploration & Development Services
S.I.C.: 1481
N.A.I.C.S.: 213115
Personnel:
Peter Elliott *(Chm)*
Graeme Smith *(Sec)*
Board of Directors:
Peter Elliott
Thomas Gilfillan
Vladimir Nikolaenko
Legal Counsel:
Steinepreis Paganin
Level 4 16 Milligan St
Perth, Australia

BLACK ROSE INDUSTRIES LTD.

145/A Mittal Towers Nariman Point
Mumbai, 400 021, India
Tel.: (91) 2243337200
Fax: (91) 2222873022
E-Mail: info@blackrosechemicals.com
Web Site: www.blackrosechemicals.com
514183—(BOM)
Rev.: $22,688,192
Assets: $10,644,931
Liabilities: $8,092,868
Net Worth: $2,552,064
Earnings: $307,273
Fiscal Year-end: 03/31/13
Business Description:
Chemical Products Mfr & Distr
S.I.C.: 2899
N.A.I.C.S.: 325998
Personnel:
C. P. Vyas *(Sec & Gen Mgr-Accts)*
Board of Directors:
Basant Kumar Goenka
Shivhari Halan
Anup Jatia
Atmaram Jatia
Sujay R. Sheth
Transfer Agent:
Satellite Corporate Services Private Limited
B-302 Sony Apartment Opp St Jude's High School Off Andheri Kurla Road
Jarimari Sakinaka, Mumbai, 400 072, India

BLACK SPARROW CAPITAL CORP.

1900 520 3rd Avenue SW
Calgary, AB, T2P 0R3, Canada
Tel.: (416) 907-5644
E-Mail: mgalloro@aloefinancial.com
Year Founded: 2011
BLC.P—(TSXV)
Business Description:
Investment Services
S.I.C.: 6211
N.A.I.C.S.: 523999
Personnel:
Michael Galloro *(Pres, CEO & CFO)*
William C. Guinan *(Sec)*
Board of Directors:
Michael Galloro
William C. Guinan
Wally Rudensky
Anthony Vella
Transfer Agent:
Valiant Trust Company
Suite 310 606 4th Street S.W.
Calgary, AB, Canada

BLACK SPRINGS CAPITAL CORP.

1660 1055 West Hastings Street
Vancouver, BC, V6E 2E9, Canada
Tel.: (604) 568-0199
Fax: (604) 681-4760
E-Mail: don@dsmi.ca
Year Founded: 2011
BSG.P—(TSXV)
Business Description:
Investment Services
S.I.C.: 6211
N.A.I.C.S.: 523999
Personnel:
Donald A. Sharpe *(Pres & CEO)*
Sean Dickenson *(CFO & Sec)*
Board of Directors:
Dorian Banks
Sean Dickenson
William L. Macdonald
Donald A. Sharpe
Transfer Agent:
Olympia Trust Company
Suite 1003 750 West Pender Street
Vancouver, BC, V6C 2T8, Canada

BLACK STAR PETROLEUM LIMITED

(Formerly Sunseeker Minerals Limited)
Level 1 330 Churchill Avenue
Subiaco, WA, 6008, Australia
Mailing Address:
PO Box 540
Subiaco, WA, 6904, Australia
Tel.: (61) 8 9200 4493
Fax: (61) 8 9200 4469

Black Star Petroleum Limited—(Continued)

Web Site: www.blackstarpetroleum.com.au
BSP—(ASX)
Rev.: $41,527
Assets: $17,652,828
Liabilities: $600,689
Net Worth: $17,052,139
Earnings: ($450,952)
Fiscal Year-end: 06/30/13
Business Description:
Oil & Gas Mining Services
S.I.C.: 1311
N.A.I.C.S.: 211111
Personnel:
Matthew Wood *(Chm)*
Greg Wood *(CEO)*
Jonathan Hart *(Sec)*
Board of Directors:
Matthew Wood
Brian McMaster
Tony Polglase
Greg Wood
Legal Counsel:
Steinepreis Paganin
Level 4 The Read Buildings 16 Milligan Street
6000 Perth, WA, Australia

BLACK WIDOW RESOURCES, INC.

Suite 304 65 Front Street East
Toronto, ON, M5E 1B5, Canada
Tel.: (416) 203-8636
Fax: (416) 815-1355
E-Mail: info@blackwidowresources.com
Web Site: www.blackwidowresources.com
Year Founded: 2011
BWR—(TSXV)
Assets: $224,921
Liabilities: $280,652
Net Worth: ($55,731)
Earnings: ($902,857)
Fiscal Year-end: 09/30/12
Business Description:
Metal Mining
S.I.C.: 1099
N.A.I.C.S.: 212299
Personnel:
Norman Brewster *(Chm)*
Neil Novak *(CEO)*
Daniel Crandall *(CFO)*
Carmen Diges *(Sec)*
Board of Directors:
Norman Brewster
Earl Coleman
George Duguay
Neil Novak
Allan Ringler

BLACKBERRY LIMITED

(Formerly Research In Motion Limited)
295 Phillip Street
Waterloo, ON, N2L 3W8, Canada
Tel.: (519) 888-7465
Fax: (519) 888-7884
E-Mail: investor_relations@blackberry.com
Web Site: www.blackberry.com
Year Founded: 1984
BBRY—(NASDAQ TSX)
Rev.: $11,073,000,000
Assets: $13,165,000,000
Liabilities: $3,705,000,000
Net Worth: $9,460,000,000
Earnings: ($646,000,000)
Emp.: 12,700
Fiscal Year-end: 03/02/13
Business Description:
Designer, Mfr & Marketer of Wireless Solutions
S.I.C.: 3661
N.A.I.C.S.: 334210
Personnel:
Michael Lazaridis *(Co-Founder & Vice Chm)*
James L. Balsillie *(Co-Founder)*
John S. Chen *(Chm & Interim CEO)*
James Yersh *(CFO)*
Robin Bienfait *(CIO)*
Steven E. Zipperstein *(Chief Legal Officer)*
Eric Johnson *(Pres-Global Sls)*
Ronald Allen Louks *(Pres-Device & Emerging Solutions)*
John J. Sims *(Pres-Global Enterprise Svcs)*
James S. Mackey *(Exec VP-Corp Dev & Strategic Plng)*
Mark Wilson *(Sr VP-Mktg)*
Board of Directors:
John S. Chen
Timothy David Dattels
David W. Kerr
Claudia B. Kotchka
Michael Lazaridis
Richard J. Lynch
Roger Martin
Bert Nordberg
John E. Richardson
Prem Watsa
John Wetmore

Computershare Investor Services Inc.
100 University Avenue 9th Floor
Toronto, ON, Canada
Transfer Agents:
Computershare Trust Company Inc.
Denver, CO 80202

Computershare Investor Services Inc.
100 University Avenue 9th Floor
Toronto, ON, Canada
Subsidiaries:

Certicom Corp. (1)
4701 Tahoe Blvd
Mississauga, ON, L4W 0B5, Canada
Tel.: (905) 507-4220
Fax: (905) 507-4230
E-Mail: info@certicom.com
Web Site: www.certicom.com
Sales Range: $10-24.9 Million
Emp.: 112
Hardware & Software Cryptography
S.I.C.: 7373
N.A.I.C.S.: 541512
Scott A. Vanstone *(Founder & Exec VP-Strategic Tech)*

QNX Software Systems Ltd (1)
175 Terence Matthews Crescent
Ottawa, ON, K2M 1W8, Canada
Tel.: (613) 591-0931
Fax: (631) 591-3579
Toll Free: (800) 676-0566
E-Mail: info@qnx.com
Web Site: www.qnx.com
Sales Range: $50-74.9 Million
Emp.: 200
Operating System Software
S.I.C.: 3652
N.A.I.C.S.: 334614
Dan Dodge *(Founder & CEO)*
Jennifer Camelon *(CFO & VP-Fin)*
Mike Michalyshyn *(Gen Counsel & VP-HR)*

Non-U.S. Branches:

QNX Software Systems GmbH & Co. KG (2)
Am Listholze 76
30177 Hannover, Germany (100%)
Tel.: (49) 51194091
Fax: (49) 51194091199
E-Mail: info@qnx.de
Web Site: www.qnx.com
Sales Range: $10-24.9 Million
Emp.: 15
Software Sales
S.I.C.: 3652
N.A.I.C.S.: 334614
Norbert Struck *(Mng Dir)*

QNX Software Systems Ltd. (2)
4F Sanbancho KB-6 Bldg 6 Banchi 3 Bancho
Chiyoda-ku, Tokyo, 102 0075, Japan
Tel.: (81) 335116450
Fax: (81) 335116451
E-Mail: japan_info@qnx.com
Web Site: www.qnx.com
Sales Range: $50-74.9 Million
Emp.: 264
Software
S.I.C.: 3652
N.A.I.C.S.: 334614

QNX Software Systems Ltd. (2)
Trinity House Cambridge Business Park
Cowley Road, Cambridge, CB4 0WZ, United Kingdom (100%)
Tel.: (44) 1223862077
Fax: (44) 1223862995
E-Mail: info@qnx.co.uk
Web Site: www.qnx.com
Sales Range: $1-9.9 Million
Emp.: 5
Software
S.I.C.: 3652
N.A.I.C.S.: 334614
Gary Bleaseale *(Gen Mgr)*

Plant:

BlackBerry Ltd. - Waterloo Manufacturing Facility (1)
451 Phillip Street
Waterloo, ON, N2L 3X2, Canada
Tel.: (519) 888-7465
Fax: (519) 888-0021
Mobile Phone Mfr
S.I.C.: 3663
N.A.I.C.S.: 334220

U.S. Subsidiary:

BlackBerry Corporation (1)
(Formerly Research In Motion Corporation)
122 W John Carpenter Pkwy Ste 430
Irving, TX 75039
Tel.: (972) 650-6126
Fax: (972) 650-2006
E-Mail: info@rim.com
Web Site: www.rim.com
Emp.: 50
Licensing of Telecommunications Products
S.I.C.: 4899
N.A.I.C.S.: 517919
Tom Sanchez *(VP)*

Subsidiaries:

Cellmania, Inc. (2)
82 Pioneer Way Ste 108
Mountain View, CA 94041 DE
Tel.: (650) 210-3851
Fax: (650) 210-3849
E-Mail: support@staff.cellmania.com
Web Site: www.cellmania.com
Emp.: 30
Mobile Commerce Solutions
S.I.C.: 7372
N.A.I.C.S.: 511210
Neerav Berry *(Co-Founder & COO)*

Non-U.S. Subsidiaries:

BlackBerry Australia Pty Limited (1)
(Formerly Research In Motion Australia Pty Limited)
Level 6 100 Pacific Highway
North Sydney, NSW, 2060, Australia
Tel.: (61) 2 9463 7600
Fax: (61) 2 99292820
E-Mail:
Web Site: au.blackberry.com
Emp.: 5
Wireless Telecommunication Services
S.I.C.: 4812
N.A.I.C.S.: 517210
Matthew Paul *(Mng Dir)*

BlackBerry Austria GmbH (1)
(Formerly Research In Motion Austria Gmbh)
Parkring 10
1010 Vienna, Austria
Tel.: (43) 1 51633 0
Fax: (43) 1 51633 3000
Emp.: 6
Wireless Telecommunication Services
S.I.C.: 4812
N.A.I.C.S.: 517210

BlackBerry Singapore Pte. Limited (1)
(Formerly Research In Motion Singapore Pte. Limited)
1 International Business Park The Synergy 02-12
Singapore, 609917, Singapore
Tel.: (65) 6879 8700
Wireless Telecommunication Services
S.I.C.: 4812
N.A.I.C.S.: 517210

Blackberry UK Limited (1)
(Formerly Research In Motion UK Limited)
200 Bath Road
Slough, Berkshire, SL1 3XE, United Kingdom UK
Tel.: (44) 1753667000 (100%)
Fax: (44) 1753669970
E-Mail:
Web Site: uk.blackberry.com
Emp.: 120
Designer, Mfr & Marketer of Wireless Solutions for Mobile Communications Market
S.I.C.: 3661
N.A.I.C.S.: 334210
Steven Bates *(Mng Dir-Europe Reg)*

Research In Motion South Africa Proprietary Limited (1)
Palazzo Towers West Monte Casino William Nicol Drive
Fourways, Johannesburg, 2086, South Africa
Tel.: (27) 11 510 0000
Fax: (27) 11 510 0261
Emp.: 3
Wireless Telecommunication Services
S.I.C.: 4812
N.A.I.C.S.: 517210

Scoreloop AG (1)
Landsbergerstr 110
80339 Munich, Germany
Tel.: (49) 89 203044600
Fax: (49) 89 203044639
E-Mail: info@scoreloop.com
Web Site: www.scoreloop.com
Emp.: 30
Mobile Game Publishing Services
S.I.C.: 7372
N.A.I.C.S.: 511210
Marc Gumpinger *(CEO)*
Christian van der Leeden *(CIO)*
Dominik Westner *(CTO)*

BLACKBIRD ENERGY INC.

Suite 400 570 Granville Street
Vancouver, BC, V6C 3P1, Canada
Tel.: (604) 685-7450
Fax: (604) 685-7485
E-Mail: wmacdonald@wlmlaw.ca
Web Site: www.blackbirdenergyinc.com
Year Founded: 2006
BBI—(TSXV)
Rev.: $960,352
Assets: $7,770,426
Liabilities: $1,283,143
Net Worth: $6,487,284
Earnings: ($3,832,333)
Emp.: 5
Fiscal Year-end: 07/31/13
Business Description:
Investment Services
S.I.C.: 6211
N.A.I.C.S.: 523999
Personnel:
Garth Braun *(Pres & CEO)*
Ron Schmitz *(CFO)*
Darrell Denney *(COO)*
Board of Directors:
Garth Braun
Sean Campbell
Darrell Denney
William L. Macdonald
Ron Schmitz
Transfer Agent:
Computershare Investor Services Inc.
100 University Ave 9th Floor
Toronto, ON, Canada

BLACKBIRD INTERNATIONAL CORPORATION

2910 South Sheridan Way
Oakville, ON, L6J 7J8, Canada

Tel.: (905) 829-3514
Fax: (905) 829-3045
E-Mail: info@blackbirdinternationalcorporation.com
Web Site: www.blackbirdinternationalcorporation.com
Year Founded: 2006
BBRD—(OTC)
Business Description:
Gaming & Leisure Software Products
S.I.C.: 7372
N.A.I.C.S.: 511210
Personnel:
John Pedder *(Pres)*

BLACKBURN RADIO INC
700 Richmond St Ste 100
London, ON, N6A 5C7, Canada
Tel.: (519) 679-8680
Fax: (519) 679-0711
E-Mail: jknowles54@aol.com
Web Site: www.blacburnradio.com
Sales Range: $50-74.9 Million
Emp.: 200
Business Description:
Broadcasting Holding Company
S.I.C.: 6719
N.A.I.C.S.: 551112
Personnel:
James K. Knowles *(VP-Fin)*
Subsidiary:

CFCO Radio AM **(1)**
117 Keil Dr
PO Box 100
Chatham, ON, N7M 5K1, Canada
Tel.: (519) 351-2326
Fax: (519) 354-2880
E-Mail: info@630cfco.com
Web Site: www.630cfco.com
Emp.: 10
Radio Station
S.I.C.: 4832
N.A.I.C.S.: 515112
Walter Ploegman *(Mgr-Ops)*

BLACKCOW FOOD CO., LTD.
9A5A6 Jinyuan Industrial City
Shantou, Guangdong, China
Tel.: (86) 754 88106868
Fax: (86) 754 88106699
E-Mail: blackcow@blackcow.cn
Web Site: www.blackcow.cn
Year Founded: 1998
002387—(SSE)
Sales Range: $75-99.9 Million
Emp.: 1,600
Business Description:
Soybean Milk Powder Mfr
S.I.C.: 2079
N.A.I.C.S.: 311224
Personnel:
Xiuhao Lin *(Chm)*

BLACKDOG RESOURCES LTD.
109 Simcoe View SW
Calgary, AB, T3H 4N4, Canada
Tel.: (403) 245-1726
Fax: (403) 245-9171
E-Mail: davidcor@telus.net
Web Site: www.blackdogresources.com
DOG—(TSXV)
Rev.: $2,072,487
Assets: $5,816,347
Liabilities: $4,123,408
Net Worth: $1,692,939
Earnings: ($3,548,102)
Fiscal Year-end: 12/31/12
Business Description:
Oil & Gas Exploration Services
S.I.C.: 1311
N.A.I.C.S.: 211111

Personnel:
George J. Hill *(Chm)*
David A. Corcoran *(Pres & CEO)*
James W. White *(CFO)*
Board of Directors:
George J. Hill
David A. Corcoran
Darcy Morgan
T. W. Morgan
Garth Von Hagen
Transfer Agent:
Olympia Trust Company
125 9th Avenue SE Suite 2300
Calgary, AB, T2G 0P6, Canada
Tel.: (403) 261-0900

BLACKFIN CAPITAL PARTNERS SAS
127 Avenue des Champs Elysees
75008 Paris, France
Tel.: (33) 1 75 00 02 30
Fax: (33) 1 75 00 02 39
Web Site: www.blackfincp.com
Sales Range: $25-49.9 Million
Emp.: 75
Business Description:
Private Equity Firm
S.I.C.: 6211
N.A.I.C.S.: 523999
Personnel:
Laurent Bouyoux *(Chm)*
Eric May *(Mng Dir)*
Paul Mizrahi *(Mng Dir)*
Bruno Rostain *(Mng Dir)*
Holding:

Hestis SAS **(1)**
10 Quai Leon Blum
92150 Suresnes, France
Tel.: (33) 1 71 11 32 03
E-Mail: fabrice.mayaud@hyperassur.com
Web Site: www.hyperassur.com
Insurance Services
S.I.C.: 6411
N.A.I.C.S.: 524298
Tanguy Thevenet *(Owner & CEO)*

BLACKFISH CAPITAL MANAGEMENT LTD
5 Savile Row
London, W1S 3PD, United Kingdom
Tel.: (44) 2070877970
Fax: (44) 2077343870
E-Mail: info@blackfishcapital.com
Web Site: www.blackfishcapital.com
Year Founded: 2006
Managed Assets: $1,000,000,000
Emp.: 2
Business Description:
Private Equity Firm
S.I.C.: 6211
N.A.I.C.S.: 523999
Personnel:
David Rowland *(Co-Owner)*
Jonathan Rowland *(Co-Owner)*
Non-U.S. Holding:

Banque Havilland S.A. **(1)**
35 A JK Kennedy 1855
L-2522 Luxembourg, Luxembourg
Tel.: (352) 463131
Fax: (352) 463132
E-Mail: info@banquehavilland.com
Web Site: www.banquehavilland.com
Emp.: 100
Banking Services
S.I.C.: 6029
N.A.I.C.S.: 522110
Nicholas Parker *(CEO)*
Venetia Lean *(COO)*

BLACKFOOT MOTORCYCLES LTD.
(d/b/a Blackfoot Motorsports)
6 Highfield Circle SE
Calgary, AB, T2G 5N5, Canada
Tel.: (403) 243-2636
Fax: (403) 243-8350
Toll Free: (800) 665-6735
E-Mail: sales@blackfootonline.com
Web Site: www.blackfootonline.com
Year Founded: 1970
Rev.: $14,094,020
Emp.: 65
Business Description:
Motorcycle Dealers
S.I.C.: 5571
N.A.I.C.S.: 441228
Personnel:
Doug MacRae *(Pres)*

BLACKGOLD INTERNATIONAL HOLDINGS LIMITED
311-313 Hay Street
Subiaco, WA, 6008, Australia
Tel.: (61) 8 9381 5819
Fax: (61) 8 9388 3701
Web Site: www.blackgoldglobal.net
Year Founded: 2010
BGG—(ASX)
Rev.: $92,271,702
Assets: $224,428,740
Liabilities: $98,847,353
Net Worth: $125,581,387
Earnings: $41,927,851
Fiscal Year-end: 10/31/12
Business Description:
Coal Mining & Other Related Services
S.I.C.: 1222
N.A.I.C.S.: 212112
Personnel:
Yu Guo Peng *(CEO)*
Shao Kui Chen *(CFO)*
Luke John Martino *(Sec)*
Board of Directors:
James Chi Ho Tong
Steven Teck Sin Chong
Jun Ou
Frank Chong Hee Peh
Yu Guo Peng
Guang Fu Yang
Seng Kiong Yap

Crowe Horwath
Level 6 256 St Georges Terrace
Perth, Australia
Legal Counsel:
Kings Park Corporate Lawyers
Suite 8 8 Clive Street
West Perth, Australia

Grandall Legal Group
31/F Nanzheng Building 580 Nanjing West Road
Shanghai, 200041, China

BLACKHAM RESOURCES LIMITED
Level 2 38 Richardson St
West Perth, WA, 6005, Australia
Tel.: (61) 893226418
Fax: (61) 893226398
E-Mail: info@blackhamresources.com.au
Web Site: www.blackhamresources.com.au
BLK—(ASX)
Rev.: $104,269
Assets: $10,334,326
Liabilities: $3,869,995
Net Worth: $6,464,332
Earnings: ($5,296,264)
Fiscal Year-end: 06/30/13
Business Description:
Mineral Exploration
S.I.C.: 1481
N.A.I.C.S.: 213115
Personnel:
Bryan Dixon *(Mng Dir)*
Mike Robbins *(CFO & Sec)*
Board of Directors:
Joseph Gutnick
Bryan Dixon
Greg Miles
Alan Thom

BLACKHAWK CAPITAL LLP
Centaur House Ancells Road
Fleet, Hants, GU51 2UJ, United Kingdom
Tel.: (44) 1252 762 108
E-Mail: info@blackhawkcapital.co.uk
Web Site: www.blackhawkcapital.co.uk
Year Founded: 2010
Business Description:
Private Equity Firm
S.I.C.: 6211
N.A.I.C.S.: 523999
Personnel:
Alan Watkins *(Co-Founder & Chm)*
Kevin Lewis *(Co-Founder & Mng Partner)*
Holding:

Computer Systems Integration Limited **(1)**
Newstead House Lake View Drive
Sherwood Business Park, Annesley, Notts, NG15 0DT, United Kingdom UK
Tel.: (44) 1623 726 300
Fax: (44) 1623 726 395
E-Mail: info@csiltd.co.uk
Web Site: www.csiltd.co.uk
Emp.: 130
Information Technology Systems Integration Services
S.I.C.: 7379
N.A.I.C.S.: 541519
Alan Watkins *(Chm)*
Richard Midgley *(Mng Dir)*

BLACKHAWK RESOURCE CORP.
650 816 7 Avenue SW
Calgary, AB, T2P 1A1, Canada
Tel.: (403) 663-0200
Fax: (403) 663-0999
Web Site: www.blackhawkcorp.ca
BLR—(TSXV)
Rev.: $830,464
Assets: $3,904,212
Liabilities: $875,617
Net Worth: $3,028,595
Earnings: ($1,229,766)
Fiscal Year-end: 06/30/13
Business Description:
Oil & Gas Exploration Services
S.I.C.: 1389
N.A.I.C.S.: 213112
Personnel:
David Antony *(CEO)*
Charidy Lazorko *(CFO)*
Board of Directors:
David Antony
Raymond Peter Antony
Mike Bowie
Dave Fuchs
Transfer Agent:
Olympia Trust Company
2300 125 9 Avenue SW
Calgary, AB, Canada

BLACKHEATH & BROMLEY HARRIERS AC
The Sydney Wooderson Ctr
56 Bourne Way Hayes, Bromley, Kent, BR2 7EY, United Kingdom
Tel.: (44) 2084623115
Web Site: www.bandbhac.org.uk
Sales Range: $50-74.9 Million
Emp.: 700
Business Description:
Sports Clubs & Associations
S.I.C.: 7941
N.A.I.C.S.: 711211
Personnel:
Steve Hollingdale *(Pres)*

BLACKHEATH RESOURCES INC.

#306 850 West Hastings Street
Vancouver, BC, V6C 1E1, Canada
Tel.: (604) 669-8988
Fax: (604) 669-2744
E-Mail: info@blackheathresources.com
Web Site: www.blackheathresources.com
Year Founded: 2011
BHR—(TSXV)
Business Description:
Metal Mining
S.I.C.: 1099
N.A.I.C.S.: 212299
Personnel:
James Robertson *(Pres & CEO)*
Kerry Spong *(CFO & Sec)*
Board of Directors:
Jonathan Carter
Marshall Farris
John Merfyn Roberts
James Robertson
Kerry Spong
Transfer Agent:
Computershare Investor Services Inc.
510 Burrard St
Vancouver, BC, V6C 3B9, Canada

BLACKLINE GPS CORP.

101 1215 13th Street SE
Calgary, AB, T2G 3J4, Canada
Tel.: (403) 451-0327
Fax: (403) 451-9981
E-Mail: info@blacklinegps.com
Web Site: www.blacklinegps.com
Year Founded: 2006
BLN—(TSXV)
Sls.: $2,629,171
Assets: $8,589,681
Liabilities: $1,556,182
Net Worth: $7,033,499
Earnings: ($3,103,266)
Emp.: 30
Fiscal Year-end: 10/31/12
Business Description:
Wireless Technology & GPS Systems Mfr
S.I.C.: 3663
N.A.I.C.S.: 334220
Personnel:
Cody Slater *(Chm & CEO)*
Clark L. Swanson *(Pres)*
Peter Dorrius *(CFO)*
Kevin Meyers *(COO)*
Craig Swanson *(CMO)*
Brendon Cook *(CTO)*
Board of Directors:
Cody Slater
John Finbow
Michael Hayduk
Bob Herdman
Clark L. Swanson
Transfer Agent:
Olympia Trust Company inc.
2300 125 - 9th Avenue SE
Calgary, AB, Canada
Subsidiary:

Blackline GPS Inc **(1)**
101-1215-13th St S E
Calgary, AB, T2G 3J4, Canada
Tel.: (403) 451-0325
Fax: (403) 451-9981
Commercial Tracking System Mfr
S.I.C.: 3829
N.A.I.C.S.: 334519

BLACKMAGIC DESIGN PTY. LTD.

11 Gateway Court
Port Melbourne, VIC, 3207, Australia
Tel.: (61) 396824770
Fax: (61) 396824790
Web Site: www.blackmagic-design.com
Business Description:
Video Editing Equipment Mfr
S.I.C.: 3651
N.A.I.C.S.: 334310
Personnel:
Grant Petty *(Founder & CEO)*

BLACKMORES LIMITED

20 Jubilee Avenue
Warriewood, NSW, 2102, Australia
Tel.: (61) 2 9910 5000
Fax: (61) 2 9910 5555
E-Mail: pr@blackmores.com.au
Web Site: www.blackmores.com.au
Year Founded: 1930
BKL—(ASX)
Rev.: $341,328,392
Assets: $241,222,182
Liabilities: $139,043,235
Net Worth: $102,178,947
Earnings: $26,027,490
Emp.: 800
Fiscal Year-end: 06/30/13
Business Description:
Health Product Mfr & Whslr
S.I.C.: 2833
N.A.I.C.S.: 325411
Personnel:
Marcus C. Blackmore *(Chm)*
Christine Holgate *(CEO)*
Chris Last *(CFO & Co-Sec)*
Cecile Cooper *(Co-Sec)*
Board of Directors:
Marcus C. Blackmore
Stephen J. Chapman
Verilyn C. Fitzgerald
Christine Holgate
Robert L. Stovold
Brent W. Wallace

Subsidiaries:

FIT-BioCeuticals Limited **(1)**
16/37-41 O'Riordan Street
PO Box 6454
Alexandria, NSW, 2015, Australia
Tel.: (61) 2 9080 0900
Fax: (61) 2 9080 0940
E-Mail: info@fit.net.au
Web Site: www.fit-bioceuticals.com.au
Health Care Product Whslr
S.I.C.: 5122
N.A.I.C.S.: 424210
Alan Dworkin *(CFO)*

PharmaFoods Pty Ltd **(1)**
Unit 16 37-41 O'Riordan St
Alexandria, NSW, 2015, Australia
Tel.: (61) 2 9080 0900
Fax: (61) 2 9080 0940
E-Mail: cs@fit.net.au
Web Site: www.pharmafoodsprofessional.com.au
Health Care Product Whslr
S.I.C.: 5122
N.A.I.C.S.: 424210

Non-U.S. Subsidiaries:

Blackmores (Malaysia) Sdn Bhd **(1)**
Suite 2 02 Block B No 10 Jalan Bersatu 13/4
46200 Petaling Jaya, Selangor, Malaysia
Tel.: (60) 3 7955 0993
E-Mail: healthadvisory@blackmores.com.my
Web Site: www.blackmores.com.my
Health Care Product Whslr
S.I.C.: 5122
N.A.I.C.S.: 424210
Eddy Ong *(Country Mgr)*

Blackmores (New Zealand) Limited **(1)**
14-16 Norman Spencer Drive
PO Box 76401
Manukau, Auckland, New Zealand
Tel.: (64) 9 279 7979
Fax: (64) 9 279 7999
E-Mail: customerservices@api.net.nz
Web Site: www.blackmoresnz.co.nz
Health Care Product Whslr
S.I.C.: 5122
N.A.I.C.S.: 424210

Blackmores (Singapore) Pte Limited **(1)**
6 Eu Tong Sen St
Singapore, 059817, Singapore
Tel.: (65) 6225 3933
E-Mail: healthadvisory@blackmores.com.sg
Web Site: www.blackmores.com.sg
Health Care Product Whslr
S.I.C.: 5122
N.A.I.C.S.: 424210

Blackmores (Taiwan) Limited **(1)**
Room 5A05 Taipei World Trade Centre No 5 Hsin-yi Rd Section 5
Taipei, Taiwan
Tel.: (886) 2 2345 0138
Fax: (886) 2 2345 0276
E-Mail: achen@blackmores.com.tw
Web Site: www.blackmores.com.tw
Health Care Product Whslr
S.I.C.: 5122
N.A.I.C.S.: 424210

Blackmores (Thailand) Limited **(1)**
10A B Mahanakorn Gypsum Bldg 539/2
Sri-Ayuddhaya Rd
Ratchathewi, Bangkok, 10400, Thailand
Tel.: (66) 2248 8290
Fax: (66) 2248 8293
E-Mail: onlineteam@blackmores.co.th
Web Site: www.en.blackmores.co.th
Health Care Product Whslr
S.I.C.: 5122
N.A.I.C.S.: 424210
Rananda Rich *(Country Mgr)*

FIT-BioCeuticals (NZ) Limited **(1)**
14-18 Lovell Court
Rosedale, Auckland, 0632, New Zealand
Tel.: (64) 9 415 3267
Fax: (64) 800 106 601
E-Mail: csnz@ebos.co.nz
Web Site: www.bioceuticals.com.au/nz
Health Care Product Whslr
S.I.C.: 5122
N.A.I.C.S.: 424210

BLACKPEARL RESOURCES INC.

Suite 700 444 7th Ave Southwest
Calgary, AB, T2P 0X8, Canada
Tel.: (403) 215-8313
Fax: (403) 262-5123
E-Mail: info@blackpearlresources.ca
Web Site: www.blackpearlresources.ca
Year Founded: 2002
PXX—(OMX TSX)
Rev.: $203,301,941
Assets: $617,013,065
Liabilities: $75,270,176
Net Worth: $541,742,888
Earnings: $44,731
Emp.: 44
Fiscal Year-end: 12/31/12
Business Description:
Oil & Natural Gas Exploration, Drilling & Extraction
S.I.C.: 1311
N.A.I.C.S.: 211111
Personnel:
John Hunter Craig *(Chm)*
John L. Festival *(Pres & CEO)*
Don Cook *(CFO)*
Diane Phillips *(Sec)*
Board of Directors:
John Hunter Craig
Brian D. Edgar
John L. Festival
Keith C. Hill
Victor Luhowy
Legal Counsel:
Bennett Jones
Calgary, AB, Canada
Transfer Agent:
Computershare Trust Company of Canada
530 8th Ave SW 6th Floor
Calgary, AB, T2P 3S8, Canada
Tel.: (403) 267-6800
Fax: (403) 267-6529
Subsidiary:

Pearl E&P Canada Ltd. **(1)**
5208 62nd St
Lloydminster, AB, T9V 2E4, Canada
Tel.: (780) 808-8448
Fax: (780) 808-8441
E-Mail: kevin.golem@pxx.ca
Web Site: www.blackpearlresources.ca
Emp.: 20
Oil & Gas Field Exploration Services
S.I.C.: 1311
N.A.I.C.S.: 211111
Kevin Golem *(Mgr)*

BLACKPOOL PLEASURE BEACH LTD.

Ocean Blvd Promenade S Shore
Blackpool, Lancashire, FY4 1EZ, United Kingdom
Tel.: (44) 1253341033
Web Site: www.blackpoolpleasurebeach.com
Sales Range: $50-74.9 Million
Emp.: 1,187
Business Description:
Amusement Park Operators
S.I.C.: 7996
N.A.I.C.S.: 713110
Personnel:
Amanda Thompson *(Mng Dir)*

BLACKROCK EMERGING EUROPE PLC

(Formerly The Eastern European Trust PLC)
c/o BlackRock Investment Management (UK) Limited
33 King William Street, London, EC4R 9AS, United Kingdom
Tel.: (44) 20 7743 3000
Fax: (44) 20 7743 1000
E-Mail: uk.investor@blackrock.co.uk
Web Site: www.blackrock.co.uk
BEEP—(LSE)
Rev.: $24,317,000
Assets: $214,666,000
Liabilities: $16,712,000
Net Worth: $197,954,000
Earnings: $23,212,000
Fiscal Year-end: 01/31/13
Business Description:
Investment Services
S.I.C.: 6211
N.A.I.C.S.: 523999
Personnel:
David Reid *(Fund Mgr)*
Board of Directors:
Rachel Beagles
Mark Bridgeman
Philippe Delpal
Neil England
Robert Sheppard
Legal Counsel:
Norton Rose LLP
3 More London Riverside
London, SE1 2AQ, United Kingdom
Tel.: (44) 20 7283 6000
Fax: (44) 20 7283 6500

BLACKSTAR GROUP SE

4th Floor Avantech Building St Julian's Road
San Gwann, SGN 2805, Malta
Tel.: (356) 2144 6377
Fax: (356) 2144 6330
E-Mail: info@blackstar.lu
Web Site: www.blackstar.lu
BLCK—(AIM)
Rev.: $128,990,090
Assets: $168,353,893
Liabilities: $33,961,052
Net Worth: $134,392,841
Earnings: $32,407,031

Emp.: 507
Fiscal Year-end: 12/31/12
Business Description:
Equity Investment Company
S.I.C.: 6211
N.A.I.C.S.: 523999
Personnel:
John Broadhurst Mills *(Chm)*
Bryan Moyer *(Sec)*
Board of Directors:
John Broadhurst Mills
Andrew David Bonamour
Marcel Ernzer
Richard Thomson Wight
Legal Counsel:
Paul Hastings (Europe) LLP
Ten Bishops Square Eighth Floor
London, E1 6EG, United Kingdom
Ganado & Associates Advocates
171 Old Bakery Street
Valletta, VLT 1455, Malta
Edward Nathan Sonnerbergs Inc.
150 West Street
Sandton, Johannesburg, 2196, South Africa
Tel.: (27) 11 269 7600
Fax: (27) 11 269 7899
Capita Registrars
The Registry 34 Beckenham Road
Beckenham, United Kingdom

Non-U.S. Subsidiaries:

Adreach Group (Pty) Limited **(1)**
33 A Bath Avenue
Rosebank, Johannesburg, Gauteng, 2196, South Africa
Tel.: (27) 113277110
Fax: (27) 113277112
E-Mail: sales@adreach.co.za
Web Site: www.streetpoleads.co.za
Emp.: 70
Outdoor Advertising Solutions
S.I.C.: 7312
N.A.I.C.S.: 541850
Bradley Fisher *(CEO)*
Ken Mourant *(COO)*

Ferro Industrial Products (Pty) Limited **(1)**
1 Atomic St
Brakpan, Gauteng, 1540, South Africa
Tel.: (27) 117464000
Fax: (27) 117464023
E-Mail: finance@ferrosa.co.za
Web Site: www.ferrosa.co.za
Emp.: 400
Powder Coatings Mfr
S.I.C.: 2851
N.A.I.C.S.: 325510
Ian D. Forbes *(Mng Dir)*

Kulungile Metals Group (Pty) Limited **(1)**
16 Quality Road
PO Box 995
Isando, Gauteng, 1600, South Africa ZA
Tel.: (27) 119295000
Fax: (27) 119295062
E-Mail: joyceg@kmg.co.za
Web Site: www.kulungile.co.za
Sales Range: $350-399.9 Million
Emp.: 1,000
Holding Company; Hot & Cold Rolled, Flat Rolled & Fabricated Structural Metal Products Mfr & Distr; Owned 27% by Management Employee Trust
S.I.C.: 6719
N.A.I.C.S.: 551112
Andrew David Bonamour *(Chm)*
Sampie J. van Rooyen *(CEO)*

Subsidiaries:

Global Roofing Solutions (Pty) Ltd. **(2)**
154 Monteer Road
Isando, Gauteng, 1600, South Africa ZA
Mailing Address:
PO Box 4213
Edenvale, 1610, South Africa
Tel.: (27) 115704600
Fax: (27) 119745683
E-Mail: info@globalroofs.co.za
Web Site: www.global-roofing-solutions.co.za
Sales Range: $100-124.9 Million
Emp.: 325
Holding Company; Metal Roof Covering, Wall Cladding & Floor Decking Products Mfr
S.I.C.: 6719
N.A.I.C.S.: 551112
Gavin Jacobsen *(Mng Dir)*

Unit:

Brownbuilt Metal Sections **(3)**
cnr of Tile & Paul Smit Roads
Boksburg, 1508, South Africa
Mailing Address:
PO Box 6461
Dunswart, 1508, South Africa
Tel.: (27) 118982903
Fax: (27) 118921455
Web Site: www.global-roofing-solutions.co.za
Metal Roof Covering, Wall Cladding & Floor Decking Products Mfr
S.I.C.: 3446
N.A.I.C.S.: 332323
Johan van der Westhuizen *(Gen Mgr)*

Stainless Steel & Aluminum Corporation **(2)**
Cnr Linton Jones & Brammer Streets
Industria East, Germiston, South Africa
Tel.: (27) 118716900
Fax: (27) 118739455
Web Site: www.stalcor.co.za
Hot & Cold Rolled, Flat Rolled & Fabricated Structural Steel & Aluminum Products Mfr & Distr
S.I.C.: 3312
N.A.I.C.S.: 331221
Chris Ransome *(Chm)*
Paul Miot *(Mng Dir)*

BLACKSTEEL ENERGY INC.

1800 510 5th Ave SW
Calgary, AB, T2P 3S2, Canada
Tel.: (403) 453-0060
Fax: (403) 460-6718
E-Mail: info@blacksteelenergy.com
Web Site: www.blacksteelenergy.ca
Year Founded: 2009
BEY—(TSXV)
Rev.: $4,179
Assets: $1,413,144
Liabilities: $151,510
Net Worth: $1,261,634
Earnings: ($520,206)
Fiscal Year-end: 04/30/13
Business Description:
Oil & Gas Exploration Services
S.I.C.: 1311
N.A.I.C.S.: 211111
Personnel:
Les Treitz *(Interim Pres & CEO)*
Derek Batorowski *(CFO)*
Board of Directors:
Eugene Chen
Curtis Hartzler
Greg McLean
Chris Scase
Les Treitz
Legal Counsel:
Gowlings
Calgary, AB, Canada
Transfer Agent:
Computershare Trust Company of Canada
Calgary, AB, Canada

BLACKSTONE VENTURES INC.

Suite 600 888 Dunsmuir Street
Vancouver, BC, V6C 3K4, Canada
Tel.: (604) 687-3929
Fax: (604) 682-3727
E-Mail: info@blv.ca
Web Site: www.blv.ca
Year Founded: 1989
BLV—(DEU TSXV)
Int. Income: $132
Assets: $180,841
Liabilities: $238,233
Net Worth: ($57,392)
Earnings: ($402,162)
Fiscal Year-end: 12/31/12
Business Description:
Nickel & Related Metals Exploration & Mining Services
S.I.C.: 1021
N.A.I.C.S.: 212234
Personnel:
Donald Arthur McInnes *(Chm, Pres & CEO)*
David M. Douglas *(CFO)*
Board of Directors:
Donald Arthur McInnes
John Angus Greig
Peter G. Wong
Legal Counsel:
Miller Thompson LLP
1000-840 Howe Street
Vancouver, BC, Canada V6Z 2M1
Transfer Agent:
CIBC Mellon Trust Company
1600-1066 West Hastings Street
Vancouver, BC, Canada

BLACKSTREAM ENERGY CORPORATION

(Name Changed to SunOil Ltd.)

BLACKTHORN RESOURCES LTD

Level 5 Suite 502 80 William Street
Sydney, NSW, 2011, Australia
Tel.: (61) 293579000
Fax: (61) 293321336
E-Mail: info@blackthornresources.com.au
Web Site: www.blackthornresources.com.au
BTR—(ASX)
Rev.: $1,427,677
Assets: $98,497,208
Liabilities: $3,669,234
Net Worth: $94,827,974
Earnings: ($13,043,966)
Fiscal Year-end: 06/30/13
Business Description:
Mineral Resource Properties Development & Exploration Services
S.I.C.: 1021
N.A.I.C.S.: 212234
Personnel:
Michael Oppenheimer *(Chm)*
Mark Mitchell *(CEO)*
Ravi Underwood *(CFO)*
Tony De Santis *(COO)*
Chris Brown *(Sec)*
Board of Directors:
Michael Oppenheimer
Nicole Bowman
Derek Carter
Roger Higgins
Peter Kalkandis

BLACKWALL PROPERTY FUNDS LIMITED

Level 1 50 Yeo Street
Neutral Bay, NSW, 2089, Australia
Mailing Address:
PO Box 612
Neutral Bay, NSW, 2089, Australia
Tel.: (61) 2 9033 8611
Fax: (61) 2 9033 8600
E-Mail: info@blackwallfunds.com.au
Web Site: www.blackwallfunds.com.au
BWF—(ASX)
Business Description:
Property Funds Management Services
S.I.C.: 6282
N.A.I.C.S.: 523920
Personnel:
Richard James Hill *(Chm)*
Stuart Brown *(CEO)*
Tim Brown *(CFO)*
Don Bayly *(Compliance Officer & Sec)*
Board of Directors:
Richard James Hill
Stuart Brown
Seph Glew
Robin Tedder

Subsidiaries:

Armada Holdings Pty Ltd **(1)**
2/19 Harley Crescent
Condell Park, Sydney, NSW, 2200, Australia
Tel.: (61) 2 9707 0111
Fax: (61) 2 9707 0199
Web Site: www.amarda.com.au
Pool Table & Jukebox Distr
S.I.C.: 5099
N.A.I.C.S.: 423990

Blackwall Management Services Pty Ltd **(1)**
Level 1 50 Yeo St
Neutral Bay, NSW, 2089, Australia
Tel.: (61) 290338622
Fax: (61) 290338600
Real Estate Management Services
S.I.C.: 6531
N.A.I.C.S.: 531390

TFML Limited **(1)**
L 3 50 Yeo St
Neutral Bay, NSW, 2089, Australia
Tel.: (61) 2 9033 8614
Fax: (61) 2 9033 8600
Real Estate Management Services
S.I.C.: 6531
N.A.I.C.S.: 531390
Clare Simmons *(Gen Mgr)*

BLACKWELL LTD.

Beaver House Hythe Bridge Street
Oxford, OX1 2ET, United Kingdom
Tel.: (44) 1865333000
Fax: (44) 1865791438
E-Mail: info@blackwell.co.uk
Web Site: www.blackwell.co.uk
Year Founded: 1879
Emp.: 1,500
Business Description:
Holding Company; Book Retailer & Publisher
S.I.C.: 6719
N.A.I.C.S.: 551112
Personnel:
Andrew Hutchings *(CEO-Blackwell Grp)*

U.S. Subsidiary:

Blackwell's North America Inc. **(1)**
2550 W Tyvola Rd Ste 300
Charlotte, NC 28217-4579 OR
Tel.: (503) 684-1140
Fax: (503) 639-2481
E-Mail: custserv@blackwell.com
Web Site: www.blackwell.com
Emp.: 200
Books, Periodicals & Newspapers Import Export
S.I.C.: 5192
N.A.I.C.S.: 424920
Christine Mitchell *(Mgr)*

BLACKWOOD BUILDING CENTRE LTD

33050 S Fraserway
Abbotsford, BC, V2S 2A9, Canada
Tel.: (604) 853-6471
Fax: (604) 853-6771
Year Founded: 1971
Rev.: $20,195,634
Emp.: 35
Business Description:
Building Materials Distr
S.I.C.: 5211
N.A.I.C.S.: 444190
Personnel:
Rick Neufeld *(Mgr-Sls)*

Blackwood Building Centre Ltd—(Continued)

BLACKWOOD CORP. LTD.
(Acquired by Cockatoo Coal Limited)

BLAIR BUILDING MATERIALS INC.
10445 Keele Street
PO Box 730
Maple, ON, L6A 1S7, Canada
Tel.: (416) 798-4996
Fax: (905) 832-1150
E-Mail: sales@blairbuildingmaterials.com
Web Site: www.blairbuildingmaterials.com
Year Founded: 1950
Rev.: $10,626,605
Emp.: 50
Business Description:
Building Material Products Distr
S.I.C.: 5211
N.A.I.C.S.: 444190
Personnel:
Martin Lieberman *(Pres & CEO)*

BLAMMO WORLDWIDE
154 Pearl Street
Toronto, ON, M5H 1L3, Canada
Tel.: (416) 979-7999
Fax: (416) 979-9750
E-Mail: gjp@gjpadvertising.com
Web Site: www.gjpadvertising.com
Year Founded: 1991
Sales Range: $75-99.9 Million
Emp.: 80
Business Description:
Advertising Services
S.I.C.: 7311
N.A.I.C.S.: 541810
Personnel:
Alan Gee *(Chm)*
Peter Jeffery *(CEO)*
Kevin Pfuhl *(Mng Partner-Client Dev)*
John Yorke *(Mng Partner-Bus Dev)*
Christine McNab *(Mng Dir & Partner)*
Nancy Christou *(CFO & Partner)*
Michael Murray *(Chief Creative Officer & Partner)*
Ritchie Emslie *(Chief Strategic Officer & Partner)*
Gord Cathmoir *(Partner & Head-Creative Svcs)*
Lisa Greenberg *(Partner & Dir-Creative)*
Ellen Zabitsky *(Exec VP-Client Dev)*

BLAUWHOED HOLDING B.V.
Lichtenauerlaan 80
3062 ME Rotterdam, Netherlands
Tel.: (31) 104535311
Fax: (31) 104526353
Sales Range: $200-249.9 Million
Emp.: 88
Business Description:
Real Estate Development Services
S.I.C.: 6531
N.A.I.C.S.: 531390

BLAVOD WINES AND SPIRITS PLC
3rd Floor Cardinal House 39/40
Albemarle Street
London, W1S 4TE, United Kingdom
Tel.: (44) 2073522096
Fax: (44) 2078233510
E-Mail: info@blavod.com
Web Site: www.blavodwinesandspirits.com
BES—(AIM)
Rev.: $5,977,613
Assets: $3,922,956
Liabilities: $1,084,972
Net Worth: $2,837,984
Earnings: ($1,165,516)
Emp.: 10
Fiscal Year-end: 03/31/13
Business Description:
Alcoholic Beverage Mfr & Distr
S.I.C.: 2085
N.A.I.C.S.: 312140
Personnel:
Don Goulding *(Chm)*
Sarah Bertolotti *(Sec & Dir-Fin)*
Board of Directors:
Don Goulding
Sarah Bertolotti
Mark Quinn
Legal Counsel:
Maclay Murray & Spens LLP
1 London Wall
London, United Kingdom

BLAZE INTERNATIONAL LIMITED
Level 1 8 Parliament Place
West Perth, WA, 6005, Australia
Tel.: (61) 894817833
Fax: (61) 894817835
E-Mail: blaze@blazelimited.com.au
Web Site: www.blazelimited.com.au
BLZ—(ASX)
Rev.: $19,025
Assets: $588,524
Liabilities: $78,316
Net Worth: $510,208
Earnings: ($797,884)
Fiscal Year-end: 06/30/13
Business Description:
Mineral Exploration
S.I.C.: 1481
N.A.I.C.S.: 213115
Personnel:
David Nathan Zukerman *(Sec)*
Board of Directors:
Michael Scivolo
Robert John Collins
Sol Majteles

BLB LTD
3rd Floor ECE House Annexe II 28 A
Kasturba Gandhi Marg
New Delhi, 110 001, India
Tel.: (91) 1149325600
Fax: (91) 1149325637
E-Mail: info@blblimited.com
Web Site: www.blblimited.com
532290—(BOM)
Rev.: $53,725,822
Assets: $33,439,675
Liabilities: $11,526,737
Net Worth: $21,912,938
Earnings: ($283,567)
Fiscal Year-end: 03/31/13
Business Description:
Finance Investments
S.I.C.: 6141
N.A.I.C.S.: 522291
Personnel:
Vikash Rawal *(CFO)*
Vasudha Thakur *(Sec)*
Board of Directors:
Brij Rattan Bagri
Rajesh Kumar Damani
Keshav Chand Jain
Manas Jain
Vikram Rathi
Satish Kumar Sharma
Transfer Agent:
Abhipra Capital Limited
A-387 Abhipra Complex Dilkhush Industrial Area
G.T. Karnal Rd Azadpur
New Delhi, 110 033, India

BLC BANK SAL
BLC Building Adlieh Intersection
Beirut, Lebanon
Tel.: (961) 1429000
Fax: (961) 9611398040
E-Mail: human.resourses@blcbank.com
Web Site: www.blcbank.com
Year Founded: 1950
Emp.: 150
Business Description:
Banking Services
S.I.C.: 6029
N.A.I.C.S.: 522110
Personnel:
Rida Mroueh *(CFO)*

BLD PLANTATION BHD
Level 6 Crown Towers 88 Jalan Pending
93450 Kuching, Sarawak, Malaysia
Tel.: (60) 82335311
Fax: (60) 82348311
E-Mail: bld@bld.com.my
Web Site: www.bld.com.my
BLDPLNT—(KLS)
Rev.: $627,561,380
Assets: $451,073,218
Liabilities: $229,723,657
Net Worth: $221,349,562
Earnings: $29,203,725
Fiscal Year-end: 12/31/12
Business Description:
Oil Palm Cultivation Services
S.I.C.: 0711
N.A.I.C.S.: 115112
Personnel:
Henry Lee Kong Lau *(Chm)*
Pauline Hieh Hua Lau *(Asst Fin Officer)*
Rutus Siros *(Risk Assessment Officer)*
Dominic Juan Lai Ting *(Risk Assessment Officer)*
Alvin Lee Jen Lau *(Sec)*
Board of Directors:
Henry Lee Kong Lau
Hamden Ahmad
Chon Chee Chong
Abdillah Hamid
Robert Hui Yew Lau

BLEECKER SA
39 avenue George V
75008 Paris, France
Tel.: (33) 144719494
Web Site: www.bleecker.fr
BLEE—(EUR)
Business Description:
Real Estate Investment & Management Services
S.I.C.: 6211
N.A.I.C.S.: 523999
Personnel:
Joelle Moulaire *(Chm-Supervisory Bd)*
Muriel Marcilhacy-Giraud *(Chm-Exec Bd)*
Sophie Rio-Chevalier *(Vice Chm-Supervisory Bd)*
Philippe Bucheton *(Mng Dir)*
Supervisory Board of Directors:
Joelle Moulaire
Jean-Louis Falco
Sophie Rio-Chevalier

BLESSED TEXTILES LIMITED
Plot 23/1 Sector 23 SM Farooq Road
Korangi Industrial Area
Karachi, Pakistan
Tel.: (92) 2135115177
Fax: (92) 2135063002
E-Mail: khioff@umergroup.com
Web Site: www.umergroup.com
BTL—(KAR LAH)
Sls.: $58,407,249
Assets: $42,034,655
Liabilities: $17,507,682
Net Worth: $24,526,973
Earnings: $3,997,445
Emp.: 997
Fiscal Year-end: 06/30/13
Business Description:
Yarn & Woven Fabric Mfr
S.I.C.: 2299
N.A.I.C.S.: 313110
Personnel:
Mohammad Amin *(CEO)*
Anwar Hussain *(CFO)*
Ashraf Ali *(Sec)*
Board of Directors:
Mohammad Salim
Mohammad Amin
Khurram Salim
Mohammad Shaheen
Adil Shakeel
Mohammad Shakeel
Bilal Sharif
Mohammad Sharif

BLEU OCEANE
Route De La Roche Sur Yon
85230 Challans, Vendee, France
Tel.: (33) 251687165
Fax: (33) 251689156
Web Site: www.bleu-oceane.com
Sls.: $13,400,000
Emp.: 91
S.I.C.: 2389
N.A.I.C.S.: 315240
Personnel:
Andre Dugast *(Pres)*

BLEVINS FRANKS FINANCIAL MANAGEMENT LIMITED
28 St James Square
London, SW1Y 4JH, United Kingdom
Tel.: (44) 20 7336 1000
Fax: (44) 2073895230
E-Mail: administrations@blevinsfranks.com
Web Site: www.blevinsfranks.com
Year Founded: 1975
Sales Range: $10-24.9 Million
Business Description:
Financial Management & Tax Services
S.I.C.: 6211
N.A.I.C.S.: 523110
Personnel:
Bill Blevins *(Co-Founder)*
John Stone *(Chm)*
John Simmonds *(CEO)*
Subsidiary:
Blevins Franks Tax Limited **(1)**
4 Fenchurch Avenue
London, EC3M 5BS, United Kingdom UK
Tel.: (44) 20 7336 1000
Fax: (44) 20 7336 1001
Tax Services
S.I.C.: 7291
N.A.I.C.S.: 541213

BLIGH MINING LIMITED
Suite 605 Level 6 66 Hunter Street
Sydney, NSW, 2000, Australia
Tel.: (61) 2 9224 9292
Fax: (61) 2 9224 9299
E-Mail: info@blighmining.com.au
Web Site: www.blighmining.com.au
BLH—(ASX)
Sales Range: Less than $1 Million
Business Description:
Metal Mining Services
S.I.C.: 1099
N.A.I.C.S.: 212299
Personnel:
Andrew Nutt *(Chm)*
Anne Adaley *(CFO & Sec)*
Board of Directors:
Anthony Crimmins
Andrew Nutt

Sevag Chalabian
Michael Doyle
Brett Gunter
Muhammad Iqbal
Tommy Tjiptadjaja

BLIGH RESOURCES LIMITED

Level 8 84 Pitt Street
Sydney, NSW, 2000, Australia
Tel.: (61) 2 9233 4677
Fax: (61) 2 9239 0866
E-Mail: info@blighresources.com.au
Web Site: www.blighresources.com.au
BGH—(ASX)
Rev.: $107,110
Assets: $4,236,405
Liabilities: $187,362
Net Worth: $4,049,043
Earnings: ($1,718,318)
Fiscal Year-end: 06/30/13
Business Description:
Manganese Mining
S.I.C.: 1099
N.A.I.C.S.: 212299
Personnel:
Robert John Benussi *(CEO)*
Anna Sandham *(Sec)*
Board of Directors:
Robert John Benussi
Eric Chan
Jinle Song
Peiqi Zhang
Legal Counsel:
Aura Legal Pty Ltd
Level 14 74 Castlereagh Street
Sydney, Australia

BLINA MINERALS NL

Level 4 66 Kings Park Road
West Perth, WA, 6005, Australia
Mailing Address:
PO Box 52
West Perth, WA, 6872, Australia
Tel.: (61) 8 6141 3500
Fax: (61) 8 6141 3599
E-Mail: general@blinaminerals.com.au
Web Site: www.blinadiamonds.com.au
BDI—(ASX)
Rev.: $6,029
Assets: $2,411,523
Liabilities: $2,047,582
Net Worth: $363,941
Earnings: ($1,234,150)
Fiscal Year-end: 06/30/13
Business Description:
Mineral Exploration Services
S.I.C.: 3299
N.A.I.C.S.: 327999
Personnel:
Peter G. Webse *(Sec)*
Board of Directors:
Brett F. Fraser
David Porter
Justin Virgin
Legal Counsel:
Freehills
250 St Georges Terrace
Perth, Australia

BLIND CREEK RESOURCES LTD.

15th Floor - 675 West Hastings Street
Vancouver, BC, V6B 1N2, Canada
Tel.: (604) 669-6463
Fax: (604) 669-3041
Toll Free: (800) 663-9688
E-Mail: info@blindcreekresources.com
Web Site: www.blindcreekresources.com
BCK—(TSXV)
Int. Income: $6,955
Assets: $10,784,369
Liabilities: $824,516
Net Worth: $9,959,853
Earnings: ($841,702)
Fiscal Year-end: 11/30/12
Business Description:
Metal Mining Services
S.I.C.: 1099
N.A.I.C.S.: 212299
Personnel:
J. Frank Callaghan *(Pres & CEO)*
Board of Directors:
J. Frank Callaghan
Thomas John Kennedy
Andrew Hutchinson Rees
Legal Counsel:
Gowling Lafleur Henderson LLP
Suite 2300 550 Burrard St
Vancouver, BC, Canada
Transfer Agent:
Computershare Investor Services Inc.
2nd Fl 510 Burrard St
Vancouver, BC, Canada

BLINKX PLC

Third Floor 47-50 Margaret Street
London, W1W 8SB, United Kingdom
Tel.: (44) 203 551 4710
Fax: (44) 2035514738
Web Site: www.blinkx.com
BLNX—(LSE OTC)
Rev.: $197,957,000
Assets: $178,364,000
Liabilities: $33,373,000
Net Worth: $144,991,000
Earnings: $17,356,000
Emp.: 265
Fiscal Year-end: 03/31/13
Business Description:
Online Services
S.I.C.: 4899
N.A.I.C.S.: 517919
Personnel:
Suranga Chandratillake *(Founder & Chief Strategy Officer)*
Subhransu Brian Mukherjee *(CEO)*
Edward Reginelli *(CFO)*
Julia Blystone *(CMO)*
Matthew Scheybeler *(CTO)*
Frank Pao *(Chief Bus Officer)*
Dan Slivjanovski *(Sr VP-Mktg)*
Board of Directors:
Anthony J. Bettencourt, III
Suranga Chandratillake
Ujjal Kohli
Michael Lynch
Subhransu Brian Mukherjee
Mark Opzoomer
Judy Vezmar
Deloitte LLP
City House 126-130 Holly Road
Cambridge, CB2 1ZY, United Kingdom
Legal Counsel:
Bird & Bird LLP
15 Fetter Lane
EC4A 1JP London, United Kingdom

U.S. Subsidiaries:

blinkx, Inc. (1)
One Market Plz Spear Tower Ste 1810
San Francisco, CA 94105
Tel.: (415) 655-1450
Fax: (415) 243-9905
E-Mail: sales@blinkx.com
Web Site: www.blinkx.com
Emp.: 30
Video Search Engine
S.I.C.: 2741
N.A.I.C.S.: 519130
Subhransu Brian Mukherjee *(CEO)*
Edward Reginelli *(CFO)*
Julia Blystone *(CMO)*
Matthew Scheybeler *(CTO)*
Frank Pao *(Chief Bus Officer)*

Subsidiary:

Rhythm NewMedia, Inc. (2)
800 W El Camino Real Ste 100
Mountain View, CA 94040-2573
Tel.: (650) 961-9024
Fax: (650) 961-0174
E-Mail: info@rnmd.net
Web Site: www.rhythmnewmedia.com
Sales Range: $10-24.9 Million
Mobile Advertising Solutions
S.I.C.: 7319
N.A.I.C.S.: 541890
Ujjal Kohli *(CEO)*
Dave Pomeroy *(CFO)*
Jim Morris *(CTO)*
Marc Cousineau *(Sr VP-Engrg & Product)*

Burst Media Corporation (1)
8 New England Executive Pk
Burlington, MA 01803
Tel.: (781) 272-5544
Fax: (781) 852-5163
E-Mail: press@burstmedia.com
Web Site: www.burstmedia.com
Emp.: 150
Advertising Services
S.I.C.: 7311
N.A.I.C.S.: 541810
G. Jarvis Coffin, III *(Pres & CEO)*
Steven Hill *(CFO)*
Harry Klein *(COO)*
Chuck Moran *(CMO)*
David E. Stein *(CTO)*
Donald Byrnes *(Chief Revenue Officer)*
John Babcock *(Sr VP-Sls)*
Jessica Chaset *(Sr VP-Mobile Solutions)*

Non-U.S. Subsidiary:

Burst Media Corporation Ltd. (2)
Third Floor 47 50 Margaret Street
London, W1W 8SB, United Kingdom
Tel.: (44) 203 551 4710
Fax: (44) 203 551 5329
E-Mail: salesuk@burstmedia.com
Advertising Services
S.I.C.: 7311
N.A.I.C.S.: 541810
Ian Woolley *(Mng Dir)*

Prime Visibility Media Group, Inc. (1)
1305 Walt Whitman Rd Ste 120
Melville, NY 11747
Tel.: (631) 719-7400
Fax: (631) 719-7401
Toll Free: (866) 774-6381
Web Site: www.primevisibility.com
Sales Range: $25-49.9 Million
Emp.: 50
Digital Marketing Services
S.I.C.: 8742
N.A.I.C.S.: 541613
Sandra R. Demitroff *(Pres)*

Subsidiary:

AdOn Network, Inc. (2)
1275 W Washington Ste 205
Phoenix, AZ 85281
Tel.: (602) 265-5242
Fax: (602) 297-4219
Toll Free: (866) 258-9245
E-Mail: ClientService@AdOnNetwork.com
Web Site: www.adonnetwork.com
Emp.: 35
Advertising Services
S.I.C.: 7319
N.A.I.C.S.: 541890
Bhaskar Ballapragada *(Gen Mgr)*

BLIS TECHNOLOGIES LIMITED

10 Birch Street
PO Box 5804
Dunedin, 9058, New Zealand
Tel.: (64) 34741338
Fax: (64) 34749050
E-Mail: info@blis.co.nz
Web Site: www.blis.co.nz
BLT—(NZE)
Rev.: $971,757
Assets: $3,203,199
Liabilities: $282,069
Net Worth: $2,921,130
Earnings: ($1,553,472)
Emp.: 11
Fiscal Year-end: 03/31/13
Business Description:
Healthcare Product Mfr
S.I.C.: 2834
N.A.I.C.S.: 325412
Personnel:
Peter Francis Fennessy *(Chm)*
Barry C. Richardson *(CEO)*
Mukesh Kumar *(Sec)*
Board of Directors:
Peter Francis Fennessy
Colin Ernest Dawson
Alan McKenzie
Anthony P. Offen
Bevan Hugh Wallace
Legal Counsel:
Anderson Lloyd
PO Box 1959
Dunedin, 9054, New Zealand

BLISS GVS PHARMA LTD.

102 Hyde Park Sakivihar Road
Andheri East
Mumbai, 400 072, India
Tel.: (91) 2242160000
Fax: (91) 2228563930
E-Mail: info@blissgvs.com
Web Site: www.blissgvspharma.com
BLISSGVS—(NSE)
Rev.: $76,142,890
Assets: $108,482,509
Liabilities: $58,089,992
Net Worth: $50,392,517
Earnings: $11,046,985
Fiscal Year-end: 03/31/13
Business Description:
Pharmaceutical Products Mfr
S.I.C.: 2834
N.A.I.C.S.: 325412
Personnel:
Govind G. Desai *(Chm)*
Shibroor N. Kamath *(Mng Dir)*
Sushma Yadav *(Sec)*
Board of Directors:
Govind G. Desai
Gautam R. Ashra
Shibroor N. Kamath
Shruti N. Kamath
Vibha N. Kamath
Mayank S. Mehta
S. R. Vaidya
Transfer Agent:
Universal Capital Securities Pvt. Ltd
21 Shakil Niwas Opp.Satya Saibaba Temple
Mahakali Caves Road Andheri
Mumbai, India

B.L.L. HOLDINGS LTD

(d/b/a British Loose Leaf)
8 Veridion Way
Erith, DA18 4AL, United Kingdom
Tel.: (44) 44 13 2252 6262
Fax: (44) 13 2255 8624
E-Mail: sales@bll.co.uk
Web Site: www.bll.co.uk
Emp.: 55
Business Description:
Presentation & Marketing Products Mfr
S.I.C.: 5112
N.A.I.C.S.: 424120
Personnel:
Jonathan Levy *(Mng Dir & Co-Owner)*

Subsidiary:

W.E. Baxter Limited (1)
8 Veridion Way
Erith, Kent, DA18 4AL, United Kingdom
Tel.: (44) 2086851234
Fax: (44) 2086402781
E-Mail: baxter_sales@we-baxter.co.uk
Web Site: www.we-baxter.co.uk
Emp.: 50
Ring Binder Printer Services

B.L.L. Holdings Ltd—(Continued)

S.I.C.: 2759
N.A.I.C.S.: 323111
Jonathamn Leby *(Mng Dir)*

THE BLM GROUP, INC.

120 McBrine Dr
Kitchener, ON, N2R1E7, Canada
Tel.: (519) 748-9880
Fax: (519) 748-2271
Toll Free: (800) 265-2743
E-Mail: information@blm.com
Web Site: www.blm.com
Year Founded: 1984
Sales Range: $50-74.9 Million
Emp.: 400

Business Description:
Freight Services
S.I.C.: 4213
N.A.I.C.S.: 484121

Personnel:
James D McConnell *(Pres)*

BLOCK SOLUTIONS LTD.

14 Shepherdess Walk
London, N1 7LB, United Kingdom
Tel.: (44) 84 4967 1646
Fax: (44) 84 4967 1642
E-Mail: info@block-solutions.net
Web Site: www.block-solutions.net
Year Founded: 2006
Sales Range: $10-24.9 Million
Emp.: 75

Business Description:
IT Consulting Services
S.I.C.: 7373
N.A.I.C.S.: 541512

Personnel:
Jon Pickering *(Co-Founder & Mng Dir)*
Marc Chang *(Co-Founder & Dir-Tech)*

BLOM ASA

Drammensveien 165
PO Box 34 Skoyen
0212 Oslo, Norway
Tel.: (47) 23254500
Fax: (47) 22131921
E-Mail: blom.no@blomasa.com
Web Site: www.blomasa.com
BLO—(OSL)
Rev.: $60,670,744
Assets: $77,115,314
Liabilities: $69,168,224
Net Worth: $7,947,090
Earnings: ($12,058,821)
Emp.: 585
Fiscal Year-end: 12/31/12

Business Description:
Geographic Information Services
S.I.C.: 8713
N.A.I.C.S.: 541370

Personnel:
Tom Knoff *(Chm)*
Dirk Blaauw *(CEO)*
Andreas Holter *(Mng Dir)*
Lars Bakklund *(CFO)*
Nils A. Karbo *(CTO)*

Board of Directors:
Tom Knoff
Olav Fjell
Ingvild Myhre
Siv Sandvik

Subsidiaries:

Blom Data AS (1)
Postboks 34
Skoyen, 0212 Oslo, Norway
Tel.: (47) 22131920
Fax: (47) 22131921
E-Mail: blom.no@blomasa.com
Emp.: 60
Geophysical Surveying Services
S.I.C.: 8713
N.A.I.C.S.: 541360
Dirk Blaauw *(Gen Mgr)*

Blom Geomatics AS (1)
PB 34
Skoyen, 0212 Oslo, Norway
Tel.: (47) 23254500
Fax: (47) 23 25 45 01
E-Mail: info.no@blomasa.com
Emp.: 50
Geospatial Mapping Services
S.I.C.: 8713
N.A.I.C.S.: 541370
Andreas Holter *(CEO)*

Non-U.S. Subsidiaries:

Blom Aerofilms Ltd. (1)
The Astrolabe Cheddar Business Park
Wedmore Road
Cheddar, Somerset, BS27 3EB, United Kingdom
Tel.: (44) 1934311000
E-Mail: info.uk@blomasa.com
Web Site: www.blomaerofilms.com
Emp.: 45
Geophysical Surveying Services
S.I.C.: 8713
N.A.I.C.S.: 541360
Paul Crisp *(Dir-Production)*

Blom CGR S.p.A. (1)
Via Cremonese 35/A
43100 Parma, Italy
Tel.: (39) 521994948
Fax: (39) 0521 992803
E-Mail: info.it@blomasa.com
Emp.: 150
Aircraft Maintenance & Aerial Surveying Services
S.I.C.: 4581
N.A.I.C.S.: 488190
Giovanni Banchini *(Pres & CEO)*
Renato They *(CFO)*
Luigi Lingesso *(COO)*
Armando Cavazzini *(CTO)*

Blom Czech Republic (1)
Olomoucka 1158/164A
627 00 Brno, Czech Republic
Tel.: (420) 513033050
Fax: (420) 226013895
E-Mail: info.cz@blomasa.com
Web Site: www.blom.com
Emp.: 5
Geophysical Surveying Services
S.I.C.: 8713
N.A.I.C.S.: 541360

Blom Deutschland GmbH (1)
Oscar-Frech-Strase 15
73614 Schorndorf, Baden-Wurttemberg, Germany
Tel.: (49) 7181980210
Fax: (49) 71819802129
E-Mail: info.de@blomasa.com
Web Site: www.blom.no
Emp.: 50
Aerial Photography & Digital Mapping Services
S.I.C.: 8713
N.A.I.C.S.: 541370
Werner Mayr *(Co-Mng Dir)*
Ralf Schroth *(Co-Mng Dir)*

Blom Kartta Oy (1)
Pasilanraitio 5
00240 Helsinki, Finland
Tel.: (358) 92293060
Fax: (358) 922930657
E-Mail: info.fi@blomasa.com
Web Site: www.blom.no
Emp.: 27
Aerial Photography & Digital Mapping Services
S.I.C.: 8713
N.A.I.C.S.: 541360
Hakon Andresen *(Mng Dir)*

Blom Portugal Lda. (1)
Av do Forte N 8 Edificio Pujol Fraccao K
2795 503 Carnaxide, Portugal
Tel.: (351) 214253830
Fax: (351) 214253839
E-Mail: info@blom.pt
Geophysical Surveying Services
S.I.C.: 8713
N.A.I.C.S.: 541360

Blom Romania S.R.L. (1)
IH Radulescu Street No 3-5
Targoviste, Dambovita, 130010, Romania
Tel.: (40) 245606150
Fax: (40) 245210852
E-Mail: office@blom.ro
Web Site: www.blom.ro
Emp.: 60
Geophysical Surveying Services
S.I.C.: 8713
N.A.I.C.S.: 541360
Silviu Stoica *(Gen Mgr)*

Blom Sistemas Geoespaciales S.L.U. (1)
C / Zurbano 46
28010 Madrid, Spain
Tel.: (34) 912106700
Fax: (34) 913 104 914
E-Mail: info.spain@blomasa.com
Web Site: www.blom.es/offices-es/office s/blom-spain.html
Geographic Information Services
S.I.C.: 8713
N.A.I.C.S.: 541360
Dirk Blaauw *(Pres)*

Blom SWE AB (1)
Hammarbacken 6B
191 49 Sollentuna, Stockholm, Sweden
Tel.: (46) 857824700
Fax: (46) 857824701
E-Mail: info@blomswe.com
Web Site: www.blom.com
Emp.: 14
Geophysical Surveying Services
S.I.C.: 8713
N.A.I.C.S.: 541360
Henrik Quist *(Mgr-HR)*

Blom Sweden AB (1)
Klippan 1J
414 51 Gothenburg, Sweden
Tel.: (46) 317045670
Fax: (46) 317049980
E-Mail: info.se@blomasa.com
Web Site: www.topeye.com
Emp.: 25
Geographic Information System Mapping Services
S.I.C.: 8713
N.A.I.C.S.: 541370
Hakan Sterner *(CEO)*

BlomInfo A/S (1)
Masnedoegade 20
2100 Copenhagen, Denmark
Tel.: (45) 70200226
Fax: (45) 70200227
E-Mail: blom.dk@blomasa.com
Web Site: www.blominfo.dk
Emp.: 50
Geographic Information System Mapping Services
S.I.C.: 8713
N.A.I.C.S.: 541360
Peter Normann Hansen *(Co-Mng Dir)*
Kristian Skak-Nielsen *(Co-Mng Dir)*

Compagnia Aeronautica Emiliana S.r.l. (1)
Via Cremonese 35/a
43126 Parma, Italy
Tel.: (39) 0521982261
Fax: (39) 0521 292782
E-Mail: info@caeitalia.com
Web Site: www.caeitalia.com
Aircraft & Parts Distr
S.I.C.: 5088
N.A.I.C.S.: 423860
Giovanni Banchini *(Pres)*

LTD BlomInfo Ukraine (1)
43 Demiivska Str
Kiev, Ukraine
Tel.: (380) 444675622
Fax: (380) 444675622
E-Mail: blominfo@blominfo-ukraine.com.ua
Web Site: www.blominfo-ukraine.com.ua
Geophysical Surveying Services
S.I.C.: 8713
N.A.I.C.S.: 541360

PT. Blom Nusantara (1)
CCSL Building 8th Floor Suite 8004 Jl Asia Afrika No 133-137
Bandung, West Java, 40112, Indonesia
Tel.: (62) 224221985
Fax: (62) 224221986
E-Mail: blom_nus@blom.co.id
Web Site: www.blom.co.id
Geophysical Mapping Services
S.I.C.: 8713
N.A.I.C.S.: 541360
Vilia J. Djalimun *(Sec)*

BLOM BANK, S.A.L.

Verdun Rachid Karami St BLOM Bank Building
PO Box 11-1912
Beirut, 1107 2807, Lebanon
Tel.: (961) 1743300
Telex: 94015829
Fax: (961) 1738946
E-Mail: blommail@blom.com.lb
Web Site: www.blom.com.lb
Year Founded: 1951
BLOM—(BEY)
Rev.: $1,265,324,459
Assets: $24,547,004,300
Liabilities: $22,409,149,100
Net Worth: $2,137,855,200
Earnings: $329,167,800
Emp.: 4,414
Fiscal Year-end: 12/31/12

Business Description:
Banking Services
S.I.C.: 6029
N.A.I.C.S.: 522110

Personnel:
Saad Azhari *(Chm & Gen Mgr)*
Talal A. Baba *(CFO & Asst Gen Mgr-Fin)*
Samer Azhari *(Gen Sec)*

Board of Directors:
Saad Azhari
Samer Azhari
Marwan Jaroudi
Joseph Emile Kharrat
Fadi Osseiran
Habib Rahal
Nicolas Nicolas Saade
Ghassan Ibrahim Shaker
Youssef Selim Takla

BDO Semaan Gholam & Co
Gholam Building Sioufi Street
Beirut, Lebanon

Subsidiaries:

Arope Insurance SAL (1)
PO Box 113-5686
Beirut, Lebanon (88.56%)
Tel.: (961) 1747444
Fax: (961) 1344012
E-Mail: arope@arope.com
Web Site: www.arope.com
Direct Property & Casualty Insurance Carriers
S.I.C.: 6351
N.A.I.C.S.: 524126
Fateh Bekdache *(Gen Mgr)*

BlomInvest Bank SAL (1)
Rachid Karameh St
2nd Fl Blk A Blom Banks Bldg, Beirut, Lebanon (99.88%)
Tel.: (961) 1743300
Fax: (961) 1738916
Web Site: www.blominvestement.com
Commercial Banking
S.I.C.: 6029
N.A.I.C.S.: 522110
Fadi Usayran *(Gen Mgr)*

Non-U.S. Subsidiaries:

BLOM Bank France S.A. (1)
38-40 Ave des Champs Elysees
75008 Paris, France (99.99%)
Tel.: (33) 144950606
Fax: (33) 144950600
E-Mail: blomfrance@blomfrance.fr
Web Site: www.blombankfrance.com
Emp.: 40
Commercial Banking
S.I.C.: 6029
N.A.I.C.S.: 522110
Samer Azhari *(Chm & Gen Mgr)*

BLOM Bank (Switzerland) S.A. (1)
1 rue de la Rotisserie
PO Box 3040
1211 Geneva, 3, Switzerland (100%)
Tel.: (41) 228177100

Fax: (41) 228177190
E-Mail: info@blombank.ch
Web Site: www.blombank.ch
Emp.: 21
Commercial Banking
S.I.C.: 6029
N.A.I.C.S.: 522110
Saad Azhari *(Pres)*

BLOOM & WAKE LTD

130 Wisbech Road Outwell
Wisbech, Cambs, PE14 8PF, United Kingdom
Tel.: (44) 1945772578
Fax: (44) 1945773135
E-Mail: enquiries@bloomandwake.co.uk
Web Site: www.bloomandwake.co.uk
Year Founded: 1969
Sales Range: $10-24.9 Million
Emp.: 68
Fiscal Year-end: 02/28/13
Business Description:
Electrical Contracting Services
S.I.C.: 1731
N.A.I.C.S.: 238210
Personnel:
John Wake *(Co-Founder)*

BLOOM DEKOR LIMITED

2/F Sumel SG Highway
Thaltej, Ahmedabad, Gujarat, 380 059, India
Tel.: (91) 79 26841916
Fax: (91) 79 2684 1914
Web Site: www.bloomdekor.com
Year Founded: 1994
526225—(BOM)
Rev.: $13,088,276
Assets: $10,738,340
Liabilities: $7,341,400
Net Worth: $3,396,939
Earnings: $203,255
Fiscal Year-end: 03/31/13
Business Description:
Decorative Laminates Mfr & Distr
S.I.C.: 3083
N.A.I.C.S.: 326130
Personnel:
Sunil Gupta *(Chm & Mng Dir)*
Rajkumar Chaudhary *(Compliance Officer)*
Board of Directors:
Sunil Gupta
Karan Gupta
Rupal Gupta
Chirag Mehta
Mayur Parikh
Transfer Agent:
Purva Sharegistry India Pvt. Ltd
9 shiv Shakti Ind JR Boricha Marg Lower Parel (East)
Mumbai, 400 011, India
Tel.: (91) 22 2301 6761
Fax: (91) 22 2301 2517

BLOOM INCOME & GROWTH CANADIAN FUND

150 York Street Suite 1710
Toronto, ON, M5H 3S5, Canada
Tel.: (416) 861-9941
Fax: (416) 861-9943
E-Mail: Paul@bloominvestmentcounsel.com
Year Founded: 2011
BI.UN—(TSX)
Business Description:
Investment Services
S.I.C.: 6211
N.A.I.C.S.: 523999
Personnel:
M. Paul Bloom *(Chm, Pres & Sec)*
Fiona E. Mitra *(CFO)*
Board of Directors:
M. Paul Bloom
Adina Bloom Somer
Beverley Lyons
Transfer Agent:
CIBC Mellon Trust Company
PO Box 7010
Adelaide Street Postal Station, Toronto, ON, M5C 2W9, Canada
Tel.: (416) 643-5500
Fax: (416) 643-5501
Toll Free: (800) 387-0825

BLOOM INDUSTRIES LIMITED

C-23/2 M I D C Taloja
Mahad, Maharashtra, 410 208, India
Tel.: (91) 22 27411224
Fax: (91) 22 67047747
E-Mail: bloom1989@ymail.com
Web Site: www.bloom-industries.com
Year Founded: 1989
513422—(BOM)
Rev.: $103,487
Assets: $848,805
Liabilities: $44,316
Net Worth: $804,489
Earnings: $12,908
Fiscal Year-end: 03/31/13
Business Description:
Iron & Steel Whslr
S.I.C.: 5051
N.A.I.C.S.: 423510
Personnel:
Kamal Kumar Chaudhary *(Chm)*
Sharad Kumar Gupta *(CEO)*
Rajesh Kumar Nagori *(Compliance Officer)*
Board of Directors:
Kamal Kumar Chaudhary
Ashish Chaudhary
Sharad Kumar Gupta
Vinod Kumar Jakhoria
Rohit Lohia
Rajesh Kumar Nagori
Transfer Agent:
Purva Sharegistry (India) Private Limited
9 Shiv Shakti Industrial Estate Ground Floor Sitaram Mill Compound
J R Boricha Marg Lower Parel, Mumbai, 400 011, India

BLOOM SELECT INCOME FUND

150 York Street Suite 1710
Toronto, ON, M5H 3S5, Canada
Tel.: (416) 861-9941
Fax: (416) 861-9943
E-Mail: paul@bloominvestmentcounsel.com
BLB.UN—(TSX)
Business Description:
Investment Services
S.I.C.: 6211
N.A.I.C.S.: 523999
Personnel:
M. Paul Bloom *(Chm, Pres & Sec)*
Fiona E. Mitra *(CFO)*
Board of Directors:
M. Paul Bloom
Adina Bloom Somer
Beverley Lyons

BLOOMAGE BIOTECHNOLOGY CORPORATION LIMITED

No 678 Tianchen Street High-Tech Development Zone
Jinan, Shandong, China
Tel.: (86) 531 82685886
Fax: (86) 531 82685888
Web Site: www.bloomagebio-tech.com
Year Founded: 2006
0963—(HKG)
Sls.: $43,678,349
Assets: $75,335,566
Liabilities: $15,453,881
Net Worth: $59,881,685
Earnings: $14,180,540
Emp.: 382
Fiscal Year-end: 12/31/12
Business Description:
Hyaluronic Acid Producer & Sales
S.I.C.: 2899
N.A.I.C.S.: 325998
Personnel:
Yan Zhao *(Chm)*
Aihua Liu *(CEO)*
Ping Kwan Loong *(Sec)*
Board of Directors:
Yan Zhao
Jiajun Guo
Wen Hai
Xuekun Jin
Junhong Li
Aihua Liu
Aihua Wang
Lili Zhan
Legal Counsel:
Loong & Yeung
Suites 2001 2005 20/F Jardine House
1 Connaught Place, Central, China (Hong Kong)

HSBC Trustee (Cayman) Limited
HSBC House 68 West Bay Road
PO Box 484
Georgetown, Grand Cayman, Cayman Islands
Transfer Agents:
Tricor Investor Services Limited
26th Floor Tesbury Centre 28 Queens Road East
Wanchai, China (Hong Kong)

HSBC Trustee (Cayman) Limited
HSBC House 68 West Bay Road
PO Box 484
Georgetown, Grand Cayman, Cayman Islands

BLOOMSBURY PUBLISHING PLC

50 Bedford Square
London, WC1B 3DP, United Kingdom
Tel.: (44) 20 7631 5600
Fax: (44) 20 7631 5800
E-Mail: contact@bloomsbury.com
Web Site: www.bloomsbury.com
BMY—(LSE)
Rev.: $155,526,900
Assets: $243,262,777
Liabilities: $61,947,650
Net Worth: $181,315,126
Earnings: $11,790,979
Emp.: 483
Fiscal Year-end: 02/28/13
Business Description:
Magazine & Book Publisher
S.I.C.: 2731
N.A.I.C.S.: 511130
Personnel:
Nigel Newton *(Founder & CEO)*
Anthony Salz *(Chm)*
Kevin Perry *(CTO)*
Michael Daykin *(Sec)*
Diya Kar Hazra *(Publr-Trade-India)*
Board of Directors:
Anthony Salz
Richard Charkin
Ian Cormack
Jill Jones
Nigel Newton
Stephen Page
Wendy Pallot
Legal Counsel:
Steinfeld Law
22 Manchester Square
London, United Kingdom

Reynolds Porter Chamberlain LLP
Tower Bridge House St Katherines Way
London, United Kingdom
Subsidiaries:

A&C Black Publishers Ltd. **(1)**
Alderman House 36 Soho Sq
London, W1D 3QY, United Kingdom (100%)
Tel.: (44) 2077580200
E-Mail: customerservices@acblack.com
Web Site: www.acblack.com
Book Publishers
S.I.C.: 2731
N.A.I.C.S.: 511130
Jonathan Glasspool *(Deputy Mng Dir)*

Berg Fashion Library Limited **(1)**
Oxford University Press Great Clarendon Street
Oxford, OX2 6DP, United Kingdom
Tel.: (44) 1865 353705
Fax: (44) 1865 353308
E-Mail: onlinesubscriptions@oup.com
Web Site: www.bergfashionlibrary.com
Emp.: 5,000
Online Portal Services
S.I.C.: 2741
N.A.I.C.S.: 519130
Valerie Cumming *(Chm)*

Bloomsbury Book Publishing Company Limited **(1)**
36 Soho Sq
W1D 3QY London, United Kingdom (100%)
Tel.: (44) 2074942111
Fax: (44) 2074340151
Web Site: www.bloomsbury-ir.co.uk/
Book Publishers
S.I.C.: 2731
N.A.I.C.S.: 511130

Bloomsbury Information Limited **(1)**
36 Soho Square
London, W1D 3QY, United Kingdom
Tel.: (44) 2074942111
E-Mail: qfinance1@bloomsbury.com
Web Site: www.qfinancebooks.com
Book Publishing Services
S.I.C.: 2731
N.A.I.C.S.: 511130

Bloomsbury Professional Limited **(1)**
41-43 Boltro Road
Haywards Heath, West Sussex, RH16 1BJ, United Kingdom
Tel.: (44) 1444 416119
Fax: (44) 1444 440426
E-Mail: customerservices@bloomsburyprofessional.com
Web Site: www.bloomsburyprofessional.com
Emp.: 25
Book Publishing Services
S.I.C.: 2731
N.A.I.C.S.: 511130
Martin Casimir *(Mng Dir)*

Methuen Drama Limited **(1)**
215 Vauxhall Bridge Rd
London, United Kingdom (100%)
Tel.: (44) 2078282838
Web Site: www.methuen.co.uk/publicity.html
Book Publishers
S.I.C.: 2731
N.A.I.C.S.: 511130
Peter Tummons *(Mng Dir)*

Peter Collin Publishing Limited **(1)**
36 Soho Square
London, W1D 3QY, United Kingdom (100%)
Tel.: (44) 2074942111
Fax: (44) 2074340151
E-Mail: reception@bloomsbury.com
Emp.: 60
Book Publishers
S.I.C.: 2731
N.A.I.C.S.: 511130
Nigel Newton *(Mng Dir)*

Reeds Nautical Almanac **(1)**
Adlard Coles Nautical 36 Soho Square
London, W1D 3QY, United Kingdom (100%)
Tel.: (44) 2074942111
Fax: (44) 2074390867
Web Site: www.reedsnauticalalmanac.co.uk
Book Publishers of Navigational Information
S.I.C.: 2731
N.A.I.C.S.: 511130
Andrew Du Port *(Editor)*

Non-U.S. Subsidiaries:

Bloomsbury Publishing Pty Ltd. **(1)**
Level 14 309 Kent St
Sydney, NSW, 2000, Australia
Tel.: (61) 2 9994 8969
Web Site: www.bloomsburyanz.com
Book Publishing Services
S.I.C.: 2731

Bloomsbury Publishing Plc—(Continued)

N.A.I.C.S.: 511130

BV Berlin Verlag GmbH (1)
Greifswalder Strasse 207
Berlin, 10405, Germany (100%)
Tel.: (49) 304438450
Fax: (49) 3044384595
E-Mail: info@berlinverlag.de
Web Site: www.berlinverlag.de
Emp.: 55
Book Publishers
S.I.C.: 2731
N.A.I.C.S.: 511130
Nigel Newton *(Mng Dir)*
Kathy Rooney *(Mng Dir)*

Bvt Berliner Taschenbuch Verlag GmbH (1)
Greifswalder Strasse 207
10405 Berlin, Germany (100%)
Tel.: (49) 304438450
Fax: (49) 3044384595
E-Mail: info@berlinverlag.de
Web Site: www.berlinverlag.de
Emp.: 50
Book Publishers
S.I.C.: 2731
N.A.I.C.S.: 511130
Philip Roeder *(Mgr)*

BLOWTHERM S.P.A.

Via G Reni 5
35134 Padua, Italy
Tel.: (39) 049601600
Fax: (39) 0498644915
E-Mail: info@blowtherm.com
Web Site: www.blowtherm.it
Emp.: 100
Business Description:
Mfr. of Spray Booths for Automotive Refinishing & Heating Systems
S.I.C.: 3542
N.A.I.C.S.: 333517

BLOX, INC.

(Formerly NAVA RESOURCES, INC.)
Suite 206 - 595 Howe Street
Vancouver, BC, V6C 2T5, Canada
Tel.: (778) 218-9638
Web Site: www.navaresources.com
Year Founded: 2005
BLXX—(OTCB)
Int. Income: $1
Assets: $21,189
Liabilities: $79,985
Net Worth: ($58,796)
Earnings: ($78,412)
Emp.: 1
Fiscal Year-end: 06/30/13
Business Description:
Mineral Exploration Services
S.I.C.: 1081
N.A.I.C.S.: 213114
Personnel:
Ronald Renne *(Pres & CEO)*

BLP TRAINING & SERVICES PTY. LTD.

(d/b/a BLP Group of Companies)
Building 9 The Construction Training Centre
460-492 Beaudesert Road, Salisbury, QLD, 4107, Australia
Mailing Address:
PO Box 392
Salisbury, QLD, 4107, Australia
Tel.: (61) 732768947
Fax: (61) 732768946
Web Site: www.blpts.com.au
Sales Range: $10-24.9 Million
Emp.: 5
Business Description:
Security Training & Equipment Supply Services
S.I.C.: 8299
N.A.I.C.S.: 611430
Personnel:
Darren McDonald *(Gen Mgr & Mgr-Munitions)*

BLRT GRUPP AS

Kopli 103
11712 Tallinn, Estonia
Tel.: (372) 6102408
Fax: (372) 6102999
E-Mail: blrt@blrt.ee
Web Site: www.blrt.ee
Sales Range: $350-399.9 Million
Emp.: 4,000
Fiscal Year-end: 12/31/12
Business Description:
Ship Building & Repair Services
S.I.C.: 3731
N.A.I.C.S.: 336611
Personnel:
Fjodor Berman *(Chm)*

Joint Venture:

MacGregor BLRT Baltic OU (1)
103 Kopli Str
11712 Tallinn, Estonia
Tel.: (372) 6102200
Fax: (372) 6 102 400
Cargo Handling Services
S.I.C.: 4491
N.A.I.C.S.: 488320

BLUE BLENDS FINANCE LIMITED

JBF House 2nd Floor Old Post Office Lane Kalbadevi Road
Mumbai, 400 002, India
Tel.: (91) 22 22088736
Fax: (91) 22 22080470
E-Mail: blueblends@yahoo.com
Web Site: www.blueblendsfinance.com
Year Founded: 1985
511361—(BOM)
Business Description:
Financial Management Services
S.I.C.: 6211
N.A.I.C.S.: 523999
Personnel:
Anand Arya *(Chm)*
Remedias Pinto *(Compliance officer)*
Board of Directors:
Anand Arya
Vijay Kumar Bothra
Janardan Joshi
Remedias Pinto
Pujaram Purohit
Transfer Agent:
Sharex Dynamic (India) Pvt. Ltd.
Unit-1 Luthra Ind Premises Safed Pool Andheri Kurla Rd Andheri (E)
Mumbai, India

BLUE BLENDS (INDIA) LIMITED

2nd Floor JBF House Old Post Office Lane Kalbadevi Road
Mumbai, 400 002, India
Tel.: (91) 22 22088736
Fax: (91) 22 22080470
E-Mail: blueblends@vsnl.net
Web Site: www.blueblends.com
Year Founded: 1995
502761—(BOM)
Rev.: $31,623,210
Assets: $19,960,096
Liabilities: $12,757,337
Net Worth: $7,202,759
Earnings: $3,894,153
Fiscal Year-end: 03/31/13
Business Description:
Yarn & Denim Fabric Mfr
S.I.C.: 2299
N.A.I.C.S.: 313210
Personnel:
Anand Arya *(Chm & Mng Dir)*
Suraj Dugar *(CFO & Compliance Officer)*
Board of Directors:
Anand Arya
Suraj Dugar
K. Parthasarthy
Pujaram Purohit
Shabbir K. Tambawalla
Transfer Agent:
Purva Shareregistry (India) Private Limited
9 Shiv Shakti Industrial Estate JR Boricha Marg Off NM Joshi Marg
Near Lodha Excelus Lower Parel East, Mumbai, India

BLUE CAPITAL REINSURANCE HOLDINGS LTD.

94 Pitts Bay Road
Pembroke, HM 08, Bermuda
Mailing Address:
PO Box HM 2079
Pembroke, HM HX, Bermuda
Tel.: (441) 278 5004
Fax: (441) 296 5551
E-Mail: info@bcapre.bm
Web Site: www.bcapre.bm
Year Founded: 2013
BCRH—(NYSE)
Business Description:
Insurance Holding Company
S.I.C.: 6719
N.A.I.C.S.: 551112
Personnel:
Christopher L. Harris *(Chm)*
William Pollett *(Pres & CEO)*
Michael S. Paquette *(CFO)*
Board of Directors:
Christopher L. Harris
D. Andrew Cook
Eric Lemieux
William Pollett
John R. Weale

BLUE CHIP INDIA LTD.

10 Princep Street 2nd Floor
Kolkata, 700 072, India
Tel.: (91) 33 22256851
Fax: (91) 33 2237 9053
E-Mail: info@bluechipindia.net
Web Site: www.bluechipind.net
531936—(BOM)
Rev.: $6,274,917
Assets: $1,755,650
Liabilities: $1,525,800
Net Worth: $229,851
Earnings: $28,099
Fiscal Year-end: 03/31/13
Business Description:
Financial Fund Management Services
S.I.C.: 6799
N.A.I.C.S.: 523920
Personnel:
Arihant Jain *(Mng Dir)*
Jyoti Gupta *(Compliance Officer & Sec)*
Board of Directors:
Amiya Kumar Basu
Pranab Chakraborty
Arihant Jain
Subhabrata Talukdar
Transfer Agent:
Maheshwari Datamatics Pvt. Ltd
6 Mangoe Lane 1st Floor
Kolkata, India

BLUE CHIP TEX INDUSTRIES LTD.

10 Jasville 2nd Floor Opp Liberty Cinema 9 New Marine Lines
Mumbai, 400020, India
Tel.: (91) 22 22000488
Fax: (91) 22 22006437
E-Mail: bluechiptex@gmail.com
Web Site: www.bluechiptexindustrieslimited.com
506981—(BOM)
Sales Range: $1-9.9 Million
Business Description:
Textile Products Mfr
S.I.C.: 2269
N.A.I.C.S.: 313310
Personnel:
Nand Khemani *(Mng Dir)*
Ranjit Chawdhery *(Compliance Officer)*
Board of Directors:
Ashok Khemani
Nand Khemani
Rahul Khemani
Shahin Khemani
Anil Kuamar Mandhana
Kumar Nathani

BLUE CIRCLE SERVICES LIMITED

Office No 33 Basement Mona Shopping Centre JP Road
Andheri W, Mumbai, 400 058, India
Tel.: (91) 22 65341911
Fax: (91) 22 26773832
E-Mail: blue.circl@gmail.com
Web Site: www.bluecirclelimited.com
Year Founded: 1983
508939—(BOM)
Rev.: $6,949,140
Assets: $12,068,078
Liabilities: $6,951,747
Net Worth: $5,116,331
Earnings: $228,415
Emp.: 14
Fiscal Year-end: 03/31/13
Business Description:
Financial Advisory Services
S.I.C.: 6282
N.A.I.C.S.: 523930
Personnel:
Anil Kumar Purohit *(Chm & Mng Dir)*
Pravin Sawant *(Compliance Officer)*
Board of Directors:
Anil Kumar Purohit
Kashi Prasad Bajaj
Dhruva Narayan Jha
Chandresh N. Shah
Transfer Agent:
Purva Sharegistry (India) Pvt. Ltd.
No 9 Shiv Shakti Ind. Estate Ground Fl J. R. Boricha Marg Lower Parel
Mumbai, India

BLUE COAST HOTELS LIMITED

415-417 Antriksh Bhawan 22 Kasturba Gandhi Marg
New Delhi, 110001, India
Tel.: (91) 11 23358774
Fax: (91) 11 23358776
Web Site: www.bluecoast.in
531495—(BOM)
Rev.: $18,258,581
Assets: $123,990,792
Liabilities: $80,674,326
Net Worth: $43,316,467
Earnings: ($1,411,840)
Emp.: 605
Fiscal Year-end: 03/31/13
Business Description:
Hotel Management Services
S.I.C.: 7011
N.A.I.C.S.: 721110
Personnel:
P. L. Suri *(Chm & Mng Dir)*
Suresh Gupta *(CFO & Asst VP-Fin & Accts)*
Rajesh Sharma *(Sec)*
Board of Directors:
P. L. Suri

Vijay Mohan Kaul
Ashoka Kini
Mamta Suri
Sunita Suri
Transfer Agent:
RCMC Share Registry Pvt. Ltd.
B-106 Sector-2
Noida, India

BLUE COLIBRI AG
Arnulfstrasse 58
80335 Munich, Germany
Tel.: (49) 89 3090 9690
E-Mail: welcome@bluecolibri.de
Web Site: www.bluecolibri.de
Year Founded: 2006
Business Description:
Commercial Real Estate Investment & Portfolio Management
S.I.C.: 6531
N.A.I.C.S.: 531390
Personnel:
Andreas Reinert *(CEO)*

BLUE-CON CONSTRUCTION
1915 Crumlin Side Road
London, ON, N5V 3B8, Canada
Tel.: (519) 659-2400
Web Site: www.bluecon.on.ca
Year Founded: 1976
Rev.: $10,607,284
Emp.: 60
Business Description:
Construction Services
S.I.C.: 1629
N.A.I.C.S.: 237990
Personnel:
Joe Haasen *(CEO)*
Michael E. Turek *(COO)*

BLUE DART EXPRESS LIMITED
Blue Dart Center Sahar Airport Road
Andheri East
Mumbai, 400099, India
Tel.: (91) 2228396444
Fax: (91) 2228244131
Web Site: www.bluedart.com
526612—(BOM NSE)
Rev.: $410,049,180
Assets: $194,805,342
Liabilities: $72,458,028
Net Worth: $122,347,314
Earnings: $35,357,634
Emp.: 8,390
Fiscal Year-end: 03/31/13
Business Description:
Trucking & Courier Services
S.I.C.: 4731
N.A.I.C.S.: 488510
Personnel:
Sharad Upasani *(Chm)*
Anil Khanna *(Mng Dir)*
Yogesh Dhingra *(COO & Dir-Fin)*
Tushar Gunderia *(Compliance Officer, Sec & Head-Legal & Compliance)*
Board of Directors:
Sharad Upasani
Clyde Cooper
Jerry Hsu
Anil Khanna
Suresh G. Sheth
Transfer Agent:
Link Intime India Private Limited
C-13 Pannalal Silk Mills Compound L.B.S. Marg Bhandup
Mumbai, India

BLUE ENERGY LIMITED
Level 3 410 Queen Street
PO Box 10261
Adelaide Street, Brisbane, 4000, Australia
Tel.: (61) 7 3270 8800
Fax: (61) 8 3270 8899
E-Mail: info@blueenergy.com.au
Web Site: www.blueenergy.com.au
BUL—(ASX)
Rev.: $978,532
Assets: $78,304,436
Liabilities: $1,725,718
Net Worth: $76,578,719
Earnings: ($13,522,290)
Fiscal Year-end: 06/30/13
Business Description:
Oil & Gas Exploration
S.I.C.: 1311
N.A.I.C.S.: 211111
Personnel:
John C. Ellice-Flint *(Chm)*
John Phillips *(CEO & Mng Dir)*
Stuart Owen *(CFO & Sec)*
Board of Directors:
John C. Ellice-Flint
Rodney Cameron
Karen Johnson
Jooho Maeng
John Phillips

BLUE ENSIGN TECHNOLOGIES LIMITED
Ste 202 Angela House 30-36 Bay Street
Double Bay, NSW, 2028, Australia
Tel.: (61) 2 9363 5088
Fax: (61) 2 9363 5488
E-Mail: heather@blueensigntech.com.au
Web Site: www.blueensigntech.com.au
Business Description:
Oil & Minerals Producer
S.I.C.: 1311
N.A.I.C.S.: 211111
Personnel:
John Blumer *(Chm)*
Darryl Smith *(CEO)*
Grahame Clegg *(Sec)*
Board of Directors:
John Blumer
Frank Ciotti
Cole Nelson
Darryl Smith
Colin Thomas

Subsidiary:

Queensland Shale Oil Pty. Ltd. **(1)**
Ste 202 Angela House 30-36 Bay St
Double Bay, NSW, 2028, Australia
Tel.: (61) 2 93635088
Fax: (61) 293635488
Web Site: www.blueensigntech.com.au
Emp.: 2
Oil Shale Mining Services
S.I.C.: 1389
N.A.I.C.S.: 213112
Heather Cu *(Sec)*

BLUE FALLS MANUFACTURING LTD.
4549 52nd St
Thorsby, AB, T0C 2P0, Canada
Tel.: (780) 789-2626
Fax: (780) 789-2624
E-Mail: reception@goarctic.com
Web Site: www.goarctic.com
Year Founded: 1994
Sales Range: $75-99.9 Million
Emp.: 130
Business Description:
Hot Tub Mfr
S.I.C.: 3949
N.A.I.C.S.: 339920
Personnel:
Darcy Amendt *(Pres & CEO)*

BLUE GOLD WATER TECHNOLOGIES LTD.
(Name Changed to Nanostruck Technologies Inc.)

BLUE HORIZON INDUSTRIES INC.
Suite 201 4811 48th Street
Red Deer, AB, T4N 1S6, Canada
Tel.: (403) 340-0864
Fax: (403) 343-3572
E-Mail: donallan@blue-horizon.ca
Web Site: www.blue-horizon.ca
BH—(CNSX)
Business Description:
Holding Company
S.I.C.: 6719
N.A.I.C.S.: 551112
Personnel:
Donald Allan *(Chm, Pres & CEO)*
C. Robin Ray *(CFO)*
David Allan *(Chief Strategic Officer, Health & Safety Officer & Field Mgr)*
Darcy Grahn *(Exec VP)*
Carlos Vasquez *(Sr VP-Ops)*
Board of Directors:
Donald Allan
Aric Ferguson
Nathan Hansen
Doug Lewis
C. Robin Ray

Division:

Blue Horizon Energy Inc. - Blue Horizon Contracting Division **(1)**
Suite 201 - 4811 48 Street
Red Deer, AB, Canada T4N 1S6
Tel.: (403) 340-2561
Fax: (403) 343-3572
Web Site: www.blue-horizon.ca/contracting
Plant Dismantling, Removal & Relocation Services
S.I.C.: 1796
N.A.I.C.S.: 238290

Subsidiary:

Blue Horizon Bio-Diesel Inc. **(1)**
Suite 201 - 4811 48 Street
Red Deer, AB, Canada T4N 1S6
Tel.: (403) 340-1542
Fax: (403) 343-3572
Web Site: www.blue-horizon.ca/bio-diesel
Biodiesel Plant Construction Services
S.I.C.: 1629
N.A.I.C.S.: 237990

BLUE ISLAND PLC
10 Polyfimou Strovolos Industrial Area
PO Box 26073
1666 Nicosia, Cyprus
Tel.: (357) 22 516555
Fax: (357) 22 518044
E-Mail: info@blue-island.com.cy
Web Site: www.blue-island.com.cy
Year Founded: 1993
BLUE—(CYP)
Business Description:
Fish Farming Services
S.I.C.: 0921
N.A.I.C.S.: 112511
Personnel:
Stavros Kremmos *(Chm)*
George Zaloumis *(Mng Dir)*
Board of Directors:
Stavros Kremmos
Antonakis Andronicou
Ioannis Economides
Iosif Korellis
Ioannis Kremmos
George Zaloumis
Legal Counsel:
KGMC Advocates
10 Vassilissis Freiderikis Office 202
Nicosia, Cyprus

E. Neophytou & Partners LLC
Kyriakou Matsis 10 1st Fl
Nicosia, Cyprus

BLUE LABEL TELECOM LIMITED
75 Grayston Drive Morningside Extension 05
Sandton, 2196 Johannesburg, South Africa
Mailing Address:
PO Box 652261
Benmore, 2010, South Africa
Tel.: (27) 115233030
Fax: (27) 115233001
Web Site: www.bluelabeltelecoms.com
BLU—(JSE)
Rev.: $2,120,536,257
Assets: $638,985,100
Liabilities: $276,758,420
Net Worth: $362,226,680
Earnings: $45,585,329
Emp.: 1,112
Fiscal Year-end: 05/31/13
Business Description:
Prepaid Secure Electronic Tokens Distr
S.I.C.: 6099
N.A.I.C.S.: 522320
Personnel:
Brett Levy *(Co-CEO)*
Mark Levy *(Co-CEO)*
Mark Pamensky *(COO)*
Angelo Roussos *(CIO)*
Rob Fleming *(CMO)*
David Fraser *(CTO)*
Larry Pogir *(Chm-Blue Label Data Solutions)*
Neil Barnard *(CEO-Blue Label Mobile)*
John Hawthorne *(CEO-Velociti)*
Werner van Reenen *(CEO-Blue Label Distribution)*
Etienne de Villiers *(Gen Counsel)*
Janine van Eden *(Sec)*
Board of Directors:
Laurence Nestadt
Kevin Ellerine
Gary Harlow
Neil Lazarus
Brett Levy
Mark Levy
Joe Mthimunye
Mark Pamensky
Jerry Vilakazi
Transfer Agent:
Computershare Investor Services (Pty) Ltd
70 Marshall Street
Johannesburg, South Africa

Subsidiaries:

Activi Deployment Services (Proprietary) Limited **(1)**
Unit L 7 Enterprise Bldg The Innovation Hub
Pretoria, Gauteng, 0087, South Africa
Tel.: (27) 128440072
Fax: (27) 12844007
E-Mail: accounts@activi.co.za
Web Site: www.bluelabeltelecom.com
Emp.: 25
Electronic Financial Transaction Processing Services
S.I.C.: 6099
N.A.I.C.S.: 522320
Jimmy van Der Merwe *(CFO)*

Cellfind (Proprietary) Limited **(1)**
142 16th Rd
Midrand, Gauteng, 1685, South Africa
Tel.: (27) 118488200)
Fax: (27) 113121344
E-Mail: info@cellfind.co.za
Web Site: www.cellfind.co.za
Emp.: 52
Cellular Phone Users Tracking Services
S.I.C.: 4899
N.A.I.C.S.: 517919
Niel Barnard *(CEO)*
Jacques Swanepoel *(COO)*

Blue Label Telecom Limited—(Continued)

Comm Express Services SA (Proprietary) Limited (1)
Ste 13-19 1st Fl Coldstream Ofc Park
Corner Hendrik Potgieter Ave
Van Staden Rd Little Falls, Roodepoort, Gauteng, 1175, South Africa
Tel.: (27) 112228666
Fax: (27) 119582089
E-Mail: help@commexpress.co.za
Web Site: www.commexpress.co.za
Emp.: 81
Cellular Airtime & Prepaid Cards Distr
S.I.C.: 5199
N.A.I.C.S.: 424990
Verna Bernard *(Gen Mgr)*

Content Connect Africa (Proprietary) Limited (1)
52 Grosvenor Rd Fairway Ofc Park First Fl
Gleneagles House
Bryanston, Gauteng, 2021, South Africa
Tel.: (27) 114632080
Fax: (27) 114630273
E-Mail: info@contactconnectafrica.co.za
Web Site: www.contentconnectafrica.com
Emp.: 7
Mobile Entertainment Applications Development Services
S.I.C.: 7371
N.A.I.C.S.: 541511
Antos Stella *(Gen Mgr)*

SharedPhone International (Proprietary) Limited (1)
Sharedphone House Kempground Rd
Cape Town, Western Cape, 7700, South Africa
Tel.: (27) 216747620
Fax: (27) 216830642
Web Site: www.sharedphone.co.za
Sim Card Operated Payphone Service Providers
S.I.C.: 4899
N.A.I.C.S.: 517919
Peter Berry *(Mng Dir)*
Warren Steyn *(Mng Dir)*

Transaction Junction (Proprietary) Limited (1)
Bldg 13 The Estuaries Oxbow Crescent
Century City, 7741 Cape Town, Western Cape, South Africa
Tel.: (27) 215253000
Fax: (27) 215529647
Web Site: www.transactionjunction.co.za
Emp.: 15
Transaction Processing Software Solutions
S.I.C.: 6099
N.A.I.C.S.: 522320
Pieter de Villiers *(Mgr-Quality Assurance)*

Velociti (Proprietary) Limited (1)
67 OldFort Rd
Durban, Kwazulu-Natal, 4000, South Africa
Tel.: (27) 313278200
Fax: (27) 313278499
E-Mail: enquire@velociti.biz
Web Site: www.velociti.biz
Emp.: 1,000
Call Centre Operation Services
S.I.C.: 7389
N.A.I.C.S.: 561422
John Hawthorne *(Co-CEO)*
Craig Ireland *(Co-CEO)*
Helen Murray *(Mng Dir-Intl Markets)*
Roger Gerrish *(COO)*

Virtual Voucher (Proprietary) Limited (1)
113-11th St
PO Box 73789
Fairland, Johannesburg, Gauteng, 2030, South Africa
Tel.: (27) 114789874
Fax: (27) 114789877
E-Mail: info@virtualvoucher.co.za
Web Site: www.virtualvoucher.co.za
Emp.: 5
Cellular Airtime & Prepaid Cards Distr
S.I.C.: 4812
N.A.I.C.S.: 517911
Klaus Johanson *(Gen Mgr)*

Non-U.S. Subsidiaries:

Africa Prepaid Services (Mozambique) Limitada (1)
Times Sq Block 3 Ground Fl 25 Septembro Ave
Maputo, Mozambique
Tel.: (258) 21315551
Fax: (258) 21315552
E-Mail: finance@oxigen.co.mz
Web Site: www.oxigen.co.mz
Prepaid Cards & Starter Packs Distr
S.I.C.: 5199
N.A.I.C.S.: 424990
Abraham Smit *(Grp CEO)*
Brett Stagman *(CFO)*

Blue Label Mexico S.A. de C.V (1)
Juan Salvador Agraz 44 Piso 2 Col Santa Fe
05109 Mexico, Mexico
Tel.: (52) 5542121400
Fax: (52) 5542121405
E-Mail: ventas@bluelabelmexico.com
Web Site: www.bluelabelmexico.com
Emp.: 60
Secured Electronic Transaction Processing Services
S.I.C.: 6099
N.A.I.C.S.: 522320
Neil Barnard *(CEO)*
Juan Carlos Garcia La Sienra *(CFO)*

BLUE MAX GROUP LIMITED

Unit 5 Kennet Way Canal Road
Industrial Estate
Canal Road, Trowbridge, Wiltshire, BA14 8BL, United Kingdom
Tel.: (44) 1225 715070
Fax: (44) 8452301888
E-Mail: sales@bluemaxgroup.co.uk
Web Site: www.bluemaxgroup.co.uk
Emp.: 150
Business Description:
Holding Company: Clothing Mfr & Distr of Schoolwear, Childrenswear & Menswear
S.I.C.: 6719
N.A.I.C.S.: 551112
Personnel:
Jeremy Aston-Phillips *(Dir-Sls)*

Subsidiary:

Blue Max Banner (1)
Blue Max House Harcourt Park Canal Road
Trowbridge, Wiltshire, BA14 8RL, United Kingdom
Tel.: (44) 1225715070
Fax: (44) 1225715073
E-Mail: info@bannergroup.co.uk
Web Site: www.bluemaxbanner.co.uk
Sales Range: $25-49.9 Million
Menswear, Childrenswear & School Uniform Mfr & Distr
S.I.C.: 5136
N.A.I.C.S.: 424320
Nigel Plenderleith *(Mng Dir)*

Division:

Blue Max Banner Limited (2)
Blue Max House Harcourt Park Canal Road
Trowbridge, Wiltshire, BA14 8RL, United Kingdom (100%)
Tel.: (44) 1225 715070
Web Site: www.bluemaxgroup.co.uk
Mfr & Distr of Childrenswear, Sportswear, Workwear & Leisurewear
S.I.C.: 5641
N.A.I.C.S.: 448130
Jeremy Aston-Phillips *(Dir-Sls)*

BLUE MOUNTAIN CHRYSLER LTD.

9950 Highway 26 East RR 2
Collingwood, ON, L9Y 3Z1, Canada
Tel.: (705) 445-2740
Fax: (705) 445-1650
Toll Free: (877) 345-2740
Web Site: www.bluemountainchrysler.com
Year Founded: 1974
Rev.: $17,031,410
Emp.: 39
Business Description:
New & Used Car Dealers
S.I.C.: 5511
N.A.I.C.S.: 441110
Personnel:
Kip Brown *(Gen Mgr)*

BLUE MOUNTAIN ECO TOURS INC.

11 Rocky Road
Queensborough, Kingston, Jamaica
Tel.: (876) 310 7166
Year Founded: 2010
Business Description:
Tour Operator
S.I.C.: 4725
N.A.I.C.S.: 561520
Personnel:
Donald Lindo *(Pres, CEO, CFO, Chief Acctg Officer, Treas & Sec)*
Board of Directors:
Donald Lindo

BLUE MOUNTAIN WALLCOVERINGS, INC.

15 Akron Road
Toronto, ON, M8W 1T3, Canada
Tel.: (416) 251-1678
Fax: (416) 251-8968
Web Site: www.ihdg.com
Rev.: $84,231,556
Emp.: 600
Business Description:
Residential Wall Coverings Distr & Mfr
S.I.C.: 1721
N.A.I.C.S.: 238320
Personnel:
Christopher M. Wood *(Chm)*

BLUE NOTE MINING INC.

1080 Cote du Beaver Hall Suite 2101
Montreal, QC, H2Z 1S8, Canada
Tel.: (514) 486-3095
Fax: (514) 486-1317
E-Mail: ir@bluenotemining.ca
Web Site: www.bluenotemining.ca
BNT—(TSX)
Sales Range: Less than $1 Million
Business Description:
Lead & Zinc Mining & Exploration Services
S.I.C.: 1031
N.A.I.C.S.: 212231
Personnel:
Leon Methot *(Pres & CEO)*
Daniel Bortoluzzi *(CFO)*
Board of Directors:
John Anderson
David Crevier
Paul Einarson
Leon Methot
Transfer Agent:
CIBC Mellon Trust Company
2001 University Street Suite 1600
Montreal, QC, Canada

BLUE PLANET WORLDWIDE FINANCIALS INVESTMENT TRUST PLC

Greenside House 25 Greenside Place
Edinburgh, EH1 3AA, United Kingdom
Tel.: (44) 1314666666
Fax: (44) 1314666677
E-Mail: info@bpia.eu
Web Site: www.blueplanet.eu
BPW—(LSE)
Business Description:
Investment Services
S.I.C.: 6211
N.A.I.C.S.: 523999
Personnel:
Philip Court *(Chm)*
Board of Directors:
Philip Court
D. Christopher Jones
Kenneth Christopher Murray

BLUE RIDGE CHINA

3701 Tower A Beijing Fortune Centre
No 7 Dongsanhuan Rd
Beijing, 100020, China
Tel.: (86) 10 65309900
Year Founded: 2006
Business Description:
Private Equity Firm
S.I.C.: 8099
N.A.I.C.S.: 621999
Personnel:
Justin Yue Tang *(CEO)*

BLUE RIVER RESOURCES LTD.

Suite 501 525 Seymour Street
Vancouver, BC, V6B 3H7, Canada
Tel.: (604) 682-7339
Fax: (604) 682-7321
E-Mail: griff@blueriv.com
Web Site: www.blueriv.com
Year Founded: 2008
BXR—(TSXV)
Int. Income: $1,502
Assets: $756,644
Liabilities: $313,387
Net Worth: $443,257
Earnings: ($965,338)
Fiscal Year-end: 10/31/12
Business Description:
Copper Mining
S.I.C.: 1021
N.A.I.C.S.: 212234
Personnel:
Griffin Jones *(Pres & CEO)*
Nadwynn Sing *(CFO)*
Board of Directors:
Cathy Edwards
Paul D. Gray
Balbir Johal
Griffin Jones
Richard Silas
Nadwynn Sing
Transfer Agent:
Computershare Investor Services Inc
100 University Avenue 9th Floor
Toronto, ON, Canada

BLUE SALON ESTABLISHMENT

Suhaim Bin Hamad St
PO Box 6255
Doha, Qatar
Tel.: (974) 44466111
Fax: (974) 04466112
E-Mail: bluesaln@qatar.net.qa
Web Site: www.bluesalon.com
Year Founded: 1981
Sales Range: $10-24.9 Million
Emp.: 700
Business Description:
Department Store
S.I.C.: 5311
N.A.I.C.S.: 452111
Personnel:
Ashraf Abu Issa *(Chm & CEO)*

BLUE SKY ALTERNATIVE INVESTMENTS LIMITED

2nd Floor Port Office Suites
40 Edward Street, Brisbane, QLD, 4000, Australia

Mailing Address:
PO Box 15515
Brisbane, QLD, 4002, Australia
Tel.: (61) 7 3270 7500
Fax: (61) 7 3270 7599
Web Site: www.blueskyfunds.com.au
BLA—(ASX)
Emp.: 24
Business Description:
Investment Management
S.I.C.: 6211
N.A.I.C.S.: 523110
Personnel:
John Kain *(Chm)*
Mark Sowerby *(Mng Dir)*
Jane Prior *(Sec)*
Board of Directors:
John Kain
Alexander McNab
Mark Sowerby
Tim Wilson

U.S. Subsidiary:

Blue Sky Alternative Investment LLC **(1)**
117 E 55th St
New York, NY 10022
Tel.: (646) 715-3479
Emp.: 1
Investment Management Services
S.I.C.: 6799
N.A.I.C.S.: 523920
Debra Goundrey, *(Mng Dir)*

BLUE SKY HOSTING LTD

19 Catherine Place Victoria
London, SW1E 6DX, United Kingdom
Tel.: (44) 20 4183 5854
Fax: (44) 20 7183 5855
E-Mail: info@bluesky.co.uk
Web Site: www.bluesky.co.uk
Year Founded: 1997
Business Description:
Web Hosting Services
S.I.C.: 7374
N.A.I.C.S.: 518210
Personnel:
Jackie Argent *(Dir-Ops)*

BLUE SKY URANIUM CORP.

Suite 709 837 West Hastings St
Vancouver, BC, V6C 3N6, Canada
Tel.: (604) 687-1828
Fax: (604) 687-1858
Toll Free: (800) 901-0058
E-Mail: info@blueskyuranium.com
Web Site: www.blueskyuranium.com
Year Founded: 2005
BSK—(TSXV)
Int. Income: $4,140
Assets: $3,700,853
Liabilities: $113,927
Net Worth: $3,586,926
Earnings: ($1,243,693)
Fiscal Year-end: 12/31/12
Business Description:
Uranium Exploration Services
S.I.C.: 1094
N.A.I.C.S.: 212291
Personnel:
Sean D. Hurd *(Pres & CEO)*
Michael E. Iannacone *(CFO & Sec)*
Board of Directors:
Sean D. Hurd
Ronald H. McMillan
David A. Terry
Transfer Agent:
Computershare Investor Services Inc
100 University Avenue 9th Floor
Toronto, ON, Canada

BLUE SOLUTIONS LIMITED

12b Oklands Business Centre
Oaklands Park
Wokingham, Berkshire, RG41 2FD, United Kingdom
Tel.: (44) 118 9898 222
Fax: (44) 118 9898 201
E-Mail: sales@bluesolutions.co.uk
Web Site: www.bluesolutions.co.uk
Sales Range: $1-9.9 Million
Business Description:
Software & Other Computer Products Distr
S.I.C.: 5045
N.A.I.C.S.: 423430
Personnel:
Mark Charleton *(CEO)*

BLUE SPA INCORPORATED

26/F Building A Times Plaza 2 Zongfu Road
Chengdu, 610016, China
Tel.: (86) 2866847826
Fax: (86) 2866067199
Web Site: www.bluespashop.com
Year Founded: 2009
BUES—(OTC OTCB)
Assets: $7,788
Liabilities: $82,576
Net Worth: ($74,788)
Earnings: ($24,736)
Fiscal Year-end: 05/31/13
Business Description:
Skin & Body Care Products, Fitness Apparel & Related Accessories Mfr
S.I.C.: 2844
N.A.I.C.S.: 325620
Personnel:
Law Yau Yau *(Pres, CEO, CFO, Treas & Sec)*
Board of Directors:
Law Yau Yau

BLUE SPHERE CORPORATION

35 Asuta Street
Even Yehuda, Israel 40500
Tel.: (972) 9 8917438
Web Site: www.bluespherecorporate.com
Year Founded: 2007
BLSPD—(OTC)
Assets: $606,000
Liabilities: $1,088,000
Net Worth: ($482,000)
Earnings: ($1,970,000)
Emp.: 5
Fiscal Year-end: 09/30/13
Business Description:
Project Integrator for Greenhouse Gas Emission & Renewable Energy Production
S.I.C.: 1389
N.A.I.C.S.: 213112
Personnel:
Joshua Shoham *(Chm)*
Shlomo Palas *(Pres, CEO & Sec)*
Shlomo Zakai *(CFO & Treas)*
Efim Monosov *(CTO)*
Mark Frederick Radom *(Chief Carbon Officer & Gen Counsel)*
Roy Amizur *(Exec VP)*
Board of Directors:
Joshua Shoham
Shlomo Palas
Transfer Agent:
Nevada Agency & Transfer Company
50 W Liberty Street Suite 880
Reno, NV 89501

BLUE STAR CAPITAL PLC

3 Wimpole Street
London, W1G 9SQ, United Kingdom
Tel.: (44) 207 612 7310
Fax: (44) 207 612 7311
E-Mail: info@bluestarcapital.co.uk
Web Site: www.bluestarcapital.co.uk
BLU—(LSE)
Rev.: $131,500
Assets: $2,827,570
Liabilities: $1,003,353
Net Worth: $1,824,217
Earnings: ($2,273,112)
Emp.: 1
Fiscal Year-end: 09/30/12
Business Description:
Venture Capital Funding Services
S.I.C.: 6211
N.A.I.C.S.: 523999
Personnel:
Anthony Fabrizi *(CEO)*
Board of Directors:
Geoffrey James
Anthony Fabrizi
Peter Varnish
Legal Counsel:
Rawlison Butler LLP
Griffin House 135 High Street
Crawley, United Kingdom

BLUE STAR ENTERTAINMENT TECHNOLOGIES, INC.

Plaza Neptuno Planta Baja Suite 351
Panama, Panama
Tel.: (507) 836 6917
SOLHF—(OTC OTCB)
Business Description:
Hotel Owner & Operator
S.I.C.: 7011
N.A.I.C.S.: 721110
Personnel:
Dan Bates *(CEO)*
Transfer Agent:
OTC Stock Transfer, Inc.
6364 S. Highland Dr. Suite 201
Salt Lake City, UT 84121

BLUE STAR FORD LINCOLN SALES LTD

115 Queensway East
Simcoe, ON, N3Y4M5, Canada
Tel.: (519) 426-3673
E-Mail: bluestarford@on.aibn.com
Web Site: www.bluestarford.dealerconnection.com
Year Founded: 1985
Rev.: $16,832,542
Emp.: 37
Business Description:
New & Used Car Dealers
S.I.C.: 5511
N.A.I.C.S.: 441110
Personnel:
Robert Kowtaluk *(Pres)*
Paul Gurney *(Treas & Sec)*

BLUE STAR INFOTECH LIMITED

8th Floor The Great Oasis Plot No D 13 MIDC Marol Andheri East
Mumbai, 400 093, India
Tel.: (91) 2266956969
Fax: (91) 2266973866
Web Site: www.bsil.com
BLUESTINFO—(NSE)
Rev.: $36,182,998
Assets: $23,102,323
Liabilities: $6,557,783
Net Worth: $16,544,540
Earnings: $924,868
Emp.: 741
Fiscal Year-end: 03/31/13
Business Description:
Computer Software Development Services
S.I.C.: 7371
N.A.I.C.S.: 541511
Personnel:
Suneel M. Advani *(Chm & Mng Dir)*
Ashok M. Advani *(Vice Chm)*
Sunil Bhatia *(CEO & Mng Dir)*
V. Sudharshan *(CFO, Compliance Officer & Sec)*
Douglas Gray *(Chief Solutions Officer)*
Sanjeev Sethi *(Pres-Blue Star Infotech America Inc)*
Suresh Iyer *(Exec VP & Head-Global Mktg)*
Board of Directors:
Suneel M. Advani
Ashok M. Advani
Sunil Bhatia
Prakash G. Hebalkar
K. P. T. Kutty
Naresh K. Malhotra
Suresh N. Talwar
Sanjay N. Vaswani
Transfer Agent:
Link Intime India Pvt. Ltd
C-13 Pannalal Silk Mills Compound LBS Marg
Bhandup (West)
Mumbai, India

BLUE STAR LIMITED

Kasturi Buildings Mohan T Advani Chowk Jamshedji Tata Road
Mumbai, 400 020, India
Tel.: (91) 2266654000
Fax: (91) 2266654151
Web Site: www.bluestarindia.com
Year Founded: 1943
500067—(BOM)
Rev.: $548,869,006
Assets: $400,409,270
Liabilities: $326,124,143
Net Worth: $74,285,126
Earnings: $7,243,671
Emp.: 2,698
Fiscal Year-end: 03/31/13
Business Description:
Air Conditioning & Refrigeration Systems & Products Mfr
S.I.C.: 3585
N.A.I.C.S.: 333415
Personnel:
Suneel M. Advani *(Vice Chm)*
Satish Jamdar *(Mng Dir)*
Sangameshwar Iyer *(Compliance Officer & Sec)*
Vir S. Advani *(Pres-Electro Mechanical Projects Bus)*
B. Thiagarajan *(Pres-Airconditioning & Refrigeration Products Bus)*
J. M. Bhambure *(Exec VP-R&D & Tech)*
Tojo Jose *(Exec VP-HR)*
Manek Kalyaniwala *(Exec VP-Corp Fin Svcs)*
Arun Khorana *(Exec VP-Pro Electronics & Indus Sys Div)*
P. Venkat Rao *(Exec VP-Central & Packagaed Airconditioning Products)*
Board of Directors:
Ashok M. Advani
Suneel M. Advani
Vir S. Advani
Shailesh Haribhakti
Satish Jamdar
Pradeep Mallick
M. K. Sharma
Gurdeep Singh
B. Thiagarajan
Transfer Agent:
Link Intime India Pvt Ltd
C-13 Kantilal Maganlal Estate Pannalal Silk Mills Compound L B S Marg
Bhandup West, Mumbai, India

Subsidiary:

Blue Star Design & Engineering Ltd. **(1)**
Mirchandani Business Park 4th Floor Off Ghatkopar Link Road
Mumbai, Maharashtra, 400 072, India
Tel.: (91) 2267774000
Fax: (91) 2267774001

Blue Star Limited—(Continued)

E-Mail: bsde_hq@bluestarindia.com
Web Site: www.bluestar-de.com
Emp.: 200
Computer Aided Designing Services
S.I.C.: 8711
N.A.I.C.S.: 541330
Prem Kalliath *(CEO)*
Dinesh N. Kamath *(CFO)*
Rita Kripalani *(Exec VP & Head-Delivery)*

Units:

Blue Star Ltd. **(1)**
Blue Star House 9A Ghatkopar Link Rd
Sakinaka, Mumbai, 400 072, India (100%)
Tel.: (91) 2256684000
Fax: (91) 2256654150
E-Mail: bthiagarajan@bluestarindia.com
Web Site: www.bluestarindia.com
Emp.: 200
Provider of Air Conditioning & Heating Services
S.I.C.: 3585
N.A.I.C.S.: 333415

Blue Star Ltd. **(1)**
104 Old No 46 Garuda Bldgs
Cathedral Rd, Chennai, Tamil Nadu, 600086, India (100%)
Tel.: (91) 4452444000
Fax: (91) 4428116736
Web Site: www.bluestarindia.com
Emp.: 125
S.I.C.: 3585
N.A.I.C.S.: 333415

Blue Star Ltd. **(1)**
Block 2A DLF Corporate Park DLF Qutab Enclave Phase III
Gurgaon, Haryana, 122 002, India
Tel.: (91) 1244094000
Telex: 31-75120 BSNF IN
Fax: (91) 1244094004
Web Site: www.bluestarindia.com
Emp.: 155
Air Conditioning & Heating Services
S.I.C.: 3585
N.A.I.C.S.: 333415
Kapil Mehrotra *(Gen Mgr)*

Blue Star Ltd. **(1)**
7 Hare Street
Kolkata, 700 001, India (100%)
Tel.: (91) 3322134000
Telex: 217655 BSCA IN
Fax: (91) 3322134102
E-Mail: manojv@bluestarindia.com
Web Site: www.bluestarindia.com
Emp.: 250
Provider of Air Conditioning & Heating Services
S.I.C.: 3585
N.A.I.C.S.: 333415
Rakesh Rao *(Mng Dir)*

Plants:

Blue Star Limited - Bharuch Facility **(1)**
Plot Nos 4 & 5 GIDC Industrial Estate
Narmada Nagar Post
Bharuch, Gujarat, 392 015, India
Tel.: (91) 2642 246116
Fax: (91) 2642 246026
Emp.: 450
Electrical Equipment Mfr
S.I.C.: 3585
N.A.I.C.S.: 333415
Haresh K. Khatwani *(Gen Mgr)*

Blue Star Limited - Thane Facility **(1)**
LInd Pokhran Road
Majiwada, Thane, Maharashtra, 400 601, India
Tel.: (91) 22 67924000
Fax: (91) 22 67924020
Web Site: www.bluestarindia.com
Air Conditioning & Refrigeration Systems Mfr
S.I.C.: 3585
N.A.I.C.S.: 333415

BLUE ZEN MEMORIAL PARKS INC.

8515 Place Devonshire Suite 100
town of Mount Royal
Montreal, QC, Canada
Tel.: (514) 288-0900
Fax: (514) 426-5851
BZM—(CNSX)
Assets: $2,383,087
Liabilities: $2,052,922
Net Worth: $330,166
Earnings: ($487,530)
Fiscal Year-end: 12/31/12
Business Description:
Custom Built Culture Parks in Scenic Areas that Feature Family Memorial Halls
S.I.C.: 7999
N.A.I.C.S.: 712190
Personnel:
Xianming Kong *(Chm & CEO)*
Carla Qiong Zhou *(Pres & COO)*
Edward Zhao *(CFO & Sec)*
Board of Directors:
Xianming Kong
Jiaping Jiang
Barry Sheehy
Benjamin Wu

BLUEBIRD ENERGY PLC

(Name Changed to Quoram PLC)

BLUECAT NETWORKS, INC.

4101 Yonge St Ste 502
Toronto, ON, M2P 1N6, Canada
Tel.: (416) 646-8400
Fax: (416) 225-4728
Toll Free: (866) 895-6931
Web Site: www.bluecatnetworks.com
Sales Range: $10-24.9 Million
Business Description:
IP Address Management Services
S.I.C.: 7372
N.A.I.C.S.: 511210
Personnel:
Michael Hyatt *(Co-Founder & CEO)*
Richard Hyatt *(Co-Founder, CTO & VP-Engrg)*

BLUECHIIP LIMITED

1 Dalmore Drive Caribbean Business Park
Scoresby, VIC, 3179, Australia
Tel.: (61) 397639763
Fax: (61) 397639764
E-Mail: info@bluechiip.com
Web Site: www.bluechiip.com
Year Founded: 2003
BCT—(ASX)
Rev.: $88,350
Assets: $2,511,409
Liabilities: $1,921,095
Net Worth: $590,314
Earnings: ($3,737,114)
Fiscal Year-end: 06/30/13
Business Description:
RFID Memory & Temperature Sensing Devices
S.I.C.: 3674
N.A.I.C.S.: 334413
Personnel:
Brett Schwarz *(CEO & Mng Dir)*
Jason Chaffey *(CTO)*
Lee D. Mitchell *(Sec)*
Board of Directors:
Iain M. C. Kirkwood
Joe Baini
Ron Finkel
Brett Schwarz
Legal Counsel:
Minter Ellison Lawyers
Rialto Towers Level 23 525 Collins Street
Melbourne, VIC, Australia

BLUECOM CO., LTD.

11-80 Songdo-dong Yeonsu-gu
Incheon, 406-840, Korea (South)
Tel.: (82) 32 8100500
Fax: (82) 32 8100600
Web Site: www.bluec.co.kr
Year Founded: 1990
033560—(KRS)
Sales Range: $75-99.9 Million
Emp.: 120
Business Description:
Wireless Communication Products Mfr
S.I.C.: 3663
N.A.I.C.S.: 334220
Personnel:
J.K. Kim *(Chm & CEO)*

BLUECOM DANMARK A/S

Staktoften 6
DK 2950 Vedbaek, Denmark
Tel.: (45) 45945555
Fax: (45) 45941155
E-Mail: kj@bluecom.com
Web Site: www.bluecom.com
Year Founded: 1992
Sales Range: $150-199.9 Million
Emp.: 10
Business Description:
Networking & Memory Products, CPUs, Data Storage Devices, CD-ROMs, Mother Boards, Sound & Graphics Cards, Mice & Other Peripheral Equipment Distr
Import Export
S.I.C.: 5045
N.A.I.C.S.: 423430
Personnel:
Jens Fournais *(CEO)*
Board of Directors:
Uffe Elander
Jens Fournais

BLUECREST ALLBLUE FUND LIMITED

Anson Place Mill Court La Charroterie
Saint Peter Port, GY1 1EJ, Guernsey
Tel.: (44) 1481 722260
Web Site: www.bluecrestallblue.co.uk
BABS—(LSE)
Sales Range: $75-99.9 Million
Business Description:
Investment Services
S.I.C.: 6211
N.A.I.C.S.: 523999
Board of Directors:
Richard John Crowder
Andrew Dodd
Jonathan Hooley
John Le Prevost
Paul Meader
Transfer Agents:
Anson Registrars Limited
Anson Place Mill Courtq
PO Box 426
La Charroterie, Saint Peter Port, Guernsey
Anson Administration (UK) Limited
3500 Parkway
Fareham, United Kingdom

BLUEDON INFORMATION SECURITY TECHNOLOGIES CO., LTD.

20-21F Building A 16 Keyun Road
Tianhe District, Guangzhou, 510665, China
Tel.: (86) 20 85526663
Fax: (86) 20 85526000
Web Site: www.bluedon.com
300297—(CHIN)
Sales Range: $25-49.9 Million
Emp.: 390
Business Description:
Information Security Software
S.I.C.: 7372
N.A.I.C.S.: 511210
Personnel:
Zongqing Ke *(Chm)*

BLUEDROP PERFORMANCE LEARNING INC.

18 Prescott Street
Saint John's, NL, A1C 3S4, Canada
Tel.: (709) 739-9000
Fax: (709) 739-9003
E-Mail: contact@bluedrop.com
Web Site: www.bluedrop.com
Year Founded: 1987
BPL—(TSXV)
Emp.: 120
Business Description:
Business Course Software & E-Learning Courses
S.I.C.: 7372
N.A.I.C.S.: 511210
Personnel:
Emad Rizkalla *(Founder & CEO)*
Derrick Rowe *(Chm)*
Rod Craig *(CFO)*
Tim Brown *(CTO)*
Board of Directors:
Derrick Rowe
Bernard Beckett
Bob Rae
Paul Sparkes
Lecia Stewart
Andrew Youngman
Subsidiaries:

Atlantis Systems Corp. **(1)**
Metropolitan Place 99 Wyse Road Suite 1100
Dartmouth, NS, B3A 4S5, Canada
Tel.: (902) 461-6600
Fax: (902) 461-6601
E-Mail: info@atlantissc.com
Web Site: www.atlantissc.com
Rev.: $10,608,181
Assets: $6,617,191
Liabilities: $16,080,262
Net Worth: ($9,463,070)
Earnings: $559,633
Emp.: 90
Fiscal Year-end: 12/31/12
Aerospace & Defense Parts Mfr
S.I.C.: 3812
N.A.I.C.S.: 334511
Bill Bartlett *(CFO)*
James Pyra *(COO)*
Christopher Spilman *(CTO)*
Chris Lewis *(Sr VP-Bus Dev-Brampton)*

Subsidiary:

Atlantis Systems International Inc. **(2)**
1 Kenview Blvd
Brampton, ON, L6T 5E6, Canada
Tel.: (905) 792-1981
Fax: (905) 792-7251
Web Site: www.atlantissi.com
Emp.: 100
Flight Instruments Mfr
S.I.C.: 3812
N.A.I.C.S.: 334511
Henrik Noesgaard *(CEO)*

BLUEFIN SOLUTIONS LTD.

Bldg 4 Chiswick Pk The Plz 566
Chiswick High Rd
London, W4 5YE, United Kingdom
Tel.: (44) 8702330404
Fax: (44) 8702330405
Web Site: www.bluefinsolutions.com
Year Founded: 2002
Sales Range: $10-24.9 Million
Emp.: 150
Business Description:
IT Consulting Services
S.I.C.: 8999
N.A.I.C.S.: 541690
Personnel:
James Appleby *(CEO)*
Dan Hawker *(Partner-Client)*
Philippa Holland *(COO)*
Mike Curl *(CTO)*

BLUEFIRE MINING CORP.

1400-400 Burrard Street
Vancouver, BC, V6C 3A6, Canada

Tel.: (604) 628-1168
Fax: (604) 688-0094
Year Founded: 2011
BFM—(TSXV)
Business Description:
Metal Mining
S.I.C.: 1099
N.A.I.C.S.: 212299
Personnel:
David E. De Witt *(Pres & CEO)*
Jason Tong *(CFO)*
C. Warren Beil *(Sec)*
Board of Directors:
Robert F. Blair
David E. De Witt
Daniel Gleadle
Jeffrey Tyson
Transfer Agent:
Equity Transfer & Trust
Suite 1620 1185 West Georgia Street
Vancouver, BC, Canada

BLUEFOCUS COMMUNICATION GROUP CO., LTD.
19th-20th Fl Star City Tower C
10 Jiu Xian Qiao Road
Chao Yang District, Beijing, 100016, China
Tel.: (86) 1084575288
Fax: (86) 1064357255
E-Mail: info@bluefocus.com
Web Site: www.bluefocus.com
300058—(CHIN)
Emp.: 500
Business Description:
Public Relations & Consulting Services
S.I.C.: 8743
N.A.I.C.S.: 541820
Personnel:
Yuhui Mao *(Pres)*
Wenquan Zhao *(CEO)*

BLUEGEM CAPITAL PARTNERS LLP
16 Berkeley Street
London, W1J 8DZ, United Kingdom
Tel.: (44) 20 7647 9710
Fax: (44) 20 7681 1304
E-Mail: enquiries@bluegemcp.com
Web Site: www.bluegemcp.com
Business Description:
Investment Services
S.I.C.: 6211
N.A.I.C.S.: 523999
Personnel:
Marco Capello *(Co-Founder & Mng Partner)*
Marco Anatriello *(Co-Founder & Partner)*
Emilio Di Spiezio Sardo *(Co-Founder & Partner)*
Vishesh Srivastava *(Principal)*
Board of Directors:
Marco Anatriello
Marco Capello
Emilio Di Spiezio Sardo

Holdings:

Enotria Group Limited (1)
4-8 Chandos Park Estate Chandos Road
London, NW10 6NF, United Kingdom (88.2%)
Tel.: (44) 20 8961 4411
Fax: (44) 20 8961 8773
E-Mail: info@enotria.co.uk
Web Site: www.enotria.co.uk
Wine Importer & Distr
S.I.C.: 5182
N.A.I.C.S.: 424820
Alison Levett *(CEO)*

Liberty (1)
Regent Street
London, W1B 5AH, United Kingdom UK
Tel.: (44) 2077341234
Fax: (44) 20775739876
E-Mail: marketing@liberty.co.uk
Web Site: www.liberty.co.uk
Sales Range: $125-149.9 Million
Emp.: 385
Women's Fashions, Gifts & Housewares Designer & Sales
S.I.C.: 5621
N.A.I.C.S.: 448120
Marco Capello *(Chm)*
Ed Burstell *(Mng Dir)*
Kirstie Carey *(Mng Dir)*

Subsidiary:

Liberty Retail Limited **(2)**
210-220 Regent St
London, W1B 5AH, United Kingdom (100%)
Tel.: (44) 2077341234
Fax: (44) 2075739876
Web Site: www.liberty.co.uk
Emp.: 200
Management of Retail Operations
S.I.C.: 5311
N.A.I.C.S.: 452112

BLUEHONE SECURED ASSETS LIMITED
32 Bedford Row
London, WC1R 4HE, United Kingdom
Tel.: (44) 20 7831 5088
E-Mail: enquiries@bluehone.com
Web Site: www.bluehone.com
Business Description:
Loan Services
S.I.C.: 6163
N.A.I.C.S.: 522310
Personnel:
Bob Morton *(Chm)*
Board of Directors:
Bob Morton
Carola Breusch
Bill Brown
Michael Capraro
Robert Mitchell
Transfer Agent:
Capita Registrars Limited
The Registry 34 Beckenham Road
Beckenham, Kent, BR3 4TU, United Kingdom
Tel.: (44) 20 8639 2157
Fax: (44) 20 8658 3430

BLUELINEA SA
243 bis boulevard Pereire
75017 Paris, France
Tel.: (33) 1 40 59 04 02
Fax: (33) 1 40 59 80 18
E-Mail: contact@bluelinea.com
Web Site: www.bluelinea.com
MLBLU—(EUR)
Emp.: 6
Business Description:
Electronic Surveillance & Medical Teleassistance Systems
S.I.C.: 3651
N.A.I.C.S.: 334310
Personnel:
Alexis Westermann *(Chm)*

BLUEPHOENIX SOLUTIONS LTD.
8 Maskit Street
Herzliyya, 46733, Israel
Tel.: (972) 9 9526110
Fax: (972) 9 952611
E-Mail: info@bphx.com
Web Site: www.bphx.com
Year Founded: 1987
BPHX—(NASDAQ TAE)
Rev.: $10,624,000
Assets: $19,750,000
Liabilities: $4,661,000
Net Worth: $15,089,000
Earnings: ($11,077,000)
Emp.: 108
Fiscal Year-end: 12/31/12
Business Description:
Develops & Markets Software Tools; Provides Consulting Services for the Implementation of Complex Conversion Projects for Main Frame Computer Systems
S.I.C.: 7371
N.A.I.C.S.: 541511
Personnel:
Melvin L. Keating *(Chm)*
Matt Bell *(Pres & CEO)*
Rick Rinaldo *(CFO)*
Yael Peretz *(VP, Gen Counsel & Sec)*
Board of Directors:
Melvin L. Keating
Michael Chill
Carla Corkern
Doron Elhanani
Thomas J. Jurewicz

Subsidiaries:

Liacom Systems Ltd. **(1)**
5 Hatzoref St
Holon, 58856, Israel (51%)
Tel.: (972) 35573400
Fax: (972) 35580638
E-Mail: info@liacom.co.il
Web Site: www.liacom.co.il
Emp.: 150
Computer System Design Services
S.I.C.: 7373
N.A.I.C.S.: 541512
Gebriel Sharon *(CEO)*

U.S. Subsidiaries:

BridgeQuest, Inc. **(1)**
8000 Regency Pkwy Ste 300
Cary, NC 27518-8514
Tel.: (919) 863-0318
Fax: (919) 863-0319
E-Mail: info@bridge-quest.com
Web Site: www.bridge-quest.com
Offshore Software Development Outsourcing Services
S.I.C.: 7373
N.A.I.C.S.: 541512
Len Erlikh *(Co-Founder, Chm & CTO)*
Renee Fulk *(CFO & VP)*

Zulu Software Inc. **(1)**
8000 Regency Pkwy
Cary, NC 27518
Tel.: (919) 380-5100
Web Site: www.zulusoftware.com
Legacy Software Conversion Services
S.I.C.: 7373
N.A.I.C.S.: 541512
Trevor Veary *(Co-Founder & CTO)*

Non-U.S. Subsidiaries:

BluePhoenix Solutions Italia **(1)**
Piazza Central Commerciale 44
San Felice, 20090 Segrate, Milan, Italy
Tel.: (39) 027539111
Fax: (39) 027531331
E-Mail: azecco@bphx.com
Web Site: www.bphx.com
Emp.: 10
S.I.C.: 7371
N.A.I.C.S.: 541511
Domenico Mezzapesa *(Country Mgr)*

BluePhoenix Solutions Nordic Aps **(1)**
Borupvang 2 C Fl 1 Tv
Ballerup, Denmark (100%)
Tel.: (45) 44208000
Custom Computer Programming Services
S.I.C.: 7371
N.A.I.C.S.: 541511

I-Ter/Informatica & Territorio S.p.A. **(1)**
Via Veneto 43 - A
Riccione, Rimini, Italy (100%)
Tel.: (39) 0541666611
Custom Computer Programming Services
S.I.C.: 7371
N.A.I.C.S.: 541511
Domenico Mezzapesa *(CEO)*

BLUEPLANET ENVIRONMENTAL INC.
Unit 15 565 Edward Avenue
Richmond Hill, ON, L4C 9W8, Canada
Tel.: (905) 508-2583
Fax: (905) 508-2582
E-Mail: info@blueplanetenviro.com
Web Site: www.blueplanetenviro.com
Year Founded: 2005
9BP—(DEU)
Business Description:
Clean Water Products & Solutions
S.I.C.: 8999
N.A.I.C.S.: 541620
Personnel:
Richard Lonetto *(Pres)*
Russ Pakosh *(Sr VP)*
Board of Directors:
Greg Binions
Mark Korol
Richard Lonetto
Kazumi Nishimura
Russ Pakosh

BLUEROCK DIAMONDS PLC
39 St James's Street
London, SW1A 1JD, United Kingdom
Tel.: (44) 20 7408 1067
Web Site: www.bluerockdiamonds.co.uk
Year Founded: 2012
BRD—(AIM)
Business Description:
Diamond Mining
S.I.C.: 1411
N.A.I.C.S.: 212311
Personnel:
Paul Beck *(Chm)*
Riaan Visser *(CEO)*
John Kilham *(CTO)*
David Facey *(Sec)*
Board of Directors:
Paul Beck
John Kilham
Tim Leslie
Andre Markgraaff
Jonathan Quirk
Riaan Visser

BLUEROCK VENTURES CORP.
2050-1055 West Georgia Street
Vancouver, BC, V6E 3P3, Canada
Tel.: (604) 684-2181
Fax: (604) 682-4768
E-Mail: praveen@varshneycapital.com
Year Founded: 2011
BCR.P—(TSXV)
Int. Income: $1,048
Assets: $88,861
Liabilities: $37,804
Net Worth: $51,058
Earnings: ($101,648)
Fiscal Year-end: 02/28/13
Business Description:
Investment Services
S.I.C.: 6211
N.A.I.C.S.: 523999
Personnel:
Clifford B. Mah *(CEO & CFO)*
Board of Directors:
Clifford B. Mah
Praveen Varshney
Transfer Agent:
Olympia Trust Company
Suite 1003 750 West Pender Street
Vancouver, BC, V6C 2T8, Canada

BLUERUSH MEDIA GROUP CORP.
75 Sherbourne Street Suite 112
Toronto, ON, M5A 3X9, Canada
Tel.: (416) 203-0618
Fax: (416) 848-0021
Web Site: www.bluerush.ca
Year Founded: 2003
BTV—(TSXV)

BlueRush Media Group Corp.—(Continued)

Rev.: $5,263,427
Assets: $2,719,333
Liabilities: $692,984
Net Worth: $2,026,349
Earnings: $347,641
Fiscal Year-end: 07/31/13

Business Description:
Digital Video Marketing Services
S.I.C.: 8742
N.A.I.C.S.: 541613

Personnel:
Laurence Lubin *(Pres & CEO)*
Bryce Walker *(CFO)*
Len Smofsky *(Exec VP)*

Board of Directors:
Jay Cashmore
Michael J. Churchill-Smith
Laurence Lubin
Jim Moriarty
Len Smofsky

Subsidiary:

BlueRush Digital Media Corp **(1)**
366 Adelaide St E Suite 433
Toronto, ON, M5A 3X9, Canada
Tel.: (416) 203-0618
Fax: (416) 848-0021
E-Mail: info@bluerush.ca
Emp.: 50
Digital Marketing Services
S.I.C.: 8742
N.A.I.C.S.: 541613
Sara Soumillion *(Project Mgr)*

BLUESCOPE STEEL LIMITED

Level 11 120 Collins Street
Melbourne, VIC, 3000, Australia
Tel.: (61) 396664000
Telex: AA31846; AA31880
Fax: (61) 396664111
E-Mail: Steeldirect@bluescopesteel.com
Web Site: www.bluescopesteel.com
BSL—(ASX)
Rev.: $7,597,221,630
Assets: $7,639,426,680
Liabilities: $2,991,348,050
Net Worth: $4,648,078,630
Earnings: ($65,235,460)
Emp.: 17,063
Fiscal Year-end: 06/30/13

Business Description:
Steel Plate, Slab & Coil Mfr
S.I.C.: 3312
N.A.I.C.S.: 331110

Personnel:
Graham John Kraehe *(Chm)*
Paul Francis O'Malley *(CEO & Mng Dir)*
Charlie S. R. Elias *(CFO)*
Michael G. Barron *(Chief Legal Officer & Sec)*
Patrick J. Finan *(Pres-Global Building Solutions)*
Sanjay Dayal *(CEO-Building Products)*
Robert J. Moore *(CEO-Global Building Solutions)*
Mark Vassella *(CEO-Australia & New Zealand)*

Board of Directors:
Graham John Kraehe
John Bevan
Penny Bingham-Hall
Ewen Graham Wolseley Crouch
Kenneth Alfred Dean
Daniel Bruno Grollo
Lloyd Jones
Ronald John McNeilly
Paul Francis O'Malley

Divisions:

Bluescope Steel **(1)**
5 Islands Rd
Port Kembla, NSW, 2505, Australia (100%)
Mailing Address:
PO Box 1854
Wollongong, NSW, 2500, Australia
Tel.: (61) 242757522
Telex: AA29083
Fax: (61) 242757585
Web Site: www.bluescope.com
Emp.: 8,000
S.I.C.: 1011
N.A.I.C.S.: 212210
Noel Cornish *(CEO-Australian/New Zealand Steel Mfg Businesses)*

Subsidiaries:

BlueScope Distribution Pty Ltd. **(1)**
88 Ricketts Road
Mount Waverley, VIC, 3149, Australia
Tel.: (61) 385408600
Fax: (61) 385408124
E-Mail: info@bluescopedistribution.com.au
Web Site: www.bluescopedistribution.com.au
Emp.: 170
Steel Product Mfr
S.I.C.: 3312
N.A.I.C.S.: 331110
Adam Newman *(Gen Mgr-Comml)*

BlueScope Pty Ltd. **(1)**
L 11 120 Collins St
Melbourne, VIC, 3000, Australia
Tel.: (61) 396664000
Fax: (61) 396664111
Steel Mfr
S.I.C.: 3399
N.A.I.C.S.: 331110

BlueScope Steel (AIS) Pty Ltd **(1)**
L 11 120 Collins St
Melbourne, VIC, 3000, Australia
Tel.: (61) 396664000
Fax: (61) 396664111
Steel Products Mfr
S.I.C.: 3399
N.A.I.C.S.: 331110

BlueScope Steel Asia Holdings Pty Ltd. **(1)**
L 11 120 Collins St
Melbourne, VIC, 3000, Australia
Tel.: (61) 396664000
Fax: (61) 396664111
E-Mail: hosupport@bluescopesteel.com
Web Site: www.bluescopesteel.com.au
Steel Product Mfr
S.I.C.: 3399
N.A.I.C.S.: 331110

BlueScope Steel (Finance) Ltd. **(1)**
L 11 120 Collins St
Melbourne, VIC, 3000, Australia
Tel.: (61) 396664000
Fax: (61) 396664111
Steel Mfr
S.I.C.: 3399
N.A.I.C.S.: 331110

BlueScope Steel Logistics Co Pty Ltd. **(1)**
L 11 120 Collins St
Melbourne, VIC, 3000, Australia
Tel.: (61) 396664000
Fax: (61) 396664111
Metal Products Logistics Services
S.I.C.: 4731
N.A.I.C.S.: 541614

BlueScope Water Pty Ltd. **(1)**
113 Dunheved Circuit
Saint Marys, NSW, 2760, Australia
Tel.: (61) 2 8801 9200
Fax: (61) 2 9833 9366
E-Mail: salesvic@bluescopewater.com.au
Web Site: www.bluescopewater.com
Water Tank Mfr
S.I.C.: 3443
N.A.I.C.S.: 332420

Fielders Australia Pty. Ltd. **(1)**
213 Railway Ter
Keswick, SA, 5035, Australia AU
Tel.: (61) 882923611 (100%)
Fax: (61) 882923626
E-Mail: info@fielders.com.au
Web Site: www.fielders.com.au
Emp.: 100
Providers of Household Audio & Video Equipment
S.I.C.: 3651
N.A.I.C.S.: 334310
Chris Stathy *(CEO)*

Laser Dynamics Australia Pty Ltd. **(1)**
96 Raubers Rd
Northgate, Brisbane, QLD, 4013, Australia
Tel.: (61) 7 3267 9666
Fax: (61) 7 3267 0300
Web Site: www.laserdynamics.com.au
Emp.: 20
Steel Mfr
S.I.C.: 3312
N.A.I.C.S.: 331110

Metalcorp Steel Pty Ltd. **(1)**
103 Ingram Road
Acacia Ridge, QLD, 4110, Australia
Tel.: (61) 7 3452 3888
Fax: (61) 7 3452 3899
Web Site: www.metalcorpsteel.com.au
Metal Products Mfr
S.I.C.: 3499
N.A.I.C.S.: 332999

New Zealand Steel (Aust) Pty Ltd. **(1)**
20 Council St
Hawthorn East, VIC, 3123, Australia
Tel.: (61) 398040788
Fax: (61) 396664111
Steel Product Mfr
S.I.C.: 3312
N.A.I.C.S.: 331110

Orrcon Operations Pty. Ltd. **(1)**
121 Evans Road Bldg 7
Salisbury, QLD, 4107, Australia AU
Tel.: (61) 732740660 (100%)
Fax: (61) 732740517
E-Mail: info@orrcon.com.au
Web Site: www.orrcon.com.au
Emp.: 200
Steel, Tube & Pipe Mfr & Distr
S.I.C.: 3317
N.A.I.C.S.: 331210
Leon Andrewartha *(Mng Dir)*

Pioneer Water Tanks (Australia) Pty Ltd. **(1)**
23 Clayton St
Bellevue, Perth, WA, 6056, Australia
Mailing Address:
PO Box 1874
Midland, WA, 6936, Australia
Tel.: (61) 8 9274 4577
E-Mail: info@pwtaust.com
Web Site: www.pioneertanks.com.au
Emp.: 10
Water Tanks Mfr & Distr
S.I.C.: 3443
N.A.I.C.S.: 332420
Daniel Wyatt *(Gen Mgr)*

The Roofing Centre (Tasmania) Pty Ltd. **(1)**
20 Mornington Rd
Mornington, Hobart, 7018, Australia
Tel.: (61) 3 6244 7055
Fax: (61) 3 6244 7027
Web Site: www.roofingcentretas.com.au
Residential & Industrial Roofing Services
S.I.C.: 1761
N.A.I.C.S.: 238160

U.S. Subsidiaries:

BlueScope Steel Americas LLC **(1)**
111 W Ocean Blvd Ste 1370
Long Beach, CA 90802
Tel.: (562) 491-1441
Fax: (562) 628-0111
Emp.: 10
Rolled Steel Shape Manufacturing
S.I.C.: 3312
N.A.I.C.S.: 331221
Dieter Schulz *(Pres)*

BlueScope Steel North America Corporation **(1)**
1540 Gebessee St
Kansas City, MO 64102
Tel.: (816) 968-3000
Fax: (816) 968-3720
Web Site: www.butlermfg.com
Emp.: 200
Steel Construction Products & Prefabricated Steel Building Mfr
S.I.C.: 3448
N.A.I.C.S.: 332311
Keith Mitchelhill *(Pres)*
Mark Vassella *(Pres-Australia)*

Subsidiaries:

ASC Profiles Inc. **(2)**
2110 Enterprise Blvd
West Sacramento, CA 95691-3428
Tel.: (916) 372-0933
Fax: (916) 372-0933
Toll Free: (800) 360-2477
E-Mail: info@ascprofiles.com
Web Site: www.ascprofiles.com
Emp.: 50
Steel Construction Materials & Building Mfr
S.I.C.: 3448
N.A.I.C.S.: 332311
John Cross *(Pres)*

BIEC International Inc **(2)**
1111 Main St Ste 545
Vancouver, WA 98660
Tel.: (360) 750-5791
Fax: (360) 750-5936
E-Mail: contact@biecint.com
Web Site: www.galvalume.com
Emp.: 3
Steel Sheet Mfr
S.I.C.: 3312
N.A.I.C.S.: 331110
Arif Humayun *(Pres)*

BlueScope Buildings North America Inc. **(2)**
273 Water St
Evansville, WI 53536-1433
Tel.: (608) 882-5000
Fax: (608) 882-2392
Construction Engineering Services
S.I.C.: 8711
N.A.I.C.S.: 541330

BlueScope Construction Inc. **(2)**
1540 Genessee St
Kansas City, MO 64102
Tel.: (816) 245-6000
Fax: (816) 245-6099
E-Mail: sales@bluescopeconstruction.com
Web Site: www.bucon.com
Emp.: 150
Construction Engineering Services
S.I.C.: 8711
N.A.I.C.S.: 541330
Kenny Strope *(Pres)*

Butler Manufacturing Company **(2)**
1540 Genessee St
Kansas City, MO 64102 DE
Mailing Address:
PO Box 419917
Kansas City, MO 64141-6917
Tel.: (816) 968-3000
Fax: (816) 968-3720
Web Site: www.butlermfg.com
Sales Range: $750-799.9 Million
Emp.: 4,300
Mfr of Pre-Engineered Buildings, Agricultural Buildings; Aluminum Extrusion & Finishing; Skylights & General Contracting
Import Export
S.I.C.: 3448
N.A.I.C.S.: 332311
Tom Gilligan *(Pres)*
Adam Newman *(Treas)*

Non-U.S. Subsidiaries:

BHP New Zealand Steel Ltd. **(3)**
131 Mission Bush Rd
2681 Glenbrook, S Auckland, New Zealand
Tel.: (64) 93758999
Fax: (64) 93758845
Web Site: www.nzsteel.co.nz
Emp.: 1,500
S.I.C.: 1011
N.A.I.C.S.: 212210
Simon Linge *(Gen Mgr)*

Butler (Shanghai), Inc. **(3)**
21st Bao Sheng Rd
Shanghai, Songjiang, 201600, China
Tel.: (86) 157741717
Fax: (86) 157741813
Web Site: www.butlerchina.com
Emp.: 30
Mfr. of Pre-Engineered Buildings, Agricultural Buildings; Aluminum Extrusion & Finishing; Skylights & General Contracting

S.I.C.: 3354
N.A.I.C.S.: 331318

Non-U.S. Affiliate:

Saudi Building Systems, Ltd. (3)
PO Box 8648
Jeddah, 21492, Saudi Arabia
Tel.: (966) 26370036
Fax: (966) 26352173
E-Mail: sbsmfg@saudibuilding.org
Web Site: www.saudibuilding.com
Emp.: 60
Mfr. of Pre-Engineered Metal Buildings
S.I.C.: 3448
N.A.I.C.S.: 332311
Butller Zufalli *(CEO)*

Steelscape Inc. (2)
222 W Kalama River Rd
Kalama, WA 98625-9420
Tel.: (360) 673-8200
Fax: (360) 673-8250
Web Site: www.steelscape.com
Emp.: 250
Coated Steel Coil Mfr
S.I.C.: 3312
N.A.I.C.S.: 331221
John Cross *(Pres)*

Varco Pruden Buildings, Inc. (2)
3200 Players Club Cir
Memphis, TN 38125-8843 DE
Mailing Address:
3200 Players Club Cir
Memphis, TN 38125-8843
Tel.: (901) 748-8000
Fax: (901) 748-9323
Toll Free: (800) 238-3246
E-Mail: vpsales@vp.com
Web Site: www.vp.com
Sls.: $400,000,000
Emp.: 1,800
Prefabricated Metal Building Mfr
Import Export
S.I.C.: 3448
N.A.I.C.S.: 332311
Chuck Haslebacher *(Pres)*
Skip Hannah *(CFO & VP-Fin)*

VSMA Inc (2)
1540 Genessee St
Kansas City, MO 64102-1069
Tel.: (816) 968-3000
Steel Products Mfr
S.I.C.: 3399
N.A.I.C.S.: 331110

Non-U.S. Subsidiaries:

BlueScope Acier Nouvelle Caledonie SA (1)
238 Route de la Baie des Dames
BP 3424
98846 Noumea, New Caledonia
Tel.: (687) 282 944
Fax: (687) 271 540
Steel Products Mfr
S.I.C.: 3312
N.A.I.C.S.: 331110

BlueScope Buildings (Guangzhou) Ltd. (1)
No 98 Pubei Rd Dongcheng Area Yunpu Industrial Zone Huangpu
Guangzhou, Guangdong, 510530, China
Tel.: (86) 2082251717
Fax: (86) 2082250001
Steel Product Mfr
S.I.C.: 3399
N.A.I.C.S.: 331110

BlueScope Buildings (Vietnam) Limited (1)
No 3 Road 9A Bien Hoa 2 Industrial Zone
Bien Hoa, Dong Nai, Vietnam
Tel.: (84) 61 3836245
Fax: (84) 61 3836220
Steel Product Mfr
S.I.C.: 3399
N.A.I.C.S.: 331110

BlueScope Lysaght (Brunei) Sdn Bhd (1)
Industrial Complex Beribi Phase 1 6Km Jln Gadong
Bandar Seri Begawan, BE 1118, Brunei Darussalam
Tel.: (673) 2447155
Fax: (673) 2447154
E-Mail: bluescope@brunet.bn
Emp.: 27
Roofing & Walling Material Distr
S.I.C.: 5033
N.A.I.C.S.: 423330
Sim Kean Chye *(Pres)*

BlueScope Lysaght (Chengdu) Ltd. (1)
West Avenue of Chengdu Economic And Technological Development Zone
Longquanyi District, Chengdu, Sichuan, 610100, China
Tel.: (86) 2884848686
Fax: (86) 28 84848333
Web Site: www.bluescopesteelasia.com
Steel Product Mfr
S.I.C.: 3312
N.A.I.C.S.: 331110

BlueScope Lysaght Fiji Ltd. (1)
169-171 Lakeba Street
Samabula, Suva, Fiji
Tel.: (679) 338 2388
Fax: (679) 337 0102
E-Mail: info.fiji@bluescopesteel.com.fj
Emp.: 42
Steel Product Mfr
S.I.C.: 3312
N.A.I.C.S.: 331110
Stuart Hill *(Gen Mgr)*

BlueScope Lysaght (Sabah) Sdn Bhd (1)
Lorong Kurma Off Jalan Kolombong
Kota Kinabalu, Sabah, Malaysia
Tel.: (60) 88445161
Fax: (60) 88421178
E-Mail: general@lysaghtsabah.com
Emp.: 45
Steel Product Mfr
S.I.C.: 3399
N.A.I.C.S.: 331110

BlueScope Lysaght (Shanghai) Ltd. (1)
No 855 Kangqiao Rd Kangqiao Industrial Zone
Shanghai, 201315, China
Tel.: (86) 2158120138
Fax: (86) 2158121363
Steel Product Mfr
S.I.C.: 3399
N.A.I.C.S.: 331110

Bluescope Lysaght Singapore Pte. Ltd. (1)
18 Benoi Sector
629851 Singapore, Singapore
Tel.: (65) 62641577
Fax: (65) 62650951
Web Site: www.bluescopesteel.com
Emp.: 80
Steel Products
S.I.C.: 3312
N.A.I.C.S.: 331110

BlueScope Lysaght (Thailand) Ltd. (1)
16 Soi Phaholyothin 96 Prachatipat
Thanyaburi, Pathumthani, 12130, Thailand
Tel.: (66) 25249800
Fax: (66) 2 524 9801
E-Mail: BLT.marketing@bluescopesteel.com
Web Site: www.bluescopelysaght.co.th
Emp.: 400
Steel Product Mfr
S.I.C.: 3312
N.A.I.C.S.: 331110
Wuttichart Anansuthivara *(Pres)*

BlueScope Lysaght (Vanuatu) Ltd. (1)
Route de Tagabe
PO Box 453
Port-Vila, Vanuatu
Tel.: (678) 23261
Fax: (678) 25906
E-Mail: bluescopesteelvan@vanuatu.com.vu
Steel Mfr
S.I.C.: 3312
N.A.I.C.S.: 331110
Narcisse Sumtoh *(Gen Mgr)*

BlueScope Steel Asia Pte Ltd. (1)
20 Anson Road 09-01 Twenty Anson
Singapore, 079912, Singapore
Tel.: (65) 63333378
Fax: (65) 62211995
Web Site: www.bluescopesteelasia.com
Emp.: 35
Steel Product Mfr
S.I.C.: 3312
N.A.I.C.S.: 331110
Sanjay Dayal *(CEO)*

BlueScope Steel International Limited. (1)
50 Southwark Street
SE1 1UN London, United Kingdom
Tel.: (44) 2070898800
Fax: (44) 2070898700
Emp.: 5
Steel Product Mfr
S.I.C.: 3312
N.A.I.C.S.: 331110

BlueScope Steel International Trading (Shanghai) Co.,Ltd. (1)
12 f Hsbc Tower No 1000 Lujiazui Ring Rd
Pudong New Dist, Shanghai, 200120, China
Tel.: (86) 2168411898
Fax: (86) 2168413628
Steel Mfr
S.I.C.: 3399
N.A.I.C.S.: 331110

BlueScope Steel Investment Management (Shanghai) Ltd. (1)
12 f Hsbc Tower No 1000 Lujiazui Ring Rd
Pudong New Dist, Shanghai, 200120, China
Tel.: (86) 2168411898
Fax: (86) 2168411760
Steel Mfr
S.I.C.: 3312
N.A.I.C.S.: 331110

BlueScope Steel (Malaysia) Sdn Bhd (1)
Lot 1551 Jalan Bukit Kapar
Kapar, Selangor, 42200, Malaysia
Tel.: (60) 333616888
Fax: (60) 3 3361 6889
E-Mail: enquiries@bluescopesteel.com
Web Site: www.bluescopesteel.com.my
Emp.: 500
Steel Product Mfr
S.I.C.: 3399
N.A.I.C.S.: 331110
Gan Ching Kok *(Gen Mgr)*

BlueScope Steel North Asia Ltd (1)
A6 12F No 6 Su Wei 3rd Road
Kaohsiung, Taiwan
Tel.: (886) 7 333 6900
Fax: (886) 7 333 6907
Emp.: 3
Steel Product Mfr
S.I.C.: 3399
N.A.I.C.S.: 331110

BlueScope Steel Philippines Inc (1)
603 SEDCCO I Building 120 Rada Corner Legaspi Str
Legaspi Village, Makati, 1229, Philippines
Tel.: (63) 28170121
Fax: (63) 28177832
E-Mail: mauro.cervantes@bluescopesteel.com
Emp.: 3
Steel Product Mfr
S.I.C.: 3312
N.A.I.C.S.: 331110

BlueScope Steel Southern Africa (Pty) Ltd. (1)
Ground Floor Black River Park Block D
Fir Road Observatory, Cape Town, 7700, South Africa
Tel.: (27) 21 442 5420
Fax: (27) 21 448 9132
Steel Products Distr
S.I.C.: 5051
N.A.I.C.S.: 423510

BlueScope Steel (Suzhou) Ltd (1)
12F HSBC Tower 1000 Lujiazui Ring Road
Pudong, Shanghai, 200120, China
Tel.: (86) 51 2628 31288
Fax: (86) 21 6841 3628
Steel Product Mfr
S.I.C.: 3399
N.A.I.C.S.: 331110

BlueScope Steel (Thailand) Ltd. (1)
7th Floor Bangkok Thai Tower 108 Rangnam Road
Phaya Thai Rajthevi, Bangkok, 10400, Thailand
Tel.: (66) 2333 3000
Fax: (66) 2333 3001
Web Site: www.bluescopesteel.co.th
Steel Product Mfr
S.I.C.: 3399
N.A.I.C.S.: 331110
Jason Ellis *(Pres)*

BlueScope Steel Trading NZ Ltd. (1)
Downtown House Queen St
PO Box 92121
Auckland, 1001, New Zealand
Tel.: (64) 93758999
Steel Products Mfr
S.I.C.: 3312
N.A.I.C.S.: 331110

BlueScope Steel Vietnam Limited. (1)
2nd floor Eastern Asia Bank 51 Nguyen Van Linh Street
Hai Chau District, Da Nang, Vietnam
Tel.: (84) 511 3584114
Fax: (84) 511 3584115
Steel Products Mfr
S.I.C.: 3399
N.A.I.C.S.: 331110

New Zealand Steel Development Ltd. (1)
131 Mission Bush Rd Glenbrook
Auckland, 2681, New Zealand
Tel.: (64) 93758999
Fax: (64) 93758845
Web Site: www.newzealandsteel.co.nz
Emp.: 1,300
Steel Products Mfr
S.I.C.: 3399
N.A.I.C.S.: 331110
Andrew Garry *(Gen Mgr)*

New Zealand Steel Holdings Ltd. (1)
131 Mission Bush Road Glenbrook
Auckland, 1852, New Zealand
Tel.: (64) 93758999
Fax: (64) 93758845
Steel Product Mfr
S.I.C.: 3399
N.A.I.C.S.: 331110
Simon Linge *(Pres)*

PT BlueScope Lysaght Indonesia (1)
Jl Irian Blok DD2-2 Kawasan Industri MM2100
Cibitung, Bekasi, West Java, Indonesia
Tel.: (62) 21 8998 2965
Fax: (62) 21 8998 2966
Emp.: 150
Steel Product Mfr
S.I.C.: 3312
N.A.I.C.S.: 331110

Steelcap Insurance Pte Ltd. (1)
18 Cross Street 04-00 Marsh And Mclennan Centre
Singapore, 048423, Singapore
Tel.: (65) 62208141
Fax: (65) 62208142
Steel Product Mfr
S.I.C.: 3312
N.A.I.C.S.: 331110

BLUESOURCE LTD.

122 Tooley Street
London, SE1 2TU, United Kingdom
Tel.: (44) 2079406200
Fax: (44) 2079406201
E-Mail: sales@bluesource.co.uk
Web Site: www.bluesource.co.uk
Year Founded: 2000
Sales Range: $10-24.9 Million
Emp.: 65

Business Description:
IT Services
S.I.C.: 7373
N.A.I.C.S.: 541512

Personnel:
Andy Ward *(Co-Founder & CEO)*
Andrew Mckeeve *(Co-Founder & COO)*
Matthew Edwards *(CTO)*

BLUESTAR NEW CHEMICAL MATERIALS CO., LTD.

Sixth floor West Beitucheng Road
Chaoyang District, Beijing, China
100029

Bluestar New Chemical Materials Co., Ltd.—(Continued)

Tel.: (86) 10 61958802
E-Mail: xc1-oo8@star-nm.com
Web Site: www.star-nm.com
Year Founded: 1999
600299—(SHG)
Business Description:
Chemical Product Mfr & Distr
S.I.C.: 2899
N.A.I.C.S.: 325998
Personnel:
Xiaobao Lu *(Chm)*

BLUESTAR SECUTECH INC.

14th Floor Tower A Chengjian Plaza18 Beitaipingzhuang Road
Haidian District, Beijing, 100088, China
Tel.: (86) 1082255855
Fax: (86) 1082255955
E-Mail: beijing@bstar.com.cn
Web Site: www.bstar.com.cn
Year Founded: 2006
BSST—(LSE)
Rev.: $29,507,341
Assets: $62,716,045
Liabilities: $16,531,361
Net Worth: $46,184,684
Earnings: $516,898
Emp.: 505
Fiscal Year-end: 03/31/13
Business Description:
Surveillance Equipment Mfr & Distr
S.I.C.: 3699
N.A.I.C.S.: 335999
Personnel:
Gang Xiao *(CEO)*
Antonia Dan Ping *(CFO & Sec)*
Caiguang He *(CTO)*
Jin Qing Liu *(Sr VP & Dir-Production Dept)*
Hui Dong Xing *(Sr VP & Dir-Sls Dept)*
Board of Directors:
Xiaochuan Liu
Caiguang He
Jin Qing Liu
Kean Eek Teo
Derrick Woolf
Gang Xiao
Hui Dong Xing
Legal Counsel:
Tian Yuan Law Firm
11th Fl Tower C Corporate Square No 35 Finance St
Beijing, China

Harney Westwood & Riegels
Craigmuir Chambers PO Box 71 Road Town
Tortola, Virgin Islands (British)

Edwin Coe LLP
2 Stone Buildings Lincolns Inn
London, WC2A 4AR, United Kingdom

BLUESTONE GLOBAL LIMITED

(Formerly Humanis Group Limited)
Level 2 420 St Kilda Road
Melbourne, VIC, 3004, Australia
Mailing Address:
PO Box 1052
Booragoon, WA, 6954, Australia
Tel.: (61) 3 9685 4400
Fax: (61) 8 9696 5451
E-Mail: info@bglcorporate.com
Web Site: www.bglcorporate.com
BUE—(ASX)
Rev.: $292,507,577
Assets: $65,927,339
Liabilities: $81,494,964
Net Worth: ($15,567,624)
Earnings: ($57,037,634)
Emp.: 203
Fiscal Year-end: 06/30/13
Business Description:
Recruitment, Professional Placement & Labor Hiring Services
S.I.C.: 7361
N.A.I.C.S.: 561311
Personnel:
Andrew Plympton *(Chm)*
Tony Leibowitz *(Deputy Chm)*
Justin Owen *(CFO)*
Sophie Karzis *(Sec)*
Board of Directors:
Andrew Plympton
Tony Leibowitz
Legal Counsel:
Price Sierakowski Lawyers
Level 24 Saint Martins Tower
44 Saint Georges Terrace
Perth, WA, 600, Australia
Subsidiaries:

Westaff (Australia) Pty. Ltd. **(1)**
Level 3 100 Albert Road 4th Floor
Melbourne, VIC, 3205, Australia AU
Tel.: (61) 396965451
Fax: (61) 396965451
E-Mail: contact_headoffice@westaff.com.au
Web Site: www.westaff.com.au
Sales Range: $100-124.9 Million
Emp.: 27
Temporary Help Services
S.I.C.: 7363
N.A.I.C.S.: 561320
Nigel Haworth *(Mng Dir)*

Non-U.S. Subsidiary:

Westaff NZ Limited **(2)**
Level 1 14 Oimietion Road
PO Box 21
7034 Potiny Junction, Auckland, New Zealand NZ
Tel.: (64) 95255990
Fax: (64) 953650932
E-Mail: marisa.nelson@westaff.co.nz
Web Site: www.westaff.co.nz
Sales Range: $1-9.9 Million
Emp.: 15
Temporary Help Service
S.I.C.: 7363
N.A.I.C.S.: 561320
Steve Sargent *(Gen Mgr)*

BLUESTONE RESOURCES INC.

1020 - 800 West Pender Street
Vancouver, BC, V6C 2V6, Canada
Tel.: (604) 646-4527
Fax: (604) 646-4526
E-Mail: info@bluestoneresources.ca
Web Site: www.bluestoneresources.ca
Year Founded: 2004
BSR—(TSXV)
Int. Income: $1,769
Assets: $3,427,284
Liabilities: $529,419
Net Worth: $2,897,865
Earnings: ($3,951,194)
Fiscal Year-end: 11/30/12
Business Description:
Diamond Exploration Services
S.I.C.: 1481
N.A.I.C.S.: 213115
Personnel:
John Robins *(Chm, Pres & CEO)*
Edward Low *(CFO)*
Jeff Dare *(Corp Sec)*
Board of Directors:
John Robins
Craig L. Bentham
Dave Kelsch
David McAdam
Jim Paterson
Transfer Agent:
Olympia Trust Company (Calgary)
1900 Cathedral Place 925 West Georgia Street
Vancouver, BC, Canada

BLUETAIL INC.

ul Polna 3A / lok 12
00-412 Warsaw, Poland
Tel.: (48) 604 954 380
Fax: (48) 17 871 44 25
E-Mail: info@bluetail.com
Web Site: www.bluetail.com
TBL—(DEU)
Business Description:
Holding Company; Hydroelectric Power Generation
S.I.C.: 6712
N.A.I.C.S.: 551111
Personnel:
Artur Lagodzinski *(CEO)*
Roman Gruszczynski *(COO)*

BLUEWATER POWER DISTRIBUTION CORPORATION

855 Confederation St
PO Box 2140
Sarnia, ON, N7T 7L6, Canada
Tel.: (519) 337-8201
Fax: (519) 332-3878
E-Mail: emailus@bluewaterpower.com
Web Site: www.bluewaterpower.com
Year Founded: 1917
Rev.: $47,700,000
Emp.: 73
Business Description:
Electrical Contractors
S.I.C.: 1731
N.A.I.C.S.: 238210
Personnel:
G. Firman Bentley *(Chm)*
Richard Grogan *(Vice Chm)*
Janice L. McMichael-Dennis *(Pres & CEO)*
Board of Directors:
G. Firman Bentley
Steve Bolt
Ray Curran
Brad Goodhill
Richard Grogan
Glenn Jones

BLUFOREST INC.

Ave Republica del Salvador y Shyris
Edificio Onix piso 10 C
Quito, Ecuador
Tel.: (593) 9 3762435
E-Mail: info@bluforest.com
Web Site: www.bluforest.com
Year Founded: 2008
BLUF—(OTC)
Assets: $698,962,128
Liabilities: $3,684,652
Net Worth: $695,277,476
Earnings: ($277,645,056)
Fiscal Year-end: 12/31/12
Business Description:
Carbon Offsets Marketer
S.I.C.: 5169
N.A.I.C.S.: 424690
Personnel:
Charles Miller *(Pres, CEO, CFO & Treas)*
Transfer Agent:
Signature Stock Transfer
2220 Coit Rd Ste 480
Plano, TX 75023

BLUGLASS LIMITED

74 Asquith Street
Silverwater, NSW, 2128, Australia
Tel.: (61) 293342300
Fax: (61) 297482122
E-Mail: admin@bluglass.com.au
Web Site: www.bluglass.com.au
BLG—(ASX)
Rev.: $187,696
Assets: $18,588,528
Liabilities: $741,081
Net Worth: $17,847,446
Earnings: ($1,747,316)
Emp.: 16
Fiscal Year-end: 06/30/13
Business Description:
Semiconductor Device Mfr
S.I.C.: 3674
N.A.I.C.S.: 334413
Personnel:
Giles Bourne *(CEO)*
Stuart Uhlhorn *(CFO)*
Ian Mann *(CTO & COO)*
Emmanuel Correia *(Sec)*
Board of Directors:
George Venardos
Gregory Cornelson
William Johnson
Chandra Kantamneni

BLUMETRIC ENVIRONMENTAL INC.

3108 Carp Road
PO Box 430
Ottawa, ON, K0A 1L0, Canada
Tel.: (613) 839-3053
Fax: (613) 839-5376
E-Mail: info@blumetric.ca
Web Site: www.blumetric.ca
Year Founded: 1985
BLM—(TSXV)
Rev.: $28,373,768
Assets: $17,806,007
Liabilities: $12,208,695
Net Worth: $5,597,312
Earnings: ($2,083,121)
Emp.: 50
Fiscal Year-end: 09/30/13
Business Description:
Water & Wastewater Treatment Solutions
S.I.C.: 9511
N.A.I.C.S.: 924110
Personnel:
Jordan B. Grant *(Chm)*
William M. Touzel *(Co-CEO)*
Roger M. Woeller *(Co-CEO)*
Ian W. Malone *(CFO)*
Dan L. Scroggins *(Pres-Water)*
Nell van Walsum *(Pres-Pro Svcs)*
Board of Directors:
Jordan B. Grant
Denis H. J. Douville
Murray J. Malley
Jane Pagel
William M. Touzel
Roger M. Woeller
Legal Counsel:
Miltons LLP
Ottawa, ON, Canada
Transfer Agent:
Computershare Investor Services Inc.
100 University Ave 9th Floor
Toronto, ON, Canada
Subsidiaries:

Seprotech **(1)**
2378 Holly Lane
Ottawa, ON, K1V 7P1, Canada
Tel.: (613) 523-1641
Fax: (613) 731-3087
Toll Free: (800) 353-3087
Web Site: www.seprotech.com
Wastewater Treatment Services
S.I.C.: 4941
N.A.I.C.S.: 221310

WESAtech **(1)**
3108 Carp Road
PO Box 430
Ottawa, ON, K0A 1L0, Canada
Tel.: (613) 839-3053
Fax: (613) 839-5376
E-Mail: wesacarp@wesa.ca
Web Site: www.wesa.ca
Water & Wastewater Treatment Projects Developer
S.I.C.: 1629
N.A.I.C.S.: 237110
Nell van Walsum *(Pres)*

U.S. Subsidiary:

CMS Group Inc. **(1)**
3973 75th St Ste 101
Aurora, IL 60504

Tel.: (630) 585-7767
Fax: (630) 585-7790
E-Mail: info@cmsolutionsgroup.com
Web Site: www.cmsolutionsgroup.com
Software Consulting Services
S.I.C.: 7373
N.A.I.C.S.: 541512
Mary Davolt *(Pres)*

BLUMONT GROUP LTD.

298 Tiong Bahru Road 20-02/03
Central Plaza
Singapore, 168730, Singapore
Tel.: (65) 63329488
Fax: (65) 63329489
Web Site: www.blumontgroup.com
Year Founded: 1993
A33—(SES)
Rev.: $32,283,279
Assets: $99,680,300
Liabilities: $15,136,755
Net Worth: $84,543,544
Earnings: $22,819,532
Emp.: 94
Fiscal Year-end: 12/31/12
Business Description:
Investment Holding Company
S.I.C.: 6719
N.A.I.C.S.: 551112
Personnel:
Kim Hock Neo *(Chm)*
Alexander Alan Molyneux *(Chm-Designate)*
Che Mei Sin *(Co-Sec)*
Choi Fan Toon *(Co-Sec)*
Board of Directors:
Kim Hock Neo
Boon Kok Goh
James Gee Ho Hong
Calvin Huan Kim Lim
Non-U.S. Holding:

Azarga Resources (Hong Kong) Limited (1)
Suite 4607-11 The Center 99 Queen's Road Central, China (Hong Kong) HK
Tel.: (852) 3796 7105
Fax: (852) 3796 7000
Uranium & Rare Earth Elements Exploration
S.I.C.: 1081
N.A.I.C.S.: 213114
Alexander Alan Molyneux *(Chm)*

BLUNDELL SEAFOODS LTD.

11351 River Road
Richmond, BC, V6X 1Z6, Canada
Tel.: (604) 270-3300
Fax: (604) 270-6513
E-Mail: info@blundellseafoods.com
Web Site: www.blundellseafoods.com
Year Founded: 1975
Rev.: $29,387,393
Emp.: 75
Business Description:
Seafood Products Whslr
S.I.C.: 5146
N.A.I.C.S.: 424460
Personnel:
Rick Ogilvie *(VP-Sls)*

BLUNDEN CONSTRUCTION LTD.

519 Herring Cove Rd
PO Box 280
Halifax, NS, B3J 2P3, Canada
Tel.: (902) 477-2531
Fax: (902) 477-0290
E-Mail: info@blunden.com
Web Site: www.blunden.com
Year Founded: 1949
Rev.: $11,082,640
Emp.: 50
Business Description:
Construction Services
S.I.C.: 1541
N.A.I.C.S.: 236210
Personnel:
Douglas Blunden *(Pres)*
Debra Paquin *(Sec)*

BLUO SICAV-SIF

2 rue Heinrich Heine
L 1720, Luxembourg, Luxembourg
Tel.: (352) 26302605
Fax: (352) 26302607
E-Mail: contact@blu-o.lu
Web Site: www.blu-o.lu
Business Description:
Private Equity Firm
S.I.C.: 6211
N.A.I.C.S.: 523999
Personnel:
Lothar Rafalski *(Chm)*
Board of Directors:
Lothar Rafalski
Stefan Beulertz
Hans-Michael Deml
Non-U.S. Holdings:

AlzChem Holding GmbH (1)
CHEMIEPARK TROSTBERG
Dr Albert Frank Str 32, 83303 Trostberg, Germany
Tel.: (49) 8621860
Fax: (49) 8621862911
E-Mail: info@alzchem.de
Web Site: www.alzchem.com
Emp.: 1,300
Specialty Chemical Mfr
S.I.C.: 2899
N.A.I.C.S.: 325998
Stefan Greger *(Mng Dir)*
Andreas Niedermaier *(Mng Dir)*
Ulli Seibel *(Mng Dir)*

Subsidiaries:

AlzChem Trostberg GmbH (2)
Dr Albert Frank Strasse 32
83308 Trostberg, Germany
Tel.: (49) 8621860
Fax: (49) 86212911
E-Mail: info@alzchem.com
Web Site: www.alzchem.com
Emp.: 1,000
Chemical Mfr
S.I.C.: 2899
N.A.I.C.S.: 325998
Stefan Greger *(Mng Dir-Comml)*

NIGU Chemie GmbH (2)
Beuthener Strasse 2
84478 Waldkraiburg, Germany
Mailing Address:
Postfach 16 20
84469 Waldkraiburg, Germany
Tel.: (49) 86389620
Fax: (49) 8638962287
E-Mail: info@nigu.de
Web Site: www.nigu.de
Emp.: 60
Mfr of Guanidine Salts
S.I.C.: 2899
N.A.I.C.S.: 325998
Sigmund Walz *(Gen Mgr)*

Evotape S.p.A. (1)
Via Per Binadrate 59
San Pietro Mosezzo, 28060 Novara, Italy
Tel.: (39) 0321540201
Fax: (39) 0321540255
E-Mail: info.packaging@evotape.com
Web Site: www.evotape.com
Sales Range: $50-74.9 Million
Emp.: 10
Adhesive Tape Mfr
Export
S.I.C.: 2891
N.A.I.C.S.: 325520
Martin Vorderwullbecke *(Pres)*

Pit-Stop Auto Service GmbH (1)
Seligenstadter Grund 11
D-63150 Heusenstamm, Germany De (100%)
Tel.: (49) 610496170
Fax: (49) 6104961717
E-Mail: info@pit-stop.de
Web Site: www.pit-stop.de
Emp.: 1,500
Automotive Tires, Parts & Repair Shops Operator
S.I.C.: 7538
N.A.I.C.S.: 811111
Oliver Apelt *(Chm-Mgmt Bd & Mng Dir)*
Hermann Scheck *(Member-Mgmt Bd)*

Rohner AG (1)
Gempenstrasse 6
4133 Pratteln, Switzerland
Tel.: (41) 618251111
Fax: (41) 618251271
E-Mail:
Web Site: www.rohnerchem.ch
Sales Range: $25-49.9 Million
Emp.: 230
Chemical Mfr
S.I.C.: 2899
N.A.I.C.S.: 325998
Thomas Rosatzin *(CEO)*

BLUR (GROUP) PLC

Studios 2-8 Westbourne Studios
242 Acklam Road, London, W10 5JJ, United Kingdom
Tel.: (44) 20 31764406
Web Site: www.blurgroup.com
BLUR—(AIM)
Business Description:
Business To Business Electronic Markets
S.I.C.: 7389
N.A.I.C.S.: 425110
Personnel:
Philip Letts *(CEO)*
James Davis *(CFO)*
Jon Hogg *(Chief Platform Officer)*
Dorothy Mead *(Chief Acq Officer)*
Board of Directors:
Richard Bourne-Arton
Robert Brooksbank
Kara Cardinale
Philip Letts
David Sherriff

BLUTIP POWER TECHNOLOGIES LTD.

6705 Millcreek Drive Unit 4
Mississauga, ON, L5N 5M4, Canada
Tel.: (905) 363-3634
Fax: (905) 363-0168
Toll Free: (888) 359-5697
E-Mail: info@blutipower.com
Web Site: www.blutipower.com
Year Founded: 1996
Sales Range: Less than $1 Million
Business Description:
Diesel-Powered Engine Control Solutions Developer & Mfr
S.I.C.: 3519
N.A.I.C.S.: 333618
Personnel:
Chuck Knott *(Pres & CEO)*
Fred Florence *(CFO)*

BM&FBOVESPA SA

Praca Antonio Prado 48 Centro
Sao Paulo, SP, Brazil 01010-901
Tel.: (55) 11 2565 4000
Fax: (55) 11 2565 5314
E-Mail: info@bmfbovespa.com.br
Web Site: www.bmfbovespa.com.br
Year Founded: 1890
BVMF3—(BRAZ)
Rev.: $1,015,629,878
Assets: $11,877,723,905
Liabilities: $2,328,229,488
Net Worth: $9,549,494,417
Earnings: $528,415,784
Emp.: 1,442
Fiscal Year-end: 12/31/12
Business Description:
Stock Exchange Services
S.I.C.: 6231
N.A.I.C.S.: 523210
Personnel:
Pedro Pullen Parente *(Chm)*
Marcelo Fernandez Trindade *(Vice Chm)*
Edemir Pinto *(CEO)*
Daniel Sonder *(CFO & Chief Corp Affairs Officer)*
Cicero Augusto Vieira Neto *(COO)*
Luis Otavio Saliba Furtado *(CTO & Chief Info Security Officer)*
Eduardo Refinetti Guardia *(Chief Product Officer & Chief IR Officer)*
Claudio Avanian Jacob *(Plng & IR Officer)*
Board of Directors:
Pedro Pullen Parente
Candido Botelho Bracher
Charles Peter Carey
Claudio Luiz da Silva Haddad
Jose Roberto Mendonca de Barros
Luiz Nelson Guedes de Carvalho
Jose de Menezes Berenguer Neto
Alfredo Antonio Lima de Menezes
Andre Santos Esteves
Luiz Fernando Figueiredo
Marcelo Fernandez Trindade
U.S. Subsidiary:

BM&F USA Inc. (1)
61 Broadway 26th Fl Ste 2605
New York, NY 10006-2828
Tel.: (212) 750-4197
Fax: (212) 750-4198
Investment Management Services
S.I.C.: 6211
N.A.I.C.S.: 523999

BM POLYCO LTD.

Crown Road
Enfield, Middlesex, EN1 1TX, United Kingdom
Tel.: (44) 20 8443 9010
Fax: (44) 20 8443 9011
E-Mail: sales@polyco.co.uk
Web Site: www.polyco.co.uk
Year Founded: 1979
Sales Range: $75-99.9 Million
Emp.: 132
Business Description:
Glove Mfr
S.I.C.: 3089
N.A.I.C.S.: 326199
Personnel:
Mark Holdaway *(Mng Dir)*

BMH TECHNOLOGY OY

Sinkokatu 11
PO Box 32
Sinkokatu 11, 26101 Rauma, Finland
Tel.: (358) 204866800
Fax: (358) 204866990
E-Mail: customer@bmh.fi
Web Site: www.bmh.fi
Sls.: $40,000,000
Emp.: 120
Business Description:
Mfr of Biomass Fuel & Ash Handling Systems, Waste Processing Plants & Chip & Bark Handling Systems
S.I.C.: 3553
N.A.I.C.S.: 333243
Personnel:
Peter Wallenius *(VP)*
Non-U.S. Subsidiary:

BMH Wood Technology AB (1)
Kaptensgatan 23
PO Box 12
745 21 Enkoping, Sweden
Tel.: (46) 17124374
Fax: (46) 17124371
Web Site: www.bmh.fi
Spare Parts & Repair Services
S.I.C.: 5065
N.A.I.C.S.: 423690

BML, INC.

5-21-3 Sendagaya
Shibuya-ku, Tokyo, 151-0051, Japan
Tel.: (81) 3 3350 0111

BML, Inc.—(Continued)

Fax: (81) 3 33501180
Web Site: www.bml.co.jp
Year Founded: 1955
4694—(TKS)
Sls.: $1,040,688,000
Assets: $913,517,000
Liabilities: $331,144,000
Net Worth: $582,373,000
Earnings: $40,788,000
Emp.: 3,866
Fiscal Year-end: 03/31/13

Business Description:
Laboratory Testing Services
S.I.C.: 8734
N.A.I.C.S.: 541380

Personnel:
Yutaka Arai *(Chm)*
Kazuta Fukuda *(Pres)*
Nobuki Arai *(Exec Officer)*
Masato Chikira *(Operating Officer)*
Kensuke Kondo *(Operating Officer)*
Toshiyuki Koreyasu *(Exec Officer)*
Yasuyuki Kudo *(Operating Officer)*
Masao Nakagawa *(Operating Officer)*
Takashi Otsuka *(Exec Officer)*
Kazuo Shigeta *(Operating Officer)*
Hideya Suda *(Operating Officer)*
Hiroshi Tanabe *(Exec Officer)*
Itaru Uehara *(Operating Officer)*
Katsushi Yamashita *(Operating Officer)*

Board of Directors:
Yutaka Arai
Nobuki Arai
Masato Chikira
Kazuta Fukuda
Kenji Kondo
Kensuke Kondo
Toshiyuki Koreyasu
Takashi Otsuka
Hiroshi Tanabe
Toshio Yamamura
Katsushi Yamashita

Subsidiaries:

BML Food Science Solutions, Inc. **(1)**
2-51-13 Ikebukuro
Toshima-ku, 171-0014 Tokyo, Japan
Tel.: (81) 339884602
Fax: (81) 339891646
E-Mail: tfujita@bml.co.jp
Web Site: www.bml.co.jp/eng/about_bml/group.html
All Other Miscellaneous Ambulatory Health Care Services
S.I.C.: 8099
N.A.I.C.S.: 621999
Fujita Takashi *(Mgr-Mktg)*

BML Fukushima, Inc. **(1)**
29-1 Azaippongi Oyama
Fukushima, 960-8252, Japan
Tel.: (81) 245330806
Fax: (81) 245330807
Clinical Laboratory Testing Services
S.I.C.: 8734
N.A.I.C.S.: 541380

BML Life Science Holdings, Inc. **(1)**
5-21-3 Sendagaya
Shibuya-ku, Tokyo, 151-0051, Japan
Tel.: (81) 333500259
Fax: (81) 333501180
Investment Management Services
S.I.C.: 6282
N.A.I.C.S.: 523920

BML Medical Works, Inc. **(1)**
1361-1 Matoba
Kawagoe, Saitama, 350-1101, Japan
Tel.: (81) 492320010
Fax: (81) 492320011
Emp.: 20
Medical Instruments & Materials Distr
S.I.C.: 5047
N.A.I.C.S.: 423450
Satoshi Enomoto *(Pres)*

Daiichi Clinical Laboratories, Inc. **(1)**
3-5-10 7Jo Fushiko
Higashi-ku, Sapporo, Hokkaido, 007-0867, Japan
Tel.: (81) 117872111
Fax: (81) 1 1787 2191
Clinical Laboratory Testing Services
S.I.C.: 8071
N.A.I.C.S.: 621511

Ehime Medical Laboratories, Inc. **(1)**
6-1-4 Yogonishi
Matsuyama, Ehime, 790 0046, Japan
Tel.: (81) 899650205
Fax: (81) 899650288
Clinical Laboratory Testing Services
S.I.C.: 8071
N.A.I.C.S.: 621511

Japan Clinical Service, Inc. **(1)**
1-34-5 Koenjiminami
Suginami-Ku, Tokyo, 166-0003, Japan
Tel.: (81) 333165223
Fax: (81) 353782678
Specimen Receiving Services
S.I.C.: 8734
N.A.I.C.S.: 541380

Kyodo Igaku Laboratories, Inc. **(1)**
5-20-25 Matsushima
Higashi-Ku, Fukuoka, Japan
Tel.: (81) 926221319
All Other Miscellaneous Ambulatory Health Care Services
S.I.C.: 8099
N.A.I.C.S.: 621999
Takei Akira *(Mgr)*

Labotec, Inc. (Chiba) **(1)**
1-1-12 Higashikokubunjidai
Ichihara, Chiba, 290-0074, Japan
Tel.: (81) 4 3622 8425
Fax: (81) 4 3625 0660
Clinical Laboratory Testing Services
S.I.C.: 8071
N.A.I.C.S.: 621511

Matsudo Medical Laboratories, Inc. **(1)**
23-16 Matsudoshinden
Matsudo, Chiba, 270-2241, Japan
Tel.: (81) 473664111
Fax: (81) 4 7366 5556
Clinical Laboratory Testing Services
S.I.C.: 8071
N.A.I.C.S.: 621511

Nikken Igaku, Inc. **(1)**
110-25 Wadanakacho
Fukui, 918-8235, Japan
Tel.: (81) 776303702
Fax: (81) 776300782
Emp.: 60
Clinical Laboratory Testing Services
S.I.C.: 8071
N.A.I.C.S.: 621511
Masaaki Hirose *(Pres)*

PCL Japan, Inc. **(1)**
1-22-23 Koenjiminami
Suginami-Ku, 166003 Tokyo, Japan
Tel.: (81) 333142824
Fax: (81) 333153491
E-Mail: shingo-ishiguro@bml.co.jp
Web Site: www.bml.co.jp/eng/about_bml/group.html
Emp.: 130
Medical Laboratories
S.I.C.: 8071
N.A.I.C.S.: 621511
K. Hayama *(Mng Dir)*

Tokyo Koshueisei Laboratories, Inc. **(1)**
5-7-3 Koenjiminami
Suginami-ku, Tokyo, 166-0003, Japan
Tel.: (81) 353053570
Fax: (81) 353053571
Web Site: www.tokyo-koken.co.jp
Diagnostic Testing Services
S.I.C.: 8071
N.A.I.C.S.: 621511

BMMI B.S.C.

812 Shaikh Jaber Al Ahmed Al Subah Highway
PO Box 828
Sitra, Bahrain
Tel.: (973) 17 739 444
Fax: (973) 17 731 186
E-Mail: enquiries@bmmi.com.bh
Web Site: www.bmmigroup.com
Year Founded: 1883
BMMI—(BAH)
Rev.: $239,165,109
Assets: $170,194,634
Liabilities: $40,022,726
Net Worth: $130,171,908
Earnings: $22,316,307
Emp.: 1,911
Fiscal Year-end: 12/31/12

Business Description:
Food & Beverages Retailer, Whslr & Distr
S.I.C.: 5142
N.A.I.C.S.: 424420

Personnel:
Abdulla Hassan Buhindi *(Chm)*
Abdulla Mohammed Juma *(Vice Chm)*
Gordon Boyle *(Pres & CEO)*
Ammar Aqeel *(CFO & Exec VP-Support Svcs)*
Jad Moukheiber *(Sec & Mgr-Legal Affairs)*
Mike Eastwood *(Exec VP-Beverages, Bayader & Ecommerce)*
Robert Smith *(Exec VP-Contract Svcs & Supply)*

Board of Directors:
Abdulla Hassan Buhindi
Redha Al Faraj
Shawki Ali Fakhroo
Mohammed Almoayyed
Mona Yousif Almoayyed
Jehad Yousif Ameen
Suhail Hajee
Abdulla Mohammed Juma

Subsidiary:

Alosra Supermarket W.L.L. **(1)**
PO Box 828
Manama, Bahrain
Tel.: (973) 17697558
Fax: (973) 17693128
Supermarket Operator
S.I.C.: 5411
N.A.I.C.S.: 445110

Non-U.S. Subsidiary:

BMMI Djibouti **(1)**
Warehouse No 1 Djibouti Free Zone
PO Box 795
Djibouti, Djibouti
Tel.: (253) 21 320 600
Fax: (253) 21 356 144
Emp.: 25
Logistics Consulting Services
S.I.C.: 4731
N.A.I.C.S.: 541614
Gordon Boyle, *(CEO)*

BMP BETEILIGUNGSMANAGEMENT AG

Schluterstrasse 38
D-10629 Berlin, Germany
Tel.: (49) 30 20 30 5 0
Fax: (49) 30 20 30 5 555
E-Mail: bmp@bmp.com
Web Site: www.bmp.com
Year Founded: 2005
BMA—(DEU)

Business Description:
Venture Capital & Private Equity
S.I.C.: 6211
N.A.I.C.S.: 523999

Personnel:
Christof Nesemeier *(Chm)*
Torsten Poeck *(Deputy Chm)*

Board of Directors:
Christof Nesemeier
Oliver Borrmann
Torsten Poeck
Tim Renner
Jens Spyrka
Andreas van Bon

BMP MEDIA INVESTORS AG

Schluterstrasse 38
10629 Berlin, Germany
Tel.: (49) 30 20 30 5 567
Fax: (49) 30 20 30 5 555
E-Mail: bmp@bmp.com
Web Site: www.mediainvestors.com
Year Founded: 1997
BTBA—(DEU)
Rev.: $1,685,058
Assets: $24,636,933
Liabilities: $1,741,473
Net Worth: $22,895,460
Earnings: ($2,290,616)
Emp.: 1
Fiscal Year-end: 12/31/12

Business Description:
Investment Management Services
S.I.C.: 6211
N.A.I.C.S.: 523999

Personnel:
Gerd Schmitz-Morkramer *(Chm-Supervisory Bd)*
Bernd Brunke *(Deputy Chm-Supervisory Bd)*
Oliver Borrmann *(Member-Exec Bd)*
Jens Spyrka *(Member-Exec Bd)*

Supervisory Board of Directors:
Gerd Schmitz-Morkramer
Bernd Brunke
Michael Stammler

BMP METALS INC.

18 Chelsea Ln
Brampton, ON, L6T 3Y4, Canada
Tel.: (905) 799-2002
Fax: (905) 799-2003
Toll Free: (800) 267-7796
E-Mail: solution@bmpmetals.com
Web Site: www.bmpmetals.com
Rev.: $22,866,522
Emp.: 175

Business Description:
Fabricated Metal Mfr
S.I.C.: 3499
N.A.I.C.S.: 332999

Personnel:
Robert Bedard *(Pres)*

BMS GROUP LTD.

1 America Square
London, EC3N 2LS, United Kingdom
Tel.: (44) 2074807288
Fax: (44) 2074889837
Web Site: www.bmsgroup.com
Year Founded: 1980
Emp.: 220

Business Description:
Reinsurance Brokers
S.I.C.: 6399
N.A.I.C.S.: 524130

Personnel:
Roger Cooper *(Mng Dir)*
John Hills *(Sec)*

Board of Directors:
Roger Cooper
John Hills
Paul Vincent

Legal Counsel:
Allen & Overy LLP
Apollolaan 15
NL-1070 AB Amsterdam, Netherlands

Subsidiaries:

Ballantyne McKean & Sullivan Ltd. **(1)**
1 America Sq
London, EC3N 2LS, United Kingdom
Tel.: (44) 2073745936
Fax: (44) 2074889837
Reinsurance Brokers
S.I.C.: 6399

N.A.I.C.S.: 524130
Hugo Crawley *(Chm)*
Roger Cooper *(Grp Mng Dir)*

BankServe Insurance Services Ltd. (1)
1 America Sq
London, United Kingdom
Tel.: (44) 2074800274
Fax: (44) 2073745909
E-Mail: peter.mellett@bms.com
Web Site: www.bms.com
Emp.: 200
Insurance Services
S.I.C.: 6411
N.A.I.C.S.: 524210
Peter Mellett *(Mng Dir)*

BMS Associates Ltd. (1)
1 America Sq, 17 Crosswall Rd Tower Hill
EC3N2LS London, United Kingdom
Tel.: (44) 2074807288
Fax: (44) 2074889837
Emp.: 215
Insurance Services
S.I.C.: 6411
N.A.I.C.S.: 524298
Dane Jonathan Douetil *(Grp CEO)*
John Hills *(Sec)*

BMS Facultative Ltd. (1)
1 America Sqare
London, EC3N 2LS, United Kingdom
Tel.: (44) 2074800306
Fax: (44) 2073745198
Web Site: www.bmsgroup.com
Emp.: 150
Insurance Services
S.I.C.: 6411
N.A.I.C.S.: 524298
Darren Doherty *(Mng Dir)*

BMS Harris & Dixon Ltd. (1)
1 America Square
London, EC3N 2LS, United Kingdom
Tel.: (44) 2074800350
Fax: (44) 2074800345
Web Site: www.bms.com
Emp.: 20
Insurance Services
S.I.C.: 6411
N.A.I.C.S.: 524298
Paul Daly *(Mng Dir)*

BMS Harris & Dixon Marine Ltd. (1)
1 America Sq
London, EC3 N2LS, United Kingdom
Tel.: (44) 2074800366
Fax: (44) 2074800339
E-Mail: info@bmsgroup.com
Web Site: www.bmsgroup.co.uk
Emp.: 230
Insurance Services
S.I.C.: 6411
N.A.I.C.S.: 524298
Tony Pryce *(Mng Dir)*

BMS Harris & Dixon Reinsurance Brokers Ltd. (1)
Latham House
6 Minories, London, EC3N 1AX, United Kingdom
Tel.: (44) 20 7480 0346
Fax: (44) 20 7480 0394
Insurance Services
S.I.C.: 6411
N.A.I.C.S.: 524298

BMS International Intermediaries Ltd. (1)
Latham House
Latham House, London, EC3N 1AX, United Kingdom
Tel.: (44) 20 7480 0346
Fax: (44) 20 7480 4372
Web Site: www.bmsgroup.co.uk/bms_business_units/bms_intermediaries/offices/default.asp
Insurance Services
S.I.C.: 6411
N.A.I.C.S.: 524298

BMS Management Services Ltd. (1)
No 1 America Sq
London, EC3N 2LS, United Kingdom
Tel.: (44) 2073745159
Fax: (44) 2074889837
Emp.: 125
Centralized Group Support Services
S.I.C.: 7389

N.A.I.C.S.: 561499
Ruth Gibson *(HR Officer)*
Kirsty Lloyd *(Officer-Trng)*

BMS Re Ltd. (1)
One America Sq
London, EC3N 2LS, United Kingdom
Tel.: (44) 2074807288
Fax: (44) 2078678013
Web Site: www.bmsgroup.co.uk
Emp.: 217
Non-Marine, Property & Casualty Reinsurance
S.I.C.: 6399
N.A.I.C.S.: 524130
Simon Clutterbuck *(Deputy Chm)*
Jonathan Morris *(Mng Dir)*

BMS Special Risk Services Ltd. (1)
1 America Sq
London, EC3N 2LS, United Kingdom
Tel.: (44) 2074807288
Fax: (44) 2074889837
Web Site: www.bms.com
Emp.: 231
Insurance Services
S.I.C.: 6411
N.A.I.C.S.: 524298
Paul Daly *(Mng Dir)*

U.S. Subsidiaries:

BMS Vision Re Ltd. (1)
One Corporate Dr
Shelton, CT 06484
Tel.: (203) 929-6200
Fax: (203) 929-6272
E-Mail: info@bms.com
Web Site: www.bms.com
Emp.: 6
Insurance Services
S.I.C.: 6411
N.A.I.C.S.: 524298
James M. Cornelius *(Chm)*
Lamberto Andreotti *(CEO)*
Charles Bancroft *(Exec VP & CFO)*
Paul VonAutenreid *(Sr VP & CIO)*
David Spiegler *(Chief Actuary & Exec VP)*
Lou Schmukler *(Pres-Ops)*
Sandra Leung *(Gen Counsel & Sec)*
John E. Celentano *(Sr VP-HR)*
Francis Cuss *(Sr VP-R&D)*
Brian Daniels *(Sr VP)*
Jeremy Levin *(Sr VP)*
Victor Marques *(Sr VP)*

BMS Vision Re Ltd. (1)
1101 Perimeter Dr Ste 875
Chicago, IL 60173
Tel.: (847) 277-0201
Fax: (847) 277-0211
Web Site: www.bmsgroup.co.uk/bms_companies/bms_intermediaries/offices/default.asp
Emp.: 3
Insurance Services
S.I.C.: 6411
N.A.I.C.S.: 524298

BMS Vision Re Ltd. (1)
5005 LBJ Fwy Ste 700
Dallas, TX 75244
Tel.: (972) 233-4020
Fax: (972) 233-4023
Web Site: www.bmsgroup.com
Emp.: 100
Insurance Services
S.I.C.: 6411
N.A.I.C.S.: 524298
Anne Marie Roberts *(Pres, CEO & COO)*
Sheli D. Steinert *(Sr VP)*

Non-U.S. Subsidiaries:

BMS Asia Inter-mediaries Pte., Ltd. (1)
20 Raffles Place
11-01 Raffles Towers, Singapore, Singapore
Tel.: (65) 63233326
Fax: (65) 62250068
Insurance Services
S.I.C.: 6411
N.A.I.C.S.: 524298

BMS Asia Intermediaries Ltd. (1)
Wisma UOA II
21 Jalan Pinang, Kuala Lumpur, Malaysia
Tel.: (60) 321643326
Fax: (60) 3 2163 0068
Insurance Services

S.I.C.: 6411
N.A.I.C.S.: 524298

BMS Bermuda Ltd. (1)
PO Box Number 2953
HMMX, Hamilton, Bermuda
Tel.: (441) 232 3784
Fax: (441) 232 3783
Web Site: www.bmsgroup.com
Insurance Services
S.I.C.: 6411
N.A.I.C.S.: 524298
Dean Carberry *(CEO)*
Guy Baly *(Exec VP)*
Thomas Doyle *(Sr VP)*

BMS Harris & Dixon Praha a.s. (1)
Senovazne Namesti 992/8
110 00 Prague, Czech Republic
Tel.: (420) 222247377
Fax: (420) 222245640
E-Mail: recebee@ube.com
Web Site: www.ube.com
Insurance Services
S.I.C.: 6411
N.A.I.C.S.: 524298

BMS Insurance & Reinsurance Brokers Hellas S.A. (1)
61 Akadimias Street
106 79 Athens, Greece
Tel.: (30) 2103390354
Fax: (30) 2103390356
E-Mail: info@bmshellas.com
Web Site: www.bmshellas.com
Emp.: 25
Insurance Services
S.I.C.: 6411
N.A.I.C.S.: 524298
Dimitris Tsesmetzolglou *(CEO)*
Stelios Assariotis *(Partner)*
Manolis Siatounis *(Partner)*

BMS Specialty Risks Underwriting Managers Ltd. (1)
1111 Lonsdale Avenue Suite 206
Vancouver, BC, V7M 2H4, Canada
Tel.: (604) 990-8882
Fax: (604) 990-8843
E-Mail: admin.bmsgroup@shawbiz.ca
Web Site: www.bmsgroup.co.uk
Emp.: 6
Insurance Services
S.I.C.: 6411
N.A.I.C.S.: 524298
Rose Mary MacLeod *(Office Mgr)*

BMT GROUP LIMITED

Goodrich House 1 Waldegrave Road
Teddington, Mddx, TW11 8LZ, United Kingdom
Tel.: (44) 20 8943 5544
Fax: (44) 20 8943 5347
E-Mail: enquiries@bmtmail.com
Web Site: www.bmt.org
Year Founded: 1985
Sales Range: $125-149.9 Million
Emp.: 1,300

Business Description:
Holding Company; Multi-Disciplinary Engineering, Science & Technology Consultancy Services
S.I.C.: 6719
N.A.I.C.S.: 551112

Personnel:
Neil Cross *(Chm)*
Peter Douglas French *(CEO)*

Board of Directors:
Neil Cross
Wendy Barnes
Ian Robert Davies
Peter Douglas French
Frances Heaton
Jan Kopernicki
David Keith McSweeney
Minoo Patel

Subsidiaries:

BMT Defence Services Ltd. (1)
Maritime House
210 Lower Bristol Rd, Bath, BA2 3DQ, United Kingdom
Tel.: (44) 1225473600

Fax: (44) 1225448714
E-Mail: info@bmtdsl.co.uk
Web Site: www.bmtdsl.co.uk
Emp.: 160
Naval Defence Design, Engineering & Management Support Services
S.I.C.: 8742
N.A.I.C.S.: 541611
Muir MacDonald *(Mng Dir)*

Non-U.S. Subsidiary:

BMT Defence Services (Australia) Pty. Ltd. (2)
99 King St Level 5
Melbourne, VIC, 3000, Australia
Tel.: (61) 386206180
Fax: (61) 386206105
E-Mail:
Web Site: www.bmtdesigntechnology.com.au
Emp.: 21
Naval Defence Engineering & Technology Services
S.I.C.: 8711
N.A.I.C.S.: 541330
Gordon MacDonald *(Mng Dir)*

BMT Energy and Environment (1)
Broadfold House Broadfold Road Bridge of Don
Bridge of Don, Aberdeen, AB23 8HG, United Kingdom
Tel.: (44) 1224414200
Fax: (44) 1224414250
E-Mail: enquiries@bmtcordah.com
Web Site: www.bmtcordah.com
Emp.: 25
Engineering Services
S.I.C.: 8711
N.A.I.C.S.: 541330
Neil Henderson *(Mgr-Bus Dev)*

Subsidiary:

BMT Cordah Limited (2)
Scotstown Rd Bridge of Don
Aberdeen, AB23 8HJ, United Kingdom
Tel.: (44) 1224414200
Fax: (44) 1224414250
E-Mail: enquiries@bmtcordah.com
Web Site: www.bmtcordah.com
Emp.: 25
Environmental Consulting Services
S.I.C.: 8999
N.A.I.C.S.: 541620
Norman Di Perno *(Mng Dir)*

Branches:

BMT Cordah Limited (3)
Unit 117 Pentagon Business Centre
36 Washington Street
Glasgow, Strathclyde, G3 8AZ, United Kingdom
Tel.: (44) 1412213236
Fax: (44) 1412487986
E-Mail: enquiries@bmtcordah.com
Web Site: www.bmtcordah.com
Emp.: 12
Environmental Consulting Services
S.I.C.: 8999
N.A.I.C.S.: 541620

BMT Cordah Limited (3)
113 W Regent St
G2 2RU Edinburgh, United Kingdom
Tel.: (44) 1412213236
Fax: (44) 1412487986
E-Mail: enquiries@bmtcordah.com
Web Site: www.bmtcordah.com
Emp.: 15
Environmental Consulting Services
S.I.C.: 8999
N.A.I.C.S.: 541620
Derek Schoehuys *(Mng Dir)*

U.S. Division:

BMT Energy (2)
9835 Whithorn Dr
Houston, TX 77095
Tel.: (281) 858-8090
Fax: (281) 858-8898
Web Site: www.scimar.com
Emp.: 19
Engineering Services
S.I.C.: 8711
N.A.I.C.S.: 541330

BMT Group Limited—(Continued)

BMT Fluid Mechanics Limited (1)
67 Stanton Avenue
Teddington, Middlesex, TW11 0JY, United Kingdom
Tel.: (44) 2089435544
Fax: (44) 2089433224
E-Mail: enquiries@bmtfm.com
Web Site: www.bmtfm.com
Emp.: 30
Wind Engineering & Offshore Marine Consultancy
S.I.C.: 8711
N.A.I.C.S.: 541330
Volker Buttgereit *(Mng Dir)*

BMT Reliability Consultants Ltd. (1)
12 Little Park Farm Road
Fareham, Hampshire, PO15 5SU, United Kingdom
Tel.: (44) 1489553100
Fax: (44) 1489553101
E-Mail: messages@bmtrcl.com
Web Site: www.bmtrcl.com
Emp.: 45
Engineering Consultancy Services
S.I.C.: 8711
N.A.I.C.S.: 541330
Andrew Coopel *(Mng Dir)*

U.S. Subsidiaries:

BMT Designers & Planners, Inc. (1)
2120 Washington Blvd Ste 200
Arlington, VA 22204
Tel.: (703) 920-7070
Fax: (703) 920-7177
Web Site: www.dandp.com
Emp.: 100
Engineering Consulting Services
S.I.C.: 8711
N.A.I.C.S.: 541330
Richard Celotto *(VP-Engrg)*

BMT Syntek Technologies, Inc. (1)
2120 Washington Blvd Ste 110
Arlington, VA 22204-1627 VA
Tel.: (703) 525-3403
Fax: (703) 525-0833
E-Mail: info@bmtsyntek.com
Web Site: www.BMTsyntek.com
Emp.: 30
Professional Services for Transportation, Telecommunications, Information Technology, Energy, Defense, Intelligence, Maritime, Electronics & Space Industries
S.I.C.: 8731
N.A.I.C.S.: 541712
James C. Davis *(Pres)*

Non-U.S. Subsidiaries:

BMT Asia Pacific Pte. Ltd. (1)
03-01 Harbour Front Tower Two
3 HarbourFront Place, Singapore, 099254, Singapore
Tel.: (65) 6517 6800
Fax: (65) 6271 8084
E-Mail: mail@bmtasia.com.sg
Web Site: www.bmtasia.com.sg
Emp.: 50
Maritime Transport Services
S.I.C.: 4789
N.A.I.C.S.: 488999
Per Roed *(Mng Dir)*
Anil Thapar *(Deputy Mng Dir)*

Non-U.S. Division:

BMT Asia Pacific Ltd. (2)
5th Fl ING Tower
308 Des Voeux Road, Central, China (Hong Kong)
Tel.: (852) 28152221
Fax: (852) 28153377
E-Mail: post@bmtasia.com.hk
Web Site: www.bmtasiapacific.com
Emp.: 50
Maritime Transport Services
S.I.C.: 4789
N.A.I.C.S.: 488999
Richard Colwill *(Mng Dir)*

BMT Consultants (India) Pvt. Ltd. (1)
310 Sarthik Square Opp Tej Motors
SG Highway, 380054 Ahmedabad, India
Tel.: (91) 7940028708
Fax: (91) 2940028710
E-Mail: suren.vakil@bmtindia.org
Web Site: www.bmtindia.org
Emp.: 30
Maritime Transport Services
S.I.C.: 4789
N.A.I.C.S.: 488999

BMT De Beer bv (1)
Guldenwaard 141
3078 AJ Rotterdam, Netherlands
Tel.: (31) 0104790311
Fax: (31) 104791466
E-Mail: surveyors@bmtdebeer.com
Web Site: www.bmtdebeer.com
Emp.: 15
Nautical, Cargo & Technical Surveying & Consulting Services
S.I.C.: 4491
N.A.I.C.S.: 488320
Jeroen J. De Haas *(Mng Dir)*
Susan Lawton *(Sec)*
Joan Vis Van Heemst *(Sec)*

BMT Fleet Technology Limited (1)
311 Legget Drive
Kanata, ON, K2K 1Z8, Canada
Tel.: (613) 592-2830
Fax: (613) 592-4950
E-Mail: fleet@fleetech.com
Web Site: www.fleetech.com
Emp.: 100
Maritime Transport Services
S.I.C.: 4789
N.A.I.C.S.: 488999
Darcy Byrtus *(Pres)*

Branches:

BMT Fleet Technology Limited (2)
Shoal Point
101-19 Dallas Road, Victoria, BC, V8V 5A6, Canada
Tel.: (250) 598-5150
Fax: (250) 598-5160
E-Mail: mwilliamson@fleetech.com
Web Site: www.fleetech.com
Emp.: 5
Maritime Transport Services
S.I.C.: 4789
N.A.I.C.S.: 488999
Mike Williamson *(Mng Dir)*

BMT Fleet Technology Limited (2)
611 Alexander St Ste 412
Vancouver, BC, V6A 1E1, Canada
Tel.: (604) 253-0955
Fax: (604) 253-5023
E-Mail: fleet@fleetech.com
Web Site: www.fleettech.com
Emp.: 11
Maritime Transport Services
S.I.C.: 4789
N.A.I.C.S.: 488999
Gorden Flemming *(Pres)*

BMT Fleet Technology Limited (2)
25 Kenmount Rd
Saint John's, NL, A1D 1W1, Canada
Tel.: (709) 753-5690
Fax: (709) 753-5694
Web Site: www.fleettech.com
Emp.: 14
Maritime Transport Services
S.I.C.: 4789
N.A.I.C.S.: 488999
Tony Barclay *(Mgr)*

Gee Ltd. (1)
Plot No E-1 Road No 7 Wagle Industrial Estate
Thane, Maharashtra, 400 604, India
Tel.: (91) 22 2582 1277
Fax: (91) 22 2582 8938
E-Mail: geeho@geelimited.com
Web Site: www.geelimited.com
504028—(BOM)
Rev.: $38,283,606
Assets: $23,390,126
Liabilities: $13,478,610
Net Worth: $9,911,516
Earnings: $860,191
Fiscal Year-end: 03/31/13
Welding Electrode Mfr
S.I.C.: 3548
N.A.I.C.S.: 333992
Ramkishan Agarwal *(Founder)*
G. K. Saraf *(CEO)*
Shankarlal Agarwal *(Mng Dir)*
Sanwarmul Agarwal *(Compliance Officer)*
C. Achuthan *(Pres-Intl Sls)*
O. P. Agarwal *(Pres-Mktg)*

WBM Pty. Ltd. (1)
490 Upper Edward Street
Brisbane, QLD, 4000, Australia
Tel.: (61) 738316744
Fax: (61) 738323627
Web Site: www.wbmpl.com.au
Sls.: $25,000,000
Emp.: 150
Engineering Services
S.I.C.: 8711
N.A.I.C.S.: 541330
Russ Morrison *(CEO)*

Branch:

WBM - Sydney (2)
256-258 Level 1 Norton Street
PO Box 194
Leichhardt, NSW, 2040, Australia
Tel.: (61) 297134836
Fax: (61) 297134890
E-Mail: wbmsyd@wbmpl.com.au
Web Site: www.wbmpl.com.au
Emp.: 10
Engineering Services
S.I.C.: 8711
N.A.I.C.S.: 541330
Rob Widders *(Mng Dir)*

BMTC GROUP INC.

8500 Place Marien
Montreal, QC, H1B 5W8, Canada
Tel.: (514) 648-5757
Fax: (514) 881-4056
Web Site:
Year Founded: 1989
GBT.A—(TSX)
Rev.: $712,583,117
Assets: $283,611,798
Liabilities: $86,975,756
Net Worth: $196,636,042
Earnings: $44,686,169
Emp.: 2,198
Fiscal Year-end: 12/31/12

Business Description:
Financial Management Services
S.I.C.: 6282
N.A.I.C.S.: 523920

Personnel:
Yves Des Groseillers *(Chm, Pres & CEO)*
Marie-Berthe Des Groseillers *(Sec)*

Board of Directors:
Yves Des Groseillers
Andre Berard
Lucien Bouchard
Gilles Crepeau
Charles Des Groseillers
Marie-Berthe Des Groseillers
Tony Fionda
Pierre Ouimet
Robert Pare
Serge Saucier

Transfer Agent:
Computershare Investor Services Inc.
Montreal, QC, Canada

BMW TORONTO

11 Sunlight Park Rd
Toronto, ON, M4M 1B5, Canada
Tel.: (416) 623-4269
Toll Free: (800) 988-5292
Web Site: www.bmwtoronto.ca
Rev.: $37,396,674
Emp.: 120

Business Description:
New & Used Car Dealers
S.I.C.: 5511
N.A.I.C.S.: 441110

Personnel:
Karen Willis *(CFO)*

BNP PARIBAS SA

16 boulevard des Italiens
75009 Paris, France
Tel.: (33) 140144546
Telex: 280605 280775
E-Mail: investor.relations@bnpparibas.com
Web Site: www.bnpparibas.com
Year Founded: 1966
BNP—(EUR OTC SWX)
Int. Income: $59,872,256,920
Net Worth: $127,108,063,740
Earnings: $9,844,541,210
Emp.: 190,000
Fiscal Year-end: 12/31/12

Business Description:
Bank Holding Company
S.I.C.: 6712
N.A.I.C.S.: 551111

Personnel:
Baudouin Prot *(Chm)*
Jean-Laurent Bonnafe *(CEO)*
Philippe Bordenave *(Co-COO)*
Georges Chodron de Courcel *(Co-COO)*
Francois Villeroy de Galhau *(Co-COO)*
Jacques d'Estais *(Deputy COO & Head-Investments, Personal Fin & Intl Retail Banking)*
Alain Papiasse *(Deputy COO & Head-Corp & Investment Banking)*
Fabio Gallia *(CEO/Gen Mgr-BNL)*
Maxime Jadot *(CEO-BNP Paribas Fortis)*
Eric Raynaud *(CEO-Asia Pacific)*

Board of Directors:
Baudouin Prot
Jean-Laurent Bonnafe
Pierre-Andre de Chalendar
Christophe de Margerie
Marion Guillou
Denis Kessler
Jean-Francois LePetit
Nicole Misson
Thierry Mouchard
Laurence Parisot
Michel Pebereau
Helene Ploix
Michel Tilmant
Emiel Van Broekhoven
Daniela Weber-Rey
Fields Wicker-Miurin

Mazars
61 rue Henri Regnault
Courbevoie, France

Deloitte & Associes
185 avenue Charles-de-Gaulle
Neuilly-sur-Seine, France

Subsidiaries:

Arius SA (1)
101 Avenue Francois Arago
92017 Nanterre, France
Tel.: (33) 4 78 94 79 58
Fax: (33) 4 78 94 86 85
Web Site: www.rentalsolutions.bnpparibas.com
Software Development Services
S.I.C.: 7371
N.A.I.C.S.: 541511

Artegy SAS (1)
46 Rue Arago
92800 Puteaux, France
Tel.: (33) 1 30 14 94 00
Fax: (33) 1 30 14 94 01
Truck Rental & Leasing Services
S.I.C.: 7513
N.A.I.C.S.: 532120

Arval ECL SAS (1)
119/121 Grand Rue
92318 Sevres, France
Tel.: (33) 141141818
Fax: (33) 141141871
Automobile Rental Services
S.I.C.: 7513
N.A.I.C.S.: 532120

Arval France (1)
119 121 Grande Rue
F 92320 Sevres, France (100%)
Tel.: (33) 141145728
Fax: (33) 146901042

E-Mail: contact@arvalphh.com
Web Site: www.arvalphh.fr
Emp.: 250
Long Term Vehicle Rental Company for Businesses
S.I.C.: 7519
N.A.I.C.S.: 532120

Non-U.S. Branches:

Arval Belgium (2)
Verdunstaraat 742
B 1130 Brussels, Belgium (100%)
Tel.: (32) 22400199
Fax: (32) 22452470
E-Mail: online@arval.be
Web Site: www.arval.be
Emp.: 124
Long Term Vehicle Rental Company for Businesses
S.I.C.: 7513
N.A.I.C.S.: 532120

Arval Italy (2)
Via Pisana 314 B
50018 Scandicci, Firenze, Italy (100%)
Tel.: (39) 0005573701
Fax: (39) 0557370370
E-Mail: arval@arval.it
Web Site: www.arval.it
Emp.: 300
Provider of Corporate Long Term Vehicle Rental Services
S.I.C.: 7519
N.A.I.C.S.: 532120

Arval Netherlands (2)
Duwboot 10
PO Box 536
3990 DH Houten, Netherlands (100%)
Tel.: (31) 306024444
Fax: (31) 306052459
E-Mail: info@arval.nl
Web Site: www.arval.nl
Emp.: 190
Long Term Vehicle Rental Company for Businesses
S.I.C.: 7513
N.A.I.C.S.: 532120
Jeff Bolders *(Mng Dir)*

Arval Portugal (2)
Arqui Parque Rua Dr Antonio Loureiro Borges Edificio 5 piso 4
1495-131 Alges, Portugal (100%)
Tel.: (351) 214709400
Fax: (351) 214709480
E-Mail: arval@arval.pt
Web Site: www.arval.pt
Emp.: 60
Long Term Vehicle Rental Services for Businesses & Fleet Services
S.I.C.: 7519
N.A.I.C.S.: 532120
Alain Yvon *(Gen Mgr)*

Arval Spain (2)
Louis st 3
San Sebastian De Los Reyes, Madrid, 28703, Spain (100%)
Tel.: (34) 916597065
Fax: (34) 916590524
E-Mail: arval@arval.es
Web Site: www.arval.es
Emp.: 240
Long Term Vehicle Rental Company for Businesses
S.I.C.: 7519
N.A.I.C.S.: 532120
Francoisc Xavier *(CEO)*

Non-U.S. Subsidiaries:

Arval Austria GmbH (2)
Marximum Business Park Property 4/OG3/B Modecenterstrasse 17, 1110 Vienna, Austria (100%)
Tel.: (43) 170698200
Fax: (43) 1706982099
E-Mail: sales@arval.at
Web Site: www.arval.at
Emp.: 100
Long Term Vehicle Rental Company for Businesses
S.I.C.: 7519
N.A.I.C.S.: 532120

Arval Germany GmbH (2)
Ammerthalstrasse 7
85551 Kirchheim, Munich, Germany (100%)
Tel.: (49) 89904770
Fax: (49) 8990477210
E-Mail: info@arval.de
Web Site: www.arval.de
Rev.: $305,052,960
Emp.: 150
Long Term Vehicle Rental Company for Businesses
S.I.C.: 7513
N.A.I.C.S.: 532120
Lionel Wolff *(Mng Dir)*

Arval Luxembourg (2)
36 Rte De Longwy
L8080 Bertrange, Luxembourg FR (100%)
Tel.: (352) 4491801
Fax: (352) 449190
E-Mail: info@arval.lu
Web Site: www.arval.lu
Emp.: 14
Long Term Vehicle Rental Company for Businesses
S.I.C.: 7513
N.A.I.C.S.: 532120
Gerry Wagner *(Mng Dir)*

Arval Schweiz AG (2)
Gewerbestrasse 11
6330 Cham, Switzerland (100%)
Tel.: (41) 7483700
Fax: (41) 7483707
E-Mail: Info@arvalnet.ch
Web Site: www.arval.ch
Emp.: 60
Long Term Vehicle Rental Company for Businesses
S.I.C.: 7513
N.A.I.C.S.: 532120

Arval UK Ltd. (2)
Windmill Hill Whitehill Way PHH Ctr
Swindon, SN5 6PE, United Kingdom (100%)
Tel.: (44) 793884212
Fax: (44) 1793886688
Web Site: www.arval.co.uk
Emp.: 1,300
Long Term Vehicle Rental Company for Businesses
S.I.C.: 7519
N.A.I.C.S.: 532120
Benoit Dilly *(Mng Dir)*

Arval Service Lease SA (1)
1 Boulevard Haussmann
Paris, 75009, France
Tel.: (33) 1 57 69 50 00
Fax: (33) 1 57 69 65 94
Web Site: www.arval.fr
Passenger Car Leasing Services
S.I.C.: 7515
N.A.I.C.S.: 532112

U.S. Subsidiary:

Atelier North America, Inc. (2)
2415 Third St Ste 231
San Francisco, CA 94107
Tel.: (415) 503-4156
Fax: (415) 503-4155
E-Mail: vanessa.rodriguez.atelier@gmail.com
Web Site: www.atelier.net
Emp.: 20
Internet Technology & On-Line Information Services
S.I.C.: 2741
N.A.I.C.S.: 519130
Frederic Tardy *(Pres & CEO)*

Non-U.S. Subsidiary:

Arval Service Lease Italia S. p. A. (2)
Via Pisana N 314/B
Scandicci, Florence, 50018, Italy
Tel.: (39) 0557 37 07 00
Fax: (39) 0557 37 03 70
E-Mail: arvi.info@arval.it
Web Site: www.arval.it
Emp.: 900
Car Leasing Services
S.I.C.: 7515
N.A.I.C.S.: 532112
Philippe Andre Georges Noubel *(Pres)*

Arval Trading SAS (1)
Parc d'Activites La Ravoire
74371 Pringy, France
Tel.: (33) 4 50 05 28 28
Fax: (33) 4 50 05 39 38
Web Site: www.arval-trading.net
Emp.: 35
New & Used Car Dealer
S.I.C.: 5511
N.A.I.C.S.: 441110
Michael Benabdallah *(Gen Mgr)*

Atelier Services (1)
1 Boulevard Haussmann
75009 Paris, France (98.5%)
Mailing Address:
5, Avenue Kleber
75116 Paris, France
E-Mail: infos@atelier.fr
Web Site: www.atelier.fr
Minority Holdings Manager for Quoted Companies on the French Stock Exchange
S.I.C.: 6719
N.A.I.C.S.: 551112
Olivier Dulac *(Pres)*
Louis Treussard *(Dir Gen)*
Laila Benali *(Bus Officer)*
Isabelle Leguillon *(Comm Officer)*

Auguste Thouard Expertise, SAS (1)
28/32 Rue Jacques Ibert
Levallois-Perret, 92300, France
Tel.: (33) 1 47 59 20 00
Fax: (33) 1 47 59 22 69
Web Site: www.auguste-thouard.fr
Real Estate Management Services
S.I.C.: 6531
N.A.I.C.S.: 531390

Autovalley, SAS (1)
1 Boulevard Haussmann
Paris, 75009, France
Tel.: (33) 1 60 87 29 20
E-Mail: contact@autovalley.fr
Web Site: www.autovalley.fr
New & Used Car Dealer
S.I.C.: 5511
N.A.I.C.S.: 441110

Banque de Bretagne (1)
18 Quai Dugay Trouin
35084 Rennes, Cedex, France (100%)
Tel.: (33) 299017777
Fax: (33) 299017510
E-Mail: jocalyne.regnier@banque.de.bretagne.com
Web Site: www.bdbretagne.com
Emp.: 500
Private Banking Services
S.I.C.: 6099
N.A.I.C.S.: 522320
Jocalyne Regnier *(Mng Dir)*

B*capital (1)
21 Boulevard haussmann
75009 Paris, France (100%)
Tel.: (33) 140175000
Fax: (33) 140175050
E-Mail: clientele@b-capital.com
Web Site: www.b-capital.com
Emp.: 214
Stock Brokerage
S.I.C.: 6211
N.A.I.C.S.: 523120
Biraud Frederic *(Mgr)*

Subsidiary:

Portzamparc societe de Bourse S.A. (2)
13 Rue De La Brasserie
Nantes, 44100, France
Tel.: (33) 240449400
Fax: (33) 240697762
Securities Brokerage Services
S.I.C.: 6211
N.A.I.C.S.: 523120

Beau Sevran Invest SCI (1)
21 Avenue Kleber
75116 Paris, France
Tel.: (33) 8 99 96 77 62
Investment Management Services
S.I.C.: 6799
N.A.I.C.S.: 523920

BNP Paribas Arbitrage (1)
8 Rue De Sofia
75018 Paris, France (100%)
Tel.: (33) 140142299
Fax: (33) 140144440
E-Mail: info@bnp.com
Web Site: www.bnp.com
Emp.: 700
Arbitrage
S.I.C.: 6211
N.A.I.C.S.: 523999
Gavgani Berniad *(COO)*

BNP Paribas Asset Management S.A.S. (1)
14 Rue Bergere
75009 Paris, France FR
Tel.: (33) 158972525 (100%)
Telex: 220 464
E-Mail: info@bnpparibas.com
Web Site: www.bnpparibas-am.com
Emp.: 3,000
Financial Services
S.I.C.: 6099
N.A.I.C.S.: 522320
Christian Dargnat *(CEO)*
Philippe Marchessaux *(Head-Asset Mgmt & CEO-Investment Partners)*

Division:

BNP Paribas Private Equity (2)
14 rue Bergere
75009 Paris, France (100%)
Tel.: (33) 1 5897 2525
Telex: 283419
Web Site: www.bnppe.com
Private Equity Firm
S.I.C.: 6211
N.A.I.C.S.: 523999
Francois Petit-Jean *(Chm)*
Stephanie Egoian *(Chief Investment Officer)*

U.S. Subsidiary:

BNP Paribas Asset Management Inc. (2)
200 Park Ave
New York, NY 10166 NY
Tel.: (212) 681-3180
Fax: (212) 681-3188
E-Mail: christel.turcat@americas.bnpparibas.com
Web Site: www.am.bnpparibas.com
Rev.: $720,000
Emp.: 120
Investment & Asset Management Services
S.I.C.: 6282
N.A.I.C.S.: 523920
Jennifer Mccassrey *(Office Mgr)*

Subsidiaries:

BNP Paribas Investment Partners - Boston (3)
75 State St 6th Fl
Boston, MA 02109 MA
Tel.: (617) 478-7200
Fax: (617) 439-9789
Web Site: www.bnpparibas-ip.com
Emp.: 60
Asset Management & Investment Banking Services
S.I.C.: 6282
N.A.I.C.S.: 523920
John J. Barletta *(CFO & Treas)*

Non-U.S. Subsidiary:

Fischer Francis Trees & Watts UK Limited (4)
5 Aldermanbury Square
London, EC2V 7BP, United Kingdom UK
Tel.: (44) 2075952000
Fax: (44) 2075952555
E-Mail: ingrid.furtado@bnpparibas.com
Web Site: www.fftw.com
Emp.: 6,000
Investment Fund Asset Management Services
S.I.C.: 6282
N.A.I.C.S.: 523920

Fischer, Francis, Trees & Watts, Inc. (3)
200 Park Ave 46th Fl
New York, NY 10166 NY
Tel.: (212) 681-3000 (100%)
Web Site: www.fftw.com
Emp.: 120
Fixed Income Investment Portfolio Management Services
S.I.C.: 6799
N.A.I.C.S.: 523920
Robert Harrison *(CEO)*
Guy Williams *(Chief Investment Officer)*

BNP Paribas SA—(Continued)

Subsidiary:

BNP Paribas Investment Partners (Hong Kong) Limited (3)
30/F Three Exchange Square
8 Connaught Place, Central, China (Hong Kong) HK
Tel.: (852) 2533 0000
Fax: (852) 2521 2520
Web Site: www.bnpparibas-ip.com.hk
Emp.: 100
Asset Management & Investment Banking Services
S.I.C.: 6799
N.A.I.C.S.: 523920
Vincent Camerlynck *(CEO-Asia Pacific)*

Non-U.S. Subsidiary:

BNP Paribas Asset Management Asia Limited (2)
30/F Three Exchange Square
8 Connaught Place, Central, China (Hong Kong) (100%)
Tel.: (852) 2533 0000
Fax: (852) 25212520
Web Site: www.bnpparibas-ip.com.hk
Emp.: 100
Fund Management & Investment Advice
S.I.C.: 6282
N.A.I.C.S.: 523930
Tan Feng Cheng *(Mng Dir)*

Non-U.S. Subsidiaries:

BNP Paribas Asset Management Singapore Limited (3)
20 Collyer Quay Ste 01-01 Tung Ctr
Singapore, 049319, Singapore SG
Tel.: (65) 62101288
Fax: (65) 62243459
Investment & Asset Management Services
S.I.C.: 6799
N.A.I.C.S.: 523920

PT BNP Paribas Investment Partners (3)
World Trade Center Building 5th Floor
Jl Jend Sudirman Kav 29-31, Jakarta, 12920, Indonesia Id
Tel.: (62) 212521574
Fax: (62) 212521594
E-Mail: vivian.Secakusuma@bnpparibas-ip.co.id
Web Site: www.bnpparibas-ip.co.id
Emp.: 55
Investment Fund Asset Management Services
S.I.C.: 6282
N.A.I.C.S.: 523920
Vivian Secakusuma *(Dir-Mktg)*

Subsidiary:

PT ABN AMRO Manajemen Investasi (4)
Jakarta Stock Exchange Building Tower 2 11th Floor
Jl Jend Sudirman Kav 52-53, Jakarta, 12190, Indonesia Id
Tel.: (62) 215156000
Asset Management & Investment Banking Services
S.I.C.: 6799
N.A.I.C.S.: 523920

Non-U.S. Affiliate:

Fortis Haitong Investment Management Co., Ltd. (3)
36-37 Floor Bank of East Asia Tower 66 Hua Yuan Shi Qiao Road
Pudong, Shanghai, 200120, China CN
Tel.: (86) 21 3865 0999 (49%)
Fax: (86) 21 5878 1634
Web Site: www.hftfund.com
Investment Fund Management Services
S.I.C.: 6799
N.A.I.C.S.: 523920
Ren Can Tian *(CEO)*
Ming Zhang *(Chief Compliance Officer)*
Hong Chen *(Chief Investment Officer & Deputy Gen Mgr)*

Non-U.S. Subsidiaries:

BNP Paribas Asset Management India Private Ltd (2)
BNP Paribas House 1 North Avenue Maker Maxity Bandra Kurla Complex
Bandra E, Mumbai, 400 051, India
Tel.: (91) 22 3370 4000
Fax: (91) 22 3370 4294
E-Mail: customer.care@bnpparibasmf.in
Web Site: www.bnpparibasmf.in
Asset Management Services
S.I.C.: 6282
N.A.I.C.S.: 523920
Rajan Ray *(Chm)*
Nikhil Johri *(Mng Dir & CEO)*
Viji Krishnan *(COO)*
Anand Shah *(CIO)*

BNP Paribas Asset Management (2)
Level 4 60 Castlereagh Street
Sydney, NSW, 2000, Australia (100%)
Mailing Address:
GPO Box 269
Sydney, NSW, 2001, Australia
Tel.: (61) 296196099
Fax: (61) 296196951
E-Mail: asset.mgt@bnpparibas.com.au
Web Site: www.bnpparibas.com.au
Emp.: 9
Fund Management
S.I.C.: 6282
N.A.I.C.S.: 523920
Robert Harrison *(Mng Dir)*

BNP Paribas Investment Partners Japan Ltd. (2)
Grand Tokyo North Tower 1-9-1 Marunouchi
Chiyoda-ku, Tokyo, 100-6740, Japan JP
Tel.: (81) 3 6377 2800 (100%)
Fax: (81) 3 5218 5888
E-Mail: info@am.japan.bnpparibas.com
Web Site: www.am.japan.bnpparibas.com
Emp.: 39
Establishment & Management of Mutual Funds
S.I.C.: 6282
N.A.I.C.S.: 523920

Fortis Portfoy Yonetimi A.S. (2)
Buyukdere Caddesi 1 Levent Plaza
A Blok Kat 7 Sisli, 34330 Istanbul, Turkey TR
Tel.: (90) 2122818160
Fax: (90) 2122819368
E-Mail: hr@fortisportfoy.com.tr
Web Site: www.fortisinvestments.com
Emp.: 18
Investment Fund Asset Management Services
S.I.C.: 6799
N.A.I.C.S.: 523920
Alt Keler *(Mng Dir)*

Non-U.S. Joint Ventures:

SAIB BNP Paribas Asset Management Co., Ltd. (2)
PO Box 5556
Riyadh, 11432, Saudi Arabia
Tel.: (966) 14742121
Fax: (966) 14749314
E-Mail: info@saibbnpp.com
Web Site: www.saibbnpp.com
Asset Management & Investment Services; Owned by Saudi Investment Bank & by BNP Paribas S.A.
S.I.C.: 6282
N.A.I.C.S.: 523920
Radi S. Al-Haddad *(CEO)*
Ivan Saldanha *(Deputy CEO)*
Zahoor Amanullah *(CFO)*
Fazal J. Seyyed *(Chief Investment Officer)*

TKB BNP Paribas Investment Partners JSC (2)
69/71 lit A Marata Street
191119 Saint Petersburg, Russia RU
Tel.: (7) 8123327332 (50%)
Fax: (7) 8123246557
Web Site: www.tkb-bnpparibasip.info
Investment Fund Asset Management Services
S.I.C.: 6282
N.A.I.C.S.: 523920
Vladimir Kirillov *(CEO)*
Tanya Landwehr *(CFO & Head-Comml Dev & Intl Sls)*
Vladimir Tsuprov *(Chief Investment Officer)*

BNP Paribas Assurance (1)
8 rue du Port
Nanterre, Cedex, 92728, France
Tel.: (33) 141426956
Web Site: www.bnpbaribascardif.com
Life & Property & Casualty Insurance
S.I.C.: 6311
N.A.I.C.S.: 524113
Stanislas Chevalet *(COO & Head-Digital, Brokers Channel, Efficiency Tech & Ops)*

Division:

Cardif (2)
41 Ave Friedland
PO Box 366
75367 Paris, Cedex, France (100%)
Tel.: (33) 153538888
Fax: (33) 153538899
E-Mail: cardif.paris@cardif.fr
Web Site: www.cardif.fr
Emp.: 2,000
Insurance & Financing Services
S.I.C.: 6411
N.A.I.C.S.: 524298
Pierre de Villeneuve *(Chm & CEO)*

Non-U.S. Branches:

Cardif Germany (3)
Friolzheimer Str 6
70499 Stuttgart, Germany (100%)
Tel.: (49) 711820550
Fax: (49) 71182055499
E-Mail: info@cardif.de
Web Site: www.cardif.de
Emp.: 100
Insurance & Financing Services
S.I.C.: 6411
N.A.I.C.S.: 524298
David Furtwaengler *(Mng Dir)*

Cardif Spain (3)
Calle Hulian Camarillo 21 4th Fl
28037 Madrid, Spain (100%)
Tel.: (34) 915903001
Fax: (34) 915903007
Web Site: www.cardif.es
Emp.: 60
Insurance & Finance Services
S.I.C.: 6411
N.A.I.C.S.: 524298
Ignacio Sainz *(Mng Dir)*

Cardif Vie & Cardif RD (3)
Chaussee de Mons 1424
Anderlecht, B 1170 Brussels, Belgium (100%)
Tel.: (32) 25280000
Fax: (32) 025280001
E-Mail: info@cardif.be
Web Site: www.cardif.be
Emp.: 16
Group Insurance
S.I.C.: 6321
N.A.I.C.S.: 524114

Cardif (3)
Via Tolmezzo 15
Corner Piazza San Babila, 20122 Milan, Italy (100%)
Tel.: (39) 02772241
Fax: (39) 0276008149
E-Mail: info@it.cardif.com
Web Site: www.cardif.com
Emp.: 120
Insurance & Credit Services
S.I.C.: 7299
N.A.I.C.S.: 812990
Isabella Fumagalli *(CEO)*

Subsidiary:

Cardif Vita SpA (4)
Via Tolmezzo 15 Palazzo C
20132 Milan, Italy (100%)
Tel.: (39) 02724271
Fax: (39) 0289010872
E-Mail: info@cardifvita.it
Web Site: www.cardifvita.it
Sales Range: $1-4.9 Billion
Life Insurance Services
S.I.C.: 6311
N.A.I.C.S.: 524113
Niccolo Pandolfini *(Pres)*
Isabella Fumagalli *(CEO)*

Cardif (3)
Ave 5 Dve Otubro 206 6th Fl
1050 065 Lisbon, Portugal (100%)
Tel.: (351) 213825540
Fax: (351) 213825544
E-Mail: cardifportugal@cardif.com
Web Site: www.cardif.com
Emp.: 30
Group Insurance & Asset Management
S.I.C.: 6321
N.A.I.C.S.: 524114
Migueal Ibeero *(Gen Mgr)*

Cardif (3)
Rotenturmstrasse 16 18
1010 Vienna, Austria (100%)
Tel.: (43) 15339878
Fax: (43) 1533987850
E-Mail: info@cardif.com
Web Site: www.cardif.at
Emp.: 15
Insurance & Finance Services
S.I.C.: 6411
N.A.I.C.S.: 524298
Ddolfjanj Drodhahn *(Head-Country)*

Cardif (3)
Hoevestein 28
PO Box 4006
4900 CS Oosterhout, Netherlands (100%)
Tel.: (31) 162486000
Fax: (31) 162486001
E-Mail: info@cardif.com
Web Site: www.cardif.nl
Sales Range: $300-349.9 Million
Emp.: 125
Insurance & Financing Services
S.I.C.: 6411
N.A.I.C.S.: 524298
Cees Dejong *(Pres)*

Non-U.S. Joint Venture:

SBI Life Insurance Company Limited (2)
2nd Floor Turner Morrison Bldg G N Vaidya Marg
Fort, Mumbai, 400 023, India
Tel.: (91) 2266392000
Fax: (91) 2222632113
E-Mail: info@sbilife.co.in
Web Site: www.sbilife.co.in
Life Insurance Services; Joint Venture of BNP Paribas Assurance & State Bank of India
S.I.C.: 6311
N.A.I.C.S.: 524113
Atanu Sen *(CEO & Mng Dir)*

BNP Paribas BDDI Participations (1)
1 Boulevard Haussmann
75009 Paris, France
Tel.: (33) 8 20 82 00 01
Financial Planning Services
S.I.C.: 6282
N.A.I.C.S.: 523930

BNP Paribas Developpement SA (1)
20 Rue Chauchat
75009 Paris, France
Tel.: (33) 1 40 14 55 78
Fax: (33) 1 40 14 29 68
Financial Management Services
S.I.C.: 6211
N.A.I.C.S.: 523999

BNP Paribas Equity Strategies S.N.C. (1)
41 Avenue de l'Opera
75002 Paris, France
Tel.: (33) 8 20 82 00 01
Securities Brokerage Services
S.I.C.: 6211
N.A.I.C.S.: 523120

BNP Paribas Factor (1)
Le Metropole 46 A 52 Rue
92823 Puteaux, Cedex, France (100%)
Tel.: (33) 141971600
Fax: (33) 141972309
Web Site: www.bnpparibasfactor.com
Emp.: 180
Factoring
S.I.C.: 6159
N.A.I.C.S.: 522298
Patrick De Villepin *(Dir Gen)*

BNP Paribas Fin AMS (1)
1 Boulevard Haussmann
75009 Paris, France
Tel.: (33) 825334335
Financial Planning Services
S.I.C.: 6282
N.A.I.C.S.: 523930

BNP Paribas Home Loan SFH (1)
1 Boulevard Haussmann
Paris, 75009, France
Tel.: (33) 1 40 14 85 75

Fax: (33) 1 40 14 61 22
Mortgage Loan Brokerage Services
S.I.C.: 6163
N.A.I.C.S.: 522310
Valerie Brunerie *(Chm & CEO)*
Alain Deforge *(Mng Dir)*

BNP Paribas Immobilier Promotion Immobilier d'Entreprise (1)
13 Boulevard Du Fort De Vaux
Paris, 75017, France
Tel.: (33) 1 55 65 20 50
Fax: (33) 1 55 65 20 51
Web Site: www.realestate.bnpparibas.fr/bnppre/promotion/services-cfo6_11220
Property Development Services
S.I.C.: 6531
N.A.I.C.S.: 531312

BNP Paribas Immobilier Residentiel Promotion Mediterranee (1)
Azurea-Immeuble Le Phoenix 455
Promenade Des Anglais
Nice, 06000, France
Tel.: (33) 4 92 29 25 30
Real Estate Management & Development Services
S.I.C.: 6531
N.A.I.C.S.: 531390

BNP Paribas Immobilier Residentiel Promotion Sud Ouest (1)
23 Parvis Chartrons
33300 Paris, France
Tel.: (33) 5 56 23 86 52
Fax: (33) 5 56 51 10 33
Real Estate Management Services
S.I.C.: 6531
N.A.I.C.S.: 531390

BNP Paribas Immobilier Residentiel Residences Services BSA (1)
7 Avenue de la Gare
BP 35157
26958 Valence, France
Tel.: (33) 4 75 40 80 25
Fax: (33) 4 75 81 11 68
Real Estate Management Services
S.I.C.: 6531
N.A.I.C.S.: 531390

BNP Paribas Immobilier Residentiel Residences Services Sofiane (1)
1 Rue Lesage
26000 Valence, France
Tel.: (33) 8 99 96 36 39
Real Estate Management Services
S.I.C.: 6531
N.A.I.C.S.: 531390

BNP Paribas Immobilier Residentiel S.A.S. (1)
1 Place Occitane
Toulouse, 31000, France
Tel.: (33) 561111600
Fax: (33) 561213606
Real Estate Development Services
S.I.C.: 6531
N.A.I.C.S.: 531390

BNP Paribas Immobilier Residentiel Transaction & Conseil (1)
13 Boulevard du Fort de Vaux13 Boulevard du Fort de Vaux
Paris, 75017, France
Tel.: (33) 1 55 65 29 30
Fax: (33) 1 55 65 20 61
Real Estate Development Services
S.I.C.: 6531
N.A.I.C.S.: 531390

BNP Paribas Lease Group (1)
Le Metropole 46-52 rue Arago
F-92823 Puteaux, Cedex, France (100%)
Tel.: (33) 141972000
Telex: 615221
Fax: (33) 141971829
Web Site: www.leasegroup.bnpparibas.com
Emp.: 1,500
Holding Company; Leasing Equipment & Vehicles
S.I.C.: 7377
N.A.I.C.S.: 532420
Philippe Bissmuth *(Gen Mgr)*

Non-U.S. Subsidiaries:

BNP Paribas Lease Group SA Belgium (2)
Chaussee De La Hulpe 150
B 1170 Brussels, Belgium (100%)
Tel.: (32) 26635790
Fax: (32) 26757598
E-Mail: info@bnpparibas.com
Web Site: www.leasegroup.be
Emp.: 16
Credit, Financial & Property Leasing Services
S.I.C.: 6159
N.A.I.C.S.: 522298

BNP Paribas Lease Group SA EFC (2)
Torre Ejesur Calle Retama 3 Planta 9
28045 Madrid, Spain (100%)
Tel.: (34) 914682048
Fax: (34) 915277327
Web Site: www.bnpparibas-leasegroup.es
Emp.: 60
Financial Services; Lease & Rental Services
S.I.C.: 6282
N.A.I.C.S.: 523930
Javier Iregoien *(Gen Mgr)*

BNP Paribas Lease Group Sp. z o.o. (2)
Ul Zielna 41-43
00078 Warsaw, Poland (100%)
Tel.: (48) 226972560
Fax: (48) 226972569
E-Mail: contact@bnpparibas.pl
Web Site: www.leasegroup.pl
Emp.: 40
Leasing Services
S.I.C.: 7363
N.A.I.C.S.: 561330
Rafal Leszczynski *(Gen Mgr)*

BNP Paribas Leasing Solutions (2)
Northern Cross Basing View
Basingstoke, Hampshire, RG21 4HL, United Kingdom (100%)
Tel.: (44) 845 226 7367
Fax: (44) 845 226 7368
E-Mail: enquiries.leasingsolutions@uk.bnpparibas.com
Web Site: leasingsolutions.bnpparibas.co.uk/
Emp.: 337
Equipment Leasing, Long Term Rental Solutions & IT Asset Management Services
S.I.C.: 6099
N.A.I.C.S.: 522320
Tristan Watkins *(Country Mgr)*

BNP Paribas Real Estate Consult France (1)
167 Quai de la Bataille de Stalingrad
92867 Issy-les-Moulineaux, France
Tel.: (33) 1 55 65 28 02
Fax: (33) 1 55 65 28 00
Real Estate Management Services
S.I.C.: 6531
N.A.I.C.S.: 531390

BNP Paribas Real Estate Financial Partner (1)
167 Quai De La Bataille De Stalingrad
Issy-les-Moulineaux, France
Tel.: (33) 155652424
Fax: (33) 1 55 65 27 06
Real Estate Investment Services
S.I.C.: 6531
N.A.I.C.S.: 531390

BNP Paribas Real Estate Investment Management (1)
167 quai de la bataille de Stalingrad
92867 Issy-les-Moulineaux, France
Tel.: (33) 1 55 65 26 94
Fax: (33) 1 46 42 72 54
E-Mail: reim-bnpparibas@bnpparibas.com
Web Site: www.reim.bnpparibas.co.uk/pages/articles/fiche.php?s_code=reim_contact&r=1084&l=fr&t=bnppre&tfime=1&l=fr
Real Estate Development Services
S.I.C.: 6531
N.A.I.C.S.: 531390

BNP Paribas Real Estate, S.A. (1)
167 quai de la Bataille de Stalingrad
92867 Issy-les-Moulineaux, France
Tel.: (33) 1 55 65 20 04
Fax: (33) 1 55 65 20 00
Web Site: www.realestate.bnpparibas.com
Real Estate Development Services
S.I.C.: 6531
N.A.I.C.S.: 531390
Patrick Delcol *(CEO-Central & Eastern Europe)*
Christoph Scharf *(CEO-Retail Svcs)*

BNP Paribas Real Estate Transaction France S.A. (1)
167 Quai de la Bataille de Stalingrad
92867 Issy-les-Moulineaux, France
Tel.: (33) 1 47 59 25 47
Web Site: www.realestate.bnpparibas.fr
Real Estate Management Services
S.I.C.: 6531
N.A.I.C.S.: 531390

BNP Paribas Wealth Management (1)
33 rue du Quatre Septembre
75078 Paris, France
Tel.: (33) 1 40 14 40 02
E-Mail: pressoffice.paris@bnpparibas.com
Web Site: www.wealthmanagement.bnpparibas.com
Asset Management Services
S.I.C.: 6282
N.A.I.C.S.: 523920
Mignonne Cheng *(Head-Global Asian Markets)*

CamGestion (1)
14 Rue Bergere
75009 Paris, France
Tel.: (33) 1 58 97 60 00
Fax: (33) 1 58 97 60 16
E-Mail: contact@camgestion.fr
Web Site: www.camgestion.fr
Emp.: 49
Asset Management Services
S.I.C.: 6282
N.A.I.C.S.: 523920
Christian Dargnat *(Chm)*
Philippe Forni *(CEO)*
Thierry Bordier *(Deputy CEO)*

Cardif I-Services (1)
1 Boulevard Haussmann
75009 Paris, France
Tel.: (33) 1 45 25 25 25
General Insurance Services
S.I.C.: 6411
N.A.I.C.S.: 524210

Cecoville SAS (1)
21 Avenue Kleber
75116 Paris, France
Tel.: (33) 1 40 67 53 98
Financial Planning Services
S.I.C.: 6282
N.A.I.C.S.: 523930

Centre Jaude Clermont SAS (1)
21 Avenue Kleber
75116 Paris, France
Tel.: (33) 1 45 25 25 25
Emp.: 100
Financial Management Services
S.I.C.: 6211
N.A.I.C.S.: 523999

Cetelem (1)
20 Ave Georges Pompidou
92 595 Levallois-Perret, Cedex, France
Tel.: (33) 146399939
Fax: (33) 146394842
Web Site: www.cetelem.fr
Emp.: 10,000
Provider of Financial Services
S.I.C.: 6159
N.A.I.C.S.: 522298
Bruno Salmon *(COO)*

Non-U.S. Subsidiaries:

Banco Cetelem S.A. (2)
Cl Retama 3
28045 Madrid, Spain (100%)
Tel.: (34) 913370700
Fax: (34) 915289140
E-Mail: info@bancocetelem.es
Web Site: www.bancocetelem.es
Emp.: 300
Consumer Credit Banking Services
S.I.C.: 6159
N.A.I.C.S.: 522298
Luis Fernandez Nieto *(Mng Dir)*

Cetelem Belgium (2)
1 Blvd Anspach
B 1000 Brussels, Belgium (60%)
Tel.: (32) 22501714
Fax: (32) 22501769
E-Mail: cetelem@cetelem.be
Web Site: www.cetelem.be
Emp.: 220
Consumer Financing; Trade & Credit Cards
S.I.C.: 6159
N.A.I.C.S.: 522298

Cetelem SFAC (2)
Rue Tomas Fonseca Torrede
Lisboa Twr G, 1600 Lisbon, Portugal (100%)
Tel.: (351) 217215894
Fax: (351) 217215796
E-Mail: joana.nunes@cetelem.pt
Web Site: www.cetelem.pt
Emp.: 700
Consumer Finance Services
S.I.C.: 6141
N.A.I.C.S.: 522291
Miguel Cadaca *(Gen Mgr)*

Cetelem Taiwan (2)
13 Fl 130 Sect 3 Nanking
Meng Shen East Rd Sec 3, Taipei, 104, Taiwan (100%)
Tel.: (886) 227776020
Fax: (886) 227760909
Web Site: www.cetelem.com.tw
Consumer Finance Services
S.I.C.: 6141
N.A.I.C.S.: 522291

Cetelem UK Ltd. (2)
Leo House Railway Approach
Wallington, SM6 ODY, United Kingdom (100%)
Tel.: (44) 2082547179
Fax: (44) 2086699511
E-Mail: info@halifaxcetelem.co.uk
Web Site: www.halifaxcetelem.com
Emp.: 100
Consumer Financing
S.I.C.: 6141
N.A.I.C.S.: 522291

Findomestic Banca S.p.A (2)
Via Jacopo da Diacceto 48
50123 Florence, Italy
Tel.: (39) 05527011
Fax: (39) 0552701309
E-Mail: findomestic@findomestic.com
Web Site: www.findomestic.it
Emp.: 2,000
Business Banking Services
S.I.C.: 6099
N.A.I.C.S.: 522320

Magyar Cetelem Bank Zrt. (2)
55-57 Terez Korut
1062 Budapest, Hungary (100%)
Tel.: (36) 61 458 6070
Fax: (36) 14586091
E-Mail: cetelem@cetelem.hu
Web Site: www.cetelem.hu
Emp.: 250
Consumer Finance Services
S.I.C.: 6141
N.A.I.C.S.: 522291
Janos Lendvai *(CEO)*

CMV Mediforce S.A. (1)
5 Avenue Kleber
75116 Paris, France
Tel.: (33) 1 46 39 99 39
Fax: (33) 1 42 98 11 42
E-Mail: support@cmvmediforce.fr
Web Site: www.cmvmediforce.fr
Financial Management Services
S.I.C.: 6211
N.A.I.C.S.: 523999
Gerard Chaurand *(Chm)*

CNH Capital Europe S.A.S. (1)
52 Rue Arago
92800 Puteaux, France
Tel.: (33) 8 10 81 06 60
Financial & Consumer Credit Services
S.I.C.: 6211
N.A.I.C.S.: 523999

Cofiparc SNC (1)
1 Boulevard Haussmann
75009 Paris, France
Tel.: (33) 1 47 56 38 60
Web Site: www.cofiparc.fr
Financial Planning Services
S.I.C.: 6282
N.A.I.C.S.: 523930

Cofiplan S.A (1)
5 Avenue Kleber
75116 Paris, France
Tel.: (33) 1 46 39 99 39
Fax: (33) 1 42 98 11 42

BNP Paribas SA—(Continued)

Financial Planning Services
S.I.C.: 6282
N.A.I.C.S.: 523930

Compagnie d Investissements de Paris C.I.P (1)
1 Boulevard Haussmann
75009 Paris, France
Tel.: (33) 140147342
Fax: (33) 140147974
Investment Management Services
S.I.C.: 6282
N.A.I.C.S.: 523920

Compagnie pour le Financement des Loisirs - Cofi loisirs (1)
9 Rue Jean Mermoz
75008 Paris, France
Tel.: (33) 1 53 65 73 30
Fax: (33) 1 53 65 73 40
Emp.: 30
Financial Management Services
S.I.C.: 6211
N.A.I.C.S.: 523999
Jean-Baptiste Souchier *(Mng Dir)*

Cortal Consors (1)
24 Rue Des Deux Gares
92855 Rueil-Malmaison, France
Tel.: (33) 147380909
Fax: (33) 47389696
E-Mail: bienvenue@mail.cortalconsors.fr
Web Site: www.cortalconsors.fr
Emp.: 500
Savings & Investments for Private Clients
S.I.C.: 6035
N.A.I.C.S.: 522120
Olivier Le Grand *(Pres)*

Non-U.S. Subsidiaries:

BNP Paribas Personal Investors (2)
27 Avenue
27 Monterey, 2163 Monterey, Luxembourg (100%)
Mailing Address:
BP 390
2013 Luxembourg, Luxembourg
Tel.: (352) 25372537
Fax: (352) 253738
E-Mail: info@personal-investors.lu
Web Site: www.bnpparibas-personalinvestors.lu
Sales Range: $1-9.9 Million
Emp.: 20
Savings & Investments for Private Investors
S.I.C.: 6211
N.A.I.C.S.: 523110
Awada Philip *(Gen Mgr)*

Cortal Consors Belgium (2)
Rue Royale 145
B 1000 Brussels, Belgium (100%)
Tel.: (32) 22251919
Fax: (32) 22181206
E-Mail: info@cortalconsors.be
Web Site: www.cortal.be
Emp.: 50
Saving & Investment Services for Private Investors
S.I.C.: 6282
N.A.I.C.S.: 523930

Cortal Consors S.A. (2)
Pahnof Strasse 55
PO Box 1743
90006 Nuremberg, D 90402, Germany
Mailing Address:
Postfacht 1743
BLZ 760 30080 Nuremberg, Germany
Tel.: (49) 9113690
Fax: (49) 9113691000
E-Mail: infoservice@cortalconsors.de
Web Site: www.cortalconsors.de
Emp.: 700
Online Brokerage Service
Export
S.I.C.: 6221
N.A.I.C.S.: 523140
Olivier le Grand *(Mng Dir)*
Franz Baur *(CIO)*

Domofinance SA (1)
5 Avenue Kleber
75116 Paris, France
Tel.: (33) 1 46 39 99 39
Fax: (33) 1 42 98 11 42
E-Mail: contact.marketing@domofinance.com
Web Site: www.domofinance.com
Financial Management Services
S.I.C.: 6211
N.A.I.C.S.: 523999

Non-U.S. Subsidiary:

BNP Paribas Real Estate (2)
Blvd Louis Schmidt
1040 Brussels, Belgium
Tel.: (32) 22379999
Fax: (32) 322905959
E-Mail: info@bnpparibа.com
Web Site: www.bnpparibа.com
Emp.: 60
Real Estate Investment Trust
S.I.C.: 6726
N.A.I.C.S.: 525990
Frederic Van de Putte *(Mng Dir)*

F G Ingenierie et Promotion Immobiliere (1)
506 Av Du Prado
13008 Camblanes-et-Meynac, France
Tel.: (33) 4 91 22 23 42
Fax: (33) 4 91 22 04 16
Real Estate Management Services
S.I.C.: 6531
N.A.I.C.S.: 531390

Fidem (1)
23 Rue De La Foret
Illkirch-Graffenstaden, 67400, France
Tel.: (33) 388320978
Web Site: www.fidem.fr
Real Estate Management Services
S.I.C.: 6531
N.A.I.C.S.: 531390

Fimapierre (1)
23 Rue L Amiral D Estaing
75116 Paris, France
Tel.: (33) 1 53 67 29 00
Emp.: 100
Financial Management Services
S.I.C.: 6211
N.A.I.C.S.: 523999
Michel Alain Marcel Lacomme *(Chm)*

Financiere BNP Paribas SAS (1)
1 Boulevard Haussmann
75009 Paris, France
Tel.: (33) 8 20 82 00 01
Financial Planning Services
S.I.C.: 6282
N.A.I.C.S.: 523930

Financiere Paris Haussmann (1)
1 Boulevard Haussmann
75009 Paris, France
Tel.: (33) 8 99 96 26 48
Financial Planning Services
S.I.C.: 6282
N.A.I.C.S.: 523930

Friedland Participation et Gestion S.A. (1)
30 Quai de Dion Bouton
92800 Puteaux, France
Tel.: (33) 8 99 96 77 60
Financial Planning Services
S.I.C.: 6282
N.A.I.C.S.: 523930

Gestion et Location Holding S.A.S. (1)
41 Avenue de l'Opera
75002 Paris, France
Tel.: (33) 1 41 14 18 18
Investment Management Services
S.I.C.: 6282
N.A.I.C.S.: 523920

GIE Groupement Auxiliaire de Moyens (1)
1 Boulevard Haussmann
75009 Paris, France
Tel.: (33) 142479000
Fax: (33) 1 47 38 49 70
Financial Planning Services
S.I.C.: 6282
N.A.I.C.S.: 523930

Holding Gondomar 3 SAS (1)
21 Avenue Kleber
75116 Paris, France
Tel.: (33) 1 46 08 28 19
Real Estate Management Services
S.I.C.: 6531
N.A.I.C.S.: 531390

JCB Finance SAS (1)
3 rue du Vignolle
95842 Sarcelles, France
Tel.: (33) 1 34 29 20 60
Fax: (33) 1 41 97 18 29
E-Mail: france.jcbfinance@jcb.com
Emp.: 6
Financial Management Services
S.I.C.: 6211
N.A.I.C.S.: 523999
Wolfgang Pinner *(Pres)*

Kle Projet 1 SAS (1)
Place St-Clair Centre Commercial B
14200 Herouville-Saint-Clair, France
Tel.: (33) 2 31 23 75 12
Real Estate Property Leasing Services
S.I.C.: 6519
N.A.I.C.S.: 531190

Kleber la Perouse SNC (1)
21 Av Kleber
75116 Paris, France
Tel.: (33) 1 45 53 62 82
Real Estate Management Services
S.I.C.: 6531
N.A.I.C.S.: 531390

Klecar Europe Sud SCS (1)
21 Avenue Kleber
75116 Paris, France
Tel.: (33) 1 40 67 53 85
Fax: (33) 1 40 67 57 40
Emp.: 540
Real Estate Leasing Services
S.I.C.: 6519
N.A.I.C.S.: 531190
Laurent Morel *(Pres)*

Klecar France SNC (1)
21 Avenue Kleber
75116 Paris, France
Tel.: (33) 1 40 67 57 40
Fax: (33) 1 40 67 55 62
Real Estate Management Services
S.I.C.: 6531
N.A.I.C.S.: 531390

Klepierre SA (1)
21 Avenue Kleber
75116 Paris, France (50.5%)
Tel.: (33) 140675740
Fax: (33) 140675562
Web Site: www.klepierre.com
LI—(EUR)
Rev.: $1,335,563,527
Assets: $17,404,705,969
Liabilities: $12,530,595,942
Net Worth: $4,874,110,027
Earnings: $352,551,154
Emp.: 1,467
Fiscal Year-end: 12/31/12
Real Estate Services
S.I.C.: 6531
N.A.I.C.S.: 531210
David Simon *(Chm-Supervisory Bd)*
Laurent Morel *(Chm-Exec Bd)*
Vivien Levy-Garboua *(Vice Chm-Supervisory Bd)*
Jean-Michel Gault *(Deputy CEO & Member-Exec Bd)*
Jean-Marc Jestin *(COO & Member-Exec Bd)*
Sandrine Quesnel *(CMO & Chief Comm Officer)*
Marie-Therese Dimasi *(Chief Legal Officer & Chief HR Officer)*
Frederic de Klopstein *(Chief Investment Officer)*
Bernard Deslandes *(Chief Dev Officer)*
Bruno Valentin *(Chief Acctg, Mgmt Reporting & IT Sys Officer)*
Eric Degouy *(Chief Property Mgmt Officer)*
Gontran Thuring *(Chief Leasing Officer)*

Subsidiaries:

Klemurs SCA (2)
21 ave Kleber
75116 Paris, France (84.1%)
Tel.: (33) 140675740
Fax: (33) 140675562
Web Site: www.klemurs.fr
KMU—(EUR)
Sales Range: $50-74.9 Million
Property Management Services
S.I.C.: 6531
N.A.I.C.S.: 531311
Steven Fivel *(Chm-Supervisory Bd)*

Klepierre Conseil SNC (2)
21 Avenue Kleber
Paris, 75116, France
Tel.: (33) 1 40 67 57 40
Real Estate Management Services
S.I.C.: 6531
N.A.I.C.S.: 531390

Klepierre Creteil SCI (2)
21 Avenue Kleber
75116 Paris, France
Tel.: (33) 1 40 67 57 40
Fax: (33) 1 40 67 55 62
Financial Management Services
S.I.C.: 6099
N.A.I.C.S.: 522320

Klepierre Finance SAS (2)
21 Avenue Kleber
75116 Paris, France
Tel.: (33) 1 40 67 57 40
Investment Management Services
S.I.C.: 6799
N.A.I.C.S.: 523920

Non-U.S. Subsidiaries:

Klepierre Athinon Fonciere (2)
3 Str Tompra
Agia Paraskevi, Athens, 15342, Greece
Tel.: (30) 2106062100
Fax: (30) 2106062111
Real Estate Management Services
S.I.C.: 6531
N.A.I.C.S.: 531390

Klepierre CZ SRO (2)
Plzenska 233/8
Prague, 150 00, Czech Republic
Tel.: (420) 251 101 061
Emp.: 40
Real Estate Leasing Services
S.I.C.: 6519
N.A.I.C.S.: 531190
David Pazitka *(Gen Mgr)*

Klepierre Larissa Ltd. (2)
3 Str Tompra
Agia Paraskevi, Athens, 15342, Greece
Tel.: (30) 2106062100
Fax: (30) 2106062111
Real Estate Property Leasing Services
S.I.C.: 6519
N.A.I.C.S.: 531190

Klepierre Makedonia Fonciere (2)
3 Stratigou Tompra
Agia Paraskevi, 15342 Athens, Greece
Tel.: (30) 2106062100
Fax: (30) 2106062111
Real Estate Management Services
S.I.C.: 6531
N.A.I.C.S.: 531390

Klepierre NEA Efkarpia Fonciere (2)
3 Str Tompra
Agia Paraskevi, Athens, 15342, Greece
Tel.: (30) 2106062100
Fax: (30) 2106062111
Real Estate Management Services
S.I.C.: 6531
N.A.I.C.S.: 531390

Klepierre Nordica BV (2)
Reguliersdwarsstraat 90
Amsterdam, 1017 BN, Netherlands
Tel.: (31) 205215645
Fax: (31) 205215629
Investment Management Services
S.I.C.: 6282
N.A.I.C.S.: 523920

Klepierre Plzen AS (2)
Radcicka 2861/2
301 00 Plzen, Czech Republic
Tel.: (420) 374809300
Real Estate Development Services
S.I.C.: 6531
N.A.I.C.S.: 531390

Klepierre Poznan SP z.o.o (2)
Armii Ludowej 26
Warsaw, 00-609, Poland
Tel.: (48) 223566950
Real Estate Development Services
S.I.C.: 6531
N.A.I.C.S.: 531390

Klepierre Praha SRO (2)
Novodvorska 1800/136
142 00 Prague, Czech Republic
Tel.: (420) 225437100
Fax: (420) 225437110
E-Mail: plazanovodvorska@segec.cz
Web Site: www.plazanovodvorska.cz
Shopping Center Operator
S.I.C.: 6512
N.A.I.C.S.: 531120
Jakub Vychodil *(Gen Mgr)*

La Rive SCI (1)
203 Rue de la Rive
42320 La Grand-Croix, France
Tel.: (33) 4 27 77 69 22
Real Estate Management Services
S.I.C.: 6531
N.A.I.C.S.: 531390

Meunier Promotion (1)
13 Blvd Fort De Vua
75017 Paris, France (100%)
Tel.: (33) 155652004
Fax: (33) 155652000
E-Mail: info@meunier-promotion.fr
Web Site: www.meunier-promotion.fr
Emp.: 250
Real Estate Developer & Housing Project Manager
S.I.C.: 6531
N.A.I.C.S.: 531390
Philippe Zivkovic *(Pres)*

Natiobail 2 S.A. (1)
46 A 52 Rue Arago
Puteaux, 92800, France
Tel.: (33) 141972000
Fax: (33) 141971829
Financial Credit Services
S.I.C.: 6159
N.A.I.C.S.: 522298

Natiocredibail SA (1)
Imm Le Metropole 46-52 46 Rue Arago
92800 Puteaux, France
Tel.: (33) 1 41 97 20 00
Fax: (33) 1 41 97 18 29
Financial Planning Services
S.I.C.: 6282
N.A.I.C.S.: 523930

Natiocredimurs SNC (1)
Imm Le Metropole 46-52 46 Rue Arago
Puteaux, Hauts-de-Seine, 92800, France
Tel.: (33) 1 41 97 20 00
Fax: (33) 1 41 97 18 29
Financial Management Services
S.I.C.: 6211
N.A.I.C.S.: 523999

Norrsken Finance SA (1)
1 Boulevard Haussmann
75009 Paris, France
Tel.: (33) 8 20 30 33 33
Web Site: www.norrsken.fr
Investment Advisory Services
S.I.C.: 6282
N.A.I.C.S.: 523930

Opera Rendement SCPI (1)
4 Avenue Pablo Picasso
92000 Nanterre, France
Tel.: (33) 1 47 24 34 25
Real Estate Management Services
S.I.C.: 6531
N.A.I.C.S.: 531390

Paricomi 2 (ex-Paricomi) (1)
46 52 Rue Arago
Puteaux, France
Tel.: (33) 141972000
Fax: (33) 141971329
Financial Management Services
S.I.C.: 6211
N.A.I.C.S.: 523999

Parilease SAS (1)
41 Avenue de L Opera
Paris, 75002, France
Tel.: (33) 142980761
Fax: (33) 142981203
Financial Management Services
S.I.C.: 6211
N.A.I.C.S.: 523999

Pommeraie Parc SC (1)
21 Avenue Kleber
75116 Paris, France
Tel.: (33) 8 99 96 35 45
Real Estate Management Services
S.I.C.: 6531
N.A.I.C.S.: 531390

Portzamparc Gestion (1)
10 rue Meurisboite
44100 Nantes, France
Tel.: (33) 240449400
Fax: (33) 240697821
E-Mail: contact@portzamparc.fr
Web Site: www.portzamparc.fr
Real Estate Development Services
S.I.C.: 6531
N.A.I.C.S.: 531390

Prets et Services SAS (1)
1 Boulevard Haussmann
75009 Paris, France
Tel.: (33) 141424896
Fax: (33) 141420701
Mortgage Loan Brokerage Services
S.I.C.: 6163
N.A.I.C.S.: 522310

Same Deutz-Fahr Finance SAS (1)
46 A 52 Rue Arago
Puteaux, 92800, France
Tel.: (33) 141972000
Fax: (33) 141971829
E-Mail: contactls@bnpparibas.com
Financial Management Services
S.I.C.: 6211
N.A.I.C.S.: 523999

SCI Champvernier (1)
30 Quai de Dion Bouton
92800 Puteaux, France
Tel.: (33) 8 99 96 77 56
Financial Planning Services
S.I.C.: 6282
N.A.I.C.S.: 523930

SCI FLIF Chateau Landon (1)
30 Quai de Dion Bouton
92800 Puteaux, France
Tel.: (33) 8 99 96 77 60
Real Estate Management Services
S.I.C.: 6531
N.A.I.C.S.: 531390

SCI FLIF Evry 2 (1)
30 Quai de Dion Bouton
92800 Puteaux, France
Tel.: (33) 8 99 96 77 60
Real Estate Management Services
S.I.C.: 6531
N.A.I.C.S.: 531390

SCI FLIF Le Gallo (1)
30 Quai de Dion Bouton
92800 Puteaux, France
Tel.: (33) 8 99 96 77 60
Real Estate Management Services
S.I.C.: 6531
N.A.I.C.S.: 531390

Sesame Conseil SAS (1)
13 Boulevard du Fort de Vaux
75017 Paris, France
Tel.: (33) 1 53 59 32 32
Fax: (33) 1 53 59 32 33
E-Mail: contact.sesame@sesameconseil.com
Web Site: www.sesameconseil.fr
Real Estate Management Services
S.I.C.: 6531
N.A.I.C.S.: 531390

Societe des Centres d'Oc et d'Oil - SCOO SC (1)
Centre Commercial Les Arcades
93160 Noisy-le-Grand, France
Tel.: (33) 1 49 31 01 72
Fax: (33) 1 43 05 09 37
Real Estate Management Services
S.I.C.: 6531
N.A.I.C.S.: 531390

Societe Orbaisienne de Participations (1)
1 Boulevard Haussmann
75009 Paris, France
Tel.: (33) 8 99 96 77 63
Investment Management Services
S.I.C.: 6799
N.A.I.C.S.: 523920

Taitbout Participation 3 Snc (1)
1 Boulevard Haussmann
75009 Paris, France
Tel.: (33) 8 99 96 77 55
Investment Management Services
S.I.C.: 6282
N.A.I.C.S.: 523920

UCB Locabail immobilier 2 (1)
46 Rue Aragola Defense
92800 Puteaux, France
Tel.: (33) 141424142
Financial Credit Services
S.I.C.: 6159
N.A.I.C.S.: 522298

Affiliate:

Banexi Ventures Partners (1)
13-15 rue Taitbout
75009 Paris, France
Tel.: (33) 1 73 02 89 69
Fax: (33) 140149896
E-Mail: contact@banexiventures.com
Web Site: www.banexiventures.com
Emp.: 10
Investing & Company Restructuring
S.I.C.: 6211
N.A.I.C.S.: 523999
Michel Dahan *(Chm & Gen Partner)*
Philippe Mere *(Gen Partner-Electronics)*
Sophie Pierrin-Lepinard *(Gen Partner-Healthcare)*
Philippe Herbert *(Partner-IT)*
Jacqueline Renard *(Sec)*

Joint Venture:

Lafayette Services LaSer (1)
66 Rue Des Archives
75003 Paris, France
Tel.: (33) 44544700
E-Mail: contact@laser.fr
Web Site: www.laser.fr
Consumer Credit & Loyalty Card Schemes.
S.I.C.: 6141
N.A.I.C.S.: 522210
Philippe Lemoine *(Chm & Co-CEO)*
Michel Philippin *(Co-CEO)*

Subsidiary:

Cofinoga S.A. (2)
66 Rue Des Archives
75003 Paris, France
Tel.: (33) 556554750
Fax: (33) 556126371
Web Site: www.cofinoga.fr
Emp.: 2,500
Consumer Credit Services
S.I.C.: 6141
N.A.I.C.S.: 522210
Philippe Lemoine *(Pres)*

Non-U.S. Subsidiary:

LaSer Polska (2)
ul Suwak 3
02 676 Warsaw, Poland
Tel.: (48) 22 591 45 45
Fax: (48) 22 256 47 01
E-Mail: media@laserpolska.com
Web Site: www.laserpolska.com
Consumer Finance Services
S.I.C.: 6141
N.A.I.C.S.: 522210

U.S. Subsidiary:

BNP Paribas North America (1)
The Equitable Tower 787 7th Ave
New York, NY 10019
Tel.: (212) 841-3000
Fax: (212) 841-2146
Web Site: www.usa.bnpparibas.com
Emp.: 2,000
S.I.C.: 6029
N.A.I.C.S.: 522110
Marc Badner *(Mng Dir-Credit Sls)*
Sean Farrell *(Mng Dir-Rates & Credit Short Duration Products)*
Kevin Stocklin *(Mng Dir & Head-US CDO Origination & Structuring)*
Catherine Flax *(Mng Dir & Head-Commodity Derivatives-Americas)*
Mallory Brooks *(Mng Dir)*
Patrick McKee *(Mng Dir)*
Keith Price *(Mng Dir)*
Sean Reddington *(Mng Dir)*

Group:

BNP Cooper-Neff Group (2)
555 Croton Rd Fl 4
King of Prussia, PA 19406
Tel.: (610) 491-1400
Fax: (610) 491-1700
E-Mail: cninfo@cooperneff.com
Web Site: www.cooperneff.com
Emp.: 150
Provider of Banking Services
S.I.C.: 6211
N.A.I.C.S.: 523110

Branches:

BNP Paribas-Chicago (2)
155 N Wacker Dr Ste 4450
Chicago, IL 60606
Tel.: (312) 977-2200
Telex: 4330167 PARIBAS CGO
Fax: (312) 977-1380
Web Site: www.bnpparibas.com
Emp.: 50
International Bankers
S.I.C.: 6029
N.A.I.C.S.: 522110

BNP Paribas-Dallas (2)
100 Crescent Ct Ste 500
Dallas, TX 75201
Tel.: (214) 969-0380
Telex: 730179 PARIBAS
Fax: (214) 969-0260
Web Site: www.bnpparibas.com
Emp.: 15
International Bankers
S.I.C.: 7359
N.A.I.C.S.: 532490
Samuel M. Hocking *(Global Co-Head-Prime Brokerage Sls)*

BNP Paribas-Houston (2)
1200 Smith St Ste 3100
Houston, TX 77002-4308
Tel.: (713) 982-1100
Telex: 792604/05
Fax: (713) 659-3832
Web Site: www.bnpparibas.com
Emp.: 55
International Bankers
S.I.C.: 6159
N.A.I.C.S.: 522293
David Dodd *(Head-Oil & Gas Bus)*

BNP Paribas-New York (2)
The Equitable Tower 787 7th Ave
New York, NY 10019
Tel.: (212) 841-2000
Telex: 239108
Fax: (212) 841-3251
E-Mail: hrconnect@americasbnpparibas.com
Web Site: usa.bnpparibas.com
Emp.: 1,400
Financial Services
S.I.C.: 6211
N.A.I.C.S.: 523120
Namuk Cho *(Mng Dir & Head-Flow, Hybrids & Exotics-America)*

BNP Paribas-San Francisco (2)
1 Frnt St Fl 23
San Francisco, CA 94111
Tel.: (415) 772-1300
Telex: 82874 PARIBAS SFO
Fax: (415) 391-3390
Web Site: www.usa.bnpparibas.com
Emp.: 50
International Bankers
S.I.C.: 6029
N.A.I.C.S.: 522110
Frances Kawaguchi *(VP & Mgr-Admin)*

Subsidiaries:

1897 Services Corporation (2)
180 Montgomery St
San Francisco, CA 94104
Tel.: (415) 765-4800
Financial Planning Services
S.I.C.: 6282
N.A.I.C.S.: 523930

BancWest Corporation (2)
999 Bishop St 29th Fl
Honolulu, HI 96813
Tel.: (808) 525-7000
Fax: (808) 525-7086
Web Site: www.bancwestcorp.com
Emp.: 12,554
Financial Services
S.I.C.: 6029
N.A.I.C.S.: 522110

BNP Paribas SA—(Continued)

J. Michael Shepherd *(CEO)*
Thibault Fulconis *(CFO & Exec VP)*

Subsidiaries:

Bancwest Investment Services. Inc. (3)
13505 California Street Plz W
Omaha, NE 68154
Tel.: (402) 918-4063
Fax: (402) 827-3108
Commercial Banking Services
S.I.C.: 6029
N.A.I.C.S.: 522110

Bank of the West (3)
180 Montgomery St
San Francisco, CA 94104 CA
Tel.: (925) 942-8300 (100%)
Fax: (925) 943-1224
Toll Free: (800) 488-BANK
Web Site: www.bankofthewest.com
Emp.: 10,700
Banking Services
S.I.C.: 6029
N.A.I.C.S.: 522110
J. Michael Shepherd *(Chm & CEO)*
Steve Glenn *(Vice Chm & Chief Admin Officer)*
Maura Markus *(Pres & COO)*
Kirsten Garen *(CIO & Exec VP)*
Ann von Germeten *(CMO)*
William Even *(Sr Exec VP & Chief Credit Officer)*
Mike Boub *(Pres-BW Insurance Agency)*
Vanessa Washington *(Gen Counsel, Sec & Exec VP)*
Scott Germer *(Sr Exec VP & Mgr-Risk)*
Donald Duggan *(Sr Exec VP-Ops & Sys)*
Andrew Harmening *(Sr Exec VP-Reg Banking Grp)*
Paul T. Wible *(Sr Exec VP-Natl Fin Grp)*
Susan H. Fowler *(Exec VP & Dir-HR)*
Ross Biatek *(Exec VP & Gen Auditor)*
Robert Dalrymple *(Exec VP-Great Plains Div)*
Mark Glasky *(Exec VP)*
James R. Kennedy *(Exec VP)*
Martin Resch *(Exec VP)*
Roger Sturdevant *(Exec VP)*
John Thomason *(Exec VP)*
Norma J. Waters *(Exec VP & Specialty Products Head-Retail & Bus Banking)*
Gina Wolley *(Exec VP)*
Hamed Farhadi *(Sr VP & Head-Global Trade Solutions)*
Christy Schmitt *(Sr VP & Mgr-Retail Small Bus Segment)*
Ralph Anthony *(Sr VP-Fin Integration & Tax)*
Mark Beecher *(Sr VP-Sls & Mktg)*
Art Crawford *(Sr VP-Consumer Fin Admin)*
Brian Katz *(Sr VP)*
Edward Mora *(Sr VP-Wealth Mgmt Grp)*
Lori Rivers *(Sr VP-Sys & Project Office)*

Subsidiaries:

Essex Credit Corporation (4)
12677 Alcosta Blvd Ste 200
San Ramon, CA 94583-4407
Tel.: (925) 274-1235
Fax: (925) 979-9505
Toll Free: (866) ESSEX-4U
E-Mail: sales@essexcredit.com
Web Site: www.essexcredit.com
Emp.: 50
Credit Services for the Pleasure Boating & Recreational Vehicle Market
S.I.C.: 6159
N.A.I.C.S.: 522298
Jesse Bragg *(CEO)*

The Bankers Club, Inc. (3)
999 Bishop St
Honolulu, HI 96813
Tel.: (808) 525-6171
Financial Management Services
S.I.C.: 6211
N.A.I.C.S.: 523999

Bishop Street Capital Management Corporation (3)
1st Hawaiian Ctr 999 Bishop St Ste 2806
Honolulu, HI 96813
Tel.: (808) 525-6246
Fax: (808) 525-8110
Investment Management Services
S.I.C.: 6211
N.A.I.C.S.: 523999

First Hawaiian Bank (3)
999 Bishop St
Honolulu, HI 96813-4423 DE
Mailing Address: (100%)
PO Box 3200
Honolulu, HI 96847-0001
Tel.: (808) 525-7000
Fax: (808) 525-5798
Toll Free: (888) 844-4444
Web Site: www.fhb.com
Emp.: 2,100
Bank Holding Company
S.I.C.: 6029
N.A.I.C.S.: 522110
Donald G. Horner *(Chm)*
Albert M. Yamada *(Vice Chm & CFO)*
Gary L. Caulfield *(Vice Chm-Info Mgmt & Ops Grp)*
Anthony R. Guerrero, Jr. *(Vice Chm-Retail Banking)*
Bob Harrison *(Pres & CEO)*
William E. Atwater *(Gen Counsel, Sec & Exec VP)*
Edward Y. W. Pei *(Exec VP-Consumer Banking)*
Chris Dods *(Sr VP & Mgr-Mktg Comm)*
Brent Helgeson *(Sr VP & Mgr-Dealer Div)*
Rachel Hanlon *(Sr VP-Private Banking Div)*
Shigeo Hone *(Sr VP-Bus Dev-Japan)*
Michael Nishida *(Sr VP-PC & Network Svcs)*
Wesley Young *(Sr VP-Branch Residential Loans)*

Subsidiaries:

FH Center, Inc. (4)
999 Bishop St
Honolulu, HI 96813-4423 HI
Tel.: (808) 525-7000 (100%)
Fax: (808) 844-3699
Web Site: www.fhb.com
Real Estate Holding & Development
S.I.C.: 6159
N.A.I.C.S.: 522293
Donald P. Horner *(Chm & CEO)*

FHB Properties, Inc. (4)
999 Bishop St
Honolulu, HI 96813-4423 HI
Tel.: (808) 525-7000 (100%)
Fax: (808) 844-3699
Web Site: www.fhb.com
Sales Range: $300-349.9 Million
Emp.: 20
Bank Properties Company
S.I.C.: 6512
N.A.I.C.S.: 531120
Donald G. Horner *(Chm, Pres & CEO)*

FHI International, Inc. (4)
999 Bishop St
Honolulu, HI 96813-4423 HI
Tel.: (808) 525-7000 (100%)
Fax: (808) 844-3699
Sales Range: $1-9.9 Million
Holding Company
S.I.C.: 6159
N.A.I.C.S.: 522293
Donald G Horner *(Pres & CEO)*
Albert Yamada *(CFO)*

First Hawaiian Capital 1 (4)
1188 Bishop St Ste 3403
Honolulu, HI 96813
Tel.: (808) 524-5738
Business Trust
S.I.C.: 6733
N.A.I.C.S.: 525920

First Hawaiian Insurance, Inc. (4)
999 Bishop St
Honolulu, HI 96813-2311 HI
Tel.: (808) 525-6212 (100%)
Fax: (808) 525-6177
E-Mail: bfarias@fhb.com
Web Site: www.fhb.com
Emp.: 15
Provider of Insurance Services
S.I.C.: 6411
N.A.I.C.S.: 524210
Donald G. Horner *(Chm & CEO)*
Brandt G. Farias *(Exec VP-Mktg Comm)*
Michael G. Taylor *(Sr VP)*

First Hawaiian Leasing, Inc. (4)
1580 Kapiolani Blvd 3rd Fl
Honolulu, HI 96814 HI
Tel.: (808) 943-4905 (100%)
Fax: (808) 943-4975
Emp.: 16
Commercial Equipment & Vehicle Sales Financing & Leasing Services
S.I.C.: 6159
N.A.I.C.S.: 522220
Keethe Koyanagi *(Pres)*

Subsidiary:

FHL Lease Holding Company Inc. (5)
1580 Kapiolani Blvd 3rd Fl
Honolulu, HI 96814
Tel.: (808) 943-4905
Fax: (808) 943-4975
Investment Management Services
S.I.C.: 6211
N.A.I.C.S.: 523999
Manny Valbuena *(VP)*

Real Estate Delivery, Inc. (4)
999 Bishop St
Honolulu, HI 96813-4423 HI
Tel.: (808) 525-7000 (100%)
Fax: (808) 844-3699
Hold Title to Certain Real Property Acquired by the Bank in Ordinary Business Activities
S.I.C.: 6531
N.A.I.C.S.: 531210

BNP Commodity Futures Inc. (2)
787 7th Ave
New York, NY 10019-6018 NY
Tel.: (212) 841-3366
Fax: (212) 841-3137
E-Mail: cfi@americas.bnpparibas.com
Web Site: www.cfi.bnpparibas.com
Emp.: 40
Commodity Futures Brokers
S.I.C.: 6221
N.A.I.C.S.: 523130
Tom Walsh *(VP-Ops)*

BNP Paribas Brokerage Services, Inc (2)
555 Croton Rd Fl 4
King of Prussia, PA 19406 (100%)
Tel.: (212) 841-3101
Fax: (610) 491-1700
E-Mail: info@bnppbs.com
Web Site: www.bnppbs.com
Emp.: 150
Brokerage Service
S.I.C.: 6211
N.A.I.C.S.: 523120

BNP Paribas Capital Services Inc. (2)
1209 Orange St
Wilmington, DE 19801
Tel.: (302) 658-7581
Capital Investment Services
S.I.C.: 6799
N.A.I.C.S.: 523910

BNP Paribas Capstar Partners Inc. (2)
2711 Centerville Rd Ste 400
Wilmington, DE 19808
Tel.: (302) 636-5401
Capital Investment Services
S.I.C.: 6799
N.A.I.C.S.: 523910

BNP Paribas Financial Services LLC (2)
555 Croton Rd Fl 4
King of Prussia, PA 19406
Tel.: (610) 491-1400
Financial Management Services
S.I.C.: 6211
N.A.I.C.S.: 523999

BNP Paribas Leasing Corporation (2)
100 Crescent Ct 500
Dallas, TX 75201
Tel.: (972) 788-9191
Commercial Equipment Leasing Services
S.I.C.: 7359
N.A.I.C.S.: 532490

BNP Paribas Mortgage Corporation (2)
787 7th Ave Fl 27
New York, NY 10019
Tel.: (212) 841-2000
Mortgage Loan Brokerage Services
S.I.C.: 6163
N.A.I.C.S.: 522310

BNP Paribas Prime Brokerage Inc. (2)
787 7th Ave The Equitable Tower
New York, NY 10019
Tel.: (212) 841-3000
Web Site: www.primebroker.com
Securities Brokerage Services
S.I.C.: 6211
N.A.I.C.S.: 523120
Anthony Carroll *(VP-Mktg)*

BNP Paribas RCC Inc. (2)
525 Washington Blvd
Jersey City, NJ 73101
Tel.: (201) 850-5737
Financial Investment Services
S.I.C.: 6211
N.A.I.C.S.: 523999
Umang Sukhia *(VP & Head-Bus Intelligence)*

BNP Paribas Securities Corp. (2)
787 7th Ave 31st Fl
New York, NY 10019-6018 NY
Tel.: (212) 841-3000
Fax: (212) 841-2146
Web Site: www.usa.bnpparibas.com
Rev.: $311,901,000
Emp.: 2,000
Security Brokers
S.I.C.: 6211
N.A.I.C.S.: 523120
David Brunner *(Pres)*
Everett Sehenk *(CEO)*

BNP Paribas VPG Medianews Group LLC (2)
1209 Orange St
Wilmington, DE 19801
Tel.: (302) 658-7581
Financial Planning Services
S.I.C.: 6282
N.A.I.C.S.: 523930

BW Insurance Agency, Inc. (2)
520 Main Ave
Fargo, ND 58124
Tel.: (701) 271-6630
Fax: (701) 271-6631
Emp.: 12
Property & Casualty Insurance Services
S.I.C.: 6351
N.A.I.C.S.: 524126
Mike Boub *(Pres)*

Center Club, Inc. (2)
100 Light St 16th Fl
Baltimore, MD 21202
Tel.: (410) 727-7788
Fax: (410) 783-0166
E-Mail: info@centerclub.org
Web Site: www.centerclub.org
Club Operator
S.I.C.: 8641
N.A.I.C.S.: 813410
Frank Walsh *(Controller)*

Claas Financial Services Inc. (2)
1209 Orange St
Wilmington, DE 19801
Tel.: (302) 658-7581
Financial Planning Services
S.I.C.: 6282
N.A.I.C.S.: 523930

Community Service, Inc. (2)
100 S Cherokee
Morrilton, AR 72110
Tel.: (501) 354-4589
Fax: (501) 354-5410
Toll Free: (800) 489-1209
Web Site: www.communityserviceinc.com
Emp.: 30
Social Development Program Administrative Services
S.I.C.: 9441
N.A.I.C.S.: 923130
John Gibson *(Chm)*
J. J. Magie *(Vice Chm)*

Fauchier Partners Corporation (2)
444 Madison Ave 29th Fl
New York, NY 10022
Tel.: (212) 319-8002
Fax: (212) 319-8003

Web Site: www.fauchierpartners.com
Investment Advisory Services
S.I.C.: 6282
N.A.I.C.S.: 523930

French American Banking Corp. (2)
787 7th Ave
New York, NY 10019 NY
Tel.: (212) 841-3000
Fax: (212) 841-2146
Web Site: www.bnpparibas.com
Emp.: 400
Commercial Banks Nec
S.I.C.: 6029
N.A.I.C.S.: 522110
Laurent Chouraki *(Chm)*
Everett Schenk *(CEO)*

Harewood Asset Management (US) Inc. (2)
555 Croton Rd 4th Fl
King of Prussia, PA 19406
Tel.: (610) 491-1400
Fax: (610) 491-1700
Asset Management Services
S.I.C.: 6799
N.A.I.C.S.: 523920

Margaret Inc. (2)
680 Makani Rd
Makawao, HI 96768
Tel.: (808) 572-0028
Investment Management Services
S.I.C.: 6799
N.A.I.C.S.: 523920

Ursus Real estate inc (2)
24405 Village Walk Pl
Murrieta, CA 92562
Tel.: (951) 677-8035
Real Estate Management Services
S.I.C.: 6531
N.A.I.C.S.: 531390

Non-U.S. Group:

Fortis Bank SA/NV (1)
Warandeberg 3
1000 Brussels, Belgium BE
Tel.: (32) 25651111 (74.93%)
Fax: (32) 25654222
E-Mail: info@bnpparibasfortis.com
Web Site: www.bnpparibasfortis.com
Int. Income: $12,406,302,720
Assets: $366,500,167,180
Liabilities: $335,099,405,760
Net Worth: $31,400,761,420
Earnings: $733,662,650
Emp.: 37,160
Fiscal Year-end: 12/31/12
Banking, Investment & Insurance Services
S.I.C.: 6029
N.A.I.C.S.: 522110
Herman Daems *(Chm)*
Maxime Jadot *(Chm-Exec Bd & CEO)*
Georges Chodron de Courcel *(Vice Chm)*
Filip R.J. Dierckx *(Vice Chm-Exec Bd, COO & Head-Grp Functions)*
Emmanuel Buttin *(CFO)*
Thomas Mennicken *(Member-Exec Bd & Chief Risk Officer)*
Dominique Remy *(Member-Exec Bd & Head-Corp & Investment Banking & Structured Fin)*
Peter Vandekerckhove *(Member-Exec Bd & Head-Retail & Private Banking-Belgium)*
Luc Haegemans *(Sec)*

Divisions:

BNP Paribas Fortis Merchant Banking (2)
Rue Montagne du Parc 3
1000 Brussels, Belgium
Tel.: (32) 2 565 1111
Fax: (32) 2 565 1013
E-Mail: merchantbanking@fortisbank.com
Web Site: www.merchant.fortisbank.com
Emp.: 3,000
Commercial & Investment Banking, Trade Financing, Clearing, Custody & Fund Services
S.I.C.: 6029
N.A.I.C.S.: 522110
Harris Antoniou *(CEO-Energy & Commodities & Transportation)*

Subsidiaries:

Alpha Credit SA/NV (2)
Rue Ravenstein 60
PO Box 15
B-1000 Brussels, Belgium BE
Tel.: (32) 25080223
Fax: (32) 25080384
E-Mail: info@acred.be
Web Site: www.acred.be
Emp.: 100
Consumer Credit Services
S.I.C.: 6099
N.A.I.C.S.: 522390
Bart Vervenne *(CEO)*

Fortis Commercial Finance (Belgium) N.V. (2)
Steenweg op Tielen 51
2300 Turnhout, Belgium BE
Tel.: (32) 14405411
Fax: (32) 14405600
E-Mail: info.be@bnpparibasfortisfactor.com
Web Site: www.factor.bnpparibasfortis.be
Emp.: 160
Commercial Finance, Factoring, Credit Management, Debt Administration & Other Financial Services
S.I.C.: 6159
N.A.I.C.S.: 522298
Marc Fossiprez *(Mng Dir)*

Fortis Finance Belgium S.C.R.L. (2)
Rue Montagne du Parc 3
1000 Brussels, Belgium
Tel.: (32) 2 228 61 11
Fax: (32) 2 565 42 22
Investment Management Services
S.I.C.: 6282
N.A.I.C.S.: 523920

Fortis Private Banking - Brussels (2)
Tervurenlaan 270
1150 Brussels, Belgium
Tel.: (32) 25659271
Fax: (32) 25659242
Web Site: www.privatebanking.fortis.com
Emp.: 136
Private Banking Services
S.I.C.: 6091
N.A.I.C.S.: 523991

Fortis Private Equity Belgium NV (2)
Warandeberg 3 1KA1A
1000 Brussels, Belgium
Tel.: (32) 2 565 97 69
Fax: (32) 2 565 99 75
Web Site: www.bva.be/Member-List-Fortis-Private-Equity.html
Investment Banking Services
S.I.C.: 6211
N.A.I.C.S.: 523110

Fortis Private Equity Expansion Belgium NV (2)
Warandeberg 3
Brussels, 1000, Belgium
Tel.: (32) 24334032
Management Consulting Services
S.I.C.: 8742
N.A.I.C.S.: 541611

Joint Venture:

Banque de La Poste S.A./Bank van De Post N.V. (2)
Boulevard Anspach 1
1000 Brussels, Belgium BE
Tel.: (32) 25456211
Fax: (32) 25456262
E-Mail: quality@bpo.be
Web Site: www.bpo.be
Emp.: 170
Retail Banking Services; Owned 50% by La Poste S.A./De Post N.V. & 50% by Fortis Bank SA/NV
S.I.C.: 6035
N.A.I.C.S.: 522120
David Moucheron *(Chm-Mgmt Bd & CEO)*
Marc Van der Schueren *(Member-Mgmt Bd)*

U.S. Subsidiaries:

Fortis Capital Corp. (2)
275 Madison Ave Ste 2218
New York, NY 10016-1101 CT
Tel.: (212) 418-8700
E-Mail: info@us.fortis.com
Web Site: www.fortisbank.com
Emp.: 75
Securities & Commodities Investment Services
S.I.C.: 6211
N.A.I.C.S.: 523110
Waldo Abbot *(CEO)*

Non-U.S. Subsidiaries:

BGL BNP Paribas S.A. (2)
50 avenue JF Kennedy
L-2951 Luxembourg, Luxembourg LU
Tel.: (352) 42422000 (65.96%)
Fax: (352) 42422001
Web Site: www.bgl.lu
Sales Range: $5-14.9 Billion
Emp.: 3,507
Personal, Commercial, Investment & Private Banking & Other Financial Services
S.I.C.: 6029
N.A.I.C.S.: 522110
Carlo Thill *(Co-Chm-Mgmt Bd)*
Eric Martin *(Co-Chm-Mgmt Bd)*
Marc Lenert *(Member-Mgmt Bd)*
Christian Schaack *(Member-Mgmt Bd)*
Robert Scharfe *(Member-Mgmt Bd)*
Thierry Schuman *(Member-Mgmt Bd)*
Jean-Louis Margue *(Sec)*

Division:

BGL Luxembourg (3)
10A Boulevard Royal
L-2093 Luxembourg, Luxembourg
Tel.: (352) 46461
Fax: (352) 46469170
Web Site: www.bgl.lu
Wealth Management & Private Banking Services
S.I.C.: 6099
N.A.I.C.S.: 523991
Eric Martin *(Mng Dir)*

Subsidiary:

Fortis Lease Group S.A. (3)
16 rue Edward Steichen
L-2951 Luxembourg, Luxembourg LU
Tel.: (352) 26434789 (100%)
Fax: (352) 26434788
E-Mail: info@fortislease.com
Web Site: www.fortislease.com
Emp.: 10
Holding Company; Commercial Leasing & Factoring Services
S.I.C.: 6719
N.A.I.C.S.: 551112
Claude Crespin *(CEO)*
Karol Sindt *(Sec)*

Subsidiary:

BNP Paribas Leasing Solutions (4)
16 rue Edward Steichen
2540 Luxembourg, Luxembourg LU
Tel.: (352) 4799 8505 (100%)
Fax: (352) 4799 5181
E-Mail: christelle.bouichou@bgl.lu
Web Site: leasingsolutions.bnpparibas.com
Emp.: 25
Commercial Leasing & Rental Solutions for Professional Equipment & Real Estate Assets
S.I.C.: 7359
N.A.I.C.S.: 532490
Robert Christophory *(Gen Mgr)*

Non-U.S. Subsidiaries:

Fortis Lease (Belgium) S.A. (4)
Gentsesteenweg Chaussee de Gand 1440
1082 Brussels, Belgium BE
Tel.: (32) 25060211
Fax: (32) 25119960
E-Mail: info.de@fortislease.com
Web Site: www.fortislease.com
Sls.: $10,693,791
Emp.: 150
Commercial Leasing & Factoring Services
S.I.C.: 6022
N.A.I.C.S.: 522190
Mark Schrauwen *(Head-Sls Dept)*

Subsidiaries:

Fortis Lease Car & Truck S.A. (5)
Chaussee de Gand 1440
Brussels, 1082, Belgium
Tel.: (32) 25060211
Fax: (32) 25119960
Commercial Equipment & Vehicle Leasing Services
S.I.C.: 7513
N.A.I.C.S.: 532120

Fortis Lease Group Services S.A. (5)
Chaussee de Gand 1440
Brussels, 1082, Belgium
Tel.: (32) 25060211
Fax: (32) 25119960
Commercial Equipment Leasing Services
S.I.C.: 7359
N.A.I.C.S.: 532490

Fortis Lease (China) Co., Ltd. (4)
No 2 Jian Guo Men Wai Avenue
Unit 2201A Tower C Yintai Ctr
Chaoyang District, Beijing, China CN
Tel.: (86) 1085171868 (100%)
Fax: (86) 1085171869
E-Mail: info.cn@bnpparibas-china.com
Web Site: www.leasegroup.bnpparibas.com
Emp.: 8
Commercial Leasing & Factoring Services
S.I.C.: 6022
N.A.I.C.S.: 522190

Fortis Lease France S.A. (4)
30 quai de Dion Bouton
F-92824 Paris, Cedex, France FR
Tel.: (33) 155677800 (100%)
Fax: (33) 155677801
E-Mail: info.fr@fortislease.com
Web Site: www.fortislease.com
Commercial Leasing & Factoring Services
S.I.C.: 6022
N.A.I.C.S.: 522190
Olivier de Ryck *(Dir Gen)*

Fortis Lease Hungaria (4)
Dunavirag St 2
1139 Budapest, Hungary (100%)
Tel.: (36) 12886000
Fax: (36) 1301 9010
E-Mail: info@Leasegroup.hu
Web Site: www.leasingsolutions.bnpparibas.com
Emp.: 25
Commercial Leasing & Factoring Services
S.I.C.: 6022
N.A.I.C.S.: 522190
Ferenc Nagy *(Gen Mgr)*

Fortis Lease (Malaysia) Sdn. Bhd (4)
G8 Faber Tower
Kuala Lumpur, 58100, Malaysia
Tel.: (60) 379804750
Fax: (60) 379810131
Financial Leasing Services
S.I.C.: 6141
N.A.I.C.S.: 522220

Fortis Lease Nederland N.V. (4)
Hambakenwetering 4
NL-5231 DC 's-Hertogenbosch, Netherlands NL
Mailing Address:
PO Box 2375
NL-5202 CJ 's-Hertogenbosch, Netherlands
Tel.: (31) 736399400
Fax: (31) 736399415
E-Mail: info.nl@fortislease.com
Web Site: www.fortislease.com
Emp.: 65
Commercial Leasing & Factoring Services
S.I.C.: 6022
N.A.I.C.S.: 522190

Fortis Lease Norge AS (4)
Brynsalleen 4
Postboks 6344
NO-0604 Oslo, Norway NO
Tel.: (47) 24099900 (100%)
Fax: (47) 24099901
Commercial Leasing & Factoring Services
S.I.C.: 6022
N.A.I.C.S.: 522190
Peer William Velde *(Gen Mgr)*

Fortis Lease Operativ Lizing Zartkoruen Mukodo Reszvenytarsasag (4)
Fay Utca 1/B
Budapest, 1139, Hungary
Tel.: (36) 12886000
Commercial Equipment & Vehicle Leasing Services
S.I.C.: 7519
N.A.I.C.S.: 532120

Fortis Lease Polska Sp. z o.o. (4)
Ul Suwak 3
02-676 Warsaw, Poland PL
Tel.: (48) 225669650 (100%)
Fax: (48) 22 566 9651
E-Mail: info.pl@fortislease.com
Web Site: www.fortislease.com

BNP Paribas SA—(Continued)

Commercial Leasing & Factoring Services
S.I.C.: 6022
N.A.I.C.S.: 522190
Janusz Rafal Piskorski *(Dir Gen)*

Fortis Lease Romania IFN S.A. **(4)**
40-44 Banu Antonache St 1st fl
Bucharest, Romania RO
Tel.: (40) 212000650 (100%)
Fax: (40) 212000663
Web Site: www.fortislease.com
Emp.: 20
Commercial Leasing & Factoring Services
S.I.C.: 6022
N.A.I.C.S.: 522190

Fortis Lease UK Ltd. **(4)**
Camelford 10th Fl 89 Albert Embankment
London, Lancs, SE1 7TP, United Kingdom UK
Tel.: (44) 1412218471 (100%)
Fax: (44) 2920853537
E-Mail: info.uk@fortislease.com
Web Site: www.fortislease.com
Emp.: 75
Commercial Leasing & Factoring Services
S.I.C.: 6022
N.A.I.C.S.: 522190
Stephen Grey *(Gen Mgr)*

Joint Venture:

Internaxx Bank S.A. **(3)**
46a Ave JF Kennedy
L-2958 Luxembourg, Luxembourg LU
Tel.: (352) 26032003
Fax: (352) 26032043
E-Mail: info@internaxx.lu
Web Site: www.internaxx.lu
Emp.: 40
Online Brokerage Services; Owned 75% by The Toronto-Dominion Bank & 25% by BGL BNP Paribas S.A.
S.I.C.: 6211
N.A.I.C.S.: 523120
Anne Marie Jung *(Gen Mgr)*

Non-U.S. Subsidiaries:

Societe Alsacienne de Developpement et d'Expansion S.A. **(3)**
4 allee de la Robertsau
F-67084 Strasbourg, Cedex, France FR
Tel.: (33) 388455151 (100%)
Fax: (33) 388604420
E-Mail: info@sade-financement.com
Web Site: www.sade-financement.com
Emp.: 22
Real Estate Investment & Financing Services
S.I.C.: 6531
N.A.I.C.S.: 531390
Antoine Gilliot *(Gen Dir)*

Direct Life & Pension Services Limited **(2)**
Metro House Northgate
Chichester, West Sussex, PO191BE, United Kingdom (100%)
Tel.: (44) 1243817905
Fax: (44) 1243536535
E-Mail: info@directlife.co.uk
Web Site: www.directlifecorporate.co.uk
Emp.: 150
Direct Life Insurance Carriers
S.I.C.: 6311
N.A.I.C.S.: 524113
Rob Quayle *(Mng Dir)*

Fortis Bank Polska S.A. **(2)**
ul Suwak 3
PL-02 676 Warsaw, Poland PL
Mailing Address: (99.29%)
PO Box 15
02-676 Warsaw, Poland
Tel.: (48) 225669000
Fax: (48) 225669010
E-Mail: info@pl.fortisbank.com
Web Site: www.bnpparibasfortis.pl
Sales Range: $300-349.9 Million
Emp.: 1,000
Personal & Commercial Banking Services
S.I.C.: 6029
N.A.I.C.S.: 522110
Camille Fohl *(Chm-Supervisory Bd)*
Jos Clijster *(Deputy Chm-Supervisory Bd)*
Antoni Potocki *(Deputy Chm-Supervisory Bd)*
Frederic Amoudru *(Pres)*
Philippe Van Hellemont *(VP & Chief Risk Officer)*
Jan Bujak *(Sr VP)*
Jacek Oblekowski *(VP-Retail Banking)*
Jaromir Pelczarski *(VP-Ops & Support Svcs)*
Michel Thebault *(VP-Personal Fin Bus Line)*

Subsidiaries:

Fortis Private Investments Polska S.A. **(3)**
ul Fredry 8
PL-00-097 Warsaw, Poland PL
Tel.: (48) 225669800 (100%)
Fax: (48) 225669810
E-Mail: info@fpip.com.pl
Web Site: www.fpip.pl
Securities Brokerage & Investment Management Services
S.I.C.: 6211
N.A.I.C.S.: 523120
Malgorzata Dominiczak-Zielinska *(Chm-Exec Bd)*
Marek Krzysztof Fido *(Member-Exec Bd)*

Fortis Banque S.A. **(2)**
29-30 Quai de Dion Bouton
F-92824 Puteaux, Cedex, France FR
Tel.: (33) 155678900
Fax: (33) 155678080
E-Mail: info@fortisbank.com
Web Site: www.fr.fortisbank.com
Emp.: 250
Retail, Merchant & Investment Banking & Wealth Management Services
S.I.C.: 6029
N.A.I.C.S.: 522110
Francois Villeroy de Galhau *(Chm-Supervisory Bd)*
Petit Bruno *(Chm-Mgmt Bd)*
Camille Fohl *(Vice Chm-Supervisory Bd)*
Didier Kunstlinger *(Dir Gen-Fortis House)*
Michel Mikolajczak *(Dir-Credit & Chief Risk Officer)*
Patrick Bony *(Dir-Network-France)*

Fortis Commercial Finance A/S **(2)**
Kanalgaden 3 1 SAL
Albertslund, 2620 Albertslund, Denmark
Tel.: (45) 43 30 88 00
Fax: (45) 43 30 88 02
E-Mail: info.dk@fortiscomfin.com
Web Site: www.fortiscomfin.com
Commercial Finance, Factoring, Credit Management, Debt Administration & Other Financial Services
S.I.C.: 6159
N.A.I.C.S.: 522298

Fortis Commercial Finance AB **(2)**
Norra Valgatan 70
S 211 22 Malmo, Sweden
Tel.: (46) 40 97 14 50
Fax: (46) 40 97 18 50
E-Mail: info.se@fortiscomfin.com
Web Site: www.fortiscomfin.com
Commercial Finance, Factoring, Credit Management, Debt Administration & Other Financial Services
S.I.C.: 6159
N.A.I.C.S.: 522298

Fortis Commercial Finance Asia Ltd. **(2)**
26/F Fortis Tower
77-79 Gloucester Road, Hong Kong, China (Hong Kong)
Tel.: (852) 28 76 34 00
Fax: (852) 21 67 83 17
E-Mail: fortiscomfin.asia@fortiscomfin.com
Web Site: www.fortiscomfin.com
Commercial Finance, Factoring, Credit Management, Debt Administration & Other Financial Services
S.I.C.: 6159
N.A.I.C.S.: 522298

Fortis Commercial Finance GmbH **(2)**
Willstatterstrasse 15
PO Box 110438
D-40549 Dusseldorf, Germany De
Tel.: (49) 21153840
Fax: (49) 2115384192
E-Mail: info.de@fortiscomfin.com
Web Site: www.commercialfinance.fortis.com
Emp.: 72
Commercial Finance, Factoring, Credit Management, Debt Administration & Other Financial Services
S.I.C.: 6159
N.A.I.C.S.: 522298
Thorsten Koenig *(Gen Mgr)*

Fortis Commercial Finance Ltd. **(2)**
Westcombe House 2-4 Mount Ephraim
Tunbridge Wells, Kent, TN4 8AS, United Kingdom UK
Tel.: (44) 1892703500
Fax: (44) 1892703500
E-Mail: info.uk@fortiscomfin.com
Web Site: www.fortiscomfin.com
Commercial Finance, Factoring, Credit Management, Debt Administration & Other Financial Services
S.I.C.: 6159
N.A.I.C.S.: 522298

Fortis Commercial Finance S.A. **(2)**
16 rue Edward Steichen
Batiment Codic D, 2540 Luxembourg, Luxembourg LU
Tel.: (352) 47995282
Fax: (352) 47995292
E-Mail: info.lu@fortiscomfin.lu
Web Site: www.fortiscomfin.com
Commercial Finance, Factoring, Credit Management, Debt Administration & Other Financial Services
S.I.C.: 6159
N.A.I.C.S.: 522298

Fortis Commercial Finance S.A.S. **(2)**
8/10 rue Godefroy Hall B
92819 Puteaux, France FR
Tel.: (33) 155677400
Fax: (33) 155677456
E-Mail: info.fr@fortiscomfin.com
Web Site: www.fortiscomfin.com
Commercial Finance, Factoring, Credit Management, Debt Administration & Other Financial Services
S.I.C.: 6159
N.A.I.C.S.: 522298

Fortis Commercial Finance Sp. z o.o. **(2)**
ul Cybernetyki 19 B
02 677 Warsaw, Poland PL
Tel.: (48) 22 431 69 30
E-Mail: info.pl@fortiscomfin.com
Web Site: www.fortiscomfin.com
Commercial Finance, Factoring, Credit Management, Debt Administration & Other Financial Services
S.I.C.: 6159
N.A.I.C.S.: 522298

Fortis Commercial Finance S.p.A. **(2)**
Viale Fulvio Testi 124
20092 Cinisello Balsamo, MI, Italy IT
Tel.: (39) 0230 4181
Fax: (39) 0230 418788
E-Mail: info.it@fortiscomfin.com
Web Site: www.fortiscomfin.com
Commercial Finance, Factoring, Credit Management, Debt Administration & Other Financial Services
S.I.C.: 6159
N.A.I.C.S.: 522298

Fortis Commercial Finance Spain S.A.U. **(2)**
C/Golfo de Salonica 27-6B
28033 Madrid, Spain
Tel.: (34) 91 767 06 79
Fax: (34) 91 383 91 26
E-Mail: info.es@fortiscomfin.com
Web Site: www.fortiscomfin.com
Commercial Finance, Factoring, Credit Management, Debt Administration & Other Financial Services
S.I.C.: 6159
N.A.I.C.S.: 522298

Fortis Holding Malta BV **(2)**
Prins Bernhardplein 200
Amsterdam, 1097 JB, Netherlands
Tel.: (31) 205214777
Investment Management Services
S.I.C.: 6282
N.A.I.C.S.: 523920

Fortis Investment Management Chile SA **(2)**
Mariano Sanchez Fontecilla 310 Piso 16
Las Condes, Chile
Tel.: (56) 27873302
Investment Management Services
S.I.C.: 6282
N.A.I.C.S.: 523920

Fortis Private Investment Management Limited **(2)**
5 Aldermanbury Square
London, EC2V 7HR, United Kingdom UK
Tel.: (44) 2073694800 (100%)
Fax: (44) 2073694888
E-Mail: fortisprivatebanking@fortis.com
Web Site: www.privatebanking.fortis.com
Private Banking & Wealth Management Services
S.I.C.: 6099
N.A.I.C.S.: 523991
Mark Rushton *(Head-Corp Dev & Mktg)*

Non-U.S. Subsidiaries:

Fortis Wealth Management (Taiwan) Co., Ltd. **(3)**
71F No 7 XinYi Road Sec 5
Taipei, Taiwan TW
Tel.: (886) 287292000 (100%)
Fax: (886) 2 8101 2060
Web Site: www.privatebanking.fortis.com
Emp.: 36
Private Banking & Wealth Management Services
S.I.C.: 6733
N.A.I.C.S.: 523991
Morris Ho *(Mgr)*

Von Essen GmbH & Co. KG Bankgesellschaft **(2)**
Huyssenallee 86-88
D-45128 Essen, Germany De
Tel.: (49) 20181180 (100%)
Fax: (49) 2018118161
E-Mail: info@vonessenbank.de
Web Site: www.vonessenbank.de
Personal & Commercial Banking Services
S.I.C.: 6029
N.A.I.C.S.: 522110
Ralf Dreher *(Chm-Mgmt Bd)*
Thorsten Wolff *(Member-Mgmt Bd)*

Non-U.S. Branches:

BNP Paribas Athens Branch **(1)**
94 Vassilissis Sofias Ave & 1 Kerasountos St
115 28 Athens, Greece
Mailing Address:
PO Box 171 58
100 24 Athens, Greece
Tel.: (30) 2107468206
Telex: 210 759 et 222 457
Fax: (30) 2107486726
E-Mail: bnpa@otenet.gr
Web Site: www.bnpparibas.gr
Emp.: 100
International Banking Services
S.I.C.: 6159
N.A.I.C.S.: 522298

BNP Paribas-Brussels Branch **(1)**
489 Ave Louise
1050 Brussels, Belgium (100%)
Tel.: (32) 25180811
Telex: 21628
Fax: (32) 25180934
E-Mail: info@bnpparibas.be
Web Site: www.bnpparibas.be
Emp.: 100
Private & Corporate Banking & International Services
S.I.C.: 6022
N.A.I.C.S.: 522190
Andre Boulanger *(CEO)*

BNP Paribas Frankfurt Branch **(1)**
Aurope Allee 12
60327 Frankfurt am Main, Germany (100%)
Mailing Address:
Postfach 10 03 61
60003 Frankfurt am Main, Germany
Tel.: (49) 6971930
Fax: (49) 6971932640
E-Mail: Info.de@bnpparibas.com
Web Site: www.bnpparibas.de

Emp.: 400
Retail, Commercial & International Banking Services
S.I.C.: 6159
N.A.I.C.S.: 522298
Joachim Von Schorlemer *(Mng Dir)*

BNP Paribas-Manama Branch (1)
Bahrain Financial Harbour W Tower 3rd Fl
Manama, Bahrain
Tel.: (973) 17531152
Telex: 8595
Fax: (973) 17866667
E-Mail: bnpbur@batelco.com.bh
Web Site: www.bahrain.bnpparibas.com
Emp.: 400
Off Shore Banking Services
S.I.C.: 6159
N.A.I.C.S.: 522298
Eric Cohu *(Gen Mgr)*

BNP Paribas Martinique (1)
72 Avenue des Caraibes
97200 Fort-de-France, Martinique
Mailing Address:
PO Box 588
97207 Fort-de-France, Martinique
Tel.: (596) 596 59 4600
Telex: 912619
Fax: (596) 596 63 7142
E-Mail:
Web Site: www.bnpparibas.mq
Full Banking Services
S.I.C.: 6099
N.A.I.C.S.: 522320

BNP Paribas - Mexico Representative Office (1)
Av Paseo de las Palmas No 425 Piso 14
Torre Optima 3
Col Lomas de Chapultepec, 11000 Mexico, DF, Mexico
Tel.: (52) 55 5003 9400
Fax: (52) 55 5003 9490
Web Site: www.bnpparibas.com.mx
Corporate & Investment Banking
S.I.C.: 6029
N.A.I.C.S.: 522110

BNP Paribas Mumbai Branch (1)
French Bank Bldg
62 Homji St, Fort Mumbai, 400 001, India (100%)
Tel.: (91) 2266501300
Fax: (91) 2222665490
E-Mail: info@bnpparibas.co.in
Web Site: www.bnpparibas.co.in
Emp.: 200
Retail & International Banking Services
S.I.C.: 6159
N.A.I.C.S.: 522293
Jacques Michel *(CEO & Country Mgr)*

BNP Paribas New Delhi Branch (1)
East Towers (Sood Towers) 1st Floor
25 Barakhamba Road, New Delhi, 110 001, India
Tel.: (91) 1141796600
Telex: 31.65.350 PARBIN
Fax: (91) 1123324188
Web Site: www.bnpparibas.co.in/en/locations/agencies.asp
Retail & International Banking Services
S.I.C.: 6159
N.A.I.C.S.: 522298

Non-U.S. Division:

BNP Paribas - South East Asia (1)
20 Collyer Quay Tung Ctr
Singapore, 049319, Singapore (100%)
Tel.: (65) 62103888
Telex: 24315
Fax: (65) 62103861
Web Site: www.bnpparibas.com.sg
Emp.: 1,200
Full Service & International Banking Services
S.I.C.: 6099
N.A.I.C.S.: 522320

Subsidiaries:

BNP Paribas Asia Private Banking (2)
Tung Ctr 18th Fl 20 Collyer Quay 0101
Singapore, 49319, Singapore (100%)
Tel.: (65) 62103888
Fax: (65) 62243459
E-Mail: pba.sg@asia.bnpparibas.com
Web Site: www.bnpparibas.com.sg
Emp.: 100
Private Banking Services
S.I.C.: 6022
N.A.I.C.S.: 522190

BNP Paribas (Singapore) Pte. Ltd. (2)
20 Collyer Quay Tung Ctr
Singapore, 49319, Singapore (100%)
Tel.: (65) 62101288
Telex: RS 24315
Fax: (65) 62243459
Web Site: www.bnpparibas.com.sg
Emp.: 800
Provider of Banking Services
S.I.C.: 6099
N.A.I.C.S.: 522320
Pierre Veyres *(CEO)*

BNP Prime Peregrine (Securities) PTE Ltd. (2)
20 Collyer Quay 01 01 Tung Centre
49319 Singapore, Singapore (100%)
Tel.: (65) 62101288
Fax: (65) 62243459
Web Site: www.bnpparibas.com.sg
Emp.: 100
International Security & Investment Services
S.I.C.: 6282
N.A.I.C.S.: 523930

Non-U.S. Subsidiaries:

BNP Paribas Bangkok (2)
990 Abdulrahim Pl 29th Fl
Rama IV Rd, Bangkok, 10500, Thailand (100%)
Tel.: (66) 6626361900
Telex: 87214 NABAPAR TH
Fax: (66) 6626361935
Web Site: www.bnpparibas.co.th
Emp.: 75
Offshore & Commercial Banking Services
S.I.C.: 6029
N.A.I.C.S.: 522110

Subsidiary:

BNP Paribas Peregrine Thailand (3)
29th Fl Abdulrahim Pl
Bangkok, 10500, Thailand (100%)
Tel.: (66) 26361900
Fax: (66) 26361935
Web Site: www.bnpparibas.co.th
Emp.: 75
Investment Banking Services
S.I.C.: 6211
N.A.I.C.S.: 523110

BNP Paribas China Group (2)
19 F China World Trade Ctr Tower 1
1 Jianguomenwai Ave, Beijing, 100004, China (100%)
Tel.: (86) 1065350888
Fax: (86) 1065053686
Web Site: www.bnpparibas.com.cn
Banking Services
S.I.C.: 6099
N.A.I.C.S.: 522320
Laurent Ling *(Head-Fin Institutions Grp)*

Subsidiaries:

BNP Paribas Beijing (3)
13 F N Tower Shanghai Stock Exchange Bldg
Beijing, 200120 30120, China (100%)
Tel.: (86) 158405500
Telex: 33318
Fax: (86) 2158889232
Web Site: www.bnpparibas.com.cn
Emp.: 50
Provider of Banking Services; Joint Venture of BNP Paribas (50%) & Industrial & Commercial Bank of China (50%)
S.I.C.: 6099
N.A.I.C.S.: 522320

BNP Paribas Guangzhou (3)
Unit 1001-1002 TP Plaza
109 9 Liuhua Road, Guangzhou, Guangdong, 510010, China
Tel.: (86) 2086695822
Fax: (86) 2086695733
Web Site: www.bnpparibas.com.cn/en/
Retail & International Banking Services
S.I.C.: 6159
N.A.I.C.S.: 522298

BNP Paribas Shanghai (3)
25 F Shanghai World Financial Center 100 Century Avenue
Pudong New Area, 200120 Shanghai, China (100%)
Tel.: (86) 2128962888
Telex: 33269 PARSH CN
Fax: (86) 2128962897
Web Site: www.bnpparibas.com.cn
Retail & International Banking Services
S.I.C.: 6159
N.A.I.C.S.: 522298
Annick De Kermadec Bentzmann *(Exec Gen Mgr)*

Non-U.S. Subsidiary:

BNP Paribas Hong Kong (3)
61st 2 International Finance Ctr# 8 Finance St
Central, China (Hong Kong) (100%)
Tel.: (852) 29098888
Fax: (852) 28652523
Web Site: www.bnpparibas.com.hk
Emp.: 1,500
Retail & International Banking Services
S.I.C.: 6099
N.A.I.C.S.: 522320
Mignonne Cheng *(CEO)*

Non-U.S. Subsidiaries:

BNP Paribas Macau (3)
61 Avda Almeida Ribeiro Central Plaza 5 andar C
Macau, China (Macau) (100%)
Tel.: (853) 28562777
Telex: 88299
Fax: (853) 28560626
E-Mail: sanco.sze@asia.bnpparibas.com
Web Site: bank.bnpparibas.com
Sales Range: $1-9.9 Million
Emp.: 100
Retail & International Banking Services
S.I.C.: 6029
N.A.I.C.S.: 522110
Sanco Sze *(Branch Mgr)*

BNP Paribas Peregrine (3)
63rd Fl 2 Intl Fin Ctr 8 Finance St
Central, China (Hong Kong) (100%)
Tel.: (852) 29098888
Fax: (852) 28652523
E-Mail: communication.hk@asia.bnpparibas.com
Web Site: www.bnpparibas.com.hk
Emp.: 1,200
Fund Management & Investment Advice
S.I.C.: 6282
N.A.I.C.S.: 523930
Lavina Chan *(Head-Corp Comm)*

BNP Paribas (Japan) Limited (2)
GranTokyo North Tower 1-9-1 Marunouchi
Chiyoda-ku, Tokyo, 100-6740, Japan
Tel.: (81) 363771000
Telex: 24825
Web Site: www.jp.bnpparibas.com
Corporate, Institutional & International Banking Services
S.I.C.: 6029
N.A.I.C.S.: 522110
Jean-Laurent Bonnafe *(CEO)*

Subsidiaries:

BNP Paribas Securities (Japan) Limited (3)
Tokyo Sankei Bldg 18th Fl
1 7 2 Otemachi Chiyoda Ku, Tokyo, 100 0004, Japan
Tel.: (81) 3 5290 1000
Fax: (81) 3 5290 1133
Web Site: www.jp.bnpparibas.com
Emp.: 100
Investment Banking Services
S.I.C.: 6211
N.A.I.C.S.: 523110
Yusuke Yasuda *(Gen Mgr & Head-Territory)*

BNP Paribas-Manila Offshore Branch (2)
30th Fl Philamlife Tower
PO Box 2265 MCPO
8767 Paseo De Roxas, 1262 Makati, 1262, Philippines
Tel.: (63) 28148730
Fax: (63) 28857076
Web Site: www.bnpparibas.com.ph
Emp.: 12
Offshore Banking Services
S.I.C.: 6159
N.A.I.C.S.: 522298
Peter Labrie *(Head-Territory)*

BNP Paribas Peregrine Securities Inc. (2)
30th Fl Philamlife Tower 8767 Paseo de Roxas
PO Box 2265 MCPO
1262 Makati, Metro Manila, Philippines
Tel.: (63) 28148700
Fax: (63) 28857076
Web Site: www.bnpparibas.com.ph
Investment Banking Services
S.I.C.: 6211
N.A.I.C.S.: 523110
Patricio Dumlao *(Country Head)*

BNP Paribas South Korea (2)
24th FL Taepyeongno Building 310
Taepyeongno 2-ga Jung-Gu, Seoul, 100 767, Korea (South) (100%)
Tel.: (82) 23171700
Telex: 26539/22227
Fax: (82) 27572530
E-Mail: bnppseoul@asia.bnpparibas.com
Web Site: www.bnpparibas.co.kr
Emp.: 100
Banking Services
S.I.C.: 6099
N.A.I.C.S.: 522320

BNP Paribas Sydney (2)
60 Castlereagh St
Sydney, New South Wales, 2000, Australia (100%)
Mailing Address:
GPO Box 269
Sydney, NSW, 2001, Australia
Tel.: (61) 292168633
Fax: (61) 292213026
E-Mail: finance@bnpparibas.com.au
Web Site: www.bnpparibas.com.au
Emp.: 750
Corporate, Institutional & Retail Banking Services
S.I.C.: 6099
N.A.I.C.S.: 522320
R. Mahout *(CEO)*

BNP Paribas Taiwan (2)
71-72F Taipei 101 Tower 7 Xin Yi Road Sec 5
Taipei, 110, Taiwan (100%)
Mailing Address:
PO Box 81-69
Taipei, Taiwan
Tel.: (886) 287583101
Telex: 22000 BNPTPE
Fax: (886) 287583102
E-Mail: shirley.penq@asia.bnpparibas.com
Web Site: www.bnpparibas.com.tw
Retail & International Banking Services
S.I.C.: 6029
N.A.I.C.S.: 522110
Olivier Rousselet *(Country Mgr)*

Cardif Societe Vie Taiwan (2)
18th Floor No 270, Chung Hsiao East Road 2nd Floor, 106 Taipei, Taiwan (100%)
Tel.: (886) 266363456
Fax: (886) 266363457
E-Mail: services@tw.cardif.com
Web Site: www.tw.cardif.com
Emp.: 100
Insurance & Finance Services
S.I.C.: 6411
N.A.I.C.S.: 524298
Elsa Lee *(Gen Mgr)*

PT Bank BNP Paribas Indonesia (2)
Menara Batavia 20th Fl Jalan KH Mas Mansyur Kav 126
Jakarta, 10220, Indonesia (100%)
Mailing Address:
PO Box 1655
JKT 10016 Jakarta, Indonesia
Tel.: (62) 215722288
Telex: 65105
Fax: (62) 215722280
Web Site: www.bnpparibas.co.id
Emp.: 50
Commercial Banking Services for Large Indonesian Companies & Multinationals
S.I.C.: 6029
N.A.I.C.S.: 522110
Baudouin Prot *(CEO)*

BNP Paribas SA—(Continued)

Subsidiaries:

Bank BNP Lippo Utama Leasing **(3)**
Menara Batavia 20th Fl
PO Box 1655
Jl KH Mas Mansyur Kav 126, Jakarta, 10220, Indonesia (100%)
Tel.: (62) 215722288
Telex: 65072
Fax: (62) 215722308
E-Mail: emiliechambert@asia.bnpparibas.com
Web Site: www.bnpparibas.co.id
Long Term Finance Facilities
S.I.C.: 6159
N.A.I.C.S.: 522298

BNP Paribas Peregrine **(3)**
Menara Batavia 20th Floor
Jl KH Mas Mansyur Kav 126, Jakarta, 10220, Indonesia (100%)
Tel.: (62) 2157900500
Fax: (62) 2157900501
Web Site: www.bnpparibas.co.id
Emp.: 25
Capital Markets Products
S.I.C.: 6799
N.A.I.C.S.: 523910

Non-U.S. Subsidiaries:

Ace Leasing BV **(1)**
Hambakenwetering 4
's-Hertogenbosch, 5231 DC, Netherlands
Tel.: (31) 73 5118667
Fax: (31) 73 6420896
Securities Brokerage Services
S.I.C.: 6211
N.A.I.C.S.: 523120

Agrilease BV **(1)**
Hambakenwetering 4
's-Hertogenbosch, 5231 DC, Netherlands
Tel.: (31) 73 6399437
Fax: (31) 73 6399415
Emp.: 70
Consumer Leasing Services
S.I.C.: 6141
N.A.I.C.S.: 522291
Raf Ramaekers *(Gen Mgr)*

Alandes BV **(1)**
Fred Roeskestraat 123-1hg
Amsterdam, 1076 EE, Netherlands
Tel.: (31) 205771177
Fax: (31) 20 6258274
Financial Planning Services
S.I.C.: 6282
N.A.I.C.S.: 523930

Albury Asset Rentals Ltd. **(1)**
Northern Cross
Basingstoke, Hampshire, RG21 4HL, United Kingdom
Tel.: (44) 1256 377176
Financial Planning Services
S.I.C.: 6282
N.A.I.C.S.: 523930

Alfred Berg Administration A/S **(1)**
Amaliegade 3
1256 Copenhagen, Denmark
Tel.: (45) 33 96 10 00
Fax: (45) 33 96 10 99
Web Site: www.alfredberginvest.dk
Financial Planning Services
S.I.C.: 6282
N.A.I.C.S.: 523930

Alfred Berg Asset Management AB **(1)**
Nybrokajen No 5
Box 70447
107 25 Stockholm, Sweden
Tel.: (46) 8 5623 47 00
Fax: (46) 8 611 69 35
E-Mail: info@alfredberg.com
Web Site: www.alfredberg.com
Asset Management Services
S.I.C.: 6282
N.A.I.C.S.: 523920
Tomas Scherp *(Head-DP Sls & Country Mgr)*

Alfred Berg Fonder AB **(1)**
Nybrokajen 5
Box 70447
107 25 Stockholm, Sweden
Tel.: (46) 856234700
Fax: (46) 856234960
Investment Management Services
S.I.C.: 6282
N.A.I.C.S.: 523920
Oerjan Nordgren *(CEO)*

Alfred Berg Fondsmaeglerselskab A/S **(1)**
Amaliegade 3
1256 Copenhagen, Denmark
Tel.: (45) 33 96 10 00
Fax: (45) 33 96 10 99
E-Mail: info@alfredberg.com
Web Site: www.alfredberg.com
Emp.: 24
Financial Management Services
S.I.C.: 6211
N.A.I.C.S.: 523999
Soren Rytoft *(CEO)*

Alfred Berg Forvaltning AS **(1)**
Olav V's gate 5
0111 Oslo, Norway
Tel.: (47) 22005100
Fax: (47) 22005105
Asset Management Services
S.I.C.: 6799
N.A.I.C.S.: 523920

Alfred Berg Holding AB **(1)**
Nybrokajen 5
10725 Stockholm, Sweden
Mailing Address:
Box 70447
107 25 Stockholm, Sweden
Tel.: (46) 856234700
Telex: 13354 bergs
Fax: (46) 57436350
E-Mail: info@alfredberg.com
Web Site: www.alfredberg.se
Emp.: 400
Managing Finances
S.I.C.: 6282
N.A.I.C.S.: 523930
Tomas Scherp *(Gen Mgr)*

Alfred Berg Kapitalforvaltning AB **(1)**
Nybrokajen 5
Stockholm, 111 48, Sweden
Tel.: (46) 856234700
Fax: (46) 5623 49 60
Emp.: 70
Financial Investment Services
S.I.C.: 6211
N.A.I.C.S.: 523999
Vincent Trouillard *(Gen Mgr)*

Alfred Berg Kapitalforvaltning AS **(1)**
Olav V's Gate 5
Postboks 1294
Vika, 0111 Oslo, Norway
Tel.: (47) 22 00 51 00
Fax: (47) 22 00 51 05
E-Mail: kundesenter.no@alfredberg.com
Web Site: www.alfredberg.no
Investment Management Services
S.I.C.: 6282
N.A.I.C.S.: 523920

Alfred Berg Kapitalforvaltning Finland AB **(1)**
Pohjoisesplanadi 37a
Helsinki, 00100, Finland
Tel.: (358) 9228321
Fax: (358) 9 2283 2689
Web Site: www.alfredberg.fi
Investment Management Services
S.I.C.: 6799
N.A.I.C.S.: 523920

All In One Vermietung GmbH **(1)**
Ignaz Kock-Strasse 9
1210 Vienna, Austria
Tel.: (43) 127158000
Fax: (43) 1271580012
Financial Leasing Services
S.I.C.: 6141
N.A.I.C.S.: 522220

Amanda Storesenter AS **(1)**
Longhammarveien 27
5536 Haugesund, Norway
Tel.: (47) 52 71 97 00
Fax: (47) 52 71 94 30
Web Site: www.amanda.no
Shopping Mall Operator
S.I.C.: 6512
N.A.I.C.S.: 531120

Aramea Asset Management AG **(1)**
Kleine Johannisstrasse 4
20457 Hamburg, Germany
Tel.: (49) 40 866 488 0
Fax: (49) 40 866 488 499
E-Mail: info@aramea-ag.de
Web Site: www.aramea-ag.de
Asset Management Services
S.I.C.: 6282
N.A.I.C.S.: 523920

Artegy Ltd. **(1)**
5 Ohio Avenue Central Park Salford Quays
M50 2GT Manchester, United Kingdom
Tel.: (44) 8452 666010
Fax: (44) 8452 666043
E-Mail:
Web Site: www.artegy.co.uk
Truck Rental & Leasing Services
S.I.C.: 7519
N.A.I.C.S.: 532120

Artigiancassa Spa **(1)**
Via Crescenzo of Monte 25/45
00153 Rome, Italy
Tel.: (39) 658451
Fax: (39) 065899672
E-Mail: artigiancassa@artigiancassa.it
Web Site: www.artigiancassa.it
Financial Institution
S.I.C.: 6029
N.A.I.C.S.: 522110

Arval Benelux BV **(1)**
Duwboot 10
Houten, 3991 CD, Netherlands
Tel.: (31) 306 02 44 44
Fax: (31) 306 05 24 59
E-Mail: info@arval.nl
Web Site: www.arval.nl
Emp.: 200
Car Leasing Services
S.I.C.: 7515
N.A.I.C.S.: 532112
Hubertus Ter Braak *(Principal)*

Arval BV **(1)**
Duwboot 10
3991 CD Houten, Netherlands
Tel.: (31) 30 602 44 44
Fax: (31) 30 605 24 59
E-Mail: info@arval.nl
Web Site: www.arval.nl
Emp.: 207
Car Leasing Services
S.I.C.: 7515
N.A.I.C.S.: 532112
Jeff Bolders *(Gen Mgr)*

Arval India Private Ltd. **(1)**
BNP Paribas House 1 North Avenue Maker Maxity Bandra Kurla Complex
Bandra East, Mumbai, 400 051, India
Tel.: (91) 22 6196 4100
Fax: (91) 22 6196 4196
E-Mail: info@arval.in
Web Site: www.arval.in
Emp.: 60
Commercial Car Leasing Services
S.I.C.: 7515
N.A.I.C.S.: 532112
Stefano Berlenghi *(CEO)*
Vivek Mulye *(CFO)*
Gabriel Paulot *(CFO)*
Armelle Gervals *(Sec & Head-Bus Support)*

Arval Magyarorszag Kft. **(1)**
Bocskai Ut 134-146
1113 Budapest, Hungary
Tel.: (36) 1 279 3300
Fax: (36) 1 279 3329
E-Mail: info@arval.hu
Web Site: www.arval.hu
Emp.: 35
Automobile Leasing Services
S.I.C.: 7513
N.A.I.C.S.: 532120
Peter Hegedus *(Head-Ops)*

Arval Maroc **(1)**
Zenith Millenium Sidi Maarouf Lotissement Taoufik - Imm 3/4
20190 Casablanca, Morocco
Tel.: (212) 5 22 87 98 00
Fax: (212) 5 22 87 98 01
Web Site: www.arval.ma
Automotive Financial Leasing Services
S.I.C.: 6141
N.A.I.C.S.: 522220
Philippe Chabot *(Gen Mgr)*

Arval OOO **(1)**
19 Leninskaya Sloboda
Moscow, 115280, Russia
Tel.: (7) 495 644 22 70
Fax: (7) 495 644 22 71
E-Mail: info@arval.ru
Web Site: www.arval.ru
S.I.C.: 7519
N.A.I.C.S.: 532120
Ekaterina Zveinik *(Dir-Mktg & External Comm)*

Arval PHH Holdings UK Ltd. **(1)**
Arval Centre Windmill Hill
Swindon, SN5 6PE, United Kingdom
Tel.: (44) 17 93 88 70 00
Investment Management Services
S.I.C.: 6799
N.A.I.C.S.: 523920

Arval PHH Service Lease CZ s.r.o **(1)**
Na Pankraci 1683/127
Prague, 140 00, Czech Republic
Tel.: (420) 261109011
Fax: (420) 261109012
Emp.: 85
Automobile Leasing Services
S.I.C.: 7515
N.A.I.C.S.: 532112
Gregor Bilik *(Mng Dir)*

Arval Service Gmbh **(1)**
Kuhnehofe 3
Hamburg, 22761, Germany
Tel.: (49) 40853500
Fax: (49) 40 8509911
Passenger Car Rental Services
S.I.C.: 7514
N.A.I.C.S.: 532111

Non-U.S. Subsidiary:

Lavoro Bank AG **(2)**
Lowenstr 56
CH 8001 Zurich, Switzerland
Tel.: (41) 442179595
Telex: 812907 LAVR CH
Fax: (41) 442211241
E-Mail: lavoro@lavoro.ch
Web Site: www.bnpparibas.ch
Int. Income: $1,419,302
Emp.: 6
Commercial Banking Services
S.I.C.: 6029
N.A.I.C.S.: 522110
Philippe Cottier *(VP)*

Arval Service Lease SA **(1)**
Sebastian
San Sebastian de los Reyes, Madrid, 28703, Spain
Tel.: (34) 91 659 72 00
Fax: (34) 91 659 03 80
Web Site: www.arval.es
Passenger Car Leasing Services
S.I.C.: 7515
N.A.I.C.S.: 532112

Arval Slovakia, s.r.o. **(1)**
Galvaniho 15/A
821 04 Bratislava, Slovakia
Tel.: (421) 2 5710 8000
Fax: (421) 2 5710 8001
Emp.: 55
Passenger Car Leasing Services
S.I.C.: 7515
N.A.I.C.S.: 532112

Banca Nazionale del Lavoro S.p.A. **(1)**
Via Vittorio Veneto 119
00187 Rome, Italy (99.14%)
Tel.: (39) 0647021
Fax: (39) 0666479378
E-Mail: redazionebnl@bnlmail.com
Web Site: www.bnl.it
Sales Range: $1-4.9 Billion
Emp.: 16,000
Commercial Banking Services
S.I.C.: 6029
N.A.I.C.S.: 522110
Luigi Abete *(Chm)*
Fabio Gallia *(CEO)*
Jean-Laurent Bonnafe *(Mng Dir)*

Banco BNP Paribas Brasil **(1)**
Av Juscelino Kubitscheck 510 Andar
045343906 Sao Paulo, Brazil (100%)
Tel.: (55) 1138413100

Fax: (55) 1138413122
E-Mail: bnpparibas@br.bnpparibas.com
Web Site: www.bnpparibas.com.br
Emp.: 200
Retail & International Banking Services
S.I.C.: 6159
N.A.I.C.S.: 522293
Louis Bazire *(Pres)*

Banco BNP Paribas Personal Finance SA (1)
Rua Tomas da Fonseca Torres de Lisboa
Torre G - 15
1600-209 Lisbon, Portugal
Tel.: (351) 21 721 58 00
Fax: (351) 21 721 58 77
Web Site: www.cetelem.pt
Emp.: 600
Financial Management Services
S.I.C.: 6211
N.A.I.C.S.: 523999
Jean Francois Marie Deullin *(Pres)*

Bank BNP Paribas Luxembourg (1)
33 Rue De Gasperich
20085 Luxembourg, Luxembourg (100%)
Tel.: (352) 2696000
Telex: 3447/2228
Fax: (352) 46469160
Web Site: www.bnpparibas.lu
Emp.: 600
Retail Banking Services
S.I.C.: 6159
N.A.I.C.S.: 522298
Eric Martin *(Head-Territory)*

Bank Insinger de Beaufort NV (1)
Herengracht 537
1017 BV Amsterdam, Netherlands
Tel.: (31) 20 5215 000
Fax: (31) 20 5215 009
E-Mail: info@insinger.com
Web Site: www.insinger.com
Financial Management Services
S.I.C.: 6211
N.A.I.C.S.: 523999
Peter Sieradzki *(CEO)*
Mark Selles *(Deputy CEO)*
Rob Mooij *(COO)*

Bank Insinger de Beaufort Safe Custody NV (1)
Herengracht 537
1017 BV Amsterdam, Netherlands
Tel.: (31) 20 5215000
Financial Management Services
S.I.C.: 6211
N.A.I.C.S.: 523999

Banque Internationale pour le Commerce et l'Industrie au Mali (1)
Immeuble Nimagala Boulevard de Peuple
BPB 72
Bamako, Mali
Tel.: (223) 223 33 68
Telex: 2780
Fax: (223) 223 33 73
E-Mail: SecretariatDirection@bicim.com
Web Site: bank.bnpparibas.com
Sales Range: $25-49.9 Million
Emp.: 71
Full Banking Services
S.I.C.: 6099
N.A.I.C.S.: 522320
Scott Moore *(CFO)*

Banque Internationale pour le Commerce et l'Industrie de la Guinee (1)
Ave de la Republique
BP 1484
Conakry, Papua New Guinea
Tel.: (675) 41 45 15
Telex: 99522175
Fax: (675) 41 39 62
E-Mail: dg.bicigui@biasy.net
Web Site: www.biciguinet.net
Full Banking Services
S.I.C.: 6099
N.A.I.C.S.: 522320
Bernard Deleuze *(CEO)*
Philippe Tauvron *(Corp Sec)*
Jean-Paul Le Bailly *(Sr Exec VP-Corp)*
Manga Fode Toure *(Sr Exec VP)*

Banque Internationale pour le Commerce et l'Industrie du Gabon (1)
Avenue du Colonel Parant
BP 2241 Libreville, Gabon
Tel.: (241) 762613
Telex: 5226 GO
Fax: (241) 744034
E-Mail: bicignet@bnpparibas.com
Web Site: www.bicig-gabon.com
Commercial & Institutional Banking Services
S.I.C.: 6029
N.A.I.C.S.: 522110

Banque Internationale pour le Commerce, l'Industrie et l'Agriculture du Burkina (1)
479 Avenue du Docteur Kwame N'Krumah
BP 08
Ouagadougou, 1, Burkina Faso (100%)
Tel.: (226) 50325600
Telex: BICIACOMI 5203
Fax: (226) 50311955
E-Mail: info@biciab.bf
Web Site: www.biciabnet.net
Full Banking Services
S.I.C.: 6099
N.A.I.C.S.: 522320
Jean-Pierre Bajon-Arnal *(Gen Mgr)*

Banque Marocaine du Commerce et de l'Industrie Offshore (1)
26 Place Des Nations Unies
Casablanca, Morocco
Tel.: (212) 522461000
Commercial Banking Services
S.I.C.: 6029
N.A.I.C.S.: 522110

Banque Marocaine pour le Commerce et l'Industrie S.A. (1)
26 Place des Nations Unies
Casablanca, 20000, Morocco Ma
Tel.: (212) 2246 1000 (66.21%)
Telex: 21967
Fax: (212) 2229 9406
E-Mail: bmci-monde@bnpparibas.com
Web Site: www.bmci.ma/
Sales Range: $400-449.9 Million
Emp.: 1,909
Personal, Commercial & Investment Banking Services
S.I.C.: 6029
N.A.I.C.S.: 522110
Mourad Cherif *(Chm-Supervisory Bd & Pres)*
Jacques Ardant *(Chm-Mgmt Bd & Pres)*
Rachid Marrakchi *(Dir Gen)*
Alain Dallard *(Sec & Member-Mgmt Bd)*
Guillaume Curnier *(Member-Mgmt Bd & Dir-Individual & Prof Investors)*
Mohamed Kettani-Hassani *(Member-Mgmt Bd & Dir-Institutional Rels)*
Najib Raihani *(Member-Mgmt Bd)*

BCI Mer Rouge (1)
Pl Lagarde
BP 2122
Djibouti, Djibouti (51%)
Tel.: (253) 350857
Telex: 5821
Fax: (253) 354260
E-Mail: bcimr@africa.bnpparibas.com
Web Site: www.bcimr.dj
Emp.: 235
Commercial Banking
S.I.C.: 6029
N.A.I.C.S.: 522110

Belgolaise SA (1)
Cantersteen 1
1000 Brussels, Belgium
Tel.: (32) 2 312 26 86
Fax: (32) 2 312 26 75
Web Site: www.belgolaise.com
Commercial Banking Services
S.I.C.: 6029
N.A.I.C.S.: 522110

BICI-BAIL de Cote d'Ivoire (1)
Avenue Franchet et d Esperey
BP 01
1298 Abidjan, 01, Cote d'Ivoire
Tel.: (225) 20201600
Telex: 23870 BICICOMI
Fax: (225) 20201700
Web Site: www.bicici.org
Emp.: 24
Provider of Leasing Services
S.I.C.: 7363
N.A.I.C.S.: 561330

Bieffe 5 SPA (1)
Via Iacopo Da Diacceto 48
Florence, 50123, Italy
Tel.: (39) 05527011
Financial Planning Services
S.I.C.: 6282
N.A.I.C.S.: 523930

BMOI (1)
Place de l'Independance Antaninarenina bis Antananarivo
PO Box 25
Antananarivo, Madagascar (55.64%)
Tel.: (261) 202234609
Fax: (261) 202234610
E-Mail: karine.rabefaritra@africa.bnpparibas.com
Web Site: www.bmoi.mg
Retail & International Banking Services
S.I.C.: 6029
N.A.I.C.S.: 522110
Gaston Ramenason *(Chm)*

BNP Factor - Portugal (1)
Av Da Boavista 3523
Apartado 1281, 4104 Porto, Portugal (95%)
Tel.: (351) 226191600
Fax: (351) 226191699
E-Mail: bnpfactor@mail.telepac.pt
Web Site: www.bnpfactor.pt
Emp.: 30
Factoring Services
S.I.C.: 6159
N.A.I.C.S.: 522298

BNP Jersey Trust Corp. Limited (1)
BNP House Anley Street
PO Box 158
Saint Helier, JE4 8RD, Jersey (100%)
Tel.: (44) 1534815200
Fax: (44) 1534739279
Trust Services
S.I.C.: 6091
N.A.I.C.S.: 523991

BNP Pacific (Australia) Ltd. (1)
60 Castlereagh St
Sydney, NSW, 2000, Australia
Tel.: (61) 2 9216 8633
Fax: (61) 2 9231 7660
Commercial Banking Services
S.I.C.: 6029
N.A.I.C.S.: 522110

BNP Paribas Abu Dhabi (1)
Al Bateen Area Street No 32
PO Box 2742
Abu Dhabi, United Arab Emirates (100%)
Tel.: (971) 26938888
Telex: 22331
Fax: (971) 26938844
Web Site: eau.bnpparibas.com
Retail, Commercial & Corporate Banking Services
S.I.C.: 6029
N.A.I.C.S.: 522110

BNP Paribas Andes (1)
Avenida Caraval y Moreyra 380 Piso 11
San Isidro, Lima, 27, Peru (99.99%)
Tel.: (51) 1 215 1700
Telex: 25138 PE
Fax: (51) 1 441 3165
E-Mail: bnp.andes@americas.bnpparibas.com
Web Site: www.bnpparibas.com.pe/en/contact/contact.asp
Emp.: 28
Retail & International Banking Services
S.I.C.: 6099
N.A.I.C.S.: 522320
Sergio Zanelli *(Treas)*

BNP Paribas Argentina (1)
Bouchard 547 26th Fl
1106 Buenos Aires, Argentina (100%)
Tel.: (54) 1143180318
Fax: (54) 1143111368
E-Mail: info@bnpparibas.com.ar
Web Site: www.bnpparibas.com.ar
Emp.: 280
Corporate & International Banking Services
S.I.C.: 6099
N.A.I.C.S.: 522320
Tullio Lanari *(Dir Gen)*

BNP Paribas Bank JSC (1)
5 Lesnaya Str
125047 Moscow, Russia RU
Tel.: (7) 495 785 60 00
Telex: 413 209 PARBM SU
Fax: (7) 495 785 60 01
Web Site: www.bnpparibas.ru
Representative Office
S.I.C.: 6159
N.A.I.C.S.: 522298
Jean-Pierre Autelli *(CEO & Country Mgr-Russia)*
Margarita Travkina *(Deputy CEO)*

BNP Paribas Bulgaria EAD (1)
2 Tsar Osvoboditel Blvd
PO Box 11
1000 Sofia, Bulgaria (100%)
Tel.: (359) 029218650
Telex: 22295
Fax: (359) 9218625
E-Mail: bulgaria_bnpparibas@bnpparibas.com
Web Site: www.bulgaria.bnpparibas.com
Emp.: 100
Banking Services
S.I.C.: 6159
N.A.I.C.S.: 522298
Ullrich-Gunther Schubert *(CEO)*

BNP Paribas (Canada) Inc. (1)
1981 McGill College Ave
Montreal, QC, H3A 2W8, Canada
Tel.: (514) 285-6000
Telex: 527137
Fax: (514) 285-6278
Web Site: www.bnpparibas.ca
Emp.: 275
Banking Services
S.I.C.: 6159
N.A.I.C.S.: 522298
Anne Marie Verstraeten *(Pres)*

BNP Paribas Canada-Quebec (1)
925 Chemin St Louis Ste 350
Quebec, QC, G1S 1C1, Canada (100%)
Tel.: (418) 684-7575
Fax: (418) 684-7585
E-Mail: line.poulin@america.bnpparibas.com
Web Site: www.bnpparibas.ca
Emp.: 3
Provider of Banking Services
S.I.C.: 6099
N.A.I.C.S.: 522320
Chantale Goyette *(Mgr-Relationship-Investor Relationship Mgmt)*

BNP Paribas Canada-Toronto (1)
155 Wellington St W Ste 3110 RBC Centre
Box 149
Toronto, ON, M5V 3K2, Canada (100%)
Tel.: (416) 365-9600
Fax: (416) 947-0086
Web Site: www.bnpparibas.ca
Emp.: 50
International Banking Services
S.I.C.: 6099
N.A.I.C.S.: 522320
Simon Segall *(CEO)*

BNP Paribas Canada (1)
155 Wellington St W Ste 3110
Toronto, ON, M5V 3H1, Canada (100%)
Tel.: (416) 365-9600
E-Mail:
Web Site: www.bnpparibas.ca
Emp.: 20
International Banking Services
S.I.C.: 6159
N.A.I.C.S.: 522293
Abhoy Vaidya *(Mng Dir)*

BNP Paribas (Canada) (1)
2001 Univ St Bureau 900
Montreal, QC, H3A 2A6, Canada
Tel.: (514) 285-6000
Fax: (514) 285-6278
Web Site: www.bnpparibas.ca
Emp.: 200
Provider of Banking Services
S.I.C.: 6099
N.A.I.C.S.: 522320
Anne Marie Verstraeten *(Pres & CEO)*

BNP Paribas Capital (Asia Pacific) Ltd. (1)
63 F Two International Finance Centre
Central, China (Hong Kong)
Tel.: (852) 28251888
Venture Capital Funding Services
S.I.C.: 6799
N.A.I.C.S.: 523910

BNP Paribas Capital Investments Ltd. (1)
33 Wigmore St
London, W1U 1QX, United Kingdom

BNP Paribas SA—(Continued)

Tel.: (44) 2075954267
Capital Investment Services
S.I.C.: 6799
N.A.I.C.S.: 523910

BNP Paribas Capital (Singapore) Ltd. **(1)**
20 Collyer Quay 01-01 Tung Centre
Singapore, 049319, Singapore
Tel.: (65) 6210 1288
Fax: (65) 6210 1983
Commercial Banking & Financial Services
S.I.C.: 6029
N.A.I.C.S.: 522110

BNP Paribas Cardif Emeklilik Anonim Sirketi **(1)**
Askerocagi Cad Suzer Plaza Kat 15
Elmadag
Sisli, 34367 Istanbul, Turkey
Tel.: (90) 212 393 3000
Fax: (90) 212 393 3053
Web Site: www.cardif.com.tr/bireyselemeklilik/cardif-emeklilik-fonlari
Financial Management Services
S.I.C.: 6211
N.A.I.C.S.: 523999

BNP Paribas (China) Ltd. **(1)**
25/F Shanghai World Financial Center 100 Century Avenue
Pudong New Area, Shanghai, 200120, China
Tel.: (86) 21 2896 2888
Fax: (86) 21 2896 2800
Web Site: www.bnpparibas.com.cn
Commercial Banking & Financial Advisory Services
S.I.C.: 6029
N.A.I.C.S.: 522110
Laurent Couraudon *(Chm)*
Clarence T'ao *(CEO)*

BNP Paribas CMG Ltd. **(1)**
10 Harewood Ave
London, NW1 6AA, United Kingdom
Tel.: (44) 20 7595 2000
Fax: (44) 20 7595 2555
Financial Management Services
S.I.C.: 6211
N.A.I.C.S.: 523999

BNP Paribas Columbia **(1)**
Carrera 8A No 99-51 Torre A Oficina 707
World Trade Center
Bogota, Colombia (100%)
Tel.: (57) 12184097
Fax: (57) 12 184236
Web Site: www.bnpparibas.com.co/en/locations/agencies.asp
Emp.: 7
Global Banking & Financial Services
S.I.C.: 6022
N.A.I.C.S.: 522190

BNP Paribas Commodity Futures Ltd. **(1)**
10 Harewood Avenue
London, NW1 6AA, United Kingdom
Tel.: (44) 20 7595 2000
Fax: (44) 20 7595 5100
Investment Management Services
S.I.C.: 6282
N.A.I.C.S.: 523920

BNP Paribas Dubai **(1)**
Twin Towers 19th Fl Beniyas Rd
PO Box 7233
Deira, Dubai, United Arab Emirates (100%)
Tel.: (971) 42106767
Telex: 45755
Fax: (971) 42225849
E-Mail: paribas@emirates.net.ae
Emp.: 120
Provider of Retail, Commercial & Corporate Banking Services
S.I.C.: 6029
N.A.I.C.S.: 522110
Michael Pereira *(Gen Mgr)*

BNP Paribas Dublin **(1)**
5 Georges Dock IFSC
Dublin, 1, Ireland (100%)
Tel.: (353) 16125000
Telex: 90641
Fax: (353) 16125100
E-Mail: dublin.desk@bnpparibas.com
Web Site: www.bnpparibas.ie
Emp.: 200
Retail & International Banking Services
S.I.C.: 6159
N.A.I.C.S.: 522298
Gilles de Decker *(CEO & Country Head)*
Michael Bermingham *(CFO)*
Jean-Francois Gloux *(COO)*

BNP Paribas E & B Ltd. **(1)**
10 Harewood Avenue
London, NW1 6AA, United Kingdom
Tel.: (44) 2075952000
Fax: (44) 20 7595 2555
Financial Planning Services
S.I.C.: 6282
N.A.I.C.S.: 523930

BNP Paribas El Djazair S.P.A. **(1)**
8 Rue de Cirta
Hydra, 16035, Algeria
Tel.: (213) 21 60 39 42
Fax: (213) 21 60 39 29
Web Site: www.bnpparibas.dz
Commercial Banking Services
S.I.C.: 6029
N.A.I.C.S.: 522110

BNP Paribas Energy Trading Canada Corp **(1)**
335 8th Ave Sw Suite 1230
Calgary, AB, T2P 1C9, Canada
Tel.: (403) 691-8800
Fax: (403) 691-8890
Emp.: 7
Natural Gas Transmission Services
S.I.C.: 4922
N.A.I.C.S.: 486210

BNP Paribas Espana S.A. **(1)**
Ribera del Loira 28
ES-28042 Madrid, Spain ES
Tel.: (34) 913888000 (99%)
Telex: 22124
Fax: (34) 913888554
E-Mail: infgeneral.es@bnpparibas.com
Web Site: www.bnpparibas.es
Emp.: 2,000
Investment Banking
S.I.C.: 6211
N.A.I.C.S.: 523110
Mato Ramiro *(Mgr)*

BNP Paribas FIN AMS Asia Limited **(1)**
63/F Two Ifc
Central, China (Hong Kong)
Tel.: (852) 29098888
Real Estate Management Services
S.I.C.: 6531
N.A.I.C.S.: 531390

BNP Paribas Finance (Hong-Kong) Ltd. **(1)**
59-63/F Two Intl Finance Ctr
Central, China (Hong Kong)
Tel.: (852) 29098888
Investment Management Services
S.I.C.: 6799
N.A.I.C.S.: 523920

BNP Paribas Finance PLC **(1)**
20 - 21 St James Street
London, SW1A 1ES, United Kingdom
Tel.: (44) 20 75952000
Fax: (44) 20 79290310
Financial Management Services
S.I.C.: 6211
N.A.I.C.S.: 523999

BNP Paribas Fleet Holdings Ltd. **(1)**
Arval Centre
Swindon, Wiltshire, SN5 6PE, United Kingdom
Tel.: (44) 1793 887000
Investment Management Services
S.I.C.: 6282
N.A.I.C.S.: 523920

BNP Paribas Fortis Factor NV **(1)**
Steenweg Op Tielen 51
Turnhout, Antwerpen, 2300, Belgium
Tel.: (32) 14405411
Fax: (32) 14405600
Emp.: 150
Credit Card Management Services
S.I.C.: 6159
N.A.I.C.S.: 522298

BNP Paribas Fortis Funding SA **(1)**
67 Boulevard Grande-Duchesse Charlotte
Luxembourg, 1331, Luxembourg
Tel.: (352) 264 49 416
Fax: (352) 263 83 509
Commercial Banking Services
S.I.C.: 6029
N.A.I.C.S.: 522110

BNP Paribas Fund Services Australasia Ltd. **(1)**
Level 6 60 Castlereagh Street
Sydney, NSW, 2000, Australia
Tel.: (61) 2 9222 0000
Web Site: www.securities.bnpparibas.com
Investment Advisory Services
S.I.C.: 6282
N.A.I.C.S.: 523930

BNP Paribas Fund Services Dublin Ltd. **(1)**
Trinity Point 10-11 Leinster Street South
Dublin, Ireland
Tel.: (353) 1 612 6400
Fax: (353) 1 612 6427
Web Site: www.bnpparibas.ie/en/locations/agencies.asp
Portfolio Management Services
S.I.C.: 6282
N.A.I.C.S.: 523920
Paul Daly *(Mng Dir)*

BNP Paribas Guyane **(1)**
2 Place Victor Schoelcher
Boite Postal n 35
97300 Cayenne, French Guiana (100%)
Tel.: (594) 594396300
Telex: 910423
Fax: (594) 5 94 30 23 08
E-Mail: bnpg@bnpparibas.com
Web Site: bank.bnpparibas.com
Emp.: 35
Provider of Banking Services
S.I.C.: 6099
N.A.I.C.S.: 522320

BNP Paribas Hungaria Bank RT **(1)**
Roosevelt Ter 7 8
1051 Budapest, Hungary (100%)
Tel.: (36) 13746300
Fax: (36) 12693967
E-Mail: info.hu@bnpparibas.com
Web Site: www.bnpparibas.hu
Emp.: 140
Retail & International Banking Services
S.I.C.: 6159
N.A.I.C.S.: 522293
Gyorgy Takacs *(Exec Dir-Treasury)*

BNP Paribas India Solutions Private Ltd. **(1)**
Unit No 601 Infinity Building No 4 Off Film City Road
Malad East, Mumbai, 400097, India
Tel.: (91) 22 67831000
E-Mail: cvispl.cmit@asia.bnpparibas.com
Web Site: www.indiasolutions.bnpparibas.co.in
Corporate & Investment Banking Services
S.I.C.: 6211
N.A.I.C.S.: 523110
Jacques Andre Rene Michel *(CEO)*
Harshal Vora *(COO & Chief Admin Officer)*
Christian Geuravetian *(COO)*

BNP Paribas Investment Partners Asia Ltd **(1)**
8 Connaught Place 30/F Three Exchange Square
Central, China (Hong Kong)
Tel.: (852) 2533 0000
Web Site: www.bnpparibas-ip.com.hk
Investment Management Services
S.I.C.: 6282
N.A.I.C.S.: 523920

BNP Paribas Investment Partners (Australia) Ltd **(1)**
60 Castlereagh Street
Sydney, NSW, 2000, Australia
Tel.: (61) 2 9619 6291
Fax: (61) 2 9006 9051
Web Site: www.bnpparibas-ip.com.au
Commercial Banking Services
S.I.C.: 6029
N.A.I.C.S.: 522110
David Grybas *(CEO)*
Seda Sadik *(CFO)*

BNP Paribas Investment Partners Belgium SA **(1)**
55 rue du Progres
1210 Brussels, Belgium
Tel.: (32) 2274 83 11
Fax: (32) 22 74 82 28
E-Mail: communications.be@bnpparibas-ip.com
Web Site: www.bnpparibas-ip.com
Investment Management Services
S.I.C.: 6211
N.A.I.C.S.: 523999
Olivier Lafont *(CEO)*

BNP Paribas Investment Partners BSC **(1)**
Bahrain Financial Harbour 4th Floor West Tower Financial Centre
PO Box 5253
Manama, Bahrain
Tel.: (973) 17 866160
Fax: (973) 17 866174
Investment Management Services
S.I.C.: 6799
N.A.I.C.S.: 523920

BNP Paribas Investment Partners Luxembourg SA **(1)**
33 Rue de Gasperich H2O Building Bloc B
5826 Hesperange, Luxembourg
Tel.: (352) 26 46 30 01
Fax: (352) 26 46 91 71
Web Site: www.bnpparibas-ip.lu
Asset Management Services
S.I.C.: 6282
N.A.I.C.S.: 523920

BNP Paribas Investment Partners Netherlands NV **(1)**
Burgerweeshuispad 201 Tripolis Building
1076 GR Amsterdam, Netherlands
Tel.: (31) 20 527 52 75
Fax: (31) 20 527 52 50
E-Mail: client.service.benelux@bnpparibas-ip.com
Web Site: www.bnpparibas-ip.nl
Emp.: 200
Investment Management Services
S.I.C.: 6282
N.A.I.C.S.: 523920
Graham Miller *(Controller-Fin)*

BNP Paribas Investment Partners NL Holding NV **(1)**
Oval Tower De Entree 99-197
Amsterdam, 1101 HE, Netherlands
Tel.: (31) 206 28 93 93
Web Site: www.bnpparibas-ip.nl
Investment Management Services
S.I.C.: 6799
N.A.I.C.S.: 523920

BNP Paribas Investment Partners Singapore Ltd **(1)**
20 Collyer Quay 08-01 Tung Centre
Singapore, 049319, Singapore
Tel.: (65) 6210 3976
Fax: (65) 6210 3960
E-Mail: sing_enquiries@asia.bnpparibas.com
Web Site: www.bnpparibas-ip.com.sg
Emp.: 30
Investment Management Services
S.I.C.: 6799
N.A.I.C.S.: 523920
Puay-Lit Tan *(Deputy CEO & Head-Institutional Bus-South & Southeast Asia)*

BNP Paribas Investment Partners UK Ltd **(1)**
5 Aldermanbury Square
EC2V 7BP London, United Kingdom
Tel.: (44) 207 595 2000
Fax: (44) 20 7595 5075
E-Mail: moneymarketfunds@bnpparibas-ip.com
Web Site: www.bnpparibas-ip.co.uk
Investment Management Services
S.I.C.: 6211
N.A.I.C.S.: 523999
Colin Graham *(Chief Investment Officer & Head-Tactical Asset Allocation & Res)*

BNP Paribas Islamic Issuance BV **(1)**
Reguliersdwarsstraat 90
Amsterdam, 1017 BN, Netherlands
Tel.: (31) 205215645
Financial Management Services
S.I.C.: 6211
N.A.I.C.S.: 523999

BNP Paribas Istanbul **(1)**
Mete Caddesi 16 3
Istanbul, 34437, Turkey (100%)

Tel.: (90) 2122930032
Fax: (90) 2122514385
E-Mail: info@turkey.bnpparibas.com
Web Site: www.turkey.bnpparibas.com
Emp.: 5
Representative Office
S.I.C.: 6022
N.A.I.C.S.: 522190
Metin Togay *(Head-Territory-Turkey)*

BNP Paribas Le Caire (1)
3 Latin America Street
Garden City, Cairo, Egypt
Tel.: (20) 27948323
Telex: 93722 BACAP UN
Fax: (20) 27942218
E-Mail: bnpegypt@africa.bnpparibas.com
Web Site: www.egypt.bnpparibas.com
Corporate & International Banking Services
S.I.C.: 6029
N.A.I.C.S.: 522110
Guy Devernay *(Sec Gen)*

BNP Paribas Lease Group GmbH & Co KG (1)
Ignaz Kock Strasse 9
1210 Vienna, Austria
Tel.: (43) 1 2724312 213
Fax: (43) 1 2724312 220
E-Mail: austria.bplg@bnpparibas.com
Web Site: www.leasingsolutions.bnpparibas.at
Emp.: 70
Equipment Leasing Services
S.I.C.: 7359
N.A.I.C.S.: 532490
Alexander Wodniansky *(Mgr)*

BNP Paribas Lease Group Lizing RT (1)
Honved U 20/A
1055 Budapest, Hungary
Tel.: (36) 1 3019000
Fax: (36) 1 3019010
Emp.: 40
Asset Management Services
S.I.C.: 6282
N.A.I.C.S.: 523920
Pfeningberger Andras *(Mng Dir)*

BNP Paribas Lease Group Luxembourg SA (1)
16 Rue Edward Steichen
2540 Luxembourg, Luxembourg
Tel.: (352) 47 99 85 05
Fax: (352) 47 99 51 81
E-Mail: bplg.sales@bgl.lu
Emp.: 20
Financial Leasing Services
S.I.C.: 6211
N.A.I.C.S.: 523999
Christelle Bouichou *(Acct Mgr)*

BNP Paribas Lease Group (Rentals) Ltd. (1)
St James Court St James Parade
Bristol, BS1 3LH, United Kingdom
Tel.: (44) 845 345 0915
Fax: (44) 845 345 0925
E-Mail: enquiries@bnpparibas-leasegroup.co.uk
Financial Planning Services
S.I.C.: 6282
N.A.I.C.S.: 523930

BNP Paribas Leasing Solutions NV (1)
Hambakenwetering 4
's-Hertogenbosch, 5231 DC, Netherlands
Tel.: (31) 73 63 99 400
Web Site: www.leasingsolutions.bnpparibas.nl/pid218-contacten.html
Financial Leasing Services
S.I.C.: 6211
N.A.I.C.S.: 523999

BNP Paribas Leasing Solutions Zrt (1)
Dunavirag U 2
1138 Budapest, Hungary
Tel.: (36) 1 577 6700
Fax: (36) 1 577 6709
E-Mail: info@leasegroup.hu
Web Site: www.leasingsolutions.bnpparibas.hu
Emp.: 34
Financial Leasing Services
S.I.C.: 6141
N.A.I.C.S.: 522220

Andras Pfeningberger *(Mng Dir)*

Subsidiary:

BNP Paribas Bank N.V. (2)
Herengracht 595
1017 CE Amsterdam, Netherlands NL
Tel.: (31) 205501212 (100%)
Fax: (31) 206253921
E-Mail: bnpparibas.ams@bnpparibas.com
Web Site: www.bnpparibas.nl
Emp.: 100
Cross Border Financing Services
S.I.C.: 6159
N.A.I.C.S.: 522298
Andre Boulanger *(Gen Mgr)*

BNP Paribas Netherlands (1)
Herengracht 595
1017 CE Amsterdam, Netherlands NL
Mailing Address: (100%)
PO Box 10042
1001EA Amsterdam, Netherlands
Tel.: (31) 205501212
Telex: 14217 Naparni
Fax: (31) 206253921
E-Mail: bnpparibas.ams@bnpparibas.com
Web Site: www.bnpgparibas.nl
Emp.: 100
Corporate & International Banking Services
S.I.C.: 6099
N.A.I.C.S.: 522320
Andre Boulanger *(Gen Mgr)*

BNP Paribas Nouvelle Caledonie (1)
37 Ave Henri Lafleur
BP K3
98849 Noumea, Cedex, New Caledonia (100%)
Tel.: (687) 258400
Telex: 3022
Fax: (687) 258459
E-Mail: bnp.nc@bnpparibas.com
Web Site: www.bnpparibas.nc
Emp.: 165
Retail Banking Services
S.I.C.: 6159
N.A.I.C.S.: 522298
Patrick Soulajes *(Mgr)*

BNP Paribas Panama (1)
Edificio Omanco No 200 Via Espana
Panama Zona 1, Panama, 1, Panama (100%)
Tel.: (507) 2648555
Fax: (507) 2636559
E-Mail: bnpparibas.panama@americas.bnpparibas.com
Web Site: www.bnpparibas.pa
Emp.: 130
Full Banking Services
S.I.C.: 6099
N.A.I.C.S.: 522320
Thierry Dingreville *(Gen Mgr)*

BNP Paribas Personal Finance BV (1)
Marten Meesweg 97
Rotterdam, 3068 AV, Netherlands
Tel.: (31) 10 286 58 00
Fax: (31) 10 286 58 29
E-Mail: info@bnpparibas-pf.nl
Web Site: www.bnpparibas-pf.nl
Emp.: 26
Mortgage Loan Brokerage Services
S.I.C.: 6163
N.A.I.C.S.: 522310

BNP Paribas Personal Finance EAD (1)
Residential Complex Mladost 4 Business Park Sofia Building 14
1766 Sofia, Bulgaria
Tel.: (359) 700 11 8 11
Fax: (359) 2 489 99 98
E-Mail: contacts@bnpparibas-pf.bg
Web Site: www.bnpparibas-pf.bg
Financial Management Services
S.I.C.: 6211
N.A.I.C.S.: 523999

BNP Paribas Personal Finance SPA (1)
Via Gustavo Fara 39
Milan, 20124, Italy
Tel.: (39) 0267602332
Fax: (39) 02 66 90 389
Web Site: www.bnpparibas.it
Financial Management Services

S.I.C.: 6211
N.A.I.C.S.: 523999

BNP Paribas Portugal (1)
Avenida 5 De Outubro 206
1050-065 Lisbon, Portugal
Tel.: (351) 217910200
Fax: (351) 217955617
E-Mail: csd_portugal@bnpparibas.com
Web Site: www.bnp.pt
Emp.: 150
Commercial Bank
S.I.C.: 6029
N.A.I.C.S.: 522110
Mary Cludi Delmont *(Sec)*

BNP Paribas Principal Investments Japan Ltd. (1)
GranTokyo North Tower 1-9-1 Marunouchi
Chiyoda-ku, Tokyo, 100-6742, Japan
Tel.: (81) 3 6377 2000
Fax: (81) 3 5218 5858
Investment Management Services
S.I.C.: 6211
N.A.I.C.S.: 523999

BNP Paribas Private Bank Plc (1)
10 Harewood Ave
London, NW1 6AA, United Kingdom (100%)
Tel.: (44) 2075952000
Fax: (44) 2075952555
E-Mail: privatebank.london@bnpparibas.com
Emp.: 100
Provider of Private Banking Services
S.I.C.: 6022
N.A.I.C.S.: 522190

BNP Paribas Private Bank Switzerland S.A. (1)
Pl de Hollande 2
1211 Basel, Geneve, Switzerland (100%)
Tel.: (41) 227878111
Fax: (41) 582122222
Web Site: www.bnpparibas.ch
Emp.: 110
International Banking Services
S.I.C.: 6099
N.A.I.C.S.: 522320
Pascal Boris *(CEo)*

BNP Paribas Qatar (1)
Rayyan Rd
Doha, Qatar (100%)
Mailing Address:
PO Box 2636
Doha, Qatar
Tel.: (974) 4433844
Telex: 4268 PARIBA DH
Fax: (974) 4410861
E-Mail: qatar.paribas@paribas.com
Web Site: qatar.bnpparibas.com
Emp.: 140
Retail & International Banking Services
S.I.C.: 6159
N.A.I.C.S.: 522298

BNP Paribas Real Estate Advisory & Property Management Luxembourg SA (1)
Axento Building Avenue J F Kennedy 44
Luxembourg, 1855, Luxembourg
Tel.: (352) 34 94 84
Fax: (352) 34 94 73
Web Site: www.realestate.bnpparibas.co.in/pages/articles/fiche.php?s_code=bnppi_implantations_lu&p=lu&s_wbg_menu=333&l=en
Emp.: 20
Property Management Services
S.I.C.: 6531
N.A.I.C.S.: 531311
Martin Heyse *(Mng Dir)*

BNP Paribas Real Estate Advisory & Property Management UK Ltd. (1)
5 Aldermanbury Square
London, EC2V 7BP, United Kingdom
Tel.: (44) 20 7338 4000
E-Mail: realestate.press@bnpparibas.com
Web Site: www.realestate.bnpparibas.co.uk
Real Estate Property Management Services
S.I.C.: 6531
N.A.I.C.S.: 531390
John Slade *(CEO)*
Mark England *(Mng Dir)*
Simon Bailey *(COO)*

BNP Paribas Real Estate Advisory Belgium SA (1)
Boulevard Louis Schmidtlaan 2 B3
1040 Brussels, Belgium
Tel.: (32) 2 646 49 49
Fax: (32) 2 646 46 50
Web Site: www.realestate.bnpparibas.be
Emp.: 60
Real Estate Development Services
S.I.C.: 6531
N.A.I.C.S.: 531390
Frederic van de Putte *(CEO)*
Sebastien Sohl *(CFO)*
Bart van den Berg *(COO)*

BNP Paribas Real Estate Advisory Italy SPA (1)
Via Carlo Bo 6
20122 Milan, Italy
Tel.: (39) 02 3211 5310
Fax: (39) 02 32 11 53 69
E-Mail: milano.advisory@bnpparibas.com
Web Site: www.realestate.bnpparibas.it
Emp.: 220
Real Estate Management Services
S.I.C.: 6531
N.A.I.C.S.: 531390
Roberto Nicosia *(Mng Dir)*

BNP Paribas Real Estate Advisory Spain SA (1)
Calle Velazquez 95
28006 Madrid, Spain
Tel.: (34) 914 459 607
Fax: (34) 91 454 96 15
Web Site: www.realestate.bnpparibas.es
Real Estate Property Management Services
S.I.C.: 6531
N.A.I.C.S.: 531390

BNP Paribas Real Estate Consult GmbH (1)
Schleusenbrucke 1 Neuer Wall 25
Hamburg, 20354, Germany
Tel.: (49) 40 348 48 101
Fax: (49) 40 348 48 100
Emp.: 9
Real Estate Advisory Services
S.I.C.: 6531
N.A.I.C.S.: 531390
Wolfgang Schneider *(Mng Dir)*

BNP Paribas Real Estate Facilities Management Ltd. (1)
5 Aldermanbury Square
London, EC2V 7BP, United Kingdom
Tel.: (44) 20 7338 4400
Fax: (44) 20 7430 2628
Real Estate Management Services
S.I.C.: 6531
N.A.I.C.S.: 531390

BNP Paribas Real Estate GmbH (1)
Goetheplatz 4
60311 Frankfurt, Germany
Tel.: (49) 69 2 98 99 0
Fax: (49) 69 2 92 91 4
E-Mail: frankfurt.realestate@bnpparibas.com
Web Site: www.realestate.bnpparibas.de
Real Estate Development Services
S.I.C.: 6531
N.A.I.C.S.: 531390

BNP Paribas Real Estate Holding GmbH (1)
Fritz-Vomfelde-Strasse 34
Dusseldorf, 40547, Germany
Tel.: (49) 211 301 82 00
Fax: (49) 211 301 82 10 00
Real Estate Brokerage Services
S.I.C.: 6531
N.A.I.C.S.: 531210

BNP Paribas Real Estate Investment Management Ltd. (1)
5 Aldermanbury Square
London, EC2V 7BP, United Kingdom
Tel.: (44) 20 7338 4000
Fax: (44) 20 7430 2628
E-Mail: reim-bnpparibas@bnpparibas.com
Web Site: www.reim.bnpparibas.co.uk
Emp.: 185
Real Estate Management Services
S.I.C.: 6531
N.A.I.C.S.: 531390
Gerardine Davies *(Head-Investment Mgmt)*

BNP Paribas SA—(Continued)

Subsidiaries:

Banca UCB S.p.A. (2)
Via G Fara 39
20124 Milan, Italy IT
Tel.: (39) 02676021 (100%)
Fax: (39) 02 66 90 389
Web Site: www.bancaucb.com
Emp.: 18
Provider of Banking & Home Finance Services
S.I.C.: 6099
N.A.I.C.S.: 522320

BNP Lease Group S.p.A. (2)
Via Le Della Liberazione 16-18
20124 Milan, Italy (100%)
Tel.: (39) 02673331
Fax: (39) 026733400
E-Mail: bplg_it_leasegroup@bnpparibas.com
Web Site: www.leasegroup.it/
Leasing Services
S.I.C.: 6726
N.A.I.C.S.: 525990

BNP Paribas Asset Management SGR SpA (2)
Via Ansperto 5
20123 Milan, Italy (100%)
Tel.: (39) 0272475101
Telex: 310641 NAPAR-I
Fax: (39) 272475230
E-Mail: marco.barbero@bnpparibas.com
Emp.: 30
Asset Management Services
S.I.C.: 6531
N.A.I.C.S.: 531390

BNP Paribas-Succursale Italia (2)
Piazza San Fedele 2
20121 Milan, Italy
Tel.: (39) 02 7247 1
Fax: (39) 02 7247 6465
Web Site: www.bnpparibas.it/en/contact/
Financial Services
S.I.C.: 6099
N.A.I.C.S.: 522320
Fabio Gallia *(Head-BNP Paribas & Chm & CEO-BNL)*

BNP Paribas Real Estate Investment Management Luxembourg SA (1)
Axento Building Avenue J F Kennedy 44
1855 Luxembourg, Luxembourg
Tel.: (352) 26 26 06 41
Fax: (352) 26 26 06 26
E-Mail: reimlux@bnpparibas.com
Web Site: www.realestate.bnpparibas.lu
Emp.: 15
Real Estate Management Services
S.I.C.: 6531
N.A.I.C.S.: 531390
Sven Rein *(Mng Dir)*

BNP Paribas Real Estate Jersey Ltd. (1)
3rd Floor Dialogue House 2-6 Anley Street
Saint Helier, Jersey
Tel.: (44) 1534 629001
Fax: (44) 1534 629011
Web Site: www.realestate.bnpparibas.je
Real Estate Management Services
S.I.C.: 6531
N.A.I.C.S.: 531390
Chris Daniels *(Mng Dir)*

BNP Paribas Real Estate Property Developpement UK Ltd. (1)
5 Aldermanbury Square
London, EC2V 7HR, United Kingdom
Tel.: (44) 20 7338 4000
Real Estate Property Management Services
S.I.C.: 6531
N.A.I.C.S.: 531390

BNP Paribas Real Estate Property Management Belgium (1)
Boulevard Louis Schmidtlaan 2 B3
Brussels, 1040, Belgium
Tel.: (32) 22379999
Fax: (32) 22905969
Web Site: www.realestate.bnpparibas.be
Emp.: 70
Real Estate Management Services
S.I.C.: 6531
N.A.I.C.S.: 531390
Bert Leerschool *(Acct Mgr)*

BNP Paribas Real Estate Property Management GmbH (1)
Fritz-Vomfelde-Str 34
Dusseldorf, Nordrhein-Westfalen, 40547, Germany
Tel.: (49) 211301820
Real Estate Development Services
S.I.C.: 6531
N.A.I.C.S.: 531390

BNP Paribas Real Estate Property Management Italy SrL (1)
Via Carlo Bo 11
20143 Milan, Italy
Tel.: (39) 02 36 66 04 01
Fax: (39) 02 36 66 04 99
E-Mail: contact-pm.italia@bnpparibas.com
Emp.: 30
Real Estate Property Management Services
S.I.C.: 6531
N.A.I.C.S.: 531390
Vincenzo Noviello *(Mng Dir)*

BNP Paribas Real Estate (1)
20 Merrion Road Ballsbridge
Dublin, 4, Ireland (50%)
Tel.: (353) 1 661 1233
Fax: (353) 1 678 9981
E-Mail: Dublin.reception@bnpparibas.com
Web Site: www.realestate.bnpparibas.ie
Emp.: 200
Property Management & Banking Services
S.I.C.: 6029
N.A.I.C.S.: 522110
Patrick Curran *(Mng Dir)*

BNP Paribas Reunion (1)
Angle des rues J Chatel et Rontounay
Saint-Denis, 93200, Reunion
Tel.: (262) 33892705705
Telex: 916133RE
E-Mail: contactreunion@bnpparibas.com
Web Site: reunion.bnpparibas.net
Full Banking Services
S.I.C.: 6029
N.A.I.C.S.: 522110

BNP Paribas SAE (1)
Plot 85 - Block G 90th Street Fifth Settlement City Centre Sector A
Cairo, Egypt
Tel.: (20) 2 19267
E-Mail: egypt.customercare@bnpparibas.com
Web Site: www.egypt.bnpparibas.com
Commercial Banking & Financial Services
S.I.C.: 6029
N.A.I.C.S.: 522110
Jany Gerometta *(Mng Dir)*
Marc Dapra *(COO)*
Shahinaz Foda *(Deputy Mng Dir & Head-Treas & Wealth Mgmt)*
Pierre Delhaise *(Deputy Mng Dir & Head-Corp)*

BNP Paribas Securities (Asia) Ltd. (1)
63/F Two International Finance Centre 8 Finance Street
Central, China (Hong Kong)
Tel.: (852) 2909 8888
Fax: (852) 2865 2523
Securities Brokerage Services
S.I.C.: 6211
N.A.I.C.S.: 523120
Angely Yip *(Dir-Sls-North Asia)*

BNP Paribas Securities Korea Company Ltd. (1)
22nd Floor Taepyeongno Building 310 Taepyeongno 2-ga
Jung-gu, Seoul, 100-767, Korea (South)
Tel.: (82) 2 2125 0500
Securities Brokerage Services
S.I.C.: 6211
N.A.I.C.S.: 523120
Hyungho Choi, *(CEO)*

BNP Paribas Securities Services (Holdings) Ltd. (1)
Liberte House 19-23 La Motte Street
PO Box 451
Saint Helier, Jersey JE4 5RL
Tel.: (44) 1534 813800
Fax: (44) 1534 849321
Emp.: 200
Investment Management Services
S.I.C.: 6211
N.A.I.C.S.: 523999
Frank Roden *(CEO)*

BNP Paribas Securities Services (1)
Trinity Point 10-11 Leinster St South
Dublin, 2, Ireland (100%)
Tel.: (353) 1 612 6400
E-Mail: ireland.clientdevelopment@bnpparibas.com
Web Site: www.bnpparibas.com
Emp.: 70
Investment Management Services
S.I.C.: 6211
N.A.I.C.S.: 523999
Paul Daly *(Mng Dir)*

BNP Paribas Securities (Singapore) Pte Ltd. (1)
20 Collyer Quay 01-01 Tung Centre
Singapore, 049319, Singapore
Tel.: (65) 6210 1988
Fax: (65) 6210 1980
Web Site: www.bnpparibas.com.sg/en/contact/
Securities Brokerage Services
S.I.C.: 6211
N.A.I.C.S.: 523120

BNP Paribas Securities (Taiwan) Co Ltd. (1)
3/F 52 Min Sheng East Road Sec 4
Taipei, Taiwan
Tel.: (886) 2 2719 8530
Fax: (886) 2 2175 7000
Securities Brokerage Services
S.I.C.: 6211
N.A.I.C.S.: 523120

BNP Paribas Services (Hong Kong) Ltd. (1)
23/F Two Ifc
Central, China (Hong Kong)
Tel.: (852) 28251888
Financial Planning Services
S.I.C.: 6282
N.A.I.C.S.: 523930

BNP Paribas Succursale Italia (1)
Piazza San Fedele 2
20121 Milan, Italy
Tel.: (39) 0272471
Telex: 335624/335628 PAR/BMII
Fax: (39) 0272476465
E-Mail: info@bnpparibas.com
Web Site: www.bnpparibas.it/it/information/legal_information.asp
Retail & International Banking Services
S.I.C.: 6159
N.A.I.C.S.: 522298
Fedrick Lavenier *(Dir-HR)*

BNP Paribas (Suisse) SA (1)
Place de Hollande 2
Case Postale, CH-1211 Geneva, Switzerland (99%)
Tel.: (41) 582122111
Telex: 962286
Fax: (41) 582122222
Web Site: www.bnpparibas.ch
Emp.: 1,500
International Banking Services
S.I.C.: 6211
N.A.I.C.S.: 523110
Pascal Boris *(CEO)*
Jean Clamon *(Head-Compliance, Internal Control Coord & Mng Dir)*

Non-U.S. Branch:

BNP Paribas Suisse S.A. (2)
La Plaiderie House
P O Box 224
Saint Peter Port, GY1 3NU, Guernsey (100%)
Tel.: (44) 1481712171
Telex: 419 14 03 PARIBA G
Fax: (44) 1481712172
Web Site: www.bnpparibas.ch/
Emp.: 4
International & Offshore Banking Services
S.I.C.: 6159
N.A.I.C.S.: 522298

BNP Paribas Tel-Aviv (1)
Weizaman 4 Beic Asia
64239 Tel Aviv, Israel (100%)
Tel.: (972) 35258686
Fax: (972) 36970555
Web Site: www.bnpparibas.co.il
Emp.: 50
Representative Office
S.I.C.: 6022
N.A.I.C.S.: 522190
Pierre Bonin *(Chm)*

BNP Paribas Trust Company (Guernesey) Ltd. (1)
BNP Paribas House St Julians Avenue
Saint Peter Port, Guernsey GY1 3WE
Tel.: (44) 1481750800
Financial Planning Services
S.I.C.: 6282
N.A.I.C.S.: 523930

BNP Paribas UK Holdings Ltd. (1)
10 Harewood Ave
London, NW1 6AA, United Kingdom (100%)
Tel.: (44) 2075952000
Telex: 883412
Fax: (44) 2075952555
E-Mail: info@bnpparibas.com
Web Site: www.bnpparibas.co.uk/en/contact/contact.asp
Emp.: 100
Bank Holding
S.I.C.: 6712
N.A.I.C.S.: 551111
Ludovic de Moncille *(CEO)*

BNP Paribas UK Treasury Ltd. (1)
10 Harewood Avenue
Camden Town, London, NW1 6AA, United Kingdom
Tel.: (44) 2075952000
Fax: (44) 2075952555
Financial Management Services
S.I.C.: 6211
N.A.I.C.S.: 523999

Subsidiary:

BNP Paribas London Branch (2)
10 Harewood Ave
NW1 6AA London, United Kingdom (100%)
Tel.: (44) 2075952000
Telex: 883412
Fax: (44) 02075952555
E-Mail: info@bnpparibas.com
Web Site: www.bnpparibas.co.uk
Emp.: 1,000
Banking
S.I.C.: 6159
N.A.I.C.S.: 522298
Stefano Blotto *(Mgr-Institutional Rels)*

BNP Paribas Uruguay S.A. (1)
Casilla De Correo 6729
Correo Central, Montevideo, 11000, Uruguay (100%)
Tel.: (598) 29162768
Fax: (598) 29164922
E-Mail: uruguay@bnpparibas.com.ar
Emp.: 3
Trade Finance; International Private Banking
S.I.C.: 6159
N.A.I.C.S.: 522293

BNP Paribas Wealth Management Monaco (1)
15-17 Avenue d'Ostende
98000 Monaco, Monaco
Tel.: (377) 93 15 68 00
Fax: (377) 93 15 68 01
Web Site: www.wealthmanagement.bnpparibas.mc
Wealth Management Services
S.I.C.: 6282
N.A.I.C.S.: 523920

BNP Paribas ZAO (1)
1 Bolshoi Gnezdnikovski Pereoulok Street 2
Moscow, 125009, Russia
Tel.: (7) 495 660 9181
Fax: (7) 495 660 9182
Web Site: www.bnpparibas.ru
Commercial Banking Services
S.I.C.: 6029
N.A.I.C.S.: 522110
Margarita Travkina *(CFO)*

BNP PB Real Estate Advisory & Property Management Hungary Ltd (1)
Alkotas U 53
1123 Budapest, Hungary
Tel.: (36) 1 487 5501
Fax: (36) 1 487 5542
E-Mail: office.hungary@bnpparibas.com

Web Site: www.realestate.bnpparibas.hu
Emp.: 15
Property Management Services
S.I.C.: 6531
N.A.I.C.S.: 531312
Csongor Csukas *(Chm)*

Bruun s Galleri AS (1)
Arne Jacobsens Alle 20
2300 Copenhagen, Denmark
Tel.: (45) 87419805
Real Estate Property Leasing Services
S.I.C.: 6519
N.A.I.C.S.: 531190

Bryggen Vejle AS (1)
Arne Jacobsens Alle 20
2300 Copenhagen, Denmark
Tel.: (45) 97404666
Real Estate Management Services
S.I.C.: 6531
N.A.I.C.S.: 531390

Capucine BV (1)
Herengracht 477
1017 BS Amsterdam, Netherlands
Tel.: (31) 205501212
Financial Planning Services
S.I.C.: 6282
N.A.I.C.S.: 523930

Cardif Biztosito Magyarorszag Zrt (1)
Korhaz U 6-12
Budapest, 1033, Hungary
Tel.: (36) 6 1 501 2300
Fax: (36) 6 1 501 2301
E-Mail: cardif@cardif.hu
Web Site: www.cardif.hu
General Insurance Services
S.I.C.: 6411
N.A.I.C.S.: 524210

Cardif Colombia Seguros Generales S.A. (1)
Calle 113 No 7-80
Bogota, Colombia
Tel.: (57) 1744 4040
Fax: (57) 1742 4012
General Insurance Services
S.I.C.: 6411
N.A.I.C.S.: 524210
Jorge Hernandez Rodriguez *(Pres)*

Cardif del Peru Sa Compania de Seguros (1)
Av Enrique Canaval y Moreyra 380 Of 1101
Lima, Peru
Tel.: (51) 1 6151700
General Insurance Services
S.I.C.: 6411
N.A.I.C.S.: 524210

Cardif Mexico Seguros de Vida SA de CV (1)
Av Paseo de las Palmas Num 425 Desp 502 y 504
Lomas de Chapultepec, Mexico, 11000, Mexico
Tel.: (52) 55 2282 2000
Fax: (52) 55 2282 2001
Web Site: www.cardif.com.mx
General Insurance Services
S.I.C.: 6411
N.A.I.C.S.: 524210

Cetelem Algerie SPA (1)
92 Chemin Gacem Mohamed
16209 El Mouradia, Algeria
Tel.: (213) 21 69 64 14
Fax: (213) 21 69 64 05
Web Site: dz.cetelem.com
Consumer Financial Services
S.I.C.: 6141
N.A.I.C.S.: 522291

Cetelem IFN SA (1)
Calea Victoriei Nr 155 Bl D1 tronson 5 Etaj 8 Sector 1
Bucharest, 010073, Romania
Tel.: (40) 21 312 0220
Fax: (40) 21 312 0219
E-Mail: office@cetelem.ro
Web Site: www.cetelem.ro
Consumer Credit Services
S.I.C.: 6141
N.A.I.C.S.: 522291

Cetelem Servicios SA de CV (1)
Paseo De La Reforma 115 Piso 5
Mexico, 11000, Mexico
Tel.: (52) 5511000300
Management Consulting Services
S.I.C.: 8742
N.A.I.C.S.: 541611

Cetelem Slovensko A.S. (1)
Panenska 7
Bratislava, 812 36, Slovakia
Tel.: (421) 259342100
E-Mail:
Web Site: www.cetelem.sk
Consumer Credit Services
S.I.C.: 6141
N.A.I.C.S.: 522291

CNH Capital Europe BV (1)
Hambakenwetering 4
's-Hertogenbosch, 5231 DC, Netherlands
Tel.: (31) 736399400
Fax: (31) 20 6977573
Consumer Credit Services
S.I.C.: 6141
N.A.I.C.S.: 522291

Cobema SA (1)
Rue de Champles 61-63
1301 Wavre, Belgium
Tel.: (32) 10 24 37 68
Fax: (32) 10 24 38 44
Financial Planning Services
S.I.C.: 6282
N.A.I.C.S.: 523930

Cofhylux SA (1)
Avenue J F Kennedy 50
2951 Luxembourg, Luxembourg
Tel.: (352) 47 99 24 57
Fax: (352) 47 99 27 90
Real Estate Development Services
S.I.C.: 6531
N.A.I.C.S.: 531390

Commerz Finanz GmbH (1)
Schwanthalerstr 31
Munich, 80336, Germany
Tel.: (49) 89551130
Fax: (49) 89 55113180
E-Mail: info@commerzfinanz.com
Web Site: www.commerzfinanz.com
Commercial Banking Services
S.I.C.: 6029
N.A.I.C.S.: 522110

Compagnie Financiere de la Cote d'Ivoire (1)
Rue Gourgas 15 F Tour BICICI
01 LP 1566
Abidjan, 1, Cote d'Ivoire
Tel.: (225) 20 21 27 32
Telex: 22228 BICICOMI
Fax: (225) 20 21 26 43
Investment Banking Services
S.I.C.: 6099
N.A.I.C.S.: 522320

Compagnie Financiere Ottomane SA (1)
44 Avenue J-F Kennedy
1855 Luxembourg, Luxembourg
Tel.: (352) 22 18 54
Financial Planning Services
S.I.C.: 6282
N.A.I.C.S.: 523930

Cooperleasing SpA (1)
Via Marconi 1
40122 Bologna, Italy
Tel.: (39) 051 276411
Fax: (39) 051 223004
E-Mail: cooperleasing@cooperleasing.it
Web Site: www.cooperleasing.it
Commercial Banking Services
S.I.C.: 6029
N.A.I.C.S.: 522110

Credirama SPA (1)
Viale Belfiore 26
Florence, 50144, Italy
Tel.: (39) 0553374820
Commercial Banking Services
S.I.C.: 6029
N.A.I.C.S.: 522110

Credit pour Habitations Sociales (1)
Jagersveld 4
1170 Brussels, Belgium
Tel.: (32) 2 673 33 00
Fax: (32) 2 675 42 41
Financial Management Services
S.I.C.: 6211
N.A.I.C.S.: 523999

Cspl 2002 Kft (1)
II Rakoczi F Ut 154-170
Budapest, 1214, Hungary
Tel.: (36) 1 425 8004
Financial Planning Services
S.I.C.: 6282
N.A.I.C.S.: 523930

Detaljhandelshuset i Hyllinge AB (1)
Kyrktorget 19
Partille, 433 33, Sweden
Tel.: (46) 850899900
Real Estate Property Leasing Services
S.I.C.: 6519
N.A.I.C.S.: 531190

Duna Plaza Zrt (1)
Vaci Ut 178
Budapest, 1138, Hungary
Tel.: (36) 1 465 1600
Fax: (36) 1 465 1620
E-Mail: dunaplaza@segece.hu
Web Site: www.dunaplaza.hu
Shopping Center Operator
S.I.C.: 6512
N.A.I.C.S.: 531120

Effico Portugal (1)
Rua Tomas da Fonseca Centro Empresarial Torres de Lisboa
Torre G-9 Andar, 1600-209 Lisbon, Portugal
Tel.: (351) 21 780 60 00
Fax: (351) 21 780 60 66
E-Mail: comercial@effico.pt
Web Site: www.effico.pt
Asset Management Services
S.I.C.: 6211
N.A.I.C.S.: 523999

Ejesur S.A. (1)
Calle Retama 3
Madrid, 28045, Spain
Tel.: (34) 914368500
Fax: (34) 915289231
Real Estate Management Services
S.I.C.: 6531
N.A.I.C.S.: 531390

Farmandstredet ANS (1)
Stoperigata 1
0250 Oslo, Norway
Tel.: (47) 23213500
Fax: (47) 23213580
Real Estate Property Leasing Services
S.I.C.: 6519
N.A.I.C.S.: 531190

Farmandstredet Eiendom AS (1)
Stoperigata 1
Oslo, 0250, Norway
Tel.: (47) 23213500
Fax: (47) 23213580
Real Estate Property Leasing Services
S.I.C.: 6519
N.A.I.C.S.: 531190

Fastighets AB Allum (1)
Kyrktorget 19
Partille, 433 33, Sweden
Tel.: (46) 850899900
Real Estate Property Leasing Services
S.I.C.: 6519
N.A.I.C.S.: 531190

Fastighets AB Borlange Kopcentrum (1)
Kyrktorget 19
Partille, 433 33, Sweden
Tel.: (46) 243248111
Real Estate Property Leasing Services
S.I.C.: 6519
N.A.I.C.S.: 531190

Fastighets AB Centrum Vasterort (1)
Kyrktorget 19
Partille, 433 33, Sweden
Tel.: (46) 850899900
Real Estate Management & Development Services
S.I.C.: 6531
N.A.I.C.S.: 531390

Fastighets AB CentrumInvest (1)
PO Box 200
Partille, 433 33, Sweden
Tel.: (46) 850899900
Real Estate Property Leasing Services
S.I.C.: 6519
N.A.I.C.S.: 531190

Fastighets AB Hageby Centrum (1)
Vastra Tradgardsgatan 2
Stockholm, 111 53, Sweden
Tel.: (46) 850899900
Fax: (46) 11 14 59 10
Real Estate Property Leasing Services
S.I.C.: 6531
N.A.I.C.S.: 531390

Fastighets AB Lantmateribacken (1)
Kyrktorget 19
Partille, 433 33, Sweden
Tel.: (46) 850899976
Real Estate Property Leasing Services
S.I.C.: 6519
N.A.I.C.S.: 531190

Fastighets AB Marieberg Centrum (1)
Kyrktorget 19
433 33 Partille, Sweden
Tel.: (46) 850899900
Real Estate Property Leasing Services
S.I.C.: 6519
N.A.I.C.S.: 531190

Fastighets AB Overby Kopcentrum (1)
Ladugardsvagen 14
Trollhattan, 461 70, Sweden
Tel.: (46) 520472550
Real Estate Property Leasing Services
S.I.C.: 6519
N.A.I.C.S.: 531190

Fastighets AB P Akanten (1)
Kyrktorget 19
Partille, 433 33, Sweden
Tel.: (46) 850899900
Real Estate Property Leasing Services
S.I.C.: 6519
N.A.I.C.S.: 531190

Fastighets AB P Brodalen (1)
Kyrktorget 19
Partille, 433 33, Sweden
Tel.: (46) 850899900
Real Estate Property Leasing Services
S.I.C.: 6519
N.A.I.C.S.: 531190

Fastighets AB Sollentuna Centrum (1)
Sollentunavagen 163c
Sollentuna, 191 47, Sweden
Tel.: (46) 86233370
E-Mail: info.sollentuna@steenstrom.com
Web Site: www.sollentunacentrum.se
Real Estate Property Leasing Services
S.I.C.: 6519
N.A.I.C.S.: 531190

Fastighets AB Uddevallatorp (1)
Kyrktorget 19
Partille, 433 33, Sweden
Tel.: (46) 850899900
Real Estate Property Leasing Services
S.I.C.: 6519
N.A.I.C.S.: 531190

Fimestic Expansion SA (1)
Calle Retama 3
Madrid, 28045, Spain
Tel.: (34) 913370700
Fax: (34) 914067509
Financial Planning Services
S.I.C.: 6282
N.A.I.C.S.: 523930

Financial Telemarketing Services Ltd. (1)
Pinnacle House A1 Barnet Way
Borehamwood, Hertfordshire, WD6 2XX, United Kingdom
Tel.: (44) 20 8324 3300
Fax: (44) 20 8953 6222
E-Mail: info@fts-ltd.com
Web Site: www.fts-ltd.com
Debt Collection & Telemarketing Services
S.I.C.: 7322
N.A.I.C.S.: 561440
Neil Sullivan *(Mng Dir)*

Findomestic Banka a.d (1)
115a Bulevar Mihaila Pupina Str
11070 Belgrade, Serbia
Tel.: (381) 11 333 6000
Fax: (381) 11 3331 766
E-Mail: corporate@findomestic.rs
Web Site: www.findomestic.rs

BNP Paribas SA—(Continued)

Commercial Banking Services
S.I.C.: 6029
N.A.I.C.S.: 522110
Angelo Scatigna *(Chm-Exec Bd)*
Vladimir Markovic *(Vice Chm-Exec Bd)*

Fund Channel SA **(1)**
5 Allee Scheffer
Luxembourg, 2520, Luxembourg
Tel.: (352) 26 73 45 00
Fax: (352) 26 73 45 33
E-Mail: info@fund-channel.com
Web Site: www.fund-channel.com
Emp.: 80
Investment Management Services
S.I.C.: 6211
N.A.I.C.S.: 523999

Fundamentum Asset Management S.A. **(1)**
8 Rue Du Fort Rheinsheim
2419 Luxembourg, Luxembourg
Tel.: (352) 26 44 40 40
Fax: (352) 26 44 40 44
Asset Management Services
S.I.C.: 6799
N.A.I.C.S.: 523920

FundQuest MM Ltd. **(1)**
5 Aldermanbury Square
London, EC2V 7BP, United Kingdom
Tel.: (44) 20 7595 2000
Fax: (44) 20 7063 7340
E-Mail: clientservices@fundquest.co.uk
Web Site: www.fundquest.com
Investment Management Services
S.I.C.: 6799
N.A.I.C.S.: 523920

FundQuest UK Ltd. **(1)**
5 Aldermanbury Square
London, EC2V 7BP, United Kingdom
Tel.: (44) 20 7595 2000
Fax: (44) 20 7063 7340
E-Mail: clientservices@fundquest.co.uk
Web Site: www.fundquest.com
Asset Management Services
S.I.C.: 6282
N.A.I.C.S.: 523920
Helen Oxley *(Head-Bus Dev & Assoc Dir)*

Geneve Credit & Leasing SA **(1)**
Boulevard Du Pont-D'arve 28
Geneva, 1205, Switzerland
Tel.: (41) 223166600
Fax: (41) 22 316 66 01
E-Mail: info@gcl-sa.ch
Web Site: www.gcl-sa.ch
Financial Planning Services
S.I.C.: 6282
N.A.I.C.S.: 523930

Gulskogen Prosjekt & Eiendom AS **(1)**
Stoperigata 1
0250 Oslo, Norway
Tel.: (47) 23 21 35 00
Fax: (47) 23 21 35 80
Real Estate Management Services
S.I.C.: 6531
N.A.I.C.S.: 531390

Hamar Storsenter AS **(1)**
Stoperigaten 1
Oslo, 0250, Norway
Tel.: (47) 23 21 35 00
Fax: (47) 23 21 35 80
Real Estate Property Leasing Services
S.I.C.: 6519
N.A.I.C.S.: 531190

Hovlandbanen AS **(1)**
Stoperigata 1
0250 Oslo, Norway
Tel.: (47) 23 21 35 00
Fax: (47) 23 21 35 80
Real Estate Property Leasing Services
S.I.C.: 6519
N.A.I.C.S.: 531190

Humberclyde Commercial Investments Ltd. **(1)**
Northern Cross
Basingstoke, Hampshire, RG21 4HL, United Kingdom
Tel.: (44) 1256 377 377
Fax: (44) 1256 377 300
Financial Management Services
S.I.C.: 6211
N.A.I.C.S.: 523999

Humberclyde Finance Ltd. **(1)**
Northern Cross
Basingstoke, Hampshire, RG21 4HL, United Kingdom
Tel.: (44) 1256 377377
Fax: (44) 1256 377 300
Financial Management Services
S.I.C.: 6211
N.A.I.C.S.: 523999

Humberclyde Investments Ltd. **(1)**
Northern Cross
Basingstoke, Hampshire, RG21 4EB, United Kingdom
Tel.: (44) 1256 377200
Agriculture Financing & Leasing Services
S.I.C.: 6211
N.A.I.C.S.: 523999

Immoparibas Royale-Neuve SA **(1)**
Ave de la Porte-Neuve 21
2227 Luxembourg, Luxembourg
Tel.: (352) 26962000
Fax: (352) 26969700
Investment Management Services
S.I.C.: 6799
N.A.I.C.S.: 523920

Insinger de Beaufort Asset Management NV **(1)**
Herengracht 537
1017 BV Amsterdam, Netherlands
Tel.: (31) 20 5215 000
Fax: (31) 20 5215 009
Asset Management Services
S.I.C.: 6282
N.A.I.C.S.: 523920

Insinger de Beaufort Associates BV **(1)**
Parklaan 60
Eindhoven, 5613 BH, Netherlands
Tel.: (31) 402655255
Fax: (31) 20 5215009
Investment Management Services
S.I.C.: 6282
N.A.I.C.S.: 523920

Insinger de Beaufort Consulting BV **(1)**
Herengracht 537
Amsterdam, 1017 BV, Netherlands
Tel.: (31) 205215450
Fax: (31) 168 419511
Investment Management Services
S.I.C.: 6282
N.A.I.C.S.: 523920

Kanizsa 2002 Kft. **(1)**
Europa Tanacs Utca 2
Nagykanizsa, 8800, Hungary
Tel.: (36) 93537700
Real Estate Management Services
S.I.C.: 6531
N.A.I.C.S.: 531390

Klecar Foncier Espana SA **(1)**
Avenida de La Vega 1 - Ed 1 Plt P Arroyo Vega
Alcobendas, 28108, Spain
Tel.: (34) 914532308
Real Estate Development Services
S.I.C.: 6531
N.A.I.C.S.: 531390

Klein Haneveld Consulting BV **(1)**
Herengracht 537
Amsterdam, 1017 BV, Netherlands
Tel.: (31) 205215450
Fax: (31) 70 3603909
Investment Advisory Services
S.I.C.: 6282
N.A.I.C.S.: 523930

KS Markedet **(1)**
Stoperigata 1
Oslo, 0250, Norway
Tel.: (47) 23123500
Real Estate Property Leasing Services
S.I.C.: 6519
N.A.I.C.S.: 531190

Le Sphinx Assurances Luxembourg SA **(1)**
Rue de Merl 74
2146 Luxembourg, Luxembourg
Tel.: (352) 26 89 03 21
General Insurance Services
S.I.C.: 6411
N.A.I.C.S.: 524210
Barbara Bavay *(Gen Mgr)*

Leveraged Finance Europe Capital V BV **(1)**
Fred Roeskestraat 123-1hg
Amsterdam, 1076 EE, Netherlands
Tel.: (31) 205771177
Securities Brokerage Services
S.I.C.: 6211
N.A.I.C.S.: 523120

LocaFit SpA **(1)**
Viale Della Liberazione 16/18
20124 Milan, Italy
Tel.: (39) 02 67 3331
Fax: (39) 02 67 333 400
Web Site: www.locafit.it
Financial Institution
S.I.C.: 6029
N.A.I.C.S.: 522110

Locatrice Italiana SPA **(1)**
Viale Della Liberazione 16/18
Milan, 20124, Italy
Tel.: (39) 02 67 33 31
Fax: (39) 02 67 33 32 89
Passenger Car Rental Services
S.I.C.: 7514
N.A.I.C.S.: 532111

Manitou Finance Ltd. **(1)**
34 Blackmoor Road
Verwood, Dorset, BH31 6BB, United Kingdom
Tel.: (44) 1202 825331
Fax: (44) 1202 813 027
Financial Planning Services
S.I.C.: 6282
N.A.I.C.S.: 523930

Meunier Hispania SA **(1)**
Calle Maria De Molina 54 - Plt Octava
Madrid, 28006, Spain
Tel.: (34) 914315074
Real Estate Management Services
S.I.C.: 6531
N.A.I.C.S.: 531390

Miskolc 2002 Kft. **(1)**
Vaci ut 178
1125 Budapest, Hungary
Tel.: (36) 46503000
Fax: (36) 46416121
E-Mail: Miskolcplaza@segece.hu
Web Site: www.miskolcplaza.hu
Commercial Building Leasing Services
S.I.C.: 6512
N.A.I.C.S.: 531120

Nerstranda AS **(1)**
Stoperigata 1
Oslo, 0250, Norway
Tel.: (47) 23213500
Fax: (47) 23 21 35 80
Real Estate Property Leasing Services
S.I.C.: 6519
N.A.I.C.S.: 531190

Nordbyen Senter AS **(1)**
Stoperigata 1
Oslo, 0250, Norway
Tel.: (47) 90 89 59 00
Real Estate Property Leasing Services
S.I.C.: 6519
N.A.I.C.S.: 531190

Norsk Kjopesenterforvaltning AS **(1)**
Stoperigata 1
0250 Oslo, Norway
Tel.: (47) 23 21 35 00
Fax: (47) 23 21 35 80
Real Estate Property Management Services
S.I.C.: 6531
N.A.I.C.S.: 531390

North Man Sverige AB **(1)**
Kyrktorget 19
Partille, 433 33, Sweden
Tel.: (46) 850899900
Real Estate Property Leasing Services
S.I.C.: 6519
N.A.I.C.S.: 531190

Omega Capital Europe PLC **(1)**
4th Floor 25-28 Adelaide Road
Dublin, Ireland
Tel.: (353) 1 605 3000
Fax: (353) 1 605 3010
Securities Brokerage Services
S.I.C.: 6211
N.A.I.C.S.: 523120
Brendan Roche *(Mgr)*

Omega Capital Investments Plc **(1)**
4th Floor 25-28 Adelaide Road
Dublin, Ireland
Tel.: (353) 1 605 3000
Securities Brokerage Services
S.I.C.: 6211
N.A.I.C.S.: 523120

Os Alle 3 AS **(1)**
Stoperigata 1
Oslo, 0250, Norway
Tel.: (47) 23213500
Fax: (47) 23 21 35 80
Real Estate Property Leasing Services
S.I.C.: 6519
N.A.I.C.S.: 531190

Paribas Asia Equity Ltd. **(1)**
Rm 63 1/F Ifc Two
Central, China (Hong Kong)
Tel.: (852) 21085600
Fax: (852) 229701362
Securities Brokerage Services
S.I.C.: 6211
N.A.I.C.S.: 523120

Partille Lexby AB **(1)**
Kyrktorget 19
Partille, 433 33, Sweden
Tel.: (46) 850899900
Real Estate Property Leasing Services
S.I.C.: 6519
N.A.I.C.S.: 531190
John Wilner Ivan Andersson *(Mgr)*

Phedina Hypotheken 2010 BV **(1)**
Reguliersdwarsstraat 90
Amsterdam, 1017 BN, Netherlands
Tel.: (31) 205215629
Securities Brokerage Services
S.I.C.: 6211
N.A.I.C.S.: 523120

Pinnacle Insurance plc **(1)**
Pinnacle House A1 Barnet Way
Borehamwood, Hertfordshire, WD6 2XX, United Kingdom UK (100%)
Tel.: (44) 20 8207 9000
Fax: (44) 20 8953 6222
E-Mail: info@cardifpinnacle.com
Web Site: www.cardifpinnacle.com
Emp.: 576
Insurance & Pension Funds
S.I.C.: 6371
N.A.I.C.S.: 524292
Gerard Binet *(Chm)*
Paul Glen *(CEO)*
Natalie Atkinson *(Chief Underwriting Officer)*

Non-U.S. Subsidiary:

Cardif Polska S.A. **(2)**
Pl Pilsudskiego 2
00 073 Warsaw, Poland (100%)
Tel.: (48) 225290123
Fax: (48) 225290111
E-Mail: cardif@cardif.pl
Web Site: www.cardif.pl
Emp.: 100
Insurance & Finance Services
S.I.C.: 6411
N.A.I.C.S.: 524298
M. Jan Rosciszewski *(Chm-Exec Bd)*

Pinnacle Underwriting Limited **(1)**
Pinnacle House A1 Barnet Way
Borehamwood, Hertfordshire, WD6 2XX, United Kingdom
Tel.: (44) 2082079250
Insurance Underwriting Services
S.I.C.: 6411
N.A.I.C.S.: 524298

PinnAfrica Insurance **(1)**
Pinnafrica Life Ltd Bldg B Curzon Pl
Turnberry Ofc Pk No 48
PO Box 98758
Bryanston, 2021, South Africa (100%)
Tel.: (27) 112441300
Fax: (27) 112441301
E-Mail: info@cardifpinnacle.co.za
Web Site: www.cardifpinnacle.co.za
Emp.: 30
Consumer Credits Insurance Services
S.I.C.: 6159

N.A.I.C.S.: 522298

PT BNP Paribas Securities Indonesia (1)
Menara BCA - 35th Floor Grand Indonesia
Jalan M H Thamrin No 1
Jakarta, 10310, Indonesia
Tel.: (62) 21 2358 6586
Fax: (62) 21 2358 7587
Web Site: www.bnpparibas.co.id/en/contact/contact.asp
Investment Banking Services
S.I.C.: 6211
N.A.I.C.S.: 523110

Pyrotex SARL (1)
AV J-F Kennedy 44
1855 Luxembourg, Luxembourg
Tel.: (352) 27848877
Investment Management Services
S.I.C.: 6282
N.A.I.C.S.: 523920

Reconfiguration BV (1)
Herengracht 450
Amsterdam, 1017 CA, Netherlands
Tel.: (31) 205554466
Asset Management Services
S.I.C.: 6282
N.A.I.C.S.: 523920

Sadyba Best Mall Sp zoo (1)
Ul Powsinska 31
02-903 Warsaw, Poland
Tel.: (48) 22 310 30 00
Fax: (48) 22 310 30 10
E-Mail: sadyba@segece.pl
Web Site: www.sadyba.pl
Shopping Mall Operator
S.I.C.: 6512
N.A.I.C.S.: 531120
Elzbieta Werner *(Gen Mgr)*

S.C BNP Paribas Real Estate Advisory S.A (1)
11 Ion Campineanu Street 6th floor 1st District
010031 Bucharest, Romania
Tel.: (40) 21 312 70 00
Fax: (40) 21 312 70 01
E-Mail: office.romania@bnpparibas.com
Web Site: realestate.bnpparibas.com.ro
Emp.: 20
Real Estate Advisory Services
S.I.C.: 6531
N.A.I.C.S.: 531390
Philippe Mer *(Pres)*
Alessandro Gallinella *(Mng Dir)*

Segece Ceska Republika SRO (1)
Plzenska 16/3217
Smichov, 150 00 Prague, Czech Republic
Tel.: (420) 257 090 600
Fax: (420) 257 320 495
E-Mail: ricepce@segece.cz
Web Site: www.segece.cz
Emp.: 40
Real Estate Property Leasing Services
S.I.C.: 6519
N.A.I.C.S.: 531190
David Pazitka *(Gen Mgr)*

Segece Espana SLU (1)
Avenida de la Vega 1 Edificio 1 3 planta
28108 Alcobendas, Spain
Tel.: (34) 91 453 23 70
Fax: (34) 91 453 23 20
Commercial Building Leasing Services
S.I.C.: 6512
N.A.I.C.S.: 531120

Segece Hellas Real Estate Management SA (1)
94 Vassilissis Sofias Avenue & 1 Kerasountos Str
115 28 Athens, Greece
Tel.: (30) 210 74 68 061
Fax: (30) 210 77 99 729
Real Estate Development Services
S.I.C.: 6531
N.A.I.C.S.: 531390
Thomas Aquizerate *(Gen Mgr)*

Segece Italia SRL (1)
Via Gadames 7
20151 Milan, Italy
Tel.: (39) 02 32113 1
Fax: (39) 02 32113 410
E-Mail: info@segece.it
Web Site: www.segece.it
Shopping Mall Management Services
S.I.C.: 6512
N.A.I.C.S.: 531120

Segece Magyarorszag KFT (1)
Vaci Ut 178
1138 Budapest, Hungary
Tel.: (36) 1 577 11 00
Fax: (36) 1 577 11 01
E-Mail: marketing@segece.hu
Web Site: www.segece.hu
Shopping Mall Management Services
S.I.C.: 6513
N.A.I.C.S.: 531110
Bout Frederic *(Mng Dir)*

Segece Polska SP. z.o.o. (1)
Al Armii Ludowej 26/9 C
00-609 Warsaw, Poland
Tel.: (48) 22 35 66 950
Fax: (48) 22 35 66 951
E-Mail: office@segece.pl
Web Site: www.segece.pl
Shopping Center Operator
S.I.C.: 6512
N.A.I.C.S.: 531120

Segece Portugal SA (1)
Avenida do Forte N 3 Edificio Suecia III - Piso 0
2790-073 Carnaxide, Portugal
Tel.: (351) 21 425 09 00
Fax: (351) 21 425 09 18
E-Mail: comercial@segece.pt
Web Site: www.segece.pt
Shopping Mall Management & Development Services
S.I.C.: 6531
N.A.I.C.S.: 531390

Non-U.S. Unit:

BNP Paribas CIB (2)
5 George's Dock IFSC
Dublin, 1, Ireland (100%)
Tel.: (353) 1 612 50 00
Fax: (353) 1 612 51 00
E-Mail: dublin.queries@bnpparibas.com
Web Site: www.bnpparibas.ie
Emp.: 580
Insurance & Finance Services
S.I.C.: 6411
N.A.I.C.S.: 524298
Derek Crummy *(Mng Dir)*

Stavanger Storsenter AS (1)
Stoperigata 1
0250 Oslo, Norway
Tel.: (47) 23 21 35 00
Fax: (47) 23 21 35 80
Real Estate Property Leasing Services
S.I.C.: 6519
N.A.I.C.S.: 531190

Steen & Strom Holding AB (1)
Vastra Tradgardsgaten 2
Stockholm, 111 53, Sweden
Tel.: (46) 8 508 99 900
Fax: (46) 8 508 99 901
Emp.: 350
Investment Management Services
S.I.C.: 6282
N.A.I.C.S.: 523920
Jan Ove Holmen *(Mgr)*

Storm Holding Norway AS (1)
Stoperigata 1
0250 Oslo, Norway
Tel.: (47) 23 21 35 00
Fax: (47) 23 21 35 80
Investment Management Services
S.I.C.: 6282
N.A.I.C.S.: 523920

Stovner Senter AS (1)
Stoperigata 1
0250 Oslo, Norway
Tel.: (47) 23 21 35 00
Fax: (47) 23 21 35 80
Real Estate Property Leasing Services
S.I.C.: 6519
N.A.I.C.S.: 531190

Szeged Plaza Kft. (1)
Kossuth Lajos Sugarut 119
Szeged, 6724, Hungary
Tel.: (36) 62553801
Fax: (36) 62 553 810
E-Mail: szegedplaza@segece.hu
Web Site: www.szegedplaza.hu
Commercial Building Leasing Services
S.I.C.: 6512
N.A.I.C.S.: 531120

Szolnok Plaza Kft. (1)
Vaci ut 178
Budapest, 1138, Hungary
Tel.: (36) 15771100
Fax: (36) 15771001
E-Mail: szolnokplaza@segece.hu
Web Site: www.szolnokplaza.hu
Emp.: 100
Shopping Mall Operator
S.I.C.: 6512
N.A.I.C.S.: 531120
Mardivirin Alphonse *(Mng Dir)*

Tasaciones Hipotecarias SA (1)
Calle Maria De Molina 54
Madrid, 28006, Spain
Tel.: (34) 914549700
E-Mail: operacionesvinculadas@tasacionesh.es
Web Site: www.tasacionesh.es
Agriculture Financing & Leasing Services
S.I.C.: 6211
N.A.I.C.S.: 523999

TEB Cetelem (1)
Yener Quarter Gayrettepe Sokak No 1 Floor 3-4
34349 Istanbul, Besiktas, Turkey (100%)
Tel.: (90) 212 355 2000
Fax: (90) 216 636 3900
E-Mail: info@tebcetelem.com.tr
Web Site: tebcetelem.com.tr/iletisim.aspx
Emp.: 77
Consumer Finance Services
S.I.C.: 6141
N.A.I.C.S.: 522291

TEB Tuketici Finansman AS (1)
Gayrettepe Mahallesi Yener Sok No 1
Besiktas, Istanbul, Turkey
Tel.: (90) 212 355 20 00
Fax: (90) 216 636 39 00
E-Mail: info@tebcetelem.com.tr
Web Site: www.tebcetelem.com.tr
Financial Management Services
S.I.C.: 6211
N.A.I.C.S.: 523999

Textainer Marine Containers Ltd. (1)
Century House 16 Par-la-Ville Road
Hamilton, HM HX, Bermuda
Tel.: (441) 296 2500
Fax: (441) 295 4164
Marine Cargo Container Leasing & Management Services
S.I.C.: 4491
N.A.I.C.S.: 488320

Thunderbird Investments PLC (1)
4th Floor 25-28 Adelaide Road
Dublin, Ireland
Tel.: (353) 1 605 3000
Fax: (353) 1 605 3010
Securities Brokerage Services
S.I.C.: 6211
N.A.I.C.S.: 523120

Torvbyen Senter AS (1)
Stoperigata 1
Oslo, 0250, Norway
Tel.: (47) 23213500
Fax: (47) 23 21 35 80
Real Estate Property Leasing Services
S.I.C.: 6519
N.A.I.C.S.: 531190

Torvbyen Utvikling AS (1)
Stoperigata 1
0250 Oslo, Norway
Tel.: (47) 23 21 35 00
Fax: (47) 23 21 35 80
Real Estate Property Leasing Services
S.I.C.: 6519
N.A.I.C.S.: 531190

Torvhjornet Lillestrom ANS (1)
Stoperigata 1
0250 Oslo, Norway
Tel.: (47) 23213500
Real Estate Property Leasing Services
S.I.C.: 6519
N.A.I.C.S.: 531190

Tour El Ghazal-BNPI (1)
Ring Fouad Chehab
Place Tabaris, Beirut, 1608, Lebanon (100%)
Tel.: (961) 1200600
Telex: BNPI 40316 LE
Fax: (961) 1200603
E-Mail: bnpi.liban@bnpi.com.lb
Web Site: www.bnpi-liban.bnpparibas.com
Commercial Banking Services
S.I.C.: 6029
N.A.I.C.S.: 522110

Turk Ekonomi Bankasi A.S. (1)
TEB Kampus C ve D Blok Saray Mah
Sokullu Cad No 7A-7B
Umraniye, Istanbul, 34768, Turkey
Tel.: (90) 2166353535
Fax: (90) 2166363636
E-Mail: info@teb.com.tr
Web Site: www.teb.com.tr
TEBNK—(IST)
Int. Income: $2,362,977,504
Assets: $25,740,210,074
Liabilities: $22,811,980,502
Net Worth: $2,928,229,572
Earnings: $323,127,771
Emp.: 9,288
Fiscal Year-end: 12/31/12
Banking Services
S.I.C.: 6029
N.A.I.C.S.: 522110
Yavuz Canevi *(Chm)*
Akin Akbaygil *(Deputy Chm)*
Jean-Paul Sabet *(Deputy Chm)*
Philippe Bernard Dumel *(COO & Asst Gen Mgr)*
Didier Van Hecke *(Chief Risk Officer)*

Subsidiaries:

Fortis Faktoring A.S. (2)
Buyukdere Cad No 100-102 Maya Akar Center B Blok
2 nci Zemin Kat No 7-8
Esentepe, 34394 Istanbul, Turkey
Tel.: (90) 212 337 68 00
Fax: (90) 212 337 68 99
E-Mail: info.tr@fortiscomfin.com
Web Site: www.fortiscomfin.com
Commercial Finance, Factoring, Credit Management, Debt Administration & Other Financial Services
S.I.C.: 6159
N.A.I.C.S.: 522298

TEB Faktoring Inc. (2)
Setustu Haktan
Merkezi No 39 1 Kabatas, 34427 Istanbul, Turkey
Tel.: (90) 2122935746
Fax: (90) 2122494479
E-Mail: tebfaktoring@teb.com.tr
Web Site: www.tebfaktoring.com.tr
International & Domestic Factoring Service Provider
S.I.C.: 6159
N.A.I.C.S.: 522293
Cagatay Baydar *(Gen Mgr)*

TEB Investment Securities, Inc (2)
Old Buyukdere Cad No 14
4 Park Plz Maslak, 34398 Istanbul, Turkey
Tel.: (90) 2123451111
Fax: (90) 2123450745
E-Mail: tebyatirim@teb.com
Web Site: www.tebyatirim.com.tr
Capital markets activities
S.I.C.: 6211
N.A.I.C.S.: 523110
Seyfettin Ata Koseoglu *(Gen Mgr)*

TEB Leasing Inc (2)
No 103 3 Mecidiyekoy
Buyukdere Cad Sarli Merkezi, Istanbul, Turkey
Tel.: (90) 212 393 69 00
Fax: (90) 212 252 55 01
Web Site: www.tebleasing.com
Financial Services
S.I.C.: 6099
N.A.I.C.S.: 522320
Kagan Living *(Gen Mgr)*

Non-U.S. Subsidiary:

The Economy Bank N V (2)
Prof W H Keesomlaan 5
Park Plaza K 5, 80670 Amstelveen, North Holland, Netherlands
Tel.: (31) 205039010
Fax: (31) 204260383
E-Mail: info@tebnv.nl
Web Site: www.tebnv.nl

BNP Paribas SA—(Continued)

Emp.: 50
International services to the Dutch Bank
S.I.C.: 6029
N.A.I.C.S.: 522110
Ozden Basaran Odabasi *(Mng Dir)*
Orkun Mungan *(Sr Dir-Mgmt Bd)*

UCB Ingatlanhitel RT **(1)**
Terez Krt 55-57 II Emelet
Budapest, 1062, Hungary
Tel.: (36) 1 238 9800
Fax: (36) 1 238 9801
E-Mail: info@ingatlanhitel.hu
Web Site: www.ingatlanhitel.hu
Mortgage Loan Brokerage Services
S.I.C.: 6163
N.A.I.C.S.: 522310

UCI Union de Creditos Imobiliarios **(1)**
Ave Eng Duarte Pacheco Torre 2 12 Andar Amoreiras
1070 102 Lisbon, Portugal (50%)
Tel.: (351) 213835000
Fax: (351) 2138350004
E-Mail: uci@uci.pt
Web Site: www.uci.com
Emp.: 60
Real Estate Credit & Finance Services
S.I.C.: 6159
N.A.I.C.S.: 522292
Pedro Megre *(Gen Mgr)*

UCI **(1)**
Calle Retama 3 Planta 7
Torre Ejesur, 28045 Madrid, Spain (100%)
Tel.: (34) 913373737
Fax: (34) 913373738
E-Mail: uci@uci.es
Web Site: www.uci.es
Emp.: 583
Mortgage Services
S.I.C.: 6163
N.A.I.C.S.: 522310
Roberto Colomer *(Gen Mgr)*

UEB (Switzerland) **(1)**
15 17 Quai Des Bergues
PO Box 1211
1211 Geneva, Switzerland (100%)
Tel.: (41) 229063002
Fax: (41) 229063012
Emp.: 600
Private Banking Services
S.I.C.: 6022
N.A.I.C.S.: 522190

Ukrainian Leasing Company **(1)**
8 Illinska Street Entrance 1 Floor 3
04070 Kiev, Ukraine
Tel.: (380) 44 501 35 91
Fax: (380) 44 501 35 95
E-Mail: office@ulc.com.ua
Web Site: www.ulc.com.ua
Financial Leasing Services
S.I.C.: 6159
N.A.I.C.S.: 522220

UkrSibbank **(1)**
2/12 Andriivska Str
Kiev, 04070, Ukraine
Tel.: (380) 44 590 06 90
E-Mail: info@ukrsibbank.com
Web Site: www.ukrsibbank.com
Commercial Banking Services
S.I.C.: 6029
N.A.I.C.S.: 522110
Camille Fohl *(Chm-Supervisory Bd)*
Jean-Adrien Lemierre *(Deputy Chm-Supervisory Bd)*
Viktor Pynzenyk *(Deputy Chm-Supervisory Bd)*

Subsidiary:

JSC Ukrsib Asset Management **(2)**
8 Illinska Str Entrance 5 3d Floor
Kiev, 04070, Ukraine
Tel.: (380) 44 537 50 74
Fax: (380) 44 5 37 50 74
E-Mail: funds@ukrsibfunds.com
Web Site: www.ukrsibfunds.com
Emp.: 20
Asset Management Services
S.I.C.: 6799
N.A.I.C.S.: 523920
Maxim Kuprin *(Chm-Mgmt Bd)*
Olena Korenyuk *(Deputy Chm-Mgmt Bd & Dir-Sls)*
Anna Tykha *(Deputy Chm-Mgmt Bd & Dir-Project Dev & Bus Support)*
Volodymyr Hryniv *(Deputy Chm-Mgmt Bd & Portfolio Mgr)*

Union Bancaire pour le Commerce et l'Industrie **(1)**
139 Avenue de la Liberte
1002 Tunis, Tunisia (50%)
Tel.: (216) 71842000
Telex: 14990
Fax: (216) 1849338
Web Site: www.ubci.com.tn
Private Banking Services
S.I.C.: 6159
N.A.I.C.S.: 522298

United European Bank & Trust (Nassau) Ltd. **(1)**
Scotia Bank Building 3rd Floor Bay Street
PO Box N-4883
Nassau, Bahamas
Tel.: (242) 3265935
Telex: 20596
Fax: (242) 3265871
Emp.: 9
Offshore Private & Commercial Banking & Trust Services
S.I.C.: 6029
N.A.I.C.S.: 522110
Denis Madaule *(CEO)*

Utexam Logistics Ltd. **(1)**
5 George's Dock IFSC
Dublin, Ireland
Tel.: (353) 1 612 5000
Fax: (353) 1 612 5100
Logistics Consulting Services
S.I.C.: 4731
N.A.I.C.S.: 541614

Vastra Torp Mark AB **(1)**
PO Box 200
Partille, 433 24, Sweden
Tel.: (46) 850899900
Real Estate Property Leasing Services
S.I.C.: 6519
N.A.I.C.S.: 531190

Vela ABS S.r.l **(1)**
Via Vittorio Alfieri 1
Conegliano, Treviso, 31015, Italy
Tel.: (39) 0438360926
Fax: (39) 0438360962
Investment Banking Services
S.I.C.: 6211
N.A.I.C.S.: 523999

Vela Home SRL **(1)**
Via Vittorio Alfieri 1
Conegliano, 31015, Italy
Tel.: (39) 0438360926
Fax: (39) 0438360962
Real Estate Management Services
S.I.C.: 6531
N.A.I.C.S.: 531390
Luigi Bussi *(Chm)*

Vela Lease SRL **(1)**
Via Vittorio Alfieri 1
Conegliano, Treviso, 31015, Italy
Tel.: (39) 0438360403
Financial Management Services
S.I.C.: 6211
N.A.I.C.S.: 523999

Viola Finanza SRL **(1)**
Via Vittorio Alfieri 1
Conegliano, Treviso, 31015, Italy
Tel.: (39) 0438360926
Fax: (39) 0438360962
Financial Management Services
S.I.C.: 6211
N.A.I.C.S.: 523999

Warranty Direct Ltd **(1)**
Quadrant House 20 Broad Street Mall
Reading, RG1 7QE, United Kingdom
Tel.: (44) 8450 521 175
Fax: (44) 8450 521 177
E-Mail: contact@warrantydirect.co.uk
Web Site: www.warrantydirect.co.uk
Automotive Insurance Coverage Services
S.I.C.: 6411
N.A.I.C.S.: 524298
Duncan McClure Fisher *(Mng Dir)*

Non-U.S. Affiliate:

Banque de Wallis et Futuna **(1)**
BP 59
98600 Mata-Utu, Wallis and Futuna
Tel.: (681) 72 21 24
Fax: (681) 72 21 56
Commercial Banking Services
S.I.C.: 6029
N.A.I.C.S.: 522110
Bertrand Creuze *(CEO)*

Non-U.S. Joint Ventures:

ERBE SA **(1)**
Rue De La Blanche Borne 12
6280 Loverval, Belgium
Tel.: (32) 71606060
Fax: (32) 71606070
E-Mail:
Web Site: www.cnp.be
Emp.: 20
Holding Company; Owned 53% by Frere-Bourgeois & 47% by BNP Paribas SA
S.I.C.: 6719
N.A.I.C.S.: 551112
Albert Frere *(Chm)*
Gilles Samyn *(Mng Dir)*

Subsidiary:

Compagnie Nationale a Portefeuille S.A. **(2)**
Rue de la Blanche Borne 12
6280 Loverval, Belgium
Tel.: (32) 71606060
Fax: (32) 71606070
E-Mail: cnp@cnp.be
Web Site: www.npm-cnp.be
Sales Range: $15-24.9 Billion
Emp.: 17,334
Holding Company
S.I.C.: 6719
N.A.I.C.S.: 551112
Gerald Frere *(Chm)*
Gilles Samyn *(Vice Chm & CEO)*
Roland Borres *(CFO)*
Jean-Charles d'Aspremont Lyden *(Chief Compliance Officer)*
Maximilien de Limburg Stirum *(Chief Investment Officer)*
Victor Delloye *(Gen Counsel)*

Joint Venture:

TRASYS S.A **(3)**
Tarhulpsestaanveg No C 1660
B 1200 Hoeilaart, Belgium BE
Tel.: (32) 27737111
Fax: (32) 27737900
E-Mail: info@trasys.be
Web Site: www.trasys.be
Emp.: 600
IT & Software Business Support Services
S.I.C.: 7371
N.A.I.C.S.: 541511
Chris de Hous *(CEO)*
Philippe Mestdag *(CFO)*

Non-U.S. Subsidiaries:

TRASYS Greece **(4)**
3 Arkadias St
11526 Athens, Attica, Greece
Tel.: (30) 2107769800
Fax: (30) 2107769801
E-Mail: info@trasys.gr
Web Site: www.trasys.gr
Emp.: 30
IT & Software Business Support Services
S.I.C.: 7371
N.A.I.C.S.: 541511
Phillip Mestbag *(CFO)*

TRASYS Luxembourg **(4)**
Route d'Arlon 283
8011 Strassen, Luxembourg
Tel.: (352) 261110
Fax: (352) 26111033
E-Mail: info@trasys.be
Web Site: www.trasys.lu
Emp.: 29
IT & Software Business Support Services
S.I.C.: 7371
N.A.I.C.S.: 541511
Pascal Desart *(Country Mgr)*

Subsidiary:

TRASYS Charleroi **(4)**
Terhulp Sesteenwg 6C
1560 Hoeilaart, Belgium BE
Tel.: (32) 71378211
Fax: (32) 78931400
E-Mail: info@trasys.be
Web Site: www.trasys.be
Emp.: 130
IT & Software Business Support Services
S.I.C.: 7371
N.A.I.C.S.: 541511
Chris De Hous *(CEO, Pres & Gen Mgr)*

Non-U.S. Subsidiary:

Agesca Nederland NV **(3)**
Veerkade 5
3016 DE Rotterdam, Netherlands NL
Tel.: (31) 102183703
Fax: (31) 10414938
E-Mail: patricia.ottervanger@agesca.eu
Holding Company
S.I.C.: 6719
N.A.I.C.S.: 551112

Joint Venture:

Parjointco N.V. **(4)**
Veerkade 5
Rotterdam, 3016DE, Netherlands NL
Tel.: (31) 4139154
Fax: (31) 4149384
Holding Company; Joint Venture Between Power Financial Europe BV and Agesca Netherland NV
S.I.C.: 6719
N.A.I.C.S.: 551112

Non-U.S. Holding:

Pargesa Holding S.A. **(5)**
11 Grand Rue
CH 1204 Geneva, Switzerland
Tel.: (41) 228177777
Fax: (41) 228177770
E-Mail: info@pargesa.ch
Web Site: www.pargesa.ch
PARG—(SWX)
Rev.: $5,305,289,528
Assets: $23,687,296,380
Liabilities: $6,399,180,348
Net Worth: $17,288,116,032
Earnings: $1,098,100,168
Emp.: 17,000
Fiscal Year-end: 12/31/12
Holding Company
S.I.C.: 6719
N.A.I.C.S.: 551112
Paul Desmarais, Jr. *(Chm)*
Andre de Pfyffer *(Vice Chm)*
Paul Desmarais, Jr. *(Vice Chm)*
Baron Frere *(Vice Chm)*
Gerald Frere *(Vice Chm)*
Arnaud Vial *(Mng Dir)*
Andrew Allender *(Deputy Mng Dir & Fin Dir)*
Fabienne Rudaz Bovard *(Treas)*

Non-U.S. Subsidiary:

Entremont S.A. **(3)**
25 Faubourg Des Balmettes
BP 29
F 74001 Annecy, Cedex 1, France
Tel.: (33) 450337474
Telex: 385063 f
Fax: (33) 450337450
Web Site: www.entremont.fr
Emp.: 3,700
Producer of Cheese
Import Export
S.I.C.: 2022
N.A.I.C.S.: 311513
Jacque Entremont *(Pres & Gen Dir)*

BNP RESOURCES INC.

Sun Life Plaza 144- 4th Avenue S W
Suite 1600
Calgary, AB, T2P 3N4, Canada
Tel.: (403) 695-1090
Fax: (403) 265-0413
E-Mail: info@bnpresources.com
Web Site: www.bnpresources.com
Year Founded: 2005
BNX.A—(TSXV)
Rev.: $53,357
Assets: $1,113,716
Liabilities: $1,293,091
Net Worth: ($179,375)
Earnings: ($602,251)
Emp.: 1
Fiscal Year-end: 12/31/12

Business Description:
Oil & Gas Exploration Services
S.I.C.: 1389
N.A.I.C.S.: 213112
Personnel:
Gregory Bilcox *(Pres & CEO)*
Toby Schulz *(CFO & Sec)*
Board of Directors:
Gregory Bilcox
John Brown
James E. Doody
Transfer Agent:
Computershare Trust Company
Calgary, AB, Canada

BNR UDYOG LTD.

218 Maheshwari Chambers 6-35-650
Somajiguda, Hyderabad, Andhra Pradesh, 500082, India
Tel.: (91) 40 23375791
E-Mail: info@bnrul.com
Web Site: www.bnrul.com
530809—(BOM)
Business Description:
Medical Transcription Services
S.I.C.: 8099
N.A.I.C.S.: 621999
Personnel:
B. N. Rathi *(Chm)*
Kamal Rathi *(Mng Dir)*
Board of Directors:
B. N. Rathi
T. Bharadwaj
B. Priyadarshini
J. Vikramdev Rao
Kamal Rathi

BOA GROUP S.A.

(d/b/a Groupe Bank of Africa)
Avenue Cheick Zayed Hamdallaye
Immeuble Tomota
BP E 3291
Bamako, Mali
Tel.: (223) 229 4829
Fax: (223) 229 4830
E-Mail: information@boaholding.com
Web Site: www.boaholding.com
Year Founded: 1988
Sales Range: $400-449.9 Million
Emp.: 4,000
Business Description:
Bank Holding Company
S.I.C.: 6712
N.A.I.C.S.: 551111
Personnel:
Mohamed Bennani *(Chm & Mng Dir)*
Board of Directors:
Mohamed Bennani
Driss Benjelloun
Brahim Benjelloun-Touimi
Paulin Laurent Cossi
Laurent Demay
Paul Derreumaux
Azeddine Guessous
Ramz Hamzaoui
Bernardus A.M. Zwinkels

Affiliate:

Bank of Africa - Mali **(1)**
418 Avenue de la Marne
BP 2249
Bozola, Bamako, Mali ML
Tel.: (223) 2070 0500 (20.43%)
Fax: (223) 2070 0560
E-Mail: information@boamali.com
Web Site: www.boamali.com
Sales Range: $25-49.9 Million
Emp.: 300
Retail & Commercial Banking
S.I.C.: 6029
N.A.I.C.S.: 522110
Paul Derreumaux *(Chm)*
Mamadou Sene *(Mng Dir)*

Non-U.S. Affiliates:

Bank of Africa - Benin **(1)**
Avenue Jean-Paul II 08
BP 0879
Cotonou, Benin (14.43%)
Tel.: (229) 2131 3228
Fax: (229) 2131 3117
E-Mail: information@boabenin.com
Web Site: www.boabenin.com
Sales Range: $75-99.9 Million
Emp.: 413
Retail & Commercial Banking
S.I.C.: 6029
N.A.I.C.S.: 522110
Paulin Laurent Cossi *(Chm)*
Cheikh Tidiane N'diaye *(Mng Dir)*

Bank of Africa - Burkina Faso **(1)**
770 Avenue du President Aboubacar Sangoule Lamizana 01
BP 1319
Ouagadougou, 01, Burkina Faso
Tel.: (226) 50308870
Fax: (226) 5030 8874
E-Mail: information@boaburkinafaso.com
Web Site: www.boaburkinafaso.com
Sales Range: $25-49.9 Million
Emp.: 195
Retail & Commercial Banking
S.I.C.: 6029
N.A.I.C.S.: 522110
Lassine Diawara *(Chm)*
Laurent R. Basque *(Mng Dir)*

Bank of Africa - Cote d'Ivoire **(1)**
Angle Avenue Terrasson de Fougeres Rue Gourgas 01
BP 4132
Abidjan, 01, Cote d'Ivoire (7.19%)
Tel.: (225) 2030 3400
Fax: (225) 2030 3401
E-Mail: information@boacoteivoire.com
Web Site: www.boacoteivoire.com
Sales Range: $25-49.9 Million
Emp.: 206
Retail & Commercial Banking
S.I.C.: 6029
N.A.I.C.S.: 522110
Paul Derreumaux *(Chm)*
Lala Moulaye *(Mng Dir)*

Bank of Africa - Kenya Ltd. **(1)**
Reinsurance Plaza Taifa Road
PO Box 69562
400 Nairobi, Kenya KE
Tel.: (254) 20 327 5000 (10%)
Fax: (254) 20 221 4166
E-Mail: headoffice@boakenya.com
Web Site: www.boakenya.com
Int. Income: $85,680,475
Assets: $703,661,075
Liabilities: $634,334,456
Net Worth: $69,326,619
Earnings: $8,552,184
Emp.: 216
Fiscal Year-end: 12/31/12
Retail & Commercial Banking
S.I.C.: 6029
N.A.I.C.S.: 522110
Kwame Ahadzi *(Mng Dir)*
Jean-Geo Pastouret *(Deputy Mng Dir)*
Anne Gitau *(Sec)*

Non-U.S. Affiliates:

Bank of Africa - Tanzania Limited **(2)**
NDC Development House Ohio Street/ Kivukoni Front
PO Box 3054
Dar es Salaam, Tanzania TZ
Tel.: (255) 222110104 (34.14%)
Fax: (255) 222113740
E-Mail: boa@boatanzania.com
Web Site: www.boatanzania.com
Sales Range: $10-24.9 Million
Emp.: 201
Retail & Commercial Banking
S.I.C.: 6029
N.A.I.C.S.: 522110
Fulgence Kazaura *(Chm)*
Kobby Andah *(Mng Dir)*

Bank of Africa - Uganda Ltd. **(2)**
Bank of Africa House Plot 45 Jinja Road
PO Box 2750
Kampala, Uganda UG
Tel.: (256) 414230436 (50.01%)
Fax: (256) 414 230 902
E-Mail: boa@boa-uganda.com
Web Site: www.boa-uganda.com
Emp.: 287
Retail & Commercial Banking
S.I.C.: 6029
N.A.I.C.S.: 522110
John Carruthers *(Chm)*
Edigold Monday *(Mng Dir)*
Rehmah Nabunya *(Sec)*

Bank of Africa - Madagascar **(1)**
2 Place de l'Independance
BP 183
Antananarivo, 101, Madagascar
Tel.: (261) 2022 391 00
Fax: (261) 2022 294 08
E-Mail: boa@boa.mg
Web Site: www.boa.mg
Sales Range: $50-74.9 Million
Emp.: 874
Retail & Commercial Banking
S.I.C.: 6029
N.A.I.C.S.: 522110
Paul Derreumaux *(Chm)*
Jacques Dilet *(Mng Dir)*

BOADICEA RESOURCES LIMITED

Suite 2 25 Koornang Road
Carnegie, VIC, 3163, Australia
Tel.: (61) 3 9569 3467
Fax: (61) 3 9572 3762
Web Site: www.boadicearesources.com.au
BOA—(ASX)
Business Description:
Gold Exploration
S.I.C.: 1041
N.A.I.C.S.: 212221
Personnel:
Clarke Dudley *(Chm & CEO)*
Board of Directors:
Clarke Dudley
Nicholas Kempton
Eugene Odachowski

BOAI NKY PHARMACEUTICALS LTD.

(d/b/a NKY)
9 Zhongshan Road
Boai, Jiaozuo, Henan, 454450, China
Tel.: (86) 391 8696320
Fax: (86) 391 8692950
E-Mail: sales@china-pvp.com
Web Site: www.china-pvp.com
300109—(CHIN)
Emp.: 400
Business Description:
Polymers for Pharmaceuticals & Personal Care Products Mfr
S.I.C.: 2899
N.A.I.C.S.: 325998
Personnel:
Haijiang Yang *(Chm)*

Subsidiary:

Tianjin Boai NKY International Ltd **(1)**
Suites 1808-9 Guohua Building 857 Dagu-Nan Road
Hexi District, Tianjin, 300200, China
Tel.: (86) 22 58316066
Fax: (86) 22 58316068
E-Mail: sales@china-pvp.com
Web Site: www.china-pvp.com
Polymers Mfr
S.I.C.: 3081
N.A.I.C.S.: 326113

BOARDROOM LIMITED

50 Raffles Place 32-01 Singapore Land Tower
Singapore, 048623, Singapore
Tel.: (65) 65365355
Fax: (65) 65361360
Web Site: www.boardroomlimited.com
B10—(SES)
Rev.: $49,683,000
Assets: $82,601,971
Liabilities: $30,796,639
Net Worth: $51,805,333
Earnings: $6,486,664
Emp.: 500
Fiscal Year-end: 06/30/13
Business Description:
Accounting & Payroll Services
S.I.C.: 8721
N.A.I.C.S.: 541214
Personnel:
Kim Poh Jin Teo *(CEO)*
Soon Keong Cheng *(CFO)*
Rhett Tregunna *(CEO-Boardroom Pty Limited)*
San-Ju Tan *(Sec)*
Board of Directors:
Geok Khim Goh
Christopher Grubb
Spencer Tien Chye Lee
Lye Mun Mak
Cheok Lim Sim
Sebastian Cher Liang Tan
Kim Poh Jin Teo
Thomas Liang Huat Teo
William Tien Leong Wong

Subsidiaries:

Boardroom Business Solutions Pte. Ltd. **(1)**
50 Raffles Place #32-01 Singapore Land Tower
Singapore, 048023, Singapore
Tel.: (65) 65364866
Fax: (65) 65361360
Web Site: www.boardroomltd.com
Emp.: 200
Accounting Services
S.I.C.: 8721
N.A.I.C.S.: 541219

Boardroom Communications Pte. Ltd. **(1)**
50 Raffles St Hecks 32-01 Singapore Lane Tower
Singapore, 048623, Singapore
Tel.: (65) 62309798
Fax: (65) 65321633
Web Site: www.boardroomlimited.com
Emp.: 250
Business Consulting Services
S.I.C.: 8748
N.A.I.C.S.: 541618
Kin Teo *(CEO)*

Non-U.S. Subsidiaries:

Boardroom Corporate Services (HK) Limited **(1)**
12th Floor The Lee Gardens
33 Hysan Avenue
Causeway Bay, China (Hong Kong)
Tel.: (852) 2598 5234
Fax: (852) 2598 7500
Accounting & Payroll Services
S.I.C.: 8721
N.A.I.C.S.: 541214
Patrick Ming Hon Fu *(COO)*

Boardroom Corporate Services (Johor) Sdn Bhd **(1)**
Suite 7E Level 7 Menara Ansar
65 Jalan Trus
80000 Johor Bahru, Malaysia
Tel.: (60) 7 222 5615
Fax: (60) 7 221 0891
Accounting & Payroll Services
S.I.C.: 8721
N.A.I.C.S.: 541214

Boardroom Corporate Service (KL) Sdn. Bhd. **(1)**
Lot 6.05 Level 6 KPMG Tower 8 First Avenue Bandar Utama
47800 Petaling Jaya, Selangor Darul Ehsan, Malaysia
Tel.: (60) 377201188
Fax: (60) 377201111
Web Site: www.boardroomlimited.com
Emp.: 30
Accounting & Trade Support Services
S.I.C.: 8721
N.A.I.C.S.: 541219

Boardroom Limited—(Continued)

Samantha Yit Chan Tai *(Mng Dir)*

Boardroom Corporate Services (Penang) Sdn Bhd (1)
Suite 2-1 2nd Floor Menara Penang Garden 42A
10050 Penang, Malaysia
Tel.: (60) 4 229 4390
Fax: (60) 4 226 5860
E-Mail: tze-en.ong@boardroomlimited.com
Web Site: www.boardroomlimited.com
Emp.: 15
Accounting & Payroll Services
S.I.C.: 8721
N.A.I.C.S.: 541214

Boardroom LSC Beijing Limited (1)
Unit 404 Block B No 92A Jian Guo Road
Shimao Tower Chaoyang District
Beijing, 100022, China
Tel.: (86) 10 8580 9177
Fax: (86) 10 8580 9178
Accounting & Payroll Services
S.I.C.: 8721
N.A.I.C.S.: 541214

Boardroom LSC China Limited (1)
Unit 701 No 227 Huangpi Bei Road
Central Plaza Huangpu District, Shanghai, 200003, China
Tel.: (86) 21 6375 8100
Fax: (86) 21 6375 8101
Web Site: www.boardroomlimited.com
Payroll & Accounting Services
S.I.C.: 8721
N.A.I.C.S.: 541214
Rena Yi Ping Lim *(Exec Dir)*

Boardroom Pty Limited (1)
Level 7 207 Kent Street
Sydney, NSW, 2000, Australia
Tel.: (61) 2 9290 9600
Fax: (61) 2 9279 0664
Web Site: www.boardroom.com.au
Payroll & Accounting Services
S.I.C.: 8721
N.A.I.C.S.: 541214
Rhett Tregunna *(CEO)*

BOARDWALK REAL ESTATE INVESTMENT TRUST

(d/b/a Boardwalk Rental Communities)
1501 First Street Southwest Suite 200
Calgary, AB, T2R OW1, Canada
Tel.: (403) 531-9255
Fax: (403) 531-9565
E-Mail: investor@bwalk.com
Web Site: www.bwalk.com
Year Founded: 1984
BEI.UN—(TSX)
Sales Range: $400-449.9 Million

Business Description:
Real Estate Investment Trust
S.I.C.: 6726
N.A.I.C.S.: 525990

Personnel:
Sam Kolias *(Chm & CEO)*
Roberto A. Geremia *(Pres)*
William Wong *(CFO)*
Michael Guyette *(CIO & VP-Ops-Southern Alberta & BC)*
Dean Burns *(Gen Counsel & Sec)*
William Chidley *(Sr VP-Corp Dev)*
Van Kolias *(Sr VP-Quality Control)*

Legal Counsel:
Stikeman Elliott
4300 Bankers Hall West 888 3 Street SW
Calgary, AB, T2P 5C5, Canada

Butlin Oke Roberts & Nobles
100 1501 1 Street SW
Calgary, AB, T2R 0W1, Canada

Transfer Agent:
Computershare Trust Company of Canada
530 8th Ave SW 6th Floor
Calgary, AB, T2P 3S8, Canada
Tel.: (403) 267-6800
Fax: (403) 267-6529

BOART LONGYEAR LTD.

26 Butler Boulevard Burbridge Business Park
Adelaide, SA, 5950, Australia
Tel.: (61) 883758375
Fax: (61) 883758497
E-Mail: infoAP@boartlongyear.com
Web Site: www.boartlongyear.com
BLY—(ASX)
Rev.: $2,011,507,000
Assets: $2,250,738,000
Liabilities: $1,115,321,000
Net Worth: $1,135,417,000
Earnings: $68,164,000
Emp.: 9,162
Fiscal Year-end: 12/31/12

Business Description:
Drilling Equipment Mfr
S.I.C.: 3532
N.A.I.C.S.: 333131

Personnel:
Richard T. O'Brien *(Pres & CEO)*
Jeffrey Olsen *(CFO)*
Fabrizio Rasetti *(Gen Counsel, Co-Sec & Sr VP)*
Paul Wesley Blewett *(Co-Sec)*
M. Bradley Baker *(Sr VP-HR)*
Alan Sides *(Sr VP-Global Drilling Svcs)*

Board of Directors:
Barbara S. Jeremiah
Bruce Robert Brook
Roger A. Brown
W. Peter Day
Roy Alexander Franklin
Tanya D. Fratto
David McLemore
Peter St. George

Subsidiaries:

Boart Longyear Australia Pty Ltd (1)
26 Burbridge Business Park
Adelaide, SA, 5950, Australia
Tel.: (61) 883758375
Fax: (61) 883758498
E-Mail: infoat@boartlongyear.com
Emp.: 100
Mineral Exploration Services
S.I.C.: 1481
N.A.I.C.S.: 213115
Kent Hoots *(VP)*

Subsidiaries:

Aqua Drilling & Grouting Pty Ltd (2)
184 Holt Parade
Thomastown, VIC, 3074, Australia
Tel.: (61) 3 9464 2677
Fax: (61) 3 9464 2240
E-Mail: info_aus@boartlongyear.com
Mineral Exploration Services
S.I.C.: 1481
N.A.I.C.S.: 213115

Grimwood Davies Pty Ltd (2)
26-28 Leviathan Street
Kalgoorlie, WA, 6432, Australia
Tel.: (61) 8 9093 2058
Fax: (61) 8 9093 2633
E-Mail: infoap@boartlongyear.com
Web Site: www.grimwood.com.au
Emp.: 200
Mineral Drilling Services
S.I.C.: 1481
N.A.I.C.S.: 213115
Kent Hoots *(Gen Mgr)*

Boart Longyear Investments Pty Ltd (1)
919-929 Marion Rd
Mitchell Park, SA, 5043, Australia
Tel.: (61) 883758375
Fax: (61) 883770539
Mineral Exploration Services
S.I.C.: 1481
N.A.I.C.S.: 213115
Steve Singalli *(VP)*

Boart Longyear Management Pty Ltd (1)
919 Marion Rd
Mitchell Park, SA, 5043, Australia
Tel.: (61) 883758375
Fax: (61) 883758498
E-Mail: infoat@boartlongyear.com
Web Site: www.boartlongyear.com
Mineral Exploration Services
S.I.C.: 1481
N.A.I.C.S.: 213115
Kent Hoots *(VP)*

Corporate Headquarters:

Boart Longyear International Holdings Inc. (1)
2640 W 1700 S
Salt Lake City, UT 84104-4240 UT
Tel.: (801) 972-6430
Fax: (801) 977-3374
E-Mail: info@boartlongyear.com
Web Site: www.boartlongyear.com
Mfr. & Supplier of Tools & Equipment for Exploration & Mining
Import Export
S.I.C.: 1481
N.A.I.C.S.: 213115

Subsidiaries:

Boart Longyear Company Inc. (2)
10808 S River Frnt Pkwy Ste 600
South Jordan, UT 84095
Tel.: (801) 972-6430
Fax: (801) 977-3374
E-Mail: info@boartlongyear.com
Web Site: www.boartlongyear.com
Sls.: $148,951,008
Emp.: 600
Nonmetallic Mineral Services
Import Export
S.I.C.: 1481
N.A.I.C.S.: 213115
Kent BroadHead *(CIO)*
Fabrizio Rasetti *(Gen Counsel, Sr VP & Sec)*
Brad Baker *(Sr VP-HR)*

Division:

Boart Longyear Drilling Services (3)
605 Union Pacific Way
Elko, NV 89801
Mailing Address:
PO Box 2748
Elko, NV 89803-2748
Tel.: (775) 738-1980
Fax: (775) 753-9229
E-Mail: info@boartlongyear.com
Web Site: www.boartlongyear.com
Sls.: $11,400,000
Emp.: 170
Drilling Services
S.I.C.: 1381
N.A.I.C.S.: 213111

Prosonic Corporation (2)
27819 State Route 7
Marietta, OH 45750
Tel.: (740) 373-2190
Fax: (740) 373-5003
Mineral Exploration Services
S.I.C.: 1481
N.A.I.C.S.: 213115
Jim Mconbx *(Office Mgr)*

Non-U.S. Subsidiaries:

Boart Longyear Alberta Limited (2)
2442 South Sheridan Way
Mississauga, ON, L5J 2M7, Canada
Tel.: (905) 822-7922
Fax: (905) 822-8358
Mineral Mining & Drilling Services
S.I.C.: 1499
N.A.I.C.S.: 212399
Steve Deck *(VP)*

Boart Longyear BV (2)
Columbusweg 8
Venlo, 5928 LC, Netherlands
Tel.: (31) 77 850 5850
Fax: (31) 77 850 5851
Emp.: 15
Mineral Exploration Services
S.I.C.: 1481
N.A.I.C.S.: 213115

Subsidiaries:

Boart Longyear EMEA Cooperatief U.A (3)
Columbusweg 8
5928 LC Venlo, Limburg, Netherlands
Tel.: (31) 778505850
Mineral Exploration Services
S.I.C.: 1481
N.A.I.C.S.: 213115

Boart Longyear International BV (3)
Columbusweg 8
Venlo, Limburg, 5928 LC, Netherlands
Tel.: (31) 778505850
Fax: (31) 773960231
Mineral Exploration Services
S.I.C.: 1481
N.A.I.C.S.: 213115

Non-U.S. Subsidiaries:

BLI Zambia Ltd (4)
PO Box 703000
Ndola, Zambia
Tel.: (260) 212 65 0953
Fax: (260) 212 65 0954
Mineral Exploration Services
S.I.C.: 1499
N.A.I.C.S.: 212399

Boart Longyear GmbH & Co. KG (4)
Meininger Weg 14
Eiterfeld, Hessen, 36132, Germany De
Tel.: (49) 6672868500
Fax: (49) 6672868590
E-Mail: infode@boartlongyear.com
Emp.: 60
Mineral Exploration Services
S.I.C.: 1481
N.A.I.C.S.: 213115
Thomas Heinmann *(Gen Mgr)*

Boart Longyear S.A. (4)
Avda De Los Metales No 7
Leganes, 28914 Madrid, Spain
Tel.: (34) 916940011
Fax: (34) 916937620
E-Mail: infoes@boartlongyear.es
Web Site: www.boartlongyear.es
Diamond Core Mining Drills Mfr
S.I.C.: 3532
N.A.I.C.S.: 333131

Longyear South Africa (Pty) Ltd (4)
Sycade House Cnr 14th Avenue Hendrick Potgie
Florida, 1709, South Africa
Tel.: (27) 117679300
Fax: (27) 117679301
E-Mail: andre.heerden@boartlongyear.com
Emp.: 42
Mineral Drilling Services
S.I.C.: 1481
N.A.I.C.S.: 213115
Andre Heerden *(Gen Mgr)*

Boart Longyear Netherlands BV (3)
Columbusweg 8
Venlo, Limburg, 5928 LC, Netherlands
Tel.: (31) 778505850
Mineral Exploration Services
S.I.C.: 1481
N.A.I.C.S.: 213115

Boart Longyear Canada (2)
2088 Rte 106
Allison, NB, E1G 4K9, Canada
Tel.: (506) 858-9977
Fax: (506) 857-8456
Emp.: 20
Mineral Exploration Services
S.I.C.: 1481
N.A.I.C.S.: 213115
Raymond Leblanc *(Gen Mgr)*

Boart Longyear Drilling Products Company (Wuxi) Ltd (2)
Inside Of Baode Industrial Park No 55 Xinmei Road
New District, Wuxi, 214028, China
Tel.: (86) 51085342766
Fax: (86) 51085346036
Mineral Exploration Services
S.I.C.: 1481
N.A.I.C.S.: 213115

Boart Longyear Inc. (2)
1111 Main St West
North Bay, ON, P1B 8H6, Canada
Tel.: (705) 474-2800
Fax: (705) 474-2373
E-Mail: info@boartlongyear.com
Web Site: www.boartlongyear.com
Emp.: 250
Third Party Contract Drilling; Diamond Core Drilling Equipment Mfr

S.I.C.: 3541
N.A.I.C.S.: 333517

Boart Longyear Ltda. (2)
Ac cel callc 928 501
Huechurava, Santiago, Chile
Tel.: (56) 25207900
Fax: (56) 3616319
E-Mail: infochile@boartlongyear.com
Web Site: www.boartlongyear.com
Emp.: 30
Diamond Core Drilling Equipment Mfr
S.I.C.: 3532
N.A.I.C.S.: 333131
Luies Delsolar *(Mgr)*

Boart Longyear Limited (2)
49 Changlor Road Hai Ya
Mueang Chiang Mai, Chiang Mai, 50100, Thailand TH
Tel.: (66) 53203871
Fax: (66) 53 203 873
Emp.: 20
Mineral Exploration Services
S.I.C.: 1481
N.A.I.C.S.: 213115

Boart Longyear (NZ) Limited (2)
9 Rawson Way Takanini
Auckland, 2243, New Zealand
Tel.: (64) 92679100
Fax: (64) 92678100
Emp.: 120
Mineral Mining Services
S.I.C.: 1499
N.A.I.C.S.: 212399
Paul Currie *(Gen Mgr)*

Boart Longyear SAC (2)
Av Defensores Del Morro 2066 Chorrillos
Lima, 9, Peru
Tel.: (51) 12034200
Fax: (51) 12523899
E-Mail: infoperu@boartlongyear.com
Web Site: www.boartlongyear.com
Mineral Drilling Services
S.I.C.: 1481
N.A.I.C.S.: 213115

P.T. Boart Longyear (2)
Jl Suci No 12 B Rt 001 Rw 03 Kel Susukan Ciracas
Jakarta, Indonesia
Tel.: (62) 2187798007
Fax: (62) 21 8779 8006
Emp.: 100
Oil & Gas Drilling Services
S.I.C.: 1381
N.A.I.C.S.: 213111
Michael Mahony *(Gen Mgr)*

BOB BELL CHEVROLET LTD

3850 48 Ave
Camrose, AB, T4V 3Z8, Canada
Tel.: (780) 672-2355
Fax: (780) 672-4772
E-Mail: mwchevrolet@gmail.com
Web Site: www.mwchevrolet.com
Year Founded: 1988
Rev.: $15,010,868
Emp.: 20
Business Description:
New & Used Car Dealers
S.I.C.: 5511
N.A.I.C.S.: 441110
Personnel:
Will MClellan *(Mng Partner)*

BOBST GROUP S.A.

Route Des Faraz 3
1031 Prilly, Switzerland
Tel.: (41) 216212111
Telex: 454 821 BOB ch
Fax: (41) 216212070
E-Mail: investors@bobstgroup.com
Web Site: www.bobstgroup.com
Year Founded: 1890
BOB—(SWX)
Sls.: $1,363,936,684
Assets: $1,768,465,820
Liabilities: $1,168,579,764
Net Worth: $599,886,056
Earnings: $4,641,076
Emp.: 5,124
Fiscal Year-end: 12/31/12
Business Description:
Packaging & Printing Machines & Equipment Mfr & Distr
Import Export
S.I.C.: 3555
N.A.I.C.S.: 333244
Personnel:
Charles Gebhard *(Chm)*
Thierry de Kalbermatten *(Vice Chm)*
Jean-Pascal Bobst *(CEO)*
Attilio Tissi *(CFO)*
Santoro Joseph *(Treas)*
Markus Niederhauser *(Sec)*
Board of Directors:
Charles Gebhard
Ulf Berg
Thierry de Kalbermatten
Michael William Oliver Garrett
Alain Guttmann
Hans Rudolf Widmer

Divisions:

Bobst S.A. (1)
Case Postale
1001 Lausanne, Switzerland (100%)
Tel.: (41) 216212111
Fax: (41) 216212040
E-Mail: advertising.bobst@bobstgroup.com
Web Site: www.bobstgroup.com
Emp.: 2,000
Internal Subcontractor
S.I.C.: 3555
N.A.I.C.S.: 333244
Jean-Pascal Bobst *(CEO)*
Thomas Ehreiser *(CFO)*

Subsidiary:

Asitrade AG (1)
Niklaus Wengi Strasse 109
2540 Grenchen, Solothurn, Switzerland (100%)
Tel.: (41) 326442500
Fax: (41) 326442501
E-Mail: remo.trusser@bobs.com
Web Site: www.bobs.com
Emp.: 80
Mfr. of Machines for the Production of Single-Face Microflute Board & Laminators
S.I.C.: 3569
N.A.I.C.S.: 333999

U.S. Subsidiary:

Bobst Group North America, Inc. (1)
146 Harrison Ave
Roseland, NJ 07068-1239 (100%)
Tel.: (973) 226-8000
Fax: (973) 226-8625
Web Site: www.bobstgroup.us
Emp.: 100
Printing Presses & Electronic Equipment Mfr
S.I.C.: 5084
N.A.I.C.S.: 423830
Jean-Pascal Bobst *(CEO)*

Non-U.S. Subsidiaries:

Bobst (Africa & Middle East) Ltd. (1)
76 Rue 8603
Z I La Charguia I, 2035 Tunis, Tunisia (100%)
Tel.: (216) 71809001
Fax: (216) 71807004
Web Site: www.bobstgroup.com
Emp.: 45
Sale of Printing & Packaging Machinery
S.I.C.: 5084
N.A.I.C.S.: 423830

Bobst Brasil Ltda. (1)
Av Henri Bobst 401 Barrio da Ponte
CP 22
13250-000 Itatiba, Brazil (100%)
Tel.: (55) 145349300
Telex: 114 67 17
Fax: (55) 1145240058
E-Mail: zendas.dr@bobstgroup.com
Web Site: www.bobst.com
Emp.: 9
Printing & Packaging Machines & Equipment Sales
S.I.C.: 5084
N.A.I.C.S.: 423830
Dirceu Fumachi *(Mng Dir)*

Bobst Central Europe Limited (1)
Technicka 15
CZ 616 00 Brno, Czech Republic (100%)
Tel.: (420) 541191311
Fax: (420) 541191315
E-Mail: sales.cz@bobstgroup.com
Web Site: www.bobst.com
Rev.: $680,220
Emp.: 11
S.I.C.: 3541
N.A.I.C.S.: 333517
Libor Panus *(Gen Mgr)*

Bobst Group Benelux N.V. (1)
Kantorenpark Den Helder
Potvlietlaan 3, 2600 Berchem, Belgium (100%)
Tel.: (32) 32700450
Fax: (32) 32700468
E-Mail: sales.be@bobstgroup.com
Web Site: www.bobstgroup.be
Rev.: $44,829,200
Emp.: 35
Sales of Printing & Packaging Machinery
S.I.C.: 5084
N.A.I.C.S.: 423830
Ronnie Simon *(Mgr-Fin)*

Bobst Group Central Europe spol. s r.o. (1)
Technicka 15
616 00 Brno, Czech Republic
Tel.: (420) 5 4119 1311
Fax: (420) 5 4119 1315
Corrugated Paper Board Distr
S.I.C.: 5085
N.A.I.C.S.: 423840
Libor Panus *(Gen Mgr)*

Bobst Group Deutschland GmbH (1)
Mollsfeld 21
PO Box 40644
40670 Meerbusch, Germany (100%)
Tel.: (49) 21599190
Fax: (49) 2159919100
E-Mail: astrid.franzkne@bobstgroup.com
Web Site: www.bobstgroup.de
Emp.: 100
Sales & Service of Printing & Packaging Machinery
S.I.C.: 3555
N.A.I.C.S.: 333244
Astrid Franzkne *(Sec)*

Bobst Group Hong Kong Ltd. (1)
Rm 1706 17th Fl Olympia Plz 255 King's Rd
North Point, China (Hong Kong) (100%)
Tel.: (852) 28313333
Fax: (852) 28335828
Emp.: 8
S.I.C.: 3542
N.A.I.C.S.: 333517
Johnny Yang *(Gen Mgr)*

Bobst Group Iberica, S.L. (1)
C/Avila 112 2 B
8018 Barcelona, Spain
Tel.: (34) 93 343 37 99
Fax: (34) 93 476 30 30
Web Site: www.bobstgroup.es
Corrugated Board & Flexible Materials Distr
S.I.C.: 5085
N.A.I.C.S.: 423840

Bobst Group Italia S.p.A. (1)
Via Pisa 250
20099 Milan, Sesto San Giovanni, Italy (100%)
Tel.: (39) 2262381
Telex: 320 539
Fax: (39) 022440476
E-Mail: sales.it@bobstgroup.com
Web Site: www.bobstgroup.com
Emp.: 60
Sales of Printing & Packaging Machines & Equipment
S.I.C.: 5084
N.A.I.C.S.: 423830

Bobst Group Japan Ltd. (1)
6-1-1 Heiwajima TRC Center Bldg 8F
Ota-ku, Tokyo, 143 0006, Japan (100%)
Tel.: (81) 364042090
Telex: 25 22 579 BOBST J
Fax: (81) 364042151
E-Mail: sales.jp@bobstgroup.com
Web Site: www.bobstgroup.jp
Emp.: 20
Sales of Printing & Packaging Machines & Equipment
S.I.C.: 5084
N.A.I.C.S.: 423830

Bobst Group Latinoamerica do Sul Ltda (1)
Av Henri Bobst 401 - Bairro da Ponte
CP 22
13251-716 Itatiba, Sao Paulo, Brazil
Tel.: (55) 11 4534 9300
Fax: (55) 11 4524 0058
Corrugated Box Mfr & Distr
S.I.C.: 2653
N.A.I.C.S.: 322211

Bobst Group Latinoamerica Norte S.A. de CV, (1)
San Francisco 624 - Piso 1
Colonia Del Valle, 3100 Mexico, Mexico
Tel.: (52) 55 5340 0970
Fax: (52) 55 5340 0980
E-Mail: humberto.sanchez@bobst.com
Web Site: www.bobst.com
Emp.: 3
Corrugated Board & Paper Products Distr
S.I.C.: 5085
N.A.I.C.S.: 423840
Humberto Sanchez *(Gen Mgr)*

Bobst Group Malaysia Sdn. Bhd. (1)
Block D1 Level 3 Unit 23-3 jalan Pju 1/41
Dataran Prima
Aman Suria, 47301 Petaling Jaya, Malaysia (100%)
Tel.: (60) 378049281
Fax: (60) 378049255
Web Site: www.bobst.co.id
Emp.: 20
Sales & Service of Printing & Packaging Machinery
S.I.C.: 5084
N.A.I.C.S.: 423830

Bobst Group Polska Sp. Z o.o. (1)
ul Niciarniana 2/6
92-208 Lodz, Poland
Tel.: (48) 42 616 26 00
Fax: (48) 42 616 26 01
Web Site: www.bobstgroup.pl
Emp.: 2
Corrugated Board & Packaging Material Distr
S.I.C.: 5085
N.A.I.C.S.: 423840
Libor Panus *(Gen Mgr)*

Bobst Group Scandinavia ApS (1)
Hojnaesvej 81
2610 Rodovre, Denmark
Tel.: (45) 36 36 20 50
Fax: (45) 36 36 20 51
Web Site: www.bobstgroup.dk
Corrugated Board Distr
S.I.C.: 5085
N.A.I.C.S.: 423840
Craig Moran *(Dir-Bus)*

Bobst Group Singapore Pte Ltd (1)
Yishun Post Office
PO Box 194
Singapore, 917607, Singapore
Tel.: (65) 6353 8028
Fax: (65) 6353 8060
Web Site: www.bobstgroup.sg
Corrugated Board & Packaging Materials Distr
S.I.C.: 5085
N.A.I.C.S.: 423840

Bobst Group Thailand Ltd (1)
123 Suntowers Building A Fl 21-07
Vibhavadee-Rangsit Rd
Jomphon Jatujak, Bangkok, 10900, Thailand
Tel.: (66) 26 177 851
Fax: (66) 26 177 850
Web Site: www.bobst.co.th
Corrugated Board & Packaging Materials Distr
S.I.C.: 5085
N.A.I.C.S.: 423840

Bobst Group (UK & Ireland) Ltd (1)
Unit 10 Broad Ground Road
Lakeside, Redditch, B98 8YP, United Kingdom
Tel.: (44) 1527 519 700

Bobst Group S.A.—(Continued)

Fax: (44) 1527 519 701
E-Mail: sales.uk@bobstgroup.com
Web Site: www.bobstgroup.co.uk
Corrugated Board & Packaging Products Distr
S.I.C.: 5085
N.A.I.C.S.: 423840
Craig Moran *(Bus Dir)*

Bobst Group (UK Holdings) Ltd **(1)**
Ravensbank House Ravensbank Drive
Redditch, Worcestershire, B98 9NA, United Kingdom
Tel.: (44) 1527 519710
Fax: (44) 1527 519701
E-Mail: sales.uk@bobst.com
Web Site: www.bobst.com
Emp.: 6
Investment Management Services
S.I.C.: 6211
N.A.I.C.S.: 523999
Neil Eric Jones *(Mng Dir)*

Bobst Group Vostok LLC **(1)**
1st Kozhevnichesky Per House 6 Build 1 of 405
115114 Moscow, Russia
Tel.: (7) 495 933 01 01
Fax: (7) 495 933 01 02
Web Site: www.bobst.com
Emp.: 30
Corrugated Board & Packaging Materials Distr.
S.I.C.: 5085
N.A.I.C.S.: 423840
Victor Rashnikov *(Gen Mgr)*

Bobst Hong Kong Ltd. **(1)**
Rm 1706-07 17/F Olympia Plz 255 King's Rd
250 King's Road, North Point, China (Hong Kong) (100%)
Tel.: (852) 28313333
Fax: (852) 28335828
E-Mail: sales.hk@bobst.com
Web Site: www.bobst.com
Sales Range: $1-9.9 Million
Emp.: 9
Printing & Packaging Machinery
S.I.C.: 5084
N.A.I.C.S.: 423830
Yang Johnny *(Gen Mgr)*

Bobst India Private Ltd. **(1)**
Gut No 82 126 132 VK Amboli
Post Ambadvet Ghotawade
Taluka Mulshi, Pune, 412 108, India
Tel.: (91) 2039878000
Fax: (91) 2039878025
E-Mail: bobstind@vsnl.com
Web Site: www.bobstgroup.com
Emp.: 300
Equipment & Services for Packaging Manufacturers
S.I.C.: 3559
N.A.I.C.S.: 333249
Upendra Degnurkar *(Pres)*

Bobst (Latinoamerica Norte y Caribe) S.A. de C.V. **(1)**
San Francisco 624 col. Del Valle
03100 Mexico, Mezzanine, Mexico
Tel.: (52) 5553400970
Fax: (52) 5553400980
E-Mail: salesmx@bobstgroup.com
Emp.: 30
S.I.C.: 3541
N.A.I.C.S.: 333517

Bobst (SEA) Pte Ltd **(1)**
28 Canberra Dr
12 Fl Unit 20, Singapore, 768429, Singapore (100%)
Tel.: (65) 63538028
Fax: (65) 63538060
Emp.: 6
Sales & Service of Printing & Packaging Machinery
S.I.C.: 5084
N.A.I.C.S.: 423830

Bobst Services Ltd. **(1)**
123 Suntowers Bldg A Fl 21 Unit 2101
Viphavadee Rangsit Rd, 10900 Bangkok, Ladayo Jatujak, Thailand (100%)
Tel.: (66) 261778515
Fax: (66) 26177850
E-Mail: sale.th@bobstgroup.com
Web Site: www.bobst.com
Emp.: 10
S.I.C.: 3541
N.A.I.C.S.: 333517

Bobst (Shanghai) Ltd **(1)**
Unit 2502 Shanghai Square 138 Middle Huaihai Road
200021 Shanghai, China
Tel.: (86) 21 5774 3366
Fax: (86) 21 6375 6741
Corrugated Board & Packaging Material Distr
S.I.C.: 5085
N.A.I.C.S.: 423840

Bobst (Taiwan) Ltd. **(1)**
1st Floor No 12 Lane 361 Fu-Hsing N Road
Taipei, 105, Taiwan (100%)
Tel.: (886) 225147928
Fax: (886) 227184104
E-Mail: bobst@ethome.com
Web Site: www.bobstgroup.com.tw
Sales Range: Less than $1 Million
Emp.: 3
Sales & Service of Printing & Packaging Machinery
S.I.C.: 5084
N.A.I.C.S.: 423830
F. F. Chen *(Gen Mgr)*

General Vacuum Equipment Ltd **(1)**
Pilsworth Road
Heywood, Lancashire, OL10 2TL, United Kingdom
Tel.: (44) 1706 622 442
Fax: (44) 1706 622 772
E-Mail: sales.general@bobstgroup.com
Vacuum Web Coating Distr
S.I.C.: 5162
N.A.I.C.S.: 424610

Martin S.A. **(1)**
22 Rue Decomberousse
69628 Villeurbanne, France (100%)
Tel.: (33) 472147474
Telex: 300 549
Fax: (33) 478263998
E-Mail: martin@martin-corrugated.com
Web Site: www.martin-corrugated.com
Sls.: $218,088,000
Emp.: 650
Mfr & Distr of Machines & Equipment in Packaging & Printing
S.I.C.: 3555
N.A.I.C.S.: 333244
Daniel Gordan *(Dir-Ops)*

PT Bobst Group Indonesia **(1)**
Jl Panjang No 5 5Th Floor Suite 501
Wisma AKR
11530 Jakarta, Indonesia
Tel.: (62) 21 531 1050
Fax: (62) 21 531 1180
Corrugated Board & Flexible Materials Distr
S.I.C.: 5085
N.A.I.C.S.: 423840

Rotomec SpA **(1)**
Casale Asti Km 5
I 15020 San Giorgio, Monferrato, Italy
Tel.: (39) 01424071
Telex: 210371 rotmec i
Fax: (39) 0142806501
Web Site: www.valmetconverting.com
Emp.: 400
Mfr. of Laminating Machines, Rotogravure Printing Machines, Coating Machines
S.I.C.: 3553
N.A.I.C.S.: 333243

Schiavi S.p.A. **(1)**
Strada Della Bosella 14/16
29121 Piacenza, Italy (50%)
Tel.: (39) 0523493111
Fax: (39) 0523493352
E-Mail: info.schiavi@bobstgroup.com
Web Site: www.bobstgroup.com
Emp.: 50
Mfr & Sale of Machinery for Flexible Packaging
S.I.C.: 3565
N.A.I.C.S.: 333993

Steuer GmbH **(1)**
Schurwaldstrasse 15
73765 Neuhausen auf den Fildern, Germany
Tel.: (49) 7158 98 70 0
Fax: (49) 7158 98 70 48
Corrugated Board Mfr
S.I.C.: 2653
N.A.I.C.S.: 322211

BOCKSTAEL CONSTRUCTION LIMITED

1505 Dugald Rd
Winnipeg, MB, R2J 0H3, Canada
Tel.: (204) 233-7135
Fax: (204) 231-0979
E-Mail: bcladmin@bockstael.com
Web Site: www.bockstael.com
Year Founded: 1912
Rev.: $29,215,682
Emp.: 50
Business Description:
Construction Services
S.I.C.: 1542
N.A.I.C.S.: 236220
Personnel:
John P. Bockstael *(CEO)*
Larry R. Bockstael *(CFO & Dir-Bus Dev)*

BOCONCEPT HOLDING A/S

Morupvej 16
7400 Herning, Denmark
Tel.: (45) 7013 1366
Fax: (45) 9626 7216
E-Mail: boconcept@boconcept.com
Web Site: www.boconcept.com
BOCON B—(CSE)
Rev.: $185,073,348
Assets: $96,001,660
Liabilities: $54,873,809
Net Worth: $41,127,852
Earnings: $2,045,102
Emp.: 586
Fiscal Year-end: 04/30/13
Business Description:
Furniture Stores
S.I.C.: 5712
N.A.I.C.S.: 442110
Personnel:
Viggo Molholm *(Chm-Supervisory Bd)*
Ebbe Pelle Jacobsen *(Vice Chm-Supervisory Bd)*
Torben Paulin *(CEO & Member-Exec Bd)*
Hans Barslund *(CFO & Member-Exec Bd)*
Supervisory Board of Directors:
Viggo Molholm
Poul Braendgaard
Rolf Eriksen
Ebbe Pelle Jacobsen
Morten Windfeldt Jensen
Joan Bjornholdt Nielsen

BOCS BREMEN OVERSEAS CHARTERING AND SHIPPING GMBH

Martinistrasse 29
D-28195 Bremen, Germany
Tel.: (49) 421369115
Fax: (49) 4213691199
E-Mail: bocs.bremen@bocs.de
Web Site: www.bocs.de
Year Founded: 1990
Rev.: $98,737,452
Emp.: 1
Business Description:
Water Transportation Services
S.I.C.: 4449
N.A.I.C.S.: 483211
Personnel:
Ilse Fliege *(Pres)*

BODAL CHEMICALS LTD.

Plot No 123-124 Phase - I GIDC Vatva
Ahmedabad, Gujarat, 382 445, India
Tel.: (91) 79 2583 5437
Fax: (91) 79 2583 6052
Web Site: www.bodal.com
524370—(BOM)
Rev.: $98,909,843
Assets: $88,331,123
Liabilities: $78,945,990
Net Worth: $9,385,133
Earnings: ($4,324,529)
Fiscal Year-end: 03/31/13
Business Description:
Dyes Mfr & Distr
S.I.C.: 2816
N.A.I.C.S.: 325130
Personnel:
Suresh J. Patel *(Chm, CEO & Mng Dir)*
Mayur B. Padhya *(CFO)*
Ashutosh B. Bhatt *(Compliance Officer & Sec)*
Board of Directors:
Suresh J. Patel
Sunil K. Mehta
Ankit S. Patel
Bhavin S. Patel
Bipin R. Patel
Surendra N. Shah
Transfer Agent:
Sharepro Services (India) Pvt. Ltd.
416-420 4th Floor Devnandan Mall Opp. Sanyash Ashram Ellisbridge
Ahmedabad, India

BODARD CONSTRUCTION MODULAIRE

ZA Sud BP 24
85150 La Mothe Achard, France
Tel.: (33) 251062222
Fax: (33) 251062711
E-Mail: contact@bodard-construction.com
Web Site: www.bodard-construction.com
Sales Range: $10-24.9 Million
Emp.: 87
Business Description:
Modular Construction Products Mfr
S.I.C.: 3441
N.A.I.C.S.: 332312
Personnel:
Pascal Boutet *(Dir-Mktg)*

BODEGAS RIOJANAS, S.A.

Ctra Estacion 1-21
Cenicero, 26350 La Rioja, Spain
Tel.: (34) 941 45 40 50
Fax: (34) 941 45 45 29
E-Mail: info@bodegasriojanas.com
Web Site: www.bodegasriojanas.com
Year Founded: 1890
RIO—(MAD)
Sales Range: $1-9.9 Million
Business Description:
Wine Mfr
S.I.C.: 2084
N.A.I.C.S.: 312130
Personnel:
Luis Zapatero Gonzalez *(Chm)*

BODISEN BIOTECH, INC.

Room 2001 FanMei Building No 1
Naguan Zhengjie
Xi'an, Shaanxi, China 710068
Tel.: (86) 2987074957
Fax: (86) 2987074958
E-Mail: info@bodisen.com
Web Site: www.bodisen.com
Year Founded: 2001
BBCZ—(AIM OTCB)
Rev.: $8,055,958
Assets: $22,695,066
Liabilities: $2,789,366
Net Worth: $19,905,700
Earnings: ($16,369,802)
Emp.: 132
Fiscal Year-end: 12/31/12

Business Description:
Fertilizer, Pesticide & Insecticide Mfr
S.I.C.: 2879
N.A.I.C.S.: 325320
Personnel:
Lin Wang *(Chm, Pres & CEO)*
Junyan Tong *(CFO)*
Chuangjun Yang *(COO)*
Board of Directors:
Lin Wang
Bo Chen
Chenglin Guo
Qiong Wang

BODYCOTE PLC

Springwood Court, Springwood Close
Tytherington Business Park
Macclesfield, Cheshire, SK10 2XF, United Kingdom
Tel.: (44) 1625505300
Fax: (44) 1625505313
E-Mail: info@bodycote.com
Web Site: www.bodycote.com
Year Founded: 1953
BOY—(LSE)
Rev.: $928,306,662
Assets: $1,251,745,254
Liabilities: $455,151,378
Net Worth: $796,593,876
Earnings: $105,812,430
Emp.: 5,700
Fiscal Year-end: 12/31/12
Business Description:
Heat Treatment, Hot Isostatic Pressing, Metallurgical Coatings & Material Testing Services
S.I.C.: 3398
N.A.I.C.S.: 332811
Personnel:
Ute S. Ball *(Sec)*
Board of Directors:
Alan M. Thomson
John A. Biles
David F. Landless
Eva Lindqvist
R. Rajagopal
J. Vogelsang
Legal Counsel:
Herbert Smith LLP
London, United Kingdom
Eversheds LLP
Manchester, United Kingdom

Subsidiaries:

Bodycote Heat Treatments Ltd. **(1)**
Springwood Court Tytherington Business Park
Macclesfield, Cheshire, SK10 2XF, United Kingdom (100%)
Tel.: (44) 1625505300
Fax: (44) 1625505312
E-Mail: info@bodycote.com
Emp.: 50
Heat Treatment of Metal
S.I.C.: 3398
N.A.I.C.S.: 332811
Simon Blantern *(VP-Sls)*

Bodycote H.I.P. Ltd. **(1)**
Sheffield Rd
Sheepsbridge, Chesterfield, Derbyshire, S41 9ED, United Kingdom (100%)
Tel.: (44) 246260888
Fax: (44) 246260889
E-Mail: sales@hip-bodycote.co.uk
Web Site: www.hip.bodycote.com
Emp.: 60
Hot Isostatic Pressing
S.I.C.: 3398
N.A.I.C.S.: 332811
Paul Clouth *(Dir)*

Bodycote Metallurgical Coatings Ltd. **(1)**
Shakespeare St
Wolverhampton, West Midlands, WV1 3LR, United Kingdom (100%)
Tel.: (44) 1902452915
Fax: (44) 1902351917
E-Mail: sales.bmc@bodycote.co.uk
Web Site: www.mc.bodycote.com
Emp.: 35
Metal Coating & Electroplating
S.I.C.: 3471
N.A.I.C.S.: 332813
John Gust *(Acct Mgr)*

U.S. Subsidiaries:

Bodycote IMT Inc. **(1)**
155 River St
Andover, MA 01810-5923
Tel.: (978) 470-1620
Fax: (978) 475-2951
Metal Heat Treating Services
S.I.C.: 3398
N.A.I.C.S.: 332811

Bodycote International Inc. **(1)**
155 River St
Andover, MA 01810
Tel.: (978) 470-1620
Fax: (978) 475-2951
Web Site: www.bodycote.com
Sls.: $54,000,000
Emp.: 1,000
Metal Heat Treating
S.I.C.: 3398
N.A.I.C.S.: 332811
Ed Tenerini *(Pres)*

Subsidiaries:

Bodycote K-Tech, Inc. **(2)**
111 K-Tech Ln
Hot Springs National Park, AR 71913
Tel.: (501) 760-1696
Fax: (501) 760-1695
Web Site: www.ktech-ceramics.com
Emp.: 22
Metal Coating Mfr
S.I.C.: 2851
N.A.I.C.S.: 325510
Jeff Carr *(Gen Mgr)*

Bodycote Thermal Processing **(2)**
1975 N Ruby St
Melrose Park, IL 60160-1109 DE
Tel.: (708) 344-4080
Fax: (708) 344-4010
E-Mail: timotyh.veenbaas@bodycote.com
Web Site: www.bodycote.com
Emp.: 1,119
Heat Treating of Metal
Import Export
S.I.C.: 3398
N.A.I.C.S.: 332811
Darius Szczekocki *(Gen Mgr)*

Bodycote Thermal Processing **(2)**
12700 Park Central Dr Ste 700
Dallas, TX 75251 (100%)
Tel.: (214) 904-2420
Fax: (214) 904-2424
E-Mail: jeanne.clark@bodycote.com
Web Site: www.htna.bodycote.com
Emp.: 1,200
Heat Treatment of Metals
S.I.C.: 3398
N.A.I.C.S.: 332811
Stephen C. Harris *(CEO)*

Unit:

Bodycote Hot Isostatic Pressing **(2)**
155 River St
Andover, MA 01810-5923 (100%)
Tel.: (978) 470-1620
Fax: (978) 475-2951
E-Mail: admund@bodycote.com
Web Site: www.na.bodycote.com
Emp.: 70
Hot Isostatic Pressing
S.I.C.: 3398
N.A.I.C.S.: 332811
Ed Tenerini *(Pres)*

Non-U.S. Subsidiaries:

Bodycote Argentina SA **(1)**
Hipolito Yrigoyen Ruta 202 3288
San Fernando, Buenos Aires, Argentina
Tel.: (54) 1147460053
Fax: (54) 1147467800
Metal Heat Treatment Services
S.I.C.: 3398
N.A.I.C.S.: 332811

Bodycote Brasimet Processamento Termico S.A. **(1)**
Av Das Nacoes Unidas 11633 - Cj 163 - 16o Floor
04578-000 Sao Paulo, Brazil
Tel.: (55) 11 2755 7200
Fax: (55) 11 2755 7240
E-Mail: info.br@bodycote.com
Web Site: brazil.bodycote.com
Metal Heat Treatment Services
S.I.C.: 3398
N.A.I.C.S.: 332811

Bodycote CMK AB **(1)**
Gammelbackavagen 6
P O Box 431
SE 691 Karlskoga, Sweden (100%)
Tel.: (46) 58681055
Fax: (46) 58658515
E-Mail: info@bodycote.com
Web Site: mt.bodycote.com
Emp.: 45
Materials Testing Services
S.I.C.: 8734
N.A.I.C.S.: 541380

Bodycote Coating Centrum BV **(1)**
AE Venlo Groethofstraat 27
NL 5916 PB Venlo, Netherlands (100%)
Tel.: (31) 773559292
Fax: (31) 773513499
Web Site: www.mc.bodycote.com
Emp.: 120
Metal Coating & Electroplating
S.I.C.: 3471
N.A.I.C.S.: 332813
Cor Brugmans *(Mgr)*

Bodycote France **(1)**
Parc Technologique de Lyon
Ilena Park Bat B2
117 Allee des Parcs, 69792 Saint Priest, France (100%)
Tel.: (33) 437238200
Fax: (33) 437238201
Web Site: www.fbi.bodycote.com
Emp.: 30
Heat Treatment & Coating of Metals
S.I.C.: 3398
N.A.I.C.S.: 332811
Joel Perrissez *(COO)*
Guy Prunel *(Div Pres-WEG)*

Bodycote Hardiff B.V. **(1)**
Paramariboweg 45
7333 PA Apeldoorn, Netherlands (100%)
Mailing Address:
P.O. Box 7347
7301 BN Apeldoorn, Netherlands
Tel.: (31) 555426392
Fax: (31) 555423116
E-Mail: apeldoorn@bodycote.com
Web Site: www.plc.bodycote.com
Emp.: 25
Heat Treatment of Metals
S.I.C.: 3398
N.A.I.C.S.: 332811
Wim Gerritsen *(Mng Dir)*

Bodycote Hardiff GmbH **(1)**
Max-Planck-Str 9
86899 Landsberg, Germany
Tel.: (49) 8191 9179 0
Fax: (49) 8191 9179 13
E-Mail: landsberg@bodycote.com
Emp.: 21
Metal Heat Treatment Services
S.I.C.: 3398
N.A.I.C.S.: 332811
Christoph Berndes *(Plant Mgr)*

Bodycote Hardingscentrum BV **(1)**
Groethofstraat 27
5916 PA Venlo, Netherlands
Tel.: (31) 773559292
Fax: (31) 773559233
E-Mail: venlo@bodycote.com
Metal Heat Treatment Services
S.I.C.: 3398
N.A.I.C.S.: 332811
Cor Brugmans *(Plant Mgr)*

Bodycote Heiss-Isostatisches Pressen GmbH **(1)**
Kolbinger Str 7
83527 Haag, Germany
Tel.: (49) 8072 3754 0
Fax: (49) 8072 3754 25
Web Site: www.bodycote.com
Emp.: 38
Powder Metallurgical Component Mfr
S.I.C.: 3499
N.A.I.C.S.: 332117
Gerhard Huber *(Gen Mgr)*

Bodycote HIP GmbH **(1)**
Kolbinger Str 7
Haag Winden, D 83527 Munich, Germany (100%)
Tel.: (49) 807237540
Fax: (49) 8072375420
E-Mail: info.imt@bodycote.de
Web Site: www.hip.bodycote.com
Emp.: 40
Hot Isostatic Pressing
S.I.C.: 3398
N.A.I.C.S.: 332811
Elwart Gan *(Mng Dir)*
Wolfram Graf *(Mng Dir)*

Bodycote HIP NV **(1)**
Industriepark Noord 7
9100 Saint-Niklaas, Oost-Vlaanderen, Belgium (100%)
Tel.: (32) 37806800
Fax: (32) 37665164
E-Mail: bodycoteimt@bodycoteimt.de
Web Site: www.hip.bodycote.com
Emp.: 22
Hot Isostatic Pressing
S.I.C.: 3398
N.A.I.C.S.: 332811

Bodycote Hokezelo KFT **(1)**
Orczy Ut 46
Budapest, 1089, Hungary
Tel.: (36) 13138680
Fax: (36) 13339324
E-Mail: Budapest@bodycote.com
Web Site: www.bodycote.com
Emp.: 6
Metal Heat Treatment Services
S.I.C.: 3398
N.A.I.C.S.: 332811

Bodycote Hot Isostatic Pressing AB **(1)**
Stalvagen 1
PO Box 209
735 31 Surahammar, Sweden (100%)
Tel.: (46) 22034800
Fax: (46) 22033118
E-Mail: info.hip@bodycote.com
Web Site: www.bodycote.se
Emp.: 47
Hot Isostatic Pressing
S.I.C.: 3398
N.A.I.C.S.: 332811
Anas Zubair *(Mgr-Production)*

Bodycote HT S.r.o **(1)**
CTPark Brno Turanka 100
Slatina, 627 00 Brno, Czech Republic
Tel.: (420) 516 102 427
Fax: (420) 516 102 428
E-Mail: info-cz@bodycote.com
Web Site: www.bodycote.cz
Metal Treatment Services
S.I.C.: 3398
N.A.I.C.S.: 332811
Borys Bachraty *(Mgr)*

Bodycote IMT NV **(1)**
Industriepark Noord 7
9100 Saint-Nicolas, Belgium
Tel.: (32) 37773751
Fax: (32) 37665164
E-Mail: hip.belgium@bodycote.com
Web Site: www.bodycote.com
Emp.: 22
Metal Heat Treatment Services
S.I.C.: 3398
N.A.I.C.S.: 332811
Diego Bergantinos *(Gen Mgr)*

Bodycote Istas Isil Islem Sanayi ve Ticaret AS **(1)**
Taskahve Mevkii
Kemalpasa, Izmir, Turkey
Tel.: (90) 232 8770300
Fax: (90) 232 8770305
E-Mail: izmir@bodycote.com
Web Site: www.istasas.com.tr
Metal Heat Treatment Services
S.I.C.: 3398
N.A.I.C.S.: 332811

Bodycote Italia Srl **(1)**
Via Parini
Gorgonzola, 20064 Milan, Italy (100%)
Tel.: (39) 0295304218
Fax: (39) 0295302820
E-Mail: gorgonzola@bodycote.com
Web Site: www.fbi.bodycote.com

Bodycote plc—(Continued)

Emp.: 15
Heat Treating & Coating of Metals
S.I.C.: 3398
N.A.I.C.S.: 332811
Stefano de Donato *(Head-Technical Production)*

Bodycote Japan K.K. (1)
Nagoya Lucent Tower 40F 6-1 Ushijima-cho
Nishi-ku, Nagoya, Aichi, Japan 451-6040
Tel.: (81) 52 912 5518
Fax: (81) 52 569 4702
E-Mail: japan.sales@bodycote.com
Web Site: www.bodycote.co.jp
Metal Heat Treatment & Joining Services
S.I.C.: 3398
N.A.I.C.S.: 332811

Bodycote Lampokasittely Oy (1)
Vasaratie 2
Vaasa, 65350, Finland
Tel.: (358) 207 466 360
Fax: (358) 207 466 369
E-Mail: bodycote.vaasa@bodycote.fi
Emp.: 1
Metal Heat Treatment Services
S.I.C.: 3398
N.A.I.C.S.: 332811

Bodycote (Ningbo) Heat Treatment Co. Limited (1)
94 Xiayu Rd Jiangnan Community Industrial Zone Jiangdong North Road
Jiangdong District, Ningbo, Zhejiang, China
Tel.: (86) 574 87781519
Fax: (86) 574 87781520
Web Site: www.bodycote.cn
Metal Heat Treatment Services
S.I.C.: 3398
N.A.I.C.S.: 332811

Bodycote Polska Sp z.o.o (1)
Ul Handlowa 2
41-807 Zabrze, Poland
Tel.: (48) 32 273 82 74
Fax: (48) 32 273 82 75
E-Mail: zabrze@bodycote.com
Web Site: internet.bodycote.org
Metal Heat Treatment Services
S.I.C.: 3398
N.A.I.C.S.: 332811

Bodycote Polymer AB (1)
Studsvik Industriomrade
611 82 Nykoping, Sweden (100%)
Tel.: (46) 55221476
Fax: (46) 55263125
E-Mail: mtweb@bodycotemt.com
Web Site: www.mt.bodycote.com
Sales Range: Less than $1 Million
Emp.: 18
Materials Testing Services
S.I.C.: 8734
N.A.I.C.S.: 541380
Goran Lindstrom *(Mng Dir)*

Bodycote Rheintal Warmebehandlung AG (1)
Im Alten Riet 123
FL-9494 Schaan, Liechtenstein (100%)
Tel.: (423) 2374600
Fax: (423) 2392102
E-Mail: schaan@bodycote.li
Web Site: www.plc.bodycote.com
Emp.: 60
Vacuum Hardening, Vacuum Brazing, Carbonotriding & Carburizing
S.I.C.: 3398
N.A.I.C.S.: 332811
Karl Schrittwieser *(Grp Dir)*

Bodycote SAS (1)
Zi Les Granges
Ambazac, 87240, France
Tel.: (33) 555568513
Fax: (33) 555568551
Web Site: www.bodycote.com
Emp.: 25
Metal Heat Treatment Services
S.I.C.: 3398
N.A.I.C.S.: 332811
David Dublanche *(Gen Mgr)*

Bodycote Schweiz Warmebehandlung AG (1)
Steinackerstrasse 39
8902 Urdorf, Switzerland
Tel.: (41) 44 735 60 35
Fax: (41) 44 735 60 36
E-Mail: urdorf@bodycote.ch
Web Site: internet.bodycote.org
Metal Heat Treatment Services
S.I.C.: 3398
N.A.I.C.S.: 332811
Rene Sami *(Gen Mgr)*

Bodycote Singapore Pte Ltd (1)
7 Tuas Avenue 8
Singapore, 639222, Singapore
Tel.: (65) 6576 9888
Fax: (65) 6863 9022
Web Site: www.bodycote.com.sg
Thermal Spray Coating Services
S.I.C.: 3479
N.A.I.C.S.: 332812
Kenny Wong *(Gen Mgr)*

Bodycote Thermal Processing Canada, Inc. (1)
9 Shirley Ave
Kitchener, ON, N2B2E6, Canada
Tel.: (519) 744-6301
Fax: (519) 744-6347
Aerospace Equipment Mfr
S.I.C.: 3728
N.A.I.C.S.: 336413

Bodycote Tratamente Termice SRL (1)
Zizinului 119 Parc Industrial Carfil
500407 Brasov, Romania
Tel.: (40) 268 330 910
Fax: (40) 268 323 918
E-Mail: brasov@bodycote.com
Web Site: www.plc.bodycote.com
Metal Heat Treatment Services
S.I.C.: 3398
N.A.I.C.S.: 332811
Nicusor Ruscu *(Plant Mgr)*

Bodycote Trattamenti Termici SPA (1)
Via Carso 89
24040 Madone, Bergamo, Italy
Tel.: (39) 035 9956 11
Fax: (39) 035 9958 57
E-Mail: madone@bodycote.com
Emp.: 5
Metal Heat Treatment Services
S.I.C.: 3398
N.A.I.C.S.: 332811
Genesio Tresoldi *(Plant Mgr)*

Bodycote Varmebehandling A/S (1)
Herlev Hovedgade 15 A
DK 2730 Herlev, Denmark (100%)
Tel.: (45) 70150600
Fax: (45) 64461891
E-Mail: info@bodycote.dk
Web Site: www.bodycote.dk
Emp.: 16
Metal Heat Treatment & Coating
S.I.C.: 3398
N.A.I.C.S.: 332811
Ksinc Apahamshen *(Gen Mgr)*

Bodycote Varmebehandling AB (1)
Spadegatan 23
PO Box 124
S 42423 Angered, New Gothenberg, Sweden (100%)
Tel.: (46) 313321900
Fax: (46) 313319087
E-Mail: anders.larsson@bodycote.com
Web Site: www.bodycote.se
Emp.: 200
Heat Treatment of Metals
S.I.C.: 3398
N.A.I.C.S.: 332811
Goran Jonsson *(CEO)*

Bodycote Warmebehandlung GmbH (1)
Buchwiesen 6
D 73061 Ebersbach, Germany (100%)
Tel.: (49) 71631030
Fax: (49) 7163103401
E-Mail: info@bodycote.de
Web Site: www.ceg.bodycote.org
Emp.: 500
Heat Treatment of Metals
S.I.C.: 3398
N.A.I.C.S.: 332811
Jan Elwart *(Mng Dir)*

Bodycote Warmebehandlung Marchtrenk GmbH (1)
Linzer Strasse 108
A4614 Marchtrenk, Austria (100%)
Tel.: (43) 7243533150
Fax: (43) 72435331585
E-Mail: office@marchtrenk.bodycote.at
Web Site: www.bodycote.at
Emp.: 20
Metal Heat Treatment & Coating
S.I.C.: 3398
N.A.I.C.S.: 332811
Gerald Gerhartiter *(Gen Mgr)*

Bodycote Warmebehandlung Wien GmbH (1)
Hosnedlgasse 20
1220 Vienna, Austria
Tel.: (43) 1 25 83 54 1
Fax: (43) 1 25 91 68 8
E-Mail: wien@bodycote.com
Web Site: internet.bodycote.org
Metal Heat Treating Services
S.I.C.: 3398
N.A.I.C.S.: 332811

Bodycote Wuxi Technology Co. Limited (1)
No 6 Xiqin Road Wuxi National High-Tech Development Zone
Wuxi, Jiangsu, 214028, China
Tel.: (86) 510 88156388
Fax: (86) 510 88157388
Web Site: www.bodycote.cn
Heat Treatment Services
S.I.C.: 3398
N.A.I.C.S.: 332811
Tony Wu *(Dir-Ops)*

Bodycote Ytbehandling AB (1)
PO Box 47
641 21 Katrineholm, Sweden (100%)
Tel.: (46) 15077800
Fax: (46) 15077810
E-Mail: fredrik.hultgren@bodycote.se
Web Site: www.bodycote.se
Emp.: 35
S.I.C.: 1799
N.A.I.C.S.: 562910

Nitrion GmbH (1)
Georg-Hardt-Strasse 8-10
Otterfing, 83624, Germany
Tel.: (49) 80 24 47 70 0
Fax: (49) 80 24 47 70 30
Web Site: www.nitrion.com
Emp.: 35
Metal Heat Treating Services
S.I.C.: 3398
N.A.I.C.S.: 332811
Horst Schiff *(Mgr)*

Nitruvid SAS (1)
Zone Industrielle Du Val 9 Rue Jean Poulmarch
95100 Argenteuil, France
Tel.: (33) 130259515
Fax: (33) 130259516
Web Site: www.nitruvid.com
Metal Heat Treatment Services
S.I.C.: 3398
N.A.I.C.S.: 332811

Techmeta SA (1)
141 Route Des Machurettes
74370 Metz-Tessy, France
Tel.: (33) 4 50 27 20 90
Fax: (33) 4 50 27 33 18
Web Site: www.techmeta.fr
Emp.: 74
Electron Beam Equipment Mfr
S.I.C.: 3548
N.A.I.C.S.: 333992
Franck Oudot *(Gen Mgr)*

BODYPOWER SPORTS PLC

(d/b/a Fitness Superstore)
13 Gate Lodge Close
Round Spinney, Northampton, NN3 8RJ, United Kingdom
Tel.: (44) 1604 673000
Fax: (44) 1604 673001
E-Mail: sales@bodypower.co.uk
Web Site: www.fitness-superstore.co.uk
Year Founded: 1994
Sales Range: $25-49.9 Million
Business Description:
Fitness Equipment Retailer
S.I.C.: 5941
N.A.I.C.S.: 451110
Personnel:
Paul D. Walker *(CEO)*

BOE TECHNOLOGY GROUP CO., LTD.

10 Jiuxianqiao Rd
Chaoyang, Beijing, 100015, China
Tel.: (86) 1064318888
Fax: (86) 1064366264
E-Mail: pr@boe.com.cn
Web Site: www.boe.com.cn
Year Founded: 1993
000725—(SSE)
Sales Range: $900-999.9 Million
Emp.: 12,900
Business Description:
Semiconductors & Electronics Mfr
S.I.C.: 3674
N.A.I.C.S.: 334413
Personnel:
Dongsheng Wang *(Chm & CEO)*
Yanshun Chen *(Vice Chm & Pres)*
Yun Sun *(CFO & Sr VP)*
Xiaodong Liu *(COO & Exec VP)*
Yanjun Wang *(CIO & Exec VP)*
Youmei Dong *(CTO & Exec VP)*
Ying Song *(Chief HR Officer & Exec VP)*
Liqiong Feng *(Chief Counsel & Sr VP)*
Board of Directors:
Dongsheng Wang
Yanshun Chen
Ansheng Dong
Jianxin Geng
Jinghua Gui
Guojian Han
Guoping Ji
Xinqing Liang
Zhongcan Ouyang
Jiaheng Wang
Hanyuan Yuan

Subsidiaries:

Beijing BOE Chatani Electronics Co., Ltd. (1)
No 8 Xihuanzhong Rd
BDA, Beijing, 100176, China
Tel.: (86) 1067855825
Fax: (86) 1067855886
Flat Screen Products Mfr
S.I.C.: 3679
N.A.I.C.S.: 334419

Beijing BOE Optoelectronics Technology Co., Ltd. (1)
No.8 Xihuanzhong Rd
BDA, Beijing, 100176, China
Tel.: (86) 1067855688
Fax: (86) 1067855276
Web Site: www.boe.com.cn/en/Technology/Entering/glqy.asp
TFT Products Mfr
S.I.C.: 3679
N.A.I.C.S.: 334419

Beijing BOE Special Display Technology Co., Ltd. (1)
No 11 Di Ze Rd
BDA, Beijing, 100176, China
Tel.: (86) 1067821777
Fax: (86) 1067821755
E-Mail: wangwei2@boe.com.cn
Web Site: www.boe.com.cn/EN/Technology/Entering/glqy1.asp
Network Research & Development Services
S.I.C.: 8731
N.A.I.C.S.: 541712

Beijing BOE Vacuum Technology Co., Ltd. (1)
No 10 Jiuxianqiao Rd
Chaoyang, Beijing, 100015, China
Tel.: (86) 1084567146
Fax: (86) 1084567146
E-Mail: jiaojianwei@boe.com.cn
Web Site: www.hfboe.com.cn
Emp.: 380
Vacuum Electronic Products Mfr
S.I.C.: 3679

N.A.I.C.S.: 334419
Jian-wei Jiao *(Mgr-HR)*

BOE (Hebei) Mobile Technology Co., Ltd. (1)
Gu an Industrial Zone
Langfang, Hebei, 065500, China
Tel.: (86) 1064316698
Fax: (86) 10 58411555
Flat Screen Products Mfr
S.I.C.: 3679
N.A.I.C.S.: 334419
Xiaodong Liu *(VP)*

BOE Hyundai LCD (Beijing) Display Technology Co., Ltd. (1)
No 10 Jiuxianqiao Rd
Chaoyang, Beijing, 100015, China
Tel.: (86) 1064316698
Fax: (86) 1064325754
E-Mail: lxdong@boe.com.cn
Web Site: www.boe.com.cn/en/Technolo gy/Entering/glqy.asp
Emp.: 200
LCD Products Mfr
S.I.C.: 3679
N.A.I.C.S.: 334419
Xiaodong Liu *(Gen Mgr)*

BOE Land Co., Ltd. (1)
No 10 Jiuxianqiao Rd
Chaoyang, 100015 Beijing, China
Tel.: (86) 1059756288
Fax: (86) 1064389365
Web Site: www.boe.com.cn/EN/Technolo gy/Entering/glqy1.asp
Emp.: 300
Commercial Facilities Leasing Services
S.I.C.: 6512
N.A.I.C.S.: 531120
Grace Liu *(Mgr-Sls)*

BOE Semi-conductor Co., Ltd. (1)
No 10 Jiuxianqiao Rd
Chaoyang, Beijing, 100016, China
Tel.: (86) 1064371448
Fax: (86) 10 64372408
Web Site: www.boe.com.cn/EN/Technolo gy/Entering/glqy1.asp
Semiconductor Products Mfr
S.I.C.: 3674
N.A.I.C.S.: 334413

K-Tronics (Suzhou) Technology Co., Ltd. (1)
No 1700 Zhongshan North Road Songling Town
Wujiang, Jiangsu, 518000, China
Tel.: (86) 51263456336
Fax: (86) 51263456210
Liquid Crystal Displays Mfr
S.I.C.: 3679
N.A.I.C.S.: 334419

Suzhou BOE Chatani Electronics Co., Ltd. (1)
No 2 Haitang St
Suzhou Industrial Park Zone, Suzhou, 215021, China
Tel.: (86) 51287180800
Fax: (86) 51287180261
Web Site: www.boe.com.cn/en/Technolo gy/Entering/glqy.asp
Flat Screen Products Mfr
S.I.C.: 3679
N.A.I.C.S.: 334419

Xiamen BOE Electronics Co., Ltd. (1)
No 1 Xianghong St
Torch High tech Zone, Xiamen, 361101, China
Tel.: (86) 51287180800
Fax: (86) 51287180809
Web Site: www.boe.com.cn/en/Technolo gy/Entering/glqy.asp
LCD Products Mfr
S.I.C.: 3679
N.A.I.C.S.: 334419

Zhejiang BOE Display Technology Co., Ltd. (1)
E Renmin Rd
C 1 Bridge, Shaoxing, Zhejiang, 312000, China
Tel.: (86) 575 88648166
Fax: (86) 575 88645722
E-Mail: supply@zboe.cn
Web Site: www.zboe.cn
Monitor & Related Parts Mfr
S.I.C.: 3575
N.A.I.C.S.: 334118

Non-U.S. Subsidiary:

BOE (Korea) Co., Ltd. (1)
Rm 1112 1113 Hyundai Ofc Bldg
Sunae dong Bundang gu, Seongnam, Gyeonggi, 463 020, Korea (South)
Tel.: (82) 317788060
Fax: (82) 317788063
Web Site: www.boe.com.cn/en/Technolo gy/Entering/glqy.asp
Emp.: 25
LCD Products Mfr
S.I.C.: 3679
N.A.I.C.S.: 334419
J. Lee *(Gen Mgr)*

BOER POWER HOLDINGS LIMITED

Unit 1805 18th Floor Infinitus Plaza
199 Des Voeux Road Central
Hong Kong, China (Hong Kong)
Tel.: (852) 25422128
Fax: (852) 25447272
E-Mail: quoter@wuxi-power.com
Web Site: www.wuxi-power.com
Year Founded: 1985
1685—(HKG)
Sls.: $193,989,844
Assets: $380,248,935
Liabilities: $104,223,709
Net Worth: $276,025,226
Earnings: $46,724,298
Emp.: 1,294
Fiscal Year-end: 12/31/12

Business Description:
Electrical Switchgear Mfr
S.I.C.: 3613
N.A.I.C.S.: 335313

Personnel:
Yixiang Qian *(Chm & CEO)*
Liang Huang *(CFO)*
Lingxia Jia *(COO)*
Yuk Chun Kwok *(Sec)*

Board of Directors:
Yixiang Qian
Liang Huang
Lingxia Jia
Zhongming Qian
Jianrong Tang
Chi Tat Yeung
Saibin Zha
Huaqiao Zhang
Jianfeng Zhao

Appleby Trust (Cayman) Ltd.
Clifton House 75 Fort Street
PO Box 1350
Grand Cayman, Cayman Islands

Transfer Agent:
Appleby Trust (Cayman) Ltd.
Clifton House 75 Fort Street
PO Box 1350
Grand Cayman, Cayman Islands

BOERLIND GESELLSCHAFT FUER KOSMETISCHE ERZEUGNISSE MBH

Lindenstr 15
75365 Calw, Germany
Tel.: (49) 705160000
Fax: (49) 7051600060
E-Mail: mail@boerlind.com
Web Site: www.boerlind.de
Year Founded: 1959
Rev.: $28,967,400
Emp.: 158

Business Description:
Cosmetics Mfr
S.I.C.: 2844
N.A.I.C.S.: 325620

Personnel:
Annemarie Linder *(Founder)*
Michael Lindner *(CEO)*

BOERO BARTOLOMEO S.P.A.

Via Macaggi 19
16121 Genoa, Italy
Tel.: (39) 01055001
Fax: (39) 0105500300
E-Mail: info@attivamarine.com
Web Site: www.gruppoboero.it
BOE—(ITA)
Sales Range: $150-199.9 Million
Emp.: 364

Business Description:
Paints & Resins Mfr
S.I.C.: 2851
N.A.I.C.S.: 325510

Personnel:
Andreina Boero *(Chm)*

Subsidiaries:

BOAT S.p.A., (1)
Via Macaggi 19
16121 Genoa, Italy
Tel.: (39) 01055005
Fax: (39) 0105500288
Web Site: www.boat.it
Emp.: 30
Marine Protective Coatings Mfr & Whslr
S.I.C.: 2851
N.A.I.C.S.: 325510
Massimo Zanone *(Mng Dir)*

Yacht Systems S.r.l (1)
Piazza Niccolo
Tommaseo 4, 34121 Trieste, Italy
Tel.: (39) 0403783911
Fax: (39) 0403783906
E-Mail: info@venezianiyacht.it
Web Site: www.venezianiyacht.it
Marine Paints Mfr
S.I.C.: 2851
N.A.I.C.S.: 325510

Non-U.S. Subsidiary:

Boero Colori France S.a.r.l (1)
Park Activity Gambe Torte Lot No 1-2855
Route de la Feneri, 06580 Pegomas, Alpes Maritimes, France
Tel.: (33) 492389088
Fax: (33) 492389106
E-Mail: boero.france@boeroyachtpaint.com
Web Site: www.boero-france.com
Emp.: 15
Marine Yacht Paints
S.I.C.: 2851
N.A.I.C.S.: 325510
Aocco Earera *(Mgr)*

BOERSE BERLIN AG

Fasanenstrasse 85
10623 Berlin, Germany
Tel.: (49) 303110910
Fax: (49) 3031109178
E-Mail: info@berlinerboerse.de
Web Site: www.boerse-berlin.de
Emp.: 20

Business Description:
Stock Exchange Operations
S.I.C.: 6231
N.A.I.C.S.: 523210

Personnel:
Artur Fischer *(CEO)*
Joerg Walter *(Co-CEO-Exchange Svcs)*

BOG'ART S.R.L.

Strasse Brezoianu 27
010131 Bucharest, Romania
Tel.: (40) 213103238
Fax: (40) 213103283
E-Mail: office@bogart.ro
Web Site: www.bogart.ro
Year Founded: 1991
Sales Range: $25-49.9 Million
Emp.: 500

Business Description:
Engineering Services
S.I.C.: 8711
N.A.I.C.S.: 541330

Personnel:
Raul Doicescu *(CEO)*

Board of Directors:
Mihaela Doicescu
Raul Doicescu
Sorin Greu

Subsidiaries:

ALUSYSTEM SRL (1)
Armoniei Street No 27/A
Timisoara, Timis, 3600291, Romania
Tel.: (40) 256 309 760
Fax: (40) 256 242 340
E-Mail: office.tm@alusystem.ro
Web Site: www.alusystem.ro
Emp.: 50
Facade Construction Services
S.I.C.: 1629
N.A.I.C.S.: 237990

BOG'ART FASHION SRL (1)
Str Stefan Mihaileanu 36
Bucharest, Muntenia, 021068, Romania
Tel.: (40) 21 320 4733
Fax: (40) 21 320 4734
E-Mail: session@bogart.ro
Emp.: 40
Fashion Designing Services
S.I.C.: 7389
N.A.I.C.S.: 541490

CONS CONSTRUCT SRL (1)
Brezoianu 27 Sector 1
Bucharest, Romania
Tel.: (40) 21 307 12 77
Fax: (40) 21 312 32 83
E-Mail: office@consconstruct.ro
Web Site: www.consconstruct.ro
Building Construction Services
S.I.C.: 1541
N.A.I.C.S.: 236210

S.C.BOG'ART BUILDING MANAGEMENT S.R.L. (1)
Sector 3 Calea Dudesti nr 124
Bucharest, Romania
Tel.: (40) 21 326 79 79
E-Mail: office@bogartfacility.ro
Web Site: www.bogartfacility.ro
Building Management Services
S.I.C.: 7349
N.A.I.C.S.: 561790

S.C. BOG'ART STEEL S.R.L. (1)
Str Nicolae Teclu nr 55 Sector 3
Bucharest, 032368, Romania
Tel.: (40) 31 102 05 84
Fax: (40) 31 102 05 85
E-Mail: office.steel@bogart.ro
Web Site: www.bogartsteel.ro
Structured Steel Product Mfr
S.I.C.: 3312
N.A.I.C.S.: 331110

S.C.BOG'ART VEST s.r.l. (1)
Str Armoniei nr 27A
Timisoara, 300291, Romania
Tel.: (40) 256 435 929
Fax: (40) 256 435 926
E-Mail: timisoara@bogart.ro
Web Site: www.bogartvest.ro
Emp.: 67
Building Construction Services
S.I.C.: 1629
N.A.I.C.S.: 236210

TONI TRADING SRL (1)
46 Tomis Blvd
Constanta, Romania
Tel.: (40) 755 743 432
E-Mail: office@tonis.ro
Web Site: www.tonis.ro
Online Shopping Services
S.I.C.: 5961
N.A.I.C.S.: 454111

BOGAWANTALAWA TEA ESTATES PLC

No 540 Thimbirigasyaya Rd
5 Colombo, Sri Lanka
Tel.: (94) 112510100
Fax: (94) 112510178
E-Mail: info@bpl.lk
Web Site: www.bplteas.com
BOPL—(COL)
Sales Range: $25-49.9 Million
Emp.: 14,853

Bogawantalawa Tea Estates PLC—(Continued)

Business Description:
Tea Mfr & Distr
S.I.C.: 2095
N.A.I.C.S.: 311920
Personnel:
Dinesh Jamnadas Ambani *(Chm)*
Magage Sarath Wimal Fernando *(CEO)*
Board of Directors:
Dinesh Jamnadas Ambani
Lalithkumar Jamnadas Ambani
Romesh Dias Bandaranaike
Magage Sarath Wimal Fernando
Carl Michael Oscarsson Haglind

BOGDAN CORPORATION

Ul Elektrikov 29A
04176 Kiev, Ukraine
Tel.: (380) 443527496
Web Site: www.bogdan.ua
Sales Range: $1-4.9 Billion
Business Description:
Motor Vehicle Mfr
S.I.C.: 3711
N.A.I.C.S.: 336211
Personnel:
Oleg Svinarchuk *(Pres)*

BOHAE BREWERY CO., LTD.

9Fl Owner's Tower 16-5 Sunae-Dong Bundang-Gu, Seongnam, Kyunggi-Do, 463-825, Korea (South)
Tel.: (82) 31 719 3907
Fax: (82) 31 719 3909
Web Site: www.bohae.co.kr
Year Founded: 1950
000890—(KRS)
Business Description:
Liquor Mfr
S.I.C.: 2084
N.A.I.C.S.: 312130
Personnel:
Min Ho Jung *(CEO)*

BOHAI INDUSTRIAL INVESTMENT FUND MANAGEMENT COMPANY LTD.

26F Tower B ICTC No 59 Machang Road
Tianjin, Hexi, 300203, China
Tel.: (86) 2283867800
Fax: (86) 2283867810
E-Mail: bohaifund@bohaicapital.com
Web Site: www.bohaicapital.com
Year Founded: 2006
Business Description:
Private Equity Investments
S.I.C.: 6211
N.A.I.C.S.: 523999
Personnel:
Li Lihui *(Chm)*
Wang Liuzhi *(Vice Chm)*
Li Xiangsheng *(CEO)*
Zhu Hui *(CFO)*
Board of Directors:
Li Lihui
Wang Liuzhi

BOHAI PHARMACEUTICALS GROUP, INC.

9 Daxin Road
Zhifu District, Yantai, Shangdong, 264000, China
Tel.: (86) 535 6857928
Web Site: www.bohaipharma.com
BOPH—(OTCB)
Rev.: $151,792,917
Assets: $165,624,398
Liabilities: $57,234,844
Net Worth: $108,389,554
Earnings: $19,123,517
Emp.: 827
Fiscal Year-end: 06/30/13
Business Description:
Herbal Pharmaceutical Mfr & Distr
S.I.C.: 2834
N.A.I.C.S.: 325412
Personnel:
Hongwei Qu *(Chm, Pres & CEO)*
Chunhong Jiang *(Treas & Sec)*
Board of Directors:
Hongwei Qu
Thomas Tan
Chengde Wang

BOHLE AG

Dieselstrasse 10
D-42781 Haan, Germany
Tel.: (49) 212955680
Fax: (49) 21295568281
E-Mail: info@bohle.de
Web Site: www.bohle.de
Year Founded: 1923
Rev.: $74,156,770
Emp.: 226
Business Description:
Glass Processing Tools Machinery & Accessories Mfr
S.I.C.: 3231
N.A.I.C.S.: 327215
Personnel:
Heinrich Ostendarp *(Chm)*

BOILERMECH HOLDINGS BERHAD

Lot 875 Jalan Subang 8 Taman Perindustrian Subang
47620 Subang Jaya, Selangor Darul Ehsan, Malaysia
Tel.: (60) 3 8023 9137
Fax: (60) 3 8023 2127
E-Mail: invest@boilermech.com
Web Site: www.boilermech.com
BOILERM—(KLS)
Sales Range: $50-74.9 Million
Emp.: 98
Business Description:
Boiler Mfr
S.I.C.: 3559
N.A.I.C.S.: 332410
Personnel:
Yew Cheong Leong *(Mng Dir)*
Bee Hwee Tan *(Co-Sec)*
Wai Foong Wong *(Co-Sec)*
Board of Directors:
Song Kun Chia
Lik Khai Chia
Mohd Yusof Hussian
Yew Cheong Leong
Teng Lum Low
Wee Voo Wong
Legal Counsel:
Naqiz & Partners
42A Lorong Dungun Damansara Heights
Kuala Lumpur, Malaysia
Subsidiary:

Boilermech Sdn Bhd (1)
Lot 875 Jalan Subang 8 Taman
Perindustrian Subang
47620 Subang Jaya, Selangor, Malaysia
Tel.: (60) 38023 9137
Fax: (60) 38023 2127
E-Mail: sales@boilermech.com
Web Site: www.boilermech.com
Power Boiler Mfr
S.I.C.: 3443
N.A.I.C.S.: 332410

BOIRON GROUP

20 rue de la Liberation
69110 Sainte-Foy-les-Lyon, France
Tel.: (33) 472164000
Fax: (33) 478596916
E-Mail: finances@boiron.fr
Web Site: www.boiron.com
BOI—(EUR)
Sls.: $762,327,994
Assets: $779,810,704
Liabilities: $303,055,175
Net Worth: $476,755,529
Earnings: $66,805,032
Emp.: 3,924
Fiscal Year-end: 12/31/12
Business Description:
Homeopathic Medical Product Mfr
S.I.C.: 2833
N.A.I.C.S.: 325411
Personnel:
Thierry Boiron *(Chm)*
Board of Directors:
Thierry Boiron
Jacky Abecassis
Christian Boiron
Michele Boiron
Michel Bouissou
Jean-Pierre Boyer
Christine Boyer-Boiron
Stephanie Chesnot
Bruno Grange
Francois Marchal

Ernst & Young et Autres
41 rue Ybry
F-92576 Neuilly-sur-Seine, France

U.S. Subsidiary:

Boiron USA Inc. (1)
6 Campus Blvd
Newtown Square, PA 19073
Tel.: (610) 325-7464
Fax: (610) 325-7480
Web Site: www.boironusa.com
Sales Range: $25-49.9 Million
Emp.: 90
Homeopathic Medical Products
S.I.C.: 2833
N.A.I.C.S.: 325411
Janick Boudazin *(Pres & CEO)*

Subsidiary:

Boiron Inc (2)
6 Campus Blvd
Newtown Square, PA 19073-3200
Tel.: (610) 325-7464
Fax: (610) 325-7480
Web Site: www.boironusa.com
Emp.: 60
Pharmaceutical Preparartions Mfr & Distr
S.I.C.: 2834
N.A.I.C.S.: 325412
Christian Boiron *(Chm)*
Janick Boudazin *(Pres & CEO)*

Non-U.S. Subsidiaries:

Boiron CZ S.r.o (1)
Pobrezni 3/620
186 00 Prague, Czech Republic
Tel.: (420) 224835090
Fax: (420) 222326502
E-Mail: info@boiron.cz
Web Site: www.boiron.cz
Emp.: 28
Homeopathy Medicines Mfr
S.I.C.: 2834
N.A.I.C.S.: 325412
Leona Mejzrova *(Gen Mgr)*

Boiron Hungaria Kft (1)
Ady Endre utca 8
Budapest, Hungary 1024
Tel.: (36) 1 365 1430
Fax: (36) 1 209 0793
E-Mail: boiron@boiron.hu
Web Site: www.boiron.hu
Pharmaceutical Preparations Mfr & Distr
S.I.C.: 2834
N.A.I.C.S.: 325412
Thierry Boiron *(CEO)*

Boiron Medicamentos Homeopaticos Ltda (1)
Rua Joaquim Floriano 1120
Sao Paulo, 04534-004, Brazil
Tel.: (55) 1137075857
Fax: (55) 1130788429
E-Mail: boiron@boiron.com.br
Web Site: www.boiron.com.br
Emp.: 30
Pharmaceutical Preparations Mfr & Distr
S.I.C.: 2834
N.A.I.C.S.: 325412

Boiron Portugal Ltda (1)
Edif Mar do Oriente Fraccao 2 4 Lote1 07 1Y
Alameda dos Oceanos, Lisbon, Portugal
Tel.: (351) 21 193 2091
Fax: (351) 21 193 1718
Pharmaceutical Preparations Mfr & Distr
S.I.C.: 2834
N.A.I.C.S.: 325412
Fernando Vitorino *(Gen Mgr)*

Boiron RO Srl (1)
Rue Dr No 40 Etage 1 Sector 5
Bucharest, 050454, Romania
Tel.: (40) 21 410 0546
Fax: (40) 21 410 2024
E-Mail: office@boiron.ro
Emp.: 15
Pharmaceuticals Whslr
S.I.C.: 5122
N.A.I.C.S.: 424210
Silvia Mainescu *(Gen Mgr)*

Boiron Russie o.o.o (1)
Orlikov Pereulok business Centre Orlikov
Plaza Building 2 Flow 6
Moscow, 103050, Russia
Tel.: (7) 495-956-0810
Fax: (7) 495-956-0814
E-Mail: info@boiron.ru
Web Site: www.boiron.ru
Emp.: 50
Pharmaceutical Preparartions Mfr & Distr
S.I.C.: 2834
N.A.I.C.S.: 325412

Boiron SK S.r.o (1)
Tomasikova 29
82 101 Bratislava, Slovakia
Tel.: (421) 2 49 102 214
Fax: (421) 2 44 640 101
E-Mail: boiron@boiron.sk
Web Site: www.boiron.sk
Homeopathic Medicines Mfr
S.I.C.: 2834
N.A.I.C.S.: 325412

Boiron Sociedad Iberica de Homeopatia (1)
27 Avenida De Valdelaparra Parque Empresarial
28108 Alcobendas, Madrid, Spain
Tel.: (34) 914840438
Fax: (34) 916612408
E-Mail: homeopatia@boiron.es
Web Site: www.boiron.es
Emp.: 100
Pharmaceutical Preparation Mfr
S.I.C.: 2834
N.A.I.C.S.: 325412
Blasco Pascal *(CEO)*

Boiron SP z.o.o (1)
Ul Raszynska 13
05-500 Piaseczno, Poland
Tel.: (48) 227026670
Fax: (48) 22 702 66 71
E-Mail: boiron@boiron.pl
Web Site: www.boiron.pl
Homeopathic Medicines Mfr
S.I.C.: 2834
N.A.I.C.S.: 325412
Jacek Sroczynski *(Pres & Gen Dir)*

Boiron Srl (1)
Via Cassanese 100
20090 Segrate, Milan, Italy
Tel.: (39) 0226990382
Fax: (39) 0226990306
E-Mail: info@boiron.it
Web Site: www.boiron.it
Pharmaceutical Preparation Mfr
S.I.C.: 2834
N.A.I.C.S.: 325412

Boiron Suisse SA (1)
Route De La Galaise 32 Plan Les Ouates
Plan-les-Ouates, Geneva, 1228, Switzerland
Tel.: (41) 22 884 1414
Fax: (41) 22 743 1044
Pharmaceutical Preparations Mfr & Distr
S.I.C.: 2834
N.A.I.C.S.: 325412

Boiron TN SARL (1)
1 Rue du Laurier Cite Taieb M hiri
La Goulette, Tunis, Tunisia

Tel.: (216) 70 727 161
Fax: (216) 70 727 173
Pharmaceuticals Mfr & Distr
S.I.C.: 2834
N.A.I.C.S.: 325412

UNDA S.A (1)
5 Rue Carli
1140 Brussels, Belgium
Tel.: (32) 27267070
Fax: (32) 2 726 7458
E-Mail: info@unda.be
Web Site: www.unda.be
Emp.: 200
Homeopathic Medicine Preparations Mfr
S.I.C.: 2834
N.A.I.C.S.: 325412
Marc Cooremans *(Dir-Informatiics)*

BOISERIES RAYMOND INC

11 880 56e avenue
Montreal, QC, H1E 2L6, Canada
Tel.: (514) 494-1141
Fax: (514) 494-9666
E-Mail: boiseries@boiseriesraymond.com
Web Site: www.boiseriesraymond.com
Year Founded: 1958
Rev.: $36,238,655
Emp.: 175
Business Description:
Interior Finishing Items Mfr & Supplier
S.I.C.: 2541
N.A.I.C.S.: 337212
Personnel:
Raymond Waechter *(Founder)*

BOISSET, LA FAMILLE DES GRANDS VINS

5 quai Dumorey
21700 Nuits-St-Georges, France
Tel.: (33) 3 8062 6161
Fax: (33) 3 8062 3738
E-Mail: presse@boisset.fr
Web Site: www.boisset.com
Year Founded: 1961
Sales Range: $150-199.9 Million
Emp.: 700
Business Description:
Holding Company; Vineyards, Wineries & Distilleries Operator; Wine & Distilled Alcoholic Beverage Distr Import Export
S.I.C.: 6719
N.A.I.C.S.: 551112
Personnel:
Jean-Claude Boisset *(Chm, Pres & CEO)*
Gilles Seguin *(CFO & COO)*
Jean-Charles Boisset *(VP & Pres-America)*

U.S. Subsidiaries:

Buena Vista Carneros Winery Inc. (1)
27000 Ramal Rd
Sonoma, CA 95476-9791
Mailing Address:
PO Box 182
Sonoma, CA 95476-0182
Tel.: (707) 252-7117
Fax: (707) 252-0392
Toll Free: (800) 678-8504
Web Site: www.buenavistawinery.com
Emp.: 102
Wine Producer
Import Export
S.I.C.: 2084
N.A.I.C.S.: 312130

Jean-Claude Boisset Wines U.S.A., Inc. (1)
849 Zinfandel Ln
Saint Helena, CA 94574 CA
Tel.: (415) 289-4500
Fax: (415) 339-0236
Toll Free: (800) 878-1123
E-Mail: info@boisset.com
Web Site: www.boissetfamilyestates.com
Emp.: 40
Holding Company; Vineyards, Wineries, & Wine Distr
Import Export
S.I.C.: 6719
N.A.I.C.S.: 551112
Jean-Charles Boisset *(Pres)*

Unit:

DeLoach Vineyards (2)
1791 Olivet Rd
Santa Rosa, CA 95401
Tel.: (707) 526-9111
Fax: (707) 526-4151
E-Mail: deloach@deloachvineyards.com
Web Site: www.deloachvineyards.com
Sales Range: $10-24.9 Million
Vineyard & Winery
S.I.C.: 2084
N.A.I.C.S.: 312130
Lisa Heisinger *(Grp VP-Ops & Gen Mgr)*

BOISSY

Route Du Puy
43150 Laussonne, Haute Loire, France
Tel.: (33) 471051184
Fax: (33) 471050328
E-Mail: accueil@boissysa.com
Sls.: $10,900,000
Emp.: 159
S.I.C.: 3199
N.A.I.C.S.: 316998
Personnel:
Albert Boissy *(Chm)*
Board of Directors:
Albert Boissy

BOKWANG TS CO.

408-1 Jung-ri Seokjeok-myeon
Chilgok-gun
Seoul, Gyeongsangbuk-do, Korea (South)
Tel.: (82) 544712354
Fax: (82) 544737173
Web Site: www.bksa.co.kr
Business Description:
Mobile Phone Metal Parts Services
S.I.C.: 3663
N.A.I.C.S.: 334220
Personnel:
Sung-wook Son *(Pres)*

Subsidiary:

Bokwang Hi-Tech Co., Ltd (1)
1108 Woram-dong
Dalseo-gu, Daegu, Korea (South)
Tel.: (82) 53 583 2354
Fax: (82) 53 583 9376
Web Site: www.bkts.co.kr
Mobile Accessories Mfr
S.I.C.: 3663
N.A.I.C.S.: 334220
Son Sung-Wook *(CEO)*

BOLAN CASTINGS LIMITED

Main RCD Highway District Lasbella
Hub Chowki, Balochistan, Pakistan
Tel.: (92) 853364033
Fax: (92) 853363292
E-Mail: bclhub@bclpk.com
Web Site: www.bolancastings.com
BCL—(KAR)
Sls.: $17,686,718
Assets: $13,618,732
Liabilities: $7,945,425
Net Worth: $5,673,306
Earnings: $231,818
Emp.: 201
Fiscal Year-end: 06/30/13
Business Description:
Automotive Castings & Foundry
S.I.C.: 3499
N.A.I.C.S.: 332999
Personnel:
Sirajuddin Khan *(CEO)*
Imran Siddiqui *(CFO)*
Arafat Mushir *(Sec)*
Board of Directors:
Sikandar M. Khan
Laeeq Uddin Ansari
Latif Khalid Hashmi
Sirajuddin Khan
Javed Munir
Muhammad Imran Rafiq
Sohail Bashir Rana
Muhammad Saleem

BOLD ENERGY INC.

(See Under LOT78, INC.)

BOLD STROKE VENTURES INC.

LW3 1185 The High Street
Coquitlam, BC, V3B 0A9, Canada
Tel.: (604) 475-0590
E-Mail: rob_sim@shaw.ca
Year Founded: 2011
BSV.P—(TSXV)
Business Description:
Investment Services
S.I.C.: 6211
N.A.I.C.S.: 523999
Personnel:
Robert A. Sim *(Pres & CEO)*
Nikolaos Tsimidis *(CFO & Sec)*
Board of Directors:
Kinder S. Deo
Garnet C. Klatt
Ioanna Kotsiris
Robert A. Sim
Nikolaos Tsimidis
Transfer Agent:
Computershare Investor Services Inc.
510 Burrard Street 2nd Floor
Vancouver, BC, V6C 3B9, Canada

BOLD VENTURES INC.

Suite 1000 15 Toronto Street
Toronto, ON, M5C 2E3, Canada
Tel.: (416) 864-1456
Fax: (416) 864-1443
E-Mail: info@boldventuresinc.com
Web Site: www.boldventuresinc.com
BOL—(TSXV)
Int. Income: $313,680
Assets: $6,628,886
Liabilities: $167,173
Net Worth: $6,461,713
Earnings: ($486,298)
Fiscal Year-end: 10/31/13
Business Description:
Holding Company; Mineral Exploration
S.I.C.: 6719
N.A.I.C.S.: 551112
Personnel:
Richard E. Nemis *(Pres & CEO)*
Rodger D. Roden *(CFO)*
John D. Harvey *(COO)*
William R. Johnstone *(Sec)*
David B. Graham *(Exec VP)*
Board of Directors:
Ian A. Brodie-Brown
Jim Glover
David B. Graham
John D. Harvey
William R. Johnstone
Richard E. Nemis
Gary Frank J. Zak
Legal Counsel:
Gardiner Roberts LLP
Scotia Plaza 40 King Street West Suite 3100
Toronto, ON, Canada
Transfer Agent:
Computershare Inc.
100 University Avenue 9th Floor
Toronto, ON, Canada

BOLERO RESOURCES CORP.

(See Under Canada Carbon Inc.)

BOLIDEN AB

Klarabergsviadukten 90
PO Box 44
SE 101 20 Stockholm, Sweden
Tel.: (46) 86101500
Fax: (46) 8315545
E-Mail: info.boliden@boliden.com
Web Site: www.boliden.com
BOL—(OMX)
Rev.: $6,192,154,800
Assets: $6,197,418,000
Liabilities: $2,644,912,800
Net Worth: $3,552,505,200
Earnings: $506,815,200
Emp.: 4,795
Fiscal Year-end: 12/31/12
Business Description:
Copper, Zinc, Lead & Precious Metals Mining & Smelting
S.I.C.: 1021
N.A.I.C.S.: 212234
Personnel:
Anders Ullberg *(Chm)*
Lennart Evrell *(Pres & CEO)*
Mikael Staffas *(CFO)*
Patrick Ammerlaan *(Pres-Metals)*
Kerstin Konradsson *(Pres-Smelters)*
Jan Mostrom *(Pres-Mines)*
Marianne Lindholm *(Gen Counsel & Sr VP)*
Sune Lundin *(Sr VP-Strategy & Bus Dev)*
Henrik Ostberg *(Sr VP-Corp Responsibility)*
Board of Directors:
Anders Ullberg
Roland Antonsson
Marie Berglund
Staffan Bohman
Tom Erixon
Lennart Evrell
Marie Holmberg
Ola Holmstrom
Ulla Litzen
Michael Gson Low
Einar Mikkelsen
Ditte Kilsgaard Moller
Hans-Goran Olvebo
Leif Ronnback

Non-U.S. Subsidiaries:

Boliden Harjavalta Oy (1)
Teollisuuskatu 1
FI 29200 Pori, Finland (100%)
Tel.: (358) 25358111
Fax: (358) 25358239
E-Mail: info@boliden.com
Emp.: 1,000
Steel Works
S.I.C.: 2999
N.A.I.C.S.: 324199
Jyrki Makkonen *(Exec Mgr)*

Boliden Harjavalta Oy (1)
Linnoikustie
PO Box 287
FIN 02601 Harjavalta, Finland (100%)
Tel.: (358) 25358111
Telex: 721461 uto fi
Fax: (358) 95472532
E-Mail: info.market@boliden.com
Web Site: www.boliden.com
Emp.: 400
Marketing & Raw Material Purchases of Nickel
S.I.C.: 1021
N.A.I.C.S.: 212234

Boliden Tara Mines Limited (1)
Knockumber House Knockumber Rd
Navan, Co Meath, Ireland (100%)
Tel.: (353) 469079800
Telex: 43559 tara ei
Fax: (353) 469079899
Emp.: 680
Zinc Mining
S.I.C.: 1031
N.A.I.C.S.: 212231
Stefan Romedahl *(Gen Mgr)*

Boliden AB—(Continued)

Boliden Kokkola Oy (1)
Outokummuntie 8
67800 Kokkola, Finland (100%)
Tel.: (358) 6 828 6111
Telex: 76113 okla sf
Fax: (358) 6 828 6005
E-Mail: info.kokkola@boliden.com
Emp.: 522
Zinc Smelting
S.I.C.: 3369
N.A.I.C.S.: 331529
Manu Myllymaki *(Mgr)*

BOLLIN GROUP LTD.

Suite 4 Bailey Court Green Street
Macclesfield, SK10 1JQ, United Kingdom
Tel.: (44) 1625 869754
Fax: (44) 1625 440092
E-Mail: info@bollingroup.com
Web Site: www.bollingroup.com
Year Founded: 1989
Sales Range: $75-99.9 Million
Emp.: 316
Business Description:
Consumer Product Whslr
S.I.C.: 5411
N.A.I.C.S.: 445110
Personnel:
Stephen Cann *(CEO)*

BOLOGNESI EMPREENDIMENTOS LTDA.

(d/b/a Grupo Bolognesi)
Avenida Plinio Brasil Milano 607
Higienopolis, Porto Alegre, RS, CEP 90520-002, Brazil
Tel.: (55) 51 3025 8100
E-Mail: bolognesi@bolognesi.com.br
Web Site: www.bolognesi.com.br
Year Founded: 1973
Business Description:
Residential Construction Services
S.I.C.: 1531
N.A.I.C.S.: 236117
Personnel:
Ronaldo Bolognesi *(CEO)*

Holding:

Multiner S.A. (1)
Avenida Almirante Barroso 52 19th andar
CEP 20031-918 Rio de Janeiro, RJ, Brazil BR
Tel.: (55) 21 2272 5500 (55%)
Fax: (55) 21 2272 5555
E-Mail: ri@multiner.com.br
Web Site: www.multiner.com.br
Holding Company; Electric Power Generation Plants Operator
S.I.C.: 6719
N.A.I.C.S.: 551112
Paulo Cesar Rutzen *(Chm & CEO)*
Antonio Alvaro Rodrigues Frade *(CFO & IR Officer)*
Giancarlo Porto Bratkowski *(COO)*

BOLSA DE COMERCIO DE BUENOS AIRES

Domingo Faustino Sarmiento 299
Buenos Aires, Argentina
Tel.: (54) 11 4316 7000
Web Site: www.bcba.sba.com.ar
Year Founded: 1854
Business Description:
Securities & Commodity Exchanges
S.I.C.: 6231
N.A.I.C.S.: 523210
Personnel:
Adelmo J.J. Gabbi *(Chm)*

BOLSA DE COMERCIO DE SANTIAGO

(d/b/a Santiago Stock Exchange)
La Bolsa 64
Santiago, Chile
Tel.: (56) 23993000
Fax: (56) 23801959
E-Mail: info@bolsadesantiago.com
Web Site: www.bolsadesantiago.com
Sales Range: $1-9.9 Million
Emp.: 120
Business Description:
Stock Exchange Services
S.I.C.: 6231
N.A.I.C.S.: 523210
Personnel:
Pablo Yrarrazaval Valdes *(Pres)*
Jose Antonio Martinez Zugarramurdi *(CEO)*
Andres Araya Falcone *(CIO)*
Rodrigo Serrano Bombal *(Sec)*
Board of Directors:
Bernardo Matte Larrain
Luis Enrique Yarur Rey
Alvaro Saieh Bendeck
Leonidas Vial Echeverria
Alfredo Ureta Vial
Luis Enrique Yarur King
Pablo Yrarrazaval Valdes

BOLSA DE VALORES DE CARACAS

Calle Sorocaima entre Ave Venezuela y Tamanaco
Caracas, 1060, Venezuela
Tel.: (58) 2129055511
Fax: (58) 2129522640
E-Mail: bvc@caracasstock.com
Web Site: www.bolsadecaracas.com
Emp.: 65
Business Description:
Stock Exchange Services
S.I.C.: 6231
N.A.I.C.S.: 523210
Personnel:
Marcel Apeloig *(Pres)*
Victor Julio Flores Rojas *(Pres)*

BOLSA DE VALORES DE LIMA S.A.

Pasaje Acuna 106
Lima, 1, Peru
Tel.: (51) 16193333
Fax: (51) 16193354
E-Mail: foviedo@bvl.com.pe
Web Site: www.bvl.com.pe
Sales Range: $1-9.9 Million
Emp.: 110
Business Description:
Stock Exchange Services
S.I.C.: 6231
N.A.I.C.S.: 523210
Personnel:
Roberto Hoyle *(Pres)*

BOLSA DE VALORES DE PANAMA S.A.

Ave Federico Boyd y Calle 49
Panama, Panama
Tel.: (507) 2691966
Fax: (507) 2692457
E-Mail: bvp@panabolsa.com
Web Site: www.panabolsa.com
Emp.: 14
Business Description:
Stock Exchange Services
S.I.C.: 6231
N.A.I.C.S.: 523210
Personnel:
Fernando Aramburu *(Treas)*
Eugenia de Jimenez *(Sec)*
Roberto Brenes Perez *(Exec VP & Gen Mgr)*
Board of Directors:
Roberto Alfaro
Fernando Aramburu
Ignacio Arias
Leopoldo Arosemena
Rodrigo Cardoze
Jose Anibal Castillo
Felipe Chapman
Juan R. De Dianous
Eugenia de Jimenez
Ivan Diaz
Mario Fabrega
Joseph Fidanque, Jr.
Arturo Gerbaud
Carlos Henriquez
Marielena Garcia Maritano
Jaime Sosa
Ivan Zarak

BOLSA MEXICANA DE VALORES, S.A.B. DE C.V.

(d/b/a The Mexican Stock Exchange)
Paseo de la Reforma 255 Col
Cuauhtemoc, 06500 Mexico, Mexico
Tel.: (52) 55 5342900
E-Mail: cinforma@bmv.com.mx
Web Site: www.bmv.com.mx
BOLSAA—(MEX)
Sales Range: Less than $1 Million
Business Description:
Stock Exchange Services
S.I.C.: 6231
N.A.I.C.S.: 523210
Personnel:
Luis Manuel Enrique Tellez Kuenzler *(Chm & CEO)*
Board of Directors:
Luis Manuel Enrique Tellez Kuenzler
Eduardo Valdes Acra
Rafael McGregor Anciola
Alvaro Garcia Pimentel Caraza
Diego Ramos Gonzalez de Castilla
Javier Arrigunaga Gomez del Campo
Francisco Gil Diaz
Alfonso Gonzalez Migoya
Jose Luis Guerrero Alvarez
Luis Manuel Enrique Tellez Kuenzler
Alberto Navarro Rodriguez
Fernando Ruiz Sahagun
Eduardo Tricio Haro
Alfredo Thorne Vetter

BOLSA NACIONAL DE VALORES, S.A.

Santa Forum
Apartado Postal 03-6155
Santa Ana, Costa Rica
Tel.: (506) 22044848
Fax: (506) 5062204485
E-Mail: servicioalcliente@bolsacr.com
Web Site: www.bolsacr.com
Emp.: 90
Business Description:
Stock Exchange Services
S.I.C.: 6231
N.A.I.C.S.: 523210
Personnel:
Jose Brenes *(CEO)*
Euillermo Masis *(Treas)*
Luis Gamboa *(Sec)*

BOLSAS Y MERCADOS ESPANOLES, SOCIEDAD HOLDING DE MERCADOS SISTEMAS FINANCIEROS, S.A.

Plaza de la Lealtad 1
28014 Madrid, Spain
Tel.: (34) 917095000
Fax: (34) 915891344
E-Mail: info@grupobme.es
Web Site: www.bolsasymercados.es
BME—(MAD OTC)
Rev.: $393,228,373
Assets: $49,245,673,056
Liabilities: $48,689,932,349
Net Worth: $555,740,707
Earnings: $182,470,651
Fiscal Year-end: 12/31/12
Business Description:
Stock Exchange Services
S.I.C.: 6231
N.A.I.C.S.: 523210
Personnel:
Antonio J. Zoido Martinez *(Chm & CEO)*
Tomas Muniesa Arantegui *(Second Vice Chm)*
Jose Andres Barreiro Hernandez *(First Vice Chm)*
Margarita Prat Rodrigo *(Fourth Vice Chm)*
Luis Maria Cazorla Prieto *(Sec)*
Board of Directors:
Antonio J. Zoido Martinez
Jose Antonio Alvarez Alvarez
Tomas Muniesa Arantegui
Jose Andres Barreiro Hernandez
Pablo Forero Calderon
Ignacio Benjumea Cabeza de Vaca
Alvaro Cuervo Garcia
Rosa Maria Garcia Garcia
Ramiro Mato Garcia-Ansorena
Joan Hortala i Arau
Ricardo Laiseca Asla
Karel Lannoo
Margarita Prat Rodrigo
Manuel Olivencia Ruiz
D. Javier Alonso Ruiz-Ojeda

Subsidiaries:

Bolsa de Barcelona (1)
Passeig de Gracia 19
08007 Barcelona, Spain
Tel.: (34) 934013555
Fax: (34) 934013650
E-Mail: informacion@borsabcn.es
Web Site: www.borsabcn.es
Emp.: 63
Stock Exchange Services
S.I.C.: 6231
N.A.I.C.S.: 523210
Joan Hortala i Arau *(Chm)*

Bolsa de Bilbao (1)
C Jose Maria Olabarri 1
48001 Bilbao, Spain
Tel.: (34) 944034400
Fax: (34) 944034430
E-Mail: bolsabilbao@bolsabilbao.es
Web Site: www.bolsabilbao.es
Emp.: 50
Stock Exchange Services
S.I.C.: 6231
N.A.I.C.S.: 523210
Jose Luis Damborenea *(CEO)*

Infobolsa, S.A. (1)
Tramontana No 2 BIS
Las rozas, 28230 Madrid, Spain
Tel.: (34) 917095600
Fax: (34) 917095688
E-Mail: infobolsa@nfobolsa.es
Web Site: www.infobolsa.es
Emp.: 50
Holding Company
S.I.C.: 6719
N.A.I.C.S.: 551112

Sociedad Rectora de la Bolsa de Valores de Barcelona, S.A. (1)
Paseo Gracia 19
08007 Barcelona, Spain (100%)
Tel.: (34) 934013555
Fax: (34) 934013625
E-Mail: info@borsabcn.es
Web Site: www.borsabcn.es
Emp.: 7
Securities & Commodity Exchanges
S.I.C.: 6231
N.A.I.C.S.: 523210

Sociedad Rectora de la Bolsa de Valores de Valencia, S.A. (1)
Calle Libreros 2
Valencia, 46002, Spain (100%)
Tel.: (34) 963870100
Securities & Commodity Exchanges
S.I.C.: 6231
N.A.I.C.S.: 523210
Angel Torre *(Pres)*

BOLTON BERHAD
(Name Changed to Symphony Life Berhad)

BOLZONI S.P.A.
Casoni di Podenzano
29027 Piacenza, Italy
Tel.: (39) 0523 555511
Fax: (39) 0523 524087
E-Mail: sales.it@bolzoni-auramo.com
Web Site: www.bolzoni-auramo.com
BLZ—(ITA)
Sls.: $161,054,433
Assets: $134,420,459
Liabilities: $79,056,526
Net Worth: $55,363,934
Earnings: $2,338,297
Emp.: 735
Fiscal Year-end: 12/31/12
Business Description:
Lift Truck Attachments & Industrial Material Handling Equipment Mfr
S.I.C.: 3559
N.A.I.C.S.: 333249
Personnel:
Emilio Bolzoni *(Chm)*
Roberto Scotti *(CEO)*
Board of Directors:
Emilio Bolzoni
Claudio Berretti
Franco Bolzoni
Raimondo Cinti
Pier Luigi Magnelli
Paolo Mazzoni
Luigi Pisani
Giovanni Salsi
Roberto Scotti
Karl-Peter Staack
Davide Turco

Non-U.S. Subsidiaries:

AURAMO OY (1)
Valimotie 22
PO Box 78
01511 Vantaa, Finland
Tel.: (358) 982931
Fax: (358) 9 87 01 037
E-Mail: sales.fi@bolzoni-auramo.com
Web Site: www.bolzoni-auramo.com
Fork Lift Trucks Mfr
S.I.C.: 3537
N.A.I.C.S.: 333924

Bolzoni Auramo AB (1)
PO Box 172
801 03 Gavle, Sweden
Tel.: (46) 26647230
Fax: (46) 26647235
E-Mail: sales.se@bolzoni-auramo.com
Web Site: www.bolzoni-auramo.se
Lift Truck Attachments Distr
S.I.C.: 5013
N.A.I.C.S.: 423120
Lars Petersson *(Gen Mgr)*

Bolzoni Auramo Australia Pty Ltd (1)
PO Box 7198
Baulkham Hills, NSW, 2153, Australia
Tel.: (61) 296592224
Fax: (61) 2 9659 22 25
E-Mail: sales.au@bolzoni-auramo.com
Web Site: www.bolzoni-auramo.com
Fork Lift Trucks Mfr
S.I.C.: 3537
N.A.I.C.S.: 333924

Bolzoni Auramo BV (1)
Waterbeemd 6a Industrieterrein nr 8955
5705 DN Helmond, Netherlands
Tel.: (31) 492509777
Fax: (31) 492382844
E-Mail: sales.benelux@bolzoni-auramo.com
Web Site: www.bolzoni-auramo.com
Fork Lift Truck Mfr
S.I.C.: 3537
N.A.I.C.S.: 333924

Bolzoni Auramo Canada Ltd (1)
90C Brunswick Blvd
Dollard des Ormeaux, QC, H9B 2C5, Canada
Tel.: (514) 685-7871
Fax: (514) 685-5238
Toll Free: (800) 685-7871
E-Mail: sales.ca@bolzoni-auramo.com
Web Site: www.bolzoni-auramo.us/index.aspx?rn=53&did=795
Fork Lift Truck Mfr
S.I.C.: 3537
N.A.I.C.S.: 333924

Bolzoni Auramo GmbH (1)
Muhlenstr 74
41352 Korschenbroich, Germany
Tel.: (49) 2161999360
Fax: (49) 2161 999 36 99
E-Mail: sales.de@bolzoni-auramo.com
Web Site: www.bolzoni-auramo.de
Fork Lift Trucks Mfr
S.I.C.: 3537
N.A.I.C.S.: 333924
Gunter Onkelbach *(Gen Mgr)*

Bolzoni Auramo Polska Sp Zoo (1)
Tokarska 9C
20-210 Lublin, Poland
Tel.: (48) 814465491
Fax: (48) 814465490
E-Mail: sales.pl@bolzoni-auramo.com
Web Site: www.bolzoni-auramo.com.pl
Emp.: 11
Lift Truck Attachments Distr
S.I.C.: 5013
N.A.I.C.S.: 423120
Amma Kalinin *(Mgr-Mktg)*

Bolzoni Auramo S.A.R.L. (1)
Rue Avogadro Technopole de Forbach-Sud
57600 Forbach, France
Tel.: (33) 387846540
Fax: (33) 387846545
E-Mail: sales.fr@bolzoni-auramo.com
Web Site: www.bolzoni-auramo.fr
Lift Truck Attachments Distr
S.I.C.: 5013
N.A.I.C.S.: 423120

Bolzoni Auramo S.L. (1)
Polig Industrial Riera de Caldes C dels Basters 12-14 - Apdo 62
8184 Palau de Plegamans, Barcelona, Spain
Tel.: (34) 938648633
Fax: (34) 938 648 350
E-Mail: sales.es@bolzoni-auramo.com
Web Site: www.bolzoni-auramo.es
Emp.: 9
Lift Truck Attachments Distr
S.I.C.: 5013
N.A.I.C.S.: 423120
Antonio Fanchez *(Gen Mgr)*

Bolzoni Limited (1)
Unit 10 Taurus Park Europa Boulevard West Brook
Warrington, Cheshire, WA5 7ZT, United Kingdom
Tel.: (44) 1925624570
Fax: (44) 1925 62 45 78
E-Mail: sales.uk@bolzoni-auramo.com
Web Site: www.bolzoni-auramo.com
Emp.: 10
Fork Lift Trucks Mfr
S.I.C.: 3537
N.A.I.C.S.: 333924
Ken Smith *(Mng Dir)*

Hans H. MEYER GmbH (1)
Werk 1 Gittertor 14
38259 Salzgitter, Germany
Tel.: (49) 53 41 803 100
Fax: (49) 53 41 803 196
E-Mail: info@meyer-sz.de
Web Site: www.meyer-world.com
Emp.: 145
Fork Lift Trucks Mfr
S.I.C.: 3537
N.A.I.C.S.: 333924
Mathias Kromker *(Dir-Sls & Svc)*

MEYER SARL (1)
Z A La Butte 3 Rue Gutenberg
91620 Nozay, France
Tel.: (33) 1 64493378
Fax: (33) 1 64493004
Emp.: 10
Fork Lift Trucks Mfr & Distr
S.I.C.: 3537
N.A.I.C.S.: 333924
Thomas Auringer *(Mng Dir)*

BOMBARDIER INC.
800 Rene Levesque Blvd West
Montreal, QC, H3B 1Y8, Canada
Tel.: (514) 861-9481
Fax: (514) 861-7769
E-Mail: info@bombardier.com
Web Site: www.bombardier.com
Year Founded: 1902
BBD—(OTC TSX)
Rev.: $16,768,000,000
Assets: $25,790,000,000
Liabilities: $24,413,000,000
Net Worth: $1,377,000,000
Earnings: $598,000,000
Emp.: 71,700
Fiscal Year-end: 12/31/12
Business Description:
Business Aircraft, Regional Aircraft, Amphibious Aircraft, Pilot Training, Mass Transit Vehicles, Snowgrooming Vehicles, Tracked Vehicles for Utility Work, All-Terrain Vehicles & Electric Neighborhood Vehicles
Export
S.I.C.: 3721
N.A.I.C.S.: 336411
Personnel:
Laurent Beaudoin *(Chm)*
J. R. Andre Bombardier *(Vice Chm)*
Jean-Louis Fontaine *(Vice Chm)*
Pierre Beaudoin *(Pres & CEO)*
Pierre Alary *(CFO & Sr VP)*
Guy C. Hachey *(Pres/COO-Aerospace)*
Daniel Desjardins *(Gen Counsel, Sec & Sr VP)*
Richard C. Bradeen *(Sr VP)*
John Paul Macdonald *(Sr VP-HR & Pub Affairs)*
Steve Ridolfi *(Sr VP-Strategy, Mergers & Acq)*
Board of Directors:
Laurent Beaudoin
Pierre Beaudoin
Andre Berard
Joanne Bissonnette
J. R. Andre Bombardier
Martha Finn Brooks
L. Denis Desautels
Thierry Desmarest
Jean-Louis Fontaine
Sheila S. M. Fraser
Daniel Johnson
Jean C. Monty
Carlos Eduardo Represas
Jean-Pierre Rosso
Heinrich Weiss
Transfer Agent:
Computershare Investor Services Inc.
100 University Ave 9th Floor
Toronto, ON, Canada

Division:

Bombardier Inc. - Bombardier Aerospace Division (1)
400 Cote-Vertu Road West
Dorval, QC, H4S 1Y9, Canada
Tel.: (514) 855-5000
Fax: (514) 855-7401
Toll Free: (866) 855-5001
Web Site: www.bombardier.com
Aircraft Mfr
S.I.C.: 3721
N.A.I.C.S.: 336411

Subsidiaries:

Bombardier Aerospace (1)
400 Chemin De La Cote Vertu W
Dorval, QC, H4S 1Y9, Canada (100%)
Tel.: (514) 855-5000
Fax: (514) 855-4381
Web Site: www.aerospace.bombardier.com
Rev.: $6,972,768,256
Emp.: 57,000
Mfr. of Civil Aircraft
Export
S.I.C.: 3721
N.A.I.C.S.: 336411
Guy C. Hachey *(Pres & COO)*
Mike Arcamone *(Pres-Comml Aircraft)*
Eric Martel *(Pres-Bus Aircraft)*
Michel Ouellette *(Pres-Customer Svcs, Specialized & Amphibious Aircraft)*
Charles R. Fuller *(Sr VP-Comml Aircraft)*
Raymond Jones *(Sr VP-Sls, Mktg & Asset Mgmt-Comml Aircraft)*

Divisions:

Bombardier Inc.-De Havilland (2)
123 Garratt Blvd
Downsview, ON, M3K 1Y5, Canada (100%)
Tel.: (416) 633-7310
Fax: (416) 375-4546
Web Site: www.bombardier.com
Emp.: 2,600
S.I.C.: 3721
N.A.I.C.S.: 336411
Steve Aliment *(VP-Comml)*

U.S. Divisions:

Bombardier - Learjet (2)
1919 14th St Ste 800
Boulder, CO 80302-5327 CO
Tel.: (303) 546-0017
Fax: (303) 447-1150
E-Mail: info@learjet.com
Web Site: www.learjet.com
Emp.: 2
Aircraft Dealers
S.I.C.: 5571
N.A.I.C.S.: 441228

Bombardier - Learjet (2)
1 Learjet Way
Wichita, KS 67209-2924 DE
Mailing Address:
PO Box 7707
Wichita, KS 67277-7707
Tel.: (316) 946-2000
Telex: 417441
Fax: (316) 946-2163
Emp.: 2,500
Mfr of Business Jet Aircraft; Modification, Maintenance & Sub-Contracting for Major Aerospace Manufacturers
Export
S.I.C.: 3721
N.A.I.C.S.: 336411
Christopher Krawshaw *(Treas & VP-Fin)*

Bombardier Aerospace (2)
2400 Aviation Way
Bridgeport, WV 26330-9729 WV
Tel.: (304) 842-6300 (100%)
Fax: (304) 848-5160
Web Site: www.bombardier.com
Emp.: 330
Aircraft Servicing & Repairing
S.I.C.: 4581
N.A.I.C.S.: 488190
Guy C. Hachey *(Pres & COO)*
Tim White *(Sr VP-Sls-West)*

Non-U.S. Subsidiary:

Bombardier Aerospace Belfast (2)
Airport Rd
Belfast, BT3 9DZ, United Kingdom (100%)
Tel.: (44) 2890458444
Fax: (44) 2890733396
E-Mail: info@aero.bombardier.com
Web Site: www.aero.bombardier.com
Emp.: 5,000
Aircraft Mfr
S.I.C.: 3519
N.A.I.C.S.: 333618
Michael Ryan *(VP & Gen Mgr)*

Bombardier Inc.-Real Estate Services (1)
2505 Rue Des Nations Ste 200
Saint Laurent, QC, H4R 3C8, Canada (100%)
Tel.: (514) 335-9511
Fax: (514) 335-7007
Web Site: www.boisfranc.com
Sales Range: $10-24.9 Million
Emp.: 5
Real Estate Lot Seller
S.I.C.: 6531
N.A.I.C.S.: 531390
Alfred N. Corriveau *(Pres)*
Michelle Gauthier *(Sec)*

Bombardier Inc.—(Continued)

Bombardier Transportation North America Inc (1)
1101 Parent Street
Saint-Bruno, QC, J3V 6E6, Canada
Tel.: (450) 441-2020
Fax: (450) 441-1515
Transportation Services
S.I.C.: 4789
N.A.I.C.S.: 488999

U.S. Subsidiaries:

Bombardier Capital Incorporated (1)
261 Mountain View Dr
Colchester, VT 05446 (100%)
Tel.: (904) 288-1000
Fax: (802) 764-5244
Toll Free: (800) 949-5568
Web Site: www.bombardier.com
Emp.: 1,100
Lending, Leasing & Asset Management Services to A Customer Base In Retail, Mortgage, Inventory, Commercial & Industrial Financing Markets
S.I.C.: 6159
N.A.I.C.S.: 522220

Subsidiaries:

Bombardier Credit Receivables Corporation (2)
261 Mountain View Dr
Colchester, VT 05446-5823
Tel.: (802) 764-5232
Fax: (802) 764-5244
Web Site: www.bombardier.com
S.I.C.: 3519
N.A.I.C.S.: 333618

RJ Finance Corp. One (2)
261 Mountain View Dr
Colchester, VT 05446-5823
Tel.: (802) 764-5232
Fax: (802) 764-5244
Web Site: www.bombardier.com
Finance Agency
S.I.C.: 6163
N.A.I.C.S.: 522310

Non-U.S. Subsidiaries:

Bombardier Capital International B.V. (2)
Deboelelaan 7
Amsterdam, HJ 1083, Netherlands
Tel.: (31) 206239263
Fax: (31) 16311059
Emp.: 2
S.I.C.: 3519
N.A.I.C.S.: 333618

Bombardier Corp. (1)
3400 Waterview Pkwy Ste 400
Richardson, TX 75080 TX
Tel.: (972) 720-2400
Fax: (972) 720-2473
Web Site: www.services.bombardier.com
Rev.: $8,700,000
Emp.: 800
Aircraft & Parts
S.I.C.: 5088
N.A.I.C.S.: 423860
Pierre Beaudoin *(Pres & CEO)*

Bombardier Transportation (Holdings) USA Inc. (1)
1501 Lebanon Church Rd
Pittsburgh, PA 15236-1406
Tel.: (412) 655-5700
Fax: (412) 655-5566
Investment Management Services
S.I.C.: 6211
N.A.I.C.S.: 523999

Non-U.S. Subsidiaries:

Bombardier European Holdings, S.L.U. (1)
Rambla de Catalunya 43-30 Izq
08007 Barcelona, Spain
Tel.: (34) 93 487 4187
Fax: (34) 93 488 0358
Web Site: www.bombardier.com
Emp.: 15
Railway Signal Equipment Mfr
S.I.C.: 3291
N.A.I.C.S.: 327910

Bombardier European Investments, S.L. (1)
Edif Louis Pasteur-Avda Del Juncal 22-24 4 Plta
San Sebastian de los Reyes, 28703 Madrid, Spain
Tel.: (34) 91 657 9100
Fax: (34) 91 6614610
Emp.: 15
Railway Transportation Equipment Mfr
S.I.C.: 3799
N.A.I.C.S.: 336999
Javier Mng Dir *(Mng Dir)*

Bombardier (Mauritius) Ltd (1)
5th Floor Ebene Esplanade 24 CyberCity
Ebene, Mauritius
Tel.: (230) 210 9000
Fax: (230) 4012301
Web Site: www.bombardiermauritius.com
Emp.: 1
Transportation Services
S.I.C.: 4789
N.A.I.C.S.: 488999

Bombardier Transpaortation Israel Ltd. (1)
11 Menachem Begin Street
PO Box 3463
Ramat Gan, 52136, Israel
Tel.: (972) 3 612 1106
Fax: (972) 3 612 1107
Emp.: 15
Railway Transportation Services
S.I.C.: 4789
N.A.I.C.S.: 488210
Yael Dror *(Gen Mgr)*

Bombardier Transport France S.A.S. (1)
1 Place Des Ateliers
59154 Crespin, France
Tel.: (33) 3 27 23 53 00
Fax: (33) 3 27 35 16 24
Emp.: 2,000
Railcar Mfr
S.I.C.: 3743
N.A.I.C.S.: 336510
Tonna Christian *(Dir)*

Division:

Bombardier Transport France S.A.S. - Services Division (2)
Les Collines de l Arche Immeuble Opera E
92057 Paris, France
Tel.: (33) 1 41 45 0808
Fax: (33) 1 47 73 7451
Web Site: www.bombardier.com
Emp.: 1
Railroad Rolling Stock Mfr
S.I.C.: 3743
N.A.I.C.S.: 336510
Laurent Troger *(Pres)*

Bombardier Transportation Australia Pty. Ltd. (1)
3rd Floor North Tower John Oxley Center
339 Coronation Drive
Milton, Brisbane, QLD, 4064, Australia
Tel.: (61) 738582400
Fax: (61) 733672422
Emp.: 6
Rail Transportation Services
S.I.C.: 4789
N.A.I.C.S.: 488210

Bombardier Transportation Austria GmbH (1)
Hermann Gebauer Strasse 5
1220 Vienna, 1220, Austria
Tel.: (43) 1 25 110 0
Fax: (43) 1 25 110 300
Emp.: 65
Light Rail Vehicle Mfr & Distr
S.I.C.: 3519
N.A.I.C.S.: 333618
Bruno Kittner *(Gen Mgr)*

Bombardier Transportation Brasil Ltda. (1)
Av Das Nacoes Unidas 4 777 Conjunto 7 A
Sao Paulo, 05477-000, Brazil
Tel.: (55) 1135384700
Fax: (55) 1135384700
Transportation Equipment Mfr
S.I.C.: 3799
N.A.I.C.S.: 336999

Bombardier Transportation (China) Ltd. (1)
Room 2003-2005 Suite A China Shine Plaza No 9 Lin He Xi Road
Tian He District, Guangzhou, Guangdong, v, China
Tel.: (86) 20 3810 8791
Fax: (86) 20 3847 8259
Web Site: www.cn.bombardier.com
Transport Equipment Parts & Accessories Mfr
S.I.C.: 2396
N.A.I.C.S.: 336360

Bombardier Transportation Denmark A/S (1)
Toldbodgade 39
8900 Randers, Denmark
Tel.: (45) 86 42 53 00
Fax: (45) 86 41 57 00
Web Site: www.dk.bombardier.com
Emp.: 4
Railroad Rolling Stock Renovation
S.I.C.: 3743
N.A.I.C.S.: 336510
Kette Nortentost *(Plant Mgr)*

Bombardier Transportation Equipment (Suzhou) Co., Ltd. (1)
1 Qiming Road Free Trade Zone Suzhou Industrial Park
Suzhou, Jiangsu, 215121, China
Tel.: (86) 512 6733 3200
Fax: (86) 512 6733 3211
Emp.: 22
Propulsion & Controls Machinery Mfr
S.I.C.: 3559
N.A.I.C.S.: 333249
Monika David *(Gen Mgr)*

Bombardier Transportation GmbH (1)
Schoneberger Ufer 1
10785 Berlin, Germany
Tel.: (49) 30986070
Fax: (49) 30986072000
Web Site: www.bombardier.com
Sales Range: $1-4.9 Billion
Emp.: 31,570
Rail Vehicles for Urban & Mainline Operations, Modernization of Rolling Stock & Operations & Maintenance Services
S.I.C.: 3743
N.A.I.C.S.: 336510
Lutz Bertling *(Pres & COO)*

Subsidiaries:

Bombardier Transportation (Bahntechnologie) Germany GmbH (2)
Kablower Weg 89
12526 Berlin, Germany (100%)
Tel.: (49) 3067931509
Fax: (49) 30 67 93 13 09
Emp.: 160
Light Rail & Locomotives Mfr
S.I.C.: 3519
N.A.I.C.S.: 333618

Bombardier Transportation GmbH & Co. KG (2)
Julicher Str 213 237
D 52070 Aachen, Germany (100%)
Tel.: (49) 24118210
Fax: (49) 2411821214
Web Site: www.transportation.bombardier.com
Emp.: 500
Train & Railway Equipment Mfr
S.I.C.: 3519
N.A.I.C.S.: 333618
Dirk Reuters *(Gen Mgr)*

Non-U.S. Subsidiaries:

Bombardier Transportation AB (2)
Ostra Ringvagan 2
S 72173 Vasteras, Sweden
Tel.: (46) 21317000
Telex: 40720 ASEAVAS
Fax: (46) 108528200
Web Site: www.bombardier.com
Emp.: 2,000
Railway Equipment & Weather Data Systems Mfr
S.I.C.: 3621
N.A.I.C.S.: 335312
Klas Wahlberg *(Mng Dir)*

Bombardier Transportation AG (2)
Zurcher Strasse 39
8401 Winterthur, Switzerland
Tel.: (41) 522641010
Telex: 896131 slmch
Fax: (41) 522641101
E-Mail: elias.kwasnicki@ch.transport.bombardier.com
Web Site: www.transportation.bombardier.com
Emp.: 50
Locomotives & Gears Mfr
S.I.C.: 3519
N.A.I.C.S.: 333618
Elias Kwasnicki *(Gen Mgr)*

Bombardier Transportation Belgium (2)
Vaartdijkstraat 5
8200 Brugge, Belgium (100%)
Tel.: (32) 50401111
Fax: (32) 5041818
Web Site: www.bombardier.com
Sales Range: $250-299.9 Million
Emp.: 800
Mfr. of Locomotives, Railway Freight & Passenger Cars, Subway Cars & Light Rail Vehicles
S.I.C.: 3743
N.A.I.C.S.: 336510
Paul Troch *(Gen Mgr)*

Bombardier Transportation Czech Republic A/S (2)
Sv Cecha 1205
CR 47001 Ceska Lipa, Czech Republic
Tel.: (420) 487802111
Fax: (420) 487802103
E-Mail: info@bombardier.com
Web Site: www.bombardier.com
Emp.: 1,000
Component Mfr for Rolling Stock
S.I.C.: 3519
N.A.I.C.S.: 333618
Jiri Madera *(Gen Mgr)*

Bombardier Transportation SA (2)
Zone Industrielle A 26
CH 1844 Villeneuve, Switzerland (100%)
Tel.: (41) 219670505
Fax: (41) 219670500
Web Site: www.transportbombardier.com
Emp.: 300
Locomotives & Gears Mfr
S.I.C.: 3519
N.A.I.C.S.: 333618
Neil Karby *(Controller)*

Bombardier Transportation UK Ltd. (2)
Litchurch Lane
Derby, DE24 8AD, United Kingdom (100%)
Tel.: (44) 1332344666
Fax: (44) 1332266271
Web Site: www.transportation.bombardier.com
Sales Range: $25-49.9 Million
Emp.: 1,800
Transportation Equipment
S.I.C.: 4731
N.A.I.C.S.: 488510

Bombardier Transportation (2)
1101 Parent St
Saint-Bruno, QC, J3V 6E6, Canada (100%)
Tel.: (450) 441-2020
Fax: (450) 441-1515
Web Site: www.bombardier.com
Sls.: $1,158,210,048
Emp.: 600
Mfr. of Passenger Rail & Freight Cars; Urban, Suburban & Intercity Vehicles as Well as TurnKey Rail Transit Systems Worldwide
S.I.C.: 3743
N.A.I.C.S.: 336510
Raymond Bachant *(Pres)*
Genevieve Lacroix *(Sec)*

Division:

Bombardier, Inc.-Transit Systems (3)
5095 Taylor Kidd Blvd County Rd 23
Millhaven, ON, K7M 6J9, Canada (100%)
Mailing Address:
PO Box 220
Kingston, ON, K7M 6R2, Canada
Tel.: (613) 384-3100
Fax: (613) 384-5244

E-Mail: gerri.stubinsky@ca.transport.bombardier.com
Emp.: 220
Street Car Engineering Design Services
S.I.C.: 3519
N.A.I.C.S.: 333618
Michael Fetsko *(VP)*

U.S. Subsidiaries:

Bombardier Mass Transit Corporation (3)
71 Wall St
Plattsburgh, NY 12901-3755
Tel.: (518) 566-0150
Fax: (518) 566-0151
E-Mail: info@bombardier.com
Emp.: 350
Locomotive Mfr
S.I.C.: 3519
N.A.I.C.S.: 333618

Bombardier Transit Corporation (3)
261 Mountain View Dr
Burlington, VT 05446 (100%)
Tel.: (802) 764-5232
Fax: (802) 764-5244
Toll Free: (800) 949-5568
Web Site: www.bombardiertransportation.com
Emp.: 4
Manufactures of Rail Cars
S.I.C.: 8999
N.A.I.C.S.: 541690

Bombardier Transportation (3)
5727 Northwest 7th St Box 294
Miami, FL 33126
Tel.: (305) 871-4220
Fax: (305) 871-9273
Emp.: 12
S.I.C.: 8712
N.A.I.C.S.: 541310

Bombardier Transportation (3)
1501 Lebanon Church Rd
Pittsburgh, PA 15236-1406 PA
Tel.: (412) 655-5700 (100%)
Fax: (412) 655-5316
Sales Range: $1-9.9 Million
Emp.: 1,200
Production of Railroad Vehicles & Equipment
S.I.C.: 3743
N.A.I.C.S.: 336510
Michael Fetsko *(VP-Automated People Movers-Sys Div)*

Non-U.S. Subsidiaries:

Bombardier Mexico, S.A. De C.V. (3)
Isaac Newton 1650
Parque Industrial AJ Bermudez, Chihuahua, 32470, Mexico (100%)
Tel.: (52) 6923700
Fax: (52) 6923737
Emp.: 350
S.I.C.: 3519
N.A.I.C.S.: 333618

Bombardier-Wien Schienenfahrzeuge AG (3)
Donaufelder Strasse 73 79
1211 Vienna, Austria
Tel.: (43) 125110
Telex: (47) 114791
Fax: (43) 1251108
Emp.: 600
Light Rail Vehicles Mfr
S.I.C.: 8742
N.A.I.C.S.: 541611

Bombardier (3)
Pl Des Ateliers
59154 Crespin, France
Tel.: (33) 327235300
Fax: (33) 327351624
Emp.: 2,000
Mfr. of Double-Decker, Self-Propelled Commuter Cars, Subway Cars, Turbo Trains & Cars for the French High-Speed TGV train
S.I.C.: 3743
N.A.I.C.S.: 336510
Jean Berze *(Pres)*

Bombardier Transportation Holdings (Thailand) Ltd. (1)
3354/16-19 Manorom Bldg 6th floor Rama 4 Rd Klongton Klontoey
10110 Bangkok, Thailand
Tel.: (66) 2 672 8290
Fax: (66) 2 249 8519
Web Site: www.bombardier.com
Investment Management Services
S.I.C.: 6799
N.A.I.C.S.: 523920

Bombardier Transportation (Holdings) UK Ltd. (1)
Derby Carriage Works
Derby, DE24 8AD, United Kingdom
Tel.: (44) 1332 344666
Fax: (44) 1332 266271
Emp.: 180
Railroad Equipment Mfr
S.I.C.: 3743
N.A.I.C.S.: 336510
Andy Derbyshire *(Gen Dir)*
Hiroshi Fujii *(Gen Dir)*

Bombardier Transportation Korea Ltd. (1)
4th Fl Samwha Bldg 21 Sokong-dong
Joong-ku, 100-070 Seoul, Korea (South)
Tel.: (82) 2 776 6133
Fax: (82) 2 776 6020
E-Mail: btkoea6@kornet.net
Emp.: 2
Railroad Rolling Stock Mfr
S.I.C.: 3743
N.A.I.C.S.: 336510
Wonhee Lee *(Dir-Fin)*

Bombardier Transportation (Malaysia) Sdn. Bhd. (1)
Unit 2A-22-2 Level 22 Block 2A Plz Sentral
Jalan Stesen Sentral 5
Kuala Lumpur Sentral, 50470 Kuala Lumpur, Malaysia
Tel.: (60) 3 2261 4369
Fax: (60) 3 2261 4368
Web Site: www.bombardier.com
Transportation Services
S.I.C.: 4789
N.A.I.C.S.: 488999

Bombardier Transportation MAV Hungary Kft. (1)
Allomas Satany 19
2120 Dunakeszi, Hungary
Tel.: (36) 27 542 100
Fax: (36) 27 342 997
Web Site: www.bombardier.com
Railroad Rolling Stock Mfr
S.I.C.: 3743
N.A.I.C.S.: 336510

Bombardier Transportation (Netherland) B.V. (1)
De Ruyterkade 6
Amsterdam, 1013 AA, Netherlands
Tel.: (31) 20 344 5720
Fax: (31) 20 344 5728
Emp.: 21
Transportation Services
S.I.C.: 4789
N.A.I.C.S.: 488999
Roger Hall *(Mgr-Sls)*

Bombardier Transportation Norway AS (1)
Stasjonsveien 1
PO Box 83
2011 Strommen, Norway
Tel.: (47) 63 80 9600
Fax: (47) 63 80 9601
Web Site: www.bombardier.com
Transportation Equipment Mfr
S.I.C.: 3799
N.A.I.C.S.: 336999

Bombardier Transportation (Obsluga Klienta) Polska Sp. z.o.o. (1)
ul Aleksandrowska 67/93
91-205 Lodz, Poland
Tel.: (48) 42 613 2666
Fax: (48) 42 613 2699
Web Site: www.bombardier.com
Transportation Equipment Mfr
S.I.C.: 3799
N.A.I.C.S.: 336999

Bombardier Transportation Polska Sp. z.o.o. (1)
ul Fabryczna 12
53-609 Wroclaw, Poland
Tel.: (48) 71 356 2317
Fax: (48) 71 355 5731
Web Site: www.bombardier.com
Emp.: 500
Transportation Equipment Mfr
S.I.C.: 3799
N.A.I.C.S.: 336999
Krzysztof Gablankowski *(Gen Mgr)*

Bombardier Transportation Portugal, S.A. (1)
Edificio Art
1998-028 Lisbon, Portugal
Tel.: (351) 21 496 9110
Fax: (351) 21 496 9200
Web Site: www.bombardier.com
Emp.: 10
Railway Equipment Mfr
S.I.C.: 3699
N.A.I.C.S.: 335999
Mario Dominguez *(Chm & Pres)*

Bombardier Transportation (Propulsion & Controls) Germany GmbH (1)
Am Rathenaupark
16761 Hennigsdorf Berlin, Germany
Tel.: (49) 3302 89 0
Fax: (49) 3302892088
Emp.: 250
Railroad Rolling Stock Mfr
S.I.C.: 3743
N.A.I.C.S.: 336510
Ragnar Joris *(Chm)*

Bombardier Transportation (Rail Engineering) Polska Sp. z o.o (1)
ul Ogrodowa 58
00-876 Warsaw, Poland
Tel.: (48) 22 520 2122
Fax: (48) 22 520 2120
Web Site: www.bombardier.com
Emp.: 50
Railroad Rolling Stock Mfr
S.I.C.: 3743
N.A.I.C.S.: 336510
Krzysztof Meczkowski *(Mgr-Sls)*

Bombardier Transportation (Rolling Stock) UK Ltd (1)
Derby Carriage Works Litchurch Lane
Derby, DE24 8AD, United Kingdom
Tel.: (44) 1332257500
Fax: (44) 1332371950
Emp.: 200
Railroad Equipment Mfr
S.I.C.: 3743
N.A.I.C.S.: 336510
Dennis Moss *(Mng Dir)*

Bombardier Transportation Romania SRL (1)
90 Calea 13 Septembrie Grand Offices 2nd Floor Sector 5
50726 Bucharest, Romania
Tel.: (40) 21 403 44 25
Fax: (40) 21 403 44 23
Emp.: 3
Transportation Services
S.I.C.: 4789
N.A.I.C.S.: 488999
Mircea Marian *(Country Mgr)*

Bombardier Transportation (Rus) Ltd. (1)
26 Denisovsky Per
Moscow, 105005, Russia
Tel.: (7) 495 775 1830
Fax: (7) 495 775 1832
Web Site: www.bombardier.com
Emp.: 8
Transportation Services
S.I.C.: 4789
N.A.I.C.S.: 488999
Nikolay Sannikov *(Dir-Transportation)*

Bombardier Transportation (Shared Services) Philippines Inc. (1)
14th Fl TGU Tower JM Del Mar Avenue
Corner Salinas Drive Asiatown
I T Park Apas, Cebu, 6000, Philippines
Tel.: (63) 32 505 1920
Fax: (63) 32 505 1902
Web Site: www.bombardier.com
Emp.: 156
Financial Management Services
S.I.C.: 6211
N.A.I.C.S.: 523999
Heiko Kaeffer *(Gen Mgr)*

Bombardier Transportation Shared Services Romania SRL (1)
Power Business Center Calea Dorobantilor Nr 18-20
400117 Cluj-Napoca, Romania
Tel.: (40) 264 502 900
Fax: (40) 264 502 902
Emp.: 30
Transportation Services
S.I.C.: 4789
N.A.I.C.S.: 488999

Bombardier Transportation (Signal) Germany GmbH (1)
Wolfenbutteler Strasse 86 / Oberbergstr 5
Braunschweig, 38102, Germany
Tel.: (49) 5312240
Fax: (49) 5312241065
Emp.: 15
Electric & Electronic Component Mfr
S.I.C.: 3291
N.A.I.C.S.: 327910
Johann Konigshofer *(Gen Mgr)*

Bombardier Transportation South Africa (Pty.) Ltd (1)
22 Milkyway Avenue Linbro Business Park
Marlboro Drive
Johannesburg, Gauteng, 2196, South Africa
Tel.: (27) 11 997 8899
Fax: (27) 11 997 8501
Web Site: www.bombardier.com
Emp.: 22
Transportation Services
S.I.C.: 4789
N.A.I.C.S.: 488999
Calvin Feher *(Gen Mgr)*

Bombardier Transportation (Switzerland) Ltd. (1)
Brown Boveri-Strasse 5
CH-8050 Zurich, Switzerland
Tel.: (41) 44 318 33 33
Fax: (41) 44 318 30 80
E-Mail: info@ch.transport.bombardier.com
Web Site: www.bombardier-transportation.ch
Emp.: 900
Rail Transportation Equipment Distr
S.I.C.: 5088
N.A.I.C.S.: 423860
Stephane Wettstein *(Mng Dir & Chief Country Mgr)*

Bombardier Transportation (ZWUS) Polska Sp. z o.o. (1)
Ul Modelarska 12
40-142 Katowice, Poland
Tel.: (48) 32 730 5000
Fax: (48) 32 730 5700
E-Mail: komunikacja.zwus@pl.transport.bombardier.com
Emp.: 50
Rail Transportation Services
S.I.C.: 4789
N.A.I.C.S.: 488210
Slawomir Nalewajka *(Gen Mgr)*

THE BOMBAY BURMAH TRADING CORPORATION LIMITED

9 Wallace Street Fort
Mumbai, Maharashtra, 400 001, India
Tel.: (91) 22 22079351
Fax: (91) 22 22071612
E-Mail: bbtcl@bom2.vsnl.net.in
Web Site: www.bbtcl.com
501425—(BOM)
Rev.: $1,226,107,767
Assets: $634,553,173
Liabilities: $276,504,485
Net Worth: $358,048,689
Earnings: $24,523,247
Fiscal Year-end: 03/31/13

Business Description:
Tea Plantation Production Services & Tea Distr
S.I.C.: 0139
N.A.I.C.S.: 111998

Personnel:
Nusli N. Wadia *(Chm)*
Anil Kumar Hirjee *(Vice Chm)*
Ashok Panjwani *(Mng Dir)*

The Bombay Burmah Trading Corporation Limited—(Continued)

Ness N. Wadia *(Mng Dir)*
Nitin H. Datanwala *(Compliance Officer, Sec & VP)*
Board of Directors:
Nusli N. Wadia
Madhav Laxman Apte
Vinita Bali
Patrick Kennedy Cassels
Anil Kumar Hirjee
Ashok Panjwani
B. N. B. Tao
Darius Erach Udwadia
Jehangir N. Wadia
Ness N. Wadia
Legal Counsel:
Udwadia Udeshi & Argus Partners
Elphinstone House 1st Floor 17 Murzban Road
Mumbai, India
Crawford Bayley & Co.
State Bank Building 4th Floor Hutatma Chowk Fountain
Mumbai, India
Transfer Agent:
Sharepro Services (India) Private Limited
13 AB Samhita Warehousing Complex II Floor
Sakinaka Telephone Lane
Off Andheri Kurla Rd Sakinaka, Mumbai, India

Subsidiary:

Electromags Autmotive Products Private Limited **(1)**
342/343 2nd Cross Street Nehru Nagar
Kottivakkam, Chennai, 600 096, India
Tel.: (91) 44 2492 9277
Fax: (91) 44 2492 9336
E-Mail: enquiry@eapl.co.in
Web Site: www.electromags.com
Automobile Parts Mfr
S.I.C.: 3711
N.A.I.C.S.: 336111

Non-U.S. Subsidiary:

Island Horti-Tech Holdings Pte. Limited **(1)**
Plot 3 Joan Road
Singapore, Singapore 298897
Tel.: (65) 62549867
Fax: (65) 62538989
Emp.: 5
Investment Management Services
S.I.C.: 6282
N.A.I.C.S.: 523920
Gadgil Jayant *(Mng Dir)*

Subsidiary:

Island Landscape & Nursery Pte Ltd **(2)**
Plot 13 Joan Road / Thomson Road PSA Nursery
Singapore, 298897, Singapore
Tel.: (65) 6254 9867
Fax: (65) 6253 8989
E-Mail: enquiries@islandgroup.com.sg
Web Site: www.islandgroup.com.sg
Landscaping & Nursery Services
S.I.C.: 0783
N.A.I.C.S.: 561730
Bipin Krishna *(Sr Mgr-Production)*

BOMBAY CYCLE & MOTOR AGENCY LIMITED

534 SVP Road Opera House
Mumbai, Maharashtra, 400 007, India
Tel.: (91) 22 4028 7104
Fax: (91) 22 23634527
E-Mail: investors@bcma.in
Web Site: www.bcma.in
501430—(BOM)
Rev.: $1,220,286
Assets: $2,736,640
Liabilities: $1,350,805
Net Worth: $1,385,835
Earnings: $182,079
Fiscal Year-end: 03/31/13
Business Description:
Automobile Sales & Maintenance Services
S.I.C.: 5012
N.A.I.C.S.: 423110
Personnel:
Chirag C. Doshi *(Chm)*
Mahendra J. Kharwa *(Sr Accts Officer-Hospitality Div)*
T. D. Lal *(Compliance Officer)*
Board of Directors:
Chirag C. Doshi
Chakor L. Doshi
T. D. Lal
Sanjay P. Muthe
Kanika G. Sanger
Transfer Agent:
TSR Darashaw Ltd.
6-10 Haji Moosa Patrawala Industrial Estate 20 Dr E Moses Road
Near Famous Studio Mahalaxmi, Mumbai, India

BOMBAY OXYGEN CORPORATION LIMITED

22/B Mittal Tower 210
Nariman Point, Mumbai, 400021, India
Tel.: (91) 22 66107503
Fax: (91) 22 66107513
E-Mail: bomoxy@mtnl.net.in
Web Site: www.bomoxy.com
Year Founded: 1960
509470—(BOM)
Rev.: $5,177,388
Assets: $38,226,032
Liabilities: $2,142,928
Net Worth: $36,083,104
Earnings: ($1,240,363)
Fiscal Year-end: 03/31/13
Business Description:
Industrial Gas Mfr
S.I.C.: 2813
N.A.I.C.S.: 325120
Personnel:
B. P. Mehta *(Compliance Officer)*
Board of Directors:
Shyam M. Ruia
Ajit M. Ghelani
Nirmal P. Jhunjhunwala
Ibrahim A. Rahimtoola
Amay S. Ruia
Mohan Bir Singh

BOMBAY RAYON FASHIONS LIMITED

D1st Floor Oberoi Gardens Estate
Chandivali Farms Road
Chandivali, Mumbai, 400072, India
Tel.: (91) 2239858800
Fax: (91) 2228476992
Web Site: www.bombayrayon.com
BRFL—(NSE)
Rev.: $615,941,442
Assets: $1,492,872,318
Liabilities: $954,615,330
Net Worth: $538,256,988
Earnings: $23,983,344
Emp.: 22,534
Fiscal Year-end: 03/31/13
Business Description:
Textile Garments Mfr & Distr
S.I.C.: 2299
N.A.I.C.S.: 313310
Personnel:
Aman Agrawal *(Vice Chm)*
Naseer Ahmed *(Vice Chm)*
Prashant Agrawal *(Mng Dir)*
Prachi Deshpande *(Compliance Officer & Sec)*
Board of Directors:
Janardan D. Agrawal
Aman Agrawal
M. M. Agrawal
Prashant Agrawal
Naseer Ahmed
A. Arumugham
A. R. Mundra
Babu Nambiar
Mukul Sarkar
Suresh Vishwasrao
Transfer Agent:
Intime Spectrum Registry Limited
C 13 Pannalal Silk Mills Compounds L B S Marg Bhandup West
Mumbai, India

Non-U.S. Subsidiary:

DPJ Clothing Ltd. **(1)**
Unit 4 Wadsworth Business Centre
Greenford, London, UB6 7LQ, United Kingdom
Tel.: (44) 20 8998 0777
Fax: (44) 20 8991 2515
E-Mail: office@dpjcloth.co.uk
Emp.: 1
Apparel & Accessories Distr
S.I.C.: 5137
N.A.I.C.S.: 424330

BOMBAY STOCK EXCHANGE LIMITED

Phiroze Jeejeebhoy Towers Dalal St
Mumbai, 400001, India
Tel.: (91) 2222721233
Fax: (91) 2222721919
E-Mail: vinay.dhopavkar@bseindia.com
Web Site: www.bseindia.com
Year Founded: 1875
Sales Range: $25-49.9 Million
Business Description:
Stock Exchange Services
S.I.C.: 6231
N.A.I.C.S.: 523210
Personnel:
Ashish Kumar Chauhan *(CEO & Mng Dir)*
L. P. Aggarwal *(CFO)*
Board of Directors:
S. S. Bolar
Ishaat Hussain
S. Jambunathan
Prakash R. Kacholia
Jitesh Khosla
Vivek Kulkarni
Balkishan Mohta
Andreas Preuss
S. Ramadorai
Sudipto Sarkar
Siddharth J. Shah
P. P. Vora

BOMBAY SWADESHI STORES LTD.

B wing 1st Floor Todi Estate Sunmill Compound
Lower Parel W, Mumbai, 400 013, India
Tel.: (91) 22 40318888
Fax: (91) 22 40318800
E-Mail: support@bombaystore.com
Web Site: www.thebombaystore.com
531276—(BOM)
Business Description:
Departmental Stores Operating Services
S.I.C.: 5311
N.A.I.C.S.: 452111
Personnel:
Milan Dalal *(Chm)*
Asim Dalal *(Mng Dir)*
John Varughese *(Compliance Officer)*

BOMBRIL S.A.

Via Anchieta Km 14 S/N - Bairro Rudge Ramos
Distrito Industrial, Sao Bernardo do Campo, Sao Paulo, Brazil 09696-000
Tel.: (55) 11 4366 1001
Fax: (55) 11 4366 1001
E-Mail: exportacao@bombril.com.br
Web Site: www.bombril.com.br
Year Founded: 1948
BOBR3—(BRAZ)
Emp.: 2,500
Business Description:
Household Products Mfr
S.I.C.: 2844
N.A.I.C.S.: 325611
Personnel:
Pedro de Souza Dias Brandi *(Dir-IR)*

BONA FILM GROUP LIMITED

11/F Guan Hu Garden 3 105 Yao Jia Yuan Road
Chaoyang District, Beijing, 100025, China
Tel.: (86) 10 5928 3663
Fax: (86) 10 5928 3383
Web Site: www.bonafilm.cn
Year Founded: 2003
BONA—(NASDAQ)
Rev.: $142,282,919
Assets: $316,565,660
Liabilities: $126,920,070
Net Worth: $189,645,590
Earnings: ($1,568,382)
Emp.: 984
Fiscal Year-end: 12/31/12
Business Description:
Motion Picture Distr & Production
S.I.C.: 7829
N.A.I.C.S.: 512120
Personnel:
Doong Yu *(Chm, CEO & Founder)*
Amy W. Xu *(CFO)*
Jeffrey Chan *(COO)*
Board of Directors:
Doong Yu
Jeffrey Chan
Jack Q. Gao
Jieceng Lian
Peixin Xu

BONANZA RESOURCES CORP.

14727 129th Street
Edmonton, AB, T6V 1C4, Canada
Tel.: (780) 887-4998
Year Founded: 2012
Business Description:
Quartz & Other Mineral Mining
S.I.C.: 3299
N.A.I.C.S.: 327999
Personnel:
Wayne Cadence *(Pres, CEO, CFO, Treas & Sec)*
Board of Directors:
Wayne Cadence

BONAPARTE RESOURCES INC.

5384B Imperial Street
Burnaby, BC, V5J 1E6, Canada
Tel.: (604) 484-8750
Fax: (604) 599-0222
E-Mail: info@bonaparteresources.ca
Web Site: www.bonaparteresources.ca
Year Founded: 2007
BON—(TSXV)
Int. Income: $99
Assets: $139,608
Liabilities: $103,399
Net Worth: $36,209
Earnings: ($1,735,691)
Fiscal Year-end: 08/31/13
Business Description:
Mineral Exploration Services
S.I.C.: 1081
N.A.I.C.S.: 213114
Personnel:
T. Randall Saunders *(Pres, CEO & Sec)*
Robert Jamieson *(CFO)*
Board of Directors:
Mike England
Robert Jamieson

Tom McCandless
William Pettigrew
T. Randall Saunders

Legal Counsel:
Clark Wilson LLP
HSBC Building 800 - 885 West Georgia Street
Vancouver, BC, V6C 3H1, Canada

Transfer Agent:
Computershare Investor Services Inc.
3rd Floor 510 Burrard St
V6C 3B9 Vancouver, BC, Canada

BONATLA PROPERTY HOLDINGS LIMITED

31 8th Street
Houghton, Johannesburg, 2198, South Africa
Mailing Address:
PO Box 787133
Sandton, 2146, South Africa
Tel.: (27) 11 442 4944
Fax: (27) 11 442 4943
Web Site: www.bonatla.com
BNT—(JSE)
Rev.: $3,296,826
Assets: $58,483,439
Liabilities: $16,391,640
Net Worth: $42,091,799
Earnings: ($3,055,665)
Fiscal Year-end: 12/31/12

Business Description:
Investment Management Services
S.I.C.: 6211
N.A.I.C.S.: 523999

Personnel:
Niki G. Vontas *(CEO)*

Board of Directors:
Mackie H. Brodie
C. Douglas
R. L. Rainier
W. Voigt
Niki G. Vontas

Transfer Agent:
Computershare Investor Services (Pty) Limited
Ground Floor 70 Marshall Street
Johannesburg, South Africa

BONAVISTA ENERGY CORPORATION

1500 525 - 8th Ave SW
Calgary, AB, T2P 1G1, Canada
Tel.: (403) 213-4300
Fax: (403) 262-5184
E-Mail: inv_rel@bonavistaenergy.com
Web Site: www.bonavistaenergy.com
BNP—(TSX)
Rev.: $827,512,704
Assets: $4,038,556,145
Liabilities: $1,766,336,761
Net Worth: $2,272,219,384
Earnings: $63,818,072
Emp.: 350
Fiscal Year-end: 12/31/12

Business Description:
Oil & Gas Services
S.I.C.: 3533
N.A.I.C.S.: 333132

Personnel:
Keith A. J. MacPhail *(Chm)*
Ronald J. Poelzer *(Vice Chm)*
Jason E. Skehar *(Pres & CEO)*
Glenn A. Hamilton *(CFO & Sr VP)*
Grant A. Zawalsky *(Sec)*

Board of Directors:
Keith A. J. MacPhail
Ian S. Brown
Michael Manuel Kanovsky
Harry Louis Knutson
Sue Lee
Margaret M. McKenzie
Ronald J. Poelzer
Jason E. Skehar
Christopher P. Slubicki
Walter C. Yeates

Legal Counsel:
Burnet, Duckworth & Palmer LLP
Suite 1400 350 7th Avenue Southwest
Calgary, AB, T2P 3N9, Canada
Tel.: (403) 263-3050

Transfer Agent:
Valiant Trust Company
550 6th Avenue Southwest Suite 510
Calgary, AB, T2P 0S2, Canada

BOND INTERNATIONAL SOFTWARE PLC

Courtlands Parklands Avenue
Goring, W Sussex, BN12 4NG, United Kingdom
Tel.: (44) 1903707070
Fax: (44) 1903707080
E-Mail: info@bond.co.uk
Web Site: www.bondinternationalsoftware.com
BDI—(LSE)
Rev.: $56,012,678
Assets: $79,553,575
Liabilities: $25,813,495
Net Worth: $53,740,080
Earnings: $1,501,905
Emp.: 499
Fiscal Year-end: 12/31/12

Business Description:
Staffing & Recruitment Software Developer
S.I.C.: 7372
N.A.I.C.S.: 511210

Personnel:
Steve Russell *(CEO)*
Richard Hall *(Sec)*

Board of Directors:
Martin Baldwin
Richard Hall
Bruce A. Morrison
Tim Richards
Steve Russell

Legal Counsel:
Memery Crystal LLP
44 Southampton Buildings Memery
London, WC2A 1AP, United Kingdom

Coole & Haddock
5 The Steyne
BN11 3DT Worthing, United Kingdom

Subsidiaries:

Bond International Software (HR) Limited (1)
Gatwick House Peeks Brook Lane
Horley, Surrey, RH6 9ST, United Kingdom
Tel.: (44) 1342834242
Fax: (44) 1293787178
E-Mail: sirah.woodman@bond.co.uk
Web Site: www.bondinternationalsoftware.com
Emp.: 15
Software Solutions Provider
S.I.C.: 7371
N.A.I.C.S.: 541511
Nicola Crook *(Mgr)*

Bond International Software (UK) Limited (1)
Courtlands Parklands Avenue
Goring, W Sussex, BN12 4NG, United Kingdom
Tel.: (44) 1903707070
Fax: (44) 1903707080
E-Mail: sales@bond.co.uk
Web Site: www.bondinternationalsoftware.com
Emp.: 150
Staffing & Recruitment Software Solutions
S.I.C.: 7371
N.A.I.C.S.: 541511
Tim Richards *(Mng Dir)*

Division:

Bond Teamspirit (2)
Warwick House 48 Collingwood Road
Witham, Essex, CM8 2DZ, United Kingdom
Tel.: (44) 1376519413
Fax: (44) 1376520471
E-Mail: sales@teamspiritsoftware.co.uk
Web Site: www.teamspiritsoftware.co.uk
Emp.: 30
Staffing & Recruitment Software Solutions
S.I.C.: 7371
N.A.I.C.S.: 541511
Roger Moore *(Mng Dir)*

Gowi Services Limited (1)
Courtlands Parklands Ave Goring By Sea
Goring, West Sussex, BN12 4NG, United Kingdom
Tel.: (44) 1903707070
Fax: (44) 1903707080
E-Mail: info@gowigroup.co.uk
Emp.: 150
Software Solutions Provider
S.I.C.: 7371
N.A.I.C.S.: 541511
Tim Richard *(Mng Dir)*

U.S. Subsidiary:

Bond International Software Inc. (1)
1805 Old Alabama Rd Ste 340
Roswell, GA 30076
Tel.: (770) 246-2300
Fax: (770) 449-3638
Toll Free: (800) 318-4983
E-Mail: sales@bond-us.com
Web Site: www.bond-us.com
Emp.: 54
Computer Software Systems Analysis & Design
S.I.C.: 7371
N.A.I.C.S.: 541511
Steve Taylor *(Pres & CEO)*
Anne Bailey *(CFO)*
Dave Williams *(COO)*
Tim Giehll *(Chief Mktg & Strategy Officer)*

Branches:

Bond International Software Inc. (2)
2051 Killebrew Dr Ste 520
Bloomington, MN 55425
Tel.: (952) 854-3050
Fax: (952) 854-0555
Toll Free: (800) 456-5660
E-Mail: sales@bond-us.com
Web Site: www.bond-us.com
Emp.: 28
Staffing Software Solutions
S.I.C.: 7371
N.A.I.C.S.: 541511
Steve Taylor *(Pres & CEO)*

Bond International Software Inc. (2)
8720 Stony Point Pkwy Ste 100
Richmond, VA 23235
Tel.: (804) 266-3300
Fax: (804) 262-5500
Toll Free: (800) 882-2663
E-Mail: sales@bond-us.com
Web Site: www.bond-us.com
Emp.: 40
Staffing Software Solutions
S.I.C.: 7372
N.A.I.C.S.: 511210
Steve Taylor *(Pres & CEO)*

Non-U.S. Subsidiaries:

Bond International Japan K.K. (1)
First Square East 4F Otemachi 1-5-1
Chiyoda-Ku, Tokyo, 100 0004, Japan
Tel.: (81) 352191232
Fax: (81) 352191201
Web Site: www.bond-jp.com
Emp.: 5
Staffing & Recruitment Software Solutions
S.I.C.: 7371
N.A.I.C.S.: 541511
Koichi Sukuda *(Pres)*

Bond International Software China Limited (1)
1104 Crawford House 70 Queen's Road
Central, China (Hong Kong)
Tel.: (852) 28927605
Fax: (852) 61242262499
E-Mail: sales@bondadapt.com.au
Web Site: www.bondadapt.com.au
Emp.: 5
Staffing & Recruitment Software Solutions
S.I.C.: 7371
N.A.I.C.S.: 541511
Cody Wong *(Gen Mgr)*

Bond International Software Limited (1)
5 Newport Dr Fall River
Halifax, NS, Canada
Tel.: (804) 266-3300
Fax: (804) 262-5500
Toll Free: (800) 882-2663
Staffing & Recruitment Software Solutions
S.I.C.: 7371
N.A.I.C.S.: 541511

Bond International Software Pty Limited (1)
8-10 Victoria Street Suite 2
Wollongong, NSW, 2500, Australia
Tel.: (61) 2 4226 1600
Fax: (61) 2 4226 2499
Software Solutions Provider
S.I.C.: 7371
N.A.I.C.S.: 541511

BONDFIELD CONSTRUCTION COMPANY LIMITED

407 Basaltic Road
Concord, ON, Canada L4K 4W8
Tel.: (416) 667-8422
Fax: (416) 667-8462
E-Mail: info@bondfield.com
Web Site: www.bondfield.com
Rev.: $37,900,000
Emp.: 150

Business Description:
Construction Services
S.I.C.: 1542
N.A.I.C.S.: 236220

Personnel:
Ralph Aquino *(Pres)*

BONDIOLI & PAVESI S.P.A.

Via 23 Aprile 35 A
46029 Suzzara, Italy
Tel.: (39) 3765141
Telex: 300 513 BYPY I
Fax: (39) 0376514444
E-Mail: bypy@bypy.it
Web Site: www.bypy.it
Year Founded: 1950
Emp.: 800

Business Description:
Motion Transmission Components Designer, Mfr & Sales
S.I.C.: 3714
N.A.I.C.S.: 336350

Personnel:
Edy Bondioli *(Pres)*

U.S. Subsidiary:

Bondioli & Pavesi Inc. (1)
10252 Sycamore Dr
Ashland, VA 23005-8137 (100%)
Tel.: (804) 550-2224
Telex: 827-303 ASLD
Fax: (804) 550-2837
E-Mail: info@bypyusa.com
Web Site: www.bondioliepavesi.com
Emp.: 30
Sales of P.T.O. Drive Shafts for Agricultural Machinery & Gear Boxes & Hydraulic Components
S.I.C.: 5083
N.A.I.C.S.: 423820
Franco Laghi *(Pres)*

Non-U.S. Subsidiaries:

Bondioli & Pavesi-France S.A. (1)
1 Rue Panhard
PO Box 1
91830 Le Coudray-Montceaux, France (100%)
Tel.: (33) 164938463
Telex: 600972 F BYPYFRA
Fax: (33) 164939446
Web Site: www.bondioli-pavesi.com
Emp.: 25
Trade of P.T.O. Drive Shafts, Gear Boxes, Hydraulic Components & Other Implements
S.I.C.: 3714
N.A.I.C.S.: 336350
Pascal Moreliere *(Mgr)*

Bondioli & Pavesi GmbH Deutschland (1)
Odenwaldstrasse 7
64521 Gross-Gerau, 64521, Germany (100%)

Bondioli & Pavesi S.p.A.—(Continued)

Tel.: (49) 615298160
Telex: 4191179 BYPY D
Fax: (49) 6152981665
E-Mail: info@bypy.de
Web Site: www.bypy.de
Emp.: 40
Trade of P.T.O. Drive Shafts, Gear Boxes, Hydraulic Components & Other Implements
S.I.C.: 3714
N.A.I.C.S.: 336350

Bondioli & Pavesi GS.M.B.H (1)
Siebenhirtenstrasse 13A
A1235 Vienna, Austria (100%)
Tel.: (43) 18692260
Fax: (43) 1869479640
Farm Machinery
S.I.C.: 3523
N.A.I.C.S.: 333111

Bondioli y Pavesi Iberica S.A. (1)
Poligono De Malpica II Calle F
PO Box 5062
50057 Zaragoza, Espagna, Spain (100%)
Tel.: (34) 976588150
Fax: (34) 976588151
E-Mail: bondiolipavesi@bypy-iberica.com
Web Site: www.bypy-iberica.com
Emp.: 28
Trade of P.T.O. Drive Shafts, Gear Boxes, Hydraulic Components & Other Implements
S.I.C.: 3714
N.A.I.C.S.: 336350

BONDPARTNERS SA

(d/b/a BPL)
Ave de l'Elysee 22-24 Case Postale 174
1001 Lausanne, Switzerland
Tel.: (41) 216134343
Fax: (41) 216179715
E-Mail: bpl@bpl-bondpartners.ch
Web Site: www.bpl-bondpartners.ch
Year Founded: 1972
BON—(SWX)
Rev.: $208,281
Assets: $142,299,106
Liabilities: $60,891,446
Net Worth: $81,407,660
Earnings: ($5,045,954)
Emp.: 31
Fiscal Year-end: 12/31/12

Business Description:
Securities Brokerage Services
S.I.C.: 6211
N.A.I.C.S.: 523120

Personnel:
Henri Plomb, Sr. *(Chm & CEO)*
Paolo Argenti *(Settlement Officer)*
Oscar Fernandez *(Trading Officer)*
Jean-Michel Gavriliuc *(Admin Officer)*
Fabio Pervangher *(Trading Officer)*
Pierre Rapin *(Trading Officer)*
Claude Wanner *(Acctg Officer)*
Christian Plomb, Jr. *(Sec)*

Board of Directors:
Henri Plomb, Sr.
Stephane Bise
Edgar Brandt
Regis Menetrey
Christian Plomb, Jr.
Antonie Spillmann
Jean-Luc Strohm

BONDUELLE SCA

Rue Nicolas Appert
BP 30173
F-59653 Villeneuve d'Ascq, France
Tel.: (33) 3 20 43 60 60
Fax: (33) 3 20 43 60 00
E-Mail: groupebonduelle@bonduelle.com
Web Site: www.bonduelle.com
BON—(EUR)
Rev.: $2,552,537,553
Assets: $2,272,022,649
Liabilities: $1,593,894,896
Net Worth: $678,127,753
Earnings: $69,902,570
Emp.: 9,758
Fiscal Year-end: 06/30/13

Business Description:
Fresh, Frozen & Canned Vegetable Products
S.I.C.: 2033
N.A.I.C.S.: 311421

Personnel:
Isabelle Danjour *(Chm-Supervisory Bd)*
Christophe Bonduelle *(Chm-Mgmt Bd)*
Daniel Bracquart *(Vice Chm-Supervisory Bd)*
Gregory Sanson *(CFO)*
Benoit Bonduelle *(CEO-Dev)*
Pascal Bredeloux *(CEO-Bonduelle Fresh Europe)*
Philippe Carreau *(CEO-Bonduelle Europe Long Life)*
Daniel Vielfaure *(CEO-Americas)*

Supervisory Board of Directors:
Isabelle Danjour
Louis Bonduelle
Daniel Bracquart
Martin Ducroquet
Matthieu Duriez
Elisabeth Minard
Yves Tack
Marie-France Tisseau

Deloitte & Associes
67 rue de Luxembourg
59777 Lille, France

BONE MEDICAL LIMITED

Level 3 46 Ord St
West Perth, WA, 6005, Australia
Mailing Address:
PO Box 154
Nedlands, WA, 6909, Australia
Tel.: (61) 8 9468 0154
Fax: (61) 8 9322 4946
E-Mail: query@bone-ltd.com
Web Site: www.bone-ltd.com
Year Founded: 2002
BNE—(ASX)
Rev.: $5
Assets: $8,501
Liabilities: $2,614,977
Net Worth: ($2,606,476)
Earnings: ($1,927,764)
Fiscal Year-end: 06/30/13

Business Description:
Bone Strengthening Biopharmaceutical Research & Mfr
S.I.C.: 2836
N.A.I.C.S.: 325414

Personnel:
Roger New *(Founder & Chief Scientific Officer)*
Peter Young *(CEO & Mng Dir)*
Mark Clements *(Sec)*

Board of Directors:
Roger New
Peter Brooks
Leon Ivory
Peter Young

Legal Counsel:
Gilbert & Tobin
1202 Hay Street
West Perth, Australia

BONG AB

Hans Michelsensgatan 9 5th floor
SE-211 20 Malmo, Sweden
Tel.: (46) 40 17 60 00
Fax: (46) 40 17 60 39
E-Mail: mail@bong.com
Web Site: www.bong.com
BONG—(OMX)
Rev.: $456,030,119
Assets: $330,808,374
Liabilities: $267,780,161
Net Worth: $63,028,213
Earnings: ($8,415,702)
Emp.: 2,218
Fiscal Year-end: 12/31/12

Business Description:
Envelope Mfr
S.I.C.: 2678
N.A.I.C.S.: 322230

Personnel:
Stephane Hamelin *(Chm)*
Anders Davidsson *(Pres, CEO & Interim Mgr-Bus-Nordic & East)*
Hakan Gunnarsson *(CFO)*
Ove Hansson *(CIO)*

Board of Directors:
Stephane Hamelin
Anders Davidsson
Mikael Ekdahl
Ulrika Eriksson
Peter Harrysson
Christian W. Jansson
Eric Joan
Christer Muth

Subsidiaries:

Bong Ljungdahl Sverige AB (1)
Emmabodavagen
823
38228 Nybro, Sweden (100%)
Tel.: (46) 48144000
Fax: (46) 48117977
E-Mail: ake.adem@bong.se
Web Site: www.bong.se
Emp.: 150
Stationery Tablet & Related Product Mfr
S.I.C.: 2678
N.A.I.C.S.: 322230
Oke Aden *(Gen Mgr)*

Bong Sverige AB (1)
Uddevagen 3
291 25 Kristianstad, Sweden
Tel.: (46) 44 20 70 00
Fax: (46) 44 20 70 90
Web Site: www.bong.se
Emp.: 150
Paperboard Mfr
S.I.C.: 2631
N.A.I.C.S.: 322130
Anders Davidsson *(Gen Mgr)*

ProPac International AB (1)
Hans Michelsensgatan 9
211 20 Malmo, Sweden
Tel.: (46) 40 17 60 00
Fax: (46) 40 17 60 39
Emp.: 22
Packaging Products Distr
S.I.C.: 5085
N.A.I.C.S.: 423840
Morgan Bosson *(Mng Dir-Sls)*

Non-U.S. Subsidiaries:

Bong Belgium S.A. (1)
Bergensesteenweg 93
7060 Brussels, Belgium
Tel.: (32) 67347650
Fax: (32) 67347677
E-Mail: info@bong.com
Web Site: www.bong.com
Emp.: 100
Stationery Tablet & Related Product Mfr
S.I.C.: 2678
N.A.I.C.S.: 322230
Bart Bouckaert *(Mng Dir)*

Bong Bjornbak AS (1)
Baldersbuen 2
PO Box 179
2640 Hedehusene, Denmark (100%)
Tel.: (45) 46565555
Fax: (45) 46590255
E-Mail: post@bong.dk
Web Site: www.bong.dk
Emp.: 40
Stationery & Office Supplies Merchant Whslr
S.I.C.: 5112
N.A.I.C.S.: 424120
Mogens Hallager *(CEO)*

Bong Caly Swiat Kopert Sp z o.o. (1)
ul Ustronna 14
60-012 Poznan, Poland
Tel.: (48) 61 822 07 60
Fax: (48) 61 828 71 29
E-Mail: koperty@bong.pl
Web Site: www.bong.pl
Envelope Mfr
S.I.C.: 2678
N.A.I.C.S.: 322230

Bong Eesti Ou (1)
Joe tn 17
79808 Kohila, Estonia (100%)
Tel.: (372) 4890140
Fax: (372) 4890141
E-Mail: bongeesti@bong.com
Emp.: 55
Stationery Tablet & Related Product Mfr
S.I.C.: 2678
N.A.I.C.S.: 322230
Mart Sepping *(Mng Dir)*

Bong GmbH (1)
Industriestr 77
42327 Wuppertal, Germany
Tel.: (49) 20274970
Fax: (49) 20274971999
E-Mail: info@bong.de
Web Site: www.bong.de
Emp.: 100
Mail Handling Machinery Mfr
S.I.C.: 3559
N.A.I.C.S.: 333249
Thomas Kraemer *(Gen Mgr)*

Bong Latvija SIA (1)
Krasta iela 97a
1019 Riga, Latvia (100%)
Tel.: (371) 7241339
Fax: (371) 7241343
E-Mail: girts.maurins@bonglatvija.lv
Web Site: www.bong.com
Emp.: 2
Stationery & Office Supplies Merchant Whslr
S.I.C.: 5112
N.A.I.C.S.: 424120
Girts Maurins *(Mng Dir)*

Bong Netherlands BV (1)
Rivium 1e Straat 68
2909 LE Capelle aan den IJssel, Netherlands
Tel.: (31) 10 288 1408
Fax: (31) 72 567 8901
Envelope Mfr
S.I.C.: 2679
N.A.I.C.S.: 322299
Gaap Kwakkel *(Gen Mgr)*

Bong Norge AS (1)
Bekkeveien 161
3173 Vear, Norway
Tel.: (47) 33 30 54 00
Fax: (47) 33 30 54 01
E-Mail: mail-no@bong.com
Web Site: www.bong.no
Envelope Mfr
S.I.C.: 2678
N.A.I.C.S.: 322230

Bong Polska S.P. z.o.o. (1)
ul Kolejowa 362-364
05-092 Dzikow Nowy, Poland
Tel.: (48) 227516652
Fax: (48) 227512277
E-Mail: koperty@bong.pl
Web Site: www.bong.pl
Emp.: 60
Stationery Tablet & Related Product Mfr
S.I.C.: 2678
N.A.I.C.S.: 322230
Tomasz Ciesla *(Mng Dir)*

BONG RCT GmbH (1)
Industriestrasse 77
42327 Wuppertal, Germany
Tel.: (49) 20274970
Fax: (49) 20274971999
E-Mail: info@bong.de
Web Site: www.bong.de
Emp.: 220
Stationery Tablet & Related Product Mfr
S.I.C.: 2678
N.A.I.C.S.: 322230
Elmar Schatzlein *(Mng Dir)*

Bong Suomi OY (1)
Tuottotie 33
PO Box 816
33960 Tampere, Finland
Tel.: (358) 32418111

Fax: (358) 32418112
E-Mail: kari.lahteenmaki@bong.com
Web Site: www.bongsuomi.fi
Emp.: 50
Stationery Tablet & Related Product Mfr
S.I.C.: 2678
N.A.I.C.S.: 322230
Kari Lahteenmaki *(Mng Dir)*

Bongs Konvolutter AS (1)
Bekkevejen 161 3173 Vear
Postboks 2074, 3103 Tonsberg, Norway
Tel.: (47) 33305400
Fax: (47) 33305401
E-Mail: mail-no@bong.no
Web Site: www.bong.no
Emp.: 250
Stationery Tablet & Related Product Mfr
S.I.C.: 2678
N.A.I.C.S.: 322230
Terje Lokem *(Mgr)*

Curtis 1000 France Sarl (1)
23 Avenue du Val de Beaute
94736 Nogent-sur-Marne, France
Tel.: (33) 1 48 73 49 55
Fax: (33) 1 48 77 87 24
E-Mail: info@curtis.fr
Web Site: www.curtis.fr
Envelope Mfr
S.I.C.: 2679
N.A.I.C.S.: 322299

Egaa Offset A/S (1)
Skejby Nordlandsvej 305
8200 Arhus, Denmark
Tel.: (45) 87434282
Fax: (45) 87434283
E-Mail: ordre@egaa-offset.dk
Web Site: www.egaa-offset.dk
Envelope Mfr
S.I.C.: 2679
N.A.I.C.S.: 322299

ENVEL EUROPA S.A (1)
Placa Gal La Placidia 7 esc D 8
08006 Barcelona, Spain
Tel.: (34) 932 41 88 50
Fax: (34) 932 40 24 11
Web Site: www.bongljungdahl.se/en/contacts/choose-country/portugal/
Envelope Mfr
S.I.C.: 2678
N.A.I.C.S.: 322230

Excelsior Enveloppen BV (1)
Galileistraat 63
1704 SE Heerhugowaard, Netherlands
Tel.: (31) 72 56 78 900
Fax: (31) 72 56 78 901
E-Mail: ee@excelsior-enveloppen.nl
Web Site: www.excelsiorenveloppen.nl
Envelope Mfr
S.I.C.: 2679
N.A.I.C.S.: 322299

Lober Druck und Kuvert GmbH (1)
Beethovenstrasse 24-26
86368 Gersthofen, Germany
Tel.: (49) 821297880
Fax: (49) 8212978830
E-Mail: info@lopa.eu
Web Site: www.lopa.eu
Emp.: 100
Other Commercial Printing
S.I.C.: 2759
N.A.I.C.S.: 323111
Stefan Lopa *(Gen Mgr)*

Petersen Allpa GmbH (1)
Hermann-Krum-Strasse 9-11
88319 Aitrach, Germany
Tel.: (49) 7565 9809 0
Fax: (49) 7565 5544
E-Mail: kontakt@petersenallpa.de
Web Site: www.petersenallpa.de
Emp.: 150
Envelopes & Mailers Mfr
S.I.C.: 2679
N.A.I.C.S.: 322299
Melanie Burkhardt *(Mgr-Natl Mktg)*

PK Koperty Sp. z o. o (1)
ul Zawila 56
Krakow, 30-390, Poland
Tel.: (48) 12 252 02 00
Fax: (48) 12 252 02 02
E-Mail: info@pfluger-koperty.pl
Web Site: www.pfluger-koperty.pl
Emp.: 13
Envelope Mfr
S.I.C.: 2678
N.A.I.C.S.: 322230
Krzysztof Kubasiak *(Gen Mgr)*

Postac LLC (1)
Domostroiteley pr 17
248000 Kaluga, Russia
Tel.: (7) 4842 76 44 68
Fax: (7) 4842 76 44 69
Envelope Mfr
S.I.C.: 2678
N.A.I.C.S.: 322230

SE (Envelope Manufacturing) Ltd (1)
Anglers Business Centre Nottingham Road
Spondon, Derby, DE21 7NJ, United Kingdom
Tel.: (44) 1332667790
Fax: (44) 1332 674767
Emp.: 7
Envelope Mfr
S.I.C.: 2679
N.A.I.C.S.: 322299
Tomy Larkin *(Mgr)*

Surrey Envelopes Ltd (1)
Unit 7 Nelson Trading Estate Morden Road
London, SW19 3BL, United Kingdom
Tel.: (44) 2085450099
Fax: (44) 20 8544 0832
E-Mail: info@surrey-envelopes.com
Web Site: www.surrey-envelopes.com
Envelope Mfr
S.I.C.: 2679
N.A.I.C.S.: 322299

Tycon S.A (1)
Zone Industrielle Rolach Halle 5
5280 Sandweiler, Luxembourg
Tel.: (352) 35 75 04 1
Fax: (352) 35 75 04 55
E-Mail: info@tycon.lu
Web Site: www.tycon.lu
Emp.: 30
Envelope Mfr
S.I.C.: 2678
N.A.I.C.S.: 322230
Mark Peterson *(Gen Mgr)*

Venlop B.V. (1)
Rudolf Dieselweg 3
5928 RA Venlo, Netherlands
Tel.: (31) 77 382 60 35
Fax: (31) 77 382 36 59
E-Mail: info@venlop.nl
Web Site: www.venlop.nl
Envelope Mfr
S.I.C.: 2679
N.A.I.C.S.: 322299

BONGRAIN S.A.

42 Rue Rieussec
78223 Viroflay, France
Telex: 840620
Fax: (33) 130240383
Web Site: www.bongrain.com
Year Founded: 1956
BH—(EUR)
Sls.: $5,497,865,974
Assets: $4,091,352,557
Liabilities: $2,466,763,639
Net Worth: $1,624,588,918
Earnings: $99,036,381
Emp.: 18,870
Fiscal Year-end: 12/31/12

Business Description:
Dairy Products Mfr & Distr
Export
S.I.C.: 2021
N.A.I.C.S.: 311512

Personnel:
Alex Bongrain *(Chm)*
Francois Wolfovski *(CFO & Deputy Mng Dir)*
Yannick Piveteau *(Treas)*
Robert Brzusczak *(Exec VP)*
Jean-Paul Torris *(Exec VP)*

Board of Directors:
Alex Bongrain
Armand Bongrain
Dominique Damon
Michel Godet
Bernard Houlot
Martine Liautaud
Elisabeth Lulin
Ignacio Osbourne
Xavier Paul-Renard
Jean-Michel Strasser
Tom Swartele

Befec-Price Waterhouse
Tour AIG-34 place de Corolles
92908 Paris, La Defense 2, Cedex, France

Subsidiaries:

Alliance Laitiere Europeenne S.A (1)
65 Avenue De Segur
75007 Paris, France
Tel.: (33) 134586300
Fax: (33) 130240383
Dairy Products Mfr
S.I.C.: 2023
N.A.I.C.S.: 311514

Bongrain Europe SAS (1)
42 Rue Rieussec
Viroflay, 78220, France
Tel.: (33) 134586300
Fax: (33) 130240383
Dairy Products Mfr & Sales
S.I.C.: 2023
N.A.I.C.S.: 311514

Bongrain-Gerard SAS (1)
4 Rue Eugene Gerard
BP 1
88530 Le Tholy, France (99.96%)
Tel.: (33) 329238200
Telex: 960.956
Fax: (33) 329238227
Web Site: www.capricedesdieux.com
Sales Range: $150-199.9 Million
Emp.: 300
Dairy Products & Gourmet Foods Producer & Distr
Export
S.I.C.: 2022
N.A.I.C.S.: 311513
Christopher Trouvost *(Mgr-Mktg-Export)*

Bongrain International (1)
42 Rue Rieussec
78229 Viroflay, France (100%)
Tel.: (33) 134586300
Fax: (33) 130240383
Web Site: www.bongrain.com
Emp.: 250
Wholesaler of Dairy Products
S.I.C.: 5499
N.A.I.C.S.: 445299

Compagnie Laitiere Europeenne S.A (1)
Conde Sur Vire
Paris, 50890, France
Tel.: (33) 2 33 06 65 00
Fax: (33) 2 33 06 67 15
Dairy Products Mfr
S.I.C.: 2023
N.A.I.C.S.: 311514

Fromagerie Perreault S.A. (1)
6 rue de Bellitourne Aze
BP 70416
53204 Chateau-Gontier, Cedex, France (99.96%)
Tel.: (33) 2 43 09 53 00
Fax: (33) 2 43 09 53 01
Web Site: www.bongrain.com
Production, Sales & Marketing of Soft Cheeses & Milk Products
S.I.C.: 2022
N.A.I.C.S.: 311513

Fromarsac S.A.S. (1)
Fromarsac BP 5
24430 Razac-sur-l'Isle, France (100%)
Tel.: (33) 553036400
Fax: (33) 553041213
Web Site: www.bongrain.com
Emp.: 400
Production, Sales & Marketing of Cream Cheese
S.I.C.: 2022
N.A.I.C.S.: 311513

Fruisec S.A.S. (1)
La Morelie
24120 Terrasson, France (100%)
Tel.: (33) 553514400
Fax: (33) 553500571
E-Mail: fruisec@wanadow.fr
Web Site: www.fruisec.com
Emp.: 40
Trading & Processing of Nuts
S.I.C.: 2068
N.A.I.C.S.: 311911
Allan Chaumont *(Mng Dir)*

Pareco S.N.C. (1)
Immeuble I Alliance
42 Rue Rieussec, Viroflay, 78222, France (100%)
Tel.: (33) 134586541
Fax: (33) 130241914
E-Mail: geanphilippe.moreau@bongrain.com
Web Site: www.bongrain.com
Emp.: 37
Mfr. & Distribution of Dairy Products
S.I.C.: 5499
N.A.I.C.S.: 445299
Albert Delenarre *(Mng Dir)*

U.S. Subsidiary:

BC-USA, Inc. (1)
400 S Custer Ave
New Holland, PA 17557-9220 (55.01%)
Tel.: (717) 355-8500
Fax: (717) 355-8561
Web Site: www.alouettecheese.com
Sls.: $120,000,000
Emp.: 500
Cheese Products Mfr
Export
S.I.C.: 2022
N.A.I.C.S.: 311513
John Crisci *(VP-Ops)*

Subsidiary:

Advanced Food Products LLC (2)
402 S Custer Ave
New Holland, PA 17557
Tel.: (717) 355-8667
Fax: (717) 355-8848
E-Mail: info@afpllc.com
Web Site: www.afpllc.com
Emp.: 200
Aseptically Canned Puddings, Cheese Sauces & Nutritional Beverages Mfr
Export
S.I.C.: 2099
N.A.I.C.S.: 311999
Miroslav Hosek *(Pres & CEO)*

Subsidiary:

Advanced Food Products LLC (3)
600 1st Ave W
Clear Lake, WI 54005-8510
Tel.: (715) 263-2956
Fax: (715) 263-3184
E-Mail: info@afpllc.com
Web Site: www.afpllc.com
Emp.: 85
Natural, Processed & Imitation Cheese
S.I.C.: 2032
N.A.I.C.S.: 311422
Chuckie DeSmith *(Plant Mgr)*

Non-U.S. Subsidiary:

Mantequerias Arias S. A. (1)
Pedro Peieira No 8 9 th Fl
28020 Madrid, Spain (100%)
Tel.: (34) 914174740
Fax: (34) 915558508
E-Mail: export@mantequeriasarias.com
Web Site: www.arias.es
Emp.: 600
Milk, Butter & Cheese Producer
S.I.C.: 2021
N.A.I.C.S.: 311512
Javaer Rosa *(Gen Mgr)*

BONGSHIN CO., LTD.

No 530 Gajua Dong Su Gu
404250 Incheon, Korea (South)
Tel.: (82) 325908800
Fax: (82) 325781712
E-Mail: sw231@bongshin.co.kr
Web Site: www.bongshin.co.kr
Year Founded: 1936
Sales Range: $350-399.9 Million
Emp.: 250

Business Description:
Marine Transportation Services; Industrial Equipment & Cast Iron Products Mfr

Bongshin Co., Ltd.—(Continued)

S.I.C.: 4412
N.A.I.C.S.: 483111
Personnel:
Junghee Lim *(Pres)*

BONHAMS 1793 LTD.

101 New Bond St
London, W1S 1SR, United Kingdom
Tel.: (44) 2074477447
Fax: (44) 2076298876
E-Mail: info@bonhams.com
Web Site: www.bonhams.com
Year Founded: 1793
Sales Range: $50-74.9 Million
Emp.: 481
Business Description:
Fine Art, Antiques & Collectibles Auction Services
S.I.C.: 5999
N.A.I.C.S.: 453920
Personnel:
Robert Brookes *(Chm)*
James Knight *(Mng Dir)*
Josephine Olley *(Sr Press Officer)*
Matthew Girling *(CEO-Europe)*

U.S. Subsidiary:

Bonhams & Butterfields (1)
220 San Bruno Ave
San Francisco, CA 94103
Tel.: (415) 861-7500
Fax: (415) 861-8951
Web Site: www.bonhams.com
Emp.: 250
Fine Art, Antiques & Collectibles Auction Services
S.I.C.: 5999
N.A.I.C.S.: 453920
Malcolm Barber *(CEO)*
Patrick Meade *(Sr VP-Bus Devel)*

BONHEUR ASA

Fred Olsens Gate 2
N-0152 Oslo, Norway
Tel.: (47) 22341000
Fax: (47) 22412415
E-Mail: Bonheur@fredolsen.no
Web Site: www.bonheur.net
Year Founded: 1895
BON—(OSL)
Rev.: $1,855,806,666
Assets: $5,357,875,023
Liabilities: $3,115,900,130
Net Worth: $2,241,974,893
Earnings: $246,856,605
Emp.: 4,333
Fiscal Year-end: 12/31/12
Business Description:
Shipping, Offshore & Energy & Tourist Industries Services
S.I.C.: 4789
N.A.I.C.S.: 488999
Personnel:
Thomas Fredrik Olsen *(Chm)*
Anette S. Olsen *(Mng Dir)*
Board of Directors:
Thomas Fredrik Olsen
Anna Synnove Bye
Andreas C. Mellbye
Pauline Walsh

Subsidiaries:

First Olsen AS (1)
PO Box 581
Sentrum, 0106 Oslo, Norway
Tel.: (47) 22341180
Fax: (47) 22341182
E-Mail: first@fredolsen.no
Marine Shipping Services
S.I.C.: 4731
N.A.I.C.S.: 488510
Per-Oscar Lund *(Pres)*

First Olsen Tankers Ltd. AS (1)
Strandgaten 5
PO Box 581
Sentrum, 0106 Oslo, Norway
Tel.: (47) 22341180
Fax: (47) 22412415
E-Mail: first@fredolsen.no
Web Site: www.fotl.no
Emp.: 10
Marine Shipping Services
S.I.C.: 4412
N.A.I.C.S.: 483111
Rolf Normann *(Mng Dir)*

Fred. Olsen Fly og Luftmateriell A/S (1)
Prinsensgate 2B
0152 Oslo, Norway
Tel.: (47) 22341388
Fax: (47) 22008888
Emp.: 3
Aircraft Parts Distr
S.I.C.: 5088
N.A.I.C.S.: 423860

Fred. Olsen Marine Services AS (1)
Prinsens Gate 2b
0512 Oslo, Norway
Tel.: (47) 22341100
Fax: (47) 22421314
E-Mail: foms@foms.no
Web Site: www.fredolsen-marine.com
Marine Support Services
S.I.C.: 4491
N.A.I.C.S.: 488320

Fred. Olsen Renewables A/S (1)
Fred Olsens Gate 2
0152 Oslo, Norway
Tel.: (47) 91888112
Fax: (47) 22412415
E-Mail: renewables@fredolsen.no
Web Site: www.fredolsen-renewables.com
Electric Power Generation Services
S.I.C.: 4939
N.A.I.C.S.: 221118

Fred. Olsen Travel A/S (1)
Prinsensgate 2B
0152 Oslo, Norway
Tel.: (47) 22341111
Fax: (47) 22341059
E-Mail: info@fredolsentravel.com
Web Site: www.fredolsentravel.com
Emp.: 15
Travel & Tour Operating Agencies
S.I.C.: 4725
N.A.I.C.S.: 561520

Ganger Rolf ASA (1)
Fred Olsens gate 2
0152 Oslo, Norway (49.5%)
Tel.: (47) 22341000
Fax: (47) 22411745
E-Mail: pos@fredooson.no
Web Site: www.ganger-rolf.com
Sales Range: $50-74.9 Million
Emp.: 200
Shipping Services & Offshore Drilling Operations; Holding Company
S.I.C.: 6719
N.A.I.C.S.: 551112
Anette S. Olsen *(Mng Dir)*

Joint Venture:

Fred. Olsen Production ASA (2)
Fred Olsens Gate 2
0152 Oslo, Norway (50%)
Tel.: (47) 22341000
Fax: (47) 22429946
E-Mail: fpso@fredolsen.no
Web Site: www.fpso.no
Rev.: $113,314,000
Fiscal Year-end: 12/31/12
Oil & Gas Vessel Leasing Services; Owned 50% by Bonheur ASA & 50% by Ganger Rolf ASA
S.I.C.: 1389
N.A.I.C.S.: 213112
Eirik Barclay *(CEO)*
Brad Neve *(CFO)*
Nils Herman Kiar *(Sr VP-Tech & Engrg)*

Knock Holding II A/S (1)
Fred Olsens gate 2
0152 Oslo, Norway
Tel.: (47) 22341000
Fax: (47) 22429946
Investment Management Services
S.I.C.: 6282
N.A.I.C.S.: 523920
Annet Olsen *(Gen Mgr)*

Knock Tankers Ltd. (1)
Strandgaten 5
PO Box 743
Sentrum, 0106 Oslo, Norway
Tel.: (47) 22341200
Fax: (47) 22422441
E-Mail: knock@knock.no
Web Site: www.fotl.no/?aid=9055599
Commercial Chartering Services
S.I.C.: 4731
N.A.I.C.S.: 488510

Oceanlink Ltd. (1)
c/o Oceanlink Management AS Tollbugata
PO Box 581
Vika, 0121 Oslo, Norway
Tel.: (47) 22838983
Fax: (47) 22838090
Web Site: www.oceanlink.no
Marine Shipping Services
S.I.C.: 4412
N.A.I.C.S.: 483111

Non-U.S. Subsidiaries:

Fred. Olsen Cruise Lines Ltd. (1)
Fred Olsen House 42 White House Road
Ipswich, Sufflok, IP1 5LL, United Kingdom
Tel.: (44) 1473742424
Fax: (44) 1473 292201
E-Mail: customer.services@fredolsen.co.uk
Web Site: www.fredolsencruise.com
Emp.: 200
Cruise Line Services
S.I.C.: 4481
N.A.I.C.S.: 483112
Mike Rodwell *(Mng Dir)*

Fred. Olsen Renewables Ltd. (1)
64-65 Vincent Square
London, SW1P 2NU, United Kingdom
Tel.: (44) 2079310975
Fax: (44) 2079317449
Emp.: 6
Energy Renewable Services
S.I.C.: 9631
N.A.I.C.S.: 926130
Jeremy Dowler *(Sec)*

BONIFAZ GOLD PLC

88 Wood Street 10th Floor
London, EC2V 7RS, United Kingdom
Tel.: (44) 208 528 1071
E-Mail: info@bonifazgold.com
Web Site: www.bonifazgold.com
BOG—(DEU)
Emp.: 52
Business Description:
Gold Mining
S.I.C.: 1041
N.A.I.C.S.: 212221
Personnel:
Oscar Bonifaz Gutierrez *(Chm)*
Oscar Antonio Bonifaz Paz *(CEO)*
Luis Fernando Quiroga *(CFO)*
Board of Directors:
Oscar Bonifaz Gutierrez
Roberto Sergio Bonifaz Paz
Pedro Pablo Hinojosa Flores
Tony Sharp

BONITASOFT SA

32 rue Gustave Eiffel
38000 Grenoble, France
Tel.: (33) 4 76 49 40 66
Fax: (33) 4 76 49 40 66
E-Mail: jobs@bonitasoft.com
Web Site: www.bonitasoft.com
Emp.: 100
Business Description:
Business Process Management Software Developer
S.I.C.: 7372
N.A.I.C.S.: 511210
Personnel:
Miguel Valdes-Faurac *(Co-Founder & CEO)*
Charles Souillard *(Co-Founder, VP-Engrg & CTO)*
Rodrigue Le Gall *(Co-Founder & Chief Svcs Officer)*
Arnaud Debains *(CFO)*
Jean-Luc Solans *(Chief Strategy Officer)*
Board of Directors:
Bertrand Diard
Philippe Granger
Claire Houry
Xavier Lorphelin
Miguel Valdes-Faurac

BONJOUR HOLDINGS LIMITED

10/F Bonjour Tower 3 Yuk Yat Street
To Kwa Wan
Kowloon, China (Hong Kong)
Tel.: (852) 23808010
E-Mail: corporate@bonjourhk.com
Web Site: www.bonjourhk.com
0653—(HKG)
Sls.: $362,073,418
Assets: $118,013,751
Liabilities: $76,141,622
Net Worth: $41,872,128
Earnings: $28,674,096
Emp.: 1,730
Fiscal Year-end: 12/31/12
Business Description:
Cosmetics Whslr
S.I.C.: 5122
N.A.I.C.S.: 446120
Personnel:
Wilson Heng Chun Ip *(Chm & CEO)*
Pui Wan Ip Chung *(Vice Chm)*
Ka Fai Cheung *(CFO)*
Wai Leung Yick *(COO)*
Rosina Kwok Chu Ha *(Pres-Bonjour Beauty Limited)*
Chun Chung Kwong *(Sec)*
Board of Directors:
Wilson Heng Chun Ip
Ho Ming Chow
Pui Wan Ip Chung
Hang Fong Lo
Chi Wai Wong
Kwok Li Yip

Computershare Hong Kong Investor Services Limited
Shops 1712-1716 17th Floor Hopewell Centre
183 Queens Road East
Wanchai, China (Hong Kong)

Transfer Agents:
Royal Bank of Canada Trust Company (Cayman) Limited
4th Floor Royal Bank House 24 Shedden Road
Georgetown, Cayman Islands

Computershare Hong Kong Investor Services Limited
Shops 1712-1716 17th Floor Hopewell Centre
183 Queens Road East
Wanchai, China (Hong Kong)

BONNIER AB

(d/b/a The Bonnier Group)
Kungsgatan 49
SE-113 90 Stockholm, Sweden
Tel.: (46) 87364000
Fax: (46) 87280028
E-Mail: info@bonnier.se
Web Site: www.bonnier.se
Year Founded: 1804
Sales Range: $1-4.9 Billion
Emp.: 12,000
Business Description:
Holding Company; Multimedia Publishing & Production Services
S.I.C.: 6719
N.A.I.C.S.: 551112
Personnel:
Carl-Johan Bonnier *(Chm)*
Jonas Bonnier *(Pres & CEO)*
Casten Almqvist *(CEO-Bus Press)*
Goran Ohrn *(CFO)*
Torsten Larsson *(Pres-Brdcst & Entertainment)*
Maria Curman *(CEO-Books)*

Divisions:

Bonnier Books AB (1)
Sveavagen 56
Box 3159
SE-103 63 Stockholm, Sweden SE
Tel.: (46) 86968000 (100%)
Fax: (46) 86968630
E-Mail: bonnierforlagen@bok.bonnier.se
Web Site: www.bok.bonnier.se
Sales Range: $800-899.9 Million
Emp.: 250
Holding Company; Book Publisher
S.I.C.: 6719
N.A.I.C.S.: 551112
Maria Curman *(CEO)*

Division:

Bonnierforlagen AB (2)
Sveavagen 56
PO Box 3159
SE-103 63 Stockholm, Sweden SE
Tel.: (46) 86968000 (100%)
Fax: (46) 86968630
Web Site: www.bok.bonnier.se
Emp.: 200
Book Publisher
S.I.C.: 2731
N.A.I.C.S.: 511130
Jacob Dalborg *(Mng Dir)*

Subsidiary:

Albert Bonniers Forlag AB (3)
Sveavagen 56
Box 3159
SE-103 63 Stockholm, Sweden SE
Tel.: (46) 86968620 (100%)
Fax: (46) 86968361
E-Mail: info@abforlag.bonnier.se
Web Site: www.albertbonniersforlag.se
Book Publisher
S.I.C.: 2731
N.A.I.C.S.: 511130
Anna Borne Minberger *(CEO)*
Jesper Monthan *(Deputy Mng Dir)*

Non-U.S. Subsidiary:

Bonnier Media Deutschland GmbH (2)
Georgenstrasse 4
80799 Munich, Germany
Tel.: (49) 89 38 18 01 0
Fax: (49) 89 38 18 01 20
E-Mail:
Book Publishing
S.I.C.: 2731
N.A.I.C.S.: 511130
Hartmut Jedicke *(CEO)*

Subsidiary:

Ullstein Buchverlage Gmbh (3)
Friedrichstrasse 126
10117 Berlin, Germany (100%)
Tel.: (49) 30 23456 300
Fax: (49) 30 23456 303
E-Mail: info@ullstein-buchverlage.de
Web Site: www.ullstein-buchverlage.de
Emp.: 100
Book Publishing
S.I.C.: 2731
N.A.I.C.S.: 511130
Alexander Lorbeer *(Mng Dir)*

Bonnier Business Press AB (1)
Torsgatan 21
SE-113 90 Stockholm, Sweden SE
Tel.: (46) 857365000 (100%)
Fax: (46) 8 5736 5220
Web Site: www.bonnierbusinesspress.com
Sales Range: $250-299.9 Million
Emp.: 5
Holding Company; Business Newspaper, Magazine & Internet Publisher
S.I.C.: 6719
N.A.I.C.S.: 551112
Anders Eriksson *(Pres & CEO)*

Subsidiary:

Dagens Industri AB (2)
Torsgatan 21
SE-113 90 Stockholm, Sweden SE
Tel.: (46) 857365000 (100%)
Fax: (46) 857365220
E-Mail: reg@di.se
Web Site: www.di.se
Emp.: 200
Business Newspaper & Internet Publisher
S.I.C.: 2711
N.A.I.C.S.: 511110
Peter Fellman *(Deputy Editor-in-Chief)*

Non-U.S. Subsidiary:

Borsen A/S (2)
Montergade 19
1140 Copenhagen, K, Denmark DK
Tel.: (45) 33320102
Fax: (45) 33122445
E-Mail: online@borsen.dk
Web Site: borsen.dk
Sales Range: $25-49.9 Million
Emp.: 250
Business Newspaper & Internet Publisher
S.I.C.: 2711
N.A.I.C.S.: 511110
Caster Almqvist *(Chm)*
Anders Krap Johansen *(CEO)*

Bonnier Entertainment AB (1)
Kungsgatan 49
SE-113 90 Stockholm, Sweden SE
Tel.: (46) 87364000 (100%)
Fax: (46) 87364039
E-Mail: info@bonnier.se
Web Site: www.bonnier.se
Sales Range: $550-599.9 Million
Holding Company; Music Publishing; Radio, Television, & Motion Picture Production & Broadcasting Services
S.I.C.: 6719
N.A.I.C.S.: 551112
Torsten Larsson *(CEO)*

Subsidiary:

TV4 Gruppen (2)
Tegeluddsvagen 3-5
SE 115 79 Stockholm, Sweden SE
Tel.: (46) 84594000 (100%)
Fax: (46) 84594444
Web Site: www.tv4.se
Emp.: 450
Television Broadcaster
S.I.C.: 4833
N.A.I.C.S.: 515120
Jan Scherman *(CEO)*
Torsten Larsson *(Chm-Bonnier)*

Subsidiary:

C More Entertainment AB (3)
Tegeluddsvagen 7
SE-115 84 Stockholm, Sweden SE
Tel.: (46) 84592800 (65%)
Fax: (46) 84592801
E-Mail: info@cmore.se
Web Site: www.cmore.se
Emp.: 50
Television Broadcasting Network
S.I.C.: 4841
N.A.I.C.S.: 515210
Johan Kleberg *(Mng Dir)*

Bonnier Magazine Group AB (1)
Kungsgatan 49
SE-113 90 Stockholm, Sweden SE
Tel.: (46) 87364000 (100%)
Fax: (46) 87364031
E-Mail: info@bonnier.se
Web Site: www.bonnier.se
Sales Range: $650-699.9 Million
Holding Company; Magazine & Internet Publisher
S.I.C.: 6719
N.A.I.C.S.: 551112
Jonas Bonnier *(CEO)*

U.S. Subsidiary:

Bonnier Corporation (2)
460 N Orlando Ave Ste 200
Winter Park, FL 32789 DE
Tel.: (407) 628-4802
Fax: (407) 628-7061
Web Site: www.bonniercorp.com
Sales Range: $350-399.9 Million
Emp.: 1,200
Magazine Publisher
S.I.C.: 2721
N.A.I.C.S.: 511120
Jonas Bonnier *(Chm)*
Dave Freygang *(CEO)*
Randall Koubek *(CFO)*
Elizabeth Burnham Murphy *(CMO-Men's Grp)*
Sean Holzman *(Chief Brand Dev Officer)*
David Ritchie *(Chief Content Officer)*
Jeremy Thompson *(Gen Counsel)*
Eric Zinczenko *(Exec VP)*

Divisions:

Bonnier Active Media, Inc. (3)
2 Park Ave 9th Fl
New York, NY 10016-5675 NY
Tel.: (212) 779-5000
Fax: (212) 779-5599
Web Site: www.bonniercorp.com
Emp.: 700
Magazine & Internet Publisher
S.I.C.: 2721
N.A.I.C.S.: 511120
Slaton L. White *(Editor-SHOT Business)*

Units:

Field & Stream Magazine (4)
2 Park Ave 9th Fl
New York, NY 10016
Tel.: (212) 779-5316
Fax: (212) 779-5118
Web Site: www.fieldandstream.com
Outdoors Magazine & Internet Publisher
S.I.C.: 2721
N.A.I.C.S.: 511120
Mike Toth *(Exec Editor)*

Popular Science Magazine (4)
2 Park Ave 9th Fl
New York, NY 10016
Tel.: (212) 779-5000
Fax: (212) 779-5108
Web Site: www.popsci.com
Emp.: 30
Science Magazine & Internet Publisher
S.I.C.: 2721
N.A.I.C.S.: 511120
Mark Jannot *(Editor-in-Chief)*

The Parenting Group, Inc. (3)
2 Park Ave 10th Fl
New York, NY 10016 DE
Tel.: (212) 779-5000
Fax: (212) 779-5200
Web Site: www.parenting.com
Magazine & Internet Publisher
S.I.C.: 2721
N.A.I.C.S.: 511120
Heather Gumbley *(Assoc Publr-Mktg)*

Unit:

Babytalk Magazine (4)
2 Park Ave 10th Fl
New York, NY 10016
Tel.: (212) 779-5000
Web Site: www.parenting.com
Post-Pregnancy Parenting Advice Magazine Publisher
S.I.C.: 2721
N.A.I.C.S.: 511120

TransWorld Media (3)
2052 Corte Del Nogal Ste 100
Carlsbad, CA 92011 NY
Tel.: (760) 722-7777
Fax: (760) 722-0653
E-Mail: business@transworld.net
Web Site: www.transworld.net
Enthusiast Magazine & Internet Publisher
S.I.C.: 2721
N.A.I.C.S.: 511120
Adam Cozens *(Publr-SNOWboarding & Bus)*

Division:

TransWorld Media (4)
2052 Corte Del Nogal Ste 100
Carlsbad, CA 92011
Tel.: (760) 722-7777
Web Site: www.transworld.net
Magazine & Internet Publisher
S.I.C.: 2721
N.A.I.C.S.: 511120
Donn Maeda *(Editor-in-Chief-Motocross)*

Unit:

TransWorld Business Magazine (4)
2052 Corte Del Nogal Ste 100
Carlsbad, CA 92011-1491
Tel.: (760) 722-7777
Fax: (760) 722-0653
E-Mail: Mike@transworld.com
Web Site: www.business.transworld.net
Emp.: 80
Board-Sports Magazine & Internet Publisher
S.I.C.: 2721
N.A.I.C.S.: 511120
Rob Campbell *(Publr)*

Working Mother Media, Inc. (3)
2 Park Ave Fl 10
New York, NY 10016-5604 DE
Tel.: (212) 351-6400
Fax: (212) 351-6487
E-Mail: privacy@workingmother.com
Web Site: www.workingmother.com
Sales Range: $50-74.9 Million
Emp.: 150
Business Association, Conferences Organizer, Magazine Publisher & Internet Portal
S.I.C.: 2721
N.A.I.C.S.: 511120
Carol Evans *(Pres)*
Joan Sheridan Labarge *(VP & Grp Publr-Working Mother Media)*
Kim Sealy *(Publr)*

Division:

The National Association for Female Executives (4)
2 Park Ave
New York, NY 10016 DE
Tel.: (212) 351-6451 (100%)
Fax: (212) 219-7801
Toll Free: (800) 927-6233
Web Site: www.nafe.com
Sales Range: $10-24.9 Million
Emp.: 19
Female Executives Association & Magazine Publisher
Import Export
S.I.C.: 8611
N.A.I.C.S.: 813910
Betty Spence *(Pres)*
Carol Evans *(CEO)*

Units:

Islands Magazine (3)
460 N Orlando Ave Ste 200
Winter Park, FL 32789
Tel.: (407) 628-4802
Fax: (407) 628-7061
Web Site: www.islands.com
Emp.: 500
Travel Magazine & Internet Publisher
S.I.C.: 2721
N.A.I.C.S.: 511120
Ken G. Leandro *(Publr)*

MotorBoating (3)
460 N Orlando Ave Ste 200
Winter Park, FL 32789
Tel.: (407) 628-4802
Fax: (407) 628-7061
E-Mail: editor@motorboating.com
Web Site: www.motorboating.com
Sales Range: $100-124.9 Million
Motor Boating Digital Magazine Publisher
S.I.C.: 2741
N.A.I.C.S.: 519130
Glenn Hughes *(VP & Grp Publr)*
Sally Helme *(Grp Publr)*
John McEver *(Publr)*

Bonnier Newspapers (1)
Sveavagen 53
10544 Stockholm, Sweden
Tel.: (46) 87364000
Web Site: www.bonnier.se
Sales Range: $800-899.9 Million
Newspaper Publisher
S.I.C.: 2711
N.A.I.C.S.: 511110
Jonas Bonnier *(CEO)*
Mats Carleson *(CEO)*

Mag+ AB (1)
Sveavagen 53
113 90 Stockholm, Sweden
Tel.: (46) 8 736 53 00
E-Mail: sales@magplus.com
Web Site: www.magplus.com
Magazine Related Mobile Media Platform
S.I.C.: 7372
N.A.I.C.S.: 511210
Gregg Hano *(CEO)*
Mats Jansson *(CFO)*
Michael Freudenthal *(COO)*
Staffan Ekholm *(Exec VP)*

BONSO ELECTRONICS INTERNATIONAL INC.

Unit 1404 14th Floor Cheuk Nang Centre 9 Hillwood Road
Tsimshatsui, Kowloon, China (Hong Kong)
Tel.: (852) 26055822
Fax: (852) 26941724
E-Mail: info@bonso.com
Web Site: www.bonso.com
Year Founded: 1980
BNSO—(NASDAQ)
Sls.: $30,386,000
Assets: $27,123,000
Liabilities: $16,537,000
Net Worth: $10,586,000
Earnings: ($754,000)
Emp.: 1,127
Fiscal Year-end: 03/31/13

Business Description:
Electronic Weighing Scales & Balances Mfr & Exporter
S.I.C.: 3829
N.A.I.C.S.: 333997

Personnel:
Anthony So *(Chm, Pres, CEO & Treas)*
Albert So *(CFO & Sec)*

Board of Directors:
Anthony So
Kim Wah Chung
Woo Ping Fok
J. Stewart Jackson, IV
Henry F. Schlueter

Transfer Agent:
Computershare
1745 Gardena Avenue #200
Glendale, CA 91204

Subsidiary:

Bonso Electronics Limited **(1)**
Unit 1404 14/F Cheuk Nang Centre 9 Hillwood Road
Tsim Tsa Tsui, Kowloon, China (Hong Kong)
Tel.: (852) 2605 5822
Fax: (852) 2691 1724
E-Mail: info@bonso.com
Web Site: www.bonso.com
Emp.: 1,200
Communication Equipment Mfr
S.I.C.: 3669
N.A.I.C.S.: 334290
Andrew So *(Deputy Chm & Dir-Ops)*

Non-U.S. Subsidiary:

Bonso Electronics (Shenzhen) Co. Limited **(2)**
132 Da Yang Road Da Yang Synthetical Develop District
Fu Yong, Shenzhen, China 518103
Tel.: (86) 755 27311888
Fax: (86) 755 27311999
Web Site: www.bonso.com
Emp.: 2,500
Communication Equipment Mfr
S.I.C.: 3669
N.A.I.C.S.: 334290

BONSOIR OF LONDON LTD.

Unit 3, Northern Way, Cropmead
Crewkerne, TA18 7HJ, United Kingdom
Tel.: (44) 8450712331
Fax: (44) 1460785507
E-Mail: sales@bonsoirdirect.com
Web Site: www.bonsoirdirect.com
Sales Range: $50-74.9 Million
Emp.: 186

Business Description:
Online Nightwear & Linens Shop
S.I.C.: 5699
N.A.I.C.S.: 315240

BONTAN CORPORATION INC.

(Name Changed to Portage Biotech Inc.)

BONTERRA ENERGY CORP.

Suite 901 1015 4th Street SW
Calgary, AB, T2R 1J4, Canada
Tel.: (403) 262-5307
Fax: (403) 265-7488
E-Mail: info@bonterraenergy.com
Web Site: www.bonterraenergy.com
Year Founded: 1981
BNE—(TSX)
Rev.: $134,965,054
Assets: $417,421,801
Liabilities: $255,121,197
Net Worth: $162,300,604
Earnings: $33,012,398
Emp.: 32
Fiscal Year-end: 12/31/12

Business Description:
Oil & Gas Exploration Services
S.I.C.: 1311
N.A.I.C.S.: 211111

Personnel:
George F. Fink *(Chm & CEO)*
Robb D. Thompson *(CFO & Sec)*

Board of Directors:
George F. Fink
Gary J. Drummond
Randy M. Jarock
Carl Roland Jonsson
F. W. Woodward

Legal Counsel:
Borden Ladner Gervais LLP
Calgary, AB, Canada

Olympia Transfer Services Inc.
Suite 920 120 Adelaide Street West
Toronto, ON, Canada

Transfer Agents:
Olympia Trust Company
125 9th Avenue SE Suite 2300
Calgary, AB, T2G 0P6, Canada
Tel.: (403) 261-0900

Olympia Transfer Services Inc.
Suite 920 120 Adelaide Street West
Toronto, ON, Canada

BONTERRA RESOURCES INC.

9285 203B Street
Langley, BC, V1M 2L9, Canada
Tel.: (604) 290-6152
Fax: (604) 888-1892
Web Site: www.bonterraresources.com
BTR—(TSXV)
Sales Range: Less than $1 Million
Emp.: 4

Business Description:
Precious & Base Metals Mining & Exploration Services
S.I.C.: 1099
N.A.I.C.S.: 212299

Personnel:
Navjit Dhaliwal *(Pres & CEO)*
Jerry A. Minni *(CFO)*

Board of Directors:
Robert Bryce
Robert Gagnon
Jerry A. Minni
Hans Rasmussen

Legal Counsel:
Clark Wilson LLP
800-885 West Georgia Street
Vancouver, BC, Canada V6C 3H1

Transfer Agent:
Pacific Corporate Trust Company
625 Howe St
Vancouver, BC, Canada V6C 3B9

BONVESTS HOLDINGS LIMITED

541 Orchard Road 16-00 Liat Towers
Singapore, 238881, Singapore
Tel.: (65) 67325533
Fax: (65) 67383092
E-Mail: investorrelations@bonvests.com.sg
Web Site: www.bonvests.com.sg
B28—(SES)
Rev.: $133,616,632
Assets: $740,572,193
Liabilities: $149,968,120
Net Worth: $590,604,073
Earnings: $20,211,232
Emp.: 2,106
Fiscal Year-end: 12/31/12

Business Description:
Holding Company; Property Development & Investment; Food & Beverage Ownership & Management; Hotel Ownership & Management & Waste Management & Contract Cleaning of Buildings
S.I.C.: 6719
N.A.I.C.S.: 551112

Personnel:
Henry Ngo *(Chm & Mng Dir)*
Soon Soo Foo *(Sec)*

Board of Directors:
Henry Ngo
Heng Ching Chew
Gary Xie
Tom Lat Shing Yee
Wee Kiong Yeo

Divisions:

Bon-Food Pte Ltd **(1)**
541 Orchard Rd 04 01-02 Liat Twr
238881 Singapore, Singapore
Tel.: (65) 67385555
Fax: (65) 67336228
E-Mail: marketing@bonfresh.com.sg
Web Site: www.bon-food.com.sg
Emp.: 40
Food Service Contractors
S.I.C.: 5812
N.A.I.C.S.: 722310

Bonfresh Pte Ltd **(1)**
541 Orchard Rd # 05-04 Liat Twr
238881 Singapore, Singapore
Tel.: (65) 67385555
Fax: (65) 67336228
E-Mail: marketing@bonfresh.com.sg
Web Site: www.bonfresh.com.sg
Emp.: 40
Food Service Contractors
S.I.C.: 5812
N.A.I.C.S.: 722310
Brenda Sim *(Mgr-HR)*

Sheraton Towers Singapore **(1)**
39th Scotts Rd
228230 Singapore, Singapore
Tel.: (65) 67376888
Fax: (65) 67371072
E-Mail: sheraton.towers.singapore@sheraton.com
Web Site: www.sheratonsingapore.com
Emp.: 300
Hotels & Motels
S.I.C.: 7011
N.A.I.C.S.: 721110
Steven Long *(Gen Mgr)*

Subsidiary:

Colex Holdings Limited **(1)**
20 Jalan Tukang
Jurong Town, Singapore, 619257, Singapore
Tel.: (65) 62687711
Fax: (65) 62641219
E-Mail: wastemgt@colex.com.sg
Web Site: www.colex.com.sg
567—(SES)
Rev.: $36,855,739
Assets: $19,075,618
Liabilities: $3,931,553
Net Worth: $15,144,064
Earnings: $1,595,275
Emp.: 150
Fiscal Year-end: 12/31/12
Waste Management Services
S.I.C.: 4959
N.A.I.C.S.: 562998
Henry Ngo *(Chm)*
Soon Soo Foo *(Sec)*

Non-U.S. Division:

The Residence Mauritius **(1)**
Coastal Rd Belle Mare
Port Louis, Mauritius
Tel.: (230) 4018888
Fax: (230) 4155888
E-Mail: residence@intnet.mu
Web Site: www.theresidence.com
Emp.: 400
Hotels & Motels
S.I.C.: 7011
N.A.I.C.S.: 721110
Frederic Chretien *(Mng Dir)*

BOOKER GROUP PLC

Equity House Irthlingborough Road
Wellingborough, Northants, NN8 1LT, United Kingdom
Tel.: (44) 1933 371000
Fax: (44) 1933 371010
E-Mail: info@bookergroup.com
Web Site: www.bookergroup.com
BOK—(LSE OTC)
Rev.: $6,304,841,538
Assets: $1,750,958,823
Liabilities: $901,142,874
Net Worth: $849,815,949
Earnings: $131,238,999
Emp.: 9,658
Fiscal Year-end: 03/29/13

Business Description:
Consumer Goods Whslr & Distr
S.I.C.: 5411
N.A.I.C.S.: 445110

Personnel:
Charles A. Wilson *(CEO)*
Mark Chilton *(Gen Counsel & Sec)*

Board of Directors:
Richard Rose
Helena Andreas
Mark Aylwin
Lord Bilimoria
Andrew Cripps
Guy Farrant
Stewart Charles Gilliland
Karen Jones
Jonathan Prentis
Bryn Alan Hywel Satherley
Charles A. Wilson

Legal Counsel:
Clifford Chance LLP
10 Upper Bank Street
London, E14 5JJ, United Kingdom
Tel.: (44) 20 7006 1000
Fax: (44) 20 7006 5555

Subsidiaries:

Booker Cash & Carry Ltd. **(1)**
Equity House Irthlingborough Road
Wellingborough, Northamptonshire, NN8 1LT, United Kingdom
Tel.: (44) 1905454336
Fax: (44) 1933371567
E-Mail: info@bookergroup.com
Web Site: www.booker.co.uk
Cash & Carry Whslr
S.I.C.: 5099
N.A.I.C.S.: 423990
Charles Willson *(CEO)*
Guy Farrant *(Mng Dir)*

Booker Direct Limited **(1)**
Frobisher Way Hatfield Business Park
Hatfield, Hertfordshire, AL10 9TR, United Kingdom
Tel.: (44) 1933371000
Fax: (44) 2076896247
Web Site: www.booker.com
Emp.: 500
Food & Beverages Whslr
S.I.C.: 5149
N.A.I.C.S.: 424490
David McCallum *(Gen Mgr)*

Division:

Ritter Courivaud Limited **(2)**
4 Westlinks
Alperton Lane, Wembley, Middlesex, HA0 1ER, United Kingdom
Tel.: (44) 20 8991 4350
Fax: (44) 20 8991 4383
Web Site: www.rittercourivaud.co.uk
Fine Foods Importer & Distr
S.I.C.: 5141
N.A.I.C.S.: 424410

Booker Ltd (1)
Equity House
Irthlingborough Rd, Wellingborough, NN8 1LT, United Kingdom
Tel.: (44) 933371000
Fax: (44) 933371010
E-Mail: feedback@booker.co.uk
Web Site: www.booker.co.uk
Emp.: 9,719
Food Products Retailer & Distr
Import
S.I.C.: 5149
N.A.I.C.S.: 424490

Makro Self Service Wholesalers Ltd. (1)
Liverpool Road Barton Moss
Eccles, Manchester, M30 7RT, United Kingdom
Tel.: (44) 161 788 8448
Telex: 667340 mak ho g
Fax: (44) 161 788 4749
E-Mail: customer.services@makro.co.uk
Web Site: www.makro.co.uk
Sales Range: $1-4.9 Billion
Emp.: 3,700
Self-Service Wholesale Stores
S.I.C.: 5411
N.A.I.C.S.: 445110
Juergen Schwarze *(Mng Dir)*

BOOKOFF CORPORATION LIMITED

2-14-20 Kobuchi Minami-ku
Sagamihara, Kanagawa, Japan 252-0344
Tel.: (81) 427691511
Fax: (81) 427692013
Web Site: www.bookoff.co.jp
3313—(TKS)
Sls.: $843,380,307
Assets: $434,006,804
Liabilities: $266,259,873
Net Worth: $167,746,931
Earnings: $11,638,968
Fiscal Year-end: 03/31/13

Business Description:
Secondhand Book Sales
S.I.C.: 5942
N.A.I.C.S.: 451211

Personnel:
Nobuyuki Matsushita *(Pres & CEO)*
Shingo Koganei *(Mng Exec Officer)*
Shinya Aruga *(Exec Officer)*
Shunsuke Hirayama *(Exec Officer)*
Yasutaka Horiuchi *(Exec Officer)*
Ryosuke Hosaka *(Exec Officer)*
Yohei Miyazaki *(Exec Officer)*
Naoki Notsu *(Exec Officer)*
Takeshi Tsuchihashi *(Exec Officer)*
Hiroyuki Ueda *(Exec Officer)*

Board of Directors:
Mayumi Hashimoto
Hiroyuki Hijikata
Yasutaka Horiuchi
Shingo Koganei
Nobuyuki Matsushita
Yohei Miyazaki
Katsuo Nakano
Noriyuki Nobayashi
Yoshitaka Sato
Takayuki Suzuki

U.S. Subsidiary:

BOOKOFF U.S.A. Inc. (1)
49 W 45th St 5& 6 th Ave
New York, NY 10017
Tel.: (212) 685-1410
Fax: (212) 685-3667
Web Site: www.bookoffusa.com
Emp.: 25
Book Publishers
S.I.C.: 2731
N.A.I.C.S.: 511130
Sato Hiroshi *(Pres)*

BOOKOOK SECURITIES CO., LTD.

Yeouido-dong
Yeongdeungpo-gu, Seoul, Korea (South)
Tel.: (82) 15887744
Fax: (82) 15887744
Web Site: www.bookook.co.kr
Year Founded: 1954
001270—(KRS)
Sales Range: $250-299.9 Million

Business Description:
Securities Brokerage Services
S.I.C.: 6211
N.A.I.C.S.: 523120

Personnel:
Ok-Soo Chang *(Pres & CEO)*
Jeong-Don Jeon *(Mng Dir)*

BOOM LOGISTICS LIMITED

Level 6 55 SouthBank Boulevard
Southbank, VIC, 3006, Australia
Tel.: (61) 392072500
Fax: (61) 392072400
Web Site: www.boomlogistics.com.au
BOL—(ASX)
Rev.: $352,633,093
Assets: $509,612,953
Liabilities: $183,108,433
Net Worth: $326,504,519
Earnings: ($2,580,240)
Emp.: 1,000
Fiscal Year-end: 06/30/13

Business Description:
Lifting Solutions & Crane Sales & Services
S.I.C.: 7353
N.A.I.C.S.: 532412

Personnel:
Brenden Clive Mitchell *(CEO & Mng Dir)*
Iona MacPherson *(CFO & Sec)*
Paul Martinez *(CIO & Dir-Strategy)*

Board of Directors:
Rodney John Robinson
Fiona Rosalyn Vivienne Bennett
Terrence Charles Francis
Terrance Alexander Hebiton
Brenden Clive Mitchell

Subsidiaries:

Boom Logistics (QLD) Pty Ltd (1)
Level 6 55 Southbank Blvd
Southbank, VIC 3006, Australia
Tel.: (61) 392072500
Fax: (61) 392072400
E-Mail: boomlogistics@boomlogistics.com.au
Web Site: www.boomlogistics.com.au/
Emp.: 32
Crane Sales & Services
S.I.C.: 3536
N.A.I.C.S.: 333923
Rosanna Hammond *(Mgr-HR)*

Sherrin Hire Pty Ltd (1)
184 Curtin Ave W
Eagle Farm, Brisbane, QLD, 4009, Australia
Tel.: (61) 738681555
Fax: (61) 738686895
E-Mail: sherrin@boomsherrin.com.au
Web Site: www.boomsherrin.com.au
Emp.: 40
Travel Towers & Access Equipments Providing Services
S.I.C.: 1796
N.A.I.C.S.: 238290
Terese Withington *(Gen Mgr)*

Division:

Boom Sherrin (1)
30 32 Twp Dr
W Burleigh, Gold Coast, 4219, Australia
Tel.: (61) 755206299
Fax: (61) 755206499
Web Site: www.boomsherrin.com.au
Travel Towers & Access Equipments Providing Services
S.I.C.: 1796
N.A.I.C.S.: 238290
Terese Withington *(Gen Mgr)*

BOOMER VENTURES INC.

Posada del Rey Via Italia Punta Paitilla
Panama, Panama
Tel.: (507) 6004 1546
Year Founded: 2012

Business Description:
Search Engine Development
S.I.C.: 2741
N.A.I.C.S.: 519130

Personnel:
Alicia Itzel Rivera Tristan *(Pres, CEO & CFO)*

Board of Directors:
Alicia Itzel Rivera Tristan

BOOMERANG PLUS PLC

The Media Centre Culverhouse Cross
Cardiff, CF5 6XJ, United Kingdom
Tel.: (44) 2920 671500
Fax: (44) 2920 590626
E-Mail: enquires@boomerang.co.uk
Web Site: www.boomerang.co.uk
Sales Range: $25-49.9 Million
Emp.: 188

Business Description:
Broadcasting & Cable TV Services
S.I.C.: 7812
N.A.I.C.S.: 512110

Personnel:
Huw Eurig Davies *(CEO)*
Gareth Rees *(Mng Dir)*

Legal Counsel:
Osborne Clarke
One London Wall
London, United Kingdom

Hugh James
114-116 St. Mary Street
Cardiff, Australia

Subsidiaries:

Boom Films Limited (1)
218 Penarth Rd
Cardiff, South Glamorgan, CF11 8NN, United Kingdom
Tel.: (44) 2920550550
Fax: (44) 29020590551
E-Mail: enquiries@boomerang.co.uk
Web Site: www.boomerang.tv
Emp.: 150
Movie Production Services
S.I.C.: 7812
N.A.I.C.S.: 512110
Huw Davies *(Mng Dir)*

Boom Freesports Limited (1)
218 Penarth Rd
Cardiff, South Glamorgan, CF11 8NN, United Kingdom
Tel.: (44) 2920550550
Fax: (44) 2920550551
E-Mail: enquiries@boomerang.co.uk
Web Site: www.boomerang.tv
Emp.: 100
Rights Management Services
S.I.C.: 8742
N.A.I.C.S.: 541611
Gareth Rees *(Mng Dir)*

Boom Talent Limited (1)
218 Penarth Rd
Cardiff, South Glamorgan, CF11 8NN, United Kingdom
Tel.: (44) 2920550565
Fax: (44) 2920550551
E-Mail: info@boomtalent.co.uk
Web Site: www.boomtalent.co.uk
Actors Casting Services
S.I.C.: 7361
N.A.I.C.S.: 561311
Sioned James *(Mng Dir)*

Cynhyrchiadau Alfresco Productions Cyfyngedig (1)
The Media Centre
Culverhouse Cross, Cardiff, South Glamorgan, CF5 6XJ, United Kingdom
Tel.: (44) 2920550550
Fax: (44) 2920590626
E-Mail: alfresco@alfrescotv.co.uk
Web Site: www.alfrescotv.co.uk
Television Programme Production Services
S.I.C.: 7812
N.A.I.C.S.: 512110
Ronw Protheroe *(Mgr)*

Fflic Cyfyngedig (1)
59 Mount Stuart Sq
Cardiff, South Glamorgan, CF10 5LR, United Kingdom
Tel.: (44) 29 20 409 000
Fax: (44) 29 20 409 001
E-Mail: post@fflic.co.uk
Emp.: 15
Lifestyle & Children Programme Production Services
S.I.C.: 7812
N.A.I.C.S.: 512110
Gwenda Griffith *(Mng Dir)*

Indus Films Limited (1)
17 Cathedral Rd
Cardiff, South Glamorgan, CF11 9LJ, United Kingdom
Tel.: (44) 2920399555
Fax: (44) 2920399777
E-Mail: info@indusfilms.com
Web Site: www.indusfilms.com
Emp.: 20
Adventure & Environmental Program Production Services
S.I.C.: 7812
N.A.I.C.S.: 512110
Gwenllian Hughes *(Head-Bus & Production)*

Mwnci Cyfyngedig (1)
20 Cathedral Rd
Pontcanna, Cardiff, South Glamorgan, CF11 9LJ, United Kingdom
Tel.: (44) 2920399800
Fax: (44) 2920399700
E-Mail: reception@gorillagroup.tv
Web Site: www.gorillagroup.tv
Emp.: 60
Television Programme Post Production Services
S.I.C.: 7819
N.A.I.C.S.: 512191
Richard Moss *(Mng Dir)*

Teledu Apollo Cyfyngedig (1)
21a Allensbank Rd
Cardiff, South Glamorgan, CF14 3PN, United Kingdom
Tel.: (44) 29 20 251 811
Fax: (44) 29 20 251 821
E-Mail: apollo@teleduapollo.tv
Emp.: 5
Television Programme Production Services
S.I.C.: 7812
N.A.I.C.S.: 512110
Dafydd Sion *(Mgr)*

Non-U.S. Subsidiary:

Boom Extreme Publishing Limited (1)
25 allee du Moura lot 8B
64200 Biarritz, France
Tel.: (33) 559412145
Television Programme Production Services
S.I.C.: 7812
N.A.I.C.S.: 512110

BOOMI INTERNATIONAL OY

Sinikalliontie 10
FI-02630 Espoo, Finland
Tel.: (358) 975115000
Fax: (358) 975115050
E-Mail: info@buumi.net
Web Site: www.mobileavenue.fi
Sales Range: $1-9.9 Million

Business Description:
Mobile Content Services
S.I.C.: 7374
N.A.I.C.S.: 518210

Personnel:
Pepe Forsberg *(CEO)*
Frank Bahrke *(CTO)*

BOOMSENSE TECHNOLOGY CO., LTD.

803 Building 4 Zhuyu International Plaza 9
Beijing, 100048, China
Tel.: (86) 10 88857070
Fax: (86) 10 88556111
Web Site: www.boomsense.com
300312—(CHIN)
Sales Range: $50-74.9 Million

Boomsense Technology Co., Ltd.—(Continued)

Emp.: 1,540

Business Description:
Wireless Network Optimization System & Equipment
S.I.C.: 3663
N.A.I.C.S.: 334220

Personnel:
Qingwen Zhang *(Chm)*

BOON EDAM B.V.

Ambachtstraat 4
PO Box 40
1135 ZG Edam, Netherlands
Tel.: (31) 299380808
Fax: (31) 299372859
E-Mail: info@boonedam.nl
Web Site: www.boonedam.com
Year Founded: 1903
Sales Range: $50-74.9 Million
Emp.: 900

Business Description:
Mfr. of Revolving Doors
S.I.C.: 3442
N.A.I.C.S.: 332321

Personnel:
Niels Huber *(Chm)*

U.S. Subsidiary:

Boon Edam Thompson Inc **(1)**
402 McKinney Pkwy
Lillington, NC 27546 (100%)
Tel.: (910) 814-3800
Fax: (910) 814-3899
Toll Free: (800) 658-8776
E-Mail: reception@boonedam.us
Web Site: www.boonedam.us
Emp.: 80
Mfr. of Revolving Doors
S.I.C.: 3442
N.A.I.C.S.: 332321
Dan Camp *(CFO)*

BOON KOON GROUP BERHAD

51-13A Menara BHL Bank Jalan Sultan Ahmad Shah
10050 Penang, Malaysia
Tel.: (60) 42289700
Fax: (60) 42279800
E-Mail: bkgb@boonkoon.com
Web Site: www.boonkoon.com
BKOON—(KLS)
Rev.: $47,283,064
Assets: $47,092,337
Liabilities: $32,458,757
Net Worth: $14,633,580
Earnings: ($2,231,261)
Fiscal Year-end: 03/31/13

Business Description:
Commercial Vehicles Mfr
S.I.C.: 3089
N.A.I.C.S.: 326199

Personnel:
Boon Koon Goh *(Chm)*
Boon Leong Goh *(CEO)*
Wai Hong Chee *(Co-Sec)*
Li Ling Foo *(Co-Sec)*

Board of Directors:
Boon Koon Goh
Poh Gin Ang
Boon Leong Goh
Kok Loon Ho
Mureli Navaratnam
Mohd Kamal Omar

BOOST CAPITAL CORP.

36 Lombard Street Suite 700
Toronto, ON, M5C 2X3, Canada
Tel.: (416) 366-6691
Fax: (416) 363-9608
Year Founded: 2011
BST.P—(TSXV)

Business Description:
Investment Management Services
S.I.C.: 6799
N.A.I.C.S.: 523920

Personnel:
Martin Doane *(CEO & CFO)*

BOOSTER CO., LTD.

1142 Nowon-ri Iwol-dong
Jincheon, Chungcheongbuk-do, 365-822, Korea (South)
Tel.: (82) 435362005
Fax: (82) 435369109
E-Mail: booster@booster.co.kr
Web Site: www.booster.co.kr
Year Founded: 1973
008470—(KRS)

Business Description:
Boilers Mfr & Marketing
S.I.C.: 3443
N.A.I.C.S.: 332410

Personnel:
Byung-Hee Lee *(CEO)*

BOOTH SECURITIES LTD.

Garden Works Charleywood Road
Knowsley, Liverpool, L33 7SG, United Kingdom
Tel.: (44) 151 549 1910
Fax: (44) 151 549 1719
E-Mail: enquiries@boothmech.co.uk
Web Site: www.boothmech.co.uk
Rev.: $55,458,760
Emp.: 452

Business Description:
Investment Holding Company
S.I.C.: 6719
N.A.I.C.S.: 551112

Personnel:
Shaun Maclean *(CEO)*

Subsidiary:

Gas Maintenance and Training Limited **(1)**
19 Rotherham Rd
Swallownest, Sheffield, South Yorkshire, S26 4UR, United Kingdom
Tel.: (44) 114 294 2040
E-Mail: info@gasmaint.com
Web Site: www.gasmaint.com
Emp.: 50
Gas Maintenance, Repair & Installation Services
S.I.C.: 1711
N.A.I.C.S.: 238220
Kevin Wilson *(Mgr)*

BOPARAN HOLDINGS LIMITED

Unit 3 Bevan Way
Alpha Business Park, Smethwick, W Midlands, B66 1AW, United Kingdom
Tel.: (44) 1215550202
Year Founded: 1998
Sales Range: $550-599.9 Million
Emp.: 3,325

Business Description:
Holding Company
S.I.C.: 6719
N.A.I.C.S.: 551112

Personnel:
Baljinder K. Boparan *(Co-Owner)*
Ranjit S. Boparan *(Co-Owner)*
Ranjit Singh *(CEO)*

Subsidiary:

2 Sisters Food Group Limited **(1)**
Dial Lane
West Bromwich, Birmingham, W Midlands, B70 0EB, United Kingdom UK
Tel.: (44) 121 555 6661
Fax: (44) 870 458 9900
E-Mail: enquiries@2sfg.co.uk
Web Site: www.2sfg.com
Sales Range: $1-4.9 Billion
Emp.: 16,000
Holding Company; Poultry, Chilled, Frozen & Bakery Foods Mfr & Distr
S.I.C.: 6719
N.A.I.C.S.: 551112
Ranjit Singh *(Founder & CEO)*

Subsidiaries:

Avana Bakeries Ltd. **(2)**
Unit 8/9 Wern Trading Estate
Rogerstone, Newport, NP10 9YB, United Kingdom (100%)
Tel.: (44) 1633 466400
Fax: (44) 1633 466466
E-Mail: avana@rhm.com
Emp.: 900
Flour Confectionery, Cakes, Puddings, Puff Pastry, Chilled Desserts & Frozen Confectionery Mfr
S.I.C.: 2051
N.A.I.C.S.: 311812
Gill McComas *(Mng Dir)*

Northern Foods Limited **(2)**
2180 Century Way Thorpe Park
Leeds, LS15 8ZB, United Kingdom UK
Tel.: (44) 1133900110
Fax: (44) 1133900211
E-Mail: enquiries@northernfoods.com
Web Site: www.northernfoods.com
Sales Range: $1-4.9 Billion
Emp.: 9,472
Holding Company; Frozen, Chilled & Bakery Foods Mfr & Whslr
S.I.C.: 6719
N.A.I.C.S.: 551112
Julian Slade *(Mng Dir)*
Garry Walsh *(Mng Dir)*
John Coppola *(Chief Scientific Officer)*
Carol Williams *(Sec)*

Subsidiaries:

Cavaghan & Gray Carlisle **(3)**
Brunel House
Brunel Way, Carlisle, Cumbria, CA1 3NQ, United Kingdom (100%)
Tel.: (44) 1228518200
Fax: (44) 1228518215
Web Site: www.northernfoods.com
Emp.: 900
Production of Chilled Ready Meals & Meal Accompaniments
S.I.C.: 2099
N.A.I.C.S.: 311999
Willie Agnew *(Mgr-Ops)*

Dalepak Foods **(3)**
Dale House
Leeming Bar, Northallerton, DL7 9UL, United Kingdom (100%)
Tel.: (44) 1677424111
Fax: (44) 1677424443
E-Mail: info@dalepak.co.uk
Web Site: www.dalepak.co.uk
Sls.: $54,895,044
Emp.: 200
Mfr. of Meat Products
S.I.C.: 5147
N.A.I.C.S.: 311612
Alan Harris *(Gen Mgr)*

Fox's Biscuits Ltd. **(3)**
Wellington St
Batley, W Yorkshire, WF17 5JA, United Kingdom (100%)
Tel.: (44) 924444333
Telex: 55 7792
Fax: (44) 924470200
E-Mail: info@foxs-buscuits.co.uk
Web Site: www.foxs-biscuits.co.uk
Sls.: $78,367,500
Emp.: 2,492
Mfr. of Biscuits
S.I.C.: 2052
N.A.I.C.S.: 311821
Colin Smith *(Mng Dir)*

Branches:

Fox's Biscuits - Preston **(4)**
Whitworth St Wesham
Kirkham, Lancs, PR4 3AX, United Kingdom UK (100%)
Tel.: (44) 1772683501
Fax: (44) 1772682762
Web Site: www.sfg.com
Emp.: 3,500
Mfr. of Biscuits
S.I.C.: 2052
N.A.I.C.S.: 311821

Fox's Biscuits - Staffordshire **(4)**
Dove Valley Bakeries
Cheadle Road, Uttoxeter, ST14 7BT, United Kingdom (100%)
Tel.: (44) 1889563131
Telex: 36438 ELKBIS G
Fax: (44) 1889565379
Web Site: www.northernfoods.com
Emp.: 700
Production of Sweet & Semi-Sweet Biscuits
S.I.C.: 2052
N.A.I.C.S.: 311821
Kevin Hand *(Mgr)*

Gunstones Bakery **(3)**
Stubley Lane
Dronfield, Sheffield, S18 1PF, United Kingdom (100%)
Tel.: (44) 1246414651
Fax: (44) 1246291353
E-Mail: martin.husseltee@northernfoods.com
Web Site: www.northernfoods.com
Emp.: 1,300
Sandwiches & Specialty Bakery Products Mfr
S.I.C.: 2051
N.A.I.C.S.: 311812

Matthew Walker Ltd. **(3)**
Heanor Gate Rd
Heanor, DE75 7RJ, United Kingdom (60%)
Tel.: (44) 1773760121
Fax: (44) 1773537273
Web Site: www.traditional-christmas-puddings.co.uk
Emp.: 200
Christmas Puddings Mfr
S.I.C.: 2099
N.A.I.C.S.: 311999

Northern Foods plc-Technical Services **(3)**
Farnsworth House
Lenton Ln, Nottingham, Nottinghamshire, NG7 2NS, United Kingdom (100%)
Tel.: (44) 159868231
Fax: (44) 1159851175
Web Site: www.northernfoods.co.uk
Emp.: 80
Provider of Auditing, Buying, Engineering & Testing Services for Food Manufacturing
S.I.C.: 8734
N.A.I.C.S.: 541380

Pennine Foods **(3)**
Drakehouse Crescent
Sheffield, S20 7JG, United Kingdom (100%)
Tel.: (44) 142476864
Fax: (44) 142475790
Web Site: www.northernfoods.com
Emp.: 700
Mfr. of Ready Made Meals
S.I.C.: 2041
N.A.I.C.S.: 311211

The Pizza Factory **(3)**
Gateside Rd
PO Box 102
Nottingham, NG7 2NN, United Kingdom (100%)
Tel.: (44) 1159868204
Fax: (44) 1159850301
Web Site: www.northern-foods.com
Emp.: 400
Produces Pizzas & Quiches
S.I.C.: 2099
N.A.I.C.S.: 311991

Walter Hollands **(3)**
Baxenden
523 Manchester Road, Accrington, Lancashire, BB5 2SA, United Kingdom (100%)
Tel.: (44) 1706213591
Fax: (44) 1706228044
E-Mail: lean.holcroft@northernfoods.com
Web Site: www.northernfoods.com
Emp.: 460
Mfr. of Pies, Pasties & Puddings
S.I.C.: 2099
N.A.I.C.S.: 311999
Mark Higgins *(Dir-Bus)*

Non-U.S. Subsidiary:

Green Isle Food Ltd. **(3)**
IDA Industrial Estate
Monread Road, Naas, Kildare, Ireland (100%)

Tel.: (353) 45848000
Fax: (353) 45897001
Web Site: www.northern-foods.co.uk
Emp.: 500
Mfr. of Frozen Foods
S.I.C.: 2038
N.A.I.C.S.: 311412
Ian Meadows *(Mng Dir)*

BORA BORA RESOURCES LIMITED

30 Ledgar Road
Balcatta, WA, 6021, Australia
Tel.: (61) 8 9240 2836
Fax: (61) 8 9240 2406
E-Mail: info@boraboraresources.com.au
Web Site: www.boraboraresources.com.au
BBR—(ASX)
Business Description:
Gold & Other Metal Mining
S.I.C.: 1041
N.A.I.C.S.: 212221
Personnel:
Patrick Douglas Ford *(Chm)*
Nelson Reynolds *(Sec)*
Board of Directors:
Patrick Douglas Ford
Andrew Lorne Johnstone
Nelson Reynolds

BORA CORPORATION

10F-6 No 2 Fuhsing North Road
Taipei, 104, Taiwan
Tel.: (886) 2 8772 5598
Fax: (886) 2 8772 5698
Web Site: www.bora-corp.com
Year Founded: 2009
Business Description:
Holding Company; Pharmaceutical Research, Development, Mfr & Distr
S.I.C.: 6719
N.A.I.C.S.: 551112
Personnel:
Bobby Sheng *(Chm & CEO)*

Subsidiary:

Hoan Pharmaceuticals (1)
6F No 164 Fuxing North Road
Zhongshan District, Taipei, 10487, Taiwan
Tel.: (886) 2 2713 3260
Fax: (886) 2 2712 7347
E-Mail: hoane@hatcopharma.com
Web Site: www.hoanpharma.com
Pharmaceutical Developer, Mfr & Distr
S.I.C.: 2834
N.A.I.C.S.: 325412
Bobby Sheng *(Chm & CEO)*

Plant:

Bora Corp. - T'ainan Factory (1)
No 54 Gong-Yeh West Road
Guan Tyan Hsiang, T'ainan, Hsien, Taiwan
Tel.: (886) 6 698 5180
Fax: (886) 6 698 7539
Emp.: 63
Pharmaceutical Products Mfr
S.I.C.: 2834
N.A.I.C.S.: 325412

BORAL LIMITED

Level 39 AMP Centre 50 Bridge Street
Sydney, NSW, 2000, Australia
Mailing Address:
GPO Box 910
Sydney, NSW, 2001, Australia
Tel.: (61) 292206300
Fax: (61) 292336605
E-Mail: info@boral.com.au
Web Site: www.boral.com.au
Year Founded: 1946
BLD—(ASX OTC)
Rev.: $5,428,715,740
Assets: $6,582,320,440
Liabilities: $3,045,954,090
Net Worth: $3,536,366,350
Earnings: ($214,359,970)
Emp.: 12,610
Fiscal Year-end: 06/30/13
Business Description:
Construction Materials Mfr & Distr Import Export
S.I.C.: 3271
N.A.I.C.S.: 327331
Personnel:
Michael P. Kane *(CEO & Mng Dir)*
Rosaline Ng *(CFO)*
Robert Gates *(Chief Admin Officer)*
Al Borm *(Pres/CEO-Boral Industries Inc)*
Damien M. Sullivan *(Gen Counsel)*
Dominic Millgate *(Sec)*
Board of Directors:
Robert L. Every
Catherine Michelle Brenner
Brian James Clark
Eileen Joy Doyle
Michael P. Kane
Richard A. Longes
John Marlay
Paul Ashley Rayner
Legal Counsel:
Murphy & Moloney
Capita Building 9 Castlereogh Street
2000 Sydney, NSW, Australia
Tel.: (61) (02) 2211433

Subsidiaries:

Boral Australian Gypsum Ltd (1)
29 Caldwell St Garbutt
Townsville, QLD, 4814, Australia
Tel.: (61) 747795255
Fax: (61) 747793080
Emp.: 5
Construction Materials Distr
S.I.C.: 5032
N.A.I.C.S.: 423320
Rodney Pearse *(Mng Dir)*

Subsidiary:

Lympike Pty Ltd (2)
71 Milperra Rd
Revesby, NSW, 2212, Australia
Tel.: (61) 297923022
Fax: (61) 297743781
Emp.: 20
Construction Materials Distr
S.I.C.: 5032
N.A.I.C.S.: 423320
Mark Nuner *(Gen Mgr)*

Boral Building Materials Pty Ltd (1)
L 39 Amp Ctr 50 Bridge St
Sydney, NSW, 2000, Australia
Tel.: (61) 292206300
Fax: (61) 292336605
Construction Materials Mfr
S.I.C.: 3297
N.A.I.C.S.: 327120

Subsidiary:

Boral International Pty Ltd (2)
L 39 Amp Ctr 50 Bridge St
Sydney, NSW, 2000, Australia
Tel.: (61) 292206300
Fax: (61) 292336605
E-Mail: info@boral.com.au
Web Site: www.boral.com.au
Emp.: 80
Construction Materials Mfr
S.I.C.: 3255
N.A.I.C.S.: 327120

Non-U.S. Subsidiary:

Boral Concrete (Thailand) Ltd (3)
12 Floor PB Tower 1000/51 Sukhumvit 71
North Klongton
Watana, Bangkok, 10110, Thailand
Tel.: (66) 22788800
Fax: (66) 2 728 8801
E-Mail: callcenter@boral.co.th
Web Site: www.boral.co.th
Concrete Products Distr
S.I.C.: 5032
N.A.I.C.S.: 423320

U.S. Subsidiary:

Boral Construction Materials LLC (2)
4395 Washington St
Denver, CO 80216-3573
Tel.: (303) 292-1771
Fax: (303) 295-0470
Construction Materials Mfr & Distr
S.I.C.: 3271
N.A.I.C.S.: 327331

Subsidiary:

BCM Oklahoma LLC (3)
1400 S Holly Ave
Yukon, OK 73099
Tel.: (405) 354-8824
Web Site: www.boraloklahoma.com
Construction Material Mfr & Distr
S.I.C.: 5032
N.A.I.C.S.: 423320
Tom Turnipseed *(Gen Mgr-Boral Aggregates)*

Boral Concrete Products Pty. Ltd. (1)
Level 39 AMP Ctr 50 Bridge Street
Sydney, NSW, 2000, Australia (100%)
Tel.: (61) 292206300
Fax: (61) 292336605
E-Mail: info@boral.com.au
Web Site: www.boral.com.au
Emp.: 13,000
Mfr. & Distribution of Concrete Masonry Products & Manufacturer of Precast Concrete Floor & Wall Panels
S.I.C.: 1741
N.A.I.C.S.: 238140
Mike Kane *(CEO & Mng Dir)*

Boral Construction Materials Ltd (1)
Greystanes House Clunies Ross Street
Prospect, NSW, Australia
Tel.: (61) 363361333
Construction Materials Distr
S.I.C.: 5032
N.A.I.C.S.: 423320
Joseph Goss *(Mng Dir-Boral Construction Materials & Cement)*

Subsidiaries:

Bayview Pty Ltd (2)
251 Salmon St
Port Melbourne, VIC, 3207, Australia
Tel.: (61) 292206300
Fax: (61) 292336605
E-Mail: info@boral.com.au
Emp.: 40
Construction Material Mfr & Sales
S.I.C.: 3271
N.A.I.C.S.: 327331
Steven Caust *(Gen Mgr)*

Boral Bricks Pty Ltd (2)
L 39 Amp Centre 50 Bridge St
Sydney, NSW, 2000, Australia
Tel.: (61) 292206300
Fax: (61) 292336605
Construction Materials Mfr
S.I.C.: 3271
N.A.I.C.S.: 327331

Boral Building Products Ltd (2)
L 39 50 Bridge Rd
Sydney, NSW, 2000, Australia
Tel.: (61) 292206300
Fax: (61) 292336605
E-Mail: info@boral.com.au
Web Site: www.boral.com.au
Emp.: 80
Construction Materials Mfr & Distr
S.I.C.: 3271
N.A.I.C.S.: 327331

Boral Masonry Ltd (2)
Clunies Ross St
Prospect, NSW, 2145, Australia
Tel.: (61) 298402333
Fax: (61) 298402344
Construction Materials Distr
S.I.C.: 5032
N.A.I.C.S.: 423320

Subsidiary:

Boral Hollostone Masonry (South Aust) Pty Ltd (3)
Main North Road
Pooraka, Adelaide, SA, 5095, Australia
Tel.: (61) 882623529
Fax: (61) 882623529
Emp.: 5
Building Materials Retailer
S.I.C.: 5251
N.A.I.C.S.: 444130
Charlie Condo *(Gen Mgr)*

Boral Recycling Pty Ltd (2)
End Of Reconciliation Road
Prospect, NSW, 2148, Australia
Tel.: (61) 290335000
Fax: (61) 296048585
E-Mail: jessica.briggs@boral.com.au
Web Site: www.boral.com.au
Emp.: 30
Building Materials Distr
S.I.C.: 5032
N.A.I.C.S.: 423320
Charlie Bounassif *(Gen Mgr)*

Boral Resources (SA) Ltd (2)
1 Station Place
Hindmarsh, SA, 5007, Australia
Tel.: (61) 884250400
Fax: (61) 883403010
Construction Materials Distr
S.I.C.: 5032
N.A.I.C.S.: 423320

Subsidiary:

Road Surfaces Group Pty Ltd (3)
18 Oak St
Barcaldine, Rockhampton, QLD, 4725, Australia
Tel.: (61) 746511585
Fax: (61) 746511770
Emp.: 3,000
Construction Materials Distr
S.I.C.: 5032
N.A.I.C.S.: 423320
Graham Jones *(Mgr-Rockhampton Div)*

Boral Resources (WA) Ltd (2)
63-69 Abernethy Rd
Belmont, WA, 6104, Australia
Tel.: (61) 894580400
Fax: (61) 9333402
Web Site: boral.com.au
Emp.: 50
Construction Materials Distr
S.I.C.: 5032
N.A.I.C.S.: 423320

Subsidiary:

Boral Contracting Pty Ltd (3)
2 Craig Rd
Kalgoorlie, WA, 6430, Australia
Tel.: (61) 893333400
Fax: (61) 893333402
E-Mail: kate.ludgate@borel.co.au
Web Site: www.borel.com
Emp.: 10
Construction Materials Mfr
S.I.C.: 3271
N.A.I.C.S.: 327331

Boral Shared Business Services Pty Ltd (2)
L 39 50 Bridge St
Sydney, NSW, 2000, Australia
Tel.: (61) 292206300
Fax: (61) 292336605
Emp.: 20
Construction Materials Mfr & Distr
S.I.C.: 3271
N.A.I.C.S.: 327331
Mike Kane *(Gen Mgr)*

Boral Windows Systems Ltd (2)
188 Canterbury Road
Bayswater, VIC, 3153, Australia
Tel.: (61) 3 9721 0700
Glass Products Mfr
S.I.C.: 3211
N.A.I.C.S.: 327211

De Martin & Gasparini Pty Ltd (2)
16 Hill Road
Homebush Bay, NSW, 2127, Australia
Tel.: (61) 297485100
Fax: (61) 297480041
E-Mail: dmg@boral.com.au
Web Site: www.boral.com.au
Emp.: 150
Building Materials Distr
S.I.C.: 5032
N.A.I.C.S.: 423320

Boral Limited—(Continued)

Louie Mazzarolo *(Mng Dir)*

Subsidiaries:

De Martin & Gasparini Concrete Placers Pty Ltd (3)
Bennelong Rd
Homebush, NSW, 2140, Australia
Tel.: (61) 297485100
Fax: (61) 297480041
Concrete Product Mfr
S.I.C.: 3273
N.A.I.C.S.: 327320

De Martin & Gasparini Contractors Pty Ltd (3)
C/Lvl 39 50 Bridge St
PO Box 524
Sydney, NSW, 2000, Australia
Tel.: (61) 297485100
Concrete Product Mfr
S.I.C.: 3273
N.A.I.C.S.: 327320

De Martin & Gasparini Pumping Pty Ltd (3)
16 Hill Rd
Homebush Bay, NSW, 2127, Australia
Tel.: (61) 297485100
Fax: (61) 297480041
Concrete Product Mfr
S.I.C.: 3273
N.A.I.C.S.: 327320

Midland Brick Limited (2)
102 Great Northern Hwy
Middle Swan, Perth, WA, 6056, Australia
Tel.: (61) 8 9273 5522
Fax: (61) 8 9273 5523
E-Mail: midlandbrick@boral.com.au
Web Site: www.midlandbrick.com.au
Emp.: 100
Construction Material Mfr
S.I.C.: 3271
N.A.I.C.S.: 327331

Boral Investments Pty Ltd (1)
L 39 Amp Ctr 50 Bridge St
Sydney, NSW, Australia
Tel.: (61) 292206300
Fax: (61) 292336605
E-Mail: info@boral.com.au
Web Site: www.boral.com.au
Emp.: 100
Investment Management Services
S.I.C.: 6211
N.A.I.C.S.: 523999
Penny Berger *(Gen Mgr-IR)*

Subsidiary:

Boral Resources (Qld) Pty Ltd (2)
147 Coronation Dr
Milton, QLD, 4064, Australia
Tel.: (61) 738677600
Fax: (61) 738677488
Construction Material Mfr & Whslr
S.I.C.: 3271
N.A.I.C.S.: 327331

Subsidiary:

Allens Asphalt Pty Ltd (3)
22 Lear Jet Drive
PO Box 1106
Caboolture, QLD, 4510, Australia
Tel.: (61) 7 5495 8166
Fax: (61) 7 5498 9774
E-Mail: asphalt@allensasphalt.com.au
Web Site: www.allensasphalt.com.au
Road Construction Equipment Rental Services
S.I.C.: 7519
N.A.I.C.S.: 532120

Boral Resources Ltd. (1)
Clunies Ross Street
Prospect, NSW, 2148, Australia (100%)
Tel.: (61) 290335000
Fax: (61) 290334004
E-Mail: info@boralresources.com.au
Web Site: www.boralresources.com.au
Emp.: 120
Quarrying, Sand Extraction, Premixed Concrete
S.I.C.: 1442
N.A.I.C.S.: 212321
R. Pearse *(Gen Mgr)*

Boral Resources (Vic) Pty Ltd (1)
251 7th St
Port Melbourne, VIC, 3207, Australia
Tel.: (61) 395087111
Fax: (61) 398462584
Emp.: 200
Construction Materials Mfr
S.I.C.: 3255
N.A.I.C.S.: 327120

Subsidiary:

Bayview Quarries Pty Ltd (2)
L 39 50 Bridge St
Sydney, NSW, 2000, Australia
Tel.: (61) 292206300
Fax: (61) 292336605
E-Mail: info@boral.com.au
Construction Materials Mfr
S.I.C.: 3255
N.A.I.C.S.: 327120
Mark Selwiy *(CEO)*

Concrite Pty Ltd (1)
Level 1 36 Eton Street
Sutherland, NSW, 2232, Australia
Tel.: (61) 2 9545 6111
Fax: (61) 2 9545 6444
E-Mail: enquiries@concrite.com.au
Web Site: www.concrite.com.au
Concrete Mfr & Distr
S.I.C.: 3273
N.A.I.C.S.: 327320
Donn Jeffrey Eagleson *(Pres)*

Oberon Softwood Holdings Pty Ltd (1)
89 Saint Hilliers Road
Auburn, NSW, 2144, Australia
Tel.: (61) 2 92206300
Construction Materials Distr
S.I.C.: 5211
N.A.I.C.S.: 444190

U.S. Subsidiary:

Boral Industries Inc. (1)
200 Manville Ct E Ste 310
Roswell, GA 30076 (100%)
Tel.: (770) 645-4500
Fax: (770) 645-2888
Web Site: www.boralbricks.com
Sls.: $440,000,000
Emp.: 2,400
Holding Company
S.I.C.: 3255
N.A.I.C.S.: 327120
Tom Zimmerman *(Dir-Sls & Mktg-TruExterior Trim)*

Subsidiaries:

Boral Bricks Inc. (2)
1630 Arthern Rd
Augusta, GA 30901-9270
Mailing Address:
PO Box 195713
Augusta, GA 30913
Tel.: (706) 722-6831
Fax: (706) 722-8222
Web Site: www.boralbricks.com
Emp.: 67
Mfr. & Distribution of Clay Facing Bricks
S.I.C.: 3255
N.A.I.C.S.: 327120
Bob Kepford *(CEO)*

Boral Material Technologies Inc. (2)
45 NE Loop 410 Ste 700
San Antonio, TX 78216
Tel.: (210) 349-4069
Fax: (210) 349-8512
Toll Free: (800) 964-0951
Web Site: www.boralmti.com
Emp.: 150
Fly Ash & Coal Combustion Products Marketer
S.I.C.: 5169
N.A.I.C.S.: 424690
Gary Shelton *(Pres)*

Division:

Boral Material Technologies Inc. (3)
PO Box 355
Maricopa, AZ 85355 AZ
Tel.: (602) 861-5100 (100%)
Fax: (623) 512-4901
Web Site: www.boralmti.com
Emp.: 1
Fly Ash Distr
S.I.C.: 5169
N.A.I.C.S.: 424690
Terry Peterson *(Pres)*

Boral Timber Inc (2)
6 Campbell CtCt
Novato, CA 94947-3858
Tel.: (415) 209-6192
Timber Logging Services
S.I.C.: 0811
N.A.I.C.S.: 113110

Ready Mixed Concrete Co. (2)
4395 Washington St
Denver, CO 80216
Tel.: (303) 429-5850
Fax: (303) 429-0470
Web Site: www.concretecolorado.com
Sls.: $24,000,000
Emp.: 100
Ready-Mixed Concrete
S.I.C.: 3273
N.A.I.C.S.: 327320

Subsidiary:

Boral Best Block LLC (3)
8227 Blakeland Dr
Littleton, CO 80125
Tel.: (303) 791-3334
Fax: (303) 791-2947
Toll Free: (877) 444-3334
E-Mail:
Web Site: www.coloradobestblock.com
Emp.: 35
Construction Material Distr
S.I.C.: 5032
N.A.I.C.S.: 423320

U.S. Joint Venture:

MonierLifetile LLC (1)
7575 Irvine Ctr Dr Ste 100
Irvine, CA 92618-2930
Tel.: (949) 756-1605
Fax: (949) 756-2401
Toll Free: (800) 571-8453
Web Site: www.monierlifetile.com
Emp.: 800
Concrete Roof Tile Mfr & Whslr; Owned by Boral Limited & by MONIER Group GmbH
Export
S.I.C.: 3259
N.A.I.C.S.: 327120
Christian Doelle *(VP-Sls & Mktg)*

Non-U.S. Subsidiaries:

Boral Building Products (NZ) Ltd (1)
8 Kelly Pl
Albany, 5632, New Zealand
Tel.: (64) 94141075
Fax: (64) 94141073
Web Site: www.midlandbrick.co.nz
Emp.: 5
Building Materials Distr
S.I.C.: 5039
N.A.I.C.S.: 423390
Brent Whalan *(Mgr)*

Boral Investments BV (1)
Nieuwe Stationsstraat 10
Arnhem, Gelderland, 6811 KS, Netherlands
Tel.: (31) 263201169
Fax: (31) 26320 3121
Real Estate Management Services
S.I.C.: 6531
N.A.I.C.S.: 531390

CMI Springs (1)
7A Carmont Pl
Mt Wellington, NIL Auckland, New Zealand NZ
Tel.: (64) 95794089 (100%)
Fax: (64) 95792595
E-Mail: info@cmisprings.co.nz
Web Site: www.cmilimited.com.au
Emp.: 50
Mfr. & Maintainance of Elevators & Escalators; Scaffolding & Material Handling Systems
S.I.C.: 1799
N.A.I.C.S.: 238290
Jeff Leong *(Gen Mgr)*

BORALEX INC.

36 Lajeunesse Street
Kingsey Falls, QC, J0A 1B0, Canada
Tel.: (819) 363-5860
Fax: (819) 363-5866
E-Mail: info@boralex.com
Web Site: www.boralex.com
Year Founded: 1982
BLX—(TSX)
Rev.: $183,190,928
Assets: $1,222,516,371
Liabilities: $882,194,738
Net Worth: $340,321,633
Earnings: ($5,232,521)
Emp.: 200
Fiscal Year-end: 12/31/12

Business Description:
Electricity Production
S.I.C.: 4939
N.A.I.C.S.: 221111

Personnel:
Bernard Lemaire *(Chm)*
Patrick Lemaire *(Pres & CEO)*
Jean-Francois Thibodeau *(CFO & VP)*
Sylvain Aird *(Chief Legal Officer & VP-Europe)*
Guy D'Aoust *(Treas & Dir-Fin)*

Board of Directors:
Bernard Lemaire
Germain Benoit
Alain Ducharme
Robert F. Hall
Edward H. Kernaghan
Patrick Lemaire
Richard Lemaire
Yves Rheault
Alain Rheaume
Michelle Samson-Doel
Pierre Seccareccia

Transfer Agent:
Computershare Investor Services Inc.
1500 University Street Suite 700
Montreal, QC, H3A 3SB, Canada

Subsidiaries:

Boralex Power Inc. (1)
404 Marie-Victorin Boulevard
Kingsey Falls, QC, J0A 1BO, Canada
Tel.: (819) 363-5860
Fax: (819) 363-5866
E-Mail: info@boralex.com
Emp.: 45
Electricity Producer
S.I.C.: 4931
N.A.I.C.S.: 221122
Bernard Lemaire *(Chm & CEO)*
Robert Hall *(Sec)*

Subsidiary:

Kingsey Cogeneration (2)
36 Lagaunesse St
Kingsey Falls, QC, J0A 1B0, Canada
Tel.: (819) 363-5860
Fax: (819) 363-5866
E-Mail: reception.blx.tf@boralex.com
Web Site: www.boralex.com
Emp.: 30
Electricity Producer
S.I.C.: 2631
N.A.I.C.S.: 322130
Denis Aubut *(Gen Mgr-Hydro & Cogeneration)*

Non-U.S. Subsidiary:

Boralex S.A.S. (1)
2 rue du Priez
Lille, Nord, 59000, France
Tel.: (33) 328365495
Fax: (33) 328365496
Emp.: 38
Electric Power Generation Services
S.I.C.: 4911
N.A.I.C.S.: 221118
Patrick Gecostre *(Gen Mgr)*

BORAX MORARJI LIMITED

53/57 Laxmi Inds Building Mumbai GPO
Fort, Mumbai, Maharashtra, 400001, India
Tel.: (91) 22 22679224

E-Mail: investorcare@boraxmorarji.com
Web Site: www.boraxmorarji.com
Year Founded: 1963
506315—(BOM)
Rev.: $11,855,143
Assets: $11,562,304
Liabilities: $9,471,938
Net Worth: $2,090,366
Earnings: ($541,127)
Emp.: 300
Fiscal Year-end: 03/31/13
Business Description:
Boron Product Mfr & Wind Power Generation Services
S.I.C.: 1474
N.A.I.C.S.: 212391
Personnel:
Bimal L. Goculdas *(Mng Dir)*
Dilip S. Nagle *(Compliance Officer & Sec)*
Board of Directors:
L. N. Goculdas
S. K. Diwanji
Bimal L. Goculdas
Mitika L. Goculdas
S. V. Joshi
Ranjan Sanghi

BORBET GMBH

Hauptstr 5
D 59969 Hallenberg, Germany
Tel.: (49) 29843010
Fax: (49) 2984301110
E-Mail: info@borbet.de
Web Site: www.borbet.de
Year Founded: 1881
Sales Range: $800-899.9 Million
Emp.: 2,800
Business Description:
Aluminium Wheel Mfr
S.I.C.: 3714
N.A.I.C.S.: 336390
Personnel:
Peter Wilhelm Borbet *(Pres)*
U.S. Subsidiary:

BORBET Alabama Inc. (1)
979 W Veterans Blvd
Auburn, AL 36832
Tel.: (334) 502-9400
Fax: (334) 502-9494
E-Mail: info@borbet-alabama.us
Web Site: www.borbet.de/en/about_borbet/locations/borbet_alabama_usa.php
Emp.: 200
Aluminium Wheel Mfr
S.I.C.: 3714
N.A.I.C.S.: 336390

BORBONESE SPA

Via Nazionale 99
Pianoro, 40065 Bologna, Italy
Tel.: (39) 051770111
Fax: (39) 051775450
E-Mail: customerservice@borbonese.com
Web Site: www.borbonese.com
Sales Range: $25-49.9 Million
Emp.: 100
Business Description:
Women's Clothing & Accessories Designer, Mfr & Retailer
S.I.C.: 2389
N.A.I.C.S.: 315990
Personnel:
Carlo Morsini *(CEO)*

BORCH TEXTILE GROUP A/S

Strudsbergsvej 4
DK 4200 Slagelse, Denmark
Tel.: (45) 58524550
Fax: (45) 58501035
E-Mail: info@borchtextile.dk
Web Site: www.borchtextile.dk
Sales Range: $10-24.9 Million
Emp.: 150
Business Description:
Clothing Mfr
S.I.C.: 5699
N.A.I.C.S.: 315220
Personnel:
Niels Mosegaard *(Chm)*
Ulrich Mosegaard *(CEO)*

BORD NA MONA PLC

Main Street
Newbridge, Co Kildare, Ireland
Tel.: (353) 45439000
Fax: (353) 45439001
Web Site: www.bordnamona.ie
Sls.: $573,629,960
Assets: $876,145,321
Liabilities: $642,899,830
Net Worth: $233,245,491
Earnings: $12,427,841
Emp.: 2,044
Fiscal Year-end: 03/27/13
Business Description:
Peat Production & Power Generation Services
S.I.C.: 4931
N.A.I.C.S.: 221112
Personnel:
John Horgan *(Chm)*
Gabriel D'Arcy *(Mng Dir)*
Paddy Rowland *(Press Officer)*
Joe Coleman *(Treas)*
Gerry Ryan *(Sec & Head-Land & Property)*
Board of Directors:
John Horgan
Paudge Bennett
Denise Cronin
Gabriel D'Arcy
Paddy Fox
Pat McEvoy
Gerard O'Donoghue
Colm O'Gogain
David Taylor
Elaine Treacy
Barry Walsh
Subsidiaries:

AES (Ireland) Limited (1)
1 Monread Commercial Park
Monread Road, Naas, Co Kildare, Ireland
Tel.: (353) 45 843800
Fax: (353) 45 981621
Web Site: www.aesirl.ie
Energy Generation Services
S.I.C.: 4931
N.A.I.C.S.: 221112

AES Portlaoise (1)
Kyletalesha
Portlaoise, County Laoise, Ireland
Tel.: (353) 578662122
Fax: (353) 578662540
E-Mail: info@aesirl.ie
Web Site: www.aesirl.ie
All Other Miscellaneous Waste Management Services
S.I.C.: 4959
N.A.I.C.S.: 562998
Paul Hennessey *(CEO)*

AES Tullamore (1)
Cappincur
Tullamore, Ireland (100%)
Tel.: (353) 579321755
Fax: (353) 579351628
E-Mail: info@aesirl.ie
Web Site: www.aesirl.ie
Emp.: 50
All Other Miscellaneous Waste Management Services
S.I.C.: 4959
N.A.I.C.S.: 562998
Paul Hennessey *(Gen Mgr)*

Bord na Mona Energy Tech/Admin (1)
Leabeg Boora
Tullamore, Ireland
Tel.: (353) 579345900
Fax: (353) 579345179
Web Site: www.bnm.ie/environmental/index.jsp?&1nID=113&pID=130&nID=150
Emp.: 100
Other Electric Power Generation
S.I.C.: 4911
N.A.I.C.S.: 221118
Gerry Ryan *(Sec)*

Bord na Mona Environmental Limited (1)
Main St
Newbridge, Ireland (100%)
Tel.: (353) 45439000
Fax: (353) 45432312
E-Mail: ed.info@bnm.ie
Web Site: www.bnm.ie/environmental/index.jsp?pID=113&nID=119
Emp.: 260
All Other Miscellaneous Waste Management Services
S.I.C.: 4959
N.A.I.C.S.: 562998
Colm O'Gogain *(Head-Strategic Infrastructure)*

Edenderry Power Limited (1)
Co Offaly Ballykilleen
Edenderry, Ireland
Tel.: (353) 469733800
Fax: (353) 469733801
E-Mail: info@edenderrypower.ie
Web Site: www.edenderrypower.ie
Emp.: 45
Other Electric Power Generation
S.I.C.: 4911
N.A.I.C.S.: 221118
Tom Egan *(CEO)*

Suttons Limited (1)
Monahan Rd
Cork, Ireland
Tel.: (353) 214963900
Fax: (353) 214318230
E-Mail: info@bnm.ie
Web Site: www.bordnamona.ie
Emp.: 12
Coal & Other Mineral & Ore Whslr
S.I.C.: 5052
N.A.I.C.S.: 423520
Michael Coleman *(CEO)*

Suttons Oil Limited (1)
Monahan Rd
Cork, Ireland (100%)
Tel.: (353) 214911700
Fax: (353) 214911701
E-Mail: info@bnm.ie
Web Site: www.bordnamona.com
Emp.: 12
Petroleum & Petroleum Products Merchant Whslr (except Bulk Stations & Terminals)
S.I.C.: 5172
N.A.I.C.S.: 424720
Joe O'Mahony *(CEO)*

U.S. Subsidiary:

Bord na Mona Environmental Products US Inc. (1)
PO Box 77457
Greensboro, NC 27417 (100%)
Tel.: (336) 547-9338
Fax: (336) 547-8559
E-Mail: info@bnm-us.com
Web Site: www.bnm-us.com
Emp.: 20
Administration Air & Water Resource & Solid Waste Management Programs
S.I.C.: 9511
N.A.I.C.S.: 924110
Shane Keaney *(Pres)*

Non-U.S. Subsidiaries:

Acorn Environmental Systems Limited (1)
Somerset Bridge Bridgwater
TA66LL Somerset, United Kingdom (100%)
Tel.: (44) 1278439325
Fax: (44) 1278439324
E-Mail: info@anua.com
Web Site: www.anua.com
Emp.: 25
All Other Miscellaneous Waste Management Services
S.I.C.: 4959
N.A.I.C.S.: 562998
Anton Bolton *(Mgr-Comml)*

Brightwater Engineering Limited (1)
Brightwater House
Unit 2 Business Ctr East Ave 1, SG62HB
Letchworth, United Kingdom (100%)
Tel.: (44) 1462485005
Fax: (44) 1462485003
Web Site: www.brightwater.uk.com
Emp.: 40
Engineering Services
S.I.C.: 8711
N.A.I.C.S.: 541330

BORDEAUX INDEX LTD.

10 Hatton Garden
London, EC1N 8AH, United Kingdom
Tel.: (44) 20 7269 0703
Fax: (44) 20 7269 0701
E-Mail: sales@bordeauxindex.com
Web Site: www.bordeauxindex.com
Year Founded: 1997
Sales Range: $100-124.9 Million
Emp.: 100
Fiscal Year-end: 03/31/13
Business Description:
Wine Merchant
S.I.C.: 5182
N.A.I.C.S.: 424820
Personnel:
Gary Boom *(Mng Dir)*
Board of Directors:
Gary Boom
Andrew Bruce
Sam Gleave
Sebastian Rowe
Colin West
Non-U.S. Subsidiaries:

Bordeaux Index (Hong Kong) Ltd. (1)
27/F Tai Yip Building 141 Thomson Road
Wanchai, China (Hong Kong)
Tel.: (852) 2504 1122
Fax: (852) 2504 1121
E-Mail: sales@bordeauxindex.com
Web Site: www.bordeauxindex.com
Emp.: 8
Wine Distr
S.I.C.: 5182
N.A.I.C.S.: 424820
Doug Rumsam *(Mng Dir)*

Bordeaux Index (Singapore) Ltd. (1)
237 Alexandra Road 07-04 The Alexcier
Singapore, 159929, Singapore
Tel.: (65) 6474 7310
Fax: (65) 6476 1519
Web Site: www.bordeauxindex.com
Wine Distr
S.I.C.: 5182
N.A.I.C.S.: 424820

BORDER CHEMICAL CO., LTD.

2147 Portage Avenue
Winnipeg, MB, R3J 0L4, Canada
Tel.: (204) 837-1383
Fax: (204) 832-7244
Year Founded: 1959
Rev.: $18,336,138
Emp.: 63
Business Description:
Chemical Products Distr & Mfr
S.I.C.: 2899
N.A.I.C.S.: 325998
Personnel:
Patricia B. Smerchanski *(CEO)*
Barbara L. Nicolson *(Sec)*

BORDER MANAGEMENT, INC.

968 240th Street
Langley, BC, V2Z 2Y3, Canada
Tel.: (604) 539-9680
Fax: (604) 539-7234
E-Mail: evanwilliam@shaw.ca
Web Site: www.bordermanagementinc.com
Year Founded: 2006
BRDN—(OTCB)

BORDER MANAGEMENT, INC.—(Continued)

Business Description:
Management & Consulting Service
S.I.C.: 8742
N.A.I.C.S.: 541611
Personnel:
Qi Sun *(Pres)*
Da Zhi Yan *(Treas)*
Bin Sun *(Sec)*
Board of Directors:
Bin Sun
Qi Sun
Da Zhi Yan
Transfer Agent:
Island Stock Transfer
Saint Petersburg, FL 33701

BORDER PETROLEUM CORP.

2000 840-7th Avenue SW
Calgary, AB, T2P 3G2, Canada
Tel.: (403) 538-8448
Fax: (403) 444-5042
E-Mail: info@borderpetroleum.com
Web Site: www.borderpetroleum.com
BOR—(OTC TSXV)
Rev.: $3,091,908
Assets: $33,654,969
Liabilities: $5,654,888
Net Worth: $28,000,080
Earnings: ($17,578,140)
Emp.: 6
Fiscal Year-end: 03/31/13
Business Description:
Oil & Gas Exploration Services
S.I.C.: 1389
N.A.I.C.S.: 213112
Personnel:
Al J. Kroontje *(Chm & Interim CEO)*
John Aihoshi *(CFO)*
Steven Thompson *(COO)*
Douglas Murray Stuve *(Sec)*
Board of Directors:
Al J. Kroontje
Thomas Jackson
Harold R. Jamieson
Eric G. Panchy
Douglas Murray Stuve
Steven Thompson
Legal Counsel:
Burstall Winger LLP
1600-333 7 Avenue SW
Calgary, AB, Canada
Transfer Agent:
CIBC Mellon Trust Company
PO Box 46205 Postal Station A
Toronto, ON, Canada

BORDER TIMBERS LIMITED

Aberdeen Road
PO Box 458
Mutare, Zimbabwe
Tel.: (263) 20 64224
Fax: (263) 20 64142
E-Mail: btlinfo@border.co.zw
Web Site: www.bordertimbers.com
BRDR—(ZIM)
Rev.: $24,122,232
Assets: $163,588,257
Liabilities: $55,990,432
Net Worth: $107,597,825
Earnings: $1,192,325
Emp.: 2,311
Fiscal Year-end: 06/30/13
Business Description:
Timber Mfr
S.I.C.: 2499
N.A.I.C.S.: 321999
Personnel:
Kenneth R.R. Schofield *(Chm)*
Heinrich B.A.J. von Pezold *(Deputy Chm)*
Erhard Kuhn *(Mng Dir)*
Board of Directors:
Kenneth R.R. Schofield
R.E. Breschini
S. Dube
E. Hwenga
Erhard Kuhn
S. Mattinson
E. Mlambo
B. Mtetwa
Heinrich B.A.J. von Pezold
Ruediger von Pezold

BORDERS & SOUTHERN PETROLEUM PLC

33 St James's Square
London, SW1Y 4JS, United Kingdom
Tel.: (44) 20 7661 9348
Fax: (44) 20 7661 8055
E-Mail: info@bordersandsouthern.com
Web Site: www.bordersandsouthern.com
Year Founded: 2004
BOR—(LSE)
Rev.: $2,023,224
Assets: $316,011,637
Liabilities: $3,705,764
Net Worth: $312,305,873
Earnings: ($1,280,504)
Emp.: 6
Fiscal Year-end: 12/31/12
Business Description:
Oil & Gas Exploration Services
S.I.C.: 1389
N.A.I.C.S.: 213112
Personnel:
Howard Kevin Obee *(CEO)*
William Slack *(Sec)*
Board of Directors:
David Harry Williamson Dobson
Peter William Fleming
Christopher Nigel Hurst-Brown
Howard Kevin Obee
Stephen James Douglas Posford
Legal Counsel:
SNR Denton UK LLP
One Fleet Place
London, United Kingdom

BORDEX PACKAGING B.V.

Schumanpark 67
7336 AS Apeldoorn, Netherlands
Tel.: (31) 55 599 65 00
Fax: (31) 55 599 65 18
E-Mail: sales@bordexpackaging.nl
Web Site: www.bordexpackaging.com
Year Founded: 1977
Sales Range: $10-24.9 Million
Emp.: 15
Business Description:
Plastic Packaging Products Mfr
S.I.C.: 2671
N.A.I.C.S.: 326112
Personnel:
Bert Hengeveld *(Owner & Mng Dir)*

BORE TECH AB

C/O GenerPro AB Terminalvagen 24
SE-721 36 Vasteras, Sweden
Tel.: (46) 31617130
Fax: (46) 31155107
E-Mail: office@borevind.se
Web Site: www.borevind.se
BORE—(DEU OMX)
Sales Range: Less than $1 Million
Emp.: 4
Business Description:
Renewable Energy Investment Services
S.I.C.: 6211
N.A.I.C.S.: 523999
Personnel:
Brad Mikkelsen *(Chm)*
Christian Widing *(Mng Dir)*
Nils Lindgren *(CFO & Mgr-Investments)*
Board of Directors:
Brad Mikkelsen
Bo Andersson
Anette Asklin
Mats Rydehell
Semida Silveira
Mats Swensson
Subsidiary:

Boreinvest AB (1)
Little Boom 5 Ctr
411 04 Gothenburg, Sweden
Tel.: (46) 31617130
Emp.: 5
Investment Management Services
S.I.C.: 6282
N.A.I.C.S.: 523920
Christian Widing *(Mng Dir)*

BOREALIS EXPLORATION LIMITED

Suite 2F/2 Eurolife Building 1 Corral Road
PO Box 575
Gibraltar, Gibraltar
Tel.: (350) 20059995
Fax: (350) 20059059
E-Mail: pr@borealis.gi
Web Site: www.borealis.com
BOREF—(OTC)
Assets: $12,046,941
Liabilities: $7,701,210
Net Worth: $4,345,731
Earnings: ($5,691,909)
Emp.: 50
Fiscal Year-end: 03/31/13
Business Description:
Holding Company; Technology Research & Development Services for Energy Industry
S.I.C.: 6719
N.A.I.C.S.: 551112
Personnel:
Rodney T. Cox *(Chm & CEO)*
Isaiah W. Cox *(Pres & COO)*
James Magdych *(CIO)*
Board of Directors:
Rodney T. Cox
Isaiah W. Cox
Nechama J. Cox
David M. Goldenberg
Wayne S. Marshall
Jan Vana
Transfer Agent:
OTR, Inc.
1001 SW 5th Ave Ste 1550
Portland, OR 97204
Tel.: (503) 225-0375

BOREK CONSTRUCTION, LTD.

Mile 2 Hart Highway 9690 223
Willowbrook Rd
P O Box 870
Dawson Creek, BC, V1G 4H8, Canada
Tel.: (250) 782-5561
Fax: (250) 782-5623
Web Site: www.borekltd.com
Year Founded: 1957
Rev.: $26,170,430
Emp.: 160
Business Description:
Construction & Engineering Services
S.I.C.: 1629
N.A.I.C.S.: 237990
Personnel:
Rosella D. Borek *(Pres)*

BORGERS AG

Borgersstrasse 2 10
D 46397 Bocholt, Germany
Tel.: (49) 28713450
Fax: (49) 2871345291
E-Mail: info@borgers-group.com
Web Site: www.borgers.de
Sales Range: $700-749.9 Million
Emp.: 5,052
Business Description:
Automobile Textile Component Mfr
S.I.C.: 2396
N.A.I.C.S.: 336360
Personnel:
Werner Borgers *(CEO)*
Meinolf Nothe *(CFO)*

BORGESTAD ASA

Gunnar Knudsensvei 144
3712 Skien, Norway
Mailing Address:
PO Box 1093
3905 Porsgrunn, Norway
Tel.: (47) 35542400
Fax: (47) 35542401
E-Mail: borgestad@borgestad.com
Web Site: www.borgestad.com
BOR—(OSL)
Rev.: $1,870,713
Assets: $95,853,209
Liabilities: $49,207,561
Net Worth: $46,645,648
Earnings: ($3,630,116)
Emp.: 15
Fiscal Year-end: 12/31/12
Business Description:
Property Development Services
S.I.C.: 6552
N.A.I.C.S.: 237210
Personnel:
Bertel O. Steen, Jr. *(Chm)*
Christen Knudsen *(CEO)*
Jan Erling Nilsen *(CFO & COO)*
Lill Sanni *(Sr VP-Acctg)*
Board of Directors:
Bertel O. Steen, Jr.
Gudmund Bratrud
Sissel Grefsrud
Jacob Moller
Hilde Westlie

Non-U.S. Subsidiary:

Borgestad Poland Sp.zo.o (1)
Lipowa 3
44 100 Gliwice, Silesian, Poland
Tel.: (48) 327192628
Fax: (48) 327192610
E-Mail: gzmokimdergarten@gzmokimdergarten.pl
Nursery Management Services
S.I.C.: 5261
N.A.I.C.S.: 444220
Urbanska Magdalena Ewa *(Chm)*

BORNEO OIL BERHAD

1st 2nd Floor Victoria Point Jalan
OKK Awang Besar
87000 Labuan, Malaysia
Tel.: (60) 87410509
Fax: (60) 87410515
E-Mail: bornoilkk@gmail.com
Web Site: www.borneo-oil.com.my
BORNOIL—(KLS)
Rev.: $10,929,787
Assets: $66,404,862
Liabilities: $6,159,360
Net Worth: $60,245,502
Earnings: ($2,652,253)
Fiscal Year-end: 01/31/13
Business Description:
Hotel Management & Property Development Services
S.I.C.: 6531
N.A.I.C.S.: 531312
Personnel:
Chee Kee Chin *(Co-Sec)*
Siew Kim Chin *(Co-Sec)*
Board of Directors:
John Yan Hong Lee
Michael Kai Wah Moo
Kok Chor Tan
Kiew Leong Teo

BOROMIR PROD SA BUZAU
Nr 37 Santierului
Buzau, Romania
Tel.: (40) 238 436 646
Fax: (40) 238 446 705
E-Mail: office@boromir.ro
Web Site: www.boromir.ro
SPCU—(BUC)
Sls.: $35,095,439
Assets: $43,947,037
Liabilities: $12,282,320
Net Worth: $31,664,717
Earnings: ($593,307)
Emp.: 751
Fiscal Year-end: 12/31/12
Business Description:
Fresh Pastry & Cakes Mfr
S.I.C.: 2053
N.A.I.C.S.: 311813
Personnel:
Sava Constantin *(Pres & Gen Mgr)*

BOROSIL GLASS WORKS LTD.
Khanna Construction House 44 R G
Thadani Marg
Worli, Mumbai, 400 018, India
Tel.: (91) 2224930362
Fax: (91) 22 24950561
E-Mail: borosil@borosil.com
Web Site: www.borosil.com
502219—(BOM)
Rev.: $29,590,211
Assets: $122,122,572
Liabilities: $5,833,796
Net Worth: $116,288,776
Earnings: $3,677,724
Emp.: 181
Fiscal Year-end: 03/31/13
Business Description:
Laboratory Glassware Mfr & Distr
S.I.C.: 3229
N.A.I.C.S.: 327212
Personnel:
B. L. Kheruka *(Chm)*
Shreevar Kheruka *(Mng Dir)*
Lovelina Cecil Faroz *(Compliance Officer & Sec)*
Board of Directors:
B. L. Kheruka
S. Bagai
P. K. Kheruka
Shreevar Kheruka
Naveen Kumar Kshatriya
U. K. Mukhopadhyay
V. Ramaswami
Dinesh N. Vaswani
Transfer Agent:
Universal Capital Securities Pvt. Ltd
21 Shakil Niwas Mahakali Caves Road Andheri East
Mumbai, India

BORR COMPANY
Elektravagen 10
126 30 Hagersten, Sweden
Tel.: (46) 87445065
Fax: (46) 87445064
E-Mail: info@borrcompany.se
Web Site: www.borrcompany.se
Emp.: 50
Business Description:
Construction Services
S.I.C.: 1389
N.A.I.C.S.: 213112
Personnel:
Nicholas Johansson *(Pres)*
Subsidiary:

R.A.D.i Sverige AB/ABVAC **(1)**
Elektravagen 10
12630 Hagersten, Sweden
Tel.: (46) 8178350
Fax: (46) 4687445064
Web Site: www.radsweden.com
Emp.: 80
Power Line Construction
S.I.C.: 1629
N.A.I.C.S.: 237130
Carreta Broby *(Mng Dir)*

BORREGAARD ASA
Hjalmar Wessels vei 10
1721 Sarpsborg, Norway
Mailing Address:
PO Box 162
1701 Sarpsborg, Norway
Tel.: (47) 69118000
Fax: (47) 69118770
E-Mail: borregaard@borregaard.com
Web Site: www.borregaard.com
BRG—(OSL)
Sales Range: $800-899.9 Million
Emp.: 1,100
Business Description:
Specialty Chemicals, Fine Chemicals; Specialty Chemical Pulp
S.I.C.: 2899
N.A.I.C.S.: 325998
Personnel:
Jan Anders Oksum *(Chm)*
Per Arthur Sorlie *(Pres & CEO)*
Per Bjarne Lyngstad *(CFO & Sr VP)*
Bjorn Erik Amundsen *(Exec VP-Ingredients & Pharma)*
Tom Erik Foss-Jacobsen *(Exec VP-ChemCell)*
Morten Harlem *(Exec VP-LignoTech)*
Dag Arthur Aasbo *(Sr VP-HR & Comm)*
Tuva Barnholt *(Sr VP-Sourcing & Pur)*
Gisle Lohre Johansen *(Sr VP-Bus Dev)*
Board of Directors:
Jan Anders Oksum
Terje Andersen
Roy Kare Appelgren
Asmund Dybedahl
Ragnhild Anker Eide
Bente Seljebakken Klausen
Jan Erik Korssjsen
Kristine Ryssdal
Ragnhild Wiborg

BORSA DE BARCELONA
Paseo De Gracia 19
08007 Barcelona, Spain
Tel.: (34) 934013555
Fax: (34) 934013625
E-Mail: informacion@borsabcn.es
Web Site: www.borsabcn.es
Year Founded: 1970
Sales Range: $10-24.9 Million
Emp.: 63
Business Description:
Securities Trading Services
S.I.C.: 6231
N.A.I.C.S.: 523210
Personnel:
Joan Hortala Arau *(Chm)*
Board of Directors:
Joan Hortala Arau
Luis Badia Almirall
Jose Maria Antunez Xaus
Pedro Mateu Ardanuy
Pablo Ciguela Ibanez
Pedro Estruch Jane
Juan Pablo Jimeno Moreno
Enrique Garcia Palacio
Jorge Harmat Perez
Pedro Perello Pons
Jose Antonio Perez Ramo
Jose Luis Negron Rodriguez
Arturo Mas-Sarda Romagosa
Luis Hausmann Tarrida
Luis Rodriguez Vega
Subsidiary:

Centro de Calculo de Bolsa S.A. **(1)**
Street Gracia 19
08012 Barcelona, Spain
Tel.: (34) 93 401 3555
Data Processing Services
S.I.C.: 7379
N.A.I.C.S.: 518210

BORSA INSTANBUL A.S.
(d/b/a Istanbul Stock Exchange)
Resitpasa Mahallesi Tuncay Artun Caddesi
Emirgan, 34467 Istanbul, Turkey
Tel.: (90) 2122982100
Fax: (90) 2122982500
E-Mail: international@borsalstanbul.com
Web Site: www.borsaistanbul.com
Year Founded: 1986
Sales Range: $100-124.9 Million
Emp.: 450
Business Description:
Stock Exchange Services
S.I.C.: 6231
N.A.I.C.S.: 523210
Personnel:
Ibrahim M. Turhan *(Chm & CEO)*
Osman Akyuz *(Deputy Chm)*
Ali Coplu *(CIO)*
Ali Sir Yardim *(Chief Regulatory Officer)*
Mustafa Baltaci *(Exec VP)*
Ceti Ali Donmez *(Exec VP)*
Seyfettin Saglam *(Exec VP)*
Aydin Seyman *(Exec VP)*
Mustafa Kemel Yilmaz *(Exec VP)*
Huseyin Zafer *(Exec VP)*
Board of Directors:
Ibrahim M. Turhan
Osman Akyuz
Mustafa Buyukabaci
Seyit Ahmet Iskin
Huseyin Kelezoglu
Isinsu Kestelli
K. Attila Koksal
Talat Ulussever
Meliksah Utku

BORUJERD TEXTILE CO (PUBLIC JOINT STOCK)
No 65 West Farzan St Afrigha Blvd
Tehran, Iran
Tel.: (98) 21 8794431
Fax: (98) 21 878 3564
E-Mail: info@borujerdtextile.com
Web Site: borujerdtextile.com
Year Founded: 1983
BROJ—(THE)
Business Description:
Textile Product Mfr
S.I.C.: 2389
N.A.I.C.S.: 314999
Personnel:
J. Soleimani *(Pres)*
Ch. Asefi *(Mng Dir)*
Board of Directors:
M. Arisian
Ch. Asefi
M. Samieinejad
B. Shafiei
J. Soleimani

BORUSSIA DORTMUND GMBH & CO. KGAA
Rheinlanddamm 207-209
44137 Dortmund, Germany
Tel.: (49) 231 9020 745
Fax: (49) 231 9020 85746
E-Mail: aktie@bvb.de
Web Site: www.bvb.de
BVB—(DEU)
Rev.: $369,844,053
Assets: $390,335,453
Liabilities: $144,785,968
Net Worth: $245,549,485
Earnings: $71,694,322
Emp.: 299
Fiscal Year-end: 06/30/13
Business Description:
Sports Club Services
S.I.C.: 7941
N.A.I.C.S.: 711211
Personnel:
Gerd Pieper *(Chm-Supervisory Bd)*
Hans-Joachim Watzke *(Chm-Mgmt Bd)*
Harald Heinze *(Vice Chm-Supervisory Bd)*
Thomas Tress *(Mng Dir & Member-Mgmt Bd)*
Supervisory Board of Directors:
Gerd Pieper
Bernd Geske
Harald Heinze
Christian Kullmann
Friedrich Merz
Peer Steinbruck
Subsidiaries:

BVB Beteiligungs-GmbH **(1)**
Rheinlanddamm 207
44137 Dortmund, Germany
Tel.: (49) 23190200
Investment Management Services
S.I.C.: 6282
N.A.I.C.S.: 523920

BVB Merchandising GmbH **(1)**
Felicitasstrasse 2
44263 Dortmund, Germany
Tel.: (49) 231434443
Fax: (49) 231434455
Football Club Operator
S.I.C.: 7941
N.A.I.C.S.: 711211

BVB Stadion GmbH **(1)**
Rheinlanddamm 207-209
Dortmund, 44137, Germany
Tel.: (49) 23190200
Football Club Operator
S.I.C.: 7941
N.A.I.C.S.: 711211

BVB Stadion Holding GmbH **(1)**
Mauritiuswall 35
44263 Dortmund, Germany
Tel.: (49) 231434443
Fax: (49) 2314278201
Investment Management Services
S.I.C.: 6799
N.A.I.C.S.: 523920

BVB Stadionmanagement GmbH **(1)**
Strobelallee 50
44139 Dortmund, Germany
Tel.: (49) 23190200
Fax: (49) 2319020105
Football Club Operator
S.I.C.: 7941
N.A.I.C.S.: 711211

Sports & Bytes GmbH **(1)**
Rheinlanddamm 207-209
44137 Dortmund, Germany
Tel.: (49) 231 9020 0
Fax: (49) 231 9020 989
E-Mail: info@sportsandbytes.de
Web Site: www.sportsandbytes.de
Online Marketing Services
S.I.C.: 2741
N.A.I.C.S.: 519130
Carsten Cramer, *(Co-CEO)*
Thomas Tress *(Co-CEO)*

BORYUNG MEDIENCE CO., LTD.
13F/14F Boryung Bldg 66-21
Wonnam-dong
Jongno-gu, Seoul, Korea (South)
Tel.: (82) 27088300
Web Site: www.medience.co.kr
Year Founded: 1979
014100—(KRS)
Business Description:
Healthcare Product Development & Sales
S.I.C.: 3999
N.A.I.C.S.: 339999
Personnel:
Eun Jung Kim *(CEO)*

Boryung Medience Co., Ltd.—(Continued)

Subsidiaries:

Boryung Co., Ltd. (1)
Boryung Bldg 66-21 Wonnam-dong
Jongno-gu, Seoul, Korea (South)
Tel.: (82) 2 708 8000
E-Mail: info@boryung.co.kr
Web Site: www.boryung.co.kr
Pharmaceutical Products Mfr
S.I.C.: 2834
N.A.I.C.S.: 325412
Tae Hun Kim *(Mgr)*

Soo & Soo, Ltd. (1)
5/F Boryung Bldg 66 - 21 Wonnam-Dong
Seoul, 110-750, Korea (South)
Tel.: (82) 27404210
Fax: (82) 27649305
Web Site: www.boryung.co.kr/englishV2/about/about35.asp
Emp.: 30
Medical Device Mfr & Distr
S.I.C.: 5047
N.A.I.C.S.: 423450

Plant:

Boryung Co., Ltd. - Ansan Factory (1)
1122-3 Shingil-dong
Danwon-gu, 425-839 Ansan, Gyeonggi-do, Korea (South)
Tel.: (82) 31 491 5171
Fax: (82) 31 491 0464
Web Site: www.boryung.co.kr/englishV2/about/about71.asp
Emp.: 200
Pharmaceutical Products Mfr
S.I.C.: 2834
N.A.I.C.S.: 325412
Yong-Bin Kim *(Gen Mgr)*

BORYUNG PHARMACEUTICAL

Boryung Bldg 66-21 Wonnam-dong
Jongno-gu, Seoul, Korea (South)
Tel.: (82) 2 708 8000
Web Site: www.boryung.co.kr
Year Founded: 1963
003850—(KRS)
Sales Range: Less than $1 Million
Business Description:
Pharmaceutical Product Mfr
S.I.C.: 2834
N.A.I.C.S.: 325412
Personnel:
Kwang-ho Kim *(Co-CEO)*
Seung-ho Kim *(Co-CEO)*

BORZA TA' MALTA

(d/b/a Malta Stock Exchange)
Garrison Chapel Castille Place
Valletta, VLT 1063, Malta
Tel.: (356) 21244051
Fax: (356) 25696316
E-Mail: borza@borzamalta.com.mt
Web Site: www.borzamalta.com.mt
Rev.: $3,268,705
Emp.: 50
Business Description:
Stock Exchange Services
S.I.C.: 6231
N.A.I.C.S.: 523210
Personnel:
Arthur Galea Salomone *(Chm)*
Eileen V. Muscat *(CEO)*

B.O.S. BETTER ONLINE SOLUTIONS LTD.

20 Freiman Street
Rishon le Zion, 75100, Israel
Tel.: (972) 3 9541000
Fax: (972) 3 9541003
E-Mail: contactbos@boscom.com
Web Site: www.boscorporate.com
BOSC—(NASDAQ TAE)
Rev.: $24,503,000
Assets: $18,049,000
Liabilities: $14,893,000
Net Worth: $3,156,000
Earnings: ($549,000)
Emp.: 59
Fiscal Year-end: 12/31/12
Business Description:
Middleware Connectivity Device Mfr
S.I.C.: 3575
N.A.I.C.S.: 334118
Personnel:
Edouard Cukierman *(Chm)*
Avidan Zelicovsky *(Pres)*
Yuval Viner *(CEO)*
Eyal Cohen *(CFO)*
Board of Directors:
Edouard Cukierman
Joel Adler
David Golan
Luis Gutierrez Roy
Ronen Zavlik

U.S. Subsidiary:

Lynk USA, Inc. (1)
6280 Manchester Blvd Ste 200
Buena Park, CA 90621-2294
Tel.: (714) 443-4000
Fax: (714) 522-6362
Toll Free: (800) 461-1992
E-Mail: info@telelynk.com
Web Site: www.telelynk.com
S.I.C.: 7373
N.A.I.C.S.: 541512

BOS EQUIPEMENT HOTELIER

Z I Des Salines Royales 57 Rue Des Acacias
73600 Moutiers, Savoie, France
Tel.: (33) 479240066
Web Site: www.equipement-hotel-restaurant.com
Sls.: $18,300,000
Emp.: 91
S.I.C.: 5084
N.A.I.C.S.: 423830
Personnel:
Jean Bos *(Pres)*
Board of Directors:
Alain Ronchietto

BOSA PROPERTIES INC.

1100-838 West Hastings Street
Vancouver, BC, V6C 0A6, Canada
Tel.: (604) 299-1363
Fax: (604) 299-6460
E-Mail: media@bosaproperties.com
Web Site: www.bosaproperties.com
Year Founded: 1961
Emp.: 400
Business Description:
Construction Services
S.I.C.: 1542
N.A.I.C.S.: 236220
Personnel:
Robert Bosa *(Founder)*
Colin Bosa *(CEO)*

BOSAL INTERNATIONAL NV

Dellestraat 20
3560 Lummen, Belgium
Tel.: (32) 13530800
Fax: (32) 13531411
E-Mail: info.bi@eur.bosal.com
Web Site: www.bosal.com
Sales Range: $650-699.9 Million
Emp.: 5,646
Business Description:
Automotive Exhaust Systems & Parts Mfr
S.I.C.: 3714
N.A.I.C.S.: 336390
Personnel:
Aag Goudriaan *(CEO)*
Johan Van de ven *(Mng Dir)*
Joop van Boesschoten *(CFO)*
Dirk Dessers *(COO)*
Board of Directors:
Dirk Dessers
Jean-Paul Janssens
Manfred Nowak

U.S. Subsidiary:

Bosal USA, Inc. (1)
14 Troy Hills Rd
Whippany, NJ 07981
Tel.: (973) 428-9822
Fax: (973) 428-8856
Web Site: www.bosalusa.com
Emp.: 50
Car Exhaust Systems Mfr
S.I.C.: 3714
N.A.I.C.S.: 336390
Jeff Berman *(Mng Dir)*

U.S. Plants:

Bosal International - Georgia (1)
1 Bosal Way
Lavonia, GA 30553
Tel.: (706) 356-2889
Fax: (706) 356-2895
Emp.: 50
Car Exhaust Systems Mfr
S.I.C.: 3714
N.A.I.C.S.: 336390
Clive Smith *(Mng Dir)*

Bosal International North America (1)
1476 Seaver Way
Ypsilanti, MI 48197
Tel.: (734) 547-7000
Fax: (734) 547-2988
Web Site: www.bosalna.com
Emp.: 300
Mfr of Car Exhaust Systems & Accessories
S.I.C.: 3714
N.A.I.C.S.: 336390
John Miles *(Pres)*

Non-U.S. Subsidiaries:

Bosal Africa (Pty) Ltd. (1)
Koedoespoort Industrial Sites
PO Box 1652
Rooibok Avenue, Pretoria, 001, South Africa
Tel.: (27) 123911000
Fax: (27) 3330659
E-Mail: normag@bosal.co.za
Web Site: www.bosal.co.za
Emp.: 50
Mfr of Automotive Exhaust Systems & Accessories
S.I.C.: 3714
N.A.I.C.S.: 336390
Norma Groenewald *(Mgr-HR)*

Bosal Canada, Ltd. (1)
1150 Gardiners Rd
Kingston, ON, K7P 1R7, Canada
Tel.: (613) 384-4150
Fax: (613) 384-8877
Web Site: www.bosalna.com
Emp.: 4
Car Exhaust Systems Mfr
S.I.C.: 3714
N.A.I.C.S.: 336390
Joe Mercanti *(Mgr-Sls)*

Bosal Mexico AM (1)
Acceso 1 No 126
Fracc Ind La Montana, CP 76150
Queretaro, Mexico
Tel.: (52) 4422385500
Fax: (52) 4422100571
E-Mail: clagunes@bosal.usa.com
Web Site: www.bosalna.com
Emp.: 160
Car Exhaust Systems Mfr
S.I.C.: 3714
N.A.I.C.S.: 336390
Arturo Perez *(Mng Dir)*

Bosal Nederland BV (1)
Kamerlingh Onnesweg 5
4131 PK Vianen, Zuid-Holland, Netherlands NL
Tel.: (31) 347362911
Fax: (31) 347362725
E-Mail: info.bnl@bur.bosal.com
Web Site: www.bosal.nl/BOSALINFORMATIE/Corporateinformation/Contact/tabid/344/Default.aspx
Sls.: $886,200,000
Emp.: 6,020
Automotive Exhaust Systems & Parts Mfr
S.I.C.: 3714
N.A.I.C.S.: 336390
H. H. Van Der Linden *(Mng Dir)*

BOSCH LIMITED

Hosur Road
Post Box No 3000
Bengaluru, 560030, India
Tel.: (91) 8022222393
Fax: (91) 8022272728
E-Mail: rbin.corporate@in.bosch.com
Web Site: www.boschindia.com
BOSCHLTD—(NSE)
Sls.: $1,693,109,880
Assets: $1,465,383,060
Liabilities: $432,093,240
Net Worth: $1,033,289,820
Earnings: $177,668,820
Emp.: 12,313
Fiscal Year-end: 12/31/12
Business Description:
Automotive Technology
S.I.C.: 3825
N.A.I.C.S.: 334515
Personnel:
V. K. Viswanathan *(Chm)*
Soumitra Bhattacharya *(Mng Dir)*
Karthik S. *(Sec)*
Board of Directors:
V. K. Viswanathan
Bhaskar Bhat
Soumitra Bhattacharya
Prasad Chandran
Renu Sud Karnad
Bernhard Steinruecke
Peter Tyroller
Transfer Agent:
Integrated Enterprises (I) Limited
30 Ramana Residency 4th Cross Sampige Road Malleshwaram
Bengaluru, India

BOSCUS CANADA INC

900 Ave Selkirk
Pointe-Claire, QC, H9R 3S3, Canada
Tel.: (514) 694-9805
Fax: (514) 694-9221
Web Site: www.boscus.com
Year Founded: 1981
Rev.: $187,599,499
Emp.: 42
Business Description:
Lumber Distr
S.I.C.: 5031
N.A.I.C.S.: 423310
Personnel:
Dary Laflamme *(Pres & Owner)*

BOSHART INDUSTRIES INC.

25 Whaley Ave
PO Box 310
Perth East, ON, N0K 1M0, Canada
Tel.: (519) 595-4444
Fax: (519) 595-4380
Toll Free: (800) 561-3164
Web Site: www.boshart.com
Year Founded: 1955
Rev.: $24,865,040
Emp.: 85
Business Description:
Industrial Valves Mfr & Distr
S.I.C.: 3491
N.A.I.C.S.: 332911
Personnel:
Gary Boshart *(Pres)*
Archie Mulder *(Sr VP-Ops & IT)*
Julie Storey *(Sr VP-Sls & Mktg)*

U.S. Subsidiary:

Flomatic Corporation (1)
15 Pruyn's Island Dr
Glens Falls, NY 12801-4424 (100%)
Tel.: (518) 761-9797
Fax: (518) 761-9798
Toll Free: (800) 833-2040
E-Mail: flomatic@flomatic.com
Web Site: www.flomatic.com

Emp.: 50
Valves Mfr
S.I.C.: 3491
N.A.I.C.S.: 332911
Bo Anderson *(Pres)*

BOSHIWA INTERNATIONAL HOLDING LIMITED

Pudong Wai Gaoqiao Free Trade Zone
No 78 Taigu Road, Shanghai, China
Tel.: (86) 21 5866 1484
Fax: (86) 21 5866 1477
Web Site: www.boshiwa.cn
Year Founded: 1997
Sales Range: $200-249.9 Million
Emp.: 2,097
Business Description:
Apparel Whlsr
S.I.C.: 5137
N.A.I.C.S.: 424330
Personnel:
Zheng Yong Zhong *(Chm & CEO)*
Xiao Qing Zhang *(CFO & VP)*
Li Ping Chen *(COO)*
Yi Hao Lv *(Chief Admin Officer & VP)*
Wah Wai Lo *(Sec)*
Board of Directors:
Zheng Yong Zhong
Li Ping Chen
Pei Qi Chen
Chang Jian Jiang
Zhi Qiang Li
Ge Wu

Butterfield Fulcrum Group (Cayman) Limited
Butterfield House 68 Fort Street 609
Georgetown, Grand Cayman, KY1 1107, Cayman Islands
Transfer Agent:
Butterfield Fulcrum Group (Cayman) Limited
Butterfield House 68 Fort Street 609
Georgetown, Grand Cayman, KY1 1107, Cayman Islands

BOSIDENG INTERNATIONAL HOLDINGS LIMITED

Room 1703A 17th Floor Harcourt House 39 Gloucester Road
Wanchai, China (Hong Kong)
Tel.: (852) 28666918
Fax: (852) 28666930
Web Site: company.bosideng.com
3998—(HKG OTC)
Rev.: $1,481,203,020
Assets: $1,940,067,932
Liabilities: $782,739,570
Net Worth: $1,157,328,362
Earnings: $167,207,734
Emp.: 5,327
Fiscal Year-end: 03/31/13
Business Description:
Apparel Products Distribution & Mfr
S.I.C.: 2241
N.A.I.C.S.: 313220
Personnel:
Dekang Gao *(Chm & CEO)*
Yun Kuen Mak *(CFO & Sec)*
Dong Mei *(Exec VP-Ops Mgmt)*
Board of Directors:
Dekang Gao
Binggen Dong
Miaoqin Gao
Qiaolian Huang
Shengyuan Kong
Jie Lian
Yun Kuen Mak
Dong Mei
Wai Fung Ngai
Jinsong Rui
Yao Wang

Legal Counsel:
DLA Piper
Hong Kong, China (Hong Kong)
Butterfield Fund Services (Cayman) Limited
Butterfield House 68 Fort Street PO Box 705
Georgetown, Cayman Islands
Transfer Agents:
Computershare Hong Kong Investor Services Limited
Shops 1712-1716 17th Floor Hopewell Centre
183 Queens Road East
Wanchai, China (Hong Kong)
Butterfield Fund Services (Cayman) Limited
Butterfield House 68 Fort Street PO Box 705
Georgetown, Cayman Islands

BOSIG HOLDING GMBH & CO. KG

Brunnenstr 75-77
73333 Gingen an der Fils, Germany
Tel.: (49) 7162 40 99 0
Fax: (49) 7162 40 99 200
E-Mail: info@bosig.de
Web Site: www.bosig.de
Business Description:
Bulding Material Mfr
S.I.C.: 2891
N.A.I.C.S.: 325520
Personnel:
Oliver Schmid *(Mng Dir)*

BOSS POWER CORP.

Suite 611 675 West Hastings Street
Vancouver, BC, V6B 1N2, Canada
Tel.: (604) 688-8115
Fax: (604) 669-2543
E-Mail: info@bosspower.ca
Web Site: www.bosspower.ca
Year Founded: 1981
BPU—(TSXV)
Int. Income: $20,327
Assets: $2,241,857
Liabilities: $118,603
Net Worth: $2,123,254
Earnings: ($451,782)
Fiscal Year-end: 12/31/12
Business Description:
Mineral Exploration Services
S.I.C.: 1081
N.A.I.C.S.: 213114
Personnel:
Ronald K. Netolitzky *(Chm & Acting CEO)*
Karen A. Allan *(CFO)*
Board of Directors:
Ronald K. Netolitzky
John H. Bowles
Douglas B. Brooks
Legal Counsel:
Fasken Martineau
2900-550 Burrard Street
Vancouver, BC, Canada
Transfer Agent:
Computershare Trust Company of Canada
510 Burrard St 2nd Fl
Vancouver, BC, Canada

BOSS RESOURCES LIMITED

Suite 23 513 Hay St
Subiaco, WA, 6008, Australia
Mailing Address:
PO Box 1311
Subiaco, WA, 6904, Australia
Tel.: (61) 8 6143 6730
Fax: (61) 8 9388 8824
E-Mail: info@bossresources.com.au
Web Site: www.bossresources.com.au
BOE—(ASX)
Rev.: $100,402
Assets: $8,497,932
Liabilities: $125,893
Net Worth: $8,372,039
Earnings: ($14,015,920)
Fiscal Year-end: 06/30/13
Business Description:
Oil & Minerals Exploration Services
S.I.C.: 1311
N.A.I.C.S.: 211111
Personnel:
Oonagh Malone *(Sec)*
Board of Directors:
Evan Cranston
Thomas Gladwin-Grove
Peter Williams
Legal Counsel:
Bellanhouse Legal
Suite 1 6 Richardson Street
West Perth, WA, 6005, Australia

BOSSARD HOLDING AG

Steinhauserstrasse 70
6301 Zug, Switzerland
Tel.: (41) 417496611
Fax: (41) 417496622
E-Mail: bossard@bossard.com
Web Site: www.bossard.com
BOS—(SWX)
Sls.: $525,730,296
Assets: $406,151,354
Liabilities: $352,068,787
Net Worth: $54,082,567
Earnings: $46,310,383
Emp.: 1,551
Fiscal Year-end: 12/31/12
Business Description:
Holding Company; Engineering & Logistic Services
S.I.C.: 6719
N.A.I.C.S.: 551112
Personnel:
Thomas Schmuckli *(Chm)*
Anton Lauber *(Deputy Chm)*
David Dean *(CEO)*
Stephan Zehnder *(CFO)*
Robert Ang *(CEO-Asia)*
Daniel Bossard *(CEO-North & Eastern Europe)*
Beat Grob *(CEO-Central Europe)*
Steen Hansen *(CEO-America)*
Board of Directors:
Thomas Schmuckli
Urs Fankhauser
Anton Lauber
Stefan Michel
Maria Teresa Vacalli
Helen Wetter-Bossard

Subsidiaries:

KVT-Fastening AG **(1)**
Lagerstrasse 8
8953 Dietikon, Switzerland
Tel.: (41) 44 743 33 33
Fax: (41) 44 740 65 66
E-Mail: info-CH@kvt-fastening.com
Web Site: www.kvt-fastening.com
Sales Range: $125-149.9 Million
Emp.: 230
Fastening Equipment Mfr
S.I.C.: 3499
N.A.I.C.S.: 332999
Frank Hilgers *(CEO)*
Roland von Arb, *(Mng Dir)*

U.S. Subsidiaries:

Bossard North America, Inc. **(1)**
6521 Production Dr
Cedar Falls, IA 50613 DE
Tel.: (319) 277-5520
Fax: (319) 277-2964
Toll Free: (800) 772-2738
E-Mail: bnasales@bossard.com
Web Site: www.bossard.com
Industrial Fasteners, Nuts, Bolts & Screws Distr
S.I.C.: 5085
N.A.I.C.S.: 423840
Steen Hansen *(CEO)*

Branch:

Bossard North America, Inc. - Milwaukee **(2)**
3801 W Green Tree Rd
Milwaukee, WI 53209
Tel.: (414) 247-1100
Fax: (414) 247-8809
E-Mail: eallen@bossard.com
Web Site: www.bossard.com
Sls.: $11,700,000
Emp.: 66
Industrial Fasteners, Nuts, Bolts & Screws Distr
S.I.C.: 5085
N.A.I.C.S.: 423840
David Dean *(CEO)*

Non-U.S. Subsidiary:

Bossard Australia Pty Ltd **(1)**
70 Swann Drive
Melbourne, VIC, 3030, Australia
Tel.: (61) 3 9368 5050
Fastening & Connecting Components Distr
S.I.C.: 5099
N.A.I.C.S.: 423990

BOSSINI INTERNATIONAL HOLDINGS LIMITED

Level 1 The Long Beach 8 Hoi Fai Road
Tai Kok Tsui, Kowloon, China (Hong Kong)
Tel.: (852) 2371 1688
Fax: (852) 2786 0869
E-Mail: IR@bossini.com
Web Site: www.bossini.com
Year Founded: 1987
592—(HKG)
Rev.: $324,588,685
Assets: $139,826,546
Liabilities: $45,873,060
Net Worth: $93,953,486
Earnings: $2,863,851
Emp.: 2,700
Fiscal Year-end: 06/30/13
Business Description:
Apparel Store Operator
S.I.C.: 5699
N.A.I.C.S.: 448150
Personnel:
Man Kuen Tsin *(Chm)*
Edmund Tak Cheong Mak *(CEO)*
Suk May Wong *(Sec)*
Board of Directors:
Man Kuen Tsin
Paul Cheuk Him Chan
Raymond Man Chun Lee
Mei Han Leung
Edmund Tak Cheong Mak
Yat Ming Sin
Butterfield Fulcrum Group (Bermuda) Limited
Rosebank Centre 11 Bermudiana Road
Pembroke, Bermuda
Transfer Agent:
Butterfield Fulcrum Group (Bermuda) Limited
Rosebank Centre 11 Bermudiana Road
Pembroke, Bermuda

BOSTON PIZZA INTERNATIONAL, INC.

5500 Parkwood Way Ste 200
Richmond, BC, Canada
Tel.: (604) 270-1108
Fax: (604) 270-4168
E-Mail: forresterj@bostonpizza.com
Web Site: www.bostonpizza.com
Emp.: 100
Business Description:
Pizza Restaurant Franchisor
S.I.C.: 5499
N.A.I.C.S.: 445299
Personnel:
George C. Melville *(Co-Owner & Co-Chm)*

Boston Pizza International, Inc.—(Continued)

Walter James Treliving *(Co-Owner & Co-Chm)*
Mark G. Pacinda *(Pres)*
Mike Cordoba *(CEO)*
Wes Bews *(CFO)*
Ken Otto *(COO)*
Board of Directors:
George C. Melville
Walter James Treliving

BOSTONAIR LTD
1 Wood Lane Mews
Beverley, E Yorkshire, HU17 8DA, United Kingdom
Tel.: (44) 1482 679757
Fax: (44) 1482 679091
E-Mail: admin@bostonair.co.uk
Web Site: www.bostonair.co.uk
Year Founded: 1997
Sales Range: $25-49.9 Million
Emp.: 200
Business Description:
Aviation Industry Recruitment Services
S.I.C.: 7361
N.A.I.C.S.: 561311
Personnel:
Mark Parkes *(Mng Dir)*

BOSUN TOOLS CO., LTD.
10 Haihe Road National High-Tech Industry Development Zone
Shijiazhuang, 050035, China
Tel.: (86) 31185960663
Fax: (86) 31185383171
E-Mail: sales@bosuntools.com
Web Site: www.bosuntools.com
002282—(SSE)
Emp.: 1,860
Business Description:
Diamond & Small Machine Tools Mfr
S.I.C.: 3541
N.A.I.C.S.: 333517
Personnel:
Huairong Chen *(Chm)*

BOTANECO CORP.
134 2985 23rd Avenue Northeast
Calgary, AB, T1Y 7L3, Canada
Tel.: (403) 668-6685
E-Mail: info@advitech.com
Web Site: www.advitech.com
Year Founded: 1997
BOT—(TSXV)
Rev.: $1,925,191
Assets: $4,664,080
Liabilities: $4,775,139
Net Worth: ($111,059)
Earnings: ($2,999,866)
Fiscal Year-end: 12/31/12
Business Description:
Proprietary Natural Ingredients Developer, Mfr & Sales
S.I.C.: 8731
N.A.I.C.S.: 541712
Personnel:
David Edwards *(Chm)*
Nam Fong Han *(CEO & COO)*
Board of Directors:
David Edwards
Aki Georgacacos
David D. Guebert
Nam Fong Han
Louis Lacasse
Legal Counsel:
McCarthy Tetrault LLP
1150 rue Claire-Fontaine 7th Floor
Quebec, QC, G1R 5G4, Canada
Transfer Agent:
Computershare Investor Services Inc.
1500 University Street Suite 700
Montreal, QC, H3A 3SB, Canada

BOTHRA METALS & ALLOYS LTD
Bothra House Room 15 3rd Floor 5 Assembly Lane
Dady SethAgyari Lane
Kalbadevi, Mumbai, Maharashtra, 400002, India
Tel.: (91) 22 67472763
E-Mail: bmal_2001@bothrametals.com
Web Site: www.bothrametals.com
535279—(BOM)
Sales Range: $10-24.9 Million
Business Description:
Metals & Alloys Mfr
S.I.C.: 3499
N.A.I.C.S.: 332999
Personnel:
Sunderlal Bothra *(Mng Dir)*
Abhishek Pareek *(CFO)*

BOTSWANA DEVELOPMENT CORPORATION LIMITED
Moedi Plot 50380 Gaborone International Showgrounds
Private Bag 160
Gaborone, Botswana
Tel.: (267) 3651300
Fax: (267) 3904193
E-Mail: enquiries@bdc.bw
Web Site: www.bdc.bw
Year Founded: 1970
Emp.: 80
Business Description:
Commercial & Industrial Development
S.I.C.: 9532
N.A.I.C.S.: 925120
Personnel:
Maria Mmasolo Nthebolan *(Mng Dir)*
Board of Directors:
T. Dikgaka
Ina Kandjii
Nightingale Kwele
Ntetleng M. Masisi
Odirile Merafhe
Banny Molosiwa
Shabani Ndzinge
Maria Mmasolo Nthebolan
S.M. Sekwakwa

Joint Venture:

Cresta Marakanelo (Pvt) Ltd **(1)**
Plot 50676 Fairground Office Park Phase 2 Block D Unit 2
Private Bag 00272
Gaborone, Botswana
Tel.: (267) 3912222
Fax: (267) 3904329
E-Mail: saleshq@cresta.co.bw
Web Site: www.crestamarakanelo.com
Emp.: 200
Hotel Owner & Operator
S.I.C.: 7011
N.A.I.C.S.: 721110
Maria Mmasolo Nthebolan *(Chm)*
Tawanda Makaya *(Mng Dir)*
Valentine Mganga *(CFO)*

BOTSWANA DIAMONDS PLC
162 Clontarf Road
Dublin, 3, Ireland
Tel.: (353) 18332833
Fax: (353) 18333505
E-Mail: info@botswanadiamonds.co.uk
Web Site: www.botswanadiamonds.co.uk
BOD—(AIM)
Rev.: $777
Assets: $10,125,949
Liabilities: $974,632
Net Worth: $9,151,318
Earnings: ($786,749)
Emp.: 7
Fiscal Year-end: 06/30/13
Business Description:
Diamond Exploration Services
S.I.C.: 1411
N.A.I.C.S.: 212311
Personnel:
John J. Teeling *(Chm)*
James Michael Finn *(Sec & Dir-Fin)*
Board of Directors:
John J. Teeling
Robert Bouquet
James Michael Finn
David Horgan
Legal Counsel:
SNR Denton UK LLP
One Fleet Place
London, United Kingdom
McEvoy Partners
Connaught House Burlington Road
Dublin, Ireland

BOTSWANA METALS LIMITED
Suite 5 Level 1 310 Whitehorse Road
Balwyn, VIC, 3103, Australia
Tel.: (61) 398307676
Fax: (61) 398363056
E-Mail: info@botswanametals.com.au
Web Site: www.botswanametals.com.au
BML—(ASX)
Rev.: $94,769
Assets: $7,770,200
Liabilities: $175,197
Net Worth: $7,595,003
Earnings: ($1,834,112)
Fiscal Year-end: 06/30/13
Business Description:
Metal Mining Services
S.I.C.: 1099
N.A.I.C.S.: 212299
Personnel:
Patrick John Volpe *(Chm)*
Richard Charles Baker *(Sec)*
Board of Directors:
Patrick John Volpe
Massimo Livio Cellante
Paul Woolrich
Legal Counsel:
Mills Oakley Lawyers
Level 6 530 Collins Street
Melbourne, Australia

BOTSWANA STOCK EXCHANGE
Off Block 6 plot 64511 Fairgrounds
Private Bag 00417
Gaborone, Botswana
Tel.: (267) 3180201
Fax: (267) 3180175
Web Site: www.bse.co.bw
Emp.: 15
Business Description:
Stock Exchange Services
S.I.C.: 6231
N.A.I.C.S.: 523210
Personnel:
Dudu Garekwe *(Mgr-Listings)*

BOU KHALIL SOCIETE MODERNE SARL
Faubourg St Jean
BP 40020
Bifurc Palais Presidentiel, Baabda, Lebanon
Tel.: (961) 5454880
Fax: (961) 5454979
E-Mail: bkmarkets@boukhalil.com
Web Site: www.boukhalil.com
Year Founded: 1935
Emp.: 450
Business Description:
Supermarkets & Pharmacies
S.I.C.: 5411
N.A.I.C.S.: 445110

BOUBYAN BANK K.S.C.
(Acquired by National Bank of Kuwait S.A.K.)

BOUBYAN PETROCHEMICAL CO. KSC
Al-Khaleejia Building 5th Floor Sharq
PO Box 2383
Kuwait, 13024, Kuwait
Tel.: (965) 22446684
Fax: (965) 22414100
E-Mail: info@boubyan.com
Web Site: www.boubyan.com
BPCC—(KUW)
Sls.: $96,811,765
Assets: $1,457,957,536
Liabilities: $465,103,090
Net Worth: $992,854,446
Earnings: $93,123,752
Emp.: 220
Fiscal Year-end: 04/30/13
Business Description:
Petrochemicals Mfr
S.I.C.: 2869
N.A.I.C.S.: 325110
Personnel:
Marzouk Ali Al Ghanim *(Chm)*
Dabbous Mubarak Al-Dabbous *(Deputy Chm)*
Board of Directors:
Marzouk Ali Al Ghanim
Saad Abdullah Al Hanyan
Saoud Abdulaziz Al-Babtain
Dabbous Mubarak Al-Dabbous
Khalid Abdulaziz Al-Muraikhi

Joint Venture:

EQUATE Petrochemical Company K.S.C.C. **(1)**
PO Box 4733
Safat, Kuwait, 13048, Kuwait
Tel.: (965) 1898888
Fax: (965) 25765733
E-Mail: pemarket@equate.com
Web Site: www.equate.com
Sales Range: $750-799.9 Million
Emp.: 1,000
Petrochemical Products Mfr; Owned 45% by Petrochemical Industries Company, 45 % by The Dow Chemical Company & 10% by Boubyan Petrochemical Company
S.I.C.: 2899
N.A.I.C.S.: 325998
Mohammad Husain *(Pres & CEO)*
Salah Al-Kahrji *(CFO)*
Tareq Al-Kandari *(Sr Exec VP-Corp Bus Dev)*
Adel Al-Munifi *(Sr Exec VP-Corp Comm & Client Affairs)*
Abeer Al-Omar *(Sr Exec VP-Admin & Corp Svcs)*
Pieter Platteeuw *(Sr VP)*

Non-U.S. Subsidiary:

Muna Noor Manufacturing and Trading Co. L.L.C **(1)**
Al Ghubrah
PO Box 1070
Muscat, Oman
Tel.: (968) 2469 2211
Fax: (968) 2469 6644
Petrochemical Mfr
S.I.C.: 2869
N.A.I.C.S.: 325110

BOUCHER AND JONES FUELS
155 Roger St
Waterloo, ON, N2J 1B1, Canada
Tel.: (519) 743-3669
Fax: (519) 743-5419
E-Mail: frontoffice@boucherandjones.com
Web Site: www.boucherandjones.com
Year Founded: 1960
Rev.: $10,868,119
Emp.: 30

Business Description:
Fuel Whslr
S.I.C.: 5172
N.A.I.C.S.: 424720
Personnel:
Bruce Boucher *(Founder)*
Greg Cusimano *(Pres)*

BOUCLAIR INC.
152 Alston Avenue
Pointe-Claire, QC, H9R 6B4, Canada
Tel.: (514) 426-0115
Fax: (514) 426-3504
Toll Free: (800) 268-2524
E-Mail: info@bouclair.com
Web Site: www.bouclair.com
Year Founded: 1970
Rev.: $62,000,000
Emp.: 1
Business Description:
Home Decorating Stores
S.I.C.: 5719
N.A.I.C.S.: 442299
Personnel:
Adam Goldberg *(Pres)*

BOULDER STEEL LIMITED
Unit 12 North Ryde Link Business Park
PO Box 1293
277-283 Lane Cove Road, North Ryde, NSW, 2113, Australia
Tel.: (61) 294131811
Fax: (61) 294192818
E-Mail: admin@bouldersteel.com.au
Web Site: www.bouldersteel.com.au
BGD—(ASX OTC)
Emp.: 5
Business Description:
Gold Ore Mining
S.I.C.: 1041
N.A.I.C.S.: 212221
Personnel:
Daniel George Owen *(Sec)*
Board of Directors:
Detlef Sulzer
Jurgen Alexander Lang
Legal Counsel:
Dibbs Barker
Level 8 Angel Pl 123 Pitt St
Sydney, Australia

BOULE DIAGNOSTICS AB
Vastberga alle 32
SE-126 30 Hagersten, Sweden
Tel.: (46) 8 7447700
Fax: (46) 8 7447720
E-Mail: info@boule.se
Web Site: www.boule.se
BOUL—(OMX)
Rev.: $42,616,595
Assets: $42,605,759
Liabilities: $11,692,973
Net Worth: $30,912,786
Earnings: $1,696,453
Emp.: 165
Fiscal Year-end: 12/31/12
Business Description:
Hematology Diagnostic Systems Mfr; Hematology Reagents & Consumables
S.I.C.: 3841
N.A.I.C.S.: 339112
Personnel:
Lars-Olof Gustavsson *(Chm)*
Ernst Westman *(Pres & CEO)*
Fredrik Alpsten *(CFO)*
Andrew Swanson *(Pres/CEO-DCS)*
Claes Blanche *(CEO-Boule Medical AB)*
Board of Directors:
Lars-Olof Gustavsson
Britta Dalunde
Eva-Lotta Kraft
Ake Nygren
Gosta Oscarsson
Subsidiary:
Boule Medical AB **(1)**
Vastberga Alle 32
Box 42056
126 30 Hagersten, Sweden
Tel.: (46) 8 744 77 00
Fax: (46) 8 744 77 20
Electromedical Apparatus Mfr
S.I.C.: 3845
N.A.I.C.S.: 334510
Ernst Westman *(CEO)*
U.S. Subsidiary:
Clinical Diagnostics Solutions Inc. **(1)**
1800 NW 65th Ave
Plantation, FL 33313
Tel.: (954) 791-1773
Fax: (954) 791-7118
E-Mail: customerservice@cdsolinc.com
Web Site: www.cdsolinc.com
Chemical Products Mfr
S.I.C.: 2899
N.A.I.C.S.: 325998
Non-U.S. Subsidiary:
Boule Medical (Beijing) Co. Ltd **(1)**
Development Zone
Shunyi District, 101 300 Beijing, China
Tel.: (86) 10 8945 1945
Fax: (86) 10 8945 1987
Electromedical Apparatus Mfr
S.I.C.: 3845
N.A.I.C.S.: 334510

BOULEVARD BREWING CO.
(Acquired by Fibemi NV)

BOULEVARD HOLDINGS, INC.
1704 Peak Tower 107 Leviste Street
Salcedo Village
Makati, 1227, Philippines
Tel.: (63) 27531405
Fax: (63) 27532188
E-Mail: inquiry@boulevardholdings.com
Web Site: www.boulevardholdings.com
BHI—(PHI)
Rev.: $3,042,701
Assets: $42,650,366
Liabilities: $3,113,007
Net Worth: $39,537,359
Earnings: ($22,174)
Emp.: 125
Fiscal Year-end: 05/31/13
Business Description:
Hotel Management Services
S.I.C.: 7011
N.A.I.C.S.: 721110
Personnel:
Jose Marcel E. Panlilio *(Chm, Pres & CEO)*
Lorenzo R. Tanada III *(Vice Chm)*
Lyra Gracia Y. Lipae-Fabella *(Corp Info Officer & Sec)*
Mauro B. Badiola *(Corp Info Officer & VP-Fin)*
Joselito V. Cabrera *(Treas)*
Board of Directors:
Jose Marcel E. Panlilio
Alfonso S. Anggala
Victor V. Benavidez
Joselito V. Cabrera
Christopher M. Gotanco
Reynaldo Y. Maulit
Ricardo S. Pascua
Goran Carl Perning
Lorenzo R. Tanada III
Subsidiary:
Fridays Holdings, Inc. **(1)**
Boracay Island
Malay, Aklan, Philippines
Tel.: (63) 362886200
Fax: (63) 362886222
E-Mail: info@fridaysboracay.com
Web Site: www.fridaysboracay.com
Emp.: 124
Resort Management Services
S.I.C.: 7011
N.A.I.C.S.: 721110
Patrick Murray *(Gen Mgr)*

BOUNCE ENERGY, INC.
(Acquired by Centrica plc)

BOUNDARY BEND LIMITED
151 Broderick Road
PO Box 92
Lara, VIC, 3212, Australia
Tel.: (61) 3 5272 9500
Fax: (61) 3 5272 9599
E-Mail: bbl@boundarybend.com
Web Site: www.boundarybend.com
Rev.: $68,482,644
Assets: $242,626,933
Liabilities: $107,960,518
Net Worth: $134,666,415
Earnings: $55,692,950
Emp.: 100
Fiscal Year-end: 06/30/13
Business Description:
Olive Oil Producer
S.I.C.: 0179
N.A.I.C.S.: 111339
Personnel:
Robert D. McGavin *(Chm)*
Paul C. Riordan *(Mng Dir)*
Samuel J. Beaton *(CFO & Sec)*
Board of Directors:
Robert D. McGavin
Craig P. Ball
Tim A. Jonas
Leandro M. Ravetti
Paul C. Riordan
Tim F. Smith
Jonathan West

BOUNTY MINING LIMITED
Suite 1002 Level 10 60 Pitt Street
Sydney, NSW, 2000, Australia
Mailing Address:
PO Box H305
Australia Square, Sydney, NSW, 1215, Australia
Tel.: (61) 2 8965 0200
Fax: (61) 2 8965 0214
Web Site: www.bounty.com.au
BNT—(ASX)
Rev.: $20,507,620
Assets: $11,130,265
Liabilities: $11,617,114
Net Worth: ($486,849)
Earnings: $972,425
Emp.: 41
Fiscal Year-end: 06/30/13
Business Description:
Coal Mining Contract Services; Mining Solutions & Equipment to Mine Owners
S.I.C.: 1241
N.A.I.C.S.: 213113
Personnel:
Gary Cochrane *(Chm & CEO)*
Eryl Baron *(CFO & Sec)*
Board of Directors:
Gary Cochrane
Julie Garland McLellan
Robert Stewart
Legal Counsel:
Watson Mangioni
Level 13 50 Carrington Street
Sydney, Australia
McCullough Robertson
Level 11 66 Eagle Street
Brisbane, QLD, 4000, Australia
Subsidiary:
InCoal Pty Ltd **(1)**
Off Construction Road
PO Box 7288
Vales Point Mannering Park, Belmont, NSW, 2259, Australia (100%)
Tel.: (61) 2 4358 7055
Fax: (61) 2 8249 8101
Coal Mining Contract Services
S.I.C.: 1241
N.A.I.C.S.: 213113
Amon Mahon *(Gen Mgr)*

BOUNTY OIL & GAS NL
Level 7 283 George Street
Sydney, NSW, 2000, Australia
Tel.: (61) 292992007
Fax: (61) 292997300
E-Mail: corporate@bountyoil.com
Web Site: www.bountyoil.com
Year Founded: 1999
BUY—(ASX)
Rev.: $3,196,923
Assets: $36,049,894
Liabilities: $2,275,688
Net Worth: $33,774,206
Earnings: ($1,559,991)
Emp.: 2
Fiscal Year-end: 06/30/13
Business Description:
Crude Petroleum & Natural Gas Production, Exploration & Development
S.I.C.: 1311
N.A.I.C.S.: 211111
Personnel:
Philip F. Kelso *(CEO)*
J. Gary Higginbotham *(CFO & Sec)*
Board of Directors:
Graham C. Reveleigh
J. Gary Higginbotham
Charles Ross
Legal Counsel:
Gadens Lawyers
77 Castlereagh Street
Sydney, Australia

BOUNTY UK LTD.
29 Broadwater Rd
Welwyn Garden City, Hertfordshire, AL7 3BQ, United Kingdom
Tel.: (44) 1707294000
Fax: (44) 1707294001
E-Mail: bountybusiness@bounty.com
Web Site: www.bountybusiness.co.uk
Emp.: 500
Business Description:
Advertising Agency
S.I.C.: 7319
N.A.I.C.S.: 541890
Personnel:
Zoe Tibell *(Dir-Fin & Ops)*

BOURBON
Avenida Paulista 287
01311-000 Sao Paulo, Brazil
Tel.: (55) 140138616
Fax: (55) 140284031
E-Mail: ser@coretronic.com
Web Site: bourbon-online.com
Sales Range: $1-4.9 Billion
Emp.: 3,000
S.I.C.: 1389
N.A.I.C.S.: 213112
Personnel:
Jacques de Chateauvieux *(Chm)*
Christian Lefevre *(CEO)*
Laurent Renard *(CFO & Exec VP)*
Gael Bodenes *(COO & Exec VP)*
Christian Munier *(Exec VP)*
Board of Directors:
Jacques de Chateauvieux
Henri de Chateauvieux
Victoire de Margerie
Guy Dupont
Marc Francken
Christian Munier
Philippe Sautter

BOURBON TAY NINH JOINT STOCK COMPANY
Tan Hung Village - Tan Chau District
Ho Chi Minh City, Tay Ninh, Vietnam
Tel.: (84) 66 3753250
Fax: (84) 66 3839834
E-Mail: sbttninh@hcm.vnn.vn
Web Site: www.bourbontn.com.vn
SBT—(HOSE)
Sales Range: $50-74.9 Million
Business Description:
Sugar Mfr
S.I.C.: 2061
N.A.I.C.S.: 311314
Personnel:
Van Thanh Dang *(Co-Chm)*
Bich Ngoc Huynh *(Co-Chm)*
Ba Chu Nguyen *(CEO)*
Board of Directors:
Van Thanh Dang
Bich Ngoc Huynh

BOURNE LEISURE GROUP LTD.
1 Park Lane
Hemel Hempstead, Herts, HP2 4YL, United Kingdom
Tel.: (44) 1442234067
Fax: (44) 1442230368
E-Mail: ownersexclusive@bourne-leisure.co.uk
Web Site: www.bourneleisuregroup.co.uk
Emp.: 5,000
Business Description:
Package Holiday Provider
S.I.C.: 7011
N.A.I.C.S.: 721199
Personnel:
John Kirk *(Mng Dir)*
Subsidiaries:

Butlin's Limited (1)
1 Park Ln
Hemel Hempstead, Herts, HP2 4YL, United Kingdom UK
Tel.: (44) 1442230300
Fax: (44) 1442203368
Web Site: www.butlinsonline.co.uk
Emp.: 200
Holiday Centers & Holiday Hotels Operator
S.I.C.: 7011
N.A.I.C.S.: 721110
Richard Bages *(Mng Dir)*

Haven Leisure Ltd. (1)
1 Park Ln
Hemel Hempstead, Hertfordshire, HP2 4YL, United Kingdom UK
Tel.: (44) 1442230300 (100%)
Fax: (44) 1442230368
E-Mail: purchasing@pourne-leisure.co.uk
Web Site: www.havenholidays.com
Emp.: 750
Operation of Caravan Parks in the United Kingdom, France & Spain
S.I.C.: 7033
N.A.I.C.S.: 721211
Peter Harris *(Mng Dir)*

Warner Leisure Ltd. (1)
1 Park Ln
Hemel Hempstead, Hertfordshire, HP2 4YL, United Kingdom UK
Tel.: (44) 1442230300 (100%)
Fax: (44) 1442330368
Web Site: www.warnerholidays.co.uk
Emp.: 750
Adult Only Holidays in the United Kingdom
S.I.C.: 7011
N.A.I.C.S.: 721199
Patti Henri *(Dir-Sls & Mktg)*

BOURSE REGIONALE DES VALEURS MOBILIERS
(d/b/a BRVM)
18 Rue Joseph Anoma
BP 3802 Abidjan, 01, Cote d'Ivoire
Tel.: (225) 20326685
Fax: (225) 20326684
E-Mail: brvm@brvm.org
Web Site: www.brvm.org
Year Founded: 1996
Business Description:
Stock Exchange Services
S.I.C.: 6231
N.A.I.C.S.: 523210
Personnel:
Felix Edoh Kossi Amenounve *(Dir Gen)*
Abdelkader N'Diaye *(Sec)*

BOUSSARD & GAVAUDAN HOLDING LIMITED
Calder House 1 Dover St
London, W1S 4LA, United Kingdom
Tel.: (44) 207 514 0707
Fax: (44) 7921 126 934
E-Mail: eg@bgam-uk.com
Web Site: www.bgholdingltd.com
BGHL—(EUR LSE)
Rev.: $76,536,349
Assets: $856,584,662
Liabilities: $84,208,816
Net Worth: $772,375,846
Earnings: $55,772,113
Fiscal Year-end: 12/31/12
Business Description:
Investment Services
S.I.C.: 6211
N.A.I.C.S.: 523999
Personnel:
Christopher Fish *(Chm)*
Board of Directors:
Christopher Fish
Andrew Henton
Sameer Sain
Nicolas Wirz
Legal Counsel:
Stibbe N.V.
Strawinskylaan 2001
1077 ZZ Amsterdam, Netherlands
Herbert Smith LLP
Exchange House Primrose Street
London, EC2A 2HS, United Kingdom
Carey Olsen
7 New Street
Saint Peter Port, Guernsey Channel Islands
Non-U.S. Holding:

GFI Informatique S.A. (1)
Immeuble La Porte du Parc 145 Boulevard Victor Hugo
93400 Saint-Ouen, France
Tel.: (33) 144045000
Fax: (33) 144045900
Web Site: www.gfi.fr
GFI—(EUR)
Rev.: $898,343,665
Assets: $798,990,934
Liabilities: $545,321,351
Net Worth: $253,669,582
Earnings: $16,257,695
Emp.: 9,011
Fiscal Year-end: 12/31/12
Information Technology Services
S.I.C.: 7373
N.A.I.C.S.: 541512
Vincent Rouaix *(Pres)*

Subsidiaries:

GFI Chrono Time S.A.S. (2)
12 rue Rouget-de-Lisle
Issy-les-Moulineaux, Hauts-de-Seine, France
Tel.: (33) 146623333
Fax: (33) 549795339
Business & Human Resources Management Software Development Services
S.I.C.: 7371
N.A.I.C.S.: 541511

GFI Consulting S.A.S. (2)
15 rue Beaujon
75008 Paris, France
Tel.: (33) 153934444
Fax: (33) 153934401
E-Mail: ce-gfic@yahoo.fr
Web Site: www.ce-gfic.com
Human Resource Management Software Development Services
S.I.C.: 7371
N.A.I.C.S.: 541511

GFI Infogen Systems S.A.S. (2)
3 rue Collange
92300 Levallois-Perret, Hauts-de-Seine, France
Tel.: (33) 141400656
Fax: (33) 144045907
E-Mail: contact@gfi.fr
Web Site: www.infogen.gfi.fr
Emp.: 90
Enterprise Resource Planning Software Publishing Services
S.I.C.: 7372
N.A.I.C.S.: 511210

GFI Informatique-Production S.A. (2)
158 Avenue de Verdun
92130 Issy-les-Moulineaux, Hauts-de-Seine, France
Tel.: (33) 2 40321818
Fax: (33) 2 40321899
Database Management Software Development Services
S.I.C.: 7371
N.A.I.C.S.: 541511

GFI Progiciels S.A.S. (2)
12 rue Rouget-de-Lisle
92130 Issy-les-Moulineaux, Hauts-de-Seine, France
Tel.: (33) 146623000
Fax: (33) 146620688
Business Management Software Development Services
S.I.C.: 7371
N.A.I.C.S.: 541511

Informatique et Services S.A.S. (2)
145 Boulevard Victor Hugo
93400 Saint-Ouen, Seine-Saint-Denis, France
Tel.: (33) 144045000
Fax: (33) 144045900
Emp.: 8,000
Data Processing Services
S.I.C.: 7379
N.A.I.C.S.: 518210
Yves Roy *(Pres)*

Nemausic S.A. (2)
151 rue Gilles Roberval CS72023
30900 Nimes, Gard, France
Tel.: (33) 466287878
Fax: (33) 466287879
E-Mail: contact@nemausic.fr
Web Site: www.nemausic.fr
Financial & Business Management Software Development Services
S.I.C.: 7371
N.A.I.C.S.: 541511

Non-U.S. Subsidiaries:

GFI Informatica (2)
56 Calle de Serrano Galvache Edificio Encina Planta 7
28033 Madrid, Spain
Tel.: (34) 91 383 63 20
Fax: (34) 91 383 28 65
E-Mail:
Web Site: www.gfi.es
Emp.: 1,500
Biometrics Software Development & Consulting Services
S.I.C.: 7371
N.A.I.C.S.: 541511
Carlos Munoz *(CEO & Dir Gen)*

GFI Benelux S.A. (2)
Technologielaan 11,
3001 Heverlee, Walloon Brabant, Belgium
Tel.: (32) 10237311
Fax: (32) 16381100
E-Mail: info@gfi.be
Web Site: www.gfi.be
Emp.: 100
Business Management Software Development Services
S.I.C.: 7371
N.A.I.C.S.: 541511
Bruno Hannon *(Mgr-Fin)*

GFI Business Solutions Inc. (2)
75 Queen Street
Montreal, QC, H3C 2M6, Canada
Tel.: (514) 288-7161
Fax: (514) 843-4095
E-Mail: info@gfisolutions.com
Web Site: www.gfisolutions.com
Sales Range: $25-49.9 Million
Emp.: 1,000
Integrated Enterprise Resource Planning Software Mfr
S.I.C.: 3652
N.A.I.C.S.: 334614

GFI Informatique Maroc (2)
Casablanca Nearshore Parc 2 2 - 3eme etage
Casablanca, 20190, Morocco
Tel.: (212) 522949779
Fax: (212) 522 36 94 14
E-Mail: gfimaroc@gfimaroc.com
Web Site: www.gfimaroc.com
Financial Software Development Services
S.I.C.: 7371
N.A.I.C.S.: 541511
Saloua Karkri-Belkeziz *(Mng Dir)*

GFI International S.A. (2)
Chemin des Aulx 10
1228 Plan-les-Ouates, Geneva, Switzerland
Tel.: (41) 227062711
Fax: (41) 22 706 27 00
E-Mail: info@gfi.ch
Web Site: www.gfi.ch
Emp.: 15
Business & Human Resources Management Software Development Services
S.I.C.: 7371
N.A.I.C.S.: 541511
Vincent Rouaix *(Chm)*

GFI Maroc Offshore (2)
Parc Casa Nearshore Sh 1 3 1100 Bd Al Qods
Sidi Maarouf, 20190 Casablanca, Morocco
Tel.: (212) 522949780
Fax: (212) 522369414
Software Development & Consulting Services
S.I.C.: 7371
N.A.I.C.S.: 541511
Saloua Karkri-Belkeziz *(Mgr)*

GFI Portugal (2)
Edificio Atlantis Ave D Joao II Lote 1 06 2 2 Piso 4 Parque das Nacoes
1050-047 Lisbon, Portugal
Tel.: (351) 499950
Fax: (351) 210435586
E-Mail: geral@gfi.pt
Web Site: www.gfi.pt
Emp.: 600
Public Administration, Healthcare, Media & Communications, Financial Services, Industry & Utilities, Transportation & Logistics Consulting & Outsourcing Services
S.I.C.: 4731
N.A.I.C.S.: 541614
Nuno Santos *(Mng Dir)*

Grupo Corporativo GFI Informatica S.A. (2)
C/ Serrano Galvache 56 Planta septima Edificio Encina
28033 Madrid, Spain
Tel.: (34) 913836320
Fax: (34) 913832865
E-Mail: reception@gfi.es
Web Site: www.gfi.es/web/gfi-es/contactolegal
Emp.: 150
Business Management Software Development Services
S.I.C.: 7371
N.A.I.C.S.: 541511
Angel Alonso *(Dir Gen)*

Grupo Corporativo GFI Norte S.L. (2)
C Licenciado Poza 55 - 2a pta
48013 Bilbao, Vizcaya, Spain
Tel.: (34) 944241825
Fax: (34) 944354186
E-Mail: norte@gfi-info.com
Web Site: www.gfi.es
Emp.: 250
Software Consulting Services
S.I.C.: 7372
N.A.I.C.S.: 511210
Jose Echezarra *(Dir Gen)*

Savac Consultores S.L. (2)
Maximo Aguirre 18 Bis 3
48011 Bilbao, Vizcaya, Spain
Tel.: (34) 94 439 54 38
Fax: (34) 94 427 26 53
E-Mail: gestion@savac.es
Web Site: www.savac.es
Healthcare Software Development Services
S.I.C.: 7371
N.A.I.C.S.: 541511
Blanca Tato *(Project Mgr)*

BOUSTEAD HEAVY INDUSTRIES CORPORATION BERHAD

17th Fl Menara Boustead 69 Jalan Raja Chulan
50200 Kuala Lumpur, Malaysia
Tel.: (60) 320787770
Fax: (60) 320316089
Web Site: www.bhic.com.my
BHIC—(KLS)
Rev.: $212,006,183
Assets: $488,404,376
Liabilities: $375,347,398
Net Worth: $113,056,978
Earnings: ($36,816,890)
Fiscal Year-end: 12/31/12

Business Description:
Engineering Services
S.I.C.: 8711
N.A.I.C.S.: 541330

Personnel:
Lodin Wok Kamaruddin *(Chm)*
Ahmad Ramli Mohd Nor *(Deputy Chm & Mng Dir)*
Ahmad Nordin Mohammad *(CFO)*
Lilyrohayu Ab Hamid *(Co-Sec)*
Suzana Sanudin *(Co-Sec)*

Board of Directors:
Lodin Wok Kamaruddin
David William Berry
Azzat Kamaludin
Ahmad Ramli Mohd Nor
Ishak Osman
Abd Malik A. Rahman

BOUSTEAD HOLDINGS BERHAD

28th Fl Menara Boustead No 69 Jalan Raja Chulan
50200 Kuala Lumpur, Malaysia
Tel.: (60) 321419044
Fax: (60) 321481866
Web Site: www.boustead.com.my
BSTEAD—(KLS OTC)
Rev.: $3,348,423,912
Assets: $4,553,923,416
Liabilities: $2,789,189,144
Net Worth: $1,764,734,272
Earnings: $169,764,184
Emp.: 17,079
Fiscal Year-end: 12/31/12

Business Description:
Holding Company; Oil Palm Cultivation, Property, Finance, Investment & Pharmaceutical Services
S.I.C.: 0711
N.A.I.C.S.: 115112

Personnel:
Lodin Wok Kamaruddin *(Deputy Chm & Grp Mng Dir)*
Sharifah Malek *(Sec)*

Board of Directors:
Mohd Ghazali Mat
Abdul Rahman Ahmad
Azzat Kamaludin
Lodin Wok Kamaruddin
Ghazali Mohd Ali
Francis Leh Kiah Tan

Subsidiaries:

Pharmaniaga Berhad (1)
No 7 Lorong Keluli 1B Kawasan Perindustrian Bukit Raja Selatan
PO Box 2030
Seksyen 7, 40000 Shah Alam, Selangor, Malaysia (86.8%)
Tel.: (60) 3 3342 9999
Fax: (60) 3 3341 7777
Web Site: www.pharmaniaga.com
PHARMA—(KLS)
Rev.: $594,304,500
Assets: $400,989,102
Liabilities: $241,012,346
Net Worth: $159,976,756
Earnings: $20,726,184
Emp.: 1,845
Fiscal Year-end: 12/31/12
Pharmaceutical Mfr
S.I.C.: 2834
N.A.I.C.S.: 325412
Farshila Emran *(Mng Dir)*
Norai'ni Mohamed Ali *(CFO)*
Mohamed Iqbal Abdul Rahman *(COO)*
Sharifah Malek *(Co-Sec)*
Nor Azrina Zakaria *(Co-Sec)*

Divisions:

Pharmaniaga Logistics Sdn Bhd (2)
No 7 Lorong Keluli 1B Kawasan Perindustrian Bukit Raja Selatan
Seksyen 7, 40000 Shah Alam, Selangor Darul Ehsan, Malaysia
Tel.: (60) 3 3342 9999
Fax: (60) 3 3341 7777
Pharmaceutical Mfr
S.I.C.: 2834
N.A.I.C.S.: 325412

Branch:

Pharmaniaga Logistics Sdn Bhd-Juru (3)
1/3/5 Lorong IKS
Juru 8
Taman Peridustrian Ringan Juru, 14100 Penang, Malaysia
Tel.: (60) 4 508 3330
Fax: (60) 4 508 3111
Pharmaceutical Logistics Services & Distr
S.I.C.: 4731
N.A.I.C.S.: 541614

Subsidiary:

Pharmaniaga Biomedical Sdn Bhd (3)
No 7 Lorong Keluli 1B
Kawasan Perindustrian Bukit Raja Selatan
Seksyen 7, 40000 Shah Alam, Malaysia
Tel.: (60) 3 3342 9999
Fax: (60) 3 3341 7777
Pharmaceutical Mfr
S.I.C.: 2834
N.A.I.C.S.: 325412

Pharmaniaga Manufacturing Berhad (2)
11A Jalan P1 Kawasan Perusahaan Bangi
43650 Bandar Baru Bangi, Malaysia
Tel.: (60) 3 8925 7880
Fax: (60) 3 8925 6177
Pharmaceutical Mfr
S.I.C.: 2834
N.A.I.C.S.: 325412

Subsidiaries:

Pharmaniaga LifeScience Sdn Bhd (3)
Lot 7 Jalan PPU 3
Taman Perindustrian Puchong Utama
47100 Puchong, Selangor Darul Ehsan, Malaysia
Tel.: (60) 3 8061 2006
Fax: (60) 3 8061 2875
Pharmaceutical Mfr
S.I.C.: 2834
N.A.I.C.S.: 325412

Pharmaniaga Research Centre Sdn Bhd (3)
11A Jalan P1
Kawasan Perusahaan Bangi
4360 Bandar Baru Bangi, Selangor Darul Ehsan, Malaysia
Tel.: (60) 3 8925 7880
Fax: (60) 3 8925 6177
Pharmaceutical Research
S.I.C.: 8731
N.A.I.C.S.: 541712

Pharmaniaga Marketing Sdn Bhd (2)
No 7 Lorong Keluli 1B Kawasan Perindustrian Bukit Raja Selatan
Seksyen 7, 40000 Shah Alam, Selangor Darul Ehsan, Malaysia
Tel.: (60) 3 3342 9999
Fax: (60) 3 3341 7777
Pharmaceutical Products Marketing
S.I.C.: 8742
N.A.I.C.S.: 541613

Subsidiaries:

Pharmaniaga Biovention Sdn Bhd (2)
No 7 Lorong Keluli 1B Kawasan Perindustrian Bukit Raja Selatan
Seksyen 7, 40000 Shah Alam, Selangor Darul Ehsan, Malaysia
Tel.: (60) 3 3342 9999
Fax: (60) 3 3341 7777
Pharamaceutical Mfr
S.I.C.: 2834
N.A.I.C.S.: 325412

Pharmaniaga International Corporation Sdn Bhd (2)
No 7 Lorong Keluli 1B
Kawasan Perindustrian Bukit Raja Selatan
Seksyen 7, 40000 Shah Alam, Malaysia
Tel.: (60) 3 3342 9999
Fax: (60) 3 3341 7777
Phramaceutical Mfr
S.I.C.: 2834
N.A.I.C.S.: 325412

Non-U.S. Subsidiary:

PT Millennium Pharmacon International Tbk (3)
Panin Bank Centre
9th Floor Jl-Jendral Sudiman
10270 Jakarta, Senayan, Indonesia
Tel.: (62) 21 727 88906
Fax: (62) 21 722 8090
E-Mail: support@mpi-indonesia.co.id
Web Site: www.mpi-indonesia.co.id
Healthcare Products Distr
S.I.C.: 5047
N.A.I.C.S.: 423450
Andrew Loke Pak Keong *(Pres & Dir)*

UAC Berhad (1)
Level 10 Menara UAC 12 Jalan PJU 7/5
Mutiara Damansara
Petaling Jaya, Selangor Darul Ehsan, 47800, Malaysia
Tel.: (60) 377219393
Fax: (60) 377219300
E-Mail: uac@uac.com.my
Web Site: www.uac.com.my
Sales Range: $50-74.9 Million
Emp.: 653
Cement Mfr & Distr
S.I.C.: 3241
N.A.I.C.S.: 327310
Hock Fee Koo *(CEO & Mng Dir)*
Lee Choo Ooi *(CFO)*
Long Puang Tey *(COO)*
Sharifah Malek *(Sec)*

BOUSTEAD SINGAPORE LIMITED

67 Ubi Avenue 1 02-01 StarHub Green North Wing
Singapore, 408942, Singapore
Tel.: (65) 67470016
Fax: (65) 67418689
E-Mail: corporate@boustead.com.sg
Web Site: www.boustead.sg
Year Founded: 1828
F9D—(SES)
Rev.: $415,526,157
Assets: $491,399,650
Liabilities: $238,515,534
Net Worth: $252,884,116
Earnings: $68,401,766
Emp.: 711
Fiscal Year-end: 03/31/13

Business Description:
Holding Company; Engineering & IT Services
S.I.C.: 6719
N.A.I.C.S.: 551112

Personnel:
Fong Fui Wong *(Chm & CEO)*
Kai Keong Loh *(CFO)*
David Miller *(Mng Dir-Boustead International Heaters Ltd)*
Michael Teo *(CEO-Boustead Salcon Water Solutions Pte Ltd)*
Steven Koh *(Deputy Mng Dir-Ops-Boustead Projects Pte Ltd)*
Yu Wei Wong *(Deputy Mng Dir-Boustead Projects Pte Ltd)*
Alvin Kok *(Sec)*
Shiok Faun Chan *(Sr VP-Fin)*
Wee Leong Yeo *(Sr VP-Internal Audit)*

Board of Directors:
Fong Fui Wong
Ngien Cheong Chong
Boon Seong Goh
John Kok Min Lim
Kai Keong Loh
Widati Ernawan Putri
Godfrey Ernest Scotchbrook
Yu Loon Wong

Divisions:

Controls & Electric Pte. Ltd. (1)
30 Gul Dr
Jurong, Singapore, 629478, Singapore (100%)
Tel.: (65) 68613377
Fax: (65) 68618408
E-Mail: sales@bousted.com.sg
Web Site: www.bousteadco.com.sg
Emp.: 40
Designer, Supplier, Installer & Commissioner of Instrumentation Systems
S.I.C.: 3625
N.A.I.C.S.: 335314
Dev Lodh *(Mng Dir)*

Subsidiaries:

Boustead Information Technology Pte Ltd (1)
67 Ubi Ave 1 #02-01 StarHub Green North Wing
Singapore, 408942, Singapore (100%)
Tel.: (65) 67428622
Fax: (65) 67421922
E-Mail: corporate@boustead.co.sg
Web Site: www.boustead.sg
Emp.: 20
Information Technology Services
S.I.C.: 7373
N.A.I.C.S.: 541512

Boustead Infrastructures Pte. Ltd. (1)
67 Ubi Avenue 1 02-05 StarHub Green
Singapore, Singapore
Tel.: (65) 6747 3313
Fax: (65) 6747 0112
Web Site: www.bousteadinfrastructures.com
Engineering Services
S.I.C.: 8711
N.A.I.C.S.: 541330

Boustead Maxitherm Energy Pte Ltd (1)
67 Ubi Avenue 1 02-01 StarHub Green North Wing
Singapore, 408942, Singapore
Tel.: (65) 67470016
Fax: (65) 67418689
Web Site: www.bousteadmaxitherm.com
Solid Waste Energy Recovery Services
S.I.C.: 4959
N.A.I.C.S.: 562998

Boustead Projects Investments Pte Ltd (1)
StarHub Green 02-01 67 Ubi Avenue 1
Singapore, 408942, Singapore
Tel.: (65) 67483945
Fax: (65) 67489250
Waste Water Engineering Services
S.I.C.: 8711
N.A.I.C.S.: 541330

Boustead Projects Pte. Ltd. (1)
67 Ubi Ave 1 02 03
Starhub Green, Singapore, 408942, Singapore SG
Tel.: (65) 67483945 (51%)

Boustead Singapore Limited—(Continued)

Fax: (65) 67489250
E-Mail: corporate@boustead.sg
Web Site: www.bousteadco.com.sg
Emp.: 25
Project Management, Design & Construction Services & Property-Related Activities
S.I.C.: 1542
N.A.I.C.S.: 236220
Thomas Chu *(CEO)*

Boustead Salcon Pte Ltd **(1)**
67 Ubi Avenue 1 02-01 StarHub Green
Singapore, 408942, Singapore
Tel.: (65) 6747 0016
Fax: (65) 6741 8689
Engineering Services
S.I.C.: 8711
N.A.I.C.S.: 541330

Boustead Salcon Water Solutions Pte Ltd **(1)**
67 Ubi Avenue 1 02-02 StarHub Green
Singapore, 408942, Singapore
Tel.: (65) 68469988
Fax: (65) 6747 8878
E-Mail: enquiry@bousteadsalcon.com
Web Site: www.bousteadsalcon.com
Wastewater Treatment Solutions
S.I.C.: 4959
N.A.I.C.S.: 562998

Esri Singapore Pte Ltd **(1)**
67 Ubi Avenue 1 StarHub Green North Wing 02-06
Singapore, 408942, Singapore
Tel.: (65) 67428622
Fax: (65) 6742 1922
E-Mail: connect@esrisingapore.com.sg
Web Site: www.esrisingapore.com.sg
Mapping Software Development & Hosting Services
S.I.C.: 7371
N.A.I.C.S.: 541511
Leslie Wong *(CEO)*

ESRI South Asia Pte Ltd **(1)**
Starhub Green 67 Ubi Avenue 1 Unit 02-01
67 Ubi Ave 1, Singapore, 408942, Singapore (100%)
Tel.: (65) 67428622
Fax: (65) 67421922
E-Mail: sales@esrisa.com
Web Site: www.esrisa.com
Emp.: 20
Provides GIS-Related Solutions
S.I.C.: 7373
N.A.I.C.S.: 541512
Lesley Wong *(Gen Mgr)*

Non-U.S. Subsidiaries:

BIH Heaters Malaysia Sdn Bhd **(1)**
14th Floor Surian Tower No1 Jalan PJU 7/3
Mutiara Damansara, 47810 Petaling Jaya, Selangor, Malaysia
Tel.: (60) 3 7491 6100
Fax: (60) 3 7491 6200
Web Site: www.bihl.com
Emp.: 50
Solid Waste Recovery Services
S.I.C.: 4953
N.A.I.C.S.: 562213
Pul Miller *(Gen Mgr)*

Boustead International Heaters Canada Limited **(1)**
Suite 200 809 Manning Road NE
Calgary, AB, T2E 7M9, Canada
Tel.: (403) 781-7070
Fax: (403) 781-7074
Solid Waste Recovery Services
S.I.C.: 4953
N.A.I.C.S.: 562213

Boustead International Heaters Limited **(1)**
Europa House Woodlands Court
Albert Drive, Burgess Hill, West Sussex, RH15 9TN, United Kingdom (100%)
Tel.: (44) 1444237500
Telex: 87285
Fax: (44) 1444237501
E-Mail: sales@bihl.com
Web Site: www.bihl.com
Emp.: 60
Mfr of Heaters & Associated Products
S.I.C.: 3433
N.A.I.C.S.: 333414
Nigel Woodhouse *(Mng Dir)*

ESRI Australia Pty. Ltd. **(1)**
Level 3 111 Elizabeth St
Brisbane, QLD, 4000, Australia
Tel.: (61) 732184100
Fax: (61) 732111310
E-Mail: defence@esriaustralia.com.au
Web Site: www.esriaustralia.com.au/esri/default.html
Emp.: 66
Military Services to Defense Industries
S.I.C.: 9199
N.A.I.C.S.: 921190
Brett Sundock *(Mng Dir)*

ESRI Malaysia Sdn Bhd **(1)**
Suite 301 Block A4 Leisure Commerce Square
9 Jalan PJ S8/9, 46150 Petaling Jaya, Selangor, Malaysia
Tel.: (60) 3 7874 9930
Fax: (60) 3 7874 9932
E-Mail: info@esrimalaysia.com.my
Web Site: www.esrimalaysia.com.my
Emp.: 20
Geographic Information System Services
S.I.C.: 7389
N.A.I.C.S.: 519190
Daniel Boey *(Gen Mgr)*

ESRI South Asia Sdn. Bhd. **(1)**
Ste 301Block A4 Leisure Commerce Sq
No9 Jalan PJS 8 9, 46150 Petaling Jaya, Selangor, Malaysia (100%)
Tel.: (60) 378749930
Fax: (60) 378749932
Web Site: www.esrimalaysia.com.my
Emp.: 18
Geographic Information System Technology Whslr
S.I.C.: 5045
N.A.I.C.S.: 423430
Ooi Siewthing *(Head-Fin)*

MapData Services Pty Ltd **(1)**
Level 1 110 Pacific Highway
Greenwich, NSW, 2065, Australia
Tel.: (61) 284362800
Fax: (61) 2 8436 2888
E-Mail: info@mapdataservices.com
Web Site: www.mapdataservices.com
Geospatial Database Development & Online Map Hosting Services
S.I.C.: 7371
N.A.I.C.S.: 541511

PT Boustead Maxitherm Industries **(1)**
Graha Pratama Building 15th Floor Jalan Letjend
MT Haryono Kav 15 Tebet, Jakarta, 12810, Indonesia
Tel.: (62) 2183793678
Fax: (62) 2183793648
E-Mail: marketing@bousteadmaxitherm.com
Web Site: www.bousteadmaxitherm.com
Solid Waste Recovery Services
S.I.C.: 4953
N.A.I.C.S.: 562213

PT ESRI Indonesia **(1)**
Graha Pratama Lt 7 JL MT Haryono Kav 15
Jakarta, Selatan, 12810, Indonesia
Tel.: (62) 2183792177
Fax: (62) 2183792178
E-Mail: support@esriindonesia.co.id
Web Site: www.esriindonesia.co.id
Geographic Information System Services
S.I.C.: 7389
N.A.I.C.S.: 519190

Tianjin University of Commerce-Boustead Informatics, Ltd. **(1)**
28 Jinjing Rd
Xiqing District, Tianjin, 300384, China
Tel.: (86) 2223799800
Fax: (86) 2223618680
E-Mail: boustead@public.tpt.tj.cn
Web Site: www.boustead.edu.cn
Emp.: 100
Educational Services
S.I.C.: 8221
N.A.I.C.S.: 611310

BOUTHILLETTE PARIZEAU

9825 Verville St
Montreal, QC, H3L 3E1, Canada
Tel.: (514) 383-3747
Fax: (514) 383-8760
E-Mail: info@bpa.ca
Web Site: www.bpa.ca
Year Founded: 1956
Rev.: $11,998,403
Emp.: 200

Business Description:
Engineering & Consulting Services
S.I.C.: 8711
N.A.I.C.S.: 541330

Personnel:
Claude Decary *(Gen Mgr)*

BOUTIQUE JACOB INC.

6125 chemin de la Cote de Liesse
Saint Laurent, QC, H4T 1C8, Canada
Tel.: (514) 731-8877
Fax: (514) 731-6223
Web Site: www.jacob.ca
Year Founded: 1977
Rev.: $60,189,091
Emp.: 750

Business Description:
Women's Apparel Stores
S.I.C.: 5621
N.A.I.C.S.: 448120

Personnel:
Joseph Basmaji *(Owner & Pres)*

BOUVET ASA

Sandakerveien 24c Bygning D11
PO Box 4430
Nydalen, 0403 Oslo, Norway
Tel.: (47) 23406000
Fax: (47) 23406001
E-Mail: info@bouvet.no
Web Site: www.bouvet.no
BOUVET—(OSL)
Rev.: $186,482,866
Assets: $74,259,292
Liabilities: $25,762,298
Net Worth: $48,496,994
Earnings: $10,236,251
Emp.: 881
Fiscal Year-end: 12/31/12

Business Description:
Information Technology Consulting Services
S.I.C.: 7379
N.A.I.C.S.: 541519

Personnel:
Age Danielsen *(Chm)*
Randi Helene Roed *(Vice Chm)*
Sverre Hurum *(CEO)*
Erik Stubo *(CFO)*

Board of Directors:
Age Danielsen
Axel Borge
Grethe Hoiland
Ingebrigt Steen Jensen
Kay Vare Johnsen
Sissel Johnsen Mannsaker
Randi Helene Roed

Non-U.S. Subsidiary:

Bouvet Sverige AB **(1)**
Sodergatan 14
211 34 Malmo, Scania, Sweden
Tel.: (46) 406366000
Information Technology Consulting Services
S.I.C.: 8742
N.A.I.C.S.: 541611

Subsidiaries:

Bouvet Stockholm AB **(2)**
Svetsarvagen 15 2 Tr
17141 Solna, Stockholm, Sweden
Tel.: (46) 406366000
E-Mail: info@bouvet.se
Web Site: www.bouvet.se
Information Technology Consulting Services
S.I.C.: 8999
N.A.I.C.S.: 541690
Jonna Norden *(Mng Dir)*

Bouvet Syd AB **(2)**
Sodergatan 3
211 34 Malmo, Sweden
Tel.: (46) 406366000
Web Site: www.bouvet.se/kontakta-oss/malmoe.aspx
Software Support Services
S.I.C.: 7389
N.A.I.C.S.: 561499

BOUYER LEROUX SA

L'Etablere
49280 La Seguiniere, France
Tel.: (33) 2 41 63 76 16
Fax: (33) 2 72 62 70 88
E-Mail: info@bouyer-leroux.fr
Web Site: www.bouyer-leroux.com
Sales Range: $150-199.9 Million
Emp.: 740

Business Description:
Building Material Mfr
S.I.C.: 3255
N.A.I.C.S.: 327120

Personnel:
Roland Besnard *(Pres)*

BOUYGUES S.A.

32 avenue Hoche
75008 Paris, France
Tel.: (33) 144201000
Telex: 250637 F
Fax: (33) 130603140
E-Mail: contacts@bouyguestelecom.fr
Web Site: www.bouygues.com
Year Founded: 1952
EN—(LUX)
Rev.: $45,159,964,990
Assets: $49,477,132,180
Liabilities: $35,910,430,920
Net Worth: $13,566,701,260
Earnings: $980,011,760
Emp.: 133,780
Fiscal Year-end: 12/31/12

Business Description:
General Contracting, Civil Engineering, Public Works, Roads, Buildings, Water Distribution, TV Channel & Cellular Phone Network Services
S.I.C.: 8711
N.A.I.C.S.: 541330

Personnel:
Martin Bouygues *(Chm & CEO)*
Olivier Bouygues *(Deputy CEO)*
Philippe Marien *(CFO & Chm-Bouygues Telecom)*
Francois Bertiere *(Chm/CEO-Immobilier)*
Yves Gabriel *(Chm/CEO-Construction)*
Herve Le Bouc *(Chm/CEO-Colas)*
Nonce Paolini *(Chm/CEO-TF1)*
Olivier Roussat *(CEO-Telecom)*
Jean-Francois Guillemin *(Sec)*
Jean-Claude Tostivin *(Sr VP-HR & Admin)*

Board of Directors:
Martin Bouygues
Yves Gabriel
Herve Le Bouc
Nonce Paolini
Francois Bertiere
Francis Bouygues
Olivier Bouygues
Jean-Paul Chifflet
Georges Chodron de Courcel
Anne-Marie Idrac
Patrick Kron
Helman le Pas de Secheval
Colette Lewiner
Sandra Nombret
Jean Peyrelevade
Francois-Henri Pinault

Rose-Marie Van Lerberghe
Michele Vilain
Ernst & Young Audit
Paris, France

Subsidiaries:

Bouygues Construction (1)
Challenger 1 avenue Eugene Freyssinet
Guyancourt, 78061 Saint-Quentin-en-Yvelines, France (100%)
Tel.: (33) 130603300
Fax: (33) 130604861
E-Mail: communication@bouygues-construction.com
Web Site: www.bouygues-construction.com
Sls.: $14,323,248,800
Assets: $12,488,419,090
Liabilities: $11,379,175,010
Net Worth: $1,109,244,080
Earnings: $352,696,540
Emp.: 51,100
Fiscal Year-end: 12/31/12
Construction & Civil Engineering
S.I.C.: 1629
N.A.I.C.S.: 237990
Yves Gabriel *(Chm & CEO)*
Philippe Amequin *(Deputy CEO-Bouygues Travaux Publics)*
Philippe Bonnave *(Deputy CEO)*
Benoit de Ruffray *(Deputy CEO-Bouygues Batiment International)*
Pascal Grange *(Deputy CEO)*
Philippe Fabie *(Chm/CEO-Bouygues Batiment Ile-de-France)*
Olivier-Marie Racine *(Chm/CEO-Bouygues Batiment International)*
Jean-Philippe Trin *(Chm/CEO-Bouygues Energies & Services)*
Christian Gazaignes *(CEO-Bouygues Travaux Publics)*
Charles Paradis *(CEO-Bouygues Construction Concessions)*
Daniel Rigout *(CEO-Specialist Civil Works)*
Jean-Marc Kiviatkowski *(Gen Counsel)*
Gaetan Desruelles *(Exec VP-R&D, Innovation & Sustainable Construction)*
Philippe Dalle Nogare *(Exec VP-Info Sys)*

Subsidiaries:

Bouygues Batiment Ile-de-France (2)
Challenger 1 Avenue Eugene Freyssinet
78061 Saint-Quentin-en-Yvelines, France (100%)
Tel.: (33) 130603400
Fax: (33) 130604861
E-Mail: info.idf@bouygues-construction.com
Web Site: www.bouygues-construction.com
Sales Range: $1-4.9 Billion
Emp.: 5,000
Residential & Commercial Construction
S.I.C.: 1531
N.A.I.C.S.: 236117
Philippe Fabie *(Chm & CEO)*

Bouygues Batiment International (2)
1 Ave Eugene Freyssinet
78065 Saint-Quentin-en-Yvelines, France (100%)
Tel.: (33) 130605600
Fax: (33) 130604861
E-Mail: communication.bi@bouygues-construction.com
Web Site: www.bouygues-construction.com
Sales Range: $1-4.9 Billion
Emp.: 11,500
Residential & Commercial Constructrion & Development
S.I.C.: 1542
N.A.I.C.S.: 236220
Olivier-Marie Racine *(CEO)*

Bouygues Entreprises France-Europe (2)
1 avenue Eugene Freyssinet
78065 Saint-Quentin-en-Yvelines, France (100%)
Tel.: (33) 130603300
Fax: (33) 130604861
Web Site: www.bouygues-construction.com
Sales Range: $1-4.9 Billion
Emp.: 9,100
Constructrion & Engineering Services
S.I.C.: 1629
N.A.I.C.S.: 237990
Philippe Bonnave *(CEO)*

Bouygues Travaux Publics (2)
1 avenue Eugene Freyssinet
78065 Saint-Quentin-en-Yvelines, France (100%)
Tel.: (33) 130605700
Fax: (33) 130604861
E-Mail: bouyguestp@bouygues-construction.com
Web Site: www.bouygues-construction.com
Sales Range: $1-4.9 Billion
Emp.: 3,000
Civil Engineering Services & Construction
S.I.C.: 1629
N.A.I.C.S.: 237990
Christian Gazaignes *(CEO)*

Non-U.S. Subsidiary:

Bouygues (UK) Ltd. (2)
Elizabeth House 39 York Rd
London, SE1 7NQ, United Kingdom
Tel.: (44) 2074010020
Fax: (44) 2074010030
E-Mail: info@bouygues-uk.com
Web Site: www.bouygues-uk.com
Emp.: 500
Construction Services
S.I.C.: 1542
N.A.I.C.S.: 236220

Bouygues Immobilier (1)
3 Boulevard Gallieni
92000 Issy-les-Moulineaux, Cedex, France (100%)
Tel.: (33) 155382525
Fax: (33) 147129645
E-Mail: contact@bouygues-immobilier.com
Web Site: www.bouygues-immobilier.com
Sales Range: $1-4.9 Billion
Emp.: 300
Developer of Commercial & Residential Real Estate
S.I.C.: 1542
N.A.I.C.S.: 236220
Francois Bertiere *(Chm & CEO)*

Non-U.S. Subsidiary:

Bouygues Inmobiliaria S.A. (2)
Calle Via de Los Poblados
Madrid, 28033, Spain
Tel.: (34) 913756030
Fax: (34) 917638602
Web Site: www.bouygues-inmobiliaria.com
Construction Engineering Services
S.I.C.: 8711
N.A.I.C.S.: 541330

Bouygues Relais SNC (1)
32 Avenue Hoche
75008 Paris, France
Tel.: (33) 1 30 60 23 11
Fax: (33) 1 30 60 48 61
Financial Management Consulting Services
S.I.C.: 8742
N.A.I.C.S.: 541611

Bouygues Telecom (1)
Arcs de Seine
1 Pl Abel Gance, 92640 Boulogne-Billancourt, France FR
Tel.: (33) 139267500 (89.5%)
Fax: (33) 139267501
E-Mail: contacts@bouyguestelecom.fr
Web Site: www.bouyguestelecom.fr
Sales Range: $1-4.9 Billion
Emp.: 6,950
Cellular Telecommunications Services
S.I.C.: 4812
N.A.I.C.S.: 517210
Frederic Ruciak *(Mgr-Mktg)*

Brezillon SA (1)
8 Rue De Deportes
60400 Noyon, France
Tel.: (33) 344932121
Fax: (33) 384932161
Industrial Building Construction Services
S.I.C.: 1541
N.A.I.C.S.: 236210

Colas SA (1)
7 Place Rene Clair
92653 Boulogne-Billancourt, France(96.7%)
Tel.: (33) 147617500
Fax: (33) 147617600
E-Mail: communication@colas.fr
Web Site: www.colas.com
RE—(EUR)
Rev.: $17,548,672,120
Assets: $11,206,865,250
Liabilities: $7,782,208,770
Net Worth: $3,424,656,480
Earnings: $417,312,700
Emp.: 66,489
Fiscal Year-end: 12/31/12
Road Construction & Infrastructure Maintenance
S.I.C.: 1622
N.A.I.C.S.: 237310
Herve Le Bouc *(Chm & CEO)*
Benoit Chauvin *(Chm/CEO-Spac)*
Philippe Durand *(Chm/CEO-Colas Sud-Ouest)*
Christophe Guy *(Chm/CEO-Colas Est)*
Joel Hamon *(Chm/CEO-Colas Nord-Picardie)*
Thierry Meline *(Chm/CEO-Colas Midi-Mediterranee)*
Bernard Sala *(Chm/CEO-Colas Ile-de-France-Normandie)*
Jean Vidal *(Chm/CEO-Colas Centre-Ouest)*
Georges Ausseil *(Deputy Mng Dir-United States)*
Martine Bourdon *(Deputy Mng Dir-Colas Nord-Picardie)*
Jean-Paul Brossard *(Deputy Mng Dir)*
Philippe Decarnin *(Deputy Mng Dir)*
Daniel Dupuy *(Deputy Mng Dir-Colas Midi-Mediterranee)*
Patrick Guenole *(Deputy Mng Dir-Railways)*
Richard Rueda *(Deputy Mng Dir-Colas Rhone-Alpes-Auvergne)*
Pascal Trouf *(Deputy Mng Dir-Colas Est)*
Thierry Montouche *(Sec)*

Subsidiaries:

Aximum (2)
41 Boulevard De La Republique
BP 76
78403 Chatou, France
Tel.: (33) 130156900
Web Site: www.aximum.fr
Road Construction Engineering Services
S.I.C.: 1622
N.A.I.C.S.: 237310

Colas Rail (2)
44 Rue Jean Mermoz
78600 Maisons-Laffitte, France
Tel.: (33) 134938300
Fax: (33) 1 34 93 82 99
Web Site: www.colasrail.com
Emp.: 100
Railway Track Construction Services
S.I.C.: 1629
N.A.I.C.S.: 237990
Guenole Patrick *(Mgr)*

Somaro (2)
3 Rue Des Beaunes
PO Box 76
784 WW Chatou, France (100%)
Tel.: (33) 130156900
Fax: (33) 130719163
Web Site: www.smaro.com
Emp.: 60
Installer & Maintainer of Highway Safety Equipment
S.I.C.: 5047
N.A.I.C.S.: 423450

U.S. Subsidiary:

Colas Inc. (2)
163 Madison Ave Ste 500
Morristown, NJ 07960
Tel.: (973) 656-4819
Fax: (973) 290-9088
E-Mail: fchaignon@colasinc.com
Web Site: www.colas.com
Roads Construction Engineering Services
S.I.C.: 1622
N.A.I.C.S.: 237310
Jean Vidal *(COO)*

Non-U.S. Subsidiaries:

Colas Belgium SA (2)
Rue Nestor Martin 313
1082 Brussels, Belgium
Tel.: (32) 24820630
Fax: (32) 24692356
E-Mail: info@colas.be
Web Site: www.colas.be
Emp.: 60
Road Construction Engineering Services
S.I.C.: 1611
N.A.I.C.S.: 237310
Derdaele Yvo *(Gen Mgr)*

Non-U.S. Subsidiary:

Colas Gabon (3)
BP 3985
Libreville, Gabon
Tel.: (241) 76 15 95
Fax: (241) 76 00 14
Construction Engineering Services
S.I.C.: 8711
N.A.I.C.S.: 541330

COLAS-HUNGARIA Zrt. (2)
Korhaz u 6-12
1033 Budapest, Hungary
Tel.: (36) 1 883 1000
Fax: (36) 1 883 1010
E-Mail: hungaria@colashun.hu
Web Site: www.colas.hu
Emp.: 600
Construction Engineering Services
S.I.C.: 8711
N.A.I.C.S.: 541330
Alain Boubees *(Gen Mgr)*

Colas Martinique (2)
BP 564 97242
Fort-de-France, cedex, Martinique
Tel.: (596) 596707070
Fax: (596) 596707080
E-Mail: taatlto@martinique.colas.fr
Emp.: 100
Road & Highway Construction Engineering Services
S.I.C.: 1611
N.A.I.C.S.: 237310
Ladouc Medharea *(Gen Mgr)*

Colas Polska Sp.z.o.o (2)
Ul Nowa 49
62-070 Paledzie, Poland
Tel.: (48) 61 894 54 60
Fax: (48) 61 894 54 65
E-Mail: colas@colas.pl
Web Site: www.colas.pl
Roads Construction Engineering Services
S.I.C.: 1622
N.A.I.C.S.: 237310
Lorecki Marek *(Gen Mgr)*

DTP Terrassement SA (1)
1 Avenue Eugene Freyssinet
78280 Saint-Quentin-en-Yvelines, France
Tel.: (33) 130603851
Fax: (33) 130604861
Emp.: 4,500
Construction Engineering Services
S.I.C.: 8711
N.A.I.C.S.: 541330

DV Construction SA (1)
Le Seville 22 Avenue Pythagore
Merignac, 33700, France
Tel.: (33) 557532525
Fax: (33) 556434777
Web Site: www.dv-construction.fr
Construction Engineering Services
S.I.C.: 8711
N.A.I.C.S.: 541330

ETDE SA (1)
19 Rue Stephenson
78063 Saint-Quentin-en-Yvelines, France
Tel.: (33) 180615000
Fax: (33) 1 39 41 68 00
Web Site: www.etde.fr
Telecommunication Networking Services
S.I.C.: 4899
N.A.I.C.S.: 517919

Non-U.S. Subsidiaries:

David Webster Limited (2)
Field House Station Approach
Harlow, CM20 2FB, United Kingdom
Tel.: (44) 1279645100
Fax: (44) 1279645101
E-Mail: infra@etde.co.uk
Web Site: www.etde.co.uk
Emp.: 40
Street Lighting Installation Services
S.I.C.: 1731
N.A.I.C.S.: 238210
Bruno Bodin *(Chm)*
Edward Peeke *(Mng Dir)*
John Barker *(Deputy Mng Dir)*
Xavier Plumley *(Sec)*

Bouygues S.A.—(Continued)

Ecovert FM (2)
Elizabeth House 39 York Road
London, SE1 7NQ, United Kingdom
Tel.: (44) 207 401 0020
Fax: (44) 207 401 0030
E-Mail: comm@ecovertfm.co.uk
Web Site: www.ecovertfm.co.uk
Emp.: 400
Building Maintenance & Engineering Services
S.I.C.: 8711
N.A.I.C.S.: 541330

ETDE Contracting Ltd (2)
One Didsbury Point
Didsbury, Manchester, M20 2EA, United Kingdom
Tel.: (44) 1612491000
Fax: (44) 1612491001
Web Site: www.etde-contracting.co.uk
Emp.: 60
Construction Engineering Services
S.I.C.: 8711
N.A.I.C.S.: 541330
Serge Bordonnat *(Mng Dir)*
Steve Weir *(Sec & Dir-Comml)*

Eurosport SA (1)
3 Rue Gaston Et Rene Caudron
Issy-les-Moulineaux, France
Tel.: (33) 140938000
Fax: (33) 140938100
Web Site: www.eurosport.com
Emp.: 600
Television Broadcasting Services
S.I.C.: 4833
N.A.I.C.S.: 515120

Subsidiary:

La Chaine Info (2)
1 Quai Du Point Du Jour
Boulogne-Billancourt, 92100, France
Tel.: (33) 141412345
Fax: (33) 141412840
Television Broadcasting Services
S.I.C.: 4833
N.A.I.C.S.: 515120

Exprimm IT (1)
16 Avenue Du Quebec Silic 712
91961 Villebon-sur-Yvette, France
Tel.: (33) 160928400
Fax: (33) 160928409
Web Site: www.exprimm-it.fr
Telecommunication Networking Services
S.I.C.: 4899
N.A.I.C.S.: 517919
Eric Hohbauer *(Gen Mgr)*

GFC Construction SA (1)
5-7 Avenue De Poumeyrol
69647 Caluire-et-Cuire, France
Tel.: (33) 4 72 81 18 18
Fax: (33) 4 86 06 03 17
Web Site: www.gfc-construction.fr
Emp.: 300
Industrial Building Construction Services
S.I.C.: 1541
N.A.I.C.S.: 236210

Norpac SA (1)
Parc Scientifique de la Haute Borne 1 avenue de l'Horizon
59651 Villeneuve d'Ascq, France
Tel.: (33) 357634000
Fax: (33) 320472803
Construction ServiceCivil Engineering Services
S.I.C.: 1629
N.A.I.C.S.: 237990

Pertuy Construction SA (1)
20 Rue Blaise Pascal
54320 Maxeville, France
Tel.: (33) 383932323
Fax: (33) 383981748
Web Site: www.pertuy-construction.com
Civil Engineering Services
S.I.C.: 1629
N.A.I.C.S.: 237990

Quille SA (1)
4 Rue Saint Eloi
BP 1048
76172 Rouen, France
Tel.: (33) 235144864
Fax: (33) 235144910
Web Site: www.quille.fr
Construction Engineering Services
S.I.C.: 8711
N.A.I.C.S.: 541330

SMAC SA (1)
40 Rue Fanfan La Tulipe
92653 Boulogne-Billancourt, France
Tel.: (33) 147617200
Fax: (33) 147617210
E-Mail: info@smac-sa.com
Web Site: www.smac-sa.com
Asphalt Products Mfr
S.I.C.: 2951
N.A.I.C.S.: 324121

Subsidiary:

Societe de la Raffinerie de Dunkerque (2)
Route de l'Ouvrage Ouest
BP 4519
Dunkirk, 59381, France
Tel.: (33) 3 28 29 50 00
Fax: (33) 3 28 29 50 21
Oil Refining Services
S.I.C.: 2911
N.A.I.C.S.: 324110

Sodearif SA (1)
1 Avenue Eugene Freyssinet
78280 Guyancourt, France
Tel.: (33) 130604859
Fax: (33) 130605008
E-Mail: renseignemeng@sodearif.com
Web Site: www.sodearif.com
Emp.: 100
Real Estate Development Services
S.I.C.: 6531
N.A.I.C.S.: 531390
Thierry Roulet *(Gen Mgr)*

Non-U.S. Subsidiaries:

Acieroid Sa (1)
Avenida de la Granvia n 179
L'Hospitalet de Llobreat, 08908 Barcelona, Spain
Tel.: (34) 932616300
Fax: (34) 932616320
Web Site: www.acieroid.es
Real Estate Development Services
S.I.C.: 6531
N.A.I.C.S.: 531390

Colas Canada Inc (1)
4984 Place De La Savane Bureau 150
Montreal, QC, H4P 2M9, Canada
Tel.: (514) 807-8282
Fax: (514) 223-0568
E-Mail: info@colascanada.ca
Web Site: www.colascanada.ca
Emp.: 12
Roads Construction Engineering Servicesb
S.I.C.: 1611
N.A.I.C.S.: 237310
Louis R. Gabanna *(Pres)*

COLAS CZ, a.s. (1)
Kolbenova 259 9
190 00 Prague, Czech Republic
Tel.: (420) 286003511
Fax: (420) 286003500
E-Mail: colas@colas.cz
Web Site: www.colas.cz
Roads Construction Services
S.I.C.: 1611
N.A.I.C.S.: 237310
Francis Grass *(Gen Mgr)*

Colas Danmark A/S (1)
Fabriksparken 40
2600 Glostrup, Denmark
Tel.: (45) 45989898
Fax: (45) 45830612
E-Mail: colas@colas.dk
Web Site: www.colas.dk
Emp.: 25
Construction Engineering Services
S.I.C.: 8711
N.A.I.C.S.: 541330
Hans Oluf Krog *(Mng Dir)*

Colas Ltd (1)
Wallage Lane
Rowfant, Crawley, West Sussex, RH10 4NF, United Kingdom
Tel.: (44) 1342 711000
Fax: (44) 1342 711099
E-Mail: info@colas.co.uk
Web Site: www.colas.co.uk
Civil Engineering Services
S.I.C.: 1629
N.A.I.C.S.: 237990

ETDE Gabon (1)
BP 305
Libreville, Gabon
Tel.: (241) 76 20 80
Fax: (241) 76 20 98
Web Site: www.etde.fr/pages/fra/implantations.asp?choix=INT
Construction Engineering Services
S.I.C.: 8711
N.A.I.C.S.: 541330

ETDE Hungary Zrt (1)
Pesti ut 1/b
9027 Gyor, Hungary
Tel.: (36) 96 512 772
Fax: (36) 96 512 773
E-Mail: etde@etde.hu
Web Site: www.etde.hu
Emp.: 80
Construction Engineering Services
S.I.C.: 8711
N.A.I.C.S.: 541330
Zsolt Hennel *(Mng Dir)*

Grands Travaux Ocean Indien (GTOI) SA (1)
Z I N 2
BP 32016
97824 Le Port, Reunion
Tel.: (262) 2 62 42 85 85
Fax: (262) 2 62 71 05 21
Web Site: www.gtoi.fr
Roads Construction Engineering Services
S.I.C.: 1611
N.A.I.C.S.: 237310

Karmar SA (1)
6 Wyscigowa Avenue
02-681 Warsaw, Poland
Tel.: (48) 223214400
Fax: (48) 22 321 44 10
Web Site: www.karmar.com.pl
Construction Engineering Services
S.I.C.: 8711
N.A.I.C.S.: 541330
Wlodzimierz Bogiel *(Pres)*
Carlos Suarez *(Co-VP)*
Robert Zoledowski *(Co-VP)*
Damien Lefebvre *(Member-Mgmt Bd)*

Losinger Construction AG (1)
Sagestrasse 76 Case Postale 624
3098 Koniz, Switzerland
Tel.: (41) 584567500
Fax: (41) 584567599
E-Mail: bern@losinger-marazzi.ch
Web Site: www.losinger-marazzi.ch
Emp.: 800
Construction Services
S.I.C.: 1542
N.A.I.C.S.: 236220
Jacky Gillmann *(Mng Dir)*

Marazzi Generalunternehmung AG (1)
Sagestrasse 76
3098 Koniz, Switzerland
Tel.: (41) 58 456 3500
Fax: (41) 58 456 3508
E-Mail: bern@marazzi.ch
Web Site: www.marazzi.ch
Construction Engineering Services
S.I.C.: 8711
N.A.I.C.S.: 541330

Marazzi Holding AG (1)
Worbstrasse 46
Muri, 3074, Switzerland
Tel.: (41) 584563500
Fax: (41) 584563508
Construction Engineering Services
S.I.C.: 8711
N.A.I.C.S.: 541330

Prader Losinger SA (1)
Route De Vissigen 110
Case Postale 4192
1950 Sion, Switzerland
Tel.: (41) 27 203 43 61
Fax: (41) 27 203 43 89
E-Mail: info@praderlosinger.ch
Web Site: www.praderlosinger.ch
Construction Engineering Services
S.I.C.: 8711
N.A.I.C.S.: 541330

Uniservice SA (1)
Rue Du Conseil-General 3
Geneva, 1204, Switzerland
Tel.: (41) 227892421
Fax: (41) 227892827
Construction Engineering Services
S.I.C.: 8711
N.A.I.C.S.: 541330

VSL International Ltd (1)
Saegestrasse 76
Koniz, 3098, Switzerland
Tel.: (41) 584563000
Fax: (41) 584563095
Web Site: www.vsl.com
Construction Engineering Services
S.I.C.: 8711
N.A.I.C.S.: 541330

Warings Construction Group Holding Ltd (1)
Gatcombe House Hilsea
Portsmouth, Hampshire, PO2 0TU, United Kingdom
Tel.: (44) 2392694900
Fax: (44) 2392694948
Construction Engineering Services
S.I.C.: 8711
N.A.I.C.S.: 541330

BOVA FRANCE

Zae Les Grandes Vignes 5 Rue Du Pont De La Breche
95190 Goussainville, Val d'Oise, France
Tel.: (33) 134388940
Sls.: $18,100,000
Emp.: 26
S.I.C.: 5511
N.A.I.C.S.: 441110
Personnel:
Nadine Da Silva *(Mgr-Personnel)*
Board of Directors:
Christian Giraudon

BOVIS HOMES GROUP PLC

The Manor House North Ash Road
New Ash Green
Longfield, Kent, DA3 8HQ, United Kingdom
Tel.: (44) 1474876200
Fax: (44) 1474876201
Web Site: www.bovishomesgroup.co.uk
BVS—(LSE)
Rev.: $672,040,012
Assets: $1,622,406,196
Liabilities: $423,963,559
Net Worth: $1,198,442,637
Earnings: $64,525,052
Emp.: 639
Fiscal Year-end: 12/31/12
Business Description:
Real Estate & Housing Development Services
S.I.C.: 6531
N.A.I.C.S.: 531390
Personnel:
David James Ritchie *(CEO)*
Martin Trevor Digby Palmer *(Sec)*
Board of Directors:
Ian Tyler
Jonathan Hill
Colin Peter Holmes
Alastair Lyons
David James Ritchie
John Anthony Warren

Subsidiary:

Bovis Homes Limited (1)
The Manor House N Ash Rd
New Ash Green Longfield, Longfield, Kent, DA3 8HQ, United Kingdom
Tel.: (44) 1474876200
Fax: (44) 1474876201
E-Mail: info.southeast@bovishomes.co.uk
Web Site: www.bovishomes.co.uk
Emp.: 100
Building Construction Services
S.I.C.: 1522

N.A.I.C.S.: 236116
David Ritchie *(CEO)*

BOW CYCLE & MOTOR COMPANY LTD.

1110 9th Ave SW
Calgary, AB, T2P 1M1, Canada
Tel.: (403) 288-5421
Fax: (403) 286-4014
Web Site: www.bowcycle.com
Year Founded: 1956
Rev.: $15,639,775
Emp.: 35
Business Description:
Motorcycle, Snowmobile, Lawn Mower & ATV Dealers
S.I.C.: 5571
N.A.I.C.S.: 441228
Personnel:
Todd Starchuk *(Mng Partner)*
James Sibthorpe *(Partner)*

BOW PLANNING GROUP INC

5700 ch De La Cote-De-Liesse
H4T 1B1 Montreal, QC, Canada
Tel.: (514) 735-5551
Fax: (514) 735-0751
Web Site: www.bow-group.com
Sales Range: $75-99.9 Million
Emp.: 200
Business Description:
Plastic Pipe & Fittings Manufacturing
S.I.C.: 3084
N.A.I.C.S.: 326122
Personnel:
Pat Chiasson *(Pres)*

BOWA-ELECTRONIC GMBH & CO. KG

Heinrich Hertz Strasse 4 10
72810 Gomaringen, Germany
Tel.: (49) 707260020
Fax: (49) 7072600233
E-Mail: info@bowa.de
Web Site: www.bowa-automotive.com
Year Founded: 1977
Rev.: $41,736,564
Emp.: 188
Business Description:
Automotive Parts Mfr
S.I.C.: 3714
N.A.I.C.S.: 336390
Personnel:
Thomas Krober *(Mng Dir)*

BOWATER BUILDING PRODUCTS LTD.

(d/b/a Bowater Windows)
Water Orton Ln Minworth
Sutton Coldfield, W Midlands, B76 9BW, United Kingdom
Tel.: (44) 1217493000
Fax: (44) 1213523026
Web Site: www.bowaterprojects.com
Year Founded: 1969
Emp.: 400
Business Description:
PVC Window & Door Mfr
S.I.C.: 3089
N.A.I.C.S.: 326199
Personnel:
David Jones *(Mng Dir)*

BOWE SYSTEC AG

Werner-Von-Siemens Strasse 1
D-86159 Augsburg, Germany
Tel.: (49) 82157020
Fax: (49) 8215702234
E-Mail: marketing@boewe-systec.de
Web Site: www.boewe-systec.de
Year Founded: 1945
BSY—(DEU)
Sales Range: $550-599.9 Million
Emp.: 3,578
Business Description:
Cutting & Inserting Systems Mfr
S.I.C.: 3553
N.A.I.C.S.: 333243
Personnel:
Klaus Wendlandt *(CFO & Member-Mgmt Bd)*
Peter Goebel *(Member-Mgmt Bd)*
Supervisory Board of Directors:
Claus D. Bunk
Adolf G. Coenenberg
Gerd Finkbeiner
Roland Hormann
Rolf-Dieter Leister
Hans-Joachim Rohler
Alfred Seifert

Subsidiary:

BOWE CARDTEC GmbH **(1)**
Balhorner Feld 28
D-33106 Paderborn, Germany
Tel.: (49) 5251180860
Fax: (49) 52511808699
E-Mail: info@boewe-cardtec.de
Web Site: www.boewe-cardtec.de
Emp.: 65
Supplier of Plastic Card Personalization Systems & Products
S.I.C.: 3555
N.A.I.C.S.: 333244
Stefan Oing *(Mng Dir)*
Stefan Oeing *(Member-Exec Bd)*

Non-U.S. Subsidiary:

Lasermax Roll Systems AB **(1)**
Langgatan 21
S 341 32 Ljungby, Sweden (100%)
Tel.: (46) 37225600
Fax: (46) 37282837
E-Mail: info@lasermaxroll.se
Web Site: www.lasermaxroll.com
Emp.: 225
Automated Paper Handling, Monitoring & Processing Equipment Mfr
S.I.C.: 3554
N.A.I.C.S.: 333243
AnnaPia Johansson *(CFO)*
Jeff Kewin *(Exec VP-Sls & Mktg)*

U.S. Subsidiary:

Lasermax Roll Systems, Inc. **(2)**
53 3rd Ave
Burlington, MA 01803
Tel.: (781) 229-2266
Fax: (781) 229-0486
E-Mail: info@rollsys.com
Web Site: www.rollsys.com
Emp.: 180
Paper Industry Machinery Mfr
S.I.C.: 3554
N.A.I.C.S.: 333243
Harold Regan *(CFO)*

BOWIM S.A.

ul Niwecka 1 E
41-200 Sosnowiec, Poland
Tel.: (48) 32 392 93 00
Fax: (48) 32 392 93 80
E-Mail: firma@bowim.pl
Web Site: www.bowim.pl
Year Founded: 1995
BOW—(WAR)
Sales Range: $300-349.9 Million
Emp.: 440
Business Description:
Steel Product Distr
S.I.C.: 5051
N.A.I.C.S.: 423510
Personnel:
Feliks Rozek *(Chm-Supervisory Bd)*
Jan Kidala *(Vice Chm-Supervisory Bd)*
Supervisory Board of Directors:
Feliks Rozek
Tadeusz Borysiewicz
Bernadetta Fuchs
Mieczyslaw Sylwester Halk
Jan Kidala
Sobieslaw Szefer
Aleksandra Wodarczyk

Subsidiaries:

Betstal Sp. z o.o. **(1)**
ul Mechanikow 9
44-109 Gliwice, Poland
Tel.: (48) 32 734 55 86
E-Mail: biuro@betstal-zbrojarnia.pl
Web Site: www.betstal.bowim.pl
Iron Rod Mfr
S.I.C.: 3322
N.A.I.C.S.: 331511

Bowim-Podkarpacie Sp. z o.o. **(1)**
ul Cieplownicza 8a
35-322 Rzeszow, Poland
Tel.: (48) 17 852 73 88
E-Mail: rzeszow@bowim.pl
Web Site: www.podkarpacie.bowim.pl
Iron Rod Mfr
S.I.C.: 3321
N.A.I.C.S.: 331511

BOWKER BLACKBURN LTD.

Trident Park
Trident Way, Blackburn, Lancashire, BB1 3NU, United Kingdom
Tel.: (44) 12 5487 2222
Fax: (44) 12 5423 6373
Web Site: www.bowkerbmw.com
Sales Range: $50-74.9 Million
Emp.: 35
Business Description:
New & Used Motor Vehicle Dealer
S.I.C.: 5511
N.A.I.C.S.: 441110
Personnel:
Chris Eccles *(Gen Mgr-Sls)*

BOWLER METCALF LIMITED

Harris Drive
Ottery, 7800 Cape Town, South Africa
Mailing Address:
PO Box 92
Ottery, 7808 Cape Town, South Africa
Tel.: (27) 21 704 2223
Fax: (27) 21 704 2224
E-Mail: investorrelations@bowler.co.za
Web Site: www.bowlermetcalf.co.za
Year Founded: 1972
Rev.: $72,649,792
Assets: $57,400,396
Liabilities: $10,001,171
Net Worth: $47,399,225
Earnings: $6,418,841
Emp.: 603
Fiscal Year-end: 06/30/13
Business Description:
Plastic Product Mfr & Whslr
S.I,C.: 3089
N.A.I.C.S.: 326199
Personnel:
Paul Friederich Sass *(CEO)*
Grant Andrew Bohler *(CFO)*
Louis Vern Rowles *(Sec)*
Board of Directors:
Brian James Frost
Grant Andrew Bohler
Michael Brain
Sarah Jane Gillett
Finlay Craig MacGillivray
Michael Allan Olds
Paul Friederich Sass

BOWLEVEN PLC

The Cube 45 Leith Street
Edinburgh, EH1 3AT, United Kingdom
Tel.: (44) 131 524 5678
Fax: (44) 131 524 5690
E-Mail: info@bowleven.com
Web Site: www.bowleven.co.uk
BO2—(AIM DEU)
Rev.: $516,000
Assets: $585,587,000
Liabilities: $15,568,000
Net Worth: $570,019,000
Earnings: ($11,081,000)
Emp.: 74
Fiscal Year-end: 06/30/13
Business Description:
Oil & Gas Exploration Services
S.I.C.: 1389
N.A.I.C.S.: 213112
Personnel:
Kevin Hart *(CEO)*
Peter G. Wilson *(Gen Counsel & Sec)*
Board of Directors:
Ronnie Hanna
David Clarkson
Caroline Cook
Kevin Hart
Tim Sullivan
Chief Tabetando
Philip Tracy
Ed Willett
Peter G. Wilson
Legal Counsel:
Shepherd & Wedderburn LLP
1 Exchange Crescent Conference Sq
Edinburgh, United Kingdom

BOWMAN POWER GROUP LTD

Ocean Quay Belvidere Rd
Southampton, Hants, SO14 5QY, United Kingdom
Tel.: (44) 23 8023 6700
Fax: (44) 23 8035 2596
Web Site: www.bowmanpower.com
Year Founded: 2004
Sales Range: $10-24.9 Million
Emp.: 62
Business Description:
Power Generator Mfr
S.I.C.: 3621
N.A.I.C.S.: 335312
Personnel:
Tony Davies *(Founder)*
Toby King *(CEO)*
David Lamb *(CFO)*
Jonathon McGuire *(CTO)*
Board of Directors:
Peter Ward
Tony Davies
Wolfgang Hanrieder
Tim Lewin
Lars McBride
Arild Nerdrum

BOWMORE EXPLORATION LTD.

2140 Saint Mathieu Street
Montreal, QC, H3H 2J4, Canada
Tel.: (514) 861-4441
Fax: (514) 861-1333
E-Mail: info@bowmorexploration.com
Web Site: www.bowmorexploration.com
Year Founded: 2000
BOW—(TSXV)
Assets: $7,711,746
Liabilities: $1,790,123
Net Worth: $5,921,624
Earnings: ($1,868,499)
Fiscal Year-end: 12/31/12
Business Description:
Gold Exploration & Development Services
S.I.C.: 1041
N.A.I.C.S.: 212221
Personnel:
Paul A. Dumas *(Pres & CEO)*
Martin Nicoletti *(CFO)*
Richard Grass *(Sec)*
Board of Directors:
Claude Charron
Paul A. Dumas
Eduardo Perlicz

Bowmore Exploration Ltd.—(Continued)

Sean Roosen
Robert Wares

Legal Counsel:
Gowling Lafleur Henderson LLP
Suite 2300-550 Burrard Street
Vancouver, BC, Canada

Transfer Agent:
CIBC Mellon Trust Company
Montreal, QC, Canada

BOWOOD ENERGY INC.
(See Under LGX Oil + Gas Inc.)

BOX UK LIMITED
6a Poland Street
London, W1F 8PT, United Kingdom
Tel.: (44) 20 7439 1900
Fax: (44) 20 7681 1889
E-Mail: info@boxuk.com
Web Site: www.boxuk.com
Year Founded: 1998
Sales Range: $1-9.9 Million
Emp.: 50

Business Description:
Software Publisher
S.I.C.: 7372
N.A.I.C.S.: 511210

Personnel:
Benno Wasserstein *(Mng Dir)*

Division:

Box UK Limited (1)
Westgate Court Westgate Street
Cardiff, CF10 1DD, United Kingdom
Tel.: (44) 29 2022 8822
Fax: (44) 29 2022 8820
Software Publisher
S.I.C.: 7372
N.A.I.C.S.: 511210

BOXXER GOLD CORP.
Suite 650 340 - 12 Ave S W
Calgary, AB, T2R 1L5, Canada
Tel.: (403) 264-4811
Fax: (403) 264-2920
Toll Free: (855) 444-4811
Web Site: www.boxxergold.com
BXX—(TSXV)
Assets: $11,956,625
Liabilities: $199,926
Net Worth: $11,756,699
Earnings: ($528,931)
Fiscal Year-end: 12/31/12

Business Description:
Mineral Exploration Services
S.I.C.: 1081
N.A.I.C.S.: 213114

Personnel:
Elmer B. Stewart *(Pres & CEO)*
Brian C. Harder *(CFO)*
John L. Maslanyk *(CIO & VP)*

Board of Directors:
William T. Kilbourne
Denis Pelletier
Gerald Lynn Roe
Elmer B. Stewart
Mary Webster
David Yancie

Transfer Agent:
Olympia Trust Company
2300 125 9 Avenue SW
Calgary, AB, Canada

BOYAA INTERACTIVE INTERNATIONAL LTD
Floor 9 B-C Section Building No 1001
Zhongshan Road
Shenzhen, 518000, China
Tel.: (86) 755 8663 0020
Web Site: www.boyaa.com
434—(HKG)
Sales Range: $75-99.9 Million
Emp.: 540

Business Description:
Online Game Publisher
S.I.C.: 2741
N.A.I.C.S.: 511199

Personnel:
Wei Zhang *(Chm & CEO)*

BOYD GROUP INCOME FUND
3570 Portage Avenue
Winnipeg, MB, R3K 0Z8, Canada
Tel.: (204) 895-1244
Fax: (204) 895-1283
E-Mail: info@boydgroup.com
Web Site: www.boydgroup.com
Year Founded: 2002
BYD.UN—(OTC TSX)
Sls.: $431,826,338
Assets: $223,216,368
Liabilities: $181,861,023
Net Worth: $41,355,345
Earnings: $7,018,945
Emp.: 3,280
Fiscal Year-end: 12/31/12

Business Description:
Unincorporated, Open-Ended Mutual Fund Trust
S.I.C.: 6722
N.A.I.C.S.: 525910

Personnel:
Allan F. Davis *(Chm)*
Brock W. Bulbuck *(Pres & CEO)*
Dan Dott *(CFO & VP)*
Kevin Comrie *(CMO)*
Eddie Cheskis *(CEO-Glass & Chief Strategy Officer-US Ops)*
Timothy O'Day *(Pres/COO-US Ops)*
Eric Danberg *(Pres-Ops-Canada)*
Rex Dunn *(Pres-True2Form Collision Repair Centers)*
Clark Plucinski *(Exec VP-Sls & Mktg-True2Form Collision Repair Centers)*
Gary Bunce *(Sr VP-Mktg & Sls-US Ops)*

Legal Counsel:
Thompson Dorfman Sweatman
2200 201 Portage Avenue
Winnipeg, MB, Canada

Transfer Agent:
Valiant Trust Company
606 4th Street SW Suite 310
Calgary, AB, T2P 1T1, Canada
Tel.: (403) 233-2801
Fax: (403) 233-2857

Subsidiary:

The Boyd Group Inc. (1)
3570 Portage Ave
Winnipeg, MB, Canada MB
Tel.: (204) 895-1244
Fax: (204) 895-1283
E-Mail: info@boydgroup.com
Emp.: 50
Collision Repair Facility Operator
S.I.C.: 7539
N.A.I.C.S.: 811198
Brock W. Bulbuck *(Pres & CEO)*
Dan Dott *(CFO & VP)*

U.S. Subsidiary:

The Boyd Group (U.S.) Inc. (2)
8250 N Skokie Blvd
Skokie, IL 60077
Tel.: (847) 679-0510
Automotive Repair & Maintenance Services
S.I.C.: 7538
N.A.I.C.S.: 811111
Timothy O'Day *(Pres & COO)*
Eddie Cheskis *(Chief Strategy Officer-US Ops & CEO-US Glass)*

Subsidiary:

The Gerber Group, Inc. (3)
8250 N Skokie Blvd
Skokie, IL 60077 DE
Tel.: (847) 679-0510
Fax: (847) 679-0740
E-Mail:
Holding Company; Automotive Glass & Collision Repair Services
S.I.C.: 6719
N.A.I.C.S.: 551112
Gary Bunce *(Sr VP-Sls-Mktg)*

Subsidiaries:

Cars Collision Center, LLC (4)
8250 N Skokie Blvd
Skokie, IL 60077 IL
Tel.: (847) 679-0510
Fax: (847) 679-0740
Web Site: www.gerbercollision.com
Sales Range: $50-74.9 Million
Automotive Repair Services
S.I.C.: 7532
N.A.I.C.S.: 811121
Larry Jaskowiak *(VP-Ops)*

Subsidiaries:

Gerber Collision & Glass (Kansas), Inc. (5)
5617 W Kellogg St
Wichita, KS 67209
Tel.: (316) 945-7007
Fax: (316) 945-1578
Toll Free: (877) 743-7237
Web Site: www.gerbercollision.com
Emp.: 7
Automotive Repair & Maintenance Services
S.I.C.: 7538
N.A.I.C.S.: 811111
Russell Southards *(Gen Mgr)*

Pearl Auto Body - Denver, Inc. (5)
2228 S Colorado Blvd
Denver, CO 80222 CO
Tel.: (303) 691-2639
Fax: (303) 758-7989
E-Mail: denver@pearlautobody.com
Web Site: www.pearlautobody.com
Sales Range: $1-9.9 Million
Auto Body Repair Services
S.I.C.: 7532
N.A.I.C.S.: 811121
Dave Call *(Gen Mgr)*

True2Form Collision Repair Centers, Inc. (5)
4853 Galaxy Pkwy Ste E
Cleveland, OH 44128
Tel.: (216) 755-1191
Fax: (216) 755-1192
Toll Free: (888) 223-8783
E-Mail: corp@true2form.com
Web Site: www.true2form.com
Emp.: 12
Automobiles Collision Repair Services
S.I.C.: 7538
N.A.I.C.S.: 811111
Rex Dunn *(Pres)*

Subsidiary:

True2form Collision Repair Centers, LLC (6)
4853 Galaxy Pkwy Ste E
Cleveland, OH 44128 OH
Tel.: (216) 755-1191
Fax: (216) 378-0586
Web Site: www.true2form.com
Sls.: $40,000,000
Emp.: 15
Automotive Repair Services
S.I.C.: 7532
N.A.I.C.S.: 811121
Rex Dunn *(Pres)*

Glass America, Inc. (4)
150 N Michigan Ave Ste 1580
Chicago, IL 60601 DE
Tel.: (312) 781-6450
E-Mail: company.info@glassusa.com
Web Site: www.glassusa.com
Sales Range: $25-49.9 Million
Automotive Glass Replacement Shops
S.I.C.: 7536
N.A.I.C.S.: 811122
Scott Wills *(CFO)*

BOYNER BUYUK MAGAZACILIK A.S.
Buyukdere Caddesi Noramin Is Merkezi No 237 E Maslak
Istanbul, Turkey
Tel.: (90) 2123357500
Fax: (90) 2122766880
E-Mail: info@boyner.com.tr
Web Site: www.boyner.com.tr
BOYNR—(IST)
Sales Range: $350-399.9 Million
Emp.: 2,595

Business Description:
Department Store Operator
S.I.C.: 5311
N.A.I.C.S.: 452112

Personnel:
R. Asly Karadeniz *(Gen Mgr)*

BOYUAN CONSTRUCTION GROUP, INC.
Boyuan Building No 6 East Road
Jiaxing, Zheijiang, China 314201
Tel.: (86) 57385581278
Fax: (86) 57385580288
E-Mail: renshu@zjboyuan.com
Web Site: www.boyuangroup.com
BOY—(TSX)
Rev.: $209,207,276
Assets: $194,346,927
Liabilities: $107,171,270
Net Worth: $87,175,657
Earnings: $7,945,727
Emp.: 5,000
Fiscal Year-end: 06/30/13

Business Description:
Construction Services
S.I.C.: 1542
N.A.I.C.S.: 236220

Personnel:
Cai Liang Shou *(Founder, Chm, Pres & CEO)*
Paul F. Y. Law *(CFO)*
Shu Ren *(Sec)*

Board of Directors:
Cai Liang Shou
John Duffy
Francis Nyon Seng Leong
Manhong Liu
Fang Lixin
Shu Ren
Wei Tang

Transfer Agent:
Computershare Trust Company of Canada
600-530 8th Avenue SW
Calgary, AB, Canada

BOZLU HOLDING
Mongeri Binasi 19 Mayis Mahallesi Dr Sevket Bey Sokak No 5
Sisli, Istanbul, 34370, Turkey
Tel.: (90) 212 231 0303
Fax: (90) 212 219 8222
Web Site: www.bozluholding.com.tr

Business Description:
Holding Company
S.I.C.: 6719
N.A.I.C.S.: 551112

Personnel:
Sukru Bozluolcay *(Chm & CEO)*
Aydin Kucuk *(Gen Mgr & Chm-Tech Grp)*
Ismail Dernek *(Chm-Health Grp)*

Holdings:

Epsilon Electronics Industry and Trade Inc. (1)
Mongeri Binasi 19 Mayis Mahallesi Dr Sevket Bey Sokak No 5
Sisli, 34360 Istanbul, Turkey
Tel.: (90) 212 219 56 57
Fax: (90) 212 219 42 88
E-Mail: info@epsilonelektronik.com
Web Site: www.epsilonelektronik.com
Sales, Marketing & Maintenance in Nuclear Medicine & Radiotherapy
S.I.C.: 5046
N.A.I.C.S.: 423440

MNT Healthcare Services and Trade Inc. (1)
Mongeri Binasi 19 Mayis Mahallesi Dr Sevket Bey Sokak No 5
Sisli, 34360 Istanbul, Turkey

Tel.: (90) 212 444 4668
Fax: (90) 212 219 82 22
Web Site: www.mnt.com.tr
Nuclear Medicine Services
S.I.C.: 8734
N.A.I.C.S.: 541380

Molecular Imaging Industry and Trading Co. Inc. (1)
Mongeri Binasi 19 Mayis Mahallesi Dr Sevket Bey Sokak No 5
34360 Istanbul, Turkey
Tel.: (90) 212 231 0303
Fax: (90) 212 219 8222
E-Mail: info@molimg.com
Web Site: www.molimg.com
Molecular Medicine Research, Development & Production
S.I.C.: 8731
N.A.I.C.S.: 541712
Dilek Turhan *(Branch Mgr)*

Solar Enerji Teknolojileri Ve Metal Sanayi Ticaret A.S. (1)
NOSAB Ihlamur Cd No 26
Nilufer, Bursa, 16140, Turkey
Tel.: (90) 224 411 99 49
Fax: (90) 224 411 24 04
E-Mail: info@solentek.com.tr
Web Site: www.solentek.com.tr
Emp.: 10
Solar Energy Technologies & Contract Services for Metal Industry
S.I.C.: 3499
N.A.I.C.S.: 332999
Rachel Mills *(Gen Mgr)*

Varinak Oncological Systems Sales and Service Inc. (1)
19 Mayis District Dr Sevket Bey Street No 5
Istanbul, Turkey
Tel.: (90) 212 444 8677
Fax: (90) 212 219 56 60
Web Site: www.varinak.com
Medical Equipment Distr
S.I.C.: 5047
N.A.I.C.S.: 423450

Joint Venture:

Epsilon Landauer Dozimetri Teknolojileri Sanayi ve Ticaret A.S. (1)
19 Mayis Mahallesi Dr Sevket Bey Sk No 5
Sisli, Istanbul, Turkey
Tel.: (90) 212 247 65 99
Fax: (90) 212 219 42 88
E-Mail: info@epsilonlandauer.com.tr
Web Site: www.epsilonlandauer.com.tr
Radiation Dose Measurement & Tracking Equipment Mfr & Services
S.I.C.: 3829
N.A.I.C.S.: 334519

B.P. MARSH & PARTNERS PLC

2nd Floor 36 Broadway
London, SW1H 0BH, United Kingdom
Tel.: (44) 2072333112
Fax: (44) 2072220294
E-Mail: enquiries@bpmarsh.co.uk
Web Site: www.bpmarsh.co.uk
BPM—(AIM)
Rev.: $12,989,660
Assets: $101,494,651
Liabilities: $13,915,124
Net Worth: $87,579,527
Earnings: $8,965,629
Emp.: 16
Fiscal Year-end: 01/31/13

Business Description:
Financial Services
S.I.C.: 6726
N.A.I.C.S.: 525990

Personnel:
Brian Marsh *(Chm)*
Sinead O'Haire *(Sec)*

Board of Directors:
Brian Marsh
Stephen Clarke
Natasha Dunbar
Camilla Kenyon
Philip Mortlock
Jonathan Newman
Campbell Scoones
Daniel Topping

Legal Counsel:
Michelmores LLP
Woodwater House Pynes Hill
EX25WR Exeter, United Kingdom

BP PLASTICS HOLDING BHD.

5A Jalan Wawasan 2 Kawasan Perindustrian Sri Gading
83300 Batu Pahat, Johor, Malaysia
Tel.: (60) 74557633
Fax: (60) 74557699
E-Mail: enquiry@bpplas.com
Web Site: www.bpplas.com
BPPLAS—(KLS)
Rev.: $72,235,470
Assets: $63,303,306
Liabilities: $13,935,290
Net Worth: $49,368,016
Earnings: $3,169,076
Emp.: 330
Fiscal Year-end: 12/31/12

Business Description:
Plastic Mfr
S.I.C.: 2671
N.A.I.C.S.: 326112

Personnel:
Chun Yow Lim *(Chm & Mng Dir)*
Siew Chuan Chua *(Sec)*

Board of Directors:
Chun Yow Lim
Chin Liong Boo
Shiow Hoe Hey
Chin Koon Koh
Kim Hock Lim
See Khim Tan

BP PLC

1 Saint James's Square
London, SW1Y 4PD, United Kingdom
Tel.: (44) 2074965311
Fax: (44) 2074964573
E-Mail: ir@bp.com
Web Site: www.bp.com
Year Founded: 1909
BP—(EUR LSE NYSE)
Rev.: $396,217,000,000
Assets: $305,690,000,000
Liabilities: $175,283,000,000
Net Worth: $130,407,000,000
Earnings: $23,758,000,000
Emp.: 83,900
Fiscal Year-end: 12/31/13

Business Description:
Holding Company; Petroleum & Natural Gas Exploration, Drilling, Extraction, Refinement, Pipeline Transportation & Distribution; Petroleum Products Mfr; Alternative Energy Developer; Retail Gasoline Service Station Franchisor
S.I.C.: 6719
N.A.I.C.S.: 551112

Personnel:
Carl-Henric Svanberg *(Chm)*
Mike Petrucci *(Pres & CEO-BP Solar)*
Robert W. Dudley *(Grp CEO)*
Brian Gilvary *(CFO)*
Mike Gibbs *(CIO)*
John Graham *(Pres-BP Wind Energy)*
Iain C. Conn *(CEO-Mktg & Refining)*
H. Lamar McKay *(CEO-Upstream)*
Rupert Bondy *(Grp Gen Counsel)*
Mark Bly *(Exec VP-Safety & Operational Risk)*
Mike C. Daly *(Exec VP-Exploration)*
Bob Fryar *(Exec VP-Safety & Operational Risk)*
Dev Sanyal *(Exec VP)*
Rashid Javanshir *(Sr VP-Strategy & Integration)*

Board of Directors:
Carl-Henric Svanberg
Paul M. Anderson
Frank L. Bowman
Antony Burgmans
Cynthia Blum Carroll
William M. Castell
Iain C. Conn
George A. David
Ian E. L. Davis
Ann Dowling
Robert W. Dudley
Brian Gilvary
Phuthuma Freedom Nhleko
Andrew B. Shilston

Transfer Agent:
JPMorgan Chase Bank, N.A.
1 Chase Manhattan Plaza Floor 58
New York, NY 10005

Subsidiaries:

Air BP Limited (1)
Sunbury Business Park
Chertsey Road, Sunbury, Middlesex, TW16 7LN, United Kingdom
Tel.: (44) 1932762000
Fax: (44) 1932739308
Sales Range: $300-349.9 Million
Aviation Fuel, Lubricants & Specialty Products Supplier
S.I.C.: 5172
N.A.I.C.S.: 424720
Tony Hayward *(CEO)*

U.S. Subsidiaries:

Air BP Americas (2)
150 W Warrenville Rd Bldg 200
Naperville, IL 60563
Tel.: (888) 274-3578
E-Mail: AirBPGANA@bp.com
Web Site: www.bp.com
Aviation Fuel Distr
S.I.C.: 5172
N.A.I.C.S.: 424720

Air BP Puerto Rico (2)
Base Muniz Area/Fuel Terminal
Carolina, PR 00979
Tel.: (787) 253-2100
Fax: (787) 253-2190
Web Site: www.bp.com
Emp.: 35
Petroleum Product Distr
S.I.C.: 5172
N.A.I.C.S.: 424720
Steve Hermann *(Gen Mgr)*

Non-U.S. Subsidiaries:

Air BP Argentina S.A. (2)
Av Alicia Moreau de Justo 140
Piso 3, Buenos Aires, C1107AAD, Argentina
Tel.: (54) 41145000
Web Site: www.bp.com
Emp.: 11
Petroleum Products Whslr
S.I.C.: 5172
N.A.I.C.S.: 424720

Air BP Brasil S.A. (2)
Ave Rouxinol 55 5th Floor
Moema Office Tower, 04516 000 Sao Paulo, Brazil
Tel.: (55) 1130549306
Fax: (55) 30549313
Web Site: www.bp.com
Storage & Distribution of Aviation Fuels & Lubricants
S.I.C.: 5172
N.A.I.C.S.: 424720
Ana Campos *(Mgr-Fin)*

Air BP Canada Limited (2)
5915 Airport Rd Ste 820
Mississauga, ON, L4V 1T1, Canada ON (100%)
Tel.: (905) 671-4568
Fax: (905) 671-1617
Web Site: www.airbp.com
Emp.: 5
Petroleum Fuel & Lubricant Distr
S.I.C.: 5172
N.A.I.C.S.: 424720
Valerio Ferro *(Pres)*

Air BP China (2)
2101-03 21/F R&F Center 10 Hua Xia Road
Guangzhou, China 510623
Tel.: (86) 20 81136888
Fax: (86) 20 81136899
Web Site: www.bp.com
Aviation Fuel Distr
S.I.C.: 5172
N.A.I.C.S.: 424720

Air BP Eastern Mediterranian Ltd (2)
41-49 Ayiou Nicolaou Street Nimeli Court
2nd Floor Office 27
Engomi, 2408 Nicosia, Cyprus
Tel.: (357) 2236 2300
Fax: (357) 2265 8848
Web Site: www.bp.com
Emp.: 50
Aviation Fuel Distr
S.I.C.: 5172
N.A.I.C.S.: 424720
Pambos Charalambous *(Gen Mgr)*

Air BP Italia S.p.A. (2)
Via Lazio 20/C - Int 4
00187 Rome, Italy
Tel.: (39) 06 42034440
Fax: (39) 06 42013021
Web Site: www.bp.com
Emp.: 15
Petroleum Product Distr
S.I.C.: 5172
N.A.I.C.S.: 424720

Air BP Moscow (2)
Novinsky Blvd 8 Floor 18
121099 Moscow, Russia
Tel.: (7) 495 7876037
Fax: (7) 495 7876026
Web Site: www.bp.com
Aviation Fuel Distr
S.I.C.: 5172
N.A.I.C.S.: 424720

AIR BP Sales Romania SRL (2)
Str Aurel Vlaicu nr 59 Aeroportul International Henri Coanda Bucuresti
075100 Otopeni, Ilfov, Romania
Tel.: (40) 21 201 47 48
Fax: (40) 21 201 47 49
E-Mail: office@airbp.ro
Emp.: 21
Aviation Fuel Distr
S.I.C.: 5172
N.A.I.C.S.: 424720
Cristian Savuica *(Gen Mgr)*

Air BP Sweden AB (2)
Sankt Goeransgatan 57
PO Box 8107
104 20 Stockholm, Sweden
Tel.: (46) 87722320
Fax: (46) 87722321
E-Mail: airbpsweden@bp.com
Web Site: www.airbp.com
Emp.: 15
Aviation Fuel, Lubricants & Specialty Products Supplier
S.I.C.: 5172
N.A.I.C.S.: 424720
Peter Lindenmo *(Pres)*

Air BP Switzerland (2)
Baarerstrasse 139
6302 Zug, Switzerland
Tel.: (41) 58 456 92 50
Fax: (41) 58 456 95 55
Web Site: www.bp.com
Aviation Fuel Distr
S.I.C.: 5172
N.A.I.C.S.: 424720

BP Alternative Energy International Ltd. (1)
Chertsey Road
Sunbury-on-Thames, TW16 7LN, United Kingdom
Tel.: (44) 19 3276 2000
Fax: (44) 19 3276 2999
Electric Power Generation Services
S.I.C.: 4911
N.A.I.C.S.: 221118

BP Capital Markets plc (1)
Breakspear Park Breakspear Way
Hemel Hempstead, HP2 4UL, United Kingdom
Tel.: (44) 14 4223 2323
Fax: (44) 14 4222 5225
Investment Management Services
S.I.C.: 6211
N.A.I.C.S.: 523999
Gary Admans *(Gen Mgr)*

BP plc—(Continued)

Non-U.S. Subsidiary:

Yangtze River Acetyls Co. Ltd. (2)
27F Metropolitian Plaza 68 Zourong Rd
Yuzhong District
Chongqing, 400010, China
Tel.: (86) 2363810694
Fax: (86) 2363810294
Web Site: www.bp.com
Emp.: 200
Inorganic Chemicals Mfr
S.I.C.: 2819
N.A.I.C.S.: 325180
Daihong Yuan *(Gen Mgr)*

BP Chemicals Ltd. (1)
1 St James Sq
London, SW1Y 4PD, United Kingdom UK
Tel.: (44) 2074964000 (100%)
Telex: 266883
Fax: (44) 2079485000
Web Site: www.bp.com
Emp.: 200
Chemicals Mfr & Distr
S.I.C.: 5169
N.A.I.C.S.: 424690

BP Exploration Operating Company Limited (1)
Gathering Station Thrashers Lane
Corfe Castle, Wareham, Dorset, BH20 5JR, United Kingdom
Tel.: (44) 1929 476 190
Fax: (44) 1929 476 072
Web Site: www.bp.com
Holding Company; Oil & Gas Exploration
S.I.C.: 6719
N.A.I.C.S.: 551112

Subsidiaries:

BP Exploration Company Limited (2)
Chertsey Rd
Sunbury-on-Thames, Mddx, TW16 7LN, United Kingdom (100%)
Tel.: (44) 1932 762000
Fax: (44) 1932 762999
Web Site: www.bp.com
Emp.: 200
Exploration for & Production of Oil & Gas
S.I.C.: 1311
N.A.I.C.S.: 211111
Peter Denis Sutherland *(Chm)*

BP (2)
124 Welhead Ave Stony Wood Park
Dyce, Aberdeen, AB21 7PB, United Kingdom (100%)
Tel.: (44) 1224832000
Fax: (44) 1224832550
Web Site: www.bp.com
Emp.: 700
Petroleum Exploration & Production
S.I.C.: 1311
N.A.I.C.S.: 211111
Trevor Garlick *(Pres-North Sea Reg)*

Non-U.S. Subsidiaries:

BP Exploration (Faroes) Limited (2)
Ground Floor 640 e/f
Skansavegur 1, Torshavn, Faroe Islands
Tel.: (298) 353130
Web Site: www.bp.com
Oil & Gas Exploration
S.I.C.: 1311
N.A.I.C.S.: 211111

BP Exploration Operating Co. Ltd. (2)
Villa A15 An Phu Compound
District 2, Ho Chi Minh City, Vietnam
Tel.: (84) 838999375
Fax: (84) 838999391
Web Site: www.bp.com
Emp.: 187
Oil & Gas Exploration & Production
S.I.C.: 1311
N.A.I.C.S.: 211111

BP Global Investments Ltd. (1)
20 Canada Square
London, E14 5NJ, United Kingdom
Tel.: (44) 20 7948 4000
Investment Management Services
S.I.C.: 6211
N.A.I.C.S.: 523999

BP International Ltd. (1)
20 Canada Square Canary Wharf
London, E14 5NJ, United Kingdom (100%)
Tel.: (44) 2074964000
Fax: (44) 2079485000
Web Site: www.bpintl.com
Emp.: 200
Integrated Oil Operations
S.I.C.: 1311
N.A.I.C.S.: 211111

BP Marine Limited (1)
Sunbury Business Park Building D First Floor
Chertsey Road, Sunbury-on-Thames, Middlesex, TW16 7LN, United Kingdom
Tel.: (44) 1932762000
Fax: (44) 1932762999
E-Mail: helpdesk.bpmarine@bp.com
Web Site: www.bpmarine.com
Sales Range: $50-74.9 Million
Supplier of Fuels, Lubricants & Technical Services to the Marine Industry
S.I.C.: 5172
N.A.I.C.S.: 424720

Non-U.S. Unit:

BP Marine (2)
Hasselager Centervej 15
8560 Viby, Denmark
Tel.: (45) 80889499
Fax: (45) 102491133
Supplier of Fuels, Lubricants & Technical Services to the Marine Industry
S.I.C.: 5172
N.A.I.C.S.: 424720

BP Oil U.K. (1)
Witan Gate House 500 600 Witan Gate
Milton Keynes, MK9 1ES, United Kingdom UK
Tel.: (44) 1908853000 (100%)
Fax: (44) 1908853999
Web Site: www.bp.com
Emp.: 1,500
Refining & Marketing Services
S.I.C.: 2911
N.A.I.C.S.: 324110

Joint Venture:

British Pipeline Agency Ltd. (2)
5-7 Alexandra Road
Hemel Hempstead, Herts, HP2 5BS, United Kingdom UK
Tel.: (44) 1442242200
Fax: (44) 1442214077
E-Mail: business@bpa.co.uk
Web Site: www.bpa.co.uk
Emp.: 100
Gas Pipelines Operator & Engineering Services; Owned 50% by Shell U.K. Ltd. & 50% by BP Oil U.K.
S.I.C.: 1629
N.A.I.C.S.: 237120
Peter Davis *(Mng Dir & Gen Mgr)*

Non-U.S. Subsidiary:

Duckhams Oils Ireland Limited (2)
Unit 1 Site 9 Northwest Business Park
Ballycoolin Blanchardstown, Dublin, 15, Ireland
Tel.: (353) 1 885 2150
Fax: (353) 1 824 2071
Web Site: www.bp.com
Emp.: 27
Oil & Lubricants Marketing
S.I.C.: 5172
N.A.I.C.S.: 424720

Castrol Limited (1)
Wakefield House Pipers Way
Swindon, SN3 1RE, United Kingdom UK
Tel.: (44) 1793512712
Web Site: www.castrol.com
Emp.: 400
Lubricant & Specialist Chemical Mfr & Distr Import Export
S.I.C.: 2992
N.A.I.C.S.: 324191
Mike Johnson *(CEO)*

Subsidiaries:

Castrol Overseas Ltd. (2)
Wakefield House
Pipers Way, Swindon, Wiltshire, SN3 1RE, United Kingdom
Tel.: (44) 1793512712
Fax: (44) 1793513506
Web Site: www.castrol.com
Emp.: 380
Lubricant & Specialist Chemical Mfr & Distr
S.I.C.: 2992
N.A.I.C.S.: 324191
Mick Johnson *(VP)*

Castrol (U.K.) Limited (2)
Wakefield House
Pipers Way, Swindon, Wiltshire, SN3 1RE, United Kingdom (100%)
Tel.: (44) 793511521
Fax: (44) 1793513506
Web Site: www.castrol.co.uk
Emp.: 700
Lubricant & Specialist Chemical Mfr & Distr
S.I.C.: 2992
N.A.I.C.S.: 324191
Mike Johnson *(VP)*

Lubricants UK Ltd (2)
Wakefield House
Pipers Way, Swindon, Wiltshire, SN3 1RE, United Kingdom (100%)
Tel.: (44) 1793511521
Fax: (44) 1793513506
Web Site: www.castrol.com
Sales Range: $500-549.9 Million
Emp.: 300
Lubricant & Petroleum Product Mfr
S.I.C.: 2992
N.A.I.C.S.: 324191
Paul Watman *(VP)*

U.S. Subsidiary:

Remet Corporation (2)
210 Commons Rd
Utica, NY 13502-6300 NY
Tel.: (315) 797-8700
Fax: (315) 797-4477
E-Mail: info@remet.com
Web Site: www.remet.com
Emp.: 50
Mfr. of Equipments for Chemicals and Heavy Industrial
S.I.C.: 5169
N.A.I.C.S.: 424690
John Paraszczak *(Pres)*

Non-U.S. Subsidiaries:

BP France Lubrifiants Industriels & Services (2)
Immeuble Le Cervier 12 Avenue des Beguines Cergy Saint Christophe
95688 Cergy-Pontoise, France
Tel.: (33) 1 34 22 40 00
Fax: (33) 1 34 22 44 17
Web Site: www.castrol.com
Emp.: 300
Lubricant Mfr & Distr
S.I.C.: 2992
N.A.I.C.S.: 324191
Anne-Marie Redon *(Mgr-Customer Svc)*

BP Fuels & Lubricants (2)
Drammensveien 167
PO Box 153
0212 Oslo, Norway (100%)
Tel.: (47) 22511220
Fax: (47) 22511270
E-Mail: marineorder@castrol.com
Web Site: www.castrol.com
Emp.: 35
Marketing of Lubricating Oils
S.I.C.: 5172
N.A.I.C.S.: 424720
Jarle Myrbo *(Gen Mgr)*

BP Korea Ltd. (2)
3 F Yousung Bldg 830-67 Yeoksam Dong
Kangnam Ku, Seoul, 135 936, Korea (South) (100%)
Tel.: (82) 25594002
Fax: (82) 25579402
Web Site: www.bp.com
Emp.: 50
Lubricants Distr
S.I.C.: 5172
N.A.I.C.S.: 424720

Subsidiary:

BP Korea Marketing Ltd (3)
2nd Fl Woojin Building 76-4 Jamwon Dong
Seochu gu, Seoul, 137 909, Korea (South)
Tel.: (82) 234793800
Fax: (82) 234793981
Web Site: www.bp.com
Emp.: 45
Petroleum & Petroleum Products Whslr
S.I.C.: 5172
N.A.I.C.S.: 424720

BP Southern Africa (Pty). Ltd. (2)
10 Junction Ave Parktown
Johannesburg, 2193, South Africa (100%)
Tel.: (27) 11 488 5111
Fax: (27) 11 643 7269
Web Site: www.castrol.com
Emp.: 100
Lubricants Distr & Developer
S.I.C.: 5172
N.A.I.C.S.: 424720
Priscillah Mabelane *(CEO)*
Alph Ngapo *(COO)*

Castrol Australia Pty. Ltd. (2)
132 Mccredie Rd
Guildford, NSW, 2161, Australia AU
Tel.: (61) 297954800 (100%)
Fax: (61) 297954814
E-Mail: info@castrol.com.au
Web Site: www.castrol.com.au
Emp.: 100
Lubricants Distr
S.I.C.: 5172
N.A.I.C.S.: 424720
Bratt Davis *(Gen Mgr)*

Castrol Austria GmbH (2)
IZ NOE SUED Strasse 6
Postfach 104
2355 Wiener Neudorf, Austria (100%)
Tel.: (43) 22366950
Fax: (43) 48000
E-Mail: slx@castrol.com
Web Site: www.castrol.at/
Emp.: 220
Lubricants Distr
S.I.C.: 5172
N.A.I.C.S.: 424720
Gustav Trubatsch *(Pres)*

Castrol Brasil Limitada (2)
Avenue Tambore 448
Alphaville, Barueri, SP, CEP 06460-000, Brazil (100%)
Tel.: (55) 11 4133 7899
Web Site: www.castrol.com
Emp.: 25
Lubricants Distr
S.I.C.: 5172
N.A.I.C.S.: 424720

Castrol Canada Inc. (2)
3620 Lakeshore Blvd W
Toronto, ON, M8W 1P2, Canada (100%)
Tel.: (416) 201-0844
Fax: (416) 252-7315
Toll Free: (800) 462-0835
E-Mail: wakefieldorders@wakefieldcanada.ca
Web Site: www.wakefieldcanada.ca
Emp.: 150
Lubricants Distr
S.I.C.: 5172
N.A.I.C.S.: 424720

Castrol Chile SA (2)
Eliodoro Yanez 1572
Santiago, 6640659, Chile (100%)
Tel.: (56) 22358444
Fax: (56) 22356070
Web Site: www.castrol.com
Emp.: 60
Lubricants Distr
S.I.C.: 5172
N.A.I.C.S.: 424720

Castrol Colombia Limitada (2)
Diagonal 24C No 96-25
Bogota, Colombia
Tel.: (57) 1 415 9288
Fax: (57) 1 415 0160
Web Site: www.castrol.com
Emp.: 70
Petroleum & Petroleum Products Whslr
S.I.C.: 5172
N.A.I.C.S.: 424720

Castrol Croatia d.o.o. (2)
Buniceva 5
Zagreb, 10000, Croatia
Tel.: (385) 16002222
Fax: (385) 16002200
E-Mail: castrol.croatia@bp.com

Web Site: www.castrol.com
Emp.: 17
Motor Oil & Lubricants Sales & Distr
S.I.C.: 2992
N.A.I.C.S.: 324191

Castrol Espana S.A.U. (2)
Pl Arroyo de la Vega Avda Bruselas 36
Alcobendas, 28108 Madrid, Spain (100%)
Tel.: (34) 902107001
Fax: (34) 902107002
E-Mail: nadcad@bp.com
Web Site: www.castrol.com
Emp.: 500
Lubricants Distr
S.I.C.: 5172
N.A.I.C.S.: 424720

Castrol France SA (2)
Immeuble Le Cergier 12 Ave Ges Beguines
95866 Cergy, Pontoise, France (100%)
Tel.: (33) 134227600
Fax: (33) 134224417
Web Site: www.bp-france.fr
Emp.: 200
Lubricants Distr
S.I.C.: 5172
N.A.I.C.S.: 424720
Remy Delphin *(Mng Dir)*

Castrol Hellas S.A. (2)
26 Kifissias Ave
Maroussi, 151 25 Athens, Greece
Tel.: (30) 2106887111
Fax: (30) 2106857701
Web Site: www.castrol.com
Lubricants Distr
S.I.C.: 5172
N.A.I.C.S.: 424720
Cristoginnis Sotiris *(Mng Dir)*

Castrol Hungary Ltd (2)
Soroksari Road 30-34 E
1095 Budapest, Hungary
Tel.: (36) 1 799 0350
Fax: (36) 1 799 0351
E-Mail: informacio@castrol.com
Web Site: www.castrol.hu
Emp.: 30
Lubricant Distr
S.I.C.: 5172
N.A.I.C.S.: 424720

Castrol India Limited (2)
Technopolis Knowledge Park
Mahakali Caves Road Andheri Ea, Mumbai, 400093, India In
Tel.: (91) 2256984100
Fax: (91) 2256984101
Web Site: www.castrol.com
Sales Range: $250-299.9 Million
Emp.: 1,200
Oil & Lubricants Mfg & Distr
S.I.C.: 2992
N.A.I.C.S.: 324191

Castrol Industria (2)
Lagoas Park - Edificio 3
2780-689 Porto Salvo, Portugal
Tel.: (351) 21 389 10 00
Fax: (351) 21 389 14 96
Web Site: www.castrol.com
Petroleum & Lubricant Distr
S.I.C.: 5172
N.A.I.C.S.: 424720
Pablo Garcia Legaz *(Country Mgr-Sls)*

Castrol Industrie Schwitzerland (2)
Baarerstrasse 139
6302 Zug, Switzerland
Tel.: (41) 840 141 816
Fax: (41) 840 141 818
Petroleum & Lubricant Distr
S.I.C.: 5172
N.A.I.C.S.: 424720
Benedikt Hans, *(Mgr-Sls)*

Castrol Ireland Ltd. (2)
Suite12 Plz 212
Ballycoolin Blanchardstown, Dublin, 15, Ireland (100%)
Tel.: (353) 8665100
Fax: (353) 8665101
Web Site: www.castrol.co.uk
Emp.: 9
Lubricants Distr
S.I.C.: 5172
N.A.I.C.S.: 424720

Castrol Italiana SpA (2)
Via Anton Chekov 50 2
20151 Milan, Italy (100%)
Tel.: (39) 02334461
Fax: (39) 0233446300
Web Site: www.castrol.com
Emp.: 80
Lubricants Distr
S.I.C.: 5172
N.A.I.C.S.: 424720

Castrol K.K. (2)
14F NakanoSakaue Sunbright Twin 46-1
Honcho 2-chome
Nakano-ku, Tokyo, 164 0012, Japan (100%)
Tel.: (81) 353711034
Fax: (81) 3 5371 1049
Web Site: www.castroljapan.com
Lubricants Distr
S.I.C.: 5172
N.A.I.C.S.: 424720

Castrol Lubricants (CR), s.r.o. (2)
V Parku 2294/2
148 00 Prague, Czech Republic
Tel.: (420) 296 770 311
Fax: (420) 296 770 302
Lubricating Oil & Grease Mfr
S.I.C.: 2992
N.A.I.C.S.: 324191

Castrol (Malaysia) Sdn. Bhd. (2)
Level 35 Menara Maxis
Kuala Lumpur City Ctr, 50088 Kuala Lumpur, Malaysia
Tel.: (60) 320595555
Fax: (60) 320595533
Web Site: www.castrol.com
Emp.: 400
Lubricants Distr
S.I.C.: 5172
N.A.I.C.S.: 424720
Ng Yook Leng *(Sec & Dir-Fin)*

Castrol Nederland B.V. (2)
Rivium Boulevard 301
2909 LK Capelle aan den IJssel, Netherlands (100%)
Mailing Address:
PO Box 1131
3000BC Rotterdam, Netherlands
Tel.: (31) 102494444
Fax: (31) 102494430
E-Mail: industrienl@castrol.com
Web Site: www.castrol.com
Emp.: 50
Lubricants Distr
S.I.C.: 5172
N.A.I.C.S.: 424720

Castrol NZ Ltd. (2)
6 Monier Place Penrose
PO Box 62291
Auckland, New Zealand NZ
Tel.: (64) 96390000 (100%)
Fax: (64) 96239446
Web Site: www.castrol.co.nz
Emp.: 60
Lubricants Distr
S.I.C.: 5172
N.A.I.C.S.: 424720
Greg Bond *(Bus Mgr)*

Castrol Pakistan Pvt. Ltd. (2)
3rd Floor Bahria Complex-1 24-MT Khan Road
PO Box 3767
Karachi, Pakistan
Tel.: (92) 21 35829000
Fax: (92) 21 3561063
Oil & Gas Exploration Services
S.I.C.: 1389
N.A.I.C.S.: 213112
Hussain Zaidi *(Project Mgr)*

Castrol Philippines, Inc. (2)
30F LKG Tower 6801 Ayala Avenue
1226 Makati, Metro Manila, Philippines
Tel.: (63) 2 884 1478
Fax: (63) 2 884 1615
Web Site: www.castrol.com
Lubricant Distr
S.I.C.: 5172
N.A.I.C.S.: 424720

Castrol (Shenzhen) Co. Ltd. (2)
No 29 Mawan Road
Nanshan District, Shenzhen, 518054, China
Tel.: (86) 7556390238
Fax: (86) 7556391578
Emp.: 50
Oil & Gas Refining
S.I.C.: 2911
N.A.I.C.S.: 324110

Castrol Singapore Pte. Ltd. (2)
1 Harbour Front Ave #02-01
Keppel Bay Tower, Singapore, 098632, Singapore (100%)
Tel.: (65) 6371 8254
Fax: (65) 6371 8989
Web Site: www.castrol.com
Emp.: 30
Lubricants Distr
S.I.C.: 5172
N.A.I.C.S.: 424720

Castrol Slovenija d.o.o. (2)
Brdnikova 44
Ljubljana, Slovenia
Tel.: (386) 12425200
Fax: (386) 1 24 25250
E-Mail: castrol.slovenija@bp.com
Web Site: www.castrol.com
Sales Range: $25-49.9 Million
Emp.: 20
Motor Oil & Lubricants Whslr
S.I.C.: 2992
N.A.I.C.S.: 324191

Castrol Slovensko, s.r.o. (2)
Roznavska 24
Bratislava, 821 04, Slovakia
Tel.: (421) 248777300
Fax: (421) 248777350
E-Mail: info.sk@castrol.sk
Web Site: www.castrol.sk
Emp.: 13
Oil & Lubricating Products Whslr
S.I.C.: 5172
N.A.I.C.S.: 424720
Ida Matulikova *(Office Mgr)*

Castrol (Switzerland) AG (2)
Bqurerstr 139
6302 Zug, Switzerland (100%)
Tel.: (41) 17522323
Fax: (41) 17522390
E-Mail: castrol.switzerland@castrol.com
Web Site: www.castrol.ch
Lubricants Distr
S.I.C.: 7389
N.A.I.C.S.: 425120

Deutsche Castrol Vertriebsgesellschaft mbH (2)
Max Born Strasse 2
D 22761 Hamburg, Germany (100%)
Tel.: (49) 40359401
Fax: (49) 4035945420
E-Mail: presse@castrol.com
Web Site: www.castrol.de
Emp.: 300
Lubricants Distr
S.I.C.: 5172
N.A.I.C.S.: 424720
Carina Rytacik *(Sec)*

Enkor d.o.o. (2)
Buniceva 5
Zagreb, 10000, Croatia
Tel.: (385) 16183823
Fax: (385) 16184493
Web Site: www.enkor.hr/content/view/24/29/
Emp.: 11
Oil & Lubricants Distr
S.I.C.: 5172
N.A.I.C.S.: 424720

Latin Energy Argentina (2)
Juramento 2059 Piso 9
C1428DNG Buenos Aires, Argentina
Tel.: (54) 11 4789 7900
Fax: (54) 11 4789 7950
E-Mail: recepcion@bp.com
Web Site: www.castrol.com
Sales Range: $25-49.9 Million
Emp.: 40
Oil & Grease Mfg
S.I.C.: 2992
N.A.I.C.S.: 324191

Nordic Lubricants A/S (2)
Hasselager Centervej 15
DK 8260 Viby, Denmark (100%)
Tel.: (45) 70807056
Fax: (45) 70 80 70 53
E-Mail: denmark.ils@castrol.com
Web Site: www.castrol.dk
Emp.: 70
Lubricants & Services Distr
S.I.C.: 5172
N.A.I.C.S.: 424720
Nina Veyhe *(Sec)*

Nordic Lubricants AB (2)
St Goransgatan 57
PO Box 49104
100 28 Stockholm, Sweden (100%)
Tel.: (46) 84411100
Fax: (46) 86510135
E-Mail: sweden.consumer@castrol.com
Web Site: www.castrol.com
Emp.: 95
Lubricants Distr
S.I.C.: 5172
N.A.I.C.S.: 424720
Johan Anderssen *(Mng Dir)*

Optimol Oelwerke Industrie GmbH & Co. KG (2)
Erkelenzer Str 20
41179 Monchengladbach, Germany
Tel.: (49) 21619090
Mfr. of Lubricants & Greases
S.I.C.: 2992
N.A.I.C.S.: 324191

PT Castrol Indonesia (2)
Perkantoran Hijau Arkadia Tower B Lt 9 Jl Let Jen TB
Simatupang Kav 88, Jakarta, 12520, Indonesia (100%)
Tel.: (62) 2178843878
Fax: (62) 2178843870
E-Mail: pressinquiryjkt@se1.bp.com
Web Site: www.castrol.com
Emp.: 1,200
Lubricants Distr
S.I.C.: 5172
N.A.I.C.S.: 424720
Tantri Yuliandini *(Sr Comm Officer)*

Non-U.S. Joint Venture:

Castrol Vietnam Ltd. (2)
4th Floor Sun Wah Tower
115 Nguyen Hue Street District, Ho Chi Minh City, Vietnam
Tel.: (84) 88219153
Fax: (84) 8 8218152
Web Site: www.castrol.com
Emp.: 200
Oil & Lubricants Mfr & Distr; Owned 60% by Castrol Ltd. & 40% by Saigon Petroleum Service Company
S.I.C.: 2992
N.A.I.C.S.: 324191

U.S. Subsidiaries:

BP America, Inc. (1)
501 Westlake Park Blvd
Houston, TX 77079-2604 DE
Tel.: (281) 366-2000
Web Site: www.bp.com
Emp.: 7,500
Oil Exploration & Production; Gas & Power & Alternative Energy Businesses
S.I.C.: 1311
N.A.I.C.S.: 211111
John Minge *(Chm & Pres)*
David Nagel *(Exec VP)*
Geoff Morrell *(Sr VP-Comm & External Affairs)*

Group:

BP Corporation North America Inc. (2)
150 W Warrenville Rd
Naperville, IL 60563 IN
Tel.: (630) 836-5000 (100%)
Web Site: www.bp.com
Holding Company; Regional Managing Office
S.I.C.: 6719
N.A.I.C.S.: 551112
Mukta Tandon *(Brand Comm Mgr-Americas)*

Branches:

BP Corporation North America Inc. (3)
28100 Torch Pkwy
Warrenville, IL 60555-3938
Tel.: (630) 836-5001
Web Site: www.bp.com
Holding Company; Oil Wells, Petroleum Pipelines & Refineries Operator; Petroleum Products Distr
S.I.C.: 6719
N.A.I.C.S.: 551112

BP plc—(Continued)

Kenneth Kaminski *(Mgr-Shareholder Svcs)*

BP Corporation North America Inc. (3)
Hwy 185 E
Port O Connor, TX 77982 TX
Mailing Address: (100%)
PO Box 364
Port O Connor, TX 77982-0364
Tel.: (361) 983-2641
Fax: (337) 735-5282
Emp.: 2
Petroleum Refining
S.I.C.: 2911
N.A.I.C.S.: 324110

BP Corporation North America Inc. (3)
4519 Grandview Rd
Blaine, WA 98230-9640
Tel.: (360) 371-1500
Fax: (360) 371-1450
Emp.: 1,100
Petroleum Refining
S.I.C.: 2911
N.A.I.C.S.: 324110
Mike Abendhoff *(Dir-Pub Affairs)*

Divisions:

BP Alternative Energy North America, Inc. (3)
700 Lousiana St Fl 33
Houston, TX 77002 DE
Tel.: (713) 354-2166
Web Site: www.bp.com
Alternative Fuels & Energy Generation Technologies Research & Development
S.I.C.: 8731
N.A.I.C.S.: 541712
Katrina Landis *(CEO)*

Division:

BP Biofuels North America LLC (4)
501 Westlake Park Blvd
Houston, TX 77079 DE
Tel.: (281) 366-2000
Web Site: www.bp.com
Biofuel Research & Development
S.I.C.: 8731
N.A.I.C.S.: 541711
Philip New *(CEO)*

Subsidiaries:

BP Biofuels Louisiana LLC (5)
11107 Campbell Wells Rd E Hwy 90
Jennings, LA 70546 LA
Tel.: (337) 785-4500
Fax: (337) 785-4546
Sales Range: $200-249.9 Million
Emp.: 100
Cellulosic Ethanol & Other Biofuels Developer & Mfr
S.I.C.: 2836
N.A.I.C.S.: 325414
Gregory Powers *(Exec VP)*

Vercipia Biofuels Texas, LLC (5)
5100 W Lemon St Ste 114
Tampa, FL 33609-1108 DE
Tel.: (813) 574-0600 (100%)
Fax: (813) 287-1852
Toll Free: (866) 369-5119
E-Mail: bizdev@vercipia.com
Web Site: www.vercipia.com
Cellulosic Ethanol Developer & Mfr
S.I.C.: 8731
N.A.I.C.S.: 541711
John Doyle *(VP-Project Tech)*

BP Pipelines North America Inc. (3)
28100 Torch Pkwy
Warrenville, IL 60555 OK
Tel.: (219) 472-2323
Operation of Crude Petroleum Pipelines
S.I.C.: 2911
N.A.I.C.S.: 324110
Lemar McKay *(Pres)*

Branches:

BP Oil Pipeline Company (4)
4421 Bradley Rd
Cleveland, OH 44109-3771 OH
Tel.: (216) 351-2211
Fax: (216) 912-2635
Emp.: 20
Crude Petroleum Pipeline Operation
S.I.C.: 4612
N.A.I.C.S.: 486110

BP Pipelines North America Inc. (4)
15600 W Bruns Rd
Manhattan, IL 60442-9537 IL
Tel.: (815) 478-6100 (100%)
Fax: (815) 478-5752
Emp.: 20
Petroleum Pipeline Operation
S.I.C.: 4613
N.A.I.C.S.: 486910
Leon Li *(Engr-Mechanical)*

BP Pipelines North America Inc. (4)
4000 Hwy 56
Houma, LA 70363-7817 LA
Tel.: (985) 580-2424 (100%)
Fax: (985) 580-2422
Web Site: www.bppipelines.com
Emp.: 13
Crude Petroleum Pipeline Operation
S.I.C.: 4613
N.A.I.C.S.: 486910

BP Pipelines North America Inc. (4)
33632 Hwy 24
Salisbury, MO 65281 MO
Mailing Address:
PO Box 11
Salisbury, MO 65281-0011
Tel.: (660) 388-5445
Fax: (660) 388-6137
Emp.: 3
Crude Petroleum Pipeline Operation
S.I.C.: 4613
N.A.I.C.S.: 486910
Joe Akkos *(Supvr)*

BP Pipelines North America Inc. (4)
200 Westlake Park Blvd
Houston, TX 77079-2663 NM
Tel.: (505) 396-2817
Emp.: 20
Crude Petroleum Pipeline Operation
S.I.C.: 4613
N.A.I.C.S.: 486910

BP Products North America Inc. (3)
150 W Warrenville Rd
Naperville, IL 60563-8473 OH
Tel.: (630) 420-4300
E-Mail: linda.bartman@bp.com
Emp.: 200
Petroleum Products Distr
S.I.C.: 2911
N.A.I.C.S.: 324110
Linda Bartman *(Mgr-Mktg Comm)*

Branches:

BP Products North America Inc. (4)
195 NE 183rd St
Miami, FL 33179-4443 FL
Tel.: (305) 651-0957
Fax: (305) 651-7817
Emp.: 6
Natural Gas Distribution
S.I.C.: 4924
N.A.I.C.S.: 221210

BP Products North America Inc. (4)
100 E Standard Oil Rd
Rochelle, IL 61068 IL
Mailing Address: (100%)
PO Box 440
Rochelle, IL 61068-0440
Tel.: (815) 562-7023
Fax: (815) 562-6114
Emp.: 4
Petroleum Products Distr
S.I.C.: 5172
N.A.I.C.S.: 424720
Jack Cowart *(Office Mgr)*

BP Products North America Inc. (4)
28301 Ferry Rd
Warrenville, IL 60555 IL
Tel.: (630) 420-4300
Emp.: 70
Petroleum Terminals
S.I.C.: 4613
N.A.I.C.S.: 486910

BP Products North America Inc. (4)
28100 Torch Pkwy 4th Fl
Warrenville, IL 60555-3938 IL
Tel.: (630) 836-5100
Fax: (630) 836-5513
Toll Free: (866) 273-4732
Web Site: www.bpdirect.com
Emp.: 175
Petroleum Products Distr
S.I.C.: 5171
N.A.I.C.S.: 424710

BP Products North America Inc. (4)
2815 Indianapolis Blvd
Whiting, IN 46394-2197 IN
Mailing Address:
PO Box 710
Whiting, IN 46394-0710
Tel.: (219) 473-3500
Emp.: 3,000
Plastics Materials & Resins Mfr
S.I.C.: 2911
N.A.I.C.S.: 324110
Nick Spencer *(Branch Mgr)*

BP Products North America Inc. (4)
Riley Rd Indiana Harbor
East Chicago, IN 46312 IN
Tel.: (219) 473-3480 (100%)
Fax: (219) 473-5169
Emp.: 22
Refined Petroleum Pipeline Operation
S.I.C.: 4613
N.A.I.C.S.: 486910

BP Products North America Inc. (4)
2500 N Tibbs Ave
Indianapolis, IN 46222-2127 IN
Mailing Address:
PO Box 22348
Indianapolis, IN 46222-0348
Tel.: (317) 926-5471
Fax: (317) 923-6854
Emp.: 6
Petroleum Products Distr
S.I.C.: 5172
N.A.I.C.S.: 424720

BP Products North America Inc. (4)
205 Marion Ave
River Rouge, MI 48218-1695 MI
Mailing Address:
PO Box 18057
Detroit, MI 48218-0057
Tel.: (313) 842-2114
Fax: (313) 842-2637
Emp.: 30
Petroleum Product Distr
S.I.C.: 5172
N.A.I.C.S.: 424720

BP Products North America Inc. (4)
2303 S Church St
Burlington, NC 27215-5331 NC
Tel.: (336) 229-5125 (100%)
Emp.: 4
Gasoline Service Station Operation
S.I.C.: 6099
N.A.I.C.S.: 522320

BP Products North America Inc. (4)
1636 Commerce Rd
Richmond, VA 23224-7502 VA
Mailing Address:
PO Box 24008
Richmond, VA 23224-0008
Tel.: (804) 232-2347
Fax: (804) 232-1279
Emp.: 4
Petroleum Products Distr
S.I.C.: 5172
N.A.I.C.S.: 424720

Castrol North America Inc. (3)
1500 Valley Rd
Wayne, NJ 07470-2040 NJ
Tel.: (973) 633-2200
Fax: (973) 633-9867
E-Mail: webmaster@castrolna.com
Web Site: www.castrolusa.com
Emp.: 200
Lubricant & Oil Mfr & Distr
S.I.C.: 2992
N.A.I.C.S.: 324191

Subsidiaries:

BP Castrol Consumer North America Inc. (4)
1500 Valley Dr
Wayne, NJ 07470 (100%)
Tel.: (973) 633-2200
Fax: (973) 633-9867
Toll Free: (800) 462-0835
Web Site: www.castrolusa.com
Emp.: 300
Lubricant Mfr & Distr
S.I.C.: 2992
N.A.I.C.S.: 324191
Peter Miller *(CFO)*

Branch:

Castrol North America Auto (5)
801 Wharf St
Richmond, CA 94804-3557 CA
Tel.: (510) 236-6312
Fax: (510) 236-4331
Emp.: 35
Auto Oils & Lubricants Mfr & Distr
S.I.C.: 2992
N.A.I.C.S.: 324191

BP Lubricants USA Inc. (4)
9300 Pulaski Hwy
Baltimore, MD 21220-2418 MD
Tel.: (410) 574-5000
Fax: (410) 682-9408
Web Site: www.bp.com
Emp.: 95
Commercial Lubricant Mfr & Distr
Export
S.I.C.: 2992
N.A.I.C.S.: 324191
Marci Drand *(Pres)*

Branches:

BP Lubricants USA Inc. (5)
1981 S Westport Dr
Port Allen, LA 70767-6128 LA
Tel.: (225) 382-8500 (100%)
Fax: (225) 343-2658
Web Site: www.castrol.com
Emp.: 83
Auto Oils & Lubricants Mfr & Distr
S.I.C.: 2992
N.A.I.C.S.: 324191
Paul Waterman *(CEO)*

Castrol Industrial North America Inc. (4)
150 W Warrenville Rd
Naperville, IL 60563
Tel.: (630) 892-8881
Fax: (630) 961-6247
Toll Free: (877) 641-1600
Web Site: www.castrolindustrial.com
Emp.: 300
Industrial Lubricants & Specialist Chemicals Mfr & Distr
S.I.C.: 2992
N.A.I.C.S.: 324191

Branches:

Castrol Industrial North America (5)
775 Louis Dr
Warminster, PA 18974-2827 PA
Tel.: (215) 443-5220
Fax: (215) 443-0780
Toll Free: (800) 464-3070
Web Site: www.castrol.com
Emp.: 50
Industrial Lubricants & Specialist Chemicals Mfr & Distr
S.I.C.: 2992
N.A.I.C.S.: 324191

Subsidiary:

LubeCon Systems, Inc. (5)
201 N Webster St
White Cloud, MI 49349-0824 MI
Mailing Address:
PO Box 824
White Cloud, MI 49349-0824
Tel.: (231) 689-0002
Fax: (231) 689-0372
Toll Free: (800) LUBECON
E-Mail: catina.metcalf@castrol.com
Web Site: www.lubecon.com
Emp.: 40
Mfr. of Automatic Lubricating Systems for Conveyors, Robotics & Machinery, Manufacturer Of Dry Film Lubricants, Gear Oil, Heavy Duty Greases, Manufacturer Of Hand Held Grease Guns, Transfer Pumps & Sprayers
Import Export
S.I.C.: 5171
N.A.I.C.S.: 424710

Non-U.S. Subsidiary:

BP Canada Energy Company (3)
240 4th Ave SW
PO Box 200
Calgary, AB, T2P 2H8, Canada (100%)
Tel.: (403) 233-1313
Fax: (403) 233-5610
Web Site: www.bp.com
Emp.: 1,500
Oil Exploration & Production
S.I.C.: 1311
N.A.I.C.S.: 211111
Doug Dickson *(Mgr-HR)*

Subsidiaries:

BP America - West (2)
6 Centerpoint Dr
La Palma, CA 90623
Tel.: (714) 670-5400
Web Site: www.bp.com
Emp.: 400
Petroleum Refining Services
Import Export
S.I.C.: 2911
N.A.I.C.S.: 324110

Subsidiary:

BP Carson Refinery (3)
2350 E 200 23St
Carson, CA 90810 (100%)
Tel.: (310) 549-6204
Web Site: www.arco.com
Emp.: 5,000
Crude Oil Production
S.I.C.: 1311
N.A.I.C.S.: 211111

Branches:

Arco AM PM (4)
25330 3rd St
San Bernardino, CA 92410-5147 CA
Tel.: (909) 889-3436
Fax: (909) 889-9396
Emp.: 4
Gasoline Station
S.I.C.: 5411
N.A.I.C.S.: 445120
Suresh Patel *(Mgr)*

Subsidiaries:

Arco (4)
3296 El Cajon Blvd
San Diego, CA 92104-1429 CA
Tel.: (619) 282-7024 (100%)
Fax: (619) 282-7026
Emp.: 6
Gasoline Service Stations
S.I.C.: 5541
N.A.I.C.S.: 447190

BP West Coast Products LLC (4)
4 Centerpoint Dr
La Palma, CA 90623 CA
Tel.: (714) 670-5400
Fax: (714) 670-5426
E-Mail: info@bp.com
Web Site: www.ampm.com
Emp.: 400
Crude Oil Production
S.I.C.: 1311
N.A.I.C.S.: 211111
Don Sterenk *(Gen Mgr)*

Branch:

BP West Coast Products (5)
2395 S Riverside Ave
Bloomington, CA 92316-2931 CA
Tel.: (909) 877-2464
Fax: (909) 877-1034
Emp.: 35
Non Local Liquid Petroleum Transport
S.I.C.: 5172
N.A.I.C.S.: 424720
Bob Grider *(Terminal Mgr)*

BP Chemicals, Inc. (2)
150 W Warrenville Rd B6
Naperville, IL 60563-8473 OH
Tel.: (630) 420-4300 (100%)
Fax: (630) 961-7920
Toll Free: (877) 701-2726
E-Mail: chem_americas@bp.com
Emp.: 800
Industrial Chemical Mfr; Holding Company
S.I.C.: 2899
N.A.I.C.S.: 325199

Subsidiaries:

BP Amoco Chemical Company (3)
1401 Finley Is Rd
Decatur, AL 35601 AL
Mailing Address:
PO Box 2215
Decatur, AL 35609-2215
Tel.: (256) 340-5200
Fax: (256) 340-5313
Emp.: 820
Industrial Organic Chemical Mfr
S.I.C.: 2869
N.A.I.C.S.: 325199

BP Amoco Chemical Company (3)
610 Spring St
Atlanta, GA 30308 GA
Tel.: (404) 876-6755
Fax: (404) 876-6766
Emp.: 25
Service Station
S.I.C.: 5541
N.A.I.C.S.: 447190
Daniel Ngugi *(Gen Mgr)*

BP Amoco Chemical Company (3)
2401 5th Ave S
Texas City, TX 77590 TX
Mailing Address:
PO Box 401
Texas City, TX 77592-0401
Tel.: (409) 945-1011
Fax: (409) 942-8889
Emp.: 3,000
Petroleum Refining
S.I.C.: 2911
N.A.I.C.S.: 324110

BP Chemicals Inc. (3)
1306 Amoco Dr
Wando, SC 29492-7879 SC
Tel.: (843) 884-6151
Emp.: 325
Petroleum Refining
S.I.C.: 2911
N.A.I.C.S.: 324110

BP Energy Company (2)
501 W Lake Pk Blvd
Houston, TX 77079 TX
Mailing Address: (100%)
PO Box 219276
Houston, TX 77218-9276
Tel.: (281) 366-2000
Fax: (281) 366-2139
Web Site: www.bp.com
Emp.: 500
Natural Gas Production
S.I.C.: 4911
N.A.I.C.S.: 221122

Branch:

BP Energy Co. (3)
69 Winn St
Burlington, MA 01803-4870 MA
Tel.: (781) 272-9181 (100%)
Fax: (781) 221-3030
Emp.: 2
Natural Gas Distribution
S.I.C.: 4924
N.A.I.C.S.: 221210

BP Oil Co. (2)
4101 Winfield Rd
Warrenville, IL 60555-3521 (100%)
Tel.: (630) 821-2222
Web Site: www.bp.com
Emp.: 150
Crude Petroleum Production & Refining; Petroleum Product Distr; Gasoline Service Stations
S.I.C.: 2911
N.A.I.C.S.: 324110

Subsidiaries:

BP Exploration (Alaska) Inc. (3)
900 E Benson Blvd
Anchorage, AK 99508-4254 DE
Mailing Address: (100%)
PO Box 196612
Anchorage, AK 99519-6612
Tel.: (907) 561-5111
Fax: (907) 564-4920
E-Mail: info@bp.com
Web Site: www.bp.com
Emp.: 1,692
Oil & Gas Exploration & Production
S.I.C.: 1311
N.A.I.C.S.: 211111
Don Kaneckfer *(VP & Dir-External Affairs)*

BP Oil Company (3)
3250 SR 133
Bethel, OH 45106-8320 OH
Tel.: (937) 378-6001 (100%)
Fax: (513) 734-2024
Emp.: 6
Oil Well Operation
S.I.C.: 5171
N.A.I.C.S.: 424710
Scott Schneider *(Mgr)*

BP Pipelines (Alaska) Inc. (3)
900 E Benson Blvd
Anchorage, AK 99508-4254 DE
Tel.: (907) 561-5111
Emp.: 3,000
Crude Petroleum Pipeline Operation
S.I.C.: 4612
N.A.I.C.S.: 486110

Branch:

BP Oil Pipeline (4)
930 Tennessee Ave
Cincinnati, OH 45229-1006 OH
Tel.: (513) 825-5250 (100%)
Fax: (513) 825-0344
Emp.: 25
Crude Petroleum Pipeline Operation
S.I.C.: 4612
N.A.I.C.S.: 486110

Joint Venture:

BP Husky Refinery (3)
4001 Cedar Point Rd
Oregon, OH 43616-1310 OH
Mailing Address:
PO Box 696
Toledo, OH 43697-0696
Tel.: (419) 698-6200
Fax: (419) 698-6408
Emp.: 500
Petroleum Refining Services; Owned by BP plc & Husky Energy, Inc.
S.I.C.: 2911
N.A.I.C.S.: 324110

BP Oil Shipping Company (2)
4850 E 49th St
Cleveland, OH 44125
Mailing Address:
PO Box 39636
Solon, OH 44139-0636
Tel.: (216) 271-8003
Toll Free: (877) 728-1815
Sls.: $83,965,562
Emp.: 333
Oil Tanker Operation
S.I.C.: 4424
N.A.I.C.S.: 483113

Branches:

BP Oil Shipping Company USA (3)
2827 Bethel Rd
Columbus, OH 43220-2226 OH
Tel.: (614) 326-0565 (100%)
Fax: (614) 326-0570
Emp.: 12
Oil Tanker Operation
S.I.C.: 4424
N.A.I.C.S.: 483113

BP Oil Shipping Company USA (3)
5502 Mahoning Ave
Youngstown, OH 44515-2315 OH
Tel.: (330) 799-7961 (100%)
Emp.: 7
Oil Tanker Operation
S.I.C.: 4424
N.A.I.C.S.: 483113
Dan McCracken *(Gen Mgr)*

Melzer's Fuel Service Inc. (3)
7669 E Derry St
Painesville, OH 44077 OH
Tel.: (440) 354-3545
Fax: (440) 354-3669
Web Site: www.melzersfuel.com
Emp.: 11
Bulk Shipping Services
S.I.C.: 5171
N.A.I.C.S.: 424710
Andrew Melzer *(VP)*

BP Oil Supply Company Inc. (2)
28301 Ferry Rd
Warrenville, IL 60555-3018 (100%)
Tel.: (630) 836-4201
Fax: (630) 836-4201
E-Mail: info@bp.com
Web Site: www.bp.com
Emp.: 50
Petroleum Products Distr
S.I.C.: 5172
N.A.I.C.S.: 424720

Branches:

BP Oil Supply Company Inc. (3)
2441 S Reynolds Rd
Toledo, OH 43614-1420 OH
Tel.: (419) 381-1181
Fax: (419) 872-3488
Emp.: 5
Petroleum Products Distr
S.I.C.: 5172
N.A.I.C.S.: 424720
Christine Paul *(Store Mgr)*

Units:

BP America Production Co. (2)
2906 County Rd 307
Durango, CO 81303-6725 CO
Tel.: (970) 247-6900
Fax: (970) 247-6910
Emp.: 40
Oil Well Operation
S.I.C.: 1311
N.A.I.C.S.: 211111

BP America Production Co. (2)
2225 W Oklahoma Ave
Ulysses, KS 67880-8416 KS
Tel.: (620) 356-1237
Fax: (620) 356-6950
E-Mail: info@bp.com
Emp.: 100
Crude Petroleum Production & Refining
S.I.C.: 1311
N.A.I.C.S.: 211111
Christy Hard *(Gen Mgr)*

BP America Production Co. (2)
5968 Parlange Ln
Livonia, LA 70755-3003 LA
Tel.: (225) 637-4942
Fax: (225) 637-3041
Emp.: 30
Oil Well Operation
S.I.C.: 1311
N.A.I.C.S.: 211111

BP America Production Co. (2)
716 Cemetary Rd
Zachary, LA 70791-6724 LA
Tel.: (225) 654-0782
Emp.: 2
Oil Well Operation
S.I.C.: 1311
N.A.I.C.S.: 211111

BP America Production Co. (2)
200 Energy Ct
Farmington, NM 87401-1010 NM
Tel.: (505) 326-9200
Fax: (505) 326-9262
Emp.: 100
Oil Well Operation
S.I.C.: 1311
N.A.I.C.S.: 211111
Kelly Heart *(Mgr)*

BP America Production Co. (2)
509 South Boston Ave
Tulsa, OK 74103-4602 OK
Tel.: (918) 581-3011
Emp.: 200
Oil Well Operation
S.I.C.: 1311
N.A.I.C.S.: 211111

BP America Production Co. (2)
369 Terrapin Neck Rd
Marshall, TX 75670 TX
Mailing Address:
PO Box 959
Hallsville, TX 75650-0959
Tel.: (903) 935-1161
Fax: (903) 927-5939
Emp.: 13
Oil Well Operation

BP plc—(Continued)

S.I.C.: 1311
N.A.I.C.S.: 211111
Gary Burns *(Gen Mgr)*

Plants:

BP America, Inc. - Cooper River Plant (2)
1306 Amoco Dr
Charleston, SC 29492-7879
Tel.: (843) 884-6151
Polyester Resin Mfr
S.I.C.: 2821
N.A.I.C.S.: 325211

BP Company North America Inc. (1)
501 WestLake Park Blvd
Houston, TX 77079
Tel.: (281) 366-2000
Petroleum Refining Services
S.I.C.: 2911
N.A.I.C.S.: 324110

Non-U.S. Subsidiaries:

Amoco Argentina Oil Co. (1)
Ave Leandro N Alem 1180
1001 Buenos Aires, Argentina (100%)
Tel.: (54) 141096000
Emp.: 270
Crude Oil Exploration & Production
S.I.C.: 1311
N.A.I.C.S.: 211111

BP Algeria (1)
Lotissement No 16 Les Cretes
Hydra, 16035 Algiers, Algeria
Tel.: (213) 21481029
Fax: (213) 21 481 037
Web Site: www.bp.com
Emp.: 156
Petroleum & Petroleum Products Distr
S.I.C.: 5172
N.A.I.C.S.: 424720

BP Angola (1)
4 February St
Towres Atlantic Bldg, Luanda, Angola
Tel.: (244) 0222637440
E-Mail: jose.patricio@bp.com
Web Site: www.angola.bp.com
Emp.: 600
Petroleum & Gas Exploration & Production
S.I.C.: 1311
N.A.I.C.S.: 211111
Jose Patricio *(Pres)*

BP Asia Pacific (Malaysia) (1)
Level 26 Quill 7 KL Sentral
Kuala Lumpur, 50470, Malaysia
Tel.: (60) 3 2272 7272
Web Site: www.bp.com
Emp.: 380
Petroleum & Petroleum Products Mfr & Whslr
S.I.C.: 5172
N.A.I.C.S.: 424720
Peter Wentworth *(CEO)*

Joint Venture:

BP Petronas Acetyls Sdn Bhd (2)
Kompleks Pentadbiran Petrokimia Petronas Kemaman
24300 Terengganu, Kertih, Malaysia
Tel.: (60) 9 8305 300
Fax: (60) 9 8305 321
Web Site: www.petronas.com.my
Emp.: 500
Acetid Acid Mfg; Owned 70% by BP plc & 30% by Petroliam Nasional Berhad
S.I.C.: 2819
N.A.I.C.S.: 325180
Shamsul Azhar Abbas *(Pres & CEO)*

BP Australia Capital Markets Limited (1)
L 29 Tower Melbourne Central 360 Elizabeth St
Melbourne, VIC, 3000, Australia
Tel.: (61) 3 9268 4844
General Insurance Services
S.I.C.: 6411
N.A.I.C.S.: 524298

BP Australia Pty. Ltd. (1)
717 Bourke Street Docklands
Victoria, 3008, Australia AU
Mailing Address: (100%)
GPO Box 5222 BB
Melbourne, VIC, 3001, Australia
Tel.: (61) 392684111
Fax: (61) 392683321
E-Mail: aucustcare@bp.com
Web Site: www.bp.com.au
Emp.: 600
Petroleum Products Distr; Gasoline Service Stations; Petroleum Refining
S.I.C.: 5172
N.A.I.C.S.: 424720
Peri Hunter *(Brand Dir-Mktg)*

BP Australia Pty. Ltd. (1)
717 Bourke St
3008 Melbourne, VIC, Australia AU
Tel.: (61) 392684111 (100%)
Fax: (61) 392683321
E-Mail: reception.elite@se1.bp.com
Web Site: www.bp.com.au
Emp.: 490
Petroleum Additives & Synthetic Fabrics Producer
S.I.C.: 5172
N.A.I.C.S.: 424720
Paul Wterman *(Pres)*

BP Austria Aktiengesellschaft (1)
IZ No Sud Strasse 6 Obj 17
2355 Vienna, Austria
Tel.: (43) 223668550
Fax: (43) 2236685548000
E-Mail: bpaustria@bp.com
Web Site: www.bp.com
Emp.: 137
Petroleum Products Whslr
Import Export
S.I.C.: 5172
N.A.I.C.S.: 424720
Johann Strassl *(CEO)*

Subsidiary:

BP Austria Marketing GmbH (2)
Schwarzenbergplatz 13
A 1041 Vienna, Austria
Tel.: (43) 150161380
Fax: (43) 150161432
E-Mail: bpplus@at.bp.com
Web Site: www.bp.com
Petroleum & Petroleum Products Whslr; Gas Service Stations
S.I.C.: 5541
N.A.I.C.S.: 447190

Subsidiaries:

BP Gas Austria GmbH Nfg. OHG (3)
Ziegeleistrasse 19
5020 Salzburg, Austria
Tel.: (43) 6628734510
Fax: (43) 662882736
E-Mail: bpgasaustria@bp.com
Emp.: 30
Liquefied Petroleum Gas Whslr
S.I.C.: 5989
N.A.I.C.S.: 454310
Andreas Kubek *(Mng Dir)*

BP Schmierstoffe GmbH Nfg. OHG (3)
IZ NO Sud Strasse 6
Obj 17, A 2355 Wiener Neudorf, Austria
Tel.: (43) 223668550
Fax: (43) 22365566
E-Mail: bplubesat@bp.com
Web Site: www.bp.com
Emp.: 31
Petroleum Products & Lubricants Whslr
S.I.C.: 5172
N.A.I.C.S.: 424720

BP Azerbaijan (1)
2 Neftchilar prospecti (Bailov)
Villa Petrolea, AZ1003 Baku, Azerbaijan
Tel.: (994) 412979000
Fax: (994) 412979602
Web Site: www.bp.com
Emp.: 1,500
Petroleum & Natural Gas Exploration, Refining & Production
S.I.C.: 1311
N.A.I.C.S.: 211111
Gordon Birrell *(Pres-Azerbaijan, Georgia & Turkey)*

BP Belgium NV/SA (1)
Archimedes Building 11 Rond Point R Schuman
1040 Brussels, Belgium BE
Tel.: (32) 22878080
Fax: (32) 22878044
Web Site: www.bp.com
Emp.: 10
Chemicals Mfr & Distr
S.I.C.: 2899
N.A.I.C.S.: 325998
Emmanuel Haton *(Dir-European Govt Affairs)*

Division:

BP Marine (2)
Uitbreidingstraat 60-62
B 2600 Berchem, Belgium
Tel.: (32) 32868250
Fax: (32) 32868269
E-Mail: gijsmeerburg@bp.com
Web Site: www.bp.com
Emp.: 40
Supplier of Fuels, Lubricants & Technical Services to the Marine Industry
S.I.C.: 5172
N.A.I.C.S.: 424720
Gijs Meerburg *(Mng Dir)*

Non-U.S. Subsidiary:

Westbit AB (2)
PO Box 16
642 21 Flen, Sweden
Tel.: (46) 15713980
Fax: (46) 157 13981
Web Site: www.bp.com
Emp.: 2
Marketing of Bitumen to the Road Construction Industry
S.I.C.: 5172
N.A.I.C.S.: 424720

BP Brasil Ltda (1)
Av Rio Branco 1-10 andar -Centro
20090 003 Rio de Janeiro, Brazil
Tel.: (55) 2125174400
Fax: (55) 2125174400
E-Mail: info@bp.com
Web Site: www.bp.com
Emp.: 620
Oil & Gas Exploration, Production & Sales
S.I.C.: 1311
N.A.I.C.S.: 211111

BP - Castrol (Thailand) Limited (1)
23rd Floor Rajanakarn Building 183 South Sathon Road
Yannawa Sathon, Bangkok, 10120, Thailand
Tel.: (66) 2 684 3555
Fax: (66) 2 684 3640
Lubricating Oil Mfr
S.I.C.: 2992
N.A.I.C.S.: 324191

BP Chembel N.V. (1)
Amocolaan 2
BE-2440 Geel, Belgium BE
Tel.: (32) 14864211 (100%)
Telex: 846-32375
Fax: (32) 14867637
E-Mail: infogeel@bp.com
Web Site: www.bpgeel.be
Emp.: 400
Chemicals Mfr & Distr
S.I.C.: 2899
N.A.I.C.S.: 325998
Patrick Van Acker *(Mng Dir)*

BP Chemical Trelleborg AB (1)
Strandridareg 1
PO Box 302
231 21 Trelleborg, Sweden
Tel.: (46) 41052300
Fax: (46) 41052310
Web Site: www.bp.com
Emp.: 54
Polystyrene Mfr
S.I.C.: 2821
N.A.I.C.S.: 325211
Peter Anderson *(Pres)*

BP (China) Holdings Limited (1)
Unit 2001 20F West Tower World Financial Centre No 1 East 3rd Ring
Middle Road Chaoyang District, Beijing, 100020, China
Tel.: (86) 10 6589 3888
Fax: (86) 10 8587 9711
Web Site: www.bp.com
Investment Management Services
S.I.C.: 6282
N.A.I.C.S.: 523920

BP Danmark A/S (1)
Hasselager Centervej 15
DK 8260 Viby, Denmark
Tel.: (45) 89487700
Fax: (45) 89487711
E-Mail: post@bpgas.dk
Web Site: www.bp.dk
Emp.: 65
Petroleum & Petroleum Products, Fuels, Petrochemicals & Gas Whslr
S.I.C.: 5172
N.A.I.C.S.: 424720
Per Offersen *(Mng Dir)*

Subsidiaries:

BP Gas A/S (2)
Hasselager Centervej 15
DK 8260 Viby, Denmark
Tel.: (45) 89487700
Fax: (45) 89487711
E-Mail: post@bpgas.dk
Web Site: www.bp.dk
Emp.: 60
Petroleum Products Whslr
Import
S.I.C.: 5172
N.A.I.C.S.: 424720
Per Offersen *(Mng Dir)*

BP Lubricants A/S (2)
Hasselager Centervej 15
DK-8260 Viby, J, Denmark
Tel.: (45) 70807055
Fax: (45) 70247106
E-Mail: info@bp.com
Web Site: www.bp.com
Emp.: 16
Petroleum Products & Lubricants Whslr
S.I.C.: 5172
N.A.I.C.S.: 424720
Anne Sonderby *(Mgr-HR)*

BP Lubricants Danmark (2)
Islands Brygge 43
DK 2300 Copenhagen, Denmark
Tel.: (45) 70247101
Fax: (45) 70247106
E-Mail: kundeservice@bp.com
Web Site: www.bp.com
Emp.: 5
Petrochemicals Whslr
S.I.C.: 5172
N.A.I.C.S.: 424720

BP Egypt (1)
14 Road 252
Digla Maadi, Cairo, Egypt (100%)
Tel.: (20) 25199915
Fax: (20) 27062143
E-Mail: bpegypt@bp.com
Emp.: 100
Petroleum Exploration & Production
S.I.C.: 1311
N.A.I.C.S.: 211111

Subsidiaries:

BP Exploration and Production Egypt LLC (2)
14 Road 252
Degla Maadi, Cairo, Egypt
Tel.: (20) 25199915
Fax: (20) 27062460
Web Site: www.bp.com
Emp.: 250
Petroleum & Gas Exploration & Production
S.I.C.: 1311
N.A.I.C.S.: 211111

BP Marketing Egypt Ltd (2)
42 Road 17
Digla Maadi, Cairo, Egypt
Tel.: (20) 25199915
Fax: (20) 27062143
Web Site: www.bp.com
Petroleum & Petroleum Products Marketing
S.I.C.: 5172
N.A.I.C.S.: 424720

BP Energy Company-Trinidad & Tobago (1)
5 & 5A Queens Park West Plaza
Port of Spain, Trinidad & Tobago (100%)
Tel.: (868) 6232862
Fax: (868) 6285058
Petroleum Exploration & Production
S.I.C.: 1311
N.A.I.C.S.: 211111
Brian Gregory *(Reg Mgr)*

Bp Energy Do Brazil Ltda (1)
Av Atlantica n 1 130 7 andar
Copacabana, 22021-000 Rio de Janeiro, Brazil
Tel.: (55) 21 2127 2999
Fax: (55) 21 2127 2985
Petroleum Product Distr
S.I.C.: 5172
N.A.I.C.S.: 424720

BP Espana S.A.U. (1)
Avenida De Bruselas 36 Parque Empresarial
Arroyo de la Vega, 28108 Madrid, Alcobendas, Spain (100%)
Tel.: (34) 902107001
Fax: (34) 902107002
E-Mail: bpesp@bp.com
Web Site: www.bp.com
Sales Range: $150-199.9 Million
Emp.: 500
Petroleum Exploration & Production & Petroleum Products Whslr
S.I.C.: 1311
N.A.I.C.S.: 211111
Luis Javier Navarro *(Pres)*

Subsidiaries:

BP Oil Espana S.A. (2)
Avenida de Bruselas 36 Parque Empresarial Arroyo de la Vega
Alcobendas, 28108 Madrid, Spain
Tel.: (34) 902107001
Fax: (34) 902107002
Web Site: www.bp.com
Emp.: 300
Petroleum Products Marketing; Gasoline Service Stations
S.I.C.: 5172
N.A.I.C.S.: 424720

Subsidiaries:

BP Gas Espana S.A. (3)
Avenida de Bruselas 36 Parque Empresarial Arroyo de la Vega
Alcobendas, 28108 Madrid, Spain
Tel.: (34) 902107001
Fax: (34) 902107002
Web Site: www.bpesp.com
Natural Gas Distr
S.I.C.: 1389
N.A.I.C.S.: 213112
Jorge Lanza *(Pres)*

BP Oil Refineria de Castellon, S.A.U. (3)
Poligono Industrial El Serrallo
El Grao, 12100 Castellon de la Plana, Spain
Tel.: (34) 964347000
Fax: (34) 902884785
E-Mail: bprefineriabecartellon@bp.com
Web Site: www.bp.com
Emp.: 450
Petroleum Refining
S.I.C.: 2911
N.A.I.C.S.: 324110
Emilio Marin *(Mgr)*

BP Solar Espana, S.A.U. (2)
Pl Tres Cantos Zona Oeste s/n
28760 Madrid, Tres Cantos, Spain
Tel.: (34) 918071600
Fax: (34) 918071601
E-Mail: infobpsolar@bp.com
Web Site: www.bp.com
Emp.: 538
Solar Cells & Modules Production
S.I.C.: 3825
N.A.I.C.S.: 334515
Miguel Balbuena *(Pres)*

BP Europa SE Oddzial w Polsce (1)
Ul Jasnogorska 1
31-358 Krakow, Poland
Tel.: (48) 12 619 1200
Fax: (48) 12 619 1205
Web Site: www.bp.com
Petroleum Product Distr
S.I.C.: 5172
N.A.I.C.S.: 424720

BP Europa SE Zweigniederlassung BP Austria AG (1)
IZ No-Sud Strasse 6 Obj 17
2355 Wiener Neudorf, Austria
Tel.: (43) 2236 6855 0
Fax: (43) 2236 6855 48000
E-Mail: bpaustria@bp.com
Web Site: www.bp.com
Emp.: 200
Petroleum Product Distr
S.I.C.: 5172
N.A.I.C.S.: 424720
Wolfgang Steinbrecher *(Plant Mgr)*

BP Europa SE Zweigniederlassung BP Gas Austria (1)
Franz Broetzner Strasse 7/6
5071 Salzburg, Austria
Tel.: (43) 662 873451
Fax: (43) 662 882736
E-Mail: bpgasaustria@bp.com
Web Site: www.bp.com
Oil & Gas Exploration Services
S.I.C.: 1389
N.A.I.C.S.: 213112

BP Europa SE (1)
Wittener Str 45
44789 Bochum, Germany
Tel.: (49) 234 315 0
Fax: (49) 234 315 2679
Web Site: www.bp.com
Petroleum Product Distr
S.I.C.: 5172
N.A.I.C.S.: 424720
Wilhelm Bonse-Geuking *(Chm-Supervisory Bd)*
Michael Schmidt *(Chm-Mgmt Bd)*
Sabine Dietrich *(Member-Mgmt Bd)*
Ludger Dohm *(Member-Mgmt Bd)*
Guy Moeyens *(Member-Mgmt Bd)*

Joint Venture:

Ruhr Oel GmbH (2)
Pawwiker Strasse 30
45896 Gelsenkirchen, Germany
Tel.: (49) 2093660
Telex: 824881-0 vo d
Fax: (49) 2093662646
E-Mail: marerrueter@bpge.de
Web Site: www.bprp.de
Emp.: 4,000
Pipeline Transportation & Distribution Services; Joint Venture of BP plc (50%) & OAO Rosneft Oil Company (50%)
S.I.C.: 4923
N.A.I.C.S.: 486210

Subsidiary:

DHC Solvent Chemie GmbH (3)
Timmerhellstrasse 28
45478 Mullheim, Germany
Tel.: (49) 208 99 40 0
Telex: 856658 hydro d
Fax: (49) 208 99 40 150
E-Mail: info@dhc-solvent.de
Web Site: www.dhc-solvent.de
Emp.: 63
Solvents & Other Oil-Based Products Mfr
S.I.C.: 2999
N.A.I.C.S.: 324199
Johannes Bremer *(Mng Dir)*

BP Exploration (Alpha) Limited (1)
Unit No 71 & 73 7th Floor 2nd North Avenue Maxity Bandra Kurla Complex
Bandra E, Mumbai, 400051, India
Tel.: (91) 22 7177 7000
Fax: (91) 22 7177 7001
Web Site: www.bp.com
Petroleum Extraction Services
S.I.C.: 1311
N.A.I.C.S.: 211111
V. V. Narayanan *(Mgr-HR-Upstream & Gas)*

BP Exploration (Caspian Sea) Ltd (1)
Villa Petrolea 2 Neftchilar Prospekti
Bayil, AZ1003 Baku, Azerbaijan
Tel.: (994) 124979000
Fax: (994) 124979602
Web Site: www.bp.com
Oil & Gas Exploration Services
S.I.C.: 1389
N.A.I.C.S.: 213112
Gordon Birrell *(Pres)*

BP Exploration Operating Co Ltd (1)
Khidma Tower 6th Floor Khalidiyah 32nd Street
PO Box 46600
Abu Dhabi, United Arab Emirates
Tel.: (971) 2 493 5555
Fax: (971) 2 493 5556
Web Site: www.bp.com
Oil & Gas Exploration Services
S.I.C.: 1389
N.A.I.C.S.: 213112

Bp Finance Australia Pty Ltd (1)
L 29 The Tower Melbourne Central 360 Elizabeth St
Melbourne, VIC, 3000, Australia
Tel.: (61) 392683889
Business Management Services
S.I.C.: 8741
N.A.I.C.S.: 561110

BP France SA (1)
12 Avenue Des Beguines
95866 Cergy, Ile De France, France (100%)
Tel.: (33) 134224000
Fax: (33) 134224417
Web Site: www.bp-france.fr
Emp.: 250
Oil Refineries
S.I.C.: 2911
N.A.I.C.S.: 324110
Eric Menut *(Dir-Fin)*

BP Global Investment Salalah & Co LLC (1)
Raysut
PO Box 2309
211 Salalah, Oman
Tel.: (968) 23 219156
Fax: (968) 23 219302
E-Mail: albrm1@bp.com
Web Site: www.bp.com
Petroleum Product Distr
S.I.C.: 5172
N.A.I.C.S.: 424720
Anil Kumar *(Mgr-Sls)*

BP Hong Kong Limited (1)
22nd Fl Devon House
979 Kings Rd Taikoo Pl, Hong Kong, China (Hong Kong) HK (100%)
Tel.: (852) 25868899
Telex: 75657 AMOCO HX
Fax: (852) 25868981
Web Site: www.bp.com
Emp.: 50
Petroleum Products Distr
S.I.C.: 5172
N.A.I.C.S.: 424720

BP Hungary Ltd (1)
Puskas Tivadar utca 11
H 2040 Budaors, Hungary
Tel.: (36) 23505350
Fax: (36) 23505351
Web Site: www.bp.com
Emp.: 60
Lubricants & Aviation Fuels Distr
S.I.C.: 5172
N.A.I.C.S.: 424720
Gyula Varsan *(Sr Mgr)*

BP India Services Pvt. Ltd (1)
15th Floor Dr Gopal Das Bhawan 28 Barakhamba Road
New Delhi, 110 001, India
Tel.: (91) 11 4375 5000
Fax: (91) 11 4375 5001
Web Site: www.bp.com
Oil & Gas Extraction Services
S.I.C.: 1389
N.A.I.C.S.: 213112
Anshul Mathur *(Gen Mgr)*

Subsidiary:

BP Magyarorszag Kft (2)
Puskas Tivadar u 11
2040 Budaors, Hungary
Tel.: (36) 23505350
Fax: (36) 23505351
E-Mail: info@bp.com
Web Site: www.bp.com
Emp.: 100
Oil & Lubricants Distr
S.I.C.: 5172
N.A.I.C.S.: 424720
Zoltan Hegedus *(Mng Dir)*

BP Italia SPA (1)
Via Anton Cechov 50/2
20151 Milan, Italy
Tel.: (39) 02 3344 51
Fax: (39) 02 3344 5200
Web Site: www.bp.com
Petroleum & Lubricating Oil Mfr & Distr
S.I.C.: 2992
N.A.I.C.S.: 324191

BP Japan KK (1)
3F Petro House
4 5 21 Kojimachi Chiyoda Ku, Tokyo, 102 0083, Japan (100%)
Tel.: (81) 332387310
Fax: (81) 332387302
Petroleum Products Distr
S.I.C.: 5172
N.A.I.C.S.: 424720

BP Kuwait Limited (1)
Sahab Tower 13th Floor
PO Box 29335
Mhd Thunayan Al-Ghanim Street, 13039 Salhiya, Kuwait
Tel.: (965) 2403316
Fax: (965) 2403317
Web Site: www.bp.com
Petroleum & Petroleum Products Whslr; Oil & Gas Exploration & Production
S.I.C.: 5172
N.A.I.C.S.: 424720

BP Luxembourg S.A. (1)
Aire de Capellen
8309 Capellen, Luxembourg
Tel.: (352) 3981991
Fax: (352) 397046
E-Mail: nicole.slim@bp.com
Emp.: 22
Petroleum Products Whslr; Gasoline Service Stations
S.I.C.: 5541
N.A.I.C.S.: 447190
Romaen Horrstmrrann *(Mng Dir)*

BP Mexico S.A. de C.V. (1)
Av Santa Fe No 505 Flr 10 Col Cruz Manca Santa Fe
05390 Mexico, Mexico MX
Tel.: (52) 5550632000
Fax: (52) 5552924847
E-Mail: ext.affairs.mexico@bp.com
Web Site: www.bp.com
Emp.: 900
Petroleum Refining & Petroleum Products Marketing; Petrochemicals Mfr; Convenience Stores
S.I.C.: 2911
N.A.I.C.S.: 324110

BP Middle East Ltd. (1)
6th Fl City Tower 2 Sheikh Zayed Rd
Dubai, United Arab Emirates
Tel.: (971) 43317999
Fax: (971) 43318530
Web Site: www.bp.com
Sales Range: $125-149.9 Million
Emp.: 60
Petroleum & Gas Exploration & Oil Refining; Petroleum Products Marketing; Petrochemicals Mfg
S.I.C.: 2911
N.A.I.C.S.: 324110
Chris Papet *(Gen Mgr)*

BP Mozambique Limited (1)
Avenida dos Martires de Inhaminga 170 8th Fl Andar
AZ Sociecydade de Geografia, 269 A
Maputo, Mozambique
Tel.: (258) 21325021
Fax: (258) 21326042
E-Mail: bp@mz.bp.com
Web Site: www.bp.co.za
Emp.: 143
Petroleum & Petroleum Products Whslr; Gasoline Service Stations
S.I.C.: 5172
N.A.I.C.S.: 424720
Martinho Guambe *(Gen Mgr)*

BP Nederland Holdings B.V. (1)
Rivium Boulevard 301
PO Box 1131
3000 BC Rotterdam, Netherlands
Tel.: (31) 102491000
Fax: (31) 102491150
E-Mail: info@bp.nl
Web Site: www.bp.nl
Emp.: 100
Holding Company
S.I.C.: 6719
N.A.I.C.S.: 551112
H. Muilerman *(Mng Dir)*

BP plc—(Continued)

Subsidiary:

BP Nederland B.V. (2)
Rivium Boulevard 301
PO Box 1131
2909 LK Capelle aan den IJssel, Netherlands
Tel.: (31) 102491000
Fax: (31) 102491150
E-Mail: reception.rotterdam@bp.com
Web Site: www.bp.nl
Emp.: 150
Petroleum Products Whslr
S.I.C.: 5172
N.A.I.C.S.: 424720
S. Gunnewijk *(Mgr-HR)*

Subsidiaries:

BP Energy Marketing B.V. (3)
Rivium Boulevard 301
2909 LK Capelle aan den IJssel, Netherlands
Mailing Address:
Postbus 1131
Rotterdam, 3000 BC, Netherlands
Tel.: (31) 102491000
Fax: (31) 102491150
E-Mail: reception@rotterdam.com
Web Site: www.bp.com
Petroleum Products Research & Marketing
S.I.C.: 5172
N.A.I.C.S.: 424720
Hendrik Muilerman *(Gen Mgr)*

Netherlands Refining Company B.V. (3)
D'Arcyweg 76
Haven 6425, 3198 NA Rotterdam, Netherlands
Mailing Address:
PO Box 1033
3810 AA Rozenburg, Netherlands
Tel.: (31) 1812500911
Fax: (31) 181 263 3014
Sales Range: $300-349.9 Million
Emp.: 600
Petroleum Refining; Owned 69% by BP Nederland B.V. & 31% by Texaco
S.I.C.: 2911
N.A.I.C.S.: 324110

BP Norge AS (1)
Godesetdalen 8
NO 4065 Stavanger, Norway (100%)
Tel.: (47) 52013000
Fax: (47) 52013001
E-Mail: bpnorge@bp.com
Web Site: www.bp.no
Rev.: $69,922,448
Emp.: 500
Petroleum Exploration & Production
S.I.C.: 1311
N.A.I.C.S.: 211111
Repecca Wilec *(Mng Dir)*

BP Oil Australia Pty. Ltd. (1)
L 17 717 Bourke St
Docklands, Melbourne, VIC, Australia
Tel.: (61) 392684111
Petroleum Product Mfr & Distr
S.I.C.: 2992
N.A.I.C.S.: 324191
Paul Waterman *(CEO)*

BP Oil Hellenic SA (1)
Kifissias 26 & Paradisou 2
Marousi, 15125 Athens, Greece
Tel.: (30) 2106887777
Fax: (30) 2106887697
E-Mail: bphellas@bp.com
Web Site: www.bp.com
Sales Range: $1-4.9 Billion
Emp.: 420
Petroleum & Petroleum Products Whslr
S.I.C.: 5172
N.A.I.C.S.: 424720
Helen Priga *(Mgr-HR)*

BP Oil New Zealand Limited (1)
20 Customhouse Quay
Wellington, 6001, New Zealand
Tel.: (64) 4 495 5000
Fax: (64) 4 495 5400
E-Mail: GANZCustomerEnquiries@bp.com
Web Site: www.bp.com
Rev.: $1,895,292,000
Emp.: 1,760
Fuel & Lubricant Distr
S.I.C.: 5172
N.A.I.C.S.: 424720
Matt Elliott *(Mng Dir)*

BP Oil Thailand (1)
24th Floor Rajanakarn Building 183 South Sathon Road
Bangkok, 10120, Thailand TH
Tel.: (66) 26843789
Fax: (66) 26843666
Web Site: www.castrol.com
Emp.: 450
Petroleum & Gas Exploration, Production & Sales; Petrochemical Mfg
S.I.C.: 1311
N.A.I.C.S.: 211111
Christopher Young Cho Ping *(CEO)*
Keits Hales *(Mng Dir)*

Subsidiary:

BP Castrol (Thailand) Limited (2)
23rd Fl Rajanakarn Bldg 183 S Sathon Rd
Bangkok, 10120, Thailand
Tel.: (66) 26843555
Fax: (66) 26843640
Web Site: www.bp.co
Emp.: 150
Oil & Petroleum Products Mfr
S.I.C.: 2992
N.A.I.C.S.: 324191
Keith Hales *(CEO)*

BP Pakistan Exploration & Production Inc. (1)
4th Floor Bahria Complex 1
MT Khan Road, Karachi, Pakistan
Tel.: (92) 215611194
Fax: (92) 215610634
Web Site: www.bp.com
Emp.: 250
Petroleum & Gas Exploration, Development & Production
S.I.C.: 1311
N.A.I.C.S.: 211111
Tariq Khamisani *(Pres)*

BP Petrolleri A.S. (1)
Sary Kanarya Sokak No 14
Kozyatagi, 34742 Istanbul, Turkey TR
Tel.: (90) 2165712000
Fax: (90) 2165712450
E-Mail: info@bp.com
Web Site: www.bp.com.tr
Emp.: 300
Petroleum & Gas Exploration & Production; Lubricants & Petroleum Products Whslr; Gasoline Service Stations
S.I.C.: 1311
N.A.I.C.S.: 211111
Richard Harding *(Gen Mgr)*

BP Philippines, Inc. (1)
30th Floor LKG Tower
6801 Ayala Avenue, Makati, 1226, Philippines
Tel.: (63) 28841478
Fax: (63) 28841911
Web Site: www.bp.com
Sales Range: $350-399.9 Million
Emp.: 50
Petroleum & Petroleum Products Marketing & Distribution
S.I.C.: 5172
N.A.I.C.S.: 424720

BP Polska Sp. z o.o. (1)
Ul Jasnogorska 1
31 358 Krakow, Poland PL
Tel.: (48) 126191200
Fax: (48) 126191205
E-Mail: dorota.adamska@bp.com
Web Site: www.bp.pl
Emp.: 300
Gasoline Service Stations; Petroleum Products Whslr
S.I.C.: 5172
N.A.I.C.S.: 424720
Jerzy Brniak *(CEO)*

BP Shanghai Trading Co. Ltd. (1)
9th Floor Plaza 66
1266 Nanjing West Road, Shanghai, 200040, China CN
Tel.: (86) 21 3227 4888
Fax: (86) 21 6288 0350
Sales Range: $25-49.9 Million
Emp.: 150
Petroleum Products Whslr
S.I.C.: 5172
N.A.I.C.S.: 424720

BP Singapore Pte. Limited (1)
1 Harbour Front Avenue 02-01 Keppel Bay Tower
Singapore, 098632, Singapore SG
Tel.: (65) 63718888
Fax: (65) 63718855
Web Site: www.bp.com
Sales Range: $1-4.9 Billion
Emp.: 500
Oil Production & Marketing of Petroleum & Petrochemical Products
S.I.C.: 5172
N.A.I.C.S.: 424720
Pek Hak Bin *(Pres)*

BP South-West Pacific Limited (1)
Level 7 Vanua House
Suva, Fiji
Tel.: (679) 3311622
Fax: (679) 3300933
E-Mail: info@bp.com
Emp.: 150
Petroleum & Petroleum Products Whslr
S.I.C.: 5172
N.A.I.C.S.: 424720
Richard Champion *(Gen Mgr)*

BP Southeast Asia Ltd. (1)
49 Hai Ba Trung Street 7th Floor Hanoi Towers
10000 Hanoi, Vietnam
Tel.: (84) 48265325
Fax: (84) 48266156
E-Mail: huong.anguyen_thi_quynh@se1.bp.com
Web Site: www.bp.com
Emp.: 20
Oil & Gas Exploration, Production & Sales; Petrochemical Mfg
S.I.C.: 1311
N.A.I.C.S.: 211111

BP Southern Africa Pty Ltd. (1)
Portswood Ridge
Cape Town, 8002, South Africa ZA (100%)
Tel.: (27) 214082911
Fax: (27) 214082509
E-Mail: info@bp.com
Web Site: www.bpsouthernafrica.com
Emp.: 1,300
Petroleum Refining & Distr; Gasoline Service Stations
S.I.C.: 2911
N.A.I.C.S.: 324110
Rams Ramashia *(Chm & Mng Dir)*

BP Swaziland (Pty) Limited (1)
Shop No 3 Nkosingiphile Building
PO Box 1161
8th Street, Matsapha, Swaziland
Tel.: (268) 87660
Fax: (268) 87665
Petroleum & Petroleum Products Whslr; Gasoline Service Stations
S.I.C.: 5172
N.A.I.C.S.: 424720

BP Switzerland (1)
Baarerstrasse 139
6302 Zug, Switzerland
Tel.: (41) 584569111
Fax: (41) 584569119
E-Mail: info@ch.bp.com
Web Site: www.bpswitzerland.ch
Sls.: $1,863,199,744
Emp.: 134
Petroleum Products, Fuel Oils and Petrochemicals Whslr; Gas Service Stations
S.I.C.: 5172
N.A.I.C.S.: 424720

BP Taiwan Marketing Limited (1)
7th Floor No 71 Sec 3 Mingsheng East Road
Taipei, 104, Taiwan
Tel.: (886) 2 8175 6800
Fax: (886) 2 2503 0734
Lubricating Oil Mfr
S.I.C.: 2992
N.A.I.C.S.: 324191

BP Trinidad and Tobago llc (1)
5-5a Queen's Park West
Port of Spain, Trinidad & Tobago
Tel.: (868) 623 2862
Fax: (868) 627 7863
E-Mail: bptt@bp.com
Web Site: www.bp.com
Emp.: 700
Oil & Gas Exploration Services
S.I.C.: 1389
N.A.I.C.S.: 213112
Shiva McMahon *(CFO)*
David Godfrey *(Chief Procurement Officer)*

BP Venezuela (1)
Edificio Centro Seguros Suramerica Pisos 3 y 5 El Rosal
Caracas, 1060, Venezuela
Tel.: (58) 2129019000
Fax: (58) 2129019033
Web Site: www.bp.com
Emp.: 374
Oil & Gas Refining
S.I.C.: 1311
N.A.I.C.S.: 211111

BP Zimbabwe (Pvt) Limited (1)
Block 1 Tendeseka Office Park
PO Box 982
S Machel Ave East Eastlea, Harare, Zimbabwe
Tel.: (263) 4701572
Fax: (263) 4701596
Web Site: www.bp.com
Oil & Gas Distribution; Gasoline Service Stations
S.I.C.: 5541
N.A.I.C.S.: 447190

Burmah Castrol Australia Pty ltd. (1)
L7 717 Bourke St
Docklands, Melbourne, VIC, 3008, Australia
Tel.: (61) 392684200
Lubricating Oil & Grease Mfr
S.I.C.: 2992
N.A.I.C.S.: 324191

Chemcolor-Beta d.d. (1)
Avenija Dubrovnik 10
Zagreb, Croatia
Tel.: (385) 16520567
Fax: (385) 16520562
E-Mail: chemcolor1@zg.htnet.hr
Sales Range: $25-49.9 Million
Emp.: 5
Lubricants Marketing Services
S.I.C.: 5172
N.A.I.C.S.: 424720
Igor Boskovic *(Mng Dir)*

China American Petrochemical Co., Ltd. (1)
4F 260 Tun Hua North Rd
Taipei, ROC, Taiwan TW (50%)
Tel.: (886) 27156688
Telex: 785-21872
Fax: (886) 27131099
E-Mail: service@capco.com.tw
Web Site: www.capco.com.tw
Emp.: 577
Mfr. & Sale of Chemical Products
S.I.C.: 2899
N.A.I.C.S.: 325998

Comercio de Combustiveis e Lubrificantes S.A. (1)
Lagoa's Park Edificio 3
2740-244 Porto Salvo, Portugal
Tel.: (351) 213891000
Fax: (351) 213891600
E-Mail: relacc@ec1.bp.com
Web Site: www.bp.pt
Emp.: 400
Petroleum & Petroleum Products Whslr
S.I.C.: 5172
N.A.I.C.S.: 424720
Saffano Gofdo *(Chm & CEO)*

Deutsche BP AG (1)
Wittener Str 45
44789 Bochum, Germany (100%)
Tel.: (49) 2343150
Telex: 8 24 881
Fax: (49) 2343152679
E-Mail: info@aral.de
Web Site: www.bpdeutschland.de
Emp.: 1,200
Oil & Gas Production; Petroleum Product Mfr & Distr
Import Export
S.I.C.: 2911
N.A.I.C.S.: 324110
Uwe Sranke *(Chm)*
Micheal Schmidt *(Mng Dir)*

Subsidiaries:

Aral Waerme Service GmbH (2)
Alexander Von Humboldt Str 1
45896 Gelsenkirchen, Germany (100%)
Tel.: (49) 2096060
Fax: (49) 2096067870
E-Mail: info@bprp.de
Web Site: www.bprp.de
Emp.: 3,100
Petroleum Product Distr
S.I.C.: 5169
N.A.I.C.S.: 424690

BP Europa SE (2)
Wittener Strasse 45
44789 Bochum, Germany (100%)
Tel.: (49) 234 315 0
Fax: (49) 234 315 2679
E-Mail: info@de.bp.com
Web Site: www.deutschebp.de
Emp.: 500
Petroleum Products Mfr & Distr
S.I.C.: 2999
N.A.I.C.S.: 324199
Michael Schmidt *(CEO)*

Subsidiary:

BP Refining & Petrochemicals GmbH (3)
Wittener Str 45
44789 Bochum, Germany (100%)
Tel.: (49) 2343150
Fax: (49) 69222212734
E-Mail: infobprp@de.bp.com
Web Site: www.bprp.de
Emp.: 1,200
Refinery Operation
S.I.C.: 2911
N.A.I.C.S.: 324110
Michael Schmidt *(Mng Dir)*
Bernhard Hautkappe *(Mng Dir)*

Holdings:

Erdoel-Raffinerie-Emsland GmbH & Co. KG (2)
Raffinerie Str 1
49808 Lingen, Germany (100%)
Tel.: (49) 5916110
Fax: (49) 5916112300
E-Mail: info@ere.de.bp.com
Web Site: www.bp.lingen.de
Emp.: 700
Oil Refinery Operation
S.I.C.: 1623
N.A.I.C.S.: 237120
Kline Eggebrecht *(Mng Dir)*

Nord-West Oelleitung GmbH (2)
Zum Oelhafendamm 207
26384 Wilhelmshaven, Germany (25.64%)
Tel.: (49) 442162460
Telex: 253348 nwoel d
Fax: (49) 442162381
E-Mail: nwo@nwowhv.de
Web Site: www.nwowhv.de
Emp.: 130
Crude Petroleum Terminal Operation
S.I.C.: 5172
N.A.I.C.S.: 424720
Lars Bergmann *(Mng Dir)*
Rudolf Schultze *(Mng Dir)*

Jovo Arco Energy Co, Ltd (1)
Huandao West Road
Gaolan'gang Zhuhai, Zhuhai, 519050, China
Tel.: (86) 7567268222
Fax: (86) 7567268801
Emp.: 116
Petroleum Products Whslr
S.I.C.: 5172
N.A.I.C.S.: 424720

Non-U.S. Affiliate:

Empresa Petrolera Chaco S.A. (1)
Edificio Centro Empresarial Equipetrol Piso 6 Ave San Martin
Santa Cruz, Santa Cruz, Bolivia
Tel.: (591) 33453700
Fax: (591) 33663050
E-Mail: rafael.martinez@ypfbchaco.com.bo
Web Site: www.ypfbchaco.com.bo
Emp.: 300
Oil & Gas Exploration & Production; Owned 50% by Bolivian Pension Funds, 30% by BP plc & 20% by Bridas Corporation
S.I.C.: 1311
N.A.I.C.S.: 211111
Rafael Martinez *(Mng Dir)*

Non-U.S. Joint Ventures:

Bahia de Bizkaia Electricidad S.L. (1)
Punta Ceballos 8
48508 Zierbena, Spain ES
Tel.: (34) 94 636 6000
Fax: (34) 94 636 6004
E-Mail: info@bbe.es
Web Site: www.bbe.es
Electricity Generation Services
S.I.C.: 4911
N.A.I.C.S.: 221112

BP Fujian Limited (1)
17E Metropolitan Financial Plaza
43 Dongjie Road Gulou District, Fuzhou, Fujian, China
Tel.: (86) 5917676007
Fax: (86) 5917676005
Web Site: www.bp.com
Emp.: 300
Liquefied Petroleum Gas Distr
S.I.C.: 5989
N.A.I.C.S.: 454310

BP Malawi Limited (1)
8 Independence Drive
PO Box 469
Blantyre, Malawi
Tel.: (265) 1 824244
Fax: (265) 1 825118
Web Site: www.bp.com
Petroleum Products Marketing
S.I.C.: 5172
N.A.I.C.S.: 424720

BP PetroChina Jiangmen Fuels Co. Ltd. (1)
Room 1101 11th Flr CTS Ctr No 219
Zhongshan Wu Rd
Guangzhou, 510030, China
Tel.: (86) 2083966988
Fax: (86) 02083278416
Emp.: 200
Petroleum & Petroleum Products Whslr
S.I.C.: 5172
N.A.I.C.S.: 424720

BP Tanzania Limited (1)
Bandari Road
PO BOX 9043
Kurasini, Dar es Salaam, Tanzania
Tel.: (255) 222112725
Fax: (255) 222112726
Web Site: www.bp.com
Emp.: 225
Petroleum & Petroleum Products Whslr; Gasoline Service Stations; Owned 50% by BP plc & 50% by Tanzanian Government
S.I.C.: 5172
N.A.I.C.S.: 424720
Arness Siame *(Mgr-HR)*

BP Zhuhai Chemical Company Limited (1)
Da Ping Harbour Lin Gang Industrial Zone
Nanshui Town, Zhuhai, Guangdong, 519050, China
Tel.: (86) 7567269888
Fax: (86) 7567269788
Emp.: 250
Plastic Materials & Resins Mfr
S.I.C.: 2821
N.A.I.C.S.: 325211

Castrol BP Petco Co., Ltd. (1)
7th Floor Central Plaza 17 Le Duan District 1
Ho Chi Minh City, Vietnam
Tel.: (84) 8 3821 9153
Fax: (84) 8 3821 9152
Web Site: www.bp.com
Emp.: 190
Petroleum & Gas Exploration, Production & Sales; Owned 65% by BP plc & 35% by Petrolimex
S.I.C.: 1311
N.A.I.C.S.: 211111

Pan American Energy LLC (1)
Av Leandro N Alem 1180
1001 Buenos Aires, Argentina
Tel.: (54) 1143104100
Fax: (54) 1143104319
E-Mail: info@panamericanenergy.com
Web Site: www.panamericanenergy.com
Sales Range: $1-4.9 Billion
Emp.: 1,500
Oil & Natural Gas Exploration & Production
S.I.C.: 1311
N.A.I.C.S.: 211111
Denis Kellener *(CFO)*

Subsidiary:

Axion Energy (2)
(Formerly Esso Petrolera Argentina S.R.L.)
Carlos Maria Della Paolera 265 Piso 19
Buenos Aires, Argentina AR
Tel.: (54) 11 4705 7000
Web Site: www.axionenergy.com
Sales Range: $600-649.9 Million
Emp.: 400
Producing, Refining & Marketing of Petroleum Products & Industrial Lubricants
S.I.C.: 2911
N.A.I.C.S.: 324110

Peninsular Aviation Services Co. Ltd. (1)
Haya Al-Salama District Hadiqat Rami Street 23
PO Box 6369
21442 Jeddah, Saudi Arabia
Tel.: (966) 26396222
Fax: (966) 26822580
E-Mail: pasco-corporate@shell.com
Web Site: www.shell.com
Emp.: 90
Aviation Services; Owned 50% by Saudi Arabian Markets Ltd., 25% by BP plc & 25% by The Shell Petroleum Co. Ltd.
S.I.C.: 4581
N.A.I.C.S.: 488119
Navased Puri *(Gen Mgr)*

Samsung BP Chemicals Co., Ltd. (1)
22-23F Samsung Electronics Bldg
Seocho2-Dong, Seoul, Seocho-Gu, 1320-10, Korea (South) Ks
Tel.: (82) 22550900
Fax: (82) 22550996
Web Site: www.samsungbp.co.kr
Emp.: 200
Production & Supply of Fine Chemicals, Including Acetic Acid Production & Vinyl Acetate Monomer; 51% Owned by BP plc & 49% by Samsung Group
S.I.C.: 5172
N.A.I.C.S.: 424720
O.K. Park *(Pres)*

Shanghai SECCO Petrochemical Co., Ltd. (1)
29/30F A Building Far East International Plaza
No 299 Xian Xia Road, Shanghai, 200051, China CN
Tel.: (86) 2152574688
Fax: (86) 2162097070
E-Mail: contacts@secco.com.cn
Web Site: www.secco.com.cn
Emp.: 500
Petrochemical Products Mfr; Owned 50% by BP plc & 50% by China Petrochemical Corporation
S.I.C.: 2869
N.A.I.C.S.: 325110
Xin Hua *(Dir-Fin)*

Tata BP Solar India Limited (1)
Plot No 78 Electronic City
Hosur Road, Bengaluru, 560 100, India
Tel.: (91) 8056601300
Fax: (91) 80 2852 0972
Web Site: www.tatabpsolar.com
Emp.: 500
Mfr of Solar Cells, Solar PV Modules & Systems & Solar Thermal Systems for Solar Energy; Owned 51% by BP plc & 49% by Tata Group
S.I.C.: 4911
N.A.I.C.S.: 221121
D. Guru *(Acting CEO)*

BPE UNTERNEHMENSBETEILI GUNGEN GMBH

(d/b/a BPE Private Equity GmbH)
Schleusenbrucke 1
20354 Hamburg, Germany
Tel.: (49) 403615700
Fax: (49) 4036157070
E-Mail: info@bpe.de
Web Site: www.bpe.de
Managed Assets: $201,973,500

Business Description:
Private Equity Firm
S.I.C.: 6211
N.A.I.C.S.: 523999

Personnel:
Stephan Gummert *(Partner)*

Holding:

StrikoWestofen GmbH (1)
Fritz Kotz Str 2 4
51674 Wiehl, Germany De
Mailing Address:
Postfach 1160
51655 Wiehl, Germany
Tel.: (49) 226170910
Fax: (49) 2617091107
E-Mail: info@strikowestofen.com
Web Site: www.strikowestofen.com
Sales Range: $50-74.9 Million
Emp.: 145
Furnace Installatiosn & Die Casting Services
S.I.C.: 8711
N.A.I.C.S.: 541330
Ludger Greskotter *(Mng Dir)*

BPH ENERGY LIMITED

14 View St
Perth, WA, 6006, Australia
Tel.: (61) 893288366
Fax: (61) 893288733
E-Mail: admin@bphenergy.com.au
Web Site: www.bphenergy.com.au
BPH—(ASX)
Sales Range: Less than $1 Million

Business Description:
Biomedical Researcher & Developer
S.I.C.: 8731
N.A.I.C.S.: 541711

Personnel:
David Breeze *(Chm & Mng Dir)*
Deborah Ambrosini *(Sec)*

Board of Directors:
David Breeze
Deborah Ambrosini
Hock Goh

BPL LIMITED

11th KM Arakere Bannerghatta Road
Bengaluru, 560076, India
Tel.: (91) 8026484314
Web Site: www.bpl.in
Year Founded: 1963
BPL—(NSE)
Rev.: $27,010,039
Assets: $84,629,761
Liabilities: $13,884,522
Net Worth: $70,745,239
Earnings: ($1,608,275)
Emp.: 392
Fiscal Year-end: 03/31/13

Business Description:
Household Appliance Mfr
S.I.C.: 3639
N.A.I.C.S.: 335228

Personnel:
Ajit G. Nambiar *(Chm-Supervisory Bd & Mng Dir)*
Manoj Nambiar *(CFO)*
Dinesh Karunakaran *(COO-BPL Telecom Pvt Ltd)*
K. Vishwanath *(Chief Admin Officer)*
Shailesh Mudaliar *(Chief HR Officer)*
Srinath Maniyal M. *(Compliance Officer, Sec & Head-Secretarial)*

Supervisory Board of Directors:
Subhash Bathe
Anju Chandrasekhar
Suray L. Mehta
Ajit G. Nambiar
S. Prabhala
K. S. Prasad

BPL Limited—(Continued)

K. Jayabharath Reddy

Transfer Agent:
Karvy Computershare Private Limited
Plot No 17-24 Near Image Hospital Vittal Rao Nagar Madhapur
Hyderabad, India

BPOST SA

(Formerly La Poste S.A./De Post N.V.)
Centre Monnaie/Muntcentrum
PO Box 5000
1000 Brussels, Belgium
Tel.: (32) 22762210
Fax: (32) 22762149
E-Mail: press.relations@bpost.be
Web Site: www.bpost.be
BPOST—(EUR OTC)
Rev.: $3,251,942,869
Emp.: 29,922
Fiscal Year-end: 12/31/12

Business Description:
Physical & Electronic Postal Services
S.I.C.: 4311
N.A.I.C.S.: 491110

Personnel:
Martine Durez *(Chm)*
Johny Thijs *(CEO)*
Pierre Winand *(CFO)*

Board of Directors:
Martine Durez
Francois Cornelis
Sophie Dutordoir
Arthur Goethals
Bruno Holthof
Luc Lallemand
Laurent Levaux
K.B. Pedersen
Johny Thijs
Caroline Ven
Bjarne Wind

Subsidiaries:

Belgian Post International SA/NV **(1)**
EMC Bldg 829 C
Brucargo, 1931 Zaventem, Belgium BE
Tel.: (32) 22762500
Fax: (32) 22762510
E-Mail: sales.international@post.be
Web Site: www.belgianpostinternational.be
Emp.: 400
International Postal Services
S.I.C.: 4311
N.A.I.C.S.: 491110
Ezes Roose *(Mgr-Comml)*

Certipost SA/NV **(1)**
Ninovesteenweg 196
9320 Erembodegem, Belgium BE
Tel.: (32) 53601111 (100%)
Fax: (32) 53601101
E-Mail: sales@staff.certipost.be
Web Site: www.certipost.be
Emp.: 90
Electronic Document Exchange & Security Services
S.I.C.: 7389
N.A.I.C.S.: 519190
Gert Roeckx *(CEO)*
Dirk Matheussen *(CIO)*

Deltamedia SA/NV **(1)**
Industrielaan 24
1740 Ternat, Belgium BE
Tel.: (32) 2568 0300 (100%)
Fax: (32) 2568 0359
E-Mail: info@deltamedia.be
Web Site: www.deltamedia.be
Emp.: 80
Newspaper, Magazine & Other Printed Materials Distr & Sales
S.I.C.: 5963
N.A.I.C.S.: 454390

Euro-Sprinters SA/NV **(1)**
Noordersingel 13
2140 Antwerp, Belgium BE
Tel.: (32) 70233533 (100%)
Fax: (32) 70233032
E-Mail: info@eurosprinters.be
Web Site: www.eurosprinters.com
Sales Range: $1-9.9 Million
Emp.: 20
Courier Services
S.I.C.: 4513
N.A.I.C.S.: 492110
Yves Remy *(Gen Mgr)*

eXbo Services International SA/NV **(1)**
Willebroekkaai 22
1000 Brussels, Belgium BE
Tel.: (32) 2763200 (100%)
Fax: (32) 2763210
Web Site: www.exbo.be
Emp.: 50
Document & Mailroom Solutions
S.I.C.: 7389
N.A.I.C.S.: 561410
Eric Piers *(Mng Dir)*

SPEOS Belgium SA/NV **(1)**
Rue Bollinckxstraat 26-32
1070 Brussels, Belgium BE
Tel.: (32) 25580200 (100%)
Fax: (32) 25207037
E-Mail: info@speos.be
Web Site: www.speos.be
Emp.: 200
Document Production & Distribution Services
S.I.C.: 7389
N.A.I.C.S.: 561410
Stephane Raymakers *(Mng Dir)*

Taxipost SA/NV **(1)**
Centre Monnaie/Muntcentrum 13th Floor
1000 Brussels, Belgium BE
Tel.: (32) 2201 2345 (100%)
Web Site: www.taxipost.be
Emp.: 1,000
Express Mail Services
S.I.C.: 4311
N.A.I.C.S.: 491110

Joint Venture:

Banque de La Poste S.A./Bank van De Post N.V. **(1)**
Boulevard Anspach 1
1000 Brussels, Belgium BE
Tel.: (32) 25456211
Fax: (32) 25456262
E-Mail: quality@bpo.be
Web Site: www.bpo.be
Emp.: 170
Retail Banking Services; Owned 50% by La Poste S.A./De Post N.V. & 50% by Fortis Bank SA/NV
S.I.C.: 6035
N.A.I.C.S.: 522120
David Moucheron *(Chm-Mgmt Bd & CEO)*
Marc Van der Schueren *(Member-Mgmt Bd)*

BPP COMMUNICATIONS LTD.

(d/b/a Bell Pottinger Private)
6th Floor Holborn Gate 330 High Holborn
London, WC1V 7QD, United Kingdom
Tel.: (44) 20 7861 3800
Fax: (44) 2078613902
E-Mail: info@bell-pottinger.co.uk
Web Site: www.bell-pottinger.co.uk
Year Founded: 2012
Emp.: 200

Business Description:
Holding Company
S.I.C.: 6719
N.A.I.C.S.: 551112

Personnel:
Tim Bell *(Co-Owner)*
Piers Pottinger *(Co-Owner)*
James Henderson *(CEO)*
Paul Barker *(Partner-Fin & Corp Practice-Consumer Indus)*
Tim Wilkinson *(Chm-Middle East)*

Holdings:

Bell Pottinger Public Affairs Ltd. **(1)**
6th Floor Holborn Gate
26 Southhampton Buildings, London, WC2A 1QB, United Kingdom
Tel.: (44) 20 7861 2400
Fax: (44) 20 7861 2401
E-Mail: pbingle@bell-pottinger.co.uk
Web Site: www.bppa.co.uk
Emp.: 45
Advertising Agency
S.I.C.: 8743
N.A.I.C.S.: 541820
Tim Collins *(Chm)*

Pelham Bell Pottinger **(1)**
6th Floor Holborn Gate
330 High Holborn, London, WC1V 7QD, United Kingdom
Tel.: (44) 20 7861 3232
Fax: (44) 20 7861 3233
E-Mail: pr@pelhambellpottinger.co.uk
Web Site: www.pelhambellpottinger.co.uk
Emp.: 32
Advertising Agency
S.I.C.: 7311
N.A.I.C.S.: 541810
James Henderson *(CEO)*
Gavin Davis *(Mng Dir)*

BPTP LIMITED

BPTP Crest Plot 15 Udyog Vihar Phase IV
Gurgaon, 122015, India
Tel.: (91) 124 385 2787
Fax: (91) 124 385 2999
E-Mail: sales@bptp.com
Web Site: www.bptp.com
Emp.: 800

Business Description:
Residential & Commercial Real Estate Developer
S.I.C.: 1531
N.A.I.C.S.: 236117

Personnel:
Kabul Chawla *(Chm & Mng Dir)*
Amit Mandahar *(CTO)*
Ajay Seth *(Sr VP-Mktg)*

Board of Directors:
Kabul Chawla
Anupam Bansal
Bhupindar Singh Lamba
Rakesh Narang
Banarsi Lal Passi
Bryan Taft Souther Gill
Peter James Succoso
Sudhanshu Tripathi

BR INDUSTRIER AS

Forusbeen 210
4313 Sandnes, Norway
Tel.: (47) 5163 1710
Fax: (47) 5163 1711
Web Site: www.br-industrier.no
Year Founded: 2000
Emp.: 700

Business Description:
Holding Company; Industrial Engineering Services
S.I.C.: 6719
N.A.I.C.S.: 551112

Personnel:
Bjorn Rygg *(CEO)*

Subsidiary:

OneCo AS **(1)**
Sagmyra 25
4623 Kristiansand, Norway NO
Mailing Address:
Postboks 5504
Voiebyen, 4677 Kristiansand, Norway
Tel.: (47) 9100 9100
E-Mail: post@oneco.no
Web Site: www.oneco.no
Sales Range: $100-124.9 Million
Emp.: 350
Energy Industry & Infrastructure Electrical Engineering & Automation Services
S.I.C.: 8711
N.A.I.C.S.: 541330
Marvin Jensen *(CEO)*
Trond Larsen *(CFO & CTO)*
Arnstein Moy *(CMO & Head-Bus Dev)*

BR MALLS PARTICIPACOES S.A.

Av Afrano de Melo Franco 290-Salas 102 103
22430-060 Rio de Janeiro, RJ, Brazil
Tel.: (55) 21 3138 9900
Fax: (55) 21 3138 9901
E-Mail: gd-ri@brmalls.com.br
Web Site: www.brmalls.com.br
BRML3—(BRAZ)

Business Description:
Shopping Mall Operator
S.I.C.: 6512
N.A.I.C.S.: 531120

Personnel:
Richard Paul Matheson *(Chm)*
Carlos Medeiros *(Vice Chm & CEO)*
Leandro Lopes *(CFO)*
Ruy Kameyama *(COO)*
Luiz Alberto Quinta *(Chief Dev Officer)*

Board of Directors:
Richard Paul Matheson
Jose Marcio Camargo
Jose Ecio Pereira da Costa, Jr.
Ricardo Dias da Cruz Affonso Ferreira
Goncalo Cristovam Meirelles de Araujo Dias
Carlos Medeiros
Luiz Alberto Quinta

BR PROPERTIES S.A.

Rua Funchal 418 15 andar Cj 1502
Vila Olimpia
04551 060 Sao Paulo, Brazil
Tel.: (55) 1132011000
Fax: (55) 1132011003
Web Site: www.brpr.com.br
BRPR3—(BRAZ OTC)
Sales Range: $125-149.9 Million

Business Description:
Real Estate Development Service
S.I.C.: 6513
N.A.I.C.S.: 531110

Personnel:
Claudio Bruni *(CEO)*
Pedro Marcio Daltro dos Santos *(CFO & IR Officer)*
Marco Antonio Cordeiro *(COO)*
Martin Jaco *(Chief Investment Officer)*

Board of Directors:
Antonio Carlos Augusto Ribeiro Bonchristiano
Antonio Carlos Borges Camanho
Sheila Periard Henrique Silva
Marcio Tabatchnik Trigueiro

BRAC BANK LIMITED

1 Gulshan Ave Gulshan-1
Dhaka, 1212, Bangladesh
Tel.: (880) 28859202
Fax: (880) 29860395
E-Mail: enquiry@bracbank.com
Web Site: www.bracbank.com
BRACBANK—(DHA)
Int. Income: $216,997,199
Assets: $2,233,304,132
Liabilities: $2,091,245,249
Net Worth: $142,058,882
Earnings: $8,663,330
Emp.: 7,403
Fiscal Year-end: 12/31/12

Business Description:
Banking Services
S.I.C.: 6211
N.A.I.C.S.: 523110

Personnel:
Mahbubur Rahman *(CEO & Mng Dir)*
Nawed Iqbal *(CTO)*
Nabil Mustafizur Rahman *(Chief Credit Officer)*
Rais Uddin Ahmad *(Chief Anti Money Laundering Compliance Officer, Sec & Head-Legal)*
Ishtiaq Mohiuddin *(Deputy Mng Dir)*
Mohammad Mamdudur Rashid *(Deputy Mng Dir)*

Board of Directors:
Fazle Hasan Abed

Tamara Hasan Abed
Muhammad A. Ali
Zahida Ispahani
Nihad Kabir
Shib Narayan Kairy
Mahbubur Rahman
Hafiz G. A. Siddiqi

BRAC SYSTEMS INC.

3614 Poirier
Ville St Laurent, Montreal, QC, H4R 2J5, Canada
Tel.: (514) 856-2722
Fax: (514) 856-2723
Toll Free: (866) 494-2722
E-Mail: info@bracsystems.com
Web Site: www.bracsystems.com
BAAC—(DEU)
Sales Range: $1-9.9 Million
Emp.: 8
Business Description:
Greywater Recycling System Mfr
S.I.C.: 4941
N.A.I.C.S.: 221310
Personnel:
Dennis Yasar *(Pres & CEO)*

BRACCO S.P.A.

Via Egdio Folli 50
20134 Milan, Italy
Tel.: (39) 221771
Fax: (39) 0226410673
E-Mail: info@bracco.com
Web Site: www.bracco.com
Year Founded: 1927
Sales Range: $750-799.9 Million
Emp.: 2,300
Business Description:
Medical Imaging & Diagnostic Equipment & Pharmaceutical Mfr
Export
S.I.C.: 2834
N.A.I.C.S.: 325412
Personnel:
Diana Bracco *(Chm & CEO)*
Subsidiaries:

Bracco Imaging S.p.A. **(1)**
Via per Ceriano
20020 Milan, Italy
Tel.: (39) 0296141
Fax: (39) 0226410678
Web Site: www.braccoimaging.com
Emp.: 300
Pharmaceutical Mfr
S.I.C.: 2834
N.A.I.C.S.: 325412
Mirezao Zernatte *(Mng Dir)*

U.S. Subsidiary:

Bracco Diagnostics Inc. **(2)**
107 College Rd E
Princeton, NJ 08540-6612 DE
Mailing Address: (100%)
PO Box 5225
Princeton, NJ 08543-5225
Tel.: (609) 514-2200
Fax: (609) 514-2424
Toll Free: (800) 631-5245
Emp.: 250
Medical Contrast Imaging Pharmaceutical Developer & Mfr
S.I.C.: 2834
N.A.I.C.S.: 325412
Ed Smith *(VP-Sls)*

Non-U.S. Subsidiary:

Bracco Imaging Deutschland GmbH **(2)**
Max Stromeyer Strasse 116
78467 Konstanz, Germany De
Tel.: (49) 75313631000
Fax: (49) 75313631001
E-Mail: kontrastmittel@bracco.com
Web Site: www.braccoimaging.de
Emp.: 50
Pharmaceutical Development & Manufacturing
S.I.C.: 2834
N.A.I.C.S.: 325412
Thilo Schneider *(Mng Dir)*

Non-U.S. Joint Venture:

Bracco-Eisai Co., Ltd. **(2)**
3-11-6 Ohtsuka
Bunkyo-ku, Tokyo, 112-0012, Japan JP
Tel.: (81) 3 5319 3381 (49%)
Fax: (81) 3 5319 3387
E-Mail: murao@bracco-eisai.co.jp
Sales Range: $1-9.9 Million
Emp.: 50
Medical Contrast Imaging Products Mfr & Distr
Import
S.I.C.: 2834
N.A.I.C.S.: 325412
Neil Foust *(Gen Mgr)*

Centro Diagnostico Italiano S.p.A. **(1)**
Via Saint Bon 20
20147 Milan, Italy
Tel.: (39) 02483171
E-Mail: info@cdi.it
Web Site: www.cdi.it
Diagnostic Medical Services
S.I.C.: 8071
N.A.I.C.S.: 621512
Maurizio Guizzardi *(Mng Dir)*
Cinzia Arsini *(Chief HR Officer & Head-Quality, Customer Svc & Org Dev)*

U.S. Subsidiaries:

ACIST Medical Systems, Inc. **(1)**
7905 Fuller Rd
Eden Prairie, MN 55344
Tel.: (952) 941-3507
Fax: (950) 995-9300
Toll Free: (888) 667-6648
Web Site: www.acist.com
Emp.: 100
Medical Chemical Injection Systems Developer & Mfr
S.I.C.: 3841
N.A.I.C.S.: 339112
Thomas Morizio *(Pres & COO)*
Fulvio Renoldi Bracco *(CEO)*

Bracco Research USA Inc **(1)**
305 College Rd E
Princeton, NJ 08540-6608 (100%)
Tel.: (609) 514-2409
Fax: (609) 514-2446
Web Site: www.bracco.com
Emp.: 48
Research & Development of Drugs
S.I.C.: 5999
N.A.I.C.S.: 453998
Adrian Nunn *(Pres)*

Non-U.S. Subsidiary:

Bracco International B.V. **(1)**
Strawinskylaan 3051
1077 ZX Amsterdam, Netherlands
Tel.: (31) 203012150
Fax: (31) 203012216
Web Site: www.bracco.com
Emp.: 2
Pharmaceutical & Medical Diagnostic Equipment Developer & Mfr
S.I.C.: 2834
N.A.I.C.S.: 325412
Tatjana Kabulova *(Mgr)*

BRADES RESOURCE CORP.

2200-1055 West Hastings Street
Vancouver, BC, V6E 2E9, Canada
Tel.: (604) 684-6264
Fax: (604) 684-6242
Year Founded: 2006
BRA—(TSXV)
Assets: $601,959
Liabilities: $72,947
Net Worth: $529,011
Earnings: ($269,683)
Fiscal Year-end: 04/30/13
Business Description:
Metal Mining
S.I.C.: 1099
N.A.I.C.S.: 212299
Personnel:
Brian Biles *(Pres & CEO)*
Cyrus H. Driver *(CFO)*
Christopher Cherry *(Sec)*
Board of Directors:
Brian Biles
Tony Chan
Harrison Cookenboo
Robert Dardi
Cyrus H. Driver

BRADESPAR S.A.

Av Paulista
1450 9 Andar Cerqueria Cesar
01310-917 Sao Paulo, Brazil
Tel.: (55) 21786300
Fax: (55) 21786315
E-Mail: bradespar@bradespar.com
Web Site: www.bradespar.com.br
BRAP4—(BRAZ EUR)
Sales Range: $1-4.9 Billion
Emp.: 14
Business Description:
Investment Company
S.I.C.: 6153
N.A.I.C.S.: 522210
Personnel:
Lazaro De Mello Brandaeo *(Chm)*
Antoenio Bornia *(Vice Chm)*
Joaeo Moises De Oliveira *(CEO)*
Renato Da Cruz Gomes *(Exec Officer)*
Luiz Mauricio Leuzinger *(Exec Officer)*
Board of Directors:
Lazaro De Mello Brandaeo
Ricardo Abecassis Espirito Santo Silva
Denise Aguiar Alvarez Valente
Joaeo Aguiar Alvarez
Antoenio Bornia
Francisco Ravara Cary
Subsidiaries:

Cia Paulista de Forca e Luz Ltda **(1)**
Rodovia Campinas Mogi-Mirim
Km 2 5 Jardim Santana, Campinas, 13088-900, Brazil
Tel.: (55) 1937568704
Fax: (55) 1937568392
E-Mail: cpfl@cpfl.com.br
Web Site: www.cpfl.com.br
Electric Power Distribution
S.I.C.: 4939
N.A.I.C.S.: 221122
Wilson Pinto Ferreira, Jr. *(Pres & CEO)*

Cia Piratininga de Forca e Luz Ltda **(1)**
Rod Campinas Mogi-Mirim km 2 5
Jardim Santana, Campinas, Brazil
Tel.: (55) 1937568704
Fax: (55) 1937568436
E-Mail: cpfl@cpfl.com.br
Web Site: www.cpfl.com.br
Electric Power Distribution
S.I.C.: 4939
N.A.I.C.S.: 221122
Wilson Serreira, Jr. *(CEO)*

RGE Rio Grande Energia S.A. **(1)**
Rua Sao Luiz 77 8th Floor
Porto Alegre, Brazil
Tel.: (55) 5132183210
Fax: (55) 5132183110
Web Site: www.rge-rs.com.br
Electric Power Distribution
S.I.C.: 4911
N.A.I.C.S.: 221122
Wilson Pinto Ferreira, Jr. *(Pres)*

BRADFORD GREENHOUSES LTD.

4346 County Rd 90 R R 2
Barrie, ON, L4M 4S4, Canada
Tel.: (705) 725-9913
Fax: (705) 725-1845
E-Mail: cs.barrie@bradfordgreenhouses.com
Web Site: www.bradfordgreenhouses.com
Year Founded: 1975
Rev.: $10,433,394
Emp.: 120
Business Description:
Flower Shop Chemicals & Fertilizers Distr
S.I.C.: 0181
N.A.I.C.S.: 111422
Personnel:
Len Ferragine *(Owner)*

BRADFORDS BUILDING SUPPLIES LTD.

96 Hendford Hill
Yeovil, Somerset, BA20 2QR, United Kingdom
Tel.: (44) 1935845245
Fax: (44) 1935845242
E-Mail: bradfords@bradfords.co.uk
Web Site: www.bradfords.co.uk
Year Founded: 1770
Sales Range: $100-124.9 Million
Emp.: 485
Business Description:
Building Supplies Retailer
S.I.C.: 5251
N.A.I.C.S.: 444130
Personnel:
Andrew Merriam *(Chm)*
Dennis J. Smith *(Mng Dir)*

BRADKEN LTD.

20 McIntosh Drive
Mayfield, NSW, 2304, Australia
Tel.: (61) 249268200
Fax: (61) 249268201
E-Mail: bradken@bradken.com.au
Web Site: www.bradken.com
Year Founded: 1922
BKN—(ASX)
Rev.: $1,372,906,308
Assets: $1,682,586,123
Liabilities: $885,056,572
Net Worth: $797,529,551
Earnings: $69,755,048
Emp.: 5,800
Fiscal Year-end: 06/30/13
Business Description:
Mfr. of Ferrous Castings; Provides Specialist Engineering & Machining Services to the Railway, Mining, Sugar, Petrochemical & Metals Processing Industries
S.I.C.: 8711
N.A.I.C.S.: 541330
Personnel:
Brian W. Hodges *(CEO & Mng Dir)*
Steven Perry *(CFO & Sec)*
John Saad *(CTO)*
Board of Directors:
Nicholas F. H. Greiner
Phillip J. Arnall
Eileen Joy Doyle
Brian W. Hodges
Gregory R. Laurie
Peter I. Richards
David Smith
Subsidiaries:

Bradken Holdings Pty Limited **(1)**
2 Maud St
Mayfield West, Mayfield, NSW, 2304, Australia
Tel.: (61) 249412600
Fax: (61) 249675003
E-Mail: bradken@bradken.com
Web Site: www.bradken.com
Emp.: 100
Mining Equipments Distr
S.I.C.: 5082
N.A.I.C.S.: 423810
Brian Hodges *(Mng Dir)*

Cast Metal Services Pty Limited **(1)**
275 Toombul Road
Northgate, Brisbane, QLD, 4013, Australia
Tel.: (61) 732666266
Fax: (61) 732666366
E-Mail: sales@castmetal.com.au
Web Site: www.castmetal.com.au

Bradken Ltd.—(Continued)

Emp.: 20
Metal Products Mfr
S.I.C.: 3499
N.A.I.C.S.: 332999
Glenn Pearcy *(Mgr)*

Bradken Resources Wundowie Foundry Pty. Ltd. (1)
Hawke Ave
PO Box 127
Wundowie, Perth, WA, 6560, Australia
Tel.: (61) 895736300
Fax: (61) 895736424
E-Mail:
Web Site: www.bradken.com.au
Sales Range: $10-24.9 Million
Emp.: 60
General Iron & Industrial Castings & Wear Resistant Blocks Mfr
S.I.C.: 3369
N.A.I.C.S.: 331529
William E. Pearce *(Mng Dir)*

U.S. Subsidiaries:

Bradken - Atlas L.P. (1)
3021 S Wilkeson St
Tacoma, WA 98409-7857
Tel.: (253) 475-4600
Fax: (253) 473-8710
Web Site: www.bradken.com
Emp.: 300
Steel Forging Services
S.I.C.: 3462
N.A.I.C.S.: 332111
Steven Gear *(Co-Pres)*

Bradken, Inc. (1)
12200 N Ambassador Dr
Kansas City, MO 64163-1244
Tel.: (816) 270-0700
Fax: (816) 270-0799
Web Site: www.bradken.com
Emp.: 15
Industrial Machinery Mfr
S.I.C.: 3559
N.A.I.C.S.: 333249
Tom Armstrong *(Pres & COO)*

Bradken - Primecast, Inc. (1)
1555 Il Route 75 E
Freeport, IL 61032
Tel.: (815) 235-7844
Fax: (815) 235-5299
Emp.: 6
Industrial Machinery Mfr
S.I.C.: 3559
N.A.I.C.S.: 333249

Bradken (1)
400 S 4th St
Atchison, KS 66002 KS
Tel.: (913) 367-2121
Fax: (913) 367-2155
Web Site: www.bradken.com
Sales Range: $300-349.9 Million
Emp.: 1,275
Steel, Iron & Non-Ferrous Castings & Forgings
Import Export
S.I.C.: 3325
N.A.I.C.S.: 331513
Kevin T. McDermott *(CFO & VP)*

Subsidiary:

Bradken (2)
13040 Foulks Ln
Amite, LA 70422-5738 LA
Tel.: (985) 748-5342
Fax: (985) 748-7396
Web Site: www.bradken.com
Emp.: 200
Mfr. of Steel Castings
S.I.C.: 3325
N.A.I.C.S.: 331513

Non-U.S. Subsidiary:

Bradken (2)
45 Enterprise Dr
London, ON, N6N 1C1, Canada ON
Tel.: (519) 685-3000
Fax: (519) 685-6448
E-Mail: info@bradken.com
Web Site: www.bradken.com
Emp.: 120
Industrial Machine Shop
S.I.C.: 3589
N.A.I.C.S.: 333318
Mike Matheson *(Mgr-Sls)*

Non-U.S. Subsidiaries:

Bradken UK Limited (1)
Dawes Lane
Scunthorpe, South Humberside, DN16 1DN, United Kingdom
Tel.: (44) 1142841000
Fax: (44) 1142841001
Web Site: www.bradken.com
Emp.: 150
Industrial Machinery Mfr
S.I.C.: 8711
N.A.I.C.S.: 541330
Greg Dalziel *(Mgr)*

BRADLEY AIR SERVICES LIMITED

20 Cope Dr
Kanata, ON, K2M 2V8, Canada
Tel.: (613) 254-6200
Fax: (613) 254-6398
Web Site: www.firstair.ca
Sales Range: $150-199.9 Million
Emp.: 850

Business Description:
Air Transportation Services
S.I.C.: 4512
N.A.I.C.S.: 481111
Personnel:
Chris Ferris *(Interim Pres & CEO, VP-Mktg & Sls)*

BRADMER PHARMACEUTICALS INC.

Wildeboer Dellelce Place Suite 800
365 Bay St
Toronto, ON, M5H 2V1, Canada
Tel.: (416) 361-6058
Web Site: www.bradmerpharma.com
BMR—(TSX)
Int. Income: $390
Assets: $998,907
Liabilities: $27,440
Net Worth: $971,467
Earnings: ($218,750)
Emp.: 2
Fiscal Year-end: 12/31/12

Business Description:
Developer of Cancer Treatment Products
S.I.C.: 2834
N.A.I.C.S.: 325412
Personnel:
Alan M. Ezrin *(Chm, Pres & CEO)*
Paul J. Van Damme *(CFO)*
Board of Directors:
Alan M. Ezrin
Dale J. Boden
Charles James Lilly
Robert Tessarolo
Transfer Agent:
Equity Financial Trust Company
200 University Avenue Suite 400
Toronto, ON, Canada

BRADVIN TRAILER SALES LTD.

10920 87 Avenue
Grande Prairie, AB, T8V 8K4, Canada
Tel.: (780) 539-6260
Fax: (780) 539-4247
Toll Free: (800) 665-0509
Web Site: www.bradvin.com
Year Founded: 1980
Rev.: $11,737,568
Emp.: 40

Business Description:
Heavy Load Truck, Trailers Sales & Repair Service
S.I.C.: 3711
N.A.I.C.S.: 336120
Personnel:
Brad Willsey *(Gen Mgr)*

BRADY & MORRIS ENGINEERING CO. LTD.

Brady House 12/14 Veer Nariman Road
Fort, Mumbai, 400 001, India
Tel.: (91) 22 22048361
Fax: (91) 22 22041855
E-Mail: bradymum@bradys.in
Web Site: www.bradymorris.in
505690—(BOM)
Sales Range: $1-9.9 Million

Business Description:
Material Handling Equipment Mfr
S.I.C.: 3559
N.A.I.C.S.: 333249
Personnel:
Pavan G. Morarka *(Chm)*
Board of Directors:
Pavan G. Morarka
Gautam Divan
Kaushik D. Shah
Mahendra K. Shah
Rajender K. Sharma
Legal Counsel:
Hariani & Co
Mumbai, India
Transfer Agent:
Bigshare Services Pvt. Ltd.
E-2/3 Ansa Industrial Estate Sakivihar Road
Saki Naka Andheri E
Mumbai, India

BRADY EXPLORATION PLC

2nd Floor 10 Chiswell Street
London, EC1Y 4UQ, United Kingdom
Tel.: (44) 7747 020600
Fax: (44) 207 681 2190
E-Mail: info@bradyexploration.com
Web Site: www.bradyexploration.com
BRDY—(AIM)
Sales Range: $1-9.9 Million
Emp.: 64

Business Description:
Investment Services
S.I.C.: 6211
N.A.I.C.S.: 523999
Personnel:
Cliff J. Cavender *(Mng Dir & Sec)*
Board of Directors:
Alex Borrelli
Nicholas Lee
Legal Counsel:
Duane Morris
2nd Floor 10 Chiswell Street
London, United Kingdom

BRADY PLC

281 Cambridge Science Park Milton Road
Cambridge, CB4 0WE, United Kingdom
Tel.: (44) 1223 479 479
Fax: (44) 1223 472 510
E-Mail: info@bradyplc.com
Web Site: www.bradyplc.com
Year Founded: 1985
BRY—(LSE)
Rev.: $44,434,903
Assets: $94,323,095
Liabilities: $28,613,576
Net Worth: $65,709,519
Earnings: $724,894
Emp.: 250
Fiscal Year-end: 12/31/12

Business Description:
Holding Company; Commodity Trading Software Publisher
S.I.C.: 6719
N.A.I.C.S.: 551112
Personnel:
Robert Brady *(Founder)*
Gavin Lavelle *(CEO)*
Martin Thorneycroft *(CFO & Sec)*
Jon Hobbs *(CTO)*
Stephen Butcher *(CEO-Metals)*
Robert de Picciotto *(CEO-Physicals)*
Patrik Egervall *(CEO-Energy)*
John W. Underwood *(CEO-Recycling)*
Board of Directors:
Paul Fullagar
Robert James Beveridge
Robert Brady
Pat Brazel
Robert de Picciotto
Peter Harverson
Gavin Lavelle
Martin Thorneycroft
Legal Counsel:
K&L Gates
One New Change
London, EC4M 9AF, United Kingdom

Subsidiary:

Commodities Software (UK) Limited (1)
281 Cambridge Science Park Milton Road
Cambridge, CB4 0WE, United Kingdom UK
Tel.: (44) 1223 479 479 (100%)
Fax: (44) 1223 472 510
E-Mail: reception@bradyplc.com
Web Site: www.bradyplc.com
Emp.: 50
Commodities Trading Software Publisher
S.I.C.: 7372
N.A.I.C.S.: 511210
Gavin Lavelle *(CEO)*

U.S. Subsidiary:

Systems Alternatives International LLC (1)
1705 Indian Wood Cir
Maumee, OH 43537 OH
Tel.: (419) 891-1100
Fax: (419) 891-1045
E-Mail:
Web Site: www.bradyplc.com
Industrial Recycling Systems Software Publisher
S.I.C.: 7372
N.A.I.C.S.: 511210
John W. Underwood *(CEO)*

Non-U.S. Subsidiary:

Brady Energy Norway AS (1)
Storgt 7
PO Box 154
NO 1751 Halden, Norway
Tel.: (47) 69709600
Fax: (47) 69709601
E-Mail:
Emp.: 100
Developer of Commodity Trading Software
S.I.C.: 7372
N.A.I.C.S.: 511210
Knut H. H. Johansen *(CEO)*
Kent Moberg *(CFO)*
Anette Nordskog *(Exec VP & Head-Bus Dev)*

U.S. Subsidiary:

Brady Energy US, Inc. (2)
199 S Los Robles Ave Ste 610
Pasadena, CA 91101
Tel.: (626) 535-9888
Fax: (626) 229-9868
Emp.: 6
Distr of Commodity Trading Software
S.I.C.: 5045
N.A.I.C.S.: 423430
Kare Thoresen *(Product Mgr-Market Settlement)*

Non-U.S. Subsidiary:

Brady Energy Canada, Inc. (2)
251 Consumers Rd 12th Fl
Toronto, ON, M2J 4R3, Canada
Tel.: (416) 640-6396
Fax: (416) 774-2475
E-Mail:
Emp.: 4
Distr of Commodity Trading Software
S.I.C.: 5045
N.A.I.C.S.: 423430

BRAEBURY HOMES
366 King Street E Suite 400
Kingston, ON, K7K 6Y3, Canada
Tel.: (613) 546-3400
Fax: (613) 546-4213
E-Mail: headoffice@braeburyhomes.com
Web Site: www.braeburyhomes.com
Year Founded: 1983
Rev.: $10,259,504
Emp.: 47
Business Description:
Home Builders
S.I.C.: 1521
N.A.I.C.S.: 236115
Personnel:
Peter Splinter *(Owner & Pres)*
Maria Throop *(CFO)*

BRAEMAR SHIPPING SERVICES PLC
35 Cosway Street
London, NW1 5BT, United Kingdom
Tel.: (44) 2075352650
Fax: (44) 2072249038
E-Mail: corporate.enquiries@braemar.com
Web Site: www.braemarseascope.com
BMS—(LSE)
Rev.: $227,060,840
Assets: $173,012,799
Liabilities: $62,710,447
Net Worth: $110,302,351
Earnings: $10,816,557
Emp.: 920
Fiscal Year-end: 02/28/13
Business Description:
Holding Company; Marine Services
S.I.C.: 4731
N.A.I.C.S.: 488510
Personnel:
James Kidwell *(CEO)*
Martin Beer *(Sec)*
Board of Directors:
Graham Hearne
Martin Beer
John Denholm
Alastair Farley
James Kidwell
David Moorhouse
Denis Petropoulos
Legal Counsel:
Nabarro
Lacon House 84 Theobolds Road
London, United Kingdom
Subsidiaries:

Braemar Container Shipping & Chartering Limited (1)
35 Cosway Street
London, NW1 5BT, United Kingdom (100%)
Tel.: (44) 2075352867
Fax: (44) 2075352601
E-Mail: teu@braemarseascope.com
Web Site: www.braemarseascope.com
Emp.: 170
Navigational Services to Shipping
S.I.C.: 4499
N.A.I.C.S.: 488330
Peter Cazalet *(Chm)*
Alan Marsh *(CEO)*

Braemar Falconer (1)
2nd Floor Centurion House 37 Jewry Street
London, EC3N 2ER, United Kingdom
Tel.: (44) 207 265 1818
Fax: (44) 207 680 1992
E-Mail: surveys@braemarfalconer.co.uk
Marine Engineering Services
S.I.C.: 8711
N.A.I.C.S.: 541330
Brian Cushing *(Mgr-Marine-Europe)*

Braemar Howells Limited (1)
The MPSC Milford Haven
Dyfed, Pembrokeshire, SA733AQ, United Kingdom (100%)
Tel.: (44) 1646697041
Fax: (44) 164663705
E-Mail: info@braemarhowells.com
Web Site: www.braemarhowells.com
Emp.: 10
Process Physical Distribution & Logistics Consulting Services
S.I.C.: 4731
N.A.I.C.S.: 541614
Simon Rickaby *(Mng Dir)*

Braemar Seascope Limited (1)
35 Cosway St
London, NW1 5BT, United Kingdom
Tel.: (44) 2075352650
E-Mail: london@seascope.co.uk
Web Site: www.seascope.co.uk
Ship Chartering Services
S.I.C.: 4449
N.A.I.C.S.: 483211
Alan Marsh *(Chm)*

Subsidiary:

Cory Brothers Shipping Agency Limited (2)
Cory House 21 Berth
Tilbury, Essex, RM18 7JT, United Kingdom (100%)
Tel.: (44) 1375843461
Fax: (44) 1375842854
E-Mail: coreythames@cory.co.uk
Web Site: www.cory.co.uk
Emp.: 50
Freight Transportation Arrangement Services
S.I.C.: 4731
N.A.I.C.S.: 488510

Subsidiaries:

Gorman Cory Shipping Limited (3)
Claremont Bldg Old Clatterbridge Rd
Wirral, Bebington, CH63 4JB, United Kingdom
Tel.: (44) 1513340530
Fax: (44) 1513340560
E-Mail: coryliverpool@cory.co.uk
Web Site: www.cory.co.uk
Emp.: 8
Marine Cargo Handling
S.I.C.: 4491
N.A.I.C.S.: 488320

Morrison Shipping (3)
90 Giles St
Edinburgh, Leith, EH6 6BZ, United Kingdom
Tel.: (44) 1315546631
Fax: (44) 1315548504
E-Mail: info@morrisonshipping.com
Web Site: www.morrisontours.co.uk
Emp.: 12
Navigational Services to Shipping
S.I.C.: 4499
N.A.I.C.S.: 488330

Planetwide Limited (3)
4 Capricorn Ctr
Cranes Farm Rd, Basildon, Essex, SS143JJ, United Kingdom
Tel.: (44) 1268530600
Fax: (44) 1268530666
E-Mail: planet@planetwide-ltd.co.uk
Web Site: www.planetwide-ltd.co.uk
Freight Transportation Arrangement
S.I.C.: 4731
N.A.I.C.S.: 488510
John van Bergen *(Mng Dir)*

Non-U.S. Subsidiary:

Cory Brothers Shipping Pte Limited (3)
1 Pickering Street 08-02B Great Eastern Centre
Singapore, Singapore
Tel.: (65) 63393637
Fax: (65) 6338 0177
E-Mail: enquiries@cory.sg
Freight Forwarding Services
S.I.C.: 4731
N.A.I.C.S.: 488510

Non-U.S. Subsidiaries:

Braemar Seascope (Dry Cargo) Pte Limited (2)
1 Pickering Street
Singapore Land Twr, 068898 Singapore, Singapore (100%)
Tel.: (65) 65330198
Fax: (65) 65331632
Emp.: 12
Marine Cargo Handling
S.I.C.: 4491
N.A.I.C.S.: 488320

Braemar Seascope India Private Limited (2)
405 Vyapar Bhavan 49 P D'Mello Road
Carnac Bunder
Mumbai, 400 009, India
Tel.: (91) 22 6529 2440
E-Mail: mumbai@braemarseascope.co.in
Ship Chartering Services
S.I.C.: 4489
N.A.I.C.S.: 483212

Braemar Seascope Pty Limited (2)
Lvl 5 432 St Kilda Rd
Melbourne, VIC, 3000, Australia (100%)
Tel.: (61) 398672177
Fax: (61) 398675962
E-Mail: melbourne@braemarseacope.com.au
Web Site: www.braemarseascope.com.au
Emp.: 50
Navigational Services to Shipping
S.I.C.: 4499
N.A.I.C.S.: 488330

Subsidiary:

Braemar Falconer Pty Limited (3)
Unit 4 Churchill Court 335 Hay Street
Subiaco, WA, 6008, Australia
Tel.: (61) 893828190
Fax: (61) 8 9382 8269
Marine Engineering Services
S.I.C.: 8711
N.A.I.C.S.: 541330
Alex Burns *(Area Mgr)*

Braemar Steege Holdings Limited (1)
35 Cosway Street
London, NW1 5BT, United Kingdom
Tel.: (44) 20 7265 1566
Emp.: 15
Investment Management Services
S.I.C.: 6211
N.A.I.C.S.: 523999
Geoff Thomas *(Mng Dir)*

Braemar Steege Limited (1)
3rd Floor 11-13 Crosswall
London, EC3N 2JY, United Kingdom
Tel.: (44) 20 7265 1566
Fax: (44) 20 7709 0030
Web Site: www.braemarsteege.com
Emp.: 12
Marine Engineering Services
S.I.C.: 8711
N.A.I.C.S.: 541330
Nigel Carpenter *(CEO)*
Geoff Thomas *(Mng Dir)*

U.S. Subsidiaries:

Braemar Steege Inc (2)
10000 Memorial Dr Ste 100
Houston, TX 77024
Tel.: (713) 688-5353
Fax: (713) 688-3355
Web Site: www.braemarsteege.com
Marine Shipping Services
S.I.C.: 4412
N.A.I.C.S.: 483111

Braemar Steege, LLC (2)
1000 Memorial Dr
Houston, TX 77024
Tel.: (832) 203-5238
Fax: (713) 793-6999
Web Site: www.braemarsteege.com
Emp.: 10
Marine Engineering Services
S.I.C.: 8711
N.A.I.C.S.: 541330

Non-U.S. Subsidiaries:

Braemar Steege Canada Limited (2)
840-7th Ave SW Ste 820
Calgary, AB, T2P 3G2, Canada
Tel.: (403) 538-5450
Fax: (403) 538-5464
Marine Engineering Services
S.I.C.: 8711
N.A.I.C.S.: 541330

Braemar Steege Rio de Janeiro (2)
Rua Dalcidio Jurandire 255 Conj 311/312
Barra da Tijuca, Rio de Janeiro, 22631-250, Brazil
Tel.: (55) 2135932008
Fax: (55) 2135972008
E-Mail: info@braemar.com
Web Site: www.braemar.com
Emp.: 7
Marine Engineering Services
S.I.C.: 8711
N.A.I.C.S.: 541330
Jaime Talbot *(COO)*

Braemar Steege SA de CV (2)
Melchor Ocampo 430 Col Romero de Terreros
Mexico, 04310, Mexico
Tel.: (52) 55 5645 1132
Fax: (52) 55 5645 1132
E-Mail: eduardo.azuara@uorumaveuspers.com
Marine Engineering Services
S.I.C.: 8711
N.A.I.C.S.: 541330

Braemar Steege Shanghai (2)
440-442 The Bund 12 Zhong Shan Dong Yi Road
Shanghai, 200002, China
Tel.: (86) 21 6321 2233
Fax: (86) 21 6321 2244
Emp.: 10
Marine Engineering Services
S.I.C.: 8711
N.A.I.C.S.: 541330

Braemar Technical Services Ltd (1)
Marlow House 1A Lloyd's Avenue
London, EC3N 3AL, United Kingdom
Tel.: (44) 207 648 9650
Fax: (44) 207 929 5564
E-Mail: enquiries@bmtmarinerisk.com
Web Site: www.bmtmarinerisk.com
Emp.: 30
Marine Consulting Services
S.I.C.: 8711
N.A.I.C.S.: 541330
Nigel Clark *(Mng Dir)*

Fred. Olsen Freight Limited (1)
Cory House Haven Exchange
Felixstowe, IP11 2QX, IP11 2QX, United Kingdom
Tel.: (44) 1394 674822
Fax: (44) 1394 674244
Web Site: www.fredolsenfreight.com
Emp.: 95
Freight Forwarding Services
S.I.C.: 4731
N.A.I.C.S.: 488510
John Van Bergen *(Gen Mgr)*

Wavespec Limited (1)
Wavespec Ltd
Fullbridge MillFullbridge, Maldon, Essex, CM9 4LE, United Kingdom
Tel.: (44) 1621840447
Fax: (44) 1621840457
E-Mail: inbox@wavespec.com
Web Site: www.wavespec.com
Emp.: 30
Marine Engineering Consulting Services
S.I.C.: 8711
N.A.I.C.S.: 541330
J. G. Green *(Mng Dir)*

U.S. Subsidiary:

BRAEMAR WAVESPEC USA Inc. (2)
10000 Memorial Dr Ste 150
Houston, TX 77024
Tel.: (713) 820-9600
Fax: (713) 820-9319
E-Mail: houston@wavespec.com
Web Site: www.wavespec.com
Marine Engineering Services
S.I.C.: 8711
N.A.I.C.S.: 541330

Non-U.S. Subsidiaries:

Braemar Falconer Pte Limited (1)
1 Pickering St 08-01 Great Eastern Ctr
Singapore, Singapore
Tel.: (65) 62229282
Fax: (65) 62257159
E-Mail: surveys.offshoes.sg@braemar.com
Web Site: www.braemar.com

Braemar Shipping Services plc—(Continued)

Emp.: 100
Marine Engineering Services
S.I.C.: 8711
N.A.I.C.S.: 541330
Michael Yew Wah Chan *(Grp Mng Dir & Dir-Technical)*
Michael Tuck Lock Kwan *(Deputy Mng Dir)*

Non-U.S. Subsidiaries:

Braemar Falconer (India) Private Ltd **(2)**
209 & 210 2nd Floor Sai Commercial Centre B K S Devshi Marg
Govandi Station Road Govandi, Mumbai, 400088, India
Tel.: (91) 22 2550 8140
Fax: (91) 22 2550 7065
E-Mail: surveys@braemarfalconer.co.in
Emp.: 8
Marine Engineering Services
S.I.C.: 8711
N.A.I.C.S.: 541330
Vishal Subhash Sharma *(Area Mgr)*

Braemar Falconer Vietnam Co Limited **(2)**
Suite 550 Petrovietnam Towers 8 Hoang Dieu Street
Vung Tau, Vietnam
Tel.: (84) 64 3832 178
Fax: (84) 64 3839 420
E-Mail: surveys@braemarfalconer.com.vn
Emp.: 17
Marine Consulting Services
S.I.C.: 8742
N.A.I.C.S.: 541611
Pham Tuan Anh *(Gen Dir-Loss Adjuster & Sr Engr)*

Braemar Falconer Sdn Bhd **(1)**
Level 16 Menara Genesis No 33 Jalan Sultan Ismail
50250 Kuala Lumpur, Malaysia
Tel.: (60) 321412494
Fax: (60) 3 2144 5995
E-Mail: surveys@braemarfalconer.com.my
Emp.: 17
Marine Engineering Services
S.I.C.: 8711
N.A.I.C.S.: 541330
Abdul Aziz Suleiman *(Mng Dir)*

Braemar Falconer (Shanghai) Pte Ltd **(1)**
Shanghai Bund International Tower 99
Huangpu Road 1101
Shanghai, 200080, China
Tel.: (86) 21 6309 5610
Fax: (86) 21 6309 5611
E-Mail: surveys@braemarfalconer.com.cn
Web Site: www.braemaroffshore.com
Marine Engineering Services
S.I.C.: 8711
N.A.I.C.S.: 541330
Arthur Seah *(Area Mgr)*

Braemar Steege Pte. Ltd. **(1)**
Wisma Kodel 2nd Floor Jl HR Rasuna Said Kav B-4
Jakarta, 12920, Indonesia
Tel.: (62) 21 527 6302
Fax: (62) 21 527 6303
Web Site: www.braemarsteege.com
Emp.: 2
Marine Engineering Services
S.I.C.: 8711
N.A.I.C.S.: 541330
Made Arcana *(Gen Mgr)*

Braemar Steege Pte Limited **(1)**
1 Pickering Street 08-01 Great Eastern Centre
Singapore, Singapore
Tel.: (65) 62255772
Fax: (65) 6225 7177
Web Site: www.braemarsteege.com
Marine Engineering Services
S.I.C.: 8711
N.A.I.C.S.: 541330

PT Braemar Falconer **(1)**
Wisma Kodel 2nd Floor Jalan H R Rasuna Said Kav B-4
Jakarta, 12920, Indonesia
Tel.: (62) 21 527 6306
Fax: (62) 21 527 6307
E-Mail: surveys.offshore.id@braemar.com
Web Site: www.braemaroffshore.com
Emp.: 20
Marine Engineering Services
S.I.C.: 8711
N.A.I.C.S.: 541330
Arthur Morgan *(Area Mgr)*

Non-U.S. Joint Venture:

Braemar Quincannon Pte Limited **(1)**
802 Robinnnson Road 22 Fl 04
068898 Singapore, Singapore (50%)
Tel.: (65) 65330069
Fax: (65) 65363459
E-Mail: ship@braemarquincannon.com.sg
Web Site: www.braemarseascope.com
Emp.: 30
Deep Sea Freight Transportation
S.I.C.: 4412
N.A.I.C.S.: 483111
Mark Sorgo *(Mng Dir)*

BRAEVAL MINING CORPORATION

150 York Street Suite 410
Toronto, ON, M5H 3S5, Canada
Tel.: (416) 848-9504
Fax: (416) 363-9813
E-Mail: info@braevalmining.com
Web Site: www.braevalmining.com
Year Founded: 2010
BVL—(TSX)
Rev.: $76,897
Assets: $20,223,057
Liabilities: $641,025
Net Worth: $19,582,032
Earnings: ($5,397,570)
Fiscal Year-end: 12/31/12
Business Description:
Gold & Other Metal Mining
S.I.C.: 1041
N.A.I.C.S.: 212221
Personnel:
John Burzynski *(Chm)*
Jose Vizquerra Benavides *(Pres & CEO)*
Blair Zaritsky *(CFO)*
Board of Directors:
John Burzynski
Patrick Anderson
Keith D. McKay
Jose Vizquerra Benavides
Robert Wares
Transfer Agent:
Equity Financial Trust Company
200 University Avenue Suite 400
Toronto, ON, M5H 4H1, Canada
Tel.: (416) 361-0152
Fax: (416) 361-0470
Toll Free: (866) 393-4891

BRAGANZA AS

Karenslyst Alle 2
PO Box 700 Skoyen, N 0214 Oslo, Norway
Tel.: (47) 22547150
Fax: (47) 22547156
Web Site: www.braganza.no
Business Description:
Investment Holding Company
S.I.C.: 6211
N.A.I.C.S.: 523999
Personnel:
Per G. Braathen *(Chm)*
Geir Stormorken *(Mng Dir)*
Trond Johannessen *(CFO)*
Board of Directors:
Per G. Braathen
Lars A. Christensen
Bjorn Froling
Vagn Ove Sorensen
Geir Stormorken

Non-U.S. Holding:

Braathens Aviation **(1)**
Jager Hills 18
PO Box 37
SE 201 20 Malmo, Sweden
Tel.: (46) 406602300
Fax: (46) 406602849
E-Mail: info@braathens.com
Web Site: www.braathens.com
Sales Range: $200-249.9 Million
Emp.: 600
Aviation Services
S.I.C.: 4512
N.A.I.C.S.: 481111
Anders Ehrling *(CEO)*
Oyvind Thon *(CFO)*
Birgitta Lundquist *(Sec)*

Subsidiary:

Malmo Aviation AB **(2)**
Jagershillgatan 18
PO Box 37
SE 201 20 Malmo, Sweden
Tel.: (46) 406602900
Fax: (46) 406602849
E-Mail: info@malmoaviation.se
Web Site: www.malmoaviation.se
Sales Range: $150-199.9 Million
Emp.: 550
Air Transportation Services
S.I.C.: 4512
N.A.I.C.S.: 481111
Per G. Braathen *(Owner & Chm)*
Bengt Roswall *(CEO)*

BRAGG GROUP OF COMPANIES

4881 Main St
Oxford, NS, B0M 1P0, Canada
Tel.: (902) 447-2100
Fax: (902) 447-3376
Business Description:
Holding Company
S.I.C.: 6719
N.A.I.C.S.: 551112
Personnel:
John Bragg *(Co-Founder & Pres)*
Judy Bragg *(Co-Founder)*

Holdings:

EastLink Cable Systems **(1)**
PO Box 8660 Station A
Halifax, NS, B3K 5M3, Canada Ca
Tel.: (902) 488-5283
Fax: (902) 454-9159
Toll Free: (888) 345-1111, ext. 4
Web Site: www.eastlink.ca
Sales Range: $150-199.9 Million
Emp.: 1,500
Cable Network; Telecommunications Services
S.I.C.: 4899
N.A.I.C.S.: 517919
Deborah Shaffner *(Pres & COO)*
Lee Bragg *(CEO)*

Branch:

EastLink **(2)**
17 Duffy Place
Saint John's, NL, A1B 4L1, Canada Ca
Tel.: (709) 754-3775
Fax: (709) 754-3883
Web Site: www.eastlink.ca
Sales Range: $100-124.9 Million
Emp.: 50
Cable Television Services; Telecommunications
S.I.C.: 4841
N.A.I.C.S.: 515210
Dave Weir *(Dir-Inter-Carrier Relations)*

Oxford Frozen Foods Limited **(1)**
4881 Main St
PO Box 220
Oxford, NS, B0M 1P0, Canada
Tel.: (902) 447-2100
Fax: (902) 447-3245
E-Mail: sales@oxfordfrozenfoods.com
Web Site: www.oxfordfrozenfoods.com
Sales Range: $150-199.9 Million
Emp.: 600
Frozen Foods Mfr
S.I.C.: 2037
N.A.I.C.S.: 311411
John Bragg *(Pres & Co-CEO)*
David Hoffman *(Co-CEO)*
Sandro Bertossi *(COO)*

BRAHIM'S HOLDINGS BERHAD

10th Floor Menara Hap Seng 1 3
Jalan P Ramlee
50250 Kuala Lumpur, Malaysia
Tel.: (60) 323824288
Fax: (60) 323824170
E-Mail: info@brahimsgroup.com
Web Site: www.brahimsgroup.com
BRAH—(KLS)
Rev.: $64,481,334
Assets: $111,558,656
Liabilities: $35,992,138
Net Worth: $75,566,518
Earnings: $4,976,690
Fiscal Year-end: 12/31/12
Business Description:
Holding Company
S.I.C.: 6719
N.A.I.C.S.: 551112
Personnel:
Ibrahim Haji Ahmad *(Chm)*
Kee Kuang Goh *(CEO)*
Lee Kuan Lim *(Co-Sec)*
Chia Tyng Pang *(Co-Sec)*
Board of Directors:
Ibrahim Haji Ahmad
Wah Cheng
Kah Hoe Choo
Joon Hai Goh
Mohamed Zamry Mohamed Hashim
Mohd Ibrahim Mohd Zain
Legal Counsel:
Azhar & Wong
Penthouse 16th Floor Heritage House 33 Jalan Yap Ah Shak
Kuala Lumpur, Malaysia

BRAHMAPUTRA INFRAPROJECT LIMITED

(Name Changed to Brahmaputra Infrastructure Limited)

BRAHMAPUTRA INFRASTRUCTURE LIMITED

(Formerly Brahmaputra Infraproject Limited)
(d/b/a Brahmaputra Group)
Brahmaputra House A-7 Mahipalpur
NH-8 Mahipalpur Crossing, New Delhi, 110 037, India
Tel.: (91) 11 42290200
Fax: (91) 11 41687880
E-Mail: delhi@brahmaputragroup.com
Web Site: www.brahmaputragroup.com
535693—(BOM)
Sales Range: $10-24.9 Million
Emp.: 2,000
Business Description:
Civil Engineering & Construction Services
S.I.C.: 1629
N.A.I.C.S.: 237990
Personnel:
Sanjay Kumar Mozika *(Co-Mng Dir)*
Manoj Kumar Prithani *(Co-Mng Dir)*
Sanjeev Kumar Prithani *(Co-Mng Dir)*
Parimesh Manocha *(Compliance Officer & Sec)*
Board of Directors:
Satish Chander Gupta
Om Kumar
Viresh Shankar Mathur
Sanjay Kumar Mozika
Manoj Kumar Prithani
Sanjeev Kumar Prithani
Suneet Kumar Todi
Transfer Agent:
Link Intime India Pvt Limited
A-40 2nd Floor Naraina Industrial Area Phase-II
Near Batra Banquet
New Delhi, India

BRAI-COST S.P.A.
Zona Industriale Vascigliano
I-05039 Vascigliano di Stroncone
Terni, Italy
Tel.: (39) 0744607349
Fax: (39) 0744607650
E-Mail: info@brai.it
Web Site: www.brai.it
Business Description:
Roofing & Structure Waterproofing Products Mfr
S.I.C.: 2821
N.A.I.C.S.: 325211

BRAIN RESOURCE LIMITED
Level 12 235 Jones Street
Ultimo, NSW, 2007, Australia
Mailing Address:
PO Box 737
Broadway, NSW, 2007, Australia
Tel.: (61) 2 9213 6666
Fax: (61) 2 9211 2710
E-Mail: info@brainresource.com
Web Site: www.brainresource.com
BRC—(ASX OTC)
Rev.: $4,081,071
Assets: $34,718,016
Liabilities: $16,468,917
Net Worth: $18,249,099
Earnings: ($1,521,134)
Emp.: 30
Fiscal Year-end: 06/30/13
Business Description:
Medical Data for Brain Health Solutions
S.I.C.: 2741
N.A.I.C.S.: 511140
Personnel:
Evian Gordon *(Chm & CEO)*
Dan Segal *(COO)*
Gregory A. Bayer *(CEO-Ops-US)*
Robert Waring *(Sec)*
Board of Directors:
Evian Gordon
Nestor Hinzack
Russell Jamison
Dan Segal
Arthur Toga

BRAINJUICER GROUP PLC
1 Cavendish Place
London, W1G 0QF, United Kingdom
Tel.: (44) 2070431000
Fax: (44) 2074731010
E-Mail: info@brainjuicer.com
Web Site: www.brainjuicer.com
BJU—(AIM)
Rev.: $32,883,976
Assets: $18,074,974
Liabilities: $6,482,985
Net Worth: $11,591,989
Earnings: $1,639,303
Emp.: 148
Fiscal Year-end: 12/31/12
Business Description:
Online Market Research Services
S.I.C.: 8732
N.A.I.C.S.: 541910
Personnel:
John Kearon *(Founder & CEO)*
James Geddes *(CFO & Sec)*
Alex Batchelor *(COO)*
Tom Ewing *(Digital Culture Officer)*
Susan Casserly Griffin *(Exec VP-Mktg & Bus Dev)*
Rene Huey-Lipton *(Exec VP-North America)*
Alex Hunt *(Exec VP-Mid & West-US)*
Brent Snider *(Exec VP-Eastern-US)*
Board of Directors:
Ken Ford
Alex Batchelor
Graham Blashill
Robert Brand
James Geddes
John Kearon
Legal Counsel:
Taylor Wessing LLP
5 New Street Square
London, United Kingdom

BRAINPAD INC.
5-2-5 Higashi-gotanda Shinagawa-ku
Tokyo, 141-0022, Japan
Tel.: (81) 3 57914210
E-Mail: sato@brainpad.co.jp
Web Site: www.brainpad.co.jp
Year Founded: 2004
3655—(TKS)
Sales Range: $10-24.9 Million
Emp.: 80
Business Description:
Data Processing & Computer Programming Services
S.I.C.: 7374
N.A.I.C.S.: 518210
Personnel:
Takafumi Kusano *(Pres)*

BRAINS II INC.
165 Konrad Cres
Markham, ON, L3R 9T9, Canada
Tel.: (905) 946-8700
Fax: (905) 946-1949
Toll Free: (800) 272-4672
E-Mail: info@brainsii.com
Web Site: www.brainsii.com
Sales Range: $1-9.9 Million
Emp.: 250
Business Description:
Computer Equipment, Training, Services & Maintenance
S.I.C.: 7378
N.A.I.C.S.: 811212
Personnel:
Charles G. Hanna *(CEO)*

BRAINSWAY LTD.
19 Hartum Street Bynet Building 1st Floor
Har Hotzvim, Jerusalem, Israel 91451
Tel.: (972) 2 581 3140
Fax: (972) 2 581 2517
E-Mail: infobr@brainsway.com
Web Site: www.brainsway.com
BRIN—(TAE)
Sales Range: Less than $1 Million
Emp.: 36
Business Description:
Medical Device Mfr
S.I.C.: 3841
N.A.I.C.S.: 339112
Personnel:
David Zacut *(Chm)*
Avner Hagai *(Pres)*
Uzi Sofer *(CEO)*
Yael Zeiger *(CFO)*
Ronen Segal *(CTO)*
Board of Directors:
David Zacut
Daniel Azriel
Uri Elmaliach
Yanai Giora
Avner Hagai
Yuval Lavi
Gavriel Magen
Eli Rosenbaum
Yiftach Roth
Uzi Sofer
Orly Uri

THE BRAINY BRANDS COMPANY, INC.
9 Hayarden Street
Yashresh, 76838, Israel
Tel.: (972) 6787621100
Web Site: www.thebrainybrandscompany.com
Year Founded: 2007
TBBC—(OTC)
Sales Range: Less than $1 Million
Emp.: 10
Business Description:
Educational & Entertainment Products for Children
S.I.C.: 3944
N.A.I.C.S.: 339930
Personnel:
Dennis Fedoruk *(Pres)*
Paul W. Harrison *(CEO)*
Young Ronda Bush *(COO)*
Board of Directors:
Dennis Fedoruk
Paul W. Harrison
Derek Schwerzler

BRAIT S.E.
4th Floor Avantech Building
St Julian's Road, San Gwann, SGN 2805, Malta
Tel.: (356) 21 446 377
Fax: (356) 21 446 330
Web Site: www.brait.com
BRAIT—(JSE LUX)
Rev.: $393,081,640
Assets: $1,721,751,430
Liabilities: $24,231,060
Net Worth: $1,697,520,370
Earnings: $370,196,750
Emp.: 66,000
Fiscal Year-end: 03/31/13
Business Description:
Investment & Financial Services
S.I.C.: 6211
N.A.I.C.S.: 523999
Personnel:
Bryan Moyer *(Sec)*
Board of Directors:
Phillip Jabulani Moleketi
Colin Denis Keogh
Richard John Koch
Lawrence Leon Porter
Christopher Stefan Seabrooke
Hermanus Roelof Willem Troskie
Christoffel Hendrick Wiese
Legal Counsel:
M Partners S.a r.l.
56 rue Charles Martel
Luxembourg, Luxembourg

Computershare Investor Services (Pty) Ltd
70 Marshall Street
Johannesburg, South Africa
Transfer Agents:
Maitland Luxembourg SA
58 rue Charles Martel
Luxembourg, Luxembourg

Computershare Investor Services (Pty) Ltd
70 Marshall Street
Johannesburg, South Africa
Non-U.S. Subsidiaries:

Brait International Ltd (1)
Suite 520 5th Floor
Barkly Wharf, Port Louis, Mauritius (100%)
Tel.: (230) 2136909
Fax: (230) 2136913
E-Mail: d.boodhoo@brait.intnet.mu
Web Site: brait.com
Emp.: 6
Miscellaneous Financial Investment Activities
S.I.C.: 6211
N.A.I.C.S.: 523999
Dhanraj Boodhoo *(CEO)*

Brait South Africa Limited (1)
Private Bag X1 Northlands
2116 Johannesburg, South Africa
Tel.: (27) 115071000
Fax: (27) 115071001
E-Mail: vboswell@brait.com
Web Site: www.brait.com
Emp.: 40
Miscellaneous Financial Investment Activities
S.I.C.: 6211
N.A.I.C.S.: 523999
Anthony Barr *(CEO)*

Iceland Foods Ltd. (1)
Second Avenue
Deeside Industrial Park, Deeside, Flintshire, CH5 2NW, United Kingdom
Tel.: (44) 1244830100
Fax: (44) 1244 814531
E-Mail: enquiries@iceland.co.uk
Web Site: www.iceland.co.uk
Sales Range: $1-4.9 Billion
Emp.: 24,000
Grocery Stores Owner & Operator
S.I.C.: 5411
N.A.I.C.S.: 445110
Malcolm Walker *(Founder, Chm & CEO)*

THE BRAJ BINANI GROUP
Mercantile Chambers 12 J N Heredia Marg Ballard Estate
400 001 Mumbai, India
Tel.: (91) 22 2269 0506
Fax: (91) 22604960
E-Mail: mumbai@binani.net
Web Site: www.binaniindustries.com
Emp.: 2,000
Business Description:
Holding Company
S.I.C.: 6719
N.A.I.C.S.: 551112
Personnel:
Braj Binani *(Chm)*

Holding:

Binani Industries Limited (1)
601 Axis Mall Block - C Plot No CF9 Action Area - IC New Town Rajarhat
Kolkata, 700156, India
Tel.: (91) 3340161800
Fax: (91) 3340161812
E-Mail: binanical@vsnl.net
Web Site: www.binaniindustries.com
500059—(BOM)
Rev.: $904,046,961
Assets: $1,207,718,553
Liabilities: $1,162,389,662
Net Worth: $45,328,891
Earnings: ($38,652,155)
Fiscal Year-end: 03/31/13
Holding Company
S.I.C.: 6719
N.A.I.C.S.: 551112
Sunil Sethy *(Vice Chm & Mng Dir)*
Krishna K. Saraf *(Pres, Compliance Officer & Sec)*
Atul P. Falgunia *(Sr VP-Secretarial-Mumbai)*

Subsidiaries:

Asian Industry and Information Services Pvt Ltd. (2)
Peltham House 1st Floor Ballard Estate 10 J N Heredia Marg
Mumbai, Maharashtra, 400001, India
Tel.: (91) 2222660623
Magazine Publishing Services
S.I.C.: 2721
N.A.I.C.S.: 511120
Bina Verma *(Mng Dir)*

Binani Cement Limited (2)
Mercantile Chambers 12 J N Heredia Marg Ballard Estate
Mumbai, 400001, India
Tel.: (91) 2222690506
Fax: (91) 2222690003
E-Mail: mumbai@binani.net
Web Site: www.binaniindustries.com
BINANICEM—(NSE)
Rev.: $557,743,436
Assets: $740,751,962
Liabilities: $598,156,057
Net Worth: $142,595,905
Earnings: $8,681,522
Emp.: 1,750
Fiscal Year-end: 03/31/13
Cement Production & Sales
S.I.C.: 3297
N.A.I.C.S.: 327120
Jotirmoy Ghose *(Mng Dir)*
Atul P. Falgunia *(Compliance Officer & Sec)*
R. S. Joshi *(Pres-Corp Affairs)*

The Braj Binani Group—(Continued)

Darshan Lal *(Pres-Tech)*
R. P. Sharma *(Pres-Works)*
Bhadresh Khara *(Exec VP-Mktg)*

Binani Energy Pvt. Ltd (2)
Mercantile Chambers 12 Ballard Estate
J N Heredia Marg, Mumbai, 400 001, India
Tel.: (91) 2222690506
Cement Mfr
S.I.C.: 3241
N.A.I.C.S.: 327310

Binani Metals Ltd. (2)
12 J N Heredia Marg Ballard Estate
Mumbai, Maharashtra, 400001, India
Tel.: (91) 2222617491
Fax: (91) 2222619577
E-Mail: contact@binanimetals.co.in
Cement Mfr
S.I.C.: 3241
N.A.I.C.S.: 327310

U.S. Subsidiary:

CPI Binani, Inc. (2)
1700 Wilkie Dr
Winona, MN 55987 MN
Mailing Address:
PO Box 108
Winona, MN 55987
Tel.: (507) 452-2881
Fax: (507) 452-1007
Toll Free: (800) 239-2881
E-Mail: sales@cpibinani.com
Web Site: www.compositeproducts.com
Emp.: 90
Thermoplastic Composite Mfr
S.I.C.: 3089
N.A.I.C.S.: 326199
Derek Mazula *(Pres)*
Ron Hawley *(CEO)*

Non-U.S. Subsidiaries:

Bhumi Resources (Singapore) Pte Limited. (2)
29 04B Clifford Centre 24 Raffles Place
Singapore, 048621, Singapore
Tel.: (65) 65356065
Fax: (65) 65356064
Portland Cement Mfr & Sales
S.I.C.: 3241
N.A.I.C.S.: 327310

Binani Cement Factory LLC (2)
B-233 Jebel Ali Industrial Area 2
PO Box 37608
Dubai, United Arab Emirates
Tel.: (971) 14 8801063
Fax: (971) 14 8801542
Cement Mfr
S.I.C.: 3241
N.A.I.C.S.: 327310

Krishna Holdings Pte. Ltd. (2)
29 04B Clifford Centre 24 Raffles Place
Singapore, 048621, Singapore
Tel.: (65) 65356065
Fax: (65) 65356064
E-Mail: binanisgp@gmail.com
Investment Management Services
S.I.C.: 6211
N.A.I.C.S.: 523999

Mukundan Holdings Ltd (2)
29 04 B Clifford Centre 24 Raffles Place
Singapore, 048621, Singapore
Tel.: (65) 65356065
Fax: (65) 65356064
Cement Mfr
S.I.C.: 3241
N.A.I.C.S.: 327310

Murari Holdings Ltd. (2)
29 04B Clifford Centre 24 Raffles Place
Singapore, 048621, Singapore
Tel.: (65) 65356065
Fax: (65) 65356064
E-Mail: binanisgb@mail.com
Web Site: www.binani.com
Emp.: 5
Investment Management Services
S.I.C.: 6211
N.A.I.C.S.: 523999
Muthu Ram *(Gen Mgr)*

Shandong Binani Rong An Cement Co. Ltd. (2)
Fujiazhuang Village
Dongguan Town, Rizhao, Shandong, 276500, China
Tel.: (86) 633 6567222
Fax: (86) 633 6567111
Cement Mfr
S.I.C.: 3241
N.A.I.C.S.: 327310

BRAKES AUTO (INDIA) LIMITED

1011 Embassy Centre
Nariman Point, Mumbai, 400 021, India
Tel.: (91) 22 2282 3367
Fax: (91) 22 2282 3368
E-Mail: sales@BrakesAutoIndia.com
Web Site: www.brakesautoindia.com
Year Founded: 1980
520115—(BOM)

Business Description:
Fabric & Information Technology Product Distr
S.I.C.: 5131
N.A.I.C.S.: 424310

Personnel:
Suresh Sharma *(Chm & Mng Dir)*
Hemant Kokatay *(Compliance Officer)*

Board of Directors:
Suresh Sharma
Indresh Khanna
Daljeet Singh Matharu
Rajen Navnital
Giriraj Prasad Sharma
Sachin Sharma

Transfer Agent:
Purva Sharegistry (India) Pvt. Ltd.
9 Shiv Shakti Industrial Estate JR Boricha Marg
Off NM Joshi Marg
Near Lodha Excelus Lower Parel (East),
Mumbai, 400 011, India

BRALORNE GOLD MINES LTD.

Suite 900 570 Granville Street
Vancouver, BC, V6C 3P1, Canada
Tel.: (604) 682-3701
Fax: (604) 682-3600
E-Mail: ir@bralorne.com
Web Site: www.bralorne.com
BPM—(DEU OTC TSXV)
Int. Income: $2,569
Assets: $31,910,927
Liabilities: $1,030,708
Net Worth: $30,880,218
Earnings: ($1,116,755)
Fiscal Year-end: 01/31/13

Business Description:
Gold Mining Services
S.I.C.: 1041
N.A.I.C.S.: 212221

Personnel:
Gary R. Robertson *(Chm)*
Matthew Ball *(Pres & COO)*
William G. Kocken *(CEO)*
Annie Chan *(CFO)*
Johnathon Smith *(IR Officer)*
Dorothy Chin *(Sec)*

Board of Directors:
Gary R. Robertson
Matthew Ball
William C. Glasier
Patrick Kinsella
William G. Kocken
David Wolfin

Legal Counsel:
Salley Bowes Harwardt
1750 - 1185 West Georgia Street
Vancouver, BC, Canada

Transfer Agent:
Computershare Investor Services Inc
100 University Avenue 9th Floor
Toronto, ON, Canada

BRAMBLES LIMITED

Level 40 Gateway Building 1
Macquarie Place
Sydney, NSW, 2000, Australia

Mailing Address:
PO Box 4173
Sydney, NSW, 2001, Australia
Tel.: (61) 292565222
Telex: AA 21307
Fax: (61) 292565299
E-Mail: info@brambles.com
Web Site: www.brambles.com
Year Founded: 1875
BXB—(ASX)
Rev.: $5,889,900,000
Assets: $7,951,900,000
Liabilities: $4,926,500,000
Net Worth: $3,025,400,000
Earnings: $640,600,000
Emp.: 18,037
Fiscal Year-end: 06/30/13

Business Description:
Industrial Support Services
S.I.C.: 7389
N.A.I.C.S.: 541420

Personnel:
Thomas Joseph Gorman *(CEO)*
Zlatko Todorcevski *(CFO)*
Jean K. Holley *(CIO)*
Peter Mackie *(Pres-Pallets)*
Wolfgang Orgeldinger *(Pres-RPCs)*
Douglas Allen Pertz *(Pres-Recall)*
Jason Rabbino *(Pres-Containers)*
Robert Nies Gerrard *(Sec)*
Nick Smith *(Sr VP-HR)*

Board of Directors:
Graham Kraehe
Christine Cross
Douglas Gordon Duncan
Tony Froggatt
Thomas Joseph Gorman
David Gosnell
Tahira Hassan
Stephen Johns
Carolyn Kay
Luke Mayhew
Brian Schwartz

Legal Counsel:
Freehill Hollingdale & Page
MLC Centre Martin Place
Sydney, NSW, 2000, Australia
Tel.: (61) 2 225 5000

Division:

CHEP Asia-Pacific (1)
Level 6 Building C 11 Talavera Road
Ryde, NSW, 2113, Australia
Tel.: (61) 298562437
Fax: (61) 298562404
Web Site: www.chep.com
Emp.: 90
Regional Management Office; Pallet & Container Collection, Reconditioning & Rental Services
S.I.C.: 8741
N.A.I.C.S.: 551114
Phillip Austin *(Gen Mgr)*

Subsidiaries:

CHEP Australia Limited (2)
Level 6 Building C 11 Talavera Road
Ryde, NSW, 2113, Australia AU
Tel.: (61) 298562437 (100%)
Telex: 24631 CHEPSYD
Fax: (61) 2 9856 2404
Web Site: www.chep.com
Emp.: 100
Pallet & Container Collection, Reconditioning & Rental Services
S.I.C.: 7359
N.A.I.C.S.: 532490
Howard Wiggin *(Mng Dir)*

CHEP Pallecon Solutions Pty Ltd (2)
(Formerly CEVA Pallecon)
1/66 Christina Road
Villawood, NSW, 2163, Australia
Tel.: (61) 287174500
Fax: (61) 287174501
E-Mail:
Web Site: www.chep.com
Emp.: 50
Materials Handling Services
S.I.C.: 4731
N.A.I.C.S.: 541614

Non-U.S. Subsidiaries:

CHEP India Pvt. Ltd. (2)
3rd Floor Aver Plaza Opp Citi Mall New Link Road
Andheri W, Mumbai, 400 053, India In
Tel.: (91) 2267839400 (100%)
Fax: (91) 2267839472
E-Mail: sales@chep.com
Web Site: www.chep.com
Emp.: 50
Pallet & Container Collection, Reconditioning & Rental Services
S.I.C.: 7359
N.A.I.C.S.: 532490
Devdip Purkayastha *(Pres)*

CHEP (Malaysia) Sdn Bhd (2)
Suite 6 06 Penthouse Wisma Academy
4A Jalan 19/1, Petaling Jaya, Selangor DE, 46300, Malaysia MY
Tel.: (60) 379563633 (100%)
Fax: (60) 379563966
Web Site: www.chep.com
Emp.: 25
Pallet & Container Collection, Reconditioning & Rental Services
S.I.C.: 7359
N.A.I.C.S.: 532490
Fabariah Mahat *(Sec)*

CHEP New Zealand (2)
1 Nesdale Ave Manukau
Auckland, 2025, New Zealand (30%)
Tel.: (64) 92790170
Fax: (64) 92793939
E-Mail: enquiries@chep.com
Web Site: www.chep.com
Emp.: 50
Pallet & Container Collection, Reconditioning & Rental Services
S.I.C.: 7359
N.A.I.C.S.: 532490
Owen Kinnaiid *(Pres)*

CHEP (Shanghai) Co., Ltd. (2)
Level 40 Ste 8-12 2 Grand Gateway
3 Hongqiao Rd XuHui, Shanghai, 200030, China CN
Tel.: (86) 2161272488 (100%)
Fax: (86) 2161272466
E-Mail: jasmine.zhu@chep.com
Web Site: www.chep.com
Emp.: 120
Pallet & Container Collection, Reconditioning & Rental Services
S.I.C.: 7359
N.A.I.C.S.: 532490
John Wan *(Pres)*

CHEP Singapore Pte. Ltd. (2)
89 Science Pk Dr Ste 04-01 The Rutherford
Singapore, 118261, Singapore SG
Tel.: (65) 62682763
Fax: (65) 62614423
Web Site: www.chep.com
Emp.: 4
Pallet & Container Collection, Reconditioning & Rental Services
S.I.C.: 7359
N.A.I.C.S.: 532490
Lars Amstrup *(Pres)*

U.S. Division:

CHEP Americas (1)
8517 S Park Cir
Orlando, FL 32819-9040
Tel.: (407) 370-2437
Fax: (407) 363-5354
E-Mail: chep@brambles.com
Web Site: www.chep.com
Regional Management Office; Pallet & Container Collection, Reconditioning & Rental Services
S.I.C.: 8741
N.A.I.C.S.: 551114
Donna Slyster *(CIO-Global & Grp Sr VP)*
Jim Ritchie *(Pres-USA)*
Matt Phelps *(Grp Sr VP-Process Tech & Product Engrg-Global)*

Subsidiary:

CHEP USA (2)
8517 S Park Cir
Orlando, FL 32819-9030 (100%)
Tel.: (407) 370-2437

Fax: (407) 363-5354
E-Mail: info@ascomusa.com
Web Site: www.chepusa.com
Sales Range: $25-49.9 Million
Emp.: 550
Pallet & Container Collection, Reconditioning & Rental Services
S.I.C.: 7359
N.A.I.C.S.: 532490

Non-U.S. Subsidiaries:

CHEP Canada, Inc. (2)
7400 East Dandro Crescent
Mississauga, ON, L5N 8C6, Canada Ca
Tel.: (905) 790-2437 (100%)
Fax: (905) 790-6545
Web Site: www.chep.com
Emp.: 100
Pallet & Container Collection, Reconditioning & Rental Services
S.I.C.: 7359
N.A.I.C.S.: 532490
Michael F. Dimond *(Pres)*

CHEP Chile SA (2)
Ave Cerro Coloroda 5240 Twr 2 Fl15
Santiago, Chile (100%)
Tel.: (56) 23873400
Fax: (56) 23816411
E-Mail: chep.chile@chep.com
Web Site: www.chepchile.com
Emp.: 33
Pallet & Container Collection, Reconditioning & Rental Services
S.I.C.: 7359
N.A.I.C.S.: 532490
Juan Cristoval Gonzales *(Gen Mgr)*

CHEP Mexico SA de CV (2)
Blvd Manuel Avila Camacho 24 Piso 22 y 23
11000 Mexico, Mexico MX
Tel.: (52) 5585031100 (100%)
E-Mail: chep.mexico@chep.com
Web Site: www.chep.com
Emp.: 150
Pallet & Container Collection, Reconditioning & Rental Services
S.I.C.: 7359
N.A.I.C.S.: 532490
Arturo Cabrera *(Pres-Latin America)*

U.S. Subsidiary:

Brambles USA Inc. (1)
180 Technology Pkwy Ste 600
Norcross, GA 30092
Tel.: (770) 776-1900
Holding Company; Regional Managing Office
S.I.C.: 6719
N.A.I.C.S.: 551112
Jason Rabbino *(Grp Pres-Containers)*

Subsidiaries:

LeanLogistics Inc (2)
1351 S Waverly Rd
Holland, MI 49423
Tel.: (866) 584-7280
Fax: (616) 738-6462
E-Mail: sales@leanlogistics.com
Web Site: www.leanlogistics.com
Supply Chain Management Services
S.I.C.: 7389
N.A.I.C.S.: 561990
Jeff Potts *(Co-Founder & Sr VP-Bus Dev)*
Matt Ahearn *(Pres)*
Steve Pietenpol *(CFO)*
Chris Timmer *(COO)*
Mark Gaddy *(Sr VP-Sls)*
Rick Tucker *(Sr VP-Global Technologies)*

Non-U.S. Division:

CHEP EMEA (1)
Rotherwick House 3 Thomas More Street
London, E1W 1YZ, United Kingdom
Tel.: (44) 1932833089
Fax: (44) 207 702 1612
Web Site: www.chep.com
Regional Management Office; Pallet & Container Collection, Reconditioning & Rental Services
S.I.C.: 8741
N.A.I.C.S.: 551114

Division:

CHEP Europe (2)
Unit 2 Weybridge Business Park
Addlestone Road, Weybridge, Surrey, KT15 2UP, United Kingdom (100%)
Tel.: (44) 1932833115
Fax: (44) 1932850144
Web Site: www.chep.com
Emp.: 130
Regional Managing Office; Pallet & Container Collection, Reconditioning & Rental Services
S.I.C.: 8741
N.A.I.C.S.: 551114
Peter Mackie *(Pres)*

Subsidiary:

CHEP UK Limited (3)
Weybridge Business Park Addlestone Rd Unit 2
Addlestone, Surrey, KT15 2UP, United Kingdom UK
Tel.: (44) 932850085 (100%)
Fax: (44) 932850144
Web Site: www.chep.com
Emp.: 150
Pallet & Container Collection, Reconditioning & Rental Services
S.I.C.: 7359
N.A.I.C.S.: 532490
Tom Gorman *(CEO)*

Non-U.S. Subsidiaries:

CHEP Benelux Nederland BV (3)
Bedrijvenlaan 1
2800 Mechelen, Belgium NL
Mailing Address: (100%)
Postbus 51
4000 AB Tiel, Netherlands
Tel.: (32) 15799700
Fax: (32) 15799799
E-Mail: info@chep.com
Web Site: www.chep.com
Emp.: 30
Pallet & Container Collection, Reconditioning & Rental Services
S.I.C.: 7359
N.A.I.C.S.: 532490
Oliver Legendre *(Gen Mgr)*

CHEP Benelux N.V. (3)
Pedro Colomalaan 15
2880 Bornem, Belgium (100%)
Tel.: (32) 80039152
Fax: (32) 15799853
E-Mail: info.benelux@chep.com
Web Site: www.chep.com
Emp.: 90
Pallet & Container Collection, Reconditioning & Rental Services
S.I.C.: 7359
N.A.I.C.S.: 532490
Sandra Debock *(Mgr-HR)*

CHEP Denmark (3)
Bjerggade 7
2600 Koge, Denmark (100%)
Tel.: (45) 70207222
Fax: (45) 70207223
E-Mail: info@chep.com
Web Site: www.chep.com
Emp.: 7
Pallet & Container Collection, Reconditioning & Rental Services
S.I.C.: 7359
N.A.I.C.S.: 532490
Torben Lunt *(Mgr)*

CHEP Deutschland GmbH (3)
Siegburgirstrasse 229b
50679 Cologne, Germany De
Tel.: (49) 221935710 (100%)
Fax: (49) 22193571134
E-Mail: germany@chep.com
Web Site: www.chep.com
Emp.: 150
Pallet & Container Collection, Reconditioning & Rental Services
S.I.C.: 7359
N.A.I.C.S.: 532490
Isabel Bohme *(Mgr-Mktg Comm)*

Unit:

CHEP Deutschland Automotive Pool (4)
Karl Scheurer Str 2A
50354 Hurth, Germany (100%)
Tel.: (49) 223368700
Fax: (49) 22336870510
E-Mail: customerservice_ac@chep.com
Web Site: www.chep.com
Emp.: 100
S.I.C.: 4731
N.A.I.C.S.: 488510

CHEP Espana SA (3)
Bia Belos Coblavos 3,2
28033 Madrid, Spain ES
Tel.: (34) 915579400 (100%)
Fax: (34) 915579480
E-Mail: chepeu.accountspayable@chep.com
Web Site: www.chep.com
Emp.: 200
Pallet & Container Collection, Reconditioning & Rental Services
S.I.C.: 7359
N.A.I.C.S.: 532490
Laura Mador *(Gen Mgr)*

CHEP Finland (3)
Auritia 8E
01510 Vantaa, Finland
Tel.: (358) 98256800
Fax: (358) 982568070
Web Site: www.chep.com
Emp.: 5
Pallet & Container Collection, Reconditioning & Rental Services
S.I.C.: 7359
N.A.I.C.S.: 532490
Mia Frollnder-Uls *(Gen Mgr)*

CHEP France S.A. (3)
1 Rue Mozart
F-92112 Clichy, France FR
Mailing Address: (100%)
BP 85
92110 Clichy, France
Tel.: (33) 149687777
Fax: (33) 147308074
Web Site: www.chep.com
Emp.: 200
Pallet & Container Collection, Reconditioning & Rental Services
S.I.C.: 7359
N.A.I.C.S.: 532490
Pierre Yves Corbiere *(Country Gen Mgr)*

CHEP Italia SRL (3)
Viale Fulvio Testi 280-3
20126 Milan, Italy IT
Tel.: (39) 0266154811 (100%)
Fax: (39) 0266154825
E-Mail: customerservice.italy@chep.com
Web Site: www.chep.com
Emp.: 70
Pallet & Container Collection, Reconditioning & Rental Services
Import Export
S.I.C.: 7359
N.A.I.C.S.: 532490
Luca Rossi *(Country Mgr)*

CHEP Norway (3)
Lorenskogveien 75
PO Box 28
1471 Skarer, Norway (100%)
Tel.: (47) 67977482
Fax: (47) 67977485
Web Site: www.chep.com
Emp.: 5
Pallet & Container Collection, Reconditioning & Rental Services
S.I.C.: 7359
N.A.I.C.S.: 532490

CHEP Osterreich Gmbh (3)
Mariahilfer Strasse 123
1060 Vienna, Austria (100%)
Tel.: (43) 159999448
Fax: (43) 159999336
E-Mail: chep.austria@chep.com
Web Site: www.chep.com
Emp.: 12
Pallet & Container Collection, Reconditioning & Rental Services
S.I.C.: 7359
N.A.I.C.S.: 532490
Frank Hoerandner *(Gen Mgr)*

CHEP Portugal (3)
Ave das Descobertas 59 3rd Fl Piso
2780053 Paco d'Arcos, Oeiras, Portugal (100%)
Tel.: (351) 214468100
Fax: (351) 214412966
E-Mail: info@chep.com
Web Site: www.chep.com
Emp.: 40
Pallet & Container Collection, Reconditioning & Rental Services
S.I.C.: 7359
N.A.I.C.S.: 532490
Maria Carvalho *(Mgr)*

CHEP Schweiz BV (3)
Rheinst No 47
Rheinstrasse 47, 4127 Birsfelden, Switzerland
Tel.: (41) 613759220
Fax: (41) 613759229
E-Mail: chepschweiz@bluewin.ch
Web Site: www.chep.com
Pallet & Container Collection, Reconditioning & Rental Services
S.I.C.: 7359
N.A.I.C.S.: 532490

CHEP Sweden (3)
Danyik Ctr Haftholmsyagem 28
131 05 Nacka, Sweden (100%)
Tel.: (46) 87558510
Fax: (46) 87558513
Web Site: www.chep.com
Emp.: 5
Pallet & Container Collection, Reconditioning & Rental Services
S.I.C.: 7359
N.A.I.C.S.: 532490
Bo Saoecerg *(Gen Mgr)*

Non-U.S. Subsidiary:

CHEP South Africa (Pty) Ltd. (2)
131 Jan Hosmeyr Road
PO Box 1053
3630 Wandsbeck, 3631, South Africa ZA
Tel.: (27) 312679300 (100%)
Fax: (27) 312678900
E-Mail: info@chepsa.com
Web Site: www.chepsa.com
Emp.: 100
Pallet & Container Pooling
S.I.C.: 2448
N.A.I.C.S.: 321920
Jurie Welman *(Pres)*

Non-U.S. Subsidiaries:

Brambles Enterprises Limited (1)
Unit 2 Weybridge Business Pk
Addlestone, Surrey, KT15 2UP, United Kingdom
Tel.: (44) 1932 833115
Fax: (44) 1932 850144
Pallet Rental & Leasing Services
S.I.C.: 7359
N.A.I.C.S.: 532490

Brambles U.K. Limited (1)
Unit 2 Weybridge Business Park Addlestone Road
Addlestone, Surrey, KT15 2UP, United Kingdom UK
Tel.: (44) 1932 850 085 (100%)
Emp.: 50
Waste Services
S.I.C.: 4959
N.A.I.C.S.: 562998

IFCO Systems N.V. (1)
Evert van de Beekstraat 310
1118 CX Schiphol, Netherlands
Tel.: (31) 206541854
Fax: (31) 20654180
E-Mail: info@ifcosystems.de
Web Site: www.ifcosystems.de
Sales Range: $750-799.9 Million
Emp.: 3,849
Logistics Systems; Pallets & Round-Trip Container Pools Mfr
S.I.C.: 4731
N.A.I.C.S.: 541614
Bernd Malmstrom *(Chm-Supervisory Bd)*
Wolfgang Orgeldinger *(CEO)*
Michael W. Nimtsch *(CFO)*
David S. Russell *(Pres-North America)*

U.S. Subsidiary:

IFCO Systems North America, Inc. (2)
13100 NW Freeway Ste 625
Houston, TX 77040 TX
Tel.: (713) 332-6145
Fax: (713) 332-6146
E-Mail: info.na@ifcosystems.com
Web Site: www.ifcosystems.com
Emp.: 80
International Logistics Services
Import Export

Brambles Limited—(Continued)

S.I.C.: 2449
N.A.I.C.S.: 321920
Dan Walsh *(Pres)*
Rich Hamlin *(CFO & Sr VP)*
Fred Heptinstall *(Sr VP-Global Bus Dev)*
Chris Tiesman *(Sr VP-Fin & Acctg)*

Subsidiaries:

RPC Management Services (3)
3030 Rocky Point Dr Ste 300
Tampa, FL 33607 DE
Tel.: (813) 463-4100
Fax: (813) 286-2070
E-Mail: info.na@no-spam.ifcosystems.com
Web Site: www.ifcosystems.com
Emp.: 40
Reusable Plastic Containers Mfr Export
S.I.C.: 7629
N.A.I.C.S.: 811219
Dorothy Patrick *(Mgr-Customer Svcs)*

Unitpool AG (1)
Steinackerstrasse 2
8302 Kloten, Switzerland
Tel.: (41) 43 255 4141
Fax: (41) 43 255 4142
E-Mail: sales@unitpool.com
Web Site: www.unitpool.com
Emp.: 20
Aviation Pooling Services
S.I.C.: 4581
N.A.I.C.S.: 488190
Ludwig Bertsch *(Chm)*
David Harman *(CEO)*
Andreas Ernst *(CFO)*

BRAMMER PLC

St Ann's House 1 Old Market Place
Knutsford, Cheshire, WA16 6PD, United Kingdom
Tel.: (44) 1565756800
Fax: (44) 1565756890
E-Mail: enquiries@brammer.plc.uk
Web Site: www.brammer.biz
Year Founded: 1920
BRAM—(LSE)
Rev.: $1,010,113,884
Assets: $539,801,322
Liabilities: $348,707,232
Net Worth: $191,094,090
Earnings: $31,269,942
Emp.: 3,109
Fiscal Year-end: 12/31/12

Business Description:
Bearings, Power Transmission Products & Motion Control Equipment, Equipment Management, Calibration & Rental Services for Instruments, Test Equipment & Computer Products Distr
Import Export
S.I.C.: 5084
N.A.I.C.S.: 423830

Personnel:
Ian R. Fraser *(CEO)*
Steven Hodkinson *(Sec & Dir-Secretarial, Legal & HR)*

Board of Directors:
Bill H. Whiteley
Ian R. Fraser
Terry Garthwaite
Charles Irving-Swift
Duncan J. Magrath
Paul Thwaite

Legal Counsel:
Addleshaw Booth & Co.
100 Barbirolli Square
Manchester, M2 3AR, United Kingdom

Non-U.S. Subsidiaries:

Brammer France (1)
3 rue de la Haye
67300 Schiltigheim, France (100%)
Tel.: (33) 388404088
Fax: (33) 388404077
E-Mail: info@roulementservice.fr
Web Site: www.brammer.biz
Emp.: 60
Mfr & Distr of Bearings, Sprockets & Various Mechanical Parts
S.I.C.: 3542
N.A.I.C.S.: 333517
Carrier Bruno *(Dir-Dev)*

Brammer GmbH (1)
Industriestrasse 19
76189 Karlsruhe, Germany DE
Tel.: (49) 7219543210
Fax: (49) 7219543222
E-Mail: karlsruhe@brammer.biz
Web Site: www.thf.de
Emp.: 450
Engineering Parts Distr
S.I.C.: 7389
N.A.I.C.S.: 425120

Branches:

THF GmbH & Co. KG (2)
Am Broegel 1A 13
42111 Wuppertal, Germany De
Tel.: (49) 20289070
Fax: (49) 2028907161
Web Site: www.thf.de
Emp.: 20
Engineering Parts Distr
S.I.C.: 7389
N.A.I.C.S.: 425120

BRAMMER SAFETY SUPPLY, INC.

(Acquired by Descours & Cabaud SA)

BRAMPTON BRICK LIMITED

225 Wanless Drive
Brampton, ON, L7A 1E9, Canada
Tel.: (905) 840-1011
Fax: (905) 840-1535
E-Mail: sales@bramptonbrick.com
Web Site: www.bramptonbrick.com
BBL.A—(TSX)
Rev.: $96,480,575
Assets: $204,118,031
Liabilities: $67,964,129
Net Worth: $136,153,901
Earnings: $1,476,120
Emp.: 210
Fiscal Year-end: 12/31/12

Business Description:
Brick Mfr
S.I.C.: 3271
N.A.I.C.S.: 327331

Personnel:
Jeffrey G. Kerbel *(Pres & CEO)*
Trevor M. Sandler *(CFO & VP-Fin)*
David R. Carter *(Exec VP)*
Frank J. Buck *(Sr VP-Strategic Dev)*
J. Bradley Duke *(Sr VP-Mfg)*

Board of Directors:
Rudolph P. Bratty
Douglas J. Buhler
Jim V. De Gasperis
P. David Grant
Howard C. Kerbel
Jeffrey G. Kerbel
John M. Piecuch
Peter R. Smith
Kenneth M. Tanenbaum

Transfer Agent:
CIBC Mellon Trust Company
PO Box 700 Station B
Montreal, QC, Canada

Subsidiaries:

Atlas Block Co. Limited. (1)
15288 Hwy 12
PO Box 670
Midland, ON, L4R 4P4, Canada
Tel.: (705) 534-7219
Fax: (705) 534-4125
Toll Free: (877) 755-5604
Web Site: www.atlasblock.com
Rev.: $20,930,548
Emp.: 180
Concrete Products Mfr
S.I.C.: 3271
N.A.I.C.S.: 327331
Don Gordon *(Co-Pres & CEO)*
Laura Gordon *(Co-Pres)*

Oaks Concrete Products Ltd (1)
455 Rodick Rd
Markham, ON, L6G 1B2, Canada
Tel.: (905) 475-5900
Fax: (905) 479-2894
Web Site: www.oakspavers.com
Emp.: 50
Construction Machinery Mfr
S.I.C.: 3531
N.A.I.C.S.: 333120
Christina Donnley *(Mgr)*

U.S. Subsidiaries:

Brampton Brick Inc (1)
1256 E County Rd 950 N
Farmersburg, IN 47850-8055
Tel.: (812) 397-2190
Brick & Structural Clay Tile Mfr
S.I.C.: 3255
N.A.I.C.S.: 327120

Oaks Concrete Products Inc (1)
51744 Pontiac Trl
Wixom, MI 48393
Tel.: (248) 684-5004
Fax: (248) 684-2726
Toll Free: (800) 709-6257
Web Site: www.oakspavers.com
Emp.: 10
Concrete Bricks Mfr
S.I.C.: 3255
N.A.I.C.S.: 327120
David Carter *(Pres)*

BRANCO RESOURCES LTD.

4005 1011 West Cordova Street
Vancouver, BC, V6C 0B2, Canada
Tel.: (604) 408-1990
E-Mail: sokhie@snjcapital.com
Year Founded: 2012
BNL.P—(TSXV)

Business Description:
Investment Services
S.I.C.: 6211
N.A.I.C.S.: 523999

Personnel:
Sokhie Puar *(Pres, CEO & Sec)*
Clive Brookes *(CFO)*

Board of Directors:
Clive Brookes
Heather Conley
John Hewlett
Sokhie Puar

THE BRAND AGENCY PTY. LTD.

Level 3 11 Harvest Tce
W, Perth, 6005, Australia
Tel.: (61) 8 9322 4433
Fax: (61) 8 9322 5663
E-Mail: contact@brandagency.com.au
Web Site: www.brandagency.com.au
Year Founded: 1991
Emp.: 70

Business Description:
Advertising Services
S.I.C.: 7311
N.A.I.C.S.: 541810

Personnel:
Neil Weeks *(Owner)*
Ken James *(Chm & Mng Dir)*

Branches

The Brand Agency-Melbourne (1)
Level 8 190 Queen St
Melbourne, VIC, 3000, Australia
Tel.: (61) 3 9602 2011
Fax: (61) 3 9602 2224
E-Mail: contact@brandagency.com.au
Web Site: www.brandagency.com.au
Advertising Services
S.I.C.: 7311
N.A.I.C.S.: 541810
Jude Robert *(Mng Partner)*

TBA Communications (1)
Level 12 7 City Rd
Auckland Central, Auckland, 1140, New Zealand
Tel.: (64) 9 369 1306
Fax: (64) 9 369 1239
E-Mail: contact@brandagency.com.au
Web Site: www.brandagency.com.au
Emp.: 8
Advertising Services
S.I.C.: 7311
N.A.I.C.S.: 541810
Stewart Carruthers *(Gen Mgr)*

BRAND DEVELOPMENT COMPANY LIMITED

50 Long Acre
London, WC2E 9JR, United Kingdom
Tel.: (44) 207 497 9727
Fax: (44) 207 497 3581
E-Mail: info@brandevo.com
Year Founded: 1985
Sales Range: $10-24.9 Million
Emp.: 4

Business Description:
Advertising
S.I.C.: 7311
N.A.I.C.S.: 541810

Personnel:
P. Morgan *(Mng Dir)*

BRAND MARVEL WORLDWIDE CONSUMER PRODUCTS CORPORATION

Suite 860 605 Robson Street
Vancouver, BC, V6B 5J3, Canada
Tel.: (604) 669-6168
Fax: (604) 669-6180
Web Site: www.beijingmarvel.com
Year Founded: 1986
BMW—(TSXV)
Sls.: $1,126,671
Assets: $5,725,956
Liabilities: $11,749,074
Net Worth: ($6,023,118)
Earnings: ($3,003,671)
Fiscal Year-end: 12/31/12

Business Description:
Wet Wipe Product Mfr & Distr
S.I.C.: 2297
N.A.I.C.S.: 313230

Personnel:
Yongliang Liao *(Chm & CEO)*
Danny Chi Tak Hon *(CFO)*
Loren D. Currie *(Sec)*

Board of Directors:
Yongliang Liao
Loren D. Currie
Danny Chi Tak Hon
Yang Li
David Mao

BRAND NEW VINTAGE LIMITED

Level 1 259 Unley Road
Malvern, SA, 5061, Australia
Tel.: (61) 882714321
Fax: (61) 827124831
E-Mail: info@brandnewvintage.com.au
Web Site: www.brandnewvintage.com.au
BNV—(ASX)
Rev.: $7,643,957
Assets: $11,338,161
Liabilities: $8,192,195
Net Worth: $3,145,965
Earnings: ($207,107)
Fiscal Year-end: 06/30/13

Business Description:
Wine Mfr & Sales
S.I.C.: 2084
N.A.I.C.S.: 312130

Personnel:
Sam Atkins *(CEO & Mng Dir)*
Dainis Zakis *(Sec & Mgr-Fin)*

Board of Directors:
Graham Keys
Sam Atkins

Theo J. Eversteyn
Frank Joseph Kraps

Subsidiary:

Sticks Yarra Valley Pty. Ltd. (1)
179 Glenview Rd
Yarra Glen, Victoria, 3775, Australia
Tel.: (61) 397301022
Fax: (61) 397301131
E-Mail: info@sticks.com.au
Web Site: www.sticks.com.au
Emp.: 12
Wines Mfr & Distr
S.I.C.: 2084
N.A.I.C.S.: 312130
Rebecca Farrow *(Mgr-Sls & Mktg)*

BRAND PARTNERSHIP LTD.

Southfork Industrial Est
Dartmouth Way, Leeds, LS11 5JL, United Kingdom
Tel.: (44) 132706061
Fax: (44) 132706146
Emp.: 350
Business Description:
Dehydrated Food Product Mfr
S.I.C.: 2034
N.A.I.C.S.: 311423

Subsidiary:

Telford Foods Ltd. (1)
10 Halesfield Business Park
Telford, Shropshire, TF7 4LY, United Kingdom (100%)
Tel.: (44) 1952422000
Telex: 35317 TFOODS
Fax: (44) 1952422021
E-Mail: p.radford@telfordfoods-uk.com
Mfr of Muesli & Breakfast Cereals, Packet Soups & Sauce Mixes, Gravy Powder, Powdered Drinks & Desserts
S.I.C.: 2043
N.A.I.C.S.: 311230

BRAND REALTY SERVICES LTD.

G-10 & 11 Sector-18
Noida, 201301, India
Tel.: (91) 120 4608152
Fax: (91) 120 4319966
E-Mail: info@brandrealty.in
Web Site: www.brandrealty.in
Year Founded: 2006
531203—(BOM)
Business Description:
Real Estate Development Services
S.I.C.: 6531
N.A.I.C.S.: 531390
Personnel:
Aruna Manchanda *(Chm)*
Board of Directors:
Aruna Manchanda
Surendra Kancheti
Yogesh Kumar
Kamal Manchanda
Transfer Agent:
Link Intime India Private Limited
A-40 2nd Floor Naraina Industrial Area Phase-II
New Delhi, India

BRANDALLEY UK LIMITED

3 Thomas More Square
London, E98 1XY, United Kingdom
Tel.: (44) 20 3060 1651
E-Mail: customerservice@brandalley.co.uk
Web Site: www.brandalley.co.uk
Sales Range: $10-24.9 Million
Business Description:
Internet Retailer
S.I.C.: 5961
N.A.I.C.S.: 454111
Personnel:
Sven Lung *(Chm)*
Rob Feldmann *(CEO)*

BRANDENBURG ENERGY CORP.

1100 - 789 West Pender Street
Vancouver, BC, V6C 1H2, Canada
Tel.: (604) 669-9330
Fax: (604) 669-9335
Web Site: www.brandenburgcorp.com
Year Founded: 2007
BBM—(TSXV)
Assets: $544,047
Liabilities: $767,881
Net Worth: ($223,834)
Earnings: ($522,780)
Fiscal Year-end: 08/31/13
Business Description:
Investment Services
S.I.C.: 6211
N.A.I.C.S.: 523999
Personnel:
Robert M. Findlay *(Pres & CEO)*
Keith Margetson *(CFO)*
Board of Directors:
Robert M. Findlay
Oleg-Serguei Schkoda
Chris Verrico
Legal Counsel:
Boughton Law Corporation
700-595 Burrard Street
PO Box 49290
Vancouver, BC, Canada
Transfer Agent:
Computershare
300 510 Burrard Street
Vancouver, BC, V6C 3A8, Canada

BRANDHOUSE RETAILS LTD

Marathon NextGen B2 5th Floor GK
Marg Lower Parel
Mumbai, 400 013, India
Tel.: (91) 22 24824500
Fax: (91) 22 24931685
E-Mail: customercare@brandhouseretails.com
Web Site: www.brandhouseretails.com
533059—(BOM)
Rev.: $151,074,284
Assets: $124,121,722
Liabilities: $106,312,680
Net Worth: $17,809,042
Earnings: ($10,289,496)
Fiscal Year-end: 03/31/13
Business Description:
Fashion Wear Retailer
S.I.C.: 5699
N.A.I.C.S.: 448150
Personnel:
Nitin S. Kasliwal *(Chm & Mng Dir)*
Dipesh U. Gosar *(Compliance Officer & Sec)*
Board of Directors:
Nitin S. Kasliwal
Vijay Kalantri
Jagadeesh S. Shetty
Haribhakti & Co
18, Haribhakti Colony,
Race Course Cir, Vadodara, 390 007, India
Tel.: (91) 265 234 0091
Fax: (91) 265 231 4495
Transfer Agent:
Datamatics Financial Services Ltd
Plot No B 5 Part B Crosslane MIDC Marol
Andheri East
Mumbai, India

BRANDPROTECT INC.

5090 Explorer Drive Suite 203
Mississauga, ON, L4W 4T9, Canada
Tel.: (905) 271-3725
Fax: (905) 267-3163
Toll Free: (866) 721-3725
E-Mail: onlinesales@brandprotect.com
Web Site: www.brandprotect.com
Year Founded: 2001
Sales Range: $1-9.9 Million
Emp.: 30
Business Description:
Data Protection Services
S.I.C.: 7382
N.A.I.C.S.: 561621
Personnel:
Elias Vamvakas *(Chm)*
Roberto Drassinower *(Pres & CEO)*
Alan Peck *(CFO)*
Frankie Wong *(CTO)*
Board of Directors:
Elias Vamvakas
Joseph C. Canavan
Tom Davidson
Roberto Drassinower
David Folk
Ken Nickerson
Alan Peck

BRANDS EUROPEAN SHOE TRADE

Parc Des Moulins 41 Rue Albert Samain
59650 Villeneuve d'Ascq, Nord, France
Tel.: (33) 320050480
Fax: (33) 320672529
Sls.: $15,900,000
Emp.: 4
S.I.C.: 5139
N.A.I.C.S.: 424340
Personnel:
Nicolas Dewaele *(Pres)*

BRANDT & WALTHER GMBH

Torneestrasse 5
D-28865 Lilienthal, Germany
Tel.: (49) 429846620
Fax: (49) 4298466211
E-Mail: info@poliboy.de
Web Site: www.poliboy.de
Year Founded: 1930
Rev.: $41,382,000
Emp.: 2
Business Description:
Cleaning Products Mfr
S.I.C.: 3999
N.A.I.C.S.: 339999
Personnel:
Torsten Emigholz *(Co-Mng Dir)*
Jorn Christian Herrmann *(Co-Mng Dir)*

BRANDWELLS CONSTRUCTION

Park House Church Lane
St George, Bristol, BS5 7AG, United Kingdom
Tel.: (44) 1179517611
Fax: (44) 1179354073
E-Mail: mailbox@brandwells.co.uk
Web Site: www.brandwells-construction.co.uk
Year Founded: 1973
Rev.: $14,893,483
Emp.: 100
Business Description:
Building Construction Services
S.I.C.: 1542
N.A.I.C.S.: 236220
Personnel:
Andy Dowden *(Founder & Mng Dir)*

BRANKAMP SYSTEM-PROZESSAUTOMATION GMBH

Max-Planck-Str 9
40699 Erkrath, Germany
Tel.: (49) 211250760
Fax: (49) 211208402
E-Mail: bpd@brankamp.com
Web Site: www.brankamp.com
Year Founded: 1977
Rev.: $10,345,500
Emp.: 65
Business Description:
Process Monitoring Systems Distr
S.I.C.: 5085
N.A.I.C.S.: 423840
Personnel:
Klaus Brankamp *(Founder)*

BRANNON STEEL

14 Tilbury Court
Brampton, ON, Canada
Tel.: (905) 453-4730
Fax: (905) 453-4483
Toll Free: (800) 387-2508
E-Mail: info@brannonsteel.com
Web Site: www.brannonsteel.com
Year Founded: 1968
Rev.: $18,431,218
Emp.: 170
Business Description:
Carbon Steel Supplier
S.I.C.: 3398
N.A.I.C.S.: 332811
Personnel:
Kirk Brannon *(Pres)*

BRASIL BROKERS PARTICIPACOES S.A.

Av Das Americas 500 - Bloco 19/sala 303/304
22640904 Rio de Janeiro, Brazil
Tel.: (55) 21 3433 3001
Fax: (55) 21 3433 3065
E-Mail: ri@brbrokers.com.br
Web Site: www.brbrokers.com.br
BBRK3—(BRAZ)
Sales Range: $150-199.9 Million
Emp.: 632
Business Description:
Real Estate Brokerage Services
S.I.C.: 6531
N.A.I.C.S.: 531390
Personnel:
Silvio Roberto Vieira Almeida *(Dir-IR)*

BRASIL ECODIESEL INDUSTRIA E COMERCIO DE BIOCOMBUSTIVEIS E OLEOS VEGETAIS SA

(d/b/a Brasil Ecodiesel)
Praia de Botofogo no 501 sala 701B
Torre Corcovado Centro
Empresarial Murisco Botofogo, Rio de Janeiro, 22250-040, Brazil
Tel.: (55) 2125 465031
Fax: (55) 2125 465040
Web Site: www.brasilecodiesel.com.br
ECOD3—(BRAZ)
Sales Range: $150-199.9 Million
Business Description:
Producer of Biodiesel
S.I.C.: 1389
N.A.I.C.S.: 213112
Personnel:
Carlos Antonio Rocca *(Chm)*
Wagner Pinheiro de Oliveira *(Vice Chm)*
Bento do Amaral Peixoto Moreira Franco *(CEO)*
Eduardo de Come *(CFO)*

BRASIL INSURANCE PARTICIPACOES E ADMINISTRACAO S.A

Alameda Santos 1787 5 andar - Cerqueira Cesar
Sao Paulo, Brazil
Tel.: (55) 1131752900
Fax: (55) 2124951065
E-Mail: contato@brasilinsurance.com.br

Brasil Insurance Participacoes e Administracao S.A—(Continued)

Web Site: www.brinsurance.com.br
Year Founded: 2010
BRIN3—(BRAZ)
Rev.: $112,139,607
Assets: $396,119,017
Liabilities: $147,091,342
Net Worth: $249,027,675
Earnings: $57,810,848
Fiscal Year-end: 12/31/12
Business Description:
Insurance Brokerage Services
S.I.C.: 6411
N.A.I.C.S.: 524298
Personnel:
Bruno Padilha de Lima Costa *(Chm)*
Antonio Jose Lemos Ramos *(CEO)*
Luis Eduardo Fischman *(CFO, Control Officer & IR Officer)*
Jose Ricardo Brun Fausto *(COO)*
Marcio Silva Chaves *(Ops officer)*
Board of Directors:
Bruno Padilha de Lima Costa
Luiz Carlos Almeida Braga Nabuco de Abreu
Marcelo de Andrade Casado
Fabio Franchini
Armando Zara Pompeu
Subsidiaries:

BASE BRASIL B.I. Corretora de Seguros Ltda. **(1)**
Avenida Presidente Vargas 3131 s/n sl 1605
Rio de Janeiro, Brazil
Tel.: (55) 21 4007 1315
Insurance Brokerage Services
S.I.C.: 6411
N.A.I.C.S.: 524210

PROMOVE Corretora de Seguros Ltda. **(1)**
Rua Alvaro Alvim 1061 Vila Pauliceia
09693-000 Sao Bernardo do Campo, Sao Paulo, Brazil
Tel.: (55) 11 2588 2100
E-Mail: promove@promoveseguros.com.br
Web Site: www.promoveseguros.com.br
Insurance Brokerage Services
S.I.C.: 6411
N.A.I.C.S.: 524210

YORK BRUKAN B.I. Assessoria Administracao e Corretagem de Seguros Ltda. **(1)**
Av 09 de Julho 5 049 - Conj - 1a
Jd Paulista, 01407 200 Sao Paulo, Brazil
Tel.: (55) 11 3032 6003
Fax: (55) 11 30326003
E-Mail: yorkseguros@yorkseguros.com.br
Emp.: 22
Insurance Brokerage Services
S.I.C.: 6411
N.A.I.C.S.: 524210
Marcio Chaves *(Gen Mgr)*

BRASILAGRO - COMPANHIA BRASILEIRA DE PROPRIEDADES AGRICOLAS

1309 Avenida Brigadeiro Faria Lima
5th Floor
Sao Paulo, 01452-002, Brazil
Tel.: (55) 1130355350
Fax: (55) 1130355366
Web Site: www.brasil-agro.com
AGRO3—(BRAZ)
Rev.: $91,317,903
Assets: $379,163,569
Liabilities: $90,431,517
Net Worth: $288,732,052
Earnings: $14,130,524
Emp.: 229
Fiscal Year-end: 06/30/13
Business Description:
Agriculture, Livestock & Property Management Services
S.I.C.: 0139
N.A.I.C.S.: 111998
Personnel:
Eduardo S. Elsztain *(Chm)*
Robert Gibbins *(Vice Chm)*
Julio Cesar de Toledo Piza Neto *(CEO & IR Officer)*
Andre Guillaumon *(COO)*
Gustavo Javier Lopez *(Chief Admin Officer)*
Mario Aguirre *(Chief Technical Agriculture Officer)*
Board of Directors:
Eduardo S. Elsztain
Gabriel Pablo Blasi
Joao de Almeida Sampaio Filho
Alejandro G. Elsztain
Robert Gibbins
Isaac Selim Sutton
Saul Zang

BRASSERIE DE TAHITI SA

17th Pl Notre
Papeete, French Polynesia
Tel.: (689) 467600
Fax: (689) 467639
E-Mail: hinano@mail.ps
Web Site: www.brasseriedetahiti.fp
Sales Range: $50-74.9 Million
Emp.: 400
Business Description:
Alcoholic Beverages Distr
S.I.C.: 5181
N.A.I.C.S.: 424810
Personnel:
Jean Pierre Fourcade *(Pres)*

BRASSEUR TRANSPORT INC.

1250 Rue Industrielle
La Prairie, QC, J5R 5G4, Canada
Tel.: (450) 444-7079
Fax: (450) 444-9268
Toll Free: (800) 363-8323
E-Mail: info@brasseurtransport.com
Web Site: www.brasseurtransport.com
Year Founded: 1953
Rev.: $12,836,939
Emp.: 100
Business Description:
Truck Transportation Services
S.I.C.: 4212
N.A.I.C.S.: 484110
Personnel:
Michel Brasseur *(Owner)*

BRASSO NISSAN

195 Glendeer Circle SE
Calgary, AB, T2H 2S8, Canada
Tel.: (403) 253-5555
Fax: (403) 252-1990
Toll Free: (888) 284-0832
Web Site: www.brassonissan.com
Year Founded: 1969
Rev.: $19,871,280
Emp.: 55
Business Description:
New & Used Car Dealers
S.I.C.: 5511
N.A.I.C.S.: 441110
Personnel:
Einar Brasso *(Pres)*

BRATIM SA

160 Str Carierei
500052 Brasov, Romania
Tel.: (40) 268 332 770
Fax: (40) 268 331 673
E-Mail: assistant@bratim.ro
Web Site: www.bratim.ro
BRAY—(BUC)
Emp.: 190
Business Description:
Heating & Plumbing Contractor
S.I.C.: 1711
N.A.I.C.S.: 238220
Personnel:
Eugen Radu Craciun *(Pres & Gen Mgr)*

BRAUEREI FOHRENBURG GMBH & CO.

Fohrenburgstrasse 5
PO Box 192
A 6700 Bludenz, Austria
Tel.: (43) 55526060
Fax: (43) 555260650
E-Mail: fohrenburg@fohrenburg.at
Web Site: www.fohrenburg.at
Year Founded: 1881
Sales Range: $25-49.9 Million
Emp.: 150
Business Description:
Beer, Alcohol-Free Beer & Soft Drinks Import Export
S.I.C.: 2082
N.A.I.C.S.: 312120
Personnel:
Hans Steiner *(Pres)*
Sabine Treinel *(CMO)*

BRAUEREI MAX LEIBINGER GMBH

Friedhofstrasse 20 36
88212 Ravensburg, Germany
Tel.: (49) 75136990
Fax: (49) 751369990
E-Mail: info@leibinger.de
Web Site: www.leibinger.de
Year Founded: 1894
Rev.: $18,382,574
Emp.: 50
Business Description:
Brewery Mfr
S.I.C.: 2082
N.A.I.C.S.: 312120
Personnel:
Michael Leibinger *(Mng Partner)*
Regina Rist *(Sec)*

BRAUEREI ZOLLER-HOF GRAF-FLEISCHHUT GMBH & CO.KG

Leopoldstr 40
72488 Sigmaringen, Germany
Tel.: (49) 75717210
Fax: (49) 757172130
E-Mail: info@zoller-hof.de
Web Site: www.zoller-hof.de
Year Founded: 1845
Rev.: $25,518,155
Emp.: 70
Business Description:
Beer Mfr
S.I.C.: 2082
N.A.I.C.S.: 312120
Personnel:
Ralf Rakel *(Mng Dir)*

BRAVADA GOLD CORPORATION

Suite 1100 1199 West Hastings Street
Vancouver, BC, V6E 3T5, Canada
Tel.: (604) 684-9384
Fax: (604) 688-4670
Toll Free: (888) 456-1112
E-Mail: info@mnxltd.com
Web Site: www.bravadagold.com
Year Founded: 2009
BVA—(TSXV)
Int. Income: $132
Assets: $584,482
Liabilities: $1,234,864
Net Worth: ($650,382)
Earnings: ($8,784,492)
Fiscal Year-end: 07/31/13
Business Description:
Gold Mining Services
S.I.C.: 1041
N.A.I.C.S.: 212221
Personnel:
Lawrence Page *(Chm)*
Joseph A. Kizis, Jr. *(Pres & CEO)*
Graham Thatcher *(CFO)*
Arie Page *(Sec)*
Board of Directors:
Lawrence Page
Paul E. Dircksen
Richard Hughes
John R. Kerr
Joseph A. Kizis, Jr.
G. Ross McDonald
Michael Rowley
Legal Counsel:
Jeffrey T.K. Fraser Law Corporation
Suite 950 1199 West Hastings Street
Vancouver, BC, Canada

BRAVEHEART INVESTMENT GROUP PLC

Merlin House Necessity Brae
Perth, PH2 0PF, United Kingdom
Tel.: (44) 1738587555
Fax: (44) 1738587666
E-Mail: mail@braveheartgroup.co.uk
Web Site: www.braveheartgroup.co.uk
BRH—(LSE)
Rev.: $5,272,586
Assets: $8,992,525
Liabilities: $1,855,115
Net Worth: $7,137,410
Earnings: $106,713
Emp.: 28
Fiscal Year-end: 03/31/13
Business Description:
Financial Services
S.I.C.: 6799
N.A.I.C.S.: 523920
Personnel:
Geoffrey C. B. Thomson *(CEO)*
Aileen Brown *(CFO & Sec)*
Paul Millar *(Chief Investment Officer-WhiteRock Capital Partners)*
Carolyn Smith *(Chief Investment Officer)*
Stephen Hart *(Legal Counsel)*
Board of Directors:
Jeremy H. Delmar-Morgan
Aileen Brown
Ken Brown
Edward Cunningham
Carolyn Smith
Geoffrey C. B. Thomson
Legal Counsel:
Maclay Murray & Spens LLP
Quartermile One, 15 Lauriston Place
Edinburgh, United Kingdom
Subsidiaries:

Strathclyde Innovation Fund LP **(1)**
The Cherrybank Ctr Cherrybank Gardens
Perth, Scotland, PH2 0PF, United Kingdom
Tel.: (44) 1738587555
Fax: (44) 1738587666
E-Mail: mail@braveheart-ventures.co.uk
Web Site: www.braveheart-ventures.co.uk
Emp.: 7
Investment Management Services
S.I.C.: 6211
N.A.I.C.S.: 523999
Jeoffrey Thomson *(CEO)*

Viking Fund Managers Ltd. **(1)**
Metic House Ripley Dr
Normanton, West Yorkshire, WF6 1QT, United Kingdom
Tel.: (44) 1924227237
Fax: (44) 1924892207
Web Site: www.vikingfund.co.uk
Fund Management Services
S.I.C.: 6799
N.A.I.C.S.: 523920
Andrew Burton *(Mng Dir)*

BRAVENETMEDIA.COM
100-200 Jensen Ave Ste 101
Parksville, BC, V9P 2H5, Canada
Mailing Address:
PO Box 1722
Parksville, BC, V9P 2H5, Canada
Tel.: (250) 954-3203
Fax: (250) 954-2164
E-Mail: melanie@bravenetmedia.com
Web Site: www.bravenetmedia.com
Year Founded: 1997
Sales Range: $10-24.9 Million
Emp.: 40
Business Description:
Free Webmaster Tools
S.I.C.: 7373
N.A.I.C.S.: 541512
Personnel:
David M. Shworan *(CEO)*

BRAVIA CAPITAL HONG KONG LIMITED
6511 13 The Center 99 Queens Road
Hong Kong, China (Hong Kong)
Tel.: (852) 26772104
E-Mail: info@braviacapital.com
Web Site: www.braviacapital.com
Business Description:
Private Equity Firm
S.I.C.: 6211
N.A.I.C.S.: 523999
Personnel:
Bharat Bhise *(CEO)*
Non-U.S. Joint Venture:

Seaco Services Ltd. (1)
21 St Thomas Street
London, SE1 9RY, United Kingdom
Tel.: (44) 20 7939 5600
Fax: (44) 2079395650
E-Mail: info.reefers@seacoglobal.com
Web Site: www.seacoglobal.com
Emp.: 100
Marine Containers Leasing Services
S.I.C.: 7359
N.A.I.C.S.: 532411
David G. Amble *(CEO)*

U.S. Subsidiary:

Seaco America LLC (2)
7200 NW 19 St Ste 500
Miami, FL 10036-2711
Tel.: (305) 597-2120
Fax: (305) 591-7214
Web Site: www.seacoglobal.com
Emp.: 25
Marine Containers Leasing Services
S.I.C.: 7359
N.A.I.C.S.: 532411
Juan Mejia *(Office Mgr)*

Non-U.S. Subsidiaries:

Seaco Asia Pte Ltd. (2)
Fuji Xerox Towers #29-01
80 Anson Road, Singapore, 79907, Singapore
Tel.: (65) 6595 1900
E-Mail: csa.singapore@seacoglobal.com
Web Site: www.seacoglobal.com
Emp.: 40
Marine Containers Leasing Services
S.I.C.: 7359
N.A.I.C.S.: 532411

Seaco China Ltd. (2)
Suite 812 Ocean Centre 5 Canton Road
Tsimshatsui, Kowloon, China (Hong Kong)
Tel.: (852) 2525 8613
E-Mail: csa.hongkong@seacoglobal.com
Web Site: www.seacoglobal.com
Marine Containers Leasing Services
S.I.C.: 7359
N.A.I.C.S.: 532411

Seaco France SARL (2)
16 rue Antonin Raynaud
92300 Levallois-Perret, France
Tel.: (33) 147459810
Telex: 641174
Fax: (33) 147459806
E-Mail:
Web Site: www.seacoglobal.com
Emp.: 3
Marine Containers Leasing Services
S.I.C.: 7359
N.A.I.C.S.: 532411

Seaco International Leasing GmbH (2)
Cremon 32
20457 Hamburg, Germany
Tel.: (49) 408080310
Fax: (49) 4080803112
E-Mail:
Web Site: www.seacoglobal.com
Emp.: 10
Marine Containers Leasing Services
S.I.C.: 7359
N.A.I.C.S.: 532411
Mike Cooper *(Mng Dir)*
Wolf Herrns *(Mng Dir)*

Seaco Italia srl (2)
Via Aurelia 136
57017 Livorno, Stagno, Italy
Tel.: (39) 0586950028
Fax: (39) 0586950177
Web Site: www.seacoglobal.com
Sales Range: $1-9.9 Million
Emp.: 3
Marine Containers Leasing Services
S.I.C.: 7359
N.A.I.C.S.: 532411

BRAVURA VENTURES CORP.
551 Howe Street Suite 200
Vancouver, BC, V6C 2C2, Canada
Tel.: (604) 628-4880
Fax: (604) 683-8605
E-Mail: info@bravuracorp.com
Web Site: www.bravuracorp.com
Year Founded: 2010
BVQ—(TSXV)
Assets: $425,250
Liabilities: $36,332
Net Worth: $388,917
Earnings: ($238,023)
Fiscal Year-end: 01/31/13
Business Description:
Metal Mining Services
S.I.C.: 1099
N.A.I.C.S.: 212299
Personnel:
Brook Bellian *(Pres & Interim CEO)*
Anthony Jackson *(CFO)*
Quinn P. Field-Dyte *(Sec)*
Board of Directors:
Brook Bellian
Quinn P. Field-Dyte
Anthony Jackson
Marc S. LeBlanc
Jerry A. Minni
Michael A. Petrina
Legal Counsel:
Axium Law Corporation
Suite 3350 - 1055 Dunsmuir Street
Vancouver, BC, Canada
Transfer Agent:
Computershare Trust Company of Canada
510 Burrard St 2nd Fl
Vancouver, BC, Canada

BRAWN BIOTECH LTD.
4/4B Asaf Ali Road II Floor
Delhi Stock Exchange Building
New Delhi, 110002, India
Tel.: (91) 11 3291 1528
Fax: (91) 11 2327 5208
E-Mail: solution@brawnpharma.com
Web Site: brawnbiotech.com
530207—(BOM)
Sales Range: $350-399.9 Million
Emp.: 300
Business Description:
Pharmaceutical Products Mfr
S.I.C.: 2834
N.A.I.C.S.: 325412
Personnel:
Brij Raj Gupta *(Chm & Mng Dir)*
Amit Bansal *(Sec)*
Board of Directors:
Brij Raj Gupta
Brij Bala Gupta
Urmila Gupta
Manohar Lal
Mahesh Kumar Nanchal
Bal Kishan Sharma
Transfer Agent:
RCMC Share Registry Private Ltd.
B-106 Sector 2
Noida, 201301, India

BRAZIL FAST FOOD CORP.
Rua Voluntarios da Patria 89-9 andar
CEP 22270010 Botafogo, RJ, Brazil
Tel.: (55) 2125367500
Fax: (55) 2125609472
Web Site: www.bffc.com.br
Year Founded: 1992
BOBS—(OTC)
Rev.: $121,072,000
Assets: $69,195,000
Liabilities: $39,158,000
Net Worth: $30,037,000
Earnings: $10,114,000
Fiscal Year-end: 12/31/12
Business Description:
Fast Food Restaurant Owner & Franchiser
S.I.C.: 5812
N.A.I.C.S.: 722513
Personnel:
Guillermo Hector Pisano *(Chm)*
Ricardo Figueiredo Bomeny *(Pres & CEO)*
Board of Directors:
Guillermo Hector Pisano
Marcos Gouvea de Souza
Marcos Rocha
Gilberto Tomazoni
Gustavo Alberto Villela Filho

BRAZIL PHARMA S.A.
Avenida Presidente Juscelino Kubitschek 1830 - 2 floor - Tower 4
Itaim Bibi, Sao Paulo, Brazil 04543-900
Tel.: (55) 11 2117 5200
Fax: (55) 11 2117 5290
E-Mail: ri@brph.com.br
Web Site: www.brasilpharma.com.br
Year Founded: 2009
BPHA3—(BRAZ)
Rev.: $1,142,567,936
Assets: $1,235,034,249
Liabilities: $578,560,139
Net Worth: $656,474,110
Earnings: $1,265,199
Fiscal Year-end: 12/31/12
Business Description:
Pharmaceutical Product Whslr
S.I.C.: 5122
N.A.I.C.S.: 424210
Personnel:
Carlos Daniel Rizzo da Fonseca *(Chm)*
Roberto Martins de Souza *(Vice Chm)*
Jose Ricardo Mendes da Silva *(CEO & IR Officer)*
Sara Fantato Rezende Souza *(CFO)*
Carlos Alberto Castro Dutra *(Chief Investment Officer)*
Renato de Vicq Telles da Silva Lobo *(Ops Officer)*
Gabriel Simoes Guioto Ribeiro *(People & Mgmt Officer)*
Cristina Caiuby Salles *(Legal Officer)*
Rodrigo Silveira *(Integration Officer)*
Board of Directors:
Carlos Daniel Rizzo da Fonseca
Alvaro Jose da Silveira
Roberto Martins de Souza
Jose Luiz Depieri
Marcelo Kalim
Alexandre Fabiano Panarello

BRAZIL RESOURCES INC.
1111 West Hastings Street Suite 320
Vancouver, BC, V6E 2J3, Canada
Tel.: (805) 630-1001
Fax: (604) 682-3591
E-Mail: info@brazilresources.com
Web Site: www.brazilresources.com
Year Founded: 2009
BRI—(OTC TSXV)
Int. Income: $100,022
Assets: $17,196,697
Liabilities: $796,519
Net Worth: $16,400,178
Earnings: ($4,510,236)
Fiscal Year-end: 11/30/12
Business Description:
Gold Ore Exploration & Mining Services
S.I.C.: 1081
N.A.I.C.S.: 213114
Personnel:
Amir Adnani *(Chm)*
Stephen P. Swatton *(Pres & CEO)*
Patrick Obara *(CFO)*
Board of Directors:
Amir Adnani
Gloria Ballesta
Herb Dhaliwal
Mario Garnero
David Tok Pay Kong
Patrick Obara
Stephen P. Swatton
Legal Counsel:
McMillian LLP
1500 1055 W Georgia St
Vancouver, BC, Canada
Transfer Agent:
Computershare
510 Burrard St 2nd Floor
Vancouver, BC, Canada

BRAZILIAN FINANCE & REAL ESTATE S.A.
Av Paulista 1374 - 15 e 16 floors
Edificio Brazilian Financial Center
Bela Vista, Sao Paulo, SP, 01310-916, Brazil
Tel.: (55) 11 4081 4499
Fax: (55) 11 4081 4695
E-Mail: bfre@grupopan.com
Web Site: www.bfre.com.br
BFRE11—(BRAZ)
Business Description:
Real Estate Financial Services
S.I.C.: 6531
N.A.I.C.S.: 531390
Personnel:
Willy Otto Jordan Neto *(Dir-IR)*

BRAZILIAN GOLD CORPORATION
(Acquired & Absorbed by Brazil Resources Inc.)

BRAZILIAN METALS GROUP LIMITED
14th Floor 191 St Georges Terrace
Perth, WA, 6000, Australia
Tel.: (61) 8 9424 9390
Fax: (61) 8 9321 5932
E-Mail: enquiry@bmgl.com.au
Web Site: www.bmgl.com.au
BMG—(ASX)
Rev.: $97,406
Assets: $4,088,505
Liabilities: $226,565
Net Worth: $3,861,940
Earnings: ($20,869,458)
Fiscal Year-end: 06/30/13
Business Description:
Iron Ore Exploration Services
S.I.C.: 1011

Brazilian Metals Group Limited—(Continued)

N.A.I.C.S.: 212210
Personnel:
Bruce Alexander McCracken *(Mng Dir)*
Michael Green *(COO)*
Fleur Hudson *(Sec)*
Board of Directors:
Christopher John Eager
Malcolm John Castle
Michael Green
Bruce Alexander McCracken
Legal Counsel:
Jackson McDonald
Level 25 140 St Georges Terrace
Perth, WA, 6000, Australia

BRAZIRON LIMITED

Suite 5 Level 3 38 Richardson Street
West Perth, WA, 6005, Australia
Tel.: (61) 8 9485 0039
Fax: (61) 8 9485 0069
E-Mail: braziron@braziron.com
Web Site: www.braziron.com
BZL—(ASX)
Rev.: $497,121
Assets: $11,392,739
Liabilities: $907,139
Net Worth: $10,485,601
Earnings: ($22,343,047)
Fiscal Year-end: 12/31/12
Business Description:
Iron Ore Mining & Exploration Services
S.I.C.: 1011
N.A.I.C.S.: 212210
Personnel:
Robert Brierley *(Chm & Mng Dir)*
Bradley William George *(CEO)*
Jamie Morton *(CFO & Sec)*
Board of Directors:
Robert Brierley
Walt Guidice
Pedro Jacobi
Neil O'Loughlin
Youzhi Wei
Legal Counsel:
Tacey Goss PS
330 112th NE Ste 301
Bellevue, WA 98004
Steinepreis Paganin
Level 4 The Read Buildings 16 Milligan Street
6000 Perth, WA, Australia
Conyers Dill & Pearman Limited
Clarendon House 2 Church Street
Hamilton, Bermuda

BRD - GROUPE SOCIETE GENERALE S.A.

BRD Tower 1-7 Ion Mihalache
Boulevard Sector 1
011171 Bucharest, Romania
Tel.: (40) 213016100
Fax: (40) 213016636
E-Mail: communication@brd.ro
Web Site: www.brd.ro
BRD—(BUC)
Rev.: $979,770,346
Assets: $15,042,656,731
Liabilities: $13,269,714,421
Net Worth: $1,772,942,310
Earnings: ($89,400,732)
Emp.: 8,496
Fiscal Year-end: 12/31/12
Business Description:
Banking & Financial Services
S.I.C.: 6211
N.A.I.C.S.: 523110
Personnel:
Philippe Charles Lhotte *(Chm, CEO & Member-Mgmt Bd)*
Petre Bunescu *(Deputy CEO & Member-Mgmt Bd)*
Claudiu Cercel *(Deputy CEO & Member-Mgmt Bd)*
Didier Colin *(Deputy CEO & Member-Mgmt Bd)*
Gabriela Gavrilescu *(Deputy CEO & Member-Mgmt Bd)*
Jean-Luc Grasset *(Deputy CEO & Member-Mgmt Bd)*
Board of Directors:
Philippe Charles Lhotte
Didier Charles Maurice Alix
Anne-Marion Bouchacourt
Petre Bunescu
Sorin Marian Coclitu
Ioan Cuzman
Jean-Louis Mattei
Dumitru Popescu
Bernardo Sanchez-Incera

BREADTALK GROUP LTD.

171 Kampong Ampat 05 01 KA Foodlink
Singapore, 368330, Singapore
Tel.: (65) 62856116
Fax: (65) 62851661
E-Mail: enquiry@breadtalk.com
Web Site: www.breadtalk.com
5DA—(SES)
Rev.: $362,197,393
Assets: $288,577,239
Liabilities: $214,876,117
Net Worth: $73,701,122
Earnings: $10,977,641
Emp.: 7,000
Fiscal Year-end: 12/31/12
Business Description:
Holding Company
S.I.C.: 6719
N.A.I.C.S.: 551112
Personnel:
George Meng Tong Quek *(Founder & Chm)*
Eng Lock Oh *(CEO)*
Lawrence Yeo *(CFO)*
Tong Pak Goh *(Pres-Chm Office Special Projects)*
William Cheng *(CEO-Restaurant Div)*
Henry Heng Hwee Chu *(CEO-Bakery Div)*
Jenson Chin Hock Ong *(CEO-Food Atrium Div)*
Frankie Swee Heng Quek *(CEO-Asean Reg)*
James Seng Hwa Quek *(CEO-China Reg & Bakery Div)*
Cher Liang Tan *(Sec)*
Board of Directors:
George Meng Tong Quek
Soo Sen Chan
Kian Min Ong
Khee Giap Tan
Subsidiaries:

BreadTalk International Pte. Ltd. (1)
171 Kampong Ampat 05 05 KA Foodlink
Singapore, Singapore
Tel.: (65) 62856116
Fax: (65) 62851661
E-Mail: enquiry@breadtalk.com
Baked Goods Mfr
S.I.C.: 2053
N.A.I.C.S.: 311813
James Quek *(VP)*

BreadTalk Pte Ltd. (1)
171 Kampong Ampat Unit 05-05
KA Food Link, 368330 Singapore, Singapore
Tel.: (65) 62856116
Fax: (65) 62851661
E-Mail: enquiry@breadtalk.com
Web Site: www.breadtalk.com
Emp.: 700
Bakery & Retail Servies
S.I.C.: 5461
N.A.I.C.S.: 311811
Yeo Lawrence *(CFO)*

Subsidiary:

Taster Food Pte Ltd (2)
290 Orchard Road B1 03 Paragon
Singapore, 238859, Singapore
Tel.: (65) 68368336
Fax: (65) 68873933
Restaurant Operation Services
S.I.C.: 5812
N.A.I.C.S.: 722511
Chong Loke Ken *(Area Mgr)*

Food Republic Pte Ltd (1)
30 Tai Seng Street
Singapore, 534013, Singapore
Tel.: (65) 62760521
Fax: (65) 62760519
E-Mail: foodrep@breadtalk.com
Restaurant Operation Services
S.I.C.: 5812
N.A.I.C.S.: 722511

Ramen Play Pte. Ltd. (1)
313 Somerset 230 Orchard Rd B3 04
Singapore, Singapore
Tel.: (65) 66340051
Fax: (65) 66340052
E-Mail: info@ramenplay.com.sg
Web Site: www.ramenplay.com.sg
Emp.: 80
Restaurants Operation Services
S.I.C.: 5812
N.A.I.C.S.: 722513
Amanda Chiew *(VP)*

Non-U.S. Subsidiaries:

BreadTalk Concept Hong Kong Limited (1)
Rm C 69 Ground Fl Olympian City Phase 2
Lin Cheung Rd
Mongkok, Kowloon, China (Hong Kong)
Tel.: (852) 22734569
Fax: (852) 22734569
Baked Goods Mfr
S.I.C.: 2053
N.A.I.C.S.: 311813

ML Breadworks Sdn Bhd (1)
Level 6 Wisma KLIH 126 Jln Bukit Bintang
Kuala Lumpur, 55100, Malaysia (90%)
Tel.: (60) 387390118
Fax: (60) 3 2145 1113
Commercial Bakeries
S.I.C.: 2052
N.A.I.C.S.: 311812
Jo-Ann Yeoh *(Mng Dir)*

Shanghai BreadTalk Co., Ltd. (1)
Floor 2 3 An Sheng Business Building No 77 Fenyang Road
Xuhui District, Shanghai, China
Tel.: (86) 2154666565
Fax: (86) 2154658828
Baked Goods Retailer
S.I.C.: 2051
N.A.I.C.S.: 311812

BREAKAWAY RESOURCES LIMITED

(Acquired & Absorbed by Minotaur Exploration Ltd.)

BREAKER RESOURCES NL

Suite 2 20 Altona Street
West Perth, WA, 6005, Australia
Tel.: (61) 8 9226 3666
Fax: (61) 8 9226 3668
E-Mail: breaker@breakerresources.com.au
Web Site: www.breakerresources.com.au
Year Founded: 2010
BRB—(ASX)
Business Description:
Gold Mining
S.I.C.: 1041
N.A.I.C.S.: 212221
Personnel:
Tom Sanders *(Chm)*
Graeme Smith *(Sec)*
Board of Directors:
Tom Sanders
Mark Edwards
Michael Kitney

BREAKING POINT DEVELOPMENTS INC.

109 Scenic Park Place Northwest
Calgary, AB, T3L 1N8, Canada
Tel.: (403) 863-4578
E-Mail: windlem@hotmail.com
Year Founded: 2007
Business Description:
Investment Services
S.I.C.: 6211
N.A.I.C.S.: 523999
Personnel:
Michael D. Windle *(Pres & CEO)*
Ken Johnston *(CFO)*
Scott Reeves *(Sec)*
Board of Directors:
Doug Hassell
Ken Johnston
Don McIvor
Michael D. Windle

BRECO ANTRIEBSTECHNIK BREHER GMBH & CO. KG

Kleiststr 53
32457 Porta Westfalica, Germany
Tel.: (49) 573176700
Fax: (49) 5731767016
E-Mail: info@breco.de
Web Site: www.breco.de
Year Founded: 1967
Rev.: $11,173,140
Emp.: 250
Business Description:
Timing Belts Mfr
S.I.C.: 3086
N.A.I.C.S.: 326150
Personnel:
Thomas Schlinkmeier *(Co-Mng Dir)*
Thomas Steinert *(Co-Mng Dir)*

BREDERODE S.A.

Dreve Richelle 161 Bte 1
1410 Waterloo, Belgium
Tel.: (32) 2 352,00 90
Fax: (32) 2 352 00 99
E-Mail: info@brederode.eu
Web Site: www.brederode.eu
BREB—(EUR)
Emp.: 6
Business Description:
Financial Investment Services
S.I.C.: 6211
N.A.I.C.S.: 523999
Personnel:
Pierre van der Mersch *(Chm)*
Gerard Cotton *(Co-Mng Dir)*
Luigi Santambrogio *(Co-Mng Dir)*
Axel van der Mersch *(Co-Mng Dir)*
Board of Directors:
Pierre van der Mersch
Bruno Colmant
Gerard Cotton
Michel Delloye
Luigi Santambrogio
Alain Siaens
Axel van der Mersch

BREEDON AGGREGATES LIMITED

Elizabeth House 9 Castle St
Saint Helier, JE2 3RT, Jersey
Tel.: (44) 1537 700 000
Fax: (44) 1534700007
E-Mail: info@breedonaggregates.com
Web Site: www.breedonaggregates.com
BREE—(AIM)
Rev.: $273,938,906
Assets: $312,105,607
Liabilities: $186,790,525
Net Worth: $125,315,082
Earnings: $8,349,706
Emp.: 805
Fiscal Year-end: 12/31/12
Business Description:
Aggregates Mfr
S.I.C.: 3272

N.A.I.C.S.: 327390
Personnel:
Peter Tom *(Chm)*
Simon Vivian *(CEO)*
Board of Directors:
Peter Tom
Susie Farnon
Ian Peters
Simon Vivian
David Warr
David Williams
Legal Counsel:
Carey Olsen
47 Esplande
Saint Helier, Jersey
Transfer Agent:
Capita Registrars (Jersey) Limited
The Registry 34 Beckenham Road
Beckenham, United Kingdom
Non-U.S. Subsidiaries:

Breedon Aggregates England Limited (1)
Breedon Quarry Breedon-on-the-Hill
Derby, DE73 8AP, United Kingdom UK
Tel.: (44) 1332 862254 (100%)
Fax: (44) 1332 864320
E-Mail: sales@breedonaggregates.com
Web Site: www.breedonaggregates.com
Emp.: 400
Aggregate Mining & Products Distr
S.I.C.: 1429
N.A.I.C.S.: 212319
Simon Vivian *(CEO)*

Breedon Aggregates Scotland Limited (1)
Clatchard Quarry Cupar Road
Newburgh, Dundee, KY146JJ, United Kingdom UK
Tel.: (44) 1337840429 (100%)
E-Mail: enquiries@breedonaggregates.com
Web Site: www.breedonaggregates.com
Emp.: 400
Aggregate Mining & Products Distr
S.I.C.: 1429
N.A.I.C.S.: 212319
Simon Vivian *(CEO)*

BREEN INTERNATIONAL PTE. LTD.

(Formerly Oakwell-Breen Pte. Ltd.)
No 8 Aljunied Avenue 3 Oakwell Building
Singapore, 389933, Singapore
Tel.: (65) 6744 3455
Fax: (65) 6745 9366
E-Mail: Sales.sg@breenintl.com
Web Site: www.breenintl.com
Year Founded: 1995
Emp.: 7
Business Description:
Marketer & Distr of Engineered Products & Work Services for Utilities & Infrastructure Industries
S.I.C.: 5085
N.A.I.C.S.: 423840
Personnel:
Cheng Chai Tan *(Mng Dir)*
Non-U.S. Subsidiary:

Breen International Sdn Bhd (1)
(Formerly Oakwell-Breen Sdn Bhd)
No 24-1 Jalan Puteri 5/1 Bandar Puteri
47100 Puchong, Selangor Darul Ehsan, Malaysia
Tel.: (60) 3 8060 3027
Fax: (60) 3 8060 3319
E-Mail: sales.my@breenintl.com
Emp.: 10
Engineered Products Sales & Maintenance Services
S.I.C.: 5084
N.A.I.C.S.: 423830
Eric Yong *(Gen Mgr)*

BREITLING S.A.

Schlachthausstrasse 2
PO Box 1132
2540 Grenchen, Switzerland
Tel.: (41) 326545454
Fax: (41) 326545400
E-Mail: breitling@breitling.com
Web Site: www.breitling.com
Year Founded: 1884
Emp.: 360
Business Description:
Watch Mfr
S.I.C.: 3829
N.A.I.C.S.: 334519
Personnel:
Theodore Schneider *(Chm & CEO)*
Ernest Schneider *(Pres)*
U.S. Subsidiary:

BREITLING USA INC. (1)
206 Danbury Rd Ste 1
Wilton, CT 06897-4004
Tel.: (203) 762-1180
Fax: (203) 762-1178
E-Mail: sales@breitlingusa.com
Chronograph Wrist Watch Distr
S.I.C.: 5094
N.A.I.C.S.: 423940

Non-U.S. Subsidiaries:

BREITLING CHINA LIMITED (1)
Westgate Mall Office Tower 27th Floor Unit 2704-06A 1038 Nanjing West
200041 Shanghai, China
Tel.: (86) 21 6352 2670
E-Mail: customer.service@breitling-china.com
Emp.: 13
Chronograph Wrist Watch Distr
S.I.C.: 5094
N.A.I.C.S.: 423940
Kenneth Yuen, *(Gen Mgr)*

BREITLING DO BRASIL (1)
Barra Da Tijuca
CP 37029
22621-971 Rio de Janeiro, Brazil
Tel.: (55) 21 3982 5445
Fax: (55) 21 3982 5444
E-Mail: info@breitlingbrasil.com.br
Emp.: 14
Chronograph Wrist Watch Distr
S.I.C.: 5094
N.A.I.C.S.: 423940
David Szpiro, *(Mng Dir)*

BREITLING FRANCE S.A.R.L. (1)
64 Rue Pierre Charron
75008 Paris, France
Tel.: (33) 1 56436700
Fax: (33) 1 56436705
E-Mail: contact@breitling.fr
Chronograph Wrist Watch Distr
S.I.C.: 5094
N.A.I.C.S.: 423940

BREITLING ITALIA SRL (1)
Via Della Moscova 3
20121 Milan, Italy
Tel.: (39) 02 00 69 10 10
Fax: (39) 02 00 69 10 60
E-Mail: info@breitling.it
Chronograph Wrist Watch Distr
S.I.C.: 5094
N.A.I.C.S.: 423940

BREITLING JAPAN LTD (1)
Shibakoen Bldg 2-2-22 Shibakoen
Minato-Ku
Tokyo, 105-0011, Japan
Tel.: (81) 3 3436 0011
Fax: (81) 3 3436 0012
E-Mail: sales@breitling-japan.com
Web Site: www.breitling.co.jp
Chronograph Wrist Watch Distr
S.I.C.: 5094
N.A.I.C.S.: 423940

BREM HOLDING BERHAD

3rd Fl Brem House Crystal Crown Hotel
No 12 Lorong Utara A Off Jalan Utara
46200 Petaling Jaya, Selangor Darul Ehsan, Malaysia
Tel.: (60) 379587888
Fax: (60) 379581533
E-Mail: corporate@bremholding.com
Web Site: www.bremholding.com
BREM—(KLS)
Sales Range: $25-49.9 Million
Business Description:
Property Development & Investment Services
S.I.C.: 6513
N.A.I.C.S.: 531110
Personnel:
Yahaya Shafie *(Chm)*
Chai Kaa Khoo *(Mng Dir)*
Chooi Yoong Chow *(Sec)*
Board of Directors:
Yahaya Shafie
Chai Kaa Khoo
Hui Keam Khoo
Yew Hwa Low
Abu Sujak Mahmud
Miow Song Wong

BREMBO S.P.A.

Viale Europa 2
24040 Stezzano, BG, Italy
Tel.: (39) 0356052111
Fax: (39) 035605518
E-Mail: press@brembo.it
Web Site: www.brembo.it
Year Founded: 1961
BRE—(ITA)
Sls.: $1,869,341,470
Assets: $1,639,775,062
Liabilities: $1,102,487,653
Net Worth: $537,287,409
Earnings: $104,691,641
Emp.: 6,937
Fiscal Year-end: 12/31/12
Business Description:
Automotive Braking Components & Systems Mfr
S.I.C.: 3714
N.A.I.C.S.: 336340
Personnel:
Alberto Bombassei *(Chm)*
Matteo Tiraboschi *(Deputy Chm & CFO)*
Andrea Abbati Marescotti *(Mng Dir & Gen Mgr)*
Giorgio Ascanelli *(CTO & Head-Advanced Res & Technical Dev)*
Board of Directors:
Alberto Bombassei
Cristina Bombassei
Giovanni Cavallini
Giancarlo Dallera
Giovanna Dossena
Andrea Abbati Marescotti
Umberto Nicodano
Pasquale Pistorio
Gianfelice Rocca
Pierfrancesco Saviotti
Matteo Tiraboschi

Subsidiaries:

Brembo SGL Carbon Ceramic Brakes S.p.A. (1)
Viale Europa 2
Stezzano, 24040 Bergamo, Italy
Tel.: (39) 0355097111
Fax: (39) 035605930
E-Mail: ir@brembo.it
Web Site: www.brembo.it
Motor Vehicle & Motorbike Brake Systems & Parts Mfr
S.I.C.: 3714
N.A.I.C.S.: 336340

Brembo North America, Inc. (1)
47765 Halyard Dr
Plymouth, MI 48170
Tel.: (734) 468-2100
Fax: (734) 468-2161
Web Site: www.brembo.com
Emp.: 40
Motor Vehicle Brake Systems Mfr
S.I.C.: 3714
N.A.I.C.S.: 336340
Daniel Sandberg *(Pres & CEO)*

Subsidiary:

Brembo North America, Inc. (2)
29991 E M 60
Homer, MI 49245-9753 MI
Tel.: (517) 568-4398
Fax: (517) 568-4207
Web Site: www.brembo.com
Sales Range: $100-124.9 Million
Emp.: 150
Automotive Brake Components
S.I.C.: 3714
N.A.I.C.S.: 336340
Jayson Wolf *(Plant Mgr)*

Non-U.S. Subsidiary:

Brembo Rassini S.A. de C.V. (3)
Platon 100 Parque Indus Kalos
PO Box KM17
Apodaca, CP 66600, Mexico MI
Tel.: (52) 8183697800
Fax: (52) 8183697841
Web Site: www.brembo.com
Emp.: 110
Brake Rotors & Drums
S.I.C.: 3714
N.A.I.C.S.: 336340
Zan Sanzberg *(Pres)*

Softia S.r.l. (1)
Via Iseo 43
Erbusco, 25030 Brescia, Italy (100%)
Tel.: (39) 0307724141
Fax: (39) 0307724140
E-Mail: info@softia.it
Web Site: www.softia.it
Emp.: 8
Software Reproduction
S.I.C.: 3652
N.A.I.C.S.: 334614
Vittorio Taglietti *(Mng Dir)*

Non-U.S. Subsidiaries:

AP Racing Ltd. (1)
Wheler Rd Seven Stars Indust Est
Coventry, West Midlands, CV3 4LB, United Kingdom (100%)
Tel.: (44) 2476639595
Fax: (44) 2476639559
Web Site: www.apracing.com
Emp.: 120
Motor Vehicle Parts Mfr
S.I.C.: 3714
N.A.I.C.S.: 336390
Charles Bolton *(Mng Dir)*

Brembo do Brasil Ltda. (1)
Distr Ind Baneirinhas Av Fausto Ribeiro Silva
1265 Betim, Brazil
Tel.: (55) 32540990
Fax: (55) 35398509
Business Service Centers
S.I.C.: 7334
N.A.I.C.S.: 561439

Brembo Japan Co. Ltd. (1)
No 14-1 kamiikedai 2-Chome
Tokyo, Ohta-ku, 145-0064, Japan
Tel.: (81) 337269199
Fax: (81) 337267605
E-Mail: info@brembo.jp
Emp.: 15
Motor Vehicle Supplies & New Parts Whslr
S.I.C.: 5013
N.A.I.C.S.: 423120
Savio Casablanca *(Mng Dir)*

Brembo Scandinavia A.B. (1)
PO Box 5296
40225 Gothenburg, Sweden
Tel.: (46) 707481665
Web Site: www.brembo.com
Emp.: 1
Motor Vehicle Supplies & New Parts Whslr
S.I.C.: 5013
N.A.I.C.S.: 423120

Brembo UK Ltd. (1)
Greenhill Industrial Estate
Kidderminster, DY10 2RN, United Kingdom
Tel.: (44) 1562512502
Fax: (44) 1562820933
E-Mail: brembo@jordans.co.uk
Web Site: www.jordans.co.uk
New Car Dealers
S.I.C.: 5511
N.A.I.C.S.: 441110

Brembo S.p.A.—(Continued)

Corporacion Upwards 98 S.A. (1)
Calle La Habana 15 Plgo Ind Centro Via
50196 Zaragoza, Spain
Tel.: (34) 976144560
Fax: (34) 976144466
Emp.: 90
Motor Vehicle Parts Whslr
S.I.C.: 5013
N.A.I.C.S.: 423120

BRENNTAG AG

Stinnes-Platz 1
45472 Mulheim an der Ruhr, Germany
Tel.: (49) 20878280
Fax: (49) 2087828698
E-Mail: info@brenntag.de
Web Site: www.brenntag.com
Year Founded: 1874
BNR—(DEU OTC)
Sls.: $13,044,252,683
Assets: $7,687,303,785
Liabilities: $5,006,810,081
Net Worth: $2,680,493,704
Earnings: $455,274,694
Emp.: 12,988
Fiscal Year-end: 12/31/12

Business Description:
Industrial & Specialty Chemical Distr
S.I.C.: 5169
N.A.I.C.S.: 424690

Personnel:
Stefan Zuschke *(Chm-Supervisory Bd)*
Thomas Ludwig *(Deputy Chm-Supervisory Bd)*
Steven Holland *(CEO)*
George Muller *(CFO & Member-Mgmt Bd)*
Hubertus Spethmann *(Press Officer & VP-Corp Comm)*
Karsten Beckmann *(CEO-EMEA)*
Jurgen Buchsteiner *(Member-Mgmt Bd)*
William Fidler *(Member-Mgmt Bd)*

Supervisory Board of Directors:
Stefan Zuschke
Stephen Clark
Edgar Fluri
Thomas Ludwig
Doreen Nowotne
Andreas Rittstieg

Subsidiaries:

Brenntag Beteiligungs GmbH (1)
Stinnes-Platz 1
Mulheim an der Ruhr, 45472, Germany
Tel.: (49) 20878280
Fax: (49) 2087828698
Chemical Products Distr
S.I.C.: 5169
N.A.I.C.S.: 424690

Brenntag Foreign Holding GmbH (1)
Stinnes-Platz 1
Mulheim an der Ruhr, 45472, Germany
Tel.: (49) 20878280
Fax: (49) 2087828698
Investment Management Services
S.I.C.: 6211
N.A.I.C.S.: 523999

Brenntag Germany Holding GmbH (1)
Stinnes-Platz 1
Mulheim an der Ruhr, 45472, Germany
Tel.: (49) 20878280
Fax: (49) 208 7828698
E-Mail: info@brenntag.de
Investment Management Services
S.I.C.: 6211
N.A.I.C.S.: 523999

Branches:

Brenntag GmbH (2)
Am Rohrenwerk 46
47259 Duisburg, Germany
Tel.: (49) 20375820
Telex: 857312
Fax: (49) 20375826001
E-Mail: info@brenntag.de
Web Site: www.brenntag.de
Emp.: 150
Distr of Industrial & Specialty Chemicals
S.I.C.: 5169
N.A.I.C.S.: 424690
Uwe Schulteua *(Gen Mgr)*

Brenntag GmbH (2)
Am Fieseler Werk 9
34253 Lohfelden, Germany
Tel.: (49) 561951070
Telex: 857674
Fax: (49) 5619510733
E-Mail: info@brenntag.de
Web Site: www.brenntag.de
Emp.: 40
Chemical Preparations
S.I.C.: 2899
N.A.I.C.S.: 325998

Brenntag GmbH (2)
Am Nordseekai 22
73207 Plochingen, Germany
Tel.: (49) 715370150
Telex: 8579355
Fax: (49) 7153701550
E-Mail: brenntag@brenntag-gmbh.de
Web Site: www.brenntag.de
Sales Range: $150-199.9 Million
Emp.: 8,300
Distr of Industrial & Specialty Chemicals
S.I.C.: 5169
N.A.I.C.S.: 424690
Uwe Schueltke *(Mng Dir)*

Brenntag GmbH (2)
Merkurstrasse 47
67663 Kaiserslautern, Germany
Tel.: (49) 631535620
Telex: 8579388
Fax: (49) 6315356239
Web Site: www.brenntag.de
Emp.: 100
Distr of Industrial & Specialty Chemicals
S.I.C.: 5169
N.A.I.C.S.: 424690
Cosimo Alemanno *(Mgr)*

BRENNTAG International Chemicals GmbH (1)
Stinnes-Platz 1
Mulheim an der Ruhr, 45472, Germany
Tel.: (49) 20878280
Fax: (49) 2087828407
E-Mail: international-chemical@brenntag.de
Web Site: www.brenntag.com
Emp.: 6
Chemical Products Distr
S.I.C.: 5169
N.A.I.C.S.: 424690
Dimitry Martsynkovsky *(Gen Mgr)*

Brenntag Real Estate GmbH (1)
Stinnes-Platz 1
Mulheim an der Ruhr, 45472, Germany
Tel.: (49) 208782 80
Fax: (49) 5352628 50 28
Real Estate Development Services
S.I.C.: 6531
N.A.I.C.S.: 531390

CVB Albert Carl GmbH & Co. KG (1)
Oberlandstrasse 22-25
12099 Berlin, Germany
Tel.: (49) 30 62 89 32 0
Fax: (49) 30 62 89 32 50
E-Mail: berlin@cvh.de
Web Site: www.cvh.de
Emp.: 18
Chemical Products Distr
S.I.C.: 5169
N.A.I.C.S.: 424690
Alfons Bogaerts *(Gen Mgr)*

CVH Chemie-Vertrieb GmbH & Co.Hannover KG (1)
Podbielskistrasse 22
30163 Hannover, Germany
Tel.: (49) 5 11 9 65 35 111
Fax: (49) 5 11 9 65 35 240
E-Mail: hannover@cvh.de
Web Site: www.cvh.de
Emp.: 3
Chemical Products Distr
S.I.C.: 5169
N.A.I.C.S.: 424690
Lutz Meyer *(Gen Mgr)*

CVH Chemie-Vertrieb Verwaltungsgesellschaft mbH (1)
Podbielskistr 22
Hannover, 30163, Germany
Tel.: (49) 511965350
Fax: (49) 51196535246
Chemical Products Distr
S.I.C.: 5169
N.A.I.C.S.: 424690

CVM Chemie-Vertrieb Magdeburg GmbH & Co. KG (1)
Geschwister-Scholl-Strasse 127
Elbe, 39218 Schonebeck, Germany
Tel.: (49) 39 28 45 64 09
Fax: (49) 39 28 45 64 50
E-Mail: magdeburg@cvh.de
Emp.: 12
Chemical Products Distr
S.I.C.: 5169
N.A.I.C.S.: 424690
Axel Lenz *(Gen Mgr)*

CVP Chemie-Vertrieb Berlin GmbH (1)
Oberlandstr 22-25
Berlin, 12099, Germany
Tel.: (49) 306289320
Fax: (49) 306268161
Chemical Products Distr
S.I.C.: 5169
N.A.I.C.S.: 424690

ROSEA Grundstucks-Vermietungsgesellschaft mbH & Co. (1)
Mercedesstr 6
40470 Dusseldorf, Germany
Tel.: (49) 211 77080
Fax: (49) 211 77083156
Real Estate Development Services
S.I.C.: 6531
N.A.I.C.S.: 531390

U.S. Subsidiaries:

Brenntag Latin America, Inc. (1)
5300 Memorial Dr 11th Fl
Houston, TX 77007
Tel.: (713) 880-5400
Fax: (713) 880-3396
E-Mail: blasales@brenntagla.com
Web Site: www.brenntagla.com
Emp.: 60
Specialty & Industrial Chemical Distr
S.I.C.: 2899
N.A.I.C.S.: 325998
German Torres *(COO)*

Non-U.S. Subsidiaries:

Brenntag Argentina S.A. (2)
Av Corrientes 345 8 flr
C1043AAD Buenos Aires, Argentina
Tel.: (54) 1152785500
Fax: (54) 1152785500
E-Mail: info@brenntagla.com
Web Site: www.brenntagla.com
Specialty & Industrial Chemical Distr
S.I.C.: 2899
N.A.I.C.S.: 325998

Brenntag Bolivia SRL (2)
Km 10 5 Carretera al Norte
Santa Cruz, Bolivia
Tel.: (591) 33853121
Fax: (591) 33853123
E-Mail: projas@brenntagla.com
Web Site: www.brenntagla.com
Emp.: 15
Specialty & Industrial Chemical Mfr
S.I.C.: 2899
N.A.I.C.S.: 325998
Pablo Rojas *(Gen Mgr)*

Brenntag Brasil Ltda. (2)
Rua Alexandre Dumas 1 658 9 andar
Chacara Sto Antonio, 04717 004 Sao Paulo, Brazil
Tel.: (55) 1155452100
Fax: (55) 1151828281
E-Mail: cjunior@brenntagla.com
Web Site: www.brenntag.com
Emp.: 200
Specialty & Industrial Chemical Distr
S.I.C.: 2899
N.A.I.C.S.: 325998
Luciano Foreste *(Mgr-Comm)*

Brenntag Caribe S.A. (2)
Ave Isabel Aguilar 209
Herrera, Santo Domingo, Dominican Republic
Tel.: (809) 5318060
Fax: (809) 5318070
Web Site: www.brenntag.com
Emp.: 50
Specialty & Industrial Chemical Mfr
S.I.C.: 2899
N.A.I.C.S.: 325998
Marcus Brocker *(Gen Mgr)*

Brenntag Chile Ltda. (2)
Camino Lo Sierra 02966 San Bernardo
Casilla 3275
Santiago, Chile
Tel.: (56) 24402400
Fax: (56) 24402425
E-Mail: faguilera@brenntagla.com
Web Site: www.brenntagla.com
Emp.: 70
Specialty & Industrial Chemical Distr
S.I.C.: 2899
N.A.I.C.S.: 325998
Francisco Aguilera Chaves *(Gen Mgr)*

Brenntag Colombia S. A. (2)
Carrera Troncal de Occidente km. 19
Mosquera, Bogota, Colombia
Tel.: (57) 12940420
Fax: (57) 1 294 0463
E-Mail: servicientecolombia@brenntagla.com
Web Site: www.brenntagla.com
Specialty & Industrial Chemical Distr
S.I.C.: 2899
N.A.I.C.S.: 325998
Alvaro Pinzon Gutierrez *(Gen Mgr)*

Brenntag Ecuador S. A. (2)
Carretera a Daule Km 9 5
Guayaquil, Ecuador
Tel.: (593) 2110500
Fax: (593) 2110351
E-Mail: gvallarino@brenntagla.com
Emp.: 105
Specialty & Industrial Chemical Distr
S.I.C.: 2899
N.A.I.C.S.: 325998
Gustavo Vallarino Marcos *(Gen Mgr)*

Brenntag Guatemala S. A. (2)
23 Avenida 40 19 Zona 12
Guatemala, Guatemala
Tel.: (502) 24237777
Fax: (502) 24237779
E-Mail: jgomez@brenntagla.com
Web Site: www.brenntagla.com
Emp.: 48
Specialty & Industrial Chemical Distr
S.I.C.: 2899
N.A.I.C.S.: 325998

Brenntag Mexico, S. A. de C. V. (2)
Ave Tejecotes lote 8 Manzana 4 Bodega G
Parque Industrial
CP 54769 Mexico, San Martin, Mexico
Tel.: (52) 5558996400
Fax: (52) 55 5899 6442
E-Mail: infomexico@brenntagla.com
Web Site: www.brenntagla.com
Specialty & Industrial Chemical Distr
S.I.C.: 2899
N.A.I.C.S.: 325998

Brenntag Nicaragua, S.A. (2)
Kilometro 10 1/2 Carretera nueva a Leon
Frente a Unilever, A.P. 4074 Managua, Nicaragua
Tel.: (505) 2690794
Fax: (505) 2690796
E-Mail: infonicaragua@brenntagla.com
Web Site: www.brenntagla.com
Specialty & Industrial Chemical Distr
S.I.C.: 2899
N.A.I.C.S.: 325998
Luis Carlos Cardena Sarmiento *(Gen Mgr)*

Brenntag Peru A. C. (2)
Calle Los Plasticos 277 Urbanizacion Ind
Vulcano Ate Vitarte
Lima, Peru
Tel.: (51) 13134800
Fax: (51) 13134802
E-Mail: infoperu@brenntagla.com
Web Site: www.brenntagla.com
Specialty & Industrial Chemical Distr
S.I.C.: 2899
N.A.I.C.S.: 325998

Luis Carlos Cavena *(Gen Mgr)*

Brenntag North America, Inc. (1)
5083 Pottsville Pike
Reading, PA 19612-3788
Mailing Address:
5083 Pottsville Pike
Reading, PA 19605-9724
Tel.: (610) 926-6100
Telex: 9023 71
Fax: (610) 926-0420
E-Mail: brenntag@brenntag.com
Web Site: www.brenntagnorthamerica.com
Industrial & Specialty Chemical Mfr & Distr
S.I.C.: 5169
N.A.I.C.S.: 424690
Markus Klahn *(CEO)*
H. Edward Boyadjian *(CFO & Exec VP)*
James Doyle *(Exec VP)*
Robert L. Moser *(Sr VP-Global Accts)*

Division:

Brenntag Specialties, Inc. (2)
1000 Coolidge St
South Plainfield, NJ 07080 DE
Tel.: (908) 561-6100
Fax: (908) 253-5041
Toll Free: (800) 732-0562
E-Mail: bsi@brenntag.com
Web Site: www.brenntagspecialties.com
Emp.: 400
Specialty Pigments, Coatings, Adhesives, Resins & Chemicals Mfr & Distr
S.I.C.: 2819
N.A.I.C.S.: 325130
Theodore Hubbard *(Exec VP)*

Unit:

Brenntag Specialties (3)
5700 Tacony St
Philadelphia, PA 19135
Tel.: (215) 537-1000
Fax: (215) 537-8575
Toll Free: (800) 423-7423
E-Mail: bsi@brenntag.com
Web Site: www.brenntagspecialties.com
Emp.: 20
Specialty Pigments, Coatings, Adhesives, Resins & Chemicals Distr
S.I.C.: 5169
N.A.I.C.S.: 424690
Cas Kleczko *(Sr Acct Mgr-Central & Northern NJ)*

Subsidiaries:

Altivia Corporation (2)
1100 Louisiana St Ste 4800
Houston, TX 77002
Tel.: (713) 658-9000
Fax: (713) 658-0102
Toll Free: (866) 258-4842
E-Mail: sales@altivia.com
Web Site: www.altivia.com
Sales Range: $75-99.9 Million
Emp.: 150
Cyclic Crudes & Intermediates
S.I.C.: 2869
N.A.I.C.S.: 325199
J. Michael Jusbasche *(CEO)*
Fred Stahelin *(CFO)*
Louis G. Huey *(COO)*

Brenntag Great Lakes, LLC (2)
4420 N Harley Davidson Ave Ste A
Wauwatosa, WI 53225
Tel.: (262) 252-3550
Fax: (262) 252-5250
E-Mail: bglsales@brenntag.com
Web Site: www.brenntagnorthamerica.com
Emp.: 100
Industrial & Specialty Chemical Mfr
S.I.C.: 2899
N.A.I.C.S.: 325998
Jim Holcomb *(Pres)*

Brenntag Mid-South, Inc. (2)
1405 Hwy 136 W
Henderson, KY 42420
Mailing Address:
PO Box 20
Henderson, KY 42419
Tel.: (270) 830-1200
Fax: (270) 827-3990
E-Mail: mid-south.info@brenntag.com
Web Site: www.brenntag.com
Emp.: 300
Specialty & Industrial Chemical Distr
S.I.C.: 2869
N.A.I.C.S.: 325199
Joel Hopper *(Pres)*

Brenntag Northeast, Inc. (2)
81 W Huller Ln
Reading, PA 19605
Tel.: (610) 926-4151
Fax: (610) 926-4160
E-Mail: northeast.salesadmin@brenntag.com
Web Site: www.brenntagnortheast.com
Specialty & Industrial Chemical Mfr & Distr
S.I.C.: 2899
N.A.I.C.S.: 325998
Denny Eisenhofer *(VP-Ops)*

Brenntag Pacific, Inc. (2)
10747 Patterson Pl
Santa Fe Springs, CA 90670-4043
Tel.: (562) 903-9626
Fax: (562) 903-9622
E-Mail: cs.bp@brenntag.com
Web Site: www.brenntagnorthamerica.com
Emp.: 80
Industrial Chemical Distr
S.I.C.: 5169
N.A.I.C.S.: 424690
Steve Pozzi *(Pres)*

Branches:

Brenntag Pacific, Inc. - Fairbanks (3)
4199 Lathrop St
Fairbanks, AK 99701
Tel.: (907) 929-9324
Web Site: www.brenntag.com
Emp.: 50
Chemicals & Allied Products Whslr
S.I.C.: 5169
N.A.I.C.S.: 424690

Brenntag Pacific, Inc. - South Gate (3)
4545 Ardine St
South Gate, CA 90280-2534 CA
Tel.: (323) 832-5000
Fax: (323) 773-0909
Web Site: www.brenntagpacific.com
Emp.: 325
Industrial & Specialty Chemical Distr
S.I.C.: 5169
N.A.I.C.S.: 424690
Debbie Thiere *(Dir-HR)*

Brenntag Southeast, Inc. (2)
2000 E Pettigrew St
Durham, NC 27703
Tel.: (919) 596-0681
Fax: (919) 596-6438
E-Mail: southeast.durham@brenntag.com
Web Site: www.brenntagsoutheast.com
Emp.: 250
Industrial & Specialty Chemical Mfr
S.I.C.: 2899
N.A.I.C.S.: 325998
Gil Steadman *(Pres)*

Brenntag Southwest, Inc. (2)
610 Fisher Rd
Longview, TX 75604
Tel.: (903) 759-7151
Fax: (903) 759-7548
E-Mail: brenntag@brenntag.com
Web Site: www.brenntagsouthwest.com
Emp.: 65
Industrial & Specialty Chemical Mfr & Distr
S.I.C.: 2899
N.A.I.C.S.: 325998
Kevin Kessing *(VP-Natl Acct)*

Branches:

Brenntag Southwest, Inc. - Borger (3)
Highway 207 S
Borger, TX 79007
Tel.: (806) 342-0163
Web Site: www.brenntagsouthwest.com
Emp.: 50
Other Chemical & Allied Products Merchant Whslr
S.I.C.: 5169
N.A.I.C.S.: 424690
Ron Morton *(Mgr)*

Brenntag Southwest, Inc. - Lancaster (3)
704 E Wintergreen Rd
Lancaster, TX 75134
Tel.: (972) 218-3500
Web Site: www.brenntagsouthwest.com
Emp.: 50
Industrial Chemical Distr
S.I.C.: 5169
N.A.I.C.S.: 424690
Kelly Hancock *(Principal)*

Coastal Chemical Co., LLC (2)
3520 Veterans Memorial Dr
Abbeville, LA 70510
Mailing Address:
PO Box 820
Abbeville, LA 70511
Tel.: (337) 898-0001
Fax: (337) 892-1185
Toll Free: (800) 535-3862
Web Site: www.coastalchem.com
Industrial & Specialty Chemical Distr
S.I.C.: 2899
N.A.I.C.S.: 325998

Brenntag Puerto Rico, Inc. (1)
Plaza Bairoa Local 206 Bairoa Industrial Park State Rd 1
Caguas, PR 00725
Tel.: (787) 286-0480
Fax: (787) 743-1498
E-Mail: infopuertorico@brenntagla.com
Web Site: www.brenntagla.com
Emp.: 10
Chemical Products Distr
S.I.C.: 5169
N.A.I.C.S.: 424690
Samuel Cruz *(Gen Mgr)*

Non-U.S. Subsidiaries:

Akashi SDN. BHD. (1)
Pt 55 64 & 65 Jalan Hulu Tinggi 26/6 Section 26
Shah Alam, Selangor, 40400, Malaysia
Tel.: (60) 351918811
Fax: (60) 351918899
Chemical Products Distr
S.I.C.: 5169
N.A.I.C.S.: 424690

Alliance Chimie Algerie SPA (1)
Hai Benchoubane N 42
Rouiba, Algiers, 16000, Algeria
Tel.: (213) 770 9150 05
Fax: (213) 21 81 07 65
Chemical Products Distr
S.I.C.: 5169
N.A.I.C.S.: 424690

Alliance Tunisie S.A.R.L. (1)
21 Rue 8602 Zone Industriel Charguia I
Ariana, 2035, Tunisia
Tel.: (216) 71771678
Fax: (216) 71770048
Chemical Products Distr
S.I.C.: 5169
N.A.I.C.S.: 424690

Brenntag Australia Pty. Ltd. (1)
270 Ferntree Gully Rd
Notting Hill, Melbourne, VIC, 3168, Australia
Tel.: (61) 395012700
Logistics Consulting Services
S.I.C.: 4731
N.A.I.C.S.: 541614

Brenntag Austria Holding GmbH (1)
Linke Wienzeile 152
Vienna, 1060, Austria
Tel.: (43) 1599950
Fax: (43) 15970200
E-Mail: office@brenntag.at
Web Site: www.brenntag-cee.com
Emp.: 30
Investment Management Services
S.I.C.: 6211
N.A.I.C.S.: 523999
Tomper Scruger *(Gen Mgr)*

Brenntag Bangladesh Ltd. (1)
Latif Tower 6th & 7th Floors 47-Kawran Bazar
Tejgaon, Dhaka, 1215, Bangladesh
Tel.: (880) 2 911 9758
Fax: (880) 2 911 9737
E-Mail: info-bangladesh@brenntag-asia.com
Chemical Products Distr
S.I.C.: 5169
N.A.I.C.S.: 424690

Brenntag Bulgaria Ltd (1)
J k Drujba 2 ul Obikolna No 21 et 1
1582 Sofia, Bulgaria
Tel.: (359) 29265600
Fax: (359) 28793270
E-Mail: info@brenntag.bg
Web Site: www.brenntag.com
Emp.: 30
Specialty & Industrial Chemical Mfr & Distr
S.I.C.: 2899
N.A.I.C.S.: 325998
Irina Tolumska *(Gen Mgr)*

Brenntag Canada Inc. (1)
43 Jutland Road
Toronto, ON, M8Z 2G6, Canada
Tel.: (416) 259-8231
Fax: (416) 259-5333
E-Mail: sales@brenntag.ca
Web Site: www.brenntag.ca
Emp.: 70
Specialty & Industrial Chemical Mfr & Distr
S.I.C.: 2899
N.A.I.C.S.: 325998
Mike Staley *(Pres)*

Brenntag CEE GmbH (1)
Linke Wienzeile 152
1060 Vienna, Austria
Tel.: (43) 5 9995 0
Fax: (43) 5 9995 1275
E-Mail: office@brenntag-cee.com
Web Site: www.brenntag-cee.com
Chemical Products Distr
S.I.C.: 5169
N.A.I.C.S.: 424690
Arno Schober *(Mgr-AdBlue Div)*

Brenntag Chemical Distribution (Ireland) Ltd. (1)
Unit 405 Greenogue Business Pk
Rathcoole 24
Dublin, Ireland
Tel.: (353) 1 4013500
Fax: (353) 1 4013501
E-Mail: dublin.sales@brenntag.ie
Web Site: www.brenntag.ie
Emp.: 17
Chemical Products Distr
S.I.C.: 5169
N.A.I.C.S.: 424690
Tony Smith *(Gen Mgr)*

Brenntag Chile Comercial e Industrial Ltda. (1)
Camino de la Sierra
02966 Santiago, Chile
Tel.: (56) 2 440 2400
Fax: (56) 2 440 2425
Web Site: www.brenntagla.com
Chemical Products Distr
S.I.C.: 5169
N.A.I.C.S.: 424690

Brenntag Colours Ltd. (1)
High Level Way
Halifax, HX1 4PN, United Kingdom
Tel.: (44) 1422 358431
Fax: (44) 1422 330867
E-Mail: enquiry@brenntag.co.uk
Web Site: www.brenntag.co.uk
Emp.: 4
Chemical Products Distr
S.I.C.: 5169
N.A.I.C.S.: 424690
Vicky Riley *(Mgr-Customer Svc-Europe)*

Brenntag Cooperatief U.A. (1)
Donker Duyvisweg 44
3316 BM Dordrecht, Netherlands
Tel.: (31) 786544944
Fax: (31) 786544919
Specialty Chemicals Distr
S.I.C.: 5169
N.A.I.C.S.: 424690

Brenntag Dutch C.V. (1)
Industrieweg 1
Loosdrecht, 1231 KG, Netherlands
Tel.: (31) 35 5889300
Fax: (31) 35 5824364
E-Mail: info@brenntag.nl
Web Site: www.brenntag.nl
Emp.: 7
Chemical Products Distr
S.I.C.: 5169
N.A.I.C.S.: 424690
Glen Grindlay *(Gen Mgr)*

Brenntag El Salvador S.A. de C.V. (1)
Blvd Del Ejercito Nacional Km 7 1/2
Complejo Industrial Regina Nave 9
PO Box 2373
Soyapango, San Salvador, El Salvador

Brenntag AG—(Continued)

Tel.: (503) 2251 5600
Fax: (503) 2251 5624
Web Site: www.brenntagla.com
Chemical Products Distr
S.I.C.: 5169
N.A.I.C.S.: 424690

Brenntag France Holding SAS (1)
90 Avenue Du Progres
Chassieu, 69680, France
Tel.: (33) 4 72 22 15 00
Fax: (33) 4 78 90 84 43
Investment Management Services
S.I.C.: 6211
N.A.I.C.S.: 523999

BRENNTAG (Holding) B.V. (1)
Donker Duyvisweg 44
Dordrecht, 3316 BM, Netherlands
Tel.: (31) 78 654 4944
Fax: (31) 78 654 4948
E-Mail: info@brenntag.nl
Web Site: www.brenntag.nl
Emp.: 10
Investment Management Services
S.I.C.: 6211
N.A.I.C.S.: 523999

BRENNTAG HOLDING S.p.A. (1)
Via Cusago 150/4
Milan, 20153, Italy
Tel.: (39) 02483330
Fax: (39) 0248333201
Investment Management Services
S.I.C.: 6211
N.A.I.C.S.: 523999

Brenntag Hong Kong Limited (1)
Unit A 18th Floor Manulife Tower 169
Electric Road
North Point, China (Hong Kong)
Tel.: (852) 3752 8010
Fax: (852) 3752 8011
E-Mail: info-hkg@brenntag-asia.com
Chemical Products Distr
S.I.C.: 5169
N.A.I.C.S.: 424690

BRENNTAG Hrvatska d.o.o. (1)
Radnicka Cesta 173p
Zagreb, 10000, Croatia
Tel.: (385) 12405710
Fax: (385) 12405711
E-Mail: office@brenntag.hr
Chemical Products Distr
S.I.C.: 5169
N.A.I.C.S.: 424690

Brenntag Hungaria Kft. (1)
Banyaleg utca 45
1225 Budapest, Hungary
Tel.: (36) 1 889 5100
Fax: (36) 1 889 5111
E-Mail: office@brenntag.hu
Web Site: www.brenntag-cee.com
Chemical Products Distr
S.I.C.: 5169
N.A.I.C.S.: 424690

Brenntag India Private Ltd. (1)
Ackruti Centre Point 301 3rd Floor MIDC
Central Road
Andheri East, Mumbai, 400 093, India
Tel.: (91) 22 424 82 100
Fax: (91) 22 424 82 164
Emp.: 4
Chemical Products Distr
S.I.C.: 5169
N.A.I.C.S.: 424690
Sanjay Gupta *(Mng Dir)*

Brenntag Ingredients Inc. (1)
4th Floor Builders Centre Building 170
Salcedo St
Legaspi Village, Makati, 12291229, Philippines
Tel.: (63) 2 812 9385
Fax: (63) 2 810 5897
E-Mail: info-phils@brenntag-asia.com
Web Site: www.brenntag-asiapacific.com
Emp.: 88
Chemical Products & Ingredients Distr
S.I.C.: 5169
N.A.I.C.S.: 424690
Aldwin Jacinto Mitra *(Reg Mgr-Water Treatment, Oil, Gas & Lubricants Market)*

Brenntag Ingredients (India) Private Limited (1)
301 Akruti Center Point 3rd Floor MIDC
Central Road
Andheri East, Mumbai, 400 093, India
Tel.: (91) 22 42482100
Fax: (91) 22 6710 0210
Emp.: 6
Specialty Chemicals Mfr
S.I.C.: 2899
N.A.I.C.S.: 325998
Sanjay Gupta *(Mng Dir)*

Brenntag Ingredients (Thailand) Public Company Ltd. (1)
1168 98 100 Lumpini Tower 33rd Fl
Rama IV Rd Kwang Thungmakamek,
Bangkok, Khet Sathorn, 10120,
Thailand (100%)
Tel.: (66) 26895999
Fax: (66) 268958889
Web Site: www.eac.co.th
Emp.: 155
Chemicals Distr
S.I.C.: 5169
N.A.I.C.S.: 424690

Non-U.S. Subsidiary:

EAC Industrial Ingredients, Inc. (2)
170 Salcedo St 4th Fl Builders Ctr Bldg
Legaspi, Makati, 1229, Philippines (100%)
Tel.: (63) 28129385
Fax: (63) 28105897
Web Site: www.brenntag-asia.com
Emp.: 80
Industrial Chemicals Distr
S.I.C.: 2899
N.A.I.C.S.: 325998
Rolando Catacutan *(Country Mgr)*

Brenntag Inorganic Chemicals (Thetford) Ltd. (1)
Albion House Rawdon Park Green Lane
Yeadon, Leeds, West Yorkshire, LS19 7XX, United Kingdom
Tel.: (44) 1842 753662
Chemical Products Mfr & Distr
S.I.C.: 2819
N.A.I.C.S.: 325180

Brenntag Kimya Ticaret Limited Sirketi (1)
Kavacik Mah Ekinciler Cad Muhtar Sok No1
K 1-6
Beykoz, 34805 Istanbul, Turkey
Tel.: (90) 216 331 3966
Fax: (90) 216 331 3936
E-Mail: info@brenntag.com.tr
Web Site: www.brenntag-cee.com
Chemical Products Distr
S.I.C.: 5169
N.A.I.C.S.: 424690

Brenntag Ljubljana d.o.o. (1)
16 Letaliska Cesta
Ljubljana, 1000, Slovenia
Tel.: (386) 15483495
Fax: (386) 15483475
E-Mail: office@brenntag.si
Web Site: www.brenntag.si
Emp.: 15
Chemical Products Distr
S.I.C.: 5169
N.A.I.C.S.: 424690

Brenntag Malaysia SDN. BHD. (1)
Lot Pt 55 64 & 65 Jalan Hulu Tinggi 26/6
Seksyen 26
40400 Shah Alam, Selangor Darul Ehsan, Malaysia
Tel.: (60) 3 5191 8811
Fax: (60) 3 5191 8899
E-Mail: info-malaysia@brenntag-asia.com
Web Site: www.brenntag-asiapacific.com
Chemical Products Distr
S.I.C.: 5169
N.A.I.C.S.: 424690

Brenntag Nederland B.V. (1)
Donker Duyvisweg 44
3316 BM Dordrecht, Netherlands
Mailing Address:
Postbus 79
3300 AB Dordrecht, Netherlands
Tel.: (31) 786544944
Fax: (31) 786544919
E-Mail: info@brenntag.nl
Web Site: www.brenntag.nl
Emp.: 300
Distr of Specialty Chemicals
S.I.C.: 5169
N.A.I.C.S.: 424690

Brenntag Nordic A/S (1)
Borupvang 5B
2750 Ballerup, Denmark
Tel.: (45) 43 29 28 00
Fax: (45) 43 29 27 00
E-Mail: main@brenntag-nordic.com
Web Site: www.brenntag-nordic.com
Emp.: 55
Chemical Products Distr
S.I.C.: 5169
N.A.I.C.S.: 424690
Michael Pieters *(Mng Dir)*
Fleischer Rene *(Mng Dir)*
Torsten Walz *(Mng Dir)*

Brenntag Nordic AB (1)
Koksgatan 18
Box 50 121
202 11 Malmo, Sweden
Tel.: (46) 40 28 73 00
Fax: (46) 40 93 28 74
E-Mail: main@brenntag-nordic.com
Web Site: www.brenntag-nordic.com
Emp.: 6
Specialty Chemicals Distr
S.I.C.: 5169
N.A.I.C.S.: 424690
Lars Nilzen *(Mng Dir)*

BRENNTAG Nordic AS (1)
Torvlia 2
Borgenhaugen, 1740 Sarpsborg, Norway
Tel.: (47) 69 10 25 00
Fax: (47) 69 10 25 01
E-Mail: main@brenntag-nordic.com
Web Site: www.brenntag-nordic.com
Emp.: 2
Chemical Products Distr
S.I.C.: 5169
N.A.I.C.S.: 424690
Helge Lundh *(Mng Dir)*

BRENNTAG Nordic OY (1)
Ayritie 16
1510 Vantaa, Finland
Tel.: (358) 95 49 56 40
Fax: (358) 95 49 56 411
E-Mail: info@brenntag-nordic.com
Web Site: www.brenntag-nordic.com
Emp.: 2
Chemical Products Distr
S.I.C.: 5169
N.A.I.C.S.: 424690
Minna Helkioe *(Mgr-Environment & Quality)*

Brenntag N.V. (1)
Nijverheidslaan 38
8540 Deerlijk, Belgium
Tel.: (32) 56776944
Telex: 85268
Fax: (32) 56775711
E-Mail: info@brenntag.be
Web Site: www.brenntag.be
Emp.: 100
Distr of Industrial & Specialty Chemicals
S.I.C.: 5169
N.A.I.C.S.: 424690
Pierre Claeys *(Mgr-Sls & Mktg)*

Brenntag Philippines Inc. (1)
4th Floor Builders Centre Building 170
Salcedo Street
Salcedo Village, Makati, 1227, Philippines
Tel.: (63) 28129385
Fax: (63) 28105897
Chemical Products Distr
S.I.C.: 5169
N.A.I.C.S.: 424690

BRENNTAG Polska Sp. z o.o. (1)
ul J Bema 21
47-224 Kedzierzyn-Kozle, Poland
Tel.: (48) 77 47 21 500
Fax: (48) 77 47 21 600
E-Mail: biuro@brenntag.pl
Web Site: www.brenntag.pl
Specialty Chemicals Distr
S.I.C.: 5169
N.A.I.C.S.: 424690
Zenon Maslona *(Chm-Mgmt Bd)*
Marek Jarawka *(Member-Mgmt Bd)*
Jerzy Jasinski *(Member-Mgmt Bd)*
Andrzej Wojtas *(Member-Mgmt Bd)*

Brenntag Portugal Lda. (1)
Estrada De Albarraque Linho
Manique De Cima, 2710 297 Sintra, Portugal
Tel.: (351) 219248800
Telex: 401/12186
Fax: (351) 219248845
Web Site: www.brenntag.pt
Sales Range: $10-24.9 Million
Emp.: 39
Distr of Industrial & Specialty Chemicals
S.I.C.: 5169
N.A.I.C.S.: 424690

BRENNTAG PORTUGAL-PRODUTOS QUIMICOS Lda. (1)
Estrada de Albarraque Linho
Sintra, Portugal
Tel.: (351) 21 924 88 00
Fax: (351) 21 924 88 45
E-Mail: brenntag@brenntag.pt
Web Site: www.brenntag.es/en/contacts/ContactsPortugal/Cosm__ticos_PT.html
Specialty Chemicals Distr
S.I.C.: 5169
N.A.I.C.S.: 424690

Brenntag PTE. LTD. (1)
7 International Business Park 02-01
Techquest
Singapore, 609919, Singapore
Tel.: (65) 6500 1100
Fax: (65) 6425 5020
E-Mail: info-sin@brenntag-asia.com
Web Site: www.brenntag-asiapacific.com
Emp.: 2
Chemical Products Distr
S.I.C.: 5169
N.A.I.C.S.: 424690
Qunsheng Ye *(Gen Mgr)*

Brenntag Pty. Ltd. (1)
Building 25 Omnico Business Park 270
Ferntree Gully Road
Notting Hill, Melbourne, VIC, 3168, Australia
Tel.: (61) 3 9501 2700
Fax: (61) 3 9501 2707
E-Mail: info-aus@brenntag-asia.com
Chemical Products Distr
S.I.C.: 5169
N.A.I.C.S.: 424690

BRENNTAG Quimica S.A. (1)
C/ Torre de los Herberos 10 Pol Ind La Isla
41703 Dos Hermanas, Sevilla, Spain
Tel.: (34) 954 9194 00
Fax: (34) 954 91 94 43
E-Mail: central@brenntag.es
Web Site: www.brenntag.es
Emp.: 145
Industrial & Specialty Chemicals Distr
S.I.C.: 5169
N.A.I.C.S.: 424690

Brenntag Schweizerhall AG (1)
Elsasserstrasse 231
4013 Basel, Switzerland
Tel.: (41) 61 3268 111
Fax: (41) 61 3268 208
E-Mail: info@brenntag.ch
Web Site: www.brenntag.ch
Emp.: 150
Chemical Products Distr
S.I.C.: 5169
N.A.I.C.S.: 424690
Hans-Peter Brader *(CEO)*
Peter Hochuli *(CFO)*
Wolfram Heymann *(COO & Head-Product & Procurement Mgmt)*

Brenntag (Shanghai) Chemical Trading Co., Limited (1)
Unit 08A 20th Floor Jinmao Tower 88
Century Avenue
Pudong New District, Shanghai, China
200121
Tel.: (86) 21 5047 2500
Fax: (86) 21 5047 2505
E-Mail: info@brenntagchina.cn
Web Site: www.brenntagchina.cn
Chemical Products Distr
S.I.C.: 5169
N.A.I.C.S.: 424690

Brenntag Singapore PTE. LTD. (1)
7 International Business Park 02-01
Techquest
Singapore, 609919, Singapore
Tel.: (65) 6500 1100

Fax: (65) 6425 5020
E-Mail: info-sin@brenntag-asia.com
Web Site: www.brenntag-asiapacific.com
Chemical Products Distr
S.I.C.: 5169
N.A.I.C.S.: 424690

BRENNTAG SLOVAKIA s.r.o. (1)
Glejovka 15
902 03 Pezinok, Slovakia
Tel.: (421) 33 648 57 68
Fax: (421) 33 641 38 67
E-Mail: office@brenntag.sk
Web Site: www.brenntag.sk
Chemical Products Distr
S.I.C.: 5169
N.A.I.C.S.: 424690
Rudolf Bezak V. R. *(Exec Dir)*

BRENNTAG S.p.A. (1)
Via Cusago 150/4
20153 Milan, Italy
Tel.: (39) 02 48 333 0
Fax: (39) 02 48 333 201
E-Mail: infobrenntag@brenntag.it
Web Site: www.brenntag.it
Chemical Products Distr
S.I.C.: 5169
N.A.I.C.S.: 424690

Brenntag (Taiwan) Co. Ltd. (1)
Rm 808 Asia Enterprise Ctr
142 Min Chuan E Rd Section 3, Taipei, 105, Taiwan
Tel.: (886) 225455685
Telex: 785/23983 BRTG
Fax: (886) 227191758
E-Mail: brtg8008@ms6.hinet.net
Web Site: www.brenntag.com
Distr of Industrial & Specialty Chemicals
S.I.C.: 5169
N.A.I.C.S.: 424690

Brenntag (Thailand) Co. Ltd. (1)
1168/98-100 Lumpini Tower 33rd Floor
Rama IV Road Thungmahamek
Bangkok, Thailand
Tel.: (66) 2 689 5999
Fax: (66) 2 689 5888 9
E-Mail: info-thai@brenntag-asia.com
Industrial Chemical Products Distr
S.I.C.: 5169
N.A.I.C.S.: 424690

Brenntag UK and Ireland Limited (1)
Albion House Rawdon Park
Green Lane, Leeds, LS19 7XX, United Kingdom
Tel.: (44) 113 3879 200
Fax: (44) 113 3879 280
E-Mail: enquiry@brenntag.co.uk
Web Site: www.brenntag.co.uk
Emp.: 100
Chemical Products Distr
S.I.C.: 5169
N.A.I.C.S.: 424690
Clare Waters *(Mng Dir-Distr & Inorganics)*

Brenntag (UK) Ltd. (1)
Pensnett House
Kingswinford, W Midlands, DY6 7PP, United Kingdom
Tel.: (44) 1384400222
Telex: 51/924629
Fax: (44) 1384400020
E-Mail: sales@brenntag.co.uk
Web Site: www.brenntag.co.uk
Sales Range: $50-74.9 Million
Emp.: 30
Distr of Industrial & Specialty Chemicals
S.I.C.: 5169
N.A.I.C.S.: 424690

Brenntag Vastgoed B.V. (1)
Donker Duyvisweg 44
Dordrecht, 3316 BM, Netherlands
Tel.: (31) 786544944
Fax: (31) 786544919
E-Mail: info@brenntag.com
Web Site: www.brenntag.com
Emp.: 7
Chemical Products Distr
S.I.C.: 5169
N.A.I.C.S.: 424690

Dipol Baltija SIA (1)
Lielvarzi Ciedri
Riga, 2123, Latvia
Tel.: (371) 67803297
Fax: (371) 67035359

Specialty Chemicals Distr
S.I.C.: 5169
N.A.I.C.S.: 424690

Eurochem Service Polska Sp. z o.o. (1)
ul Migdalowa 4/52
02-796 Warsaw, Poland PL
Tel.: (48) 22 54 47 898
Fax: (48) 77 40 56 014
E-Mail: biuro@eurochemservice.pl
Web Site: www.eurochemservice.pl
Emp.: 3
Industrial Chemicals Distr
S.I.C.: 5169
N.A.I.C.S.: 424690

Forchem Sp. z o.o. (1)
Ul Heroldow 15 B lok 1
01-991 Warsaw, Poland
Tel.: (48) 22 896 00 51
Fax: (48) 22 896 00 54
E-Mail: biuro@forchem.com.pl
Web Site: www.forchem.pl
Construction Chemicals Mfr
S.I.C.: 2899
N.A.I.C.S.: 325998

HCI Central Europe Holding B.V. (1)
Donker Duyvisweg 44
Dordrecht, 3316 BM, Netherlands
Tel.: (31) 786544944
Fax: (31) 786544948
E-Mail: info@brenntag.com
Web Site: www.brenntag.com
Emp.: 7
Investment Management Services
S.I.C.: 6211
N.A.I.C.S.: 523999

H.C.I Chemicals Nederland B.V. (1)
Industrieweg 1
Loosdrecht, 1231 KG, Netherlands
Tel.: (31) 355889300
Fax: (31) 355889309
Web Site: www.brenntag.com
Emp.: 80
Chemical Products Distr
S.I.C.: 5169
N.A.I.C.S.: 424690
Gustaaf Oorthuys *(Gen Mgr)*

Holanda Venezuela C.A. (1)
Zona Industrial Carabobo 8va Transversal
Parcela 15-A y 15-B
Valencia, Venezuela
Tel.: (58) 241 200 7200
Fax: (58) 241 200 7200
E-Mail: infovenezuela@brenntagla.com
Web Site: www.brenntagla.com
Industrial Chemical Products Distr
S.I.C.: 5169
N.A.I.C.S.: 424690

Inversiones Quimicas S.A. (1)
Boulevard del Norte Km 5 Frente a Sedac
Carretera a Pto Cortes, San Pedro Sula, Honduras
Tel.: (504) 551 7060
Fax: (504) 551 8213
E-Mail: infohonduras@brenntagla.com
Chemical Products Distr
S.I.C.: 5169
N.A.I.C.S.: 424690

Metausel SAS (1)
90 Avenue Du Progres
69680 Chassieu, France
Tel.: (33) 388 33 44 04
Fax: (33) 388 33 78 48
Industrial Chemicals Distr
S.I.C.: 5169
N.A.I.C.S.: 424690
Bruno Mardon *(Gen Mgr)*

Natural World S.r.l. (1)
Via Rambaldo Jacchia 8
48022 Lugo, Ravenna, Italy
Tel.: (39) 0545 27100
Fax: (39) 0545 33739
E-Mail: naturalworld@naturalworld.it
Web Site: www.naturalworld.it
Food Products Ingredient Distr
S.I.C.: 5145
N.A.I.C.S.: 424450
Elena Resta *(Gen Mgr)*

OOO BRENNTAG (1)
1st Volkonsky Pereulok 13 Bldg 2 Fl 6
109028 Moscow, Russia

Tel.: (7) 495 739 57 27
Fax: (7) 495 739 57 07
E-Mail: office@brenntag.com.ru
Chemical Products Distr
S.I.C.: 5169
N.A.I.C.S.: 424690

Pelican Chemical Traders Ltd. (1)
Building Clarendon House Street 2 Church Street
PO Box HM 1888
Hamilton, Bermuda
Tel.: (441) 292 4000
Chemical Products Distr
S.I.C.: 5169
N.A.I.C.S.: 424690

PHU Elmar Sp. z o.o. (1)
ul Torunska 114
Bydgoszcz, 85 123, Poland
Tel.: (48) 523704670
Fax: (48) 523704671
Logistics Consulting Services
S.I.C.: 4731
N.A.I.C.S.: 541614

Poldiplast Ltd. (1)
42/44 Shelkovichnaya Str
Kiev, 1601, Ukraine
Tel.: (380) 44 4905860
Fax: (380) 44 4905861
Emp.: 3
Specialty Chemicals Mfr
S.I.C.: 2869
N.A.I.C.S.: 325199
Richard Roth *(Gen Mgr)*

PT Brenntag Indonesia (1)
Graha Pratama Building 17th Floor Jl MT Haryono Kav 15
South Jakarta, Jakarta, 12810, Indonesia
Tel.: (62) 21 8379 0755
Fax: (62) 21 8379 0760
E-Mail: info-indonesia@brenntag-asia.com
Web Site: www.brenntag-asiapacific.com
Chemical Products Distr
S.I.C.: 5169
N.A.I.C.S.: 424690

PT EAC Indonesia (1)
Graha Pratama 17th Floor Jl Letjen MT Haryono Kav 15 Pancoran
Tebet, Jakarta, 12810, Indonesia
Tel.: (62) 21 83790755
Fax: (62) 21 83790760
Chemical Products Mfr
S.I.C.: 2899
N.A.I.C.S.: 325998

Quimicos Holanda Costa Rica S.A. (1)
200 Mts Al Norte de la Cenada Barreal de la Heredia
San Jose, Costa Rica
Tel.: (506) 2508 5300
Fax: (506) 2293 0019
E-Mail: infocostarica@brenntagla.com
Chemical Products Distr
S.I.C.: 5169
N.A.I.C.S.: 424690

Romana Chimici S.p.A. (1)
Localita Paduni
03012 Anagni, Frosinone, Italy
Tel.: (39) 0775 77481
Fax: (39) 0775 768250
Web Site: www.brenntag.it/en/contatti.html
Emp.: 50
Chemical Products Distr
S.I.C.: 5169
N.A.I.C.S.: 424690
Pasquale Specchioli *(Gen Mgr)*

S I A BRENNTAG LATVIA (1)
Dominante Park Warehouse Nr 2 Ciedri Lielvarzi
Kekavas Pagasts, Kekava, 2123, Latvia
Tel.: (371) 678 032 80
Fax: (371) 678 476 71
E-Mail: brenntag@brenntag.lv
Web Site: www.brenntag.lv
Chemical Products Distr
S.I.C.: 5169
N.A.I.C.S.: 424690
Tomasz Grzegorz Wronka *(CEO)*

Societe commerciale Tardy et Cie. S.a.r.l. (1)
21 Boulevard De L Europe
Vitrolles, 13127, France

Tel.: (33) 442462242
Fax: (33) 442795779
Emp.: 3
Chemical Products Distr
S.I.C.: 5169
N.A.I.C.S.: 424690
Jean-Yves Parayre *(Gen Mgr)*

Tride Rus OOO (1)
1st Volkonsky per 13 bld 2 floor6
Moscow, 127473, Russia
Tel.: (7) 4957395727
Chemical Products Distr
S.I.C.: 5169
N.A.I.C.S.: 424690

UAB Brenntag Lietuva (1)
Palemono G 171 D
52107 Kaunas, Lithuania
Tel.: (370) 37 759095
Fax: (370) 37 760209
E-Mail: info@brenntag.lt
Web Site: www.brenntag.lt
Specialty Chemicals Distr
S.I.C.: 5169
N.A.I.C.S.: 424690
Tomasz Grzegorz Wronka *(Gen Mgr)*

Water Treatment Solution Ltd. (1)
Boothes Lane
Sandbach, CW11 3PZ, United Kingdom
Tel.: (44) 1270 758285
Fax: (44) 1270 758234
Water Treatment Services
S.I.C.: 4971
N.A.I.C.S.: 221310

BRENTRIDGE FORD SALES

5604 41 Ave
Wetaskiwin, AB, T9A 3M7, Canada
Tel.: (780) 352-6048
Fax: (780) 352-8272
Toll Free: (877) 477-3673
E-Mail: brentridge@telus.net
Web Site: www.brentridgeford.dealerconnection.com
Sales Range: $10-24.9 Million
Emp.: 31

Business Description:
New & Used Car Dealers
S.I.C.: 5511
N.A.I.C.S.: 441110

Personnel:
Chris Harquail *(Gen Mgr-Sls)*

BREUNING GMBH

Luisen strasse 60
Pforzheim, 75172, Germany
Tel.: (49) 72319320
Fax: (49) 7231932200
E-Mail: info@breuning.de
Web Site: www.breuning.com
Year Founded: 1927
Emp.: 300

Business Description:
Jewelry Mfr
S.I.C.: 3914
N.A.I.C.S.: 339910

Personnel:
Marcus Breuning *(Mng Dir)*

U.S. Subsidiary:

Breuning Inc. (1)
PO Box 465945
Lawrenceville, GA 30042
Tel.: (678) 377-1673
Fax: (678) 377-1674
E-Mail: info@breuning.us
Web Site: www.breuning.com
Emp.: 6
Mfr. of Jewelry
S.I.C.: 3911
N.A.I.C.S.: 339910
Marcus Breuning *(Pres)*

BREVILLE GROUP LIMITED

Building 2 Port Air Industrial Estate
1A Hale St
Botany, NSW, 2019, Australia
Tel.: (61) 2 9384 8100
Fax: (61) 2 9700 1249

Breville Group Limited—(Continued)

Web Site: www.brevillegroup.com.au
BRG—(ASX OTC)
Rev.: $507,030,629
Assets: $352,696,661
Liabilities: $143,030,309
Net Worth: $209,666,352
Earnings: $51,825,717
Fiscal Year-end: 06/30/13

Business Description:
Kitchen Appliances
S.I.C.: 3631
N.A.I.C.S.: 335221

Personnel:
Jonathan Lord *(CEO)*
Mervyn Cohen *(CFO & Sec)*

Board of Directors:
Steven Fisher
Sally Herman
Dean Warwick Howell
Steven Klein
Lawrence Myers
Samuel Scott Weiss

BREWERS RETAIL INC

(dba The Beer Store)
5900 Explorer Dr
Mississauga, ON, L4W 5L2, Canada
Tel.: (905) 361-1005
Fax: (905) 361-4289
Toll Free: (888) 948-2337
E-Mail: customerservice@thebeerstore.ca
Web Site: www.thebeerstore.ca
Sales Range: $1-4.9 Billion
Emp.: 1,900

Business Description:
Beer Retail Services
S.I.C.: 5181
N.A.I.C.S.: 424810

Personnel:
Ted Moroz *(Pres)*

BREWIN DOLPHIN HOLDINGS PLC

12 Smithfield Street
London, EC1A 9BD, United Kingdom
Tel.: (44) 20 7246 1000
Fax: (44) 2032013001
E-Mail: info@brewin.co.uk
Web Site: www.brewin.co.uk
BRW—(LSE)
Rev.: $471,313,976
Assets: $914,622,720
Liabilities: $546,372,851
Net Worth: $368,249,869
Earnings: $35,345,475
Emp.: 1,960
Fiscal Year-end: 09/29/13

Business Description:
Investment & Brokerage Services
S.I.C.: 6211
N.A.I.C.S.: 523110

Personnel:
David Nicol *(CEO)*
Louise Meads *(Sec)*

Board of Directors:
Simon Edward Callum Miller
Ian Dewar
Stephen Ford
Angela Knight
Stephen Mark Jeffrey Lamport
David Nicol
Andrew Karl Thomas Westenberger
Michael John Ross Williams
Paul Wilson

Legal Counsel:
Lawrence Graham LLP
4 More London Riverside
London, England, SE1 2AU, United Kingdom

Subsidiaries:

Brewin Dolphin Securities (1)
12 Smithfield St
London, EC1A 9BD, United Kingdom
Tel.: (44) 2072484400
Fax: (44) 8452131001
E-Mail: info@brewin.co.uk
Web Site: www.brewin.co.uk
Emp.: 500
Securities Trading Services
S.I.C.: 6211
N.A.I.C.S.: 523110

Brewin Nominees Limited (1)
12 Smithfield Street
London, EC1A 9BD, United Kingdom (100%)
Tel.: (44) 2072484400
Fax: (44) 2032013001
Web Site: www.brewin.co.uk
Securities Brokerage
S.I.C.: 6211
N.A.I.C.S.: 523120

BRF - BRASIL FOODS S.A.

1400 R Hungria 5th Floor
Jd America, 01455000 Sao Paulo, SP, Brazil
Tel.: (55) 11 2322 5052
Fax: (55) 11 232257400
Web Site: www.brasilfoods.com
Year Founded: 1934
BRFS—(BRAZ NYSE)
Rev.: $14,027,423,886
Assets: $15,136,586,647
Liabilities: $7,966,748,818
Net Worth: $7,169,837,829
Earnings: $403,644,934
Emp.: 113,991
Fiscal Year-end: 12/31/12

Business Description:
Farms, Slaughterhouses, Animal-Feed Factories, Incubators & Meat Processing Stations Owner & Operator
S.I.C.: 2011
N.A.I.C.S.: 311611

Personnel:
Nildemar Secches *(Co-Chm)*
Claudio Eugenio Stiller Galeazzi *(CEO)*
Leopoldo Viriato Saboya *(CFO, Chief Admin Officer & Chief IR Officer)*
Fabio Medeiros Martins da Silva *(Officer-Dairy Ops)*

Board of Directors:
Nildemar Secches
Decio da Silva
Pedro De Andrade Faria
Jose Carlos Reis de Magalhaes Neto
Paulo Assuncao de Souza
Luis Carlos Fernandes Afonso
Manoel Cordeiro Silva Filho
Walter Fontana Filho
Luiz Fernando Furlan
Allan Simoes Toledo
Jose Julio Cardoso de Lucena *(Chm & CEO)*

Subsidiaries:

Perdigao Agroindustrial S.A. (1)
Av Escola Politecnica 760
Jaguare, 05350-901 Sao Paulo, Brazil
Tel.: (55) 1137185301
Fax: (55) 1137185287
Web Site: www.perdigao.com.br
Meat Markets
S.I.C.: 5421
N.A.I.C.S.: 445210

Sadia S.A. (1)
Rua Senador Attilio Fontana 86 Centro
Concordia, SC, 89700-000, Brazil
Tel.: (55) 49 4443000
Telex: 11-71373
Fax: (55) 49 4430001
E-Mail: grm@sadia.com.br
Web Site: www.sadia.com.br
SDIA3—(BRAZ MAD)
Sales Range: $5-14.9 Billion
Emp.: 60,580
Refrigerated & Frozen Foods Distr, Pork & Poultry Producer, Meat Products Exporter
Import Export
S.I.C.: 2011
N.A.I.C.S.: 311611

Subsidiaries:

BRF-Americas Markets Division (2)
Rua Hungria 1400
Sao Paulo, Brazil (76.31%)
Tel.: (55) 11 2322 5801
Telex: 494 492225
Web Site: www.sadia.com
Rev.: $994,851,000
Emp.: 200
Processed Products of Pork and Poultry, Soya Bean Crushing, Soybean Meal & Refined Oil
Import Export
S.I.C.: 0259
N.A.I.C.S.: 112390
Fernanda Pires *(Gen Mgr)*

Non-U.S. Subsidiary:

Sadia Uruguay S.A. (2)
Miraflores 1445 103
Montevideo, Uruguay
Tel.: (598) 2 601 3925
Emp.: 4
Processed Meat Distr
S.I.C.: 5147
N.A.I.C.S.: 424470

Sino dos Alpes Alimentos Ltda. (1)
Rua Reinaldo Noschang 322
Bom Retiro do Sul, Rio Grande do Sul, 95870-000, Brazil
Tel.: (55) 51 3762 1100
Fax: (55) 51 3762 1014
Meat Processing Services
S.I.C.: 2013
N.A.I.C.S.: 311613

U.S. Subsidiary:

Highline International Ltd. (1)
511 N 103rd St
Seattle, WA 98133-9201
Tel.: (206) 781-8736
Restaurants
S.I.C.: 5812
N.A.I.C.S.: 722511

Non-U.S. Subsidiaries:

BRF Brasil Foods PTE Ltd. (1)
350 Orchard Rd 13-01 Shaw Hse
Singapore, 238868, Singapore
Tel.: (65) 67337343
Fax: (65) 67332765
Emp.: 8
Meat Products Distr
S.I.C.: 5147
N.A.I.C.S.: 424470

Perdigao France SARL (1)
1 Ave Du Braden
29000 Quimper, France
Tel.: (33) 298644500
Fax: (33) 2986447500
E-Mail: swmuriel.troussey@brazilfoods.com
Web Site: www.perdigao.com
Emp.: 4
Management Consulting Services
S.I.C.: 8748
N.A.I.C.S.: 541618
Christophe Vasseur *(Gen Mgr)*

Perdigao Holland B.V. (1)
Het Sterrenbeeld 21
5215 MK 's-Hertogenbosch, Netherlands
Tel.: (31) 736104501
Fax: (31) 736104504
Business Service Centers
S.I.C.: 7334
N.A.I.C.S.: 561439

Perdigao International Ltd. (1)
City Tower 2
Dubai, United Arab Emirates
Tel.: (971) 3291155
Business Service Centers
S.I.C.: 7334
N.A.I.C.S.: 561439

Perdigao UK Ltd. (1)
Theobald Ct Theobald Street
Borehamwood, WD64RN, United Kingdom
Tel.: (44) 2082362330
Fax: (44) 2082362330
Business Service Centers
S.I.C.: 7334
N.A.I.C.S.: 561439

Plusfood B.V. (1)
Houtwal 30
8431 EX Oosterwolde, Netherlands
Tel.: (31) 51656 67 00
Fax: (31) 51651 68 05
Web Site: www.plusfood.com
Holding Company; Poultry Processing & Food Products Distr
S.I.C.: 6719
N.A.I.C.S.: 551112

Subsidiary:

Plusfood Holland B.V. (2)
Houtwal 30
8431 EX Oosterwolde, Netherlands
Tel.: (31) 516 566 700
Fax: (31) 516 516 805
E-Mail: info@plusfood.nl
Web Site: www.plusfood.nl
Emp.: 200
Poultry Processing & Food Products Distr
S.I.C.: 2015
N.A.I.C.S.: 311615
Hans Deboer *(Mgr-Pur)*

Subsidiary:

Plusfood Groep B.V. (3)
Houtwal 30
Oosterwolde, 8431 EX, Netherlands
Tel.: (31) 516 566 700
Fax: (31) 516 516 805
Chicken Feed Mfr
S.I.C.: 2048
N.A.I.C.S.: 311119

Non-U.S. Subsidiaries:

Plusfood Germany GmbH (2)
Speditionstrass 15
40221 Dusseldorf, Germany
Tel.: (49) 211 91324 600
Fax: (49) 211 91324 601
E-Mail: info@plusfood.de
Web Site: www.plusfood.de
Emp.: 12
Food Products Mfr
S.I.C.: 2099
N.A.I.C.S.: 311991
Steffen Neubauer *(Gen Mgr)*

Plusfood Hungary Trade and Service LLC (2)
Terez Krt 55-57
1062 Budapest, Hungary
Tel.: (36) 1 412 1236
Fax: (36) 1 412 1238
E-Mail: info@plusfood.hu
Web Site: www.plusfood.hu
Meat Food Products Distr
S.I.C.: 5147
N.A.I.C.S.: 424470
Thomas Toki *(Gen Mgr)*

Plusfood Italy SRL (2)
Via Giardino Giusti 2
37129 Verona, Italy
Tel.: (39) 045 8004039
Fax: (39) 045 8003954
Emp.: 9
Chicken Meat Mfr & Distr
S.I.C.: 2015
N.A.I.C.S.: 311615
Giuseppe Grigolini *(Gen Mgr)*

Plusfood UK Ltd. (2)
Bell House Seebeck Place Knowlhill
Milton Keynes, MK5 8FR, United Kingdom
Tel.: (44) 1908 685 000
Fax: (44) 1908 685 017
E-Mail: info@plusfood.co.uk
Web Site: www.plusfood.co.uk
Chicken Meat Mfr & Distr
S.I.C.: 2015
N.A.I.C.S.: 311615

Subsidiary:

Plusfood Wrexham Ltd. (3)
Miners Road
Wrexham, LL12 0PJ, United Kingdom
Tel.: (44) 1978 852161
Fax: (44) 1978854029
Frozen Foods Mfr
S.I.C.: 2038
N.A.I.C.S.: 311412

BRGM SA
3 Avenue Claude Guillermin
PO Box 6009
45060 Orleans, Cedex, France
Tel.: (33) 238643434
Fax: (33) 238643518
E-Mail: webmaster@brgm.fr
Web Site: www.brgm.fr
Sls.: $90,458,056
Emp.: 855
Business Description:
Engineering & Environmental Services
S.I.C.: 8711
N.A.I.C.S.: 541330
Personnel:
Jean-Francois Rocchi *(Chm)*
F. Demarcq *(Mng Dir)*
Subsidiaries:

BRGM (1)
3 Ave Claude Guillemin
PO Box 6009
45060 Orleans, France (100%)
Tel.: (33) 238643439
Fax: (33) 238643518
E-Mail: webmaster@brgm.fr
Web Site: www.brgm.fr
Emp.: 850
Engineering Services
S.I.C.: 8711
N.A.I.C.S.: 541330
Didier Houssin *(Mng Dir)*

CFG Services SA (1)
3 Ave Claude Guillemin
Orleans, France (100%)
Tel.: (33) 238643122
Fax: (33) 238643283
E-Mail: ghougueres@cfg.brgm.fr
Web Site: www.cfgservices.fr
Emp.: 40
Engineering Services
S.I.C.: 8711
N.A.I.C.S.: 541330
Burno Lanouille *(Pres)*
Gerard Hougueres *(Mng Dir)*

IRIS Instruments SA (1)
1 Ave Buffon
PO Box 16007
Loiret, 45060 Orleans, Cedex 2, France (51%)
Tel.: (33) 238638100
Fax: (33) 238638182
E-Mail: info@iris-instruments.com
Web Site: www.iris-instruments.com
Emp.: 20
Instrument Mfr for Measuring & Testing Electricity & Electrical Signals
S.I.C.: 3825
N.A.I.C.S.: 334515

BRI-CHEM CORP.
2125 64 Avenue
Edmonton, AB, T6P 1Z4, Canada
Tel.: (780) 455-8667
Fax: (780) 451-4420
E-Mail: info@brichem.com
Web Site: www.brichem.com
BRY—(TSX)
Sls.: $159,110,853
Assets: $128,482,114
Liabilities: $77,062,094
Net Worth: $51,420,019
Earnings: $4,863,263
Emp.: 132
Fiscal Year-end: 12/31/12
Business Description:
Drilling Fluid Chemicals & Steel Products Wholesale Distr
S.I.C.: 2899
N.A.I.C.S.: 325998
Personnel:
Don Caron *(Chm, Pres & CEO)*
Jason Theiss *(CFO)*
Trent Abraham *(Pres-Fluids Div)*
Neil Rasmussen *(Pres-Steel Div)*
Board of Directors:
Don Caron
Brian Campbell
Eric Sauze
Albert Sharp
Transfer Agent:
Computershare Company of Canada
Suite 600 530 - 8th Avenue S.W
Calgary, AB, Canada
Subsidiaries:

Bri-Steel Corporation (1)
2125 64th Avenue
Edmonton, AB, T6P 1Z4, Canada
Tel.: (780) 469-6603
Fax: (780) 469-6986
E-Mail: info@bri-steel.com
Web Site: www.bri-steel.com
Emp.: 5
Steel Piping Products Mfr & Distr
S.I.C.: 3317
N.A.I.C.S.: 331210
Neil Rasmussen *(Pres)*

Bri-Chem Supply Ltd. (1)
15 53016 Hwy 60
Acheson, AB, T7X 5A7, Canada
Tel.: (780) 455-8667
Fax: (780) 451-4420
Web Site: www.brichemsupply.com
Drilling Fluid Chemicals Distr
S.I.C.: 5169
N.A.I.C.S.: 424690

Sodium Solutions Inc. (1)
15 53016 Hwy 60
Acheson, AB, T7X 5A7, Canada
Tel.: (780) 482-1312
Fax: (780) 451-5193
Web Site: www.sodiumsolutions.com
Specialty Chemicals Distr
S.I.C.: 5169
N.A.I.C.S.: 424690

BRIAN KURTZ TRUCKING LTD.
RR 2 6960 Speedvale Avenue West
Breslau, ON, N0B 1M0, Canada
Tel.: (519) 836-5821
Fax: (519) 836-2488
Toll Free: (800) 265-2835
E-Mail: operations@kurtztrucking.com
Web Site: www.kurtztrucking.com
Year Founded: 1980
Rev.: $13,000,000
Emp.: 100
Business Description:
Truck Transportation Services
S.I.C.: 4213
N.A.I.C.S.: 484121
Personnel:
Brian Kurtz *(Pres & CEO)*

BRICK BREWING COMPANY LIMITED
400 Bingemans Centre Drive
Kitchener, ON, N2B 3X9, Canada
Tel.: (519) 742-2732
Fax: (519) 742-9874
E-Mail: info@brickbeer.com
Web Site: www.brickbeer.com
BRB—(TSX)
Rev.: $35,556,063
Assets: $45,153,836
Liabilities: $15,738,255
Net Worth: $29,415,581
Earnings: $724,673
Emp.: 145
Fiscal Year-end: 01/31/13
Business Description:
Beer Mfr
S.I.C.: 2082
N.A.I.C.S.: 312120
Personnel:
Peter J. Schwartz *(Chm)*
George H. Croft *(Pres & CEO)*
Sean Byrne *(CFO)*
Russell Tabata *(COO)*
Board of Directors:
Peter J. Schwartz
John H. Bowey
George H. Croft
Stan G. Dunford
Edward H. Kernaghan
Lawrence Macauley
David R. Shaw
Legal Counsel:
Wildeboer Dellelce LLP
Wildeboer Dellelce Place 365 Bay Street Suite 800
Toronto, ON, Canada
Transfer Agent:
Computershare Investor Services Inc.
100 University Ave 9th Floor
Toronto, ON, Canada

BRICKWORKS LIMITED
738 - 780 Wallgrove Road
Horsley Park, NSW, 2175, Australia
Mailing Address:
PO Box 6550
Wetherill Park, NSW, 1851, Australia
Tel.: (61) 298307800
Fax: (61) 296201328
E-Mail: info@brickworks.com.au
Web Site: www.brickworks.com.au
Year Founded: 1934
BKW—(ASX)
Rev.: $632,043,029
Assets: $2,470,606,512
Liabilities: $678,299,764
Net Worth: $1,792,306,748
Earnings: $88,750,447
Emp.: 89
Fiscal Year-end: 07/31/13
Business Description:
Clay Products Mfr & Distr; Investments
S.I.C.: 3255
N.A.I.C.S.: 327120
Personnel:
Lindsay R. Partridge *(Mng Dir)*
Alexander J. Payne *(CFO)*
Iain H. Thompson *(Sec)*
Board of Directors:
Robert D. Millner
Brendan P. Crotty
David N. Gilham
Michael J. Millner
Lindsay R. Partridge
Robert J. Webster
Subsidiaries:

The Austral Brick Company Pty. Limited (1)
738 - 780 Wallgrove Rd
Horsley Park, NSW, 2175, Australia
Tel.: (61) 298307700
Fax: (61) 298313771
E-Mail: infosouthwales@australbricks.com.au
Web Site: www.australbricks.com.au
Emp.: 250
Pavers & Brick Mfr
S.I.C.: 3271
N.A.I.C.S.: 327331
Lindsay R. Partridge *(Mng Dir)*

Austral Bricks (NSW) Pty Ltd (1)
Group Administration Office 738-780 Wallgrove Rd
Horsley Park, NSW, 2175, Australia
Tel.: (61) 299159100
Fax: (61) 298307818
E-Mail: info@australbricks.com.au
Web Site: www.australbricks.com.au
Building Products Mfr
S.I.C.: 3272
N.A.I.C.S.: 327390
Lindsay Partridge *(Gen Mgr)*

Austral Bricks (Tasmania) Pty Ltd. (1)
Cressy Rd
7301 Longford, Tasmania, Australia (100%)
Tel.: (61) 363911511
Fax: (61) 363974550
E-Mail: infotas@australbricks.com.au
Web Site: www.australbrick.com.au
Emp.: 30
Clay Refractory Mfr
S.I.C.: 3259
N.A.I.C.S.: 327120
Lyndsiy Pirtrodgu *(Pres)*

Austral Bricks (WA) Pty Ltd (1)
Harper Street
Caversham, WA, 6055, Australia
Tel.: (61) 8 9261 9999
Fax: (61) 8 9261 9988
E-Mail: infowa@australbricks.com.au
Web Site: www.australbricks.com
Construction Materials Mfr
S.I.C.: 3271
N.A.I.C.S.: 327331
Peter Scott *(Gen Mgr)*

Austral Masonry (QLD) Pty Ltd (1)
105 Gardner Road
Rochedale, Brisbane, QLD, 4123, Australia
Tel.: (61) 7 3347 2111
Fax: (61) 7 3343 2899
Concrete Block & Brick Mfr
S.I.C.: 3271
N.A.I.C.S.: 327331
Lindsay Partridge *(Mng Dir)*

Austral Precast Pty Ltd (1)
33-41 Cowpasture Road
Wetherill Park, NSW, 2164, Australia
Tel.: (61) 2 9604 9444
Fax: (61) 2 9604 9477
E-Mail:
Web Site: www.australprecast.com
Concrete Products Mfr
S.I.C.: 3273
N.A.I.C.S.: 327320
Lindsay Partridge *(Mng Dir)*

Auswest Timbers (ACT) Pty Ltd (1)
21 Geelong St
Fyshwick, ACT, 2609, Australia
Tel.: (61) 262393901
Fax: (61) 262393905
Sawmill Operating Services
S.I.C.: 2421
N.A.I.C.S.: 321113

Auswest Timbers Holdings Pty Ltd (1)
5 158 Francisco St
Belmont, WA, 6104, Australia
Tel.: (61) 897761002
Fax: (61) 894785622
Emp.: 70
Timber Products Mfr
S.I.C.: 2439
N.A.I.C.S.: 321213
Gary Addison *(Gen Mgr)*

Auswest Timbers Pty Ltd. (1)
Unit 5 158 Francisco St
6104 Belmont, WA, Australia (100%)
Tel.: (61) 894785955
Fax: (61) 894785622
Web Site: www.auswesttimber.com.au
Emp.: 6
Clay Refractory Mfr
S.I.C.: 3255
N.A.I.C.S.: 327120
Gary Addison *(Mng Dir)*
Lindsay Hartley *(Mng Dir)*

Brickworks Building Products Pty Ltd (1)
738-780 Wallgrove Rd
Horsley Park, NSW, 2175, Australia
Tel.: (61) 298307800
Fax: (61) 298307797
E-Mail: info@brickworks.com.au
Web Site: www.brickworks.com.au
Emp.: 100
Concrete Products Mfr
S.I.C.: 3255
N.A.I.C.S.: 327120
Lindsay Partridge *(Mng Dir)*

Bristile Guardians Pty Ltd. (1)
Harper St
Caversham, WA, 6055, Australia (100%)
Tel.: (61) 892619999
Fax: (61) 892619988
Web Site: www.bristile.com.au
Structural Clay Product Mfr
S.I.C.: 3255
N.A.I.C.S.: 327120
Peter Scott *(Gen Mgr-Western Australia)*

Bristile Ltd. (1)
Harper St
Caversham, WA, 6055, Australia AU

Brickworks Limited—(Continued)

Mailing Address:
Locked Bag 100
Midland, WA, 6936, Australia
Tel.: (61) 892619999
Fax: (61) 892619988
E-Mail: corporate@bristile.com.au
Emp.: 920
Mfr. & Distributor of Building & Other Products; General Transport Export
S.I.C.: 1542
N.A.I.C.S.: 236220

Bristile Operations Pty Ltd. (1)
Harper Street
6055 Caversham, WA, Australia (100%)
Tel.: (61) 892619999
Fax: (61) 893771931
Web Site: www.bristileroofing.com
Emp.: 50
Structural Clay Product Mfr
S.I.C.: 3255
N.A.I.C.S.: 327120
Peter Scott *(Gen Mgr)*

Bristile Roofing (East Coast) Pty Ltd. (1)
164 Viking Drive
PO Box 3040 Darra
4076 Wacol, QLD, Australia (100%)
Tel.: (61) 732122444
Fax: (61) 732122499
E-Mail: michiel.monro@bristileroofing.com.au
Web Site: www.bristileroofing.com.au
Emp.: 100
Concrete Product Mfr
S.I.C.: 3272
N.A.I.C.S.: 327390
Lindsay Partridge *(Mng Dir)*
Alex Tiyne *(CFO)*

Bristile Roofing Pty. Ltd. (1)
Harper Street
6055 Caversham, WA, Australia (100%)
Tel.: (61) 892619999
Fax: (61) 892619988
Web Site: www.bristileroofing.com
Emp.: 50
Innovative Roofing Products Mfr, Designer & Distr
S.I.C.: 1761
N.A.I.C.S.: 238160
Peter Scott *(Gen Mgr)*

Christies Sands Pty Ltd (1)
Harper St
Caversham, WA, 6055, Australia
Tel.: (61) 892619999
Fax: (61) 892619988
E-Mail: info@christies.com
Emp.: 40
Building Materials Whslr
S.I.C.: 5039
N.A.I.C.S.: 423390
Peter Scott *(Gen Mgr)*

Clifton Brick Holdings Pty Ltd (1)
Harper St
Caversham, WA, 6055, Australia
Tel.: (61) 892619999
Fax: (61) 892619988
Bricks Mfr
S.I.C.: 3259
N.A.I.C.S.: 327120

Clifton Brick Manufacturers Pty Ltd. (1)
Harper St
6055 Caversham, WA, Australia (100%)
Tel.: (61) 892619999
Fax: (61) 892619988
E-Mail: peter.scotts@austrilbricks.com.au
Web Site: www.austrilbricks.com.au
Emp.: 85
Structural Clay Product Mfr
S.I.C.: 3259
N.A.I.C.S.: 327120
Peter Scotts *(Gen Mgr-Western Australia)*

Eureka Tiles Pty Ltd. (1)
Cnr Charlesworth And Stawell Station
3350 Ballarat, VIC, Australia (100%)
Tel.: (61) 1300387352
Fax: (61) 1300765792
E-Mail: info@eureka-tiles.com.au
Web Site: www.eureka-tiles.com.au
Emp.: 50
Ceramic Wall & Floor Tile Mfr
S.I.C.: 3297
N.A.I.C.S.: 327120
Mark Schosiald *(Mng Dir)*

GB Masonry Pty. Ltd. (1)
Bruce Highway & Woondum Road
Gympie, QLD, 4570, Australia
Tel.: (61) 754835144
Fax: (61) 754835352
E-Mail: sales@gbmasonry.com.au
Web Site: www.gbmasonry.com.au
Emp.: 35
Producer of Masonry Supplies
S.I.C.: 3271
N.A.I.C.S.: 327331
Rupert Hohls *(Plant Mgr)*

Hallett Roofing Services Pty Ltd (1)
Harper St
Caversham, WA, 6055, Australia
Tel.: (61) 298307800
Fax: (61) 298307797
E-Mail: info@australbricks.com.au
Web Site: www.australbricks.com.au
Emp.: 10
Roofing Metal Sheet Work Mfr
S.I.C.: 3444
N.A.I.C.S.: 332322
Lindy Partridge *(Gen Mgr)*

International Brick & Tile Pty Ltd (1)
10 Bonner Dr
Malaga, WA, 6090, Australia
Tel.: (61) 298307800
Fax: (61) 296201328
Brick & Structural Clay Tile Mfr
S.I.C.: 3259
N.A.I.C.S.: 327120
Alexander James Payne *(CFO)*

Metropolitan Brick Company Pty Ltd (1)
10 Bonner Dr
Malaga, WA, 6090, Australia
Tel.: (61) 298307800
Concrete Products Distr
S.I.C.: 5032
N.A.I.C.S.: 423320

Nubrik (NRT) Pty Ltd. (1)
Harper Street
6055 Caversham, WA, Australia (100%)
Tel.: (61) 892619999
Fax: (61) 892619988
Web Site: www.nubrik.com
Emp.: 50
Structural Clay Product Mfr
S.I.C.: 3255
N.A.I.C.S.: 327120
Peter Scott *(Gen Mgr)*

Nubrik Pty Ltd (1)
Harper St
Caversham, WA, 6055, Australia
Tel.: (61) 892619999
Fax: (61) 892619988
Concrete Products Mfr
S.I.C.: 3271
N.A.I.C.S.: 327331
Lindsay Partridge *(Mng Dir)*

Terra Timbers Pty Ltd (1)
15 Power Station Rd
Bairnsdale, VIC, 3875, Australia
Tel.: (61) 351526600
Fax: (61) 351531800
Timber Products Distr
S.I.C.: 5099
N.A.I.C.S.: 423990
Gary Addison *(Gen Mgr)*

Triffid Investments Pty Ltd. (1)
Harper St
6055 Caversham, WA, Australia (100%)
Tel.: (61) 892619999
Fax: (61) 892619988
Structural Clay Product Mfr
S.I.C.: 3259
N.A.I.C.S.: 327120

BRICORAMA S.A.

21a boulevard Jean Monnet
94357 Villiers-sur-Marne, Cedex, France
Tel.: (33) 1 77 61 56 04
Fax: (33) 1 77 61 55 32
E-Mail: recrutement@bricorama.fr
Web Site: www.bricorama.fr
ALBRI—(EUR)
Sls.: $985,800,291
Assets: $814,836,701
Liabilities: $424,716,635
Net Worth: $390,120,066
Earnings: $20,327,167
Emp.: 4,593
Fiscal Year-end: 12/31/12

Business Description:
Hardware Store Operator
S.I.C.: 5251
N.A.I.C.S.: 444130

Personnel:
Jean-Claude Bourrelier *(Chm & CEO)*
Christian Roubaud *(Dir-Fin & Admin)*

Board of Directors:
Jean-Claude Bourrelier
Didier Cantreau
Jacky Leclercq
Christian Roubaud
Olivier Vergniere

BRIDAS CORPORATION

Leandro N Alem Av 1180
1001 Buenos Aires, Argentina
Tel.: (54) 1143104100
Fax: (54) 1143104445
Web Site: www.bridascorp.com
Year Founded: 1948
Emp.: 1,300

Business Description:
Oil & Gas Holding Company
S.I.C.: 6719
N.A.I.C.S.: 551112

Personnel:
Carlos A. Bulgheroni *(Chm & Pres)*
Alejandro Pedro Bulgheroni *(Vice Chm & Exec VP)*

Board of Directors:
Carlos A. Bulgheroni
Silvestre Asurey
Glenn A. Nelle
Miles Watson

Joint Venture:

Pan American Energy LLC (1)
Av Leandro N Alem 1180
1001 Buenos Aires, Argentina
Tel.: (54) 1143104100
Fax: (54) 1143104319
E-Mail: info@panamericanenergy.com
Web Site: www.panamericanenergy.com
Sales Range: $1-4.9 Billion
Emp.: 1,500
Oil & Natural Gas Exploration & Production
S.I.C.: 1311
N.A.I.C.S.: 211111
Denis Kellener *(CFO)*

Subsidiary:

Axion Energy (2)
(Formerly Esso Petrolera Argentina S.R.L.)
Carlos Maria Della Paolera 265 Piso 19
Buenos Aires, Argentina AR
Tel.: (54) 11 4705 7000
Web Site: www.axionenergy.com
Sales Range: $600-649.9 Million
Emp.: 400
Producing, Refining & Marketing of Petroleum Products & Industrial Lubricants
S.I.C.: 2911
N.A.I.C.S.: 324110

Non-U.S. Affiliate:

Empresa Petrolera Chaco S.A. (1)
Edificio Centro Empresarial Equipetrol Piso 6 Ave San Martin
Santa Cruz, Santa Cruz, Bolivia
Tel.: (591) 33453700
Fax: (591) 33663050
E-Mail: rafael.martinez@ypfbchaco.com.bo
Web Site: www.ypfbchaco.com.bo
Emp.: 300
Oil & Gas Exploration & Production; Owned 50% by Bolivian Pension Funds, 30% by BP plc & 20% by Bridas Corporation
S.I.C.: 1311
N.A.I.C.S.: 211111
Rafael Martinez *(Mng Dir)*

BRIDGE ENERGY ASA

(Acquired by Spike Exploration Holding AS)

BRIDGEHOUSE CAPITAL LTD.

35 Davies St 5th Fl,55 baker 7 fl
London, W1U 8EW, United Kingdom
Tel.: (44) 2074958801
Fax: (44) 2074958802
E-Mail: info@bridgehousecapital.com
Web Site: www.bridgehousecapital.com
Emp.: 10

Business Description:
Private Equity Firm
S.I.C.: 6211
N.A.I.C.S.: 523999

Holding:

Global Marine Systems Limited (1)
New Saxon House 1 Winsford Way
Boreham Interchange, Chelmsford, Essex, CM2 5PD, United Kingdom UK
Tel.: (44) 1245702000
Fax: (44) 1245702210
E-Mail: contactus@globalmarinesystems.com
Web Site: www.globalmarinesystems.com
Emp.: 125
Submarine Cable Installation & Maintenance Services
S.I.C.: 1629
N.A.I.C.S.: 237130
Andrew Ruhan *(Chm)*
Gabriel Ruhan *(CEO)*
Ian Douglas *(Mng Dir)*

U.S. Subsidiary:

Global Marine Systems (Americas) Inc. (2)
100 Cummings Center Ste 435P
Beverly, MA 01915 (100%)
Tel.: (978) 922-7706
Fax: (978) 922-7708
Web Site: www.globalmarinesystems.com
Emp.: 2
Installation of Submarine Fibre Optic Cables, Maintenance
S.I.C.: 3354
N.A.I.C.S.: 331318

BRIDGELINE ROPES INC.

70 Dundas St
Deseronto, ON, K0K 1X0, Canada
Tel.: (613) 396-9990
Fax: (613) 396-9996
Web Site: www.bridgeline.ca
Year Founded: 1978
Emp.: 35

Business Description:
Mfr of Braided & Twisted Nylon, Polyester & Polypropylene Rope for the Marine, Agricultural & Industrial Markets.
S.I.C.: 2298
N.A.I.C.S.: 314994

Personnel:
Keith Bridges *(Pres)*

BRIDGEMERE UK PLC

(d/b/a Bridgemere Group)
Bridgemere House Chester Road
Preston Brook, Cheshire, WA7 3BD, United Kingdom
Tel.: (44) 1928797900
Fax: (44) 1928797800
E-Mail: info@bridgemere-group.co.uk
Web Site: www.bridgemere-group.co.uk

Business Description:
Investment Holding Company
S.I.C.: 6719
N.A.I.C.S.: 551112

Personnel:
Steve P. Morgan *(Chm)*

Board of Directors:
Steve P. Morgan
Vincent Fairclough
Ashley Lewis

Holding:

Wolverhampton Wanderers Football Club (1986) Limited (1)
Molineux Stadium Waterloo Road
Wolverhampton, W Midlands, WV1 4QR, United Kingdom UK
Tel.: (44) 8712222220
Fax: (44) 1902 687 006
E-Mail: info@wolves.co.uk
Web Site: www.wolves.co.uk
Emp.: 250
Professional Soccer Club
S.I.C.: 7941
N.A.I.C.S.: 711211
Steve P. Morgan *(Chm)*
Jack Hayward *(Pres)*
Jez Moxey *(CEO)*

BRIDGEPOINT ADVISERS LIMITED

30 Warwick Street
London, W1B 5AL, United Kingdom
Tel.: (44) 2074323500
Fax: (44) 2074323600
E-Mail: london@bridgepoint.eu
Web Site: www.bridgepoint.eu
Business Description:
Private Equity Firm
S.I.C.: 6211
N.A.I.C.S.: 523999
Personnel:
William Jackson *(Mng Partner)*
Raoul Hughes *(COO & Partner)*
Guy Weldon *(Partner & Chief Investment Officer)*
Michael Black *(Partner & Head-Media & Tech)*
Stephen Green *(Partner & Head-Fin Svcs)*
Rob Moores *(Partner & Head-Healthcare Investments-Europe)*
Graham Oldroyd *(Partner & Head-Mfg & Industrials)*
John Barber *(Partner-Investor Svcs)*
Michael Davy *(Partner)*
Martin Dunn *(Partner-Investor Svcs)*
Patrick Fox *(Partner)*
Alastair Gibbons *(Partner)*
Vince Gwilliam *(Partner)*
James Murray *(Partner-Mktg & External Affairs)*
Kevin Reynolds *(Joint Mng Partner-BDC & Partner-Bridgepoint)*
Rod Selkirk *(Joint Mng Partner-BDC & Partner-Bridgepoint)*
Charles Barter *(Gen Counsel, Chief Legal & Compliance Officer)*
Affiliate:

Bridgepoint Advisers UK Limited (1)
30 Warwick Street
London, W1B 5AL, United Kingdom UK
Tel.: (44) 2074323500
Fax: (44) 2074323600
E-Mail: info@bridgepoint.eu
Web Site: www.bridgepoint.eu
Private Equity Firm
S.I.C.: 6211
N.A.I.C.S.: 523999
William Jackson *(Grp Mng Partner)*
Raoul Hughes *(Grp COO & Partner)*
John Barber *(Partner & Grp Co-Head-Investor Svcs)*
Michael Black *(Partner & Grp Co-Head-Media & Tech Investments-Europe)*
Christopher Busby *(Partner & Grp Head-Bus Svcs Investments-Europe)*
Michael Davy *(Partner & Grp Head-Operational Support Grp)*
Stephen Green *(Partner & Grp Head-Fin Svcs Investments-Europe)*
Rob Moores *(Partner & Grp Head-Healthcare Investments-Europe)*
Graham Oldroyd *(Partner & Grp Head-Mfg & Indus Investments-Europe)*
Guy Weldon *(Partner & Head-Investments-UK)*
Patrick Fox *(Partner-Operational Support Grp)*
Alastair Gibbons *(Partner-Bus Dev & Cross-Border Investments)*
Vince Gwilliam *(Partner-Consumer Investments-Europe)*
James Murray *(Partner-Mktg & Comm)*
Kevin Reynolds *(Partner)*
Rod Selkirk *(Partner)*

Division:

Bridgepoint Development Capital Limited (2)
30 Warwick Street
London, W1B 5AL, United Kingdom UK
Tel.: (44) 2074323500
Fax: (44) 2074323600
E-Mail: devcap@bridgepoint.eu
Web Site: www.bridgepoint.eu/developmentcapital
Emp.: 30
Venture Capital Investment Firm
S.I.C.: 6211
N.A.I.C.S.: 523999
Kevin Reynolds *(Co-Mng Partner)*
Rod Selkirk *(Co-Mng Partner)*

Holding:

Shimtech Industries Group Limited (3)
30 Warwick Street
London, W1B 5AL, United Kingdom UK
Tel.: (44) 208 571 0055 (Bridgepoint)
Fax: (44) 208 573 3973
E-Mail: enquiries@shimtechgroup.com
Web Site: www.shimtechgroup.com
Sales Range: $25-49.9 Million
Holding Company; Aerospace Shim Mfr
S.I.C.: 6719
N.A.I.C.S.: 551112
Clive Snowdon *(Chm)*

Subsidiaries:

Attewell Limited (4)
7 A-B Millington Rd
Hayes, Middlesex, UB3 4AZ, United Kingdom
Tel.: (44) 2085710055
Fax: (44) 2085717139
E-Mail: sales@hampsongroup.com
Web Site: www.attewell.co.uk
Emp.: 50
Engineering Services
S.I.C.: 8711
N.A.I.C.S.: 541330
Matt Giggle *(Mng Dir)*

Pillar Seals & Gaskets Limited (4)
Willowbrook Road
Ham Bridge Trading Estate West, BN14 8NA Worthing, United Kingdom UK
Tel.: (44) 1903207101
Fax: (44) 1903821176
E-Mail:
Emp.: 20
Gasket Packing & Sealing Device Mfr
S.I.C.: 3053
N.A.I.C.S.: 339991
Jhon Nighy *(Mng Dir)*

U.S. Subsidiaries:

Bolsan Company, Inc. (4)
163 Linnwood Rd
Eighty Four, PA 15330 (100%)
Tel.: (724) 225-0446
Fax: (724) 225-8268
E-Mail: sales@bolsan.com
Web Site: www.bolsan.com
Emp.: 15
Fabricated Metal Product Mfr
S.I.C.: 3499
N.A.I.C.S.: 332999
Chris Fetcher *(Mng Dir)*

Lamsco West, Inc. (4)
24823 Anza Dr
Santa Clarita, CA 91355
Tel.: (661) 295-8620
Fax: (661) 295-8626
E-Mail: sales@lamscowest.com
Web Site: www.lamscowest.com
Laminated Plastics Plate Sheet & Shape Mfr
S.I.C.: 3083
N.A.I.C.S.: 326130
Gladden Baldwin *(Pres)*

Holdings:

Care UK plc (2)
Connaught House 850 The Crescent
Colchester Business Park, Colchester, Essex, CO4 9QB, United Kingdom
Tel.: (44) 1206752552
E-Mail: enquiries@careuk.com
Web Site: www.careuk.com
Sales Range: $700-749.9 Million
Emp.: 280
Specialist Care Outsourcing Services for Nursing, Residential & Homecare to Elderly, Mentally Ill & Adults With Learning Difficulties
S.I.C.: 8059
N.A.I.C.S.: 623210
Mike Parish *(CEO)*

Subsidiaries:

Althea Park Limited (3)
10 Lansdown
Stroud, GL5 1BB, United Kingdom
Tel.: (44) 1453767093
Fax: (44) 1453756439
E-Mail:
Web Site: www.careuk.com
Emp.: 75
Health Care Services
S.I.C.: 8082
N.A.I.C.S.: 621610
Martin Davies *(Mgr-Ops)*

Care UK Clinical Services Limited (3)
Connaught House 850 The Crescent
Colchester Business Park, Colchester, Essex, CO4 9QB, United Kingdom
Tel.: (44) 1206752552
Web Site: guildhallwalkgp.co.uk/index.php?page=useful-links
Health & Social Care Services
S.I.C.: 8011
N.A.I.C.S.: 621491

Care UK Community Partnerships Group Limited (3)
Connaught Hse 850 The Crescent
Colchester Business Park, Colchester, CO4 9QB, United Kingdom
Tel.: (44) 1206752552
Fax: (44) 1206517193
Emp.: 200
Health Care Services
S.I.C.: 8082
N.A.I.C.S.: 621610

Care UK Mental Health Partnerships Limited (3)
Connaught House 850 The Crescent
Colchester Business Park, Colchester, CO4 9QB, United Kingdom
Tel.: (44) 1206752552
Web Site: www.careuk.com
Emp.: 200
Health Care Services
S.I.C.: 8082
N.A.I.C.S.: 621610
Mike Parish *(Gen Mgr)*

Partnership Health Group Limited (3)
Rosebery House
3rd Fl 41 Springfield Rd, Chelmsford, CM2 6QZ, United Kingdom
Tel.: (44) 1245351749
Fax: (44) 1245351614
Web Site: www.partnershiphealth.co.uk
Health Care Services
S.I.C.: 8011
N.A.I.C.S.: 621491

LGC Limited (2)
Queens Road
Teddington, Middlesex, TW11 0LY, United Kingdom
Tel.: (44) 2089437000
Fax: (44) 2089432767
E-Mail: info@lgcgroup.com
Web Site: www.lgc.co.uk
Sales Range: $200-249.9 Million
Emp.: 600
Laboratory Services, Measurement Standards, Reference Materials & Proficiency Testing Services
S.I.C.: 8071
N.A.I.C.S.: 621511
David Richardson *(CEO)*

Quilter & Co. Limited (2)
Saint Helens
1 Undershaft, London, EC3A 8BB, United Kingdom UK
Tel.: (44) 20 4662 6262
Fax: (44) 20 7726 8826
E-Mail: info@quilter.com.uk
Web Site: www.quilter.com
Sales Range: $5-14.9 Billion
Emp.: 330
Investment Management Services
S.I.C.: 6282
N.A.I.C.S.: 523920
Chris Meares *(Chm)*
Martin Baines *(CEO)*
Stephen Vakil *(Mng Dir)*
Mark Macleod *(CFO)*
Duncan Gwyther *(Chief Investment Officer)*

Wiggle Ltd. (2)
3 Optima Northarbour Spur
Portsmouth, PO6 3TU, United Kingdom
Tel.: (44) 2392 314 811
Fax: (44) 2392 373 664
E-Mail: sales@wiggle.co.uk
Web Site: www.wiggle.co.uk
Sales Range: $125-149.9 Million
Sporting Goods Retailer
S.I.C.: 5941
N.A.I.C.S.: 451110
Andrew Bond *(Chm)*
Humphrey Cobbold *(CEO)*

Non-U.S. Affiliates:

Bridgepoint AB (1)
Master Samuelsgatan 1
111 44 Stockholm, Sweden SE
Tel.: (46) 854516820
Fax: (46) 854516821
E-Mail: info@bridgepoint.eu
Web Site: www.bridgepoint.eu
Emp.: 11
Private Equity Firm
S.I.C.: 6211
N.A.I.C.S.: 523999
Hakan Johansson *(Partner-Healthcare Investments-Europe)*
Mikael Lovgren *(Partner-Nordic Investments)*

Holding:

Gambro Healthcare AB (2)
Scheelevagen 34
PO Box 101 01
SE-220 10 Lund, Sweden SE
Tel.: (46) 46169000
Fax: (46) 46169696
E-Mail: ghccommunications@gambro.com
Web Site: www.gambrohealthcare.com
Sales Range: $300-349.9 Million
Emp.: 900
Dialysis Clinic Services
S.I.C.: 8092
N.A.I.C.S.: 621492
Annette Kumlien *(CFO & VP)*

Bridgepoint GmbH (1)
Neue mainzer Strasse 28
D-60311 Frankfurt am Main, Germany De
Tel.: (49) 692108770
Fax: (49) 6921087777
E-Mail: info@bridgepoint.eu
Web Site: www.bridgepoint.eu
Emp.: 10
Private Equity Firm
S.I.C.: 6211
N.A.I.C.S.: 523999
Uwe Kolb *(Partner)*

Holdings:

CABB GmbH (2)
Am Unisys Park 1
65843 Sulzbach, Germany
Tel.: (49) 6930527772
Fax: (49) 6930527778
E-Mail: contact@cabb-chemicals.com
Web Site: www.cabb-chemicals.com
Sales Range: $400-449.9 Million
Emp.: 750
Chemical Mfr
S.I.C.: 2899
N.A.I.C.S.: 325998
Martin Wienkenhover *(CEO)*

Bridgepoint Advisers Limited—(Continued)

Non-U.S. Subsidiaries:

CABB AG **(3)**
Dungerstrasse 81
4133 Pratteln, Switzerland
Tel.: (41) 618253111
Fax: (41) 618218027
E-Mail: contact@cabb-chemicals.com
Web Site: www.cabb-chemicals.com
Sales Range: $150-199.9 Million
Emp.: 360
Chemical Mfr
S.I.C.: 2899
N.A.I.C.S.: 325998
Joerg Schrickel *(Mgr-Mktg)*

CABB Oy **(3)**
Tammasaarenkatu 3
FI 00180 Helsinki, Finland FI
Mailing Address:
High Tech Center Helsinki
PO Box 660
FI 00181 Helsinki, Finland
Tel.: (358) 467100600
Fax: (358) 467100701
E-Mail: info@cabb-chemicals.fi
Web Site: www.kemfine.com
Sales Range: $100-124.9 Million
Emp.: 190
Chemical Mfr
S.I.C.: 2899
N.A.I.C.S.: 325998
Ulf Bjorkqvist *(CEO)*
Ari Tasa *(CFO)*

KPS AG **(2)**
Beta-Strasse 10H
85774 Munich, Germany De
Tel.: (49) 89356310
Fax: (49) 89356313300
E-Mail: kontakt@kps-consulting.com
Web Site: www.kps-consulting.com
Sales Range: $10-24.9 Million
Emp.: 120
Holding Company; Information Technology Consultancy Software & Services
S.I.C.: 6719
N.A.I.C.S.: 551112
Michael Tsifidaris *(Chm-Supervisory Bd)*
Dietmar Mueller *(Member-Mgmt Bd)*

Branch:

KPS Consulting **(3)**
Gewerbepark Eschberger Weg
D-66121 Saarbrucken, Germany De
Tel.: (49) 681950900 (100%)
Fax: (49) 6819509099
E-Mail: info@kps-consulting.com
Web Site: www.kps-consulting.com
Document Management & Data Processing Services
S.I.C.: 7374
N.A.I.C.S.: 518210
Wolfgang Sandmaier *(Mng Dir)*

Rodenstock GmbH **(2)**
Elsenheimer St 33 Munich
0687 Munich, Germany
Tel.: (49) 8972020
Fax: (49) 897202629
E-Mail: dialog@rodenstock.com
Web Site: www.rodenstock.com
Sales Range: $400-449.9 Million
Emp.: 400
Mfr. & Marketer of Ophthalmic Frames & Lenses
Import Export
S.I.C.: 3851
N.A.I.C.S.: 339115
Giancarlo Galli *(CEO)*
Oliver Kastalio *(CEO)*
Olaf Goettgenf *(Mng Dir)*
Werner Mueller *(Sr VP-Res)*

Non-U.S. Holdings:

Rodenstock Australia Pty. Ltd. **(3)**
100 108 Asquith Street
Silverwater, NSW, 2128, Australia AU
Tel.: (61) 297480988
Fax: (61) 297482284
E-Mail: optics@rodenstock.com.au
Emp.: 25
Ophthalmic Products Mfr
S.I.C.: 3231
N.A.I.C.S.: 327215
Craig Chick *(Gen Mgr)*

Rodenstock Canada Inc. **(3)**
172 Towers Road Unit 30
Vaughan, ON, L4L 8A7, Canada
Tel.: (905) 851-7183
Fax: (905) 265-2893
Toll Free: (800) 387-7750
E-Mail: customerservice@rodenstock.ca
Web Site: www.rodenstock.ca
Emp.: 25
Spectacle Frames & Ophthalmic Lenses
S.I.C.: 3827
N.A.I.C.S.: 333314
Jeremy Carvalho *(Gen Mgr-Ops)*

Rodenstock Osterreich GmbH **(3)**
Mariahilfer Str 116
PO Box 82
1072 Vienna, Austria
Tel.: (43) 159900200
Fax: (43) 159900150
E-Mail: info@rodenstock.com
Emp.: 70
Provider of Ophthalmic Products
S.I.C.: 3231
N.A.I.C.S.: 327215
Moritzer Clemens *(Gen Mgr)*

Non-U.S. Holdings:

CTL Logistics S.A. **(2)**
Aleja Armii Ludowej 26
00-609 Warsaw, Poland
Tel.: (48) 225493200
Fax: (48) 225493203
E-Mail: info@ctl.pl
Web Site: www.ctl.pl
Sales Range: $300-349.9 Million
Emp.: 2,550
Logistics & Freight Transportation Services
S.I.C.: 4731
N.A.I.C.S.: 541614
Marek Dziemianczyk *(Gen Dir & Chm-Mgmt Bd)*
Jacek Bieczek *(Mng Dir)*
Matthias Raith *(Head-European Dev)*

Infinitas Learning Holding B.V. **(2)**
Het Spoor 8-14
NL-3994 AK Houten, Netherlands NL
Tel.: (31) 306383520
Fax: (31) 306383599
E-Mail: info@infinitaslearning.com
Web Site: www.infinitaslearning.com
Sales Range: $400-449.9 Million
Emp.: 1,500
Holding Company; Educational Books, CD-ROMs & Other Materials Publisher
S.I.C.: 6719
N.A.I.C.S.: 551112
Clice Hay-Smith *(CEO)*

Subsidiary:

Infinitas Learning Netherlands B.V. **(3)**
Het Spoor 8-14
3994 AK Houten, Netherlands NL
Tel.: (31) 306383520
Fax: (31) 306383599
E-Mail: info@infinitaslearning.com
Web Site: www.infinitaslearning.com
Sales Range: $400-449.9 Million
Emp.: 450
Educational Books, CD-ROMs & Other Materials Publisher
S.I.C.: 2731
N.A.I.C.S.: 511130
Clive Hay-Smith *(CEO)*
Jos Wilschut *(CTO)*
Harold Roelofs *(Chief Production Officer)*

Subsidiary:

Wolters-Noordhoff Groningen **(4)**
Winschotordiap 70 A
9723 AB Groningen, Netherlands
Tel.: (31) 505226922
Fax: (31) 505277599
E-Mail: info@noordhoff.nl
Web Site: www.noordhoff.nl
Emp.: 450
Publisher for Subject Areas in Primary Education, General Secondary Education, Vocational Education & Tertiary Education; Provider of Books, Educational Services, Tools & Materials
S.I.C.: 2721
N.A.I.C.S.: 511120
Erjan Holl *(Mng Dir)*

Non-U.S. Subsidiaries:

Bildungsverlag EINS GmbH **(4)**
Sieglarer Str 2
53842 Troisdorf, Germany
Tel.: (49) 22413976805
Fax: (49) 22413976888
E-Mail: info@bv-1.de
Web Site: www.bildungsverlag1.de
Emp.: 150
Trade & Professional Book Publisher
S.I.C.: 2731
N.A.I.C.S.: 511130
Wilmar Diepgrond *(CEO)*

digital spirit GmbH **(4)**
Markgrafenstr 62-63
10969 Berlin, Germany
Tel.: (49) 3084191140
Fax: (49) 3084191499
E-Mail: dialog@digital-spirit.de
Web Site: www.digital-spirit.de
Emp.: 50
Developer of Corporate Training & Education Programs
S.I.C.: 8299
N.A.I.C.S.: 611430
Matthias Boldin *(Dir-Content Production)*

Liber AB **(4)**
Markgrafenstr 62-63
S-11398 Stockholm, Sweden SE
Tel.: (46) 86909000
Fax: (46) 86909300
Web Site: www.liber.se
Emp.: 100
Educational Support Services
S.I.C.: 7389
N.A.I.C.S.: 561499
Jerker Nilsson *(CEO)*

Nelson Thornes Ltd. **(4)**
Delta Pl 27 Bath Rd
Cheltenham, Gloucestershire, GL53 7TH, United Kingdom UK
Tel.: (44) 12422780100
Telex: 929365 Nelson G
Fax: (44) 1242221914
E-Mail: cservices@nelsonthornes.com
Web Site: www.nelsonthornes.com
Emp.: 260
Educational Book Publisher
S.I.C.: 2731
N.A.I.C.S.: 511130
Mary O'Connor *(Mng Dir)*

Bridgepoint Ltd. Sti. **(1)**
Visnezade Mahallesi Suleyman Seba Caddesi BJK Plaza no 48
A blok 9 kat D 93-94
Akaretler, Istanbul, Turkey TR
Tel.: (90) 2123108252
E-Mail: info@bridgepoint.eu
Web Site: www.bridgepoint.eu
Private Equity Firm
S.I.C.: 6211
N.A.I.C.S.: 523999
Jason McGibbon *(Head-Investments-Turkey & Dir-Consumer Investments-Europe)*

Bridgepoint S.A. **(1)**
Calle de Rafael Calvo 39A 4 andar
ES-28010 Madrid, Spain ES
Tel.: (34) 917022490
Fax: (34) 913196092
E-Mail: info@bridgepoint.eu
Web Site: www.bridgepoint.eu
Private Equity Firm
S.I.C.: 6211
N.A.I.C.S.: 523999
Jose Maria Maldonado *(Partner & Head-Investments-Spain)*

Bridgepoint S.A.S. **(1)**
37-39 rue de la Bienfaisance
75008 Paris, France FR
Tel.: (33) 144292100
Fax: (33) 144292110
Web Site: www.bridgepoint-capital.com
Emp.: 20
Private Equity Firm
S.I.C.: 6211
N.A.I.C.S.: 523999
Benoit Bassi *(Partner & Head-Investments-France)*
Xavier Robert *(Partner & Grp Co-Head-Media/Tech Investments-Europe)*
Vincent Briancon *(Partner-Consumer & Healthcare Investments-Europe)*

Holdings:

Compagnie du Ponant SA **(2)**
408 avenue du Prado
13008 Marseille, France FR
Tel.: (33) 488 666 400
Web Site: www.ponant.com
Sales Range: $100-124.9 Million
Emp.: 580
Yacht Cruise Line
S.I.C.: 4481
N.A.I.C.S.: 483112
Herve Bellaiche *(Exec VP-Sls)*

FDS Group SA **(2)**
250 bis rue du Faubourg Saint-Honore
75008 Paris, France
Tel.: (33) 1 48 88 88 87
E-Mail: kchaise@flexitallicgroup.com
Web Site: www.flexitallicgroup.com
Sales Range: $250-299.9 Million
Emp.: 1,250
Holding Company; Industrial Sealing Products Mfr
S.I.C.: 6719
N.A.I.C.S.: 551112
Remi Toledano *(Pres & CEO)*

U.S. Subsidiaries:

Custom Rubber Products, Inc. **(3)**
2625 Bennington St
Houston, TX 77093
Tel.: (713) 691-2211
Fax: (713) 691-3005
E-Mail: crpadmin@customrubber.com
Web Site: www.customrubber.com
Sales Range: $1-9.9 Million
Emp.: 63
Plastic Products Mfr
S.I.C.: 3069
N.A.I.C.S.: 326299
Russell Molina *(Pres & CEO)*

The Flexitallic Group, Inc. **(3)**
6915 Hwy 225
Deer Park, TX 77536 DE
Tel.: (281) 604-2400
Fax: (281) 604-2415
Toll Free: (800) 527-1935
E-Mail: flexmarketing@flexitallic.com
Web Site: www.flexitallic.com
Emp.: 390
Sealing Products Mfr
Export
S.I.C.: 3053
N.A.I.C.S.: 339991
Gregory English *(CFO & VP-Admin)*
Ray Cole *(CIO)*
Gordon Hambley *(Chief Acctg Officer)*

Subsidiary:

Flexitallic LP **(4)**
6915 Hwy 225
Deer Park, TX 77536-2414 (100%)
Tel.: (281) 604-2400
Fax: (281) 604-2415
Web Site: www.flexitallic.com
Emp.: 205
Mfr of Spiral Wound Gaskets, Sheet Materials & Heat Exchangers
Import Export
S.I.C.: 3053
N.A.I.C.S.: 339991
Ross Simmons *(VP-Mfg)*

Non-U.S. Subsidiary:

Flexitallic Ltd. **(4)**
Scandinavia Mill
Hunsworth Lane, Cleckheaton, West Yorkshire, BD19 4LN, United Kingdom (100%)
Tel.: (44) 1274 851 273
Fax: (44) 1274 864 984
E-Mail: enquiries@flexitallic.eu
Web Site: www.flexitallic.eu
Emp.: 110
Mfr & Marketer of Industrial Static Sealing Products for Oil & Gas, Pipeline, Refining, Petrochemical, Pulp & Paper & Energy Industries
S.I.C.: 3053
N.A.I.C.S.: 339991
Philip Kelshaw *(Mng Dir)*

Non-U.S. Subsidiary:

AGS Flexitallic, Inc. **(3)**
4340 78 Avenue
Edmonton, AB, T6B 3J5, Canada

Tel.: (780) 466-5050
Fax: (780) 465-1177
E-Mail: info@agsflexitallic.com
Web Site: www.agsflexitallic.com
Sales Range: $25-49.9 Million
Emp.: 150
Gaskets & Other Sealing Device Mfr
S.I.C.: 3053
N.A.I.C.S.: 339991
Mario Keca *(Dir-Ops)*

Groupe Moniteur Holding (2)
17 rue d Uzes
75002 Paris, France
Tel.: (33) 140133030
Fax: (33) 140133070
Web Site: www.groupemoniteur.fr
Holding Company; Periodical & Commercial Journal Publisher
S.I.C.: 6719
N.A.I.C.S.: 551112
Olivier de La Chaise *(Deputy Chief Officer)*

Subsidiaries:

Group Moniteur (3)
17 Rue d Uzes
75002 Paris, France
Tel.: (33) 140133030
Fax: (33) 140133070
Web Site: www.groupemoniteur.fr
Periodical Publisher
S.I.C.: 2721
N.A.I.C.S.: 511120
Guillaume Prot *(Pres)*

Subsidiary:

Editions du Moniteur (4)
17 Rue D'Uzes
F 75002 Paris, France
Tel.: (33) 141961550
Telex: 680876 F
Web Site: www.editionsdumoniteur.com
Publisher of Books on Architecture, Construction, Economics; Bookstores
S.I.C.: 2731
N.A.I.C.S.: 511130

Groupe Territorial (3)
BP 215
38506 Voiron, France
Tel.: (33) 476657136
Fax: (33) 476050163
E-Mail: info@territorial.fr
Web Site: www.territorial.fr
Emp.: 80
Periodical Publisher
S.I.C.: 2721
N.A.I.C.S.: 511120
Perinel Hugues *(Gen Mgr)*

Prosys (3)
23 rue du Capitaine Ferber
92130 Issy-les-Moulineaux, France
Tel.: (33) 141232777
E-Mail: contact@prosys.fr
Web Site: www.prosys.fr
Construction Project Management & Document Organization Services
S.I.C.: 7389
N.A.I.C.S.: 561499

Vecteur Plus (3)
1 rue Galilee
44341 Bouguenais, Cedex, France
Tel.: (33) 251112626
Fax: (33) 251112627
E-Mail: contact@vecteurplus.com
Web Site: www.vecteurplus.com
Emp.: 230
Periodical Publishing
S.I.C.: 2721
N.A.I.C.S.: 511120

Histoire d'Or S.A.S. (2)
2 Rue de Valenciennes
75010 Paris, France
Tel.: (33) 1 44 65 13 14
Fax: (33) 1 44 65 13 42
Web Site: www.histoiredor.fr
Sales Range: $450-499.9 Million
Emp.: 2,700
Jewelry Stores
S.I.C.: 5944
N.A.I.C.S.: 448310
Eric Belmonte *(CEO)*

U.S. Holdings:

Designed Metal Connections, Inc. (2)
14800 S Figueroa St
Gardena, CA 90248-1719 DE
Tel.: (310) 323-6200
Fax: (310) 329-2505
E-Mail: customerservice@permaswage.com
Web Site: www.permaswage.com
Sales Range: $50-74.9 Million
Emp.: 508
Tube, Pipe & Cable Fittings Systems Mfr
S.I.C.: 3494
N.A.I.C.S.: 332919
Andrew Roberts *(CEO)*

Bridgepoint Sp. z o.o. (1)
ul Rondo ONZ 1
PL-00 124 Warsaw, Poland PL
Tel.: (48) 225448282
Fax: (48) 225448299
E-Mail: info@bridgepoint.eu
Web Site: www.bridgepoint.eu
Emp.: 6
Private Equity Firm
S.I.C.: 6211
N.A.I.C.S.: 523999
Khai Tan *(Partner & Head-Investments-Central & Eastern Europe)*

Bridgepoint S.p.A. (1)
Via Gabba Fratelli 1/A
IT-20121 Milan, MI, Italy IT
Tel.: (39) 02806951
Fax: (39) 0286452424
E-Mail: info@bridgepoint.eu
Web Site: www.bridgepoint.eu
Emp.: 9
Private Equity Firm
S.I.C.: 6211
N.A.I.C.S.: 523999

BRIDGEPORT VENTURES INC.

36 Toronto Street Suite 1000
Toronto, ON, M5C 2C5, Canada
Tel.: (416) 350-2173
Fax: (416) 350-3510
E-Mail: info@bridgeportventures.net
Web Site: www.bridgeportventures.net
Year Founded: 2007
BPV—(TSX)
Emp.: 5
Business Description:
Metal Mining Services
S.I.C.: 1099
N.A.I.C.S.: 212299
Personnel:
Hugh Snyder *(Chm)*
Shastri Ramnath *(Pres & CEO)*
Carmelo Marrelli *(CFO)*
Board of Directors:
Hugh Snyder
John McBridge
Jon North

BRIDGESTONE CORPORATION

10-1 Kyobashi 1-chome
Chuo-ku, Tokyo, 104-8340, Japan
Tel.: (81) 335636811
Fax: (81) 335674615
Web Site: www.bridgestone.com
Year Founded: 1931
5108—(NGO TKS)
Sls.: $33,437,118,000
Assets: $33,431,761,000
Liabilities: $17,821,727,000
Net Worth: $15,610,034,000
Earnings: $1,577,928,000
Emp.: 143,448
Fiscal Year-end: 12/31/12
Business Description:
Rubber Tires, Tubes, Shock Absorbers, Conveyor Belts, Hoses, Foam Rubber, Polyurethane Foam & Golf Balls Mfr & Whslr
Import Export
S.I.C.: 3011
N.A.I.C.S.: 326211
Personnel:
Masaaki Tsuya *(Chm & CEO)*
Kazuhisa Nishigai *(COO)*
Yuichiro Takenami *(CIO-IT, Network & Corp Comm & VP-Global Innovation)*
Shuichi Ishibashi *(CMO-Global Mktg Strategy & Advance Bus Plng & VP)*
Shingo Kubota *(Chief Compliance Officer, Gen Counsel & VP)*
Yoshiyuki Morimoto *(CTO & Sr VP)*
Shinichi Yochi *(Chief Risk Officer, Chief Human Rights Officer & VP)*
Yoichi Sato *(Chief Quality Officer & VP-Quality, Safety & Disaster Prevention)*
Asahiko Nishiyama *(Sr VP-Japan Tire Bus & Original Equipment Tire Sls)*
Narumi Zaitsu *(Sr VP-Intl Tire Bus Ops)*
Board of Directors:
Masaaki Tsuya
Scott Trevor Davis
Takao Enkawa
Sakie Tachibana Fukushima
Yoshiyuki Morimoto
Kimiko Murofushi
Kazuhisa Nishigai
Narumi Zaitsu
Transfer Agent:
Sumitomo Mitsui Trust Bank, Limited
4-1 Marunouchi 1-chome Chiyoda-ku
Tokyo, Japan
Subsidiaries:

Asahi Carbon Co., Ltd (1)
2 Kamomejima-machi
Niigata, 950 0883, Japan (99.4%)
Tel.: (81) 252741211
Fax: (81) 252754658
E-Mail: soumu.kyouyu@asahi-carbon.com
Web Site: www.asahicarbon.co.jp
Emp.: 165
Carbon Black Production & Sales
S.I.C.: 2819
N.A.I.C.S.: 325180

Bridgestone Cycle Co., Ltd. (1)
3-1-1 Nakazuma
Ageo, Saitama, 362-0072, Japan (100%)
Tel.: (81) 487732221
Telex: 2224943 BSC J
Fax: (81) 487752299
Web Site: www.bscycle.co.jp
Bicycles & Industrial Machinery Mfr & Sales
S.I.C.: 3751
N.A.I.C.S.: 336991

Subsidiaries:

Bridgestone Cycle East Japan Sales Co., Ltd. (2)
2-31-6 Shimo-Shakujii
Nerima-ku, Tokyo, Japan
Tel.: (81) 3 3995 2311
Web Site: www.bscycle.co.jp/en/corporate/06.html
Bicycle Distr
S.I.C.: 5012
N.A.I.C.S.: 423110

Bridgestone Cycle West Japan Sales Co., Ltd. (2)
1-4-25 Hamadera Ishizucho Nisi
Nishi-ku, Sakai, Osaka, Japan
Tel.: (81) 72 245 1111
Fax: (81) 72 244 9541
Web Site: www.bscycle.co.jp/en/corporate/06.html
Bicycle & Parts Distr
S.I.C.: 5091
N.A.I.C.S.: 423910

Plants:

Bridgestone Cycle Co., Ltd. - Ageo Plant (2)
3-1-1 Nakazuma
Ageo, Saitama, 3628520, Japan
Tel.: (81) 48 773 2221
Fax: (81) 48 772 5220
Web Site: www.bscycle.co.jp/en/corporate/06.html
Emp.: 800
Bicycle & Parts Mfr
S.I.C.: 3751
N.A.I.C.S.: 336991

Bridgestone Cycle Co., Ltd. - Asahi Plant (2)
1500 Saitsumachi
Tosu, Saga, Japan
Tel.: (81) 942 82 5111
Bicycle Mfr
S.I.C.: 3751
N.A.I.C.S.: 336991

Bridgestone Diversified Chemical Products Co., Ltd. (1)
3-4-4 Nihombashimuromachi Jp Bldg 4f
Tokyo, 103-0022, Japan
Tel.: (81) 332705661
Specialty Chemicals Mfr
S.I.C.: 2899
N.A.I.C.S.: 325998

Bridgestone Diversified Products West Co., Ltd. (1)
2-4-2 Shimmachi Nishi-Ku Naniwasujishia Bldg 13f
Osaka, 550-0013, Japan
Tel.: (81) 665348700
Automobile Tire Mfr
S.I.C.: 3011
N.A.I.C.S.: 326211

Bridgestone Finance Corporation (1)
1-7-1 Kyobashi Bridgestone Bldg 6f
Tokyo, 104-0031, Japan
Tel.: (81) 335636815
Financial Management Services
S.I.C.: 6211
N.A.I.C.S.: 523999

Bridgestone Flowtech Corporation (1)
1-3-1 Minami-shinozaki
Kazocd, Saitama, 347-0017, Japan (100%)
Tel.: (81) 480651121
Fax: (81) 480651072
Web Site: www.bsft.co.jp
Emp.: 400
Industrial Hydraulic Hoses Mfr & Sales
S.I.C.: 3052
N.A.I.C.S.: 326220
Shingo Kato *(Gen Mgr)*

BRIDGESTONE RIHGA, LTD. (1)
45-1 Ebisujimacho
Sakai-Ku, Sakai, 590-0985, Japan
Tel.: (81) 722241121
Fax: (81) 722241120
E-Mail: ski-room@agoraregency-sakai.com
Web Site: www.agoraregency-sakai.com
Emp.: 20
Automotive Tire Mfr
S.I.C.: 3011
N.A.I.C.S.: 326211
Harold Linssen *(Gen Mgr)*

Bridgestone Sports Co., Ltd. (1)
Omori Bellport East Building 6-22-7 Minami-oi
Shinagawa-ku, Tokyo, 140-0013, Japan (100%)
Tel.: (81) 357632500
Fax: (81) 357632540
E-Mail: info@bs-sports.co.jp
Web Site: www.bs-sports.co.jp
Emp.: 100
Sporting Goods Mfr & Sales
S.I.C.: 3949
N.A.I.C.S.: 339920
Kawano Hisashi *(Pres)*

U.S. Subsidiary:

Bridgestone Golf, Inc. (2)
15320 Industrial Park Blvd Ne
Covington, GA 30014-6428 (100%)
Tel.: (770) 787-7400
Fax: (770) 786-6416
Web Site: www.bridgestonegolf.com
Emp.: 175
Golf Equipment Mfr & Sales
S.I.C.: 3949
N.A.I.C.S.: 339920
Stan Murphy *(VP-Mktg)*

Plants:

Bridgestone Corporation - Amagi Plant (1)
2011 Oaza-ota
Asakura, Fukuoka, 838-0051, Japan

Bridgestone Corporation—(Continued)

Tel.: (81) 946227111
Fax: (81) 946227122
Automotive Tire Mfr
S.I.C.: 3011
N.A.I.C.S.: 326211

Bridgestone Corporation - Hofu Plant (1)
100 Hamakata
Hofu, Yamaguchi, 747-0833, Japan
Tel.: (81) 835228111
Automotive Tire Mfr
S.I.C.: 3011
N.A.I.C.S.: 326211

Bridgestone Corporation - Kumamoto Plant (1)
600 Kawasaki
Tamana, Kumamoto, 865-0007, Japan
Tel.: (81) 968740111
Automotive Tire Mfr
S.I.C.: 3011
N.A.I.C.S.: 326211

Bridgestone Corporation - Kuroiso Plant (1)
10 Kaminakano
Nasushiobara, Tochigi, 329-3154, Japan
Tel.: (81) 287653211
Fax: (81) 287652084
Automotive Tire Mfr
S.I.C.: 3011
N.A.I.C.S.: 326211

Bridgestone Corporation - Kurume Plant (1)
105 Kyomachi
Kurume, 830-0028, Japan
Tel.: (81) 942330111
Automotive Tire Mfr
S.I.C.: 3011
N.A.I.C.S.: 326211

Bridgestone Corporation - Nasu Plant (1)
3-1 Higashiyamatocho
Nasushiobara, Tochigi, 325-0041, Japan
Tel.: (81) 287632311
Fax: (81) 287643591
Emp.: 847
Automotive Tire Mfr
S.I.C.: 3011
N.A.I.C.S.: 326211

Bridgestone Corporation - Seki Plant (1)
20 Shinhasama
Seki, 501-3923, Japan
Tel.: (81) 575234111
Automobile Tire Mfr
S.I.C.: 3011
N.A.I.C.S.: 326211

Bridgestone Corporation - Shimonoseki Plant (1)
3-1 Chofuminatomachi
Shimonoseki, Yamaguchi, 752-0953, Japan
Tel.: (81) 832451251
Fax: (81) 832452901
Automotive Tire Mfr
S.I.C.: 3011
N.A.I.C.S.: 326211

Bridgestone Corporation - Tochigi Plant (1)
800 Shimonakano
Nasushiobara, Tochigi, 329-3146, Japan
Tel.: (81) 287653111
Automotive Tire Mfr
S.I.C.: 3011
N.A.I.C.S.: 326211

Bridgestone Corporation - Tokyo Plant (1)
3-1-1 Ogawa Higashi-Cho
Kodaira, Tokyo, 187-0031, Japan
Tel.: (81) 423426555
Automobile Tire Mfr
S.I.C.: 3011
N.A.I.C.S.: 326211

Bridgestone Corporation - Tosu Plant (1)
1000 Todorokimachi
Tosu, Saga, 841-0061, Japan
Tel.: (81) 942835111
Automotive Tire Mfr
S.I.C.: 3011
N.A.I.C.S.: 326211

Bridgestone Corporation - Yokohama Plant (1)
1 Kashiocho
Totsuka-Ku, Yokohama, Kanagawa, 244-0812, Japan
Tel.: (81) 458241111
Automobile Tire Mfr
S.I.C.: 3011
N.A.I.C.S.: 326211

U.S. Subsidiaries:

Bandag Incorporated (1)
2905 N Hwy 61
Muscatine, IA 52761 IA
Tel.: (563) 262-1400
Toll Free: (800) 822-6324
E-Mail: webmaster@bandag.com
Web Site: www.bandag.com
Sales Range: $900-999.9 Million
Emp.: 3,362
Tire Treads Mfr
S.I.C.: 7534
N.A.I.C.S.: 326212
Kurk Danielson *(Pres)*
Troy Geuther *(Treas & VP-Fin)*

Affiliate:

Belleroc (2)
1325 N 31st Ave
Melrose Park, IL 60160-2907 IL
Tel.: (708) 681-5363
Fax: (708) 681-5393
Web Site: www.belleroc.com
Tire Sales, Retreading & Repair Services
Import Export
S.I.C.: 5014
N.A.I.C.S.: 441320
Dan Sickafoose *(Pres)*

Subsidiaries:

Belleroc (3)
2505 Thornwood St SW
Grand Rapids, MI 49509
Tel.: (616) 538-0250
Fax: (616) 538-1121
Web Site: www.belleroc.com
Sales Range: $10-24.9 Million
Emp.: 40
Tire Sales, Retreading & Repair Services
S.I.C.: 5014
N.A.I.C.S.: 441320
Dan Taylor *(Reg Mgr)*

Tredroc Tire Services (3)
875 Ralston Rd
Machesney Park, IL 61115-1609
Tel.: (815) 636-8000
Fax: (815) 636-1186
Web Site: www.tredroc.com
Sls.: $2,500,000
Emp.: 17
Tire Retreading & Repair Services
Import Export
S.I.C.: 7534
N.A.I.C.S.: 326212
Glen Parks *(CFO)*

Bridgestone Americas, Inc. (1)
535 Marriott Dr
Nashville, TN 37214-3672 NV
Tel.: (615) 937-1000 (100%)
Fax: (615) 937-3621
Web Site: www.bridgestone-firestone.com
Emp.: 900
Holding Company
Import Export
S.I.C.: 3011
N.A.I.C.S.: 326211
Asahiko Nishiyama *(Chm)*
Gary Garfield *(Pres & CEO)*
Eduardo Minardi *(COO)*
Tim Walsh *(CIO)*
Ken Weaver *(Pres-Comml Tire Sls-US & Canada)*
Eugene Stephens *(Treas)*
Christine Karbowiak *(Exec VP)*

Divisions:

Bridgestone Americas, Inc. - Center for Research & Technology (2)
1659 S Main St
Akron, OH 44301
Tel.: (330) 379-7570
Fax: (330) 379-7530
Web Site: www.ba-thecenter.com
Emp.: 60
Research & Development Services
S.I.C.: 8731
N.A.I.C.S.: 541712
Yasutaka Enoki *(Pres)*

Bridgestone Americas Tire Operations, LLC (2)
535 Marriott Dr
Nashville, TN 37214-5092 DE
Mailing Address: (100%)
PO Box 140990
Nashville, TN 37214-5092
Tel.: (615) 937-1000
Fax: (615) 937-3621
Toll Free: (800) 668-0345
Web Site: www.bridgestone-firestone.com
Emp.: 1,000
Tire Mfr & Sales
S.I.C.: 3011
N.A.I.C.S.: 326211
Philip Dobbs *(CMO-North America)*
Gordon Knapp *(Pres-Consumer Tire)*
Saul Solomon *(Pres-Latin America)*

Divisions:

Bridgestone Americas, Inc. - Akron (3)
10 E Firestone Blvd
Akron, OH 44317-0001
Tel.: (330) 379-7000
Fax: (330) 379-6386
Web Site: www.bf.usa.com
Emp.: 100
Tire Research & Product Development Services
S.I.C.: 8731
N.A.I.C.S.: 541712

Bridgestone Americas, Inc. - Business Technology Group Division (3)
535 Marriott Dr
Nashville, TN 37214
Tel.: (615) 937-1000
Fax: (615) 937-3621
Software Management Services
S.I.C.: 7371
N.A.I.C.S.: 541511

Bridgestone Americas Tire Operations, LLC - Agricultural Tire, U.S. & Canada Commercial Tire Sales Division (3)
730 E 2nd St
Des Moines, IA 50309
Tel.: (515) 283-1440
Fax: (515) 283-1610
Automobile Tire Mfr
S.I.C.: 3011
N.A.I.C.S.: 326211

Bridgestone Americas Tire Operations, LLC - Akron Technical Center Division (3)
10 E Firestone Blvd
Akron, OH 44317
Tel.: (330) 379-6640
Web Site: www.bridgestone-firestone.com
Tire Research & Development Services
S.I.C.: 8731
N.A.I.C.S.: 541712

Bridgestone Americas Tire Operations, LLC - Bridgestone Bandag Tire Solutions Division (3)
2905 N Hwy 61
Muscatine, IA 52761
Tel.: (563) 262-1400
Fax: (563) 262-1069
Automobile Tire Mfr & Whslr
S.I.C.: 3011
N.A.I.C.S.: 326211

Bridgestone Americas Tire Operations, LLC - Des Moines (3)
4600 NW 2nd Ave Ste 100
Des Moines, IA 50313
Tel.: (515) 283-1440
Fax: (515) 283-1610
Web Site: www.bridgestone-firestone.com
Emp.: 2,500
Agricultural & Forestry Tire Mfr
S.I.C.: 5014
N.A.I.C.S.: 423130
Eduardo Minardi *(Chm, Pres & CEO)*

Plant:

Firestone Agricultural-Des Moines (4)
2nd Ave & Hoffman Rd
Des Moines, IA 50313
Tel.: (515) 243-1211
Fax: (515) 235-4060
Web Site: www.firestone.com
Emp.: 1,600
Agricultural Tire Mfr
S.I.C.: 3011
N.A.I.C.S.: 326211
Nobel Smith *(Plant Mgr)*

Bridgestone Americas Tire Operations, LLC - Off Road Tire, U.S. & Canada Tire Sales Division (3)
535 Marriott Dr
Nashville, TN 37214
Tel.: (615) 937-1000
Fax: (615) 937-3621
Automobile Tire Distr
S.I.C.: 5014
N.A.I.C.S.: 423130

Bridgestone Americas Tire Operations, LLC - Original Equipment, U.S. & Canada Consumer Tire Sales Division (3)
39500 High Pointe Blvd Ste 200
Novi, MI 48375
Tel.: (248) 348-2202
Fax: (248) 348-2040
Web Site: www.bridgestone-firestone.com
Automotive Tire Mfr
S.I.C.: 3011
N.A.I.C.S.: 326211

Bridgestone Americas Tire Operations, LLC - Replacement Tire Sales, U.S. & Canada Consumer Tire Sales Division (3)
535 Marriott Dr
Nashville, TN 37214
Tel.: (615) 937-1000
Fax: (615) 937-3621
Automobile Tire Whslr
S.I.C.: 5014
N.A.I.C.S.: 423130

Bridgestone Americas Tire Operations, LLC - Texas Proving Ground Division (3)
199 Firestone Rd
Fort Stockton, TX 79735
Tel.: (432) 336-4800
Fax: (432) 336-4821
Web Site: www.bridgestone-firestone.com
Emp.: 20
Automobile Testing Ground Operator
S.I.C.: 8734
N.A.I.C.S.: 541380
Juan De Hoyos *(Gen Mgr)*

Bridgestone/Firestone Off Road Tire Division (3)
535 Marriott Dr Ste 800
Nashville, TN 37214-5039
Tel.: (615) 937-5700
Fax: (615) 937-5799
Toll Free: (800) 905-2367
Web Site: www.bfor.com
Heavy-Duty Tire Distr
S.I.C.: 5014
N.A.I.C.S.: 441320
Shawn Rasey *(Pres)*

Bridgestone/Firestone Original Equipment Division (3)
39500 High Pointe Blvd Ste 200
Novi, MI 48375-5505
Tel.: (248) 348-2030
Fax: (248) 208-3635
Web Site: www.bridgestone-firestone.com
Emp.: 30
Tire Sales to Automotive Manufacturing Businesses
S.I.C.: 5014
N.A.I.C.S.: 441320

Firestone Tube Division (3)
2700 E Main St
Russellville, AR 72801
Mailing Address:
PO Box 10730
Russellville, AR 72812

Tel.: (479) 968-1443
Fax: (479) 964-0292
Toll Free: (800) 553-6008
Web Site: www.firestonetubes.com
Emp.: 75
Tire Tube Mfr
S.I.C.: 3011
N.A.I.C.S.: 326211
Ron Keeneth *(Controller)*

Subsidiaries:

Bridgestone Americas Center for Research and Technology, LLC (3)
1200 Firestone Pkwy
Akron, OH 44317
Tel.: (330) 379-7570
Fax: (330) 379-7530
Web Site: www.ba-thecenter.com
Tire Polymer Research & Development Services
S.I.C.: 8731
N.A.I.C.S.: 541712

Kendon Corporation (3)
3904 S Hoyt Ave
Muncie, IN 47302
Tel.: (765) 282-1515
Fax: (765) 282-9359
Toll Free: (800) 223-6653
Web Site: www.kendon-national.com
Hub Assemblies & Rim Mfr
S.I.C.: 3714
N.A.I.C.S.: 336390
Melvin Hershey *(Pres)*

U.S., Canada and Monterrey Manufacturing Group (3)
535 Marriott Dr
Nashville, TN 37214
Tel.: (615) 937-1000
Fax: (615) 937-3621
Web Site: www.bridgestone-firestone.com
Automobile Tire Mfr
S.I.C.: 3011
N.A.I.C.S.: 326211

White Tire (3)
1615 2nd Ave
Muscatine, IA 52761
Tel.: (563) 288-2200
Fax: (563) 288-2215
Automobile Tire Retreading Services
S.I.C.: 7534
N.A.I.C.S.: 326212

Plants:

Bridgestone Americas Tire Operations, LLC - Abilene Manufacturing Facility (3)
4750 FM 18
Abilene, TX 79602
Tel.: (325) 677-1861
Fax: (325) 734-6040
Web Site: www.bridgestone-firestone.com
Emp.: 150
Tread Rubber & Retreading Materials Mfr
S.I.C.: 3069
N.A.I.C.S.: 326299
Valentin Fernandez *(Gen Mgr)*

Bridgestone Americas Tire Operations, LLC - Aiken County Manufacturing Facility (3)
1 Bridgestone Pkwy
Graniteville, SC 29829
Tel.: (803) 232-2000
Fax: (803) 663-0965
Automobile Tire Mfr
S.I.C.: 3011
N.A.I.C.S.: 326211

Bridgestone Americas Tire Operations, LLC - Akron Manufacturing Facility (3)
10 E Firestone Blvd
Akron, OH 44317
Tel.: (330) 379-7000
Fax: (330) 379-7441
Web Site: www.bridgestone-firestone.com
Racing Tire Mfr
S.I.C.: 3011
N.A.I.C.S.: 326211

Bridgestone Americas Tire Operations, LLC - Bloomington-Normal Manufacturing Facility (3)
Ft Jesse Rd & Veterans Pkwy
Normal, IL 61761
Tel.: (309) 452-4411
Fax: (309) 454-0201
Web Site: www.bridgestone-firestone.com
Off Road Tire Mfr
S.I.C.: 3011
N.A.I.C.S.: 326211

Bridgestone Americas Tire Operations, LLC - Des Moines Manufacturing Facility (3)
2nd Ave & Hoffman Rd
Des Moines, IA 50313
Tel.: (515) 243-1211
Fax: (515) 235-4060
Web Site: www.bridgestone-firestone.com
Tractor Tire Mfr
S.I.C.: 3011
N.A.I.C.S.: 326211

Bridgestone Americas Tire Operations, LLC - Griffin Manufacturing Facility (3)
801 Greenbelt Pkwy
Griffin, GA 30223
Tel.: (770) 233-8000
Fax: (770) 233-8035
Web Site: www.bridgestone-firestone.com
Emp.: 150
Tread Rubber & Retreading Material Mfr
S.I.C.: 3069
N.A.I.C.S.: 326299
Gary Betz *(Mgr)*

Bridgestone Americas Tire Operations, LLC - LaVergne Manufacturing Facility (3)
1201 Bridgestone Pkwy
La Vergne, TN 37086
Tel.: (615) 793-7581
Fax: (615) 793-1758
Automotive Tire Mfr
S.I.C.: 3011
N.A.I.C.S.: 326211

Bridgestone Americas Tire Operations, LLC - Long Beach Manufacturing Facility (3)
2500 E Thompson St
Long Beach, CA 90805
Tel.: (562) 531-3880
Fax: (562) 630-4941
Web Site: www.bridgestone-firestone.com
Emp.: 60
Tread Rubber & Retreading Material Mfr
S.I.C.: 3069
N.A.I.C.S.: 326299
Manuel Navarrette *(Mgr)*

Bridgestone Americas Tire Operations, LLC - Muscatine Manufacturing Facility (3)
2905 N Hwy 61
Muscatine, IA 52761
Tel.: (563) 262-1400
Fax: (563) 262-1069
Retreading Machinery Mfr
S.I.C.: 3559
N.A.I.C.S.: 333249

Bridgestone Americas Tire Operations, LLC - Oxford Manufacturing Facility (3)
505 W Industry Dr
Oxford, NC 27565
Tel.: (919) 693-8855
Fax: (919) 603-5210
Web Site: www.bridgestone-firestone.com
Emp.: 186
Tread Rubber & Retreading Materials Mfr
S.I.C.: 3069
N.A.I.C.S.: 326299
Mark Averette *(Gen Mgr)*

Bridgestone Americas Tire Operations, LLC - Warren County Manufacturing Facility (3)
725 Bridgestone Dr
Morrison, TN 37357
Tel.: (931) 668-5500
Fax: (931) 668-5646
Web Site: www.bridgestone-firestone.com
Truck & Bus Tires Mfr
S.I.C.: 3011
N.A.I.C.S.: 326211

Bridgestone Americas Tire Operations, LLC - Wilson Manufacturing Facility (3)
3001 Firestone Pkwy
Wilson, NC 27893
Tel.: (252) 291-4275
Fax: (252) 246-7331
Web Site: www.bridgestone-firestone.com
Light Truck Tire Mfr
S.I.C.: 3011
N.A.I.C.S.: 326211

Non-U.S. Plants:

Bridgestone Americas Tire Operations, LLC - Joliette Manufacturing Facility (3)
1200 Firestone Blvd
Joliette, QC, J6E 2W5, Canada
Tel.: (450) 756-1061
Fax: (450) 756-1826
Automotive Tire Mfr
S.I.C.: 3011
N.A.I.C.S.: 326211

Bridgestone Americas Tire Operations, LLC - Sao Paulo Facility (3)
Av Queiros dos Santos 1717
Sao Paulo, 09015-901, Brazil
Tel.: (55) 11 4433 1666
Fax: (55) 11 4433 1074
E-Mail: recepcao@bsbr.com.br
Web Site: www.bridgestone-firestone.com
Emp.: 300
Automotive Tire Mfr
S.I.C.: 3011
N.A.I.C.S.: 326211

Bridgestone/Firestone Information Services Company (2)
1200 Ofc Main St
Akron, OH 44310-0001
Tel.: (330) 379-7000
Fax: (330) 379-7290
E-Mail: lastnamefirstname@bfis.com
Web Site: www.bfis.com
Emp.: 100
Data Services
S.I.C.: 7379
N.A.I.C.S.: 518210
Dennis George *(Pres & Gen Mgr)*

Subsidiaries:

BFS Diversified Products, LLC (2)
250 W 96th St
Indianapolis, IN 46260 (100%)
Tel.: (317) 575-7000
Fax: (317) 575-7100
Toll Free: (800) 428-4442
Web Site: www.firestonebpco.com
Emp.: 500
Roofing Materials, Synthetic Rubber & Textiles Mfr
S.I.C.: 2295
N.A.I.C.S.: 313320
Ken Weaver *(Chm, Pres, CEO & CFO)*

Divisions:

Firestone Building Products Division (3)
250 W 96th St
Indianapolis, IN 46260 (100%)
Tel.: (317) 575-7000
Fax: (317) 575-7100
Web Site: www.firestonebpco.com
Emp.: 200
Roofing & Insulation Mfr
S.I.C.: 3061
N.A.I.C.S.: 326291
Phil LaDuke *(Dir-Accts Svc-Natl)*

Plants:

Firestone Building Products-Beech Grove (4)
3525 S Arlington Ave
Indianapolis, IN 46203-6102 (100%)
Tel.: (317) 784-1161
Fax: (317) 781-9222
Web Site: www.bridgestone-firestone.com
Emp.: 60
Roofing Mfr
S.I.C.: 5014
N.A.I.C.S.: 441320

Firestone Building Products-Kingstree (4)
Old Lake City Hwy
Kingstree, SC 29556-9804
Tel.: (843) 382-5040
Fax: (843) 382-5048
E-Mail: support@sharonstair.com
Web Site: www.sharonstair.com
Emp.: 300
Rubber Roofing Mfr
S.I.C.: 5014
N.A.I.C.S.: 441320

Firestone Building Products-Prescott (4)
1406 Hwy 371 N
Prescott, AR 71857-3903
Tel.: (870) 887-2673
Fax: (870) 887-1409
Web Site: www.firestonebpco.com
Emp.: 500
Roofing, Flashing & Seam Tape Mfr
S.I.C.: 3069
N.A.I.C.S.: 326299
Ray Oxley *(Plant Mgr)*

Firestone Fibers & Textiles Division (3)
100 Firestone Ln
Kings Mountain, NC 28086
Tel.: (704) 734-2100
Fax: (704) 734-2104
Web Site: www.firestonefibers.com
Emp.: 350
Tire Cord & Industrial Fabric Mfr
S.I.C.: 2299
N.A.I.C.S.: 313110
Tim Dunn *(Pres)*

Plants:

Firestone Fibers & Textiles Company, LLC - Gastonia Manufacturing Facility (4)
1101 W 2nd Ave
Gastonia, NC 28052
Tel.: (704) 734-2100
Fax: (704) 734-2930
Web Site: www.bridgestone-firestone.com
Fiber Textile Products Mfr
S.I.C.: 2389
N.A.I.C.S.: 314999

Firestone Fibers & Textiles-Kings Mountain (4)
100 Firestone Ln
Kings Mountain, NC 28086-1369
Tel.: (704) 734-2102
Fax: (704) 734-2101
Web Site: www.bridgestonecorporation.com
Emp.: 300
Tire Cord & Industrial Fabric Mfr
S.I.C.: 2296
N.A.I.C.S.: 314994
Fred Padgett *(Plant Mgr)*

Non-U.S. Plant:

Firestone Textiles-Woodstock (4)
1200 Dundas St E
PO Box 486
Woodstock, ON, N4S 7Y9, Canada
Tel.: (519) 537-6231
Telex: 64-5629
Fax: (519) 421-5659
E-Mail: don.bacher@firestone-textile.com
Web Site: www.firestone-textile.com
Emp.: 270
Tire Cord Fabrics & Textiles Mfr
Export
S.I.C.: 2296
N.A.I.C.S.: 314994
Bob Galway *(Gen Mgr)*

Firestone Industrial Products Division (3)
250 W 96th St
Indiana, IN 46260 (100%)
Tel.: (317) 818-8600
Fax: (317) 818-8645
Web Site: www.firestoneindustrial.com
Emp.: 100
Vehicular Suspension Systems & Industrial Air Springs Mfr
S.I.C.: 3493
N.A.I.C.S.: 332613
John Geary *(Dir-Mktg)*

Plants:

Firestone Industrial Products Company-Dyersburg (4)
1901 Sylvan Rd
Dyersburg, TN 38024-1703
Tel.: (731) 286-5054

Bridgestone Corporation—(Continued)

Fax: (901) 286-2462
Web Site: www.firestoneip.com
Emp.: 130
Mfr of Air Springs for Motor Vehicles & Industrial Uses
S.I.C.: 3714
N.A.I.C.S.: 336390
Mike Kroeger *(Plant Mgr)*

Firestone Industrial Products-Williamsburg (4)
1 Firestone Blvd
Williamsburg, KY 40769-9338
Tel.: (606) 549-0528
Fax: (606) 549-0611
E-Mail: info@firestoneindustrial.com
Web Site: www.firestoneindustrial.com
Emp.: 100
Airsprings Mfr
S.I.C.: 2399
N.A.I.C.S.: 315990
Lynn Taylor *(Gen Mgr)*

Firestone Synthetic Rubber & Latex-Orange (4)
Farm Rd 1006
Orange, TX 77630
Mailing Address:
PO Box 1269
Orange, TX 77630
Tel.: (409) 883-1776
Fax: (409) 924-4750
Web Site: www.firestone.com
Emp.: 300
Synthetic Rubber Mfr
S.I.C.: 2869
N.A.I.C.S.: 325199
Nelson Bernard *(Controller)*

Non-U.S. Subsidiaries:

Firestone Industrial Products de Costa Rica, S.A. (4)
500 Mts Noreste del Cruce La Suiza y Turrialba Pavones
Turrialba, Cartago, Costa Rica
Tel.: (506) 2558 4200
Fax: (506) 2558 4201
Emp.: 145
Air Spring Mfr
S.I.C.: 3728
N.A.I.C.S.: 336413
Alvaro Murillo *(Mgr)*

Firestone Industrial Products Poland Sp. z o.o. (4)
Berzyna 80
64-200 Wolsztyn, Poland
Tel.: (48) 68 347 51 00
Fax: (48) 68 347 51 01
Web Site: www.bridgestone-firestone.com
Air Spring Mfr
S.I.C.: 3728
N.A.I.C.S.: 336413
Powell Jada *(Gen Mgr)*

Firestone Produtos Industriais Av. (4)
Queiros dos Santos 1717
09015 311 Santo Andre, Sao Paulo, Brazil
Tel.: (55) 11 4433 1166
Fax: (55) 11 4994 7328
Industrial Machinery Mfr
S.I.C.: 3559
N.A.I.C.S.: 333249

Non-U.S. Plant:

Firestone Industrial Products, LLC - Arnhem Manufacturing Facility (4)
Delta 160
6825 MV Arnhem, Netherlands
Tel.: (31) 26 352 98 98
Fax: (31) 26 352 98 97
Web Site: www.bridgestone-firestone.com
Emp.: 30
Industrial Machinery Mfr
S.I.C.: 3559
N.A.I.C.S.: 333249
Piotr Bogaczynski *(Mng Dir)*

Subsidiary:

UNA-CLAD by Firestone (3)
1001 Lund Blvd
Anoka, MN 55303-1089
Tel.: (763) 576-9595
Fax: (763) 576-9596
E-Mail: info@unaclad.com
Web Site: www.unaclad.com
Emp.: 200
Mfr. of Architectural Metal Products
S.I.C.: 5051
N.A.I.C.S.: 423510
John Bernardi *(Pres)*

Bridgestone Aircraft Tire (USA), Inc. (2)
802 Ayerszille Rd
Mayodan, NC 27027-1889 (100%)
Tel.: (336) 548-8100
Fax: (336) 548-7441
Web Site: ap.bridgestone.co.jp/contacts/contacts.html
Emp.: 150
Aircraft Tire Retread & Sales
S.I.C.: 5014
N.A.I.C.S.: 441320
Ron Wise *(Mgr-HR)*

Bridgestone Retail Operations, LLC (2)
333 East Lake St
Bloomingdale, IL 60108 (100%)
Tel.: (630) 259-9000
Fax: (630) 259-9158
Web Site: www.bridgestone-firestone.com
Emp.: 23,000
Tires & Automotive Components Sales & Automotive Repair Services
S.I.C.: 7538
N.A.I.C.S.: 811111
Stuart Crum *(Pres)*

Division:

Bridgestone/Firestone Credit Card Division (3)
6275 Eastland Rd
Brook Park, OH 44142
Tel.: (216) 362-5000
Fax: (216) 362-5069
Credit Card & Collection Services
S.I.C.: 6062
N.A.I.C.S.: 522130

Subsidiary:

Credit First National Association (3)
6275 Eastland Rd
Brook Park, OH 44142
Tel.: (216) 362-5000
Fax: (216) 362-5069
Commercial Banking Services
S.I.C.: 6029
N.A.I.C.S.: 522110
Rose Marie Boll *(Mgr-Collection)*

Unit:

GCR Tire Centers (3)
2601 N 32nd Ave
Phoenix, AZ 85009-1505 AZ
Tel.: (602) 269-1351
Fax: (602) 484-9279
E-Mail: info@gcrtires.com
Web Site: www.gcrtires.com
Emp.: 25
Tire Saves
S.I.C.: 5014
N.A.I.C.S.: 423130
Mark Gagnon *(Gen Mgr)*

Firestone Building Products Company, LLC (2)
250 W 96th St
Indianapolis, IN 46260
Tel.: (317) 575-7000
Fax: (317) 575-7100
Toll Free: (800) 428-4442
Web Site: www.firestonebpco.com
Commercial Roofing System Mfr
S.I.C.: 3444
N.A.I.C.S.: 332322
Tim Dunn *(Pres)*

Subsidiaries:

Firestone Diversified Products, LLC (3)
250 W 96th St
Indianapolis, IN 46260
Tel.: (317) 575-7000
Fax: (317) 575-7100
Extruded Rubber Product Mfr
S.I.C.: 3069
N.A.I.C.S.: 326299

Firestone Energy Solutions (3)
250 W 96th St
Indianapolis, IN 46260
Tel.: (317) 853-4680
Fax: (317) 428-5719
Toll Free: (888) 793-0012
Solar Power Generation Services
S.I.C.: 4911
N.A.I.C.S.: 221114

Firestone GenFlex Roofing Systems, LLC (3)
250 W 96th St
Indianapolis, IN 46260
Tel.: (800) 443-4272
Fax: (877) 777-2909
E-Mail: info@fbpe.be
Web Site: www.genflex.com
Roofing System Mfr
S.I.C.: 3444
N.A.I.C.S.: 332322
Tim Dunn *(Pres & CEO)*

Plants:

Firestone Building Products Company, LLC - Bristol Manufacturing Facility (3)
780 James P Casey Rd
Bristol, CT 06010
Tel.: (860) 584-9000
Fax: (860) 584-4666
Web Site: www.bridgestone-firestone.com
Insulation & Roofing Materials Mfr
S.I.C.: 3444
N.A.I.C.S.: 332322

Firestone Building Products Company, LLC - Corsicana Manufacturing Facility (3)
4201 E Hwy 31
Corsicana, TX 75109-9697
Tel.: (903) 874-1003
Fax: (903) 874-1008
Web Site: www.bridgestone-firestone.com
Insulation Material Mfr
S.I.C.: 3999
N.A.I.C.S.: 339999

Firestone Building Products Company, LLC - DeForest Manufacturing Facility (3)
612 N Stevenson Rd
De Forest, WI 53532
Tel.: (608) 846-4440
Fax: (608) 846-0391
Web Site: www.bridgestone-firestone.com
Insulation & Roofing Materials Mfr
S.I.C.: 3444
N.A.I.C.S.: 332322

Firestone Building Products Company, LLC - Florence Manufacturing Facility (3)
8170 Holton Dr
Florence, KY 41042
Tel.: (859) 291-4900
Fax: (859) 727-3842
Web Site: www.bridgestone-firestone.com
Insulation & Roofing Materials Mfr
S.I.C.: 3999
N.A.I.C.S.: 339999

Firestone Building Products Company, LLC - Indianapolis Manufacturing Facility (3)
3525 S Arlington
Indianapolis, IN 46203
Tel.: (317) 784-1161
Fax: (317) 781-4181
Web Site: www.bridgestone-firestone.com
Insulation & Roofing Materials Mfr
S.I.C.: 3444
N.A.I.C.S.: 332322

Firestone Building Products Company, LLC - Jacksonville Manufacturing Facility (3)
6831 Stuart Ave
Jacksonville, FL 32254
Tel.: (904) 783-3110
Fax: (904) 783-6177
Web Site: www.bridgestone-firestone.com
Insulation & Residential Sheeting Materials Mfr
S.I.C.: 3999
N.A.I.C.S.: 339999

Firestone Building Products Company, LLC - Prescott Manufacturing Facility (3)
1406 Hwy 371 N
Prescott, AR 71857
Tel.: (870) 887-2673
Fax: (870) 887-1409
Web Site: www.bridgestone-firestone.com
Building Materials Mfr
S.I.C.: 3444
N.A.I.C.S.: 332322

Firestone Building Products Company, LLC - Salt Lake City Manufacturing Facility (3)
3790 W 2555 S
Salt Lake City, UT 84120
Tel.: (801) 972-6650
Fax: (801) 974-0205
Web Site: www.bridgestone-firestone.com
Emp.: 20
Insulation & Roofing Materials Mfr
S.I.C.: 3999
N.A.I.C.S.: 339999
Michael McCrea *(Mgr)*

Firestone Building Products Company, LLC - Tuscumbia Manufacturing Facility (3)
393 Denton Cir
Tuscumbia, AL 35674
Tel.: (256) 381-4001
Fax: (256) 314-1887
Roofing Construction Services
S.I.C.: 1761
N.A.I.C.S.: 238160

Firestone Building Products Company, LLC - Wellford Manufacturing Facility (3)
320 Innovation Way
Wellford, SC 29385-8900
Tel.: (864) 439-5641
Fax: (864) 439-5642
Web Site: www.bridgestone-firestone.com
Building Products Mfr
S.I.C.: 3271
N.A.I.C.S.: 327331

Firestone Building Products Company, LLC - Youngwood Manufacturing Facility (3)
Buncher Commerce Park Bldg 102 Ave A
Youngwood, PA 15697
Tel.: (724) 755-1100
Fax: (724) 755-0101
Web Site: www.bridgestone-firestone.com
Emp.: 40
Insulation Materials & Metal Sheet Mfr
S.I.C.: 3444
N.A.I.C.S.: 332322
Scott Thompson *(Mgr)*

Firestone Natural Rubber Company, LLC (2)
535 Marriott Dr
Nashville, TN 37214-0990
Tel.: (615) 937-1000
Fax: (615) 493-2744
E-Mail: donationcargo@firestonenaturalrubber.com
Web Site: www.firestonenaturalrubber.com
Rubber Products Mfr
S.I.C.: 3061
N.A.I.C.S.: 326291

Firestone Polymers, LLC (2)
381 W Wilbeth Rd
Akron, OH 44301
Tel.: (800) 282-0222
Fax: (330) 379-7875
E-Mail: info@firestonepolymers.com
Web Site: www.firesyn.com
Industrial Chemical Mfr
S.I.C.: 2819
N.A.I.C.S.: 325180
Theresa Graves *(Dir-R&D)*

Plants:

Firestone Polymers, LLC - Lake Charles Plant (3)
Hwy 108 S
Lake Charles, LA 70601
Tel.: (337) 882-1211
Fax: (337) 882-6051
Synthetic Rubber Mfr
S.I.C.: 2822

N.A.I.C.S.: 325212

Firestone Polymers, LLC - Orange Plant (3)
5713 Farm Rd 1006
Orange, TX 77630
Tel.: (409) 924-4500
Fax: (409) 924-4750
Synthetic Rubber Mfr
S.I.C.: 2822
N.A.I.C.S.: 325212

Non-U.S. Subsidiaries:

Bridgestone Canada, Inc. (2)
5770 Hurontario St Suite 400
Mississauga, ON, L5R 3G5, Canada
Tel.: (905) 890-1990
Fax: (905) 890-1991
Toll Free: (800) 267-1318
Web Site: www.bridgestone-firestone.ca
Emp.: 1,900
Automotive Tire Mfr & Distr
S.I.C.: 3011
N.A.I.C.S.: 326211

Bridgestone Chile, S.A. (2)
Avda Kennedy 5735 - Piso 12 - Of 1202
Las Condes, Santiago, Chile
Tel.: (56) 2 460 7200
Fax: (56) 2 460 7208
Web Site: www.bridgestone-firestone.com
Automobile Tire Distr
S.I.C.: 5014
N.A.I.C.S.: 423130

Bridgestone de Mexico, S.A.de C.V. (2)
Darwin 74 Col Anzures Del M Hidalgo
11590 Mexico, Mexico
Tel.: (52) 55 5626 6600
Fax: (52) 55 5254 4778
Web Site: www.bridgestone-firestone.com
Automobile Tire Mfr & Distr
S.I.C.: 3011
N.A.I.C.S.: 326211

Bridgestone Argentina S.A.I.C. (2)
Antartida Argentina 2715
Llavallol, 1836 Buenos Aires, Argentina Ar
Tel.: (54) 11 4231 3669 (100%)
Fax: (54) 11 4231 7337
Web Site: www.firestone.com.ar
Emp.: 1,000
Tires & Automotive Components Mfr & Sales
S.I.C.: 3011
N.A.I.C.S.: 326211

Bridgestone/Firestone Canada, Inc. (2)
5770 Hurontario St Ste 400
Mississauga, ON, L5R 3G5, Canada (100%)
Tel.: (905) 890-1990
Fax: (905) 890-1991
Web Site: www.bridgestone.ca
Emp.: 90
Tires & Automotive Components Sales
S.I.C.: 3011
N.A.I.C.S.: 326211
David Scheklesky *(Dir-Mktg)*

Bridgestone/Firestone Chile, S.A. (2)
Ave Kennedy 5735 12th Fl Ste 1202
Santiago, Chile (89.7%)
Tel.: (56) 24607200
Fax: (56) 24607208
E-Mail: pedidos@bridgestone.com
Web Site: www.bridgestone.cl
Emp.: 23
Tire Mfr & Sales
S.I.C.: 3011
N.A.I.C.S.: 326211
Sergio Naqashima *(Gen Mgr)*

Bridgestone/Firestone de Costa Rica, S.A. (2)
Km 11 Autopista General Canas La Ribera de Belen
Heredia, 4018, Costa Rica (98.6%)
Tel.: (506) 22097300
Fax: (506) 22097301
E-Mail: servicioalcliente@bfcr.co.cr
Web Site: www.bfcr.co.cr
Emp.: 1,000
Tire Mfr & Sales
S.I.C.: 3011
N.A.I.C.S.: 326211

Oscar Rodriguez *(Gen Mgr)*

Bridgestone/Firestone de Mexico, S.A. de C.V. (2)
Darwin 74 Col Anzures del Miguel Hidalgo
11590 Mexico, Mexico MX
Tel.: (52) 5556266600 (100%)
E-Mail: mpacheco@bfmx.com.mx
Web Site: www.bridgestone.com.mx
Emp.: 1,150
Tire Mfr & Sales
S.I.C.: 3011
N.A.I.C.S.: 326211
Miguel Pac200heco *(Mgr-Mktg)*

Bridgestone/Firestone do Brasil Industria e Comercio Ltda (2)
Av Queiroz dos Santos 1717
Bairro Casa Branca, 09015-901 Santo Andre, SP, Brazil (100%)
Tel.: (55) 44331666
Fax: (55) 49926655
E-Mail: central@bfbr.com.br
Web Site: www.bfbr.com.br
Emp.: 5,000
Tires & Automotive Components Mfr & Sales
S.I.C.: 3011
N.A.I.C.S.: 326211
Marcio Surlan *(Gen Mgr-Mktg)*

Bridgestone/Firestone Venezolana C.A. (2)
Carrera Valencia-Los Guayos
Valencia, Venezuela VE
Tel.: (58) 2418747758 (100%)
Fax: (58) 2418747989
E-Mail: info@bfvz.com
Web Site: www.bfvz.com
Emp.: 1,111
Tire Mfr & Sales
S.I.C.: 3011
N.A.I.C.S.: 326211
Carlos Mejias *(Gen & Pres)*

BRIDGESTONE OFF-THE-ROAD TIRE LATIN AMERICA S.A (2)
La Concepcion 322 Piso 7
PO Box 283-T
Santiago, Chile
Tel.: (56) 28989000
Fax: (56) 28989080
Web Site: www.bridgestone.com
Automotive Tire Mfr
S.I.C.: 3011
N.A.I.C.S.: 326211

BRIDGESTONE OFF-THE-ROAD TIRE PERU S.A.C (2)
Av Jorge Chavez 263 Office 402
Miraflores, Lima, 9, Peru
Tel.: (51) 1 612 6600
Fax: (51) 1 612 6610
Emp.: 16
Automotive Tire Distr
S.I.C.: 5014
N.A.I.C.S.: 423130
Takumi Sadohara *(Gen Mgr)*

Non-U.S. Plant:

Bridgestone do Brasil Industria e Comercio Ltda. - Sao Paulo Plant (2)
Av Queiros dos Santos 1717
Sao Paulo, Brazil 09015-901
Tel.: (55) 11 4433 1666
Fax: (55) 11 4433 1074
Automotive Tire Mfr
S.I.C.: 3011
N.A.I.C.S.: 326211

Bridgestone APM Company (1)
PO Box 1505
Findlay, OH 45839 (100%)
Tel.: (419) 423-9552
Fax: (419) 423-1232
Emp.: 25
Antivibration Components for Automobiles Mfr & Sales
S.I.C.: 2822
N.A.I.C.S.: 325212
Todd Hole *(Gen Mgr-HR)*

Firestone Metal Products Company, LLC (1)
1001 Lund Blvd
Anoka, MN 55303
Tel.: (800) 426-7737
Fax: (763) 576-9596
Metal Product Mfr
S.I.C.: 3499
N.A.I.C.S.: 332999

Plants:

Firestone Metal Products Company, LLC - Anoka Manufacturing Facility (2)
1001 Lund Blvd
Anoka, MN 55303
Tel.: (800) 426-7737
Fax: (763) 576-9596
Roofing Construction Services
S.I.C.: 1761
N.A.I.C.S.: 238160

Firestone Metal Products Company, LLC - College Park Manufacturing Facility (2)
3511 Naturally Fresh Blvd Ste 400
College Park, GA 30349
Tel.: (404) 974-3450
Fax: (404) 974-3455
Web Site: www.bridgestone-firestone.com
Metal Sheet, Roofing & Wall Panel Mfr
S.I.C.: 3444
N.A.I.C.S.: 332322
Jason Lakatos *(Mgr)*

Firestone Metal Products Company, LLC - Jackson Manufacturing Facility (2)
1085 Mendell Davis Dr
Jackson, MS 39272
Tel.: (800) 426-7737
Fax: (763) 576-9596
Construction Engineering Services
S.I.C.: 1629
N.A.I.C.S.: 237990

Firestone Metal Products Company, LLC - Las Vegas Manufacturing Facility (2)
4272 Corporate Ctr Dr
North Las Vegas, NV 89030
Tel.: (702) 880-8012
Fax: (702) 642-4538
Web Site: www.bridgestone-firestone.com
Metal Products Mfr
S.I.C.: 3499
N.A.I.C.S.: 332999

Firestone Metal Products Company, LLC - Warren Manufacturing Facility (2)
2050 Morrissey
Warren, MI 48091
Tel.: (888) 466-8833
Fax: (763) 576-9596
Web Site: www.bridgestone-firestone.com
Metal Sheet Mfr
S.I.C.: 3444
N.A.I.C.S.: 332322

Tires Plus Total Car Care (1)
2021 Sunnydale Blvd
Clearwater, FL 33765-1202 (64.4%)
Tel.: (727) 441-3727
Web Site: www.tiresplus.com
Emp.: 6,000
Tire Dealerships Operator; Automotive Repair
S.I.C.: 5014
N.A.I.C.S.: 441320
Stu Watterson *(Pres)*

Non-U.S. Subsidiaries:

Bridgestone Aircraft Tire Company (Asia) Limited (1)
22-24 Dai Wang Street
Tai Po Industrial Estate, Tai Po, China (Hong Kong) (100%)
Tel.: (852) 26648303
Fax: (852) 26647577
E-Mail: baa@bridgestone-baa.com
Web Site: www.bridgestone.com
Emp.: 25
Aircraft Tires Retread & Sales
S.I.C.: 3011
N.A.I.C.S.: 326211
Willy Cheng *(Gen Mgr)*

Bridgestone Aircraft tire Company (China) Limited (1)
180 Tashan Qingdao Economic & Technical Development Zone
266500 Qingdao, China
Tel.: (86) 532 8098 2990
Fax: (86) 532 8098 2977
Emp.: 88
Aircraft Tire Mfr
S.I.C.: 3728
N.A.I.C.S.: 336413

Bridgestone Asia Pacific Pte. Ltd. (1)
83 Clemenceau Avenue 11-05/08
Singapore, 239920, Singapore
Tel.: (65) 63039559
Fax: (65) 63039599
E-Mail: mediaenquiries@bridgestone.com.sg
Web Site: www.bridgestone-asiapacific.com
Emp.: 10
Automotive Tire Distr
S.I.C.: 5014
N.A.I.C.S.: 423130

Bridgestone Australia Ltd. (1)
Level 1 196 Greenhill Road
Eastwood, SA, 5063, Australia AU
Mailing Address: (60.3%)
GPO Box 2200
Adelaide, SA, 5001, Australia
Tel.: (61) 882060200
Telex: 82105
Fax: (61) 882060299
E-Mail: headoffice@bsal.com.au
Web Site: www.bridgestone.com.au
Emp.: 150
Tire Mfr & Sales
S.I.C.: 3011
N.A.I.C.S.: 326211
Shojiro Hara *(Chm & CEO)*
Dean J. Leech *(Sec)*

Subsidiary:

Bridgestone Earthmover Tyres Pty. Ltd. (2)
223 Rookwood Road
Yagoona, NSW, 2199, Australia (100%)
Tel.: (61) 297226111
Fax: (61) 297226199
E-Mail: businessplanning@bsem.com.au
Web Site: www.bridgestone-earthmover.com.au
Emp.: 35
Off-the-Road Tires Sales for Mining & Construction Vehicles
S.I.C.: 5014
N.A.I.C.S.: 441320
Takashi Yokoyama *(Mng Dir)*

Bridgestone Diversified Products (China) Co., Ltd. (1)
Rm 1016 Genway Bldg No 188 Wangdun Road Suzhou Industrial Park
Suzhou, Jiangsu, 215123, China
Tel.: (86) 512 6258 1088
Fax: (86) 512 6258 5808
E-Mail: Bsdc-sales@bsdc.bridgestone.com.cn
Conveyor Belt Mfr
S.I.C.: 3535
N.A.I.C.S.: 333922

Bridgestone Diversified Products East Co., Ltd. (1)
1201 Ilsin Bldg 541 Dohwa-dong
Mapo-gu, Seoul, 121-701, Korea (South)
Tel.: (82) 2 565 2048
Fax: (82) 2 3210 2488
E-Mail: info_kr@bridgestone-dpe.co.jp
Web Site: www.bridgestone-dpe.co.jp
Emp.: 2
Extruded Rubber Product Mfr
S.I.C.: 3061
N.A.I.C.S.: 326291
Yonggi Cho *(Gen Mgr)*

Bridgestone Diversified Products East Co., Ltd. (1)
6F-2 No 41 Nanking W Rd
Taipei, Taiwan
Tel.: (886) 2 2556 3459
Fax: (886) 2 2556 3487
E-Mail: info_tw@bridgestone-dpe.co.jp
Web Site: www.bridgestone.com
Conveyor Belt Mfr
S.I.C.: 3535
N.A.I.C.S.: 333922

Bridgestone Engineered Products of Asia, Sdn Bhd. (1)
L1-E-3B Enterprise 4 Lebuhraya
Puchong-Sg Besi
Bukit Jalil, 57000 Kuala Lumpur, Malaysia

Bridgestone Corporation—(Continued)

Tel.: (60) 3 8996 2670
Fax: (60) 3 8996 2690
E-Mail: info@bridgestone.com.my
Emp.: 4
Conveyor Belt Mfr
S.I.C.: 3535
N.A.I.C.S.: 333922
Bukhary Yaakub *(Dir-Fin)*

Bridgestone Europe NV/SA (1)
Kleine Kloosterstraat 10
1932 Zaventem, Belgium BE
Tel.: (32) 27146700 (100%)
Fax: (32) 27146709
E-Mail: reception.bseu@bridgestone-eu.com
Web Site: www.bridgestone-eu.com
Emp.: 400
Holding Company
S.I.C.: 6719
N.A.I.C.S.: 551112
Eduardo Minardi *(Chm)*
Toru Tsuda *(Pres & CEO)*

Subsidiary:

Bridgestone Aircraft Tire (Europe) S.A. (2)
Route de Bavay
Frameries, 7080, Belgium (100%)
Tel.: (32) 65673761
Fax: (32) 32065678104
Web Site: www.bridgestone-eu.com
Aircraft Tires Retread & Sales
S.I.C.: 5014
N.A.I.C.S.: 441320
Mac Ohashi *(Pres & CEO)*
Vancromerugge Thierry *(Pres)*

Non-U.S. Subsidiaries:

B. GJERDE (2)
Jerikoveien 22
1067 Oslo, Norway
Tel.: (47) 2 230 6577
Fax: (47) 2 232 0550
Automobile Tire Mfr
S.I.C.: 3011
N.A.I.C.S.: 326211

Bridgestone Benelux B.V. (2)
Distriboulevard 15
NL 4761-RZ Moerdijk, Netherlands (100%)
Tel.: (31) 168385110
Fax: (31) 168385111
E-Mail: bs-netherlands@bridgestone.eu
Web Site: www.bridgestone.eu
Emp.: 60
Tire Sales
S.I.C.: 5014
N.A.I.C.S.: 441320
Peter Van-der-Wal *(Gen Mgr)*

BRIDGESTONE DENMARK A/S (2)
Sigma 1 Soften
8382 Hinnerup, Denmark
Tel.: (45) 8764 6664
Fax: (45) 8764 6665
E-Mail: dk@bridgestone.eu
Automotive Tire Mfr
S.I.C.: 3011
N.A.I.C.S.: 326211

Bridgestone Deutschland GmbH (2)
Du Pont Strasse 1
61352 Bad Homburg, Germany De
Tel.: (49) 617240801 (100%)
Fax: (49) 6172408490
E-Mail: contect@bridgestone.de
Web Site: www.bridgestone.de
Emp.: 300
Tire & Automotive Component Sales
S.I.C.: 5014
N.A.I.C.S.: 441320
Des Collins *(VP-Sls-Mktg)*

BRIDGESTONE FINLAND Oy (2)
Korpivaarantie 1
01450 Vantaa, Finland
Tel.: (358) 9 8578 61
Fax: (358) 9 8578 6251
E-Mail: contact.finland@bridgestone-eu.com
Emp.: 20
Automotive Tire Mfr
S.I.C.: 3011
N.A.I.C.S.: 326211

Bridgestone France S.A. (2)
Parc d Activities du Moulin de Massy
23 Rue du Saule Trapu, 91882 Massy, Cedex, France (100%)
Tel.: (33) 169192700
Fax: (33) 169192701
E-Mail: contact.bsfr@bridgestone.eu
Web Site: www.bridgestone-eu.com
Sales Range: $150-199.9 Million
Emp.: 50
Tires & Automotive Parts Mfr & Sales
S.I.C.: 3011
N.A.I.C.S.: 326211

Plant:

Bridgestone France S.A.S - Bethune Plant (3)
575 Avenue George Washington
Boite Postale 3
62401 Bethune, France
Tel.: (33) 3 21 64 78 60
Fax: (33) 3 64 77 31
E-Mail:
Emp.: 130
Automotive Tire Mfr
S.I.C.: 3011
N.A.I.C.S.: 326211
Bruno Capron *(Mng Dir)*

Bridgestone Hispania S.A. (2)
St Islagraciosi no 3 1st Fl
028703 Madrid, Spain ES
Tel.: (34) 916233023 (99.7%)
Fax: (34) 916230044
Web Site: www.bridgestone.eu
Emp.: 4,500
Tire Mfr & Sales
S.I.C.: 3011
N.A.I.C.S.: 326211
Thomas Zumarraga *(Mng Dir)*

Plants:

Bridgestone Hispania S.A - Bilbao Plant (3)
Apartado 406
48080 Bilbao, Spain
Tel.: (34) 94 448 50 00
Fax: (34) 94 448 57 14
Automotive Tire Mfr
S.I.C.: 3011
N.A.I.C.S.: 326211
Kepa Hernandez *(Mgr)*

Bridgestone Hispania S.A - Burgos Plant (3)
Apartado 300
9080 Burgos, Spain
Tel.: (34) 947 479 800
Fax: (34) 947 479 822
Web Site: www.bridgestone.eu
Emp.: 130
Automotive Tire Mfr
S.I.C.: 3011
N.A.I.C.S.: 326211
Camilla Sjodahl *(Gen Mgr)*

Bridgestone Hispania S.A - Puente San Miguel Plant (3)
Apartado 4 - Puente San Miguel
Torrelavega, 39530, Spain
Tel.: (34) 94 281 25 00
Fax: (34) 94 281 25 60
Emp.: 50
Automotive Tire Mfr
S.I.C.: 3011
N.A.I.C.S.: 326211
Adolfo Llorens *(Plant Mgr)*

Bridgestone Industrial Ltd. (2)
2nd Fl W CP House 97-107 Uxbridge Rd
London, W55 TL, United Kingdom (100%)
Tel.: (44) 2085678080
Fax: (44) 2085672066
E-Mail: info@bsil.co.uk
Web Site: www.info.bsil.co.uk
Emp.: 11
Engineered Rubber Products Sales
S.I.C.: 2394
N.A.I.C.S.: 314910

BRIDGESTONE IRELAND Ltd. (2)
Unit 10 Fingal Bay Business Park
Balbriggan
Dublin, Ireland
Tel.: (353) 1 84100
Fax: (353) 1 8415245
E-Mail: ireland@bridgestone-eu.com
Web Site: www.bridgestone.ie
Emp.: 5
Automotive Tire Distr
S.I.C.: 5014
N.A.I.C.S.: 423130
Pat Curran *(Mng Dir)*

Bridgestone Italia S.p.A. (2)
Via delle Margherite 40
Zona Industriale, I-70026 Modugno, BA, Italy IT
Tel.: (39) 0805063111 (100%)
Fax: (39) 0805063333
Web Site: www.bridgestone-eu.com
Emp.: 1,060
Tire Mfr & Sales
S.I.C.: 3011
N.A.I.C.S.: 326211

Bridgestone Nederland B.V. (2)
Distriboulevard 15
4761 RZ Moerdijk, Netherlands
Tel.: (31) 168 38 51 10
Fax: (31) 168 38 51 11
Automotive Tire Mfr
S.I.C.: 3011
N.A.I.C.S.: 326211

Bridgestone Portugal Lda. (2)
Urbanizacao do Passil Lote 96 A
2890-118 Alcochete, Portugal (100%)
Tel.: (351) 212307350
Fax: (351) 212307391
E-Mail: info@bridgestone.com
Web Site: www.bridgestone.eu
Emp.: 64
Tire Sales
S.I.C.: 5014
N.A.I.C.S.: 441320
Jose Barroco *(Mng Dir)*

Bridgestone Poznan Sp. z.o.o. (2)
Ul Baltycka 65
61-017 Poznan, Poland
Tel.: (48) 61 873 40 22
Fax: (48) 61 873 40 11
E-Mail: poz@bridgestone.eu
Emp.: 1,500
Automotive Tire Mfr
S.I.C.: 3011
N.A.I.C.S.: 326211
Piotr Kozlowski *(Plant Mgr)*

Subsidiary:

Bridgestone Stargard Sp. z.o.o (3)
Ul Most Kamienny 7
73-110 Stargard Szczecinski, Poland
Tel.: (48) 91 472 34 00
Fax: (48) 91 472 31 01
Emp.: 60
Automotive Tire Mfr
S.I.C.: 3011
N.A.I.C.S.: 326211
Hiroyuki Ozaki *(Gen Mgr)*

Bridgestone Romania S.R.L. (2)
Dacia Blvd No 153-155 Floor 3 Section S2
District 2, Bucharest, 202065, Romania
Tel.: (40) 21 210 21 79
Fax: (40) 21 210 21
E-Mail: contact.romania@bridgestone.eu
Emp.: 8
Automotive Tire Mfr
S.I.C.: 3011
N.A.I.C.S.: 326211
Andy Davies *(Mng Dir)*

Bridgestone Slovakia s.r.o. (2)
Michalska 9
811 01 Bratislava, Slovakia
Tel.: (421) 220 633 218
Fax: (421) 220 633 219
E-Mail: objednavke@bridgestone.eu
Web Site: www.bridgestone.eu
Emp.: 3
Automotive Tire Distr
S.I.C.: 5014
N.A.I.C.S.: 423130
Mitchell Palas *(Mgr-Slovakia & Czech)*

Bridgestone Sweden AB (2)
Box 9074
S-850 09 Sundsvall, Sweden (100%)
Tel.: (46) 60515200
Fax: (46) 60566121
Web Site: www.bridgestone.se
Emp.: 41
Tire Sales
S.I.C.: 5014
N.A.I.C.S.: 441320

Bridgestone U.K. Ltd. (2)
Athena Drive Tachbrook Park
Warwick, CV34 6UX, United Kingdom (100%)
Tel.: (44) 1926488500
Fax: (44) 1926488600
E-Mail: info@bridgestone.eu
Web Site: www.bridgestone.eu
Emp.: 150
Tire & Automotive Component Sales
S.I.C.: 5014
N.A.I.C.S.: 441320
John McNaught *(Mng Dir)*

Bridgestone India Private Limited (1)
Plot No 12 Kheda Growth Centre Post Sagore
Pithampur, Dhar, Madhya Pradesh, 454 774, India
Tel.: (91) 7292 423333
Fax: (91) 7292 255039
E-Mail: customer-care@bridgestone.co.in
Web Site: www.bridgestone.co.in
Emp.: 900
Automobile Tire Mfr
S.I.C.: 3011
N.A.I.C.S.: 326211
H. Tanigawa *(Mng Dir)*

Bridgestone Middle East & Africa FZE. (1)
Jebel Ali Free Zone
PO Box 16813
Dubai, United Arab Emirates
Tel.: (971) 4 8833933
Fax: (971) 4 8833978
Web Site: www.bridgestone-mea.com
Emp.: 90
Automotive Tire Distr
S.I.C.: 5014
N.A.I.C.S.: 423130
Sakuma Sakuma *(Pres)*

Bridgestone Natural Rubber (Thailand) Co., Ltd. (1)
129/2 Moo 3
Songkhla, 90120, Thailand
Tel.: (66) 74456111
Fax: (66) 74456060
Industrial Rubber Mfr
S.I.C.: 3069
N.A.I.C.S.: 326299

Bridgestone New Zealand Ltd. (1)
40 Paisley Place
Mount Wellington, Auckland, New Zealand (100%)
Tel.: (64) 9195300
Fax: (64) 99195304
E-Mail: information@bridgestone.co.nz
Web Site: www.bridgestone.co.nz
Emp.: 750
Tire Mfr & Sales
S.I.C.: 3011
N.A.I.C.S.: 326211
Heath Barclay *(Mgr-Mktg)*

Bridgestone Singapore Pte. Ltd. (1)
16 Raffles Quay Ste 32-02 Hong Leong Bldg
Singapore, 048581, Singapore (100%)
Tel.: (65) 62202811
Fax: (65) 62245218
Web Site: www.bridgestone.com
Emp.: 30
Natural Rubber Whslr
S.I.C.: 5199
N.A.I.C.S.: 424990

Bridgestone South Africa Holdings (Pty) Ltd. (1)
PO Box 515
1600 Isando, South Africa (93.7%)
Tel.: (27) 119237500
Fax: (27) 113924710
E-Mail: info@bridgestone.co.za
Web Site: www.bridgestone.co.za
Emp.: 2,000
Tire Mfr & Sales
S.I.C.: 3011
N.A.I.C.S.: 326211

Bridgestone Taiwan Co., Ltd. (1)
1 Chuang Ching Rd
Hsinchu Industrial Zone, Hsin-chu, 303, Taiwan TW
Tel.: (886) 35981621 (80%)
Telex: 20352
Fax: (886) 35981888
E-Mail: bridgestone@mail.bridgestone.com.tw
Web Site: www.bridgestone.com.tw
Emp.: 400

Tire Mfr & Sales
S.I.C.: 3011
N.A.I.C.S.: 326211

Bridgestone Tire Manufacturing (Thailand) Co., Ltd. (1)
700/622 Moo 4 Amata Nakorn Industrial Estate Phan Thong
Chon Buri, 20160, Thailand
Tel.: (66) 3821030001
Fax: (66) 38210302
Automobile Tire Mfr
S.I.C.: 3011
N.A.I.C.S.: 326211

BRIDGESTONE TYRE SALES SINGAPORE PTE. LTD. (1)
10 Science Park Road 02-08 The Alpha
Singapore, 117684, Singapore
Tel.: (65) 6777 4181
Fax: (65) 6777 3493
Web Site: www.bridgestone.com.sg
Emp.: 2
Automotive Tire Distr
S.I.C.: 5014
N.A.I.C.S.: 423130
Shinsuke Nomura *(Mng Dir)*

BRIDGESTONE TYRES (P.N.G) PTY. LTD (1)
Milfordhaven Road
PO Box 459
Lae, Morobe, 411, Papua New Guinea
Tel.: (675) 472 1822
Fax: (675) 472 6436
Emp.: 15
Automobile Tire Distr
S.I.C.: 5014
N.A.I.C.S.: 423130
Jon Seeto *(Gen Mgr)*

PT. Bridgestone Engineered Products Indonesia (1)
Wisma Slipi 12th Floor Jl Let Jend S Parman Kav 12
Jakarta, 11480, Indonesia
Tel.: (62) 21 5366 1971
Fax: (62) 21 5366 1975
E-Mail: bseain_sales@bsea-in.com
Emp.: 2
Conveyor Belt Distr
S.I.C.: 5085
N.A.I.C.S.: 423840
Herman Gunawan *(Mgr-Sls)*

P.T. Bridgestone Tire Indonesia (1)
18th Fl Wisma Nusantara Bldg Jalan MH Thamrin 59
Jakarta, 10350, Indonesia (51%)
Tel.: (62) 213900909
Fax: (62) 2131936345
Web Site: www.bridgestone.co.id
Emp.: 1,300
Tire Mfr & Sales
S.I.C.: 3011
N.A.I.C.S.: 326211

Thai Bridgestone Co., Ltd. (1)
16th Fl Abdulrahim Pl
10500 Bangkok, Thailand TH
Tel.: (66) 26361505 (67.2%)
Telex: 82809
Fax: (66) 26361543
E-Mail: webadmin@bridgestone.co.th
Web Site: www.bridgestone.co.th
Emp.: 165
Tire Mfr & Sales
S.I.C.: 3011
N.A.I.C.S.: 326211

Non-U.S. Joint Venture:

Brisa Bridgestone Sabanci Lastik Sanayi ve Ticaret A.S. (1)
Alikahya
41220 Kocaeli, Turkey TR
Tel.: (90) 2623164000
Fax: (90) 2623164040
E-Mail: brisa.info@brisa.com.tr
Web Site: www.brisa.com.tr
Emp.: 1,300
Tire Mfr & Distr; Owned 42.9% by Bridgestone Corporation & 57.1% by Haci Omer Sabanci Holding S.A.
S.I.C.: 3011
N.A.I.C.S.: 326211

BRIDGETEC CORP.

14-15F Korea teacher pension B/D
27 Yeouinaru-Ro
Youngdeungpo-Gu, Seoul, Korea (South) 150-742
Tel.: (82) 2 3430 4114
Fax: (82) 2 564 9980
E-Mail: sales@bridgetec.co.kr
Web Site: www.bridgetec.co.kr
Year Founded: 1999
064480—(KRS)
Business Description:
Software Development Services
S.I.C.: 7371
N.A.I.C.S.: 541511
Personnel:
Sang Ho Lee *(CEO)*

BRIERTY LIMITED

Level 2 72 Melville Parad
South Perth, WA, 6151, Australia
Mailing Address:
Locked Bag 2001
South Perth, WA, 6951, Australia
Tel.: (61) 8 9267 8000
Fax: (61) 3 0073 5152
E-Mail: info@brierty.com.au
Web Site: www.brierty.com.au
BYL—(ASX)
Rev.: $304,726,862
Assets: $157,726,472
Liabilities: $103,000,513
Net Worth: $54,725,960
Earnings: $10,641,038
Emp.: 532
Fiscal Year-end: 06/30/13
Business Description:
Transport Infrastructure
S.I.C.: 3792
N.A.I.C.S.: 336214
Personnel:
Peter McBain *(Mng Dir)*
Ian Sydney *(CFO)*
John Sicard *(Sec)*
Board of Directors:
Dalton Leslie Gooding
Alan Robert Brierty
Ken Hellsten
Peter McBain
Richard O'Shannassy
Legal Counsel:
Clifford Chance
Level 7 190 St George's Terrace
Perth, Australia

BRIGADE ENTERPRISES LTD.

29th & 30th Floors World Trade Center Brigade Gateway Campus
26/1 Dr Rajkumar Road, Bengaluru, 560 055, India
Tel.: (91) 8041379200
Fax: (91) 8022210784
E-Mail: enquiry@brigadegroup.com
Web Site: www.brigadegroup.com
532929—(BOM)
Rev.: $154,736,694
Assets: $5,481,443,700
Liabilities: $3,224,106,000
Net Worth: $2,257,337,700
Earnings: $11,127,708
Emp.: 424
Fiscal Year-end: 03/31/13
Business Description:
Property Developers
S.I.C.: 8711
N.A.I.C.S.: 541330
Personnel:
M. R. Jaishankar *(Chm & Mng Dir)*
K. Suresh *(CFO)*
P. Om Prakash *(Sec)*
Board of Directors:
M. R. Jaishankar
M. R. Gurumurthy
P. V. Maiya
K. R. S. Murthy
Githa Shankar
M. R. Shivram
P. M. Thampi
Transfer Agent:
Karvy Computershare Private Limited
Plot No 17 to 24 Vittalrao Nagar Madhapur
Hyderabad, India

BRIGADIER GOLD LIMITED

200 Front Street West Suite 2300
Toronto, ON, M5V 1RS, Canada
Tel.: (416) 410-7956
Fax: (905) 707-1520
E-Mail: info@brigadiergold.com
Web Site: www.brigadiergold.com
BRG—(TSXV)
Assets: $89,085
Liabilities: $232,891
Net Worth: ($143,806)
Earnings: ($1,852,329)
Fiscal Year-end: 12/31/12
Business Description:
Gold Exploration Services
S.I.C.: 1041
N.A.I.C.S.: 212221
Personnel:
Grant Hall *(Pres & CEO)*
Herb Kokotow *(CFO & Treas)*
Board of Directors:
William J. Dynes
Grant Hall
Denis Hayes
Herb Kokotow
Alick Ryder
Legal Counsel:
Davis LLP
1 First Canadian Pl Suite 6000 PO Box 367
100 King St West
Toronto, ON, Canada
Transfer Agent:
Equity Financial Trust Company
200 University Avenue Suite 400
Toronto, ON, Canada

BRIGHOLME INTERIORS GROUP

4118 14th Avenue
Markham, ON, L3R 0J3, Canada
Tel.: (905) 475-0043
Fax: (905) 475-3390
Toll Free: (888) 822-3111
E-Mail: inquiry@brigholme.com
Web Site: www.brigholme.com
Year Founded: 1961
Sales Range: $10-24.9 Million
Emp.: 35
Business Description:
Household & Industrial Furniture Mfr
S.I.C.: 2512
N.A.I.C.S.: 337121
Personnel:
Ralph Wilson *(Owner)*
Joe Williams *(Pres)*

BRIGHT FOOD (GROUP) CO., LTD.

No 7 Lane 263 Huashan Road
Shanghai, China
Tel.: (86) 21 6247 4500
Fax: (86) 21 6247 3474
Web Site: www.brightfood.com
Year Founded: 2006
Business Description:
Holding Company; Diversified Food Mfr
S.I.C.: 6719
N.A.I.C.S.: 551112
Personnel:
Zongnan Wang *(Chm)*
Shu Min Cao *(Pres & CEO)*

Subsidiary:

Bright Dairy & Food Co., Ltd. (1)
578 Wuzhong Road
Shanghai, 201103, China
Tel.: (86) 21 54584520
Fax: (86) 21 64013337
E-Mail: brightdairy@brightdairy.com
Web Site: www.brightdairy.com
600597—(SHG)
Emp.: 2,594
Development, Production & Sales of Milk & Dairy Products
S.I.C.: 2026
N.A.I.C.S.: 311511
Benheng Guo *(Pres)*

Non-U.S. Subsidiary:

Weetabix Limited (2)
Weetabix Mills
Burton Latimer, Kettering, Northants, NN15 5JR, United Kingdom UK
Tel.: (44) 1536722181 (60%)
Fax: (44) 1536726148
Web Site: www.weetabix.co.uk
Sales Range: $700-749.9 Million
Emp.: 1,800
Cereal Mfr
Export
S.I.C.: 2043
N.A.I.C.S.: 311230
Giles Turrell *(CEO)*

U.S. Subsidiary:

The Weetabix Company, Inc. (3)
300 Nickerson Rd
Marlborough, MA 01752
Tel.: (508) 683-3600
Fax: (978) 365-7268
Web Site: www.weetabixusa.com
Emp.: 240
Cereal Mfr
S.I.C.: 2043
N.A.I.C.S.: 311230
Richard Cachion *(VP-Sls)*

Non-U.S. Subsidiary:

Weetabix of Canada Limited (3)
N Industrial Park
PO Box 2020
Cobourg, ON, K9A 5P5, Canada
Tel.: (905) 372-5441
Fax: (905) 372-7261
Web Site: www.weetabix.ca
Emp.: 200
Cereal Mfr
S.I.C.: 2043
N.A.I.C.S.: 311230
Teresa Owen *(Mgr-HR)*

Affiliates:

Shanghai Haibo Co., Ltd. (1)
829 Yishan Road
Shanghai, 200233, China
Tel.: (86) 2161132800
Fax: (86) 2161132878
E-Mail: hbgf@hb600708.com
Web Site: www.hb600708.com
600708—(SHG)
Sales Range: $1-4.9 Billion
Emp.: 12,768
Rental Car Services
S.I.C.: 7514
N.A.I.C.S.: 532111
Guowei Zhuang *(Chm)*
Zhongxin Chen *(Vice Chm)*
Yuping Tang *(Pres)*

Shanghai Maling Aquarius Co., Ltd. (1)
400 North Road
Shanghai, 200082, China
Tel.: (86) 21 65957558
Fax: (86) 21 65452699
Web Site: www.shanghaimaling.com
600073—(SHG)
Sales Range: $300-349.9 Million
Meat, Fish, Fruits & Vegetables Processing & Distribution
S.I.C.: 5146
N.A.I.C.S.: 311612
Haiming Zhou *(Chm)*

Non-U.S. Subsidiary:

Manassen Foods Australia Pty. Ltd. (1)
8 Interchange Drive
Eastern Creek, NSW, 2766, Australia
Tel.: (61) 2 9421 3100

Bright Food (Group) Co., Ltd.—(Continued)

Fax: (61) 94213101
E-Mail: enquiries@manassen.com.au
Web Site: www.manassen.com.au
Emp.: 10
Grocery Product Distr
S.I.C.: 5149
N.A.I.C.S.: 424490
Fernando Arnedo *(CEO)*

BRIGHT LED ELECTRONICS CORP.

3F No 19 H-Ping Rd
Panchiao, Taipei, Taiwan
Tel.: (886) 229591090
Fax: (886) 229547006
E-Mail: services@brtled.com
Web Site: www.brtled.com
3031—(TAI)
Sales Range: $75-99.9 Million

Business Description:
Light Emitting Diode Mfr
S.I.C.: 3674
N.A.I.C.S.: 334413

Personnel:
Sandy Lian *(Pres)*

Non-U.S. Subsidiaries:

Bright LED Europe GmbH (1)
Sven Hedin Str 11
28211 Bremen, Germany
Tel.: (49) 4212428793
Fax: (49) 4213365341
Web Site: www.brtled.com
Light Emitting Diode Products Distr
S.I.C.: 5065
N.A.I.C.S.: 423690
Frank Muller *(Owner)*

Mainbright Enterprises Ltd. (1)
Unit 5 11F Hung Tai Ind Building 37-39 Hung To Road
Kwun Tong, Kowloon, China (Hong Kong)
Tel.: (852) 27979568
Fax: (852) 23416439
E-Mail: brtledhk@biznetvigator.com
Light Emitting Diode Mfr & Distr
S.I.C.: 3674
N.A.I.C.S.: 334413

Non-U.S. Plant:

Bright Led Electronics Corp. - China Factory (1)
No 8 Gaolong East Road
Gao Bu Town, Dongguan, Guang Dong, 523000, China
Tel.: (86) 76988731855
Fax: (86) 769 88733355
Light Emitting Diode Mfr
S.I.C.: 3679
N.A.I.C.S.: 334419

BRIGHT ORIENT (HOLDING) LTD.

133 Xiangnan Road
Nanshan, Shenzhen, China
Tel.: (86) 755 2640 2448
Fax: (86) 755 2640 2350
E-Mail: bohl@bohl.com.cn
Web Site: www.bohl.com.cn
5DT—(SES)
Sales Range: $50-74.9 Million
Emp.: 1,380

Business Description:
Garments & Textile Related Products Mfr & Distr
S.I.C.: 2399
N.A.I.C.S.: 315990

Personnel:
Jian Jun Du *(Chm, Pres & Mng Dir)*
Hong Cheng *(CFO)*
Beng Hong Ong *(Sec)*

Transfer Agent:
BACS Private Limited
63 Cantonment Rd
Singapore, 089758, Singapore
Tel.: (65) 323 6200

BRIGHT PACKAGING INDUSTRY BERHAD

No 23 Jalan Delima 1/3 Subang Hi-Tech Industrial Park
40000 Shah Alam, Selangor, Malaysia
Tel.: (60) 356351949
Fax: (60) 356351984
E-Mail: marketing@brightpack.net
Web Site: www.brightpack.net
BRIGHT—(KLS)
Rev.: $17,123,880
Assets: $17,652,523
Liabilities: $2,324,654
Net Worth: $15,327,868
Earnings: $2,266,030
Fiscal Year-end: 08/31/13

Business Description:
Aluminum Foil Packaging Materials Mfr
S.I.C.: 3353
N.A.I.C.S.: 331315

Personnel:
Mustapha Muhamad *(Chm)*
Hong Peng Ang *(Co-Sec)*
Wei Fong Wong *(Co-Sec)*

Board of Directors:
Mustapha Muhamad
Ali Abbas Alhabshee
Lay Chieng Ang
Jun Fei Lye
Wee Keat Tee
Siew Lee Yeong

BRIGHT SMART SECURITIES & COMMODITIES GROUP LIMITED

10th Floor Wing On House 71 Des Voeux Road
Central, China (Hong Kong)
Tel.: (852) 25371371
Fax: (852) 25378031
E-Mail: online@bsgroup.com.hk
Web Site: www.bsgroup.com.hk
1428—(HKG)
Sls.: $35,239,550
Assets: $410,912,005
Liabilities: $313,235,513
Net Worth: $97,676,492
Earnings: $11,892,563
Emp.: 245
Fiscal Year-end: 03/31/13

Business Description:
Securities & Commodities Brokerage Services
S.I.C.: 6211
N.A.I.C.S.: 523120

Personnel:
Peter Mow Lum Yip *(Chm)*
Nelson Kai Fung Chan *(CEO)*
Jacquelyn Wing Yan Yip *(Mng Dir)*
Priscilla Wan Mei Li *(CFO)*
Kwan Pak Chan *(Sec)*

Board of Directors:
Peter Mow Lum Yip
Nelson Kai Fung Chan
Wilson Wing Shing Chan
Francis Sze Chi Kwok
Joseph Kwok Fai Ling
Wai Sun Szeto
Yun Kong Yu

Legal Counsel:
K&L Gates LLP
44/F., Edinburgh Tower, 15 Queen's Road.
Central, China (Hong Kong)

Appleby
8th Floor, Bank of America Tower, 12 Harcourt Road
Central, China (Hong Kong)

Appleby Trust (Cayman) Ltd.
Clifton House 75 Fort Street
PO Box 1350
Grand Cayman, Cayman Islands

Transfer Agent:
Appleby Trust (Cayman) Ltd.
Clifton House 75 Fort Street
PO Box 1350
Grand Cayman, Cayman Islands

BRIGHTHOUSE GROUP PLC.

5 Hercules Way Leavesden Park
Watford, WD25 7GS, United Kingdom
Tel.: (44) 1923 488200
Fax: (44) 1923 488202
E-Mail: investor.relations@brighthouse.co.uk
Web Site: www.brighthouse.co.uk
Year Founded: 1994
Sales Range: $400-449.9 Million
Emp.: 2,285

Business Description:
Household Product Whslr
S.I.C.: 5064
N.A.I.C.S.: 423620

Personnel:
Leo McKee *(CEO)*

BRIGHTLITE NOMINEES PROPRIETARY LIMITED

5 Bastow Place
Mulgrave, VIC, 3170, Australia
Tel.: (61) 395690911
Fax: (61) 385611566
E-Mail: recption@beaconlighting.com.au
Web Site: www.beaconlighting.com.au
Sales Range: $50-74.9 Million
Emp.: 500

Business Description:
Outdoor Lighting Fixtures Mfr
S.I.C.: 3645
N.A.I.C.S.: 335121

Personnel:
Ian Robinson *(CEO)*

BRIGHTOIL PETROLEUM HOLDINGS LIMITED

33F 118 Connaught Road West
Hong Kong, China (Hong Kong)
Tel.: (852) 28343188
Fax: (852) 28343938
E-Mail: inquiry@bwoil.hk
Web Site: www.bwoil.com
0933—(HKG)
Rev.: $7,150,124,436
Assets: $2,489,061,115
Liabilities: $1,599,689,741
Net Worth: $889,371,374
Earnings: ($93,056,767)
Emp.: 330
Fiscal Year-end: 06/30/13

Business Description:
Fuel oil Sales
S.I.C.: 5171
N.A.I.C.S.: 424710

Personnel:
Kwong Lam Sit *(Founder, Chm & CEO)*
Danny Yih Lin Tan *(CFO)*
Wa Ying Cheung *(Sec)*

Board of Directors:
Kwong Lam Sit
Hsin Kang Chang
Zhujiang Dai
Chan Lam Kwong
Hon Chuen Lau
Justin Sawdon Stewart Murphy
Danny Yih Lin Tan
Bo Tang

MUFG Fund Services (Bermuda) Limited
26 Burnaby Street
Hamilton, Bermuda

BRIGHTON MINING GROUP LIMITED

34 Charles Street
PO Box 742
South Perth, WA, 6151, Australia
Tel.: (61) 8 9368 1200
Fax: (61) 8 9474 1333
E-Mail: info@brightonmininggroup.com.au
Web Site: www.brightonmininggroup.com.au
BTN—(ASX)
Assets: $6,310,784
Liabilities: $2,560,457
Net Worth: $3,750,326
Earnings: ($1,330,812)
Fiscal Year-end: 06/30/13

Business Description:
Gold Mining Services
S.I.C.: 1041
N.A.I.C.S.: 212221

Personnel:
Jonathan Remta *(Mng Dir)*
Michael Cooper *(Sec)*

Board of Directors:
Peter Remta
Jonathan Remta
Kim Thomas

BRIGHTSIDE GROUP PLC

MMT Centre Severn Bridge
Aust, Bristol, Avon, BS35 4BL, United Kingdom
Tel.: (44) 1454 635860
Fax: (44) 1454 634187
E-Mail: info@brightsidegroup.co.uk
Web Site: www.brightsidegroup.co.uk
BRT—(LSE)
Rev.: $144,095,999
Assets: $217,908,855
Liabilities: $91,339,816
Net Worth: $126,569,038
Earnings: $20,031,714
Emp.: 971
Fiscal Year-end: 12/31/12

Business Description:
Financial Services
S.I.C.: 6282
N.A.I.C.S.: 523930

Personnel:
Martyn Holman *(CEO)*
David Herrmann *(Compliance Officer & Sec)*
Alan Sanderson *(CEO-Insurance Broking Div)*

Board of Directors:
Christopher Fay
Paul Chase-Gardener
Martyn Holman
Helen Molyneux
Stuart Palmer
Julian Telling

Legal Counsel:
Manches LLP
Aldwych House 81 Aldwych
London, United Kingdom

Subsidiaries:

Group Direct Limited (1)
MMT Ctr Severn Bridge
Aust, Bristol, BS35 4BL, United Kingdom
Tel.: (44) 1454636807
Fax: (44) 1452190532
E-Mail: enquiries@cvd-insurance.co.uk
Sls.: $42,921,000
Emp.: 500
Management Services
S.I.C.: 8741
N.A.I.C.S.: 551114

Subsidiaries:

Commercial Vehicle Direct Insurance Services Ltd (2)
MMT Ctr Severn Bridge
Aust, Bristol, BS35 4BL, United Kingdom
Tel.: (44) 8452190604

Fax: (44) 8452190515
E-Mail: enquiries@cvd-insurance.co.uk
Web Site: www.cvd-insurance.co.uk
Vehicle Insurance Services
S.I.C.: 6351
N.A.I.C.S.: 524126
Arron Banks *(Co-Founder)*
John Gannon *(Co-Founder)*
David Herrmann *(Sec)*

Panacea Finance Limited (2)
MMT Ctr Severn Bridge
Aust, Bristol, BS35 4BL, United Kingdom
Tel.: (44) 8452190530
Fax: (44) 1454634585
E-Mail: customerservice@panaceafinance.co.uk
Web Site: www.panaceafinance.co.uk
Emp.: 30
Customized Financial Services
S.I.C.: 6726
N.A.I.C.S.: 525990
Simon Pearce *(Mng Dir)*

Injury QED Limited (1)
Ground Fl Helmont House Churchill Way
Cardiff, Wales, CF10 2HE, United Kingdom
Tel.: (44) 8454819950
Fax: (44) 845 481 0845
E-Mail: mail@injuryqed.co.uk
Web Site: www.injuryqed.co.uk
Emp.: 25
Medico Legal Reporting Services
S.I.C.: 8071
N.A.I.C.S.: 621512
Neil Startup *(Dir-Ops)*

BRIGHTTALK LIMITED

16 St Martins Le Grand
London, EC1A 4EN, United Kingdom
Tel.: (44) 2073978533
Fax: (44) 2073978400
E-Mail: support@brighttalk.com
Web Site: www.brighttalk.com
Year Founded: 2002
Sales Range: $10-24.9 Million
Emp.: 50
Business Description:
Online Event Solutions
S.I.C.: 7372
N.A.I.C.S.: 511210
Personnel:
Charlie Blackburn *(Chm, Co-Founder & COO)*
Paul Heald *(Co-Founder & CEO)*
Jan McDaniel *(CMO)*
Dorian Logan *(CTO)*
Board of Directors:
Charlie Blackburn
Chuck Dietrich
Graham Elliott
Paul Heald
Richard Heald
Russ Pyle

U.S. Subsidiary:

BrightTALK Inc. (1)
501 Folsom St 2nd Fl
San Francisco, CA 94105
Tel.: (415) 625-1500
Fax: (415) 625-1555
Online Event Solutions
S.I.C.: 7372
N.A.I.C.S.: 511210
Paul Heald *(CEO)*
John Eichhorn *(CFO)*

BRIGITTE FRANCE

Rue Ettore Bugatti
67201 Strasbourg, Bas Rhin, France
Tel.: (33) 388770088
Web Site: www.brigitte-france.fr/kontakt.php?url=020373739323234363d34696
Rev.: $11,300,000
Emp.: 24
S.I.C.: 5961
N.A.I.C.S.: 454113
Personnel:
Board of Directors:
Suzanne Kircher

BRIGUS GOLD CORP.

(Acquired & Absorbed by Primero Mining Corp.)

BRIKOR LIMITED

Maharaj Attorneys 3 Rydall Vale
Crescent La Lucia Office Park
Durban, South Africa
Mailing Address:
PO Box 884
Nigel, 1490, South Africa
Tel.: (27) 11 739 9000
Fax: (27) 11 739 9021
Web Site: www.brikor.net
BIK—(JSE)
Rev.: $24,993,434
Assets: $30,159,447
Liabilities: $26,448,214
Net Worth: $3,711,233
Earnings: $3,678,169
Emp.: 556
Fiscal Year-end: 02/28/13
Business Description:
Clay Brick & Aggregate Mfr
S.I.C.: 3255
N.A.I.C.S.: 327120
Personnel:
Garnett van Niekerk Parkin *(Acting Chm & CEO)*
Board of Directors:
Garnett van Niekerk Parkin
Hanleu Botha
Colin Bongane Madolo
Ramasela Joyce Magoele
Baldwin Sipho Ngubane

BRILLIANCE CHINA AUTOMOTIVE HOLDINGS LIMITED

Suites 1602-1605 Charter House 8
Connaught Road
Central, China (Hong Kong)
Tel.: (852) 25237227
Fax: (852) 25268472
E-Mail: cba@brillianceauto.com
Web Site: www.brillianceauto.com
Year Founded: 1992
1114—(HKG OTC)
Rev.: $939,755,170
Assets: $2,550,742,771
Liabilities: $1,089,565,494
Net Worth: $1,461,177,277
Earnings: $355,354,281
Emp.: 6,400
Fiscal Year-end: 12/31/12
Business Description:
Automobile & Truck Mfr
S.I.C.: 3711
N.A.I.C.S.: 336111
Personnel:
Xiao An Wu *(Chm)*
Yumin Qi *(Pres & CEO)*
Zuming Qian *(CFO)*
Eva Yee Wah Lam *(Sec)*
Lisa Ng *(Sr VP)*
Board of Directors:
Xiao An Wu
Bo Jiang
Xiaoyang Lei
Yumin Qi
Jian Song
Chengxu Tan
Shiping Wang
Bingjin Xu

Appleby Management (Bermuda) Limited
Argyle House 41A Cedar Avenue
Hamilton, Bermuda

Transfer Agents:
Computershare Hong Kong Investor Services Limited
Room 1712-1716 17th Floor Hopewell Centre
183 Queen's Road East
Hong Kong, China (Hong Kong)

Appleby Management (Bermuda) Limited
Argyle House 41A Cedar Avenue
Hamilton, Bermuda

Non-U.S. Subsidiary:

Shenyang Brilliance JinBei Automobile Co Ltd. (1)
No 39 Dongwang St
Dadong Distr, Shenyang, 110044, China
Tel.: (86) 2431666631
Fax: (86) 2431660143
E-Mail: customer@brilliance-auto.com
Web Site: www.brilliance-auto.com
Emp.: 7,000
Automobile Mfr
S.I.C.: 3711
N.A.I.C.S.: 336111
Yumin Qi *(Chm)*

BRILLIANT CIRCLE HOLDINGS INTERNATIONAL LIMITED

18/F 111 Leighton Road Causeway Bay
Hong Kong, China (Hong Kong)
Tel.: (852) 39157888
Fax: (852) 39157800
E-Mail: enquiry@brilliantcircle.com
Web Site: www.bcghk.cn
1008—(HKG)
Rev.: $250,090,788
Assets: $599,765,148
Liabilities: $279,678,237
Net Worth: $320,086,911
Earnings: $59,714,682
Emp.: 2,384
Fiscal Year-end: 12/31/12
Business Description:
Printing Services
S.I.C.: 2759
N.A.I.C.S.: 323111
Personnel:
Tak Tsoi *(Chm)*
David Xiao Ming Cai *(CEO)*
Chung Hang Yau *(CFO & Sec)*
Song Qin *(COO)*
Board of Directors:
Tak Tsoi
David Xiao Ming Cai
Yttox Chung Yin Kiong
Andy Ying Hung Lam
Tin Nang Lui
Song Qin
Xing He Sean
Simon Man Ho Siu

Butterfield Fulcrum Group (Cayman) Limited
Butterfield House 68 Fort Street 609
Georgetown, Grand Cayman, KY1 1107, Cayman Islands

Transfer Agents:
Tricor Investor Services Limited
26th Floor Tesbury Centre 28 Queens Road East
Wanchai, China (Hong Kong)

Butterfield Fulcrum Group (Cayman) Limited
Butterfield House 68 Fort Street 609
Georgetown, Grand Cayman, KY1 1107, Cayman Islands

Subsidiary:

CT Printing Limited (1)
Ste 23012 23 F Tower 2 Nina Tower
8 Yeung UK Rd, Tsuen Wan, China (Hong Kong)
Tel.: (852) 28519288
Fax: (852) 28518972
E-Mail: sales@ctprinting.com.hk
Web Site: www.ctprinting.com.hk/html/contact_info.php
Emp.: 20
Books & Paper Mfr
S.I.C.: 5192
N.A.I.C.S.: 424920
William Chan *(Mgr-Sls)*

BRILLIANT RESOURCES INC.

Suite 220 9797 45th Avenue
Edmonton, AB, T6E 5V8, Canada
Tel.: (780) 437-6624
Fax: (780) 439-7308
E-Mail: info@brilliantmining.com
Web Site: www.brilliantmining.com
BLT—(TSXV)
Rev.: $85,239
Assets: $30,635,731
Liabilities: $246,677
Net Worth: $30,389,054
Earnings: ($3,002,456)
Fiscal Year-end: 09/30/12
Business Description:
Mineral Exploration Services
S.I.C.: 1081
N.A.I.C.S.: 213114
Personnel:
John Williamson *(Chm & CEO)*
Sean Mager *(CFO)*
Board of Directors:
John Williamson
Allan J. Bezanson
John Hawkrigg
Courtenay Wolfe
Transfer Agent:
Olympia Trust Company
Suite 2300 125 9th Ave SE
Calgary, AB, Canada

BRILONER LEUCHTEN GMBH

Im Kissen 2
59929 Brilon, Germany
Tel.: (49) 296197120
Fax: (49) 29619712195
E-Mail: mail@briloner.de
Web Site: www.briloner.de
Rev.: $31,726,200
Emp.: 150
Business Description:
Residential Lighting Product Whslr
S.I.C.: 5063
N.A.I.C.S.: 423610
Personnel:
Hans-Walter Hustadt *(Mng Dir)*

BRIMSTONE INVESTMENT CORPORATION LTD.

1st Floor Slade House Boundary Terraces 1 Mariendahl Lane
Newlands, 7700 Cape Town, South Africa
Tel.: (27) 216831444
Fax: (27) 216831285
E-Mail: info@brimstone.co.za
Web Site: www.brimstone.co.za
Year Founded: 1998
BRT—(JSE)
Rev.: $217,420,922
Assets: $639,534,329
Liabilities: $312,254,893
Net Worth: $327,279,436
Earnings: $94,064,357
Emp.: 3,267
Fiscal Year-end: 12/31/12
Business Description:
Holding Company; Financial Services, Healthcare & Industrial Services
S.I.C.: 6719
N.A.I.C.S.: 551112
Personnel:
Fred Robertson *(Chm)*
Mustaq A. Brey *(CEO)*
Michael O'Dea *(CFO)*
Mi Khan *(CIO)*
Tiloshani Moodley *(Sec)*

Brimstone Investment Corporation Ltd.—(Continued)

Board of Directors:
Fred Robertson
Mustaq A. Brey
Lawrie Z. Brozin
P. Leon Campher
Mzwandile Hewu
Nazeem Khan
Mpho K. Ndebele
Liyaqat Parker
Felicia D. Roman

Transfer Agent:
Computershare Investor Services Pty ltd
70 Marshall Street Johannesburg 2001 PO Box 61051
Marshalltown, South Africa

Subsidiaries:

House of Monatic (Pty) Ltd. (1)
364 Victoria Road
Salt River, Cape Town, Western Cape, 7925, South Africa
Tel.: (27) 214429402
Fax: (27) 214429596
E-Mail: info@monatic.co.za
Web Site: www.monatic.co.za
Emp.: 800
Corporate Wear Mfr
S.I.C.: 2389
N.A.I.C.S.: 315210
Mike Maurer *(Mng Dir)*

Lion of Africa Holdings Company (Pty) Ltd (1)
Sunridge Park 62 Wierda Road East
Wierda Valley
Sandton, Gauteng, 2196, South Africa
Tel.: (27) 21 674 0450
Fax: (27) 21 683 1113
General Insurance Services
S.I.C.: 6311
N.A.I.C.S.: 524113

Oceana SPV (Pty) Ltd. (1)
25 Jan Smuts St
Cape Town, Western Cape, 8001, South Africa
Tel.: (27) 214101400
Fax: (27) 214158601
E-Mail: info@oceana.co.za
Web Site: www.oceana.co.za
Fish Products Whslr
S.I.C.: 5146
N.A.I.C.S.: 424460
Francois Kuttel *(CEO)*

Holding:

Sea Harvest Corporation Limited (1)
1st Floor Block C Boulevard Office Park
Searle Street
PO Box 761
Woodstock, 7925 Cape Town, 8000, South Africa
Tel.: (27) 216487900
Fax: (27) 214655883
E-Mail: info@seaharvest.co.za
Web Site: www.seaharvest.co.za
Food Service Contractors
S.I.C.: 5812
N.A.I.C.S.: 722310
George Bezuidenhout *(Mng Dir)*

BRINGSPRING SCIENCE & TECHNOLOGY CO., LTD.

62 Heping North Avenue
Heping District, Shenyang, 110002, China
Tel.: (86) 24 86905851
Fax: (86) 24 86907731
E-Mail: bringspring_hr@bringspring.com
Web Site: www.bringspring.com
300290—(CHIN)
Emp.: 310

Business Description:
IT Services
S.I.C.: 7379
N.A.I.C.S.: 541519

Personnel:
Yongquan Fu *(Chm)*

Subsidiary:

Liaoning Bringspring Financial Service Co., Ltd (1)
F5 & F6 Ruyi Building Jinshajiang Rd
Fanhe District, Tieling, China
Tel.: (86) 24 72256409
Financial Data Management Services
S.I.C.: 7374
N.A.I.C.S.: 518210

BRINQUEDOS ESTRELA S/A

R Gomes de Carvalho 1327 - 10 Andar
4547005 Sao Paulo, Brazil
Tel.: (55) 11 2102 7001
Fax: (55) 11 2102 7090
Web Site: www.estrela.com.br
Year Founded: 1937
ESTR3—(BRAZ)
Sales Range: $50-74.9 Million
Emp.: 657

Business Description:
Toy Mfr & Whslr
S.I.C.: 3942
N.A.I.C.S.: 339930

Personnel:
Carlos Antonio Tilkian *(Dir-IR)*

BRINTONS LIMITED

No 6 Site Stourport Rd
Kidderminster, Worcestershire, DY11 7PZ, United Kingdom
Tel.: (44) 1562820000
Fax: (44) 1562515597
E-Mail: solutions@brintons.net
Web Site: www.brintons.net
Year Founded: 1800
Sales Range: $150-199.9 Million
Emp.: 1,000

Business Description:
Carpet & Rug Mfr
S.I.C.: 2273
N.A.I.C.S.: 314110

Personnel:
Duccio Baldi *(CEO)*

U.S. Subsidiary:

Brintons USA Inc. (1)
1000 Cobb Pl Blvd Bldg 200 Ste 200
Kennesaw, GA 30144
Tel.: (678) 594-9300
Fax: (678) 594-9301
E-Mail: brintons@brintonsusa.com
Web Site: www.brintons.net
Sales Range: $25-49.9 Million
Emp.: 10
Carpet & Rug Mfr
S.I.C.: 2273
N.A.I.C.S.: 314110
Johnny Massey *(VP-Mktg)*

Non-U.S. Subsidiaries:

Barrington Carpets Inc. (1)
Unit 1110 11th Floor W Twr
Philippine Stock Exchange Orti, Manila, Philippines (100%)
Tel.: (63) 26370942
Fax: (63) 26373196
E-Mail: bcarpets@blbpdsl.net
Emp.: 25
Carpet & Rug Mills
S.I.C.: 2273
N.A.I.C.S.: 314110
Geraldine Jamias *(Mng Dir)*

Brintons Carpets Asia Pvt Ltd. (1)
309 ABC City Mall University Rd
411007 Pune, MH, India (100%)
Tel.: (91) 2066208071
Fax: (91) 2025511755
Web Site: www.brintons.net
Emp.: 75
Carpet & Rug Mills
S.I.C.: 2273
N.A.I.C.S.: 314110

Brintons France S.a.r.l. (1)
95 Rue du Faubourg
Saint Honore, 75008 Paris, France
Tel.: (33) 158183360
Fax: (33) 158183361
E-Mail: brintons.france@wanadoo.fr
Carpet & Rugs Mfr
S.I.C.: 2273
N.A.I.C.S.: 314110

Brintons Industria de Alcatifas Ltda (1)
Rebordinho
Campia, 3670-056 Coimbra, Portugal
Tel.: (351) 232750060
Fax: (351) 232750069
E-Mail: bridal@brintons.pt
Web Site: www.brintons.net
Emp.: 253
Carpet & Rug Mills
S.I.C.: 2273
N.A.I.C.S.: 314110
Elisio Mota *(Mng Dir)*

Brintons Pty. Ltd. (1)
3 Westside Ave Unit 35
Port Melbourne, VIC, 3207, Australia AU
Mailing Address: (100%)
PO Box 788
Geelong, VIC, 3219, Australia
Tel.: (61) 352263200
Fax: (61) 352290355
E-Mail: geelong@brintons.com.au
Web Site: www.brintons.com.au
Sales Range: $25-49.9 Million
Emp.: 100
Carpet & Rug Mfr
S.I.C.: 2273
N.A.I.C.S.: 314110
Chrish Paxton *(CEO)*

BRIONOR RESOURCES INC.

1935 rue La Corne
Saint-Bruno, QC, J3V 5A1, Canada
Tel.: (450) 441-9177
Fax: (450) 653-3721
Year Founded: 2009
BNR—(TSXV)
Assets: $1,634,555
Liabilities: $159,945
Net Worth: $1,474,610
Earnings: ($320,842)
Fiscal Year-end: 08/31/13

Business Description:
Mineral Exploration Services
S.I.C.: 1099
N.A.I.C.S.: 212299

Personnel:
Robert Ayotte *(Chm)*
Lewis Lawrick *(Pres & CEO)*
Errol Farr *(CFO)*

Board of Directors:
Robert Ayotte
Michael J. Byron
Brian Gavin
Lewis Lawrick

BRISA AUTO-ESTRADAS DE PORTUGAL, S.A.

Quinta da Torre da Aguilha - Edificio Brisa
2785-599 Sao Domingos de Rana, Portugal
Tel.: (351) 214448500
Fax: (351) 214449592
E-Mail: contacto@brisa.pt
Web Site: www.brisa.pt
Year Founded: 1972
BRI—(EUR)
Rev.: $839,446,035
Assets: $6,626,457,209
Liabilities: $4,814,259,309
Net Worth: $1,812,197,900
Earnings: $61,953,436
Emp.: 2,253
Fiscal Year-end: 12/31/12

Business Description:
Highway & Street Construction Services
S.I.C.: 1622
N.A.I.C.S.: 237310

Personnel:
Vasco Maria Guimaraes Jose de Mello *(Chm & CEO)*
Joao Pedro Stilwell Rocha e Melo *(Vice Chm)*
Joao Pedro Ribeiro de Azevedo Coutinho *(CFO & Exec Dir)*
Tiago Severim de Melo Alves dos Santos *(Sec)*

Board of Directors:
Vasco Maria Guimaraes Jose de Mello
Michael Gregory Allen
Daniel Alexandre Miguel Amaral
Joao Pedro Ribeiro de Azevedo Coutinho
Luis Eduardo Brito Freixial de Goes
Maria Margarida de Lucena Correa de Aguiar
Antonio Jose Fernandes de Sousa
Antonio Nunes de Sousa
Rui Alexandre Pires Diniz
Joao Pedro Stilwell Rocha e Melo
Jorge Manuel Pereira Caldas Goncalves
Antonino Lo Bianco
Graham Peter Wilson Marr
Martin Wolfgang Johannes Rey

Subsidiaries:

Brisa Assistencia Rodoviaria, S.A. (1)
Edificio Brisa
Quinta Da Torre Da Aguilha, 2785599S AO
Cascais, Portugal (100%)
Tel.: (351) 214448500
Fax: (351) 214449592
E-Mail: contact@brisa.pt
Web Site: www.brisa.com
All Other Support Activities for Transportation
S.I.C.: 4789
N.A.I.C.S.: 488999

Brisa Internacional, SGPS, S.A. (1)
Edificio Brisa
Quinta Da Torre Da Aguilha, Cascais, Portugal (100%)
Tel.: (351) 214449100
Fax: (351) 214445672
Other Holding Companies Offices
S.I.C.: 6719
N.A.I.C.S.: 551112

BRISA O&M, S.A. (1)
Quinta Da Torre Da Agullha Edificio Brisa
Sao Domingos de Rana, 2785-599, Portugal
Tel.: (351) 214448500
Fax: (351) 214449590
Civil Engineering Construction Services
S.I.C.: 1611
N.A.I.C.S.: 237310

Brisa - Servicos Viarios, SGPS, S.A. (1)
Quinta da Torre Da Aguilha
Edificio Brisa Domingos De Ran, Cascais, Portugal (100%)
Tel.: (351) 214448500
Fax: (351) 214445698
E-Mail: contact@brisa.pt
Web Site: www.brisa.pt/PresentationLayer/conteudo.aspx?menuid=199&exmenuid=174
Other Holding Companies Offices
S.I.C.: 6719
N.A.I.C.S.: 551112

CONTROLAUTO - CONTROLO TECNICO AUTOMOVEL, S.A. (1)
Rua Alfredo L Vilaverde 15-B-s 7 Alto da Loba-Paco de Arcos
2770-009 Paco d'Arcos, Portugal
Tel.: (351) 214 418 376
Fax: (351) 214 418 363
E-Mail: controlauto@controlauto.pt
Web Site: www.controlauto.pt
Automotive Control & Maintenance Services
S.I.C.: 7532
N.A.I.C.S.: 811121
Zosa Enjra *(Gen Mgr)*

Iteuve Portugal, Lda (1)
R Fernao Lopes
2750-663 Cascais, Portugal
Tel.: (351) 214812920
Fax: (351) 214812939
E-Mail: scorreiaer@Iteuve.pt

Web Site: www.controlauto.com
Emp.: 60
All Other Automotive Repair & Maintenance
S.I.C.: 7549
N.A.I.C.S.: 811198
Vrlbamrm Manvas *(Mng Dir)*

M. CALL, S.A. (1)
Taguspark Edificio Mcall Tecnologia III
Corpo 5
2740-257 Porto Salvo, Portugal
Tel.: (351) 707 50 30 40
E-Mail: geral@mcall.pt
Web Site: www.mcall.pt
Business Process Outsourcing Services
S.I.C.: 7389
N.A.I.C.S.: 561499

Toitorres Inspeccoes, S.A. (1)
Estrada Nacional 8 Km 43 9
2564 909 Lisbon, Portugal
Tel.: (351) 261315680
Fax: (351) 261315795
Web Site: www.controlauto.pt
Emp.: 10
Advertising Agencies
S.I.C.: 7311
N.A.I.C.S.: 541810
Nuno Henriques *(Mng Dir)*

U.S. Subsidiaries:

BRISA NORTH AMERICA, INC (1)
1420 Peachtree St N E 220
Atlanta, GA 30309-3049
Tel.: (404) 835-8400
Road & Building Construction Services
S.I.C.: 1622
N.A.I.C.S.: 237310

BRISA UNITED STATES, LLC (1)
2755 Nothwoods Pkwy
Norcross, GA 30071
Tel.: (404) 835-8400
Fax: (404) 835-8401
Emp.: 7
Highway & Street Construction Services
S.I.C.: 1622
N.A.I.C.S.: 237310
Victor Saltao *(CEO)*

Non-U.S. Subsidiaries:

BRISA INTERNACIONAL, BV (1)
Zwet 1/C Westland
2295 KZ Kwintsheul, Zuid-Holland, Netherlands
Tel.: (31) 70 3350350
Fax: (31) 70 3859777
Investment Management Services
S.I.C.: 6211
N.A.I.C.S.: 523999

BRISCOE GROUP LIMITED

36 Taylors Road Morningside
PO Box 884
Auckland, New Zealand
Tel.: (64) 98153737
Fax: (64) 98153738
E-Mail: briscoegroup@briscoes.co.nz
Web Site: www.briscoegroup.co.nz
BGR—(NZE)
Rev.: $378,911,574
Assets: $160,562,547
Liabilities: $52,940,250
Net Worth: $107,622,297
Earnings: $25,501,716
Emp.: 72
Fiscal Year-end: 01/27/13

Business Description:
Homeware & Sports Goods Retailer
S.I.C.: 5941
N.A.I.C.S.: 451110

Personnel:
Rodney Adrian Duke *(Deputy Chm & Mng Dir)*
Geoffrey Peter Scowcroft *(CFO)*
Peter William Burilin *(COO)*
Alaister John Wall *(Deputy Mng Dir)*

Board of Directors:
Rosanne Philippa O'Loghlen Meo
Rodney Adrian Duke
Stuart Hamilton Johnstone
Alaister John Wall

Subsidiaries:

Briscoes (New Zealand) Limited (1)
36 Taylors Road
Morningside, Auckland, 1025, New Zealand
Tel.: (64) 98153737
Fax: (64) 98153738
E-Mail: receptionb@briscoegroup.co.nz
Web Site: www.briscoes.co.nz
Household Appliances & Utensils Retailer
S.I.C.: 5722
N.A.I.C.S.: 443141
Rodney Duke *(Mng Dir)*

The Sports Authority Limited (1)
Unit 14 16-18 Taylors Road
Morningside, Auckland, 1025, New Zealand
Tel.: (64) 98450980
Fax: (64) 98450981
E-Mail: contact@briscoegroup.co.nz
Web Site: www.rebelsport.co.nz
Sport Goods Distr
S.I.C.: 5091
N.A.I.C.S.: 423910
Rodney Duke *(Mng Dir)*

BRISIO INNOVATIONS INC.

(Formerly Netco Silver Inc.)
580 Hornby Street Suite 490
Vancouver, BC, V6C 3B6, Canada
Tel.: (604) 644-0072
Fax: (604) 683-7589
E-Mail: support@brisio.com
Web Site: www.brisio.com
Year Founded: 1993
BZI—(CNSX)
Rev.: $1,218
Assets: $76,949
Liabilities: $116,012
Net Worth: ($39,063)
Earnings: ($1,270,629)
Fiscal Year-end: 12/31/12

Business Description:
Software Applications
S.I.C.: 7372
N.A.I.C.S.: 511210

Personnel:
Paul Andreola *(Pres & CEO)*
Scott MacEachern *(CFO & Sec)*

Board of Directors:
Paul Andreola
Colin Bowkett
Steve Vestergaard

Transfer Agent:
Computershare Investor Services Inc.
100 University Avenue 8th Floor
Toronto, ON, M5J 2Y1, Canada
Tel.: (514) 982-7555

BRISTA CORP.

Stigu iela 26 dz 2
LV- 2101 Mezares, Babites Pagasts, Latvia
Tel.: (371) 27196113
E-Mail: bristacorp@gmail.com
Year Founded: 2012

Business Description:
Crumb Rubber Tiles Mfr
S.I.C.: 3069
N.A.I.C.S.: 326299

Personnel:
Andrejs Levaskovics *(Pres, Treas & Sec)*

Board of Directors:
Andrejs Levaskovics

BRITANNIA SUPERFINE LTD.

Chaucer Industrial Estate Dittons Road
Lewes, East Sussex, BN26 6JF, United Kingdom
Tel.: (44) 1323 485 155
Fax: (44) 1323 483 927
E-Mail: sales@britannia-superfine.com
Web Site: www.britannia-superfine.com
Year Founded: 1953
Sales Range: $25-49.9 Million
Emp.: 106

Business Description:
Confectionery Mfr
S.I.C.: 2064
N.A.I.C.S.: 311352

Personnel:
Colin Manser *(Mng Dir)*

BRITANNICA RESOURCES CORP.

153A Ave Perreault
Val d'Or, QC, Canada
Tel.: (819) 825-9311
Fax: (819) 825-1199
E-Mail: info@brrgold.com
Web Site: www.brrgold.com
BRR—(TSXV)

Business Description:
Mineral Exploration Services
S.I.C.: 1081
N.A.I.C.S.: 213114

Personnel:
Jeffrey A. Cocks *(Pres, CEO, CFO & Sec)*

Board of Directors:
Jeffrey A. Cocks
Eugene Gauthier
Benita Silas

Transfer Agent:
Computershare Trust Company of Canada
510 Burrard St 3rd Fl
Vancouver, BC, V6C 3B9, Canada

BRITCON

Midland Rd
Scunthorpe, South Lincolnshire, DN16 1DQ, United Kingdom
Tel.: (44) 1724280022
Fax: (44) 1724270616
E-Mail: enquiries@britcon.co.uk
Web Site: www.britcon.co.uk
Sales Range: $50-74.9 Million
Emp.: 120

Business Description:
Engineering Services, Industrial & Commercial Buildings Constructor
S.I.C.: 8711
N.A.I.C.S.: 541330

Personnel:
Shaun Hunt *(Mng Dir)*

BRITHOL MICHCOMA MOZAMBIQUE LIMITED

Ave Mao Tse Tung 346
Maputo, Mozambique
Tel.: (258) 21493865
Telex: 6-659 bmcl mo
Fax: (258) 21494037
E-Mail: britholmichcoma@brithol.com
Web Site: www.brithol.com
Year Founded: 1990
Sales Range: $1-9.9 Million
Emp.: 400

Business Description:
Office Equipment, Computers & Electronics & Hotels Distr & Importer; Printing Services
S.I.C.: 3589
N.A.I.C.S.: 333318

Personnel:
Lucas Manhica *(Mgr)*

BRITISH AMERICAN INVESTMENT CO. (MTIUS) LTD.

25 Pope Hennessy St
Port Louis, Mauritius
Tel.: (230) 202 3600
Fax: (230) 208 3713
E-Mail: info@bainvestment.intnet.mu
Web Site: www.britishamericaninvestment.com
Sales Range: $500-549.9 Million

Business Description:
Investment Holding Company
S.I.C.: 6719
N.A.I.C.S.: 551112

Personnel:
J. Nicholas Ashford-Hodges *(Chm)*
Seemadree Rajanah *(COO)*

Board of Directors:
J. Nicholas Ashford-Hodges
Claudio A.S. Feistritzer
Dawood A. Rawat
Ishack A. Rawat
Moussa I. Rawat
Sulleman A. Rawat

Subsidiary:

Bramer Corporation Limited (1)
25 Pope Hennessy Street
Port Louis, Mauritius
Tel.: (230) 202 3600
Web Site: www.bramercorporation.com
Financial Services
S.I.C.: 6029
N.A.I.C.S.: 522110
Tarun Ghulati, *(Pres & CEO)*

Subsidiary:

Bramer Banking Corporation Ltd. (2)
26 Bourbon Street
Port Louis, Mauritius
Tel.: (230) 405 4400
Fax: (230) 211 4900
E-Mail: info@bramerbank.mu
Web Site: www.bramerbank.mu
BBC—(MAU)
Int. Income: $15,747,870
Assets: $342,454,802
Liabilities: $304,523,291
Net Worth: $37,931,511
Earnings: $520,742
Fiscal Year-end: 12/31/12
Banking Services
S.I.C.: 6029
N.A.I.C.S.: 522110
Thomas St. John Neville Bates *(Chm)*
Tarun Ghulati *(Vice Chm)*
M. Ashraf Esmael *(CEO)*
Iqra Maudarbocus *(Sr VP-Legal Svcs & Compliance)*
Deepak Mohadeb *(Sr VP-Recovery & Revenue Control)*
Ramesh Motee *(Sr VP-Ops)*
Issa Soormally *(Sr VP-Sls)*

BRITISH AMERICAN TOBACCO PLC

Globe House 4 Temple Place
London, WC2R 2PG, United Kingdom
Tel.: (44) 20 7845 1000
Telex: 915195
Fax: (44) 20 7240 0555
E-Mail: press_office@bat.com
Web Site: www.bat.com
Year Founded: 1902
BTI—(JSE LSE NYSEMKT)
Sls.: $72,445,190,880
Assets: $43,157,257,830
Liabilities: $30,871,960,920
Net Worth: $12,285,296,910
Earnings: $6,509,833,380
Emp.: 87,485
Fiscal Year-end: 12/31/12

Business Description:
Holding Company; Tobacco Products Mfr & Distr
Import Export
S.I.C.: 6719
N.A.I.C.S.: 551112

Personnel:
Richard Burrows *(Chm)*
Nicandro Durante *(CEO)*
John Patrick Daly *(COO)*
John Benedict Stevens *(CIO & Dir-Fin)*
Neil R. Withington *(Gen Counsel & Dir-Legal & Security)*
Nicola Snook *(Sec)*

British American Tobacco plc—(Continued)

Board of Directors:
Richard Burrows
John Patrick Daly
Karen M. A. de Segundo
Ann Frances Godbehere
Savio Kwan
Robert Earl Lerwill
Christine J. M. Morin-Postel
Gerard Murphy
Kieran Charles Poynter
Anthony Ruys
Nicholas V. Scheele
John Benedict Stevens
Richard Tubb

Subsidiaries:

B.A.T. International Finance p.l.c. (1)
Globe House 4 Temple Place
London, WC2R 2PG, United Kingdom
Tel.: (44) 20 7845 1000
Financial Management Services
S.I.C.: 6211
N.A.I.C.S.: 523999

B.A.T (U.K. and Export) Ltd. (1)
Globe Ho 4 Temple Pl
London, WC2R 2PG, United Kingdom
Tel.: (44) 20 7845 1000
Fax: (44) 20 7240 0555
Cigarette Mfr
S.I.C.: 2131
N.A.I.C.S.: 312230
Nicandro Durante *(CEO)*

British American Tobacco (Brands) Ltd. (1)
Globe House 4 Temple Place
London, WC2R 2PG, United Kingdom
Tel.: (44) 20 7845 1000
Fax: (44) 20 7240 0555
Web Site: www.bat.com
Cigarette Mfr
S.I.C.: 2131
N.A.I.C.S.: 312230
Nicandro Durante *(CEO)*

British American Tobacco (GLP) Ltd. (1)
Globe House 4 Temple Pl
London, WC2R 2PG, United Kingdom
Tel.: (44) 20 784 51000
Fax: (44) 2072400555
E-Mail: uk_hr_helpline@bat.com
Web Site: www.bat.com
Tobacco Products Whslr
S.I.C.: 5194
N.A.I.C.S.: 424940

British-American Tobacco (Holdings) Ltd. (1)
Globe Ho 4 Temple Pl
London, WC2R 2PG, United Kingdom
Tel.: (44) 20 7845 1000
Fax: (44) 2072400555
Web Site: www.bat.com
Investment Management Services
S.I.C.: 6211
N.A.I.C.S.: 523999

British American Tobacco (Investments) Ltd. (1)
Globe House 4 Temple Place
London, WC2R 2PG, United Kingdom
Tel.: (44) 20 7845 1000
Fax: (44) 2072400555
E-Mail: uk_hr_helpline@bat.com
Web Site: www.bat.com
Investment Management Services
S.I.C.: 6211
N.A.I.C.S.: 523999

Non-U.S. Subsidiary:

West Indian Tobacco Limited (2)
Eastern Main Road
Champs Fleurs, Trinidad & Tobago TT
Tel.: (868) 662 2271
Fax: (868) 663 5451
Web Site: www.westindiantobacco.com
WCO—(TRI)
Sls.: $170,732,686
Assets: $66,226,077
Liabilities: $31,109,782
Net Worth: $35,116,295
Earnings: $53,958,512
Emp.: 199
Fiscal Year-end: 12/31/12
Cigarette Mfr
S.I.C.: 2131
N.A.I.C.S.: 312230
Anthony E. Phillip *(Chm)*
Jean-Pierre S. du Coudray *(Mng Dir)*
Danielle F. Chow *(Sec)*

British American Tobacco UK Ltd. (1)
Oxford House Oxford Road
Aylesbury, Bucks, HP21 8SZ, United Kingdom
Tel.: (44) 1296335000
Fax: (44) 1296335999
Web Site: www.bat.com
Emp.: 800
Tobacco Products Distr
Import
S.I.C.: 5194
N.A.I.C.S.: 424940

Unit:

British American Tobacco Research & Development (1)
Regents Park Road
Millbrook, Southampton, SO15 8TL, United Kingdom (100%)
Tel.: (44) 2380777155
Fax: (44) 2380780332
Web Site: www.bat-science.com
Emp.: 800
Tobacco Product Research & Development
S.I.C.: 8731
N.A.I.C.S.: 541712
Nicky Snook *(Sec)*

Non-U.S. Subsidiaries:

B.A.T. (Cyprus) Ltd. (1)
PO Box 21563
Nicosia, 1510, Cyprus (100%)
Tel.: (357) 22746000
Fax: (357) 22437053
Emp.: 80
Cigarette Mfr
S.I.C.: 2131
N.A.I.C.S.: 312230

B.A.T. Sucursal Costa Rica (1)
225 Metros Al Este De La Firestone Flores
Heredia, 284 3007, Costa Rica (100%)
Tel.: (506) 2091717
Fax: (506) 2091770
Web Site: www.batcentralamerica.com
Emp.: 75
Cigarette Mfr
S.I.C.: 2131
N.A.I.C.S.: 312230

PT Bentoel Internasional Investama Tbk (1)
Plaza Bapindo Citibank Tower 2nd Floor
Jl Jend Sudirman Kav 54 55, Jakarta, 12190, Indonesia
Tel.: (62) 21 526 8388
Fax: (62) 21 526 8389
Web Site: www.bentoel.co.id
LFV—(DEU)
Cigarette Mfr
S.I.C.: 2131
N.A.I.C.S.: 312230
Christoph von Brockhusen *(Pres)*

British Aamerican Tobacco Holdings (The Netherlands) B.V. (1)
PO Box 246
1180 AE Amstelveen, North Holland, Netherlands NL (100%)
Tel.: (31) 205005800
Fax: (31) 205406910
Web Site: www.bat.nl
Emp.: 250
Holding Company; Tobacco Production
S.I.C.: 6719
N.A.I.C.S.: 551112
Saimon Welford *(Gen Mgr)*

Holding:

British American Tobacco The Netherlands B.V. (2)
Handelsweg 53 A
1181 ZA Amstelveen, Netherlands NL (100%)
Tel.: (31) 205406911
Fax: (31) 205406910
E-Mail: reception@bat.com
Web Site: www.batnl.nl
Emp.: 250
Tobacco Products Distr
S.I.C.: 5993
N.A.I.C.S.: 453991
Simon Welford *(Mng Dir)*

Subsidiaries:

British American Tobacco Finance BV (3)
Hambelswed 53 A
1083 HJ Amstelveen, Netherlands (100%)
Tel.: (31) 206445366
Fax: (31) 0205406910
E-Mail: info@britishamerican.com
Web Site: www.britishamerican.com
Emp.: 150
Tobacco Products Exporter
S.I.C.: 5993
N.A.I.C.S.: 453991
Christoph von Brockhusen *(Gen Mgr)*

Koninklijke Theodorus Niemeyer B.V. (3)
Paterswoldseweg 43
9700 AA Groningen, Netherlands (100%)
Tel.: (31) 503664911
Fax: (31) 503664452
E-Mail: info@niemeyer.nl
Web Site: www.niemeyer.nl
Emp.: 350
Distributor of Tobacco
S.I.C.: 5993
N.A.I.C.S.: 453991
Com Crembrs *(Mng Dir)*

British American Tobacco Australasia Ltd. (1)
Private Bag 1 Maroubra
2035 Sydney, New South Wales, Australia (100%)
Tel.: (61) 293701500
Telex: 20116
Fax: (61) 93701188
Web Site: www.bata.com.au
Emp.: 1,500
Mfr. of Cigar & Cigarette Tobacco
S.I.C.: 2131
N.A.I.C.S.: 312230
David Crow *(Mng Dir)*

British American Tobacco Australia Ltd. (1)
Private Bag No 1
Maroubra, Sydney, 2035, Australia
Tel.: (61) 29370 1500
Fax: (61) 29370 1188
E-Mail: info@bata.com.au
Web Site: www.bata.com.au
Tobacco Products Mfr
S.I.C.: 2131
N.A.I.C.S.: 312230
Tim Every-Burns *(Chm)*
David Crow *(Mng Dir)*

British American Tobacco Bangladesh Co. Ltd. (1)
New DOHS Rd Mohakhali
Dhaka, 1206, Bangladesh (65%)
Mailing Address:
PO Box 6069
Mohakhali, Dhaka, 1206, Bangladesh
Tel.: (880) 28822791
Fax: (880) 28822786
E-Mail: info@bat.com
Web Site: www.bat.com
Emp.: 130
Cigarette Mfr
S.I.C.: 2131
N.A.I.C.S.: 312230
Alan Davy *(Mng Dir)*

British American Tobacco Belgium S.A. (1)
Rue De Koninck 38
B 1080 Brussels, Belgium BE (100%)
Tel.: (32) 24131211
Fax: (32) 24131422
Web Site: www.bat.be
Emp.: 170
Cigarette Mfr
S.I.C.: 2131
N.A.I.C.S.: 312230
Christoph von Brockhusen *(CEO)*

British American Tobacco Denmark (1)
Tobaksvejen 4
DK-2860 Soborg, Denmark
Tel.: (45) 39556300
Fax: (45) 39556303
E-Mail: info_dk@bat.com
Web Site: www.bat.com
Sales Range: $1-4.9 Billion
Emp.: 1,866
Cigarette Manufacturer
S.I.C.: 2131
N.A.I.C.S.: 312230
Christian Hother Sorensen *(Mng Dir)*
Jacob Bjerre *(Sr VP-Leaf Tobacco)*
Peter Dalsberg *(Sr VP-Supply Chain)*
Kristian Kornerup *(Sr VP-Export)*
Lars Wassberg *(Sr VP-Intl Trade Svcs)*
Peter Willumsen *(Sr VP-Sls & Mktg)*

British American Tobacco Espana, S.A. (1)
P Castellana 259 - D Planta 25
28046 Madrid, Spain
Tel.: (34) 91 555 1904
Fax: (34) 91 555 2185
E-Mail: info_es@bat.com
Web Site: www.bat.com.es
Cigarette Mfr & Distr
S.I.C.: 2131
N.A.I.C.S.: 312230

British American Tobacco Finland Oy (1)
Pitk Nsillanranta 3 A 00530
530 Helsinki, Finland FI
Mailing Address: (100%)
PO Box 22
00531 Helsinki, Finland
Tel.: (358) 9731311
Fax: (358) 73131252
E-Mail: mikel.brunberg@bat.fi
Web Site: www.bat.fi
Emp.: 100
Cigarette Mfr
S.I.C.: 2131
N.A.I.C.S.: 312230
Mikel Brunberg *(Country Mgr)*

British American Tobacco France SAS (1)
29-31 rue de l'Abreuvoir
92513 Boulogne-Billancourt, France
Tel.: (33) 155199200
Fax: (33) 155199500
E-Mail: contactez_nous@bat.com
Web Site: www.batfrance.com
Emp.: 150
Tobacco Products Mfr & Whslr
S.I.C.: 2131
N.A.I.C.S.: 312230
Ricardo Oberlander *(Gen Mgr)*

British-American Tobacco (Germany) GmbH (1)
Alsterufer 4
20354 Hamburg, Germany (100%)
Tel.: (49) 40415101
Fax: (49) 4041513231
Web Site: www.bat.de
Emp.: 2,200
Cigarettes & Fine-Cut Tobacco Mfr
Import Export
S.I.C.: 2131
N.A.I.C.S.: 312230
Adrianus Schenk *(Mng Dir)*

British American Tobacco Hellas S.A. (1)
27 Ag Thoma Street Marousi
151 24 Athens, Greece
Tel.: (30) 210 819 85 00
Fax: (30) 210 622 08 67
Cigarette Mfr
S.I.C.: 2131
N.A.I.C.S.: 312230

British American Tobacco Holdings South Africa (Pty) Ltd. (1)
25 Du Toit Street
Cape Town, Western Cape, 7599, South Africa
Tel.: (27) 218883500
Fax: (27) 218727321
Investment Management Services
S.I.C.: 6211
N.A.I.C.S.: 523999

British American Tobacco Holdings (The Netherlands) B.V. (1)
Handelsweg 53a
Amstelveen, North Holland, 1181 ZA, Netherlands

Tel.: (31) 206445366
Fax: (31) 20540691
Web Site: www.britishamericantobacco.com
Emp.: 300
Investment Management Services
S.I.C.: 6211
N.A.I.C.S.: 523999

British American Tobacco (Hong Kong) Ltd. (1)
Unit 1 25/F Island Place Tower
510 Kings Road, North Point, China (Hong Kong) HK
Tel.: (852) 36561288
Fax: (852) 29079988
Web Site: www.bathongkong.com
Emp.: 90
Tobacco Products Distr
S.I.C.: 5192
N.A.I.C.S.: 424920
Bartholomeus Alkemade *(Chm)*

British American Tobacco (Industrie) GmbH (1)
Alsterufer 4
20354 Hamburg, Germany
Tel.: (49) 40 4151 01
Fax: (49) 40 4151 3231
E-Mail: service@bat.de
Web Site: www.bat.de
Tobacco Product Mfr & Whslr
S.I.C.: 2131
N.A.I.C.S.: 312230

British American Tobacco International Ltd. (1)
Zahlerweg 4
6301 Zug, Switzerland
Tel.: (41) 417697676
Fax: (41) 417697680
Web Site: www.bati.com
Emp.: 120
Tobacco Products Whslr
S.I.C.: 5194
N.A.I.C.S.: 424940
Jose Benitec *(Gen Mgr)*

British American Tobacco Italia S.p.A. (1)
Via Amsterdam 147
144 Rome, Italy
Tel.: (39) 06 52871
Fax: (39) 06 52879020
Web Site: www.batitalia.com
Tobacco Products Mfr & Whslr
S.I.C.: 2131
N.A.I.C.S.: 312230

British American Tobacco Japan, Ltd. (1)
Atago Mori Tower 22/F 2-5-1 Atago
Minato-ku, Tokyo, 105 6222, Japan JP (100%)
Tel.: (81) 364023000
Fax: (81) 364023001
E-Mail: infojapan@bat.com
Web Site: www.batj.com
Emp.: 100
Cigarette Manufacturing
S.I.C.: 2131
N.A.I.C.S.: 312230
Andrew Colchin *(Pres)*

British American Tobacco Korea Ltd. (1)
42nd Floor Star Tower 737 Yeoksam-dong
Kangnam, 135-984, Korea (South)
Tel.: (82) 2 2112 7100
Fax: (82) 2 2112 7109
Web Site: www.batkorea.com
Tobacco Products Mfr
S.I.C.: 2131
N.A.I.C.S.: 312230
Stephan Liechti *(Pres)*

British American Tobacco Korea Manufacturing Ltd. (1)
889 Yoochun-Ri Sanam-Myeon
Sacheon, Gyeongsangnam-do, 64942, Korea (South)
Tel.: (82) 558517500
Fax: (82) 558517699
Web Site: www.batkorea.com
Emp.: 20
Tobacco Product Mfr & Whslr
S.I.C.: 2131
N.A.I.C.S.: 312230
Sung Ju Han *(Mgr-Factory)*

British American Tobacco Mexico (1)
Francisco 1 Madero 2750 Pte
Monterrey, Nuevo Leon, 64000, Mexico
Tel.: (52) 8181224000
Fax: (52) 8181224097
Web Site: www.batmexico.com.mx
Emp.: 150
Cigarette Mfr & Distr
S.I.C.: 2131
N.A.I.C.S.: 312230
Andrea Martinit *(Gen Mgr)*

British American Tobacco Nederland B.V. (1)
Handelsweg 53 A
1181 ZA Amstelveen, Netherlands
Tel.: (31) 20 540 69 11
Fax: (31) 20 540 69 10
Web Site: www.batbenelux.com
Emp.: 300
Tobacco Product Mfr & Whslr
S.I.C.: 2131
N.A.I.C.S.: 312230

British American Tobacco (New Zealand) Ltd. (1)
14th Floor Gen-i Tower 66 Wyndham Street
Auckland, New Zealand
Tel.: (64) 9 357 9430
Fax: (64) 9 357 9431
Web Site: www.batnz.com
Tobacco Product Mfr & Whslr
S.I.C.: 2131
N.A.I.C.S.: 312230

British American Tobacco Polska Trading Sp. z.o.o. (1)
ul Ilzecka 26
02-135 Warsaw, Poland
Tel.: (48) 22 575 43 00
Fax: (48) 22 575 43 09
Tobacco Products Whslr
S.I.C.: 5194
N.A.I.C.S.: 424940

British-American Tobacco (Singapore) Pte. Ltd. (1)
15 Senoko Loop
Singapore, 758168, Singapore (100%)
Tel.: (65) 63388998
Fax: (65) 63388181
Web Site: www.bat.com
Emp.: 300
Cigarette Mfr & Distr
S.I.C.: 2131
N.A.I.C.S.: 312230

British American Tobacco South Africa (1)
25 Du Toit St
Stellenbosch, 7600, South Africa (100%)
Mailing Address:
PO Box 631
Cape Town, 8000, South Africa
Tel.: (27) 218883500
Fax: (27) 218872503
E-Mail: info@batsa.co.za
Web Site: www.batsa.co.za
Emp.: 2,000
Tobacco Products Mfr
S.I.C.: 2131
N.A.I.C.S.: 312230
Brian Finch *(CEO)*
John Taylor *(Mng Dir)*

British American Tobacco Sweden AB (1)
Warfvinges Vag 31
Box 30244
104 25 Stockholm, Sweden
Tel.: (46) 8 546 730 00
Fax: (46) 8 546 730 20
Web Site: www.batsweden.se
Tobacco Products Whslr
S.I.C.: 5194
N.A.I.C.S.: 424940
Stephane Croce *(Mng Dir)*

British American Tobacco Switzerland (1)
Case Postale 186
CH 1000 Lausanne, Switzerland (100%)
Tel.: (41) 216141614
Fax: (41) 216171409
E-Mail: info@bat.com
Web Site: www.bat.ch
Emp.: 120
Tobacco & Tobacco Products Distr
S.I.C.: 5993
N.A.I.C.S.: 453991
Rals Wittenberg *(Gen Mgr)*

British American Tobacco Tutun Mamulleri Sanayi ve Ticaret A.S. (1)
Veko Giz Plaza B Blok K 18 3 Meydan Sokak
Istanbul, 34398, Turkey
Tel.: (90) 2123678000
Fax: (90) 2122903130
Tobacco Products Mfr & Distr
S.I.C.: 2131
N.A.I.C.S.: 312230
Sabio Lima *(Gen Mgr)*

British American Tobacco Vietnam Ltd. (1)
12th Floor Diamond Plaza
34 Le Duan Boulevard
District 1, Ho Chi Minh City, Vietnam VN
Tel.: (84) 8 8219 888
Fax: (84) 8 8219 338
Web Site: www.batvietnam.com
Tobacco Production & Cigarette Manufacturing
S.I.C.: 2131
N.A.I.C.S.: 312230
Paul Lageweg *(Gen Dir)*

C.A. Cigarrera Bigott Sucs. (1)
Apartado 186
Caracas, 1010-A, Venezuela (100%)
Tel.: (58) 212 203 7511
Telex: 25368 bigott
Fax: (58) 212 237 8539
E-Mail: presidencia_bigott@bat.com
Web Site: www.bigott.com.ve
Emp.: 1,300
Cigarette Mfr
Export
S.I.C.: 2131
N.A.I.C.S.: 312230

Carreras Limited (1)
Twickenham Park
PO Box 100
Spanish Town, Jamaica
Tel.: (876) 7499800
Fax: (876) 7499810
E-Mail: carreras@bat.com
Web Site: www.carrerasltd.com
CAR—(JAM)
Rev.: $129,882,442
Assets: $74,885,178
Liabilities: $35,750,459
Net Worth: $39,134,720
Earnings: $69,370,769
Emp.: 90
Fiscal Year-end: 03/31/13
Tobacco Products
S.I.C.: 2131
N.A.I.C.S.: 312230
Richard Lewis *(Chm)*
Marcus Steele *(Mng Dir)*
Patrice Gray *(Sec & Dir-Fin)*

Demerara Tobacco Co. Ltd. (1)
PO Box 10262
Georgetown, Guyana (70.25%)
Tel.: (592) 2251900
Fax: (592) 2269322
Sales Range: $10-24.9 Million
Emp.: 17
Cigars & Cigarette Mfr
S.I.C.: 2131
N.A.I.C.S.: 312230
Malissa Sylvester *(Gen Mgr)*

Fiedler & Lundgren AB (1)
Stenaldersgatan 23
PO Box 9041
200 39 Malmo, Sweden
Tel.: (46) 406303950
Fax: (46) 406702070
E-Mail: info@flsnus.se
Web Site: www.fiedlerlundgren.se
Emp.: 90
Smokeless Tobacco Product Mfr
S.I.C.: 2131
N.A.I.C.S.: 312230
Leif Hansson *(Mng Dir)*

Imperial Tobacco Canada Limited (1)
3711 Saint-Antoine Street
Montreal, QC, H4C 3P6, Canada (100%)
Mailing Address:
P.O. Box 6500
Montreal, QC, H3C 3L6, Canada
Tel.: (514) 932-6161
Telex: 55-60673
Fax: (514) 939-0432
Web Site: www.imperialtobaccocanada.com
Emp.: 400
Cigarettes, Tobacco & Tobacco Products Mfr & Distr
Export
S.I.C.: 2131
N.A.I.C.S.: 312230
Benjamin Kemball *(Pres & CEO)*

Nobleza Piccardo SAIC y F (1)
Casilla De Correo 899
1000 Buenos Aires, Argentina (90%)
Tel.: (54) 1147248444
Fax: (54) 1147248495
Web Site: www.noblezapiccardo.com
Emp.: 1,100
Mfr. of Cigarettes
S.I.C.: 2131
N.A.I.C.S.: 312230

Pakistan Tobacco Co. Ltd. (1)
Silver Sq Plot No 15 F-11 Markaz
Islamabad, 44000, Pakistan (63%)
Tel.: (92) 5120832000
Fax: (92) 2224217
Web Site: www.ptc.com.pk
Emp.: 200
Cigarette Mfr & Distr
S.I.C.: 1411
N.A.I.C.S.: 212311
Graeme Amey *(CEO)*

P.J. Carroll & Co. Ltd. (1)
Burton Hall Park
Sandyford, Dublin, 18, Ireland (100%)
Tel.: (353) 12052300
Telex: 93629
Fax: (353) 2958105
Web Site: www.pjcarroll.ie
Emp.: 100
Cigarette & Pipe Tobacco Mfr
S.I.C.: 2131
N.A.I.C.S.: 312230

Souza Cruz, S.A. (1)
Rua Candelaria 66
PO Box 160
20091-900 Rio de Janeiro, Brazil (100%)
Tel.: (55) 2138499000
Telex: 212 2629
Fax: (55) 2138499643
E-Mail: souzacruz@souzacruz.com.br
Web Site: www.souzacruz.com.br
Emp.: 5,816
Holding Company; Tobacco, Pulp, Paper
Export
S.I.C.: 6719
N.A.I.C.S.: 551112
Juliana Barreto *(Mgr-Media Rels)*

Tabacalera Hondurena SA (1)
Zona Catao Blvd Sur S
PO Box 64
San Pedro Sula, Honduras (100%)
Tel.: (504) 5566161
Fax: (504) 5566189
Web Site: www.batca.com
Emp.: 21
Cigarette & Snuff Mfr
S.I.C.: 2131
N.A.I.C.S.: 312230

Tabacalera Istmena SA (1)
Apartado A 3
Panama, 9A, Panama (100%)
Tel.: (507) 2788600
Fax: (507) 2788656
E-Mail: ervin_olivares@bat.com
Web Site: www.batca.com
Emp.: 75
Cigarette Mfr
S.I.C.: 2131
N.A.I.C.S.: 312230
Cesar Agurcia *(Mgr-Territory)*

Tabacalera Nicaraguense S.A. (1)
Km 7 1/2 Carretera Norte
Managua, Nicaragua (60%)
Tel.: (505) 2 2631900
Fax: (505) 2 2631642
Web Site: www.batcentralamerica.com
Emp.: 100
Cigarette & Snuff Mfr
S.I.C.: 2131
N.A.I.C.S.: 312230

Non-U.S. Affiliate:

British American Tobacco (Malaysia) Berhad (1)
Virginia Park Jalan University
46200 Petaling Jaya, Malaysia (50%)

British American Tobacco plc—(Continued)

Tel.: (60) 379566899
Fax: (60) 379558416
E-Mail: cora_malaysia@bat.com
Web Site: www.batmalaysia.com
Cigarette Mfr & Distr
S.I.C.: 2131
N.A.I.C.S.: 312230
William Toh Ah Wah *(Mng Dir)*

BRITISH & MALAYAN TRUSTEES LTD

1 Coleman Street No 08 01
The Adelphi, Singapore, 179803, Singapore
Tel.: (65) 65354922
Fax: (65) 65351258
E-Mail: enquiry@bmtrust.com
Web Site: www.bmtrust.com
B08—(SES)
Rev.: $3,220,538
Assets: $14,762,891
Liabilities: $1,239,824
Net Worth: $13,523,066
Earnings: $442,450
Fiscal Year-end: 06/30/13

Business Description:
Trustee & Advisory Services
S.I.C.: 6282
N.A.I.C.S.: 523930

Personnel:
Kah-Lian Siew *(Acting CEO, Head-Legal & Compliance & Mgr-Resident)*
Angela Ho *(Co-Sec & Controller-Fin)*
Chee Mei Sin *(Co-Sec)*

Board of Directors:
Colin Yung-Shih Lee
Roxanne Davies
William Cornelius Lexmond
Nigel David Stead

BRITISH ARAB COMMERCIAL BANK LIMITED

8-10 Mansion House Place
London, EC4N 8BJ, United Kingdom
Tel.: (44) 2076487777
Telex: 22961
Fax: (44) 2076003318
E-Mail: enquiries@bacb.co.uk
Web Site: www.bacb.co.uk
Year Founded: 1972
Sales Range: $200-249.9 Million
Emp.: 141

Business Description:
Banking Services
S.I.C.: 6029
N.A.I.C.S.: 522110

Personnel:
Andrew Dixon *(Chm)*
Michael Parr *(CEO)*
Crispian Denby *(CFO & Sec)*
Rollo Greenfield *(COO)*
Jon Bowen *(Treas)*

BRITISH BROADCASTING CORPORATION

Broadcasting House
Portland Place, London, W1A 1AA, United Kingdom
Tel.: (44) 8700100222
Fax: (44) 1413075770
E-Mail: info@bbc.co.uk
Web Site: www.bbc.co.uk
Year Founded: 1936
Rev.: $8,058,011,367
Assets: $6,236,774,139
Liabilities: $6,331,215,681
Net Worth: ($94,441,542)
Earnings: $518,480,907
Emp.: 21,282
Fiscal Year-end: 03/31/13

Business Description:
TV, Radio & Internet Broadcasting Services
S.I.C.: 4833
N.A.I.C.S.: 515120

Personnel:
Tony Hall *(Dir Gen & Member-Mgmt Bd)*
John Linwood *(CTO)*
Pat Younge *(Chief Creative Officer)*
Blair McQuade *(Chief Comml Officer-Australasia)*
Tim Davie *(CEO-Worldwide, Member-Mgmt Bd & Dir-Global)*
Anne Bulford *(Member-Mgmt Bd & Mng Dir-Ops & Fin)*
Lucy Adams *(Member-Mgmt Bd & Dir-HR)*
Philip Almond *(Member-Mgmt Bd & Dir-Mktg)*
Helen Boaden *(Member-Mgmt Bd & Dir-Radio)*
Danny Cohen *(Member-Mgmt Bd & Dir-Television)*
Rhodri Talfan Davies *(Member-Mgmt Bd & Dir-Cymru Wales)*
James Harding *(Member-Mgmt Bd & Dir-News & Current Affairs)*
Peter Johnston *(Member-Mgmt Bd & Dir-Northern Ireland)*
Ken MacQuarrie *(Member-Mgmt Bd & Dir-Scotland)*
James Purnell *(Member-Mgmt Bd & Dir-Strategy & Digital)*
Ralph Rivera *(Member-Mgmt Bd & Dir-Future Media)*
Peter Salmon *(Member-Mgmt Bd & Dir-North)*
Alan Yentob *(Member-Mgmt Bd & Dir-Creative)*
David Jordan *(Member-Mgmt Bd-Editorial Policy & Standards)*
Sarah Jones *(Gen Counsel-Ops)*

Board of Directors:
Lucy Adams
Helen Boaden
Simon Burke
Danny Cohen
Sally Margaret Davis
Tony Hall
James Harding
Brian McBride
James Purnell
Dame Fiona Reynolds

Subsidiaries:

BBC Symphony Orchestra **(1)**
BBC Maida Vale Studios
Delaware Rd, London, W9 2LG, United Kingdom
Tel.: (44) 2077652956
Fax: (44) 2072863251
E-Mail: bbcso@bbc.co.uk
Emp.: 130
Symphony Orchestra Services
S.I.C.: 7929
N.A.I.C.S.: 711130
Kate Finch *(Head-Mktg, Learning & Publ)*

BBC Worldwide Limited **(1)**
BBC Worldwide Limited Media Centre
201 Wood Lane, London, W127 TQ, United Kingdom
Tel.: (44) 2084332000
E-Mail: bbcworldwide@bbc.co.uk
Web Site: www.bbcworldwide.com
Rev.: $1,762,171,782
Assets: $1,210,841,643
Liabilities: $738,160,146
Net Worth: $472,681,497
Earnings: $201,517,404
Emp.: 2,333
Fiscal Year-end: 03/31/13
Commercial Arm of the British Broadcasting Corporation; Magazines, Videos, Multimedia & Other Merchandise Publisher; Television Programming & Network Services
S.I.C.: 2721
N.A.I.C.S.: 511120
Tim Davie *(CEO)*
Philip Vincent *(CFO)*
Daniel Heaf *(Chief Digital Officer)*
Amanda Hill *(Chief Brands Officer)*
Helen Jackson *(Chief Content Officer)*
Paul Dempsey *(Pres-Global Markets)*
Herb Scannell *(Pres-North America)*
Martyn Freeman *(Gen Counsel)*
Jane Earl *(Sec)*
Ian McDonough *(Exec VP-Central Europe, Eastern Europe, Middle East & Africa)*
Fred Medina *(Exec VP-Latin America)*
Sunita Rajan *(Exec VP-Adv Sls-Asia, Australia & New Zealand)*
David Weiland *(Exec VP-Western Europe)*
Joyce Yeung *(Exec VP-Asia)*

Subsidiary:

Dovetail Services (UK) Limited **(2)**
800 Guillat Ave
Kent Science Park, Sittingbourne, Kent, ME9 8GU, United Kingdom (100%)
Tel.: (44) 8448150855
Fax: (44) 1795414555
E-Mail: contact@dovetailservices.com
Web Site: www.dovetailservices.com
Emp.: 300
Subscription Marketing & Fulfilment Services
S.I.C.: 7389
N.A.I.C.S.: 561499
Julian Thorne *(Mng Dir)*

Joint Ventures:

DTV Services Limited **(2)**
Broadcast Centre BC3 D5
201 Wood Lane, London, W12 7TP, United Kingdom
Tel.: (44) 8708809980
Web Site: www.freeview.co.uk
Holding Company; Digital Television Services
S.I.C.: 6719
N.A.I.C.S.: 551112

UKTV Interactive Limited **(2)**
160 Great Portland St
London, W1W 5QA, United Kingdom UK
Tel.: (44) 2072996200
Fax: (44) 2072996000
Web Site: www.uktv.co.uk
Rev.: $325,856,992
Emp.: 900
Television Broadcasting; Owned 50% by British Broadcasting Corporation & 50% by NTL Incorporated
S.I.C.: 4833
N.A.I.C.S.: 515120
Matthee Littlesort *(COO)*

U.S. Subsidiary:

BBC Worldwide America Inc. **(2)**
1120 Ave Of Americas Fl 5
New York, NY 10036
Tel.: (212) 705-9300
Fax: (212) 894-4403
E-Mail: info@bbcamerica.com
Web Site: www.bbcamerica.com
Emp.: 90
Radio & TV Broadcaster
S.I.C.: 7812
N.A.I.C.S.: 512110
Herb Scannell *(Pres)*
Fred Medina *(Mng Dir & Exec VP-Latin America & Hispanic)*
Ann Sarnoff *(COO)*
Mark Gall *(Exec VP-Ad Sls)*
Soumya Sriraman *(Exec VP-Home Entertainment & Licensing)*
Matt Stein *(Sr VP-Mktg, Promo & Creative Svcs)*

Subsidiary:

New Video Channel LLC **(3)**
1120 Ave of the Americas
New York, NY 10036
Tel.: (212) 705-9300
Fax: (212) 894-4403
E-Mail: info@bbcamerica.com
Web Site: www.bbcamerica.com
Emp.: 150
Cable & Satellite Broadcaster of British Television Programs in the United States
S.I.C.: 4841
N.A.I.C.S.: 515210
Valerie Bruce *(Sr VP-Bus Affairs)*
Richard De Croce *(Sr VP-Programming)*

Non-U.S. Subsidiary:

Lonely Planet Publications Pty Limited **(2)**
90 Maribyrnong Street
Footscray, VIC, 3011, Australia AU
Tel.: (61) 383798000 (100%)
Fax: (61) 383798111
E-Mail: reception@onelyplanet.com.au
Web Site: www.lonelyplanet.com
Sales Range: $75-99.9 Million
Emp.: 300
Travel Guidebook Publisher; Travel Services
S.I.C.: 2731
N.A.I.C.S.: 511130
Maureen Wheeler *(Co-Founder)*
Tony Wheeler *(Co-Founder)*

BRITISH COLUMBIA FERRY SERVICES INC

Suite 500 - 1321 Blanshard Street
Victoria, BC, V8W 0B7, Canada
Tel.: (250) 381-1401
Fax: (250) 978-1119
Toll Free: (888) 223-3779
E-Mail: customerservice@bcferries.com
Web Site: www.bcferries.com
Rev.: $781,670,489
Assets: $1,813,372,794
Liabilities: $1,477,495,424
Net Worth: $335,877,370
Earnings: $15,415,262
Emp.: 4,500
Fiscal Year-end: 03/31/13

Business Description:
Ferry Services
S.I.C.: 4489
N.A.I.C.S.: 483212

Personnel:
Donald P. Hayes *(Chm)*
Mike Corrigan *(Pres & CEO)*
Rob Clark *(CFO & Exec VP)*
Pierre Vorster *(CIO & VP)*
M. Alana Gallaher *(Treas)*
Cynthia M. Lukaitis *(Sec & VP)*
Glen N. Schwartz *(Exec VP-HR & Corp Dev)*

Board of Directors:
Donald P. Hayes
Jane M. Bird
John A. Horning
Guy D. Johnson
Brian G. Kenning
Gordon R. Larkin
Maureen V. Macarenko
P. Geoffrey Plant
Graham M. Wilson

BRITISH COLUMBIA INVESTMENT MANAGEMENT CORPORATION

301- 2940 Jutland Road
Victoria, BC, V8T 5K6, Canada
Tel.: (250) 356-0263
Fax: (250) 387-7874
E-Mail: communications@bcimc.com
Web Site: www.bcimc.com
Rev.: $200,738,363
Assets: $54,118,425
Liabilities: $49,122,480
Net Worth: $4,995,945
Earnings: $834,977
Emp.: 192
Fiscal Year-end: 03/31/13

Business Description:
Public Funds Investment Management Services
S.I.C.: 6211
N.A.I.C.S.: 523999

Personnel:
Rick Mahler *(Chm)*
Doug Pearce *(CEO & Chief Investment Officer)*
Steve Barnett *(COO)*

Robert des Trois Maisons *(Gen Counsel & Sr VP-Legal Affairs)*
Dean Atkins *(Sr VP-Mortgages)*
Paul Flanagan *(Sr VP-Fixed Income)*
Mary Garden *(Sr VP-Real Estate)*
Lynn Hannah *(Sr VP-Consulting & Client Svcs)*
Carol Iverson *(Sr VP-HR)*
Shauna Lukaitis *(Sr VP-Trade Mgmt & Compliance)*
Michelle Ostermann *(Sr VP-Res & Risk Measurement)*
Gina Pala *(Sr VP-IT)*
Bryan Thomson *(Sr VP-Equity Investments)*
Lincoln Webb *(Sr VP-Private Placements)*
David Woodward *(Sr VP-Fin)*
Board of Directors:
Rick Mahler
Joan Axford
Dennis Blatchford
Ron McEachern
John Wilson
Ken Woods
Cheryl Yaremko

Holdings:

Corix Group (1)
1188 W Georgia St Ste 1160
Vancouver, BC, V6E 4A2, Canada
Tel.: (604) 273-4987
Fax: (604) 697-6703
E-Mail: brett.hodson@corix.com
Web Site: www.corix.com
Emp.: 1,400
Utility Infrastructure System Design, Construction & Management Services; Owned by CAI Capital Management Inc. & British Columbia Investment Management Corporation
S.I.C.: 1623
N.A.I.C.S.: 237110
Brett Hodson *(CEO)*

Delta Hotels Limited (1)
77 King St W Ste 2300
Toronto, ON, M5K 1G8, Canada
Tel.: (416) 874-2000
Fax: (416) 874-2001
Toll Free: (800) 266-1133
E-Mail: info@deltahotels.com
Web Site: www.deltahotels.com
Emp.: 7,000
Hotels & Resorts Operator
S.I.C.: 7011
N.A.I.C.S.: 721110
Ken Greene *(CEO)*
Josef Ebner *(Mng Dir & Reg VP-Delta Chelsea)*
David Bird *(Sr VP-Ops)*
Bill Pallett *(Sr VP-HR)*

Subsidiary:

Delta Grand Okanagan Resort and Conference Centre (2)
1310 Water Street
Kelowna, BC, V1Y 9P3, Canada
Tel.: (250) 763-4500
Fax: (250) 763-4565
Toll Free: (800) 465-4651
E-Mail: dbibby@deltahotels.com
Web Site: www.deltagrandokanagan.com
Emp.: 300
Hotel & Conference Hall Operations
S.I.C.: 7011
N.A.I.C.S.: 721110
Daneil Bibby *(Gen Mgr)*

Parkbridge Lifestyle Communities Inc. (1)
Ste 1500 500 4th Ave SW
Calgary, AB, T2P 2V6, Canada AB
Tel.: (403) 215-2100
Fax: (403) 215-2115
E-Mail: info@parkbridge.com
Web Site: www.parkbridge.com
Sales Range: $100-124.9 Million
Emp.: 380
Land Lease Communities & Destination R.V. Resorts Owner & Operator
S.I.C.: 6519
N.A.I.C.S.: 531190
Joseph F. Killi *(Chm)*
Iain Stewart *(Exec VP-Asset Mgmt)*
Bill Wells *(Sr VP-Dev)*

Subsidiaries:

Albion Sun Vista Development Corporation (2)
6600 Mitch Owens Rd
Greely, Ottawa, ON, K4P 1M5, Canada
Tel.: (613) 822-4530
Fax: (613) 822-4531
Toll Free: (877) 860-4889
E-Mail: rbilczuk@rogers.com
Web Site: www.albionwoods.ca
Single Family Home Construction & Development
S.I.C.: 1521
N.A.I.C.S.: 236115
Rob Bilczuk *(Gen Mgr)*

Bailey's Bay Resort Ltd. (2)
78 Lindsay Rd
Box 8620
Peterborough, ON, K9J 6X3, Canada
Tel.: (705) 748-9656
Fax: (705) 748-0615
E-Mail: baileysbayinfo@parkbridge.ca
Web Site: www.baileysbayresort.ca
Emp.: 25
RV Camping Resort
S.I.C.: 7033
N.A.I.C.S.: 721211
Garry Smith *(Mgr-Resort)*

Bay Port Yachting Centre (2)
156 Marina Park Avenue
PO Box 644
Midland, ON, L4R 4P4, Canada
Tel.: (705) 527-7678
Fax: (705) 527-4190
Toll Free: (888) 229-7678
E-Mail: bayport@bayportyc.com
Web Site: www.bayportyc.com
Emp.: 50
Marina
S.I.C.: 4493
N.A.I.C.S.: 713930
Scott Cain *(Mgr-Ops)*

Beaver Narrows (2)
433 Beaver Rd
PO Box 60
Omemee, ON, K0L 2W0, Canada
Tel.: (705) 799-6221
Fax: (705) 799-6220
E-Mail: info@beavernarrows.ca
Web Site: parkbridge.ca/prop/cottagerv/beavernarrows/contactus.aspx
Emp.: 10
RV Resort
S.I.C.: 7033
N.A.I.C.S.: 721211
Glenna Beattie *(Mgr-Resort)*

Bluewater Country (2)
5700 Blackwell Side Road
Sarnia, ON, N7W 1B7, Canada
Tel.: (519) 542-7800
Fax: (519) 542-4377
Toll Free: (800) 934-9996
E-Mail: info@bwcountry.com
Web Site: www.bwcountry.com
Emp.: 10
Single Family Home Construction & Development
S.I.C.: 1521
N.A.I.C.S.: 236115

Cherry Hill at Vineland (2)
3515 Rittenhouse Road
Vineland, ON, L0R 2C0, Canada
Tel.: (905) 562-7763
Fax: (905) 562-0912
Toll Free: (800) 479-9777
E-Mail: cherryhill@parkbridge.ca
Emp.: 4
Single Family Home Construction & Development
S.I.C.: 1521
N.A.I.C.S.: 236115
Jason Wakem *(Mgr-Community)*

Our Ponderosa Family Campground & Golf Resort (2)
9338 W Ipperwash Rd
Lambton Shores, ON, N0N 1J0, Canada
Tel.: (519) 786-2031
Fax: (519) 786-5031
E-Mail: camping@ourponderosa.com
Web Site: www.ourponderosa.com
Emp.: 25
RV & Golf Resort
S.I.C.: 7033
N.A.I.C.S.: 721211
Jenny Barbash *(Reg Mgr)*

Parkbridge GP Inc. (2)
Concession 8 West
Freelton, ON, L0R 1K0, Canada
Tel.: (905) 659-2050
Fax: (905) 659-3516
Toll Free: (800) 856-4318
E-Mail: antrimgelnsales@cogeco.net
Emp.: 50
Single Family Construction & Development
S.I.C.: 1521
N.A.I.C.S.: 236115
Bill Wells *(VP)*

Parkland Village (2)
53222 Range Rd 272
Spruce Grove, AB, T7X 3N4, Canada
Tel.: (780) 962-0403
Fax: (780) 962-0406
E-Mail: plvsales@countryhillshomes.com
Web Site: www.parkbridge.ca/prop/allage/parkland/locationcontactus.aspx
Single Family Home Construction & Development
S.I.C.: 1521
N.A.I.C.S.: 236115
Rick Lebouthillier *(VP)*

Pioneer Point (2)
2560 Westview Road
Lakefield, ON, K0L 2H0, Canada
Tel.: (705) 657-8831
Fax: (705) 657-9281
E-Mail: pioneerpoint@nexicom.net
Web Site: www.parkbridge.ca/prop/cottagerv/pioneerpoint/contactus.aspx
RV Resort
S.I.C.: 7033
N.A.I.C.S.: 721211
Grant Loosemore *(Gen Mgr)*

Ranch Estates (2)
100 Ranchwood Lane
Strathmore, AB, T1P 1M8, Canada
Tel.: (403) 934-5630
Fax: (403) 934-5636
E-Mail: ranchestates@parkbridge.com
Web Site: parkbridge.ca/prop/ResCom/ranchestates/home.aspx
Emp.: 1
Single Family Homes
S.I.C.: 1521
N.A.I.C.S.: 236115

Sama (2)
Highway 7 East RR 3
Havelock, ON, K0L 1Z0, Canada
Tel.: (705) 778-2341
Fax: (705) 778-2997
E-Mail: samapark@parkbridge.ca
Emp.: 5
Single Family Home Construction & Development
S.I.C.: 1521
N.A.I.C.S.: 236115
Diane Cox *(Gen Mgr)*

Wasaga Pines Resort (2)
1780 County Rd 92 Ste K
Elmvale, ON, L0L 1P0, Canada
Tel.: (705) 322-2727
Fax: (705) 322-5284
E-Mail: wasagapines@rogers.com
Web Site: www.parkbridge.ca
RV Resort
S.I.C.: 7033
N.A.I.C.S.: 721211
Len Gorski *(Gen Mgr)*

Affiliate:

Canadian Hotel Income Properties Real Estate Investment Trust (1)
The Burrard Bldg Ste 1600
1030 W Georgia St, Vancouver, BC, V6E 2Y3, Canada BC
Tel.: (604) 646-2447
Fax: (914) 646-2404
Sales Range: $300-349.9 Million
Emp.: 3,000
Real Estate Investment Trust Services & Hotel Management
S.I.C.: 6726
N.A.I.C.S.: 525990

Subsidiary:

SilverBirch Hotels & Resorts (2)
1600 1030 W Georgia Street
The Burrard Building, Vancouver, BC, V6E 2Y3, Canada (100%)
Tel.: (604) 646-2447
Fax: (604) 646-2404
Toll Free: (800) 431-.0070
Web Site: www.silverbirchhotels.com
Emp.: 50
Business Services
S.I.C.: 7389
N.A.I.C.S.: 561499
Steve Giblin *(Pres & CEO)*
Christine Maassen *(Sr VP-HR)*
Robb Walker *(Sr VP-Ops)*

Joint Venture:

TimberWest Forest Corp. (1)
3rd Fl 856 Homer St
Vancouver, BC, V6B 2W5, Canada
Tel.: (604) 654-4600
Fax: (604) 654-4571
Web Site: www.timberwest.com
Sales Range: $250-299.9 Million
Emp.: 80
Logging & Lumbermill Services
S.I.C.: 2411
N.A.I.C.S.: 113310
David L. Emerson *(Chm)*
Brian E. Frank *(Pres & CEO)*
John B. Mitchell *(Chief Forester Officer)*
Brenda Blue *(Sec & Dir-Fin)*

U.S. Joint Venture:

Puget Energy, Inc. (1)
10885 NE 4th St Ste 1200
Bellevue, WA 98004-5591 WA
Mailing Address:
PO Box 97034
Bellevue, WA 98009-9734
Tel.: (425) 454-6363
Fax: (425) 424-6537
Toll Free: (888) 225-5773
E-Mail: durga.waite@pse.com
Web Site: www.pugetenergy.com
Rev.: $3,187,297,000
Assets: $12,906,575,000
Liabilities: $9,226,896,000
Net Worth: $3,679,679,000
Earnings: $285,728,000
Fiscal Year-end: 12/31/13
Holding Company; Electric Power & Gas Distr
S.I.C.: 4911
N.A.I.C.S.: 221122
William S. Ayer *(Chm)*
Kimberly J. Harris *(Pres & CEO)*
Daniel A. Doyle *(CFO & Sr VP)*
Michael J. Stranik *(Chief Acctg Officer & Controller)*
Don E. Gaines *(Treas & VP-Fin)*

Subsidiary:

Puget Sound Energy, Inc. (2)
10885 NE 4th St Ste 1200
Bellevue, WA 98004-5591 WA
Mailing Address:
PO Box 97034
Bellevue, WA 98009-9734
Tel.: (425) 454-6363
Fax: (425) 424-6537
Web Site: www.pse.com
Rev.: $3,187,335,000
Assets: $10,808,888,000
Liabilities: $7,368,131,000
Net Worth: $3,440,757,000
Earnings: $356,129,000
Emp.: 2,700
Fiscal Year-end: 12/31/13
Electric Power & Natural Gas Distribution & Generation Services
S.I.C.: 4939
N.A.I.C.S.: 221122
William S. Ayer *(Chm)*
Kimberly J. Harris *(Pres & CEO)*
Daniel A. Doyle *(CFO & Sr VP)*
Rudiger H. Wolf *(CIO & VP)*
Jennifer L. O'Connor *(Gen Counsel, Sec, Sr VP, Chief Ethics & Compliance Officer)*
Eric M. Markell *(Chief Strategy Officer & Sr VP)*
Marla D. Mellies *(Sr VP & Chief Admin Officer)*

British Columbia Investment Management Corporation—(Continued)

James W. Eldredge *(Chief Acctg Officer, VP & Controller)*
Steve R. Secrist *(VP, Gen Counsel & Chief Ethics & Compliance Officer)*
Donald E. Gaines *(Treas & VP-Fin)*
Paul M. Wiegand *(Sr VP-Energy Ops)*

Subsidiaries:

Hydro Energy Development Corp. **(3)**
10885 NE 4th St Ste 1200
Bellevue, WA 98004 WA
Tel.: (425) 456-2570
Fax: (425) 456-3128
Emp.: 3
Small Hydro Development
S.I.C.: 6794
N.A.I.C.S.: 533110
Martin Thompson *(VP)*

Puget Western, Inc. **(3)**
19515 North Creek Pkwy Ste 310
Bothell, WA 98011-8200 WA
Tel.: (425) 487-6550
Fax: (425) 487-6565
Web Site: www.pugetwestern.com
Emp.: 5
Real Estate Holding & Developing
S.I.C.: 6552
N.A.I.C.S.: 237210
Gus Erikson *(Pres)*

Non-U.S. Joint Venture:

Open Grid Europe GmbH **(1)**
Kallenbergstrasse 5
D-45141 Essen, Germany De
Tel.: (49) 201 3642 0
Fax: (49) 201 3642 13900
E-Mail: info@open-grid-europe.com
Web Site: www.open-grid-europe.com
Holding Company; Natural Gas Pipeline Transportation Services
S.I.C.: 6719
N.A.I.C.S.: 551112
Stephan Kamphues *(Chm-Mgmt Bd)*
Jurgen Fuhlrott *(Mng Dir)*
Thomas Huwener *(Mng Dir)*
Ulrich Ronnacker *(Mng Dir)*
Wolfgang Anthes *(Member-Mgmt Bd)*
Jorg Bergmann *(Member-Mgmt Bd)*

Subsidiaries:

Mittelrheinische Erdgastransportleitungsgesellschaft mbH **(2)**
Neuer Markt 29
42781 Haan, Germany De
Mailing Address:
Postfach 1253
42756 Haan, Germany
Tel.: (49) 212993530
Fax: (49) 212952572
Emp.: 3
Natural Gas Pipeline Transportation Services
S.I.C.: 4923
N.A.I.C.S.: 486210
Jochen Schafer *(Mng Dir)*

PLEdoc Gesellschaft fur Dokumentationserstellung und -pflege mbH **(2)**
Schnieringshof 10-14
D-45329 Essen, Germany De
Tel.: (49) 201 3659 0
Fax: (49) 201 3659 163
E-Mail: info@pledoc.de
Web Site: www.pledoc.de
Emp.: 130
Technical Consulting Services
S.I.C.: 8999
N.A.I.C.S.: 541690
Anne-Kathrin Wirtz *(Mng Dir & Member-Mgmt Bd)*
Matthias Lenz *(Member-Mgmt Bd)*

Joint Venture:

MEGAL Mittel-Europaische-Gasleitungsgesellschaft mbH & Co. KG **(2)**
Kallenbergstrasse 5
D-45141 Essen, Germany De
Tel.: (49) 201 3642 0
Fax: (49) 201 3642 13900
E-Mail: info@open-grid-europe.com
Web Site: www.open-grid-europe.com
Natural Gas Pipeline Transportation Services
S.I.C.: 4922
N.A.I.C.S.: 486210
Hans Jurgen Plattner *(Mng Dir)*

BRITISH COLUMBIA TRANSIT

(d/b/a BC Transit)
520 Gorge Road East
Victoria, BC, V8W 2P3, Canada
Tel.: (250) 385-2551
Fax: (250) 995-5639
E-Mail: info@bctransit.com
Web Site: www.bctransit.com
Rev.: $264,633,969
Assets: $1,160,641,608
Liabilities: $1,100,734,011
Net Worth: $59,907,597
Earnings: ($211,726)
Emp.: 700
Fiscal Year-end: 03/31/13
Business Description:
Passenger Transportation System
S.I.C.: 4131
N.A.I.C.S.: 485210
Personnel:
Kevin D. Mahoney *(Chm)*
Manuel Achadinha *(Pres & CEO)*
Mike Davis *(COO & VP-Ops)*
Brian Anderson *(CIO & VP-Bus Dev)*
Board of Directors:
Kevin D. Mahoney
Susan M. Brice
Kelly A. Cairns
Bob de Clark
Carol Hamilton
Peter Milobar
Mary Sjostrom

BRITISH CONTROLLED OILFIELDS LIMITED

1155 Rue University Suite 1310
Montreal, QC, H3B 3A7, Canada
Tel.: (514) 871-9571
Fax: (514) 397-0816
Year Founded: 1918
BCO—(TSXV)
Rev.: $96,493
Assets: $3,328,852
Liabilities: $21,848
Net Worth: $3,307,004
Earnings: ($187,878)
Fiscal Year-end: 12/31/12
Business Description:
Investment Management Services
S.I.C.: 6282
N.A.I.C.S.: 523920
Personnel:
Michael A. Salberg *(Pres & CEO)*
Robert Salberg *(CFO)*
Harry J. F. Bloomfield *(Sec)*
Board of Directors:
Harry J. F. Bloomfield
Anita M. G. Hecht
Michael A. Salberg
Robert Salberg
Transfer Agent:
Computershare Trust Company of Canada
Montreal, QC, Canada

BRITISH CONVERTING SOLUTIONS, LTD.

Youngs Industrial Estate
Stanbridge Road, Leighton Buzzard, Bedfordshire, LU7 4QB, United Kingdom
Tel.: (44) 1727 866233
Fax: (44) 1727 862847
Business Description:
Box Mfr
S.I.C.: 2657
N.A.I.C.S.: 322212
Personnel:
Barry Tabor *(Mng Dir)*

BRITISH EMPIRE SECURITIES AND GENERAL TRUST PLC

Springfield Lodge Colchester Road
Chelmsford, Essex, CM2 5PW, United Kingdom
Tel.: (44) 2076472900
Fax: (44) 2076472901
Web Site: www.british-empire.co.uk
BTEM—(LSE)
Sales Range: $125-149.9 Million
Business Description:
Closed-End Investment Trust
S.I.C.: 6733
N.A.I.C.S.: 525920
Personnel:
Joe Bauernfreund *(Mgr-Fund)*
Board of Directors:
Strone Macpherson
Steven Andrew Ralph Bates
Susan Noble
Nigel Rich
Andrew Robson
Legal Counsel:
Herbert Smith
Exchange Square Primrose Street
London, United Kingdom
Transfer Agent:
Equiniti Limited
Aspect House Spencer Road
Lancing, West Sussex, BN99 6DA, United Kingdom
Tel.: (44) 121 415 7005
Fax: (44) 871 384 2100

BRITISH FILM INSTITUTE

21 Stephen Street
London, W1T 1LN, United Kingdom
Tel.: (44) 2072551444
Web Site: www.bfi.org.uk
Year Founded: 1933
Sales Range: $25-49.9 Million
Emp.: 493
Business Description:
Film & Television Education Exhibition & Distr; National Film Archive of the UK
S.I.C.: 7829
N.A.I.C.S.: 512120
Personnel:
Gregory Dyke *(Chm)*
Amanda Nevill *(CEO)*
Board of Directors:
Gregory Dyke
Charles Cecil
Shami Chakrabarti
Pete Czernin
Peter Foy
Christopher Frayling
Ashley Highfield
Amanda Nevill
Howard Newby
Jonathan Ross
David Thompson
Andrea Wong
Cy Young
Subsidiary:

BFI (Big Screen) Limited **(1)**
21 Stephen Street
London, W1T 1LN, United Kingdom
Tel.: (44) 2072551444
Motion Picture Production & Distribution Services
S.I.C.: 7812
N.A.I.C.S.: 512110

THE BRITISH LAND COMPANY PLC

York House 45 Seymour Street
London, W1H 7LX, United Kingdom
Tel.: (44) 2074864466
Telex: 28411
Fax: (44) 2079355552
E-Mail: info@britishland.com
Web Site: www.britishland.com
BLND—(LSE)
Sales Range: $1-4.9 Billion
Emp.: 179
Business Description:
Real Estate Investment Trust
S.I.C.: 6726
N.A.I.C.S.: 525990
Personnel:
John Gildersleeve *(Chm)*
Chris Grigg *(CEO)*
Anthony Braine *(Sec)*
Board of Directors:
John Gildersleeve
Aubrey Adams
Lucinda M. Bell
Simon A. Borrows
Anthony Braine
Chris Grigg
Dido Harding
William Jackson
Charles Maudsley
Timothy M. Roberts
Andrew Turnbull
Subsidiaries:

The British Land Corporation Ltd. **(1)**
45 Seymour Street
London, 1H 7LX, United Kingdom
Tel.: (44) 2074864466
Telex: 28411
Fax: (44) 2079355552
E-Mail: info@britishland.com
Emp.: 200
Property Trading & Development
S.I.C.: 6221
N.A.I.C.S.: 523130

British Land Developments Ltd. **(1)**
45 Seymour St York House
45 Seymour Street, London, W1H 7LX, United Kingdom
Tel.: (44) 2074864466
Fax: (44) 2079355552
E-Mail: info@britishland.com
Emp.: 170
Land Developer
S.I.C.: 6552
N.A.I.C.S.: 237210

British Land Financing Ltd. **(1)**
York House 45 Seymour St
London, W1H 7LX, United Kingdom
Tel.: (44) 2074864466
Fax: (44) 2079355552
E-Mail: info@britishland.com
Emp.: 300
Land Financing Services
S.I.C.: 6726
N.A.I.C.S.: 525990

British Land Properties Ltd. **(1)**
York House
45 Seymour Street W, London, W1H7 LX, United Kingdom
Tel.: (44) 2074864466
Fax: (44) 2079355552
E-Mail: info@britishland.com
Web Site: www.britishland.com
Emp.: 200
Land Developer
S.I.C.: 6552
N.A.I.C.S.: 237210

British Land Retail Warehouses Limited **(1)**
York House 45 Seymour Street
London, W1H 7JT, United Kingdom
Tel.: (44) 2074864466
Fax: (44) 2074672995
Real Estate Management Services
S.I.C.: 6531
N.A.I.C.S.: 531390

Broadgate Estates Ltd. **(1)**
Exchange House 12 Exchange Square
London, EC2A 2BQ, United Kingdom
Tel.: (44) 2075054000
Fax: (44) 2073829854
E-Mail: info@broadgateestates.co.uk
Web Site: www.broadgateestates.co.uk

Emp.: 150
Land Developer
S.I.C.: 6552
N.A.I.C.S.: 237210
Steve Whyman *(Mng Dir)*

St. Stephens Shopping Centre Limited (1)
The Management Suite 110 Ferensway
Kingston upon Hull, HU2 8LN, United Kingdom
Tel.: (44) 1482 313 960
Fax: (44) 1482 333 624
E-Mail: enquiries@ststephens-hull.com
Web Site: www.ststephens-hull.com
Shopping Mall Management Services
S.I.C.: 6512
N.A.I.C.S.: 531120
Jim Harris *(Mgr-Centre)*

Non-U.S. Subsidiaries:

British Land Investments Netherlands BV (1)
Atrium Bldg Strawinskylaan 3085
1077 ZX Amsterdam, Netherlands (100%)
Tel.: (31) 206429848
E-Mail: dutchofficeadmin@britishland.com
Emp.: 5
Property Trading & Development
S.I.C.: 6331
N.A.I.C.S.: 524126
Arend J. van der Marel *(Mng Dir)*

THE BRITISH LIBRARY

Saint Pancras 96 Euston Road
London, NW1 2DB, United Kingdom
Tel.: (44) 843 2081144
E-Mail: customer-services@bl.uk
Web Site: www.bl.uk
Rev.: $199,151,628
Assets: $1,118,664,803
Liabilities: $39,605,435
Net Worth: $1,079,059,368
Earnings: $2,615,304
Emp.: 1,636
Fiscal Year-end: 03/31/13

Business Description:
Library Services
S.I.C.: 8231
N.A.I.C.S.: 519120

Personnel:
Baroness Blackstone *(Chm)*
Roly Keating *(CEO)*
Steve Morris *(CFO)*
Phil Spence *(COO)*
Richard Boulderstone *(Chief Digital Officer)*

Board of Directors:
Baroness Blackstone
Dawn Airey
David Barclay
Robert Black
Kenneth Calman
Robert Fellowes
Wendy Hall
Roly Keating
Mike Lynch
Kate McLuskie
Stephen Page
Patrick Plant
Maggie Semple

BRITISH LINEN ADVISERS HOLDINGS

8 Frederick's Pl
London, EC2R 8HY, United Kingdom
Tel.: (44) 20 7710 8800
Fax: (44) 20 7710 8813
Sales Range: $1-9.9 Million
Emp.: 25

Business Description:
Holding Company: Banking Services
S.I.C.: 6719
N.A.I.C.S.: 551112

Non-U.S. Subsidiaries:

Brilliant Lighting Pty Ltd (1)
956 Stud Rd
PO Box 2529
Rowville, VIC, 3178, Australia
Tel.: (61) 397652555
Fax: (61) 397630277
E-Mail: briliant-lighting@blinklighting.com
Web Site: www.blinklighting.com
Sales Range: $1-9.9 Million
Emp.: 35
Mfr of Residential Lighting Fixtures
Import
S.I.C.: 3645
N.A.I.C.S.: 335121
Norman Cyril Levin *(CEO)*

L'Eclairage Technique S.A. (1)
41 Rue Lafayette
Laxou, 54528, France
Mailing Address:
PO Box 69
Laxou, 54520, France
Tel.: (33) 383393828
Fax: (33) 383393895
E-Mail: export@eclatec.com
Web Site: www.eclatec.com
Emp.: 120
Mfr of Lighting Fixtures
Import Export
S.I.C.: 3648
N.A.I.C.S.: 335129
Vincent Carru *(Pres)*

THE BRITISH PLASTICS FEDERATION

6 Bath Pl
London, EC2A 3JE, United Kingdom
Tel.: (44) 2074575000
Fax: (44) 2074575045
E-Mail: bpf@bpf.co.uk
Web Site: www.bpf.co.uk
Year Founded: 1933
Sales Range: $100-124.9 Million
Emp.: 18

Business Description:
Trade Association for UK Plastics Industry
S.I.C.: 8611
N.A.I.C.S.: 813910

Personnel:
Philip Watkinn *(Pres)*
Peter Davis *(Dir Gen)*

BRITISH POLYTHENE INDUSTRIES PLC

96 Port Glasgow Road
Greenock, PA15 2UL, United Kingdom
Tel.: (44) 1475501000
Fax: (44) 1475743143
E-Mail: enquiries@bpipoly.com
Web Site: www.bpipoly.com
BPI—(LSE)
Sls.: $756,006,123
Assets: $363,552,558
Liabilities: $272,111,667
Net Worth: $91,440,891
Earnings: $21,794,202
Emp.: 2,292
Fiscal Year-end: 12/31/12

Business Description:
Industrial & Consumer Packaging Mfr
S.I.C.: 2671
N.A.I.C.S.: 326112

Personnel:
Cameron McLatchie *(Chm)*
John Langlands *(CEO)*

Board of Directors:
Cameron McLatchie
Hamish McLeod Grossart
David Harris
John Langlands
Jamie Lindsay
Ron Marsh
Ian Russell
David Warnock

Legal Counsel:
Maclay Murray & Spens LLP
1 George Square
Glasgow, United Kingdom

Subsidiaries:

BPI plc (1)
The Moor Road
Sevenoaks, Kent, TN14 5EQ, United Kingdom
Tel.: (44) 1732450001
Fax: (44) 1732740043
E-Mail: info@bpifilms.com
Web Site: www.bpifilms.com
Emp.: 80
Plastic Products Mfr
S.I.C.: 3089
N.A.I.C.S.: 326199
Garry Buchalter *(Dir-Ops)*

British Polythene Limited (1)
Worcester Road
Leominster, Herefordshire, HR6 0QA, United Kingdom
Tel.: (44) 1568617220
Fax: (44) 1568611435
E-Mail: sales@bpiagri.com
Web Site: www.bpiagri.com
Emp.: 250
Polythene Products Mfr
S.I.C.: 3081
N.A.I.C.S.: 326113
Barry Buckley *(Dir-Sls)*

Non-U.S. Subsidiaries:

AT Films Inc. (1)
4605-101 Ave
Edmonton, AB, T6B 3R4, Canada
Tel.: (780) 450-7760
Fax: (780) 450-7777
E-Mail: info@atfilmsinc.com
Web Site: www.atfilmsinc.com
Emp.: 80
Polythene Film Products Mfr
S.I.C.: 3081
N.A.I.C.S.: 326113
Calvin Mazurenko *(Mng Dir)*

BPI Europe B V (1)
Bruchterweg 88
7772BJ Hardenberg, Netherlands (100%)
Tel.: (31) 523288888
Fax: (31) 523288240
E-Mail: indupac@indupac.com
Web Site: www.indupac.com
Emp.: 6
Religious Organizations
S.I.C.: 8661
N.A.I.C.S.: 813110
R. De Gonge *(Mng Dir)*

Combipac BV (1)
Bruchterweg 88
7772BJ Hardenberg, Netherlands (100%)
Tel.: (31) 523288888
Fax: (31) 523288240
E-Mail: indupac@indupac.com
Web Site: www.indupac.com
Emp.: 170
Religious Organizations
S.I.C.: 8661
N.A.I.C.S.: 813110
Rick Degonge *(Mng Dir)*

Irish Polythene Industries Ltd (1)
Toughers Business Park
Kildare, Ireland (100%)
Tel.: (353) 45431777
Fax: (353) 454444620
E-Mail: enquiries@irishpolyagri.com
Web Site: www.bpipoly.com
Emp.: 10
Plastics Materials & Basic Forms & Shapes Whslr
S.I.C.: 5162
N.A.I.C.S.: 424610
Shaun Connor *(CEO)*

BRITISH SKY BROADCASTING GROUP PLC

(d/b/a BSkyB Group)
Grant Way
Isleworth, TW7 5QD, United Kingdom
Tel.: (44) 20 7705 3000
Fax: (44) 20 7705 3060
E-Mail: corporate.communications@bskyb.com
Web Site: www.sky.com
BSY—(LSE OTC)
Rev.: $11,426,163,150
Assets: $10,020,595,050
Liabilities: $8,422,353,570
Net Worth: $1,598,241,480
Earnings: $1,546,124,910
Emp.: 19,413
Fiscal Year-end: 06/30/13

Business Description:
Holding Company; Television Broadcasting, Multimedia Entertainment Publishing & Telecommunications Services
S.I.C.: 6719
N.A.I.C.S.: 551112

Personnel:
Jeremy Darroch *(CEO)*
Andrew Griffith *(CFO & Mng Dir-Comml Bus)*
Didier Lebrat *(CTO)*
Amy Holland *(Mgr-Consumer PR-Products Svcs & Brand)*
James Conyers *(Gen Counsel)*
Chris Taylor *(Sec)*

Board of Directors:
Nicholas Ferguson
Chase Carey
Tracy Jayne Clarke
Jeremy Darroch
David F. DeVoe
Martin James Gilbert
Adine Grate
Andrew Griffith
Andrew Higginson
Dave Lewis
James Rupert Murdoch
Matthieu Pigasse
Daniel Rimer
Arthur M. Siskind
Andrew J. Sukawaty

Legal Counsel:
Herbert Smith Freehills LLP
Exchange House Primrose Street
London, EC2A 2HS, United Kingdom

Subsidiaries:

Amstrad Limited (1)
Brentwood House 130 Kings Rd
Brentwood, Essex, CM14 4EQ, United Kingdom UK
Tel.: (44) 1277228888 (100%)
Fax: (44) 1277211350
E-Mail: info@amstrad.com
Web Site: www.amstrad.com
Sales Range: $150-199.9 Million
Emp.: 88
Office & Consumer Electronic Products Mfr
Import Export
S.I.C.: 3663
N.A.I.C.S.: 334220
Alun Webber *(Mng Dir)*

Non-U.S. Subsidiary:

Amstrad International Ltd. (2)
Unit 2701 27 Fl Well Tech Ctr
9 Pat Tat Street San Po Kong, Kowloon, China (Hong Kong)
Tel.: (852) 27517879
Fax: (852) 27955832
E-Mail: psuen@amstrad.com.hk
Emp.: 100
Office & Consumer Electronic Products Mfr
S.I.C.: 3663
N.A.I.C.S.: 334220

British Sky Broadcasting Limited (1)
Grant Way
Isleworth, Mddx, TW7 5QD, United Kingdom UK
Tel.: (44) 20 7705 3000
Fax: (44) 20 7705 3060
Web Site: www.sky.com
Television Broadcasting
S.I.C.: 4833
N.A.I.C.S.: 515120
Jeremy Darroch *(CEO)*
Mike Darcey *(COO)*

BSkyB Publications Limited (1)
Grant Way
Isleworth, Mddx, TW7 5QD, United Kingdom UK

British Sky Broadcasting Group plc—(Continued)

Tel.: (44) 2077053000
Fax: (44) 2077053030
Multimedia Publishing Services
S.I.C.: 2741
N.A.I.C.S.: 511199

Subsidiaries:

Challenge TV (2)
1 Braham Street
London, E1 8EP, United Kingdom UK
Tel.: (44) 20 7032 8000 (100%)
E-Mail: mysky@bskyb.com
Web Site: www.challenge.co.uk
Digital Television Broadcasting
S.I.C.: 4833
N.A.I.C.S.: 515120

Sky Living (2)
123 Buckingham Palace Road 2nd Floor
London, SW1W 9SL, United Kingdom UK
Tel.: (44) 20 7032 2000
Fax: (44) 207299600
E-Mail: enquiries@livingtv.co.uk
Web Site: www.sky.com
Emp.: 50
Television Broadcasting
S.I.C.: 4833
N.A.I.C.S.: 515120

The Cloud Networks Limited (1)
Third Floor 4 Victoria Square
Saint Albans, AL1 3TF, United Kingdom
Tel.: (44) 20 7710 6500
E-Mail: marketing@thecloud.net
Web Site: www.thecloud.net
Sales Range: $10-24.9 Million
Emp.: 70
Wireless Broadband Services
S.I.C.: 4899
N.A.I.C.S.: 517919
Niall Murphy *(Founder)*
Steve Nicholson *(CEO)*
Vince Russell *(Mng Dir)*
Jonathan Apps *(CFO)*
Paul Gooch *(COO)*

Sky Home Communications Limited (1)
(Formerly Be Un Limited)
260 Bath Road
Slough, SL1 4DX, United Kingdom UK
Tel.: (44) 2074795000
Fax: (44) 8707319130
E-Mail: finance@beunlimited.co.uk
Web Site: www.bethere.co.uk
Internet Service Provider
S.I.C.: 4899
N.A.I.C.S.: 517919
Chris Stening *(Mng Dir)*

Joint Venture:

DTV Services Limited (1)
Broadcast Centre BC3 D5
201 Wood Lane, London, W12 7TP, United Kingdom
Tel.: (44) 8708809980
Web Site: www.freeview.co.uk
Holding Company; Digital Television Services
S.I.C.: 6719
N.A.I.C.S.: 551112

THE BRITISH STANDARDS INSTITUTION

389 Chiswick High Rd
London, W4 4AL, United Kingdom
Tel.: (44) 2089969001
Fax: (44) 2089967001
E-Mail: cservices@bsigroup.com
Web Site: www.bsigroup.com
Year Founded: 1901
Rev.: $402,087,234
Assets: $265,478,649
Liabilities: $186,672,078
Net Worth: $78,806,571
Earnings: $36,797,457
Emp.: 2,796
Fiscal Year-end: 12/31/12

Business Description:
Quality Testing Services
Export
S.I.C.: 9199
N.A.I.C.S.: 921190

Personnel:
Howard Kerr *(CEO)*
Todd VanderVen *(Pres-America)*
Tony Wales *(Sec & Dir-Legal Affairs)*

Board of Directors:
David Brown
Keith Clarke
Tom Gorrie
Howard Kerr
Anthony Lea
John J. Regazzi
Lucinda Riches
Craig Smith
Scott Steedman

Subsidiary:

BSI Assurance UK Limited (1)
Kitemark Court Davy Avenue Knowlhill
Milton Keynes, MK5 8PP, United Kingdom
Tel.: (44) 845 080 9000
E-Mail: cservices@bsigroup.com
Business Support Services
N.A.I.C.S.: 561499
Mike Inman *(Mgr-Green Deal Product Technical)*

U.S. Division:

BSI Inc. (1)
12110 Sunset Hills Rd Ste 200
Reston, VA 20190-3223
Tel.: (703) 437-9000
Fax: (703) 437-9001
Toll Free: (800) 862-4977
Web Site: www.bsiamericas.com
Emp.: 70
Non-Profit Organization for Standards, Quality Services & Inspection
S.I.C.: 7389
N.A.I.C.S.: 541990
Todd Vanderven *(Pres)*
Reg Blake *(Mng Dir)*

Non-U.S. Subsidiaries:

BSI Brasil (1)
Rua Gomes de Carvalho 1069-18 andar
Vila Olimpia, Sao Paulo, 04547-004, Brazil
Tel.: (55) 11 2148 9600
Fax: (55) 11 2148 9601
E-Mail: bsibrasil@bsibrasil.com.br
Web Site: www.bsibrasil.com.br
Business Support Services
N.A.I.C.S.: 561499
Carlos Pitanga *(Pres)*

BSI Group (Australia and New Zealand) Pty Ltd (1)
Suite 2 Level 7 15 Talavera Road
Macquarie Park, NSW, 2113, Australia
Tel.: (61) 1300 237 808
Fax: (61) 1300 730 135
E-Mail: sales.aus@bsigroup.com
Web Site: www.bsigroup.com
Business Support Services
N.A.I.C.S.: 561499
Stephanie Vincent *(Gen Mgr-Compliance & Risk)*

BSI Group Canada Inc (1)
6205B Airport Rd Suite 414
Mississauga, ON, L4V 1E3, Canada
Tel.: (416) 620-9991
Fax: (416) 620-9911
Toll Free: (800) 862-6752
E-Mail: inquiry.canada@bsigroup.com
Web Site: www.bsigroup.ca
Business Support Services
N.A.I.C.S.: 561499
Anne-Marie Pizzitelli *(Mgr-Mktg)*

BSI Group Deutschland GmbH (1)
Hanauer Landstrasse 115
60314 Frankfurt am Main, Germany
Tel.: (49) 69 2222 8 9200
Fax: (49) 69 2222 8 9300
E-Mail: info.de@bsigroup.com
Web Site: www.bsigroup.com
Business Support Services
N.A.I.C.S.: 561499
Holly-Anna Evans *(Mgr-Sls)*

BSI Group Eurasia Certification Services Co. Ltd (1)
Degirmen Sk No 16 Ar Plaza Ofis 61/62 A
Blok Kozyatagi
Istanbul, Turkey
Tel.: (90) 216 445 90 38
Fax: (90) 216 463 26 26
E-Mail: bsi.eurasia@bsigroup.com
Web Site: www.bsi-turkey.com
Business Support Services
N.A.I.C.S.: 561499
Ozlem Unsal *(Mng Dir)*

BSI Group France Sarl (1)
3 rue Chauveau Lagarde
75008 Paris, France
Tel.: (33) 1 55 34 11 40
Fax: (33) 1 40 26 99 74
E-Mail: contact.france@bsigroup.com
Web Site: www.bsigroup.com
Business Support Services
N.A.I.C.S.: 561499

BSI Group India Private Ltd (1)
The MIRA Corporate Suites A-2 Plot 1&2
Ishwar Nagar
Mathura Road, New Delhi, 110065, India
Tel.: (91) 11 2692 9000
Fax: (91) 11 2692 9001
E-Mail: india.marketing@bsigroup.com
Web Site: www.bsigroup.co.in
Business Support Services
N.A.I.C.S.: 561499
Kapil Mahajan *(Head-Bus & Reg Mgr-Sls)*

BSI Group Italia SRL (1)
Via Fara 35
20124 Milan, Italy
Tel.: (39) 02 667909201
Fax: (39) 02 66981396
E-Mail: marketing.italy@bsigroup.com
Web Site: www.bsigroup.it
Business Support Services
N.A.I.C.S.: 561499
Rasa Kildisaite *(Mgr-Ops)*

BSI Group Japan KK (1)
Seizan Bldg 5F 2-12-28 Kita-Aoyama
Minato-ku, Tokyo, 107-0061, Japan
Tel.: (81) 6 6244 0770
Fax: (81) 6 6244 0550
Web Site: www.bsigroup.jp
Business Support Services
N.A.I.C.S.: 561499

BSI Group Korea Ltd (1)
21F Jongno Tower Building 6 Jongno 2-ga
Jongno-gu, Seoul, Korea (South)
Tel.: (82) 2 777 4123 4
Fax: (82) 2 777 4446
E-Mail: bsikorea@bsigroup.com
Web Site: www.bsigroup.co.kr
Business Support Services
N.A.I.C.S.: 561499

BSI Group Mexico S dr RL de CV (1)
Torre Mayor Av Paseo de la Reforma No 505 Piso 50-Suite A
Col Cuauhtemoc, Mexico, 06500, Mexico
Tel.: (52) 55 5241 1370
Web Site: www.bsigroup.com.mx
Business Support Services
N.A.I.C.S.: 561499
Nancy Guel *(Acct Mgr-Dev)*

BSI Group Polska Spolka z.o.o. (1)
ul Krolewska 16
00-103 Warsaw, Poland
Tel.: (48) 22 330 61 80
Fax: (48) 22 390 44 70
E-Mail: infopoland@bsigroup.com
Web Site: www.bsigroup.pl
Business Support Services
N.A.I.C.S.: 561499
Michal Krajewski *(Mgr-Client)*

BSI Group Singapore Pte Ltd (1)
1 Robinson Road 15-01 AIA Tower
Singapore, 048542, Singapore
Tel.: (65) 6270 0777
Fax: (65) 6270 2777
E-Mail: sgp@bsigroup.com
Web Site: www.bsigroup.com
Business Support Services
N.A.I.C.S.: 561499
Owen Xu *(Gen Mgr)*

BSI Group (Thailand) Co., Ltd (1)
127/25 Panjathani Tower Floor 20th Nonsee Road Chongnonsee
Yannawa, Bangkok, 10120, Thailand
Tel.: (66) 2 294 4889 92
Fax: (66) 2 294 4467
E-Mail: infothai@bsigroup.com
Web Site: www.bsigroup.co.th
Business Support Services
N.A.I.C.S.: 561499
Kwang Noi *(Mgr-Client)*

BSI Healthcare Saudi Arabia (1)
854 Olaya Street
Al Ghadir, Riyadh, Saudi Arabia
Tel.: (966) 1 210 7732
Business Support Services
N.A.I.C.S.: 561499

BSI Services Malaysia Sdn. Bhd. (1)
B-08-01 East Level 8 Block B PJ8 No 23
Jalan Barat Section 8, 46050 Petaling Jaya, Selangor, Malaysia
Tel.: (60) 3 7960 7801
Fax: (60) 3 7960 5801
E-Mail: info.malaysia@bsigroup.com
Web Site: www.bsigroup.com.my
Business Support Services
N.A.I.C.S.: 561499
Nicklaus Au *(Mgr-Bus Dev)*

BSI Vietnam Co., Ltd (1)
Unit 301-303 Saigon Software Park 123
Truong Dinh
Ward 7 Dist 3, Ho Chi Minh City, Vietnam
Tel.: (84) 8 39320 778
Fax: (84) 8 39320 779
E-Mail: info.vietnam@bsigroup.com
Web Site: www.bsigroup.com.vn
Business Support Services
N.A.I.C.S.: 561499
Duyenanh Le *(Country Mgr)*

NCS International Pty. Ltd. (1)
Unit 8 8 Greenhill Road
Wayville, SA, 5034, Australia
Tel.: (61) 8 8372 7807
Fax: (61) 8 8357 9552
Web Site: www.ncsi.com.au
Business Support Services
N.A.I.C.S.: 561499

PT BSI Group Indonesia (1)
Menara Bidakara 2-17th Floor Unit 5 Jl
Jend Gatot Subroto Kav 71-73
Komplek Bidakara Pancoran, Jakarta, 12870, Indonesia
Tel.: (62) 21 8379 3174 77
Fax: (62) 21 8379 3287
Web Site: www.bsigroup.com
Business Support Services
N.A.I.C.S.: 561499
Yuan Handayana *(Mng Dir)*

BRITISH UNITED PROVIDENT ASSOCIATION LTD.

(d/b/a BUPA)
BUPA House 15 - 19 Bloomsbury Way
London, WC1A 2BA, United Kingdom
Tel.: (44) 2076562000
Fax: (44) 2076562700
Web Site: www.bupa.com
Year Founded: 1947
Rev.: $13,224,816,531
Assets: $15,530,895,789
Liabilities: $7,922,034,498
Net Worth: $7,608,861,291
Earnings: $708,627,423
Emp.: 62,000
Fiscal Year-end: 12/31/12

Business Description:
Holding Company; Health Care Products & Services
S.I.C.: 6719
N.A.I.C.S.: 551112

Personnel:
Alexander P. Leitch *(Chm)*
Stuart Fletcher *(CEO)*
Evelyn Bourke *(CFO)*
Yasmin Jetha *(CIO)*
Theresa Heggie *(CMO & Chief Strategy Officer)*
Paul Newton *(Chief Legal Officer)*
Denise Collis *(Chief People Officer)*
Paul Zollinger-Read *(Chief Medical Officer)*
Nicholas Beazley *(Sec & Dir-Strategy)*

Board of Directors:

Alexander P. Leitch
M. Bottomley
Evelyn Bourke
Peter Cawdron
Lawrence Churchill
Rita Clifton
Stuart Fletcher
John Lorimer
George Mitchell
John Tooke

U.S. Subsidiary:

Health Dialog Services Corp. (1)
60 State Ste 1100
Boston, MA 02109
Tel.: (617) 406-5200
Fax: (617) 406-5201
Toll Free: (800) 893-5532
E-Mail: publicrelations@healthdialog.com
Web Site: www.healthdialog.com
Sales Range: $75-99.9 Million
Emp.: 150
Health Care Management Programs
S.I.C.: 8742
N.A.I.C.S.: 541611
George Bennett *(Chm)*
Christopher McKown *(Pres)*
Robert Mandel *(CEO)*
Bill Pelzar *(CIO)*
Peter Goldbach *(Chief Medical Officer)*
Jeffrey Doctoroff *(Gen Counsel & Sr VP)*
William Brennan *(Sr VP-Content Svcs & Product Dev)*
Mary Jane Favazza *(Sr VP-Client Ops)*
David Morris *(Sr VP-Sls & Svc)*
Craig Russell *(Sr VP-Strategic Initiatives)*

Subsidiary:

Health Dialog Analytic Solutions Corp. (2)
2 Monument Sq
Portland, ME 04101
Tel.: (207) 822-3700
Fax: (207) 771-5511
E-Mail: info@healthdialog.com
Web Site: www.healthdialog.com
Emp.: 150
Medical Analytical Solutions
S.I.C.: 8731
N.A.I.C.S.: 541712
James Tugendhat *(CEO)*

Non-U.S. Subsidiary:

Quality HealthCare Medical Services Limited (1)
3/F Skyline Tower 39 Wang Kwong Road
Kowloon Bay, Kowloon, China (Hong Kong) HK
Tel.: (852) 2975 3200 (100%)
E-Mail: info@qhms.com
Web Site: www.qhms.com
Emp.: 400
Contract Healthcare Services & Medical Centers Network Operator
S.I.C.: 8049
N.A.I.C.S.: 621399
Paul Li *(CEO)*

Subsidiaries:

Quality HealthCare Medical Centre Limited (2)
3/F Skyline Tower 39 Wang Kwong Road
Kowloon Bay, Kowloon, China (Hong Kong) HK
Tel.: (852) 2975 3200 (100%)
E-Mail: info@qhms.com
Web Site: www.qhms.com
Emp.: 200
HMO Medical Centers Operator
S.I.C.: 8011
N.A.I.C.S.: 621491

Quality HealthCare Nursing Agency Limited (2)
3/F Skyline Tower 39 Wang Kwong Road
Kowloon Bay, Kowloon, China (Hong Kong) HK
Tel.: (852) 2975 3200 (100%)
E-Mail: info@qhms.com
Web Site: www.qhms.com
Private Nursing Services
S.I.C.: 8049
N.A.I.C.S.: 621399

Quality HealthCare Physiotherapy Services Limited (2)
3/F Skyline Tower 39 Wang Kwong Road
Kowloon Bay, Kowloon, China (Hong Kong) HK
Tel.: (852) 2975 3200 (100%)
E-Mail: info@qhms.com
Web Site: www.qhms.com
Physiotherapy Services
S.I.C.: 8049
N.A.I.C.S.: 621340

BRITVIC PLC

Breakspear Park Breakspear Way
Hemel Hempstead, HP2 4TZ, United Kingdom
Tel.: (44) 1217111102
Fax: (44) 1245267147
E-Mail: pressoffice@britvic.co.uk
Web Site: www.britvic.com
BVIC—(LSE)
Rev.: $1,975,362,336
Assets: $1,612,803,792
Liabilities: $1,554,473,688
Net Worth: $58,330,104
Earnings: $90,246,576
Emp.: 3,337
Fiscal Year-end: 09/30/12
Business Description:
Holding Company; Soft Drink Mfr
S.I.C.: 6719
N.A.I.C.S.: 551112
Personnel:
Simon Litherland *(CEO)*
Matt Barwell *(CMO)*
Steve Nightingale *(Exec-IR)*
Board of Directors:
Gerald Corbett
Joanne Averiss
John Gibney
Ben Gordon
Bob Ivell
Ian McHoul
Michael Shallow

Subsidiary:

Britvic Soft Drinks Ltd. (1)
Britvic House Broomfield Road
Chelmsford, CM1 1TU, United Kingdom UK
Tel.: (44) 1245261871 (100%)
Fax: (44) 1245261871
Web Site: www.britvic.co.uk
Soft Drink Mfr & Distr
Export
S.I.C.: 2086
N.A.I.C.S.: 312111
Paul Moody *(CEO)*
Simon Litherland *(Mng Dir)*

Non-U.S. Subsidiary:

Britvic Ireland (1)
Kylemore Park West
Dublin, 10, Ireland
Tel.: (353) 16161200
Fax: (353) 16161395
E-Mail: info@britvic.ie
Web Site: www.britvic.ie
Emp.: 550
Bottled Water Mfr & Distr
Import Export
S.I.C.: 2086
N.A.I.C.S.: 312112
Dave Fitzgerald *(Mng Dir)*

BRIXTON ENERGY CORP.

325 1500 14th Street SW
Calgary, AB, T3C 1C9, Canada
Tel.: (403) 269-8424
Fax: (403) 269-8477
Web Site: www.brixtonenergy.com
Year Founded: 1980
BRX—(TSXV)
Business Description:
Oil & Gas Exploration Services
S.I.C.: 1389
N.A.I.C.S.: 213112
Personnel:
Richard Saxon *(Pres & CEO)*
Miroslava Antoniouk *(CFO & Sec)*
Board of Directors:
Matthew Dodwell
Joseph Brian Henry
Richard Saxon
Transfer Agent:
Computershare Investor Services Inc
100 University Avenue 9th Floor
Toronto, ON, Canada

BRIXTON METALS CORPORATION

409 Granville St Suite 1411
Vancouver, BC, V6C 1T2, Canada
Tel.: (604) 630-9707
Fax: (888) 863-3810
Toll Free: (888) 863-3801
E-Mail: info@brixtonmetals.com
Web Site: www.brixtonmetals.com
Year Founded: 2008
BBB—(TSXV)
Assets: $4,101,863
Liabilities: $45,323
Net Worth: $4,056,540
Earnings: ($3,052,090)
Fiscal Year-end: 09/30/13
Business Description:
Mineral Exploration Services
S.I.C.: 1081
N.A.I.C.S.: 213114
Personnel:
Gary Thompson *(Co-Founder, Chm & CEO)*
Cale Moodie *(Co-Founder & CFO)*
Sorin Posescu *(Sr VP-Geology)*
Board of Directors:
Gary Thompson
Jim Defer
Cale Moodie
Don Poirier
George Salamis
Legal Counsel:
Blake, Cassels & Graydon LLP
595 Burrard St Suite 2600
Vancouver, BC, Canada
Transfer Agent:
TMX Equity Transfer Services
200 University Avenue Suite 400
Toronto, ON, M5H 4H1, Canada

BRL TRUST SERVICOS FIDUCIARIOS E PARTICIPACOES LTDA.

Rua Iguatemi 151 19th Floor
01451-011 Itaim, SP, Brazil
Tel.: (55) 11 3133 0350
Fax: (55) 11 3133 0360
Web Site: www.brltrust.com.br
Year Founded: 2005
Business Description:
Trust Services & Fund Management
S.I.C.: 6733
N.A.I.C.S.: 523991
Personnel:
Rodrigo Boccaner Gomes *(Partner)*
Mauricio da Costa Ribeiro *(Partner)*

BROAD INVESTMENTS LIMITED

15 Whiting Street
Artarmon, NSW, 2064, Australia
Tel.: (61) 294250000
Fax: (61) 294250099
E-Mail: info@broadinvestments.com.au
Web Site: www.broadinvestments.com.au
BRO—(ASX)
Rev.: $3,263,958
Assets: $840,069
Liabilities: $1,424,794
Net Worth: ($584,724)
Earnings: ($1,397,595)
Emp.: 8
Fiscal Year-end: 06/30/13
Business Description:
Mobile Applications Sales
S.I.C.: 4899
N.A.I.C.S.: 517919
Personnel:
Vaz Hovanessian *(Chm, CEO, CFO & Sec)*
Board of Directors:
Vaz Hovanessian
Neil Gibson
Johannes Scholtz
Legal Counsel:
Weir & Strempel
50 Strathalbyn St
Kew, Australia

Subsidiary:

Mirrus Pty Ltd (1)
Unit 2 16 Silcon
Tullamarine, Victoria, 3043, Australia
Tel.: (61) 383312200
Fax: (61) 390775864
E-Mail: info@mirrus.com.au
Web Site: www.mirrus.com.au
Emp.: 130
Outsourcing Services
S.I.C.: 7389
N.A.I.C.S.: 561499
Michael Saliba *(Gen Mgr)*

BROADCAST INITIATIVES LTD.

9th Floor HDIL Towers
Anant Kanekar Marg
Bandrai E, 400051 Mumbai, Maharashtra, India
Tel.: (91) 2226583500
Fax: (91) 2226350996
Web Site: www.liveindia.tv
BROADCAST—(BOM)
Sales Range: $1-9.9 Million
Business Description:
Television Broadcasting Services
S.I.C.: 4833
N.A.I.C.S.: 515120
Personnel:
Supriya Kanse *(CEO & CFO)*
Ashok Kumar Gupta *(Mng Dir)*
Balakrishna Swamy *(Compliance Officer & Sec)*
Board of Directors:
Gautam Adhikari
Markand Adhikari
Ashok Kumar Gupta
M. S. Kapur
Deepak Sharma
Waryam Singh
Transfer Agent:
Link Intime India Pvt. Ltd.
C-13 Pannalal Silk Mills Compound
LBS Marg
Bhandup, Mumbai, 400 078, India
Tel.: (91) 22 2596 3838
Fax: (91) 22 2594 6969

Subsidiary:

Sri Adhikari Brothers Media Limited (1)
HDIL Mi Marathi Big Hall Rd White House
Bldg 2nd Fl Off LBS Rd
Kurla W, Mumbai, Maharashtra, 400 070, India
Tel.: (91) 2267882000
Fax: (91) 2267882077
E-Mail: liveindia.tv@gmail.com
Web Site: www.liveindia.tv.com
Emp.: 250
Television Programs Production Services
S.I.C.: 7819
N.A.I.C.S.: 512199
Kunal Walawalkar *(Mgr-HR)*

BROADGRAIN COMMODITIES INC.

18 King St East Suite 900
Toronto, ON, M5C 1C4, Canada

BroadGrain Commodities Inc.—(Continued)

Tel.: (416) 504-0070
Fax: (416) 504-0080
Toll Free: (877) 804-0070
E-Mail: broadgrain@broadgrain.com
Web Site: www.broadgrain.com
Sales Range: $600-649.9 Million
Emp.: 100

Business Description:
Agricultural Commodity Processing, Storage & Marketing Service
S.I.C.: 4221
N.A.I.C.S.: 493130

Subsidiary:

Lakeside Global Grains Inc. **(1)**
Junction Highways 6 & 16
Wynyard, SK, S0A 4TO, Canada
Tel.: (306) 554-3030
Fax: (306) 554-3010
Web Site: www.lakesideglobal.ca
Sales Range: $1-9.9 Million
Emp.: 8
Agricultural Commodity Processing, Storage & Marketing Service
S.I.C.: 4221
N.A.I.C.S.: 493130
Bob Waldbauer *(Mgr-Special Crops)*

BROADLEAF CO., LTD.
4-13-14 Higashishinagawa
Shinagawa-ku, Tokyo, 140-0002, Japan
Tel.: (81) 3 5781 3100
Web Site: www.broadleaf.co.jp
3673—(TKS)
Rev.: $172,061,956
Emp.: 840
Fiscal Year-end: 12/31/12

Business Description:
Software Publisher
S.I.C.: 7372
N.A.I.C.S.: 511210

Personnel:
Akira Kojima *(Pres & CEO)*

BROADVECTOR LIMITED
123 Camberwell Road Level 1
Hawthorn, VIC, 3123, Australia
Tel.: (61) 3 9811 9966
E-Mail: info@broadvector.com
Web Site: www.broadvector.com

Business Description:
Biotechnology Product Developer & Researcher
S.I.C.: 8731
N.A.I.C.S.: 541711

Personnel:
Wayne A. Millen *(Chm)*
Malcolm J. Booth *(CFO & Sec)*
Gerald W. Both *(Chief Scientific Officer)*

Board of Directors:
Wayne A. Millen
Andrew L. Smith

BROADVIEW PRESS INC.
815 First St SW Ste 412
Calgary, AB, T2P 1N3, Canada
Tel.: (705) 743-8990
Fax: (519) 767-1643
E-Mail: customerservice@broadviewpress.com
Web Site: www.broadviewpress.com
Year Founded: 2003
Sales Range: $1-9.9 Million
Emp.: 30

Business Description:
Academic Publisher
S.I.C.: 2731
N.A.I.C.S.: 511130

Personnel:
Don Le Pan *(Pres & CEO)*
Carol Richardson *(CFO & Controller)*

Board of Directors:
Susan Bennett
Roy MacLaren
JoAnn McCaig
Janet D. Sisson
Thomas H. B. Symons

BROADWAY INDUSTRIAL GROUP LIMITED
65 Chulia Street 48-03/04 OCBC Centre
Singapore, 049513, Singapore
Tel.: (65) 62360088
Fax: (65) 62266119
E-Mail: bwe@pacific.net.sg
Web Site: www.bigl.com.cn
Year Founded: 1969
B69—(SES)
Rev.: $498,548,315
Assets: $431,135,977
Liabilities: $261,371,181
Net Worth: $169,764,796
Earnings: $19,757,002
Emp.: 12,000
Fiscal Year-end: 12/31/12

Business Description:
Holding Company; Foam Plastics & Packaging Products Mfr
S.I.C.: 6719
N.A.I.C.S.: 551112

Personnel:
Sheung Sze Wong *(Chm)*
Syn Pau Lew *(Deputy Chm)*
Ai Ling Chang *(Co-Sec)*
San-Ju Tan *(Co-Sec)*

Board of Directors:
Sheung Sze Wong
Richard Yee Ming Eu
Chow Soon Lee
Po Lo Lee
Syn Pau Lew
Ah Hoy Ng
Richard An Kai Tsiang

Non-U.S. Subsidiaries:

Chongqing Broadway Foam Applications & Total Packaging Co., Ltd. **(1)**
No 798 North Biqing Road Bicheng Street
Bishan County, Chongqing, 402760, China
Tel.: (86) 23 6430 2133
Fax: (86) 23 6430 2132
Web Site: www.bigl.com.cn/contact.htm
Emp.: 90
Foam Plastics & Packaging Products Mfr
S.I.C.: 3086
N.A.I.C.S.: 326140
Patrick Leo *(Dir-Engrg Chinese Grp)*

Shanghai Broadway Packaging & Insulation Materials Co., Ltd. **(1)**
No 8 Guxu Road
Pudong New District, Shanghai, 201209, China
Tel.: (86) 2158632133
Fax: (86) 21 5863 4874
Foam Plastics & Packaging Products Mfr
S.I.C.: 2671
N.A.I.C.S.: 322220

Shenzhen Broadway Total Packaging Solution Co., Ltd. **(1)**
Block 34 East Juhuang Industrial Park
Dasan Village
Bao An District, Shenzhen, 518110, China
Tel.: (86) 75529561539
Fax: (86) 755 2944 3320
Foam Plastics & Packaging Products Mfr
S.I.C.: 3086
N.A.I.C.S.: 326140

BROBOT PETROLEUM LTD.
Thorpe Road
Melton Mowbray, Leicestershire, LE13 1SH, United Kingdom
Tel.: (44) 1664480000
Fax: (44) 1664410504
E-Mail: sales@brobot.co.uk
Web Site: www.brobot.co.uk
Year Founded: 1978
Rev.: $208,862,554
Emp.: 275

Business Description:
Fuels Lubricants & Oil Distr
S.I.C.: 5989
N.A.I.C.S.: 454310

Personnel:
V C Bootle *(Founder)*

BROCCOLINI CONSTRUCTION INC.
16740 Transcanada Hwy 3rd Floor
Kirkland, QC, H9H 4M7, Canada
Tel.: (514) 737-0076
Fax: (514) 737-2728
Web Site: www.broccolini.com
Year Founded: 1949
Rev.: $17,151,025
Emp.: 60

Business Description:
Real Estate Development & Construction Services
S.I.C.: 1521
N.A.I.C.S.: 236115

Personnel:
John Broccolini *(Pres)*

BROCK FORD SALES
4500 Drummond Rd
Niagara Falls, ON, L2E6C7, Canada
Tel.: (905) 357-5410
Toll Free: (800) 461-3323
Web Site: www.brockfordsales.com
Rev.: $29,735,173
Emp.: 60

Business Description:
New & Used Car Dealers
S.I.C.: 5511
N.A.I.C.S.: 441110

Personnel:
John Dill *(Gen Mgr)*

BROCKMAN MINING LIMITED
Level 1 117 Stirling Highway
Nedlands, WA, 6009, Australia
Tel.: (61) 8 9389 3000
Fax: (61) 8 9389 3033
E-Mail: Inquiry@brockmanmining.com
Web Site: www.brockmanmining.com
159—(ASX HKG)
Rev.: $20,445,796
Assets: $502,567,538
Liabilities: $147,110,931
Net Worth: $355,456,607
Earnings: ($61,488,776)
Emp.: 581
Fiscal Year-end: 06/30/13

Business Description:
Investment Holding Company; Iron Ore & Copper Mining; Limousine Rental & Airport Shuttle Services
S.I.C.: 6719
N.A.I.C.S.: 551112

Personnel:
Peter Joseph Kin Luk *(CEO)*
Derek Humphry *(CFO)*
Danny Chi Yan Leung *(Pres-Perryville Grp)*
Russell Tipper *(CEO-Ops-Australia)*
Graeme Carlin *(Gen Counsel)*
Jason Kam Kwan Chan *(Sec)*

Board of Directors:
Sze Hoi Kwai
Warren Talbot Beckwith
Jason Kam Kwan Chan
Eddie Kwok Kuen Lau
Zhengui Lui
Peter Joseph Kin Luk
Ross Stewart Norgard
Uwe Henke Von Parpart
Danny Kwok Cheung Yip

Butterfield Fulcrum Group (Bermuda) Limited
26 Burnaby Street
Hamilton, HM 11, Bermuda

Transfer Agents:
Tricor Secretaries Limited
26th Floor Tesbury Centre 28 Queen's Road East
Wanchai, China (Hong Kong)

Butterfield Fulcrum Group (Bermuda) Limited
26 Burnaby Street
Hamilton, HM 11, Bermuda

Subsidiary:

Parklane Limousine Service Limited **(1)**
Unit 702 7/F Yue Hwa International Building
No 1 Kowloon Park Drive
Kowloon, China (Hong Kong)
Tel.: (852) 2730 0662
Fax: (852) 2735 5860
E-Mail: info@hongkonglimo.com
Web Site: www.hongkonglimo.com
Emp.: 221
Limousine Services
S.I.C.: 4119
N.A.I.C.S.: 485320
Danny Leung *(Gen Mgr)*

Subsidiary:

Airport Shuttle Services Limited **(2)**
Unit 702 7/F Yue Hwa International Building
No 1 Kowloon Park Drive
Kowloon, China (Hong Kong)
Tel.: (852) 2730 0662
Fax: (852) 2735 5860
Web Site: www.hongkonglimo.com
Airport Limousine Services
S.I.C.: 4111
N.A.I.C.S.: 485999

Non-U.S. Subsidiaries:

Brockman Resources Limited **(1)**
117 Stirling Highway Level 1
Nedlands, WA, 6009, Australia AU
Tel.: (61) 8 9389 3000
Fax: (61) 8 9389 3033
E-Mail: brockman@brockman.com.au
Web Site: www.brockman.com.au
Emp.: 16
Minerals Acquisition & Exploration
S.I.C.: 1481
N.A.I.C.S.: 213115
Russell Tipper *(CEO)*
Derek Humphry *(CFO)*
Graeme Carlin *(Gen Counsel)*
Tara A. Robson *(Sec)*

Subsidiary:

Brockman Iron Pty. Ltd. **(2)**
Level 1 117 Stirling Hwy
Nedlands, WA, 6009, Australia
Tel.: (61) 893893000
Fax: (61) 893893033
E-Mail: brockman@brockman.com.au
Web Site: www.brockman.com.au
Emp.: 20
Iron Ore Mining Services
S.I.C.: 1011
N.A.I.C.S.: 212210
Kevin Watpers *(Mgr-Project Dev)*

Guangzhou Parklane Limousine Service Ltd **(1)**
Room No 16-17 16th Floor Zhong Xin Building
Baogang Haizhu, Guangzhou, Guangdong, 510240, China
Tel.: (86) 2062378441
Fax: (86) 2062378440
E-Mail: infogz@parklanelimochina.com
Web Site: www.parklanelimochina.com
Emp.: 30
Limousine Services
S.I.C.: 4119
N.A.I.C.S.: 485320
Grace Yang *(Gen Mgr)*

Parklane Limousine Service (Shanghai) Ltd **(1)**
Jiang Hua Road 369 24 Room C
200050 Shanghai, China
Tel.: (86) 2161382222
Fax: (86) 21 61382223
E-Mail: infosh@parklanelimochina.com
Limousine Services
S.I.C.: 4119
N.A.I.C.S.: 485320

BRODOGRADILISTE VIKTOR LENAC D.D.

Martinscica bb
PO Box 210
51000 Rijeka, Croatia
Tel.: (385) 51405555
Fax: (385) 51217033
E-Mail: viktor.lenac@lenac.hr
Web Site: www.lenac.hr
VLEN-R-B—(ZAG)
Sales Range: $50-74.9 Million
Emp.: 580
Business Description:
Ship Repair Services
S.I.C.: 3731
N.A.I.C.S.: 336611
Personnel:
Karlo Radolovic *(Chm-Supervisory Bd)*
Robert Skific *(Chm-Mgmt Bd)*
Ive Mustac *(Vice Chm-Supervisory Bd)*
Davor Lukes *(Member-Mgmt Bd)*
Sandra Uzelac *(Member-Mgmt Bd)*
Supervisory Board of Directors:
Karlo Radolovic
Damir Bacinovic
Anton Brajkovic
Lenko Milin
Ive Mustac

Subsidiary:

Viktor Servisi d.o.o. (1)
Martinscica bb
51000 Rijeka, Croatia
Tel.: (385) 51217002
Fax: (385) 51 21 72 29
E-Mail: viktor.servisi@lenac.hr
Emp.: 14
Ship Repairing Services
S.I.C.: 3731
N.A.I.C.S.: 336611
Vladimir Bruketa *(Gen Mgr)*

BRODRENE HARTMANN A/S

hartmannsvej 2
DK-6270 Tonder, Denmark
Tel.: (45) 74 7285 00
Fax: (45) 74 7285 29
E-Mail: bhtonder@hartmann-packaging.com
Web Site: www.hartmann.dk
HART—(CSE)
Rev.: $278,493,876
Assets: $205,862,904
Liabilities: $97,610,832
Net Worth: $108,252,072
Earnings: $16,683,300
Emp.: 1,506
Fiscal Year-end: 12/31/12
Business Description:
Mfr of Moulded-Fibre Packaging
S.I.C.: 4783
N.A.I.C.S.: 488991
Personnel:
Agnete Raaschou-Nielsen *(Chm)*
Walther V. Paulsen *(Vice Chm)*
Michael Rohde Pedersen *(Pres, CEO & Member-Exec Bd)*
Niels Hermansen *(Mng Dir)*
Marianne Rorslev Bock *(CFO & Member-Exec Bd)*
Torben Rosenkrantz-Theil *(Pres-North America)*
Tom Wrensted *(Grp Dir-Fin & Treas)*
Ruth Pedersen *(Sec)*
Board of Directors:
Agnete Raaschou-Nielsen
Jan Peter Antonisen
Niels Hermansen
Jorn Morkeberg Nielsen
Steen Parsholt
Walther V. Paulsen
Niels Christian Petersen

Non-U.S. Subsidiaries:

Aropac S.r.l (1)
Via Ugofoscolo 11
Carmignano Di Brenta, IT 35010 Padua, Italy (100%)
Tel.: (39) 0495958340
Fax: (39) 0495958562
E-Mail: info@hartmannitaliana.it
Web Site: www.hartmannitaliana.it
Emp.: 3
S.I.C.: 4783
N.A.I.C.S.: 488991

Hartmann-Babolna Packaging Kft. (1)
Hartmann 1
HU 2941 Acs, Hungary (100%)
Tel.: (36) 34595100
Fax: (36) 34595101
E-Mail: hba@hartman-packaging.com
Web Site: wwwhartman-packaging.com
Emp.: 500
S.I.C.: 4783
N.A.I.C.S.: 488991
Attila Vincze *(Gen Mgr)*

Hartmann Bilokalnik Ambalaza d.o.o. (1)
Dravska BB
HR 48000 Koprivnica, Croatia (100%)
Tel.: (385) 48658800
Fax: (385) 48658808
E-Mail: hbi@hartmann.dk
Web Site: www.hartmann-bilokalnik.hr
Emp.: 200
S.I.C.: 4783
N.A.I.C.S.: 488991

Hartmann CZ s.r.o. (1)
Gabinova 867
CZ 152 00 Prague, 5, Czech Republic
Tel.: (420) 251813090
Fax: (420) 251811949
E-Mail: pucek@ptu.cz
Web Site: www.hartmann-cz.cz
Emp.: 1
S.I.C.: 4783
N.A.I.C.S.: 488991

Hartmann France S.a.r.l. (1)
Le Bailliage Du Roi 3 Rue Du Bailliage
FR 78000 Versailles, France (100%)
Tel.: (33) 139512141
Fax: (33) 130215083
Web Site: www.hartmann-france.fr
Emp.: 7
S.I.C.: 4783
N.A.I.C.S.: 488991

Hartmann-Hungary Kft. (1)
Hartmann u 1
2941 Acs, Hungary
Tel.: (36) 34 595 100
Fax: (36) 34 595 101
E-Mail: hba@hartmann-packaging.com
Web Site: www.hartmann.dk/Contact%20Us/Egg%20Packaging%20Sales.aspx
Packaging Product Mfr
S.I.C.: 2671
N.A.I.C.S.: 322220

Hartmann-Mai Ltd. (1)
10 Haorzim St
PO Box 13456
Industrial Zone, IL 42138 Netanya, Israel (100%)
Tel.: (972) 98621845
Fax: (972) 98624467
Emp.: 50
S.I.C.: 4783
N.A.I.C.S.: 488991

Hartmann Papirna Ambalaza d.o.o. (1)
Dravska bb
48000 Koprivnica, Croatia
Tel.: (385) 48 65 88 00
Fax: (385) 48 65 88 08
E-Mail: hbi@hartmann-packaging.com
Emp.: 20
Packaging Paper Products Mfr
S.I.C.: 2671
N.A.I.C.S.: 322220
Melita Baci *(Gen Mgr)*

HARTMANN Polska Sp. Z.o.o. (1)
Ul Mala 5
Gorzow Wlkp, PL 66 400 Opole, Poland (100%)
Tel.: (48) 957281982
Fax: (48) 957281984
E-Mail: kki@hartmannpackaging.com
Web Site: www.hartmannpackaging.com
Emp.: 9
S.I.C.: 4783
N.A.I.C.S.: 488991
Krzusztof Kloczkowski *(Gen Mgr)*

Hartmann-Schwedt GmbH (1)
Kuhheide 32
DE 16303 Schwedt an der Oder, Germany (100%)
Tel.: (49) 333226550
Fax: (49) 3332265529
Web Site: www.hartmann.dk/Contact%20Us/Factories.aspx
Emp.: 91
S.I.C.: 4783
N.A.I.C.S.: 488991
Andreas Mascheck *(Mng Dir)*

HARTMANN (UK) Ltd. (1)
Exchange House Exchange Sq
Beccles, Norwich, Suffolk, NR34 9HH, United Kingdom (100%)
Tel.: (44) 1502717101
Fax: (44) 1502713831
E-Mail: sl@hartmann-packaging.com
Web Site: www.hartmann-packaging.com
Emp.: 5
S.I.C.: 4783
N.A.I.C.S.: 488991
Sam Luckey *(Gen Mgr)*

Hartmann-Varkaus Oy (1)
Satakunnankatu 10
Varkaus, 78300, Finland (100%)
Tel.: (358) 20461460
Fax: (358) 204632146
E-Mail: jol@hartmann-packaging.com
Web Site: www.hartmann.dk
Emp.: 40
Egg Packaging
S.I.C.: 4783
N.A.I.C.S.: 488991
Touli Lehtonen *(Mng Dir)*

Hartmann Verpackung AG (1)
Buggenrain 5
Adligenswil, CH 6043 Lucerne, Switzerland (100%)
Tel.: (41) 413707038
Fax: (41) 413707028
Web Site: www.hartmann-suisse.ch
S.I.C.: 4783
N.A.I.C.S.: 488991

Hartmann Verpackung GmbH (1)
Mergenthaler Allee 77
65760 Eschborn, Germany (100%)
Tel.: (49) 61969320
Fax: (49) 6196932109
E-Mail: hartmannverpackung@hartmann-packaging.com
Web Site: www.hartmann-packaging.de
Emp.: 35
S.I.C.: 4783
N.A.I.C.S.: 488991
Ronald Rebmamnn *(Mng Dir)*

Nihon Hartmann K.K. (1)
August House 3F 3 23 5 Uehara Shibuya Ku
Tokyo, 151 0064, Japan (100%)
Tel.: (81) 334653011
Fax: (81) 334653380
Emp.: 3
S.I.C.: 4783
N.A.I.C.S.: 488991

BROKERS TRUST INSURANCE GROUP INC.

2780 Highway 7 Suite 201
Concord, ON, L4k 3R9, Canada
Tel.: (905) 760-1515
Fax: (905) 760-0240
Toll Free: (800) 405-2299
Web Site: www.brokerstrust.ca
Year Founded: 1963
Rev.: $27,300,714
Emp.: 50
Business Description:
Insurance & Risk Management Solutions
S.I.C.: 6411
N.A.I.C.S.: 524210
Personnel:
John Fil *(Gen Mgr)*

BROMBERGS BOKFORLAG

Hantverkargatan 26
PO Box 12886
Stockholm, 11298, Sweden
Tel.: (46) 856262080
Fax: (46) 8 657 19 95
E-Mail: info@brombergs.se
Web Site: www.brombergs.se
Emp.: 5
Business Description:
Publishing House
S.I.C.: 2731
N.A.I.C.S.: 511130
Personnel:
Dorothea Bromberg *(Mng Dir)*

BROME LAKE DUCKS LTD

40 Centre Road
PO Box 3430
Knowlton, QC, J0E 1V0, Canada
Tel.: (450) 242-3825
Fax: (450) 243-0497
Toll Free: (888) 956-1977
E-Mail: info@bromelakeducks.com
Web Site: www.bromelakeducks.com
Year Founded: 1912
Rev.: $29,561,283
Emp.: 170
Business Description:
Duck Food Mfr
S.I.C.: 2015
N.A.I.C.S.: 311615
Personnel:
Claude Trottier *(Pres & COO)*

BROMI MASKIN AB

Foretagsvagen 29 Hus 11
23237 Arlov, Sweden
Tel.: (46) 40537550
Fax: (46) 40434897
E-Mail: info@bromi.se
Web Site: www.bromi.se
Sls.: $11,706,200
Emp.: 16
Business Description:
Industrial Machinery & Equipment
S.I.C.: 5084
N.A.I.C.S.: 423830
Personnel:
Martin Paland *(Pres)*

BROMPTON SPLIT BANC CORP.

Suite 2930 Bay-Wellington Tower
Brookfield Place 181 Bay Street
Toronto, ON, M5J 2T3, Canada
Tel.: (416) 642-9050
Fax: (416) 642-6001
Year Founded: 2005
SBC—(TSX)
Rev.: $5,376,883
Assets: $152,728,487
Liabilities: $74,453,889
Net Worth: $78,274,598
Earnings: $403,330
Fiscal Year-end: 12/31/12
Business Description:
Financial Investment Services
S.I.C.: 6211
N.A.I.C.S.: 523999
Personnel:
Mark A. Caranci *(Pres & CEO)*
Transfer Agent:
Equity Financial Trust Company
Toronto, ON, Canada

BRONCO BILLY CO., LTD.

1-75 Heiwagaoka Meito-ku
Nagoya, 465-0097, Japan

Bronco Billy Co., Ltd.—(Continued)

Tel.: (81) 527758000
Fax: (81) 527764141
Web Site: www.bronco.co.jp
Year Founded: 1978
3091—(JAS NGO TKS)
Sales Range: $75-99.9 Million
Emp.: 160
Business Description:
Restaurant Owner & Operator
S.I.C.: 5812
N.A.I.C.S.: 722511
Personnel:
Yasuhiro Takeichi *(Pres)*

BRONSSTADET AB

Linnegatan 18
114 47 Stockholm, Sweden
Tel.: (46) 8 120 510 00
E-Mail: info@bronsstadet.se
Web Site: www.bronsstadet.se
Year Founded: 2001
Sales Range: $25-49.9 Million
Business Description:
Investment Holding Company
S.I.C.: 6719
N.A.I.C.S.: 551112
Personnel:
Peter Gyllenhammer *(Owner & Chm)*
Martin Hansson *(CEO)*

Divisions:

Browallia AB **(1)**
Linnegatan 18
SE-114 38 Stockholm, Sweden SE
Tel.: (46) 84428564 (100%)
Fax: (46) 87370379
E-Mail: info@browallia.se
Web Site: www.browallia.se
Emp.: 1
Investment Management & Business Support Services
S.I.C.: 6282
N.A.I.C.S.: 523920
Jan Gustav Lennart Holmstrom *(CEO)*

Non-U.S. Holding:

Darby Glass Ltd. **(2)**
Sunningdale Rd
Scunthorpe, North Lincolnshire, DN17 2SS, United Kingdom
Tel.: (44) 1724280044
Fax: (44) 1724868295
E-Mail: sales@darbyglass.co.uk
Web Site: www.darbyglass.co.uk
Sales Range: $25-49.9 Million
Emp.: 65
Glass Mfr
S.I.C.: 3229
N.A.I.C.S.: 327212
Philip Corke *(CEO)*
Adrian Edwards *(Mng Dir)*

Division:

Pro-Glass Ltd **(3)**
Sunningdale Road
Scunthorpe, North Lincolnshire, DN17 2SS, United Kingdom
Tel.: (44) 1724280044
Fax: (44) 1724868295
E-Mail: pro-glass@darbyglass.co.uk
Web Site: www.darbyglass.co.uk/proglassho me.php
Glass Mfr
S.I.C.: 3211
N.A.I.C.S.: 327211

Galjaden Fastigheter AB **(1)**
Grev Turegatan 27
SE-114 38 Stockholm, Sweden SE
Tel.: (46) 84428560 (95%)
Fax: (46) 87370379
E-Mail: info@galjaden.se
Web Site: www.galjaden.se
Emp.: 10
Commercial Property Acquisition, Development & Management Services
S.I.C.: 6726
N.A.I.C.S.: 525990
Martin Hansson *(CEO)*

Non-U.S. Subsidiary:

International Fibres Group (Holdings) Limited **(1)**
Old Mills Whitehall Grove
Drighlington, Bradford, BD11 1BY, United Kingdom UK
Tel.: (44) 1132859020
Fax: (44) 1132859033
Web Site: www.fibresgroup.com
Sales Range: $125-149.9 Million
Emp.: 327
Holding Company; Specialty Coatings, Fibers & Umbrella Frames Mfr
S.I.C.: 6719
N.A.I.C.S.: 551112
Ian Powell *(CEO)*

Subsidiary:

Drake Extrusion Ltd. **(2)**
Old Mills Moor Top
Drighlington, BD111BY Bradford, United Kingdom UK
Tel.: (44) 1132852202 (100%)
Fax: (44) 1132852575
E-Mail: sales@drakeuk.com
Web Site: www.drakeuk.com
Emp.: 90
Noncellulosic Organic Fiber Mfr
S.I.C.: 2823
N.A.I.C.S.: 325220
Colin Porteous *(Mng Dir)*

U.S. Subsidiary:

Drake Extrusion, Inc. **(2)**
790 Industrial Park Dr
Ridgeway, VA 24148 (100%)
Tel.: (276) 632-0159
Fax: (276) 656-4990
Web Site: www.drakeextrusion.com
Emp.: 200
Noncellulosic Organic Fiber Mfr
S.I.C.: 2823
N.A.I.C.S.: 325220
Geoff Schofield *(VP-Sls & Mktg)*

Non-U.S. Subsidiary:

Asota GmbH **(2)**
Schachermayerstrasse 22
4020 Linz, Austria (100%)
Tel.: (43) 73269850
Fax: (43) 73269855526
E-Mail: office@asota.com
Web Site: www.asota.com
Emp.: 100
Noncellulosic Organic Fiber Mfr
S.I.C.: 2823
N.A.I.C.S.: 325220
Helmut Rankl *(Mng Dir)*

BRONZE INFRA-TECH LIMITED

158 Lenin Sarani 3rd Floor Suite 7B
Kolkata, 700 012, India
Tel.: (91) 33 22158486
Fax: (91) 9133221584
E-Mail: investorcell@bronzeinfratech.com
Web Site: www.bronzeinfratech.com
534731—(BOM)
Business Description:
Land Development, Construction & Infrastructure Projects
S.I.C.: 6552
N.A.I.C.S.: 237210
Personnel:
Manoj Kumar Bajaj *(Chm & Mng Dir)*
Sweety Bhawsinghka *(CFO)*
Shilpi Agarwal *(Compliance Officer & Sec)*
Board of Directors:
Manoj Kumar Bajaj
Niraj Jewrajka
Sumit Sharma
Punit Sureka

BROOKEMONT CAPITAL INC.

701 West Georgia St Suite 1470
PO Box 10112
Vancouver, BC, V7Y 1C6, Canada
Tel.: (604) 899-9150
Web Site: www.brookemontcapital.com
Year Founded: 2007
BKT—(TSXV)
Assets: $729,355
Liabilities: $782,769
Net Worth: ($53,414)
Earnings: ($4,074,646)
Fiscal Year-end: 07/31/13
Business Description:
Mineral Exploration Services
S.I.C.: 1081
N.A.I.C.S.: 213114
Personnel:
Conrad Clemiss *(Pres, CEO & Sec)*
Negar Adam *(CFO)*
Board of Directors:
Conrad Clemiss
Jim Nelson
Daniel Terrett
Gregory R. Thomson
Transfer Agent:
Computershare Investor Services Inc.
100 University Ave 9th Floor
Toronto, ON, Canada

THE BROOKER GROUP PUBLIC COMPANY LIMITED

26/F The Trendy Office Building, 10/190-193 Soi Sukhumvit 13
Sukhumvit Road Klong Toey Nua
Wattana, Bangkok, 10110, Thailand
Tel.: (66) 2168 7100
Fax: (66) 2168 7111 2
E-Mail: info@brookergroup.com
Web Site: www.brookergroup.com
BROOK—(THA)
Rev.: $18,039,796
Assets: $29,887,211
Liabilities: $1,847,770
Net Worth: $28,039,441
Earnings: $12,748,112
Fiscal Year-end: 12/31/12
Business Description:
Independent Research & Consulting Services
S.I.C.: 8742
N.A.I.C.S.: 541611
Personnel:
Narongchai Akrasanee *(Chm)*
Chan Bulakul *(Vice Chm & CEO)*
Nongnuch Panyasuwannakul *(Sr Ops Officer)*
Anake Kamolnate *(Sec & Exec VP)*
Amornsakdi Ketcharoon *(Sr VP-Bus, Fin, Consultancy & Investments)*
Board of Directors:
Narongchai Akrasanee
Chan Bulakul
Varut Bulakul
Anake Kamolnate
Robert William McMillen
Kirin Narula
Phongchai Sethiwan
Chaipatr Srivisarvacha
Peter Weldon
Punnee Worawuthichongsathit
Legal Counsel:
Weerawong, Chinnavat & Peangpanor Ltd
22nd floor Mercury Tower 540 Ploenchit Road
Lumpini
Bangkok, Thailand

Subsidiary:

Binswanger Brooker (Thailand) Limited **(1)**
26th Fl Trendy Ofc Bldg 10 190 193
Sukhumvit Soi 13 Wattana, Bangkok, Thailand
Tel.: (66) 21687100
Fax: (66) 21687111
E-Mail: angkana@brookergroup.com
Web Site: www.binswangerbrooker.com
Emp.: 30
Real Estate Brokerage & Consulting Services
S.I.C.: 6531
N.A.I.C.S.: 531390
Nigel J. Cornick *(CEO)*

BROOKFIELD ASSET MANAGEMENT INC.

Suite 300 Brookfield Place 181 Bay Street
PO Box 762
Toronto, ON, M5J 2T3, Canada
Tel.: (416) 363-9491
Telex: 6524254
Fax: (416) 363-9642
E-Mail: inquiries@brookfield.com
Web Site: www.brookfield.com
Year Founded: 1912
BAM—(EUR NYSE TSX)
Rev.: $18,697,000,000
Assets: $108,644,000,000
Liabilities: $64,393,000,000
Net Worth: $44,251,000,000
Earnings: $2,747,000,000
Emp.: 24,000
Fiscal Year-end: 12/31/12
Business Description:
Holding Company; Natural Resources, Power Generation, Real Estate & Financial Services
S.I.C.: 6719
N.A.I.C.S.: 551112
Personnel:
Frank J. McKenna *(Chm)*
Craig Noble *(CEO & Portfolio Mgr)*
James Bruce Flatt *(CEO)*
Joseph S. Freedman *(Sr Mng Partner)*
Harry A. Goldgut *(Sr Mng Partner)*
Richard Legault *(Sr Mng Partner)*
Barry Blattman *(Sr Mng Partner-Rels & Strategic Transactions)*
Jeffrey Miles Blidner *(Sr Mng Partner-Strategic Plng)*
Brian W. Kingston *(Sr Mng Partner-Australian Ops)*
Cyrus Madon *(Sr Mng Partner-Private Equity & Fin)*
Lori Pearson *(Mng Partner-HR)*
Luiz Ildefonso Simoes Lopes *(Sr Mng Partner-Brazil)*
Leo Van den Thillart *(Mng Partner-Private Funds Grp)*
Brian D. Lawson *(CFO & Sr Mng Partner)*
George Eugene Myhal *(COO & Sr Mng Partner)*
Richard B. Clark *(CEO-Property Grp)*
Keith G. Smith *(Sr VP-Private Funds Grp)*
Katherine Vyse *(Sr VP-IR)*
Andrew Willis *(Sr VP-Comm & Media)*
Board of Directors:
Frank J. McKenna
Jack L. Cockwell
Marcel R. Coutu
John Trevor Eyton
James Bruce Flatt
Robert James Harding
V. Maureen Kempston Darkes
David W. Kerr
Lance M. Liebman
Philip B. Lind
Jack M. Mintz
Youssef Assad Nasr
James A. Pattison
George S. Taylor
Legal Counsel:
Tory Tory Deslauriers & Binnington
Maritime Life Tower Ste 3000 TD Centre 79
Wellington St W
PO Box 270
Toronto, ON, M5K 1N2, Canada
Tel.: (416) 865-0040

Fax: (416) 865-7380

BNY Mellon Shareowner Services LLC
Jersey City, NJ 07310

Transfer Agents:

CIBC Mellon Trust Company
PO Box 7010
Adelaide Street Postal Station, Toronto, ON, M5C 2W9, Canada
Tel.: (416) 643-5500
Fax: (416) 643-5501
Toll Free: (800) 387-0825

BNY Mellon Shareowner Services LLC
Jersey City, NJ 07310

Subsidiaries:

Brookfield Bridge Lending Fund Inc (1)
181 Bay St Ste 300
Brookfield Place, Toronto, ON, M5J 2T3, Canada
Tel.: (416) 363-9491
Investment Firm
S.I.C.: 6211
N.A.I.C.S.: 523999

Subsidiary:

Second Wave Petroleum Inc. (2)
800 202 6th Avenue SW
Calgary, AB, T2P 2R9, Canada AB
Tel.: (403) 451-0165 (100%)
Fax: (403) 451-0166
E-Mail: info@secondwavepetroleum.com
Web Site: www.secondwavepetroleum.com
Rev.: $48,720,933
Assets: $219,743,833
Liabilities: $133,664,556
Net Worth: $86,079,277
Earnings: ($15,074,212)
Emp.: 20
Fiscal Year-end: 12/31/12
Oil & Gas Exploration & Production Services
S.I.C.: 1311
N.A.I.C.S.: 211111
Colin B. Witwer *(Pres & CEO)*

Brookfield Office Properties Inc. (1)
Brookfield Pl 181 Bay St Suite 330
Toronto, ON, M5J 2T3, Canada Ca
Tel.: (416) 369-2300 (50.7%)
Fax: (416) 369-2301
Web Site: www.brookfieldofficeproperties.com
BPO—(NYSE TSX)
Rev.: $2,195,000,000
Assets: $27,479,000,000
Liabilities: $14,515,000,000
Net Worth: $12,964,000,000
Earnings: $1,468,000,000
Emp.: 1,895
Fiscal Year-end: 12/31/12
Commercial Real Estate Investment, Property Development & Management Services
S.I.C.: 6726
N.A.I.C.S.: 525990
Richard B. Clark *(Co-Chm)*
John E. Zuccotti *(Co-Chm)*
Thomas F. Farley *(Pres & Global COO)*
Dennis H. Friedrich *(CEO)*
Bryan K. Davis *(CFO)*
Brett M. Fox *(Chief Admin Officer, Chief Compliance Officer & Gen Counsel)*
G. Mark Brown *(Global Chief Investment Officer)*
Mitchell E. Rudin *(Pres/CEO-Property Ops-US)*
T. Jan Sucharda *(Pres/CEO-Property Ops-Canada)*
Martin Jepson *(Sr VP-Dev & Investment-London)*
Philip Wharton *(Sr VP-Dev-US Comml Ops)*
Gordon E. Widdes *(Sr VP-IT)*

Subsidiaries:

Brookfield Residential Services Ltd. (2)
3190 Steeles Avenue East Suite 200
Markham, ON, L3R 1G9, Canada
Tel.: (416) 510-8700
Fax: (416) 510-8880
Toll Free: (800) 949-0274
Web Site: www.brookfieldresidential.com
Property Management Services
S.I.C.: 6531
N.A.I.C.S.: 531311
Sandro J. Zuliani *(Pres & COO)*
John M. Oakes *(CEO)*
Tracy Gregory *(CFO)*

Royal LePage Real Estate Services Ltd. (2)
39 Wynford Dr
Toronto, ON, M3C 3K5, Canada
Tel.: (416) 510-5800
Fax: (416) 510-5790
Toll Free: (877) 757-4545
Web Site: www.royallepage.ca
Real Estate Management Services
S.I.C.: 6531
N.A.I.C.S.: 531210

Affiliate:

Brookfield Canada Office Properties (2)
Bay Wellington Tower Brookfield Place 181 Bay Street Suite 330
PO Box 770
Toronto, ON, M5J 2T3, Canada (40.5%)
Tel.: (416) 359-8555
Fax: (416) 359-8596
Web Site: www.brookfieldofficepropertiescanada.com
BOXC—(NYSE TSX)
Rev.: $512,019,702
Assets: $5,132,721,672
Liabilities: $2,115,274,560
Net Worth: $3,017,447,112
Earnings: $524,345,550
Fiscal Year-end: 12/31/12
Real Estate Investment Trust
S.I.C.: 6531
N.A.I.C.S.: 531390
Thomas F. Farley *(Chm)*
T. Jan Sucharda *(Pres & CEO)*
Bryan K. Davis *(CFO)*
Deborah R. Rogers *(Legal Counsel, Sec & Sr VP)*
D. Cameron Black *(Legal Counsel-Western & VP)*
Elliott S. Feintuch *(Legal Counsel-Eastern & VP)*
Stefan Dembinski *(Sr VP-Asset Mgmt-Eastern)*
Ian Parker *(Sr VP-Asset Mgmt-Western)*
Ryk Stryland *(Sr VP-Dev)*
T. Nga Trinh *(Sr VP-Investments)*

Subsidiaries:

Brookfield Properties Management Corporation (3)
10303 Jasper Ave NW Ste C4
Edmonton, AB, G5J 3N6, Canada (100%)
Tel.: (780) 426-2678
Fax: (780) 425-8777
Web Site: www.brookfieldproperties.com
Emp.: 15
Real Estate Agents & Brokers Offices
S.I.C.: 6531
N.A.I.C.S.: 531210
Thomas F. Farley *(Pres & CEO)*

U.S. Subsidiaries:

Brookfield Financial Properties, L.P. (2)
Brookfield Pl 250 Vesey St 15th Fl
New York, NY 10281 DE
Tel.: (212) 417-7000 (99.4%)
Fax: (212) 417-7214
Web Site: www.brookfieldofficeproperties.com
Emp.: 100
Real Estate Development & Management
S.I.C.: 6512
N.A.I.C.S.: 531120
John E. Zuccotti *(Chm)*
Heather S. Goldman *(Mng Dir & Global Head-Mktg & Bus Dev-Investment Mgmt)*
Paul Schulman *(COO)*
Kathleen G. Kane *(Sr VP-Property Ops & Gen Counsel-Property Ops)*
Lawrence F. Graham *(Exec VP-Property Ops-United States)*
Edward F. Beisner *(Sr VP-Property Ops & Controller-Property Ops)*
Jeremiah B. Larkin *(Sr VP-Property Ops & Dir-Leasing-Property Ops)*
Grant Berlin *(Sr VP)*
Joshua J. Sirefman *(Sr VP-US Dev)*

Subsidiaries:

33 South 6th Street LLC (3)
33 S 6th St
Minneapolis, MN 55402
Tel.: (612) 372-1234
E-Mail: tstefans@brookfieldproperties.com
Web Site: www.brookfieldofficeproperties.com
Property Management Services
S.I.C.: 6799
N.A.I.C.S.: 523920
Ted Zwieg *(VP-Ops)*

BOP 1801 California Street LLC (3)
1801 California St Ste 200
Denver, CO 80202-2658
Tel.: (612) 372-1500
Real Estate Development Services
S.I.C.: 6531
N.A.I.C.S.: 531390

Brookfield Republic Plaza LLC (3)
370 17th St
Denver, CO 80202-5695
Tel.: (303) 595-7050
Fax: (303) 595-7003
Web Site: www.brookfieldofficeproperties.com
Emp.: 24
Real Estate Development Services
S.I.C.: 6531
N.A.I.C.S.: 531390
Kit McPhail-Bowman *(Gen Mgr)*

Brookfield Properties, Inc. (2)
Brookfield Pl 250 Vesey St 15th Fl
New York, NY 10281 DE
Tel.: (212) 417-7000
Real Estate Investment Trust
S.I.C.: 6726
N.A.I.C.S.: 525990
Kit McPhail-Bowman *(Gen Mgr)*

Subsidiaries:

1201 Louisiana Co. L.P. (3)
1201 Louisiana St Ste 304
Houston, TX 77002
Tel.: (416) 646-2473
Fax: (713) 650-8506
Property Management Services
S.I.C.: 6799
N.A.I.C.S.: 523920

1600 Smith Co. LLC (3)
1600 Smith St
Houston, TX 77002
Tel.: (713) 951-7400
Fax: (713) 951-7462
Property Management Services
S.I.C.: 6799
N.A.I.C.S.: 523920
Laura Krupowicz *(Mgr-Property)*

2401P Co. LLC (3)
2401 Pennsylvania Ave N
Washington, DC 20037-1730
Tel.: (202) 659-5929
Fax: (202) 659-5054
Emp.: 2
Real Estate Development Services
S.I.C.: 6531
N.A.I.C.S.: 531390
Beronica Jimenez *(Gen Mgr)*

BOP 650 Mass LLC (3)
750 9th St NW
Washington, DC 20001-4524
Tel.: (202) 467-7760
Real Estate Development Services
S.I.C.: 6531
N.A.I.C.S.: 531390

BOP Landmark Square Co. LLC (3)
111 W Ocean Blvd
Long Beach, CA 90802
Tel.: (562) 495-5000
Fax: (562) 495-1629
Property Management Services
S.I.C.: 6799
N.A.I.C.S.: 523920

Brookfield Properties 75 State Co. LLC (3)
75 State St
Boston, MA 02109
Tel.: (617) 443-2800
Fax: (617) 443-2899
Property Management Services
S.I.C.: 6282
N.A.I.C.S.: 523920

EYP Realty, LLC (3)
725 S Figueroa St Ste 1850
Los Angeles, CA 90017-5524
Tel.: (213) 955-7170
Fax: (213) 955-7163
Emp.: 12
Real Estate Development Services
S.I.C.: 6531
N.A.I.C.S.: 531390

One Allen Center Co. LLC (3)
2975 Regent Blvd
Irving, TX 75063
Tel.: (713) 651-1515
Fax: (713) 951-0209
Web Site: www.brookfieldofficeproperties.com
Real Estate Development Services
S.I.C.: 6531
N.A.I.C.S.: 531390
James Sinclair *(Mgr-Property)*

Sunrise Tech Park Co. LLC (3)
750 9th St Nw 700
Washington, DC 20001-4590
Tel.: (202) 467-7700
Real Estate Development Services
S.I.C.: 6531
N.A.I.C.S.: 531390

Two Ballston Plaza Co. LLC (3)
1110 N Glebe Rd
Arlington, VA 22201
Tel.: (703) 351-7900
Web Site: www.brookfieldofficeproperties.com
Property Management Services
S.I.C.: 6531
N.A.I.C.S.: 531311
Colleen Dolby *(Gen Mgr)*

Brookfield Properties Management LLC (2)
3 World Financial Ctr 11
New York, NY 10281-1013
Tel.: (212) 693-8150
Fax: (212) 693-8150
Properties Management Services
S.I.C.: 6531
N.A.I.C.S.: 531312

Brookfield Properties (US) LLC (2)
555 Nicollet Mall 50
Minneapolis, MN 55402-1059
Tel.: (612) 372-1230
Fax: (612) 372-1239
Real Estate Development Services
S.I.C.: 6531
N.A.I.C.S.: 531390

Brookfield Residential Properties Inc. (1)
4906 Richard Road Southwest
Calgary, AB, T3E 6L1, Canada ON
Tel.: (403) 231-8900 (72.5%)
Fax: (403) 231-8960
E-Mail: info@brookfieldrp.com
Web Site: www.brookfieldrp.com
BRP—(NYSE TSX)
Rev.: $1,340,370,000
Assets: $2,815,193,000
Liabilities: $1,507,798,000
Net Worth: $1,307,395,000
Earnings: $92,539,000
Emp.: 770
Fiscal Year-end: 12/31/12
Real Estate Services
S.I.C.: 6531
N.A.I.C.S.: 531390
Robert L. Stelzl *(Chm)*
Alan Norris *(Pres & CEO)*
Craig J. Laurie *(CFO & Exec VP)*
David Allen *(Pres-Calgary Land)*
Stephen P. Doyle *(Pres-San Diego)*
Robert Hubbell *(Pres-Washington D.C.)*
Shane D. Pearson *(Corp Counsel & Sr VP)*
Michael Dutczak *(Exec VP-Special Situations)*
David Harvie *(Exec VP-Austin)*
Don Merlo *(Exec VP-Corp Dev-Phoenix)*
Tom Morton *(Sr VP-Denver)*
Rich Westren *(Sr VP-Edmonton Land)*

Division:

Brookfield Residential Property Services (2)
3190 Steles Ave E Ste 200
Markham, ON, L3R 1G9, Canada

Brookfield Asset Management Inc.—(Continued)

Tel.: (416) 510-8700
Fax: (416) 510-8880
Web Site: www.brookfieldrps.com
Emp.: 50
Real Estate & Relocation Services
S.I.C.: 6531
N.A.I.C.S.: 531390
John Oakes *(Pres)*

Unit:

Brookfield Global Relocation Services (3)
900 S Frontage Rd Ste 200
Woodridge, IL 60517 NJ
Tel.: (630) 972-2250
Fax: (630) 972-2287
Toll Free: (866) 465-0323
Web Site: www.brookfieldgrs.com
Emp.: 70
Global Relocation & Assignment Management Services
S.I.C.: 8999
N.A.I.C.S.: 541612
Traci Morris *(CEO)*
Maggie Ryan *(Exec VP-Global Ops)*
Cynthia D. Salter *(Exec VP-Client Svcs)*
Scott T. Sullivan *(Exec VP-Global Sls & Mktg)*
Michael Schaetzle *(Sr VP)*
Eric M. Stern *(Sr VP-Global Ops-EMEA & APAC)*

Subsidiaries:

Brookfield Homes Ontario Ltd. (2)
7303 Warden Avenue Suite 100
Markham, ON, L3R 5Y6, Canada (100%)
Tel.: (905) 477-5111
Fax: (905) 477-9001
E-Mail: info@brookfieldhomes.ca
Web Site: www.brookfieldhomes.ca
Sales Range: $10-24.9 Million
Emp.: 50
Housing Developments
S.I.C.: 9531
N.A.I.C.S.: 925110
Sid J. Kerrigan *(Pres)*

Brookfield Residential (Alberta) LP (2)
200-10414 103 Ave
Edmonton, AB, T5J 0J1, Canada
Tel.: (780) 423-1910
Fax: (780) 421-4653
Real Estate Development Services
S.I.C.: 6531
N.A.I.C.S.: 531390

U.S. Subsidiaries:

Brookfield Homes Corporation (2)
8500 Executive Park Ave Ste 300
Fairfax, VA 22031 DE
Tel.: (703) 270-1700
Fax: (703) 270-1401
E-Mail: infosf@brookfieldhomes.com
Web Site: www.brookfieldhomes.com
Emp.: 271
Real Estate Development Company
S.I.C.: 1521
N.A.I.C.S.: 236115
Robert C. Hubbell *(Pres)*

Brookfield Special Situations Partners Ltd. (1)
Ste 1700 335 8th Ave SW
Calgary, AB, T2P 1C9, Canada
Tel.: (403) 770-7220
Private Equity Firm
S.I.C.: 6211
N.A.I.C.S.: 523999
Jim Reid *(Partner)*

Holdings:

Ainsworth Lumber Co. Ltd. (2)
Suite 3194 Bentall 4 1055 Dunsmuir Street
PO Box 49307
Vancouver, BC, V7X 1L3, Canada BC
Tel.: (604) 661-3200 (53.5%)
Fax: (604) 661-3201
Toll Free: (877) 661-3200
E-Mail: info@ainsworth.ca
Web Site: www.ainsworth.ca
ANS—(OTC TSX)
Sls.: $406,624,755
Assets: $830,188,606
Liabilities: $447,218,544
Net Worth: $382,970,061
Earnings: $28,202,335
Emp.: 600
Fiscal Year-end: 12/31/12
Forest Products Mfr
S.I.C.: 5031
N.A.I.C.S.: 423310
J. Peter Gordon *(Chm)*
James Lake *(Pres & CEO)*
Rick Eng *(CFO & VP-Fin)*

Subsidiaries:

Ainsworth GP Ltd. (3)
1055 Dunsmuir St Ste 3194
Vancouver, BC, V7X 1L3, Canada
Tel.: (604) 661-3200
Oriented Strand Board Mfr
S.I.C.: 2439
N.A.I.C.S.: 321213

Ember Resources Inc. (2)
32400 300W Ave SW
Calgary, AB, T2P 3C4, Canada
Tel.: (403) 270-0803
Fax: (403) 270-2850
E-Mail: info@emberresources.com
Web Site: www.emberresources.com
Sales Range: $25-49.9 Million
Emp.: 31
Gas Production
S.I.C.: 4924
N.A.I.C.S.: 221210
Doug A. Dafoe *(Pres & CEO)*
Bruce Ryan *(CFO & VP-Fin)*
Kent D. Kufeldt *(Sec)*

Hammerstone Corporation (2)
2681 Hochwald Court SW
Calgary, AB, T3E 7M3, Canada AB
Tel.: (403) 297-1680
Fax: (403) 355-2224
E-Mail: info@hammerstonecorp.com
Web Site: www.hammerstonecorp.com
Emp.: 15
Limestone & Other Mineral Mining & Quarrying
S.I.C.: 1422
N.A.I.C.S.: 212312
Terry Owen *(Pres)*

IPICO, Inc. (2)
4480 Harvester Road
Burlington, ON, L7L 4X2, Canada
Tel.: (905) 631-6310
Fax: (905) 631-6614
E-Mail: sales@ipico.com
Web Site: www.ipico.com
Sales Range: $1-9.9 Million
Emp.: 32
Radio-Frequency Identification Equipment Designer & Mfr
S.I.C.: 3663
N.A.I.C.S.: 334220
Gordon Westwater *(Pres & CEO)*
Ted Irwin *(CFO)*

U.S. Subsidiary:

Mercury Sports Group, Inc. (3)
311 SW Water St Ste 206
Peoria, IL 61602 (70%)
Tel.: (309) 672-6442
Fax: (309) 672-6432
E-Mail: sports@ipico.com
Web Site: www.ipicosports.com
Emp.: 20
Sports Timing & Tracking System Developer
S.I.C.: 3663
N.A.I.C.S.: 334220
Gordon Westwater *(Pres & CEO)*

Non-U.S. Subsidiary:

IPICO South Africa (Pty) Ltd. (3)
Scientia Techno Park Building C Unit 20
Meiring Naude Street, Pretoria, 0020, South Africa
Tel.: (27) 123497620
Fax: (27) 123491118
Emp.: 9
Sports Timing & Tracking System Services
S.I.C.: 3663
N.A.I.C.S.: 334220
Marius Van Dyk *(Mgr)*

MAAX Bath Inc. (2)
160 Saint Joseph Blvd
Lachine, QC, H8S 2L3, Canada QC
Tel.: (514) 844-4155
Fax: (888) 361-2045
Toll Free: (800) 463-6229
E-Mail: info@maax.com
Web Site: www.maax.com
Sales Range: $350-399.9 Million
Emp.: 1,800
Kitchen Cabinets, Bathroom Fixtures, Spas & Accessories Mfr
Import Export
S.I.C.: 2434
N.A.I.C.S.: 337110
Mark A. Gold *(Pres & CEO)*

Subsidiaries:

MAAX Canada Inc. (3)
4225 Spallumcheen Road
Armstrong, BC, V0E 1B6, Canada Ca
Tel.: (250) 546-8701
Fax: (250) 546-3755
Emp.: 250
Bathroom Plumbing Fixture Mfr
S.I.C.: 3432
N.A.I.C.S.: 332913
Louis Bourgoin *(VP-North American-Ops)*

U.S. Branches:

MAAX Inc.-Bremen (3)
1001 N Oak Dr
Plymouth, IN 46563-3416
Tel.: (574) 546-3298
Fax: (574) 546-5361
Emp.: 150
Bathroom Plumbing Fixture Mfr
S.I.C.: 3432
N.A.I.C.S.: 332913

MAAX Inc.-Minneapolis (3)
7767 Elm Creek Blvd Ste 310
Maple Grove, MN 55369 MN
Tel.: (763) 424-3335
Fax: (763) 424-9808
Toll Free: (800) 328-2531
E-Mail: minneapoliscustomercare@maax.com
Web Site: www.maax.com
Emp.: 120
Sauna & Acrylic Spa Mfr
S.I.C.: 3088
N.A.I.C.S.: 326191

MAAX Inc.-Plymouth (3)
1001 N Oak Dr
Plymouth, IN 46563-3428 IN
Tel.: (574) 936-3838
Fax: (574) 936-9824
Web Site: www.maax.com
Emp.: 700
Plastic Plumbing Fixtures Mfr
Import Export
S.I.C.: 3088
N.A.I.C.S.: 326191
Dan Stewart *(VP & Gen Mgr-HR)*

MAAX Inc.-Valdosta (3)
1625 James P Rogers Rd
Valdosta, GA 31601
Tel.: (229) 247-2364
Fax: (229) 247-7137
E-Mail: email@maax.com
Web Site: www.maax.com
Emp.: 45
Bathroom Plumbing Fixture Mfr
S.I.C.: 3432
N.A.I.C.S.: 332913
Jason Wells *(Gen Mgr)*

U.S. Subsidiaries:

MAAX-KSD LLC (3)
505 Keystone Rd
Southampton, PA 18966
Tel.: (215) 825-5250
Fax: (215) 355-7048
Toll Free: (800) 355-5397
Web Site: www.keystonebath.com
Emp.: 75
Shower Doors & Medicine Cabinets Mfr
S.I.C.: 2434
N.A.I.C.S.: 337110
Daniel Stewart *(Gen Mgr)*

MAAX Spas Arizona, Inc. (3)
25605 S Arizona Ave
Chandler, AZ 85248 AZ
Tel.: (480) 895-0598
Fax: (480) 895-7926
E-Mail: info@colemanspas.com
Web Site: www.colemanspas.com
Emp.: 150
Sauna & Acrylic Spas Mfr
Export
S.I.C.: 3088
N.A.I.C.S.: 326191

MediSolution Ltd. (2)
110 Blvd Cremazie W 12th Fl
Montreal, QC, H2P 1B9, Canada ON
Tel.: (514) 850-5000 (60%)
Fax: (514) 850-5005
Toll Free: (800) 361-4187 (Customer Support)
E-Mail: info@medisolution.com
Web Site: www.medisolution.com
Sales Range: $25-49.9 Million
Emp.: 302
Healthcare & Service Industry Information Technology Software & Services
S.I.C.: 7372
N.A.I.C.S.: 511210
Cyrus Madon *(Chm)*
Angelos Vlasopoulos *(CFO & VP)*
Louise Cardinal *(Sr VP-Sls & Mktg)*

NBS Technologies Inc. (2)
703 Evans Ave Ste 400
Toronto, ON, M9C 5E9, Canada ON
Tel.: (416) 621-1911
Fax: (416) 621-8875
E-Mail: info@nbstech.com
Web Site: www.nbstech.com
NBS—(TSX)
Sales Range: $50-74.9 Million
Emp.: 222
Credit Card & Plastic Card Related Services
Export
S.I.C.: 6153
N.A.I.C.S.: 522210
Bryan Hills *(Pres & CEO)*

U.S. Subsidiaries:

Equinox Payments, LLC (3)
8901 Et Raintree Dr Ste 400
Scottsdale, AZ 85260 DE
Tel.: (480) 551-7800
Fax: (480) 551-7811
Toll Free: (877) 497-3726
E-Mail: info@equinoxpayments.com
Web Site: www.equinoxpayments.com
Sales Range: $450-499.9 Million
Emp.: 1,431
End-to-End Electronic Payment Solutions, Including Card Payment Systems, Peripherals, Network Products, Ascendent Software & E-Commerce Payment Solutions
S.I.C.: 6099
N.A.I.C.S.: 522320
Patrick Hazel *(Chm & CEO)*
J. Norman Stout *(Chm)*
Clint Jones *(Pres)*
Karen Diepolz *(VP & CFO)*
William Rossiter *(VP & CMO)*
Douglas J. Reich *(Chief Compliance Officer, Gen Counsel, Sec & Sr VP)*
Lance Nakamura *(VP & CTO)*

Subsidiaries:

Hypercom North America (4)
4170 Ashford Dunwoody Road Ste 150
Atlanta, GA 30319
Tel.: (404) 531-7100
Fax: (404) 531-7285
Web Site: www.hypercom.com
Sales Range: $125-149.9 Million
End-to-End Electronic Payment Solutions, Including Card Payment Systems, Peripherals, Network Products, Ascendent Software & E-Commerce Payment Solutions
S.I.C.: 3577
N.A.I.C.S.: 334118

Hypercom (4)
Rodval Bldg 90 Calle San Martin Ste 201
Guaynabo, PR 00968
Tel.: (787) 641-1525
Fax: (787) 641-1533
Toll Free: (800) 837-4366
E-Mail: puertoricoservices@verifone.com
Web Site: www.verifone.com
Sales Range: $125-149.9 Million
Emp.: 50
End-to-End Electronic Payment Solutions, Including Card Payment Systems,

Peripherals, Network Products, Ascendent Software & E-Commerce Payment Solutions
S.I.C.: 3575
N.A.I.C.S.: 334118

Non-U.S. Holding:

NBS Technologies Ltd. (3)
41 Moorfield Road
Slyfield Industrial Estate, Guildford, Surrey, GU1 1RU, United Kingdom
Tel.: (44) 1483563200
Fax: (44) 1483511189
E-Mail: nbstech@nbstech.com
Web Site: www.nbstech.com
Emp.: 10
Business Support Services
S.I.C.: 7389
N.A.I.C.S.: 561499

U.S. Holding:

Longview Fibre Company (2)
300 Fibre Way
Longview, WA 98632-7411 WA
Mailing Address:
PO Box 639
Longview, WA 98632-0639
Tel.: (360) 425-1550
Fax: (360) 230-5135
E-Mail: info@longfibre.com
Web Site: www.longviewfibre.com
Sales Range: $700-749.9 Million
Emp.: 2,400
Real Estate Investment Trust; Kraft Paper & Containerboard Mills Operator & Packaging Products Mfr; Timber Tract Operator
Import Export
S.I.C.: 6726
N.A.I.C.S.: 525990
Randy Nebel *(Pres-Mfg Div)*

Non-U.S. Holding:

Wynyard Properties Holdings Limited (2)
(Formerly Thakral Holdings Ltd.)
Level 12 301 George Street
Sydney, NSW, 2000, Australia AU
Tel.: (61) 2 9272 8888
Fax: (61) 2 9272 8755
E-Mail:
Web Site: www.wynyardproperties.com
Sales Range: $200-249.9 Million
Emp.: 1,200
Holding Company; Real Estate Developement Services; Hotel Owner & Operator
S.I.C.: 6719
N.A.I.C.S.: 551112
Anthony Francis Story *(CFO & Co-Sec)*

Subsidiaries:

Hilton on the Park Melbourne (3)
192 Wellington Parade
Melbourne, VIC, 3002, Australia
Tel.: (61) 394192000
Fax: (61) 394192001
E-Mail: melbourne@hilton.com
Web Site: www.hiltonmelbourne.com.au
Hotel & Spa Services
S.I.C.: 7011
N.A.I.C.S.: 721110
Andreas Boettger *(Gen Mgr)*

Sovereign AOC Operations Pty Limited (3)
(Formerly AOC Operations Pty Limited)
L 12 301 George Street
Sydney, NSW, 2000, Australia
Tel.: (61) 292728888
Fax: (61) 292728755
Property Development Services
S.I.C.: 6531
N.A.I.C.S.: 531311

Sovereign Australia On Collins Pty Limited (3)
(Formerly Australia On Collins Pty Limited)
Level 12 301 George Street
Sydney, NSW, 2000, Australia
Tel.: (61) 292728888
Fax: (61) 292728752
E-Mail: info@thakral.com.au
Web Site: www.thakral.com.au/
Emp.: 30
Nonresidential Property Managers
S.I.C.: 6531
N.A.I.C.S.: 531312
John Hudson *(Mng Dir)*

Sovereign Brighton Hotel Pty Limited (3)
(Formerly Thakral Brighton Hotel Pty Limited)
Level 12 Thakral House 301 George Street
Sydney, NSW, 2000, Australia
Tel.: (61) 292728888
Fax: (61) 92728888
Web Site: www.thakral.com.au
Emp.: 50
Hotel Management Services
S.I.C.: 7011
N.A.I.C.S.: 721110
Anthony Story *(CEO)*

Sovereign Goldsea Pty Limited (3)
(Formerly Goldsea Pty Limited)
Oasis Shopping Centre Victoria Ave
Broadbeach, Gold Coast, QLD, 4218, Australia
Tel.: (61) 755923900
Fax: (61) 755920271
Property Development Services
S.I.C.: 6531
N.A.I.C.S.: 531311
David Clare *(Mgr)*

Sovereign Operations Pty Limited (3)
(Formerly Thakral Operations Pty Limited)
Level 12 301 George Street
Sydney, NSW, 2000, Australia
Tel.: (61) 292728888
Fax: (61) 92728755
E-Mail: info@wynyardproperties.com.au
Web Site: www.wynyardproperties.com.au
Emp.: 30
Nonresidential Property Managers
S.I.C.: 6531
N.A.I.C.S.: 531312
John Hudson *(Mng Dir)*

Sovereign Pacific Bay Investments Pty Limited (3)
(Formerly Pacific Bay Investments Pty Limited)
Bay Drive (Cnr Pacific Hwy)
Coffs Harbour, NSW, Australia
Tel.: (61) 266597000
Fax: (61) 266597100
E-Mail: stay@pacificbayresort.com.au
Web Site: www.pacificbayresort.com.au
Emp.: 130
Hotels & Motels
S.I.C.: 7011
N.A.I.C.S.: 721110
Dene Zahner *(Gen Mgr)*

Sovereign Pacific Bay Property Management Pty Limited (3)
(Formerly Pacific Bay Property Management Pty Limited)
L 12 301 George Street
Sydney, NSW, 2000, Australia
Tel.: (61) 2 9272 8888
Fax: (61) 92728755
Property Management Services
S.I.C.: 6531
N.A.I.C.S.: 531311

Sovereign Palm Cove Development Nominees Pty Limited (3)
(Formerly Palm Cove Development Nominees Pty Limited)
PO Box 53
Palm Cove, 4879, Australia
Tel.: (61) 740598400
Fax: (61) 740592979
Nominee Services
S.I.C.: 7389
N.A.I.C.S.: 541199

Sovereign Property Fund Pty Limited (3)
Level 12 Wynyard House 301 George Street
Sydney, NSW, 2000, Australia
Tel.: (61) 292728888
Real Estate Management Services
S.I.C.: 6531
N.A.I.C.S.: 531390

Sovereign Robina Pty Limited (3)
(Formerly THL Robina Pty Limited)
Level 12
301 George Street, Sydney, NSW, Australia
Tel.: (61) 292728888
Fax: (61) 292728755
E-Mail: info@thakral.com.au
Emp.: 20
Land Subdivision
S.I.C.: 6552
N.A.I.C.S.: 237210
Anthony Story *(COO)*

Sovereign Wynyard Finance Pty Limited (3)
(Formerly Thakral Finance Pty Limited)
Level 12 Thakral House 301 George Street
Sydney, NSW, 2000, Australia
Tel.: (61) 292728888
Property Management Services
S.I.C.: 6531
N.A.I.C.S.: 531311

Wynyard Properties Pty Limited (3)
14 Carrington St
Sydney, NSW, 2000, Australia
Tel.: (61) 292991000
Fax: (61) 92903819
Hotels
S.I.C.: 7011
N.A.I.C.S.: 721110
Michael Smith *(Mng Dir)*

Western Wind Energy Corporation (1)
1326-885 W George Street
1041 HSBC Building, Vancouver, BC, V6C 3E8, Canada BC
Tel.: (604) 685-9463
Fax: (604) 685-9441
E-Mail: info@westernwindenergy.com
Web Site: www.westernwindenergy.com
Sales Range: $1-9.9 Million
Emp.: 9
Wind Power Services
S.I.C.: 4939
N.A.I.C.S.: 221111
J. Michael Boyd *(Chm , Exec VP-Bus Dev)*
Jeffrey J. Ciachurski *(CEO)*
Claus Andrup *(Sec)*
Steven R. Mendoza *(Exec VP & Chief Engrg)*
Chris Thompson *(Sr VP-Project Fin)*

U.S. Subsidiaries:

Aero Energy LLC (2)
885 W Georgia St
Vancouver, BC, V6C 3E8, Canada (100%)
Tel.: (604) 685-9463
Fax: (604) 685-9441
Wind Energy Services
S.I.C.: 4939
N.A.I.C.S.: 221122
Jeff Ciachurski *(CEO)*

Western Wind Energy US Corporation (2)
6619 N Scottsdale Rd
Scottsdale, AZ 85250 (100%)
Tel.: (480) 296-2040
Web Site: www.westernwindenergy.com
Emp.: 1
Wind Energy Services
S.I.C.: 4911
N.A.I.C.S.: 221122
Steve Mendoza *(Exec VP)*

Holding:

Insignia Energy Ltd. (1)
2300 500 4th Ave SW
Calgary, AB, T2P 2V6, Canada AB
Tel.: (403) 536-8132
Fax: (403) 514-6940
E-Mail: info@insigniaenergy.ca
Web Site: www.insigniaenergy.ca
Rev.: $38,194,224
Assets: $140,653,830
Liabilities: $34,339,415
Net Worth: $106,314,415
Earnings: ($17,755,185)
Emp.: 15
Fiscal Year-end: 12/31/12
Oil & Gas Exploration Services
S.I.C.: 1311
N.A.I.C.S.: 211111
Jeffrey D. Newcommon *(Pres & CEO)*
Danny G. Geremia *(CFO & VP-Fin)*
Glen Fischer *(COO)*
C. Steven Cohen *(Sec)*

Affiliates:

Brookfield High Yield Strategic Income Fund (1)
Brookfield Place 181 Bay Street Suite 300
PO Box 762
Toronto, ON, M5J 2T3, Canada ON
Tel.: (416) 363-9491
Fax: (416) 363-2856
E-Mail: andrew.willis@brookfield.com
BHY.UN—(TSX)
Closed-End Investment Fund
S.I.C.: 6726
N.A.I.C.S.: 525990
George Eugene Myhal *(Pres & CEO)*
Jonathan C. Tyras *(CFO, Treas & Sec)*

Brookfield Investments Corporation (1)
Brookfield Place Suite 300 181 Bay Street
Toronto, ON, M5J 2T3, Canada Ca
Tel.: (416) 363-9491
Fax: (416) 365-9642
Web Site: www.brookfieldinvestments.com
BRN.PR.A—(TSXV)
Rev.: $76,000,000
Assets: $2,332,000,000
Liabilities: $1,201,000,000
Net Worth: $1,131,000,000
Earnings: $48,000,000
Fiscal Year-end: 12/31/12
Real Estate Investment Trust
S.I.C.: 6726
N.A.I.C.S.: 525990
Edward C. Kress *(Chm & Pres)*
Derek Gorgi *(CFO & VP)*
Loretta M. Corso *(Sec & VP)*

Brookfield New Horizons Income Fund (1)
Brookfield Place 181 Bay Street Suite 300
Toronto, ON, M5J 2T3, Canada ON
Tel.: (416) 393-9491
Fax: (416) 363-2856
E-Mail: sshah@brookfield.com
BIF.UN—(CNSX)
Rev.: $181,713
Assets: $140,941,090
Liabilities: $2,932,376
Net Worth: $138,008,714
Earnings: ($922,428)
Fiscal Year-end: 12/31/12
Closed-End Investment Fund
S.I.C.: 6726
N.A.I.C.S.: 525990
George Eugene Myhal *(Pres & CEO)*
Jonathan C. Tyras *(Mng Dir, CFO & Gen Counsel)*
Gail Cecil *(Mng Dir)*

Royal Oak Ventures Inc. (1)
Brookfield Place 181 Bay Street Suite 300
PO Box 762
Toronto, ON, M5J 2T3, Canada ON
Tel.: (416) 359-8590 (100%)
ROV—(CNSX)
Rev.: $902,570
Assets: $34,404,026
Liabilities: $85,486
Net Worth: $34,318,541
Earnings: ($367,787)
Fiscal Year-end: 12/31/12
Investment Holding Company
S.I.C.: 6719
N.A.I.C.S.: 551112
Brian G. Kenning *(Chm)*
James Reid *(Pres & CEO)*
Derek E. Gorgi *(CFO & VP)*
Alan J. Hutchison *(Sec)*

U.S. Subsidiary:

Brookfield Investment Management Inc. (1)
3 World Financial Ctr 200 Vesey St 10th Fl
New York, NY 10281-1010 DE
Tel.: (212) 549-8400
Fax: (212) 549-8300
E-Mail: funds@brookfield.com
Web Site: www.brookfieldim.com
Emp.: 70
Investment Advisory & Management Services
S.I.C.: 6282
N.A.I.C.S.: 523930
Jonathan C. Tyras *(Mng Dir, CFO & Gen Counsel)*
Heather S. Goldman *(Mng Dir & Head-Mktg & Bus Dev-Global)*

Brookfield Asset Management Inc.—(Continued)

Kim Gordon Redding *(Chief Investment Officer & Head-Registered Fund Platform)*
Seth Gelman *(Chief Compliance Officer & Dir-Compliance Dept)*
Gregory Bordner *(Chief Risk Officer & Dir-Quantitative Analysis Dept)*

Subsidiaries:

Crystal River Capital Advisors, LLC (2)
200 Vesey St 10th Fl
New York, NY 10281-1010 (100%)
Tel.: (212) 549-8400
Fax: (212) 549-8300
Investment Management Services
S.I.C.: 6211
N.A.I.C.S.: 523999

Affiliate:

Crystal River Capital, Inc. (3)
3 World Financial Center 200 Vesey St 10th Fl
New York, NY 10281-1010 MD
Tel.: (212) 549-8400
Fax: (212) 549-8300
E-Mail:
Web Site: www.crystalriverreit.com
Sales Range: $50-74.9 Million
Real Estate Investment Trust
S.I.C.: 6726
N.A.I.C.S.: 525990

Industrial Developments International, Inc. (2)
1100 Peachtree St Ste 1100
Atlanta, GA 30309 DE
Tel.: (404) 479-4000
Fax: (404) 479-4115
Web Site: www.idi.com
Managed Assets: $2,000,000,000
Emp.: 215
Industrial Real Estate Development, Property Management & Leasing Services
S.I.C.: 6531
N.A.I.C.S.: 531390
Greg Gregory *(Vice Chm)*
Timothy J. Gunter *(Pres & CEO)*
Linda Booker *(CFO & Sr VP)*
David R. Birdwell *(COO & Exec VP)*
Matt O'Sullivan *(Chief Dev Officer & Exec VP)*
G. Bryan Blasingame *(Sr VP-Investments & Dir-Dispositions)*
Greg J. Ryan *(Sr VP-Investments & Dir-Acq)*
Brian T. Mee *(Sr VP-Strategic Dev Svcs)*
S. Michael Parks *(Sr VP-Natl Bus Dev Grp)*
Paul Phillips *(Sr VP-Investment Mgmt)*

Division:

IDI Services Group, LLC (3)
1100 Peachtree St Ste 1100
Atlanta, GA 30309 GA
Tel.: (404) 479-4000 (100%)
Fax: (404) 479-4142
E-Mail: info@idisg.com
Web Site: www.idisg.com
Emp.: 100
Commercial Property Management & Leasing Services
S.I.C.: 6531
N.A.I.C.S.: 531312
Bob Tardy *(VP-Natl Leasing & Mktg)*

Verde Realty (2)
5847 San Felipe Ste 4400
Houston, TX 77057 MD
Tel.: (713) 338-3000
Fax: (713) 335-1437
Toll Free: (888) 411-8277
E-Mail: info@verderealty.com
Web Site: www.verderealty.com
Sales Range: $75-99.9 Million
Real Estate Investment Trust
S.I.C.: 6726
N.A.I.C.S.: 525990
C. Ronald Blankenship *(CEO)*
Shawn Warren *(Chief Acctg Officer & VP-Fin)*
Mary Jane Anderson *(Treas & VP-Fin)*
David C. Dressler, Jr. *(Exec VP-Investments)*
Rafael Garcia-Rovirosa *(Sr VP-Mktg & Leasing)*

Affiliates:

BROOKFIELD GLOBAL LISTED INFRASTRUCTURE INCOME FUND INC. (2)
Three World Financial Center 200 Vesey Street
New York, NY 10281-1010 MD
Tel.: (212) 549-8000
Toll Free: (800) 497-3746
INF—(NYSE)
Rev.: $8,654,697
Assets: $219,231,539
Liabilities: $53,350,151
Net Worth: $165,881,388
Earnings: $5,026,680
Fiscal Year-end: 12/31/12
Closed-End Investment Fund
S.I.C.: 6726
N.A.I.C.S.: 525990
Rodman L. Drake *(Chm)*
Kim Gordon Redding *(Pres)*
Angela W. Ghantous *(Treas)*
Jonathan C. Tyras *(Sec)*

Brookfield Mortgage Opportunity Income Fund Inc. (2)
Brookfield Pl 250 Vesey St
New York, NY 10281-1023 MD
Tel.: (212) 549-8400
Toll Free: (800) 282-0429
BOI—(NYSE)
Closed-End Investment Fund
S.I.C.: 6726
N.A.I.C.S.: 525990
Rodman L. Drake *(Chm)*
Steven Pires *(Treas)*
Jonathan C. Tyras *(Sec)*

Brookfield Realty Capital Corp. (2)
Three World Financial Center 200 Vesey St 10th Fl
New York, NY 10281-1010 MD
Tel.: (212) 417-7000
Web Site: www.brookfield.com
Real Estate Investment Trust
S.I.C.: 6726
N.A.I.C.S.: 525990
Barry S. Blattman *(Chm)*
William M. Powell *(Pres & CEO)*
Lowell G. Baron *(CFO & Treas)*
Jonathan C. Tyras *(Gen Counsel, Sec & VP)*

Non-U.S. Subsidiaries:

Brookfield Brasil, S.A. (1)
Rua Lauro Mueller No 116 21 Andar
Botafogo, 22290-160 Rio de Janeiro, Brazil BR
Tel.: (55) 2135277800 (100%)
Fax: (55) 2135277799
Web Site: www.brookfieldbr.com
Emp.: 14,000
Holding Company; Real Estate, Financial & Services, Natural Resources & Agribusiness
S.I.C.: 6719
N.A.I.C.S.: 551112
Renato Cassim Cavalini *(Mng Partner & Sr VP)*
Sergio L. Campos *(Mng Partner & VP)*
Tim Formuziewich *(Mng Partner)*
Luiz I. Simoes Lopes *(Sr Mng Partner-Brookfield Asset Mgmt & CEO-Brazil)*
Paulo Cesar C. Garcia *(Gen Counsel)*

Brookfield Infrastructure L.P. (1)
7 Reid St 4th Fl
Hamilton, HM 11, Bermuda
Tel.: (441) 296 4480
Asset Management Services
S.I.C.: 6282
N.A.I.C.S.: 523920

Brookfield Multiplex Group Limited (1)
Level 22 135 king st
Sydney, NSW, 2000, Australia AU
Tel.: (61) 292565000 (100%)
Fax: (61) 293222001
E-Mail: info@brookfieldmultiplex.com
Web Site: www.brookfieldmultiplex.com
Sales Range: $1-4.9 Billion
Emp.: 2,000
Holding Company; Property Development, Facilities Management, Fund Management & Construction
S.I.C.: 6719
N.A.I.C.S.: 551112
Ross A. McDiven *(CEO)*
Michael Jothy *(CFO)*

Subsidiaries:

Brookfield Multiplex Capital Limited (2)
Level 22 135 Kings St
Sydney, NSW, 2000, Australia AU
Tel.: (61) 292565000
Fax: (61) 293222001
E-Mail: information@au.brookfield.com
Web Site: www.brookfieldmultiplex.com
Emp.: 500
Property Fund Management
S.I.C.: 6531
N.A.I.C.S.: 531390
Michael Jothy *(CFO)*
Mark Wilson *(CEO-Funds Mgmt & Infrastructure-Asia Pacific)*

Units:

Brookfield Multiplex Property Trust (3)
Level 22 135 King St
Sydney, NSW, 2000, Australia
Tel.: (61) 292565000
Fax: (61) 93222001
E-Mail: information@au.brookfield.com
Web Site: www.brookfieldmultiplex.com
Emp.: 400
Real Estate Investments
S.I.C.: 6531
N.A.I.C.S.: 531390

Multiplex European Property Fund (3)
Level 22 135 Kings Street
Sydney, NSW, 2000, Australia
Tel.: (61) 293222000
Fax: (61) 293222001
Web Site: www.au.brookfield.com
MUE—(ASX)
Rev.: $42,407,217
Assets: $390,705,174
Liabilities: $384,935,066
Net Worth: $5,770,108
Earnings: $4,461,230
Emp.: 200
Fiscal Year-end: 06/30/13
Property Fund Management Services
S.I.C.: 6722
N.A.I.C.S.: 525910
Neil Olofsson *(Sec)*

Non-U.S. Branches:

Brookfield Multiplex Capital - New Zealand (3)
66 Wyndham Street Level 8
Auckland, New Zealand
Tel.: (64) 93002000
Fax: (64) 93002100
Web Site: www.brookfieldmultiplexcapital.com
Emp.: 50
Property Fund Management Services
S.I.C.: 6531
N.A.I.C.S.: 531390
Kym Wall *(Mng Dir)*

Brookfield Multiplex Developments (2)
Level 22 135 King Street
Sydney, NSW, 2000, Australia
Tel.: (61) 292565000
Fax: (61) 293222001
E-Mail: information@brookfieldmultiplex.com
Web Site: www.brookfieldmultiplex.com
Emp.: 200
Property Developers
S.I.C.: 6531
N.A.I.C.S.: 531390
George Kostis *(Mgr)*

Non-U.S. Subsidiary:

Nasa Multiplex LLC (2)
Level 17 Al Attar Business Tower
Sheikh Zayed Road, Dubai, United Arab Emirates
Tel.: (971) 58500
Fax: (971) 43158600
E-Mail: bmxuae@mea.brookfield.com
Web Site: www.brookfieldmultiplex.com
Construction Management Services
S.I.C.: 1541
N.A.I.C.S.: 236210

Brookfield Renewable Energy Partners L.P. (1)
73 Front Street 5th Floor
Hamilton, HM 12, Bermuda BM
Tel.: (441) 295 1443 (68%)
Web Site: www.brookfieldrenewable.com
BEP—(NYSE TSX)
Rev.: $1,706,000,000
Assets: $16,977,000,000
Liabilities: $9,441,000,000
Net Worth: $7,536,000,000
Earnings: $215,000,000
Emp.: 1,169
Fiscal Year-end: 12/31/13
Electric Power Generation & Distribution
S.I.C.: 4911
N.A.I.C.S.: 221122
Jeffrey Miles Blidner *(Chm)*
Richard Legault *(Pres & CEO)*
Sachin Shah *(CFO)*

Subsidiaries:

Brookfield Energy Marketing, LP. (2)
181 Bay St
Ste 300, Toronto, ON, M5J 2T3, Canada
Tel.: (819) 561-8659
Fax: (819) 561-7188
Web Site: www.brookfieldpower.com
Emp.: 80
Electric Power Distribution
S.I.C.: 4931
N.A.I.C.S.: 221122
Patricia Bood *(VP & Sec)*

Non-U.S. Subsidiary:

Brookfield Renewable Power Preferred Equity Inc. (2)
Brookfield Place 181 Bay Street Suite 300
PO Box 762
Toronto, ON, M5J 2T3, Canada
Tel.: (416) 359-1955
Fax: (416) 363-2856
BRF—(TSX)
Investement Management Services
S.I.C.: 6282
N.A.I.C.S.: 523920
Richard J. Legault, *(Pres & CEO)*

Non-U.S. Joint Venture:

Arteris S.A. (1)
(Formerly Obrascon Huarte Lain Brasil S.A.)
Rua Joaquim Floriano 913 - 6th Floor
Itaim Bibi, 04534-013 Sao Paulo, Brazil
Tel.: (55) 11 3074 2404
Fax: (55) 11 3074 2405
E-Mail:
Web Site: www.ohlbrasil.com.br
OHLB3—(RIO)
Rev.: $1,534,105,056
Assets: $2,975,157,314
Liabilities: $2,184,648,765
Net Worth: $790,508,549
Earnings: $198,510,080
Emp.: 1,302
Fiscal Year-end: 12/31/12
Toll Management Services
S.I.C.: 1611
N.A.I.C.S.: 237310
Sergio Silva de Freitas *(Chm)*
David Antonio Diaz Almazan *(CEO)*
Felipe Ezquerra Plasencia *(Deputy CEO)*
Maria de Castro Michielin *(Legal Officer)*
Luis Manuel Eusebio Inigo *(Exec Officer)*
Paulo Pacheco Fernandes *(Exec Officer)*
Alessandro Scotoni Levy *(IR Officer)*
Marcio Augusto Travain *(Admin & Fin Officer)*

BROOKFIELD INCORPORACOES S.A.

Av Paisagista Jose Silva de Azevedo Neto 200
22775056 Rio de Janeiro, Brazil
Tel.: (55) 21 3127 9200
Fax: (55) 21 3127 9200
E-Mail: ri@br.brookfield.com
Web Site: www.br.brookfield.com
Year Founded: 1970
BISA3—(BRAZ)

Sales Range: $1-4.9 Billion
Emp.: 6,001
Business Description:
Real Estate Development Services
S.I.C.: 6531
N.A.I.C.S.: 531390
Personnel:
Luiz Ildefonso Simoes Lopes *(Chm)*
Nicholas Vincent Reade *(CEO)*
Sergio Leal Campos *(CFO)*
Denise Goulart *(Gen Counsel)*
Board of Directors:
Luiz Ildefonso Simoes Lopes
Omar Carneiro da Cunha
Mario Cezar de Andrade
Joel Korn
Antonio Fernando Maia
Marcilio Marques Moreira
George Myhal
Nicholas Vincent Reade
Benjamin Vaughan

BROOKFIELD INFRASTRUCTURE PARTNERS L.P.
73 Front Street
Hamilton, HM 12, Bermuda
Mailing Address:
7 Reid Street 4th Floor
Hamilton, HM 11, Bermuda
Tel.: (441) 294 3309
Web Site: www.brookfieldinfrastructure.com
BIP—(NYSE TSX)
Rev.: $2,004,000,000
Assets: $19,718,000,000
Liabilities: $11,910,000,000
Net Worth: $7,808,000,000
Earnings: $291,000,000
Fiscal Year-end: 12/31/12
Business Description:
Infrastructure Asset Owner & Operator
S.I.C.: 6719
N.A.I.C.S.: 551112
Personnel:
Derek Pannell *(Chm)*
Samuel P.S. Pollock *(CEO)*
Bahir Manios *(CFO)*
Board of Directors:
Derek Pannell
Jeffrey Miles Blidner
John A. Fees
David Hamill
Arthur Jacobson, Jr.
Don Mackenzie
Rafael Miranda Robredo
Anne C. Schaumburg
Danesh Varma
Transfer Agent:
Computershare Trust Company N.A.
New York, NY 10021
Non-U.S. Holdings:

Brookfield Rail Pty. Ltd. (1)
2-10 Adams Drive
Welshpool, WA, 6106, Australia AU
Mailing Address:
GPO Box S1411
Perth, WA, 6846, Australia
Tel.: (61) 892122800
Fax: (61) 921222922
Web Site: www.brookfieldrail.com
Emp.: 100
Railroad Infrastructure Management Services
S.I.C.: 4789
N.A.I.C.S.: 488210
Paul Larsen *(CEO)*

Oy Rauma Stevedoring Ltd. (1)
Hakunintie 23
FIN 26101 Rauma, Finland FI
Tel.: (358) 283121 (100%)
Fax: (358) 28312444
E-Mail: headoffice.rst@raumasteve.fi
Web Site: www.raumastevedoring.fi
Sales Range: $100-124.9 Million
Emp.: 620
Port Operator & Marine Cargo Handling Services
S.I.C.: 4491
N.A.I.C.S.: 488310
Matti Esko *(Mng Dir)*

PD Ports Ltd. (1)
17-27 Queen's Square
Middlesbrough, TS2 1AH, United Kingdom UK
Tel.: (44) 1642877200 (100%)
Fax: (44) 01642877056
E-Mail: enquiries@pdports.co.uk
Web Site: www.pdports.co.uk
Sales Range: $250-299.9 Million
Emp.: 1,246
Holding Company; Port Operation & Logistic Services
S.I.C.: 6719
N.A.I.C.S.: 551112
David Robinson *(CEO)*
Alison Smiles *(Sec)*

Holding:

PD Ports Group Limited (2)
17-27 Queens Square
Middlesbrough, TS2 1AH, United Kingdom UK
Tel.: (44) 01642877000 (100%)
Fax: (44) 1642877056
E-Mail: enquries@pdports.co.uk
Web Site: www.pdports.co.uk
Emp.: 30
Holding Company; Port Operation & Logistic Services
S.I.C.: 6719
N.A.I.C.S.: 551112
David Robinson *(Grp CEO)*
Dermot Russell *(Grp CFO)*
Jerry Hopkinson *(Grp COO)*

Subsidiaries:

PD Port Services Ltd. (3)
Spurn House
Immingham, Lincs, DN40 2NR, United Kingdom UK
Tel.: (44) 1469552700 (100%)
Fax: (44) 1469552737
E-Mail: ageny@pdports.co.uk
Web Site: www.pdports.co.uk
Emp.: 1,000
Port Operation Services
S.I.C.: 4491
N.A.I.C.S.: 488310
Jerry Hopkinson *(COO)*

Unit:

PD Logistics (3)
1 Pk Ave
Felixstowe, Suffolk, IP11 4HF, United Kingdom UK
Tel.: (44) 1394675541
Fax: (44) 1394676095
Web Site: www.pdlogistics.com
Emp.: 50
General Freight Warehousing & Distribution Services
S.I.C.: 4225
N.A.I.C.S.: 493110
Malcolm Dodd *(Gen Mgr)*

BROOKFIELD PROPERTY PARTNERS L.P.
73 Front Street 5th Floor
Hamilton, Bermuda HM 12
Tel.: (441) 2943304
Fax: (441) 296 4475
Web Site: www.brookfieldpropertypartners.com
Year Founded: 2013
BPY.UN—(TSX)
Business Description:
Real Estate Management Services
S.I.C.: 6531
N.A.I.C.S.: 531390
Personnel:
Richard B. Clark *(CEO)*

BROOKFIELD REAL ESTATE SERVICES INC.
39 Wynford Drive
Don Mills, Toronto, ON, M3C 3K5, Canada
Tel.: (416) 510-5800
E-Mail: info@brookfieldresinc.com
Web Site: www.brookfieldresinc.com
Year Founded: 2010
BRE—(OTC TSX)
Rev.: $36,300,616
Assets: $99,825,453
Liabilities: $97,740,993
Net Worth: $2,084,460
Earnings: $2,954,227
Fiscal Year-end: 12/31/12
Business Description:
Real Estate Brokers
S.I.C.: 6531
N.A.I.C.S.: 531210
Personnel:
George Eugene Myhal *(Chm)*
Philip Soper *(Pres & CEO)*
Kevin Cash *(CFO & Sr VP)*
Board of Directors:
George Eugene Myhal
Lorraine D. Bell
Simon P. Dean
Allen Karp
Gail Kilgour

BROOKFIELD SOUNDVEST SPLIT TRUST
100 Sparks Street 9th Floor
Ottawa, ON, K1P 5B7, Canada
Tel.: (613) 236-7361
Fax: (613) 236-6130
Year Founded: 2005
BSD—(TSX)
Rev.: $2,925,927
Assets: $48,434,598
Liabilities: $40,381,555
Net Worth: $8,053,043
Earnings: ($386,608)
Fiscal Year-end: 12/31/12
Business Description:
Financial Investment Services
S.I.C.: 6211
N.A.I.C.S.: 523999
Personnel:
Kevin Charlebois *(CEO)*
Transfer Agent:
Computershare Investor Services Inc
100 University Avenue
Toronto, ON, Canada

BROOKS FORGINGS LTD.
Doulton Road
Cradley Heath, B645QJ Warley, West Midlands, United Kingdom
Tel.: (44) 1384563356
Fax: (44) 1384563357
E-Mail: a.brooks@brooksforgings.co.uk
Web Site: www.brooksforgings.co.uk
Sls.: $3,500,000
Emp.: 50
Business Description:
Plumbing & Heating Equipment & Supplies (Hydronics) Merchant Wholesalers
S.I.C.: 5074
N.A.I.C.S.: 423720
Personnel:
Steven Clive Brooks *(Mng Dir)*
Sylvia M. Brooks *(Sec)*

BROOKS LABORATORIES LIMITED
Suite No 203-204 Eco House
Vishveshwar Nagar Goregaon (East)
Mumbai, 400 063, India
Tel.: (91) 22 29275901
Fax: (91) 22 29275905
E-Mail: cs@brookslabs.net
Web Site: www.brookslabs.net
Year Founded: 2002
533543—(BOM NSE)
Rev.: $14,854,005
Assets: $24,409,724
Liabilities: $4,867,253
Net Worth: $19,542,471
Earnings: $1,324,471
Emp.: 216
Fiscal Year-end: 03/31/13
Business Description:
Pharmaceutical Mfr
S.I.C.: 2834
N.A.I.C.S.: 325412
Personnel:
Atul Ranchal *(Chm)*
Durga Sankar Maity *(CEO & Dir-Technical)*
Rajesh Mahajan *(Mng Dir)*
Ashima Banodha *(Compliance Officer & Sec)*
Board of Directors:
Atul Ranchal
Rajnish Kumar Bedi
Rajesh Mahajan
Durga Sankar Maity
Bhaskar Sharma
Transfer Agent:
Link Intime India Pvt. Ltd
C-13 Pannalal Silk Mills Compound LBS Marg
Bhandup (West)
Mumbai, India

BROOKS MACDONALD GROUP PLC
111 Park Street Mayfair
London, W1K 7JL, United Kingdom
Tel.: (44) 20 7499 6424
Fax: (44) 20 7499 5718
E-Mail: info@brooksmacdonald.com
Web Site: www.brooksmacdonald.com
BRK—(AIM)
Rev.: $99,746,377
Assets: $135,341,994
Liabilities: $44,438,062
Net Worth: $90,903,932
Earnings: $12,681,699
Emp.: 363
Fiscal Year-end: 06/30/13
Business Description:
Financial Services
S.I.C.: 6282
N.A.I.C.S.: 523920
Personnel:
Christopher A. J. Macdonald *(Co-Founder & CEO)*
Jonathan M. Gumpel *(Co-Founder)*
Richard H. Spencer *(Co-Founder)*
Simon J. Jackson *(Sec & Dir-Fin)*
Board of Directors:
Christopher J. Knight
Colin R. Harris
Nicholas Ian Holmes
Simon J. Jackson
Christopher A. J. Macdonald
Diane Seymour-Williams
Andrew William Shepherd
Richard H. Spencer
Simon P. Wombwell
Legal Counsel:
Macfarlanes LLP
20 Cursitor Street
London, EC4A 1LT, United Kingdom
Tel.: (44) 20 7831 9222
Subsidiaries:

Braemar Group plc (1)
Richmond House
Heath Road, Hale, Cheshire, WA14 2XP, United Kingdom
Tel.: (44) 1619294969
Fax: (44) 1619290111
E-Mail: info@braemar-group.co.uk
Web Site: www.braemar-farming.co.uk
Sales Range: $1-9.9 Million
Emp.: 34
Financial, Investment & Property Management Services
S.I.C.: 6211

Brooks Macdonald Group plc—(Continued)

N.A.I.C.S.: 523999
William Martin Robinson *(Chm)*
Jonathan Stewart Murphy *(Mng Dir)*
Orla Ball *(Corp Counsel)*

Divisions:

Braemar Estates (Residential) Limited (2)
Richmond House
Heath Road, Hale, Cheshire, WA14 2XP, United Kingdom
Tel.: (44) 1619292300
E-Mail: info@braemar-estates.com
Web Site: www.braemar-estates.com
Emp.: 40
Residential Property Management Services
S.I.C.: 6531
N.A.I.C.S.: 531311
Neil Roberts *(Mng Dir)*

Braemar Securities Limited (2)
Richmond House
1A Heath Rd, Hale, Cheshire, WA14 2XP, United Kingdom
Tel.: (44) 1619292303
Fax: (44) 1619290111
E-Mail: info@bm-funds.com
Web Site: www.bm-funds.com
Fund Management Services
S.I.C.: 6722
N.A.I.C.S.: 525910
William Martin Robinson *(CEO)*

Brooks Macdonald Asset Management Limited (1)
111 Park St
Mayfair, London, W1K 7JL, United Kingdom
Tel.: (44) 2074996424
Fax: (44) 2074995718
E-Mail: info@bm-am.com
Web Site: www.bm-am.com
Emp.: 150
Investment Management Services
S.I.C.: 6211
N.A.I.C.S.: 523999
Chris Macdonald *(CEO)*
Nick Holmes *(Mng Dir)*
Andrew Shepherd *(Mng Dir)*
Richard Spencer *(Chief Investment Officer)*

Subsidiary:

Brooks Macdonald Asset Management (Tunbridge Wells) Limited (2)
2 Mt Ephraim Rd
Tunbridge Wells, Kent, TN1 1EE, United Kingdom
Tel.: (44) 1892554900
Fax: (44) 1892554999
E-Mail: tunbridgewells@brooksmacdonald.com
Web Site: www.bm-am.com
Emp.: 12
Asset & Pension Fund Management Services
S.I.C.: 6211
N.A.I.C.S.: 523999
Cheryl Bennette *(Mgr-HR)*

BROOKWATER VENTURES INC.

Suite 1100 505 3rd Street SW
Calgary, AB, T2P 3E6, Canada
Tel.: (403) 441-1156
Fax: (403) 263-3041
Web Site: brookwaterventures.com
BW—(TSXV)
Int. Income: $5,463
Assets: $21,753
Liabilities: $5,595,001
Net Worth: ($5,573,247)
Earnings: ($4,004,381)
Fiscal Year-end: 07/31/13

Business Description:
Oil & Gas Exploration Services
S.I.C.: 1389
N.A.I.C.S.: 213112

Personnel:
Ahmed S. Said *(Pres & CEO)*
Paul Bozoki *(CFO)*
Neil Said *(Sec)*

Board of Directors:
Peter Boot
Scott Moore
Ahmed S. Said

Transfer Agent:
CIBC Mellon Trust Company
PO Box 721
Agincourt, ON, Canada

BROOKWELL LIMITED

11 New Street
Saint Peter Port, GY1 2PF, Guernsey
Tel.: (44) 1481726034
E-Mail: info@brookwelllimited.com
Web Site: www.brookwelllimited.com
Year Founded: 2008
BKW—(AIM)

Business Description:
Investment Services
S.I.C.: 6211
N.A.I.C.S.: 523999

Board of Directors:
Paul A. Clarke
Colin D. Ferbrache
Alasdair R. McLaren
Philip D. Soulsby

Legal Counsel:
Mourant Ozannes
1 Le Marchant Street
186
Saint Peter Port, Guernsey

Debevoise & Plimpton LLP
Tower 42 One Broad Street
London, United Kingdom

BROSE FAHRZEUGTEILE GMBH & CO. KG

(d/b/a The Brose Group)
Ketschendorfer Strasse 38-50
D-96450 Coburg, Germany
Tel.: (49) 9561210
Fax: (49) 9561211429
E-Mail: info@brose.com
Web Site: www.brose.com
Year Founded: 1908
Emp.: 8,790

Business Description:
Motor Vehicle Doors & Seats
S.I.C.: 3714
N.A.I.C.S.: 336340

Personnel:
Michael Stoschek *(Chm)*
Jurgen Otto *(CEO)*
Gary Tan *(Pres-Asia/Pacific)*
Jan Kowal *(Pres-North America)*
Klaus Deller *(Exec VP-Pur & Dev)*
Dietmar Meister *(Exec VP-Central Admin)*
Thomas Spangler *(Exec VP-Production)*

Supervisory Board of Directors:
Wolf-Dieter Kirchner
Franz-Josef Kortum
Gunther Schuh

U.S. Subsidiary:

Brose North America, Inc. (1)
3933 Automation Ave
Auburn Hills, MI 48326
Tel.: (248) 339-4000
Fax: (248) 339-4099
E-Mail: detroit@brose.com
Web Site: www.brose.com
Emp.: 325
Motor Vehicle Parts & Accessories Mfr
S.I.C.: 3714
N.A.I.C.S.: 336390
Michael Stoscheck *(Owner)*
Jan Kowal *(Chm)*
John Dunn *(Pres)*

Subsidiaries:

Brose Chicago, Inc. (2)
12543 S. Burley Ave
Chicago, IL 60633
Tel.: (773) 371-4750
Fax: (773) 371-4900
E-Mail: chicago@brose.net
Motor Vehicle Parts & Accessories Mfr
S.I.C.: 3714
N.A.I.C.S.: 336390

Brose Tuscaloosa, Inc. (2)
10100 Brose Dr
Vance, AL 35490
Tel.: (205) 562-4800
Fax: (205) 562-4900
E-Mail: tuscaloosa@brose.net
Motor Vehicle Parts & Accessories Mfr
S.I.C.: 3714
N.A.I.C.S.: 336390

Non-U.S. Subsidiaries:

Brose Bratislava, spol. s r.o. (1)
Priemyselny park Lozorno 1006
900 55 Bratislava, Slovakia
Tel.: (421) 260261100
Fax: (421) 260261711
E-Mail: bratislava@brose.com
Web Site: www.brose.com
Emp.: 30
Motor Vehicle Parts & Accessories Mfr
S.I.C.: 3714
N.A.I.C.S.: 336390

Brose Canada Inc (1)
1500 Max Brose Drive
London, ON, N6N 1P7, Canada
Tel.: (519) 644-5200
Fax: (519) 644-5290
E-Mail: london@brose.net
Emp.: 600
Motor Vehicle Parts & Accessories Mfr
S.I.C.: 3714
N.A.I.C.S.: 336390

Brose Changchun Automotive Systems Co., Ltd (1)
No 1177 Wen Zhou Street
Economical & Technological Development Zone, 130033 Changchun, China
Tel.: (86) 43184991000
Fax: (86) 43184991100
E-Mail: changchun@brose.com
Web Site: www.brose.net
Motor Vehicle Design Services
S.I.C.: 3714
N.A.I.C.S.: 336390

Brose CZ spol. s r.o. (1)
Prumyslovy park 302
74221 Koprivnice, Czech Republic
Tel.: (420) 556844118
Fax: (420) 556844411
E-Mail: ostrava@brose.com
Web Site: www.brose.com.de
Emp.: 50
Motor Vehicle Parts & Accessories Mfr
S.I.C.: 3714
N.A.I.C.S.: 336390
Michael Daniel *(Chm)*

Brose do Brasil Ltda. (1)
Av Sul 151
Campo Largo da Roseira, CEP 83183-000 Curitiba, Brazil
Tel.: (55) 4133812000
Fax: (55) 4133812096
E-Mail: curitiba@brose.com
Web Site: www.brose.net
Motor Vehicle Parts & Accessories Mfr
S.I.C.: 3714
N.A.I.C.S.: 336390
Michael Stoscheck *(Chm)*

Brose France S.A.S. (1)
Parc d'Activites Actipole
134 Avenue Joseph Kessel, 78960 Voisins-le-Bretonneux, France
Tel.: (33) 130120980
Fax: (33) 130489803
E-Mail: paris@brose.com
Web Site: www.brose.net
Emp.: 25
Motor Vehicle Parts & Accessories Mfr
S.I.C.: 3714
N.A.I.C.S.: 336390
Kurt Sauernheimer *(Pres)*

Brose Gent bvba (1)
Skaldenstraat 121
Bus A2
9042 Gent, Belgium
Tel.: (32) 92180888
Fax: (32) 92180889
E-Mail: gent@brose.com
Web Site: www.brose.com
Emp.: 120
Motor Vehicle Parts & Accessories Mfr
S.I.C.: 3714
N.A.I.C.S.: 336390

Brose Korea Ltd. (1)
12th Floor KANC 906-10 Iui-dong
Yeongtong-gu Suwon-si, Ansan, Gyeonggi-Do, 443-270, Korea (South)
Tel.: (82) 315466160
Fax: (82) 315466190
Web Site: www.brose.net
Motor Vehicle Parts & Accessories Mfr
S.I.C.: 3714
N.A.I.C.S.: 336390

Brose Limited (1)
Colliery Ln
Exhall, CV7 9NW, United Kingdom
Tel.: (44) 2476646410
Fax: (44) 2476646410
E-Mail: coventry@brose.com
Web Site: www.brose.com
Emp.: 270
Motor Vehicle Parts & Accessories Mfr
S.I.C.: 3714
N.A.I.C.S.: 336390
Michael Stoscheck *(Chm)*

Brose Mexico, S.A. de C. V. (1)
Calle 2 No 7
Fracc Ind Benito Juarez
C P 76120 Queretaro, Mexico
Tel.: (52) 42118500
Fax: (52) 4 217 1751
E-Mail: queretaro@brose.net
Web Site: www.brose.net
Motor Vehicle Parts & Accessories Mfr
S.I.C.: 3714
N.A.I.C.S.: 336390

Brose S. A. (1)
C Illes Balears 2-6
8730 Barcelona, Spain
Tel.: (34) 938917300
Fax: (34) 938917301
E-Mail: sta.margarida@brose.com
Web Site: www.brose.com
Emp.: 300
Motor Vehicle Parts & Accessories Mfr
S.I.C.: 3714
N.A.I.C.S.: 336390
Michael Stoscheck *(Chm)*

Brose Shanghai Automotive Systems Co., Ltd. (1)
No 585 Tashan Rd Anting Industrial Zone
Tashan Rd, Shanghai, China
Tel.: (86) 2139575555
Fax: (86) 2169502906
E-Mail: shbrose@shbrose.com
Web Site: www.shbrose.com
Electrical Motor Vehicle Parts & Accessories Mfr
S.I.C.: 3714
N.A.I.C.S.: 336390
Michael Stoscheck *(Chm)*

Brose Sistemas de Fechaduras para Automoveis, Unipessoal Lda. (1)
Apartado 116
3465168 Tondela, Portugal
Tel.: (351) 232811001
Fax: (351) 232811009
E-Mail: tondela@brose.com
Emp.: 100
Motor Vehicle Parts & Accessories Mfr
S.I.C.: 3714
N.A.I.C.S.: 336390
Michael Stoscheck *(Chm)*

Brose Sweden AB (1)
Flygfaltsgatan 4
423 37 Torslanda, Sweden
Tel.: (46) 317257000
Fax: (46) 0317257038
E-Mail: goeteborg@brose.net
Web Site: www.brose.net
Emp.: 70
Motor Vehicle Parts & Accessories Mfr
S.I.C.: 3714
N.A.I.C.S.: 336390
Michael Stoscheck *(Chm)*

RG Brose Automotive Components (Pty.) Ltd. (1)
6 Spruit Ave
PO Box 899
Industrial Sites, Brits, 0250, South Africa

Tel.: (27) 122502385
Fax: (27) 122502723
E-Mail: rgbrose@rgbrose.co.za
Web Site: www.rgbrose.co.za
Emp.: 120
Motor Vehicle Window Regulator & Door Module Mfr
S.I.C.: 3714
N.A.I.C.S.: 336390
Michael Stoscheck *(Chm)*

BROTHER ENTERPRISES HOLDING CO., LTD.

3 Caijiashi Bridge Lianmin Villiage
Zhouwangmiao Town, Haining, Zhejiang, 314407, China
Tel.: (86) 573 87015331
Fax: (86) 573 87015333
Web Site: www.brother.com.cn
Year Founded: 1989
002562—(SSE)
Sales Range: $75-99.9 Million
Emp.: 410

Business Description:
Vitamin Products & Leather Chemicals Mfr
S.I.C.: 2899
N.A.I.C.S.: 325998

Personnel:
Zhida Qian *(Chm & Gen Mgr)*
Xiaofeng Qian *(CFO)*

BROTHER INDUSTRIES, LTD.

(d/b/a Brother Group)
15-1 Naeshiro-cho Mizuho-ku
Nagoya, 467-8561, Japan
Tel.: (81) 528242511
Telex: J59743
Fax: (81) 52 811 6826 (Plant)
Web Site: www.brother.com
Year Founded: 1908
6448—(NGO TKS)
Sls.: $5,676,737,000
Assets: $4,636,445,000
Liabilities: $1,569,964,000
Net Worth: $3,066,481,000
Earnings: $196,086,000
Emp.: 31,694
Fiscal Year-end: 03/31/13

Business Description:
Home & Office Typewriters, Printers, Word Processors, Facsimile Machines, Sewing Machines & Other Various Electrical Appliances Mfr & Distr
Export
S.I.C.: 3589
N.A.I.C.S.: 333318

Personnel:
Toshikazu Koike *(Pres)*
Yoshitsugu Asai *(Mng Exec Officer)*
Munetaka Fujii *(Exec Officer)*
Tomoyuki Hasegawa *(Mng Exec Officer)*
Chikamasa Hattori *(Exec Officer)*
Tadashi Ishiguro *(Grp Mng Exec Officer)*
Hiroshi Ishikawa *(Grp Mng Exec Officer)*
Shigeki Ishikawa *(Sr Mng Exec Officer)*
Takafumi Kamenouchi *(Mng Exec Officer)*
Jun Kamiya *(Mng Exec Officer)*
Shunsuke Katayama *(Grp Mng Exec Officer)*
Tasuku Kawanabe *(Exec Officer)*
Mitsuyasu Kyuno *(Exec Officer)*
Yumio Matsumoto *(Mng Exec Officer)*
Yuji Miwa *(Exec Officer)*
Ichiro Sasaki *(Mng Exec Officer)*
Masahiko Suzuki *(Exec Officer)*
Yuichi Tada *(Grp Exec Officer)*
Hiroyuki Wakahara *(Exec Officer)*

Board of Directors:
Koichi Fukaya
Tomoyuki Hasegawa
Shigehiko Hattori
Yukihisa Hirano
Shigeki Ishikawa
Toshikazu Koike
Atsushi Nishijo

Transfer Agent:
Mitsubishi UFJ Trust and Banking Corporation
Marunouchi1-4-5 Chiyoda-ku
Tokyo, Japan

Subsidiaries:

Bellezza Club Japan Inc. **(1)**
15-1 Naeshirocho
Mizuho-Ku, Nagoya, Aichi, 467-0841, Japan
Tel.: (81) 528243270
Electrical Equipment Distr
S.I.C.: 5063
N.A.I.C.S.: 423610

BETOP STAFF, LTD. **(1)**
1-1 Kawagishi-icchome
Mizuho-ku, Nagoya, Aichi, 467-8562, Japan
Tel.: (81) 52 824 3260
Web Site: www.betop.co.jp
Human Resource Consulting Services
S.I.C.: 8999
N.A.I.C.S.: 541612

BROTHER ENTERPRISE, LTD. **(1)**
1-1 Kawagishi-icchome
Mizuho-ku, Nagoya, Aichi, 467-8562, Japan
Tel.: (81) 528243239
Web Site: www.brother-enterprise.co.jp
Amusement Equipment Mfr
S.I.C.: 3589
N.A.I.C.S.: 333318

Brother Finance (Japan), Ltd. **(1)**
15-1 Naeshiro-cho
Mizuho-ku, Nagoya, 467-8561, Japan JP
Tel.: (81) 52 824 2117 (100%)
Web Site: www.brother.com
International Trade Financing Services
S.I.C.: 6159
N.A.I.C.S.: 522293

Brother International Corporation - Japan **(1)**
1-1Kawagishi 1 Mizuho-ku Nagoya
Aichi, 467-0845, Japan JP
Tel.: (81) 528242072 (100%)
Fax: (81) 81528243390
Web Site: www.brother.com
Emp.: 3,000
Regional Export & Sales Managing Office
S.I.C.: 8741
N.A.I.C.S.: 551114
Toyomi Ido *(Pres)*

Non-U.S. Subsidiaries:

Brother International (Australia) Pty. Ltd. **(2)**
11 Talavera Rd Macquarie Park
Macquarie Park, NSW, 2113, Australia AU
Tel.: (61) 298874344
Fax: (61) 298889707
E-Mail: info@brother.com.au
Web Site: www.brother.com.au
Emp.: 80
Office Equipment & Sewing Machines Whslr
S.I.C.: 5044
N.A.I.C.S.: 423420
Yoshi Sugimoto *(Mng Dir)*

Brother International (HK) Limited **(2)**
Unit 620 6th Floor Ocean Centre
5 Canton Rd Tsimshatsui, Kowloon, China (Hong Kong) HK
Tel.: (852) 27210689 (100%)
Fax: (852) 27230287
E-Mail: inquiry@brother.com.hk
Web Site: www.brother.com.hk
Emp.: 40
Office Equipment & Sewing Machines Whslr
S.I.C.: 5044
N.A.I.C.S.: 423420

Brother International (India) Pte. Ltd. **(2)**
703-705 Powai Plaza
Hiranandani Business Park
Powai, Mumbai, 400 076, India In
Tel.: (91) 2240988900 (100%)
Fax: (91) 2240988989
Web Site: www.brother.in
Emp.: 35
Office Equipment & Sewing Machines Whslr
S.I.C.: 5044
N.A.I.C.S.: 423420
Toshiyuki Takamure *(Dir)*

Brother International (Malaysia) Sdn. Bhd. **(2)**
T1-5 5th Fl Tower 1 Jaya 33
No 3 Jalan Semangat, 46100 Petaling
Jaya, Selangor, Malaysia MY
Tel.: (60) 378849999 (100%)
Fax: (60) 378849988
E-Mail: atyourside@brother.com.my
Web Site: www.brother.com.my
Emp.: 40
Office Equipment & Sewing Machines Whslr
S.I.C.: 5044
N.A.I.C.S.: 423420
Sew Kok Meng *(Gen Mgr-Fin)*

Brother International (NZ) Limited **(2)**
1E Quadrant Dr Gracefield Lower Hutt
PO Box 38294
5045 Wellington, 6009, New Zealand NZ
Tel.: (64) 45890284 (100%)
Fax: (64) 45890287
E-Mail: brother@brother.co.nz
Web Site: www.brother.co.nz
Emp.: 40
Office Equipment & Sewing Machines Whslr
S.I.C.: 5044
N.A.I.C.S.: 423420
Graham Walshe *(Chm)*

Brother International Philippines Corporation **(2)**
6th Floor Marajo Tower 312 26th Street West
corner 4th Avenue
Bonifacio, Taguig, Philippines PH
Tel.: (63) 25819800
Fax: (63) 2 581 9811
Web Site: www.brother.com.ph
Office Equipment & Sewing Machines Whslr
S.I.C.: 5044
N.A.I.C.S.: 423420

Brother International Singapore Pte. Ltd. **(2)**
152 Beach Road 25 01 04 Gateway E
Singapore, 189721, Singapore SG
Tel.: (65) 65383998 (100%)
Fax: (65) 65387003
E-Mail: customerservice@brother.com.sg
Web Site: www.brother.com.sg
Emp.: 90
Office Equipment & Sewing Machines Whslr
S.I.C.: 5044
N.A.I.C.S.: 423420
Takeo Shimazu *(Mng Dir)*

BROTHER LIVING SERVICE CO., LTD. **(1)**
1-1 Kawagishi-icchome
Mizuho-ku, Nagoya, Aichi, 467-8562, Japan
Tel.: (81) 52 824 2140
Web Site: www.brother.com
Building Maintenance & Security Services
S.I.C.: 0783
N.A.I.C.S.: 561730

BROTHER LOGITEC LTD. **(1)**
4-20 Tobeshita-icchome Minami-ku
Nagoya, Aichi, 457-0842, Japan
Tel.: (81) 528242356
Fax: (81) 528112523
Web Site: www.brother.com
Logistics Consulting Services
S.I.C.: 4731
N.A.I.C.S.: 541614

Brother Real Estate, Ltd. **(1)**
15-1 Naeshiro-cho
Mizuho-ku, Nagoya, Aichi, 467-8561, Japan
Tel.: (81) 528243431
Fax: (81) 528114322
Web Site: www.brother-bre.co.jp
Emp.: 17
Real Estate Management Services
S.I.C.: 6531
N.A.I.C.S.: 531390

Brother Sales, Ltd. **(1)**
15-1 Naeshiro-cho
Mizuho-ku, Nagoya, 467-8561, Japan JP
Tel.: (81) 528243311 (100%)
Fax: (81) 528243031
Web Site: www.brother.jp
Emp.: 3,000
Office Equipment & Sewing Machines Whslr
S.I.C.: 5044
N.A.I.C.S.: 423420

MIE BROTHER PRECISION INDUSTRIES, LTD. **(1)**
1480 Higashino Saiku Meiwa-cho
Taki-gun, Mie, 515-0321, Japan JP
Tel.: (81) 596522811
Fax: (81) 596522105
Web Site: www.brother.com
Computer Peripheral Equipment Mfr
S.I.C.: 3575
N.A.I.C.S.: 334118

Standard Corp. **(1)**
4-1 Shibakoen-nichome
Minato-ku, Tokyo, 105-0011, Japan
Tel.: (81) 3 6848 8181
Fax: (81) 3 5785 8811
E-Mail: campaign@standard-k.co.jp
Web Site: www.standard-k.co.jp
Restaurant Operating Services
S.I.C.: 5812
N.A.I.C.S.: 722511

Xing Inc. **(1)**
18-1 Shioiri-cho
Mizuho-ku, Nagoya, 467-0851, Japan JP
Tel.: (81) 528251901 (89%)
Fax: (81) 528251903
Web Site: www.xing.co.jp
Emp.: 1,200
Karaoke Network Content Data Services
S.I.C.: 7379
N.A.I.C.S.: 518210
Atsushi Yoshida *(Pres)*

U.S. Subsidiary:

Brother International Corporation - USA **(1)**
100 Somerset Corporate Blvd
Bridgewater, NJ 08807-0911 DE
Mailing Address: (100%)
PO Box 6911
Bridgewater, NJ 08807-0911
Tel.: (908) 704-1700
Fax: (908) 704-8235
Web Site: www.brother-usa.com
Emp.: 1,100
Office Equipment & Sewing Machines Whslr
Import Export
S.I.C.: 5044
N.A.I.C.S.: 423420
Tadashi Ishiguro *(Pres)*
Anthony Melfi *(CFO)*
Dean F. Shulman *(Sr VP)*

Subsidiaries:

Brother Industries (U.S.A.), Inc. **(2)**
7819 N Brother Blvd
Memphis, TN 38133 DE
Tel.: (901) 377-7777 (100%)
Fax: (901) 356-4085
Web Site: www.brother-usa.com
Emp.: 1,200
Electronic Typewriters & Word Processors Mfr
S.I.C.: 3589
N.A.I.C.S.: 333318
Toru Uchibayafhi *(Pres)*

BROTHER MOBILE SOLUTIONS, INC. **(2)**
100 Technology Dr Ste 250A
Broomfield, CO 80021
Tel.: (303) 460-1655, ext. 1655
Fax: (303) 460-1628
Toll Free: (800) 543-6144
E-Mail: mobilemedia@brother.com
Web Site: www.brother-usa.com
Mobile Software Development Services
S.I.C.: 7371
N.A.I.C.S.: 541511

Non-U.S. Subsidiaries:

Brother International Corporation (Canada) Ltd. **(2)**
1 Rue Hotel De Ville
Dollard Des Ormeaux, Montreal, QC, H9B3H6, Canada Ca
Tel.: (514) 685-0600 (100%)
Fax: (514) 685-0700
Toll Free: (800) 361-6466

Brother Industries, Ltd.—(Continued)

E-Mail: info@brother.ca
Web Site: www.brother.ca
Emp.: 110
Office Equipment & Sewing Machines Whslr
S.I.C.: 5044
N.A.I.C.S.: 423420
Martin Featherston *(Pres)*

Brother International Corporation de Argentina S.R.L. **(2)**
Chiclana 2975
C1259AAB Buenos Aires, Argentina Ar
Tel.: (54) 1143086600 (100%)
Fax: (54) 1143086601
Web Site: www.brother.com.ar
Office Equipment & Sewing Machines Whslr
S.I.C.: 5044
N.A.I.C.S.: 423420

Brother International Corporation do Brazil, Ltda. **(2)**
Ave Paulista 854 15th Fl
Edificio Top Ctr Bela Vista, 01216 Sao Paulo, Brazil BR
Tel.: (55) 1133713555 (100%)
Telex: 55-11-36621 bipa br
Fax: (55) 11 3283 0802
E-Mail: mkt@brother.com.br
Web Site: www.brother.com.br
Emp.: 38
Office Equipment & Sewing Machines Whslr
S.I.C.: 5044
N.A.I.C.S.: 423420

Brother International de Chile, Ltda. **(2)**
Avenida Presidente Riesco 5335 Oficina 501
Las Condes, Santiago, Chile CL
Tel.: (56) 4116500 (100%)
Fax: (56) 4116510
Web Site: www.brotherlatinamerica.com
Sales Range: $10-24.9 Million
Emp.: 16
Office Equipment & Sewing Machines Whslr
S.I.C.: 5044
N.A.I.C.S.: 423420

Brother International de Mexico, S.A. de C.V. **(2)**
Nemesio Diez Riega No 8
Lote 4 Parque Ind, 11570 Mexico, DF, Mexico MX
Tel.: (52) 5585038700 (100%)
Fax: (52) 017282825288
E-Mail: cervicio@brother.com.mx
Web Site: www.brother.com.mx
Emp.: 60
Office Equipment & Sewing Machines Whslr
Import
S.I.C.: 5044
N.A.I.C.S.: 423420
Javier Pastor *(Mng Dir)*

Non-U.S. Subsidiaries:

BROTHER CENTRAL AND EASTERN EUROPE GmbH **(1)**
Pfarrgasse 58
1230 Vienna, Austria
Tel.: (43) 1 61007
Fax: (43) 1 61007 100
Web Site: www.brother.com
Industrial Electronic Machinery Mfr
S.I.C.: 3559
N.A.I.C.S.: 333249

Brother (China) Ltd. **(1)**
Unit 2303 Tower A City Center of Shanghai
100 Zunyi Road, Shanghai, 200051, China CN
Tel.: (86) 2162371228 (100%)
Fax: (86) 2132283641
Web Site: www.brother-cn.net
Emp.: 100
Office Equipment & Sewing Machines Whslr
S.I.C.: 5044
N.A.I.C.S.: 423420
Hashimoto Yasuhiro *(Mng Dir)*

Brother Corporation (Asia) Ltd. **(1)**
Unit 606 6/F Exchange Tower 33 Wang Chiu Road
Kowloon Bay, Hong Kong, China (Hong Kong) HK
Tel.: (852) 27234198 (100%)
Fax: (852) 27231776
Emp.: 20
Holding Company; Printers & Other Office Machinery Mfr
S.I.C.: 6719
N.A.I.C.S.: 551112

Non-U.S. Subsidiaries:

Brother Industries (Shenzhen) Ltd. **(2)**
G02414-1 Baochangli Bonded Transportation Industrial Park
Baolong Industrial Estate
Longgang District, Shenzhen, 518 116, China CN
Tel.: (86) 75584639697 (100%)
Fax: (86) 75584639745
Web Site: www.brother.com
Multi-Function Office Machinery Mfr
S.I.C.: 3589
N.A.I.C.S.: 333318

Brother Technology (Shenzhen) Ltd. **(2)**
No 6 Gold Garden Ind Nanling Buji
Longgang District, Shenzhen, Guangdong, China CN
Tel.: (86) 75528709987 (100%)
Fax: (86) 75528700981
Emp.: 6,000
Printers, Facsimile Machines & Other Office Equipment Mfr
S.I.C.: 3555
N.A.I.C.S.: 333244
Hiroyuki Wakahara *(Mng Dir)*

Brother Finance (U.K.) plc **(1)**
4th Floor N Ste Warwick House
65-66 Queen Street, London, EC4R 1EB, United Kingdom UK
Tel.: (44) 2072489948 (100%)
Fax: (44) 2072489938
E-Mail: email@brotherfinance.co.uk
Web Site: www.brother.com
Emp.: 4
International Trade Financing Services
S.I.C.: 6159
N.A.I.C.S.: 522293
Seo Takeshi *(Mgr)*

Brother Holding (Europe) Ltd. **(1)**
Brother House 1 Tame Street
Audenshaw, Manchester, M34 5JE, United Kingdom
Tel.: (44) 161 330 6531
Fax: (44) 161 330 5520
Web Site: www.brother.com
Emp.: 220
Computer Peripheral Equipment Mfr & Distr
S.I.C.: 3575
N.A.I.C.S.: 334118
Yuji Ishiguro *(Mng Dir)*

BROTHER IBERIA, S.L.U. **(1)**
Parque Emp San Fernando Av Castilla No 2 Edificio A
San Fdo de Henares, 28830 Madrid, Spain ES
Tel.: (34) 916557570
Fax: (34) 916763412
E-Mail: bentas@brother.es
Web Site: www.brother.es
Emp.: 70
Industrial Machinery Mfr
S.I.C.: 3559
N.A.I.C.S.: 333249

Brother Industries Technology (M) Sdn. Bhd. **(1)**
17 Jalan Firma 2 Kawasan Perindustrian Tebrau
81100 Johor Bahru, Johor Darul Takzim, Malaysia
Tel.: (60) 73543888
Fax: (60) 73543666
Web Site: www.brother.com
Emp.: 2,500
S.I.C.: 3579
N.A.I.C.S.: 339940

Brother Industries Technology (Malaysia) Sdn. Bhd. **(1)**
17 Jalan Firma 2 Kawasan Perindustrian Tebrau
Johor Darul Takzim, 81100 Johor Bahru, Johor, Malaysia
Tel.: (60) 7 3543 888
Fax: (60) 7 3543 666
Web Site: www.brother.com.my
Emp.: 1,800
Industrial Machinery Mfr
S.I.C.: 3559
N.A.I.C.S.: 333249

Brother Industries (U.K.) Ltd. **(1)**
Unit 1 Vauxhall Industrial Estate
Ruabon, Wrexham, LL14 6HA, United Kingdom UK
Tel.: (44) 1978813400 (100%)
Fax: (44) 1978 813 493
Web Site: www.brother.com
Emp.: 150
Office Machines Mfr
S.I.C.: 3589
N.A.I.C.S.: 333318
Phil Mack *(Gen Mgr)*

Non-U.S. Subsidiary:

Brother Industries (Slovakia) s.r.o. **(2)**
Oslobodítelov 929/15
963 01 Krupina, Slovakia Sk
Tel.: (421) 455251400 (100%)
Fax: (421) 455251450
Emp.: 170
Used Toner Cartridge Recycling Services
S.I.C.: 4953
N.A.I.C.S.: 562920
Andy Dutton *(Mgr)*

Brother Industries (Vietnam) Ltd. **(1)**
No 63 Tu Xuong Street
Ward 7 District 3, Ho Chi Minh City, Vietnam VN
Tel.: (84) 862908787 (100%)
Fax: (84) 862908786 /862908788
Web Site: www.brother.com.vn
Emp.: 500
Printers, Facsimile Machines & Multi-Fucntion Office Machinery Mfr
Export
S.I.C.: 3589
N.A.I.C.S.: 333318
Hachiro Hasegawa *(Mng Dir)*

BROTHER INTERNATIONAL DEL PERU S.A.C. **(1)**
Alcanfores 199 Oficina 203
Miraflores, Lima, Peru
Tel.: (51) 1 626 9200
Fax: (51) 1 626 9205
E-Mail: info@brother.com.pe
Web Site: www.brother.com
Emp.: 7
Industrial Machinery Mfr
S.I.C.: 3559
N.A.I.C.S.: 333249
Geneva Miranda *(Office Mgr)*

Brother International Europe Ltd. **(1)**
Brother House 1 Tame Street
Manchester, M34 5JE, United Kingdom UK
Tel.: (44) 1613306531 (100%)
Fax: (44) 1613305520
Web Site: www.brother.co.uk
Emp.: 250
Regional Sales Managing Office
S.I.C.: 8741
N.A.I.C.S.: 551114
Yuji Ishiguro *(Mng Dir)*
Debby Glimshaw *(Sec)*

Subsidiary:

Brother UK Ltd. **(2)**
Shepley Street Guide Bridge
Audenshaw, Manchester, M34 5JD, United Kingdom UK
Tel.: (44) 1613306531 (100%)
Telex: 669092
Fax: (44) 1613083281
Web Site: www.brother.co.uk
Emp.: 300
Office Equipment & Sewing Machines Whslr
S.I.C.: 5044
N.A.I.C.S.: 423420
Phil Jones *(Mng Dir)*

Non-U.S. Subsidiaries:

Brother Finland Oy **(2)**
Honkanummentie 2
PL 53
FI-01261 Vantaa, Finland FI
Tel.: (358) 9875921 (100%)
Fax: (358) 98751133
Web Site: www.brother.fi
Office Equipment & Sewing Machines Whslr
S.I.C.: 5044
N.A.I.C.S.: 423420
John Manelius *(Mng Dir)*

Brother France S.A.S. **(2)**
Parc Des Reflets Paris Nord II
165 Ave Du Bois De La Pie, BP 46061
Roissy-en-Brie, 95913, France FR
Tel.: (33) 49906000 (100%)
Fax: (33) 149901061
E-Mail: info@brother.fr
Web Site: www.brother.fr
Emp.: 140
Office Equipment & Sewing Machines Whslr
S.I.C.: 5044
N.A.I.C.S.: 423420
Andreas Gerber *(Chm)*

Brother Iberia, S.L.U. - Portugal **(2)**
Rua da Garagem 7
2795-510 Carnaxide, Lisboa, Portugal
Tel.: (351) 21 425 4050
Fax: (351) 21 416 0200
Web Site: www.brother.pt
Emp.: 2
Office Equipment & Sewing Machines Whslr
S.I.C.: 5044
N.A.I.C.S.: 423420

Brother International (Austria) GmbH **(2)**
Pfarrgasse 58
1230 Vienna, Austria AT
Tel.: (43) 161007 (100%)
Fax: (43) 1 61007 100
E-Mail: office@brother.at
Web Site: www.brother.at
Sales Range: $1-9.9 Million
Emp.: 20
Office Equipment & Sewing Machines Whslr
S.I.C.: 5044
N.A.I.C.S.: 423420

Brother International Corporation (Ireland) Ltd. **(2)**
Boeing Rd Airways Industrial Estate
Santry, Dublin, 17, Ireland IE
Tel.: (353) 12411900 (100%)
Fax: (353) 18424517
E-Mail: info@brother.ie
Web Site: www.brother.ie
Emp.: 24
Office Equipment & Sewing Machines Whslr
S.I.C.: 5044
N.A.I.C.S.: 423420
Tony Jackson *(Gen Mgr)*

Brother International (Danmark) A/S **(2)**
Baldershoj 22
2635 Ishoj, Denmark DK
Tel.: (45) 43313131 (100%)
Telex: 62226
Fax: (45) 43313143
E-Mail: info@brother.dk
Web Site: www.brother.dk
Emp.: 32
Office Equipment & Sewing Machines Whslr
Import
S.I.C.: 5044
N.A.I.C.S.: 423420

Brother International GmbH **(2)**
Im Rosengarten 14
D 61118 Bad Vilbel, Germany De
Tel.: (49) 61018050 (100%)
Telex: 85007
Fax: (49) 6101805333
E-Mail: brother@brother.de
Web Site: www.brother.de
Emp.: 200
Office Equipment Whslr
S.I.C.: 5044
N.A.I.C.S.: 423420
Lothar Harbich *(Mng Dir)*

Brother International (Gulf) FZE **(2)**
Jebel Ali Free Zone
PO Box 16851
Dubai, United Arab Emirates AE
Tel.: (971) 048835878 (100%)
Fax: (971) 048835387
E-Mail: bicgulf@brother.ae
Web Site: www.brother.ae
Emp.: 40
Office Equipment & Sewing Machines Whslr
S.I.C.: 5044
N.A.I.C.S.: 423420

Sunil Heryani *(Gen Mgr-Admin & Fin)*

Brother International Hungary Kft. (2)
Hungaria Krt 179 187
H-1146 Budapest, Hungary HU
Tel.: (36) 13827453
Fax: (36) 13827455
E-Mail: info@brother.hu
Web Site: www.brother.hu
Emp.: 7
Office Equipment & Sewing Machines Whslr
S.I.C.: 5044
N.A.I.C.S.: 423420

Brother International (Nederland) B.V. (2)
Zanderij 25-27
1185 ZM Amstelveen, Netherlands NL
Tel.: (31) 205451251 (100%)
Fax: (31) 206436495
E-Mail: info@brother.nl
Web Site: www.brother.nl
Emp.: 51
Office Equipment & Sewing Machines Whslr Import
S.I.C.: 5044
N.A.I.C.S.: 423420
Michelle Stassen *(Mng Dir)*

Brother International S.A. (Pty) Ltd. (2)
21 De Havilland Crescent
Persequor Technopark, Pretoria, South Africa ZA
Tel.: (27) 12 349 1410
Fax: (27) 12 349 1232
Web Site: www.brother.co.za
Office Equipment & Sewing Machines Whslr
S.I.C.: 5044
N.A.I.C.S.: 423420

Brother International s.r.o. (2)
Veveri 102
CZ-616 00 Brno, Czech Republic CZ
Tel.: (420) 541426911 (100%)
Fax: (420) 541212463
E-Mail: info@brother.cz
Web Site: www.brother.cz
Emp.: 2
Office Equipment & Sewing Machines Whslr
S.I.C.: 5044
N.A.I.C.S.: 423420

Brother International Sweden A.B. (2)
Holda Lindgrensg 6B
421 31 Vastra Frolunda, Sweden SE
Tel.: (46) 317341200 (100%)
Fax: (46) 317341250
E-Mail: info@brother.se
Web Site: www.brother.se
Sales Range: Less than $1 Million
Emp.: 20
Office Equipment & Sewing Machines Whslr
S.I.C.: 5044
N.A.I.C.S.: 423420
Mats Svensson *(Mng Dir)*

Brother Internationale Industriemaschinen GmbH (2)
Dusseldorfer Strasse 7-29
D-46446 Emmerich am Rhein, Germany De
Mailing Address: (100%)
Postfach 100253
D-46446 Emmerich am Rhein, Germany
Tel.: (49) 28226090
Fax: (49) 282260950
E-Mail: info@brother-ism.com
Web Site: www.brother-ism.com
Sales Range: $10-24.9 Million
Emp.: 28
Industrial Sewing & Embroidery Machines Distr
S.I.C.: 5084
N.A.I.C.S.: 423830

Brother Italia S.p.A. (2)
Segreen Business Park
Via san bovio 3 San Felice, 20090 Segrate, Milano, Italy IT
Tel.: (39) 029500191 (100%)
Fax: (39) 02950019260
E-Mail: brother@brother.it
Web Site: www.brother.it
Emp.: 40
Office Equipment Whslr
S.I.C.: 5044
N.A.I.C.S.: 423420
Marcello Acquaviva *(Mng Dir)*

Brother LLC (2)
Schepkina St 33 Business Ctr Etmia
129090 Moscow, Russia RU
Tel.: (7) 4955105050 (100%)
Fax: (7) 4955105052
E-Mail: info@brother.ru
Web Site: www.brother.ru
Office Equipment & Sewing Machines Whslr
S.I.C.: 5044
N.A.I.C.S.: 423420

Brother Norge A.S. (2)
Oluf Onsums Vei 11
PO Box 93
Manglerud, NO-0612 Oslo, Norway NO
Tel.: (47) 22577500 (100%)
Fax: (47) 22577509
E-Mail: brother@brother.no
Web Site: www.brother.no
Rev.: $14,128,660
Emp.: 32
Office Equipment & Sewing Machines Whslr
S.I.C.: 5044
N.A.I.C.S.: 423420

Brother (Schweiz) A.G. (2)
Taefernstrasse 30
5405 Baden, Daettwil, 5, Switzerland CH
Tel.: (41) 564841111 (100%)
Fax: (41) 564841122
E-Mail: info@brother.ch
Web Site: www.brother.ch
Rev.: $51,026,016
Emp.: 100
Office Equipment & Sewing Machines Whslr
S.I.C.: 5044
N.A.I.C.S.: 423420
Martin Weber *(Mng Dir)*

N.V. Brother International (Belgium) S.A. (2)
Industrialaan 32 Groot Bijaarden
1702 Brussels, Belgium BE
Tel.: (32) 24674211
Fax: (32) 24674444
E-Mail: info@brother.be
Web Site: www.brother.be
Sales Range: $25-49.9 Million
Emp.: 50
Office Equipment & Sewing Machines Whslr
S.I.C.: 5044
N.A.I.C.S.: 423420
Stanilms Brocorens *(Gen Mgr)*

BROTHER INTERNATIONAL KOREA CO., LTD. (1)
2F Changwoo bldg 553 Dogok-dong
Gangnam-gu, Seoul, Korea (South)
Tel.: (82) 56452000
Fax: (82) 2 572 4368
Web Site: www.brother-korea.com
Industrial Electronic Machinery Mfr
S.I.C.: 3559
N.A.I.C.S.: 333249

Brother Nordic A/S (1)
Baldershoej 22
2635 Ishoj, Denmark
Tel.: (45) 43313131
Fax: (45) 43313143
Web Site: www.brother.dk
Industrial Electronic Machinery Mfr
S.I.C.: 3559
N.A.I.C.S.: 333249

BROTHER POLSKA Sp. z o.o (1)
ul Garazowa 7
02-651 Warsaw, Poland
Tel.: (48) 22 607 76 60
Fax: (48) 22 607 76 63
Web Site: www.brother.pl
Industrial Electronic Machinery Mfr
S.I.C.: 3559
N.A.I.C.S.: 333249

Brother Sewing Machine (Shanghai) Co., Ltd. (1)
2201 Yongsheng Road
Jiading Industrial Zone, Shanghai, 201821, China CN
Tel.: (86) 21 6952 0891 (100%)
Fax: (86) 21 6952 0893
Sewing Machine Mfr
S.I.C.: 3559
N.A.I.C.S.: 333249

Brother Sewing Machine Xian Co., Ltd. (1)
No 91 Hong Guang Road
Xi'an, Shaanxi, China CN
Tel.: (86) 2984271487 (100%)
Fax: (86) 2984271936
E-Mail: kozo.tamagawa@brother.co.jp
Web Site: www.brother.com
High-End Industrial Sewing Machine Mfr
S.I.C.: 3559
N.A.I.C.S.: 333249

BROTHER SEWING MACHINES EUROPE GmbH (1)
Im Rosengarten 1111
61118 Bad Vilbel, Germany
Tel.: (49) 6101 9814 0
Fax: (49) 6101 9814 2299
E-Mail: info@brothersewing.eu
Web Site: www.brothersewing.de
Industrial Sewing Machine Distr
S.I.C.: 5084
N.A.I.C.S.: 423830
Koji Kadomura *(Mng Dir)*

BROTHER SOFTWARE DEVELOPMENT (HANGZHOU) LTD. (1)
25F Xiao Hong Building 1777 Bin Sheng Road
Bin Jiang District, Hangzhou, 310052, China
Tel.: (86) 571 8659 1639
Fax: (86) 571 8659 1687
Software Development Services
S.I.C.: 7371
N.A.I.C.S.: 541511

PT BROTHER INTERNATIONAL SALES INDONESIA (1)
Wisma 46 Kota BNI 22nd Fl Suite 22 04/05
Jl Jend Sudirman kav 1
Jakarta, 10220, Indonesia
Tel.: (62) 21 5744477
Fax: (62) 21 5749830
E-Mail: indonesia@brother.co.id
Web Site: www.brother.co.id
Emp.: 25
Industrial Electronic Machinery Distr
S.I.C.: 5084
N.A.I.C.S.: 423830
Deny Santosa *(Gen Mgr)*

Taiwan Brother Industries, Ltd. (1)
76 Kai Fa Rd
Kaohsiung, Taiwan TW
Tel.: (886) 73613111 (100%)
Fax: (886) 73613319
E-Mail: yusw@brother-tw.com
Web Site: www.taiwanbrother.com
Emp.: 300
Household Appliances Mfr
S.I.C.: 5722
N.A.I.C.S.: 443141
Ito Noboru *(Gen Mgr)*

Xian Brother Industries Co., Ltd. (1)
No 20 Gao Xin Road 3
Development Zone of Hi-Tech Industries, Xi'an, Shaanxi, China CN
Tel.: (86) 29 8831 5753 (100%)
Fax: (86) 29 8831 4514
Web Site: www.brother.com
Emp.: 300
Industrial Sewing Machines Mfr
S.I.C.: 3559
N.A.I.C.S.: 333249
Tsuyoshi Miyazawa *(Chm & CEO)*

Zhuhai Brother Industries Co., Ltd. (1)
254 Gang Chang Road Congbei
Zhuhai, Guangdong, China CN
Tel.: (86) 7568610224 (100%)
Fax: (86) 8610134
E-Mail: aiyc@brother.com.cn
Web Site: www.brother.com.cn
Emp.: 3,000
S.I.C.: 3579
N.A.I.C.S.: 339940

BROTOMATIC S.L.
C San Miguel de Acha 2 - Pab 3
01010 Vitoria, Alava, Spain
Tel.: (34) 945249411
Fax: (34) 945227832
E-Mail: broto@brotomatic.es
Web Site: www.brotomatic.es
Business Description:
Industrial Equipment & Services
S.I.C.: 5084
N.A.I.C.S.: 423830

BROUWER CLAIMS CANADA & CO. INC.
510-1100 Melville St
Vancouver, BC, V6E 4A6, Canada
Tel.: (604) 681-2381
Fax: (604) 681-6388
Toll Free: (877) 909-9933
Web Site: www.scm-claimspro.ca
Year Founded: 1956
Rev.: $32,517,411
Emp.: 90
Business Description:
Insurance Claims Services
S.I.C.: 6411
N.A.I.C.S.: 524298
Personnel:
Rodney H. Murrell *(Pres & COO)*
Mark Smith *(Sr VP)*

BROWALLIA INTERNATIONAL B.V.
Amsterdijk 166
PO Box 74120
1070 BC Amsterdam, Netherlands
Tel.: (31) 206446125
Fax: (31) 206423185
Emp.: 200
Business Description:
Holding Company
S.I.C.: 6719
N.A.I.C.S.: 551112

BROWN & NEWIRTH LTD.
Elma House Beaconsfield Close
Hatfield, Herts, AL10 8YG, United Kingdom
Tel.: (44) 1707255000
Fax: (44) 1707255055
E-Mail: sales@bnrings.com
Web Site: www.brownandnewirth.com
Year Founded: 1967
Emp.: 50
Business Description:
Jewelry Designer, Mfr & Whslr
S.I.C.: 3911
N.A.I.C.S.: 339910
Personnel:
John Ball *(Dir)*

Non-U.S. Subsidiary:

Abbeycrest Thailand Ltd. (1)
12th Floor Bangkok Gem & Jewellery Tower
322 Surawong Road, 10500 Bangkok, Thailand (100%)
Tel.: (66) 22 367 133
Fax: (66) 22367135
E-Mail: sales@abbeycrestinternational.com
Web Site: www.abbeycrest.co.th
Emp.: 60
Jewelry Mfr
S.I.C.: 3911
N.A.I.C.S.: 339910
Mark Robinson *(Mng Dir)*

BROWN BROS FORD LINCOLN SALES & SERVICE
270 S E Marine Drive
Vancouver, BC, V5X 2S6, Canada
Tel.: (604) 321-5100
Fax: (604) 321-3791
Web Site: www.brownbros.dealerconnection.com
Rev.: $61,035,355
Emp.: 121
Business Description:
New & Used Car Dealers
S.I.C.: 5511

Brown Bros Ford Lincoln Sales & Service—(Continued)

N.A.I.C.S.: 441110
Personnel:
Leanne Braun *(Mgr-Fin Svcs)*

BROWN WINDOW CORPORATION
185 Snow Blvd
Concord, ON, Canada
Tel.: (905) 738-6045
Fax: (905) 738-1342
Toll Free: (877) 662-6662
E-Mail: info@brownwindow.com
Web Site: www.brownwindow.com
Rev.: $10,417,645
Emp.: 70
Business Description:
Vinyl & Wooden Windows & Doors Mfr
S.I.C.: 2431
N.A.I.C.S.: 321911
Personnel:
Eros Gerardi *(Pres)*

BROWNE & CO.
100 Esna Pk Dr
Markham, ON, L3R 1E3, Canada
Tel.: (905) 475-6104
Fax: (905) 475-5843
E-Mail: info@browneco.com
Web Site: www.browneco.com
Sales Range: $250-299.9 Million
Emp.: 200
Business Description:
Designs, Manufactures, Markets & Imports Kitchen & Tableware
S.I.C.: 3421
N.A.I.C.S.: 332215
Personnel:
Michael Browne *(Pres)*
Division:

Duncan Kitchen Grips Inc. **(1)**
100 Esna Park Drive
Markham, ON, L3R 1E3, Canada
Tel.: (905) 752-3128
Fax: (905) 754-0966
Toll Free: (866) 849-4715
E-Mail: info@kitchengrips.com
Web Site: www.kitchengrips.com
Mfr & Retailer of Kitchen Gloves, Pot Holders, Oven Mitts & Barbecue Mitts
S.I.C.: 3421
N.A.I.C.S.: 332215
Terri-Lynn Harrison *(Mgr-Customer Svc-North America)*

BROWNS' CHEVROLET
12109 8th St
Dawson Creek, BC, VIG 5A5, Canada
Tel.: (250) 782-9155
Fax: (250) 782-1238
Toll Free: (800) 663-8080
Web Site: www.brownschev.com
Year Founded: 1982
Rev.: $13,602,054
Emp.: 45
Business Description:
New & Used Car Dealers
S.I.C.: 5511
N.A.I.C.S.: 441110
Personnel:
Alvie Shearer *(Controller & Mgr-Acctg)*

BROWNSTONE ENERGY INC.
The Exchange Tower 130 King Street West Suite 2500
Toronto, ON, M5X 1A9, Canada
Tel.: (416) 941-8900
Fax: (416) 941-1090
E-Mail: info@brownstoneenergy.com
Web Site: www.brownestoneenergy.com
BWN—(OTC TSXV)
Rev.: $212,503
Assets: $30,270,849
Liabilities: $3,529,884
Net Worth: $26,740,965
Earnings: ($40,615,837)
Fiscal Year-end: 06/30/13
Business Description:
Oil & Gas Exploration Services
S.I.C.: 1311
N.A.I.C.S.: 211111
Personnel:
Sheldon Inwentash *(Chm & CEO)*
Jonathan Schroeder *(Pres & COO)*
Gerald Morris Feldman *(CFO)*
Board of Directors:
Sheldon Inwentash
Steven M. Mintz
Kevin O'Connor
Jonathan Schroeder
Michael D. Sweatman
Transfer Agent:
Equity Financial Trust Company
200 University Avenue Suite 300
Toronto, ON, M5H 4H1, Canada

B.R.R. GUARDIAN MODARABA
1900-B Saima Trade Towers II
Chundrigar Road
Karachi, 74000, Pakistan
Tel.: (92) 21 32271874
Fax: (92) 2132271912
E-Mail: brr@firstdawood.com
Web Site: www.firstdawood.com
BRR—(KAR)
Rev.: $4,072,231
Assets: $30,508,051
Liabilities: $22,383,172
Net Worth: $8,124,880
Earnings: $541,042
Emp.: 25
Fiscal Year-end: 06/30/13
Business Description:
Investment & Financial Management Services
S.I.C.: 6282
N.A.I.C.S.: 523920
Personnel:
Rafique Dawood *(Chm)*
Ayaz Dawood *(CEO)*
Tariq Masood *(CFO)*
Tahir Mehmood *(Sec)*
Board of Directors:
Rafique Dawood
Ayaz Dawood
Mohammad Shahid Murtaza
Farouq Habib Rahimtoola

BRS VENTURES LTD.
999 West Hastings Street Suite 1040
Vancouver, BC, V6C 2W2, Canada
Tel.: (604) 290-1642
Fax: (604) 922-4706
E-Mail: stephen@hiscoventures.com
Year Founded: 2007
BVRH—(CNSX)
Assets: $179,086
Liabilities: $28,543
Net Worth: $150,543
Earnings: ($56,632)
Fiscal Year-end: 10/31/12
Business Description:
Investment Services
S.I.C.: 6211
N.A.I.C.S.: 523999
Personnel:
Luke Norman *(CEO & CFO)*
Board of Directors:
Robert G. McMorran
Luke Norman

BRUCE POWER, INC.
177 Tie Rd R R 2
Tiverton, Kincardine, ON, N0G 2T0, Canada
Tel.: (519) 361-2673
E-Mail: info@brucepower.com
Web Site: www.brucepower.com
Year Founded: 2000
Emp.: 3,720
Business Description:
Nuclear Electric Power Generation
S.I.C.: 4939
N.A.I.C.S.: 221113
Personnel:
Duncan Hawthorne *(Pres & CEO)*
Board of Directors:
Duncan Hawthorne

BRUCE R SMITH LIMITED
Railroad 2
Simcoe, ON, N3Y 4K1, Canada
Tel.: (519) 426-0904
Fax: (519) 428-2690
Toll Free: (800) 265-8070
Web Site: www.brsmith.com
Year Founded: 1947
Rev.: $49,477,473
Emp.: 500
Business Description:
Transportation Services
S.I.C.: 4789
N.A.I.C.S.: 488999
Personnel:
John H. Smith *(Pres & CEO)*
Beth Knoll *(Chief Admin Officer)*

BRUMBY RESOURCES LIMITED
Unit 3 49 Ord Street
West Perth, WA, 6005, Australia
Mailing Address:
PO Box 231
West Perth, WA, 6872, Australia
Tel.: (61) 894868333
Fax: (61) 893225123
E-Mail: admin@brumbyresources.com.au
Web Site: www.brumbyresources.com.au
BMY—(ASX)
Rev.: $70,853
Assets: $1,578,968
Liabilities: $129,923
Net Worth: $1,449,045
Earnings: ($2,446,726)
Emp.: 7
Fiscal Year-end: 06/30/13
Business Description:
Minerals Exploration & Development
S.I.C.: 1011
N.A.I.C.S.: 212210
Personnel:
Alison Morley *(CEO)*
Kimberley Arnold Hogg *(Sec)*
Board of Directors:
Geoffrey Michael Jones
Tom Henderson
John Hutton
Legal Counsel:
Steinepreis Paganin
Level 4 16 Milligan St
Perth, Australia
Transfer Agent:
Computershare Investor Services Pty. Limited
Level 2 45 Saint George's Terrace
Perth, WA, 6000, Australia
Tel.: (61) 8 9323 2000
Fax: (61) 8 9323 2033

BRUN AUTOMOBILES S.A.
710 avenue de l'Europe
69400 Villefranche-sur-Saone, France
Tel.: (33) 474620085
Web Site:
Sls.: $12,300,000
Emp.: 23
Business Description:
Automobile Dealer for Opel
S.I.C.: 5511
N.A.I.C.S.: 441110
Personnel:
Daniel Brun *(Pres)*

BRUNEL & FAMILY HOUSING ASSOCIATION LTD.
87 Manningham Lane
BD13BN Bradford, West Yorkshire, United Kingdom
Tel.: (44) 8456500913
Fax: (44) 1274826001
Web Site: www.housingnet.co.uk
Sales Range: $25-49.9 Million
Emp.: 215
Business Description:
Construction & Management of Housing Accommodation
S.I.C.: 9531
N.A.I.C.S.: 925110
Personnel:
P. Geoghegan *(Chm)*

BRUNEL INTERNATIONAL N.V.
John M Keynesplein 33
1066 ep Amsterdam, Netherlands
Tel.: (31) 20 312 5000
Fax: (31) 20 614 1199
E-Mail: info@brunel.nl
Web Site: www.brunel.net
BRNL—(EUR)
Rev.: $1,664,578,244
Assets: $564,762,739
Liabilities: $209,158,471
Net Worth: $355,604,267
Earnings: $59,873,603
Emp.: 11,775
Fiscal Year-end: 12/31/12
Business Description:
Business Consulting & Project Management Placement Services
S.I.C.: 7361
N.A.I.C.S.: 561311
Personnel:
Daan van Doorn *(Chm-Supervisory Bd)*
Aat Schouwenaar *(Vice Chm-Supervisory Bd)*
Jan Arie van Barneveld *(CEO & Member-Mgmt Bd)*
Rob van der Hoek *(CFO & Member-Mgmt Bd)*
Supervisory Board of Directors:
Daan van Doorn
Ing Jan Bout
Aat Schouwenaar
Subsidiaries:

Brunel Energy Europe BV **(1)**
Rethodam Airport
2909 LE Capelle aan den IJssel, Netherlands (100%)
Tel.: (31) 102666444
Fax: (31) 102666379
E-Mail: energy@brunel.net
Web Site: www.brunel.nl
Emp.: 200
Business Support Services
S.I.C.: 7389
N.A.I.C.S.: 561499
Jan van Barneveld *(CEO)*

Brunel Energy Holding BV **(1)**
Rivium Straat 121
2909 Capelle aan den IJssel, Netherlands (100%)
Tel.: (31) 102666400
Fax: (31) 102666379
E-Mail: info@brunel.net
Web Site: www.brunel.nl
Emp.: 55
Business Support Services
S.I.C.: 7389
N.A.I.C.S.: 561499

Jan van Barneveld *(CEO)*

Brunel Nederland BV (1)
Hullenbergweg 385-411
1066 EP Amsterdam, Netherlands (100%)
Tel.: (31) 203125000
Fax: (31) 203125099
E-Mail: info@brunel.nl
Web Site: www.brunel.nl
Emp.: 2,550
Employment Placement Agencies
S.I.C.: 7361
N.A.I.C.S.: 561311
Jan van Barneveld *(CEO)*

U.S. Subsidiary:

Brunel Energy Inc. (1)
5333 Westheimer Rd Ste 840
Houston, TX 77056-5407 (100%)
Tel.: (713) 339-9339
Fax: (713) 339-2778
E-Mail: a.braccogartner@brunel.nl
Web Site: www.brunelenergy.net
Emp.: 25
Employment Placement Agencies
S.I.C.: 7361
N.A.I.C.S.: 561311
Bracco Gartner *(Mng Dir)*

Non-U.S. Subsidiaries:

Brunel Energy Canada Inc (1)
Ste 635 - 8 Avenue SW
Calgary, AB, T2P 3M3, Canada (100%)
Tel.: (403) 539-5009
Fax: (403) 294-9594
Web Site: www.brunelenergy.net
Emp.: 10
Employment Placement Agencies
S.I.C.: 7361
N.A.I.C.S.: 561311
Michael McKinnon *(Gen Mgr)*

Brunel Energy L.L.C. (1)
Office 105 1st Floor Business Centre Building
PO Box 5658
Khalid Bin Waleed St, Dubai, United Arab Emirates
Tel.: (971) 43974778
Fax: (971) 43974757
E-Mail: energy-uae@brunel.net
Web Site: www.brunelenergy.net
Emp.: 1,000
Oil & Gas Operations
S.I.C.: 1389
N.A.I.C.S.: 213112
Aloysious Harrdwijn *(Reg Dir)*

Brunel Energy Malaysia Sdn Bhd (1)
25-2 Level 25 Menara Standard
30 Jalan Sultan Ismail, 50250 Kuala Lumpur, Malaysia
Tel.: (60) 321443451
Fax: (60) 327132283
E-Mail: energy@brunel.com.my
Web Site: www.brunelenergy.net
Emp.: 9
Engineering Services
S.I.C.: 8711
N.A.I.C.S.: 541330
Ganeashan Periasamy *(Mgr)*

Brunel Energy Nigeria Ltd (1)
Eshrow House No 7 Onikepoakande Street
Off Admiralty Way Road 12
Lekki Phase 1, Victoria Island, Lagos, Nigeria
Tel.: (234) 1271 4023
Fax: (234) 1271 4022
Human Resource Consulting Services
S.I.C.: 8999
N.A.I.C.S.: 541612
Mitch Sonariwo *(Country Mgr)*

Brunel Energy Pty Ltd (1)
Level 2, 101 St George's Terrace
6000 Perth, WA, Australia
Tel.: (61) 893219600
Fax: (61) 894295642
E-Mail: energy@brunel.com.au
Web Site: www.brunel.net
Emp.: 40
Drilling Oil & Gas Wells
S.I.C.: 1381
N.A.I.C.S.: 213111
Craig Follett *(Gen Mgr)*

Brunel Energy Qatar W.L.L. (1)
Office No 3108 F1 Bldg 3 Al Waab city
Comml District Salwa Rd
PO Box 24936
Jaun St Al Saad, Doha, Qatar
Tel.: (974) 4320422
Fax: (974) 44666375
E-Mail: energy@brunelqatar.com
Web Site: www.brunel.net
Emp.: 200
Support Activities for Oil & Gas Operations
S.I.C.: 1389
N.A.I.C.S.: 213112

Brunel Engineering Consultants NV (1)
Blareenbeerglaan 3 A
2800 Mechelen, Belgium
Tel.: (32) 15273333
Fax: (32) 15273332
E-Mail: info@brunel.be
Web Site: www.brunel.be
Emp.: 120
Engineering Services
S.I.C.: 1622
N.A.I.C.S.: 237310
Wouter Gansen *(Dir-Brunel Engrg)*

Brunel GmbH (1)
Hermann-Kohl-Str 1
Bremen, Germany (100%)
Tel.: (49) 421169410
Fax: (49) 4211694141
E-Mail: contact@brunel.de
Web Site: www.brunel.de
Emp.: 60
Regulation Licensing & Inspection of Commercial Sectors
S.I.C.: 9651
N.A.I.C.S.: 926150
Banrnivald Jen arei *(CEO)*

Brunel ICt NV (1)
Blarenberglaan 3A
2800 Mechelen, Belgium
Tel.: (32) 15273333
Fax: (32) 15273332
E-Mail: info@brunel.be
Web Site: www.brunel.be
Emp.: 120
Highway & Street Construction
S.I.C.: 8711
N.A.I.C.S.: 541330
Sandra Schuerewegen *(Mng Dir)*

Brunel International France Sarl (1)
56 Boulevard de la Mission Marchand
92400 Courbevoie, France
Tel.: (33) 1 49 05 02 40
Fax: (33) 1 55 70 04 84
E-Mail: energy@brunel.net
Web Site: www.brunelenergy.net
Human Resource Consulting Services
S.I.C.: 8999
N.A.I.C.S.: 541612

Brunel International South East Asia Pte Ltd (1)
77 Robinson Rd #10-03
628896 Singapore, Singapore
Tel.: (65) 65322480
Fax: (65) 65322536
E-Mail: mailbox@brunel.net
Web Site: www.brunel.com.sg
Emp.: 70
Management Consulting Services
S.I.C.: 8748
N.A.I.C.S.: 541618
Sil Hoeve *(Gen Mgr)*

Brunel International UK Ltd (1)
Corunna House 39
Cadogan Street, Glasgow, G27 AB, United Kingdom (100%)
Tel.: (44) 1413023032
Fax: (44) 1413023001
E-Mail: energy@brunel-uk.com
Web Site: www.brunelenergy.net
Emp.: 20
Employment Placement Agencies
S.I.C.: 7361
N.A.I.C.S.: 561311
Stuart Mills *(Mgr-Ops)*

Brunel Oil & Gas Services WLL (1)
Bldg No 3 Office No 3108 Al Waab City
Commercial District Salwa Road
Doha, Qatar
Tel.: (974) 44 666 275
Fax: (974) 44 666 375
E-Mail: energy-qatar@brunel.net
Web Site: www.brunel.net
Emp.: 30
Oil & Gas Industry Recruitment Consulting Services
S.I.C.: 4731
N.A.I.C.S.: 541614
John Deneys *(Reg Mgr)*

Brunel Technical Services Pte Ltd (1)
77 Robinson Rd 10-03
068896 Singapore, Singapore (100%)
Tel.: (65) 65341352
Fax: (65) 65322535
E-Mail: energy-singapore@brunel.com.sg
Web Site: www.brunel.com.sg
Emp.: 100
Scientific & Technical Consulting Services
S.I.C.: 8999
N.A.I.C.S.: 541690
William Anderson *(CEO)*

Brunel Technical Services Pty Ltd (1)
L 2 101 Saint Georges Terrace
Perth, WA, 6000, Australia
Tel.: (61) 8 9429 5600
Fax: (61) 8 9429 5642
Emp.: 60
Technical Consulting Services
S.I.C.: 8999
N.A.I.C.S.: 541690
Denise Freeman *(Gen Mgr)*

Brunel Technical Services (Thailand) Limited (1)
4-25-26 Moo 10 Sukhumvit Road
Tombol Tungsukhla, 20230 Chon Buri, Thailand (100%)
Tel.: (66) 384015913
Fax: (66) 38401594
E-Mail: betes@brunel.co.th
Web Site: www.brunel.co.th
Emp.: 400
Professional Scientific & Technical Services
S.I.C.: 7389
N.A.I.C.S.: 541990
Glenn Waters *(Gen Mgr)*

Car Synergies GmbH (1)
Dinnendahlstrasse 9
44809 Bochum, Germany (100%)
Tel.: (49) 23441710
Fax: (49) 2344171100
E-Mail: contact@carsynergies.de
Web Site: www.carsynergies.de
Emp.: 35
Business Support Services
S.I.C.: 7389
N.A.I.C.S.: 561499
Peter Bolz *(CEO)*

Multec Canada Ltd (1)
200 Ronson Dr Ste 320
Toronto, ON, M9W 5Z9, Canada (100%)
Tel.: (416) 244-2402
Fax: (416) 244-6883
Toll Free: (888) 244-8466
E-Mail: toronto@brunel.net
Web Site: www.brunel.net
Emp.: 36
Employment Placement Agencies
S.I.C.: 7361
N.A.I.C.S.: 561311
Arjan De Vries *(Pres)*

BRUNELLO CUCINELLI S.P.A.

Via dell'Industria 5
Solomeo, 06073 Corciano, Perugia, Italy
Tel.: (39) 075 6970079
Web Site: www.brunellocucinelli.com
BC—(ITA)
Business Description:
Luxury Clothing & Accessories
S.I.C.: 2389
N.A.I.C.S.: 315240
Personnel:
Brunello Cucinelli *(Chm & CEO)*
Moreno Ciarapica *(CFO)*
Fabio Gnocchi *(Chief Comml Officer)*
Board of Directors:
Brunello Cucinelli
Moreno Ciarapica
Cassian Folsom
Candice Koo
Giovanna Manfredi
Matteo Marzotto
Andrea Pontremoli
Riccardo Stefanelli
Enrico Vitali

BRUNO'S CONTRACTING (THUNDER BAY) LTD.

665 Hewitson St
Thunder Bay, ON, P7B 5V5, Canada
Tel.: (807) 623-1855
Fax: (807) 623-0360
Web Site: www.brunoscontracting.com
Year Founded: 1973
Rev.: $31,369,738
Emp.: 200
Business Description:
Building Contractors
S.I.C.: 1542
N.A.I.C.S.: 236220
Personnel:
Silvio Di Gregorio *(Treas & Sec)*

BRUSHMAN (INDIA) LIMITED

B-95/3 Phase - 1 Naraina Industrial Area
New Delhi, 110028, India
Tel.: (91) 11 25891453
Fax: (91) 11 25798187
E-Mail: info@brushmanindia.com
Web Site: www.brushmanindia.com
Year Founded: 1993
590061—(BOM)
Business Description:
Paintbrushes Mfr
S.I.C.: 3991
N.A.I.C.S.: 339994
Personnel:
Kapil Kumar *(Mng Dir)*

BRYDOL LTD.

Unit Q Hunting Gate East Portway Industrial Estate
Andover, Hampshire, SP10 3SJ, United Kingdom
Tel.: (44) 1264 339740
Fax: (44) 1264 339746
E-Mail: sales@brydol.co.uk
Web Site: www.brydol.co.uk
Emp.: 15
Business Description:
Joinery & Shopfitting Mfr
S.I.C.: 3559
N.A.I.C.S.: 333249
Personnel:
Michael Bryden *(CEO)*

BRYEN & LANGLEY LTD.

48 60 Footscray Rd
Eltham, London, SE9 2SU, United Kingdom
Tel.: (44) 2088507775
Fax: (44) 2088506772
E-Mail: info@bryen-langley.com
Web Site: www.bryen-langley.com
Sales Range: $50-74.9 Million
Emp.: 189
Business Description:
Construction & Maintainance Services
S.I.C.: 1629
N.A.I.C.S.: 237990
Personnel:
Alan Escudier *(Dir-Construction)*

BRYMOR CONTRACTORS LTD.

Brymor House Parklands Business Park Forest Rd
Denmead, Waterlooville, Hampshire, PO7 6XP, United Kingdom
Tel.: (44) 2392261515

Brymor Contractors Ltd.—(Continued)

Fax: (44) 2392240666
E-Mail: office@brymor.co.uk
Web Site: www.brymor.co.uk
Sales Range: $50-74.9 Million
Emp.: 150
Business Description:
Building Contractors
S.I.C.: 1799
N.A.I.C.S.: 238190
Personnel:
Stephen J. Morton *(Chm)*

BRYTEX BUILDING SYSTEMS INC.

5610 97 Street
Edmonton, AB, T6E 3J1, Canada
Tel.: (780) 437-7970
Fax: (780) 437-5022
E-Mail: brytex@brytex.com
Web Site: www.brytex.com
Year Founded: 1987
Rev.: $36,400,952
Emp.: 100
Business Description:
Metal Building Construction
S.I.C.: 3448
N.A.I.C.S.: 332311
Personnel:
Al Stix *(Pres)*

BRZ INVESTIMENTOS S.A.

Rua Leopoldo Couto de Magalhaes Jr 758
Cj 52 Itaim Bib, 4542000 Sao Paulo, Brazil
Tel.: (55) 1135388000
Fax: (55) 1135388099
E-Mail: marcus.martino@brzinvestimentos.com.br
Web Site: www.brzinvestimentos.com.br
BRZ13B—(BRAZ)
Emp.: 50
Business Description:
Financial & Asset Management Investment Services
S.I.C.: 6211
N.A.I.C.S.: 523999
Personnel:
Nelson Rozental *(Chm)*
Marcos Pessoa de Queiroz Falcao *(CEO)*
Marcus Marques Martino *(CFO & Dir-IR)*
Board of Directors:
Nelson Rozental
Antonio Carlos Augusto R. Bonchristiano
Marcos Pessoa de Queiroz Falcao
Mariano Ceppas Figueiredo
Danilo Gamboa
Fersen Lamas Lambranho
Marcus Marques Martino

BS FINANCIAL GROUP INC.

937 3 Beomil Dong
Dong Gu, Busan, 601060, Korea (South)
Tel.: (82) 516 203118
Fax: (82) 516 203040
Web Site: www.bsfng.com
Year Founded: 2011
138930—(KRS)
Business Description:
Bank Holding Company
S.I.C.: 6712
N.A.I.C.S.: 551111
Personnel:
Jang-ho Lee *(CEO)*
Subsidiaries:

Busan Bank, Ltd. **(1)**
830-38 Bomil-dong
Busan, Dong-gu, 601-060, Korea (South)
Tel.: (82) 516423300
Fax: (82) 516698481
E-Mail: josh@busanbank.co.kr
Web Site: www.busanbank.co.kr
Sales Range: $1-4.9 Billion
Emp.: 3,398
Banking Services
S.I.C.: 6029
N.A.I.C.S.: 522110
Jang-ho Lee *(Chm, Pres & CEO)*
Shin-won Kang *(Mng Dir & VP)*
Young-rok Lim *(Mng Dir & VP)*
Se-hwan Sung *(Mng Dir & VP)*
Jae-joo Cha *(Exec VP)*
Jae-young Chung *(Exec VP)*
Jae-woong Kim *(Exec VP)*
Chang-yoeul Lee *(Exec VP)*
Ji-ho Lee *(Exec VP)*
Yong-jin Yoon *(Exec VP)*

Busan Credit & Information Co., Ltd. **(1)**
378-11 Gaya 1-Dong
Busanjin-Gu, Busan, Korea (South) (100%)
Tel.: (82) 518905000
Fax: (82) 518952342
Emp.: 15
Credit Services
S.I.C.: 6159
N.A.I.C.S.: 522298

PB Futures Co., Ltd. **(1)**
10th Floor Pusan Chamber of Commerce & Industry Building
853-1 Bumcheon 1-Dong
Busanjin-Gu, Busan, Korea (South) (100%)
Tel.: (82) 0232151560
Fax: (82) 027862998
Web Site: www.pbfutures.com
Emp.: 25
Investment Banking Services
S.I.C.: 6211
N.A.I.C.S.: 523999

BS INVESTIMENTI SGR S.P.A

(d/b/a BS Private Equity)
Via dell Orso 8
20121 Milan, Italy
Tel.: (39) 027621131
Fax: (39) 0276211340
E-Mail: info@bspeg.com
Web Site: www.bspeg.com
Emp.: 25
Business Description:
Private Equity Firm
S.I.C.: 6211
N.A.I.C.S.: 523999
Personnel:
Paolo Baretta *(Mng Partner)*
Antonio Perricone *(Mng Partner)*
Lidia Carbonetti *(Partner)*
Alessandra Gavirati *(Partner)*
Paolo Pendenza *(Partner)*
Ugo Pivato *(Partner)*
Luciana Russo *(Partner)*
Maria Scozzafava *(Partner)*
Francesco Sironi *(Partner)*

Holding:

Mediacontech S.p.A. **(1)**
Via Messina 38 Torre A
20154 Milan, Italy IT
Tel.: (39) 0234594900 (78.37%)
Fax: (39) 0118015955
E-Mail: marketing@mediacontech.com
Web Site: www.mediacontech.com
MCH—(ITA)
Sales Range: $125-149.9 Million
Emp.: 600
Television Content Development & Media Management Services
S.I.C.: 4833
N.A.I.C.S.: 515120
Andrea Frecchiami *(Chm)*
Enzo Badalotti *(CEO)*

Subsidiaries:

Euphon Communications S.p.A. **(2)**
Via Nizza 294
10137 Turin, Italy
Tel.: (39) 0113811111
Fax: (39) 0118015933
E-Mail: jobopportunities@euphon.it
Web Site: www.euphon.it
Sales Range: $25-49.9 Million
Emp.: 521
Audio Video Communications Systems Design Services
S.I.C.: 3651
N.A.I.C.S.: 334310
Andrea Frecchiami *(Pres)*

Videe S.p.A. **(2)**
Via Roggiuzzole 3
33170 Pordenone, Italy IT
Tel.: (39) 0434361016 (50.1%)
Fax: (39) 0434551115
E-Mail: info@videe.it
Web Site: www.videe.it
Sales Range: $1-9.9 Million
Emp.: 20
Motion Picture & Video Production
S.I.C.: 7812
N.A.I.C.S.: 512110
Bruno Mercuri *(Pres & CEO)*
Paola Montanari *(Mng Dir)*

Non-U.S. Subsidiary:

Mikros Image S.A. **(2)**
120 rue Danton
92300 Levallois-Perret, France FR
Tel.: (33) 155631100
Fax: (33) 155631101
E-Mail: info@mikrosimage.fr
Web Site: www.mikrosimage.fr
Sales Range: $10-24.9 Million
Emp.: 150
Motion Picture & Video Production
S.I.C.: 7812
N.A.I.C.S.: 512110
Maurice Prost *(CEO)*
Pascal Buron *(COO)*

Subsidiary:

Plus Gros Le Logo **(3)**
120 rue Danton
92300 Levallois-Perret, France FR
Tel.: (33) 155631200
Fax: (33) 155631205
E-Mail: info@mikrosimage.fr
Web Site: www.mikrosimage.fr
Emp.: 100
Postproduction for the Advertising Business
S.I.C.: 7819
N.A.I.C.S.: 512191
Lionel Gujlair *(Gen Mgr)*

BS TRANSCOMM LIMITED

(d/b/a BS Group)
504 Trendset Towers Road 2
Banjara Hills, Hyderabad, Andhra Pradesh, 500034, India
Tel.: (91) 40 6666 6204
Fax: (91) 40 6666 7268
E-Mail: info@bsgroup.in
Web Site: www.bsgroup.in
BSTRANSCOM—(BOM NSE)
Sales Range: $75-99.9 Million
Emp.: 300
Business Description:
Telecommunication & Power Structures Mfr
S.I.C.: 1623
N.A.I.C.S.: 237130
Personnel:
Rajesh Agarwal *(Chm & Mng Dir)*
Tarun Nanda *(CEO)*
Board of Directors:
Rajesh Agarwal
A. Gopalakrishnan Iyer

BSA LIMITED

7 Figtree Drive
Sydney, NSW, 2127, Australia
Tel.: (61) 287482400
Fax: (61) 287482577
E-Mail: corporate@bsa.com.au
Web Site: www.bsa.com.au
BSA—(ASX)
Rev.: $494,142,978
Assets: $184,862,287
Liabilities: $106,918,418
Net Worth: $77,943,870
Earnings: $3,921,422
Emp.: 1,000
Fiscal Year-end: 06/30/13
Business Description:
Communications & Technical Service Solutions; Satellite Installation Services
S.I.C.: 4899
N.A.I.C.S.: 517410
Personnel:
Graham Seppelt *(Sec)*
Board of Directors:
Ross Johnston
Daniel Collis
Michael Givoni
Mark Lowe
Paul Teisseire
Subsidiaries:

Triple 'M' Fire **(1)**
Quad 4 Level 1 8 Parkview Dr
Homebush Bay, NSW, 2127, Australia
Tel.: (61) 297636200
Fax: (61) 297636201
E-Mail: TMFAdmin@triple-m.com.au
Web Site: www.triple-m.com.au
Fire Protection Solutions
S.I.C.: 9224
N.A.I.C.S.: 922160
Mark Lowe *(Mng Dir)*

Triple M Mechanical Services Pty Ltd **(1)**
Triple M Industrial Estate
Unit 5/47 Day Street North, Silverwater, NSW, 2128, Australia AU
Tel.: (61) 297378711
Fax: (61) 297636201
E-Mail: tms@triple-m.com.au
Web Site: www.triple-m.com.au
Mechanical Engineering Services
S.I.C.: 8711
N.A.I.C.S.: 541330
Mark Lowe *(Mng Dir)*

Triple M Mechanical Services Pty Ltd **(1)**
56 Overlord Place
4110 Acacia Ridge, QLD, Australia AU
Tel.: (61) 732721177
Fax: (61) 732722199
E-Mail: tmq@triple-m.com.au
Web Site: www.triple-m.com.au
Emp.: 60
Mechanical Engineering Services
S.I.C.: 8711
N.A.I.C.S.: 541330
Mark Lowe *(Mng Dir)*

BSB SA

(d/b/a BSB Group)
Boulevard Baudouin 1er 25 1348 Ottignies
Louvain-la-Neuve, Belgium
Tel.: (32) 10483480
Fax: (32) 10483499
E-Mail: investors@bsb.com
Web Site: www.bsb.com
Year Founded: 1995
BSB—(EUR)
Rev.: $49,471,748
Assets: $30,757,292
Liabilities: $22,833,736
Net Worth: $7,923,557
Earnings: ($9,903,773)
Emp.: 344
Fiscal Year-end: 12/31/12
Business Description:
IT Consulting & Business Software Publisher
S.I.C.: 8742
N.A.I.C.S.: 541611
Personnel:
Badreddine Ouali *(Chm)*
Jean Martin *(CEO)*
Olivier Tordeurs *(CFO)*
Miguel Danckers *(Sec & Dir-HR)*
Board of Directors:
Badreddine Ouali
Pierre De Muelenaere
Marwan Hanifeh

Michel Isaac
Jean Martin
Vincent Werbrouck

Subsidiary:

Business Solutions Builders (Belgium) SA (1)
Boulevard Baudouin Ier 25 Ottignies
Louvain-la-Neuve, 1348, Belgium
Tel.: (32) 10483480
Fax: (32) 10483499
E-Mail: bsbbelgium@bsb.com
Emp.: 100
IT Services & Financial Software Publishers
S.I.C.: 7372
N.A.I.C.S.: 511210
Jean Martin *(CEO)*

BSC DRUKARNIA OPAKOWAN SA

Ul Zmigrodzka 37
60-171 Poznan, Poland
Tel.: (48) 618676061
Fax: (48) 618676066
E-Mail: relacje-inwestorskie@bsc-packaging.com
Web Site: www.bsc-packaging.com
BSC—(WAR)
Sales Range: $25-49.9 Million

Business Description:
Packaging Products Mfr
S.I.C.: 2672
N.A.I.C.S.: 322220
Personnel:
Janusz Schwark *(Chm)*

BSEL INFRASTRUCTURE REALTY LIMITED

737 7th Floor The Bombay Oilseeds & Oils Exchange Premises Co-op Sty Plot No 2 3 & 4 Vashi, Navi Mumbai, Maharashtra, 400 705, India
Tel.: (91) 2265123124
E-Mail: info@bsel.com
Web Site: www.bsel.com
BSELINFRA—(NSE)
Rev.: $372,970
Assets: $114,378,807
Liabilities: $52,929,536
Net Worth: $61,449,271
Earnings: ($93,013)
Fiscal Year-end: 03/31/13

Business Description:
Real Estate Development Services
S.I.C.: 6531
N.A.I.C.S.: 531390
Personnel:
Disha Devrukhkar *(CEO & Compliance Officer)*
Vijay Chauhan *(CFO)*
Board of Directors:
Kirit Kanakiya
Disha Devrukhkar
Dippal Muchhala
Hitesh Vora

Transfer Agent:
Sharex Dynamic (India) Pvt. Ltd.
Unit No 1 Luthra Industrial Premises Andheri-Kurla Road
Safed Pool Andheri E, 400 072 Mumbai, India

BSI STEEL LIMITED

Erf 24 Farm Waterval M61
Kliprivier, 1451 Gauteng, South Africa
Mailing Address:
PO Box 124396
Alrode, 1451 Gauteng, South Africa
Tel.: (27) 11 861 7600
Fax: (27) 11 861 7611
Web Site: www.bsisteel.com
Rev.: $313,311,798
Assets: $175,261,545
Liabilities: $114,295,796
Net Worth: $60,965,748
Earnings: $3,251,140
Fiscal Year-end: 03/31/13

Business Description:
Steel Products Mfr & Distr
S.I.C.: 3317
N.A.I.C.S.: 331210
Personnel:
William Battershill *(Chm)*
Grant Mackenzie *(CEO)*
Jerry Govender *(COO)*
Board of Directors:
William Battershill
Ivan Clarke
Jerry Govender
Butana Khoza
Richard Lewis
Grant Mackenzie
Craig Parry
Nigel Payne
James Waller

Legal Counsel:
Venn Nemeth & Hart Inc
281 Pietermaritzburg St
Pietermaritzburg, South Africa

Transfer Agent:
Computershare Investor Services (Pty) Limited
Ground Floor 70 Marshall Street
Johannesburg, South Africa

BSL LIMITED

26 Industrial Area Gandhi Nagar
Post Box No 17
Bhilwara, Rajasthan, 31001, India
Tel.: (91) 1482246801
Fax: (91) 1482246807
E-Mail: info@bslsuitings.com
Web Site: www.bslltd.com
BSL—(NSE)
Rev.: $54,904,022
Assets: $49,452,076
Liabilities: $37,659,616
Net Worth: $11,792,460
Earnings: $64,167
Fiscal Year-end: 03/31/13

Business Description:
Formal Suits Mfr
S.I.C.: 2329
N.A.I.C.S.: 315220
Personnel:
Arun Churiwal *(Chm & Mng Dir)*
Praveen Jain *(CFO, Compliance Officer & Sec)*
Board of Directors:
Arun Churiwal
Shekhar Agarwal
Salil Bhandari
A. N. Choudhary
Nivedan Churiwal
Ravi Jhunjhunwala
Sushil Jhunjhunwala

Transfer Agent:
MCS Ltd
Sri Venkatesh Bhawan F-65 1st Floor Okhla Industrial Area Phase-I
New Delhi, India

BSM GROUP LIMITED

BSM Center 119/122
Amin Market, Chittagong, Bangladesh
Tel.: (880) 31624372
Fax: (880) 31610841
E-Mail: info@modernbd.com
Web Site: www.modernbd.com
Emp.: 60

Business Description:
Holding Company
S.I.C.: 6719
N.A.I.C.S.: 551112
Personnel:
Abul Bashar Chowdhury *(Chm)*

Subsidiary:

Modern Poly Industries Ltd. (1)
BSM Center 119/122
Amin Market, Chittagong, Bangladesh
Tel.: (880) 31624372
Fax: (880) 31620545
E-Mail: info@modernbd.com
Web Site: www.modernbd.com
Sales Range: $10-24.9 Million
Emp.: 400
Polyester Yarn
S.I.C.: 2399
N.A.I.C.S.: 313110
Abul Bashar Chowdhury *(Chm)*
Abu Sufian Chowdhury *(Mng Dir)*

BSM TECHNOLOGIES INC.

75 International Blvd Suite 100
Toronto, ON, M9W 6L9, Canada
Tel.: (905) 265-1200
Fax: (905) 265-1288
Toll Free: (866) 578-4315
E-Mail: ir@bsmtechnologies.com
Web Site: www.bsmtechnologies.com
Year Founded: 1996
GPS—(TSXV)
Rev.: $13,780,678
Assets: $9,532,850
Liabilities: $3,949,761
Net Worth: $5,583,090
Earnings: $1,537,459
Emp.: 40
Fiscal Year-end: 09/30/12

Business Description:
After-Market, Wireless, High Security Vehicle Surveillance Products & Monitoring Services
S.I.C.: 4812
N.A.I.C.S.: 517210
Personnel:
Frank Maw *(Chm)*
Aly Rahemtulla *(Pres & CEO)*
Louis De Jong *(CFO)*
Eric Moran *(COO)*
Alban Hoxha *(CTO)*
Lisa Hunter *(Exec VP-Mktg)*
Owen Moore *(Exec VP-Sls)*
Board of Directors:
Frank Maw
Pierre Belanger
John K. Bell
Aly Rahemtulla
Greg Rokos
David Yach

Transfer Agent:
Computershare Investor Services
100 University Avenue 11th Floor
Toronto, ON, M5J 2Y1, Canada
Tel.: (416) 263-9200
Toll Free: (800) 564-6253

Subsidiary:

Datacom Wireless Corporation (1)
440 Armand-Frappier Boulevard Suite 350
Laval, QC, H7V 4B4, Canada Ca
Tel.: (450) 781-6000
Fax: (450) 781-6001
Toll Free: (888) 776-3333
E-Mail: services@datacom.com
Web Site: www.datacom.com
Emp.: 53
Wireless Communications & Satellite Based Tracking Solutions for Fleet Management, Theft Prevention & Recovery
S.I.C.: 4899
N.A.I.C.S.: 517410
Claude Bergeron *(CTO & VP)*

Non-U.S. Subsidiary:

SecTrack N.V. (1)
Bredastraat 123
2060 Antwerp, Belgium
Tel.: (32) 32291717
Fax: (32) 3 229 17 19
E-Mail: support@sectrack.be
Web Site: www.sectrack.be
Emp.: 30
Satellite Communication Services
S.I.C.: 3663
N.A.I.C.S.: 334220
Luc Martens *(CEO)*
Fred Marsh *(Mng Dir)*

BSP INCORPORATED

Shinagawa Intercity A-29 2-15-1
Kounan Minato-ku
Tokyo, 108-6029, Japan
Tel.: (81) 3 5463 6381
Fax: (81) 3 5463 6392
Web Site: www.bsp.jp
Year Founded: 1982
3800—(JAS)
Sls.: $43,241,000
Assets: $88,770,000
Liabilities: $11,396,000
Net Worth: $77,374,000
Earnings: $7,799,000
Emp.: 227
Fiscal Year-end: 03/31/13

Business Description:
Information Technology Services
S.I.C.: 7389
N.A.I.C.S.: 519190
Personnel:
Hiroki Takefuji *(Pres)*
Board of Directors:
Yukihiro Akiyama
Norimi Eto
Akihiro Furukawa
Eiji Masuda
Hiroki Takefuji
Harumi Watanabe

Non-U.S. Subsidiary:

BSP (Shanghai) Inc. (1)
Room 2001-2002 Sheng Kang Liao Shi Building 738 Shang Cheng Road
PuDong New District, Shanghai, China
Tel.: (86) 21 5058 8268
Web Site: www.bsp-sh.cn
Emp.: 28
Software Development Services
S.I.C.: 7371
N.A.I.C.S.: 541511
Hiroki Takefuji, *(Chm)*

BSRM STEELS LIMITED

Ali Mansion 1207/1099 Sadarghat Road
Chittagong, Bangladesh
Tel.: (880) 312854901
Fax: (880) 31610101
E-Mail: mail@bsrm.com
Web Site: www.bsrm.com
Year Founded: 1952
BRSMSTEEL—(DHA)
Rev.: $473,688,452
Assets: $331,865,502
Liabilities: $252,044,338
Net Worth: $79,821,164
Earnings: $12,394,944
Emp.: 176
Fiscal Year-end: 12/31/12

Business Description:
Steel Mfr
S.I.C.: 3312
N.A.I.C.S.: 331110
Personnel:
Alihussain Akberali *(Chm)*
Aameir Alihussain *(Mng Dir)*
Shekar Ranjan Kar *(CFO & Sec)*
Board of Directors:
Alihussain Akberali
Sabeen Aameir
Aameir Alihussain
Mono Ranjan Dey
Tehseen Zohair Taherali
Zohair Taherali

BSW TIMBER LTD.

East End
Berwick-upon-Tweed, Berwickshire, TD4 6JA, United Kingdom
Tel.: (44) 1896 849255
Fax: (44) 1896 848308
E-Mail: sales@bsw.co.uk
Web Site: www.bsw.co.uk
Year Founded: 1848
Sales Range: $250-299.9 Million
Emp.: 909

Business Description:
Sawmill Operator
S.I.C.: 2421

BSW Timber Ltd.—(Continued)

N.A.I.C.S.: 321113
Personnel:
Tony Hackney *(CEO)*

BT GROUP PLC

BT Centre 81 Newgate Street
London, EC1A 7AJ, United Kingdom
Tel.: (44) 20 7356 5000
Telex: 883051
Fax: (44) 20 7356 5520
E-Mail: btgroup@bt.com
Web Site: www.btplc.com
Year Founded: 1984
BT—(LSE NYSE)
Rev.: $28,454,067,930
Assets: $39,207,453,540
Liabilities: $39,621,227,520
Net Worth: ($413,773,980)
Earnings: $3,302,295,390
Emp.: 87,900
Fiscal Year-end: 03/31/13
Business Description:
Holding Company; Communications Products & Services
S.I.C.: 6719
N.A.I.C.S.: 551112
Personnel:
Michael Rake *(Chm)*
Ian Livingston *(CEO)*
Clive Selley *(CEO)*
Tony Chanmugam *(Grp Dir-Fin)*
Haruno Yoshida *(Pres-Japan)*
Luis Alvarez *(CEO-Global Svcs)*
Gavin E. Patterson *(CEO-Retail)*
Daniel Fitz *(Gen Counsel & Sec)*
Board of Directors:
Michael Rake
Tony Ball
Patricia Hewitt
Phil Hodkinson
Ian Livingston
Gavin E. Patterson
Karen A. Richardson
Nick Rose
Jasmine Whitbread

Subsidiaries:

BT Convergent Solutions Limited **(1)**
Cassini House Hanborough Business Park
Witney, Oxon, OX29 8SD, United Kingdom
Tel.: (44) 1993 885900
Fax: (44) 1993 886651
Emp.: 30
Telecommunication Services
S.I.C.: 4899
N.A.I.C.S.: 517919
Neil Pemberton *(Gen Mgr)*

BT Fleet Limited **(1)**
Parkside Business Park
Mile Lane, Coventry, CV1 2TR, United Kingdom
Tel.: (44) 800 028 4387
E-Mail: reading@btfleet.com
Web Site: www.btfleet.com
Emp.: 940
Fleet Management Services
S.I.C.: 7389
N.A.I.C.S.: 561499

Holdings:

British Telecommunications plc **(1)**
BT Centre 81 Newgate Street
London, EC1A 7AJ, United Kingdom UK
Tel.: (44) 2073565000 (100%)
Fax: (44) 207356099
Web Site: www.btplc.com
Rev.: $28,454,066,930
Assets: $70,398,431,040
Liabilities: $39,684,399,120
Net Worth: $30,714,031,920
Earnings: $3,619,732,680
Fiscal Year-end: 03/31/13
Communications Products & Services
S.I.C.: 4813
N.A.I.C.S.: 517110
Michael Rake *(Chm)*
Ian Livingston *(CEO)*
Michael J. Boustridge *(CEO-Americas & Asia Pacific)*
Jeff Kelly *(CEO-Global Svcs)*

Divisions:

BT Global Services **(2)**
BT Centre 81 Newgate St
EC1A 7AJ London, United Kingdom UK
Tel.: (44) 2073565000 (100%)
Web Site: www.btglobalservices.com
Sales Range: $15-24.9 Billion
Emp.: 37,000
Multi-Site Corporate Network Information Technology Services
S.I.C.: 4899
N.A.I.C.S.: 517919
Luis Alvarez *(CEO)*
Nigel Perks *(Chief HR Officer)*
Maggy McClelland *(Pres-Bus Dev)*
Tanuja Randery *(Pres-Strategy & Mktg)*
Tom Regent *(Pres-Global Sls)*

Non-U.S. Subsidiary:

BT Frontline Pte. Ltd. **(3)**
750 Chai Chee Road 02-01/02/03 The Oasis
Technopark at Chai Chee, 469000
Singapore, Singapore SG
Tel.: (65) 67737227 (100%)
Fax: (65) 67794455
E-Mail: marcom@frontline.com.sg
Web Site: www.frontline.com.sg
Emp.: 5,000
IT Consulting & Services
S.I.C.: 8999
N.A.I.C.S.: 541690
Lim Chin Hu *(CEO)*
Wong Wai Meng *(Mng Dir)*
Chiam Heng Huat *(CFO)*
Steve Ting *(Chm-BT South East Asia)*
Stephen Yeo *(CEO-Southeast Asia)*

BT Retail **(2)**
BT Centre 81 Newgate St
London, EC1A 7AJ, United Kingdom
Tel.: (44) 2073565000
Fax: (44) 2073556679
Web Site: www.bt.com
Sales Range: $15-24.9 Billion
Residential & Commercial Communications Products & Services
S.I.C.: 4813
N.A.I.C.S.: 517110
Gavin Patterson *(CEO)*
Duncan Ingram *(Mng Dir-Customer Svc)*
Stratis Scleparis *(CTO)*

BT Wholesale **(2)**
BT Centre 81 Newgate Street
London, EC1A 7AJ, United Kingdom
Tel.: (44) 2073565000
Fax: (44) 2073565520
E-Mail: btwholesale.direct@bt.com
Web Site: www.btwholesale.com
Sales Range: $5-14.9 Billion
Communications Network Voice & Internet Services
S.I.C.: 4813
N.A.I.C.S.: 517110
Nigel Stagg *(CEO)*
Neil Taylor *(CFO)*

Openreach **(2)**
BT Centre 81 Newgate Street
London, EC1A 7AJ, United Kingdom
Tel.: (44) 2073565000
Fax: (44) 192543444978
Web Site: www.openreach.co.uk
Sales Range: $5-14.9 Billion
Emp.: 100
Communications Network Development, Maintenance & Support Services
S.I.C.: 7622
N.A.I.C.S.: 811213
Joe Garner *(CEO)*
Warren Clements *(CFO)*
Nigel Cheek *(Gen Counsel)*

Subsidiaries:

BT Conferencing **(2)**
81 Newgate St
London, EC1A 7AJ, United Kingdom
Tel.: (44) 2073565000
E-Mail: cceo@bt.com
Web Site: www.bt.com
Audio, Video & Web Collaboration Services
S.I.C.: 7389
N.A.I.C.S.: 561499
Philip Kenny *(Global CIO)*

Subsidiary:

BT Conferencing, Inc. **(3)**
150 Newport Ave Ext Ste 400
North Quincy, MA 02171
Tel.: (781) 849-8136
Web Site: www.btconferencing.com
Emp.: 1,000
Audio, Video & Web Conferencing Services
S.I.C.: 7389
N.A.I.C.S.: 561499
Jack Blaeser *(Pres & Gen Mgr)*
Jeff Prestel *(CEO)*

Subsidiary:

BT Conferencing Video Inc. **(4)**
11400 Westmoor Cr Ste 225
Westminster, CO 80021
Tel.: (303) 448-7800
Fax: (303) 448-7803
Web Site: www.btconferencing.com
Video Conferencing Services
S.I.C.: 7389
N.A.I.C.S.: 561499

Subsidiary:

BT Conferencing Video Inc. **(5)**
1000 1st Ave Ste 400
King of Prussia, PA 19406-1333
Tel.: (610) 382-1000
Fax: (610) 382-1099
Toll Free: (888) 448-7726
Web Site: www.vspan.com
Sls.: $26,000,000
Emp.: 250
Video Conferencing Services
S.I.C.: 7389
N.A.I.C.S.: 561499

BT Lynx Ltd. **(2)**
3 Midland Way Barlborough Links
Chesterfield, Derbyshire, S43 4XA, United Kingdom UK
Tel.: (44) 1246574000
Fax: (44) 1246819401
E-Mail: enquiries@btengageit.com
Web Site: www.btengageit.com
Sales Range: $75-99.9 Million
Emp.: 600
Information Technology Products, Consulting & Technology Services
S.I.C.: 7371
N.A.I.C.S.: 541511
Richard Lowe *(CEO)*

BT Property Ltd. **(2)**
BT Ctr 81 Newgate St
London, EC1A 7AJ, United Kingdom
Tel.: (44) 2073565000
Fax: (44) 203565099
Web Site: www.bt.com
Emp.: 20
Property Holding Company
S.I.C.: 6512
N.A.I.C.S.: 531120
Michael Rlke *(Chm)*

BT Redcare Group **(2)**
Monument 11-13 Great Tower St
London, EC3R 5AQ, United Kingdom
Tel.: (44) 800800828
Fax: (44) 2079296490
E-Mail: redcare@bt.com
Web Site: www.redcare.bt.com
Emp.: 150
Remote Monitoring & Tracking Systems Developer & Mfr
S.I.C.: 3812
N.A.I.C.S.: 334511
Mark Chamberlain *(Dir-Mktg)*

Division:

BT Redcare **(3)**
H1 Newgate Street BT Centre
London, EC1A 7AJ, United Kingdom UK
Tel.: (44) 8708506696
Fax: (44) 8708506697
E-Mail: redcare@bt.com
Web Site: www.redcare.bt.com
Emp.: 85
Wireless Data Communication Security Services
S.I.C.: 4812
N.A.I.C.S.: 517210
Kevin McNulty *(CEO)*

ESPN Sports Media Limited **(2)**
3 Queen Caroline Street
Hammersmith, London, W6 9PE, United Kingdom UK
Tel.: (44) 20 7766 8473
E-Mail:
Web Site: www.espn.co.uk/
Sales Range: $75-99.9 Million
Sports Cable Channel
S.I.C.: 4841
N.A.I.C.S.: 515210
Amory B. Schwartz *(CEO)*

PlusNet Plc **(2)**
Internet House
2 Tenter Street, S1 4BY Sheffield, United Kingdom UK
Tel.: (44) 8451400200
E-Mail: reception@plus.net
Web Site: www.plus.net
Emp.: 200
Internet Services
S.I.C.: 4899
N.A.I.C.S.: 517919
Jamie Ford *(CEO)*
Roy Robinson *(Officer-Pub Rels)*

Scoot **(2)**
Eaglescliffe Logistics Ctr
Durham Ln
Stockton-on-Tees, TS16 0RW, United Kingdom
Tel.: (44) 642881088
Fax: (44) 642881099
E-Mail: info@scoot.co.uk
Web Site: www.scoot.co.uk
Consumer Information Services
S.I.C.: 7373
N.A.I.C.S.: 541512

U.S. Subsidiaries:

BT Ignite **(2)**
11440 Commerce Pk Dr
Reston, VA 20191
Tel.: (703) 755-6000
Fax: (703) 755-6502
Web Site: www.btamericas.com
Emp.: 450
Global Telecommunications Supplier
S.I.C.: 8999
N.A.I.C.S.: 541690

BT Infonet **(2)**
2160 E Grand Ave
El Segundo, CA 90245 DE
Tel.: (310) 335-4700
Fax: (310) 335-4507
Web Site: www.bt.com
Global Communications Import Export
S.I.C.: 4899
N.A.I.C.S.: 517919
Peter C. Sweers *(COO)*
John C. Hoffman *(Exec VP-Comm-Sls & Svc)*
Antti Kaunonen *(Sr VP-Mktg)*

Ribbit Corp. **(2)**
800 W El Camino Real Ste 250
Mountain View, CA 94040-2587
Tel.: (650) 644-3600
Fax: (650) 941-1295
Web Site: www.ribbit.com
Telecommunications Carrier Infrastructure Services
S.I.C.: 4899
N.A.I.C.S.: 517919
Ted Griggs *(Co-Founder & CEO)*
Peter Leong *(Co-Founder & VP-Engrg)*
Don Thorson *(CMO)*

Non-U.S. Subsidiaries:

BT Australasia Pty Limited **(2)**
Level 11 BT Tower 1 Market Street
Sydney, NSW, 2000, Australia (100%)
Tel.: (61) 292691000
Fax: (61) 292691098
E-Mail: reception.sydney@bt.com
Web Site: www.globalservices.bt.com
Emp.: 110
Telecommunication Services Provider
S.I.C.: 4813
N.A.I.C.S.: 517110
Simon Gatward *(COO)*

Subsidiary:

First State Computing Pty Ltd. (3)
Level 7, Underwood House 37-49 Pitt Street
Sydney, NSW, 2000, Australia
Computer Software Developer
S.I.C.: 3652
N.A.I.C.S.: 334614

BT Espana S.A. (2)
Salvador De Madariaga 1 Planta 3
Madrid, 28027, Spain (100%)
Tel.: (34) 912708000
Fax: (34) 912708888
E-Mail: marketing.spain@bt.com
Web Site: www.bt.com
Emp.: 600
Telecommunication Services Provider
S.I.C.: 4813
N.A.I.C.S.: 517110
Jacinto Cavestany *(CEO)*

BT Hong Kong Limited (2)
38 F Porset House Taikoo Pl
979 Kings Rd, Quarry Bay, China (Hong Kong) (100%)
Tel.: (852) 25323606
Fax: (852) 28100164
E-Mail: ines.chin@bt.com
Web Site: www.bt.com
Emp.: 100
Telecommunication Services
S.I.C.: 4813
N.A.I.C.S.: 517110
Kevin Taylor *(Pres)*

BT Italia SpA (2)
Via Tucidide 56
Torre 7, 20134 Milan, Italy (100%)
Tel.: (39) 02752921
Fax: (39) 0275292778
Web Site: www.italia.bt.com
Sales Range: $800-899.9 Million
Emp.: 1,300
Communications Services & Solutions
S.I.C.: 4813
N.A.I.C.S.: 517110
Corrado Sciolla *(Pres-Europe & Latin America)*

Subsidiaries:

ERP Tech S.p.A. (3)
Via Darwin 85
20019 Settimo Milanese, Italy (100%)
Tel.: (39) 02311828
Fax: (39) 0234536022
E-Mail: info@erptech.it
Web Site: www.erptech.it
Emp.: 50
Management Consulting Services
S.I.C.: 8748
N.A.I.C.S.: 541618
Gieseppe Bewia *(CEO)*

SPC Italia Srl (3)
Via Vittor Pisani 31
20124 Milan, Italy (100%)
Tel.: (39) 02674971
Fax: (39) 0267497415
Web Site: www.spcitalia.it
Data Processing Services
S.I.C.: 7379
N.A.I.C.S.: 518210

Tikit Group plc (1)
12 Gough Square
London, EC4A 3DW, United Kingdom UK
Tel.: (44) 2074003737
Fax: (44) 2074003738
E-Mail: enquiries@tikit.com
Web Site: www.tikit.com
Emp.: 197
Software Development Services
S.I.C.: 7371
N.A.I.C.S.: 541511
Tim Springham *(CEO)*
Simon Hill *(COO)*

U.S. Subsidiary:

BT INS Inc (1)
1600 Memorex Dr Ste 200
Santa Clara, CA 95050-2842
Tel.: (408) 330-2700
Fax: (408) 330-2701
Web Site: www.ins.com
Network Consulting Services
S.I.C.: 8748
N.A.I.C.S.: 541618

Non-U.S. Subsidiaries:

BT Communications do Brasil Limitada (1)
Km 9 - Chacara Assay - Condominio Tech Town Unidade 27
Hortolandia, Sao Paulo, 13186 904, Brazil
Tel.: (55) 19 3031 9600
Fax: (55) 19 3031 9604
Telecommunication Services
S.I.C.: 4899
N.A.I.C.S.: 517919

BT (Germany) GmbH & Co. OHG (1)
Barthstrasse 4
Munich, 80339, Germany
Tel.: (49) 8926000
Fax: (49) 89 2600 9930
E-Mail: information@bt.com
Web Site: www.bt.com
Telecommunication Software Development Services
S.I.C.: 7371
N.A.I.C.S.: 541511

BT Global Communications India Private Limited (1)
502 5th Floor Raheja Titanium II Off Western Express Highway
Jogeshwari E, Mumbai, 400 063, India
Tel.: (91) 2242430000
Fax: (91) 2267655181
Telecommunication Services
S.I.C.: 4899
N.A.I.C.S.: 517919

BT LatAm Brasil Ltda (1)
SP 101 - Campinas/Monte Mor Km 9 5
Cond Tech Town-Unid 27
Hortolandia, Sao Paulo, 13030-040, Brazil
Tel.: (55) 1930319600
Fax: (55) 1930319600
Data Processing Services
S.I.C.: 7379
N.A.I.C.S.: 518210
Javier Semerene *(VP-Latin America)*

BT Singapore Pte Ltd (1)
750B Chai Chee Road 02-02/04
Technopark
Chai Chee, Singapore, 469002, Singapore
Tel.: (65) 6290 7100
Fax: (65) 6293 9500
Telecommunication Services
S.I.C.: 4899
N.A.I.C.S.: 517919

BT Switzerland AG (1)
Richtistrasse 5
Wallisellen, Zurich, 8304, Switzerland
Tel.: (41) 445432111
Fax: (41) 445432110
Telecommunication Services
S.I.C.: 4899
N.A.I.C.S.: 517919

BT HOLDING AG

Stadtturmstrasse 19
CH-5400 Baden, Switzerland
Tel.: (41) 562005050
Business Description:
Investment Holding Company
S.I.C.: 6719
N.A.I.C.S.: 551112
Personnel:
Peter Wanner *(Chm)*

Holding:

AZ Medien AG (1)
Neumattstrasse 1
5001 Aarau, Switzerland CH
Tel.: (41) 58 200 5858
Fax: (41) 58 200 5022
E-Mail: info@azmedien.ch
Web Site: www.azmedien.ch
Emp.: 761
Multimedia Holding Company
S.I.C.: 6719
N.A.I.C.S.: 551112
Peter Wanner *(Chm)*
Philip Funk *(Vice Chm)*
Axel Wustmann *(CEO)*

Subsidiaries:

Aargauer Zeitung AG (2)
Neumattstrasse 1
5001 Aarau, Switzerland CH
Tel.: (41) 582005858 (100%)
Web Site: www.aargauerzeitung.ch
Newspaper Publisher
S.I.C.: 2711
N.A.I.C.S.: 511110
Peter Wanner *(Publr)*

AZ Anzeiger AG (2)
Zuchwilerstrasse 21
CH-4501 Solothurn, Switzerland CH
Tel.: (41) 326247511 (100%)
Web Site: www.azeiger.ch
Newspaper Publisher
S.I.C.: 2711
N.A.I.C.S.: 511110
Dietrich Berg *(Mng Dir)*

AZ Fachverlage AG (2)
Neumattstrasse 1
CH-5001 Aarau, Switzerland CH
Tel.: (41) 582005858 (100%)
Fax: (41) 582005644
Web Site: www.azmedien.ch/unternehmen/adressen.php
Magazines Publisher
S.I.C.: 2721
N.A.I.C.S.: 511120
Dietrich Berg *(Mng Dir)*

Radio 24 AG (2)
Limmatstrasse 183
CH-8005 Zurich, Switzerland
Tel.: (41) 444482424
Fax: (41) 444482490
E-Mail: info@radio24.ch
Web Site: www.radio24.ch
Emp.: 50
Radio Broadcasting Station
S.I.C.: 4832
N.A.I.C.S.: 515112
Karin Muller *(Mng Dir)*

Radio 32 AG (2)
Zuchwilerstrasse 21
CH-4501 Solothurn, Switzerland CH
Tel.: (41) 582004232 (61.3%)
Fax: (41) 582004239
E-Mail: info@radio32.ch
Web Site: www.radio32.ch
Emp.: 32
Radio Broadcasting Station
S.I.C.: 4832
N.A.I.C.S.: 515112
Karin Fluckiger *(Editor-in-Chief)*

Solothurner Zeitung AG (2)
Zuchwilerstrasse 21
CH-4501 Solothurn, Switzerland CH
Tel.: (41) 582004774 (100%)
Web Site: www.solothurnerzeitung.ch
Newspaper Publisher
S.I.C.: 2711
N.A.I.C.S.: 511110
Peter Wanner *(Publr)*

Tele M1 AG (2)
Neumattstrasse 1
CH-5001 Aarau, Switzerland CH
Tel.: (41) 582004600 (100%)
Web Site: www.telem1.ch
Emp.: 50
Television Broadcasting Station
S.I.C.: 4833
N.A.I.C.S.: 515120
Marc Friedli *(Mng Dir)*

Weiss Medien AG (2)
Obere Bahnhofstrasse 5
CH-8910 Affoltern am Albis, Switzerland CH
Tel.: (41) 582005700 (100%)
Fax: (41) 582005701
Web Site: www.affolteranzeiger.ch
Newspaper Publisher
S.I.C.: 2711
N.A.I.C.S.: 511110
Barbara Roth-Herzig *(Mng Dir & Head-Adv Sls)*

BT INVESTMENT MANAGEMENT LIMITED

Level 14 The Chifley Tower 2 Chifley Square
Sydney, NSW, 2000, Australia
Mailing Address:
GPO Box 7072
Sydney, NSW, 2001, Australia
Tel.: (61) 2 9220 2000
Fax: (61) 2 9220 2307
E-Mail: enquiries@btim.com.au
Web Site: www.btim.com.au
BTT—(ASX)
Rev.: $273,697,144
Assets: $799,007,249
Liabilities: $213,914,993
Net Worth: $585,092,256
Earnings: $53,402,415
Emp.: 220
Fiscal Year-end: 09/30/13
Business Description:
Investment Management Services
S.I.C.: 6799
N.A.I.C.S.: 523920
Personnel:
Emilio Gonzalez *(CEO & Mng Dir)*
Cameron Williamson *(CFO)*
Jennifer Davies *(Chief Risk Officer)*
Merryn Hunt *(Bus Dev Officer-VIC, SA & TAS)*
Olivera Milevska *(Bus Dev Officer-NSW, ACT & WA)*
Carolyn Stephens *(Bus Dev Officer-QLD & NT)*
Gavin Rochussen *(CEO-J O Hambro Capital Management)*
Chris Millard *(Sec)*
Board of Directors:
James Evans
Meredith Brooks
Brad Cooper
Andrew Fay
Emilio Gonzalez

BTA BANK JSC

(Filed Ch 15 Bankruptcy #12-13081 on 07/17/12 in U.S. Bankruptcy Ct, Southern Dist of NY, NY)
97 Zholdasbekova str md Samal-2
050051 Almaty, Kazakhstan
Tel.: (7) 7272505100
Fax: (7) 7272500224
E-Mail: pr@bta.kz
Web Site: www.bta.kz/en/
BTAS—(KAZ)
Sales Range: $1-4.9 Billion
Business Description:
Banking Services
S.I.C.: 6029
N.A.I.C.S.: 522110
Personnel:
Yelena Bakhmutova *(Chm)*
Kadyrzhan Damitov *(Chm-Mgmt Bd)*
Zhuldyz Akhmetkaliyeva *(Mng Dir)*
Rimma Ilyasova *(Mng Dir)*
Viktor Romanyuk *(Mng Dir)*
Arman Shakenov *(Mng Dir)*
Zhandos Yessenbay *(Mng Dir)*
Board of Directors:
Yelena Bakhmutova
Kadyrzhan Damitov
Raikhan Imambayeva
Konstantin Korischenko
Mira Koshkimbayeva
Yury Voicehovsky

Subsidiaries:

Insurance Company London-Almaty JSC (1)
9th Floor 3B Block Nurly Tau Business Center
19/1 Al-Farabi Ave, 050059 Almaty, Kazakhstan
Tel.: (7) 7273110777
Fax: (7) 3110777
E-Mail: info@laic.kz
Web Site: www.laic.kz
LNAT—(KAZ)
Sales Range: $1-9.9 Million
Emp.: 90
Insurance Services

BTA Bank JSC—(Continued)

S.I.C.: 6411
N.A.I.C.S.: 524298
Yergali Nurlanovich Begimbetov *(Chm-Mgmt Bd)*
Anna Alexandrovna Nekrukova *(Deputy Chm-Mgmt Bd)*
Gulmira Mamaevna Prmanshayeva *(Deputy Chm-Mgmt Bd)*
Larissa Alexandrovna Slozhenikina *(Deputy Chm-Mgmt Bd)*
David Anthony Wansbrough-Jones *(Member-Mgmt Bd)*

Joint Stock Company Eximbank Kazakhstan (1)
80 Bogenbai Batyr Str
050010 Almaty, Kazakhstan
Tel.: (7) 7272663093
Fax: (7) 7272663910
E-Mail: info@eximbank.kz
Web Site: www.eximbank.kz
EXBNB1—(KAZ)
Int. Income: $46,282,791
Assets: $504,881,664
Liabilities: $423,691,970
Net Worth: $81,189,693
Earnings: $3,348,746
Emp.: 233
Fiscal Year-end: 12/31/12
Commercial Banking Services
S.I.C.: 6029
N.A.I.C.S.: 522110
Alexander Y. Klebanov *(Chm)*
Dmitriy A. Prikhozhan *(Chm-Mgmt Bd)*
Nataliya G. Rimer *(Deputy Chm-Mgmt Bd)*
Altynai K. Dzhaksymbetova *(Member-Mgmt Bd)*
Krivtsova Tatyana Leonidovna *(Member-Mgmt Bd)*
Salikhov Yevgeniy Rashidovich *(Member-Mgmt Bd)*

BTB REAL ESTATE INVESTMENT TRUST

2155 rue Crescent Suite 300
Montreal, QC, H3G 2C1, Canada
Tel.: (514) 286-0188
Fax: (514) 286-0011
E-Mail: mleonard@btbreit.com
Web Site: www.btbreit.com
Year Founded: 2006
BTB.DB.B—(TSX)
Rev.: $47,830,254
Assets: $501,907,537
Liabilities: $377,875,709
Net Worth: $124,031,828
Earnings: $17,859,557
Emp.: 38
Fiscal Year-end: 12/31/12

Business Description:
Real Estate Investment Services
S.I.C.: 6726
N.A.I.C.S.: 525990

Personnel:
Jocelyn Proteau *(Chm)*
Michel Leonard *(Pres & CEO)*
Benoit Cyr *(CFO & VP)*

Legal Counsel:
De Grandpre Chait
1000 rue de la Gauchetiere Ouest
Montreal, QC, H3B 4W5, Canada

Computershare Investor Services Inc.
Montreal, QC, Canada

Transfer Agents:
Computershare Trust Company of Canada
1500 University Suite 700
Montreal, QC, Canada

Computershare Investor Services Inc.
Montreal, QC, Canada

Subsidiaries:

Complexe Lebourgneuf Phase II Inc. (1)
815 Boulevard Lebourgneuf
Quebec, QC, G2J 1C3, Canada
Tel.: (418) 627-2566
Real Estate Development Services
S.I.C.: 6531
N.A.I.C.S.: 531390

Gestion immobiliere BTB Inc. (1)
1001 Sherbrooke E Bur 800
Montreal, QC, H2L 1L3, Canada
Tel.: (514) 439-4001
Real Estate Development Services
S.I.C.: 6531
N.A.I.C.S.: 531390

BTG PACTUAL HOLDING S.A.

(d/b/a BTG Pactual Group)
Av Brigadeiro Faria Lima 3 729 9th andar
Itaim Bibi, 04538-133 Sao Paulo, SP, Brazil
Tel.: (55) 11 3383 2000
Fax: (55) 11 3383 2001
E-Mail: ri@btgpactual.com
Web Site: www.btgpactual.com
Year Founded: 2008
BBTG—(BRAZ EUR)
Sales Range: $1-4.9 Billion
Emp.: 1,300

Business Description:
Financial Holding Company
S.I.C.: 6712
N.A.I.C.S.: 551111

Personnel:
Andre Santos Esteves *(Chm & CEO)*
Marcelo Kalim *(CFO)*

Board of Directors:
Andre Santos Esteves
Persio Arida
Juan Garcia Canizares
John Huw Gwili Jenkins
Marcelo Kalim
William Thomas Royan
Roberto Sallouti
Claudio Eugenio Stiller Galeazzi

Subsidiary:

Banco BTG Pactual S.A. (1)
Praia de Botafogo 501 6th Andar
Torre Corcovado Botafogo, 22250-040 Rio de Janeiro, RJ, Brazil BR
Tel.: (55) 21 3262 9600 (72.91%)
Web Site: www.btgpactual.com
BPAC3—(BRAZ)
Rev.: $4,931,354,655
Assets: $74,168,727,097
Liabilities: $67,167,607,538
Net Worth: $7,001,119,559
Earnings: $1,601,390,198
Fiscal Year-end: 12/31/12
Investment Banking, Securities Brokerage & Investment Advisory Services
S.I.C.: 6211
N.A.I.C.S.: 523110
Andre Santos Esteves *(Chm, Pres & CEO)*
Marcelo Kalim *(CFO)*
Roberto Sallouti *(COO)*
Andre Fernandes Lopes Dias *(Chief Risk Officer)*
Joao Marcello Dantas Leite *(IR Officer & Head-Fin & Tax)*
Antonio Carlos Canto Porto Filho *(Chm-Wealth Mgmt)*
Jonathan David Bisgaier *(Gen Counsel)*

Holding:

B&A Mineracao S.A. (1)
Avenida do Contorno 5919 5 andar
Savassi, 30110-035 Belo Horizonte, Brazil BR
Tel.: (55) 31 2552 1588
Web Site: www.bamineracao.com
Holding Company; Fertilizer Minerals, Iron Ore & Copper Mining
S.I.C.: 6719
N.A.I.C.S.: 551112
Roger Agnelli *(Chm)*
Eduardo Ledsham *(CEO)*

Subsidiary:

B&A Fertilizers Limited (2)
Avenida do Contorno 5919 5 andar
Savassi, 30110-035 Belo Horizonte, Brazil VG
Tel.: (55) 31 2552 1588
Fertilizer Mineral Mining
S.I.C.: 1479
N.A.I.C.S.: 212393
Roger Agnelli *(Chm)*
Eduardo Ledsham *(CEO)*

Affiliate:

BTG Pactual Participations Ltd. (1)
Av Brigadeiro Faria Lima 3 477 14th andar
Itaim Bibi, 04538-133 Sao Paulo, SP, Brazil BM
Tel.: (55) 11 3383 2000 (5.17%)
Web Site: www.btgpactual.com
BBTG11—(BRAZ)
Sales Range: $200-249.9 Million
Holding Company; Open & Closed-End Investment Fund Management Services
S.I.C.: 6719
N.A.I.C.S.: 551112
Andre Santos Esteves *(Chm & CEO)*
Marcelo Kalim *(CFO)*
Roberto Balls Sallouti *(COO)*

Affiliate:

Stigma Participacoes S.A. (2)
(Formerly BTG Pactual Stigma Participacoes S.A.)
Av Brigadeiro Faria Lima 3 729 9th Floor
04538-133 Sao Paulo, SP, Brazil BR
Tel.: (55) 11 3383 2000
Investment Banking Services
S.I.C.: 6211
N.A.I.C.S.: 523110
Andre Santos Esteves *(CEO)*

BTG PLC

5 Fleet Place
London, EC4M 7RD, United Kingdom
Tel.: (44) 2075750000
Fax: (44) 2075750010
E-Mail: info@btgplc.com
Web Site: www.btgplc.com
BTG—(LSE)
Rev.: $369,080,073
Assets: $851,711,097
Liabilities: $171,037,107
Net Worth: $680,673,990
Earnings: $25,900,356
Emp.: 569
Fiscal Year-end: 03/31/13

Business Description:
Pharmaceutical & Medical Equipment Developer
S.I.C.: 2834
N.A.I.C.S.: 325412

Personnel:
Louise Makin *(CEO)*
Rolf Soderstrom *(CFO)*
Peter Stratford *(CTO-Interventional Medicine)*
Guenter R. Janhofer *(Chief Medical Officer & Head-Dev)*
John Sylvester *(Chief Comml Officer-Interventional Medicine)*
Jeffrey Klimaski *(Corp Ethics & Compliance Officer)*
Paul Mussenden *(Gen Counsel & Sec)*
Matthew Gantz *(Exec VP-US)*

Board of Directors:
Garry Watts
Giles Kerr
Melanie G. Lee
Louise Makin
Ian F. R. Much
William James O'Shea
Rolf Soderstrom
Richard Wohanka

Subsidiaries:

Biocompatibles International Plc (1)
Chapman House Farnham Business Park
Weydon Lane, Farnham, Surrey, GU9 8QL, United Kingdom
Tel.: (44) 1252732732
Fax: (44) 1252732777
E-Mail: info@biocompatibles.com
Web Site: www.biocompatibles.com
Sales Range: $25-49.9 Million
Emp.: 200
Biotechnology Industry; Develops, Manufactures & Markets Implantable Products for Patients with Liver & Prostate Cancer
S.I.C.: 3841
N.A.I.C.S.: 339112
Gerry Brown *(Chm)*

Division:

Biocompatibles International Plc - Oncology Products Division (2)
Chapman House Farnham Business Park
Weydon Lane, Farnham, Surrey, GU9 8QL, United Kingdom
Tel.: (44) 1252732732
Fax: (44) 1252732777
E-Mail: marketing@biocompatibles.com
Web Site: www.biocompatibles.com
Emp.: 80
Oncology Products Distr
S.I.C.: 5047
N.A.I.C.S.: 423450
Peter Stratford *(Mng Dir)*
John Sylvester *(Mng Dir)*

Subsidiary:

Biocompatibles UK Limited (2)
Chapman House Farnham Business Park
Farnham, Surrey, GU9 8QL, United Kingdom
Tel.: (44) 1252732732
Fax: (44) 1252732777
E-Mail: info@biocompatibles.com
Web Site: www.biocompatibles.com
Emp.: 160
Oncology Products Distr
S.I.C.: 5047
N.A.I.C.S.: 423450

Subsidiary:

Biocompatibles International Limited (3)
Chapman House Farnham Business Park
Farnham, GU9 8QT, United Kingdom
Tel.: (44) 1252732732
Fax: (44) 1252732777
E-Mail: info@biocompatibles.com
Web Site: www.biocompatibles.com
Emp.: 90
Pharmaceutical Products Mfr & Distr
S.I.C.: 2834
N.A.I.C.S.: 325412
Peter Stratford *(Mng Dir)*

U.S. Subsidiary:

BrachySciences Inc. (2)
115 Hurley Rd Bldg 3C
Oxford, CT 06478
Tel.: (203) 262-0571
Fax: (203) 262-8968
Toll Free: (866) 789-4215
E-Mail: orders@brachysciences.com
Web Site: www.brachysciences.com
Sales Range: $10-24.9 Million
Emp.: 50
Developer, Mfr & Distr of Brachytherapy Implants
S.I.C.: 3841
N.A.I.C.S.: 339112

Non-U.S. Subsidiary:

CellMed AG (2)
Industriestrasse 19
63755 Alzenau, Germany
Tel.: (49) 602391810
Fax: (49) 6023918133
E-Mail: contact@cellmed.com
Web Site: www.cellmed.com
Emp.: 45
Therapeutic Drug Products Mfr
S.I.C.: 3841
N.A.I.C.S.: 339112

British Technology Group Inter-Corporate Licensing Ltd (1)
5 Fleet Pl
London, EC4M 7RD, United Kingdom
Tel.: (44) 2075750000
Fax: (44) 2075750010
E-Mail: info@btgplc.com
Web Site: www.btgplc.com
Emp.: 50
Commercial Sectors Regulation Licensing & Inspection
S.I.C.: 9651

N.A.I.C.S.: 926150
Louise Makin *(CEO)*

BTG International (Holdings) Ltd (1)
5 Fleet Place
London, EC4M 7RD, United Kingdom
Tel.: (44) 2075750000
Fax: (44) 2075750010
Emp.: 65
Health Care Services
S.I.C.: 5999
N.A.I.C.S.: 446199

BTG International Ltd. (1)
5 Fleet Place
London, EC4M 7RD, United Kingdom
Tel.: (44) 2075750000
Fax: (44) 2075750010
E-Mail: info@btgplc.com
Emp.: 60
Drug & Technology Development Services
S.I.C.: 8731
N.A.I.C.S.: 541712
Louise Makin *(CEO)*

BTG Investment (Holdings) Ltd. (1)
Suite 4 5th Floor 4-19 Berkeley Square House
Berkeley Square, London, W1J 6BR, United Kingdom
Tel.: (44) 2076474900
Fax: (44) 2076474901
E-Mail: btg-ir@btginvest.com
Web Site: www.btginvest.com
Business & Investment Services
S.I.C.: 7389
N.A.I.C.S.: 561499

Protherics UK Limited (1)
Blaenwaun Ffostrasol
Llandysul, Ceredigion, SA44 5JT, United Kingdom
Tel.: (44) 1239 851 122
Fax: (44) 1239 858 800
Web Site: www.btgplc.com
Emp.: 120
Health Care Pharmaceutical Products Mfr
S.I.C.: 2834
N.A.I.C.S.: 325412

U.S. Subsidiaries:

Biocompatibles Inc. (1)
115 Hurley Rd Bldg 3C
Oxford, CT 06478
Tel.: (203) 262-4198
E-Mail: orders@biocompatiblesinc.com
Web Site: www.biocompatibles.com
Pharmaceutical Products Distr
S.I.C.: 5122
N.A.I.C.S.: 424210
Jim Matons *(Pres)*

BTG International Inc. (1)
5 Tower Bridge Ste 800 300 Barr Harbor Dr
West Conshohocken, PA 19428
Tel.: (610) 278-1660
Fax: (610) 278-1605
E-Mail: info.us@btgplc.com
Web Site: www.btgplc.com
Emp.: 20
Database & Directory Publishers
S.I.C.: 2741
N.A.I.C.S.: 511140
Louise Makin *(CEO)*

Protherics Inc. (1)
5214 Maryland Way Ste 405
Brentwood, TN 37027
Tel.: (615) 327-1027
Fax: (615) 320-1212
Pharmaceutical Products Mfr
S.I.C.: 2834
N.A.I.C.S.: 325412

Protherics Utah Inc. (1)
615 Arapeen Dr
Salt Lake City, UT 84108-1267
Tel.: (801) 583-8077
Pharmaceutical Products Mfr
S.I.C.: 2834
N.A.I.C.S.: 325412

Non-U.S. Subsidiary:

BTG Australasia Pty Limited (1)
RSD Turretfield RC Holland Road
Rosedale, SA, Australia
Tel.: (61) 885249700
Fax: (61) 885249113
Pharmaceutical Products Mfr
S.I.C.: 2834
N.A.I.C.S.: 325412

BTHC X, INC.

2 Argyrokastrou Street Voula
16673 Athens, Greece
Tel.: (30) 2108992896
Year Founded: 2006
BTXI—(OTC)
Liabilities: $189,171
Net Worth: ($189,171)
Earnings: ($62,363)
Fiscal Year-end: 12/31/12

Business Description:
Investment Services
S.I.C.: 6211
N.A.I.C.S.: 523999

Personnel:
George Syllantavos *(Pres, Treas & Sec)*

Transfer Agent:
Securities Transfer Corporation
2591 Dallas Pkwy Ste 102
Frisco, TX 75034
Tel.: (469) 633-0101
Fax: (469) 633-0088

BTHC XV, INC.

c/o Underground Grand Canyon
Yishui County, Linyi, Shandong, China 276400
Tel.: (86) 539 2553919
Year Founded: 2006
BTXV—(OTCB)
Sales Range: $10-24.9 Million
Emp.: 156

Business Description:
Tourism Development Services
S.I.C.: 7999
N.A.I.C.S.: 713990

Personnel:
Shanjiu Zhang *(Chm, Pres & CEO)*
Xinbo Yu *(CFO, Treas & Sec)*
Rongguang Chen *(COO)*
Xianghai Kong *(Chief Admin Officer)*

BTI SYSTEMS INC.

1000 Innovation Dr Ste 200
Ottawa, ON, K2K 3E7, Canada
Tel.: (613) 248-9154
Fax: (613) 287-1886
Toll Free: (866) 626-9154
E-Mail: Info@btisystems.com
Web Site: www.btisystems.com
Sales Range: $25-49.9 Million
Emp.: 250

Business Description:
Packet Optical Solutions
S.I.C.: 7372
N.A.I.C.S.: 511210

Personnel:
Robert Ferchat *(Chm)*
Steven Waszak *(Pres & CEO)*
Ken Taylor *(CFO)*
Gary Southwell *(CTO-EMEA)*
Peter Allen *(Treas)*
Jonathan Boocock *(Exec VP-Engrg)*
Sally Bament *(Sr VP-Global Mktg)*
Paul Crann *(Sr VP-Product Mgmt & Bus Dev)*
Thomas Nolette *(Sr VP-Global Ops)*

Board of Directors:
Robert Ferchat
William I. Campbell
Richard Charlebois
George Chase
Neil Ferris
Dave Furneaux
J. Ian Giffen
Paul Smelters
Steven Waszak

BTM RESOURCES BERHAD

No 101 3rd Floor Wisma Kam Choon
Jalan Kampong Tiong
20000 Kuala Terengganu, Terengganu Darul Ima, Malaysia
Tel.: (60) 96223633
Fax: (60) 96235795
E-Mail: btmres@po.jaring.my
Web Site: www.btmresources.com.my
BTM—(KLS)
Rev.: $1,521,697
Assets: $7,922,334
Liabilities: $4,198,545
Net Worth: $3,723,789
Earnings: ($684,229)
Fiscal Year-end: 12/31/12

Business Description:
Timber Lamination Boards Mfr
S.I.C.: 2421
N.A.I.C.S.: 321113

Personnel:
Tu Sang Yong *(Mng Dir)*
Seok Tian Chong *(Sec)*
Ji Keng Heng *(Sec)*
Mary Margaret Pelly *(Sec)*

Board of Directors:
Abdul Aziz Abdul Rahman
Show Tong Choong
Mohamed Iqbal M. M. Mohamed Ganey
Khairuddin Mohd Hussin
Emmy Yong
Tu Sang Yong

BTS GROUP AB

(d/b/a BTS Sweden)
Grevgatan 34
114 53 Stockholm, Sweden
Tel.: (46) 858707000
Fax: (46) 858707001
E-Mail: gabriela.pettersfon@bts.com
Web Site: www.bts.com
Year Founded: 1985
BTS B—(OMX OTC)
Sls.: $119,280,830
Assets: $80,267,051
Liabilities: $29,715,098
Net Worth: $50,551,952
Earnings: $9,867,107
Emp.: 385
Fiscal Year-end: 12/31/12

Business Description:
Business Acumen Education Simulations & Services
S.I.C.: 8299
N.A.I.C.S.: 611430

Personnel:
Michael Grindfors *(Chm)*
Henrik Ekelund *(Pres & CEO)*
Stefan Brown *(CFO & VP)*
Jonas Akerman *(Pres-BTS North America)*
Todd Ehrlich *(COO-BTS USA, Exec VP & Global Head-Dev Process)*
Rommin Adl *(Mng Dir-BTS Interactive, Exec VP & Head-Global Mktg)*
Ted Fawle *(Mng Dir-BTS Asia & Exec VP)*
Philios Andreou *(Exec VP & Head-Iberia & Mexico)*
Peter Mulford *(Exec VP & Head-Strategic Alignment & Bus Acumen Practice)*
Dan Parisi *(Exec VP & Head-BTS USA Western)*
Stefan af Petersens *(Exec VP-Acq & Key Acct Contacts)*
Thomas Ahlerup *(Sr VP-Investor & Corp Comm)*

Board of Directors:
Michael Grindfors
Henrik Ekelund
Stefan Gardefjord
Mariana Burenstam Linder
Dag Sehlin

Subsidiaries:

BTS STOCKHOLM (1)
Grevgatan 34
114 53 Stockholm, Sweden
Tel.: (46) 8 58 70 70 00
Fax: (46) 8 58 70 70 01
E-Mail: bts@bts.com
Emp.: 20
Corporate Training & Development Services
S.I.C.: 8299
N.A.I.C.S.: 611430
Katrin Fagerberg *(Gen Mgr-Northern Europe)*

BTS Sverige AB (1)
Grevgatan 34
114 53 Stockholm, Sweden
Tel.: (46) 858707000
Fax: (46) 858707001
E-Mail: info@bts.com
Web Site: www.bts.com
Emp.: 35
Corporate Training & Development Solutions
S.I.C.: 8299
N.A.I.C.S.: 611430
Anna Sandberg *(Gen Mgr)*

U.S. Subsidiaries:

BTS CHICAGO Limited (1)
33 N LaSalle St Ste 1210
Chicago, IL 60602
Tel.: (312) 263-6250
Fax: (312) 263-6110
Web Site: www.bts.com
Emp.: 13
Corporate Training & Development Solutions
S.I.C.: 8299
N.A.I.C.S.: 611430
Steve Toomey *(Sr VP)*

BTS SAN FRANCISCO (1)
456 Montgomery St Ste 900
San Francisco, CA 94104-2808
Tel.: (415) 362-4200
Fax: (415) 362-4270
E-Mail: jodeline.kushima@bts.com
Web Site: www.bts.com
Emp.: 40
Corporate Training & Development Services
S.I.C.: 8299
N.A.I.C.S.: 611430
Gina Brice *(Office Mgr)*

BTS STAMFORD (1)
300 First Stamford Pl
Stamford, CT 06902
Tel.: (203) 316-2740
Fax: (203) 316-2750
Web Site: www.bts.com
Corporate Training & Development Solutions
S.I.C.: 8299
N.A.I.C.S.: 611430

BTS United States (1)
300 First Stamford Pl
Stamford, CT 06902
Tel.: (203) 316-2740
Fax: (203) 316-2750
E-Mail: reception.stamford@bts.com
Web Site: www.bts.com
Emp.: 25
Developer of Business Acumen Education Simulations & Services
S.I.C.: 8299
N.A.I.C.S.: 611430
Jonas Ackerman *(Pres-North America)*

Subsidiaries:

Advantage Performance Group (2)
700 Larkstur Landing Cr Ste 125
Larkspur, CA 94939
Tel.: (415) 925-6832
Fax: (415) 925-9512
E-Mail: contact@advantageperformance.com
Web Site: www.advantageperformance.com
Sales Range: $10-24.9 Million
Emp.: 7
Employee Performance Improvement Services
S.I.C.: 8299
N.A.I.C.S.: 611430
Annika McCrea *(Pres & CEO)*

BTS Group AB—(Continued)

BTS Philadelphia (2)
6 Tower Bridge Ste 540 181 Washington St
Conshohocken, PA 19428
Tel.: (484) 391-2900
Fax: (484) 391-2900
Toll Free: (800) 445-7089
Web Site: www.smginc.com
Emp.: 10
Business Management Solutions
S.I.C.: 7389
N.A.I.C.S.: 561499
Rommin Adl *(Pres & CEO)*

BTS Scottsdale (2)
9455 E Ironwood Square Dr Ste 100
Scottsdale, AZ 85258
Tel.: (480) 948-2777
Fax: (480) 948-2928
E-Mail: info@bts.com
Web Site: www.bts.com
Sales Range: $10-24.9 Million
Emp.: 30
Employee Performance Improvement Services
S.I.C.: 8299
N.A.I.C.S.: 611430

Non-U.S. Subsidiaries:

BTS Australasia (1)
Suite 103 Level
1109 Pitt Street, Sydney, NSW, 2000, Australia
Tel.: (61) 292338833
Fax: (61) 292338655
Web Site: www.bts.com.au
Business Management Solutions
S.I.C.: 8748
N.A.I.C.S.: 541618

BTS BILBAO (1)
Simon Bolivar 27 10 dpt 19
Bilbao, 48010, Spain
Tel.: (34) 94 423 5594
Fax: (34) 94 423 6897
Corporate Training & Development Solutions
S.I.C.: 8299
N.A.I.C.S.: 611430

BTS Brussels NV (1)
Rue d'Arenberg 44
1000 Brussels, Belgium
Tel.: (32) 2 27 415 10
E-Mail: info@bts.com
Emp.: 4
Corporate Training & Development Services
S.I.C.: 8299
N.A.I.C.S.: 611430
Bjorn Gustafsson *(Gen Mgr)*

BTS Business Consulting (Thailand) Co.,Ltd. (1)
Thai CC Building Suite 181 18th Floor 889 South Sathorn Road
Yannawa Sathorn, Bangkok, 10120, Thailand
Tel.: (66) 2672 3780
Fax: (66) 2672 3665
Web Site: www.bts.com
Emp.: 3
Business Management Services
S.I.C.: 7389
N.A.I.C.S.: 561499
Isra Smitabindu *(Gen Mgr)*

BTS Consulting (Shanghai) Co., Ltd. (1)
Suite 506B West Office Tower 1515 Nan Jing West Road Shanghai Centre
1376 Nanjing Road West, Shanghai, 200040, China
Tel.: (86) 21 6289 8688
Fax: (86) 21 6289 8311
Corporate Training & Development Services
S.I.C.: 8299
N.A.I.C.S.: 611430

BTS do Brasil Ltda (1)
Av Brig Faria Lima 3729-5th Floor
04538-905 Sao Paulo, Brazil
Tel.: (55) 11 3443 6295
Fax: (55) 11 3443 6201
Corporate Training & Development Solutions
S.I.C.: 8299
N.A.I.C.S.: 611430

BTS in Amsterdam bv (1)
Rieker Business Park Thomas R
Malthusstraat 1-3
1066 JR Amsterdam, Netherlands
Tel.: (31) 20 615 15 14
Fax: (31) 20 388 00 65
Web Site: www.bts.com
Corporate Training & Development Services
S.I.C.: 8299
N.A.I.C.S.: 611430

BTS Management SA (1)
C/o Lkm Associates sarl rue du Nant 8
1207 Geneva, Switzerland
Tel.: (41) 22 807 24 00
Fax: (41) 22 807 24 01
Corporate Training & Development Services
S.I.C.: 8299
N.A.I.C.S.: 611430

BTS MEXICO (1)
Moliere No 13 -P H
11560 Mexico, Mexico
Tel.: (52) 55 5281 6972
E-Mail: office.managermx@bts.com
Web Site: www.bts.com
Emp.: 13
Corporate Training & Development Services
S.I.C.: 8299
N.A.I.C.S.: 611430
Ruth Valdes *(Gen Mgr)*

BTS SEOUL (1)
Room 506 Tower Crystal Building 1008-1 Daechi-dong
Gangnam-gu, Seoul, 135-280, Korea (South)
Tel.: (82) 2 539 7676
Fax: (82) 2 553 3700
Emp.: 3
Corporate Training & Development Services
S.I.C.: 8299
N.A.I.C.S.: 611430
Yunho Chung *(Gen Mgr)*

BTS South Africa (1)
2671 West Ave Lakefield Office Park Bldg C
Centurion, Gauteng, South Africa
Tel.: (27) 126636909
Fax: (27) 126636887
E-Mail: elsie.mogale@bts.com
Emp.: 15
Business Management Solutions
S.I.C.: 8748
N.A.I.C.S.: 541618
Deon Greyling *(Mng Dir)*

BTS TAIPEI (1)
12F Building A No 25 Ren Ai Road Section 4
Taipei, Taiwan
Tel.: (886) 987 80 29 30
Business Consulting Services
S.I.C.: 7389
N.A.I.C.S.: 561499

BTS TOKYO (1)
Embassy of Sweden Compound 1-10-3-901 Roppongi
Minato-ku, Tokyo, 106-0032, Japan
Tel.: (81) 3 3560 3692
Fax: (81) 3 3560 3693
Web Site: www.bts.com
Corporate Training & Development Solutions
S.I.C.: 8299
N.A.I.C.S.: 611430

BTS United Kingdom (1)
37 Kensington High St
London, W85 5ED, United Kingdom
Tel.: (44) 2073481800
Fax: (44) 2073481801
Web Site: www.bts.com
Emp.: 15
Business Management Solutions
S.I.C.: 8748
N.A.I.C.S.: 541618
Joel Sigrist *(Mng Dir)*

Business Training Solutions S.L. (1)
Calle Simon Bolivar 27-1 of 19
Bilbao, 48013, Spain
Tel.: (34) 944235594
Fax: (34) 944236897
Emp.: 9
Corporate Training & Development Solutions
S.I.C.: 8299
N.A.I.C.S.: 611430
Philios Andreou *(Exec VP)*

Catalysts for Profitability and Growth Ltd (1)
267 W Ave
Centurion, 46, South Africa
Tel.: (27) 126636909
Fax: (27) 126636887
Web Site: www.bts.com
Emp.: 14
Corporate Training & Development Services
S.I.C.: 8299
N.A.I.C.S.: 611430
Deon Greyling *(Mng Dir)*

BTS GROUP HOLDINGS PUBLIC COMPANY LIMITED

15th floor TST Tower 21 Soi Choei Phuang Viphavadi-Rangsit Road Chomph
Chatuchak, Bangkok, 10900, Thailand
Tel.: (66) 2 273 8611
Fax: (66) 2 273 8610
E-Mail: info@btsgroup.co.th
Web Site: www.btsgroup.co.th
Year Founded: 1968
BTS—(OTC THA)
Rev.: $222,418,817
Assets: $2,220,739,859
Liabilities: $544,271,956
Net Worth: $1,676,467,903
Earnings: $90,648,146
Emp.: 3,420
Fiscal Year-end: 03/31/13

Business Description:
Mass Transit Solution Services
S.I.C.: 4111
N.A.I.C.S.: 485999

Personnel:
Keeree Kanjanapas *(Chm)*
Surayut Thavikulwat *(CFO)*
Rangsin Kritalug *(COO & Exec Dir)*
Chayada Yodyingtammakul *(Sec & Dir-Legal)*

Board of Directors:
Keeree Kanjanapas
Anat Arbhabhirama
Amorn Chandara-Somboon
Henry Ying Chew Cheong
Kavin Kanjanapas
Chi Keung Kong
Rangsin Kritalug
Surapong Laoha-Unya
Phisal Thepsithar
Paul Tong
Suchin Wanglee
Charoen Wattansin

Legal Counsel:
Weerawong, Chinnavat & Peangpanor Ltd
22nd floor Mercury Tower 540 Ploenchit Road Lumpini
Bangkok, Thailand

Subsidiaries:

888 Media Co., Ltd. (1)
21 TST Tower 9th Floor Viphavadi-Rangsit Road Chomphon
Chatuchak, Bangkok, 10900, Thailand
Tel.: (66) 2273 8884
Fax: (66) 2273 8883
Advertising Management Services
S.I.C.: 7319
N.A.I.C.S.: 541890

Bangkok Mass Transit System Plc. (1)
1000 BTS Building Phahonyothin Road Chomphon
Chatuchak, Bangkok, 10900, Thailand
Tel.: (66) 2617 7300
Fax: (66) 2617 7133
Mass Transit Services
S.I.C.: 4111
N.A.I.C.S.: 485113
Keeree Kanjanapas *(Chm)*
Kong Chi Keung *(CFO)*
Surapong Laoha-Unya *(COO)*

Bangkok Smartcard System Co., Ltd. (1)
21 TST Tower 19th Floor Viphavadi-Rangsit Road
Chomphon Jatujak, Bangkok, 10900, Thailand
Tel.: (66) 2 617 8338
Fax: (66) 2 617 8339
Financial Transaction Processing Services
S.I.C.: 6099
N.A.I.C.S.: 522320

DNAL Co., Ltd. (1)
21 Soi Choei Phuang Viphavadi-Rangsit Road
Jompol Jatujak, Bangkok, 10900, Thailand
Tel.: (66) 2 273 8833
Fax: (66) 2 273 8131
Office Building Rental Services
S.I.C.: 6512
N.A.I.C.S.: 531120

Sam Pao Petch Co., Ltd. (1)
100-100/1 Moo 4 Bangna-Trad Road Km 14
Bangchalong, Bang Phli, Samutprakarn, 10540, Thailand
Tel.: (66) 2336 1938 9
Fax: (66) 2336 1985
Real Estate Management Services
S.I.C.: 6531
N.A.I.C.S.: 531390

Thana City Golf & Sports Club Co., Ltd. (1)
100/2 Moo 4 Bangna-Trad Highway Km 14
Banchalong, Bang Phli, Samut Prakarn, 10540, Thailand
Tel.: (66) 2 336 1968 72
Fax: (66) 2 336 0570
E-Mail: golfconcierge@thanacitygolf.com
Web Site: www.thanacitygolf.com
Golf Club Operator
S.I.C.: 7999
N.A.I.C.S.: 713910

BTU CAPITAL CORP.

125A 1030 Denman Street
Vancouver, BC, V6G 2M6, Canada
Tel.: (604) 818-2617
Fax: (604) 648-9013
Year Founded: 2008
BTU.P—(TSXV)
Assets: $3,177
Liabilities: $197,426
Net Worth: ($194,249)
Earnings: ($110,423)
Fiscal Year-end: 04/30/13

Business Description:
Investment Services
S.I.C.: 6211
N.A.I.C.S.: 523999

Personnel:
Michael B. England *(CEO)*
Philip Taneda *(CFO)*

Board of Directors:
Michael B. England
Jianxing Qian
Philip Taneda

Transfer Agent:
Computershare Investor Services Inc.
100 University Ave 9th Floor
Toronto, ON, Canada

BUCCANEER ENERGY LIMITED

Level 9 25 Bligh Street
Sydney, NSW, 2000, Australia
Tel.: (61) 2 9233 2520
Fax: (61) 2 9233 2530
E-Mail: info@buccenergy.com
Web Site: www.buccenergy.com
BCC—(ASX)
Rev.: $28,585,897
Assets: $176,376,466
Liabilities: $139,962,281
Net Worth: $36,414,185
Earnings: ($28,056,543)
Emp.: 16
Fiscal Year-end: 06/30/13

Business Description:
Oil & Gas Exploration Services
S.I.C.: 1381

N.A.I.C.S.: 213111
Personnel:
Dean Lloyd Gallegos *(Chm & Dir-Fin)*
Curtis D. Burton *(CEO & Mng Dir)*
Ron Huff *(CFO)*
Clint Wainwright, Jr. *(Chief Dev Officer & Chief Exploration Officer)*
John T. Young, Jr. *(Chief Restructuring Officer)*
Andy Rike *(Pres-Buccaneer Alaska, LLC)*
Bruce David Burrell *(Sec)*
Board of Directors:
Dean Lloyd Gallegos
Curtis D. Burton
Brian Moller
Patrick O'Connor
Alan Stein
Gavin Wilson
Legal Counsel:
HopgoodGanim Lawyers
Level 8 Waterfront Place 1 Eagle Street
Brisbane, QLD, Australia

BUCHANAN FOREST PRODUCTS, LTD.
233 South Court Street
McIntyre Centre, Thunder Bay, ON, P7B 2X9, Canada
Tel.: (807) 345-0571
Fax: (807) 345-4004
Business Description:
Lumber Mfr
S.I.C.: 2421
N.A.I.C.S.: 321912
Personnel:
Bucky Henson *(Pres)*

BUCHANS MINERALS CORPORATION
(Acquired & Absorbed by Minco PLC)

BUCHER INDUSTRIES AG
Murzlenstrasse 80
CH-8166 Niederweningen, Switzerland
Tel.: (41) 438158080
Fax: (41) 438158081
E-Mail: info@bucherind.com
Web Site: www.bucherind.com
Year Founded: 1984
BUCN—(BER DEU STU SWX)
Rev.: $166,882,300
Assets: $1,482,250,663
Liabilities: $802,357,853
Net Worth: $679,892,810
Earnings: $44,711,910
Emp.: 10,166
Fiscal Year-end: 12/31/12
Business Description:
Holding Company; Mechanical & Vehicle Mfr & Engineering
S.I.C.: 6719
N.A.I.C.S.: 551112
Personnel:
Rolf Broglie *(Chm)*
Philip Mosimann *(CEO)*
Roger Baillod *(CFO)*
Michael Hausermann *(Pres-Bucher Municipal Div)*
Martin Jetter *(Pres-Emhart Glass Div)*
Michel Siebert *(Pres-Kuhn Grp)*
Daniel Waller *(Pres-Bucher Hydraulics Div)*
Board of Directors:
Rolf Broglie
Ernst Bartschi
Claude R. Cornaz
Anita Hauser
Michael Hauser
Heinrich Spoerry
Subsidiaries:

Bucher-Guyer AG (1)
Murzlenstrasse 80
8166 Niederweningen, Switzerland (100%)
Tel.: (41) 448572211
Fax: (41) 448572702
E-Mail: info@bucherschoerling.com
Web Site: www.bucherindustries.com
Emp.: 500
Mfr. of Vehicles & Agricultural Vehicles
S.I.C.: 3711
N.A.I.C.S.: 336112
Michael Haeusermann *(Mng Dir)*

Divisions:

Bucher-Guyer AG All-Terrain Vehicles (2)
Murzlenstrasse 80
CH 8166 Niederweningen, Switzerland (100%)
Tel.: (41) 448572211
E-Mail: info@bucherguyer.ch
Web Site: www.bucherguyer.ch
Emp.: 450
Mfr. of Vehicles & Agricultural Vehicles
S.I.C.: 3711
N.A.I.C.S.: 336111
Roger Baillod *(CFO)*

Bucher-Guyer AG Food Tech (2)
Niederweningen ZH
CH 8166 Niederweningen, Switzerland (100%)
Tel.: (41) 448572211
Fax: (41) 448572341
E-Mail: gl@bucherguyer.ch
Web Site: www.bucherguyer.ch
Emp.: 70
S.I.C.: 2034
N.A.I.C.S.: 311423
Hartmut Haverland *(Mng Dir)*

Bucher-Guyer AG Municipal Vehicles (2)
Murzlenstrasse 80
8166 Niederweningen, Switzerland (100%)
Tel.: (41) 438158080
Fax: (41) 438158081
E-Mail: info@bucherind.com
Web Site: www.bucherguyer.ch
Emp.: 550
Mfr. & Retailer of Municipal Vehicles
S.I.C.: 3711
N.A.I.C.S.: 336111

Bucher Landtechnik AG (2)
Murzlenstrasse 80
CH 8166 Niederweningen, Switzerland (100%)
Tel.: (41) 448572211
Fax: (41) 448572249
E-Mail: bucher_landtechnik@bucherguyer.ch
Web Site: www.bucherguyer.ch
Sales Range: $25-49.9 Million
Emp.: 450
Importer of Tractors
S.I.C.: 3537
N.A.I.C.S.: 333924

Bucher Management AG (1)
Flughafenstrasse 90
8058 Zurich, Switzerland
Tel.: (41) 43 815 80 80
Fax: (41) 43 815 80 81
E-Mail: info@bucherind.com
Emp.: 22
Business Management Consulting Services
S.I.C.: 8742
N.A.I.C.S.: 541611
Philip Mosimann *(CEO)*

Bucher Schorling AG (1)
Murzlenstrasse 80
8166 Niederweningen, Switzerland
Tel.: (41) 44 857 22 11
Fax: (41) 44 857 24 10
E-Mail: info@bucherschoerling.com
Web Site: www.bucherschoerling.com
Emp.: 450
Street Sweeping Truck Mfr & Distr
S.I.C.: 3711
N.A.I.C.S.: 336120
Michael Hausermann *(Gen Mgr)*

Non-U.S. Subsidiaries:

Beam A/S (2)
Salten Skovvej 4-6
DK-8653 Them, Denmark
Tel.: (45) 86 84 76 00
Fax: (45) 86 84 77 34
E-Mail: sales@beamsweepers.com
Web Site: www.beamsweepers.com
Emp.: 80
Street Sweeper Mfr
S.I.C.: 3569
N.A.I.C.S.: 333999

Bucher-Schoerling GmbH (2)
Schoerlingstrasse 3
D 30453 Hannover, Germany (100%)
Tel.: (49) 51121490
Fax: (49) 5112149115
E-Mail: info@bucherschoerling.de
Web Site: www.bucherschoerling.de
Emp.: 25
S.I.C.: 3711
N.A.I.C.S.: 336111
Stefan Zulaman *(Mng Dir)*

Bucher Schorling Korea Ltd (2)
Sihwa Industrial Complex Chungwang-Dong 3Ma 819Ho
Siheung, Kyunggi-do, 429-450, Korea (South)
Tel.: (82) 31 498 89 61 3
Fax: (82) 31 498 89 85
E-Mail: info@bucherschoerling.co.kr
Emp.: 2
Truck Mfr
S.I.C.: 3711
N.A.I.C.S.: 336120
Jaewook Ha *(Gen Mgr)*

Giletta S.p.A. (2)
Via A De Gasperi 1
12036 Revello, Italy IT
Tel.: (39) 0175 258 800 (60%)
Fax: (39) 0175 258 825
Web Site: www.giletta.com
Snow Removal Equipment Mfr
S.I.C.: 3569
N.A.I.C.S.: 333999

Gmeiner GmbH (2)
Daimlerstrasse 18
92533 Wernberg-Koblitz, Germany
Tel.: (49) 9604 93267 0
Fax: (49) 9604 93267 49
E-Mail: info@gmeiner-online.de
Emp.: 4
Winter Maintenance Equipment Mfr & Distr
S.I.C.: 3589
N.A.I.C.S.: 333318
Wilfried Muller *(Gen Mgr)*

Johnston Sweepers Ltd (2)
Curtis Road
Dorking, Surrey, RH4 1XF, United Kingdom
Tel.: (44) 1306 884722
Fax: (44) 1306 884151
E-Mail: dorking@johnstonsweepers.com
Web Site: www.johnstonsweepers.com
Emp.: 45
Outdoor Surface Cleansing Equipment Mfr
S.I.C.: 3589
N.A.I.C.S.: 333318
Chris Mitchell *(Mgr-Bus Support)*

U.S. Subsidiary:

Johnston North America Inc (3)
606 Performance Rd Ste A & B
Mooresville, NC 28115
Tel.: (704) 658-1333
Fax: (704) 658-1377
E-Mail: info@johnstonnorthamerica.com
Web Site: www.johnstonnorthamerica.com
Emp.: 13
Outdoor Surface Cleaning Equipment Distr
S.I.C.: 5087
N.A.I.C.S.: 423850
Bob O'Hara *(Gen Mgr)*

Non-U.S. Subsidiaries:

New Motion Limited (3)
Workshop 2 13/f Wah Lai Industrial Centre No 10-14 Kwei Tei Street
Fotan, New Territories, China (Hong Kong)
Tel.: (852) 3102 7606
Fax: (852) 2657 8880
E-Mail: sales@newmotion.com.hk
Web Site: www.newmotion.com.hk
Emp.: 15
Cleaning Machine & Equipment Distr
S.I.C.: 5087
N.A.I.C.S.: 423850
Franco Martegani *(Mng Dir)*

P T Nasaral Kekal Medal (3)
Wisma Sawah Besar Mendawai I No 64-66
Kebayoran Baro, 12130 Jakarta, Indonesia
Tel.: (62) 21723 1877
Fax: (62) 21724 4037
Emp.: 1
Cleaning Equipment Distr
S.I.C.: 5082
N.A.I.C.S.: 423810
Alex Takarianto *(Gen Mgr)*

MacDonald Johnston Ltd. (2)
65-73 Nantilla Road
Clayton North, Melbourne, VIC, 3168, Australia
Tel.: (61) 3 9271 6400
Fax: (61) 3 9271 6480
E-Mail: information@macdonaldjohnston.com.au
Web Site: www.mje.com.au
Emp.: 260
Side Loader Bodies Mfr
S.I.C.: 3711
N.A.I.C.S.: 336211
David Waldron *(Gen Mgr)*

SIA Bucher Schoerling Baltic SA (2)
105 Ganibu Street
3601 Ventspils, Latvia
Tel.: (371) 63661050
Fax: (371) 63661051
Emp.: 17
Transportation Equipment Mfr
S.I.C.: 3799
N.A.I.C.S.: 336999
Niklaus Huser *(Gen Mgr)*

Bucher Unipektin Ltd (1)
Murzlenstrasse 80
8166 Niederweningen, Switzerland
Tel.: (41) 44 857 23 00
Fax: (41) 44 857 23 41
E-Mail: info@bucherunipektin.com
Web Site: www.bucherunipektin.com
Vacuum Evaporator Mfr & Installation Services
S.I.C.: 3494
N.A.I.C.S.: 332919
Hartmut Haverland *(Gen Mgr)*

Non-U.S. Subsidiaries:

Bucher Unipektin Co. Ltd. (2)
Asian Game Village Huiyuan Apartment Room E1102 No 8 Beichendong Lu
Chaoyang District, Beijing, 100101, China
Tel.: (86) 10 6499 13 88
Fax: (86) 10 8498 13 98
E-Mail: info@bucherunipektin.com
Web Site: www.bucheralimentech.com
Emp.: 6
Soft Drink Mfr
S.I.C.: 2086
N.A.I.C.S.: 312111
Gerardo Paciello *(Gen Mgr)*

Emhart Glass S.A. (1)
Hinterbergstrasse 22
PO Box 2251
6330 Cham, Switzerland (100%)
Tel.: (41) 417494200
Fax: (41) 417494271
Web Site: www.emhartglass.com
Emp.: 60
Industrial Equipment, Controls & Glass Parts Supplier
S.I.C.: 5085
N.A.I.C.S.: 423840
Martin Jetter *(Pres)*

Subsidiary:

Emhart Glass International SA (2)
Hinterbergstrasse 22
Steinhausen, 6312, Switzerland
Tel.: (41) 417494200
Fax: (41) 417494271
Emp.: 75
Glass Equipment Distr
S.I.C.: 5131
N.A.I.C.S.: 424310

U.S. Subsidiaries:

Emhart Glass Inc (2)
123 Great Pond Dr
Windsor, CT 06095-0220
Tel.: (860) 298-7340
Fax: (860) 298-7395
E-Mail: info@emhartglass.com
Web Site: www.emhartglass.com
Glass Container Parts Mfr & Distr
S.I.C.: 3231

Bucher Industries AG—(Continued)

N.A.I.C.S.: 327215

Emhart Glass Manufacturing Inc. (2)
123 Great Pond Dr
Windsor, CT 06095 (100%)
Mailing Address:
PO Box 220
Windsor, CT 06095-0220
Tel.: (860) 298-7340
Fax: (860) 298-7395
Web Site: www.emhartglass.com
Emp.: 64
Mfr. of Container Glass
S.I.C.: 3221
N.A.I.C.S.: 327213
Stephen Austin *(VP-R&D)*

Branch:

Emhart Glass Manufacturing Inc. (3)
13075 US Hwy 19 N
Clearwater, FL 33764-7225 DE
Tel.: (727) 535-5502 (100%)
Fax: (727) 532-8513
Emp.: 25
Automated Inspection Equipment
S.I.C.: 3565
N.A.I.C.S.: 333993

Non-U.S. Subsidiaries:

Emhart Glass GmbH (2)
Hammfelddamm 4B
41460 Neuss, Germany (100%)
Tel.: (49) 213135950
Fax: (49) 21313595125
Web Site: www.emhartglass.com
Emp.: 20
Marketing of Industrial Supplies
S.I.C.: 5085
N.A.I.C.S.: 423840
Martin Jeter *(Mng Dir)*

Emhart Glass Japan Co Ltd. (2)
Parale Mitsui Bldg 15F 8 Higashida-cho
Kawasaki-ku, Kawasaki, 210-0005, Japan
Tel.: (81) 44 222 7371
Fax: (81) 44 222 4868
Web Site: www.emhartglass.com
Emp.: 5
Glass Products Distr
S.I.C.: 5199
N.A.I.C.S.: 424310

Emhart Glass Ltd. (2)
First Avenue The Village
Trafford Park, Manchester, M17 1JZ, United Kingdom (50%)
Tel.: (44) 1618761700
Fax: (44) 1618761701
Web Site: www.gemhartglass.com
Emp.: 17
Industrial Equipment Supplier
S.I.C.: 5085
N.A.I.C.S.: 423840
Mike Curry *(Mng Dir)*

Emhart Glass OOO (2)
Privolnaya Str 70
Moscow, 109431, Russia
Tel.: (7) 499 746 13 40
Fax: (7) 499 746 13 41
Web Site: www.emhartglass.com
Emp.: 6
Glass Processing Machinery Distr
S.I.C.: 5084
N.A.I.C.S.: 423830
Francois Laenen *(Gen Dir)*

Emhart Glass Pte. Ltd. (2)
200 Pandan Loop 07 03
Singapore, 128388, Singapore (100%)
Tel.: (65) 67781466
Fax: (65) 67789433
Web Site: www.emhartglass.com
Emp.: 13
Marketing of Industrial Supplies
S.I.C.: 5085
N.A.I.C.S.: 423840
Vincent Pang *(Mng Dir)*

Emhart Glass Sdn Bhd (2)
No 20 Jalan Mahir 5
Taman Perindustrian Cemerlang, 81800 Ulu Tiram, Johor, Malaysia
Tel.: (60) 78631122
Fax: (60) 78637717
E-Mail: kk.wong@emhartglass.com
Web Site: www.emhartglass.com
Emp.: 100
Glass Container Mfr
S.I.C.: 3221
N.A.I.C.S.: 327213
K. K. Wong *(Product Mgr)*

Emhart Glass S.r.l. (2)
Localita Colletto
Casella Postale 35, 17058 Dego, Savona, Italy (100%)
Tel.: (39) 01951661
Fax: (39) 0195166302
Web Site: www.emhartglass.com
Emp.: 30
Equipment, Controls & Parts Supplier to the Glass Container Industry
S.I.C.: 5085
N.A.I.C.S.: 423840

Emhart Glass Sweden AB (2)
University Aly 1
PO Box 710
85121 Sundsvall, Sweden (100%)
Tel.: (46) 60199100
Fax: (46) 60199261
E-Mail: christer.hermansson@emhartglass.com
Web Site: www.emhartglass.com
Emp.: 400
Marketing of Industrial Supplies
S.I.C.: 5085
N.A.I.C.S.: 423840
Bertil Bjugard *(Mng Dir)*

Non-U.S. Subsidiaries:

Bucher Beteiligungen GmbH (1)
Industriestrasse 1
79771 Klettgau, Germany
Tel.: (49) 7742 8520
Fax: (49) 7742 7116
Investment Management Services
S.I.C.: 6211
N.A.I.C.S.: 523999

Bucher Hydraulics GmbH (1)
Industriestrasse 1
79771 Klettgau, Germany (100%)
Tel.: (49) 77428520
Fax: (49) 77427116
E-Mail: info.de@bucherhydraulics.com
Web Site: www.bucherhydraulics.com
Sales Range: $400-449.9 Million
Emp.: 1,700
Mobile & Industrial Hydraulics
S.I.C.: 3594
N.A.I.C.S.: 333996
Daniel Waller *(CEO)*

Subsidiary:

Bucher Hydraulics Dachau GmbH (2)
Ohmstr 9
Dachau, 85521, Germany
Tel.: (49) 813131170
Fax: (49) 81312251
E-Mail: info.dah@bucherhydraulics.com
Emp.: 30
Fluid Power Pump & Motor Mfr
S.I.C.: 3594
N.A.I.C.S.: 333996
Georg Disson *(Gen Mgr)*

U.S. Subsidiary:

Bucher Hydraulics (2)
1363 Michigan St NE
Grand Rapids, MI 49503-2003 MI
Tel.: (616) 458-1306
Fax: (616) 458-0079
E-Mail: info.mi@bucherhydraulics.com
Web Site: www.monarchhyd.com
Sales Range: $50-74.9 Million
Emp.: 250
Fluid Power Pumps & Motors
Import Export
S.I.C.: 3594
N.A.I.C.S.: 333996
Dan Vaughan *(CEO-Bucher Hydraulics-North America)*

Non-U.S. Subsidiaries:

Bucher Hidrolik Sistemleri Tic. Ltd. (2)
ISTOC33 Ada No 31-33
Mahmutbey, 34550 Istanbul, Turkey
Tel.: (90) 212 659 0488
Fax: (90) 212 659 0489
E-Mail: info.tr@bucherhydraulics.com
Hydraulic Equipment Distr
S.I.C.: 5084
N.A.I.C.S.: 423830
Avni Bezmez *(Gen Mgr)*

Bucher Hydraulics AG (2)
Industriestrasse 15
CH 6345 Neuheim, Switzerland (100%)
Tel.: (41) 417570333
Fax: (41) 417570319
E-Mail: info.nh@bucherhydraulics.com
Web Site: www.bucherhydraulics.com
Emp.: 200
S.I.C.: 3511
N.A.I.C.S.: 333611

Subsidiary:

Bucher Hydraulics Fruhgen AG (3)
Schwandistrasse 25
CH 3714 Frutigen, Switzerland (100%)
Tel.: (41) 336726111
Fax: (41) 336726103
E-Mail: info.ch@bucherhydraulics.com
Web Site: www.bucherhydraulics.com
Emp.: 230
S.I.C.: 3511
N.A.I.C.S.: 333611
Aurelo Lemos *(Mng Dir)*

Bucher Hydraulics Co., Ltd (2)
No 22 Ding Hwu 5th Street
Kuasun Shiang, Taoyuan, Taiwan
Tel.: (886) 33 28 77 28
Fax: (886) 33 28 83 89
E-Mail: info.tw@bucherhydraulics.com
Web Site: www.bucherhydraulics.com
Hydraulic Cylinder Mfr
S.I.C.: 3593
N.A.I.C.S.: 333995
Timothy Lin *(Gen Mgr)*

Bucher Hydraulics Corp (2)
460 Newbold Street
London, ON, N6E 1K3, Canada
Tel.: (519) 686-5900
Fax: (519) 686-8976
E-Mail: info.ca@bucherhydraulics.com
Web Site: www.fluidpack.com
Emp.: 25
Hydraulic Component Mfr & Distr
S.I.C.: 3593
N.A.I.C.S.: 333995
Chris Countryman *(Gen Mgr)*

Bucher Hydraulics Corporation (2)
460 Newbold Street
London, ON, N6E 1K3, Canada
Tel.: (519) 686-5900
Fax: (519) 686-8976
Web Site: www.fluidpack.com
Emp.: 12
Hydraulic Assemblies
S.I.C.: 7699
N.A.I.C.S.: 811310
Chris Countryman *(Gen Mgr)*

Bucher Hydraulics KK (2)
Sakae-Cho 723-1-102
Yoshikawa, Saitama-Ken, 342-0050, Japan
Tel.: (81) 48 984 3713
Fax: (81) 48 984 3717
E-Mail: info.jp@bucherhydraulics.com
Web Site: www.bucherhydraulics.com
Hydraulic Equipment Mfr
S.I.C.: 3593
N.A.I.C.S.: 333995

Bucher Hydraulics Ltd (2)
Unit 9 Eastboro Fields
Hemdale, Nuneaton, Warwickshire, CV11 6GL, United Kingdom
Tel.: (44) 2476 35 35 61
Fax: (44) 2476 35 35 72
E-Mail: info.uk@bucherhydraulics.com
Hydraulic Equipment Distr
S.I.C.: 5084
N.A.I.C.S.: 423830

Bucher Hydraulics Pvt Ltd. (2)
35 Pace City - 1 Sector - 37
Gurgaon, 122 001, India
Tel.: (91) 124 47 00 100
Fax: (91) 124 40 39 499
E-Mail: info.in@bucherhydraulics.com
Web Site: www.bucherhydraulics.com
Hydraulic Equipment Distr
S.I.C.: 5084
N.A.I.C.S.: 423830

Bucher Hydraulics SAS (2)
50 Rue de l'Ile Napoleon
68173 Rixheim, France
Tel.: (33) 3 89 64 22 44
Fax: (33) 3 89 65 28 78
E-Mail: info.fr@bucherhydraulics.com
Hydraulic Component Distr
S.I.C.: 5084
N.A.I.C.S.: 423830

Bucher Hydraulics S.p.A. (2)
Via P Colletta N 5
I 42100 Reggio nell'Emilia, Italy (100%)
Tel.: (39) 0522928411
Fax: (39) 522513211
E-Mail: info@bucherhydraulics.com
Web Site: www.bucherhydraulics.it
Sales Range: $25-49.9 Million
Emp.: 200
S.I.C.: 3511
N.A.I.C.S.: 333611

Bucher Hydraulics (2)
Dawang Comprehensive Economic Development Zone
Zhaoqing, China
Tel.: (86) 7583642371
Fax: (86) 7583642373
E-Mail: info.ss@bucherhydraulics.com
Web Site: www.bucherhydraulics.com
Hydraulics Mfr
S.I.C.: 3594
N.A.I.C.S.: 333996

Suzhou Bucher Hydraulics Co. Ltd (2)
No 168 Shexing Road Fenghu Developing Zone
Wujiang, Jiangsu, 215214, China
Tel.: (86) 512 6322 1299
Fax: (86) 512 6322 1033
E-Mail: info.cn@bucherhydraulics.com
Web Site: www.bucherhydraulics.com
Hydraulic Cylinder Mfr
S.I.C.: 3593
N.A.I.C.S.: 333995

Bucher Vaslin SA (1)
Rue Gaston Bernier
F 49290 Chalonnes-sur-Loire, France (100%)
Tel.: (33) 241745050
Fax: (33) 241745051
E-Mail: commercial@buchervaslin.com
Web Site: www.buchervaslin.com
Emp.: 200
Wine Production Equipment Mfr
S.I.C.: 3556
N.A.I.C.S.: 333241

Subsidiary:

Bucher Vaslin MS SA (2)
Espace Entreprise Mediter Allee Alfred Nobel
66600 Rivesaltes, France
Tel.: (33) 468382390
Fax: (33) 468382399
Web Site: www.buchervaslin.com
Emp.: 39
Grapes Reception Equipment Mfr
S.I.C.: 3556
N.A.I.C.S.: 333241
Salon Christophe *(Gen Mgr)*

U.S. Subsidiary:

Bucher Vaslin North America, Inc (2)
350 Morris St Ste E
Sebastopol, CA 95472
Tel.: (707) 823-2883
Fax: (707) 823-6954
E-Mail: info.northamerica@buchervaslin.com
Web Site: www.bvnorthamerica.com
Emp.: 10
Food Product Machinery Mfr
S.I.C.: 3556
N.A.I.C.S.: 333241
Mea Leeman *(Dir-Sls & Mktg-Napa Valley)*

Non-U.S. Subsidiaries:

Bucher-Alimentech Ltd (2)
13b Gabador Place Mt Wellington
1060 Auckland, New Zealand
Tel.: (64) 95731333
Fax: (64) 95731334
E-Mail: foodtech@bucheralimentech.com
Food Processing Machinery Mfr

S.I.C.: 3556
N.A.I.C.S.: 333241
Chris Miller *(Gen Mgr)*

Bucher Vaslin Sudamerica (2)
Neptuno 1339 - Quinta Normal
Santiago, Chile
Tel.: (56) 2 773 3960
Fax: (56) 2 773 3960
Emp.: 3
Wine Making Machinery Mfr
S.I.C.: 3559
N.A.I.C.S.: 333249
Gallardo Osvaldo *(Gen Mgr)*

Contifonte SA (1)
4 Impasse des Fabriques
BP 50060
67706 Saverne, France
Tel.: (33) 3 88 01 81 05
Fax: (33) 3 88 01 81 06
Web Site: www.contifonte.fr
Rev.: $15,063,846
Emp.: 75
Agricultural Machinery Mfr
S.I.C.: 3523
N.A.I.C.S.: 333111
Michel Siepert *(Gen Mgr)*

KUHN S.A. (1)
4 Impasse des Fabriques
BP 50060
F-67706 Saverne, Cedex, France FR
Tel.: (33) 388018100 (99%)
Fax: (33) 388018101
E-Mail: info@kuhn.com
Web Site: www.kuhn.com
Sales Range: $800-899.9 Million
Emp.: 3,200
Mfr. of Agricultural Machinery
S.I.C.: 3523
N.A.I.C.S.: 333111
Michael Siebert *(Pres & CEO)*

Subsidiaries:

Kuhn-Audureau SA (2)
Rue Quanquese
85260 La Copechagniere, France
Tel.: (33) 2 51 41 47 00
Fax: (33) 2 51 41 41 03
E-Mail: kuhn-audureau@kuhn.com
Web Site: www.kuhn.com
Emp.: 20
Agricultural Machinery Mfr
S.I.C.: 3523
N.A.I.C.S.: 333111

Kuhn-Blanchard SAS (2)
24 rue de Nantes
44680 Chemere, France
Tel.: (33) 240 21 30 24
Fax: (33) 240 64 80 11
Web Site: www.bucherind.com
Agricultural & Forestry Machinery Mfr
S.I.C.: 3523
N.A.I.C.S.: 333111

Kuhn Group SAS (2)
4 Impasse Des Fabriques
67700 Saverne, France
Tel.: (33) 3 88 01 81 00
Fax: (33) 3 88 01 81 01
Industrial Machinery Distr
S.I.C.: 5084
N.A.I.C.S.: 423830

KUHN Huard S.A. (2)
Rue Du Quebec
44142 Chateaubriant, France FR
Tel.: (33) 240557700 (90%)
Fax: (33) 240557710
Web Site: www.kuhn.com
Sales Range: $50-74.9 Million
Emp.: 350
Agricultural Machinery Mfr
S.I.C.: 3523
N.A.I.C.S.: 333111

Kuhn MGM SAS (2)
Parc De La Faisanderie
67700 Monswiller, France
Tel.: (33) 388018100
Agricultural Machinery & Equipment Mfr
S.I.C.: 3523
N.A.I.C.S.: 333111

U.S. Subsidiary:

KUHN North America, Inc. (2)
1501 W 7th Ave
Brodhead, WI 53520-1637 DE
Tel.: (608) 897-2131
Fax: (608) 897-2561
Web Site: www.kuhnnorthamerica.com
Emp.: 300
Farm Machinery & Equipment
Import Export
S.I.C.: 3523
N.A.I.C.S.: 333111
Thierry Krier *(Pres & CEO)*

Subsidiary:

Kuhn Krause, Inc. (3)
305 S Monroe St
Hutchinson, KS 67501 KS
Mailing Address:
PO Box 2707
Hutchinson, KS 67504-2707
Tel.: (620) 663-6161
Fax: (620) 663-6943
Toll Free: (800) 957-2873
E-Mail: sales@krauseco.com
Web Site: www.krauseco.com
Sales Range: $50-74.9 Million
Emp.: 230
Farm Equipment Mfr
Export
S.I.C.: 3523
N.A.I.C.S.: 333111
Rod Hagman *(Dir-Engrg)*

Non-U.S. Subsidiaries:

Kuhn do Brasil S/A (2)
Rua Arno Pini 1380
Passo Fundo, Rio Grande do Sul, 99050 130, Brazil
Tel.: (55) 54 3316 6200
Fax: (55) 54 3316 6250
Emp.: 48
Agricultural Machinery Mfr
S.I.C.: 3523
N.A.I.C.S.: 333111
Mario Wagner *(Gen Dir)*

Kuhn Farm Machinery Ltd (2)
Stafford Park 7
Telford, Shrops, TF3 3BQ, United Kingdom
Tel.: (44) 1952 239 300
Fax: (44) 1952 290 091
E-Mail: info.uk@kuhn.co.uk
Web Site: www.kuhn.co.uk
Emp.: 3
Agricultural Machinery Distr
S.I.C.: 5083
N.A.I.C.S.: 423820
Sian Pritchard *(Gen Mgr)*

Kuhn Farm Machinery Pty Ltd (2)
313 - 325 Foleys Road
Deer Park, VIC, 3023, Australia
Tel.: (61) 3 9982 1490
Fax: (61) 3 8348 5999
Web Site: www.kuhn.com.au
Agricultural Machinery Mfr
S.I.C.: 3523
N.A.I.C.S.: 333111

Kuhn Farm Machinery Sarl (2)
16 Mechnikova Str Office Ste 311-312
Kiev, 1601, Ukraine
Tel.: (380) 44 2293875
Fax: (380) 44 2293875
E-Mail: info@kuhn.ua
Web Site: www.kuhn.com
Emp.: 1
Agricultural Machinery Mfr
S.I.C.: 3523
N.A.I.C.S.: 333111
Viktor Sych *(Gen Dir)*

Kuhn-Geldrop B.V. (2)
Nuenenseweg 165
5667 KP Geldrop, Netherlands
Tel.: (31) 40 28 93 300
Fax: (31) 40 28 53 215
Web Site: www.bucherind.com
Emp.: 400
Farm Machinery & Equipment Mfr
S.I.C.: 3523
N.A.I.C.S.: 333111
Theodor Sanden *(Gen Mgr)*

Kuhn Iberica SA (2)
Carretera A-131 Km 100
22005 Huesca, Spain
Tel.: (34) 974234440
Fax: (34) 974234439
E-Mail: info@kuhn.es
Farm Machinery Distr
S.I.C.: 5083
N.A.I.C.S.: 423820

Kuhn Italia Srl. (2)
Via Cerca per Colturano 8
20077 Melegnano, Italy
Tel.: (39) 02 982161
Fax: (39) 02 98216212
Agricultural Machinery Distr
S.I.C.: 5083
N.A.I.C.S.: 423820

Kuhn Maschinen-Vertrieb GmbH (2)
Industriestr 14
39291 Schopsdorf, Germany
Tel.: (49) 39225 960 0
Fax: (49) 39225 960 20
Web Site: www.kuhn.de
Agricultural Machinery Distr
S.I.C.: 5083
N.A.I.C.S.: 423820
Armin Rau *(Mng Dir)*

Kuhn Maszyny Rolnicze Sp. z.o.o (2)
Jelonek K/Poznania - ul Orzechowa
62-002 Suchy Las, Poland
Tel.: (48) 61 812 52 35
Fax: (48) 61 811 70 10
Emp.: 37
Farm Machinery & Equipment Distr
S.I.C.: 5083
N.A.I.C.S.: 423820
Artur Szymczak *(Mng Dir)*

Kuhn Vostok LLC (2)
9 Str 1 Ofis 322 Varshavskoe Shosse
Moscow, 117105, Russia
Tel.: (7) 4957868112
Fax: (7) 4957858272
E-Mail: info@kuhn.ru
Web Site: www.kuhn.ru
Emp.: 25
Agricultural Machinery & Equipment Distr
S.I.C.: 5083
N.A.I.C.S.: 423820

BUCHER LEICHTBAU AG

Industriestrasse 1a
CH-8117 Fallanden, Switzerland
Tel.: (41) 44 806 24 24
Fax: (41) 44 806 24 20
E-Mail: bucher@bucher-group.com
Web Site: www.bucher-group.com
Business Description:
Aircraft Equipment Mfr
S.I.C.: 3728
N.A.I.C.S.: 336413
Personnel:
Beat Burlet *(Acting CEO & Dir-Sls & Mktg)*

U.S. Subsidiary:

Bucher Aerospace Corp. (1)
1310 Industry St Ste 100
Everett, WA 98203 WA
Tel.: (425) 355-2202
Fax: (425) 355-2204
Web Site: www.bucher-group.com
Emp.: 50
Aircraft Component Mfr
S.I.C.: 3728
N.A.I.C.S.: 336413
Francisco Aguilera *(CEO)*

BUCHERER AG

Langensandstrasse 27
CH-6002 Lucerne, Switzerland
Tel.: (41) 413697000
Fax: (41) 413697364
E-Mail: info@bucherer.com
Web Site: www.bucherer.com
Year Founded: 1888
Emp.: 1,100
Business Description:
Watch & Jewelry Mfr & Retailer
S.I.C.: 5094
N.A.I.C.S.: 423940
Personnel:
Joerg G. Bucherer *(Chm)*
Guido Zumbuhl *(CEO)*

BUCK-CHEMIE GMBH

Hertzstrasse 1
D-71083 Herrenberg, Germany
Tel.: (49) 703297690
Fax: (49) 703277176
E-Mail: info@buck-chemie.de
Web Site: www.buck-chemie.de
Year Founded: 1966
Rev.: $18,374,869
Emp.: 47
Business Description:
Cleaning Consumer Goods Mfr
S.I.C.: 2819
N.A.I.C.S.: 325180
Personnel:
Edgar Jaeschke *(Gen Mgr)*

BUCKING HORSE ENERGY INC.

Ste 900 609 West Hastings Street
Vancouver, BC, V6B 4W4, Canada
Tel.: (604) 331-3398
Fax: (604) 688-4712
Web Site: www.buckinghorseenergy.com
Year Founded: 2006
BUC.H—(TSXV)
Sales Range: $10-24.9 Million
Business Description:
Petroleum Exploration & Development
S.I.C.: 1389
N.A.I.C.S.: 213112
Personnel:
Gordon Nielsen *(Interim CFO)*
Board of Directors:
Vinko Barcot, Jr.
Ray Deere
Michael Schoen
Transfer Agent:
Computershare Investor Services Inc
510 Burrard Street 3rd Floor
Vancouver, BC, V6C 3B9, Canada

U.S. Subsidiary:

Arrowhead Resources (U.S.A.) Ltd. (1)
3964 Crystal Bridge Dr
Carbondale, CO 81623
Tel.: (970) 704-0471
Fax: (970) 704-1767
Oil & Gas Field Exploration Services
S.I.C.: 1389
N.A.I.C.S.: 213112
Christopher Schultze *(Pres)*

BUCKINGHAM EXPLORATION INC.

(Name Changed to Tierra Grande Resources Inc.)

BUCKINGHAMSHIRE BUILDING SOCIETY

High Street
Chalfont Saint Giles, Bucks, HP8 4QB, United Kingdom
Tel.: (44) 1494 879500
Fax: (44) 1494 876256
E-Mail: info@bucksbs.co.uk
Web Site: www.bucksbs.co.uk
Year Founded: 1907
Rev.: $11,705,697
Assets: $338,787,712
Liabilities: $319,727,261
Net Worth: $19,060,451
Earnings: $2,060,973
Emp.: 30
Fiscal Year-end: 12/31/12
Business Description:
Mortgage Lender
S.I.C.: 6163
N.A.I.C.S.: 522310
Personnel:
Ivan James Gould *(CEO)*
Judith Williams *(Sec)*

Buckinghamshire Building Society—(Continued)

Board of Directors:
Robin Thomas Bailey
Sharon Lesley Constancon
Ivan James Gould
Stephen Scott Nichols
Rajeshkumar Kantilal Patel
Ian George Powell
Sanaya Homi Robinson
Michael John Stannard

BUCKLAND CUSTOMS BROKERS LTD.
73 Gaylord Road
Saint Thomas, ON, N5P 3R9, Canada
Tel.: (519) 631-4944
Fax: (519) 633-8038
Toll Free: (800) 991-4944
E-Mail: opsho@bucklandcustoms.com
Web Site: www.bucklandcustoms.com
Year Founded: 1945
Rev.: $21,350,380
Emp.: 175
Business Description:
Consulting & Brokerage Services
S.I.C.: 6211
N.A.I.C.S.: 523120
Personnel:
Shirley Smith *(Pres)*
Craig Smith *(CEO)*

BUCKWOLD WESTERN LTD.
75 24th Street East
Saskatoon, SK, S7K 0K3, Canada
Tel.: (306) 652-1660
Fax: (306) 665-1817
Web Site: www.buckwold.com
Year Founded: 1925
Rev.: $22,250,769
Emp.: 145
Business Description:
Floor Covering Products Distr
S.I.C.: 5211
N.A.I.C.S.: 444190
Personnel:
Bruce Buckwold *(Pres)*

BUCUR OBOR SA
(See Under S.C. Bucur Obor S.A.)

BUDAPEST PROPERTY UTILIZATION AND DEVELOPMENT PLC.
Bajcsy Zsilinszky Ut 57
1065 Budapest, Hungary
Tel.: (36) 13322200
Fax: (36) 13672800
E-Mail: info@bif.hu
Web Site: www.bif.hu
Year Founded: 1994
BIF—(BUD)
Rev.: $11,027,119
Assets: $111,024,737
Liabilities: $46,463,661
Net Worth: $64,561,076
Earnings: ($922,085)
Emp.: 44
Fiscal Year-end: 12/31/12
Business Description:
Real Estate Management Services
S.I.C.: 6531
N.A.I.C.S.: 531390
Personnel:
Kristof Nobilis *(Chm)*
Zoltan Speder *(Vice Chm)*
Gabor Angel *(CEO)*
Eniko Martonne Uhrin *(CFO)*
Board of Directors:
Kristof Nobilis
Eniko Martonne Uhrin
Marton Olah
Zoltan Speder
Anna Ungar

BUDDHA AIR PVT. LTD.
Jawalakhel Lalitpur
PO Box 2167
Kathmandu, Nepal
Tel.: (977) 015521015
Fax: (977) 015537726
E-Mail: buddhaair@buddhaair.com
Web Site: www.buddhaair.com
Emp.: 700
Business Description:
Air Transportation Services
S.I.C.: 4512
N.A.I.C.S.: 481111
Personnel:
Surendra B. Basnet *(Chm)*
Birendra B. Basnet *(Mng Dir)*

BUDDS' BMW
2454 South Service Road West
Oakville, ON, L6L 5M9, Canada
Tel.: (905) 827-6047
Fax: (905) 825-9887
Toll Free: (866) 434-2833
Web Site: www.buddsbmw.com
Year Founded: 1973
Rev.: $23,973,621
Emp.: 50
Business Description:
New & Used Car Dealers
S.I.C.: 5511
N.A.I.C.S.: 441110
Personnel:
Scott Johnson *(Gen Mgr-Sls)*

BUDERIM GINGER LIMITED
50 Pioneer Road
PO Box 231
Yandina, QLD, 4561, Australia
Mailing Address:
PO Box 231
Yandina, QLD, 4561, Australia
Tel.: (61) 800067686
Fax: (61) 754467520
E-Mail: buderimg@buderimginger.com
Web Site: www.buderimginger.com
BUG—(ASX)
Sls.: $79,305,894
Assets: $71,798,606
Liabilities: $35,863,872
Net Worth: $35,934,734
Earnings: $1,917,464
Emp.: 416
Fiscal Year-end: 12/31/12
Business Description:
Ginger Production, Processing & Distribution
S.I.C.: 2034
N.A.I.C.S.: 311423
Personnel:
Murray Richardson *(CEO)*
Karon Lesley Rogers *(CFO)*
Andrew Bond *(Sec)*
Board of Directors:
Stephen John Morrow
Shane Tyson Templeton
George Vasili
Margaret Walker
Legal Counsel:
Thomsons Lawyers
Waterfront Place 1 Eagle Street
Brisbane, Australia
Subsidiaries:

Buderim Baking Company Pty Ltd (1)
60-62 Maroochydore Rd Kunda Pk
Maroochydore, Queensland, 4556, Australia
Tel.: (61) 754455011
Fax: (61) 754456606
Emp.: 50
Bakery Products Mfr
S.I.C.: 5461
N.A.I.C.S.: 445291
David Dippelsman *(Gen Mgr)*

Buderim Ginger (Overseas) Holdings Pty Ltd (1)
50 Pioneer Rd
Yandina, QLD, 4561, Australia
Tel.: (61) 754467100
Fax: (61) 754467520
Emp.: 80
Ginger Supplies
S.I.C.: 0182
N.A.I.C.S.: 111419

Non-U.S. Subsidiary:

Frespac Ginger (Fiji) Ltd (2)
Lot 13 Wailada Estate
PO Box 15128
Lami, Suva, Fiji
Tel.: (679) 3362863
Fax: (679) 3361225
E-Mail: info@frespac.com.fj
Emp.: 100
Ginger Supplies
S.I.C.: 0182
N.A.I.C.S.: 111419
Sathish Kumar *(Mgr-Factory)*

Buderim Macadamias Pty Ltd (1)
1 Northcott Crescent
Alstonville, NSW, 2477, Australia
Tel.: (61) 266286185
Fax: (61) 266286183
E-Mail: marketing@agrimac.com.au
Web Site: www.agrimac.com.au/
Emp.: 50
Macadamia Nut Farming Services
S.I.C.: 0173
N.A.I.C.S.: 111335
Darren Burton *(Gen Mgr)*

U.S. Subsidiaries:

Buderim Ginger America, Inc. (1)
850 Montgomery Ste 350
San Francisco, CA 94133
Tel.: (201) 560-1170
Confectionery Ginger Mfr
S.I.C.: 0182
N.A.I.C.S.: 111419

Buderim Macadamias of Hawaii, LLC (1)
89-406 Mamalahoa Hwy
Captain Cook, HI 96704
Tel.: (808) 328-2435
Fax: (808) 328-2080
Web Site: www.macfarms.com
Emp.: 150
Macadamia Nut Farming Services
S.I.C.: 0173
N.A.I.C.S.: 111335
Mark Crawford *(VP)*

Non-U.S. Subsidiary:

Buderim Ginger (UK) Ltd (1)
306 Stafford Rd
Croydon, Surrey, CR0 4NH, United Kingdom
Tel.: (44) 2086818459
Fax: (44) 2086808049
E-Mail: sales@buderimginger.co.uk
Web Site: www.buderimginger.co.uk
Confectionery Ginger Mfr
S.I.C.: 0182
N.A.I.C.S.: 111419

BUDGET RENT-A-CAR OF B.C. LTD
3840 Mcdonald Road
Richmond, BC, V7B 1L8, Canada
Tel.: (604) 668-7100
Web Site: www.budgetbc.com
Year Founded: 1965
Rev.: $22,084,017
Emp.: 150
Business Description:
Automobile Renting & Leasing
S.I.C.: 7514
N.A.I.C.S.: 532111
Personnel:
Sydney Belzberg *(Chm)*

BUDOPOL-WROCLAW S.A.
ul Raclawicka 15/19
53-149 Wroclaw, Poland
Tel.: (48) 717993906
Fax: (48) 717993905
E-Mail: sekretariat@budopol.wroc.pl
BDL—(WAR)
Sales Range: $25-49.9 Million
Business Description:
Residential & Commercial Construction Services
S.I.C.: 1521
N.A.I.C.S.: 236115
Personnel:
Janusz Konopka *(Chm-Supervisory Bd)*
Miroslaw Motyka *(Chm-Mgmt Bd)*
Andrzej Kostrzewa *(Vice Chm-Mgmt Bd)*
Marzanna Adamska *(Member-Mgmt Bd)*
Supervisory Board of Directors:
Janusz Konopka
Luiza Berg
Henryk Jukowski
Miroslaw Kadlubowski
Adam Michalski
Zbigniew Walas

BUDUCNOST A.D. SUBOTICA
Losinjska 8
24000 Subotica, Serbia
Tel.: (381) 24 546 317
Fax: (381) 24 553 166
E-Mail: adbudsub@gmail.com
Web Site: www.buducnost.co.rs
BDSU—(BEL)
Business Description:
Wood Furniture Mfr
S.I.C.: 2521
N.A.I.C.S.: 337211
Personnel:
Ana Sujic *(Dir-Comml)*

BUDVAR CENTRUM SA
ul Przemyslowa 36
98-220 Zdunska Wola, Poland
Tel.: (48) 438243132
Fax: (48) 438243133
E-Mail: info@budvar.pl
Web Site: www.budvar.pl
Year Founded: 1997
BDV—(WAR)
Sales Range: $10-24.9 Million
Emp.: 300
Business Description:
PVC, Wooden & Aluminum Window & Door Mfr
S.I.C.: 3442
N.A.I.C.S.: 332321
Personnel:
Marek Trzcinski *(Chm-Mgmt Bd)*

BUECHL HANDELS-UND BETEILIGUNGS-KG
Im Gewerbepark C 30
93059 Regensburg, Germany
Tel.: (49) 9 41 46 46 40
Fax: (49) 9 41 4 64 64 10
E-Mail: info@bueechl.de
Web Site: www.bueechl.de
Business Description:
Engineering Services
S.I.C.: 8711
N.A.I.C.S.: 541330
Subsidiary:

Michael Glatt Maschinenbau GmbH (1)
Industriestrasse 2
Abensberg, 93326 Kelheim, Bavaria, Germany
Tel.: (49) 944391140
Fax: (49) 9443911499
E-Mail: info@glattistgutgmbh.de

Web Site: www.glattistgutgmbh.de
Sales Range: $10-24.9 Million
Emp.: 80
Mfr of Pressure Containers & Other Apparatus for Chemicals, Pharmaceuticals & Biotechnology Industries
S.I.C.: 3499
N.A.I.C.S.: 332999
Georg Hochreiter *(Mng Dir)*
Jens Otto *(Mng Dir)*

BUETTNER S.A.

R Edgar Von Buettner 941
88355350 Brusque, SC, Brazil
Tel.: (55) 47 3211 4078
Fax: (55) 47 3211 4013
Web Site: www.buettner.com.br
Year Founded: 1898
BUET3—(BRAZ)
Sales Range: $25-49.9 Million
Emp.: 743
Business Description:
Textile Product Mfr & Whslr
S.I.C.: 2392
N.A.I.C.S.: 314120
Personnel:
Fabricio Pozzi Colzani *(Dir-IR)*

BUFFALO DAVID BITTON

(d/b/a The Buffalo Group)
400 Sauve W
Montreal, QC, H3L 1Z8, Canada
Tel.: (514) 388-3551
Fax: (514) 388-1972
E-Mail: info@buffalojeans.com
Web Site: www.buffalojeans.com
Year Founded: 1985
Sales Range: $100-124.9 Million
Emp.: 300
Business Description:
Denim Apparel Designer, Mfr & Retailer
S.I.C.: 5699
N.A.I.C.S.: 448190
Personnel:
Gaby Bitton *(Pres)*

BUHLER AG

Bahnhofstrasse
CH 9240 Uzwil, Switzerland
Tel.: (41) 719551111
Fax: (41) 719553379
E-Mail: buhler.uzwil@buhlergroup.com
Web Site: www.buhlergroup.com
Year Founded: 1860
Rev.: $2,637,858,080
Assets: $2,560,902,564
Liabilities: $1,511,371,796
Net Worth: $1,049,530,768
Earnings: $173,446,724
Emp.: 10,346
Fiscal Year-end: 12/31/12
Business Description:
Food Processing Systems; Chemical Process Engineering; Die Casting; Manufacturing & Logistics
Export
S.I.C.: 2099
N.A.I.C.S.: 311999
Personnel:
Urs Buhler *(Chm)*
Calvin Grieder *(Chm-Exec Bd & CEO)*
Andreas R. Herzog *(CFO & Member-Exec Bd)*
Samuel Schar *(Member-Exec Bd & Head-Advanced Matls Div)*
Bruno Mendler *(Member-Exec Bd-Grain Processing Div)*
Martin Menrath *(Member-Exec Bd-Mfg & Logistics Div)*
Stefan Scheiber *(Member-Exec Bd-Food Processing Div)*
Board of Directors:
Urs Buhler
Calvin Grieder
Konrad Hummler
Hans J. Loliger
Ruth Metzler-Arnold
Josef M. Muller
Peter Quadri
U.S. Subsidiaries:

Buhler Aeroglide **(1)**
100 Aeroglide Dr
Cary, NC 27511-6900 NC
Mailing Address:
PO Box 29505
Raleigh, NC 27626-0505
Tel.: (919) 851-2000
Telex: 579421
Fax: (919) 851-6029
E-Mail: sales@aeroglide.com
Web Site: www.aeroglide.com
Sales Range: $50-74.9 Million
Emp.: 220
Designer & Mfr of Industrial Drying & Cooling Equipment
Export
S.I.C.: 3556
N.A.I.C.S.: 333241
Hans-Joerg III *(Pres & CEO)*
Michael Williams *(CFO & VP)*

Non-U.S. Subsidiary:

Buhler Aeroglide U.K. **(2)**
2 St Mary's Hill
Stamford, Lincs, PE9 2DW, United Kingdom
Tel.: (44) 1780767007
Fax: (44) 1780767008
E-Mail: aerosales@aeroglide.com
Web Site: www.aeroglide.com
Emp.: 10
Mfr of Termal Processing Equipment
S.I.C.: 3559
N.A.I.C.S.: 333249

Buhler Inc. **(1)**
13105 12th Ave N
Plymouth, MN 55441 MN
Mailing Address:
PO Box 9497
Minneapolis, MN 55440-9497
Tel.: (763) 847-9900
Fax: (763) 847-9911
Web Site: www.buhlerusa.com
Emp.: 170
Mfr. & Wholesaler of Industrial Food Processing Machinery & Equipment; Manufacturer of Bulk Conveying & Dust Control Systems & Machinery
S.I.C.: 3556
N.A.I.C.S.: 333241
Rene Steiner *(Pres)*

IdraPrince, Inc. **(1)**
670 Windcrest Dr
Holland, MI 49423
Tel.: (616) 394-8248
Fax: (616) 394-1250
E-Mail: info@idraprince.com
Web Site: www.prince-machine.com
Emp.: 230
Mfr. of Die Casting Machines
S.I.C.: 3542
N.A.I.C.S.: 333517

BUHLER INDUSTRIES INC.

1260 Clarence Avenue
Winnipeg, MB, R3T 1T2, Canada
Tel.: (204) 661-8711
Fax: (204) 654-2503
E-Mail: info@buhler.com
Web Site: www.buhlerindustries.com
BUI—(TSX)
Rev.: $309,328,734
Assets: $254,977,417
Liabilities: $92,360,547
Net Worth: $162,616,870
Earnings: $17,888,971
Emp.: 1,073
Fiscal Year-end: 09/30/13
Business Description:
Farm Equipment Mfr
S.I.C.: 3524
N.A.I.C.S.: 333112
Personnel:
Dmitry Udras *(Chm)*
Dmitry Lyubimov *(Pres)*
Yury Ryazanov *(CEO, Treas & Sec)*
Willy Janzen *(CFO)*
Grant Adolph *(COO)*
Min Lee *(CIO)*
Board of Directors:
Dmitry Udras
Konstantin Babkin
John Buhler
Oleg Gorbunov
Yury Ryazanov
Allan Stewart
Legal Counsel:
Thompson Dorfman Sweatman LLP
Winnipeg, MB, Canada
Transfer Agent:
Computershare Trust Company of Canada
Calgary, AB, Canada

BUILD INVESTMENTS GROUP JSC

Bokehana 24
010000 Astana, Kazakhstan
Tel.: (7) 7172360360
E-Mail: infosales@bi-group.kz
Web Site: www.bi-group.kz
Sales Range: $75-99.9 Million
Business Description:
Construction & Related Industries Investment Services
S.I.C.: 6211
N.A.I.C.S.: 523999
Personnel:
Askhat Omarov *(Chm-Mgmt Bd)*

BUILD KING HOLDINGS LIMITED

Units 601-605A 6/F Tower B Manulife Financial Centre
223 Wai Yip Street Kwun Tong, Kowloon, China (Hong Kong)
Tel.: (852) 22723680
Fax: (852) 23753655
E-Mail: info@buildking.hk
Web Site: www.buildking.hk
0240—(HKG)
Rev.: $214,211,095
Assets: $137,115,888
Liabilities: $99,457,459
Net Worth: $37,658,429
Earnings: $2,594,990
Emp.: 915
Fiscal Year-end: 12/31/12
Business Description:
Construction Business
S.I.C.: 6159
N.A.I.C.S.: 522292
Personnel:
Derek Wei Peu Zen *(Chm, CEO & Mng Dir)*
Desmond Kam Chuen Chang *(Sec)*
Board of Directors:
Derek Wei Peu Zen
Anthony Chi Hung Chan
Desmond Kam Chuen Chang
Leslie Chi Pang Cheng
Joseph Ming Kuen Chow
David Howard Gem
David Tai Wai Ho
James Chi Ming Ng
Butterfield Fulcrum Group (Bermuda) Limited
26 Burnaby Street
Hamilton, HM 11, Bermuda
Transfer Agents:
Tricor Progressive Limited
26/F Tesbury Centre 28 Queen's Road
Wanchai, China (Hong Kong)
Butterfield Fulcrum Group (Bermuda) Limited
26 Burnaby Street
Hamilton, HM 11, Bermuda

BUILDERS CAPITAL MORTGAGE CORP.

405 1210 8th Street Southwest
Calgary, AB, T2R 1L3, Canada
Tel.: (403) 685-9888
Fax: (403) 225-9470
E-Mail: info@builderscapital.ca
Web Site: www.builderscapital.ca
Year Founded: 2013
BCF—(TSXV)
Business Description:
Mortgage Investment Services
S.I.C.: 6211
N.A.I.C.S.: 523999
Personnel:
Sandy L. Loutitt *(Chm, Pres & CEO)*
John Strangway *(CFO)*
Board of Directors:
Sandy L. Loutitt
John A. Drummond
Victor P. Harwardt
Michael Matishak
David E.T. Pinkman
John Strangway
Brent J. Walter

BUILDERSMART PUBLIC COMPANY LIMITED

905 7 Soi 51 Rama 3 Road
Bangpongpang
Yannawa, Bangkok, 10120, Thailand
Tel.: (66) 26834900
Fax: (66) 26834949
E-Mail: customercare@buildersmart.com
Web Site: www.buildersmart.com
Year Founded: 1999
BSM—(THA)
Rev.: $14,459,580
Assets: $8,034,450
Liabilities: $4,433,223
Net Worth: $3,601,227
Earnings: $462,325
Fiscal Year-end: 12/31/12
Business Description:
Construction Material Distr
S.I.C.: 5039
N.A.I.C.S.: 423390
Personnel:
Suresh Subramaniam *(Chm & CEO)*
Sunchai Nuengsit *(Vice Chm)*
Board of Directors:
Suresh Subramaniam
Christopher John Carrias
Sunchai Nuengsit
Anek Pichetpongsa
Mark David Remijan
Theerathon Tharachai
Shiun Moh Yang
Non-U.S. Subsidiaries:

Builders Box (India) PVT. Ltd **(1)**
Unit G5-6 26 Race Course Road
Bengaluru, Karnataka, 560 001, India
Tel.: (91) 80 412 26 332
Fax: (91) 80 412 26 331
E-Mail: dsengupta@bboxxindia.com
Construction Material Distr
S.I.C.: 5032
N.A.I.C.S.: 423320

BuilderSmart (Vietnam) Limited **(1)**
90A/B 73 Ly Thuong Kiet
Ho Chi Minh City, Vietnam
Tel.: (84) 8 3864 3525
Fax: (84) 8 3864 3524
E-Mail: vn-info@buildersmart.com
Construction Material Distr
S.I.C.: 5032
N.A.I.C.S.: 423320

BuilderSmart Construction Systems PVT Ltd **(1)**
Prince Greenwoods Walnut A-401 A-404 4th Floor
Ambattur, Chennai, 600058, India
Tel.: (91) 95 00123029
E-Mail: in-info@buildersmart.com

BuilderSmart Public Company Limited—(Continued)

Building Material Distr
S.I.C.: 5211
N.A.I.C.S.: 444190

BUILDEX VENTURE CAPITAL CORPORATION

3030 boul Le Carrefour
Bureau 1002
Laval, QC, H7T 2P5, Canada
Tel.: (450) 681-7744
Fax: (450) 681-8400
E-Mail: ic@seguinracine.com
Year Founded: 2010
BUX.P—(TSXV)

Business Description:
Investment Services
S.I.C.: 6211
N.A.I.C.S.: 523999

Personnel:
Alain Larochelle *(Pres & CEO)*
Roger Boucher *(CFO)*
Pierre-Hubert Seguin *(Sec)*

Board of Directors:
Stephane Beshro
Roger Boucher
Paul Forest
Alain Larochelle
Pierre-Hubert Seguin

Transfer Agent:
CIBC Mellon Trust Company
Montreal, QC, Canada

BUILDMAX LIMITED

515 Pretoria Road Fairleads AH
Benoni, 1512, South Africa
Tel.: (27) 861 691 177
Fax: (27) 126850441
E-Mail: info@buildmax.co.za
Web Site: www.buildmax.co.za
BDM—(JSE)
Rev.: $132,524,008
Assets: $139,181,998
Liabilities: $74,535,399
Net Worth: $64,646,598
Earnings: $5,768,970
Emp.: 1,845
Fiscal Year-end: 02/28/13

Business Description:
Coal Mining Contractor & Construction Materials Supplier
S.I.C.: 1629
N.A.I.C.S.: 236210

Personnel:
Terry P. Bantock *(CEO)*
Kobus van Biljon *(CEO-Mining Svcs)*
Gillian Hope Miller *(Sec)*

Board of Directors:
Colin J. M. Wood
Terry P. Bantock
Colin B. Brayshaw
Christiaan Stephanus Els
M. David Lamola
Dennis J. Mack
Jackie Mathebula
Malcolm W. McCulloch
Graeme Montgomery
Bulelani T. Ngcuka

Subsidiaries:

Buildmax Aggregates and Quarries (Pty) Limited **(1)**
Unit 19 First Fl E Block Cambridge Ofc Highveld Park
Centurion, Gauteng, 0067, South Africa
Tel.: (27) 116220544
Fax: (27) 116222291
Building Materials Distr
S.I.C.: 5211
N.A.I.C.S.: 444190

Buildmax Management Services (Pty) Limited **(1)**
Unit 19 1st Fl E Cambridge Ofc Park
Pretoria, Gauteng, 1400, South Africa
Tel.: (27) 126850440
Fax: (27) 126850441
E-Mail: info@buidmax.co.za
Emp.: 7
Construction Materials Whslr
S.I.C.: 5032
N.A.I.C.S.: 423320
Paul de Klerk *(CEO)*

Crushco (Pty) Limited **(1)**
Private Bag X02 1514
Rynsfield, Benoni, 1514, South Africa
Tel.: (27) 118285722
Fax: (27) 119642360
Emp.: 70
Sand & Gravel Quarrying Services
S.I.C.: 1442
N.A.I.C.S.: 212321
Titus Alogeier *(Mgr)*

Diesel Power Open Cast Mining (Pty) Limited **(1)**
126 Tenth Rd Kew
Sandton, Johannesburg, Gauteng, 2090, South Africa
Tel.: (27) 11 882 2665
Fax: (27) 11 882 3045
Mining & Earthmoving Contract Services
S.I.C.: 1081
N.A.I.C.S.: 213114
Michael Watson *(Mng Dir)*

Vukuza Earth Works (Pty) Limited **(1)**
516 Pretoria Rd
Benoni, Gauteng, 1501, South Africa
Tel.: (27) 119689300
Fax: (27) 119681143
Contract Mining Services
S.I.C.: 1481
N.A.I.C.S.: 213115
Kobus Van Biljon *(Mgr-Fin)*

Wit Deep Sand and Stone (Pty) Limited **(1)**
320 Main Reef Rd Knights
Germiston, Gauteng, 1413, South Africa
Tel.: (27) 861 948 3337
Fax: (27) 866 738 382
E-Mail: orders@witdeep.co.za
Construction Materials Distr
S.I.C.: 5211
N.A.I.C.S.: 444190
Geoff Jordaan *(Mng Dir)*
Gillian Miller *(Sec)*

BUKIT SEMBAWANG ESTATES LTD

250 Tanjong Pagar Road 09-01 St Andrew's Centre
Singapore, 088541, Singapore
Tel.: (65) 68900333
Fax: (65) 65361858
E-Mail: bsel@bukitsembawang.sg
Web Site: www.bukitsembawang.sg
Year Founded: 1967
B61—(SES)
Rev.: $287,159,489
Assets: $1,009,968,922
Liabilities: $71,098,810
Net Worth: $938,870,112
Earnings: $92,824,954
Fiscal Year-end: 03/31/13

Business Description:
Holding Company
S.I.C.: 6719
N.A.I.C.S.: 551112

Personnel:
Chee Seng Ng *(CEO)*
Guat Ngoh Tan *(Sec)*

Board of Directors:
Samuel Chin Huat Guok
Chien Shih Lee
Chee Seng Ng
Swee Siong Tan
Eddie Tang
Kim Yam Teo

Subsidiaries:

Bukit Sembawang Rubber Company Limited **(1)**
250 Tanjong Pagar Rd Unit X09-01
St Andrews Centre, Singapore, 088541, Singapore
Tel.: (65) 68900333
Fax: (65) 65361858
E-Mail: bsel@bukitsembawang.com.sg
Web Site: www.bukitsembawang.com.sg
Emp.: 20
Financial & Investments Services
S.I.C.: 6211
N.A.I.C.S.: 523999
Chee Seng Ng *(Gen Mgr)*

Subsidiaries:

Singapore United Estates (Private) Limited **(2)**
250 Tanjong Pagar Rd 09-01
St Andrew's Ctr, Singapore, 088541, Singapore
Tel.: (65) 68900333
Fax: (65) 65361858
E-Mail: bsel@bukitsembawang.sg
Emp.: 30
Property Development Services
S.I.C.: 6519
N.A.I.C.S.: 531190

Singapore United Rubber Plantations Limited **(2)**
250 Tanjong Pagar Rd
09-01 St.Andrews Ctr, 088541 Singapore, Singapore
Tel.: (65) 68900333
Fax: (65) 65361858
E-Mail: bsel@bukitsembawang.sg
Emp.: 30
Financial & Investments Services
S.I.C.: 6211
N.A.I.C.S.: 523999
Chee Seng Ng *(CEO)*

Bukit Sembawang View Pte Ltd **(1)**
250 Cheng yung Paga Rd 6 09-01
St.Andrew tower
Singapore, 088541, Singapore
Tel.: (65) 68900333
Fax: (65) 65361858
E-Mail: bsel@bukitsembawang.sg
Web Site: www.bukitsembawang.sg
Emp.: 25
Property Development Services
S.I.C.: 6519
N.A.I.C.S.: 531190
Ng Chee *(Mng Dir)*

BUKWANG PHARMACEUTICAL CO., LTD.

398-1 Daebang-dong
Dongjak-gu, Seoul, Korea (South) 156-811
Tel.: (82) 28288114
Fax: (82) 28288029
Web Site: www.bukwang.co.kr
Year Founded: 1960
003000—(KRS)

Business Description:
Pharmaceutical Products Mfr & Sales
S.I.C.: 2834
N.A.I.C.S.: 325412

Personnel:
Dong yeon Kim *(Chm)*
Chang soo Jung *(Vice Chm)*
Sung Koo Lee *(Pres & CEO)*

Board of Directors:
Dong yeon Kim
Chang soo Jung
Chung Ho Kim
Tae Hyun Kim
Chang Hwi Koo
Sung Koo Lee
Won Tae Park
Chul Ho Rim
In Myoung Yeo

BULGARIAN AMERICAN CREDIT BANK AD

2 Slavyanska Str
Sofia, Bulgaria
Tel.: (359) 2965 83 58
Web Site: www.bacb.bg
5BN—(BUL)

Business Description:
Financial & Insurance Services
S.I.C.: 6099
N.A.I.C.S.: 522320

Personnel:
Tzvetelina Borislavova Karagyozova *(Chm-Supervisory Bd)*
Vassil Stefanov Simov *(Chm-Mgmt Bd)*
Marshall L. Miller *(Deputy Chm-Supervisory Bd)*
Ilian Petrov Georgiev *(Member-Mgmt Bd)*
Silvia Kirilova *(Member-Mgmt Bd)*

Supervisory Board of Directors:
Tzvetelina Borislavova Karagyozova
Jason Lyle Cook
Martin Boychev Ganev
Evgeni Ivanov
Kiril Manov
Marshall L. Miller

Subsidiary:

Imoti Direct REIT **(1)**
16 Krakra Str
Sofia, 1504, Bulgaria
Tel.: (359) 2 9658 345
Fax: (359) 2 9445 010
E-Mail: zmihailova@bacb.bg
Web Site: www.imoti-direct.bg
Investment Management Services
S.I.C.: 6799
N.A.I.C.S.: 523920
Daniela Atanasova Handjieva *(Chm)*
Yordan Nikolov Chompalov *(Vice Chm)*

BULGARIAN NATIONAL BANK

1 Alexander Battenberg Square
1000 Sofia, Bulgaria
Tel.: (359) 291459
Fax: (359) 29802425
E-Mail: press_office@bnbank.org
Web Site: www.bnb.bg
Sales Range: $350-399.9 Million
Emp.: 932

Business Description:
Banking Services
S.I.C.: 6011
N.A.I.C.S.: 521110

Personnel:
Dimitar Kostov *(Deputy Governor-Banking Dept)*
Petko Krastev *(Sec)*

Board of Directors:
Dimitar Kostov
Oleg Nedyalkov
Nikolay Nenovsky
Statty Stattev

BULGARIAN RIVER SHIPPING J.S.CO.

Otetz Paisii sq No 2
7000 Ruse, Bulgaria
Tel.: (359) 82 833777
Fax: (359) 82 822130
E-Mail: main@brp.bg
Web Site: www.brp.bg
5BR—(BUL)

Business Description:
Transportation Services
S.I.C.: 4789
N.A.I.C.S.: 488999

Personnel:
Diana Ivanova Pavlova *(Dir-IR)*

BULGARIAN STOCK EXCHANGE - SOFIA AD

6 Tri ushi St
1303 Sofia, Bulgaria
Tel.: (359) 2 937 09 34
Fax: (359) 2 937 09 46
E-Mail: bse@bse-sofia.bg
Web Site: www.bse-sofia.bg
Year Founded: 1997
BSO—(BUL)
Rev.: $1,985,568
Assets: $8,552,636
Liabilities: $1,206,378
Net Worth: $7,346,258

Earnings: $416,935
Emp.: 30
Fiscal Year-end: 12/31/12
Business Description:
Security Exchange
S.I.C.: 6231
N.A.I.C.S.: 523210
Personnel:
Asen Yagodin *(Chm)*
Vasil Golemanski *(Vice Chm & Co-CEO)*
Ivan Takev *(Co-CEO & Dir-IT)*
Board of Directors:
Asen Yagodin
Lyubomir Boyadzhiev
Georgi Bylgarski
Vasil Golemanski
Ivan Takev

Subsidiary:

Balkan Services Ltd. (1)
31 Ekzarh Yossif Str
1000 Sofia, Bulgaria
Tel.: (359) 2 9809599
Fax: (359) 2 9811517
E-Mail: info@balkanservices.com
Web Site: www.balkanservices.com
Information Technology Consulting Services
S.I.C.: 7373
N.A.I.C.S.: 541512
Philip Mutafis *(Mng Partner)*
Vladimir Rashev, *(Mng Partner)*

BULGARTABAC HOLDING A.D.

62 Graf Ignatiev Str
1000 Sofia, Bulgaria
Tel.: (359) 29306803
Fax: (359) 29306830
E-Mail: info@bulgartabac.bg
Web Site: www.bulgartabac.bg
57B—(BUL)
Rev.: $328,104,606
Assets: $421,344,259
Liabilities: $166,737,091
Net Worth: $254,607,168
Earnings: $61,372,832
Emp.: 2,109
Fiscal Year-end: 12/31/12
Business Description:
Holding Company; Tobacco Products Mfr & Retailer
S.I.C.: 6719
N.A.I.C.S.: 551112
Personnel:
Alexander Jurjevich Romanov *(Chm)*
Docho Minev Karadochev *(Chm-Mgmt Bd)*
Yarov Nikolaev Draganov *(Vice Chm)*
Georgi Serafimov Kostov *(Deputy Chm-Mgmt Bd)*
Korneliya Petrova Ninova *(Mng Dir)*
Nikolay Simeonov Malinov *(Member-Mgmt Bd)*
Rumen Andonov Porojanov *(Member-Mgmt Bd)*
Asen Yosifov Shehov *(Member-Mgmt Bd)*
Board of Directors:
Alexander Jurjevich Romanov
Ventzislav Zlatkov Cholakov
Angel Dimitrov Dimitrov
Yarov Nikolaev Draganov
Miglena Petrova Hristova

Subsidiaries:

Blagoevgrad-BT AD (1)
ul Pokrovnishko Shosse 1
2700 Blagoevgrad, Bulgaria
Tel.: (359) 73884826
Fax: (359) 73884815
E-Mail: blbt@blagoevgrad-bt.com
Web Site: www.blagoevgrad-bt.com
Emp.: 930
Tobacco Products Mfr
S.I.C.: 2131
N.A.I.C.S.: 312230
George Kaosteov *(Gen Mgr)*

Bulgartabac-Trading AD (1)
62 Graf Ignatiev St
1000 Sofia, Bulgaria
Tel.: (359) 29306847
E-Mail: m.kancheva@bulgartabac.bg
Tobacco Products Mfr
S.I.C.: 2131
N.A.I.C.S.: 312230
Mariana Kancheva *(Gen Mgr)*

Pleven-BT AD (1)
Selo Yasen Plains vlg
Pleven, 5850, Bulgaria
Tel.: (359) 64903258
Fax: (359) 64903193
E-Mail: pbt@pleven-bt.com
Web Site: www.pleven-bt.com
Tobacco Processing Services
S.I.C.: 2131
N.A.I.C.S.: 312230

Sofia-BT A.D. (1)
Bul Tzar Boris III 134
Sofia, 1618, Bulgaria
Tel.: (359) 28189350
Fax: (359) 28558011
E-Mail: sofiabt@sofia.bulgartabac.bg
Web Site: www.sofia-bt.com
Emp.: 500
Cigarette Mfr
S.I.C.: 2131
N.A.I.C.S.: 312230
Dilyana Mihaylova *(Gen Mgr)*

Yambol-Tabac A.D. (1)
7 Yambolen St
8600 Yambol, Yambol, Bulgaria
Tel.: (359) 46 661782
Tobacco Products Mfr
S.I.C.: 2131
N.A.I.C.S.: 312230

BULL S.A.

Rue Jean Jaures
BP 68
78340 Les Clayes-sous-Bois, France
Tel.: (33) 130807000
Fax: (33) 130807373
Web Site: www.bull.com
Year Founded: 1931
BULL—(EUR)
Rev.: $1,730,097,684
Assets: $1,178,167,984
Liabilities: $906,107,027
Net Worth: $272,060,957
Earnings: $35,673,505
Emp.: 9,300
Fiscal Year-end: 12/31/12
Business Description:
Computer Integrated Systems Design; IT Consultancy Services Import Export
S.I.C.: 7373
N.A.I.C.S.: 541512
Personnel:
Philippe Vannier *(Chm & CEO)*
Marie-Piere de Bailliencourt *(Deputy CEO)*
Board of Directors:
Philippe Vannier
Valerie Irene Amelie Monique Bernis
Marc Blanchet
Henri Conze
Marc Heriard Dubreuil
Dominique Lesourd
Anne Marechal
Jean-Francois Rambicur
Alexandra Soto
Philippe Vassor

Deloitte & Associes
185 avenue Charles-de-Gaulle
Neuilly-sur-Seine, France

Subsidiaries:

AGARIK SAS (1)
20 rue Dieumegard
93400 Saint-Ouen, France
Tel.: (33) 140105878
Fax: (33) 140105878
Web Site: www.agarik.com
Web Hosting Services
S.I.C.: 7374
N.A.I.C.S.: 518210

Amesys S.A. (1)
1030 Avenue Guillibert de la Lauziere
ZI Des Milles, F-13080 Aix-en-Provence, France FR
Mailing Address: (100%)
BP 20140
F-13794 Aix-en-Provence, Cedex 03, France
Tel.: (33) 442607000
Fax: (33) 442600026
Web Site: www.amesys.fr
Emp.: 750
Information Technology Products Developer & Technical Services
S.I.C.: 7373
N.A.I.C.S.: 541512
Beno T. Guegan *(Dir-Fin)*

Subsidiary:

Amesys International SAS (2)
1030 Avenue Guilibert the Lauziere
BP 20140
13794 Les Milles, Aix-en-Provence, France
Tel.: (33) 442607015
Fax: (33) 442607048
Emp.: 2
Software Development Services
S.I.C.: 7371
N.A.I.C.S.: 541511
Hicham El Merini *(Pres)*

Non-U.S. Subsidiary:

Amesys Canada inc. (2)
137 rue Saint-Pierre App 206
Montreal, QC, H2Y 3T5, Canada
Tel.: (514) 875-9755
Computer Equipment Repair & Maintenence Services
S.I.C.: 7699
N.A.I.C.S.: 811212

Bull International S.A.S (1)
Avenue Jean-Jaures
Les Clayes-sous-Bois, 78340, France
Tel.: (33) 130807000
Fax: (33) 130807373
Web Site: www.bull.fr
Software Development Services
S.I.C.: 7371
N.A.I.C.S.: 541511
Philippe Vannier *(Gen Dir)*

Non-U.S. Subsidiaries:

Bull Algerie (2)
Rue Yahia El-Mazouni Lotissement la Fumee Villa N 16A
El-Biar, Algiers, 16000, Algeria
Tel.: (213) 21798854
Fax: (213) 21798863
Web Site: www.bull.com
Internet Publishing Services
S.I.C.: 2741
N.A.I.C.S.: 519130

Bull d.o.o (2)
Koturaska 69
10000 Zagreb, Croatia
Tel.: (385) 16311255
Fax: (385) 16170813
E-Mail: info@bull.hr
Emp.: 3
Software Development Services
S.I.C.: 7371
N.A.I.C.S.: 541511
Ivan Giljanovic *(Gen Mgr)*

Bull Indian Ocean Ltd. (2)
1st Floor Beau Bebe Building Trianon
Quatre Bornes, 230, Mauritius
Tel.: (230) 467 0889
Fax: (230) 446 70889
Emp.: 1
Security Software Development Services
S.I.C.: 7371
N.A.I.C.S.: 541511
Eric Coquelin *(Gen Mgr)*

S.A. Bull N.V. (2)
Chausse de La Hulpe 120
1160 Brussels, Belgium
Tel.: (32) 26616111
Fax: (32) 26616891
Web Site: www.bull.com
Information Technology Consulting Services
S.I.C.: 7373
N.A.I.C.S.: 541512
Saskia Van Uttelen *(CEO)*

Subsidiary:

CSB Consulting Limited (3)
Rue Charles Lemaire 1
1160 Brussels, Belgium
Tel.: (32) 22091640
Fax: (32) 22172732
E-Mail: info@csbconsulting.com
Web Site: www.csbconsulting.com
Emp.: 98
Software Consulting Services
S.I.C.: 7373
N.A.I.C.S.: 541512

Tuscan Connects Ltd. (2)
2 Beevor Court Pontefract Road
Barnsley, South Yorkshire, S71 1HG, United Kingdom
Tel.: (44) 1226773295
Fax: (44) 1226773289
Software Development Services
S.I.C.: 7371
N.A.I.C.S.: 541511

UAB Bull Baltija (2)
7 Konstitucijos Ave
09308 Vilnius, Lithuania
Tel.: (370) 52487460
Fax: (370) 52487462
Web Site: www.bull.com
Emp.: 20
Software Development Services
S.I.C.: 7371
N.A.I.C.S.: 541511
Saulius Eiva *(Gen Mgr)*

Elexo S.A. (1)
20 Rue De Billancourt
92100 Boulogne, France
Tel.: (33) 141221000
Fax: (33) 141221001
E-Mail: info@elexo.fr
Emp.: 25
Computer Peripheral Equipment Distr
S.I.C.: 5045
N.A.I.C.S.: 423430

Evidian SA (1)
Rue Jean Jaures BP 68
78340 Les Clayes-sous-Bois, France (100%)
Tel.: (33) 130803700
Fax: (33) 130807676
Web Site: www.evidian.com
Emp.: 1,000
Security Software Services
S.I.C.: 7371
N.A.I.C.S.: 541511
Gruno Penna *(Mng Dir)*

U.S. Subsidiary:

Evidian Systems Inc (2)
111 John St Ste 1622
New York, NY 10038
Tel.: (646) 233-1239
Fax: (646) 304-2295
E-Mail: info@evidian.com
Web Site: www.evidian.com
Software Development Services
S.I.C.: 7371
N.A.I.C.S.: 541511

Non-U.S. Subsidiaries:

Eutelia (2)
Via Ai Laboratori Olivetti 79
20010 Pregnana Milanese, Milan, MI, Italy
Tel.: (39) 0246545248
Fax: (39) 0223033901
E-Mail: info@evidian.com
Web Site: www.evidian.com
Emp.: 1
Computer Hardware & Software Systems Designer
S.I.C.: 7373
N.A.I.C.S.: 541512

Evidian GmbH (2)
Von-der-Wettern-Strasse 27
51149 Cologne, Germany (100%)
Tel.: (49) 22033051325
Fax: (49) 22033051842
Web Site: www.evidian.com
Security Software Services

Bull S.A.—(Continued)

S.I.C.: 7371
N.A.I.C.S.: 541511

HRBC (1)
20 rue Dieumegard
93406 Saint-Ouen, France
Tel.: (33) 149455283
Fax: (33) 149455283
Human Resource Consulting Services
S.I.C.: 8999
N.A.I.C.S.: 541612

S.A.S. SIRUS (1)
152 Avenue du Prado
Marseille, 13008, France
Tel.: (33) 491255474
Fax: (33) 491255476
Emp.: 20
Social Program Software Development Services
S.I.C.: 7371
N.A.I.C.S.: 541511
Eric Spriet *(Mng Dir)*

Seres SA (1)
20 Rue Dieumegard
93406 Saint-Ouen, France (34%)
Tel.: (33) 149455700
Fax: (33) 149455701
Web Site: www.seres.fr
Electronic Data Services; Joint Venture of SOFIPOST (66%) & Bull SA (34%)
S.I.C.: 7379
N.A.I.C.S.: 518210

Societe Europeenne de Renovation et Reparation Informatique de Belfort (1)
25 Rue Albert Camus
PO Box 355
90006 Belfort, France (100%)
Tel.: (33) 382022800
Fax: (33) 384545554
E-Mail: contact@serrib.com
Web Site: www.serrib.com
IT Maintenance Services
S.I.C.: 7378
N.A.I.C.S.: 811212

U.S. Subsidiaries:

Bull Corporation of America (1)
285 Billerica Rd
Chelmsford, MA 01824
Tel.: (978) 294-6000
Fax: (978) 244-0085
Web Site: www.bull.com
Computer Services
S.I.C.: 5045
N.A.I.C.S.: 423430

Bull HN Information Systems Inc (1)
285 Billerica Rd Ste 200
Chelmsford, MA 01824 (80%)
Tel.: (978) 294-6000
Fax: (978) 244-0062
Web Site: www.bull.com
Emp.: 400
Computer Products & Services
S.I.C.: 3571
N.A.I.C.S.: 334111
James Custer *(Dir-Sls & Mktg)*

Non-U.S. Subsidiary:

Bull Data Systems N.V. (2)
Hogehilweg 21
PO Box 22859
1101 CB Amsterdam, Zuidoost, Netherlands (100%)
Tel.: (31) 204302111
Fax: (31) 204302930
Web Site: www.bull.nl
Emp.: 150
Computer Integrated Systems Design
S.I.C.: 7374
N.A.I.C.S.: 518210
Dick Sens *(Mng Dir)*

Subsidiary:

Bull Nederland N.V (3)
Dalsteindreef 141
1112 XG Amsterdam, Netherlands
Tel.: (31) 204302111
Fax: (31) 204302911
E-Mail: helpdesk@bull.nl
Web Site: www.bull.nl
Emp.: 110
Designer & Developer of Software & IT Infrastructure solutions
S.I.C.: 7371
N.A.I.C.S.: 541511
Deck Fens *(Gen Mgr)*

Non-U.S. Subsidiaries:

Bull AG (1)
EURO PLAZA Gebaude G Am Euro Platz 2
A 1120 Vienna, Austria (100%)
Tel.: (43) 1891360
Fax: (43) 1891363317
E-Mail: info@bull.at
Web Site: www.bull.at
Emp.: 40
Data Processing, Hosting & Related Services
S.I.C.: 7374
N.A.I.C.S.: 518210
Erich Strobl *(Mng Dir)*

Bull Cameroon (1)
Immeuble Abili Zone Industrielle d'Oloumi
BP 2260
Libreville, Gabon (100%)
Tel.: (241) 05 30 6000
Fax: (241) 03 30 6000
E-Mail: info@cameroon.bull.net
Web Site: www.bull.com
Emp.: 10
Data & Logistics Management
S.I.C.: 7379
N.A.I.C.S.: 518210

Bull Computers N.V. (1)
De Cuserstraat 91
1112 XJ Amsterdam, Netherlands (100%)
Tel.: (31) 204302111
Fax: (31) 204302930
E-Mail: info@bull.nl
Web Site: www.bull.nl
Emp.: 125
S.I.C.: 7374
N.A.I.C.S.: 518210
Dick Fens *(Gen Mgr)*

Bull Cote d'Ivoire (1)
Av Nogues
BP 1580
01 Abidjan, Cote d'Ivoire (100%)
Tel.: (225) 20213904
Fax: (225) 20211270
Web Site: www.evidian.com
Emp.: 20
S.I.C.: 7379
N.A.I.C.S.: 518210
Boukary Ouedraogo *(Mgr)*

Bull Cyprus Ltd (1)
70 Makarios III Avenue
PO Box 27269
Nicosia, Cyprus
Tel.: (357) 22374188
Fax: (357) 22374003
Designer of Information Technology Infrastructure
S.I.C.: 7379
N.A.I.C.S.: 518210

Bull do Brasil Sistemas de Informacao Ltda (1)
Rua Angelica 903
Baixo Santa Cecilia, 12907-000 Sao Paulo, Brazil
Tel.: (55) 138244700
Fax: (55) 138244500
Emp.: 200
Designer of Information Technology Infrastructure Systems & Consulting Services
S.I.C.: 7373
N.A.I.C.S.: 541512

Subsidiary:

Bull Limited (2)
Angelica Ave 903
01227 901 Sao Paulo, SP, Brazil (100%)
Tel.: (55) 11 3824 4700
Fax: (55) 11 3824 4500
E-Mail: jose.saintmartin@bull.com.br
Web Site: www.bull.com.br
Emp.: 200
Computer Integration Systems Designer
S.I.C.: 7374
N.A.I.C.S.: 518210
Alberto Lemos Araujo *(Gen Mgr)*

Non-U.S. Subsidiaries:

Bull Argentina SA (2)
Carlos Pellegrini 1363 Piso 2
1011 Buenos Aires, Argentina (100%)
Tel.: (54) 1143252016
Fax: (54) 1143255626
Web Site: www.bull.com
Emp.: 50
Distributor of Computer Hardware & Systems Integration Services
S.I.C.: 7373
N.A.I.C.S.: 541512
Roberto Furio *(Mng Dir)*

Bull Uruguay SA (2)
Av Dr Luis A De Herrerra 2802
1160 Montevideo, Uruguay (100%)
Tel.: (598) 24871169
Fax: (598) 24870587
Web Site: www.bull.com
Emp.: 100
S.I.C.: 7374
N.A.I.C.S.: 518210
Roberto Fureo *(Gen Mgr)*

Bull Egypte (1)
World Trade Center
11-13 Corniche El Nil, Cairo, Egypt (100%)
Web Site: www.bull.com
Computer Integrated Systems Design
S.I.C.: 7379
N.A.I.C.S.: 518210

Bull Espana SA (1)
Paseo de las Doce Estrellas No 2
Campo de las Naciones, 28042 Madrid, Spain
Tel.: (34) 913939392
Fax: (34) 913939395
Web Site: www.bull.es/contacto/contactar.htm
Designer & Developer of Servers & Software
S.I.C.: 7379
N.A.I.C.S.: 518210

Subsidiary:

Data System SA (2)
Paseo de las Doce Estrellas No 2
Campo de las Naciones, 28042 Madrid, Spain
Tel.: (34) 91 393 9393
Fax: (34) 91 393 9395
Web Site: www.bull.com
Designer & Developer of Servers & Software Products
S.I.C.: 7374
N.A.I.C.S.: 518210

Bull Gabon (1)
Immeuble Ex-Sonagar
BP 2260
Libreville, Gabon (100%)
Tel.: (241) 760761
E-Mail: paul.marolleau@bull.net
Web Site: www.bull.net
Emp.: 15
S.I.C.: 7379
N.A.I.C.S.: 518210
Paul Marolleau *(Mgr)*

Bull GmbH (1)
Von-der-Wettern Strasse 27
PO Box 51149
51149 Cologne, Germany (100%)
Tel.: (49) 22033050
Fax: (49) 2203305
E-Mail: info@bull.de
Web Site: www.bull.de
Emp.: 230
Designer & Developer of Servers & Software
S.I.C.: 7374
N.A.I.C.S.: 518210
Uli Richartz *(Dir-Mktg)*

Subsidiary:

science+computing A.G. (2)
Hagellocher Weg 73
72070 Tubingen, Germany
Tel.: (49) 707194570
Fax: (49) 70719457211
E-Mail: info@science-computing.de
Web Site: www.science-computing.de
Rev.: $35,228,257
Emp.: 30
Information Technology Consulting Services
S.I.C.: 7373
N.A.I.C.S.: 541512
Philippe Miltin *(Chm-Supervisory Bd)*
Gerd-Lothar Leonhart *(Chm-Exec Bd & Mgr-Mktg & Sls)*
Bernd Finkbeiner *(Mgr-IT Svcs)*
Michael Heinrichs *(Mgr-Fin)*
Ingrid Zech *(Mgr-HR)*
Arno Steitz *(Member-Exec Bd)*

Non-U.S. Subsidiaries:

Bull GmbH (2)
Euro Plaza Gebaude G Am Euro Platz 2
1120 Vienna, Austria
Tel.: (43) 1891360
Fax: (43) 1891363317
E-Mail: info@bull.at
Web Site: www.bull.at
Emp.: 28
Software Development Services
S.I.C.: 7371
N.A.I.C.S.: 541511
Michael Heinrichs *(CFO)*

Bull (Schweiz) AG (2)
Wallisellerstrasse 116
8152 Opfikon, Switzerland
Tel.: (41) 43 455 8090
Fax: (41) 43 455 8099
E-Mail: info@bull.ch
Web Site: www.bull.com
Emp.: 30
Software Development Services
S.I.C.: 7371
N.A.I.C.S.: 541511

Bull Information Systems (Hong Kong) Ltd. (1)
Ste 2401 24 Fl Chinachem Exchange Sq 1
Hoi Wan St
Quarry Bay, China (Hong Kong) (100%)
Tel.: (852) 28367512
Fax: (852) 28367583
Emp.: 3
Designer & Developer of Software and Servers
S.I.C.: 3652
N.A.I.C.S.: 334614

Non-U.S. Subsidiaries:

Bull Information Systems Co. Limited (Beijing) (2)
11 Floor Jing Guang Centre Office Building
Hu Jia Lou
Mail Box 8806
100020 Beijing, Chaoyang District, China
Tel.: (86) 10 6597 8001
Fax: (86) 10 6597 8021
Web Site: www.bull.com
Designer & Developer of Servers & Software Products
S.I.C.: 7379
N.A.I.C.S.: 518210

Bull Information Systems Taiwan Ltd. (2)
7 Floor 3 No 207 Section 3 Beishin Road
Shindian City, Taipei, 231, Taiwan (100%)
Tel.: (886) 289131298
Fax: (886) 289131267
Web Site: www.bull.com
Emp.: 70
Computer Integrated Systems Design; IT Consultancy Services
S.I.C.: 7374
N.A.I.C.S.: 518210

Bull Information Systems Ireland (1)
29-31 South William Street
Dublin, Ireland
Tel.: (353) 1 6794278
Fax: (353) 1 6790098
Emp.: 10
Software Development Services
S.I.C.: 7371
N.A.I.C.S.: 541511
Noel O'Duill *(Gen Mgr)*

Bull Information Systems Nigeria Ltd (1)
89, A Ajose
Adeogun St 401 Rd
Victoria Island, Lagos, Nigeria (100%)
Tel.: (234) 12619023
Fax: (234) 12614224
Web Site: www.bull.com
Computer Integrated Systems Design; IT Consultancy Services

S.I.C.: 7374
N.A.I.C.S.: 518210

Bull International N.V. (1)
Dalsteindreef 141
1112 XJ Diemen, Netherlands
Tel.: (31) 204302111
Fax: (31) 204302911
E-Mail: info@bull.nl
Web Site: www.bull.nl
Emp.: 100
Computer Integrated Systems Design
S.I.C.: 7374
N.A.I.C.S.: 518210
Dick Fens *(Gen Mgr)*

Non-U.S. Subsidiary:

Bull Italia SpA (2)
Via Egeo 100 106
00144 Rome, Italy
Tel.: (39) 06830331
Fax: (39) 0683033517
Web Site: www.bull.it
Emp.: 200
Designer of Information Technology Infrastructure & Services
S.I.C.: 7371
N.A.I.C.S.: 541511

Bull Madagascar S.A. (1)
12 Rue Indira Gandhi
BP 252
Tsaralalana, 101 Antananarivo, Madagascar (100%)
Tel.: (261) 2222407
Fax: (261) 202223373
Web Site: www.bull.com
Emp.: 26
S.I.C.: 7374
N.A.I.C.S.: 518210

Bull Middle East Pte. Ltd. (1)
18 Kyriakou Matsis Ave
PO Box 27299
Nicosia, 1643, Cyprus (100%)
Tel.: (357) 22 449933
Fax: (357) 22 449931
Web Site: www.bull.com
Designer of Information Technology Infrastructure Systems
S.I.C.: 7379
N.A.I.C.S.: 518210

Bull Morocco (1)
Technopark Rte Nouacar 2 Fl
BP 2218
20150 Casablanca, Morocco (100%)
Tel.: (212) 22529030
Fax: (212) 22505810
Web Site: www.bull.com
Emp.: 50
S.I.C.: 7379
N.A.I.C.S.: 518210

Bull PFS S.A. (1)
40 Rue Pafebruch
8308 Capellen, Luxembourg
Tel.: (352) 4569451
Fax: (352) 458017
E-Mail: info@bull.com
Web Site: www.bull.com
Emp.: 45
Software Development Services
S.I.C.: 7371
N.A.I.C.S.: 541511
Georg Schlegel *(Country Mgr)*

Bull Polska sp. z.o.o. (1)
Saski Crescent ul Krolewska 16
00-103 Warsaw, Poland
Tel.: (48) 224334900
Fax: (48) 222106570
Software Development Services
S.I.C.: 7371
N.A.I.C.S.: 541511
Miron Niewiadomski *(Mgr-PR)*

Bull SAL (1)
69 Rue Jal El Dib
PO Box 60208
Secteur 1, Beirut, Lebanon (95%)
Tel.: (961) 4712855
Fax: (961) 4712856
E-Mail: info@bull.com.lb
Web Site: www.bull.com
Emp.: 15
Computer Integrated Systems Design; IT Consultancy Services
S.I.C.: 7374
N.A.I.C.S.: 518210
Francois Lorho *(Gen Mgr)*

CSB Consulting Limited (1)
Orco House 40 Parc Activites de Capellen
8308 Capellen, Luxembourg
Tel.: (352) 26187598
Fax: (352) 4569456312
Information Technology Consulting Services
S.I.C.: 7373
N.A.I.C.S.: 541512

Evidian UK (1)
Maxted Road
Hemel Hempstead, Herts, HP2 7DZ, United Kingdom
Tel.: (44) 1442 411258
Software Development Services
S.I.C.: 7371
N.A.I.C.S.: 541511

W. Schraml Softwarehaus GmbH (1)
Einsteinstrasse 39 A
82152 Martinsried, Germany (40%)
Tel.: (49) 898941350
Fax: (49) 8989413530
E-Mail: info@schramlsoft.de
Web Site: www.schramlsoft.de
Emp.: 15
Custom Computer Programming Services
S.I.C.: 7371
N.A.I.C.S.: 541511
Wolfking Schraml *(Mng Dir)*

BULLABULLING GOLD LIMITED

Level 2 55 Carringotn St
Nedlands, WA, 6009, Australia
Tel.: (61) 8 9386 4086
Fax: (61) 8 9389 8327
E-Mail: info@bullabullinggold.com
Web Site: www.bullabullinggold.com
Year Founded: 2011
BAB—(AIM ASX)
Business Description:
Gold Exploration & Mining Services
S.I.C.: 1081
N.A.I.C.S.: 213114
Personnel:
Peter Mansell *(Chm)*
Brett Lambert *(Mng Dir)*
David Maxwell McArthur *(CFO)*
Board of Directors:
Peter Mansell
Ronnie Beevor
Brett Lambert
David Maxwell McArthur
Timothy Carl Netscher

BULLETIN RESOURCES LIMITED

Unit A8 Level 1 435 Roberts Road
Subiaco, WA, 6008, Australia
Mailing Address:
PO Box 894
Subiaco, WA, 6904, Australia
Tel.: (61) 8 9388 6921
Fax: (61) 8 6316 3337
E-Mail: admin@bulletinresources.com
Web Site: www.bulletinresources.com
Year Founded: 2010
BNR—(ASX)
Rev.: $250,214
Assets: $1,563,091
Liabilities: $497,616
Net Worth: $1,065,474
Earnings: ($3,993,165)
Fiscal Year-end: 06/30/13
Business Description:
Gold Mining Services
S.I.C.: 1041
N.A.I.C.S.: 212221
Personnel:
Frank Sibbel *(Chm)*
Craig Nelmes *(Sec)*
Board of Directors:
Frank Sibbel
Andrew Beckwith
Michael Fitzgerald
Legal Counsel:
Steinepreis Paganin
Level 4 The Read Buildings 16 Milligan Street
Perth, Australia

BULLION GOLD RESOURCES CORP.

(Formerly TIEX Inc.)
102 - 1949 Beach Avenue
Vancouver, BC, V1Y 8H2, Canada
Tel.: (604) 763-4848
Fax: (604) 683-6350
Web Site: www.bulliongold.ca
Year Founded: 2005
BGD—(TSXV)
Sales Range: Less than $1 Million
Business Description:
Mineral Exploration Services
S.I.C.: 1081
N.A.I.C.S.: 213114
Personnel:
Terry Severs *(CEO)*
Randy Minhas *(CFO)*
Board of Directors:
Wade N. Black
John Bucklc
Kurt J. Hoffman
David Mark
Terry Severs

BULLMAN MINERALS INC.

Suite 308 595 Howe Street
Vancouver, BC, V6C 2T5, Canada
Tel.: (604) 718-2800
Fax: (604) 718-2808
Year Founded: 2010
BUL—(TSXV)
Rev.: $770
Assets: $65,180
Liabilities: $13,548
Net Worth: $51,632
Earnings: ($108,706)
Fiscal Year-end: 11/30/12
Business Description:
Financial Managament Services
S.I.C.: 6211
N.A.I.C.S.: 523999
Personnel:
Peter Yue *(CEO, CFO & Sec)*
Board of Directors:
Garnet Dawson
Don H. C. Ho
Peter Yue
Transfer Agent:
Computershare Investor Services Inc.
510 Burrard Street 2nd Floor
Vancouver, BC, V6C 3B9, Canada

BULLOCK CONSTRUCTION LIMITED

Northgate Aldridge
Walsall, West Midlands, WS9 8TU, United Kingdom
Tel.: (44) 1922 458 311
Fax: (44) 1922 459 589
E-Mail: bcl-marketing@bullock.co.uk
Web Site: www.bullock.co.uk
Year Founded: 1955
Sales Range: $10-24.9 Million
Emp.: 604
Business Description:
Contstruction Engineering Services
S.I.C.: 8711
N.A.I.C.S.: 541330
Personnel:
Ian Burnett *(CEO)*
Martyn Vitty *(Sec & Dir-Fin)*
Board of Directors:
Richard Baker
Martyn Vitty

BULVESTA HOLDING AD

Vitosha VEC Simeonovo 999
1700 Sofia, Bulgaria
Tel.: (359) 2 962 87 68
Fax: (359) 2 962 87 58
E-Mail: b.v.h@vivesta-bg.com
Web Site: www.bulvesta-bg.com
5BV—(BUL)
Business Description:
Investment Management Services
S.I.C.: 6282
N.A.I.C.S.: 523930
Personnel:
Victor Angelov Serov *(Chm & Exec Mgr)*
Board of Directors:
Victor Angelov Serov
Krasimir Kocev

BUMI ARMADA BERHAD

Level 21 Menara Perak 24 Jalan Perak
50450 Kuala Lumpur, Malaysia
Tel.: (60) 3 2171 5799
Fax: (60) 3 2163 5799
Web Site: www.bumiarmada.com
ARMADA—(KLS)
Rev.: $544,079,617
Assets: $2,272,406,571
Liabilities: $1,037,128,324
Net Worth: $1,235,278,247
Earnings: $127,238,863
Emp.: 621
Fiscal Year-end: 12/31/12
Business Description:
Marine Transportation Services
S.I.C.: 4412
N.A.I.C.S.: 483111
Personnel:
Hassan Assad Basma *(CEO)*
Navdeep Jain *(Deputy CFO)*
Kenneth Murdoch *(CFO)*
Chakib Abi-Saab *(CIO)*
Madhusudanan Madasery Balan *(Chief Talent Officer)*
Khien Ngoh Lo *(Gen Counsel)*
Noor Hamiza Abd Hamid *(Co-Sec)*
Ann Nee Chew *(Co-Sec)*
Massimiliano Bellotti *(Sr VP-T&I)*
Eric Guan Huat Choong *(Sr VP-Strategic Procurement)*
Jonathan Edward Duckett *(Sr VP-Corp Plng)*
Andrew Day Lamshed *(Sr VP-Floating Production Sys)*
Adriaan Petrus Van De Korput *(Sr VP-Major Projects)*
Yam Khoon Wee *(Sr VP-OSV)*
Board of Directors:
Tunku Ali Redhauddin Tuanku Muhriz
Hassan Assad Basma
Chee Beng Chan
Ghee Keong Lim
Ahmad Fuad Md Ali
Alexandra Elisabeth Johanna Maria Schaapveld
Saiful Aznir Shahabudin
Andrew Philip Whittle

Subsidiary:

Bumi Armada Engineering Sdn Bhd (1)
Level 21 Menara Perak 24 Jalan Perak
50450 Kuala Lumpur, Malaysia
Tel.: (60) 3 21715799
Fax: (60) 3 21715770
E-Mail: bumiarmada@bumiarmada.com
Web Site: www.bumiarmada.com
Offshore Engineering Services
S.I.C.: 8711
N.A.I.C.S.: 541330

BUMI PLC

Atlas House 3rd floor 173 Victoria Street
London, SW1E 5NH, United Kingdom
Tel.: (44) 207 201 7500
Fax: (44) 207 201 7501
E-Mail: info@bumiplc.com

Bumi plc—(Continued)

Web Site: www.bumi-plc.com
BUMI—(LSE)
Rev.: $1,531,000,000
Assets: $5,141,000,000
Liabilities: $3,182,000,000
Net Worth: $1,959,000,000
Earnings: ($2,541,000,000)
Emp.: 1,245
Fiscal Year-end: 12/31/12
Business Description:
Holding Company; Coal Mining
S.I.C.: 6719
N.A.I.C.S.: 551112
Personnel:
Samin Tan *(Chm)*
Julian Michael Horn-Smith *(Deputy Chm)*
Nick von Schirnding *(CEO)*
Scott Andrew Merrillees *(CFO)*
Paul Vickers *(Gen Counsel & Sec)*
Board of Directors:
Samin Tan
Richard Gozney
Graham Ian Holdaway
Julian Michael Horn-Smith
Scott Andrew Merrillees
Alexander Ramlie
Amir Sambodo
Steven Shapiro
Nick von Schirnding
Legal Counsel:
Freshfields Bruckhaus Deringer LLP
65 Fleet Street
London, United Kingdom

BUMITAMA AGRI LTD.

10 Anson Road 11-19 International Plaza
Singapore, 079903, Singapore
Tel.: (65) 6222 1332
Fax: (65) 6222 1336
Web Site: www.bumitama-agri.com
P8Z—(SES)
Rev.: $352,554,600
Assets: $908,912,700
Liabilities: $380,206,500
Net Worth: $528,706,200
Earnings: $90,182,000
Fiscal Year-end: 12/31/12
Business Description:
Crude Palm Oil & Palm Kernel Production
S.I.C.: 0119
N.A.I.C.S.: 111120
Personnel:
Gunawan Hariyanto Lim *(Chm & CEO)*
Hariyanto Lim Gunardi *(Deputy CEO)*
Sie Eddy Kurniawan *(CFO)*
Johannes Tanuwijaya *(Chief Strategy Officer)*
Busarakham Koshikaporn *(Co-Sec)*
Lei Mui Toh *(Co-Sec)*
Board of Directors:
Gunawan Hariyanto Lim
Christopher Chun Guan Chua
Hariyanto Lim Gunardi
Yeow Chor Lee
Chan Hwa Ong
Boon Hoo Tan

BUMRUNGRAD HOSPITAL PUBLIC COMPANY LIMITED

33 Sukhumvit 3 Soi Nana Nua
Wattana, Bangkok, 10110, Thailand
Tel.: (66) 2 667 1000
Fax: (66) 2 667 2525
E-Mail: info@bumrungrad.com
Web Site: www.bumrungrad.com
BH—(THA)
Rev.: $465,199,434
Assets: $525,499,909
Liabilities: $247,620,840
Net Worth: $277,879,070
Earnings: $88,372,647
Emp.: 4,700
Fiscal Year-end: 12/31/12
Business Description:
Hospital Service
S.I.C.: 8062
N.A.I.C.S.: 622110
Personnel:
Chai Sophonpanich *(Chm)*
Chanvit Tanphiphat *(Vice Chm)*
Dennis Michael Brown *(CEO)*
Linda Lisahapanya *(Mng Dir)*
Kenneth Beasley Love, Jr. *(Acting CFO-Bumrungrad International Hospital)*
Karen Carter *(COO)*
Kamonsak Reungjarearnrung *(Chief Admin Officer-Bumrungrad International Hospital)*
Varanya Seupsuk *(Chief Admin Officer-Bumrungrad International Hospital)*
Artirat Charukitpipat *(Chief People Officer-Bumrungrad International Hospital)*
Phawinee Rujpattanakul *(Chief Nursing Officer-Bumrungrad International Hospital)*
James Matthew Banner *(CEO-Bumrungrad International Hospital)*
Banphot Kittikinglert *(Sec)*
Board of Directors:
Chai Sophonpanich
Sinn Anuras
Prin Chirathivat
Dhanit Dheandhanoo
Aruni Kettratad
Linda Lisahapanya
Chanvit Tanphiphat
Chong Toh
Sophavadee Uttamobol
Suvarn Valaisathien
Soradis Vinyaratn

Subsidiary:

Bumrungrad Medical Center Ltd. (BMC) **(1)**
33 Sukhumvit 3 Soi Nana Nua
Klongtoey Nua, Bangkok, 10110, Thailand (100%)
Tel.: (66) 26671000
Fax: (66) 26672525
E-Mail: info@bumrungrad.com
Web Site: www.bumrungrad.com
Emp.: 4,000
Gen Medical & Surgical Hospitals
S.I.C.: 8062
N.A.I.C.S.: 622110
Curtis Schroeder *(CEO)*

BUNDESDRUCKEREI GMBH

Oranienstrasse 91
D 109 69 Berlin, Germany
Tel.: (49) 3025980
Fax: (49) 3025982205
E-Mail: info@bundesdruckerei.de
Web Site: www.bundesdruckerei.de
Sales Range: $500-549.9 Million
Emp.: 1,682
Business Description:
Mfr of Secure Identification Systems;
S.I.C.: 7373
N.A.I.C.S.: 541512
Personnel:
Detlef Bachler *(Vice Chm-Supervisory Bd)*
Ulrich Hamann *(CEO)*
Christian Helfrich *(CFO)*
Supervisory Board of Directors:
Detlef Bachler
Claudia Eckert
Hans Georg Fabritius
Werner Gatzer
Bettina Grat
August Hanning
Bruno Kahl
Andreas Kohn
Joerg Plantikow
Joachim Rosemann
Matthias von Fintel

BUNKA SHUTTER CO., LTD.

1-17-3 Nishikata Bunkyo-ku
Tokyo, 113-8535, Japan
Tel.: (81) 358447200
Fax: (81) 358447201
Web Site: www.bunka-s.co.jp
Year Founded: 1955
5930—(TKS)
Sls.: $1,242,142,000
Assets: $1,052,524,000
Liabilities: $620,466,000
Net Worth: $432,058,000
Earnings: $74,074,000
Emp.: 3,296
Fiscal Year-end: 03/31/13
Business Description:
Shutter Mfr
S.I.C.: 3442
N.A.I.C.S.: 332321
Personnel:
Kingo Iwabe *(Chm)*
Tetsuya Mogi *(Pres)*
Satoru Fujiyama *(Mng Operating Officer)*
Atsushi Kushiro *(Sr Operating Officer)*
Hiroyuki Ogura *(Sr Operating Officer)*
Yoshinori Shimamura *(Sr Operating Officer)*
Toshihiko Shiozaki *(Exec Operating Officer)*
Yoshio Yabuki *(Mng Operating Officer)*
Board of Directors:
Kingo Iwabe
Satoru Fujiyama
Atsushi Kushiro
Tetsuya Mogi
Hiroyuki Ogura
Yoshinori Shimamura
Toshihiko Shiozaki
Yoshio Yabuki

Subsidiaries:

Aiwa Insurance Service Co., Ltd. **(1)**
TM21 Bldg 1-53-2 Itabashi
Itabashi-ku, Tokyo, Japan
Tel.: (81) 359444350
Fax: (81) 359444352
Casualty Insurance Services
S.I.C.: 6351
N.A.I.C.S.: 524126

Bunka Kougei Co., Ltd. **(1)**
2-6-5 Shibashimo
Kawaguchi, Saitama, 333-0848, Japan
Tel.: (81) 482684711
Fax: (81) 48 268 3533
E-Mail: hp_support@b-kougei.com
Web Site: www.b-Kougei.com
Household Furnitures Retailer
S.I.C.: 5021
N.A.I.C.S.: 423210

Bunka Panel Kogyo Co., Ltd. **(1)**
5-16-8 Minami Suita
Suita, Osaka, 564-0043, Japan
Tel.: (81) 663396115
Shutters Mfr
S.I.C.: 3442
N.A.I.C.S.: 332321

BX Koun Co., Ltd. **(1)**
37-2 Shimobutai Aza
Inuyama, Aichi, 484-0953, Japan
Tel.: (81) 568670661
Web Site: www.bunka-s.co.jp/english/outline/index.html
Household Furnitures Retailer
S.I.C.: 5712
N.A.I.C.S.: 442110

Okinawa Bunka Shutter Co., Ltd **(1)**
667 Aza Nesabu
Tomigusuku, Okinawa, Japan
Tel.: (81) 988506116
Fax: (81) 988506141
Emp.: 40
Metal Service Centers & Other Metal Merchant Whslr
S.I.C.: 5051
N.A.I.C.S.: 423510
Sayoko Takara *(Mng Dir)*

Shinsei Seiki Co., Ltd **(1)**
687 Kamodani-cho
Kasai, Hyogo, Japan
Tel.: (81) 790441161
Fax: (81) 790442271
Web Site: www.shinseiseiki.co.jp
Emp.: 100
Metal Service Centers & Other Metal Merchant Whslr
S.I.C.: 5051
N.A.I.C.S.: 423510
Kiyokazu Kokado *(Pres)*

Tenpal Co., Ltd. **(1)**
2nd Floor Shinjuku Toho Bldg
1-29-8 Takadanobaba, Tokyo, Japan
Tel.: (81) 332074901
Fax: (81) 332078631
E-Mail: info@tenpal.co.jp
Web Site: www.tenpal.co.jp
Emp.: 100
Canvas & Related Product Mills
S.I.C.: 2394
N.A.I.C.S.: 314910
Koga Akihiro *(Pres)*

TR Kenzai Co., Ltd. **(1)**
753 Aza Nishihara Hiratsuka
Ageo, Saitama, 362-0011, Japan
Tel.: (81) 48 771 3710
Web Site: www.bunka-s.co.jp/english/outline/index.html
Home Remodeling Services
S.I.C.: 1522
N.A.I.C.S.: 236118

Yutori Form Co., Ltd. **(1)**
1-42-18 Itabashi
Itabashi-ku, Tokyo, 173-0004, Japan
Tel.: (81) 369055321
Fax: (81) 3 6905 5328
Web Site: www.yutoriform.com
Emp.: 350
Remodeling Services
S.I.C.: 1522
N.A.I.C.S.: 236118
Hiroaki Oosawa *(Pres)*

Non-U.S. Subsidiary:

BUNKA-VIET NAM Co., Ltd. **(1)**
Plot C9 Thang Long Industrial Park II
Yen My, Hung Yen, Vietnam
Tel.: (84) 3213974580
Fax: (84) 3213974581
E-Mail: info@bunkavietnam.com
Web Site: www.bunka.vn
Emp.: 33
Shutters & Door Mfr & Whslr
S.I.C.: 3442
N.A.I.C.S.: 332321
Sato Eiichiro *(Mng Dir)*

BUNZL PLC

York House 45 Seymour Street
London, W1H 7JT, United Kingdom
Tel.: (44) 2077255000
Fax: (44) 2077255001
Web Site: www.bunzl.com
Year Founded: 1940
BNZL—(LSE)
Rev.: $8,463,730,968
Assets: $4,645,007,748
Liabilities: $3,246,546,453
Net Worth: $1,398,461,295
Earnings: $308,435,337
Emp.: 11,738
Fiscal Year-end: 12/31/12
Business Description:
Holding Company; Outsourcing & Distribution Services
Import Export
S.I.C.: 6719
N.A.I.C.S.: 551112
Personnel:
Michael J. Roney *(CEO)*

Patrick L. Larmon *(Pres/CEO-North America)*
Paul N. Hussey *(Gen Counsel & Sec)*
Board of Directors:
Philip Graham Rogerson
Peter Johnson
Patrick L. Larmon
Brian May
Meinie Oldersma
Jean-Charles Pauze
Michael J. Roney
David Sleath
Eugenia M. Ulasewicz

Subsidiary:

Bunzl UK Ltd (1)
Ellerslie Square Industrial Estate Unit 9
London, SW2 5DZ, United Kingdom
Tel.: (44) 2077339771
Fax: (44) 20 7473 5897
Janitorial Services
S.I.C.: 7349
N.A.I.C.S.: 561720

Unit:

Greenham (1)
Greenham House 671 London Rd
Isleworth, Mddx, TW7 4EX, United Kingdom (100%)
Tel.: (44) 2085601244
Fax: (44) 2085688423
E-Mail: national.sales@greenham.co.uk
Web Site: www.greenham.com
Emp.: 900
Personal Protection Equipment, Construction Tools, Cleaning & Hygiene & Maintenance Products Supplier
S.I.C.: 7389
N.A.I.C.S.: 425120
C. Budge *(Mng Dir)*

U.S. Subsidiaries:

Bunzl USA Holdings Corporation (1)
1 City Place Dr Ste 200
Saint Louis, MO 63141
Tel.: (314) 997-5959
Fax: (314) 997-1405
Web Site: www.bunzldistribution.com
Emp.: 150
Packaging Materials Distr
S.I.C.: 5113
N.A.I.C.S.: 424130
Patrick Larmon *(Pres & CEO)*

Subsidiary:

Bunzl USA, Inc. (2)
One Cityplace Dr Ste 200
Saint Louis, MO 63141
Tel.: (314) 997-5959
Fax: (314) 997-1405
Toll Free: (888) 997-5959
Web Site: www.bunzldistribution.com
Emp.: 100
Fabricated Plastic Products Mfr; Outsourced Service Provider
S.I.C.: 5113
N.A.I.C.S.: 424130
Patrick L. Larmon *(Pres & CEO)*
Daniel Lett *(Gen Counsel)*

Subsidiaries:

Bunzl Distribution USA Inc. (3)
701 Emerson Rd Ste 500
Saint Louis, MO 63141-6754 DE
Tel.: (314) 997-5959 (100%)
Fax: (314) 997-1405
Web Site: www.bunzldistribution.com
Food Product Packaging Distr
S.I.C.: 5113
N.A.I.C.S.: 424130
Pat Larmon *(Pres & CEO)*
Mark Brasher *(Pres-Specialty Bus & Ops)*
Derek Goodin *(Exec VP-IT)*
Pat Oliverio *(Exec VP-Opers)*
Earl Engleman *(Sr VP-Corp Strategic Sourcing)*
Jane Jennewein *(Sr VP-Fin)*

Bunzl Phoenix (3)
6718 S Harl Ave Ste 106
Tempe, AZ 85283-4375
Tel.: (480) 730-9100
Fax: (480) 730-9200
Web Site: www.bunzldistribution.com
Sls.: $27,537,985
Emp.: 34
Provider of Janitorial Supplies & Related Plastic Products
S.I.C.: 5087
N.A.I.C.S.: 423850
Wally Dougles *(Gen Mgr)*

Bunzl USA (3)
3366 Walden Ave
Depew, NY 14043-2437 NY
Tel.: (716) 685-6001
Fax: (716) 685-6020
Web Site: www.bunzldistribution.com
Sales Range: $150-199.9 Million
Emp.: 60
Wholesale Distributor of Paper Products & Janitorial Supplies
Export
S.I.C.: 5113
N.A.I.C.S.: 424130

R3, LLC (3)
701 Emerson Rd
Saint Louis, MO 63141
Tel.: (314) 997-5959
Fax: (314) 997-1405
Toll Free: (800) 877-7778
Web Site: www.r3redistribution.com
Emp.: 3,500
Industrial, Food Service & Janitorial Supplies Distr
S.I.C.: 5085
N.A.I.C.S.: 423840
Patrick L. Larmon *(Pres & CEO)*

Subsidiaries:

R3 AWM (4)
2301 Lunt Ave
Elk Grove Village, IL 60007-5625 IL
Tel.: (847) 952-9000
Fax: (847) 952-9292
Web Site: www.morganscott.com
Emp.: 80
Redistributor of Paper, Plastic Aluminum & Allied Products
S.I.C.: 5085
N.A.I.C.S.: 423840
Bob Katz *(Exec VP-Mktg)*

R3 Metro South TEC (4)
1000 Amboy Ave
Perth Amboy, NJ 08861-1916 NJ
Tel.: (732) 969-8700
Fax: (732) 969-6089
Sales Range: $1-9.9 Million
Emp.: 35
Hardware & Paper Product Distr
S.I.C.: 5072
N.A.I.C.S.: 423710
David Holtzman *(Pres)*

R3 Safety (4)
105 American Way
Wilmington, OH 45177
Tel.: (937) 382-6911
Fax: (937) 382-0557
E-Mail: united@uasi.com
Web Site: www.uasi.com
Emp.: 60
Welding Machinery & Equipment Distr
S.I.C.: 5084
N.A.I.C.S.: 423830
Joseph Sodini *(VP & Gen Mgr)*

SAS Safety Corp (3)
3031 Gardenia Ave
Long Beach, CA 90807
Tel.: (562) 427-2775
Fax: (562) 427-4836
Toll Free: (800) 262-0200
E-Mail: sales@sassafety.com
Web Site: www.sassafety.com
Sales Range: $25-49.9 Million
Emp.: 60
Industrial Safety Apparel & Accessories Mfr & Distr
S.I.C.: 2399
N.A.I.C.S.: 315990
Ken Watson *(Pres & COO)*
George J. Heuser *(CEO)*
Traci S. Gomez *(CFO)*

Non-U.S. Subsidiaries:

Bunzl Australasia Ltd (1)
Suite 8 9-11 Compark Circuit
PO Box 379
Mulgrave, VIC, 3170, Australia
Tel.: (61) 395903000
Fax: (61) 395903099
E-Mail: info@bunzl.com.au
Web Site: www.bunzl.com.au
Emp.: 21
Consumer Products Distr
S.I.C.: 5099
N.A.I.C.S.: 423990
Kin Hetherington *(Mng Dir)*

Bunzl Holding GmbH (1)
Buschgrundstr 23
45894 Gelsenkirchen, Nordrhein-Westfalen, Germany
Tel.: (49) 209 93030
Fax: (49) 209 349352
Emp.: 150
Investment Management Services
S.I.C.: 6211
N.A.I.C.S.: 523999
Hans-Georg Wieskus *(Mng Dir)*

Bunzl Outsourcing Services BV (1)
Rondebeltweg 82
Almere, 1329 BG, Netherlands
Tel.: (31) 365478600
Fax: (31) 365478677
E-Mail: info@bunzl.nl
Web Site: www.bunzl.nl
Emp.: 100
Business Outsourcing Services
S.I.C.: 7389
N.A.I.C.S.: 561439
Wilco Wieling *(Gen Mgr)*

BUONGIORNO S.P.A.
(Acquired by Nippon Telegraph & Telephone Corporation)

BURBANK AUSTRALIA PTY LTD
Burbank Business Pk Aberdeen Rd
Altona, VIC, 3018, Australia
Tel.: (61) 393280333
Fax: (61) 393280222
E-Mail: info@burbank.com.au
Web Site: www.burbank.com.au
Sales Range: $25-49.9 Million
Emp.: 267
Business Description:
Single Family Home Builder
S.I.C.: 1521
N.A.I.C.S.: 236115
Personnel:
Anthony E. Sanfilippo *(CEO)*

BURBERRY GROUP PLC
Horseferry House Horseferry Road
London, SW1P 2AW, United Kingdom
Tel.: (44) 2033673000
Fax: (44) 2073182666
E-Mail: investor.relations@burberry.com
Web Site: www.burberry.com
Year Founded: 1856
BRBY—(LSE)
Rev.: $3,156,526,923
Assets: $2,757,756,198
Liabilities: $1,095,079,686
Net Worth: $1,662,676,512
Earnings: $409,351,968
Emp.: 8,867
Fiscal Year-end: 03/31/13
Business Description:
Apparel Mfr & Retailer
Export
S.I.C.: 5699
N.A.I.C.S.: 448150
Personnel:
John Wilfred Peace *(Chm)*
Angela Ahrendts *(CEO)*
Carol Fairweather *(CFO)*
John Smith *(COO)*
John Douglas *(CIO)*
Sarah Manley *(CMO)*
Christopher Bailey *(Chief Creative Officer)*
Mark Taylor *(Chief People Officer)*
Michael Mahony *(Chief Corp Affairs Officer & Gen Counsel)*
Roberto Canevari *(Chief Supply Chain Officer)*
Paul Price *(Chief Mdsg Officer)*
Steve Sacks *(Chief Customer Officer)*
Jan Heppe *(Pres-Americas)*
Andrew Maag *(CEO-Europe, Middle East, India & Africa)*
Pascal Perrier *(CEO-Asia Pacific)*
Emilio Foa *(CFO-Europe & Sr VP-Emerging Markets)*
Marco Gentile *(COO-Europe & Sr VP-Southern Europe)*
Catherine Sukmonowski *(Sec)*
Simona Cattaneo *(Sr VP-Beauty)*
Yvonne Chan *(Sr VP-Beauty & Partnership Bus-Asia Pacific)*
Jon Ehlen *(Sr VP-Beauty & Partner Bus-Americas)*
Fabrizio Fabbro *(Sr VP-Product Dev)*
Alessandro Fabrini *(Sr VP-Licensing)*
Stephen Gilbert *(Sr VP-Architecture)*
Donald Kohler *(Sr VP-Plng)*
Jenna Littler *(Sr VP-Mktg & Comm-Europe, Middle East, India & Africa)*
Matthew McEvoy *(Sr VP-Strategy & New Bus Dev)*
Marianne Naberhaus *(Sr VP-Wholesale Americas)*
Edouard Roche *(Sr VP-Mdsg-Europe)*
Board of Directors:
John Wilfred Peace
Angela Ahrendts
Philip Bowman
Ian Carter
Jeremy Darroch
Carol Fairweather
Stephanie George
Matthew Key
John Smith
David Alan Tyler

U.S. Subsidiary:

Burberry Limited (1)
444 Madison Ave
New York, NY 10022 NY
Tel.: (212) 707-6500
Fax: (212) 246-9440
E-Mail: info@burberry.com
Web Site: www.burberry.com
Emp.: 250
Apparel for Men & Women Mfr
S.I.C.: 5621
N.A.I.C.S.: 448120
John Pearce *(Chm)*
Euginia Ulasewicz *(Pres & COO)*
Virginie Costa *(CFO)*

BURCKHARDT COMPRESSION HOLDING AG
Im Link 5
PO Box 65
CH-8404 Winterthur, Switzerland
Tel.: (41) 522625500
Fax: (41) 522620051
E-Mail: info@burckhardtcompression.com
Web Site: www.burckhardtcompression.com
Year Founded: 2002
BCHN—(SWX)
Sls.: $395,761,820
Net Worth: $364,883,554
Earnings: $71,911,854
Emp.: 891
Fiscal Year-end: 03/31/13
Business Description:
Reciprocating Compressor Mfr
S.I.C.: 3563
N.A.I.C.S.: 333912
Personnel:
Marcel Pawlicek *(CEO)*
Rolf Braendli *(CFO & VP)*
Board of Directors:
Urs Fankhauser

Burckhardt Compression Holding AG—(Continued)

Hans Hess
Monika Krusi Schadle
Urs Leinhauser
Valentin Vogt

Subsidiaries:

Burckhardt Compression AG (1)
Im Link 5
Winterthur, 8404, Switzerland
Tel.: (41) 52 262 55 00
Fax: (41) 52 262 00 51
Reciprocating Compressors Mfr
S.I.C.: 3563
N.A.I.C.S.: 333912

U.S. Subsidiary:

Burckhardt Compression (US) Inc. (2)
7240 Brittmore Rd Ste 100
Houston, TX 77041
Tel.: (281) 582-1050
Fax: (281) 582-1060
E-Mail: rudolf.buschauer@burckhardtcompression.com
Web Site: www.burckhardtcompression.com
Sls.: $3,996,000
Emp.: 25
Reciprocating Compressor Sales & Servicing
S.I.C.: 5084
N.A.I.C.S.: 423830
Rudolf Buschauer *(Pres)*

Subsidiary:

Selltech Compressor, Pump & Engine Products, Inc. (3)
25048 Anza Dr
Valencia, CA 91355
Tel.: (661) 257-6026
Fax: (661) 257-4706
Web Site: www.selltechcompressor.com
Compressor Valve Repair & Maintenance Service
S.I.C.: 7699
N.A.I.C.S.: 811310
Jeff van Scoy *(Gen Mgr)*

Non-U.S. Subsidiaries:

Burckhardt Compression (Brasil) Ltda. (2)
Rua Zelia 431
09861-710 Sao Paulo, Brazil (100%)
Tel.: (55) 1143442310
Fax: (55) 1143562721
E-Mail: info@burckhardtcompression.co.br
Web Site: www.burckhardtcompression.com
Emp.: 20
Air & Gas Compressor Mfr
S.I.C.: 3586
N.A.I.C.S.: 333913

Burckhardt Compression (Canada) Inc. (2)
7956 Torbram Road Unit 9-C
Brampton, ON, L6T 5A2, Canada (100%)
Tel.: (905) 458-1623
Fax: (905) 458-1573
E-Mail: tim.lillak@burckhardtcomopression.com
Web Site: www.burckhardtcomopression.ca
Emp.: 5
Appliance Repair & Maintenance
S.I.C.: 7699
N.A.I.C.S.: 811412
Tim Lillak *(Mng Dir)*

Burckhardt Compression (Deutschland) GmbH (2)
Kruppstrasse 1a
41469 Neuss, Germany (100%)
Tel.: (49) 213791700
Fax: (49) 2137917030
E-Mail: info.deutschland@burckhardtcompression.de
Emp.: 50
Oil & Gas Field Machinery & Equipment Mfr
S.I.C.: 3533
N.A.I.C.S.: 333132
Olas Goaaes *(VP)*

Burckhardt Compression (Espana) S.A. (2)
Avenida de los Pirineos 25 Nave
28046 Madrid, Spain (100%)
Tel.: (34) 915675727
Fax: (34) 915675787
E-Mail: info.spain@burckhardtcompression.com
Emp.: 15
Oil & Gas Field Machinery & Equipment Mfr
S.I.C.: 3533
N.A.I.C.S.: 333132
Javier Gamboa *(Mng Dir)*

Burckhardt Compression (France) S.A.S (2)
28-30 Bd Roger Salengro
F-78712 Mantes-la-Jolie, France (100%)
Mailing Address:
Boite Postale 1031
F-78202 Mantes-la-Jolie, Cedex, France
Tel.: (33) 134777373
Fax: (33) 175720340
E-Mail: info@burckhardtcompression.com
Web Site: www.burckhardtcompression.com
Emp.: 11
Air & Gas Compressor Mfr
S.I.C.: 3586
N.A.I.C.S.: 333913
Francois Bouziguet *(Gen Mgr)*

Burckhardt Compression (India) Pvt. Ltd. (2)
Gate No 304 Village Kondhapuri Pune-Nagar Road Tal Shirur
Pune, Maharashtra, 412 209, India
Tel.: (91) 2137 669 400
Fax: (91) 2137 669 496
E-Mail: info.india@burckhardtcompression.com
Web Site: www.bc-india.com
Emp.: 30
Reciprocating Compressors Mfr
S.I.C.: 3559
N.A.I.C.S.: 333249
Narasimha Rao *(Mng Dir)*

Burckhardt Compression (Italia) S.r.l. (2)
Viale Emilia 83
Milano, 20093 Milan, Italy (100%)
Tel.: (39) 022540891
Fax: (39) 022531615
E-Mail: info.italia@burckhardtcompression.com
Web Site: www.burckhardtcompression.com
Emp.: 15
Ship Building & Repairing
S.I.C.: 3731
N.A.I.C.S.: 336611
Tullio Buonocore *(Mng Dir)*

Burckhardt Compression (Japan) Ltd. (2)
Yamazaki Bldg 4th floor 3-7-2 Irifune
Chuo-ku
104-0042 Tokyo, Japan (100%)
Tel.: (81) 335378870
Fax: (81) 335378877
E-Mail: info.japan@burckhardtcompression.com
Web Site: www.burckhardtcompression.com
Emp.: 7
Air & Gas Compressor Mfr
S.I.C.: 3563
N.A.I.C.S.: 333912
Mamoru Tanaka *(Mng Dir)*

Burckhardt Compression (Middle East) FZE (2)
7 Liu 15 Jebel Ali Freezone
PO Box 262944
Dubai, United Arab Emirates
Tel.: (971) 4 887 0042
Fax: (971) 4 887 0052
E-Mail: info_dubai@burckhardtcompression.com
Web Site: www.burckhardtcompression.com
Emp.: 15
Reciprocating Compressor Mfr
S.I.C.: 3563
N.A.I.C.S.: 333912

Burckhardt Compression (Shanghai) Co. Ltd. (2)
Rm 517 Fuxing Plaza
No 109 Yandang Road, 200020 Shanghai, China (100%)
Tel.: (86) 2150720880
Fax: (86) 2150720383
E-Mail: keven.li@burckhardtcompression.com
Web Site: www.burckhardtcompression.com
Emp.: 30
Oil & Gas Field Machinery & Equipment Mfr
S.I.C.: 3533
N.A.I.C.S.: 333132

Burckhardt Compression (UK) Ltd. (2)
Units 1 & 2 Arena 14 Bicester Park
Charbridge Lane
OX26 4SS Bicester, Oxfordshire, United Kingdom (100%)
Tel.: (44) 1869326800
Fax: (44) 1869326808
Web Site: www.burckhardtcompression.com
Emp.: 18
Air & Gas Compressor Mfr
S.I.C.: 3563
N.A.I.C.S.: 333912
Colin Webb *(Mng Dir)*

MT Sealing Technology Inc (1)
Aspstrasse 8
8472 Seuzach, Switzerland
Tel.: (41) 523205060
Fax: (41) 523351174
E-Mail: info@mt-switzerland.ch
Web Site: www.mt-switzerland.ch
Emp.: 4
Sealing Component Mfr
S.I.C.: 3053
N.A.I.C.S.: 339991
Rose Mary MacLeod *(Gen Mgr)*

Non-U.S. Subsidiary:

PROGNOST Systems GmbH (1)
PO Box 1905
48409 Rheine, Germany
Tel.: (49) 59 71 8 08 19 0
Fax: (49) 59 71 8 08 19 42
E-Mail: info@prognost.com
Web Site: www.prognost.com
Emp.: 45
Reciprocating Compressors Mfr
S.I.C.: 3585
N.A.I.C.S.: 333415
Eike Drewes *(Mng Dir)*

U.S. Subsidiary:

PROGNOST Systems Inc. (2)
1020 Bay Area Blvd Ste 105
Houston, TX 77058
Tel.: (281) 480-9300
Fax: (281) 480-9302
E-Mail: infousa@prognost.com
Web Site: www.prognost.com
Monitoring Diagnostic System Mfr
S.I.C.: 2835
N.A.I.C.S.: 325413
Edward D. Morrison *(Gen Mgr)*

BURCON NUTRASCIENCE CORPORATION

1946 West Broadway
Vancouver, BC, V6J 1Z2, Canada
Tel.: (604) 733-0896
Fax: (604) 733-0896
E-Mail: info@burcon.ca
Web Site: www.burcon.ca
Year Founded: 1998
BUR—(NASDAQ TSX)
Rev.: $30,128
Assets: $10,451,524
Liabilities: $763,884
Net Worth: $9,687,639
Earnings: ($5,512,360)
Emp.: 24
Fiscal Year-end: 03/31/13

Business Description:
Plant-Based Protein Products Researcher & Mfr
S.I.C.: 8731
N.A.I.C.S.: 541712

Personnel:
Allan Yap *(Chm & CEO)*
Johann F. Tergesen *(Pres & COO)*
Jade Cheng *(CFO)*
Randy Willardsen *(Sr VP-Process)*

Board of Directors:
Allan Yap
Bradford Allen
Alan Yiu Lun Chan
Rosanna Mei Wah Chau
Matthew Hall
David Lorne John Tyrrell

Legal Counsel:
Stikeman Elliott
Park Place 1700 666 Burrard Street
Vancouver, BC, V6C 2X8, Canada

Computershare Investor Services Inc.
510 Burrard St 2nd Floor
Vancouver, BC, V6C 3B9, Canada
Tel.: (604) 661-9400

Transfer Agents:
Computershare Trust Company, N.A.
Denver, CO 80401

Computershare Investor Services Inc.
510 Burrard St 2nd Floor
Vancouver, BC, V6C 3B9, Canada
Tel.: (604) 661-9400

Subsidiary:

Burcon NutraScience (MB) Corp. (1)
1388 Waller Ave
Winnipeg, MB, R3T 1P9, Canada
Tel.: (204) 475-6207
Fax: (204) 284-6407
E-Mail: info@burcon.ca
Web Site: www.burcon.ca/contact_us
Emp.: 15
Physical Research & Development Services
S.I.C.: 8731
N.A.I.C.S.: 541712
Martin Schweizn *(VP)*

BURE EQUITY AB

Nybrogatan 6
114 34 Stockholm, Sweden
Tel.: (46) 86140020
Fax: (46) 86140038
E-Mail: info@bure.se
Web Site: www.bure.se
BURE—(OMX)
Rev.: $127,895,760
Assets: $377,433,360
Liabilities: $50,387,400
Net Worth: $327,045,960
Earnings: ($25,650,360)
Emp.: 659
Fiscal Year-end: 12/31/12

Business Description:
Holding Company
S.I.C.: 6719
N.A.I.C.S.: 551112

Personnel:
Patrik Tigerschiold *(Chm)*
Hakan Larsson *(Vice Chm)*
Henrik Blomquist *(CEO)*
Agneta Schein *(Asst CEO)*
Andreas Berglin *(CFO)*

Board of Directors:
Patrik Tigerschiold
Hans Biorck
Carl Bjorkman
Eva Gidlof
Hakan Larsson
Mathias Uhlen

Subsidiaries:

Celemiab Group AB (1)
Nordenskioldsgatan 8
Malmo, 211 19, Sweden
Tel.: (46) 406602700
Fax: (46) 406602701
Emp.: 15
Marketing Consulting Services
S.I.C.: 8742
N.A.I.C.S.: 541613
Kjell Lindqvist *(Gen Mgr)*

Citat AB (1)
PO Box 30159
10425 Stockholm, Sweden (100%)
Tel.: (46) 850661750
Fax: (46) 850610880
E-Mail: info@citat.se
Web Site: www.citat.se/
Emp.: 150
Plate Work Mfr
S.I.C.: 3443
N.A.I.C.S.: 332313
Dan Sehlberg *(Pres & CEO)*

CR&T Ventures AB (1)
Goteborg
Gothenburg, Sweden (100%)
Tel.: (46) 317086400
Securities & Commodity Exchanges
S.I.C.: 6231
N.A.I.C.S.: 523210
Berlin Carlson *(Mgr-Acct)*

IT Gymnasiet Sverige AB (1)
Origovagen 4
Gothenburg, Sweden (100%)
Tel.: (46) 317341190
Fax: (46) 31473112
Emp.: 20
Colleges Universities & Professional Schools
S.I.C.: 8221
N.A.I.C.S.: 611310
Ulf Sjulander *(Mng Dir)*

Mercuri International Group AB (1)
Gustav III Boulevard 42 Solna
41263 Gothenburg, Sweden (100%)
Tel.: (46) 31687200
Fax: (46) 31682198
E-Mail: info@mercury.se
Web Site: www.mercury.se
Emp.: 34
Holding Company
S.I.C.: 6719
N.A.I.C.S.: 551112
Nicole Dereumaux *(CEO)*

Vittra AB (1)
Adolf Fredriks Kyrkogata 2
111 37 Stockholm, Sweden (100%)
Tel.: (46) 771191090
E-Mail: info@vittra.se
Web Site: www.vittra.se
Emp.: 41
Elementary & Secondary Schools
S.I.C.: 8211
N.A.I.C.S.: 611110

BURELLE S.A.

1 rue Francois 1er
F-75800 Paris, France
Tel.: (33) 140876500
Fax: (33) 140879680
E-Mail: investor.relations@burelle.com
Web Site: www.burelle.fr
BUR—(EUR)
Sales Range: $1-4.9 Billion
Emp.: 10,000

Business Description:
Holding Company
S.I.C.: 6719
N.A.I.C.S.: 551112

Personnel:
Jean Burelle *(Pres & Gen Dir)*

Subsidiaries:

Compagnie Plastic Omnium S.A. (1)
1 Rue Du Parc
Levallois, 92593 Perret, Cedex, France (54.7%)
Tel.: (33) 140876400
Fax: (33) 140879662
Web Site: www.plasticomnium.com
POM—(EUR)
Rev.: $6,469,923,215
Assets: $4,242,725,335
Liabilities: $3,142,896,368
Net Worth: $1,099,828,967
Earnings: $244,333,894
Emp.: 21,034
Fiscal Year-end: 12/31/12
Plastic Components Mfr for Automotive, Medical, Pharmaceutical, Waste Management, Recreational Equipment & Recycling Industries
S.I.C.: 3089
N.A.I.C.S.: 326199
Laurent Burelle *(Chm & CEO)*
Rodolphe Lapillonne *(CFO & Exec VP)*
Paul Henry Lemarie *(Co-COO)*
Jean-Michel Szczerba *(Co-COO)*
Michel Kempinski *(Chm-Environment)*
Eric Auzepy *(Pres-Auto Exterior)*
Pierre Lecocq *(Pres-Auto Inergy)*
Jean-Luc Petit *(Sec & VP-Legal Affairs)*
Philippe Hugon *(Exec VP-HR)*
Adeline Mickeler *(Exec VP-Corp Plng & M&A)*

Subsidiaries:

Inergy Automotive Systems S.A. (2)
18 Rue de Calais
75009 Paris, France
Tel.: (33) 156022162
Fax: (33) 145261108
Web Site: www.inergyautomotive.com
Sales Range: $1-4.9 Billion
Emp.: 4,000
Automotive Fuel Systems Mfr
S.I.C.: 3714
N.A.I.C.S.: 336310
Pierre Lecocq *(CEO)*

Subsidiary:

Inergy Automotive Systems France (3)
92 rue du Marechal Leclerc
PO Box 80259
Venette, 60202 Compiegne, Cedex, France
Tel.: (33) 344903456
Fax: (33) 344905058
Web Site: www.inergyautomotive.com
Emp.: 500
Mfr. of Automotive Fuel Systems
S.I.C.: 3089
N.A.I.C.S.: 326199
Pierre Lecocq *(CEO)*

U.S. Subsidiary:

Inergy Automotive Systems Inc. (3)
1549 W Beecher St
Adrian, MI 49221
Tel.: (517) 265-1100
Fax: (517) 265-1135
Web Site: www.inergyautomotive.com
Sls.: $93,000,000
Emp.: 170
Plastic Automotive Parts
S.I.C.: 3089
N.A.I.C.S.: 326199

Non-U.S. Subsidiaries:

Inergy Automotive Systems Belgium NV (3)
310 Rue De Ransbeek
1120 Brussels, Belgium (50%)
Tel.: (32) 22642855
Fax: (32) 22643075
E-Mail: info@inergyautomotive.com
Web Site: www.inergyautomotive.com
Emp.: 50
Mfr. of Automotive Fuel Systems; Joint Venture of Plastic Omnium & Solvay S.A.
S.I.C.: 3089
N.A.I.C.S.: 326199
Philippe Convain *(VP)*

Inergy Automotive Systems (Belgium) N.V. (3)
Grensstraat 12
2200 Herentals, Belgium (100%)
Tel.: (32) 14849540
Fax: (32) 14849541
E-Mail: mieks.gebruers@inergyautomotive.com
Web Site: www.inergyautomotive.com
Emp.: 80
Automotive Fuel Systems
S.I.C.: 3714
N.A.I.C.S.: 336310
Peter Wijnants *(Gen Mgr)*

Inergy Automotive Systems Germany GmbH (3)
Max Planck Strasse 27
D 61184 Karben, Germany (100%)
Tel.: (49) 603992900
Fax: (49) 6039929039
E-Mail: info@inergyautomotive.com
Web Site: www.inergyautomotive.com
Emp.: 250
Mfr. of Automotive Fuel Systems; Joint Venture of Plastic Omnium & Solvay S.A.
S.I.C.: 3089
N.A.I.C.S.: 326199
Ulrich Seibt *(Mng Dir)*

Inergy Automotive Systems Germany GmbH (3)
Kesterbacher Str 23
65479 Raunheim, Hessen, Germany (50%)
Tel.: (49) 614291340
Fax: (49) 6142913440
Web Site: www.inergyautomotive.com
Emp.: 10
Mfr. of Automotive Fuel Systems; Joint Venture of Plastic Omnium & Solvay S.A.
S.I.C.: 3089
N.A.I.C.S.: 326199
Dieter Bruess *(Gen Mgr)*

Inergy Automotive Systems Germany GmbH (3)
Essener Strasse
99819 Grossenlupnitz, Thuringen, Germany (100%)
Tel.: (49) 893692085192
Fax: (49) 893692085142
E-Mail: inergy@inergyautomotive.com
Web Site: www.inergyautomotive.com
Emp.: 50
Mfr. of Automotive Fuel Systems; Joint Venture of Plastic Omnium & Solvay S.A.
S.I.C.: 3089
N.A.I.C.S.: 326199
Ulrech Saibt *(Mgr)*

Inergy Automotive Systems Mexico S.A. de C.V. (3)
Blvd Industria De La Transformacion 3150
Parque Industrial Saltillo, 25900 Ramos Arizpe, Coahuila, Mexico (100%)
Tel.: (52) 8444382200
Fax: (52) 844 438 22 32
E-Mail: receptionist.ramos@inergyautomotive.com
Web Site: www.inergyautomotive.com
Emp.: 250
Mfr. of Automotive Fuel Systems; Joint Venture of Plastic Omnium & Solvay S.A.
S.I.C.: 3089
N.A.I.C.S.: 326199
Albreto Calderon *(Gen Mgr)*

Inergy Automotive Systems U.K. Ltd. (3)
Halesfield 6
Telford, Stropshire, TF7 4RQ, United Kingdom (100%)
Tel.: (44) 1952685588
Fax: (44) 1952685545
Emp.: 50
Mfr. of Fuel Systems
S.I.C.: 3714
N.A.I.C.S.: 336310

Ludoparc S.A. (2)
131 151 Rue Du 1 Er Mai
92000 Nanterre, France (100%)
Tel.: (33) 155669898
Fax: (33) 155669899
Web Site: www.plasticomnium.com
Emp.: 70
Playground Equipment Mfr.
S.I.C.: 3949
N.A.I.C.S.: 339920

Metroplast SA (2)
Rue Denis Papin
71100 Chalon-sur-Saone, France (100%)
Tel.: (33) 385971200
Fax: (33) 385414697
E-Mail: info@plasticomnium.com
Web Site: www.plasticomnium.com
Emp.: 50
Plastics Products
S.I.C.: 3089
N.A.I.C.S.: 326199
Lesevere Oliser *(Mgr)*

Plastic Omnium Auto Exterieur SA (2)
1 rue du Parc
92593 Levallois-Perret, France (100%)
Tel.: (33) 140876400
Fax: (33) 147397898
Web Site: www.plasticomnium.com
Emp.: 200
Motor Vehicle Plastic Parts
S.I.C.: 3089
N.A.I.C.S.: 326199
Andre Poirson *(Mng Dir)*

Plastic Omnium Medical SA (2)
1 Rue du Parc
PO Box 7020
92593 Perret, France (100%)
Tel.: (33) 472767778
Fax: (33) 472734692
Web Site: www.plasticomnium.com.fr
Emp.: 300
Plastics Products Mfr.
S.I.C.: 3089
N.A.I.C.S.: 326199

Plastic Omnium Systemes Urbains SA (2)
19 Ave Jules Carteret
PO Box 7020
69342 Lyon, France (100%)
Tel.: (33) 472767778
Fax: (33) 472767764
Web Site: www.plasticomnium.com
Plastics Products
S.I.C.: 3089
N.A.I.C.S.: 326199

Produits Plastiques Performants - 3P (2)
1 rue du Parc
92593 Levallois-Perret, France (100%)
Tel.: (33) 140876400
Fax: (33) 147397898
E-Mail: Lvulelle@plasticomnium.com
Web Site: www.plasticomnium.com
Emp.: 800
Plastics Products
S.I.C.: 3089
N.A.I.C.S.: 326199

Transit SA (2)
19 Ave Jules Carteret
PO Box 7020
69342 Lyon, France (100%)
Tel.: (33) 472767778
Fax: (33) 472734692
Web Site: www.plasticomnium.com
Wholesale of Plastic Products
S.I.C.: 5113
N.A.I.C.S.: 424130

U.S. Subsidiaries:

EPSCO International Inc. (2)
717 Georgia Ave
Deer Park, TX 77536-2513
Tel.: (281) 930-1340
Fax: (281) 476-8139
Web Site: www.epscointl.com
Emp.: 50
Distributor of Plastic Pipe
S.I.C.: 5074
N.A.I.C.S.: 423720
Jeff Duncombe *(Owner)*

Plastic Omnium, Inc (2)
5100 Old Pearman Dairy Rd
Anderson, SC 29625-1314
Tel.: (864) 260-0000
Fax: (864) 231-7537
Web Site: www.plasticomnium.com
Emp.: 400
Mfr. of Automobile Bumpers
S.I.C.: 3089
N.A.I.C.S.: 326199

Plastic Omnium Industries Inc. (2)
1050 Wilshire Dr
Troy, MI 48084
Tel.: (248) 458-0700
Fax: (248) 637-7877
Web Site: www.plasticomnium.com
Plastics Products Mfr
S.I.C.: 5013
N.A.I.C.S.: 423120

Non-U.S. Subsidiaries:

3P GmbH-Performance Plastic Products (2)
Max Planck Str 27
D 61184 Karben, Germany
Tel.: (49) 603948040
Fax: (49) 603948481
Web Site: www.plasticomnium.com
Emp.: 4
Plastics Products
S.I.C.: 3089
N.A.I.C.S.: 326199
Serge Aeig *(Mng Dir)*

3P- Productos Plasticos Performantes SA (2)
Pista De Silla Km 6 700
P O Box 428
46080 Valencia, Spain (100%)
Tel.: (34) 963896800
Fax: (34) 961270940
Web Site: www.plasticomnium.com
Emp.: 120
Plastics Products
S.I.C.: 3089

Burelle S.A.—(Continued)

N.A.I.C.S.: 326199

3P SpA (2)
Via Kennedy 38
Rodano Millepini, 20090 Milan, Italy (100%)
Tel.: (39) 0295328283
Fax: (39) 0295328339
Web Site: www.3pcorporate.com
Emp.: 8
Plastics Products
S.I.C.: 3089
N.A.I.C.S.: 326199

Plastic Omnium AB (2)
PO Box 104
Vannhogsgatan 11, S 23122 Trelleborg, Sweden (100%)
Tel.: (46) 41012460
Fax: (46) 41010515
E-Mail: info@plasticomnium.se
Web Site: www.plasticomnium.se
Emp.: 6
Plastics Products
S.I.C.: 3089
N.A.I.C.S.: 326199
Christophe Gence *(Gen Mgr)*

Plastic Omnium AG (2)
Baselstrasse 61
4124 Basel, Switzerland (100%)
Tel.: (41) 615603634
Fax: (41) 614812632
Web Site: www.plasticomnium.com
Emp.: 40
Plastics Products
S.I.C.: 3089
N.A.I.C.S.: 326199

Plastic Omnium Automotive Ltd (2)
Westminster Industrial Est Huntington Way
Measham, Swadlincote, Terbyshira, DE12 7DS, United Kingdom (100%)
Tel.: (44) 530273849
Fax: (44) 1530273863
Web Site: www.plasticomnium.com
Emp.: 150
Automotive Plastic Products
S.I.C.: 3089
N.A.I.C.S.: 326199

Plastic Omnium BV (2)
Nikkelstraat 31
4823 DZ Breda, Netherlands
Tel.: (31) 76 54 25 055
Fax: (31) 76 54 25 033
Web Site: www.plasticomnium.com
Plastics Products Mfr
S.I.C.: 3089
N.A.I.C.S.: 326199

Plastic Omnium Do Brasil Ltda (2)
Avenida Hilario Jose SIgnorini 201 Distrito Industrial Una II Bairro
Itaim, 12095-193 Taubate, SP, Brazil
Tel.: (55) 12 2125 0900
Fax: (55) 12 2125 0915
Web Site: www.plasticomnium.com
Plastics Products Mfr
S.I.C.: 3089
N.A.I.C.S.: 326199

Plastic Omnium Entsorgungstechnik GmbH (2)
Essener Strasse
99819 Grossenlupnitz, Germany (100%)
Tel.: (49) 369208510
Fax: (49) 3692086153
Web Site: www.plasticomnium.com
Emp.: 200
Plastics Products
S.I.C.: 3089
N.A.I.C.S.: 326199
Plaus Schmittbetz *(Mng Dir)*

Plastic Omnium Equipamientos Exteriores SA (2)
Calle Gobelas 47-49
La Florida, 28023 Madrid, Spain (100%)
Tel.: (34) 917082970
Fax: (34) 917080305
E-Mail: posusa@plasticomnium.com
Web Site: www.plasticomnium.com
Emp.: 20
Plastics Products
S.I.C.: 3089
N.A.I.C.S.: 326199
Arderius Alegandro *(Gen Mgr)*

Plastic Omnium SA (2)
Rua Da Bela Vista Lt 2 R C Bairro Massapes Aboboda
S Domingos De Rana, 2785 254 Lisbon, Portugal (100%)
Tel.: (351) 214446817
Fax: (351) 214446818
Web Site: www.plasticomnium.com
Emp.: 17
Plastics Products
S.I.C.: 3089
N.A.I.C.S.: 326199

Plastic Omnium SA (2)
Calle Galvarino Gallardo 1754
Providencia, Santiago, 6640677, Chile (100%)
Tel.: (56) 22360000
Fax: (56) 22359377, ext. 22369000
Web Site: www.plasticomnium.com
Emp.: 53
Plastics Products
S.I.C.: 3089
N.A.I.C.S.: 326199

Plastic Omnium Sistemas Urbanos SA (2)
Calle Gobelas 47-49
La Florida, 28023 Madrid, Spain (100%)
Tel.: (34) 917082970
Fax: (34) 917080305
E-Mail: posusa@plasticomnium.com
Web Site: www.plasticomnium.com
Emp.: 20
Plastics Products
S.I.C.: 3089
N.A.I.C.S.: 326199
Arderius Alejandro *(Gen Mgr)*

Posedo Co., Ltd. (2)
140-2 Daejeon Ri Hapdeok-Eub Tangjin-Goon
Seoul, Korea (South) (100%)
Tel.: (82) 41 362 2390
Fax: (82) 41 362 9762
Web Site: www.posedo.co.kr
Emp.: 10
Plastics Products Mfr
S.I.C.: 3089
N.A.I.C.S.: 326199

Signature S.A. (1)
63 Rue Edouard Colone
92027 Nanterre, Cedex, France FR
Tel.: (33) 140874300 (100%)
Fax: (33) 155466079
E-Mail: ciesignatture@ciesignature.com
Web Site: www.ciesignature.com
Emp.: 400
Signs, Safety Equipment & Road Marking Mfr; Road Management Services
S.I.C.: 3993
N.A.I.C.S.: 339950
Oliver Duquen *(Mng Dir)*

Subsidiary:

Euroliners (2)
Zone Industrielle de Boulay 30 Rte du General de Rascas
57220 Boulay, France (100%)
Tel.: (33) 387794838
Fax: (33) 387791204
Web Site: www.euroliners.com
Emp.: 27
Mfr. of Road Marking Machines
S.I.C.: 3531
N.A.I.C.S.: 333120

Non-U.S. Subsidiary:

Berlack GmbH (2)
Kusterkamp 1
D-25355 Barmstedt, Germany De
Tel.: (49) 412392190
Fax: (49) 4123921919
E-Mail: info@berlack.de
Web Site: www.berlack.de
Emp.: 16
Road Marking Products Mfr
S.I.C.: 3579
N.A.I.C.S.: 339940
Philip Werdiere *(Mng Dir)*

BUREY GOLD LIMITED

Level 1 Suite 5 The Business Centre
55 Salvado Road
Subiaco, WA, 6008, Australia
Tel.: (61) 8 9381 2299
Fax: (61) 8 9380 6761
Web Site: www.bureygold.com
Year Founded: 2005
BYR—(ASX)
Rev.: $189,918
Assets: $17,056,748
Liabilities: $258,759
Net Worth: $16,797,989
Earnings: ($2,911,495)
Emp.: 15
Fiscal Year-end: 06/30/13

Business Description:
Gold Ore Mining
S.I.C.: 1041
N.A.I.C.S.: 212221

Personnel:
Klaus Eckhof *(CEO & Mng Dir)*
Susmit Mohanlal Shah *(Sec)*

Board of Directors:
Ron Norbert Gajewski
Klaus Eckhof
Susmit Mohanlal Shah
Kevin Thomson

Legal Counsel:
Cullen Babington Hughes Pty Ltd
229 Stirling Highway
6010 Claremont, Australia

BURG-WACHTER KG

Altenhofer Weg 15
58300 Wetter, Germany
Tel.: (49) 2335 965
Fax: (49) 2335 965 390
E-Mail: info@burg-waechter.de
Web Site: www.burg-waechter.de
Emp.: 700

Business Description:
Locks, Mailboxes & Safe Mfr & Distr
S.I.C.: 3429
N.A.I.C.S.: 332510

Personnel:
Dietmar Luling *(Mng Dir)*

Subsidiary:

Sanyo Video Vertrieb AG (1)
An der Strusbek 31
22926 Ahrensburg, Germany
Tel.: (49) 410247980
Fax: (49) 4102479810
E-Mail: info@santec-video.com
Web Site: www.santec-video.com
Rev.: $11,380,050
Emp.: 34
Security System Services
S.I.C.: 7382
N.A.I.C.S.: 561621
Lars Christian Diestel *(CEO)*

BURGAN COMPANY FOR WELL DRILLING, TRADING & MAINTENANCE KSCC

Al-Shuaiba Industrial Area Wafra Exit 306
Street 10 Block 3 Plot 78
Fahaheel, 64022, Kuwait

Mailing Address:
PO Box 47143
Fahaheel, 64022, Kuwait
Tel.: (965) 23261378
Fax: (965) 23261348
E-Mail: info@burgandrilling.com
Web Site: www.burgandrilling.com
Year Founded: 1970
ABAR—(KUW)
Sales Range: $150-199.9 Million
Emp.: 1,500

Business Description:
Oil Well Drilling & Maintenance Services
S.I.C.: 1381
N.A.I.C.S.: 213111

Personnel:
Ahmed Al-Hamad *(Chm & Mng Dir)*
Faisal Abdul Latif Al-Hamad *(Vice Chm)*

Board of Directors:
Ahmed Al-Hamad
Tareq Al-Adasani
Faisal Abdul Latif Al-Hamad
Mohammed Ali Al-Jazzaf
Yousef Al-Oumi
Abdul Hussain Shehab

BURGBAD AKTIENGESELLSCHAFT

Bad Fredeburg Kirchplatz 10
57392 Schmallenberg, Germany
Tel.: (49) 297496170
Fax: (49) 2974 9617278
E-Mail: info@burgbad.de
Web Site: www.burgbad.com
BUB4—(DEU)
Sales Range: $100-124.9 Million
Emp.: 628

Business Description:
Interior & Bathroom Furnishings Mfr
S.I.C.: 3269
N.A.I.C.S.: 327110

Personnel:
Erdal Karamercan *(Chm-Supervisory Bd)*
Karl-Heinz Wennrich *(Chm-Mgmt Bd)*
Husamettin Onanc *(Deputy Chm-Supervisory Bd)*
Jorg Loew *(Member-Mgmt Bd)*
Annelie Ruddies-Warwitz *(Member-Mgmt Bd)*

Supervisory Board of Directors:
Peter Lammerskitten
Klaus Weisshaar
Stephen Gockeler
Levent Avni Ersalman
Haluk Bayraktar
Husamettin Onanc
Erdal Karamercan

BURGER KING RESTAURANTS OF CANADA INC.

401 The W Mall Ste 700
Etobicoke, ON, M9C 5J4, Canada
Tel.: (416) 626-6464
Fax: (416) 626-6464
Toll Free: (877) 271-0493
Web Site: www.burgerking.ca
Year Founded: 1989
Sales Range: $10-24.9 Million
Emp.: 20

Business Description:
Fast Food Restaurants Franchisor & Operator
S.I.C.: 5812
N.A.I.C.S.: 722513

Personnel:
Jason Keown *(Sr Dir-Mktg)*

BURGESS ARCHITECTURAL PRODUCTS LIMITED

Brookfield Rd
Hinckley, Leicestershire, LE10 2LL, United Kingdom
Tel.: (44) 1455618787
Fax: (44) 1455251061
E-Mail: info@burgessceilings.co.uk
Web Site: www.burgessceilings.co.uk
Emp.: 50

Business Description:
Metal Ceiling Tiles Mfr
S.I.C.: 3449
N.A.I.C.S.: 332323

Personnel:
Rob Burke *(Mng Dir)*

BURGO GROUP S.P.A.

Via Luigi Burgo 8
10099 San Mauro Torinese, Turin, Italy
Tel.: (39) 0112233111
Fax: (39) 0112233444
Web Site: www.burgo.com
Emp.: 4,983

Business Description:
Graphics Paper & Flexible Packaging Papers Mfr
S.I.C.: 2621
N.A.I.C.S.: 322122
Personnel:
Giorgo Cefis *(Chm & Pres)*
Aldo Marchi *(Vice Chm)*
Girolamo Marchi *(CEO & Mng Dir)*
Board of Directors:
Giorgo Cefis
Enrico Benaglio
Alessandro Bertani
Fabio Buscarini
Aldo Marchi
Girolamo Marchi
Gianni Mion
Alberto C. Motta, Jr.
Renato Pagliro
Alfonso Sonato

Subsidiaries:

Burgo Distribuzione Srl (1)
Via dei Missaglia 97-edificio B1
20142 Milan, Italy
Tel.: (39) 02893941
Fax: (39) 0289394282
Web Site: www.burgodistribuzione.com
Paper Product Whslr
N.A.I.C.S.: 424110
Gianluigi Magarini *(Dir-Comml)*

Burgo Energia Srl (1)
Corso Giulio Cesare 268-Edificio A
10154 Turin, Italy
Tel.: (39) 011 22 333 22
Fax: (39) 011 22 334 20
E-Mail: info@burgoenergia.com
Web Site: www.burgoenergia.it
Electric Power Generation Services
N.A.I.C.S.: 221111
Giancarlo Mallarino *(Area Mgr-Resellers & Indirect Sls Channel)*

Comecart Spa (1)
Via Valle Po 88
12100 Cuneo, Italy
Tel.: (39) 0171 410410
Fax: (39) 0171 411158
E-Mail: factory@comecart.it
Web Site: www.comecart.it
Paper Machinery Mfr
N.A.I.C.S.: 333243
Davide Fusta *(Mgr-Quality Sys)*

Joint Venture:

Italmaceri S.r.l. (1)
Strada Lanzo 237
I-101 48 Turin, Italy
Tel.: (39) 011 22 82 911
Fax: (39) 011 22 60 890
E-Mail: info.italmaceri@sca.com
Emp.: 32
Wastepaper Collection & Processing
S.I.C.: 5093
N.A.I.C.S.: 423930

U.S. Subsidiary:

Burgo North America Inc (1)
1 Landmark Sq
Stamford, CT 06901
Tel.: (203) 569-9000
Fax: (203) 569-9006
Emp.: 10
Paper Product Whslr
N.A.I.C.S.: 424110
Giovanni Cattoni, *(Mng Dir)*

Non-U.S. Subsidiary:

Burgo UK ltd (1)
Office G Old Stratford Business Park
Falcon Drive
Old Stratford, Milton Keynes, MK19 6FG, United Kingdom
Tel.: (44) 1908 265800
Emp.: 10
Paper Product Whslr
N.A.I.C.S.: 424110
Jeremy Martin, *(Mng Dir)*

BURKHALTER HOLDING AG
Hohlstrasse 475
8048 Zurich, Switzerland
Tel.: (41) 444324777
Fax: (41) 444324823
E-Mail: info@burkhalter.ch
Web Site: www.burkhalter.ch
Year Founded: 1959
BRKN—(SWX)
Rev.: $516,831,303
Assets: $275,989,679
Liabilities: $142,754,101
Net Worth: $133,235,578
Earnings: $27,047,759
Emp.: 2,827
Fiscal Year-end: 12/31/12
Business Description:
Electrotechnical & Telecommunication Engineering Systems Distr & Installer
S.I.C.: 3699
N.A.I.C.S.: 335999
Personnel:
Marco Syfrig *(CEO)*
Zeno Bohm *(CFO)*
Board of Directors:
Gaudenz F. Domenig
Willy Huppi
Marco Syfrig
Peter Weigelt

Subsidiaries:

Alpha-Plan AG Rothrist (1)
Helblingstrasse 4
4852 Rothrist, Aargau, Switzerland
Tel.: (41) 627851085
Fax: (41) 627851075
E-Mail: info@alpha-plan.ch
Web Site: www.alpha-plan.ch
Emp.: 16
Electrical Engineering Services
S.I.C.: 8711
N.A.I.C.S.: 541330
Heinz Glanzmann *(Mng Dir)*
Claudio Meneghini *(Deputy Mng Dir)*

Bassi Elektro AG (1)
Poststrasse 141
7050 Arosa, Graubunden, Switzerland
Tel.: (41) 813787878
Fax: (41) 813787870
E-Mail: info@bassiarosa.ch
Web Site: www.bassiarosa.ch
Emp.: 20
Electrical Engineering Services
S.I.C.: 8711
N.A.I.C.S.: 541330
Karl Butzerin *(Mng Dir)*

Baumann Electro AG (1)
Breitfeldstrasse 10
9015 Saint Gallen, Switzerland
Tel.: (41) 713118888
Fax: (41) 71 311 50 20
E-Mail: info@baumann-electro.ch
Web Site: www.baumann-electro.ch
Electrical Engineering Services
S.I.C.: 8711
N.A.I.C.S.: 541330
Thomas Baumann *(Mng Dir)*

Burkhalter Automation AG (1)
Muttenzerstrasse 143
4133 Pratteln, Basel, Switzerland
Tel.: (41) 616993939
Fax: (41) 616993900
E-Mail: info@buat.ch
Web Site: www.burkhalter-automation.ch
Emp.: 18
Industrial Automation Services
S.I.C.: 7389
N.A.I.C.S.: 561990
Heinz Wiskotf *(Mng Dir)*

Burkhalter Technics AG (1)
Hohlstrasse 475
8048 Zurich, Switzerland
Tel.: (41) 444321111
Fax: (41) 444323633
E-Mail: info.buag@burkhalter.ch
Web Site: www.burkhalter-technics.ch
Emp.: 500
Electrical Engineering Services
S.I.C.: 8711
N.A.I.C.S.: 541330
Kasper Adrian *(Project Mgr)*

Caviezel AG (1)
Bramabuelstrasse 4A
Davos Platz, 7270 Davos, Graubunden, Switzerland
Tel.: (41) 81 410 00 00
Fax: (41) 81 410 00 05
E-Mail: info@caviezel-ag.ch
Web Site: www.caviezel-ag.ch
Emp.: 60
Electrical Engineering Services
S.I.C.: 8711
N.A.I.C.S.: 541330
Reto Mueller *(Mng Dir)*

Eigenmann AG (1)
Frauenfelderstrasse 13
9542 Munchwilen, Aargau, Switzerland
Tel.: (41) 719600666
Fax: (41) 71 960 06 67
E-Mail: info@eigenmann-elektro.ch
Web Site: www.eigenmann-elektro.ch
Electrical Engineering Services
S.I.C.: 8711
N.A.I.C.S.: 541330

Electra Buin SA (1)
Sotcha 680
7550 Scuol, Graubunden, Switzerland
Tel.: (41) 812586300
Fax: (41) 812586309
E-Mail: buin@buin.ch
Web Site: www.buin.ch
Emp.: 25
Electrical Engineering Services
S.I.C.: 8711
N.A.I.C.S.: 541330

Elektro Arber AG (1)
Romanshornerstrasse 2
8280 Kreuzlingen, Thurgau, Switzerland
Tel.: (41) 716868050
Fax: (41) 71 686 80 58
E-Mail: info@arber.ch
Web Site: www.arber.ch
Emp.: 110
Electrical Engineering Services
S.I.C.: 8711
N.A.I.C.S.: 541330
Andreas Haueter *(Mng Dir)*

Elektro-Bau AG Rothrist (1)
Helblingstrasse 4
4852 Rothrist, Aargau, Switzerland
Tel.: (41) 627852424
Fax: (41) 62 785 24 44
E-Mail: info@elektro-bau.ch
Web Site: www.elektro-bau.ch
Electrical Engineering Services
S.I.C.: 8711
N.A.I.C.S.: 541330

Elektro Burkhalter AG (1)
Eymattstrasse 7
3027 Bern, Switzerland
Tel.: (41) 319963333
Fax: (41) 31 996 33 66
E-Mail: bube.info@burkhalter.ch
Web Site: www.burkhalter-biel.ch
Emp.: 130
Electrical Engineering Services
S.I.C.: 8711
N.A.I.C.S.: 541330

Elektro Gutzwiller AG (1)
Muhlemattstrasse 25
4104 Oberwil, Basel, Switzerland
Tel.: (41) 614061010
Fax: (41) 614061007
E-Mail: info@elektro-gutzwiller.ch
Web Site: www.elektro-gutzwiller.ch
Emp.: 25
Electrical Engineering Services
S.I.C.: 8711
N.A.I.C.S.: 541330
Heinz Lussi *(Gen Mgr)*

Elektro Pizol AG (1)
Bahnhofstrasse 23
7323 Wangs, Switzerland
Tel.: (41) 817237766
Fax: (41) 81 723 67 92
E-Mail: info@elektro-pizol.ch
Web Site: www.elektro-pizol.ch
Emp.: 13
Electrical Engineering Services
S.I.C.: 8711
N.A.I.C.S.: 541330
Paul Moser *(Mng Dir)*

Elektro Ruegg AG (1)
Voa Sporz 12
7078 Lenzerheide, Graubunden, Switzerland
Tel.: (41) 813851717
Fax: (41) 81 385 17 19
E-Mail: info@ruegg-elektro.ch
Web Site: www.ruegg-elektro.ch
Emp.: 15
Electrical Engineering Services
S.I.C.: 8711
N.A.I.C.S.: 541330

Elektro Schmidlin AG (1)
Prattelerstrasse 35
4132 Muttenz, Switzerland
Tel.: (41) 614657878
Fax: (41) 61 465 78 72
E-Mail: info@elektro-schmidlin.ch
Web Site: www.elektro-schmidlin.ch
Electrical Engineering Services
S.I.C.: 8711
N.A.I.C.S.: 541330

Elektro Siegrist AG (1)
Dorfstrasse 2
5082 Kaisten, Aargau, Switzerland
Tel.: (41) 628742626
Fax: (41) 62 874 26 49
E-Mail: info@siegrist-elektro.ch
Web Site: www.siegrist-elektro.ch
Emp.: 34
Electrical Engineering Services
S.I.C.: 8711
N.A.I.C.S.: 541330

Elektrohuus von Allmen AG (1)
Gsteigstrasse
3780 Gstaad, Switzerland
Tel.: (41) 337487748
Fax: (41) 337487749
E-Mail: info@elektrohuus.ch
Web Site: www.elektrohuus.ch
Emp.: 40
Electrical Engineering Services
S.I.C.: 8711
N.A.I.C.S.: 541330
Caviezel Tarcisius *(Chm)*
Schar Hans *(Mng Dir)*

Elettro Celio SA (1)
Via del Tiglio 6
6512 Giubiasco, Ticino, Switzerland
Tel.: (41) 918573641
Fax: (41) 91 857 48 01
E-Mail: info@celio.ch
Web Site: www.celio.ch
Emp.: 30
Electrical Engineering Services
S.I.C.: 8711
N.A.I.C.S.: 541330
Celio Marco *(Mng Dir)*

Fritz Wegmann Elektrische Anlagen AG (1)
Henauerstrasse 11
Niederuzwil, 9244 Uzwil, Switzerland
Tel.: (41) 719500529
Fax: (41) 71 950 05 21
E-Mail: info@elektro-wegmann.ch
Web Site: www.elektro-wegmann.ch
Electrical Engineering Services
S.I.C.: 8711
N.A.I.C.S.: 541330
Thomas Baumann *(Mng Dir)*

Grichting & Valterio Electro SA (1)
54 Rue Oscar Bider
1951 Sion, Valais, Switzerland
Tel.: (41) 27 948 14 14
Fax: (41) 27 948 14 15
E-Mail: sion@grichting-valterio.ch
Web Site: www.grichting-valterio.ch
Emp.: 100
Electrical Engineering Services
S.I.C.: 8711
N.A.I.C.S.: 541330

Marcel Hufschmid AG (1)
Industriestrasse 55
6302 Zug, Switzerland
Tel.: (41) 417696969
Fax: (41) 417696970
E-Mail: info@hufschmid-elektro.ch
Web Site: www.hufschmid-elektro.ch
Emp.: 120
Electrical Engineering Services
S.I.C.: 8711
N.A.I.C.S.: 541330
Letter Hans *(Mng Dir)*

Oberholzer AG (1)
Pfaffikerstrasse 34
8623 Wetzikon, Zurich, Switzerland
Tel.: (41) 844667788

Burkhalter Holding AG—(Continued)

Fax: (41) 44 943 67 67
E-Mail: info@oberholzer.ch
Web Site: www.oberholzer.ch
Emp.: 90
Electrical Engineering Services
S.I.C.: 8711
N.A.I.C.S.: 541330

Otto Hermann AG (1)
Sankt Karli Strasse 2
6004 Lucerne, Switzerland
Tel.: (41) 413172222
Fax: (41) 413172220
E-Mail: info@hermann-elektro.ch
Web Site: www.hermann-elektro.ch
Emp.: 20
Electrical Engineering Services
S.I.C.: 8711
N.A.I.C.S.: 541330
Foehn Roger *(Mng Dir)*
Kaeppeli Pius *(Deputy Mng Dir)*

Peter & Barbisch AG (1)
Malervastrasse 5
7320 Sargans, Saint Gallen, Switzerland
Tel.: (41) 81 723 62 63
Fax: (41) 81 723 79 39
E-Mail: info@peter-barbisch.ch
Web Site: www.peter-barbisch.ch
Emp.: 17
Electrical Engineering Services
S.I.C.: 8711
N.A.I.C.S.: 541330

Schachenmann & Co. AG (1)
Barenfelserstrasse 40
4007 Basel, Switzerland
Mailing Address:
Postfach 569
4007 Basel, Switzerland
Tel.: (41) 616992233
Fax: (41) 616922009
E-Mail: info@schachenmann.ch
Web Site: www.schachenmann.ch
Emp.: 100
Provider of Electrical Services
S.I.C.: 1731
N.A.I.C.S.: 238210

Schachenmann & Co. AG (1)
Bettingerstrasse 7
4127 Birsfelden, Switzerland
Tel.: (41) 613789800
Fax: (41) 613789801
E-Mail: info@schachenmann.ch
Web Site: www.schachenmann.ch
Emp.: 100
Provider of Electrical Services
S.I.C.: 1731
N.A.I.C.S.: 238210
Peter Rombach *(Mng Dir)*

Schild Elektro AG (1)
Hauptstrasse 121
3818 Grindelwald, Bern, Switzerland
Tel.: (41) 339528888
Fax: (41) 33 952 88 89
E-Mail: info@schild-elektro.ch
Web Site: www.schild-elektro.ch
Emp.: 20
Electrical Engineering Services
S.I.C.: 8711
N.A.I.C.S.: 541330

Schonholzer AG (1)
Kalchbuhlstrasse 18
7000 Chur, Graubunden, Switzerland
Tel.: (41) 81 257 12 12
Fax: (41) 81 257 12 13
E-Mail: info@schoenholzer-elektro.ch
Web Site: www.schoenholzer-elektro.ch
Emp.: 60
Electrical Engineering Services
S.I.C.: 8711
N.A.I.C.S.: 541330

Schultheis-Mockli AG (1)
Froschenweidstrasse 10
8404 Winterthur, Zurich, Switzerland
Tel.: (41) 522350101
Fax: (41) 52 235 01 02
E-Mail: info@b-smwt.ch
Web Site: www.schultheismoeckli.ch
Electrical Engineering Services
S.I.C.: 8711
N.A.I.C.S.: 541330

Sedelec SA Lausanne (1)
Av des Boveresses 48
1010 Lausanne, Vaud, Switzerland
Tel.: (41) 216512000
Fax: (41) 21 653 76 00
E-Mail: info@sedelec-lsne.ch
Emp.: 70
Electrical Engineering Services
S.I.C.: 8711
N.A.I.C.S.: 541330
Alain Viaccoz *(Mng Dir)*

Sedelec SA (1)
Rue Blavignac 1
1227 Carouge, Geneva, Switzerland
Tel.: (41) 228698000
Fax: (41) 223482820
E-Mail: info@sedelec.ch
Web Site: www.sedelec.ch
Emp.: 300
Electrical Engineering Services
S.I.C.: 8711
N.A.I.C.S.: 541330
Schaller Eric *(Mng Dir)*

Triulzi AG (1)
Via dal Bagn 2
7500 Sankt Moritz-Bad, Graubunden, Switzerland
Tel.: (41) 818373666
Fax: (41) 818373660
E-Mail: info@triulzi.ch
Web Site: www.triulzi.ch
Emp.: 45
Electrical Engineering Services
S.I.C.: 8711
N.A.I.C.S.: 541330
Marco Triulzi *(Mng Dir)*

TZ Stromag (1)
Kantonsstrasse 132
3902 Brig, Valais, Switzerland
Tel.: (41) 279222070
Fax: (41) 279222075
E-Mail: info@stromag.ch
Web Site: www.stromag.ch
Electrical Engineering Services
S.I.C.: 8711
N.A.I.C.S.: 541330

Vuadens Controles SA (1)
Rue Oscar Bider 54
1950 Sion, Valais, Switzerland
Tel.: (41) 273228480
Fax: (41) 273228481
Electrical Engineering Services
S.I.C.: 8711
N.A.I.C.S.: 541330

BURKI VERPACKUNGSTECHNIK AG

Niedermattstrasse 14
Oberbipp, Bern, 4538, Switzerland
Tel.: (41) 326365353
Fax: (41) 326365359
E-Mail: info@buerkiat.ch
Web Site: www.buerkiat.ch
Sales Range: $10-24.9 Million
Emp.: 10
Business Description:
Real Estate Agents & Brokers Offices
S.I.C.: 6531
N.A.I.C.S.: 531210
Personnel:
Markus Frey *(CEO)*

BURLESON ENERGY LIMITED

Level 6 9 Barrack Street
Sydney, NSW, 2000, Australia
Mailing Address:
GPO Box 92
Sydney, NSW, 2001, Australia
Tel.: (61) 2 8252 6177
Fax: (61) 2 8252 6178
E-Mail: info@burlesonenergyltd.com
Web Site: www.burlesonenergyltd.com
BUR—(ASX)
Rev.: $1,522,605
Assets: $3,038,059
Liabilities: $115,423
Net Worth: $2,922,636
Earnings: $1,268,612
Fiscal Year-end: 06/30/13
Business Description:
Oil & Gas Exploration & Production
S.I.C.: 1381
N.A.I.C.S.: 213111
Personnel:
Michael Sandy *(Chm)*
Alex Sundich *(CFO)*
Kevin Lynn *(Sec)*
Board of Directors:
Michael Sandy
Andrew Kugler Jr
Alex Sundich
Legal Counsel:
HWL Ebsworth Lawyers
Level 14 Australia Sq 264 278 George St
Sydney, Australia

BURNABY IMPORT AUTO SALES LTD

(d/b/a Wolfe Mazda)
1595 Boundary Rd
Vancouver, BC, V5K 5C4, Canada
Tel.: (604) 294-4299
Fax: (604) 294-2081
E-Mail: mazdainfo@destinationauto.ca
Web Site: www.wolfemazda.com
Year Founded: 1986
Rev.: $12,954,798
Emp.: 628
Business Description:
New & Used Car Dealers
S.I.C.: 5511
N.A.I.C.S.: 441110
Personnel:
John Wolfe *(Pres)*

BURNAC CORPORATION

44 St Clair Avenue West
Toronto, ON, M4V 3C9, Canada
Tel.: (416) 964-3600
Fax: (416) 964-5840
E-Mail: info@burnac.com
Web Site: www.burnac.com
Year Founded: 1964
Rev.: $19,127,889
Emp.: 60
Business Description:
Real Estate Services
S.I.C.: 6531
N.A.I.C.S.: 531390
Personnel:
Joseph Burnett *(Chm)*
Ted Burnett *(Pres)*
Ronald McEachern *(Treas & VP)*
Lorne Burnett *(Exec VP)*

BURNCO ROCK PRODUCTS LTD

155 Glendeer Cir SE Ste 200
PO Box 1480
Station T, Calgary, AB, T2H 2P9, Canada
Tel.: (403) 255-2600
Fax: (403) 255-0323
Toll Free: (877) 528-7626
E-Mail: burnco@burnco.com
Web Site: www.burnco.com
Sales Range: $75-99.9 Million
Emp.: 550
Business Description:
Ready Mix Concrete Mfr
S.I.C.: 3273
N.A.I.C.S.: 327320
Personnel:
Scott M Burns *(Chm & CEO)*

BURNPUR CEMENT LIMITED

Gujarat Mansion 14 Bentinck Street
2nd Floor Suit No 7
Kolkata, West Bengal, 700 0001, India
Tel.: (91) 3322623167
Fax: (91) 3330250828
E-Mail: info@burnpurcement.com
Web Site: www.burnpurcement.com
Year Founded: 1980
BURNPUR—(NSE)
Rev.: $15,572,434
Assets: $33,805,259
Liabilities: $16,426,394
Net Worth: $17,378,865
Earnings: $587,179
Fiscal Year-end: 03/31/13
Business Description:
Cement Mfr & Distr
S.I.C.: 3241
N.A.I.C.S.: 327310
Personnel:
Ashok Gutgutia *(Vice Chm & Mng Dir)*
Ashish Roychowdhury *(CEO)*
Sudhansu Sekhar Panigrahi *(Compliance Officer & Sec)*
Board of Directors:
Prem Prakash Sharma
Ansul Agarwal
Manoj Kumar Agarwal
Prem Prakash Agarwal
Ashok Gutgutia
Bal Krishan Ladha
Subrata Mookherjee
Transfer Agent:
Niche Technologies Pvt. Ltd
D 511 Bagree Market 71 B R B Basu Road
700001 Kolkata, India

BURNSTONE VENTURES INC.

Suite 615 - 800 West Pender Street
Vancouver, BC, V6E 3T5, Canada
Tel.: (604) 687-2038
Fax: (604) 687-3141
E-Mail: info@burnstoneventures.com
Web Site: www.burnstoneventures.com
BVE—(TSXV)
Int. Income: $7,151
Assets: $1,617,930
Liabilities: $60,237
Net Worth: $1,557,693
Earnings: ($1,732,176)
Emp.: 10
Fiscal Year-end: 03/31/13
Business Description:
Mineral Mining & Exploration Services
S.I.C.: 1041
N.A.I.C.S.: 212221
Personnel:
Douglas Fulcher *(Pres & CEO)*
David Slater-Kinghorn *(CFO)*
Eugene Beukman *(Sec & VP-Admin)*
Board of Directors:
Eugene Beukman
Douglas Fulcher
Gordon Keevil
Emmet McGrath
Michael McInnis
Transfer Agent:
Computershare Trust Company of Canada
9th Floor 100 University Avenue
Toronto, ON, Canada

BURNT TREE GROUP LTD.

Burnt Tree House Knight Way
Battlefield Enterprise Park
Shrewsbury, Shropshire, SY1 3AB, United Kingdom
Tel.: (44) 1743457600
Fax: (44) 1743457648
Web Site: www.burnt-tree.co.uk
Sales Range: $50-74.9 Million
Emp.: 300
Business Description:
Car Rental Services
S.I.C.: 7514
N.A.I.C.S.: 532111
Personnel:
Richard Metcalfe *(CEO)*

BURO HAPPOLD ENGINEERS, LTD.
Camden Mill 230 Lower Bristol Rd
Bath, BA2 3DQ, United Kingdom
Tel.: (44) 1225320600
Fax: (44) 8707874148
E-Mail: enquires@burohappold.com
Web Site: www.burohappold.com
Year Founded: 1976
Emp.: 1,600
Business Description:
Engineering Services
S.I.C.: 8711
N.A.I.C.S.: 541330
Personnel:
Paul Westbury *(CEO)*

BURROWES
1570 de Montarville Blvd suite B
Boucherville, QC, J4B 5Y3, Canada
Tel.: (450) 655-6023
Fax: (450) 641-3860
Toll Free: (800) 939-7757
E-Mail: info@burrowes.ca
Web Site: www.burrowes.ca
Rev.: $27,126,824
Emp.: 60
Business Description:
Insurance Agencies
S.I.C.: 6411
N.A.I.C.S.: 524298
Personnel:
John Burrowes *(Pres)*

BURSA DE VALORI BUCURESTI
34-36 Carol St 14th Fl
District 2, Bucharest, 2, Romania
Tel.: (40) 213079500
Fax: (40) 213079519
E-Mail: bvb@bvb.ro
Web Site: www.bvb.ro
Emp.: 53
Business Description:
Stock Exchange Services
S.I.C.: 6231
N.A.I.C.S.: 523210
Personnel:
lucian Anghel *(Pres)*
Board of Directors:
Ionescu Dana-Mirela
Adrian Manaila
Sergiu Oprescu
Petru Prunea
Nilas Rares-Doralin

BURSA MALAYSIA BERHAD
15th Floor Exchange Square Bukit Kewangan
Kuala Lumpur, 50200, Malaysia
Tel.: (60) 320347000
Fax: (60) 327326437
E-Mail: enquiries@bursamalaysia.com
Web Site: www.bursamalaysia.com
Year Founded: 1973
BURSA—(KLS)
Rev.: $140,049,057
Assets: $720,913,101
Liabilities: $428,663,910
Net Worth: $292,249,190
Earnings: $51,728,068
Emp.: 626
Fiscal Year-end: 12/31/12
Business Description:
Stock Exchange Services
S.I.C.: 6231
N.A.I.C.S.: 523210
Personnel:
Tajuddin Atan *(CEO)*
Omar Ali Merican *(COO)*
Chai Kin Leong *(Acting CIO-Tech & Sys)*
Aishah Md Lassim *(Chief HR Officer)*
Kong Khai Chua *(Chief Market Ops Officer)*
Selvarany Rasiah *(Chief Regulatory Officer-Regulation)*
Kim Seng Chong *(CEO-Bursa Malaysia Derivatives)*
Suzanne Soo Yong Hong *(Co-Sec)*
Yong Hazadurah Md. Hashim *(Co-Sec)*
Board of Directors:
Mohamed Dzaiddin Abdullah
Puteh Rukiah Abd Majid
Muhamad Abdul Kadir
Abdul Samad Alias
Tajuddin Atan
Tek Kuang Cheah
Leong Huat Ong
Thillainathan Ramasamy
Md Tap Salleh
Puan Wah Wong
Izham Yusoff
Saiful Bahri Zainuddin
Subsidiaries:

Bursa Malaysia Derivatives Berhad **(1)**
2nd Fl Exchange Square Bukit Kewangan
50200 Kuala Lumpur, Malaysia
Tel.: (60) 3 2034 7000
Fax: (60) 3 2732 5258
E-Mail: futures@bursamalaysia.com
Web Site: www.bursamalaysia.com
Securities Services
S.I.C.: 6211
N.A.I.C.S.: 523999
Tajuddin Atan *(Chm)*
Chong Kim Seng *(CEO)*

Bursa Malaysia Information Sdn Bhd **(1)**
11th Floor Exchange Square
Bukit Kewangan, 50200 Kuala Lumpur, Malaysia
Tel.: (60) 3 2034 7084
Fax: (60) 3 2026 3699
E-Mail: infoservices@bursamalaysia.com
Emp.: 5
Securities Services
S.I.C.: 6211
N.A.I.C.S.: 523999
Lee Siew Tin *(VP)*

Bursa Malaysia IT Sdn Bhd **(1)**
4th Floor Exchange Square
Bukit Kewangan, 50200 Kuala Lumpur, Malaysia
Tel.: (60) 3 20267099
Fax: (60) 3 20263716
Web Site: www.klse.com
Securities Services
S.I.C.: 6211
N.A.I.C.S.: 523999

Bursa Malaysia Property Sdn Bhd **(1)**
15th Floor Exchange Square
Bukit Kewangan, 50200 Kuala Lumpur, Malaysia
Tel.: (60) 320347000
Fax: (60) 60327326437
E-Mail: yong@bursamalaysia.com
Web Site: www.klse.com
Emp.: 600
Securities Services
S.I.C.: 6211
N.A.I.C.S.: 523999
Dato Yusli Mohamed Yusoff *(CEO)*
Yong Hazadurah Md Hashim *(Sec)*

Labuan International Financial Exchange Inc. **(1)**
Unit B Level 7 Main Ofc Tower Financial Park Complex
Jalan Merdeka, 87000 Labuan, Malaysia (100%)
Tel.: (60) 87451359
Fax: (60) 87451379
E-Mail: cust-mgmt@lfx.com.my
Web Site: www.lfx.com.my
Sales Range: $25-49.9 Million
Emp.: 6
Securities Services
S.I.C.: 6211
N.A.I.C.S.: 523999
Goban Arasu *(Mng Dir)*

Malaysia Derivatives Exchange Berhad **(1)**
10th Floor Exchange Square
Bukit Kewangan, 50200 Kuala Lumpur, Malaysia
Tel.: (60) 320347000
Fax: (60) 320264122
Web Site: www.klse.com.my/
Securities Services
S.I.C.: 6211
N.A.I.C.S.: 523999
Tajuddin Atan *(Chm)*
Chong Kim Seng *(CEO)*

Malaysian Central Depository Sdn Bhd **(1)**
6th Floor Exchange Square
Bukit Kewangan, 50200 Kuala Lumpur, Malaysia
Tel.: (60) 320262099
Fax: (60) 3 20263719
Securities Services
S.I.C.: 6211
N.A.I.C.S.: 523999

Securities Clearing Automated Network Services Sdn Bhd **(1)**
6th Fl Exchange Square
Bukit Kewngan, 50200 Kuala Lumpur, Malaysia
Tel.: (60) 3 20268099
Fax: (60) 3 20263715
Securities Services
S.I.C.: 6211
N.A.I.C.S.: 523999

Yayasan Bursa Malaysia **(1)**
15th Floor Exchange Square
Bukim Kewangan, 50200 Kuala Lumpur, Malaysia
Tel.: (60) 320347000
Fax: (60) 320263687
E-Mail: aidura@bursamalaysia.com
Securities Services
S.I.C.: 6211
N.A.I.C.S.: 523999
Aidura Haron *(Head-Community Investment)*

BURSEI DE VALORI A MOLDOVEI
(d/b/a Moldova Stock Exchange)
Stefan cel Mare Blvd 73 Room 352
MD2001 Chisinau, Moldova
Tel.: (373) 22277594
Fax: (373) 22277358
E-Mail: postmaster@moldse.md
Web Site: www.moldse.md
Year Founded: 1994
Emp.: 20
Business Description:
Stock Exchange Services
S.I.C.: 6231
N.A.I.C.S.: 523210
Personnel:
Sergiu Cebotari *(Chm)*
Corneliu Dodu *(Pres)*

BURU ENERGY LIMITED
Level 2 88 William Street
Perth, WA, 6000, Australia
Mailing Address:
PO Box 7794
Cloisters Square, Perth, WA, 6850, Australia
Tel.: (61) 892151800
Fax: (61) 892151899
E-Mail: info@buruenergy.com
Web Site: www.buruenergy.com.au
BRU—(ASX OTC)
Rev.: $5,648,182
Assets: $186,963,161
Liabilities: $52,982,448
Net Worth: $133,980,713
Earnings: ($18,150,256)
Emp.: 72
Fiscal Year-end: 06/30/13
Business Description:
Petroleum Exploration Services
S.I.C.: 1311
N.A.I.C.S.: 211111
Personnel:
Keiran John Wulff *(Mng Dir)*
Christopher J. Bath *(CFO & Sec)*
Board of Directors:
Graham Riley
Peter Jones
Eric Streitberg
Keiran John Wulff

BURWILL HOLDINGS LIMITED
Unit 1402 14/F Office Tower
Convention Plaza 1 Harbour Road
Wanchai, China (Hong Kong)
Tel.: (852) 28777368
Fax: (852) 28777037
E-Mail: contactcentre@burwill.com
Web Site: www.burwill.com
0024—(HKG)
Sls.: $633,959,980
Assets: $439,034,647
Liabilities: $214,277,762
Net Worth: $224,756,884
Earnings: ($59,034,342)
Emp.: 534
Fiscal Year-end: 12/31/12
Business Description:
International Steel Trading
S.I.C.: 3324
N.A.I.C.S.: 331512
Personnel:
Shing Chan *(Chm & Mng Dir)*
Mark Yin *(Pres/Gen Mgr-Steel Processing)*
Guojian Zhang *(Pres/Gen Mgr-Comml Property Investment-Yangzhou Times Square)*
Wai Lam Kwok *(Sec & Controller-Fin)*
Board of Directors:
Shing Chan
Ming Fai Chan
Bun Chang
Shu Ming Cui
Shenglan Huang
Wai Lam Kwok
Ting Lau
Mike Kai Man Sham
Hoi Tung Sit
Virginia Pui Shan Tung
Dawei Yang
Mark Yin

Butterfield Fulcrum Group (Bermuda) Limited
26 Burnaby Street
Hamilton, HM 11, Bermuda
Transfer Agent:
Boardroom Corporate & Advisory Services Pte. Ltd.
50 Raffles Place 32-01 Singapore Land Tower
Singapore, Singapore

Subsidiaries:

Burwill Resources Limited **(1)**
Rm 1402 14 F Convention Plz Ofc Tower 1
Harbour RdWanchai
Wanchai, China (Hong Kong)
Tel.: (852) 28777368
Fax: (852) 28772282
E-Mail: bwr@burwill.com
Emp.: 150
Steel Products Distr
S.I.C.: 5051
N.A.I.C.S.: 423510
Sham Kai Man *(Mng Dir)*

Burwill Steel Pipes Limited **(1)**
Unit 1402 Ofc Tower Convention Plz 1
Harbour Rd
Wanchai, China (Hong Kong)
Tel.: (852) 26778839
Fax: (852) 26821079
E-Mail: sales.bsp@burwill.com
Web Site: www.burwill-bsp.com
Emp.: 50
Steel Processing Services
S.I.C.: 3399
N.A.I.C.S.: 331221
Mark Yin *(Pres)*

BURZA CENNYCH PAPIEROV V BRATISLAVE, A.S.
Vysoka 17
PO Box 151
814 99 Bratislava, Slovakia
Tel.: (421) 249236111
Fax: (421) 249236103
E-Mail: info@bsse.sk
Web Site: www.bsse.sk
Sales Range: $1-9.9 Million
Emp.: 30
Business Description:
Stock Exchange Services
S.I.C.: 6231
N.A.I.C.S.: 523210
Personnel:
Vladimir Kocourek *(Chm)*
Anna Bubenikova *(Chm-Supervisory Bd)*
Maria Hurajova *(Vice Chm)*
Board of Directors:
Vladimir Kocourek
Ivan Gransky
Maria Hurajova
Elena Kohutikova
Robert Kopal
Pavol Kristof
Emilia Palkova
Tomas Pavlak
Tibor Pongracz
Juraj Sipko
Dusan Tomasec
Supervisory Board of Directors:
Anna Bubenikova
Rastislav Matejsko
Jozef Mihalik
Todor Todorov
Jan Vaculciak

BUSAN CITY GAS CO., LTD.
(Formerly Pusan City Gas Co., Ltd.)
545 Namcheon-1 Dong
Suyeong-Gu, Busan, 613-713, Korea (South)
Tel.: (82) 51 6071011
Fax: (82) 51 6239870
Web Site: www.pusancitygas.com
Year Founded: 1981
015350—(KRS)
Sales Range: $900-999.9 Million
Emp.: 276
Business Description:
Liquefied Natural Gas Distr
S.I.C.: 4924
N.A.I.C.S.: 221210
Personnel:
Yong-Woo Cho *(CEO)*

BUSAN TEXTILE INDUSTRY CO., LTD.
5 6th Floor Bubang Extension Bldg
156 Samseong-dong
Gangnam-gu, Seoul, Korea (South)
Tel.: (82) 2 2008 7200
Fax: (82) 2 565 8746
Web Site: www.busantex.co.kr
Year Founded: 1934
025270—(KRS)
Business Description:
Textile & Apparel Mfr
S.I.C.: 2299
N.A.I.C.S.: 313310
Personnel:
Choon-Ho Roh *(CEO)*

BUSH PHARMACEUTICALS LTD.
1 Oaza-Takeno
Kawagoe, Saitama, Japan
Tel.: (81) 49 233 4651
Fax: (81) 49 233 4655
Web Site: www.bush-seiyaku.co.jp
Year Founded: 1998
Sales Range: $150-199.9 Million
Business Description:
Contract Pharmaceutical Mfr
S.I.C.: 2834
N.A.I.C.S.: 325412
Personnel:
Takayuki Kasai *(Pres)*

BUSHVELD MINERALS LIMITED
Suite 3A #5 Fricker Road
Illovo, Johannesburg, 2116, South Africa
Tel.: (27) 11 268 6555
Fax: (27) 11 268 5170
Web Site: www.bushveldminerals.com
BMN—(AIM)
Assets: $86,849,129
Liabilities: $314,503
Net Worth: $86,534,626
Earnings: ($3,559,623)
Fiscal Year-end: 02/28/13
Business Description:
Holding Company; Iron Ore Mining
S.I.C.: 6719
N.A.I.C.S.: 551112
Personnel:
Fortune Mojapelo *(CEO)*
Anthony Viljoen *(COO)*
Board of Directors:
Ian Watson
Jeremy Friedlander
Fortune Mojapelo
Geoffrey Sproule
Anthony Viljoen
Non-U.S. Subsidiary:

Lemur Resources Limited (1)
Suite 1 Ground Floor 83 Havelock Street
West Perth, WA, 6005, Australia AU
Tel.: (61) 8 9486 4768 (54.39%)
Fax: (61) 8 9322 5230
E-Mail: enquiries@lemurresources.com
Web Site: www.lemurresources.com.au
LMR—(ASX)
Rev.: $1,062,639
Assets: $30,512,457
Liabilities: $808,662
Net Worth: $29,703,794
Earnings: ($698,535)
Fiscal Year-end: 12/31/12
Coal Mining
S.I.C.: 1222
N.A.I.C.S.: 212112
Anthony Viljoen *(CEO)*
Dale Hanna *(CFO)*
Shannon Coates *(Sec)*

BUSINESS & DECISION SA
153 rue de Courcelles
75107 Paris, France
Tel.: (33) 156212121
Fax: (33) 156212122
E-Mail: finance@businessdecision.com
Web Site: www.businessdecision.com
Year Founded: 1992
BND—(EUR)
Sls.: $299,361,285
Assets: $212,429,665
Liabilities: $130,971,572
Net Worth: $81,458,093
Earnings: $2,300,605
Emp.: 2,416
Fiscal Year-end: 12/31/12
Business Description:
Business Consulting, Data Engineering & Customer Relationship Management Services
S.I.C.: 8742
N.A.I.C.S.: 541611
Personnel:
Patrick Bensabat *(Chm & Mng Dir)*
Christophe Dumoulin *(Vice Chm & Deputy Mng Dir)*
Emmanuel Parodi *(CFO)*
Board of Directors:
Patrick Bensabat
Michele Bensabat
Christophe Dumoulin
Copernic SARL
5 rue Crevaux
Paris, France
Subsidiaries:

Exens (1)
153 rue de Courcelles
75817 Paris, France
Tel.: (33) 1 56 21 21 21
Fax: (33) 1 56 21 21 22
Web Site: www.exens.fr
Enterprise Resource Planning Software Development Services
S.I.C.: 7371
N.A.I.C.S.: 541511
Jean-Francois Danquigny *(Mgr)*

SARL Business & Decision Alliance (1)
153 rue de Courcelles
75817 Paris, France
Tel.: (33) 1 56 21 21 21
Fax: (33) 1 56 21 21 22
Business Planning Software Development Services
S.I.C.: 7371
N.A.I.C.S.: 541511

SARL Business & Decision Lille (1)
11/13/15 square Dutilleul
59000 Lille, Nord, France
Tel.: (33) 320344488
Fax: (33) 3 20 34 44 80
Web Site: www.businessdecision.com
Business Planning Software Development Services
S.I.C.: 7371
N.A.I.C.S.: 541511

SCI Mangin (1)
386 rue Gen Leclerc
60170 Carlepont, Oise, France
Tel.: (33) 3 44 75 34 64
Engineering Services
S.I.C.: 8711
N.A.I.C.S.: 541330

U.S. Subsidiary:

Inforte Corp. (1)
940 W Valley Rd Ste 1000
Wayne, PA 19087-1800 DE
Tel.: (312) 540-0900
Fax: (312) 540-0855
Toll Free: (800) 340-0200
Sales Range: $25-49.9 Million
Emp.: 253
Business Consulting Services
S.I.C.: 8999
N.A.I.C.S.: 541690
Andreas Wilmsmeier *(Mng Dir-Germany)*

Non-U.S. Subsidiaries:

BD Chine (1)
Office 402 Baiyan Building No 238
Beisihuan Zhong Road
Haidian District, Beijing, China
Tel.: (86) 10 823 32 835
Fax: (86) 10 823 32 062
E-Mail: info.cn@businessdecision.com
Web Site: www.businessdecision.cn
Emp.: 28
Business Planning Software Development Services
S.I.C.: 7371
N.A.I.C.S.: 541511
Zixiong Wang *(Gen Mgr)*

BD Espana (1)
Calle Princesa 25
28008 Madrid, Spain
Tel.: (34) 915159547
Fax: (34) 914113773
Emp.: 30
Business Planning Software Development Services
S.I.C.: 7371
N.A.I.C.S.: 541511
Mariagose Torres *(Mgr)*

BD Israel Ltd. (1)
20 Hamagshimim Str Kiryat Matalon
Petah Tiqwa, 49170, Israel
Tel.: (972) 39213550
Fax: (972) 39215087
E-Mail: info@businessdecision.com
Emp.: 22
Business Planning Software Development Services
S.I.C.: 7371
N.A.I.C.S.: 541511
Michael Ben-Shabat *(CEO)*

BD Italie (1)
4 via dei Caudini
00185 Rome, Italy
Tel.: (39) 06 96 52 79 73
Fax: (39) 06 96 52 79 74
Business Planning Software Development Services
S.I.C.: 7371
N.A.I.C.S.: 541511

BD Maroc (1)
265 Bd Zerktouni 2eme etage N 22
20050 Casablanca, Morocco
Tel.: (212) 5 22 94 11 94
Fax: (212) 522 95 19 11
E-Mail: bouchra.challal@businessdecision.com
Emp.: 25
Business Planning Software Development Services
S.I.C.: 7371
N.A.I.C.S.: 541511
David Tuledano *(Mgr)*

BD Mauritius (1)
7th Floor BG Court Rue Saint Jean et Avenue d'Epinay
Quatre Bornes, Mauritius
Tel.: (230) 4660931
Fax: (230) 4650696
E-Mail: info@businessdecision.mu
Emp.: 35
Software Development & Consulting Services
S.I.C.: 7371
N.A.I.C.S.: 541511

Business & Decision AG (1)
Lowenstrasse 12
8001 Zurich, Switzerland
Tel.: (41) 44 390 37 21
Fax: (41) 44 390 37 22
E-Mail: info@businessdecision.com
Web Site: www.businessdecision.ch
Emp.: 15
Business Planning Software Development Services
S.I.C.: 7371
N.A.I.C.S.: 541511
Sami Jaballah *(Mng Dir-Geneva Branch)*

Business & Decision Benelux SA (1)
Sint Lambertusstraat Rue Saint Lambert 141
1200 Brussels, Belgium
Tel.: (32) 25100540
Fax: (32) 27741199
E-Mail: info@businessdecision.be
Web Site: www.businessdecision.be
Emp.: 300
Business Management Software Development Services
S.I.C.: 7371
N.A.I.C.S.: 541511
Ada Sekyirm *(CEO)*

Non-U.S. Subsidiary:

BD Luxembourg (2)
4 rue d'Orange
2267 Luxembourg, Luxembourg
Tel.: (352) 26458650
Fax: (352) 26458659
Web Site: www.businessdecision.lu
Emp.: 35
Business Planning Software Development Services
S.I.C.: 7371
N.A.I.C.S.: 541511
Pierre Daussenbach *(Mng Dir)*

Business & Decision Netherlands BV (1)
Wattbaan 52A
3439 ML Nieuwegein, Utrecht, Netherlands
Tel.: (31) 308200333
Fax: (31) 306308075
E-Mail: admin.nl@businessdecision.com
Web Site: www.businessdecision.nl
Emp.: 40

Business Planning Software Development Services
S.I.C.: 7371
N.A.I.C.S.: 541511
Michael Gomes *(Mgr-Practice)*

Business & Decision Software India (P) Ltd (1)
2nd Floor NDK Trust 13th Main off 100 Ft Road
Hall II Stage
Indiranagar, Bengaluru, 560 038, India
Tel.: (91) 8041256369
Web Site: www.businessdecision.co.uk/1652-india.htm
Consulting Services
S.I.C.: 8999
N.A.I.C.S.: 541690

BUSINESS BRAIN SHOWA-OTA INC.

21F Hibiya Central Bldg 1-2-9
Nishishimbashi Minato-ku
Tokyo, 105-0003, Japan
Tel.: (81) 3 3507 1300
Fax: (81) 3 3507 1301
Web Site: www.bbs.co.jp
Year Founded: 1967
9658—(JAS)
Sls.: $175,758,000
Assets: $113,300,000
Liabilities: $56,540,000
Net Worth: $56,760,000
Earnings: $5,104,000
Emp.: 896
Fiscal Year-end: 03/31/13

Business Description:
Management Consulting Services
S.I.C.: 8748
N.A.I.C.S.: 541618

Personnel:
Toshihiko Ishikawa *(Pres & CEO)*

Subsidiaries:

ISS Inc. (1)
4710-3 Tomitsuka-cho Naka-ku
Hamamatsu-Shi, Shizuoka, 432-8002, Japan
Tel.: (81) 53 456 1595
Fax: (81) 53 456 1632
Web Site: www.mics-i.co.jp
Staff Recruitment Services
S.I.C.: 7361
N.A.I.C.S.: 561311
Chikahisa Ioka *(CFO)*

PLM Japan Inc. (1)
5F Hibiya Central Bldg Nishishimbashi 1-2-9
Minato-ku, Tokyo, 105-0003, Japan
Tel.: (81) 3 3507 134
Fax: (81) 3 3507 1341
Web Site: www.plmj.jp
Software Development Services
S.I.C.: 7371
N.A.I.C.S.: 541511

BUSINESS CENTRIC SERVICES GROUP

130 Old Street
London, EC1V 9BD, United Kingdom
Tel.: (44) 845 880 8820
E-Mail: clients@bcsg.com
Web Site: www.bcsg.com
Year Founded: 2006
Sales Range: $10-24.9 Million
Emp.: 100

Business Description:
Information Technology Consultancy Services
S.I.C.: 7373
N.A.I.C.S.: 541512

Personnel:
John Davis *(Mng Dir)*
Phil Bircumshaw *(CTO)*

BUSINESS CONNEXION GROUP LIMITED

Business Connexion Park 789 16th Rd Randjespark
PO Box X48
Halfway House, Midrand, Gauteng, 1685, South Africa
Tel.: (27) 112665111
Fax: (27) 112661088
E-Mail: info@bcx.co.za
Web Site: www.bcx.co.za
BCX—(JSE)
Rev.: $689,561,966
Assets: $440,018,693
Liabilities: $171,844,418
Net Worth: $268,174,275
Earnings: $26,025,542
Emp.: 7,000
Fiscal Year-end: 08/31/13

Business Description:
Holding Company; Information & Communication Technology Products & Services
S.I.C.: 6719
N.A.I.C.S.: 551112

Personnel:
Benjamin Mophatlane *(CEO)*
Vanessa Olver *(Deputy CEO & Grp Exec-Svcs Div)*
Lawrence Weitzman *(CFO)*
Matthew Blewett *(COO)*
Andy Brauer *(CTO)*
Jane Canny *(Grp Exec-UCS Div)*
Grace Dipale *(Grp Exec-HR)*
Themba Gumbi *(Grp Exec-Bus Dev-Pub Sector)*
John Jenkins *(Grp Exec-Bus Dev-Private Sector)*
Isaac Mophatlane *(Grp Exec-Canoa Div)*
Douglas Woolley *(Grp Exec-Tech Div)*
Rodwell Zvarayi *(Grp Exec-Intl Div)*
Johan de Koker *(Sec)*

Board of Directors:
Anthony Ruiters
John Bester
Alex Darko
Mike Ettling
John Jenkins
Jenitha John
Nkenke Kekana
Mamoroke Lehobye
Benjamin Mophatlane
Vanessa Olver
Dean C. Sparrow
Lawrence Weitzman

Transfer Agent:
Computershare Investor Services (Pty) Limited
Ground Floor 70 Marshall Street
Johannesburg, South Africa

Subsidiaries:

Accsys (Proprietary) Limited (1)
Sandhavon Ofc Park Pongola Crescent
Eastgate Ext 17
Sandton, Gauteng, 2199, South Africa
Tel.: (27) 117198000
Fax: (27) 117198060
E-Mail: support@accsys.co.za
Web Site: www.accsys.co.za
Emp.: 70
Human Resource Software Development Services
S.I.C.: 7371
N.A.I.C.S.: 541511
Teryl Schroenn *(CEO)*
Liam Terblanche *(CIO)*

Business Connexion (Pty) Limited (1)
Business Connexion Park - South Block B
789 16th Road Randjespark, Midrand, South Africa (100%)
Tel.: (27) 112665111
Fax: (27) 112665123
E-Mail: clive.vanrooyen@bcx.co.za
Web Site: www.bcx.co.za/live/content.php?Category_ID=32
Emp.: 3,500
Custom Computer Programming Services
S.I.C.: 7371
N.A.I.C.S.: 541511
Benjamin Mophatlane *(CEO)*

Subsidiaries:

Business Connexion Communications (Pty) Limited (2)
789 Business Connexion Park 16 Road
Randjespark Halfway House
Midrand, Gauteng, 4685, South Africa
Tel.: (27) 112665111
Fax: (27) 112560504
Communication & Web Hosting Services
S.I.C.: 4899
N.A.I.C.S.: 517919
Vanessa Olver *(CEO)*

Business Connexion Technology Holdings (Pty) Limited (2)
789 16th Road Randjespark
Midrand, 1685, South Africa
Tel.: (27) 112661000
Fax: (27) 112666647
Business Management Software Development Services
S.I.C.: 7371
N.A.I.C.S.: 541511

Nanoteq (Pty) Limited (2)
1 Pieter St
PO Box 7991
0046 Centurion, South Africa (100%)
Tel.: (27) 126727000
Fax: (27) 126651343
E-Mail: info@nanoteq.com
Web Site: www.nanoteq.com
Emp.: 60
Custom Computer Programming Services
S.I.C.: 7371
N.A.I.C.S.: 541511
Mike Zenter *(CEO)*

Non-U.S. Subsidiaries:

Business Connexion Limited (2)
Connexion House 4 Arlington Court Whittle Way Arlington Business Park
Stevenage, Hertfordshire, SG1 2FS, United Kingdom
Tel.: (44) 8456781122
E-Mail: info@bcx.uk.com
Web Site: www.bcx.uk.com
Emp.: 25
Software Support Services
S.I.C.: 7371
N.A.I.C.S.: 541511
Leetile Benjamin Mophatlane *(CEO)*
Marius W. Schoeman *(CFO)*
Andy J. Brauer *(CTO)*

Business Connexion Mozambique Limitada (2)
Rua de Kassuende No 140
Bairro da Polana, Maputo, Mozambique
Tel.: (258) 21495530
Fax: (258) 21494831
E-Mail: info-bcxmoz@bcx.co.mz
Emp.: 50
Business Management Software Development Services
S.I.C.: 7371
N.A.I.C.S.: 541511
Celia Hofmeister *(Mng Dir)*

Business Connexion Namibia (Pty) Limited (2)
Corner Jan Jonker Road & Thorer Street
PO Box 6702
Windhoek, Namibia
Tel.: (264) 612040000
Fax: (264) 612040009
E-Mail: bcx@bcx.com.na
Web Site: www.bcx.com.na
Emp.: 80
Internet & Telecommunication Services
S.I.C.: 4813
N.A.I.C.S.: 517110
Ferdi Graupe *(CEO)*

Business Connexion Networks (Nigeria) Limited (2)
Adebola House 228A Awolowo Road
Lagos, Nigeria
Tel.: (234) 702 5337 980
Fax: (234) 1 463 8325
Business Management Software Development Services
S.I.C.: 7371
N.A.I.C.S.: 541511

Business Connexion Tanzania Limited (2)
Mikocheni Lucy Lameck St Plot 6
Kinondoni District, Dar es Salaam, 766384, Tanzania
Tel.: (255) 222780606
Fax: (255) 222780504
E-Mail: info@bcx.co.tz
Web Site: www.bcx.co.za
Emp.: 30
Business Management Software Development Services
S.I.C.: 7371
N.A.I.C.S.: 541511
Joram Ngowi *(Mgr-Ops)*

CEB Maintenance Africa (Proprietary) Limited (1)
5 Monza Rd
Westmead, Pinetown, KwaZulu-Natal, 3610, South Africa
Tel.: (27) 317003332
Fax: (27) 317003355
E-Mail: cebdbn@cebmain.co.za
Web Site: www.ceb.co.za
Emp.: 400
Information Technology Support Services
S.I.C.: 7373
N.A.I.C.S.: 541512
Desmond Poulter *(Mng Dir)*

UCS Solutions (Proprietary) Limited (1)
2nd Fl ABB Park The Crescent 3 Eglin Rd
Sunninghill, Johannesburg, Gauteng, 2157, South Africa
Tel.: (27) 115189000
Fax: (27) 118034017
E-Mail: info@ucs-solutions.co.za
Web Site: www.ucs-solutions.co.za
Emp.: 500
Business Management Solutions
S.I.C.: 8741
N.A.I.C.S.: 561110
Richard Newton *(CEO)*

Branch:

UCS Solutions (2)
7th Fl Newlands Terraces 8 Boundary Rd
PO Box 27
Rondebosch, Cape Town, 7701, South Africa (100%)
Tel.: (27) 216804000
Fax: (27) 216804040
E-Mail: info@ucs-solutions.co.za
Web Site: www.ucs-solutions.co.za
Emp.: 100
Provider of Networking Services
S.I.C.: 7373
N.A.I.C.S.: 541512
Richard Newton *(CEO)*

Non-U.S. Subsidiary:

Q Data Europe Limited (1)
Gate House Fretherne Road
AL86NS Welwyn Garden City, United Kingdom (100%)
Tel.: (44) 1707395885
Fax: (44) 1707395880
E-Mail: info@qdataeurope.com
Web Site: www.qdataeurope.com
Emp.: 55
Other Management Consulting Services
S.I.C.: 8748
N.A.I.C.S.: 541618

BUSINESS CREATION HOLDINGS B.V.

Tower A Fl 5 Strawimskylaan 509
1077 XX Amsterdam, Netherlands
Tel.: (31) 206724438
Fax: (31) 206724439
E-Mail: info@businesscreation.com
Web Site: www.businesscreation.com
Year Founded: 1982
Emp.: 25

Business Description:
Business Redevelopment Consultant
S.I.C.: 8748
N.A.I.C.S.: 541618

Personnel:
Andreas Ezinga *(Owner & Mng Dir)*

Business Creation Holdings B.V.—(Continued)

U.S. Division:

Global Imaging (1)
51 Industrial Dr
North Smithfield, RI 02896-8032 DE
Mailing Address: (100%)
PO Box 278
Slatersville, RI 02876-0278
Tel.: (401) 762-3800
Fax: (401) 767-4437
Web Site: www.nimaging.com
Emp.: 50
Mfr. of Electron Tubes
S.I.C.: 3679
N.A.I.C.S.: 334419
Bill Ulmschneider *(Pres & COO)*

Divisions:

Narragansett Imaging (2)
51 Industrial Dr
North Smithfield, RI 02896-0278
Mailing Address:
PO Box 278
Slatersville, RI 02876-0278
Tel.: (401) 762-3800
Fax: (401) 767-4407
E-Mail: info@nimaging.com
Web Site: www.nimaging.com
Optical Devices
S.I.C.: 3679
N.A.I.C.S.: 334419
Frank Epps *(Co-Owner)*

Solid State & Active Devices Division (2)
One Providence Pike
Slatersville, RI 02876-0278
Tel.: (401) 762-3800
Mfr. of Solid State Imaging Modules
S.I.C.: 5051
N.A.I.C.S.: 423510

BUSINESS DEVELOPMENT BANK OF CANADA
5 Place Ville Marie Suite 400
Montreal, QC, H3B 5E7, Canada
Tel.: (514) 283-5904
Fax: (877) 329-9232
Toll Free: (877) 232-2269
E-Mail: info@bdc.ca
Web Site: www.bdc.ca
Year Founded: 1944
Int. Income: $962,003,610
Assets: $18,075,165,248
Liabilities: $14,154,544,606
Net Worth: $3,920,620,642
Earnings: $465,510,500
Emp.: 2,000
Fiscal Year-end: 03/31/13
Business Description:
Commercial Banking
S.I.C.: 6029
N.A.I.C.S.: 522110
Personnel:
Samuel L. Duboc *(Chm)*
Jean-Rene Halde *(Pres & CEO)*
Charles Cazabon *(Mng Partner-GO Capital)*
Robert Simon *(Sr Mng Partner-IT Venture Fund)*
Paul Buron *(CFO & Exec VP)*
Chantal Belzile *(CIO & Sr VP)*
Philip Hould *(Branding & Sponsorship Officer)*
Francois Laurin *(Treas)*
Louise Paradis *(Sec & Sr VP-Legal Affairs)*
Pierre Dubreuil *(Exec VP-Fin & Consulting)*
Jerome Nycz *(Exec VP-Subordinate Fin & Venture Capital)*
Michel Bergeron *(Sr VP-Mktg & Pub Affairs)*
Patrice Bernard *(Sr VP-Fin & Consulting-Quebec)*
Gina Gale *(Sr VP-Fin & Consulting-Atlantic)*
Mary Karamanos *(Sr VP-HR)*
Patrick Latour *(Sr VP-Fin & Consulting-Prairies & West)*
Peter Lawler *(Sr VP-Fin & Consulting-Ontario)*
Andre St-Pierre *(Sr VP-Credit Risk Mgmt)*
Board of Directors:
Samuel L. Duboc
Eric Boyko
Michael Calyniuk
Sue Fawcett
Shahir Guindi
Jean-Rene Halde
Brian Hayward
Jean Martel
Prashant Shanker Pathak
Rick Perkins
Rosemary Zigrossi

BUSINESS MONITOR INTERNATIONAL LTD.
(Acquired by Fimalac S.A.)

BUSINESS ONLINE PUBLIC COMPANY LIMITED
900/8-10 SVOA Tower 11th 12th 14th Floor Rama III Road Bangpongpang
Yannawa, Bangkok, 10120, Thailand
Tel.: (66) 26573999
Fax: (66) 26573900
E-Mail: info@bol.co.th
Web Site: www.bol.co.th
BOL—(THA)
Rev.: $12,623,999
Assets: $14,109,077
Liabilities: $5,193,049
Net Worth: $8,916,028
Earnings: $2,829,553
Emp.: 142
Fiscal Year-end: 12/31/12
Business Description:
Business Information Services
S.I.C.: 7389
N.A.I.C.S.: 561499
Personnel:
Noravat Suwarn *(Chm)*
Min Intanate *(Chm-Exec Bd)*
Chamaiporn Apikulvanich *(CEO & Gen Mgr)*
Kanyapan Buranarom *(CFO)*
Chaiyaporn Kiatnuntavimon *(COO & Sec)*
Board of Directors:
Noravat Suwarn
Chamaiporn Apikulvanich
Min Intanate
Prayoon Rattanachaiyanont
Suteera Sripaibulya
Anant Tangtatswas
Wilson Yong Peng Teo
Khiam Boon Teoh
Manida Zinmerman

Subsidiaries:

iBOL Co., Ltd. (1)
900/21 25 Fl Rama III Rd Bangpongpang
Yannawa, Bangkok, 10120, Thailand
Tel.: (66) 2657 3988
Fax: (66) 2657 3900
Information Technology Consulting Services
S.I.C.: 7373
N.A.I.C.S.: 541512

D&B (Thailand) Co., Ltd. (1)
900/8-10 SVOA Tower Rama III Rd Bangpongpang
Yannawa, Bangkok, 10120, Thailand
Tel.: (66) 2657 3939
Fax: (66) 2657 3901
Credit Reporting Services
S.I.C.: 7323
N.A.I.C.S.: 561450
Jack Min Intanate, *(Chm)*

BUSINESS TELECOM NYRT.
Mindszenti krt 27
6000 Kecskemet, Hungary
Tel.: (36) 76585027
Fax: (36) 76777999
Web Site: www.btel.hu
BTEL—(BUD)
Business Description:
Telecommunications
S.I.C.: 4813
N.A.I.C.S.: 517110
Personnel:
Krisztian Takacs *(Chm & CEO)*
Judit Kurdik-Tasnadi-Szekely *(CFO)*
Gabor Takacs *(CMO)*
Board of Directors:
Krisztian Takacs
Andrea Borsuk
Dezso Kormendi
Attila Sokvari
Ilona Szoke
Gabor Takacs
Milan Toth
Laszlo Pal Varga

BUSINESSWORLD PUBLISHING CORP.
(Acquired by Philippine Long Distance Telephone Company)

BUSS-SMS-CANZLER GMBH
Kaiserstrasse 13-15
Butzbach, 35510, Germany
Tel.: (49) 6033850
Telex: 4 184 481 sms d
Fax: (49) 603385249
E-Mail: info@sms-vt.com
Web Site: www.sms-vt.com
Year Founded: 1919
Sales Range: $25-49.9 Million
Emp.: 171
Business Description:
Developer & Mfr of Thermal Separation Components & Systems
S.I.C.: 3559
N.A.I.C.S.: 333249
Personnel:
Harald Bechmann *(Mng Dir)*

BUSSEYS AND SABBERTON BROS. LTD.
95 Whiffler Road
Norwich, Norfolk, NR3 2EU, United Kingdom
Tel.: (44) 1603909986
Fax: (44) 1603254010
E-Mail: marketing@busseys.co.uk
Web Site: www.busseys.co.uk
Year Founded: 1911
Rev.: $67,264,010
Emp.: 210
Business Description:
New & Used Car Dealers
S.I.C.: 5511
N.A.I.C.S.: 441110
Personnel:
Charlers Bussey *(Chm)*
David Bussey *(Mng Dir)*

BUSY BEE CLEANING SERVICES LTD.
Units 5/6 Kingsmill Park London Rd
Loudwater, High Wycombe, Bucks, HP10 9UB, United Kingdom
Tel.: (44) 1494530077
Fax: (44) 01494530037
E-Mail: enquiries@busybeecleaning.co.uk
Web Site: www.busybeecleaning.co.uk
Sales Range: $150-199.9 Million
Emp.: 1,500
Business Description:
Building Cleaning Services
S.I.C.: 7342
N.A.I.C.S.: 561710
Personnel:
Gary C. Stevens *(Founder & Mng Dir)*

BUT SON CEMENT PACKING JOINT STOCK COMPANY
Km 2 Van Cao Str
Nam Dinh, Vietnam
Tel.: (84) 350383 9353
Fax: (84) 350384 0395
Web Site: www.baobibutson.com.vn
Year Founded: 2003
BBS—(HNX)
Business Description:
Cement Sack Mfr
S.I.C.: 2671
N.A.I.C.S.: 322220
Personnel:
Pham Van Minh *(Mgr)*

THE BUTCHER ENGINEERING ENTERPRISES LIMITED
2755 Lauzon Parkway
Windsor, ON, Canada N8T 3H5
Tel.: (519) 944-9200
Fax: (519) 944-8338
E-Mail: info1@butcherent.com
Web Site: www.butcherengineering.com
Year Founded: 1943
Rev.: $69,555,960
Emp.: 850
Business Description:
Packaging & Painting Services
S.I.C.: 4783
N.A.I.C.S.: 488991
Personnel:
William Spencer *(Pres)*

BUTCHER'S PET CARE LTD.
Baker Group House
Crick, Northamptonshire, NN6 7TZ, United Kingdom
Tel.: (44) 1788 825 872
Fax: (44) 1788 822 960
E-Mail: consumerservice@butcherspetcare.com
Web Site: www.butcherspetcare.com
Year Founded: 1987
Sales Range: $100-124.9 Million
Emp.: 259
Business Description:
Pet Food Mfr
S.I.C.: 2047
N.A.I.C.S.: 311111
Personnel:
Francis Powell *(Dir-Fin)*

BUTLER CAPITAL PARTNERS SA
30 cours Albert 1er
75008 Paris, France
Tel.: (33) 1 45 61 55 80
Fax: (33) 1 45 61 97 94
E-Mail: contact@butlercapitalpartners.com
Web Site: www.butlercapitalpartners.com
Business Description:
Private Equity Firm
S.I.C.: 6211
N.A.I.C.S.: 523999
Personnel:
Walter Butler *(Pres)*

Holdings:

ANOVO S.A. (1)
16 rue Joseph Cugnot
ZI de Bracheux, 60000 Beauvais, France
Tel.: (33) 344897900
Fax: (33) 344051696
E-Mail: contact@anovo.com
Web Site: www.anovo.com

Sales Range: $450-499.9 Million
Emp.: 5,200
Electronics Equipment Repair & Recycling Services
S.I.C.: 7622
N.A.I.C.S.: 811213
Claude Cormerais *(Gen Dir)*

Subsidiaries:

A Novo Beauvais S.A. (2)
16 Rue Joseph Cugnot
ZI le Bracheux, 60000 Beauvais, France (100%)
Tel.: (33) 344897900
Fax: (33) 344051696
Web Site: www.anovo.com
Emp.: 4,000
Electronics Equipment Repair & Recycling Services
S.I.C.: 7629
N.A.I.C.S.: 811213
Frederick Flipo *(Mng Dir)*

A Novo Groupe S.A. (2)
31 Rue des Peupliers
92100 Boulogne-Billancourt, France
Tel.: (33) 158170070
Fax: (33) 158170099
Web Site: www.anovo.com
Emp.: 6,000
Electronics Equipment Repair & Recycling Services
S.I.C.: 7622
N.A.I.C.S.: 811213
Jean De La Villardiere *(CEO)*

Non-U.S. Subsidiaries:

A Novo Andes SA (2)
Vista Alegre 2303 Cerrillos
Santiago, Chile (87.86%)
Tel.: (56) 23805000
Electronics Equipment Repair & Recycling Services
S.I.C.: 7622
N.A.I.C.S.: 811213
Olivier Ragu *(Gen Mgr)*

A Novo Arce SL (2)
Calle Pitagoras 13
28906 Getafe, Spain (100%)
Tel.: (34) 916653720
Fax: (34) 916019309
Electronics Equipment Repair & Recycling Services
S.I.C.: 7622
N.A.I.C.S.: 811213

A Novo Belgique B.V. (2)
Boulevard millenium 7
Garocentre, 7110 Houdeng-Goegnies, Belgium
Tel.: (32) 64237111
Fax: (32) 64237171
E-Mail: belgium.administration@anovo.com
Web Site: www.anovo.com
Emp.: 30
Electronics Equipment Repair & Recycling Services
S.I.C.: 7629
N.A.I.C.S.: 811213
Alain Moucheron *(Gen Mgr)*

A Novo Comlink Espana SL (2)
Parque Tecnologico de Andalucia
Charles Darwin S-N, 29590 Malaga, Spain (100%)
Tel.: (34) 952020020
Fax: (34) 952020400
E-Mail: droldan@anovo.com
Web Site: www.anovo.com
Emp.: 300
Communications Equipment Mfr
S.I.C.: 3669
N.A.I.C.S.: 334290
Bomimi Ricardo *(Mng Dir)*

A Novo Logitec SA (2)
Chemin De Familleureux 2040
La Louviere, Belgium (100%)
Tel.: (32) 64237111
Emp.: 40
Electronics Equipment Repair & Recycling Services
S.I.C.: 7629
N.A.I.C.S.: 811213
Frank Roth *(Mng Dir)*

A Novo Polska Sp.zo.o. (2)
Ul Lukasiewicza 7B
Wolomin, 05200 Warsaw, Poland (100%)
Tel.: (48) 227767041
Fax: (48) 227768055
E-Mail: sekretariat@anovo.pl
Web Site: www.a-novo.pl
Emp.: 100
Electronics Equipment Repair & Recycling Services
S.I.C.: 7622
N.A.I.C.S.: 811213
Monika Kwiatkowska *(Mng Dir)*

A Novo Services Solutions Limited (2)
Unit C 7 Station Rd Business Park
Dublin, Ireland (100%)
Tel.: (353) 14579787
Fax: (353) 14579790
Emp.: 20
Electronics Equipment Repair & Recycling Services
S.I.C.: 7629
N.A.I.C.S.: 811213
Owen Kavanagh *(Mng Dir)*

A Novo Suisse SA (2)
Centre de Reparation GSM
Draizes 5 Case postale, 2002 Neuchatel, Switzerland
Tel.: (41) 844810110
Fax: (41) 327303864
E-Mail: vmelan@a-novo.ch
Web Site: www.anovo.com
Emp.: 60
Electronics Equipment Repair & Recycling Services
S.I.C.: 7622
N.A.I.C.S.: 811213
Beat Scheurer *(Mng Dir)*

A Novo U.K. Ltd. (2)
71 Bilton Way
Enfield, Middlesex, EN3 7EP, United Kingdom (100%)
Tel.: (44) 2084438600
Fax: (44) 2084438750
E-Mail: sales_u@anovo.com
Web Site: www.anovo.com
Emp.: 180
Electronics Equipment Repair & Recycling Services
S.I.C.: 7622
N.A.I.C.S.: 811213
Kevin Coleman *(CEO)*

Sernam S.A. (1)
33 Ave Claude Gedussy
92 110 Clichy, France
Tel.: (33) 146529000
Fax: (33) 146529001
Web Site: www.sernam.fr
Sales Range: $450-499.9 Million
Emp.: 2,100
Courier Services
S.I.C.: 4215
N.A.I.C.S.: 492110
Philippe Chevalier *(Pres)*

Subsidiaries:

Sernam Centre S.A. (2)
5 Boulevard De Quebec
Orleans, France (100%)
Tel.: (33) 238524545
Fax: (33) 238524559
E-Mail: src206045@sernam.fr
Web Site: www.sernam.fr/reseau/InfosRegions.aspx?ID=1
Emp.: 30
Freight Transportation Arrangement
S.I.C.: 4731
N.A.I.C.S.: 488510
Mrlrpert Bergrang *(Mng Dir)*

Sernam Est S.A. (2)
1 Chemin De La Rompure
Champigneulles, 54250 Nancy, France (100%)
Tel.: (33) 383396565
Fax: (33) 3833396502
Emp.: 40
Freight Transportation Arrangement
S.I.C.: 4731
N.A.I.C.S.: 488510
Jacques Pierson *(Mng Dir)*

Sernam IDF S.A. (2)
142-176 Avenue de Stalingrad
92700 Colombes, France (100%)
Tel.: (33) 146529000
Fax: (33) 146529001
Freight Transportation Arrangement
S.I.C.: 4731
N.A.I.C.S.: 488510

Sernam Nord S.A. (2)
Tarcdunelanpoys Ruegessaules
59811 Lesquin, France
Tel.: (33) 320494200
Fax: (33) 0320595250
E-Mail: info@sernam.sr
Web Site: www.sernam.sr
Emp.: 50
Freight Transportation Arrangement
S.I.C.: 4731
N.A.I.C.S.: 488510
Ettyenne Georgge *(Gen Mgr)*

Sernam Ouest S.A. (2)
ZA de la Hallerais
Vern-sur-Seiche, France (100%)
Tel.: (33) 299327000
Fax: (33) 299327059
E-Mail: bpl@sernam.fr
Web Site: www.sernam.fr/en/reseau/InfosRegions.aspx?ID=5
Freight Transportation Arrangement
S.I.C.: 4731
N.A.I.C.S.: 488510

BUTTE ENERGY INC.

Suite 800 906 12th Avenue SW
Calgary, AB, T2R 1K7, Canada
Tel.: (403) 244-5340
Fax: (403) 245-5156
Web Site: www.butteenergy.com
Year Founded: 1992
BEN—(TSXV)
Rev.: $212,936
Assets: $7,278,176
Liabilities: $8,668,762
Net Worth: ($1,390,586)
Earnings: ($1,883,333)
Fiscal Year-end: 12/31/12

Business Description:
Petroleum & Gas Extraction Services
S.I.C.: 1311
N.A.I.C.S.: 211111

Personnel:
Victor Redekop *(Chm)*
Tyron Pfeifer *(Pres & CEO)*
Chris Reimchen *(CFO)*

Board of Directors:
Victor Redekop
Charles Baker
Gerry Gilbert
Chris Reimchen
Cuneyt Tirmandi

Legal Counsel:
Borden Ladner Gervais LLP
Calgary, AB, Canada

Transfer Agent:
Olympia Trust Company
Calgary, AB, Canada

BUTTERFLY GANDHIMATHI APPLIANCES LIMITED

34 2nd Floor Rajivgandhi Salai
Egattur Village OMR
Chennai, Tamil Nadu, 603013, India
Tel.: (91) 44 49005100
Fax: (91) 44 24343522
E-Mail: gmal@butterflyindia.com
Web Site: www.butterflyindia.com
517421—(BOM)
Rev.: $149,617,170
Assets: $100,406,040
Liabilities: $63,087,467
Net Worth: $37,318,573
Earnings: $6,196,624
Emp.: 2,525
Fiscal Year-end: 03/31/13

Business Description:
Kitchen Products Mfr
S.I.C.: 5046
N.A.I.C.S.: 423440

Personnel:
V. M. Lakshminarayanan *(Chm & Mng Dir)*
V. M. Seshadri *(Mng Dir)*
D. Krishnamurthy *(Compliance Officer & Sec)*

Board of Directors:
V. M. Lakshminarayanan
V. M. Balasubramaniam
A. Balasubramanian
K. Ganesan
V. M. Gangadharam
D. Krishnamurthy
K. J. Kumar
V. M. Kumaresan
V. R. Lakshminarayanan
M. Padmanabhan
R. S. Prakash
G. S. Samuel
V. M. Seshadri
T. R. Srinivasan

Transfer Agent:
GNSA Infotech Ltd
STA Department Nelson Chambers 4th Fl F Block 115 Nelson Manickam Road
Aminjikarai, Chennai, 600 029, India

Subsidiary:

LLM Appliances Limited (1)
Seshachalam Center No 636/1 9th Floor Annasalai
Nandanam, Chennai, Tamil Nadu, 600 035, India
Tel.: (91) 44 42287600
Fax: (91) 44 42287655
E-Mail: llmalmktg@butterflyindia.com
Emp.: 250
Home Appliance Mfr
S.I.C.: 3639
N.A.I.C.S.: 335228
T. R. Ramesh Babu *(Asst Mgr-Fin)*

BUTWAL POWER COMPANY LIMITED

Ganga Devi Marga 313 Buddha Nagar
PO Box 11728
Kathmandu, Nepal
Tel.: (977) 14784026
Fax: (977) 14780994
E-Mail: info@bpc.com.np
Web Site: www.bpc.com.np
BPCL—(NEP)
Emp.: 297

Business Description:
Hydropower Generating Services
S.I.C.: 4939
N.A.I.C.S.: 221111

Personnel:
Padma Jyoti *(Chm)*
Ranjan Lohar *(CEO)*
Murali Prasad Sharma *(Sec)*

Board of Directors:
Padma Jyoti
Bijay Bahadur Shrestha
Bijaya Krishna Shrestha
Pradeep Kumar Shrestha
Ratna Sansar Shrestha
Anup Kumar Upadhayay

BUXTON RESOURCES LIMITED

Suite 1 First Floor 14 - 16 Rowland Street
Subiaco, WA, 6008, Australia
Tel.: (61) 893806063
Fax: (61) 893814056
E-Mail: info@buxtonresources.com.au
Web Site: www.buxtonresources.com.au
BUX—(ASX)
Rev.: $445,570
Assets: $4,319,964
Liabilities: $448,422
Net Worth: $3,871,542
Earnings: ($2,179,955)
Emp.: 8
Fiscal Year-end: 06/30/13

Buxton Resources Limited—(Continued)

Business Description:
Minerals Mining Services
S.I.C.: 1481
N.A.I.C.S.: 213115
Personnel:
Anthony Maslin *(Mng Dir)*
Sam Wright *(Sec)*
Board of Directors:
Seamus Cornelius
Stuart Fogarty
Xingzhou Liu
Anthony Maslin
Julian Stephens
Legal Counsel:
Norman Waterhouse Lawyers
Level 15 45 Pirie St
Adelaide, Australia

BUZZ TELECOMMUNICATIONS SERVICES INC.

5450 Cote des Neiges Suite 522
Montreal, QC, H3T 1Y6, Canada
Tel.: (514) 788-1499, ext. 202
Fax: (514) 397-2375
Toll Free: (866) 692-2899
E-Mail: service@buzztelecom.ca
Web Site: www.buzztelecom.ca
Year Founded: 2004
BZZ—(TSXV)
Sales Range: $1-9.9 Million
Business Description:
Telecommunication Services
S.I.C.: 4899
N.A.I.C.S.: 517919
Personnel:
Rafi Hazan *(Co-Founder, CFO & Sec)*
Michel Bensoussan *(Co-Founder & COO)*
Elie Hazan *(Co-Founder & CTO)*
Mazen Haddad *(Chm, Pres & CEO)*
Board of Directors:
Mazen Haddad
Guy Charette
Rafi Hazan
Douglas McMullen
Transfer Agent:
Computershare Investor Services Inc.
100 University Avenue 8th Floor
Toronto, ON, M5J 2Y1, Canada
Tel.: (514) 982-7555

Subsidiary:

Triple 5 Communications Inc (1)
5450 Cote-Des-Neiges Ste 522
Montreal, QC, H3T 1Y6, Canada
Tel.: (514) 831-2424
Fax: (514) 397-2375
Emp.: 8
Telecommunication Services
S.I.C.: 4899
N.A.I.C.S.: 517919
Rafi Hazan *(Mng Dir)*

BUZZI UNICEM SPA

via Luigi Buzzi 6
15033 Casale Monferrato, Italy
Tel.: (39) 0142 433411
Fax: (39) 0142 433464
E-Mail: info@buzziunicem.it
Web Site: www.buzziunicem.it
Year Founded: 1872
BZU—(ITA)
Sls.: $3,787,376,602
Assets: $7,811,396,428
Liabilities: $4,307,823,424
Net Worth: $3,503,573,004
Earnings: $2,645,224
Emp.: 10,894
Fiscal Year-end: 12/31/12
Business Description:
Engineering & Construction Services
S.I.C.: 3531
N.A.I.C.S.: 333120
Personnel:
Sandro Buzzi *(Chm)*
Enrico Buzzi *(Vice Chm)*
Agostino Pieressa *(IR Officer)*
Michele Buzzi *(CEO-Ops)*
Pietro Buzzi *(CEO-Fin)*
Board of Directors:
Sandro Buzzi
Wolfgang Bauer
Paolo Burlando
Enrico Buzzi
Michele Buzzi
Pietro Buzzi
Veronica Buzzi
York Dyckerhoff
Ester Faia
Gianfelice Mario Rocca
Aldo Fumagalli Romario
Maurizio Sella
Marco Weigmann

Subsidiary:

Dyckerhoff AG (1)
Biebricher Strasse 69
65203 Wiesbaden, Germany (91.2%)
Mailing Address:
Postfach 2247
65012 Wiesbaden, Germany
Tel.: (49) 6116760
Fax: (49) 6116761040
E-Mail: info@dyckerhoff.com
Web Site: www.dyckerhoff.com
DYK—(DEU)
Sls.: $2,158,458,401
Assets: $4,316,967,957
Liabilities: $2,101,682,335
Net Worth: $2,215,285,622
Earnings: $46,907,294
Emp.: 6,808
Fiscal Year-end: 12/31/12
Producer, Marketer, & Distr of Cement, Concrete & Finishing Products
S.I.C.: 5211
N.A.I.C.S.: 444190
Gunnar Gremlin *(Chm-Supervisory Bd)*
Wolfgang Bauer *(Chm-Mgmt Bd)*
Klaus-Dieter Becker *(Vice Chm-Supervisory Bd)*
Allesandro Buzzi *(Vice Chm-Supervisory Bd)*
Michele Buzzi *(Member-Mgmt Bd-Bus Dev)*
Stefan Fink *(Member-Mgmt Bd-Fin & Controlling Unit)*
Stefan John *(Member-Mgmt Bd-Bus Svcs Unit)*

Subsidiaries:

Deuna Zement GmbH (2)
Industriestr 7
D 37355 Deuna, Germany
Mailing Address:
Postfach 7
D-37352 Niederorschel, Germany
Tel.: (49) 3607680
Fax: (49) 3607682255
E-Mail: info@deuna-zement.com
Web Site: www.deuna-zement.com
Sales Range: $1-9.9 Million
Emp.: 146
Mfr of Cement
S.I.C.: 3241
N.A.I.C.S.: 327310
Wilandg Garhrard *(Mng Dir)*
Berward Deudeko *(Mng Dir)*

Dyckerhoff Ausbauprodukte Service GmbH (2)
Dienstleistungszentrum Dresden
Am Wuesteberg 2, D-01723 Dresden, Kesselsdorf, Germany
Tel.: (49) 3520462610
Fax: (49) 35 20462660
E-Mail: dlzdresden@dyckerhoff.com
Web Site: www.dyckerhoff.com
Producer, Marketer, & Distributor of Cement, Concrete & Finishing Products
S.I.C.: 3241
N.A.I.C.S.: 327310

Dyckerhoff Ausbauprodukte Service GmbH (2)
Wusteberg 2
D 01723 Rostock, Kesselsdorf, Germany
Tel.: (49) 520440401
Fax: (49) 52 04 4 04
E-Mail: dlzrostock@dyckerhoff.com
Producer & Distr of Cement, Concrete & Finishing Products
S.I.C.: 3241
N.A.I.C.S.: 327310

Dyckerhoff Beton GmbH (2)
Biebricher Strasse 69
65203 Wiesbaden, Germany
Mailing Address:
PO Box 2247
65012 Wiesbaden, Germany
Tel.: (49) 6116760
Fax: (49) 6116761040
E-Mail: beton@dyckerhoff.com
Web Site: www.dyckerhoff.com
Emp.: 350
Producer of Cement, Concrete & Finishing Products
S.I.C.: 3272
N.A.I.C.S.: 327332
Wolfgang Bauer *(Gen Mgr)*

Branch:

Dyckerhoff Beton GmbH & Co. KG - Rhein-Ruhr (3)
An der Wachsfabrik 17
50996 Cologne, Germany (100%)
Tel.: (49) 2236962220
Fax: (49) 22369622248
E-Mail: verkauf-nl-koeln-bonn@dyckerhoff.com
Web Site: www.beton-union.de
Emp.: 20
Cement Mfr & Supplier
S.I.C.: 3241
N.A.I.C.S.: 327310

Dyckerhoff Transportbeton GmbH (2)
Biebricher St 69
PO Box 47
65203 Wiesbaden, Germany (100%)
Tel.: (49) 6116760
Fax: (49) 1676199561
E-Mail: info@dyckerhoff.com
Web Site: www.transportbeton.de
Emp.: 600
Cement & Concrete Distr
S.I.C.: 3241
N.A.I.C.S.: 327310
Jurgen Lose *(Chm)*
Wolfgang Bauer *(CEO)*

Dyckerhoff Weiss Marketing-und Vertriebs-GmbH & Co. KG (2)
Biebricher Strasse 69
65203 Wiesbaden, Germany (100%)
Mailing Address:
Postfach 22 47
65012 Wiesbaden, Germany
Tel.: (49) 611609091
Fax: (49) 6116763175
E-Mail: info@dyckerhoff-weis.com
Web Site: www.Dyckerhoff.com
Emp.: 400
Cement Mfr
S.I.C.: 3241
N.A.I.C.S.: 327310
Wolfgang Bauer *(CEO)*

Dyckerhoff Zement GmbH (2)
Biebricher Str 69
65203 Wiesbaden, Germany (100%)
Mailing Address:
PO Box 2247
65012 Wiesbaden, Germany
Tel.: (49) 6116760
Fax: (49) 6116761040
E-Mail: info@dyckerhoff.com
Web Site: www.dyckerhoff.com
Emp.: 400
Mfr. of Cement
S.I.C.: 3241
N.A.I.C.S.: 327310
Wolfgang Bauer *(CEO)*

Leschuplat GmbH (2)
Linderhauser Str 135
D 42279 Wuppertal, Germany
Tel.: (49) 202758860
Fax: (49) 202758890
E-Mail: info@leschuplast-glt.de
Web Site: www.leschuplast.de
Emp.: 10
Mfr. of Cement
S.I.C.: 3241
N.A.I.C.S.: 327310

RHEBAU Rheinische Beton- und Bauindustrie GmbH & Co. KG (2)
Dusseldorfer Strasse 118
41541 Dormagen, Germany (100%)
Tel.: (49) 213377030
Fax: (49) 213377037
Web Site: www.rhebau.de
Emp.: 100
Mfr. of Cement
S.I.C.: 3241
N.A.I.C.S.: 327310

Sudwest Lacke & Farben GmbH & Co. KG (2)
Iggelheimer Strasse 13
67459 Boehl-Iggelheim, Germany (100%)
Mailing Address:
Postfach 12 41
67456 Boehl-Iggelheim, Germany
Tel.: (49) 63247090
Fax: (49) 6324709175
E-Mail: info@suedwest.de
Web Site: www.suedwest.de
Rev.: $20,638,200
Emp.: 120
Paints, Stripper, Protective Coatings & Finishing Products
S.I.C.: 5211
N.A.I.C.S.: 444190
Hansgoerd Vonrhade *(Mng Dir)*

TUBAG Trass-Zement-Steinwerke GmbH (2)
Bundesstrasse
D 56638 Kruft, Germany
Mailing Address:
Postfach 11 80
D-56638 Kruft, Germany
Tel.: (49) 265281104
Fax: (49) 265281161
Web Site: www.dykerhoff.de
Emp.: 100
Mfr. of Cement
S.I.C.: 3241
N.A.I.C.S.: 327310

U.S. Subsidiary:

Buzzi Unicem USA Inc. (2)
100 Brodhead Rd
Bethlehem, PA 18017-8989
Tel.: (610) 866-4400
Fax: (610) 866-9430
Web Site: www.buzziunicemusa.com
Emp.: 100
Portland Cement, Masonry Cement, & Ready-mixed Concrete
S.I.C.: 1422
N.A.I.C.S.: 212312
Dave Nepereny *(Pres & CEO)*

Branch:

Buzzi Unicem USA (3)
10401 N Meridian St Ste 400
Indianapolis, IN 46290 DE
Tel.: (610) 882-5000
Fax: (317) 805-3250
Web Site: www.buzziunicem.com
Emp.: 40
Mfr. & Importer of Cement, Clinker & Ready Mixed Concrete
Import
S.I.C.: 3241
N.A.I.C.S.: 327310
John White *(VP-Logistics)*

Non-U.S. Subsidiaries:

Cement Hranice a.s. (2)
Akciova Spolecnost
Belontinska 288, CZ 75339 Hranice, Czech Republic
Tel.: (420) 581829111
Fax: (420) 581829240
E-Mail: cement@cement.cz
Web Site: www.cement.cz
Emp.: 200
Cement Mfr
S.I.C.: 3241
N.A.I.C.S.: 327310
Jaronier Chmele *(Gen Mgr)*

Cementos Hispania s.a. (2)
Avda de Felipe II 15
E-28009 Madrid, Spain
Tel.: (34) 914314540
Fax: (34) 915778596

E-Mail: hispania@dyckerhoff.com
Web Site: www.dyckerhoff.com
Cement Mfr
S.I.C.: 3241
N.A.I.C.S.: 327310

Ciments Luxembourgeois S.A. (2)
50 S Rue Fandel Fomain
4002 Esch-sur-Alzette, Luxembourg (100%)
Tel.: (352) 5525251
Fax: (352) 557061
E-Mail: info@cimalux.lu
Web Site: www.cimalux.lu
Sales Range: $10-24.9 Million
Emp.: 150
Mfr. of Cement
S.I.C.: 3241
N.A.I.C.S.: 327310
Jean-Paul Proth *(Mng Dir)*

Dyckerhoff Polska Sp. z o.o. (2)
ul Zakladowa 3
Sitkowka, PL 26 052 Nowiny, Poland
Tel.: (48) 413466000
Fax: (48) 413466488
E-Mail: biuro@dyckerhoff.pl
Web Site: www.dyckerhoff.pl
Emp.: 200
Building Material Producer
S.I.C.: 5211
N.A.I.C.S.: 444190
Christoph Kocic *(Mng Dir)*

Dyckerhoff Transportbeton Praha s.r.o. (2)
Ostrovni 12 1708
11000 Prague, Czech Republic
Tel.: (420) 224930972
Web Site: www.dyckerhoff.com
Mfr. of Concrete
S.I.C.: 3271
N.A.I.C.S.: 327331

Materiaux S.A. (2)
2A Rue Kalchesbreck
PO Box 2492
L 1852 Luxembourg, Luxembourg
Tel.: (352) 438811
Fax: (352) 439254
E-Mail: info@materiaux.com
Web Site: www.cimentslux.lu
Mfr. of Cement
S.I.C.: 3241
N.A.I.C.S.: 327310

OAO Sucholoshskzement (2)
Ul Kunarskaja 20
Swerdlowsker Gebiet, RUS 623520
Yekaterinburg, Suchoi Log, Russia
Tel.: (7) 3437379038
Fax: (7) 3437343532
E-Mail: info@sl-cement.ru
Web Site: www.sl-cement.ru/online/en/Home.html
Emp.: 1,000
Producer & Distr of Cement, Concrete & Finishing Products
S.I.C.: 3241
N.A.I.C.S.: 327310
Vladimir Alekseyevich Nikolaev *(Gen Dir)*

Vynex S.A. (2)
Lieu-Dit la Foulerie
F-08350 Thelonne, France
Tel.: (33) 324545959
Fax: (33) 330324265001
Web Site: www.vynex.fr/Historique.html
Emp.: 300
Building & Repair
S.I.C.: 1542
N.A.I.C.S.: 236220

BVE HOLDING SE

Am Wollelager 8
27749 Delmenhorst, Germany
Tel.: (49) 422115493011
Fax: (49) 42219248364
E-Mail: mesar-ts@bve-group.eu
Web Site: www.bve-group.eu
BV6—(DEU)
Business Description:
Holding Company
S.I.C.: 6719
N.A.I.C.S.: 551112
Personnel:
Karl-Heinz Klarmann *(Chm)*
Sarah Stoppe-Ramadan *(Vice Chm)*
Board of Directors:
Karl-Heinz Klarmann
Sylvia Kolsch
Sarah Stoppe-Ramadan
Subsidiary:

Mesar Beratung (1)
Am Wollelager 8 Technologiezentrum
27749 Delmenhorst, Germany
Tel.: (49) 42222093180
Fax: (49) 42222093189
E-Mail: post@mesar-beratung.com
Web Site: www.mesar-beratung.com
Financial Advisory Services
S.I.C.: 6282
N.A.I.C.S.: 523930
Karl Heinz Klarmann *(Mgr)*

BW MARITIME PTE LTD.

Mapletree Business City 18-01 10
Pasir Panjang Road
Singapore, 117438, Singapore
Tel.: (65) 63372133
Fax: (65) 63371623
Web Site: www.bwshipping.com
Business Description:
Holding Company; Marine Operations
S.I.C.: 6719
N.A.I.C.S.: 551112
Personnel:
Stephen Yue-Kuo Pan *(Chm)*
Subsidiary:

BW LPG Limited (1)
10 Pasir Panjang Road Mapletree Business City #18-01
Singapore, 117438, Singapore BM
Tel.: (65) 6434 5840 (45%)
Web Site: www.bwlpg.com
BWLPG—(OSL)
LPG Carrier
S.I.C.: 1389
N.A.I.C.S.: 213112
Andreas Sohmen-Pao *(Chm)*
John B. Harrison *(Vice Chm)*
Nicholas Murray Gleeson *(CEO)*
Vijay Kamath *(CFO)*
Andrew Hoare *(Chief Comml Officer)*

Non-U.S. Subsidiary:

BW Gas ASA (1)
Drammensveien 106
0273 Oslo, Norway
Mailing Address:
PO Box 2800
Solli, 0204 Oslo, Norway
Tel.: (47) 22120505
Telex: 71172
Fax: (47) 22120500
E-Mail: bwgas@bwgas.com
Web Site: www.bwgas.com
Sales Range: $550-599.9 Million
Emp.: 3,790
Gas & Marine Transportation Services
S.I.C.: 4499
N.A.I.C.S.: 488330
Helmut Sohmen *(Chm)*
Andreas Sohmen Pao *(Vice Chm & CEO)*
Yngvil Asheim *(Exec VP-Fleet Mgmt)*

Non-U.S. Subsidiaries:

Bergesen D.Y. Philippines, Inc. (2)
5th Fl Urban Bldg
405 Sen Gil Puyat Ave, Makati, Metro
Manila, 1209, Philippines (100%)
Tel.: (63) 28952469
Telex: 45991
Fax: (63) 28959870
E-Mail: management.philippines@bergesen.no
Web Site: www.bergesen.no
Emp.: 40
Shipping Services
S.I.C.: 4499
N.A.I.C.S.: 488330
Rolando Adoradle *(Pres)*

BW OFFSHORE LIMITED

Drammensveien 149
0277 Oslo, Norway
Mailing Address:
PO Box 33
0212 Skoyen, Norway
Tel.: (47) 23130000
Fax: (47) 23130001
E-Mail: bwoffshore@bwoffshore.com
Web Site: www.bwoffshore.com
BWO—(OSL)
Rev.: $909,400,000
Assets: $3,423,800,000
Liabilities: $2,296,700,000
Net Worth: $1,127,100,000
Emp.: 2,280
Fiscal Year-end: 12/31/12
Business Description:
Floating Production Services for Oil & Gas Industry
S.I.C.: 1389
N.A.I.C.S.: 213112
Personnel:
Helmut Sohmen *(Chm)*
Ronny Johan Langeland *(Vice Chm)*
Carl K. Arnet *(CEO)*
Knut R. Saethre *(CFO)*
Stuart Bannerman *(COO)*
Thyl Kint *(CTO)*
Claude Rouxel *(Chief Bus Dev Officer)*
Board of Directors:
Helmut Sohmen
Ronny Johan Langeland
Christophe Pettenati-Auziere
Maarten R. Scholten
Andreas Sohmen-Pao
Clare Spottiswoode
Non-U.S. Subsidiaries:

BW Offshore Cyprus Ltd (1)
Ariadne House 333 28th October Street
3106 Limassol, Cyprus
Tel.: (357) 25 814 038
Fax: (357) 25 814 039
E-Mail:
Floating Production Services for Oil & Gas Industry
S.I.C.: 1389
N.A.I.C.S.: 213112
Knut Borgen *(Mgr)*

BW Offshore do Brasil Ltda (1)
Rua Lauro Muller 116 Sala 1106
Torre do Rio Sul Botafogo, Rio de Janeiro, 22290-160, Brazil
Tel.: (55) 2125432339
Fax: (55) 22448383
E-Mail: reception@bwoffshore.com
Emp.: 50
Floating Production Services for Oil & Gas Industry
S.I.C.: 1389
N.A.I.C.S.: 213112

BW Offshore Nigeria Ltd. (1)
South Atlantic petroleum towers 8th floor
Osborne Estate
PO Box 50655
Falomo Ikoyi, Lagos, 234, Nigeria
Tel.: (234) 18990750
E-Mail: lagos@bwoffshore.com
Floating Production Services for Oil & Gas Industry
S.I.C.: 1389
N.A.I.C.S.: 213112

BW Offshore Singapore Pte. Ltd. (1)
30 Pasir Panjang Road
17-01 Mapletree Business City, Singapore, 117400, Singapore
Tel.: (65) 63250388
Fax: (65) 63231263
Web Site: www.bwoffshore.com
Emp.: 250
Floating Production Services for Oil & Gas Industry
S.I.C.: 1389
N.A.I.C.S.: 213112
Carl Arnet *(CEO)*

BWA GROUP PLC

50 Broadway Westminster
London, SW1H 0BL, United Kingdom
Tel.: (44) 7836 238172
E-Mail: enquiries@bwagroupplc.com
Web Site: www.bwagroupplc.com
BWAP—(ISDX)
Rev.: $15,793
Assets: $185,004
Liabilities: $124,356
Net Worth: $60,648
Earnings: ($105,553)
Fiscal Year-end: 04/30/13
Business Description:
Investment Services
S.I.C.: 6211
N.A.I.C.S.: 523999
Personnel:
James Montford Victor Butterfield *(Sec)*
Board of Directors:
Richard Godfrey Battersby
Michael Alexander Borrelli
James Montford Victor Butterfield
Legal Counsel:
Bircham Dyson Bell
50 Broadway
London, United Kingdom

BWG HOMES ASA

Vika Atrium Munkedamsveien 45
Elevator D 5th Floor
PO Box 1817
0123 Oslo, Norway
Tel.: (47) 23246000
Fax: (47) 23246013
E-Mail: post@bwghomes.no
Web Site: www.bwghomes.no
Year Founded: 1926
BWG—(OSL)
Rev.: $628,870,388
Assets: $958,001,608
Liabilities: $563,140,612
Net Worth: $394,860,996
Earnings: ($31,574,067)
Emp.: 1,014
Fiscal Year-end: 12/31/12
Business Description:
Home Construction & Land Development
S.I.C.: 1521
N.A.I.C.S.: 236115
Personnel:
Roar Engeland *(Chm)*
Daniel Kjorberg Siraj *(Vice Chm)*
Ole Feet *(CEO)*
Arnt Eriksen *(CFO)*
Mikael Olsson *(CEO-BWG Homes AB)*
Board of Directors:
Roar Engeland
Charlotte Axelsson
Hege Bomark
Lars Nilsen
Tore Morten Randen
Lars Orjan Reinholdsson
Daniel Kjorberg Siraj
Magne Staalstrom
Subsidiaries:

Block Watne AS (1)
PO Box 1817 Vika
NO-123 Oslo, Norway NO
Tel.: (47) 23246000 (100%)
Fax: (47) 23246001
E-Mail: post@blockwatne.no
Web Site: www.blockwatne.no
Emp.: 50
Land Acquisition & Development & Housing Construction
S.I.C.: 1521
N.A.I.C.S.: 236115
Ole Feet *(CEO)*

Hetlandhus AS (1)
PO Box 1817 Vika
NO-0123 Oslo, Norway NO
Tel.: (47) 22012000 (100%)
Fax: (47) 22012001
Web Site: www.hetlandhus.no
Prefabricated Module Housing Mfr
S.I.C.: 2452

BWG Homes ASA—(Continued)

N.A.I.C.S.: 321992
Aursnes Borre Lidvard *(Mng Dir)*

Non-U.S. Subsidiary:

BWG Homes AB (1)
Myresjo
SE-574 85 Vetlanda, Sweden SE
Tel.: (46) 38396300 (100%)
Fax: (46) 38391440
E-Mail: info@smalandsvillan.se
Web Site: www.smalandsvillan.se
Emp.: 300
House Components & Load-Bearing Structures Mfr
S.I.C.: 1531
N.A.I.C.S.: 236117
Mikael Olsson *(CEO)*
Jonas Karlsson *(Deputy CEO & CFO)*

Subsidiaries:

Myresjohus AB (2)
Scateonvagen 4
SE 574 85 Vetlanda, Sweden SE
Tel.: (46) 38396000 (100%)
Fax: (46) 38391440
E-Mail: info@myresjohus.se
Web Site: www.myresjohus.se
Sales Range: $125-149.9 Million
Emp.: 450
Building Material Mfr
S.I.C.: 5211
N.A.I.C.S.: 444190
Mikael Olsson *(Mng Dir)*

SmalandsVillan AB (2)
Vaxjovagen
Vrigstad, 570 03 Savsjo, Jonkoping, Sweden
Tel.: (46) 38234550
Fax: (46) 383 962 05
E-Mail: info@smalandsvillan.se
Web Site: www.smalandsvillan.se
Villa Rental & Leasing Services
S.I.C.: 6519
N.A.I.C.S.: 531190
David Carlsson *(Mgr-Ops)*

BWIN.PARTY DIGITAL ENTERTAINMENT PLC

711 Europort
Gibraltar, Gibraltar
Tel.: (350) 20078700
Fax: (350) 78790
Web Site: www.bwinparty.com
Year Founded: 1997
BPTY—(LSE VIE)
Rev.: $1,079,089,872
Assets: $1,474,594,618
Liabilities: $574,141,505
Net Worth: $900,453,113
Earnings: ($87,097,199)
Emp.: 3,000
Fiscal Year-end: 12/31/12

Business Description:
Gaming Web Site Operator
S.I.C.: 7999
N.A.I.C.S.: 713290

Personnel:
Simon Duffy *(Chm)*
Rod Perry *(Deputy Chm)*
Norbert Teufelberger *(CEO)*
Martin Weigold *(CFO)*
Robert Hoskin *(Sec)*

Board of Directors:
Simon Duffy
Per Afrell
Manfred Bodner
Sylvia Coleman
Helmut Kern
Lewis Moonie
Rod Perry
Georg Riedl
Norbert Teufelberger
Martin Weigold

BDO Fidecs Chartered Accountants Limited
Montagu Pavilion 8-10 Queensway
PO Box 575
Gibraltar, Gibraltar

Legal Counsel:
Hassans
57/63 Line Wall Road
Gibraltar, Gibraltar

Freshfields Bruckhaus Deringer
65 Fleet St
London, United Kingdom

Transfer Agent:
Capita Registrars
The Registry 34 Beckenham Road
Beckenham, United Kingdom

Subsidiaries:

ElectraWorks Limited (1)
711 Europort
Gibraltar, Gibraltar
Tel.: (350) 2 007 9000
Online Gaming Services
S.I.C.: 7389
N.A.I.C.S.: 561990

iGlobalMedia Marketing (Gibraltar) Limited (1)
711 Europort
Gibraltar, Gibraltar
Tel.: (350) 20078700
Fax: (350) 20048521
Internet Advertising Services
S.I.C.: 2741
N.A.I.C.S.: 519130

PKR Services Limited (1)
711 Europort
Gibraltar, Gibraltar
Tel.: (350) 200 72800
E-Mail: info@pkrser.com
Web Site: www.pkrser.com
Financial Transaction Processing Services
S.I.C.: 6099
N.A.I.C.S.: 522320

Non-U.S. Subsidiaries:

Cashcade Limited (1)
One New Change 3rd Floor
London, EC4M9AF, United Kingdom
Tel.: (44) 20 7337 0100
Fax: (44) 2073370101
E-Mail: enquiries@cashcade.co.uk
Web Site: www.cashcade.co.uk
Emp.: 170
Online Gaming Software Development Services
S.I.C.: 7371
N.A.I.C.S.: 541511
Nick Wann *(Gen Mgr)*

iGlobalMedia Marketing (Israel) Limited (1)
48 Menachem Begin Road
Tel Aviv, Israel
Tel.: (972) 3 637 4455
Fax: (972) 3 637 4454
Marketing Consulting Services
S.I.C.: 8742
N.A.I.C.S.: 541613

Non-U.S. Subsidiary:

iGlobalMedia Marketing (UK) Limited (2)
Phoenix House
London, EC4N 7BP, United Kingdom
Tel.: (44) 20 7337 0100
Fax: (44) 20 7337 0101
Emp.: 140
Marketing Consulting Services
S.I.C.: 8742
N.A.I.C.S.: 541613
John Mayes *(Sec)*

IVY Comptech Private Limited (1)
5th Floor, 'B' Block, Divyasree Omega, Hitech City Road
Kondapur, Hyderabad, Andhra Pradesh, 500 081, India
Tel.: (91) 4044721000
Fax: (91) 4066565825
E-Mail: info@ivycomptech.com
Web Site: www.ivycomptech.com
Emp.: 800
Online Gaming Software Development Services
S.I.C.: 7371
N.A.I.C.S.: 541511
Sudhakar Prasad *(Mng Dir & CTO)*
Ananth Krishnan C. Subramanian *(CFO)*

BWK GMBH UNTERNEHMENSBETEILIGUNGS GESELLSCHAFT

Thouretstrasse 2
D 70173 Stuttgart, Germany
Tel.: (49) 7112255760
Fax: (49) 7112257610
E-Mail: stuttgart@bwku.de
Web Site: www.bwku.de
Emp.: 14

Business Description:
Investment Services
Export
S.I.C.: 6211
N.A.I.C.S.: 523999

Personnel:
Armin Schuler *(Mng Dir)*

BWT AKTIENGESELLSCHAFT

Walter Simmer Strasse 4
A-5310 Mondsee, Austria
Tel.: (43) 623250110
Fax: (43) 4362324058
E-Mail: office@bwt-group.com
Web Site: www.bwt-group.com
BWT—(VIE)
Rev.: $676,179,710
Assets: $474,847,063
Liabilities: $248,135,747
Net Worth: $226,711,317
Earnings: $19,414,464
Emp.: 2,726
Fiscal Year-end: 12/31/12

Business Description:
Water Technology Services
S.I.C.: 4499
N.A.I.C.S.: 488390

Personnel:
Leopold Bednar *(Chm-Supervisory Bd)*
Andreas Weissenbacher *(Chm-Exec Bd & CEO)*
Wolfgang Hochsteger *(Deputy Chm-Supervisory Bd)*
Gerhard Speigner *(CFO & Member-Mgmt Bd)*

Supervisory Board of Directors:
Leopold Bednar
Gerda Egger
Wolfgang Hochsteger
Ekkehard Reicher
Helmut Schutzeneder

Subsidiaries:

Aqua Service GmbH (1)
VogelsangstraBe 3
Mondsee, 5310 Salzburg, Austria
Tel.: (43) 62325010
Fax: (43) 62324058
E-Mail: office@aquaservice.at
Web Site: www.aquaservice.at
Emp.: 2,000
Sewage Treatment Facilities
S.I.C.: 4952
N.A.I.C.S.: 221320
Andras Weissenbachcr *(Mng Dir)*

arcana pool systems gmbh (1)
Brunner Strasse 186
Gerasdorf Bei, 2201 Vienna, Austria
Tel.: (43) 2246 28555
Fax: (43) 2246 28555 10
E-Mail: office@arcanapoolsystems.at
Swimming Pool Equipment Distr
S.I.C.: 5091
N.A.I.C.S.: 423910

BWT Austria GmbH (1)
Walter-Simmer-Strasse 4
5310 Mondsee, Austria
Tel.: (43) 6232 5011 0
Fax: (43) 6232 4058
E-Mail: office@bwt.at
Web Site: www.bwt.at
Emp.: 30
Water Treatment Services
S.I.C.: 4941
N.A.I.C.S.: 221310
Roland D'leteren *(Gen Mgr)*

BWT water + more GmbH (1)
Walter Simmer-Strasse 4
5310 Mondsee, Austria
Tel.: (43) 6232 5011 1164
Fax: (43) 62324058
E-Mail: infowm@bwt-group.com
Emp.: 45
Water Treatment Services
S.I.C.: 4941
N.A.I.C.S.: 221310
Andreas Weissenbacher *(Gen Mgr)*

P & LS Beteiligungs GmbH (1)
Walter-Simmer-Strasse 4
5310 Mondsee, Austria
Tel.: (43) 6232 5011 0
Water Treatment Services
S.I.C.: 4971
N.A.I.C.S.: 221310

P & LS Holding GmbH (1)
Walter-Simmer-Str 4
5310 Mondsee, Austria
Tel.: (43) 623250110
E-Mail: office@christaqua.com
Web Site: www.christaqua.com
Investment Management Services
S.I.C.: 6211
N.A.I.C.S.: 523999
Henrik Forslund *(Member-Mgmt Bd)*
Gerhard Speigner *(Member-Mgmt Bd)*
Andreas Weissenbacher *(Member-Mgmt Bd)*

Non-U.S. Subsidiaries:

Best Water Technology (Ireland) Ltd. (2)
Unit 2A Ashbourne Business Park
Ashbourne, Co. Meath, Ireland IE
Tel.: (353) 18498700
Fax: (353) 18498701
Emp.: 15
Water & Wastewater Sterilization Services
S.I.C.: 4971
N.A.I.C.S.: 221310
Patrick Archer *(Mng Dir)*

BWT Pharma & Biotech AB (2)
Kantyxegatan 25A
21376 Malmo, Sweden
Tel.: (46) 40315440
Fax: (46) 40315449
E-Mail: info@christ.se
Web Site: www.christ.se
Emp.: 20
Water Treatment & Management Engineering
S.I.C.: 8711
N.A.I.C.S.: 541330
Kyle Monsson *(Mng Dir)*

BWT Pharma & Biotech GmbH (2)
Carl-Benz-Strasse 4
D-74321 Bietigheim-Bissingen, Germany De
Tel.: (49) 7142 3737 500
Fax: (49) 7142 3737 700
E-Mail:
Web Site: www.bwt-pharma.com
Emp.: 60
Water Treatment & Management Engineering
S.I.C.: 8711
N.A.I.C.S.: 541330
Stephan Stautmeaster *(Mng Dir)*

BWT UK Limited (2)
BWT House The Gateway Centre
Coronation Road
High Wycombe, Buckinghamshire, HP12 3SU, United Kingdom
Tel.: (44) 1494 838100
Fax: (44) 1494 838101
E-Mail: enquiries@bwt-uk.co.uk
Web Site: www.bwt-uk.co.uk
Water Treatment Services
S.I.C.: 4941
N.A.I.C.S.: 221310

Christ Nishotech Water Systems Pte. Ltd. (2)
Plot No W159 MIDC Pawane
TTC Industrial Area, 400705 Mumbai, 400 705, India In
Tel.: (91) 2227619274 (50%)
Fax: (91) 2227619278
E-Mail: info@christ-nishotech.com
Web Site: www.christ-nishotech.com

Water Treatment & Management Engineering
S.I.C.: 8711
N.A.I.C.S.: 541330
Sheb Kurawabwala *(Mng Dir)*

Christ Pharma & Life Science Shanghai Ltd. (2)
No 799 Yuyang Rd
Cangquiao Ind Zone, 201600 Shanghai, China
Tel.: (86) 21 59867200
Fax: (86) 21 59867201
E-Mail: info@sh.austar.com.cn
Web Site: www.christ-austar.com
Emp.: 120
Service Industry Machinery Mfr
S.I.C.: 3589
N.A.I.C.S.: 333318
Michael Lee *(Gen Mgr)*

Non-U.S. Subsidiaries:

Anna International Limited (1)
Suite 2a Level 5
Plaza Commercial Centre, Sliema, Malta
Tel.: (356) 21335174
Other Miscellaneous Durable Goods Whslr
S.I.C.: 5099
N.A.I.C.S.: 423990

BWT Hungaria Kft (1)
Keleti 7
2040 Budaors, Hungary
Tel.: (36) 23415305
Fax: (36) 23430482
E-Mail: bwtchrist@bwtchrist.hu
Web Site: www.bwtchrist.hu
Emp.: 20
Other Commercial & Service Industry Machinery Mfr
S.I.C.: 3589
N.A.I.C.S.: 333318
Gyula Patro *(Mng Dir)*

BWT Belgium n.v. (1)
Leuvensesteenweg 633
1930 Zaventem, Belgium
Tel.: (32) 27580310
Fax: (32) 27580333
E-Mail: bwt@bwt.be
Web Site: www.bwt.be
Emp.: 40
Other Support Activities for Water Transportation
S.I.C.: 4499
N.A.I.C.S.: 488390

BWT Ceska Republika s.r.o. (1)
Lipova 196 - Cestlice
Prague, Czech Republic
Tel.: (420) 272680300
Fax: (420) 272680299
E-Mail: info@bwt.cz
Sewage Treatment Facilities
S.I.C.: 4952
N.A.I.C.S.: 221320

BWT France SAS (1)
103 rue Charles Michels
93206 Saint Denis, France
Tel.: (33) 1 49 22 45 00
Fax: (33) 1 49 22 45 45
E-Mail: bwt@bwt.fr
Water Treatment Services
S.I.C.: 4971
N.A.I.C.S.: 221310

BWT International Trading Ltd (1)
Tower Gate Place Tal-Qroqq Street
Msida, MSD 1703, Malta
Tel.: (356) 2131 3060
Fax: (356) 2131 3064
E-Mail: International.trading@bwtmalta.com.mt
Water Treatment & Distr
S.I.C.: 4971
N.A.I.C.S.: 221310
John Tsaila *(Gen Mgr)*

BWT Ireland Ltd. (1)
Unit 2A Ashbourne Business Park
Ashbourne, Meath, Ireland
Tel.: (353) 1 849 87 00
Fax: (353) 1 849 87 01
E-Mail: office@christaqua.com
Web Site: www.christaqua.com
Emp.: 20
Water Treatment Services
S.I.C.: 4971
N.A.I.C.S.: 221310
Patrick Archer *(Gen Mgr)*

BWT Malta Holdings Ltd. (1)
Tower Gate Pl Tal-Qroqq St
Msida, MSD 1703, Malta
Tel.: (356) 2131 3060
Fax: (356) 2131 3064
Investment Management Services
S.I.C.: 6211
N.A.I.C.S.: 523999
John Psaila *(Mng Partner)*

BWT Nederland BV (1)
Energieweg 9
2382 NA Zoeterwoude, Netherlands
Tel.: (31) 88 750 90 00
Fax: (31) 88 750 90 90
E-Mail: sales@bwtnederland.nl
Web Site: www.bwtnederland.nl
Emp.: 49
Water Treatment Services
S.I.C.: 4971
N.A.I.C.S.: 221310
Jan Aufenacker *(Mng Dir)*

BWT Polska Sp. z.o.o. (1)
Ul Polczynska 116
01-304 Warsaw, Poland
Tel.: (48) 22 533 57 00
Fax: (48) 22 533 57 19
E-Mail: bwt@bwt.pl
Water Treatment Services
S.I.C.: 4971
N.A.I.C.S.: 221310

Non-U.S. Subsidiary:

BWT Ukraine Ltd. (2)
Radyshcheva Lane 8 Kiev
4073 Kiev, Ukraine
Tel.: (380) 44 390 76 18
Fax: (380) 44 390 76 19
E-Mail: info@bwt.com.ua
Web Site: www.bwt.ua
Emp.: 11
Water Treatment Services
S.I.C.: 4941
N.A.I.C.S.: 221310
Evgeniy Doroshenko *(Gen Mgr)*

BWT Wassertechnik GmbH (1)
Industriestr 7
Schriesheim, 69198 Heidelberg, Germany
Tel.: (49) 6203730
Fax: (49) 6203102
E-Mail: info@bwt.ge
Web Site: www.bwt.ge
Emp.: 300
Other Commercial & Service Industry Machinery Mfr
S.I.C.: 3589
N.A.I.C.S.: 333318
lutz Huepner *(Mng Dir)*

Subsidiaries:

BWT water+more Deutschland GmbH (2)
Spiegelgasse 13
65183 Wiesbaden, Germany
Tel.: (49) 611 58019 0
Fax: (49) 611 58019 22
E-Mail: info@water-and-more.de
Web Site: www.water-and-more.com
Emp.: 1
Water Treatment Services
S.I.C.: 4971
N.A.I.C.S.: 221310
Frank Neuhausen *(Gen Mgr)*

Non-U.S. Subsidiaries:

BWT water and more Iberica S.L. (3)
TCM 2 6 Pl Ofic 20 Avda Ernest Lluch 32
8302 Mataro, Spain
Tel.: (34) 937023 204
Fax: (34) 937 023 205
E-Mail: info@water-and-more.de
Water Treatment Services
S.I.C.: 4941
N.A.I.C.S.: 221310

BWT water+more Italia srl (3)
Viale Giulio Cesare 20
24124 Bergamo, Italy
Tel.: (39) 035 210738
E-Mail: info@water-and-more.de
Water Treatment Services
S.I.C.: 4971
N.A.I.C.S.: 221310

hobby-pool technologies GmbH (2)
Rodgener Str 8-9
Ot Grosszoberitz, 06780 Zorbig, Germany
Tel.: (49) 34956 3998 0
Fax: (49) 34956 3998 57
E-Mail: info@hobbypooltechnologies.de
Swimming Pool Products Distr
S.I.C.: 5091
N.A.I.C.S.: 423910

BWT Water Technology (Shanghai) Co. Ltd. (1)
248 Xintuan Rd 12 Workshop Qingpu Ind Zone
201707 Shanghai, China
Tel.: (86) 21 5986 7100
Fax: (86) 21 5986 7101
E-Mail: info@bwt.cn
Emp.: 5
Water Treatment Services
S.I.C.: 4971
N.A.I.C.S.: 221310
Oliver Wake *(Gen Mgr)*

Christ Aqua Ecolife AG (1)
Neuhofweg 53
Aesch, 4147 Lucerne, Switzerland
Tel.: (41) 617558899
Fax: (41) 617558990
E-Mail: info@bwt-aqua.ch
Web Site: www.bwt-aqua.ch
Emp.: 180
General Purpose Machinery Mfr
S.I.C.: 3569
N.A.I.C.S.: 333999
Ravasio Enrico *(Mng Dir)*

Cilit SA (1)
C/ Silici 71-73 Poligono Industrial del Este
8940 Barcelona, Spain
Tel.: (34) 934740494
Fax: (34) 934744730
E-Mail: cilit@cilit.com
Water Treatment Services
S.I.C.: 4941
N.A.I.C.S.: 221310

Cillichemie Italiana Srl (1)
Via Plinio 59
20129 Milan, Italy
Tel.: (39) 02 2046343
Fax: (39) 02 201058
E-Mail: cillichemie@cibemi.it
Emp.: 100
Water Treatment Services
S.I.C.: 4971
N.A.I.C.S.: 221310
Lorenzo Tadini *(Mng Dir)*

Culligan International (UK) Ltd. (1)
Culligan House The Gateway Center
Coronation Road, High Wycombe, Buckinghamshire, HP12 3SU, United Kingdom (100%)
Tel.: (44) 1494838100
Fax: (44) 1494 523833
E-Mail: sales@culligan.co.uk
Web Site: www.culligan.co.uk
Water Conditioning & Purification Equipment & Related Products
S.I.C.: 3589
N.A.I.C.S.: 333318

FuMA-Tech GmbH (1)
Am Grubenstollen 11
66386 Saint Ingbert, Germany
Tel.: (49) 689492650
Fax: (49) 6894926599
E-Mail: info@fumatech.de
Web Site: www.fumatech.com
Emp.: 25
Support Activities for Water Transportation
S.I.C.: 4499
N.A.I.C.S.: 488390
Bernd Bauer *(Mng Dir)*

HOH Birger Christensen AS (1)
Roykenveien 142 A
Postboks 136
N-1371 Asker, Norway
Tel.: (47) 67177000
Fax: (47) 67177001
E-Mail: firmapost@bwtwater.no
Web Site: www.hoh.no
Emp.: 35
Water Supply and Irrigation Systems
S.I.C.: 4971
N.A.I.C.S.: 221310

HOH Separtec OY (1)
Varppeenkatu 28 19
21201 Raisio, Finland
Tel.: (358) 24367300
Fax: (358) 24367355
E-Mail: hoh@hoh.fi
Web Site: www.hoh.fi
Emp.: 14
Commercial & Service Industry Machinery Mfr
S.I.C.: 3589
N.A.I.C.S.: 333318
Mika Makela *(Mgr-Sls)*

HOH Vattenteknik AB (1)
Kantyxegatan 25
PO Box 9226
S-200 39 Malmo, Sweden
Tel.: (46) 406914500
Fax: (46) 40212055
E-Mail: info@vattenteknik.se
Web Site: www.vattenteknik.se
Emp.: 35
Commercial & Service Industry Machinery Mfr
S.I.C.: 3589
N.A.I.C.S.: 333318
Paul Morin *(Mng Dir)*

HOH Water Technology A/S (1)
Geminivej 24
2670 Greve, Denmark
Tel.: (45) 43600500
Fax: (45) 43600900
E-Mail: hoh@hoh.dk
Web Site: www.hoh.com
Emp.: 100
Consumer Electronics Repair & Maintenance
S.I.C.: 7622
N.A.I.C.S.: 811211
Henick Forslund *(CEO)*

OOO BWT (1)
Ul Kasatkina 3a
129301 Moscow, Russia
Tel.: (7) 495 686 62 64
Fax: (7) 495 686 74 65
E-Mail: info@bwt.ru
Emp.: 10
Water Treatment Services
S.I.C.: 4941
N.A.I.C.S.: 221310

WTA - Wassertechnischer Anlagenbau Plauen GmbH (1)
Reissiger Gewerbering Eleven
8525 Plauen, Germany
Tel.: (49) 37 41 55 84 0
Fax: (49) 37 41 55 84 99
E-Mail: info@wta-plauen.de
Water Treatment Services
S.I.C.: 4941
N.A.I.C.S.: 221310

BYBLOS BANK S.A.L.

Byblos Bank Tower Elias Sarkis Ave
Ashrfieh
Beirut, Lebanon
Mailing Address:
PO Box 11-5605
Beirut, Lebanon
Tel.: (961) 1335200
Fax: (961) 1339436
E-Mail: byblosbk@byblosbank.com.lb
Web Site: www.byblosbank.com
Year Founded: 1950
BYBL—(BEY LSE)
Rev.: $828,584,900
Assets: $16,672,635,850
Liabilities: $15,052,961,950
Net Worth: $1,619,673,900
Earnings: $163,970,300
Emp.: 2,572
Fiscal Year-end: 12/31/12

Business Description:
Banking Services
S.I.C.: 6029
N.A.I.C.S.: 522110

Byblos Bank S.A.L.—(Continued)

Personnel:
Francois Semaan Bassil *(Chm & Gen Mgr)*
Semaan Francois Bassil *(Vice Chm & Gen Mgr)*
Board of Directors:
Francois Semaan Bassil
Henri Toufic Azzam
Semaan Francois Bassil
Faisal M. Ali El Tabsh
Sami F. Haddad
Marie-Helene Loison
Bassam Albert Nassar
Arthur G. Nazarian
Baron Guy Louis Quaden
Abdulhadi A. Shayif
Ahmad Toufic Tabbarah
Alain Clovis Tohme

BDO Semaan Gholam & Co
Gholam Building Sioufi Street
Beirut, Lebanon

Subsidiary:

Byblos Bank Invest S.A.L (1)
Byblos Tower Elias
Sarkis Avenue, Beirut, Lebanon
Tel.: (961) 1335200
Web Site: www.byblosbank.com
Commercial Banking
S.I.C.: 6029
N.A.I.C.S.: 522110
Sami Haddad *(Gen Mgr)*

Non-U.S. Subsidiaries:

Byblos Bank Africa ltd. (1)
El Amarat - Street 21 8121
Khartoum, Sudan
Tel.: (249) 183566444
Fax: (249) 183566454
E-Mail: Byblosbankafrica@byblosbank.com
Web Site: www.byblosbank.com.lb/africa/index.shtml
Emp.: 60
Commercial Banking
S.I.C.: 6029
N.A.I.C.S.: 522110
Fuad Negga *(Gen Mgr)*

Byblos Bank Europe S.A. (1)
Rue Montoyer 10
Box 3
1000 Brussels, Belgium
Tel.: (32) 25510020
Fax: (32) 25130526
E-Mail: byblosbankeurope@byblosbankeur.com
Web Site: www.byblosbank.com
Emp.: 55
Commercial Banking
S.I.C.: 6029
N.A.I.C.S.: 522110
Fouad Nicolas Trad *(Gen Mgr)*

Byblos Bank Syria S.A. (1)
Amine Loutfi Hafez St
Al Sham, 5424 Damascus, Syria
Tel.: (963) 113348240
Fax: (963) 113348207
E-Mail: byblosbanksyria@byblosbank.com
Web Site: www.byblosbank.com.lb/aboutbbkgroup/bbk_sa/board/index.shtml
Emp.: 201
Commercial Banking
S.I.C.: 6029
N.A.I.C.S.: 522110

BYCO PETROLEUM PAKISTAN LIMITED

The Harbour Front 9th Floor Dolmen City
HC-3 Block 4 Marine Drive
Clifton, Karachi, 75600, Pakistan
Tel.: (92) 21 111 222 081
Fax: (92) 21 111 888 081
Web Site: www.byco.com.pk
BYCO—(KAR)
Sales Range: $50-74.9 Million
Emp.: 500
Business Description:
Crude Oil Refining & Marketing
S.I.C.: 2911
N.A.I.C.S.: 324110
Personnel:
Waqar Hassan Siddique *(Chm)*
Hamid Imtiaz Hanfi *(Vice Chm & Head-Supervisory Secretariat)*
Amir Abbassciy *(CEO)*
Roshan B. Mehri *(CFO & Head-Treasury)*
Muhammad Qaiser Jamal *(Pres-Oil Refining Bus)*
Mohammad Wasi Khan *(Pres-Chemical Mfg Bus)*
Shahana Ahmed Ali *(Sec & Head-Corp Svcs & Legal)*
Board of Directors:
Waqar Hassan Siddique
Amir Abbassciy
Hamid Imtiaz Hanfi
Muhammad Raza Hasnani
Tariq Kirmani
Aziz Moolji
Samia Roomi
Kashif Shah
Matteo Stefanel
Abdullah Yusuf

BYD COMPANY LIMITED

No 3009 BYD Road
Pingshan, Shenzhen, 518118, China
Tel.: (86) 75589888888
Fax: (86) 755 84202222
E-Mail: li.tang1@byd.com
Web Site: www.byd.com.cn
1211—(HKG)
Rev.: $7,049,899,293
Assets: $11,120,740,142
Liabilities: $7,285,406,809
Net Worth: $3,835,333,333
Earnings: $33,817,577
Emp.: 166,000
Fiscal Year-end: 12/31/12
Business Description:
Electronic Component Mfr
S.I.C.: 3691
N.A.I.C.S.: 335911
Personnel:
Chuan-Fu Wang *(Chm & Pres)*
Jun-qing Dong *(Chm-Supervisory Bd)*
Jing-sheng Wu *(CFO & VP)*
Qian Li *(Sec)*
Board of Directors:
Chuan-Fu Wang
Dong Li
Lian-he Li
Xiang-yang Lu
Chang-qi Wu
Zuo-quan Xia
Supervisory Board of Directors:
Jun-qing Dong
Yong-zhao Li
Zhen Wang
Chen Yan
Hui-bin Zhang
Transfer Agent:
Computershare Hong Kong Investor Services Limited
17M Floor Hopewell Centre 183 Queen's Road East
Wanchai, China (Hong Kong)

Subsidiary:

BYD (H.K.) Co., Limited (1)
Unit 1712 17 F Tower 2 Grand Cent Plz No 138 Shatin Rural Comt Rd
Sha Tin, New Territories, China (Hong Kong)
Tel.: (852) 23055128
Fax: (852) 23055028
Nickel & Lithium Batteries Sales
S.I.C.: 3691
N.A.I.C.S.: 335911

U.S. Subsidiary:

BYD America Corporation (1)
1500 W Shure Dr Ste 250
Arlington Heights, IL 60004-1465
Tel.: (847) 690-9999
Fax: (847) 690-0228
Toll Free: (877) 585-6868
Storage Batteries Mfr & Sales
S.I.C.: 3691
N.A.I.C.S.: 335911

Non-U.S. Subsidiaries:

BYD Electronic Hungary Kft (1)
Ipari Park Puskas Tivadar Ut 8
Koppanymonostor, 2903, Hungary
Tel.: (36) 34540840
Fax: (36) 34340299
Mobile Handset Components Mfr & Sales
S.I.C.: 3663
N.A.I.C.S.: 334220

BYD Europe B.V. (1)
Vareseweg 53
3047 AA Rotterdam, Netherlands
Tel.: (31) 102070888
Fax: (31) 102070880
E-Mail: eu@byd.com
Web Site: www.byd.com
Emp.: 35
Nickel & Lithium Batteries Distr
S.I.C.: 5063
N.A.I.C.S.: 423610
Stella K. Li *(Principal)*

BYD Japan Co., Ltd. (1)
Thefifthyasuta Bldg 5 F 2-20-3 Tsuruya-cho
Yokohama, Kanagawa, 221-0835, Japan
Tel.: (81) 452906550
Fax: (81) 453191506
Rechargeable Batteries Whslr
S.I.C.: 5063
N.A.I.C.S.: 423610
Xuelang Liu *(Pres)*

Shanghai BYD Company Limited (1)
No 999 Xiangjing Rd
Songjiang Dist, Shanghai, 201611, China
Tel.: (86) 21 57778888
Fax: (86) 21 57775000
Lithium Batteries Mfr & Sales
S.I.C.: 3692
N.A.I.C.S.: 335912

Non-U.S. Plant:

BYD Company Limited - Huizhou Plant 2 (1)
Xiangshui River Econ Develop Zone Daya Bay
Huizhou, Guangdong, 516083, China
Tel.: (86) 7525118888
Ferrous Batteries Mfr
S.I.C.: 3691
N.A.I.C.S.: 335911

BYD ELECTRONIC INTERNATIONAL CO LTD

1712 17th Floor Tower 2 Grand Central Plaza
138 Shatin Rural Committee Road, Sha Tin, New Territories, China (Hong Kong)
Tel.: (852) 23055128
Fax: (852) 23055028
Web Site: www.byd-electronic.com
0285—(HKG)
Rev.: $2,238,340,895
Assets: $1,888,535,245
Liabilities: $577,320,945
Net Worth: $1,311,214,299
Earnings: $60,195,572
Emp.: 55,000
Fiscal Year-end: 12/31/12
Business Description:
Telecommunication Services
S.I.C.: 3661
N.A.I.C.S.: 334210
Personnel:
Ke Li *(CEO)*
Ai-yun Zhu *(CFO)*
Yi-Zao Sun *(COO)*
Hon-Wan Cheung *(Co-Sec)*
Qian Li *(Co-Sec)*
Board of Directors:
Chuan-Fu Wang
Yuk-Tong Chan
Ke Li
Ping Liang
Antony Francis Mampilly
Yi-Zao Sun
Jing-Sheng Wu
Transfer Agent:
Computershare Hong Kong Investor Services Limited
Shops 1712-1716 17th Floor Hopewell Centre
183 Queens Road East
Wanchai, China (Hong Kong)

THE BYKE HOSPITALITY LIMITED

Shree Shakambhari Corporate Park
Plot No 156-158
Chakravarti Ashok Society JB Nagar
Andheri E, Mumbai, 400 099, India
Tel.: (91) 22 6707 9666
Fax: (91) 22 6707 9696
E-Mail: investors.care@thebyke.com
Web Site: www.thebyke.com
Year Founded: 1990
531373—(BOM)
Rev.: $18,804,556
Assets: $21,069,135
Liabilities: $7,635,683
Net Worth: $13,433,452
Earnings: $1,438,081
Fiscal Year-end: 03/31/13
Business Description:
Hotel Management Services
S.I.C.: 7011
N.A.I.C.S.: 721110
Personnel:
Anil Patodia *(CEO & Mng Dir)*
Swati Gupta *(Compliance Officer & Sec)*
Board of Directors:
Ram Ratan Bajaj
Anil Patodia
Pramod Patodia
Satyanarayan Sharma
Bharat Thakkar
Ramesh Vohra
Transfer Agent:
Sharepro Services (India) Pvt Ltd
13AB Samhita Warehousing Complex 2nd Fl
Sakinaka Telephone Exchange Ln
Off Andheri-Kurla Road Sakinaka Andheri East, Mumbai, 400 072, India

BYOTROL PLC

Riverside Works Collyhurst Road
Manchester, M40 7RU, United Kingdom
Tel.: (44) 1925742000
Fax: (44) 1925742029
E-Mail: info@byotrol.com
Web Site: www.byotrol.co.uk
BYOT—(LSE)
Rev.: $3,459,831
Assets: $4,091,880
Liabilities: $1,901,160
Net Worth: $2,190,720
Earnings: ($2,745,059)
Emp.: 22
Fiscal Year-end: 03/31/13
Business Description:
Microbial Technology Products Mfr
S.I.C.: 3999
N.A.I.C.S.: 339999
Personnel:
Gary Millar *(CEO)*
Denise Keenan *(Sec & Dir-Fin)*
Board of Directors:
Nicholas Martel
Till Medinger
Gary Millar
Legal Counsel:
Field Fisher Waterhouse LLP
35 Vine Street
London, United Kingdom

Subsidiary:

Byotrol Technology Limited (1)
Vanguard House Keckwick Lane
Daresbury, WA4 4AB, United Kingdom

Tel.: (44) 161 277 9518
Fax: (44) 192 574 2029
E-Mail: info@byotrol.com
Emp.: 2
Household Cleaning & Personal Care Products Distr
S.I.C.: 5169
N.A.I.C.S.: 424690
Gary Millar *(CEO)*

U.S. Subsidiary:

Byotrol Inc. (1)
100 Corporate Dr Ste J
Spartanburg, SC 29303-5008
Tel.: (864) 278-8017
Fax: (864) 578-6770
E-Mail: info@byotrol.com
Web Site: www.byotrol.co.uk/contact-us.html
Emp.: 7
Household Cleaning & Personal Care Products Distr
S.I.C.: 5169
N.A.I.C.S.: 424690
Shea Phillips *(Gen Mgr)*

BYRON ENERGY LIMITED

(Formerly Trojan Equity Limited)
Level 4 480 Collins Street
Melbourne, VIC, 3000, Australia
Tel.: (61) 3 8610 6583
Fax: (61) 3 8610 6334
E-Mail: info@byronenergy.com.au
Web Site: www.byronenergy.com.au
BYE—(ASX)
Sales Range: $1-9.9 Million

Business Description:
Oil & Gas Exploration Services
S.I.C.: 1311
N.A.I.C.S.: 211111

Personnel:
Doug Battersby *(Chm)*
Maynard Smith *(CEO)*
Nick Filipovic *(CFO & Sec)*
Prent Kallenberger *(COO)*

Board of Directors:
Doug Battersby
Prent Kallenberger
Charles Sands
Maynard Smith
Paul Young

BYTE COMPUTER SA

98 Kallirois Street
117 41 Athens, Greece
Tel.: (30) 210 900 2000
Fax: (30) 210 924 4084
E-Mail: xtsenes@byte.gr
Web Site: www.byte.gr
Year Founded: 1990
BYTE—(ATH)
Sls.: $27,771,152
Assets: $36,785,214
Liabilities: $16,845,600
Net Worth: $19,939,614
Earnings: ($2,984,964)
Emp.: 161
Fiscal Year-end: 12/31/12

Business Description:
Information Technology Consulting Services
S.I.C.: 7373
N.A.I.C.S.: 541512

Personnel:
Spyros Vyzantios *(Chm & CEO)*
Nikolitsa Vyzantios *(Vice Chm)*

Board of Directors:
Spyros Vyzantios
Konstantinos Fotinopoulos
Stavroula Giannakopoulou
Anastasia Louis
Vasillios Lyberopoulos
Nikolitsa Vyzantios
Konstantinos Xirotiris

Non-U.S. Subsidiaries:

BYTE Bulgaria Ltd. (1)
Quarter Mladost 3 51 Aleksandar Malinov blv
Entry 3 Floor 6 App 7, 1712 Sofia, Bulgaria
Tel.: (359) 2 872 9313
E-Mail: info@bytebulgaria.com
Computer Consulting Services
S.I.C.: 7379
N.A.I.C.S.: 541519

BYTE IT Srl (1)
Cal;ea Dorobanti nr 42 sector 1
Bucharest, Romania
Tel.: (40) 21 2023604
Fax: (40) 21 2240152
E-Mail: inforo@bytecomputer.eu
Web Site: www.byteromania.com
Computer Consulting Services
S.I.C.: 7379
N.A.I.C.S.: 541519

BYTE POWER GROUP LIMITED

Suite 13 76 Doggett Street
Newstead, QLD, 4006, Australia
Tel.: (61) 736201688
Fax: (61) 736201689
E-Mail: info@bytepowergroup.com
Web Site: www.bytepowergroup.com
Year Founded: 1989
BPG—(ASX)
Rev.: $6,713,509
Assets: $1,436,840
Liabilities: $8,515,312
Net Worth: ($7,078,472)
Earnings: $25,036
Emp.: 5
Fiscal Year-end: 06/30/13

Business Description:
Information Technology & Telecommunications Facilites, Products & Network Management Solutions
S.I.C.: 7389
N.A.I.C.S.: 541990

Personnel:
Alvin Phua *(Chm & CEO)*
Ethel Lau *(Sec)*

Board of Directors:
Alvin Phua
Marc Higgins
Horward Shi
Raphael Wai Mun Tham

Legal Counsel:
Hopgood Ganim
Level 8 Waterfront Place 1 Eagle Street
Brisbane, QLD, 4000, Australia

Subsidiaries:

Byte Power Pty Ltd (1)
1/75 Longland Street
4006 Newstead, QLD, Australia (100%)
Tel.: (61) 736201688
Fax: (61) 736201689
E-Mail: txu@bytepower.com
Web Site: www.bytepower.com.au
Emp.: 10
Information Technology Products & Services
S.I.C.: 5045
N.A.I.C.S.: 423430

Byte Power Technologies Pty Ltd (1)
Unit 1 75 Longland Street
Newstead, QLD, 4006, Australia (100%)
Tel.: (61) 736201688
Fax: (61) 736201689
E-Mail: info@bytepower.com.au
Web Site: www.bytepower.com.au
Emp.: 10
Software Development & Integration Services for the Telecommunications & Corporate Communications Markets
S.I.C.: 7372
N.A.I.C.S.: 511210
Alvin Phua *(CEO & Mng Dir)*

Power Tech Systems Pty Ltd (1)
Unit 8 101 Wedgewood Road
Hallam, VIC, 3173, Australia (100%)
Tel.: (61) 397086866
Fax: (61) 397086500
E-Mail: info@ptech.com.au
Web Site: www.ptech.com.au
Power Supply Products Mfr & Distr
S.I.C.: 3612
N.A.I.C.S.: 335311
Alvin Phua *(CEO)*

Non-U.S. Subsidiaries:

Byte Power (Hong Kong) Limited (1)
Room 2104 Island Palace Tower
510 Kings Road, North Point, China (Hong Kong) (83.4%)
Tel.: (852) 2907 9838
Fax: (852) 2559 2102
Web Site: www.bytepowergroup.com
Software Development & Integration Services for the Telecommunications & Corporate Communications Markets
S.I.C.: 7372
N.A.I.C.S.: 511210

Byte Power Technology (Intl) Pte Ltd (1)
Marina Bay Financial Center Tower Two
Level 39 10 Marina Boulevard
Singapore, Singapore (100%)
Tel.: (65) 68186302
Web Site: www.bytepowergroup.com
Software Development & Integration Services for the Telecommunications & Corporate Communications Markets
S.I.C.: 7372
N.A.I.C.S.: 511210

BYTE SOFTWARE HOUSE S.P.A.

Via Oropa 28
10153 Turin, Italy
Tel.: (39) 0118185611
Fax: (39) 0118185677
E-Mail: info@bytesh.com
Web Site: www.bytesh.com
Year Founded: 1974
Sales Range: $50-74.9 Million
Emp.: 500

Business Description:
Information Technology Services
S.I.C.: 7371
N.A.I.C.S.: 541511

Personnel:
Robarto Gamarro *(Pres)*

BYTEK AUTOMOBILES INC.

1325 St Laurent Blvd
Ottawa, ON, K1G 0Z7, Canada
Tel.: (613) 745-6885
Fax: (613) 745-7749
Toll Free: (866) 409-8148
Web Site: www.bytekvolkswagen.com
Year Founded: 1970
Rev.: $16,848,000
Emp.: 35

Business Description:
New & Used Car Dealers
S.I.C.: 5511
N.A.I.C.S.: 441110

Personnel:
Jill Blanke *(VP-Ops)*

BYUCKSAN ENGINEERING & CONSTRUCTION CO., LTD.

13 25 Yeouido Dong
Yeongdeungpo Gu
150870 Seoul, Korea (South)
Tel.: (82) 27675114
Fax: (82) 27675205
Web Site: www.becco.co.kr
Year Founded: 1958
002530—(KRS)
Sales Range: $1-4.9 Billion
Emp.: 580

Business Description:
Architectural & Civil Engineering Services
S.I.C.: 8712
N.A.I.C.S.: 541310

Personnel:
Hee Cheol Kim *(Chm)*
Seong Gak Jang *(CEO)*

Board of Directors:
Hee Cheol Kim
Seong Gak Jang
Min Young Jung

U.S. Subsidiary:

Byucksan America Inc. (1)
4060 W Wash Blvd
Los Angeles, CA 90018
Tel.: (323) 735-3479
Civil Engineering Services
S.I.C.: 8711
N.A.I.C.S.: 541330

BYWATERS LTD

Lea Riverside Twelvetrees Crescent
Bow
London, E3 3JG, United Kingdom
Tel.: (44) 2070016000
Fax: (44) 2070016001
E-Mail: customerservices@bywaters.co.uk
Web Site: www.bywaters.co.uk
Year Founded: 1952
Rev.: $41,201,221
Emp.: 273

Business Description:
Recycling & Resource Management Services
S.I.C.: 4959
N.A.I.C.S.: 562998

Personnel:
Peter Johnson *(Chm)*
John S. Glover *(Mng Dir)*
Michael Pusey *(Deputy Mng Dir)*

BZ BANK AKTIENGESELLSCHAFT

Egglirain 15
8832 Munchwilen, Switzerland
Tel.: (41) 17866111
Fax: (41) 17866115
E-Mail: info@bzbank.ch
Web Site: www.bzbank.ch
Sales Range: $1-9.9 Million
Emp.: 16

Business Description:
Private Bank
S.I.C.: 6029
N.A.I.C.S.: 522110

Personnel:
Heinz Haeberli *(Chm)*
Nils Engel *(Pres)*
Dieter Golei *(CFO & Exec VP)*
Ralph Stadler *(Exec VP)*

Board of Directors:
Heinz Haeberli
Nils Engel
Dieter Goldi
Kurt Schiltknecht
Ralph Stadler

Subsidiaries:

BZ Fund Management Aktiengesellschaft (1)
Egglirain 24
8832 Munchwilen, Switzerland
Tel.: (41) 447866600
Fax: (41) 447866699
E-Mail: info@bzfund.ch
Web Site: www.bzfund.ch
Emp.: 4
Securities & Commodity Exchanges
S.I.C.: 6231
N.A.I.C.S.: 523210
Joe Manko *(Mng Dir)*

Intershop Holding AG (1)
Pulse 5 Giessereistrasse No 18
8031 Zurich, Switzerland (100%)
Tel.: (41) 445441000
Fax: (41) 445441001
E-Mail: intershop@intershop.ch
Web Site: www.intershop.ch
Emp.: 36
Real Estate Investment Company
S.I.C.: 6726
N.A.I.C.S.: 525990
Dieter Marmet *(Pres)*
Cyrill M. Schneuwly *(CEO)*

C & C CONSTRUCTIONS LIMITED
Plot No 70 Sector 32
Gurgaon, Haryana, 122001, India
Tel.: (91) 1244536666
Fax: (91) 1244536799
E-Mail: candc@candcinfrastructure.com
Web Site: www.candcinfrastructure.com
Year Founded: 1996
CANDC—(NSE)
Rev.: $186,741,691
Assets: $670,447,854
Liabilities: $614,607,265
Net Worth: $55,840,588
Earnings: ($47,154,736)
Emp.: 1,043
Fiscal Year-end: 06/30/13
Business Description:
Highways & Bridge Construction Services
S.I.C.: 1622
N.A.I.C.S.: 237310
Personnel:
Gurjeet Singh Johar *(Chm)*
Charanbir Singh Sethi *(Mng Dir)*
Tapash K. Majumdar *(CFO)*
Deepak Nathani *(Compliance Officer & Sec)*
Board of Directors:
Gurjeet Singh Johar
Rajendra Mohan Aggarwal
Anand Bordia
Amrit Pal Singh Chadha
Sanjay Gupta
Kanwal Monga
Ramesh Chandra Rekhi
Charanbir Singh Sethi
Rajbir Singh
Tarlochan Singh
Transfer Agent:
Bigshare Services Pvt. Ltd.
E-2/3 Ansa Industrial Estate Sakivihar Road
Saki Naka Andheri E
Mumbai, India
Subsidiary:

C & C Towers Ltd (1)
Sector- 57 Mohali Phase- 6 ISBT
Commercial Complex Gate No 5
Opposite Verka Milk Plant, Mohali, Punjab, 140 501, India
Tel.: (91) 172 4242300
Fax: (91) 172 4242333
E-Mail: querymjunc@candcinfrastructure.com
Emp.: 18
Construction Engineering Services
S.I.C.: 8711
N.A.I.C.S.: 541330
C. V. S. Sehgal *(Gen Mgr)*

C&C GROUP PLC
3rd Floor Block 71 The Plaza
Parkwest Business Park, Dublin, 12, Ireland
Tel.: (353) 16161100
Fax: (353) 16546272
E-Mail: info@candcgroupplc.com
Web Site: www.candcgroupplc.com
GCC—(ISE)
Rev.: $974,761,697
Assets: $1,615,807,851
Liabilities: $566,199,102
Net Worth: $1,049,608,749
Earnings: $119,405,279
Emp.: 1,001
Fiscal Year-end: 02/28/13
Business Description:
Alcoholic & Non-Alcoholic Beverages & Snacks Mfr
S.I.C.: 5182
N.A.I.C.S.: 424820
Personnel:
Stephen Glancey *(CEO)*
Kenny Neison *(CFO)*
Paul Walker *(Gen Counsel & Sec)*
Board of Directors:
Brian Stewart
Joris Brams
Stewart Gilliland
Stephen Glancey
John Hogan
Richard Holroyd
Kenny Neison
Breege O'Donoghue
Tony Smurfit
Legal Counsel:
McCann FitzGerald
Riverside One Sir John Rogerson's Quay
Dublin, Ireland
Subsidiaries:

Bulmers Ltd (1)
Annerville Clonmel
Tipperary, Ireland
Tel.: (353) 526172100
Fax: (353) 5272256
E-Mail: info@bulmers.ie
Web Site: www.bulmers.ie
Cider Mfr
S.I.C.: 2086
N.A.I.C.S.: 312111
Paul O'Sullivan *(Mng Dir)*

C & C International Ltd (1)
3rd Fl Block 71 The Plaza
Parkwest Business Park, Dublin, 12, Ireland
Tel.: (353) 16161100
Fax: (353) 6546272
E-Mail: info@www.candcgroup.ie
Emp.: 40
Beverage Sales & Distr
S.I.C.: 5182
N.A.I.C.S.: 424820
Joris Brams *(Mng Dir)*

M. & J. Gleeson Investments Ltd. (1)
16 Cherry Orchard Industrial Estate
Ballyfermot, Dublin, 10, Ireland
Tel.: (353) 1 6269787
Fax: (353) 1 6260512
E-Mail: info@gleesongroup.ie
Web Site: www.gleesongroup.ie
Sales Range: $300-349.9 Million
Beverage Distr
S.I.C.: 5182
N.A.I.C.S.: 424820
Stephen Meleady *(Gen Mgr)*

Subsidiary:

Gilbey's of Ireland, Ltd. (2)
Nangor House
Nangor Road, Dublin, 12, Ireland (100%)
Tel.: (353) 1 429 2200
Telex: 93451
Fax: (353) 1 429 2230
Rev.: $181,773,000
Emp.: 110
Wine Distr
S.I.C.: 5182
N.A.I.C.S.: 424820
Sally-Anne Cooney *(Gen Mgr)*

U.S. Subsidiary:

Vermont Hard Cider Company, LLC (1)
153 Pond Ln
Middlebury, VT 05753
Tel.: (802) 388-0700
Fax: (802) 388-0600
E-Mail: gmbinfo@gmbeverage.com
Web Site: www.woodchuck.com
Emp.: 35
Hard Cider Mfr & Distr
S.I.C.: 2082
N.A.I.C.S.: 312120
Dan Rowell *(Interim CEO)*

C&G BEAULIEU GROUP INC.
368 Grand Boulevard Est
Saint-Basile-Le-Grand, QC, J3N 1M4, Canada
Tel.: (450) 653-9581
Fax: (450) 653-3417
Web Site: www.cgbeaulieu.net
Year Founded: 1974
Emp.: 100
Business Description:
Construction Services
S.I.C.: 1542
N.A.I.C.S.: 236220
Personnel:
Gaetan Beaulieu *(Pres)*

C&G DISTRIBUTING INC.
(Acquired by Anheuser-Busch InBev N.V./S.A. & Name Changed to Anheuser-Busch Sales of Lima)

C&G INDUSTRIAL HOLDINGS LIMITED
Ping Lin Industrial Development Zone
Tie Shan Town
Xinluo District, Longyan, Fujian, China
Tel.: (86) 5972340388
Fax: (86) 5972340688
D79—(SES)
Sales Range: $75-99.9 Million
Emp.: 620
Business Description:
Holding Company; Polyethylene Terephthalate Textile Products Mfr & Distr
S.I.C.: 3089
N.A.I.C.S.: 326199
Personnel:
Chik Tsan Lam *(Chm)*
Junyi Cai *(CEO)*

C&G SYSTEMS INC.
Tennoz Central Tower 19th floor 2-2-24 Higashi-shinagawa Shinagawa-ku
Tokyo, 140-0002, Japan
Tel.: (81) 368640777
Fax: (81) 368640778
E-Mail: sales@cgsys.co.jp
Web Site: www.cgsys.co.jp
Year Founded: 2007
6633—(JAS)
Sls.: $37,261,389
Assets: $40,613,782
Liabilities: $16,263,577
Net Worth: $24,350,205
Earnings: $1,548,745
Emp.: 221
Fiscal Year-end: 12/31/12
Business Description:
Software Development & Distr
S.I.C.: 7371
N.A.I.C.S.: 541511
Personnel:
Shuji Yamaguchi *(Chm)*
Seiichi Shiota *(Pres)*
Hiroyuki Tomono *(Mng Dir)*
Katsuhito Kasuga *(Corp Officer)*
Satoru Koizumi *(Corp Officer)*
Tetsuo Tsuchiya *(Corp Officer)*
Kenju Waku *(Corp Officer)*
Board of Directors:
Shuji Yamaguchi
Takao Fujita
Tatsuo Kamiya
Sotaro Ohno
Kiyoshi Sakon
Seiichi Shiota
Kazuhiko Terasaki
Hiroyuki Tomono
Masaaki Yoshida
U.S. Subsidiary:

Tritech International, LLC (1)
1710 Todd Farm Dr
Elgin, IL 60123
Tel.: (847) 888-0333
E-Mail: info@tritech-intl.com
Web Site: www.usatritech.wix.com
Industrial Mold Mfr
S.I.C.: 3544
N.A.I.C.S.: 333511

Non-U.S. Subsidiary:

CGS NORTH AMERICA INC. (1)
2160 Fasan Drive
Windsor, ON, N0R 1L0, Canada
Tel.: (519) 737-6009
Fax: (519) 737-1647
E-Mail: info@camtool.net
Web Site: www.camtool.net
Software Publishing Services
S.I.C.: 7372
N.A.I.C.S.: 511210

C&J CLARK LTD.
(d/b/a Clarks)
40 High St
Street, Somerset, BA16 0EQ, United Kingdom
Tel.: (44) 1458442251
Telex: 44102
Fax: (44) 1458447547
E-Mail: customercare@clarks.com
Web Site: www.clarks.co.uk
Year Founded: 1825
Sales Range: $1-4.9 Billion
Emp.: 14,000
Business Description:
Men's, Women's & Children's Shoes Mfr & Retailer
Import Export
S.I.C.: 2389
N.A.I.C.S.: 316210
Personnel:
Thomas O'Neill *(Chm)*
Melissa Potter *(CEO)*
U.S. Subsidiary:

Clarks Companies North America (1)
156 Oak St
Newton Upper Falls, MA 02464-1440
Tel.: (617) 964-1222
Fax: (617) 243-4300
E-Mail:
Web Site: www.clarksusa.com
Emp.: 1,000
Retailer of Shoes
Import
S.I.C.: 5139
N.A.I.C.S.: 424340
Ritch Haag *(Sr VP-Ops)*
Margaret Newville *(Sr VP-Mktg)*
Sharon Schuler *(Sr VP-Fin-Americas)*

Divisions:

Bostonian Wholesale Division (2)
156 Oak St
Newton Upper Falls, MA 02464
Tel.: (617) 964-1222
Fax: (866) 575-8515
E-Mail: jobs@bostonianshoe.com
Web Site: www.bostonianshoe.com
Emp.: 300
Shoe Wholesaling
S.I.C.: 8051
N.A.I.C.S.: 623110
Jim Salzano *(Pres)*

Clarks Companies - IT Division (2)
620 S Union St
Kennett Square, PA 19348-3534 DE (100%)
Tel.: (610) 444-6550
Fax: (610) 444-3567
Emp.: 40
Information Technology Services
S.I.C.: 7379
N.A.I.C.S.: 541519
Jim Salzano *(Pres)*

Non-U.S. Subsidiary:

C&J Clark Canada, Ltd. (1)
2881 Brighton Rd
Oakville, ON, L6H 6C9, Canada (100%)
Tel.: (905) 829-1825
Fax: (905) 829-1839
Web Site: www.clarkscanada.com
Emp.: 26
Shoes Distr
S.I.C.: 5139
N.A.I.C.S.: 424340
George Molyneux *(Sr VP & Gen Mgr)*

C&S PAPER CO., LTD.
136 West Rainbow Boulevard
Zhongshan, Guangdong, China
Tel.: (86) 760 88553333

Fax: (86) 760 23886886
Web Site: www.zhongshungroup.com
002511—(SSE)
Emp.: 4,500
Business Description:
Household Paper Products Mfr
S.I.C.: 2676
N.A.I.C.S.: 322291
Personnel:
Yingzhong Deng *(Chm)*

C & T REINFORCING STEEL CO (1987) LIMITED
93 Passmore Avenue
Scarborough, ON, Canada M1V 4S9
Tel.: (416) 291-7349
Fax: (416) 291-0698
Web Site: www.ctsteel.com
Rev.: $13,215,632
Emp.: 85
Business Description:
Reinforcing Steel Supplier
S.I.C.: 1791
N.A.I.C.S.: 238120
Personnel:
Sam Costa *(Pres)*

C. BROWN & SONS (STEEL) LTD
Cochrane House Pedmore Road
Dudley, W Midlands, DY2 0RL, United Kingdom
Tel.: (44) 1384 480048
Fax: (44) 1384 263838
E-Mail: sales@cbrownsteels.co.uk
Web Site: www.cbrownsteels.co.uk
Year Founded: 1946
Sales Range: $75-99.9 Million
Emp.: 150
Business Description:
Steel Mfr & Distr
S.I.C.: 3325
N.A.I.C.S.: 331513
Personnel:
Neville Brown *(Mng Dir)*
Division:
C. Brown & Sons (Steel) Ltd (1)
Brenton Business Complex Bond Street
Bury, Lancs, BL9 7BE, United Kingdom
Tel.: (44) 161 763 1454
Fax: (44) 161 763 1455
Steel Mfr
S.I.C.: 3325
N.A.I.C.S.: 331513

C. C. MARINE DISTRIBUTORS INC.
460 Harry Walker Parkway South
Newmarket, ON, L3Y 8E3, Canada
Tel.: (905) 830-0000
Fax: (905) 830-9433
Toll Free: (800) 387-5780
E-Mail: info@ccmarine.ca
Web Site: www.ccmarine.ca
Rev.: $11,011,189
Emp.: 36
Business Description:
Transportation Service
S.I.C.: 4424
N.A.I.C.S.: 483113
Personnel:
Rick Chang *(VP)*

C CHENG HOLDINGS LIMITED
15/F North Tower World Finance Centre
Harbour City
Tsim Sha Tsui, Kowloon, China (Hong Kong)
Tel.: (852) 2574 1633
Fax: (852) 2572 4908
E-Mail: ccheng@cchengholdings.com
Web Site: www.cchengholdings.com
8320—(HKG)
Rev.: $34,594,964
Earnings: $3,511,051
Emp.: 550
Fiscal Year-end: 12/31/12
Business Description:
Architectural & Ladscaping Services
S.I.C.: 8712
N.A.I.C.S.: 541310
Personnel:
Ronald Liang *(Chm)*
Chin Shing Fu *(CEO)*
Wing Sze Yu *(Sec)*
Board of Directors:
Ronald Liang
Chin Shing Fu
Xiao He
Kin Nang Lo
Wai Hung Lo
Kwok Fai Ng
Julius Wang
Jun You Wang
Chi Hang Yu

C. CHRISTOPHEL MASCHINENHANDEL & VERMITTLUNGEN GMBH
Taschenmacherstrasse 31-33
23556 Lubeck, Germany
Tel.: (49) 451899470
Fax: (49) 4518994749
E-Mail: mail@christophel.com
Web Site: www.christophel.com
Year Founded: 1984
Rev.: $25,243,020
Emp.: 24
Business Description:
Construction Machinery Supplier
S.I.C.: 5082
N.A.I.C.S.: 423810
Personnel:
Rudiger Christophel *(Mng Dir)*

C-COM SATELLITE SYSTEMS INC.
2574 Sheffield Road
Ottawa, ON, K1B 3V7, Canada
Tel.: (613) 745-4110
Fax: (613) 745-7144
E-Mail: info@c-comsat.com
Web Site: www.c-comsat.com
Year Founded: 1997
CMI—(TSXV)
Rev.: $13,305,280
Assets: $16,440,460
Liabilities: $1,204,249
Net Worth: $15,236,210
Earnings: $2,649,551
Fiscal Year-end: 11/30/12
Business Description:
Vehicle Mounted Antennas Mfr
S.I.C.: 3999
N.A.I.C.S.: 339999
Personnel:
Leslie Klein *(Pres & CEO)*
Jim Fowles *(CFO)*
Bilal Awada *(CTO)*
Shane McLean *(Sec)*
Board of Directors:
Eli Fathi
Leslie Klein
Walter Edward Koenig
Ronald Leslie
Transfer Agent:
Computershare Investor Services Inc
100 University Avenue 9th Floor
Toronto, ON, Canada

C DUGARD LTD
75 Old Shoreham Road
Hove, East Sussex, BN3 7BX, United Kingdom
Tel.: (44) 1273732286
Fax: (44) 1273203835
E-Mail: info@dugard.co.uk
Web Site: www.dugard.com
Year Founded: 1939
Rev.: $13,452,048
Emp.: 53
Business Description:
Machine Tools Mfr
S.I.C.: 3541
N.A.I.C.S.: 333517
Personnel:
Bob Dugard *(Chm)*
Eric Dugard *(Mng Dir)*

C. HAFNER GMBH + CO. KG
Bleichstrasse 13-17
75173 Pforzheim, Germany
Tel.: (49) 72319200
Fax: (49) 7231920207
E-Mail: info@c-hafner.de
Web Site: www.c-hafner.de
Year Founded: 1850
Rev.: $57,934,800
Emp.: 181
Business Description:
Metals Recovery & Processing Services
S.I.C.: 5094
N.A.I.C.S.: 423940
Personnel:
Birgitta Hafner *(Co-Mng Dir)*
Philipp Reisert *(Co-Mng Dir)*

C J O'SHEA GROUP LTD
1 Granard Business Centre Bunns Lane Mill Hill
London, NW7 2DZ, United Kingdom
Tel.: (44) 2089593600
Fax: (44) 2089590184
E-Mail: info@oshea.co.uk
Web Site: www.cjoshea.co.uk
Year Founded: 1966
Rev.: $155,741,806
Emp.: 175
Business Description:
Construction Services
S.I.C.: 1542
N.A.I.C.S.: 236220
Personnel:
Crohan O'Shea *(Founder & Chm)*

C LEVEL III INC.
181 Bay Street Suite 4400
Toronto, ON, M5J 2T3, Canada
Tel.: (514) 987-5081
Fax: (514) 987-1213
E-Mail: jean-francois.pelland@mcmillan.ca
Web Site: www.clevel.com
Year Founded: 2011
CLV.P—(TSXV)
Business Description:
Investment Services
S.I.C.: 6211
N.A.I.C.S.: 523999
Personnel:
Daniel Pharand *(Pres, CEO & CFO)*
Jean-Francois Pelland *(Sec)*
Board of Directors:
Robert Daigle
Scott Kelly
Jean-Francois Pelland
Daniel Pharand
George Wesley Roberts
Transfer Agent:
Olympia Transfer Services Inc.
Suite 920 120 Adelaide Street West
Toronto, ON, Canada

C. MAHENDRA EXPORTS LTD.
Tower C Office No CC-6011 Bharat Diamond Bourse Bandra Kurla Complex
Bandra East, Mumbai, 400 051, India
Tel.: (91) 22 26725555
Fax: (91) 22 26754560
E-Mail: bkc@cmahendra.com
Web Site: www.cmahendra.com
Year Founded: 1978
CMAHENDRA—(BOM NSE)
Rev.: $776,943,557
Assets: $625,928,605
Liabilities: $433,112,726
Net Worth: $192,815,878
Earnings: $29,358,292
Emp.: 368
Fiscal Year-end: 03/31/13
Business Description:
Diamond & Jewelry Distr & Exporter
S.I.C.: 5094
N.A.I.C.S.: 423940
Personnel:
Mahendra Chandulal Shah *(Chm)*
Champak Kirtilal Mehta *(Mng Dir)*
Babulal V. Virvadia *(CFO)*
Ashish Kumar Shrivastava *(Compliance Officer & Sec)*
Board of Directors:
Mahendra Chandulal Shah
Kailashchandra Chowdhary
Vittala Sooru Hegde
Champak Kirtilal Mehta
Prabodh Nagardas Shah
Sandeep Mahendra Shah
Transfer Agent:
Link Intime India Private Limited
C-13 Pannalal Silk Mills Compound LBS Road
Bhandup W
Mumbai, India
Plant:
C. Mahendra Exports Ltd. - Diamond Factory (1)
No 37 AK Road Opp to Umiya Temple
395001 Surat, Gujarat, India
Tel.: (91) 26125464
Fax: (91) 2612558547
E-Mail: adminkadampalli@cmahendra.com
Web Site: www.cmahendra.com
Emp.: 1,200
Diamond Mfr
S.I.C.: 3911
N.A.I.C.S.: 339910
Nitin Patel *(Mgr)*

C-QUADRAT INVESTMENT AG
Stubenring 2
A-1010 Vienna, Austria
Tel.: (43) 1 515 66 0
Fax: (43) 151566159
E-Mail: C-QUADRAT@investmentfonds.at
Web Site: www.c-quadrat.at
C81—(DEU VIE)
Rev.: $62,069,206
Assets: $69,439,487
Liabilities: $31,007,680
Net Worth: $38,431,807
Earnings: $321,735
Emp.: 83
Fiscal Year-end: 12/31/12
Business Description:
Investment Fund Services
S.I.C.: 6722
N.A.I.C.S.: 525910
Personnel:
Marcus D. Mautner Markhof *(Chm-Supervisory Bd)*
Franz Fuchs *(Deputy Chm-Supervisory Bd)*
Thomas Riess *(Member-Mgmt Bd-Sls, HR & Admin)*
Alexander Schutz *(Member-Mgmt Bd-Fin, Acctg, Controlling, Corp Comm & IR)*
Supervisory Board of Directors:
Marcus D. Mautner Markhof
Hubert Cussigh
Franz Fuchs
Harry Ploemacher
Walter Schmidt
Fritz Schweiger

C-QUADRAT Investment AG—(Continued)

C Y FOUNDATION GROUP LIMITED

Unit 3503B-5 35/F 148 Electric Road
North Point, China (Hong Kong)
Tel.: (852) 35763309
Fax: (852) 35763963
E-Mail: contactus@cyfoundation.com
Web Site: www.cyfoundation.com
1182—(HKG)
Sls.: $8,625,981
Assets: $31,061,218
Liabilities: $9,067,764
Net Worth: $21,993,454
Earnings: ($8,408,314)
Emp.: 514
Fiscal Year-end: 03/31/13

Business Description:
Online Entertainment Services
S.I.C.: 2741
N.A.I.C.S.: 519130

Personnel:
Kar Loon Sneah *(Chm)*
Balakrishnan Narayanan *(CEO)*
Gloria Pui Ki Cheung *(Sec)*

Board of Directors:
Kar Loon Sneah
Hoon Leum Goh
Rudy Cheok Kei Io
Hock Meng Lai
Balakrishnan Narayanan
Kwok Lun Ng
Peng Tak Yong
Lin Zheying

Butterfield Fulcrum Group (Bermuda) Limited
26 Burnaby Street
Hamilton, HM 11, Bermuda

Transfer Agents:
Tricor Secretaries Limited
26th Floor Tesbury Centre 28 Queen's Road East
Wanchai, China (Hong Kong)

Butterfield Fulcrum Group (Bermuda) Limited
26 Burnaby Street
Hamilton, HM 11, Bermuda

C+G INFORMATIONSTECHNOLOGIE GMBH

Seligenstadter Grund 7
63150 Heusenstamm, Germany
Tel.: (49) 6104945555
Fax: (49) 6104945166
E-Mail: info@cg-infogmbh.com
Web Site: www.cg-infogmbh.com
Year Founded: 1995
Rev.: $13,120,410
Emp.: 60

Business Description:
Computer Equipment Whslr
S.I.C.: 5045
N.A.I.C.S.: 423430

Personnel:
Ortwin Hutter *(Founder & Mng Dir)*

C2C INDUSTRIAL PROPERTIES INC.

(Acquired by Dundee Corporation & Name Changed to DIR Industrial Properties Inc.)

C4U TECHNOLOGIES LTD.

Hill House 2 Heron Square
Richmond, Surrey, TW9 1EP, United Kingdom
Tel.: (44) 20 8439 9577
E-Mail: contact@c4utech.com
Web Site: www.c4utech.com
Year Founded: 2001

Business Description:
Medical Software
S.I.C.: 7372
N.A.I.C.S.: 511210

Personnel:
Torsten Bolbjerg *(Co-Founder & CEO)*
Monica Bolbjerg *(Co-Founder & CIO)*

Non-U.S. Subsidiary:

C4U Technologies ApS **(1)**
Havnegade 39
1058 Copenhagen, Denmark
Tel.: (45) 4976 7000
Medical Software
S.I.C.: 7372
N.A.I.C.S.: 511210

C.A. BANCORP INC.

225a MacPherson Avenue Suite 201
Toronto, ON, M4V 1A1, Canada
Toll Free: (800) 439-5136
E-Mail: info@cabancorp.com
Web Site: www.cabancorp.com
Year Founded: 2005
BKP—(TSXV)
Sales Range: $1-9.9 Million
Emp.: 13

Business Description:
Merchant Banking & Alternative Asset Management Services
S.I.C.: 6211
N.A.I.C.S.: 523110

Personnel:
Robert Wolf *(Chm)*
Helen Martin *(Gen Counsel & Sec)*

Board of Directors:
Robert Wolf
Bradd Gold
Gaetano Muzio
Roy Pottle

Transfer Agent:
Computershare Investor Services Inc.
100 University Ave 9th Floor
Toronto, ON, Canada

CA IMMOBILIEN ANLAGEN AG

(d/b/a CA Immo)
Mechelgasse 1
A-1030 Vienna, Austria
Tel.: (43) 4315325907500
Fax: (43) 4315325907510
E-Mail: office@caimmo.com
Web Site: www.caimmo.com
CAI—(VIE)
Rev.: $378,120,307
Assets: $7,926,843,967
Liabilities: $5,482,546,559
Net Worth: $2,444,297,408
Earnings: $65,371,361
Emp.: 375
Fiscal Year-end: 12/31/12

Business Description:
Real Estate Services
S.I.C.: 6531
N.A.I.C.S.: 531210

Personnel:
Wolfgang Ruttenstorfer *(Chm-Supervisory Bd)*
Bruno Ettenauer *(CEO)*
Florian Nowotny *(CFO)*
Bernhard H. Hansen *(Chief Dev Officer)*

Supervisory Board of Directors:
Wolfgang Ruttenstorfer
Helmut Bernkopf
Waldemar Jud
Barbara A. Knoflach
Reinhard Madlencnik
Franz Zwickl

Subsidiaries:

CA Immo Asset Management GmbH **(1)**
Rennweg 16 Eingang Mechel Alley 1
1030 Vienna, Austria
Tel.: (43) 15325907
Fax: (43) 15325907510
E-Mail: office@caimmoag.com
Web Site: www.caimmoag.com
Emp.: 100
Business Management Services
S.I.C.: 8748
N.A.I.C.S.: 541618
Bruno Ettenauer *(Gen Mgr)*

CA Immo BIP Liegenschaftsverwaltung GmbH **(1)**
Mechelgasse 1
1030 Vienna, Austria
Tel.: (43) 15325907
Fax: (43) 15325907510
E-Mail: office@caimmoag.com
Emp.: 65
Alcoholic Beverages Whslr
S.I.C.: 5181
N.A.I.C.S.: 424810
Vvolfhrt Fromvveld *(CFO)*

CA Immo Galleria Liegenschaftsverwaltung GmbH **(1)**
Mechel Alley 1
Vienna, 1030, Austria
Tel.: (43) 15325907
Fax: (43) 15325907510
E-Mail: office@caimmoag.com
Emp.: 100
Housing Construction Services
S.I.C.: 1531
N.A.I.C.S.: 236117
Wolfhard Fromwal *(Mgr)*

CA Immo Rennweg 16 GmbH **(1)**
Freyung 3 36
1030 Vienna, Austria
Tel.: (43) 15325907
Fax: (43) 15325907510
E-Mail: office@caimmoag.com
Web Site: www.caimoag.com
Emp.: 100
Investment Management Services
S.I.C.: 8748
N.A.I.C.S.: 541618
Bruno Ettenauer *(CEO)*

CA Immobilien Anlagen Beteiligungs GmbH & Co Finanzierungs OEG **(1)**
Mechel Alley 1
1030 Vienna, Austria
Tel.: (43) 15325907
Fax: (43) 15325907510
E-Mail: office@caimmoag.com
Web Site: www.caimmo.com
Emp.: 100
Business Management Services
S.I.C.: 8748
N.A.I.C.S.: 541618
Vvolfhard Fromyyalt *(Mng Dir)*

CA Immobilien Anlagen Beteiligungs GmbH **(1)**
Freyung 3 2 11
1030 Vienna, Austria
Tel.: (43) 15325907
Web Site: www.caimmoag.com
Emp.: 80
Investment Management Services
S.I.C.: 8748
N.A.I.C.S.: 541618
Bruno Ettenauer *(Mng Dir)*

Europolis AG **(1)**
Kohlmarkt 8-10
1010 Vienna, Austria
Tel.: (43) 13197200
Fax: (43) 13197200111
E-Mail: vienna@europolis.com
Web Site: www.europolis.com
Emp.: 30
Real Estate Investment & Asset Management
S.I.C.: 6211
N.A.I.C.S.: 523999
Thomas Kurzmann *(COO)*

SQUARE S Holding GmbH **(1)**
Mechelgasse 1
Vienna, Austria
Tel.: (43) 15325907
Fax: (43) 15325907510
Web Site: www.caemmoat.com
Investment Management Services
S.I.C.: 8748
N.A.I.C.S.: 541618

Non-U.S. Subsidiaries:

omniCon Verwaltungs GmbH **(1)**
Hedderichstrasse 55-57
60594 Frankfurt am Main, Germany
Tel.: (49) 6103 3001610
Chemical & Rubber Products Mfr
S.I.C.: 2822
N.A.I.C.S.: 325212

omniPro Gesellschaft fur Projektmanagement mbH **(1)**
Im Steingrund 8
Dreieich, Germany
Tel.: (49) 61033001610
Fax: (49) 61033001616
E-Mail: info@omnipro.de
Web Site: www.omnipro.de
Business Management Services
S.I.C.: 8748
N.A.I.C.S.: 541618

TM Immo d.o.o **(1)**
Djordja Stanojevic 14
11070 Belgrade, Serbia
Tel.: (381) 113189120
Fax: (381) 113187924
E-Mail: srejic@caimmo.rs
Emp.: 6
Business Management Services
S.I.C.: 8748
N.A.I.C.S.: 541618
Milos Srejic *(Mng Dir)*

VIADOR GmbH **(1)**
Hedderichstr 55-57
60594 Frankfurt am Main, Germany
Tel.: (49) 69606270
Fax: (49) 6976806891
Web Site: www.viador.eu
Real Estate Management Services
S.I.C.: 6531
N.A.I.C.S.: 531390

Vivico Berlin Schoneberger Ufer Verwaltungs GmbH **(1)**
Hedderichstr 55-57
Frankfurt am Main, Germany
Tel.: (49) 69606270
Fax: (49) 6960627383
E-Mail: office@vivico.de
Web Site: www.vivico.de
Business Management Services
S.I.C.: 8748
N.A.I.C.S.: 541618

Vivico Berlin Unter den Linden GmbH & Co. KG **(1)**
Europa Allee 22
Frankfurt am Main, Germany
Tel.: (49) 69606270
Fax: (49) 7680679431
E-Mail: info@camo.de
Web Site: www.camo.de
Emp.: 100
Business Management Services
S.I.C.: 8748
N.A.I.C.S.: 541618
Bernard Hansen *(Mgr)*

Vivico Frankfurt TL Hotel Verwaltungs-GmbH **(1)**
Hedderichstr 55-57
60594 Frankfurt am Main, Germany
Tel.: (49) 69606270
Real Estate Management Services
S.I.C.: 6531
N.A.I.C.S.: 531390

Vivico Munchen Perlach Grundstucksverwertungs GmbH **(1)**
Hedderichstr 55-57
Frankfurt am Main, Germany
Tel.: (49) 69606270
Web Site: www.vivico.de
Business Management Services
S.I.C.: 8748
N.A.I.C.S.: 541618

C.A. SPENCER INC.

2930 Dagenais Boulevard West
Laval, QC, H7P 1T1, Canada
Tel.: (450) 622-2420
Fax: (450) 628-2632
Toll Free: (800) 361-0789
E-Mail: email@caspencer.ca
Web Site: www.caspencer.ca

Year Founded: 1908
Rev.: $27,246,148
Emp.: 70
Business Description:
Hardwood Products Mfr
S.I.C.: 2861
N.A.I.C.S.: 325194
Personnel:
Claude Cadrin *(Pres)*

C.A. SPERATI PLC

(Formerly C.A. Sperati (The Special Agency) PLC)
54 Westcombe Hill
Greenwich, London, SE10 0LR, United Kingdom
Tel.: (44) 20 8858 7069
Fax: (44) 20 8853 5349
E-Mail: sales@casperatiplc.com
Web Site: www.casperatiplc.com
Year Founded: 1856
SPR—(LSE)
Sls.: $333,451
Assets: $266,872
Liabilities: $744,983
Net Worth: ($478,111)
Earnings: ($488,674)
Emp.: 7
Fiscal Year-end: 10/31/13
Business Description:
Button & Buckle Whslr
S.I.C.: 5131
N.A.I.C.S.: 424310
Personnel:
Jason Drummond *(Chm)*
I. Granger *(Mng Dir)*
Valerie Beeny *(Sec)*
Board of Directors:
Jason Drummond
Oliver Fattal
Nilesh Jagatia

CAB CAKARAN CORPORATION BERHAD

Plot 21 Lorong Jelawat 4 Seberang Jaya Industrial Park
Seberang Jaya Perai, 13700 Penang, Malaysia
Tel.: (60) 4 398 2233
Fax: (60) 4 398 0137
E-Mail: cab@cab.com.my
Web Site: www.cab.com.my
CAB—(KLS)
Rev.: $175,290,557
Assets: $110,178,437
Liabilities: $61,016,496
Net Worth: $49,161,941
Earnings: $459,336
Fiscal Year-end: 09/30/12
Business Description:
Food Processing, Poultry Farming & Marine Products Mfr
S.I.C.: 3519
N.A.I.C.S.: 333618
Personnel:
Ah Bee Chuah *(Chm)*
Hoon Phong Chuah *(Mng Dir)*
Siew Cheng Chew *(Co-Sec)*
Chit Geok Gunn *(Co-Sec)*
Board of Directors:
Ah Bee Chuah
Kim Keow Chan
Chee Khong Chew
Hoon Phong Chuah
Choon Aik Goh
Ahmad Fazil Hashim
Choo Gee Loo
Seng Bee Ng

CABBEEN FASHION LIMITED

No 379 Shougouling Road
Tianhe District, Guangzhou, 510507, China
Tel.: (86) 20 38163000
Fax: (86) 20 38163311
E-Mail: media@cabbeen.com
Web Site: www.cabbeen.com
2030—(HKG)
Business Description:
Casual Menswear Mfr & Sales
S.I.C.: 2329
N.A.I.C.S.: 315220
Personnel:
Ziming Yang *(Chm)*
Siu Keung Ng *(CEO)*
Board of Directors:
Ziming Yang
Honghui Chen
Rongqin Ke
Ming Shu Leung
Siu Keung Ng
Dongliang Tian
Yung Kwok Tsui
Qiang Wei

CABCHARGE AUSTRALIA LIMITED

152-162 Riley Street
Sydney, NSW, 2010, Australia
Tel.: (61) 2 9332 9222
Fax: (61) 2 9332 9270
E-Mail: info@cabcharge.com.au
Web Site: www.cabcharge.com.au
Year Founded: 1976
CAB—(ASX OTC)
Rev.: $204,904,997
Assets: $597,265,026
Liabilities: $243,856,611
Net Worth: $353,408,415
Earnings: $63,143,965
Emp.: 595
Fiscal Year-end: 06/30/13
Business Description:
Electronic Taxi Fare Payment Systems Developer & Mfr
S.I.C.: 4789
N.A.I.C.S.: 488999
Personnel:
Reginald Lionel Kermode *(Chm & CEO)*
Chip Beng Yeoh *(CFO & Co-Sec)*
Sai Kancharla *(Deputy CFO)*
Andrew Skelton *(Corp Counsel & Co-Sec)*
Board of Directors:
Reginald Lionel Kermode
Ian Alexander Armstrong
Russell Balding
Neill Ford
Philip Franet
Donnald McMichael
Subsidiaries:

Black Cabs Combined Pty Ltd **(1)**
35 Downing Street
Oakleigh, Melbourne, VIC, 3166, Australia
Tel.: (61) 392773700
Fax: (61) 392773800
Web Site: www.13cabs.com.au
Emp.: 200
Taxi Services
S.I.C.: 4121
N.A.I.C.S.: 485310
Simon Purssey *(Mgr-Client Svcs)*

Combined Communications Network Pty Ltd **(1)**
9-13 O Riordan Street
Alexandria, NSW, 2015, Australia (100%)
Tel.: (61) 290202244
Fax: (61) 290202111
E-Mail: info@ccnetwork.com.au
Web Site: www.ccnetwork.com.au
Emp.: 200
Taxi Service
S.I.C.: 4121
N.A.I.C.S.: 485310
Frederick Lukabyo *(CEO)*

EFT Solutions Pty Ltd **(1)**
1/9 Apollo Street
Warriewood, Sydney, NSW, 2102, Australia
Tel.: (61) 290202180
Fax: (61) 2 9979 4302
E-Mail: info@eftsolutions.com.au
Web Site: www.eftsolutions.com.au
Software Development Consulting Services
S.I.C.: 7373
N.A.I.C.S.: 541512

Newcastle Taxis Ltd **(1)**
3/7 Chauncer St
Hamilton, Newcastle, NSW, 2303, Australia
Tel.: (61) 249405955
Fax: (61) 249405959
E-Mail: info@newcastletaxis.com.au
Web Site: www.newcastletaxis.com.au
Emp.: 30
Taxi Services
S.I.C.: 4121
N.A.I.C.S.: 485310
John Woods *(Mgr)*

Taxi Combined Services Pty Ltd **(1)**
9-13 O Riordan St
NSW Alexandria, Australia (100%)
Tel.: (61) 290202244
Fax: (61) 290202111
E-Mail: klynn@ccnetwork.com.au
Web Site: www.taxicombined.com.au
Emp.: 200
Taxi Service
S.I.C.: 4121
N.A.I.C.S.: 485310
Frederick Lukabyo *(CEO)*

Yellow Cabs of Sydney Pty Ltd **(1)**
9-13 O Riordan Street
NSW Alexandria, Australia (100%)
Tel.: (61) 290202244
Fax: (61) 290202111
E-Mail: info@ccnetwork.com.au
Web Site: www.yellowcabs.com
Emp.: 200
Taxi Service
S.I.C.: 4121
N.A.I.C.S.: 485310
Frederick Lukabyo *(CEO)*

Joint Venture:

ComfortDelGro Cabcharge Pty. Ltd. **(1)**
29 Foundry Rd,
Seven Hills, NSW, 2147, Australia
Tel.: (61) 298900000
Fax: (61) 298915900
Web Site: www.cdcbus.com
Emp.: 120
Passenger Bus Service Operator; Joint Venture of ComfortDelGro Corporation Limited (51%) & Cabcharge Australia Limited (49%)
S.I.C.: 4111
N.A.I.C.S.: 485113

CABLE & WIRELESS COMMUNICATIONS PLC

3rd Floor 26 Red Lion Square
London, WC1R 4HQ, United Kingdom
Tel.: (44) 207 315 4000
Web Site: www.cwc.com
CWC—(LSE)
Rev.: $1,942,000,000
Assets: $3,670,000,000
Liabilities: $3,418,000,000
Net Worth: $252,000,000
Earnings: $178,000,000
Emp.: 5,549
Fiscal Year-end: 03/31/13
Business Description:
Telecommunications Services
S.I.C.: 4813
N.A.I.C.S.: 517110
Personnel:
Richard Lapthorne *(Chm)*
Phil Bentley *(CEO)*
Geoff Houston *(CEO-Bahamas)*
Denis Martin *(CEO-Monaco & Islands)*
Jorge Nicolau *(CEO-Panama)*
Vandy Poon *(CEO-Macau)*
Garry Sinclair *(CEO-Jamaica)*
Clare Underwood *(Sec)*
Board of Directors:
Richard Lapthorne
Simon Ball
Nick Cooper
Mark Hamlin
Alison Platt
Ian P. Tyler
Subsidiary:

Cable & Wireless Limited **(1)**
26 Red Lion Square 3rd Floor
London, WC1R 4HQ, United Kingdom
Tel.: (44) 2073154000
Fax: (44) 2073155000
E-Mail: info@cwplc.com
Web Site: www.cw.com
Telecommunications Services
S.I.C.: 4813
N.A.I.C.S.: 517110

Non-U.S. Joint Venture:

Telecom Vanuatu Limited **(2)**
Telecom House
Father Walter Lini Highway, Port-Vila, Vanuatu (50%)
Tel.: (678) 22185
Fax: (678) 22628
E-Mail: sales@tvl.net.vu
Web Site: www.tvl.vu
Emp.: 100
Telecommunication Services
S.I.C.: 4899
N.A.I.C.S.: 517919
Catherine Rumillat *(Mng Dir)*

Non-U.S. Subsidiaries:

Cable & Wireless International Finance BV **(1)**
Fred Roeskestraat 123
Amsterdam, 1076 EE, Netherlands
Tel.: (31) 205996300
Fax: (31) 203059201
Telecommunication Services
S.I.C.: 4899
N.A.I.C.S.: 517919

Cable & Wireless Panama SA **(1)**
Condominio Plaza Internacional Torre C Via Espana
Panama, Panama
Tel.: (507) 800 2102
Fax: (507) 264 5743
E-Mail: cwp@cwpanama.com
Web Site: www.cwpanama.com
Sales Range: $600-649.9 Million
Telecommunication Services
S.I.C.: 4813
N.A.I.C.S.: 517110
Jorge Nicolau *(CEO)*

Companhia de Telecomunicacoes de Macau, S.A.R.L **(1)**
Rua de Lagos Telecentro
Taipa, China (Macau) Mo
Tel.: (853) 28833833 (51%)
Web Site: www.ctm.net
Sales Range: $300-349.9 Million
Telecommunications Services
S.I.C.: 4813
N.A.I.C.S.: 517110
Vandy Poon *(CEO)*

Sable International Finance Limited **(1)**
PO Box 709
Georgetown, KY1-1107, Cayman Islands
Tel.: (345) 94 9 4544
Telecommunication Services
S.I.C.: 4899
N.A.I.C.S.: 517919

Non-U.S. Unit:

LIME **(1)**
Ground Floor Cedar Court Wildey
Saint Michael, Barbados
Tel.: (246) 292 5050
Web Site: www.time4lime.com
Sales Range: $800-899.9 Million
Telecommunications Services
S.I.C.: 4813
N.A.I.C.S.: 517110
Tony Rice *(CEO)*
Chris Dehring *(Chief Comml Officer)*

Non-U.S. Subsidiaries:

Bahamas Telecommunications Company Limited **(2)**
John F. Kennedy Drive
Nassau, Bahamas

Cable & Wireless Communications plc—(Continued)

Tel.: (242) 2255282
Fax: (242) 3267474
Sales Range: $350-399.9 Million
Telecommunications Services
S.I.C.: 4813
N.A.I.C.S.: 517110
Tony Rice *(Chm)*
Geoff Houston *(CEO)*

Cable & Wireless (West Indies) Ltd. (2)
Telecoms House
PO Box 77
The Valley, Anguilla
Tel.: (264) 18008042994
Web Site: www.anguillanet.com
Telecommunication Services
S.I.C.: 4813
N.A.I.C.S.: 517110

Non-U.S. Unit:

LIME Caribbean (2)
2 6 Carlton Crescent
Kingston, 10, Jamaica (82%)
Tel.: (876) 9269700
Fax: (876) 9689696
E-Mail: customer.services@cwjamaica.com
Web Site: www.time4lime.com
LIME—(JAM)
Sales Range: $200-249.9 Million
Telecommunication Services
S.I.C.: 4813
N.A.I.C.S.: 517110
Christopher Dehring *(Chm)*
Garfield Sinclair *(CEO-Jamaica & Cayman)*
Kamina Johnson Smith *(Sec)*

CABLE BAHAMAS LTD.

Robinson Road at Marathon
PO Box CB 13050
Nassau, Bahamas
Tel.: (242) 601 6780
Fax: (242) 601 8990
E-Mail: info@cablebahamas.com
Web Site: www.cablebahamas.com
Year Founded: 1994
CAB—(BISX)
Rev.: $111,188,157
Assets: $220,249,418
Liabilities: $126,782,803
Net Worth: $93,466,615
Earnings: $21,400,607
Emp.: 400
Fiscal Year-end: 12/31/12
Business Description:
Cable Television, Internet & Voice Telecommunications Services
S.I.C.: 4813
N.A.I.C.S.: 517110
Personnel:
Anthony Butler *(Pres & CEO)*
Judith Smith *(Corp Counsel-Legal)*
Barry Williams *(Sr VP-Fin)*
Board of Directors:
Philip Keeping
Anthony Butler
Franklyn Butler, II
Troy D'Arville
Gary Kain

U.S. Subsidiary:

U.S. Metropolitan Telecom, LLC (1)
24017 Production Cir
Bonita Springs, FL 34135 FL
Tel.: (239) 325-4105
Toll Free: (877) 244-0242
Web Site: www.usmetrotel.com
Emp.: 15
Telecommunications Products & Services
S.I.C.: 4813
N.A.I.C.S.: 517110
Frank Mambuca *(Pres & CEO)*
Scott Tonarelli *(Sr VP-Bus & Network Ops)*

Subsidiary:

Orlando Telephone Company, Inc. (2)
4558 35th St Ste 100
Orlando, FL 32811 FL
Tel.: (407) 996-8900
E-Mail: care@summit-broadband.com
Web Site: www.summit-broadband.com
Telecommunications Reseller
S.I.C.: 4812
N.A.I.C.S.: 517911
Richard W. Pardy *(Pres & CEO)*

CABLE CORPORATION OF INDIA LTD.

Laxmi Building 4th Floor 6 Shoorji Vallabhdas Marg
Ballard Estate, Mumbai, 400001, India
Tel.: (91) 22 66144000
Fax: (91) 22 66144113
E-Mail: customercare@cablecorporation.com
Web Site: www.cablecorporation.com
500077—(BOM)
Rev.: $39,658,914
Assets: $62,299,962
Liabilities: $35,168,526
Net Worth: $27,131,436
Earnings: $3,370,572
Fiscal Year-end: 03/31/13
Business Description:
Electric Cable Mfr
S.I.C.: 3678
N.A.I.C.S.: 334417
Personnel:
Maadhav Digraskar *(CEO & Mng Dir)*
Surendra Khemka *(CFO, Compliance Officer & Sec)*
Board of Directors:
G. D. Bhingarkar
Abhijit Datta
Maadhav Digraskar
Mukul Kasliwal
Rohan H. Khatau
N. B. Pasta
Rajiv Saxena
R. Sridharan
C. Sundershyam
Transfer Agent:
Link Intime India Pvt. Ltd
C-13 Pannalal Silk Mills Compound LBS Marg
Bhandup (West)
Mumbai, India

THE CABLESHOPPE INC.

1410 Birchmount Road
Toronto, ON, M1P 2E3, Canada
Tel.: (416) 293-3634
Fax: (416) 293-5258
Web Site: www.thecableshoppe.com
Year Founded: 1991
Rev.: $15,727,375
Emp.: 100
Business Description:
Telecommunications Services
S.I.C.: 4899
N.A.I.C.S.: 517919
Personnel:
Monty Muthulingam *(Co-Chm)*
Stan Muthulingam *(Co-Chm)*
Enn Vaher *(Exec VP-Bus Dev)*

CABLUL ROMANESC SA

293 Republicii Bvd
598052 Ploiesti, Romania
Tel.: (40) 244598052
Fax: (40) 244598632
E-Mail: info@cablul-romanesc.ro
Web Site: www.cablul-romanesc.ro
CABZ—(BUC)
Rev.: $4,669,177
Assets: $10,992,402
Liabilities: $9,617,891
Net Worth: $1,374,510
Earnings: ($1,955,926)
Emp.: 118
Fiscal Year-end: 12/31/12
Business Description:
Steel Wire Ropes Mfr
S.I.C.: 2296
N.A.I.C.S.: 314994
Personnel:
Spiridon Kontogiannis *(Gen Mgr)*

CABO DRILLING CORP.

20 Sixth Street
New Westminster, BC, V3L 2Y8, Canada
Tel.: (604) 527-4201
Fax: (604) 527-9126
E-Mail: info@cabo.ca
Web Site: www.cabo.ca
Year Founded: 1996
CBE—(TSXV)
Rev.: $42,279,405
Assets: $37,327,715
Liabilities: $13,750,540
Net Worth: $23,577,175
Earnings: ($561,731)
Emp.: 500
Fiscal Year-end: 06/30/13
Business Description:
Oil & Gas Drilling Services
S.I.C.: 1381
N.A.I.C.S.: 213111
Personnel:
John A. Versfelt *(Chm, Pres & CEO)*
Calvin Lucyshyn *(CFO & Controller)*
Darren K. Timmer *(Sec)*
Board of Directors:
John A. Versfelt
Terry Aimone
Peter Freeman
Tom Oliver
Robert W. Schellenberg
Transfer Agent:
Computershare Trust Company of Canada
2nd Floor 510 Burrard Street
V6C3B9 Vancouver, BC, Canada

Subsidiaries:

Cabo Drilling (Atlantic) Corp (1)
171 Little Bay Rd
PO Box 488
Springdale, NL, A0J 1T0, Canada
Tel.: (709) 673-3801
Fax: (709) 673-3839
E-Mail: caboatlantic@cabo.ca
Emp.: 50
Core Drilling Services
S.I.C.: 1381
N.A.I.C.S.: 213111
Art Clarke *(Gen Mgr)*

Cabo Drilling (International) Inc. (1)
21 Goodfish Rd
Kirkland Lake, ON, P2N 1H7, Canada
Tel.: (705) 567-9311
Fax: (705) 567-1126
E-Mail: caboontario@cabo.ca
Web Site: www.cabo.ca
Drilling Services
S.I.C.: 1081
N.A.I.C.S.: 213114
Pierre Germain *(Gen Mgr)*

Cabo Drilling (Ontario) Corp. (1)
34 Duncan Avenue
PO Box 998
Kirkland Lake, ON, P2N 3L3, Canada
Tel.: (705) 567-9311
Fax: (705) 567-3014
E-Mail: caboontario@cabo.ca
Emp.: 130
Oil Drilling Services
S.I.C.: 1381
N.A.I.C.S.: 213111
Pierre Germain *(Gen Mgr)*

Cabo Drilling (Pacific) Corp. (1)
19469-92 Ave
Surrey, BC, V4N 4G6, Canada
Tel.: (604) 888-0033
Fax: (604) 888-2269
Toll Free: (800) 663-0093
E-Mail: cabopacific@cabo.ca
Emp.: 20
Drilling Services
S.I.C.: 1381
N.A.I.C.S.: 213111
John Versfelt *(Pres)*

Forages Cabo Inc. (1)
3000 Boulevard Industriel
Chambly, QC, J3L 4X3, Canada
Tel.: (450) 572-1400
Fax: (450) 572-1084
E-Mail: foragescabo@cabo.ca
Emp.: 20
Geothermal Drilling Services
S.I.C.: 1629
N.A.I.C.S.: 237110
Pierre Germain *(Gen Mgr)*

Petro Drilling Company Limited (1)
Bayers Road RPO
PO Box 22100
Halifax, NS, B3L 4T7, Canada
Tel.: (902) 453-2577
Fax: (902) 453-2578
E-Mail: info.ns@petrodrilling.ca
Web Site: www.petrodrilling.ca
Oil Drilling Services
S.I.C.: 1381
N.A.I.C.S.: 213111
Frank Nolan *(Pres)*

Non-U.S. Subsidiary:

Cabo Drilling (Panama) Corp., (1)
Aerea Especial Economica Panama
Pacifico Andrews Boulevard
Edificio 466, Panama, Panama
Tel.: (507) 3162226
Fax: (507) 3161919
E-Mail: cabopanama@cabo.ca
Web Site: www.cabo.ca/Divisions.aspx?pid=46
Emp.: 100
Drilling Services
S.I.C.: 1381
N.A.I.C.S.: 213111
Herb Butler *(Gen Mgr)*

CABRAL RESOURCES LIMITED

Suite 2 Level 5 20 Bond Street
Sydney, NSW, 2000, Australia
Tel.: (61) 292320211
Fax: (61) 292320233
E-Mail: reception@cabralresources.com.au
Web Site: www.cabralresources.com.au
CBS—(ASX)
Rev.: $293,807
Assets: $18,402,727
Liabilities: $560,426
Net Worth: $17,842,302
Earnings: ($3,860,525)
Fiscal Year-end: 06/30/13
Business Description:
Mineral Resources Exploration Services
S.I.C.: 5052
N.A.I.C.S.: 423520
Personnel:
James Jingzhong Li *(Pres & Exec Gen Mgr-Asia)*
Michael Joseph Bogue *(CEO & Mng Dir)*
Carolyn Patman *(Sec)*
Board of Directors:
Michael Joseph Bogue
James Jingzhong Li
Bruno Maia
Legal Counsel:
Tozzini Freire Teixeira E Silva
R. Borges Lagoa 1328
Sao Paulo, Brazil

Ashurst
Level 36 Grosvenor Place 225 George Street
Sydney, 2000, Australia

Subsidiary:

Northern Yeelirrie Pty Limited (1)
Currency House Se 603 L 6 23-25 Hunter St
Sydney, NSW, Australia
Tel.: (61) 2 9232 0211
Iron Ore Mining Services
S.I.C.: 1011
N.A.I.C.S.: 212210

CAC CORPORATION
24-1 Hakozaki-cho Nihonbashi
Chuo-ku, Tokyo, 103-0015, Japan
Tel.: (81) 366678000
Fax: (81) 356413200
E-Mail: admin@cac.co.jp
Web Site: www.cac.co.jp
Year Founded: 1966
4725—(TKS)
Sales Range: $500-549.9 Million
Emp.: 1,305
Business Description:
Business Information & Computer Services
S.I.C.: 8999
N.A.I.C.S.: 541519
Personnel:
Toshio Shimada *(Pres & CEO)*
Subsidiaries:

Arm Systex Co.,Ltd. (1)
St 2-chome 3rd 14 Akira Hunaba Bill 4th Floor
Chuo-Ku, 541-0053 Osaka, Japan
Tel.: (81) 649646228
Fax: (81) 649646268
Data Processing Services
S.I.C.: 7374
N.A.I.C.S.: 518210

CAC Knowledge Co., Ltd. (1)
4-1 Nihombashiyokoyamacho
Nisshinyokoyamacho Building 4f
Chuo-ku, Tokyo, 103-0003, Japan
Tel.: (81) 358477561
Fax: (81) 356402731
Business Process Outsourcing Services
S.I.C.: 7389
N.A.I.C.S.: 561499

CAC MARUHA NICHIRO SYSTEMS CORPORATION (1)
1-28-25 Shinkawa Tokyo Daiya Building 3gokan 6f
Chuo-ku, Tokyo, 104-0033, Japan
Tel.: (81) 335527432
Fax: (81) 335527547
Information Technology Consulting Services
S.I.C.: 7373
N.A.I.C.S.: 541512

CAC Maruha Systems Corporation (1)
Tokyo Dia Bldg 3go-Kan
Chuo-Ku, Tokyo, Japan
Tel.: (81) 335527432
Data Processing Hosting & Related Services
S.I.C.: 7374
N.A.I.C.S.: 518210

CAC Orbis Corporation (1)
Edobori Yatanibiru Bldg 8th Fl
Osaka, Japan
Tel.: (81) 664458888
Fax: (81) 0664460939
Web Site: www.orbis-corp.jp
Emp.: 100
Custom Computer Programming Services
S.I.C.: 7371
N.A.I.C.S.: 541511
Makase Koji *(Pres)*

U.S. Subsidiaries:

CAC America Corporation (1)
457th Ave Ste 808
New York, NY 10123 (100%)
Tel.: (212) 482-8340
Fax: (212) 482-8344
E-Mail: info@cacamerica.com
Web Site: www.cacamerica.com
Emp.: 50
Business Information & Computer Services
S.I.C.: 7379
N.A.I.C.S.: 541519
Takayuki Havihara *(Pres)*

Non-U.S. Subsidiaries:

CAC EUROPE LIMITED (1)
60 Lombard Street
London, EC3V 9EA, United Kingdom
Tel.: (44) 2074648435
Fax: (44) 20 7464 8833
E-Mail: info@caceurope.com
Web Site: www.caceurope.com
Computer Software Consulting Services
S.I.C.: 7373
N.A.I.C.S.: 541512

CAC Shanghai Corporation (1)
3rd Floor Chamtime International Finance Center
1589 Century Ave, Shanghai, Pudong, 200122, China
Tel.: (86) 2161940080
Fax: (86) 2161940081
Web Site: www.cacshanghai.com
Business Information & Computer Services
S.I.C.: 7379
N.A.I.C.S.: 541519
Bin Cheng *(Pres & CEO)*

GoldenTech Computer Technology (Suzhou) Co.,Ltd. (1)
103 Sutong Rd Suzhou Industrial Park
215021 Suzhou, China
Tel.: (86) 51267630301
Fax: (86) 51267610910
E-Mail: golden@goldentech.com
Web Site: www.goldentech.com
Emp.: 100
Software & Systems Development
S.I.C.: 3652
N.A.I.C.S.: 334614
Zhu Jian Ting *(Mgr)*

CACANSKA BANKA A.D. CACAK
1 Pivarska St
32000 Cacak, Serbia
Tel.: (381) 32 302 100
Fax: (381) 32225 048
E-Mail: office@cacanskabanka.co.rs
Web Site: www.cacanskabanka.co.rs
CCNBPB—(BEL)
Int. Income: $25,050,012
Assets: $393,655,764
Liabilities: $332,774,812
Net Worth: $60,880,952
Earnings: $598,205
Emp.: 389
Fiscal Year-end: 12/31/12
Business Description:
Banking Services
S.I.C.: 6036
N.A.I.C.S.: 522120
Personnel:
Sanja Jevtovic *(Chm)*
Dragan Jovanovic *(Chm-Exec Bd)*
Vera Leko *(Vice Chm)*
Aleksandar Calovic *(Vice Chm-Exec Bd)*
Milanka Mandic *(Member-Exec Bd)*
Board of Directors:
Sanja Jevtovic
Anthony Paul Tekla Bendien
Jasmina Bogicevic
Vera Leko
Dorde Pjevic
Andrzej Witak

CACHE EXPLORATION INC.
Suite 147 350 B2-125 The Queensway
Etobicoke, ON, M8Y 1H6, Canada
Tel.: (416) 867-1101
Fax: (416) 876-1222
E-Mail: info@cacheexploration.com
Web Site: www.cacheexploration.com
Year Founded: 2005
CAY.P—(TSXV)
Assets: $49,776
Liabilities: $36,689
Net Worth: $13,086
Earnings: ($344,836)
Emp.: 2
Fiscal Year-end: 09/30/13
Business Description:
Investment Services
S.I.C.: 6211
N.A.I.C.S.: 523999
Personnel:
George A. Brown *(Pres & CEO)*
Carmen Yuen *(CFO & Sec)*
Board of Directors:
George A. Brown
Driffield Cameron
David R. Lentz
Asha Reeves
Legal Counsel:
Boughton & Company
Suite 700 595 Burrard Street
PO Box 49290
Vancouver, BC, V7X 1S8, Canada
Transfer Agent:
Computershare
200 - 510 Burrard Street
Vancouver, BC, Canada

CACHET PHARMACEUTICAL CO., LTD.
1 Building 11 Kunminghu South Road
Haidian District, Beijing, 100195, China
Tel.: (86) 1088433464
Fax: (86) 1088447731
E-Mail: cachet@cachet.cn
Web Site: www.cachet.com.cn
002462—(SSE)
Emp.: 1,200
Business Description:
Pharmacy Owner & Operator
S.I.C.: 5912
N.A.I.C.S.: 446110
Personnel:
Yuanwei Ding *(Chm)*

CACOLA FURNITURE INTERNATIONAL LIMITED
Changlang Ave Long Road
Changping Town
523577 Dongguan, Guangdong, China
Tel.: (86) 769 83912388
Fax: (86) 769 83332645
E-Mail: cacola@cacola.com
Web Site: www.cacola.com
D2U—(SES)
Sales Range: $50-74.9 Million
Business Description:
Leather Furniture Mfr
S.I.C.: 2512
N.A.I.C.S.: 337121
Personnel:
Ming Chow Tat *(Chm)*
Kan Yen Yeo *(Vice Chm & Exec Dir)*
Zhou Lin Zhou *(CEO)*
Board of Directors:
Ming Chow Tat
Siu Fan Cheuk
Heng Lau Kay
Jeow Ho Soo
Kan Yen Yeo
Min Zong Zhou
Zhou Lin Zhou

CAD IT S.P.A.
Via Torricelli 44A
37136 Verona, Italy
Tel.: (39) 0458211111
Fax: (39) 0458211110
E-Mail: caditgroup@caditgroup.com
Web Site: www.caditgroup.com
Year Founded: 1977
CAD—(ITA)
Rev.: $69,547,181
Assets: $114,482,335
Liabilities: $35,073,113
Net Worth: $79,409,222
Earnings: $4,774,865
Emp.: 604
Fiscal Year-end: 12/31/12
Business Description:
Information Technology Services
S.I.C.: 7373
N.A.I.C.S.: 541512
Personnel:
Giuseppe Dal Cortivo *(Chm & Co-CEO)*
Giampietro Magnani *(Vice Chm & Co-CEO)*
Luigi Zanella *(Vice Chm & Co-CEO)*
Paolo Dal Cortivo *(Co-CEO)*
Board of Directors:
Giuseppe Dal Cortivo
Jorg Karsten Brand
Paolo Dal Cortivo
Lamberto Lambertini
Giampietro Magnani
Maurizio Rizzoli
Francesco Rossi
Luigi Zanella
Subsidiaries:

Bit Groove S.r.l. (1)
Viale Montegrappa 306
59100 Prato, Italy
Tel.: (39) 0574562813
Fax: (39) 0574 577 814
E-Mail: info@bitgroove.it
Web Site: www.bitgroove.it
Business Planning Software Development Services
S.I.C.: 7371
N.A.I.C.S.: 541511

CAD S.r.l. (1)
Via Torricelli 44A
37136 Verona, Italy
Tel.: (39) 0458211111
Fax: (39) 0458211110
E-Mail: cadit@cadit.it
Emp.: 600
Information Technology Services
S.I.C.: 7389
N.A.I.C.S.: 519190
Giuseppe Dal Cortivo *(Mng Dir)*

Cesbe S.r.l. (1)
Centro Studi Bancari Europei
Via Torricelli 44-A, 37136 Verona, Italy (52%)
Tel.: (39) 0458211111
Fax: (39) 0458211110
E-Mail: cesbe@cesbe.it
Web Site: www.cesbe.it
Emp.: 300
Educational Support Services
S.I.C.: 8299
N.A.I.C.S.: 611710
Paolo Dal Cortivo *(CEO)*

ELIData S.r.l. (1)
Via Sanadolo 19
Castiglione d Adda, 26823 Lodi, Italy (51%)
Tel.: (39) 0377901448
Fax: (39) 0377 909692
E-Mail: info@elidata.it
Web Site: www.elidata.it
Computer & Computer Peripheral Equipment & Software Merchant Whslr
S.I.C.: 5045
N.A.I.C.S.: 423430

Netbureau S.r.l. (1)
via Morigi 13
20123 Milan, Italy (10%)
Tel.: (39) 028550131
Fax: (39) 0285501355
E-Mail: info@netbureau.it
Web Site: www.netbureau.it
Software Publishers511210
S.I.C.: 7372
N.A.I.C.S.: 511210

S.G.M. S.r.l. (1)
Via Torricelli 44/A
37136 Verona, VR, Italy (100%)
Tel.: (39) 0458211111
Fax: (39) 0458211110
E-Mail: cadit@cadit.it
Web Site: www.cadit.it
Testing Laboratories
S.I.C.: 8734
N.A.I.C.S.: 541380

Smart Line S.r.l. (1)
Viale Montegrappa 306
Prato, 59100, Italy
Tel.: (39) 057 452011

CAD IT S.p.A.—(Continued)

Fax: (39) 0574 520100
E-Mail: smartline@smart-line.it
Web Site: www.smart-line.it
Tax Collection Software Development Services
S.I.C.: 7371
N.A.I.C.S.: 541511

Tecsit S.r.l. (1)
Via Silvio D amico 40
00145 Rome, Italy (70%)
Tel.: (39) 0654225625
Fax: (39) 065412861
E-Mail: info@tecsit.it
Web Site: www.tecsit.it
Switchgear & Switchboard Apparatus Mfr
S.I.C.: 3613
N.A.I.C.S.: 335313

CADAC GROUP HOLDING B.V.

Nieuw Eyckholt 282
NL-6419 Heerlen, Netherlands
Mailing Address:
Postbus 2759
NL-6401 DG Heerlen, Netherlands
Tel.: (31) 454001000
Fax: (31) 454001001
E-Mail: info@cadac.com
Web Site: www.cadac.com
Emp.: 400
Business Description:
Holding Company; Digital Design Information Software Publisher, Whslr & Support Services
S.I.C.: 6719
N.A.I.C.S.: 551112
Personnel:
Jan Baggen *(CEO)*
Astrid van de Sande *(CFO)*
Paul Smeets *(CTO)*
John Limpens *(Chief Procurement Officer)*
Board of Directors:
F.J.A.M. Pistorius
M.A.J. Verhagen
Subsidiaries:

Cadac Group B.V. (1)
Nieuw Eyckholt 282
NL-6419 DJ Heerlen, Netherlands NL
Mailing Address: (100%)
Postbus 2759
NL-6419 DJ Heerlen, Netherlands
Tel.: (31) 454001000
Fax: (31) 454001001
E-Mail: info@cadac.com
Web Site: www.cadac.com
Emp.: 175
Digital Design Information Software Publisher & Whslr
S.I.C.: 7372
N.A.I.C.S.: 511210
Jan Baggen *(Founder & CEO)*
Astrid van de Sande *(CFO)*
Paul Smeets *(CTO)*
John Limpens *(Chief Procurement Officer)*

NedGraphics B.V. (1)
Ir DS Tuijnmanweg 10
NL-4131 PN Vianen, Netherlands NL
Tel.: (31) 347329600 (60%)
Fax: (31) 347329666
E-Mail: cadgis.info@nedgraphics.nl
Web Site: www.nedgraphics.nl
Emp.: 80
Design & Geographic Information Software Developer, Publisher & Distr
S.I.C.: 7372
N.A.I.C.S.: 511210
Richard Goossens *(Pres)*

CADAN RESOURCES CORPORATION

Suite 1720 1111 West Georgia Street
Vancouver, BC, V6E 4M3, Canada
Tel.: (604) 687-0760
Fax: (604) 628-5001
E-Mail: info@cadanresources.com
Web Site: www.cadanresources.com
CXD—(TSXV)
Sales Range: Less than $1 Million
Business Description:
Metal Exploration Services
S.I.C.: 1081
N.A.I.C.S.: 213114
Personnel:
Yuzheng Xie *(Chm)*
Robert Gordon Butchart *(Pres)*
Peter Cunningham *(CEO & COO)*
Derick Sinclair *(CFO)*
Monita Faris *(Sec)*
Board of Directors:
Yuzheng Xie
Robert Gordon Butchart
Peter Cunningham
Doug Evans
Francois Marland
Legal Counsel:
Fortun Narvasa & Salazar
Manila, Philippines
Transfer Agent:
Computershare Trust Company of Canada
Vancouver, BC, Canada
Tel.: (604) 661-9400
Fax: (604) 669-1548
Subsidiaries:

Philco Holdings Inc. (1)
7 Hamilton Crt
Cobourg, ON, K9A 1V2, Canada
Tel.: (905) 372-9429
Investment Management Services
S.I.C.: 6211
N.A.I.C.S.: 523999

Tribal Holdings Inc. (1)
179 Charlotte St
Peterborough, ON, K9J 2T7, Canada
Tel.: (905) 982-1130
Fax: (705) 876-8298
E-Mail: tribalvoices@sympatico.ca
Emp.: 2
Investment Management Services
S.I.C.: 6211
N.A.I.C.S.: 523999
Joerg Leinhaas *(Office Mgr)*

CADENCE CAPITAL LIMITED

11 131 Macquarie Street
Sydney, NSW, 2000, Australia
Tel.: (61) 282982444
Fax: (61) 282982499
E-Mail: info@cadencecapital.com.au
Web Site: www.cadencecapital.com.au
CDM—(ASX)
Sls.: $61,369,470
Assets: $176,688,198
Liabilities: $5,385,084
Net Worth: $171,303,114
Earnings: $11,861,545
Fiscal Year-end: 06/30/13
Business Description:
Security Consulting Services
S.I.C.: 8999
N.A.I.C.S.: 541690
Personnel:
Karl Siegling *(Chm, Mng Dir, Chief Investment Officer & Sec)*
Wayne Davies *(COO)*
Board of Directors:
Karl Siegling
James Chirnside
Wayne Davies
Ronald Hancock

CADEX ELECTRONICS INC.

22000 Fraserwood Way
Richmond, BC, Canada V6W 1J6
Tel.: (604) 231-7777
Fax: (604) 231-7755
Toll Free: (800) 565-5228
E-Mail: info@cadex.com
Web Site: www.cadex.com
Year Founded: 1980
Rev.: $13,305,662
Emp.: 55
Business Description:
Battery Charging & Analyzing Equipment Mfr
S.I.C.: 3825
N.A.I.C.S.: 334515
Personnel:
Isidor Buchmann *(Founder & CEO)*
Paul Buchmann *(Pres & COO)*

CADILA HEALTHCARE LIMITED

(d/b/a Zydus Cadila)
Zydus Tower Satellite Cross Roads
Ahmedabad, 380015, India
Tel.: (91) 7926868100
Fax: (91) 7926862365
Web Site: www.zyduscadila.com
532321—(BOM)
Rev.: $1,185,577,380
Assets: $1,366,805,880
Liabilities: $798,777,360
Net Worth: $568,028,520
Earnings: $127,907,460
Emp.: 12,192
Fiscal Year-end: 03/31/13
Business Description:
Pharmaceutical Company
S.I.C.: 2834
N.A.I.C.S.: 325412
Personnel:
Pankaj R. Patel *(Chm & Mng Dir)*
Nitin D. Parekh *(CFO)*
Upen H. Shah *(Compliance Officer & Sec)*
Jyotindra B. Gor *(Chief Accts Officer)*
Sharvil P. Patel *(Deputy Mng Dir)*
Board of Directors:
Pankaj R. Patel
Nitin Raojibhai Desai
Humayun Dhanrajgir
Apurva S. Diwanji
Mukesh M. Patel
Sharvil P. Patel
Transfer Agent:
Sharepro Services (India) Private Limited
13 AB Samhita Warehousing Complex II Floor
Sakinaka Telephone Lane
Off Andheri Kurla Rd Sakinaka, Mumbai, India
Subsidiaries:

Dialforhealth India Ltd. (1)
8th Fl N G Tower Satellite Cross Rd
Ahmedabad, Gujarat, 380 015, India
Tel.: (91) 7926868600
Fax: (91) 7926868601
E-Mail: info@dialforhealth.net
Web Site: www.dialforhealth.net
Emp.: 100
Health Information Resource Services
S.I.C.: 9651
N.A.I.C.S.: 926150
Pankaj Patel *(Mng Dir)*

Zydus Animal Health Limited (1)
Astron Tech Park 5th Floor Satellite Cross Roads
Ahmedabad, Gujarat, 380 015, India (100%)
Tel.: (91) 79 26868681
Fax: (91) 79 26868687
E-Mail: enquiry@zydusahl.com
Web Site: www.zydusahl.com
Emp.: 55
Animal Healthcare Products Mfr
S.I.C.: 2834
N.A.I.C.S.: 325412
Pankaj R. Patel *(Chm & Mng Dir)*
Arun Atrey *(Mng Dir)*

Zydus Wellness Limited (1)
Zydus Tower Satellite Cross Roads
Ahmedabad, Gujarat, 380015, India
Tel.: (91) 7926868100
Fax: (91) 7926862253
E-Mail: info@zyduswellness.in
Web Site: www.zyduswellness.in
ZYDUSWELL—(NSE)
Rev.: $760,065,840
Assets: $647,268,480
Liabilities: $166,359,420
Net Worth: $480,909,060
Earnings: $180,041,940
Fiscal Year-end: 03/31/13
Pharmaceutical Products Mfr
S.I.C.: 2834
N.A.I.C.S.: 325412
Elkana N. Ezekiel *(Mng Dir)*
Amit B. Jain *(CFO)*
Dhaval N. Soni *(Compliance Officer & Sec)*

Joint Venture:

Zydus Nycomed Healthcare Private Ltd. (1)
C 4 MIDC Village Pawne
Thane-Belapur Road, Vashi, Navi Mumbai, 400 705, India
Tel.: (91) 2227682666
Fax: (91) 2227670223
E-Mail: hr@zydusnycomed.com
Web Site: www.zydusnycomed.com
Emp.: 240
Pharmaceuticals Mfr
S.I.C.: 2834
N.A.I.C.S.: 325412
Ravi Chandran *(Mng Dir)*

U.S. Subsidiaries:

Zydus Healthcare (USA) LLC. (1)
73 Route 31 N
Pennington, NJ 08534-3601
Tel.: (609) 275-5125
Fax: (609) 514-1002
Pharmaceutical Preparations Mfr & Whslr
S.I.C.: 2834
N.A.I.C.S.: 325412

Zydus Pharmaceuticals USA Inc. (1)
73 Route 31 N
Pennington, NJ 08534-3601
Tel.: (609) 275-5125
Fax: (609) 275-0499
E-Mail: sales@zydususa.com
Web Site: www.zydususa.com
Emp.: 20
Pharmaceutical Products Mfr & Sales
S.I.C.: 2834
N.A.I.C.S.: 325412
Joseph D Renner *(CEO)*

Non-U.S. Subsidiaries:

Quimica E Farmaceutica NIKKHO Do Brasil Ltda. (1)
Rua Jaime Perdigao 431 445 Ilha Do Governador
Rio de Janeiro, 21920-240, Brazil
Tel.: (55) 21 3393 4266
Fax: (55) 21 3393 1343
Toll Free: 8002829911
E-Mail: nikkho@nikkho.com.br
Web Site: www.nikkho.com.br
Pharmaceutical Preparations Mfr
S.I.C.: 2834
N.A.I.C.S.: 325412
Amit Dave *(CEO)*

Simayla Pharmaceuticals (Pty) Ltd. (1)
Block 15 The Boardwalk Ofc Park 107 Haymeadow St
PO Box 1646
Faerie Glen, Pretoria, Gauteng, 0043, South Africa
Tel.: (27) 129910730
Fax: (27) 129916796
E-Mail: desrael@simayla.co.za
Web Site: www.simayla.co.za
Emp.: 32
Pharmaceutical Products Mfr & Sales
S.I.C.: 2834
N.A.I.C.S.: 325412
Renacea Hahl *(CEO)*

Zydus France SAS. (1)
Zac Les Hautes Patures 25 rue Des Peupliers
92000 Nanterre, France
Tel.: (33) 141191850
Fax: (33) 146495873
E-Mail: contact@zydusfrance.com
Web Site: www.zydusfrance.com
Emp.: 22
Pharmaceutical Products Mfr
S.I.C.: 2834

N.A.I.C.S.: 325412
Josiane Peyrepeyry *(Pres)*
Francoise Mothe *(Dir Gen)*

Zydus Healthcare Brasil Ltda. (1)
Alameda Jau N 1905 - Cj 41 E 47 Jardim Paulista
Sao Paulo, 01420-002, Brazil
Tel.: (55) 1130864180
Fax: (55) 30694185
Toll Free: 8002821127
E-Mail: silvio@zydusbrasil.com.br
Web Site: www.zydusbrasil.com.br
Generic Drugs Supplier
S.I.C.: 5122
N.A.I.C.S.: 424210
Amit Dave *(Pres)*

THE CADILLAC FAIRVIEW CORPORATION LIMITED

20 Queen St W 5th Fl
Toronto, ON, M5H 3R4, Canada
Tel.: (416) 598-8200
Fax: (416) 598-8607
Web Site: www.cadillacfairview.com
Emp.: 1,700
Business Description:
Real Estate Manager
S.I.C.: 6531
N.A.I.C.S.: 531210
Personnel:
Robert W. Korthals *(Chm)*
Scot Adams *(CIO & Sr VP)*
John M. Sullivan *(Exec VP-Dev)*
Rudy Adlaf *(Sr VP-Architecture & Design)*
Wayne L. Barwise *(Sr VP-Dev)*
Clive Baxter *(Sr VP-Toronto Eaton Centre Portfolio)*
Norm Blouin *(Sr VP-Eastern Canada Portfolio)*
Alan Carlisle *(Sr VP-US Portfolio)*
Linda Gray *(Sr VP-Ontario Portfolio)*
David E. Handley *(Sr VP-Project Mgmt)*
Scott Pennock *(Sr VP-Toronto Office Portfolio)*
Ron Wratschko *(Sr VP-Western Portfolio)*
Board of Directors:
Robert W. Korthals
Jalynn Hamilton Bennett
Robert G. Bertram
John P. Curtin, Jr.
Robert P. Kelly
Thomas Knowlton
James W. Leech
Peter W. Mills
Allan J. Reesor
Subsidiary:

Sherway Gardens (1)
25 W Mall
Toronto, ON, M9C 1B8, Canada (100%)
Tel.: (416) 621-1070
Fax: (416) 620-7918
Web Site: www.sherwaygardens.ca
Emp.: 100
Retail & Commercial Properties
S.I.C.: 6531
N.A.I.C.S.: 531312
Andy Traynor *(Gen Mgr)*

CADILLAC MINING CORPORATION

3741 West 36th Avenue
Vancouver, BC, V6N 2S3, Canada
Tel.: (604) 684-7300
Fax: (604) 531-9512
Web Site: www.cadillacmining.com
Year Founded: 2004
CQX—(TSXV)
Assets: $1,443,583
Liabilities: $1,070,953
Net Worth: $372,630
Earnings: ($255,569)
Fiscal Year-end: 08/31/13
Business Description:
Mineral Properties Exploration Services
S.I.C.: 1081
N.A.I.C.S.: 213114
Personnel:
Victor F. Erickson *(Pres & CEO)*
Justin Blanchet *(CFO & Sec)*
Board of Directors:
Andre J. Audet
David W. Childs
Victor F. Erickson
Elmer B. Stewart
Transfer Agent:
Equity Transfer & Trust Company
400-200 University Avenue
Toronto, ON, Canada

CADILLAC VENTURES INC.

65 Front Street East Suite 200
Toronto, ON, M5E 1B5, Canada
Tel.: (416) 203-7722
Fax: (416) 203-7782
E-Mail: info@cadillacventures.com
Web Site: www.cadillacventures.com
Year Founded: 1995
CDC—(TSXV)
Rev.: $9,424
Assets: $23,313,042
Liabilities: $900,357
Net Worth: $22,412,685
Earnings: ($1,614,566)
Emp.: 2
Fiscal Year-end: 05/31/13
Business Description:
Gold Mining Services
S.I.C.: 1041
N.A.I.C.S.: 212221
Personnel:
Peter Gleeson *(Chm)*
Norman E. Brewster *(Pres & CEO)*
Leo O'Shaughnessy *(CFO)*
Board of Directors:
Peter Gleeson
Norman E. Brewster
James Burke
Jesus Fernandez Lopez
Neil Novak
Bing Pan
Maurice Stekel
Jeremy Weir
Transfer Agent:
Equity Financial Trust Company
200 University Avenue Suite 400
Toronto, ON, Canada
Subsidiary:

Cadillac Ventures Holdings Inc. (1)
181 Bay St Ste 2840
Toronto, ON, M5J 2T3, Canada
Tel.: (416) 203-7722
Fax: (416) 203-7782
Investment Management Services
S.I.C.: 6211
N.A.I.C.S.: 523999

CADIZ HOLDINGS LIMITED

4th Floor The Terraces 25 Protea Road
Claremont, 7708, South Africa
Tel.: (27) 216704600
Fax: (27) 216704651
E-Mail: info@cadiz.co.za
Web Site: www.cadiz.co.za
CDZ—(JSE)
Rev.: $17,439,721
Assets: $630,088,418
Liabilities: $554,924,483
Net Worth: $75,163,935
Earnings: $570,675
Emp.: 115
Fiscal Year-end: 03/31/13
Business Description:
Financial Services
S.I.C.: 8742
N.A.I.C.S.: 541611
Personnel:
Fraser Shaw *(CEO, COO & Dir-Fin)*
Dan Ahern *(CEO-Cadiz Securities)*
Frank Cadiz *(CEO-Cadiz Asset Mgmt)*
Robbie Gonsalves *(CEO-Cadiz Corp Solutions)*
Charl Schmahl *(Sec)*
Board of Directors:
Peter-Paul Ngwenya
Ray Cadiz
Greg Fury
Bryan Kent
Gando Matyumza
Totsie Memela-Khambula
Steven Saunders
Fraser Shaw
Transfer Agent:
Computershare Investor Services 2004 (Pty) Limited
70 Marshall Street
61051
Johannesburg, South Africa
Subsidiaries:

Cadiz Asset Management (Pty) Ltd (1)
4th Fl The Ter 25 Protea Rd
Claremont, Western Cape, 7700, South Africa
Tel.: (27) 216704600
Fax: (27) 216704651
E-Mail: cam@cadiz.co.za
Emp.: 150
Asset Management Services
S.I.C.: 6531
N.A.I.C.S.: 531390
Frank Cadiz *(Mng Dir)*

Cadiz Special Projects Limited (1)
1 Oakdale Rd
Cape Town, Western Cape, 7700, South Africa
Tel.: (27) 216578300
Fax: (27) 216578301
E-Mail: info@cadiz.co.za
Real Estate Asset Management Services
S.I.C.: 6531
N.A.I.C.S.: 531390
Frank Cadiz *(Mng Dir)*

Penryth Finance and Risk (Pty) Ltd (1)
1 Oakdale Rd
Cape Town, Western Cape, 7700, South Africa
Tel.: (27) 216578300
Fax: (27) 216578301
E-Mail: info@cadiz.co.za
Emp.: 180
Financial Management Services
S.I.C.: 8742
N.A.I.C.S.: 541611
Ram Barkai *(CEO)*

CADMAN RESOURCES INC.

Suite 700 - 350 Bay Street
Toronto, ON, M5H 2S6, Canada
Tel.: (416) 304-9935
E-Mail: info@cadmanresourcesinc.com
Web Site: www.cadmanresourcesinc.com
Year Founded: 2007
CUZ—(CNSX)
Rev.: $902
Assets: $185,875
Liabilities: $156,369
Net Worth: $29,505
Earnings: ($430,873)
Fiscal Year-end: 12/31/12
Business Description:
Gold Mining
S.I.C.: 1041
N.A.I.C.S.: 212221
Personnel:
Boris Ziger *(Chm & CEO)*
Derek Bartlett *(Pres)*
Richard Tong *(CFO)*
Board of Directors:
Boris Ziger
Derek Bartlett
Alex Johnston
Monty C. Ritchings

CADOGAN PETROLEUM PLC

Ibex House 42 47 Minories
London, EC3N 1DX, United Kingdom
Tel.: (44) 2074878301
Fax: (44) 2074878402
E-Mail: info@cadoganpetroleum.com
Web Site: www.cadoganpetroleum.com
Year Founded: 2004
CAD—(LSE)
Rev.: $5,653,000
Assets: $207,976,000
Liabilities: $13,699,000
Net Worth: $194,277,000
Earnings: ($93,136,000)
Emp.: 164
Fiscal Year-end: 12/31/12
Business Description:
Oil & Gas Exploration Services
S.I.C.: 1311
N.A.I.C.S.: 211111
Personnel:
Bertrand des Pallieres *(CEO)*
Adelmo Schenato *(COO)*
Laurence Sudwarts *(Sec)*
Board of Directors:
Zev Furst
Bertrand des Pallieres
Gilbert Lehmann
Adelmo Schenato
Chicco Testa
Legal Counsel:
Baker & McKenzie LLP
100 New Bridge Street
EC4V6JA London, United Kingdom
Subsidiary:

Cadogan Petroleum Holdings Ltd (1)
5th Floor 4-5 Grosvenor Place
London, SW1X 7HJ, United Kingdom
Tel.: (44) 20 7245 0801
Oil & Gas Drilling Services
S.I.C.: 1381
N.A.I.C.S.: 213111
Non-U.S. Subsidiaries:

Cadogan Bitlyanske BV (1)
Claude Debussylaan 24
Amsterdam, 1082 MD, Netherlands
Tel.: (31) 205222555
Oil & Gas Exploration Services
S.I.C.: 1389
N.A.I.C.S.: 213112

Cadogan Delta BV (1)
Claude Debussylaan 24
Amsterdam, 1082 MD, Netherlands
Tel.: (31) 205222555
Oil & Gas Exploration Services
S.I.C.: 1389
N.A.I.C.S.: 213112

Cadogan Petroleum Holdings BV (1)
Claude Debussylaan 24
Amsterdam, 1082 MD, Netherlands
Tel.: (31) 205222555
Oil & Gas Exploration Services
S.I.C.: 1389
N.A.I.C.S.: 213112

LLC Astroinvest-Energy (1)
Bud 5a Kv 2 Vul Pogrebnyaka
Zen'kov, 38100, Ukraine
Tel.: (380) 532503060
Fax: (380) 532503080
Oil & Gas Exploration Services
S.I.C.: 1389
N.A.I.C.S.: 213112

LLC Industrial Company Gazvydobuvannya (1)
3 Myru Street
Poltava, 36022, Ukraine
Tel.: (380) 532503060
Fax: (380) 532503080
Oil & Gas Exploration Services
S.I.C.: 1389

Cadogan Petroleum plc—(Continued)

N.A.I.C.S.: 213112

CADUCEUS SOFTWARE SYSTEMS CORP.

42A High Street
Sutton Coldfield, W Midlands, United Kingdom
Tel.: (44) 121 695 9585
Year Founded: 2006
CSOC—(OTC)

Business Description:
Software Services
S.I.C.: 7372
N.A.I.C.S.: 511210

Personnel:
Derrick Gidden *(Pres, CEO, CFO, Treas & Sec)*

Board of Directors:
Derrick Gidden
Oswald Huggins

Transfer Agent:
Island Stock Transfer
100 2nd Ave S Suite 705S
Saint Petersburg, FL 33701
Tel.: (727) 289-0010

CAE INC.

8585 Cote de Liesse
Saint Laurent, QC, H4T 1G6, Canada
Tel.: (514) 341-6780
Fax: (514) 341-7699
Toll Free: (800) 760-0667
E-Mail: investor.relations@cae.com
Web Site: www.cae.com
Year Founded: 1947
CAE—(NYSE TSX)
Rev.: $2,091,915,090
Assets: $3,855,505,374
Liabilities: $2,727,789,684
Net Worth: $1,127,715,690
Earnings: $141,548,448
Emp.: 7,686
Fiscal Year-end: 03/31/13

Business Description:
Simulation, Modelling & Training Solutions for Civil Aviation & Military
Import Export
S.I.C.: 5063
N.A.I.C.S.: 423610

Personnel:
James F. Hankinson *(Chm)*
Stephane Lefebvre *(CFO & VP-Fin)*
Gene Colabatistto *(Pres-Military Products, Trng & Svcs Grp)*
Jeffrey G. Roberts *(Pres-Civil Simulation Products, Trng & Svcs)*
Hartland J. A. Paterson *(Gen Counsel, Sec & VP-Legal)*
Eric Bussieres *(Treas & VP-Fin-Civil)*

Board of Directors:
James F. Hankinson
Brian E. Barents
H. Garfield Emerson
Michael M. Fortier
Paul Ernest Gagne
Edward Randolph Jayne, II
Robert Lacroix
John P. Manley
Marc Parent
Peter J. Schoomaker
Andrew J. Stevens
Katharine Berghuis Stevenson
Lawrence N. Stevenson
Kathleen E. Walsh

Transfer Agent:
Computershare Trust Company of Canada
100 University Avenue 9th Floor
Toronto, ON, M5J 2Y1, Canada
Tel.: (416) 663-9097
Fax: (416) 263-9694

Subsidiaries:

CAE Healthcare Inc. **(1)**
8585 Cote de Liesse
Saint Laurent, QC, H4T 1G6, Canada
Tel.: (514) 341-6780
Fax: (514) 341-7699
Toll Free: (877) 223-6273
E-Mail: caehealthcare@cae.com
Web Site: www.cae.com
Medical Training & Simulation Systems Developer
S.I.C.: 8299
N.A.I.C.S.: 611699
Michael Bernstein *(Pres)*
Robert Amyot *(Chief Medical Officer & VP-Medical Programs)*

U.S. Subsidiary:

Medical Education Technologies, Inc. **(2)**
6300 Edgelake Dr
Sarasota, FL 34240
Tel.: (941) 377-5562
Fax: (941) 377-5590
E-Mail: info@meti.com
Web Site: www.meti.com
Sales Range: $50-74.9 Million
Emp.: 200
Medical Education & Simulation Technology Solutions
S.I.C.: 8299
N.A.I.C.S.: 611699
Dina Dennis *(VP-Sls)*

CAE Mining Canada Inc. **(1)**
8585 Cote de Liesse
Saint Laurent, QC, H4T 1G8, Canada
Tel.: (514) 341-6780
Web Site: www.cae.com
Mining Operation Planning Technology Developer
S.I.C.: 1081
N.A.I.C.S.: 213114
Nick Beaton *(CEO)*

Presagis **(1)**
4700 de la Savane Suite 300
Montreal, QC, H4P 1T7, Canada
Tel.: (514) 341-3874
Fax: (514) 341-8018
Toll Free: (800) 361-6424
E-Mail: info@presagis.com
Web Site: www.presagis.com
Sales Range: $10-24.9 Million
Emp.: 120
Simulation Software Development
S.I.C.: 7372
N.A.I.C.S.: 511210
Jean-Michel Briere *(VP-Sls, Mktg & Client Svcs)*

U.S. Subsidiary:

Presagis USA **(2)**
1301 W George Bush Fwy Ste 120
Richardson, TX 75080
Tel.: (972) 943-2400
Fax: (469) 467-4563
Web Site: www.presagis.com
Emp.: 75
3D Simulation Technologies & Software Mfr
S.I.C.: 7371
N.A.I.C.S.: 541511
Douglas Price *(Dir-Res)*

U.S. Subsidiary:

CAE USA, Inc. **(1)**
4908 Tampa W Blvd
Tampa, FL 33634-2411 FL
Mailing Address: (100%)
PO Box 15000
Tampa, FL 33684-5000
Tel.: (813) 885-7481
Fax: (813) 887-1439
E-Mail: info@cae.com
Web Site: www.cae.com
Rev.: $100,000,000
Emp.: 425
High Fidelity Flight Simulators
Import Export
S.I.C.: 3589
N.A.I.C.S.: 333318
Michael E. Ryan *(Chm)*
Raymond Duquette *(Pres & Gen Mgr)*
Alain Raquepas *(CFO & VP-Fin)*
David Allman *(Gen Counsel)*
John Atkinson *(Treas & Dir-Fin)*

Non-U.S. Subsidiary:

Medium Support Helicopter Aircrew Training Facility (MSHATF) **(2)**
RAF Benson
Wallingford, Oxon, OX10 6AA, United Kingdom UK
Tel.: (44) 1491 828 000 (80%)
Fax: (44) 1491 2828 080
E-Mail: caeats@caeats.co.uk
Web Site: www.cae.com
Emp.: 5
Military Helicopter Simulation Training
S.I.C.: 8249
N.A.I.C.S.: 611512
Ian Bell *(Gen Mgr)*

Non-U.S. Subsidiaries:

CAE Australia Pty Ltd. **(1)**
Unit 40 Slough Avenue
PO Box 6650
Silverwater, NSW, 2128, Australia (100%)
Tel.: (61) 297484844
Fax: (61) 297140300
E-Mail: caeaus@cae.com.au
Web Site: www.cae.com.au
Emp.: 100
Supplier of Integrated Sensor Stimulation Products & Systems for Military Radar Testing; Commercial & Military Flight Simulators & Control Systems
S.I.C.: 3769
N.A.I.C.S.: 336419
Mathew Eastlei *(Head-Fin)*

CAE Elektronik GmbH **(1)**
Steinfurt 11
52222 Stolberg, Germany DE
Tel.: (49) 24021060 (100%)
Telex: 832 220 caegd
Fax: (49) 2402106270
E-Mail: info@cae.de
Web Site: www.cae.de
Emp.: 600
Flight Simulation & Training Systems
S.I.C.: 8249
N.A.I.C.S.: 611512
Ulrich Aderhold *(Mng Dir)*

CAE India Private Limited **(1)**
108 Gavipuram Guttahalli
Bengaluru, 560 019, India
Tel.: (91) 80 2660 3805
Fax: (91) 80 2660 4111
E-Mail: drramesh@macmet.com
Web Site: www.macmet-technologies.com
Manufactures, Maintains & Upgrades Full-Flight Simulators, Tank & Gunnery Trainers & Naval Trainers & Develops Software for Simulation Applications
S.I.C.: 7379
N.A.I.C.S.: 541519

CAE UK plc **(1)**
Innovation Dr
Burgess Hill, W Sussex, RH15 9TW, United Kingdom UK
Tel.: (44) 1444247535 (100%)
Fax: (44) 1444244895
E-Mail: cae_plc@cae.co.uk
Web Site: www.cae.co.uk
Emp.: 150
Military Simulation & Training
S.I.C.: 9711
N.A.I.C.S.: 928110
Ian Bell *(Mng Dir)*

Oxford Aviation Academy Limited **(1)**
Oxford Airport - Langford Lane
Kidlington, Oxford, OX5 1QX, United Kingdom
Tel.: (44) 1865841234
Fax: (44) 1865378797
E-Mail: enquiries@oaa.com
Web Site: www.oaa.com
Emp.: 500
Flight Training
S.I.C.: 8249
N.A.I.C.S.: 611512
Brian Simpson *(CEO)*

Subsidiary:

Oxford Aviation Academy UK Limited **(2)**
Fleming Way
Crawley, W Sussex, SK7 1QR, United Kingdom UK
Tel.: (44) 1293 543541
Fax: (44) 1293 547063
E-Mail: info@oaa.com
Web Site: www.oaa.com
Emp.: 800
Flight Training Systems
S.I.C.: 8249
N.A.I.C.S.: 611512

Non-U.S. Subsidiary:

PARC Aviation, Ltd. **(2)**
Saint John's Court Swords Rd
Santry, Dublin, 9, Ireland
Tel.: (353) 18161747
Telex: 33784 PARC EI
Fax: (353) 18161766
E-Mail: flight.crew@cae.com
Web Site: www.cae.parcaviation.com
Emp.: 40
Aviation Specialist Personnel & Support Solutions
Export
S.I.C.: 7361
N.A.I.C.S.: 561311
Sean Butler *(CEO)*

Non-U.S. Joint Venture:

Rotorsim S.r.l. **(1)**
Via Indipendenza 2
21018 Sesto Calende, Italy
Tel.: (39) 0331 915 062
Helicopter Flight Training Services
S.I.C.: 8249
N.A.I.C.S.: 611512

CAERUS RESOURCE CORPORATION

(See Under Angel Gold Corp.)

CAESARS GROUP

Al Muttawa Bldg 16 2nd Fl Block 1
Salhiya St
PO Box 5592
Kuwait, 13056, Kuwait
Tel.: (965) 2450504
Fax: (965) 2421361
E-Mail: caesars@caesarsgroup.net
Web Site: www.caesarsgroup.net
Year Founded: 1973
Sls.: $15,000,000
Emp.: 1,000

Business Description:
Holding Company; Operator of Restaurants; Foodstuff Distr; Travel Agency Services; Corrugated Cartons & Paper Products Mfr; Chemicals Distr; Industrial Equipment, Testing Equipment & Building Materials Distr
S.I.C.: 6719
N.A.I.C.S.: 551112

Personnel:
Lawrence D'Souza *(Co-Owner & Mng Dir)*
Ghazi Al Abdul Razzak *(Co-Owner & Mng Dir)*

Subsidiaries:

Al Afrah Al Sharqiya General Trading and Contracting Company W.L.L. **(1)**
PO Box 5592
Safat, Kuwait, Kuwait
Tel.: (965) 22450504
Fax: (965) 22421361
E-Mail: alafrah@caesarsgroup.net
Web Site: www.caesarsgroup.net
Polyester Resins & Fiberglass Distr
S.I.C.: 5085
N.A.I.C.S.: 423840
M. Varghese *(Mng Dir)*

Caesar Pac Carton & Paper Products Co. **(1)**
PO Box 5592
Safat, Kuwait, Kuwait
Tel.: (965) 4610077
Fax: (965) 4610177
E-Mail: caesarpac@caesarsgroup.net
Web Site: www.caesarpac.com
Folding Paperboard Box Mfr
S.I.C.: 2679
N.A.I.C.S.: 322299

Caesars General Trading and Contracting Company W.L.L. **(1)**
PO Box 5592
Safat, Kuwait, Kuwait
Tel.: (965) 2450504

Fax: (965) 2421 361
Emp.: 550
Trading & Contracting Services
S.I.C.: 1542
N.A.I.C.S.: 236220

Caesars Holidays (1)
PO Box 5592
Safat, 13056 Kuwait, Kuwait
Tel.: (965) 22450504
Fax: (965) 22421361
E-Mail: nricustomerservice@coxandkings.com
Web Site: www.caesarsgroup.net
Travel Services, Tour Packages & Hotel Reservations
S.I.C.: 4729
N.A.I.C.S.: 561599

Caesars Travel Company (1)
PO Box 5592
Safat, Kuwait, Kuwait
Tel.: (965) 2450504
Fax: (965) 2421361
E-Mail: ctravels@qualitynet.net
Web Site: www.caesarsgroup.net
Travel Services
S.I.C.: 4729
N.A.I.C.S.: 561599
P. N. J. Kumar *(Gen Mgr)*

CAESARSTONE SDOT-YAM LTD.

Kibbutz Sdot-Yam
MP Menashe, Caesarea, 3780400, Israel
Tel.: (972) 4 636 4555
Fax: (972) 4 636 4400
E-Mail: sherut@caesarstone.com
Web Site: www.caesarstone.com
CSTE—(NASDAQ)
Rev.: $296,564,000
Assets: $321,049,000
Liabilities: $97,132,000
Net Worth: $223,917,000
Earnings: $40,367,000
Emp.: 883
Fiscal Year-end: 12/31/12

Business Description:
Quartz Countertops Mfr
S.I.C.: 3281
N.A.I.C.S.: 327991

Personnel:
Maxim Ohana *(Chm)*
Yosef Shiran *(CEO)*
Giora Wegman *(Deputy CEO)*
Yair Averbuch *(CFO)*
David Cullen *(CEO-Australia)*
Michal Baumwald Oron *(Gen Counsel)*

Board of Directors:
Maxim Ohana
Irit Ben-Dov
Ofer Borovsky
Dori Brown
Gal Cohen
Shachar Degani
Oded Goldstein
Yonathan Melamed
Moshe Ronen
Eitan Shachar
Boaz Shani

Transfer Agent:
American Stock Transfer & Trust Co.
6201 15th Ave
Brooklyn, NY 11219
Tel.: (718) 921-8124

U.S. Subsidiary:

Caesarstone US (1)
6840 Hayvenhurst Ave Ste 100
Van Nuys, CA 91406
Tel.: (818) 779-0099
E-Mail: info@caesarstoneus.com
Web Site: www.caesarstoneus.com
Quartz Countertop Mfr
S.I.C.: 3281
N.A.I.C.S.: 327991
Sagi Cohen *(CEO)*

Non-U.S. Subsidiaries:

Caesarstone Australia Pty Ltd (1)
Unit 3/1 Secombe Place
Moorebank, NSW, 2170, Australia
Tel.: (61) 1300 119 119
E-Mail: sales@caesarstone.com.au
Web Site: www.caesarstone.com.au
Emp.: 7
Quartz Countertop Mfr
S.I.C.: 3281
N.A.I.C.S.: 327991
David Cullen *(CEO)*

Caesarstone Canada Inc. (1)
8899 Jane Street
Concord, ON, L4K 2M6, Canada
Tel.: (416) 479-8400
Fax: (416) 479-8401
E-Mail: info@caesarstone.ca
Web Site: www.caesarstone.ca
Quartz Countertop Mfr
S.I.C.: 3281
N.A.I.C.S.: 327991
Fernando Mammoliti *(CEO)*

Caesarstone South East Asia Pte Ltd (1)
10 Bukit Batok Crescent #08-07 The Spire
Singapore, 658079, Singapore
Tel.: (65) 6316 1938
Fax: (65) 6565 9838
E-Mail: info@caesarstone.sg
Web Site: www.caesarstone.sg
Quartz Countertop Mfr
S.I.C.: 3281
N.A.I.C.S.: 327991

CAFCA LIMITED

54 Lytton Road
PO Box 1651
Harare, Zimbabwe
Tel.: (263) 4 754075
Fax: (263) 4 754080
Web Site: www.cafca.co.zw
Year Founded: 1947
CAC—(JSE)
Rev.: $23,119,929
Assets: $13,354,485
Liabilities: $4,512,224
Net Worth: $8,842,261
Earnings: $1,672,039
Fiscal Year-end: 09/30/12

Business Description:
Cable Mfr & Whslr
S.I.C.: 3357
N.A.I.C.S.: 335929

Personnel:
Robert Neill Webster *(Mng Dir)*

Board of Directors:
Piniel Mkushi
Edwin Tavengwa Zinyoro Chidzonga
Alan Ernest Dickson
Alvord Mabena
Thomas Alexander Taylor
Robert Neill Webster

CAFE DE CORAL HOLDINGS LIMITED

No 5-13 Wo Shui Street Fo Tan
Sha Tin, New Territories, China (Hong Kong)
Tel.: (852) 26936218
Fax: (852) 26950245
E-Mail: gcc@cafedecoral.com
Web Site: www.cafedecoral.com
Year Founded: 1986
0341—(HKG)
Rev.: $824,517,777
Assets: $569,151,515
Liabilities: $111,166,892
Net Worth: $457,984,623
Earnings: $70,399,866
Emp.: 17,000
Fiscal Year-end: 03/31/13

Business Description:
Holding Company; Restaurant Operator
S.I.C.: 6719
N.A.I.C.S.: 551112

Personnel:
Sunny Hoi Kwong Lo *(CEO)*
Mike Hung Chun Lim *(CFO)*
Kelvin Siu Min Chen *(Pres/CEO-Manchu WOK)*
Helen Oi Chun Li *(Sec)*

Board of Directors:
Michael Yue Kwong Chan
Albert Siu Cheung Au
Michael Ngai Min Choi
Samuel Tung Wah Hui
Larry Lam Kwong Kwok
Aubrey Kwok Sing Li
Anita Pik Ling Lo
Ian Ming Shing Lo
Peter Tak Shing Lo
Sunny Hoi Kwong Lo

Legal Counsel:
Mayer Brown JSM
16th-19th Floors Prince's Building
10 Chater Road, Central, China (Hong Kong)
Tel.: (852) 2843 2211
Fax: (852) 2845 9121

Subsidiaries:

Barson Development Limited (1)
10th Fl Cafe De Coral Ctr
Sha Tin, China (Hong Kong) (100%)
Tel.: (852) 26936218
Fax: (852) 26901756
E-Mail: gcc@cafedecoral.com
Other Real Estate Property Lessors
S.I.C.: 6519
N.A.I.C.S.: 531190
Michael Chan *(Pres)*

Bloomcheer Limited (1)
Cafe De Coral Ctr
Sha Tin, China (Hong Kong) (100%)
Tel.: (852) 26936218
Fax: (852) 26950245
Web Site: www.cafetecoral.com
Full-Service Restaurants
S.I.C.: 5812
N.A.I.C.S.: 722511

Cafe de Coral Fast Food Limited (1)
Cafe De Coral Centre No 5-13 Wo Shui Street Fo Tan
New Territories, Sha Tin, China (Hong Kong) (100%)
Tel.: (852) 26936218
Fax: (852) 26950245
Web Site: www.cafedecoral.com
Emp.: 70
Full-Service Restaurants
S.I.C.: 5812
N.A.I.C.S.: 722511

Cafe de Coral Group Limited (1)
10th Floor Cafe De Coral Center
Sha Tin, China (Hong Kong) (100%)
Tel.: (852) 26936218
Fax: (852) 26950245
E-Mail: gcc@cafedecoral.com
Web Site: www.cafedecoral.com
Full-Service Restaurants
S.I.C.: 5812
N.A.I.C.S.: 722511
Sunny Lo *(Mng Dir)*

Eldoon Limited (1)
10/f Cafe De Coral Center 5 Wo Shui St Fotan
Sha Tin, New Territories, China (Hong Kong)
Tel.: (852) 26936218
Fax: (852) 26073215
Catering Services
S.I.C.: 5812
N.A.I.C.S.: 722320

Exo Enterprises Limited (1)
Cafe De Coral Ctr
Sha Tin, China (Hong Kong) (100%)
Tel.: (852) 26936218
Fax: (852) 26950245
E-Mail: oad@cafedecoral.com
Full-Service Restaurants
S.I.C.: 5812
N.A.I.C.S.: 722511

Kater International Limited (1)
Cafe de Coral Centre No 5-13 Wo Shui St Fo Tan
Sha Tin, China (Hong Kong)
Tel.: (852) 26936218
Fax: (852) 26950245
Full-Service Restaurants
S.I.C.: 5812
N.A.I.C.S.: 722511

Luckyview Enterprises Limited (1)
10/f Cafe De Coral Center 5 Wo Shui St Fo Tan
Sha Tin, New Territories, China (Hong Kong)
Tel.: (852) 26936218
Fax: (852) 26950245
E-Mail: ccc@cafedecoral.com
Fast Food Restaurant Operators
S.I.C.: 5812
N.A.I.C.S.: 722511

Scanfoods Limited (1)
9th Floor Cafe De Coral Centre
Sha Tin, China (Hong Kong) (100%)
Tel.: (852) 27302323
Fax: (852) 26902145
Web Site: www.scanfoods.com.hk
Meat & Meat Product Whslr
S.I.C.: 5147
N.A.I.C.S.: 424470

Yumi Yumi Caterers Limited (1)
10th Floor Cafe De Coral Ctr
Sha Tin, China (Hong Kong) (100%)
Tel.: (852) 26936218
Fax: (852) 26950245
Full-Service Restaurants
S.I.C.: 5812
N.A.I.C.S.: 722511

U.S. Subsidiaries:

China Inn Restaurants, Inc. (1)
285 Main St
Pawtucket, RI 02860-2907 (100%)
Tel.: (401) 723-3960
Full-Service Restaurants
S.I.C.: 5812
N.A.I.C.S.: 722511

Dai Bai Dang Restaurants Inc (1)
165 E Paseo Del Centro
Fresno, CA 93720-4320
Tel.: (559) 448-8894
Fax: (559) 448-8896
Web Site: www.daibaidang.com
Restaurant Operation Services
S.I.C.: 5812
N.A.I.C.S.: 722511

Non-U.S. Subsidiaries:

Manchu Wok (Canada) Inc. (1)
85 Citizen Court Unit 9
Markham, ON, L6G 1A8, Canada (100%)
Tel.: (905) 946-7200
Fax: (905) 946-7201
Web Site: www.manchuwok.com
Emp.: 35
Full-Service Restaurants
S.I.C.: 5812
N.A.I.C.S.: 722511
Kelvin Chen *(Mng Dir)*

Shenzhen Cafe de Coral Catering Company Limited (1)
G/F Dexing Building 1048 Jianshe Road
Shenzhen, 518001, China
Tel.: (86) 75582330173
Catering Services
S.I.C.: 5812
N.A.I.C.S.: 722320

CAFE SOLUVEL BRASILIA SA

R Sara 17
20220070 Rio de Janeiro, Brazil
Tel.: (55) 35 2106 1900
Fax: (55) 35 2106 1904
CAFE3—(BRAZ)
Sales Range: $1-9.9 Million
Emp.: 205

Business Description:
Coffee Mfr & Whslr
S.I.C.: 2099
N.A.I.C.S.: 311920

Personnel:
Ruy Barreto *(Dir-IR)*

CAFFE NERO GROUP LTD.

3 Neal St
London, WC2H 9PU, United Kingdom

Caffe Nero Group Ltd.—(Continued)

Tel.: (44) 2075205150
Fax: (44) 2073790858
E-Mail: enqueries@caffenero.com
Web Site: www.caffenero.com
Sales Range: $150-199.9 Million
Emp.: 1,969

Business Description:
Coffee Retailer
S.I.C.: 2099
N.A.I.C.S.: 311920

Personnel:
Gerry Ford *(Chm)*

Board of Directors:
Gerry Ford
Benedict Price

CAFFYNS PLC

4 Meads Road
Eastbourne, East Sussex, BN20 7DR, United Kingdom
Tel.: (44) 1323730201
Fax: (44) 1323739680
E-Mail: registrar@caffyns.co.uk
Web Site: www.caffynsplc.co.uk
CFYN—(LSE)
Rev.: $260,527,575
Assets: $105,905,608
Liabilities: $81,718,782
Net Worth: $24,186,826
Earnings: $2,035,705
Emp.: 425
Fiscal Year-end: 03/31/13

Business Description:
Automobile Dealership Operator
S.I.C.: 5511
N.A.I.C.S.: 441110

Personnel:
Simon G. M. Caffyn *(CEO)*
Sarah J. Caffyn *(Sec & Dir-HR)*

Board of Directors:
Richard Wright
Sarah J. Caffyn
Simon G. M. Caffyn
Andrew R. Goodburn
Mark S. Harrison
Nick W. Hollingworth

Legal Counsel:
Taylor Wessing LLP
Carmelite 50 Victoria Embankment
London, United Kingdom

CAFOM SA

(d/b/a Groupe Cafom)
3 avenue Hoche
75008 Paris, France
Tel.: (33) 1 41 60 19 24
Fax: (33) 1 48 91 19 13
E-Mail: contact@cafom.com
Web Site: www.cafom.com
CAFO—(EUR)
Sales Range: $300-349.9 Million
Emp.: 640

Business Description:
Household Goods Retailer
S.I.C.: 5399
N.A.I.C.S.: 452990

Personnel:
Herve Giaoui *(Chm & CEO)*

Subsidiary:

Habitat International **(1)**
La Maison Blanche Rte De Quarante Sous
F 78630 Orgeval, France
Tel.: (33) 139224444
Fax: (33) 139754389
Web Site: www.habitat.net
Emp.: 80
Furniture Retail
S.I.C.: 5712
N.A.I.C.S.: 442110

Subsidiary:

Habitat France SA **(2)**
33 avenue de Wagram
75017 Paris, France (100%)
Tel.: (33) 155374450
Fax: (33) 155374483
E-Mail: service.presse@habitat.fr
Web Site: www.habitat.fr
Emp.: 15
Retail Furnishings & Fittings
S.I.C.: 5719
N.A.I.C.S.: 442299
Andrea Segura *(Pres)*

CAG HOLDING GMBH

Keisslergasse 26
Vienna, 0012, Austria
Tel.: (43) 1415650
Fax: (43) 141565284
E-Mail: office@stoelzle.com
Web Site: www.stoelzle.com
Emp.: 500

Business Description:
Investment Holding Company
S.I.C.: 6719
N.A.I.C.S.: 551112

Personnel:
Johannes Scheck *(Mng Dir)*

Non-U.S. Holdings:

Glanzstoff Bohemia s.r.o. **(1)**
Terezinska 60
Lovosice, 41002, Czech Republic
Tel.: (420) 416 575 120
Fax: (420) 416 575 107
E-Mail: info@glanzstoff.cz
Web Site: www.glanzstoff.com
Emp.: 50
Textile Viscose Filament Yarns Mfr
S.I.C.: 2399
N.A.I.C.S.: 313110
Georg Feith *(Member-Exec Bd)*
Milan Grmela *(Member-Exec Bd)*
Roman Konig *(Member-Exec Bd)*

Sicrem S.p.A. **(1)**
Via GB Pirelli 56
I-26026 Pizzighettone, Lombardy, Italy IT
Tel.: (39) 0372738011
Fax: (39) 0372743938
E-Mail: info.sicrem@glanzstoff.com
Web Site: www.glanzstoff.com
Emp.: 134
Tire Reinforcement Fabrics Mfr
S.I.C.: 2298
N.A.I.C.S.: 314994
Ferdinando Prestini *(Mgr)*

Textilcord Steinfort S.A. **(1)**
Rue Schwarzenhof
BP 11
L-8401 Steinfort, Luxembourg LU
Tel.: (352) 3998811
Fax: (352) 399881213
E-Mail: direction@textilcord.lu
Web Site: www.glanzstoff.com
Sales Range: $125-149.9 Million
Emp.: 110
Tire Reinforcement Fabrics Mfr
S.I.C.: 2298
N.A.I.C.S.: 314994
Jose Beaudoint *(Gen Mgr)*

CAHYA MATA SARAWAK BERHAD

Wisma Mahmud Jalan Sungai Sarawak
93100 Kuching, Sarawak, Malaysia
Tel.: (60) 82 238 888
Fax: (60) 82 338 611
E-Mail: www@hq.cmsb.com.my
Web Site: www.cmsb.com.my
Year Founded: 1974
CMSB—(KLS)
Rev.: $394,673,035
Assets: $701,827,501
Liabilities: $148,651,711
Net Worth: $553,175,790
Earnings: $54,640,326
Emp.: 2,018
Fiscal Year-end: 12/31/12

Business Description:
Investment Services
S.I.C.: 6211
N.A.I.C.S.: 523999

Personnel:
Richard Alexander John Curtis *(Mng Dir)*
Hizam Alsagoff *(CFO)*
David Koah Wi Ling *(Gen Counsel)*
Denise Swee Pheng Koo *(Sec)*

Board of Directors:
Anwar Jamalullail
Ahmed Alwee Alsree
Mahmud Abu Bekir Taib
Richard Alexander John Curtis
Kevin How Kow
Hubert Chong Hui Thian
Michael Kuok Ngie Ting
Ali Tuanku Yubi
Mohd Zahidi Zainuddin

Subsidiaries:

CMS Capital Sdn. Bhd. **(1)**
Level 6 Wisma Mahmud Jalan Sg
93100 Kuching, Sarawak, Malaysia
Tel.: (60) 82238888
Fax: (60) 82333828
Management Services
S.I.C.: 8741
N.A.I.C.S.: 551114
Richard Curtis *(CEO)*

CMS Clinker Sdn. Bhd. **(1)**
Lot 571 Jalan Mambong Off Jalan Puncak Borneo
93250 Kuching, Sarawak, Malaysia
Tel.: (60) 82610229
Fax: (60) 82610227
E-Mail: clinker@clinker.cmsb.com.my
Web Site: www.cmsb.com.my
Emp.: 200
Clinker Mfr
S.I.C.: 3241
N.A.I.C.S.: 327310
Lim Kimbeng *(Gen Mgr)*

CMS Concrete Products Sdn. Bhd. **(1)**
Lot 212 Block 17 KCLD Jalan Old Airport
93250 Kuching, Sarawak, Malaysia
Tel.: (60) 82618718
Fax: (60) 82614406
Web Site: www.cmsb.com.my/concrete
Emp.: 45
Ready Mix Concrete Mfr
S.I.C.: 3273
N.A.I.C.S.: 327320
Sie Ang Lau *(Mgr)*

CMS Infra Trading Sdn. Bhd. **(1)**
No 2128 Sublot 2 Jalan Utama Pending
93450 Kuching, Sarawak, Malaysia
Tel.: (60) 82348949
Fax: (60) 82348952
Emp.: 16
Water Management Products Distr
S.I.C.: 5074
N.A.I.C.S.: 423720
Talib Zulpilip *(Chm)*

CMS Penkuari Sdn. Bhd. **(1)**
9th Mile Kuching-Serian Road
93250 Kuching, Sarawak, Malaysia
Tel.: (60) 82614913
Fax: (60) 82614923
Web Site: www.cmsb.my/contacts/co nstr_mat_SBU.htm
Emp.: 28
Crushed Stone Aggregates Whslr
S.I.C.: 5032
N.A.I.C.S.: 423320
Gohchii Bing *(Mng Dir)*

CMS Premix Sdn. Bhd. **(1)**
Lot 353 Block 17 7th Mile Penrissen Road
93250 Kuching, Sarawak, Malaysia
Tel.: (60) 82614208
Fax: (60) 82614626
Web Site: www.cmsb.com.my/premix/
Emp.: 20
Premix Concrete Mfr & Distr
S.I.C.: 3273
N.A.I.C.S.: 327320
Chan Fok Hong *(Gen Mgr)*

CMS Property Development Sdn. Bhd. **(1)**
Level 5 Wisma Mahmud Jalan Sungai Sarawak
93100 Kuching, Sarawak, Malaysia
Tel.: (60) 82237777
Fax: (60) 82252652
E-Mail: info@cmsproperty.com.my
Web Site: www.cmsproperty.com.my
Emp.: 28
Commercial & Residential Property Development Services
S.I.C.: 6531
N.A.I.C.S.: 531210
Joseph Lee *(Mgr-Dev)*

CMS Quarries Sdn. Bhd. **(1)**
7th Mile Kuching-Serian Rd
93250 Kuching, Sarawak, Malaysia
Tel.: (60) 82615605
Fax: (60) 82615598
Web Site: www.cmsb.com.my/quarries/co ntactus.htm
Emp.: 150
Crushed Stone Aggregates Mfr
S.I.C.: 3532
N.A.I.C.S.: 333131
Goh Chii Bing *(Gen Mgr)*

PPES Works (Sarawak) Sdn. Bhd. **(1)**
1st-4th Floor Lot 621-623 Section 62 Jalan Padungan
93100 Kuching, Sarawak, Malaysia
Tel.: (60) 82340588
Fax: (60) 82340695
E-Mail: works@cmsb.com.my
Web Site: www.cmsb.com.my/works
Emp.: 100
Public Utility Construction & Engineering Services
S.I.C.: 1623
N.A.I.C.S.: 237990
Mazlin Darus *(Gen Mgr)*

Projek Bandar Samariang Sdn. Bhd. **(1)**
No 5574 Jln Sultan Tengah Bandar Baru Semariang
93050 Kuching, Sarawak, Malaysia
Tel.: (60) 82311887
Fax: (60) 82313887
E-Mail: sales@cmsp.cmsb.com.my
Web Site: www.cmsproperty.com.my
Emp.: 24
Commercial Property Development Services
S.I.C.: 6531
N.A.I.C.S.: 531210
Ashley Ang *(Asst Mgr-Mktg)*

CAI LAY VETERINARY PHARMACEUTICAL JOINT STOCK COMPANY

560 National Road 1A
Cai Lay, Tien Giang, Vietnam
Tel.: (84) 73 826 385
Fax: (84) 7 3382 6363
Web Site: www.cailayvet.com.vn
Year Founded: 1990
MKV—(HNX)

Business Description:
Pharmaceutical Products Mfr
S.I.C.: 2834
N.A.I.C.S.: 325412

Personnel:
Tran Van Se *(Chm & Gen Mgr)*

Board of Directors:
Tran Van Se
Hoang Son Tran

CAI PRIVATE EQUITY

Royal Bank Plaza South Tower
200 Bay Street Suite 2320, Toronto, ON, M5J 2J1, Canada
Tel.: (416) 306-9810
Fax: (416) 306-9816
E-Mail: pgottsegen@caifunds.com
Web Site: www.caifunds.com
Year Founded: 1989
Emp.: 20

Business Description:
Private Equity Firm
S.I.C.: 6211
N.A.I.C.S.: 523999

Personnel:
Allan D. L. Weinstein *(Mng Partner-New York)*
Mark Piotrowski *(Mng Dir)*

Branches:

CAI Capital Management Inc. (1)
3429 Rue Drummond Ste 200
Montreal, QC, H3G 1X6, Canada
Tel.: (514) 849-1642
Fax: (514) 849-1788
Emp.: 12
Private Equity Firm
S.I.C.: 6211
N.A.I.C.S.: 523999
David M. Culver *(Founder & Partner)*

CAI Capital Management Inc. (1)
Ste 2833 Bentall Three
595 Burrard St, Vancouver, BC, V7X 1KB, Canada
Tel.: (604) 637-3411
Fax: (604) 694-2524
Emp.: 7
Private Equity Firm
S.I.C.: 6211
N.A.I.C.S.: 523999
Tracey L. McVicar *(Mng Dir)*

Holdings:

Corix Group (1)
1188 W Georgia St Ste 1160
Vancouver, BC, V6E 4A2, Canada
Tel.: (604) 273-4987
Fax: (604) 697-6703
E-Mail: brett.hodson@corix.com
Web Site: www.corix.com
Emp.: 1,400
Utility Infrastructure System Design, Construction & Management Services; Owned by CAI Capital Management Inc. & British Columbia Investment Management Corporation
S.I.C.: 1623
N.A.I.C.S.: 237110
Brett Hodson *(CEO)*

Plastube Inc. (1)
590 Rue Simonds South
Granby, QC, J2J 1E1, Canada QC
Tel.: (450) 378-2633
Fax: (450) 378-1378
E-Mail: pauline.gelipeau@plastube.com
Web Site: www.plastube.com
Emp.: 200
Mfr. of Plastic Packaging Products
S.I.C.: 3089
N.A.I.C.S.: 326199
Paul Goodman *(Pres & CEO)*

CAIAC FUND MANAGEMENT AG

Haus Atzig Industriestrasse 2
PO Box 27
Bendern, 9487 Gamprin, Liechtenstein
Tel.: (423) 375 83 33
Fax: (423) 375 83 38
E-Mail: info@caiac.li
Web Site: www.caiac.li
Business Description:
Fund Management Services
S.I.C.: 6282
N.A.I.C.S.: 523930
Personnel:
Thomas Jahn *(CEO & Chm-Exec Bd)*
Michael Wiederin *(COO)*
Susanna Jahn *(Chief Admin Officer)*
Hans Messmer *(Chief Investment Officer)*
Raimond Schuster *(Member-Exec Bd)*
Board of Directors:
Roland Mueller
Gerhard Lehner
Dietmar Loretz

CAIANO AS

Strandgaten 92
5528 Haugesund, Norway
Tel.: (47) 52709070
Fax: (47) 52709077
E-Mail: post@caiano.no
Web Site: www.caiano.no
Emp.: 19
Business Description:
Investment Holding Company
S.I.C.: 6719
N.A.I.C.S.: 551112
Personnel:
Kristian Eidesvik *(Chm)*

Holdings:

Reach Subsea ASA (1)
(Formerly Green Reefers ASA)
Killingoy Offshore Base Hall B
Skillebekkgata 1B, 5523 Haugesund, Norway (54.56%)
Mailing Address:
Postboks 1393
5507 Haugesund, Norway
Tel.: (47) 4000 7710
E-Mail: post@reachsubsea.no
Web Site: reachsubsea.com
REACH—(OSL)
Rev.: $644,324
Assets: $9,170,944
Liabilities: $1,166,843
Net Worth: $8,004,102
Earnings: ($994,902)
Fiscal Year-end: 12/31/12
Logistics Management Services
S.I.C.: 4731
N.A.I.C.S.: 541614
Rune Lande *(Chm)*
Kare Johannes Lie *(Mng Dir)*
Birgitte Wendelbo Johansen *(CFO)*
Morten Roth Stranden *(COO)*

Wilson ASA (1)
Bradbenken 1
5835 Bergen, Norway (90.1%)
Mailing Address:
Postboks 4145
Sandvika, Norway
Tel.: (47) 55308200
Fax: (47) 55310590
Web Site: www.wilsonship.no
WILS—(OSL)
Sales Range: $300-349.9 Million
Emp.: 1,600
Water Transportation Management Services
S.I.C.: 4449
N.A.I.C.S.: 483211
Kristian Eidesvik *(Chm)*
Oyvind Gjerde *(CEO)*
Petter Berge *(CFO)*

Subsidiaries:

Euro Container Lines AS (2)
Bradbenken 1
5835 Bergen, Norway
Mailing Address:
Postboks 4145
Sandvika, Norway
Tel.: (47) 5530 8350
E-Mail: ecl@wilsonship.no
Web Site: www.ecl.no
Marine Transportation Services
S.I.C.: 4491
N.A.I.C.S.: 488320

Wilson Agency Norge AS (2)
Hammaren 23
4056 Tananger, Norway
Tel.: (47) 9414 8560
E-Mail: agency.rogaland@wilsonship.no
Marine Transportation Services
S.I.C.: 4491
N.A.I.C.S.: 488320

Wilson EuroCarriers AS (2)
Bradbenken 1
5835 Bergen, Norway
Mailing Address:
Postboks 4145
Sandvika, Norway
Tel.: (47) 5530 8200
E-Mail: wec.chart@wilsonship.no
Marine Transportation Services
S.I.C.: 4491
N.A.I.C.S.: 488320

Wilson Management AS (2)
Bradbenken 1
5835 Bergen, Norway
Mailing Address:
Postboks 4145
Sandvika, Norway
Tel.: (47) 5530 8200
Marine Transportation Services
S.I.C.: 4491
N.A.I.C.S.: 488320

Wilson Ship Management AS (2)
Bradbenken 1
5835 Bergen, Norway
Mailing Address:
Postboks 4145
Sandvika, Norway
Tel.: (47) 5530 8200
E-Mail: shipmanagement@wilsonship.no
Marine Transportation Services
S.I.C.: 4491
N.A.I.C.S.: 488320

Non-U.S. Subsidiaries:

Nesskip hf. (2)
IS-170 Seltjarnarnes
Reykjavik, Iceland
Tel.: (354) 563 9900
Fax: (354) 563 9919
E-Mail: nesskip@nesskip.is
Web Site: www.nesskip.is
Marine Transportation Services
S.I.C.: 4491
N.A.I.C.S.: 488320

NSA Schifffahrt und Transport GmbH (2)
Michaelisstr 24
D-20459 Hamburg, Germany
Tel.: (49) 40 703 83580
Fax: (49) 40 364915
E-Mail: agency@nsa.hamburg.de
Web Site: www.nsa-fracht.de
Marine Transportation Services
S.I.C.: 4491
N.A.I.C.S.: 488320

Wilson Agency B.V. (2)
Directiekade 15
3089 JA Rotterdam, Netherlands
Tel.: (31) 10 2952 888
Fax: (31) 10 4722 401
E-Mail: rotterdam@wilsonagency.nl
Web Site: www.wilsonagency.nl
Marine Transportation Services
S.I.C.: 4491
N.A.I.C.S.: 488320

Wilson Crewing Agency Ltd. (2)
29/1 K Marks Str
Arkhangelsk, 163000, Russia
Tel.: (7) 8182 650357
E-Mail: wca@wilsonship.no
Web Site: www.wilson-crewing.com
Marine Transportation Services
S.I.C.: 4491
N.A.I.C.S.: 488320

Wilson Crewing Agency Odessa Ltd. (2)
7 Mayakovskogo Lane
Odessa, 65000, Ukraine
Tel.: (380) 48 723 4175
E-Mail: wca.odessa@wilsonship.no
Web Site: www.wilson-crewing.com
Marine Transportation Services
S.I.C.: 4491
N.A.I.C.S.: 488320

Wilson Murmansk Ltd. (2)
Lenina 102 Office 24
Murmansk, 183012, Russia
Tel.: (7) 8152 458296
Fax: (7) 8152 451671
Marine Transportation Services
S.I.C.: 4491
N.A.I.C.S.: 488320

Wilson NRL Transport GmbH (2)
Dammstrasse 13
47119 Duisburg, Germany
Tel.: (49) 203 809 570
Fax: (49) 203 809 5730
E-Mail: dbg.chart@wilsonship.de
Web Site: www.wilsonship.de
Marine Transportation Services
S.I.C.: 4491
N.A.I.C.S.: 488320

CAINVEST INTERNATIONAL BANK LTD.

Harbour Place 5th Floor 103 South Church Street
PO Box 1353 GT
Georgetown, KY1-1108, Cayman Islands
Tel.: (345) 747 5555
Fax: (345) 747 5554
E-Mail: bank@cainvest.com
Web Site: www.cainvest.com
Year Founded: 1994
CIB—(CAY)
Business Description:
Banking Services
S.I.C.: 6029
N.A.I.C.S.: 522110
Personnel:
Mauricio Charles Cohab *(Chm)*
Garry John Wilkins *(Mng Dir)*
Charles Aboulafia *(CFO)*
Starr Alexander Wood *(Deputy Mng Dir)*
Board of Directors:
Mauricio Charles Cohab
Charles Aboulafia
Alvaro Dominguez
Garry John Wilkins
Starr Alexander Wood

CAIRN ENERGY PLC

50 Lothian Road
Edinburgh, EH3 9BY, United Kingdom
Tel.: (44) 1314753000
Fax: (44) 1314753030
Web Site: www.cairnenergy.com
CNE—(LSE OTC)
Sales Range: $1-4.9 Billion
Emp.: 1,259
Business Description:
Explorer & Producer of Oil & Gas
S.I.C.: 1311
N.A.I.C.S.: 211111
Personnel:
William B. B. Gammell *(Chm)*
Simon John Thomson *(CEO)*
Michael John Watts *(Deputy CEO)*
Board of Directors:
William B. B. Gammell
Alexander Berger
James W. Buckee
Todd Hunt
Mary Jacqueline Sheppard
Simon John Thomson
Ian P. Tyler
Michael John Watts
Legal Counsel:
Shepherd & Wedderburn LLP
1 Exchange Crescent Conference Sq
Edinburgh, United Kingdom

Subsidiaries:

Cairn Energy Hydrocarbons Limited (1)
50 Lothian Rd
Edinburgh, Scotland, EH3 9BY, United Kingdom
Tel.: (44) 1314753000
E-Mail: pr@carinenergy.com
Web Site: www.carinenergy.com
Oil & Gas Exploration Services
S.I.C.: 1311
N.A.I.C.S.: 211111

Cairn Energy Lumbini Limited (1)
50 Lothian Road
Edinburgh, EH3 9BY, United Kingdom
Tel.: (44) 1314753030
Fax: (44) 1314753030
Emp.: 180
Oil & Gas Exploration Services
S.I.C.: 1389
N.A.I.C.S.: 213112

Cairn UK Holdings Limited (1)
PO Box 258
Northwich, Cheshire, CW9 8TE, United Kingdom UK
Tel.: (44) 1606331101 (100%)
Fax: (44) 1606556217
Holding Company
S.I.C.: 6719
N.A.I.C.S.: 551112

Capricorn Energy Limited (1)
50 Lothian Road
Edinburgh, EH3 9BY, United Kingdom

Cairn Energy plc—(Continued)

Tel.: (44) 1314753000
Fax: (44) 1314753030
Holding Company; Oil & Gas Exploration Services
S.I.C.: 6719
N.A.I.C.S.: 551112

CAIRNS HOLDINGS LIMITED

Cairns Food Complex 1 Upton Rd
Ardbennie
PO Box 1813
Harare, Zimbabwe
Tel.: (263) 4620411
Fax: (263) 4620431
E-Mail: info@cairnsfoods.co.zw
Web Site: www.cairnsfoods.co.zw
CAIRNS—(ZIM)
Sales Range: $1-9.9 Million

Business Description:
Food Products, Beverages & Wine Mfr & Distr
S.I.C.: 2099
N.A.I.C.S.: 311991

Personnel:
C. M.B. Utete *(Chm)*
D. A. Ellman-Brown *(Deputy Chm)*
P. Chigumira *(Grp CEO)*

Board of Directors:
C. M.B. Utete
P. Chigumira
D. A. Ellman-Brown
P. Fitzpatrick
K. M. Gaynor
S. Gweshe
M. Kereke
H. H. Patel
Z. L. Rusike
T. C. Sithole

CAIRO & ALEXANDRIA STOCK EXCHANGES

4A El Sherifien St
11513 Cairo, Egypt
Tel.: (20) 223928698
Fax: (20) 2 23924214
E-Mail: webmaster@egyptse.com
Web Site: www.egyptse.com

Business Description:
Stock Exchange Services
S.I.C.: 6231
N.A.I.C.S.: 523210

Personnel:
Mohamed Abdel Salam *(Chm)*

Board of Directors:
Mohamed Abdel Salam
Hassan Abdallah
Ossama Amer
Mohamed Dakroury
Hussein Lotfy El Sherbiny
Khaled El Taweel
Alaa El Din Hassouna
Tarek Kandil
Ahmed Saad Abdel Latif
Mahmoud Abdel Latif
Mohammad Maher
Hamdy Mahran
Mohamed Ozalp
Sameh Abou Zaid

Subsidiary:

Egypt for Information Dissemination **(1)**
Block 72 off 90 Axis El Tagmoaa El Khames
New Cairo, Helwan, Egypt (100%)
Tel.: (20) 226145000
E-Mail: info@egidegypt.com
Web Site: www.egidegypt.com
Stock Exchange Services
S.I.C.: 6211
N.A.I.C.S.: 523999
Maher Asham *(CEO)*

Affiliate:

Misr for Central Clearing, Depository & Registry SAE **(1)**
70 El Gamhouria Street
Cairo, Egypt (35%)
Tel.: (20) 25971581
Fax: (20) 25971523
E-Mail: customer.support@mcsd.com.eg
Web Site: www.mcsd.com.eg
Stock Exchange Services
S.I.C.: 6211
N.A.I.C.S.: 523999
Mohamed Soliman Abdel Salam *(Chm)*

CAIRO COMMUNICATION S.P.A.

Via Tucidide 56
21034 Milan, Italy
Tel.: (39) 02748131
Fax: (39) 02 70100102
E-Mail: info@cairocommunication.it
Web Site: www.cairocommunication.it
CAI—(ITA)
Rev.: $421,956,987
Emp.: 720
Fiscal Year-end: 12/31/12

Business Description:
Book & Magazine Publisher; Internet Site Operator; Advertising Space & Time Sales
Export
S.I.C.: 2731
N.A.I.C.S.: 511130

Personnel:
Urbano Cairo *(Chm)*
Uberto Fornara *(CEO)*
Marco Pompignoli *(CFO)*

Board of Directors:
Urbano Cairo
Roberto Cairo
Uberto Fornara
Marco Janni
Antonio Magnocavallo
Marco Pompignoli
Roberto Rezzonico
Mauro Sala

Subsidiaries:

Cairo Editore S.p.A. **(1)**
Corso Magenta 55
20123 Milan, Italy (100%)
Tel.: (39) 02460709
Fax: (39) 02460702
Web Site: www.cairoeditore.it/component/option,com_jbook/Itemid,124/catid,99/id,243/task,view/
Emp.: 75
All Other Publishers
S.I.C.: 2741
N.A.I.C.S.: 511199
Urbano Cairo *(Pres)*

Cairo Pubblicita S.p.A **(1)**
Via Tucidide 56
Milan, Italy (100%)
Tel.: (39) 027481111
Web Site: www.cairocommunication.it/Contatti/Mario-Cargnelutti.html
Emp.: 50
Television Broadcasting
S.I.C.: 4833
N.A.I.C.S.: 515120
Urbano Cairo *(Pres)*

Cairo Publishing Srl **(1)**
Corso Magenta 55
20123 Milan, Italy (100%)
Tel.: (39) 02433131
Fax: (39) 0243313550
E-Mail: info@cairoeditore.it
Emp.: 100
All Other Publishers
S.I.C.: 2741
N.A.I.C.S.: 511199
Urbano Cairo *(Pres)*

Cairo Sport Srl **(1)**
Via Tucidide 56
Milan, Italy (100%)
Tel.: (39) 027481111
Web Site: www.cairocommunication.it/Contatti/Mario-Cargnelutti.html
Emp.: 25
Advertising Agencies
S.I.C.: 7311
N.A.I.C.S.: 541810
Urbano Cairo *(Pres)*

Editoriale Giorgio Mondadori Spa **(1)**
Corso Magenta 55
20123 Milan, Italy (100%)
Tel.: (39) 02460709
Fax: (39) 02460702
Web Site: www.cairoeditore.it/component/option,com_jbook/Itemid,124/catid,99/id,243/task,view/
Emp.: 75
All Other Publishers
S.I.C.: 2741
N.A.I.C.S.: 511199
Urbano Cairo *(Pres)*

IL Trovatore Srl **(1)**
Via Tucidide 56
Milan, Italy (100%)
Tel.: (39) 027481111
Emp.: 30
Software Publishers
S.I.C.: 7372
N.A.I.C.S.: 511210
Urbano Cairo *(Pres)*

CAIRO RESOURCES INC.

Suite 1400 570 Granville Street
Vancouver, BC, V6C 3P1, Canada
Tel.: (604) 646-1553
E-Mail: msadhra@sadhrachow.com
Year Founded: 2010
QAI.P—(TSXV)

Business Description:
Investment Services
S.I.C.: 6211
N.A.I.C.S.: 523999

Personnel:
Kal Malhi *(Pres & CEO)*
Michael Sadhra *(CFO & Sec)*

Board of Directors:
Kal Malhi
Rauni Malhi
Michael Sadhra

Transfer Agent:
Computershare Investor Services Inc.
3rd Floor 510 Burrard St
V6C 3B9 Vancouver, BC, Canada

CAISSE DE DEPOT ET PLACEMENT DU QUEBEC

1000 Pl Jean-Paul-Riopelle
Montreal, QC, H2Z 2B3, Canada
Tel.: (514) 842-3261
Telex: 55-61874
Fax: (514) 842-4833
Toll Free: (866) 330-3936
E-Mail: info@lacaisse.com
Web Site: www.lacaisse.com
Year Founded: 1965
Sales Range: $1-4.9 Billion
Emp.: 700

Business Description:
Public Investment Portfolio Management
S.I.C.: 6799
N.A.I.C.S.: 523920

Personnel:
Robert Tessier *(Chm)*
Michael Sabia *(Pres & CEO)*
Maarika Paul *(CFO & Sr VP)*
Normand Provost *(COO & Exec VP-Private Equity)*
Roland Lescure *(Chief Investment Officer & Exec VP)*
Claude Bergeron *(Chief Risk Officer & Exec VP)*
Daniel Fournier *(Pres-Real Estate Grp & Exec VP-Real Estate)*
Marie Giguere *(Sec & Exec VP-Legal Affairs)*
Jean-Luc Gravel *(Exec VP-Equity Markets Investment Mgmt)*
Rashad Kaldany *(Exec VP-Emerging Markets)*
Pierre Miron *(Exec VP-Ops & IT)*

Board of Directors:
Robert Tessier
Louise Charette
Michele Desjardins
Rita Dionne-Marsolais
Denys Jean
A. Michel Lavigne
Jean Pierre Ouellet
Real Raymond
Francois R. Roy
Michael Sabia
Ouma Sananikone

Subsidiaries:

Capital CDPQ **(1)**
1000 Pl Jean Paul Riopelle
Montreal, QC, H2Z 2B3, Canada
Tel.: (514) 842-3261
E-Mail: mdias@lacaisse.com
Web Site: www.lacaisse.com
Emp.: 600
S.I.C.: 6411
N.A.I.C.S.: 524298
Michael Sabia *(Pres & CEO)*

Capital International CDPQ **(1)**
1001 Sq Victoria
Montreal, QC, H2Z 2A8, Canada (100%)
Tel.: (514) 842-3261
Fax: (514) 842-4833
E-Mail: info@lacaisse.com
Web Site: www.lacaisse.com
Emp.: 1,500
Investments & International Networking
S.I.C.: 6211
N.A.I.C.S.: 523110
Michael Sabia *(Pres)*

CDP Capital Financing Inc. **(1)**
1000 Place Jean Paul Riopelle
Montreal, QC, H2Z 2B3, Canada
Tel.: (514) 842-3261
Fax: (514) 842-4833
Web Site: www.lacaisse.com
Emp.: 800
Holding Company
S.I.C.: 6719
N.A.I.C.S.: 551112
Michael Sabia *(CEO)*

CDP Capital Real Estate Advisory **(1)**
1000 Pl Jean Paul Riopelle Ste A 300
Montreal, QC, H2Z 2B6, Canada (100%)
Tel.: (514) 875-3360
Fax: (514) 875-3327
E-Mail: sitq@cdpcapital.com
Web Site: www.cdpcapital.com
Emp.: 800
Management of a Portfolio Targeting Residential Properties & Non-Traditional Real Estate Investmentst
S.I.C.: 6531
N.A.I.C.S.: 531210
Andre Landry *(Mgr)*

CDP Capital Technologies **(1)**
1000 Pl Jean Paul Riopelle
Montreal, QC, H2Z 2B3, Canada
Tel.: (514) 847-2000
Fax: (514) 847-2628
Web Site: www.cdpcapital.com
Emp.: 500
Investor of Telecommunications, Media, Cultural Industries & Technologies
S.I.C.: 4813
N.A.I.C.S.: 517110

CDP Technologies **(1)**
1000 Gean Paul Riopelle
Montreal, QC, H2Z2B3, Canada
Tel.: (514) 847-2613
Fax: (514) 842-4833
E-Mail: info@lacaisse.com
Web Site: www.sofinov.lacaisse.com
Emp.: 800
S.I.C.: 6411
N.A.I.C.S.: 524298

CDPQ Mortgage Corporation **(1)**
65 Steamme St 13th Fl
Quebec, QC, G1R 3X5, Canada (100%)
Tel.: (418) 656-6572
Fax: (418) 656-6577
E-Mail: luc.blier@mcap.com
Web Site: www.mcap.com
Emp.: 2

Mortgage Loans & Securities
S.I.C.: 6163
N.A.I.C.S.: 522310

Centre CDP Capital (1)
1000 Pl Jean Paul Riopelle
Montreal, QC, H2Z 2B3, Canada
Tel.: (514) 842-3261
Fax: (514) 842-4833
Toll Free: (866) 330-3936
E-Mail: info@lacaisse.com
Web Site: www.lacaisse.com
Emp.: 50
Insurance Services
S.I.C.: 6411
N.A.I.C.S.: 524298
Michael Savia *(Pres & CEO)*
Ginette Depelteau *(Sr VP)*

Ivanhoe Cambridge, Inc. (1)
1001 Victoria Sq Ste C 500
Montreal, QC, H2Z 2B5, Canada (100%)
Tel.: (514) 841-7600
Fax: (514) 841-7762
E-Mail: hlbrault@ivanhoecambridge.com
Web Site: www.ivanhoecambridge.com
Emp.: 400
Operator & Manager of Shopping Centers
S.I.C.: 6512
N.A.I.C.S.: 531120
Daniel Fournier *(Chm & CEO)*
Kim D. McInnes *(Pres)*
Paul S. Chehab *(Chief Investment Officer & Sr VP)*
Claude Gendron *(Gen Counsel & Exec VP-Legal Affairs)*
Lorna Telfer *(Sec & Exec VP-Legal Affairs)*
Rita-Rose Gagne *(Exec VP-Growth Markets)*
Mario D. Morroni *(Exec VP-Strategy & Capital Allocation)*
Brian Castle *(Sr VP-China)*
Jean Eastern *(Sr VP-Canada-Eastern)*

Subsidiaries:

Ivanhoe Cambridge, Inc. (2)
95 Wellington St W Ste 300
Toronto, ON, M5J2R2, Canada (100%)
Tel.: (416) 369-1200
Fax: (416) 369-1327
Web Site: www.ivanhoecambridge.com
Emp.: 170
Shopping Center Space Leasing
S.I.C.: 6513
N.A.I.C.S.: 531110
Kim D. Mcinnes *(Pres & CEO)*

Sentinel Self-Storage Corporation (2)
Ste 1970 Sun Light Pl 10123 99th St
Edmonton, AB, T5J 3H1, Canada (100%)
Tel.: (780) 424-8945
Fax: (780) 426-3924
E-Mail: kbodoanl@sentinel.ca
Web Site: www.sentinel.ca
Emp.: 8
Self-Service, Mini-Warehousing Business
S.I.C.: 4225
N.A.I.C.S.: 493110
Karen Bodoanl *(Gen Mgr)*

U.S. Subsidiary:

The Shops at Mary Brickell Village (2)
901 S Miami Ave Ste 206
Miami, FL 33130
Tel.: (305) 381-6130
Fax: (305) 381-6128
Web Site: www.marybrickellvillage.com
Shopping Center
S.I.C.: 5999
N.A.I.C.S.: 453998
Fernando Perez *(Gen Mgr)*

U.S. Affiliate:

Donahue Schriber Realty Group, Inc. (2)
200 E Baker St Ste 100
Costa Mesa, CA 92626 (50%)
Tel.: (714) 545-1400
Fax: (714) 545-4222
E-Mail: info@donahueschriber.com
Web Site: www.donahueschriber.com
Emp.: 110
Real Estate Investment Trust
S.I.C.: 6512
N.A.I.C.S.: 531120
Patrick S. Donahue *(Chm & CEO)*
Lawrence P. Casey *(Pres & COO)*
David W. Mossman *(Chief Investment Officer & Exec VP)*
Mark L. Whitfield *(Exec VP)*

SITQ (1)
1001 Sq Victoria Ste C 500
Montreal, QC, H2Z 2B5, Canada (100%)
Tel.: (514) 287-1852
Fax: (514) 841-7762
Toll Free: (800) 599-IMMO
Web Site: www.ivanhoecambridge.com
Emp.: 400
Industrial & Office Building & Shopping Center Owner & Manager
S.I.C.: 6512
N.A.I.C.S.: 531120
William R. C. Tresham *(Pres & CEO)*
Michel Cyr *(Sr VP-Dev)*
Pierre Lefebvre *(Sr VP-HR & Pub Affairs)*
Yvon Tessier *(Sr VP-Investments)*

Subsidiary:

Bentall Capital LP (2)
Four Bentall Centre
1055 Dunsmuir Street
Ste 1800, Vancouver, BC, V7X 1B1, Canada BC
Tel.: (604) 661-5000 (100%)
Fax: (604) 661-5055
Web Site: www.bentallkennedy.com
Emp.: 1,000
Real Estate Services
S.I.C.: 6531
N.A.I.C.S.: 531210
Gary Whitelaw *(Pres & CEO-Bentall Kennedy Group)*
Remco Daal *(Pres & COO)*
Andy Clydesdale *(Pres & COO-Retail Svcs)*
Lawrence Neilson *(CFO)*
Paul Zemla *(Chief Investment Officer)*
David Barry *(Exec VP & Mgr-Portfolio)*

Subsidiaries:

Bentall LP (3)
55 University Ave Ste 300
Toronto, ON, M5J 2H7, Canada (100%)
Tel.: (416) 681-3400
Fax: (416) 681-3405
Web Site: www.bentallkennedy.com
Emp.: 150
Real Estate Investment Manager
S.I.C.: 6531
N.A.I.C.S.: 531210
Gary Whitelaw *(Pres & CEO)*
Malcolm Leitch *(COO)*
Paul Zemla *(Chief Investment Officer)*
David Barry *(Exec VP & Portfolio Mgr)*

Bentall Real Estate LLP (3)
2630 Skymark St
PO Box 103
Mississauga, ON, L4W SL6, Canada (100%)
Tel.: (905) 624-3330
Fax: (905) 624-2141
Web Site: www.bentall.com
Emp.: 4
S.I.C.: 6411
N.A.I.C.S.: 524298

Bentall Real Estate Services LP (3)
55 University Ave Ste 300
Toronto, ON, M5J 2H7, Canada (100%)
Tel.: (416) 681-6250
Fax: (416) 681-3405
Web Site: www.bentall.com
Emp.: 150
Office & Industrial Real Estate Manager & Lessor
S.I.C.: 6531
N.A.I.C.S.: 531210
Stuart Wanlin *(VP)*

Bentall Retail Services LP (3)
55 University Ave Ste 300
Toronto, ON, M5J 2H7, Canada (100%)
Tel.: (416) 681-3400
Fax: (416) 681-3405
Web Site: www.bentallkennedy.com
Emp.: 150
Retail Real Estate Investor, Acquirer, Repositioner, Lessor & Manager
S.I.C.: 6531
N.A.I.C.S.: 531210
Martin Kaefer *(Sr VP-Leasing)*

U.S. Subsidiaries:

Bentall Capital US Inc. (3)
1215 1 St Ave Ste 2410
Seattle, WA 98161
Tel.: (206) 315-3818
Fax: (206) 315-3819
Web Site: www.bentall.com
Emp.: 60
Real Estate Services
S.I.C.: 6531
N.A.I.C.S.: 531210
Gary Carpenter *(COO & Exec VP)*

Bentall Residential LLC (3)
8105 Irvine Centre Dr Ste 830
Irvine, CA 92618
Tel.: (949) 753-0555
Fax: (949) 753-7590
Web Site: www.bentall.com
Emp.: 3
Real Estate Services
S.I.C.: 6519
N.A.I.C.S.: 531190

The Praedium Group LLC (3)
825 3rd Ave 36th Fl
New York, NY 10022
Tel.: (212) 224-5600
Fax: (212) 224-5611
Web Site: www.praediumgroup.com
Emp.: 25
Real Estate Services
S.I.C.: 6531
N.A.I.C.S.: 531390
Russell Appel *(Pres)*
A. Floyd Lattin *(Chief Investment Officer)*
Christopher Hughes *(Principal)*
Laura Schaffer *(Gen Counsel & Dir-Legal)*
Ronald Strobl *(Treas & Dir-Fin)*

Sodemex (1)
65 Sainte Anne St
Quebec, QC, G1R 3X5, Canada (100%)
Tel.: (418) 684-8168
Fax: (418) 684-8166
Emp.: 2
Private Investments in Junior Exploration Companies
S.I.C.: 6211
N.A.I.C.S.: 523110
Denis Landry *(Pres)*

T2C2 (1)
1550 Rue Metcalfe
Bureau 502, Montreal, QC, H3A 1X6, Canada (100%)
Tel.: (514) 842-9849
Fax: (514) 842-1505
Web Site: www.t2c2capital.com
Emp.: 6
Provider of Marketing Services for New Technologies
S.I.C.: 8742
N.A.I.C.S.: 541613
Bernard Coupal *(Pres)*

Holdings:

Trencap L.P. (1)
1000 place Jean Paul Riopelle
Montreal, QC, H2Z 2B3, Canada (51.1%)
Tel.: (514) 847-2126
Holding Company
S.I.C.: 6719
N.A.I.C.S.: 551112

Holding:

Noverco Inc. (2)
1000 place Jean Paul Riopelle
Montreal, QC, H2Z 2B3, Canada (50.4%)
Tel.: (514) 847-2126
Holding Company; Gas Distribution
S.I.C.: 6719
N.A.I.C.S.: 551112

Holding:

Gaz Metro Inc. (3)
1717 Du Havre St
Montreal, QC, H2K 2X3, Canada (100%)
Tel.: (514) 598-3444
Fax: (514) 598-3144
E-Mail: info@gazmetro.com
Web Site: www.gazmetro.com
Emp.: 1,500
Holding Company
S.I.C.: 6719
N.A.I.C.S.: 551112
Louie Desa Lorimier *(Dir-Sls)*

Subsidiary:

Gaz Metro Limited Partnership (4)
1717 rue du Havre
Montreal, QC, H2K 2X3, Canada Ca
Tel.: (514) 598-3321 (71%)
Fax: (514) 598-3725
Toll Free: (800) 361-4005
E-Mail: info@gazmetro.com
Web Site: www.gazmetro.com
GZM—(TSX)
Sales Range: $1-4.9 Billion
Emp.: 1,400
Natural Gas Distr
Export
S.I.C.: 4924
N.A.I.C.S.: 221210
Sophie Brochu *(Pres & CEO)*
Pierre Despars *(CFO & Exec VP)*

Subsidiaries:

Climatisation et Chauffage Urbains de Montreal (CCUM) (5)
1350 Nobel
Boucherville, QC, J4B 5H3, Canada
Tel.: (514) 398-9773
Fax: (514) 398-9776
E-Mail: info@gazmetplus.com
Web Site: www.ccum.com
Emp.: 20
Superheated Steam Distr
S.I.C.: 4961
N.A.I.C.S.: 221330
Jean-Claude Claude Michel *(Pres)*

Gaz Metro Plus Inc. (5)
1350 Nobel
Boucherville, QC, J4B 5H3, Canada
Tel.: (450) 641-6300
Fax: (450) 641-6313
E-Mail: info@gazmetplus.com
Web Site: www.gazmetplus.com
Sales Range: $10-24.9 Million
Emp.: 200
Provider of Equipment Rental & Technical Services
S.I.C.: 7353
N.A.I.C.S.: 532412
Luc Genier *(Pres)*

TelDig Systems, Inc. (5)
575 Saint Joseph E
Quebec, QC, G1K 3B7, Canada
Tel.: (418) 948-1314
Fax: (418) 948-1322
Toll Free: (800) 501-5554
E-Mail: sales@teldig.com
Web Site: www.teldig.com
Emp.: 23
Damage Protection for Buried Infrastructure Systems
S.I.C.: 4924
N.A.I.C.S.: 221210
Jacque Therrien *(Pres)*

Affiliates:

Aqua-Rehab, Inc. (5)
2145 Rue Michelin
Laval, QC, H7L 5B8, Canada
Tel.: (450) 687-3472
Fax: (450) 687-4570
E-Mail: adm@aquarehab.com
Web Site: www.aquarehab.com
Sales Range: $1-9.9 Million
Emp.: 65
Trenchless Rehabilitation of Underground Infrastructures
S.I.C.: 8299
N.A.I.C.S.: 611710
George Dorval *(Pres)*

Natural Gas Technology Centre (5)
1350 Nobel St Ste 150
Boucherville, QC, J4B 5H3, Canada
Tel.: (450) 449-4774
Fax: (450) 449-4994
E-Mail: ctgn@ctgn.qc.ca
Web Site: www.ctgn.qc.ca
Sales Range: $1-9.9 Million
Emp.: 20
Research Center on Natural Gas Applications
S.I.C.: 4924
N.A.I.C.S.: 221210
Stephane Brunet *(Gen Mgr)*

Caisse de Depot et Placement du Quebec—(Continued)

Joint Venture:

Trans Quebec & Maritimes Pipeline Inc. (5)
6300 Auteuil Ave Ste 525
Brossard, QC, J4Z 3T2, Canada
Tel.: (450) 462-5300
Fax: (450) 462-5388
Toll Free: (888) 810-8800
E-Mail: ssbbaughamt@gazoductqm.com
Web Site: www.gazoductqm.com
Emp.: 4
Natural Gas Distr
S.I.C.: 4923
N.A.I.C.S.: 486210
Patrick Cabana *(CEO)*

U.S. Subsidiary:

Northern New England Energy Corporation (5)
PO Box 467
Burlington, VT 05402-0700
Tel.: (802) 658-6555
E-Mail: dgilbert@nneec.com
Web Site: www.nneec.com
Natural Gas Distr
S.I.C.: 4924
N.A.I.C.S.: 221210
Sophie Brochu *(Pres & CEO)*
A. Donald Gilbert *(Sr VP-Fin)*

Subsidiaries:

Green Mountain Power Corporation (6)
163 Acorn Ln
Colchester, VT 05446-6612 VT
Tel.: (802) 864-5731
Fax: (802) 655-8445
Toll Free: (888) 835-4672
E-Mail: callcenter@gmpvt.com
Web Site: www.greenmountainpower.biz
Sales Range: $200-249.9 Million
Emp.: 192
Electricity Supplier
S.I.C.: 4931
N.A.I.C.S.: 221122
Mary G. Powell *(Pres & CEO)*
Dawn D. Bugbee *(CFO & VP)*
Donald J. Rendall, Jr. *(Gen Counsel, Sec & VP)*

Subsidiaries:

Vermont Electric Power Company, Inc. (7)
366 Pinnacle Ridge Rd
Rutland, VT 05701 VT
Tel.: (802) 773-9161
Fax: (802) 770-6440
E-Mail: info@velco.com
Web Site: www.velco.com
Emp.: 100
Distr of Electric Energy & Operator of Power Transmission Infrastructure
S.I.C.: 4911
N.A.I.C.S.: 221121

Vermont Yankee Nuclear Power Corporation (7)
185 Old Ferry Rd
Brattleboro, VT 05301-9787
Tel.: (802) 257-5271
Fax: (802) 258-2128
Web Site: www.safecleanreliable.com
Emp.: 650
Electric Power Distribution Services
S.I.C.: 4911
N.A.I.C.S.: 221122
Mike Romeo *(Dir-Nuclear Safety Assurance)*

Vermont Gas Systems, Inc. (6)
85 Swift St
South Burlington, VT 05403-7306
Mailing Address:
PO Box 467
Burlington, VT 05402
Tel.: (802) 863-4511
Fax: (802) 863-8872
E-Mail: customerservice@vermontgas.com
Web Site: www.vermontgas.com
Sales Range: $50-74.9 Million
Emp.: 113
Natural Gas Distr
S.I.C.: 4924
N.A.I.C.S.: 221210
A. Donald Gilbert, Jr. *(Pres & CEO)*
Tim Keese *(CFO & VP-Fin)*
Nancy Rossi *(Sec)*

Non-U.S. Joint Venture:

SPIE SA (1)
Parc Saint-Christophe
10 avenue de l'Enterprise, 95863 Cergy, Cedex, France
Tel.: (33) 134226931
E-Mail: communication@spie.com
Web Site: www.spie.com
Sales Range: $1-4.9 Billion
Emp.: 29,000
Engineering Services
Import Export
S.I.C.: 8711
N.A.I.C.S.: 541330
Gauthier Louette *(Chm & CEO)*
Denis Chene *(CFO)*
Emmanuel Martin *(CEO-Sud-Est)*

Subsidiaries:

SPIE Communications SA (2)
10 avenue de l'Enterprise
Pole Vinci, 95800 Cergy-Pontoise, France
Tel.: (33) 141464146
Fax: (33) 141464147
E-Mail: infos@spie.fr
Web Site: www.spiecom.globalsysteme.com
Emp.: 2,200
Telecommunications Mfr
S.I.C.: 4812
N.A.I.C.S.: 517210
Gilles Brazey *(Mng Dir)*

SPIE Communications (2)
ZA Pre Catelan 1 rue Delesalle
F 59110 La Madeleine, France
Tel.: (33) 320125900
Fax: (33) 320125989
E-Mail: p.spriet@spie.com
Web Site: www.spie.com
Emp.: 2,000
Telephone Equipment Distr
S.I.C.: 5065
N.A.I.C.S.: 423690

CAISSE DES DEPOTS ET CONSIGNATIONS

(d/b/a Caisse des Depots Group)
56 rue de Lille
75356 Paris, France
Tel.: (33) 158500000
Fax: (33) 158500138
Web Site: www.caissedesdepots.fr
Year Founded: 1816
Int. Income: $7,492,782,220
Assets: $385,876,938,160
Liabilities: $333,834,005,960
Net Worth: $52,042,932,200
Earnings: ($1,544,056,990)
Emp.: 35,000
Fiscal Year-end: 12/31/12

Business Description:
Holding Company; Financial, Insurance, Real Estate, Service Industry & Private Equity Services
S.I.C.: 6719
N.A.I.C.S.: 551112

Personnel:
Nicolas Jachiet *(Chm & CEO-Egis)*
Jean-Marc Janaillac *(Chm & CEO-Transdev)*
Henri Emmanuelli *(Chm-Supervisory Bd)*
Jean-Pierre Jouyet *(CEO)*
Antoine Gosset-Grainville *(Deputy CEO & Deputy Gen Dir)*
Olivier Mareuse *(CFO & Dir-Fin)*
Jean Bensaid *(CEO-CDC Infrastructure)*
Pierre Ducret *(CEO-CDC Climat)*
Jean-Yves Andre Aime Gilet *(CEO-Fonds Stratrgique d'Investissement)*
Andre Laurent Michelson *(Sec)*

Supervisory Board of Directors:
Henri Emmanuelli
Jean Arthuis
Franck Borotra
Ramon Fernandez
Arlette Grosskost
Daniel Houri
Francois Lavondes
Martin Malvy
Francois Marc
Christian Noyer
Jean Picq

Mazars
Courbevoie, France

Subsidiaries:

CDC Enterprises Capital Investissement (1)
41 ave de Sievland
F-75007 Paris, France (100%)
Tel.: (33) 158509091
Fax: (33) 158508969
E-Mail: beagrixe.lafore@qualium.com
Web Site: www.qualium.com
Emp.: 32
Holding Company; Private Equity & Venture Investment Services
S.I.C.: 6719
N.A.I.C.S.: 551112
Jean Eichenlaub *(Pres)*

Subsidiaries:

CDC Capital Investissement (2)
148 rue de l'Universite
F-75007 Paris, France (100%)
Tel.: (33) 158509091
Fax: (33) 0158508969
E-Mail: info@cdcci.fr
Web Site: www.cdcci.fr
Managed Assets: $1,982,085,000
Emp.: 40
Private Equity Firm
S.I.C.: 6211
N.A.I.C.S.: 523999
Rene Maury *(Pres & CEO)*

Holding:

Genoyer S.A. (3)
9/11 Groupe Agvnoyer 911 Roag rue de Lisbonne Zone Industrielle
BP 600 61
13742 Vitrolles, France FR
Tel.: (33) 442794000
Fax: (33) 442794079
E-Mail: sales@genoyer.com.fr
Web Site: www.genoyer.com
Sales Range: $500-549.9 Million
Emp.: 1,200
Oil, Gas & Chemical Industry Steel Piping Products & Services
S.I.C.: 3494
N.A.I.C.S.: 332919

Subsidiaries:

RTI (4)
Zone Artisanale 22 route de Creton
Les Culs Menaux, 18110 Vasselay, France (100%)
Tel.: (33) 248697420
Fax: (33) 248697429
E-Mail: pbaudon@rtiindustrie.com
Web Site: www.genoyer.com
Steel Pipe Fittings Mfr
S.I.C.: 3498
N.A.I.C.S.: 332996

SBS (4)
Rue de la Gare
BP 6
F-42130 Boen, France (100%)
Tel.: (33) 477968000
Fax: (33) 477968050
E-Mail: aperonnet@genoyer.sr
Web Site: www.sbs-forge.com
Emp.: 90
Forged Steel Flanges Mfr
S.I.C.: 3494
N.A.I.C.S.: 332919
Bernard Giry *(Gen Dir)*

U.S. Subsidiaries:

Genoyer Group, Inc. (4)
16360 Park 10 Pl Ste 300
Houston, TX 77084 (100%)
Tel.: (281) 578-2718
Fax: (281) 578-2455
E-Mail: houston@genoyer.com
Web Site: www.genoyer.com
Emp.: 15
Industrial Pipe Products Distr
S.I.C.: 5084
N.A.I.C.S.: 423830
Penny Henson *(Office Mgr)*

Non-U.S. Subsidiaries:

Bon Accord Caspian (4)
13 km Salyan Highway
Shikh District, Baku, AZ1023, Azerbaijan
Tel.: (994) 124474336
Fax: (994) 124474337
E-Mail: zeynel@alikve.org
Web Site: www.genoyer.com
Emp.: 20
Piping Equipment Warehousing & Distr
S.I.C.: 5084
N.A.I.C.S.: 423830
Ilgar Akhundov *(Mng Dir)*

Phoceenne Asia Pte. Ltd. (4)
171 Chin Swee Road
11-09 San Centre, Singapore, 169877, Singapore SG
Tel.: (65) 64382444 (100%)
Fax: (65) 64388084
E-Mail: singapor@genoyer.com
Web Site: www.genoyer.com
Emp.: 3
Industrial Pipe Products Distr
S.I.C.: 5084
N.A.I.C.S.: 423830

Phoceenne Chili Ltda. (4)
Napoleon 3 200 Oficina 805
Las Condes, Santiago, Chile CL
Tel.: (56) 22429888 (100%)
Fax: (56) 3771066
E-Mail: santiago@genoyer.com
Web Site: www.genoyer.com
Emp.: 2
Industrial Pipe Products Distr
S.I.C.: 5084
N.A.I.C.S.: 423830
Gorhe Watqamf *(Gen Mgr)*

Phoceenne S.A. (4)
Plaza de Castilla 3
Planta 8aA, 28046 Madrid, Spain ES
Tel.: (34) 913237662 (100%)
Fax: (34) 913142544
E-Mail: madrid@genoyer.com
Web Site: www.genoyer.com
Emp.: 10
Industrial Pipe Products Distr
S.I.C.: 5084
N.A.I.C.S.: 423830

PT Phoceenne Indonesie (4)
Permata Plaza 11th Floor
Jalan MH Thamrin #57, Jakarta, 10 350, Indonesia (100%)
Tel.: (62) 213903330
Fax: (62) 213903329
E-Mail: jakarta@genoyer.com
Web Site: www.genoyer.com
Industrial Pipe Products Distr
S.I.C.: 5084
N.A.I.C.S.: 423830

Special Flange Services, Ltd. (4)
Elevator Road
Trafford Park, Manchester, M17 1BR, United Kingdom UK
Tel.: (44) 1618764422 (100%)
Fax: (44) 1618764401
E-Mail: sales@sfsltd.co.uk
Web Site: www.genoyer.com
Metal Flanges Mfr
S.I.C.: 3494
N.A.I.C.S.: 332919

Vilmar S.A. (4)
1 Platforma Industriala Street
240050 Ramnicu Valcea, Romania RO
Tel.: (40) 250703800 (100%)
Fax: (40) 250703807
E-Mail: office@vilmar.ro
Web Site: www.vilmar.ro
Emp.: 740
Metal Valves, Flanges & Pipe Fittings Mfr
S.I.C.: 3494
N.A.I.C.S.: 332919
Kelifa Guemra *(Gen Mgr)*

CDC Innovation (2)
63 Avenue des Champs Elysees
F-75008 Paris, France (100%)

Tel.: (33) 140769900
Fax: (33) 145612478
E-Mail: businessplan@cdcinnovation.com
Web Site: www.cdcinnovation.com
Emp.: 12
Private Equity Firm
S.I.C.: 6211
N.A.I.C.S.: 523999
Chantal Parpex *(Pres & Mng Partner)*
Valery Huot *(Mng Partner)*
Franck Noiret *(Gen Partner)*
Bertrand Limoges *(Principal)*

CDC Entreprises Holding (1)
137 st of university
BP 174
75007 Paris, Cedex 15, France (100%)
Tel.: (33) 158507171
Fax: (33) 158507774
E-Mail: contact-cdcenterprises@cdcenterprises.fr
Web Site: www.cdcenterprises.fr
Sales Range: $1-4.9 Billion
Emp.: 150
Holding Company; Public Interest Equity & Venture Investment Services
S.I.C.: 6719
N.A.I.C.S.: 551112
Jerome Gallot *(Pres)*
Pascal Lagarde *(CEO)*
Dominique Phelouzat *(CFO)*
Philippe Kunter *(Sec)*

Subsidiary:

CDC Enterprises (2)
137 rue de l Universite
BP 174
75007 Paris, Cedex 15, France (100%)
Tel.: (33) 158507171
Fax: (33) 015850074
E-Mail: contact-cdcenterprises@cdcenterprises.fr
Web Site: www.cdcenterprises.fr
Emp.: 100
Equity Investment Firm
S.I.C.: 6211
N.A.I.C.S.: 523999
Jerome Gallot *(Pres)*
Pascal Lagarde *(CEO)*
Dominique Phelouzat *(CFO)*
Philippe Kunter *(Sec)*

Egis S.A. (1)
11 avenue du Centre
78286 Saint-Quentin-en-Yvelines, Cedex, France
Tel.: (33) 130484415
Fax: (33) 130484986
E-Mail: dircom@groupegis.com
Web Site: www.groupegis.com
Infrastructure Engineering Services
S.I.C.: 8711
N.A.I.C.S.: 541330
Nicolas Jachiet *(Chm & CEO)*
Philippe Segretain *(Chm)*

Fonds Strategique d'Investissement S.A. (1)
56 rue de Lille
F-75007 Paris, France FR
Tel.: (33) 158501515 (51%)
E-Mail: jean.pierre.jouyet@caissedesdepots.fr
Web Site: www.fonds-fsi.fr
Sales Range: $900-999.9 Million
Private Equity Firm
S.I.C.: 6211
N.A.I.C.S.: 523999
Augustin de Romanet de Beaune *(Chm)*

Joint Venture:

TDF S.A.S. (2)
106 avenue Marx Dormoy
92541 Montrouge, France
Tel.: (33) 155951000
Web Site: www.tdf-group.com
Sales Range: $1-4.9 Billion
Emp.: 4,500
Television, Radio, Telecommunications & Satellite Communications Infrastructure Operator
S.I.C.: 4833
N.A.I.C.S.: 515120
Olivier Huart *(CEO)*

Icade S.A. (1)
Millenaire 1 35 Rue de la Gare
75168 Paris, Cedex 19, France (61.6%)
Tel.: (33) 141577000
Fax: (33) 141578000
E-Mail: info@icade.fr
Web Site: www.icade.fr
ICAD—(EUR)
Rev.: $2,027,735,871
Assets: $10,504,029,893
Liabilities: $6,514,520,481
Net Worth: $3,989,509,412
Earnings: $83,058,689
Emp.: 1,712
Fiscal Year-end: 12/31/12
Real Estate Investment Trust
S.I.C.: 6726
N.A.I.C.S.: 525990
Serge Grzybowski *(Chm & CEO)*
Romain Fremont *(Deputy Mng Dir-Icade Svcs)*
Magali Michel *(Deputy Mng Dir-Icade Property Mgmt)*

Subsidiaries:

Capri Atlantique (2)
70 Cours De Verdun
33000 Bordeaux, France (100%)
Tel.: (33) 556000111
Fax: (33) 556000120
E-Mail: bordeaux@capri-immo.fr
Web Site: www.capri-immo.fr
Property Development Company
S.I.C.: 1522
N.A.I.C.S.: 236118

Capri Lyon Mediterranee (2)
103 Ave De Saxe
69003 Lyon, France (100%)
Tel.: (33) 472601080
Fax: (33) 472601099
Web Site: www.capri-immo.fr/programme-1.asp?PROID=773
Emp.: 150
Property Development Group
S.I.C.: 1522
N.A.I.C.S.: 236118

Compagnie la Lucette S.A. (2)
7 rue Scribe
75009 Paris, France FR
Tel.: (33) 1 42 25 86 86 (100%)
Fax: (33) 1 42 25 86 70
Web Site: www.compagnielalucette.com
Sales Range: $125-149.9 Million
Emp.: 40
Commercial, Office & Industrial Real Estate, Developer & Manager
S.I.C.: 6519
N.A.I.C.S.: 531190
Thomas Guyot *(Mng Dir)*
Emmanuel Gey *(CFO)*

EMGP (2)
50 Ave Du Pres Wilson
St Denis La Plaine, 93214 Paris, Cedex, France (100%)
Tel.: (33) 149464840
Fax: (33) 149464841
E-Mail: contact@emgp.fr
Web Site: www.emgp.fr
Property Leasing Services
S.I.C.: 6512
N.A.I.C.S.: 531120

GFF (Ile de France) (2)
Tour Franklin La Defence 8
92042 Paris, Cedex, France (100%)
Tel.: (33) 44948686
Fax: (33) 144948687
E-Mail: gff-idf@gff.fr
Web Site: www.gff.fr
Property Management & Consultancy Services
S.I.C.: 9199
N.A.I.C.S.: 921190

Icade Capri S.A. (2)
204 Ave De Colmar
67100 Strasbourg, France
Tel.: (33) 388237464
Fax: (33) 388237460
E-Mail: icade.capri-est@icade.fr
Web Site: www.capriimmo.fr
Emp.: 15
Property Development Company
S.I.C.: 1522
N.A.I.C.S.: 236118
Sommer Clement *(Mng Dir)*

Promomidi (2)
13 Rue Paul Mesple
BP 1257
Toulouse, Cedex, 31100, France
Tel.: (33) 534613060
Fax: (33) 534613079
Web Site: www.capri-immo.fr
Property Development Group
S.I.C.: 1522
N.A.I.C.S.: 236118

SCIC Habitat (2)
Latrium
6 Pl Abel Gance, 92100 Boulogne-Billancourt, France (100%)
Tel.: (33) 146944711
Fax: (33) 146945882
Web Site: www.scichabitat.fr
Constructor of Affordable Housing & Property Management Services
S.I.C.: 9531
N.A.I.C.S.: 925110

Services Conseil Expertise Territoire S.A. (2)
102 Ave du France
75646 Paris, France
Tel.: (33) 155033000
Fax: (33) 155033001
E-Mail: remi.deneijs@scet.esr
Web Site: www.scet.fr
Emp.: 500
Property Consultancy Group
S.I.C.: 9199
N.A.I.C.S.: 921190
Remi de Nijs *(CEO)*

Silic SA (2)
31 Boulevard des Bouvets
92000 Nanterre, France (100%)
Tel.: (33) 153897979
Fax: (33) 153897950
E-Mail: nanterre@socomie.fr
Web Site: www.silic.fr
SIL—(EUR)
Rev.: $247,409,892
Assets: $2,925,670,300
Liabilities: $2,344,807,368
Net Worth: $580,862,932
Earnings: $16,975,204
Emp.: 96
Fiscal Year-end: 12/31/12
Property Management & Investment Services
S.I.C.: 6211
N.A.I.C.S.: 523999
Sabine Schimel *(CEO)*
Bruno Meyer *(Deputy Mng Dir)*
Jerome Lucchini *(Sec)*

Subsidiary:

Socomie (3)
Batiment Bruges
50 Ave Robert Schuman, Rungis, France
Tel.: (33) 145125020
Fax: (33) 145125080
E-Mail: rungis@socomie.fr
Web Site: www.socomie.fr
Emp.: 100
Property Management Services
S.I.C.: 6531
N.A.I.C.S.: 531312
Philippe Lemoine *(CEO)*

Novethic (1)
56 rue de Lille
75007 Paris, France
Tel.: (33) 158509814
Fax: (33) 158500030
E-Mail: info@novethic.fr
Web Site: www.novethic.fr
Investment Consultants
S.I.C.: 6282
N.A.I.C.S.: 523930
Anne Catherine Husson Traore *(Dir Gen)*

Societe Nationale Immobiliere (1)
125 avenue de Lodeve
BP 6068
34074 Montpellier, Cedex 1, France (100%)
Tel.: (33) 467759640
Fax: (33) 467759643
Web Site: www.groupesni.fr
Property Management Services
S.I.C.: 6513
N.A.I.C.S.: 531110
Francis Mayer *(Chm-Supervisory Bd)*
Andre Yche *(Chm-Mgmt Bd)*

Transdev S.A. (1)
(Formerly Veolia Transdev S.A.)
32 Boulevard Gallieni
F-92442 Issy-les-Moulineaux, France
Tel.: (33) F-92445
Web Site: www.veoliatransdev.com
Sales Range: $5-14.9 Billion
Emp.: 37,000
Passenger Transportation Services
S.I.C.: 4119
N.A.I.C.S.: 485999
Jean-Marc Janaillac *(Chm & CEO)*

U.S. Subsidiaries:

SuperShuttle International, Inc. (2)
14500 N Northsight Blvd Ste 329
Scottsdale, AZ 85260 DE
Tel.: (480) 609-3000
Fax: (480) 607-9317
Toll Free: (800) 258-3826
E-Mail: mlofaro@supershuttle.net
Web Site: www.supershuttle.com
Sales Range: $25-49.9 Million
Emp.: 1,000
Airport Transportation Services
S.I.C.: 4111
N.A.I.C.S.: 485119
R. Brian Weir *(Pres & CEO)*
Thomas C. LaVoy *(CFO & Sec)*
Dave Bird *(Sr VP-Ops)*

Subsidiary:

Golden Touch Transportation of New York (3)
45-02 Ditmars Blvd
Astoria, NY 11105
Tel.: (718) 886-5204
Fax: (718) 661-4341
E-Mail: allgoldentouch@gttny.com
Web Site: www.goldentouchtransportation.com
Sales Range: $25-49.9 Million
Emp.: 100
Scheduled Air Transportation
Import Export
S.I.C.: 4119
N.A.I.C.S.: 485999
Thomas Herrschaft *(Pres)*

Veolia Transportation, Inc. (2)
720 E Butterfield Ste 300
Lombard, IL 60148
Tel.: (630) 571-7070
Fax: (630) 571-6454
Toll Free: (800) 225-8880
E-Mail: info@veoliatransportation.com
Web Site: www.veoliatransportation.com
Sales Range: $900-999.9 Million
Emp.: 90
Passenger & Freight Transportation Services
S.I.C.: 4111
N.A.I.C.S.: 485113
Mark Joseph *(CEO)*
Ken Westbrook *(Pres/COO-Transit)*
Ron Hartman *(CEO-Rail)*
Alan B. Moldawer *(Gen Counsel & Exec VP)*
Dick Alexander *(Sr VP-Bus Dev)*
Bill McCloud *(Sr VP-Client Rels)*
Mike Murray *(Sr VP-Transit-Northeast)*

Subsidiaries:

Veolia Transportation, Inc. (3)
720 E Butterfield Rd Ste 300
Lombard, IL 60148
Tel.: (630) 571-7070
Fax: (630) 495-1302
Web Site: www.veoliatransportation.com
Emp.: 100
Passenger Transport Services Operator
S.I.C.: 4119
N.A.I.C.S.: 485999
Jan Hoistmann *(CFO)*

Veolia Transportation, Inc. (3)
2100 Huntingdon Ave
Baltimore, MD 21211 MD
Tel.: (410) 727-7300
Fax: (410) 385-8484
Web Site: www.veoliatransportation.com
Emp.: 500
Passenger & Freight Transportation Services
S.I.C.: 4111
N.A.I.C.S.: 485999
Mark Joseph *(Vice Chm & CEO)*
Benoit Papy *(CFO)*
Alan B. Moldawer *(Gen Counsel & Exec VP)*
Ronald J. Hartman *(Exec VP-Rail)*

Caisse des Depots et Consignations—(Continued)

Non-U.S. Subsidiaries:

Connex Melbourne (2)
Level 24 1 Spring Street
Melbourne, VIC, 3000, Australia
Tel.: (61) 396102400
Fax: (61) 396102600
Web Site: www.connexmelbourne.com.au
Emp.: 2,500
Passenger Transport Services Operator
S.I.C.: 4111
N.A.I.C.S.: 485999
Alan Chaplin *(Mng Dir)*

London United Busways (2)
Busways House
Wellington Rd, Twickenham, Middlesex, TW2 5NX, United Kingdom
Tel.: (44) 2084006665
Fax: (44) 2089432688
E-Mail: customer@lonutd.co.uk
Web Site: www.londonutd.co.uk
Emp.: 2,000
Bus Operating Company
S.I.C.: 4131
N.A.I.C.S.: 485210
Nigel Stevens *(Mng Dir)*

Transdev plc (2)
4th Floor Zone G7
Palestra
197 Blackfairs Road, London, SE 8NJ, United Kingdom
Tel.: (44) 8453007000
Fax: (44) 207279914
E-Mail: customerservices@tfl-buses.co.uk
Web Site: www.transdevplc.co.uk
Sales Range: $250-299.9 Million
Emp.: 3,895
Public Transportation
S.I.C.: 4119
N.A.I.C.S.: 485999

Veolia Transport AB (2)
Lofstroms Alle 6A
PO Box 1820
17124 Sundbyberg, Sweden
Tel.: (46) 86295000
Fax: (46) 8290096
E-Mail: info@veolia-transport.se
Web Site: www.veolia-transport.se
Emp.: 130
Passenger Transport Services Operator
S.I.C.: 4111
N.A.I.C.S.: 485999
Cyril Carneel *(CEO)*
Gunnar Schon *(CEO)*

Non-U.S. Subsidiaries:

Veolia Transport Belgium (3)
Groenendaallaan 387
2030 Antwerp, Belgium
Tel.: (32) 35443370
Fax: (32) 35443377
E-Mail: info@veolia-transport.be
Web Site: www.veolia-transport.be
Sales Range: $100-124.9 Million
Emp.: 11
Passenger Transport Services Operator
S.I.C.: 4111
N.A.I.C.S.: 485999
Luc Jullet *(Mng Dir)*

Veolia Transport Finland Oy (3)
Tuupakantie 7 A
01740 Vantaa, Finland
Tel.: (358) 98789170
Fax: (358) 958609510
E-Mail: info@veolia-transport.fi
Web Site: www.veolia-transport.fi
Emp.: 10
Passenger Transport Services Operator
S.I.C.: 4111
N.A.I.C.S.: 485999
Pa..ivi Katagisto *(Mgr-Sls)*

Veolia Transport Nederland BV (3)
Mastbosstraat 12
PO Box 3306
4800 DH Breda, Netherlands
Tel.: (31) 765281000
Fax: (31) 765221191
Web Site: www.connex.se
Emp.: 4,033
Passenger Transport Services Operator
S.I.C.: 4119
N.A.I.C.S.: 485999

Veolia Transport Norge AS (3)
Klubbgaten 1
NO 4013 Stavanger, Norway
Tel.: (47) 51564100
Fax: (47) 51564101
E-Mail: post@veolia-transport.no
Web Site: www.veolia-transport.no
Emp.: 2,000
Passenger Transport Services Operator
S.I.C.: 4111
N.A.I.C.S.: 485999
Kjetil Sorsvoll *(Mng Dir)*

Veolia Transport Polska Sp. z o.o. ul. (3)
Ul Slominskiego15509
00 195 Warsaw, Poland
Tel.: (48) 226375170
Fax: (48) 226375169
E-Mail: info@connex.se
Web Site: www.connex.se
Sales Range: $25-49.9 Million
Emp.: 12
Passenger Transport Services Operator
S.I.C.: 4111
N.A.I.C.S.: 485999
Tomasz Rochowicz *(Gen Mgr)*

Veolia Transport Praha s.r.o. (3)
U Seradiste 9
10 Prague, CR 101 40, Czech Republic
Tel.: (420) 271724253
Fax: (420) 234125999
E-Mail: info.praha@veolia-transport.cz
Web Site: www.connex.cz
Emp.: 1,500
Passenger Transport Services Operator
S.I.C.: 4119
N.A.I.C.S.: 485999
Petr Cihak *(Gen Mgr)*

Veolia Verkher GmbH (3)
Georgenstrasse 22
10117 Berlin, Germany
Tel.: (49) 3020073343
Fax: (49) 3020073200
E-Mail: post@veolia-verkher.de
Web Site: www.veolia-verkher.de
Emp.: 4,000
Passenger Transport Services Operator
S.I.C.: 4111
N.A.I.C.S.: 485999

Veolia Transport Australasia (2)
Level 24 1 Spring Street
Melbourne, VIC, 3000, Australia
Tel.: (61) 386817500
Fax: (61) 399461330
E-Mail: info@veoliatransport.com.au
Web Site: www.veoliatransport.com.au
Emp.: 2,000
Passenger Transport Services Operator
S.I.C.: 4119
N.A.I.C.S.: 485999

Subsidiary:

Veolia Transport Sydney Pty Ltd (3)
220 Pyrmont Street
Sydney, 2000, Australia
Tel.: (61) 285845288
Fax: (61) 296600955
E-Mail: reception@veoliatransportsydney.com.au
Web Site: www.veoliatransport.com.au
Passenger Transport Services Operator
S.I.C.: 4111
N.A.I.C.S.: 485999

Veolia Transport Ireland (2)
Luas Depot Red Cow Roundabout
Clondalkin, Dublin, 22, Ireland
Tel.: (353) 14614910
Fax: (353) 14673046
E-Mail: info@veolia-transport.ie
Web Site: www.veolia-transport.ie
Emp.: 350
Passenger Transport Services Operator
S.I.C.: 4111
N.A.I.C.S.: 485999
Nigel Stevens *(CEO)*

Joint Venture:

Saur SA (1)
1 Ave Eugene Freyssinet
78064 Saint-Quentin-en-Yvelines, France
Tel.: (33) 130602260
Fax: (33) 130602789
Web Site: www.saur.com
Sales Range: $1-4.9 Billion
Emp.: 12,400
Water Treatment & Sanitation Services
S.I.C.: 4953
N.A.I.C.S.: 562219
Joel Seche *(Chm)*
Olivier Brousse *(Mng Dir & Pres)*
Patrick Barthelemy *(Deputy Mng Dir)*

Subsidiaries:

Coved (2)
1 rue Antoine Lavoisier
78064 Guyancourt, France
Tel.: (33) 130602260
Fax: (33) 130606569
E-Mail: dircom@saur.fr
Web Site: www.saur.com
Sales Range: $550-599.9 Million
Emp.: 2,800
Sanitation Management Services
S.I.C.: 4959
N.A.I.C.S.: 562998
Brousse Olivier *(Mng Dir)*

Stereau SAS (2)
1 rue Antoine Lavoisier
78064 Saint-Quentin-en-Yvelines, France
Tel.: (33) 130606491
Fax: (33) 130606439
Web Site: www.stereau.fr
Emp.: 30
Water Treatment Services
S.I.C.: 4953
N.A.I.C.S.: 562219
Christophe Peltzer *(CFO)*
Jacques Tessier *(COO)*

Units:

Caisse des Depots et Consignations - Banking Services (1)
56 Auedelille
F-75356 Paris, SP, France (100%)
Tel.: (33) 158500000
Web Site: www.caissedesdepots.fr
Emp.: 9,500
Banking Services
S.I.C.: 6011
N.A.I.C.S.: 521110
Pierre Ducret *(Pres)*

Caisse des Depots et Consignations - Local & Regional Development (1)
72 avenue Pierre Mendes-France
F-75914 Paris, Cedex 13, France (100%)
Tel.: (33) 158507661
Web Site: www.caissedesdepots.fr
Community & Public Works Development Services
S.I.C.: 9532
N.A.I.C.S.: 925120
Philippe Braidy *(Sr Exec VP)*

Subsidiary:

Alteau S.A. (2)
43 Rue Boissiere
F-75116 Paris, France FR
Tel.: (33) 153704540 (51%)
Fax: (33) 153704547
E-Mail: info@alteau.fr
Web Site: www.alteau.fr
Sales Range: $10-24.9 Million
Emp.: 150
Public & Commercial Water & Sanitation Systems Management
S.I.C.: 9511
N.A.I.C.S.: 924110
Patrice Millet *(CEO)*

CAISSE NATIONALE DES CAISSES D'EPARGNE ET DE PREVOYANCE

(d/b/a Groupe Caisse d'Epargne)
50 avenue Pierre Mendes
75201 Paris, Cedex 13, France
Tel.: (33) 158404142
Fax: (33) 158404800
Web Site:
Year Founded: 1999
Sales Range: $5-14.9 Billion
Emp.: 51,200

Business Description:
Bank Holding Company; Savings, Commercial, Investment Banking & Real Estate Services
S.I.C.: 6712
N.A.I.C.S.: 551111

Personnel:
Yves Toublanc *(Chm-Supervisory Bd)*
Steve Gentili *(Vice Chm-Supervisory Bd)*
Alain Lemaire *(CEO)*
Guy Cotret *(Exec Dir-HR, Banking Ops & IT)*

Supervisory Board of Directors:
Yves Toublanc
Catherine Amin-Garde
Francois Audibert
Joel Bourdin
Jean-Marc Carceles
Dominique Courtin
Jean-Pierre Deramecourt
Bruno Dugelay
Jean-Marc Espalioux
Steve Gentili
Eric Grimonprez
Serge Huber
Jean Levallois
Alain Maire
Benoit Mercier
Jacques Moreau
Nicole Moreau
Jean-Francois Paillisse
Bernard Sirol
Michel Sorbier

Subsidiary:

Banque BCP S.A.S. (1)
14 avenue Franklin Roosevelt
F-75008 Paris, France (80.1%)
Tel.: (33) 1 44 20 51 19
Fax: (33) 1 44 20 50 53
Web Site: www.banquebcp.fr
Emp.: 500
Banking Services
S.I.C.: 6029
N.A.I.C.S.: 522110

Joint Venture:

BPCE S.A. (1)
50 Avenue Pierre Mendes France
75013 Paris, France FR
Tel.: (33) 158404142
Fax: (33) 158404800
E-Mail: investor.relations@bpce.fr
Web Site: www.bpce.fr
Emp.: 127,000
Bank Holding Company
S.I.C.: 6712
N.A.I.C.S.: 551111
Philippe Dupont *(Chm-Supervisory Bd)*
Francois Perol *(Chm-Mgmt Bd)*
Yves Toublanc *(Vice Chm-Supervisory Bd)*
Nicolas Duhamel *(CFO & Member-Mgmt Bd)*
Olivier Klein *(Member-Mgmt Bd & CEO-Comml Banking)*
Philippe Queuille *(Member-Mgmt Bd & CEO-Ops & Organization)*
Jean-Luc Vergne *(Member-Mgmt Bd & CEO-HR)*

Subsidiaries:

Credit Foncier de France (2)
19 rue des Capucines
BP 65
75050 Paris, Cedex 1, France
Tel.: (33) 142448000
Fax: (33) 142448699
E-Mail: admin@creditfoncier.fr
Web Site: www.creditfoncier.fr
Sales Range: $1-4.9 Billion
Real Estate Banking Services
S.I.C.: 6159
N.A.I.C.S.: 522292

Subsidiary:

Compagnie de Financement Foncier (3)
4 quai de Bercy
94224 Charenton-le-Pont, France
Tel.: (33) 1 57 44 72 27
Fax: (33) 1 57 44 92 88
E-Mail: ir@creditfoncier.fr
Web Site: www.foncier.fr
CFF—(ASX)

Rev.: $6,864,736,030
Assets: $135,670,093,983
Liabilities: $133,160,353,866
Net Worth: $2,509,740,117
Earnings: $178,476,565
Fiscal Year-end: 12/31/12
Financial Management Services
S.I.C.: 6211
N.A.I.C.S.: 523999
Thierry Dufour *(Chm & CEO)*
Sandrine Guerin *(Deputy CEO)*

Mancelle d'Habitation SA (2)
11 rue du Donjon
72055 Le Mans, France
Tel.: (33) 2 43 74 45 45
Fax: (33) 2 43 74 45 40
E-Mail: contact@mancelle-habitation.fr
Web Site: www.mancelle-habitation.fr
Banking Services
S.I.C.: 6029
N.A.I.C.S.: 522110

Subsidiary:

Manceliere Logement Soc Economie Mixte (3)
10 rue Hippolyte Lecornue
72015 Le Mans, Cedex 2, France
Tel.: (33) 2 43 43 74 33
Fax: (33) 2 43 43 74 36
Web Site: www.manceliere-logement.fr
Sales Range: $10-24.9 Million
Emp.: 16
Real Estate Management Services
S.I.C.: 6513
N.A.I.C.S.: 531110
Annick Vignez *(VP)*

Natixis, S.A. (2)
30 avenue Pierre Mendes
75013 Paris, France FR
Mailing Address:
BP 4
F-75060 Paris, Cedex 02, France
Tel.: (33) 158323000
Fax: (33) 158199393
E-Mail: relinvest@natixis.fr
Web Site: www.natixis.com
KN—(EUR)
Rev.: $8,717,796,920
Assets: $711,275,842,900
Liabilities: $658,104,820,240
Net Worth: $53,171,022,660
Earnings: $1,274,822,990
Emp.: 20,198
Fiscal Year-end: 12/31/12
Bank Holding Company; Investment & Commercial Banking, Private Equity, Insurance & Asset Management Services
S.I.C.: 6712
N.A.I.C.S.: 551111
Francois Perol *(Chm)*
Laurent Mignon *(CEO & Member-Mgmt Bd)*
Jacques Sudre *(Chief Compliance Officer)*
Christian Le Hir *(Chief Legal Officer)*
Andre-Jean Olivier *(Member-Mgmt Bd & Sec)*
Luc-Emmanuel Auberger *(Member-Mgmt Bd-Ops & IS)*
Aline Bec *(Member-Mgmt Bd-Info Sys Pur Logistics)*
Alain Delouis *(Member-Mgmt Bd-HR)*
De Doan Tran *(Member-Mgmt Bd-Corp & Investment Banking)*
Olivier Perquel *(Member-Mgmt Bd-Wholesale Banking-Fin & Global Markets)*
Pierre Servant *(Member-Mgmt Bd-Investment Solutions)*

Divisions:

Natixis - Corporate & Investment Banking (3)
47 quai d'Austerlitz
F-75648 Paris, Cedex 13, France
Tel.: (33) 158551515
Fax: (33) 158552002
Web Site: www.natixis.com
Sales Range: $5-14.9 Billion
Corporate & Investment Banking Services
S.I.C.: 6211
N.A.I.C.S.: 523110
Jean-Marc Moriani *(CEO)*
Christophe Lanne *(COO)*

Subsidiaries:

Natixis Finance (4)
30 Avenue Pierre Mendes
75013 Paris, France
Tel.: (33) 158192400
Fax: (33) 158198549
Web Site: www.natixis.com
Emp.: 400
Commercial Banking Services to Agribusiness; Foreign Exchange; Credit & Cash Management Services
S.I.C.: 6159
N.A.I.C.S.: 522298
Daniel Giroux *(CEO)*

Natixis Lease (4)
4 place de la Coupole
F-94676 Charenton-le-Pont, Cedex, France
Tel.: (33) 158328080
Fax: (33) 158328081
E-Mail: contact@lease.natexis.fr
Web Site: www.lease.natixis.fr
Emp.: 50
Mobile & Property Lease Financing Services
S.I.C.: 6159
N.A.I.C.S.: 522294
Francois Brabander *(CEO)*
Henri Doumerc *(Mng Dir)*

U.S. Subsidiaries:

Natixis Bleichroeder Inc. (4)
1345 Ave of the Americas
New York, NY 10105-4300 NY
Tel.: (212) 698-3000
Fax: (212) 299-4444
Web Site: www.natexisblr.us/en/index.html
Emp.: 50
Investment Banking & Securities Brokerage Services
S.I.C.: 6211
N.A.I.C.S.: 523120

Natixis North America Inc. (4)
9 W 57th St 36th Fl
New York, NY 10019 DE
Tel.: (212) 891-6100
Web Site: www.cm.natixis.com
Holding Company
S.I.C.: 6719
N.A.I.C.S.: 551112
Philippe Becret *(CIO)*

Holding:

Natixis Capital Markets Inc. (5)
9 W 57th St 36th Fl
New York, NY 10019
Tel.: (212) 891-6100
Fax: (212) 891-6295
Web Site: www.cm.natixis.com
Corporate Investment Banking & Risk Management Services
S.I.C.: 6211
N.A.I.C.S.: 523110
Mitch Karig *(VP-Mktg Comm)*

Subsidiaries:

Natixis Real Estate Capital Inc. (6)
9 West 57th St 36th Fl
New York, NY 10019
Tel.: (212) 891-5700
Fax: (212) 891-5777
E-Mail: realestate@cm.natixis.com
Web Site: www.re.natixis.com
Emp.: 25
Commercial Real Estate Financing Services
S.I.C.: 6163
N.A.I.C.S.: 522310
Greg Murphy *(Head-Fin & Real Estate)*

Natixis Securities North America Inc. (6)
9 W 57th St 35th Fl
New York, NY 10019 NY
Tel.: (212) 891-6100
Fax: (212) 891-6260
Web Site: www.sp.natixis.com
Securities Broker & Dealer
S.I.C.: 6211
N.A.I.C.S.: 523120

Non-U.S. Branches:

Natixis - Bogota (4)
Carrera 15 n 91-30- of 601
Bogota, Colombia
Tel.: (57) 16231631
Fax: (57) 16234190
E-Mail: servicioalcliente@coface.com.co
Web Site: www.coface.com.co
Emp.: 30
Commercial Banking Services
S.I.C.: 6029
N.A.I.C.S.: 522110

Natixis - Buenos Aires (4)
Cerrito 1294 6th Fl
C1010AAZ Buenos Aires, Argentina
Tel.: (54) 1148160388
Fax: (54) 1148160427
E-Mail: sandra.smimmo@ar.natixis.com
Web Site: www.natixis.com
Emp.: 45
Commercial Banking Services
S.I.C.: 6029
N.A.I.C.S.: 522110

Natixis - Cairo (4)
50 rue Abdel Khalek Sarwat
Cairo, Egypt
Tel.: (20) 223904667
Fax: (20) 223915705
Web Site: www.natixis.com
Emp.: 2
Commercial Banking Services
S.I.C.: 6029
N.A.I.C.S.: 522110

Natixis Corporate Solutions Asia (4)
9 Raffles Place #60-01 Republic Plaza
Singapore, 048619, Singapore
Tel.: (65) 68231188
Telex: 28277 BFCE SG
Fax: (65) 68231199
Web Site: www.natixis.com
Emp.: 20
Commercial & Corporate Banking Services
S.I.C.: 6029
N.A.I.C.S.: 522110
Jenny Ong *(Mng Dir)*

Natixis - Hanoi (4)
Prime Center 53 Quang Trung
Room 16-02 16th Floor, Hanoi, Vietnam
Tel.: (84) 49433667
Telex: 805 811563
Fax: (84) 4 9433 665
Web Site: www.natixis.com
Commercial Banking Services
S.I.C.: 6029
N.A.I.C.S.: 522110

Natixis - Ho Chi Minh (4)
173 Vo Thi Sau
3e arrondissement, Ho Chi Minh City, Vietnam
Tel.: (84) 89320827
Fax: (84) 89320844
Web Site: www.natixis.com
Commercial Banking Services
S.I.C.: 6029
N.A.I.C.S.: 522110

Natixis - Hong Kong (4)
Level 23 Two Pacific Place
88 Queensway, Hong Kong, China (Hong Kong)
Tel.: (852) 28280999
Telex: 80186 BFCEX HX
Fax: (852) 25839801
E-Mail: hongkong.info@ap.natixis.com
Web Site: www.natixis.com
Rev.: $128,210
Emp.: 50
Commercial Banking Services
S.I.C.: 6029
N.A.I.C.S.: 522110

Natixis - Kuala Lumpur (4)
Marketing Office Suite 16-5 Level 16th
Menara Weld 76
Jalan Raja Chulan, MY 50200 Kuala Lumpur, Malaysia
Tel.: (60) 60320263900
Fax: (60) 60320263901
E-Mail: rizal.abdullah@ap.natixis.com
Web Site: www.natixis.com
Emp.: 7
Commercial Banking Services
S.I.C.: 6029
N.A.I.C.S.: 522110

Natixis - Labuan (4)
Unit Level 9 Main Office Tower
Financial Park Labuan Complex
Jalan Merdeka, 87000 Labuan, Malaysia
Tel.: (60) 87582009
Fax: (60) 87583009
Web Site: www.natixis.com
Commercial Banking Services
S.I.C.: 6029
N.A.I.C.S.: 522110

Natixis - London (4)
Cannon Bridge House
25 Dowgate Hill, London, EC4R 2YA, United Kingdom
Tel.: (44) 2032169000
Fax: (44) 2032169201
Web Site: www.natixis.com
Emp.: 200
Commercial Banking Services
S.I.C.: 6029
N.A.I.C.S.: 522110
Olivier Allard *(Head-Capital Markets)*

Non-U.S. Subsidiaries:

Natixis Algerie Sp.A. (4)
62 chemin Mohamed Drareni
Hydra, 16035, Algeria
Tel.: (213) 2154 9015 (-9020)
Fax: (213) 2154 9193
E-Mail: Nasr-Eddine.Bouharaoua@algerie.natixis.com
Web Site: www.natixis.com
Commercial Banking Services
S.I.C.: 6029
N.A.I.C.S.: 522110

Natixis Luxembourg S.A. (4)
51 avenue JF Kennedy
L-1855 Luxembourg, Luxembourg LU
Tel.: (352) 253418315
Fax: (352) 253418342
E-Mail: luxembourgnatixis@luxembourgnatixis.lu
Web Site: www.natixis.com
Emp.: 9
Bank Holding Company; Investment & Commercial Banking Services
S.I.C.: 6712
N.A.I.C.S.: 551111

Natixis Global Asset Management S.A. (3)
21 quai d'Austerlitz
F-75634 Paris, Cedex 13, France
Tel.: (33) 178409000
Fax: (33) 178406500
E-Mail: christian.silianoff@globalam.natixis.com
Web Site: www.globalam.natixis.com
Emp.: 2,800
Financial & Real Estate Asset Management Services
S.I.C.: 6719
N.A.I.C.S.: 551112
Laurent Mignon *(Chm)*
Pierre Servant *(Global CEO)*
Jamal Saab *(Mng Dir & Head-MENA)*
Geoffroy Sartorius *(CFO & Exec VP)*
Pascal Delaunay *(Chief Compliance Officer)*
Herve Guinament *(Pres/CEO-Intl Distr)*
John T. Hailer *(Pres/CEO-Americas & Asia)*
Pascal Voisin *(CEO-Natixis Asset Mgmt)*
Jeffrey D. Plunkett *(Gen Counsel & Exec VP)*
Beverly M. Bearden *(Exec VP-HR)*
Caren Leedom *(Exec VP-Global Comm)*

Division:

Natixis Global Asset Management (France) (4)
21 quai d'Austerlitz
F-75634 Paris, Cedex 13, France
Tel.: (33) 178409000
Fax: (33) 178406500
Web Site: www.globalam.natixis.com
Sales Range: $400-449.9 Billion
Holding Company; Financial & Real Estate Asset Management Services
S.I.C.: 6719
N.A.I.C.S.: 551112
Pascal Voisin *(CEO)*

Subsidiaries:

AEW Europe (5)
21 quai d''Austerlitz
F-75634 Paris, France
Tel.: (33) 178409200
Fax: (33) 178406601
Web Site: www.aeweurope.com
Managed Assets: $22,463,630,000
Emp.: 270
Real Estate Investment Management Services
S.I.C.: 6726
N.A.I.C.S.: 525990

Caisse Nationale des Caisses d'Epargne et de Prevoyance—(Continued)

Mireille Chetioui *(CFO & Sec)*
Rob Wilkinson *(Chief Investment Officer)*
Coralie Auguet *(Gen Counsel)*

Subsidiary:

NAMI-AEW Europe **(6)**
1-1 rue des Italiens
F-75009 Paris, France
Tel.: (33) 178403300
Web Site: www.namiaeweurope.com
Real Estate Fund Management Services
S.I.C.: 6531
N.A.I.C.S.: 531390
Alain Pivert *(Dir Gen)*
Philippe Agenis-Nevers *(Deputy Dir Gen)*

Non-U.S. Subsidiary:

AEW Europe-London **(6)**
33 Jermyn Street
London, SW1Y 6DN, United Kingdom UK
Tel.: (44) 2070164800
Fax: (44) 470164842
E-Mail: enquiries@curzonglobal.com
Emp.: 80
Real Estate Investment Management Services
S.I.C.: 6726
N.A.I.C.S.: 525990
Ric Lewis *(CEO & Chief Investment Officer-AEW Europe)*

Natixis Asset Management S.A. **(5)**
21 quai d'Austerlitz
F-75634 Paris, Cedex 13, France
Tel.: (33) 178408000
Fax: (33) 178406000
Web Site: www.am.natixis.com
Asset Management Services
S.I.C.: 6799
N.A.I.C.S.: 523920
Pascal Voisin *(CEO)*
Dominique Sabassier *(Deputy Mng Dir)*

Subsidiary:

Natixis Multimanager **(6)**
21 quai d'Austerlitz
75634 Paris, Cedex, 13, France
Tel.: (33) 178403200
Fax: (33) 178403299
E-Mail: rh@am.natixis.com
Web Site: www.multimanager.natixis.com
Mutual Fund & Other Asset Multimanagement Services
S.I.C.: 6722
N.A.I.C.S.: 525910
Dominique Mourocq *(CEO & CIO)*
Brigitte Minard *(CFO)*

U.S. Division:

Natixis Global Asset Management, L.P. **(4)**
399 Boylston St 13th Fl
Boston, MA 02116-3305 DE
Tel.: (617) 449-2100
Fax: (617) 247-1447
Web Site: www.globalam.natixis.com
Sales Range: $250-299.9 Billion
Emp.: 1,400
Holding Company; Financial & Real Estate Asset Management Services
S.I.C.: 6719
N.A.I.C.S.: 551112
John T. Hailer *(Pres & CEO)*
Faith Yando *(Sr VP)*

Subsidiaries:

AEW Capital Management, L.P. **(5)**
World Trade Center E 2 Seaport Ln
Boston, MA 02210-2021
Tel.: (617) 261-9000
Fax: (617) 261-9555
Web Site: www.aew.com
Managed Assets: $26,000,000,000
Emp.: 150
Real Estate Investment Management Services
S.I.C.: 6726
N.A.I.C.S.: 525990
Jeffrey Davis Furber *(CEO & Mng Dir)*
James J. Finnegan *(Mng Dir, Gen Counsel & Chief Compliance Officer)*
Pamela J. Herbst *(Mng Dir & Head-Direct Investment Grp)*
Michael J. Acton *(Mng Dir & Dir-Res)*
Robert J. Plumb *(Mng Dir & Dir-Acq)*
Marc L. Davidson *(Mng Dir & Portfolio Mgr-Partners Funds)*
Matthew A. Troxell *(Mng Dir & Sr Portfolio Mgr-Construction & Mgmt-Real Estate)*

AlphaSimplex Group, LLC **(5)**
One Cambridge Ctr 7th Fl
Cambridge, MA 02142 DE
Tel.: (617) 475-7100
Fax: (617) 588-1925
Web Site: www.alphasimplex.com
Emp.: 25
Investment Management Services
S.I.C.: 6722
N.A.I.C.S.: 525910
Andrew W. Lo *(Founder, Chm & Chief Scientific Officer)*
Arnout M. Eikeboom *(Chief Compliance Officer)*

Capital Growth Management, L.P. **(5)**
1 International Pl 45th Fl
Boston, MA 02110
Mailing Address:
PO Box 8511
Boston, MA 02266-8511
Tel.: (617) 737-3225
Fax: (617) 261-0572
Toll Free: (800) 345-4048
E-Mail: staff@cgmfunds.com
Web Site: www.cgmfunds.com
Sales Range: $75-99.9 Million
Emp.: 20
Mutual Funds & Advisory Accounts Management Services
S.I.C.: 6722
N.A.I.C.S.: 525910
Robert L. Kemp *(Co-Founder & Pres)*
G. Kenneth Heebner *(Co-Founder & VP/ Portfolio Mgr)*
David C. Fietze *(Chief Compliance Officer)*
Jem A. Hudgins *(Treas)*
Leslie A. Lake *(Sec & VP-Admin)*

Gateway Investment Advisers, L.P. **(5)**
312 Walnut St Fl 35
Cincinnati, OH 45202-9834 DE
Tel.: (513) 719-1100
Fax: (513) 719-1199
Web Site: www.gia.com
Sales Range: $5-14.9 Billion
Emp.: 25
Investment & Portfolio Management Services
S.I.C.: 6722
N.A.I.C.S.: 525910
J. Patrick Rogers *(Pres, CEO & Portfolio Mgr)*
Paul R. Stewart *(CIO, Sr VP & Portfolio Mgr)*
Geoffrey Keenan *(Exec VP)*

Hansberger Global Investors, Inc. **(5)**
401 E Las Olas Blvd Ste 1700
Fort Lauderdale, FL 33301
Tel.: (954) 522-5150
Fax: (954) 713-2525
Web Site: www.hansberger.com
Managed Assets: $7,400,000,000
Emp.: 60
Investment Management Services
S.I.C.: 6211
N.A.I.C.S.: 523110
Ron Holt *(CEO & Co-Chief Investment Officer-Value Team)*
David Lemanski *(Chief Admin Officer)*
Susan Moore-Wester *(Chief Compliance Officer)*
Andrew Powers *(Sr VP & Mng Dir-IT)*
Mary Foglia *(Sr VP & Dir-Trading)*
Moira McLachlan *(Sr VP-Res-Fort Lauderdale)*
Evelyn Orley *(Sr VP-Mktg-Western US)*
Sharon Pelletier *(Sr VP-Investment Ops & Acct Admin)*

Non-U.S. Branch:

Hansberger Global Investors **(6)**
5500 N Service Rd 11th Fl
Burlington, ON, L7L 6W6, Canada
Tel.: (905) 331-5770
Fax: (905) 331-5776
Web Site: www.hansberger.com
Emp.: 10
Investment Management Services
S.I.C.: 6211
N.A.I.C.S.: 523110
Thomas R.H. Tibbles *(Mng Dir & Chief Investment Officer-Growth Team)*
Barry A. Lockhart *(Deputy Mng Dir-Canada)*
Trevor Graham *(Sr VP-Res)*
Patrick Tan *(Sr VP-Res)*

Harris Associates, L.P. **(5)**
2 N La Salle St Ste 500
Chicago, IL 60602-3790
Tel.: (312) 621-0600
Fax: (312) 621-9929
Web Site: www.harrisassoc.com
Sales Range: $50-74.9 Billion
Emp.: 190
Investment & Portfolio Management Services
S.I.C.: 6211
N.A.I.C.S.: 523110
Robert M. Levy *(Chm, Chief Investment Officer & Partner)*
David G. Herro *(Chief Investment Officer-Intl Equity & Partner)*
Janet L. Reali *(Partner & Gen Counsel)*
Michael J. Neary *(Partner & Mng Dir-Mktg & Client Rels)*
Robert A. Taylor *(Partner & Dir-Intl Res & Portfolio Mgr)*
Henry R. Berghoef *(Partner, Mgr-Portfolio & Dir-Res)*
Edward S. Loeb *(Partner & Portfolio Mgr)*
Michael J. Mangan *(Partner & Portfolio Mgr)*
Clyde S. McGregor *(Partner & Portfolio Mgr)*
William C. Nygren *(Partner & Portfolio Mgr)*
Edward A. Studzinski *(Partner & Portfolio Mgr)*
Judson H. Brooks *(Partner)*
Anthony P. Coniaris *(Partner)*
M. Colin Hudson *(Partner)*
John R. Raitt *(Partner)*
Thomas E. Herman *(CFO)*
John N. Desmond *(COO)*
Dermot Putnam *(CIO)*
Richard J. Gorman *(Chief Compliance Officer)*
Colin P. McFarland *(Chief Compliance Officer)*

Loomis, Sayles & Company, L.P. **(5)**
1 Financial Ctr
Boston, MA 02111-2621
Tel.: (617) 482-2450
Fax: (617) 482-1985
Toll Free: (800) 343-2029
Web Site: www.loomissayles.com
Sales Range: $100-149.9 Billion
Emp.: 200
Securities Investment & Fund Management Services
S.I.C.: 6211
N.A.I.C.S.: 523110
Dan Fuss *(Vice Chm)*
Robert J. Blanding *(CEO)*
Kevin Charleston *(CFO)*
Mark Baribeau *(CIO & VP)*
Lauriann Kloppenburg *(Chief Strategy Officer)*
Jae Park *(Chief Investment Officer)*
David Waldman *(Deputy Chief Investment Officer)*
Jean Loewenberg *(Gen Counsel)*

Natixis Global Associates, LLC **(5)**
399 Bolston St
Boston, MA 02116
Tel.: (617) 449-2600
Fax: (617) 449-2688
Web Site: www.ga.natixis.com
Emp.: 500
Holding Company; Financial Investment Advisory & Distribution Services
S.I.C.: 6719
N.A.I.C.S.: 551112
David Giunta *(Pres & CEO)*
Matthew Coldren *(Exec VP-Global Relationships & Retirement Strategy Grp)*

Subsidiaries:

Natixis Asset Management Advisors, L.P. **(6)**
399 Bolston St
Boston, MA 02116
Tel.: (617) 449-2600
Fax: (617) 449-2688
Web Site: www.ga.natixis.com
Investment Advisory Services
S.I.C.: 6282
N.A.I.C.S.: 523930
David Giunta *(Pres & CEO)*
Coleen Downs Dinneen *(Gen Counsel, Sec & Exec VP)*

Natixis Distributors, L.P. **(6)**
399 Bolston St
Boston, MA 02116
Tel.: (617) 449-2600
Fax: (617) 449-2688
Toll Free: (800) 283-1155
Web Site: www.ga.natixis.com
Managed Assets: $10,000,000,000
Financial Distribution Services
Import Export
S.I.C.: 6371
N.A.I.C.S.: 524292
David Giunta *(Pres & CEO-U.S.)*
Sharon Wratchford *(Exec VP-Admin & Ops-Global Distr)*
Faith Yando *(Sr VP-PR)*

Non-U.S. Branch:

Natixis Global Associates International **(6)**
21 Quai d'Austerlitz
F-75013 Paris, Cedex 13, France
Tel.: (33) 178409600
Fax: (33) 178406000
Web Site: www.ga.natixis.com
Investment Advisory & Distribution Services
S.I.C.: 6282
N.A.I.C.S.: 523930
Herve Guinamant *(Pres & CEO)*
Fabrice Chemouny *(Exec VP & Head-Intl Mktg & Strategy)*

Reich & Tang Asset Management, LLC **(5)**
1411 Broadway Ste 28
New York, NY 10018-3496
Tel.: (617) 449-2100
Web Site: www.reichandtang.com
Emp.: 200
Portfolio Management Services
Import Export
S.I.C.: 6282
N.A.I.C.S.: 523920
Michael Lydon *(Pres)*
Richard De Sanctis *(CFO & Exec VP)*

Divisions:

Reich & Tang Capital Management **(6)**
1411 Broadway
New York, NY 10018
Tel.: (212) 830-5200
Fax: (212) 830-5468
Toll Free: (800) 676-6779
E-Mail: cminfo@rnt.com
Web Site: www.reichandtang.com
Emp.: 100
Asset Management & Investment Services
S.I.C.: 6799
N.A.I.C.S.: 523920
Naomi Friedland-Wechsler *(Gen Counsel & Exec VP)*
Sandra Arcaro *(Sr VP-Portfolio Admin)*

Division:

Global Investment Advisors **(7)**
12 E 49th St # 36
New York, NY 10017-1028
Tel.: (212) 830-5460
Fax: (212) 974-2057
Web Site: www.reichandtang.com
Fixed Income Assets Management Services
S.I.C.: 6799
N.A.I.C.S.: 523920
Christopher Brancazio *(Chief Compliance Officer)*

Reich & Tang Funds **(6)**
1411 Broadway Rm 2800
New York, NY 10018-3450
Tel.: (212) 830-5200
Fax: (212) 330-5477
Web Site: www.reichandtang.com
Emp.: 80
Short-Term Money Market Funds Management Services

S.I.C.: 6722
N.A.I.C.S.: 525910
Michael P. Lydon *(Pres & CEO)*

Snyder Capital Management, L.P. (5)
1 Market Plz Steuart Tower Ste 1200
San Francisco, CA 94105
Tel.: (415) 392-3900
Fax: (415) 391-9437
Emp.: 13
Small & Mid-Cap Equities Investment Management
S.I.C.: 6722
N.A.I.C.S.: 525910
Peter Eisele *(Pres)*
Walter Niemasik, Jr. *(CEO)*
Sonja L. Commer *(Chief Compliance Officer)*

Vaughan Nelson Investment Management, L.P. (5)
600 Travis St Ste 6300
Houston, TX 77002-3071
Tel.: (713) 224-2545
Fax: (713) 228-4292
Web Site: www.vaughannelson.com
Emp.: 50
Investment Management Services
S.I.C.: 6799
N.A.I.C.S.: 523920
Eugene H. Vaughan *(Chm)*
Lee Alan Lahourcade *(Pres & CEO)*
Jay Wagner *(CIO)*
Richard B. Faig *(Dir-Fin, Admin & Chief Compliance Officer)*

Subsidiary:

Vaughan Nelson Trust Company (6)
600 Travis St Ste 6300
Houston, TX 77002
Tel.: (713) 224-2545
Fax: (713) 247-9534
E-Mail: info@vaughannelson.com
Web Site: www.vaughannelson.com
Emp.: 50
Financial Trust Services
S.I.C.: 6733
N.A.I.C.S.: 523991
Richard Faig *(Pres)*
Mark E. Farrell *(Sr VP)*

Westpeak Global Advisors, L.P. (5)
1470 Walnut St Ste 101
Boulder, CO 80302-5114
Tel.: (303) 786-7700
Fax: (303) 786-7411
Web Site: www.westpeak.com
Emp.: 7
Equity Investment & Management Services
S.I.C.: 6211
N.A.I.C.S.: 523110
Khalid Ghayur *(CEO & Chief Investment Officer)*
Deborah A. Gamel *(CFO & Chief Compliance Officer)*
Eric D. Krawetz *(Chief Admin Officer)*
Ronan G. Heaney *(Sr VP & Dir-Res)*
Stephen C. Platt *(Sr VP & Dir-Portfolio Mgmt)*

Natixis - Private Equity & Private Banking (3)
5-7 rue de Monttessuy
F-75007 Paris, France
Tel.: (33) 158323000
Fax: (33) 158324248
Web Site: www.privatebanking.natixis.com
Emp.: 3,000
Private Equity & Private Banking Services
S.I.C.: 6211
N.A.I.C.S.: 523999
Nicolas Homassel *(CEO)*

Subsidiaries:

Banque Privee Saint Dominique (4)
12-14 Rond Point des Champs Elysees
F-75382 Paris, Cedex 08, France
Tel.: (33) 156888000
Fax: (33) 156888199
E-Mail: alexandra.ellert@banque-bpsd.fr
Web Site: www.bpsd.fr
Emp.: 125
Private Banking & Wealth Management Services
S.I.C.: 6282
N.A.I.C.S.: 523920
Jacques-Antoine Allain *(COO)*

Natixis Private Equity (4)
5-7 rue de Monttessuy
F-75340 Paris, Cedex 07, France
Tel.: (33) 158192000
Fax: (33) 158192010
Web Site: www.natixis-pe.com
Emp.: 250
Private Equity Firm
S.I.C.: 6211
N.A.I.C.S.: 523999
Jean-Louis Delvaux *(Deputy CEO & Chm-Intl)*
Jean Duhau de Berenx *(CEO)*
Francois Baubeau *(COO)*

Division:

Natixis Private Equity International (5)
5-7 rue de Monttessuy
F-75340 Paris, Cedex 07, France
Tel.: (33) 158192350
E-Mail: Jeanfrancois.helfer@npeim.com
Web Site: www.natixis-pe.com
Emp.: 7
Private Equity Firm
S.I.C.: 6211
N.A.I.C.S.: 523999
Jean-Louis Delvaux *(Chm)*
Jean-Francois Helfer *(Chm-Mgmt Bd)*
Jean de Severac *(Mng Dir)*
Francois Feige *(Member-Mgmt Bd)*

Subsidiaries:

Initiative & Finance (5)
96 avenue d'Lena
F-75783 Paris, Cedex 16, France
Tel.: (33) 156899700
Fax: (33) 147208690
E-Mail: info@initiative-finance.com
Web Site: www.initiative-finance.com
Emp.: 20
Equity Investment Firm
S.I.C.: 6211
N.A.I.C.S.: 523999
Jean-Bernard Meurisse *(Pres)*
Valerie Bouillier *(Partner)*
Matthieu Douchet *(Partner)*
Thierry Giron *(Partner)*
Jean-Michel Laveu *(Partner)*

iXEN S.A. (5)
5-7 rue de Monttessuy
F-75340 Paris, Cedex 07, France
Tel.: (33) 1 5819 2000
Fax: (33) 1 5819 2010
Emp.: 10
Private Equity Firm
S.I.C.: 6211
N.A.I.C.S.: 523999
Caroline Remus *(Chm-Mgmt Bd)*
Yves Roucaud *(CEO)*
Veronique Bernard *(CFO)*

Natixis Investissement Partners (5)
5-7 rue de Monttessuy
F-75340 Paris, Cedex 07, France
Tel.: (33) 158192100
Fax: (33) 1 5819 2110
E-Mail: contact@ni-partners.com
Web Site: www.ni-partners.com
Emp.: 15
Private Equity Firm
S.I.C.: 6211
N.A.I.C.S.: 523999
Jean-Paul Bernardini *(Chm-Mgmt Bd)*
Philippe Taranto *(Assoc Dir)*
Vincent Lardoux *(Member-Mgmt Bd)*
Jean-Pierre Magagnin *(Sec)*

Naxicap Partners SA (5)
5-7 rue de Monttessuy
F-75340 Paris, Cedex 07, France
Tel.: (33) 158192220
Fax: (33) 158192230
E-Mail: contact@naxicap.fr
Web Site: www.naxicap.fr
Emp.: 50
Equity Investment Firm
S.I.C.: 6211
N.A.I.C.S.: 523999
Eric Aveillan *(Mng Dir)*

nempartners (5)
5-7 rue de Monttessuy
F-75340 Paris, Cedex 07, France
Tel.: (33) 158192130
Fax: (33) 158192140
E-Mail: info@nem-partners.com
Web Site: www.nem-partners.com
Emp.: 15
Equity Investment Firm
S.I.C.: 6211
N.A.I.C.S.: 523999
Eric Girardin *(Dir-Publ)*

Seventure Partners (5)
5-7 Rue de Monttessuy
F-75340 Paris, Cedex 07, France
Tel.: (33) 158192270
Fax: (33) 158192280
E-Mail: contact@seventure.fr
Web Site: www.seventure.fr
Managed Assets: $584,044,800
Emp.: 19
Equity Investment Firm
S.I.C.: 6211
N.A.I.C.S.: 523999
Jean-Patrick Demonsang *(Chm-Mgmt Bd)*
Isabelle de Cremoux *(Partner & Dir-Life Sciences Dept)*
Emmanuel Fiessinger *(Partner)*
Didier Piccino *(Partner)*
Bruno Rivet *(Partner)*
Ioana Simionescu *(Partner)*
Thi Than Vu *(CFO)*
Sylvie Padrazzi *(Sec)*

Spef LBO (5)
5-7 rue de Monttessuy
F-75340 Paris, Cedex, France
Tel.: (33) 158192250
Fax: (33) 158192260
E-Mail: contact@spef-lbo.fr
Web Site: www.spef-lbo.fr
Emp.: 10
Equity Investment Firm
S.I.C.: 6211
N.A.I.C.S.: 523999
Jacques Vachelard *(Chm-Mgmt Bd)*
Laurent Allegot *(Mng Dir)*
Arnaud Leclercq *(Member-Mgmt Bd)*

Ventech (5)
5-7 rue de Monttessuy
F-75007 Paris, Cedex 07, France
Tel.: (33) 158192150
Fax: (33) 158192160
E-Mail: contact@ventech.fr
Web Site: www.ventech.fr
Managed Assets: $474,536,400
Emp.: 16
Equity Investment Firm
S.I.C.: 6211
N.A.I.C.S.: 523999
Alain Caffi *(Chm & Gen Partner)*
Jean Bourcereau *(Gen Partner)*
Alain Cassi *(Gen Partner)*
Mounia Chaoui *(Gen Partner)*
Eric Huet *(Gen Partner)*

Affiliate:

EPF Partners (5)
11/13 avenue de Friedland
F-75008 Paris, France
Tel.: (33) 156436520
Fax: (33) 156436530
E-Mail: contact@epf-partners.com
Web Site: www.epf-partners.com
Managed Assets: $438,033,600
Emp.: 12
Private Equity Firm
S.I.C.: 6211
N.A.I.C.S.: 523999
Christian d'Argoubet *(Gen Mgr)*

Non-U.S. Subsidiaries:

Finatem Beteiligungsgesellschaft (5)
feldbergstrasse 5
D-60323 Frankfurt am Main, Germany
Tel.: (49) 695095640
Fax: (49) 6950956430
E-Mail: info@finatem.de
Web Site: www.finatem.de
Emp.: 11
Private Equity Firm
S.I.C.: 6211
N.A.I.C.S.: 523999
Christophe Hemmerle *(Founder, Mng Dir & Partner)*
Robert Hennigs *(Mng Dir & Partner)*
Eric Jungblut *(Partner & Dir-Investment)*
Irmgard Schade *(Partner & Dir-Investment)*

MCH Private Equity Asesores, S.L. (5)
Plaza de Colon 2 Torre I Planta 15
28046 Madrid, Spain ES
Tel.: (34) 914264444
Fax: (34) 914264440
E-Mail: mch@mch.es
Web Site: www.mch.es
Emp.: 20
Private Equity Firm
S.I.C.: 6211
N.A.I.C.S.: 523999
Jose Maria Munoz *(Co-Founder & Mng Partner)*
Jaime Hernandez Soto *(Co-Founder & Mng Partner)*
Andres Pelaez Collado *(Mng Partner)*
Andres Pelaez *(Mng Dir)*
Idoya Aguirre *(Gen Counsel)*

Non-U.S. Affiliate:

Axxon Group (5)
Ladeira de Nossa Senhora 311
Gloria, 22211-100 Rio de Janeiro, RJ, Brazil
Tel.: (55) 2132350770
Fax: (55) 2132350772
E-Mail: axxon@axxongroup.com.br
Web Site: www.axxongroup.com.br
Managed Assets: $150,000,000
Emp.: 20
Private Equity Firm
S.I.C.: 6211
N.A.I.C.S.: 523999
Nicolas Wollak *(Founder & Partner)*
Jose Augusto de Carvalho *(Partner)*

Non-U.S. Joint Ventures:

Cape-Natixis S.G.R. S.p.A. (5)
Monte Rosa No 88
I-20149 Milan, Italy
Tel.: (39) 027636131
Fax: (39) 0277331617
E-Mail: info@cape.it
Web Site: www.cape.it
Emp.: 25
Private Equity Funds Management Services
S.I.C.: 6211
N.A.I.C.S.: 523999
Simone Cimino *(Founder, Chm & Mng Partner)*
Marco Visarma *(CEO & Mng Partner)*
Guido De Vecchi *(Mng Partner)*
Annamaria Petrillo *(Partner)*
Emanuela Trezzi *(Partner)*
Maddalena De Liso *(CFO)*

Krokus Private Equity Sp. z o.o. (5)
Al Jana Pawla II 25
00-854 Warsaw, Poland PL
Tel.: (48) 226534700
Fax: (48) 226534707
E-Mail: biuro@krokuspe.pl
Web Site: www.krokuspe.pl
Emp.: 10
Private Equity Firm
S.I.C.: 6211
N.A.I.C.S.: 523999
Witold Radwanski *(CEO & Partner)*
Marzena Tomecka *(CFO & Partner)*
Robert Bozyk *(Partner)*
Piotr Oskroba *(Partner)*

Natixis - Receivables Management (3)
30 Ave Tierr Menges France
F-75013 Paris, France
Tel.: (33) 158323000
Web Site: www.natixis.fr
Receivables Management, Credit Insurance, Factoring & Collections Services
S.I.C.: 6099
N.A.I.C.S.: 522390
Jerome Cazes *(CEO)*

Subsidiaries:

Coface S.A. (4)
12 cours Michelet
La Defense 10, F-92800 Puteaux, France FR
Tel.: (33) 149022000
Fax: (33) 1 4902 2741
E-Mail: info@coface.com
Web Site: www.coface.com
Sales Range: $1-4.9 Billion
Emp.: 7,000

Caisse Nationale des Caisses d'Epargne et de Prevoyance—(Continued)

Credit Insurance & Credit Management Services
S.I.C.: 6159
N.A.I.C.S.: 522298
Jean-Marc Pillu *(CEO)*
Daniel Garcia *(CIO)*
Carole Lytton *(Officer-Legal & Compliance)*
Thierry Coldefy *(Sec & Head-HR & Fin)*

Subsidiary:

Coface Services (5)
1 rue de l'Union
92843 Rueil-Malmaison, France
Tel.: (33) 147524360
Fax: (33) 147524361
Web Site: www.cofaceservices.fr
Emp.: 800
Business Intelligence & Receivables Management Services
S.I.C.: 6099
N.A.I.C.S.: 522390
Jerome Cazes *(Chm)*
Jacques Romand *(Deputy Mng Dir & Dir-HR/Admin)*

U.S. Subsidiary:

Coface North America Holding Company (5)
1350 Broadway Ste 2000
New York, NY 10018
Tel.: (212) 389-6500
Fax: (917) 322-0433
E-Mail: cofaceusa@coface.com
Web Site: www.coface-usa.com
Sales Range: $100-124.9 Million
Emp.: 360
Holding Company; Credit Insurance & Credit Management Services
S.I.C.: 6719
N.A.I.C.S.: 551112
Michael Ferrante *(Chm & CEO)*

Subsidiary:

Coface North America, Inc. (6)
Windsor Corp Park Bldg 100 Ste 350 50 Millstone Rd
East Windsor, NJ 08520
Tel.: (609) 469-0400
E-Mail: cofaceusa@coface.com
Web Site: www.coface-usa.com
Credit Insurance & Credit Management Services
S.I.C.: 6159
N.A.I.C.S.: 522298
Mike Ferrante *(Chm & CEO)*
Val Goldstein *(Exec VP-Credit Mgmt Div)*

Divisions:

Coface Credit Management North America, Inc. (7)
50 Millstone Rd Windsor Corp Park Bldg 100 Ste 360
East Windsor, NJ 08520
Tel.: (609) 469-0400
Fax: (609) 490-1580
Web Site: www.coface-usa.com
Credit Management Services
S.I.C.: 6159
N.A.I.C.S.: 522298
Val Goldstein *(Exec VP)*

Coface North America Insurance Company, Inc. (7)
50 Millstone Rd Windsor Corp Park Bldg 100 Ste 360
East Windsor, NJ 08520
Tel.: (609) 469-0400
Fax: (609) 490-1581
E-Mail: insurance@coface-usa.com
Web Site: www.coface-usa.com
Corporate Credit & Political Risk Insurance Services
S.I.C.: 6399
N.A.I.C.S.: 524130
Cristina Lane *(VP-Comml-Political Risk Insurance)*

Unit:

Coface North America Political Risk (8)
1350 Broadway Ste 2000
New York, NY 10018
Tel.: (212) 389-6470
Fax: (212) 322-0430
E-Mail: political_risk@coface-usa.com
Web Site: www.coface-usa.com
Political Risk Insurance Services
S.I.C.: 6733
N.A.I.C.S.: 525190
Cristina Lane *(VP-Comml)*

Subsidiary:

Coface Collections North America, Inc. (7)
2400 Veterans Blvd Ste 300
Kenner, LA 70062
Tel.: (504) 469-9545
Fax: (504) 471-0948
Toll Free: (800) 509-6060
Web Site: www.coface-usa.com
Sales Range: $10-24.9 Million
Emp.: 107
Commercial Debt Collection Services
S.I.C.: 7322
N.A.I.C.S.: 561440
Thomas E. Brenan *(Pres)*
Cliff Sanders *(Exec VP-Bus Dev)*
Don Beetcher *(Sr VP)*
James McDermott *(Sr VP)*

Non-U.S. Subsidiaries:

Coface Central Europe Holding AG (5)
Stubenring 24
1010 Vienna, Austria AT
Tel.: (43) 1515540
Fax: (43) 15124415
Web Site: www.cofacecentraleurope.com
Sales Range: $200-249.9 Million
Emp.: 640
Holding Company; Credit Insurance & Credit Management Services
S.I.C.: 6159
N.A.I.C.S.: 522298
Martina Dobringer *(Chm-Supervisory Bd & CEO)*
Christian Berger *(Member-Mgmt Bd)*

Coface Holding AG (5)
Isaac-Fulda-Allee 1
55124 Mainz, Germany De
Mailing Address:
Postfach 1209
55002 Mainz, Germany
Tel.: (49) 61313230
Fax: (49) 6131372766
E-Mail:
Web Site: www.coface.de
Sales Range: $400-449.9 Million
Emp.: 700
Holding Company; Credit Insurance & Credit Management Services
S.I.C.: 6719
N.A.I.C.S.: 551112
Norbert Langenbach *(Member-Mgmt Bd)*
Anna Saylor *(Sec)*

Subsidiary:

Coface Kreditversicherung AG (6)
Isaac-Fulda-Allee 1
D-55124 Mainz, Germany De
Mailing Address:
Postfach 1209
D-55002 Mainz, Germany
Tel.: (49) 61313230
Fax: (49) 6131372766
E-Mail: info@coface.de
Web Site: www.coface.de
Emp.: 6,000
Credit Insurance Services
S.I.C.: 6399
N.A.I.C.S.: 524130
Stefan Brauel *(Member-Mgmt Bd)*
Norbert Langenbach *(Member-Mgmt Bd)*

Non-U.S. Branch:

Coface Danmark (6)
Bulowsevej 3
1870 Frederiksberg, Denmark
Tel.: (45) 33862500
Fax: (45) 33862505
E-Mail: info@coface.dk
Web Site: www.coface.dk
Emp.: 8
Credit Insurance & Credit Management Services
S.I.C.: 6159
N.A.I.C.S.: 522298
Vagn Thorsager *(Gen Mgr)*

Non-U.S. Holding:

Coface Austria Holding AG (6)
Stubenring 24
1010 Vienna, Austria AT
Tel.: (43) 1515540
Fax: (43) 15124415
E-Mail: office@coface.at
Web Site: www.coface.at
Sales Range: $75-99.9 Million
Emp.: 115
Holding Company; Credit Insurance & Credit Management Services
S.I.C.: 6719
N.A.I.C.S.: 551112
K. R. Martina Dobringer *(Chm)*
Benoit Claire *(Chm-Supervisory Bd)*
Susanne Krones *(Mng Dir)*
Christian Berger *(Member-Mgmt Bd)*

Subsidiaries:

Coface Austria Bank AG (7)
Stubenring 24
1010 Vienna, Austria AT
Tel.: (43) 1515540
Fax: (43) 15124415
E-Mail: info@coface.at
Web Site: www.coface.at
Emp.: 130
Factoring Services
S.I.C.: 6099
N.A.I.C.S.: 522390
Gabriele Duker *(Member-Mgmt Bd)*
Rudolf Kandioler *(Member-Mgmt Bd)*

Coface Austria Kreditversicherung AG (7)
Stubenring 24
1010 Vienna, Austria AT
Tel.: (43) 1515540
Fax: (43) 151554221
Web Site: www.coface.at
Credit Insurance & Credit Management Services
S.I.C.: 6159
N.A.I.C.S.: 522298
Martina Dobringer *(Chm)*
Christian Berger *(Member-Mgmt Bd)*
Gabriele Duker *(Member-Mgmt Bd)*

Coface Italia S.p.A. (5)
Via Giovanni Spadolini 4
I-20141 Milan, Italy IT
Tel.: (39) 0248335111
Fax: (39) 0248335404
E-Mail: info@coface.it
Web Site: www.coface.it
Sales Range: $200-249.9 Million
Emp.: 180
Holding Company; Credit Insurance & Credit Management Services
S.I.C.: 6719
N.A.I.C.S.: 551112
Riccardo Carradori *(Mng Dir)*

Subsidiary:

Coface Assicurazioni S.p.A. (6)
Via Giovanni Spadolini 4
I 20141 Milan, Italy IT
Tel.: (39) 0248335111
Fax: (39) 0248335404
E-Mail: info@coface.it
Web Site: www.coface.it
Emp.: 100
Credit Insurance Services
S.I.C.: 6399
N.A.I.C.S.: 524130
Massimo Coletti *(Deputy Mng Dir)*
Ernesto De Martinis *(Deputy Mng Dir)*

Coface UK Holding Ltd. (5)
15 Appold St
London, EC2A 2DL, United Kingdom UK
Tel.: (44) 2073257500
Fax: (44) 1923478101
E-Mail: enquiries@cofaceuk.com
Web Site: www.cofaceuk.com
Sales Range: $75-99.9 Million
Emp.: 180
Holding Company; Credit Management Services
S.I.C.: 6719
N.A.I.C.S.: 551112
Xavier Denecker *(Mng Dir)*

Subsidiaries:

Coface Receivables Finance Limited (6)
Egale 1 80 St Albans Rd
Watford, Herts, WD17 1RP, United Kingdom UK
Tel.: (44) 1923478100
Fax: (44) 1923659091
Emp.: 100
Receivables Management Services
S.I.C.: 6099
N.A.I.C.S.: 522390
Frederic Bourgeois *(Mng Dir)*

Coface UK Services Limited (6)
15 Appold Street
London, EC2A 2DL, United Kingdom UK
Tel.: (44) 2073257500
Fax: (44) 2073257699
E-Mail: enquiries@cofaceuk.com
Web Site: www.cofaceuk.com
Emp.: 30
Credit Intermediation Services
S.I.C.: 6159
N.A.I.C.S.: 522298
Xavier Denecker *(Mng Dir)*

Natixis Factor S.A. (4)
10-12 Avenue Winston Churchill
F-94676 Charenton-le-Pont, Cedex, France
Tel.: (33) 158328000
Fax: (33) 158328100
Web Site: www.factor.natixis.com
Emp.: 475
Factoring & Credit Insurance Services
S.I.C.: 6022
N.A.I.C.S.: 522190
Gils Berrous *(Chm)*
Philippe Petiot *(CEO)*

Subsidiaries:

Natixis Assurances S.A. (3)
115 rue Reaumur CS 40230
75086 Paris, Cedex 02, France FR
Tel.: (33) 158199000
Fax: (33) 158199140
E-Mail: service.clients@assurances.natixis.fr
Web Site: www.assurances.natixis.fr
Sales Range: $1-4.9 Billion
Emp.: 310
Holding Company; Life, Personal Risk & Other Insurance Carrier
S.I.C.: 6719
N.A.I.C.S.: 551112
Nathalie Broutele *(Dir Gen)*
Laurent Doubrovine *(Mng Dir)*
Jean Marches *(CEO-Life Insurance Div)*
Veronique Necker *(Sec General-Quality/Gen Svcs Dept)*
Bernard Paris *(Exec VP-Legal & Tax)*

Subsidiary:

Vitalia Vie (4)
115 rue Reaumur CS 40230 75086
F-75606 Paris, Cedex 02, France
Tel.: (33) 158199381
Fax: (33) 158199220
Life Insurance Carrier
S.I.C.: 6311
N.A.I.C.S.: 524113

Natixis Interepargne S.A. (3)
5 Ave Ge la liberge
BP 4 75060
F-94220 Paris, Cedex, France
Tel.: (33) 158194300
Fax: (33) 158324001
Web Site: www.interepargne.natixis.fr
Employee Savings Plans Management Services
S.I.C.: 6726
N.A.I.C.S.: 525990
Didier Trupin *(CEO & Mng Dir)*

SLIB S.A. (3)
22 28 Rue Joubert
75012 Paris, France
Tel.: (33) 170369700
Fax: (33) 170369701
Web Site: www.slib.fr
Emp.: 100
Investment Banking Software Publisher & Information Technologies Management
S.I.C.: 7372
N.A.I.C.S.: 511210
Philippe Cognet *(CEO)*

Societe de Banque Francaise et Internationale (3)
30 Ave Pierre Mendes
F-75013 Paris, France
Tel.: (33) 158323000
Fax: (33) 178406000
Web Site: www.natixis.com
Emp.: 2,000
Commercial Bank
S.I.C.: 6029
N.A.I.C.S.: 522110
Laurent Mignon *(Mng Dir)*

Thermocompact SA (3)
route de Sarves
BP 21
Zone Industrielle Metz-Tessy, 74371 Pringy, France
Tel.: (33) 4 50 27 20 02
Fax: (33) 4 50 27 17 37
E-Mail: thermo@thermocompact.com
Web Site: www.thermocompact.com
Sls.: $29,300,000
Emp.: 247
Metal Heat Treating
S.I.C.: 3398
N.A.I.C.S.: 332811
Jean-Claude Cornier *(Chm)*
Gilles Mollard *(CEO)*
Philippe Descaillot *(Mng Dir)*

Subsidiary:

Banque Palatine S.A. (2)
42 rue d'Anjou
F 75382 Paris, Cedex 08, France (100%)
Tel.: (33) 155279494
Fax: (33) 147544791
Web Site: www.palantine.fr
Sls.: $248,378,000
Banking Services
S.I.C.: 6029
N.A.I.C.S.: 522110
Katia Gely *(Dir-Comm)*

Non-U.S. Joint Venture:

CIFG Holding, Ltd. (1)
44 Church Street
Hamilton, HM 12, Bermuda BM
Tel.: (441) 294 8730
Fax: (441) 294 8729
Web Site: www.cifg.com
Sales Range: $200-249.9 Million
Emp.: 120
Holding Company; Reinsurance Carriers
S.I.C.: 6719
N.A.I.C.S.: 551112
John Salvatore Pizzarelli *(CEO)*
Michael Stuart Knopf *(Gen Counsel & Mng Dir)*
James Joseph O'Keefe, III *(CFO)*

Holding:

CIFG Guaranty, Ltd. (2)
44 Church Street
Hamilton, HM 12, Bermuda
Tel.: (441) 294 8730
Fax: (441) 294 8729
Web Site: www.cifg.com
Reinsurance Carrier
S.I.C.: 6399
N.A.I.C.S.: 524130
Gabriel Topor *(Chief Underwriting Officer)*

U.S. Subsidiary:

CIFG Assurance North America, Inc. (3)
850 3rd Ave 10th Fl
New York, NY 10022
Tel.: (212) 909-3939
Fax: (212) 909-3958
Web Site: www.cifg.com
Premiums: $40,986,384
Assets: $757,899,775
Liabilities: $380,844,775
Net Worth: $377,055,000
Earnings: ($212,191,154)
Emp.: 70
Fiscal Year-end: 12/31/12
Primary Financial Guaranty Reinsurance Carrier
S.I.C.: 6399
N.A.I.C.S.: 524130
David A. Buzen *(Pres, CFO & COO)*
Lawrence P. English *(CEO)*
Jessica Stern *(Mng Dir & Head-Global HR & Facilities)*
Maurice Toledano *(Deputy CFO-Europe)*
Michael Stuart Knopf *(Gen Counsel)*

Non-U.S. Subsidiary:

CIFG Europe S.A. (3)
19 boulevard Malesherbes
75008 Paris, France FR
Tel.: (33) 155273748
Fax: (33) 155273756
E-Mail: c.bertrand@cifg.com
Web Site: www.cifg.com
Rev.: $2,917,150
Assets: $106,152,235
Liabilities: $57,108,570
Net Worth: $49,043,665
Earnings: ($1,766,175)
Emp.: 3
Fiscal Year-end: 12/31/12
Primary Financial Guaranty Reinsurance Carrier
S.I.C.: 6399
N.A.I.C.S.: 524130
Maurice Toledano *(Deputy CFO)*

CAIXA ECONOMICA MONTEPIO GERAL

rua Aurea 219 a 241
PT-1100-062 Lisbon, Portugal
Tel.: (351) 21 724 16
Web Site: www.montepio.pt
MPIO—(EUR)
Rev.: $579,534,262
Emp.: 4,867
Fiscal Year-end: 12/31/12

Business Description:
Banking Services
S.I.C.: 6029
N.A.I.C.S.: 522110

Personnel:
Jose de Almeida Serra *(Chm-Supervisory Bd)*
Antonio Tomas Correia *(Chm-Exec Bd)*
Jorge Humberto Barros Luis *(Member-Exec Bd)*
Pedro Miguel de Almeida Alves Ribeiro *(Member-Exec Bd)*
Fernando Paulo Pereira Magalhaes *(Member-Exec Bd)*

Supervisory Board of Directors:
Jose de Almeida Serra
Alvaro Cordeiro Damaso
Eduardo Jose da Silva Farinha
Gabriel Jose dos Santos Fernandes
Alvaro Joao Duarte Pinto Correia
Eugenio Oscar Garcia Rosa
Antonio Goncalves Ribeiro
Luisa Maria Xavier Machado
Vitor Jose Melicias Lopes
Carlos Morais Beato
Maria Manuela Silva

CAIXA GERAL DE DEPOSITOS S.A.

Avenida Joao XXI 63
1000-300 Lisbon, Portugal
Tel.: (351) 217953000
Fax: (351) 217905050
E-Mail: cgd@cgd.pt
Web Site: www.cgd.pt
Year Founded: 1876
Rev.: $6,830,867,893
Assets: $157,308,717,167
Liabilities: $147,508,537,206
Net Worth: $9,800,179,961
Earnings: ($465,736,011)
Emp.: 23,205
Fiscal Year-end: 12/31/12

Business Description:
Banking Services
S.I.C.: 6211
N.A.I.C.S.: 523110

Personnel:
Fernando Manuel Barbosa Faria de Oliveira *(Chm)*
Jose Agostinho Martins de Matos *(Vice Chm & CEO)*
Ana Paula Rogenes Perez Lopes Pargana Calado *(Deputy Sec)*
Joao Manuel Travassos Dias Garcia *(Acting Sec)*

Board of Directors:
Fernando Manuel Barbosa Faria de Oliveira
Eduardo Manuel Hintze da Paz Ferreira
Norberto Emilio Sequeira da Rosa
Nuno Maria Pinto de Magalhaes Fernandes Thomaz
Jose Agostinho Martins de Matos
Joao Nuno de Oliveira Jorge Palma
Alvaro Jose Barrigas do Nascimento
Jose Pedro Cabral dos Santos
Rodolfo Vasco Castro Gomes Mascarenhas Lavrador

Affiliates:

Caixa-Imobiliario-Sociedade de Gestao e Investimento Imobiliario S.A. (1)
Ave Zuao 2163
1000063 Lisbon, Portugal (100%)
Tel.: (351) 217953000
Fax: (351) 00351218456939
Emp.: 500
Real Estate Management
S.I.C.: 6531
N.A.I.C.S.: 531210

Caixa Leasing & Factoring, IFIC, SA (1)
Av 5 Outubro 175 12 andar
1050 053 Lisbon, Portugal (100%)
Tel.: (351) 217807940
Fax: (351) 217807799
E-Mail: contacto@clf.pt
Web Site: www.clf.pt
Rev.: $75,000,000
Emp.: 200
Financial Leasing & Banking Services
S.I.C.: 6159
N.A.I.C.S.: 522298
Paulo Pinheiro *(Gen Mgr)*

Caixagest (1)
Ave Joao XXI 63 2nd Floor
Allas
1000-3000 Lisbon, Portugal (88.3%)
Tel.: (351) 217905457
Fax: (351) 217905475
E-Mail: caixagest@cgd.pt
Web Site: www.caixagest.pt
Rev.: $34,575,892
Emp.: 150
Fund Management Company
S.I.C.: 6282
N.A.I.C.S.: 523920
Joao Faria *(Pres)*

Caixagest (1)
Avda Joao XXI NO 63 2nd Fl
1000300 Lisbon, Portugal (100%)
Tel.: (351) 217905457
Fax: (351) 217905765
E-Mail: caixagest@caixagest.pt
Web Site: www.caixagest.pt
Emp.: 100
S.I.C.: 6159
N.A.I.C.S.: 522298
Antonio Vaz *(Mng Dir)*

Fidelidade (1)
Largo Do Calharix 30
1100 Lisbon, Portugal (100%)
Tel.: (351) 213237000
Fax: (351) 213103010
Insurance
S.I.C.: 6399
N.A.I.C.S.: 524128

Fundimo, S.A. (1)
Av Joao XXI 63 2 Fl
1000 Lisbon, Portugal (100%)
Tel.: (351) 217905450
Fax: (351) 217905474
E-Mail: fundimo@cgd.pt
Web Site: www.fundimo.pt
Rev.: $3,703,187
Emp.: 30
Real Estate Investment Fund
S.I.C.: 6726
N.A.I.C.S.: 525990
George Madeira *(Mng Dir)*

Imoleasing-Socciedade de Locacao Financiera Imobiliaria SA (1)
Av 5 de Outubro 175-12
1050 053 Lisbon, Portugal (68.4%)
Tel.: (351) 217807940
Fax: (351) 217807799
E-Mail: contactto@cls.pt
Web Site: www.imoleasing.pt
Rev.: $73,041,176
Emp.: 39
Finance Leasing Services
S.I.C.: 6159
N.A.I.C.S.: 522220
Paul Pnairo *(Pres)*

Locapor - Companhia Portuguesa Locacao Financeria Mobiliaria, S.A. (1)
Ave 5 de Outubro 175 12
1050053 Lisbon, Portugal (62%)
Tel.: (351) 217807940
Fax: (351) 217807799
E-Mail: contacto@clf.pt
Web Site: www.clf.pt
Rev.: $208,541,825
Emp.: 100
Finance Leasing
S.I.C.: 6141
N.A.I.C.S.: 522220
Paulo Pinheiro *(Pres)*

Non-U.S. Subsidiaries:

Caixa Geral de Depositos (France) (1)
85 Ave Marceau
75116 Paris, France (100%)
Tel.: (33) 00140695400
Telex: 630172 CAIXA F
Fax: (33) 140700309
E-Mail: cgdon-line@cgd.fr
Web Site: www.cgd.fr
Sales Range: $450-499.9 Million
Emp.: 500
International Banking
S.I.C.: 6159
N.A.I.C.S.: 522293

Mercantile Bank Holdings Limited (1)
142 West Street 1st Floor
Sandton, 2196, South Africa
Tel.: (27) 113020300
Fax: (27) 113020729
Web Site: www.mercantile.co.za
Int. Income: $59,017,924
Assets: $808,746,983
Liabilities: $621,771,907
Net Worth: $186,975,077
Earnings: $17,106,632
Emp.: 420
Fiscal Year-end: 12/31/12
International Banking & Financial Services
S.I.C.: 6159
N.A.I.C.S.: 522293
Karl R. Kumbier *(CEO)*
F. J. Schutte *(Sec)*

Non-U.S. Affiliates:

Banco Caixa Geral, S.A. (1)
Avda Madrid 83
28902 Madrid, Spain (100%)
Tel.: (34) 91 682 5431
Fax: (34) 91 683 7194
E-Mail: vetere@bancocaixageral.es
Web Site: www.bancocaixageral.es
Rev.: $56,587,000
Emp.: 250
International Banking
S.I.C.: 6159
N.A.I.C.S.: 522293

CAJA DE AHORROS Y PENSIONES DE BARCELONA

(d/b/a la Caixa Group)
Avenida Diagonal 621-629
ES-08028 Barcelona, Spain
Tel.: (34) 934046000
Fax: (34) 934047456
Web Site: www.lacaixa.es
Year Founded: 1990
Sales Range: $15-24.9 Billion

Caja de Ahorros y Pensiones de Barcelona—(Continued)

Emp.: 27,818
Business Description:
Bank Holding Company
S.I.C.: 6712
N.A.I.C.S.: 551111
Personnel:
Isidro Faine Casas *(Chm)*
Salvador Gabarro Serra *(First Deputy Chm)*
Javier Godo Muntanola *(Second Deputy Chm)*
Juan Maria Nin Genova *(Pres & CEO)*
Alejandro Garcia-Bragado Dalmau *(Sec)*
Juan Antonio Alcaraz Garcia *(Sr Exec VP)*
Marcelino Armenter Vidal *(Sr Exec VP)*
Antonio Massanell Lavilla *(Sr Exec VP)*
Tomas Muniesa Arantegui *(Sr Exec VP)*
Ignacio Alegre de Miquel *(Exec VP-IT Svcs)*
Ignacio Alvarez-Rendueles *(Exec VP-Intl)*
Xavier Coll Escursell *(Exec VP-HR)*
Luis Deulofeu Fuguet *(Exec VP-Global Risk)*
Jesus Escolano Cebolla *(Exec VP-Risk & Foreign Ops)*
Jaime Lanaspa Gatnau *(Exec VP-Welfare Projects)*
Sebastia Sastre Papiol *(Exec VP-Legal Svcs)*
Joaquin Vilar Barrabeig *(Exec VP-Acctg & Mgmt Control)*
Board of Directors:
Isidro Faine Casas
Eva Aurin Pardo
Victoria Barber Willems
Teresa Bassons Boncompte
Montserrat Cabra Martorell
Salvador Gabarro Serra
Javier Godo Muntanola
Josep-Delfi Guardia Canela
Monika Hapsburg Lothringen
Francesc Homs Ferret
Xavier Ibarz Alegria
Dolors Llobet Maria
Juan Jose Lopez Burniol
Mario Lopez Martinez
Estefania J. Martin Puente
Miquel Noguer Planas
Justo B. Novella Martinez
Ana Robles Gordaliza
Leopoldo Rodes Castane
Josep Joan Simon Carreras
Josep Francesc Zaragoza Alba

Subsidiary:

Criteria CaixaHolding, S.A. (1)
Avenida Diagonal 621-629
ES-08028 Barcelona, Spain ES
Tel.: (34) 934046000
Web Site: www.caixaholding.es
Real Estate & Equity Investment Holding Company
S.I.C.: 6719
N.A.I.C.S.: 551112

Holding:

CaixaBank, S.A. (1)
Avenida Diagonal 621
08028 Barcelona, Spain ES
Tel.: (34) 934092121 (81.5%)
Fax: (34) 933309727
E-Mail: inversores@criteria.com
Web Site: www.caixabank.com
CABK—(MAD OTC)
Rev.: $12,355,149,606
Assets: $468,863,033,597
Liabilities: $438,289,935,185
Net Worth: $30,573,098,411
Earnings: $307,940,426
Emp.: 32,625
Fiscal Year-end: 12/31/12
Investment Banking Services
S.I.C.: 6211
N.A.I.C.S.: 523999
Isidre Faine Casas *(Chm)*
Juan Maria Nin Genova *(Deputy Chm & CEO)*
Francisco Reynes Massanet *(Mng Dir)*
Alejandro Garcia-Bragado Dalmau *(Gen Sec)*

Subsidiaries:

VidaCaixa Grupo, S.A.U. (2)
Juan Gris 20-26
ES-08014 Barcelona, Spain ES
Tel.: (34) 93 227 8700 (100%)
Fax: (34) 93 298 9005
Web Site: www.vidacaixa-segurcaixaadeslas.es
Premiums: $5,846,871,315
Assets: $59,922,860,796
Liabilities: $55,111,649,216
Net Worth: $4,811,211,580
Earnings: $1,062,856,408
Emp.: 32,625
Fiscal Year-end: 12/31/12
Holding Company; Insurance Products & Services
S.I.C.: 6719
N.A.I.C.S.: 551112
Ricardo Fornesa Ribo *(Chm)*
Tomas Muniesa Arantegui *(Vice Chm & CEO)*
Jorge Mercader Miro *(Vice Chm)*
Antonio Trueba de Sinety *(Mng Dir)*
Jordi Arenillas *(Asst Mng Dir-Economic-Fin)*
Ernesto Moreno Caballero *(Asst Mng Dir-Investments)*
Adolfo Feijoo Rey *(Sec)*

Subsidiaries:

AgenCaixa, S.A. (3)
Juan Gris 20-26
ES-08014 Barcelona, Spain ES
Tel.: (34) 93 227 8700 (99%)
Web Site: www.agencaixa.com
Insurance Agency
S.I.C.: 6411
N.A.I.C.S.: 524210

VidaCaixa, S.A. de Seguros y Reaseguros (3)
Juan Gris 20-26
ES-08014 Barcelona, Spain ES
Tel.: (34) 932278700 (100%)
Fax: (34) 932989008
Web Site: www.vidacaixa.com
Life & Health Insurance & Pension Products & Services
S.I.C.: 6411
N.A.I.C.S.: 524298
Tomas Muniesa Arantegui *(Chm)*

Affiliate:

SegurCaixa Adeslas, S.A. de Seguros y Reaseguros (3)
General Almirante 2-4-6
ES-08014 Barcelona, Spain ES
Tel.: (34) 932278700 (49.92%)
Web Site: www.segurcaixa.com
Title, Property, Casualty & Other Non-Life Insurance Products & Services
S.I.C.: 6411
N.A.I.C.S.: 524298
E. Condie *(Sr Dir-Motor Vehicle Insurance Bus)*

CAL BANK LIMITED

23 Independence Avenue
PO Box 14596
Accra, Ghana
Tel.: (233) 302 680068
Fax: (233) 302 680081
E-Mail: calbank@calbank.net
Web Site: www.calbank.net
CAL—(GHA)
Sales Range: $25-49.9 Million
Emp.: 319
Business Description:
Banking Services
S.I.C.: 6029
N.A.I.C.S.: 522110
Personnel:
Paarock Asuman VanPercy *(Chm)*
Frank Brako Adu, Jr. *(Mng Dir & CEO)*
Philip Owiredu *(CFO)*
Board of Directors:
Paarock Asuman VanPercy
Frank Brako Adu, Jr.
Charles Asare
Leonora Awua-Kyerematen
James Chamberlain Brenner
Eduardo Gutierrez
Ernest Benjamin Kakra Essamuah
Philip Owiredu
Malcolmn Dermot Pryor
Kobina Quansah
Legal Counsel:
Reindorf Chambers
61 Jones Nelson Road
Adabraka, Accra, Ghana

Agyemang & Associates
3rd Floor America House
Tudu, Accra, Ghana

Non-U.S. Subsidiary:

CAL Investments Limited (1)
4 Farm St Mayfair
London, W1J 5RD, United Kingdom
Tel.: (44) 2073993380
Fax: (44) 2073993381
Web Site: www.calinvestments.com
Investment Management Services
S.I.C.: 8748
N.A.I.C.S.: 541618
Martin H.J. Smetsers *(Mng Dir)*

CAL-COMP ELECTRONICS (THAILAND) PCL

191/54 191/57 18th Floor CTI Tower
Rachadapisek Road
Klongtoey, Bangkok, 10110, Thailand
Tel.: (66) 2261 5033
Fax: (66) 2661 9396
E-Mail: info@calcomp.co.th
Web Site: www.calcomp.co.th
Year Founded: 1989
CCET—(TAI THA)
Rev.: $4,696,340,734
Assets: $1,905,152,291
Liabilities: $1,398,870,594
Net Worth: $506,281,697
Earnings: $39,722,385
Emp.: 16,937
Fiscal Year-end: 12/31/12
Business Description:
Electronic Products Mfr
S.I.C.: 3679
N.A.I.C.S.: 334419
Personnel:
Sheng-Hsiung Hsu *(Chm)*
Shyh-Yong Shen *(Vice Chm)*
Khongsit Choukitcharoen *(Mng Dir)*
Sunadda Jaypong *(Sec)*
Board of Directors:
Sheng-Hsiung Hsu
Zuei-Wei Chang
Thanasak Chanyapoon
William Hang Man Chao
Khongsit Choukitcharoen
Sheng-Chieh Hsu
Alan Kam
Charng-Chyi Ko
Shyh-Yong Shen

Plants:

Cal-Comp Electronics - Mahachai (1)
60 Moo 8 Sethakij Road Klon Maduea
Kratoom Bean, Samut Sakhon, 74110, Thailand
Tel.: (66) 34472000
Fax: (66) 34848994
Web Site: www.calcomp.co.th
Electronics Products Mfr
S.I.C.: 3679
N.A.I.C.S.: 334419

Cal-Comp Electronics - Petchaburi (1)
138 Moo 4 Phetchakasam Rd
Sapung, Khao Yoi, Phetchaburi, 76140, Thailand
Tel.: (66) 32 447756
Fax: (66) 32 447619
Web Site: www.calcomp.co.th
Electronics Products Mfr
S.I.C.: 3679
N.A.I.C.S.: 334419

U.S. Subsidiaries:

SMS Technologies, Inc. (1)
9877 Waples St
San Diego, CA 92121
Tel.: (858) 587-6900
Fax: (858) 457-2069
E-Mail: info@calcompusa.com
Web Site: www.calcompusa.com
Sales Range: $50-74.9 Million
Emp.: 150
Electronic Components Mfr
S.I.C.: 3679
N.A.I.C.S.: 334419
Jack Chang *(Pres)*
Elliot Shev *(Sr VP-Sls & Mktg)*

Total Electronics, LLC (1)
1 Technology Way
Logansport, IN 46947
Tel.: (574) 739-2929
Web Site: www.totalems.com
Electronic Component Mfr
S.I.C.: 3679
N.A.I.C.S.: 334419
Matt Price *(Dir-New Bus Dev)*

Non-U.S. Subsidiaries:

Cal-Comp Electronics and Communications Company Limited (1)
A Bldg No 147 Sec 3 Beishen Rd
Wanshuen Tsuen
Shenkeng Shiang, Taipei, 222, Taiwan (100%)
Tel.: (886) 277058001
E-Mail: IR@calcomp.com.tw
Web Site: www.calcomp.com.tw/eng/contact/contact.php
Emp.: 100
Computer Peripheral Equipment & Software Whslr
S.I.C.: 5045
N.A.I.C.S.: 423430

Cal-Comp Electronics (Suzhou) Company Limited (1)
No 2288 Jiangxing E Rd
Wujiang Economic Development Z, Nanjing, China (100%)
Tel.: (86) 51263407000
Fax: (86) 51263407995
E-Mail: mariamiu@calcompelectronics.com
Emp.: 7,000
Electronic Component Mfr
S.I.C.: 3679
N.A.I.C.S.: 334419
Chi-Tien Lai *(VP)*

Cal-Comp Optical Electronics (Suzhou) Company Limited (1)
No 2288 Jiangxing E Rd
Wujiang Economic Development Z, Nanjing, China (100%)
Tel.: (86) 51263407000
Fax: (86) 51263407995
Emp.: 7,000
Electronic Computer Mfr
S.I.C.: 3571
N.A.I.C.S.: 334111
Chi-Tien Lai *(VP)*

Power Digital Communication Co., Ltd. (1)
17B-23L Banwol Ind Com 491-1 Mongnae-dong
Ansan-si Danwon-gu, Seoul, Korea (South)
Tel.: (82) 25696767
Fax: (82) 25696768
Web Site: www.dpc.co.kr
Electronic Component Mfr
S.I.C.: 3679
N.A.I.C.S.: 334419

Zakang, Inc. (1)
C-402 Pundang Techno Park 151 Yatap-Dong
Pundang-Ku, Seongnam, Korea (South) (100%)

Tel.: (82) 317899013
Fax: (82) 317890515
E-Mail: admin@zakang.co.kr
Web Site: www.zakang.co.kr
Emp.: 40
Cellular & Wireless Telecommunications
S.I.C.: 4812
N.A.I.C.S.: 517210
S. Yio *(Pres)*

Non-U.S. Holding:

Logistar International Holding Company Limited (1)
Beaufort House
PO Box 438
Tortola, Virgin Islands (British) (100%)
Tel.: (284) 4942616
Fax: (284) 4942704
Holding Company
S.I.C.: 6719
N.A.I.C.S.: 551112

Subsidiary:

Wise Sigma International Holding Company Limited (2)
Beaufort House
PO Box 438
Tortola, Virgin Islands (British)
Tel.: (284) 4942616
Fax: (284) 4942704
Holding Company
S.I.C.: 6719
N.A.I.C.S.: 551112

CALA GROUP LIMITED

Adam House 5 Mid New Cultins
Edinburgh, EH11 4DU, United Kingdom
Tel.: (44) 1315355200
Fax: (44) 1315355201
Web Site: www.cala.co.uk
Year Founded: 1875
Emp.: 377

Business Description:
Residential & Commercial Property Developer
S.I.C.: 1542
N.A.I.C.S.: 236220

Personnel:
Alan D. Brown *(CEO)*
Moira R. Sibbald *(Legal Counsel & Sec)*

Board of Directors:
Anthony M. Fry
Alan D. Brown
Michael J. Freshney
Robert J. Millar
Mike Pacitti
J. Graham G. Reid

Legal Counsel:
Pinsent Masons LLP
Princes Exchange 1 Earl Grey Street
Edinburgh, United Kingdom

Subsidiaries:

CALA Finance Limited (1)
Adam House 5 Mid New Cultins
Edinburgh, EH11 4DU, United Kingdom
Tel.: (44) 01315355200
Fax: (44) 1315355201
E-Mail: calafinance@cala.co.uk
Web Site: www.vcamillerrobertson.com
Emp.: 50
Funding for Construction Builders
S.I.C.: 6726
N.A.I.C.S.: 525990
Irene Levery *(Mgr)*

CALA Homes (East) Limited (1)
14 Albyn Terrace
Aberdeen, AB10 1YP, United Kingdom
Tel.: (44) 1224633446
Fax: (44) 1224626972
E-Mail: cala.homes.aberdeen@cala.co.uk
Web Site: www.cala.co.uk/homes/contact.aspx
Residential Housing Development
S.I.C.: 1521
N.A.I.C.S.: 236115
Kevin Whitaker *(Mng Dir)*

CALA Homes (Midlands) Limited (1)
Brook House Birmingham Rd
Henley-in-Arden, Warks, B95 5QR, United Kingdom
Tel.: (44) 1216291300
Fax: (44) 1564797641
E-Mail: cala.homes.midlands@cala.co.uk
Web Site: www.cala.co.uk/homes/contact.aspx
Emp.: 50
Residential Housing Development
S.I.C.: 1521
N.A.I.C.S.: 236115
Darren Humphreys *(Mng Dir)*

CALA Homes (South) Limited (1)
Cala House 54
The Causeway, Staines-upon-Thames, TW18 3AX, United Kingdom
Tel.: (44) 1784225300
Fax: (44) 1784225301
E-Mail: cala.homes.south@cala.co.uk
Web Site: www.cala.co.uk/group/company/registered_offices.aspx
Emp.: 35
Residential Housing Development
S.I.C.: 1521
N.A.I.C.S.: 236115
Michael Freshney *(Chm)*
Graham Dunningham *(Mng Dir)*

CALA Homes (West) Limited (1)
Cairnlee House Callendar Business Pk
Callendar Rd, Falkirk, FK1 1XE, United Kingdom
Tel.: (44) 1324600000
Fax: (44) 1324600001
E-Mail: cala.homes.scotlandwest@cala.co.uk
Web Site: www.cala.co.uk/homes/contact.aspx
Emp.: 100
Residential Housing Development
S.I.C.: 1521
N.A.I.C.S.: 236115
Alestair White *(Mng Dir)*

CALA Homes (Yorkshire) Limited (1)
Victoria House Lawnswood Business Park
Redvers Close, Leeds, LS16 6SS, United Kingdom
Tel.: (44) 1132399500
Fax: (44) 113 239 9545
Residential Housing Development
S.I.C.: 1521
N.A.I.C.S.: 236115

CALAC TRUCKING LTD.

202 Edson Street
Saskatoon, SK, S7J 0P9, Canada
Tel.: (306) 242-0155
Fax: (306) 242-7716
Rev.: $40,636,138
Emp.: 320

Business Description:
Road Transportation & Trucking Services
S.I.C.: 4213
N.A.I.C.S.: 484121

Personnel:
Timothy Mckechnie *(Pres & CEO)*

CALANCE CORPORATION

Suite No 20 Greenwood Plaza
Greenwood City Sec 45
Gurgaon, 122002, India
Tel.: (91) 124 4047951
Fax: (91) 124 4047953
E-Mail: cspl@calance.com
Web Site: www.calance.com
Sales Range: $10-24.9 Million
Emp.: 75
Fiscal Year-end: 03/31/13

Business Description:
IT Services
S.I.C.: 7373
N.A.I.C.S.: 541512

Personnel:
Amit Govil *(Co-Founder, Chm & CEO)*
Sunil Chopra *(Co-Founder & COO)*
Archie Galbraith *(Sr VP & Gen Mgr-Health & Life Sciences)*

U.S. Subsidiary:

Partners Consulting Services, Inc. (1)
2855 Michelle Dr Ste 190
Irvine, CA 92606-1026
Tel.: (714) 573-7450
Fax: (714) 573-7470
Toll Free: (866) 736-5500
E-Mail: info@partnersconsulting.com
Web Site: www.partnersconsulting.com
Emp.: 100
IT and Staffing Services
Import Export
S.I.C.: 7373
N.A.I.C.S.: 541512
Chad Decatur *(Sr Mgr-Sys Ops)*

Subsidiary:

Consultants' Choice, Inc. (2)
2211 Norfolk Ste 1100
Houston, TX 77098 TX
Tel.: (713) 263-1400
Fax: (713) 263-1375
E-Mail:
Web Site: www.cpsg-inc.com
Sales Range: $10-24.9 Million
Emp.: 100
IT Consulting Services
S.I.C.: 7373
N.A.I.C.S.: 541512
Stephen Rossi *(Controller)*

CALAPAN VENTURES INC.

4th Floor 20 Lansbergh Place 170
Tomas Morato Avenue
Corner Scout Castor Street, Quezon City, 1103, Philippines
Tel.: (63) 23733038
Fax: (63) 23738491
E-Mail: info@h2o.ph
Web Site: www.h2o.ph
Emp.: 50

Business Description:
Holding Company; Water Supply
S.I.C.: 6719
N.A.I.C.S.: 551112

Personnel:
Jolly L. Ting *(Chm)*

CALATA CORPORATION

Cagayan Valley Road Banga 1st Plaridel
Bulacan, 3004, Philippines
Tel.: (63) 44 795 0136
Fax: (63) 44 795 1979
E-Mail: info@calatacorp.com
Web Site: www.calatacorp.com
CAL—(PHI)
Sales Range: $25-49.9 Million
Emp.: 110

Business Description:
Agricultural Products Including Agrochemicals, Feeds, Fertilizers & Veterinary Medicines Distr
S.I.C.: 5191
N.A.I.C.S.: 424910

Personnel:
Joseph H. Calata *(Chm, Pres & CEO)*
Benison Paul De Torres *(CFO & COO)*
Jose Marie E. Fabella *(Sec)*

Board of Directors:
Joseph H. Calata
Benison Paul De Torres
Baltazar N. Endriga
Jose Marie E. Fabella
Harvey S. Keh
Jaime C. Laya
George A. Nava
Jose A. Zaide

CALBEE, INC.

Marunouchi Trust Tower Main 22nd Floor 1-8-3 Marunouchi Chiyoda-Ku
Tokyo, 100-0005, Japan
Tel.: (81) 352206222
Web Site: www.calbee.co.jp
Year Founded: 1949
2229—(TKS)
Sls.: $1,973,521,000
Assets: $1,372,723,000
Liabilities: $353,188,000
Net Worth: $1,019,535,000
Earnings: $103,851,000
Emp.: 3,352
Fiscal Year-end: 03/31/13

Business Description:
Snack Food Mfr
S.I.C.: 2052
N.A.I.C.S.: 311919

Personnel:
Akira Matsumoto *(Chm & CEO)*
Shuji Ito *(Pres & COO)*
Koichi Kikuchi *(CFO & Gen Mgr-Info Sys Grp)*
Makoto Ehara *(Sr Exec Officer)*
Masakazu Fujii *(Sr Exec Officer)*
Shoji Tobayama *(Sr Exec Officer)*
Haruhiko Sekiguchi *(Exec VP)*

Board of Directors:
Akira Matsumoto
Umran Beba
Kazuo Ichijo
Shuji Ito
Koji Kioka
Yuzaburo Mogi
Hong-Ming Wei

U.S. Subsidiary:

Calbee America, Inc. (1)
2600 Maxwell Way
Fairfield, CA 94534 (100%)
Tel.: (707) 427-2500
Fax: (707) 427-2900
E-Mail: info@calbeeamerica.com
Web Site: www.calbeeamerica.com
Emp.: 60
Snack Food Mfr & Distr
S.I.C.: 2096
N.A.I.C.S.: 311919
Gene Jensen *(Pres)*

CALCIALIMENT

ZI de la Gare
22690 Pleudihen-sur-Rance, France
Tel.: (33) 296832142
Fax: (33) 296833150
E-Mail: contact@calcialiment.fr
Web Site: www.calcialiment.com
Sales Range: $10-24.9 Million
Emp.: 51

Business Description:
Animal Feed Mfr
S.I.C.: 2048
N.A.I.C.S.: 311119

Personnel:
Francois Lognone *(Dir-Publication)*

CALCITECH LTD.

10 route de l'aeroport
1215 Geneva, Switzerland
Tel.: (41) 227883092
Fax: (41) 22 788 3092
E-Mail: nick@calcitech.com
Web Site: www.calcitech.com
CLKTF—(OTC)
Rev.: $96,000
Assets: $10,322,000
Liabilities: $5,355,000
Net Worth: $4,967,000
Earnings: ($731,000)
Emp.: 4
Fiscal Year-end: 12/31/12

Business Description:
Chemical Mfr
S.I.C.: 2899
N.A.I.C.S.: 325998

Personnel:
Roger A. Leopard *(Chm, Pres & CEO)*

Board of Directors:
Roger A. Leopard

CalciTech Ltd.—(Continued)

Michael James Brindley Brickell
John O'Kelly-Lynch

CALCOM VISION LTD.

B-16 Side C Surajpur Industrial Area
Noida, Uttar Pradesh, 201306, India
Tel.: (91) 120 2569761
Fax: (91) 120 2569769
E-Mail: support@calcomindia.com
Web Site: www.calcomindia.com
517236—(BOM)
Rev.: $3,620,770
Assets: $2,227,729
Liabilities: $5,565,986
Net Worth: ($3,338,257)
Earnings: ($57,104)
Emp.: 240
Fiscal Year-end: 03/31/13

Business Description:
Television Mfr
S.I.C.: 3651
N.A.I.C.S.: 334310

Personnel:
Sushil Kumar Malik *(Chm & Mng Dir)*
Aijaz Ghaffar *(Vice Chm)*
Anil Vaish *(Compliance Officer)*

Board of Directors:
Sushil Kumar Malik
S. K. Bhattacharya
Aijaz Ghaffar
Bharat Bhusan Jain
Hamidulla Khan

Transfer Agent:
Abhipra Capital Limited
Ground Fl Abhipra Complex Dilkhush Industrial Area A-387 GT Karnal Rd
Delhi, India

CALCUTTA STOCK EXCHANGE ASSOCIATION LTD.

7 Lyons Range
Kolkata, 700 001, India
Tel.: (91) 3322104470
Fax: (91) 22313021
E-Mail: cseadmn@cse-india.com
Web Site: www.cse-india.com
Emp.: 125

Business Description:
Stock Exchange Services
S.I.C.: 6231
N.A.I.C.S.: 523210

Personnel:
Dhiraj Chakraborty *(Deputy Gen Mgr-Acct-Admin)*

CALDERA RESOURCES INC.

1155 blvd Rene-Levesque West Ste 2500
Montreal, QC, H3B 2K4, Canada
Tel.: (514) 813-9200
Fax: (514) 221-4386
E-Mail: bmavridis@calderaresources.com
Web Site: www.calderaresources.com
Year Founded: 1950
CDR—(TSXV)

Business Description:
Gold Exploration Services
S.I.C.: 1041
N.A.I.C.S.: 212221

Personnel:
Bill Mavridis *(Pres)*

Legal Counsel:
Newhouse Strategic Counsel
1155 Rene-Leveque West Suite 2500
Montreal, QC, H3B 2K4, Canada

Transfer Agent:
Equity Transfer & Trust Company
200 University Avenue Ste 400
Toronto, ON, M5H 4H1, Canada
Tel.: (416) 361-0152
Fax: (416) 361-0470

Co-Headquarters:

Caldera Resources Inc. (1)
1 Charles Street Suite 8
Perth, WA, 6152, Australia
Tel.: (61) 893682800
Fax: (61) 893677705
E-Mail: calderares@bigpond.com
Web Site: www.calderares.com
Diamond Mining
S.I.C.: 1499
N.A.I.C.S.: 212399
John L. Daniels *(Chm)*
Christopher W. Reindler *(Pres & CEO)*

THE CALDWELL PARTNERS INTERNATIONAL INC.

165 Avenue Road Suite 600
Toronto, ON, M5R 3S4, Canada
Tel.: (416) 920-7702
Fax: (416) 922-8646
E-Mail: leaders@caldwellpartners.com
Web Site: www.caldwellpartners.com
Year Founded: 1970
CWL—(TSX)
Rev.: $33,600,852
Assets: $22,598,418
Liabilities: $12,433,949
Net Worth: $10,164,470
Earnings: ($280,218)
Emp.: 107
Fiscal Year-end: 08/31/13

Business Description:
Executive Search & Consulting Services
S.I.C.: 8999
N.A.I.C.S.: 541612

Personnel:
G. Edmund King *(Chm)*
John N. Wallace *(Pres & CEO)*
Jim Bethmann *(Mng Partner-Dallas)*
Gerry Cameron *(Mng Partner-New York)*
Mercedes Chatfield-Taylor *(Mng Partner-San Francisco)*
Darin A. DeWitt *(Mng Partner-Los Angeles)*
Jodie Emery *(Mng Partner-Stamford)*
Les Gombik *(Mng Partner-Calgary)*
Kristin Hebert *(Mng Partner-San Francisco)*
Paul Heller *(Mng Partner-New York)*
Jeff Lemming *(Mng Partner-Atlanta)*
Neal Maslan *(Mng Partner-Los Angeles)*
Harry Parslow *(Mng Partner-Vancouver)*
Elan Pratzer *(Mng Partner-Toronto)*
Drew Railton *(Mng Partner-Vancouver)*
Peter Reed *(Mng Partner-Stamford)*
Smooch Repovich Reynolds *(Mng Partner-Los Angeles)*
Denise Tobin *(Mng Partner-Toronto)*
John Wasley *(Mng Partner-Los Angeles)*
Dave Winston *(Mng Partner-Dallas)*
Michael Ballenger *(Partner-San Francisco)*
Scott Bilby *(Partner-New York)*
Kelly Blair *(Partner-Toronto)*
Michael DeCosta *(Partner-Stamford)*
Jeff Freeborough *(Partner-Toronto)*
Mike Gooley *(Partner-Toronto)*
Constance Kassouf *(Partner-New York)*
Sean McLean *(Partner-Calgary)*
Avo Oudabachian *(Partner-Toronto)*
Heather Ring *(Partner-Toronto)*
Richard Stein *(Partner-New York)*
C. Christopher Beck *(CFO & Sec)*

Board of Directors:
G. Edmund King
Paul Daoust
Richard D. Innes
John N. Wallace
Kathryn A. Welsh

Legal Counsel:
Miller Thomson LLP
Toronto, ON, Canada

Transfer Agent:
Valiant Trust Company
Suite 2950, 130 King Street West
Toronto, ON, Canada

Subsidiaries:

Caldwell Interim Executives Inc. (1)
165 Ave Rd
Toronto, ON, M5R 3S4, Canada
Tel.: (416) 920-7702
Human Resource Consulting Services
S.I.C.: 8999
N.A.I.C.S.: 541612

Prince Arthur Advertising Inc. (1)
165 Ave Rd
Toronto, ON, M5R 3S4, Canada
Tel.: (416) 920-7702
Fax: (416) 922-8646
Toll Free: (888) 366-3827
Web Site: www.caldwellpartners.com
Advertising Agencies & Consultants
S.I.C.: 7311
N.A.I.C.S.: 541810
John Wallace *(Pres & CEO)*

CALEDONIA INVESTMENTS PLC

Cayzer House 30 Buckingham Gate
London, SW1E 6NN, United Kingdom
Tel.: (44) 2078028080
Fax: (44) 2078028090
E-Mail: enquiries@caledonia.com
Web Site: www.caledonia.com
CLDN—(LSE)
Rev.: $514,058,895
Assets: $2,179,104,342
Liabilities: $164,246,160
Net Worth: $2,014,858,182
Earnings: $319,174,509
Emp.: 767
Fiscal Year-end: 03/31/13

Business Description:
Investment Services
S.I.C.: 6211
N.A.I.C.S.: 523999

Personnel:
William P. Wyatt *(CEO)*
Graeme P. Denison *(Sec & Assoc Dir)*

Board of Directors:
Roderick D. Kent
Charles M. Allen-Jones
Stuart Bridges
Charles W. Cayzer
James M. B. Cayzer-Colvin
Richard Goblet d'Alviella
Charles H. Gregson
Stephen Anthony King
Robert B. Woods
William P. Wyatt

Legal Counsel:
Freshfields Bruckhaus Deringer LLP
65 Fleet Street
London, United Kingdom

Capita Registrars
The Registry 34 Beckenham Road
Beckenham, United Kingdom

Subsidiaries:

The Amber Chemical Company Ltd. (1)
Amber House Showground Road
Bridgwater, TA6 6AJ, United Kingdom (100%)
Tel.: (44) 1278500004
Fax: (44) 1278446585
E-Mail: abc@amberchemical.com
Web Site: www.amberchemical.com
Emp.: 50
Organic Chemical Mfr
S.I.C.: 2869
N.A.I.C.S.: 325199
Joachim Roeser *(CEO & Mng Dir)*

Subsidiary:

ACC Silicones Ltd. (2)
Amber House Showground Road
Bridgwater, TA6 6AJ, United Kingdom (100%)
Tel.: (44) 1278411400
Fax: (44) 1278411444
E-Mail: info@acc-silicones.com
Web Site: www.acc-silicones.com
Emp.: 45
Space Research & Technology
S.I.C.: 9661
N.A.I.C.S.: 927110
Maurizio Macchi *(Mng Dir)*

Caledonia Group Services Ltd (1)
Cayzer House
London, United Kingdom (100%)
Tel.: (44) 2078028080
Fax: (44) 2078028090
E-Mail: enquiries@caledonia.com
Web Site: www.caledonia.com
Emp.: 50
Miscellaneous Financial Investment Activities
S.I.C.: 6211
N.A.I.C.S.: 523999
Will Wyatt *(CEO)*

Caledonia Treasury Ltd (1)
Cayzer House 30 Buckingham Gate
London, SW1E 6NN, United Kingdom
Tel.: (44) 2078028080
Investment Management Services
S.I.C.: 6211
N.A.I.C.S.: 523999

Edinmore Holdings Ltd. (1)
2 Rutland Square
Edinburgh, EH1 2AS, United Kingdom UK (100%)
Tel.: (44) 1312298800
Fax: (44) 1312294827
Web Site: www.edinmore.co.uk
Investment Holding Company
S.I.C.: 6719
N.A.I.C.S.: 551112

Edinmore Investments Ltd (1)
Cayzer House 30 Buckingham Gate
London, SW1E 6NN, United Kingdom
Tel.: (44) 2078028080
Fax: (44) 2078028090
Real Estate Management Services
S.I.C.: 6531
N.A.I.C.S.: 531390

Sloane Club Holdings Ltd. (1)
52 Lower Sloane St
SW1W 8BS London, United Kingdom (100%)
Tel.: (44) 2077309131
Fax: (44) 2077306146
E-Mail: reservations@sloaneclub.co.uk
Web Site: www.sloaneclub.co.uk
Emp.: 75
Miscellaneous Financial Investment Activities
S.I.C.: 6211
N.A.I.C.S.: 523999
Tim Ingran *(CEO)*

Sterling Industries PLC (1)
DL Group Buliding George Smith Way
Yeovil, DA22 8QR, United Kingdom (100%)
Tel.: (44) 1935478850
Fax: (44) 1935478852
E-Mail: info@sterling-industries.com
Web Site: www.sterling-industries.com
Emp.: 4
Engineering Services
S.I.C.: 8711
N.A.I.C.S.: 541330
William Wiatt *(Mng Dir)*

U.S. Subsidiaries:

Siovation (1)
1270 Progress Center Ave Ste 200
Lawrenceville, GA 30043
Mailing Address:
PO Box 768
Lawrenceville, GA 30046
Tel.: (770) 339-4460
Fax: (770) 339-4464
Toll Free: (800) 822-4460
E-Mail: orders@siovation.com
Web Site: www.siovation.com

Emp.: 20
Cleaning Products Mfr
S.I.C.: 2842
N.A.I.C.S.: 325612
Bernie Cobb *(Pres)*

CALEDONIA MINING CORPORATION

Suite 1201 67 Yonge Street
Toronto, ON, M5E 1J8, Canada
Tel.: (416) 369-9835
Fax: (416) 369-0449
E-Mail: info@caledoniamining.com
Web Site: www.caledoniamining.com
CAL—(AIM OTC TSX)
Rev.: $74,771,178
Assets: $71,397,475
Liabilities: $16,111,076
Net Worth: $55,286,398
Earnings: $7,313,999
Emp.: 850
Fiscal Year-end: 12/31/12

Business Description:
Gold Mining Services
S.I.C.: 1041
N.A.I.C.S.: 212221

Personnel:
Leigh Alan Wilson *(Chm)*
Stefan E. Hayden *(Pres & CEO)*
Steve Curtis *(CFO & VP-Fin)*
Dana Roets *(COO)*

Board of Directors:
Leigh Alan Wilson
Steve Curtis
Stefan E. Hayden
Johan Andries Holtzhausen
James Johnstone
John Lawson Kelly
Richard J. Patricio

Legal Counsel:
Tupper, Jonsson & Yeadon
1710-1177 West Hastings Street
Vancouver, BC, Canada

Borden Ladner Gervais LLP
Suite 4100 Scotia Plaza 40 King Street West
Toronto, ON, Canada

Transfer Agent:
Equity Transfer & Trust Company
200 University Avenue Ste 400
Toronto, ON, M5H 4H1, Canada
Tel.: (416) 361-0152
Fax: (416) 361-0470

Non-U.S. Subsidiaries:

Caledonia Holdings Zimbabwe (Limited) **(1)**
6th Floor Red Bridge East Gate Robert Mugabe Road
PO Box CY1277
Causeway, Harare, Zimbabwe
Tel.: (263) 4701151
Fax: (263) 4701153
E-Mail: harare.info@caledoniazim.com
Web Site: www.caledoniazim.com
Emp.: 600
Mining Services
S.I.C.: 1099
N.A.I.C.S.: 212299
Patrick Mubzuca *(Sr Mgr-Stores)*

Caledonia Holdings Zimbabwe (Private) Limited **(1)**
Causeway
PO Box CY1277
Harare, Zimbabwe
Tel.: (263) 4701151
Fax: (263) 4701153
E-Mail: harare@caledoniazim.com
Web Site: www.caledoniamining.com
Emp.: 3
Precious Metal Mining Services
S.I.C.: 1041
N.A.I.C.S.: 212221
Caxton Mangezi *(Gen Mgr)*

Eersteling Gold Mining Corporation Limited **(1)**
24 9th Street Houghton Estate
Johannesburg, Gauteng, 2198, South Africa
Tel.: (27) 114472499
Fax: (27) 114472554
Gold Mining Services
S.I.C.: 1041
N.A.I.C.S.: 212221
Trevor Tearton *(VP)*

Greenstone Management Services (Pty) Ltd. **(1)**
PO Box 834
Saxonwold, 2134, South Africa
Tel.: (27) 114472499
Fax: (27) 114472554
E-Mail: info@caledoniamining.com
Emp.: 10
Mining Sevices
S.I.C.: 1099
N.A.I.C.S.: 212299
Stefan Hayden *(CEO)*

CALEDONIAN TRUST PLC

61a North Castle Street
Edinburgh, EH2 3LJ, United Kingdom
Tel.: (44) 1312200416
Fax: (44) 1312200417
E-Mail: webmail@caledoniantrust.com
Web Site: www.caledoniantrust.com
CNN—(AIM)
Rev.: $527,483
Assets: $32,552,325
Liabilities: $5,418,544
Net Worth: $27,133,781
Earnings: ($97,916)
Emp.: 8
Fiscal Year-end: 06/30/13

Business Description:
Real Estate Development & Investment Services
S.I.C.: 6531
N.A.I.C.S.: 531390

Personnel:
I. Douglas Lowe *(Chm & CEO)*
Michael J. Baynham *(Sec)*

Board of Directors:
I. Douglas Lowe
Michael J. Baynham
Roderick J. Pearson

Subsidiaries:

Caledonian City Developments Ltd. **(1)**
61a N Castle St
Edinburgh, Scotland, EH2 3LJ, United Kingdom
Tel.: (44) 191 2221010
Fax: (44) 131 2200417
Emp.: 2
Property Development Services
S.I.C.: 6531
N.A.I.C.S.: 531311
Michael J Baynham *(Sec)*

Caledonian Scottish Developments Ltd. **(1)**
61A N Castle St
Edinburgh, Scotland, EH2 3LJ, United Kingdom
Tel.: (44) 1312200416
Fax: (44) 1312200417
Property Development Services
S.I.C.: 6531
N.A.I.C.S.: 531311
Michael J Baynham *(Sec)*

South Castle Properties Ltd. **(1)**
61a N Castle St
Edinburgh, Scotland, EH2 3LJ, United Kingdom
Tel.: (44) 1312200416
Fax: (44) 1312200417
E-Mail: mail@caledoniantrust.com
Web Site: www.caledoniantrust.com
Emp.: 2
Property Investment Services
S.I.C.: 6531
N.A.I.C.S.: 531311
Michael J Baynham *(Sec)*

West Castle Properties Ltd. **(1)**
61A N Castle St
Edinburgh, Scotland, EH2 3LJ, United Kingdom
Tel.: (44) 1312200416
Fax: (44) 1312200417
E-Mail: mail@caledoniantrust.com
Web Site: www.caledoniantrust.com
Property Investment Services
S.I.C.: 6531
N.A.I.C.S.: 531311
Michael Baynham *(Gen Mgr)*

CALEFFI - S.P.A.

Via Belfiore 24
46049 Viadana, MN, Italy
Tel.: (39) 03757881
Fax: (39) 0375788288
E-Mail: info@caleffionline.it
Web Site: www.caleffionline.it
Year Founded: 1967
CLF—(ITA)
Sales Range: $75-99.9 Million
Emp.: 191

Business Description:
Home Furnishing Mfr & Retailer
S.I.C.: 2391
N.A.I.C.S.: 314120

Personnel:
Giuliana Caleffi *(Chm)*
Guido Ferretti *(CEO)*
Giovanni Bozzetti *(CFO)*

Board of Directors:
Giuliana Caleffi
Rita Federici Caleffi
Guido Ferretti
Roberto Negrini

CALEFFI S.P.A.

SR 229 N 25
I-28010 Fontaneto D'Agogna, NO, Italy
Tel.: (39) 03228491
Fax: (39) 0322863723
E-Mail: info@caleffi.it
Web Site: www.caleffi.it
Year Founded: 1961
Sales Range: $350-399.9 Million
Emp.: 912

Business Description:
Hydronic Systems Mfr & Distr
Import Export
S.I.C.: 5074
N.A.I.C.S.: 423720

Personnel:
Marco Caleffi *(Chm)*

U.S. Subsidiary:

Caleffi North America, Inc. **(1)**
3883 W Milwaukee Rd
Milwaukee, WI 53208
Tel.: (414) 421-1000
Fax: (414) 238-2366
E-Mail: sales@caleffi.com
Web Site: www.caleffi.us
Emp.: 16
Hydronic Systems Distr
S.I.C.: 5074
N.A.I.C.S.: 423720
Mark Olson *(Gen Mgr)*

Non-U.S. Subsidiaries:

Altecnic Ltd. **(1)**
Mustang Drive
Stafford, ST16 1GW, United Kingdom
Tel.: (44) 1785218200
Fax: (44) 1785218201
E-Mail: sales@altecnic.co.uk
Web Site: www.altecnic.co.uk
Emp.: 50
Hydronic Systems Distr
S.I.C.: 5074
N.A.I.C.S.: 423720
Allan Sherwin *(Mng Dir)*

Caleffi Armaturen GmbH **(1)**
Daimlerstrasse 3
63165 Muhlheim, Germany
Tel.: (49) 610890910
Fax: (49) 6108909170
E-Mail: info@caleffi.de
Web Site: www.caleffi.de
Emp.: 30
Hydronic Systems Distr
S.I.C.: 5074
N.A.I.C.S.: 423720
Thomas Brennecke *(Mng Dir)*

Caleffi France Consulting **(1)**
45 Avenue Gambetta
26000 Valence, France
Tel.: (33) 475599586
Fax: (33) 475841561
E-Mail: infos@caleffi.fr
Web Site: www.caleffi.fr
Emp.: 10
Hydronic Systems Distr
S.I.C.: 5074
N.A.I.C.S.: 423720

Caleffi Internationa N.V. **(1)**
Moesdijk 10-12
PO Box 10357
6000 GJ Weert, Netherlands
Tel.: (31) 495547733
Fax: (31) 495548402
E-Mail: info@caleffi.nl
Web Site: www.caleffi.nl
Emp.: 20
Hydronic Systems Distr
S.I.C.: 5074
N.A.I.C.S.: 423720
Walter Schincariol *(Mgr)*

Caleffi Lda. **(1)**
Urbanizacao das Australias lote 17
Milheiros Ap 1214, 4417-909 Maia, Codex, Portugal
Tel.: (351) 229619410
Fax: (351) 229619420
E-Mail: info@caleffi.pt
Web Site: www.caleffi.pt
Emp.: 100
Hydronic Systems Distr
S.I.C.: 5074
N.A.I.C.S.: 423720
Jorge Hamig Aires Pereira *(Gen Mgr)*

CALFRAC WELL SERVICES LTD.

411 - 8th Ave S W
Calgary, AB, T2P 1E3, Canada
Tel.: (403) 266-6000
Fax: (403) 266-7381
Toll Free: (866) 770-3722
E-Mail: info@calfrac.com
Web Site: www.calfrac.com
CFW—(OTC TSX)
Rev.: $1,585,676,608
Assets: $1,515,702,570
Liabilities: $739,612,509
Net Worth: $776,090,061
Earnings: $95,784,761
Emp.: 3,700
Fiscal Year-end: 12/31/12

Business Description:
Oil & Gas Services
S.I.C.: 1389
N.A.I.C.S.: 213112

Personnel:
Ronald P. Mathison *(Chm)*
Douglas R. Ramsay *(Vice Chm & CEO)*
Fernando Aguilar *(Pres & COO)*
Michael J. McNulty *(CFO)*
Lindsay Robert Link *(Pres-Operating Div-United States)*
Rob Montgomery *(Pres-Canada)*
Robert L. Sutherland *(Pres-Russia)*
B. Mark Paslawski *(Gen Counsel, Sec & VP)*
Gordon A. Dibb *(Exec VP)*
Dwight M. Bobier *(Sr VP-Tech Svcs)*
Laura A. Cillis *(Sr VP-Fin)*
Stephen T. Dadge *(Sr VP-Health, Safety & Environment)*
Tom J. Medvedic *(Sr VP-Corp Dev)*

Board of Directors:
Ronald P. Mathison
Kevin R. Baker
James S. Blair
Gregory S. Fletcher
Lorne A. Gartner
Douglas R. Ramsay
R. Timothy Swinton

Legal Counsel:
Bennet Jones LLP
Calgary, AB, Canada

Calfrac Well Services Ltd.—(Continued)

Transfer Agent:
Computershare Investor Services Inc
100 University Avenue 9th Floor North Tower
Toronto, ON, Canada

Subsidiary:

Calfrac Well Services Corp. **(1)**
411-8 Ave SW
Calgary, AB, T2P 1E3, Canada
Tel.: (403) 266-6000
Fax: (403) 266-7381
Toll Free: (866) 770-3722
E-Mail:
Web Site: www.Calfrac.com
Emp.: 120
Oil & Gas Wells Drilling Services
S.I.C.: 1381
N.A.I.C.S.: 213111
Doug Ramsay *(CEO)*

CALGARY CO-OPERATIVE ASSOCIATION LIMITED

110 151 86th Avenue SE
Calgary, AB, T2H 3A5, Canada
Tel.: (403) 219-6025
Fax: (403) 299-5445
E-Mail: info@calgarycoop.com
Web Site: www.calgarycoop.com
Year Founded: 1956
Sls.: $1,156,998,525
Assets: $454,121,019
Liabilities: $115,074,713
Net Worth: $339,046,306
Earnings: $49,373,967
Emp.: 3,500
Fiscal Year-end: 11/03/12
Business Description:
Food, Drugs & Petroleum Retailer; General Merchandise Stores
S.I.C.: 5399
N.A.I.C.S.: 452990
Personnel:
Terry Geib *(Chm)*
Laura Sullivan *(Vice Chm)*
Deane Collinson *(CEO)*
Barry Heinrich *(CFO)*
Board of Directors:
Terry Geib
Johanna Bates
Stuart Cantrill
Myra D'Souza Kormann
Peggy LeSueur
Elaine Smith
Rick Smith
Laura Sullivan
Lisa Wise

Subsidiary:

Calgary Co-op Home Health Care Limited **(1)**
9309 MacLeod Trail SW
Calgary, AB, T2J 0P6, Canada
Tel.: (403) 252-2266
Fax: (403) 259-8384
Emp.: 50
Home Health Care Services
S.I.C.: 8082
N.A.I.C.S.: 621610
Linda Kealey, *(Gen Mgr)*

CALGARY FLAMES LIMITED PARTNERSHIP

555 Saddledome Rise SE Station M
PO Box 1540
Calgary, AB, T2G 2W1, Canada
Tel.: (403) 777-2177
Fax: (403) 777-2171
E-Mail: customerservice@calgaryflames.com
Web Site: www.calgaryflames.com
Year Founded: 1980
Emp.: 950
Business Description:
Professional Hockey Team & Multi-Purpose Entertainment Facility
S.I.C.: 7941
N.A.I.C.S.: 711211
Personnel:
Alvin G. Libin *(Owner)*
Byron J. Seaman *(Owner)*
Daryl K. Seaman *(Co-Owner)*
Ken King *(Pres)*
Brian Burke *(Pres-Hockey Ops)*
Michael Holditch *(Sr VP-Hockey Ops & Asst Gen Mgr)*
Board of Directors:
Alvin G. Libin
Allan P. Markin

CALGARY METAL RECYCLING INC.

3415 Ogden Road SE
Calgary, AB, T2G 4N4, Canada
Tel.: (403) 262-4542
Fax: (403) 262-1114
E-Mail: info@calgarymetal.com
Web Site: www.calgarymetal.com
Year Founded: 1918
Rev.: $10,323,021
Emp.: 70
Business Description:
Metal Recycling Services
S.I.C.: 4953
N.A.I.C.S.: 562920

CALGARY TENT & AWNING LTD.

Bay 142 1220 28th Street NE
Calgary, AB, Canada
Tel.: (403) 273-8368
Fax: (403) 248-7482
Toll Free: (888) 855-8368
E-Mail: info@calgarytent.com
Web Site: www.calgarytent.com
Year Founded: 1928
Sales Range: $10-24.9 Million
Emp.: 10
Business Description:
Commercial & Residential Textile Products Mfr
S.I.C.: 7389
N.A.I.C.S.: 541490
Personnel:
Marty Way *(Pres)*

CALGRO M3 HOLDINGS LIMITED

33 Ballyclare Drive Ballywoods Office Park Cedarwood House 1st floor
Bryanston, Sandton, South Africa
Mailing Address:
Private Bag X33
Craighall, 2024, South Africa
Tel.: (27) 861 225476
Fax: (27) 86 509 6133
E-Mail: info@calgrom3.com
Web Site: www.calgrom3.com
Year Founded: 1995
CGRE—(JSE)
Rev.: $89,180,616
Assets: $90,378,730
Liabilities: $53,812,892
Net Worth: $36,565,838
Earnings: $10,198,605
Emp.: 440
Fiscal Year-end: 02/28/13
Business Description:
Residential Building Development Services
S.I.C.: 1521
N.A.I.C.S.: 236115
Personnel:
Ben Pierre Malherbe *(CEO)*
Deon Noel Steyn *(COO)*
Wayne Williams *(Chief Legal Officer & Sec)*
Board of Directors:
Pumla Fundiswa Radebe
Mduduzi Edward Gama
John Braidwood Gibbon
Willem Jakobus Lategan
Ben Pierre Malherbe
Hatla Ntene
Ralph Bruce Patmore
Deon Noel Steyn
Frederik Johannes Steyn
Transfer Agent:
Computershare Investor Services (Pty) Ltd
70 Marshall Street
Johannesburg, South Africa

CALHOME PROPERTIES

12 800 MacLeod Trail S
Calgary, AB, T2G 2M3, Canada
Tel.: (403) 268-1450
Fax: (403) 268-1948
Year Founded: 1978
Rev.: $43,047,000
Emp.: 100
Business Description:
Engineering Construction Services
S.I.C.: 1629
N.A.I.C.S.: 237990
Personnel:
Jim Anderson *(Mgr-House)*

CALIAN TECHNOLOGIES LTD.

340 Legget Drive Suite 101
Ottawa, ON, K2K 1Y6, Canada
Tel.: (613) 599-8600
Fax: (613) 599-8650
Toll Free: (877) 225-4264
E-Mail: ir@calian.com
Web Site: www.calian.com
Year Founded: 1982
CTY—(TSX)
Rev.: $235,399,521
Assets: $103,455,739
Liabilities: $35,612,050
Net Worth: $67,843,689
Earnings: $14,076,398
Emp.: 2,400
Fiscal Year-end: 09/30/12
Business Description:
Management Consulting, Information Technology, Systems Integration, Outsourcing & Staffing Services
S.I.C.: 8999
N.A.I.C.S.: 541690
Personnel:
Kenneth J. Loeb *(Chm)*
Raymond Basler *(Pres & CEO)*
Jacqueline Gauthier *(CFO, Sec & VP)*
Kevin Ford *(Pres-Bus & Tech Svcs Div)*
Patrick Thera *(Pres-Sys Engrg Div)*
Board of Directors:
Kenneth J. Loeb
Raymond Basler
C. William Hewson
David Tkachuk
Richard Vickers
George Weber
Transfer Agent:
CIBC Mellon Trust Company
PO Box 7010
Adelaide Street Postal Station, Toronto, ON, M5C 2W9, Canada
Tel.: (416) 643-5500
Fax: (416) 643-5501
Toll Free: (800) 387-0825

Subsidiary:

Calian Ltd. **(1)**
340 Legget Drive Suite 101
Ottawa, ON, K2K 1Y6, Canada (100%)
Tel.: (613) 599-8600
Fax: (613) 599-8650
E-Mail: info@calian.com
Web Site: www.calian.com
Emp.: 80
Provider of Technical & Professional Services
S.I.C.: 7389
N.A.I.C.S.: 541990

Branch:

Calian Ltd. - Toronto **(2)**
55 City Centre Dr Ste 503
Mississauga, ON, L5B 1M3, Canada
Tel.: (905) 848-2818
Fax: (905) 848-4944
Toll Free: (877) 225-4264
Web Site: www.calian.com
Business Software Development Services
S.I.C.: 7371
N.A.I.C.S.: 541511

Division:

Calian Ltd. - SED Systems Division **(2)**
18 Innovation Blvd
PO Box 1464
Saskatoon, SK, S7K 3P7, Canada
Tel.: (306) 931-3425
Fax: (306) 933-1486
E-Mail: marketing@sedsystems.ca
Web Site: www.sedsystems.ca
Sls.: $61,129,200
Emp.: 300
Satellite Telemetry Operation Services
S.I.C.: 4899
N.A.I.C.S.: 517919
Patrick Thera *(Pres)*

U.S. Subsidiary:

Calian Technology (U.S.) Ltd. **(1)**
200 12th St S Ste 1101
Arlington, VA 22202
Tel.: (703) 418-0636
Fax: (703) 392-0980
Web Site: www.calian.com
Emp.: 40
Technical & Professional Services
S.I.C.: 7389
N.A.I.C.S.: 541990
Michael Niggel *(CEO)*

CALIBRE GROUP LTD

Calibre House Level 2 50 St Georges Terrace
Perth, WA, 6000, Australia
Mailing Address:
PO Box Z5426
Perth, WA, 6831, Australia
Tel.: (61) 8 9265 3000
Fax: (61) 8 9265 3012
E-Mail: enquiries@calibregroup.com
Web Site: www.calibregroup.com
Year Founded: 2002
CGH—(ASX)
Business Description:
Engineering Services
S.I.C.: 8711
N.A.I.C.S.: 541330
Personnel:
Ray Horsburgh *(Chm)*
Peter Reichler *(Mng Dir)*
Michael Silbert *(Chief Legal Counsel & Sec)*
Board of Directors:
Ray Horsburgh
Peter Housden
Brian Macdonald
Ray Munro
Geoff Tomlinson
Alex Williams

CALIBRE MINING CORP.

Suite 1620 - 1066 West Hastings Street
Vancouver, BC, V6E 3X1, Canada
Tel.: (604) 681-9944
Fax: (604) 681-9955
E-Mail: calibre@calibremining.com
Web Site: www.calibremining.com
CXB—(OTC TSXV)
Int. Income: $39,001
Assets: $16,803,926
Liabilities: $172,295
Net Worth: $16,631,631
Earnings: ($2,663,460)
Fiscal Year-end: 12/31/12

Business Description:
Gold, Silver & Copper Exploration Services
S.I.C.: 1041
N.A.I.C.S.: 212221
Personnel:
Douglas B. Forster *(Chm)*
Gregory F. Smith *(Pres & CEO)*
Paulo Santos *(CFO)*
Board of Directors:
Douglas B. Forster
Edward Farrauto
Blayne Johnson
John Reynolds
George Salamis
Gregory F. Smith

CALICO RESOURCES CORP.

Suite 2300 1066 West Hastings Street
Vancouver, BC, V6E 3X2, Canada
Tel.: (604) 681-6855
Fax: (604) 408-8893
Web Site: www.calicoresources.com
CKB—(OTC TSXV)
Business Description:
Metal Mining
S.I.C.: 1099
N.A.I.C.S.: 212299
Personnel:
Arden Buck Morrow *(Chm, Pres & CEO)*
Alexander S. Peck *(CFO)*
Pamela White *(Sec)*
Board of Directors:
Arden Buck Morrow
Roderick Chisholm
Nicholas Glass
Kevin Milledge
Allan W. Williams
Transfer Agent:
Olympia Trust Company
Suite 1003 750 West Pender Street
Vancouver, BC, V6C 2T8, Canada

CALIDA HOLDING AG

Industrie Muenigen
CH-6210 Sursee, Switzerland
Tel.: (41) 419254525
Fax: (41) 419254284
E-Mail: info@calida.com
Web Site: www.calida-group.com
CALN—(SWX)
Rev.: $219,222,844
Assets: $187,464,932
Liabilities: $43,190,069
Net Worth: $144,274,863
Earnings: $22,225,357
Emp.: 1,586
Fiscal Year-end: 12/31/12
Business Description:
Holding Company; Men's & Women's Clothing Mfr
S.I.C.: 6719
N.A.I.C.S.: 551112
Personnel:
Thomas Lustenberger *(Chm-Supervisory Bd)*
Alfred M. Niederer *(Vice Chm-Supervisory Bd)*
Felix Sulzberger *(CEO)*
Thomas Stocklin *(CFO)*
Daniel Gemperle *(COO & CIO)*
Supervisory Board of Directors:
Thomas Lustenberger
Marco Gadola
Beat Gruring
Erich Kellenberger
Alfred M. Niederer
Felix Sulzberger
Marianne Tesler
Subsidiaries:

Calida AG (1)
Industrie Munigen Sursee
6210 Lucerne, Switzerland (100%)
Tel.: (41) 9254525
Fax: (41) 9254284
E-Mail: info@calida.com
Emp.: 300
Womens & Girls Cut & Sew Lingerie Loungewear & Nightwear Mfr
S.I.C.: 2389
N.A.I.C.S.: 315240
Andreas Lindemann *(Mng Dir)*

Non-U.S. Subsidiaries:

Aubade Italia S.R.L. (1)
Via Magnaghi 2/8
16129 Genoa, Italy (100%)
Tel.: (39) 59553669
Web Site: aubade.it/
Womens & Girls Cut & Sew Lingerie Loungewear & Nightwear Mfr
S.I.C.: 5699
N.A.I.C.S.: 315240
Paulo Gallitto *(Mng Dir)*

Aubade Paris SAS (1)
10 Rue du Colonel Driant
75001 Paris, France (100%)
Tel.: (33) 170992000
Fax: (33) 170992026
E-Mail: conso@aubadepro.com
Web Site: www.aubade.com
Emp.: 130
Womens & Girls Cut & Sew Lingerie Loungewear & Nightwear Mfr
S.I.C.: 5699
N.A.I.C.S.: 315240
Philippe Bernaug *(Mng Dir)*
Felix Sulzberger *(Mng Dir)*

Aubade Paris (UK) Ltd. (1)
1 Pury Hill Cottage
Alderton Rd Paulerspury Nort, Towcester, United Kingdom (100%)
Tel.: (44) 1327811289
Fax: (44) 1327811461
Web Site: www.aubade.com
Emp.: 3
Womens & Girls Cut & Sew Lingerie Loungewear & Nightwear Mfr
S.I.C.: 2389
N.A.I.C.S.: 315240
Laura Mclellan *(Mng Dir)*

Belaubade SA (1)
Avenue Victor Olivier 19
Brussels, Belgium (100%)
Tel.: (32) 25233890
Piece Goods Notions & Other Dry Goods Whslr
S.I.C.: 5131
N.A.I.C.S.: 424310

Lafuma SA (1)
6 Rue Victor Lafuma
BP 60
26140 Anneyron, France (50.6%)
Tel.: (33) 475313131
Fax: (33) 475315726
E-Mail: infos-finance@lafuma.fr
Web Site: www.groupe-lafuma.com
LAF—(EUR)
Sales Range: $300-349.9 Million
Emp.: 2,001
Outdoor Garments, Backpacks, Tents, Sleeping Bags, Footwear & Camping Equipment Mfr
S.I.C.: 3949
N.A.I.C.S.: 339920
Philippe Joffard *(Chm & CEO)*

Subsidiaries:

Eider (2)
Parc Altais Annecy 70 Rue Cassiopee
74650 Chavanod, France
Tel.: (33) 450102360
Fax: (33) 450102370
E-Mail: contact@eider.com
Web Site: www.eider.com
Emp.: 50
Clothing & Footwear Mfr
S.I.C.: 2389
N.A.I.C.S.: 316210
Thibaut Cornet *(Gen Mgr)*

Lafprom S.A.S. (2)
5 rue de la Terrasse
Paris, F 75017, France
Tel.: (33) 145006540
Fax: (33) 148871267
Emp.: 1,000
Clothing & Furnishings Whslr
S.I.C.: 5611
N.A.I.C.S.: 448110
Philippe Joffrard *(CEO)*

Non-U.S. Subsidiary:

Lafprom Hong Kong Ltd (3)
1 F Chinachem Hollywood Ctr
1 13 Hollywood Rd, Central, China (Hong Kong)
Tel.: (852) 25266632
Fax: (852) 25379908
Web Site: www.lafuma.com
Men Clothing Stores
S.I.C.: 5611
N.A.I.C.S.: 448110

Millet (2)
21 Rue du Pre Faucon PAE les Glaisins
74943 Annecy-le-Vieux, Cedex, France
Tel.: (33) 450695959
Fax: (33) 450695960
E-Mail: millet@millet.fr
Web Site: www.millet.fr
Emp.: 70
Mountain Clothing & Backpacks Mfr
S.I.C.: 2393
N.A.I.C.S.: 314910
Frederick Ducruet *(Gen Mgr)*

U.S. Subsidiary:

Lafuma America (2)
140 Old Laramie Trl Ste 3
Lafayette, CO 80026
Tel.: (303) 527-1460
Fax: (303) 527-1464
Toll Free: (800) 514-4807
E-Mail: lafuma@lafumausa.com
Web Site: www.lafumausa.com
Emp.: 15
Clothing & Footwear Mfr
S.I.C.: 2389
N.A.I.C.S.: 316210
Guillaume Linossier *(Gen Mgr)*

Non-U.S. Subsidiaries:

Lafuma BV (2)
PlesmanStraat 1
PO Box 180
3830 Leusden, Netherlands
Tel.: (31) 334320499
Fax: (31) 334320944
E-Mail: infonl@lafuma.com
Web Site: www.lafuma.com
Emp.: 5
Fashion Womenswear Mfr
S.I.C.: 5137
N.A.I.C.S.: 424330
Ingrid Portman *(Mng Dir)*

Lafuma Group GmbH (2)
Fabrikstr 35
73266 Bietigheim-Bissingen, Germany
Tel.: (49) 702395110
Fax: (49) 7023951171
E-Mail: germany@lafuma.fr
Web Site: www.lafuma.com
Emp.: 15
Backpacks & Tents Mfr
S.I.C.: 2393
N.A.I.C.S.: 314910
Oliver Schroer *(Gen Mgr)*

Lafuma Hungaria (2)
Hard Istvanu 1 1st
9600 Sarvar, Hungary
Tel.: (36) 95320651
Fax: (36) 95323112
E-Mail: lafuma.hungaria@mail.datanet.hu
Emp.: 230
Sportswear Producer
S.I.C.: 5136
N.A.I.C.S.: 424320

CALIFORNIA SOFTWARE COMPANY LTD.

Robert V Chandran Tower 149
Velachery Tambaram Main Road
Pallikaranai, Chennai, Tamil Nadu, 600 100, India
Tel.: (91) 4442829000
Fax: (91) 4442829012
Web Site: www.calsoftgroup.com
532386—(BOM)
Sls.: $9,590,121
Assets: $27,484,311
Liabilities: $25,726,045
Net Worth: $1,758,266
Earnings: ($510,502)
Emp.: 204
Fiscal Year-end: 03/31/13
Business Description:
Enterprise Software Products
S.I.C.: 7371
N.A.I.C.S.: 541511
Personnel:
Bhavesh Rameshlal Chauhan *(CEO & Mng Dir)*
Jitendra Kumar Pal *(Compliance Officer & Sec)*
Board of Directors:
Bhavesh Rameshlal Chauhan
P. J. George
K. Chandra Pratap
Transfer Agent:
Integrated Enterprises (India) Ltd
2nd Floor Kences Towers 1 Ramakrishna Street
North Usman Road T Nagur, Chennai, 600017, India

CALIN TECHNOLOGY CO., LTD.

24 Chien Kuo Rd
Tan Tzu District, Taichung, 42760, Taiwan
Tel.: (886) 4 25353658
Fax: (886) 4 25352916
Web Site: www.calin.com.tw
4976—(TAI)
Business Description:
Optical Glass Lens Mfr
S.I.C.: 3827
N.A.I.C.S.: 333314
Personnel:
Yuan-Chyuan Lee *(Chm)*

CALLABONNA RESOURCES LIMITED

Level 17 530 Collins Street
Melbourne, VIC, 3000, Australia
Tel.: (61) 3 9618 2590
Fax: (61) 3 9620 5200
E-Mail: info@callabonna.com.au
Web Site: www.callabonna.com.au
CUU—(ASX)
Rev.: $5,900
Assets: $1,049,568
Liabilities: $178,563
Net Worth: $871,005
Earnings: ($620,780)
Emp.: 1
Fiscal Year-end: 06/30/13
Business Description:
Mineral Exploration Services
S.I.C.: 1099
N.A.I.C.S.: 212299
Personnel:
Michael Raetz *(Acting Mng Dir)*
Ian Hobson *(CFO & Sec)*
Board of Directors:
Phillip Harman
Hyunsoo Kim
Jeffrey Williams
Legal Counsel:
Baker & McKenzie
Level 19 181 William Street
Melbourne, Australia

CALLAGHAN INNOVATION RESEARCH LIMITED

(Formerly Industrial Research Limited)
69 Gracefield Road
PO Box 31310
Lower Hutt, 5040, New Zealand
Tel.: (64) 4 931 3000
Web Site: www.callaghaninnovation.govt.nz

Callaghan Innovation Research Limited—(Continued)

Year Founded: 1992
Emp.: 500
Business Description:
Scientific Research & Development, Research Funding & Business Consulting Services
S.I.C.: 8731
N.A.I.C.S.: 541712
Personnel:
Mary Quin *(CEO)*
Board of Directors:
Sue Suckling
Michelle Allan
Robin Hapi
Peter Hunter
Richard Janes
Paul Lockey
Peter Maire
Craig Richardson

CALLIDEN GROUP LIMITED

Level 7 100 Arthur Street
North Sydney, NSW, 2060, Australia
Tel.: (61) 295511111
Fax: (61) 295511155
E-Mail: customerservice@calliden.com.au
Web Site: www.calliden.com.au
CIX—(ASX)
Premiums: $179,241,200
Assets: $376,025,111
Liabilities: $276,138,784
Net Worth: $99,886,327
Earnings: $1,134,847
Emp.: 200
Fiscal Year-end: 12/31/12
Business Description:
Insurance Services
S.I.C.: 6411
N.A.I.C.S.: 524298
Personnel:
Nicholas George Kirk *(CEO)*
Anthony Dijanosic *(CFO)*
Dimi Boubolas *(Exec-Svcs)*
Stephen J. Fay *(Exec-Insurance Bus)*
Mike Hooton *(Exec-Agency Svcs)*
Nicholas John Victor Geddes *(Sec)*
Board of Directors:
Richard James Hill
Anthony Vincent Connon
Nicholas George Kirk
Maurice William Loomes
Jack Theseus Lowenstein
John Ian Messenger
Gordon Geoffrey Marsden Smith

Subsidiaries:

ARGIS Limited (1)
Level 1 467 Kiewa St
Albury, New South Wales, 2640, Australia
Tel.: (61) 260512611
Fax: (61) 260512630
Web Site: www.argis.com.au
Insurance Underwriting Agencies
S.I.C.: 6411
N.A.I.C.S.: 524298

Dawes Underwriting Australia Pty. Limited (1)
Level 1 4 Eastern Rd
Turramurra, New South Wales, 2074, Australia
Tel.: (61) 295511065
Fax: (61) 2 9144 6900
Automobile Insurance Services
S.I.C.: 6399
N.A.I.C.S.: 524128

Mansions of Australia Limited (1)
Level 7 100 Arthur St
North Sydney, NSW, 2060, Australia
Tel.: (61) 295511080
E-Mail: info@mansions.com.au
Web Site: www.mansions.com.au
Property Insurance Services
S.I.C.: 6331
N.A.I.C.S.: 524126
Rachel Adams *(Mgr-Bus Dev)*

CALLINAN ROYALTIES CORPORATION

1110 - 555 West Hastings Street
Vancouver, BC, V6B 4N4, Canada
Tel.: (604) 605-0885
Fax: (604) 605-0886
E-Mail: info@callinan.com
Web Site: www.callinan.com
Year Founded: 1927
CAA—(TSXV)
Rev.: $16,695,614
Assets: $46,632,007
Liabilities: $1,169,043
Net Worth: $45,462,964
Earnings: $8,798,223
Emp.: 6
Fiscal Year-end: 06/30/13
Business Description:
Mineral Properties Exploration Services
S.I.C.: 1081
N.A.I.C.S.: 213114
Personnel:
Brian C. Irwin *(Chm)*
Roland Butler *(Pres & CEO)*
Tamara Edwards *(CFO & Sec)*
Board of Directors:
Brian C. Irwin
Glenn R. Brown
Roland Butler
David Caulfield
Raymond Goldie
G. Ross McDonald
Legal Counsel:
Boughton Law Corporation
700-595 Burrard Street
PO Box 49290
Vancouver, BC, Canada
Transfer Agent:
Canadian Stock Transfer
1600 1066 W Hastings Street
Vancouver, BC, V6E 3X1CANS, Canada

CALLINEX MINES INC.

Suite 1110 - 555 W Hastings Street
Vancouver, BC, V6B 4N4, Canada
Tel.: (604) 605-0885
Fax: (604) 605-0886
E-Mail: info@callinex.ca
Web Site: www.callinex.ca
Year Founded: 2011
CNX—(OTC TSXV)
Rev.: $46,491
Assets: $32,406,219
Liabilities: $5,749,819
Net Worth: $26,656,400
Earnings: ($2,506,380)
Fiscal Year-end: 09/30/13
Business Description:
Metal Mining Services
S.I.C.: 1099
N.A.I.C.S.: 212299
Personnel:
Mike Muzylowski *(Chm & CEO)*
Tamara Edwards *(CFO)*
Board of Directors:
Mike Muzylowski
Nico O. Civelli
Michael Louie
A. Gordon Slade

CALLISTA PRIVATE EQUITY GMBH & CO. KG

Konrad-Zuse-Platz 8
81829 Munich, Germany
Tel.: (49) 89 207042430
Web Site: www.callista-pe.de
Business Description:
Private Equity Firm
S.I.C.: 6211
N.A.I.C.S.: 523999
Personnel:
Olaf Meier *(CEO)*
Marc Zube *(COO)*

CALLOWAY REAL ESTATE INVESTMENT TRUST

700 Applewood Crescent Suite 200
Vaughan, ON, L4K 5X3, Canada
Tel.: (905) 326-6400
Fax: (905) 326-0783
Web Site: www.callowayreit.com
CWT.UN—(OTC TSX)
Sales Range: $500-549.9 Million
Emp.: 106
Business Description:
Real Estate Investment Trust
S.I.C.: 6726
N.A.I.C.S.: 525990
Personnel:
J. Huw Thomas *(Pres & CEO)*
Mario Calabrese *(Interim CFO)*
Marc Charlebois *(COO)*
Rudy Gobin *(Exec VP-Asset Mgmt)*
Legal Counsel:
Osler, Hoskin & Harcourt LLP
Toronto, ON, Canada
Transfer Agent:
Computershare Trust Company of Canada
Toronto, ON, Canada

CALMENA ENERGY SERVICES INC.

The Dome Tower Suite 700 333 7th Avenue SW
Box 71
Calgary, AB, T2P 2Z1, Canada
Tel.: (403) 225-3879
Fax: (403) 366-2066
E-Mail: pbalkwill@calmena.com
Web Site: www.calmena.com
CEZ—(TSX)
Rev.: $162,943,734
Assets: $228,950,639
Liabilities: $99,963,621
Net Worth: $128,987,017
Earnings: ($11,061,455)
Emp.: 943
Fiscal Year-end: 12/31/12
Business Description:
Oil & Gas Exploration Services
S.I.C.: 1311
N.A.I.C.S.: 211111
Personnel:
Hank B. Swartout *(Chm)*
John R. King *(Pres & CEO)*
Peter J. Balkwill *(CFO & VP-Fin)*
Bill J. Beattie *(Sr VP-Directional Drilling)*
Marwan Bitar *(Sr VP-Middle East & North Africa)*
Mike Carter *(Sr VP-Canada)*
David Mears *(Sr VP-Brazil)*
Board of Directors:
Hank B. Swartout
Chris J. Bloomer
John A. Brussa
M. Bruce Chernoff
John R. King
David J. Rain
Legal Counsel:
Burnet, Duckworth & Palmer LLP
Suite 1400 350 7th Avenue Southwest
Calgary, AB, T2P 3N9, Canada
Tel.: (403) 263-3050
Transfer Agent:
Valiant Trust Company
Calgary, AB, Canada

CALMONT LEASING LTD

14610 Yellowhead Tr NW
Edmonton, AB, T5L 3C5, Canada
Tel.: (780) 454-0491
Fax: (780) 451-5768
Toll Free: (888) 557-7318
E-Mail: info@calmontedm.ca
Web Site: www.calmontedm.ca
Year Founded: 1977
Rev.: $51,558,355
Emp.: 270
Business Description:
New & Used Truck Dealers
S.I.C.: 7519
N.A.I.C.S.: 532120
Personnel:
Darren Currie *(Pres)*

CALOREX HEAT PUMPS LTD

The Causeway
Maldon, Essex, CM9 4XD, United Kingdom
Tel.: (44) 1621856611
Fax: (44) 1621850871
E-Mail: sales@calorex.com
Web Site: www.calorex.com
Rev.: $27,258,523
Emp.: 150
Business Description:
Heat Pump Mfr
S.I.C.: 3561
N.A.I.C.S.: 333911
Personnel:
Richard Carrington *(Mng Dir)*

CALORIC ANLAGENBAU GMBH

D-82166
D-82166 Grafelfing, Germany
Tel.: (49) 89898190
Fax: (49) 8989819104
E-Mail: info@caloric.de
Web Site: www.caloric.de
Year Founded: 1965
Rev.: $25,067,147
Emp.: 50
Business Description:
Gas Generating Plant Mfr
S.I.C.: 3569
N.A.I.C.S.: 333999
Personnel:
Florian von Linde *(Mng Dir)*

CALS REFINERIES LIMITED

21 Basant Lok Complex Vasant Vihar
New Delhi, 110 057, India
Tel.: (91) 11 40534750
Fax: (91) 11 40537914
E-Mail: info@calsrefineries.com
Web Site: www.cals.in
Year Founded: 1984
526652—(BOM)
Rev.: $204,682
Assets: $120,282,700
Liabilities: $18,679,421
Net Worth: $101,603,279
Earnings: ($1,443,524)
Fiscal Year-end: 03/31/13
Business Description:
Oil Refining Services
S.I.C.: 2911
N.A.I.C.S.: 324110
Personnel:
Deep Kumar Rastogi *(Chm)*
D. Sundararajan *(Mng Dir)*
Suvindra Kumar *(Compliance Officer & Sec)*
Board of Directors:
Deep Kumar Rastogi
R. Rajagopalan
Sameer Rajpal
Alexander Walter Schweickhardt
D. Sundararajan
Transfer Agent:
MCS Limited
F-65 1st Floor Okhla Industrial Area Phase I
New Delhi, 110 020, India

CALSONIC KANSEI CORPORATION

2-1917 Nisshin-cho Kita-ku
Saitama, 331-8501, Japan
Tel.: (81) 486602111
Telex: TOKYO 232-2174
Web Site: www.calsonickansei.co.jp
Year Founded: 1938
7248—(TKS)
Sls.: $8,369,570,000
Assets: $3,715,833,000
Liabilities: $2,112,770,000
Net Worth: $1,603,063,000
Earnings: $64,427,000
Emp.: 18,818
Fiscal Year-end: 03/31/13

Business Description:
Automotive Parts Mfr
Import Export
S.I.C.: 3714
N.A.I.C.S.: 336390

Personnel:
Katsumi Nakamura *(Chm)*
Hiroshi Moriya *(Pres & CEO)*
Seiichi Kakizawa *(CFO & Exec VP)*
Shingo Yamamoto *(CIO & Exec VP)*
Akira Fujisaki *(Exec VP)*
Kosaku Hosokawa *(Exec VP)*
Shigeo Shingyoji *(Exec VP)*
James Davies *(Sr VP)*
Koji Furukawa *(Sr VP)*
Katsuhiko Gima *(Sr VP)*
Eric Huch *(Sr VP)*
Masayoshi Kikojima *(Sr VP)*
Katsuyuki Narita *(Sr VP)*
Noboru Noda *(Sr VP)*
Yukihide Oishi *(Sr VP)*
Hiroyuki Osawa *(Sr VP)*
Hirotada Sumino *(Sr VP)*
Akihiro Tsurujima *(Sr VP)*
Hideaki Watanabe *(Sr VP)*
Toshimasa Yamane *(Sr VP)*

Board of Directors:
Katsumi Nakamura
Akira Fujisaki
Seiichi Kakizawa
Hiroshi Moriya
Shigeo Shingyoji

U.S. Subsidiary:

Calsonic Kansei North America, Inc. **(1)**
One Calsonic Way
Shelbyville, TN 37160 (100%)
Tel.: (931) 684-4490
Web Site: www.calsonic.com
Emp.: 2,300
Holding Company
S.I.C.: 3714
N.A.I.C.S.: 336390
Masaharu Sato *(Pres)*

Plant:

Calsonic Kansei North America, Inc. **(2)**
9 Holland
Irvine, CA 92618 (100%)
Mailing Address:
PO Box 350
Shelbyville, TN 37162-0350
Tel.: (949) 855-8050
Fax: (949) 951-1827
Web Site: www.calsonic.com
Emp.: 300
Automobile Electro-Mechanical System Mfr
S.I.C.: 3714
N.A.I.C.S.: 336390

Non-U.S. Subsidiaries:

Calsonic Kansei (China) Holding Company **(1)**
18F Maxdo Center 8 Xing Yi Road Hong Qiao Development Zone
Shanghai, 200336, China
Tel.: (86) 2152080707
Web Site: www.calsonickansei.co.jp/english/company/overseas.html
Electronic Component Mfr
S.I.C.: 3679
N.A.I.C.S.: 334419

Calsonic Kansei (Guangzhou) Corp. **(1)**
18 Qichacheng Donfeng Dadao
Guangzhou, 510800, China
Tel.: (86) 2086733188
Web Site: www.calsonickansei.co.jp/english/company/overseas.html
Electronic Component Mfr
S.I.C.: 3679
N.A.I.C.S.: 334419

Calsonic Kansei Mexicana, S.A. de R.L. de C.V. **(1)**
Circuito Aguascalientes Oriente 127 Parque Ind Del Valle de
Aguascalientes, 20900, Mexico
Tel.: (52) 449 910 0100
Web Site: www.calsonickansei.co.jp/english/company/overseas.html
Electronic Component Mfr
S.I.C.: 3679
N.A.I.C.S.: 334419

Calsonic Kansei (Shanghai) Corp. **(1)**
Bid No 6 Huaning Road Lane 2888 No 88
Xinzhuang, Shanghai, 201108, China
Tel.: (86) 2164897868
Web Site: www.calsonickansei.co.jp/english/company/overseas.html
Electronic Component Mfr
S.I.C.: 3679
N.A.I.C.S.: 334419

CALTAGIRONE EDITORE S.P.A.

Via Barberini 28
00187 Rome, Italy
Tel.: (39) 0645412200
Fax: (39) 0645412299
E-Mail: investor.relations@caltagironeeditore.com
Web Site: www.caltagironeeditore.com
CED—(ITA)
Rev.: $263,092,772
Assets: $1,200,938,450
Liabilities: $298,168,578
Net Worth: $902,769,872
Earnings: ($82,549,837)
Emp.: 976
Fiscal Year-end: 12/31/12

Business Description:
Newspaper & Advertising Publishing Services
S.I.C.: 3275
N.A.I.C.S.: 327420

Personnel:
Francesco Gaetano Caltagirone *(Chm)*
Azzurra Caltagirone *(Deputy Chm)*
Gaetano Caltagirone *(Deputy Chm)*

Board of Directors:
Francesco Gaetano Caltagirone
Alessandro Caltagirone
Azzurra Caltagirone
Francesco Caltagirone
Gaetano Caltagirone
Massimo Confortini
Mario Delfini
Massimo Garzilli
Albino Majore
Giampietro Nattino

Subsidiaries:

Centro Stampa Veneto SpA **(1)**
Via Torino 110
Venice, 30172, Italy (99.91%)
Tel.: (39) 0416652111
Fax: (39) 041665183
E-Mail: sistemi@gazzettino.it
Web Site: www.gazzettino.it
Emp.: 120
Periodical Publishers
S.I.C.: 2721
N.A.I.C.S.: 511120
Roberto Papetti *(Mng Dir)*

Il Gazzettino SpA **(1)**
Via Torino 110
30172 Venice, Italy (99.91%)
Tel.: (39) 041665111
Fax: (39) 041665386
Web Site: www.gazzettino.it
Newspaper Publishers
S.I.C.: 2711
N.A.I.C.S.: 511110

Il Mattino SpA **(1)**
Via Chiatamone 65
80121 Naples, Italy (100%)
Tel.: (39) 0817947111
Fax: (39) 0812451546
Web Site: www.ilmattino.it
Newspaper Publishers
S.I.C.: 2711
N.A.I.C.S.: 511110
Azzurra Caltagirone *(Deputy Chm)*

Il Messaggero SpA **(1)**
Via Del Tritone 152
00187 Rome, Italy (100%)
Tel.: (39) 0647201
Fax: (39) 064720446
Web Site: www.ilmessaggero.it
Periodical Publishers
S.I.C.: 2721
N.A.I.C.S.: 511120
Roberto Napoletano *(Mng Dir)*

Imprese Tipografiche Venete SpA **(1)**
Via Torino 110
Venice, 110, Italy (99.91%)
Tel.: (39) 041665111
Newspaper Publishers
S.I.C.: 2711
N.A.I.C.S.: 511110

Piemme SpA **(1)**
Via Umberto Novaro 18
Rome, Italy (100%)
Tel.: (39) 06377081
Fax: (39) 063724830
Media Representatives
S.I.C.: 7313
N.A.I.C.S.: 541840

Societa Editrice Padana SpA **(1)**
via Torino 110
Mestre, Italy (52%)
Tel.: (39) 540 191 970
Fax: (39) 51 344 761
Publishing Services
S.I.C.: 2711
N.A.I.C.S.: 511110

Vianini Lavori S.p.A. **(1)**
Via Montello 10
00195 Rome, Italy (55%)
Tel.: (39) 06374921
Fax: (39) 063728546
E-Mail: espero.sede@vianinigroup.it
Web Site: www.vianinigroup.it
VLA—(ITA)
Rev.: $284,935,727
Assets: $1,017,957,600
Liabilities: $271,024,406
Net Worth: $746,933,194
Earnings: $8,513,179
Emp.: 41
Fiscal Year-end: 12/31/12
Provider of Construction & Civil Engineering Services
S.I.C.: 8711
N.A.I.C.S.: 541330
Vittorio Di Paola *(Chm)*
Mario Delfini *(Vice Chm)*
Franco Cristini *(CEO)*

CALTECH SURVEYS LTD.

800 110 12th Ave SW
Calgary, AB, T2R 0G7, Canada
Tel.: (403) 263-8055
Fax: (403) 263-8058
Toll Free: (888) 263-8055
E-Mail: info@caltechsurveys.com
Web Site: www.caltechsurveys.com
Year Founded: 1990
Rev.: $13,038,400
Emp.: 110

Business Description:
Oil & Natural Gas Pipeline Surveys
S.I.C.: 8713
N.A.I.C.S.: 541370

Personnel:
Harvey Goosens *(Pres)*

CALTEX AUSTRALIA LIMITED

Level 24 2 Market Street
Sydney, NSW, 2000, Australia
Tel.: (61) 292505000
Fax: (61) 292505742
E-Mail: investor@caltex.com.au
Web Site: www.caltex.com.au
Year Founded: 1941
CTX—(ASX)
Rev.: $24,241,210,359
Assets: $5,612,371,276
Liabilities: $3,361,874,000
Net Worth: $2,250,497,276
Earnings: $60,026,002
Emp.: 3,610
Fiscal Year-end: 12/31/12

Business Description:
Oil Refining & Marketing Services
S.I.C.: 2911
N.A.I.C.S.: 324110

Personnel:
Julian Segal *(CEO & Mng Dir)*
Simon Hepworth *(CFO)*
Peter Lim *(Gen Counsel & Sec)*

Board of Directors:
Elizabeth Blomfield Bryan
Trevor Bourne
Richard Brown
Barbara Burger
Greig Gailey
Ryan Krogmeier
Julian Segal
John Thorne

Subsidiaries:

Ampol Bendigo Pty Ltd **(1)**
L 12 Mlc Ctr 19-29 Martin Pl
Sydney, NSW, 2000, Australia (100%)
Tel.: (61) 299250500
Petroleum Products Whslr
S.I.C.: 5171
N.A.I.C.S.: 424710
Jagjeet S. Bindra *(Mng Dir)*
Des King *(Mng Dir)*

Ampol Metro Fuels Pty Ltd **(1)**
Allianz Center Level 28
Sydney, NSW, 2000, Australia (100%)
Tel.: (61) 292505000
Gasoline Stations & Convenience Stores
S.I.C.: 5541
N.A.I.C.S.: 447110
Jagjeet S. Bindra *(Mng Dir)*
Des King *(Mng Dir)*

Brisbane Airport Fuel Services Pty Ltd **(1)**
PO Box 738
Hamilton, QLD, Australia (100%)
Tel.: (61) 738604647
Airport Operations
S.I.C.: 4581
N.A.I.C.S.: 488119
Damian Jordan *(Mng Dir)*

Calstores Pty Ltd **(1)**
Allianz Ctr L 24 2 Market St
Sydney, NSW, 2000, Australia (100%)
Tel.: (61) 292505000
Fax: (61) 292505742
Emp.: 600
Gasoline Stations & Convenience Stores
S.I.C.: 5541
N.A.I.C.S.: 447110
Julian Segal *(Mng Dir)*

Caltex Australia Custodians Pty Ltd **(1)**
Allianz Center 2 Market St Level 24
2000 Sydney, NSW, Australia (100%)
Tel.: (61) 292505000
Fax: (61) 292505742
E-Mail: info@caltex.co.au
Emp.: 600
Oil Refining
S.I.C.: 2911
N.A.I.C.S.: 324110
Julian Segal *(Mng Dir)*

Caltex Australia Limited—(Continued)

Caltex Australia Finance Pty Ltd (1)
Allianz Center Level 24 2 North St
2000 Sydney, NSW, Australia (100%)
Tel.: (61) 292505000
Fax: (61) 292505742
Emp.: 600
Business Service Centers
S.I.C.: 7334
N.A.I.C.S.: 561439
Julian Seagal *(Mng Dir)*

Caltex Australia Investments Pty Ltd (1)
Allianz Center Level 25
2000 Sydney, NSW, Australia (100%)
Tel.: (61) 292505000
Trusts Estates & Agency Accounts
S.I.C.: 6733
N.A.I.C.S.: 525920
Des King *(Mng Dir)*

Caltex Australia Management Pty Ltd (1)
L12 Mlc Center 19-29 Martin Place
Sydney, NSW, 2000, Australia (100%)
Tel.: (61) 292505000
Fax: (61) 92505742
Web Site: www.caltex.com.au
Holding Company
S.I.C.: 6719
N.A.I.C.S.: 551112
Julian Segal *(Mng Dir)*

Caltex Australia Petroleum Pty Ltd (1)
Allianz Center Level 24 2 market
2000 Sydney, NSW, Australia (100%)
Tel.: (61) 292505000
Fax: (61) 0292505742
Web Site: www.caltex.com.au
Emp.: 600
Gasoline Stations & Convenience Stores
S.I.C.: 5541
N.A.I.C.S.: 447110
Julian Segil *(Mng Dir)*

Caltex Lubricating Oil Refinery Pty Ltd. (1)
Sir Joseph Banks Dr
Kurnell, 2231 Sydney, NSW, Australia
Tel.: (61) 296681111
Fax: (61) 296681188
Web Site: www.caltex.com.au/community_ref.asp
Emp.: 1,500
Oil & Gas Operations
S.I.C.: 1389
N.A.I.C.S.: 213112
Julian Segal *(CEO & Mng Dir)*

Caltex Petroleum Services Pty Ltd (1)
L 24-2 Market St
2000 Sydney, NSW, Australia (100%)
Tel.: (61) 292505000
Fax: (61) 292505742
Petroleum Products Whslr Not Bulk Stations & Terminals
S.I.C.: 5172
N.A.I.C.S.: 424720
Julian Segal *(Mng Dir)*

Caltex Petroleum (Victoria) Pty Ltd (1)
411 Douglas Parade
Melbourne, VIC, 3015, Australia
Tel.: (61) 392879555
Petroleum Bulk Station Operating Services
S.I.C.: 5171
N.A.I.C.S.: 424710

Caltex Refineries (NSW) Pty Ltd. (1)
2 Solander Street
Kurnell, Sydney, NSW, 2231, Australia
Tel.: (61) 296681111
Fax: (61) 296681188
E-Mail: kurnellrefineries@caltex.com.au
Web Site: www.caltex.com.au
Emp.: 600
Oil & Gas Operations
S.I.C.: 1389
N.A.I.C.S.: 213112
Julian Segal *(Mng Dir)*

Cooper & Dysart Pty Ltd (1)
119 Kurnall Rd
Welshpool, WA, Australia (100%)
Tel.: (61) 893518881
Petroleum Products Whslr
S.I.C.: 5172
N.A.I.C.S.: 424720
Des King *(Mng Dir)*

Hunter Pipe Line Company Pty Ltd (1)
L24 2 Market Street
Sydney, NSW, 2000, Australia (100%)
Tel.: (61) 292505000
Web Site: www.Caltex.com
Emp.: 600
General Warehousing & Storage
S.I.C.: 4225
N.A.I.C.S.: 493110
Julian Segil *(Mng Dir)*

Jayvee Petroleum Pty Ltd (1)
Level 24 2 Market St
Sydney, NSW, 2000, Australia (100%)
Tel.: (61) 292505000
Fax: (61) 292505018
Heating Oil Dealers
S.I.C.: 5989
N.A.I.C.S.: 454310
Julian Segal *(Mng Dir)*

Newcastle Pipe Line Company Pty Ltd (1)
L 24 2 Market St
Sydney, NSW, 2000, Australia (100%)
Tel.: (61) 292505000
Emp.: 600
Oil & Gas Operations
S.I.C.: 1389
N.A.I.C.S.: 213112
Julie Sejil *(Mng Dir)*

Solo Oil Australia Pty Ltd (1)
Aooianz L 24 2 market Street
2000 Sydney, NSW, 2000, Australia (100%)
Tel.: (61) 292505000
Fax: (61) 292505742
Emp.: 600
Trusts Estates & Agency Accounts
S.I.C.: 6733
N.A.I.C.S.: 525920
Julian Sejil *(CEO)*

South Coast Oils Pty Ltd (1)
19-29 Martin Pl
Sydney, NSW, Australia (100%)
Tel.: (61) 292505000
Petroleum Products Whslr
S.I.C.: 5172
N.A.I.C.S.: 424720
Des King *(Mng Dir)*

Sydney Metropolitan Pipeline Pty Ltd (1)
L 24 No 2 Market street
Sydney, NSW, 2000, Australia (100%)
Tel.: (61) 292505000
Fax: (61) 292505742
Web Site: www.caltex.com.au
Emp.: 600
Crude Petroleum & Natural Gas Extraction
S.I.C.: 1311
N.A.I.C.S.: 211111
Julian Segal *(Mng Dir)*

Tulloch Petroleum Services Pty Ltd (1)
L24 Market St
Sydney, NSW, Australia (100%)
Tel.: (61) 292505000
Web Site: www.tulloch.com.au
Emp.: 620
Gasoline Stations & Convenience Stores
S.I.C.: 5541
N.A.I.C.S.: 447110
Julien Segaio *(Mng Dir)*

Affiliates:

Airport Fuel Services Pty Ltd (1)
The Ulm Bldg 1 Link Road
Sydney International
Terminal, Sydney, NSW, 2020, Australia (40%)
Tel.: (61) 296673626
Fax: (61) 2 9317 3970
Web Site: www.caltex.com.au
Petroleum Products Whslr & Distr
S.I.C.: 5989
N.A.I.C.S.: 454310

Australasian Lubricants Manufacturing Company Pty Ltd (1)
1 Tanker St
Lytton, Brisbane, QLD, 4178, Australia (50%)
Tel.: (61) 733610900
Fax: (61) 733610988
E-Mail: accounts@almc.com.au
Web Site: www.almc.com.au
Emp.: 400
Petroleum Products Whslr
S.I.C.: 5172
N.A.I.C.S.: 424720
John Wyrnock *(CEO)*

Geraldton Fuel Company Pty Ltd (1)
120 Sloras Road
Geraldton, Perth, WA, Australia (50%)
Tel.: (61) 899208000
Fax: (61) 899208080
Emp.: 10
Petroleum Products Whslr
S.I.C.: 5172
N.A.I.C.S.: 424720
Ian Burrows *(Mng Dir)*

Link Energy Pty Ltd (1)
L 5 15 Ogilvie Rd
Mount Pleasant, WA, Australia (50%)
Tel.: (61) 893157888
Fax: (61) 93157814
Petroleum Products Whslr
S.I.C.: 5172
N.A.I.C.S.: 424720

South East Queensland Fuels Pty Ltd (1)
61 Ashover Rd
Rocklea, QLD, Australia (50%)
Tel.: (61) 749766800
Fuel Dealers
S.I.C.: 5989
N.A.I.C.S.: 454310

CALVALLEY PETROLEUM INC.

600 6th Avenue SW Suite 700
Calgary, AB, T2P 0S5, Canada
Tel.: (403) 297-0490
Fax: (403) 297-0499
E-Mail: inquiries@calvalleypetroleum.com
Web Site: www.calvalleypetroleum.com
Year Founded: 1996
CVI.A—(OTC TSX)
Sls.: $102,137,000
Assets: $231,605,000
Liabilities: $12,992,000
Net Worth: $218,613,000
Earnings: $25,675,000
Emp.: 154
Fiscal Year-end: 12/31/12

Business Description:
Oil & Gas Exploration & Development
S.I.C.: 8713
N.A.I.C.S.: 541360

Personnel:
Edmund M. Shimoon *(Chm & CEO)*
Gerry J. Elms *(CFO)*
Thomas E. Valentine *(Sec)*

Board of Directors:
Edmund M. Shimoon
Bernard Polge de Combret
Nikolas Perrault
Gary Robertson
Thomas H. Skupa
Kenneth Munro Stephenson
Thomas E. Valentine

Computershare Investor Services Inc.
Calgary, AB, Canada

Transfer Agents:
Computershare Investor Services Inc.
Calgary, AB, Canada

Computershare Investor Services Inc.
Montreal, QC, Canada

Non-U.S. Subsidiary:

Calvalley Petroleum (Cyprus) Ltd (1)
PO Box 7090
Hadda Area, Sana'a, Yemen
Tel.: (967) 1415555
Fax: (967) 1423580
E-Mail: nilqbal@calvalleyyemen.com
Web Site: www.calvalleypetroleum.com
Emp.: 50
Petroleum Extraction Services
S.I.C.: 1311
N.A.I.C.S.: 211111
Nadeem Iqbal *(VP-Fin)*

CALVATIS GMBH

Dr Albert Ryman Strasse 2
D 68526 Ladenburg, Germany
Tel.: (49) 62031050
Telex: 465060
Fax: (49) 6203105111
E-Mail: info@calvatis.com
Web Site: www.calvatis.com
Sales Range: $50-74.9 Million
Emp.: 120

Business Description:
Industrial Detergent & Disinfectant Mfr
S.I.C.: 2844
N.A.I.C.S.: 325611

Personnel:
Thomas Mohr *(Gen Mgr)*

Non-U.S. Subsidiaries:

Calvatis Asia Pacific Co., Ltd (1)
406 Ratchadapisek Rd Samsen Nork
Huay Kwang, Bangkok, Thailand
Tel.: (66) 2276 0163 Ext 161
Fax: (66) 2276 0127
E-Mail: info.th@calvatis.com
Web Site: www.calvatisthai.com
Disinfectant & Cleaning Equipment Mfr & Distr
S.I.C.: 2842
N.A.I.C.S.: 325612

Calvatis B.V. (1)
Cob Balkplein 1
3945 ER Cothen, Netherlands
Tel.: (31) 343 563959
Fax: (31) 343 561102
E-Mail: info.nl@calvatis.com
Emp.: 5
Detergent & Disinfectant Distr
S.I.C.: 5169
N.A.I.C.S.: 424690

Calvatis GmbH (1)
Kaiser-Josef-Platz 41
4600 Wels, Austria
Tel.: (43) 7242 42899 0
Fax: (43) 7242 42899 22
E-Mail: info.at@calvatis.com
Emp.: 12
Detergent & Disinfectant Distr
S.I.C.: 5169
N.A.I.C.S.: 424690

Calvatis Hijyen San. ve Ds Tic. Ltd. Sti. (1)
Sanayi Mah Isso San Sit R 2 Blok No 1-2
34517 Esenyurt, Istanbul, Turkey
Tel.: (90) 212 6231833
Fax: (90) 212 6231834
E-Mail: info.tr@calvatis.com
Detergent & Disinfectant Distr
S.I.C.: 5169
N.A.I.C.S.: 424690

Calvatis OOO (1)
Leninskiy Prospekt D 42 K 1
119119 Moscow, Russia
Tel.: (7) 495 9387136
Fax: (7) 495 9387024
E-Mail: info.ru@calvatis.com
Web Site: www.calvatis.ru
Detergent & Disinfectant Mfr & Distr
S.I.C.: 2841
N.A.I.C.S.: 325611

Calvatis srl (1)
Via-Carlo-Abarth 17
39012 Merano, Italy
Tel.: (39) 0473 232016
Fax: (39) 0473 256820
Detergent & Disinfectant Mfr & Distr
S.I.C.: 2844
N.A.I.C.S.: 325611

Calvatis srl (1)
str Fabricii nr 56
400620 Cluj-Napoca, Romania
Tel.: (40) 264415830
Fax: (40) 264456038
E-Mail: info.ro@calvatis.com
Emp.: 4
Detergent & Disinfectant Distr

S.I.C.: 5169
N.A.I.C.S.: 424690

Calvatis UAB (1)
B Sruogos Str 36
10220 Vilnius, Lithuania
Tel.: (370) 52 340 336
Fax: (370) 52 340 372
E-Mail: info@calvatis.lt
Emp.: 15
Detergent & Disinfectant Distr
S.I.C.: 5169
N.A.I.C.S.: 424690

CALVI HOLDING S.R.L.

Via 4 Novembre 2
23807 Lecco, Italy
Tel.: (39) 03999851
Fax: (39) 0399985240
E-Mail: calvispa@calvi.it
Web Site: www.calvi.it
Business Description:
Steel Profile Mfr
S.I.C.: 3444
N.A.I.C.S.: 332322
Personnel:
Riccardo Chini *(Chm & CEO)*

U.S. Subsidiary:

Rathbone Precision Metals, Inc. (1)
1241 Park St
Palmer, MA 01069-1606
Tel.: (413) 283-8961
Fax: (413) 283-9722
Toll Free: (888) 283-8961
E-Mail: info@rathboneprofiles.com
Web Site: www.rathboneprofiles.com
Emp.: 50
Custom, Cold-Drawn Metal Shapes Mfr
S.I.C.: 3312
N.A.I.C.S.: 331221
Dale Pretz *(Pres)*

CALYPSO URANIUM CORP.

(Acquired & Absorbed by U3O8 Corp.)

CALYSTENE

16 Rue Irene Joliot-Curie
38320 Eybens, France
Tel.: (33) 476412930
Fax: (33) 4 7641 2118
Web Site: www.calystene.com
Sales Range: $10-24.9 Million
Emp.: 35
Business Description:
Medical Software Systems Solutions
S.I.C.: 7372
N.A.I.C.S.: 511210

CALYX BIO-VENTURES INC.

450 - 400 Burrard Street
Vancouver, BC, V6C 3A6, Canada
Tel.: (604) 689-2495
Fax: (604) 689-0014
Web Site: www.calyxbio.com
Year Founded: 2008
CYX—(TSXV)
Rev.: $111,827
Assets: $2,594,760
Liabilities: $198,620
Net Worth: $2,396,140
Earnings: ($1,733,217)
Fiscal Year-end: 12/31/12
Business Description:
Holding Company; Biotechnology Products Developer
S.I.C.: 6719
N.A.I.C.S.: 551112
Personnel:
Don Konantz *(Pres & CEO)*
Kevin Rathbun *(Exec VP)*
Board of Directors:
David T. Howard
Louis P. Lacasse
Stuart MacGregor
William Hugh Notman
Richard Whittall

Affiliate:

Agrisoma Biosciences Inc. (1)
5929L Jeanne D'Arc Boulevard Suite 323
Ottawa, ON, K1C 7K2, Canada (32%)
Tel.: (613) 323-3171
E-Mail: info@agrisoma.com
Web Site: www.agrisoma.com
Agricultural Biotechnology Products Developer & Mfr
S.I.C.: 2836
N.A.I.C.S.: 325414
Steven Fabijanski *(Pres & CEO)*

CALZADA LIMITED

Wendy Townsend 2/320 Lorimer Street
Port Melbourne, VIC, 3207, Australia
Tel.: (61) 386814050
Fax: (61) 386814099
E-Mail: wtownsend@calzada.com.au
Web Site: www.calzada.com.au
CZD—(ASX)
Rev.: $290,168
Assets: $8,981,535
Liabilities: $834,522
Net Worth: $8,147,013
Earnings: ($1,560,602)
Emp.: 5
Fiscal Year-end: 06/30/13
Business Description:
Medical Device Mfr
S.I.C.: 3845
N.A.I.C.S.: 334510
Personnel:
Christopher Mews *(CFO & Sec)*
Laurent Fossaert *(CEO-Polynovo Biomaterials Pty Ltd)*
David Kenley *(CEO-Metabolic Pharmaceuticals Pty Ltd)*
Board of Directors:
David Williams
Roger Aston
David McQuillan
Bruce Rathie
Legal Counsel:
Corrs Chambers Westgarth
Perth, Australia
Subsidiaries:

Metabolic Pharmaceuticals Limited (1)
2/320 Lorimer Street
Port Melbourne, VIC, 3207, Australia
Tel.: (61) 3 8681 4050
Fax: (61) 3 8681 4099
Web Site: www.metabolic.com.au
Pharmaceutical Mfr
S.I.C.: 2834
N.A.I.C.S.: 325412
David Kenley *(CEO)*

PolyNovo Biomaterials Pty Ltd. (1)
2/230 Lorimer Street
Port Melbourne, VIC, 3207, Australia
Tel.: (61) 3 8681 4050
Fax: (61) 3 8681 4099
E-Mail: info@polynovo.com
Web Site: www.polynovo.com
Medical Materials Mfr
S.I.C.: 2834
N.A.I.C.S.: 325412
Laurent Fossaert *(CEO)*

CAM GROUP, INC.

Jixing Building 151 Shengli Avenue North
Shijiazhuang, Hebei, 050041, China
Tel.: (86) 311 8696 4264
Year Founded: 1995
CAMG—(OTC OTCB)
Sls.: $3,978,756
Assets: $4,514,299
Liabilities: $1,567,085
Net Worth: $2,947,214
Earnings: $2,485,738
Emp.: 11
Fiscal Year-end: 12/31/12
Business Description:
Advertising Services
S.I.C.: 7319
N.A.I.C.S.: 541890
Personnel:
Lijun Chen *(Chm)*
Kit Ka *(Pres, CEO, Interim Chief Acctg Officer & Sec)*
Board of Directors:
Lijun Chen
Kit Ka
Renchang Ma
Zhaohui Ma
Enrique Marchese
Guojiang Peng
Yichuan Wang
Yongli Xia
Yanhui Zhang
Transfer Agent:
Guardian Registrar & Transfer, Inc.
7951 SW 6th St Ste 216
Plantation, FL 33324-3276

CAM MEDIA S.A.

ul Tamka 16 premises U4
00-349 Warsaw, Poland
Tel.: (48) 228280885
Fax: (48) 228280886
E-Mail: biuro@cammedia.pl
Web Site: www.cammedia.pl
CAM—(WAR)
Sales Range: $10-24.9 Million
Business Description:
Advertising Services
S.I.C.: 7311
N.A.I.C.S.: 541810
Personnel:
Joanna Braulinska *(Chm-Supervisory Bd)*
Krzysztof Przybylowski *(Chm-Mgmt Bd)*
Adam Michalewicz *(Vice Chm-Mgmt Bd)*
Pawel Orlowski *(Vice Chm-Mgmt Bd)*
Supervisory Board of Directors:
Joanna Braulinska
Jerzy Drozdowski
Bartosz Foroncewicz
Robert Kozielski
Piotr Krawczynski
Andrzej Szymanski
Dariusz Werbowy

CAM RESOURCES BERHAD

10th Floor Menara Hap Seng No 1 & 3 Jalan P Ramlee
Kuala Lumpur, 50250, Malaysia
Tel.: (60) 323824288
Fax: (60) 323824170
Web Site: www.camres.com.my
CAMRES—(KLS)
Rev.: $40,653,660
Assets: $47,591,781
Liabilities: $16,931,876
Net Worth: $30,659,905
Earnings: $212,812
Fiscal Year-end: 12/31/12
Business Description:
Aluminum & Stainless Steel Mfr
S.I.C.: 3325
N.A.I.C.S.: 331513
Personnel:
Chin Yen Lee *(Chm)*
Hong Cheng Tan *(Mng Dir)*
Aileen Khor *(Co-Sec)*
Ming Toong Lim *(Co-Sec)*
Board of Directors:
Chin Yen Lee
Moi Kim Chai
Kee Loin Chan
Kay Joo Chia
Wan Kiga Hia
Poh Choo Lee
Azizul Mohd Othman
Hong Cheng Tan
Kim Hong Tan

CAMARGO CORREA S.A.

(d/b/a Camargo Correa Group)
Rua Funchal 160 Vila Olimpia
04551-903 Sao Paulo, SP, Brazil
Tel.: (55) 1138415511
Web Site: www.camargocorrea.com.br
Year Founded: 1939
Sales Range: $5-14.9 Billion
Emp.: 49,186
Business Description:
Multi-Industry Holding Company
S.I.C.: 6719
N.A.I.C.S.: 551112
Personnel:
Marcio Garcia de Souza *(Chm)*
Vitor Sarquis Hallack *(Chm-Mgmt Bd)*
Board of Directors:
Marcio Garcia de Souza
Arthur Sanchez Badin
Rodrigo Cardoso Barbosa
Marcello Antonio D'Angelo
Adalgiso Fragoso de Faria
Carla Duprat
Roberto Navarro Evangelista
Bruno Machado Ferla
Fernando Dias Gomes
Joao Carlos Orzzi Lucas
Marco Antonio Zangari

Subsidiaries:

Construcoes e Comercio Camargo Correa SA (1)
Rua Funchal 160 Vila Olimpia
CEP 04551 903, Sao Paulo, Brazil
Tel.: (55) 1138415511
Fax: (55) 1138415849
Web Site: www.cccc.camargocorrea.com.br
Engineering & Construction Services
S.I.C.: 1611
N.A.I.C.S.: 237310

InterCement Brasil S.A. (1)
Rua Funchal 160 Vila Olimpia
04551-903 Sao Paulo, SP, Brazil BR
Tel.: (55) 11 3848 7816 (99.89%)
E-Mail:
Web Site: www.intercement.com
Sales Range: $1-4.9 Billion
Emp.: 125
Cement & Concrete Mfr
S.I.C.: 3241
N.A.I.C.S.: 327310
Antonio Miguel Marques *(Mng Dir)*

VBC Energia S.A. (1)
Av Eng Luis Carlos Berrini 1297
13 andar Conjunto 132 Brooklin, Sao Paulo, Brazil
Tel.: (55) 1151027050
Fax: (55) 1155059161
Electric Power Generation
S.I.C.: 4939
N.A.I.C.S.: 221118

Affiliate:

Alpargatas S.A. (1)
Rua Funchal 160 Vila Olimpia
04551-903 Sao Paulo, SP, Brazil BR
Tel.: (55) 1138477322 (44.12%)
Telex: 36896
Fax: (55) 1138477262
E-Mail: ri@apargatas.com.br
Web Site: www.alpargatas.com.br
ALPA4—(BRAZ)
Sales Range: $1-4.9 Billion
Emp.: 15,733
Footwear, Sporting Goods & Textiles Mfr
Import Export
S.I.C.: 2389
N.A.I.C.S.: 316210
Marcio Garcia de Souza *(Chm)*
Marcio Luiz Simoes Utsch *(CEO)*
Jose Roberto Lettiere *(CFO & Dir-Fin, Admin & IR)*

Camargo Correa S.A.—(Continued)

Non-U.S. Subsidiary:

Cimpor - Cimentos de Portugal, SGPS, S.A. (1)
Rua Alexandre Herculano 35
1250-009 Lisbon, Portugal PT
Tel.: (351) 213118100 (94.1%)
Fax: (351) 213561381
E-Mail: dcom@cimpor.com
Web Site: www.cimpor.com
CPR—(EUR)
Rev.: $2,129,953,251
Assets: $9,543,678,946
Liabilities: $7,480,106,683
Net Worth: $2,063,572,263
Earnings: $69,294,101
Emp.: 9,500
Fiscal Year-end: 12/31/12
Cement Mfr
S.I.C.: 3241
N.A.I.C.S.: 327310
Daniel Proenca de Carvalho *(Chm)*
Ricardo Fonseca de Mendonca Lima *(CEO)*
Armando Sergio Antunes Silva *(CFO)*
Ana Filipa Mendes de Magalhaes Saraiva Mendes *(Sec & Head-IR)*

Subsidiaries:

Agrepor Agregados - Extraccao De Inertes S.A. (2)
Sangardao
Condeixa-A-Nova, 3151-999 Coimbra, Portugal (100%)
Tel.: (351) 239949620
Fax: (351) 239941009
E-Mail: lcarmona@cimpor.com
Emp.: 20
Dimension Stone Mining & Quarrying
S.I.C.: 1411
N.A.I.C.S.: 212311
Lizurrta Gomez *(Gen Dir)*

Alempedras - Sociedade de Britas Lda (2)
Casal Da Luz Bairro
Obidos, Lisbon, Portugal (100%)
Tel.: (351) 262959444
Nonmetallic Mineral Product Mfr
S.I.C.: 3299
N.A.I.C.S.: 327999

Bepronor - Sociedade De Betao Pronto Do Nordeste S.A. (2)
Rua Alexandre Herculano 35
1250-009 Lisbon, Portugal (100%)
Tel.: (351) 278265347
Concrete Product Mfr
S.I.C.: 3272
N.A.I.C.S.: 327390
Ricardo Manuel Simoes Bayao Horta *(Chm)*

Betabeiras - Betoes Da Beira S.A. (2)
Rua De SAo Jose 149 2
Lisbon, Portugal (88.95%)
Tel.: (351) 213472038
Ready-Mix Concrete Mfr
S.I.C.: 3273
N.A.I.C.S.: 327320

Betao Liz S.A. (2)
R Qta Paizinho-Bloco 2 1-E
2795-650 Carnaxide, Portugal (66.44%)
Tel.: (351) 214247500
Fax: (351) 214247500
Web Site: www.bpcc.pt/construction.asp
Mixed Mode Transit Systems
S.I.C.: 4111
N.A.I.C.S.: 485111

Cecisa - Comercio Internacional S.A. (2)
Rua Alexandre Herculano 35
1250-009 Lisbon, Portugal (100%)
Tel.: (351) 213118100
Fax: (351) 213561381
Durable Goods Whslr
S.I.C.: 5099
N.A.I.C.S.: 423990
Ricardo Manuel Simoes Bayao Horta *(Chm)*

Celfa - Socedade Industrial De Transformacao de Gessos S.A. (2)
Rua Alexandre Herculano 35
Lisbon, Portugal (100%)
Tel.: (351) 239501397
Gypsum Product Mfr
S.I.C.: 3275
N.A.I.C.S.: 327420
Ricardo Manuel Simoes Bayao Horta *(Chm)*

Cement Trading Activities - Comercio Internacional S.A. (2)
Rua Alexandre Herculano 35
Lisbon, 1250-009, Portugal (100%)
Tel.: (351) 219408600
Fax: (351) 213561381
Web Site: www.cempro.com
Emp.: 250
Brick Stone & Related Construction Material Merchant Whslr
S.I.C.: 5032
N.A.I.C.S.: 423320
Ricardo Manuel Simoes Bayao Horta *(Chm)*

Ciarga - Argamassas Secas S.A. (2)
Rua Alexandre Herculano 35
1250-009 Lisbon, Portugal (100%)
Tel.: (351) 213118100
Fax: (351) 213118100
Web Site: www.cimpor.pt
Brick Stone & Related Construction Material Whslr
S.I.C.: 5032
N.A.I.C.S.: 423320
Ricardo Manuel Simoes Bayao Horta *(Chm)*

Cimadjuvantes - Comercializacao E Producao De Adjuvantes Para Cimento Lda (2)
Edificio Cimpor
Pomar Velho, 1250-009 Faro, Portugal (100%)
Tel.: (351) 213118100
Fax: (351) 213561381
Chemical & Allied Products Whslr
S.I.C.: 5169
N.A.I.C.S.: 424690

Cimentacor - Cimentos Dos Acores Lda (2)
R Bento D Carreiro 6 Pico Pedr
Ribeira Grande, 9600-050 Lisbon, Portugal (75%)
Tel.: (351) 296201730
Fax: (351) 296201748
Emp.: 20
Cement Mfr
S.I.C.: 3241
N.A.I.C.S.: 327310

Cimpor Betao - Industria De Betao Pronto S.A. (2)
Av Alm Gago Coutinho
Portela Sintra, Sintra, 2710-418, Portugal (100%)
Tel.: (351) 219105540
Fax: (351) 219242516
E-Mail: jlino@cimpor.pt
Asphalt Paving Mixture & Block Mfr
S.I.C.: 2951
N.A.I.C.S.: 324121

Cimpor Betao - Sociedade Gestora De Participacoes Sociais S.A. (2)
Rua Alexandre Herculano 35
1250-009 Lisbon, Portugal (100%)
Tel.: (351) 213118100
E-Mail: dre@cimpor.com
Web Site: www.cimpor.com
Holding Company
S.I.C.: 6719
N.A.I.C.S.: 551112
Luis Filipe Sequeira Martins *(Exec Dir)*

Cimpor - Industria De Cimentos S.A. (2)
Rua Alexandre Herculano 35
1250-009 Lisbon, Portugal (100%)
Tel.: (351) 213118100
Fax: (351) 213561381
Cement Mfr
S.I.C.: 3241
N.A.I.C.S.: 327310
Ricardo Manuel Simoes Bayao Horta *(Chm)*

Cimpor Internacional SGPS S.A. (2)
Rua Alexandre Herculano 35
Lisbon, 1250-009, Portugal (100%)
Tel.: (351) 213118100
Fax: (351) 500722900
E-Mail: realista@Cimpor.com
Web Site: www.Cimpor.com
Emp.: 200
Holding Company
S.I.C.: 6719
N.A.I.C.S.: 551112
Ricardo Manuel Simoes Bayao Horta *(Chm)*

Cimpor Investimentos SGPS S.A. (2)
Rua Alexandre Herculano 35
Lisbon, Portugal (100%)
Tel.: (351) 213118100
Holding Company
S.I.C.: 6719
N.A.I.C.S.: 551112
Ricardo Manuel Simoes Bayao Horta *(Chm)*

Cimpor Portugal SGPS S.A. (2)
Rua Alexandre Herculano 35
Lisbon, Portugal (100%)
Tel.: (351) 213118100
Fax: (351) 213118225
Holding Company
S.I.C.: 6719
N.A.I.C.S.: 551112
Filipa S. Mendes *(Head-IR)*

Cimpor - Servicos De Apoio A Gestao De Empresas S.A. (2)
Rua Alexandre Herculano 35
1250-009 Lisbon, Portugal (100%)
Tel.: (351) 213118100
Fax: (351) 213118805
Web Site: www.cimpor-portugal.pt
Business Support Services
S.I.C.: 7389
N.A.I.C.S.: 561499

CIMPOR TRADING, S.A. (2)
Rua Alexandre Herculano 35
1250-009 Lisbon, Portugal
Tel.: (351) 21 311 81 00
Fax: (351) 21 311 82 25
E-Mail: CTA@cimpor.com
Web Site: www.cimportrading.com
Construction Materials Whslr
S.I.C.: 5032
N.A.I.C.S.: 423320

CIMPSHIP - TRANSPORTES MARITIMOS, S.A. (2)
Rua Ivens Edificio Dona Mecia Nr 3-B- 2-L
Funchal, 9000-046, Portugal
Tel.: (351) 291200300
Fax: (351) 291238010
Marine Transportation Services
S.I.C.: 4499
N.A.I.C.S.: 488390

Estabelecimentos Scial Do Norte S.A. (2)
Av Americo Duarte - SAo Pedro De Fins
4425-504 Maia, Portugal (100%)
Tel.: (351) 219408732
Construction Material Whslr
S.I.C.: 5039
N.A.I.C.S.: 423390

GEOFER - PRODUCAO E COMERCIALIZACAO DE BENS E EQUIPAMENTOS, S.A. (2)
Zona Industrial
Tramagal, 2206-906 Santarem, Portugal
Tel.: (351) 241899050
Fax: (351) 241899080
Emp.: 6
Cement Mfr & Distr
S.I.C.: 3241
N.A.I.C.S.: 327310

Ibera - Industria De Betao S.A. (2)
Quinta da Madeira Estrada Nac 114 km 85
Evora, 7002-505 Setubal, Portugal(66.44%)
Tel.: (351) 266758505
Fax: (351) 266758506
Emp.: 50
Ready-Mix Concrete Mfr
S.I.C.: 3273
N.A.I.C.S.: 327320
Vitor Basosa *(Gen Mgr)*

Jomatel - Empresa De Materiais de Construcao S.A. (2)
Estrada de Albarraque - Linho
Sintra, Portugal (90%)
Tel.: (351) 219239000
Fax: (351) 219239029
Mixed Mode Transit Systems
S.I.C.: 4111
N.A.I.C.S.: 485111

Kandmad - Sociedade Gestora De Participacoes Sociais Lda (2)
Avenida Arriaga 77 1 Edificio Marina Forum Sala 103
Funchal, Portugal (99.93%)
Tel.: (351) 291206430
Holding Company
S.I.C.: 6719
N.A.I.C.S.: 551112

Prediana - Sociedade De Pre-Esforcados S.A. (2)
Rua Alexandre Herculano 35
1250-009 Lisbon, Portugal (100%)
Tel.: (351) 266893908
Concrete Contractors
S.I.C.: 1771
N.A.I.C.S.: 238110
Ricardo Manuel Simoes Bayao Horta *(Chm)*

Sacopor - Sociedade De Embalagens E Sacos De Papel S.A. (2)
Quinta da Arrocazia Lote 1 - Santo Estevao
Alenquer, 2580-374 Lisbon, Portugal (100%)
Tel.: (351) 263730370
Fax: (351) 263730379
E-Mail: sacopor@cimpor.com
Emp.: 54
Nonfolding Sanitary Food Container Mfr
S.I.C.: 2652
N.A.I.C.S.: 322219
Costa Azevedo *(Mgr)*

Scoreco - Valorizacao De Residuos Lda (2)
Av Severian Falcao 8 - Edificio Cimpor
Prior Velho, 2685-378 Faro, Portugal
Tel.: (351) 219408743
Fax: (351) 219408641
Web Site: www.cimentos.com
Brick Stone & Related Construction Material Whslr
S.I.C.: 5032
N.A.I.C.S.: 423320
Alvarez Manuel Gomez *(Gen Mgr)*

SOGESSO - SOCIEDADE DE GESSOS DE SOURE, S.A. (2)
Sao Jose Do Pinheiro
Soure, 3130-544, Portugal
Tel.: (351) 239506120
Fax: (351) 239506122
Construction Machinery Whslr
S.I.C.: 5084
N.A.I.C.S.: 423830

Transviaria - Gestao De Transportes S.A. (2)
Rua Alexandre Herculano 35
1250-009 Lisbon, Portugal (100%)
Tel.: (351) 219408600
Fax: (351) 219408733
E-Mail:
General Freight Trucking
S.I.C.: 4212
N.A.I.C.S.: 484110
Ricardo Manuel Simoes Bayao Horta *(Chm)*

Non-U.S. Subsidiaries:

Amreyah Cement Compamy S.A.E. (2)
El Gharbaneyat - Borg el Arab
Alexandria, Egypt (96.39%)
Tel.: (20) 34195600
Fax: (20) 34195628
Cement Mfr
S.I.C.: 3241
N.A.I.C.S.: 327310
Luis Fernandes *(Mng Dir)*

Amreyah Cimpor Cement Company S.A.E. (2)
El Gharbaneyat - Borg el Arab
Alexandria, Egypt (97.29%)
Tel.: (20) 3 41 95 600
Fax: (20) 41 95 628
Web Site: www.cimpor.pt/artigo_generico.aspx?sid=ae6a7a1a-f9e6-4858-aa25-8513bae856ba&cntx=N9fwOXksnW3PG0AiC2ilCUBkgPIRussC
Concrete Block & Brick Mfr
S.I.C.: 3271
N.A.I.C.S.: 327331

Asment de Temara S.A. (2)
Route Principale de Casablanca
Ain Attig Temara, Rabat, Morocco (62.62%)

Tel.: (212) 377476992
Fax: (212) 37741570
Web Site: www.asment.co.ma
Cement Mfr
S.I.C.: 3241
N.A.I.C.S.: 327310

Betocim SA (2)
QI lot Azzahra oulja
Sale Rabat, Morocco
Tel.: (212) 3780 7826
Fax: (212) 3780 7831
Cement Products Mfr
S.I.C.: 3241
N.A.I.C.S.: 327310

Canteras Prebetong S.L. (2)
Cl Brasil 56
36204 Vigo, Spain (98.41%)
Tel.: (34) 986269000
Fax: (34) 986418819
Web Site: www.cimpor.es/corpnor.php?page =01-06-Localizador1
Crushed & Broken Limestone Mining & Quarrying
S.I.C.: 1422
N.A.I.C.S.: 212312

Cement Services Company S.A.E. (2)
Km 55 Alexandria - Mattrouh Road Gharbanyat
Alexandria, Egypt (98.38%)
Tel.: (20) 2034195622
Management Consulting Services
S.I.C.: 8748
N.A.I.C.S.: 541618

Cementos Cosmos S.A. (2)
Brasil 56
36204 Vigo, Spain (99.29%)
Tel.: (34) 986269000
Fax: (34) 986473951
Web Site: www.cimpor.es/corpnor.php?page =01-06-Localizador1
Cement Mfr
S.I.C.: 3241
N.A.I.C.S.: 327310

Cementos De Andalucia S.L. (2)
Avda Agrupacion Cordoba 15
Cordoba, Spain (99.54%)
Tel.: (34) 954413847
Fax: (34) 354415570
Web Site: www.cimpor.es
Emp.: 7
Construction Material Whslr
S.I.C.: 5039
N.A.I.C.S.: 423390
Evamuno De Morales *(Asst Dir)*

CEMENTOS OTORONGO, S.A.C. (2)
Calle Los Gavilanes No 159 San Isidro
Lima, 2727, Peru
Tel.: (51) 12411275
Fax: (51) 12411275
Cement & Concrete Product Mfr
S.I.C.: 3273
N.A.I.C.S.: 327320

Cimentos De Cabo Verde S.A. (2)
Estrada de Tira Chapeu C P 14-A
Sao Vicente, Cape Verde (98.65%)
Tel.: (238) 2603110
Fax: (238) 2612086
E-Mail: lezora@cimpor.com
Cement Mfr
S.I.C.: 3241
N.A.I.C.S.: 327310

CIMENTOS DE MOCAMBIQUE, S.A. (2)
Estrada Velha 56
Matola, Mozambique
Tel.: (258) 21482507
Fax: (258) 21720076
Cement Mfr & Distr
S.I.C.: 5032
N.A.I.C.S.: 423320

CIMPOR BETAO MOCAMBIQUE, S.A. (2)
Av Angola-Maputo
Maputo, Mozambique
Tel.: (258) 2140 78 68
Fax: (258) 2140 78 51
E-Mail: cimpor@cimporbetao.imoz.com
Cement Mfr
S.I.C.: 3241
N.A.I.C.S.: 327310

Cimpor Brasil Participacoes Ltda (2)
Av Maria Coelho Aguiar 215
Sao Paulo, 05805-000, Brazil (100%)
Tel.: (55) 1137413000
Fax: (55) 1137414171
Web Site: www.cimpor.com
Emp.: 100
Holding Company
S.I.C.: 6719
N.A.I.C.S.: 551112
Alexandre Lancixtra *(Pres)*

CIMPOR FINANCIAL OPERATIONS, B.V. (2)
Teleportboulevard 140
Amsterdam, 1043 EJ, Netherlands
Tel.: (31) 205405800
Fax: (31) 206447011
Financial Management Services
S.I.C.: 6211
N.A.I.C.S.: 523999

CIMPOR HORMIGON ESPANA, S.A. (2)
Avda Miguel de Fabra Parc 4 Pol Ind El Nevero
Badajoz, 06006, Spain
Tel.: (34) 924 275 200
Fax: (34) 924 275 907
Ready Mixed Concrete Mfr
S.I.C.: 3273
N.A.I.C.S.: 327320

Cimpor Inversiones S.A. (2)
Calle Brasil 56
36204 Vigo, Spain (100%)
Tel.: (34) 986269000
Fax: (34) 986269098
Financial Investment Activities
S.I.C.: 6211
N.A.I.C.S.: 523999

C.J.O.-Societe les Ciments De Jbel Oust (2)
3 Rue de Touraine - Cite Jardins
Le Belvedere, 1002 Tunis, Tunisia (100%)
Tel.: (216) 71780945
Fax: (216) 71783094
Web Site: www.cimpor.com
Cement Mfr
S.I.C.: 3241
N.A.I.C.S.: 327310

Companhia de Cimentos do Brasil Ltda (2)
Av Maria Coelho Aguiar 215 - Bloco E 8 Andar
Jardim Sao Luiz, 05805-000 Sao Paulo, Brazil (100%)
Tel.: (55) 1137413581
Fax: (55) 1137413295
Web Site: www.cimpor.com.br
Emp.: 110
Cement Mfr
S.I.C.: 3241
N.A.I.C.S.: 327310
Mota Aniew Moatems *(Dir-Comml)*

Corporacion Noroeste S.A. (2)
Brasil n 56
36204 Vigo, Spain (99.54%)
Tel.: (34) 986269000
Fax: (34) 986473951
E-Mail: info@pulmor.es
Web Site: www.pulmor.es
Emp.: 30
Management Consulting Services
S.I.C.: 8748
N.A.I.C.S.: 541618
Ricardo Manuel Simoes Bayao Horta *(Chm)*

Firmes Y Hormigones Sani S.L. (2)
Carretera Nacional 630 Gijon - Sevilha Km 308
Almendralejo, 06200 Caceres, Spain (79.63%)
Tel.: (34) 924666113
Fax: (34) 924666113
Ready-Mix Concrete Mfr
S.I.C.: 3273
N.A.I.C.S.: 327320

Hormigones Hercules S.L. (2)
Apartado 411
21080 Huelva, Spain (99.54%)
Tel.: (34) 959282471
Fax: (34) 959282584
Ready-Mix Concrete Mfr
S.I.C.: 3273
N.A.I.C.S.: 327320

Morteros De Galicia S.L. (2)
Calle Brasil 56
36204 Vigo, Spain (99.54%)
Tel.: (34) 986269000
Concrete Contractors
S.I.C.: 1771
N.A.I.C.S.: 238110

NATAL PORTLAND CEMENT COMPANY (PTY) LTD. (2)
199 Coedmore Road Bellair
PO Box 15245
Durban, 4006, South Africa
Tel.: (27) 31 450 4411
Fax: (27) 31 451 9010
E-Mail: info@cimpor.com
Web Site: www.npc.co.za
Emp.: 50
Cement Mfr & Distr
S.I.C.: 3241
N.A.I.C.S.: 327310
Simon Jensen *(Gen Mgr)*

NPC - CIMPOR (PTY) LIMITED (2)
199 Coedmore Road
PO Box 15245
Bellair, Durban, 4006, South Africa
Tel.: (27) 31 450 4411
Fax: (27) 865352771
E-Mail: info@npc-eagle.co.za
Web Site: www.npc-eagle.co.za
Emp.: 500
Cement Concrete Mfr & Distr
S.I.C.: 5032
N.A.I.C.S.: 423320
Pieter Strauss *(Gen Mgr)*

Occidental De Hormigones S.L. (2)
Poligono Ind El Nevero C/La Biela S/N
6006 Badajoz, Spain (99.54%)
Tel.: (34) 924 27 0205
Fax: (34) 924275907
Web Site: www.cimpor.es
Ready-Mix Concrete Mfr
S.I.C.: 3273
N.A.I.C.S.: 327320

Prebetong Galicia S.A. (2)
C- Brasil 56
36204 Vigo, Spain (98.41%)
Tel.: (34) 986269000
Fax: (34) 986413448
Web Site: www.cimpor.es/corpnor.php?page =01-06-Localizador1
Ready-Mix Concrete Mfr
S.I.C.: 3273
N.A.I.C.S.: 327320

Prebetong Lugo Hormigones S.A. (2)
Avenida Benigno Rivera Pg Industrial De Ceao S-N
27003 Lugo, Spain (81.57%)
Tel.: (34) 982209121
Fax: (34) 982209272
Cement Mfr
S.I.C.: 3273
N.A.I.C.S.: 327320

Prebetong Lugo S.A. (2)
Avenida Benigno Rivera S-N
27003 Lugo, Spain (81.57%)
Tel.: (34) 982209121
Fax: (34) 982209272
Ready-Mix Concrete Mfr
S.I.C.: 3273
N.A.I.C.S.: 327320

Retonoba S.A. (2)
Calle Brasil 56
36204 Vigo, Spain (100%)
Tel.: (34) 986269000
Fax: (34) 986418819
Concrete Product Mfr
S.I.C.: 3272
N.A.I.C.S.: 327390

Scanang Trading Activities-Espana S.A. (2)
Calle Brasil 56
36204 Vigo, Spain (100%)
Tel.: (34) 986269000
Concrete Product Mfr
S.I.C.: 3272
N.A.I.C.S.: 327390

Servicios Y Materiales Para La Construccion S.A. (2)
Calle Brasil 56
36204 Vigo, Spain (99.54%)
Tel.: (34) 986269000
Web Site: www.cimpor.es/corpnor.php?page =01-06-Localizador1
Construction Material Whslr
S.I.C.: 5039
N.A.I.C.S.: 423390

Sociedad De Cementos Y Materiales De Construccion De Andalucia S.A. (2)
Avda de Agrapacion Cordoba 15
14014 Cordoba, Spain (99.54%)
Tel.: (34) 957013000
Fax: (34) 957262628
Web Site: www.oficemen.com
Cement Mfr
S.I.C.: 3241
N.A.I.C.S.: 327310
Juan Jose Garcia Yuste *(Plant Mgr)*

SOUTH COAST STONE CRUSHERS (PTY) LTD. (2)
Lot 2000 Quarry Rd Uvongo Port Shepstone
Margate, KwaZulu-Natal, 4270, South Africa
Tel.: (27) 314504411
Fax: (27) 393156325
E-Mail: info@cimpor.com
Web Site: www.npc.co.za
Cement Mfr
S.I.C.: 3241
N.A.I.C.S.: 327310
Dave Kendall *(Gen Mgr-Sterkspruit Quarry)*

CAMAU FROZEN SEAFOOD PROCESSING IMPORT EXPORT CORPORATION

333 Cao Thang Str Ward 8
Ca Mau, Vietnam
Tel.: (84) 780 3831608
Fax: (84) 780 3832297
E-Mail: camimex@hcm.vnn.vn
Web Site: www.camimex.com.vn
CMX—(HOSE)

Business Description:
Seafood Export Services
S.I.C.: 2092
N.A.I.C.S.: 311710

Personnel:
Minh Hieu Le *(Chm & Gen Dir)*

Board of Directors:
Minh Hieu Le
An Ninh Nguyen
Hoang Nam Nguyen
Tan Diong Nguyen
Anh Duc Pham

CAMBIE ROOFING & DRAINAGE CONTRACTORS LTD.

1367 E North Kent St
Vancouver, BC, V5X 4T6, Canada
Tel.: (604) 261-1111
Fax: (604) 325-5580
E-Mail: info@cambieroofing.com
Web Site: www.cambieroofing.com
Year Founded: 1952
Rev.: $10,795,569
Emp.: 90

Business Description:
Roofing & Drainage Contract Services
S.I.C.: 1761
N.A.I.C.S.: 238160

Personnel:
Knute Skujins *(Pres)*

CAMBIUM GLOBAL TIMBERLAND LIMITED

26 New Street
Saint Helier, JE2 3RA, Jersey
Tel.: (44) 1534 814814
Web Site: www.cambiumfunds.com
TREE—(AIM)
Rev.: $445,382
Assets: $107,787,687
Liabilities: $12,467,271
Net Worth: $95,320,417

Cambium Global Timberland Limited—(Continued)

Earnings: ($14,071,234)
Fiscal Year-end: 04/30/13

Business Description:
Forestry Investment Services
S.I.C.: 6211
N.A.I.C.S.: 523999

Personnel:
Donald Lindsay Adamson *(Chm)*

Board of Directors:
Donald Lindsay Adamson
Svante Adde
Roger Lewis
Martin Willaume Richardson
Robert James Rickman

Legal Counsel:
Carey Olsen Corporate Finance Limited
44 Esplanade
Saint Helier, Jersey

Transfer Agent:
Capita Registrars (Jersey) Limited
PO Box 378
Saint Helier, Jersey

CAMBRIA AFRICA PLC

1 Berkeley Street Mayfair
London, WIJ8DJ, United Kingdom
Tel.: (44) 203 4022 366
Fax: (44) 203 4022 367
E-Mail: info@cambriaafrica.com
Web Site: www.cambriaafrica.com
CMB—(LSE)
Rev.: $8,487,000
Assets: $24,235,000
Liabilities: $13,494,000
Net Worth: $10,741,000
Earnings: ($11,904,000)
Emp.: 93
Fiscal Year-end: 08/31/13

Business Description:
Investment Management Services
S.I.C.: 6799
N.A.I.C.S.: 523920

Personnel:
Edzo Wisman *(CEO)*
Roy Meiring *(CEO-Hotels Div)*

Board of Directors:
Ian Perkins
Fred Jones
Itai Mazaiwana
Paul Turner
Edzo Wisman

CAMBRIA AUTOMOBILES PLC

Dorcan Way
Swindon, SN3 3RA, United Kingdom
Tel.: (44) 1793 414200
Fax: (44) 1793 414201
E-Mail: enq@cambriaautos.co.uk
Web Site: www.cambriaautomobilesplc.com
Year Founded: 2006
CAMB—(AIM)
Rev.: $657,558,077
Assets: $196,659,668
Liabilities: $155,733,417
Net Worth: $40,926,252
Earnings: $5,801,748
Emp.: 1,017
Fiscal Year-end: 08/31/13

Business Description:
Car Dealership Owner & Operator
S.I.C.: 5511
N.A.I.C.S.: 441110

Personnel:
Mark Jonathan James Lavery *(CEO)*
James Anthony Mullins *(Sec & Dir-Fin)*

Board of Directors:
Philip H. Swatman
Michael Wallace Burt
Peter Alexander Burt
Mark Jonathan James Lavery
James Anthony Mullins

Legal Counsel:
Sherrards LLP
45 Grosvenor Road
Saint Albans, AL1 3AW, United Kingdom

King & Spalding International LLP
125 Old Broad Street
London, EC2N 1AR, United Kingdom

CAMBRIAN FORD SALES INC

1615 Kingsway St
Sudbury, ON, P3A 4S9, Canada
Tel.: (705) 560-3673
Fax: (705) 560-4662
E-Mail: auto@cambrianford.com
Web Site: www.cambrianford.com
Rev.: $50,000,000
Emp.: 215

Business Description:
New & Used Car Dealers
S.I.C.: 5511
N.A.I.C.S.: 441110

Personnel:
Steve McCulloch *(Pres)*

CAMBRIDGE BROADBAND NETWORKS LIMITED

Selwyn House Cambridge Business Park Cowley Road
Cambridge, CB4 0WZ, United Kingdom
Tel.: (44) 1223703000
Fax: (44) 1223703001
E-Mail: info@cbnl.com
Web Site: www.cbnl.com
Year Founded: 2000
Sales Range: $25-49.9 Million
Emp.: 100

Business Description:
Point-to-Multipoint Wireless Transmission Equipment Mfr
S.I.C.: 3663
N.A.I.C.S.: 334220

Personnel:
Teresa M. Vega *(Chm)*
Lionel Chmilewsky *(CEO)*
William Ginn *(CFO)*
David Purle *(Sr VP-R&D)*

Board of Directors:
Teresa M. Vega
Martin Gibson
Hermann Hauser
John Naylon

CAMBRIDGE BUILDING SOCIETY

51 Newmarket Road
PO Box 232
Cambridge, CB5 8FF, United Kingdom
Tel.: (44) 845 601 3344
Fax: (44) 1223 727700
E-Mail: enquiries@cambridgebs.co.uk
Web Site: www.cambridgebs.co.uk
Rev.: $50,551,494
Assets: $1,802,506,849
Liabilities: $1,717,897,966
Net Worth: $84,608,882
Earnings: $919,147
Emp.: 144
Fiscal Year-end: 12/31/12

Business Description:
Mortgage Lending Services
S.I.C.: 6163
N.A.I.C.S.: 522310

Personnel:
Stephen Mitcham *(CEO)*
Suzanne Pattinson *(Press Officer)*
Roy Badcock *(Sec & Head-Corp Affairs)*

Board of Directors:
Ian O'Reilly
Duncan Bain
Gerald Coteman
Stuart Cruickshank
John Granger
Andy Lucas
Stephen Mitcham
Jane Pilcher
Jonathan Spence

CAMBRIDGE COGNITION HOLDINGS PLC

Tunbridge Court Tunbridge Lane
Bottisham, Cambridge, CB25 9TU, United Kingdom
Tel.: (44) 1223 810700
E-Mail: info@camcog.com
Web Site: www.cambridgecognition.com
COG—(AIM)

Business Description:
Pharmaceutical Mfr
S.I.C.: 2834
N.A.I.C.S.: 325412

Personnel:
Jane Worlock *(Chm)*
Nick Kerton *(CEO)*
Nick Walters *(CFO)*
Andrew Blackwell *(Chief Scientific Officer)*

Board of Directors:
Jane Worlock
Andrew Blackwell
Eric Dodd
Nick Kerton

CAMBRIDGE LIFE SCIENCES LTD.

14 St Thomas Place
Cambridgeshire Business Park, Ely, Cambs, CB7 4EX, United Kingdom
Tel.: (44) 1353645200
Fax: (44) 1353645250
E-Mail: info@clsdiagnostics.com
Web Site: www.cambridgelifesciences.co.uk
Year Founded: 1981
Sales Range: $10-24.9 Million
Emp.: 20

Business Description:
Pharmaceutical Products Mfr
S.I.C.: 2834
N.A.I.C.S.: 325412

Personnel:
Peter Blake *(Mng Dir)*

CAMBRIDGE PLYMOUTH CHRYSLER LTD

289 Hespeler Rd
Cambridge, ON, N1R 3H8, Canada
Tel.: (519) 621-2830
Fax: (519) 621-0588
E-Mail: cambchry@execulink.com
Web Site: www.cambridgechrysler.com
Year Founded: 1984
Rev.: $15,727,375
Emp.: 35

Business Description:
New Car Dealers
S.I.C.: 5511
N.A.I.C.S.: 441110

Personnel:
Paul Beaudoin *(Pres)*

CAMBRIDGE PRO FAB INC.

470 Franklin Blvd
Cambridge, ON, N1R 8G6, Canada
Tel.: (519) 740-6033
Fax: (519) 740-6162
Web Site: www.cambridgeprofab.com
Rev.: $10,172,559
Emp.: 80

Business Description:
Metal Fabrication & Other Industrial Equipment Mfr
S.I.C.: 3499
N.A.I.C.S.: 332999

Personnel:
George Figueiredo *(Gen Mgr)*

CAMBRIDGE SEMICONDUCTOR LIMITED

St Andrews House St Andrews Road
Cambridge, CB4 1DL, United Kingdom
Tel.: (44) 1223 446450
Fax: (44) 1223 446451
E-Mail: info@camsemi.com
Web Site: www.camsemi.com
Year Founded: 2000
Sales Range: $10-24.9 Million
Emp.: 59

Business Description:
Semiconductor Device Mfr
S.I.C.: 3674
N.A.I.C.S.: 334413

Personnel:
Gehan Amaratunga *(Co-Founder)*
Florin Udrea *(Co-Founder)*
David Baillie *(CEO)*
Martin Stephenson *(CFO)*
John Miller *(Sr VP-Bus Ops)*

CAMBRIDGE TECHNOLOGY ENTERPRISES LTD.

Plot No 8-2-269/A/2/1 to 6 1st Floor West Wing Cyber Spazio Road No 2
Banjara Hills, Hyderabad, Andhra Pradesh, 500 033, India
Tel.: (91) 4040234400
Fax: (91) 4040234600
E-Mail: innovation@ctepl.com
Web Site: www.ctepl.com
532801—(BOM)
Sls.: $16,774,306
Assets: $5,811,734
Liabilities: $1,219,561
Net Worth: $4,592,173
Earnings: ($2,510,390)
Emp.: 600
Fiscal Year-end: 03/31/13

Business Description:
Technology Services & Outsourcing Company
S.I.C.: 7371
N.A.I.C.S.: 541511

Personnel:
Stefan Hetges *(Chm & CEO)*
Arjun Chopra *(CTO)*
V. Ramana Reddy *(Sec)*
Joerg Wirthmann *(Sr VP-Sls)*

Board of Directors:
Stefan Hetges
Swaroop Dharani
Anand Mallipudi
Venkat Motaparthy

Transfer Agent:
Aarthi Consultants Private Limited
1-2-285, Domalguda
Hyderabad, India

CAMBRIDGE UNIVERSITY PRESS

UPH Shaftesbury Road
Cambridge, CB2 8BS, United Kingdom
Tel.: (44) 1223 3385331
Fax: (44) 1223315052
E-Mail: information@cambridge.org
Web Site: www.cambridge.org
Sales Range: $200-249.9 Million
Emp.: 800

Business Description:
Publishing Services
S.I.C.: 2731
N.A.I.C.S.: 511130

Personnel:
Peter Phillips *(CEO)*
Andrew Chandler *(CFO)*
Mark Maddocks *(CIO)*

U.S. Branch:

Cambridge University Press, North America (1)
32 Avenue of the Americas
New York, NY 10013-2473
Tel.: (212) 924-3900
Fax: (212) 691-3239
Toll Free: (800) 221-4512
E-Mail: information@cup.org
Web Site: www.cup.org
Emp.: 150
Publisher of Books, Publications & Journals
S.I.C.: 2731
N.A.I.C.S.: 511130
Liza Muphury *(Dir-Mktg)*

Non-U.S. Subsidiary:

Cambridge University Press Japan K.K. (1)
Sakura Building 1st Floor Nishiki-cho
1-10-1 Kanda Chiyoda-ku
Tokyo, 101-0054, Japan
Tel.: (81) 332955875
Fax: (81) 332197182
Web Site: www.cambridge.org
Book Publishers
S.I.C.: 2731
N.A.I.C.S.: 511130

CAMBUCI S.A.

Av Pedroso de Morais 1553 - 3
Andar - cj 33
Pinheiros, Sao Paulo, 05419-002, Brazil
Tel.: (55) 11 3811 4900
Fax: (55) 11 3811 4942
E-Mail: ri@cambuci.com.br
Web Site: www.cambuci.com.br
Year Founded: 1945
CAMB3—(BRAZ)
Sales Range: $125-149.9 Million
Emp.: 3,000
Business Description:
Sporting Goods Mfr
S.I.C.: 3949
N.A.I.C.S.: 339920
Personnel:
Paulo Ricardo de Oliveira *(CEO)*

CAMCO ACURA

1475 Carling Avenue
Ottawa, ON, K1Z 7L9, Canada
Tel.: (613) 728-8888
Fax: (613) 728-2045
Toll Free: (866) 980-1487
Web Site: www.camcoacura.com
Rev.: $23,803,595
Emp.: 50
Business Description:
New & Used Car Dealers
S.I.C.: 5511
N.A.I.C.S.: 441110
Personnel:
William Chu *(Gen Mgr-Sls)*

CAMCO CLEAN ENERGY PLC

(Formerly Camco International Ltd.)
31 Clerkenwell Close Suite 413
London, EC1R 0AT, United Kingdom
Tel.: (44) 2071216100
Fax: (44) 2071216101
E-Mail: companysecretary@camcocleanenergy.com
Web Site: www.camcocleanenergy.com
CAO—(AIM)
Rev.: $25,083,863
Assets: $59,485,537
Liabilities: $44,529,661
Net Worth: $14,955,876
Earnings: ($37,377,056)
Emp.: 182
Fiscal Year-end: 12/31/12
Business Description:
Renewable & Clean Energy Services
S.I.C.: 8999
N.A.I.C.S.: 541620
Personnel:
Jeff Kenna *(Chm)*
Scott McGregor *(CEO)*
Jonathan Anthony Frank Marren *(CFO)*
Andrew Jackura *(Sr VP-Bus Dev-North America)*
Board of Directors:
Jeff Kenna
Michael Farrow
Jonathan Anthony Frank Marren
Scott McGregor
Zainul Rahim

U.S. Subsidiary:

Camco International Group Incorporated (1)
390 Interlocken Crescent Ste 490
Broomfield, CO 80021
Tel.: (720) 897-6677
Fax: (303) 410-6634
Web Site: www.camcocleanenergy.com
Emp.: 13
Carbon Management Strategy
S.I.C.: 3624
N.A.I.C.S.: 335991
Scott McGregor *(CEO)*
Jim Wiest *(Mng Dir)*

Non-U.S. Subsidiaries:

Camco International Carbon Assets Information Consulting (Beijing) Co. Limited (1)
Fl 14 Lucky Tower A No 3 N Rd E 3rd Ring Rd
Chaoyang District, Beijing, China
Tel.: (86) 1084481623
Fax: (86) 1084482432
Emp.: 30
Business Service Providers
S.I.C.: 7334
N.A.I.C.S.: 561439

Camco Services (UK) Limited (1)
172 Tottenham Court Rd
London, W1T 7NS, United Kingdom
Tel.: (44) 2071216100
Fax: (44) 2071216101
Web Site: www.camcoglobal.com
Emp.: 20
Environmental Engineering Services
S.I.C.: 8711
N.A.I.C.S.: 541330
Petra Ernst- Gutierrez *(Mgr-Mktg)*

Camco Ventures (China) Limited (1)
14th Floor Lucky Tower A No 3 North Road
East 3rd Ring Road
Chaovang District, Beijing, 100027, China
Tel.: (86) 1084481623
Fax: (86) 1084482432
Emp.: 50
Environmental Engineering Services
S.I.C.: 8711
N.A.I.C.S.: 541330

Camco Ventures Limited (1)
Overmoor Farm Neston
Corsham, Wiltshire, SN13 9TZ, United Kingdom
Tel.: (44) 1225812102
Fax: (44) 1225812103
Emp.: 30
Gas Emission Reduction Services
S.I.C.: 8734
N.A.I.C.S.: 541380
Doug Smith *(Mng Dir)*

Carbon Asset Management International GmbH (1)
Burggasse 116
PO Box 1070
Vienna, Austria
Tel.: (43) 152520200
Fax: (43) 4059898298
Emp.: 5
Asset Management & Investment Services
S.I.C.: 6794
N.A.I.C.S.: 533110

EPES Limited (1)
Overmoor Farm
Neston, SN13 9TZ Corsham, United Kingdom
Tel.: (44) 1225 812 102
Environmental Consulting Services
S.I.C.: 8999
N.A.I.C.S.: 541620

ESD Bulgaria Limited (1)
38 Dondukov Blv Fl 2
Sofia, 1000, Bulgaria
Tel.: (359) 29817041
Fax: (359) 29808306
E-Mail: esdb@esdb.bg
Web Site: www.esdb.bg
Emp.: 9
Environmental Consulting Services
S.I.C.: 8999
N.A.I.C.S.: 541620
Alexander Penchev *(Mng Dir)*

ESD Partners Limited (1)
Overmoor Farm
Corsham, SN13 9TZ, United Kingdom
Tel.: (44) 1225812102
Fax: (44) 1225812103
Emp.: 20
Management Consulting Services
S.I.C.: 8748
N.A.I.C.S.: 541618
Charlotte Challis *(Office Mgr)*

CAMCO INTERNATIONAL LTD.

(Name Changed to Camco Clean Energy plc)

CAMDEN MOTORS GROUP LTD.

77-283 Grovebury Rd
Leighton Buzzard, Beds, LU7 4TE, United Kingdom
Tel.: (44) 8707606100
Fax: (44) 1525252226
Year Founded: 1932
Sales Range: $1-4.9 Billion
Emp.: 900
Business Description:
New & Used Motor Vehicle Retailer
S.I.C.: 5511
N.A.I.C.S.: 441110
Personnel:
Paul Dunkley *(CEO)*
David Hammond *(CEO-Camden Ventures)*

CAMDON CONSTRUCTION LTD

6780 76th Street
Red Deer, AB, T4P 4G6, Canada
Tel.: (403) 343-1233
Fax: (403) 342-2422
Toll Free: (800) 615-3381
E-Mail: info@camdon.ca
Web Site: www.camdon.ca
Year Founded: 1984
Rev.: $17,002,568
Emp.: 60
Business Description:
Building Construction Services
S.I.C.: 1542
N.A.I.C.S.: 236220
Personnel:
Tim Katakami *(Partner)*
Scott McQuaig *(Partner)*
Troy Spelt *(Partner)*
George Wilson *(Partner)*

CAMECO CORPORATION

2121 11th Street West
Saskatoon, SK, S7M 1J3, Canada
Tel.: (306) 956-6200
Fax: (306) 956-6201
E-Mail: employment@cameco.com
Web Site: www.cameco.com
CCJ—(NYSE TSX)
Rev.: $2,193,265,530
Assets: $7,230,159,744
Liabilities: $2,419,182,250
Net Worth: $4,810,977,494
Earnings: $285,711,803
Emp.: 7,949
Fiscal Year-end: 12/31/13
Business Description:
Ownership & Operation of Uranium Mines
S.I.C.: 1094
N.A.I.C.S.: 212291
Personnel:
Timothy S. Gitzel *(Pres & CEO)*
Grant Isaac *(CFO & Sr VP)*
Bob Steane *(COO & Sr VP)*
Sean Quinn *(Chief Legal Officer, Sec & Sr VP)*
Ken Seitz *(Chief Comml Officer & Sr VP)*
Alice Wong *(Chief Corp Officer & Sr VP)*
Board of Directors:
A. Neil McMillan
Ian D. Bruce
Daniel Camus
John H. Clappison
Joe F. Colvin
James R. Curtiss
Donald H. F. Deranger
Catherine A. Gignac
Timothy S. Gitzel
James K. Gowans
Nancy E. Hopkins
A. Anne McLellan
Victor J. Zaleschuk

American Stock Transfer & Trust Company, LLC
6201 15th Ave
Brooklyn, NY 11219

Transfer Agents:
CST Trust Company
PO Box 700 Station B
Montreal, QC, Canada

American Stock Transfer & Trust Company, LLC
6201 15th Ave
Brooklyn, NY 11219

Subsidiary:

Cameco Fuel Manufacturing Inc (1)
200 Dorset St E
Port Hope, ON, L1A 3V4, Canada
Tel.: (905) 885-4537
Fax: (905) 372-3748
Web Site: www.cameco.com
Emp.: 300
Fuel Mfr
S.I.C.: 2911
N.A.I.C.S.: 324110

Non-U.S. Subsidiary:

NUKEM GmbH (1)
Industriestrasse 13
D 63755 Alzenau, Germany De (100%)
Mailing Address:
P.O. Box 1313
D-63754 Alzenau, Germany
Tel.: (49) 60239106
Fax: (49) 602391188
E-Mail: info@nukem.de
Web Site: www.nukem.de
Emp.: 300
Uranium Trading, Conversion & Enrichment Services
S.I.C.: 7389
N.A.I.C.S.: 425120
Beate Scheffler *(Dir-Comm)*

U.S. Subsidiary:

NUKEM, Inc. (2)
39 Old Ridgebury Rd
Danbury, CT 06810-5100 DE (100%)
Tel.: (203) 778-9420
Fax: (203) 778-9430
E-Mail: info@nukeminc.com
Web Site: www.nukeminc.com
Emp.: 25
Uranium Trading, Conversion & Enrichment Services
S.I.C.: 7389
N.A.I.C.S.: 425120
Jeffrey R. Faul *(Pres & CEO)*
Timothy Y. McGraw *(Exec VP)*

CAMEL GROUP CO., LTD.
No 83 Wudang Rd
Wuhan, Hubei, China
Tel.: (86) 710 7615058
E-Mail: camel@chinacamel.com
Web Site: www.chinacamel.com
Year Founded: 1980
601311—(SHG)
Business Description:
Battery Mfr & Whslr
S.I.C.: 3691
N.A.I.C.S.: 335911
Personnel:
Guoben Liu *(Chm)*

CAMELEON SOFTWARE SA
Le Galilee 185 Rue Galilee
31670 Labege, France
Tel.: (33) 811707878
Fax: (33) 561397888
Web Site: www.cameleon-software.com
Year Founded: 1987
CAM—(EUR)
Sls.: $14,044,592
Earnings: $807,702
Emp.: 64
Fiscal Year-end: 12/31/12
Business Description:
Computer Software Developer
S.I.C.: 7372
N.A.I.C.S.: 511210
Personnel:
Jacques Soumeillan *(Pres & CEO)*
Francoise Asparre *(Deputy CEO & Sr VP-Pro Svc)*
Thibault de Bouville *(CFO)*
Sylvie Rouge *(Sr VP-Product Mktg)*
Board of Directors:
Francoise Asparre
Thibault de Bouville
Amelie Faure
Philippe Gaillard
Jacques Soumeillan
Mike Sutton

CAMELLIA PLC
Linton Park Linton
Maidstone, Kent, ME17 4AB, United Kingdom
Tel.: (44) 1622 746655
Fax: (44) 1622 747422
E-Mail: office@camellia.co.uk
Web Site: www.camellia.plc.uk
Year Founded: 1889
CAM—(LSE)
Rev.: $413,030,134
Assets: $1,074,128,825
Liabilities: $515,848,231
Net Worth: $558,280,594
Earnings: $71,181,759
Emp.: 71,043
Fiscal Year-end: 12/31/12
Business Description:
Holding Company
S.I.C.: 6719
N.A.I.C.S.: 551112
Personnel:
Malcolm C. Perkins *(Chm)*
C. J. Ames *(Mng Dir & Mng Dir-Ops-UK)*
P. J. Field *(Mng Dir & Mng Dir-Banking & Fin Svcs)*
J. A. Morton *(Sec)*
Board of Directors:
Malcolm C. Perkins
C. J. Ames
M. Dunki
P. J. Field
Anil K. Mathur
D. A. Reeves
C. J. Relleen
C. P. T. Vaughan-Johnson
F. Vuilleumier

Subsidiaries:

Abbey Metal Finishing Company Limited (1)
Unit 2 Dodwells Bridge Industrial Estate
Dodwells Road
Hinckley, LE10 3BZ, United Kingdom
Tel.: (44) 2476350444
Fax: (44) 2476641299
E-Mail: info@amfin.co.uk
Web Site: www.amfin.co.uk
Emp.: 70
Electroplating Plating Polishing Anodizing & Coloring
S.I.C.: 3471
N.A.I.C.S.: 332813
Paul Bennett *(Mng Dir)*

Affish Limited (1)
Linton Park Linton
Maidstone, Kent, ME17 4AB, United Kingdom
Tel.: (44) 1622746655
Fax: (44) 1622747422
E-Mail: camellia@camellia.uk
Web Site: www.camellia.plc.uk
Emp.: 12
Holding Company
S.I.C.: 6719
N.A.I.C.S.: 551112
Malcolm C. Perkins *(Chm)*

AJT Engineering Limited (1)
Craigshaw Crescent West Tullos
Aberdeen, AB12 3TB, United Kingdom
Tel.: (44) 1224871791
Fax: (44) 1224890251
E-Mail: info@ajt-engineering.co.uk
Web Site: www.ajt-engineering.co.uk
Emp.: 75
Engineering Services
S.I.C.: 8711
N.A.I.C.S.: 541330
William Boyd *(Mng Dir)*

AKD Engineering Limited (1)
Horn Hill
Lowestoft, Suffolk, NR33 0PX, United Kingdom
Tel.: (44) 1502527800
Fax: (44) 1502527846
E-Mail: info@akd-engineering.co.uk
Web Site: www.akd-engineering.co.uk
Emp.: 100
Fabricated Metal Product Mfr
S.I.C.: 3499
N.A.I.C.S.: 332999
Mark Jones *(Mng Dir)*

Bordure Limited (1)
Linton Park Linton
Maidstone, Kent, ME174AB, United Kingdom
Tel.: (44) 1622746655
Fax: (44) 1622747422
E-Mail: camellia@camellia.co.uk
Web Site: www.camellia.plc.uk
Emp.: 12
Holding Company
S.I.C.: 6719
N.A.I.C.S.: 551112
Malcolm C. Perkins *(Chm)*

British Metal Treatments Limited (1)
Battery Rd
Great Yarmouth, Norfolk, NR30 3NN, United Kingdom
Tel.: (44) 1493844153
Fax: (44) 1493330303
E-Mail: info@bmtgalv.co.uk
Web Site: www.bmtgalv.co.uk
Emp.: 20
Precision Turned Product Mfr
S.I.C.: 3451
N.A.I.C.S.: 332721
David Cowley *(Mng Dir)*

Duncan Lawrie Limited (1)
1 Hobart Place
London, SW1W 0HU, United Kingdom
Tel.: (44) 2072451234
Fax: (44) 2072456276
E-Mail: london@duncanlawrie.com
Web Site: www.duncanlawrie.com
Emp.: 100
Financial Investment Services
S.I.C.: 6211
N.A.I.C.S.: 523999
Peter Field *(Mng Dir)*

Subsidiaries:

Douglas Deakin Young Limited (2)
1 Hobart Pl
London, SW1W 0HU, United Kingdom
Tel.: (44) 2072451234
Fax: (44) 2072013031
E-Mail: london@duncanlawrie.com
Web Site: www.duncanlawrie.com
Emp.: 100
Financial Investment Services
S.I.C.: 6211
N.A.I.C.S.: 523999
Matthew Parden *(Mng Dir)*

Duncan Lawrie (2)
11-12 Queen Sq
Bristol, BS1 4NT, United Kingdom
Tel.: (44) 1179271500
Fax: (44) 1179271501
E-Mail: bristol@duncanlawrie.com
Web Site: www.duncanlawrie.com
Emp.: 8
Business Services
S.I.C.: 7389
N.A.I.C.S.: 561499
Matthew Parden *(Mng Dir)*

Duncan Lawrie (2)
11-12 Queen Square
Bristol, BS1 4NT, United Kingdom
Tel.: (44) 1179271500
Fax: (44) 1179271501
E-Mail: bristol@duncanlawrie.com
Web Site: www.duncanlawrie.com
Emp.: 35
Private Banking Services
S.I.C.: 6029
N.A.I.C.S.: 522110
Wayne Mathews *(Mng Dir)*
Matthew Parden *(Mng Dir)*

Non-U.S. Subsidiaries:

Duncan Lawrie (IOM) Limited (2)
14-15 Mount Havelock
IM12QG Douglas, Isle of Man
Tel.: (44) 1624662200
Fax: (44) 1624676315
E-Mail: iom@duncanlawrie.com
Web Site: www.duncanlawrie.com
Emp.: 30
Financial Investment Services
S.I.C.: 6211
N.A.I.C.S.: 523999
Nigel Gautrey *(Mng Dir)*

Duncan Lawrie Offshore Services Limited (2)
14-15 Mt Havelock
IM12QG Douglas, Isle of Man
Tel.: (44) 1624662200
Fax: (44) 1624612980
E-Mail: iom@duncanlawrie.com
Web Site: www.duncanlawrie.com
Emp.: 100
Financial Investment Services
S.I.C.: 6211
N.A.I.C.S.: 523999
Peter Field *(CEO)*

Lawrie Group Plc (1)
Wrotham Place Wrotham
Sevenoaks, Kent, TN1 57AE, United Kingdom
Tel.: (44) 1732884488
Fax: (44) 1732885724
Holding Company
S.I.C.: 6719
N.A.I.C.S.: 551112
Peter Leggatt *(Mng Dir)*

Linton Park Plc (1)
Linton Park Linton
Maidstone, Kent, ME17 4AB, United Kingdom
Tel.: (44) 1622746655
Fax: (44) 1622747422
E-Mail: camellia@lintonpark.plc.uk
Web Site: www.camellia.plc.uk
Emp.: 12
Holding Company
S.I.C.: 6719
N.A.I.C.S.: 551112
Malcolm C. Perkins *(Chm)*

Robertson Bois Dickson Anderson Limited (1)
Linton Park Linton
Maidstone, Kent, ME17 4AB, United Kingdom
Tel.: (44) 1622746655
Fax: (44) 1622747422
E-Mail: office@camellia.plc.uk
Web Site: www.camellia.plc.uk
Emp.: 12
Holding Company
S.I.C.: 6719
N.A.I.C.S.: 551112
Malcolm C. Perkins *(Chm)*

Unochrome Industries Limited (1)
Linton Park Linton
Maidstone, Kent, ME17 4AB, United Kingdom
Tel.: (44) 1622746655
Fax: (44) 1622747422
E-Mail: camellia@lintonpark.plc.uk
Web Site: www.camellia.com
Emp.: 15
Holding Company
S.I.C.: 6719
N.A.I.C.S.: 551112
Malcolm C. Perkins *(Chm)*

Non-U.S. Subsidiaries:

Affish B.V. (1)
Burg Vd Lelystraat 2
Woudrichem, 4285ZH Utrecht, Netherlands
Tel.: (31) 183303484
Fax: (31) 183303375
E-Mail: sales@affish.nl
Web Site: www.affish.nl
Emp.: 8
Fish & Seafood Whslr
S.I.C.: 5146
N.A.I.C.S.: 424460
Gaab Buys *(Mgr)*

Eastern Produce Cape (Pty) Limited (1)
Linton Park Wines
PO Box 1234
Wellington, 7654 Cape Town, South Africa
Tel.: (27) 218731625
Fax: (27) 0218735460
E-Mail: info@lintonparkwines.co.za
Web Site: www.lintonparkwines.com
Emp.: 45
Grape Vineyards
S.I.C.: 0172
N.A.I.C.S.: 111332
Malcolm C. Perkins *(Mng Dir)*

Eastern Produce Kenya Limited (1)
3rd Floor New Rehema House
PO Box 45560
0100 Nairobi, Kenya
Tel.: (254) 204440115
Fax: (254) 204449635
E-Mail: mail@easternproduce.co.ke
Web Site: www.easternproduce.co.ke
Emp.: 35
Coffee & Tea Mfr
S.I.C.: 2099
N.A.I.C.S.: 311920
Graham McLean *(Mng Dir)*

Eastern Produce South Africa (Pty) Limited (1)
7 Windsor St
0850 Tzaneen, South Africa
Tel.: (27) 153073120
Fax: (27) 153074381
E-Mail: genihegouwa@mweb.co.zi
Web Site: www.easternproduce.com
Emp.: 30
Roasted Nuts & Peanut Butter Mfr
S.I.C.: 2068
N.A.I.C.S.: 311911
J. A. de Kock *(Mng Dir)*

Goodricke Group Limited (1)
Camellia House
14 Gurusaday Road, 700019 Kolkata, WB, India
Tel.: (91) 3322871816
Fax: (91) 3322877089
E-Mail: goodricke@goodricke.com
Web Site: www.camellia.plc.uk
Emp.: 100
Coffee & Tea Mfr
S.I.C.: 2095
N.A.I.C.S.: 311920
Subrata Banerjee *(Sec)*

Subsidiaries:

Amgoorie India Limited (2)
Camellia House
14 Gurusaday Road, 700019 Kolkata, WB, India

Tel.: (91) 3322873067
Fax: (91) 3322877089
E-Mail: goodricke@goodricke.com
Web Site: www.goodricke.com
Emp.: 100
Coffee & Tea Mfr
S.I.C.: 2095
N.A.I.C.S.: 311920
Arun Singh *(Mng Dir)*

Koomber Tea Company Limited **(2)**
Camellia House
14 Gurusaday Road, 700019 Kolkata, WB, India
Tel.: (91) 3322873067
Fax: (91) 3322877089
Web Site: www.goodricke.com
Coffee & Tea Mfr
S.I.C.: 2095
N.A.I.C.S.: 311920

Tiru Tea Company Limited **(1)**
Camellia House
14 Gurusaday Rd, 700019 Kolkata, WB, India
Tel.: (91) 3322871816
Fax: (91) 228725777089
Web Site: www.camellia.plc.uk
Coffee & Tea Mfr
S.I.C.: 2095
N.A.I.C.S.: 311920

United Leasing Company Limited **(1)**
Camellia House 22 Kazi Nazrul Islam Avenue, 1000 Dhaka, Bangladesh
Tel.: (880) 29669006
Fax: (880) 29662596
E-Mail: webmail@ulc.com.bd
Web Site: www.ulc.com.bd
Emp.: 1,000
Insurance Services
S.I.C.: 6411
N.A.I.C.S.: 524298
Syed Ehsan *(Mng Dir)*

Wylax International B.V. **(1)**
Burg Vd Lelystraat 2
Woudrichem, 4285 Utrecht, Netherlands
Tel.: (31) 183301333
Fax: (31) 183303375
E-Mail: info@wylax.nl
Web Site: www.wylax.nl
Emp.: 50
Fish & Seafood Whslr
S.I.C.: 5146
N.A.I.C.S.: 424460

CAMELOT CORPORATION
(Name Changed to Comjoyful International Company)

CAMELOT GHANA LIMITED
PO Box M191
Accra, Ghana
Tel.: (233) 21773120
Fax: (233) 21773043
E-Mail: camelot@camelotprint.com
Web Site: www.camelotprint.com
Year Founded: 1977
CMLT—(GHA)
Emp.: 60
Business Description:
Pre-Printed, Customized Forms & Security Printing
S.I.C.: 2759
N.A.I.C.S.: 323111
Personnel:
Sam Mensah *(Chm)*
Elisabeth Joyce Villars *(CEO & Mng Dir)*
Board of Directors:
Sam Mensah
Edward K. Akyea-Djamson
Suganthan E. Allotey
Dzifa Amegashie
Elisabeth Joyce Villars
John Colin Villars
John Theophilus Warmann
Non-U.S. Subsidiary:

Camelot Security Solutions Limited **(1)**
14th Floor New Africa House 31 Marina
Lagos, Nigeria
Tel.: (234) 8079215440
E-Mail: cssl@camelotprint.com
Security Printing Services
S.I.C.: 2759
N.A.I.C.S.: 323111
Elizabeth Joyce Villars *(Founder)*
Sam Mensah *(Chm)*
John Colin Villars *(Mng Dir)*

CAMELOT INFORMATION SYSTEMS INC.
Beijing Publishing House A6 North Third Ring Road
Xicheng District, Beijing, 100120, China
Tel.: (86) 10 82019000
Fax: (86) 10 82019100
E-Mail: hotline@camelotchina.com
Web Site: www.camelotchina.com
CIS—(NYSE)
Rev.: $254,063,000
Assets: $288,928,000
Liabilities: $85,655,000
Net Worth: $203,273,000
Earnings: ($40,402,000)
Emp.: 6,085
Fiscal Year-end: 12/31/12
Business Description:
IT Services & Solutions
S.I.C.: 7379
N.A.I.C.S.: 541519
Personnel:
Simon Yiming Ma *(Chm & CEO)*
Bo Chen *(Vice Chm)*
Heidi Chou *(Co-Pres)*
Jacob Qian *(Co-Pres)*
Jan-Kung Roh *(CTO)*
Yang Xiao Chun *(Sr VP-Japan Offshore Svcs)*
Board of Directors:
Simon Yiming Ma
Bo Chen
Shang-Wen Hsiao
David Dahu Wang
Jian Wang
Joanna Wang
Yuhui Wang

CAMELOT MANAGEMENT CONSULTANTS AG
Theodor-Heuss-Anlage 12
68165 Mannheim, Germany
Tel.: (49) 621 86298 0
Fax: (49) 621 86298 250
E-Mail: office@camelot-mc.com
Web Site: www.camelot-mc.com
Year Founded: 1996
CTK—(DEU)
Business Description:
Business Management Consulting Services
S.I.C.: 8742
N.A.I.C.S.: 541611
Personnel:
Libor Kotlik *(Mng Partner)*
Josef Packowski *(Mng Partner)*
Jorma Gall *(Partner)*
Andreas Gmur *(Partner)*
Michael Jarosch *(Partner)*
Christoph Lieth *(Partner)*
Sven Mandewirth *(Partner)*
Marcus Meissner *(Partner)*
Harald Munzberg *(Partner)*
Marko Schmidt *(Partner)*
Patrick Wolf *(Partner)*

CAMEO COMMUNICATION, INC.
7F No 32 Chung Shin Rd
221 Hsi-chieh, Taipei, Taiwan
Tel.: (886) 226499800
Fax: (886) 226499983
Web Site: www.cameo.com.tw
6142—(TAI)
Sales Range: $200-249.9 Million
Business Description:
Wireless Adapters & Routers Mfr
S.I.C.: 3661
N.A.I.C.S.: 334210
Personnel:
Jerry Chien *(Chm)*
Victor Lee *(CFO)*

CAMERON BALLOONS LTD.
Saint Johns St
Bedminster, Bristol, BS3 4NH, United Kingdom
Tel.: (44) 1179637216
Fax: (44) 1179661168
E-Mail: enquiries@cameronballoons.co.uk
Web Site: www.cameronballoons.co.uk
Year Founded: 1970
Emp.: 63
Business Description:
Hot-Air Balloon Mfr
S.I.C.: 3721
N.A.I.C.S.: 336411
Personnel:
Alan R. Noble *(Mng Dir)*
U.S. Subsidiary:

Cameron Balloons U.S. **(1)**
7399 Newman Blvd
Dexter, MI 48130 (100%)
Mailing Address:
PO Box 3672
Ann Arbor, MI 48106-3672
Tel.: (734) 426-5525
Fax: (734) 426-5026
E-Mail: hotline@cameronballoons.com
Web Site: www.cameronballoons.com
Sales Range: $1-9.9 Million
Emp.: 15
Hot-Air Balloon Mfr
Import Export
S.I.C.: 3721
N.A.I.C.S.: 336411
Dave Moody *(Mgr-Engrg)*

CAMERONS BREWERY LTD.
Lion Brewery Waldon St
Hartlepool, Cleveland, TS24 7QS, United Kingdom
Tel.: (44) 1429852000
Fax: (44) 1429852011
Web Site: www.cameronsbrewery.com
Emp.: 100
Business Description:
Alcoholic Beverages
S.I.C.: 5181
N.A.I.C.S.: 424810
Personnel:
Christopher David Soley *(Gen Mgr)*

CAMEROON AIRLINES SA
3 Avenue du General de Gaulle
BP 4092
Douala, Cameroon
Tel.: (237) 342 2525
Fax: (237) 343 3543
Web Site: www.cameroon-airlines.com
Year Founded: 1961
Rev.: $70,180,000
Emp.: 1,400
Business Description:
Air Transportation Services
S.I.C.: 4512
N.A.I.C.S.: 481111

CAMEX EQUIPMENT SALES & RENTALS INC.
1511 Sparrow Drive
Nisku, AB, Canada
Tel.: (780) 955-2770
Fax: (780) 955-3735
Toll Free: (877) 955-2770
E-Mail: info@camex.ca
Web Site: www.camex.ca
Year Founded: 1992
Rev.: $27,500,000
Emp.: 90
Business Description:
Oil Field Equipment Services
S.I.C.: 1389
N.A.I.C.S.: 213112
Personnel:
Pat Wilson *(Pres & CEO)*

CAMEX LIMITED
Camex House Stadium - Commerce Road Navrangpura
Ahmedabad, Gujarat, 380 009, India
Tel.: (91) 79 66307200
Fax: (91) 79 26462123
E-Mail: info@camexltd.com
Web Site: www.camexltd.com
Year Founded: 1986
524440—(BOM)
Sales Range: $25-49.9 Million
Business Description:
Textile & Leather Product Mfr
S.I.C.: 2299
N.A.I.C.S.: 314999
Personnel:
Chandraprakash Chopra *(Chm & CEO)*

CAMEXIP S.A.
9 Republcii St
2064 Baicoi, Romania
Tel.: (40) 44260347
Fax: (40) 44260838
E-Mail: camexip@camexipsa.ro
Web Site: www.camexipsa.ro
CAXY—(BUC)
Sales Range: $1-9.9 Million
Emp.: 120
Business Description:
Industrial Equipment Mfr
S.I.C.: 7699
N.A.I.C.S.: 811310
Personnel:
George State *(Pres & Mng Dir)*
Madalina Barbu *(Asst Mng Dir)*

CAMFIL AB
(d/b/a Camfil Farr Group)
Industrigatan 3
619 33 Trosa, Sweden
Tel.: (46) 15653600
Fax: (46) 15616724
E-Mail: info@camfil.se
Web Site: www.camfilfarr.com
Sls.: $753,148,440
Assets: $653,348,880
Liabilities: $474,415,560
Net Worth: $178,933,320
Earnings: $52,771,320
Emp.: 3,484
Fiscal Year-end: 12/31/12
Business Description:
Mfr of Air Filters & Purification Equipment
S.I.C.: 3564
N.A.I.C.S.: 333413
Personnel:
Jan Eric Larson *(Chm)*
Johan Markman *(Vice Chm)*
Alan O'Connell *(Pres)*
Tomas Brane *(CIO)*
Jan-Erik Dantoft *(CTO)*
Erik Markman *(Program Officer & VP-Comm)*
Johan Ryrberg *(Exec VP)*
Board of Directors:
Jan Eric Larson
Eric Giertz
Dan Larson
Mats Lonnqvist
Erik Markman
Johan Markman

Camfil AB—(Continued)

Carl Wilhelm Ros
Christer Stavstrom
Magnus Yngen

U.S. Subsidiary:

Camfil Farr, Inc. (1)
2121 E Paulhan St
Compton, CA 90220-6433 DE
Tel.: (310) 668-6300
Fax: (310) 608-2268
Toll Free: (800) 333-7320
Web Site: www.camfilfarr.com
Sales Range: $300-349.9 Million
Emp.: 500
Mfr. of Air Filtration Equipment, (HVAC) Engine Air Cleaners & Dust Collection Systems
Import Export
S.I.C.: 3564
N.A.I.C.S.: 333413
John Johnston *(Pres)*

Subsidiary:

Farr Air Polllution Control Company (2)
3505 S Airport Rd
Jonesboro, AR 72401 (100%)
Tel.: (870) 933-8048
Fax: (870) 933-8381
Web Site: www.farrapc.com
Emp.: 70
Mfr. of Air Filtration Equipment
S.I.C.: 3564
N.A.I.C.S.: 333413
Lee Morgan *(Pres)*

Plants:

Camfil Farr (2)
500 Industrial Ave
Corcoran, CA 93212-9629
Mailing Address:
500 Industrial Ave
Corcoran, CA 93212-9629
Tel.: (559) 992-5118
Fax: (559) 992-5286
Web Site: www.camfilfarr.com
Emp.: 25
Mfr. of Commercial & Industrial Air Filtration Systems
S.I.C.: 3564
N.A.I.C.S.: 333413

Camfil Farr (2)
500 S Main St
Crystal Lake, IL 60014-6205
Tel.: (815) 459-6600
Fax: (815) 459-5390
Web Site: www.cfhvachpp.com
Emp.: 100
Mfr. of Commercial & Industrial Air Filtration Equipment
S.I.C.: 3569
N.A.I.C.S.: 333999

Camfil Farr (2)
1008 1st St W
Conover, NC 28613 (100%)
Tel.: (828) 465-2880
Fax: (828) 464-9650
Toll Free: (800) 262-2716
Web Site: www.camfilfarr.com
Emp.: 150
Mfr. of Commercial & Industrial Air Filtration Equipment
S.I.C.: 3564
N.A.I.C.S.: 333413

Non-U.S. Branches:

Camfil Ltd. (2)
Knowsley Road
Haslingden, Lancashire, BB4 4EG, United Kingdom (100%)
Tel.: (44) 1706 23800
Fax: (44) 1706 226736
E-Mail: filtersales@camfil.co.uk
Web Site: www.camfilfarr.com
Sls.: $10,746,000
Emp.: 60
Mfr of Commercial & Industrial Filters & Filtration Systems
S.I.C.: 3564
N.A.I.C.S.: 333413

Camfil Farr (2)
2785 Francis Hughes
Laval, QC, H7L 3J6, Canada (100%)
Tel.: (450) 629-3030
Fax: (450) 662-6035
Web Site: www.camfilfarr.com
Sales Range: $10-24.9 Million
Emp.: 200
Mfr. of Commercial & Industrial Filters & Filtration Systems
S.I.C.: 3564
N.A.I.C.S.: 333413
Steve Leduc *(Pres)*

CAMFIN S.P.A.

Via Gaetano Negri 8
20213 Milan, Italy
Tel.: (39) 0272583400
Fax: (39) 0235374305
E-Mail: ir@gruppocamfin.it
Web Site: www.gruppocamfin.it
Year Founded: 1915
CMF—(ITA)
Emp.: 100

Business Description:
Investment Holding Company
S.I.C.: 6719
N.A.I.C.S.: 551112

Personnel:
Marco Tronchetti Provera *(Chm)*
Carlo Alessandro Puri Negri *(Deputy Chm)*
Enrico Parazzini *(CEO)*
Roberto Rivellino *(Sec)*

Board of Directors:
Marco Tronchetti Provera
Georgio Luca Bruno
Allesandro Foti
Nicoletta Greco
Roberto Haggiag
Vittorio Malacalza
Mario Notari
Enrico Parazzini
Alberto Pirelli
Carlo Alessandro Puri Negri
Mauro Rebutto
Roberto Rivellino
Arturo Sanguinetti
Giuseppe Tronchetti Provera
Luigi Tronchetti Provera
Raffaele Bruno Tronchetti Provera

Subsidiaries:

Cam Immobiliare S.p.A. (1)
Via Sempione 230
20016 Pero, Italy (100%)
Tel.: (39) 02353741
Fax: (39) 0235374305
Web Site: www.gruppocamfin.it/inglese/pag44.asp
Activities Related to Real Estate
S.I.C.: 6531
N.A.I.C.S.: 531390

Cam Partecipazioni S.p.A. (1)
Viale Piero e Alberto Pirelli 25
20126 Milan, MI, Italy (100%)
Tel.: (39) 0272582400
Fax: (39) 02 72582433
Energy & Environmental Services
S.I.C.: 8999
N.A.I.C.S.: 541620

Perhopolis S.r.l. (1)
Via Sempione 230
20016 Pero, Italy (100%)
Tel.: (39) 02353741
Fax: (39) 0235374305
Activities Related to Real Estate
S.I.C.: 6531
N.A.I.C.S.: 531390

Pirelli & C Ambiente S.p.A. (1)
Via Sempione 230
20016 Pero, Italy (100%)
Tel.: (39) 02353741
Fax: (39) 0235374305
Activities Related to Real Estate
S.I.C.: 6531
N.A.I.C.S.: 531390

Joint Venture:

Cam Petroli S.r.l. (1)
Via Sempione 230
20016 Pero, Italy (50%)
Tel.: (39) 02353741
Fax: (39) 0235374305
Web Site: www.gruppocamfin.it/inglese/pag44.asp
Petroleum Bulk Stations & Terminals
S.I.C.: 5171
N.A.I.C.S.: 424710

CAMILION SOLUTIONS, INC

123 Commerce Valley Dr E 6th Fl
Markham, ON, L3T 7W8, Canada
Tel.: (905) 482-3450
Fax: (905) 482-2805
Toll Free: (866) 226-4546
Web Site: www.camilion.com
Year Founded: 2001
Sales Range: $10-24.9 Million

Business Description:
Financial Services Industry Product Development & Management Solutions
S.I.C.: 7372
N.A.I.C.S.: 511210

Personnel:
Ross Orrett *(Pres & CEO)*
Dave Conte *(CFO)*
Neil Ohm *(CTO)*
Susan Hutt *(Sr VP-R&D)*

Board of Directors:
David Adderley
Brian Antonen
G. Raymond Chang
Ross Orrett
Andrew Pinkerton
Rick Stuckey

CAMINHOS DE FERRO PORTUGUESES, EP

Calcada do Duque 20
1294 Lisbon, Portugal
Tel.: (351) 21 321 5700
Fax: (351) 21 321 5879
Web Site: www.cp.pt
Year Founded: 1927
Sales Range: $300-349.9 Million
Emp.: 5,126

Business Description:
Railroad Operator
S.I.C.: 4011
N.A.I.C.S.: 482111

Personnel:
Ernesto Jorge Sanchez Martins de Brito *(Chm)*
Jose Luis Areal Alves de Cunha *(Sr VP)*
Carlos Fernando Moreira de Cavalho *(Sr VP)*
Edita Rodrigues Vinhas *(Sr VP)*

CAMINO MINERALS CORPORATION

999 West Hastings Street Suite 1510
Vancouver, BC, V6C 2W2, Canada
Tel.: (604) 683-8218
Fax: (604) 683-8350
Toll Free: (866) 338-0047
E-Mail: info@caminominerals.com
Web Site: www.caminominerals.com
Year Founded: 2009
COR—(TSXV)
Int. Income: $26,580
Assets: $8,953,420
Liabilities: $182,876
Net Worth: $8,770,545
Earnings: ($1,971,925)
Fiscal Year-end: 07/31/13

Business Description:
Metal Mining Services
S.I.C.: 1099
N.A.I.C.S.: 212299

Personnel:
R. E. Gordon Davis *(Chm & CEO)*
Alexander Cheong *(CFO)*

Board of Directors:
R. E. Gordon Davis
James W. Tutton
David Harold Watkins

Transfer Agent:
Computershare Investor Services Inc.
100 University Ave 9th Floor
Toronto, ON, Canada

CAMINOS DE LAS SIERRAS S.A.

Av Italia 700
5101 Cordoba, Argentina
Tel.: (54) 351 498 2400
Fax: (54) 351 498 1170
Web Site: www.camsierras.com.ar
Sales Range: $25-49.9 Million

Business Description:
Road & Bridge Construction Services
S.I.C.: 1611
N.A.I.C.S.: 237310

CAMIRA FABRICS LTD.

Hopton Mills
Mirfield, West Yorkshire, WF14 8HE, United Kingdom
Tel.: (44) 1924490591
Fax: (44) 1924495605
E-Mail: info@camirafabrics.com
Web Site: www.camirafabrics.com
Sales Range: $50-74.9 Million
Emp.: 250

Business Description:
Upholstery Fabric Mfr
S.I.C.: 2299
N.A.I.C.S.: 313210

Personnel:
Abdul Ali *(Dir-Sls-United Kingdom)*

CAMISHA RESOURCES CORP.

(Name Changed to Prima Fluorspar Corp.)

CAMLIN FINE SCIENCES LTD.

WICEL Plot No F/ 11 & F/12 MIDC
Marol Central Road
Opp SEEPZ Main Gate Andheri East, Mumbai, Maharashtra, 400 093, India
Tel.: (91) 2267001000
Fax: (91) 2228324404
E-Mail: sales@camlinfs.com
Web Site: www.camlinfs.com
532834—(BOM)
Rev.: $71,164,770
Assets: $68,501,277
Liabilities: $56,379,194
Net Worth: $12,122,082
Earnings: $2,803,878
Emp.: 220
Fiscal Year-end: 03/31/13

Business Description:
Bulk Drugs, Fine Chemicals & Food Grade Products Mfr
S.I.C.: 2833
N.A.I.C.S.: 325411

Personnel:
Ashish S. Dandekar *(Mng Dir)*
Dattatraya R. Puranik *(CFO)*
Arpita S. Patwardhan *(Compliance Officer & Deputy Sec)*

Board of Directors:
Dilip D. Dandekar
Ashish S. Dandekar
Abeezar E. Faizullabhoy
Sharad M. Kulkarni
Bhargav A. Patel
Dattatraya R. Puranik
Pramod M. Sapre

Transfer Agent:
Sharepro Services (India) Pvt Ltd
13AB Samhita Warehousing Complex 2nd Fl
Sakinaka Telephone Exchange Ln
Off Andheri-Kurla Road Sakinaka Andheri East, Mumbai, 400 072, India

Subsidiaries:

Chemolutions Chemicals Ltd. (1)
ICC Chambers 3rd Fl Saki Vihar Rd
Powai, Mumbai, Maharashtra, 400 072, India
Tel.: (91) 2228479609
Fax: (91) 2228479601
E-Mail: sales@camlinfine.com
Emp.: 40
Food Grade Antioxidants Mfr
S.I.C.: 2899
N.A.I.C.S.: 325998
Ashis Dandekar *(Mgr Dir)*

Sangam Laboratories Ltd (1)
ICC Chambers 3rd flr Saki Vihar Rd
Powai, Mumbai, Maharashtra, 400 072, India
Tel.: (91) 22 2847 9609
Fax: (91) 22 2847 9601
E-Mail: sales@sangamlab.com
Web Site: www.sangamlab.com
Emp.: 20
Bulk Drug Mfrs
S.I.C.: 5122
N.A.I.C.S.: 424210

CAMMSYS CO., LTD
11-82 Songdo-dong Yeonsu-gu
Incheon, Korea (South)
Tel.: (82) 328502000
Fax: (82) 328172078
Web Site: www.cammsys.net
Year Founded: 1993
050110—(KRS)
Business Description:
Semiconductor Fabrication Equipment Mfr & Sales
S.I.C.: 3559
N.A.I.C.S.: 333242
Personnel:
Heon Bok Lee *(Pres & CEO)*

CAMOZZI GROUP
Via Eritrea 20-I
25126 Brescia, Italy
Tel.: (39) 03037921
Fax: (39) 302600430
E-Mail: info@camozzi.com
Web Site: www.camozzi.com
Year Founded: 1964
Sales Range: $100-124.9 Million
Emp.: 3,000
Business Description:
Machine Tool Mfr
S.I.C.: 3541
N.A.I.C.S.: 333517
Personnel:
Attilio Camozzi *(Chm & Pres)*
Ettore Camozzi *(CEO)*

U.S. Holding:

Ingersoll Machines Tools, Inc. (IMTA) (1)
707 Fulton Ave
Rockford, IL 61103-4069 IL
Mailing Address:
PO Box 246
Ford City, PA 16226-0246
Tel.: (815) 987-6000
Fax: (815) 987-6725
E-Mail: info@ingersoll.com
Web Site: www.ingersoll.com
Emp.: 200
Special Machine Tools Mfr
S.I.C.: 3541
N.A.I.C.S.: 333517
Tino Oldani *(Pres & CEO)*

CAMP WAHANOWIN
227 Eglinton Ave W
Toronto, ON, M4R 1A9, Canada
Tel.: (416) 482-2600
Toll Free: (800) 701-3132
E-Mail: info@wahanowin.com
Web Site: www.wahanowin.com
Year Founded: 1955
Rev.: $11,368,860
Emp.: 300
Business Description:
Camp & Vacation Services
S.I.C.: 7032
N.A.I.C.S.: 721214
Personnel:
Harold Nashman *(Founder)*

CAMPAIGN MONITOR PTY LTD
Suite 201 3/5 Stapleton Avenue
Sutherland, Sydney, NSW, 2232, Australia
Tel.: (61) 2 9521 5312
Web Site: www.campaignmonitor.com
Year Founded: 2004
Sales Range: $1-9.9 Million
Emp.: 55
Business Description:
Email Campaign Software
S.I.C.: 7372
N.A.I.C.S.: 511210
Personnel:
David Greiner *(Co-Founder)*
Ben Richardson *(Co-Founder)*

CAMPBELL FORD
1500 Carling Ave
Ottawa, ON, K1Z 0A3, Canada
Tel.: (613) 725-3611
Fax: (613) 725-1893
Web Site: www.campbellford.com
Year Founded: 1920
Rev.: $43,681,143
Emp.: 100
Business Description:
New & Used Car Dealers
S.I.C.: 5511
N.A.I.C.S.: 441110
Personnel:
Gordon Hoddinott *(Pres)*

CAMPBELL POOLS INC.
4490 County Road 17
Alfred, ON, K0B 1A0, Canada
Tel.: (613) 679-1213
Fax: (613) 679-4408
E-Mail: alfred@campbellpools.ca
Web Site: www.campbellpools.ca
Year Founded: 1989
Sales Range: $10-24.9 Million
Emp.: 35
Business Description:
Swimming Pool Accessories Distr
S.I.C.: 5099
N.A.I.C.S.: 423990
Personnel:
Tom Campbell *(Pres)*
Harry Martyniuk *(Sec)*

CAMPBELLS/BEWLEY GROUP
Northern Cross Malahide Rd
Dublin, 17, Ireland
Tel.: (353) 18160606
Fax: (353) 18160601
E-Mail: info@bewleys.ie
Web Site: www.bewleys.com
Year Founded: 1924
Sales Range: $125-149.9 Million
Emp.: 152
Business Description:
Confectioneries, Coffees & Teas; Restaurants; Catering Import Export
S.I.C.: 2066
N.A.I.C.S.: 311352
Personnel:
John Cahill *(CEO)*
Michael O'Sullivan *(Sec)*

Divisions:

Bewley's Ltd. (1)
Northern Cross Malahide Rd
Dublin, 17, Ireland (100%)
Tel.: (353) 18160606
Fax: (353) 18160601
E-Mail: info@bewleys.ie
Web Site: www.bewleys.com
Emp.: 250
Provider of Coffee, Tea & Bakery Products
S.I.C.: 5461
N.A.I.C.S.: 311811
Jim Corbett *(Mng Dir)*

Campbell Catering Limited (1)
Northern Cross Malahide Rd
Dublin, 17, Ireland
Tel.: (353) 18160606
Fax: (353) 8160681
E-Mail: info@campbellcatering.ie
Web Site: www.campbellcatering.com
Emp.: 1,800
Contract & Commercial Catering
S.I.C.: 5812
N.A.I.C.S.: 722320
Pat Cronin *(Dir-Fin)*

Subsidiary:

Bewley's Oriental Cafes Limited (1)
Northern Cross Malahide Rd
Dublin, 17, Ireland (100%)
Tel.: (353) 18160606
Fax: (353) 18160601
E-Mail: info@bewleys.ie
Web Site: www.bewleys.ie
Emp.: 200
Operator of Retail Cafe & Shop Units
S.I.C.: 7299
N.A.I.C.S.: 812990
Jim Coobett *(Mng Dir)*

CAMPER & NICHOLSONS MARINA INVST. LTD.
31 33 Le Pollet
Saint Peter Port, GY1 3YR, Guernsey
Tel.: (44) 2075238000
Web Site: www.cnmarinas.com
CNMI—(LSE)
Rev.: $14,860,099
Assets: $76,442,378
Liabilities: $44,957,467
Net Worth: $31,484,911
Earnings: ($7,071,387)
Fiscal Year-end: 12/31/12
Business Description:
Investment company
S.I.C.: 6282
N.A.I.C.S.: 523920
Personnel:
Christopher Lewinton *(Chm)*
Clive Peter Whiley *(Interim CEO)*
James Beaver *(COO)*
Board of Directors:
Christopher Lewinton
Trevor Ash
Martin Bralsford
Elizabeth Kan
Roger Lewis
Clive Peter Whiley
Legal Counsel:
Stephenson Harwood
One St. Paul's Churchyard
London, EC4M 85H, United Kingdom
Tel.: (44) 81 329 4422

Carey Olsen
7 New Street
Saint Peter Port, Guernsey Channel Islands

Non-U.S. Subsidiaries:

Camper & Nicholsons Marinas Ltd. (1)
15 Petersham Rd
Richmond, Surrey, TW10 6TP, United Kingdom
Tel.: (44) 2083348046
Fax: (44) 2034053229
E-Mail: mail@cnmarinas.com
Web Site: www.cnmarinas.com
Emp.: 15
Marinas Management Services
S.I.C.: 4493
N.A.I.C.S.: 713930
Nick Maris *(CEO)*

CAMPHOR & ALLIED PRODUCTS LTD.
Jehangir Building 133 M G Road
Mumbai, 400 001, India
Tel.: (91) 22 43214000
Fax: (91) 22 43214099
E-Mail: sales_bom@camphor-allied.com
Web Site: www.camphor-allied.com
500078—(BOM)
Rev.: $43,848,379
Assets: $48,873,424
Liabilities: $30,847,019
Net Worth: $18,026,405
Earnings: $4,438,124
Emp.: 206
Fiscal Year-end: 03/31/13
Business Description:
Aroma Chemicals Mfr
S.I.C.: 2899
N.A.I.C.S.: 325998
Personnel:
Anil K. Bodani *(Chm)*
Dharmil A. Bodani *(Mng Dir)*
Nirmala Agarwal *(Compliance Officer & Sec)*
Board of Directors:
Anil K. Bodani
Dharmil A. Bodani
Shyamal A. Bodani
Prakash Mehta
Harshvardhan Piramal
Ranjeet A. Puranik
Devendra Singh Raghava
Transfer Agent:
Sharex Dynamic (India) Pvt. Ltd
Unit 1 Luthra Indus Premises Andheri Kurla Road Safed Pool Andheri E
Mumbai, India

CAMPINE N.V.
Nijverheidsstraat 2
2340 Beerse, Belgium
Tel.: (32) 14 60 15 11
Fax: (32) 14 61 29 85
E-Mail: info@campine.be
Web Site: www.campine.be
Year Founded: 1912
CAMB—(EUR)
Rev.: $201,825
Assets: $96,472
Liabilities: $65,630
Net Worth: $30,842
Earnings: $3,320
Emp.: 171
Fiscal Year-end: 12/31/12
Business Description:
Chemical Product Mfr
S.I.C.: 2819
N.A.I.C.S.: 325180
Personnel:
Friedrich-Wilhelm Hempel *(Chm)*
Geert Krekel *(Mng Dir)*
Board of Directors:
Friedrich-Wilhelm Hempel
Patrick De Groote
Andre Hempel
Geert Krekel
Hans Orgs
Martine Reynaers

CAMPION MARINE INC.
200 Campion Rd
Kelowna, BC, V1X 7S8, Canada
Tel.: (250) 765-7795
Fax: (250) 765-8883
E-Mail: askus@campionboats.com
Web Site: www.campionboats.com
Year Founded: 1974
Rev.: $17,388,990
Emp.: 50
Business Description:
Boat Builders Repair & Maintenance
S.I.C.: 3732
N.A.I.C.S.: 336612
Personnel:
Brock Elliott *(Gen Mgr)*

CAMPOFRIO FOOD GROUP, S.A.

Avda Europa 24 Parque Empresarial La Moraleja
28108 Alcobendas, Madrid, Spain
Tel.: (34) 914842700
Fax: (34) 916615345
E-Mail: cfg@campofriofg.com
Web Site: www.campofriofoodgroup.es
CFG—(BAR MAD)
Sls.: $2,582,419,835
Assets: $2,991,343,203
Liabilities: $2,200,425,251
Net Worth: $790,917,952
Earnings: $21,163,139
Emp.: 8,039
Fiscal Year-end: 12/31/12

Business Description:
Pork Processor
S.I.C.: 2099
N.A.I.C.S.: 311999

Personnel:
Pedro Ballve Lantero *(Chm)*
Yiannis Petrides *(Vice Chm)*
Robert Alair Sharpe, II *(CEO)*
Paulo Soares *(CFO & Chief IST Officer)*
Jaime Lobera *(CMO & Chief Sls Officer)*
Remedios Orrantia *(Chief Legal Officer & Chief HR Officer)*
Morten Jensen *(Chief Supply Integrated Chain Officer)*
Fernando Valdes Bueno *(Pres-Markets)*
Dirk Jacxsens *(Pres-Market Challengers Div)*
Olivier Maes *(CEO-Groupe Aoste-France)*
Athos Maestri *(CEO-Fiorucci)*
Wouter Meijerink *(CEO-Stegeman)*
Emmanuelle Bely *(Gen Counsel & Sr VP-Corp Dev)*
Alfredo Sanfeliz Mezquita *(General Counsel & Sr VP-Legal Affairs)*
Karl-Heinz Kiesel *(Sr VP-Ops)*

Board of Directors:
Pedro Ballve Lantero
Guillermo de la Dehesa Romero
Juan Jose Guibelalde Inurritegui
Karim Michael Khairallah
Caleb Samuel Kramer
Joseph W. Luter, IV
Luis Serrano Martin
Yiannis Petrides
Charles Larry Pope
Robert Alair Sharpe, II

Subsidiaries:

Campofrio Alimentacion **(1)**
Avda Isla Graciosa n 1 3 planta
Edificio Ancora, 28703 Madrid, Spain
Tel.: (34) 914842700
Fax: (34) 914848564
Meat Product Mfr
S.I.C.: 5147
N.A.I.C.S.: 311612

Carnes Selectas 2000 S.A. **(1)**
Calle Bureba Pg Ind Gamonal Villimar S/n
Burgos, 09007, Spain
Tel.: (34) 947490100
Fax: (34) 947490133
Processed Meat Products Mfr
S.I.C.: 2099
N.A.I.C.S.: 311999

La Montanera, S.A. **(1)**
Exdisa 64 S.L.
c/Les Astes de Sant
Macari, 3-25300 Tarrega, Lleida, Spain (100%)
Tel.: (34) 902103739
Fax: (34) 973501477
Web Site: www.lamontanera.es
Livestock Whslr
S.I.C.: 5154
N.A.I.C.S.: 424520

Navidul Extremadura S.A. **(1)**
Avenida Extremadura Km 250
Trujillo, Caceres, 21200, Spain
Tel.: (34) 927659029
Fax: (34) 927659132
Processed Pork Meat Mfr
S.I.C.: 5147
N.A.I.C.S.: 311612

Non-U.S. Subsidiaries:

Aoste Filiale (Suisse) Sarl **(1)**
Rue Jacques-Grosselin 8
1345 Geneva, Switzerland
Tel.: (41) 22 3017626
Fax: (41) 22 3017627
Food Products Mfr
S.I.C.: 2099
N.A.I.C.S.: 311999
Lober Mauer *(Gen Mgr)*

Campofrio Portugal, S.A. **(1)**
Estrada Nacional 249 km 14
2725397 Mem Martins, Portugal (100%)
Tel.: (351) 219179400
Fax: (351) 219161994
E-Mail: reception@campofrio.pt
Web Site: www.campofrio.pt
Emp.: 30
Meat & Meat Product Whslr
S.I.C.: 5147
N.A.I.C.S.: 424470
Sentra Portugal *(Gen Mgr)*

CESARE FIORUCCI S.p.a **(1)**
Viale Cesare Fiorucci 11 Loc Santa Palomba
00040 Pomezia, Roma, Italy
Tel.: (39) 06 911 931
Fax: (39) 0691 19 33 72
E-Mail: informazioni@fioruccifood.it
Web Site: www.fioruccifood.it
Specialty Food Mfr & Distr
S.I.C.: 2038
N.A.I.C.S.: 311412

CFG Deutschland GmbH **(1)**
Im Teelbruch 67
45219 Essen, Germany
Tel.: (49) 205487870
Fax: (49) 20548787100
E-Mail: kontakt@cfgdeutschland.de
Web Site: www.aoste.de
Emp.: 50
Meat Product Mfr
S.I.C.: 5147
N.A.I.C.S.: 311612
Volkel Baltes *(CEO)*

Groupe Aoste **(1)**
523 Cours du Troisieme Millenaire Parc Mail
69800 Saint Priest, France
Tel.: (33) 472148500
Web Site: www.groupeaoste.fr
Emp.: 3,000
Meat Product Mfr
S.I.C.: 5147
N.A.I.C.S.: 311612
Olivier Maes *(CEO)*

Subsidiaries:

Jean Caby **(2)**
BP 80359
29403 Landivisiau, Cedex, France (100%)
Tel.: (33) 298686868
Fax: (33) 298686899
Web Site: www.emerson.com
Sales Range: $500-549.9 Million
Emp.: 600
Meat Processing & Products
S.I.C.: 5147
N.A.I.C.S.: 311612
Christian Cruvelier *(Gen Mgr)*

Jean Caby **(2)**
40 rue de la Gare
BP 12
59872 Saint-Andre-lez-Lille, Cedex, France
Tel.: (33) 320405700
Fax: (33) 320405733
E-Mail: commercial@groupeaouste.com
Web Site: www.groupeaouste.com
Sls.: $374,384,384
Emp.: 600
Processed Meats Mfr & Marketer
S.I.C.: 5147
N.A.I.C.S.: 311612

Imperial Meat Products N.V. **(1)**
Grote Baan 200
B-9920 Lovendegem, Belgium
Tel.: (32) 93700211
Fax: (32) 93725000
Web Site: www.imperial.be
Sales Range: $25-49.9 Million
Emp.: 670
Meat & Meat Products Producer
S.I.C.: 5147
N.A.I.C.S.: 311612
Bart Martens *(Plant Mgr)*

Industrias de Carnes Nobre S.A. **(1)**
PO Box 23
Aveiro, 2040-998, Portugal
Tel.: (351) 243909200
Fax: (351) 3512439092
E-Mail: info.nobre@nobre.pt
Web Site: www.nobre.pt
Sales Range: $450-499.9 Million
Emp.: 700
Meat Products Producer
S.I.C.: 5147
N.A.I.C.S.: 311612
Rui Silva *(CEO)*
Paolo Soares *(CEO)*

Stegeman B.V. **(1)**
Rigastraat 17
7418 EW Deventer, Netherlands
Tel.: (31) 570505505
Fax: (31) 570505509
E-Mail: info@stegeman.nl
Web Site: www.stegeman.nl
Emp.: 560
Meat Product Mfr
S.I.C.: 5147
N.A.I.C.S.: 311612
Router Mering *(CEO)*

Tabco-Campofrio **(1)**
Str Diditel nr 9 Sector4
4040337 Bucharest, Romania
Tel.: (40) 213301283
Web Site: www.tabco-campofrio.ro
Emp.: 683
Meat Product Mfr
S.I.C.: 5147
N.A.I.C.S.: 311612
Ovidiu Wencz *(CEO)*

Tradi France S.A. **(1)**
Lieu Dit Les Trois Francs
Peyrolles-en-Provence, France
Tel.: (33) 442577700
Fax: (33) 442670081
Sales Range: $75-99.9 Million
Emp.: 126
Meat Products Mfr
S.I.C.: 5147
N.A.I.C.S.: 424470

Non-U.S. Plants:

Campofrio Food Group, S.A. - Manufacturing Pitesti **(1)**
Pitesti Abatorului Street no 30 jud Arges, Romania
Tel.: (40) 248 615 252
Fax: (40) 248 615 333
Processed Meat Mfr
S.I.C.: 5147
N.A.I.C.S.: 311612

Campofrio Food Group, S.A. - Manufacturing Tulcea **(1)**
Tulcea Str Prislav no 177 jud
Tulcea, Romania
Tel.: (40) 240 517 940
Fax: (40) 240 517 533
Processed Meat Mfr
S.I.C.: 5147
N.A.I.C.S.: 311612

LUIGI UGOLOTTI S.r.l. **(1)**
Stabilimento di Felino Via Calestano 68
43035 Felino, Parma, Italy
Tel.: (39) 05 21 85 90 11
Food Products Distr
S.I.C.: 5142
N.A.I.C.S.: 424420

CAMPOSTANO GROUP S.P.A.

Via Paleocapa 6/3
17100 Savona, Italy
Tel.: (39) 01984131
Fax: (39) 019812112
E-Mail: infocampostano@campostano.com
Web Site: www.campostano.com
Emp.: 200

Business Description:
Freight Forwarding, Shipping & Terminal Operation Services
S.I.C.: 4731
N.A.I.C.S.: 488510

Personnel:
Paolo Campostano *(Pres)*

Subsidiary:

Forest S.p.A. **(1)**
Ponte Somalia Ponente
16149 Genoa, Italy
Tel.: (39) 010415341
Fax: (39) 0106454728
E-Mail: forest@campostano.com
Web Site: www.campostano.com
Emp.: 11
Shipping Services
S.I.C.: 7389
N.A.I.C.S.: 425120

CAMROST-FELCORP INC.

250 Davisville Avenue Ste 401
Toronto, ON, M4S 1H2, Canada
Tel.: (416) 486-1961
Fax: (416) 486-6653
E-Mail: astroud@camrost.com
Web Site: www.camrost.com
Year Founded: 1976
Rev.: $12,780,908
Emp.: 40

Business Description:
Residential & Industrial Building Construction Services
S.I.C.: 1542
N.A.I.C.S.: 236220

Personnel:
David Feldman *(Founder, Pres & CEO)*

CAMSON BIO TECHNOLOGIES LTD.

C-7 7th Floor Corporate Block
Golden Enclave Old Airport Road
Bengaluru, 560 017, India
Tel.: (91) 80 40768900
Fax: (91) 80 25202285
E-Mail: info@camsonbiotechnologies.com
Web Site: www.camsonbiotechnologies.com
590076—(BOM)
Rev.: $25,278,264
Assets: $43,195,635
Liabilities: $13,147,364
Net Worth: $30,048,270
Earnings: $4,408,471
Emp.: 200
Fiscal Year-end: 03/31/13

Business Description:
Agricultural Fertilizer Mfr
S.I.C.: 2875
N.A.I.C.S.: 325314

Personnel:
Santosh Nair *(CEO)*
Dhirendra Kumar *(Mng Dir)*
Rohit Sareen *(COO)*
Ekta Gandhi Thakurel *(Sec)*

Board of Directors:
Gulshan Kumar Khanna
Dhirendra Kumar
B. C. Madappa
Krishnaswamy Ramaswamy
A. N. Singh
Anirudh Kumar Singh
Virendra Kumar Singh

Transfer Agent:
Integrated Enterprises (India) Ltd
30 Ramana Residency 4th Cross Sampige Road Malleswaram
Bengaluru, India

CAN AM PRODUCE & TRADING LTD
886 Malkin Ave
Vancouver, BC, V6A 2K6, Canada
Tel.: (604) 253-8834
Fax: (604) 253-8682
Year Founded: 1991
Rev.: $13,911,192
Emp.: 42
Business Description:
Fruits & Vegetables Whslr
S.I.C.: 5145
N.A.I.C.S.: 424450
Personnel:
Jim J. Su *(Corp Sec & Mgr-Credit)*

CAN ART ALUMINUM EXTRUSION INC.
85 Parkshore Drive
Brampton, ON, L9T4A8, Canada
Tel.: (905) 791-1464
Fax: (905) 791-9151
Web Site: www.canart.com
Year Founded: 1989
Rev.: $35,285,170
Emp.: 200
Business Description:
Aluminum Extrusions & Fabrication Services
S.I.C.: 3354
N.A.I.C.S.: 331318
Personnel:
Bill MacDonald *(Pres)*

CAN BOW MOTORS LTD.
707 Railway Ave
Canmore, AB, T1W 1P2, Canada
Tel.: (403) 678-4222
Fax: (403) 678-4176
Toll Free: (888) 542-6064
Web Site: www.can-bow.com
Year Founded: 1977
Rev.: $10,005,000
Emp.: 29
Business Description:
New & Used Car Dealers
S.I.C.: 5511
N.A.I.C.S.: 441110
Personnel:
Kenny Pauls, Jr. *(Gen Mgr-Sls)*

CAN-CELL INDUSTRIES INC.
14735 124 Avenue
Edmonton, AB, T5L 3B2, Canada
Tel.: (780) 447-1255
Fax: (780) 447-1034
Toll Free: (800) 661-5031
Web Site: www.can-cell.com
Year Founded: 1976
Rev.: $22,070,400
Emp.: 160
Business Description:
Building Hardware Products Mfr & Distr
S.I.C.: 2891
N.A.I.C.S.: 325520
Personnel:
Harold Tiemstra *(Pres)*

CAN-DER CONSTRUCTION LTD
(d/b/a Christenson Developments)
5410 97 St
Edmonton, AB, T6E 5C1, Canada
Tel.: (780) 436-2980
Fax: (780) 434-3655
Year Founded: 1970
Rev.: $27,134,149
Emp.: 50
Business Description:
Building Construction Services
S.I.C.: 1542
N.A.I.C.S.: 236220
Personnel:
Greg Christenson *(Owner & Pres)*

CAN-FITE BIOPHARMA LTD
10 Bareket Street Kiryat Matalon
PO Box 7537
Petah Tiqwa, 49170, Israel
Tel.: (972) 3 9241114
Fax: (972) 3 9249378
E-Mail: info@canfite.co.il
Web Site: www.canfite.com
Year Founded: 1994
CANF—(NYSEMKT TAE)
Rev.: $145,356
Assets: $1,641,366
Liabilities: $2,352,025
Net Worth: ($710,659)
Earnings: ($5,880,599)
Emp.: 8
Fiscal Year-end: 12/31/12
Business Description:
Biopharmaceutical Mfr
S.I.C.: 2834
N.A.I.C.S.: 325412
Personnel:
Ilan Cohn *(Chm)*
Pnina Fishman *(CEO)*
Motti Farbstein *(CFO & COO)*
Board of Directors:
Ilan Cohn
Yechezkel Barenholz
Pnina Fishman
Liora Lev
Gil Oren
Guy Regev
Avraham Sartani
Subsidiary:

OphthaliX Inc. (1)
10 Bareket St
Petah Tiqwa, Israel 49170 DE
Tel.: (972) 3 9241114
Fax: (972) 3 9249378
E-Mail: info@ophthalix.com
Web Site: www.ophthalix.com
OPLI—(OTC)
Rev.: $648,000
Assets: $2,286,000
Liabilities: $669,000
Net Worth: $1,617,000
Earnings: ($1,863,000)
Fiscal Year-end: 12/31/12
Pharmaceutical Preparation Mfr
S.I.C.: 2834
N.A.I.C.S.: 325412
Pnina Fishman *(Chm)*
Ilan Cohn *(Vice Chm)*
Barak Singer *(CEO)*
Itay Weinstein *(CFO)*

CAN (OFFSHORE) LTD
(d/b/a CAN Group)
Hareness Road
Altens, Aberdeen, AB12 3LE, United Kingdom
Tel.: (44) 1224 870100
Fax: (44) 1224 870101
E-Mail: info@cangroup.net
Web Site: www.cangroup.net
Year Founded: 1977
Sales Range: $100-124.9 Million
Emp.: 1,000
Business Description:
Engineering, Inspection & Maintenance Services
S.I.C.: 8711
N.A.I.C.S.: 541330
Personnel:
Michael Freeman *(Mng Dir)*
Subsidiaries:

CAN Geotechnical Ltd (1)
Smeckley Wood Close Chesterfield Trading Estate
Chesterfield, Derbyshire, S41 9PZ, United Kingdom
Tel.: (44) 1246 261111
Fax: (44) 1246 261626
E-Mail: info@can.ltd.uk
Web Site: www.can.ltd.uk
Emp.: 3
Rock Faces, Soil Slopes & Retaining Walls Stabilization Services
S.I.C.: 8999
N.A.I.C.S.: 541620
Gerald Borcherds *(Mng Dir)*

CAN London Ltd (1)
Unit A Springhead Enterprise Park
Springhead Road
Northfleet, Kent, DA11 8HB, United Kingdom
Tel.: (44) 1474 538100
Fax: (44) 1474 538101
E-Mail: info@canlondon.co.uk
Web Site: www.can.ltd.uk
Emp.: 5
Environmental Construction & Maintenance Services
S.I.C.: 8711
N.A.I.C.S.: 541330
Sean Cadogan *(Gen Mgr)*

CAN Structures Ltd (1)
Smeckley Wood Close Chesterfield Trading Estate
Chesterfield, Derbyshire, S41 9PZ, United Kingdom
Tel.: (44) 1246 261111
Fax: (44) 1246 261626
E-Mail: info@can.ltd.uk
Web Site: www.can.ltd.uk
Environmental Construction & Maintenance Services
S.I.C.: 8711
N.A.I.C.S.: 541330
James Wong *(Dir-Ops)*

U.S. Subsidiaries:

CAN USA, Inc. (1)
1800 Jutland Dr
Harvey, LA 70058
Tel.: (504) 328-1567
Fax: (504) 341-0608
E-Mail: ropeaccess@can-usa.net
Web Site: www.can-usa.net
Emp.: 100
Engineering, Inspection & Maintenance Services
S.I.C.: 8711
N.A.I.C.S.: 541330
Clayton Hinyup *(Pres)*

CAN USA, Inc. (1)
171 Lodi St
Hackensack, NJ 07601
Tel.: (201) 996-9287
Fax: (201) 996-9285
Emp.: 100
Engineering, Inspection & Maintenance Services
S.I.C.: 8711
N.A.I.C.S.: 541330
Mike Freeman *(Pres)*

Non-U.S. Subsidiaries:

CAN AS (1)
Slettestrandveien 4
4032 Stavanger, Norway
Tel.: (47) 51 81 18 18
Fax: (47) 48 24 48 00
E-Mail: post@can.no
Web Site: www.can.as
Engineering, Inspection & Maintenance Services
S.I.C.: 8711
N.A.I.C.S.: 541330
Lars-Erik Berntzen *(Mng Dir)*

CAN Global Angola LDA (1)
Suite 15 Sonils Building Boavista Street
Luanda, Angola
Tel.: (244) 226 430 677
Fax: (244) 226 430 680
E-Mail: angola@cangroup.net
Engineering, Inspection & Maintenance Services
S.I.C.: 8711
N.A.I.C.S.: 541330

CAN Middle East L.L.C. (1)
PO Box 52892
Abu Dhabi, United Arab Emirates
Tel.: (971) 2 644 1338
Fax: (971) 2 644 3949
E-Mail: cangroup@emirates.net.ae
Engineering, Inspection & Maintenance Services
S.I.C.: 8711
N.A.I.C.S.: 541330

CAN-ONE BERHAD
2B-4 Level 4 Jalan SS 6/6 Kelana Jaya
47301 Petaling Jaya, Selangor Darul Ehsan, Malaysia
Tel.: (60) 378048590
Fax: (60) 378801605
E-Mail: can1@canone.com.my
Web Site: www.canone.com.my
CANONE—(KLS)
Rev.: $255,790,717
Assets: $324,992,002
Liabilities: $190,122,769
Net Worth: $134,869,233
Earnings: $58,411,734
Fiscal Year-end: 12/31/12
Business Description:
Tin Cans & Plastic Jerry Cans Mfr
S.I.C.: 3411
N.A.I.C.S.: 332431
Personnel:
Jin Hoe Yeoh *(Mng Dir)*
Marc Francis Min Chang Yeoh *(COO)*
Bee Keng Tan *(Sec)*
Board of Directors:
William Maurice Samson
Razmi Alias
Khay Leong Chee
Ewe Lin See
Beng Wah Tan
Jin Beng Yeoh
Jin Hoe Yeoh
Marc Francis Min Chang Yeoh

CAN THO PESTICIDES JOINT STOCK COMPANY
Km 14 Highway 91
Phuoc Thoi Ward
O Mon District, Can Tho, Vietnam
Tel.: (84) 7103861770
Fax: (84) 7103861798
E-Mail: info@tstcantho.com.vn
Web Site: www.tstcantho.com.vn
CPC—(HNX)
Emp.: 190
Business Description:
Pesticides & Agricultural Chemicals Mfr
S.I.C.: 2879
N.A.I.C.S.: 325320
Personnel:
Trung Van Nguyen *(Chm)*

CANA-DATUM MOULDS LTD.
55 Goldthorne Avenue
Toronto, ON, M8Z 5S7, Canada
Tel.: (416) 252-1212
Fax: (416) 252-3539
E-Mail: contact@cana-datum.com
Web Site: www.cana-datum.com
Year Founded: 1986
Rev.: $14,541,430
Emp.: 140
Business Description:
Precision Tools & Dies Mfr
S.I.C.: 3451
N.A.I.C.S.: 332721
Personnel:
Ignacio Musalem *(Gen Mgr)*

CANA VENTURE CAPITAL CORP.
308 138 18th Avenue SE
Calgary, AB, T2G 5P9, Canada
Tel.: (403) 366-5220
E-Mail: ryan@canaventure.com
Year Founded: 2011

Cana Venture Capital Corp.—(Continued)

Business Description:
Investment Services
S.I.C.: 6211
N.A.I.C.S.: 523999
Personnel:
Ryan Danard *(Pres, CEO & CFO)*
Christopher Robbins *(Sec)*
Board of Directors:
Leonard Danard
Robert Danard
Ryan Danard
Christopher Robbins
Transfer Agent:
Olympia Trust Company
125 9th Avenue SE Suite 2300
Calgary, AB, T2G 0P6, Canada
Tel.: (403) 261-0900

CANACCORD FINANCIAL INC.

Pacific Centre 609 Granville Street
Suite 2200
PO Box 10337
Vancouver, BC, V7Y 1H2, Canada
Tel.: (604) 643-7300
Fax: (604) 643-7606
Toll Free: (800) 663-1899
E-Mail: investor.relations@canaccord.com
Web Site: www.canaccord.com
Year Founded: 1950
CF—(AIM TSX)
Rev.: $792,355,210
Assets: $4,575,973,058
Liabilities: $3,517,011,743
Net Worth: $1,058,961,315
Earnings: ($18,662,725)
Emp.: 2,060
Fiscal Year-end: 03/31/13
Business Description:
Investment Services
S.I.C.: 6211
N.A.I.C.S.: 523999
Personnel:
Peter M. Brown *(Founder)*
David J. Kassie *(Chm)*
Paul D. Reynolds *(Pres & CEO)*
Jens Mayer *(Co-Mng Dir, Exec VP & Head-Investment Banking-Global)*
Jeff Barlow *(Co-Mng Dir & Head-Investment Banking-US)*
Dvai Ghose *(Co-Mng Dir & Head-Res-Canada)*
Barry Goldberg *(Mng Dir & Head-Mergers, Acq & Restructuring-Global)*
Edward Hirst *(Mng Dir & Head-Investment Banking-Global)*
Ken Knowles *(Co-Mng Dir & Head-Fixed Income)*
Graham Saunders *(Co-Mng Dir & Head-Institutional Equity Sls)*
Brad Kotush *(CFO & Exec VP)*
Andrew Jappy *(CIO)*
Bruce Maranda *(Chief Compliance Officer, Exec VP & Dir-Compliance-Global)*
Howard Robert Balloch *(Chm-Canaccord Genuity-Asia)*
Daniel Daviau *(Pres-Canaccord Genuity Inc)*
Matthew Gaasenbeek *(Pres-Canaccord Genuity-Canada)*
Stuart Raftus *(Pres- Genuity Wealth Mgmt)*
Alexis de Rosnay *(CEO-Ops-UK & Europe)*
Peter O'Malley *(CEO-Canaccord Genuity-Asia)*
Peter Virvilis *(Treas & Exec VP-Ops)*
Scott Davidson *(Exec VP & Head-Corp Dev & Strategy-Global)*
Martin MacLachlan *(Sr VP-Legal Affairs)*
Board of Directors:
David J. Kassie
Charles N. Bralver
Peter M. Brown
Massimo C. Carello
William J. Eeuwes
Michael D. Harris
Terrence A. Lyons
Paul D. Reynolds
Dipesh J. Shah

Computershare Investor Services Inc.
100 University Ave 9th Floor
Toronto, ON, Canada
Transfer Agents:
Computershare Investor Services Inc.
100 University Ave 9th Floor
Toronto, ON, Canada

Computershare Investor Services Inc
Vancouver, BC, Canada

Subsidiaries:

Canaccord Capital Corporation (USA), Inc. **(1)**
609 Granville St Ste 2200
Vancouver, BC, V7Y 1H2, Canada (100%)
Tel.: (604) 643-7300
Fax: (604) 643-7606
Toll Free: (800) 663-8061
Emp.: 550
Broker/Dealer
S.I.C.: 6799
N.A.I.C.S.: 523910
Vicki Hammil *(Sec)*

Canaccord Genuity Corp. **(1)**
Pacific Centre 609 Granville Street Ste 2200
PO Box 10337
Vancouver, BC, V7Y 1H2, Canada
Tel.: (604) 643-7300
Fax: (604) 643-7606
Web Site: www.canaccordgenuity.com
Emp.: 700
Investment Banking Services
S.I.C.: 6211
N.A.I.C.S.: 523110
Matthew Gaasenbeek *(Pres)*
Gerhard Gleich *(Mng Dir & Head-Frankfurt)*

U.S. Subsidiary:

Canaccord Genuity Inc. **(2)**
99 High St
Boston, MA 02110 DE
Tel.: (617) 371-3900
Fax: (617) 371-3793
Toll Free: (800) 225-6201
Web Site: www.canaccordgenuity.com
Emp.: 225
Brokerage & Investment Financial Services
S.I.C.: 6211
N.A.I.C.S.: 523120
Daniel Daviau *(Pres)*
Geoffrey A. Richards *(Mng Dir & Head-Special Situations & Restructuring)*

Subsidiary:

Canaccord Genuity Securities LLC **(3)**
350 Madison Ave
New York, NY 10017 DE
Tel.: (212) 389-8000 (100%)
Fax: (212) 389-8881
Web Site: www.canaccordgenuity.com
Emp.: 50
Institutional & Private Client Stockbroking, Market Making, Corporate Finance, Fund Management & Financial Information Services
S.I.C.: 6726
N.A.I.C.S.: 525990
Daniel Daviau *(Pres)*
Henry Erbe *(Sr Mng Dir & Head-Capital Markets Grp-US)*
Michael Brill *(Mng Dir & Head-Fixed Income Banking-Investment Banking)*
Gregory Miller *(Mng Dir)*

Non-U.S. Subsidiaries:

Canaccord Genuity Limited **(2)**
88 Wood Street
London, EC2V 7QR, United Kingdom UK
Tel.: (44) 2075238000
Fax: (44) 2075238131
Web Site: www.canaccordgenuity.com
Institutional & Private Client Stockbroking, Market Making, Corporate Finance, Fund Management & Financial Information Services
S.I.C.: 6211
N.A.I.C.S.: 523110
Paul D. Reynolds *(Chm)*
Giles Fitzpatrick *(Pres)*
Alexis de Rosnay *(CEO)*
Darren Ellis *(COO)*
Neil Darke *(CEO-Europe)*

Subsidiaries:

Canaccord Genuity Hawkpoint Limited **(3)**
41 Lothbury
London, EC2R 7AE, United Kingdom UK
Tel.: (44) 2076654500
Fax: (44) 2076654600
E-Mail:
Sales Range: $50-74.9 Million
Emp.: 125
Corporate Financial Advisory Services
S.I.C.: 6282
N.A.I.C.S.: 523930

Canaccord Genuity Securities Limited **(3)**
88 Wood Street
London, EC2V 7QR, United Kingdom UK
Tel.: (44) 20 7523 8000 (100%)
Fax: (44) 20 7050 6501
Web Site: www.canaccordgenuity.com
Emp.: 80
Investment Advisory, Asset Management & Securities Brokerage Services
S.I.C.: 6799
N.A.I.C.S.: 523930
Giles Fitzpatrick *(Pres)*
Alexis de Rosnay *(CEO)*
Damien Hackett *(Mng Dir & Head-Res-UK)*
Angelo Sofocleous *(Mng Dir & Head-Trading-UK)*
Darren Ellis *(COO)*

CANACOL ENERGY LTD.

Eighth Avenue Place 4500 525 - Eighth Avenue South West
Calgary, AB, T2P 1G1, Canada
Tel.: (403) 561-1648
Fax: (403) 228-6419
E-Mail: kflick@canacolenergy.com
Web Site: www.canacolenergy.com
CNE—(COLO TSX)
Rev.: $147,666,000
Assets: $476,335,000
Liabilities: $229,837,000
Net Worth: $246,498,000
Earnings: ($120,612,000)
Emp.: 216
Fiscal Year-end: 06/30/13
Business Description:
Oil & Gas Exploration Services
S.I.C.: 1311
N.A.I.C.S.: 211111
Personnel:
Michael John Hibberd *(Chm)*
Charle Gamba *(Pres & CEO)*
George Gramatke *(CFO)*
Mark Holliday *(COO)*
Anthony Zaidi *(Gen Counsel & VP-Bus Dev)*
Board of Directors:
Michael John Hibberd
Luis Baena
Jason Bednar
Greg Elliott
Charle Gamba
Stuart P. Hensman
Gary Petersen
David Winter
Transfer Agent:
Olympia Trust Company
Suite 2300 125 9th Ave SE
Calgary, AB, Canada

CANADA CARBON INC.

(Formerly Bolero Resources Corp.)
Suite 605 1166 Alberni Street
Vancouver, BC, V6E 3Z3, Canada
Tel.: (604) 638-0971
Fax: (604) 638-0973
E-Mail: info@canadacarbon.com
Web Site: www.canadacarbon.com
Year Founded: 1985
CCB—(TSXV)
Assets: $1,688,465
Liabilities: $76,170
Net Worth: $1,612,295
Earnings: ($6,144,134)
Fiscal Year-end: 12/31/12
Business Description:
Carbon Exploration Services
S.I.C.: 1099
N.A.I.C.S.: 212299
Personnel:
R. Bruce Duncan *(Chm & CEO)*
Olga Nikitovic *(CFO)*
Board of Directors:
R. Bruce Duncan
Bruce Coventry
Greg Lipton
Legal Counsel:
Aird & Berlis LLP
181 Bay Street Suite 1800
Toronto, ON, M2J 2T9, Canada
Transfer Agent:
Computershare Trust Company of Canada
510 Burrard St 2nd Fl
Vancouver, BC, Canada

CANADA DRUGS LTD.

24 Terracon Pl
Winnipeg, MB, R2J 4G7, Canada
Tel.: (204) 654-5194
Fax: (204) 258-7009
Toll Free: (800) 226-3784
E-Mail: info@canadadrugs.com
Web Site: www.canadadrugs.com
Year Founded: 2001
Sales Range: $25-49.9 Million
Emp.: 250
Business Description:
Online & Mail Order Pharmacy
S.I.C.: 5912
N.A.I.C.S.: 446110
Personnel:
Kris Thorkelson *(Founder & Pres)*
Ron Sigurdson *(CFO)*

CANADA ENERGY PARTNERS INC.

1680-200 Burrard Street
Vancouver, BC, V6C 3L6, Canada
Tel.: (604) 909-1154
Fax: (604) 488-0319
E-Mail: info@canadaenergypartners.com
Web Site: www.canadaenergypartners.com
Year Founded: 2006
CE—(TSXV)
Int. Income: $4,537
Assets: $75,959,570
Liabilities: $8,518,639
Net Worth: $67,440,931
Earnings: ($567,930)
Emp.: 2
Fiscal Year-end: 04/30/13
Business Description:
Natural Gas Exploration & Development Services
S.I.C.: 1389
N.A.I.C.S.: 213112
Personnel:
John Graham Proust *(Chm & Interim CFO)*
Benjamin M. Jones *(Pres & CEO)*
Eileen Au *(Sec)*
Board of Directors:
John Graham Proust
Jonathan Bahnuik
Kyle R. Burnett
Benjamin M. Jones

Legal Counsel:
Axium Law Corporation
Suite 3350 - 1055 Dunsmuir Street
Vancouver, BC, Canada
Transfer Agent:
Computershare
3rd Floor 510 Burrard Street
V6C 3B9 Vancouver, BC, Canada

CANADA FLUORSPAR INC.

10060 Kennedy Road
Markham, ON, L6C1N9, Canada
Tel.: (208) 755-6989
Fax: (208) 765-8520
Toll Free: (800) 823-8095
Web Site: www.canadafluorspar.com
Year Founded: 1993
CFI—(TSXV)
Sales Range: Less than $1 Million
Business Description:
Mineral Properties Exploration Services
S.I.C.: 1081
N.A.I.C.S.: 213114
Personnel:
Richard Carl *(Chm)*
Lindsay Edward Gorrill *(Pres & CEO)*
Paul Coombs *(CFO)*
Board of Directors:
Richard Carl
William Assini
Lisa Brody
Senator George Furey
Lindsay Edward Gorrill
Andrew Krusen
Leo Power
Richard Rowe
Gordon Stollery
Transfer Agent:
Equity Financial Trust Company
Toronto, ON, Canada

CANADA FORGINGS INC.

130 Hagar St
PO Box 308
Station Main, Welland, ON, L3B 5P8, Canada
Tel.: (905) 735-1220
Fax: (905) 735-6992
E-Mail: sales@canforge.com
Web Site: www.canforge.com
Year Founded: 1912
Sales Range: $10-24.9 Million
Emp.: 115
Business Description:
Open & Closed Die Forgings & Seamless Rolled Rings Mfr
Export
S.I.C.: 3462
N.A.I.C.S.: 332111
Personnel:
G. Guilbeault *(Pres)*

CANADA GARDENWORKS LTD.

(d/b/a GardenWorks)
6250 Lougheed Hwy
Burnaby, BC, V5B 2Z9, Canada
Tel.: (604) 299-0621
Fax: (604) 299-4403
Web Site: www.gardenworks.ca
Year Founded: 1984
Rev.: $12,757,336
Emp.: 260
Business Description:
Garden & Floral Stores
S.I.C.: 5261
N.A.I.C.S.: 444220
Personnel:
Bruce Meyers *(Pres & CEO)*
Leanne Johnson *(COO)*

CANADA GOLD CORPORATION

1500-1199 West Hastings Street
Vancouver, BC, V6E 3T5, Canada
Tel.: (604) 685-5851
Fax: (604) 685-7349
Web Site: www.canadagold.com
CI—(TSXV)
Assets: $14,254
Liabilities: $226,664
Net Worth: ($212,410)
Earnings: ($1,025,364)
Fiscal Year-end: 12/31/12
Business Description:
Mineral Properties Exploration Services
S.I.C.: 1081
N.A.I.C.S.: 213114
Personnel:
Dave McMillan *(Chm)*
Chad McMillan *(Pres & CEO)*
Board of Directors:
Dave McMillan
Al Fabbro
Chad McMillan
Legal Counsel:
Morton & Company
Suite 1200-750 W Pender Street
Vancouver, BC, Canada
Transfer Agent:
Computershare
709 - 510 Burrard Street
Vancouver, BC, Canada
Non-U.S. Subsidiary:

Canada Gold Colombia S.A.S. **(1)**
Calle 16 41 210 Of 806
Medellin, Colombia
Tel.: (57) 46041981
Fax: (57) 46041981111
Gold Ore Mining Services
S.I.C.: 1041
N.A.I.C.S.: 212221
Ian Park *(Gen Mgr)*

CANADA IRON INC.

170 University Ave Ste 900
Toronto, ON, M5H 3B3, Canada
Tel.: (416) 346-1008
E-Mail: info@canadaironinc.com
Web Site: www.canadaironinc.com
Business Description:
Mineral Resource Company Engaged in the Acquisition, Exploration & Development of Quality Iron Ore
S.I.C.: 1011
N.A.I.C.S.: 212210
Personnel:
Tony Dwyer *(Chm)*
Gary Handley *(Pres & CEO)*
Ying Xiong *(Officer-Administration)*
Board of Directors:
Tony Dwyer
Gary Handley
Mike Kraemer

CANADA LAND LIMITED

15th Floor Yat Chau Building 262
Des Voeux Road
Central, China (Hong Kong)
Tel.: (852) 28544333
Fax: (852) 25410389
E-Mail: canland@canadaland.com.hk
Web Site: www.canadaland.com.hk
Year Founded: 1972
Sales Range: $1-9.9 Million
Emp.: 110
Business Description:
Real Estate Operations
S.I.C.: 6531
N.A.I.C.S.: 531210
Personnel:
William Shue Lam Yip *(Chm)*
Derrick Siu Ming Yip *(Sec)*
Board of Directors:
William Shue Lam Yip
Yuk Wah Chow
M. B. Lee
Eva Loke Moy Yip
Legal Counsel:
Guangzhou Foreign Economic Law Office
18th Floor Guangdong Holdings Tower 555
Dongfeng Rd
Guangzhou, China

Guangdong Kings Law Firm
Room A802 China Shine Building No 9 Lin He Xi Lu
Tian He, Guangzhou, China

Fred Kan & Co
Suite 3104-7 31st Floor Central Plaza 18 Harbour Road
Hong Kong, China (Hong Kong)

Computershare Investor Services Pty Limited
Yarra Falls 452 Johnston Street
Abbotsford, VIC, 3067, Australia

CANADA LANDS COMPANY LIMITED

1 University Ave Ste 1200
Toronto, ON, M5J 2P1, Canada
Tel.: (416) 952-6100
Fax: (416) 952-6200
Toll Free: (888) 252-5263
E-Mail: info@clc.ca
Web Site: www.clc.ca
Year Founded: 1956
Sales Range: $150-199.9 Million
Emp.: 100
Business Description:
Offices of Bank Holding Companies
S.I.C.: 6712
N.A.I.C.S.: 551111
Personnel:
Grant B. Walsh *(Chm)*
John McBain *(Pres & CEO)*
Jurgen Dirks *(CFO & VP-Fin)*
Jack Robinson *(COO)*
Antoinette Bozac *(Gen Counsel & VP-HR & Legal Affairs)*
Robert A Howald *(Sr VP-Real Estate)*
Board of Directors:
Grant B. Walsh
W. Michael Evans
Llyord S. D. Fogler
Clint Hames
Wayne MacIntosh
Alana McPhee
Louise N. Pelletier

CANADA LITHIUM CORP.

(Name Changed to RB Energy Inc.)

CANADA MORTGAGE & HOUSING CORPORATION

700 Montreal Road
Ottawa, ON, K1A 0P7, Canada
Tel.: (613) 748-2000
Fax: (613) 748-2098
E-Mail: chic@cmhc-schl.gc.ca
Web Site: www.cmhc.ca
Year Founded: 1946
Rev.: $11,190,677,160
Assets: $290,293,600,800
Liabilities: $276,531,393,900
Net Worth: $13,762,206,900
Earnings: $1,705,738,320
Emp.: 1,900
Fiscal Year-end: 12/31/12
Business Description:
Mortgage Financing Services
Export
S.I.C.: 6163
N.A.I.C.S.: 522310
Personnel:
Robert P. Kelly *(Chm)*
Douglas A. Stewart *(Interim Pres)*
Evan Siddall *(CEO)*
Brian Naish *(CFO & VP)*
Pierre Serre *(Chief Risk Officer & VP)*
Kate Munroe *(Media Rels Officer)*
Charles Sauriol *(Sr Media Rels Officer)*
Sebastien Gignac *(Gen Counsel & Sec)*
Board of Directors:
Robert P. Kelly
Michael Gendron
Sandra Hanington
Brian Johnston
Rennie Pieterman
Andre G. Plourde
Louise Poirier-Landry
Bruce Shirreff

CANADA PENSION PLAN INVESTMENT BOARD

(d/b/a CPP Investment Board)
One Queen Street East Suite 2500
Toronto, ON, M5C 2W5, Canada
Tel.: (416) 868-4075
Fax: (416) 868-8689
Toll Free: (866) 557-9510
E-Mail: contact@cppib.com
Web Site: www.cppib.ca
Year Founded: 1997
Rev.: $16,635,918,720
Assets: $210,381,350,940
Liabilities: $28,213,269,660
Net Worth: $182,168,081,280
Earnings: $16,148,848,920
Emp.: 906
Fiscal Year-end: 03/31/13
Business Description:
Professional Investment Management Services
S.I.C.: 6371
N.A.I.C.S.: 524292
Personnel:
Robert M. Astley *(Chm)*
Mark D. Wiseman *(Pres & CEO)*
Benita M. Warmbold *(CFO)*
Nicholas Zelenczuk *(COO)*
Pierre Lavallee *(Chief Talent Officer & Sr VP)*
Mark Machin *(Pres-CPPIB Asia Inc)*
John H. Butler *(Gen Counsel, Sec & Sr VP)*
Graeme M. Eadie *(Sr VP & Head-Real Estate Investments)*
Andre Bourbonnais *(Sr VP-Private Investments)*
Edwin D. Cass *(Sr VP)*
Michel Leduc *(Sr VP-Comm & Pub Affairs)*
Donald M. Raymond *(Sr VP)*
Eric M. Wetlaufer *(Sr VP-Pub Market Investments)*
Board of Directors:
Robert M. Astley
Ian A. Bourne
Robert L. Brooks
Pierre Choquette
Michael Goldberg
Nancy Hopkins
Douglas William Mahaffy
Heather E. L. Munroe-Blum
Karen H. Sheriff
Kathleen Taylor
D. Murray Wallace
Jo Mark Zurel

Joint Venture:

Livingston International Inc. **(1)**
405 The West Mall Ste 400
Toronto, ON, M9C 5K7, Canada ON
Tel.: (416) 626-2800
Fax: (416) 622-3890
E-Mail: info@livingstonintl.com
Web Site: www.livingstonintl.com
Sales Range: $250-299.9 Million
Emp.: 350
Customs Brokerage, Logistics & Transportation Services; Owned by Sterling Partners & by Canada Pension Plan Investment Board
S.I.C.: 4731
N.A.I.C.S.: 488510

Canada Pension Plan Investment Board—(Continued)

Roy Coburn *(Pres)*
Peter Luit *(CEO)*
Chris McMullen *(CFO)*

Subsidiary:

Advantex Express Inc. (2)
1935 Drew Road Unit 14
Mississauga, ON, L5S 1M7, Canada
Tel.: (905) 677-0340
Fax: (905) 677-8764
Toll Free: (877) 677-4999
E-Mail: accounting.toronto@advantex.ca
Web Site: www.advantex.ca
Rev.: $45,199,915
Emp.: 118
Freight Forwarding & Customs Brokerage Services
S.I.C.: 4731
N.A.I.C.S.: 488510
Greg Richard *(Pres)*

U.S. Subsidiaries:

Livingston International (2)
1 Commercial Pl Ste 300
Norfolk, VA 23510-1754 VA
Tel.: (757) 446-1500
Fax: (757) 446-1538
E-Mail:
Sales Range: $10-24.9 Million
Emp.: 100
Customhouse Brokers
S.I.C.: 4731
N.A.I.C.S.: 488510

U.S. Holdings:

Air System Components, Inc. (1)
1401 N Plano Rd
Richardson, TX 75081
Tel.: (972) 680-9126
Fax: (214) 575-3372
Web Site: www.airsysco.com
Emp.: 300
Heating, Air Conditioning & Ventilation System Components Mfr
S.I.C.: 3585
N.A.I.C.S.: 333415

Units:

PennBarry (2)
605 Shiloh Rd
Plano, TX 75074 DE
Tel.: (972) 212-4700
Telex: 83-4545
E-Mail: pennbarrysales@pennbarry.com
Web Site: www.pennbarry.com
Emp.: 550
Ventilators & Air-Moving Equipment Mfr
S.I.C.: 3585
N.A.I.C.S.: 333415
Vince Snyder *(VP)*

Titus (2)
605 Shiloh Rd
Plano, TX 75074
Tel.: (972) 212-4800
Fax: (972) 212-4877
E-Mail: titus@titus-hvac.com
Web Site: www.titus-hvac.com
Emp.: 60
Architectural & Ornamental Metal Work Mfr
S.I.C.: 4225
N.A.I.C.S.: 493110
Terry O'Halloran *(Grp Pres)*

Hart & Cooley, Inc. (1)
5030 Corporate Exchange Blvd
Grand Rapids, MI 49512
Tel.: (616) 656-8200
Fax: (800) 223-8461
Toll Free: (800) 433-6341
E-Mail: info@hartcool.com
Web Site: www.hartandcooley.com
Emp.: 800
Air Distribution Products Mfr
S.I.C.: 3822
N.A.I.C.S.: 334512
Bernard Roy *(Pres)*
Curt Monhart *(Exec VP-Mktg & Sls)*

Koch Filter Corporation (1)
625 W Hill St
Louisville, KY 40208 KY
Mailing Address:
PO Box 3186
Louisville, KY 40201
Tel.: (502) 634-4796
Fax: (502) 637-2280
Toll Free: (800) 757-5624
E-Mail: info@kochfilter.com
Web Site: www.kochfilter.com
Sales Range: $25-49.9 Million
Emp.: 250
Air Filter & Filtration Products Mfr
S.I.C.: 3564
N.A.I.C.S.: 333413
Mark Mattingly *(VP-Sls & Mktg)*

Ruskin Company (1)
3900 Doctor Greaves Rd
Grandview, MO 64030-1134
Tel.: (816) 761-7476
Fax: (816) 765-8955
Web Site: www.ruskin.com
Emp.: 570
Air, Fire & Smoke Dampers, Louvres & Fibreglass Products Mfr
S.I.C.: 3822
N.A.I.C.S.: 334512
Tom Edwards *(Pres)*

Divisions:

Lau Industries (2)
4509 Springfield St
Dayton, OH 45431-0943
Tel.: (937) 253-2000
Fax: (937) 252-9169
E-Mail: info@lauparts.com
Web Site: www.lauparts.com
Emp.: 20
Fans & Blowers Mfr
S.I.C.: 3564
N.A.I.C.S.: 333413
Anna Schlotterbeck *(Mgr-Sls & Mktg)*

Rooftop Systems Inc. (2)
1625 Diplomat Dr
Carrollton, TX 75006
Tel.: (972) 247-7447
Fax: (972) 243-0940
Toll Free: (800) 552-4822
Web Site: www.rooftopsystems.com
Sales Range: $25-49.9 Million
Emp.: 350
Air Ducts & Sheet Metal Mfr
S.I.C.: 5039
N.A.I.C.S.: 423390

Swartwout Division (2)
3900 Doctor Greaves Rd
Grandview, MO 64030-1134
Tel.: (816) 761-7476
Fax: (816) 765-8955
E-Mail: swartwout@swartwout.com
Web Site: www.swartwout.com
Emp.: 115
Ventilators, Louvers, Heat & Smoke Units & Roof Curbs Mfr
S.I.C.: 1799
N.A.I.C.S.: 238990
Tom Edwards *(Pres)*

Selkirk Corporation (1)
1301 W President Bush Hwy Ste 330
Richardson, TX 75080
Mailing Address:
1301 W President George Bush Hwy Ste 330
Richardson, TX 75080-1139
Tel.: (972) 943-6100
Fax: (972) 943-6137
Toll Free: (800) 992-8368
E-Mail: sales@selkirkinc.com
Web Site: www.selkirkinc.com
Emp.: 1,200
Chimneys & Venting Products Mfr
S.I.C.: 5074
N.A.I.C.S.: 423720
Curt Monhart *(Exec VP-Sls & Mktg)*

Non-U.S. Subsidiary:

Selkirk Canada Corporation (2)
375 Green Rd
Stoney Creek, ON, L8E 4A5, Canada
Tel.: (905) 662-6600
Fax: (866) 835-9624
Toll Free: (888) 735-5475
E-Mail: info@selkirkcanada.com
Web Site: www.selkirkcorp.com
Emp.: 15
Chimney Pipes, Venting & Fireplace Mfr
S.I.C.: 3272
N.A.I.C.S.: 327390
John Vukanovich *(Pres-Mktg)*

U.S. Joint Ventures:

99 Cents Only Stores (1)
4000 Union Pacific Ave
Los Angeles, CA 90023-3202 CA
Tel.: (323) 980-8145
Fax: (323) 980-8160
E-Mail: IR@99only.com
Web Site: www.99only.com
Sls.: $1,668,651,000
Assets: $1,757,237,000
Liabilities: $1,118,267,000
Net Worth: $638,970,000
Earnings: ($8,909,000)
Emp.: 13,700
Fiscal Year-end: 03/30/13
Discount Merchandise Retailer
S.I.C.: 5399
N.A.I.C.S.: 452990
David Gold *(Chm)*
Stephane Gonthier *(Pres & CEO)*
Frank Schools *(CFO & Sr VP)*
James G. Parros *(Sr VP-Logistics)*

Cequel Communications, LLC (1)
12444 Powerscourt Dr
Saint Louis, MO 63131 DE
Tel.: (314) 965-2020
Fax: (314) 965-0050
Toll Free: (800) 999-6845
Web Site: www.suddenlink.com
Sales Range: $1-4.9 Billion
Emp.: 6,100
Digital Cable TV, High-Speed Internet & Home Security Services
S.I.C.: 4841
N.A.I.C.S.: 515210
Jerald L. Kent *(Chm & CEO)*
Mary E. Meduski *(CFO & Exec VP)*
Thomas P. McMillin *(COO & Exec VP)*
Robert L. Putnam *(CIO & Sr VP)*
Jerry Dow *(CMO & Chief Sls Officer)*
Terry M. Cordova *(CTO & Sr VP)*
James B. Fox *(Chief Acctg Officer & Sr VP)*
Katherine Payne *(Chief Programming Officer & Sr VP)*
Kevin A. Stephens *(Pres-Comml & Adv Ops)*
Craig L. Rosenthal *(Gen Counsel & Sr VP)*
Ralph G. Kelly *(Treas & Sr VP)*
Wendy Knudsen *(Sec & Exec VP)*
Peter M. Abel *(Sr VP-Corp Comm)*
John E. Fuhler *(Sr VP-Fiscal Ops)*
Gregg Graff *(Sr VP-Sls)*
Gibbs Jones *(Sr VP-Customer Experience)*
Patricia L. McCaskill *(Sr VP-Programming & Chief Programming Officer)*
Mary R. Meier *(Sr VP-Mktg)*
Douglas G. Wiley *(Sr VP-HR)*

Subsidiary:

Perimeter Technology Center, Inc. (2)
4100 Perimeter Ctr Dr Ste 300
Oklahoma City, OK 73112
Tel.: (405) 917-3700
Toll Free: (888) 782-2656
E-Mail: sales@perimetercenter.com
Web Site: www.perimetercenter.com
Sales Range: $1-9.9 Million
Emp.: 20
Commercial Data Center Services, Monitored & Managed Network Services & Professional Engineering Services
S.I.C.: 7374
N.A.I.C.S.: 518210
R. Todd Currie *(Founder, Treas & VP-Ops)*
John W. Parsons *(CEO)*
Brad Thomas *(Sec & VP-Tech)*

Neiman Marcus Group LTD Inc. (1)
(Formerly Neiman Marcus, Inc.)
1618 Main St
Dallas, TX 75201 DE
Tel.: (214) 743-7600
Fax: (214) 742-4904
E-Mail: investor_relations@neimanmarcus.com
Web Site: www.neimanmarcusgroup.com
Rev.: $4,648,249,000
Assets: $5,300,241,000
Liabilities: $4,469,203,000
Net Worth: $831,038,000
Earnings: $163,699,000
Emp.: 15,700
Fiscal Year-end: 08/03/13
Holding Company; Online & Specialty Store Fashion & Gift Retailer
S.I.C.: 6719
N.A.I.C.S.: 551112
Karen W. Katz *(Pres & CEO)*
James E. Skinner *(CFO, COO & Exec VP)*
Michael R. Kingston *(CIO & Sr VP)*
Wanda Gierhart *(CMO & Sr VP)*
T. Dale Stapleton *(Chief Acctg Officer & Sr VP)*
Joseph Weber *(Chief HR Officer & Sr VP)*
James J. Gold *(Pres-Specialty Retail)*
John E. Koryl *(Pres-Direct)*
Joshua Schulman *(Pres-Bergdorf Goodman)*
Tracy M. Preston *(Gen Counsel & Sr VP)*
Stacie R. Shirley *(Sr VP-Fin & Treas)*
Ken Downing *(Sr VP & Dir-Fashion)*
Wayne A. Hussey *(Sr VP-Properties & Store Dev)*
Thomas J. Lind *(Sr VP-Program Mgmt)*
Michael West *(Sr VP-Distr, Logistics & Fulfillment)*

Subsidiaries:

Bergdorf Goodman, Inc. (2)
754 Fifth Ave
New York, NY 10019-2503
Tel.: (212) 753-7300
Fax: (646) 735-5202
Toll Free: (800) 558-1855
Web Site: www.bergdorfgoodman.com
Emp.: 1,300
Retail Specialty Stores
S.I.C.: 5621
N.A.I.C.S.: 448120
Joshua Schulman *(Pres)*
James J. Gold *(CEO)*
Tracy Margolies *(Sr VP & Gen Mgr-Mdse)*
Elizabeth Hui von der Golt *(Sr VP & Gen Mgr-Mdse-Jewelry)*

Neiman Marcus Stores (2)
1618 Main St
Dallas, TX 75201
Tel.: (214) 743-7600
Fax: (214) 573-5992
Toll Free: (800) 937-9146
Web Site: www.neimanmarcus.com
Emp.: 14,700
Speciality Retailing Men's, Women's & Children's Clothing & Accessories Import
S.I.C.: 5311
N.A.I.C.S.: 452111
James E. Skinner *(CFO)*
Wanda Gierhart *(CMO)*

Non-U.S. Subsidiary:

Quality Call Care Solutions, Inc. (2)
Westmount Center Suite 700
Edmonton, AB, T5M 3L7, Canada ON
Tel.: (780) 378-4000
Fax: (780) 378-4990
E-Mail: hr@qualitycallcare.com
Telemarketing Services
S.I.C.: 7389
N.A.I.C.S.: 561422
Kathie Kinisky *(Dir-Cust Svcs)*

Puget Energy, Inc. (1)
10885 NE 4th St Ste 1200
Bellevue, WA 98004-5591 WA
Mailing Address:
PO Box 97034
Bellevue, WA 98009-9734
Tel.: (425) 454-6363
Fax: (425) 424-6537
Toll Free: (888) 225-5773
E-Mail: durga.waite@pse.com
Web Site: www.pugetenergy.com
Rev.: $3,187,297,000
Assets: $12,906,575,000
Liabilities: $9,226,896,000
Net Worth: $3,679,679,000
Earnings: $285,728,000
Fiscal Year-end: 12/31/13
Holding Company; Electric Power & Gas Distr
S.I.C.: 4911
N.A.I.C.S.: 221122
William S. Ayer *(Chm)*
Kimberly J. Harris *(Pres & CEO)*
Daniel A. Doyle *(CFO & Sr VP)*
Michael J. Stranik *(Chief Acctg Officer & Controller)*
Don E. Gaines *(Treas & VP-Fin)*

Subsidiary:

Puget Sound Energy, Inc. (2)
10885 NE 4th St Ste 1200
Bellevue, WA 98004-5591 WA
Mailing Address:
PO Box 97034
Bellevue, WA 98009-9734
Tel.: (425) 454-6363
Fax: (425) 424-6537
Web Site: www.pse.com
Rev.: $3,187,335,000
Assets: $10,808,888,000
Liabilities: $7,368,131,000
Net Worth: $3,440,757,000
Earnings: $356,129,000
Emp.: 2,700
Fiscal Year-end: 12/31/13
Electric Power & Natural Gas Distribution & Generation Services
S.I.C.: 4939
N.A.I.C.S.: 221122
William S. Ayer *(Chm)*
Kimberly J. Harris *(Pres & CEO)*
Daniel A. Doyle *(CFO & Sr VP)*
Rudiger H. Wolf *(CIO & VP)*
Jennifer L. O'Connor *(Gen Counsel, Sec, Sr VP, Chief Ethics & Compliance Officer)*
Eric M. Markell *(Chief Strategy Officer & Sr VP)*
Marla D. Mellies *(Sr VP & Chief Admin Officer)*
James W. Eldredge *(Chief Acctg Officer, VP & Controller)*
Steve R. Secrist *(VP, Gen Counsel & Chief Ethics & Compliance Officer)*
Donald E. Gaines *(Treas & VP-Fin)*
Paul M. Wiegand *(Sr VP-Energy Ops)*

Subsidiaries:

Hydro Energy Development Corp. (3)
10885 NE 4th St Ste 1200
Bellevue, WA 98004 WA
Tel.: (425) 456-2570
Fax: (425) 456-3128
Emp.: 3
Small Hydro Development
S.I.C.: 6794
N.A.I.C.S.: 533110
Martin Thompson *(VP)*

Puget Western, Inc. (3)
19515 North Creek Pkwy Ste 310
Bothell, WA 98011-8200 WA
Tel.: (425) 487-6550
Fax: (425) 487-6565
Web Site: www.pugetwestern.com
Emp.: 5
Real Estate Holding & Developing
S.I.C.: 6552
N.A.I.C.S.: 237210
Gus Erikson *(Pres)*

Non-U.S. Holdings:

Airwave Solutions Ltd. (1)
Charter Court 50 Windsor Rd
Slough, Berks, SL1 2EJ, United Kingdom UK
Tel.: (44) 1753557387
Fax: (44) 1753557425
E-Mail: alliance.programme@airwavesolutions.co.uk
Web Site: www.airwavesolutions.co.uk
Sales Range: $400-449.9 Million
Emp.: 1,000
Secure Digital Radio Network Used by Emergency Personnel
S.I.C.: 3663
N.A.I.C.S.: 334220
Richard Bobbett *(CEO)*
Parminder Dost *(CFO)*

Subsidiary:

Arqiva Limited (2)
Wireless House Warwick Technology Park
Warwick, CV34 6DD, United Kingdom
Tel.: (44) 1926416000
Fax: (44) 1926416600
Web Site: www.arqiva.com
Sales Range: $500-549.9 Million
Emp.: 250
Mobile Telecommunication Infrastructure Services
S.I.C.: 4812
N.A.I.C.S.: 517210
John Cresswell *(CEO)*
Phil Moses *(CFO)*
Cameron Rejali *(CTO)*

Joint Venture:

Digital One Ltd. (2)
30 Leicester Square
London, WC2H 7LA, United Kingdom
Tel.: (44) 2072998670
Fax: (44) 20 7388 4601
E-Mail: info@digitalone.co.uk
Web Site: www.ukdigitalradio.com
Emp.: 6
Digital Radio Broadcasting; Owned by Canada Pension Plan Investment Board & by Lydian Capital Advisors S.A.
S.I.C.: 2741
N.A.I.C.S.: 519130
Glyn Jones *(Acting CEO)*

Non-U.S. Joint Ventures:

Anglian Water Group Limited (1)
Anglian House Ambury Road
Huntingdon, Cambs, PE29 3NZ, United Kingdom JE
Tel.: (44) 1480323000
Fax: (44) 1480323115
E-Mail: enquiries@awg.com
Web Site: www.awg.com
Sls.: $2,203,899,195
Assets: $13,509,404,589
Liabilities: $13,347,053,577
Net Worth: $162,351,012
Earnings: ($75,805,920)
Emp.: 5,967
Fiscal Year-end: 03/31/13
Holding Company; Water Supply, Sewerage & Property Development Services
S.I.C.: 6719
N.A.I.C.S.: 551112
Claire Russell *(Sec)*

Subsidiaries:

Anglian Water Services Limited (2)
Anglian House Ambury Road
Huntingdon, Cambs, PE29 3NZ, United Kingdom UK
Tel.: (44) 1480323000
Fax: (44) 1480323115
Web Site: www.anglianwater.co.uk
Sls.: $1,836,714,270
Assets: $13,001,189,067
Liabilities: $11,435,007,174
Net Worth: $1,566,181,893
Earnings: $467,153,982
Emp.: 250
Fiscal Year-end: 03/31/13
Water Supply Distribution & Sewerage Services
S.I.C.: 4971
N.A.I.C.S.: 221310
Adrian Montague *(Chm)*
Peter Simpson *(Mng Dir & Member-Mgmt Bd)*
Claire Russell *(Member-Mgmt Bd, Sec & Dir-Legal)*
Scott Longhurst *(Member-Mgmt Bd & Mng Dir-Fin & Non Regulated Bus)*
Chris Boucher *(Member-Mgmt Bd & Dir-Info Svcs)*
Richard Boucher *(Member-Mgmt Bd & Dir-Bus Change & Strategy)*
Paul Gibbs *(Member-Mgmt Bd & Dir-Wastewater Svcs)*
Kate Kelly *(Member-Mgmt Bd & Dir-HR)*
Chris Newsome *(Member-Mgmt Bd & Dir-Asset Mgmt)*
Martyn Oakley *(Member-Mgmt Bd & Dir-Customer Svcs)*
Mark Pendlington *(Member-Mgmt Bd & Dir-Corp Affairs)*
Jean Spencer *(Member-Mgmt Bd & Dir-Regulation)*
Paul Valleley *(Member-Mgmt Bd & Dir-Water Svcs)*

AWG Property Limited (2)
47 Melville Street
Edinburgh, EH4 7HL, United Kingdom UK
Tel.: (44) 01313431000
Fax: (44) 01312004480
Web Site: www.awgproperty.co.uk
Emp.: 30
Commercial & Residential Property Investment & Development
S.I.C.: 6531
N.A.I.C.S.: 531390
Tony Donnelly *(Mng Dir)*

Pinafore Holdings B.V. (1)
Prins Bernhardplein 200
1097 JB Amsterdam, Netherlands NL
Tel.: (31) 20577 1177
Sls.: $2,947,300,000
Assets: $4,945,600,000
Liabilities: $2,914,000,000
Net Worth: $2,031,600,000
Earnings: $136,100,000
Emp.: 14,930
Fiscal Year-end: 12/31/13
Holding Company; Owned by Onex Corporation & by Canada Pension Plan Investment Board
S.I.C.: 6719
N.A.I.C.S.: 551112
James Nicol *(CEO)*
John Zimmerman *(CFO)*
Alan Power *(Pres-Indus & Automotive)*
Thomas Reeve *(Gen Counsel & Exec VP)*
Dave Carroll *(Exec VP-Bus Dev)*

Non-U.S. Subsidiary:

Tomkins Limited (2)
East Putney House
84 Upper Richmond Road, London, SW15 2ST, United Kingdom UK
Tel.: (44) 2088714544
Fax: (44) 20 8877 9700
E-Mail: ir@tomkins.co.uk
Web Site: www.tomkins.co.uk
Sales Range: $1-4.9 Billion
Emp.: 26,949
Industrial Power Systems, Automotive, Plumbing & Construction Products Mfr
S.I.C.: 3714
N.A.I.C.S.: 336390
James Nicol *(CEO)*
John W. Zimmerman *(CFO & Dir-Fin)*
Al Power *(Pres-Indus & Automotive)*

U.S. Subsidiary:

Tomkins Industries, Inc. (3)
1551 Wewatta St
Denver, CO 80202 OH
Tel.: (303) 744-1911
Fax: (303) 744-4443
Web Site: www.tomkins.co.uk
Emp.: 7,000
Holding Company; Regional Managing Office
S.I.C.: 6719
N.A.I.C.S.: 551112
Al Power *(Pres-Indus & Automotive)*

Subsidiaries:

Aquatic (4)
8101 E Kaiser Blvd Ste 200
Anaheim, CA 92808-2261
Tel.: (714) 993-1220
Fax: (714) 998-1250
Toll Free: (800) 877-2005
Web Site: www.aquaticbath.com
Emp.: 80
Bathware & Shower Products Mfr
Export
S.I.C.: 3088
N.A.I.C.S.: 326191
Gary Anderson *(Pres)*

The Gates Corporation (4)
1551 Wewatta St
Denver, CO 80202 DE
Mailing Address:
PO Box 5887
Denver, CO 80217-5887
Tel.: (303) 744-1911
Telex: 6837035
Web Site: www.gates.com
Sls.: $1,763,400,000
Emp.: 15,000
Automotive Belts, Hoses & Other Rubber Related Products Mfr
Import Export
S.I.C.: 3052
N.A.I.C.S.: 326220
James Nicol *(Chm & CEO)*
Michael Wedge *(CIO)*
Jeff Brekke *(Pres-Aftermarket-North America & Exec VP-Global Aftermarket Bus)*
Jack Ramsey *(Sr VP-Aftermarket-North America)*

Non-U.S. Subsidiaries:

Gates Argentina S.A. (5)
Av del Libertador 498 Piso 20
C1001ABR Buenos Aires, Argentina
Tel.: (54) 1140185050
Fax: (54) 1140185059
Web Site: www.gates-argentina.com.ar
Emp.: 25
Belts & Hoses Mfr
S.I.C.: 3052
N.A.I.C.S.: 326220
Diego Borsai *(Dir-Sls)*

Gates Australia Pty. Ltd (5)
1-15 Hydrive Close
Dandenong, VIC, Australia
Tel.: (61) 397979666
Fax: (61) 397979600
E-Mail: southpacsales@gates.com
Web Site: www.gatesaustralia.com.au
Sales Range: $25-49.9 Million
Emp.: 70
Hardware & Tools Distr
S.I.C.: 5072
N.A.I.C.S.: 423710
Peter King *(CEO)*

Gates Canada Inc. (5)
225 Henry St
Brantford, ON, N3S 7R4, Canada
Tel.: (519) 759-4141
Fax: (519) 759-0944
Web Site: www.gates.com
Emp.: 150
Belts & Hoses Mfr
S.I.C.: 3052
N.A.I.C.S.: 326220
Ray Osika *(VP-Automotive Div)*

Gates De Mexico S.A. De C.V. (5)
Cerrada De Galeana No 5
Fracc Industrial La Loma
54060 Tlalnepantla, Mexico MX
Tel.: (52) 553332700
Fax: (52) 5553332701
E-Mail: buzon@gates.com
Web Site: www.gates.com.mx
Emp.: 1,300
Belts & Hoses Mfr
S.I.C.: 3052
N.A.I.C.S.: 326220

Gates Do Brasil Industria E Comerico Limited (5)
Rua Dr Renato Paes de Barros 1017 8 andar
Itaim Bibi, Sao Paulo, Brazil BR
Tel.: (55) 11 3848 8122
Telex: 1121240
Fax: (55) 11 3848 8170
E-Mail: cezar.yasuoka@gatesbrasil.com.br
Web Site: www.gatesbrasil.com.br
Emp.: 75
Belts & Hoses Mfr
S.I.C.: 3052
N.A.I.C.S.: 326220

Gates Europe nv (5)
Dr Carlierlaan 30
B 9320 Erembodegem, Belgium BE
Tel.: (32) 53762711
Telex: 84612322
Fax: (32) 53762715
E-Mail: info@gates.com
Web Site: www.gates.com
Emp.: 650
Belting & Hoses Mfr
Import Export
S.I.C.: 3052
N.A.I.C.S.: 326220
Christine Baillius *(Mgr-Bus Admin)*

Subsidiaries:

Gates GmbH (6)
Eisenbahnweg 50
PO Box 1428
52068 Aachen, Germany De
Tel.: (49) 2415108327
Fax: (49) 2415108 7327
E-Mail: bewerber@gates.com
Web Site: www.gates.com
Belts & Hoses Whslr
S.I.C.: 5199
N.A.I.C.S.: 424990

Gates Hydraulics Ltd. (6)
5 Alpha Drive
Huntingdon, Cambs, PE19 8JJ, United Kingdom UK

Canada Pension Plan Investment Board—(Continued)

Tel.: (44) 1480402300
Fax: (44) 1480402352
E-Mail: info@gates.com
Web Site: www.gates.com
Emp.: 65
Belts & Hoses Mfr
S.I.C.: 3052
N.A.I.C.S.: 326220
Gary Milner *(Mgr-Sls)*

Gates PT Spain S.A. **(6)**
Poligono Industrial Les Malloles
E-08660, Balsareny, Barcelona, Spain ES
Tel.: (34) 938777000
Fax: (34) 938777049
E-Mail: immag@gates.com
Web Site: www.gates.com
Sales Range: $10-24.9 Million
Emp.: 250
Belts & Hoses Mfr
S.I.C.: 3052
N.A.I.C.S.: 326220
Marc Etaix *(Dir-Ops)*

Plews, Inc. **(4)**
1550 Franklin Grove Rd
Dixon, IL 61021 DE
Tel.: (815) 288-3344
Fax: (815) 288-3388
Toll Free: (800) 770-4639
Web Site: www.plews-edelmann.com
Emp.: 190
Automotive Parts; Brass Fittings; Steel Brake Lines; Power Steering Products; Lubrication Tools; Grease Guns; Tire Hardware & Air Accessories; Specialty Greases & Oils Mfr
Import Export
S.I.C.: 3714
N.A.I.C.S.: 336390
Gordon Hoffman *(Dir-Sls & Mktg)*

Trion, Inc. **(4)**
101 McNeill Rd
Sanford, NC 27330-9451 PA
Tel.: (919) 775-2201
Telex: 823143 Trion UF
Fax: (919) 777-6399
Toll Free: (800) 884-0002
E-Mail: customerservice@trioninc.com
Web Site: www.trioniaq.com
Sales Range: $10-24.9 Million
Emp.: 150
Electronic Air Cleaners Mfr
Import Export
S.I.C.: 3564
N.A.I.C.S.: 333413
Mike Howell *(VP-Sls & Mktg)*

Subsidiaries:

Envirco Corporation **(5)**
101 McNeill Rd
Sanford, NC 27330 NM
Tel.: (919) 775-2201
Fax: (919) 777-6399
Toll Free: (800) 884-0002
E-Mail: info@envirco.com
Web Site: www.envirco.com
Emp.: 50
Air Filtration Systems & Components Design & Mfr
S.I.C.: 3564
N.A.I.C.S.: 333413
Colin O'Connell *(VP-Sls)*

Non-U.S. Subsidiary:

Stackpole Limited **(3)**
2430 Royal Windsor Drive
Mississauga, ON, L5J 1K7, Canada
Tel.: (905) 822-6015
Fax: (905) 822-9556
Toll Free: (800) 295-1982
E-Mail: contact@stackpole.com
Web Site: www.stackpole.com
Emp.: 250
Automotive Gears Mfr
S.I.C.: 3566
N.A.I.C.S.: 333612
Dave Maginn *(Gen Mgr)*

CANADA POST CORPORATION

35 Hughes St
Fredericton, NB, E3A 2W2, Canada
Tel.: (416) 979-8822
Toll Free: (866) 607-6301
E-Mail: communications@canadapost.ca
Web Site: www.canadapost.ca
Year Founded: 1981
Rev.: $7,483,976,580
Assets: $6,976,032,360
Liabilities: $9,608,197,320
Net Worth: ($2,632,164,960)
Earnings: $93,437,880
Emp.: 68,000
Fiscal Year-end: 12/31/12

Business Description:
Postal Services
S.I.C.: 4311
N.A.I.C.S.: 491110

Personnel:
Marc A. Courtois *(Chm)*
Deepak Chopra *(Pres & CEO)*
Wayne Cheeseman *(CFO)*
Andre Turgeon *(CTO, CIO & Sr VP)*
Douglas Greaves *(Chief Investment Officer & VP-Pension Fund)*
Andre Joron *(Chief HR Officer)*
Jacques Cote *(Pres-Physical Delivery Network)*
Kerry Munro *(Pres-Digital Delivery Network)*
Bonnie Boretsky *(Gen Counsel, Sec & VP)*
Rene Desmarais *(Sr VP-Parcels)*
Stephane Dubreuil *(Sr VP-Strategy & Corp Mktg)*
Cal Hart *(Sr VP-Processing, Engrg & Infrastructure)*
Douglas Jones *(Sr VP-Delivery)*
Mary Traversy *(Sr VP-Mail)*
Philip Ventura *(Sr VP-Strategy)*

Board of Directors:
Marc A. Courtois
Alain Sans Cartier
Deepak Chopra
Thomas Cryer
A. Michel Lavigne
Sian M. Matthews
Stewart McInnes
Andrew B. Paterson
Iris G. Petten
William Herbert Sheffield
Donald Woodley

Subsidiaries:

Canada Post International Ltd. **(1)**
2701 Riverside Dr Ste C0115
Ottawa, ON, K1A 0B1, Canada
Tel.: (613) 734-9800
Fax: (613) 734-4698
E-Mail: cpi@canadapost.ca
Provider of Consulting Services, Postal Technology, Postal Transformation & e-Commerce Capabilities to the Global Postal Industry
S.I.C.: 2741
N.A.I.C.S.: 519130

Intelcom Courier **(1)**
291 Rue De La Montagne Ste 100
Montreal, QC, H3C 4K4, Canada (50%)
Tel.: (514) 937-0430
Fax: (514) 284-2386
Web Site: www.intelcomgroup.com
Sales Range: $1-9.9 Million
Emp.: 20
Provider of Delivery, Courier, Warehousing, Distribution & Logistics Management Services for Business
S.I.C.: 7389
N.A.I.C.S.: 561499
Daniel Hudon *(Founder, Pres & CEO)*

Progistix-Solutions Inc. **(1)**
Unit 300 Bldg 99 Signet Dr
North York, ON, M9L 1T6, Canada (100%)
Tel.: (416) 401-7000
Fax: (416) 401-7278
Toll Free: (888) 277-6447
E-Mail: info@progistix.com
Web Site: www.progistix.com
Emp.: 300
Provider of Logistics Services to Businesses
S.I.C.: 7389
N.A.I.C.S.: 561499

Purolator Courier Ltd. **(1)**
5995 Avebury Rd
Mississauga, ON, L5R 3T8, Canada (100%)
Tel.: (905) 712-1084
Fax: (905) 712-6696
Toll Free: (888) 744-7123
Web Site: www.purolator.ca
Sales Range: $1-4.9 Billion
Emp.: 12,500
Overnight Courier Services
S.I.C.: 4311
N.A.I.C.S.: 491110
Patrick Nangle *(Pres & CEO)*

Joint Ventures:

epost **(1)**
393 University Ave 13th Fl
Toronto, ON, M5G 2P7, Canada (100%)
Tel.: (416) 313-4100
Fax: (416) 313-4199
Toll Free: (877) 376-1212
E-Mail: service@to.epost.ca
Web Site: www.epost.ca
Provider of Online Mail Services
S.I.C.: 2741
N.A.I.C.S.: 519130

Innovapost, Inc. **(1)**
365 March Rd
Ottawa, ON, K2K 3N5, Canada
Tel.: (613) 270-6262
Fax: (613) 270-6525
E-Mail:
Web Site: www.innovapost.com
Emp.: 700
Provider of IS/IT & eBusiness Solutions to the Global Postal Industry, Particularly to the Canada Post Group of Companies
S.I.C.: 2741
N.A.I.C.S.: 519130
Andre Turgeon *(CEO)*

CANADA POWER TECHNOLOGY LIMITED

161 Watline Avenue
Mississauga, ON, L4Z 1P2, Canada
Tel.: (905) 890-6900
Fax: (905) 890-0147
Web Site: www.canadapowertech.com
Year Founded: 1987
Rev.: $10,817,105
Emp.: 35

Business Description:
Air-Cooled Engines Distr
S.I.C.: 7539
N.A.I.C.S.: 811198

Personnel:
Tim Bequiri *(Pres)*

CANADA RARE EARTH CORP.

(Formerly Rare Earth Metals Inc.)
#400 602 West Hastings Street
Vancouver, BC, V6B 1P2, Canada
Tel.: (604) 689-1280
Fax: (604) 689-1288
E-Mail: admin@canadarareearth.com
Web Site: www.canadarareearth.com
LL—(OTC TSXV)
Int. Income: $24,887
Assets: $6,822,297
Liabilities: $116,022
Net Worth: $6,706,275
Earnings: ($1,887,050)
Fiscal Year-end: 03/31/13

Business Description:
Metal Mining Services
S.I.C.: 1099
N.A.I.C.S.: 212299

Personnel:
Rojer Li *(Chm)*
Tracy A. Moore *(Pres & CEO)*
Evan Asselstine *(CFO)*

Board of Directors:
Rojer Li
Tracy A. Moore
William Randolph Purcell
Peter Shearing
Michael R. Stares

CANADA RARE EARTHS INC.

(See Under Canada Strategic Metals Inc.)

CANADA RENEWABLE BIOENERGY CORP.

Suite 2000 1066 West Hastings Street
Vancouver, BC, V6E 3X2, Canada
Tel.: (778) 373-5456
Fax: (778) 373-5460
E-Mail: jfinklestein@hotmail.ca
Web Site: www.canadarenewablebioenergy.com
Year Founded: 2007
XZX—(CNSX)
Sls.: $16,327,933
Assets: $9,885,243
Liabilities: $1,450,580
Net Worth: $8,434,662
Earnings: $2,084,183
Fiscal Year-end: 03/31/13

Business Description:
Oil & Gas Exploration Services
S.I.C.: 1311
N.A.I.C.S.: 211111

Personnel:
Xuedian Liu *(Founder, Chm, Pres & CEO)*
Xinlin Huang *(CFO & Sec)*
Robert Mukasa *(COO)*

Board of Directors:
Xuedian Liu
Ling Jin
Ian Mallmann
Paul Zhang
Jiaming Zhu

Legal Counsel:
McMillan LLP
Royal Centre 1055 West Georgia Street Suite 1500 PO Box 11117
Vancouver, BC, Canada

Transfer Agent:
Olympia Trust Company
1003 750 West Pender Street
Vancouver, BC, V6C2T8, Canada

CANADA STRATEGIC METALS INC.

(Formerly Canada Rare Earths Inc.)
1500-1199 West Hastings Street
Vancouver, BC, V6E 3T5, Canada
Tel.: (604) 685-5851
Fax: (604) 685-7349
Web Site: www.canadastrategicmetals.com
Year Founded: 1984
CJC—(TSXV)
Assets: $3,743,213
Liabilities: $937,572
Net Worth: $2,805,641
Earnings: ($1,145,939)
Fiscal Year-end: 01/31/13

Business Description:
Metal Exploration Services
S.I.C.: 1099
N.A.I.C.S.: 212299

Personnel:
Jean-Sebastien Lavallee *(Pres & CEO)*
Nathalie Laurin *(CFO & Sec)*

Board of Directors:
Jean-Sebastien Lavallee
Chad McMillan
Hugo Monette

CANADA ZINC METALS CORP.
Suite 2050-1055 West Georgia Street
PO Box 11121
Royal Centre, Vancouver, BC, V6E 3P3, Canada
Tel.: (604) 684-2181
Fax: (604) 682-4768
E-Mail: info@canadazincmetals.com
Web Site: www.canadazincmetals.com
CZX—(TSXV)
Int. Income: $195,860
Assets: $78,396,392
Liabilities: $2,384,277
Net Worth: $76,012,115
Earnings: ($1,850,732)
Fiscal Year-end: 06/30/13
Business Description:
Zinc Mining Properties Exploration & Development
S.I.C.: 1081
N.A.I.C.S.: 213114
Personnel:
Peeyush K. Varshney *(Chm, Pres & CEO)*
Praveen K. Varshney *(CFO)*
Board of Directors:
Peeyush K. Varshney
Henry M. Giegerich
Marco Strub
John Alan Thomas
Legal Counsel:
Boughton Law Corporation
Suite 700 595 Burrard Street
Vancouver, BC, Canada
Transfer Agent:
Computershare Trust Company of Canada
510 Burrard St
Vancouver, BC, Canada

CANADIAN 50 ADVANTAGED PREFERRED SHARE FUND
181 University Avenue Suite 300
Toronto, ON, M5H 3M7, Canada
Tel.: (416) 364-2839
Fax: (416) 363-2089
E-Mail: nmurdoch@cclgroup.com
CPF.UN—(TSX)
Business Description:
Investment Services
S.I.C.: 6211
N.A.I.C.S.: 523999
Personnel:
Michael W. Freund *(Chm)*
W. Neil Murdoch *(Pres & CEO)*
Darren N. Cabral *(CFO & VP)*
Board of Directors:
Michael W. Freund
Darren N. Cabral
W. Neil Murdoch
Transfer Agent:
Computershare Investor Services Inc.
Toronto, ON, Canada

CANADIAN ADVANCED TECHNOLOGY ALLIANCE
(d/b/a CATAAlliance)
388 Albert St
207 Bank St Ste 416, Ottawa, ON, K2R KN2, Canada
Tel.: (613) 236-6550
Fax: (866) 274-8189
E-Mail: info@cata.ca
Web Site: www.cata.ca
Emp.: 7
Business Description:
Technology Alliance
S.I.C.: 8611
N.A.I.C.S.: 813910
Personnel:
John Reid *(Pres & CEO)*
Clay Braziller *(Pres)*
Norm Kirkpatrick *(Pres)*
Russ Roberts *(Sr VP-Tax & Fin)*
Divisions:

Canadian Association of Internet Providers **(1)**
388 Albert St 2nd Fl
Ottawa, ON, K1R 5B2, Canada
Tel.: (613) 232-2247
Fax: (613) 236-8189
E-Mail: info@caip.ca
Web Site: www.caip.ca
Emp.: 6
Technology Trade Association
S.I.C.: 8611
N.A.I.C.S.: 813910
Tom Copeland *(Chm)*
Joanne Stanley *(Mng Dir)*
John LaCalamita *(Gen Counsel)*

CATA Biometrics Group **(1)**
388 Albert St 2nd Fl
Ottawa, ON, K1R 5B2, Canada
Tel.: (613) 236-6550
Fax: (613) 236-8189
Web Site: www.cata.ca/print/About_Cata/membershipform.html
Emp.: 8
Biometric Technology Alliance
S.I.C.: 8611
N.A.I.C.S.: 813910

CANADIAN APARTMENT PROPERTIES REAL ESTATE INVESTMENT TRUST
11 Church Street Suite 401
Toronto, ON, M5E 1W1, Canada
Tel.: (416) 861-9404
Fax: (416) 861-9209
E-Mail: ir@capreit.net
Web Site: www.capreit.net
Year Founded: 1997
CAR.UN—(OTC TSX)
Rev.: $409,954,722
Assets: $4,892,115,155
Liabilities: $2,477,427,855
Net Worth: $2,414,687,300
Earnings: $409,797,667
Emp.: 829
Fiscal Year-end: 12/31/12
Business Description:
Real Estate Investment Trust Services
S.I.C.: 6726
N.A.I.C.S.: 525990
Personnel:
Michael L. Stein *(Chm)*
Thomas Schwartz *(Pres & CEO)*
Gobal Mailwaganam *(Mng Dir & Dir-Housing & Municipal Affairs)*
Patti Baker *(Mng Dir)*
Judy Harkai *(Mng Dir)*
Scott Cryer *(CFO)*
Mark Kenney *(COO)*
Maria Amaral *(Chief Acctg Officer)*
Robert Sestito *(Chief Info Sys Officer & VP-IT)*
Corinne Pruzanski *(Gen Counsel & Sec)*
Transfer Agent:
Computershare Trust Company of Canada
9th Floor 100 University Avenue
Toronto, ON, Canada

CANADIAN ARROW MINES LIMITED
Suite 8 - 233 Brady Street East
Sudbury, ON, P3B 4H5, Canada
Tel.: (705) 673-8259
Fax: (705) 673-5450
Toll Free: (877) 673-5462
E-Mail: info@canadianarrowmines.ca
Web Site: www.canadianarrowmines.ca
Year Founded: 1938
CRO—(TSXV)
Int. Income: $60
Assets: $15,150,963
Liabilities: $843,917
Net Worth: $14,307,046
Earnings: ($841,631)
Fiscal Year-end: 12/31/12
Business Description:
Metal Mining & Exploration Services
S.I.C.: 1099
N.A.I.C.S.: 212299
Personnel:
Kim Tyler *(Pres)*
Dean MacEachern *(CEO)*
Paul D'Aloisio *(CFO)*
Board of Directors:
Paul D'Aloisio
Todd Keast
Alan Letourneau
Dean MacEachern
George Edward Pirie
Kim Tyler

CANADIAN AUTO WORKERS
205 Placer Ct
M2H 3H9 Toronto, ON, Canada
Tel.: (416) 497-4110
Fax: (416) 459-6559
Toll Free: (800) 268-5763
E-Mail: cawpres@caw.ca
Web Site: www.caw.ca
Sales Range: $100-124.9 Million
Emp.: 900
Business Description:
Labor Union
S.I.C.: 8631
N.A.I.C.S.: 813930
Personnel:
Jean-Pierre Fortin *(Dir-Quebec)*

CANADIAN BACK INSTITUTE LIMITED PARTNERSHIP
(d/b/a CBI Health Group)
Sun Life Financial Centre West Tower
3300 Bloor St W Ste 900
Toronto, ON, M8X 2X2, Canada
Tel.: (416) 231-0078
Fax: (416) 231-0091
Toll Free: (800) 463-2225
Web Site: www.cbi.ca
Business Description:
Healthcare Management Services
S.I.C.: 8049
N.A.I.C.S.: 621399
Personnel:
Christopher Szybbo *(Pres)*
Avi Barkin *(CFO)*
Dave Maxwell *(Sr VP-Ops-Western Canada)*
Cameron McInnes *(Sr VP-Ops-Central Eastern Canada)*
Subsidiary:

Care Point Medical Centres **(1)**
3993 Henning Dr
Suite 203, Burnaby, BC, V5C 6N5, Canada BC (100%)
Tel.: (604) 205-9466
Fax: (604) 205-9406
Web Site: www.carepoint.ca
Sales Range: $1-9.9 Million
Emp.: 100
Healthcare Services
S.I.C.: 8011
N.A.I.C.S.: 621111

CANADIAN BANC CAPITAL SECURITIES TRUST
181 University Avenue Suite 300
Toronto, ON, M5H 3M9, Canada
Tel.: (416) 364-2839
E-Mail: nmurdoch@cclgroup.com
Web Site: www.cclgroup.com
CSB.UN—(TSX)
Sales Range: Less than $1 Million
Emp.: 6
Business Description:
Investment Services
S.I.C.: 6211
N.A.I.C.S.: 523999
Personnel:
Michael W. Freund *(Chm & CFO)*
W. Neil Murdoch *(Pres & CEO)*
Board of Directors:
Michael W. Freund
Darren N. Cabral
W. Neil Murdoch
Transfer Agent:
Computershare Investor Services Inc.
Montreal, QC, Canada

CANADIAN BANK NOTE COMPANY LIMITED
145 Richmond Rd
Ottawa, ON, K1Z 1A1, Canada
Tel.: (613) 722-3421
Fax: (613) 722-2548
E-Mail: info@cbnco.com
Web Site: www.cbnco.com
Year Founded: 1910
Sales Range: $75-99.9 Million
Emp.: 750
Business Description:
High Security Printing Services
S.I.C.: 7389
N.A.I.C.S.: 323120
Personnel:
Douglas R. Arends *(Chm)*
Ronald G. Arends *(Pres & CEO)*
Charles R. Lavoie *(CFO & Exec VP)*
Ian Shaw *(Pres-Identification Sys)*
Michel P. Perras *(Treas, VP & Controller)*
Shirley A. Arends *(Sec & Sr VP)*
Board of Directors:
Douglas R. Arends
Shirley A. Arends
Patrick J. Lavelle
Subsidiaries:

Canadian Bank Note Design Inc. **(1)**
105 2507 12th St NE
Calgary, AB, 22E 7F5, Canada (100%)
Tel.: (403) 250-9510
Fax: (403) 250-1165
E-Mail: mcara@mcara.com
Web Site: www.mcara.com
Emp.: 70
High Security Printing Services
S.I.C.: 7389
N.A.I.C.S.: 323120
Rodger K. Grant *(Gen Mgr)*

CBN Lottery Group **(1)**
18 Auriga Dr Ste 205
Ottawa, ON, K2E 7T9, Canada (100%)
Tel.: (613) 225-3018
Fax: (613) 225-9012
E-Mail: lottery@cbnlottery.com
Web Site: www.cbnco.com
Emp.: 214
Provider of High Security Printing Services
S.I.C.: 2759
N.A.I.C.S.: 323120
Craig Bascombe *(Pres)*

McAra Printing **(1)**
105 2507 12th St NE
Calgary, AB, T2E 7L5, Canada (100%)
Tel.: (403) 250-9510
Fax: (403) 250-1165
E-Mail: mcara@mcara.com
Web Site: www.mcara.com
Emp.: 70
Printer of Government, Financial & Lottery Related Documents
S.I.C.: 7389
N.A.I.C.S.: 323120
Rodger K. Grant *(VP & Gen Mgr)*

WANN Connection Devices, Inc. **(1)**
18 Auriga Dr
Ottawa, ON, K2E 7T9, Canada (100%)
Tel.: (613) 225-9266
Fax: (613) 225-4593
E-Mail: wanninfo@cbnco.com
Web Site: www.wann.com
Emp.: 200
Developer of High Technology Devices
S.I.C.: 3669
N.A.I.C.S.: 334290

Canadian Bank Note Company Limited—(Continued)

Robert Balderson *(VP-R&D)*

Non-U.S. Subsidiaries:

Guyana Lottery Company Limited (1)
357 Lamaha Street North Cummingsburg
Georgetown, Guyana (100%)
Tel.: (592) 2260753
Fax: (592) 2259633
E-Mail: guyanalottery@ewirelessgy.com
Web Site: www.guyana-lottery.com
Emp.: 40
Provider of Lottery Services
S.I.C.: 7999
N.A.I.C.S.: 713290
Tracey Lewis *(Gen Mgr)*

THE CANADIAN BROADCASTING CORPORATION

181 Queen St
Ottawa, ON, K1P 1K9, Canada
Tel.: (613) 288-6000
Fax: (613) 288-6455
Web Site: www.cbc.ca
Year Founded: 1936
Sales Range: $500-549.9 Million
Emp.: 10,000

Business Description:
Television & Radio Networks Broadcaster
Import Export
S.I.C.: 4833
N.A.I.C.S.: 515120

Personnel:
Timothy W. Casgrain *(Chm)*
Hubert T. Lacroix *(Pres & CEO)*
Suzanne Morris *(CFO & VP)*
Steven Guiton *(Chief Regulatory Officer & VP)*
Pierre Nollet *(Chief Legal Officer, Sec & VP)*
Heather E. Conway *(Exec VP-English Language Svcs)*
Sylvain Lafrance *(Exec VP-French Svcs)*
George C.B. Smith *(Sr VP-HR & Org)*

Board of Directors:
Timothy W. Casgrain
Linda Black
Peter D. Charbonneau
George Cooper
Peter Herrndorf
Hubert T. Lacroix
Patricia A. McIver
Trina McQueen
Brian R. Mitchell
Remi Racine
Edna Turpin
John Fitzgerald Young

Subsidiary:

Radio Canada International (1)
1400 Rene-Levesque Blvd E
PO Box 6000
Montreal, QC, H2L 2M2, Canada
Tel.: (514) 597-7500
Fax: (514) 597-7760
E-Mail: info@rcinet.ca
Web Site: www.rcinet.ca
Emp.: 80
Radio Network
S.I.C.: 4832
N.A.I.C.S.: 515111
Hubert T. Lacroix *(Pres & CEO)*
Pia Marquard *(Mng Dir)*

CANADIAN COMMERCIAL CORPORATION

50 O'Connor St 11th Fl
Ottawa, ON, K1A 0S6, Canada
Tel.: (613) 996-0034
Fax: (613) 995-2121
Toll Free: (800) 748-8191 (Canada)
E-Mail: reception@ccc.ca
Web Site: www.ccc.ca
Year Founded: 1946
Rev.: $2,211,886,346
Assets: $1,165,592,822
Liabilities: $1,115,526,023
Net Worth: $50,066,799
Earnings: $1,317,077
Emp.: 130
Fiscal Year-end: 03/31/13

Business Description:
Export Contracting Services
S.I.C.: 7389
N.A.I.C.S.: 561499

Personnel:
Ray Castelli *(Chm)*
Marc Whittingham *(Pres & CEO)*
Anthony Carty *(CFO & VP-Risk & Fin)*
Martin Zablocki *(COO & Exec VP)*
Tamara Parschin-Rybkin *(Gen Counsel, Sec & VP-Legal Svcs)*

Board of Directors:
Ray Castelli
Martine Corriveau-Gougeon
Martin Gagne
Sherry Helwer
Dwayne Lucas
Scott Player
Derrick Rowe
Andrew Saxton
Stephen J. Sorocky
Norman A. Turnbull
Marc Whittingham

CANADIAN DATA PRESERVE INC.

1140-1185 West Georgia Street
Vancouver, BC, V6E 2E6, Canada
Tel.: (778) 240-7055
Fax: (604) 687-1188
Year Founded: 2010
DPC—(CNSX)
Assets: $2,884
Liabilities: $209,350
Net Worth: ($206,466)
Earnings: ($111,005)
Fiscal Year-end: 05/31/13

Business Description:
Data Preservation Services
S.I.C.: 7379
N.A.I.C.S.: 518210

Personnel:
Van H. Potter *(Pres & CEO)*
Brian Cameron *(CFO)*

Board of Directors:
Brian Cameron
Van H. Potter
Jack Saltich

Transfer Agent:
Computershare Investor Services Inc
Suite 300 510 Burrard Street
Vancouver, BC, Canada

THE CANADIAN DEPOSITORY FOR SECURITIES LIMITED

85 Richmond St W
Toronto, ON, M5H 2C9, Canada
Tel.: (416) 365-8400
Fax: (416) 365-0842
E-Mail: cdswebmaster@cds.ca
Web Site: www.cds.ca
Sales Range: $75-99.9 Million
Emp.: 400

Business Description:
Security & Commodity Services
S.I.C.: 6231
N.A.I.C.S.: 523210

Personnel:
David Wood *(Chm)*
Jean Desgagne *(Pres & CEO)*
Debbie Block *(Mng Dir-HR)*
Edward Lee *(Mng Dir-IT Dept)*
Adina Saposnik *(Mng Dir-IT Svcs)*
Steve M. Blake *(CFO)*
Brian Gill *(CIO)*
Lindsay A. Wallace *(Chief Admin Officer & VP-Strategy Dev)*
Toomas Marley *(Chief Legal Officer)*
David Stanton *(Chief Risk Officer)*
Sandra Kendall *(Sec)*

Board of Directors:
David Wood
John B. Cieslak
Charles Freedman
Norman K. J. Graham
Raymond Lafontaine
Bruce Macdonald
John K. Mitchell
Yvan Naud
Gerard J. O'Mahoney
Michael Ptasznik
Wayne Ralph

Subsidiary:

CDS Inc. (1)
85 Richmond Street West
Flr 11, Toronto, ON, M5H 2C9, Canada
Tel.: (416) 365-8400
Fax: (416) 365-0842
E-Mail: cdswebmaster@cds.ca
Web Site: www.cds.ca
Securities Related Services
S.I.C.: 6231
N.A.I.C.S.: 523210
Steve M. Blake *(CFO)*
Brian Gill *(CIO)*
Toomas Marley *(Chief Legal Officer)*

CANADIAN ENERGY SERVICES & TECHNOLOGY CORP.

Suite 1400 700 4th Avenue SW
Calgary, AB, T2P 3J4, Canada
Tel.: (403) 269-2800
Fax: (403) 266-5708
Toll Free: (888) 785-6695
E-Mail: info@ceslp.ca
Web Site: www.canadianenergyservices.com
CEU—(OTC TSX)
Rev.: $468,480,632
Assets: $352,521,241
Liabilities: $138,389,452
Net Worth: $214,131,788
Earnings: $27,702,343
Emp.: 350
Fiscal Year-end: 12/31/12

Business Description:
Drilling Fluid Systems Designer
S.I.C.: 1389
N.A.I.C.S.: 213112

Personnel:
Kyle D. Kitagawa *(Chm)*
Thomas J. Simons *(Pres & CEO)*
Craig F. Nieboer *(CFO)*
Kenneth E. Zinger *(COO)*
Scott R. Cochlan *(Sec)*

Board of Directors:
Kyle D. Kitagawa
Colin D. Boyer
Rodney L. Carpenter
John M. Hooks
James G. Sherman
Thomas J. Simons
D. Michael G. Stewart

Legal Counsel:
Torys LLP
Calgary, AB, Canada

Crowe & Dunlevy
Oklahoma City, OK 73102

Computershare Investor Services Inc.
Calgary, AB, Canada

Transfer Agents:
Computershare Investor Services Inc.
Montreal, QC, Canada

Computershare Investor Services Inc.
Calgary, AB, Canada

Division:

Clear Environmental Solutions Inc. (1)
440 840 6th Ave SW
Calgary, AB, T2P 3E5, Canada
Tel.: (403) 263-5953
Fax: (403) 263-2943
E-Mail: info@clearenv.com
Web Site: www.clearenv.com
Emp.: 16
Environmental Engineering Services
S.I.C.: 8711
N.A.I.C.S.: 541330
Gavin Grimson *(Gen Mgr)*

U.S. Subsidiary:

AES Drilling Fluids, LLC (1)
1625 Broadway Ste 1480
Denver, CO 80202
Tel.: (303) 820-2800
Fax: (303) 820-3801
Web Site: www.aesfluids.com
Emp.: 8
Oil & Gas Drilling Services
S.I.C.: 1381
N.A.I.C.S.: 213111

CANADIAN FERRO REFRACTORIES

345 Arvin Ave
Stoney Creek, ON, L8E 2M6, Canada
Tel.: (905) 662-8381
Fax: (905) 662-1240
E-Mail: mheugh@cdnferroref.ca
Web Site: www.thermatex.ca
Emp.: 9

Business Description:
Mfr of Specialty Refractories for the Steel Industry
S.I.C.: 3255
N.A.I.C.S.: 327120

Personnel:
John Flannigan *(Pres)*

CANADIAN GENERAL TOWER LIMITED

52 Middleton St
Cambridge, ON, N1R 5T6, Canada
Tel.: (519) 623-1630
Fax: (519) 740-2977
Web Site: www.cgtower.com
Year Founded: 1946
Sales Range: $200-249.9 Million
Emp.: 1,100

Business Description:
Coated Fabrics & Plastic Film Mfr
S.I.C.: 2671
N.A.I.C.S.: 322220

Personnel:
Jan Chaplin *(Pres & CEO)*

CANADIAN GOLD SEAFOOD COMPANY

209 Aerotech Drive Unit 10B
Enfield, NS, B2T 1K3, Canada
Tel.: (902) 873-3766
Fax: (902) 873-4535
Web Site: www.canadiangold.ns.ca
Year Founded: 1995
Rev.: $21,736,238
Emp.: 30

Business Description:
Seafood Processing Storage & Distr
S.I.C.: 2092
N.A.I.C.S.: 311710

Personnel:
Doug McRae *(Pres)*

CANADIAN HELICOPTERS GROUP INC.

(See Under HNZ Group Inc.)

CANADIAN HIGH YIELD FOCUS FUND

161 Bay Street 27th Floor
Toronto, ON, M5J 1S2, Canada

Tel.: (416) 285-0050
Fax: (647) 572-2201
E-Mail: kmatheson@propelcpaital.ca
Year Founded: 2011
CAH.UN—(TSX)
Int. Income: $1,998
Assets: $38,789,108
Liabilities: $790,306
Net Worth: $37,998,802
Earnings: ($575,055)
Fiscal Year-end: 12/31/12

Business Description:
Investment Services
S.I.C.: 6211
N.A.I.C.S.: 523999

Personnel:
Michael Simonetta *(Chm)*
Raj Lala *(Pres & CEO)*
Krista Matheson *(CFO, Sec & Sr VP)*

Board of Directors:
Michael Simonetta
Keith Crone
Raj Lala
Krista Matheson

Transfer Agent:
Computershare Investor Services Inc.
Montreal, QC, Canada

CANADIAN IMPERIAL BANK OF COMMERCE

(d/b/a CIBC)
Commerce Court
Toronto, ON, M5L 1A2, Canada
Tel.: (416) 980-2211
Fax: (416) 363-5347
Toll Free: (800) 465-2422
E-Mail: pas@cibc.com
Web Site: www.cibc.com
Year Founded: 1867
CM—(NYSE TSX)
Rev.: $17,036,508,780
Assets: $396,006,633,780
Liabilities: $377,687,839,200
Net Worth: $18,318,794,580
Earnings: $3,379,668,000
Emp.: 43,039
Fiscal Year-end: 10/31/13

Business Description:
Banking Services
S.I.C.: 6029
N.A.I.C.S.: 522110

Personnel:
Charles Sirois *(Chm)*
James Prentice *(Vice Chm & Sr Exec VP)*
Tom D. Woods *(Vice Chm & Sr Exec VP)*
Gerald T. McCaughey *(Pres & CEO)*
Kevin A. Glass *(CFO & Sr Exec VP)*
Richard W. Nesbitt *(COO)*
Michael G. Capatides *(Chief Admin Officer, Gen Counsel & Sr Exec VP)*
Laura Dottori-Attanasio *(Chief Risk Officer & Sr Exec VP)*
Richard E. Venn *(Sr Exec VP)*
Victor Dodig *(Sr Exec VP & Grp Head-Wealth Mgmt)*
David Williamson *(Sr Exec VP & Grp Head-Retail & Bus Banking)*

Board of Directors:
Charles Sirois
Brent S. Belzberg
Gary F. Colter
Dominic D'Alessandro
Patrick Donald Daniel
Luc Desjardins
Gordon D. Giffin
Linda S. Hasenfratz
Kevin J. Kelly
Nicholas D. Le Pan
John P. Manley
Gerald T. McCaughey
Jane L. Peverett
Leslie Rahl
Katharine Berghuis Stevenson
Martine Turcotte
Ronald W. Tysoe

Computershare Inc
250 Royall Street
Canton, MA 02021

Transfer Agents:
CST Trust Company
PO Box 700
Postal Station B, Montreal, QC, Canada

Computershare Inc
250 Royall Street
Canton, MA 02021

Subsidiaries:

CIBC Asset Management Holdings Inc. (1)
Commerce Ct W 5 Fl
Toronto, ON, M5L 1A2, Canada
Tel.: (416) 980-2211
Investment Management Services
S.I.C.: 6211
N.A.I.C.S.: 523999

CIBC Global Asset Management Inc. (1)
1000 De La Gauchetiere West Suite 3200
Montreal, QC, H3B 4W5, Canada
Tel.: (514) 875-7040
Fax: (514) 875-9364
E-Mail: cibcam-info@cibc.ca
Web Site: www.cibc.com
Emp.: 90
Investment Management Services
S.I.C.: 6799
N.A.I.C.S.: 523920
Steve Geist *(Pres & CEO)*
Suzann Pennington *(Chief Investment Officer, Mng Dir & Head-Equities)*

CIBC Investor Services Inc. (1)
800 Bay Street 2nd Floor
Toronto, ON, M5S 3A9, Canada
Tel.: (416) 980-3343
Toll Free: (800) 567-3343
E-Mail:
Web Site: www.investorsedge.cibc.com
Emp.: 200
Investment Management Services
S.I.C.: 6282
N.A.I.C.S.: 523920
Marybeth Jordan *(Pres)*

CIBC Securities, Inc. (1)
161 Bay St
Toronto, ON, M5J 2S8, Canada (100%)
Tel.: (416) 980-2211
Fax: (416) 980-6502
E-Mail: andrea.livingstone@cibc.com
Web Site: www.cibc.com
Emp.: 300
Securities Brokers
S.I.C.: 6211
N.A.I.C.S.: 523999
Gerald T. McCaughey *(Pres & CEO)*
Sonia A. Baxendale *(Sr Exec VP)*

CIBC Trust Corporation (1)
55 Yonge St 10th Fl
Toronto, ON, M5E 1J4, Canada
Tel.: (416) 861-7000
Fax: (416) 862-2272
Investment Management Services
S.I.C.: 6211
N.A.I.C.S.: 523999

The CIBC Wood Gundy Corporation (1)
Commerce Ct W 7th Fl
Toronto, ON, M5L 1A2, Canada (100%)
Mailing Address:
BCE Place
PO Box 500
Toronto, ON, M5J 2S8, Canada
Tel.: (416) 980-2211
Fax: (416) 980-2212
Toll Free: (800) 563-3193
E-Mail: info@woodgundy.com
Web Site: www.woodgundy.com
Emp.: 1,000
Investment Securities Broker
S.I.C.: 6799
N.A.I.C.S.: 523910

Subsidiaries:

CIBC Wood Gundy (2)
2200 255 Queens Avenue
London, ON, N6A 5R8, Canada ON
Tel.: (519) 663-5353
Fax: (519) 663-5037
Web Site: www.cibcwoodgundy.com
Emp.: 120
Securities Brokerage Services
S.I.C.: 6211
N.A.I.C.S.: 523120
Cheryl Spencer *(Gen Mgr)*

CIBC Wood Gundy (2)
1800 Manulise Pl 10180 St
Edmonton, AB, T5J 3S4, Canada AB
Tel.: (780) 429-8900
Fax: (780) 429-8999
Web Site: www.cibcwoodgundy.com
Emp.: 140
Securities Brokerage Services
S.I.C.: 6211
N.A.I.C.S.: 523120

CIBC World Markets Inc. (2)
161 Bay St
Toronto, ON, M5J 2S8, Canada (62.4%)
Mailing Address:
PO Box 500
Toronto, ON, M5J 2S8, Canada
Tel.: (416) 594-7000
Fax: (416) 594-7664
Web Site: www.cibcwm.com
Emp.: 2,500
Investments & Financial Services
Export
S.I.C.: 6211
N.A.I.C.S.: 523110
Enio M. Lazzer *(Mng Dir & Head-Prime Brokerage & Trading Svcs)*
Richard Phillips *(Mng Dir & Head-Global Equities)*
Monique Gravel *(Mng Dir)*

Subsidiaries:

CIBC WM Real Estate Ltd. (3)
199 Bay Street 44th Floor Commerce Court
Toronto, ON, M5L 1A2, Canada
Tel.: (416) 594-7360
Web Site: www.cibc.com
Emp.: 5
Real Estate Brokerage Services
S.I.C.: 6531
N.A.I.C.S.: 531210
Chris Bell *(Mng Dir)*

CIBC Wood Gundy Financial Services Inc. (3)
200 King Street West Suite 700
Toronto, ON, M5H 4A8, Canada
Tel.: (800) 563-3193
Web Site: www.woodgundy.com
Emp.: 300
Financial Management Services
S.I.C.: 6211
N.A.I.C.S.: 523999

U.S. Subsidiary:

CIBC World Markets Corp. (3)
425 Lexington Ave
New York, NY 10017-6232 DE
Tel.: (212) 667-7000
Fax: (212) 667-4818
Toll Free: (800) 999-6726
Web Site: www.cibc.wm.com
Securities Firm & Investment Banking
S.I.C.: 6211
N.A.I.C.S.: 523110
James J. Baranello, Jr. *(Mng Dir)*

Non-U.S. Branches:

CIBC World Markets - Australia Office (3)
Level 45 Gateway 1 Macquarie Place
Sydney, NSW, 2000, Australia
Tel.: (61) 292751300
Fax: (61) 292751310
E-Mail:
Web Site: www.cibcwm.com.au
Emp.: 13
Merchant Bank & Financial Services
S.I.C.: 6159
N.A.I.C.S.: 522298
Neil Johnson *(Mng Dir)*

CIBC World Markets - Hong Kong Office (3)
Ste 3602 Cheung Kong Ctr 2 Queen's Rd
Hong Kong, China (Hong Kong)
Tel.: (852) 28416111
Telex: 75719
Fax: (852) 28419218
E-Mail: civihk@cibcwm.com.hk
Web Site: www.cibcwm.com
Emp.: 100
Bank & Finance Company
S.I.C.: 9311
N.A.I.C.S.: 921130

CIBC World Markets - Singapore Office (3)
16 Collyer Quay 04 02 Hitachi Twr
Singapore, 49318, Singapore
Tel.: (65) 65352323
Telex: 20499
Fax: (65) 65357565
Web Site: www.cibcwm.com
Emp.: 77
Merchant Bank & Financial Services
S.I.C.: 6159
N.A.I.C.S.: 522298
Deborah Wong *(Mng Dir)*

Non-U.S. Subsidiaries:

CIBC World Markets (Japan) Inc. (3)
2-2-3 Uchisaiwaicho Hibiyakokusai Bldg 8f
Chiyoda-Ku, Tokyo, 100-0011, Japan
Tel.: (81) 355128866
Investment Management Services
S.I.C.: 6211
N.A.I.C.S.: 523999

CIBC World Markets plc (3)
150 Cheapside
London, EC2V 6ET, United Kingdom UK
Tel.: (44) 20 7234 6000 (100%)
Fax: (44) 20 7407 4127
Web Site: www.cibcwm.com
Emp.: 500
Investment Company
S.I.C.: 6799
N.A.I.C.S.: 523910

INTRIA Items Inc. (1)
155 Britannia Road East
Mississauga, ON, L5R 3E9, Canada
Tel.: (905) 755-2400
Fax: (905) 755-4799
E-Mail: Mailbox.inquiry@intria.com
Web Site: www.intriaitemsinc.com
Emp.: 150
Payment & Information Management Services
S.I.C.: 6099
N.A.I.C.S.: 522320
Robert G. Bouey *(Pres)*

Joint Venture:

CIBC Mellon (1)
320 Bay Street
Toronto, ON, M5H 4A6, Canada
Mailing Address:
PO Box 1
Toronto, ON, M5H 4A6, Canada
Tel.: (416) 643-5000
Web Site: www.cibcmellon.com
Investment Processing Services
S.I.C.: 6733
N.A.I.C.S.: 523991
Thomas S. Monahan *(Pres & CEO)*
Robert M. Shier *(COO & Sr VP)*
Mike Plantinga *(CIO)*
Kelly Hastings *(Chief Risk Officer & VP)*
Mark R. Hemingway *(Gen Counsel, Sr VP-Corp Dev & Governance)*
Rob Ferguson *(Sr VP-Capital Markets)*
David S. Linds *(Sr VP-Bus Dev & Client Relationship Mgmt)*
Sue Simone *(Sr VP-HR & Corp Comm)*

U.S. Subsidiary:

Canadian Imperial Holdings Inc. (1)
425 Lexington Ave
New York, NY 10017-3903 DE
Tel.: (212) 856-4000 (100%)
Web Site: www.cibcwm.com
Emp.: 500
Bank Holding Company
S.I.C.: 6712
N.A.I.C.S.: 551111
Gary Brown *(Pres & CEO)*

Subsidiaries:

Atlantic Trust Group, Inc. (2)
1555 Peachtree St Ste 1100
Atlanta, GA 30309 DE
Tel.: (404) 881-3400

Canadian Imperial Bank of Commerce—(Continued)

Fax: (404) 881-3401
Web Site: www.atlantictrust.com
Sales Range: $650-699.9 Million
Investment & Wealth Management Services
S.I.C.: 6282
N.A.I.C.S.: 523920
John S. Markwalter Jr. *(Chm & CEO)*
Jeffrey S. Thomas *(Vice Chm)*
Eric B. Propper *(Pres & COO)*
David L. Donabedian *(Chief Investment Officer)*
Kenneth J. Kozanda *(Chief Admin Officer)*
Lisa M. Garcia *(Chief Risk Officer)*
Linda S. Beerman *(Chief Fiduciary Officer)*
David Van Blerkom *(Sr VP & Sr Mgr-Relationship-San Francisco)*
Jennifer M. Kane *(Sr VP & Mgr-Relationship-Houston)*

Branches:

Atlantic Trust Group, Inc. - Baltimore (3)
100 E Pratt St Ste 2550
Baltimore, MD 21202-3228
Tel.: (410) 539-4660
Fax: (410) 539-4661
Web Site: www.atlantictrust.com
Sales Range: $1-9.9 Million
Emp.: 16
Investment & Wealth Management Services
S.I.C.: 6799
N.A.I.C.S.: 523920
Andrew G. Nichols *(Mng Dir & Office Head-Baltimore)*
David L. Donabedian *(Grp Chief Investment Officer)*
Roseanna M. Ritmiller *(Sr VP)*

Atlantic Trust Group, Inc. - Boston (3)
100 Federal St
Boston, MA 02110
Tel.: (617) 357-9600
Fax: (617) 357-9602
Web Site: www.atlantictrust.com
Sales Range: $50-74.9 Million
Emp.: 85
Investment & Wealth Management Services
S.I.C.: 6282
N.A.I.C.S.: 523920
Jeffrey S. Thomas *(Grp Vice Chm & Mng Dir)*
Thomas N. Riley *(Mng Dir & Office Head)*
Sidney F. Queler *(Mng Dir & Dir-Bus Dev-Natl)*
Lisa M. Garcia *(Chief Risk Officer & Dir-Fiduciary Svcs)*
J. Timothy Delaney *(Sr VP-Wealth Mgmt & Sr Mgr-Relationships)*

Subsidiary:

Stein Roe Investment Counsel, Inc. (3)
1 S Wacker Dr Fl 35
Chicago, IL 60606-4617 DE
Tel.: (312) 368-7700
Fax: (312) 368-8136
Web Site: www.atlantictrust.com
Sales Range: $25-49.9 Million
Emp.: 50
Investment Advisory Services
S.I.C.: 6282
N.A.I.C.S.: 523930
Kenneth J. Kozanda *(Grp Chief Admin Officer & Mng Dir)*
Jon E. Henderson *(Mng Dir & Co-Office Head)*
Kenneth G. Pollard *(Mng Dir & Co-Office Head)*
Gregory B. Campbell *(Sr VP)*

CIBC Inc. (2)
425 Lexington Ave
New York, NY 10017-3903 DE
Tel.: (212) 856-4000 (100%)
Fax: (212) 885-4913
E-Mail:
Web Site: www.cibc.com
Emp.: 70
Corporate Banking & Financial Services
S.I.C.: 6211
N.A.I.C.S.: 523110
Michael P. Higgins *(Mng Dir & Head-Real Estate Fin)*
Laurene Bielski Mahon *(Mng Dir & Head-Global Infrastructure Fin)*

Non-U.S. Subsidiaries:

CIBC Australia Ltd. (1)
Level 45 Gateway 1 Macquarie Place
Sydney, NSW, 2000, Australia
Tel.: (61) 292751300
Fax: (61) 292751310
Emp.: 13
Investment Management Services
S.I.C.: 6799
N.A.I.C.S.: 523920
Neil Johnson *(Mng Dir)*

CIBC Reinsurance Company Limited (1)
FCIB Head Office 3rd Floor
Saint Michael, 22026, Barbados
Tel.: (246) 367 2400
Fax: (246) 421 7150
Emp.: 12
Reinsurance Services
S.I.C.: 6399
N.A.I.C.S.: 524130
Lawrie McGill *(CEO)*

CIBC (U.K.) Holdings Limited (1)
150 Cheapside
London, EC2V 6ET, United Kingdom (100%)
Tel.: (44) 2072346000
Fax: (44) 2072346089
E-Mail: info@cibcwm.com
Web Site: www.cibcwm.com
Emp.: 300
Holding Company
S.I.C.: 6719
N.A.I.C.S.: 551112
Ed Dodig *(Gen Mgr)*

FirstCaribbean International Bank Limited (1)
PO Box 503
Warrens, Saint Michael, Barbados (87.4%)
Tel.: (246) 367-2300
Fax: (246) 424-8977
Web Site: www.cibcfcib.com
FCI—(BARB ECA JAM)
Rev.: $542,917,000
Assets: $11,500,291,000
Liabilities: $9,849,776,000
Net Worth: $1,650,515,000
Earnings: $71,869,000
Emp.: 3,400
Fiscal Year-end: 10/31/12
Corporate & Retail Banking, Credit Card & Financial Management Services
S.I.C.: 6091
N.A.I.C.S.: 523991
Michael K. Mansoor *(Chm)*
Rik Parkhill *(CEO)*
Brian Lee *(CFO)*
Derek Wilson *(CIO & Mng Dir-Tech)*
Minish Parikh *(Chief Admin Officer)*
Geoff Scott *(Chief Risk Officer)*
Mark St. Hill *(Mng Dir/Senior Coverage Officer-Barbados Operating Company)*
Ben Gillooly *(CEO-CIBC Bank & Trust Cayman)*
Brian H. Clarke *(Gen Counsel & Sec)*
David Whitcroft *(Treas)*

Subsidiary:

FirstCaribbean International Bank (Barbados) Ltd. (2)
Broad Street
PO Box 301
Bridgetown, Barbados BB
Tel.: (246) 467-1432
Fax: (246) 426-9034
Web Site: www.cibcfcib.com
Commercial & Investment Banking
S.I.C.: 6029
N.A.I.C.S.: 522110
Donna Wellington *(Mng Dir)*

CANADIAN IMPERIAL VENTURE CORP.

3rd Floor 189 Water Street
Saint John's, NL, A1C 1B4, Canada
Mailing Address:
PO Box 6232
Saint John's, NL, A1C 6J9, Canada
Tel.: (709) 739-6700
Fax: (709) 739-6605
E-Mail: info@canadianimperial.com
Web Site: www.canadianimperial.net
Year Founded: 1995
CQV—(TSXV)
Rev.: $571
Assets: $1,350,881
Liabilities: $192,795
Net Worth: $1,158,086
Earnings: ($2,002,386)
Fiscal Year-end: 11/30/12
Business Description:
Petroleum & Natural Gas Exploration Services
S.I.C.: 1389
N.A.I.C.S.: 213112
Personnel:
Gerard M. Edwards *(Pres & CEO)*
Tina Ricketts *(CFO)*
Board of Directors:
Jerome Byrne
Gerard M. Edwards
Robert G. Smiley
Legal Counsel:
Miller Thomson
Toronto, ON, Canada
Transfer Agent:
Pacific Corporate Trust Company
Vancouver, BC, Canada

Subsidiary:

Carina Energy Inc. (1)
365 Bay St
Toronto, ON, M5H 2V1, Canada
Tel.: (416) 366-5821
Uranium & Gold Mining Services
S.I.C.: 1094
N.A.I.C.S.: 212291

CANADIAN INTERNATIONAL MINERALS INC.

1128 - 789 West Pender Street
Vancouver, BC, V6C 1H2, Canada
Tel.: (604) 669-9330
Fax: (604) 669-9335
E-Mail: info@cin-v.com
Web Site: www.cdnintlminerals.com
Year Founded: 2006
CIN—(TSXV)
Int. Income: $2,139
Assets: $1,458,883
Liabilities: $357,523
Net Worth: $1,101,360
Earnings: ($3,698,382)
Fiscal Year-end: 03/31/13
Business Description:
Gold, Silver & Copper Mining & Exploration Services
S.I.C.: 1041
N.A.I.C.S.: 212221
Personnel:
Michael E. Schuss *(Pres, CEO & Sec)*
James Casey Forward *(CFO)*
Board of Directors:
Tor Bruland
Garth Evans
James Casey Forward
Michael E. Schuss
Christopher R. Verrico
Transfer Agent:
Computershare
510 Burrard St 2nd Floor
Vancouver, BC, Canada

CANADIAN LINEN & UNIFORM SERVICE CO.

75 Norfinch Dr
Toronto, ON, M3N 1W8, Canada
Tel.: (416) 849-5100
Fax: (416) 849-5102
Toll Free: (888) 258-2222
Web Site: www.canadianuniform.com
Year Founded: 1925
Sales Range: $125-149.9 Million
Emp.: 1,850
Business Description:
Linen Supply Services
S.I.C.: 7213
N.A.I.C.S.: 812331
Personnel:
Bruce Steiner *(Pres & CEO)*

CANADIAN METALS INC.

3-1940 Cuvillier Street
Montreal, QC, H1W 3Y9, Canada
Tel.: (418) 717-2553
Web Site: www.canadianmetalsinc.com
CME—(CNSX)
Business Description:
Gold Mining
S.I.C.: 1041
N.A.I.C.S.: 212221
Personnel:
David Vincent *(Pres & CEO)*
Daniel Belisle *(CFO)*
Board of Directors:
Guy Chamard
Andre Laferriere
Stephane Leblanc
David Vincent
Transfer Agent:
Computershare Investor Services Inc.
1500 University St 7th Floor
Montreal, QC, Canada

CANADIAN MINING COMPANY INC.

Suite 2300 - 1066 West Hastings St
Vancouver, BC, V6E 3X2, Canada
Tel.: (604) 684-3301
Fax: (604) 684-3451
E-Mail: info@CanadianMining.ca
Web Site: www.canadianmining.ca
CNG—(TSXV)
Assets: $808,791
Liabilities: $765,896
Net Worth: $42,895
Earnings: ($857,310)
Fiscal Year-end: 06/30/13
Business Description:
Metal Exploration Services
S.I.C.: 1081
N.A.I.C.S.: 213114
Personnel:
Ray Paquette *(Pres & CEO)*
Mark Groenewald *(CFO)*
Dianne Szigety *(Sec)*
Board of Directors:
Dave Kepkay
Ray Paquette
Edward Skoda
Transfer Agent:
CIBC Mellon Trust Company
600 The Dome Tower 333 7th Avenue S.W.
Calgary, AB, T2P 2Z1, Canada
Tel.: (800) 387-0825
Fax: (416) 643-5501

CANADIAN NATIONAL RAILWAY COMPANY

935 de La Gauchetiere Street West
Montreal, QC, H3B 2M9, Canada
Tel.: (514) 399-7091
Telex: 55 61497
Fax: (514) 399-5537
Toll Free: (888) 888-5909
E-Mail: contact@cn.ca
Web Site: www.cn.ca
Year Founded: 1919
CNI—(NYSE TSX)
Rev.: $10,575,000,000
Assets: $30,163,000,000
Liabilities: $17,210,000,000
Net Worth: $12,953,000,000
Earnings: $2,612,000,000
Emp.: 23,721
Fiscal Year-end: 12/31/13
Business Description:
Freight & Railway Transportation Services

Import Export
S.I.C.: 4011
N.A.I.C.S.: 482111
Personnel:
David G. A. McLean *(Chm)*
Robert L. Pace *(Vice Chm)*
Claude Mongeau *(Pres & CEO)*
Luc Jobin *(CFO & Exec VP)*
James Vena *(COO & Exec VP)*
James Bright *(CIO & VP-IT)*
Jean-Jacques Ruest *(CMO & Exec VP)*
Sean Finn *(Chief Legal Officer & Exec VP-Corp Svcs)*
Stephen Covey *(Chief Security Officer)*
Russell J. Hiscock *(Pres/CEO-Investment Div)*
Sunil Panray *(Treas & VP)*
Mike Cory *(Sr VP-Western Reg)*
Jeff Liepelt *(Sr VP-Southern Reg)*
Board of Directors:
David G. A. McLean
Robert L. Pace
Michael Ralph Armellino
A. Charles Baillie
Hugh John Bolton
Donald J. Carty
Gordon D. Giffin
Edith E. Holiday
V. Maureen Kempston Darkes
Denis Losier
Edward C. Lumley
Claude Mongeau
James E. O'Connor

Computershare Trust Company, N.A.
250 Royall St
Canton, MA 02021
Tel.: (781) 575-2724
Transfer Agents:
Computershare Trust Company of Canada
100 University Avenue 8th Floor
Toronto, ON, M5J 2Y1, Canada

Computershare Trust Company, N.A.
250 Royall St
Canton, MA 02021
Tel.: (781) 575-2724

U.S. Branches:

Canadian National Railway Company (1)
455 N Cityfront Plaza Dr
Chicago, IL 60611-5503 DE
Tel.: (312) 755-7500
Fax: (312) 755-7920
Web Site: www.cn.ca
Emp.: 3,500
Provider of Rail Transportation Services
S.I.C.: 4011
N.A.I.C.S.: 482111
Keith Reardon *(VP-Intermodal Svcs)*

Canadian National Railway Company (1)
17641 S Ashland Ave
Homewood, IL 60430 IL
Tel.: (708) 332-4377
Fax: (708) 332-6800
Toll Free: (888) 888-5909
E-Mail: contact@cn.ca
Web Site: www.cn.ca
Emp.: 2,000
Freight Railroad
S.I.C.: 4011
N.A.I.C.S.: 482111
Claude Mongeau *(Pres & CEO)*

U.S. Unit:

CN WorldWide North America (1)
16800 S Center St
Harvey, IL 60426 (100%)
Tel.: (708) 332-4532
Fax: (708) 332-4570
E-Mail: sales@cnworldwide.com
Web Site: www.cnworldwide.com
Transportation Management, Warehousing & Distribution Services
S.I.C.: 4789
N.A.I.C.S.: 488210

Rusty Radloff *(Asst VP-Sls)*

CANADIAN NATURAL RESOURCES LTD.

2500 855 2nd Street SW
Calgary, AB, T2P 4J8, Canada
Tel.: (403) 517-7345
Fax: (403) 517-7350
E-Mail: ir@cnrl.com
Web Site: www.cnrl.com
Year Founded: 1989
CNQ—(NYSE TSX)
Sls.: $16,098,153,900
Assets: $48,687,099,600
Liabilities: $24,549,311,940
Net Worth: $24,137,787,660
Earnings: $1,880,685,840
Emp.: 5,970
Fiscal Year-end: 12/31/12
Business Description:
Exploration, Development & Production of Crude Oil & Natural Gas
S.I.C.: 1311
N.A.I.C.S.: 211111
Personnel:
N. Murray Edwards *(Chm)*
John G. Langille *(Vice Chm)*
Steve W. Laut *(Pres)*
Tim S. McKay *(COO & Exec VP)*
Bruce E. McGrath *(Sec)*
Douglas A. Proll *(Exec VP)*
Real M. Cusson *(Sr VP-Mktg)*
Real J.H. Doucet *(Sr VP-Horizon Projects)*
Peter J. Janson *(Sr VP-Horizon Ops)*
Terry J. Jocksch *(Sr VP-Thermal)*
Allen M. Knight *(Sr VP-Intl & Corp Dev)*
Lyle G. Stevens *(Sr VP-Exploitation)*
Jeffrey W. Wilson *(Sr VP-Exploration)*
Board of Directors:
N. Murray Edwards
Catherine M. Best
Timothy W. Faithfull
Gary A. Filmon
Christopher L. Fong
Gordon D. Giffin
Wilfred A. Gobert
Steve W. Laut
Keith A.J. MacPhail
Frank J. McKenna
James Simpson Palmer
Eldon R. Smith
David A. Tuer

Computershare Investor Services LLC
New York, NY 10036
Transfer Agents:
Computershare Trust Company of Canada
530 8th Ave SW 6th Floor
Calgary, AB, T2P 3S8, Canada
Tel.: (403) 267-6800
Fax: (403) 267-6529

Computershare Investor Services LLC
New York, NY 10036

Subsidiaries:

Canadian Natural Resources (1)
5201 44th St
PO Box 6968
Bonnyville, AB, T9N 2H4, Canada CO
Tel.: (780) 826-4447 (100%)
Fax: (780) 826-1718
Emp.: 74
Oil/Gas Exploration & Production
S.I.C.: 1311
N.A.I.C.S.: 211111

CNR (ECHO) Resources Inc. (1)
855 2 St SW Suite 2500
Calgary, AB, T2P 4J8, Canada
Tel.: (403) 517-7000
Petroleum & Natural Gas Extraction Services
S.I.C.: 1311
N.A.I.C.S.: 211111

Horizon Construction Management Ltd. (1)
855 2 St SW Ste 2500
Calgary, AB, T2P 4J8, Canada
Tel.: (403) 517-6700
Oil & Gas Exploration Services
S.I.C.: 1389
N.A.I.C.S.: 213112

Non-U.S. Subsidiaries:

CNR International (Angola) Limited (1)
Rua Dos Enganos 1-1 Andar
5876 Luanda, Angola
Tel.: (244) 2396145
Fax: (244) 2442396145
E-Mail: helena.pereira@cnrinternational.com
Web Site: www.cnrinternational.com
Emp.: 17
S.I.C.: 1311
N.A.I.C.S.: 211111

CNR International (Gabon) Limited (1)
Immeuble Le Narval Bas De Gue - Gue
BP 641 Libreville, Gabon
Tel.: (241) 443 893
Fax: (241) 443 895
Oil & Gas Exploration Services
S.I.C.: 1389
N.A.I.C.S.: 213112

CNR International (South Africa) Limited (1)
Suite 1B Nautica The Waterclub Beach Road Granger Bay
Cape Town, 8005, South Africa
Tel.: (27) 214014140
Fax: (27) 214014198
Emp.: 1
Oil & Gas Exploration Services
S.I.C.: 1389
N.A.I.C.S.: 213112
Gloria Hutchinson *(Gen Mgr)*

CNR International UK Limited (1)
Walnut Tree Close
Guildford, Surrey, GU1 4US, United Kingdom (100%)
Tel.: (44) 148 340 1401
Telex: 858943
Fax: (44) 148 340 1414
Oil/Gas Exploration & Production
S.I.C.: 1311
N.A.I.C.S.: 211111
Terry J. Jocksch *(Mng Dir)*

CNR International (1)
SARL Immeuble Kharrat Angle Boul Botreau Roussel
P O Box 8707
Ave Nougoues O1, 1 Abidjan, Cote d'Ivoire (100%)
E-Mail: info@cnrinternational.com
Web Site: www.cnrinternational.com
Emp.: 30
Oil/Gas Exploration & Production
S.I.C.: 1311
N.A.I.C.S.: 211111

CANADIAN OIL RECOVERY & REMEDIATION ENTERPRISES LIMITED

141 Adelaide Street West Suite 110
Toronto, ON, M5H 3L5, Canada
Tel.: (416) 368-4027
Fax: (416) 368-4469
E-Mail: info@corre.com
Web Site: www.corre.com
Year Founded: 2007
CVR—(TSXV)
Int. Income: $25,964
Assets: $10,787,627
Liabilities: $711,593
Net Worth: $10,076,034
Earnings: ($4,016,707)
Fiscal Year-end: 12/31/12
Business Description:
Oil & Gas Exploration Services
S.I.C.: 1311
N.A.I.C.S.: 211111

Personnel:
John Lorenzo *(Chm, Pres & CEO)*
Alex Gress *(CFO & Sr VP)*
Board of Directors:
John Lorenzo
Hassan M. J. Dahlawi
Fred Di Tomaso
Alex Gress
Edward Gress
Sohail Khan
Turki Khalid Khoj
William F. Madison
James Newman
Chandrakant J. Panchal
Raymond J. Stapell

CANADIAN OIL SANDS LIMITED

2500 First Canadian Centre 350 7th Avenue SW
Calgary, AB, T2P 3N9, Canada
Tel.: (403) 218-6200
Fax: (403) 218-6201
E-Mail: invest@cdnoilsands.com
Web Site: www.cdnoilsands.com
Year Founded: 1995
COS—(OTC TSX)
Sls.: $3,881,648,100
Assets: $10,110,177,420
Liabilities: $5,622,177,120
Net Worth: $4,488,000,300
Earnings: $975,133,620
Emp.: 24
Fiscal Year-end: 12/31/12
Business Description:
Oil & Gas Producer
S.I.C.: 1389
N.A.I.C.S.: 213112
Personnel:
Donald James Lowry *(Chm)*
Ryan M. Kubik *(Pres & CEO)*
Robert P. Dawson *(CFO)*
Trudy M. Curran *(Gen Counsel, Sec & Sr VP)*
Allen R. Hagerman *(Exec VP)*
Darren K. Hardy *(Sr VP-Ops)*
Board of Directors:
Donald James Lowry
Ian A. Bourne
Gerald W. Grandey
Ryan M. Kubik
Sarah E. Raiss
John K. Read
Brant Sangster
C. E. Shultz
Wesley R. Twiss
John B. Zaozirny
Transfer Agent:
Computershare Trust Company of Canada
600 530 8th Avenue SW
Calgary, AB, T2P 3S8, Canada
Tel.: (403) 267-6555
Toll Free: (800) 558-0046

Subsidiary:

Canadian Arctic Gas Ltd. (1)
Ste 250 706 7th Ave SW
Calgary, AB, T2P 0Z1, Canada Ca
Tel.: (403) 269-7741 (100%)
Fax: (403) 261-5667
Emp.: 7
Natural Gas Exploration & Development Services
S.I.C.: 1311
N.A.I.C.S.: 211111
Marcel R. Coutu *(Chm)*

CANADIAN OREBODIES INC.

3130 Airport Road
Box 1130
Timmins, ON, P4N 7H9, Canada
Tel.: (705) 268-9000
Fax: (705) 268-5532
E-Mail: info@canadianorebodies.com

Canadian Orebodies Inc.—(Continued)

Web Site: www.canadianorebodies.com
CO—(TSXV)
Int. Income: $22,607
Assets: $18,340,461
Liabilities: $672,821
Net Worth: $17,667,640
Earnings: ($978,873)
Fiscal Year-end: 01/31/13

Business Description:
Mineral Properties Exploration Services
S.I.C.: 1081
N.A.I.C.S.: 213114

Personnel:
Gordon McKinnon *(Pres & CEO)*
Fraser Laschinger *(CFO)*

Board of Directors:
Gordon J. Cyr
John D. Harvey
Chris Hodgson
Gordon McKinnon

Transfer Agent:
Equity Financial Trust Company
200 University Avenue Suite 400
Toronto, ON, Canada

CANADIAN OVERSEAS PETROLEUM LIMITED

3200 715 - 5th Avenue SW
Calgary, AB, T2P 2X6, Canada
Tel.: (403) 262-5441
Fax: (403) 263-3251
Web Site: www.canoverseas.com
Year Founded: 2004
XOP—(TSXV)
Int. Income: $56,659
Assets: $19,894,316
Liabilities: $3,174,900
Net Worth: $16,719,416
Earnings: ($56,299,305)
Emp.: 14
Fiscal Year-end: 12/31/12

Business Description:
Oil & Gas Exploration & Development Services
S.I.C.: 1389
N.A.I.C.S.: 213112

Personnel:
Harald Horst Ludwig *(Chm)*
Arthur Millholland *(Pres & CEO)*
Christopher McLean *(CFO)*

Board of Directors:
Harald Horst Ludwig
Massimo Carello
Christopher McLean
Arthur Millholland
Richard Schmitt

Legal Counsel:
McCarthy Tetrault
Calgary, AB, Canada

McCarthy Tetrault
London, United Kingdom

Transfer Agent:
Computershare Trust Company
Calgary, AB, Canada

CANADIAN PACIFIC RAILWAY LIMITED

7550 Ogden Dale Road SE
Calgary, AB, T2C 4X9, Canada
Tel.: (403) 319-7000
Fax: (403) 319-7567
Toll Free: (888) 333-6370
E-Mail: investor@cpr.ca
Web Site: www.cpr.ca
Year Founded: 1881
CP—(NYSE TSX)
Rev.: $5,515,713,550
Assets: $15,342,911,000
Liabilities: $8,960,224,050
Net Worth: $6,382,686,950
Earnings: $786,931,250
Emp.: 15,011
Fiscal Year-end: 12/31/13

Business Description:
Rail & Intermodal Freight Transportation Services
S.I.C.: 4011
N.A.I.C.S.: 482111

Personnel:
Paul G. Haggis *(Chm)*
Keith E. Creel *(Pres & COO)*
E. Hunter Harrison *(CEO)*
Bart W. Demosky *(CFO)*
Michael Redeker *(CIO & VP)*
Jane O'Hagan *(CMO & Exec VP)*
Tracy A. Robinson *(Treas & VP)*
Guido De Ciccio *(Sr VP-Ops-Western Reg)*
Scott MacDonald *(Sr VP-Sys Ops)*
Doug McFarlane *(Sr VP-US Ops)*

Board of Directors:
Paul G. Haggis
William Albert Ackman
Gary F. Colter
Paul C. Hilal
Krystyna T. Hoeg
Richard C. Kelly
Rebecca MacDonald
John P. Manley
Anthony R. Melman
Linda J. Morgan
Madeleine Paquin
James Prentice
Hartley T. Richardson

Computershare Investor Services Inc.
100 University Ave 9th Floor
Toronto, ON, Canada

Transfer Agents:
Computershare Trust Company, N.A.
Denver, CO 80401

Computershare Investor Services Inc.
100 University Ave 9th Floor
Toronto, ON, Canada

U.S. Subsidiaries:

Canadian Pacific Railway, Soo Line Corporation **(1)**
501 Marquette Ave
Minneapolis, MN 55402 MN
Tel.: (612) 904-5994 (100%)
Toll Free: (800) 234-0013
E-Mail: investor@cpr.ca
Web Site: www8.cpr.ca/cms/English/Media/News/General/2008/Accreditation+assessment.htm
Emp.: 26
Railroad
S.I.C.: 6062
N.A.I.C.S.: 522130
Fred J. Green *(Pres & CEO)*

Cedar American Rail Holdings, Inc. **(1)**
140 N Phillips Ave
Sioux Falls, SD 57104-2828
Tel.: (605) 782-1200
Holding Company
S.I.C.: 6719
N.A.I.C.S.: 551112
Richard D. Awe *(Chief Transportation Officer)*

Subsidiaries:

Dakota, Minnesota & Eastern Railroad Corporation **(2)**
140 N Phillips Ave
Sioux Falls, SD 57104-2828 DE
Tel.: (605) 782-1200
Fax: (605) 782-1299
Sales Range: $250-299.9 Million
Emp.: 340
Railroads, Line-Haul Operating Services Import Export
S.I.C.: 4011
N.A.I.C.S.: 482111

Iowa, Chicago & Eastern Railroad Corporation **(2)**
140 N Phillips Ave
Sioux Falls, SD 57104-2828
Tel.: (605) 782-1200
Fax: (605) 782-1299
Web Site: www.dmerail.com
Railroad Freight Services
S.I.C.: 4011
N.A.I.C.S.: 482111
Clyde Mittleider *(Chief Transportation Officer)*

Delaware & Hudson Railway Company, Inc. **(1)**
200 Clifton Corporate Pkwy
Clifton Park, NY 12065-3862
Tel.: (518) 383-7200
Fax: (518) 383-7250
Railroads
S.I.C.: 4011
N.A.I.C.S.: 482111
Brent Szafrom *(Gen Mgr)*

CANADIAN PLATINUM CORP.

Suite 700 1300-8th Street SW
Calgary, AB, T2R 1B2, Canada
Tel.: (403) 294-5731
Fax: (403) 262-4860
E-Mail: bwalter@proventurelaw.com
Web Site: www.canadianplatinumcorp.com
Year Founded: 2008
CPC—(TSXV)
Rev.: $1,260
Assets: $12,363,068
Liabilities: $905,934
Net Worth: $11,457,134
Earnings: ($951,019)
Fiscal Year-end: 12/31/12

Business Description:
Investment Services
S.I.C.: 6211
N.A.I.C.S.: 523999

Personnel:
Randy Ludwar *(CFO)*

Board of Directors:
Gary Billingsley
Mason Douglas
Randy Ludwar
Brent J. Walter

Legal Counsel:
Proventure Law LLP
Suite 2 880 - 16th Avenue SW
Calgary, AB, Canada

Transfer Agent:
Olympia Trust Company
125 9th Avenue SE Suite 2300
Calgary, AB, T2G 0P6, Canada
Tel.: (403) 261-0900

CANADIAN PUREGAS EQUIPMENT LIMITED

8410 Hwy 3
PO Box 280
Dunnville, ON, N1A 2X5, Canada
Tel.: (905) 774-8600
Fax: (905) 774-6974
Toll Free: (800) 787-3547
E-Mail: info@canadianpuregas.com
Web Site: www.canadianpuregas.com
Year Founded: 1958
Sales Range: $1-9.9 Million
Emp.: 25

Business Description:
Dryers & Pressurization Systems Designer, Installer, Maintenance & Repair
S.I.C.: 3564
N.A.I.C.S.: 333413

Personnel:
Ingolf Plath *(Pres)*

CANADIAN QUANTUM ENERGY CORPORATION

Suite 500 1414 8th St SW
Calgary, AB, T2R 1J6, Canada
Tel.: (403) 532-8543
Fax: (403) 452-7743
E-Mail: info@canadianquantum.com
Web Site: www.canadianquantum.com
Year Founded: 1981
CQM—(TSXV)
Sls.: $61,556
Assets: $1,150,237
Liabilities: $2,941,226
Net Worth: ($1,790,988)
Earnings: ($3,123,920)
Fiscal Year-end: 04/30/13

Business Description:
Oil & Gas Exploration Services
S.I.C.: 1389
N.A.I.C.S.: 213112

Personnel:
Douglas Brett *(Pres & CEO)*
Michael Koenig *(CFO)*

Board of Directors:
Douglas Brett
Michael Koenig
Eric Leslie
Neil Munro

Transfer Agent:
Computershare Trust Company of Canada
9th Floor 100 University Avenue
Toronto, ON, Canada

CANADIAN REAL ESTATE INVESTMENT TRUST

N500 175 Bloor Street
Toronto, ON, M4W 3R8, Canada
Tel.: (416) 628-7771
Fax: (416) 628-7777
E-Mail: info@creit.ca
Web Site: www.creit.ca
Year Founded: 1984
REF.UN—(OTC TSX)
Rev.: $372,181,962
Assets: $3,632,200,769
Liabilities: $1,938,249,538
Net Worth: $1,693,951,231
Earnings: $79,615,038
Emp.: 140
Fiscal Year-end: 12/31/12

Business Description:
Real Estate Investment Trust
S.I.C.: 6726
N.A.I.C.S.: 525990

Personnel:
Stephen E. Johnson *(Pres & CEO)*
Rael Diamond *(CFO)*
Judith Somerville *(Sec)*
Adam E. Paul *(Exec VP-Investments & Leasing & Interim VP-Alberta)*

Transfer Agent:
CIBC Mellon Trust Company
PO Box 700 Postal Station B
Montreal, QC, Canada

CANADIAN RESOURCES INCOME TRUST

26th Floor Scotia Plaza 40 King Street West
Toronto, ON, M5W 2X6, Canada
Tel.: (416) 863-7144
Fax: (416) 863-7425
Year Founded: 1996
RTU.UN—(TSX)
Rev.: $1,533,579
Assets: $24,729,333
Liabilities: $210,110
Net Worth: $24,519,223
Earnings: $1,263,132
Fiscal Year-end: 12/31/12

Business Description:
Financial Investment Services
S.I.C.: 6211
N.A.I.C.S.: 523999

Personnel:
John B. Newman *(Chm)*

Legal Counsel:
Stikeman Elliott LLP
Toronto, ON, Canada

Transfer Agent:
Computershare Investor Services Inc
100 University Avenue
Toronto, ON, Canada

CANADIAN SATELLITE RADIO HOLDINGS INC.

(d/b/a XM Canada)
135 Liberty Street 4th Floor
Toronto, ON, M6K 1A7, Canada
Tel.: (416) 408-6000
Fax: (416) 408-6005
Toll Free: (877) 438-9677
E-Mail: commercial@xmradio.ca
Web Site: www.xmradio.ca
Year Founded: 2002
XSR—(TSX)
Emp.: 142
Business Description:
Satellite Radio Entertainment Services
S.I.C.: 4832
N.A.I.C.S.: 515111
Personnel:
Mark Redmon *(Pres & CEO)*
Michael Washinushi *(CFO, Treas & Sec)*
Board of Directors:
Dara F. Altman
Pierre Boivin
Philip Evershed
David J. Frear
Guy Johnson
Suzanne Morris
Gary Slaight
Anthony Viner
Transfer Agent:
Canadian Stock Transfer Company Inc.
320 Bay Street
PO Box 1
M5H4A6 Toronto, ON, Canada
Subsidiary:
Sirius XM Canada Inc. (1)
135 Liberty Street 4th Floor
Toronto, ON, M6K 1A7, Canada
Tel.: (416) 513-7470
Fax: (416) 513-7489
E-Mail: customercare@siriuscanada.ca
Web Site: www.sirius.ca
Satellite Radio Broadcasting Services
S.I.C.: 4832
N.A.I.C.S.: 515112

CANADIAN SILVER HUNTER INC.

360 Toronto Street Suite 1000
Toronto, ON, M5C 2C5, Canada
Tel.: (647) 348-6966
E-Mail: info@cshi.ca
Web Site: www.canadiansilverhunter.ca
Year Founded: 2006
AGH—(TSXV)
Int. Income: $10,296
Assets: $1,670,650
Liabilities: $67,174
Net Worth: $1,603,477
Earnings: ($427,213)
Fiscal Year-end: 12/31/12
Business Description:
Silver Mining Services
S.I.C.: 1044
N.A.I.C.S.: 212222
Personnel:
Jeffrey Hunter *(Pres, CEO & Sec)*
Carmelo Marrelli *(CFO)*
Board of Directors:
Robert Gordon
Jeffrey Hunter
Shastri Ramnath
Transfer Agent:
Capital Transfer Agency Inc.
105 Adelaide St West Suite 1101
Toronto, ON, M5H 1P9, Canada

CANADIAN SOLAR INC.

545 Speedvale Avenue West
Guelph, ON, N1K 1E6, Canada
Tel.: (519) 837-1881
Fax: (519) 837-2250
E-Mail: inquire.ca@canadiansolar.com
Web Site: www.canadiansolar.com
Year Founded: 2001
CSIQ—(NASDAQ)
Rev.: $1,294,829,413
Assets: $2,259,313,081
Liabilities: $1,957,729,650
Net Worth: $301,583,431
Earnings: ($195,155,097)
Emp.: 7,020
Fiscal Year-end: 12/31/12
Business Description:
Solar Power Device Mfr
S.I.C.: 3679
N.A.I.C.S.: 334419
Personnel:
Shawn Qu *(Chm, Pres & CEO)*
Michael G. Potter *(CFO & Sr VP)*
Guangchun Zhang *(COO)*
Yan Zhuang *(Chief Comml Officer & Sr VP)*
Gregory Spanoudakis *(Pres-Ops-Europe)*
Charlotte Xi Klein *(Sr VP-Global Ops)*
Board of Directors:
Shawn Qu
Lars-Eric Johansson
Robert K. McDermott
Michael G. Potter
Harry E. Ruda
U.S. Subsidiaries:
Canadian Solar (USA) Inc. (1)
12657 Alcosta Blvd Ste 130
San Ramon, CA 94583
Tel.: (925) 866-2700
Fax: (925) 866-2704
Web Site: www.canadiansolar.com
Emp.: 30
Solar Cells Mfr & Distr
S.I.C.: 3674
N.A.I.C.S.: 334413

CSI Solar Inc. (1)
3420E Shea Blvd
Phoenix, AZ 85028
Tel.: (602) 953-5242
Fax: (602) 953-5245
Solar Device Mfr
S.I.C.: 3829
N.A.I.C.S.: 334519
Robert Paterson *(Sls Coord)*
Non-U.S. Branch:
Canadian Solar Europe (1)
Mozartstrasse 1
D-87727 Babenhausen, Germany
Tel.: (49) 83333923280
Fax: (49) 83339232811
E-Mail: inquire.eu@canadian-solar.com
Web Site: www.canadian-solar.com
Emp.: 4,000
Solar Device Mfr
S.I.C.: 3829
N.A.I.C.S.: 334519
Gregory Spanoudakis *(Pres)*
Non-U.S. Subsidiaries:
Canadian Solar (Australia) Pty., Ltd. (1)
277 Lane Cove Road
Macquarie, NSW, 2113, Australia
Tel.: (61) 2 9889 4395
Fax: (61) 1298895436
Web Site: www.canadiansolar.com
Silicon Wafer Mfr
S.I.C.: 3674
N.A.I.C.S.: 334413

Canadian Solar EMEA GmbH (1)
Landberger Str 94
80339 Munich, Germany
Tel.: (49) 8951996890
Fax: (49) 89519968911
E-Mail: inquire.eu@canadiansolar.com
Web Site: www.canadiansolar.com
Emp.: 4
Solar Cells & Module Mfr
S.I.C.: 3674
N.A.I.C.S.: 334413
Ivan Rubio *(Gen Mgr)*

Canadian Solar Japan K.K. (1)
Round-Cross Shinjuku 5-Chome 8F 5-17-5
Shinjuku-ku, Tokyo, 160-0022, Japan
Tel.: (81) 35291 8591
Fax: (81) 35291 8596
Web Site: www.canadiansolar.co.jp
Emp.: 4
Solar Cells & Module Mfr & Distr
S.I.C.: 3674
N.A.I.C.S.: 334413

Canadian Solar Manufacturing (Suzhou) Inc. (1)
No 199 Lushan Rd Hi-New Zone
Suzhou, 215129, China
Tel.: (86) 51266908088
Fax: (86) 51266908085
Web Site: www.canadiansolar.com
Emp.: 300
Wafer & Solar Cells Mfr
S.I.C.: 3674
N.A.I.C.S.: 334413
Shawn Qu *(CEO)*

CSI Project Consulting GmbH (1)
Landsberger Str 94
Munich, 80339, Germany
Tel.: (49) 4305 991423
Fax: (49) 4305 9913064
Project Management Consulting Services
S.I.C.: 8748
N.A.I.C.S.: 541618

CSI Solar Technologies Inc. (1)
No 2 Changsheng Road Yangyuan Town
Changshu, 215562, China
Tel.: (86) 51252477677
Fax: (86) 51252477672
Solar Module Mfr
S.I.C.: 3674
N.A.I.C.S.: 334413

CSI Solartronics (Changshu) Co., Ltd. (1)
Xinzhuang Industrial Park Yangyuan Town
Changshu, Jiangsu, 215562, China
Tel.: (86) 51252477677
Solar Wafer & Cells Mfr
S.I.C.: 3674
N.A.I.C.S.: 334413

CANADIAN SPIRIT RESOURCES INC.

Suite 1950 Ford Tower 633 6th Avenue SW
Calgary, AB, T2P 2Y5, Canada
Tel.: (403) 539-5005
Fax: (403) 262-4177
E-Mail: info@csri.ca
Web Site: www.csri.ca
Year Founded: 1987
SPI—(TSXV)
Sls.: $1,407,648
Assets: $61,962,800
Liabilities: $1,829,116
Net Worth: $60,133,684
Earnings: ($3,426,631)
Emp.: 9
Fiscal Year-end: 12/31/12
Business Description:
Oil & Natural Gas Exploration Services
S.I.C.: 1311
N.A.I.C.S.: 211111
Personnel:
Joseph Iannicelli *(Chm)*
Phillip D. C. Geiger *(Pres & COO)*
Alfred Sorensen *(CEO & Sec)*
Dean G. Hill *(CFO & VP-Fin)*
Board of Directors:
Joseph Iannicelli
J. Richard Couillard
Donald R. Gardner
Alfred Sorensen
Transfer Agent:
Computershare Investor Services Inc.
Montreal, QC, Canada

CANADIAN TACTICAL TRAINING ACADEMY INC.

7000 Chemin Cote de Liesse Suite 8
Montreal, QC, H4T 1E7, Canada
Tel.: (514) 373-8411
Fax: (514) 303-8841
E-Mail: info@ctta-global.com
Web Site: www.ctta-global.com
Year Founded: 2001
CTTG—(OTCB)
Sales Range: Less than $1 Million
Business Description:
Tactical Training Services
S.I.C.: 8249
N.A.I.C.S.: 611519
Personnel:
Jocelyn Moisan *(Pres)*
John Giovanni Farinaccio *(Treas & VP)*
Angelo M. Marino *(Sec & VP)*
Board of Directors:
Steven W. Joe
Jocelyn Moisan
Arthur Nathaniel Sapp
Transfer Agent:
The Nevada Agency & Trust Company
50 Liberty Street Suite 880
Reno, NV 89501

CANADIAN TIRE CORPORATION LIMITED

2180 Yonge Street
PO Box 770
Station K, Toronto, ON, M4P 2VB, Canada
Tel.: (416) 480-3000
Fax: (416) 544-7715
Toll Free: (800) 387-8803
E-Mail: investor.relations@cantire.com
Web Site: www.canadiantire.ca
Year Founded: 1922
CTC—(OTC TSX)
Rev.: $11,358,865,344
Assets: $13,102,575,228
Liabilities: $8,367,461,556
Net Worth: $4,735,113,672
Earnings: $496,214,784
Emp.: 10,183
Fiscal Year-end: 12/29/12
Business Description:
Automotive Parts & Accessories Retailer
S.I.C.: 5531
N.A.I.C.S.: 441310
Personnel:
Stephen G. Wetmore *(Pres & CEO)*
Dean McCann *(CFO & Exec VP-Fin)*
Duncan Fulton *(CMO-FGL Sports Ltd & Sr VP-Comm & Corp Affairs)*
Eugene Orest Roman *(CTO & Sr VP-IT)*
Douglas B. Nathanson *(Chief HR Officer & Sr VP)*
Michael B. Medline *(Pres-FGL Sports Ltd & Mark's Work Wearhouse Ltd & Exec VP)*
Marco Marrone *(COO-Retail & Exec VP)*
Robyn A. Collver *(Gen Counsel, Sec & Sr VP)*
Candace A. MacLean *(Treas & VP)*
G. Michael Arnett *(Exec VP-Corp Dev)*
Glenn Gerard Butt *(Exec VP-Customer Experience & Automotive)*
Patrick R. Sinnott *(Exec VP-Tech & Supply Chain)*
Gregory Craig *(Sr VP-Fin)*
Kristine Freudenthaler *(Sr VP-Process Innovation)*
David R. Hicks *(Sr VP-Store Ops & Dealer Rels)*

Canadian Tire Corporation Limited—(Continued)

Allan MacDonald *(Sr VP-Mktg & Automotive)*
Reginald J. McLay *(Sr VP-Mdse Sourcing)*
David Mock *(Sr VP-Mdsg)*
John D. Salt *(Sr VP-Supply Chain)*
Kenneth Silver *(Sr VP-Corp Strategy & Real Estate)*
Board of Directors:
Maureen J. Sabia
Iain C. Aitchison
Martha G. Billes
Owen G. Billes
H. Garfield Emerson
John A. F. Furlong
James L. Goodfellow
Claude L'Heureux
Jonathan Lampe
N. Frank Potter
Timothy Robert Price
Alan P. Rossy
Peter B. Saunders
Graham W. Savage
George A. Vallance
Stephen G. Wetmore
Legal Counsel:
Cassels, Brock & Blackwell LLP
2100 Scotia Plaza 40 King St W
Toronto, ON, M5H 3C2, Canada
Tel.: (416) 869-5300
Telex: 6-23415
Fax: (416) 360-8877
Transfer Agent:
Computershare Trust Company of Canada
100 University Avenue 9th Floor
Toronto, ON, M5J 2Y1, Canada
Tel.: (416) 663-9097
Fax: (416) 263-9694

Subsidiaries:

Canadian Tire Financial Services Ltd. **(1)**
1000 East Main St.
PO Box 2000
Welland, ON, L3B 3Z3, Canada (100%)
Tel.: (905) 735-3131
Fax: (905) 735-9414
E-Mail: info@cantire.com
Web Site: www.cantire.com
Emp.: 1,200
Credit Card Services
S.I.C.: 7299
N.A.I.C.S.: 812990
Mary Louise Turner *(COO & Pres-Canadian Tire Bank)*

FGL Sports Ltd. **(1)**
824 41st Ave NE
Calgary, AB, T2E 3R3, Canada
Tel.: (403) 717-1400
Fax: (403) 717-1491
E-Mail: cjordan@forzani.com
Web Site: www.forzanigroup.com
Emp.: 12,000
Sporting Goods Stores
S.I.C.: 5941
N.A.I.C.S.: 451110
Michael Medline *(Pres)*
Gregory Craig *(CFO)*
Kristine Freudenthaler *(CIO, Chief Intergration Officer & Sr VP-IT)*
Duncan Fulton *(CMO & Sr VP-Comm)*
Richard J. White *(Chief Mdsg Officer & Sr VP)*
Jean-Stephane Tremblay *(Exec VP-Franchise)*
Richard Burnet *(Sr VP-Fin)*
Keith Lambert *(Sr VP-Supply Chain & Mdse Mgmt)*
Chad McKinnon *(Sr VP-Corp Store Ops)*

Marks Work Wearhouse Ltd. **(1)**
30 1035 64th Ave SE Ste 30
Calgary, AB, T2H 2J7, Canada AB
Tel.: (403) 255-9220 (100%)
Fax: (403) 255-6005
Toll Free: (800) 663-6275
E-Mail: customer.service@marksegain.net
Web Site: www.marks.com
Sales Range: $250-299.9 Million
Emp.: 2,863
Retailer of Women's & Men's Workwear, Casual Wear, Custom Uniforms & Related Apparel
Import
S.I.C.: 5699
N.A.I.C.S.: 448150
Michael Strachan *(Sr VP-Mdsg)*

Division:

Marks Work Wearhouse **(2)**
30 1035 64th Ave SE
Calgary, AB, T2H 2J7, Canada (100%)
Tel.: (403) 255-9220
Fax: (403) 255-6005
E-Mail: customer.service@marks.com
Web Site: www.marks.com
Emp.: 300
Operator of Retail Clothing Stores
S.I.C.: 5699
N.A.I.C.S.: 448150
Paul Wilson *(Pres)*

CANADIAN UNIVERSITIES TRAVEL SERVICE LIMITED

45 Charles St E Ste 100
Toronto, ON, M4Y 1S2, Canada
Tel.: (416) 966-2887
Fax: (416) 966-2544
Toll Free: (866) 246-9762
E-Mail: ibe-cs@travelcuts.com
Web Site: www.travelcuts.com
Sales Range: $150-199.9 Million
Emp.: 380
Business Description:
Travel Agency
S.I.C.: 4724
N.A.I.C.S.: 561510
Personnel:
Rodney Hurd *(Pres)*

CANADIAN UTILITIES & TELECOM INCOME FUND

121 King Street West Standard Life Centre Suite 2600
Toronto, ON, M5H 3T9, Canada
Tel.: (416) 681-3940
Fax: (416) 681-3901
E-Mail: droode@mulvihill.com
Year Founded: 2010
UTE.UN—(TSX)
Sales Range: Less than $1 Million
Business Description:
Closed-End Investment Fund
S.I.C.: 6726
N.A.I.C.S.: 525990
Personnel:
John P. Mulvihill *(Chm & Pres)*
John D. Germain *(CFO & Sr VP)*
David E. Roode *(Pres-Fund Svcs)*
Board of Directors:
John P. Mulvihill
Robert G. Bertram
John D. Germain
Michael M. Koerner
Robert W. Korthals
David E. Roode
Transfer Agent:
Computershare Investor Services Inc
100 University Avenue 8th Floor
Toronto, ON, Canada

CANADIAN WESTERN BANK

Suite 3000 Canadian Western Bank Place 10303 Jasper Avenue
Edmonton, AB, T5J 3X6, Canada
Tel.: (800) 836-1886
Fax: (780) 969-8326
E-Mail: InvestorRelations@cwbank.com
Web Site: www.cwbankgroup.com
Year Founded: 1984
CWB—(TSX)
Int. Income: $728,090,823
Assets: $16,772,366,851
Liabilities: $15,211,531,796
Net Worth: $1,560,835,055
Earnings: $193,294,147
Emp.: 2,044
Fiscal Year-end: 12/31/12
Business Description:
Banking
S.I.C.: 6211
N.A.I.C.S.: 523110
Personnel:
Allan W. Jackson *(Chm)*
Chris H. Fowler *(Pres & CEO)*
Tracey C. Ball *(CFO & Exec VP)*
Darrell R. Jones *(CIO & Sr VP)*
Brian J. Young *(Pres/CEO-Canadian Direct Insurance & Exec VP)*
Nick Logan *(Pres/CEO-National Leasing)*
David Schuster *(Pres/CEO-Adroit Investment Mgmt)*
Gail L. Harding *(Gen Counsel, Sec & Sr VP)*
Ricki L. Golick *(Treas & Sr VP)*
William J. Addington *(Exec VP)*
Randell W. Garvey *(Exec VP)*
M. Glen Eastwood *(Sr VP & Reg Gen Mgr)*
Richard R. Gilpin *(Sr VP-Credit Risk Mgmt)*
Carolyn J. Graham *(Sr VP)*
Michael N. Halliwell *(Sr VP & Reg Gen Mgr)*
Uve Knaak *(Sr VP-HR)*
Gregory J. Sprung *(Sr VP & Reg Gen Mgr)*
Jack C. Wright *(Sr VP)*
Board of Directors:
Allan W. Jackson
Albrecht W. A. Bellstedt
Linda M. O. Hohol
Wendy A. Leaney
Robert A. Manning
Gerald A. B. McGavin
Howard E. Pechet
Robert Lawrence Phillips
Raymond J. Protti
Ian M. Reid
H. Sanford Riley
Alan M. Rowe
Arnold J. Shell
Transfer Agent:
Valiant Trust Company
Suite 310 606 4th Street S.W.
Calgary, AB, Canada

Subsidiaries:

Canadian Direct Insurance Incorporated **(1)**
750 Cambie Street Suite 600
Vancouver, BC, V6B 0A2, Canada
Tel.: (604) 699-3678
Fax: (604) 699-3851
E-Mail: insurancegeneral@canadiandirect.ca
Web Site: www.canadiandirect.com
Emp.: 300
Insurance Services
S.I.C.: 6411
N.A.I.C.S.: 524298
Brian Young *(CEO)*

Canadian Western Financial Ltd. **(1)**
11350 Jasper Ave
Edmonton, AB, T5K 0L8, Canada
Tel.: (780) 424-4846
Fax: (780) 424-0584
E-Mail: edmontonmain@cwbank.com
Web Site: www.cwbank.com
Emp.: 50
Financial Investment Activities
S.I.C.: 6211
N.A.I.C.S.: 523999
Mike Mcinnis *(Mgr)*

Canadian Western Trust **(1)**
600 - 750 Cambie Street
Vancouver, BC, V6B 0A2, Canada BC
Tel.: (604) 685-2081 (100%)
Fax: (604) 669-6069
E-Mail: informationservices@cwt.ca
Web Site: www.cwt.ca
Emp.: 75
Trust, Deposits & Lending
S.I.C.: 6153
N.A.I.C.S.: 522210

CANADIAN ZINC CORPORATION

650 West Georgia Street Suite 1710
Vancouver, BC, V6B 4N9, Canada
Tel.: (604) 688-2001
Fax: (604) 688-2043
Toll Free: (866) 688-2001
E-Mail: invest@canadianzinc.com
Web Site: www.canadianzinc.com
Year Founded: 1965
CZN—(TSX)
Rev.: $163,019
Assets: $21,816,751
Liabilities: $4,111,267
Net Worth: $17,705,484
Earnings: ($19,751,177)
Emp.: 25
Fiscal Year-end: 12/31/12
Business Description:
Zinc & Other Mineral Exploration & Mining
S.I.C.: 1081
N.A.I.C.S.: 213114
Personnel:
John F. Kearney *(Chm, Pres & CEO)*
Trevor L. Cunningham *(CFO, Sec & VP-Fin)*
Alan B. Taylor *(COO & VP-Exploration)*
Board of Directors:
John F. Kearney
Brian Atkins
John A. MacPherson
David Nickerson
Alan B. Taylor
Transfer Agent:
Computershare Investor Services Inc
4th Floor 510 Burrard Street
Vancouver, BC, Canada

CANADREAM CORPORATION

2510 27th Street NE
Calgary, AB, T1Y 7G1, Canada
Tel.: (403) 291-1000
Fax: (403) 291-5509
Toll Free: (800) 461-7368
Web Site: www.canadream.com
Year Founded: 1995
CDN—(TSXV)
Rev.: $27,686,879
Assets: $37,364,660
Liabilities: $26,868,549
Net Worth: $10,496,111
Earnings: $604,413
Fiscal Year-end: 04/30/13
Business Description:
Recreational Vehicle Rental Services
S.I.C.: 7033
N.A.I.C.S.: 721211
Personnel:
Blaine Nicholson *(Chm)*
Brian W. Gronberg *(Pres & CEO)*
Kelly Shier *(CFO & COO)*
Board of Directors:
Blaine Nicholson
Scott Graham
Brian W. Gronberg
Todd Nicholson
Alfred Sailer
Luke Trouchet
Gerry Wood

Subsidiary:

CanaDream Inc. **(1)**
2510 27 St Ne
Calgary, AB, T1Y 7G1, Canada
Tel.: (403) 291-1000
Fax: (403) 291-5509
Toll Free: (800) 461-7368
E-Mail: reservations@canadream.com
Web Site: www.canadream.com
Emp.: 3

Recreational Vehicle Rental & Tour Operating Services
S.I.C.: 7513
N.A.I.C.S.: 532120
Brian W. Gronberg *(Mgr)*

CANAF GROUP INC.

Suite 500-666 Burrard Street
Vancouver, BC, V6C 2PC, Canada
Tel.: (604) 682-2245
Fax: (604) 929-6362
E-Mail: info@canafgroup.com
Web Site: www.canafgroup.com
Year Founded: 1996
CAF—(TSXV)
Sls.: $10,882,074
Assets: $4,029,063
Liabilities: $2,871,933
Net Worth: $1,157,130
Earnings: $327,808
Fiscal Year-end: 10/31/12

Business Description:
Mineral Exploration Services
S.I.C.: 1081
N.A.I.C.S.: 213114

Personnel:
David Way *(Chm)*
Christopher Way *(Pres & CEO)*
Zeny Manalo *(CFO)*
Richard Skeith *(Sec)*

Board of Directors:
David Way
Kevin Corrigan
Zeny Manalo
Christopher Way

Transfer Agent:
Computershares
510 Burrard Street
Vancouver, BC, Canada

Non-U.S. Subsidiary:

Quantum Screening and Crushing (Proprietary) Limited (1)
45 Harding Street
Newcastle, Kwazulu-Natal, 2940, South Africa
Tel.: (27) 343127750
Fax: (27) 343127749
Emp.: 30
Coal Products Mfr
S.I.C.: 2999
N.A.I.C.S.: 324199
Michael Hopley *(Mgr)*

Subsidiary:

Southern Coal (Proprietary) Limited (2)
45 Harding Street
Newcastle, Kwazulu-Natal, 2940, South Africa
Tel.: (27) 343127750
Fax: (27) 343127749
E-Mail: info@southern.coal.co.za
Web Site: www.southern-coal.co.za
Emp.: 3
Anthracite Mining Services
S.I.C.: 1231
N.A.I.C.S.: 212113
Sing Chan *(Gen Mgr)*

CANALASKA URANIUM LTD.

1020-625 Howe Street
Vancouver, BC, V6C 2T6, Canada
Tel.: (604) 688-3211
Fax: (604) 688-3217
E-Mail: info@canalaska.com
Web Site: www.canalaska.com
CVV—(DEU OTC OTCB TSXV)
Rev.: $23,856
Assets: $3,205,715
Liabilities: $193,834
Net Worth: $3,011,881
Earnings: ($2,345,887)
Emp.: 1
Fiscal Year-end: 04/30/13

Business Description:
Uranium Mining Services
S.I.C.: 1094
N.A.I.C.S.: 212291

Personnel:
Thomas Graham, Jr. *(Chm)*
Peter G. Dasler *(Pres & CEO)*
Harry Chan *(CFO & Controller)*
Dianne Marie Szigety *(Sec)*

Board of Directors:
Thomas Graham, Jr.
Peter G. Dasler
Victor Fern
Michael E. Riley
Jean Luc Roy
Kathleen Kennedy Townsend

Legal Counsel:
Stikeman Elliott LLP
5300 Commerce Court West 199 Bay Street
Toronto, ON, Canada

Transfer Agent:
CIBC Mellon Trust Company
1600-1066 West Hastings Street
Vancouver, BC, Canada

CANALI S.P.A.

Via Lombardia 17-19 Sovico
20050 Milan, Italy
Tel.: (39) 0392014226
Fax: (39) 0392323005
E-Mail: info@canali.it
Web Site: www.canali.it
Year Founded: 1934
Emp.: 1,500

Business Description:
Men's & Boy's Clothing
S.I.C.: 2389
N.A.I.C.S.: 315210

Personnel:
Eugenio Canali *(CEO)*

U.S. Subsidiary:

Canali USA Inc. (1)
712 5th Ave 30th Fl
New York, NY 10019
Tel.: (212) 767-0205
Fax: (212) 586-9775
E-Mail: newyork@canali.it
Emp.: 25
Men's Apparel
S.I.C.: 2399
N.A.I.C.S.: 315210

CANAM COAL CORP.

202 1201-5th Street SW
Calgary, AB, T2R 0Y6, Canada
Tel.: (403) 262-3797
Fax: (403) 262-3794
E-Mail: info@canamcoal.com
Web Site: www.canamcoal.com
COE—(OTC TSXV)
Sls.: $55,061,153
Assets: $65,593,418
Liabilities: $58,848,701
Net Worth: $6,744,717
Earnings: ($6,021,558)
Fiscal Year-end: 12/31/12

Business Description:
Coal Mining & Production Services
S.I.C.: 1222
N.A.I.C.S.: 212112

Personnel:
Jonathan R. Legg *(Chm)*
Timothy J. Bergen *(Vice Chm)*
Jos De Smedt *(Pres & CEO)*
Scott Bolton *(CFO)*

Board of Directors:
Jonathan R. Legg
Timothy J. Bergen
Jos De Smedt
Tim Nakaska
Robert N. Power
Steve Somerville

Legal Counsel:
Davis LLP
1000 250 2nd St SW
Calgary, AB, Canada

Transfer Agent:
Computershare
600 530 8th Ave SW
Calgary, AB, Canada

CANAM GROUP INC.

11535 1st Ave bureau 500
Saint-Georges, QC, G5Y 7H5, Canada
Tel.: (418) 228-8031
Fax: (418) 228-1750
E-Mail: infogroup@groupecanam.ws
Web Site: www.canamgroup.ws
Year Founded: 1960
CAM—(TSX)
Rev.: $899,985,708
Assets: $799,318,321
Liabilities: $439,299,187
Net Worth: $360,019,134
Earnings: $16,932,137
Emp.: 3,396
Fiscal Year-end: 12/31/12

Business Description:
Design & Fabrication of Steel Joists, Deck & Other Steel Components; Fabrication of Semitrailers & Forestry Equipment
S.I.C.: 3441
N.A.I.C.S.: 332312

Personnel:
Marcel C. M. Dutil *(Chm)*
Marc Dutil *(Pres & CEO)*
Rene Guizzetti *(CFO & VP)*
Mario Bernard *(Chief Mfg Officer & Exec VP)*
Mary Gordon *(Pres-Canam Steel & Controller)*
Georges Hage-Chahine *(Pres-Intl)*
Kurt Langsenkamp *(Pres-FabSouth & Steel Fabricators)*
Raymond Pomerleau *(Treas)*
Louis Guertin *(Sec & VP-Legal Affairs)*
Sean Finn *(Exec VP-Corp Svcs)*
Peter Frantz *(Sr VP-Structal-Heavy Steel Construction)*
Jean Thibodeau *(Sr VP-InteliBuild & Mgmt Info Sys)*

Board of Directors:
Marcel C. M. Dutil
Elaine Beaudoin
Anne-Marie Dutil Blatchford
Marc Dutil
Sean Finn
Pierre Lortie
Pierre Marcouiller
Normand Morin
Pierre Thabet
Jean-Marie Toulouse
Jean Turmel

Transfer Agent:
Computershare Investor Services Inc
1500 rue University bureau 700
Montreal, QC, H3A 3S8, Canada

Subsidiaries:

Finloc, Inc. (1)
11505 1st Ave Ste 500
Saint-Georges, QC, G5Y 7X3, Canada (100%)
Tel.: (418) 228-8031
Fax: (418) 228-0334
E-Mail: frederic.gagne@finloc.ws
Web Site: www.finloc.com
Emp.: 8
Private Investment Services
S.I.C.: 6211
N.A.I.C.S.: 523999
Marcel Blouin *(Pres)*

Subsidiary:

Finloc 2000 Inc. (2)
11505 1st Avenue Suite 500
Saint-Georges, QC, G5Y 7X3, Canada
Tel.: (418) 227-8384
Fax: (418) 228-0334
Web Site: www.finloc.ws
Emp.: 9
Equipment Financing Services
S.I.C.: 6153
N.A.I.C.S.: 522220
Marcel Blouin *(Pres)*

Structal-Bridges (1)
1445 rue du Grand-Tronc
Quebec, QC, G1N 4G1, Canada
Tel.: (418) 683-2561
Fax: (418) 688-8512
Web Site: www.structalbridges.ws
Emp.: 300
Bridge Construction Services
S.I.C.: 1611
N.A.I.C.S.: 237310
Robin Lapointe *(Gen Mgr)*

U.S. Plant:

Structal-Bridges (2)
386 River Rd
Claremont, NH 03743 DE
Tel.: (603) 542-5202
Fax: (603) 542-5317
Web Site: www.structalbridges.ws
Sales Range: $10-24.9 Million
Emp.: 100
Fabrication of Steel Girders for Bridges
S.I.C.: 3441
N.A.I.C.S.: 332312
Carmine Macchiagodena *(Gen Mgr)*

U.S. Subsidiaries:

Canam Steel Corporation (1)
4010 Clay St
Point of Rocks, MD 21777
Tel.: (301) 874-5141
Fax: (301) 874-5685
Emp.: 275
Steel Products Mfr
S.I.C.: 3399
N.A.I.C.S.: 331110
Michel Cyr *(Gen Mgr)*

FabSouth, LLC (1)
721 Ne 44th St
Fort Lauderdale, FL 33334-3150
Tel.: (954) 938-5853
Fax: (954) 938-5829
E-Mail: info@fabsouthllc.com
Web Site: www.fabsouthllc.com
Emp.: 600
Fabricated Steel Products Mfr
S.I.C.: 3399
N.A.I.C.S.: 331110

Non-U.S. Subsidiaries:

Canam Steel Romania S.R.L. (1)
9 Str Ionescu Crum
Brasov, 500484, Romania
Tel.: (40) 268314373
Construction Products Mfr
S.I.C.: 3441
N.A.I.C.S.: 332312

Steel Plus Limited (1)
Gn 37 B Sector 5 Salt Lake
Kolkata, West Bengal, 700091, India
Tel.: (91) 3323575862
Fax: (91) 3323575914
Emp.: 60
Steel Joists Mfr
S.I.C.: 3441
N.A.I.C.S.: 332312
Partha Pratim Ghosh *(Gen Mgr)*

Technyx Euro Services s.r.l. (1)
9 Ionescu Crum Street
500446 Brasov, Romania
Tel.: (40) 268318057
Fax: (40) 268315028
Emp.: 230
Construction Products Mfr
S.I.C.: 3441
N.A.I.C.S.: 332312
Adriana Israel *(Mgr-Admin)*

CANAMEX RESOURCES CORP.

Suite 303 505 Howe Street
Vancouver, BC, V6C 2T5, Canada
Tel.: (604) 336-8612
Fax: (604) 718-2808
E-Mail: info@canamex.us
Web Site: www.canamex.us
Year Founded: 1987
CSQ—(DEU OTC TSXV)
Assets: $8,070,710
Liabilities: $177,294
Net Worth: $7,893,415

Canamex Resources Corp.—(Continued)

Earnings: ($1,650,777)
Fiscal Year-end: 12/31/12

Business Description:
Gold Exploration Services
S.I.C.: 1041
N.A.I.C.S.: 212221

Personnel:
Robert Kramer *(Chm & CEO)*
Gregory A. Hahn *(Vice Chm, Pres & COO)*
Richard Barnett *(CFO & Sec)*

Board of Directors:
Robert Kramer
Mark Anthony Billings
W. Pierce Carson
Gregory A. Hahn
Dean W.A. Mcdonald
Mike Stark

Legal Counsel:
DuMoulin Black LLP
595 Howe Street 10th Floor
Vancouver, BC, Canada

Transfer Agent:
Computershare Canada
3rd Floor 510 Burrard Street
Vancouver, BC, V6C 3B9, Canada

CANARA BANK

112 J C Road
Bengaluru, Karnataka, 560 002, India
Tel.: (91) 8022100250
Fax: (91) 22248831
E-Mail: hosecretarial@canbank.co.in
Web Site: www.canarabank.com
Year Founded: 1906
532483—(BAN BOM NSE)
Rev.: $6,929,792,189
Assets: $77,742,720,177
Liabilities: $73,031,968,444
Net Worth: $4,710,751,733
Earnings: $555,229,857
Emp.: 42,693
Fiscal Year-end: 03/31/13

Business Description:
Banking Services
S.I.C.: 6029
N.A.I.C.S.: 522110

Personnel:
R. K. Dubey *(Chm & Mng Dir)*
B. Nagesh Babu *(Compliance Officer & Sec)*

Board of Directors:
R. K. Dubey
Rajat Bhargava
Rajinder Kumar Goel
Ashok Kumar Gupta
Meena Hemchandra
Sanjay Jain
V. S. Krishnakumar
G. V. Manimaran
G. V. Sambasiva Rao
Pradyuman Singh Rawat
Brij Mohan Sharma
Sutanu Sinha

P Chopra & Co
Bengaluru, India

Loonker & Co
Bengaluru, India

K Venkatachalam Iyer & Co
Bengaluru, India

H K Chaudhry & CO.
Bengaluru, India

A R Das & Associates
Bengaluru, India

Transfer Agent:
Karvy Computershare Private Limited
Plot No 17 to 24 Vittalrao Nagar Madhapur
Hyderabad, India

Subsidiaries:

Canbank Computer Services Limited (1)
Naveen Complex 7th Floor
14 M G Road, 560001 Bengaluru, India (100%)
Tel.: (91) 8025599789
Fax: (91) 8025599790
Web Site: www.ccslindya.com
Emp.: 90
Custom Computer Programming Services
S.I.C.: 7371
N.A.I.C.S.: 541511
B. Sivaraman *(Mng Dir)*

Canbank Factors Limited (1)
67/1, Kanakapura Main Road
Basavanagudi
560004 Bengaluru, India (80%)
Tel.: (91) 8022268268
Fax: (91) 08022420240
E-Mail: canfact.dgldgi@canbankfactors.com
Web Site: www.canbankfactors.com
Emp.: 25
Activities Related to Credit Intermediation
S.I.C.: 6099
N.A.I.C.S.: 522390
Ajith Kumar *(Mng Dir)*

Canbank Financial Services Limited (1)
Naveen Complex 6th Floor M G Road
14 M G Road, 560001 Bengaluru, India (100%)
Tel.: (91) 8025583844
Fax: (91) 80255582658
E-Mail: canfina@yahoo.com
Emp.: 2
Activities Related to Credit Intermediation
S.I.C.: 6099
N.A.I.C.S.: 522390
P. Venkateswara Rao *(Exec Dir)*

Canbank Venture Capital Fund Limited (1)
6th Flr Naveen Complex
14 M G Rd, 560001 Bengaluru, India
Tel.: (91) 8025586506
Fax: (91) 8025583909
E-Mail: info@canbankventure.com
Web Site: www.canbankventure.com
Emp.: 8
Open-End Investment Funds
S.I.C.: 6722
N.A.I.C.S.: 525910
S. Thiruvadi *(Mng Dir)*

CAN FIN HOMES LIMITED (1)
No 29/1 Sir M N Krishna Rao Road Lalbagh West
Basavanagudi, Bengaluru, 560 004, India
Tel.: (91) 8026570155
Fax: (91) 8026565746
E-Mail: development@canfinhomes.com
Web Site: www.canfinhomes.com
511196—(BOM)
Rev.: $72,805,672
Assets: $750,685,323
Liabilities: $677,976,783
Net Worth: $72,708,540
Earnings: $10,034,015
Emp.: 320
Fiscal Year-end: 03/31/13
Housing Loan Financial Services
S.I.C.: 6159
N.A.I.C.S.: 522298
C. Ilango *(Mng Dir)*
K. S. Sathyaprakash *(Compliance Officer, Sec & Asst Gen Mgr)*

CANARC RESOURCE CORP.

Suite 301 700 West Pender Street
Vancouver, BC, V6C 1G8, Canada
Tel.: (604) 685-9700
Fax: (604) 685-9744
E-Mail: info@canarc.net
Web Site: www.canarc.net
CCM—(OTC OTCB TSX)
Assets: $13,983,000
Liabilities: $929,000
Net Worth: $13,054,000
Earnings: ($1,206,000)
Emp.: 3
Fiscal Year-end: 12/31/12

Business Description:
Gold Mining
S.I.C.: 1041
N.A.I.C.S.: 212221

Personnel:
Bradford James Cooke *(Chm)*
Garry D. Biles *(Pres & COO)*
Catalin Chiloflischi *(CEO)*
Philip Yee *(CFO & VP-Fin)*
Stewart L. Lockwood *(Legal Counsel & Sec)*

Board of Directors:
Bradford James Cooke
Bruce E. Bried
W. Derek Bullock
Martin Burian
Leonard J. Harris
William L. Price

Transfer Agent:
Computershare Investor Services Inc.
3rd Floor 510 Burrard Street
Vancouver, BC, Canada

CANARE ELECTRIC CO., LTD.

4th FL WN Bldg 2-4-1 Shin-Yokohama
Kouhoku-ku, Yokohama, Kanagawa, 222-0033, Japan
Tel.: (81) 45 470 5674
Fax: (81) 45 470 5676
E-Mail: overseas@canare.co.jp
Web Site: www.canare.co.jp
Year Founded: 1970
5819—(TKS)

Business Description:
Cable Product Mfr
S.I.C.: 3357
N.A.I.C.S.: 335929

Personnel:
Masao Obase *(Pres)*

CANARGO ENERGY CORPORATION

(Filed Ch 11 Bankruptcy #916453 on 10/28/09 in U.S. Bankruptcy Ct, Southern Dist of NY, NY)
PO Box 291
Saint Peter Port, GY1 3RR, Guernsey
Tel.: (44) 1481 729 980
Fax: (44) 1481 729 982
E-Mail: info@canargo.com
Web Site: www.canargo.com
Sales Range: $1-9.9 Million
Emp.: 150

Business Description:
Holding Company; Oil & Gas Exploration Services
S.I.C.: 1311
N.A.I.C.S.: 211111

Personnel:
Vincent McDonnell *(Chm, Pres, CEO, COO & Chief Comml Officer)*
Jeffrey Wilkins *(CFO & Sec)*

Board of Directors:
Vincent McDonnell
C. Michael Ayre
Anthony J. Perry
Jeffrey Wilkins

Subsidiary:

CanArgo Limited (1)
PO Box 291
Saint Peter Port, GY1 3RR, Guernsey
Tel.: (44) 1481729980
Fax: (44) 1481729982
E-Mail: info@canargo.com
Web Site: www.canargo.com
Oil & Gas Exploration Services
S.I.C.: 1311
N.A.I.C.S.: 211111
Vincent Mcdonnel *(CEO)*

Subsidiary:

Tethys Petroleum Limited (2)
PO Box 524
Saint Peter Port, Guernsey GY1 6EL GY
Tel.: (44) 1481725911
Fax: (44) 1481725922
Web Site: www.tethyspetroleum.com
TPL—(OTC TSX)
Rev.: $38,107,000
Assets: $251,953,000
Liabilities: $31,800,000
Net Worth: $220,153,000
Earnings: ($20,904,000)
Emp.: 560
Fiscal Year-end: 12/31/12
Petroleum Investment Services
S.I.C.: 6211
N.A.I.C.S.: 523999
David B. Robson *(Chm & Pres)*
Julian Hammond *(CEO & Chief Comml Officer)*
Denise Lay *(CFO & Dir-Fin)*
Graham Wall *(COO)*
Elizabeth Anne Landles *(Chief Admin Officer, Sec & Exec VP)*
Ian Philliskirk *(Gen Counsel & VP)*
Mark Sarssam *(Sr VP)*

Non-U.S. Subsidiary:

CanArgo Georgia Ltd (2)
70 Kostava Street
Tbilisi, Georgia
Tel.: (995) 32933793
Oil & Gas Exploration Services
S.I.C.: 1311
N.A.I.C.S.: 211111

CANASIA FINANCIAL INC.

Suite 1000 888-3 Street SW
Calgary, AB, Canada
Tel.: (403) 973-0433
E-Mail: contactus@canasiafinancial.com
Web Site: www.canasiafinancial.com
Year Founded: 2008
CNA.P—(TSXV)
Rev.: $114,552
Assets: $307,835
Liabilities: $664,072
Net Worth: ($356,237)
Earnings: ($2,136,755)
Emp.: 2
Fiscal Year-end: 12/31/12

Business Description:
Investment Services
S.I.C.: 6211
N.A.I.C.S.: 523999

Personnel:
James G. Louie *(Pres & CEO)*
Jacob Sung Kyung Kim *(CFO)*

Board of Directors:
Jacob Sung Kyung Kim
James G. Louie

CANASIA INDUSTRIES CORPORATION

(Name Changed to Makena Resources Inc.)

CANASIL RESOURCES INC.

Suite 915-700 West Pender Street
Vancouver, BC, V6C 1G8, Canada
Tel.: (604) 708-3788
Fax: (604) 708-3728
E-Mail: admin@canasil.com
Web Site: www.canasil.com
CLZ—(TSXV)
Assets: $1,097,596
Liabilities: $166,529
Net Worth: $931,067
Earnings: ($1,294,923)
Emp.: 2
Fiscal Year-end: 12/31/12

Business Description:
Acquisition & Development of Mineral Properties; Gold, Silver, Copper & Zinc Mining
S.I.C.: 1041
N.A.I.C.S.: 212221

Personnel:
Bahman Yamini *(Pres & CEO)*
Kerry Melbourne Spong *(CFO & VP-Fin)*
Graham H. Scott *(Legal Counsel & Sec)*

Board of Directors:
Arthur Charles Freeze
Alvin W. Jackson

Michael McInnis
Gary D. Nordin
Bahman Yamini

Legal Counsel:
Vector Corporate Finance Lawyers
999 West Hastings Street Suite 1040
Vancouver, BC, V6C 2W2, Canada
Tel.: (604) 683-1102
Fax: (604) 683-2643

Transfer Agent:
Computershare
3rd Floor 510 Burrard Street
Vancouver, BC, Canada

Non-U.S. Subsidiary:

Minera Canasil, S.A. de C.V. **(1)**
Alheli No 142 Fracc Jardines de Durango
Durango, 34200, Mexico
Tel.: (52) 6181296082
Fax: (52) 6181296082
E-Mail: admin@canasil.com.mx
Mineral Exploration Services
S.I.C.: 1481
N.A.I.C.S.: 213115

CANBAS CO., LTD.

2-2-1 Otemachi
Numazu, 410-0801, Japan
Tel.: (81) 559543666
Fax: (81) 559543668
E-Mail: info@canbas.co.jp
Web Site: www.canbas.co.jp
4575—(TKS)
Sales Range: $1-9.9 Million
Emp.: 20

Business Description:
Cancer Pharmaceutical Researcher, Developer & Mfr
S.I.C.: 2834
N.A.I.C.S.: 325412

Personnel:
Takumi Kawabe *(Pres)*
Makoto Katozumi *(CFO)*

Board of Directors:
Makoto Katozumi
Takumi Kawabe
Kazuyoshi Sakamoto

CANBURG LIMITED

Hopton Industrial Works
London Road, Devizes, Wilts, SN10 2EU, United Kingdom
Tel.: (44) 1380729090
Fax: (44) 1380731625
E-Mail: enquiries@canburg.com
Web Site: www.canburg.com
Year Founded: 2009
Sales Range: $50-74.9 Million
Emp.: 400

Business Description:
Holding Company; Wood Household Furniture & Kitchen Cabinetry Designer, Mfr & Distr
S.I.C.: 6719
N.A.I.C.S.: 551112

Personnel:
Leo Caplan *(Owner & Chm)*

Board of Directors:
Leo Caplan
Martin Warbrick

Subsidiaries:

Mark Wilkinson Furniture Limited **(1)**
The Hopton Works Hopton Industrial Works
London Rd, Devizes, Wilts, SN10 2EU,
United Kingdom UK
Tel.: (44) 1380850007
E-Mail: enquires@mwf.com
Web Site: www.mwf.com
Sales Range: $25-49.9 Million
Emp.: 300
Wood Household Furniture & Kitchen Cabinetry Designer, Mfr & Distr
S.I.C.: 2511
N.A.I.C.S.: 337122
Mark Wilkinson *(Founder)*

Smallbone & Co (Devizes) Limited **(1)**
The Hopton Works Hopton Industrial Works
London Rd, Devizes, Wilts, SN10 2EU,
United Kingdom UK
Tel.: (44) 1380729090
Fax: (44) 1380731625
E-Mail: enquiries@smallbone.co.uk
Web Site: www.smallbone.co.uk
Sales Range: $25-49.9 Million
Emp.: 300
Wood Household Furniture & Kitchen Cabinetry Designer, Mfr & Distr; Ceramic & Stone Wall & Floor Tile Mfr & Distr
S.I.C.: 2511
N.A.I.C.S.: 337122
David King *(Gen Mgr)*

CANCANA RESOURCES CORP.

Sun Life Plaza West Tower Suite 1600 144 - 4th Ave SW
Calgary, AB, T2P 3N4, Canada
Tel.: (403) 269-2065
Fax: (888) 281-0548
E-Mail: cancanainfo@cancanacorp.com
Web Site: www.cancanacorp.com
Year Founded: 1980
CNY—(TSXV)
Assets: $1,847,749
Liabilities: $1,134,407
Net Worth: $713,342
Earnings: ($1,607,738)
Fiscal Year-end: 01/31/13

Business Description:
Mineral Properties Exploration Services
S.I.C.: 1081
N.A.I.C.S.: 213114

Personnel:
Andrew R. Male *(Pres & CEO)*
Jonathan Richards *(CFO)*

Board of Directors:
Warren Boyd
David Madill
Andrew R. Male
William Pfaffenberger

CANCEN OIL CANADA, INC.

Suite 910 521 - 3rd Avenue SW
Calgary, AB, T2P 3T3, Canada
Tel.: (403) 262-2783
Fax: (403) 263-0603
E-Mail: info@cancenoil.com
Web Site: www.cancenoilcanada.com
COI—(TSXV)
Rev.: $759,955
Assets: $21,409,420
Liabilities: $11,408,344
Net Worth: $10,001,077
Earnings: ($3,257,582)
Fiscal Year-end: 12/31/12

Business Description:
Oil Waste Disposal Services
S.I.C.: 1389
N.A.I.C.S.: 213112

Personnel:
Marvin Jones *(Chm)*
Ian Simister *(Pres)*
Brian Petersen *(CEO & Mng Dir-Capital Markets)*
Shankar Nandiwada *(CFO & Sec)*
Richard Lane *(COO)*
Jim Coughlan *(Sr VP-Sls & Bus Dev)*

Board of Directors:
Marvin Jones
Thomas Bugg
Brian Petersen
Ian Simister
Keith Talbot

Transfer Agent:
Computershare Trust Company of Canada
Proxy Department 9th Floor 100 University Avenue
Toronto, ON, Canada

CANCOM SE

Erika-Mann-Strasse 69
80636 Munich, Germany
Tel.: (49) 89540540
Fax: (49) 8954054119
E-Mail: info@cancom.de
Web Site: www.cancom.com
Year Founded: 1992
COK—(DEU)
Rev.: $755,524,451
Assets: $280,875,678
Liabilities: $172,140,143
Net Worth: $108,735,536
Earnings: $15,594,033
Emp.: 2,040
Fiscal Year-end: 12/31/12

Business Description:
Holding Company; IT Infrastructure & Professional Services
S.I.C.: 6719
N.A.I.C.S.: 551112

Personnel:
Walter von Szczytnicki *(Chm-Supervisory Bd)*
Klaus Weinmann *(Chm-Exec Bd, Pres & CEO)*
Stefan Kober *(Vice Chm-Supervisory Bd)*
Rudolf Hotter *(COO & Member-Exec Bd)*

Supervisory Board of Directors:
Stefan Kober
Lothar Koniarski
Walter Krejci
Petra Neureither
Walter von Szczytnicki
Regina Weinmann

Subsidiaries:

CANCOM IT Solutions GmbH **(1)**
Industriestrasse 3
70565 Stuttgart, Baden-Wurttemberg, Germany
Tel.: (49) 74339015
Fax: (49) 71173582290
Emp.: 10
Information Technology Solutions
S.I.C.: 7373
N.A.I.C.S.: 541512
Christian Linda *(Mgr)*

Subsidiary:

acentrix GmbH **(2)**
Ridlerstrasse 37
80339 Munich, Bavaria, Germany
Tel.: (49) 8954054520
Fax: (49) 8954054529
E-Mail: info.muenchen@acentrix.de
Web Site: www.acentrix.de
Emp.: 40
Information Technology Solutions
S.I.C.: 7373
N.A.I.C.S.: 541512
Thomas Heinz *(Mng Dir)*

CANCOM NSG GIS GmbH **(1)**
Messerschmittstr 20
D-89343 Jettingen, Bavaria, Germany
Tel.: (49) 8225 996 1381
Fax: (49) 8225 996 41381
E-Mail: info@cancom.de
Web Site: www.cancom.de
Recruitment Services
S.I.C.: 7361
N.A.I.C.S.: 561311

CANCOM NSG GmbH **(1)**
Ridlerstrasse 37
80339 Munich, Bavaria, Germany
Tel.: (49) 893681680
Fax: (49) 89368168111
E-Mail: info-nsg@cancom.de
Web Site: www.cancom.de
Emp.: 80
Information Technology Solutions
S.I.C.: 7373
N.A.I.C.S.: 541512
Hubert Schmitt *(Gen Mgr)*

CANCOM SYSDAT GmbH **(1)**
Kirchweg 2
50858 Cologne, Germany
Tel.: (49) 2219488101
Fax: (49) 2219481701
Web Site: www.cancom.de
Emp.: 150
Information Technology Solutions
S.I.C.: 7371
N.A.I.C.S.: 541511
Manfred Hoevel *(Mng Dir)*

Non-U.S. Subsidiaries:

CANCOM a+d IT Solutions GmbH **(1)**
Alfred Feierfeil Strasse 5
2380 Perchtoldsdorf, Austria
Tel.: (43) 506058200
Fax: (43) 506058209
E-Mail: info@cancom.at
Web Site: www.cancom.at
Information Technology Solutions
S.I.C.: 7373
N.A.I.C.S.: 541512
Elisabeth Hoedl *(Sec)*

CANCOM Ltd. **(1)**
Genesis House Merrow Ln
Guildford, Surrey, GU4 7BN, United Kingdom
Tel.: (44) 1483500500
Fax: (44) 1483 500 511
E-Mail: guildford.sales@cancomuk.com
Web Site: www.cancomuk.com
Information Technology Solutions
S.I.C.: 7371
N.A.I.C.S.: 541511

CANCOR MINES INC.

110 Cremazie Boulevard West Suite 430
Montreal, QC, H2P 1B9, Canada
Tel.: (514) 849-3013
Fax: (514) 384-6399
E-Mail: khobzi@cancor.ca
Web Site: www.cancor.ca
Year Founded: 1989
KCR—(CNSX)
Rev.: $18,870
Assets: $13,258,677
Liabilities: $501,887
Net Worth: $12,756,790
Earnings: ($264,700)
Fiscal Year-end: 03/31/13

Business Description:
Gold, Silver & Copper Mining
S.I.C.: 1041
N.A.I.C.S.: 212221

Personnel:
David Crevier *(Chm)*
Kamil Khobzi *(Pres & CEO)*

Board of Directors:
David Crevier
Rene Dufour
Denis Francoeur
Gabor Jellinek
Kamil Khobzi
Kenneth Lester

Legal Counsel:
Colby, Monet, Demers, Delage & Crevier
1501 McGill College Avenue Suite 2900
Montreal, QC, Canada

Transfer Agent:
Computershare Trust Company of Canada
1800 McGill College Ave 6th Fl
Montreal, QC, H3A 3K9, Canada
Tel.: (514) 982-7888

CANDAX ENERGY INC.

36 Toronto Street Suite 1000
Toronto, ON, M5C 2C5, Canada
Tel.: (416) 368-9137
Fax: (416) 364-5400
E-Mail: info@candax.com
Web Site: www.candax.com
CAX—(TSX)
Sls.: $8,659,000
Assets: $79,442,000
Liabilities: $50,387,000
Net Worth: $29,055,000

Candax Energy Inc.—(Continued)

Earnings: ($13,708,000)
Emp.: 49
Fiscal Year-end: 12/31/12

Business Description:
Energy Production & Development Services
S.I.C.: 4939
N.A.I.C.S.: 221112

Personnel:
Benoit Debray *(Chm & CEO)*
John Younger *(Pres)*
Pierre-Henri Boutant *(CFO)*
Pascal Mirville *(COO & Gen Mgr-Tunisia)*
Jo-Anne Archibald *(Sec)*

Board of Directors:
Benoit Debray
M'hamed Ali Bouleymen
Stephen Drinkwater
Jean Pouzet
Hubert Roudot
John Younger

Legal Counsel:
McCarthy Tetrault
Suite 5300T TD Bank Tower Toronto Dominion Centre 66 Wellington Street
Toronto, ON, Canada

Transfer Agent:
Equity Financial Trust Company
200 University Avenue Suite 400
Toronto, ON, Canada

Non-U.S. Subsidiaries:

Candax Madagascar Ltd. (1)
Immeuble SANTA Lot 3E Etage
Antananarivo, 101, Madagascar
Tel.: (261) 20 22 265 58
Fax: (261) 20 22 265 81
Web Site: www.candax.com
Energy Production & Development Services
S.I.C.: 4931
N.A.I.C.S.: 221112

Ecumed Petroleum Limited (1)
Rue du Lac Windermere
les Berges du Lac, 1053 Tunis, Tunisia
Tel.: (216) 71962611
Fax: (216) 71963765
Emp.: 20
Oil & Gas Explorer, Developer & Producer
S.I.C.: 1311
N.A.I.C.S.: 211111
Pascal Mirville *(Gen Mgr)*

Falcan Chaal Petroleum, Ltd (1)
Rue Du Lac Windermere Les Berges Du Lac
Tunis, 1053, Tunisia
Tel.: (216) 71962611
Fax: (216) 71963765
Emp.: 15
Natural Gas Exploration Services
S.I.C.: 1389
N.A.I.C.S.: 213112
Pascal Meirville *(Gen Mgr)*

CANDENTE COPPER CORP.

Commerce Place Suite 1650 - 400 Burrard Street
Vancouver, BC, V6C 3A6, Canada
Tel.: (604) 689-1957
Fax: (604) 685-1946
Toll Free: (877) 689-1964
E-Mail: info@candentecopper.com
Web Site: www.candentecopper.com
Year Founded: 1997
DNT—(LIM TSX)
Rev.: $157,740
Assets: $63,806,393
Liabilities: $1,617,996
Net Worth: $62,188,397
Earnings: ($3,787,252)
Emp.: 208
Fiscal Year-end: 12/31/12

Business Description:
Copper Ore Exploration & Mining Development Services
S.I.C.: 1081
N.A.I.C.S.: 213114

Personnel:
Joanne C. Freeze *(Chm & CEO)*
Sean I. Waller *(Pres)*
Cameron Dong *(CFO)*
Maria Eugenia Montagne *(Treas & Sec)*

Board of Directors:
Joanne C. Freeze
John E. Black
George Elliot
Andres J. Milla
Wolfgang P. T. Nickel
Michael Thicke
Sean I. Waller

Legal Counsel:
Gowling Lafleur Henderson LLP
Bentall 5 550 Burrard Street Suite 2300 PO Box 30
Vancouver, BC, V6C 2B5, Canada

Estudio Egusquiza S.C.R.L
Edificio Torre Parque Mar Av Larco No 1203
Miraflores, Lima, Peru

Transfer Agent:
Computershare
3rd Floor 510 Burrard Street
Vancouver, BC, Canada

Non-U.S. Subsidiary:

Canariaco Copper Peru S.A. (1)
Calle Antequera 777 -Oficina 1101
San Isidro, Lima, Peru
Tel.: (51) 511 715 2001
Fax: (51) 511 717 1233
E-Mail: peruadmin@candente.com
Copper Exploration Services
S.I.C.: 1021
N.A.I.C.S.: 212234

CANDENTE GOLD CORP.

Suite 1650 400 Burrard Street
Vancouver, BC, V6C 3A6, Canada
Tel.: (604) 689-1957
Fax: (604) 685-1946
E-Mail: info@candentegold.com
Web Site: www.candentegold.com
CDG—(TSX)
Assets: $13,893,869
Liabilities: $561,147
Net Worth: $13,332,722
Earnings: ($1,764,836)
Emp.: 9
Fiscal Year-end: 03/31/13

Business Description:
Gold Mining Services
S.I.C.: 1041
N.A.I.C.S.: 212221

Personnel:
Joanne C. Freeze *(Pres & CEO)*
G. Cameron Dong *(CFO)*
Maria Eugenia Montagne *(Treas & Sec)*

Board of Directors:
Michael Casselman
Joanne C. Freeze
Larry D. Kornze
Peter K. M. Megaw
Andres J. Milla
Kenneth G. Thomas

Legal Counsel:
Gowlings
Bentall 5 550 Burrard St. Suite 2300 30
Vancouver, BC, Canada

Transfer Agent:
Computershare
3rd Floor 510 Burrard Street
Vancouver, BC, Canada

CANDEREL MANAGEMENT INC.

2000 rue Peel Suite 900
Montreal, QC, H3A 2W5, Canada
Tel.: (514) 842-8636
Fax: (514) 982-9076
E-Mail: info@canderel.com
Web Site: www.canderel.com
Year Founded: 1975
Rev.: $31,908,797
Emp.: 100

Business Description:
Real Estate Development Services
S.I.C.: 6519
N.A.I.C.S.: 531190

Personnel:
Jonathan Wener *(Chm & CEO)*
Douglas Pascal *(Vice Chm & COO)*
Michael LaBrier *(Pres-Canderel Stoneridge-Toronto)*
Joelle Sebag *(Gen Counsel & VP)*
Richard C. Diamond *(Sr VP-Toronto)*
Daniel D. Peritz *(Sr VP-Montreal & Ottawa)*

Board of Directors:
Jonathan Wener
Douglas Pascal

CANDMARK ELECTROPTICS CO., LTD.

No 1300 Chenggong Road 6th Neighborhood
Poluow Village
Hukoku Township, Hsin-chu, 30345, Taiwan
Tel.: (886) 3 5996720
Fax: (886) 3 5996729
Web Site: www.candmark.com.tw
5259—(TAI)
Sales Range: $25-49.9 Million
Emp.: 300

Business Description:
Lenses & Glass Products for Electronic Devices
S.I.C.: 3827
N.A.I.C.S.: 333314

Personnel:
Huan Sung Wu *(Chm & Gen Mgr)*

CANDO CONTRACTING LTD.

4th Floor 740 Rosser Avenue
Brandon, MB, R7A 0K9, Canada
Tel.: (204) 725-2627
Fax: (204) 725-4100
E-Mail: info@candoltd.com
Web Site: www.candoltd.com
Year Founded: 1978
Rev.: $25,995,310
Emp.: 200

Business Description:
Heavy Construction Services
S.I.C.: 3743
N.A.I.C.S.: 336510

Personnel:
Gord Peters *(Pres)*
Brent Mills *(CEO)*
Terry Carlisle *(CFO & Controller)*

CANDORADO OPERATING COMPANY LTD.

(See Under Sunrise Resources Ltd.)

CANDOVER INVESTMENTS PLC

34 Lime Street
London, EC3M 7AT, United Kingdom
Tel.: (44) 2074899848
Fax: (44) 2072485483
E-Mail: info@candover.com
Web Site: www.candoverinvestments.com
Year Founded: 1980
CDI—(LSE)
Assets: $460,205,106
Liabilities: $250,475,394
Net Worth: $209,729,712
Earnings: ($37,587,102)
Emp.: 2
Fiscal Year-end: 12/31/12

Business Description:
Investment Trust
S.I.C.: 6733
N.A.I.C.S.: 525920

Personnel:
Malcolm Fallen *(CEO)*

Board of Directors:
Richard A. Stone
Malcolm Fallen
Michael Jay
Scott Longhurst
Jan Pieter Oosterveld

Legal Counsel:
Ashurst LLP
Broadwalk House 5 Appold Street
London, EC2A 2HA, United Kingdom

Subsidiary:

Candover Services Limited (1)
20 Old Bailey
London, EC4M 7LN, United Kingdom
Tel.: (44) 2074899848
Investment Management Services
S.I.C.: 6211
N.A.I.C.S.: 523999
Malcolm Fallen *(CEO)*

Holding:

Expro International Group Ltd. (1)
Davidson House
Forbury Square, Reading, Berks, RG1 3EU, United Kingdom UK
Tel.: (44) 1189591341
Fax: (44) 1189589000
E-Mail: enquiries@exprogroup.com
Web Site: www.exprogroup.com
Sales Range: $1-4.9 Billion
Emp.: 4,272
Gas & Oil Well Management Services
S.I.C.: 1389
N.A.I.C.S.: 213112
Charles Woodburn *(CEO)*
Chris Mawtus *(COO)*
John McAlister *(Gen Counsel)*

Division:

Tronic Products Division (2)
Subsea Excellence Ctr
Excellence Centra Subsea, Ulverston, Cumbria, LA12 9EE, United Kingdom
Tel.: (44) 1229580500
Fax: (44) 1229586604
E-Mail:
Web Site: www.siemens.com
Emp.: 300
Power & Data Connection Systems Developer & Mfr
S.I.C.: 3679
N.A.I.C.S.: 334419
Mark Jones *(CEO)*

Non-U.S. Subsidiaries:

Expro Group Malaysia Sdn Bhd (2)
13th Floor West Block Wisma Selangor Dredging 142C
Bangsar, Kuala Lumpur, 50450, Malaysia
Tel.: (60) 320847000
Fax: (60) 3 2282 1107
Web Site: www.exprogroup.com
Oil & Gas Well Management Services
S.I.C.: 1389
N.A.I.C.S.: 213112
Tengku Abdulmalik *(Mng Dir)*

Expro International B.V. (2)
Nijverheidsweg 4
Postbus 419
1780 AK Den Helder, Netherlands NL
Tel.: (31) 223677900
Fax: (31) 223677911
E-Mail: expro.denhelder@exprogroup.com
Web Site: www.exprogroup.com
Emp.: 240
Oil & Gas Well Management Services
S.I.C.: 1389
N.A.I.C.S.: 213112
Jan Van Schijndel *(Mng Dir)*

Non-U.S. Subsidiaries:

Expro Group Australia Pty Ltd (3)
Level 3 1060 Hay St
West Perth, NSW, 6005, Australia
Mailing Address:
PO Box 168
West Perth, 6872, Australia
Tel.: (61) 892135555

Fax: (61) 892135599
E-Mail: info@expro.com
Web Site: www.expro.com
Emp.: 70
Gas & Oil Well Management Services
S.I.C.: 1389
N.A.I.C.S.: 213112
Callen Souter *(Mng Dir)*

Expro Norway A/S (3)
Norsea Base
PO Box 49
Bygg 7, 4056 Tananger, Norway
Tel.: (47) 51695400
Fax: (47) 51695401
E-Mail: norge@exprogroup.com
Web Site: www.exprogroup.com
Emp.: 15
Oil & Gas Well Management Services
S.I.C.: 1389
N.A.I.C.S.: 213112
Jan Wong Schiendel *(Mng Dir)*

Subsidiary:

Matre Instruments AS (4)
Genecangen
5420 Rubbestadneset, Norway
Tel.: (47) 1229485130
Fax: (47) 53428601
E-Mail: matre.instruments@expogroup.com
Web Site: www.readmatre.no
Emp.: 60
High Pressure Connector & Measurement Systems
S.I.C.: 3825
N.A.I.C.S.: 334515
Phil Ashley *(Gen Mgr)*

U.S. Holding:

Capital Safety, Inc. (1)
3833 Sala Way
Red Wing, MN 55066-5005
Tel.: (651) 388-8282
Fax: (651) 388-5065
Toll Free: (800) 328-6146
E-Mail: info@capitalsafety.com
Web Site: www.capitalsafety.com
Sales Range: $25-49.9 Million
Emp.: 500
Fall Protection & Rescue Equipment Mfr
S.I.C.: 7382
N.A.I.C.S.: 561621
Sarah Erickson *(Gen Counsel)*

Non-U.S. Subsidiaries:

Candover France S.A.S. (1)
4 Rond Point Des Champs Elysees
F-75008 Paris, France FR
Tel.: (33) 158364350 (100%)
Fax: (33) 158364361
E-Mail: infofr@candover.com
Web Site: www.candover.com
Emp.: 3
Private Equity Firm
S.I.C.: 6211
N.A.I.C.S.: 523999
Cyril Zivre *(Dir-Investments)*

Candover Spain SL (1)
Jorge Juan 15-1 Izq
ES-28001 Madrid, Spain ES
Tel.: (34) 914322497 (100%)
Fax: (34) 914357043
Web Site: www.candover.com
Private Equity Firm
S.I.C.: 6211
N.A.I.C.S.: 523999
Javier Abad *(Head-Spain)*

Non-U.S. Holdings:

Inversiones Astrau SL (1)
Ayala 11
28001 Madrid, Spain (100%)
Tel.: (34) 914263851
Fax: (34) 914263869
E-Mail: astrau@telefonica.net
Sales Range: $1-9.9 Million
Emp.: 40
Buy-Out & Buy-In Investors & Consultants
S.I.C.: 6221
N.A.I.C.S.: 523130
Alejandro Von Der Pahlen *(Gen Mgr)*

Parques Reunidos S.A. (1)
Casa de Campo S/N
ES-28011 Madrid, Spain ES
Tel.: (34) 914632900
Fax: (34) 914632916
E-Mail: parquesreunidos@grpr.com
Web Site: www.parquesreunidos.com
Sales Range: $550-599.9 Million
Emp.: 300
Amusement, Water, Theme, Nature & Animal Parks Operator
S.I.C.: 7996
N.A.I.C.S.: 713110
Richard Golding *(Grp Pres)*
Jose Diaz *(Mng Dir)*
Richard Goldeng *(Dir Gen-Admin & Fin)*

U.S. Subsidiaries:

Kennywood Entertainment, Inc. (2)
4800 Kennywood Blvd
West Mifflin, PA 15122 PA
Tel.: (412) 461-0500
Fax: (412) 464-0719
E-Mail: kennywoodinformation@kennywood.com
Web Site: www.kennywood.com
Amusement Park Owner & Operator
S.I.C.: 7996
N.A.I.C.S.: 713110
Jerome Gibas *(Gen Mgr)*

Palace Entertainment Holdings, Inc. (2)
4590 MacArthur Blvd Ste 400
Newport Beach, CA 92660 CA
Tel.: (949) 261-0404
Fax: (949) 261-1414
E-Mail: employment@palaceentertainment.com
Web Site: www.palaceentertainment.com
Sales Range: $350-399.9 Million
Emp.: 9,000
Amusement Park Owner & Operator
S.I.C.: 7996
N.A.I.C.S.: 713110
Richard T. Golding *(Chm)*
Fernando Eiroa *(Pres & CEO)*
Russ Owens *(CFO)*
Chip Cleary *(Sr VP-Ops)*

Subsidiaries:

Raging Waters (3)
2333 S White Rd
San Jose, CA 95148-1518 CA
Tel.: (408) 238-9900
Fax: (408) 270-2022
Web Site: www.rwsplash.com
Sales Range: $1-9.9 Million
Emp.: 650
Amusement Park
S.I.C.: 7996
N.A.I.C.S.: 713110

Raging Waters (3)
111 Raging Waters Dr
San Dimas, CA 91773-3928
Tel.: (909) 802-2200
Fax: (909) 802-2219
E-Mail: extreme@ragingwaters.com
Web Site: www.ragingwaters.com
Sales Range: $1-9.9 Million
Amusement Park
S.I.C.: 7996
N.A.I.C.S.: 713110

Silver Springs, Inc. (3)
5656 E Silver Springs Blvd
Silver Springs, FL 34488 FL
Tel.: (352) 236-2121
Fax: (352) 236-1732
E-Mail: ssinfo@silversprings.com
Web Site: www.silversprings.com
Emp.: 550
Family Entertainment Parks
S.I.C.: 7996
N.A.I.C.S.: 713110
Terry Turner *(Gen Mgr)*

Water Country Corp. (3)
2300 Lafayette Rd
Portsmouth, NH 03801
Tel.: (603) 427-1112
Fax: (603) 427-6644
Web Site: www.watercountry.com
Emp.: 500
Amusement Park Operator
S.I.C.: 7996
N.A.I.C.S.: 713110

Sea Life Park Hawaii (2)
41-202 Kalanianaole Hwy 7
Waimanalo, HI 96795
Tel.: (808) 259-2500
Fax: (808) 259-7373
Web Site: www.sealifeparkhawaii.com
Sales Range: $10-24.9 Million
Emp.: 200
Marine Mammal Park & Research Center
S.I.C.: 7999
N.A.I.C.S.: 712190
Johnathan Casey *(Supvr-Reef Life)*

Stork N.V. (1)
Van gevengerlaan 121
1412 KA Utrecht, Netherlands NL
Mailing Address:
PO Box 5004
1410AA Naarden, Netherlands
Tel.: (31) 30669170
Fax: (31) 306664733
E-Mail: info.technicalservices@stork.com
Web Site: www.storktechnicalservices.com
Sales Range: $1-4.9 Billion
Emp.: 14,500
Holding Company
S.I.C.: 6719
N.A.I.C.S.: 551112
Sjoerd S. Vollebregt *(Chm & CEO)*
Pim Oomens *(CFO)*

Subsidiary:

Stork B.V. (2)
Amersfoortsestraatweg 7
1412 KA Naarden, Netherlands
Tel.: (31) 356957411
Fax: (31) 356941184
E-Mail: info@stork.com
Web Site: www.stork.com
Emp.: 45
Food Processing, Aerospace, Printing, Industrial Equipment Businesses & Management Services
S.I.C.: 3812
N.A.I.C.S.: 334511
S. J. S. Vollebregt *(Chm-Mgmt Bd)*

Subsidiaries:

Fokker Elmo (3)
Aviolandalaan 33
4631 RP Hoogerheide, Netherlands
Tel.: (31) 164617000
Fax: (31) 164617700
E-Mail: info.fokkerelmo@fokkerelmo.com
Web Site: www.fokkerelmo.com
Sales Range: $1-4.9 Billion
Emp.: 400
Supplier of Electrical Systems for Military & Commercial Aircraft
S.I.C.: 1731
N.A.I.C.S.: 238210
Jan Lagasse *(Mng Dir)*

Fokker Services B.V. (3)
Lucas Bols Straat 7
2152 CZ Nieuw-Vennep, Netherlands
Mailing Address:
PO Box 3
4630 AA Hoogerheide, Netherlands
Tel.: (31) 252627000
Telex: 78063 FOW NL
Fax: (31) 252627209
E-Mail: info.fokkerservices@fokker.com
Web Site: www.fokkerservices.com
Emp.: 650
Aerospace Design & Repair Services
S.I.C.: 3721
N.A.I.C.S.: 336411
Harold Freeburg *(Pres)*

Stork Fokker AESP (3)
Industrieweg 4
PO Box 1
3351 LB Papendrecht, Netherlands
Tel.: (31) 786419911
Fax: (31) 786419600
E-Mail: fokker@fokker.com
Web Site: www.fokker.com
Sales Range: $550-599.9 Million
Emp.: 3,100
Aircraft Components
S.I.C.: 3728
N.A.I.C.S.: 336413
Hams Buther *(Mng Dir)*

Stork Fokker AESP (3)
Industrieweg 4
3350AA Papendrecht, Denthe, Netherlands
Tel.: (31) 528285000
Fax: (31) 0528285010
E-Mail: info@fokker.com
Web Site: www.fokker.com
Emp.: 1,000
Aircraft Component Mfr
S.I.C.: 3728
N.A.I.C.S.: 336413
Roob Goossens *(Mgr-HR)*

Stork Gears & Services B.V. (3)
Pannerdenstraat 5
3087 CH Rotterdam, Netherlands
Tel.: (31) 104873500
Fax: (31) 104291129
E-Mail: webinfo.gears@stork.com
Web Site: www.stork-gears.com
Emp.: 40
Gearbox & Gear Technology Repair
S.I.C.: 7699
N.A.I.C.S.: 811219

Stork Industry Services (3)
Business Park Stain 318
6181 MC Elsloo, Netherlands
Tel.: (31) 464268888
Fax: (31) 464268999
E-Mail: industryservices.zuidoost@stork.com
Web Site: www.storkindustryservices.com
Emp.: 600
Industrial Maintenance & Project Management
S.I.C.: 7699
N.A.I.C.S.: 811310
Gijf Bers *(Dir-Bus Dev)*

Stork Industry Services (3)
Van Deventerlaan 121
3544 AD Utrecht, Netherlands
Tel.: (31) 306691700
Fax: (31) 306664733
E-Mail: info.industryservices@stork.com
Web Site: www.storkindustryservices.nl
Emp.: 1,400
Industrial Maintenance & Project Management
S.I.C.: 7699
N.A.I.C.S.: 811310
Carla Rodenberg *(Mgr-Sls & Mktg)*

Stork Maintenance Management B.V. (3)
Burgemeester Verderlaan 13
3544 AD Utrecht, Netherlands
Tel.: (31) 306691864
Fax: (31) 306691785
E-Mail: maintenance.management@stork.com
Web Site: www.storkmaintenancemanagement.com
Emp.: 130
Management Consulting Service
S.I.C.: 8748
N.A.I.C.S.: 541618
Gerard Rohaan *(Gen Mgr)*

Stork Primoteq B.V. (3)
Industrieplein 3
7553 LL Hengelo, Netherlands
Mailing Address:
PO Box 2079
7550 CB Hengelo, Netherlands
Tel.: (31) 742403000
Fax: (31) 2403899
E-Mail: info.primoteq@stork.com
Web Site: www.storkprimoteq.com
Emp.: 180
Production Equipment Mfr
S.I.C.: 7699
N.A.I.C.S.: 811310
Hans Flef *(Mng Dir)*

Stork Railway Services (3)
A Hogmanweg 130
2031 BL Haarlem, Netherlands
Tel.: (31) 235173232
Fax: (31) 235173233
E-Mail: info.railway@stork.com
Web Site: www.stork.com
Emp.: 200
Engineer, Manufacture & Overhaul Bogies for Railway Cars, Metro Cars & Trams
S.I.C.: 3743
N.A.I.C.S.: 336510

Stork Thermeq B.V. (3)
Langelermaatweg 12
7553 JD Hengelo, Netherlands
Mailing Address:
PO Box 33
7550 AA Hengelo, Netherlands
Tel.: (31) 742401724

Candover Investments plc—(Continued)

Fax: (31) 742424790
E-Mail: info.thermeq@stork.com
Web Site: www.stork-thermeq.nl
Emp.: 170
Boiler Mfr
S.I.C.: 3559
N.A.I.C.S.: 332410
Robert Nijhuis *(Gen Mgr)*

Stork Trading B.V. (3)
Industrieplein 3
7550 LL Hengelo, Netherlands
Mailing Address:
PO Box 533
7550AM Hengelo, Netherlands
Tel.: (31) 742408801
Fax: (31) 742408811
E-Mail: stork.trading@stork.com
Web Site: www.storktrading.nl
Sales Range: $50-74.9 Million
Emp.: 6
Used Power Generating Equipment Distr
S.I.C.: 5084
N.A.I.C.S.: 423830
Richard Youngman *(Gen Mgr)*

Stork Turbo Blading B.V. (3)
Kamerlingh Onnesstraat 21
8606 JN Sneek, Netherlands
Tel.: (31) 515483800
Fax: (31) 515419487
E-Mail: info.turboblading@stork.com
Web Site: www.storktechinalservices.com
Emp.: 75
Turbine Blade Mfr & Whslr
S.I.C.: 3451
N.A.I.C.S.: 332721
Jacco van Berge *(Gen Mgr)*

Affiliates:

hiTecs (3)
Veldzigt 2 A
3454PW De Meern, Netherlands
Mailing Address:
Postbus 199
3454 ZK De Meern, Netherlands
Tel.: (31) 306076030
Fax: (31) 303076031
E-Mail: info@hitecs.nl
Web Site: www.hitecs.nl
Emp.: 50
Internal Employment Agency
S.I.C.: 8999
N.A.I.C.S.: 541612
Martin Dalwel *(Pres)*

Stork GLT v.o.f. (3)
De Vosholen 97
9611 TE Sappemeer, Netherlands
Tel.: (31) 598366300
Fax: (31) 598366395
E-Mail: bart.pronk@gltplus.nl
Web Site: www.gltplus.nl
Emp.: 500
Industrial Building Construction
S.I.C.: 1541
N.A.I.C.S.: 236210
Hanns Mayar *(Pres)*

Stork Plastics Machinery B.V. (3)
Alfred Marshallstraat 2
7559 SE Hengelo, Netherlands
Mailing Address:
PO Box 195
7550AD Hengelo, Netherlands
Tel.: (31) 742405029
Fax: (31) 742405009
E-Mail: sales.spm@stork.com
Web Site: www.storkspm.com
Emp.: 180
Injection Molding Machine Mfr & Whslr
S.I.C.: 3589
N.A.I.C.S.: 333318
Lucien Van Os *(Gen Mgr)*

Non-U.S. Subsidiaries:

RBG Limited (3)
Norfolk House Pitmedden Road
Dyce, Aberdeen, AB21 0DP, United Kingdom
Tel.: (44) 1224722888
Fax: (44) 1224723406
E-Mail: contact@rbgltd.com
Web Site: www.rbgltd.com
Sales Range: $450-499.9 Million
Emp.: 500
Oil & Natural Gas Production Support Services
S.I.C.: 1389
N.A.I.C.S.: 213112
Wayne Henderson *(Dir-Sls & Comml)*

Stork Inter Iberica (3)
Calle la Ribera
Pol Ind Gamonal Villayuda, 09007 Burgos, Spain
Tel.: (34) 947474220
Fax: (34) 947471398
E-Mail: central@stork-iberica.com
Web Site: www.stork-iberica.com
Packaging Mfr
S.I.C.: 2672
N.A.I.C.S.: 322220
Oscar De Gruijter *(Gen Mgr)*

Stork Turbo Service GmbH (3)
Ohmstrasse 10
93055 Regensburg, Germany
Tel.: (49) 94191030
Fax: (49) 9419103398
E-Mail: info.turboservice@stork.com
Web Site: www.stork.com
Sales Range: $10-24.9 Million
Emp.: 400
Specialized Machinery Maintenance
S.I.C.: 7699
N.A.I.C.S.: 811310
Peter Katting *(Mng Dir)*

CANDRAFT DETAILING, INC.

889 Carnarvon Street
New Westminster, BC, V3M 1G2, Canada
Tel.: (604) 525-0055
Web Site: www.candraft.bc.ca
Emp.: 50
Business Description:
Drafting & Detailing Services
S.I.C.: 7389
N.A.I.C.S.: 541340
Personnel:
John Cooper *(Pres)*

CANDY HOOVER GROUP S.R.L.

Via Privata Eden Fumagalli
20047 Brugherio, MB, Italy
Tel.: (39) 3920861
Telex: 322455
Fax: (39) 0392086403
E-Mail: candy@candy.it
Web Site: www.candy-group.com
Year Founded: 1945
Sales Range: $500-549.9 Million
Emp.: 4,500
Business Description:
Household Appliances Mfr
Import Export
S.I.C.: 3639
N.A.I.C.S.: 335228
Personnel:
Silvano Fumagalli *(Pres)*
Aldo Fumagalli *(CEO)*
Mauro Moretti *(CFO & GM Svcs)*

Plant:

Candy Hoover Group S.r.l. - Brugherio Plant (1)
Via Comolli
20861 Brugherio, MB, Italy
Tel.: (39) 03920861
Telex: 300373/303295
Fax: (39) 0392086403
Web Site: www.candy.it
Emp.: 311
Vacuum Mfr
S.I.C.: 3639
N.A.I.C.S.: 335228

Non-U.S. Subsidiaries:

Candy Hoover Electrodomesticos SA (1)
Ahumategui Bide S N
20570 Bergara, Spain (100%)
Tel.: (34) 943037367
Fax: (34) 943037304
E-Mail: info@candy.es
Web Site: www.candy.es
Emp.: 400
Household Appliances
S.I.C.: 3639
N.A.I.C.S.: 335228
Javier Lizarraga *(COO)*

Candy Hoover Portugal, Ltda. (1)
Estrada Nacional n 10 Edificio Pratagi bloco 4-1
Alverca, 2615 129 Lisbon, Portugal (100%)
Tel.: (351) 21 318 9700
Fax: (351) 21 353 7805
Web Site: www.hoover.pt
Emp.: 14
Vacuum Cleaners Mfr
S.I.C.: 3639
N.A.I.C.S.: 335210

Candy Iberica S.A. (1)
Pasaje Tasso 8
8009 Barcelona, Spain (100%)
Tel.: (34) 932452555
Fax: (34) 932464622
Web Site: www.candy.es
Emp.: 12
S.I.C.: 3639
N.A.I.C.S.: 335228

Hoover Ltd. (1)
Pentrebach Road
Merthyr Tydfil, Mid Glamorgan, CF48 4TU, United Kingdom UK
Tel.: (44) 1685721222 (100%)
Fax: (44) 1685382946
Web Site: www.hoover.co.uk
Emp.: 100
S.I.C.: 3639
N.A.I.C.S.: 335228
Robert Mudie *(Dir-Fin)*

Subsidiaries:

Candy Domestic Appliances Limited (2)
Pentrebach Road
Merthyr Tydfil, Mid Glamorgan, CF48 4TU, United Kingdom UK
Tel.: (44) 1685 721 222 (100%)
Web Site: www.candy-domestic.co.uk
Emp.: 10
S.I.C.: 3639
N.A.I.C.S.: 335228
Maurizio Severgnini *(Mng Dir)*

Unit:

Hoover Candy Group Ltd. - Research & Development (2)
1 Forrest Gate
Tannochside Park Uddingston, Glasgow, G71 5PG, United Kingdom (100%)
Tel.: (44) 1698803653
Web Site: www.hoover.co.uk
Emp.: 28
Research & Development of Floorcare Products
S.I.C.: 3639
N.A.I.C.S.: 335210
David Kelly *(Mgr-R&D)*

Usines de Rosieres S.A.S. (1)
30 Rue Yves Lacelle
18400 Lunery, France FR
Tel.: (33) 248557800
Telex: 300373
Fax: (33) 248680175
Emp.: 637
Mfr. of Household Appliances
S.I.C.: 3631
N.A.I.C.S.: 335221

CANDYM ENTERPRISES LTD.

95 Clegg Rd
Markham, ON, L6G 1B9, Canada
Tel.: (905) 474-1555
Fax: (800) 224-8770
Toll Free: (800) 263-3551
E-Mail: info@candym.com
Web Site: www.candym.com
Rev.: $17,248,140
Emp.: 48
Business Description:
Gift Wares Mfr & Distr
S.I.C.: 5199
N.A.I.C.S.: 424990
Personnel:
Brian Matheson *(Pres)*

CANEFCO LIMITED

10 Milner Business Ct Ste 301
Scarborough, ON, M1B 3C6, Canada
Tel.: (416) 335-6556
Fax: (416) 335-6122
Web Site: www.canefco.com
Emp.: 15
Business Description:
Custom Mfr., Designer & Installer of Industrial Heat Processing Equipment, Specializing in the Aluminum Industry
S.I.C.: 3433
N.A.I.C.S.: 333414

CANELSON DRILLING INC.

700 808 4th Ave SW
Calgary, AB, T2P 3E8, Canada
Tel.: (403) 266-3922
Fax: (403) 266-3968
E-Mail: info@canelsondrilling.com
Web Site: www.canelsondrilling.com
Year Founded: 2008
CDI—(TSX)
Rev.: $227,976,499
Assets: $400,294,836
Liabilities: $100,038,173
Net Worth: $300,256,663
Earnings: $47,037,026
Emp.: 710
Fiscal Year-end: 12/31/12
Business Description:
Oil Drilling Rigs Mfr & Operator
S.I.C.: 3533
N.A.I.C.S.: 333132
Personnel:
Elson J. McDougald *(Chm)*
W. Randy Hawkings *(Pres & CEO)*
Robert Skilnick *(CFO)*
Ron Barmby *(COO & VP)*
Daniel G. Kolibar *(Sec)*
Board of Directors:
Elson J. McDougald
W. Randy Hawkings
Rodger Glen Hawkins
C. Kent Jespersen
Dale Johnson
Daniel G. Kolibar
Donald R. Seaman
Legal Counsel:
Borden Ladner Gervais LLP
Calgary, AB, Canada
Transfer Agent:
Olympia Trust Company
Calgary, AB, Canada
U.S. Subsidiary:

CanElson Drilling (US), Inc. (1)
137 Industrial Ave
Mohall, ND 58761-4101
Tel.: (701) 756-7260
Fax: (701) 756-6941
Oilfield Drilling Services
S.I.C.: 1381
N.A.I.C.S.: 213111

CANEO SA

14 Faubourg des Ancetres
BP 40269
90000 Belfort, France
Tel.: (33) 384267542
Fax: (33) 384268456
E-Mail: contact@caneo.eu
Web Site: www.caneo.eu
MLCAN—(EUR)
Business Description:
Soft Drink & Juice Mfr & Sales
S.I.C.: 2086
N.A.I.C.S.: 312111
Personnel:
Renaud Meger-Tissiere *(Co-Chm)*
Benoit Metayer *(Co-Chm)*

Board of Directors:
Renaud Meger-Tissiere
Benoit Metayer

CANERA ENERGY CORP.
800-202 6 Avenue SW
Calgary, AB, T2P 2R9, Canada
Tel.: (403) 718-6282
Year Founded: 2010
Business Description:
Crude Petroleum & Natural Gas Production Services
S.I.C.: 1311
N.A.I.C.S.: 211111
Personnel:
Paul Charron *(Pres & CEO)*
David Broshko *(CFO)*
Brian D. Evans *(Gen Counsel & VP)*

CANERECTOR INC.
23 Lesmill Rd Suite 201
North York, ON, M3B 3P6, Canada
Tel.: (416) 225-6240
Fax: (416) 225-1232
E-Mail: inquiries@canerector.com
Web Site: www.canerector.com
Year Founded: 1947
Sales Range: $500-549.9 Million
Emp.: 2,000
Business Description:
Steel Works & Blast Furnace Mfr
S.I.C.: 3567
N.A.I.C.S.: 333994
Personnel:
Cecil Hawkins *(Pres & CEO)*
Maynard Young *(CFO)*
Divisions:

Associated Valve (1)
703 19th Ave
Nisku, AB, T9E 7Z9, Canada (100%)
Tel.: (780) 436-9030
Fax: (780) 979-0444
E-Mail: info@associatedvalve.com
Web Site: www.associatedvalve.com
Emp.: 5
S.I.C.: 7389
N.A.I.C.S.: 425120
Rory Fodchuk *(Office Mgr)*

Capitol Equipment (1)
85 Talbot Street East
PO Box 606
Jarvis, ON, N0A 1J0, Canada (100%)
Tel.: (519) 587-4571
Fax: (519) 587-2165
E-Mail: capitol@kwic.com
Web Site: www.capitolequipmentrentals.com
Emp.: 30
S.I.C.: 7389
N.A.I.C.S.: 425120
Terry Furler *(Gen Mgr)*

Capitol Pipe & Steel (1)
101 261200 Wagonville Way
Rocky View, Calgary, AB, T4A 0E3, Canada (100%)
Tel.: (403) 279-2428
Fax: (403) 236-2171
Web Site: www.capitolpipe.ca
Emp.: 7
S.I.C.: 7389
N.A.I.C.S.: 425120
Paul Roberts *(Gen Mgr)*

Capitol Pipe Supports (1)
85 Talbot St E
PO Box 606
Jarvis, ON, N0A 1J0, Canada (100%)
Tel.: (519) 587-2264
Fax: (519) 587-2165
E-Mail: capitol@kwic.com
Emp.: 20
S.I.C.: 7389
N.A.I.C.S.: 425120
Terry Furler *(Gen Mgr)*

C.E. MacPherson Division of Conrex Steel Ltd. (1)
468 Rideau St
Kingston, ON, K7K 3B1, Canada (100%)
Tel.: (613) 549-2001
Fax: (613) 549-5606
Toll Free: (800) 461-2001
E-Mail: conrex@kingston.net
Web Site: www.conrex.kingston.net
Sales Range: $1-9.9 Million
Emp.: 16
S.I.C.: 7389
N.A.I.C.S.: 425120
Dave Morre *(Mgr)*

Niagara Structural Steel (1)
23 Smith St
PO Box 730
L2R6Y6 Saint Catharines, ON, L2R6Y6, Canada (100%)
Tel.: (905) 684-2022
Fax: (905) 684-3161
E-Mail: niagara@niagarastructuralsteel.com
Web Site: www.niagarastructuralsteel.com
Emp.: 70
S.I.C.: 7389
N.A.I.C.S.: 425120
Maynard Young *(Mgr-Fin)*

Niagarasteel (1)
23 Smith St
PO Box 730
Saint Catharines, ON, L2R 6Y6, Canada (100%)
Tel.: (905) 688-1943
Fax: (905) 684-6076
Web Site: www.niagarasteel.com
Sales Range: $1-9.9 Million
Emp.: 8
Steel Plate Rolling & Fabrication
S.I.C.: 7389
N.A.I.C.S.: 425120

TIW Steel Platework Inc. (1)
23 Smith Street
PO Box 730
Saint Catharines, ON, L2R 6Y6, Canada
Tel.: (905) 684-9421
Fax: (905) 684-7310
Web Site: www.tiwsteelplatework.ca
Emp.: 120
Design, Manufacture & Construction of Field Erected Steel Platework Structures
S.I.C.: 1791
N.A.I.C.S.: 238120
John Raposo *(Mgr-Gen Sls)*

Subsidiaries:

Douglas Barwick Inc. (1)
150 California Ave
PO Box 756
Brockville, ON, K6V 5W1, Canada (100%)
Tel.: (613) 342-8471
Fax: (613) 342-4432
E-Mail: dbi@douglasbarwick.com
Web Site: www.douglasbarwick.com
Emp.: 65
Stainless Steel Pipe & Pipe Fittings Mfr
S.I.C.: 3317
N.A.I.C.S.: 331210
Pierre Desormeaux *(Gen Mgr)*

Douglas Barwick (1)
599 Cure Boivin
Boisbriand, QC, J7G 2A8, Canada (100%)
Tel.: (450) 435-3643
Fax: (450) 435-5262
E-Mail: dblaval@dblaval.com
Web Site: www.douglasbarwick.com
Emp.: 40
S.I.C.: 7389
N.A.I.C.S.: 425120

Norsteel Limited (1)
234 Des Pionniers
Sept-Iles, QC, G4R 4K2, Canada (100%)
Tel.: (418) 962-7744
Fax: (418) 962-7415
E-Mail: maim@acierdunord.qc.ca
Emp.: 4
S.I.C.: 7389
N.A.I.C.S.: 425120

TIW Western, Inc. (1)
7770 44th St SE
Calgary, AB, T2C 2L5, Canada (100%)
Tel.: (403) 279-8310
Fax: (403) 279-0120
E-Mail: tiww@tiwwestern.com
Web Site: www.tiwwestern.com
Emp.: 80
S.I.C.: 7389
N.A.I.C.S.: 425120

U.S. Division:

Formweld Fittings (1)
8118 Progress Dr
Milton, FL 32583-8725
Tel.: (850) 626-4888
Fax: (850) 626-9988
E-Mail: sales@formweldfitting.com
Web Site: www.formweldfitting.com
Sales Range: $1-9.9 Million
Emp.: 20
Mfr of Buttweld Fittings
S.I.C.: 3443
N.A.I.C.S.: 332313
Chuck Hartwrg *(Pres)*

CANEXUS CORPORATION
Suite 2100 144 - 4th Avenue SW
Calgary, AB, T2P 3N4, Canada
Tel.: (403) 571-7300
Fax: (403) 571-7800
E-Mail: canexus@canexus.ca
Web Site: www.canexus.ca
Year Founded: 2005
C2X—(DEU TSX)
Sls.: $578,943,093
Assets: $898,411,180
Liabilities: $665,438,737
Net Worth: $232,972,443
Earnings: $39,608,715
Fiscal Year-end: 12/31/12
Business Description:
Specialty Chemical Mfr
S.I.C.: 2899
N.A.I.C.S.: 325998
Personnel:
Dennis G. Flanagan *(Chm)*
Richard T. McLellan *(CFO & Sr VP-Fin)*
Diane J. Pettie *(Gen Counsel, Sec & VP)*
Brian P. Bourgeois *(Sr VP-Sls & Mktg)*
Angelo Lacara, Jr. *(Sr VP-Ops)*
Board of Directors:
Dennis G. Flanagan
Stephanie L. Felesky
Hugh A. Fergusson
Douglas P. Hayhurst
Arthur N. Korpach
Richard A. Ott
Thomas A. Sugalski
Lyall C. Work
Transfer Agent:
Computershare Trust Company of Canada
Calgary, AB, Canada

CANFOR CORPORATION
100 1700 West 75th Ave
Vancouver, BC, V6P 6G2, Canada
Tel.: (604) 661-5241
Fax: (604) 661-5253
E-Mail: info@canfor.ca
Web Site: www.canfor.com
Year Founded: 1938
CFP—(TSX)
Sls.: $2,697,869,682
Assets: $2,473,022,358
Liabilities: $1,171,054,962
Net Worth: $1,301,967,396
Earnings: $41,152,428
Emp.: 3,970
Fiscal Year-end: 12/31/12
Business Description:
Holding Company; Forest Products; Pulp, Paper, Lumber & Hardboard Export
S.I.C.: 6719
N.A.I.C.S.: 551112
Personnel:
Ronald L. Cliff *(Chm)*
Donald B. Kayne *(Pres & CEO)*
Alan Nicholl *(CFO & Sr VP-Fin)*
Douglas Warstler *(Pres-Ops-US)*
Patrick Elliott *(Treas & VP)*
David M. Calabrigo *(Sec & Sr VP-Corp & Legal Affairs)*
Alistair L.W. Cook *(Sr VP-Wood Products Ops-Canada)*
Mark A. Feldinger *(Sr VP-Forestry, Environment & Energy)*
Wayne Guthrie *(Sr VP-Sls & Mktg)*
Board of Directors:
Ronald L. Cliff
Peter J. G. Bentley
Glen Clark
Michael J. Korenberg
James A. Pattison
Conrad A. Pinette
J. McNeil Singleton
Ross S. Smith
William Stinson
Transfer Agent:
Canadian Stock Transfer Company, Inc
Vancouver, BC, Canada
Division:

Canfor Corporation-Polar Division (1)
General Delivery 366 54 Hart Highway
Bear Lake, BC, V0J 3G0, Canada (100%)
Tel.: (250) 972-4700
Fax: (250) 972-4323
Web Site: www.canfor.ca
Sales Range: $50-74.9 Million
Emp.: 200
Sawmill & Planing Mill
S.I.C.: 2421
N.A.I.C.S.: 321113
Chris Barber *(Mng Dir)*

Subsidiaries:

Canadian Forest Products Ltd. (1)
100 1700 W 75th Ave
Vancouver, BC, V6P 6G2, Canada (100%)
Tel.: (604) 661-5241
Fax: (604) 661-5235
E-Mail: info@canfor.com
Web Site: www.canfor.com
Emp.: 200
Integrated Forest Products Company
S.I.C.: 0831
N.A.I.C.S.: 113210
Jim Shepherd *(Pres & CEO)*

Units:

Canadian Forest Products - Chetwynd (2)
4700 50th St
PO Box 180
Chetwynd, BC, V0C 1J0, Canada (100%)
Tel.: (250) 788-2231
Fax: (250) 788-4310
Web Site: www.canfor.ca
Emp.: 150
Timber Tracts & Sawmilling
S.I.C.: 0811
N.A.I.C.S.: 113110

Canadian Forest Products - Clear Lake (2)
Sta A
PO Box 9000
V2L 4W2 Prince George, BC, Canada (100%)
Tel.: (250) 964-5000
Fax: (250) 964-5049
E-Mail: info@canfor.ca
Web Site: www.canfor.ca
Emp.: 200
Timber Tracts & Sawmilling
S.I.C.: 0811
N.A.I.C.S.: 113110
Mark Todd *(Mgr-HR)*

Canadian Forest Products - Englewood Logging (2)
5000 Railway Ave
Woss, BC, V0N 3P0, Canada (100%)
Tel.: (250) 281-2300
Fax: (250) 281-2485
Web Site: www.canfor.ca
Emp.: 400
Logging Operations
S.I.C.: 2411
N.A.I.C.S.: 113310

Canfor Corporation—(Continued)

Canadian Forest Products - Grande Prairie (2)
9401 101st St
PO Box 100
Grande Prairie, AB, T8V 3A3, Canada (100%)
Tel.: (780) 538-7749
Fax: (780) 538-7800
Web Site: www.canfor.com
Emp.: 200
Timber Tracts & Sawmilling
S.I.C.: 0811
N.A.I.C.S.: 113110

Canadian Forest Products - Isle Pierre (2)
Bag Service 5410 Isle Pierre Rd
PO Box 6000
Prince George, BC, V2N 2K3, Canada (100%)
Tel.: (250) 441-5900
Fax: (250) 441-3308
E-Mail: melanie.burnett@canfor.com
Web Site: www.canfor.ca
Emp.: 100
Timber Tracts & Sawmilling
S.I.C.: 0811
N.A.I.C.S.: 113110
Al Stearns *(Mgr-Pharma)*

Canadian Forest Products - Prince George Pulp & Paper Mills (2)
Prince George 7689
PO Box 6000
Prince George, BC, V2N 2K3, Canada (100%)
Tel.: (250) 563-0161
Fax: (250) 561-3921
Web Site: www.canfor.ca
Emp.: 310
S.I.C.: 2621
N.A.I.C.S.: 322122
Martin Pudlas *(Gen Mgr)*

Canfor Panel & Fibre (2)
430 Canfor Ave
New Westminster, BC, V3L 5G2, Canada (100%)
Tel.: (604) 529-6300
Fax: (604) 521-3179
Web Site: www.canforpfd.com
Emp.: 144
Panel & Fiber Mat
S.I.C.: 5211
N.A.I.C.S.: 444110
Frank Turnbull *(Gen Mgr)*

U.S. Subsidiary:

Canfor U.S.A. (2)
4395 Curtis Rd
Bellingham, WA 98226-9253 ID
Tel.: (360) 647-2434 (100%)
Fax: (360) 647-2437
Web Site: www.canfor.com
Emp.: 75
Sawmill, Pulp Mill
S.I.C.: 2421
N.A.I.C.S.: 321912

Chemtrade Pulp Chemicals Limited (1)
2711 Pulp Mill Rd
PO Box 2390
Prince George, BC, V2N 2S6, Canada Ca
Tel.: (250) 565-8700 (100%)
Fax: (250) 565-8723
Web Site: www.chemtradelogistics.com
Emp.: 40
Produces Sodium Chlorate Used in the Pulp Mill Bleaching Process
S.I.C.: 2899
N.A.I.C.S.: 325998
Jamie Betts *(Plant Mgr)*

Daaquam Lumber Inc. (1)
2590 Boul Laurier Suite 740
Quebec, QC, G1V 4M6, Canada
Tel.: (418) 659-2422
Fax: (418) 659-2428
E-Mail: info@daaquam.com
Web Site: www.daaquam.com
Emp.: 20
Lumber & Stud Mfr
S.I.C.: 2499
N.A.I.C.S.: 321999
Robert Pratt *(VP)*

Plants:

Canfor Corporation - Canal Flats Sawmill Facility (1)
9006 Grainger Rd
Canal Flats, BC, V0B 1B0, Canada
Tel.: (250) 349-5294
Fax: (250) 349-5250
Emp.: 18
Lumber Products Mfr
S.I.C.: 2499
N.A.I.C.S.: 321999
Pascal Buzon *(Mng Dir)*
Mel Jones *(Mng Dir)*

Canfor Corporation - Chetwynd Sawmill Facility (1)
4700 50th Street
PO Box 180
Chetwynd, BC, V0C 1J0, Canada
Tel.: (250) 788-2231
Fax: (250) 788-4310
Web Site: www.canfor.com
Emp.: 20
Lumber Products Mfr
S.I.C.: 2499
N.A.I.C.S.: 321999
Don Kayne *(Pres)*

Canfor Corporation - Fort St John Sawmill Facility (1)
Swanson Lumber Road RR 1 Site 13 Compartment 2
Fort Saint John, BC, V1J 4M6, Canada
Tel.: (250) 787-3600
Fax: (250) 787-3622
Web Site: www.canfor.com
Lumber Products Mfr
S.I.C.: 3291
N.A.I.C.S.: 327910

Canfor Corporation - Intercontinental Pulp (CPLP) Facility (1)
2533 Prince George Pulp Mill Road
PO Box 6000
Prince George, BC, V2N 2K3, Canada
Tel.: (250) 563-0161
Fax: (250) 561-3921
Emp.: 50
Paper Products Mfr
S.I.C.: 2679
N.A.I.C.S.: 322299
Martin Pudlas *(Gen Mgr)*

Canfor Corporation - Isle Pierre Sawmill Facility (1)
5410 Isle Pierre Road Bag Service Box 6000
Prince George, BC, V2N 2K3, Canada
Tel.: (250) 441-5900
Fax: (250) 441-3308
Web Site: www.canfor.com
Emp.: 13
Lumber Products Mfr
S.I.C.: 2499
N.A.I.C.S.: 321999
Joe Kavanagh *(Gen Mgr)*

Canfor Corporation - Polar Sawmill Facility (1)
36654 Hart Highway General Delivery
Bear Lake, BC, V0J 3G0, Canada
Tel.: (250) 972-4700
Fax: (250) 972-4323
Web Site: www.canfor.com
Emp.: 22
Lumber Products Mfr
S.I.C.: 2499
N.A.I.C.S.: 321999
Jim Tazelaar *(Gen Mgr)*

Canfor Corporation - Prince George Pulp & Paper (CPLP) Facility (1)
2789 Prince George Pulp Mill Road
PO Box 6000
Prince George, BC, V2N 2K3, Canada
Tel.: (250) 563-0161
Fax: (250) 561-3627
Paper Products Mfr
S.I.C.: 2679
N.A.I.C.S.: 322299
Martin Pudlas *(Gen Mgr)*

Canfor Corporation - Quesnel Sawmill Facility (1)
1920 Brownmiller Road
Quesnel, BC, V2J 6S1, Canada
Tel.: (250) 992-5581
Fax: (250) 992-8520
Web Site: www.canfor.com
Lumber Products Mfr
S.I.C.: 2499
N.A.I.C.S.: 321999

U.S. Plants:

Canfor Corporation - Camden Plant (1)
1281 Sanders Creek Rd
Camden, SC 29020-1026
Tel.: (803) 425-1810
Fax: (803) 424-2825
Web Site: www.canfor.com
Lumber Products Mfr
S.I.C.: 2499
N.A.I.C.S.: 321999

Canfor Corporation - Graham Plant (1)
4408 Mt Herman-Rock Creek Rd
Graham, NC 27253
Tel.: (336) 376-3130
Fax: (336) 376-8403
Web Site: www.canfor.com
Lumber Products Mfr
S.I.C.: 2499
N.A.I.C.S.: 321999

Canfor Corporation - Marion Plant (1)
402 Bypass 576
Marion, SC 29571-1519
Tel.: (843) 423-1385
Fax: (843) 423-3475
Web Site: www.canfor.com
Lumber Products Mfr
S.I.C.: 2499
N.A.I.C.S.: 321999

Non-U.S. Subsidiaries:

Canfor Europe (1)
2 Ave De La Foresterie
B 1170 Brussels, Belgium BE
Tel.: (32) 26725561 (100%)
Fax: (32) 26723792
E-Mail: mats.strandberg@canfor.com
Web Site: www.canfor.ca
Emp.: 7
Sales Office for Pulp & Paper
S.I.C.: 2621
N.A.I.C.S.: 322122
Mats Strandberg *(Pres)*

Canfor Japan Corporation (1)
Toranomon Toho Bldg 4F
Tokyo, 105-0001, Japan
Tel.: (81) 335931205
Fax: (81) 335013682
E-Mail: cjc@canfor.com
Web Site: www.canfor.com.jp
Emp.: 5
Lumber & Plywood Products Marketer & Whslr
S.I.C.: 5031
N.A.I.C.S.: 423310
Jason Nomura *(Pres)*

Joint Venture:

Canfor Georgia-Pacific Japan Corporation (2)
Arco Tower 16F 1-8-1 Shimo-Meguro
Meguro-ku, Tokyo, 153-0064, Japan
Tel.: (81) 354345778
Fax: (81) 454345788
Web Site: www.canforpulp.com
Emp.: 10
Marketing Consulting Services
S.I.C.: 8742
N.A.I.C.S.: 541613

CANFOR PULP PRODUCTS INC.

230 - 1700 West 75th Ave
Vancouver, BC, V6P 6G2, Canada
Tel.: (604) 661-5241
Fax: (604) 661-5226
E-Mail: info@canforpulp.com
Web Site: www.canforpulp.com
CFX—(TSX)
Emp.: 1,159
Business Description:
Pulp & Paper Products Supplier
S.I.C.: 2679
N.A.I.C.S.: 322299
Personnel:
Charles J. Jago *(Chm)*
Joe Nemeth *(Pres & CEO)*
Terry D. Hodgins *(CFO & Sec)*
Board of Directors:
Peter J. G. Bentley
Stanley E. Bracken-Horrocks
Donald W. Campbell
Ronald L. Cliff
Charles J. Jago
Joe Nemeth
William W. Stinson
Transfer Agent:
CIBC Mellon Trust Company
Vancouver, BC, Canada

CANGOLD LIMITED

Suite 800 333 Seymour Street
Vancouver, BC, V6B 5A6, Canada
Tel.: (604) 638-8967
Fax: (604) 608-1744
E-Mail: info@cangold.ca
Web Site: www.cangold.ca
Year Founded: 2004
CLD—(TSXV)
Int. Income: $15,880
Assets: $992,766
Liabilities: $61,499
Net Worth: $931,267
Earnings: ($891,309)
Fiscal Year-end: 06/30/13
Business Description:
Mineral Properties Exploration Services
S.I.C.: 1081
N.A.I.C.S.: 213114
Personnel:
Kaare G. Foy *(Chm)*
Robert A. Archer *(Pres & CEO)*
Raakel S. Iskanius *(CFO)*
Wendy M. Ratcliffe *(Sec)*
Board of Directors:
Kaare G. Foy
Robert A. Archer
Robert F. Brown
Brian D. MacEachen
Kenneth W. Major
Transfer Agent:
Computershare Investor Services Inc
100 University Avenue 9th Floor North Tower
Toronto, ON, Canada

CANICKEL MINING LIMITED

1655-999 West Hastings Street
PO Box 35
Vancouver, BC, V6C 2W2, Canada
Tel.: (778) 372-1806
Fax: (604) 254-8863
E-Mail: info@canickel.com
Web Site: www.canickel.com
Year Founded: 1937
CML—(DEU TSX)
Rev.: $9,557,712
Assets: $39,286,824
Liabilities: $45,776,971
Net Worth: ($6,490,146)
Earnings: ($32,869,698)
Emp.: 72
Fiscal Year-end: 12/31/12
Business Description:
Nickel Mining & Exploration Services
S.I.C.: 1021
N.A.I.C.S.: 212234
Personnel:
Wenfeng Liu *(Chm & Interim CEO)*
Derek Liu *(CFO & Sec)*
Stephen Davies *(COO)*
Board of Directors:
Wenfeng Liu
Myles Gao
Raymond Lai
John Pan
Transfer Agent:
Equity Transfer & Trust Company
Toronto, ON, Canada

CANLAN ICE SPORTS CORPORATION
6501 Sprott Street
Burnaby, BC, V5B 3B8, Canada
Tel.: (604) 736-9152
Fax: (604) 736-9170
E-Mail: info@icesports.com
Web Site: www.icesports.com
Year Founded: 1956
ICE—(TSX)
Rev.: $72,387,518
Assets: $102,209,112
Liabilities: $57,550,776
Net Worth: $44,658,337
Earnings: $1,287,256
Emp.: 960
Fiscal Year-end: 12/31/12
Business Description:
Ice Rinks Development Services
S.I.C.: 7999
N.A.I.C.S.: 713940
Personnel:
W. Grant Ballantyne *(Chm)*
Joey St-Aubin *(Pres & CEO)*
Michael F. Gellard *(CFO & Sr VP)*
Mark Faubert *(Sr VP-Ops)*
Board of Directors:
W. Grant Ballantyne
Charles Allen
Frank D. Barker
Geoffrey J. Barker
William G. Bullis
Victor D'Souza
William B. Pattison
Joey St-Aubin
Legal Counsel:
Edwards, Kenny & Bray
19th Floor 1040 West Georgia Street
Vancouver, BC, V6E 4H3, Canada
Transfer Agent:
Computershare Investor Services Inc.
510 Burrard St 2nd Floor
Vancouver, BC, V6C 3B9, Canada
Tel.: (604) 661-9400
Subsidiary:

Les Quatre Glaces (1994) Inc (1)
5880 Boul Taschereau Blvd
Brossard, QC, J4W 1M6, Canada
Tel.: (450) 462-2113
Fax: (450) 462-1949
Web Site: www.Canlanicesports.com
Ice Sports Facility Operation Services
S.I.C.: 7999
N.A.I.C.S.: 711310
Joann Glive *(Gen Mgr)*

CANNON POINT RESOURCES LTD.
Suite 3123 - 595 Burrard St
PO Box 49139
Vancouver, BC, V7X 1J1, Canada
Tel.: (604) 609-6110
Fax: (604) 609-6145
Year Founded: 1978
CNP—(TSXV)
Rev.: $59,734
Assets: $4,934,773
Liabilities: $23,436
Net Worth: $4,911,337
Earnings: ($237,063)
Fiscal Year-end: 12/31/12
Business Description:
Mineral Exploration Services
S.I.C.: 1099
N.A.I.C.S.: 212299
Personnel:
Gordon Keep *(CEO)*
Peter Leitch *(CFO)*

CANNY ELEVATOR CO., LTD.
88 (Luxu) Linhu Economic Development Zone
Wujiang, Jiangsu, 215213, China
Tel.: (86) 512 63297851
Fax: (86) 512 63299709
E-Mail: export@canny-elevator.com
Web Site: www.canny-elevator.com
002367—(SSE)
Sales Range: $75-99.9 Million
Business Description:
Elevator Mfr
S.I.C.: 3534
N.A.I.C.S.: 333921
Personnel:
Youlin Wang *(Pres)*

CANOE FINANCIAL INC.
Suite 3900 350 7th Avenue SW
Calgary, AB, T2P 3N9, Canada
Tel.: (403) 571-5550
Fax: (403) 571-5554
Toll Free: (800) 459-3384
E-Mail: info@canoefinancial.com
Web Site: www.canoefinancial.com
Managed Assets: $1,795,968,000
Business Description:
Open & Closed-End Investment Fund Management Services
S.I.C.: 6799
N.A.I.C.S.: 523920
Personnel:
W. Brett Wilson *(Chm)*
Nevin G. Markwart *(Pres & CEO)*
Renata Colic *(CFO)*
Larry Herscu *(COO)*
Supriya Kapoor *(Chief Compliance Officer & Sr VP)*
Darcy Hulston *(Sr VP & Sls Dir-Natl)*
Affiliates:

EnerVest Diversified Income Trust (1)
Suite 3900 350 7th Avenue SW
Calgary, AB, T2P 3N9, Canada AB
Tel.: (403) 571-5550
Fax: (403) 571-5554
Toll Free: (800) 459-3384
E-Mail: info@canoefinancial.com
Web Site: www.canoefinancial.com
EIT.UN—(TSX)
Rev.: $58,285,357
Assets: $1,357,223,974
Liabilities: $234,275,604
Net Worth: $1,122,948,370
Earnings: $20,376,416
Fiscal Year-end: 12/31/12
Closed-End Investment Fund
S.I.C.: 6726
N.A.I.C.S.: 525990
W. Brett Wilson *(Chm)*
Nevin G. Markwart *(Pres & CEO)*
Renata Colic *(CFO)*
Larry Herscu *(COO)*
Supriya Kapoor *(Chief Compliance Officer & Sr VP)*
Regan Simpson *(Sec)*
Carrie Tuck *(Sr VP & Head-Product & Mktg)*
Darcy Hulston *(Sr VP & Dir-Natl Sls)*

CANOEL INTERNATIONAL ENERGY LTD.
Suite 1500 15th Floor Bankers Court
850 - 2nd Street SW
Calgary, AB, T2P 0R8, Canada
Tel.: (403) 938-8154
Fax: (403) 775-4474
E-Mail: info@canoelenergy.com
Web Site: www.canoelenergy.com
Year Founded: 2007
CIL—(TSXV)
Rev.: $2,460,089
Assets: $5,081,713
Liabilities: $7,168,317
Net Worth: ($2,086,604)
Earnings: ($2,093,837)
Fiscal Year-end: 03/31/13
Business Description:
Petroleum & Natural Gas Exploration Services
S.I.C.: 1389
N.A.I.C.S.: 213112
Personnel:
Andrea Cattaneo *(Pres & CEO)*
Luigi Regis Milano *(CFO)*
Board of Directors:
Erik Larre
Luigi Regis Milano
Jose Ramon Lopez Portillo
Dario Sodero
Francesco Zofrea
Transfer Agent:
Olympia Trust Company
Suite 2300 125 9th Ave SE
Calgary, AB, Canada

CANON INC.
30-2 Shimomaruko 3-Chome Ohta-ku
Tokyo, 146-8501, Japan
Tel.: (81) 3 3758 2111
Fax: (81) 3 5482 9680
Web Site: www.canon.com
Year Founded: 1937
CAJ—(DEU NGO NYSE TKS)
Sls.: $38,277,668,000
Assets: $43,510,533,000
Liabilities: $13,213,211,000
Net Worth: $30,297,322,000
Earnings: $2,556,895,000
Emp.: 197,386
Fiscal Year-end: 12/31/12
Business Description:
Cameras, Business Machines & Precision Optical Equipment Mfr Import Export
S.I.C.: 3579
N.A.I.C.S.: 333316
Personnel:
Fujio Mitarai *(Chm & CEO)*
Tsuneji Uchida *(Pres & COO)*
Yasuo Mitsuhashi *(Sr Mng Dir & CEO-Peripheral Products Ops)*
Yoroku Adachi *(Sr Mng Dir)*
Toshio Homma *(Sr Mng Dir)*
Haruhisa Honda *(Sr Mng Dir)*
Shigeyuki Matsumoto *(Sr Mng Dir)*
Masaki Nakaoka *(Sr Mng Dir)*
Masaya Maeda *(Mng Dir & CEO-Image Comm Products Ops)*
Hideki Ozawa *(Mng Dir)*
Toshizo Tanaka *(CFO & Exec VP)*
Seymour E. Liebman *(Chief Admin Officer, Gen Counsel, Sec-Admin Grp & Exec VP)*
Toshiaki Ikoma *(CTO & Exec VP)*
Kunio Watanabe *(Exec VP)*
Board of Directors:
Fujio Mitarai
Yoroku Adachi
Makoto Araki
Toshio Homma
Haruhisa Honda
Toshiaki Ikoma
Masaya Maeda
Shigeyuki Matsumoto
Yasuo Mitsuhashi
Masaki Nakaoka
Hideki Ozawa
Hiroyuki Suematsu
Toshizo Tanaka
Yasuhiro Tani
Tsuneji Uchida
Kunio Watanabe
Transfer Agent:
Mizuho Trust & Banking Co., Ltd.
2-1 Yaesu 1-Chome Chuo-ku
Tokyo, 103 8670, Japan
Tel.: (81) 332788111
Fax: (81) 332816947
Subsidiaries:

ASPAC Inc. (1)
3-17-7 Shibaura Ryoshintaiji Bldg
Minato-Ku, Tokyo, 108-0023, Japan
Tel.: (81) 3 6435 4890
Fax: (81) 3 5418 4677
Web Site: www.canon.com
Emp.: 641
Computer Software Development Services
S.I.C.: 7371
N.A.I.C.S.: 541511

Canon ANELVA Corporation (1)
5-1 Kurigi 2-chome
Asao-ku, Kawasaki, Kanagawa, 215-8550, Japan
Tel.: (81) 449805111
Fax: (81) 449864014
Web Site: www.canon-anelva.co.jp
Sales Range: $550-599.9 Million
Emp.: 1,460
Mfr of Vacuum Thin-Film Deposition & Processing Equipment
S.I.C.: 3674
N.A.I.C.S.: 334413
Junji Ichikawa *(Pres)*

Canon Chemicals, Inc. (1)
1882 Kukizaki
Tsukuba-shi, Ibaraki, 300 1294, Japan JP
Tel.: (81) 298762111 (100%)
Fax: (81) 29876009
Web Site: www.canon-kasei.co.jp
Emp.: 1,344
Mfr. of Toner Cartridgers, Chemical Products & Plastic Precision-Molded Parts
S.I.C.: 2899
N.A.I.C.S.: 325998

Canon Components, Inc. (1)
3461-1 Ooaza-nanahongi Kamisato Machi
Kodama-gun, Saitama, 369-0093, Japan JP
Tel.: (81) 495333111 (100%)
Fax: (81) 495333114
Web Site: www.canon-compo.co.jp
Emp.: 1,000
Mfr. & Sales of Contact Image Sensors, Printer Cartridges & Printed Circuits
S.I.C.: 3575
N.A.I.C.S.: 334118
Shiyuki Komatsu *(CEO & Pres)*

Canon Ecology Industry Inc. (1)
1234 Matate
Bando, Ibaraki, 306-0605, Japan
Tel.: (81) 297 36 3101
Web Site: www.canon.com
Emp.: 749
Toner Cartridge Repair & Maintenance Services
S.I.C.: 7699
N.A.I.C.S.: 811212

Canon Electronics Business Systems Inc. (1)
1248 Shimokagemori
Chichibu, Saitama, 369-1892, Japan
Tel.: (81) 494 21 1621
Emp.: 23
Laser Printer Distr
S.I.C.: 5112
N.A.I.C.S.: 424120

Canon Electronics, Inc. (1)
1248 Shimokagemori Chichibu-shi
Saitama, 369-1892, Japan JP
Tel.: (81) 494233111 (100%)
Fax: (81) 494231942
E-Mail: ir@canon-elec.co.jp
Web Site: www.canon-elec.co.jp
7739—(TKS)
Sls.: $1,159,950,000
Assets: $1,001,671,000
Liabilities: $251,449,000
Net Worth: $750,222,000
Earnings: $68,343,000
Emp.: 6,073
Fiscal Year-end: 12/31/12
Electronic Component Sales; Magnetic Components, Document Scanners, Micrographics & Handheld Information Terminals
S.I.C.: 3577
N.A.I.C.S.: 334118
Hisashi Sakamaki *(Pres & CEO)*
Takashi Ehara *(Sr Mng Dir)*
Takumi Ishizuka *(Mng Dir)*

Subsidiaries:

Asia Pacific System Research Co., Ltd. (2)
3-37-10 Takada
Toshima-ku, Tokyo, Japan
Tel.: (81) 339854311
Fax: (81) 339854310

Canon Inc.—(Continued)

Web Site: www.asia.co.jp
Computer Systems Design Services
S.I.C.: 7373
N.A.I.C.S.: 541512
Takeshi Uchiyama *(CEO)*
Kiyoshi Izeki *(Sr Exec Officer & Chief Dir-Gen Support)*
Hideki Takanabe *(Exec Officer & Dir-Bus Plng)*
Kazuhiko Wakabayashi *(Dir-Tech Support & Exec Officer & Dir Of Industrial Sys)*
Tatsuya Sakamoto *(Exec Officer)*
Masaki Hirabayashi *(Sr Exec officer)*
Kazutoshi Nanya *(Exec Officer & Dir-Plng)*
Toshiyuki Nebashi *(Exec Officer)*
Hideyuki Sato *(Sr Exec Officer)*
Shunji Uchida *(Sr Exec Officer)*

e-System Corporation (2)
1-3-11 Nihombashi Chuo-ku
Tokyo, 103-0027, Japan
Tel.: (81) 3 35169200
Fax: (81) 3 35169210
Web Site: www.e-system.co.jp
Sales Range: $50-74.9 Million
Emp.: 400
CRM Consulting, Integration, Technical Support & Application Support Services
S.I.C.: 7373
N.A.I.C.S.: 541512
Tetsuro Tahara *(Pres)*
Hidehiko Ichimura *(Mng Dir)*

Subsidiary:

EC Concierge Corporation (3)
6th Floor Asano Bldg 1-3-11 Nihonbashi Chuou-ku
103-0027 Tokyo, Japan (100%)
Tel.: (81) 335169320
Fax: (81) 335169207
Computer Facilities Management Services
S.I.C.: 7376
N.A.I.C.S.: 541513
Hirofumi Watanabe *(Pres)*

Canon Finetech Inc. (1)
5540-11 Sakatemachi
Joso-shi, Ibaraki, 303 8503, Japan JP
Tel.: (81) 297270111 (100%)
Fax: (81) 297271551
Web Site: www.canon-finetech.co.jp
Sls.: $1,741,315,257
Emp.: 1,600
Mfr. & Sales of Business Machines & Peripherals
S.I.C.: 3575
N.A.I.C.S.: 334118
Ikuo Soma *(Pres)*
Hiroshi Sugitani *(Mng Dir)*
Hisashi Kurachi *(Mng Dir)*

Subsidiary:

Nisca Corporation (2)
430-1 Kobayashi Minamikoma-gun
Fujikawa-cho, Yamanashi, 400-0593, Japan
Tel.: (81) 556 22 3929
Fax: (81) 556 22 8508
E-Mail: info@office.nisca.co.jp
Web Site: www.nisca.co.jp
Sls.: $267,688,320
Emp.: 827
Photocopying Machinery & Printer Mfr
S.I.C.: 3579
N.A.I.C.S.: 333316
Noriyoshi Ueda *(Pres)*

Plants:

Canon Finetech Inc. - Fukui Plant (2)
3-6-4 Technoport Ishibashi-cho
Fukui, 910-3138, Japan
Tel.: (81) 776 85 1300
Photocopying Machinery Mfr
S.I.C.: 3579
N.A.I.C.S.: 333316

Canon Finetech Inc. - Ibaraki Plant (2)
5540-11 Sakatemachi
Joso, Ibaraki, 303-8503, Japan
Tel.: (81) 297 27 0111
Web Site: www.canon-finetech.co.jp/en/profile/overview.html
Photographic Machinery Mfr
S.I.C.: 3579
N.A.I.C.S.: 333316

Non-U.S. Subsidiaries:

Canon Finetech Nisca Industrial Hong Kong Co., Limited (2)
Suite 1116 Shatin Galleria 18-24 Shan Mei Street
Fotan, New Territories, China (Hong Kong)
Tel.: (852) 2687 4928
Fax: (852) 2688 2728
Emp.: 7
Digital Camera & Printer Mfr
S.I.C.: 3579
N.A.I.C.S.: 333316

Canon Finetech Nisca (Shenzhen) Inc. (2)
Building A Kefa Industrial Park Xintian Community Guanlan Town
Shenzhen, 518040, China
Tel.: (86) 75583596300
Fax: (86) 75583306850
Photocopying Machinery Mfr
S.I.C.: 3579
N.A.I.C.S.: 333316

Canon i-tech Inc. (1)
9F Fuchu South Bldg 1-40-1 Miyamachi
Fuchu, Tokyo, 183-0023, Japan
Tel.: (81) 42 366 1161
Fax: (81) 42 366 8844
E-Mail: privacy@citech.co.jp
Web Site: www.citech.co.jp
Emp.: 15
Color Image Management Software Development Services
S.I.C.: 7371
N.A.I.C.S.: 541511
Masahiro Tomosada *(Pres & CEO)*

Canon Imaging Systems Inc. (1)
Plaka 2 4F 1-2 Sasaguchi
Chuou-ku, Niigata, 950-0911, Japan
Tel.: (81) 25 244 6335
Web Site: www.canon.com
Emp.: 370
Photocopying Software Development Services
S.I.C.: 7371
N.A.I.C.S.: 541511

Canon Machinery Inc. (1)
85 Minami Yamada-cho
Kusatsu, Shiga, Japan 525-8511
Tel.: (81) 77 563 8511
Fax: (81) 77 566 1824
Web Site: www.canon-machinery.co.jp
Sls.: $376,606,090
Emp.: 1,061
Electronic Component Mfr
S.I.C.: 3679
N.A.I.C.S.: 334419
Kazuo Kageyama *(Pres)*

Non-U.S. Subsidiaries:

Canon Machinery (Dalian) Co., Ltd. (2)
No 8 Huashengda 26 Development Zone
Dalian, Liaoning, 116600, China
Tel.: (86) 411 8753 1126
Fax: (86) 411 8753 1127
Emp.: 10
Photographic Machinery Mfr
S.I.C.: 3579
N.A.I.C.S.: 333316
Takahiro Tsubota *(Mng Dir)*

Canon Machinery (Malaysia) Sdn Bhd. (2)
Lot 47 Persiaran Teknologi Subang Subang Hi-Tech Industrial Park
Batu Tiga, 40000 Shah Alam, Selangor Darul Ehsan, Malaysia
Tel.: (60) 3 5633 2127
Fax: (60) 3 5637 6416
Web Site: www.canon.com.my/business/web/company/about/associate
Emp.: 95
Semiconductor Equipment Mfr
S.I.C.: 3674
N.A.I.C.S.: 334413

Canon Marketing Japan Inc. (1)
Canon S Tower 16-6 Konan 2-chome
Minato-ku
Tokyo, 108-8011, Japan
Tel.: (81) 3 67199111
Web Site: cweb.canon.jp
8060—(TKS)
Sls.: $7,493,574,000
Assets: $5,088,314,000
Liabilities: $2,293,346,000
Net Worth: $2,794,968,000
Earnings: $116,369,000
Emp.: 18,490
Fiscal Year-end: 12/31/12
Office Equipment Marketer; IT Consulting Services
S.I.C.: 5044
N.A.I.C.S.: 423420
Haruo Murase *(Chm)*
Masami Kawasaki *(Pres)*
Hisato Abe *(Exec Officer)*
Masaharu Hayashi *(Exec Officer)*
Takeshi Iwaya *(Exec Officer)*
Yoshiyuki Kurihara *(Exec Officer)*
Keiji Matsumoto *(Exec Officer)*
Koichi Mikami *(Exec Officer)*
Hiroki Morita *(Exec Officer)*
Yasuhisa Oba *(Exec Officer)*
Kazunori Asada *(Exec VP)*
Shinichi Inoue *(Sr VP)*
Akihisa Kamimori *(Sr VP)*
Akihiko Kamino *(Sr VP)*
Masahiro Sakata *(Sr VP)*
Osamu Sasaki *(Sr VP)*
Masaki Sawabe *(Sr VP)*
Yo Shibasaki *(Sr VP)*
Yutaka Usui *(Sr VP)*
Koichi Yagi *(Sr VP)*

Subsidiaries:

Canon Business Support Inc. (2)
Canon Konan Building 13-29 Konan 2-chome
Minato-ku, Tokyo, 108-8011, Japan
Tel.: (81) 367197832
Fax: (81) 367197831
E-Mail: gp-cbs-it@canon-bs.co.jp
Emp.: 724
Business Process Outsourcing Services
S.I.C.: 7389
N.A.I.C.S.: 561499

Subsidiary:

OAL Inc. (3)
2-13-29 Konan
Minato-Ku, Tokyo, 108-0075, Japan
Tel.: (81) 367199383
Business Process Outsourcing Services
S.I.C.: 7389
N.A.I.C.S.: 561499

Canon Customer Support Inc. (2)
Canon MJ Makuhari Office 16F 7-2 Nakase 1-chome
Mihama-ku, Chiba, 261-0023, Japan
Tel.: (81) 43 211 9312
Fax: (81) 43 211 9329
Emp.: 754
Business Process Outsourcing Services
S.I.C.: 7389
N.A.I.C.S.: 561499
Jill Nakamura *(Gen Mgr)*

Canon Field Assist Inc. (2)
Canon S Tower 22F 16-6 Konan 2-chome
Minato-ku, Tokyo, 108-8011, Japan
Tel.: (81) 3 6719 9872
Fax: (81) 367198165
Emp.: 100
Camera Retailer
S.I.C.: 5731
N.A.I.C.S.: 443142
Soichiro Tabe *(Gen Mgr)*

Canon MJ IT Group Holdings Inc. (2)
Nomura Fudosan Tennozu Building 4-11 Higashishinagawa 2-chome
Shinagawa-ku, Tokyo, 140-8526, Japan
Tel.: (81) 3 6701 3600
Fax: (81) 367013607
Web Site: www.canon-mj.co.jp
Emp.: 5
Investment Management Services
S.I.C.: 6282
N.A.I.C.S.: 523920

Subsidiaries:

Canon IT Solutions Inc. (3)
Nomura Fudosan Tennozu Building 4-11 Higashishinagawa 2-chome
Shinagawa-ku, Tokyo, 140-8526, Japan
Tel.: (81) 3 6701 3300
Fax: (81) 3 6701 3301
Emp.: 2,676
Software Consulting Services
S.I.C.: 7373
N.A.I.C.S.: 541512

Subsidiaries:

Canon ITS Medical Inc. (4)
2nd Floor of Building 10 No 29 No 8 Terasaki Nishimiyahara 1-chome
Yodogawa-ku, Osaka, Japan
Tel.: (81) 6 4807 1678
Fax: (81) 6 4807 1428
Medical Equipment Mfr
S.I.C.: 3841
N.A.I.C.S.: 339112

Garden Network, Ltd. (4)
6-1-15 Kachidokiys Building
Chuo-Ku, Tokyo, 104-0054, Japan
Tel.: (81) 3 6701 3630
Fax: (81) 3 6701 3631
Gas Station Management Services
S.I.C.: 8748
N.A.I.C.S.: 541618

Qualysite technologies Inc. (4)
195-3 Toyohara Mirai Hall 2
Nago, Okinawa, 905-2172, Japan
Tel.: (81) 980 50 0600
Fax: (81) 980 50 0601
E-Mail: info@qualysite.co.jp
Software Development Services
S.I.C.: 7371
N.A.I.C.S.: 541511

SuperStream Inc. (4)
Nomura Fudosan Tennozu Bldg 2-4-11 Higashi-shinagawa
Shinagawa-ku, Tokyo, 140-8526, Japan
Tel.: (81) 3 6701 3647
Fax: (81) 3 6701 3641
E-Mail: ssusers@superstream.co.jp
Web Site: www.superstream.co.jp
Emp.: 13
Software Development Services
S.I.C.: 7371
N.A.I.C.S.: 541511
Yoshio Tanimoto *(Pres & CEO)*

U.S. Subsidiary:

Canon Software America, Inc. (4)
1 Canon Plz
Lake Success, NY 11042-1198
Tel.: (516) 327-2270
Software Development Services
S.I.C.: 7371
N.A.I.C.S.: 541511

Edifist Learning Inc. (3)
Otemachi Building 2F 6-1 Otemachi 1-chome
Chiyoda-ku, Tokyo, 100-0004, Japan
Tel.: (81) 3 3282 1311
Fax: (81) 3 3282 1303
E-Mail: learning@edifist.co.jp
Emp.: 58
Information Technology Training Services
S.I.C.: 8299
N.A.I.C.S.: 611430
Toshiro Kamei *(Pres)*

Canon Print square Inc. (2)
Canon Konan Building 13-29 Konan 2-chome
Minato-ku, Tokyo, 108-8011, Japan
Tel.: (81) 3 6719 9594
Web Site: www.canon.com
Emp.: 62
Photocopying Machinery Leasing Services
S.I.C.: 7377
N.A.I.C.S.: 532420

Canon Software, Inc. (2)
3-9-7 Mita
Minato Ku, 108-8317 Tokyo, Japan JP
Tel.: (81) 334559911 (100%)
Fax: (81) 334559916
E-Mail: webmaster@canon-soft.co.jp
Web Site: www.canon-soft.co.jp
Sls.: $144,691,200
Emp.: 861
S.I.C.: 5946
N.A.I.C.S.: 443142

Subsidiary:

Canon Software Information Systems Inc. (3)
Osaka Sakaisuji Bldg 2-2-13 Bakuromachi
Chuo-ku, Osaka, 541-0059, Japan

Tel.: (81) 6 6125 4828
Fax: (81) 6 6125 4821
Web Site: www.canon-js.co.jp
Rev.: $37,513,370
Emp.: 267
Networking Software Development Services
S.I.C.: 7371
N.A.I.C.S.: 541511
Hideyuki Umezawa *(Chm)*
Akihiko Chimura *(Mng Dir)*

ELK Corporation (2)
2-17-4 Yushima
Bunkyo-ku, Tokyo, 113-0034, Japan
Tel.: (81) 3 3818 1324
Fax: (81) 3 3818 1814
E-Mail: sales-overseas@elkc.co.jp
Emp.: 337
Medical Device Mfr
S.I.C.: 3841
N.A.I.C.S.: 339112
Keiji Matsumoto *(Pres)*

Oce-Japan Corporation (2)
25 1 Nishi Shimbashi 3 Chome
Minato-ku, Tokyo, 105 0003, Japan (85%)
Tel.: (81) 354026145
Fax: (81) 354026134
Web Site: www.ocejapan.co.jp
Emp.: 100
S.I.C.: 5943
N.A.I.C.S.: 453210
Yoshiachi Yamamoto *(Gen Mgr)*

Showa Information Systems Co., Ltd. (2)
No 45 Kowa Bldg 1-15-9 Minami Aoyama
Minato-Ku, Tokyo, 107-0062, Japan JP
Tel.: (81) 3 3403 7101
Fax: (81) 3 3403 9168
E-Mail: senden@sis.co.jp
Web Site: www.sis.co.jp
Rev.: $135,876,840
Emp.: 380
Precision Printing System Mfr
S.I.C.: 3555
N.A.I.C.S.: 333244
Yuichi Nakazawa *(Co-Chm)*
Koutaro Tomiyama *(Co-Chm)*

withPhoto Inc. (2)
2-2-43 Higashi-Shinagawa
Shinagawa-ku, Tokyo, Japan
Tel.: (81) 3 3740 0531
Web Site: www.canon.com
Emp.: 10
Photographic Mail Ordering Services
S.I.C.: 5961
N.A.I.C.S.: 454113

Non-U.S. Subsidiary:

Canon Advanced Technologies Taiwan, Inc. (2)
9F-1 No 25 Puding Road
Hsin-chu, Taiwan
Tel.: (886) 3 5797 500
Fax: (886) 3 5797 511
Web Site: www.canon-at.com.tw
Emp.: 6
Semiconductor Testing Equipment Mfr
S.I.C.: 3825
N.A.I.C.S.: 334515
Yasuhisa Oba *(Chm)*
Koichiro Kawana *(Pres)*

Canon Mold Co., Ltd. (1)
6241-6 Koibuchi Kasama
Kasama, Ibaraki, 309-1703, Japan
Tel.: (81) 296 77 8171
Fax: (81) 296 77 8359
Emp.: 491
Precise Plastic Molding Mfr
S.I.C.: 3089
N.A.I.C.S.: 326199

Canon Optron, Inc. (1)
1744-1 Kanakubo
Yuki-shi, Ibaraki, 307-0015, Japan JP
Tel.: (81) 296213700 (100%)
Fax: (81) 296213770
E-Mail: optsales@canon-optron.co.jp
Web Site: www.canon-optron.co.jp
Sales Range: $25-49.9 Million
Emp.: 200
Polisher of Optical Crystals for Steppers, Cameras & Telescopes & Manufacturer of Vapor Deposition Materials
S.I.C.: 3827
N.A.I.C.S.: 333314

Takeuti Kazunori *(Pres)*

Canon Precision Inc. (1)
4-1 Seinobukuro 5-chome
Aomori, 036-8072, Japan JP
Tel.: (81) 172322911 (100%)
Fax: (81) 337250831
Web Site: www.canon-prec.co.jp
Sls.: $433,152,000
Emp.: 953
Developer & Sales of DC Micromotors & Ultrasonic Motor-Related Units
S.I.C.: 3621
N.A.I.C.S.: 335312
Omi Noboru *(Pres)*

Canon Sales Co., Inc. (1)
30-2 Shimomaruko 3 chome Ohta-ku
Tokyo, 146-8501, Japan (100%)
Tel.: (81) 3 3758 2111
E-Mail: shimada.etsuko.cp@canon-mj.co.jp
Web Site: www.canon.com
Emp.: 15,813
R&D & Corporate Administration
S.I.C.: 8731
N.A.I.C.S.: 541712

Canon Semiconductor Equipment Inc. (1)
1234 Matate
Bando-shi, Ibaraki, 306-0605, Japan JP
Tel.: (81) 297352531
Fax: (81) 297363251
Web Site: www.canon-semicon.co.jp
Emp.: 1,345
Sales of Business Machines
S.I.C.: 5112
N.A.I.C.S.: 453210

Canon System & Support (1)
Tokyo MI Bldg 2 4 Higashi Shinagawa 2 Chome
Shanagawa Ku, Tokyo, 140 8650, Japan JP
Tel.: (81) 354797878 (100%)
Fax: (81) 354622739
Web Site: www.canon-sas.co.jp
Emp.: 300
Sales & Servicer of Business Machines
S.I.C.: 5044
N.A.I.C.S.: 423420

Canon Technical Information Services Inc. (1)
30-2 Shimomaruko 3-chome
Ohta-ku, Tokyo, 146-8501, Japan
Tel.: (81) 3 3757 6241
Fax: (81) 3 7578 131
Emp.: 76
Translation Services
S.I.C.: 7389
N.A.I.C.S.: 541930

Canon Tokki Corporation (1)
10-1 Shinko-cho
Mitsuke-shi, Niigata, 954-0076, Japan
Tel.: (81) 258 61 5050
Fax: (81) 258 61 5980
Web Site: www.canon-tokki.co.jp
Emp.: 283
Vacuum Product Mfr
S.I.C.: 3679
N.A.I.C.S.: 334419
Teruhisa Teruhisa *(Chm & CEO)*
Nakaharu Kuroiwa *(Pres & COO)*

Canon Wind Inc. (1)
564-1 Sako
Oita, 870-0292, Japan
Tel.: (81) 97 524 1122
Emp.: 17
Digital Camera Parts Mfr
S.I.C.: 3579
N.A.I.C.S.: 333316

Miyazaki Daishin Canon Co., Ltd. (1)
4308 1 Ohaza Takajo Kijo-Cho
Koyu-gun, Miyazaki, 884 0101, Japan JP
Tel.: (81) 983322233 (100%)
Fax: (81) 983324173
E-Mail: yoshida@mac.canon.co.jp
Emp.: 1,500
Mfr. of Digital Video Camcorders, Digital Cameras & Surface Mount Packaging
S.I.C.: 3579
N.A.I.C.S.: 333316

Nagahama Canon Inc. (1)
1280 Kunitomomachi
Nagahama-Shi, Shiga, 526-0001, Japan JP
Tel.: (81) 749642111 (100%)
Fax: (81) 749653043
E-Mail: t.hirooka@canon-nagahama.co.jp
Web Site: www.canon-nagahama.co.jp
Emp.: 1,000
Mfr. of Chemical Products, Solar Cells & Printer Cartridges
S.I.C.: 2899
N.A.I.C.S.: 325998

Nagasaki Canon Inc. (1)
925-1 Orishikisego Hasami-cho
Higashisonogi-gun, Nagasaki, 859-3793, Japan
Tel.: (81) 956 85 1111
Web Site: www.canon.com
Emp.: 1,125
Digital Camera Mfr
S.I.C.: 3579
N.A.I.C.S.: 333316

Oita Canon Materials Inc. (1)
111 Kumano 1-chome
Kitsuki, Oita, 873-8501, Japan
Tel.: (81) 978 64 2111
Emp.: 1,736
Specialty Chemicals Mfr
S.I.C.: 2899
N.A.I.C.S.: 325998

Ueno Canon Materials Inc. (1)
410-7 Higashiomachi Mita-aza
Iga-Shi, Ueno, Mie, 518-0022, Japan JP
Tel.: (81) 595243111
Web Site: www.canon.com
Emp.: 250
Mfr of Chemical Products for Copying Machines & Printers
S.I.C.: 2899
N.A.I.C.S.: 325998

U.S. Subsidiary:

Canon U.S.A., Inc. (1)
1 Canon Plz
Lake Success, NY 11042 (100%)
Tel.: (516) 328-5000
Fax: (516) 328-5069
Toll Free: (800) 652-2666
E-Mail: pr@cusa.canon.com
Web Site: www.usa.canon.com
Sls.: $9,722,099,712
Emp.: 900
Photographic & Office Products Importer, Marketer & Distr
Import
S.I.C.: 5044
N.A.I.C.S.: 423420
Joe Adachi *(Pres & CEO)*
Kunihiko Tedo *(CFO, Sr VP & Treas-Fin & Acctg)*
Seymour E. Liebman *(Chief Admin Officer, Gen Counsel & Exec VP)*
Toru Nishizawa *(Pres/CEO-Canon US Life Sciences Inc.)*
Satoshi Nagata *(Pres-Canon Information and Imaging Solutions, Inc.)*
Yuichi Ishizuka *(Exec VP)*
Tamotsu Nakamura *(Exec VP-Imaging Sys Grp)*
Joseph Warren *(Sr VP & Gen Mgr-Corp HR)*

Division:

Canon Latin America, Inc. (2)
703 Waterford Way Ste 400
Miami, FL 33126-4675 (100%)
Tel.: (305) 260-7400
Fax: (305) 260-7409
Web Site: www.canonlatinamerica.com
Emp.: 80
Canon Sales & Marketing for Latin America
S.I.C.: 3579
N.A.I.C.S.: 333316
Taro Maruyama *(CEO)*
Kenji Kobayashi *(Pres)*

Non-U.S. Subsidiaries:

Canon Argentina S.A. (3)
San Martin 344 Piso 19
Buenos Aires, C1004AAH, Argentina (100%)
Tel.: (54) 11 5554 9800
Fax: (54) 11 5554 9899
E-Mail: info@canon.com.ar
Web Site: www.canonarg.com.ar
Sales Range: $10-24.9 Million
Emp.: 100
Sales of Business Machines
S.I.C.: 5044
N.A.I.C.S.: 423420

Canon Chile S.A. (3)
Av Manquehue Norte No 1337
Piso 1 Vitacura, Santiago, Chile CL
Tel.: (56) 23666600 (100%)
Fax: (56) 22422727
Web Site: www.canon.cl
Emp.: 130
Sales of Business Machines
S.I.C.: 5044
N.A.I.C.S.: 423420
Jun Otsuka *(Pres & Gen Mgr)*

Canon do Brasil Industrial e Comercio Limitada (3)
Avenida Do Cafe 277
6 Andar Torre B Vila Guarani, CEP 04311 002 Sao Paulo, S P, Brazil BR
Tel.: (55) 150707100 (100%)
Fax: (55) 1150707101
Web Site: www.canon.com.br
Emp.: 100
Sales of Copy & Fax Machines
S.I.C.: 5044
N.A.I.C.S.: 423420
Jun Otsuka *(Pres & CEO)*

Subsidiary:

Oce-Brasil Comercio e Industria Ltda. (4)
Ave Macoes Unidas 11857 1st Fl
04578000 Sao Paulo, Brazil BR
Tel.: (55) 1130535300 (100%)
Fax: (55) 1130535314
E-Mail: info@oce-brasil.com.br
Web Site: www.oce.com
Emp.: 60
Sales, Services & Marketing for High End Printing for the Engineering Market
S.I.C.: 2759
N.A.I.C.S.: 323111
Roel Ulidricks *(CEO)*

Canon Mexicana, S. de R.L. de C.V. (3)
Bvld Manuel Villa Camacho 138 Piso PB 15 16 y 17
Col Lomas de Chapultepec
Del Miguel Hidalgo, CP 11000 Mexico, D F, Mexico MX
Tel.: (52) 52494900 (100%)
Fax: (52) 52494901
Toll Free: 800 710 7168
E-Mail: canonmx_soporte@cusa.canon.com
Web Site: www.canon.com.mx
Emp.: 166
Sales of all Canon Products
S.I.C.: 5734
N.A.I.C.S.: 443142
Yasuhiro Suzuki *(Pres)*

Subsidiary:

Oce Mexico S.A. de C.V. (4)
Prolongacion Reforma 1236 4 To Piso Col Santa Fe
Del Cuajimalpa, 5348 Mexico, Mexico
Tel.: (52) 55 5089 8710
Fax: (52) 55 5089 8701
Web Site: www.oce-mexico.com
Emp.: 7
Document Management Software Development Services
S.I.C.: 7371
N.A.I.C.S.: 541511
Jaime Escudero *(Gen Mgr)*

Canon Panama, S.A. (3)
Ave Ricardo J Alfaro Edificio Canon 2nd Fl
PO Box 7022
Panama, Panama Pa
Tel.: (507) 2798900
Fax: (507) 2798940
E-Mail: aevesucre@canonpoinpa.com
Web Site: www.canonpoint.com
Sls.: $10,000,000
Emp.: 200
Sales of all Canon Products
S.I.C.: 5731
N.A.I.C.S.: 443142
Elsa de Sucre *(Pres)*

Canon Inc.—(Continued)

Subsidiaries:

Canon Business Process Services, Inc. (2)
(Formerly Oce Business Services, Inc.)
460 W 34th St
New York, NY 10001-2320 (100%)
Tel.: (212) 502-2100
Fax: (212) 502-2113
Toll Free: (888) 623-2668
E-Mail: CBPS-Rebranding@cbps.canon.com
Web Site: www.cbps.canon.com
Emp.: 4,500
Business Process Outsourcing Services
S.I.C.: 7389
N.A.I.C.S.: 561499
Joseph R. Marciano *(Pres & CEO)*
Stephen Mackay *(CFO)*
Walter Baransky *(COO)*
Elizabeth Halaki *(CMO)*
Michael Scordino *(Chief Legal Officer & VP-Electronic Discovery)*
Andrea Oriel *(Chief HR & Admin Officer)*

Canon Development Americas, Inc. (2)
15975 Alton Pkwy
Irvine, CA 92618
Tel.: (949) 932-3100
Fax: (949) 932-3510
Web Site: www.cda.canon.com
Emp.: 100
Digital Software Developer
S.I.C.: 5045
N.A.I.C.S.: 423430

Canon Financial Services, Inc. (2)
158 Gaither Dr Ste 200
Mount Laurel, NJ 08054
Tel.: (856) 813-1000
Fax: (856) 813-5118
Toll Free: (800) 220-0200
E-Mail: cfscustserv@cfs.canon.com
Web Site: www.cfs.canon.com
Leasing of Cannon Products
S.I.C.: 7359
N.A.I.C.S.: 532490
Kunihiko Tedo *(Pres)*

Canon Information and Imaging Solutions, Inc. (2)
1 Canon Plz
Lake Success, NY 11042
Tel.: (516) 328-5000
E-Mail: info@ciis.canon.com
Web Site: www.ciis.canon.com
Software Consulting Services
S.I.C.: 7373
N.A.I.C.S.: 541512
Tetsuhiro Minamide *(VP & Gen Mgr)*

Canon Information Technology Services Inc. (2)
850 Greenbrier Cir Ste K
Chesapeake, VA 23320-2644 VA
Tel.: (757) 579-7100
Fax: (757) 579-7109
E-Mail: chr@cits.cannon.com
Web Site: www.consumerusa.cannon.com
Rev.: $14,100,000
Emp.: 485
Technical Support Center for Canon Printers & Products
S.I.C.: 7699
N.A.I.C.S.: 811212
Yuichi Ishizuka *(Chm & CEO)*
Doris Higginbotham *(Pres)*
Doris Armstrong *(Sr VP)*

Canon Solutions America, Inc. (2)
One Canon Park
Melville, NY 11747
Tel.: (631) 330-5000
Web Site: www.csa.canon.com
Emp.: 7,000
Office Machinery Distribution & Support Services
S.I.C.: 5044
N.A.I.C.S.: 423420
Toyotsugu Kuwamura *(Pres)*

Units:

Canon Solutions America, Inc. - Burlington (3)
(Formerly Canon Business Solutions, Inc. - Burlington)
300 Commerce Sq Blvd
Burlington, NJ 08016 NY
Tel.: (609) 387-8700 (100%)
Web Site: www.solutions.canon.com
Emp.: 200
Office Products Distr
S.I.C.: 5044
N.A.I.C.S.: 423420
Melisa Boling *(Mgr-Sls-Northern Colorado)*

Canon Solutions America, Inc. - Chicago (3)
5450 N Cumberland Ave
Chicago, IL 60656-1484 (100%)
Tel.: (773) 714-8500
Fax: (713) 714-4056
Holding Company
S.I.C.: 3861
N.A.I.C.S.: 325992

Canon Solutions America, Inc. - Gardena (3)
(Formerly Canon Business Solutions, Inc. - Gardena)
110 W Walnut St
Gardena, CA 90248-3100 CA
Tel.: (310) 217-3000 (100%)
Fax: (310) 715-7050
Web Site: www.solutions.canon.com
Emp.: 250
Office Products Distr
S.I.C.: 5044
N.A.I.C.S.: 423420

Canon Solutions America, Inc. - Salt Lake City (3)
298 Mercer Way
Salt Lake City, UT 84115
Tel.: (801) 461-7600
Fax: (801) 486-4720
Web Site: www.canonbusinesssolutions.com
Sales Range: $50-74.9 Million
Emp.: 85
Office Equipment Distr
S.I.C.: 5044
N.A.I.C.S.: 423420
Eric Waite *(Dir-Mktg)*

Canon Solutions America, Inc. - Schaumburg (3)
(Formerly Canon Business Solutions, Inc. - Schaumburg)
425 N Martingale Rd Ste 100
Schaumburg, IL 60173-2212 IL
Tel.: (847) 706-3400 (100%)
Fax: (847) 706-3152
Web Site: www.solutions.canon.com
Emp.: 605
Office Products Distr
S.I.C.: 5044
N.A.I.C.S.: 423420

Canon Solutions America, Inc. - Trumbull (3)
(Formerly Oce North America Inc. - Trumbull)
100 Oakview Dr
Trumbull, CT 06611-4724 DE
Tel.: (203) 365-7000
Toll Free: (800) 945-9708
Office Equipment Distr
S.I.C.: 5044
N.A.I.C.S.: 423420
Anthony J. Marino *(Sr Assoc Gen Counsel)*
William Midgley *(Sr VP-Admin & Logistics)*

Canon U.S. Life Sciences, Inc. (2)
9800 Medical Ctr Dr
Rockville, MD 20850
Tel.: (301) 762-7070
Fax: (301) 762-0406
E-Mail: culs@culs.canon.com
Web Site: www.culs.canon.com
Emp.: 37
Clinical Diagnostic Research & Development Services
S.I.C.: 8731
N.A.I.C.S.: 541712
Toru Nishizawa *(Pres & CEO)*
Ivor Knight *(CTO & Sr VP)*

Canon USA, Inc. (2)
15955 Alton Pkwy
Irvine, CA 92618 (100%)
Tel.: (949) 753-4000
Web Site: www.usa.canon.com
Emp.: 200
Mfr. of Image Finding Systems, Cameras, Lenses & Printers
S.I.C.: 5043
N.A.I.C.S.: 423410

Canon USA, Inc. (2)
3300 N 1st St
San Jose, CA 95134-1900 CA
Tel.: (408) 468-2000 (100%)
Fax: (408) 468-2309
Web Site: www.usa.canon.com
Rev.: $1,700,000
Emp.: 10
Computer Peripherals & Software
S.I.C.: 5734
N.A.I.C.S.: 443142

Canon Virginia, Inc. (2)
12000 Canon Blvd
Newport News, VA 23606-4201 (100%)
Tel.: (757) 881-6000
Fax: (757) 881-6564
Web Site: www.canonusa.com
Emp.: 2,000
Mfr. of Copying Machines
S.I.C.: 3579
N.A.I.C.S.: 333316
Yusaku Azuma *(Pres & CEO)*
Toru Nishizawa *(Exec VP-Bus & Tech Grp)*

Subsidiary:

Custom Integrated Technology Inc. (3)
120 Enterprise Dr
Newport News, VA 23603-1368 VA
Tel.: (757) 887-0211
Fax: (757) 887-3781
Web Site: www.canon.com
Rev.: $10,100,000
Emp.: 90
Computer Printers & Copiers
S.I.C.: 3577
N.A.I.C.S.: 334118
Takayoshi Hanagata *(Pres)*

Non-U.S. Subsidiary:

Canon Canada, Inc. (2)
6390 Dixie Rd
Mississauga, ON, L5T 1P7, Canada (100%)
Tel.: (905) 795-1111
Fax: (905) 795-2020
Web Site: www.canon.ca
Emp.: 500
Marketing of Canon Products
S.I.C.: 5043
N.A.I.C.S.: 423410
Taizaburo Egawa *(Pres & CEO)*

Subsidiary:

Oce-Canada, Inc. (3)
4711 Young St Ste 1100
Toronto, ON, M2N 6K8, Canada (100%)
Tel.: (416) 224-5600
Fax: (416) 224-5778
E-Mail: info@oce.ca
Web Site: www.oce.ca
Emp.: 80
Document Management & Printing Equipment Distr
S.I.C.: 5044
N.A.I.C.S.: 423420
Patrick D'Souza *(Pres)*

Non-U.S. Groups:

Canon Europa N.V. (1)
Bovenkerkerweg 59-61
1185 XB Amstelveen, Netherlands NL
Mailing Address: (100%)
PO Box 2262
1180 EG Amstelveen, Netherlands
Tel.: (31) 205458000
Fax: (31) 205458222
E-Mail: reception.mainoffie@canon-europe.com
Web Site: www.canon-europe.com
Emp.: 20
Office & Photographic Equipment Distr
S.I.C.: 5043
N.A.I.C.S.: 423410
James Leipnik *(Chief Comm Officer)*

Subsidiary:

Canon Nederland N.V. (2)
Bovenkerkerweg 59
Amstelveen, 1185 XB, Netherlands (100%)
Tel.: (31) 235670123
Fax: (31) 235670124
E-Mail: info@canon.nl
Web Site: www.canon.nl
Emp.: 500
Sales of Business Machines
S.I.C.: 5044
N.A.I.C.S.: 423420
M. Trampe *(Mng Dir)*

Subsidiary:

Canon Nederland N.V. - 's-Hertogenbosch (3)
Brabantlaan 2
PO Box 800
5201 AV 's-Hertogenbosch, Noord-Brabant, Netherlands (100%)
Tel.: (31) 736815815
Telex: 50495
Fax: (31) 736120685
E-Mail: info-nl@oce.com
Web Site: www.oce.nl
Emp.: 1,000
Office Equipment Distr
S.I.C.: 5044
N.A.I.C.S.: 423420
Antony Verhoazen *(Chm)*

Non-U.S. Subsidiaries:

Canon Belgium N.V./S.A. (2)
Berkanlan St 3
B 1831 Diegem, Belgium BE
Tel.: (32) 27220411 (100%)
Fax: (32) 27223274
E-Mail: info@canon.be
Web Site: www.canon.be
Sls.: $90,947,976
Emp.: 300
Sales of Business Machines
S.I.C.: 5044
N.A.I.C.S.: 423420
Angelo Van Wilderen *(Dir-Fin)*

Canon CEE GmbH (2)
Oberlaaer Strasse 233
1100 Vienna, Austria
Tel.: (43) 1 680 89 0
Fax: (43) 1 680 89 333
E-Mail: office.cee@canon.at
Web Site: www.canon-cee.com
Emp.: 88
Digital Camera & Printer Scanner Distr
S.I.C.: 5043
N.A.I.C.S.: 423410
Jenny Lu *(Mng Dir)*

Canon CZ spol s.r.o. (2)
NAM NA Santince 2440
160 00 Prague, Czech Republic
Tel.: (420) 225280111
Fax: (420) 225280311
E-Mail: info@canon.cz
Web Site: www.canon.cz
Emp.: 80
Sales of Copy & Fax Machines
S.I.C.: 5044
N.A.I.C.S.: 423420
Ladislav Palecek *(Dir Gen)*

Canon Deutschland GmbH (2)
Europark Fichtenhain A10
47807 Krefeld, Germany DE
Tel.: (49) 21513450 (100%)
Fax: (49) 2151345102
Web Site: www.canon.de
Emp.: 800
Sales of Office Products, Computer Peripherals & Photographic Equipment
S.I.C.: 5112
N.A.I.C.S.: 453210
Jappe Frandsen *(Mng Dir)*

Subsidiaries:

Canon Giessen GmbH (3)
Canonstrasse 1
35394 Giessen, Germany DE
Tel.: (49) 6414060
Fax: (49) 641406101
Web Site: www.canon.de
Emp.: 200
Mfr. & Remanufacturer of Copy Machines
S.I.C.: 5044
N.A.I.C.S.: 423420
Masahiko Motohashi *(Gen Mgr)*

Oce-Deutschland GmbH (3)
Solingerstr 5 7
D 45481 Mullheim, Germany DE
Tel.: (49) 20848450 (100%)

Fax: (49) 208480950
E-Mail: info-de@oce.com
Web Site: www.oce.com
Emp.: 1,000
Service & Sales of Printing Equipment
S.I.C.: 5084
N.A.I.C.S.: 423830
Goop Fan Boerdonk *(CEO)*

Subsidiaries:

Oce-Deutschland Leasing GmbH **(4)**
Solinger Str 5-7
45481 Mullheim, Germany DE
Tel.: (49) 20848450
Fax: (49) 208480950
E-Mail: info-de@oce.com
Web Site: www.oce.de
Emp.: 300
Leasing of Printing Equipment
S.I.C.: 7359
N.A.I.C.S.: 532420
Joopvan Boerdonk *(Mng Dir)*
Danny de Grand *(CFO)*

Oce Printing Systems GmbH **(4)**
Siemens Allee 2
PO Box 1260
85586 Poing, 85581, Germany DE
Tel.: (49) 8121720 (100%)
Fax: (49) 8121724748
E-Mail: info@oce.com
Web Site: www.oce.com
Sls.: $3,220,404,480
Emp.: 1,300
Provider of Solutions for Printing Systems
S.I.C.: 2759
N.A.I.C.S.: 323111
Andre Mittelsteiner *(CEO)*

Canon Europe Ltd. **(2)**
6 Roundwood Ave
Uxbridge, Middlesex, UB11 1JA, United Kingdom (100%)
Tel.: (44) 2085888000
Fax: (44) 2085888603
Web Site: www.canon-europe.com
Emp.: 11,000
Sales of all Canon Products
S.I.C.: 5731
N.A.I.C.S.: 443142
Rokus L. van Iperen *(Pres/CEO-EMEA)*

Subsidiary:

Canon Technology Europe Ltd **(3)**
The Braccans London Road
Bracknell, Berks, RG12 2XH, United Kingdom UK
Tel.: (44) 344354700 (100%)
Fax: (44) 1344354801
Web Site: www.cre.canon.co.uk
Emp.: 100
Provider of Computer Research Services
S.I.C.: 8731
N.A.I.C.S.: 541712

Non-U.S. Subsidiaries:

Canon Espana, S.A. **(3)**
Avenida de Europa 6 Parque Empresarial La Moraleja
Alcobendas, 28108 Madrid, Spain ES
Tel.: (34) 915384500
Fax: (34) 914117780
E-Mail: info@canon.es
Web Site: www.canon.es
Emp.: 250
Cameras & Photographic Supplies Sales
S.I.C.: 5731
N.A.I.C.S.: 443142
Massimo Dutti *(Gen Mgr)*

Subsidiaries:

Oce-Espana S.A. **(4)**
Mas Blau Osona 2
El Prat De Llobregat, E 08820 Barcelona, Spain ES
Tel.: (34) 934844848 (100%)
Fax: (34) 934844828
E-Mail: oce-info@oce.es
Web Site: www.oce.es
Emp.: 225
Marketing & Sales of Office Equipment
S.I.C.: 5044
N.A.I.C.S.: 423420

Oce-Renting S.A. **(4)**
Businnes Park Mas Blau Osona 2
08820 Barcelona, Spain (100%)
Tel.: (34) 934844800
Fax: (34) 934844828
E-Mail: oce-info@oce.com
Web Site: www.oce.es
Emp.: 200
S.I.C.: 5943
N.A.I.C.S.: 453210
Eduardo De Sus *(CEO)*

Canon (Irl) Business Equipment Ltd. **(3)**
Arena Rd Sandyford Industrial Estate
Dublin, 18, Ireland IE
Tel.: (353) 1205 2400 (100%)
Fax: (353) 1205 2525
E-Mail: dublin.reception@canon.ie
Web Site: www.canon.ie
Emp.: 120
Sales of Business Machines, IT Support & Consulting
S.I.C.: 5044
N.A.I.C.S.: 423420
Greg Wilson *(Mgr-Mktg & Color Production)*

Canon Norge A.S. **(3)**
Hallagerbakken 110
PO Box 33
1201 Oslo, Norway NO
Tel.: (47) 2262 9200 (100%)
Fax: (47) 2262 9201
E-Mail: erik.mikalsen@canon.no
Web Site: www.canon.no
Emp.: 350
Sales of all Canon Products
S.I.C.: 5946
N.A.I.C.S.: 443142
Erik Mikalson *(Mng Dir)*

Canon France S.A. **(2)**
17 Quai du President Paul Doumer
92414 Courbevoie, Cedex, France FR
Tel.: (33) 1 41 997777 (100%)
Fax: (33) 1 41 997799
Web Site: www.canon.fr
Emp.: 700
Sales of Business Machines
S.I.C.: 5943
N.A.I.C.S.: 453210

Subsidiaries:

Canon Bretagne S.A. **(3)**
Les Landes De Beauge
35341 Liffre, Cedex, France FR
Tel.: (33) 299235111 (100%)
Fax: (33) 299685603
E-Mail: canon.bretagne@cb.canon.fr
Web Site: www.canon-bretagne.fr
Emp.: 700
Mfr. of Low-Speed Copy Machines & Toner Cartridges; Recycler of Toner Cartridges
S.I.C.: 5044
N.A.I.C.S.: 423420
Shungi Nakamura *(Pres)*

Canon Communication & Image France S.A. **(3)**
12 Rue De l Industrie 92
414 Courbevoie, Cedex, France FR
Tel.: (33) 141301515 (100%)
Fax: (33) 141301505
E-Mail: info@canon.fr
Web Site: www.canon.fr
Emp.: 600
Sales of Cameras & Computer Peripherals
S.I.C.: 5731
N.A.I.C.S.: 443142
Yashin Kengi *(Gen Mgr)*

Canon Research Centre France S.A.S. **(3)**
Rue De La Touche Lambert Rennes
35517 Cesson Sevigne, Atalante, France FR
Tel.: (33) 299876800 (100%)
Fax: (33) 299876899
Web Site: www.canon.fr
Emp.: 70
Developer of Image Processing Technology, Wireless Communications & Multimedia Network Infrastructures
S.I.C.: 7373
N.A.I.C.S.: 541512
Mahe Robert *(Head-Fin)*

Oce-France S.A. **(3)**
12 Avenue de l'Europe
77144 Montevrain, France FR
Tel.: (33) 820 12 04 10 (100%)
Fax: (33) 820 12 05 10
E-Mail: accueil@oce.fr
Web Site: www.oce.fr
Emp.: 600
Mfr. & Sales of Copier Products
S.I.C.: 5112
N.A.I.C.S.: 424120
Cathrine Renauv *(Mgr-HR)*

Subsidiaries:

Oce-France Financement S.A. **(4)**
32 Pacenneus NeaJran
93883 Neuilly-sur-Seine, France FR
Tel.: (33) 145925055
Fax: (33) 145925271
Web Site: www.oce.fr
Emp.: 800
Provider of Financial Services for Oce France
S.I.C.: 6211
N.A.I.C.S.: 523999

Oce P.L.T. **(4)**
1 Rue Gean Le Moyne
94015 Creteil, France FR
Tel.: (33) 148988000 (99%)
Fax: (33) 148985450
Web Site: www.oce-plt.com
Emp.: 120
Mfr. & Marketing of Graphic Plotters
S.I.C.: 2759
N.A.I.C.S.: 323111
Reneka Even *(Mgr-Site)*

Canon GmbH **(2)**
Obaalaerstrasse 233
A-1100 Vienna, Austria AT
Tel.: (43) 1680880 (100%)
Fax: (43) 168088222
E-Mail: info@canon.at
Web Site: www.canon.at
Rev.: $188,713,952
Emp.: 250
Sales of all Canon Products
S.I.C.: 5946
N.A.I.C.S.: 443142
Peter Baldaus *(Mng Dir)*

Subsidiary:

Canon East Europe Vertriebsgesellschaft mbH **(3)**
Oberlaaer Strasse 233
Vienna, 1100, Austria AT
Tel.: (43) 1680880 (100%)
Fax: (43) 168089313
E-Mail: cee_info@canon.at
Web Site: www.canon-europe.com
Sales Range: $150-199.9 Million
Emp.: 50
Copier & Fax Machine Sales
S.I.C.: 5044
N.A.I.C.S.: 423420

Non-U.S. Subsidiaries:

Canon Hungaria Kft. **(3)**
Zahony St 7
H 1031 Budapest, Hungary HU
Tel.: (36) 12375900 (100%)
Fax: (36) 12375901
E-Mail: canonhu@canon.hu
Web Site: www.canon.hu
Emp.: 80
Sales of Copy & Fax Machines
S.I.C.: 5044
N.A.I.C.S.: 423420
Laszlo Morazcsik *(Mng Dir)*

Subsidiary:

Oce-Hungaria Kft. **(4)**
Zahony 7th Street Hx Building
1031 Budapest, Hungary
Tel.: (36) 1 236 1040
Fax: (36) 1 239 3633
E-Mail: hu-sales@oce.com
Web Site: www.oce.hu
Emp.: 100
Printing & Office Solutions & Business Services
S.I.C.: 2759
N.A.I.C.S.: 323120

Canon Polska Sp. z o.o. **(3)**
ul Gottlieba Daimlera 2
02-460 Warsaw, Poland PL
Tel.: (48) 22 430 60 00 (100%)
Fax: (48) 22 430 60 11
E-Mail: serwis@canon.pl
Web Site: www.canon.pl
Emp.: 60
Sales of Copy & Fax Machines
S.I.C.: 5044
N.A.I.C.S.: 423420

Canon Slovakia s.r.o. **(3)**
Karadzicova 8 building CBC I
821 08 Bratislava, Slovakia Sk
Tel.: (421) 257104011
Fax: (421) 257104019
Web Site: www.canon.sk
Emp.: 10
Sales of Photographic Equipment
S.I.C.: 5043
N.A.I.C.S.: 423410
Ladislav Palecek *(Gen Mgr)*

Canon Italia S.p.A. **(2)**
Via Milano 8 San Donato Milanese
San Donato Milanese, 20097 Milan, Italy IT
Tel.: (39) 0282481 (100%)
Fax: (39) 0282484600
Web Site: www.canon.it
Emp.: 350
Sales of all Canon Products
S.I.C.: 5734
N.A.I.C.S.: 443142
Enrico Deluchi *(Mng Dir)*

Subsidiary:

Oce-Italia S.p.A. **(3)**
Strada Padarna Superiore 2 B
20063 Cernusco sul Naviglio, MI, Italy IT
Tel.: (39) 02927261 (100%)
Fax: (39) 0292726920
Web Site: www.oce.it
Emp.: 35
Marketing & Sales of Copiers, Printers & Plotters
S.I.C.: 5112
N.A.I.C.S.: 424120

Canon Middle East, FZ-LLC **(2)**
Dubai Internet City
PO Box 500 007
Dubai, United Arab Emirates
Tel.: (971) 43915050
Fax: (971) 43916715
E-Mail: info@canon-me.com
Web Site: www.canon-me.com
Emp.: 75
Sales of Business Machines
S.I.C.: 5044
N.A.I.C.S.: 423420
Anurag Agrawal *(Mng Dir)*

Canon Oy **(2)**
Huopalahdentie 24
PL 1
00350 Helsinki, Finland FI
Tel.: (358) 1054420 (100%)
Fax: (358) 1054430
E-Mail: pekka.bask@canon.fi
Web Site: www.canon.fi
Emp.: 380
Sales of all Canon Products
S.I.C.: 5946
N.A.I.C.S.: 443142
Harry Nystrom *(CEO)*

Subsidiaries:

Canon North-East Oy **(3)**
Huopalahdentie 24
PL1, 00351 Helsinki, Finland (100%)
Tel.: (358) 01054400
Fax: (358) 105444290
Web Site: www.canon.fi
Sales Range: $250-299.9 Million
Emp.: 45
Sales of all Canon Products
S.I.C.: 5044
N.A.I.C.S.: 423420
Pentti Nelimarkaa *(Gen Mgr)*

Oce-Finland Oy **(3)**
Keilaranta 15 B
2150 Espoo, Finland
Tel.: (358) 207 438 710
Fax: (358) 207 438 711
E-Mail: myynti@oce.com
Web Site: www.oce.com
Emp.: 15
Printing Software Development Services
S.I.C.: 7371
N.A.I.C.S.: 541511

Canon Inc.—(Continued)

Jari-Pekka Koskenmies *(Mng Dir)*

Canon (Schweiz) AG (2)
Industriestrasse 12
8305 Dietikon, Switzerland (90%)
Tel.: (41) 18356161
Fax: (41) 18356468
Web Site: www.canon.ch
Sales Range: $200-249.9 Million
Emp.: 400
Sales of all Canon Products
S.I.C.: 5734
N.A.I.C.S.: 443142
Pierre Muekly *(Gen Mgr)*

Subsidiaries:

Canon S.A. (3)
59 Route des Jeunes
CH-1211 Geneva, Switzerland
Tel.: (41) 223091811
Fax: (41) 223436538
E-Mail: info@canon.ch
Web Site: www.canon.ch
Emp.: 1,000
Sales of Canon Products
S.I.C.: 5946
N.A.I.C.S.: 443142
Markus Naegeli *(Mng Dir)*

Canon (Schweiz) AG - Glattbrugg (3)
Sagereistrasse 10
Glattbrugg, 8152, Switzerland CH
Tel.: (41) 448291111
Fax: (41) 448291348
E-Mail:
Emp.: 250
Marketing & Sales of Office Equipment & Graphics Plotters
S.I.C.: 5044
N.A.I.C.S.: 423420

Canon South Africa Pty. Ltd. (2)
Halfway House
PO Box 1782
Johannesburg, 1685, South Africa (100%)
Tel.: (27) 112654900
Fax: (27) 112654954
E-Mail: info@canon.co.za
Web Site: www.canon.co.za
Rev.: $61,758,000
Emp.: 75
Sales of Consumer Products
S.I.C.: 7359
N.A.I.C.S.: 532299
John DeVallier *(Mng Dir)*

Canon Svenska AB (2)
Gustav III Blvd 26
S 16972 Solna, Sweden SE
Tel.: (46) 87448500 (100%)
Fax: (46) 87446465
E-Mail: info@canon.com
Web Site: www.canon.se
Emp.: 200
Sales of all Canon Products
S.I.C.: 5946
N.A.I.C.S.: 443142
Bertil Widmark *(Mng Dir)*

Canon (U.K.) Ltd. (2)
Cockshot Hill Woodhatch
Reigate, Surrey, RH2 8BF, United Kingdom UK
Tel.: (44) 1737220000 (100%)
Fax: (44) 1737220022
Web Site: www.canon.co.uk
Sales Range: $250-299.9 Million
Emp.: 2,150
Digital Imaging Technology
Import
S.I.C.: 3579
N.A.I.C.S.: 333316
Caroline Price *(Partner-Strategic Bus-HR)*
Hasse Iwarsson *(Mng Dir)*

Subsidiary:

Oce (UK) Limited (3)
Oce House Chatham Way
Brentwood, Essex, CM14 4DZ, United Kingdom UK
Tel.: (44) 8706005544 (100%)
Fax: (44) 8706001113
E-Mail: salesinformation@oce.co.uk
Web Site: www.oce.co.uk
Emp.: 250
Mfr., Sales & Marketing of Copiers, Printers, Plotters & Supplies
Import Export
S.I.C.: 5112
N.A.I.C.S.: 424120
Bron Curley *(Mng Dir)*

Non-U.S. Subsidiary:

Oce-Ireland Ltd. (3)
3006 Lake Dr Citywest Bus Campus
Saggart
Dublin, 24, Ireland IE
Tel.: (353) 14039100 (100%)
Fax: (353) 102052525
E-Mail: dublin.reception@canon.ie
Web Site: www.canon.ie
Emp.: 20
Marketing & Sales of Photocopiers, Plotters & Printers
Export
S.I.C.: 5112
N.A.I.C.S.: 424120
Philip Brady *(Gen Mgr)*

I.R.I.S. Group S.A. (2)
10 rue du Bosquet
B-1348 Louvain-la-Neuve, Belgium BE
Tel.: (32) 10 45 13 64
Fax: (32) 10 45 34 43
E-Mail: info@irislink.com
Web Site: www.iriscorporate.com
Emp.: 496
Software & Technology Services
S.I.C.: 7373
N.A.I.C.S.: 541512
Pierre De Muelenaere *(Pres & CEO)*
Denis Hermesse *(CFO)*

Subsidiary:

I.R.I.S. eCommunication (3)
10 rue du Bosquet
1348 Louvain-la-Neuve, Belgium
Tel.: (32) 10832450
Fax: (32) 10452291
E-Mail: info@irisecom.com
Web Site: www.irisecom.com
Emp.: 20
Developer & Marketer of Advanced Web Content Management Solutions for Professional Associations, Companies & Industries
S.I.C.: 7379
N.A.I.C.S.: 541519

U.S. Subsidiary:

I.R.I.S. Inc. (3)
955 NW 17th Ave Unit A
Delray Beach, FL 33445
Tel.: (561) 921-0847
Fax: (561) 921-0854
E-Mail:
Web Site: www.irisusa.com
Emp.: 8
Computer Software Design & Consulting Services
S.I.C.: 7379
N.A.I.C.S.: 541519
Jean-Marc Fontaine *(Mgr)*

Non-U.S. Subsidiaries:

I.R.I.S. Luxembourg s.a. (3)
Ecoparc - SolarWind Rue de l'Industrie 13
L 8399 Windhof, Luxembourg (100%)
Tel.: (352) 39 03 26 1
Fax: (352) 39 03 26 99
E-Mail: david.grey@iriscorporate.com
Web Site: www.iriscorporate.com
Sales Range: $10-24.9 Million
Emp.: 39
Developer & Marketer of Computer Software; Information Technology Services
S.I.C.: 7373
N.A.I.C.S.: 541512

I.R.I.S. France s.a. (3)
68 avenue de la Victoire
94310 Orly, France
Tel.: (33) 1 56 70 7070
Fax: (33) 1 56 70 7077
E-Mail:
Web Site: www.iriscorporate.com
Emp.: 15
Developer & Marketer of Computer Software; Information Technology Services
S.I.C.: 7373
N.A.I.C.S.: 541512

Serge Dahan *(Pres & Dir Gen)*

Oce Holding N.V. (1)
(Formerly Oce N.V.)
St Urbanusweg 43
5914 CA Venlo, Netherlands NL
Mailing Address: (100%)
PO Box 101
5900 MA Venlo, Netherlands
Tel.: (31) 773592222
Fax: (31) 773544700
E-Mail: info@oce.com
Web Site: www.oce.com
Sales Range: $1-4.9 Billion
Emp.: 2,100
Holding Company; Digital Document Management Technology & Services
Export
S.I.C.: 6719
N.A.I.C.S.: 551112
Peter A .F. W. Elverding *(Chm-Supervisory Bd)*
Rokus L. van Iperen *(Chm-Exec Bd & Acting CFO)*
Toshizo Tanaka *(Vice Chm-Supervisory Bd)*
Anton H. Schaaf *(COO & CTO)*
Wilfred Deherder *(CIO & Sr VP)*
F. W. T. Kool *(Sec)*
T. Egelund *(Exec VP)*
Mark Euwe *(Exec VP-Bus Svcs)*
Jan Hol *(Sr VP-Comm)*

Non-U.S. Subsidiaries:

Canon Australia Pty. Ltd. (1)
1 Thomas Holt Dr
North Ryde, NSW, 2113, Australia AU
Tel.: (61) 298052000 (100%)
Fax: (61) 298833650
E-Mail: business.sal@canon.com.au
Web Site: www.canon.com.au
Emp.: 600
Sales of Office Machines, Photographic Equipment & Computer Peripherals
S.I.C.: 5112
N.A.I.C.S.: 453210
Takanobu Nakamasu *(Mng Dir)*

Division:

Canon Professional Printing (2)
(Formerly Oce-Australia Limited)
Level 3 Building 1 195 Wellington Road
Clayton, VIC, 3168, Australia AU
Mailing Address: (100%)
PO Box 363
Ferntree Gully MDC, Scoresby, Vic, 3156, Australia
Tel.: (61) 397303333
Fax: (61) 397303356
E-Mail: sales@oce.com.au
Web Site: www.oce.com
Emp.: 100
Printing Equipment Distr
S.I.C.: 5044
N.A.I.C.S.: 423420
Simon Wheeler *(Mng Dir)*

Subsidiaries:

Canon Finance Australia Pty. Ltd. (2)
1 Thomas Holt Dr N Ryde
Sydney, NSW, 2113, Australia AU
Tel.: (61) 298052000 (100%)
Fax: (61) 298052703
E-Mail: info@canon.com.au
Web Site: www.canon.com.au
Emp.: 1,500
Provider of Leasing & Rental Services
S.I.C.: 6512
N.A.I.C.S.: 531120
George Lagos *(Sr Gen Mgr)*

Non-U.S. Subsidiary:

Canon Finance New Zealand Ltd. (3)
Akoringi Bus Pk 28 The Warehouse Way
PO Box 33336
Northcourt Takapuna, Auckland, 0740, New Zealand (100%)
Tel.: (64) 94890300
Fax: (64) 94890384
E-Mail: carol.r@canon.co.nz
Web Site: www.cfnz.co.nz
Emp.: 7
Provider of Leasing & Rental Services
S.I.C.: 6512
N.A.I.C.S.: 531120

Canon Information Systems Research Australia Pty. Ltd. (2)
Level 6 3 Thomas Holt Dr
PO Box 313
North Ryde, NSW, 2113, Australia AU
Tel.: (61) 298052000 (100%)
Fax: (61) 298883650
E-Mail: info@cisra.com.au
Web Site: www.research.canon.com.au
Emp.: 100
Developer of Computer Software
S.I.C.: 7373
N.A.I.C.S.: 541512
Tsukhara Huichi *(Mng Dir)*
Hayao Ozu *(Mng Dir)*

Inland Technology (2)
Unit 2 9 Gateway Crs
Orange, NSW, 2800, Australia AU
Tel.: (61) 263626811 (100%)
Fax: (61) 263628662
E-Mail: info@inlandtechnology.com
Web Site: www.inlandtechnology.com.au
Emp.: 9
Sales of Business Machines
S.I.C.: 5044
N.A.I.C.S.: 423420
Laurence Breen *(Principal)*

Non-U.S. Subsidiary:

Canon New Zealand Ltd. (2)
Akoranga Business Pk Akoranga Dr N Cote Takapuna
Auckland, New Zealand (100%)
Tel.: (64) 94890300
Fax: (64) 94890380
E-Mail: info@canon.co.nz
Web Site: www.canon.co.nz
Emp.: 130
Sales of all Canon Products
S.I.C.: 5946
N.A.I.C.S.: 443142
Craig Manson *(Mng Dir)*

Canon Austria GmbH (1)
Oberlaaer Strasse 233
1100 Vienna, Austria
Tel.: (43) 1 680 88 0
Fax: (43) 1 680 88 222
E-Mail: pr@canon.at
Web Site: www.canon.com
Emp.: 324
Digital Camera Mfr
S.I.C.: 3579
N.A.I.C.S.: 333316

Canon Bulgaria EOOD (1)
121 Tzarigradsko Shausse Blvd
1784 Sofia, Bulgaria
Tel.: (359) 2 975 1630
Fax: (359) 2 975 16 36
E-Mail: infooffice@canon.bg
Emp.: 11
Digital Camera & Printer Mfr
S.I.C.: 3579
N.A.I.C.S.: 333316
Atanas Nastradinov *(Mng Dir)*

Canon (China) Co., Ltd. (1)
15F Jinbao Bldg No 89 Jinbao St
Dongcheng District, 100005 Beijing, China CN
Tel.: (86) 1085139999 (100%)
Fax: (86) 85296649
Web Site: www.canon.com.cn
Emp.: 185
Office Machines, Cameras & Computer Peripherals Sales
S.I.C.: 5044
N.A.I.C.S.: 423420
Hideki Ozawa *(Pres & CEO)*

Subsidiaries:

Oce Office Equipment (Shanghai) Co., Ltd. (2)
First Shanghai Center Phase II Building 4
Lane 180 Zhangheng Road
Pudong District, Shanghai, China
Tel.: (86) 21 38657600
Fax: (86) 21 33932120
Web Site: www.global.oce.com
Photocopier Distr
S.I.C.: 5112
N.A.I.C.S.: 424120

Canon Dalian Business Machines, Inc. (1)
Dalian Economic And Technical Development Zone

No 23 Huai He West Road, Dalian, 116600, China CN
Tel.: (86) 41187613333 (50%)
Fax: (86) 41187647241
E-Mail: invest@dalian-gov.net
Web Site: www.canon.com
Emp.: 184
Mfr. & Recycler of Toner Cartridges
S.I.C.: 3861
N.A.I.C.S.: 325992

Canon Danmark A/S (1)
Knud Hojgaards Vej 1
2860 Soborg, Denmark
Tel.: (45) 7015 5005
Fax: (45) 7015 5025
E-Mail: canon@canon.dk
Web Site: www.canon.dk
Emp.: 205
Digital Camera & Printer Mfr
S.I.C.: 3579
N.A.I.C.S.: 333316

Canon Electronics Vietnam Co., Ltd. (1)
Road 206 Section B Pho Noi A Industrial Park
Van Lam District, Yen My, Hung Yen, Vietnam
Tel.: (84) 321 3587311
Fax: (84) 3213587315
Emp.: 120
Electronic Component Mfr
S.I.C.: 3679
N.A.I.C.S.: 334419
Wayne Hartley *(Gen Dir)*

Canon Emirates LLC (1)
Showroom No 1 Office 1 & 2 Indigo Central Building 6 Sheikh Zayed Road
PO Box 1700
Dubai, United Arab Emirates
Tel.: (971) 4 350 2500
Fax: (971) 4 350 6656
E-Mail: info@canon-emirates.ae
Web Site: www.canon-emirates.ae
Emp.: 89
Photocopying Machinery Mfr
S.I.C.: 3579
N.A.I.C.S.: 333316

Canon Engineering Hong Kong Co., Ltd. (1)
5th Floor Trade Square 681 Cheung Sha Wan Road
Kowloon, China (Hong Kong)
Tel.: (852) 2759 2662
Fax: (852) 2759 6690
E-Mail: reception@cehk.canon.com.hk
Emp.: 122
Electronic Component Mfr
S.I.C.: 3679
N.A.I.C.S.: 334419
Osamu Izawa *(Mng Dir)*

Canon Eurasia A.S. (1)
Degirmen Sokak Nida Kule Is Merkezi No 18/10 K 2 Kozyatagi
Kadikoy, 34742 Istanbul, Turkey
Tel.: (90) 216 571 68 00
Fax: (90) 216 571 68 99
E-Mail: info@canon.com.tr
Web Site: www.canon.com.tr
Emp.: 12
Digital Camera & Printer Mfr
S.I.C.: 3579
N.A.I.C.S.: 333316
Roman Troedthandl *(Mng Dir)*

Canon Hi-Tech (Thailand) Ltd. (1)
Hi Tech Indus Estate 89 Moo 1 Bhan Lain Bang Pa-in, Phra Nakhon Si Ayutthaya, 13160, Thailand (100%)
Tel.: (66) 35350080
Fax: (66) 35350100
Web Site: www.canon.co.th
Emp.: 6,000
S.I.C.: 8711
N.A.I.C.S.: 541330
Kitanura Peki *(Pres)*

Canon HongKong Co., Ltd. (1)
19th Fl Metropolis Tower 10 Metropolis Drive
Hunghom, Kowloon, China (Hong Kong) HK
Tel.: (852) 21702828
Fax: (852) 27239684
Web Site: www.canon.com.hk
Emp.: 700
Marketer of All Canon Products
S.I.C.: 5731
N.A.I.C.S.: 443142
Hisahiro Minokawa *(Pres)*

Subsidiaries:

Canon Electronic Business Machines (H.K.) Co., Ltd. (2)
17th Fl Tower 1 Ever Gain Plz 88 Container Port Road
Kwai Chung, NT, China (Hong Kong) HK
Tel.: (852) 23058400
Fax: (852) 23181719
Web Site: www.canon-ebm.hk
Emp.: 100
Mfr. & Marketing of Personal Information Products
S.I.C.: 7373
N.A.I.C.S.: 541512
Fujio Mitarai *(Pres)*

Oce (Hong Kong China) Ltd. (2)
3711 218 Tower 1 Millennium City 1 Kwun Tong Rd Kwun Tong Tower
Hong Kong, China (Hong Kong) HK
Tel.: (852) 25776064 (100%)
Fax: (852) 25778957
E-Mail: webmaster@oce.com.hk
Web Site: www.oce.com
Sales Range: $10-24.9 Million
Emp.: 50
Sales of Office Equipment
S.I.C.: 5044
N.A.I.C.S.: 423420

Canon Inc., Taiwan (1)
18 Chen Kuo Road Tan Tzu Hsiang Taichung Hsien Taichung
Export Processing Zone, Tanzte, 427, Taiwan
Tel.: (886) 425322123
Fax: (886) 4 2533 1900
Web Site: www.canon.com.tw
Emp.: 1,600
Mfr. of Compact Cameras, EF Lenses & Lens Units for Image Scanners & Multimedia Projectors
S.I.C.: 3827
N.A.I.C.S.: 333314

Canon India Pvt. Ltd. (1)
2nd Floor Tower A & B Cyber Greens DLF Phase III, Gurgaon, Haryana, 122002, India (100%)
Tel.: (91) 124 516 0000
Web Site: www.canon.co.in
Emp.: 160
Sales of Copy Machines & Software
S.I.C.: 5044
N.A.I.C.S.: 423420
Alok Bharadwaj *(Pres & Exec VP)*

Canon Information Technologies Philippines, Inc. (1)
Techno Plaza One 18 Orchard Road Eastwood, Quezon City, 1110, Philippines
Tel.: (63) 2 421 1000
Fax: (63) 2 421 1050
E-Mail: sales@canon.com.ph
Emp.: 40
Application Software Development Services
S.I.C.: 7371
N.A.I.C.S.: 541511
Lu Xueli *(Pres)*

Canon Korea Consumer Imaging Inc. (1)
Canon Bldg 5F 168-12 Samseong-dong Gangnam-gu, Seoul, 135-090, Korea (South)
Tel.: (82) 2 2191 8500
Fax: (82) 2 2191 8575
E-Mail: ga@canon-ci.co.kr
Web Site: www.canon-ci.co.kr
Emp.: 90
Digital Camera Mfr
S.I.C.: 3579
N.A.I.C.S.: 333316
Dong-Hwan Kang *(CEO)*

Canon Luxembourg S.A. (1)
Rue des Joncs 21
1818 Howald, Luxembourg
Tel.: (352) 48 47 961
Fax: (352) 48 47 96235
E-Mail: contact@canon.lu
Emp.: 35
Digital Camera & Printer Mfr
S.I.C.: 3579
N.A.I.C.S.: 333316

Canon Marketing (Malaysia) Sdn. Bhd. (1)
Block D Peremba Sq Saujana Resort Section U2
40150 Shah Alam, Selangor Darul Ehsen, Malaysia MY
Tel.: (60) 378446000 (100%)
Fax: (60) 378468843
E-Mail: helpdesk@cmm.canon.com.my
Web Site: www.canon.com.my
Emp.: 500
Sales of all Canon Products
S.I.C.: 5731
N.A.I.C.S.: 443142
Melvyn Ho *(Pres & CEO)*

Subsidiary:

Oce (Malaysia) Sdn. Bhd. (2)
301 Level 3 Wisma Academy Lot 4A Jalan 19/1
46300 Petaling Jaya, Selangor Darul Ehsan, Malaysia
Tel.: (60) 379668000
Fax: (60) 379556125
E-Mail: info.malaysia@oce.com
Web Site: www.oce.com
Emp.: 60
Professional Printing Services
S.I.C.: 2759
N.A.I.C.S.: 323111

Canon Marketing (Philippines), Inc. (1)
2153 Marvin Plaza Bldg
Chino Roces Ave
Makati City, Manila, Philippines (100%)
Tel.: (63) 2 812 6047
Fax: (63) 28120067
E-Mail: info@canon.com.ph
Web Site: www.canon.com.ph
Sales Range: $10-24.9 Million
Emp.: 170
Sales of Business Machines
S.I.C.: 5044
N.A.I.C.S.: 423420

Canon Marketing (Taiwan) Co., Ltd. (1)
19th Fl No 100 Roosevelt Rd
Taipei, 100, Taiwan (100%)
Tel.: (886) 266328888
Fax: (886) 277255869
E-Mail: service@cntw.canon.com.tw
Web Site: www.canon.com.tw
Emp.: 100
Sales of Business Machines
S.I.C.: 5044
N.A.I.C.S.: 423420
Satoshi Yahata *(CEO)*

Canon Marketing (Thailand) Co., Ltd. (1)
179 34-45 Bangkok City Tower 9th-10th Fl
Bangkok, 10120, Thailand TH
Tel.: (66) 23449999 (55%)
Fax: (66) 23449910
E-Mail: cmt-info@canon.co.th
Web Site: www.canon.co.th
Emp.: 600
Sales of all Canon Products
S.I.C.: 5731
N.A.I.C.S.: 443142
Wataru Nishioka *(Pres & CEO)*

Canon Optical Industrial Equipment Service (Shanghai) Inc. (1)
Room 1604-1607 16F Harbour Ring Plaza
No 18 Middle Xi Zang Road
Shanghai, 200001, China
Tel.: (86) 21 5385 2211
Fax: (86) 21 5385 2033
Emp.: 94
Electronic Component Mfr
S.I.C.: 3679
N.A.I.C.S.: 334419

Canon Optical Industrial Equipment (Shanghai) Inc. (1)
Room 1604-1607 16F Harbour Ring Plaza
No 18 Middle Xi Zang Road
Shanghai, 200001, China
Tel.: (86) 21 5385 2211
Fax: (86) 21 5385 2033
Web Site: www.canon.com
Emp.: 46
Semiconductor Equipment Mfr
S.I.C.: 3674
N.A.I.C.S.: 334413
Makino Akira *(Pres)*

Canon Opto (Malaysia) Sdn. Bhd. (1)
2495 Mk. 1 Lorong Perusahaan Baru 2 Zon Perusahaan Prai
Prai, 13600 Penang, Malaysia MY
Tel.: (60) 43900077 (50%)
Fax: (60) 351914475
Web Site: www.canon.com.my/section/contactus/
Emp.: 2,700
Mfr. of Optical Lenses, Video Camcorder Lenses & Compact Cameras
S.I.C.: 3827
N.A.I.C.S.: 333314

Canon Portugal S.A. (1)
Rua Alfredo da Silva 14
Alfragide, Amadora, 2610-016, Portugal
Tel.: (351) 214 704 000
Fax: (351) 214 704 002
E-Mail: info@canon.pt
Emp.: 174
Digital Camera & Printer Mfr
S.I.C.: 3579
N.A.I.C.S.: 333316

Subsidiary:

Oce Portugal Equipamentos Graficos S.A. (2)
Edificio Canon Rua Alfredo da Silva 14
Miraflores, Amadora, Alfragide, 2610-016, Portugal (100%)
Tel.: (351) 214125700
Fax: (351) 214125800
E-Mail: sandra.alamo@oce.com
Web Site: www.oce.pt
Emp.: 56
S.I.C.: 5112
N.A.I.C.S.: 453210
Luc Wyjnhoven *(Gen Mgr)*

Canon Ru LLC (1)
Serebryanicheskaya Naberezhnaya 29 8th Floor
Business Center Silver City, 109028
Moscow, Russia
Tel.: (7) 495 258 5600
Fax: (7) 495 258 5601
Web Site: www.canon.com
Emp.: 189
Digital Camera & Printer Mfr
S.I.C.: 3579
N.A.I.C.S.: 333316

Canon Semiconductor Engineering Korea Inc. (1)
6th Floor Dong-heung Building Samsung-Dong
Kangnam-gu, Seoul, 135-090, Korea (South) Ks
Tel.: (82) 2 556 2389
Web Site: www.canon.com
Emp.: 118
Sales of Semiconductor Equipment
S.I.C.: 5065
N.A.I.C.S.: 423690

Canon Semiconductor Equipment Taiwan, Inc. (1)
9F 2 No 25 Pu Ding Road
Hsin-chu, 300, Taiwan TW
Tel.: (886) 36686600 (100%)
Fax: (886) 3 668 6969
E-Mail: webmaster@cset.canon.com.tw
Web Site: wwwcset.canon.com.tw/hitech/en/contacts.html
Sales Range: $75-99.9 Million
Emp.: 150
Sales of Semiconductor Equipment
S.I.C.: 5065
N.A.I.C.S.: 423690

Canon Singapore Pte. Ltd. (1)
1 Harbour Front Ave No 04-01 Keppel BayTower
Singapore, 098632, Singapore
Tel.: (65) 67998888
Fax: (65) 67998882
E-Mail: general@canon.com.sg
Web Site: www.canon.com.sg
Emp.: 1,000
Sales of Business Machines

Canon Inc.—(Continued)

S.I.C.: 5044
N.A.I.C.S.: 423420
Yoroku Adachi *(Chm)*
Kensaku Konishi *(Pres & CEO)*

Subsidiaries:

TECH Semiconductor Singapore Pte. Ltd. **(2)**
No 1 Woodlands Industrial Park D Street 1
Singapore, 738799, Singapore SG
Tel.: (65) 6365 1998
Fax: (65) 6365 7528
E-Mail: hrmanager@techsemicon.com.sg
Web Site: www.techsemiconductor.com.sg
Emp.: 1,807
Mfr. of Semiconductors
S.I.C.: 3674
N.A.I.C.S.: 334413

Canon Vietnam Co., Ltd. **(1)**
A-1 Thang Long Industrial Park
Dong Anh District, Hanoi, Vietnam
Tel.: (84) 4 38812111
Fax: (84) 4 38811284
E-Mail: canonscvn@yahoo.com.vn
Web Site: www.canon-cvn.com.vn
Emp.: 22,747
Printer & Toner Cartridge Mfr
S.I.C.: 3577
N.A.I.C.S.: 334118
Katsuyoshi Soma *(Gen Dir)*

Subsidiary:

Canon Marketing Vietnam Company Limited **(2)**
10th Fl & 11th Fl President Pl 93 Nguyen Du Dist 1
District 1, Ho Chi Minh City, Vietnam
Tel.: (84) 8 38200 466
Fax: (84) 8 38200 477
E-Mail: cmv@canon.com.vn
Web Site: www.canon.com.vn
Emp.: 2
Photographic Equipment Distr
S.I.C.: 5043
N.A.I.C.S.: 423410
Noriji Yoshida *(Gen Dir)*

Canon Zhongshan Business Machines Co., Ltd. **(1)**
No 2 Huan Mao 3 Road Zhongshan Torch Hi-Tech
Industrial Development Zone, Zhongshan, Guangdong, China
Tel.: (86) 760 89957888
Fax: (86) 760 89957888
Web Site: www.canon.com
Emp.: 6,297
Photocopying Machinery Mfr
S.I.C.: 3579
N.A.I.C.S.: 333316

Canon Zhuhai, Inc. **(1)**
No 2323 Middle of Jiuzhou Road
Zhuhai, Guangdong, 519020, China
Tel.: (86) 756 8888101
Web Site: www.canon.com
Emp.: 11,996
Digital Camera & Printer Mfr
S.I.C.: 3579
N.A.I.C.S.: 333316

OPTOPOL Technology S.A. **(1)**
ul Zabia 42
42-400 Zawiercie, Poland
Tel.: (48) 32 6709173
Fax: (48) 32 6700048
E-Mail: info@optopol.com.pl
Web Site: www.optopol.com
Emp.: 20
Diagnostic Equipment Mfr & Distr
S.I.C.: 3845
N.A.I.C.S.: 334510
Yukiaki Hashimoto *(Chm-Supervisory Bd)*
Shinya Tanaka *(Chm-Mgmt Bd)*
Norman Eley *(Vice Chm-Supervisory Bd)*
Jaroslaw Jaronski *(Vice Chm-Mgmt Bd)*
Hideki Shiokawa *(Member-Mgmt Bd)*
Thomas Antes *(Sec-Supervisory Bd)*

Tianjin Canon Co., Ltd. **(1)**
1 Xijiang Street Jiefangnan Road
Hexi District, Tianjin, 300221, China
Tel.: (86) 22 8824 2111
Digital Camera & Printer Mfr
S.I.C.: 3579
N.A.I.C.S.: 333316

CANONICAL GROUP LIMITED

5th Floor Blue Fin Building 110
Southwark Street
London, SE1 0SU, United Kingdom
Tel.: (44) 20 7630 2401
Web Site: www.canonical.com
Year Founded: 2004
Emp.: 400
Business Description:
Software Development & Support Services
S.I.C.: 7372
N.A.I.C.S.: 511210
Personnel:
Mark Shuttleworth *(Founder)*
Jane Silber *(CEO)*

CANPAR INDUSTRIES LTD.

2400 555 West Hastings Street
Vancouver, BC, V6B 4N5, Canada
Tel.: (604) 681-7336
Fax: (604) 681-8906
Web Site: www.canparindustries.com
Year Founded: 1932
Rev.: $35,212,705
Emp.: 100
Business Description:
Wood Products Mfr
S.I.C.: 2493
N.A.I.C.S.: 321219
Personnel:
Brian P. Bailley *(Asst Gen Mgr & Dir-Sls & Mktg)*

CANPRO CONSTRUCTION LTD.

555 Dupplin Road
Victoria, BC, V8Z 1C2, Canada
Tel.: (250) 475-0975
Fax: (250) 475-0976
E-Mail: canpro@direct.ca
Web Site: www.canpro-ltd.com
Year Founded: 1984
Rev.: $13,852,619
Emp.: 15
Business Description:
Building Construction Services
S.I.C.: 1542
N.A.I.C.S.: 236220
Personnel:
Don Wagner *(Owner)*

CANSO CREDIT INCOME FUND

100 York Boulevard Suite 550
Richmond Hill, ON, L4B 1J8, Canada
Tel.: (416) 640-4275
Fax: (905) 881-1466
PBY.UN—(TSX)
Assets: $224,917,340
Liabilities: $1,551,158
Net Worth: $223,366,182
Earnings: ($2,069,872)
Fiscal Year-end: 12/31/12
Business Description:
Closed-End Investment Fund
S.I.C.: 6726
N.A.I.C.S.: 525990
Personnel:
Richard Usher-Jones *(Pres & CEO)*
Timothy Hicks *(CFO & Chief Investment Officer)*
Raj Vijh *(COO & VP)*
Brenda Burns *(Sec)*
Transfer Agent:
CIBC Mellon Trust Company
PO Box 7010
Adelaide Street Postal Station, Toronto, ON, M5C 2W9, Canada
Tel.: (416) 643-5500
Fax: (416) 643-5501
Toll Free: (800) 387-0825

CANSO ENTERPRISES LTD.

Avenue Javier Rojo Gomez 630
Leyes de Reforma
Istapalapa, Mexico, 09310, Mexico
Tel.: (52) 55 10843026
Year Founded: 2013
Business Description:
Metal Mining
S.I.C.: 1099
N.A.I.C.S.: 212299
Personnel:
Jim Burns *(Pres, CEO, CFO, Principal Acctg Officer, Treas & Sec)*
Board of Directors:
Jim Burns
German Martinez

CANSO FORD SALES

9 MacIntosh Ave
Port Hawkesbury, NS, B9A 3K4, Canada
Tel.: (902) 625-1338
E-Mail: cansofordsales@ns.aliantzinc.ca
Web Site: www.cansoford.ca
Year Founded: 1979
Rev.: $11,561,746
Emp.: 26
Business Description:
Used & New Car Dealers
S.I.C.: 5511
N.A.I.C.S.: 441110
Personnel:
Robert MacKeigan *(Pres)*

CANSTAR RESOURCES INC.

56 Temperance Street Suite 1000
Toronto, ON, M5H 3V5, Canada
Tel.: (647) 557-3442
Fax: (647) 557-3448
E-Mail: info@canstarresources.com
Web Site: www.canstarresources.com
ROX—(TSXV)
Assets: $3,154,182
Liabilities: $154,855
Net Worth: $2,999,326
Earnings: ($439,452)
Fiscal Year-end: 06/30/13
Business Description:
Mineral Exploration Services
S.I.C.: 1081
N.A.I.C.S.: 213114
Personnel:
Dennis H. Peterson *(Chm)*
Danniel J. Oosterman *(Pres & CEO)*
Jack Hurley *(CFO)*
Board of Directors:
Dennis H. Peterson
William S. Deluce
John E. Hurley
David Palmer
T. Patrick Reid
Legal Counsel:
Peterson Law Professional Corporation
390 Bay Street Suite 806
Toronto, ON, Canada
Transfer Agent:
Equity Financial Trust Company
200 University Avenue Suite 300
Toronto, ON, M5H 4H1, Canada

CANTABIL RETAIL INDIA LIMITED

B-47 Lawrence Rd Industrial Area
New Delhi, 110035, India
Tel.: (91) 1127156381
Fax: (91) 1127156383
E-Mail: info@cantabilinternational.com
Web Site: www.cantabilinternational.com
CANTABIL—(BOM NSE)
Sales Range: $25-49.9 Million
Business Description:
Clothing Mfr & Retailer
S.I.C.: 5699
N.A.I.C.S.: 448190
Personnel:
Vijay Bansal *(Chm & Mng Dir)*
Rajesh Rohilla *(CFO)*
Poonam Chahal *(Sec)*

CANTERRA MINERALS CORPORATION

Suite 1410 650 West Georgia Street
PO Box 11584
Vancouver, BC, V6B 4N8, Canada
Tel.: (604) 687-6644
Fax: (604) 687-1448
E-Mail: info@canterraminerals.com
Web Site: www.canterraminerals.com
CTM—(TSXV)
Int. Income: $13,828
Assets: $9,792,144
Liabilities: $73,801
Net Worth: $9,718,343
Earnings: ($2,364,517)
Emp.: 10
Fiscal Year-end: 12/31/12
Business Description:
Minerals Exploration & Mining
S.I.C.: 1499
N.A.I.C.S.: 212399
Personnel:
Randy C. Turner *(Pres & CEO)*
J. Christopher Mitchell *(CFO)*
Louis G. Montpellier *(Sec)*
Board of Directors:
James E. Eccott
James D. Excell
John McDonald
Mike Muzylowski
Randy C. Turner
Legal Counsel:
Gowling Lafleur Henderson LLP
Bentall 5 2300 550 Burrard Street
PO Box 49122
Vancouver, BC, Canada
Transfer Agent:
Computershare
100 University Avenue 11th Floor
Toronto, ON, Canada

CANTEX MINE DEVELOPMENT CORP.

203 - 1634 Harvey Ave
Kelowna, BC, V1Y 6G2, Canada
Tel.: (250) 860-8582
Fax: (250) 860-1362
E-Mail: info@cantex.ca
Web Site: www.cantex.ca
CD—(TSXV)
Int. Income: $7,763
Assets: $3,665,366
Liabilities: $3,749,881
Net Worth: ($84,515)
Earnings: ($2,252,683)
Fiscal Year-end: 07/31/13
Business Description:
Mineral Exploration Services
S.I.C.: 1081
N.A.I.C.S.: 213114
Personnel:
Charles Fipke *(Chm)*
Chad Ulansky *(Pres & CEO)*
Jennifer Irons *(CFO & Sec)*
Keiven Bauer *(COO)*
Board of Directors:
Charles Fipke
Vernon Frolick
Katherine MacDonald
Chad Ulansky
Legal Counsel:
Lang Michener LLP
Suite 1500 1055 West Georgia Street
Vancouver, BC, Canada

Transfer Agent:
Canadian Stock Transfer Company Inc
600 The Dome Tower, 333 7th Ave SW
Calgary, AB, Canada

CANTILLANA SA/NV

Pontstraat 84
Deurle, B-9831 Sint-Martens-Latem, Belgium
Tel.: (32) 9280 7780
Fax: (32) 9280 7787
Web Site: www.cantillana.com
Year Founded: 1875
Emp.: 250
Business Description:
Plaster & Mortar Mfr
S.I.C.: 3259
N.A.I.C.S.: 327120
Personnel:
Piet Bogaert *(Sls Dir)*

Non-U.S. Subsidiaries:

Cantillana B.V. (1)
Munnikenlandse Maaskade 2a
Poederoijen, 5307 TE Zaltbommel, Netherlands NL
Tel.: (31) 183 44 7800
Fax: (31) 183 44 7809
Web Site: www.cantillana.com
Plaster & Mortar Mfr
S.I.C.: 3259
N.A.I.C.S.: 327120

Cantillana SAS (1)
ZI des Iscles 785 Avenue de la Durance
13160 Chateaurenard, France FR
Mailing Address:
BP 3
59536 Wavrin, Cedex, France
Tel.: (33) 4 9094 2060
Fax: (33) 4 9094 7550
E-Mail: francois.femaux@cantillana.com
Web Site: www.cantillana.com
Sales Range: $1-9.9 Million
Emp.: 50
Plaster & Mortar Mfr
S.I.C.: 3297
N.A.I.C.S.: 327120
Marc Nuytens *(Dir-Pur)*

CANTINE RIUNITE & CIV S.C.AGR.

Via Brodolini 24
IT-42040 Campegine, RE, Italy
Tel.: (39) 0522905711
Fax: (39) 0522905777
E-Mail: comita@riunite.it
Web Site: www.riunite.it
Year Founded: 1950
Sales Range: $600-649.9 Million
Emp.: 1,500
Business Description:
Holding Company; Wineries & Wine Whslr
S.I.C.: 6719
N.A.I.C.S.: 551112
Personnel:
Corrado Casoli *(Chm)*

Subsidiary:

Gruppo Italiano Vini S.p.A. (1)
Villa Belvedere
Frazione Di Bardolino, IT-37010 Calmasino, Veneto, Italy IT
Tel.: (39) 0456269600
Fax: (39) 0457235772
E-Mail: giv@giv.it
Web Site: www.gruppoitalianovini.com
Emp.: 330
Holding Company; Wineries & Wine Whslr
S.I.C.: 6719
N.A.I.C.S.: 551112
Corrado Casoli *(Chm)*
Rolando Chiossi *(Vice Chm & Head-Fin Ops)*

Subsidiary:

Bigi S.p.A. (2)
Localita Ponte Giulio no 3
IT-05018 Orvieto, Terni, Italy IT
Tel.: (39) 0763315888
Fax: (39) 0763316376
E-Mail: bigi@giv.it
Web Site: www.cantinebigi.it
Emp.: 21
Winery & Wine Whslr
S.I.C.: 2084
N.A.I.C.S.: 312130
Luigi Bigi *(Founder)*

U.S. Holding:

Frederick Wildman & Sons Ltd. (2)
307 E 53rd St
New York, NY 10022-4985 DE
Tel.: (212) 355-0700 (75%)
Fax: (212) 355-4719
Toll Free: (800) RED-WINE
E-Mail: info@frederickwildman.com
Web Site: www.frederickwildman.com
Emp.: 75
French & Italian Wines Importer Import
S.I.C.: 5182
N.A.I.C.S.: 424820
Richard Cacciato *(Pres & CEO)*
Rocco Lombardo *(COO & Sr VP)*

CANTONI MOTOR S.A.

Grazynskiego 22
43-300 Bielsko-Biala, Poland
Tel.: (48) 8138700
Fax: (48) 8138701
E-Mail: motor@cantonigroup.com
Web Site:
Emp.: 20
Business Description:
Electric Motor Mfr
S.I.C.: 3621
N.A.I.C.S.: 335312
Personnel:
Luca Cantoni *(Chm)*
Board of Directors:
Luca Cantoni

Subsidiaries:

Besel S.A. (1)
Ul Elektryczna 8
49-300 Brzeg, Poland
Tel.: (48) 774162861
Fax: (48) 774166868
E-Mail: besel@cantonimotor.com.pl
Web Site: www.besel.pl
Emp.: 100
Electric Motor Mfr
S.I.C.: 3621
N.A.I.C.S.: 335312

Celma S.A. (1)
Ul 3 Maja 19
43 400 Cieszyn, Poland
Tel.: (48) 338519100
Fax: (48) 338521344
E-Mail: celma@cantonimotor.com.pl
Web Site: www.motors.celma.pl
Electric Motor Mfr
S.I.C.: 3621
N.A.I.C.S.: 335312
Mariusz Kozica *(Pres)*

Emit S.A. (1)
Narutowicza 72
99 320 Zychlin, Poland
Tel.: (48) 242851014
Fax: (48) 242852005
E-Mail: info@emit-motor.com.pl
Web Site: www.emit-motor.com.pl
Emp.: 400
Low & High Voltage Induction Motors Mfr
S.I.C.: 3621
N.A.I.C.S.: 335312
Wlodzimierz Kesicki *(Chm)*
Ewa Falacinska *(Vice Chm)*

Fenes S.A. (1)
gen Franciszka Kleeberga 2
08 110 Siedlce, Poland
Tel.: (48) 256325251
Fax: (48) 256327946
E-Mail: fenes@fenes.com.pl
Web Site: www.fenes.com.pl
Emp.: 200
Cutting Tools for Metalworking & Woodworking Mfr
S.I.C.: 3549
N.A.I.C.S.: 333519
Dariusz Piatek *(Pres)*

Indukta S.A. (1)
ul Grazynskiego 22
43 300 Bielsko-Biala, Poland
Tel.: (48) 338272000
Fax: (48) 338272098
E-Mail: indukta@cantonigroup.com
Web Site: www.indukta.com.pl
Emp.: 500
Electric Motor Mfr
S.I.C.: 3621
N.A.I.C.S.: 335312
Mariusz Kozica *(Pres)*

Subsidiary:

Ema-Elfa Sp.zo.o. (2)
Ul Pocztowa 7
63500 Ostrzeszow, Poland
Tel.: (48) 627303051
Fax: (48) 627303306
E-Mail: emaelfa@ema-elfa.home.pl
Web Site: www.ema-elfa.home.pl
Emp.: 100
Motor Accessories Supplier
S.I.C.: 5063
N.A.I.C.S.: 423610
Wlodzimierz Kesicki *(Chm)*

CANTRONIC SYSTEMS INC.

67A Clipper Street
Coquitlam, BC, V3K 6X2, Canada
Tel.: (604) 516-6667
Fax: (604) 516-6618
Toll Free: (866) 391-6970
E-Mail: info@cantronics.com
Web Site: www.cantronics.com
Year Founded: 2005
Sales Range: $10-24.9 Million
Emp.: 300
Business Description:
Infrared Imaging Camera & Night Vision Surveillance Systems Mfr & Distr
S.I.C.: 7382
N.A.I.C.S.: 561621
Personnel:
James Zahn *(CEO)*
Kevin Tao Su *(CFO)*

Subsidiary:

AIRT Academy of Infrared Training Inc. (1)
67A Clipper St
Coquitlam, BC, V3K 6X2, Canada
Tel.: (604) 516-6646
Fax: (604) 516-6674
E-Mail: airt@infraredtraining.net
Web Site: www.infraredtraining.net
Emp.: 15
Training Services
S.I.C.: 8299
N.A.I.C.S.: 611430
Helen Leung *(Mng Dir)*
James Zahn *(Mng Dir)*

U.S. Subsidiary:

QWIP Technologies, Inc. (1)
499 Nibus St Ste D
Brea, CA 92821
Tel.: (866) 391-6970
E-Mail: info@cantronics.com
Web Site: www.cantronics.com
Surveillance Equipments Mfr & Sales
S.I.C.: 3812
N.A.I.C.S.: 334511
Alex Hong *(Dir-Engrg & Bus Dev)*

Non-U.S. Subsidiaries:

Actiontop Electronics (Shenzhen) Co. Ltd (1)
2Fl C D Building Hongmen Technology Park Jihua Road Buji Town
Longgang District, Shenzhen, Guangdong, 518129, China
Tel.: (86) 75589390905
Fax: (86) 755 89580546
E-Mail: sales@actiontop.cn
Web Site: www.actiontop.com
Surveillance Equipments Mfr
S.I.C.: 3812
N.A.I.C.S.: 334511
Alec Weingart *(CEO & Pres)*

Beijing Advanced VideoInfo Technology Co., Ltd (1)
Jiahuiyua Huaao International Building B Area 10th Floor
Beijing, 100097, China
Tel.: (86) 10 58930606
Fax: (86) 10 58931006
Web Site: www.avinfo.cn
Emp.: 80
Surveillance Equipments Mfr & Distr
S.I.C.: 3812
N.A.I.C.S.: 334511
Bonny Lu *(Mgr)*

Subsidiary:

Liaoning Daoheng Technology Co., Ltd (2)
No 9 d1 1F Baike Mansion Kehuan Road
Shenyang, Liaoning, 110000, China
Tel.: (86) 2483601302
Surveillance Equipments Mfr
S.I.C.: 3812
N.A.I.C.S.: 334511

Cantronic Security Systems (China) Co., Ltd (1)
F 17 Multimedia Plaza No 757 Guangzhong West Road
Shanghai, 200072, China
Tel.: (86) 21 6630 6600
Fax: (86) 21 6630 9997
E-Mail: sales@cantronics.com.cn
Web Site: www.cantronics.com.cn
Surveillance Equipment Mfr
S.I.C.: 3669
N.A.I.C.S.: 334290
James Zahn *(CEO)*

Cantronic Systems Inc. (1)
F.17 Multimedia Plaza No. 757 Guangzhong W. Road
Pudong District, Shanghai, 200122, China
Tel.: (86) 2166306600
Fax: (86) 2166309997
E-Mail: sales@cantronics.com.cn
Web Site: www.cantronics.com
Infrared Imaging Camera & Night Vision Surveillance Systems Mfr & Distr
S.I.C.: 5043
N.A.I.C.S.: 423410

Shenzhen Huanghe Digital Technology Co. Ltd (1)
6th Floor 1st Building Yuehai Industrial Park Yuehai Road
Nanshan, Shenzhen, Guangdong, 518054, China
Tel.: (86) 75533631190
Fax: (86) 75533631150
E-Mail: sales@histream.cn
Web Site: www.histream.cn
Surveillance Equipments Mfr
S.I.C.: 3812
N.A.I.C.S.: 334511

CANUC RESOURCES CORPORATION

121 Richmond Street West Suite 402
Toronto, ON, M5H 2K1, Canada
Tel.: (416) 867-1300
Fax: (416) 364-2595
E-Mail: info@canucresources.ca
Web Site: www.canucresources.ca
Year Founded: 1997
CDA—(TSXV)
Sls.: $185,621
Assets: $668,998
Liabilities: $325,756
Net Worth: $343,242
Earnings: ($7,914,758)
Emp.: 3
Fiscal Year-end: 12/31/12
Business Description:
Gold Mining Services
S.I.C.: 1041
N.A.I.C.S.: 212221
Personnel:
Hubert J. Mockler *(Vice Chm)*
Gary Lohman *(Pres & CEO)*
Christopher R. Chadder *(CFO)*
Board of Directors:

Canuc Resources Corporation—(Continued)

Christopher J. Berlet
Richard W. Brissenden
Gary Lohman
John Lynch
Hubert J. Mockler

Transfer Agent:
Equity Transfer & Trust Company
200 University Avenue Ste 400
Toronto, ON, M5H 4H1, Canada
Tel.: (416) 361-0152
Fax: (416) 361-0470

CANUSA AUTOMOTIVE WAREHOUSING INC.

257 Hamilton Crescent
Dorchester, ON, N0L 1G4, Canada
Tel.: (519) 268-7070
Fax: (519) 268-8375
Toll Free: (866) 860-1231
Web Site: www.canusa.on.ca
Year Founded: 1981
Rev.: $21,384,980
Emp.: 140

Business Description:
Automobile Parts Mfr & Distr
S.I.C.: 5995
N.A.I.C.S.: 446130

Personnel:
Ivor Jones *(Pres)*

CANUSA WOOD PRODUCTS LIMITED

1281 W Georgia St Ste 203
Vancouver, BC, V6E 3J7, Canada
Tel.: (604) 687-2254
Fax: (604) 682-4691
Toll Free: (877) 822-6872
E-Mail: canusa@canusawoodproducts.com
Web Site: www.canusawoodproducts.com
Year Founded: 1975
Sales Range: $10-24.9 Million
Emp.: 15
Fiscal Year-end: 03/31/13

Business Description:
Timber & Panel Products Importer
S.I.C.: 5031
N.A.I.C.S.: 423310

Personnel:
Douglas Hay *(CEO)*

CANWEALTH MINERALS CORPORATION

1376 Perrot Boulevard
L'Ile Perrot, QC, J7V 7P2, Canada
Tel.: (514) 425-2020
Web Site: www.canwealthminerals.com
Year Founded: 2006
Assets: $69,123
Liabilities: $266,287
Net Worth: ($197,164)
Earnings: ($169,061)
Fiscal Year-end: 12/31/12

Business Description:
Gold & Other Precious Metal Mining
S.I.C.: 1041
N.A.I.C.S.: 212221

Personnel:
Garth McIntosh *(Chm, Pres & CEO)*

Board of Directors:
Garth McIntosh

CANYON COPPER CORP.

Suite 408 - 1199 West Pender Street
Vancouver, BC, V6E 2R1, Canada
Tel.: (604) 331-9326
Toll Free: (888) 331-9326
E-Mail: info@canyoncc.com
Web Site: www.canyoncc.com
Year Founded: 2000
CNC—(OTC TSXV)
Rev.: $230,346
Assets: $44,117
Liabilities: $66,510
Net Worth: ($22,393)
Earnings: ($605,616)
Fiscal Year-end: 06/30/13

Business Description:
Copper Mining Services
S.I.C.: 1021
N.A.I.C.S.: 212234

Personnel:
Benjamin Ainsworth *(Pres, CEO & Sec)*
Kurt James Bordian *(CFO & Treas)*

Board of Directors:
Benjamin Ainsworth
John R. Kerr
James Ernest Yates

CANYON CREEK FOOD COMPANY LTD.

8704 - 53rd Avenue
Edmonton, AB, T6E 5G2, Canada
Tel.: (780) 463-2991
Fax: (780) 463-5511
Toll Free: (888) 217-1246
Web Site: www.canyoncreekfood.com
CYF—(TSXV)
Rev.: $1,200,089
Assets: $1,520,618
Liabilities: $10,208,911
Net Worth: ($8,688,293)
Earnings: ($2,004,283)
Fiscal Year-end: 05/31/13

Business Description:
Food Product Mfr
S.I.C.: 2099
N.A.I.C.S.: 311999

Personnel:
Brian Halina *(Chm)*
Terence Alty *(Pres & CEO)*
Belva Rode *(CFO)*

Board of Directors:
Brian Halina
Terence Alty
David Harbinson
Scott Reeves

CANYON CREEK TOYOTA INC.

370 Canyon Meadows Dr SE
Calgary, AB, T2J 7C6, Canada
Tel.: (403) 278-6066
Fax: (403) 278-6223
E-Mail: info@canyoncreektoyota.com
Web Site: www.canyoncreektoyota.com
Rev.: $30,865,457
Emp.: 62

Business Description:
New & Used Car Dealers
S.I.C.: 5511
N.A.I.C.S.: 441110

Personnel:
Mark Kerr *(Mgr-Fin Svcs)*

CANYON RESOURCES LTD

353 Rokeby Road
Subiaco, WA, 6008, Australia

Mailing Address:
PO Box 270
West Perth, WA, 6872, Australia
Tel.: (61) 8 6143 4256
Fax: (61) 8 9324 1502
E-Mail: info@canyonresources.com.au
Web Site: www.canyonresources.com.au
CAY—(ASX)
Rev.: $275,554
Assets: $8,590,081
Liabilities: $529,284
Net Worth: $8,060,798
Earnings: ($2,672,893)
Emp.: 11
Fiscal Year-end: 06/30/13

Business Description:
Gold Mining Services
S.I.C.: 1041
N.A.I.C.S.: 212221

Personnel:
Matthew Shackleton *(Founder)*
Phillip Gallagher *(Mng Dir)*
Phillip MacLeod *(Sec)*

Board of Directors:
Rhoderick Grivas
Phillip Gallagher
Matthew Shackleton

Legal Counsel:
Steinepreis Paganin
Level 4 The Read Building 16 Milligan Street
Perth, WA, 6000, Australia
Tel.: (61) 8 9321 4000
Fax: (61) 8 9321 4333

CANYON SERVICES GROUP INC.

Suite 2900 Bow Valley III 255 5th Avenue SW
Calgary, AB, T2P 3G6, Canada
Tel.: (403) 355-2300
Fax: (403) 355-2211
E-Mail: info@canyontech.ca
Web Site: www.canyontech.ca
FRC—(TSX)
Rev.: $351,007,348
Assets: $403,684,444
Liabilities: $67,929,339
Net Worth: $335,755,106
Earnings: $54,083,634
Emp.: 800
Fiscal Year-end: 12/31/12

Business Description:
Oil Field Services
S.I.C.: 1311
N.A.I.C.S.: 211111

Personnel:
Raymond Peter Antony *(Chm)*
Bradley P. D. Fedora *(Pres & CEO)*
Barry J. O'Brien *(CFO & VP-Fin)*
Todd G. Thue *(COO)*
Jeremy Matthies *(Gen Counsel)*
A. J. Peskunowicz *(Exec VP)*

Board of Directors:
Raymond Peter Antony
Bradley P. D. Fedora
Douglas C. Freel
Stan G. P. Grad
Neil MacKenzie
Richard E. Peterson
Scott Ratushny

Legal Counsel:
Blakes, Cassels & Graydon LLP
Calgary, AB, Canada

Transfer Agent:
Olympia Trust Company
125 9th Avenue SE Suite 2300
Calgary, AB, T2G 0P6, Canada
Tel.: (403) 261-0900

Subsidiary:

Canyon Technical Services Ltd. (1)
255 5th Ave SW
Calgary, AB, T2P 3G6, Canada
Tel.: (403) 355-2300
Fax: (403) 355-2211
Web Site: www.canyontech.ca
Emp.: 50
Oil & Gas Field Exploration Services
S.I.C.: 1311
N.A.I.C.S.: 211111
Brad Fedora *(Pres)*
Barry O'Brien *(CFO & VP-Fin)*
Todd Thue *(COO)*
A J Peskunowicz *(Exec VP)*

CAP ENERGY LTD

25 Dover Street
London, W1S 4LX, United Kingdom
Tel.: (44) 207 491 9196
E-Mail: info@capenergyplc.com
Web Site: www.capenergy.co.uk
CAPP—(ISDX)
Assets: $511,837
Liabilities: $574,876
Net Worth: ($63,039)
Earnings: ($64,269)
Emp.: 3
Fiscal Year-end: 12/31/12

Business Description:
Oil & Gas Exploration
S.I.C.: 1311
N.A.I.C.S.: 211111

Personnel:
Lina Haidar *(CEO & COO)*
Pierantonio Tassini *(COO)*
Chanelle George *(Sec)*

Board of Directors:
Timothy Hearley
Lina Haidar
Alexander Haly
Pierantonio Tassini

Legal Counsel:
Fox Williams LLP
10 Dominion St
London, United Kingdom

CAP-EX VENTURES LTD.

Suite 1240 1140 West Pender Street
Vancouver, BC, V6E 4G1, Canada
Tel.: (604) 681-8030
Fax: (604) 681-8039
E-Mail: info@cap-ex.ca
Web Site: www.cap-ex.ca
Year Founded: 2007
CEV—(DEU OTC TSXV)

Business Description:
Iron Ore Exploration & Mining Services
S.I.C.: 1011
N.A.I.C.S.: 212210

Personnel:
Andrew W. Bowering *(Chm)*
Paul Sandor Bozoki *(CFO)*
Valery Zamuner *(Chief Legal Officer & Sec)*
Brian K. Penney *(Chm-Ops)*

Board of Directors:
Andrew W. Bowering
Troy Gill
Graham Harris
Brett Matich
Gary Norris
Brian K. Penney

Legal Counsel:
CD Farber Law Corp.
Suite 2602 1111 Beach Avenue
Vancouver, BC, V6E 1T9, Canada

Transfer Agent:
Equity Financial Trust Company
200 University Avenue Suite 400
Toronto, ON, Canada

CAP PARTS AG

Elterleiner Strasse 15
09481 Scheibenberg, Germany
Tel.: (49) 373496980
Fax: (49) 3734969825
E-Mail: capparts@capparts.de
Web Site: www.capparts.de
Year Founded: 1933
Rev.: $13,448,194
Emp.: 90

Business Description:
Electronic Device Packaging Products Mfr
S.I.C.: 3269
N.A.I.C.S.: 327110

Personnel:
Hans-Gerd Meixner *(CEO)*

CAP S.A.

Gertrudis Echenique 220 Las Condes
Santiago, Chile
Tel.: (56) 28186000
Fax: (56) 28186116

Web Site: www.cap.cl
CAP—(SGO)
Rev.: $2,470,003,000
Assets: $5,166,626,000
Liabilities: $2,058,216,000
Net Worth: $3,108,410,000
Earnings: $327,506,000
Emp.: 5,454
Fiscal Year-end: 12/31/12

Business Description:
Iron Ore & Steel Mfr
S.I.C.: 3312
N.A.I.C.S.: 331110

Personnel:
Roberto De Andraca *(Chm)*
Sven Von Appen *(Vice Chm)*
Jaime Charles *(Pres & CEO)*
Raul Gamonal *(CFO & Sr Exec VP)*
Juan Pablo Cortes *(CEO-Cintac SA)*
Ivan Flores *(CEO-Acero)*
Erick Weber *(CEO-Mineria)*
Sergio Verdugo *(COO-Mining & Steel & Sr Exec VP)*
Eduardo Frei *(Legal Counsel)*
Jorge Dominquez *(Sr Exec VP-Bus Dev)*
Ernesto Escobar *(Sr Exec VP-Corp Affairs)*
Arturo Wenzel Alvarez *(Exec VP-Plng & Strategic Resources)*
Andres Del Sante *(Exec VP-Internal Control)*

Board of Directors:
Roberto De Andraca
Tokuro Furukawa
Eddie Navarrete
Hernan Orellana
Fernando Reitich
Osamn Sasaki
Sven Von Appen

Subsidiaries:

Armacero Industrial y Comercial Ltda (1)
Calle Interior N 700 Panamericana Norte Km 17 1 2
Lampa, Santiago, Chile
Tel.: (56) 2 544 99 01
Fax: (56) 2 738 73 25
E-Mail: usc@armacero.cl
Web Site: www.armacero.cl
Emp.: 140
Steel Bars Mfr
S.I.C.: 3399
N.A.I.C.S.: 331110
Fernando Miranda *(Mng Dir)*

Compania Minera del Pacifico S.A (1)
P Pablo Munoz 675
IV Region Coquimbo, La Serena, Elqui, Chile
Tel.: (56) 51208000
Fax: (56) 51208100
E-Mail: cmpsa@cmp.cl
Web Site: www.cmp.cl
Iron Mine Deposits Onwership & Operation Services
S.I.C.: 1011
N.A.I.C.S.: 212210
Jaime Charles *(Pres)*
Erick Weber *(Pres)*

Subsidiaries:

Imopac Ltda. (2)
Calle Brasil 1050
Vallenar, Chile
Tel.: (56) 51208609
Fax: (56) 51208700
Iron Ore Mining Services
S.I.C.: 1011
N.A.I.C.S.: 212210

Manganesos Atacama S.A. (2)
Vulcano N 75
IV Region, Coquimbo, Elqui, Chile
Tel.: (56) 51322299
Fax: (56) 51322299
E-Mail: manganesosatacama@manganeso.cl
Web Site: www.manganeso.cl
Manganese Ferroalloys Mfr
S.I.C.: 3312
N.A.I.C.S.: 331110

Minera Hierro Atacama S.A. (2)
Brasil N 1050
III Region, Vallenar, Huasco, Chile
Tel.: (56) 51 208 400
Fax: (56) 51 208 500
Iron Ore Mining Services
S.I.C.: 1011
N.A.I.C.S.: 212210

Petropac Ltda (1)
Pedro Pablo Munoz N 675
Region IV Coquimbo, La Serena, Elqui, Chile
Tel.: (56) 51 208153
Fax: (56) 51 208140
E-Mail: petropac@entelchile.net
Web Site: www.petropac.cl
Emp.: 10
Fuel Oil Terminals Operation Services
S.I.C.: 5171
N.A.I.C.S.: 424710
Sherman Ghirardo *(Pres)*

Non-U.S. Subsidiary:

Novacero S.A. (1)
Avenida De Los Shirys 3941
Y Rio Coca Planta Baja, Quito, Pichincha, Ecuador
Tel.: (593) 22269944
Fax: (593) 22469966
Web Site: www.novacero.com
Emp.: 54
Structured Iron & Steel Products Mfr
S.I.C.: 3312
N.A.I.C.S.: 331110
Rosalia Velez *(Reg Mgr)*

CAPARO GROUP LTD.

103 Baker St
London, W1U 6LN, United Kingdom
Tel.: (44) 2074861417
Fax: (44) 2072244109
E-Mail: info@caparo.com
Web Site: www.caparo.com
Year Founded: 1968

Business Description:
Steel Based Engineering Products; Automotive Components
S.I.C.: 3714
N.A.I.C.S.: 336330

Personnel:
Swraj Paul *(Founder & Chm)*
Angad Paul *(CEO)*

Board of Directors:
Swraj Paul
Richard Butler
David Dancaster
Jack Meyer
Dennis Morrill
Sunil Pahilajani
Akash Paul
Ambar Paul
Chris Shaw
John Smith
Colin Steele
Baroness Symons
Lord Walker
John Wood
John Wraith

Legal Counsel:
Edge & Ellison, Hatwell Pritchett & Co.
Birmingham, United Kingdom

Berwin Leighton
Adelaide House
London Bridge
London, EC4 9HA, United Kingdom
Tel.: (44) 71 623 3144

Subsidiary:

Caparo Plc (1)
103 Baker St
London, W1U 6LN, United Kingdom (100%)
Tel.: (44) 2074861417
Fax: (44) 2072244109
E-Mail: info@caparo.co.uk
Web Site: www.caparo.com
Sls.: $259,747,390
Emp.: 10
Fabricated Metal Products
S.I.C.: 3499
N.A.I.C.S.: 332999

Subsidiaries:

Caparo Atlas Fastenings (2)
Heath Rd
PO Box 6
Darlaston, W Midlands, WS10 8UL, United Kingdom (100%)
Tel.: (44) 1212242000
Telex: 339512
Fax: (44) 1212242007
E-Mail: enquiries@caparoatlasfastenings.com
Web Site: www.caparoatlasfastenings.com
Emp.: 200
Bolt & Fasteners Mfr
S.I.C.: 3452
N.A.I.C.S.: 332722
Chris Jina *(CEO)*

Caparo Industries Plc (2)
Caparo House
Popes Lane, Oldbury, West Midlands, B69 4PJ, United Kingdom (100%)
Tel.: (44) 1212024400
Fax: (44) 1212024401
E-Mail: enquiries@caparo.co.uk
Web Site: www.caparo.com
Emp.: 25
Mfr. of Automotive Products
S.I.C.: 3399
N.A.I.C.S.: 331110

Subsidiaries:

Caparo Engineering Ltd. (3)
Caparo House Popes Lane
Oldbury, West Midlands, B69 4PJ, United Kingdom (100%)
Tel.: (44) 1212024400
Fax: (44) 1212024401
E-Mail: enquries@caparo.com
Web Site: www.caparo.com
Emp.: 25
Metal Product Mfr
S.I.C.: 3499
N.A.I.C.S.: 332999

Divisions:

Caparo Modular Systems Ltd. (4)
Neachells Lane
Willenhall, WV13 3SN, United Kingdom (100%)
Tel.: (44) 1902305221
Telex: 339 621
Fax: (44) 1902307730
Web Site: www.willenhall-manufacturing.co.uk
Sls.: $11,000,000
Emp.: 50
Automobile Body Panels, Truck & Tractor Cabs
S.I.C.: 3711
N.A.I.C.S.: 336120
Bob Piosonh *(Mng Dir)*

Clydesdale Forge (4)
Brenda Road
Hartlepool, TS25 2BP, United Kingdom
Tel.: (44) 1429268101
Fax: (44) 1429233346
E-Mail: Sales@Clydesdale-Forge.co.uk
Web Site: www.clydesdale-forge.co.uk
Emp.: 100
Metal Product Mfr
S.I.C.: 3499
N.A.I.C.S.: 332999
Mike Wilson *(Mgr-Mktg)*

CMT Engineering (4)
Congreaves Road
PO Box 36
Warley, Cradley Heath, W Midlands, B64 7DQ, United Kingdom (100%)
Tel.: (44) 1384638777
Telex: 339867
Fax: (44) 138 465 249
Web Site: www.cmt-engineering.co.uk
Emp.: 138
Pipe Fittings & Insulation Mfr
S.I.C.: 3494
N.A.I.C.S.: 332919

Caparo Merchant Bar plc (3)
Caparo House
PO Box 15
Scunthorpe, DN16 1XL, United Kingdom UK
Tel.: (44) 1724853333
Telex: 527419
Fax: (44) 1724403044
E-Mail: sales@cmbplc.co.uk
Web Site: www.cmbplc.co.uk
Emp.: 180
Merchant Bar Rolling Mill
S.I.C.: 3399
N.A.I.C.S.: 331221

Caparo Precision Tubes Ltd. (2)
Popes Ln
Oldbury, W Midlands, B69 4PF, United Kingdom
Tel.: (44) 1215435700
Fax: (44) 1215435730
E-Mail: info@caparoprecisiontubes.co.uk
Web Site: www.caparoprecisiontubes.co.uk
Emp.: 250
Steel Welded Tubes, Steel Seamless Tubes, Drawn Tubes, Steel Electrical Conduits, Precision Tubes, Manipulated Tubes, Rigid Metal Framing Components, Cold-Rolled Strip Processing & Other Metal Products Mfr & Distr
S.I.C.: 3317
N.A.I.C.S.: 331210
Dave Farrow *(Mng Dir)*

Caparo Wire Limited (2)
Ash Road
Wrexham Industrial Estate, Wrexham, LL13 9JT, United Kingdom UK
Tel.: (44) 1978 666 800
Telex: 66193
Fax: (44) 1978 666 840
E-Mail: sales@caparo-wire.co.uk
Web Site: www.caparo-wire.co.uk
Emp.: 110
Mfr. of Specialized Wire for Fasteners, Ropes, Chains, Bedding & Seating
S.I.C.: 3496
N.A.I.C.S.: 332618
Phioo Earl *(Mng Dir)*

U.S. Subsidiary:

Bull Moose Tube Company (2)
1819 Clarkson Rd Ste 100
Chesterfield, MO 63017-5071 (100%)
Tel.: (636) 537-2600
Fax: (636) 537-5848
E-Mail: sales@bullmoosetube.com
Web Site: www.bullmoosetube.com
Emp.: 360
Steel Pipe Mfr
S.I.C.: 3317
N.A.I.C.S.: 331210
Jack Meyer *(Pres)*

Subsidiary:

Bull Moose Tubes (3)
29851 County Rd 20 W
Elkhart, IN 46515 (100%)
Tel.: (574) 295-8070
Fax: (877) 232-7130
Web Site: www.bullmoosetube.com
Emp.: 100
Steel Pipe Mfr
S.I.C.: 3317
N.A.I.C.S.: 331210

Non-U.S. Subsidiary:

Bull Moose Tubes Ltd. (1)
2170 Queensway Dr
Burlington, ON, L7R 3T1, Canada (100%)
Tel.: (905) 637-8261
Fax: (905) 681-8228
E-Mail: dshaver@bullmoosetube.com
Web Site: www.bullmoosetube.com
Emp.: 48
Steel Pipe Mfr
S.I.C.: 3317
N.A.I.C.S.: 331210
Swraj Paul *(Chm)*

CAPCARGO AG

Ifangstrasse 12
8302 Kloten, Switzerland
Tel.: (41) 44 578 04 00
Web Site: www.capcargo.com

Business Description:
Logistics Software Development Services

CAPcargo AG—(Continued)

S.I.C.: 7371
N.A.I.C.S.: 541511
Personnel:
Oliver Franz *(Chm)*

CAPCELLENCE MITTELSTANDSPARTNER GMBH

Caffamacherreihe 7
20355 Hamburg, Germany
Tel.: (49) 40 307 007 00
Fax: (49) 40 307 007 77
E-Mail: info@capcellence.com
Web Site: www.capcellence.com
Emp.: 15
Business Description:
Private Equity Firm
S.I.C.: 6211
N.A.I.C.S.: 523999
Personnel:
Spyros Chaveles *(Mng Partner)*

Holdings:

4WHEELS Service + Logistik GmbH (1)
Worringer Str 57
40211 Dusseldorf, Germany
Tel.: (49) 2 11 90 60 90
Fax: (49) 2 11 24 50 450
E-Mail: info@4wheels.de
Web Site: www.4wheels.de
Sales Range: $25-49.9 Million
Emp.: 330
Tire Warehousing Services
S.I.C.: 4225
N.A.I.C.S.: 493110
Robin Vogl *(CEO)*

GARDEUR GmbH (1)
Alsstrasse 155
41063 Monchengladbach, Germany
Tel.: (49) 2161 816 0
Fax: (49) 2161 183833
E-Mail: info@gardeur.de
Web Site: www.gardeur.com
Sales Range: $125-149.9 Million
Emp.: 1,600
Pants Mfr
S.I.C.: 5699
N.A.I.C.S.: 315220
Gerhard Kranzle *(CEO)*
Joachim Pelz *(CFO)*
Jens Biermann *(COO)*

CAPCOM CO., LTD.

3-1-3 Uchihirano-machi
Chuo-ku, Osaka, 540-0037, Japan
Tel.: (81) 669203600
Fax: (81) 669205100
Web Site: www.capcom.co.jp
Year Founded: 1979
9697—(OTC TKS)
Sls.: $1,034,825,000
Assets: $1,148,015,000
Liabilities: $456,907,000
Net Worth: $691,108,000
Earnings: $32,703,000
Emp.: 2,476
Fiscal Year-end: 03/31/13
Business Description:
Video Game Software & Hardware Developer
S.I.C.: 3652
N.A.I.C.S.: 334614
Personnel:
Kenzo Tsujimoto *(Chm & CEO)*
Haruhiro Tsujimoto *(Pres & COO)*
Tamio Oda *(CFO & Exec VP)*
Kazuo Kano *(Corp Officer)*
Midori Yuasa *(Corp Officer)*
Board of Directors:
Kenzo Tsujimoto
Kazuhiko Abe
Yoichi Egawa
Katsuhiko Ichii
Makoto Matsuo
Takayuki Morinaga
Tamio Oda
Haruhiro Tsujimoto
Yoshifumi Yamashita
Hiroshi Yasuda
Transfer Agent:
Mitsubishi UFJ Trust & Banking Corporation
1-5, Doujimahama 1-chome, Kita-ku
Osaka, Japan

Subsidiaries:

Captron Co., Ltd. (1)
3-1-3 Uchihirano-machi
Chuo-ku, Osaka, 540-0037, Japan (100%)
Tel.: (81) 6 6920 3626
Fax: (81) 6 6920 5126
Web Site: www.capcom.co.jp/site/privacy_05english.html
Emp.: 1,200
Developer of Video Game Software & Hardware
S.I.C.: 3942
N.A.I.C.S.: 339930
Kazuhisa Hirao *(Mgr-Audit)*

ENTERRISE CO., LTD (1)
Noe Building 2-5-1 Taitou
Taitou-ku, Tokyo, 110-0016, Japan
Tel.: (81) 358128725
Fax: (81) 358128727
Web Site: www.enterrise.co.jp
Amusement Equipment Mfr & Sales
S.I.C.: 3999
N.A.I.C.S.: 339999

Flagship Co., Ltd. (1)
6th Fl Nakano F Bldg 4 44 18 Honmachi
Nakano Ku, Tokyo, 164 0012, Japan
Tel.: (81) 353288071
Fax: (81) 333400711
S.I.C.: 3751
N.A.I.C.S.: 336991

K2 CO., LTD (1)
th Floor Shogyo Building 5-6-10 Toyosaki
Kita-ku, Osaka, 531-0072, Japan
Tel.: (81) 648024557
Fax: (81) 648024559
E-Mail: info24712@kei-two.co.jp
Web Site: www.kei-two.co.jp
Home Video Game Development Services
S.I.C.: 7371
N.A.I.C.S.: 541511

Plant:

Capcom Co., Ltd. - Ueno Facility (1)
3902 Hatta
Iga, Mie, 518-1155, Japan
Tel.: (81) 595202030
Web Site: www.capcom.co.jp/ir/english/company/address.html
Video Games Distr
S.I.C.: 5099
N.A.I.C.S.: 423990

U.S. Subsidiaries:

Capcom Entertainment, Inc. (1)
800 Concar Dr Ste 300
San Mateo, CA 94402-2649
Tel.: (650) 350-6500
Fax: (650) 350-6655
Web Site: www.capcom.com
Sales Range: $100-124.9 Million
Emp.: 100
Developer of Video Game Software & Hardware
S.I.C.: 5092
N.A.I.C.S.: 423920
Darin Johnston *(Mgr-E-Commerce & Event Sls)*

Capcom Inc (1)
800 Concar Dr Ste 300
San Mateo, CA 94402-2649
Tel.: (650) 350-6500
Web Site: www.capcom.com
Mfr of Video Games
S.I.C.: 7372
N.A.I.C.S.: 511210

Capcom USA, Inc. (1)
800 Concar Dr Ste 300
San Mateo, CA 94402-2649 (100%)
Tel.: (650) 350-6500
Fax: (650) 350-6655
Web Site: www.capcom.com
Emp.: 120
Mfr of Pinball Machines, Video Games; Operator of Arcades; Consumer Video Games Whslr
S.I.C.: 7993
N.A.I.C.S.: 713120
Tanya Shaw *(Sec)*

Non-U.S. Subsidiaries:

Capcom Asia Co., Ltd. (1)
Unit 1510 1511 N Tower
Concordia Plz 1 Science Museam,
Kowloon, China (Hong Kong) (100%)
Tel.: (852) 23661001
Fax: (852) 23661985
Web Site: www.capcomasia.com.hk
Emp.: 7
Developer of Video Game Software & Hardware
S.I.C.: 3942
N.A.I.C.S.: 339930

CAPCOM ENTERTAINMENT KOREA CO., LTD. (1)
Dong Il Highvill Office 410 1542-1 Seochodong
Seocho-gu, Seoul, 137872, Korea (South)
Tel.: (82) 25252160
Fax: (82) 25252161
Web Site: www.capcomkorea.com
Emp.: 10
Electronic Game Machines Mfr & Sales
S.I.C.: 3944
N.A.I.C.S.: 339930

CAPCOM INTERACTIVE CANADA, INC (1)
405 The West Mall
Toronto, ON, M9C 5J1, Canada
Tel.: (647) 788-1600
Fax: (647) 788-1601
Emp.: 20
Video Games Development & Publishing Services
S.I.C.: 7372
N.A.I.C.S.: 511210
Vera Dobric *(Mgr-Office)*

CE Europe Ltd. (1)
9th Fl 26 28 Hammersmith Grove
Hammersmith, London, W6 7HA, United Kingdom (100%)
Tel.: (44) 2088462550
Fax: (44) 2087414176
E-Mail: info@capcom-europe.com
Web Site: www.capcom-europe.com
Emp.: 35
Developer of Video Game Software & Hardware
S.I.C.: 3944
N.A.I.C.S.: 339930

CEG INTERACTIVE ENTERTAINMENT GmbH (1)
Barmbeker Strasse 4 B
Hamburg, 22303, Germany
Tel.: (49) 406965620
Fax: (49) 4069656222
Emp.: 15
Video Games Distr
S.I.C.: 5099
N.A.I.C.S.: 423990
Kazuhiko Aba *(Gen Mgr)*

CAPCON LIMITED

82 Saint John Street
London, EC1M 4JN, United Kingdom
Tel.: (44) 1923 242202
Fax: (44) 1923 698899
Web Site: www.capcon.co.uk
Business Description:
Investigation Services
S.I.C.: 7381
N.A.I.C.S.: 561611
Personnel:
Marcus Jones *(Mng Dir)*
Cliff Cavender *(Sec)*

Subsidiary:

Capcon Argen Limited (1)
Carlton House 19 West St
Epsom, Surrey, KT18 7RL, United Kingdom
Tel.: (44) 8700675070
Fax: (44) 8700675071
Emp.: 10
Investigations & Risk Management Services
S.I.C.: 7381
N.A.I.C.S.: 561611

CAPE ALUMINA LIMITED

Level 8 300 Adelaide Street
Brisbane, QLD, 4000, Australia
Tel.: (61) 7 3009 8000
Fax: (61) 7 7 3221 4811
E-Mail: info@capealumina.com.au
Web Site: www.capealumina.com.au
CBX—(ASX)
Rev.: $146,676
Assets: $9,739,578
Liabilities: $5,474,693
Net Worth: $4,264,885
Earnings: ($2,753,663)
Fiscal Year-end: 06/30/13
Business Description:
Bauxite Mining Services
S.I.C.: 1099
N.A.I.C.S.: 212299
Personnel:
Graeme Sherlock *(CEO & Mng Dir)*
Scott Waddell *(CFO & Sec)*
Board of Directors:
George Alfred Lloyd
Rennie Fritschy
Jijun Liu
Graeme Sherlock
Legal Counsel:
Hopgood Ganim
Level 8 Waterfront Place 1 Eagle Street
Brisbane, QLD, 4000, Australia

CAPE EMPOWERMENT TRUST LIMITED

2nd Fl Sunclare Bldg
21 Dreyer St
7700 Claremont, South Africa
Tel.: (27) 216839050
Fax: (27) 216839109
E-Mail: info@capemp.co.za
Web Site: www.capemp.co.za
CAE—(JSE)
Sales Range: $10-24.9 Million
Emp.: 10
Business Description:
Security & Services
S.I.C.: 8999
N.A.I.C.S.: 541690
Personnel:
Shaun Louis Rai *(Chm)*
Jeremy de Villiers *(Mng Dir)*
Henry Dednam *(Fin Dir & Sec)*
Board of Directors:
Shaun Louis Rai
Peter Bernard Hesseling
Theodore Dominic Rai
Haroon Takolia
Omar Valley

CAPE LAMBERT RESOURCES LTD

32 Harrogate Street
Leederville, WA, 6007, Australia
Mailing Address:
PO Box 144
West Perth, WA, 6872, Australia
Tel.: (61) 893809555
Fax: (61) 893809666
E-Mail: reception@capelam.com.au
Web Site: www.capelam.com.au
CFE—(ASX)
Rev.: $8,693,303
Assets: $254,308,489
Liabilities: $10,463,080
Net Worth: $243,845,409
Earnings: ($149,970,461)
Fiscal Year-end: 06/30/13
Business Description:
Gold & Iron Ore Mining
S.I.C.: 1041
N.A.I.C.S.: 212221

Personnel:
Antony William Paul Sage *(Chm)*
Melissa Chapman *(CFO)*
Claire Tolcon *(Legal Counsel & Sec)*
Board of Directors:
Antony William Paul Sage
Jason Brewer
Ross Joseph Levin
Timothy Paul Turner
Legal Counsel:
Steinepreis Paganin
Level 4 Next Building 16 Milligan St
Perth, Australia
Non-U.S. Subsidiaries:

Scarborough Minerals International BV (1)
Martinus Nijhofflaan 2
2624 ES Delft, Netherlands NL
Tel.: (31) 152569251
Fax: (31) 157890199
Emp.: 30
Mineral Exploration Services
S.I.C.: 1481
N.A.I.C.S.: 213115

Thrace Investments BV (1)
Martinus Nijhofflaan 2
2624 ES Delft, Netherlands
Tel.: (31) 152569251
Mineral Exploration Services
S.I.C.: 1481
N.A.I.C.S.: 213115

CAPE PLC

Drayton Hall Church Road West Drayton
West Drayton, Middlesex, UB7 7PS, United Kingdom
Tel.: (44) 1895431705
Fax: (44) 1895459999
E-Mail: investors@capeplc.com
Web Site: www.capeplc.com
CIU—(LSE)
Rev.: $1,169,306,316
Assets: $920,726,070
Liabilities: $639,612,450
Net Worth: $281,113,620
Earnings: ($314,278,710)
Emp.: 20,621
Fiscal Year-end: 12/31/12
Business Description:
Holding Company; Fire Protection & Insulation Materials for the Construction Industry Mfr
S.I.C.: 6719
N.A.I.C.S.: 551112
Personnel:
Joe Oatley *(CEO)*
Michael Speakman *(CFO)*
Christopher Judd *(Sec)*
Board of Directors:
Timothy John Crommelin Eggar
Brendan Connolly
Michael Merton
Joe Oatley
Michael Speakman
Leslie Van de Walle
Legal Counsel:
Lawrence Graham LLP
4 More London Riverside
London, England, SE1 2AU, United Kingdom
Carey Olsen
47 Esplande
Saint Helier, Jersey
Subsidiaries:

Cape Industrial Services Group Limited (1)
Cape House 3 Red Hall Avenue
Paragon Business Village, Wakefield, West Yorkshire, WF1 2UL, United Kingdom
Tel.: (44) 1709886050
Fax: (44) 1924 361605
E-Mail: reception.fieldsend@capeplc.com
Web Site: www.capeplc.com
Emp.: 50
Industrial Services
S.I.C.: 1742
N.A.I.C.S.: 238310
Steven Connolly *(Mng Dir)*

Subsidiaries:

Cape East Limited (2)
Watford, United Kingdom
Coordination of International Industrial Services Activities
S.I.C.: 1742
N.A.I.C.S.: 238310

Cape Industrial Services Limited (2)
Cape House Paragon Bus Vlg
3 Redhole Ave, Wakefield, West Yorkshire, WS1 2UL, United Kingdom (100%)
Tel.: (44) 1924876200
Fax: (44) 1924361605
Web Site: www.kpsc.com
Emp.: 70
Industrial Services
S.I.C.: 1742
N.A.I.C.S.: 238310

Non-U.S. Subsidiaries:

Cape East Private Limited (2)
3 internation bussiness park
Hex 02-22/ 23
Nordice European Center, Singapore, 609927, Singapore (100%)
Tel.: (65) 62621822
Fax: (65) 62650548
E-Mail: enquiries@capeeast.com.sg
Web Site: www.capeclc.com
Emp.: 500
Industrial Services
S.I.C.: 1742
N.A.I.C.S.: 238310
Ramaraj Ramesh *(Mgr-Ops)*

Cleton Insulation BV (2)
George Stephensonweg 15
3133 KJ Vlaardingen, Netherlands (100%)
Mailing Address:
Postbus 160
3130 AD Vlaardingen, Netherlands
Tel.: (31) 4455444
Fax: (31) 4351403
E-Mail: west@cleton.com
Web Site: www.cleton.com
Emp.: 350
Insulation Services
S.I.C.: 1742
N.A.I.C.S.: 238310

PCH Group Limited (2)
11 Juna Drive
Malaga, WA, 6090, Australia
Mailing Address:
PO Box 1400
Morley, WA, 6943, Australia
Tel.: (61) 892489000
Fax: (61) 892099099
E-Mail: admin@capeplc.com.au
Web Site: www.pchgroup.com.au
Sales Range: $75-99.9 Million
Emp.: 1,200
Management & Contracting Services for Construction & Maintenance Activities
S.I.C.: 8742
N.A.I.C.S.: 541611

Non-U.S. Subsidiary:

Cape East LLC (2)
14 Al Mussafah
PO Box 347
Abu Dhabi, United Arab Emirates (49%)
Web Site: www.capeplc.com
Industrial Services
S.I.C.: 1742
N.A.I.C.S.: 238310

DBI Industrial Services Limited (1)
15 Atherton Way Ancholme Business Park
Brigg, North Lincolnshire, DN20 8AR, United Kingdom
Tel.: (44) 1652657338
Fax: (44) 1652650194
Industrial Cleaning Services
S.I.C.: 7349
N.A.I.C.S.: 561720
Nick Sinclair *(Gen Mgr)*

Non-U.S. Subsidiaries:

Cape East Philippines Inc (1)
6th Floor NOL Tower Commerce Avenue
Madrigal Business Park
Ayala Alabang, Muntinlupa, 1780, Philippines
Tel.: (63) 2 809 9000
Fax: (63) 2 809 1639
Industrial Cleaning Services
S.I.C.: 7349
N.A.I.C.S.: 561720
Michael Harding *(Dir-Ops Offshore-Asia Pacific Rim)*

Cape East (Thailand) Limited (1)
94 Moo 10 Tungsukla
Si Racha, Chonburi, 20230, Thailand
Tel.: (66) 3849 2790
Fax: (66) 3849 2789
Industrial Cleaning Services
S.I.C.: 7349
N.A.I.C.S.: 561720
Paul Adams *(Dir-Ops)*

R B Hilton Saudi Arabia Limited (1)
Royal Commission Support Industries Park
Lot 10 Block 17 Section 3
PO Box 2081
Al Jubayl, 31951, Saudi Arabia
Tel.: (966) 3340 7910
Fax: (966) 3340 3634
Industrial Cleaning Services
S.I.C.: 7349
N.A.I.C.S.: 561720

Total Corrosion Control Pty. Ltd. (1)
Lot 424 89 Office Rd Kwinana Beach
Perth, WA, 6167, Australia AU
Tel.: (61) 894194455
Fax: (61) 894190499
Web Site: www.capeplc.com.au
Abrasive Blasting Services
S.I.C.: 7349
N.A.I.C.S.: 561790
Gerry Pore *(Gen Mgr)*

CAPE RANGE LIMITED

21 Teddington Road
Burswood, WA, 6100, Australia
Mailing Address:
PO Box 401
Belmont, WA, 6984, Australia
Tel.: (61) 895862333
Fax: (61) 893554580
E-Mail: admin@caperange.com.au
Web Site: www.caperange.com.au
CAG—(ASX)
Rev.: $8,605
Assets: $316,537
Liabilities: $1,272,763
Net Worth: ($956,226)
Earnings: ($505,573)
Fiscal Year-end: 12/31/12
Business Description:
Telecommunication Services
S.I.C.: 4899
N.A.I.C.S.: 517919
Personnel:
Wayne Johnson *(Chm)*
Michael Higginson *(Sec)*
Board of Directors:
Wayne Johnson
John Georgiopoulos
Michael Higginson

CAPELLA TELECOMMUNICATIONS INC.

747 Monaghan Road
Peterborough, ON, K9J 5K2, Canada
Tel.: (705) 748-3255
Fax: (705) 748-4535
Toll Free: (800) 668-0175
E-Mail: inquiry@capella.ca
Web Site: www.capella.ca
Year Founded: 1993
Rev.: $34,538,400
Emp.: 27
Business Description:
Telecommunication Service Provider
S.I.C.: 4899
N.A.I.C.S.: 517919
Personnel:
Laura O'Hare *(Dir-Product Mgmt)*

CAPEVIN HOLDINGS LIMITED

Millennia Park 16 Stellentia Avenue
Stellenbosch, 7600, South Africa
Mailing Address:
PO Box 456
Stellenbosch, 7599, South Africa
Tel.: (27) 21 888 3311
Web Site: www.capevin.com
CVH—(JSE)
Business Description:
Investment Management Services
S.I.C.: 6799
N.A.I.C.S.: 523920
Personnel:
C. A. Otto *(Chm)*
Board of Directors:
C. A. Otto
Aevz Botha
N. Celliers
J. J. Durand
R. M. Jansen
L. C. Verwey
Transfer Agent:
Computershare Investor Services (Pty) Ltd
70 Marshall Street
Johannesburg, South Africa

CAPEVIN INVESTMENTS LIMITED

57 Main St
7646 Paarl, South Africa
Tel.: (27) 218073911
Fax: (27) 218073000
Web Site: www.kwv.co.za
CVI—(JSE)
Sales Range: $75-99.9 Million
Emp.: 360
Business Description:
Fund Investment
S.I.C.: 6799
N.A.I.C.S.: 523910
Personnel:
Thys Loubser *(CEO)*
Albert W. Eksteen *(Sec)*
Board of Directors:
Thys du Toit
Abrie Botha
John Copelyn
Fran A. du Plessis
Neil Ellis
Marcel Golding
Mike Joubert
Thys Loubser
Khutso I. Mampeule
Keneilwe Moloko
Andre van der Veen
Leatitia van Dyk

CAPGEMINI S.A.

(d/b/a Capgemini Group)
Place de l'Etoile 11 Rue de Tilsitt
75017 Paris, France
Tel.: (33) 147545000
Fax: (33) 147545025
Web Site: www.capgemini.com
Year Founded: 1967
CAP—(EUR)
Rev.: $13,817,088,880
Assets: $14,336,710,500
Liabilities: $8,239,906,570
Net Worth: $6,096,803,930
Earnings: $484,621,200
Emp.: 125,110
Fiscal Year-end: 12/31/12
Business Description:
Holding Company; Consulting, Information Technology & Outsourcing Services
S.I.C.: 6719
N.A.I.C.S.: 551112
Personnel:
Paul Hermelin *(Chm & CEO)*
Serge Kampf *(Vice Chm)*
John Brahim *(Deputy CEO-Application Svcs)*
Lucia Sinapi-Thomas *(Deputy CFO)*
Aiman Ezzat *(CFO)*

Capgemini S.A.—(Continued)

Lanny Cohen *(Global CTO)*
Pierre-Yves Cros *(Chief Dev Officer)*
Hubert Giraud *(CEO-Bus Process Outsourcing)*
Xavier Hochet *(CEO-Consulting)*
Aruna Jayanthi *(CEO-India)*
Christopher Stancombe *(CEO-Bus Process Outsourcing)*
Jean-Baptiste Massignon *(Gen Sec)*

Board of Directors:
Paul Hermelin
Serge Kampf
Daniel Bernard
Yann Delabriere
Laurence Meary Dors
Philip A. Laskawy
Bernard Liautaud
Terrence R. Ozan
Pierre Pringuet
Bruno Roger
Lucia Sinapi-Thomas
Ruud van Ommeren

KPMG SA
Immeuble Le Palatin 3, cours du Triangle
Paris, France

Subsidiaries:

Artesys SA (1)
23 Rue du Renard
75004 Paris, France
Tel.: (33) 1 44 61 11 00
Fax: (33) 1 44 61 11 01
E-Mail: contact@artesys.eu
Web Site: www.artesys.eu
Emp.: 100
Information Technology Consulting Services
S.I.C.: 7373
N.A.I.C.S.: 541512
Eric Chenneveau *(CEO)*

Cap Sogeti 2005 S.A.S. (1)
11 Rue de Tilsitt
75017 Paris, France
Tel.: (33) 1 47 54 50 00
Fax: (33) 1 47 54 50 86
Emp.: 5
Management Consulting Services
S.I.C.: 8748
N.A.I.C.S.: 541618

Capgemini Consulting S.A.S. (1)
Tour Europlaza - 20 Avenue Andre Prothin
92927 Paris, France
Tel.: (33) 1 49 67 30 00
Fax: (33) 1 49 67 30 01
Web Site: www.capgemini-consulting.fr
Information Technology Consulting Services
S.I.C.: 7373
N.A.I.C.S.: 541512
Pierre-Yves Cros *(CEO)*

Capgemini France S.A.S. (1)
11 Rue de Tilsitt
75017 Paris, Cedex 16, France FR
Tel.: (33) 0147545000 (100%)
Fax: (33) 142273211
Web Site: www.fr.capgemini.com
Emp.: 50
Holding Company
S.I.C.: 6719
N.A.I.C.S.: 551112

Branches:

Capgemini France - Grenoble (2)
485 Avenue de l'Europe
38330 Montbonnot-Saint-Martin, France
Tel.: (33) 476526200
Fax: (33) 476526201
E-Mail:
Web Site: www.fr.capgemini.com
Emp.: 500
Information Technology Consulting Services
S.I.C.: 8999
N.A.I.C.S.: 541690

Capgemini France - Rennes (2)
3 Allee de la Croix des Hetres
CS 46412, 35064 Rennes, Cedex, France
Tel.: (33) 299125500
Fax: (33) 299125509
E-Mail: akrctueil_fennes.fr@capgemini.com
Web Site: www.fr.capgemini.com
Emp.: 300
Provider of Information Technology Consulting Services
S.I.C.: 7374
N.A.I.C.S.: 518210

Capgemini Gouvieux S.A.S. (1)
11 Rue De Tilsitt
75017 Paris, France
Tel.: (33) 1 47 54 50 00
Fax: (33) 1 47 54 50 25
Emp.: 50
Information Technology Consulting Services
S.I.C.: 7373
N.A.I.C.S.: 541512

Capgemini Outsourcing Services S.A.S. (1)
55 Quai Marcel-Dassault Cedex
Saint-Cloud, 92212, France
Tel.: (33) 1 57 58 51 00
Fax: (33) 1 57 58 51 01
Business Process Outsourcing Services
S.I.C.: 7389
N.A.I.C.S.: 561499

Capgemini Service S.A.S (1)
11 Rue de Tilsitt
75017 Paris, France
Tel.: (33) 1 47 54 50 00
Fax: (33) 1 47 54 50
Information Technology Consulting Services
S.I.C.: 7373
N.A.I.C.S.: 541512
Serge Kampf *(Chm)*

Capgemini Technology Services S.A.S. (1)
Tour Europlaza 20 Avenue Andre Prothin
92400 Courbevoie, Hauts De Seine, France
Tel.: (33) 149673000
Fax: (33) 149675212
Information Technology Consulting Services
S.I.C.: 7373
N.A.I.C.S.: 541512

Capgemini Universite (1)
Rue Du Nid De Geai
Route de chacilly, 78910 Behoust-Orgerus, France FR
Tel.: (33) 344629100 (100%)
Fax: (33) 333629494
Web Site: www.les-fontaines.com
Emp.: 30
Information Technology Consulting Services
S.I.C.: 7379
N.A.I.C.S.: 518210
Collin Jacquas *(Founder & Pres)*

IBX France S.A.R.L. (1)
20 Avenue Andra Prothin
92927 Paris, France
Tel.: (33) 149 67 54 27
Fax: (33) 149 67 42 62
Information Technology Consulting Services
S.I.C.: 7373
N.A.I.C.S.: 541512
Rolf Nuyts *(VP-Bus Dev)*

Immobiliere Les Fontaines S.A.R.L. (1)
67 Route de Chantilly
60270 Gouvieux, France
Tel.: (33) 3 44 62 91 00
Fax: (33) 3 44 62 94 94
E-Mail: contact@les-fontaines.com
Web Site: www.les-fontaines.com
Emp.: 6
Event Management Services
S.I.C.: 7999
N.A.I.C.S.: 711310
Collins Jacques *(Pres)*

Prosodie France S.A. (1)
150 Rue Gallieni
92100 Boulogne-Billancourt, France
Tel.: (33) 1 46 84 11 11
Fax: (33) 1 46 84 02 26
E-Mail: prosodie@prosodie.com
Web Site: www.prosodie.com
Emp.: 65
Information Technology Consulting Services
S.I.C.: 7373
N.A.I.C.S.: 541512
Aymar de Lencquesaing *(Chm)*
Nicolas Aidoud *(CEO)*

Sogeti (1)
Sogeti Lolisee 23-24 Rue du Gouverneur General Eboue
92130 Issy-les-Moulineaux, France (100%)
Tel.: (33) 158445566
Fax: (33) 158445570
Web Site: www.sogeti-transiciel.com
IT & Other Professional Technical Services
S.I.C.: 7373
N.A.I.C.S.: 541512
Luc-Francois Salvador *(Chm & CEO)*
Michiel Boreel *(CTO)*

Subsidiaries:

Sogeti Corporate Services SAS (2)
22-24 Rue Street Gouverneur General Eboue
75016 Issy-les-Moulineaux, France
Tel.: (33) 15500120
Fax: (33) 155001230
Emp.: 40
Information Technology Consulting Services
S.I.C.: 7373
N.A.I.C.S.: 541512

Sogeti France S.A.S. (2)
24 Rue du Gouverneur General Eboue
92130 Issy-les-Moulineaux, France
Tel.: (33) 1 55 00 12 00
Fax: (33) 1 55 00 12 30
E-Mail: institut_formation.fr@sogeti.com
Web Site: www.fr.sogeti.com
Emp.: 65
Information Technology Consulting Services
S.I.C.: 7373
N.A.I.C.S.: 541512
Stephanie La Montagne *(Acct Mgr)*

Sogeti High Tech S.A.S. (2)
24 Rue du Gouverneur Eboue
92136 Issy-les-Moulineaux, France
Tel.: (33) 1 40 93 73 00
Fax: (33) 1 55 00 12 30
E-Mail: infohightech@sogeti.com
Web Site: www.sogeti-hightech.fr
Emp.: 400
Information Technology Consulting Services
S.I.C.: 7373
N.A.I.C.S.: 541512
Christian Gleyo *(Pres)*
Dominique Lafond *(CEO)*

U.S. Subsidiary:

Sogeti USA LLC (2)
7735 Paragon Rd Ste A
Dayton, OH 45459
Tel.: (937) 433-3334
Fax: (937) 433-4048
Web Site: www.us.sogeti.com
Sales Range: $400-449.9 Million
Emp.: 2,000
IT & Other Professional Technical Services
S.I.C.: 7373
N.A.I.C.S.: 541512
Mike Pleiman *(Exec VP)*

Branches:

Sogeti USA LLC (3)
1820 NW 118th St
Des Moines, IA 50325
Tel.: (515) 282-4802
Fax: (515) 282-4922
Web Site: www.sogeti.com
Emp.: 78
Provider of IT Services
S.I.C.: 7371
N.A.I.C.S.: 541511
Brandy Reed *(VP)*

Sogeti USA LLC (3)
4 Westbrook Corporate Ctr Ste 800
Westchester, IL 60154-5755
Tel.: (708) 531-0011
Fax: (708) 531-0277
Toll Free: (800) 899-9847
E-Mail: chicagooffice@us.sogeti.com
Web Site: www.us.sogeti.com
Emp.: 30
Contract Computer Programming Services
S.I.C.: 7374
N.A.I.C.S.: 518210

Sogeti USA LLC (3)
8395 Keystone Crossing Ste 200
Indianapolis, IN 46240
Tel.: (317) 810-4400
Fax: (877) 406-9649
E-Mail: IndianapolisOffice@us.sogeti.com
Web Site: www.us.sogeti.com
Emp.: 100
IT & Other Professional Technical Services
S.I.C.: 7379
N.A.I.C.S.: 541519

Sogeti USA LLC (3)
7101 College Blvd Ste 1150
Overland Park, KS 66210
Tel.: (913) 451-9600
Fax: (877) 406-9650
E-Mail: kansascityoffice@us.sogeti.com
Web Site: www.us.sogeti.com
IT & Other Professional Technical Services
S.I.C.: 7373
N.A.I.C.S.: 541512

Sogeti USA LLC (3)
Owings Mills Corp Campus 10055 Red Run Blvd Ste 100
Owings Mills, MD 21117-4860
Tel.: (410) 581-5022
Fax: (410) 581-7815
E-Mail: baltimoreoffice@us.sogeti.com
Web Site: www.sogeti.com
Emp.: 150
Contract Computer Programming
S.I.C.: 7379
N.A.I.C.S.: 518210
John Dragunas *(VP)*

Sogeti USA LLC (3)
31555 W 14 Mile Rd Ste 301
Farmington Hills, MI 48334
Tel.: (248) 702-1900
Fax: (248) 932-2870
E-Mail: detroitoffice@us.sogeti.com
Web Site: www.us.sogeti.com
Sales Range: $1-9.9 Million
Emp.: 125
IT Services
S.I.C.: 7373
N.A.I.C.S.: 541512

Sogeti USA LLC (3)
14301 FNB Pkwy Ste 206
Omaha, NE 68154
Tel.: (402) 492-8877
Fax: (402) 492-8866
E-Mail: omahaoffice@us.sogeti.com
Web Site: www.us.sogeti.com
Emp.: 50
IT Services
S.I.C.: 7373
N.A.I.C.S.: 541512
Shawni Helms *(Mgr-Ops)*

Sogeti USA LLC (3)
10100 Innovation Dr Ste 200
Dayton, OH 45342 (100%)
Tel.: (937) 291-8100
Fax: (713) 860-7427
E-Mail: houstonoffice@us.sogeti.com
Web Site: www.us.sogeti.com
Emp.: 100
Contract Computer Programming Services
S.I.C.: 8748
N.A.I.C.S.: 541618
Mark Rizzo *(VP)*

Sogeti USA LLC (3)
8425 Pulsar Pl Ste 300
Columbus, OH 43240
Tel.: (614) 847-4477
Fax: (614) 847-4424
Toll Free: (800) 899-9849
E-Mail: columbusoffice@us.sogeti.com
Web Site: www.us.sogeti.com
Emp.: 150
IT Services
S.I.C.: 7371
N.A.I.C.S.: 541511
Mike Pleiman *(VP)*

Sogeti USA LLC (3)
4445 Lake Forest Dr Ste 550
Cincinnati, OH 45242
Tel.: (513) 563-6622
Fax: (513) 563-6774
E-Mail: cincinnatioffice@us.sogeti.com
Web Site: www.us.sogeti.com
Emp.: 250
IT & Other Professional Technical Services
S.I.C.: 7373
N.A.I.C.S.: 541512

Sogeti USA LLC (3)
Beacon Pl 6055 Rockside Woods Blvd Ste 170
Independence, OH 44131
Tel.: (216) 654-2230
E-Mail: clevelandoffice@us.sogeti.com
Web Site: www.us.sogeti.com

IT & Other Professional Technical Services
S.I.C.: 7373
N.A.I.C.S.: 541512

Sogeti USA LLC (3)
222 W Las Colinas Blvd Ste 960
Irving, TX 75039
Tel.: (972) 892-3407
Fax: (972) 892-3401
E-Mail: dallasoffice@us.sogeti.com
Web Site: www.sogeti-usa.com
Emp.: 140
Contract Computer Programming Services
S.I.C.: 8748
N.A.I.C.S.: 541618

Sogeti USA LLC (3)
8201 Greensboro Dr Ste 1002
McLean, VA 22102-3840
Tel.: (703) 734-1511
Fax: (703) 790-5824
E-Mail: washingtondcoffice@us.sogeti.com
Web Site: www.us.sogeti.com
Emp.: 12
Contract Computer Programming Services
S.I.C.: 7379
N.A.I.C.S.: 541519

Sogeti USA LLC (3)
14335 Ne 24th St Ste 200
Bellevue, WA 98007-3737
Tel.: (206) 624-4600
Fax: (206) 625-0828
E-Mail: seattleoffice@us.sogeti.com
Web Site: www.us.sogeti.com
Emp.: 70
Contract Computer Programming Services
S.I.C.: 8748
N.A.I.C.S.: 541618

Non-U.S. Subsidiaries:

Sogeti Belgium (2)
Jules Bordetlaan 160
1140 Brussels, Belgium BE
Tel.: (32) 25389292
Fax: (32) 253833587
E-Mail: info@sogeti.be
Web Site: www.sogeti.be
Emp.: 500
IT Consulting Services
S.I.C.: 7373
N.A.I.C.S.: 541512
Ytes Debeaurecard *(Mng Dir)*

Sogeti Danmark AS (2)
Carl Gustavs Gade 3 1 Th
2630 Tastrup, Denmark
Tel.: (45) 70 23 15 05
Fax: (45) 70 23 15 06
E-Mail: sgetil@sogeti.dk
Web Site: www.sogeti.dk
Information Technology Consulting Services
S.I.C.: 7373
N.A.I.C.S.: 541512
Holger Bonde *(CEO)*

Sogeti Deutschland GmbH (2)
Schiessm Strasse 72
40549 Dusseldorf, Germany (100%)
Tel.: (49) 211522850
Fax: (49) 21152285100
E-Mail: kontakt@sogeti.de
Web Site: www.sogeti.de
Emp.: 200
IT & Other Professional Technical Services
S.I.C.: 7373
N.A.I.C.S.: 541512
Maarten Galesloot *(CEO)*

Sogeti Espana SL (2)
Placa de la P93 253 0188au Edifici WTCAP 2 3 planta
08940 Cornella, Barcelona, Spain (100%)
Tel.: (34) 932530188
Fax: (34) 932530750
Web Site: www.sogeti.com
IT & Other Professional Technical Services
S.I.C.: 7373
N.A.I.C.S.: 541512

Sogeti Finland Oy (2)
Vaisalantie 6
2130 Espoo, Finland
Tel.: (358) 207 463 880
Fax: (358) 207 463 884
E-Mail: info@sogeti.fi
Web Site: www.sogeti.fi
Emp.: 7
Information Technology Consulting Services
S.I.C.: 7373
N.A.I.C.S.: 541512
Mikko Misukka *(CEO)*

Sogeti High Tech GmbH (2)
Hein-Sass-Weg 38
21129 Hamburg, Germany
Tel.: (49) 40 743 781 94
Fax: (49) 40 49 29 37 37
E-Mail: office@sogeti-hightech.de
Web Site: www.sogeti-hightech.de
Emp.: 28
Aerospace Engineering & Consulting Services
S.I.C.: 8711
N.A.I.C.S.: 541330
Dominique Lafond *(CEO)*
Arne Vieth *(Mng Dir)*

Sogeti Ireland Ltd. (2)
Plaza 256 Blanchardstown Corporate Business Park 2
Ballycoolin, Dublin, Ireland
Tel.: (353) 1 639 0100
Fax: (353) 1 639 0199
E-Mail: info.ie@sogeti.com
Web Site: www.ie.sogeti.com
Emp.: 90
Software Development Services
S.I.C.: 7371
N.A.I.C.S.: 541511
Jeff Schmalbach *(CEO)*

Sogeti Luxembourg S.A. (2)
Route de Longwy 36
8080 Bertrange, Luxembourg
Tel.: (352) 31 44 01
Fax: (352) 26 31 12 92
E-Mail: info@sogeti.lu
Web Site: www.sogeti.lu
Rev.: $52,855,600
Emp.: 50
Information Technology Consulting Services
S.I.C.: 7373
N.A.I.C.S.: 541512
Alain Gena *(Mgr-Applications Dept)*

Sogeti Nederland B.V. (2)
Lenga Dreef 17
4131 NG Vianen, Netherlands
Mailing Address:
Postbus 76
4130 EB Vianen, Netherlands
Tel.: (31) 88 660 6600
Fax: (31) 88 660 6700
E-Mail: info@sogeti.nl
Web Site: www.sogeti.nl
Emp.: 3,500
IT & Other Professional Technical Services
S.I.C.: 7373
N.A.I.C.S.: 541512

Sogeti Norge AS (2)
Storgaten 10A
155 Oslo, Norway
Tel.: (47) 40 00 50 89
Web Site: www.sogeti.no
Information Technology Consulting Services
S.I.C.: 7373
N.A.I.C.S.: 541512
Morten Lovstad *(CEO)*

SOGETI N.V./S.A. (2)
Av Jules Bordet 160
Evere, 1140, Belgium
Tel.: (32) 2 538 92 92
Fax: (32) 2 537 49 47
E-Mail: comunicacion.spain.es@sogeti.com
Information Technology Consulting Services
S.I.C.: 7373
N.A.I.C.S.: 541512

Sogeti PSF S.A. (2)
Route de Longwy 36
8080 Bertrange, Luxembourg
Tel.: (352) 31 44 01
Fax: (352) 26 31 12 92
E-Mail: sogeti@sogeti.lu
Emp.: 500
Information Technology Consulting Services
S.I.C.: 7373
N.A.I.C.S.: 541512
Philippe Margraff *(Gen Mgr)*

Sogeti Suisse SA (2)
65 rue du Port
1204 Geneva, Switzerland (100%)
Tel.: (41) 228791650
Fax: (41) 228791659
E-Mail: sogeti-geneve@sogeti.com
Web Site: www.sogeti.com
Emp.: 100
IT & Other Professional Technical Services
S.I.C.: 7373
N.A.I.C.S.: 541512
Y. Froppier *(Mng Dir)*

Sogeti Sverige AB (2)
Gustavslundsvagen 131
Box 825
161 24 Bromma, Sweden (100%)
Tel.: (46) 853682000
Fax: (46) 853682001
E-Mail: stefen.ek@sogeti.se
Web Site: www.hilti.de
Emp.: 150
IT & Other Professional Technical Services
S.I.C.: 7373
N.A.I.C.S.: 541512
Stefen Ek *(Mng Dir)*

Sogeti UK Ltd. (2)
85 London Wall 3rd Floor
London, EC2M 7AD, United Kingdom
Tel.: (44) 20 7014 8900
Fax: (44) 20 7014 8901
E-Mail: enquiries.uk@sogeti.com
Web Site: www.uk.sogeti.com
Emp.: 40
Information Technology Consulting Services
S.I.C.: 7373
N.A.I.C.S.: 541512
Edouard Paule *(CFO)*

U.S. Subsidiaries:

Capgemini Business Services USA LLC (1)
2099 S State College Blvd 600
Anaheim, CA 92806-6137
Tel.: (714) 787-1550
Fax: (714) 889-6300
Emp.: 50
Business Process Outsourcing Services
S.I.C.: 7389
N.A.I.C.S.: 561499
Robert Sherman *(Gen Mgr)*

Capgemini Financial Services International Inc. (1)
6400 Shafer Ct
Rosemont, IL 60018
Tel.: (847) 384-6100
Fax: (847) 384-0500
Information Technology Consulting Services
S.I.C.: 7373
N.A.I.C.S.: 541512

Capgemini Financial Services USA Inc. (1)
6400 Shafer Ct Ste 100
Rosemont, IL 60018-4944
Tel.: (847) 384-6100
Fax: (847) 384-0500
Financial Management Services
S.I.C.: 6211
N.A.I.C.S.: 523999

Capgemini North America Inc. (1)
623 5th Ave 33rd Fl
New York, NY 10022
Tel.: (917) 934-8000
Fax: (917) 934-8001
Web Site: www.us.capgemini.com
Information Technology Consulting Services
S.I.C.: 7373
N.A.I.C.S.: 541512
Tim Bridges *(Head-Application Svcs)*

Capgemini Technologies LLC (1)
2250 Corporate Park Dr 406
Herndon, VA 20171-2898
Tel.: (703) 673-9100
Fax: (703) 481-6457
Information Technology Consulting Services
S.I.C.: 7373
N.A.I.C.S.: 541512

Capgemini U.S. (1)
623 5th Ave 33rd Fl
New York, NY 10022 WI
Tel.: (212) 314-8000 (100%)
Fax: (212) 314-8001
E-Mail: webmaster@capgemini.com
Web Site: www.us.capgemini.com
Emp.: 3,000
Information Technology Consulting Services
S.I.C.: 8748
N.A.I.C.S.: 541618
Jerry Nuzum *(COO)*
Christopher K. Williams *(CMO & VP-North America)*
Francois-Xavier Rouxel *(CEO-Infrastructure Svcs Bus Unit)*
Michael Chayet *(Gen Counsel)*

CPM Braxis USA Corp. (1)
19495 Biscayne Blvd 708 Ste 400
Miami, FL 33180-2318
Tel.: (305) 932-6010
Information Technology Consulting Services
S.I.C.: 7373
N.A.I.C.S.: 541512

IBX North America Inc. (1)
150 N Michigan Ave
Chicago, IL 60606
Tel.: (847) 454-5998
E-Mail: info@ibxgroup.com
Web Site: www.ibx.se/locations-1.aspx
Business Process Outsourcing Services
S.I.C.: 7389
N.A.I.C.S.: 561499
Per Finnhammar *(VP)*

Kanbay International, Inc. (1)
6400 Shafer Ct Ste 100
Rosemont, IL 60018-4944
Tel.: (847) 384-6100
Fax: (847) 384-0500
E-Mail: info@capgemini.com
Web Site: www.capgemini.com
Sales Range: $125-149.9 Million
Emp.: 5,242
Microcomputer Hardware Development of Systems Software & Telecommunications Equipment Distr
S.I.C.: 7371
N.A.I.C.S.: 541511
Roy K. Stansbury *(COO-Global Indus Solutions)*

Non-U.S. Subsidiaries:

AIVE BST SPA (1)
Centro Direzionale Valecenter Via E Mattei 1/C
30020 Marcon, Venice, Italy
Tel.: (39) 041 5957511
Fax: (39) 041 5950330
E-Mail: info@aivebst.it
Web Site: www.aivebst.it
Financial Management Services
S.I.C.: 6211
N.A.I.C.S.: 523999
Andrea Falleni *(Mng Dir)*

AIVE SPA (1)
Centro Direzionale Valecenter Via E Mattei 1/c
Marcon, Venice, 30020, Italy
Tel.: (39) 0415 95 75 11
Fax: (39) 0415 95 03 30
E-Mail: aive@aive.it
Web Site: www.aive.com
Information Technology Consulting Services
S.I.C.: 7373
N.A.I.C.S.: 541512
Giuseppe Camia *(CEO)*

AIVEBS SPA (1)
Centro Direzionale Valecenter Via E Mattei 1/c
30020 Marcon, Venice, Italy
Tel.: (39) 041 5957511
Fax: (39) 041 5950330
E-Mail: marketing@aivebs.it
Web Site: www.aivebs.it
Information Technology Consulting Services
S.I.C.: 7373
N.A.I.C.S.: 541512
Franco Mazza *(Pres)*
Walter Brollo *(Co-Mng Dir)*
Giuseppe Camia *(Co-Mng Dir)*

Capgemini Asia Pacific Pte. Ltd. (1)
6 Battery Road 16-07/08
Singapore, 049909, Singapore
Tel.: (65) 6224 6620
Fax: (65) 6224 6770
Information Technology Consulting Services
S.I.C.: 7373
N.A.I.C.S.: 541512

Non-U.S. Subsidiary:

Praxis Technology Co. Ltd. (2)
Room 1506 No 800 Dongfang Road
Pudong New District, Shanghai, 200122, China

Capgemini S.A.—(Continued)

Tel.: (86) 2158205592
Information Technology Consulting Services
S.I.C.: 7373
N.A.I.C.S.: 541512

Capgemini Asia Pacific (1)
Level 7 77 Kings St
PO Box 4287
Sydney, 2000, Australia (100%)
Tel.: (61) 292934000
Fax: (61) 292934444
Web Site: www.capgemini.com.au
Emp.: 100
Holding Company
S.I.C.: 6719
N.A.I.C.S.: 551112
Paul Thorley *(CEO)*

Subsidiaries:

Capgemini Australia Pty Ltd (2)
Level 7 77 Kings St
Sydney, NSW, 2000, Australia
Tel.: (61) 292934000
Fax: (61) 292934444
E-Mail: info@capgemini.com
Web Site: www.capgemini.com
Emp.: 700
IT Services & Business Consultancy
S.I.C.: 8742
N.A.I.C.S.: 541611
Paul Thorley *(CEO)*

Capgemini Financial Services Australia Pty Ltd. (2)
Level 16 595 Collins Street
Melbourne, VIC, 3000, Australia
Tel.: (61) 3 9613 3000
Fax: (61) 3 9613 3333
Emp.: 50
Financial Investment Services
S.I.C.: 6211
N.A.I.C.S.: 523999

Non-U.S. Subsidiaries:

Capgemini Business Services Asia Ltd. (2)
501A 9 Queen Rd Central
Quarry Bay, China (Hong Kong) (100%)
Tel.: (852) 22991548
Fax: (852) 31123344
E-Mail: info.hk@capgemini.com
Emp.: 50
IT Services & Business Consultancy
S.I.C.: 8742
N.A.I.C.S.: 541611

Capgemini China (2)
Unit 803-806 Capital Tower 6 Jia Jian Guo Menwai Ave
Chao Yang District, 100 022 Beijing, China
Tel.: (86) 1065637388
Fax: (86) 1065637399
E-Mail: bjreception@capgemini.com
Web Site: www.cn.capgemini.com
Emp.: 100
IT Services & Business Consulting Services
S.I.C.: 8742
N.A.I.C.S.: 541611
Yu Huangchao *(CEO)*

Capgemini Consulting India Pvt. Ltd. (2)
SEP SEP2 B 3 Godrej Industries Complex Eastern Express Hwy
Vikhroli, Mumbai, 400 079, India (100%)
Tel.: (91) 2267557000
Fax: (91) 2267557100
E-Mail: sajedah.pal@capgemini.com
Web Site: www.in.capgemini.com
Sales Range: $1-4.9 Billion
Emp.: 3,000
IT Services & Business Consultancy
S.I.C.: 8742
N.A.I.C.S.: 541611
Salil Parekh *(Chm)*

Capgemini (Shanghai) (2)
Capgemini Center No 11 Boxia Rd
Zhangjiang High-Tech Park, 201203
Shanghai, PRC, China (100%)
Tel.: (86) 2161822688
Fax: (86) 2161822699
E-Mail: christinexie@capgemini.com
Web Site: www.capgemini.com
Emp.: 200
Consultancy & IT Services
S.I.C.: 8748
N.A.I.C.S.: 541618

Capgemini Business Services Australia Pty Ltd. (1)
Level 8 68 Grenfell Street
Adelaide, SA, 5000, Australia
Tel.: (61) 8 8113 8000
Fax: (61) 8 8113 8297
E-Mail: capgemini.marketing@au.capgemini.com
Information Technology Consulting Services
S.I.C.: 7373
N.A.I.C.S.: 541512

Capgemini Business Services Chile Ltda. (1)
Americo Vespucio 1737 Piso 6
Huechuraba, Santiago, Chile
Tel.: (56) 2 8975700
Fax: (56) 2 5807788
Financial Management Services
S.I.C.: 6211
N.A.I.C.S.: 523999

Capgemini Business Services Guatemala S.A. (1)
15 Avenida 17-30 Edificio Tetra Center 2 Nivel 2
Guatemala, Guatemala
Tel.: (502) 22230010
Business Process Outsourcing Services
S.I.C.: 7389
N.A.I.C.S.: 561499
Christian Chilliwack *(Gen Mgr)*

Capgemini Business Services (India) Ltd. (1)
4th Floor Btp Block B
Agrahara Village, Bengaluru, Karnataka, Karnataka, India
Tel.: (91) 22 67557000
Fax: (91) 22 67557100
E-Mail: processconsultancy.in@capgemini.com
Emp.: 5,000
Business Process Outsourcing Services
S.I.C.: 7389
N.A.I.C.S.: 561499
Meher B. Ghyara *(Mgr-HR)*

Capgemini Canada Inc. (1)
144-4th Ave SW 2607
Calgary, AB, T2P 3N4, Canada
Tel.: (403) 716-3636
Fax: (403) 716-3637
Web Site: www.ca.capgemini.com
Information Technology Consulting Services
S.I.C.: 7373
N.A.I.C.S.: 541512

Capgemini Consulting Osterreich AG (1)
Lassallestrasse 9B
A-1020 Vienna, Austria AT (100%)
Tel.: (43) 211630
Fax: (43) 211635000
E-Mail: contact.us@capgemini.com
Web Site: www.capgemini.com
Emp.: 260
Management Consulting, Information Technology & Outsourcing Services
S.I.C.: 8742
N.A.I.C.S.: 541611
Peter Laggner *(CEO)*
Klaus Fekete *(Mng Dir)*
Wolfgang Weber *(CFO & Dir-HR)*
Josef Matulka *(COO)*

Capgemini Consulting Slovakia d.o.o (1)
Zelezniciarska 13
81104 Bratislava, Slovakia
Tel.: (421) 44455678
Fax: (421) 44455680
Web Site: www.it.capgemini.com
Management Consulting, Information Technology & Outsourcing Services
S.I.C.: 8742
N.A.I.C.S.: 541611

Capgemini Czech Republic s.r.o (1)
Vaclavske namesti 19
110 00 Prague, Czech Republic
Tel.: (420) 224505277
Fax: (420) 224505281
E-Mail: reception.cz@capgemini.com
Web Site: www.cz.capgemini.com
Management Consulting, Information Technology & Outsourcing Services
S.I.C.: 8742
N.A.I.C.S.: 541611

Capgemini Danmark AS (1)
Delta Park 40
2665 Vallensbaek, Denmark
Tel.: (45) 70112200
Fax: (45) 70112201
Web Site: www.dk.capgemini.com
Information Technology Consulting Services
S.I.C.: 7373
N.A.I.C.S.: 541512

Capgemini Deutschland Holding GmbH (1)
potsdamer platz 5
10719 Berlin, Germany
Tel.: (49) 30887030
Fax: (49) 3088703111
E-Mail: marketing.de@capgemini.com
Web Site: www.de.capgemini.com
Holding Company; Investment Management Services
S.I.C.: 6719
N.A.I.C.S.: 551112
Hans-Peter Berger *(Gen Counsel)*

Subsidiaries:

Cap Gemini Telecom Media & Networks Deutschland GmbH (2)
Berliner Str 76
63065 Offenbach, Hessen, Germany
Tel.: (49) 21156611000
Fax: (49) 21156611111
E-Mail:
Data Processing Services
S.I.C.: 7374
N.A.I.C.S.: 518210

Capgemini Deutschland GmbH (2)
Neues Kranzler Eck Kurfurstendamm 21
D 10719 Berlin, Germany (100%)
Tel.: (49) 30887030
Fax: (49) 3088703111
E-Mail: marketing.de@capgemini.com
Web Site: www.de.capgemini.com
Sls.: $558,719,424
Emp.: 300
Consultancy & IT Services
S.I.C.: 8742
N.A.I.C.S.: 541611

Branches:

Capgemini Deutschland GmbH - Cologne (3)
Konrad Adenauer Ufer 37
D 50668 Cologne, Germany
Tel.: (49) 221912644
Fax: (49) 291264430
Web Site: www.de.capgemini.com
Consultancy & IT Services
S.I.C.: 8742
N.A.I.C.S.: 541611

Capgemini Deutschland GmbH - Hamburg (3)
Lubecker Strasse 1
D 22087 Hamburg, Germany
Tel.: (49) 40253180
Fax: (49) 4025318111
Web Site: www.de.capgemini.com
Consultancy & IT Services
S.I.C.: 8742
N.A.I.C.S.: 541611

Capgemini Deutschland GmbH - Munich (3)
Karl Str 12
80333 Munich, Germany
Tel.: (49) 8994000
Fax: (49) 8994001111
E-Mail: lisa.graf@capgemini.com
Web Site: www.de.capgemini.com
Emp.: 100
Consultancy & IT Services
S.I.C.: 8742
N.A.I.C.S.: 541611
Antino Schmiever *(Mng Dir)*

Capgemini Deutschland GmbH - Offenbach (3)
Berliner Strasse 76
63065 Offenbach, Germany
Tel.: (49) 6995150
Fax: (49) 6995151111
E-Mail: reception.off.de@capgemini.com
Web Site: www.de.capgemini.com
Emp.: 200
IT Consulting Services
S.I.C.: 8742
N.A.I.C.S.: 541611
Peter Lempp *(Office Mgr)*

Capgemini Deutschland GmbH - Stuttgart (3)
Loffelstrasse 44 46
70597 Stuttgart, Germany
Tel.: (49) 711505050
Fax: (49) 71150505333
E-Mail: entfang.str.de@capgemini.com
Web Site: www.de.capgemini.com
Emp.: 250
Consultancy & IT Services
S.I.C.: 8742
N.A.I.C.S.: 541611

Capgemini Outsourcing Services GmbH (2)
Wanheimer Str 68
Dusseldorf, Nordrhein-Westfalen, 40468, Germany
Tel.: (49) 21156611000
Fax: (49) 21156611111
E-Mail: ts-ak-internet-ripe.de@capgemini.com
Web Site: www.capgemini.de
Emp.: 40
Business Process Outsourcing Services
S.I.C.: 7389
N.A.I.C.S.: 561499
Oliver Schwarz *(Gen Mgr)*

Capgemini do Brasil, Servicos de Consultoria e Informatica Ltda. (1)
Rua Samuel Morse 120 Conjunto 71 - 7 Andar
Sao Paulo, 04576-060, Brazil
Tel.: (55) 1155026802
Fax: (55) 1155026804
Information Technology Consulting Services
S.I.C.: 7373
N.A.I.C.S.: 541512

Capgemini Espana S.L. (1)
Calle Anabel Segura 14 Edificio Cedro
28108 Alcobendas, Spain ES
Tel.: (34) 916577000 (100%)
Fax: (34) 916612019
E-Mail: es.comuniaction@capgemini.es
Web Site: www.es.capgemini.com
Emp.: 2,000
Management Consulting, Information Technology & Outsourcing Services
S.I.C.: 8742
N.A.I.C.S.: 541611

Branches:

Capgemini Espana S.L. - Barcelona (2)
Avda Diagonal 199
08018 Barcelona, Spain
Tel.: (34) 934958600
Fax: (34) 933568803
E-Mail: es.info@capgemini.es
Web Site: www.capgemini.es
Management Consulting, Information Technology & Outsourcing Services
S.I.C.: 8742
N.A.I.C.S.: 541611

Capgemini Finland Oy (1)
Niittymaentie 9
02200 Espoo, Finland
Tel.: (358) 945 2651
Fax: (358) 9452 65900
E-Mail: tsfsupport.fi@capgemini.com
Web Site: www.fi.capgemini.com
Emp.: 600
Information Technology Consulting Services
S.I.C.: 7373
N.A.I.C.S.: 541512
Mia Andersson *(Gen Mgr)*

Capgemini India Private Ltd. (1)
Plant-2 A Wing Godrej IT Park Godrej & Boyce Compound LBS
Marg Vikhroi West, Mumbai, 400079, India
Tel.: (91) 22 67557000
Fax: (91) 22 66860600
E-Mail: processconsultancy.in@capgemini.com
Web Site: www.in.capgemini.com
Emp.: 370
Information Technology Consulting Services
S.I.C.: 7373

N.A.I.C.S.: 541512
Aruna Jayanthi *(CEO)*
Natarajan Radhakrishnan *(Sr VP & Head-Offshore-Consulting)*

Capgemini Italia SpA (1)
Via Di Torre Spaccata 140
00169 Rome, Italy
Tel.: (39) 0006231901
Fax: (39) 0623269218
Web Site: www.capgemini.it
Management Consulting, Information Technology & Outsourcing Services
S.I.C.: 8742
N.A.I.C.S.: 541611

Branches:

Capgemini Italia SpA (2)
Via Fontevivo 21/M
19125 La Spezia, Italy
Tel.: (39) 018728381
Fax: (39) 01872838228
Web Site: www.it.capgemini.com
Management Consulting, Information Technology & Outsourcing Services
S.I.C.: 8742
N.A.I.C.S.: 541611

Capgemini Italia (2)
Via Nizzoli 6
20147 Milan, Italy IT
Tel.: (39) 02414931 (100%)
Fax: (39) 0241493500
E-Mail: communication.it@capgemini.com
Web Site: www.it.capgemini.com
Management Consulting, Information Technology & Outsourcing Services
S.I.C.: 8742
N.A.I.C.S.: 541611

Capgemini Italia (2)
Via Gioberti 18
10128 Turin, Italy
Tel.: (39) 011509431
Fax: (39) 0115094371
Web Site: www.it.capgemini.com
Management Consulting, Information Technology & Outsourcing Services
S.I.C.: 8742
N.A.I.C.S.: 541611

Capgemini Italia (2)
Via Giovanni Porzio 4
80143 Naples, Italy
Tel.: (39) 0816068911
Fax: (39) 0817879880
Web Site: www.it.capgemini.com
Management Consulting, Information Technology & Outsourcing Services
S.I.C.: 8742
N.A.I.C.S.: 541611

Capgemini Magyarorszag Kft (1)
Retkoz Utca 5 BudaWest Irodak 3 Emelet
Budapest, 1118, Hungary
Tel.: (36) 1 248 4000
Fax: (36) 1 248 4001
E-Mail: hello@capgemini.hu
Web Site: www.capgemini.hu
Emp.: 6
Information Technology Consulting Services
S.I.C.: 7373
N.A.I.C.S.: 541512
Judit Mori *(Sr Project Mgr)*

Capgemini Middle East FZ LLC (1)
Al Shatha Tower Office No F27-14
PO Box 502420
Dubai, United Arab Emirates
Tel.: (971) 4 4335690
Fax: (971) 4 4231998
Information Technology Consulting Services
S.I.C.: 7373
N.A.I.C.S.: 541512

Capgemini Nederland B.V. (1)
Reykjavikplein 1
3528 BJ Utrecht, Netherlands (100%)
Tel.: (31) 306898989
Fax: (31) 306899999
E-Mail: info@capgemini.com
Web Site: www.nl.capgemini.com
Emp.: 5,000
Holding Company
S.I.C.: 6719
N.A.I.C.S.: 551112
Jeroen Groenevelt *(Mng Dir)*

Subsidiaries:

Capgemini Business services BV (2)
Reykjavikplein 1
Utrecht, 3524 KA, Netherlands
Tel.: (31) 306898989
Fax: (31) 306899999
E-Mail: info.nl@capgemini.com
Web Site: www.capgemini.com
Business Process Outsourcing Services
S.I.C.: 7389
N.A.I.C.S.: 561499
Jeroen Versteeg *(Gen Mgr)*

Capgemini Educational Services B.V. (2)
Papendorpseweg 100
3528 BJ Utrecht, Netherlands
Tel.: (31) 306896600
E-Mail: csopl.nl@capgemini.com
Web Site: www.academy.capgemini.nl
Emp.: 50
Educational Support Services
S.I.C.: 8299
N.A.I.C.S.: 611710
Ruddi De Souza *(Mng Dir)*
Onno van de Weteringh *(Mng Dir)*

Capgemini Outsourcing B.V (2)
Reykjavic Plein 1
3528 BJ Utrecht, Netherlands (100%)
Tel.: (31) 306894422
E-Mail: info@capgemini.com
Web Site: www.capgemini.nl.co
Emp.: 5,000
Outsourcing Consultancy Services
S.I.C.: 8742
N.A.I.C.S.: 541611
Peter Barbier *(Mng Dir)*

Capgemini Shared Services BV (2)
Reykjavikplein 1
Utrecht, 3524 KA, Netherlands
Tel.: (31) 306898989
Fax: (31) 306899999
E-Mail: info.nl@capgemini.com
Web Site: www.nl.capgemini.com
Business Process Outsourcing Services
S.I.C.: 7389
N.A.I.C.S.: 561499
Bernard Helders *(Gen Mgr)*

Non-U.S. Subsidiary:

Capgemini Belgium N.V/S.A (2)
Bessenveldstraat 19
1831 Diegem, Brussels, Belgium (100%)
Tel.: (32) 27081111
Fax: (32) 27081110
E-Mail: reception.desk.de@capgemini.com
Web Site: www.be.capgemini.com
Emp.: 800
Professional Techical Services; Management Consultancy
S.I.C.: 8742
N.A.I.C.S.: 541611
Urdain Boven *(CEO)*

Capgemini Norge AS (1)
Hoffsveien 1D
0275 Oslo, Norway
Tel.: (47) 24 12 80 00
Fax: (47) 24 12 80 01
Web Site: www.capgemini.com
Emp.: 700
Information Technology Consulting Services
S.I.C.: 7373
N.A.I.C.S.: 541512
Ben Hammer *(Gen Mgr)*

Capgemini Oldco Ltd (1)
1 Avenue Road
Birmingham, West Midlands, B6 4DU, United Kingdom
Tel.: (44) 121 607 1366
Software Development Services
S.I.C.: 7371
N.A.I.C.S.: 541511

Capgemini Phillipines SBOS (1)
3rd Floor One World Square McKinley Hill
Fort Bonifacio, Taguig, Philippines 1634
Tel.: (63) 2 667 6000
Fax: (63) 2 667 6199
Emp.: 200
Information Technology Consulting Services
S.I.C.: 7373
N.A.I.C.S.: 541512

Capgemini Polska Sp. Z o. o (1)
Ul Piekna 18
Warsaw, 00-549, Poland
Tel.: (48) 224 64 70 00
Fax: (48) 224 64 71 00
E-Mail: office.pl@capgemini.com
Web Site: www.pl.capgemini.com
Information Technology Consulting Services
S.I.C.: 7373
N.A.I.C.S.: 541512
Frank Wagenbauer *(Gen Mgr)*

Capgemini Portugal, Servicos de Consultoria e Informatica, SA (1)
Avenida do Colegio Militar 37-F
Torre Colombo Oreante Piso 10, 1500-180
Lisbon, Portugal PT
Tel.: (351) 214122200 (100%)
Fax: (351) 214122299
E-Mail: geral.pt@capgemini.com
Web Site: www.pt.capgemini.com
Emp.: 100
Consultancy & IT Services
S.I.C.: 8742
N.A.I.C.S.: 541611
Paulo Morgado *(Gen Mgr)*

Capgemini Retail Solutions B.V. (1)
Hoogoorddreef 15 Atlas Arena
Amsterdam Zuidoost, Amsterdam, Noord-Holland, 1101 BA, Netherlands
Tel.: (31) 203129966
Fax: (31) 206976796
Information Technology Consulting Services
S.I.C.: 7373
N.A.I.C.S.: 541512

Capgemini Schweiz AG (1)
World Trade Ctr
Leutschenbachstrasse 95, CH 8050 Zurich, Switzerland CH
Tel.: (41) 445602400 (100%)
Fax: (41) 445602500
E-Mail: info.ch@capgemini.com
Web Site: www.ch.capgemini.com
Sales Range: $10-24.9 Million
Emp.: 350
Management & Information Technology Consulting Services, Systems Integration & Technology Development, Design & Outsourcing Capabilities
S.I.C.: 8742
N.A.I.C.S.: 541611
Patrick Nicolet *(CEO)*

Branches:

Capgemini Schweiz AG (Basel) (2)
Leutschenbachstrasse 95
Zurich, CH-8050, Switzerland (100%)
Tel.: (41) 445602400
Fax: (41) 0445602500
Web Site: www.capgemini.com
Emp.: 40
Management Consulting, Information Technology & Outsourcing Services
S.I.C.: 8742
N.A.I.C.S.: 541611
Herbert Hensle *(Pres)*

Capgemini Schweiz AG (Genf) (2)
12 Ave Des Morgines
CH-1213 Geneva, Petit Lancy, Switzerland
Tel.: (41) 228795200
Fax: (41) 228795239
E-Mail: info.zlh.gh@gemini.com
Web Site: www.ch.capgemini.com
Emp.: 85,000
Management Consulting, Information Technology & Outsourcing Services
S.I.C.: 8742
N.A.I.C.S.: 541611
Herdert Hensle *(Dir)*

Capgemini Schweiz AG (2)
Amsler Laffon Str 9
CH 8201 Schaffhausen, Switzerland CH
Tel.: (41) 445602600 (100%)
Fax: (41) 526314880
E-Mail: zurich.ch@capgemini.com
Web Site: www.ch.capgemini.com
Sales Range: $10-24.9 Million
Emp.: 80
Data Processing Software Development & Related Services
S.I.C.: 7374
N.A.I.C.S.: 518210
Achim Schreiber *(Mgr-PR)*

Capgemini Services Malaysia Sdn Bhd (1)
Suite 15-10 GTower 99 Jalan Tun Razak
50400 Kuala Lumpur, Malaysia
Tel.: (60) 3 2168 1954
Fax: (60) 21681824
Web Site: www.Capgemini.com
Information Technology Consulting Services
S.I.C.: 7373
N.A.I.C.S.: 541512

Capgemini Services Romania s.r.l. (1)
Str Dr Felix 63-69 sector 1
011033 Bucharest, Romania
Tel.: (40) 21 209 80 00
Fax: (40) 31 405 51 36
E-Mail: office.ro@capgemini.com
Web Site: www.ro.capgemini.com
Information Technology Consulting Services
S.I.C.: 7373
N.A.I.C.S.: 541512
Cosmin Branzan *(CEO)*

Capgemini Slovensko, S.r.o. (1)
Karadzicova 8
821 08 Bratislava, Slovakia
Tel.: (421) 2 444 556 78
Fax: (421) 2 444 556 80
E-Mail: info.sk@capgemini.com
Web Site: www.sk.capgemini.com
Information Technology Consulting Services
S.I.C.: 7373
N.A.I.C.S.: 541512

Capgemini Suisse SA (2)
Pl Chauderon 16
CH-1003 Lausanne, Switzerland
Tel.: (41) 213175011
Fax: (41) 213175010
E-Mail: info@ch.capgemini.com
Web Site: www.ch.capgemini.com
Emp.: 50
Management Consulting, Information Technology & Outsourcing Services
S.I.C.: 8742
N.A.I.C.S.: 541611
Serge Kampf *(Chm)*

Capgemini Sverige AB (1)
Gustavlundsvagen 131
PO Box 825
Bromma, 161 24 Stockholm, Sweden SE
Tel.: (46) 853685000 (100%)
Fax: (46) 853685555
E-Mail:
Web Site: www.se.capgemini.com
Rev.: $7,391,668,065
Emp.: 1,350
Management Consulting, Information Technology & Outsourcing Services
S.I.C.: 8742
N.A.I.C.S.: 541611
Leendert Venema *(Pres)*

Capgemini Technology Services Maroc S.A. (1)
Casanearshore Shore 8 A 1100 Boulevard Al Qods
Sidi Maarouf, 20270 Casablanca, Morocco
Tel.: (212) 5 22 46 18 00
Fax: (212) 5 22 29 57 44
Web Site: www.capgemini.com
Information Technology Consulting Services
S.I.C.: 7373
N.A.I.C.S.: 541512

Capgemini UK (1)
1 Forge End
Woking, Surrey, GU21 6DB, United Kingdom (100%)
Tel.: (44) 483764764
Fax: (44) 1483786161
Web Site: www.uk.capgemini.com
Emp.: 8,000
Management Consulting, Information Technology & Outsourcing Services
S.I.C.: 8742
N.A.I.C.S.: 541611
Christine Hodgson *(Chm)*
Cliff Evans *(Chief Digital Officer)*

CPM Braxis ERP Tecnologia da Informacao Ltda. (1)
Alameda araguaia 2096
Alphaville, Barueri, 06455-000, Brazil
Tel.: (55) 1137089100
Fax: (55) 1141963455
Information Technology Consulting Services
S.I.C.: 7373
N.A.I.C.S.: 541512

CPM Braxis Outsourcing S.A. (1)
Sede Alameda Araguaia N 2 096
Alphaville Baruari, Sao Paulo, 06455-000, Brazil
Tel.: (55) 11 3708 9100

Capgemini S.A.—(Continued)

Fax: (55) 11 3708 9199
E-Mail: outsourcing@cpmbraxis.br
Business Process Outsourcing Services
S.I.C.: 7389
N.A.I.C.S.: 561499

CS Consulting GmbH (1)
Hindenburgstr 37
30175 Hannover, Germany
Tel.: (49) 511 957 94 0
Fax: (49) 511 957 94 999
E-Mail: office@cs-consulting.de
Web Site: www.cs-consulting.de
Banking Information Technology Consulting Services
S.I.C.: 7373
N.A.I.C.S.: 541512
Edmund Kuepper *(Mng Dir)*

ENTERPRIME CONSULTING SPA (1)
Centro Direzionale Valecenter Via E Mattei 1/C
30020 Marcon, Venice, Italy
Tel.: (39) 041 5957311
Fax: (39) 041 4569358
E-Mail: info@enterprime.it
Web Site: www.enterprime.it
Information Technology Consulting Services
S.I.C.: 7373
N.A.I.C.S.: 541512
Graziano Borgonovo *(Principal-Supply Chain)*

ENTERPRIME FINANCE SRL (1)
Centro Direzionale Valecenter Via E Mattei 1/C
30020 Marcon, Venice, Italy
Tel.: (39) 041 5957511
Fax: (39) 041 5950330
Financial Software Development Services
S.I.C.: 7371
N.A.I.C.S.: 541511

I&S IT-Beratung & Service GmbH (1)
Martin-Schmeisser-Weg 10
44227 Dortmund, Germany
Tel.: (49) 231 975186 0
Fax: (49) 975186420
E-Mail: info@is-do.de
Web Site: www.is-do.de
Emp.: 2
Information Technology Consulting Services
S.I.C.: 7373
N.A.I.C.S.: 541512

IBX Group AB (1)
Banergatan 16
Box 24236
104 51 Stockholm, Sweden
Tel.: (46) 8 5368 5000
Fax: (46) 8 5368 3354
E-Mail: info@ibxgroup.com
Web Site: www.ibx.se
Information Technology Consulting Services
S.I.C.: 7373
N.A.I.C.S.: 541512
Veronica Wiren *(Partner-Global HR Bus)*

Non-U.S. Subsidiaries:

IBX Danmark AS (2)
Delta Park 40
2665 Vallensbaek, Denmark
Tel.: (45) 70 11 22 00
Fax: (45) 70 11 22 01
Web Site: www.ibx.se/locations-1.aspx
Information Technology Consulting Services
S.I.C.: 7373
N.A.I.C.S.: 541512
Mads Fischer Rasmussen *(Country Mgr)*

IBX Norway A/S (2)
Hoffsveien 1D
Postboks 475
Skoyen, 0214 Oslo, Norway
Tel.: (47) 24 12 80 00
Fax: (47) 22 52 55 05
E-Mail: info@ibx.no
Web Site: www.ibx.se/locations-1.aspx
Information Technology Consulting Services
S.I.C.: 7373
N.A.I.C.S.: 541512
Herman Rovde *(Country Mgr)*

IBX Software Development s.r.l. (2)
Victoria Square 63-69 Dr J Felix Street 9th Floor Sector 1
011033 Bucharest, Romania
Tel.: (40) 21 209 80 00
Fax: (40) 31 40 55 136
Web Site: www.ibx.se/locations-1.aspx
Emp.: 100
Software Development Services
S.I.C.: 7371
N.A.I.C.S.: 541511
Dragos Metea *(Gen Mgr)*

Prosodie Iberica S.L.U. (1)
Calle Leganitos 47 5a Planta
28013 Madrid, Spain
Tel.: (34) 91 540 70 00
Fax: (34) 91 540 70 01
E-Mail: prosodie@prosodie.es
Web Site: www.prosodie.es
Software Development Services
S.I.C.: 7373
N.A.I.C.S.: 541512
Carles Molina *(Mgr-R&D)*

REALTA' INFORMATCA SRL (1)
Via Assarotti 9
10122 Turin, Italy
Tel.: (39) 011 5619585
Fax: (39) 011 5630029
E-Mail: infobox@realtainformatica.it
Web Site: www.realtainformatica.it
Information Technology Consulting Services
S.I.C.: 7373
N.A.I.C.S.: 541512

CAPILANO HONEY LIMITED

399 Archerfield Road
PO Box 531
Richlands, QLD, 4077, Australia
Tel.: (61) 7 3712 8282
Fax: (61) 7 3712 8286
E-Mail: honey@capilano.com.au
Web Site: www.capilano.com.au
CZZ—(ASX)
Rev.: $75,198,349
Assets: $57,002,181
Liabilities: $28,920,740
Net Worth: $28,081,442
Earnings: $3,591,706
Fiscal Year-end: 06/30/13
Business Description:
Honey Producer
S.I.C.: 2099
N.A.I.C.S.: 311999
Personnel:
Benjamin A. McKee *(Mng Dir)*
Dirk Kemp *(Sec & Controller-Fin)*
Board of Directors:
Trevor R. Morgan
Phillip F. McHugh
Benjamin A. McKee
Robert N. Newey
Simon L. Tregoning

CAPILLION INTERNATIONAL PTE LTD.

10 Anson Road
International Plaza #27-16,
Singapore, 079903, Singapore
Tel.: (65) 6221 6518
Fax: (65) 6224 4342
E-Mail: cs@capillion.com
Web Site: www.capillion.com
Sales Range: $50-74.9 Million
Business Description:
Content Management System, Customer Relationship Management & Internet Marketing Services
S.I.C.: 7389
N.A.I.C.S.: 561499
Personnel:
Keane Lee *(Chm)*
Jack Lan *(CEO)*
Richard Boo *(CFO)*
Julius Peh *(COO)*
Daniel Tan *(CMO)*

CAPINFO COMPANY LIMITED

12/F 23 Quantum Silver Plaza
ZhiChun Road
Haidian District, Beijing, 100191, China
Tel.: (86) 10 88511155
Fax: (86) 10 82358550
E-Mail: capinfo@capinfo.com.cn
Web Site: www.capinfo.com.cn
1075—(HKG)
Rev.: $83,570,508
Assets: $177,321,078
Liabilities: $52,360,137
Net Worth: $124,960,941
Earnings: $13,149,603
Emp.: 1,253
Fiscal Year-end: 12/31/12
Business Description:
IT Services & Software
S.I.C.: 7373
N.A.I.C.S.: 541512
Personnel:
Guojun Di *(Chm-Supervisory Bd)*
Xu Wang *(CEO)*
Jiaqing Gao *(Co-Sec & VP)*
Ching Fan Koo *(Co-Sec)*
Board of Directors:
Zhe Xu
Jing Chen
Zhiqiang Gong
Sha Hu
Lei Lu
Xiaobing Lu
Jiaren Pan
Hongyin Shi
Xu Wang
Xianggao Zeng
Kaihua Zhang
Liye Zhou
Supervisory Board of Directors:
Guojun Di
Jun Xiao
Xiangyan Xu

Deloitte Touche Tohmatsu
35F 1 Pacific Place 88 Queensway
Hong Kong, China (Hong Kong)
Legal Counsel:
Tian Yuan Law Firm
10th Floor China Pacific Insurance Plaza 28 Fengsheng Lane
Xicheng District, Beijing, 100032, China

Morrison & Foerster
33/F Edinburgh Tower The Landmark 15 Queen's Road
Central, China (Hong Kong)

China Securities Depository & Clearing Corporation Limited
No 17 Taipingqiao Street
Xicheng District, Beijing, 100033, China
Tel.: (86) 10 5937 8888
Fax: (86) 10 5859 8977
Transfer Agents:
Hong Kong Registrars Limited
Room 1712-16 17th Floor Hopewell Centre 183 Queens Road East
Wanchai, China (Hong Kong)

China Securities Depository & Clearing Corporation Limited
No 17 Taipingqiao Street
Xicheng District, Beijing, 100033, China
Tel.: (86) 10 5937 8888
Fax: (86) 10 5859 8977

CAPINTEC INC.

(Acquired by Eczacibasi Holding A.S.)

CAPITA PLC

(Formerly The Capita Group plc)
71 Victoria Street
London, SW1H 0XA, United Kingdom
Tel.: (44) 2077991525
Fax: (44) 2077991526
E-Mail: corporate@capita.co.uk
Web Site: www.capita.co.uk
Year Founded: 1984
CPI—(LSE OTC)
Rev.: $5,293,464,222
Assets: $6,101,428,986
Liabilities: $4,714,654,437
Net Worth: $1,386,774,549
Earnings: $372,712,440
Emp.: 47,590
Fiscal Year-end: 12/31/12
Business Description:
Business Process Outsourcing Services
S.I.C.: 8742
N.A.I.C.S.: 541611
Personnel:
Paul Pindar *(CEO)*
Andrew Parker *(Co-COO & Deputy CEO)*
Gordon Hurst *(Sec & Fin Dir)*
Vic Gysin *(Co-COO)*
Board of Directors:
Martin Bolland
Maggi Bell
J. Paul M. Bowtell
Vic Gysin
Gordon Hurst
Andrew Parker
Paul Pindar
Gillian Sheldon
Legal Counsel:
Herbert Smith LLP
Exchange House Primrose Street
London, EC2A 2HS, United Kingdom

Subsidiaries:

Applied Language Solutions (1)
Unit 1 Riverside Ct
Huddersfiled Rd Delph, Oldham, OL3 5FZ, United Kingdom (100%)
Tel.: (44) 8453677000
Fax: (44) 8702250262
E-Mail: marketing@appliedlanguage.com
Web Site: www.appliedlanguage.com
Sales Range: $10-24.9 Million
Emp.: 130
Language Translation Services
S.I.C.: 7389
N.A.I.C.S.: 541930
Kenny Holden *(Head-Tech)*

BDML Connect Limited (1)
The Connect Ctr Kingston Crescent
North End, Portsmouth, PO2 8QL, United Kingdom
Tel.: (44) 8706061389
Fax: (44) 8706061382
E-Mail: enquiries@bdml.co.uk
Web Site: www.bdml.co.uk
Emp.: 450
Automobile Insurance Services
S.I.C.: 6351
N.A.I.C.S.: 524126
Mark Townsend *(Mng Dir)*

Call Centre Technology Limited (1)
Oxleigh House 540 Bristol Business Park
Coldharbour Lane, Bristol, BS16 1EJ, United Kingdom
Tel.: (44) 844 2252057
Fax: (44) 117 311 3322
E-Mail: support@cctonline.co.uk
Web Site: www.cctonline.co.uk
Emp.: 60
Business Process Outsourcing Services
S.I.C.: 7389
N.A.I.C.S.: 561499
Russell Attwood *(CEO)*

Capita Business Services Limited (1)
17-19 Rochester Row
London, SW1P 1LA, United Kingdom
Tel.: (44) 8000223414
Fax: (44) 8704001099
E-Mail: webenquiries@capita-ld.co.uk
Web Site: www.capita-ld.co.uk
Training & Consultancy Services
S.I.C.: 8299
N.A.I.C.S.: 611710
Paul Pindar *(CEO)*

Capita Commercial Services Limited (1)
71 Victoria St
Westminster, London, SW1H 0XA, United Kingdom
Tel.: (44) 20 7799 1525
Fax: (44) 20 7222 6124
E-Mail: insurance@capita.co.uk
Web Site: www.capitainsuranceservices.co.uk
Business Support Services

S.I.C.: 7389
N.A.I.C.S.: 561499
Richard Holland *(Mng Dir)*

Capita Insurance Services Limited (1)
40 Dukes Place
London, EC3A 7NH, United Kingdom
Tel.: (44) 8704027570
Fax: (44) 8701624566
E-Mail: insurance@capita.co.uk
Web Site: www.capitainsuranceservices.co.uk
Emp.: 300
Commercial Insurance Management Services
S.I.C.: 6411
N.A.I.C.S.: 524298
Vic Gysin *(COO)*

Capita International Development (1)
Beacon House 27 Clarendon Road 88 Main Street
Belfast, Northern Ireland, BT1 3PR, United Kingdom
Tel.: (44) 28 9261 0930
Fax: (44) 28 92 610931
E-Mail:
Emp.: 30
Financial Consulting Services
S.I.C.: 6211
N.A.I.C.S.: 523999
Caroline Rickatson *(Mng Dir)*

Capita Life & Pensions Limited (1)
141 Castle St
Salisbury, Wiltshire, SP1 3TB, United Kingdom
Tel.: (44) 1722414888
Fax: (44) 1722414613
Emp.: 300
Pension Administration Services
S.I.C.: 6371
N.A.I.C.S.: 524292
John Graham *(Mng Dir)*

Capita Life & Pensions Regulated Services Limited (1)
141 Castle St
Salisbury, Wiltshire, SP1 3TB, United Kingdom
Tel.: (44) 1722414888
Fax: (44) 1722414613
E-Mail: capita-sip-services@capita.co.uk
Web Site: www.capitasipservices.co.uk
Emp.: 300
Pension Administration Services
S.I.C.: 6371
N.A.I.C.S.: 524292
Denise Von Roretz *(Mgr-Premises)*

Capita Resourcing Limited (1)
Kings Chase
107 King St, Maidenhead, Berkshire, SL6 1DP, United Kingdom
Tel.: (44) 1628408100
Fax: (44) 1628408101
Web Site: www.capitaresourcing.co.uk
Emp.: 100
Business Process Outsourcing Services
S.I.C.: 8742
N.A.I.C.S.: 541611
Dawn Marriott *(Mng Dir)*

Capita Secure Information Systems Limited (1)
Methuen Park Bath Road
Chippenham, SN14 0TW, United Kingdom
Tel.: (44) 8456041999
Fax: (44) 8456042999
E-Mail: csis.info@capita.co.uk
Web Site: www.capitasecureinformationsystems.co.uk
Emp.: 900
Security Software Development Services
S.I.C.: 7371
N.A.I.C.S.: 541511
Craig Rogerson *(CEO)*

Capita Symonds Limited (1)
Business Ctr CastleWay House
17 Preston New Rd, Blackburn, BB2 1AU, United Kingdom
Tel.: (44) 1254273000
Fax: (44) 1254273559
E-Mail: chris.nelhams@capita.co.uk
Web Site: www.capitasymonds.co.uk
Emp.: 550
Infrastructure Consulting Services
S.I.C.: 8712
N.A.I.C.S.: 541310
Chris Booy *(Chm)*
Graham Cowley *(COO)*

Capita Trust Company Limited (1)
7th Floor Phoenix House 18 King William Street
London, EC4N 7HE, United Kingdom
Tel.: (44) 20 7800 4100
Fax: (44) 20 7800 4180
Web Site: www.capitafiduciary.com
Financial Management Services
S.I.C.: 6211
N.A.I.C.S.: 523999
Chris Searson *(CEO)*
Bruno Beernaerts *(Co-Mng Dir-Luxembourg)*
Alain Lam *(Co-Mng Dir-Luxembourg)*
Sue Lawrence *(Mng Dir)*

Club 24 Limited (1)
Hepworth House
Leeds, LS2 8AE, United Kingdom
Tel.: (44) 8453309030
E-Mail:
Sales Range: $200-249.9 Million
Emp.: 8,000
Customer Management Outsourcing Services
S.I.C.: 8742
N.A.I.C.S.: 541611
Ian Cherry *(Mng Dir)*

ComputerLand UK Ltd. (1)
Discovery House Mere Way
Ruddington Fields, Ruddington, Nottinghamshire, NG11 6JW, United Kingdom
Tel.: (44) 1159318000
Fax: (44) 1159318222
E-Mail: infomation@computerland.co.uk
Web Site: www.computerland.co.uk
Sales Range: $125-149.9 Million
Emp.: 500
Systems Integration & Technical Support Services
S.I.C.: 7373
N.A.I.C.S.: 541512

Evolvi Rail Systems Limited (1)
Templegate House
115-123 High St, Orpington, Kent, United Kingdom
Tel.: (44) 871 521 9871
Fax: (44) 168 983 2343
Web Site: www.evolvi.co.uk
Online Rail Travelling Solution Provider
S.I.C.: 2741
N.A.I.C.S.: 519130
Ken Cameron *(Mng Dir)*

IBS OPENSystems (UK) Limited (1)
Newhouse Overbridge Square Cambridge Lane
Newbury, RG14 5UX, United Kingdom
Tel.: (44) 1635550088
Fax: (44) 0163537532
E-Mail: web@ibsopensystems.com
Web Site: www.ibsopensystems.com
Emp.: 40
Software Solutions Provider
S.I.C.: 7372
N.A.I.C.S.: 511210
Tracey Fletcher *(Mgr)*

National Dental Plan Limited (1)
Ibex House Minories
London, EC3N 1DY, United Kingdom
Tel.: (44) 2074807201
Fax: (44) 2074812842
E-Mail: ndp@nationaldental.co.uk
Web Site: www.nationaldental.co.uk
Emp.: 1
Dental Insurance Services
S.I.C.: 6321
N.A.I.C.S.: 524114
Andrew Bower *(Gen Mgr)*

Premier Medical Group Limited (1)
Eco Business Park
Ludlow, Shropshire, SY8 1ES, United Kingdom
Tel.: (44) 8456006742
Fax: (44) 158 487 9523
E-Mail: info@premiermedical.co.uk
Web Site: www.premiermedicalgroup.com
Emp.: 15
Medical Reporting & Screening Services
S.I.C.: 8099
N.A.I.C.S.: 621999
Harry Bruenjes *(Chm-Exec Bd)*
Jason Powell *(CEO)*
Bob Goodall *(Chief Medical Officer)*
Basil Nally *(Dir-Sls)*
Debbie Thornton *(Dir-HR)*
Sara Mayhew *(Grp Controller-Fin)*

Tascor Services Limited (1)
(Formerly Reliance Secure Task Management Ltd.)
Surety House 18 Concorde Road
Patchway, Bristol, BS34 5TB, United Kingdom
Tel.: (44) 1179 336 600
Fax: (44) 1179 336 699
Web Site: www.tascor.co.uk
Emp.: 2,000
Forensic Medical Services, Custody & Secure Transport Services
S.I.C.: 7382
N.A.I.C.S.: 561621
Geoff Vinall *(CEO)*

Service Birmingham Limited (1)
Birmingham City Council Council House
Victoria Sq, Birmingham, B1 1BB, United Kingdom
Tel.: (44) 1213031111
E-Mail: contact@birmingham.gov.uk
Web Site: www.birmingham.gov.uk
Emp.: 55
Professional & Management Services
S.I.C.: 8741
N.A.I.C.S.: 561110
Stephen Hughes *(CEO)*

Smiths Consulting Ltd. (1)
New Broad Street House
35 New Broad Street, London, EC2M 1NH, United Kingdom
Tel.: (44) 8454581607
Fax: (44) 2071171998
E-Mail: info@smiths-consulting.com
Web Site: www.smithsconsulting.co.uk
Sales Range: $10-24.9 Million
Emp.: 52
Management Consulting Services
S.I.C.: 8742
N.A.I.C.S.: 541611
Stephen Lee *(Mng Dir)*

Synetrix Limited (1)
Innovation Centre Keele Science Park
Keele, Staffordshire, ST5 5NB, United Kingdom
Tel.: (44) 1782 338 200
Fax: (44) 1782 629 600
E-Mail: info@synetrix.co.uk
Web Site: www.synetrix.co.uk
Software Consultancy Services
S.I.C.: 7371
N.A.I.C.S.: 541511

Team24 Limited (1)
2nd Floor Pathtrace House 91-93 High St
Banstead, Surrey, United Kingdom
Tel.: (44) 845 370 2424
Fax: (44) 845 370 2525
E-Mail: info@team24.co.uk
Web Site: www.team24.co.uk
Health Care Recruitment Services
S.I.C.: 8999
N.A.I.C.S.: 541612
Robert Stiff *(Mng Dir)*

Non-U.S. Subsidiary:

Capita International Financial Services Ltd. (1)
2 Grand Canal Square
Grand Canal Harbour, Dublin, 2, Ireland IE (100%)
Tel.: (353) 1 224 0300
Fax: (353) 1 224 0480
E-Mail: reception@capitaifs.com
Web Site: www.capitaifs.com
Emp.: 200
International Financial Services
S.I.C.: 6099
N.A.I.C.S.: 522320
Patrick Diamond *(Mng Dir)*

CAPITAL AIRPORTS HOLDING COMPANY (CAH)

28 Bldg Tianzhu Rd A Block
Tianzhu Port Industry Zone
Shunyi District, Beijing, 100621, China
Tel.: (86) 10 64563947
Fax: (86) 10 64568496
Web Site: www.cah.com.cn
Year Founded: 2002
Emp.: 50,000

Business Description:
Holding Company: Air Transportation Services
S.I.C.: 6719
N.A.I.C.S.: 551112

Personnel:
Li Peiying *(Pres)*
Wang Zuoyi *(CFO)*
Hu Jintao *(Gen Sec)*

Subsidiary:

Beijing Airport Foods Service Co., Ltd. (1)
28 Building Tianzhu Road A Blcok
Tianzhu Port Industry Zone
Shunyi District, Beijing, 100621, China
Tel.: (86) 64563947
Airport Restaurant Services
S.I.C.: 4581
N.A.I.C.S.: 488119

CAPITAL & COUNTIES PROPERTIES PLC

15 Grosvenor Street
London, W1K 4QZ, United Kingdom
Tel.: (44) 20 3214 9150
Fax: (44) 20 3214 9151
E-Mail: info@capitalandcounties.com
Web Site: www.capitalandcounties.com
Year Founded: 2010
CAPC—(LSE)
Emp.: 326

Business Description:
Property Development Services
S.I.C.: 6519
N.A.I.C.S.: 531190

Personnel:
Ian Hawksworth *(CEO)*
Anne Byrne *(Gen Counsel)*
Ruth Pavey *(Sec)*

Board of Directors:
Ian Durant
Soumen Das
Graeme Gordon
Ian Hawksworth
Ian Henderson
Andrew Huntley
Demetra Pinsent
Henry Staunton
Andrew Strang
Gary Yardley

CAPITAL & REGIONAL PLC

52 Grosvenor Gardens
London, SW1W 0AU, United Kingdom
Tel.: (44) 207 932 8000
Fax: (44) 207 802 5600
E-Mail: nanrogers@arbuthnot.co.uk
Web Site: www.capreg.com
CAL—(LSE)
Rev.: $45,325,623
Assets: $401,297,589
Liabilities: $117,657,105
Net Worth: $283,640,484
Earnings: ($25,268,640)
Emp.: 282
Fiscal Year-end: 12/30/12

Business Description:
Real Estate Investing Management Services
S.I.C.: 6211
N.A.I.C.S.: 523999

Personnel:
John Clare *(Chm)*
Hugh Y. Scott-Barrett *(CEO)*
Miles Stephenson *(CEO-Garigal Asset Mgmt)*
Falguni Desai *(Sec)*

Capital & Regional plc—(Continued)

Board of Directors:
John Clare
Mark Bourgeois
Kenneth Ford
Neno Haasbroek
Tony Hales
Philip Newton
Louis Norval
Hugh Y. Scott-Barrett
Charles Staveley

Legal Counsel:
Olswang LLP
90 High Holborn
London, United Kingdom

Subsidiaries:

Capital & Regional Property Management Limited (1)
52 Grosvenor Gardens
SW1W 0AU London, United Kingdom (100%)
Tel.: (44) 2079328000
Fax: (44) 2078025600
E-Mail: new.supplies@capreg.com
Web Site: www.capreg.com
Emp.: 60
Land Subdivision
S.I.C.: 6552
N.A.I.C.S.: 237210
Hugh Scott-Barrett *(CEO)*

Morrison Merlin Limited (1)
235 Deansgate
N34EW Manchester, United Kingdom (100%)
Tel.: (44) 1618328136
Fax: (44) 1618327876
E-Mail: gary.dunkley@x-leisure.co.uk
Emp.: 7
Land Subdivision
S.I.C.: 6552
N.A.I.C.S.: 237210
Gary Dunkley *(Gen Mgr)*

CAPITAL ASSET LEASING CORPORATION LIMITED

14th Floor Chapal Plaza Hasrat Mohani Road
Karachi, 74000, Pakistan
Tel.: (92) 21 32431181
Fax: (92) 21 32465718
E-Mail: info@calcorp.com.pk
Web Site: www.calcorp.com.pk
Year Founded: 1992
CPAL—(ISL)

Business Description:
Car Rental Business Services
S.I.C.: 7514
N.A.I.C.S.: 532111

Personnel:
Muhammad Sajid *(Chm)*
Saad Saeed Faruqui *(CEO)*
Abdul Wajid Soherwardy *(CFO & Sec)*

Board of Directors:
Muhammad Sajid
Saad Saeed Faruqui
Shahrukh Saeed Faruqui
Mustafa Jafar
Hasan Akbar Kazmi
Sajid Nasim
Ayesha Qadri

Transfer Agent:
Technology Trade (Pvt.) Ltd.
Dagia House 241-C Block-2 PECHS
Karachi, Pakistan

CAPITAL BANK

Issam Ajlouni Str Shmeisani
PO Box 941283
Amman, 11194, Jordan
Tel.: (962) 65100200
Fax: (962) 65194250
E-Mail: info@capitalbank.jo
Web Site: www.capitalbank.jo
Year Founded: 1995
EXFB—(AMM)
Sales Range: $75-99.9 Million
Emp.: 400

Business Description:
Commercial & Investment Banking Services
S.I.C.: 6029
N.A.I.C.S.: 522110

Personnel:
Bassem Khalil Salem Al-Salem *(Chm)*
Said Samih Taleb Darwazah *(Vice Chm)*
Ayman Omran Abu-Dhaim *(CFO)*
Iman Mahmmod Allan Al Damen *(Chief Credit & Risk Officer)*
Sami Mohammad Musa Khair *(Chief HR & Admin Affairs Officer)*

Board of Directors:
Bassem Khalil Salem Al-Salem
Kim Foad Sa'd Abu Jaber
Mazen Ahmad Al-Jubeir
Jawad Abdel Reda Abdel Baqi Al-Qassab
Mohammed Mousaed Al-Seif
Mohammed Ali Khaldoun Husry
Samih Taleb Daewazah
Said Samih Taleb Darwazah
Nidal Younis Mohammed Eses

Subsidiary:

Capital Investment Company (1)
Shmesani Issam Ajluni St
PO Box 940982
Amman, 11194, Jordan
Tel.: (962) 6 5200330
Fax: (962) 6 5692872
E-Mail: info@Capitalinv.jo
Web Site: www.capitalinv.jo
Emp.: 40
Financial Management Services
S.I.C.: 6211
N.A.I.C.S.: 523999

CAPITAL BANK - GRAWE GRUPPE AG

Burgring 16
Graz, 8010, Austria
Tel.: (43) 31680720
Fax: (43) 3168072390
E-Mail: pool@capitalbank.at
Web Site: www.capitalbank.at
Sales Range: $100-124.9 Million
Emp.: 111

Business Description:
Banking Services
S.I.C.: 6029
N.A.I.C.S.: 522110

Personnel:
Christian Jauk *(CEO)*

Division:

Capital Bank (1)
Wallnerstrasse 4/1
1010 Vienna, Austria
Tel.: (43) 131614
Telex: 111715
Fax: (43) 13161411
E-Mail: office.wien@capitalbank.at
Emp.: 200
Banking Services
S.I.C.: 6029
N.A.I.C.S.: 522110
Christian Jauk *(Mng Dir)*
Constantine Malmberg *(Mng Dir)*

CAPITAL BLF INC.

7250 Boulevard Taschereau Suite 200
Brossard, QC, J4W 1M9, Canada
Tel.: (450) 672-5090
Fax: (514) 626-1870
E-Mail: info@captialblf.com
Web Site: www.capitalblf.com
Year Founded: 2007
BLF—(TSXV)
Rev.: $2,949,588
Assets: $13,804,580
Liabilities: $6,490,903
Net Worth: $7,313,677
Earnings: ($407,326)
Fiscal Year-end: 12/31/12

Business Description:
Residential Buildings Rental Services
S.I.C.: 6514
N.A.I.C.S.: 531110

Personnel:
Claude Blanchet *(Chm)*
Mathieu Duguay *(Pres & CEO)*
Daniel Blanchette *(CFO)*

Board of Directors:
Claude Blanchet
Daniel Blanchette
Francois Bourbonnais
Mathieu Duguay
Dino Fuoco
Pierre Laflamme
Marc Marois
Philippe Morin

Transfer Agent:
Computershare Investor Services Inc.
100 University Ave 9th Floor
Toronto, ON, Canada

CAPITAL DEVELOPMENT AND INVESTMENT COMPANY PLC

(See Under National Development Bank PLC)

CAPITAL DGMC INC.

1100 boulevard Cremazie Est Bureau 805
Montreal, QC, H2P 2X2, Canada
Tel.: (514) 238-5091
Fax: (450) 581-0389
VTC.P—(TSXV)

Business Description:
Investment Services
S.I.C.: 6211
N.A.I.C.S.: 523999

Personnel:
Daniel Dumont *(Pres)*

CAPITAL DRILLING LTD.

23 Amoy Street
Singapore, 069858, Singapore
Tel.: (65) 62279050
Fax: (65) 62279089
E-Mail: info@capdrill.com
Web Site: www.capdrill.com
Year Founded: 2004
CAPD—(LSE)
Rev.: $128,647,591
Assets: $114,054,785
Liabilities: $38,557,609
Net Worth: $75,497,176
Earnings: $11,425,290
Emp.: 1,400
Fiscal Year-end: 12/31/12

Business Description:
Mineral Exploration & Mining Services
S.I.C.: 1481
N.A.I.C.S.: 213115

Personnel:
Jamie Boyton *(Chm & Interim CEO)*
Uno Makotsvana *(CFO)*
David Payne *(Chief Comml Officer & Sec)*

Board of Directors:
Jamie Boyton
Craig Burton
Alexander John Davidson
Tim Read
Brian Rudd

Subsidiaries:

Capital Drilling (Singapore) Pte. Ltd. (1)
23 Amoy St
Singapore, 69858, Singapore
Tel.: (65) 62279050
Fax: (65) 62279089
Web Site: www.capdrill.com
Emp.: 15
Mineral Drilling Services
S.I.C.: 1481
N.A.I.C.S.: 213115
Amit Chatterjee *(CFO)*

Supply Force International Pte Ltd (1)
23 Amoy St
Singapore, 69858, Singapore
Tel.: (65) 62279050
Fax: (65) 6562279089
Web Site: www.captdrill.com
Logistics Consulting Services
S.I.C.: 4731
N.A.I.C.S.: 541614

Non-U.S. Subsidiaries:

Capital Drilling Egypt (Limited Liability Company) (1)
52 Ahmed Fakhry
Cairo, Nasr, Egypt
Tel.: (20) 222700699
Fax: (20) 22700699, ext. 102
Mineral Drilling Services
S.I.C.: 1481
N.A.I.C.S.: 213115
Brian Rudd *(CEO)*

Capital Drilling Mozambique Limitada (1)
Rua 3 De Fevereiro No 108
Tete, Mozambique
Tel.: (258) 25 222 174
Web Site: www.capdrill.com
Mineral Drilling Services
S.I.C.: 1481
N.A.I.C.S.: 213115

Capital Drilling Perforaciones Chile Limitada (1)
El Juncal 111 2 Piso Parque Industrial Portezuelo
Quilicura, Santiago, Chile
Tel.: (56) 27386640
Fax: (56) 27386121
Web Site: www.capdrill.com
Emp.: 11
Mineral Drilling Services
S.I.C.: 1481
N.A.I.C.S.: 213115
Ismael Reinuaba *(Gen Mgr)*

Capital Drilling Zambia Limited (1)
Plot 609T Zambezi Rd
Roma, Lusaka, Zambia
Tel.: (260) 211292337
Fax: (260) 211292137
Mineral Drilling Services
S.I.C.: 1481
N.A.I.C.S.: 213115
Bert Gerritsen *(Gen Mgr)*

CAPITAL DYNAMICS AG

Bahnhofstrasse 22
CH-6301 Zug, Switzerland
Tel.: (41) 41 748 8444
Fax: (41) 41 748 8440
E-Mail: info@capdyn.com
Web Site: www.capdyn.com
Year Founded: 1999

Business Description:
Equity Investment & Portfolio Management Services
S.I.C.: 6211
N.A.I.C.S.: 523999

Personnel:
Thomas Kubr *(Vice Chm, CEO & Mng Dir)*
Stefan Ammann *(Mng Dir, CFO, COO & Head-Bus Dev)*
Katharina Lichtner *(Mng Dir & Head-Res & Investment Mgmt)*
Stefan Studer *(CTO & VP)*
Jordan Urstadt *(Gen Counsel & Dir-Legal)*

Board of Directors:
Craig Sakin
Michael Hinderer
Thomas Kubr
Katharina Lichtner

Urs Schenker

CAPITAL ENGINEERING NETWORK PUBLIC COMPANY LIMITED

900/15 SVOA Tower 19th Floor Rama III Road Kwang Bangpongpang Khet Yannawa, Bangkok, 10120, Thailand
Tel.: (66) 26826345
Fax: (66) 26826344
Web Site: www.cenplc.com
CEN—(THA)
Rev.: $66,158,476
Assets: $102,868,520
Liabilities: $24,457,475
Net Worth: $78,411,044
Earnings: $1,018,937
Emp.: 559
Fiscal Year-end: 12/31/12

Business Description:
Industrial Steel, Aluminium & Related Wire Ropes Mfr
S.I.C.: 3315
N.A.I.C.S.: 331222

Personnel:
Wutichai Leenabanchong *(Chm & CEO)*
Danusorn Choocherdwattanasak *(Sec)*

Board of Directors:
Wutichai Leenabanchong
Ukris Athrathimai
Monthon Chatuwallopkul
Chenin Chen
Pipit Jaovisidha
Theerachai Leenabanchong
Pusit Lertwattanaruk
Kanchanuth Ratanasribuathong
Wijit Techkaseam
Somchai Tongsirikool
Yanyong Wattanawongpitak
Jakkathan Yothanan

Subsidiary:

Ua Withya Public Company Limited (1)
247 Romklao Rd
Saensaeb Minburi, Bangkok, 10510, Thailand
Tel.: (66) 2543 9020
Fax: (66) 2543 9029
E-Mail: uwc@uwc.co.th
Web Site: www.uwc.co.th
UWC—(THA)
Emp.: 50
Transmission Line Towers Mfr
S.I.C.: 1629
N.A.I.C.S.: 237130
Oran Ratanatrakarn *(Mng Dir)*

CAPITAL ESTATE LIMITED

17/F Asia Orient Tower Town Place 33 Lockhart Road
Wanchai, China (Hong Kong)
Tel.: (852) 25292678
Fax: (852) 25298128
Web Site: www.capitalestate.com.hk
0193—(HKG)
Rev.: $18,151,260
Assets: $155,088,552
Liabilities: $52,174,717
Net Worth: $102,913,834
Earnings: ($21,313,114)
Emp.: 640
Fiscal Year-end: 07/31/13

Business Description:
Property & Investment Holding
S.I.C.: 6282
N.A.I.C.S.: 523920

Personnel:
Tak Hong Sio *(Chm)*
David Nin Wai Chu *(Deputy Chm)*
Stephen Nin Yiu Chu *(CEO)*
Yat Ming Hung *(Sec)*

Board of Directors:
Tak Hong Sio
David Nin Wai Chu
Stephen Nin Yiu Chu
Michael Chi Kan Lau
Kam Fai Leung
Billy Sze Kuen Li
Kwong Fat Wong

Transfer Agent:
Computershare Hong Kong Investor Services Limited
Rooms 1712-1716 17/F Hopewell Centre 183 Queen's Road East
Wanchai, China (Hong Kong)
Tel.: (852) 2862 8628
Fax: (852) 2865 0990

Non-U.S. Subsidiary:

Foshan Fortuna Hotel Company Limited (1)
B 82 Lecong Dadao Lecong Town
Shunde Dist, Foshan, Guangdong, 528315, China
Tel.: (86) 2033363233
Fax: (86) 2062614116
E-Mail: reservation@HotelFortunaFoshan.com
Hotel Management Services
S.I.C.: 7011
N.A.I.C.S.: 721110

CAPITAL EYE INVESTMENTS LIMITED

2nd Floor 30 Melrose Boulevard Melrose Arch
Melrose North, Johannesburg, South Africa
Tel.: (27) 11 712 1449
Fax: (27) 11 339 1836
Web Site: www.capitaleye.co.za
Sales Range: $150-199.9 Million
Emp.: 2,315

Business Description:
Investments in Technology
S.I.C.: 6211
N.A.I.C.S.: 523999

Personnel:
Dean Sparrow *(Chm & CEO)*
Josephine Fortuin *(CFO)*
Mark Hyslop *(Chief Legal Officer)*
Neels van Tonder *(CTO)*

Board of Directors:
Duncan Coles
John Bright
Vani Chetty
Josephine Fortuin
Neil Michelson
Mntungwa Morojele
Dean Sparrow
Peter Terblanche

Subsidiaries:

Fernridge Consulting (Proprietary) Limited (1)
26th Fl UCS Bldg 209 Smit St Corner Harrison St
PO Box 31266
Braamfontein, Johannesburg, Gauteng, 2001, South Africa
Tel.: (27) 117121715
Fax: (27) 113391833
E-Mail: admin.fernridge@fernridge.ucs.co.za
Web Site: www.fernridge.co.za
Emp.: 12
Business Consulting Services
S.I.C.: 8742
N.A.I.C.S.: 541611
Sybrand Strauss *(Mng Dir)*
Stephen Walters *(Mng Dir)*

GAAP Point-of-Sale (Proprietary) Limited (1)
Bldg 4 Constantia Park 546 16th Rd
Midrand, Gauteng, 1685, South Africa
Tel.: (27) 113156938
Fax: (27) 113156436
Web Site: www.gaap.co.za
Emp.: 51
Restaurant Software Development Services
S.I.C.: 7371
N.A.I.C.S.: 541511
J. P. d' Abbadie *(Mng Dir)*

UCS Dynamics Software Solutions (Proprietary) Limited (1)
Easirun House 18 Kleinfontein Lake Ofc Park
Benoni, Gauteng, 1501, South Africa
Tel.: (27) 114214800
Fax: (27) 114214999
E-Mail: support@ucs.co.za
Emp.: 26
Software Support Services
S.I.C.: 7373
N.A.I.C.S.: 541512

UCS Software Manufacturing (Proprietary) Limited (1)
Meerlus Bldg 263 W St
Centurion, Gauteng, 0157, South Africa
Tel.: (27) 126438300
Fax: (27) 126438333
E-Mail: info@ucssm.com
Web Site: www.ucssm.com
Emp.: 52
Retail Management Software Development Services
S.I.C.: 7371
N.A.I.C.S.: 541511
Grant Wellbeloved *(CEO)*

Ultisales Retail Software (Proprietary) Limited (1)
Meerlus Bldg 263 W Ave
Centurion, Gauteng, South Africa
Tel.: (27) 126821300
Fax: (27) 126438333
Web Site: www.ultisales.com
Emp.: 11
Retail Management Software Development Services
S.I.C.: 7371
N.A.I.C.S.: 541511
John Mccloesky *(CEO)*
Steve Mallaby *(Mng Dir)*

Universal Knowledge Software (Proprietary) Limited (1)
UCS House 21st Fl 209 Smit St
Braamfontein, Johannesburg, Gauteng, 2001, South Africa
Tel.: (27) 117121750
Fax: (27) 114039463
Web Site: www.uks.co.za
Emp.: 18
Library Management Software Development Services
S.I.C.: 7371
N.A.I.C.S.: 541511
Neesha Ramsumar *(Mng Dir)*

CAPITAL FOR COLLEAGUES PLC

1 Portland Street
Manchester, M1 3BE, United Kingdom
Tel.: (44) 161 233 4891
E-Mail: info@sbmf.co.uk
Web Site: www.capitalforcolleagues.com

Business Description:
Investment Services
S.I.C.: 6211
N.A.I.C.S.: 523999

Personnel:
Richard Bailey *(Chm)*
John Eckersley *(CEO)*

Board of Directors:
Richard Bailey
Alistair Currie
John Eckersley
Edmund Jenkins

CAPITAL MANAGEMENT AND INVESTMENT PLC

54 Baker Street
London, W1U 1FB, United Kingdom
Tel.: (44) 2077250800
Fax: (44) 2077250808
E-Mail: info@cmi-plc.co.uk
Web Site: www.cmi-plc.co.uk
Year Founded: 1999
CMIP—(AIM)
Sales Range: Less than $1 Million
Emp.: 3

Business Description:
Investment Management Services
S.I.C.: 6211
N.A.I.C.S.: 523999

Personnel:
Giles Davies *(Chm)*
Tim D. Woodcock *(Sec)*

Board of Directors:
Giles Davies
Stephen Farrugia
Nick Peter Ledbetter
Charles Nasser
Edward Spencer-Churchill
Tim D. Woodcock

Legal Counsel:
Pinsent Masons
CityPoint 1 Ropemaker Street
London, EC2Y 9AH, United Kingdom

Subsidiary:

CMI Investments Limited (1)
Watson House 54
4th Fl Baker St, London, W1U 7BU, United Kingdom
Tel.: (44) 2077250800
Fax: (44) 2077250808
Emp.: 25
Investment Management Services
S.I.C.: 8748
N.A.I.C.S.: 541618
Tim Woodcock *(Mng Dir)*

CAPITAL MERCHANT BANKING AND FINANCE LIMITED

Battisputali
Kathmandu, Nepal
Tel.: (977) 1 4471458
Fax: (977) 1 4496321
E-Mail: info@cmbfl.com.np
Web Site: www.cmbfl.com.np
Year Founded: 2002
CMB—(NEP)

Business Description:
Financial & Banking Services
S.I.C.: 6029
N.A.I.C.S.: 522110

Personnel:
Bhumi N. Shrestha *(Chm)*
Basudev Acharya *(CEO)*
Indira Rajbhandari *(CFO)*
Chandra Man Maleku *(COO)*
Maheswor Maharjan *(IT Officer)*
Suni Pradhan *(Sec)*

Board of Directors:
Bhumi N. Shrestha
Ashok Kumar Bhattarai
Suni Pradhan
Rabindra Ram Shrestha

CAPITAL MINING LIMITED

PO Box 3770
Weston Creek, ACT, 2611, Australia
Tel.: (61) 262882661
Fax: (61) 262884878
E-Mail: admin@capitalmining.com.au
Web Site: www.capitalmining.com.au
CMY—(ASX)
Rev.: $6,185
Assets: $3,802,981
Liabilities: $293,442
Net Worth: $3,509,540
Earnings: ($2,651,056)
Emp.: 1
Fiscal Year-end: 06/30/13

Business Description:
Mineral Exploration & Evaluation
S.I.C.: 1481
N.A.I.C.S.: 213115

Personnel:
Robert J. McCauley *(CEO)*
Elizabeth Hunt *(Sec)*

Board of Directors:

Capital Mining Limited—(Continued)

James Ellingford
Robert J. McCauley
Peter Torney
Legal Counsel:
Maddocks
123 Pitt Street
Sydney, NSW, 2000, Australia

CAPITAL NOMURA SECURITIES PUBLIC COMPANY LIMITED

25 Bangkok Insurance Building 15th
17th Floor South Sathorn Road
Sathorn, Bangkok, 10120, Thailand
Tel.: (66) 2638 5000
Fax: (66) 2287 6001
E-Mail: investors_relations@th.nomura.com
Web Site: www.cns.co.th
CNS—(BAK)
Rev.: $36,934,189
Assets: $306,456,198
Liabilities: $184,860,989
Net Worth: $121,595,209
Earnings: $6,228,124
Emp.: 449
Fiscal Year-end: 12/31/12
Business Description:
Investment, Securities & Other Financial Services; Owned 25.11% by Nomura Holdings Inc.
S.I.C.: 6211
N.A.I.C.S.: 523110
Personnel:
Suthep Peetakanont *(Chm)*
Shinichi Mizuno *(Pres)*
Varangkna Wasuwanich *(Sec & Head-Fin Div)*
Board of Directors:
Suthep Peetakanont
Prasit Kanchanasakdichai
Ruangsub Kovindha
Koki Miura
Shinichi Mizuno
Wattanee Phanachet
Chrisana Sae-Leiw
Naoki Sugaya
Pisit Tesabamroong
Prasert Virasathienpornkul
Nimit Wongjariyakul

CAPITAL POWER CORPORATION

1200 10423 101 St NW
Edmonton, AB, T5H 0E9, Canada
Tel.: (780) 392-5100
E-Mail: info@capitalpower.com
Web Site: www.capitalpower.com
Year Founded: 2009
CPX—(TSX)
Rev.: $1,283,279,820
Assets: $5,103,298,680
Liabilities: $2,367,755,640
Net Worth: $2,735,543,040
Earnings: $89,461,800
Emp.: 939
Fiscal Year-end: 12/31/12
Business Description:
Gas & Electric Power Distribution & Generation Services
S.I.C.: 4911
N.A.I.C.S.: 221118
Personnel:
Donald James Lowry *(Chm)*
Brian Vaasjo *(Pres & CEO)*
Stuart Lee *(CFO & Sr VP-Fin)*
Yale Loh *(Treas & VP)*
Peter Arnold *(Sr VP-HR, Health, Safety & Environment)*
Kate Chisholm *(Sr VP-Legal & External Rels)*
Bryan DeNeve *(Sr VP-Corp Dev & Comml Svcs)*
Darcy John Trufyn *(Sr VP-Ops, Engrg & Construction)*
Board of Directors:
Donald James Lowry
Albrecht Bellstedt
Doyle Beneby
William Bennett
Brian Bentz
Hugh Bolton
Richard Cruickshank
Philip Lachambre
Allister McPherson
Peggy Mulligan
Robert Phillips
Brian Vaasjo
Transfer Agent:
Computershare Trust Company of Canada
100 University Avenue 9th Floor North Tower
Toronto, ON, Canada

CAPITAL PRODUCT PARTNERS L.P.

3 Iassonos Street
Piraeus, 18537, Greece
Tel.: (30) 210 458 4950
Fax: (30) 2104284285
E-Mail: info@capitalpplp.com
Web Site: www.capitalpplp.com
CPLP —(NASDAQ)
Rev.: $171,494,000
Assets: $1,401,772,000
Liabilities: $620,346,000
Net Worth: $781,426,000
Earnings: $99,481,000
Fiscal Year-end: 12/31/13
Business Description:
Holding Company; Deep-Sea Freight Transportation Services
S.I.C.: 6719
N.A.I.C.S.: 551112
Personnel:
Evangelos M. Marinakis *(Chm)*
Ioannis E. Lazaridis *(CEO & CFO)*
Evangelos G. Bairactaris *(Sec)*
Board of Directors:
Evangelos M. Marinakis
Evangelos G. Bairactaris
Dimitris P. Christacopoulos
Pierre de Demandolx Dedons
Keith B. Forman
Ioannis E. Lazaridis
Abel L. Rasterhoff
Nikolaos Syntychakis

CAPITAL SECURITIES CORPORATION

Capital Center No 101 Sung Jen Road
Xinyi District, Taipei, 110, Taiwan
Tel.: (886) 2 4128878
E-Mail: service@capital.com.tw
Web Site: www.capital.com.tw
6005—(TAI)
Rev.: $203,383,186
Assets: $1,842,644,716
Liabilities: $856,123,353
Net Worth: $986,521,363
Earnings: $35,707,685
Emp.: 2,110
Fiscal Year-end: 12/31/12
Business Description:
Corporate Banking Services
S.I.C.: 6211
N.A.I.C.S.: 523110
Personnel:
Alex Jiunn-Chih Wang *(Chm)*
Subsidiaries:

Capital Insurance Advisory Corp. (1)
Capital Center 13F-2 No 97 Songren Road
Xinyi District, Taipei, 11073, Taiwan
Tel.: (886) 2 87896777
Fax: (886) 2 87893174
General Insurance Services
S.I.C.: 6411
N.A.I.C.S.: 524210

Capital Insurance Agency Corp. (1)
106 15F Tunhua S Road Sec 2
Taipei, 11073, Taiwan
Tel.: (886) 2 87896777
Fax: (886) 2 87893174
General Insurance Services
S.I.C.: 6411
N.A.I.C.S.: 524210

Capital Investment Management Corp. (1)
Capital Center 4F-1 No 97 Sungren Road
Shinyi Chiu
Taipei, 110, Taiwan
Tel.: (886) 2 87806789
Fax: (886) 2 87892758
Investment Management Services
S.I.C.: 6211
N.A.I.C.S.: 523999

Non-U.S. Subsidiaries:

CSC Financial Services Limited (1)
Unit 3204-07 32/F Cosco Tower 183 Queen Road
Central, China (Hong Kong)
Tel.: (852) 25309966
Fax: (852) 21046006
Financial Management Services
S.I.C.: 6211
N.A.I.C.S.: 523999

CSC Futures (HK) Ltd. (1)
Unit 3204-07 32/F Cosco Tower 183 Queen Road
Central, China (Hong Kong)
Tel.: (852) 25309966
Fax: (852) 21051193
E-Mail: sam_kao@e-capital.com.hk
Emp.: 28
Financial Investment Management Services
S.I.C.: 6211
N.A.I.C.S.: 523999
Sam Kao *(Mng Dir)*

CSC International Holdings Ltd. (1)
18F No 360 Pu Dong Nan Road New Shanghai Int'l Tower
Shanghai, 200120, China
Tel.: (86) 21 58887188
Fax: (86) 21 58882929
Investment Management Services
S.I.C.: 6211
N.A.I.C.S.: 523999

Non-U.S. Subsidiaries:

Capital Securities (Hong Kong) Ltd. (2)
Unit 3204-07 32/F Cosco Tower 183 Queen Road
Central, China (Hong Kong)
Tel.: (852) 25309966
Fax: (852) 21046006
Securities Brokerage Services
S.I.C.: 6211
N.A.I.C.S.: 523120

CSC Finance Ltd. (2)
Unit 3204-07 32/F Cosco Tower 183 Queen Road
Central, Hong Kong, China (Hong Kong)
Tel.: (852) 25309966
Fax: (852) 21046006
Financial Management Services
S.I.C.: 6211
N.A.I.C.S.: 523999

CSC Securities (HK) Ltd. (2)
Unit 3204-07 32/F Cosco Tower 183 Queen Road
Central, China (Hong Kong)
Tel.: (852) 25309966
Fax: (852) 21046006
Financial Investment Management Services
S.I.C.: 6211
N.A.I.C.S.: 523999

First Securities (HK) Limited (1)
Rm 1708-1710 17/F China Insurance Group Bldg 141 Des Voeux Road
Central, China (Hong Kong)
Tel.: (852) 25281723
Fax: (852) 25298134
E-Mail: info@firstsechk.com
Web Site: www.firstsechk.com
Emp.: 24
Securities Brokerage Services
S.I.C.: 6211
N.A.I.C.S.: 523120
James Chen *(Gen Mgr)*

CAPITAL SHOPPING CENTRES GROUP PLC

(Name Changed to Intu Properties plc)

CAPITAL SPORTS GROUP OF COMPANIES

1000 Palladium Dr
Kanata, ON, K2V 1A5, Canada
Tel.: (613) 599-0250
Fax: (613) 599-4974
E-Mail: reception@ottawasenators.com
Web Site: www.ottawasenators.com
Emp.: 200
Business Description:
Holding Company
S.I.C.: 6719
N.A.I.C.S.: 551112
Personnel:
Eugene Melnyk *(Owner & Chm)*
Cyril Leeder *(CEO)*
Subsidiaries:

Scotiabank Place (1)
1000 Palladium Drive
Kanata, ON, K2V 1A5, Canada
Tel.: (613) 599-0250
Fax: (613) 599-0150
Web Site: www.scotiabankplace.com
Sports & Entertainment Complex
S.I.C.: 7999
N.A.I.C.S.: 711310
Eugene Melnyk *(Owner)*

Ottawa Senators Hockey Club (1)
Scociabank Pl Ctr 1000 Palladium Dr
Kanata, ON, K2V 1A5, Canada Ca
Tel.: (613) 599-0250
Fax: (613) 599-0358
E-Mail: info@ottawasenators.com
Web Site: www.ottawasenators.com
Professional Hockey Franchise
S.I.C.: 7941
N.A.I.C.S.: 711211
Eugene Melnyk *(Owner)*
Cyril M. Leeder *(Pres)*
Erin Crowe *(CFO, Exec VP & Alternate Governor)*
Dave Ready *(Pres-Ottawa Senators Foundation)*
Mark Bonneau *(Sr VP)*

CAPITAL VC LIMITED

Flat 7601B 76/F International Commerce Centre
1 Austin Road West
Tsim Sha Tsui, Kowloon, China (Hong Kong)
Tel.: (852) 3106 3019
Fax: (852) 3106 0958
E-Mail: info@capital-vc.com
Web Site: www.capital-vc.com
2324—(HKG)
Sales Range: $1-9.9 Million
Emp.: 2
Business Description:
Investment Services
S.I.C.: 6799
N.A.I.C.S.: 523920
Personnel:
Kwan Pak Chan *(Sec)*
Board of Directors:
Ming Sun Chan
Duncan Tak Keung Chui
Fan Peng Kong
Kwan Lam
Ta-pei Liu
Siu Tao Shiu
Chung Hong Yau

Transfer Agent:
Tricor Tengis Limited
26/F Tesbury Centre, 28 Queens Road East
Hong Kong, China (Hong Kong)

CAPITALAND LIMITED

168 Robinson Road 30-01Capital Tower
Singapore, 068912, Singapore
Tel.: (65) 68233200
Fax: (65) 68202202
E-Mail: ask-us@capitaland.com
Web Site: www.capitaland.com
Year Founded: 1985
C31—(SES)
Rev.: $2,673,047,594
Assets: $30,595,871,255
Liabilities: $14,852,628,226
Net Worth: $15,743,243,029
Earnings: $1,066,001,207
Emp.: 7,284
Fiscal Year-end: 12/31/12

Business Description:
Hospitality & Real Estate Investment, Development & Financial Services
S.I.C.: 6726
N.A.I.C.S.: 525990

Personnel:
Peter Lim Huat Seah *(Deputy Chm)*
Ming Yan Lim *(Pres & CEO)*
Simon Chee Hwee Ho *(Deputy CEO-CapitaMalls Asia Limited)*
Olivier Lim *(Deputy CEO)*
Arthur Tao Yih Lang *(CFO)*
Seng Chai Tan *(Grp Chief Corp Officer)*
Bob Johnston *(CEO/Mng Dir-Australand Property Group)*
Lian Pang Chen *(CEO-CapitaLand Vietnam)*
Kee Hiong Chong *(CEO-The Ascott Limited)*
Lit Cheong Chong *(CEO-Reg Investments)*
Margaret Goh *(CEO-Special Projects-CapitaLand Singapore)*
Lynette Chin Yee Leong *(CEO-CapitaCommercial Trust Management Limited)*
Jason Juan Thong Leow *(CEO-CapitaLand China)*
Beng Chee Lim *(CEO-CapitaMalls Asia Limited)*
Sharon Hwee Li Lim *(CEO-CapitaMalls Malaysia REIT Management Sdn Bhd)*
Tony Tee Hieong Tan *(CEO-CapitaRetail China Trust Management Limited)*
Wilson Wee Yan Tan *(CEO-CapitaMall Trust Management Limited)*
Ronald Boon Hwee Tay *(CEO-Ascott Residence Trust Management Limited)*
Khai Meng Wen *(CEO-CapitaLand Singapore)*
Su-Lin Yong *(Inerim CEO-Quill Capita Management Sdn Bhd)*
Sai Choy Low *(Sec)*
Harold Woo *(Sr VP-IR)*

Board of Directors:
Kee Choe Ng
Amirsham Bin Abdul Aziz
Kenneth Stuart Courtis
Euleen Yiu Kiang Goh
Tsu Tau Hu
Simon Claude Israel
Stephen Ching Yen Lee
Ming Yan Lim
John Powell Morschel
Peter Lim Huat Seah
Arfat Pannir Selvam

Subsidiaries:

The Ascott Group Limited **(1)**
8 Shenton Way 13-01 Temasek Twr
Singapore, 068811, Singapore (100%)
Tel.: (65) 62208222
Fax: (65) 62272220
Web Site: www.theascottgroup.com
ASCOTT—(SES)
Sales Range: $100-124.9 Million
Emp.: 3,200
Owner & Manager of Serviced Residence Units
S.I.C.: 6513
N.A.I.C.S.: 531110
Mun Leong Liew *(Deputy Chm)*
Chin Beng Lim *(Chm)*
Jennie Chua *(Pres & CEO)*
Hazel Chew *(CFO)*
Ng Lai Leng *(Chief Corp Officer)*
Chong Kee Hiong *(CEO-Real Estate & Residence Trust Mgmt)*
Gerald Lee *(CEO-Hospitality)*
Ee Chee Hong *(CEO-China-Ascott Intl)*
Lam Chee Kin *(Secretarial & VP-Legal)*

Subsidiaries:

The Ascott Capital Pte Ltd **(2)**
8 Shenton Way 13-01 8 Shenton Way
Singapore, 068811, Singapore
Tel.: (65) 62208222
Fax: (65) 62272220
Web Site: www.the-ascott.com
Emp.: 100
Real Estate Management Services
S.I.C.: 6531
N.A.I.C.S.: 531390
Lee Chee Koon *(CEO)*

The Ascott (Europe) Pte Ltd **(2)**
8 Shenton Way 13-01 Temasek Tower
Singapore, 068811, Singapore
Tel.: (65) 62208222
Fax: (65) 62272220
Web Site: www.the-acott.com
Emp.: 110
Real Estate Management Services
S.I.C.: 6531
N.A.I.C.S.: 531390
Chong Kee Hiong *(CEO)*

Ascott International Management (2001) Pte Ltd **(2)**
8 Shenton Way 13-01
Singapore, 068811, Singapore
Tel.: (65) 62208222
Fax: (65) 62272220
Web Site: www.the-ascott.com
Emp.: 100
Property Management Services
S.I.C.: 6531
N.A.I.C.S.: 531311
Chong Kee Hiong *(CEO)*

Ascott Residence Trust Management Limited **(2)**
8 Shenton Way 13-01 8 Shenton Way
Singapore, 068811, Singapore
Tel.: (65) 63899388
Fax: (65) 63899399
Web Site: www.ascottreit.com
Residential Property Management Services
S.I.C.: 6531
N.A.I.C.S.: 531311
Ming Yan Lim *(CEO)*

Non-U.S. Subsidiaries:

Ascott Property Management (Beijing) Co., Ltd **(2)**
No 108 B Jianguo Rd
Chaoyang District, Beijing, 100022, China
Tel.: (86) 1065678100
Fax: (86) 10 6567 8122
E-Mail: ask-us@the-ascott.com
Property Management Services
S.I.C.: 6531
N.A.I.C.S.: 531311
Darren Cher *(Gen Mgr)*

Citadines Melbourne on Bourke Pty Ltd **(2)**
131-135 Bourke Street
Melbourne, 3000, Australia
Tel.: (61) 390398888
Fax: (61) 3 9039 8899
Web Site: www.citadines.com.au
Residential Property Management Services
S.I.C.: 6531
N.A.I.C.S.: 531311

CapitaCommercial Trust Management Limited **(1)**
39 Robinson Road 18-01 Robinson Point
068911 Singapore, Singapore
Tel.: (65) 65361188
Fax: (65) 65336133
E-Mail: ask-us@capitacommercial.com
Web Site: www.capitacommercial.com
Emp.: 200
Holding Company
S.I.C.: 6719
N.A.I.C.S.: 551112
Leong Lynette *(CEO)*

Subsidiary:

CapitaCommercial Trust **(2)**
39 Robinson Road 18-01 Robinson Point
Singapore, 068911, Singapore
Tel.: (65) 6536 1188
Fax: (65) 6533 6133
E-Mail: ask-us@capitacommercial.com
Web Site: www.cct.com.sg
C61U—(OTC SES)
Rev.: $304,282,602
Assets: $5,670,192,279
Liabilities: $1,852,832,038
Net Worth: $3,817,360,241
Earnings: $171,891,825
Emp.: 75
Fiscal Year-end: 12/31/12
Real Estate Investment Trust
S.I.C.: 6726
N.A.I.C.S.: 525990
Lynette Chin Yee Leong *(CEO)*
Sian Howe Chua *(Sr Exec-IR & Comm)*
Marilyn Lee *(Sr Exec-Fin)*
Yi Zhuan Lee *(Sr Exec-Asset Mgmt)*
Michelle Koh *(Sec)*

CapitaLand Commercial Limited **(1)**
39 Robinson Rd 18-01 Robinson Point
Singapore, 068911, Singapore (100%)
Tel.: (65) 65361188
Fax: (65) 65363788
E-Mail: ask_us@capitalandcommercial.com
Web Site: www.capitalandcommercial.com
Emp.: 400
Operator of Commercial Properties
S.I.C.: 6531
N.A.I.C.S.: 531312
Wen Khai Meng *(Deputy Chm)*
Chee Hong Ee *(CEO)*
Chen Lian Pang *(CEO-Southeast Asia)*

Subsidiary:

Wan Tien Realty (Pte) Ltd **(2)**
750E Chai Chee Rd 01-00
Singapore, 469005, Singapore
Tel.: (65) 64437338
Fax: (65) 64444732
E-Mail: cheicheetechnopark@ugl-premas.com
Emp.: 18
Real Estate Management Services
S.I.C.: 6531
N.A.I.C.S.: 531390
Kim Kee Ng *(Mgr)*

CapitaLand Fund Management Limited **(1)**
39 Robinson Rd 18 01 Robinson Pt
Singapore, 068911, Singapore (100%)
Tel.: (65) 65361188
Fax: (65) 65363788
E-Mail: ask_us@capitalandcommercial.com
Web Site: www.capitalandcommercial.com
Emp.: 400
Provider of Property Fund Management
S.I.C.: 6282
N.A.I.C.S.: 523920

CapitaLand GCC Holdings Pte Ltd **(1)**
39 Robinson Road 16-01 Robinson Point
Singapore, 068911, Singapore
Tel.: (65) 6622 6000
Fax: (65) 6720 8608
E-Mail: ask-us@capitalandilec.com
Emp.: 17
Real Estate Management Services
S.I.C.: 6531
N.A.I.C.S.: 531390
Wei Siong Ku *(VP)*

CapitaLand Residential Limited **(1)**
8 Shenton Way Unit 21-01
Singapore, 68811, Singapore (100%)
Tel.: (65) 68202188
Fax: (65) 68202208
E-Mail: ask-uf@capitalandresidential.com
Web Site: www.capitalandresidential.com
Emp.: 150
Developer of Condominiums
S.I.C.: 6531
N.A.I.C.S.: 531311
Wong Heang Fine *(CEO)*
Chen Lian Pang *(CEO-Southeast Asia)*
Heangfine Wong *(CEO-Capital & Residential)*
Lee Yew Kwung *(Sr VP-Project & Design Mgmt)*
Colin Wong *(Sr VP-Mktg & Sls)*

Subsidiary:

CapitaLand Residential Singapore Pte Ltd **(2)**
8 Shenton Way 21-01
Singapore, 068811, Singapore
Tel.: (65) 68202188
Fax: (65) 68202208
E-Mail: ask-us@capitalandresidential.com
Web Site: www.capitalandresidential.com
Emp.: 100
Real Estate Management Services
S.I.C.: 6531
N.A.I.C.S.: 531390
Wong Heang Fine *(CEO)*

Capital and Treasury Limited **(1)**
168 Robinson Road 30-01
Singapore, 068912, Singapore
Tel.: (65) 68233200
Fax: (65) 68202202
Real Estate Development Services
S.I.C.: 6531
N.A.I.C.S.: 531390

CapitalValue Homes Limited **(1)**
8 Shenton Way 29-03
Singapore, 068811, Singapore
Tel.: (65) 68265312
Fax: (65) 6820 1206
Web Site: www.capitavaluehomes.com
Real Estate Management Services
S.I.C.: 6531
N.A.I.C.S.: 531390
Lian Pang Chen *(CEO)*

Raffles Holdings Limited **(1)**
250 North Bridge Road
15-03/04 Raffles City Tower, Singapore, 179101, Singapore (100%)
Tel.: (65) 63985777
Fax: (65) 63985767
E-Mail: investor@rafflesholdings.com
Web Site: www.raffleshoIdings.com
Real Estate Investment & Management Services
S.I.C.: 6726
N.A.I.C.S.: 525990

Non-U.S. Subsidiaries:

Australand Holdings Limited **(1)**
Level 3 Building C
1 Homebush Bay Drive, Rhodes, NSW, 2138, Australia (59%)
Tel.: (61) 297672000
Fax: (61) 297672900
Web Site: www.australand.com.au
AUAOF—(OTC)
Sales Range: $1-4.9 Billion
Emp.: 700
Real Estate Investment, Development & Management Services
S.I.C.: 3291
N.A.I.C.S.: 327910
Olivier Lim *(Chm)*
James Glen Service *(Deputy Chm)*
Robert William Johnston *(Mng Dir)*
Kieran Pryke *(CFO)*
Michael Newsom *(Gen Counsel & Head-Risk Mgmt)*
Bev Booker *(Sec)*

Subsidiaries:

Australand Property Group Pty Limited **(2)**
L 3 1c Homebush Bay Dr
Rhodes, NSW, 2138, Australia
Tel.: (61) 297672000
Fax: (61) 297672900
Web Site: www.australand.com.au
Emp.: 150

CapitaLand Limited—(Continued)

Real Estate Management Services
S.I.C.: 6531
N.A.I.C.S.: 531390
Bob Johnston *(Mng Dir)*

Australand Property Limited (2)
Level 3 Building C
1 Homebush Bay Drive, Rhodes, NSW, 2138, Australia
Tel.: (61) 297672000
Fax: (61) 297672900
E-Mail: rmorton@australand.com.au
Web Site: www.australand.com.au
Sales Range: $600-649.9 Million
Emp.: 185
Real Estate Investment, Development & Management Services
S.I.C.: 6531
N.A.I.C.S.: 531390
Robert William Johnston *(Mng Dir)*
Kieran Pryke *(CFO)*
Michael Newsom *(Gen Counsel)*
Bev Booker *(Sec)*

Divisions:

Australand Investments Limited (3)
Level 3 Building C
1 Homebush Bay Drive, Rhodes, NSW, 2138, Australia
Tel.: (61) 297672000
Fax: (61) 297672900
E-Mail: info@australand.com.au
Web Site: www.australand.com.au
Emp.: 200
Real Estate Investment, Development & Management Services
S.I.C.: 6531
N.A.I.C.S.: 531390
Robert William Johnston *(Mng Dir)*

Australand Property Trust (3)
Level 3 Bldg C
1 Homebush Bay Dr, Rhodes, NSW, 2138, Australia
Tel.: (61) 297672000
Fax: (61) 297672900
E-Mail: info@australand.com.au
Web Site: www.australand.com.au
Emp.: 120
Real Estate Investment, Development & Management Services
S.I.C.: 6531
N.A.I.C.S.: 531390
Robert William Johnston *(Mng Dir)*

Australand Wholesale Holdings Limited (2)
L 3 1c Homebush Bay Dr
Rhodes, NSW, 2138, Australia
Tel.: (61) 297672000
Fax: (61) 2 9767 2900
Real Estate Management Services
S.I.C.: 6531
N.A.I.C.S.: 531390

Non-U.S. Subsidiary:

Australand HK Company Limited (2)
Rm 2312 23/f Lippo Centre Twr 2 89 Queensway
Admiralty, Hong Kong, China (Hong Kong)
Tel.: (852) 28109210
Fax: (852) 28109630
Real Estate Management Services
S.I.C.: 6531
N.A.I.C.S.: 531390

CapitaLand China Holdings Pte Ltd (1)
268 Xizang Road Middle
19-01 Raffles City Shanghai, 200001
Shanghai, China CN
Tel.: (86) 21 3311 4633 (100%)
Fax: (86) 21 6340 3733
Web Site: www.capitaland.com.cn/en
Holding Company; Real Estate Development
S.I.C.: 6719
N.A.I.C.S.: 551112
Liew Mun Long *(Chm)*
Jason Juan Thong Leow *(CEO)*

Subsidiary:

CapitaLand (China) Investment Co., Ltd (2)
12/f Raffles Center No 1 Dongzhimens Avenue
Dongcheng Dis, Beijing, 100007, China
Tel.: (86) 1065630828
Fax: (86) 1065630868
Real Estate Management Services
S.I.C.: 6531
N.A.I.C.S.: 531390

CapitaLand (Japan) Kabushiki Kaisha (1)
Tokyo Bldg 21F 2-7-3 Marunouchi
Chiyoda-Ku, Tokyo, 100-6421, Japan
Tel.: (81) 352190788
Fax: (81) 352190778
E-Mail: ask-japan@capitaland.com
Web Site: www.capitaland.co.jp
Real Estate Management Services
S.I.C.: 6531
N.A.I.C.S.: 531390

CapitaLand UK Management Ltd (1)
Citadines London Barbican 7-21 Goswell Road
London, EC1M 7AH, United Kingdom
Tel.: (44) 20 3119 3430
Fax: (44) 20 3119 3401
Real Estate Management Services
S.I.C.: 6531
N.A.I.C.S.: 531390

CapitaLand (Vietnam) Holdings Pte Ltd (1)
19th floor Kumho Asiana Plaza Saigon 39 Le Duan Street
District 1, Ho Chi Minh City, Vietnam
Tel.: (84) 8 3910 6182
Fax: (84) 8 3910 6186
Web Site: www.capitaland.com.vn
Emp.: 80
Real Estate Management Services
S.I.C.: 6531
N.A.I.C.S.: 531390

Capitaland - Vista Joint Venture Co., Ltd (1)
30th Floor Saigon Trade Center 37 Ton Duc Thang Street
District 1, Ho Chi Minh City, Vietnam
Tel.: (84) 8 3910 6688
Fax: (84) 8 3911 0293
E-Mail: customer_service@capitalandvista.com.vn
Web Site: www.thevista.com.vn
Real Estate Management Services
S.I.C.: 6531
N.A.I.C.S.: 531390

CAPITALGROUP LIMITED

Ground Floor 5 Eglon Street
Parnell, Auckland, New Zealand
Tel.: (64) 93090506
Fax: (64) 93090508
Web Site: www.capitalgroup.co.nz/
Year Founded: 1996
Emp.: 5

Business Description:
Private Equity Firm
S.I.C.: 6211
N.A.I.C.S.: 523999

Personnel:
Greig Allison *(Co-Founder)*
Phillip Bell *(Co-Founder)*

Non-U.S. Holding:

BBQ Factory Pty. Ltd. (1)
91 Darley Street
Mona Vale, NSW, 2103, Australia AU
Tel.: (61) 299991891
Fax: (61) 299795689
E-Mail: inquiry@bbqfactory.com.au
Web Site: www.bbqfactory.co.nz
Sales Range: $25-49.9 Million
Emp.: 100
Barbeque & Spa Pool Retailer
S.I.C.: 5999
N.A.I.C.S.: 453998
Russell Whittaker *(Owner)*

CAPITALPART PARTICIPACOES S.A.

R Iguatemi 354 - Cj 301
1451010 Sao Paulo, Brazil
Tel.: (55) 21 3231 8200
Fax: (55) 21 2262 6675
Year Founded: 1998
CPTP3B—(BRAZ)

Business Description:
Financial Investment Services
S.I.C.: 6211
N.A.I.C.S.: 523999

Personnel:
Kevin Michael Altit *(Dir-IR)*

CAPITALWORKS INVESTMENT PARTNERS

24 Central Building 3rd Fl
Gwen Way & Fredman Drive,
Sandton, 2196, South Africa
Tel.: (27) 11 301 3000
Fax: (27) 11 883 5560
E-Mail: info@capitalworksip.com
Web Site: www.capitalworksip.com

Business Description:
Investment Services
S.I.C.: 6282
N.A.I.C.S.: 523930

Personnel:
Andrew Hart *(CFO)*
Darshan Daya *(Principal)*
Shaun Frankish *(Principal)*
Beth Mandel *(Principal)*
Chad Smart *(Principal)*

CAPITAMALLS ASIA LIMITED

39 Robinson Road 18-01 Robinson Point
Singapore, 068911, Singapore
Tel.: (65) 6538 1188
Fax: (65) 6883 0831
Web Site: www.capitamallsasia.com
JS8—(HKG OTC SES)
Rev.: $466,258,276
Assets: $8,041,202,513
Liabilities: $2,585,610,251
Net Worth: $5,455,592,262
Earnings: $452,488,049
Emp.: 4,100
Fiscal Year-end: 12/31/12

Business Description:
Shopping Mall Developer, Owner & Manager
S.I.C.: 6531
N.A.I.C.S.: 531390

Personnel:
Beng Chee Lim *(CEO)*
Simon Chee Hwee Ho *(Deputy CEO)*
Kok Siong Ng *(CFO)*
Kim Sai Toh *(Deputy Chief Dev Officer)*
Simon Kam Yuen Yong *(Chief Dev Officer)*
Sharon Hwee Li Lim *(CEO-CapitaMalls Malaysia REIT Management Sdn Bhd)*
Wai Han Lock *(CEO-China)*
Tony Tee Hieong Tan *(CEO-CapitaRetail China Trust Management Limited)*
Wilson Wee Yan Tan *(CEO-CapitaMall Trust Management Limited)*
Wei-Pin Choo *(Co-Sec)*
Lee Nah Tan *(Co-Sec)*

Board of Directors:
Kee Choe Ng
Sunil Tissa Amarasuriya
Amirsham A. Aziz
Jennie Kheng Yeng Chua
Beng Chee Lim
Ming Yan Lim
Olivier Tse Ghow Lim
Choon Yong Loo
Arfat Pannir Selvam
Bob Beng Hai Tan
Kong Yam Tan

Boardroom Corporate & Advisory Services Pte. Ltd.
50 Raffles Place 32-01 Singapore Land Tower
Singapore, Singapore

CAPITEC BANK HOLDINGS LIMITED

1 Quantum Stret Techno Park
Stellenbosch, 7600, South Africa
Tel.: (27) 218095900
Fax: (27) 218801207
Web Site: www.capitecbank.co.za
CPI—(JSE)
Int. Income: $791,366,798
Assets: $4,283,329,071
Liabilities: $3,332,427,641
Net Worth: $950,901,430
Earnings: $179,231,698
Emp.: 8,308
Fiscal Year-end: 02/28/13

Business Description:
Bank Holding Company
S.I.C.: 6712
N.A.I.C.S.: 551111

Personnel:
Riaan Stassen *(Founder)*
Gerhardus Metselaar Fourie *(CEO)*
Andre Pierre du Plessis *(CFO & Dir-Fin)*
Jacobus Everhardus Carstens *(Chief Credit Officer)*
Christian George van Schalkwyk *(Sec & Exec-Risk Mgmt)*
Carl Gustav Fischer *(Exec-Mktg & Corp Affairs)*
Nathan Stephen Tlaweng Motjuwadi *(Exec-HR)*
Andre Olivier *(Exec-Card Svcs & Bus Dev)*
Christiaan Oosthuizen *(Exec-IT)*
Leonardus Venter *(Exec-Bus Support Centre)*

Board of Directors:
Michiel Scholtz du Pre le Roux
Andre Pierre du Plessis
Reitumetse Jacqueline Huntley
John David McKenzie
Nonhlanhla Sylvia Mjoli-Mncube
Petrus Johannes Mouton
Chris Adriaan Otto
Gerrit Pretorius
Riaan Stassen
Jacobus Pieter van der Merwe

CAPITOL HEALTH LIMITED

Level 3 81 Lorimer St Docklands
Melbourne, VIC, 3008, Australia
Mailing Address:
PO Box 836
Port Melbourne, VIC, 3207, Australia
Tel.: (61) 3 9348 3333
Fax: (61) 3 9646 2260
E-Mail: j.conidi@capitolhealth.com.au
Web Site: www.capitolhealth.com.au
Year Founded: 2005
CAJ—(ASX)
Rev.: $64,212,447
Assets: $59,628,615
Liabilities: $24,087,496
Net Worth: $35,541,119
Earnings: $3,780,073
Fiscal Year-end: 06/30/13

Business Description:
Diagnostic Imaging Product Mfr
S.I.C.: 8071
N.A.I.C.S.: 621512

Personnel:
John Conidi *(Mng Dir)*
Dominik Henry Kucera *(CFO)*
Kimberley Hogg *(Sec)*

Board of Directors:
John Conidi
Andrew Duncan Harrison
Dominik Henry Kucera
Steven Craig Sewell

Legal Counsel:
Steinepreis Paganin
Level 4 16 Milligan St
Perth, Australia

Subsidiary:

Capital Radiology Pty Ltd (1)
54-56 Princes Highway
Dandenong, VIC, 3175, Australia
Tel.: (61) 3 9792 2234
Fax: (61) 3 9792 2253
Web Site: www.capitalradiology.com.au
Health Care Services
S.I.C.: 8099
N.A.I.C.S.: 621999

CAPITOL W.B.C. PLC

48 Peel Street
Hull, HU3 1QR, United Kingdom
Tel.: (44) 2081234218
Fax: (44) 2087115421
E-Mail: info@wbc-capital.co.uk
Web Site: www.wbc-capitol.co.uk
8WB—(DEU)

Business Description:
Fire Prevention Products Mfr
S.I.C.: 2899
N.A.I.C.S.: 325998

Personnel:
Nedeljko Dzudzelija *(CEO)*

Transfer Agent:
Integral Transfer Agency
Toronto, ON, Canada

Non-U.S. Subsidiary:

Capitol W.B.C. d.o.o. (1)
Nikole Dobrovica St No 26/3
11070 Belgrade, Serbia
Tel.: (381) 11 318 50 85
Fax: (381) 11 2270 658
Emp.: 5
Fertilizer Mining Services
S.I.C.: 1479
N.A.I.C.S.: 212393
Nedeljko Dzudzelija *(Gen Mgr)*

CAPITON AG

Bleibtreustrasse 33
10707 Berlin, Germany
Tel.: (49) 303159450
Fax: (49) 3031594557
E-Mail: info@capiton.de
Web Site: www.capiton.de
Year Founded: 1999
Managed Assets: $636,608,832

Business Description:
Equity Investment Firm
S.I.C.: 6211
N.A.I.C.S.: 523999

Personnel:
Stefan Theis *(Sr Partner & CEO)*
Andreas Kogler *(Sr Partner)*
Alexander Kretzer *(Partner & Head-Controlling)*
Gerwin Theiler *(Partner & Dir-Fin)*
Reinhard Blei *(Sr Partner)*
Andreas Denkmann *(Partner)*
Manuel W. Hertweck *(Partner)*
Christoph Karbenk *(Partner)*
Christoph Spors *(Partner)*
Frank-Markus Winkler *(Partner)*

Holding:

nora systems GmbH (1)
Hohnerweg 2-4
D-69469 Weinheim, Germany De
Tel.: (49) 6201805666
Fax: (49) 6201883019
E-Mail: Info@nora.de
Web Site: www.nora.de
Sales Range: $200-249.9 Million
Emp.: 1,000
Rubber Floorcovering & Footwear Component Mfr & Marketer
S.I.C.: 3069
N.A.I.C.S.: 326299
Manuel W. Hertweck *(Chm-Supervisory Bd)*
Heinz Futscher *(Mng Dir)*
Christa Hoffmann *(Mng Dir)*
Philipp Leferenz *(Mng Dir)*
Andreas Mueller *(Mng Dir)*

U.S. Subsidiary:

nora systems, Inc. (2)
9 NE Blvd
Salem, NH 03079 DE
Tel.: (978) 689-0530
Fax: (978) 975-0110
E-Mail: info@nora.com
Web Site: www.norarubber.com
Sales Range: $25-49.9 Million
Emp.: 70
Rubber Floorcovering Mfr & Distr
S.I.C.: 3069
N.A.I.C.S.: 326299
Andreas Mueller *(Pres & CEO)*

CAPLIN POINT LABORATORIES LIMITED

NARBAVI No 3 Lakshmanan Street T Nagar
Chennai, Tamil Nadu, 600 017, India
Tel.: (91) 44 2815 6653
Fax: (91) 44 2815 4952
E-Mail: info@caplinpoint.net
Web Site: www.caplinpoint.net
Year Founded: 1990
524742—(BOM)
Rev.: $23,940,442
Assets: $25,010,831
Liabilities: $16,995,025
Net Worth: $8,015,806
Earnings: $2,592,597
Emp.: 300
Fiscal Year-end: 06/30/13

Business Description:
Pharmaceutical Product Mfr & Distr
S.I.C.: 2834
N.A.I.C.S.: 325412

Personnel:
M. Jayapal *(Mng Dir)*
Vivek Siddharth *(COO)*
S. Mohanraj *(Compliance Officer, Sec & VP-Fin)*
B. M. Sundaram *(Pres-Global Generics)*

Board of Directors:
C. C. Paarthipan
M. Jayapal
D. P. Mishra
Venkat Radhakrishnan
V. Thirumalai
P. T. Baby Thomas
R. Vijay Venkatraman

Transfer Agent:
Karvy Computershare (P) Limited
Plot No 17-24 Vittal Rao Nagar Madhapur
Hyderabad, India

CAPMAN PLC

Korkeavuorenkatu 32
00130 Helsinki, Finland
Tel.: (358) 207207500
Fax: (358) 207207510
E-Mail: mari.reponen@capman.com
Web Site: www.capman.com
Year Founded: 1989
CPMBV—(HEL)
Sls.: $36,755,826
Assets: $178,343,294
Liabilities: $66,547,914
Net Worth: $111,795,380
Earnings: $3,645,428
Emp.: 109
Fiscal Year-end: 12/31/12

Business Description:
Holding Company; Private Equity & Real Estate Investment Services
S.I.C.: 6719
N.A.I.C.S.: 551112

Personnel:
Heikki Westerlund *(Chm)*
Niko Haavisto *(Interim CEO & CFO)*
Jerome Bouix *(Sr Partner & Head-Bus Dev & IR)*
Kai Jordahl *(Sr Partner & Head-CapMan Buyout)*
Mika Matikainen *(Sr Partner & Head-Real Estate)*
Hans Christian Dall Nygard *(Sr Partner & Head-Russia)*
Joakim Rubin *(Sr Partner & Head-Pub Market)*
Vesa Wallden *(Sr Partner & Head-Tech)*
Markus Sjoholm *(Sr Partner & Deputy Head-Buyout)*
Goran Barsby *(Sr Partner)*
Olli Liitola *(Sr Partner)*
Tuomo Raasio *(Sr Partner)*
Petri Saavalainen *(Sr Partner)*
Ari Tolppanen *(Sr Partner)*
Johan Bennarsten *(Partner & Head-Life Science)*
Karl Aberg *(Partner)*
Anders Bjorkell *(Partner)*
Juhani Erke *(Partner)*
Natalia Boutina *(Legal Counsel & Mgr-Investment)*

Board of Directors:
Heikki Westerlund
Claes de Neergaard
Koen Dejonckheere
Karri Kaitue
Nora Kerppola
Ari Tolppanen

Subsidiaries:

CapMan Capital Management Oy (1)
Korkeavuorenkatu 32
00130 Helsinki, Finland FI
Tel.: (358) 207207500 (100%)
Fax: (358) 207207510
E-Mail: mari.reponen@capman.com
Web Site: www.capman.com
Private Equity Firm
S.I.C.: 6211
N.A.I.C.S.: 523999
Lennart Simonsen *(CEO & Sr Partner)*

Holdings:

Maintpartner Oy (2)
Ahventie 4 B
FI 02170 Espoo, Finland (78%)
Tel.: (358) 923115000
Fax: (358) 923115015
E-Mail: jouko.latvakangas@maintpartner.com
Web Site: www.maintpartner.com
Sales Range: $200-249.9 Million
Emp.: 1,750
Industrial Maintenance & Operation Services
S.I.C.: 1389
N.A.I.C.S.: 213112
Esko Makelainen *(Chm)*

Non-U.S. Subsidiary:

Maintpartner ASI Sp. z o.o. (3)
ul Jana Galla 29A
41-800 Zabrze, Poland
Tel.: (48) 322313265
Fax: (48) 322314682
E-Mail: polska@maintpartner.com
Web Site: www.maintpartner.com
Sales Range: $1-9.9 Million
Emp.: 250
Electrical Equipments Maintenance & Services
S.I.C.: 1731
N.A.I.C.S.: 238210
Grzegorz Szydlowski *(Pres)*

Walki Oy (2)
Radanvarsitie 9
PO Box 33
Valkeakoski, 37601, Finland
Tel.: (358) 205363111
Fax: (358) 205363090
E-Mail: walki@walki.com
Web Site: www.walki.com
Emp.: 220
Paper Product Services
S.I.C.: 2678
N.A.I.C.S.: 322230
Leif Frilund *(CEO)*

Non-U.S. Subsidiaries:

Walki GmbH (3)
Alte Durener Strasse 3
PO Box 1780
52428 Julich, Germany
Tel.: (49) 246168060
Fax: (49) 2461680696
E-Mail: info@walki.com
Web Site: www.walki.com
Packaging Materials
S.I.C.: 7389
N.A.I.C.S.: 561910
Wolfgang Thissen *(VP & Gen Mgr)*

Walki Ltd. (3)
Ray Ln
Garstang, Preston, PR3 1GB, United Kingdom
Tel.: (44) 995604227
Fax: (44) 1995605222
Web Site: www.walki.com
Emp.: 67
Wrappings for the Paper, Steel & Mechanical Wood-Processing Industries & Composite Materials for the Packaging Industry & Technical Purposes Mfr
S.I.C.: 2679
N.A.I.C.S.: 322299

Non-U.S. Affiliate:

Cardinal Foods AS (2)
Brynsveien 5
0667 Oslo, Norway (49%)
Tel.: (47) 22728860
Fax: (47) 22728861
E-Mail: information@cardinalfoods.no
Web Site: www.cardinalfoods.no
Sales Range: $200-249.9 Million
Emp.: 300
Poultry Products & Eggs Producer & Distr
S.I.C.: 0259
N.A.I.C.S.: 112390
Torfinn Prytz Higdem *(CEO)*

CapMan Hotels RE GP Oy (1)
Korkeavuorenkatu 32v
00130 Helsinki, Finland
Tel.: (358) 20 720 7500
Fax: (358) 207 207 510
Restaurant Operating Services
S.I.C.: 5812
N.A.I.C.S.: 722511

CapMan PSH GP Oy (1)
Korkeavuorenkatu 32
130 Helsinki, Finland
Tel.: (358) 20 720 7500
Fax: (358) 20 720 7510
Investment Management Services
S.I.C.: 6211
N.A.I.C.S.: 523999

CapMan RE II GP OY (1)
Korkeavuorenkatu 32
00130 Helsinki, Finland
Tel.: (358) 20 7207500
Fax: (358) 9 61558330
Investment Management Services
S.I.C.: 6211
N.A.I.C.S.: 523999

CapMan Real Estate Oy (1)
Korkeavuorenkatu 32
130 Helsinki, Finland
Tel.: (358) 207 207 500
Fax: (358) 207 207 510
Real Estate Development Services
S.I.C.: 6531
N.A.I.C.S.: 531390
Anders Bjoerkell *(Co-Partner)*
Olli Liitola *(Sr Partner)*
Mika Matikainen *(Sr Partner)*
Jan Mattlin *(Co-Partner)*
Tuomo Raasio *(Sr Partner)*
Heidi Lepaentalo *(CFO)*

Dividum Oy (1)
Korkeavuorenkatu 32
00130 Helsinki, Finland
Tel.: (358) 20 720 7500
Fax: (358) 20 720 7540
Emp.: 100
Real Estate Development Services
S.I.C.: 6531
N.A.I.C.S.: 531390
Lennart Simonsen *(CEO)*

Realprojekti Oy (1)
Korkeavuorenkatu 34
130 Helsinki, Finland
Tel.: (358) 10 309 1800
Fax: (358) 10 309 1801
E-Mail: info@realprojekti.fi
Web Site: www.realprojekti.fi

CapMan PLC—(Continued)

Real Estate Development & Construction Engineering Services
S.I.C.: 6531
N.A.I.C.S.: 531390
Markku Hietala *(CEO & Partner)*
Pasi Nieminen *(Partner & Acct Dir)*
Matti Karlsson *(Partner & Dir-Shopping Center)*
Vesa Olkkola *(Partner & Dir-Real Estate Dev & Plng)*

Fortaco Group Oy **(1)**
(Formerly Ruukki Engineering Oy)
Atomitie 2 C
00370 Helsinki, Finland
Tel.: (358) 10 757 6000
Fax: (358) 20 592 9088
Web Site: www.fortacogroup.com
Emp.: 2,600
Material Handling Equipment Mfr
S.I.C.: 3559
N.A.I.C.S.: 333249
Lars Hellsberg *(Pres & CEO)*
Esko Harila *(Exec VP-Fin & Svcs)*
Ville Jaakkola *(Exec VP-Sourcing & Logistics)*
Jan Nordlander *(Exec VP-Mktg & Sls)*

Non-U.S. Subsidiaries:

CapMan AB **(1)**
Grev Turegatan 30 5 Fl
PO Box 5745
114 87 Stockholm, Sweden
Tel.: (46) 854585470
Fax: (46) 854585489
E-Mail: pernilla.zirath@capman.com
Web Site: www.capman.com
Emp.: 20
Investment Company
S.I.C.: 6722
N.A.I.C.S.: 525910
Goram Barfby *(Mng Dir)*

Holding:

Cederroth International AB **(2)**
PO Box 715
Upplands Vasby, S 194 27, Sweden SE
Tel.: (46) 859096300
Fax: (46) 859096472
E-Mail: info@cederroth.com
Web Site: www.cederroth.com
Sales Range: $150-199.9 Million
Emp.: 800
Mfr. of Toiletries, Household Products & Health & Wound Care Products
S.I.C.: 7699
N.A.I.C.S.: 811490
Sarah Brandt *(Exec VP)*
Maria Lundman Hedberg *(Exec VP)*

CapMan Fund Investment SICAV-SIF **(1)**
7A Rue Robert Stumper
2557 Luxembourg, Luxembourg
Tel.: (352) 26 49 58 42 05
Fax: (352) 26 49 58 42 06
Investment Management Services
S.I.C.: 6211
N.A.I.C.S.: 523999

CapMan (Guernsey) Buyout IX GP Limited **(1)**
Western Suite Ground Floor Mill Court
La Charroterie, Saint Peter Port, GY1 3GG, Guernsey
Tel.: (44) 1481 742 400
Fax: (44) 1481 742 410
E-Mail: capman@gentoo.gg
Web Site: www.gentoo.gg
Financial Management Services
S.I.C.: 6211
N.A.I.C.S.: 523999
Chris Le Galloudec *(Gen Mgr)*

CapMan (Guernsey) Ltd. **(1)**
Hambro House St Julian's Ave
PO Box 86
Saint Peter Port, GY1 3AE, Guernsey
Tel.: (44) 481726521
Fax: (44) 1481710742
Web Site: www.capman.com
Investment Company
S.I.C.: 6722
N.A.I.C.S.: 525910

CapMan (Guernsey) Technology 2007 GP Limited **(1)**
Western Suite Ground Floor Mill Court
La Charroterie, Saint Peter Port, GY1 3GG, Guernsey
Tel.: (44) 1481 742 400
Fax: (44) 1481 742 410
E-Mail: capman@gentoo.gg
Web Site: www.capman.com
Financial Management Services
S.I.C.: 6211
N.A.I.C.S.: 523999

CapMan Mezzanine V Manager S.A. **(1)**
7A Rue Robert Stumper
2557 Luxembourg, Luxembourg
Tel.: (352) 26 49 58 42 05
Fax: (352) 26 49 58 42 06
Fund Management Services
S.I.C.: 6282
N.A.I.C.S.: 523920

CapMan Norway AS **(1)**
Dronning Mauds Gt 3
PO Box 1235
0250 Oslo, Norway (100%)
Tel.: (47) 23237575
Fax: (47) 23237579
E-Mail: kai.jordahl@capman.com
Web Site: www.capman.com
Emp.: 5
Investment Company
S.I.C.: 6722
N.A.I.C.S.: 525910
Kai Jordahl *(CEO)*

CapMan Private Equity Advisors Limited **(1)**
10 Arbat Str
119002 Moscow, Russia
Tel.: (7) 495 620 4885
Fax: (7) 495 620 4886
Web Site: www.capman.com
Private Equity Firm
S.I.C.: 6211
N.A.I.C.S.: 523999
Hans Christian Dall Nygard *(CEO & Sr Partner)*
Alberto Morandi *(Partner)*
Natalia Boutina *(Mgr-Investment & Legal Counsel)*

CapMan Public Market Manager S.A. **(1)**
7A Rue Robert Stumper
2557 Luxembourg, Luxembourg
Tel.: (352) 26 49 58 42 05
Fax: (352) 26 49 58 42 06
Emp.: 1
Venture Capital Services
S.I.C.: 6799
N.A.I.C.S.: 523910
Sella Komulaimen *(Gen Mgr)*

CapMan Sweden AB **(1)**
Box 5745
114 87 Stockholm, Sweden
Tel.: (46) 854585470
Fax: (46) 854585489
Equity Fund Management Services
S.I.C.: 6282
N.A.I.C.S.: 523920

CapMan (Sweden) Buyout VIII GP AB **(1)**
Box 5745
114 87 Stockholm, Sweden
Tel.: (46) 8 545 854 70
Fax: (46) 8 545 854 89
Fund Management Services
S.I.C.: 6282
N.A.I.C.S.: 523920

CapMan (Sweden) Technology Fund 2007 GP AB **(1)**
Box 5745
114 87 Stockholm, Sweden
Tel.: (46) 8 54585470
Financial Management Services
S.I.C.: 6211
N.A.I.C.S.: 523999

CAPPELLE PIGNENES N.V.

Kortrijkstraat 153
B 8930 Menen, Belgium
Tel.: (32) 56521200
Fax: (32) 56521262
E-Mail: sales@cappelle.be
Web Site: www.cappelle.be
Year Founded: 1890
Sales Range: $10-24.9 Million
Emp.: 250

Business Description:
Pigment Sales
S.I.C.: 5198
N.A.I.C.S.: 424950

Personnel:
Lieven Debaets *(CEO)*

Subsidiary:

Gebroeders Cappelle Freres S.A.R.L. **(1)**
Kortrijkstraat 115
8930 Menen, Belgium
Tel.: (32) 56511801
Telex: 85 661
Fax: (32) 56517632
Web Site: www.cappelle.be
S.I.C.: 2816
N.A.I.C.S.: 325180

U.S. Subsidiary:

Cappelle Inc. **(1)**
PO Box 169
Alpharetta, GA 30009
Tel.: (770) 663-8226
Telex: (0232) 91 035 07329
Fax: (770) 663-8017
Emp.: 7
S.I.C.: 2819
N.A.I.C.S.: 325180

Non-U.S. Subsidiaries:

Cappelle Freres (UK) Ltd. **(1)**
PO Box 2, 77A London Rd.
Grays, Essex, RM17 5YY, United Kingdom
Tel.: (44) 1375384084
Telex: (051) 995 484
Fax: (44) 1375371385
S.I.C.: 2816
N.A.I.C.S.: 325180

CAPRAL LIMITED

71 Ashburn Road
Bundamba, QLD, 4304, Australia
Mailing Address:
PO Box 106
Granville, QLD, 4304, Australia
Tel.: (61) 738167000
Telex: 120281
Fax: (61) 738167111
Web Site: www.capral.com.au
Year Founded: 1938
CAA—(ASX)
Rev.: $316,734,832
Assets: $223,628,407
Liabilities: $70,762,758
Net Worth: $152,865,649
Earnings: ($11,449,553)
Fiscal Year-end: 12/31/12

Business Description:
Rolling Mill, Extrusion, Aluminum Plant & Smelter
S.I.C.: 3355
N.A.I.C.S.: 331318

Personnel:
Rex Wood-Ward *(Chm)*
Philip Jobe *(CEO & Mng Dir)*
Tertius Campbell *(CFO)*
Richard Rolfe *(Gen Counsel & Sec)*

Board of Directors:
Rex Wood-Ward
Ian Blair
Anthony M. Eisen
Michael Jefferies
Philip Jobe
Graeme Pettigrew

Legal Counsel:
Allen Allen & Hemsley
19 Martin Place
Sydney, NSW, 2000, Australia
Tel.: (61) 2 229 8765

Units:

Capral Aluminium-Sheets **(1)**
71 Ashburn Rd
PO Box 12
Bundamba, QLD, 4304, Australia (100%)
Tel.: (61) 296820711
Fax: (61) 738167500
E-Mail: contact@capral-aluminium.com.au
Web Site: www.capral.com.au
Emp.: 50
S.I.C.: 3354
N.A.I.C.S.: 331318
Tony Dragicevich *(Gen Mgr)*

Non-U.S. Subsidiary:

National Aluminium Limited **(1)**
259 046 BOTINY
2163 Auckland, New Zealand
Tel.: (64) 927217006
Fax: (64) 92721701
E-Mail: sales@nalco.co.nz
Web Site: www.nalco.co.nz
Emp.: 300
S.I.C.: 3355
N.A.I.C.S.: 331318

CAPRI GLOBAL CAPITAL LIMITED

(Formerly Money Matters Financial Services Limited)
1-B Court Chambers Sir Vithaldas Thackersey Marg
New Marine Lines, Mumbai, 400020, India
Tel.: (91) 22 4354 8200
Fax: (91) 22 2201 9051
E-Mail: contact@cgcl.co.in
Web Site: cgcl.co.in
Year Founded: 1997
CGCL—(NSE)
Rev.: $372,809,143
Assets: $169,415,109
Liabilities: $2,570,775
Net Worth: $166,844,334
Earnings: $14,198,470
Fiscal Year-end: 03/31/13

Business Description:
Investment Banking Services
S.I.C.: 6211
N.A.I.C.S.: 523110

Personnel:
Quintin E. Primo, III *(Chm)*
P. H. Ravikumar *(Mng Dir)*
Arvind Hali *(COO)*
Harish Agrawal *(VP & Sec)*
Ashok Agarwal *(Sr VP-Fin, Accts & Compliance)*
Suresh Gattani *(Sr VP-Fin & Taxation)*
Gautam Munjal *(Sr VP-Ops, Sys & Accts)*

Board of Directors:
Quintin E. Primo, III
Mukesh Kacker
Sanjay Kaul
Bhagwati Prasad
Bhagyam Ramani
Beni Prrasad Rauka
P. H. Ravikumar
Rajesh Sharma

Transfer Agent:
MCS Limited
Shri Kashiram Jamnadas Bldg Ground Fl Office
No 21/22 5 P Dmello Rd Ne
Mumbai, India

CAPRICORN BUSINESS ACQUISITIONS INC.

77 King Street West Suite 3000
Toronto, ON, M5K 1G8, Canada
Tel.: (905) 709-7057
Fax: (905) 564-6518
Year Founded: 2008
CAK.P—(TSXV)
Int. Income: $690
Assets: $69,397
Liabilities: $32,606

Net Worth: $36,791
Earnings: ($80,886)
Emp.: 2
Fiscal Year-end: 04/30/13
Business Description:
Investment Services
S.I.C.: 6211
N.A.I.C.S.: 523999
Personnel:
Yvan Routhier *(Pres & CEO)*
Gary N. Hokkanen *(CFO)*
Board of Directors:
Julio DiGirolamo
Gerald Goldberg
Norman L. Goldman
Gary N. Hokkanen
Statis Rizas
Yvan Routhier
Transfer Agent:
Olympia Transfer Service Inc
Suite 920 120 Adelaide Street West
Toronto, ON, Canada

CAPRICORN SOCIETY LIMITED

172 Burswood Road
Burswood, WA, 6100, Australia
Mailing Address:
Locked Bag 436
Victoria Park, WA, 6979, Australia
Tel.: (61) 8 6250 9500
Fax: (61) 8 6250 9600
Toll Free: 800327437
E-Mail: info@capricorn.coop
Web Site: www.capricorn.coop
Rev.: $85,876,335
Assets: $225,417,693
Liabilities: $124,520,529
Net Worth: $100,897,164
Earnings: $14,525,832
Emp.: 200
Fiscal Year-end: 06/30/13
Business Description:
Automobile Service Stations
S.I.C.: 7538
N.A.I.C.S.: 811111
Personnel:
Colin Heavyside *(Chm)*
Russell Becker *(Vice Chm)*
Greg Wall *(CEO)*
Keith Halliwell *(CFO)*
David Fraser *(CEO-Automotive)*
Tremayne West *(CEO-Risk)*
Bradley Gannon *(Gen Counsel-Legal & Risk & Sec)*
Board of Directors:
Colin Heavyside
Russell Becker
Mark Coleman
Mark Cooper
Russell Green
Wayne Negus
Ross Pickering
Bruce Rathie

CAPRICORN SYSTEMS GLOBAL SOLUTIONS LIMITED

8-2-293/82A/408A Plot No 408A
Road No 22A Jubilee Hills
Hyderabad, 500 033, India
Tel.: (91) 40 23547889
Fax: (91) 40 23547889
E-Mail: contact@capricornsys-global.com
Web Site: www.capricornsys-global.com
512169—(BOM)
Rev.: $615,901
Assets: $1,281,558
Liabilities: $297,263
Net Worth: $984,295
Earnings: $8,318
Emp.: 63
Fiscal Year-end: 03/31/13
Business Description:
Software Development Services
S.I.C.: 7371
N.A.I.C.S.: 541511
Personnel:
S. Man Mohan Rao *(Mng Dir)*
D. Madhav Rao *(Compliance Officer)*
Board of Directors:
G. Ramesh Babu
Anand Deshmukh
K. V. Srinivasa Rao
S. Man Mohan Rao
Transfer Agent:
Venture Capital & Corporate Investments Pvt. Limited
12-10-167 Bharat Nagar Colony
Hyderabad, 500018, India

CAPRIHANS INDIA LIMITED

Block D Shivsagar Estate Dr A B Road Worli
Mumbai, 400 018, India
Tel.: (91) 2230478664
Fax: (91) 2224934042
E-Mail: marketing@caprihansindia.com
Web Site: www.caprihansindia.com
509486—(BOM)
Rev.: $41,468,325
Assets: $26,014,123
Liabilities: $6,404,699
Net Worth: $19,609,424
Earnings: $1,258,996
Emp.: 362
Fiscal Year-end: 03/31/13
Business Description:
PVC Films Products Mfr
S.I.C.: 3089
N.A.I.C.S.: 326199
Personnel:
Robin Banerjee *(Mng Dir)*
P. N. Srinivasan *(Compliance Officer & Asst Sec)*
K. R. Viswanathan *(Sec & Exec VP-Fin)*
Board of Directors:
Mofatraj P. Munot
Robin Banerjee
Rahul G. Divan
Krishnava S. Dutt
Suresh A. Gandhi
Rakesh Khanna
Dhaval K. Vussonji
Transfer Agent:
Link Intime India Pvt. Ltd
C-13 Pannalal Silk Mills Compound LBS Marg
Bhandup (West)
Mumbai, India

CAPRO CORP.

Floor 11 & 12 Baeksang Building 197-28
Gwanhun dong Jongno gu, Seoul, 110 300, Korea (South)
Tel.: (82) 23991200
Fax: (82) 27324214
Web Site: www.hcccapro.co.kr
Year Founded: 1969
006380—(KRS)
Sls.: $889,681
Assets: $683,212
Liabilities: $258,196
Net Worth: $425,016
Earnings: ($17,895)
Emp.: 360
Fiscal Year-end: 12/31/12
Business Description:
Caprolactam, Ammonium Sulfate & Inorganic Fertilizers Producer
S.I.C.: 2875
N.A.I.C.S.: 325314
Personnel:
Sang Gyu Lee *(Pres & CEO)*
Kye Suk Kim *(Mng Dir & Head-HR & Fin)*
Byung Ju Lee *(Mng Dir & Head-Sls, Mktg & Procurement)*
Board of Directors:
Hong Moon An
Suk Rae Cho
Young Rae Cho
Sung An Hong
Sang Gyu Lee

CAPROLACTAM CHEMICALS LIMITED

B-31 MIDC Mahad
Raigad District, Mahad, Maharashtra, 402309, India
Tel.: (91) 2145 233427
E-Mail: caprolactamcl@gmail.com
Web Site: www.caprolactam.in
Year Founded: 1992
507486—(BOM)
Rev.: $635,875
Assets: $407,379
Liabilities: $76,922
Net Worth: $330,456
Earnings: $77,950
Fiscal Year-end: 03/31/13
Business Description:
Specialty Chemicals Mfr
S.I.C.: 2899
N.A.I.C.S.: 325998
Personnel:
Zaver S. Bhanushali *(Chm & Mng Dir)*
Siddharth S. Bhanushali *(Compliance Officer)*
Board of Directors:
Vikram P. Adagale
Siddharth S. Bhanushali
Zaver S. Bhanushali
Rajesh P. Mange
Vasant Laxmidas Mange
Transfer Agent:
Purva Sharegistry (India) Pvt. Ltd.
Unit No 9 Shiv Shakti Ind Estt J R Boricha marg
Opp Kasturba Hospital Lane Lower Parel (E), Mumbai, 400 011, India

CAPS HOLDINGS LIMITED

2 Manchester Rd Southerton
PO Box ST 202
Harare, Zimbabwe
Tel.: (263) 663581
Fax: (263) 665038
Web Site: www.caps.co.zw
—(ZIM)
Business Description:
Pharmaceutical & Healthcare Services
S.I.C.: 2834
N.A.I.C.S.: 325412
Personnel:
F. Mtandah *(Chm)*
T. Munyika *(CFO)*
C. Mahari *(Sec)*
Board of Directors:
F. Mtandah
G. Cheater
M. Mutanda
J. Nderere
Bekithemba Nkomo
Y. Nxumalo
M. Vickery
Subsidiary:

CAPS HOLDINGS LIMITED - St Anne s Hospital Unit **(1)**
155 King George Road
Avondale, Harare, Zimbabwe
Tel.: (263) 4339932
Fax: (263) 4333806
Web Site: www.stannes.co.zw
Emp.: 200
Health Care Services
S.I.C.: 8099
N.A.I.C.S.: 621999

Non-U.S. Subsidiary:

CAPS Botswana Trading (PTY) LTD **(1)**
Plot 17979 Ramogononwane Road
PO Box 40282
Gaborone West, Gaborone, Botswana
Tel.: (267) 3922173
Fax: (267) 3923804
E-Mail: info@caps.co.zw
Pharmaceutical Products Whslr
S.I.C.: 5122
N.A.I.C.S.: 424210
M. Sibanda *(Gen Mgr)*

CAPSTONE INFRASTRUCTURE CORPORATION

155 Wellington Street West Suite 2930
Toronto, ON, M5V 3H1, Canada
Tel.: (416) 649-1300
Fax: (416) 649-1335
E-Mail: info@capstoneinfrastructure.com
Web Site: www.capstoneinfrastructure.com
CSE—(TSX)
Rev.: $355,471,492
Assets: $1,642,656,817
Liabilities: $1,135,251,356
Net Worth: $507,405,461
Earnings: $43,462,530
Emp.: 528
Fiscal Year-end: 12/31/12
Business Description:
Infrastructure Investment Holding Company
S.I.C.: 6719
N.A.I.C.S.: 551112
Personnel:
Vincent James Sardo *(Chm)*
Micheal Bernstein *(Pres & CEO)*
Michael Smerdon *(CFO & Exec VP)*
Stu Miller *(Gen Counsel, Sec & Exec VP)*
Jack Bittan *(Sr VP-Bus Dev)*
Sarah Borg-Olivier *(Sr VP-Comm)*
Jens Ehlers *(Sr VP-Fin)*
Rob Roberti *(Sr VP-Power Generation)*
Board of Directors:
Vincent James Sardo
Patrick J. Lavelle
Goran Mornhed
Jerry Patava
Francois R. Roy
Transfer Agent:
Computershare Investor Services Inc
1500 University Ste 700
Montreal, QC, Canada

Holding:

Renewable Energy Developers Inc. **(1)**
(Formerly Sprott Power Corp.)
Royal Bank Plz South Tower 200 Bay St Ste 2750
PO Box 90
Toronto, ON, M5J 2J2, Canada Ca
Tel.: (416) 943-8099
Fax: (416) 943-4695
E-Mail: info@sprottpower.com
Web Site: www.sprottpower.com
Renewable Energy Used in Power Generation
S.I.C.: 4931
N.A.I.C.S.: 221118
John Varghese *(Chm)*
Jeffrey Jenner *(Pres & CEO)*
Andrew Ingram *(CFO)*
Donald J. Bartlett *(COO)*
Mary Lou McDonald *(Sec)*

Subsidiaries:

Shear Wind Inc. **(2)**
Suite 305 15 Dartmouth Road
Bedford, NS, B4A 3X6, Canada
Tel.: (902) 444-7420

Capstone Infrastructure Corporation—(Continued)

Fax: (902) 444-7465
E-Mail: info@shearwind.com
Web Site: www.shearwind.com
Renewable Energy Exploration Services
S.I.C.: 4939
N.A.I.C.S.: 221118
Michael Magnus *(Pres & CEO)*
Bill Bartlett *(CFO)*
Ian Tillard *(COO)*

SP Development Limited Partnership (2)
Royal Bank Plaza South Tower 200 Bay Street Suite 2750
PO Box 90
Toronto, ON, M5J 2J2, Canada
Tel.: (416) 943-8099
Fax: (416) 943-4695
Toll Free: (877) 973-8099
E-Mail: info@sprott.com
Web Site: www.sprott.com
Renewable Energy Project Development Services
S.I.C.: 7389
N.A.I.C.S.: 561990
Jeff Jenner *(Pres & CEO)*

Non-U.S. Holding:

Bristol Water plc (1)
Bridgwater Road
Bristol, BS99 7AU, United Kingdom (70%)
Tel.: (44) 1179665881
Fax: (44) 1179633755
E-Mail: corporate.affairs@bristolwater.co.uk
Web Site: www.bristolwater.co.uk
Sales Range: $150-199.9 Million
Emp.: 446
Water Supply Services
S.I.C.: 4941
N.A.I.C.S.: 221310
John Moger Woolley *(Chm)*
Luis Garcia *(CEO)*

CAPSTONE MINING CORP.

Suite 900 999 West Hastings Street
Vancouver, BC, V6C 2W2, Canada
Tel.: (604) 684-8894
Fax: (604) 688-2180
Toll Free: (866) 684-8894
E-Mail: info@capstonemining.com
Web Site: www.capstonemining.com
Year Founded: 1987
CS—(TSX)
Rev.: $305,515,000
Assets: $1,512,710,000
Liabilities: $150,976,000
Net Worth: $1,361,734,000
Earnings: $59,592,000
Emp.: 744
Fiscal Year-end: 12/31/12

Business Description:
Copper, Silver, Zinc & Lead Mining Services
S.I.C.: 1021
N.A.I.C.S.: 212234

Personnel:
Darren M. Pylot *(Pres & CEO)*
D. James Slattery *(CFO & Sr VP)*
Gregg B. Bush *(COO & Sr VP)*
Peter T. Hemstead *(Treas & VP-Mktg)*
John J. Kim *(Sec)*
Jay K. Grewal *(Sr VP-Strategy & Stakeholder Affairs)*
Brad J. Mercer *(Sr VP-Exploration)*

Board of Directors:
George L. Brack
Lawrence I. Bell
Chantal Gosselin
GookHo Lee
Kalidas V. Madhavpeddi
Dale Canfield Peniuk
Darren M. Pylot
Richard Norman Zimmer

Transfer Agent:
Computershare Investor Services Inc.
100 University Ave 9th Floor
Toronto, ON, Canada

Subsidiaries:

Kutcho Copper Corp. (1)
Unit 2 3167 Tatlow Rd
PO Box 2871
Smithers, BC, V0J 2N0, Canada BC
Tel.: (250) 877-7898
Fax: (250) 877-7891
Gold, Copper & Other Exploration & Mining
S.I.C.: 1041
N.A.I.C.S.: 212221
Jean O'Sullivan *(Gen Mgr)*

CAPSTREAM VENTURES INC.

800 885 West Georgia Street
Vancouver, BC, V6C 3H1, Canada
Tel.: (604) 542-9458
Fax: (604) 542-0101
E-Mail: bthast@telus.net
Year Founded: 2011
CSP.P—(TSXV)

Business Description:
Investment Services
S.I.C.: 6211
N.A.I.C.S.: 523999

Personnel:
Robert Thast *(CEO & Sec)*
Robert McPhail *(CFO)*

Board of Directors:
Andrew Bowering
Kenneth Richard Holmes
Robert McPhail
Robert Thast

Transfer Agent:
Computershare Investor Services Inc.
3rd Floor 510 Burrard Street
Vancouver, BC, Canada

CAPTAIN POLYPLAST LTD.

Survey No 267 Plot No 10A & 11 NH 8B Behind Jain Manufacture
Shapar
Veraval, Rajkot, Gujarat, 360024, India
Tel.: (91) 2827 253006
Fax: (91) 2827 252056
E-Mail: info@captainpolyplast.in
Web Site: www.captainpolyplast.com
536974—(BOM)
Emp.: 400

Business Description:
HDPE Pipes & Irrigation Equipment Mfr & Distr
S.I.C.: 3089
N.A.I.C.S.: 326122

Personnel:
Ramesh Khichadia *(Chm & Mng Dir)*

Board of Directors:
Ramesh Khichadia
Gopal Khichadia
Dhanji Padmani
Ashok Patel
Harshadray Patel
Arvind Ranpariya

CAPTURE

52 Welbeck Street
London, W1G 9XP, United Kingdom
Tel.: (44) 20 3553 5555
E-Mail: hello@capturemarketing.co.uk
Web Site: www.capturemarketing.co.uk
Year Founded: 2008
Sales Range: $10-24.9 Million
Emp.: 27

Business Description:
Digital Marketing Service
S.I.C.: 8742
N.A.I.C.S.: 541613

Personnel:
Joel Hopwood *(Co-Founder & Dir-Client Svcs)*
Matt Lee *(Co-Founder & Dir-Comml)*
David Lee *(CFO)*

CAPULA LIMITED

Orion House
Stone Business Park, Stone, Staffs, ST15 0LT, United Kingdom
Tel.: (44) 1785827000
Fax: (44) 1785825900
E-Mail: sales@capula.co.uk
Web Site: www.capula.co.uk
Year Founded: 1969
Sales Range: $25-49.9 Million
Emp.: 232
Fiscal Year-end: 12/31/12

Business Description:
Information Technology Systems for Nuclear, Power Generation & Utilities Markets
S.I.C.: 7373
N.A.I.C.S.: 541512

Personnel:
Roger Turner *(CEO)*
Mike Fawcett *(COO & Dir-Fin)*

CAPVEST ASSOCIATES LLP

100 Pall Mall
London, SW1Y 5NQ, United Kingdom
Tel.: (44) 20 7389 7900
Fax: (44) 20 7389 7901
E-Mail: info@capvest.co.uk
Web Site: www.capvest.co.uk
Year Founded: 1999
Emp.: 40

Business Description:
Private Equity Firm
S.I.C.: 6211
N.A.I.C.S.: 523999

Personnel:
Seamus Fitzpatrick *(Founder)*

Non-U.S. Holdings:

RenoNorden AS (1)
Lindebergveien 3
2016 Frogner, Norway
Tel.: (47) 63 86 60 80
E-Mail: post@renonorden.no
Web Site: www.renonorden.no
Emp.: 100
Waste Collection Services
S.I.C.: 4212
N.A.I.C.S.: 562111
Svein Tore Aurland *(CEO)*

Valeo Foods Group Limited (1)
Merrywell Industrial Estate
Ballymount, Dublin, 12, Ireland
Tel.: (353) 1 4051500
Fax: (353) 1 460 1336
E-Mail: info@valeofoods.ie
Web Site: www.valeofoods.ie
Sales Range: $400-449.9 Million
Emp.: 50
Grocery Product Mfr; Owned by CapVest Limited (55%) & Origin Enterprises plc (45%)
S.I.C.: 2033
N.A.I.C.S.: 311421
Seamus Fitzpatrick *(Chm)*

Subsidiaries:

Batchelors Ltd. (2)
72 74 Bannow Rd Cabra W
PO Box 88
Dublin, 7, Ireland
Tel.: (353) 18380133
Fax: (353) 18385963
E-Mail: enquiries@bachelors.ie
Web Site: www.batchelors.ie
Emp.: 200
Canned Vegetables & Fruit Juice & Distr
Import Export
S.I.C.: 2032
N.A.I.C.S.: 311422
Eugene Heary *(Mng Dir)*

Jacob Fruitfield Food Group Ltd. (2)
Belgard Road
Tallaght, Dublin, 24, Ireland IE
Tel.: (353) 14141111
Fax: (353) 14511898
Web Site: www.jacobfruitfield.com
Sales Range: $125-149.9 Million
Emp.: 70
Candies, Chocolates, Biscuits, Jams & Sauces Mfr & Distr
S.I.C.: 2064
N.A.I.C.S.: 311340
Michael Carey *(Chm)*
Seamus Kearney *(Mng Dir & COO)*

Non-U.S. Subsidiary:

Irish Biscuits (N.I.) Limited (3)
PO Box 3
Hillsborough, Co Down, United Kingdom UK
Tel.: (44) 2892682644
Fax: (44) 2892 683 804
Biscuits, Food & Drinks Products Distr
S.I.C.: 5499
N.A.I.C.S.: 445299

Shamrock Foods Limited (2)
Marywell Industrial Estate
Ballymount Road, Dublin, Ireland
Tel.: (353) 14051500
Fax: (353) 14601336
E-Mail: info@valeofoods.ie
Web Site: www.valeofoods.ie
Emp.: 200
Dried & Dehydrated Food Mfr
S.I.C.: 2034
N.A.I.C.S.: 311423
Seamus Kearney *(Mng Dir)*

CAPVEST LIMITED

(See Under CapVest Associates LLP)

CAPVIS EQUITY PARTNERS AG

Talacker 42
CH 8022 Zurich, Switzerland
Tel.: (41) 433005858
Fax: (41) 433005859
E-Mail: info@capvis.com
Web Site: www.capvis.com
Managed Assets: $985,383,000
Emp.: 20

Business Description:
Private Equity Firm
S.I.C.: 6211
N.A.I.C.S.: 523999

Personnel:
Felix Rohner *(CFO & Partner)*
Marc Battenfeld *(Partner)*
Ueli Eckhardt *(Partner)*
Daniel Flaig *(Partner)*
Rolf Friedli *(Partner)*
Stephen Lauer *(Partner)*
Andreas Simon *(Partner)*
Eric Trueb *(Partner)*

Holding:

Lista B+L Holding AG (1)
Fabrikstrasse 1
8586 Erlen, Switzerland
Tel.: (41) 7164921110
Fax: (41) 7164922030
E-Mail: info@lista.com
Web Site: www.lista.com
Sales Range: $200-249.9 Million
Emp.: 800
Holding Company
Export
S.I.C.: 6719
N.A.I.C.S.: 551112
Juerg Henz *(Gen Mgr)*

Subsidiary:

Lista AG (2)
Fabrikstrasse 1
CH 8586 Erlen, Switzerland (100%)
Tel.: (41) 71 649 21 11
Fax: (41) 71 649 22 03
E-Mail: info@lista.com
Web Site: www.lista.com
Emp.: 200
Mfr of Storage Equipment for Industrial & Office Use
S.I.C.: 2599
N.A.I.C.S.: 337127
Frad Gamper *(CEO)*

Non-U.S. Subsidiaries:

Lista Austria GmbH (2)
Prager Strasse 245
A 1210 Vienna, Austria (100%)

Tel.: (43) 1 291 20
Fax: (43) 1 291 204
E-Mail: info.at@lista.com
Web Site: www.lista.com
Emp.: 8
Sales of Workspace Equipment & Drawer Systems
S.I.C.: 5084
N.A.I.C.S.: 423830

Lista GmbH (2)
Brueckenstrasse 1
51702 Bergneustadt, Germany
Tel.: (49) 2261 40 30
Fax: (49) 2261 40 32 22
E-Mail: info.de@lista.com
Web Site: www.lista.com
Drawer Systems & Workspace Equipment Mfr & Whslr
S.I.C.: 3499
N.A.I.C.S.: 332999

Lista Italia s.r.l. (2)
Viale Lombardia 9
24020 Colzate, BG, Italy (100%)
Tel.: (39) 02 935 70 196
Fax: (39) 02 935 70 417
E-Mail: info.it@lista.com
Web Site: www.lista.com
Emp.: 10
Sales of Drawer Systems & Workspace Equipment
S.I.C.: 5084
N.A.I.C.S.: 423830

Lista Sistemas de Almacenaje, S.A. (2)
Edificio CIM Valles planta 9
E 08130 Santa Perpetua de Mogoda, Spain (100%)
Tel.: (34) 902 181 083
Fax: (34) 902 181 084
E-Mail: info.es@lista.com
Web Site: www.lista.com
Emp.: 6
Sales of Workspace Equipment & Drawer Systems
S.I.C.: 5084
N.A.I.C.S.: 423830
Ramon Cambra *(Gen Mgr)*

Lista UK Ltd. (2)
14 Warren Yard Warren Farm Office Village
Wolverton Mill, Milton Keynes, MK12 5NW, United Kingdom (100%)
Tel.: (44) 1 908 222 333
Fax: (44) 1 908 222 433
E-Mail: info.uk@lista.com
Web Site: www.lista.com
Emp.: 6
Sales of Workspace Equipment & Drawer Systems
S.I.C.: 5084
N.A.I.C.S.: 423830
Marco van der Linden *(Gen Mgr)*

Non-U.S. Holding:

Ondal Medical Systems GmbH (1)
Wellastrasse 6
36088 Hunfeld, Germany De
Tel.: (49) 6652 81 0
Fax: (49) 6652 81 392
E-Mail: info@ondal.de
Web Site: www.ondal.de
Sales Range: $75-99.9 Million
Emp.: 450
Developer, Designer & Mfr of Carrying Systems, Sauna Systems & Isolation & Fixation Bundles for Wires & Cables for Medical Equipment
S.I.C.: 3499
N.A.I.C.S.: 332999
Andreas Muhlenbeck *(Mng Dir)*
Andreas Pahl *(Mng Dir)*

U.S. Subsidiary:

Ondal Medical Systems of America, Inc. (2)
540 Eastpark Ct Ste A
Sandston, VA 23150
Tel.: (804) 532-1440
Fax: (804) 532-1494
E-Mail: hester.john@ondal.com
Web Site: www.ondal.de
Emp.: 12
Developer, Designer & Mfr of Carrying Systems, Sauna Systems & Isolation & Fixation Bundles for Wires & Cables for Medical Equipment
S.I.C.: 3499
N.A.I.C.S.: 332999
Christoph Roeer *(Mng Dir)*

CAPXON INTERNATIONAL ELECTRONIC CO LTD

Room 1702 17th Floor CRE Building
No 303 Hennessy Road
Wanchai, China (Hong Kong)
Tel.: (852) 25981308
Fax: (852) 25981808
E-Mail: capxon@biznetvigator.com
Web Site: www.capxongroup.com
0469—(HKG)
Rev.: $154,239,379
Assets: $245,883,121
Liabilities: $122,548,168
Net Worth: $123,334,952
Earnings: ($350,264)
Emp.: 2,885
Fiscal Year-end: 12/31/12

Business Description:
Capacitors Mfr
S.I.C.: 3699
N.A.I.C.S.: 335999

Personnel:
Chin Tsun Lin *(Chm & Pres)*
Yuan Yu Lin *(CEO)*
Carol Szu Jung Hu *(CFO & Chief-Fin Ops-Taiwan)*
Yin Fung Chan *(Sec & Controller-Fin)*

Board of Directors:
Chin Tsun Lin
Chiu Yueh Chou
Chung Ching Lai
I. Chu Lin
Yuan Yu Lin
Fang Chun Liu
Hong Te Lu
Chin Chuan Tung

Legal Counsel:
Minter Ellison
15F Hutchison House 10 Harcourt Road
Central, China (Hong Kong)

Computershare Hong Kong Investor Services Limited
Shops 1712-1716 17th Floor Hopewell Centre
183 Queens Road East
Wanchai, China (Hong Kong)

Transfer Agents:
Royal Bank of Canada Trust Company (Cayman) Limited
4th Floor Royal Bank House 24 Shedden Road
Georgetown, Cayman Islands

Computershare Hong Kong Investor Services Limited
Shops 1712-1716 17th Floor Hopewell Centre
183 Queens Road East
Wanchai, China (Hong Kong)

Non-U.S. Subsidiaries:

Capxon Electronic Industrial Company Limited (1)
5F 165 Datong Rd Sec 2
Taipei, Taiwan
Tel.: (886) 286926611
Fax: (886) 686926477
Web Site: www.Capxon.com.tw
Emp.: 44
Aluminum Electrolytic Capacitors Mfr
S.I.C.: 3675
N.A.I.C.S.: 334416
Chin Tsun Lin *(Pres)*

Capxon Electronic (Shenzhen) Co. Ltd. (1)
Tang Wei Indus Section Tang Wei Vlg Gong Ming
New Guangming Dist, Shenzhen, Guangdong, 518106, China
Tel.: (86) 755 27177888
Fax: (86) 755 27177802
E-Mail: sales@capxon.com.cn
Emp.: 2,836
Capacitors Mfr & Sales
S.I.C.: 3675
N.A.I.C.S.: 334416

Capxon Europe GmbH (1)
Sandwiesenstrasse 15
72793 Pfullingen, Baden-Wurttemberg, Germany
Tel.: (49) 7121701777
Fax: (49) 7121701778
E-Mail: info@capxon-europe.de
Web Site: www.capxon-europe.com
Emp.: 3
Electronic Component Distr
S.I.C.: 5065
N.A.I.C.S.: 423690
Erwin Reutter *(Gen Mgr)*

CAR KLEEN NEW ZEALAND LTD.

Unit E 1066 Great S Rd
Penrose, Auckland, 1061, New Zealand
Tel.: (64) 92761960
Fax: (64) 92761962
E-Mail: cknz@xtra.co.nz
Emp.: 10

Business Description:
Car Wash Equipment Sales
S.I.C.: 5087
N.A.I.C.S.: 423850

Personnel:
Steve Jans *(Mng Dir)*

CAR MATE MFG. CO., LTD.

5-33-11 Nagasaki Toshima-ku
Tokyo, 171-0051, Japan
Tel.: (81) 359261211
Fax: (81) 359261227
E-Mail: int@carmate.co.jp
Web Site: www.carmate.co.jp
7297—(JAS)
Sales Range: $100-124.9 Million
Emp.: 300

Business Description:
Automotive Accessories Mfr & Sales
S.I.C.: 3714
N.A.I.C.S.: 336390

Personnel:
Takaaki Murata *(Pres)*

CAR PARKING TECHNOLOGIES LTD

(Name Changed to Smart Parking Ltd.)

CAR TELEMATICS SA

31 avenue du General Leclerc
92100 Boulogne-Billancourt, France
Tel.: (33) 8 25162016
Fax: (33) 825 163016
E-Mail: eric.felix@cartelematics.fr
Web Site: www.cartelematics.fr
Sales Range: $1-9.9 Million
Emp.: 11

Business Description:
Geolocation Services
S.I.C.: 4812
N.A.I.C.S.: 517210

Personnel:
Eric Felix *(Chm & CEO)*

CARA OPERATIONS LIMITED

6303 Airport Rd
199 Four Valley Dr
Vaughan, ON, L4V 1R8, Canada
Tel.: (905) 760-2244
E-Mail: info@cara.com
Web Site: www.cara.com
Year Founded: 1883
Sales Range: $800-899.9 Million
Emp.: 26,000

Business Description:
In-Flight Catering, Airport Restaurants, Gift Shops, Multi-Unit Restaurants, Institutional Catering, & Food Distribution
Import
S.I.C.: 5812
N.A.I.C.S.: 722320

Personnel:
M. Bernard Syron *(Chm)*
Arjen A. Melis *(Pres & Corp Dev)*
Steven Smith *(CFO)*
Rob Ramage *(Pres-Cara Airline Solutions)*
Ian C. Wilkie *(Gen Counsel, Sec & Sr VP)*
Sean Regan *(Sr VP)*

Board of Directors:
M. Bernard Syron
John T. Evans
John H. Tory

Subsidiary:

Kelseys International, Inc. (1)
6303 Airport Rd
Mississauga, ON, L4V 1R8, Canada ON
Tel.: (905) 405-6500 (61%)
Fax: (905) 405-5063
E-Mail: comments@cara.com
Web Site: www.kelseys.ca
Emp.: 75
Eating Places
S.I.C.: 5812
N.A.I.C.S.: 722513

CARACAL ENERGY INC.

Suite 2100 555 4th Ave SW
Calgary, AB, T2P-3E7, Canada
Tel.: (403) 724-7200
Fax: (403) 262-7534
E-Mail: info@caracalenergy.com
Web Site: www.caracalenergy.com
Year Founded: 2009
CRCL—(LSE)
Emp.: 113

Business Description:
Oil Exploration & Development
N.A.I.C.S.: 213111

Personnel:
Robert B. Hodgins *(Chm)*
Gary Guidry *(Pres & CEO)*
Trevor Peters *(CFO)*
J. Dean Tucker *(COO)*
Christine Antony *(VP-Legal & Gen Counsel)*

Board of Directors:
Robert B. Hodgins
Carol Bell
John Bentley
Peter Dey
Gary Guidry
Ronald W. Royal
Brooke Wade

CARACARA SILVER INC.

120 Adelaide Street West Suite 2400
Toronto, ON, M5H 1T1, Canada
Tel.: (416) 637-3523
Fax: (416) 363-8858
Web Site: www.caracarasilver.com
Year Founded: 2009
CSV—(TSXV)

Business Description:
Investment Services
S.I.C.: 6211
N.A.I.C.S.: 523999

Personnel:
Nicholas Tintor *(Pres & CEO)*
Stephen Mark Gledhill *(CFO)*
Leslie Haddow *(Sec)*

Board of Directors:
Robert G. Boaz
Anne Chopra
Stephen Coates
John Francis Cook
Nicholas Tintor

Transfer Agent:
Computershare Investor Services Inc.
510 Burrard Street 2nd Floor
Vancouver, BC, V6C 3B9, Canada

CARACAS PAPER COMPANY, S.A.

Capaco Bldg Avenida Aragua Floor 1
Urb Mendoza Foundation
Edo Aragua, Maracay, Venezuela

Caracas Paper Company, S.A.—(Continued)

Tel.: (58) 243 2311711
E-Mail: info@capaco.com
Web Site: www.capaco.com
Year Founded: 1953
Emp.: 400

Business Description:
Paper Products
S.I.C.: 2653
N.A.I.C.S.: 322211

CARAD SA
5 Falirou
185 43 Piraeus, Greece
Tel.: (30) 2104203625
Fax: (30) 2104200036
E-Mail: info@carad.gr
Web Site: www.carad.gr

Business Description:
Household Appliances Distr
S.I.C.: 5064
N.A.I.C.S.: 423620

CARAT DUCHATELET S.A.
Rue Winston Churchill 413
Liege, 4020, Belgium
Tel.: (32) 43495555
Fax: (32) 43438429
E-Mail: info@caratsecurity.com
Web Site: www.caratsecurity.com
Year Founded: 1968
Sls.: $17,447,220
Emp.: 1,000

Business Description:
Mobile Security Company
S.I.C.: 7382
N.A.I.C.S.: 561621

Personnel:
Christopher H. Letter *(CEO)*

Division:

Centigon (1)
Rue Winston Churchill 413
4020 Liege, Belgium
Tel.: (32) 43495555
Fax: (32) 43495574
E-Mail: info@caratsecurity.com
Web Site: www.caratsecurity.com
Emp.: 110
Armored Vehicle Mfr
S.I.C.: 3711
N.A.I.C.S.: 336211
Christopher H. Letter *(CEO)*

Non-U.S. Plants:

Centigon Brazil (2)
Alameda Araguaia 1801
Sao Paulo, 06455-000, Brazil
Tel.: (55) 1146894200
Fax: (55) 1146894210
E-Mail: colivieira@centigon.com
Web Site: www.centigon.com
Emp.: 80
Armored Vehicle Mfr
S.I.C.: 3711
N.A.I.C.S.: 336211
Andre Belmonte *(Gen Mgr)*

Centigon Colombia (2)
Calle 21 No 69B-05
95118 Bogota, Colombia
Tel.: (57) 14051414
Fax: (57) 14112568
Web Site: www.centigon.com
Emp.: 130
Armored Vehicle Mfr
S.I.C.: 3711
N.A.I.C.S.: 336211
Fernanado Cruz *(Gen Mgr)*

Centigon France (2)
42 rue d Armor
BP 90447
Cedex, 22404 Lamballe, France
Tel.: (33) 296501280
Fax: (33) 296347265
Web Site: www.centigon.com
Sls.: $32,600,000
Emp.: 200
Mobile Security Service
S.I.C.: 7382
N.A.I.C.S.: 561621

CARAVANE 185 INC
86 Principale
Saint-Antonin, QC, G0L 2J0, Canada
Tel.: (418) 867-2111
Fax: (418) 867-2339
Toll Free: (800) 383-2110
Web Site: www.caravane185.com
Year Founded: 1992
Rev.: $10,700,800
Emp.: 32

Business Description:
Recreational Vehicle Dealers
S.I.C.: 5561
N.A.I.C.S.: 441210

Personnel:
Gilles D'Amours *(Pres)*
Julie Chouinard *(Sec)*

CARAVEL ENERGY LIMITED
(Formerly Copper Range Limited)
Level 1 330 Churchill Avenue
Subiaco, WA, 6008, Australia
Tel.: (61) 8 9200 4268
Fax: (61) 8 9200 4469
E-Mail: info@caravelenergy.com.au
Web Site: www.caravelenergy.com.au
CRJ—(ASX)
Rev.: $21,837
Assets: $8,031,990
Liabilities: $2,335,383
Net Worth: $5,696,607
Earnings: ($2,814,027)
Fiscal Year-end: 06/30/13

Business Description:
Oil & Gas Exploration
S.I.C.: 1311
N.A.I.C.S.: 211111

Personnel:
Brian McMaster *(Chm)*
Aaron Bertolatti *(Sec)*

Board of Directors:
Brian McMaster
Roseline Emma Rasolovoahangy
Matthew Wood

Legal Counsel:
Steinepreis Paganin
Level 4 Next Building 16 Milligan St
Perth, Australia

Subsidiary:

Copper Range (SA) Pty Limited (1)
34 Stepney St
Stepney, South Australia, 5069, Australia
Tel.: (61) 883628540
Fax: (61) 892004469
E-Mail: info@copperrange.com.au
Web Site: www.copperrange.com.au
Emp.: 5
Copper Ore Mining Services
S.I.C.: 1021
N.A.I.C.S.: 212234
Mark Arundell *(Mng Dir)*

CARAVEL MINERALS LIMITED
(Formerly SILVER SWAN GROUP LIMITED)
Level 3 18 Richardson Street
West Perth, WA, 6005, Australia
Tel.: (61) 8 9426 6400
Fax: (61) 8 9426 6448
Web Site: www.caravelminerals.com.au
CVV—(ASX)
Rev.: $99,015
Assets: $6,819,870
Liabilities: $1,125,105
Net Worth: $5,694,765
Earnings: ($7,873,838)
Fiscal Year-end: 06/30/13

Business Description:
Gold & Base Metals Exploration
S.I.C.: 1041
N.A.I.C.S.: 212221

Personnel:
Marcel Hilmer *(CEO)*
Rowen Colman *(CFO)*
Simon Robertson *(Sec)*

Board of Directors:
Peter Alexander
James Harris
Marcel Hilmer
Brett McKeon

Legal Counsel:
Gilbert & Tobin
1202 Hay Street
West Perth, Australia

CARAVELLE SA
6 Place des Etats-Unis
75116 Paris, France
Tel.: (33) 1 5365 6700
Fax: (33) 1 4405 0446
E-Mail: contact@caravelle.fr
Web Site: www.caravelle.fr
Year Founded: 1995

Business Description:
Investment Holding Company
S.I.C.: 6719
N.A.I.C.S.: 551112

Personnel:
Marc-Olivier Laurent *(Chm)*
Helene Martel-Massignac *(Dir Gen)*

Board of Directors:
Marc-Olivier Laurent
Patrick Buffet
Andre Lebrun
Lorene Martel
Helene Martel-Massignac

Subsidiary:

Belambra vvf S.A. (1)
28 rue d'Arcueil
F-94253 Gentilly, Cedex, France
Tel.: (33) 155013000
Fax: (33) 155013001
Web Site: www.belambra-vvf.fr
Emp.: 200
Vacation Resort & Tour Operator
S.I.C.: 7032
N.A.I.C.S.: 721214
Olivier Colcombet *(Chm-Mgmt Bd & CEO)*

CARBERY GROUP
Carbery Ballineen
Cork, Ireland
Tel.: (353) 23 8822200
Fax: (353) 23 8847541
Web Site: www.carbery.com
Year Founded: 1965
Sales Range: $300-349.9 Million

Business Description:
Food Ingredients, Flavors & Cheese Mfr
S.I.C.: 2022
N.A.I.C.S.: 311513

Personnel:
Donal Tobin *(Chm)*

U.S. Subsidiary:

Synergy Flavors, Inc. (1)
1230 Karl Ct
Wauconda, IL 60084 IL
Tel.: (847) 487-1022
Fax: (847) 487-1066
Web Site: www.synergytaste.com
Flavoring Mfr
S.I.C.: 2087
N.A.I.C.S.: 311930
Daniel Wampler *(Pres-Coffee & Tea Flavor Div)*

Subsidiaries:

Sensus, LLC (2)
7255 Hamilton Entp Pk Dr
Hamilton, OH 45011
Tel.: (513) 892-7100
Web Site: www.sensusflavors.com
Sales Range: $1-9.9 Million
Emp.: 12
Flavor Extracts/Syrup Mfr
S.I.C.: 2099
N.A.I.C.S.: 311999
Daniel J. Wampler *(Founder & Pres)*

Sethness-Greenleaf, Inc. (2)
1826 N Lorel Ave
Chicago, IL 60639
Tel.: (773) 889-1400
Fax: (773) 889-0854
Toll Free: (800) 621-4549
E-Mail: info@synergytaste.com
Web Site: www.synergytaste.com
Sales Range: $1-9.9 Million
Emp.: 27
Flavoring Mfr
S.I.C.: 2087
N.A.I.C.S.: 311930
John Smyth *(VP-Ops)*

CARBINE RESOURCES LIMITED
Suite 23 513 Hay Street
Subiaco, WA, 6008, Australia
Tel.: (61) 861420986
Fax: (61) 893888824
E-Mail: carbine@carbineresources.com.au
Web Site: www.carbineresources.com.au
Year Founded: 2006
CRB—(ASX)
Rev.: $3,186,533
Assets: $6,776,093
Liabilities: $48,294
Net Worth: $6,727,799
Earnings: ($516,850)
Fiscal Year-end: 12/31/12

Business Description:
Gold Exploration Services
S.I.C.: 1041
N.A.I.C.S.: 212221

Personnel:
Peter Sheehan *(Mng Dir)*
Grant Mooney *(Sec)*

Board of Directors:
Evan Cranston
Grant Mooney
Peter Sheehan

Legal Counsel:
Hardy Bowen
Level 1 28 Ord Street
West West Perth, WA, 6005, Australia

CARBINE TUNGSTEN LIMITED
50 Scott Street Bungalow
PO Box 1040
Cairns, QLD, 4870, Australia
Tel.: (61) 740522400
Fax: (61) 740522444
E-Mail: info@carbinetungsten.com.au
Web Site: www.carbinetungsten.com.au
CNQ—(ASX)
Rev.: $3,147,016
Assets: $16,038,593
Liabilities: $1,330,914
Net Worth: $14,707,679
Earnings: ($5,154,765)
Emp.: 11
Fiscal Year-end: 06/30/13

Business Description:
Mineral Exploration Services
S.I.C.: 1481
N.A.I.C.S.: 213115

Personnel:
Andrew James Morgan *(CEO & Mng Dir)*
Tom Bloomfield *(Sec)*

Board of Directors:
Russell H. Krause
Anthony E. Gordon
Andrew James Morgan
Roland W. Nice

CARBIOS SACA
Biopole Clermont-Limagne
63360 Saint-Beauzire, France

Tel.: (33) 4 73 86 51 76
Web Site: www.carbios.fr
ALCRB—(EUR)
Business Description:
Chemical Recycling Services
S.I.C.: 4959
N.A.I.C.S.: 562998
Personnel:
Alain Chevallier *(Chm)*
Jean-Claude Lumaret *(CEO)*
Board of Directors:
Alain Chevallier
Gregoire Berthe
Jacqueline Lecourtier
Erik Orsenna
Alain Philippart
Philippe Pouletty

CARBON CONSCIOUS LIMITED

Suite 5 Level 1 26 Railway Road
Subiaco, WA, 6008, Australia
Tel.: (61) 892875600
Fax: (61) 892875699
E-Mail: info@carbonconscious.com.au
Web Site: www.carbonconscious.com.au
CCF—(ASX)
Rev.: $6,883,735
Assets: $22,102,767
Liabilities: $7,261,443
Net Worth: $14,841,324
Earnings: ($2,178,969)
Emp.: 9
Fiscal Year-end: 06/30/13
Business Description:
Carbon Farming
S.I.C.: 2819
N.A.I.C.S.: 325130
Personnel:
Stephen Bodeker *(CFO)*
Kent Hunter *(Sec)*
Board of Directors:
Trevor Gordon Stoney
Kent Hunter
Andrew McBain
Legal Counsel:
Hardy Bowen Lawyers
Level 1 28 Ord Street
West Perth, Australia

CARBON ENERGY LIMITED

Level 9 301 Coronation drive
Milton, QLD, 4064, Australia
Tel.: (61) 7 3156 7777
Fax: (61) 7 3156 7776
E-Mail: askus@carbonenergy.com.au
Web Site: www.carbonenergy.com.au
CNX—(ASX OTC)
Rev.: $1,946,294
Assets: $155,483,708
Liabilities: $14,779,734
Net Worth: $140,703,974
Earnings: ($37,082,427)
Emp.: 36
Fiscal Year-end: 06/30/13
Business Description:
Production Of Clean Energy & Chemicals
S.I.C.: 2833
N.A.I.C.S.: 325411
Personnel:
Morne Engelbrecht *(CEO & Mng Dir)*
Board of Directors:
Christopher David Rawlings
Max D. J. Cozijn
Morne Engelbrecht
Helen M. Garnett
Peter N. Hogan
Louis I. Rozman
Legal Counsel:
Gadens Lawyers
240 Queen St
Brisbane, Australia

CARBON FRIENDLY SOLUTIONS INC.

(Name Changed to MicroCoal Technologies Inc.)

CARBON GREEN INC.

Vysoka 26
81106 Bratislava, Slovakia
Tel.: (421) 2 52926300
E-Mail: investor@carbongreeninc.com
Web Site: www.carbongreeninc.com
CGNI—(OTC)
Sales Range: Less than $1 Million
Business Description:
Tire Recycling Services
S.I.C.: 5014
N.A.I.C.S.: 423130
Personnel:
John T. Novak *(Pres & CEO)*
David W. Thursfield *(COO)*
Peter K. Jensen *(Gen Counsel)*
Kenneth Lee *(Sec & VP-Fin)*
Board of Directors:
Peter K. Jensen
Kenneth Lee
Adi Muljo
John T. Novak
Non-U.S. Subsidiary:

True Health Studio, Inc. **(1)**
200 4255 Arbutus St
Vancouver, BC, V6J 4R1, Canada
Tel.: (604) 221-8783
Fax: (604) 221-8700
E-Mail: truehealth@truehealthstudio.com
Web Site: www.truehealthstudio.com
Chiropractic & Massaging Services
S.I.C.: 8041
N.A.I.C.S.: 621310
Marcus Wong *(Gen Mgr)*

CARBON MINERALS LIMITED

Level 7 10 Barrack Street
Sydney, NSW, 2000, Australia
Tel.: (61) 2 9299 3655
E-Mail: admin@carbonminerals.com.au
Web Site: www.carbonminerals.com.au
CRM—(ASX)
Rev.: $1,104,543
Assets: $22,219,920
Liabilities: $7,843,297
Net Worth: $14,376,623
Earnings: ($1,424,809)
Fiscal Year-end: 12/31/12
Business Description:
Natural Gas Exploration Services
S.I.C.: 1311
N.A.I.C.S.: 211111
Personnel:
Paul Lincoln Smith *(Chm, CEO & CFO)*
Steven Danielson *(Co-Sec)*
Rachel Thorn *(Co-Sec)*
Board of Directors:
Paul Lincoln Smith
Wayne Annis-Brown
Steven Danielson
Marcus Lincoln Smith
Legal Counsel:
Lincoln Smith & Co
Level 15 Suite 1505 Westfield Tower 1 520 Oxford Street
Bondi Junction, NSW, 2022, Australia

CARBON POLYMERS LIMITED

18-22 Pacific Drive
Keysborough, VIC, 3173, Australia
Tel.: (61) 2 9756 0960
Fax: (61) 2 9475 4770
E-Mail: info@carbonpolymers.com.au
Web Site: www.carbonpolymers.com.au
CBP—(ASX)
Sales Range: $1-9.9 Million
Business Description:
Carbon & Plastic Materials Recovery & Reuse Services
S.I.C.: 4953
N.A.I.C.S.: 562920
Personnel:
David Jacobs *(CFO)*
Jerry Gordon *(Sec)*
Board of Directors:
Rodger Johnston
Paul McGregor

CARBURES EUROPE, S.A.

Carretera de Fuentebravia km 0 8
Edif Hindustan Local 2
El Puerto de Santa Maria, 11500
Cadiz, Spain
Tel.: (34) 902190029
Web Site: www.carbures.com
CAR—(MAD)
Sales Range: $1-9.9 Million
Emp.: 20
Business Description:
Carbon Structures Mfr
S.I.C.: 3624
N.A.I.C.S.: 335991
Personnel:
Carlos Guillen *(Pres)*
Rafael Contreras *(CEO)*
Board of Directors:
Rafael Contreras
Carlos Guillen
Javier Sanchez
Jose Maria Tarrago
Angel Vallejo

CARCLO PLC

Springstone House 27 Dewsbury Road
PO Box 88
Ossett, West Yorkshire, WF5 9WS, United Kingdom
Tel.: (44) 1924268040
Fax: (44) 1924283226
E-Mail: investor.relations@carclo-plc.com
Web Site: www.carclo-plc.com
Year Founded: 1924
CAR—(LSE)
Rev.: $136,630,695
Assets: $214,511,802
Liabilities: $111,665,279
Net Worth: $102,846,523
Earnings: $6,511,413
Emp.: 1,073
Fiscal Year-end: 03/31/13
Business Description:
Specialty Wire, Cable & Technical Plastic Product Mfr
Import Export
S.I.C.: 3089
N.A.I.C.S.: 326199
Personnel:
Christopher Malley *(CEO)*
Eric Cook *(Sec)*
Board of Directors:
Michael Derbyshire
Robert Brooksbank
Christopher Malley
Robert Rickman
Bill Tame
KPMG Audit Plc
1 The Embankment Neville Street
Leeds, LS1 4DW, United Kingdom
Legal Counsel:
Addleshaw Goddard
Sovereign House Sovereign Street
Leeds, LS1 1HQ, United Kingdom
Subsidiaries:

Birkett Cutmaster Limited **(1)**
Middleton Business Park Cartwright Street
PO Box 30
Cleckheaton, Yorkshire, BD19 5LY, United Kingdom UK
Tel.: (44) 1274870311 (100%)
Fax: (44) 1274862754
E-Mail: bcinfo@birkett-cutmaster.co.uk
Web Site: www.birkett-cutmaster.co.uk
Emp.: 9
Industrial Equipment Wholesale
S.I.C.: 5084
N.A.I.C.S.: 423830
Bryn Pritchaid *(Mng Dir)*

Bruntons Aero Products Limited **(1)**
Units 1-3 Block 1 Inveresk Industrial Estate
Musselburgh, East Lothian, EH21 7PA, United Kingdom
Tel.: (44) 1316653888
Fax: (44) 1316532236
E-Mail: info@bruntons.co.uk
Web Site: www.bruntons.co.uk
Emp.: 40
Aerospace Product Mfr
S.I.C.: 3728
N.A.I.C.S.: 336413
Alan Hook *(Mng Dir)*

Carclo Diagnostic Solutions Ltd **(1)**
Springstone House 27 Dewsbury Road
PO Box 88
Ossett, West Yorkshire, United Kingdom WF5 9WS
Tel.: (44) 208 685 0500
Web Site: www.carclodiagnosticsolutions.com
Electromedical Apparatus Mfr
S.I.C.: 3845
N.A.I.C.S.: 334510
Martin Day *(Mgr-Mktg)*

Carclo Precision Optics **(1)**
103 Buckingham Ave
Slough, Berks, SL1 4PF, United Kingdom UK
Tel.: (44) 1753 575011 (100%)
Fax: (44) 1753 811359
E-Mail: sales@carclo-optics.com
Web Site: www.carclo-optics.com
Emp.: 15
Plastic Optical Component & Moulding Mfr
S.I.C.: 3827
N.A.I.C.S.: 333314
Neil Collis *(Mng Dir)*
Patrick Ward *(Mng Dir)*

Carclo Technical Plastics Ltd. **(1)**
111 Buckingham Ave
Berks Slough, SL1 4PF, United Kingdom UK
Tel.: (44) 01753575011 (100%)
Fax: (44) 1753811359
E-Mail: info@carclo-plc.com
Web Site: www.carclo-optics.com
Emp.: 15
Technical Plastics Mfr
S.I.C.: 3089
N.A.I.C.S.: 326199

Carclo Technical Plastics Ltd. **(1)**
Ploughland House
P O Box 14
62 George St, Wakefield, WF11ZF, United Kingdom UK
Tel.: (44) 1554749000 (100%)
Fax: (44) 1554749158
Emp.: 60
Technical Plastics Mfr
S.I.C.: 3089
N.A.I.C.S.: 326199

Non-U.S. Subsidiary:

Carclo Technical Plastics Shanghai Co. Limited **(2)**
No 21 Lianxi Road Lianxi Village Huangdu Town
Jiading District, Shanghai, 201804, China
Tel.: (86) 2169595189
Plastic Products Mfr
S.I.C.: 5162
N.A.I.C.S.: 424610

Carclo Technical Plastics Mitcham Ltd. **(1)**
47 Wates Way
Mitcham, Surrey, CR4 4HR, United Kingdom UK
Tel.: (44) 2086850500 (100%)
E-Mail: sales@carclo-usa.com
Web Site: www.carclo-ctp.co.uk/
Emp.: 150
Technical Plastics Mfr

Carclo plc—(Continued)

S.I.C.: 3089
N.A.I.C.S.: 326199
Patrick Ward *(Mng Dir)*

Carclo Technical Plastics (1)
Mossburn Ave
Harthill, Lanerkshire, ML7 5NP, United Kingdom UK
Tel.: (44) 501751447 (100%)
Fax: (44) 1501753109
Web Site: www.carclo.com
Emp.: 200
Technical Plastics Mfr
S.I.C.: 3089
N.A.I.C.S.: 326199

Conductive Inkjet Technology Limited (1)
Brookmount Ct Kirkwood Rd
Cambridge, CB4 2QH, United Kingdom
Tel.: (44) 1223424323
Fax: (44) 1223437930
E-Mail: enquiries@conductiveinkjet.com
Web Site: www.conductiveinkjet.com
Emp.: 20
Electronic Products Mfr
S.I.C.: 3679
N.A.I.C.S.: 334419

CTP Wipac Ltd. (1)
London Rd
Buckingham, Buckshire, MK18 1BH, United Kingdom UK
Tel.: (44) 1280822800 (100%)
Fax: (44) 1280822802
E-Mail: info@wipac.com
Web Site: www.wipac.com
Sls.: $29,948,560
Emp.: 170
Automotive & General Purpose Electrical & Electronic Component Mfr
S.I.C.: 3714
N.A.I.C.S.: 336340
Neil Sibley *(Mng Dir)*

Wipac Limited (1)
London Rd
Buckingham, MK18 1BH, United Kingdom
Tel.: (44) 1280 822800
Fax: (44) 1280 822802
E-Mail: info@wipac.com
Web Site: www.wipac.com
Emp.: 150
Lighting Products Mfr
S.I.C.: 3646
N.A.I.C.S.: 335122
Neil Sibley *(Mng Dir)*

U.S. Subsidiary:

Carclo Technical Plastics Ltd (1)
600 Depot St
Latrobe, PA 15650-1617 (100%)
Tel.: (724) 539-1833
Fax: (724) 539-6620
Web Site: www.ctpcarrera.com
Emp.: 60
Technical Plastic Mfr
S.I.C.: 3089
N.A.I.C.S.: 326199
Mark Charvonneau *(Pres)*

Non-U.S. Subsidiaries:

Carclo Technical Plastics (Brno) s.r.o (1)
Turanka 98/1277
Brno, 627 00, Czech Republic
Tel.: (420) 532 190 711
E-Mail: carclo@ctp-czech.com
Plastic Product Mfr
S.I.C.: 3089
N.A.I.C.S.: 326199

Estab Platt Freres S.A. (1)
108 122 Blvd De Lyon
PO Box 165
59053 Roubaix, France FR
Tel.: (33) 320893700 (100%)
Fax: (33) 320893701
E-Mail: fabien.vandekerkove@eccplatt.fr
Web Site: www.eccplatt.fr
Emp.: 40
Mfr. of Flexible Card Clothing
S.I.C.: 3499
N.A.I.C.S.: 332999
Carlos Gryspeerd *(Mng Dir)*

Jacottet Industrie SAS (1)
40 bis avenue d'Orleans
28000 Chartres, France
Tel.: (33) 237286128
Fax: (33) 2 37 28 61 25
Web Site: www.jacottet-industrie.com
Aerospace Cables Mfr
S.I.C.: 3812
N.A.I.C.S.: 334511
Alan Hook *(Mng Dir)*

CARCOUSTICS INTERNATIONAL GMBH

Neuenkamp 8
51381 Leverkusen, Germany
Tel.: (49) 21719000
Fax: (49) 2171900299
E-Mail: info@carcoustics.de
Web Site: www.carcoustics.de
Sales Range: $300-349.9 Million
Emp.: 2,219

Business Description:
Developer & Producer of Accoustics Systems For Cars
S.I.C.: 3651
N.A.I.C.S.: 334310

Personnel:
Peter Hoening *(Chm & CEO)*
Thomas Brettar *(CFO)*
Gunter Einzenhofer *(Chief Market Officer)*

U.S. Subsidiaries:

Carcoustics Tech Center North America Inc (1)
29770 Hudson Dr
Novi, MI 48377
Tel.: (248) 668-7200
Fax: (248) 926-8286
E-Mail: techconsult@carcoustics.com
Web Site: www.carcoustics.com
Audio & Video Equipment Mfr
S.I.C.: 3651
N.A.I.C.S.: 334310
Axel Boehme *(COO & VP-Sls)*

Carcoustics USA, Inc. (1)
1400 Durant Dr
Howell, MI 48843-8572
Tel.: (517) 548-6700
Fax: (517) 548-9122
E-Mail: info@carcoustics.com
Web Site: www.carcoustics.com
Sales Range: $10-24.9 Million
Emp.: 100
Developer & Producer of Accoustics Products For Cars
Import Export
S.I.C.: 3086
N.A.I.C.S.: 326150

Non-U.S. Subsidiaries:

Carcoustics Belgium N.V. (1)
GZ-Zone 9
Henry Fordlaan Z-N, 3600 Genk, Belgium
Tel.: (32) 89612582
Fax: (32) 89612561
E-Mail: infob@carcoustics.com
Web Site: www.carcoustics.com
Emp.: 50
Broadwoven Fabric Mills
S.I.C.: 2299
N.A.I.C.S.: 313210
Gunter Heinze *(Gen Mgr)*

Carcoustics de Mexico S.A. de C.V. (1)
Km 48 Carret Federal Mexico-Pachuca Los Reyes Acozac
Estado de Mexico, 76920 Queretaro, Mexico
Tel.: (52) 4423093800
Fax: (52) 4423093819
E-Mail: info@carcoustics.com
Web Site: www.carcoustics.com
Emp.: 140
Motor Vehicle Parts Mfr
S.I.C.: 3714
N.A.I.C.S.: 336390
Biedtmar Osterle *(Gen Mgr)*

Carcoustics Espana SA (1)
Poligono Industrial El Alter Carrer dels Argenters No 46
PO Box 66
46290 Valencia, Spain
Tel.: (34) 961221280
Fax: (34) 961221281
E-Mail: info@carcoustics.com
Web Site: www.carcoustics.com
Emp.: 87
Motor Vehicle Parts Mfr
S.I.C.: 3714
N.A.I.C.S.: 336390
Jose Enrique Careaga *(Gen Mgr)*

Carcoustics France S.A.R.L. (1)
13 rue de Camilles-Desmoulins
90150 Issy-les-Moulineaux, France
Tel.: (33) 1 5804 24 24
Fax: (33) 158042300
E-Mail: info@carcoustics.com
Plastics Product Mfr
S.I.C.: 3089
N.A.I.C.S.: 326199
Hubert Schneider *(Gen Mgr)*

Carcoustics South Africa (Pty) Ltd. (1)
Building BE2 Automotive Supplier Park East London Indus Dev Zone
Harbour Arterial Street
Sunnyridge, 5201 East London, South Africa
Tel.: (27) 43 701 91 00
Fax: (27) 43 736 60 81
E-Mail: info@carcoustics.com
Web Site: www.carcoustics.com
Automotive Repair & Maintenance
S.I.C.: 7549
N.A.I.C.S.: 811198
Thomas Brettar *(CFO)*

Subsidiaries:

Carcoustics Deutschland GmbH (1)
Werk Wolfsburg
Sagerbaume 9, 38448 Wolfsburg, Germany
Tel.: (49) 21719000
Fax: (49) 21 71 900 199
E-Mail: info@carcoustics.com
Web Site: www.carcoustics.com
Emp.: 100
Plastics Product Mfr
S.I.C.: 3089
N.A.I.C.S.: 326199
Werner Haberecht *(Gen Mgr)*

Carcoustics Haldensleben GmbH (1)
Jakob-Uffrecht-Str 26
Haldensleben, 39340 Magdeburg, Germany
Tel.: (49) 3904668260
Fax: (49) 3904668277
E-Mail: mschiod@carcoustics.com
Web Site: www.carcoustics.com
Emp.: 160
Audio & Video Equipment Mfr
S.I.C.: 3651
N.A.I.C.S.: 334310
Werner Haberecht *(Gen Mgr)*

CARDIA BIOPLASTICS LIMITED

Unit 18/35 Dunlop Road
Mulgrave, VIC, 3170, Australia
Tel.: (61) 395620122
Fax: (61) 395620422
E-Mail: info@cardiabioplastics.com
Web Site: www.cardiabioplastics.com
CNN—(ASX OTC)
Sls.: $5,263,204
Assets: $10,533,480
Liabilities: $1,957,951
Net Worth: $8,575,529
Earnings: ($3,188,972)
Emp.: 62
Fiscal Year-end: 06/30/13

Business Description:
Investment Services; Pharmaceuticals, Pesticides, Environmental Technology & Mining
S.I.C.: 6722
N.A.I.C.S.: 525910

Personnel:
Frank Peter Glatz *(CEO & Mng Dir)*
Alex Fernando *(COO)*
Rekha Bhambhani *(Sec & Controller-Fin)*

Board of Directors:
Richard Tegoni
Steve Bendel
Frank Peter Glatz
Gideon Meltzer

Shanghai WSP Certified Public Accountants
UDC Innovative Plaza Block A Suite 308 No 125 Jiangsu Road North
Shanghai, China

Legal Counsel:
Mills Oakley Lawyers
St James Building Level 4 121 William St
Melbourne, VIC, Australia

Subsidiaries:

Cardia Bioplastics (Australia) Pty Ltd (1)
Unit 18/35 Dunlop Road
Mulgrave, VIC, 3170, Australia
Tel.: (61) 395620122
Fax: (61) 395620422
E-Mail: info@cardiabioplastics.com
Web Site: cardiabioplastics.com.au
Resins Mfr & Whslr
S.I.C.: 2821
N.A.I.C.S.: 325211
Graeme Ward *(Gen Mgr)*

P-Fuel Limited (1)
Suite 5 310 Whitehorse Road
Balwyn, VIC, 3103, Australia
Tel.: (61) 3 9830 7946
Fax: (61) 3 9836 3056
E-Mail: info@p-fuel.com
Web Site: www.p-fuel.com
Biofuel Mfr
S.I.C.: 2999
N.A.I.C.S.: 324199

CARDIFF CAR CITY PTY LIMITED

54 MacQuarrie Rd
Cardiff, NSW, 2285, Australia
Tel.: (61) 249046777
Fax: (61) 249565405
E-Mail: reception@cardiffcarcity.com.au
Web Site: www.cardiffcarcity.com.au
Sales Range: $25-49.9 Million
Emp.: 90

Business Description:
Car Dealership Owner & Operator
S.I.C.: 5511
N.A.I.C.S.: 441110

Personnel:
James Bradstreet *(CEO)*

CARDIFF ENERGY CORP.

3920 Delbrook Ave
North Vancouver, BC, V7N 3Z8, Canada
Tel.: (604) 505-4380
E-Mail: info@cardiffenergy.com
Web Site: www.cardiffenergy.com
Year Founded: 2010
CRS—(TSXV)

Business Description:
Oil & Gas Exploration
S.I.C.: 1311
N.A.I.C.S.: 211111

Personnel:
Lorne Torhjelm *(Pres)*
Gordon Melvin Bradford *(CFO)*
Greg Campbell *(Sec)*

Board of Directors:
Gordon Melvin Bradford
Brian William Dunning
Dennis Gary Stewart
Lorne Torhjelm

Legal Counsel:
Salley Bowes Hardwardt Law Corp.
Suite 1750 - 1185 West Georgia St
Vancouver, BC, Canada

Transfer Agent:
Equity Financial Trust Company
1185 West Georgia Street Suite 1620
Vancouver, BC, Canada

THE CARDIFF PROPERTY PLC
56 Station Road
Egham, Surrey, TW20 9LF, United Kingdom
Tel.: (44) 1784437444
Fax: (44) 1784439157
E-Mail: webmaster@cardiff-property.com
Web Site: www.cardiff-property.com
CDFF—(LSE)
Sales Range: Less than $1 Million
Emp.: 5
Business Description:
Property Investment & Management
S.I.C.: 6531
N.A.I.C.S.: 531311
Personnel:
J. Richard Wollenberg *(Chm & CEO)*
David A. Whitaker *(Sec & Dir-Fin)*
Board of Directors:
J. Richard Wollenberg
Nigel D. Jamieson
David A. Whitaker
Legal Counsel:
Morgan Cole
Bradley Ct Park Pl
Cardiff, United Kingdom
Transfer Agent:
Neville Registrars Limited
Neville House 18 Laurel Lane
Halesowen, West Midlands, B63 3DA, United Kingdom
Tel.: (44) 121 585 1131
Fax: (44) 121 585 1132
Subsidiaries:

First Choice Estates plc **(1)**
56 Sta Rd
Egham, Surrey, TW20 9LF, United Kingdom
Tel.: (44) 1784437444
Fax: (44) 1784439157
E-Mail: webmaster@cardiff-property.com
Web Site: www.cardiff-property.com
Emp.: 4
Real Estate Management Services
S.I.C.: 6531
N.A.I.C.S.: 531311
Richard Wollenberg *(Chm)*

Village Residential plc **(1)**
First Choice Estate 56 Station Rd
Egham, Surrey, TW20 9LF, United Kingdom
Tel.: (44) 1784437444
Fax: (44) 01784439157
E-Mail: webmaster@cardiff-property.com
Real Estate Management Services
S.I.C.: 6531
N.A.I.C.S.: 531312
J.R. Wollenberg *(Mng Dir)*

CARDINAL ENERGY LTD.
1400 440 2nd Avenue Southwest
Calgary, AB, T2P 5E9, Canada
Tel.: (403) 216-2709
Fax: (403) 234-0603
E-Mail: info@cardinalenergy.ca
Web Site: www.cardinalenergy.ca
Year Founded: 2010
CJ—(TSX)
Rev.: $3,961,475
Assets: $80,344,698
Liabilities: $19,402,224
Net Worth: $60,942,475
Earnings: ($3,797,345)
Fiscal Year-end: 12/31/12
Business Description:
Oil & Gas Exploration
S.I.C.: 1311
N.A.I.C.S.: 211111
Personnel:
M. Scott Ratushny *(Chm & CEO)*
Douglas Smith *(CFO)*
Shane Peet *(COO)*
Board of Directors:
M. Scott Ratushny
John A. Brussa
David D. Johnson
James C. Smith
Gregory T. Tisdale

CARDINAL MEAT SPECIALISTS LTD.
3160 Caravelle Drive
Mississauga, ON, L4V 1K9, Canada
Tel.: (905) 672-1411
Fax: (905) 672-0450
Toll Free: (800) 363-1439
E-Mail: cardinalinfo@cardinalmeats.com
Web Site: www.cardinalmeats.com
Year Founded: 1966
Rev.: $41,800,000
Emp.: 100
Business Description:
Food Products Mfr
S.I.C.: 0251
N.A.I.C.S.: 112320
Personnel:
Brent Cator *(Pres)*
Mark Cator *(CEO)*

CARDINAL RESOURCES LIMITED
(Formerly Ridge Resources Ltd.)
Level 1 115 Cambridge Street
Leederville, WA, 6007, Australia
Tel.: (61) 8 9322 6600
Fax: (61) 8 9322 6610
E-Mail: info@cardinalresources.com.au
Web Site: www.cardinalresources.com.au
Year Founded: 2010
CDV—(ASX)
Rev.: $118,400
Assets: $12,994,669
Liabilities: $161,965
Net Worth: $12,832,704
Earnings: ($2,092,032)
Fiscal Year-end: 06/30/13
Business Description:
Gold Mining
S.I.C.: 1041
N.A.I.C.S.: 212221
Personnel:
Klaus Eckhof *(Chm)*
Archie Koimtsidis *(Mng Dir)*
Sarah Shipway *(Sec)*
Board of Directors:
Klaus Eckhof
Malik Easah
Archie Koimtsidis
Marcus Michael
Alec Christopher Pismiris

CARDIO3 BIOSCIENCES SA
Rue Edouard Belin 12
1435 Mont-Saint-Guibert, Belgium
Tel.: (32) 10 39 41 00
Fax: (32) 10 39 41 41
E-Mail: info@c3bs.com
Web Site: www.c3bs.com
Year Founded: 2007
CARD—(EUR)
Emp.: 40
Business Description:
Stem Cell-Based Pharmaceuticals for Cardiovascular Disease
S.I.C.: 2834
N.A.I.C.S.: 325412
Personnel:
Michel Lussier *(Chm)*
Christian Homsy *(CEO)*
Patrick Jeanmart *(CFO)*
Gaetane Metz *(COO)*
Board of Directors:
Michel Lussier
Chris Buyse
Rudy DeKeyser
Serge Goblet
Jean-Marc Heynderickx
Christian Homsy
William Wijns

CARDIOCOMM SOLUTIONS, INC.
201- 3060 Cedar Hill Road
Victoria, BC, V8T 3J5, Canada
Tel.: (250) 744-1822
Fax: (250) 744-1866
Toll Free: (877) 744-1122
E-Mail: sales@cardiocomm.com
Web Site: www.cardiocommsolutions.com
Year Founded: 1989
EKG—(OTC TSXV)
Sls.: $1,596,088
Assets: $1,015,417
Liabilities: $495,355
Net Worth: $520,062
Earnings: ($3,322,469)
Emp.: 30
Fiscal Year-end: 12/31/12
Business Description:
Cardiac Management & Diagnostic Tools Software Solutions
S.I.C.: 7372
N.A.I.C.S.: 511210
Personnel:
Anatoly Langer *(Chm)*
Etienne Grima *(CEO & Sec)*
Wendy Hsieh *(CFO)*
Wade Barnes *(CTO)*
Board of Directors:
Anatoly Langer
Etienne Grima
Simi Grosman
Yury Levin
David Newman
William E. Smith
Transfer Agent:
Computershare Investor Services Inc
4th Floor 510 Burrard Street
Vancouver, BC, Canada

CARDIOGENICS HOLDINGS INC.
6295 Northam Drive Unit 8
Mississauga, ON, L4V 1WB, Canada
Tel.: (905) 673-8501
E-Mail: info@cardiogenics.com
Web Site: www.cardiogenics.com
Year Founded: 1997
CGNH—(OTCB)
Assets: $547,950
Liabilities: $1,464,994
Net Worth: ($917,044)
Earnings: ($2,936,937)
Emp.: 7
Fiscal Year-end: 10/31/13
Business Description:
In-Vitro Diagnostic Products Mfr
S.I.C.: 2835
N.A.I.C.S.: 325413
Personnel:
J. Neil Tabatznik *(Acting Chm)*
Yahia A. Gawad *(CEO)*
James A. Essex *(CFO)*
Linda J. Sterling *(Sec)*
Board of Directors:
J. Neil Tabatznik
Yahia A. Gawad
Alexander D. G. Reid
Linda J. Sterling
Transfer Agent:
Transfer Online
512 SE Salmon Street
Portland, OR 97214
Subsidiary:

CardioGenics Exchange Co. Inc. **(1)**
6295 Northam Dr Unit 8
Mississauga, ON, L4V 1W8, Canada
Tel.: (905) 673-8501
Diagnostic Test Equipments Mfr
S.I.C.: 3845
N.A.I.C.S.: 334510

Subsidiary:

CardioGenics Inc. **(2)**
6295 Northam Dr Unit 8
Mississauga, ON, L4V 1W8, Canada
Tel.: (905) 673-8501
E-Mail: info@cardiogenics.com
Web Site: www.cardiogenics.com
Diagnostic Test Equipment Mfr
S.I.C.: 3845
N.A.I.C.S.: 334510

CARDIOME PHARMA CORP.
6190 Agronomy Road Suite 405
Vancouver, BC, V6T 1Z3, Canada
Tel.: (604) 677-6905
Fax: (604) 677-6915
Toll Free: (800) 330-9928
E-Mail: info@cardiome.com
Web Site: cardiome.com
CRME—(NASDAQ TSX)
Rev.: $789,000
Assets: $44,793,000
Liabilities: $36,934,000
Net Worth: $7,859,000
Earnings: ($18,315,000)
Emp.: 13
Fiscal Year-end: 12/31/12
Business Description:
Research Company for Cardiovascular Treatments
S.I.C.: 2834
N.A.I.C.S.: 325412
Personnel:
Robert W. Rieder *(Chm)*
William L. Hunter *(Pres & CEO)*
Jennifer Archibald *(CFO)*
Sheila M. Grant *(COO)*
Karim Lalji *(Chief Comml Officer)*
Board of Directors:
Robert W. Rieder
Jackie M. Clegg
Richard M. Glickman
William L. Hunter
Peter W. Roberts
Harold H. Shlevin

Computershare Investor Services Inc.
Montreal, QC, Canada

Computershare Investor Services Inc.
510 Burrard Street 2nd Floor
Vancouver, BC, V6C 3B9, Canada
Transfer Agent:
Computershare Trust Company of Canada
510 Burrard St 3rd Fl
Vancouver, BC, V6C 3B9, Canada

CARDNO LIMITED
Level 11 515 St Paul's Terrace
Locked Bag 4006
Fortitude Valley, QLD, 4006, Australia
Tel.: (61) 7 3369 9822
Fax: (61) 7 3369 9722
E-Mail: cardno@cardno.com.au
Web Site: www.cardno.com
Year Founded: 1945
CDD—(ASX OTC)
Rev.: $1,245,676,319
Assets: $1,181,991,504
Liabilities: $522,838,244
Net Worth: $659,153,260
Earnings: $80,907,602
Emp.: 8,021
Fiscal Year-end: 06/30/13
Business Description:
Holding Company; Infrastructure Engineering, Project Management & Environmental Consulting Services
S.I.C.: 6719
N.A.I.C.S.: 551112
Personnel:
John Marlay *(Chm)*
Andrew David Buckley *(CEO & Mng Dir)*
Graham Kenneth Yerbury *(CFO)*
Board of Directors:

Cardno Limited—(Continued)

John Marlay
Anthony Higson Barnes
Andrew David Buckley
Peter J. Cosgrove
Tonianne A. Dwyer
Trevor Charles Johnson
Ian J. Johnston
Grant Murdoch

Legal Counsel:
McCullough Robertson Lawyers
Level 11 Central Plaza Two 66 Eagle Street
Brisbane, Australia

Kirkland & Ellis LLP
300 North LaSalle
Chicago, IL 60654

Subsidiaries:

Bowler Geotechnical Pty. Ltd. (1)
229 Woodward Road
Golden Square, Bendigo, VIC, 3555, Australia
Tel.: (61) 354444810
Fax: (61) 354444812
Web Site: www.cardno.com
Emp.: 8
Geotechnical Engineering & Consulting Services
S.I.C.: 8711
N.A.I.C.S.: 541330
Andrew Buckley *(Gen Mgr)*

Subsidiaries:

Bowler Geotechnical Cairns Pty. Ltd. (2)
Shed 5 202-204 McCormack Street
Manunda, Cairns, QLD, 4870, Australia
Tel.: (61) 7 40323522
Fax: (61) 40324156
Geotechnical Engineering & Consulting Services
S.I.C.: 8711
N.A.I.C.S.: 541330
Karl Hodgson *(Mgr)*

Bowler Geotechnical (SC) Pty. Ltd. (2)
32 Hi-Tech Dr
Kunda Park, QLD, 4556, Australia
Tel.: (61) 754501544
Geotechnical Engineering & Consulting Services
S.I.C.: 8711
N.A.I.C.S.: 541330

Bowler Geotechnical Sydney West Pty. Ltd. (2)
Unit 7 68 Industry Rd
Vineyard, NSW, 2765, Australia
Tel.: (61) 296271929
Fax: (61) 296272021
Web Site: www.cardno.com
Emp.: 6
Geotechnical Engineering & Consulting Services
S.I.C.: 8711
N.A.I.C.S.: 541330
David Heathcote *(Mgr-Lab)*

Cardinal Surveys Pty. Ltd. (1)
89 Connors Road
Mackay, QLD, 4740, Australia
Tel.: (61) 749522155
Land Surveying Services
S.I.C.: 8713
N.A.I.C.S.: 541370
Rodger Louw *(Mgr-Survey)*

Cardno Alexander Browne Pty. Ltd. (1)
Locked Bag 4006
Fortitude Valley, QLD, 4006, Australia
Tel.: (61) 733699822
Fax: (61) 733699722
Engineering Consulting Services
S.I.C.: 8711
N.A.I.C.S.: 541330

Cardno Australian Underground Services Pty. Ltd. (1)
15 Teton Court
Highett, VIC, 3190, Australia
Tel.: (61) 395537236
Fax: (61) 395322688
E-Mail: enquiries@ausunderground.com.au
Web Site: www.ausunderground.com.au
Underground Works & Excavation Services
S.I.C.: 1799
N.A.I.C.S.: 238910
Matt Keppich *(Mgr)*

Cardno Bowler Pty. Ltd. (1)
Unit 7 98 Anzac Avenue
Hillcrest, Logan, QLD, 4118, Australia
Tel.: (61) 738006446
Fax: (61) 738000816
Web Site: www.cardnobowler.com.au
Emp.: 45
Geotechnical Engineering & Consulting Services
S.I.C.: 8711
N.A.I.C.S.: 541330

Cardno CCS Pty. Ltd. (1)
280 Sheridan Street
Cairns North, Cairns, QLD, 4870, Australia
Tel.: (61) 740510288
Fax: (61) 740510133
Engineering Consulting Services
S.I.C.: 8711
N.A.I.C.S.: 541330
Mark Perry *(Mgr-Bus Unit)*

Cardno Ecology Lab Pty. Ltd. (1)
Level 9 The Forum 203 Pacific Highway St Leonards
Brookvale, NSW, 2065, Australia
Tel.: (61) 299074440
Fax: (61) 294395170
E-Mail: ceo.projects@cardno.com.au
Web Site: www.cardno.com
Emp.: 15
Environmental Engineering Services
S.I.C.: 8711
N.A.I.C.S.: 541330
Peggy O'Donneoo *(Mgr)*

Cardno Emerging Markets (Australia) Pty. Ltd. (1)
854 Glenferrie Road
Hawthorn, VIC, 3122, Australia
Tel.: (61) 398192877
Fax: (61) 398194216
E-Mail: emergingmarkets.australia@cardno.com
Web Site: www.cardnoacil.com
Emp.: 40
Construction Engineering Services
S.I.C.: 8711
N.A.I.C.S.: 541330
Martin Mason *(Mgr-IT)*

Cardno Eppell Olsen Pty. Ltd. (1)
ILevel 11 Green Square - North Tower 515 St Paul's Terrace
Fortitude Valley, QLD, 4006, Australia
Tel.: (61) 733102401
Fax: (61) 7 3369 9722
Traffic Management Services
S.I.C.: 4581
N.A.I.C.S.: 488111
Paul Hatcher *(Principal)*

Cardno Holdings Pty. Ltd. (1)
Level 11 North Tower 515 St Paul's Terrace
Fortitude Valley, QLD, 4066, Australia
Tel.: (61) 733699822
Fax: (61) 733699722
E-Mail: Cardno@Cardno.com.au
Web Site: www.Cardno.com.au
Emp.: 400
Investment Management Services
S.I.C.: 6282
N.A.I.C.S.: 523920
Andrew David Buckley *(Gen Mgr)*

Cardno ITC Pty. Ltd. (1)
Level 7 33 York Street
Sydney, NSW, 2000, Australia
Tel.: (61) 294958100
Fax: (61) 294958111
E-Mail: sydney@itcgroup.net.au
Web Site: www.itcgroup.net.au
Emp.: 50
Construction Engineering Services
S.I.C.: 8711
N.A.I.C.S.: 541330
Jason Varker-Miles *(Mng Dir)*

Subsidiaries:

Cardno ITC (QLD) Pty. Ltd. (2)
Level 7 33 York Street
Sydney, NSW, 2000, Australia
Tel.: (61) 294958100
Fax: (61) 294958111
E-Mail: angela.wozniak@cardno.com.au
Web Site: www.cardnoitc.com.au
Emp.: 80
Construction Engineering Services
S.I.C.: 8711
N.A.I.C.S.: 541330
Jason Varker-Miles *(Founder & Mng Dir)*

Cardno ITC (VIC) Pty. Ltd. (2)
Level 10 271 William Street
Melbourne, VIC, 3000, Australia
Tel.: (61) 386108000
Fax: (61) 386108088
Web Site: www.cardnoitc.com.au
Emp.: 22
Engineering Consulting Services
S.I.C.: 8711
N.A.I.C.S.: 541330
Andrew David Buckley *(Mng Dir)*

Cardno ITC (WA) Pty. Ltd. (2)
Suite 5 Shafto Lane 880 Hay St
Perth, WA, 6000, Australia
Tel.: (61) 894869924
Fax: (61) 894869926
E-Mail: perth@itcgroup.net.au
Web Site: www.cardno.com
Emp.: 12
Construction Engineering Services
S.I.C.: 8711
N.A.I.C.S.: 541330
Tim Desaxe *(Mng Dir)*

Cardno Lawson Treloar Pty. Ltd. (1)
Level 3 910 Pacific Highway
Gordon, NSW, 2072, Australia
Tel.: (61) 294993000
Fax: (61) 294993033
Engineering Consulting Services
S.I.C.: 8711
N.A.I.C.S.: 541330
Roger Collins-Woolcock *(Mng Dir)*

Cardno Low & Hooke Pty. Ltd. (1)
Level 1 910 Pacific Highway
Gordon, NSW, 2072, Australia
Tel.: (61) 294967700
Fax: (61) 294993902
Emp.: 180
Engineering Consulting Services
S.I.C.: 8711
N.A.I.C.S.: 541330
Neil Lawson *(Mng Dir)*

Cardno (NSW/ACT) Pty. Ltd. (1)
Level 3 Cardno Building 910 Pacific Highway
Gordon, NSW, 2072, Australia
Tel.: (61) 294967700
Fax: (61) 294993902
Emp.: 170
Engineering Consulting Services
S.I.C.: 8711
N.A.I.C.S.: 541330

Cardno Pty. Ltd. (1)
47 Burelli Street Level 1
Wollongong, NSW, 2500, Australia
Tel.: (61) 2 4228 4133
Fax: (61) 2 4228 6811
Web Site: www.cardno.com
Emp.: 40
Civil Engineering Services
S.I.C.: 8711
N.A.I.C.S.: 541330
Andrew David Buckley *(Mng Dir)*

Cardno (Qld) Pty. Ltd. (1)
Level 11 North Tower
PO Box 359
Hervey Bay, QLD, 4211, Australia
Tel.: (61) 741245455
Engineering Consulting Services
S.I.C.: 8711
N.A.I.C.S.: 541330

Cardno Spectrum Survey Pty. Ltd. (1)
11 HARVEST Terrace
West Perth, WA, 6008, Australia
Tel.: (61) 892404444
Fax: (61) 94868664
E-Mail: perth@cardno.com.au
Web Site: www.cardno.com
Surveying & Mapping Services
S.I.C.: 8713
N.A.I.C.S.: 541370
Gavin Taylor *(Mng Dir)*

Cardno Ullman & Nolan Pty. Ltd. (1)
L 11 515 St Pauls Tce
Fortitude Valley, QLD, 4006, Australia
Tel.: (61) 731002199
Fax: (61) 733699722
E-Mail: cardno@cardno.com
Web Site: www.cardno.com
Emp.: 400
Engineering Consulting Services
S.I.C.: 8711
N.A.I.C.S.: 541330

Cardno Victoria Pty. Ltd. (1)
150 Oxford Street
Collingwood, VIC, 3066, Australia
Tel.: (61) 384157777
Fax: (61) 3733699722
Web Site: www.cardno.com
Emp.: 130
Commercial Construction Services
S.I.C.: 1629
N.A.I.C.S.: 237990
Chris Butler *(Mgr-Traffic & Transport)*

Cardno (WA) Pty. Ltd. (1)
11 Harvest Ter
West Perth, WA, 6005, Australia
Tel.: (61) 892733888
Fax: (61) 893883831
E-Mail: perth@cardno.com.au
Emp.: 100
Engineering Consulting Services
S.I.C.: 8711
N.A.I.C.S.: 541330
Gavin Taylor *(Gen Mgr)*

L.A. & S.R. Thorne Pty. Ltd. (1)
363 Montgomerie Street
Rockhampton, QLD, 4701, Australia
Tel.: (61) 7 4934 8899
Fax: (61) 7 4934 8855
Environmental Consulting Services
S.I.C.: 8999
N.A.I.C.S.: 541620

Sandhorse Pty. Ltd. (1)
Unit 3 20 Fortune Street
Geebung, Brisbane, QLD, 4034, Australia
Tel.: (61) 738653212
Engineering Consulting Services
S.I.C.: 8711
N.A.I.C.S.: 541330

XP Software Pty. Ltd. (1)
8-10 Purdue Street
Belconnen, Canberra, ACT, 2617, Australia
Tel.: (61) 262531844
Fax: (61) 262531847
E-Mail: sales@xpsoftware.com
Web Site: www.xpsoftware.com
Emp.: 10
Water Resource Software Development Services
S.I.C.: 7371
N.A.I.C.S.: 541511
Sudesh Mudaliar *(Mgr)*

U.S. Subsidiary:

XP Software Inc. (2)
5415 SW Westgate Dr Ste 150
Portland, OR 97221
Tel.: (888) 554-5022
Fax: (888) 554-5122
E-Mail: sales@xpsoftware.com
Web Site: www.xpsoftware.com
Emp.: 8
Software Development Services
S.I.C.: 7371
N.A.I.C.S.: 541511
Colby T. Manwaring *(Pres)*

U.S. Subsidiaries:

Cardno United States of America (1)
5415 SW Westgate Dr Ste 100
Portland, OR 97221
Tel.: (503) 734-1800
Fax: (503) 734-1810
Web Site: www.cardno.com
Engineering Consulting
S.I.C.: 8711
N.A.I.C.S.: 541330
Michael Landry *(CFO & Exec VP)*

Subsidiaries:

ATC Group Services Inc. (2)
221 Rue de Jean Ste 200
Lafayette, LA 70508 DE
Tel.: (337) 234-8777
Fax: (337) 235-6777
E-Mail: solutions@atcassociates.com

Web Site: www.atcassociates.com
Sales Range: $125-149.9 Million
Emp.: 1,600
Environmental Consulting, Industrial Hygiene, Geotechnical Engineering, Construction Materials Testing & Inspection Services
S.I.C.: 8999
N.A.I.C.S.: 541620
Robert Toups *(Pres & CEO)*

Cardno Emerging Markets (USA), Ltd. (2)
Colonial Pl 3rd Ste 800 2107 Wilson Blvd
Arlington, VA 22201-3096
Tel.: (703) 373-7600
Fax: (703) 373-7620
Web Site: www.cardnoem.com
Emp.: 80
Engineering Consulting Services
S.I.C.: 8711
N.A.I.C.S.: 541330
Patti Espey *(CFO)*

Cardno ENTRIX, Inc. (2)
5252 Westchester St
Houston, TX 77005-4141 TX
Tel.: (713) 666-6223
Fax: (713) 666-5227
E-Mail: hou-recruit@entrix.com
Web Site: www.entrix.com
Sales Range: $25-49.9 Million
Emp.: 250
Environmental Consulting & Natural Resource Management Services
Import Export
S.I.C.: 8999
N.A.I.C.S.: 541620
Todd M. Williams *(Pres)*
R.W. Firth, Jr. *(Exec VP & Dir-Strategic Dev)*
Dan D. Taylor *(Exec VP & Dir-Mergers & Acq)*
Douglas Campbell *(Sr VP & Dir-Fin & Acctg)*
Edgar Uribe *(Sr VP & Dir-Ops-Latin America)*

Cardno ERI, Inc. (2)
20372 N Sea Cir
Lake Forest, CA 92630
Tel.: (949) 340-1020
Fax: (949) 457-8956
Web Site: www.cardnoeri.com
Sales Range: $1-9.9 Million
Emp.: 50
Environmental Consulting Services
S.I.C.: 8999
N.A.I.C.S.: 541620
Joseph E. O Connell *(Pres)*
Steve M. Zigan *(CEO)*
Robert L. Kroeger *(VP & CFO)*
Keith A. Romstad *(VP & COO)*

Cardno Haynes Whaley, Inc. (2)
(Formerly Haynes Whaley Associates, Inc.)
3700 W Sam Houston Pkwy S Ste 100
Houston, TX 77042 TX
Tel.: (713) 868-1591
Fax: (713) 868-0046
Web Site: www.hayneswhaley.com
Sales Range: $1-9.9 Million
Emp.: 83
Structural Engineering Services
S.I.C.: 8711
N.A.I.C.S.: 541330
Larry E. Whaley *(Pres & CEO)*
Robert R. Tyler *(COO)*
Wally B. Ford *(Exec VP)*
John D. Rohrer *(Exec VP)*
Mark A. Thompson *(Exec VP)*

Cardno TBE (2)
380 Park Pl Blvd Ste 300
Clearwater, FL 33759
Tel.: (727) 531-3505
Fax: (727) 539-1294
Toll Free: (800) 861-8314
E-Mail:
Web Site: www.cardnotbe.com
Sales Range: $50-74.9 Million
Emp.: 450
Engineering Services
S.I.C.: 8711
N.A.I.C.S.: 541330
Patrick L. Beyer *(Pres)*
Craig Snyder *(COO)*

Subsidiary:

Cardno TBE (Michigan), Inc. (3)
4500 Empire Way Ste 4
Lansing, MI 48917
Tel.: (517) 322-0822
Fax: (517) 322-0862
Web Site: www.tbegroup.com
Construction Engineering Services
S.I.C.: 8711
N.A.I.C.S.: 541330

Cardno WRG, Inc. (2)
5415 SW Westgate Dr Ste 100
Portland, OR 97221
Tel.: (503) 419-2500
Fax: (503) 419-2600
Web Site: www.cardnowrg.com
Emp.: 100
Environmental Engineering Services
S.I.C.: 8711
N.A.I.C.S.: 541330
Jeff Curran *(Pres)*
Jon Reimann *(Sr Principal)*

EM-Assist, Inc. (2)
90 Blue Ravine Rd Ste 180
Folsom, CA 95630
Tel.: (916) 355-8444
Fax: (916) 355-8445
E-Mail: folsom@em-assist.com
Web Site: www.em-assist.com
Sales Range: $10-24.9 Million
Emp.: 120
Environmental Program Management & Training Solutions
S.I.C.: 8999
N.A.I.C.S.: 541620
Andreas Graham *(Chm)*
Lynn Meland *(Pres)*
Jeremy Burr *(CEO)*
Gregg Alex *(Exec VP)*

TEC, Inc. (2)
2496 Old Ivory Rd Ste 300
Charlottesville, VA 22903
Tel.: (434) 295-4446
Fax: (434) 295-5535
Web Site: www.tecinc.com
Sales Range: $50-74.9 Million
Environmental Consulting Services
S.I.C.: 8999
N.A.I.C.S.: 541620
Dick Heiderstadt *(Pres)*

Chemrisk, Inc. (1)
101 2nd St Ste 700
San Francisco, CA 94105 CA
Tel.: (415) 896-2400
Web Site: www.chemrisk.com
Emp.: 15
Business Consulting Services
S.I.C.: 8999
N.A.I.C.S.: 541690
Dennis J. Paustenbach *(Mng Partner & Founder)*

Non-U.S. Subsidiaries:

Cardno Emerging Markets (East Africa) Limited (1)
87 Rhapta Road Lantana Place
PO Box 39636
Westlands, 00623 Nairobi, Kenya
Tel.: (254) 20 444 5630
Fax: (254) 20 444 3953
E-Mail: info@cardno.uk.com
Web Site: cardnoem.agrisystems.co.uk/
Emp.: 10
Agricultural Consulting Services
S.I.C.: 8999
N.A.I.C.S.: 541690
Jayne Wachira *(Mgr)*

Cardno (PNG) Ltd. (1)
Westpac Building Waigani Drive
Port Moresby, Papua New Guinea
Tel.: (675) 3254606
Fax: (675) 3250987
E-Mail: cardnoacil@png.cardno.com.au
Web Site: www.cardnoem.com
Emp.: 42
Engineering Consulting Services
S.I.C.: 8711
N.A.I.C.S.: 541330
Christian Forsyth *(Dir-Res)*

Cardno TCB (Christchurch) (1)
155 Blenheim Road Riccarton
PO Box 13-212
Christchurch, 8142, New Zealand
Tel.: (64) 33665428
Fax: (64) 6433795227
E-Mail: ch@cardno.co.nz
Web Site: www.cardno.co.nz
Emp.: 15
Surveying & Land Development Consulting Services
S.I.C.: 0781
N.A.I.C.S.: 541320
Richard Grham *(Gen Mgr)*

Cardno UK Limited (1)
Oxford House Oxford Road
Thame, Oxfordshire, OX9 2AH, United Kingdom
Tel.: (44) 1844216500
Fax: (44) 1844261593
E-Mail: info@cardno.uk.com
Web Site: www.cardno.uk.com
Emp.: 20
Engineering Consulting Services
S.I.C.: 8711
N.A.I.C.S.: 541330

Subsidiaries:

Cardno Emerging Markets (UK) Limited (2)
Suite 3 Oxford House Oxford Road
Thame, Oxfordshire, OX9 2AH, United Kingdom
Tel.: (44) 1844216500
Fax: (44) 1844261593
E-Mail: info@cardno.uk.com
Emp.: 25
Agricultural Consulting Services
S.I.C.: 8999
N.A.I.C.S.: 541690
David Burton *(Mng Dir)*

Micro Drainage Limited (2)
Jacobs Well West Street
Newbury, Berkshire, RG14 1BD, United Kingdom
Tel.: (44) 1635582555
Fax: (44) 1635582131
E-Mail: sales@microdrainage.co.uk
Web Site: www.microdrainage.co.uk
Emp.: 20
Drainage Management Software Development Services
S.I.C.: 7371
N.A.I.C.S.: 541511
Colby Manwaring *(Mng Dir)*

CARDS OFF SA

48 rue de Miromesnil
75008 Paris, France
Tel.: (33) 146074287
Fax: (33) 142050910
E-Mail: contact@cardsoff.com
Web Site: www.cardsoff.com
MLOFF—(EUR)
Sales Range: Less than $1 Million
Emp.: 13
Business Description:
Financial Transaction Software & Systems
S.I.C.: 6099
N.A.I.C.S.: 522320
Personnel:
Philippe Mendil Mendil *(Chm & Mng Dir)*

CARE CANADA

9 Gurdwara Rd Ste 200
Ottawa, ON, K2E 7X6, Canada
Tel.: (613) 228-5600
Fax: (613) 226-5777
Toll Free: (800) 267-5232
E-Mail: info@care.ca
Web Site: www.care.ca
Rev.: $119,939,447
Assets: $38,096,811
Liabilities: $31,266,899
Net Worth: $6,829,911
Earnings: ($1,197,794)
Emp.: 56
Fiscal Year-end: 06/30/13
Business Description:
Aid & Development Organization
S.I.C.: 8322
N.A.I.C.S.: 624230
Personnel:
Louise Frechette *(Chm)*
Gillian Barth *(Pres & CEO)*
Board of Directors:
Louise Frechette
Clarence Cheng
Piers Cumberlege
Denis Durand
Lorne Hepworth
Doug Horswill
Aldea Landry
John P. Manley
Shahid Minto
Hilary M. Pearson
Martha C. Piper
Susan Smith
Ken Sunquist
Victor Thomas
Helen Wesley
Janet Yale

CARECAPITAL GROUP PLC

6th Floor 54 Baker Street
London, W1U 7BU, United Kingdom
Tel.: (44) 2070341949
Fax: (44) 2070341941
E-Mail: info@carecapital.co.uk
Web Site: www.carecapital.co.uk
CARE—(AIM)
Sales Range: $1-9.9 Million
Emp.: 14
Business Description:
Healthcare Real Estate Developer
S.I.C.: 6531
N.A.I.C.S.: 531312
Personnel:
Paul Stacey *(CEO & Mng Dir)*
Michael J. Sinclair *(Grp CEO)*
Stephen Wilden *(Sec)*
Board of Directors:
Trevor Brown
David Evans
Keith Gibbs
Margaret McDonagh
Michael J. Sinclair
Paul Stacey
Stephen Wilden
Legal Counsel:
Finers Stephens Innocent LLP
179 Great Portland Street
London, W1W 5LS, United Kingdom
Subsidiary:

CareCapital (Folkestone) Ltd (1)
54 Baker Street
London, W1U 7BU, United Kingdom
Tel.: (44) 20 7034 1949
Fax: (44) 20 7034 1941
Emp.: 5
Real Estate Management Services
S.I.C.: 6531
N.A.I.C.S.: 531390
Paul Stacey *(Gen Mgr)*

Non-U.S. Subsidiary:

CareCapital Gesundheitsimmobilien Verwaltungs GmbH (1)
Jagerstrasse 67
10117 Berlin, Germany
Tel.: (49) 30 20 64 94 01
Fax: (49) 30 20 64 94 02
E-Mail: info@care-capital.de
Web Site: www.care-capital.de
Hospital Construction Services
S.I.C.: 1629
N.A.I.C.S.: 237990

CAREER POINT INFOSYSTEMS LTD.

(d/b/a Career Point Group)
112-B Shakti Nagar
Kota, Rajasthan, 324 009, India
Tel.: (91) 744 5121491
Fax: (91) 744 2500892
E-Mail: info@careerpointgroup.com

Career Point Infosystems Ltd.—(Continued)

Web Site: www.careerpointgroup.com
CPIL—(BOM NSE)
Emp.: 440

Business Description:
Educational Support Services
S.I.C.: 8299
N.A.I.C.S.: 611710

Personnel:
Pramod Maheshwari *(Chm, CEO & Mng Dir)*
Om Maheshwari *(CFO)*
Mithilesh Dixit *(Sr VP-School & Vocational Education)*
Shailendra Maheshwari *(Sr VP-Academics & Product Dev)*

Board of Directors:
Pramod Maheshwari
Naval Maheshwari
Om Maheshwari

CAREER TECHNOLOGY (MFG.) CO., LTD.

No 248 Bo-ai St
Taipei, Shulin District, Taiwan
Tel.: (886) 286868868
Fax: (886) 286866998
E-Mail: finance@careergroups.com
Web Site: www.careergroups.com
6153—(TAI)
Sales Range: $125-149.9 Million

Business Description:
Flexible Printed Circuits Mfr
S.I.C.: 2671
N.A.I.C.S.: 326112

Personnel:
Chang Ying Tsai *(Chm)*

U.S. Subsidiary:

Career Technology (USA) Corporation (1)
18634-3 Parthenia St
Northridge, CA 91324
Tel.: (818) 701-5391
Fax: (818) 701-5361
E-Mail: sales@careertech-usa.com
Web Site: www.careertech-usa.com
Circuit Design & Fabrication Services
S.I.C.: 7389
N.A.I.C.S.: 541490

Non-U.S. Subsidiaries:

Career Electronic (Kunshan) Co., Ltd. (1)
18 Chin-Sha-Chiang South Road Kunshan Development Zone
Kunshan, Jiangshu, China
Tel.: (86) 512 5771 8998
Fax: (86) 512 5771 2898
Flexible Printed Circuit Boards Mfr
S.I.C.: 3672
N.A.I.C.S.: 334412

Career Technology (H.K.) Ltd. (1)
Room 1308 Laurels Industrial Centre 32 Tai Yau Street
San Po Kong, Kowloon, China (Hong Kong)
Tel.: (852) 23201185
Fax: (852) 2320 0067
Web Site: www.careergroups.com
Emp.: 5
Printed Circuits Distr
S.I.C.: 5065
N.A.I.C.S.: 423690
Peter Yeung *(Mgr)*

Career Technology (S) Pte. Ltd. (1)
47 Kallang Pudding Rd #11-12
Singapore, 349318, Singapore
Tel.: (65) 67458891
Fax: (65) 62591642
Web Site: www.careergroups.com
Emp.: 3
Printed Circuits Distr
S.I.C.: 5065
N.A.I.C.S.: 423690
Cecilia Chia *(Mgr)*

Elcoflex (Suzhou) Co., Ltd. (1)
Suhong Industrial Square Block A2 No 81
Suhong West Street
Suzhou, Jiangsu, 215021, China
Tel.: (86) 512 6767 1225
Fax: (86) 512 6767 1056
Web Site: www.elcoflex.com
Flexible Printed Circuits Distr
S.I.C.: 5065
N.A.I.C.S.: 423690

KJC Corporation (1)
44-15 Choong-Moo Building 702-708
Yeouido-dong
Youngdeungpo-gu, Seoul, 702-708, Korea (South)
Tel.: (82) 53633966
Fax: (82) 27804776
Web Site: www.kjcor.co.kr
Display Accessories Distr
S.I.C.: 5063
N.A.I.C.S.: 423610

Career Technology (Suzhou) Co., Ltd. (1)
28 Chungqui Road Panyang Industrial Park
Huangdai Town, Suzhou, Jiangsu, 215143, China
Tel.: (86) 512 6571 6688
Fax: (86) 512 6571 6695
Web Site: www.careergroups.com
Flexible Printed Circuits Mfr
S.I.C.: 3674
N.A.I.C.S.: 334413
Eric Hsiao *(Mgr)*

CAREERLINK CO., LTD.

2-1-1 Nishi-Shinjuku Shinjuku-ku
Tokyo, 163-0433, Japan
Tel.: (81) 3 6311 7321
Web Site: www.careerlink.co.jp
6070—(TKS)
Sales Range: $200-249.9 Million
Emp.: 280

Business Description:
Employment Placement Services
S.I.C.: 7361
N.A.I.C.S.: 561311

Personnel:
Yasuhiko Kondo *(Chm)*

CAREERS MULTILIST LIMITED

Level 4 61 Lavender Street
Milsons Point, NSW, 2061, Australia
Tel.: (61) 292674222
Fax: (61) 292671567
E-Mail: enquiries@careersmultilist.com.au
Web Site: www.careersmultilist.com.au
CGR—(ASX)
Rev.: $105,060,354
Assets: $18,015,825
Liabilities: $13,644,215
Net Worth: $4,371,610
Earnings: $798,249
Emp.: 40
Fiscal Year-end: 06/30/13

Business Description:
Employment Agencies
S.I.C.: 7361
N.A.I.C.S.: 561311

Personnel:
Daniel Riley *(Mng Dir)*
Ralph Stonell *(Sec)*

Board of Directors:
Ian Winlaw
Sue Healy
Daniel Riley
Greg Riley
Steve Rogers

Legal Counsel:
DCS Lawyers
Level 13, MLC Centre 19 Martin Place
Sydney, Australia

CAREPLUS GROUP BERHAD

Lot 120 &121 Jalan Senawang 3
Senawang Industrial Estate
70450 Seremban, Malaysia
Tel.: (60) 66772781
Fax: (60) 66772780
E-Mail: info@careplus.com
Web Site: www.careplus.com
CAREPLS—(KLS)
Rev.: $31,936,918
Assets: $39,868,582
Liabilities: $22,233,313
Net Worth: $17,635,269
Earnings: $753,215
Emp.: 120
Fiscal Year-end: 01/31/13

Business Description:
Glove Mfr
S.I.C.: 2389
N.A.I.C.S.: 315990

Personnel:
Kwee Shyan Lim *(CEO)*
Pek Hoong Shee *(Co-Sec)*
Sor Hua Tea *(Co-Sec)*

Board of Directors:
Nieng Choon Yew
Kuan Ming Foong
Kwee Shyan Lim
Teck Looi Loo
Chuan Hock Tan
Yee Peng Yew

Subsidiaries:

Careplus (M) Sdn Bhd (1)
Lot 1010 Lorong Senawang 4/3 Off Jalan Senawang Empat
Senawang Industrial Estate, 70450
Seremban, Negeri Sembilan, Malaysia
Tel.: (60) 66772781
Fax: (60) 66772780
E-Mail: careplus@po.jaring.my
Web Site: www.careplus.com.my
Emp.: 200
Gloves Mfr & Whslr
S.I.C.: 3841
N.A.I.C.S.: 339113
Kwee Shyan Lim *(Mng Dir)*

MASTERCLEAN TECHNOLOGIES (M) SDN BHD (1)
Lot 110 Lorong Senawang 4/3 Off Jalan Senawang Empat
Senawang Industrial Estate, 70450
Seremban, Negeri Sembilan, Malaysia
Tel.: (60) 66772781
Fax: (60) 66772780
Gloves Mfr & Whslr
S.I.C.: 3841
N.A.I.C.S.: 339113
Christene Yew *(Gen Mgr)*

Rubbercare Protection Products Sdn Bhd (1)
Lot 110 Lorong Senawang 4/3 Off Jalan Senawang Empat
Senawang Industrial Estate, 70450
Seremban, Negeri Sembilan, Malaysia
Tel.: (60) 66772781
Fax: (60) 66772780
E-Mail: careplus@po.jaring.my
Web Site: www.rubbercare.com.my
Emp.: 250
Rubber Gloves Mfr & Distr
S.I.C.: 3841
N.A.I.C.S.: 339113
Kwee Shyan Lim *(Mng Dir)*

CARETECH HOLDINGS PLC

5th Floor Metropolitan House 3 Darkes Lane
Potters Bar, EN6 1AG, United Kingdom
Tel.: (44) 1707 601 800
Fax: (44) 1707 655 265
E-Mail: info@caretech-uk.com
Web Site: www.caretech-uk.com
CTH—(LSE)
Rev.: $189,940,805
Assets: $520,063,949
Liabilities: $356,010,040
Net Worth: $164,053,908
Earnings: $40,484,308
Emp.: 3,284
Fiscal Year-end: 09/30/13

Business Description:
Housing Support Services
S.I.C.: 8322
N.A.I.C.S.: 624120

Personnel:
Farouq Sheikh *(Co-Founder & Chm)*
Haroon Sheikh *(Co-Founder & CEO)*
Michael Hill *(Sec & Dir-Fin)*

Board of Directors:
Farouq Sheikh
Mike Adams
James Stuart Cummings
Michael Hill
Karl Monaghan
Haroon Sheikh
Stewart Wallace

Legal Counsel:
Pinsent Masons
30 Crown Place
London, United Kingdom

Subsidiaries:

Ashcroft House Limited (1)
11 Elmstead Rd
Bexhill-on-Sea, Sussex, TN40 2HP, United Kingdom
Tel.: (44) 1424736020
Fax: (44) 1424736635
Emp.: 18
Homage Services
S.I.C.: 8051
N.A.I.C.S.: 623110
Jo Lea *(Mgr)*

Ashring House Limited (1)
Ashring House Lewes Rd Ringmer
Lewes, Sussex, BN8 5ES, United Kingdom
Tel.: (44) 1273814400
Fax: (44) 1273814400
Web Site: www.caretech-uk.com
Emp.: 11
Homage Services
S.I.C.: 8051
N.A.I.C.S.: 623110
Margaret Goodwin *(Mgr-Home)*

Beacon Care Limited (1)
The Coach House Remenham Hill
Henley-on-Thames, Oxfordshire, RG9 3EP, United Kingdom
Tel.: (44) 1707652053
Fax: (44) 1491 579738
Emp.: 200
Physically Challenged People Caring Services
S.I.C.: 8051
N.A.I.C.S.: 623110

Beech Care Limited (1)
99 Dunes Rd
Greatstone, New Romney, Kent, TN28 8SW, United Kingdom
Tel.: (44) 1797362121
Fax: (44) 1797362121
E-Mail: beech@caretech-uk.com
Emp.: 14
Physically Challenged People Caring Services
S.I.C.: 8051
N.A.I.C.S.: 623110
Sara Duncan *(Mgr)*

CareTech Community Services Limited (1)
Metropolitan House 6th Floor 3 Darkes Lane
Potters Bar, Hertfordshire, EN6 1AG, United Kingdom
Tel.: (44) 1707601800
Fax: (44) 1707662719
E-Mail: info@caretech.co.uk
Web Site: www.caretech.co.uk
Emp.: 80
Physically Challenged People Caring Services
S.I.C.: 8051
N.A.I.C.S.: 623110
Farouq Sheikh *(Mng Dir)*

Subsidiaries:

CareTech Community Services (No. 2) Limited (2)
Leighton House 33 37 Darkes Ln
Potters Bar, Hertfordshire, EN6 1BB, United Kingdom
Tel.: (44) 1707652053
Fax: (44) 1707662719
E-Mail: info@caretech-uk.com

Emp.: 50
Physically Challenged People Caring Services
S.I.C.: 8051
N.A.I.C.S.: 623110
Danielle Galvin *(Mgr-HR)*

Daisybrook Limited (2)
49 Norton Green Ln
Norton Canes, Cannock, Staffordshire, WS11 9PR, United Kingdom
Tel.: (44) 1543274848
Fax: (44) 1543495236
E-Mail: daisybrook@aol.com
Emp.: 39
Physically Challenged People Caring Services
S.I.C.: 8051
N.A.I.C.S.: 623110
Ann Pritchard *(Mgr)*

Huntsmans Lodge Limited (2)
33 Huntsmans Way
Leicester, Leicestershire, LE4 7ZG, United Kingdom
Tel.: (44) 1162611222
Fax: (44) 1162611222
Emp.: 5
Physically Challenged People Caring Services
S.I.C.: 8051
N.A.I.C.S.: 623110
Simon Moore *(Mgr)*

Kirkstall Lodge Limited (2)
56 Kirkstall Rd
Streatham, London, SW2 4HF, United Kingdom
Tel.: (44) 2086788296
Fax: (44) 2086788296
Emp.: 13
Physically Challenged People Caring Services
S.I.C.: 8051
N.A.I.C.S.: 623110
Eliza Mohungngo *(Mgr)*

Lonsdale Midlands Limited (2)
1st Fl Court House 335- 337 High St
W Bromwich, Birmingham, West Midlands, B70 8LU, United Kingdom
Tel.: (44) 1215005262
Fax: (44) 1215258492
E-Mail: midlands.enquiries@caretech-uk.com
Physically Challenged People Caring Services
S.I.C.: 8051
N.A.I.C.S.: 623110

Rosedale Children's Services Limited (2)
2 Bullace Trees Ln
Liversedge, West Yorkshire, WF15 7PF, United Kingdom
Tel.: (44) 1924407540
Fax: (44) 1924407534
E-Mail: theoakx01@btconnect.com
Emp.: 30
Physically Challenged People Caring Services
S.I.C.: 8051
N.A.I.C.S.: 623110

Emeraldpoint Limited (1)
40 Richmond Ave
Bognor Regis, Sussex, PO21 2YE, United Kingdom
Tel.: (44) 1243 822145
Physically Challenged People Caring Services
S.I.C.: 8051
N.A.I.C.S.: 623110

Glenroyd House Limited (1)
Glenroyd House 26 High Rd N
Basildon Dist, Laindon, Essex, SS15 4DP, United Kingdom
Tel.: (44) 1268541333
Fax: (44) 1268541333
Web Site: www.caretech.co.uk
Emp.: 13
Physically Challenged People Caring Services
S.I.C.: 8051
N.A.I.C.S.: 623110

One Step (Support) Limited (1)
One Step (Support) Limited
Badgemore, Henley-on-Thames, Oxfordshire, RG9 4NR, United Kingdom
Tel.: (44) 1491414455
Fax: (44) 1491413186
E-Mail: customerservices@onestepatatime.org.uk
Web Site: www.onestepatatime.org.uk
Emp.: 10
Residential Support & Family Assessment Services
S.I.C.: 8361
N.A.I.C.S.: 623990
Karen Cox *(Mgr-Ops)*

Palm Care Limited (1)
12 Hardy Rd
Greatstone, New Romney, Kent, TN28 8SF, United Kingdom
Tel.: (44) 1797367006
E-Mail: palm@caretech-uk.com
Web Site: www.palmhomecare.co.uk
Emp.: 12
Physically Challenged People Caring Services
S.I.C.: 8051
N.A.I.C.S.: 623110
Iron Shiek *(Mng Dir)*

Valeo Limited (1)
Queens Sq Leeds Rd
Huddersfield, Yorkshire, HD2 1XN, United Kingdom
Tel.: (44) 1484 480 802
Fax: (44) 1484 435 033
E-Mail: eb@valeoltd.com
Web Site: www.valeoltd.com
Emp.: 12
Residential & Domiciliary Support Services
S.I.C.: 8322
N.A.I.C.S.: 624190

CAREY GROUP PLC

Carey House Great Central Way
Wembley, Middlesex, HA9 0HR, United Kingdom
Tel.: (44) 2089000221
Fax: (44) 2089039987
E-Mail: admin@careysplc.co.uk
Web Site: www.carey-plc.co.uk
Rev.: $247,070,828
Emp.: 70
Business Description:
Construction Services
S.I.C.: 1542
N.A.I.C.S.: 236220
Personnel:
John Carey *(Chm)*
Denis Deacy *(Mng Dir)*

CARFINCO FINANCIAL GROUP INC.

#300 4245-97 St
Edmonton, AB, T6E 5Y7, Canada
Tel.: (780) 413-7549
Fax: (888) 486-7456
Toll Free: (888) 486-4356
E-Mail: carfinco@carfinco.com
Web Site: www.carfinco.com
CFN—(TSX)
Rev.: $71,808,752
Assets: $176,541,774
Liabilities: $132,573,930
Net Worth: $43,967,844
Earnings: $20,590,619
Emp.: 150
Fiscal Year-end: 12/31/12
Business Description:
Automobile Financing Services
S.I.C.: 6141
N.A.I.C.S.: 522291
Personnel:
Tracy A. Graf *(Pres & CEO)*
Stephen Dykau *(CFO)*
Troy S.F. Graf *(VP & COO)*
Rick Hewson *(Sr VP-Ops)*
Board of Directors:
Brent Channell
Tracy A. Graf
Maurice Kagan
J. Daryl MacLellan
David Prussky
David Rosenkrantz
Simon Serruya
U.S. Subsidiary:

Persian Acceptance Corp. (1)
101 Edgewater Dr Ste 112
Wakefield, MA 01880
Tel.: (978) 535-2887
Fax: (781) 213-6684
Toll Free: (888) 852-2886
Web Site: www.persianacceptance.com
Sales Range: $1-9.9 Million
Emp.: 7
Automobile Financing Services
S.I.C.: 6141
N.A.I.C.S.: 522291
Peter Miller *(Pres)*

CARGIANT LTD.

44-45 Hythe Road
London, White City, NW10 6RJ, United Kingdom
Tel.: (44) 20 8969 5511
Web Site: www.cargiant.co.uk
Year Founded: 1977
Sales Range: $500-549.9 Million
Emp.: 560
Business Description:
New & Used Car Dealer
S.I.C.: 5511
N.A.I.C.S.: 441110
Personnel:
Geoffrey Warren *(Chm)*

CARGILLS (CEYLON) PLC

No 40 York Street
Colombo, 1, Sri Lanka
Tel.: (94) 112427777
Fax: (94) 112338704
E-Mail: ccl@cargillsceylon.com
Web Site: www.cargillsceylon.com
CARG—(COL)
Rev.: $434,724,498
Assets: $279,231,251
Liabilities: $184,723,460
Net Worth: $94,507,791
Earnings: $12,793,585
Emp.: 7,832
Fiscal Year-end: 03/31/13
Business Description:
Ice Cream & Dairy Products Mfr
S.I.C.: 2023
N.A.I.C.S.: 311514
Personnel:
V. Ranjit Page *(Deputy Chm & CEO)*
M. Imtiaz Abdul Wahid *(Deputy CEO & Mng Dir)*
Prabhu S. Mathavan *(CFO)*
Sidath V. Kodikara *(COO)*
Sarath Dissanayake *(Sec)*
Board of Directors:
Louis R. Page
Jayantha Dhanapala
A. T. Priya Edirisinghe
Sanjeev E. C. Gardiner
Sidath V. Kodikara
Prabhu S. Mathavan
Sunil Mendis
Anthony A. Page
Joseph C. Page
V. Ranjit Page
Errol A. D. Perera
M. Imtiaz Abdul Wahid

CARGO CARRIERS LTD

11a Grace Road Mountainview Observatory
Houghton, 2198, South Africa
Tel.: (27) 114858700
Fax: (27) 114858781
Web Site: www.cargocarriers.co.za
CRG—(JSE)
Rev.: $81,172,949
Assets: $96,393,749
Liabilities: $52,857,669
Net Worth: $43,536,080
Earnings: $2,915,705
Emp.: 1,027
Fiscal Year-end: 02/28/13
Business Description:
Logistics, Transport & Information Technology Solutions
S.I.C.: 4212
N.A.I.C.S.: 484110
Personnel:
Murray J. Bolton *(Co-CEO & Sec)*
Garth D. Bolton *(Co-CEO)*
Shaneel Maharaj *(CFO)*
Board of Directors:
Stan G. Chilvers
Garth D. Bolton
Murray J. Bolton
Alistair E. Franklin
Beverley B. Fraser
Shaneel Maharaj
Sizakele P. Mzimela
Matsotso J. Vuso
Legal Counsel:
Werksmans Attorneys
155 Fifth Street Sandton
Johannesburg, South Africa
Transfer Agent:
Computershare Investor Services (Proprietary) Limited
70 Marshall Street
Johannesburg, South Africa

CARGOJET INC.

350 Britannia Road East Units 5 & 6
Mississauga, ON, L4Z 1X9, Canada
Tel.: (905) 501-7373
Fax: (905) 501-7447
Toll Free: (800) 753-1051
E-Mail: cs@cargojet.com
Web Site: www.cargojet.com
Year Founded: 2005
CJT—(TSX)
Rev.: $167,761,439
Assets: $112,763,498
Liabilities: $48,678,759
Net Worth: $64,084,739
Earnings: $3,530,937
Emp.: 343
Fiscal Year-end: 12/31/12
Business Description:
Air Cargo Services
S.I.C.: 4581
N.A.I.C.S.: 488190
Personnel:
Ajay K. Virmani *(Chm, Pres & CEO)*
John Kim *(CFO & Sec)*
Jamie B. Porteous *(Exec VP-Sls & Svc)*
George Sugar *(Sr VP-Flight Ops)*
Board of Directors:
Ajay K. Virmani
Terence M. Francis
Paul V. Godfrey
Jamie B. Porteous
John P. Webster
Transfer Agent:
Computershare Investor Services Inc.
Montreal, QC, Canada
Subsidiary:

Cargojet Partnership Ltd (1)
Unit 140-4840 Miller Road
Richmond, BC, V6X 2A9, Canada
Tel.: (604) 244-8868
Fax: (604) 244-8242
E-Mail: ybrbookings@cargojet.com
Emp.: 30
Scheduled Freight Air Transportation Services
S.I.C.: 4512
N.A.I.C.S.: 481112
Lyle Gibson, *(Gen Mgr)*
Holding:

Cargojet Holdings Ltd. (1)
3486 21 Street East Edmonton International Airport
Edmonton, AB, T5J 2T2, Canada

Cargojet Inc.—(Continued)

Tel.: (780) 890-8606
Fax: (780) 890-8607
E-Mail: yegbookings@cargojet.com
Emp.: 12
Investment Management Services
S.I.C.: 6282
N.A.I.C.S.: 523920
Sean Walsh, *(Gen Mgr)*

CARGOLUX AIRLINES INTERNATIONAL S.A.

Luxembourg Airport
2990 Luxembourg, Luxembourg
Tel.: (352) 4211 3925
Fax: (352) 4211 3692
E-Mail: info@cargolux.com
Web Site: www.cargolux.com
Year Founded: 1970
Rev.: $1,726,335,000
Assets: $2,222,960,000
Liabilities: $1,792,272,000
Net Worth: $430,688,000
Earnings: ($35,130,000)
Emp.: 1,599
Fiscal Year-end: 12/31/12

Business Description:
Cargo Airline
S.I.C.: 4512
N.A.I.C.S.: 481112

Personnel:
Paul Helminger *(Chm)*
Richard Forson *(Interim Pres, CEO & CFO)*
Peter van de Pas *(COO & Sr VP)*
Henning zur Hausen *(Sr VP-Legal Affairs & Compliance)*

Board of Directors:
Paul Helminger
Richard Agutter
Hussain Al-Abdulla
Akbar Al-Baker
Bettina Faulhaber
Jean-Claude Finck
George Karambilas
Einar Kristjansson
David Massaro
Adrien Ney
Patrick Nickels
Armand Seil
Francoise Thoma
Tom Weisgerber

CARGOTEC CORPORATION

Porkkalankatu 5
PO Box 61
FI-00501 Helsinki, Finland
Tel.: (358) 207774000
Fax: (358) 207774036
E-Mail: communications@cargotec.com
Web Site: www.cargotec.com
CGCBV—(HEL)
Sls.: $4,479,111,441
Assets: $4,434,014,746
Liabilities: $2,775,264,072
Net Worth: $1,658,750,674
Earnings: $120,078,364
Emp.: 10,294
Fiscal Year-end: 12/31/12

Business Description:
Cargo-Handling Solutions for Ships, Ports, Terminals & Defense Customers
S.I.C.: 4491
N.A.I.C.S.: 488320

Personnel:
Ilkka Herlin *(Chm)*
Mika Vehvilainen *(Chm-Exec Bd & Pres & CEO)*
Eeva Sipila *(CFO, Member-Exec Bd & Exec VP)*
Soili Maikinen *(CIO & Member-Exec Bd)*
Matti Sommarberg *(CTO, Exec VP & Member-Exec Bd)*
Olli Isotalo *(Pres-Kalmar & Member-Exec Bd)*
Axel Leijonhufvud *(Pres-Hiab & Member-Exec Bd)*
Eric A. Nielsen *(Pres-MacGregor Bus Area)*
Outi Aaltonen *(Member-Exec Bd, Gen Counsel & Sr VP)*
Stephen Foster *(Member-Exec Bd & Sr VP-Corp Audit)*
Anne Westersund *(Member-Exec Bd & Sr VP-Comm & Pub Affairs)*
Pasi Lehtonen *(Sr VP-Offshore Bus Segment)*

Board of Directors:
Ilkka Herlin
Jorma Eloranta
Tapio Hakakari
Peter Immonen
Antti Lagerroos
Teuvo Salminen
Anja Silvennoinen

Subsidiaries:

Cargotec Finland Oy **(1)**
Porkkalankatu 5
00501 Helsinki, Finland
Tel.: (358) 204554401
Fax: (358) 204554511
E-Mail: communications@cargotec.com
Web Site: www.cargotec.fi
Emp.: 10,000
Load Handling Equipment & Logistics Services
S.I.C.: 4491
N.A.I.C.S.: 488320

Subsidiaries:

Focolift Product Line **(2)**
Torpanmaentie 3
PO Box 6
25500 Pernio, Perino, Finland
Tel.: (358) 204552899
Fax: (358) 204552850
E-Mail: cargotec@cargotec.com
Web Site: www.focolift.com
Sales Range: $1-9.9 Million
Emp.: 31
Mfr & Sales of Tail Lifts
S.I.C.: 3537
N.A.I.C.S.: 333924
Nurmi Kalavi *(Gen Mgr)*

Loglift Jonsered AB **(2)**
Nesteentie 36
FI 21200 Raisio, Finland
Tel.: (358) 204552599
Fax: (358) 204552500
E-Mail: logliftjonsered@cargotech.com
Web Site: www.cargotech.com
Sales Range: $10-24.9 Million
Emp.: 200
Mfr Timber Cranes & Production Loaders
S.I.C.: 3536
N.A.I.C.S.: 333923
Kalevi Nurmi *(CEO)*

U.S. Subsidiary:

Cargotec USA Inc. **(2)**
12233 Williams Rd
Perrysburg, OH 43551
Tel.: (419) 482-6000
Fax: (419) 482-6001
E-Mail: us.sales@cargotec.com
Web Site: www.hiab.com
Sales Range: $50-74.9 Million
Emp.: 148
Mfr of Fork Lifts & Cranes
S.I.C.: 5084
N.A.I.C.S.: 423830
Tim Arklander *(Product Mgr)*

Non-U.S. Subsidiaries:

Cargotec Austria GmbH **(2)**
Portendorf 8
9020 Klagenfurt, Austria
Tel.: (43) 463 717 88
Fax: (43) 463 717 22
E-Mail: marketing.austria@cargotec.com
Web Site: www.kalmarind.at
Emp.: 48
Cargo Handling Equipment Distr
S.I.C.: 5084
N.A.I.C.S.: 423830
Guenter Thonhauser *(Reg Mgr-Product & Sls)*

Cargotec France S.A.S. **(2)**
38-40 Ave Roger Hennequin
PO Box 34
F 78192 Trappes, Cedex, France FR
Tel.: (33) 130511836
Fax: (33) 130517111
E-Mail: accueil.hiabsas@cargotec.com
Web Site: www.hiab.fr
Sales Range: $50-74.9 Million
Net Worth: $725,468
Emp.: 65
Mfr Cranes & Loaders & Industrial Equipment & Machinery
S.I.C.: 3536
N.A.I.C.S.: 333923
Thierry Aubry *(Pres & CEO)*

Cargotec Italia S.r.l. **(2)**
Via Al Molo Giano
I-16128 Genoa, Italy
Tel.: (39) 03351394779
Fax: (39) 10246 1194
Web Site: www.cargotec.com
Sales Range: $1-9.9 Million
Emp.: 14
Cargo Access Equipment & Engineering & Service Solutions for the Maritime Transportation Industry
S.I.C.: 4491
N.A.I.C.S.: 488320
Barbara Messina *(Gen Mgr)*

Cargotec Netherlands B.V. **(2)**
Hesselingen 42
PO Box 1086
7944 HR Meppel, Netherlands
Tel.: (31) 522253831
Fax: (31) 522260983
E-Mail: info-nl@cargotec.com
Web Site: www.hiab.nl
Emp.: 100
Mfr of Cranes, Loaders & Industrial Machinery
S.I.C.: 3537
N.A.I.C.S.: 333924
Albert Gong *(CFO)*

Cargotec Netherlands b.v. **(2)**
Doklaan 22
3081 AD Rotterdam, Netherlands
Mailing Address:
PO Box 5303
Rotterdam, Netherlands
Tel.: (31) 102832121
Fax: (31) 104293219
E-Mail: bart.van.maurik@macgregor-group.com
Web Site: www.macgregor-group.com
Sales Range: $1-9.9 Million
Emp.: 22
Cargo Access Equipment & Engineering & Service Solutions for the Maritime Transportation Industry
S.I.C.: 4491
N.A.I.C.S.: 488320
Bart Van Maurik *(Mgr-Svc)*

Cargotec Poland Sp. Z O.O. **(2)**
Ul Poznanska 94
05 850 Ozarow Mazowiecki, Poland
Tel.: (48) 227210270
Fax: (48) 227210271
E-Mail: biuro@cargotec.com
Web Site: www.hiab.pl
Emp.: 11
Engineering Services
S.I.C.: 8711
N.A.I.C.S.: 541330
Andrzej Wieclaw *(Mng Dir)*

Cargotec Rus LLC **(2)**
Naberezhnaya Obvodnogo Kanala 118A
Liter ZH Office 503, Saint Petersburg, 190005, Russia
Tel.: (7) 8 1233 75450
Fax: (7) 8 1233 75451
E-Mail: info.rus@cargotec.com
Web Site: www.cargotec.com
Emp.: 22
Bulk Handling Equipment, Hatch Covers, Cargo Cranes, Lashing Bridges, Lashing Equipment, Offshore Loading Solutions & RoRo Equipment
S.I.C.: 3531
N.A.I.C.S.: 333120
Varerly Mozhevekin *(Mgr-Sls)*

Cargotec Sweden AB **(2)**
Angsvagen 5
SE 267 25 Bjuv, Sweden SE
Mailing Address: (100%)
Box 566
26725 Bjuv, Sweden
Tel.: (46) 4285800
Fax: (46) 4285899
E-Mail: blk.sales@cargotec.com
Web Site: www.cargotec.com
Emp.: 135
Dry Bulk Material Handling Equipment
S.I.C.: 4491
N.A.I.C.S.: 488320
Michael Floren *(Exec VP-Svcs)*

Hiab AB **(2)**
Kopmanbergsvagen 5
824 83 Hudiksvall, Sweden
Tel.: (46) 65091442
Fax: (46) 65091226
E-Mail: leif.wallin@cargotec.com
Web Site: www.hiab.se
Emp.: 500
Loader Cranes Manufacturing & Marketing
S.I.C.: 3537
N.A.I.C.S.: 333924
Axel Leijonhufvud *(Pres)*
Leif Wallin *(Mng Dir)*
Carl Gustaf Goransson *(Sr VP)*

Hiab Chile S.A. **(2)**
El Juncal 071 B
Portezuelo, Santiago, Quilicura, Chile
Tel.: (56) 27386993
Fax: (56) 7386460
E-Mail: hiabchilesa@hiab.cl
Web Site: www.hiab.cl
Emp.: 45
Mfr Loader Cranes
S.I.C.: 5084
N.A.I.C.S.: 423830
Hafez Eelhejl *(Mng Dir)*

Hiab Cranes, S.L. **(2)**
Poligono Industrial de Malpica Calle E 86
50016 Zaragoza, Spain
Tel.: (34) 976579800
Fax: (34) 976571886
E-Mail: hiab.cranes@cargotec.com
Web Site: www.hiab.com
Sales Range: $50-74.9 Million
Net Worth: $379,407
Emp.: 240
Mfr Loader Cranes
S.I.C.: 3536
N.A.I.C.S.: 333923
John Lopez *(Gen Mgr)*

Hiab Denmark A/S **(2)**
Industrikrogen 14
2635 Ishoj, Denmark
Tel.: (45) 49192424
Fax: (45) 49 1924 33
Web Site: www.zepro.dk
Sales Range: Less than $1 Million
Net Worth: $1,005,100
Loader Cranes Manufacturing, Sales & Marketing
S.I.C.: 3537
N.A.I.C.S.: 333924

Hiab GmbH **(2)**
Emil Berliner Strasse 29
PO Box 101446
D 30835 Langenhagen, Germany
Tel.: (49) 51177050
Fax: (49) 5117705132
E-Mail: zentrale.langenhagen@hiab.com
Web Site: www.hiab.com
Rev.: $445,615,904
Emp.: 80
Cargo-Handling Solutions
S.I.C.: 4491
N.A.I.C.S.: 488320
Thomas Koskimaa *(Mng Dir)*

Hiab Hana Co. Ltd. **(2)**
356 Taesung-Ri Gangnae-Myon
Chongwon-gun, Chongju, Chungbuk, 363-893, Korea (South)
Tel.: (82) 43 231 6300
Fax: (82) 43 231 6200
E-Mail: hiabhana@hiabhana.com
Web Site: www.hiabhana.com
Sales Range: $10-24.9 Million
Net Worth: $796,500
Emp.: 74

Loader Cranes Mfr & Sales
S.I.C.: 3537
N.A.I.C.S.: 333924

Hiab KK (2)
3831 1 Ikonobe Cho
Tsuzuki Ku, Yokohama, Kanagawa, 224 0053, Japan
Tel.: (81) 459348291
Fax: (81) 459331993
E-Mail: hiab.japan@cargoteh.com
Web Site: www.hiab.jp
Emp.: 44
Crane Equipment Mfg & Sales
S.I.C.: 5084
N.A.I.C.S.: 423830
Fhinichi Tomioka *(Pres)*

Hiab Ltd. (2)
Cargotec Industrial Pk
Ellesmere, SY12 9JW, United Kingdom
Tel.: (44) 01691623100
Fax: (44) 1691623022
E-Mail: enquiries.uk@hiab.com
Web Site: www.hiab.co.uk
Sales Range: $25-49.9 Million
Emp.: 55
Mfr Loader Cranes & Ground Level Demountables
S.I.C.: 3536
N.A.I.C.S.: 333923

Hiab S.A. de C.V. (2)
San Andres Atoto 16 A Col San Esteban
CP 53550 Naucalpan, Edo De Mexico, Mexico
Tel.: (52) 5553587411
Fax: (52) 5553595230
Toll Free: 8002018439
E-Mail: ventas@hiab.com.mx
Web Site: www.hiab.com.mx
Sales Range: $1-9.9 Million
Emp.: 70
Mfr Crane & Loaders
S.I.C.: 3536
N.A.I.C.S.: 333923
Martha Pana *(Mng Dir)*

Hiab S.A./N.V. (2)
Parc Industriel 8
BE 1440 Wauthier Brain, Belgium BE
Tel.: (32) 23662036
Fax: (32) 23661290
E-Mail: hiab_belgium@cargotec.com
Web Site: www.hiab.be
Sales Range: $10-24.9 Million
Net Worth: $354,600
Emp.: 15
Mfr Cranes & Loaders
S.I.C.: 3536
N.A.I.C.S.: 333923
Jells Da Thomas *(Mng Dir)*

Hiab S.A. (2)
Poligono Las Fronteras
28850 Torrejon de Ardoz, Madrid, Spain
Tel.: (34) 916270100
Fax: (34) 916270106
E-Mail: susana.rivera@hiab.com
Web Site: www.hiab.com
Sales Range: $50-74.9 Million
Net Worth: $12,455,786
Emp.: 44
Loader Cranes Mfr, Sales, Marketing & Service
S.I.C.: 3537
N.A.I.C.S.: 333924
Edwardo Prat *(Mng Dir)*

LeeBur Multilift B.V. (2)
Postbus 1086
NL 5530 AC Bladel, Netherlands
Tel.: (31) 497362100
Fax: (31) 497362199
E-Mail: info@hiab.nl
Web Site: www.hiab.nl
Sales Range: $25-49.9 Million
Emp.: 45
Mfr & Sales of Cranes & Demountables
S.I.C.: 3536
N.A.I.C.S.: 333923
Johannes Roelofs *(CEO)*
Ron Van Gestel *(Mng Dir)*

Cargotec Solutions Oy (1)
Satamakaari 35
00980 Helsinki, Finland
Tel.: (358) 32658111
Cargo Handling Services
S.I.C.: 4491
N.A.I.C.S.: 488320

Kalmar Industries Oy Ab (1)
Sornaisten rantatie 23
P O Box 61
00501 Helsinki, Finland
Tel.: (358) 2045511
Fax: (358) 204554222
E-Mail: info@kalmarind.com
Web Site: www.kalmarind.com —(HEL)
Sales Range: Less than $1 Million
Emp.: 4,700
Container & Industrial Handling Applications
S.I.C.: 4731
N.A.I.C.S.: 488510
Ismo Vaiheamo *(Pres)*

Subsidiary:

Kalmar Industries Oy AB (2)
Valnetin Kapu 5
PO Box 387
Nuolialantie 62, FIN 33101 Tampere, Finland FI
Tel.: (358) 32658111
Fax: (358) 32658616
Web Site: www.kalmarind.com
Sales Range: $300-349.9 Million
Emp.: 656
Mfr of Tractors, Forklifts, Loaders, Cranes & Other Industrial Machinery
S.I.C.: 3536
N.A.I.C.S.: 333923
Kauko Autio *(Dir-Real Estate)*

Non-U.S. Subsidiaries:

Kalmar Belgium nv/sa (2)
Heizegemweg 7
2030 Antwerp, Belgium
Tel.: (32) 35410966
Fax: (32) 35412823
Mfr of Cranes, Tractors, Forklifts, & Other Industrial Machinery
S.I.C.: 7699
N.A.I.C.S.: 811310

Kalmar B.V. (2)
Tokoaan22
5303
Tokoaan22, Rotterdam, 3008 AH, Netherlands
Mailing Address:
P.O. Box 635
NL-3190 AN Hoogvliet, Netherlands
Tel.: (31) 102956464
Fax: (31) 102956777
E-Mail: kalmar.nederland@rotterdam.info
Web Site: www.kalmarind.nl
Emp.: 50
Mfr of Cranes, Loaders, Tractors, Demountables & Other Industrial Machinery
S.I.C.: 3536
N.A.I.C.S.: 333923
Martcel Coecoel *(Mng Dir)*

Kalmar Danmark A/S (2)
Oceanvej 17
8000 Arhus, Denmark
Tel.: (45) 27 101 701
Web Site: www.cargotec.com
General Industrial Machine Mfr
S.I.C.: 3593
N.A.I.C.S.: 333995

Kalmar Industries AB (2)
Torggatan 3
34010 Lidhult, Sweden SE
Tel.: (46) 37226000
Fax: (46) 37226393
E-Mail: kalmar@cargotec.com
Web Site: www.kalmarind.com
Sls.: $468,693
Emp.: 835
Mfr of Cranes, Tractors, Forklifts, & Other Industrial Machinery
S.I.C.: 3536
N.A.I.C.S.: 333923
Lotta Clausen *(VP-Mktg)*

Subsidiaries:

Cargotec Sweden AB (3)
Malaxgatan 7
164 74 Kista, Sweden
Mailing Address:
Box 1133
164 22 Kista, Sweden
Tel.: (46) 84453800
Fax: (46) 84453838
E-Mail: info@kalmarind.com
Web Site: www.kalmarind.com
Sales Range: $25-49.9 Million
Net Worth: $2,760,600
Emp.: 120
Mfr of Cranes, Forklifts, Demountables & Other Industrial Machinery
S.I.C.: 3536
N.A.I.C.S.: 333923
Jan Ohlsson *(Mng Dir)*

Kalmar Industries Sverige AB (3)
Torggatan 3
SE 341 81 Lidhult, Sweden
Tel.: (46) 37226000
Fax: (46) 37226393
E-Mail: kalmar@cargotec.com
Web Site: www.kalmarind.com
Sales Range: $200-249.9 Million
Net Worth: $13,068,924
Emp.: 400
Mfr of Cranes, Forklifts, Demountables & Industrial Machinery
S.I.C.: 3536
N.A.I.C.S.: 333923
Don Peterson *(Mng Dir)*

U.S. Division:

Ottawa Truck (3)
415 E Dundee St
Ottawa, KS 66067-1543
Tel.: (785) 242-2200
Fax: (785) 229-1167
Web Site: www.kalmarind-northamerica.com
Sales Range: $100-124.9 Million
Emp.: 305
Industrial Truck Mfr
S.I.C.: 3537
N.A.I.C.S.: 333924
Leif Wallin *(Pres)*

U.S. Subsidiaries:

Kalmar Industries Corporation (3)
21 Englehard Dr
Monroe, NJ 08831-3722
Tel.: (609) 860-0150
Fax: (609) 860-0224
E-Mail: info@kalmarind.com
Web Site: www.kalmarind.com
Emp.: 50
Inland Material Handling Equipment Service & Sales
S.I.C.: 3999
N.A.I.C.S.: 339999
Andy DePalma *(Mgr-Customer Support)*

Kalmar Industries Magnum Division (3)
1301 Cherokee Trace
White Oak, TX 75693-3530
Tel.: (903) 759-5490
Fax: (903) 297-8166
Sales Range: $1-9.9 Million
Emp.: 44
Mfr Industrial Trucks & Tractors
S.I.C.: 3537
N.A.I.C.S.: 333924

Non-U.S. Subsidiaries:

Cargotec Asia Limited (3)
2nd Fl Yoo Hoo Tower 38-42 Kwai Fung Crescent
Kwai Chung, NT, China (Hong Kong) HK
Tel.: (852) 29448383
Fax: (852) 29449966
E-Mail: kalmarasia.info@cargotec.com
Web Site: www.kalmarglobal.com
Emp.: 90
Develop, Mfr & Sell Material Handling Equipment
S.I.C.: 5039
N.A.I.C.S.: 423390
Ken Loh *(Exec VP)*

Cargotec Norway A/S (3)
Carl Bergersens vei 5
1481 Hagan, Norway NO
Tel.: (47) 67067500
Fax: (47) 67067580
E-Mail: firmapost.oslo@cargotec.com
Web Site: www.kalmar.no
Sales Range: $10-24.9 Million
Emp.: 30
Oil & Gas Field Machinery
S.I.C.: 3533
N.A.I.C.S.: 333132
Jan Ohlsson *(Mng Dir)*

Kalmar Equipment (Australia) Pty. Ltd. (3)
Ste 2 Level 2 768 Lorimer St
Melbourne, VIC, 3207, Australia
Tel.: (61) 397010311
Fax: (61) 0396818202
E-Mail: info@cargotec.com
Web Site: www.kalmar.com
Sales Range: $1-9.9 Million
Emp.: 50
Heavy Equipment Repair Services
S.I.C.: 7539
N.A.I.C.S.: 811310
Peter Mclean *(CFO)*

Kalmar France S.A. (3)
170 boulevard Jules Durand
FR 76600 Le Havre, France FR
Tel.: (33) 235248010
Fax: (33) 235136895
Web Site: www.kalmar.fr
Sales Range: $10-24.9 Million
Emp.: 35
Mfr Industrial Machinery & Equipment
S.I.C.: 3559
N.A.I.C.S.: 333249
Aubry Thierry *(Mng Dir)*

Kalmar HebeFahrzeuge HandelsgesmbH (3)
Porpendors 8
A 9020 Klagenfurt, Austria
Tel.: (43) 4637178818
Fax: (43) 46371722
E-Mail: marketing.austria@cargotec.com
Web Site: www.kalmarind.com
Sales Range: $25-49.9 Million
Emp.: 50
Mfr Industrial Heavy Equipment
S.I.C.: 3799
N.A.I.C.S.: 336999
Jurgen Wurzer *(Mng Dir)*

Kalmar Ltd. (3)
Cargotec Industrial Park
Ellesmere, SY12 9JW, United Kingdom
Tel.: (44) 8451630700
Fax: (44) 1691624687
E-Mail: enquires.uk@cargotec.com
Web Site: www.cargotec.com
Sales Range: $100-124.9 Million
Emp.: 60
Motor Vehicle Mfr
S.I.C.: 3714
N.A.I.C.S.: 336390
Ismo Leppanen *(Mng Dir)*

Kalmar South East Asia Pte. Ltd. (3)
No 2 Gul St 4
Jurong, 629234, Singapore
Tel.: (65) 68653880
Fax: (65) 68653881
Web Site: www.kalmarasia.com
Sales Range: $1-9.9 Million
Net Worth: $302,827
Emp.: 50
Heavy Industrial Equipment
S.I.C.: 3559
N.A.I.C.S.: 333249
Edward Soon Jan Houng *(Mng Dir)*

Kalmer Flurforderzeuge Vertriebs GmbH (3)
Reichsbahnstrasse 72
D 22525 Hamburg, Germany
Tel.: (49) 405473050
Fax: (49) 4054730519
E-Mail: kalmerdesales@kalmerind.com
Web Site: www.kalmerind.de
Sales Range: $25-49.9 Million
Emp.: 74
Heavy Industrial Equipment
S.I.C.: 3559
N.A.I.C.S.: 333249
Wilfreiet Rohrf *(Mng Dir)*

Kalmar Industries South Africa (Pty) Ltd (2)
Off 1100 11th Flr Mansion Hse 12 Field Str
4001 Durban, Kwazulu-Natal, South Africa
Tel.: (27) 31 327 1808
Fax: (27) 31 327 1811
Emp.: 65
Business Management Consulting Services
S.I.C.: 8742
N.A.I.C.S.: 541611
Anton Burchell *(Gen Mgr)*

Cargotec Corporation—(Continued)

Kalmar Port Machinery (Shenzhen) Co., Ltd (2)
No 191 Hua Shen Road Wai Gao Qiao
Free Trade Zone
Shanghai, 200131, China
Tel.: (86) 755 2685 6700
Fax: (86) 755 2685 6701
E-Mail: kalmarasia.info@cargotec.com
Web Site: www.kalmarasia.com
Cargo Handling Equipment Distr
S.I.C.: 5084
N.A.I.C.S.: 423830

U.S. Subsidiaries:

Cargotec Solutions LLC (1)
415 E Dundee St
Ottawa, KS 66067
Tel.: (785) 242-2200
Fax: (785) 242-8573
Heavy Duty Material Handling Equipment Mfr & Distr
S.I.C.: 3589
N.A.I.C.S.: 333318

Kalmar RT Center LLC (1)
103 Guadalupe Dr Rd No 303
Cibolo, TX 78108
Tel.: (210) 599-6541
Fax: (210) 599-4009
Toll Free: (800) 232-1236
E-Mail: sales@kalmarRT.com
Web Site: www.kalmarrt.com
Container Handling Equipment Mfr
S.I.C.: 3536
N.A.I.C.S.: 333923
Steve Speakes *(Pres & CEO)*
Bob Wills *(CFO)*

Navis Holding LLC (1)
55 Harrison St Ste 600
Oakland, CA 94607
Tel.: (510) 267-5000
Fax: (510) 267-5100
Emp.: 150
Investment Management Services
S.I.C.: 6211
N.A.I.C.S.: 523999
Bill Walsh *(CEO)*

Waltco Lift Corp. (1)
298 Northeast Ave
Tallmadge, OH 44278-1428
Tel.: (330) 633-9191
Fax: (330) 633-1418
E-Mail: sales@waltco.com
Web Site: www.waltcoliftgates.com
Emp.: 100
Hydraulic Liftgate Mfr & Distr
S.I.C.: 3536
N.A.I.C.S.: 333923
Steve Miller *(Pres)*

Non-U.S. Subsidiaries:

All Set Marine Lashing AB (1)
Gustavslundsv Gen 151A
Box 14112
167 14 Bromma, Sweden
Tel.: (46) 8 807570
Fax: (46) 8 801588
E-Mail: info@allset.se
Web Site: www.allset.se
Cargo Handling Services
S.I.C.: 4491
N.A.I.C.S.: 488320

Bromma (Malaysia) Sdn. Bhd. (1)
Lot 19 Jalan Kelebang 1/6 Zon
Perindustrian Bebas Kinta
31200 Chemor, Perak, Malaysia
Tel.: (60) 529 388 90
Fax: (60) 529 140 99
E-Mail: malaysia@bromma.com
Web Site: www.bromma.com
Emp.: 450
Crane Spreader & Rotator Mfr
S.I.C.: 3537
N.A.I.C.S.: 333924
Mika Virtanen *(Mng Dir)*

Cargotec ACT B.V. (1)
Proostwetering 26
3543 AE Utrecht, Netherlands
Tel.: (31) 302415422
Emp.: 15
Industrial Control Equipment Mfr
S.I.C.: 3625
N.A.I.C.S.: 335314
Rudi De Vos Burchart *(Gen Mgr)*

Cargotec (ARE) GULF WLL (1)
Plot No 50 Shop Nos 12 & 13 M-9
Mussafah Industrial Area n a
Abu Dhabi, United Arab Emirates
Tel.: (971) 25541690
Fax: (971) 25541601
Crane & Hydraulic Equipment Distr
S.I.C.: 5084
N.A.I.C.S.: 423830

Cargotec Argentina S.R.L. (1)
Av Pte J A Roca 610 2A
1067 Buenos Aires, Argentina
Tel.: (54) 11 4343 3545
Fax: (54) 11 4343 3548
E-Mail: cargotecargentina@kalmar.com.ar
Web Site: www.cargotecargentina.com
Cargo Handling Services
S.I.C.: 4491
N.A.I.C.S.: 488320
Marcelo Massa *(Mng Dir)*

Cargotec Australia Pty. Ltd. (1)
Suite 2 Level 2 768 Lorimer Street
Melbourne, VIC, 3207, Australia
Tel.: (61) 3 9234 7000
Fax: (61) 3 9681 8202
Web Site: www.cargotec.com
Emp.: 24
Cargo Handling Services
S.I.C.: 4491
N.A.I.C.S.: 488320
Peter McLean *(Gen Mgr)*

Cargotec Belgium NV (1)
Heizegemweg 7
2030 Antwerp, Belgium
Tel.: (32) 3 541 77 22
Fax: (32) 3 541 28 23
E-Mail: antwerp.info@cargotec.com
Web Site: www.kalmarbelgium.be
Cargo Handling Equipment Distr
S.I.C.: 5084
N.A.I.C.S.: 423830
Annick Deprez *(Mgr-HR)*

Cargotec Brazil Industria e Comercio de Equipamentos para Movimentacao de Cargas Ltda (1)
Av Santos Dummont 3365 Vicente de Carvalho Guaruja
Sao Paulo, 11460-006, Brazil
Tel.: (55) 13 3308 2222
Fax: (55) 13 3308 2224
Web Site: www.cargotec.com
Marine Cargo Handling Services
S.I.C.: 4491
N.A.I.C.S.: 488320
Alexandre Trindade *(Mgr-Svcs)*

Cargotec Chile - S.A. (1)
El Juncal 071-B Portezuelo
Quilicura, Santiago, Chile
Tel.: (56) 27386993
Fax: (56) 27386460
Web Site: www.cargotec.com
Emp.: 40
Marine Cargo Handling Services
S.I.C.: 4491
N.A.I.C.S.: 488320
Ronald Verzijl *(Gen Mgr)*

Cargotec CHS Asia Pacific Pte Ltd. (1)
No 15 Tukang Innovation Drive
Singapore, 618299, Singapore
Tel.: (65) 65973888
Fax: (65) 65973800
Web Site: www.cargotec.com
Cargo Handling Services
S.I.C.: 4491
N.A.I.C.S.: 488320

Cargotec Croatia d.o.o. (1)
Vrh Martinscice 93B
51221 Rijeka, Croatia
Tel.: (385) 51289717
Fax: (385) 51 287 154
E-Mail:
Web Site: www.cargotec.com
Emp.: 8
Cargo Handling Services
S.I.C.: 4491
N.A.I.C.S.: 488320
Neven Cop *(Mgr-Sls & Svc)*

Cargotec Cyprus Ltd. (1)
Titos Building Office 201 58 Gladstone Street
CY-3041 Limassol, Cyprus
Tel.: (357) 25763670
Fax: (357) 25763671
Web Site: www.cargotec.com
Marine Cargo Handling Services
S.I.C.: 4491
N.A.I.C.S.: 488320
Vladimir Stajduhar *(Acct Mgr-Sls)*

Cargotec Czech Republic s.r.o (1)
Sezemicka 2757/2
193 00 Prague, Czech Republic
Tel.: (420) 226 238 600
Fax: (420) 226 238 601
Web Site: www.cargotec.com
Emp.: 8
Cargo Handling Services
S.I.C.: 4491
N.A.I.C.S.: 488320
Jiri Vrkoc *(Mgr-Sls)*

Cargotec de Mexico, S.A. de C.V. (1)
San Andres Atoto 16A Col San Esteban
Naucalpan, 53550, Mexico
Tel.: (52) 55 53587411
Web Site: www.kalmarind-latinamerica.com
Marine Cargo Handling Services
S.I.C.: 4491
N.A.I.C.S.: 488320
Rafael Llamas *(Dir Gen)*

Cargotec Engineering Italy S.r.l. (1)
Via Massa Avenza 2
54100 Massa, Italy
Tel.: (39) 0585256015
Fax: (39) 0585796112
Web Site: www.cargotec.com
Emp.: 8
Marine Cargo Handling Services
S.I.C.: 4491
N.A.I.C.S.: 488320
Claudia Fontanini *(Gen Mgr)*

Cargotec Germany Gmbh (1)
Emil-Berliner-Strasse 29
30851 Langenhagen, Germany
Tel.: (49) 511 77050
Fax: (49) 511 7705132
E-Mail: hiab.Langenhagen@cargotec.com
Marine Cargo Handling Services
S.I.C.: 4491
N.A.I.C.S.: 488320
Thomas Koskimaa *(Gen Mgr)*

Cargotec Greece Ltd (1)
4-6 Efplias Str
18537 Piraeus, Greece
Tel.: (30) 2104283838
Fax: (30) 2104283839
Web Site: www.cargotec.com
Cargo Handling Services
S.I.C.: 4491
N.A.I.C.S.: 488320

Cargotec Holding Netherlands B.V. (1)
Steenwijkerstraatweg 78 7942
7942 HR Meppel, Netherlands
Tel.: (31) 52225 38 31
Fax: (31) 52224 15 81
Investment Management Sevices
S.I.C.: 6211
N.A.I.C.S.: 523999

Cargotec Holding Sweden AB (1)
70 Kungsgatan
Stockholm, 111 22, Sweden
Tel.: (46) 86775300
Investment Management Services
S.I.C.: 6211
N.A.I.C.S.: 523999

Cargotec Iberia SA (1)
C/Limite s/n Poligono Las Fronteras
28850 Torrejon de Ardoz, Spain
Tel.: (34) 916 270 100
Fax: (34) 916 270 106
E-Mail: salesspain@cargotec.com
Web Site: www.cargotec.com
Emp.: 50
Industrial Machinery Whslr
S.I.C.: 5084
N.A.I.C.S.: 423830
Eduardo Prat *(Gen Mgr)*

Cargotec India Private Limited (1)
3rd Floor Kesar Solitaire Plot No 5 Sector 19 Sanpada Palm Beach Road
Navi Mumbai, Maharashtra, 400705, India
Tel.: (91) 22 6773 6666
Fax: (91) 22 6773 6600
E-Mail: cargotec.india@cargotec.com
Web Site: www.hiab.in
Marine Cargo Handling Services
S.I.C.: 4491
N.A.I.C.S.: 488320

Cargotec Industries (China) Co., Ltd (1)
No 550 South Xin Yuan Road
Pudong, Shanghai, 201306, China
Tel.: (86) 21 6118 4800
Fax: (86) 21 6118 4808
Marine Cargo Handling Services
S.I.C.: 4491
N.A.I.C.S.: 488320
Conor Magee *(Gen Mgr)*

Cargotec Japan Ltd. (1)
9/F Suzue Baydium Building 1-15-1 Kaigan
Minato-Ku, 105-0022 Tokyo, Japan
Tel.: (81) 3 5403 1966
Fax: (81) 3 5403 1953
Web Site: www.cargotec.com
Marine Cargo Handling Services
S.I.C.: 4491
N.A.I.C.S.: 488320
Masashi Tarui *(Mgr)*

Cargotec Korea Limited (1)
173-5 Songjeong-dong
Haeundae-gu, Busan, Gwangyeoksi, 612-040, Korea (South)
Tel.: (82) 517048150
Fax: (82) 51704 0414
Web Site: www.cargotec.com
Marine Cargo Handling Services
S.I.C.: 4491
N.A.I.C.S.: 488320

Cargotec Marine GmbH (1)
Reichsbahnstrasse 72
22525 Hamburg, Germany
Tel.: (49) 40254440
Fax: (49) 4025444444
Web Site: www.cargotec.com
Marine Cargo Handling Services
S.I.C.: 4491
N.A.I.C.S.: 488320

Cargotec (Shanghai) Trading Company Limited (1)
No 191 Hua Shen Road Wai Gao Qiao
Free Trade Zone
Shanghai, 200131, China
Tel.: (86) 2158666658
Cargo Handling Services
S.I.C.: 4491
N.A.I.C.S.: 488320

Cargotec Sweden Bulk Handling AB (1)
Gunnarstorp
PO Box 566
267 25 Bjuv, Sweden
Tel.: (46) 42 85800
Fax: (46) 42 85899
Emp.: 85
Cargo Handling Services
S.I.C.: 4491
N.A.I.C.S.: 488320
Per Karlsson *(Gen Mgr)*

Cargotec Terminal Solutions (Malaysia) Sdn Bhd (1)
No 8 Lorong Sultan Hishamuddin 1 Selat
Klang Utara
Kelang, Selangor, 42000, Malaysia
Tel.: (60) 3 31762998
Cargo Handling Services
S.I.C.: 4491
N.A.I.C.S.: 488320
Collin Swee *(Mng Dir)*

Cargotec Ukraine, LLC (1)
54-A Petropavlivs ka st
04086 Kiev, Ukraine
Tel.: (380) 50 170 25 73
Fax: (380) 44 468 20 19
Web Site: www.cargotec.com
Cargo Handling Services
S.I.C.: 4491
N.A.I.C.S.: 488320

Cargotec UK Ltd. (1)
Cargotec Industrial Park
Ellesmere, SY12 9JW, United Kingdom

Tel.: (44) 169 162 3100
Fax: (44) 191 295 2188
E-Mail: enquiries.uk@cargotec.com
Web Site: www.cargotec.com
Cargo Handling Services
S.I.C.: 4491
N.A.I.C.S.: 488320

Del Equipment (UK) Ltd. (1)
Building 1 Windrush Park Road Windrush Industrial Park
Witney, Oxfordshire, OX29 7HA, United Kingdom
Tel.: (44) 1993 708811
Fax: (44) 1993 708787
E-Mail: sales@del-uk.com
Web Site: www.del-tailifts.co.uk
Emp.: 100
Tail Lift Mfr
S.I.C.: 3537
N.A.I.C.S.: 333924

Hiab Load Handling Equipment (Shanghai) Co., Ltd (1)
International Capital Plaza 12F 1318 Sichuan Road N
Shanghai, 200080, China
Tel.: (86) 21 2606 3000
Fax: (86) 21 6391 2100
Load Handling Machinery Distr
S.I.C.: 3559
N.A.I.C.S.: 333249

Hiab (Pty) Ltd (1)
Corner Fordicks & Aberdein Road Roodekop
1401 Germiston, Gauteng, South Africa
Tel.: (27) 11 865 1425
Fax: (27) 11 866 1226
Web Site: www.hiab.com
Emp.: 74
Load Handling Machinery Mfr
S.I.C.: 3559
N.A.I.C.S.: 333249
Eddie Rewitzky *(Mgr-Ops)*

Hiab Sdn Bhd (1)
27-1 Jalan Bandar 14 Pusat Bandar Puchong, Selangor, 47100, Malaysia
Tel.: (60) 3 5882 2903
Fax: (60) 3 5882 2917
E-Mail: hiab.malaysia@cargotech.com
Emp.: 12
Truck Mounted Crane & Hooklift Distr
S.I.C.: 5084
N.A.I.C.S.: 423830
P. T. Yong *(Mng Dir)*

Interhydraulik Zepro GmbH (1)
Dr Karl Grimmgasse 14
2552 Hirtenberg, Austria
Tel.: (43) 225681500
Fax: (43) 225681500 12
Web Site: www.Interhydraulik.at
Emp.: 10
Industrial Machinery Mfr & Distr
S.I.C.: 3559
N.A.I.C.S.: 333249

International MacGREGOR-Navire Holding BV (1)
Albert Plesmanweg 95 -97
3088 GC Rotterdam, Netherlands
Tel.: (31) 10 2832121
Fax: (31) 10 4293219
Emp.: 300
Investment Management Services
S.I.C.: 6211
N.A.I.C.S.: 523999
Dick Vroonland *(Gen Mgr)*

MacGregor Group AB (1)
PO Box 4113
SE 400 40 Gothenburg, Sweden
Tel.: (46) 31850700
Fax: (46) 31850946
E-Mail: marketing@macgregor-group.com
Web Site: www.macgregor-group.com
Sales Range: $450-499.9 Million
Emp.: 130
Mfr of Marine Cargo Handling & Stowage Systems
S.I.C.: 4499
N.A.I.C.S.: 488390
Mikael Makinen *(Pres)*
Declan Guerin *(CFO)*

Non-U.S. Subsidiaries:

MacGregor (ARE) LLC (2)
Al Quoz Industrial Area 4 Street 14B
Dubai, United Arab Emirates
Tel.: (971) 43413933
Fax: (971) 43413588
E-Mail: behrooz.boorang@cargotec.com
Web Site: www.macgregor-group.com
Emp.: 67
Marine Cargo Handling Services
S.I.C.: 4491
N.A.I.C.S.: 488320
Darko Bogdanovic *(Reg Mgr)*

MacGregor (AUS) Pty. Ltd. (2)
2 Gordon Place
PO Box 662
Balmain, Narellan Vale, NSW 2567, Australia
Tel.: (61) 246474149
Fax: (61) 246477003
E-Mail: michael.stacey@macgregor-group.com
Web Site: www.macgregor-group.com
Emp.: 12
Cargo Access Equipment for Ship Repair & Maintenance Services & Engineering & Service Solutions for the Maritime Transportation Industry
S.I.C.: 3535
N.A.I.C.S.: 333922
Michael Stacey *(Mng Dir)*

MacGregor (CHN) Ltd. (2)
1318 North Sichuan Road 12F International Capital Plaza
200080 Shanghai, China
Tel.: (86) 2163912798
Fax: (86) 2163912276
Web Site: www.macgregor-group.com
Emp.: 160
Engineering & Service Solutions for the Maritime Industry
S.I.C.: 3531
N.A.I.C.S.: 333120

MacGregor Conver GmbH (2)
Zum Panrepel 41
28307 Bremen, Germany
Tel.: (49) 421839183
Fax: (49) 4218391899
Web Site: www.macgregor-group.com
Sales Range: $25-49.9 Million
Emp.: 24
Engineering & Service Solutions for the Maritime Transportation Industry
S.I.C.: 3531
N.A.I.C.S.: 333120

MacGregor (CYPRUS) Ltd. (2)
Titos Bldg Office 201 58 Gladstone St
CY-3071 Limassol, Cyprus
Tel.: (357) 25 76 36 70
Fax: (357) 25 76 36 71
Cargo Handling Equipment Mfr
S.I.C.: 3536
N.A.I.C.S.: 333923
Vladimir Stajduhar *(Gen Mgr)*

Cargotec Denmark A/S (2)
Smedeholm 11
DK 2730 Herlev, Denmark
Tel.: (45) 44538484
Fax: (45) 44538410
Web Site: www.macgregor-group.com
Emp.: 15
Cargo Access Equipment for Ships & Engineering & Service Solutions for Maritime Transportation Industry
S.I.C.: 4491
N.A.I.C.S.: 488320
John Egholm Andersen *(Mgr-Svcs)*

MacGregor (ESP) S.A. (2)
Edificio Tmb 2 Fl Dock A 2 Port Of Bilbao
ES 48980 Santurce, Vizcaya, Spain
Tel.: (34) 944807339
Fax: (34) 944316945
E-Mail: ramon.iturre@cargotec.com
Web Site: www.macgregor-group.com
Sales Range: $1-9.9 Million
Emp.: 10
Cargo Access Equipment for Ships & Engineering & Service Solutions for the Maritime Transportation Industry
S.I.C.: 3531
N.A.I.C.S.: 333120
Ramon Iturre *(Gen Mgr)*

MacGregor France S.A.S (2)
5 Bis Rue De Bel Air
PO Box 437
44474 Carquefou, Cedex, France
Tel.: (33) 240305000
Fax: (33) 240305091
E-Mail:
Emp.: 40
Cargo Access Equipment for Ships & Engineering & Service Solutions for the Maritime Transportation Industry
S.I.C.: 4491
N.A.I.C.S.: 488320
Vilhelm Roberts *(Mng Dir)*

MacGregor (GBR) Ltd. (2)
83 Somerset Rd
Wirral, Pensby, CH61 8SS, United Kingdom
Tel.: (44) 7768334412
Fax: (44) 1517271460
E-Mail: paul.cooper@macgregor-group.com
Web Site: www.macgregor-group.com
Emp.: 10
Cargo Access Equipment & Engineering & Service Solutions for the Maritime Transportation Industry
S.I.C.: 4491
N.A.I.C.S.: 488320
Paul Cooper *(Mgr)*

MacGregor (GRC) E.P.E. (2)
4-6 Efplias St 4th Fl
GR 185 37 Piraeus, Greece
Tel.: (30) 2104283838
Fax: (30) 2104283839
E-Mail: dl_mcg_grc_piraeus_spares@cargotec.com
Web Site: www.macgregor-group.com
Emp.: 10
Cargo Access Equipment for Ships & Engineering & Service Solutions for the Maritime Transportation Industry
S.I.C.: 3531
N.A.I.C.S.: 333120
Agneta Dyberg *(Mng Dir)*
Athena Kanellidou *(Mng Dir)*

MacGregor (Hong Kong) Ltd. (2)
Unit 3551 12 35th Fl Tower 1 Millenium City 1
388 Kwun Tong Rd, Kowloon, China (Hong Kong)
Tel.: (852) 23941008
Fax: (852) 27877652
E-Mail: spencer.lee@macgregor-group.com
Web Site: www.macgregor-group.com
Emp.: 67
Cargo Access Equipment, Repair & Maintenance Services & Engineering & Service Solutions for the Maritime Transportation Industry
S.I.C.: 4491
N.A.I.C.S.: 488320
Spencer Lee *(Branch Mgr)*

MacGregor (HRV) d.o.o. (2)
Vrh Martinscice 93B
Kostrena, 51221 Rijeka, Croatia
Tel.: (385) 51289718
Fax: (385) 51287154
E-Mail: vladimir.stajduhar@macgregor-group.com
Web Site: www.macgregor-group.com
Emp.: 10
Cargo Access Equipment for Ships & Engineering & Service Solutions for the Maritime Transportation Industry
S.I.C.: 3531
N.A.I.C.S.: 333120
Darko Bogdanovic *(Mgr-Middle East)*

MacGregor Kayaba Ltd. (2)
9 F Suzue Baydium Bldg 1-15-1 Kaigan
Tokyo, Minato-Ku, 105 0022, Japan
Tel.: (81) 354031966
Fax: (81) 354031953
E-Mail: motoki.sudo@macgregor-group.com
Web Site: www.macgregor-group.com
Sales Range: $75-99.9 Million
Emp.: 100
Engineering & Service Solutions for the Maritime Transportation Industry
S.I.C.: 3531
N.A.I.C.S.: 333120
Ikuma Sadakane *(Pres)*

MacGregor (KOR) Ltd. (2)
173 5 Song Jeong Dong Haeungae Gu
Busan, 612 040, Korea (South)
Tel.: (82) 517040844
Fax: (82) 517040414
E-Mail: dae.won.hwang@cargotec.com
Web Site: www.macgregor-group.com
Sales Range: $1-9.9 Million
Emp.: 21
Engineering & Service Solutions for the Maritime Transportation Industry
S.I.C.: 3531
N.A.I.C.S.: 333120
Dae Won Hwang *(Gen Mgr)*

MacGregor (NOR) A/S (2)
Skur 39
PO Box 337
0050 Oslo, Vippetangen, Norway
Tel.: (47) 23103400
Fax: (47) 23103401
E-Mail: claus.bjerga@macgregor-group.com
Web Site: www.macgregor-group.com
Emp.: 6
Cargo Access Equipment for Ships & Engineering & Service Solutions for the Maritime Transportation Industry
S.I.C.: 4491
N.A.I.C.S.: 488320
Arve Plassen *(Branch Mgr)*

Subsidiary:

Aker Pusnes AS (3)
PO Box 732
4808 Arendal, Norway
Tel.: (47) 37087300
E-Mail: corporate@akerkvaerner.com
Web Site: www.akersolutions.com
Emp.: 150
Deck Machinery & Mooring Systems Designer & Supplier for Marine & Offshore Applications
S.I.C.: 4491
N.A.I.C.S.: 488320
Lies Hriokim *(Mng Dir)*
Arstein Sunde *(CFO & VP)*

Subsidiaries:

Porsgrunn Steering Gear AS (4)
Dokkveien 10
3920 Porsgrunn, Norway
Tel.: (47) 35931200
Fax: (47) 35931201
E-Mail: Porsgrunn@akersolutions.com
Web Site: www.psg.no
Emp.: 17
Rotary Vane Steering Gears Mfr
S.I.C.: 3566
N.A.I.C.S.: 333612
Rune Nygaard *(CEO)*

Non-U.S. Subsidiary:

Woodfield Systems Limited (4)
Tyler Way Swalecliffe
Whitstable, Kent, CT5 2RS, United Kingdom
Tel.: (44) 1227793351
Fax: (44) 1227793625
E-Mail: info@akersolutions.com
Web Site: www.akersolutions.com
Emp.: 60
Marine Loading Arms Mfr & Designer
S.I.C.: 3483
N.A.I.C.S.: 332993
Richard Williams *(Mng Dir)*

MacGregor Oy (2)
Hallimestarinkatu 6
PO Box 116
20780 Kaarina, Finland
Tel.: (358) 241211
Fax: (358) 24121517
E-Mail: timo.nordlin@cargotec.com
Web Site: www.macgregor-group.com
Sales Range: $10-24.9 Million
Emp.: 200
Designs Shipboard Cargo Handling Equipment & Engineering & Service Solutions for the Maritime Transportation Industry
S.I.C.: 4491
N.A.I.C.S.: 488320
Timo Nordlin *(Branch Mgr)*

MacGregor Plimsoll Offshore Services Pte Ltd (2)
48 Tuas Road Pioneer West
Singapore, 638500, Singapore
Tel.: (65) 68613922
Cargo Handling Services
S.I.C.: 4491
N.A.I.C.S.: 488320

MacGregor Plimsoll Sdn Bhd (2)
Lot 14695 Kg Jaya Batu 2 Jalan Air Putih
Kemaman, Terengganu, 24000, Malaysia

Cargotec Corporation—(Continued)

Tel.: (60) 98592129
Fax: (60) 98582272
E-Mail: ofs.sgp.salesmiri@cargotec.com
Web Site: www.cargotec.com
Emp.: 10
Cargo Handling Services
S.I.C.: 4491
N.A.I.C.S.: 488320
Melvin Go *(Mgr)*

MacGregor Plimsoll (Tianjin) Co., Ltd (2)
No.8 XinYe Street One West TEDA
Tianjin, 300462, China
Tel.: (86) 2259829200
Fax: (86) 2259829212
Load Handling Equipment Mfr
S.I.C.: 3559
N.A.I.C.S.: 333249

MacGregor (POL) Sp. z o.o. (2)
Ul Luzycka 8
PL 81 537 Gdynia, Poland
Tel.: (48) 587855110
Fax: (48) 87855111
E-Mail: romuald.tomaszewski@macgregor-group.com
Web Site: www.macgregor-group.com
Sales Range: $1-9.9 Million
Emp.: 50
Cargo Access Equipment for Ships & Engineering & Service Solutions for the Maritime Transportation Industry
S.I.C.: 3531
N.A.I.C.S.: 333120
Romuald Tomaszewski *(CEO)*

MacGregor (PRT) Lda. (2)
Av Alianca Povo MFA
Cova da Piedade
2800 Almada, Portugal
Tel.: (351) 12744359
Fax: (351) 12747592
Web Site: www.macgregor-group.com
Emp.: 46
Cargo Access Equipment & Engineering & Service Solutions for the Maritime Transportation Industry
S.I.C.: 3535
N.A.I.C.S.: 333922

MacGregor (SGP) Pte. Ltd. (2)
12 Benoi Crescent
Singapore, 629975, Singapore
Tel.: (65) 62652322
Fax: (65) 62641261
E-Mail: albert.chua.choo.huat@macgregor-group.com
Web Site: www.macgregor-group.com
Emp.: 25
Cargo Access Equipment for Ship Repair & Maintenance Services & Engineering & Service Solutions for the Maritime Transportation Industry
S.I.C.: 4491
N.A.I.C.S.: 488320

PT MacGregor Plimsoll Indonesia (2)
Puri Industrial ParkBlok D No 2 Batam Centre
Batam, Indonesia
Tel.: (62) 7787482171
Fax: (62) 7787482173
Marine Cargo Handling Services
S.I.C.: 4491
N.A.I.C.S.: 488320

Non-U.S. Joint Venture:

MacGregor BLRT Baltic OU (2)
103 Kopli Str
11712 Tallinn, Estonia
Tel.: (372) 6102200
Fax: (372) 6 102 400
Cargo Handling Services
S.I.C.: 4491
N.A.I.C.S.: 488320

MacGREGOR Hydramarine AS (1)
Andoyveien 23
Kristiansand, 4623, Norway
Tel.: (47) 91 68 60 00
Fax: (47) 38 01 87 01
Load Handling Equipment Mfr
S.I.C.: 3559
N.A.I.C.S.: 333249

MacGREGOR Plimsoll Pte Ltd (1)
48 Tuas Road
Singapore, 638500, Singapore
Tel.: (65) 68613922
Fax: (65) 68624334
Web Site: www.plimsollcorp.com
Cargo Handling Equipment Mfr
S.I.C.: 3589
N.A.I.C.S.: 333318

MacGREGOR Shanghai Trading Co., Ltd. (1)
12F International Capital Plaza 1318 North Sichuan Road
200080 Shanghai, China
Tel.: (86) 2126063000
Fax: (86) 2163912276
Cargo Handling Equipment Mfr
S.I.C.: 3589
N.A.I.C.S.: 333318
Frank Chen *(Mgr-Svc-Hatch Covers, RoRo Equipment & Winches)*

MacGREGOR (UKR) A.O. (1)
Bolshaya Arnautskaya St House 15 Room 78
Odessa, 65012, Ukraine
Tel.: (380) 48 221 0142
Fax: (380) 48 221 0612
Marine Cargo Handling Services
S.I.C.: 4491
N.A.I.C.S.: 488320

Moffett Engineering Ltd (1)
Ardee Road
Dundalk, Ireland
Tel.: (353) 429359500
Fax: (353) 429327298
Emp.: 170
Hydraulic System Mfr
S.I.C.: 3536
N.A.I.C.S.: 333923
Keith Quigley *(Gen Mgr)*

Navis India Technologies Private Limited (1)
Unit No 4 9th Floor Zenith International Tech Park Phase III
Taramani - CSIR Road, Chennai, 600 113, India
Tel.: (91) 44 4590 3000
Fax: (91) 44 4590 3100
Web Site: www.navis.com
Logistics Consulting Services
S.I.C.: 4731
N.A.I.C.S.: 541614

O'Leary's Material Handling Services Pty Ltd (1)
6 Montgomery Way
Malaga, Perth, WA, 6090, Australia
Tel.: (61) 8 9248 6674
Fax: (61) 8 9248 6694
E-Mail: admin@olearys.com.au
Web Site: www.olearys.com.au
Emp.: 15
Tail Lift Mfr & Whslr
S.I.C.: 3534
N.A.I.C.S.: 333921

Platform Crane Services Mexico S. de. R.L. (1)
Calle 61 No 1A Col Revolution Cd del Carmen
24120 Campeche, Mexico
Tel.: (52) 938 286 1528
Fax: (52) 938 286 1528
Oil & Gas Exploration Services
S.I.C.: 1389
N.A.I.C.S.: 213112
David Crockett *(Mgr)*

Z-Lyften Produktion AB (1)
Mossvagen 8
641 49 Katrineholm, Sweden
Tel.: (46) 150 489 550
Fax: (46) 150 489 551
Web Site: www.z-lyften.se
Tail Lift Mfr
S.I.C.: 3569
N.A.I.C.S.: 333999

Zepro Danmark A/S (1)
Industrikrogen 14
2635 Ishoj, Denmark
Tel.: (45) 43 99 33 00
Fax: (45) 43 99 10 15
Web Site: www.zepro.dk
Cargo Handling Equipment Distr

S.I.C.: 5084
N.A.I.C.S.: 423830

CARIBBEAN AIRLINES LIMITED

30 Edward Street
Port of Spain, Trinidad & Tobago
Tel.: (868) 6257200
E-Mail: mail@caribbean-airlines.com
Web Site: www.caribbean-airlines.com
Year Founded: 1940
Sales Range: $650-699.9 Million
Emp.: 1,984

Business Description:
Air Carrier
S.I.C.: 4512
N.A.I.C.S.: 481111

Personnel:
George M. Nicholas, III *(Chm)*
Mohan Jaikaran *(Vice Chm)*
Robert Corbie *(Acting CEO & COO)*

Board of Directors:
George M. Nicholas, III
Allan Clovis
Mohan Jaikaran
Avedanand Persad
Gizelle Russell
Venosh Sagewan-Maraj
Susan Smith

CARIBBEAN DEVELOPMENT BANK

Wildey
PO Box 408
Saint Michael, Barbados
Mailing Address:
PO Box 408
Wildey, Saint Michael, Barbados
Tel.: (246) 4311600
Fax: (246) 4267269
E-Mail: info@caribank.org
Web Site: www.caribank.org
Sales Range: $10-24.9 Million
Emp.: 200

Business Description:
Banking Services
S.I.C.: 6029
N.A.I.C.S.: 522110

Personnel:
William Warren Smith *(Pres)*
Clyde Roopchand *(Chief Plng Officer)*
Douglas Leys *(Gen Counsel)*

Board of Directors:
Isaac Anthony
Lindsey Block
Alberto de Brigard
Kathryn Dunlop
Rosamund Edwards
Pablo Facchinei
Crispin Frederick
Bentley Gibbs
Whitfield Harris, Jr.
Joseph Howard
Wang Lin
Adolfo Meisel
Ruth R. Millar
Carol Nelson
Sandra Pepera
Jin Qi
George D. Rodgers
Clyde Roopchand
John Skerritt
Locksley Smith
Uwe Wolff

CARIBBEAN DISCOVERY, S.A. DE C.V.

(d/b/a Dolphin Discovery)
Puerto Aventuras
Quintana Roo Isla Mujeres, Cancun, Mexico
Tel.: (52) 998 849 4757
Web Site: www.caribbeancoasttravel.com
Year Founded: 1990

Business Description:
Marine Mammal & Animal Park Operator
S.I.C.: 8422
N.A.I.C.S.: 712190

Personnel:
Eduardo Albor *(Pres & CEO)*

CARIBBEAN DIVERSIFIED INVESTMENTS INC.

175 Commerce Valley Drive West
Suite 310
Markham, ON, L3T 7P6, Canada
Tel.: (905) 763-3001
E-Mail: info@caribbeaninvestments.ca
Web Site: www.caribbeaninvestments.ca
Year Founded: 2011
HDC—(CNSX)

Business Description:
Investment Services
S.I.C.: 6211
N.A.I.C.S.: 523999

Personnel:
Christopher Malone *(Pres & CEO)*

CARIBOO CHEVROLET BUICK GMC LTD.

370 Mackenzie Ave S
Williams Lake, BC, V2G 1C7, Canada
Tel.: (250) 392-7185
Fax: (250) 392-4703
Toll Free: (800) 665-2409
Web Site: www.cariboogm.ca
Year Founded: 1982
Rev.: $15,217,298
Emp.: 34

Business Description:
New & Used Car Dealers
S.I.C.: 5511
N.A.I.C.S.: 441110

Personnel:
Tammy Tugnum *(Gen Mgr)*

CARIBOO ROSE RESOURCES LTD.

Suite 110 - 325 Howe Street
Vancouver, BC, V6C 1Z7, Canada
Tel.: (604) 681-7913
Fax: (604) 681-9855
Toll Free: (888) 656-6611
E-Mail: info@eastfieldgroup.com
Web Site: www.cariboorose.com
Year Founded: 2006
CRB—(TSXV)
Int. Income: $10,274
Assets: $1,012,737
Liabilities: $38,616
Net Worth: $974,122
Earnings: ($69,727)
Fiscal Year-end: 02/28/13

Business Description:
Metal Exploration Services
S.I.C.: 1081
N.A.I.C.S.: 213114

Personnel:
William Morton *(Pres & CEO)*
Don Sharp *(CFO)*
Glen Garratt *(Sec & VP)*

Board of Directors:
Glen Garratt
Ed Kimura
William Morton
Al Scott
Don Sharp
Paul Way

Legal Counsel:
Miller Thompson
1000-840 Howe Street
Vancouver, BC, Canada

Transfer Agent:
Olympia Trust Company
1900 925 W Georgia Street
Vancouver, BC, V6C 3L2, Canada

CARIBOU KING RESOURCES LTD.

Suite 1220 - 789 West Pender
Vancouver, BC, V6C 1H2, Canada
Tel.: (604) 683-3995
Fax: (604) 683-3988
Toll Free: (888) 945-4770
E-Mail: info@caribouking.com
Web Site: www.caribouking.com
Year Founded: 2007
CKR—(TSXV)
Assets: $309,943
Liabilities: $270,202
Net Worth: $39,741
Earnings: ($3,468,031)
Fiscal Year-end: 12/31/12

Business Description:
Metal Mineral Exploration Services
S.I.C.: 1099
N.A.I.C.S.: 212299

Personnel:
Tom McCandless *(Pres)*
Michael B. England *(CEO)*
John Masters *(CFO & Sec)*

Board of Directors:
Michael B. England
David Lajack
John Masters
Tom McCandless
Bernard Stannus

CARILLION PLC

Birch Street
Wolverhampton, WV1 4HY, United Kingdom
Tel.: (44) 1902422431
Telex: 336057TARCONG
Fax: (44) 1902316165
E-Mail: info@carillionplc.com
Web Site: www.carillionplc.com
CLLN—(LSE OTC)
Rev.: $6,953,298,012
Assets: $6,099,217,980
Liabilities: $4,504,924,725
Net Worth: $1,594,293,255
Earnings: $262,477,998
Emp.: 27,426
Fiscal Year-end: 12/31/12

Business Description:
Civil Engineering, Facilities Management & Infrastructure Services
S.I.C.: 8744
N.A.I.C.S.: 561210

Personnel:
Richard Howson *(CEO)*
Richard F. Tapp *(Sec)*

Board of Directors:
Philip Graham Rogerson
Richard Adam
Andrew J. H. Dougal
Philip Nevill Green
Alison Horner
Richard Howson
Steven Lewis Mogford
Vanda Murray
Ceri Powell

Legal Counsel:
Slaughter & May
One Bunhill Row
London, EC1Y 8YY, United Kingdom
Tel.: (44) 20 7600 1200
Fax: (44) 20 7600 0289

Subsidiaries:

1st Insulation Partners Limited (1)
Unit G02 Magna 34 Temple Close
Rotherham, South Yorkshire, S60 1FH, United Kingdom
Tel.: (44) 1709389300
Fax: (44) 1709389301
E-Mail: office@firstinsulation.co.uk
Web Site: www.firstinsulation.co.uk
Emp.: 25
Insulation Installation Services
S.I.C.: 1799
N.A.I.C.S.: 238290
Phil Walker *(Acct Mgr)*

AFR Limited (1)
Avoncraft House
20 Burrowfield, Welwyn Garden City, AL7 4SR, United Kingdom
Tel.: (44) 1707320207
Fax: (44) 1707320171
Central Heating & Maintenance Services
S.I.C.: 1711
N.A.I.C.S.: 238220
Alan Ring *(Mng Dir)*

Carillion (AMBS) Ltd (1)
Construction House 24 Birch St
Wolverhampton, West Midlands, WV1 4HY, United Kingdom
Tel.: (44) 1902 422431
Web Site: www.carillionplc.com
Facilities Management Services
S.I.C.: 8744
N.A.I.C.S.: 561210

Carillion (Aspire Construction) Holdings No 2 Ltd (1)
Construction House 24 Birch Street
Wolverhampton, West Midlands, WV1 4HY, United Kingdom
Tel.: (44) 1902 422431
Investment Management Services
S.I.C.: 6211
N.A.I.C.S.: 523999

Carillion Construction Ltd (1)
Radius Court
Bracknell, Berkshire, RG12 2UP, United Kingdom
Tel.: (44) 1344 828500
Fax: (44) 1344 828693
Emp.: 80
Construction Engineering Services
S.I.C.: 8711
N.A.I.C.S.: 541330
Fraser Gale *(Reg Mgr-Comml)*

Carillion CR Ltd (1)
24 Birch Street
Wolverhampton, West Midlands, WV1 4HY, United Kingdom
Tel.: (44) 845 120 8208
Web Site: www.carillionplc.com
Emp.: 100
Construction Engineering Services
S.I.C.: 8711
N.A.I.C.S.: 541330

Carillion Energy Services Limited (1)
Partnership House City W Business Park
Tyne And Wear, Newcastle upon Tyne, NE3 3AF, United Kingdom
Tel.: (44) 1912473800
Fax: (44) 191 2473802
Web Site: www.renewables.carillionenergy.com
Emp.: 150
Architectural & Engineering Activities
S.I.C.: 0781
N.A.I.C.S.: 541320
Derek Holes *(Mgr-Bus)*

Carillion Fleet Management Ltd (1)
Construction House 24 Birch Street
Wolverhampton, West Midlands, WV3 0SR, United Kingdom
Tel.: (44) 8451282999
Web Site: www.carillionplc.com
Fleet Management Services
S.I.C.: 7515
N.A.I.C.S.: 532112

Carillion Private Finance Ltd (1)
24 Birch Street
Wolverhampton, WV1 4HY, United Kingdom
Tel.: (44) 1902 316 733
Fax: (44) 1902318112
E-Mail: privatefinance@carillionplc.com
Emp.: 1
Financial Management Services
S.I.C.: 6211
N.A.I.C.S.: 523999
Kai Becker *(Mng Dir)*

Carillion Services Ltd (1)
24 Birch St
Wolverhampton, West Midlands, WV1 4HY, United Kingdom
Tel.: (44) 1902 422431
Web Site: www.carillionplc.com
Emp.: 100
Construction Engineering Services
S.I.C.: 8711
N.A.I.C.S.: 541330

Eaga Contract Services East Ltd. (1)
4 Traynor Way Whitehouse Business Park
Peterlee, Durham, SR8 2RT, United Kingdom
Tel.: (44) 191288 9940
Fax: (44) 191 288 9941
Web Site: www.howeltd.co.uk
External Wall Insulation Services
S.I.C.: 1742
N.A.I.C.S.: 238310

eaga Insurance Services Limited (1)
Lawrence House Harborough Rd Market Harborough
Bowden Bus Vlg, Leicester, Leicestershire, LE16 7SA, United Kingdom
Tel.: (44) 1858545000
Fax: (44) 1858545962
E-Mail: eisl@eaga.com
Emp.: 19
Insurance Services
S.I.C.: 6411
N.A.I.C.S.: 524210
John Moore *(Gen Mgr)*

Mico Services Limited (1)
Unit 14 Seaway Dr Seaway Pde Industrial Estate
Port Talbot, W Glamorgan, SA12 7BR, United Kingdom
Tel.: (44) 1639825770
Fax: (44) 1639825778
E-Mail: nigel.piles@eaga.co.uk
Emp.: 124
Energy Efficiency Service Provider
S.I.C.: 9631
N.A.I.C.S.: 926130
Nigel Piles *(Gen Mgr)*

Permarock Products Limited (1)
Jubilee Dr Loughborough
Leicestershire, Leicester, LE11 5TW, United Kingdom
Tel.: (44) 1509262924
Fax: (44) 1509230063
E-Mail: permarock@permarock.com
Web Site: www.permarock.com
Emp.: 38
External Wall Insulation Service Provider
S.I.C.: 1742
N.A.I.C.S.: 238310
Sean Waldrem *(Mng Dir)*

Postworth Ltd (1)
Courtyard Woodlands
Bristol, Avon, BS32 4NH, United Kingdom
Tel.: (44) 870 128 5160
Construction Engineering Services
S.I.C.: 8711
N.A.I.C.S.: 541330

TPS Consult Limited (1)
Centre Tower Whitgift Centre
Croydon, CR9 0AU, United Kingdom UK
Tel.: (44) 2082564000
Fax: (44) 2082564116
E-Mail: info@tpsconsult.co.uk
Web Site: www.tpsconsult.co.uk
Emp.: 240
Architectural & Engineering Consulting Services
S.I.C.: 8712
N.A.I.C.S.: 541310
Frank Huidobro *(Mng Dir)*

Division:

Carillion Specialist Services (2)
Centre Tower Whitgift Centre
Croydon, CR9 0AU, United Kingdom
Tel.: (44) 20 8265 4000
Fax: (44) 20 8356 4116
E-Mail: info@tpsconsult.co.uk
Web Site: www.buildingcontrolonline.com
Building Inspection Services
S.I.C.: 7389
N.A.I.C.S.: 541350
David McCullogh *(Head-Prof Standards)*

Units:

Carillion Defence (1)
24 Birch St
Wolverhampton, WV1 4HY, United Kingdom
Tel.: (44) 1902316696
Fax: (44) 1902316165
E-Mail: jiana.lester@carillionplc.com
Web Site: www.carillionplc.com
Construction & Facilities Management Services for the Defense Industry
S.I.C.: 1542
N.A.I.C.S.: 236220
Richard Lumby *(Mng Dir)*

Carillion Facilities Management (1)
Hetton Court The Oval
Hunslet, Leeds, LS10 2AU, United Kingdom (100%)
Tel.: (44) 1132705533
Fax: (44) 1132701133
E-Mail: carillionfm@carillionplc.com
Property Asset Management & Facilities Support Services
S.I.C.: 8744
N.A.I.C.S.: 561210
John Platt *(Mng Dir)*

Carillion Health (1)
24 Birch Street
Wolverhampton, WV1 4HY, United Kingdom
Tel.: (44) 1902422431
Web Site: www.carillionplc.com
Emp.: 1,000
Health Facilities Management Services
S.I.C.: 8744
N.A.I.C.S.: 561210

Carillion Piling (1)
1st Fl Radius Ct Eastern Rd
RG12 2UP Bracknell, Berks, United Kingdom
Tel.: (44) 1344828500
Fax: (44) 1344828691
E-Mail: enquiries@carillionpiling.com
Web Site: www.carillionpiling.com
Emp.: 70
Specialty Engineering & Construction Services
S.I.C.: 8711
N.A.I.C.S.: 541330
Martin Kenwright *(Mng Dir)*

Carillion Planned Maintenance (1)
12 14 Lombard Road
London, SW11 3AY, United Kingdom
Tel.: (44) 2072286400
Fax: (44) 2079243480
E-Mail: info@plannedmaintenanceengineering.co.uk
Web Site: www.plannedmaintenanceengineering.co.uk
Emp.: 60
Technical & Building Maintenance Services
S.I.C.: 8744
N.A.I.C.S.: 561210
Dominic Shorrocks *(Mng Dir)*

Non-U.S. Subsidiaries:

Carillion Alawi LLC (1)
Ruwi
PO Box 1436
Ruwi, PC 112, Oman (100%)
Tel.: (968) 24590347
Telex: 3240WIMMUSMB
Fax: (968) 24590893
E-Mail: callc@omancal.net.om
Web Site: www.carillionplc.com
Civil Engineering Contractors
S.I.C.: 1623
N.A.I.C.S.: 237110

Carillion Canada Inc (1)
7077 Keele St
Concord, ON, L4K 0B6, Canada
Tel.: (905) 532-5200
Fax: (905) 532-5299
E-Mail: info@carillion.ca
Web Site: www.carillion.ca
Highway Construction Engineering Services
S.I.C.: 1611
N.A.I.C.S.: 237310
Paul Quinless *(Exec VP-Transport & Civil Infrastructure-Roads Mgmt Div)*
Albert Barclay *(Sr VP-Construction-Building Div)*
Elaine Dray *(Sr VP-HR)*
John MacCuish *(Sr VP-Svcs-Integrated Facilities Mgmt Div)*

Carillion Construction Canada (1)
7077 Kelle St
Concord, ON, L4K 0B6, Canada (100%)
Tel.: (416) 233-5811

Carillion plc—(Continued)

Telex: 6967518
Fax: (905) 532-5299
Emp.: 80
Civil Engineering Contractors
S.I.C.: 1629
N.A.I.C.S.: 237110
Graham Brown *(Pres & CEO)*

Carillion Construction (Caribbean) Ltd. **(1)**
Southern Main Road
Couva, Trinidad & Tobago (100%)
Telex: 31345
Civil Engineering Contractors
S.I.C.: 1623
N.A.I.C.S.: 237110

Eaga Energy India Private Limited **(1)**
T2 1A & 8C Millenium City IT Park DN 62
Sector V
Salt Lake City, Kolkata, West Bengal, 700091, India
Tel.: (91) 3330128485
Fax: (91) 3330128586
E-Mail: hr@eaga.co.in
Web Site: www.eaga.co.in
Emp.: 100
IT Services & Energy Conservation
S.I.C.: 3571
N.A.I.C.S.: 334111
Deb A. Mukherjee *(Chm)*

Non-U.S. Joint Venture:

Al Futtaim Carillion **(1)**
Near Dubai Municipality Used Car Showroom Complex Aweer
Dubai, 1811, United Arab Emirates (100%)
Tel.: (971) 43331200
Telex: 47523ALWIMEM
Fax: (971) 3331018
E-Mail: afc@afcarillion.ae
Web Site: www.afcarillion.ae
Emp.: 24,000
Civil Engineering Contractors
S.I.C.: 1629
N.A.I.C.S.: 237990
Richard Howson *(Mng Dir)*
Simon Web *(Mng Dir)*

CARIMALO

La Loge Rue Jean Jaures
22600 Saint-Barnabe, Cotes-d'Armor, France
Tel.: (33) 296267461
Fax: (33) 296266561
E-Mail: contact@carimalo.fr
Web Site: www.carimalo.fr
Rev.: $10,000,000
Emp.: 48

Business Description:
Construction
S.I.C.: 1541
N.A.I.C.S.: 236210

Personnel:
Yvon Carimalo *(Pres&Gen Mgr)*

CARINDALE PROPERTY TRUST

Level 30 85 Castlereagh Street
Sydney, NSW, 2000, Australia
Tel.: (61) 2 9358 7877
Fax: (61) 2 9358 7881
E-Mail: investor@au.westfield.com
Web Site: www.carindalepropertytrust.com.au
CDP—(ASX)
Rev.: $52,396,788
Assets: $712,978,768
Liabilities: $242,379,955
Net Worth: $470,598,813
Earnings: $26,133,784
Fiscal Year-end: 06/30/13

Business Description:
Commercial Shopping Centers Real Estate Investment Trust
S.I.C.: 6726
N.A.I.C.S.: 525990

Personnel:
Maureen T. McGrath *(Co-Sec)*
Simon J. Tuxen *(Co-Sec)*

CARING PHARMACY GROUP BHD

8 Jln 1/137C Bedford Business Park
Kuala Lumpur, 58200, Malaysia
Tel.: (60) 3 7782 1988
Web Site: www.caring2u.com.my
Year Founded: 1994
5245—(KLS)
Sales Range: $75-99.9 Million
Emp.: 340

Business Description:
Pharmacies
S.I.C.: 5912
N.A.I.C.S.: 446110

Personnel:
Yeow Siang Chong *(Mng Dir)*

CARISBROOKE SHIPPING LIMITED

Bridge House 38 Medina Road
Cowes, Isle of Wight, PO31 7DA, United Kingdom
Tel.: (44) 1983 284100
Fax: (44) 1983 284199
E-Mail: operations@caship.com
Web Site: www.carisbrookeshipping.net
Sales Range: $100-124.9 Million
Emp.: 90

Business Description:
Freight Transportation
S.I.C.: 4731
N.A.I.C.S.: 488510

Personnel:
Robert Webster *(CEO)*

Non-U.S. Subsidiaries:

Carisbrooke Shipping BV **(1)**
Scheepmakerij 230
3331 MB Zwijndrecht, Netherlands
Tel.: (31) 78 625 1973
Fax: (31) 78 625 1955
Freight Transportation
S.I.C.: 4731
N.A.I.C.S.: 488510

Carisbrooke Shipping (Germany) GmbH **(1)**
Flughafenallee 26
D-28199 Bremen, Germany
Tel.: (49) 421 597 65 491
E-Mail: chartering@caship.de
Freight Transportation
S.I.C.: 4731
N.A.I.C.S.: 488510

Carisbrooke Shipping GmbH **(1)**
Ledastrasse 24
26789 Leer, Germany
Tel.: (49) 4919994341
Fax: (49) 4919994342
Freight Transportation
S.I.C.: 4731
N.A.I.C.S.: 488510

Soetermeer Fekkes - Zwijndrecht **(1)**
Scheepmakerij 230
3331 MB Zwijndrecht, Netherlands
Tel.: (31) 786251900
Fax: (31) 786251925
E-Mail: operations@sfck.nl
Web Site: www.sfck.nl
Freight Transportation
S.I.C.: 4731
N.A.I.C.S.: 488510

CARISTRAP INTERNATIONAL INC.

1760 Fortin Boulevard
Laval, QC, H7S 1NH, Canada
Tel.: (450) 667-4700
Fax: (450) 663-1520
Toll Free: (800) 361-9466
E-Mail: info@caristrap.com
Web Site: www.caristrap.com
Year Founded: 1954
Sales Range: $1-9.9 Million
Emp.: 250

Business Description:
Polyester Cord Strapping Systems Mfr
Export
S.I.C.: 2296
N.A.I.C.S.: 314994

Personnel:
Audrey Karass *(Pres)*

Non-U.S. Subsidiary:

CARISTRAP EUROPE d.o.o. **(1)**
Mihovljan bb
49252 Mihovljan, Croatia
Tel.: (385) 49 354 287
Fax: (385) 49 354 290
E-Mail: info@caristrapeurope.com
Emp.: 32
Industrial Strapping Mfr
S.I.C.: 3499
N.A.I.C.S.: 332999
Dino Celjo *(Mgr-Sls)*

CARL ALLERS ETABLISSEMENT A/S

Vigerslev Alle 18
DK 2500 Valby, Denmark
Tel.: (45) 36152000
Fax: (45) 36152696
E-Mail: info@aller.dk
Web Site: www.aller.dk
Emp.: 400

Business Description:
Holding Company
S.I.C.: 6719
N.A.I.C.S.: 551112

Personnel:
Paul Chora-Kaospy *(Pres)*

Non-U.S. Subsidiary:

Aller Norge A/S **(1)**
Postboks 1169
107 Oslo, Sentrum, Norway
Tel.: (47) 21301100
Fax: (47) 21301204
E-Mail: post@aller.no
Web Site: www.aller.no
Emp.: 420
Holding Company
S.I.C.: 6719
N.A.I.C.S.: 551112
Roger Hansen *(Mng Dir)*

Subsidiary:

Allers Familie-Journal A/S **(2)**
Stenersgata 2
N 0184 Oslo, Norway (100%)
Mailing Address:
PO Box 1169
Oslo, Sentrum, N 0107, Norway
Tel.: (47) 21301000
Fax: (47) 21301205
E-Mail: post@aller.no
Web Site: www.aller.no/Allergruppen/Kontakt/Selskapene/
Emp.: 180
Weekly Magazine Publisher
S.I.C.: 2721
N.A.I.C.S.: 511120
Per Christian Andersen *(Dir-Mktg)*

CARL BENNET AB

Arvid Wallgrens Backe 20
SE 402 33 Gothenburg, Sweden
Tel.: (46) 317416400
Fax: (46) 317416410
Web Site: www.carlbennetab.se
Sales Range: $1-4.9 Billion
Emp.: 4,311

Business Description:
Investment Holding Company
S.I.C.: 6719
N.A.I.C.S.: 551112

Personnel:
Carl Bennet *(Owner, Chm & CEO)*
Anne Lenerius *(CFO)*

Board of Directors:
Carl Bennet
Nina Bennet
Johan Stern

Holdings:

Elanders AB **(1)**
Designvagen 2
435 33 Molnlycke, Sweden (73.4%)
Mailing Address:
PO Box 137
435 23 Molnlycke, Sweden
Tel.: (46) 31 750 00 00
Fax: (46) 31 750 00 10
E-Mail: info@elanders.com
Web Site: www.elanders.com
ELANB—(OMX)
Sls.: $297,865,076
Assets: $350,032,057
Liabilities: $202,386,758
Net Worth: $147,645,299
Earnings: $6,881,015
Emp.: 1,780
Fiscal Year-end: 12/31/12
Graphics Services for Commercial Printing, Packaging & E-Commerce
S.I.C.: 2759
N.A.I.C.S.: 323111
Carl Bennet *(Chm)*
Johan Stern *(Vice Chm)*
Magnus Nilsson *(Pres & CEO)*
Andreas Wikner *(CFO)*

Subsidiaries:

AB Repronik **(2)**
Box 13033
40151 Gothenburg, Sweden (100%)
Tel.: (46) 317072970
Fax: (46) 317073115
E-Mail: info@repronik.se
Emp.: 45
Provider of Graphical Production Servcies
S.I.C.: 7336
N.A.I.C.S.: 541430

Elanders Digitaltryck AB **(2)**
PO BOX 137
43523 Molnlycke, Sweden (100%)
Tel.: (46) 317500000
Fax: (46) 317500010
E-Mail: info@elanders.com
Web Site: www.elanders.se
Emp.: 200
Provider of Graphical Media Services
S.I.C.: 7336
N.A.I.C.S.: 541430
Gunas Brannerud *(Pres)*

Elanders Gummessons AB **(2)**
Lovengatan 4
PO Box 807
52123 Falkoping, Sweden (100%)
Tel.: (46) 515723200
Fax: (46) 51516464
E-Mail: info@elanders.com
Web Site: www.elanders.com
Sls.: $19,344,040
Emp.: 75
Provider of Graphical Media Services
S.I.C.: 7336
N.A.I.C.S.: 541430
Jonas Brannerud *(CEO & Mng Dir)*

Elanders Novum AB, Stockholm **(2)**
Marieholmsgatan 10
415 02 Gothenburg, Sweden
Tel.: (46) 31840155
Fax: (46) 31250580
Web Site: www.elanders.se
Graphic Services
S.I.C.: 7336
N.A.I.C.S.: 541430

Elanders Stockholm **(2)**
Bux 518
1615 Vallingby, Sweden
Tel.: (46) 86346000
Fax: (46) 86346071
Web Site: www.elanders.com
Provider of Graphical Media Services
S.I.C.: 7336
N.A.I.C.S.: 541430

Elanders Svenskt Tryck AB **(2)**
Bruksvagen
Box 2052
Surte, 44502 Gothenburg, Sweden (100%)

Tel.: (46) 31979800
Fax: (46) 31982255
Emp.: 45
Provider of Graphical Media Services
S.I.C.: 7336
N.A.I.C.S.: 541430

Elanders Sverige AB (2)
Kallvattengatan 9
21223 Malmo, Sweden SE
Tel.: (46) 40385700 (100%)
Fax: (46) 40931868
E-Mail: info@elanders.com
Web Site: www.elanders.se/de/Kontakt/Elanders-in-Sweden/Elanders-in-Malmo/
Emp.: 50
Graphical Media Services
S.I.C.: 7336
N.A.I.C.S.: 541430
Magnus Sahlen *(Bus Mgr)*

Elanders (2)
Design Veg 2
PO Box 137
43533 Molnlycke, Sweden
Tel.: (46) 317500000
Fax: (46) 0317500010
E-Mail: info@elanders.com
Web Site: www.elanders.se
Emp.: 1,500
Provider of Graphical Development Services
S.I.C.: 7336
N.A.I.C.S.: 541430
Magnus Nilsson *(Pres)*

U.S. Subsidiary:

Midland Information Resources Inc. (2)
5440 Corporate Pk Dr
Davenport, IA 52807
Tel.: (563) 359-3696
Fax: (563) 359-1333
Toll Free: (800) 232-3696
Web Site: www.midlandcorp.com
Sales Range: $25-49.9 Million
Emp.: 192
Information Management & Digital Printing Solutions
S.I.C.: 2759
N.A.I.C.S.: 323111
Thomas Sheehan *(Pres & CEO)*

Non-U.S. Subsidiaries:

Elanders Hindson Ltd. (2)
Merlin Way New York Bus Pk
North Tyneside, Newcastle, NE27 0QG, United Kingdom (100%)
Tel.: (44) 1912800400
Fax: (44) 1912800401
Web Site: www.elanders.com
Emp.: 150
Provider of Graphical Design Services
S.I.C.: 7336
N.A.I.C.S.: 541430
Paul Jacques *(Dir-Fin)*

Elanders Polska Sp. z.o.o. (2)
Ul Mazowiecka 2
Plonsk, 9100 Warsaw, Tonsk, Poland (100%)
Tel.: (48) 236622316
Fax: (48) 236623146
E-Mail: recepcja.plonska@elanders.com
Web Site: www.elanders.com
Emp.: 60
Provider of Graphical Servcies
S.I.C.: 7336
N.A.I.C.S.: 541430
Jonas Brannerud *(Mng Dir)*

Elanders UK Ltd. (2)
32 Kings Rd
Harrogate, N Yorkshire, HG15JW, United Kingdom (100%)
Tel.: (44) 1423530362
Fax: (44) 1423230610
E-Mail: info@elanders.com
Web Site: www.elanders.co.uk
Emp.: 15
Provider of Graphical Design Services
S.I.C.: 7336
N.A.I.C.S.: 541430
Roy Hamilton *(Mng Dir)*

Lifco AB (1)
Verkmastaregatan 1
745 85 Enkoping, Sweden
Tel.: (46) 171478450
Fax: (46) 171478489
Web Site: www.lifco.se
Sales Range: $900-999.9 Million
Emp.: 2,800
Mail Order for Dental Supplies & Consumables
S.I.C.: 5961
N.A.I.C.S.: 454113
Fredrik Karlsson *(CEO)*
Therese Hoffman *(CFO)*

Subsidiaries:

Brokk AB (2)
Risbergsgatan 67
Skelleftea, Sweden
Tel.: (46) 910711800
Fax: (46) 910 711 811
E-Mail: info@brokk.com
Web Site: www.brokk.com
Remote Controlled Demolition Machinery Mfr
S.I.C.: 3531
N.A.I.C.S.: 333120
Martin Krupicka *(Mng Dir)*

U.S. Subsidiary:

Brokk, Inc. (3)
1144 Village Way
Monroe, WA 98272 WA
Tel.: (360) 794-1277
Fax: (360) 805-2521
Toll Free: (800) 621-7856
E-Mail: www.info@brokkinc.com
Web Site: www.brokkinc.com
Emp.: 15
Remote Controlled Demolition Machinery Mfr
S.I.C.: 3531
N.A.I.C.S.: 333120
Lars Lindgren *(Pres)*

Sorb Industri AB (2)
Risberggatan 67
Post Box 730
931 36 Skelleftea, 931 27, Sweden
Tel.: (46) 91017400
Fax: (46) 910711869
E-Mail: info@sorb.se
Web Site: www.sorb.se
Emp.: 900
Sawmill Equipment, Demolition, Contract Manufacturing & Business Development Services
S.I.C.: 3554
N.A.I.C.S.: 333243
Carl Bennet *(Chm)*
Fredrik Karlsson *(Mng Dir)*

Subsidiary:

Renholmen AB (3)
PO Box 10
SE 930 47 Byske, Sweden
Tel.: (46) 91240800
Fax: (46) 91261182
E-Mail: gunnar.Marklund@renholmen.se
Web Site: www.renholmen.se
Sls.: $9,892,500
Emp.: 30
Sawmill Equipment
S.I.C.: 3553
N.A.I.C.S.: 333243
Gunnar Marklund *(Mng Dir)*

Subsidiary:

Renholmen AB (4)
Strandvagen 64
PO Box 33
S 870 52 Nyland, Sweden (100%)
Tel.: (46) 612771730
Telex: 71030 hammars s
Fax: (46) 61222979
E-Mail: marknad@renholmen.se
Web Site: www.renholmen.se
Emp.: 1
S.I.C.: 2653
N.A.I.C.S.: 322211

Non-U.S. Subsidiaries:

KINSHOFER GmbH (2)
Hauptstrasse 76
83666 Waakirchen, Germany
Tel.: (49) 802188990
Fax: (49) 8021889937
E-Mail: info@kinshofer.com
Web Site: www.kinshofer.com
Emp.: 200
Construction Machinery Mfr
S.I.C.: 3531
N.A.I.C.S.: 333120
Thomas Friedrich *(Mng Dir)*

Non-U.S. Subsidiaries:

KINSHOFER Aponox Oy (3)
Terminaalitie 10
FI 13430 Hameenlinna, Finland
Tel.: (358) 757540200
Fax: (358) 757540210
E-Mail: info@kinshofer-aponox.com
Emp.: 6
Construction Machinery Mfr
S.I.C.: 3531
N.A.I.C.S.: 333120

KINSHOFER CZ s.r.o. (3)
Cs Legii 568
37810 Ceske Velenice, Czech Republic
Tel.: (420) 384795110
Fax: (420) 384795120
Emp.: 94
Construction Machinery Mfr
S.I.C.: 3531
N.A.I.C.S.: 333120

KINSHOFER France S.A.R.L. (3)
BP 20100
67213 Obernai, France
Tel.: (33) 388 3955 00
Fax: (33) 388 7906 75
E-Mail: info@kinshofer.fr
Web Site: www.kinshofer.com
Emp.: 2
Construction Machinery Mfr
S.I.C.: 3531
N.A.I.C.S.: 333120
Friedrich Thomas *(Gen Mgr)*

KINSHOFER UK Ltd. (3)
4 Milton Industrial Court Horsfield Way
Bredbury, Stockport, Cheshire, SK6 2TA, United Kingdom
Tel.: (44) 1614067046
Fax: (44) 161 406 7014
E-Mail: sales@kinshofer.co.uk
Emp.: 7
Construction Machinery Mfr
S.I.C.: 3531
N.A.I.C.S.: 333120

M+W Dental GmbH (2)
Industriestrasse 25
63654 Darmstadt, Budingen, Germany
Tel.: (49) 6042880088
Fax: (49) 88008001
E-Mail: contact@mwdental.de
Web Site: www.mwdental.de
Emp.: 200
Dental Consumables & Small Appliances Mfr
S.I.C.: 5047
N.A.I.C.S.: 423450
Reinhold Kuhn *(Mng Dir)*

Symbrio AB (1)
Ostgotagatan 12
SE 116 25 Stockholm, Sweden
Tel.: (46) 8204950
Fax: (46) 8206011
E-Mail: sales@symbrio.com
Web Site: www.symbrio.com
Purchasing & Invoicing Software Developer
S.I.C.: 7372
N.A.I.C.S.: 511210
Johan Ouchterlony *(CEO)*

Non-U.S. Subsidiary:

Symbrio AS (2)
Grenseveien 97A
Oslo, Norway
Tel.: (47) 90080730
Purchasing & Invoicing Software Developer
S.I.C.: 7372
N.A.I.C.S.: 511210

CARL FROH GMBH

Hachenerstr 157
59846 Sundern, Germany
Tel.: (49) 2935810
Telex: 84227 froh d
Fax: (49) 293581202
E-Mail: info@carl-froh.com
Web Site: www.carl-froh.de
Sales Range: $75-99.9 Million
Emp.: 180

Business Description:
Steel Tube & Component Mfr
S.I.C.: 3317
N.A.I.C.S.: 331210

Personnel:
Horst Leitner *(Mng Dir)*

CARL MAHR HOLDING GMBH

Brauweg 38
D 37073 Gottingen, Germany
Tel.: (49) 55170730
Fax: (49) 55171021
E-Mail: info@mahr.de
Web Site: www.mahr.de
Year Founded: 1861
Sales Range: $150-199.9 Million
Emp.: 1,500

Business Description:
Measuring Instruments Mfr
S.I.C.: 3823
N.A.I.C.S.: 334513

Personnel:
Carl Frieder Mahr *(Chm)*
Ulrich Kastar *(Pres & Mng Dir)*
T. Keider *(CEO)*

Subsidiaries:

Mahr Metering Systems GmbH (1)
Carl -Mahr Str 1
PO Box 1853
37073 Gottingen, Germany
Tel.: (49) 55170730
Fax: (49) 55171021
E-Mail: mahrmeteringsystems@mahr.de
Emp.: 600
Relay & Industrial Control Mfr
S.I.C.: 3625
N.A.I.C.S.: 335314

Mahr OKM GmbH (1)
Carl-Zeiss-Promenade 10
07745 Jena, Germany
Tel.: (49) 3641642696
Fax: (49) 3641643368
E-Mail: info-okm@mahr.de
Web Site: www.mahr.com
Emp.: 30
Electrical Equipment & Component Mfr
S.I.C.: 3699
N.A.I.C.S.: 335999
Holger Hage *(Mng Dir)*

U.S. Subsidiaries:

Mahr Federal, Inc. (1)
1144 Eddy St
Providence, RI 02905-4511 DE
Tel.: (401) 784-3100 (100%)
Fax: (401) 784-3246
Toll Free: (800) 343-2050
E-Mail: information@mahr.com
Web Site: www.mahr.com
Emp.: 300
Dimensional Measuring Instruments Mfr
S.I.C.: 3823
N.A.I.C.S.: 334513
Tony Picone *(Pres)*

Mahr Metering Systems Corporation (1)
1415 A Cross Beam Dr
Charlotte, NC 28217
Tel.: (704) 525-7128
Fax: (704) 525-8290
Toll Free: (800) 459-7867
E-Mail: Info@MahrMeteringSystems.com
Web Site: www.mmscusa.com
Emp.: 20
Industrial Machinery & Equipment Whslr
S.I.C.: 5084
N.A.I.C.S.: 423830
Carl Mahr *(Mng Dir)*

Non-U.S. Subsidiaries:

Mahr Austria GmbH (1)
Hirschstettnerstrasse 19-21
1220 Vienna, Austria
Tel.: (43) 120436730
Fax: (43) 1204367315
E-Mail: info-austria@mahr.com

Carl Mahr Holding GmbH—(Continued)

Web Site: www.mahr.de/index.php?Node ID=8230
Emp.: 5
Measuring & Controlling Device Mfr
S.I.C.: 3829
N.A.I.C.S.: 334519
Martin Schober *(Mng Dir)*

Mahr China Ltd. **(1)**
Unit G 14th-Floor CDW Building
388 Castle Peak Road, Tsuen Wan, China (Hong Kong)
Tel.: (852) 23579683
Fax: (852) 27639613
E-Mail: info@mahr.com.hk
Web Site: www.mahr.de/index.php?Node ID=8265&print=1
Emp.: 10
Industrial Machinery & Equipment Whslr
S.I.C.: 5084
N.A.I.C.S.: 423830
Lych Wong *(Mng Dir)*

Mahr Corporation de Mexico S.A. de C.V. **(1)**
Francisco G Sada 690
Col Chepevera Monterrey, Nuevo Leon, Mexico
Tel.: (52) 8183332010
Fax: (52) 8183472793
E-Mail: bentasmexico@mahr.com
Web Site: www.mahr.com
Emp.: 18
Industrial Machinery Mfr
S.I.C.: 3559
N.A.I.C.S.: 333249
Geogre Escarcega *(Gen Mgr)*

Mahr France Centre de Mesures Lorrain SA **(1)**
Pole de Ressources Technologiques
6 rue du Colonel Clarenthal, 54300 Metz, France
Tel.: (33) 383743349
Fax: (33) 169351912
E-Mail: info@mahr.fr
Web Site: www.mahr.de/index.php
Emp.: 5
Industrial Machinery & Equipment Whslr
S.I.C.: 5084
N.A.I.C.S.: 423830
Alain Simeon *(Mgr)*

Mahr Japan Co., Ltd. **(1)**
712-4-1 Mamedo-cho
222-0032 Yokohama, Kohoku-ku, Japan
Tel.: (81) 455403591
Fax: (81) 455406252
E-Mail: info@mahr.co.jp
Web Site: www.mahr.co.jp
Industrial Machinery & Equipment Merchant Whslr
S.I.C.: 5084
N.A.I.C.S.: 423830
Dirk Edert *(Mng Dir)*

Mahr Korea Ltd. **(1)**
Panwon B-D 6th Fl
38-30 Jangchung-dong 1-ga Chun, 100-391 Seoul, Korea (South)
Tel.: (82) 25794981
Fax: (82) 25794986
E-Mail: sales@mahr.co.kr
Web Site: www.mahr.co.kr
Emp.: 10
Industrial Machinery & Equipment Merchant Whslr
S.I.C.: 5084
N.A.I.C.S.: 423830
Jung Cho *(Gen Mgr)*

Mahr Malaysia Sdn. Bhd. **(1)**
No 130 Block B 1
Leisure Commerce Sq No 9 Jalan, 46150 Petaling Jaya, Selangor, Malaysia
Tel.: (60) 378772060
Fax: (60) 378772040
E-Mail: mahr@tm.net.my
Web Site: www.mahr.com.my
Emp.: 5
Power-Driven Handtool Mfr
S.I.C.: 3546
N.A.I.C.S.: 333991

Mahr Metrology India Private Ltd. **(1)**
Mahr Metrology India Private Ltd.
Anna Nagar East, 600102 Chennai, India
Tel.: (91) 4442170531
Fax: (91) 4442170531
E-Mail: mahrindia@mahr.com
Web Site: www.mahr.com
Emp.: 12
Electromedical & Electrotherapeutic Apparatus Mfr
S.I.C.: 3845
N.A.I.C.S.: 334510
R. Ganesan *(Mng Dir)*

Mahr S.E.A. Co. Ltd. **(1)**
c/o Mahr China Ltd Room 103A G/F Riley House
88 Lei Muk Road, Kwai Chung, China (Hong Kong)
Tel.: (852) 23579683
Fax: (852) 27639613
E-Mail: eddie.tee@mahr.com
Web Site: www.mahr.de/index.php?Node ID=176&print=1
Emp.: 12
Industrial Machinery Mfr
S.I.C.: 3559
N.A.I.C.S.: 333249

Mahr, spol s.r.o. **(1)**
Ulice Kpt Jarose 552
Probostov, 41712 Prague, Czech Republic
Tel.: (420) 417816711
Fax: (420) 417560237
E-Mail: Info-cz@mahr.com
Web Site: www.mahr.de/index.php
Emp.: 150
Cutting Tool & Machine Tool Accessory Mfr
S.I.C.: 3545
N.A.I.C.S.: 333515

Mahr U.K. plc. **(1)**
19 Drakes Mews
Crownhill, Milton Keynes, Buckingamshire, MK8 0ER, United Kingdom (100%)
Tel.: (44) 908563700
Fax: (44) 908563704
E-Mail: info@mahr.com
Web Site: www.mahr.com
Emp.: 14
Dial Indicators & Precision Instruments
S.I.C.: 7629
N.A.I.C.S.: 811219

CARL SCHAEFER GMBH & CO. KG

Altstadter Kirchenweg 23
75175 Pforzheim, Germany
Tel.: (49) 723115760
Fax: (49) 7231157650
Web Site: www.carl-schaefer.de
Year Founded: 1861
Rev.: $19,311,600
Emp.: 33
Business Description:
Metal Recovery Services
S.I.C.: 5051
N.A.I.C.S.: 423510
Personnel:
Sascha Bohnenberger *(Head-Analytical Laboratory)*

CARL-ZEISS-STIFTUNG

Carl Zeiss Strasse 22
73447 Oberkochen, Germany
Tel.: (49) 7364200
Fax: (49) 73646808
E-Mail: info@zeiss.de
Web Site: www.zeiss.de
Year Founded: 1846
Emp.: 13,667
Business Description:
Optical Instruments, Lenses & Eyecare Products Mfr
S.I.C.: 3827
N.A.I.C.S.: 333314
Personnel:
Theo Spettmann *(Chm-Supervisory Bd)*
Jurgen Domel *(Vice Chm)*
Dieter Kurz *(Pres & CEO)*
Supervisory Board of Directors:
Theo Spettmann
Gunter Stock
Karl-Heinz Schuster
Mathias Kammuller
Klaus Dieterich
Reinhard Dickehuth
Hellmuth Aeugle
Hariolf Abele
Michael Claus
Adolf G. Coenenberg
Roland Hamm
Hans-Jurgen Heinicke
Hermann-Josef Lamberti
Klaus-Dieter Vohringer
Martin Allespach
Michael Rogowski

Subsidiaries:

Carl Zeiss AG **(1)**
Carl Zeiss Strasse 22
73447 Oberkochen, Germany (100%)
Tel.: (49) 7364200
Telex: 71375155
Fax: (49) 73646808
E-Mail: info@zeiss.de
Web Site: www.zeiss.de
Emp.: 4,000
Mfr. of Lenses, Magnifying Lenses; Microscopes, Microphotographic, Microprojection & Microcinematographic Equipment; Binoculars; Telescopic Rifle Sights; Astronomical Telescopes & Equipmment; Surveying Instruments & Accessories; Camera Lenses; Medical Instruments; Precision Tools
S.I.C.: 3827
N.A.I.C.S.: 333314
Michael Kaschke *(Mng Dir)*

Subsidiaries:

Carl Zeiss Meditec AG **(2)**
Carl Zeiss Promenade 10
7745 Jena, Germany (100%)
Tel.: (49) 3641640
Fax: (49) 3641220112
E-Mail: j.griebsch@meditec.ziess
Emp.: 400
Medical Supply Mfr
S.I.C.: 3845
N.A.I.C.S.: 334510
Ulrich Krauss *(Mng Dir)*

Carl Zeiss Microscopy GmbH **(2)**
Carl Zeiss Promenade 10
07745 Jena, Germany
Tel.: (49) 551 50600
Optical Instruments, Lenses & Eyecare Products Mfr
S.I.C.: 3827
N.A.I.C.S.: 333314

Carl Zeiss Sports Optics GmbH **(2)**
Gloelstrasse 3 5
35576 Wetzlar, Germany (100%)
Tel.: (49) 64414040
Fax: (49) 6441404150
E-Mail: info.sportsoptics@zeiss.de
Web Site: www.zeiss.de
Emp.: 800
Mfr of Optical instruments
S.I.C.: 3827
N.A.I.C.S.: 333314
Erik Schumacher *(Pres)*

Joint Venture:

Zeiss Optronik GmbH **(2)**
Carl Zeiss Str 22
73447 Oberkochen, Baden Weurttenberg, Germany (100%)
Tel.: (49) 7364200
Fax: (49) 7364203911
E-Mail: marketingzeo@zeiss.de
Web Site: www.zeissoptronik.de
Sales Range: $1-4.9 Billion
Emp.: 400
S.I.C.: 3365
N.A.I.C.S.: 331524

U.S. Subsidiaries:

Carl Zeiss, Inc. **(2)**
1 Zeiss Dr
Thornwood, NY 10594-1939 NY
Tel.: (914) 747-1800
Fax: (914) 681-7482
E-Mail: microcustomer@zeiss.com
Web Site: www.zeiss.com
Sales Range: $300-349.9 Million
Emp.: 700
Distr of Scientific Instruments: Laboratory Microscopes, Surgical Microscopes & Ophthalmic Diagnostic Equipment
Import Export
S.I.C.: 5047
N.A.I.C.S.: 423450
Jim Sharp *(Pres)*

Carl Zeiss Meditec, Inc. **(2)**
5160 Hacienda Dr
Dublin, CA 94568
Tel.: (925) 557-4100
Fax: (925) 557-4101
Web Site: www.meditec.zeiss.com
Emp.: 500
Medical Optics Mfr
S.I.C.: 3827
N.A.I.C.S.: 333314
Ralf Kuschnereit *(Pres & CEO)*

Subsidiaries:

Aaren Scientific Inc. **(3)**
4290 E Brickell St Bldg A
Ontario, CA 91761-1569
Tel.: (909) 937-1033
Fax: (909) 937-1088
Toll Free: (877) 644-4657
E-Mail: info@aareninc.com
Web Site: www.aareninc.com
Sales Range: $10-24.9 Million
Emp.: 130
Optical Instruments & Intraocular Lenses Mfr
S.I.C.: 3827
N.A.I.C.S.: 333314
Charles R. Cummings *(Chm)*
Rick Aguilera *(Pres)*

Laser Diagnostic Technologies **(3)**
Ste 210 10805 Rancho Bernardo Rd
San Diego, CA 92127-5703
Tel.: (858) 673-7900
Fax: (858) 673-7909
Web Site: www.laserdiagnostic.com
Sls.: $16,000,000
Emp.: 120
Surgical & Medical Instruments
S.I.C.: 3841
N.A.I.C.S.: 339112

Carl Zeiss Sports Optics, LLC **(2)**
13017 N Kingston Ave
Chester, VA 23836-8333
Tel.: (804) 530-8300
Fax: (804) 530-8311
Toll Free: (800) 338-2984
E-Mail: lenses@zeiss.com
Web Site: www.zeiss.com
Emp.: 96
Binoculars, Riflescopes, Ophthalmic Lenses & Coatings Mfr
S.I.C.: 3851
N.A.I.C.S.: 339115
Michael A. Jensen *(Pres)*

Non-U.S. Subsidiaries:

Carl Zeiss Canada Ltd. **(2)**
45 Valleybrook D
Toronto, ON, M3B 2S6, Canada (60%)
Tel.: (416) 449-4660
Fax: (416) 449-3524
E-Mail: fsomogy@zeiss.com
Web Site: www.zeiss.ca
Sales Range: $25-49.9 Million
Emp.: 150
Production of Scientific, Medical & Optical Instruments
Import
S.I.C.: 3841
N.A.I.C.S.: 339112
Lynn Mousmanif *(Controller)*

Carl Zeiss Pty Ltd **(2)**
Tenancy Office 4 Level 1 40 52 Talavera Road
PO Box 501
North Ryde, NSW, 2113, Australia (100%)
Tel.: (61) 1300367244
Fax: (61) 290201331
E-Mail: servicedesk@zeiss.com
Web Site: www.zeiss.com.au
Emp.: 40
Surgical Instruments & Instruments for Ophthalmology
S.I.C.: 3841
N.A.I.C.S.: 339112

Schott AG (1)
Hattenbergstrasse 10
55122 Mainz, Germany (100%)
Tel.: (49) 6131660
Fax: (49) 6131662000
E-Mail: info@schott.com
Web Site: www.schott.de
Emp.: 18,616
Glass Mfr
S.I.C.: 3229
N.A.I.C.S.: 327212
Theo Spettmann *(Chm-Supervisory Bd)*
Frank Heinricht *(Chm-Mgmt Bd)*
Stephan Schaller *(Vice Chm-Mgmt Bd)*
Jurgen Dahmer *(Member-Mgmt Bd)*
Martin Heming *(Member-Mgmt Bd)*
Hans-Joachim Konz *(Member-Mgmt Bd)*
Klaus Rubenthaler *(Member-Mgmt Bd)*
Peter Scarborough *(Member-Mgmt Bd)*

Subsidiaries:

Jenaer Glaswerk GmbH (2)
Otto Schott Strasse 13
7745 Jena, Germany (100%)
Tel.: (49) 36416810
Fax: (49) 3641685100
E-Mail: jenaer.glas@schott.com
Web Site: www.schott.com
Emp.: 500
Mfr. of Glass Products
S.I.C.: 3231
N.A.I.C.S.: 327215
Klaus Schneider *(Gen Mgr)*

Schott Auer GmbH (2)
Hildesheimer Strasse 35
37581 Bad Gandersheim, Germany (100%)
Tel.: (49) 53827010
Fax: (49) 53827011
E-Mail: info.liking@schott.com
Web Site: www.schott.com
Emp.: 530
Mfr. of Optical Instruments & Lenses
S.I.C.: 3827
N.A.I.C.S.: 333314

SCHOTT Glas Export GmbH (2)
Rheinallee 145
55120 Mainz, Germany (100%)
Tel.: (49) 613132100
Fax: (49) 6131662000
E-Mail: info@schott.com
Web Site: www.schott.com
Emp.: 200
Exporter of Laboratory Glass Products
S.I.C.: 3231
N.A.I.C.S.: 327215
Jean-Yves Grandmange *(Mng Dir)*
Bernard Langner *(Mng Dir)*

SCHOTT Solar GmbH (2)
Carl Zeiss Strasse 4
63755 Alzenau, Germany De
Tel.: (49) 6023911726
Fax: (49) 6023761700
E-Mail: solar.sales@schottsolar.com
Web Site: www.schottsolar.com
Emp.: 500
Solar Energy Products & Services
S.I.C.: 3674
N.A.I.C.S.: 334413
Martin Heming *(CEO)*

U.S. Subsidiary:

SCHOTT Solar Inc. (3)
5201 Hawking Dr Se
Albuquerque, NM 87106-9705
Tel.: (978) 667-5900
Fax: (978) 663-2868
Toll Free: (800) 977-0777
E-Mail: info@schottsolar.us
Web Site: www.asepv.com
Emp.: 225
Mfr, Installation & Support of Solar Energy Systems.
S.I.C.: 8731
N.A.I.C.S.: 541712
Gerald J. Fine *(Pres & CEO)*

SCHOTT Spezialglas AG (2)
Hattenderg Strasse 10
55122 Mainz, Germany (83.9%)
Mailing Address:
Postfach 2032
31074 Gruenenplan, Germany
Tel.: (49) 61316601288
Telex: 92950 desag d
Fax: (49) 6131662000
E-Mail: info@schott.com
Web Site: www.schott.com
Emp.: 4,000
Producer of Ophthalmic Glass; Processor of Flat Glass; Manufacturer of Protective Glass for Industrial Applications
Export
S.I.C.: 3827
N.A.I.C.S.: 333314
Klaus Hofmann *(Dir-Corp PR)*

U.S. Subsidiary:

SCHOTT North America Inc (3)
400 York Ave
Duryea, PA 18642-2026 (100%)
Tel.: (570) 457-7485
Telex: 510-671-4535
Fax: (570) 457-6960
Web Site: www.us.schott.com
Emp.: 300
Production of Special Glasses
S.I.C.: 3211
N.A.I.C.S.: 327211
Linda S. Mayer *(Pres & CEO)*

U.S. Joint Venture:

SCHOTT Gemtron Corporation (2)
615 Hwy 68
Sweetwater, TN 37874-1911 TN
Tel.: (423) 337-3522
Fax: (423) 337-7979
E-Mail: salesinfo@gemtron.net
Web Site: www.gemtron.net
Emp.: 250
Mfr. of Tempered & Decorative Glass For Uses Including Shower Doors, Ovens & Shelving; Joint Venture of Schott Glaswerke & AFG Industries, Inc.
Export
S.I.C.: 3211
N.A.I.C.S.: 327211
Mark Delp *(Exec VP)*

Subsidiary:

SCHOTT Gemtron Corporation (3)
2000 Chestnut St
Vincennes, IN 47591-1760
Mailing Address:
PO Box 317
Vincennes, IN 47591-0317
Tel.: (812) 882-2680
Fax: (812) 882-7679
Web Site: www.gemtron.com
Emp.: 500
Glass Tempering & Tempered Glass; Ceramics
Import Export
S.I.C.: 3231
N.A.I.C.S.: 327215
Tim Kiger *(Gen Mgr)*

Non-U.S. Subsidiaries:

Moritex Corporation (2)
Sunny Building Ikebukuro 4-39-11 Higashi Ikebukuro
Toshima-ku, Tokyo, 170-0013, Japan
Tel.: (81) 3 6367 3620
Fax: (81) 3 3590 6618
Web Site: www.schott-moritex.com
MQX—(DEU TKS)
Sales Range: $25-49.9 Million
Optical Equipment Mfr & Whslr
S.I.C.: 3827
N.A.I.C.S.: 333314
Noboru Matsuoka *(Chm)*
Takao Sato *(Pres, CEO & COO)*
Miyuki Kanemoto *(Operating Officer)*
Tomohiro Mizuno *(Operating Officer)*

SCHOTT Brasil Ltda. Divisao Vitrofarma (2)
R Ivan de Oliveira Lima 155
20760 600 Sao Paulo, Rio de Janiero, Brazil (100%)
Tel.: (55) 2121593100
Fax: (55) 21 2159 3170
Web Site: www.schott.com
Emp.: 50
Tubing Mfr
S.I.C.: 3317
N.A.I.C.S.: 331210

SCHOTT Brazil (2)
Rua Ivan De Oliveira Lima 155
CEP 20760 600 Rio de Janeiro, Brazil (100%)
Tel.: (55) 2125993100
Fax: (55) 2125993170
E-Mail: info.vitrofarma@schott.com
Web Site: www.schott.com
Emp.: 200
Laboratory Glass Mfr
S.I.C.: 3231
N.A.I.C.S.: 327215

SCHOTT France SAS (2)
6 bis rue Fournier
92110 Clichy, France (100%)
Tel.: (33) 140873974
Fax: (33) 142707322
Web Site: www.schott.com
Emp.: 30
Optical Instruments Mfr
S.I.C.: 3827
N.A.I.C.S.: 333314
Henri Huypens *(Gen Mgr)*

SCHOTT France SAS (2)
6 bis rue Fournier
92110 Clichy, France (100%)
Tel.: (33) 140873906
Fax: (33) 1140873906
E-Mail: edwige.gullion@schott.com
Web Site: www.schott.com
Emp.: 30
Optical Instruments & Lenses Mfr
S.I.C.: 3827
N.A.I.C.S.: 333314
Udo Ungeheuer *(CEO)*

SCHOTT Iberica, S.A. Commercial Division (2)
Pi I Gibert 1-25
Apartado de Correos No. 2, 08930
Barcelona, Spain (100%)
Tel.: (34) 932283200
Fax: (34) 934620051
Web Site: www.schott.es
Emp.: 85
Producer of Ophthalmic Glass; Processor of Flat Glass; Manufacturer of Protective Glass for Industrial Applications
S.I.C.: 3211
N.A.I.C.S.: 327211
Manuel Gutierrez *(Gen Mgr)*

SCHOTT Iberica, S.A. (2)
Pi i Gibert 1 25
PO Box 2
Sant Adria de Besos, 08950 Barcelona, Spain (100%)
Tel.: (34) 934626900
Fax: (34) 934620981
E-Mail: marketing.esbcn@schott.com
Web Site: www.schott.es
Emp.: 150
Provider of Aluminum Products
S.I.C.: 3365
N.A.I.C.S.: 331524
Manuel Gutierrez *(Mng Dir)*

SFAM Societe Francaise d'Ampoules Mecaniques SARL (2)
Rte De Bordeaux
47700 Casteljaloux, France (100%)
Tel.: (33) 553930240
Fax: (33) 553931289
E-Mail: pps@schott.com
Web Site: www.schott.com
Emp.: 70
Mfr of Optical Instruments
S.I.C.: 3827
N.A.I.C.S.: 333314
Maxime Duranti *(Mgr-Plant)*

Joint Venture:

Carl Zeiss Vision International GmbH (1)
Gartenstrasse 97
73430 Aalen, Germany
Fax: (49) 7361 55578 1299
E-Mail: optics@zeiss.de
Web Site: www.vision.zeiss.com
Sales Range: $1-4.9 Billion
Emp.: 10,000
Mfr of Eyeglasses & Lenses
S.I.C.: 3827
N.A.I.C.S.: 333314
Michael Hoffmann *(CEO)*

Subsidiary:

Carl Zeiss Vision GmbH (2)
Turnstrasse 27
73430 Aalen, Germany
Tel.: (49) 7361 598 5000
Fax: (49) 7361 591 480
Web Site: vision.zeiss.com
Emp.: 8
Eyeglass Lenses Mfr
S.I.C.: 3827
N.A.I.C.S.: 333314
Spiller Rudols *(Gen Mgr)*

U.S. Subsidiary:

Carl Zeiss Vision Inc. (2)
12121 Scripps Summit Dr
San Diego, CA 92130-4682 DE
Tel.: (858) 790-7700
Fax: (858) 790-7590
Web Site: www.vision.zeiss.com
Sales Range: $650-699.9 Million
Emp.: 6,634
Plastic & Glass Eyeglass Lenses Mfr & Sales
Import Export
S.I.C.: 3851
N.A.I.C.S.: 339115
Susan Armstrong *(VP)*

Subsidiaries:

Great Lakes Coating Laboratory (3)
1784 Larchwood Dr
Troy, MI 48083-2223
Tel.: (248) 524-0550
Fax: (248) 524-0808
Web Site: www.carl-zeiss.com
Emp.: 120
Optical Goods Mfr & Sales
S.I.C.: 3827
N.A.I.C.S.: 333314

Kansas City Opthalmics LLC (3)
13731 E 42nd Ter
Independence, MO 64055
Tel.: (816) 478-4901
Emp.: 6
Optical Services
S.I.C.: 5995
N.A.I.C.S.: 446130
David Jochims *(CEO)*

Non-U.S. Subsidiaries:

Alpha Lens Company Ltd. (2)
76-77 Capitol Industrial Park Capitol Way
London, NX9 0EW, United Kingdom
Tel.: (44) 2089491901
Emp.: 50
Ophthalmic Products Mfr & Supply
S.I.C.: 3827
N.A.I.C.S.: 333314

Carl Zeiss Vision Australia Ltd. (2)
24 Heath St
Lonsdale, SA, 5160, Australia
Mailing Address:
PO Box 244
Morphett Vale, SA, 5162, Australia
Tel.: (61) 883928899
Fax: (61) 883928875
Web Site: www.vision.zeiss.com.au
Emp.: 700
Eyeglass Lense Mfr
S.I.C.: 3827
N.A.I.C.S.: 333314
Nobert Gorny *(Pres)*

Carl Zeiss Vision Brasil Industria Optica Ltda. (2)
Rua Luiz Winter 222 Duarte da Silveira
25665-431 Petropolis, RJ, Brazil
Tel.: (55) 24 2233 7012
Fax: (55) 24 2233 7096
E-Mail: andrea.costa@vision.zeiss.com
Web Site: www.lenteszeiss.com.br
Eyeglass Lenses Mfr
S.I.C.: 3827
N.A.I.C.S.: 333314
Andrea Costa *(Dir-Mktg)*

Carl Zeiss Vision (Guangzhou) Ltd. (2)
No 1389 Jui Fo West Road
Baiyun District, Guangzhou, 510555, China
Tel.: (86) 2087490088
Fax: (86) 20 8749 0733
Web Site: www.joffray.com
Eyeglass Lenses Mfr
S.I.C.: 3827
N.A.I.C.S.: 333314

Carl Zeiss Vision Ireland Ltd. (2)
Whitemill Industrial Estate
Wexford, Ireland

Carl-Zeiss-Stiftung—(Continued)

Tel.: (353) 5363700
Fax: (353) 5341671
Emp.: 450
Optical Lense Services
S.I.C.: 5995
N.A.I.C.S.: 446130

Carl Zeiss Vision Italia SPA (2)
Via SEP Mazzucchelli No 17
Castiglione Olona, 21043 Varese, Lombardia, Italy
Tel.: (39) 0331851111
Fax: (39) 0331850720
E-Mail: marketing@vision.zeiss.com
Web Site: www.zeiss.it/
Emp.: 450
Eyeglass Lenses & Magnifying Vision Mfr
S.I.C.: 3827
N.A.I.C.S.: 333314
Michele D'adamo *(Gen Mgr)*

Carl Zeiss Vision Swiss AG (2)
Helsinkistrasse 9
Basel, 4142, Switzerland
Tel.: (41) 613388100
Fax: (41) 613388101
E-Mail: info@americanoptical.ch
Web Site: www.americanoptical.ch
Emp.: 15
Optical Products Mfr & Sales
S.I.C.: 3827
N.A.I.C.S.: 333314

Carl Zeiss Vision UK Ltd. (2)
Unit 9 Holford Way
Holford, Birmingham, B6 7AX, United Kingdom
Tel.: (44) 1213324404
Fax: (44) 121 356 5618
Web Site: www.vision.zeiss.co.uk
Emp.: 279
Eyeglass Lenses Mfr
S.I.C.: 3827
N.A.I.C.S.: 333314
Andrew Leonsson *(Mng Dir)*

Carl Zeiss Vision Venezuela Industria Optica C.A. (2)
Av Francisco de Miranda
Centro Profesional Miranda
piso 2 ofc 2C, Caracas, 1060, Venezuela
Mailing Address:
PO Box 3982
Caracas, 1010-A, Venezuela
Tel.: (58) 212 264 6231
Fax: (58) 212 264 5108
Web Site: www.solaven.com
Emp.: 5
Eyeglass Lenses Mfr
S.I.C.: 3827
N.A.I.C.S.: 333314

Carl Zeiss Vision (2)
5th Fl Nissei Fushimi Machi Building
4 4 1 Fushimi Machi Chuo Ku, Osaka, 541 0044, Japan
Tel.: (81) 662022672
Fax: (81) 662022675
Emp.: 100
Eyeglass Lenses Mfr
S.I.C.: 3827
N.A.I.C.S.: 333314

Carl Zeiss Vision (2)
Avenida San Andres Atoto 165-B
Naucalpan de Juarez, Mexico, 53550, Mexico
Tel.: (52) 5555767033
Fax: (52) 5553583576
Web Site: www.aolens.com
Emp.: 100
Optical Lense Services
S.I.C.: 3827
N.A.I.C.S.: 333314

Carl Zeiss Vision (2)
Calle 7 Sur No 1111
Tijuana, 22500, Mexico
Tel.: (52) 6646233734
Fax: (52) 6646233734
Optical Lense Services
S.I.C.: 5995
N.A.I.C.S.: 446130

Non-U.S. Subsidiaries:

Carl Zeiss AB (1)
Tegeluddsvagen 76
S 10254 Stockholm, Sweden (100%)
Tel.: (46) 84592500
Fax: (46) 86602935
E-Mail: info@zeiss.se
Web Site: www.zeiss.se
Emp.: 50
Mfr. of Optical Instruments & Lenses
S.I.C.: 3827
N.A.I.C.S.: 333314
Walter Heger *(Mng Dir)*

Carl Zeiss AG (1)
Feldbachstrasse 81
8714 Feldbach, Switzerland
Tel.: (41) 55 254 7535
Fax: (41) 55 254 7530
E-Mail: zeiss@zeiss.ch
Web Site: www.zeiss.ch
Mfr of Optical Instruments & Lenses
S.I.C.: 3827
N.A.I.C.S.: 333314

Carl Zeiss Argentina S.A. (1)
Calle Nahuel Huapi 4015/25
1430 BCO Buenos Aires, Argentina (100%)
Tel.: (54) 11 4545 6661
Fax: (54) 11 4545 3355
E-Mail: info@zeiss.com.ar
Web Site: www.zeiss.com
Mfr. of Optical Instruments & Lenses
S.I.C.: 3827
N.A.I.C.S.: 333314

Carl Zeiss AS (1)
Kabelgaten 8
N0580 Oslo, Norway (100%)
Tel.: (47) 23172393
Fax: (47) 23172399
E-Mail: info@zeiss.no
Web Site: www.zeiss.no
Emp.: 20
Eyeglass Lenses & Visual Devices
S.I.C.: 3851
N.A.I.C.S.: 339115
Sturla Ekrol *(Gen Mgr)*

Carl Zeiss B.V. (1)
Trapezium 300
PO Box 310
3360 AH Sliedrecht, Netherlands (100%)
Tel.: (31) 184433400
Fax: (31) 184433500
E-Mail: info@zeiss.nl
Web Site: www.zeiss.nl
Emp.: 100
Mfr. of Optical Instruments & Lenses
S.I.C.: 3827
N.A.I.C.S.: 333314

Carl Zeiss Co. Ltd. (1)
2F BR Elitel Bldg 141-1 Sangsu-dong
Mapo-gu, Seoul, 121 828, Korea (South) (100%)
Tel.: (82) 231402600
Fax: (82) 231402699
E-Mail: korea@zeiss.co.kr
Web Site: www.zeiss.co.kr
Emp.: 50
Mfr of Optical Instruments & Lenses
S.I.C.: 3827
N.A.I.C.S.: 333314

Carl Zeiss Co. Ltd. (1)
Fl 8 Thosapol Land Bldg 230
Rajchadapisek Rd Huaykwang, Bangkok, 10310, Thailand (49%)
Tel.: (66) 227406435
Fax: (66) 22740727
E-Mail: thailand@zeiss.com.sg
Web Site: www.zeiss.com.sg
Emp.: 15
Mfr. of Optical Instruments & Lenses
S.I.C.: 3827
N.A.I.C.S.: 333314

Carl Zeiss de Mexico, S.A. de C.V. (1)
Av Miguel A De Quevedo 496
Coyoacan, Catarina, 4010, Mexico (100%)
Tel.: (52) 5559990200
E-Mail: czmexico@zeiss.org
Web Site: www.zeiss.com.mx
Emp.: 50
Mfr. of Optical Instruments & Lenses
S.I.C.: 3827
N.A.I.C.S.: 333314
Jose Manuelalonso *(Gen Mgr)*

Carl Zeiss Far East Company Limited (1)
Tower 1 13th Floor 5-7 Ever Gain Plz No 88
Container Port Rd
Kwaichung, Cheung Sha Wan, Kowloon, China (Hong Kong) (100%)
Tel.: (852) 23320402
Fax: (852) 27800650
E-Mail: czfe@zeiss.com.hk
Web Site: www.carlzeiss.com
Emp.: 40
Mfr. of Optical Instruments & Lenses
S.I.C.: 3827
N.A.I.C.S.: 333314
Bjorn Franken *(Dir-Sls & Mktg)*

Carl Zeiss GmbH (1)
Modecenterstrasse 16
A 1030 Vienna, Austria (100%)
Tel.: (43) 1795180
Fax: (43) 179518300
E-Mail: austria@zeiss.org
Web Site: www.zeiss.at
Emp.: 80
Mfr. of Optical Instruments & Lenses
S.I.C.: 3827
N.A.I.C.S.: 333314
Peter Amend *(Gen Mgr)*

Carl Zeiss Instruments s.r.l. (1)
Str Fluierului 21B
021423 Bucharest, Romania (100%)
Tel.: (40) 4253000
Fax: (40) 4253370
E-Mail: romania@zeiss.org
Web Site: www.zeiss.com
Emp.: 4
Mfr. of Optical Instruments & Lenses
S.I.C.: 3827
N.A.I.C.S.: 333314
Mircer Constantynscu *(Dir-Svcs)*

Carl Zeiss Japan Group (1)
22 Honshio-cho
Shinjuku-ku, Tokyo, 160-0003, Japan
Tel.: (81) 333550341
Web Site: www.zeiss.co.jp
Distr of Scientific Instruments: Laboratory Microscopes, Surgical Microscopes & Ophthalmic Equipment & Ophthalmic Diagnostic Equipment
S.I.C.: 5049
N.A.I.C.S.: 423490

Carl Zeiss Ltd. (1)
15-20 Woodfield Road
Welwyn Garden City, Herts, AL7 1LU, United Kingdom (100%)
Mailing Address:
PO Box 78
Welwyn Garden City, Herts, AL7 1LU, United Kingdom
Tel.: (44) 1707871200
Fax: (44) 1707871287
E-Mail: customercare@zeiss.co.uk
Web Site: www.zeiss.co.uk
Emp.: 150
Mfr of Optical Instruments & Lenses
S.I.C.: 3827
N.A.I.C.S.: 333314
Paul Adderley *(Gen Mgr)*

Carl Zeiss N.V-S.A. (1)
Ikaroslaan 49
1930 Zaventem, Belgium
Tel.: (32) 27193911
Fax: (32) 27193910
E-Mail: info@zeiss.be
Web Site: www.zeiss.be
Emp.: 40
Mfr. of Optical Instruments & Lenses
S.I.C.: 3827
N.A.I.C.S.: 333314

Carl Zeiss Opton Kft. (1)
Bocskai ut 134-146
1113 Budapest, Hungary
Tel.: (36) 6 1 309 7930
Fax: (36) 6 1 309 7940
E-Mail: zeiss@zeiss.hu
Web Site: www.zeiss.hu
Optical Instruments & Lenses Mfr
S.I.C.: 3827
N.A.I.C.S.: 333314

Carl Zeiss Pte. Ltd. (1)
50 Kaki Bukit Place 0501
415926 Singapore, Singapore (100%)
Tel.: (65) 67419600
Fax: (65) 68427117
E-Mail: info@zeiss.com.sg
Web Site: www.zeiss.com.sg
Emp.: 50
Mfr. of Optical Instruments & Lenses
S.I.C.: 3827
N.A.I.C.S.: 333314
Ven Raman *(Mng Dir)*

Carl Zeiss Pty. Ltd. (1)
363 Oak Avenue Randburg
PO Box 3003
Ferndale, 2194, South Africa
Tel.: (27) 118869510
Fax: (27) 118869592
E-Mail: info@zeiss.com
Web Site: www.zeiss.co.za
Microscopes, Binoculars, Optical Lens, Ophthalmic Products & Laboratory Products Mfr & Distr
S.I.C.: 3826
N.A.I.C.S.: 334516
Daniel Sims *(Mng Dir)*

Carl Zeiss S.A.S (1)
60 Rte De Sartrouville
BP No 66
78230 Le Pecq, France (100%)
Tel.: (33) 33134802000
Fax: (33) 34802002
E-Mail: czf@zeiss.fr
Web Site: www.zeiss.fr
Mfr of Optical Instruments
S.I.C.: 3827
N.A.I.C.S.: 333314

Carl Zeiss Sp. z o. o. (1)
Ul Mangalia 4
02 758 Warsaw, Poland (100%)
Tel.: (48) 228587819
Fax: (48) 226421587
E-Mail: zeiss@zeiss.pl
Web Site: www.zeiss.pl
Emp.: 15
Mfr. of Optical Instruments & Lenses
S.I.C.: 3827
N.A.I.C.S.: 333314

Carl Zeiss S.p.A. (1)
Viale Delle Industrie 1820
20020 Arese, Italy (100%)
Tel.: (39) 2937731
Fax: (39) 2 93773 539
E-Mail: post@zeiss.it
Web Site: www.zeiss.it
Provider of Optical Products
S.I.C.: 3231
N.A.I.C.S.: 327215

Carl Zeiss spol. s.r.o. (1)
Radlecka 14 3201
15000 Prague, Czech Republic (50%)
Tel.: (420) 233101221
Fax: (420) 233101223
E-Mail: zeiss@zeiss.cz
Web Site: www.zeiss.cz
Emp.: 55
Mfr. of Optical Products
S.I.C.: 3231
N.A.I.C.S.: 327215

Carl Zeiss spol. s.r.o. (1)
Org Ziozka Carl Zeiss
Trnavska 3, 81105 Bratislava, Slovakia (100%)
Tel.: (421) 255646791
Fax: (421) 255646783
E-Mail: zeiss@zeiss.sk
Web Site: www.zeiss.sk
Emp.: 11
Mfr. of Optical Instruments & Lenses
S.I.C.: 3827
N.A.I.C.S.: 333314

Carl Zeiss Vision Espana (1)
c/Tomas Lopez 3 4
28009 Madrid, Spain (100%)
Tel.: (34) 91 3096200
Fax: (34) 91 3096219
E-Mail: marketing.sp@vision.zeiss.com
Web Site: www.zeiss.es
Emp.: 60
Optical Instruments & Lenses Mfr
S.I.C.: 3827
N.A.I.C.S.: 333314

ICC Ukraine Ltd. (1)
10 Dovzhenko St Apt 13
3057 Kiev, Ukraine
Tel.: (380) 444555128
Fax: (380) 444555130
E-Mail: icc@zeiss.kiev.ua
Web Site: www.zeiss.com
Provider of Optical Products
S.I.C.: 3231

N.A.I.C.S.: 327215

Ooo Carl Zeiss (1)
Denisovski Per 26
105005 Moscow, Russia (100%)
Tel.: (7) 4959335151
Fax: (7) 4959335155
E-Mail: igelnik@zeiss.ru
Web Site: www.zeiss.ru
Emp.: 80
Provider of Optical Products
S.I.C.: 3231
N.A.I.C.S.: 327215

CARLAW CAPITAL IV INC.

245 Carlaw Avenue Suite 500
Toronto, ON, Canada
Tel.: (416) 399-0009
Year Founded: 2010
CLW.P—(TSXV)
Rev.: $2,726
Assets: $251,109
Liabilities: $28,597
Net Worth: $222,512
Earnings: ($74,822)
Fiscal Year-end: 12/31/12

Business Description:
Closed-End Investment Fund
S.I.C.: 6726
N.A.I.C.S.: 525990
Personnel:
Amar Bhalla *(CEO & CFO)*
Board of Directors:
Amar Bhalla
James Eaton
Richard Kimel

Transfer Agent:
Equity Financial Trust Company
200 University Avenue Suite 400
Toronto, ON, Canada

CARLIER PLASTIQUES

15 Chaussee Brunehaut
62470 Calonne-Ricouart, Pas De Calais, France
Tel.: (33) 321655454
Fax: (33) 321656995
E-Mail: contacts@carlier-plastiques.com
Web Site: www.carlier-plastiques.com
Sales Range: $25-49.9 Million
Emp.: 103

Business Description:
Plastics Product Mfr
S.I.C.: 3089
N.A.I.C.S.: 326199
Personnel:
Jean-Brice Guerin *(Gen Mgr)*

CARLIN GOLD CORPORATION

320-800 West Pender Street
Vancouver, BC, V6C 2V6, Canada
Tel.: (604) 638-1402
Fax: (604) 608-3878
E-Mail: info@carlingold.com
Web Site: www.carlingold.com
CGD—(TSXV)
Assets: $3,979,111
Liabilities: $32,385
Net Worth: $3,946,726
Earnings: ($1,273,413)
Fiscal Year-end: 12/31/12

Business Description:
Gold Exploration Services
S.I.C.: 1041
N.A.I.C.S.: 212221
Personnel:
K. Wayne Livingstone *(Pres & CEO)*
Aris Morfopoulos *(CFO)*
Board of Directors:
Robert Culbert
Brian C. Irwin
K. Wayne Livingstone
Ken Rye
Jay Sujir
Robert Thomas

Transfer Agent:
Computershare Investor Services Inc.
100 University Ave 9th Floor
Toronto, ON, Canada

CARLING CAPITAL PARTNERS PTY LTD.

3 Spring Street
Sydney, NSW, 2000, Australia
Mailing Address:
PO Box H32
Australia Square, Sydney, NSW, 1215, Australia
Tel.: (61) 2 9247 7744
Web Site: www.carlingcapitalpartners.com

Business Description:
Private Equity Firm
S.I.C.: 6211
N.A.I.C.S.: 523999
Personnel:
Maxim Carling *(Founder & Partner)*

Subsidiary:

Elysium Resources Limited (1)
(Formerly United Orogen Limited)
Suite 705 3 Spring Street
Sydney, NSW, 2000, Australia AU
Tel.: (61) 02 9247 7744
E-Mail: info@elysiumresources.com.au
Web Site: www.elysiumresources.com.au/
EYM—(ASX)
Rev.: $25,558
Assets: $653,906
Liabilities: $519,326
Net Worth: $134,580
Earnings: ($6,816,621)
Fiscal Year-end: 06/30/13
Mineral Exploration Services
S.I.C.: 1481
N.A.I.C.S.: 213115
Mark T. Ohlsson *(Sec)*

CARLING MOTORS CO. LIMITED

1638 Carling Avenue
Ottawa, ON, K2A 1C5, Canada
Tel.: (613) 729-2222
Fax: (613) 728-8901
E-Mail: sales@carlingmotorsvolvo.com
Web Site: www.carlingmotors.ca
Year Founded: 1956
Rev.: $33,696,000
Emp.: 64

Business Description:
New & Used Car Dealers
S.I.C.: 5511
N.A.I.C.S.: 441110
Personnel:
David Wharmby *(Gen Mgr)*

CARLISLE GOLDFIELDS LIMITED

401 Bay Street Suite 2702
Toronto, ON, M5H 2Y4, Canada
Tel.: (416) 278-8406
Fax: (416) 703-3695
E-Mail: info@carlislegold.com
Web Site: www.carlislegold.com
Year Founded: 2005
CGJ—(OTC TSX)
Int. Income: $3,976
Assets: $28,272,911
Liabilities: $1,980,088
Net Worth: $26,292,823
Earnings: ($2,078,496)
Emp.: 8
Fiscal Year-end: 08/31/13

Business Description:
Gold Mining Services
S.I.C.: 1041
N.A.I.C.S.: 212221
Personnel:
Bruce D. Reid *(Chm)*
Abraham Peter Drost *(Pres & CEO)*
Julio DiGirolamo *(CFO)*
Rick Adams *(COO)*
Donald A. Sheldon *(Sec)*
Board of Directors:
Bruce D. Reid
Jennifer L. Boyle
Abraham Peter Drost
James Macintosh
Donald A. Sheldon
Harold Roy Shipes
Nicholas Tintor

Legal Counsel:
Sheldon Huxtable Professional Corporation
Toronto, ON, Canada

Transfer Agent:
Equity Financial Trust Company
200 University Avenue Suite 400
Toronto, ON, Canada

CARLIT HOLDINGS CO., LTD.

1-17-10 Kyobashi
Chuo-ku, Tokyo, 104-0031, Japan
Tel.: (81) 3 6893 7070
Fax: (81) 3 6893 7050
Web Site: www.carlithd.co.jp
Year Founded: 2013
4275—(TKS)
Emp.: 741

Business Description:
Holding Company
S.I.C.: 6719
N.A.I.C.S.: 551112
Personnel:
Kazuo Deguchi *(Chm)*
Mitsuru Tomizawa *(Exec VP)*
Kenichi Hirohashi *(Mng Exec Officer)*
Hideo Yamamoto *(Exec Officer & Gen Mgr-R&D Center)*
Akinori Aoki *(Exec Officer)*
Tetsuji Banno *(Exec Officer)*
Minoru Fukuda *(Exec Officer)*
Akihide Kamiya *(Exec Officer)*
Hirofumi Kaneko *(Exec Officer)*
Masatoshi Kimura *(Exec Officer)*
Takeshi Kimura *(Exec Officer)*
Masayasu Konishi *(Exec Officer)*
Tadashi Mitsui *(Exec Officer)*
Takashi Morishita *(Exec Officer)*
Yoshiaki Shibata *(Exec Officer)*
Board of Directors:
Kazuo Deguchi
Kenichi Hirohashi
Mitsuru Tomizawa
Yukio Wakui
Hideo Yamamoto

Subsidiaries:

Carlit Sangyo Co., Ltd. (1)
2470 Handa
Shibukawa, Gunma, 377-0004, Japan JP
Tel.: (81) 279 23 8818
Fax: (81) 279 23 8863
Web Site: www.carlitsangyou.co.jp
Engineering, Construction & Termite Control Services
S.I.C.: 8711
N.A.I.C.S.: 541330
Tadashi Mitsui, *(Pres)*

Daiichi Yakuhin Kogyo Co., Ltd. (1)
1-17-10 Kyobashi
Chuo-ku, Tokyo, 104-0031, Japan JP
Tel.: (81) 3 3564 5651
Fax: (81) 3 3564 5660
Industrial Chemicals & Explosives Raw Materials Whslr
S.I.C.: 5169
N.A.I.C.S.: 424690
Satoshi Sakano, *(Pres)*

Fuji Shoji Co., Ltd. (1)
6-8-24 Nakatsu
Kita-ku, Osaka, 531-0071, Japan JP
Tel.: (81) 6 6458 2521
Fax: (81) 6 6458 3930
Web Site: www.fuji-syoji.jp
Paint Whslr & Industrial Painting Services
S.I.C.: 1721
N.A.I.C.S.: 238320
Osamu Sawamura, *(Pres)*

Japan Abrasive Grain, Ltd. (1)
1-17-10 Kyobashi
Chuo-ku, Tokyo, 104-0031, Japan JP
Tel.: (81) 3 6685 2100
Fax: (81) 3 6685 2095
Web Site: www.jag-co.net
Abrasives & Fire-Resistant Materials Mfr & Whslr
S.I.C.: 3291
N.A.I.C.S.: 327910
Akihide Kamiya, *(Pres)*

Japan Carlit Co., Ltd. (1)
1-17-10 Kyobashi
Chuo-ku, Tokyo, 104-0031, Japan JP
Tel.: (81) 3 6685 2020
Fax: (81) 3 6685 2050
Web Site: www.carlit.co.jp
Chemical & Electronic Materials Mfr & Distr
S.I.C.: 2899
N.A.I.C.S.: 325998
Mitsuru Tomizawa *(Pres)*

JC Bottling Co., Ltd. (1)
1-17-10 Kyobashi
Chuo-ku, Tokyo, 104-0031, Japan JP
Tel.: (81) 3 6228 7735
Fax: (81) 3 6228 7736
Soft Drink Bottler
S.I.C.: 2086
N.A.I.C.S.: 312111
Takeshi Kimura, *(Pres)*

Namitakiko Co., Ltd. (1)
1-13-13 Kobayashi-nishi
Taisho-ku, Osaka, 531-0071, Japan JP
Tel.: (81) 6 6553 0155
Fax: (81) 6 6553 0150
Web Site: www.namitakiko.co.jp
Fire-Resistant & Heat-Resistant Metal Materials Mfr & Whslr
S.I.C.: 3499
N.A.I.C.S.: 332999
Masatoshi Kimura, *(Pres)*

Silicon Technology Corporation (1)
1-17-10 Kyobashi
Chuo-ku, Tokyo, 104-0031, Japan JP
Tel.: (81) 3 5159 3301
Fax: (81) 3 5159 3302
Web Site: www.s-tc.co.jp
Semiconductor Silicon Wafer Mfr & Whslr
S.I.C.: 3674
N.A.I.C.S.: 334413
Masayasu Konishi, *(Pres)*

CARLO GAVAZZI HOLDING AG

Sumpfstrasse 32
CH-6312 Steinhausen, Switzerland
Tel.: (41) 417474525
Fax: (41) 417404560
E-Mail: gavazzi@carlogavazzi.ch
Web Site: www.carlogavazzi.com
GAV—(SWX)
Sls.: $149,308,812
Assets: $147,628,310
Liabilities: $38,348,240
Net Worth: $109,280,071
Earnings: $13,547,625
Emp.: 1,006
Fiscal Year-end: 03/31/13

Business Description:
Holding Company
S.I.C.: 6719
N.A.I.C.S.: 551112
Personnel:
Valeria Gavazzi *(Chm)*
Stefano Premoli Trovati *(Vice Chm)*
Anthony M. Goldstein *(CFO)*
Vittorio Rossi *(CEO-Automation Components)*
Board of Directors:
Valeria Gavazzi
Federico Foglia
Daniel Hirschi
Stefano Premoli Trovati

Carlo Gavazzi Holding AG—(Continued)

Subsidiaries:

Carlo Gavazzi AG (1)
Verkauf Schweiz-Vente
SuisseSumpfstrasse 32, 6312 Steinhausen, Switzerland (100%)
Tel.: (41) 417474535
Fax: (41) 417404540
E-Mail: verkauf_vente@carlogavazzi.ch
Web Site: www.carlogavazzi.ch
Other Management Consulting Services
S.I.C.: 8748
N.A.I.C.S.: 541618

Carlo Gavazzi Marketing Ag (1)
Sumpfstrasse 32
6312 Steinhausen, Switzerland (100%)
Tel.: (41) 417474535
Fax: (41) 417404540
Web Site: www.carlogavazzi.com
Other Management Consulting Services
S.I.C.: 8748
N.A.I.C.S.: 541618

Carlo Gavazzi Services Ag (1)
Sumpfstrasse 3
6312 Steinhausen, Switzerland (100%)
Tel.: (41) 7474525
Fax: (41) 7404560
E-Mail: gavazzi@carlogavazzi.ch
Web Site: www.carlogavazzi.com
Emp.: 9
Other Management Consulting Services
S.I.C.: 8748
N.A.I.C.S.: 541618

U.S. Subsidiary:

Carlo Gavazzi Inc. (1)
750 Hastings Ln
Buffalo Grove, IL 60089-6904 (100%)
Tel.: (847) 465-6100
Fax: (847) 465-7373
E-Mail: sales@carlogavazzi.com
Web Site: www.gavazzionline.com
Emp.: 25
Engineering Services
S.I.C.: 8711
N.A.I.C.S.: 541330
Fred Shirzadi *(Pres & CEO)*

Non-U.S. Subsidiaries:

Carlo Gavazzi AB (1)
Nattvindsgatan 1
65221 Karlstad, Sweden (100%)
Tel.: (46) 54851125
Fax: (46) 54851177
E-Mail: gavazzi@carlogavazzi.se
Web Site: www.carlogavazzi.se
Emp.: 20
Electrical & Electronic Appliance Television & Radio Set Merchant Whslr
S.I.C.: 5064
N.A.I.C.S.: 423620
Christer Boman *(Gen Mgr)*

Carlo Gavazzi AS (1)
Melkevegen 13
3919 Porsgrunn, Norway (100%)
Tel.: (47) 35930800
Fax: (47) 35930801
E-Mail: gavazzi@carlogavazzi.no
Web Site: www.carlogavazzi.no
Emp.: 14
Other Electronic Parts & Equipment Whslr
S.I.C.: 5065
N.A.I.C.S.: 423690

Carlo Gavazzi Automation (China) Co Ltd (1)
Rm 2308-2310 23/F News Building Block 1
Shennan Zhong Road, 1002 Shenzhen, China (100%)
Tel.: (86) 75583699500
Fax: (86) 75583969300
E-Mail: ben.tai@carlogavazzi.cn
Web Site: www.carlogavazzi.com
Emp.: 25
Commercial Industrial & Institutional Electric Lighting Fixture Mfr
S.I.C.: 3646
N.A.I.C.S.: 335122
Ben Tai *(Mng Dir)*

Carlo Gavazzi Automation Hong Kong Ltd (1)
Unit 3 12/F Crown Ind
Building 106 How Ming St, Kowloon, China (Hong Kong) (100%)
Tel.: (852) 23041228
Fax: (852) 23443689
Web Site: www.carlogavazzi.com
Emp.: 25
Other Electronic Component Mfr
S.I.C.: 3679
N.A.I.C.S.: 334419
Ben Tai *(Mng Dir)*

Carlo Gavazzi Automation (M) Sdn Bhd (1)
D12-06-G Block D12 Pusat Perdagangan Dana 1
Jalan PJU 1A/46, 47301 Petaling Jaya, Malaysia (100%)
Tel.: (60) 378427299
Fax: (60) 378427399
E-Mail: sales@gavazzi-asia.com
Web Site: www.gavazzi-automation.com
Emp.: 7
All Other Industrial Machinery Mfr
S.I.C.: 3559
N.A.I.C.S.: 333249
Chris Lee *(Mng Dir)*

Carlo Gavazzi Automation Singapore Pte Ltd (1)
61 Tai Seng Ave Unit 05-06
UE Print Media Hub, 534167 Singapore, Singapore (100%)
Tel.: (65) 67466990
Fax: (65) 67461980
E-Mail: info@carlogavazzi.com.sg
Web Site: www.gavazzi-automation.com.sg
Emp.: 15
Electrical & Electronic Appliance Television & Radio Set Merchant Whslr
S.I.C.: 5064
N.A.I.C.S.: 423620
Songyang Lee *(Mng Dir)*

Carlo Gavazzi Automation Spa (1)
Via Milano 13
20020 Lainate, Italy (100%)
Tel.: (39) 0293176431
Fax: (39) 0293176402
E-Mail: info@gavazzi-automation.com
Web Site: www.carlogavazzi.com
Electrical Apparatus & Equipment Wiring Supplies & Related Equipment Merchant Whslr
S.I.C.: 5063
N.A.I.C.S.: 423610

Carlo Gavazzi BV (1)
Wijkermeerweg 23
1948 Beverwijk, Netherlands (100%)
Tel.: (31) 251229345
Fax: (31) 251226055
E-Mail: info@carlogavazzi.nl
Web Site: www.carlogavazzi.com
Emp.: 7
Other Electronic Parts & Equipment Whslr
S.I.C.: 5065
N.A.I.C.S.: 423690
Paul Dekker *(Mng Dir)*

Carlo Gavazzi (Canada) Inc. (1)
Unit 8 2660 Meadowvale Blvd
Mississauga, ON, L5N 6M6, Canada
Tel.: (905) 542-0979
Fax: (905) 542-2248
E-Mail: gavazzi@carlogavazzi.com
Web Site: www.gavazzionline.com
Emp.: 15
Instrument Mfr for Measuring & Testing Electricity & Electrical Signals
S.I.C.: 3825
N.A.I.C.S.: 334515
Fred Shirzaei *(Pres-North America)*

Carlo Gavazzi Gmbh (1)
Ketzergasse 374
1230 Vienna, Austria (100%)
Tel.: (43) 18884112
Fax: (43) 18891053
E-Mail: office@carlogavazzi.at
Web Site: www.carlogavazzi.at
Emp.: 4
Other Electronic Component Mfr
S.I.C.: 3679
N.A.I.C.S.: 334419
Deiter Woss *(Mng Dir)*

CARLO GAVAZZI GmbH (1)
Pfnorstr 10-14
64293 Darmstadt, Germany
Tel.: (49) 6151 81 00 0
Fax: (49) 6151 81 00 40
E-Mail: info@gavazzi.de
Web Site: www.gavazzi.de
Electronic Component Mfr & Distr
S.I.C.: 3679
N.A.I.C.S.: 334419

Carlo Gavazzi Handel A/S (1)
Over Hadstenvej 40
8370 Hadsten, Denmark (100%)
Tel.: (45) 89606100
Fax: (45) 86981530
E-Mail: handel@gavazzi.dk
Web Site: www.gavazzi.dk
Emp.: 20
Other Electronic Parts & Equipment Whslr
S.I.C.: 5065
N.A.I.C.S.: 423690
Michael Rasmussen *(Mng Dir)*

Carlo Gavazzi Industri A/S (1)
Over Hadstenvej 40
8370 Hadsten, Denmark (100%)
Tel.: (45) 89606100
Fax: (45) 86982522
E-Mail: industri@gavazzi.dk
Web Site: www.gavazzi.dk
Emp.: 20
Semiconductor & Related Device Mfr
S.I.C.: 3674
N.A.I.C.S.: 334413
Savio Fion *(Mng Dir)*

Non-U.S. Subsidiary:

CARLO GAVAZZI INDUSTRI KAUNAS UAB (2)
Raudondvario Pl 101
47184 Kaunas, Lithuania
Tel.: (370) 37328227
Fax: (370) 37328222
E-Mail: info@gavazzi.lt
Web Site: www.gavazzi-automation.com
Emp.: 140
Industrial Automation Component Distr
S.I.C.: 5065
N.A.I.C.S.: 423690
Ernestas Greicius *(Mgr-Ops)*

Carlo Gavazzi LDA (1)
Rua dos Jeronimos 38-B
1400-212 Lisbon, Portugal (100%)
Tel.: (351) 213617060
Fax: (351) 213621373
E-Mail: carlogavazzi@carlogavazzi.pt
Web Site: www.carlogavazzi.com
Emp.: 4
Other Electronic Parts & Equipment Whslr
S.I.C.: 5065
N.A.I.C.S.: 423690
Jose Teixera *(Mng Dir)*

Carlo Gavazzi Logistics Spa (1)
Via Milano 13
20020 Lainate, Italy (100%)
Tel.: (39) 0293176431
Fax: (39) 0293176401
E-Mail: bruno.rebora@gavazziacbu.it
Web Site: www.carlogavazzi.com
Emp.: 40
Electrical Apparatus & Equipment Wiring Supplies & Related Equipment Merchant Whslr
S.I.C.: 5063
N.A.I.C.S.: 423610
Gianluigi Taglioretti *(Gen Mgr)*

Carlo Gavazzi Oy AB (1)
Petaksentie 2-4
00661 Helsinki, Finland (100%)
Tel.: (358) 97562000
Fax: (358) 975620010
E-Mail: myynti@carlogavazzi.fi
Web Site: www.carlogavazzi.com
Emp.: 6
Other Electronic Component Mfr
S.I.C.: 3679
N.A.I.C.S.: 334419
Sven Bostrom *(Mng Dir)*

Carlo Gavazzi Participation Danmark A/S (1)
Over Hadstenvej 40
8370 Hadsten, Denmark (100%)
Tel.: (45) 89606100
Fax: (45) 86982522
E-Mail: gavazzi@carlogavazzi.ind.dk
Web Site: www.carlogavazzi.com
Emp.: 25
Switchgear & Switchboard Apparatus Mfr
S.I.C.: 3613
N.A.I.C.S.: 335313
Savio Fion *(Mng Dir)*

Non-U.S. Subsidiaries:

CARLO GAVAZZI AUTOMATION (KUNSHAN) Co Ltd (2)
Kunjia Road 347 Kunshan Development Zone
215334 Kunshan, Jiangsu, China
Tel.: (86) 512 57639310
Fax: (86) 512 57639330
E-Mail: cgak@carlogavazzi.cn
Web Site: www.gavazzi-automation.com
Electronic Automation Component Mfr
S.I.C.: 3679
N.A.I.C.S.: 334419

CARLO GAVAZZI CONTROLS SpA (2)
Via Safforze 8
32100 Belluno, Italy
Tel.: (39) 04 379 31000
Fax: (39) 04 379 31021
E-Mail: controls@gavazziacbu.it
Web Site: www.gavazzi-automation.com
Electronic Component Mfr & Distr
S.I.C.: 3679
N.A.I.C.S.: 334419

CARLO GAVAZZI Ltd (2)
B42 Bulebel Industrial Estate
Zejtun, ZTN 3000, Malta
Tel.: (356) 2360 1100
Fax: (356) 2360 1111
E-Mail: customerservice@carlogavazzi.com.mt
Web Site: www.carlogavazzi.com.mt
Electronic Automation Component Mfr & Distr
S.I.C.: 3679
N.A.I.C.S.: 334419
Deborah Gaffiero *(Controller-Fin & Mgr-HR)*

CARLO GAVAZZI SA (2)
Avda Iparraguirre 80-82
48940 Leioa, Bizkaia, Spain
Tel.: (34) 94 480 40 37
Fax: (34) 94 480 10 61
E-Mail: gavazzi@gavazzi.es
Web Site: www.carlogavazzi.es
Emp.: 40
Automation Component Mfr & Distr
S.I.C.: 3559
N.A.I.C.S.: 333249
Angel Olea *(Gen Mgr)*

Carlo Gavazzi Sa (1)
Schaarbeeklei 213-3
1800 Vilvoorde, Belgium (100%)
Tel.: (32) 22574120
Fax: (32) 22574125
E-Mail: sales@carlogavazzi.be
Web Site: www.carlogavazzi.be
Emp.: 8
Other Electronic Component Mfr
S.I.C.: 3679
N.A.I.C.S.: 334419
Peter Martins *(Mng Dir)*

Carlo Gavazzi Sarl (1)
Zac Paris Nord II 69
Rue de la Belle Etoile, 95956 Roissy-en-France, Cedex, France (100%)
Tel.: (33) 149389860
Fax: (33) 148632743
E-Mail: french.team@carlogavazzi.fr
Web Site: www.gavazzi-automation.com
Emp.: 15
Other Electronic Parts & Equipment Whslr
S.I.C.: 5065
N.A.I.C.S.: 423690
Philipp Dourqui *(Pres)*

Carlo Gavazzi Spa (1)
Via Milano 13
20020 Lainate, Italy (100%)
Tel.: (39) 0293176431
Fax: (39) 0293176301
E-Mail: info@gavazziacbu.it
Web Site: www.carlogavazzi.com
Other Electronic Parts & Equipment Whslr
S.I.C.: 5065
N.A.I.C.S.: 423690

Carlo Gavazzi UK Ltd (1)
7 Springlakes Industrial Estate Deadbrook Lane
Hampshire, Aldershot, GU12 4UH, United Kingdom (100%)

Tel.: (44) 1252339600
Fax: (44) 1252326799
E-Mail: sales@carlogavazzi.co.uk
Web Site: www.carlogavazzi.com
Emp.: 14
Other Electronic Parts & Equipment Whslr
S.I.C.: 5065
N.A.I.C.S.: 423690
Alan Hickman *(Mng Dir)*

CARLSBERG A/S

(d/b/a Carlsberg Group)
100 Ny Carlsberg Vej
1799 Copenhagen, Denmark
Tel.: (45) 33273300
Fax: (45) 33274808
E-Mail: contact@carlsberg.com
Web Site: www.carlsberggroup.com
Year Founded: 1847
CARLB—(CSE)
Rev.: $16,791,516,000
Assets: $27,769,127,400
Liabilities: $14,485,613,400
Net Worth: $13,283,514,000
Earnings: $1,126,348,200
Emp.: 41,708
Fiscal Year-end: 12/31/12

Business Description:
Brewer
Import Export
S.I.C.: 2082
N.A.I.C.S.: 312120

Personnel:
Flemming Besenbacher *(Chm-Supervisory Bd)*
Jess Soderberg *(Deputy Chm-Supervisory Bd)*
Jorgen Buhl Rasmussen *(Grp CEO)*
Jorn Peter Jensen *(Deputy CEO, CFO & Member-Exec Bd)*
Anton O. Artemiev *(Pres-Baltic Reg)*
Thomas Amstutz *(CEO-Feldschlosschen Beverages Ltd)*
Alberto Frausin *(CEO-Italy)*
Alexander Grancharov *(CEO-Bulgaria)*
Carsten Hanel *(CEO-Denmark)*
Frank Massen *(CEO-Germany)*
Lars Cordi *(Treas & VP)*
Bengt Erlandsson *(Sr VP-Procurement)*
Peter Ernsting *(Sr VP-Supply Chain)*
Graham Fewkes *(Sr VP-Global Sls, Mktg & Innovation)*
Jorn Tolstrup Rohde *(Sr VP-Western Europe)*
Claudia Schlossberger *(Sr VP-HR)*
Isaac Sheps *(Sr VP-Eastern Europe)*
Anne-Marie Skov *(Sr VP-Comm & CSR)*

Supervisory Board of Directors:
Flemming Besenbacher
Hans S. Andersen
Richard Burrows
Donna Cordner
Elisabeth Fleuriot
Thomas Knudsen
Per Ohrgaard
Soren-Peter Fuchs Olesen
Bent Ole Petersen
Peter Petersen
Nina Smith
Jess Soderberg
Lars Stemmerik
Kees van der Graaf

Subsidiaries:

Alectia A/S (1)
Teknikerbyen 34
Virum, 2830, Denmark (100%)
Tel.: (45) 88191000
Fax: (45) 88191001
E-Mail: info@alectia.com
Web Site: www.alectia.com
Emp.: 550
Brewery
S.I.C.: 2082
N.A.I.C.S.: 312120
Jens Moberg *(CEO)*
Conny Sorensen *(CFO)*

Carlsberg Breweries A/S (1)
100 Ny Carlsberg Vej
1799 Copenhagen, Denmark
Tel.: (45) 33 27 33 00
Fax: (45) 33 27 47 01
E-Mail: webcommunications@carlsberg.com
Beer Mfr
S.I.C.: 2082
N.A.I.C.S.: 312120

Carlsberg Danmark A/S (1)
Vesterfaeledvej 100
1799 Copenhagen, Denmark
Tel.: (45) 33 27 33 27
Fax: (45) 33 27 47 11
E-Mail: carlsberg@carlsberg.dk
Web Site: www.carlsbergdanmark.dk
Beer Mfr
S.I.C.: 2082
N.A.I.C.S.: 312120
Jens Bekke *(Mgr-Comm)*

Carlsberg Ejendomme Holding A/S (1)
Bag Elefanterne Ny Carlsberg Vej 140
1760 Copenhagen, Denmark
Tel.: (45) 33 27 33 00
Real Estate Development Services
S.I.C.: 6531
N.A.I.C.S.: 531390
Jakob Stilov *(Dir-Real Estate)*

Carlsberg Finans A/S (1)
Ny Carlsberg Vej 100
1799 Copenhagen, Denmark (100%)
Tel.: (45) 33273300
Fax: (45) 33274808
E-Mail: carlsberg@carlsberg.com
Web Site: www.carlsberg.com
Emp.: 100
Financial Services
S.I.C.: 7389
N.A.I.C.S.: 561499
Jorgen Buhl Rasmussen *(CEO)*

Carlsberg Insurance A/S (1)
Ny Carlsberg Vej 100
1799 Copenhagen, Denmark
Tel.: (45) 33273300
Fax: (45) 33274701
E-Mail: carlsberg@carlsberg.com
Emp.: 200
General Insurance Services
S.I.C.: 6411
N.A.I.C.S.: 524298
Yutaka Usuda *(CEO)*

Carlsberg International A/S (1)
Ny Carlsberg Vej 100
1799 Copenhagen, Denmark
Tel.: (45) 33273300
Fax: (45) 33274811
E-Mail: carlsberg@carlsberg.dk
Web Site: www.carlsbergbyen.dk
Emp.: 180
Beer Mfr
S.I.C.: 2082
N.A.I.C.S.: 312120
Carsten Hanel *(Gen Mgr)*

Carlsberg Invest A/S (1)
Ny Carlsberg Vej 100
1799 Copenhagen, Denmark
Tel.: (45) 33273300
Fax: (45) 33275151
Web Site: www.carlsberg.com
Investment Management Services
S.I.C.: 6211
N.A.I.C.S.: 523999
Jorgen Rasmussen *(Pres)*

Danish Malting Group A/S (1)
Spirevej 5
DK 4760 Vordingborg, Denmark (100%)
Tel.: (45) 55975000
Fax: (45) 55975050
E-Mail: dmg@malting.dk
Web Site: www.carlsberg.dk
Sls.: $41,579,500
Emp.: 25
S.I.C.: 2082
N.A.I.C.S.: 312120
Kim G. Jorgensen *(Mng Dir)*

Ejendomsaktieselskabet af 4. marts 1982 (1)
Ny Carlsberg Vej 100
1799 Copenhagen, Denmark
Tel.: (45) 33223929
E-Mail: carlsberg@carlsberg.com
Property Management Services
S.I.C.: 6531
N.A.I.C.S.: 531312

Carlsberg Denmark A/S Fredericia (1)
Vestre Ringvej 111
7000 Fredericia, Denmark (100%)
Tel.: (45) 3327 3327
Fax: (45) 75931618
Web Site: www.carlsbergdanmark.dk
Emp.: 332
Beer Distiller
S.I.C.: 2082
N.A.I.C.S.: 312120
Finn Jakobsen *(VP)*

Non-U.S. Subsidiaries:

A/S Aldaris (1)
Tvaika street 44
Riga, 1005, Latvia
Tel.: (371) 67 023 200
Fax: (371) 67 023 224
E-Mail: aldaris@aldaris.lv
Web Site: www.aldaris.lv
Emp.: 40
Beverage Products Mfr & Distr
S.I.C.: 2082
N.A.I.C.S.: 312120
Thomas Panteli *(CEO)*

AB Svyturys (1)
Kuliu Vartu g 7
92276 Klaipeda, Lithuania (57%)
Tel.: (370) 8 46 484000
Fax: (370) 8 46 484009
Web Site: www.svyturys.lt/en
Mfr. of Beer
S.I.C.: 2082
N.A.I.C.S.: 312120
Imantas Cepulis *(Mng Dir-Brewery)*

Brasseries Kronenbourg (1)
Bp 13 68 Rte D Oberhausbergen
PO Box 13
67037 Strasbourg, Cedex, France FR
Tel.: (33) 388274488
Fax: (33) 388274206
E-Mail: info@brasseries-kronenbourg.com
Web Site: www.brasseries-kronenbourg.com
Emp.: 2,000
Brewery
S.I.C.: 2082
N.A.I.C.S.: 312120

Carlsberg Accounting Service Centre Sp. z.o.o. (1)
Male Garbary 9
61-756 Poznan, Poland
Tel.: (48) 61 844 11 00
Fax: (48) 61 844 11 00
E-Mail: ASC@carlsberg.com
Web Site: www.carlsberggroup.com
Emp.: 300
Accounting Services
S.I.C.: 8721
N.A.I.C.S.: 541219
Lars Rasmussen *(Gen Mgr)*

Carlsberg Brewery Hong Kong Limited (1)
1st Fl Delta House 3 On Yiu St Sui Lek Yuen
Sha Tin, China (Hong Kong) (51%)
Tel.: (852) 31898000
Fax: (852) 31898168
E-Mail: info@carlsberg.com.hk
Web Site: www.carlsberg.com.hk
Sales Range: $25-49.9 Million
Emp.: 200
S.I.C.: 2082
N.A.I.C.S.: 312120
Daniel Sjogren *(Mng Dir)*

Non-U.S. Subsidiaries:

Carlsberg (Singapore) Pte. Ltd. (2)
238A Thomson Road #13-08/10. Novena Square Tower A
Singapore, 307684, Singapore (100%)
Tel.: (65) 62953395
Fax: (65) 62952115
E-Mail: CarlsbergSingaporePteLtd@Carlsberg.com
Web Site: www.Carlsberg.com.sg
Emp.: 68
S.I.C.: 2082
N.A.I.C.S.: 312120
John Botia *(Mng Dir)*

Luen Heng F&B Sdn Bhd (2)
Wisma LHA No8 Jalan Kilang Midah
Taman Midah, 56000 Kuala Lumpur, Malaysia
Tel.: (60) 3 91730398
Fax: (60) 3 91730498
E-Mail: lha@luenheng.com
Web Site: www.luenheng.com
Emp.: 10
Alcoholic Beverage Mfr
S.I.C.: 2082
N.A.I.C.S.: 312120
Kenneth Soh *(Gen Mgr)*

Carlsberg Brewing Limited (1)
140 Bridge St
Northampton, NN1 1PZ, United Kingdom (100%)
Tel.: (44) 604668866
Fax: (44) 1604234444
Web Site: www.carlsberg.co.uk
Sls.: $1,500,000
Emp.: 2,867
Brewers of Beer
Import Export
S.I.C.: 5921
N.A.I.C.S.: 445310

Carlsberg Canada Inc. (1)
2650 Bristol Circle Unit 100
Oakville, ON, L6H 6Z7, Canada
Tel.: (905) 829-0299
Fax: (905) 829-2666
E-Mail: marketing@carlsberg.ca
Web Site: www.carlsberg.ca
Beverage Products Distr
S.I.C.: 5182
N.A.I.C.S.: 424820

Carlsberg Deutschland GmbH (1)
Holstenstrasse 224
22765 Hamburg, Germany
Tel.: (49) 40 38 101 0
Fax: (49) 40 38101 751
E-Mail: info@carlsberg.de
Web Site: www.carlsbergdeutschland.de
Beer Mfr
S.I.C.: 2082
N.A.I.C.S.: 312120

Carlsberg GB Limited (1)
Carlsberg Brewery 140 Bridge Street
Northampton, NN1 1PZ, United Kingdom
Tel.: (44) 1604668866
Fax: (44) 1604234444
Web Site: www.carlsberg.co.uk
Beverage Mfr
S.I.C.: 2082
N.A.I.C.S.: 312120

Carlsberg Hungary Sales Limited Liability Company (1)
Neumann Janos Utca 3
2040 Budaors, Hungary
Tel.: (36) 23 88 85 55
Fax: (36) 23 88 85 01
Web Site: www.carlsberggroup.com
Emp.: 30
Alcoholic Beverage Distr
S.I.C.: 5182
N.A.I.C.S.: 424820
Andras Ambrisko *(Dir-Sls)*

Carlsberg Importers SA (1)
Industrielaan 16-20
Ternat, 1740, Belgium (100%)
Tel.: (32) 25835000
Fax: (32) 25810608
E-Mail: info@carlsberg.be
Web Site: www.carlsberg.be
Emp.: 100
Provider of Brewing Services
S.I.C.: 2082
N.A.I.C.S.: 312120
Paul Haelterman *(Gen Mgr)*

Carlsberg India Pvt Ltd (1)
Plot No 52 Sector 32 Institutional Area
Gurgaon, Haryana, 122 001, India
Tel.: (91) 124 4554444
Fax: (91) 124 4554499
E-Mail: reception@carlsbergindia.in
Web Site: www.carlsbergindia.com
Emp.: 537
Alcoholic Beverage Distr
S.I.C.: 5182
N.A.I.C.S.: 424820

Carlsberg A/S—(Continued)

Soren Gronnegaard Lauridsen *(Mng Dir)*
Dheeraj Mishra *(CFO & Dir-Fin)*
Vikas Bhatia *(CFO)*

Subsidiary:

Parag Breweries Ltd (2)
2 J L Nehru Road
Kolkata, West Bengal, 700 013, India
Tel.: (91) 3213 251443
Alcoholic Beverage Mfr & Distr
S.I.C.: 2082
N.A.I.C.S.: 312120

Carlsberg Italia S.p.A. (1)
Via Ramazzotti 12
I 20020 Lainate, Milano, Italy (100%)
Tel.: (39) 0293536911
Fax: (39) 0293536412
E-Mail: info@carlsberg.it
Web Site: www.carlsbergitalia.it
Emp.: 200
S.I.C.: 2082
N.A.I.C.S.: 312120
Frdosen Alberto *(Mng Dir)*
Alberto Frausin *(CFO)*

Carlsberg Kazakhstan Ltd. (1)
270 B Kazybayev St
050014 Almaty, Kazakhstan
Tel.: (7) 727 3 210 100
Fax: (7) 727 3 211 100
E-Mail: carlsberg@carlsberg.kz
Web Site: www.carlsbergkazakhstan.com
Alcoholic Beverage Distr
S.I.C.: 5182
N.A.I.C.S.: 424820
Maria Gorokhova *(Mgr-Comm)*

Carlsberg Polska S. A. (1)
ul Ilzecka 24 Budynek F
02-135 Warsaw, Poland
Tel.: (48) 22 543 14 00
Fax: (48) 22 543 15 00
E-Mail: info@carlsberg.pl
Alcoholic Beverage Mfr
S.I.C.: 2082
N.A.I.C.S.: 312120

Carlsberg Sverige AB (1)
Evenemangsgatan 27
161 86 Solna, Sweden
Tel.: (46) 8 757 70 00
Fax: (46) 8 28 98 61
E-Mail: info@carlsberg.se
Web Site: www.carlsberg.se
Emp.: 120
Beverage Products Mfr & Distr
S.I.C.: 2082
N.A.I.C.S.: 312120
Gustavo Pedreira *(Gen Mgr)*

CTDD Beer Imports Ltd. (1)
5565 Av Christophe-Colomb
Montreal, QC, H2J 3H3, Canada
Tel.: (514) 938-3883
Fax: (514) 938-3666
Emp.: 3
Alcoholic Beverage Distr
S.I.C.: 5182
N.A.I.C.S.: 424820
Rob Boulet *(Gen Mgr)*

Dali Beer (Group) Limited Company (1)
13D No 308 Binjiang Road Central
Guangzhou, China
Tel.: (86) 20 34691778
Fax: (86) 20 34691994
Alcoholic Beverage Distr
S.I.C.: 5182
N.A.I.C.S.: 424820

Danish Malting Group Polska Sp. z.o.o. (1)
ul Swietokrzyska 27
09-200 Sierpc, Poland
Tel.: (48) 242758400
Fax: (48) 24 275 8410
E-Mail: dmgp@dmgp.pl
Web Site: www.dmgp.pl
Emp.: 30
Malt Mfr
S.I.C.: 2083
N.A.I.C.S.: 311213
Marcin Siemion *(Mng Dir)*

Dyland BV (1)
Gooiberg 26
Bussum, 1406 SP, Netherlands
Tel.: (31) 356919285
Beverage Products Mfr & Distr
S.I.C.: 2082
N.A.I.C.S.: 312120

Euro Distributors Sdn BHD (1)
No 55 Psn Selangor Seksyen 15
40200 Shah Alam, Selangor, Malaysia
Tel.: (60) 3 5519 1621
Fax: (60) 3 5519 1931
Emp.: 40
Beverage Products Distr
S.I.C.: 5182
N.A.I.C.S.: 424820
Soren Ravn *(Mng Dir)*

Feldschlosschen Beverages Holding Ltd. (1)
Theophil Roniger Strasse
Rheinfelden, 4310, Switzerland (100%)
Tel.: (41) 848125000
Fax: (41) 848125001
E-Mail: info@feldschloesschen.ch
Web Site: www.feldschloesschen.ch
Emp.: 1,500
Producer, Buyer & Distributer of Beer, Sweet Drinks, Mineral Water
S.I.C.: 2084
N.A.I.C.S.: 312130
Alex Myers *(Chm)*
Thomas Metzger *(CEO)*

Subsidiary:

Feldschlosschen Beverages Ltd. (2)
Theophil Roniger Strasse
Rheinfelden, 4310, Switzerland (100%)
Tel.: (41) 848125000
Fax: (41) 848125001
E-Mail: info@feldschloesschen.com
Web Site: www.feldschloesschen.com
Emp.: 700
Brewers of Beer
S.I.C.: 2082
N.A.I.C.S.: 312120
Thomas Metzger *(CEO)*

Feldschlosschen Getranke Holding AG (1)
Feldschlosschenstrasse 34
Rheinfelden, 4310, Switzerland
Tel.: (41) 84 812 50 00
Fax: (41) 84 812 50 01
E-Mail: info@feldschloesschen.ch
Web Site: www.feldschloesschen.com
Emp.: 1,700
Investment Management Services
S.I.C.: 6211
N.A.I.C.S.: 523999
Thomas Amstutz *(CEO)*

Holsten-Brauerei AG (1)
Holstenstrasse 224
Hamburg, 22765, Germany De
Tel.: (49) 40381010 (98%)
Fax: (49) 4038101751
Web Site: www.holsten.de
Sales Range: $800-899.9 Million
Emp.: 2,840
Mfr. of Beer & Non-Alcoholic Beverages
S.I.C.: 2082
N.A.I.C.S.: 312120
Frank Massen *(Chm)*

Mythos Brewery S.A. (1)
Industrial Zone
570 22 Thessaloniki, Greece
Tel.: (30) 2310568400
Fax: (30) 2310799179
Web Site: www.mythosbrewery.gr
Brewery
S.I.C.: 2082
N.A.I.C.S.: 312120
Alexander Karafilidis *(Mng Dir)*

Nuuk Imeq A/S (1)
Post Box 1075
3900 Nuuk, Greenland
Tel.: (299) 2 95 88
Fax: (299) 2 96 51
Web Site: home.tiscali.nl/beercollection/Adres/Greenland.htm
Brewers of Beer
S.I.C.: 2082
N.A.I.C.S.: 312120

OAO Baltika Breweries (1)
6 Verkhny per d 3
194292 Saint Petersburg, Russia RU
Tel.: (7) 8123259325 (100%)
Web Site: www.corporate.baltika.ru
Emp.: 12,000
Beer Producer
S.I.C.: 2082
N.A.I.C.S.: 312120
Jorgen Buhl Rasmussen *(Chm)*
Isaac Sheps *(Pres & CEO)*
Olga Golchikova *(CFO & VP-Fin)*

Oy Sinebrychoff AB (1)
Alikerauantia 40
PO Box 87
FIN 04201 Kerava, Finland (100%)
Tel.: (358) 9294991
Fax: (358) 929499464
E-Mail: sanna.askiainen@sff.fi
Web Site: www.sinebrychoff.fi
Emp.: 800
Mfr. of Beer
S.I.C.: 2082
N.A.I.C.S.: 312120
Pekke Tiainen *(Mgr)*

Non-U.S. Subsidiaries:

Carlsberg Sweden AB (2)
Arstadvagen
31122 Falkenberg, 31122, Sweden (100%)
Tel.: (46) 87577000
Fax: (46) 34617155
E-Mail: johan.boestam@carlsberg.se
Web Site: www.carlsberg.se
Emp.: 500
Brewer, Bottler & Distributor of Malt Beverages
S.I.C.: 2082
N.A.I.C.S.: 312120
Christina Kormendy *(Mgr-Mktg)*

OAO Vena (2)
1 Farforovskata Str
192171 Saint Petersburg, Russia (66%)
Tel.: (7) 8123262100
Fax: (7) 8123299148
E-Mail: post@daltika.ru
Web Site: www.vv.daltika.ru
Emp.: 7,000
Mfr. of Beer
S.I.C.: 2082
N.A.I.C.S.: 312120
Antom Artiemied *(Pres)*

Pripps Ringnes AB (1)
Bryggerivagen 10
Bromma, 168 67, Sweden
Tel.: (46) 87577000
Fax: (46) 8 28 98 61
Beverage Products Distr
S.I.C.: 5182
N.A.I.C.S.: 424820
Mark Jensen *(Mng Dir)*

Ringnes A/S (1)
Thofrvalenvenrs 9211
PO Box 7152
N 0307 Oslo, Norway
Mailing Address:
PO Box 7152
0307 Oslo, Norway
Tel.: (47) 22069500
Fax: (47) 22069730
E-Mail: johnny.ottesen@ringnes.no
Web Site: www.ringnes.no
Rev.: $439,410
Emp.: 1,500
Producers of Carbonated Soft Drinks & Beer
S.I.C.: 2086
N.A.I.C.S.: 312111
Jacek Pastuszka *(CEO)*

Saku Olletehase AS (1)
Tallinna Mnt 2
Saku, Harju, 75501, Estonia
Tel.: (372) 6 508 400
Fax: (372) 6 508 401
E-Mail: saku@saku.ee
Web Site: www.saku.ee
Emp.: 150
Beverage Products Mfr & Distr
S.I.C.: 2082
N.A.I.C.S.: 312120
Margus Kastein *(CEO & Exec Dir)*
Margit Martin *(Sec)*

Non-U.S. Affiliates:

Carlsberg Brewery Malaysia Berhad (1)
No 55 Persiaran Selangor Section 15
40200 Shah Alam, Selangor, Malaysia MY
Mailing Address: (50%)
PO Box 10617
50720 Kuala Lumpur, Malaysia
Tel.: (60) 355226688
Fax: (60) 355191931
E-Mail: info@carlsberg.com.my
Web Site: www.carlsberg.com.my
Emp.: 700
Brewer of Beers & Ales
S.I.C.: 2082
N.A.I.C.S.: 312120
Soren Ravn *(Mng Dir)*

Subsidiary:

Carlsberg Marketing Sdn BHD (2)
No 55 Persiaran Selangor Section 1
Shah Alam, Selangor, 40200, Malaysia
Tel.: (60) 355226688
Fax: (60) 355191931
E-Mail: info@carlsberg.com.my
Web Site: www.carlsbergmalaysia.com.my
Emp.: 30
Alcoholic Beverage Distr
S.I.C.: 5182
N.A.I.C.S.: 424820
Soren Ravn *(Gen Mgr)*

Carlsberg Croatia (1)
Dacea 3
48000 Koprivnica, Croatia (40%)
Tel.: (385) 48657011
Fax: (385) 48657077
E-Mail: info@carlberg.hr
Web Site: www.carlsberg.hr
Emp.: 309
Provider of Beverage Services
S.I.C.: 2082
N.A.I.C.S.: 312120
Slobodan Vuletic *(Product Dir)*

Carlsberg Malawi Brewery Limited (1)
Malimidwe Road
PO Box 406
Makata Indusrial Area, Blantyre, Malawi (49%)
Tel.: (265) 1872999
Fax: (265) 1 873 038
E-Mail: ce@sobomw.com
Web Site: www.carlsberggroup.com
Emp.: 326
S.I.C.: 2082
N.A.I.C.S.: 312120

Carlsberg Okocim SA. (1)
Ul Bokserska 66
02 690 Warsaw, Poland (45%)
Tel.: (48) 225431440
Fax: (48) 225431460
E-Mail: info@carlsberg.pl
Web Site: www.carlsberg.pl
Emp.: 150
Mfr. of Beer
S.I.C.: 2082
N.A.I.C.S.: 312120
Piopr Majchrzak *(CFO)*

Ceylon Brewery Ltd. (1)
83 George Road de Silva Mawatha
13 Colombo, Sri Lanka (8%)
Tel.: (94) 33153542
Fax: (94) 331534
E-Mail: sks@lionbrew.com
Emp.: 165
Beverages
S.I.C.: 2082
N.A.I.C.S.: 312120

Gorkha Brewery Limited (1)
Hattisar
PO Box 4140
Kathmandu, Nepal
Tel.: (977) 14444445
Fax: (977) 14444443
E-Mail: info@gorkhabrewery.com
Web Site: www.gorkhabrewery.com
Emp.: 225
Brewery Mfr
S.I.C.: 2082
N.A.I.C.S.: 312120
Rajendra Khetan *(Chm)*

Hue Brewery Ltd. (1)
Thuan An St
Hue, Vietnam (50%)

Tel.: (84) 54850166
Fax: (84) 54850171
E-Mail: huda@huda.com.vn
Web Site: www.huda.com.vn
Sales Range: $1-9.9 Million
Emp.: 297
S.I.C.: 2082
N.A.I.C.S.: 312120

South-East Asia Brewery Ltd. (1)
167B Minh Khai St
Hanoi, Vietnam (35%)
Tel.: (84) 48631871
Fax: (84) 48631307
E-Mail: info@seab.netvan.vn
Web Site: www.halida.com.vn
Emp.: 327
S.I.C.: 2082
N.A.I.C.S.: 312120

United Romanian Breweries Bereprod SRL (1)
89 Biruintei Boulevard
Com Pantelimon
Bucharest, Romania
Tel.: (40) 1 205 50 00
Fax: (40) 1 205 50 09
Web Site: www.tuborg.ro
Emp.: 750
Mfr. of Beer
S.I.C.: 2082
N.A.I.C.S.: 312120

CARLTON INVESTMENTS LIMITED

Level 22 227 Elizabeth Street
Sydney, NSW, 2000, Australia
Mailing Address:
GPO Box 1469
Sydney, NSW, 2001, Australia
Tel.: (61) 2 9373 6732
Fax: (61) 2 9373 6539
E-Mail: info@carltoninvestments.com.au
Web Site: www.carltoninvestments.com.au
Year Founded: 1938
CIN—(ASX)
Rev.: $35,228,191
Assets: $724,287,637
Liabilities: $103,354,436
Net Worth: $620,933,201
Earnings: $33,760,914
Fiscal Year-end: 06/30/13
Business Description:
Investment Management Services
S.I.C.: 6799
N.A.I.C.S.: 523920
Personnel:
Peter Horton *(CFO & Sec)*
Board of Directors:
Alan G. Rydge
Anthony J. Clark
Graeme L. Herring

CARLTON RESOURCES PLC

Suite 5 Sicilian House
Sicilian Avenue, London, WC1A 2QH, United Kingdom
Tel.: (44) 2074005740
Fax: (44) 2078318323
E-Mail: info@carltonresourcesplc.com
Web Site: www.carltonresourcesplc.com
Emp.: 4
Business Description:
Investment Services
S.I.C.: 6211
N.A.I.C.S.: 523999
Board of Directors:
Keith Coughlan
David Pettman
Legal Counsel:
Nabarro
Lacon House 84 Theobolds Road
London, United Kingdom

Memery Crystal LLP
44 Southampton Buildings Memery
London, WC2A 1AP, United Kingdom

CARLYLE MOTOR PRODUCTS LTD

Junction 9 13
Carlyle, SK, S0C 0R0, Canada
Tel.: (306) 453-6741
Fax: (306) 453-6497
E-Mail: info@carlylegm.ca
Web Site: www.carlylemotorproducts.com
Year Founded: 1986
Rev.: $16,276,095
Emp.: 23
Business Description:
New & Used Car Dealers
S.I.C.: 5511
N.A.I.C.S.: 441110
Personnel:
Garnet Goud *(Pres)*

CARMANAH TECHNOLOGIES CORPORATION

250 Bay Street
Victoria, BC, V9A 3K5, Canada
Tel.: (250) 380-0052
Fax: (250) 380-0062
Toll Free: (877) 722-8877
E-Mail: info@carmanah.com
Web Site: www.carmanah.com
Year Founded: 1996
CMH—(TSX)
Rev.: $26,442,000
Assets: $13,176,000
Liabilities: $4,480,000
Net Worth: $8,696,000
Earnings: ($3,921,000)
Emp.: 68
Fiscal Year-end: 12/31/12
Business Description:
Renewable & Energy-Efficient Technology Solutions Integrator Focusing on Solar-Powered LED Lighting, Solar Power Systems (Off Grid & Grid Tie) & LED Illuminated Signage
S.I.C.: 3674
N.A.I.C.S.: 334413
Personnel:
David Green *(Founder)*
Michael Sonnenfeldt *(Chm)*
John Simmons *(Pres & CEO)*
Roland Sartorius *(CFO & Sec)*
Board of Directors:
Michael Sonnenfeldt
Peter Berrang
Terry Holland
Jim Meekison
Daniel Nocente
John Simmons
Transfer Agent:
Computershare Investor Services Inc.
510 Burrard Street 2nd Floor
Vancouver, BC, V6C 3B9, Canada

Groups:

Carmanah Technologies Corp. - LED Illuminated Sign Group (1)
Suite 5-6025 12th Street Southeast
Calgary, AB, T2H 2K1, Canada
Tel.: (403) 252-6047
Fax: (403) 252-5580
Web Site: www.carmanah.com
LED Illuminated Signage Mfr
S.I.C.: 3648
N.A.I.C.S.: 335129

Carmanah Technologies Corp. - Power Systems Group (1)
Building 4 203 Harbour Road
Victoria, BC, V9A 3S2, Canada
Tel.: (250) 380-0052
Emp.: 300
Solar-Powered LED Lighting & Solar Power Systems (Off Grid & Grid Tie)
S.I.C.: 3612
N.A.I.C.S.: 335311
Don Hargreaves *(VP-Ops)*

CARMAT SAS

36 avenue de l'Europe CS 40533
Immeuble l'Etendard
78941 Velizy-Villacoublay, Cedex, France
Tel.: (33) 1 39 45 64 50
Fax: (33) 1 39 45 64 51
E-Mail: contact@carmatsas.com
Web Site: www.carmatsa.com
Year Founded: 2008
ALCAR—(EUR)
Rev.: $24,216
Assets: $26,515,370
Liabilities: $8,093,883
Net Worth: $18,421,487
Earnings: ($23,140,246)
Emp.: 40
Fiscal Year-end: 12/31/12
Business Description:
Implantable Artificial Heart Developer
S.I.C.: 3841
N.A.I.C.S.: 339112
Personnel:
Jean-Claude Cadudal *(Chm)*
Marcello Conviti *(CEO & Dir Gen)*
Patrick Coulombier *(Deputy CEO & COO)*
Alain Carpentier *(Pres-Scientific Council & Dir-Scientific)*
Philippe Pouletty *(CEO-Truffle Capital)*
Board of Directors:
Jean-Claude Cadudal
Andre-Michel Ballester
Alain Carpentier
Marcello Conviti
Michel Finance
Henri Lachmann
Philippe Pouletty

CARMAX MINING CORP.

3rd Floor Bellevue Centre 235 15th St
Vancouver, BC, V7T 2X1, Canada
Tel.: (604) 921-1810
Fax: (604) 921-1898
E-Mail: info@carmaxmining.com
Web Site: www.carmaxmining.com
CXM—(TSXV)
Int. Income: $6,500
Assets: $8,487,298
Liabilities: $69,579
Net Worth: $8,417,718
Earnings: ($341,906)
Fiscal Year-end: 07/31/13
Business Description:
Mineral Properties Exploration Services
S.I.C.: 1081
N.A.I.C.S.: 213114
Personnel:
Jevin Werbes *(Pres & CEO)*
Matthew G. Wright *(CFO)*
Bev Funston *(Sec)*
Board of Directors:
Hrayr Agnerian
Christopher Martin Healey
Jeff Poloni
Jevin Werbes

CARMEN ENERGY INC.

1600 510 5th Street SW
Calgary, AB, T2P 3S2, Canada
Tel.: (403) 537-5590
Fax: (403) 537-5591
E-Mail: brian.doherty@shaw.ca
Year Founded: 2009
CEI.P—(TSXV)
Sls.: $622,320
Assets: $1,307,981
Liabilities: $769,709
Net Worth: $538,272
Earnings: ($5,753,704)
Emp.: 3
Fiscal Year-end: 09/30/12
Business Description:
Investment Services
S.I.C.: 6211
N.A.I.C.S.: 523999
Personnel:
Randall Harrison *(Chm & CEO)*
H. Tyler Rice *(Pres & CFO)*
Zeno Bereznicki *(COO & VP-Ops)*
Board of Directors:
Randall Harrison
Robert J. Derkitt
Gerald D. Facciani
James A. Letwin
Archibald Jonathon Nesbitt
Transfer Agent:
Valiant Trust Company
606 4th Street SW Suite 310
Calgary, AB, T2P 1T1, Canada
Tel.: (403) 233-2801
Fax: (403) 233-2857

CARMESIN SA

1 Pantelimon Road Sector 2
PB 39-F5
73381 Bucharest, Romania
Tel.: (40) 21 2520355
Fax: (40) 21 2527686
E-Mail: office@carmesin.ro
Web Site: www.carmesin.ro
CARC—(BUC)
Emp.: 35
Business Description:
Metal Forging, Stamping, Extruding, Drawing, Rolling & Powder Metallurgy
S.I.C.: 3462
N.A.I.C.S.: 332111
Personnel:
Ion Popovici *(Gen Mgr)*

CARMEUSE S.A.

Athena Scientific Pk
B 1348 Louvain-la-Neuve, Belgium
Tel.: (32) 010481600
Web Site: www.carmeuse.be
Sales Range: $1-4.9 Billion
Emp.: 6,000
Business Description:
Crushed & Broken Limestone
S.I.C.: 3274
N.A.I.C.S.: 327410
Personnel:
Rodolphe Collinet *(CEO)*
Yves Schoonejans *(CFO)*
Yves Willems *(COO & CEO-Europe)*
J. B. De Jongh *(Gen Sec & VP-Pub Affairs)*

U.S. Subsidiary:

Carmeuse North America (1)
11 Stanwix St 21th Fl
Pittsburgh, PA 15222-1312 PA
Tel.: (412) 995-5500
Fax: (412) 995-5570
E-Mail: info@carmeusena.com
Web Site: www.carmeusena.com
Emp.: 100
Lime & Lime Related Environmental Technologies Mfr
S.I.C.: 3274
N.A.I.C.S.: 327410
Thomas Buck *(Pres & CEO)*
Bruce Inglis *(CFO)*
Patrick Worms *(CIO)*
Kevin Whyte *(Gen Counsel & VP)*
Philip Johnson *(Sr VP-Sls & Mktg)*

Subsidiaries:

Carmeuse Lime & Stone (2)
103 Holly St
Chatsworth, GA 30705
Tel.: (706) 695-1562
Fax: (706) 695-3350
Web Site: www.carmeuse.com
Emp.: 70
Industrial Filler Products Operations
S.I.C.: 1499
N.A.I.C.S.: 212399
Mark Davis *(Area Mgr-Ops)*

Carmeuse S.A.—(Continued)

Carmeuse Lime & Stone (2)
165 Steel Dr
Portage, IN 46368 IN
Tel.: (219) 787-9190
Fax: (219) 787-9397
Web Site: www.carmeusena.com
Emp.: 15
Industrial Minerals
S.I.C.: 1422
N.A.I.C.S.: 212312
Ron Vessel *(Plant Mgr)*

Carmeuse Lime & Stone (2)
2 E Bay Dr
Erie, PA 16507
Tel.: (814) 453-6721
Fax: (814) 453-5138
Web Site: www.carmeusena.com
Emp.: 25
Sand Crushed Limestone
S.I.C.: 1422
N.A.I.C.S.: 212312
Roger Davis *(Mgr-Sls)*

Carmeuse Lime & Stone (2)
11 Stanwix St Ste 21
Pittsburgh, PA 15222 PA
Tel.: (412) 995-5500
Fax: (412) 995-5570
E-Mail: info@carmeusena.com
Web Site: www.carmeusena.com
Emp.: 100
Industrial Minerals
S.I.C.: 1422
N.A.I.C.S.: 212312
Joe Bourdage *(Dir-H&S)*

Carmeuse Lime & Stone (2)
486 Clinch Vly Rd
Luttrell, TN 37779-9414 DE
Tel.: (865) 992-3841
Fax: (865) 992-6034
Toll Free: (800) 467-5463
E-Mail: info@carmeusena.com
Web Site: www.carmeusena.com
Emp.: 100
Industrial Minerals
S.I.C.: 3295
N.A.I.C.S.: 327992
Mark Davis *(Mgr-Site)*

Carmeuse Lime & Stone (2)
684 Pkwy Dr
Buchanan, VA 24066 DE
Mailing Address:
PO Box 617
Buchanan, VA 24066
Tel.: (540) 254-1241
Fax: (540) 254-2219
E-Mail: info@carmeusena.com
Web Site: www.carmeusena.com
Emp.: 75
Industrial Minerals
S.I.C.: 1422
N.A.I.C.S.: 212312
Steve Powell *(Mgr-Ops)*

Carmeuse Lime & Stone (2)
1696 Oranda Rd
Strasburg, VA 22657-3731 DE
Tel.: (540) 465-5161
Toll Free: (800) 541-3172
Industrial Minerals
S.I.C.: 1422
N.A.I.C.S.: 212312
Jim Bottom *(Plant Mgr)*

Carmeuse Lime Inc. (2)
3245 E 103rd St
Chicago, IL 60617 DE
Tel.: (773) 221-9400 (100%)
Fax: (773) 221-3501
E-Mail: info@carmeuse.na.com
Web Site: www.carmeuse.na.com
Emp.: 85
Lime Processing
S.I.C.: 1422
N.A.I.C.S.: 212312

Carmeuse N.A. (2)
11 Stanwix St 21th Fl
Pittsburgh, PA 15222-1312 DE
Tel.: (412) 995-5500 (100%)
Fax: (412) 995-5570
E-Mail: info@carmeusena.com
Web Site: www.carmeusena.com
Emp.: 100
Mfr. of Chemical & Metallurgical Lime & Lime-Related Environmental Technologies
S.I.C.: 3274
N.A.I.C.S.: 327410
Bruce Routhieaux *(VP-Sls)*

CARNA BIOSCIENCES INC.

BMA 3F 1-5-5 Minatojima-Minamimachi
Chuo-ku, Kobe, 650-0047, Japan
Tel.: (81) 783027039
Fax: (81) 783026665
E-Mail: info@carnabio.com
Web Site: www.carnabio.com
Year Founded: 2003
4572—(JAS)
Rev.: $5,619,119
Assets: $12,285,823
Liabilities: $2,597,111
Net Worth: $9,688,712
Earnings: ($4,949,934)
Emp.: 52
Fiscal Year-end: 12/31/12
Business Description:
Pharmaceutical Mfr
S.I.C.: 2834
N.A.I.C.S.: 325412
Personnel:
Kohichiro Yoshino *(Pres & CEO)*
Board of Directors:
Norio Aikawa
Shinichi Kuwahara
Tsunehisa Yanagihara
Kohichiro Yoshino

U.S. Subsidiary:

CarnaBio USA Inc. (1)
209 W Central St Ste 127
Natick, MA 01760
Tel.: (508) 650-1244
Fax: (508) 650-1722
Toll Free: (888) 645-1233
E-Mail: orders@carnabio.com
Web Site: www.carnabio.com
Emp.: 6
Biological Products Distr
S.I.C.: 2836
N.A.I.C.S.: 325414

CARNARVON PETROLEUM LIMITED

Ground Floor 1322 Hay Street
West Perth, WA, 6005, Australia
Mailing Address:
PO Box 99
West Perth, WA, 6872, Australia
Tel.: (61) 893212665
Fax: (61) 893218867
E-Mail: admin@cvn.com.au
Web Site: www.carnarvonpetroleum.com
CVN—(ASX)
Sls.: $19,074,598
Assets: $150,441,724
Liabilities: $49,537,266
Net Worth: $100,904,459
Earnings: ($8,738,008)
Emp.: 10
Fiscal Year-end: 06/30/13
Business Description:
Oil & Gas Exploration & Production Services
S.I.C.: 1311
N.A.I.C.S.: 211111
Personnel:
Adrian C. Cook *(CEO & Mng Dir)*
Philip Huizenga *(COO)*
Thomson Naude *(Sec)*
Board of Directors:
Peter J. Leonhardt
Adrian C. Cook
William A. Foster
Edward P. Jacobson

CARNATION INDUSTRIES LTD.

222 A J C Bose Road Suite 4 & 5 1st Floor
Kolkata, 700 017, India
Tel.: (91) 2287 8229
Fax: (91) 2287 9938
E-Mail: carnation.ltd@gmail.com
Web Site: www.carnationindustries.com
530609—(BOM)
Rev.: $17,002,367
Assets: $15,638,286
Liabilities: $13,217,388
Net Worth: $2,420,898
Earnings: $213,154
Fiscal Year-end: 03/31/13
Business Description:
Grey Iron, Iron Castings, Manhole Covers & Frames Mfr
S.I.C.: 3322
N.A.I.C.S.: 331511
Personnel:
Suvobrata Saha *(Co-Mng Dir)*
Ravindra Prakash Sehgal *(Co-Mng Dir)*
Sanjay Agarwal *(Compliance Officer & Sec)*
Board of Directors:
Ramesh Chandra Jha
Arun Kumar Bose
Manoj Bose
Debajyoti Chakrabarti
Suvobrata Saha
Ravindra Prakash Sehgal
Legal Counsel:
R. Ginodia & Co.
4E & F Hastings Chamber 7C Kiran Shankar Roy Road
Kolkata, India
Transfer Agent:
R&D Infotech Private Limited
1st Floor 7A Beltala Road
Kolkata, India

CARNAVALE RESOURCES LIMITED

Level 1 Suite 5 The Business Centre
55 Salvado Road, Subiaco, Western Australia, 6008, Australia
Tel.: (61) 8 9380 9098
Fax: (61) 8 9380 6761
Web Site: www.carnavaleresources.de
CAV—(ASX)
Rev.: $42,922
Assets: $1,563,401
Liabilities: $50,871
Net Worth: $1,512,530
Earnings: ($460,189)
Fiscal Year-end: 06/30/13
Business Description:
Gold & Copper Assets Developer
S.I.C.: 1021
N.A.I.C.S.: 212234
Personnel:
Ron Gajewski *(Chm)*
Paul Jurman *(Sec)*
Board of Directors:
Ron Gajewski
Rhett Brans
Peter Christie
Klaus Peter Eckhof
Legal Counsel:
Cullen Babington Hughes Pty Ltd
229 Stirling Highway
6010 Claremont, Australia
Transfer Agent:
Security Transfer Registrars Pty Limited
770 Canning Highway
PO Box 535
Applecross, WA, 6153, Australia

CARNEGIE WAVE ENERGY LIMITED

Suite 1 124 Stirling Highway North
PO Box 133
Fremantle, WA, 6159, Australia
Tel.: (61) 894864466
Fax: (61) 894864266
E-Mail: enquiries@carnegiewave.com
Web Site: www.carnegiewave.com
CWE—(ASX)
Rev.: $366,733
Assets: $92,541,357
Liabilities: $2,954,508
Net Worth: $89,586,850
Earnings: ($3,442,652)
Emp.: 28
Fiscal Year-end: 06/30/13
Business Description:
Wave Energy Technology
S.I.C.: 4931
N.A.I.C.S.: 221118
Personnel:
Michael Edward Ottaviano *(CEO & Mng Dir)*
Aidan Flynn *(CFO)*
Greg Allen *(COO)*
Jonathan Fievez *(CTO)*
Tim Sawyer *(Project Dev Officer)*
Grant Jonathan Mooney *(Sec)*
Board of Directors:
Grant Jonathan Mooney
Mike Fitzpatrick
Jeffrey Harding
John S. Leggate
Kieran O'Brien
Michael Edward Ottaviano
Legal Counsel:
Hardy Bowen
1/28 Ord Street
West Perth, WA, 6005, Australia

CARNIVAL GROUP INTERNATIONAL HOLDINGS LIMITED

(Formerly Oriental Ginza Holdings Limited)
Suites 903B 5 9/F Great Eagle Centre 23 Harbour Road
Wanchai, China (Hong Kong)
Tel.: (852) 28777722
Fax: (852) 28775522
Web Site:
0996—(HKG)
Sales Range: Less than $1 Million
Emp.: 274
Business Description:
Investment Services
S.I.C.: 6211
N.A.I.C.S.: 523999
Personnel:
Cheng Rong Zhou *(Chm)*
Transfer Agent:
Tricor Standard Limited
26/F Tesbury Centre 28 Queen's Road East
Wanchai, China (Hong Kong)
Tel.: (852) 2980 1333
Fax: (852) 2810 8185

Subsidiary:

Po Sun Piece Goods Company Limited (1)
9 Queens Rd
Central, China (Hong Kong)
Tel.: (852) 23983878
Textile & Fabrics Whslr
S.I.C.: 5131
N.A.I.C.S.: 424310

CAROL INFO SERVICES LTD.

Wockhardt Towers Bandra-Kurla Comples
Bandra East, Mumbai, 400051, India
Tel.: (91) 22 2653 4444
Fax: (91) 22 2653 4242
Web Site: www.carolinfoservices.com
Sales Range: Less than $1 Million
Emp.: 100
Business Description:
Pharmaceutical Products Mfr
S.I.C.: 2834
N.A.I.C.S.: 325412

Personnel:
G. B. Parulkar *(Chm & Mng Dir)*
Amruta Avasare *(Compliance Officer & Sec)*
Board of Directors:
G. B. Parulkar
Stephen D'Souza
Shahnawaz Khan
Suresh R. Shenoy
Transfer Agent:
Link Intime India Pvt. Ltd
C-13 Pannalal Silk Mills Compound LBS Marg
Bhandup (West)
Mumbai, India

CAROLINA CAPITAL CORP.
2075 West 37th Avenue
Vancouver, BC, V6M 1N7, Canada
Tel.: (604) 687-6991
Fax: (604) 688-2687
E-Mail: suzannewood@telus.net
Year Founded: 2010
CQC.P—(TSXV)
Int. Income: $2,959
Assets: $530,876
Net Worth: $530,876
Earnings: ($106,673)
Fiscal Year-end: 08/31/13
Business Description:
Investment Services
S.I.C.: 6211
N.A.I.C.S.: 523999
Personnel:
Stephen Hanson *(CEO)*
Suzanne Wood *(CFO)*
Board of Directors:
Donn Burchill
Stephen Hanson
Suzanne Wood
Transfer Agent:
Computershare Trust Company of Canada
510 Burrard St 3rd Fl
Vancouver, BC, V6C 3B9, Canada

CAROLYN RIVER PROJECTS LTD.
2640 Tempe Knoll Drive
North Vancouver, BC, V6C 1V5, Canada
Tel.: (604) 908-0233
Year Founded: 2004
CRPL—(OTC)
Sales Range: Less than $1 Million
Business Description:
Mineral Mining & Exploration Services
S.I.C.: 1099
N.A.I.C.S.: 212299
Personnel:
Steve Bolton *(Pres, CEO, CFO, Treas & Sec)*
Board of Directors:
Steve Bolton
Transfer Agent:
Empire Stock Transfer, Inc.
1859 Whitney Mesa Dr
Henderson, NV 89009

CARON TRANSPORTATION SYSTEMS PARTNERSHIP
301 Streambank Avenue
Sherwood Park, AB, T8H 1N1, Canada
Tel.: (780) 449-6688
Fax: (780) 449-6696
E-Mail: info@carontransport.ca
Web Site: www.carontransport.ca
Year Founded: 1990
Rev.: $38,085,752
Emp.: 300
Business Description:
Transportation Services
S.I.C.: 4619
N.A.I.C.S.: 486990
Personnel:
Bruno Muller *(Pres)*

CARPATHIAN GOLD INC.
365 Bay St Suite 300
Toronto, ON, M5H 2V1, Canada
Tel.: (416) 368-7744
Fax: (416) 363-3883
E-Mail: info@carpathiangold.com
Web Site: www.carpathiangold.com
Year Founded: 2003
CPN—(OTC TSX)
Assets: $159,763,216
Liabilities: $66,138,369
Net Worth: $93,624,847
Earnings: ($33,375,133)
Emp.: 10
Fiscal Year-end: 12/31/12
Business Description:
Mineral Exploration & Development Services
S.I.C.: 3299
N.A.I.C.S.: 327999
Personnel:
Dino Titaro *(Co-Founder, Pres & CEO)*
Guy Charette *(Co-Founder & Exec VP)*
Peter S. Lehner *(Chm)*
Rishi Tibriwal *(CFO)*
Daniel B. J. Kivari *(COO)*
Michael Kozub *(Gen Counsel & Sec)*
Randall K. Ruff *(Exec VP-Exploration)*
Board of Directors:
Peter S. Lehner
Julio L. Carvalho
Guy Charette
David C. Danziger
John Walter Wallen Hick
Patrick J. Mars
Dino Titaro
Legal Counsel:
Fraser Milner Casgrain LLP
77 King Street West Suite 400 Toronto Dominion Centre
Toronto, ON, M5K 0A1, Canada
Transfer Agent:
Equity Financial Trust Company
200 University Avenue Suite 400
Toronto, ON, Canada

CARPENE MALVOLTI S.P.A.
Via A Carpene 1
31015 Conegliano, Italy
Tel.: (39) 438364611
Fax: (39) 0438364690
E-Mail: info@carpene-malvolti.com
Web Site: www.carpene-malvolti.com
Year Founded: 1868
Sales Range: $10-24.9 Million
Emp.: 39
Business Description:
Wine, Brandy & Grappa Producer Import Export
S.I.C.: 2084
N.A.I.C.S.: 312130
Personnel:
Etile Carpene *(Chm & Pres)*

CARPENTARIA EXPLORATION LIMITED
Level 6 345 Ann Street
PO Box 10919
Adelaide Street, Brisbane, QLD, 4000, Australia
Tel.: (61) 7 3220 2022
Fax: (61) 7 3220 1291
E-Mail: info@capex.net.au
Web Site: www.carpentariaex.com.au
78A—(ASX DEU)
Rev.: $181,511
Assets: $17,274,176
Liabilities: $2,064,672
Net Worth: $15,209,504
Earnings: ($1,898,164)
Fiscal Year-end: 06/30/13
Business Description:
Mineral Exploration Services
S.I.C.: 1481
N.A.I.C.S.: 213115
Personnel:
Stuart Nicholas Sheard *(Chm)*
Quentin Hill *(Mng Dir)*
Chris Powell *(Sec)*
Board of Directors:
Stuart Nicholas Sheard
Bin Cai
Paul Cholakos
Robert William Hair
Quentin Hill
Neil Williams
Legal Counsel:
HWL Ebsworth
Level 23 Riverside Centre 123 Eagle Street
Brisbane, QLD, Australia

CARPENTER TAN HOLDINGS LIMITED
Fl 43 Future International Building Guanyinqiao
Jiangbei District, Chongqing, China
Tel.: (86) 2367562222
Fax: (86) 2367622700
E-Mail: ir@ctans.com
Web Site: www.ctans.com
837—(HKG)
Sls.: $43,201,799
Assets: $78,993,246
Liabilities: $9,082,566
Net Worth: $69,910,679
Earnings: $20,040,834
Emp.: 996
Fiscal Year-end: 12/31/12
Business Description:
Wooden Handcrafts Including Combs, Furniture & Accessories Mfr
S.I.C.: 2499
N.A.I.C.S.: 321999
Personnel:
Chuan Hua Tan *(Co-Founder, Chm & CEO)*
Cheng Qin Fan *(Co-Founder & Controller-Quality)*
Hon Wan Chan *(Sec & Controller-Fin)*
Board of Directors:
Chuan Hua Tan
Donald Kam Wing Chau
Xin Li Du
Chang Sheng Geng
Chang Liu
Cao Tan
Di Fu Tan
Ming Yang Yu
Legal Counsel:
Hastings & Co.
5th Floor Gloucester Tower 11 Pedder Street
Central, China (Hong Kong)
Butterfield Fund Services (Cayman) Limited
Butterfield House 68 Fort Street PO Box 705
Georgetown, Cayman Islands
Transfer Agents:
Tricor Investor Services Limited
26/F Tesbury Centre 28 Queen's Road East
Hong Kong, China (Hong Kong)
Butterfield Fund Services (Cayman) Limited
Butterfield House 68 Fort Street PO Box 705
Georgetown, Cayman Islands

CARPETRIGHT PLC
Harris House Purfleet Bypass
Purfleet, Essex, RM19 1TT, United Kingdom
Tel.: (44) 1708802000
Fax: (44) 708559361
E-Mail: enquiries@carpetright.co.uk
Web Site: www.carpetright.plc.uk
Year Founded: 1988
CPR—(LSE)
Rev.: $722,683,104
Assets: $407,930,607
Liabilities: $304,802,970
Net Worth: $103,127,637
Earnings: ($10,423,314)
Emp.: 3,061
Fiscal Year-end: 04/27/13
Business Description:
Retail Floor Coverings & Carpet Services
S.I.C.: 5713
N.A.I.C.S.: 442210
Personnel:
Philip C. Harris *(Founder & Chm)*
Graham Harris *(COO)*
Jeremy Sampson *(Sec & Dir-Legal)*
Board of Directors:
Philip C. Harris
David Clifford
Alan Dickinson
Graham Harris
Martin J. Harris
Sheila Valerie Noakes
Andrew Page
Neil Page
Sandra Turner
Legal Counsel:
Travers Smith
10 Snow Hill
London, EC1A 2AL, United Kingdom
Tel.: (44) 171 248 9133
Telex: 887117 Traver G
Fax: (44) 171 236 3728
Andrew Jackson
Essex House
PO Box 47
Hull, HU1 1X, United Kingdom

Subsidiaries:

Carpetright of London Limited (1)
Amberley House New Road
Rainham, RA13 8QN, United Kingdom (100%)
Tel.: (44) 1708525522
Fax: (44) 1708559361
Miscellaneous Retail Stores
S.I.C.: 5999
N.A.I.C.S.: 453998

Non-U.S. Subsidiaries:

Carpetland BV (1)
Schuttersveld 6
7514AL Enschede, Netherlands (100%)
Tel.: (31) 302631263
Fax: (31) 534332422
E-Mail: info@carpetright.nl
Web Site: www.carpetright.nl
Emp.: 500
Miscellaneous Retail Stores
S.I.C.: 5999
N.A.I.C.S.: 453998
Andy Garden *(Mng Dir)*

Carpetland NV (1)
Rue du Stalle 215
1620 Drogenbos, Belgium (100%)
Tel.: (32) 23712411
Fax: (32) 23780415
Emp.: 20
Floor Covering Stores
S.I.C.: 5713
N.A.I.C.S.: 442210
Lord Harris *(Gen Mgr)*

Fontainebleau Vastgoed BV (1)
Franciscusdreef 60
3565 AC Utrecht, Netherlands (100%)
Tel.: (31) 302631261
Fax: (31) 302631262
E-Mail: info@carpetright.nl
Web Site: www.carpetright.nl
Emp.: 25
Real Estate Propert Lessorsy
S.I.C.: 6519
N.A.I.C.S.: 531190
Andy Gordon *(Mng Dir)*

THE CARPHONE WAREHOUSE GROUP PLC
1 Portal Way
London, W3 6RS, United Kingdom

The Carphone Warehouse Group PLC—(Continued)

Tel.: (44) 2088965000
Fax: (44) 2087538009
E-Mail: cdunstone@cpw.co.uk
Web Site: www.cpwplc.com
Year Founded: 1989
CPW—(LSE)
Rev.: $16,898,403
Assets: $1,081,339,863
Liabilities: $38,060,889
Net Worth: $1,043,278,974
Earnings: $6,633,018
Emp.: 22
Fiscal Year-end: 03/31/13

Business Description:
Mobile Telecommunications Products & Services Retailer
S.I.C.: 4812
N.A.I.C.S.: 517210

Personnel:
Charles Dunstone *(Founder & Chm)*
Roger Taylor *(Deputy Chm)*
Andrew Harrison *(CEO)*
Nigel Langstaff *(CFO)*
Tim Morris *(Gen Counsel & Sec)*

Board of Directors:
Charles Dunstone
John Allwood
John Gildersleeve
Andrew Harrison
Nigel Langstaff
Baroness Morgan
Roger Taylor

Legal Counsel:
Ashurst LLP
5 Appold St
London, EC2A 2HA, United Kingdom

CARRARO S.P.A.

Via Olmo 37
35011 Padua, Italy
Tel.: (39) 0499219111
Fax: (39) 0499289111
E-Mail: webinfo@carraro.com
Web Site: www.carraro.com
CARR—(ITA)
Rev.: $137,460,278
Assets: $248,831,283
Liabilities: $153,208,946
Net Worth: $95,622,337
Earnings: ($5,565,313)
Emp.: 1,116
Fiscal Year-end: 12/31/12

Business Description:
Axles, Gears, Transmissions & Related Components Mfr for Cars, Earth-Moving Equipment, Forklifts, Tractors & Other Industrial Vehicles
S.I.C.: 3566
N.A.I.C.S.: 333612

Personnel:
Enrico Carraro *(Chm)*
Tomaso Carraro *(Vice Chm)*
Alexander Josef Bossard *(CEO)*
Enrico Gomiero *(CFO)*

Board of Directors:
Enrico Carraro
Alexander Josef Bossard
Arnaldo Camuffo
Francesco Carraro
Tomaso Carraro
Antonio Cortellazzo
Gabriele del Torchio
Marina Pittini
Marco Reboa

Subsidiaries:

A.E. Srl (1)
Via Nazionale Sannitica 35
Benevento, Italy
Tel.: (39) 0824903081
Emp.: 35
Motor Vehicle Parts Whslr
S.I.C.: 5015
N.A.I.C.S.: 423140

Elettronica Santerno S.p.A. (1)
Strada Statale Selice 47
Imola, 40026 Bologna, Italy
Tel.: (39) 0542668611
Fax: (39) 0542668600
E-Mail: info@santerno.com
Web Site: www.elettronicasanterno.it
Emp.: 66
Other Electric Power Generation
S.I.C.: 4939
N.A.I.C.S.: 221118

SIAP S.p.A. (1)
Via Monfalcone 4
35085 Maniago, Italy (73.8%)
Tel.: (39) 0427706911
Fax: (39) 0427 706935
E-Mail: siap_maniago@carraro.com
Web Site: www.siapgears.com
Sales Range: $150-199.9 Million
Emp.: 471
Gear Assembly Mfr
S.I.C.: 3566
N.A.I.C.S.: 333612

Subsidiary:

TQT S.r.l. (2)
Via Monfalcone 4
33085 Maniago, Italy (100%)
Tel.: (39) 0427706911
Fax: (39) 0427706945
Web Site: www.carraro.com
Emp.: 500
All Other Professional Scientific & Technical Services
S.I.C.: 7389
N.A.I.C.S.: 541990
Luejeno Recatto *(Mgr)*

Trenton S.p.A. (1)
Via Matilde Di Canossa 21
Frassinoro, Modena, Italy
Tel.: (39) 0536971711
Fax: (39) 0536971726
Emp.: 52
Industrial Supplies Whslr
S.I.C.: 5085
N.A.I.C.S.: 423840

U.S. Subsidiary:

Carraro North America Inc. (1)
2505 International Pkwy
Virginia Beach, VA 23452-7821
Tel.: (757) 689-3725
Fax: (757) 233-1949
E-Mail: cna@carraro.com
Web Site: www.carraro.com
Motor Vehicle Steering & Suspension Components (except Spring) Mfr
S.I.C.: 3714
N.A.I.C.S.: 336330
Marco Birtig *(Dir-Sls & Mktg-North America)*

Non-U.S. Subsidiaries:

Carraro Argentina S.A. (1)
Valentin Gomez 577
Haedo, 1714 Buenos Aires, Argentina
Tel.: (54) 1144833220
Fax: (54) 1144833221
E-Mail: info@gear-world.com
Web Site: carraro.com
Emp.: 354
Speed Changer Industrial High-Speed Drive & Gear Mfr
S.I.C.: 3566
N.A.I.C.S.: 333612

Carraro India Ltd. (1)
B2/2 MIDC Ind
Area Ranjangaon, 412210 Pune, India (100%)
Tel.: (91) 2138232101
Fax: (91) 2138562666
E-Mail: cil@carraro.com
Web Site: www.carraro.com
Machine Tool (Metal Forming Types) Mfr
S.I.C.: 3541
N.A.I.C.S.: 333517
Rajan Nanda *(Chm)*

Carraro Qingdao Ltd. (1)
The West of Kun Lun Shan Road
262555 Qingdao, Shandong, China
Tel.: (86) 53286721991
Fax: (86) 53286721919
E-Mail: qingdao@carraro.com
All Other Motor Vehicle Parts Mfr
S.I.C.: 3714
N.A.I.C.S.: 336390

Fabryca Osi Napedowych S.A. (1)
Ul Krasickiego 63/71
Radomsko, Radom, Poland (100%)
Tel.: (48) 446821471
Fax: (48) 446821480
E-Mail: marco_ferretti@carraro.com
Emp.: 300
All Other Motor Vehicle Parts Mfr
S.I.C.: 3714
N.A.I.C.S.: 336390
Ciupa Iwona *(Pres)*

O&K Antriebstechnik GmbH (1)
Nierenhofer Str 10
45525 Hattingen, Germany (100%)
Tel.: (49) 232420500
Fax: (49) 23242050310
E-Mail: ok_info@carraro.com
Web Site: www.oundkantriebstechnik.com
Emp.: 150
Speed Changer Industrial High-Speed Drive & Gear Mfr
S.I.C.: 3566
N.A.I.C.S.: 333612
Georgo Cucchi *(Mng Dir)*

CARREFOUR SA

33 Avenue Emile-Zola
92649 Boulogne-Billancourt, Cedex, France
Tel.: (33) 1 4104 2600
Telex: 601 941 F
Fax: (33) 1 4104 2601
Web Site: www.carrefour.com
Year Founded: 1959
CA—(EUR OTC)
Rev.: $105,620,498,200
Assets: $61,713,817,480
Liabilities: $50,458,490,110
Net Worth: $11,255,327,370
Earnings: $1,771,559,720
Emp.: 364,969
Fiscal Year-end: 12/31/12

Business Description:
Holding Company; Supermarkets, Hypermarkets & Convenience Stores Owner & Operator
S.I.C.: 6719
N.A.I.C.S.: 551112

Personnel:
Georges Plassat *(Chm & CEO)*
Sebastien Bazin *(Vice Chm)*
Pierre-Jean Sivignon *(CFO)*
Herve Thoumyre *(CIO)*
Jean-Christophe Deslarzes *(Chief HR Officer & Chief Org Officer)*
Eric Legros *(Exec Dir-Grp Mdse)*
Noel Prioux *(Exec Dir-France)*
Franck Tassan *(Grp Gen Counsel)*
Jerome Bedier *(Gen Sec)*

Board of Directors:
Georges Plassat
Bernard Arnault
Sebastien Bazin
Nicolas Bazire
Jean-Laurent Bonnafe
Thierry Breton
Rene Brillet
Bertrand de Montesquiou
Amaury de Seze
Charles Edelstenne
Diane Labruyere-Cuilleret
Mathilde Lemoine
Georges Ralli
Anne-Claire Taittinger

KPMG Audit
3 Cours du Triangle
Paris, France

Deloitte & Associes
185 avenue Charles-de-Gaulle
Neuilly-sur-Seine, France

Subsidiaries:

ANDEY (1)
Les Bordets
74130 Bonneville, France
Tel.: (33) 450 97 19 28
Fax: (33) 450 97 01 65
Supermarket Operating Services
S.I.C.: 5411
N.A.I.C.S.: 445110

BEARBULL SAS (1)
95 Cours Lafayette
69006 Lyon, France
Tel.: (33) 4 72 74 53 00
Fax: (33) 4 78 34 19 46
Emp.: 10
Investment Management Services
S.I.C.: 6211
N.A.I.C.S.: 523999

Bellevue Distribution SA (1)
Rue De La Poste
36000 Chateauroux, France FR
Tel.: (33) 254085240 (100%)
Grocery Distr
S.I.C.: 5149
N.A.I.C.S.: 424490
Martial Simon *(Mng Dir)*

BLO DISTRIBUTION (1)
Route de Paris Zi
Mondeville, 14120, France
Tel.: (33) 231702000
Supermarket Stores Operating Services
S.I.C.: 5411
N.A.I.C.S.: 445110

Cardadel SA (1)
58 Avenue Du Marechal Leclerc
Cosne-Cours-sur-Loire, 58200, France FR
Tel.: (33) 386266549 (100%)
Fax: (33) 386266317
Emp.: 25
Supermarket Stores Operating Services
S.I.C.: 5411
N.A.I.C.S.: 445110
Christophe Petit *(Mng Dir)*

Carrefour France (1)
102 rue de Paris
BP 83
91300 Massy, France FR
Tel.: (33) 1 6919 3000
Fax: (33) 1 6919 3099
Web Site: www.carrefour.fr
Supermarket Stores Operating Services
S.I.C.: 5411
N.A.I.C.S.: 445110

Subsidiaries:

Carrefour Administratif France (2)
66 Avenue Charles de Gaulle
92200 Neuilly-sur-Seine, France FR
Tel.: (33) 1 4641 5800 (100%)
Supermarket Stores Operating Services
S.I.C.: 5411
N.A.I.C.S.: 445110

Carrefour Drive (2)
102 rue de Paris
91300 Massy, France FR
Tel.: (33) 169193000 (100%)
Web Site: www.carrefour.fr/courses_en_ligne/carrefour_drive
Emp.: 10
Grocery Pick-up Services
S.I.C.: 7299
N.A.I.C.S.: 812990
Bruno Lebon *(Mng Dir)*

Carrefour Hypermarches (2)
1 Rue Jean Mermoz
BP75 91002 Courcouronnes, France (100%)
Tel.: (33) 160913737
Web Site: www.carrefour.fr
Owner & Operator of Hypermarkets
S.I.C.: 5411
N.A.I.C.S.: 445110
George Plassa *(Gen Mgr)*

Carrefour Import SAS (2)
102 rue de Paris
91300 Massy, France FR
Tel.: (33) 164869000 (100%)
Product Import Services
Import
S.I.C.: 7389
N.A.I.C.S.: 425120

Carrefour Property Gestion (2)
66/70 Avenue Charles de Gaulle
92200 Neuilly-sur-Seine, France FR
Tel.: (33) 1 4641 5800 (100%)

Real Estate Acquisition & Store Development
S.I.C.: 6531
N.A.I.C.S.: 531390

Carrefour Station Service (2)
Quartier Les Salles Route Nationale 7
83480 Puget-sur-Argens, France FR
Tel.: (33) 494176560 (100%)
Supermarket Stores Operating Services
S.I.C.: 5411
N.A.I.C.S.: 445110

Carrefour Systemes d'Informations France (2)
Route De Paris Zi
14120 Mondeville, France FR
Tel.: (33) 2 31 70 60 00 (100%)
Fax: (33) 2 31 83 56 19
Information Technology Support Services
S.I.C.: 7376
N.A.I.C.S.: 541513

CHALLENGER SARL (1)
35 Cours Napoleon
20000 Ajaccio, France
Tel.: (33) 495210855
Supermarket Stores Operating Services
S.I.C.: 5411
N.A.I.C.S.: 445110

Champion Supermarches France SAS (1)
4 Rue Brest
35000 Rennes, France FR
Tel.: (33) 299592893
Fax: (33) 299545860
Emp.: 5
Supermarket Stores Operating Services
S.I.C.: 5411
N.A.I.C.S.: 445110

CLAIREFONTAINE SA (1)
27 route de la Loire
44450 La Chapelle-Basse-Mer, France
Tel.: (33) 2 40333260
Fax: (33) 2 40801745
E-Mail: info@cfsa.fr
Emp.: 10
Paper Products & Stationery Material Mfr
S.I.C.: 2678
N.A.I.C.S.: 322230

CLV DISTRIBUTION (1)
3 rue Georges Clemenceau
69470 Cours-la-Ville, France
Tel.: (33) 4 74 89 72 96
Supermarket Operating Services
S.I.C.: 5411
N.A.I.C.S.: 445110

COLIBRI (1)
8 Place de la Madeleine
Paris, France
Tel.: (33) 1 42 60 59 22
Web Site: www.colibri.com
General Retail Store Operating Services
S.I.C.: 5399
N.A.I.C.S.: 452990

CONTINENT 2001 (1)
13 Quai De Marne
Epernay, 51200, France
Tel.: (33) 326532979
Supermarket Stores Operating Services
S.I.C.: 5411
N.A.I.C.S.: 445110

COSG (1)
33 Avenue Emile Zola
92100 Boulogne-Billancourt, France
Tel.: (33) 141042600
Fax: (33) 141042601
Emp.: 400
Business Management Services
S.I.C.: 8748
N.A.I.C.S.: 541618

CSF France (1)
Zone Industrielle Route De Paris
14120 Mondeville, France
Tel.: (33) 386389990
Supermarket Operating Services
S.I.C.: 5411
N.A.I.C.S.: 445110

DISTRIVAL SA (1)
9 Rue Louis Pasteur
26000 Valence, France
Tel.: (33) 475800881
Soft Drinks Distr
S.I.C.: 5149
N.A.I.C.S.: 424490

ED SAS (1)
120 rue du General Malleret Joinville
Vitry-sur-Seine, 94405, France
Tel.: (33) 1 47 18 17 17
Fax: (33) 1 47 18 17 18
Supermarket Stores Operating Services
S.I.C.: 5411
N.A.I.C.S.: 445110

Etadis (1)
32 boulevard St Michel
91150 Etampes, France FR
Tel.: (33) 1 64 94 22 72 (100%)
Fax: (33) 1 60 80 13 87
Emp.: 60
Supermarket Operating Services
S.I.C.: 5411
N.A.I.C.S.: 445110

Euromarche (1)
16 Place Vendome
75001 Paris, France FR
Tel.: (33) 1 53 45 28 60 (100%)
Fax: (33) 1 53 45 28 29
E-Mail: customers@ema-europe.com
Web Site: www.ema-europe.com
Food Product Mfr & Retailer
S.I.C.: 2099
N.A.I.C.S.: 311999

FALDIS SA (1)
167 Rue Neuve Grange
88000 Epinal, France
Tel.: (33) 329641313
Fax: (33) 329643296
Supermarket Stores Operating Services
S.I.C.: 5411
N.A.I.C.S.: 445110

Floradis (1)
11 Rue Nationale
57190 Florange, France FR
Tel.: (33) 382590259 (100%)
Supermarket Operating Services
S.I.C.: 5411
N.A.I.C.S.: 445110

Flortine (1)
Avenue Des Peupliers
27400 Louviers, France FR
Tel.: (33) 2 32 25 93 03 (100%)
Fax: (33) 2 32 40 71 33
Supermarket Operating Services
S.I.C.: 5411
N.A.I.C.S.: 445110

GEDEL SARL (1)
Avenue De Madrazes
24200 Sarlat-la-Caneda, France
Tel.: (33) 553592453
Supermarket Stores Operating Services
S.I.C.: 5411
N.A.I.C.S.: 445110

GENEDIS SAS (1)
Zone Industrielle Route de Paris
14120 Mondeville, France
Tel.: (33) 2 31 70 60 00
Fax: (33) 2 31 70 60 36
Hypermarket & Supermarket Stores Operating Services
S.I.C.: 5411
N.A.I.C.S.: 445110

GUILVIDIS (1)
Zone Industrielle Route De Paris
14120 Mondeville, France
Tel.: (33) 298581884
Supermarket Stores Operating Services
S.I.C.: 5411
N.A.I.C.S.: 445110

Guyenne et Gascogne SA (1)
60 avenue du Capitaine
Resplandy, 64101 Bayonne, Cedex, France FR
Tel.: (33) 559445500
Fax: (33) 559445519
E-Mail: info@guyenneetgascogne.fr
Web Site: www.guyenneetgascogne.com
Sales Range: $500-549.9 Million
Emp.: 2,047
Grocery Store Operator
S.I.C.: 5411
N.A.I.C.S.: 445110
Bertrand de Montesquiou *(Chm-Mgmt Bd)*
Marc Leguillette *(Sec)*

HGP SAS (1)
Zone Industrielle la Boitardiere
37400 Amboise, Indre et Loire, France
Tel.: (33) 247 30 56 40
Fax: (33) 247 30 44 39
Supermarket Stores Operating Services
S.I.C.: 5411
N.A.I.C.S.: 445110

Hyparlo S.A. (1)
100 route de Paris
BP 51
69751 Charbonnieres, Cedex, France
Tel.: (33) 4 7259 2097
Fax: (33) 4 7259 2062
Web Site: www.hyparlo.fr
HYP—(EUR)
Emp.: 4,792
Supermarket Operator
S.I.C.: 5411
N.A.I.C.S.: 445110
Jean-Michel Arlaud *(Dir Gen)*

Immobiliere Carrefour S.A.S. (1)
Route De Paris
BP 186
14120 Mondeville, Calvados, France FR
Tel.: (33) 231706000
Fax: (33) 231835619
Real Estate Acquisition & Development Services
S.I.C.: 6531
N.A.I.C.S.: 531390

IMMODIS (1)
180 rue Garibaldi
76300 Sotteville-les-Rouen, France
Tel.: (33) 2 32 18 22 88
Supermarket Stores Operating Services
S.I.C.: 5411
N.A.I.C.S.: 445110

IMOREAL (1)
90 rue Sierck
57480 Rettel, France
Tel.: (33) 3 82 83 70 67
Supermarket Stores Operator
S.I.C.: 5411
N.A.I.C.S.: 445110

Interdis SNC (1)
Zone Industrielle Route De Paris
14120 Mondeville, France FR
Tel.: (33) 169193000 (100%)
Supermarket Stores Operating Services
S.I.C.: 5411
N.A.I.C.S.: 445110

La Chartreuse (1)
Rue Saint Georges
Cahors, France FR
Tel.: (33) 565351737 (100%)
Hotel Management Services
S.I.C.: 7011
N.A.I.C.S.: 721110

LA VOULTE DISTRIBUTION (1)
Ld Camp Hannibal Av Du Onze Novembre
7800 La Voulte-sur-Rhone, France
Tel.: (33) 4 75 85 17 42
Real Estate Management Services
S.I.C.: 6531
N.A.I.C.S.: 531390

LE DAVID (1)
101 Promenade Georges-Pompidou
13008 Marseille, France
Tel.: (33) 4 91 79 99 63
Supermarket Stores Operating Services
S.I.C.: 5411
N.A.I.C.S.: 445110

Lefaubas (1)
Zone Industrielle Route De Paris
14120 Mondeville, France FR
Tel.: (33) 545781933 (100%)
Supermarket Operating Services
S.I.C.: 5411
N.A.I.C.S.: 445110

LODIAF S.A. (1)
Avenue des Peupliers
27400 Louviers, France
Tel.: (33) 232259303
Fax: (33) 232407133
Supermarket Operating Services
S.I.C.: 5411
N.A.I.C.S.: 445110

Logdis SAS (1)
Avenue Gabriel Voisin
13300 Salon-de-Provence, France FR
Tel.: (33) 4 90 17 20 00 (100%)
Supermarket Stores Operating Services
S.I.C.: 5411
N.A.I.C.S.: 445110

MAICHE DISTRIBUTION SA (1)
Place Du Champ De Foire
25120 Maiche, Doubs, France
Tel.: (33) 381643060
Fax: (33) 381643061
Supermarket Stores Operating Services
S.I.C.: 5411
N.A.I.C.S.: 445110

Maison Johanes Boubee SAS (1)
1 Rue De Grassi
33000 Bordeaux, France FR
Tel.: (33) 556488787
Fax: (33) 556488788
Wine Distr
S.I.C.: 5182
N.A.I.C.S.: 424820

MEGANE (1)
56 Avenue De La Republique
Tassin-la-Demi-Lune, Rhone, 69160, France
Tel.: (33) 478347768
Supermarket Stores Operating Services
S.I.C.: 5411
N.A.I.C.S.: 445110

MONTEL DISTRIBUTION SA (1)
Qu Saint Christophe
4000 Digne-les-Bains, France
Tel.: (33) 4 92 36 63 36
Fax: (33) 4 92 36 63 49
E-Mail: montel.distri@wanadoo.fr
Food Retail Store Operator
S.I.C.: 5499
N.A.I.C.S.: 445299

OOSHOP (1)
Zone Industrielle Route De Paris
14120 Mondeville, France
Tel.: (33) 146852031
E-Mail: client@ooshop.com
Supermarket Stores Operating Services
S.I.C.: 5411
N.A.I.C.S.: 445110

PHILIBERT SARL (1)
12 Rue De La Grange
67000 Strasbourg, France
Tel.: (33) 388326535
Fax: (33) 388322637
Toy Stores Operating Services
S.I.C.: 5945
N.A.I.C.S.: 451120

PHIVETOL SA (1)
Zone Industrielle Route De Paris
Mondeville, 14120, France
Tel.: (33) 233321813
Supermarket Operating Services
S.I.C.: 5411
N.A.I.C.S.: 445110

POULAIN DISTRIBUTION (1)
Zone Industrielle Rue De La Belle Jardiniere
Equeurdreville-Hainneville, 50120, France
Tel.: (33) 233034874
Industrial Equipment Whslr
S.I.C.: 5084
N.A.I.C.S.: 423830

PRODIM SAS (1)
Zone Industrielle Les Estroublans 29
Boulevard De L Europe
BP 30216
13746 Vitrolles, France
Tel.: (33) 4 42 10 88 00
Fax: (33) 4 42 10 88 01
Cleaning Equipment Distr
S.I.C.: 5087
N.A.I.C.S.: 423850

PROFIDIS (1)
Route De Paris
14120 Mondeville, France
Tel.: (33) 2 31 70 60 00
Fax: (33) 2 31 83 56 19
Financial Services
S.I.C.: 6211
N.A.I.C.S.: 523999

QUERCY (1)
Zac Des Grands Camps
46090 Mercues, France
Tel.: (33) 565303905
Fax: (33) 565226904
Supermarket Operating Services

Carrefour SA—(Continued)

S.I.C.: 5411
N.A.I.C.S.: 445110

ROTONDE (1)
105 Boulevard du Montparnasse
75006 Paris, Ile-de-France, France
Tel.: (33) 1 43 26 68 84
Supermarket Stores Operating Services
S.I.C.: 5411
N.A.I.C.S.: 445110

S.D.O (1)
13 Allee Du Clos Des Charmes
Collegien, 77090, France
Tel.: (33) 160060045
Fax: (33) 160370194
Supermarket Stores Operating Services
S.I.C.: 5411
N.A.I.C.S.: 445110

S.L.M. DISTRIBUTION (1)
Rte de Paris
14120 Mondeville, France
Tel.: (33) 2 31 84 44 37
Plumbing & Heating Equipment Distr
S.I.C.: 5074
N.A.I.C.S.: 423720

SOBRECO (1)
Rue Des Tournelles
74100 Annemasse, France
Tel.: (33) 450950874
Fax: (33) 450371827
Supermarket Stores Operating Services
S.I.C.: 5411
N.A.I.C.S.: 445110

SODITA (1)
1 Chemin De Geles
33320 Le Taillan-Medoc, France
Tel.: (33) 556576363
Supermarket Operating Services
S.I.C.: 5411
N.A.I.C.S.: 445110

Soessardis Sarl (1)
Rue Rouen
95420 Magny-en-Vexin, France
Tel.: (33) 1 34 67 36 30
Supermarket Stores Operating Services
S.I.C.: 5411
N.A.I.C.S.: 445110

SOREDIS SA (1)
Rue De Sierck
57480 Rettel, France
Tel.: (33) 3 82 83 70 67
Fax: (33) 3 82 83 68 28
Web Site: www.soredis.com
Supermarket Stores Operating Services
S.I.C.: 5411
N.A.I.C.S.: 445110

Soval SA (1)
78 Rue Gabriel Peri
Dombasle-sur-Meurthe, 54110, France FR
Tel.: (33) 383482320 (100%)
Fax: (33) 383469012
Supermarket Stores Operating Services
S.I.C.: 5411
N.A.I.C.S.: 445110

Sovidis (1)
7 Rue du Fougeray
35500 Vitre, France FR
Tel.: (33) 2 23 55 71 00 (100%)
Fax: (33) 2 23 55 71 09
Supermarket Stores Operating Services
S.I.C.: 5411
N.A.I.C.S.: 445110

STEMA SNC (1)
15 Cours Gambetta
Montpellier, 34000, France
Tel.: (33) 467926010
Supermarket Stores Operating Services
S.I.C.: 5411
N.A.I.C.S.: 445110

STROFI SA (1)
Zone Industrielle Route De Paris
Mondeville, 14120, France
Tel.: (33) 235200764
Supermarket Stores Operating Services
S.I.C.: 5411
N.A.I.C.S.: 445110

SUPERDIS SA (1)
Zone Industrielle Le Vaillant Lot N 13 2 Rue Jean Moulin
Le Bourget, 93350, France
Tel.: (33) 148364544
Real Estate Management Services
S.I.C.: 6531
N.A.I.C.S.: 531390

VIADIX SAS (1)
Zone Industrielle Route De Paris
Mondeville, 14120, France
Tel.: (33) 490257681
Supermarket Stores Operating Services
S.I.C.: 5411
N.A.I.C.S.: 445110

Non-U.S. Subsidiaries:

Carrefour Asia Limited (1)
14th Floor Tower 1 Admiralty
Hong Kong, China (Hong Kong) (100%)
Tel.: (852) 22834000
Fax: (852) 25376484
E-Mail: info@carrefour.com
Emp.: 100
Owner & Operator of Hypermarkets, Supermarkets, Grocery & Convenience Stores
S.I.C.: 5411
N.A.I.C.S.: 445110
Noel Priox *(CEO)*

Subsidiary:

Carrefour Global Sourcing Asia Limited (2)
18/F One Kowloon 1 Wang Yuen St
Kowloon, China (Hong Kong)
Tel.: (852) 25866400
Fax: (852) 23758096
Emp.: 11
Vegetables & Canned Fruits Distr
S.I.C.: 5148
N.A.I.C.S.: 424480

Non-U.S. Subsidiaries:

Carrefour Singapore Pte Ltd (2)
8 Temasek Blvd 04-01/2/3
Suntec Twr Three, 38988 Singapore, Singapore (100%)
Tel.: (65) 63336868
Fax: (65) 63336178
Web Site: www.carrefour.com.sg
Emp.: 120
Owner & Operator of Supermarkets, Hypermarkets, Grocery & Convenience Stores
S.I.C.: 5411
N.A.I.C.S.: 445110

Carrefour South East Asia Pte. Ltd. (2)
8 Temasek Boulevard 04-01/02/03 Suntec Tower 3
Singapore, 039192, Singapore SG
Tel.: (65) 62113102
Fax: (65) 63336178
Supermarket Stores Operating Services
S.I.C.: 5411
N.A.I.C.S.: 445110

Carrefour Taiwan (2)
Presicarre Corporation
6F-1,137 Nan King East Road
Section 2, 104 Taipei, Taiwan
Tel.: (886) 225063400
Fax: (886) 25064201
Web Site: www.carrefour.com.tw
Hypermarkets, Supermarkets, Grocery & Convenience Stores
S.I.C.: 5541
N.A.I.C.S.: 447110
David Chuang *(Project Mgr)*

Cencar Limited (Carrefour Thailand) (2)
15th Floor, Q. House Building
11 South Sethorn Road
Tungmahamek, Sathorn, 10120 Bangkok, Thailand
Tel.: (66) 26773399
Fax: (66) 26773366
Owner & Operator of Hypermarkets, Supermarkets, Grocery & Convenience Stores
S.I.C.: 5411
N.A.I.C.S.: 445110

CHENGDU YUSHENG INDUSTRIAL DEVELOPMENT CO LTD (2)
Rm 2401 Minshan Restaurant
Jinjiang, Chengdu, 610021, China
Tel.: (86) 2885583333
Supermarket Stores Operating Services
S.I.C.: 5411
N.A.I.C.S.: 445110

DIA TIANTIAN (SHANGHAI) MANAGEMENT CONSULTING SERVICE CO. LTD (2)
A G 7/F International Ship Finance Mansion
No 720 Pudong Ave
Shanghai, 200120, China
Tel.: (86) 2150368282
Fax: (86) 2150368386
Web Site: www.diatiantian.com
Emp.: 320
Management Consulting Services
S.I.C.: 8742
N.A.I.C.S.: 541611

Presicarre Corp. (2)
6th Fl 1 137 Nanking East Rd Section 2
Taipei, ROC, 106, Taiwan (59%)
Tel.: (886) 225063400
Fax: (886) 225064201
E-Mail: carrefur@ms37.hinet.net
Emp.: 100
Grocery Store Operator; Joint Venture of Carrefour SA & Uni-President Enterprises Corp.
S.I.C.: 5541
N.A.I.C.S.: 447110

WUHAN HANFU SUPERMARKET CO. LTD (2)
No 687 Hanyang Road
Wuhan, 430051, China
Tel.: (86) 27 84882020
Fax: (86) 27 84882058
Supermarket Stores Operating Services
S.I.C.: 5411
N.A.I.C.S.: 445110

XIAMEN CARREFOUR COMMERCIAL CO LTD (2)
Crossroads Of Jiahe Rd And Lianqian W Rd
Xiamen, 361000, China
Tel.: (86) 5922928888
Fax: (86) 5922928828
Supermarket Stores Operating Services
S.I.C.: 5411
N.A.I.C.S.: 445110

XUZHOU YUEJIA COMMERCIAL CO LTD (2)
No 6 Zhongshan North Road
Gulou, Xuzhou, 221005, China
Tel.: (86) 51687880001
Fax: (86) 51687880086
Supermarket Stores Operating Services
S.I.C.: 5411
N.A.I.C.S.: 445110
Lee Hill *(Gen Mgr)*

Carrefour Belgium SA (1)
Ave Des Olympiades 20
PO Box 1140
Evere, Brussels, 1140, Belgium (100%)
Tel.: (32) 27292111
Fax: (32) 27292987
Web Site: www.carrefour.eu
Emp.: 1,000
Operator of Supermarkets, Hypermarkets, Convenience Stores & Grocery Stores
S.I.C.: 5411
N.A.I.C.S.: 445110
Gerard Lavinay *(CEO)*

Subsidiaries:

Carrefour Finance SA (2)
Emile De Motlaan 19
Brussels, Belgium
Tel.: (32) 26261960
Fax: (32) 26464373
Emp.: 15
Financial Management Services
S.I.C.: 6211
N.A.I.C.S.: 523999

DE NETELAAR Sprl (2)
Mechelsesteenweg 24
Dendermonde, Belgium
Tel.: (32) 52259811
Supermarket Stores Operating Services
S.I.C.: 5411
N.A.I.C.S.: 445110

EXTENSION BEL-TEX SA (2)
Olympiadenlaan 20
Brussels, Belgium
Tel.: (32) 27292181
Fax: (32) 27292126
Supermarket Operating Services
S.I.C.: 5411
N.A.I.C.S.: 445110

FILUNIC N.V (2)
Chaussee de Louvain 580
1030 Schaarbeek, Belgium
Tel.: (32) 27341346
Supermarket Stores Operating Services
S.I.C.: 5411
N.A.I.C.S.: 445110

FOURCAR BELGIUM SA (2)
Avenue Emile De Mot 19
Brussels, 1000, Belgium
Tel.: (32) 26261960
Fax: (32) 26464373
Trade Shows Organisation Services
S.I.C.: 7389
N.A.I.C.S.: 561920

FRESHFOOD SA (2)
Avenue Des Olympiades 20
Brussels, 1140, Belgium
Tel.: (32) 56313530
Fax: (32) 56315346
Supermarket Stores Operating Services
S.I.C.: 5411
N.A.I.C.S.: 445110

QUIEVRAIN RETAIL ASSOCIATE NV (2)
Avenue Docteur Schweitzer 30
7340 Wasmes, Belgium
Tel.: (32) 65 80 32 92
Fax: (32) 65 79 36 96
Emp.: 8
Food Stores Operating Services
S.I.C.: 5499
N.A.I.C.S.: 445299
Charles Roobaert *(Mng Dir)*

ROTHIDI SA (2)
Rue De La Bruyere 215
Rixensart, Walloon Brabant, 1332, Belgium
Tel.: (32) 26 53 63 68
Fax: (32) 26 52 09 37
Supermarket Stores Operating Services
S.I.C.: 5411
N.A.I.C.S.: 445110

VANDEN MEERSSCHE NV (2)
Brusselstraat 64
Dilbeek, Brabant, 9040, Belgium
Tel.: (32) 24660682
Fax: (32) 24666799
Emp.: 2
Supermarket Operating Services
S.I.C.: 5411
N.A.I.C.S.: 445110
Helmut Huber *(Gen Mgr)*

Units:

Supertransport - Traffic Center Kontich (2)
Neerveld 1
2550 Kontich, Belgium (100%)
Tel.: (32) 34514681
Fax: (32) 34514668
E-Mail: goffarns@aosasa.com
Web Site: www.supertransport.be
Emp.: 50
Distribution Services
S.I.C.: 4731
N.A.I.C.S.: 541614
G. Offarns *(Dir)*

Supertransport - Traffic Center Nord (KDC) (2)
Drevendaal 3
St Katelijne Waver, 2860 Mechelen, Belgium (100%)
Tel.: (32) 5306580
Web Site: www.supertransport.be/contact.cfm?lang=fr
Distribution Services
S.I.C.: 4731
N.A.I.C.S.: 541614

Supertransport - Traffic Center Sud (2)
Rue De lindustrie 21
1400 Nivelles, Belgium (100%)
Tel.: (32) 67634814
Fax: (32) 67634810
Web Site: www.supertransport.be
Distribution Services

S.I.C.: 4731
N.A.I.C.S.: 541614

Supertransport - Traffic Center Vilvoorde (2)
Drevendaal 3 St Katelinje Waver
Waver, 2860 Vilvoorde, Belgium (100%)
Tel.: (32) 22572630
Fax: (32) 22572616
Distribution Services
S.I.C.: 4731
N.A.I.C.S.: 541614

Carrefour Ceska Republika (1)
Podbabska 17
Praha 6, Prague, 16624, Czech Republic (100%)
Tel.: (420) 233013300
Fax: (420) 233013393
Web Site: carrefour.czechtrade.us/
Emp.: 300
Owner & Operator of Hypermarkets, Supermarkets, Grocery & Convenience Stores
S.I.C.: 5411
N.A.I.C.S.: 445110

Carrefour China Holdings BV (1)
Overschiestraat 186 D
Amsterdam, 1062 XK, Netherlands NL
Tel.: (31) 20 669 5858
Fax: (31) 20 669 6847
Emp.: 4
Holding Company
S.I.C.: 6719
N.A.I.C.S.: 551112
Bernard Carrel-Billiard *(Mng Dir)*

Carrefour Italia SpA (1)
Via Caldera 21
20153 Milan, Italy IT
Tel.: (39) 248251 (100%)
Fax: (39) 02 98 24 0812
E-Mail: serviziocliente@carrefour.com
Web Site: www.carrefouritalia.it
S.I.C.: 5251
N.A.I.C.S.: 444130

Carrefour Latin America (1)
Cuyo 3323/3337
Martinez, 1640 Buenos Aires, Argentina
Tel.: (54) 1140037000
Fax: (54) 1140037722
E-Mail: rodolpha_demaene@carrefour.com
Web Site: www.carrefour.com.ar
Holding Company
S.I.C.: 6719
N.A.I.C.S.: 551112

Subsidiary:

Carrefour Argentina S.A. (2)
Cuyo 3323/3337
Martinez, 1640 Buenos Aires, Argentina
Tel.: (54) 1140037000
Telex: 27324
Fax: (54) 11 40 03 77 22
E-Mail: consultas@carrefour.com
Web Site: www.carrefour.com.ar
Earnings: $60,000,000
Owner & Operator of Supermarkets, Hypermarkets, Grocery & Convenience Stores
S.I.C.: 5411
N.A.I.C.S.: 445110
Daniel Fernandez *(Exec Dir)*

Non-U.S. Subsidiaries:

Carrefour Brasil (2)
213 Rua George Eastman
CEP 04719 Sao Paulo, Brazil (80%)
Tel.: (55) 11 37796000
Telex: 1157024
Fax: (55) 1137796694
Web Site: www.grupocarrefour.com.br/
Emp.: 170
Owner & Operator of Hypermarkets, Supermarkets, Grocery & Convenience Stores
S.I.C.: 5411
N.A.I.C.S.: 445110
Charles Desmartis *(CEO)*

Carrefour Monaco (1)
Avenue Albert 2BP 233
Monaco, 98004, Monaco
Tel.: (377) 92055700
Fax: (377) 92059944
Supermarket Operating Services
S.I.C.: 5411
N.A.I.C.S.: 445110

Carrefour Nederland B.V. (1)
186 D Gebouw Spring Overschiestraat
1062 XK Amsterdam, Netherlands (100%)
Tel.: (31) 206695858
Telex: 23641
Fax: (31) 206696847
E-Mail: cnbc@carrefour.com
Emp.: 4
Owner & Operator of Hypermarkets, Supermarkets, Grocery & Convenience Stores
S.I.C.: 5411
N.A.I.C.S.: 445110
F. Tassan *(Gen Mgr)*

Subsidiaries:

ALCYON BV (2)
Overschiestraat 186d Geb Spring
Amsterdam, 1062 XK, Netherlands
Tel.: (31) 206695858
Fax: (31) 206696847
Emp.: 4
Supermarket Stores Operating Services
S.I.C.: 5411
N.A.I.C.S.: 445110

CADAM BV (2)
Overschiestraat 186d
Amsterdam, 1062 XK, Netherlands
Tel.: (31) 206695858
Supermarket Stores Operating Services
S.I.C.: 5411
N.A.I.C.S.: 445110

Carrefour Property B.V. (2)
Overschiestraat 186d
Amsterdam, 1062 XK, Netherlands NL
Tel.: (31) 206695858
Property Management Services
S.I.C.: 6531
N.A.I.C.S.: 531311

FOURCAR BV (2)
Overschiestraat 186d
Amsterdam, 1062 XK, Netherlands
Tel.: (31) 206695858
Supermarket Stores Operating Services
S.I.C.: 5411
N.A.I.C.S.: 445110

FRANCOFIN BV (2)
Overschiestraat 186d
Amsterdam, 1062 XK, Netherlands
Tel.: (31) 206695858
Fax: (31) 206696847
Emp.: 4
Supermarket Stores Operating Services
S.I.C.: 5411
N.A.I.C.S.: 445110

MILDEW BV (2)
Overschiestraat 186 d
Amsterdam, 1062 XK, Netherlands
Tel.: (31) 900 9888
Hypermarket Stores Operating Services
S.I.C.: 5411
N.A.I.C.S.: 445110

SOCA BV (2)
Overschiestraat 186D
Amsterdam, 1062 XK, Netherlands
Tel.: (31) 206695858
Supermarket Stores Operating Services
S.I.C.: 5411
N.A.I.C.S.: 445110

Carrefour Polska Sp. z o.o. (1)
Al Jerozolimskie 148
02326 Warsaw, Poland PL
Tel.: (48) 225724700
Fax: (48) 228238856
Emp.: 15,397
Owner & Operator of Hypermarkets, Supermarkets, Grocery & Convenience Stores
S.I.C.: 5411
N.A.I.C.S.: 445110
Gilles Roudy *(Mng Dir-Europe)*

Subsidiaries:

Carrefour Polska Proper Sp. z o.o. (2)
ul Targowa 72
Warsaw, 03-734, Poland PL
Tel.: (48) 22 517 2110
Fax: (48) 22 517 2204
Supermarket Stores Operating Services
S.I.C.: 5411
N.A.I.C.S.: 445110

Carrefour Procurement International AG & Co. KG (1)
Schliengener Strasse 25
79379 Mullheim, Germany De
Tel.: (49) 763170040
Fax: (49) 7631700420
Supermarket Stores Operating Services
S.I.C.: 5411
N.A.I.C.S.: 445110

Carrefour Slovensko s.r.o. (1)
Panonska Cesta 16a
Bratislava, 851 04, Slovakia Sk
Tel.: (421) 268 292 111
Fax: (421) 268 292 112
Supermarket Stores Operating Services
S.I.C.: 5411
N.A.I.C.S.: 445110
Stephane Sellier *(Gen Mgr)*

Carrefour WC&C India Pvt. Ltd. (1)
2nd Floor Park Centra Sector 30
Village Silokhra, Gurgaon, Haryana, 122 001, India In
Tel.: (91) 1244752048
Fax: (91) 1244752005
E-Mail: contact_india@carrefour.com
Web Site: www.carrefour.in
Supermarket Stores Operating Services
S.I.C.: 5411
N.A.I.C.S.: 445110

Carrefour World Trade SA (1)
Route de l'Aeroport 10
Geneva, 1215, Switzerland
Tel.: (41) 227107311
Fax: (41) 227107312
Web Site: www.carrefour.com
Emp.: 18
Supermarket Stores Operating Services
S.I.C.: 5411
N.A.I.C.S.: 445110
Jean Pierre Noeel *(Mng Dir)*

Carrefoursa Turkiye Genel Mudurluk (1)
Dudullu Asfalti 1
Kucukbakkalkoy Mahallesi
Kadikoy, 34750 Istanbul, Turkey
Tel.: (90) 2166550000
Fax: (90) 216 655 00 50
Web Site: www.carrefour.com.tr/basinodasi.asp?NewId=26&CatId=9
Owner & Operator of Hypermarkets, Supermarkets, Grocery & Convenience Stores
S.I.C.: 5411
N.A.I.C.S.: 445110

Centros Comerciales Carrefour, S.A. (1)
Centra de Burgos Km 14500
28108 Madrid, Alcobendas, Spain ES
Tel.: (34) 902 20 20 00 (77%)
Telex: 42015
Fax: (34) 913331836
Web Site: www.carrefour.es
Owner & Operator of Hypermarkets, Supermarkets, Grocery & Convenience Stores
S.I.C.: 5411
N.A.I.C.S.: 445110

Subsidiaries:

Carrefour Canarias, S.A. (2)
Avenida Manuel Hermoso Rojas 16
38003 Santa Cruz de Tenerife, Spain ES
Tel.: (34) 922236000
Fax: (34) 922225167
Supermarket Stores Operating Services
S.I.C.: 5411
N.A.I.C.S.: 445110

Carrefour Espana Properties, S.L. (2)
Avenida Matapinonera S/N-Ed Abside Planta 5
Madrid, Spain ES
Tel.: (34) 916634335
Property Management Services
S.I.C.: 6531
N.A.I.C.S.: 531311

Carrefour Navarra, S.L. (2)
Avenida Baranain S/N
31008 Pamplona, Spain ES
Tel.: (34) 948194100
Fax: (34) 948171500
Supermarket Stores Operating Services
S.I.C.: 5411
N.A.I.C.S.: 445110

Carrefour Norte, S.L. (2)
Carretera Trapaga A Barakaldo S/N
48910 Sestao, Spain ES
Tel.: (34) 944729100
Fax: (34) 944729110
Supermarket Stores Operating Services
S.I.C.: 5411
N.A.I.C.S.: 445110

Distribuidora Internacional de Alimentacion S.A. (2)
Plaza Carlos Trias Beltran 7
Madrid, 28020, Spain
Tel.: (34) 914567300
Fax: (34) 915557741
E-Mail: investor.relations@diagroup.com
Web Site: www.diacorporate.com
DIA—(MAD)
Grocery Store
S.I.C.: 5411
N.A.I.C.S.: 445110
Ana Maria Llopis *(Chm)*
Ricardo Curras de Don Pablos *(Mng Dir)*

GROUP SUPECO MAXOR SL (2)
Av Angel Sallent S/N
Terrassa, 8224, Spain
Tel.: (34) 937333006
Emp.: 54
Supermarket Store Operating Services
S.I.C.: 5411
N.A.I.C.S.: 445110
Fidel Murillo *(Gen Mgr)*

INVERSIONES PRYCA, S.A. (2)
Calle Campezo 16
Madrid, 28022, Spain
Tel.: (34) 913018900
Supermarket Stores Operating Services
S.I.C.: 5411
N.A.I.C.S.: 445110

VIAJES CARREFOUR, S.L. (2)
Carretera Autovia A-1 Km 14 500
Alcobendas, 28108, Spain
Tel.: (34) 916634828
Fax: (34) 916634005
E-Mail: es.viajes.Callcenter@carrefour.com
Travel Agencies
S.I.C.: 4724
N.A.I.C.S.: 561510

Non-U.S. Subsidiary:

DIA PORTUGAL SUPERMERCADOS SA (2)
R Carlos Mardel 49 1
Lisbon, 1900-117, Portugal
Tel.: (351) 218452240
Supermarket Operating Services
S.I.C.: 5411
N.A.I.C.S.: 445110

HYPERDEMA SA (1)
C/O Daniel Schneuwly Avocat Rue De Romont 35
Fribourg, 1700, Switzerland
Tel.: (41) 263472222
Fax: (41) 263472227
Supermarket Stores Operating Services
S.I.C.: 5411
N.A.I.C.S.: 445110

PROMOHYPERMARKT AG (1)
C/O Daniel Schneuwly Rue De Romont 35
Fribourg, 1700, Switzerland
Tel.: (41) 263471630
Fax: (41) 263471631
Hypermarket & Supermarket Stores Operating Services
S.I.C.: 5411
N.A.I.C.S.: 445110

Non-U.S. Joint Ventures:

Carrefour Sabanci Ticaret Merkezi AS CarrefourSA (1)
No 1 Kucukbakkalkoy Mahallesi Dudullu Asfalti
Kadikoy, 34750 Istanbul, Turkey TR
Tel.: (90) 2166 55 0000
Fax: (90) 2166 55 0055
Web Site: www.carrefour.com.tr
Emp.: 500

Carrefour SA—(Continued)

Supermarkets & Other Stores Operator
S.I.C.: 5411
N.A.I.C.S.: 445110

CARRIANNA GROUP HOLDINGS COMPANY LIMITED

(Formerly Tak Sing Alliance Holdings Limited)
26/F Wyler Centre Phase II
200 Tai Lin Pai Road, Kwai Chung, NT, China (Hong Kong)
Tel.: (852) 2426 1021
Fax: (852) 2480 5644
E-Mail: info@carrianna.com
Web Site: www.carrianna.com
0126—(HKG)
Rev.: $96,516,367
Assets: $117,972,616,095
Liabilities: $117,498,992,932
Net Worth: $473,623,163
Earnings: $21,609,312
Emp.: 2,300
Fiscal Year-end: 03/31/13

Business Description:
Property Investment & Development Services
S.I.C.: 6531
N.A.I.C.S.: 531312

Personnel:
Kai Cheung Ma *(Founder & Chm)*
Kai Yum Ma *(Vice Chm & Mng Dir)*
Jimmy Sheung Lai Chan *(CEO)*
Yan Kwong Ng *(CFO & Sec)*

Board of Directors:
Kai Cheung Ma
Jimmy Sheung Lai Chan
Charles Ming Chi Lo
Sam Man Kit Lo
John Hung Ming Ma
Kai Yum Ma
Yan Kwong Ng
See King Wong

Legal Counsel:
King & Wood Mallesons
13th Floor Gloucester Tower The Landmark 15 Queens Road Central
Central, China (Hong Kong)

Appleby (Bermuda) Limited
Hamilton, Bermuda

HSBC Bank Bermuda Limited
6 Front Street
Hamilton, Bermuda

Transfer Agents:
Tricor Tengis Limited
26/F Tesbury Centre, 28 Queens Road East
Hong Kong, China (Hong Kong)

HSBC Bank Bermuda Limited
6 Front Street
Hamilton, Bermuda

Subsidiaries:

Carrianna (Chiu Chow) Restaurant Limited (1)
1 F 151 Gloucester Rd
Wanchai, China (Hong Kong)
Tel.: (852) 25111282
Fax: (852) 25074869
Web Site: www.carrianna.com
Restaurants Management Services
S.I.C.: 5812
N.A.I.C.S.: 722511

Tak Sing Alliance Limited (1)
26 F Wyler Ctr Phase II 200 Tai Lin Pai Rd
Kwai Chung, New Territories, China (Hong Kong)
Tel.: (852) 24261021
Fax: (852) 24805644
E-Mail: info@carrianna.com
Web Site: www.carrianna.com
Emp.: 10
Garments Mfr
S.I.C.: 2389
N.A.I.C.S.: 315210
Ma Kai Cheung *(Chm)*
Kai Yum Ma *(Vice Chm)*

CARRIE ARRAN RESOURCES INC.

141 Adelaide Street West Suite 301
Toronto, ON, M5H 3L5, Canada
Tel.: (416) 628-5940
Fax: (416) 628-5911
E-Mail: mlesko@mail.com
Web Site:
SCO—(TSXV)
Assets: $40,811
Liabilities: $95,724
Net Worth: ($54,913)
Earnings: ($442,680)
Fiscal Year-end: 07/31/13

Business Description:
Metal Mining Services
S.I.C.: 1099
N.A.I.C.S.: 212299

Personnel:
Thomas J. Pladsen *(Pres & CEO)*
Michael G. Leskovec *(CFO)*

Board of Directors:
Stephen F. Brown
Michael Byron
Brent J. Peters
Thomas J. Pladsen

Transfer Agent:
Olympia Transfer Service Inc
Suite 920 120 Adelaide Street West
Toronto, ON, Canada

CARRIERE INDUSTRIAL SUPPLY LIMITED

190 Magill Street Walden Industrial Park
Lively, ON, P3Y 1K7, Canada
Tel.: (705) 692-4784
Fax: (705) 692-5707
Toll Free: (800) 268-5350
Web Site: www.steelwear.com
Rev.: $22,271,797
Emp.: 100

Business Description:
Construction Services & Mining Machinery Provider
S.I.C.: 5082
N.A.I.C.S.: 423810

Personnel:
Jean-Marc Valade *(Gen Mgr)*

CARRIERNET GLOBAL LTD.

81 Ubi Avenue 4 03-11 UB One
Singapore, 408830, Singapore
Tel.: (65) 63099088
Fax: (65) 63050489
Web Site: www.carriernetglobal.com
Year Founded: 1984
5BI—(SES)
Rev.: $121,010,724
Assets: $11,583,282
Liabilities: $6,550,311
Net Worth: $5,032,971
Earnings: $2,581,260
Emp.: 191
Fiscal Year-end: 12/31/12

Business Description:
Liquid Crystal Displays & Electronic Modules Designer & Mfr
S.I.C.: 3679
N.A.I.C.S.: 334419

Personnel:
Peter Chuan Hui Ang *(CEO)*
Elaine Beh Pur-Lin *(Sec)*

Board of Directors:
Richard Chung Yaw Tan
Peter Chuan Hui Ang
Kok Wah Ong
Juliana Julianti Samudro
Sugiono Wiyono Sugialam

Legal Counsel:
Stamford Law Corporation
10 Collyer Quay 27-00 Ocean Financial Centre
Singapore, Singapore

Colin Ng & Partners LLP
36 Carpenter Street
Singapore, Singapore

Subsidiaries:

CarrierNet Corporation (Singapore) Pte. Ltd. (1)
300 Beach Road 29-01 The Concourse
Singapore, 199555, Singapore
Tel.: (65) 6309 9088
Fax: (65) 6305 0489
Calling Cards Distr
S.I.C.: 4812
N.A.I.C.S.: 517911

Uni 3 Pte Ltd (1)
29 Roberts Lane
Singapore, 218308, Singapore
Tel.: (65) 62966065
Fax: (65) 6296 6145
Calling Cards Distr
S.I.C.: 4812
N.A.I.C.S.: 517911

U.S. Subsidiary:

Vikay America Incorporated (1)
9311 Eton Ave
Chatsworth, CA 91311 (100%)
Tel.: (818) 772-6050
Fax: (818) 772-1167
Web Site: www.vikay.com
Emp.: 20
Liquid Crystal Modules
S.I.C.: 3575
N.A.I.C.S.: 334118
Steven Bruckner *(Mgr-Sls)*

Non-U.S. Subsidiaries:

VK Manufacturing Sdn Bhd (1)
No9-16 Jalan Biru Taman Bandar Jaya
85300 Labis Johor, Malaysia (100%)
Tel.: (60) 78961543
Fax: (60) 78961546
E-Mail: shyeo@vikay.com
Web Site: www.vikay.com
Liquid Crystal Modules
S.I.C.: 3577
N.A.I.C.S.: 334118

CARROLL SOUTH SHORE MOTORS INC.

15133 Hebbville Highway
PO Box 306
Bridgewater, NS, B4V 2W9, Canada
Tel.: (902) 543-2493
Fax: (902) 543-6232
Toll Free: (866) 913-0064
Web Site: www.carrollsouthshore.ns.ca
Year Founded: 1926
Rev.: $19,896,146
Emp.: 41

Business Description:
New & Used Car Dealers
S.I.C.: 5511
N.A.I.C.S.: 441110

Personnel:
J. Scott Carroll *(Gen Mgr)*

CARR'S MILLING INDUSTRIES PLC

Old Croft Stanwix
Carlisle, CA3 9BA, United Kingdom
Tel.: (44) 1228554600
Fax: (44) 1228554601
E-Mail: carrflour@cmiplc.co.uk
Web Site: www.carrs-milling.com
CRM—(LSE)
Emp.: 883

Business Description:
Flour Milling Services
S.I.C.: 2041
N.A.I.C.S.: 311211

Personnel:
Tim Davies *(CEO)*
Katie Sinclair *(Sec)*

Board of Directors:
Chris N. C. Holmes
Richard Inglewood
Neil Austin
A. Robert Heygate
Alistair G. M. Wannop

Legal Counsel:
Hill Dickinson LLP
1 St Paul's Square
Liverpool, L3 9SJ, United Kingdom

Atkinson Ritson
15 Fisher Street
Carlisle, CA3 8RW, United Kingdom

Division:

Bendalls Engineering (1)
Brunthill Road
CA30EH Carlisle, United Kingdom (100%)
Tel.: (44) 1228526246
Fax: (44) 1228525634
E-Mail: info@bendalls.co.uk
Web Site: www.bendalls.co.uk
Emp.: 80
Engineering Services
S.I.C.: 8711
N.A.I.C.S.: 541330
Norman Attison *(Mng Dir)*

Subsidiaries:

Carrs Agriculture Ltd. (1)
The Old Wool Mill
Lockerbie, Dumfries, DG11 1JA, United Kingdom (100%)
Tel.: (44) 1387750747
E-Mail: carrsflour@cmiplc.co.uk
Hog & Pig Farming
S.I.C.: 0213
N.A.I.C.S.: 112210

Carrs Billington Agriculture (Sales) Ltd. (1)
Montgomery Way
Rosehill Estate, Carlisle, CA1 2UY, United Kingdom (51%)
Tel.: (44) 1228520212
Fax: (44) 1228512572
E-Mail: customerservices@carrs-billington.com
Web Site: www.carrs-billington.com
Emp.: 45
Farm & Garden Machinery & Equipment Whslr
S.I.C.: 5083
N.A.I.C.S.: 423820
Chris Hormes *(Mng Dir)*

Carrs Engineering Limited (1)
Brunthill Road Kingstown Industrial Estate
Carlisle, Cumbria, CA3 0EH, United Kingdom
Tel.: (44) 1228 815350
Fax: (44) 1228 525634
Emp.: 80
Fabricated Metal Product Mfr
S.I.C.: 3499
N.A.I.C.S.: 332999
Norman Addison *(Gen Mgr)*

Carr's Flour Mills Ltd. (1)
Old Croft
Carlisle, CA3 9BA, United Kingdom (100%)
Tel.: (44) 1228554600
Fax: (44) 1228554602
E-Mail: carrsflour@cmiplc.co.uk
Web Site: www.carrs-flourmills.co.uk
Emp.: 25
Flour Milling
S.I.C.: 2041
N.A.I.C.S.: 311211
Duncan Monroe *(Mng Dir)*

Carrs Properties Limited (1)
Oldcroft Stanwix
Carlisle, Cumbria, CA3 9BA, United Kingdom
Tel.: (44) 1228 554600
Fax: (44) 1228546645
Farm Supplies Merchant Whslr
S.I.C.: 5191
N.A.I.C.S.: 424910

Forsyths of Wooler Limited (1)
Bridge End
Wooler, Northumberland, NE71 6QE, United Kingdom
Tel.: (44) 1668 281567
Fax: (44) 1668 283453
Animal Feed Distr
S.I.C.: 5191
N.A.I.C.S.: 424910
Mark Tasker Brown *(Gen Mgr)*

Scotmin Nutrition Limited (1)
13 Whitfield Drive Heathfield Industrial Estate
Ayr, KA8 9RX, United Kingdom

Tel.: (44) 1292280909
Fax: (44) 1292 280919
E-Mail: admin@scotmin.com
Web Site: www.scotmin.com
Emp.: 30
Animal Supplements Distr
S.I.C.: 5159
N.A.I.C.S.: 424590
Andrew Robertson *(Mng Dir)*

Joint Ventures:

Afgritech Limited (1)
Old Croft
Carlisle, CA3 9BA, United Kingdom (50%)
Tel.: (44) 1228554600
Fax: (44) 1228554601
E-Mail: carrsflour@cmiplc.co.uk
Other Animal Food Mfr
S.I.C.: 2048
N.A.I.C.S.: 311119
Duncan Monroe *(Mng Dir)*

Bibby Agriculture Limited (1)
1A Network House
Badgers Way Oxon Business Park,
SY35AB Shrewsbury, United Kingdom (26%)
Tel.: (44) 1743237890
Fax: (44) 1743351552
Emp.: 70
Other Animal Food Mfr
S.I.C.: 2048
N.A.I.C.S.: 311119

U.S. Subsidiary:

Animal Feed Supplement Inc. (1)
E Hwy 212 PO Box 188
Belle Fourche, SD 57717 (100%)
Tel.: (605) 892-3421
Fax: (605) 892-3473
E-Mail: jeffw@smartlic.com
Web Site: www.smartlic.com
Emp.: 50
Other Animal Food Mfr
S.I.C.: 2048
N.A.I.C.S.: 311119
Jeff Westberg *(Mng Dir)*

Non-U.S. Subsidiary:

Walischmiller Engineering GmbH (1)
Schiessstattweg 16
88677 Markdorf, Germany
Tel.: (49) 754495140
Fax: (49) 7544951499
E-Mail: info@hwm.com
Web Site: www.hwm.com
Emp.: 90
Robot Grip Tongs Mfr
S.I.C.: 3559
N.A.I.C.S.: 333249
Frau Claudia Reich *(Mng Dir)*

CARRUS CAPITAL CORPORATION

1320 - 885 West Georgia Street
Vancouver, BC, V6C 3E8, Canada
Tel.: (604) 375-5578
Fax: (604) 221-9688
Web Site: www.carruscapital.ca
CHQ—(TSXV)
Assets: $479,066
Liabilities: $269,008
Net Worth: $210,058
Earnings: ($642,735)
Emp.: 5
Fiscal Year-end: 04/30/13

Business Description:
Investment Services
S.I.C.: 6211
N.A.I.C.S.: 523999

Personnel:
Bruce A. Schmidt *(CEO)*
Ann Fehr *(CFO)*

Board of Directors:
Douglas B. Johnson
Andrew Rae
Bruce A. Schmidt

Legal Counsel:
Seed Intellectual Property Law Group
701 Fifth Ave., Ste. 6300
Seattle, WA 98104-7092

Farris, Vaughan, Wills & Murphy
26th Fl., 700 W. Georgia
Vancouver, BC, Canada

Transfer Agent:
Computershare Trust Company of Canada
510 Burrard St 3rd Fl
Vancouver, BC, V6C 3B9, Canada

CARRY TECHNOLOGY CO., LTD.

5F No 119 Jiankang Rd
235 Junghe, Taipei, Taiwan
Tel.: (886) 282213985
Fax: (886) 282272168
Web Site: www.carry.com.tw
3054—(TAI)
Sales Range: $1-9.9 Million

Business Description:
Portable Multimedia & Storage Products Mfr
S.I.C.: 3572
N.A.I.C.S.: 334112

Personnel:
Jason Chen *(Chm & Gen Mgr)*

CARRY WEALTH HOLDINGS LIMITED

2908 29th Floor Enterprise Square
Three 39 Wang Chiu Road
Kowloon, China (Hong Kong)
Tel.: (852) 23108180
Fax: (852) 23108797
E-Mail: info@carrywealth.com
Web Site: www.carrywealth.com
0643—(HKG)
Rev.: $15,826,936
Assets: $28,684,412
Liabilities: $4,399,774
Net Worth: $24,284,638
Earnings: ($9,268,410)
Emp.: 972
Fiscal Year-end: 12/31/12

Business Description:
Apparel Products Mfr
S.I.C.: 2399
N.A.I.C.S.: 315990

Personnel:
Haifeng Li *(Chm)*
James Sheng Kuang Lee *(Mng Dir)*
Yuk Lan Kung *(Sec)*

Board of Directors:
Haifeng Li
Zhong Fa Chen
Flynn Xuxian Huang
James Sheng Kuang Lee
Charlie Chak Lam Tang
Yong Xiao
Wing Yiu Yau
Feng Zhang

Butterfield Fulcrum Group (Bermuda) Limited
26 Burnaby Street
Hamilton, HM 11, Bermuda

Transfer Agents:
Tricor Abacus Limited
26/F Tesbury Centre 28 Queen's Road East
Hong Kong, China (Hong Kong)

Butterfield Fulcrum Group (Bermuda) Limited
26 Burnaby Street
Hamilton, HM 11, Bermuda

Subsidiaries:

Carry Wealth Limited (1)
Room 2701 27F One Kowloon 1 Wang Yuen Street
Kowloon Bay, Kowloon, China (Hong Kong)
Tel.: (852) 23108180
Fax: (852) 23108797
Emp.: 100
Apparel Products Mfr
S.I.C.: 2259
N.A.I.C.S.: 315190
James Lee *(Mng Dir)*

Topwell Group Development Ltd (1)
Room 2701 27F One Kowloon 1 Wang Yuen Street
Kowloon Bay, Kowloon, China (Hong Kong)
Tel.: (852) 23108180
Fax: (852) 23108797
Emp.: 100
Apparel Products Mfr
S.I.C.: 2259
N.A.I.C.S.: 315190
James Le *(Mgr)*

Non-U.S. Subsidiaries:

PT Aneka Garmentama Indah (1)
Jl Raya Cakung Cilincing Blok F 3-4
10310 Jakarta, Indonesia (95%)
Tel.: (62) 214404224
Fax: (62) 214405212
Broadwoven Fabric Mills
S.I.C.: 2299
N.A.I.C.S.: 313210

PT Caterindo Garment Industri (1)
Jl Nusantara II Blok E 2-3
Tanjung Priuk, 14310 Jakarta, Indonesia (95%)
Tel.: (62) 214356070
Fax: (62) 21498880
Men's & Boys' Clothing Mfr
S.I.C.: 5699
N.A.I.C.S.: 315220

CARS GALORE LTD.

Melton Court Gibson Lane
Melton, East Yorkshire, HU14 3HH, United Kingdom
Tel.: (44) 1482638499
Fax: (44) 1482638527
E-Mail: sales@carsgaloreonline.co.uk
Web Site: www.carsgaloreonline.co.uk
Year Founded: 2005
Sales Range: $25-49.9 Million
Emp.: 6

Business Description:
Used Automobile Purchasing & Retailing Services
S.I.C.: 5012
N.A.I.C.S.: 423110

Personnel:
Noel Parkinson *(Founder & Mng Dir)*

CARSALES.COM LIMITED

Level 4 449 Punt Road
Richmond, VIC, 3121, Australia
Tel.: (61) 390938600
Fax: (61) 390938698
E-Mail: sales@carsales.com.au
Web Site: www.carsales.com.au
CRZ—(ASX OTC)
Rev.: $225,579,219
Assets: $253,387,657
Liabilities: $94,456,986
Net Worth: $158,930,671
Earnings: $87,032,024
Emp.: 385
Fiscal Year-end: 06/30/13

Business Description:
Online Motor Vehicle Advertising Services
S.I.C.: 7319
N.A.I.C.S.: 541890

Personnel:
Greg Roebuck *(CEO & Mng Dir)*
Cameron McIntyre *(CFO & Sec)*
Ajay Bhatia *(CIO)*

Board of Directors:
Wal Pisciotta
Kim Anderson
Jeffrey Browne
Richard Collins
Patrick O'Sullivan
Greg Roebuck

Subsidiaries:

Automotive Data Services Pty. Ltd. (1)
Level 2 111 117 Devonshire St
Surry Hills, New South Wales, 2010, Australia
Tel.: (61) 293107622
Fax: (61) 293107455
E-Mail: info@redbook.com.au
Web Site: www.redbook.com.au
Emp.: 20
Data Processing Services
S.I.C.: 7374
N.A.I.C.S.: 518210
Russ Booth *(Mgr)*

Equipment Research Group Pty. Ltd. (1)
Lvl 4 449 Punt Rd
Richmond, VIC, 3122, Australia
Tel.: (61) 390938766
Fax: (61) 390938791
E-Mail: erg@carsales.com.au
Web Site: www.erginternational.com.au
Emp.: 200
Business Management Services
S.I.C.: 8742
N.A.I.C.S.: 541611

Non-U.S. Subsidiaries:

Red Book Automotive Data Services (Beijing) Limited (1)
No 6 A Gongti North Rd
Chao Yang Dist, Beijing, 100037, China
Tel.: (86) 1051799633
Fax: (86) 85236968
E-Mail: silo.young@redbookasiapacific.com
Web Site: www.redbook.net.cn
Emp.: 7
Data Processing Services
S.I.C.: 7374
N.A.I.C.S.: 518210
Amy Yin *(Gen Mgr)*

Red Book Automotive Services (M) Sdn. Bhd. (1)
A 10 5 Northpoint Offices Mid Vly City No 1
Medan Syed Putra Utara
Kuala Lumpur, 59200, Malaysia
Tel.: (60) 322824599
Fax: (60) 322824559
E-Mail: sookyee@redbookasiapacific.com
Web Site: www.redbookasiapacific.com
Emp.: 6
Data Processing Services
S.I.C.: 7379
N.A.I.C.S.: 518210
Yogananthan Muniandy *(Mgr-Sls)*

CARSON CUMBERBATCH PLC

61 Janadhipathi Mawatha
Colombo, 01, Sri Lanka
Tel.: (94) 114739200
Fax: (94) 114739300
E-Mail: carsons@carcumb.com
Web Site: www.carsoncumberbatch.com
CARS—(COL)
Rev.: $597,872,689
Assets: $1,089,136,977
Liabilities: $549,886,628
Net Worth: $539,250,349
Earnings: $75,369,436
Emp.: 15,097
Fiscal Year-end: 03/31/13

Business Description:
Investment Holding Company
S.I.C.: 6719
N.A.I.C.S.: 551112

Personnel:
Tilak de Zoysa *(Chm)*
Hariharan Selvanathan *(Deputy Chm)*
Suresh Kumar Shah *(CEO-Beverage)*
Palehenalage Chandana Priyankara Tissera *(CEO-Oil Palm)*

Board of Directors:
Tilak de Zoysa
Vijaya Prasanna Malalasekera
Faiz Mohideen
Mangala Moonesinghe
Israel Paulraj
Hariharan Selvanathan
Manoharan Selvanathan
Suresh Kumar Shah
Palehenalage Chandana Priyankara Tissera

Holdings:

Bukit Darah PLC (1)
61 Janadhipathi Mawatha
Colombo, 1, Sri Lanka

Carson Cumberbatch PLC—(Continued)

Tel.: (94) 114739200
Fax: (94) 114739300
E-Mail: carsons@carcumb.com
Web Site: www.carsoncumberbatch.com
BUKI—(COL)
Rev.: $597,859,242
Assets: $1,077,913,864
Liabilities: $550,271,443
Net Worth: $527,642,421
Earnings: $75,285,558
Fiscal Year-end: 03/31/13
Oil Palm Plantation Services
S.I.C.: 2079
N.A.I.C.S.: 311225
Hariharan Selvanathan *(Chm)*
Palehenalage Chandana Priyankara Tissera *(CEO)*
Shalike Karunasena *(CFO)*
Ruvini Fernando *(CEO-Guardian Fund Mgmt)*
Suresh Shah *(CEO-Beverage)*

Carsons Management Services (Private) Limited **(1)**
61 Janadhipathi Mawatha
Colombo, 12337, Sri Lanka
Tel.: (94) 112337665
Investment Management Services
S.I.C.: 6211
N.A.I.C.S.: 523999

Ceylon Guardian Investment Trust PLC **(1)**
No 61 Janadhipathi Mawatha
Colombo, 1, Sri Lanka
Tel.: (94) 112039200
Fax: (94) 112039300
E-Mail: carsons@carcumb.com
Web Site: www.carsoncumberbatch.com
GUAR—(COL)
Sales Range: $1-9.9 Million
Investment Management Services
S.I.C.: 6282
N.A.I.C.S.: 523920
K. Selvanathan *(Exec Dir)*

Ceylon Investment PLC **(1)**
No 61 Janadhipathi Mawatha
1 Colombo, Sri Lanka
Tel.: (94) 114739200
Fax: (94) 114739300
E-Mail: carsons@carcumb.com
Web Site: www.carsoncumberbatch.com
CINV—(COL)
Sales Range: $10-24.9 Million
Investment Management Services
S.I.C.: 6799
N.A.I.C.S.: 523920
Israel Paulraj *(Chm)*

Equity One PLC **(1)**
No 61 Janadhipathi Mawatha
Colombo, 1, Sri Lanka
Tel.: (94) 11 2039200
Fax: (94) 11 2039300
E-Mail: carsons@carcumb.com
Web Site: www.carsoncumberbatch.com
EQIT—(COL)
Sales Range: Less than $1 Million
Emp.: 15
Property Development & Management Services
S.I.C.: 6531
N.A.I.C.S.: 531312
Kurukulasuriya Calisanctus Nalake Fernando *(Exec Dir)*

Equity Two PLC **(1)**
No 61 Janadhipathi Mawatha
Colombo, 01, Sri Lanka
Tel.: (94) 114739200
Fax: (94) 114739300
E-Mail: carsons@carcumb.com
Web Site: www.carsoncumberbatch.com
ETWO—(COL)
Sales Range: Less than $1 Million
Emp.: 4
Real Estate Services
S.I.C.: 6531
N.A.I.C.S.: 531390
Chandima Rajakaruna Gunawardena *(Chm)*

Good Hope PLC **(1)**
61 Janadhipathi Mawatha
Colombo, 1, Sri Lanka
Tel.: (94) 112039200
Fax: (94) 112039300
Web Site: www.goodhopeasia.com
GOOD—(COL)
Rev.: $1,863,982
Assets: $44,949,092
Liabilities: $803,102
Net Worth: $44,145,990
Earnings: $1,150,873
Fiscal Year-end: 03/31/13
Crude Palm Oil Mfr
S.I.C.: 2079
N.A.I.C.S.: 311225
Hariharan Selvanathan *(Chm)*

Guardian Capital Partners PLC **(1)**
No 61 Janadhipathi Mawatha
Colombo, 01, Sri Lanka
Tel.: (94) 112039200
Fax: (94) 112039300
E-Mail: carsons@carcumb.com
Web Site: www.carsoncumberbatch.com
WAPO—(COL)
Rev.: $180,950
Assets: $3,840,377
Liabilities: $47,830
Net Worth: $3,792,547
Earnings: ($265,259)
Fiscal Year-end: 03/31/13
Investment Management Services
S.I.C.: 6282
N.A.I.C.S.: 523920
Israel Paulraj *(Chm)*

Indo-Malay PLC **(1)**
61 Janadhipathi Mawatha
Colombo, 1, Sri Lanka
Tel.: (94) 112039200
Fax: (94) 112039300
E-Mail: carsons@carcumb.com
Web Site: www.carsoncumberbatch.com
INDO—(COL)
Rev.: $1,918,901
Assets: $43,789,577
Liabilities: $563,913
Net Worth: $43,225,664
Earnings: $1,198,624
Fiscal Year-end: 03/31/13
Crude Palm Oil Mfr
S.I.C.: 2079
N.A.I.C.S.: 311225
Hariharan Selvanathan *(Chm)*

Pegasus Hotels of Ceylon PLC **(1)**
No 61 Janadhipathi Mawatha
Colombo, 01, Sri Lanka
Tel.: (94) 112039200
Fax: (94) 112039300
E-Mail: carsons@carcumb.com
Web Site: www.carsoncumberbatch.com
PEG—(COL)
Rev.: $3,871,494
Assets: $11,818,175
Liabilities: $1,278,459
Net Worth: $10,539,716
Earnings: $1,114,410
Emp.: 245
Fiscal Year-end: 03/31/13
Hotel Services
S.I.C.: 7011
N.A.I.C.S.: 721110
Hari Selvanathan *(Exec Dir)*

Selinsing PLC **(1)**
61 Janadhipathi Mawatha
Colombo, 1, Sri Lanka
Tel.: (94) 112039200
Fax: (94) 112039300
E-Mail: carsons@carcumb.com
Web Site: www.carsoncumberbatch.com
SELI—(COL)
Rev.: $3,240,606
Assets: $51,752,106
Liabilities: $883,698
Net Worth: $50,868,408
Earnings: $2,020,566
Fiscal Year-end: 03/31/13
Crude Palm Oil Producer
S.I.C.: 2079
N.A.I.C.S.: 311225
Manoharan Selvanathan *(Chm)*

Shalimar (Malay) PLC **(1)**
61 Janadhipathi Mawatha
Colombo, 1, Sri Lanka
Tel.: (94) 114739200
Fax: (94) 114739300
E-Mail: carsons@carcumb.com
Web Site: www.carsoncumberbatch.com
SHAL—(COL)
Rev.: $2,294,940
Assets: $44,243,424
Liabilities: $607,880
Net Worth: $43,635,544
Earnings: $1,404,687
Fiscal Year-end: 03/31/13
Crude Palm Oil Producer
S.I.C.: 2079
N.A.I.C.S.: 311225
Hariharan Selvanathan *(Chm)*

Non-U.S. Holding:

Goodhope Asia Holdings Ltd **(1)**
Robinson Rd 17-00 AIA Tower
Singapore, 048542, Singapore
Tel.: (65) 65351944
Web Site: www.goodhopeasia.com
Palm Oil Processing Services
S.I.C.: 2075
N.A.I.C.S.: 311224
Christoforus Pakadang *(Head-Risk Mgmt & Dir-Local External Rels)*

Non-U.S. Subsidiaries:

Agro Harapan Lestari Sdn. Bhd **(2)**
Suite 3 02 3rd Floor Wisma E and C 2
Lorong Dungun Kiri
Damansara Heights, Kuala Lumpur, 50490, Malaysia
Tel.: (60) 320934660
Fax: (60) 3 2093 5660
E-Mail: reachus@goodhope-sg.com
Web Site: www.goodhopeasia.com
Emp.: 50
Palm Oil Plantation Services
S.I.C.: 2075
N.A.I.C.S.: 311224
Sanjeev Abeynayake *(Gen Mgr)*

Premier Nalfin Berhad **(2)**
Level 27 Wisma Tun Sambanthan No 2
Jalan Sultan Sulaiman
50000 Kuala Lumpur, Malaysia
Tel.: (60) 322735033
Fax: (60) 322734340
E-Mail: enquiry@premium-kl.com
Web Site: www.premiumveg.com
PRNB—(KLS)
Specialty Fats Mfr for Confectionery
S.I.C.: 2079
N.A.I.C.S.: 311224
Hariharan Selvanathan *(Deputy Chm)*
Anandaraj K.R. Somasundram *(CEO)*

PT Agro Harapan Lestari **(2)**
16th Floor Unit C D Jl Jend Gatot Subroto Kav 27
Jakarta, 12950, Indonesia
Tel.: (62) 21 52892260
Fax: (62) 21 52892259
Web Site: www.goodhopeasia.com
Palm Oil Plantation Services
S.I.C.: 2079
N.A.I.C.S.: 311224

Subsidiary:

PT Agro Indomas **(3)**
Jalan P Antasari II No 26
PO Box 233
Sampit, Central Kalimantan, Indonesia
Tel.: (62) 542593560
Fax: (62) 542594500
Palm Oil Plantation Services
S.I.C.: 0721
N.A.I.C.S.: 115112

CARTAMUNDI N.V.

Vibeekstraat 22
Turnhout, 2300, Belgium
Tel.: (32) 14 42 0201
Fax: (32) 14 42 8254
E-Mail: info@cartamundi.com
Web Site: www.cartamundi.com
Year Founded: 1970
Sales Range: $100-124.9 Million
Emp.: 1,200

Business Description:
Mfr Playing, Tarot Cards & Cards for Games
S.I.C.: 3944
N.A.I.C.S.: 339930

Personnel:
Philippe de Somer *(Chm & Pres)*
Chris Van Doorslaer *(CEO & Mng Dir)*
Jean-Louis de Cartier de Marchienne *(Mng Dir)*

Board of Directors:
Philippe de Somer
John Boks
Emile de Cartier de Marchienne
Jean-Louis de Cartier de Marchienne
Frederic de Somer
Jan Jacobs

U.S. Subsidiary:

Carta Mundi, Inc. **(1)**
4809 S Westmoreland Rd
Dallas, TX 75237-1619
Tel.: (423) 279-9200
Fax: (423) 279-9201
Toll Free: (800) 892-2782
E-Mail: info@cartamundiusa.com
Web Site: www.cartamundiusa.com
Emp.: 100
Playing Cards Mfr
S.I.C.: 5092
N.A.I.C.S.: 423920
Chris Doorslaer *(CEO)*

Non-U.S. Subsidiaries:

Carta Mundi Asia Pacific Pte. Ltd. **(1)**
161B Telok Ayer St
068615 Singapore, Singapore (100%)
Tel.: (65) 62273292
Fax: (65) 62342706
E-Mail: info.asia@cartamundi.com
Emp.: 10
Game Toy & Childrens Vehicle Mfr
S.I.C.: 3942
N.A.I.C.S.: 339930
Stefan Magnus *(Mng Dir)*

Carta Mundi Hungary Kft. **(1)**
Margit Krt 43-45
1024 Budapest, Hungary (100%)
Tel.: (36) 13189430
Fax: (36) 13180918
E-Mail: info.hungary@cartamundi.com
Emp.: 3
Durable Goods Whslr
S.I.C.: 5099
N.A.I.C.S.: 423990
Peter Bako *(Mng Dir)*

Carta Mundi UK Ltd. **(1)**
Units 8-17 Sandhurst Kings Rd
Charfleets Industrial Est, Canvey, Essex, SS8OQY, United Kingdom (100%)
Tel.: (44) 1268511522
Fax: (44) 1268510337
E-Mail: info@cartamundi.co.uk
Web Site: www.cartamundi.co.uk
Emp.: 65
Retailers Stores
S.I.C.: 5999
N.A.I.C.S.: 453998
Paul Roberts *(Mng Dir)*

Spielkartenfabrik Altenburg GmbH **(1)**
Leipziger Strasse 7
Altenburg, 04600 Leipzig, Germany
Tel.: (49) 34475820
Fax: (49) 3447582109
E-Mail: info@spielkarten.com
Web Site: www.spielkarten.com
Emp.: 125
Game Toy & Childrens Vehicle Mfr
S.I.C.: 3944
N.A.I.C.S.: 339930
Gerd Matthes *(Mng Dir)*

CARTE INTERNATIONAL INC.

1995 Logan Avenue
Winnipeg, MB, R2R 0H8, Canada
Tel.: (204) 633-7220
Fax: (204) 694-0614
Web Site: www.carteinternational.com
Year Founded: 1973
Rev.: $36,516,879
Emp.: 200

Business Description:
Electrical Utilities Mfr & Distr
S.I.C.: 3677

N.A.I.C.S.: 334416
Personnel:
Brian Klaponski *(Pres & CEO)*

CARTER DODGE CHRYSLER LTD

4650 Lougheed Hwy
Burnaby, BC, V5C 4A6, Canada
Tel.: (604) 299-9181
Fax: (604) 299-3116
Toll Free: (800) 667-5877
E-Mail: info@carterdodgechrysler.com
Web Site: www.carterdodgechrysler.com
Year Founded: 1960
Rev.: $33,495,059
Emp.: 70
Business Description:
New & Used Car Dealer
S.I.C.: 5511
N.A.I.C.S.: 441110
Personnel:
Bill Mitchell *(Pres & CEO)*

CARTER MOTOR CARS LTD

(d/b/a Carter Honda)
2390 Burrard St
Vancouver, BC, V6J 3J1, Canada
Tel.: (604) 736-2821
Fax: (604) 736-2828
Toll Free: (888) 693-5985
E-Mail: info@carterhonda.com
Web Site: www.cartermotorcars.com
Year Founded: 1984
Rev.: $59,731,181
Emp.: 115
Business Description:
New & Used Car Dealers
S.I.C.: 5511
N.A.I.C.S.: 441110
Personnel:
Bill Mitchell *(Pres & CEO)*

CARTERA INDUSTRIAL REA, S.A.

C/ Hermosilla 34 1
28002 Madrid, Spain
Tel.: (34) 91 7817387
Fax: (34) 91 5774543
E-Mail: contacto@carteraindustrialrea.com
Web Site: www.carteraindustrialrea.com
REA—(MAD)
Business Description:
Investment Services
S.I.C.: 6211
N.A.I.C.S.: 523999
Personnel:
Manuel Arredondo Brana *(Gen Dir)*

CARTHEW BAY TECHNOLOGIES INC.

181 Bay Street Suite 2500
Toronto, ON, M5J 2T7, Canada
Tel.: (416) 307-4015
Fax: (416) 365-1719
E-Mail: mliik@carthewbaytechnologies.com
Web Site: www.carthewbaytechnologies.com
CWBYF—(OTC)
Sales Range: Less than $1 Million
Business Description:
Investment Services
S.I.C.: 6211
N.A.I.C.S.: 523999
Personnel:
Michael M. Liik *(Pres & CEO)*
Brian D. Clewes *(CFO, Treas & Sec)*
Board of Directors:
Christopher Besant
Richard Callander
Brian D. Clewes
Howard M. Drabinsky
Arthur E. Laudenslager
Michael M. Liik

CARTIER IRON CORPORATION

20 Adelaide Street East Suite 301
Toronto, ON, M5C 1K6, Canada
Tel.: (416) 360-8006
Fax: (416) 361-1333
E-Mail: info@cartieriron.com
Web Site: www.cartieriron.com
CFE—(CNSX)
Assets: $1,862,750
Liabilities: $241,234
Net Worth: $1,621,516
Earnings: ($352,738)
Fiscal Year-end: 12/31/12
Business Description:
Iron Ore Mining
S.I.C.: 1011
N.A.I.C.S.: 212210
Personnel:
John Langton *(Pres)*
Miles Nagamatsu *(CFO)*
Jorge Estepa *(Sec & VP)*
Board of Directors:
Alexander Horvath
Marcus Moser
Miles Nagamatsu
Legal Counsel:
Sheldon Huxtable Professional Corporation
180 Dundas Street West Suite1801
Toronto, ON, Canada
Transfer Agent:
Equity Financial Trust Company
200 University Avenue Suite 400
Toronto, ON, M5H 4H1, Canada
Tel.: (416) 361-0152
Fax: (416) 361-0470
Toll Free: (866) 393-4891

CARTIER RESOURCES INC.

1740 Sullivan Road Suite 1000
Val d'Or, QC, J9P 7H1, Canada
Tel.: (819) 874-1331
Fax: (819) 874-3113
Toll Free: (877) 874-1331
E-Mail: info@ressourcescartier.com
Web Site: www.ressourcescartier.com
Year Founded: 2006
ECR—(TSXV)
Rev.: $26,652
Assets: $13,182,583
Liabilities: $2,632,854
Net Worth: $10,549,729
Earnings: ($2,116,215)
Fiscal Year-end: 12/31/12
Business Description:
Mineral Exploration Services
S.I.C.: 1081
N.A.I.C.S.: 213114
Personnel:
Philippe Cloutier *(Chm, Pres & CEO)*
Jean-Yves Laliberte *(CFO & Sec)*
Board of Directors:
Philippe Cloutier
Jean Carriere
Mario Jacob
Jean-Yves Laliberte
Daniel Masse
Legal Counsel:
Miller Thomson Pouliot SENCRL / LLP
La Tour CIBC Floor 31st 1155 Rene-Levesque Blvd W
Montreal, QC, Canada
Transfer Agent:
Computershare Inc.
1500 University Street Suite 700
Montreal, QC, Canada

CARTIER SAADA

285-291 Industrial Area Sidi Ghanem
40110 Marrakech, Morocco
Tel.: (212) 524 336 868
Fax: (212) 524 335 074
Web Site: www.cartiersaada.com
Year Founded: 1947
CRS—(CAS)
Business Description:
Food Preservation Services
S.I.C.: 5148
N.A.I.C.S.: 424480
Personnel:
Pierre Cartier *(Chm)*

CARTIERA LUCCHESE S.P.A.

(d/b/a Lucart Group)
Via Ciarpi 77
55016 Porcari, LU, Italy
Tel.: (39) 0583 2140
Fax: (39) 0583 299051
E-Mail: info@lucartgroup.com
Web Site: www.lucartgroup.com
Year Founded: 1953
Sales Range: $550-599.9 Million
Emp.: 1,400
Business Description:
Machine-Glazed Packaging Paper, Tissue Paper & Converted Paper Products Mfr & Distr
S.I.C.: 2621
N.A.I.C.S.: 322121
Personnel:
Massimo Pasquini *(CEO)*
Subsidiaries:

Fato Professional S.p.A. **(1)**
Via Galileo Galilei 4
Torre di Mosto, IT-30020 Santo Stino di Livenza, VE, Italy IT
Tel.: (39) 390421 312 811 (100%)
Fax: (39) 0421 473 757
E-Mail: fato@fato.com
Web Site: www.fato.com
Converted Machine-Glazed Packaging & Tissue Paper Products Mfr
S.I.C.: 2679
N.A.I.C.S.: 322299
Tommaso De Luca *(Controller-Data)*

Airtissue S.r.l. **(1)**
Via Boccardo 1
IT-16121 Genoa, Italy IT
Tel.: (39) 010 55411 (100%)
Fax: (39) 010 5531764
E-Mail: info.marketing@tenderly.it
Web Site: www.tenderly.it
Sales Range: $125-149.9 Million
Emp.: 300
Tissue Paper Products Mfr
S.I.C.: 2676
N.A.I.C.S.: 322291
Fabio Patrucci *(Mgr-Fin)*

Non-U.S. Subsidiaries:

Lucart France SAS **(1)**
ZI de Torvilliers RN 60
La Riviere-de-Corps, F-10440 Troyes, France FR
Tel.: (33) 3 2579 0606 (100%)
Fax: (33) 3 2579 3838
Tissue Paper & Converted Tissue Paper Products Mfr
S.I.C.: 2621
N.A.I.C.S.: 322121

Lucart Iberica S.L.U. **(1)**
Calle Trafalgar 4 10th andar
ES-08010 Barcelona, Spain ES
Tel.: (34) 93 268 0440 (100%)
Fax: (34) 93 268 3113
Paper Products Whslr
S.I.C.: 5113
N.A.I.C.S.: 424130

Novatissue SAS **(1)**
10 Rue Maurice Mougeot
BP 35
F-88600 Laval, France FR
Tel.: (33) 3 2955 7878 (100%)
Fax: (33) 3 2955 7887
Web Site: www.novatissue.com
Emp.: 230
Tissue Paper & Converted Tissue Paper Products Mfr
S.I.C.: 2621
N.A.I.C.S.: 322121
Kraemer Herve *(Mgr)*

CARTRIDGE SAVE LIMITED

5-6 Gregson Road
Stockport, SK5 7SS, United Kingdom
Tel.: (44) 161 968 5994
Fax: (44) 845 6868 556
Web Site: www.cartridgesave.co.uk
Year Founded: 2003
Sales Range: $10-24.9 Million
Emp.: 33
Business Description:
Printer Cartridge Whslr
S.I.C.: 5112
N.A.I.C.S.: 424120
Personnel:
Ian Cowley *(Mng Dir)*

CARTU GROUP JSC

39a Chavchavadze Avenue
Tbilisi, 0162, Georgia
Tel.: (995) 32 292 5592
Fax: (995) 32 291 2279
Web Site:
Emp.: 295
Business Description:
Bank Holding Company
S.I.C.: 6712
N.A.I.C.S.: 551111
Personnel:
Nodar Javakhishvili *(Dir Gen-Cartu Bank)*
Subsidiary:

Cartu Bank JSC **(1)**
39a Chavchavadze Avenue
Tbilisi, 0162, Georgia GE
Tel.: (995) 322925592 (100%)
Fax: (995) 322912279
E-Mail: info@cartubank.ge
Web Site: www.cartubank.ge
Int. Income: $22,835,914
Assets: $251,476,348
Liabilities: $142,972,025
Net Worth: $108,504,323
Earnings: ($7,842,467)
Fiscal Year-end: 12/31/12
Retail & Commercial Banking
S.I.C.: 6029
N.A.I.C.S.: 522110
Nodar Javakhishvili *(Chm-Supervisory Bd & Dir Gen)*
Nato Khaindrava *(First Deputy Dir Gen)*
David Galuashvili *(Deputy Dir Gen)*

CARWOOD MOTOR UNITS LTD

Herald Way
Binley, Coventry, CV3 2RQ, United Kingdom
Tel.: (44) 2476449533
Fax: (44) 2476452074
E-Mail: carwood@carwood.co.uk
Web Site: www.carwood.co.uk
Year Founded: 1966
Rev.: $26,892,591
Emp.: 110
Business Description:
Vehicle Parts Mfr
S.I.C.: 3714
N.A.I.C.S.: 336390
Personnel:
Gary Carter *(Founder & Chm)*
Kevin Mulholland *(Mng Dir)*
Peter Boardman *(Sec & Dir-Fin)*

CASA DEL MAR BEACH RESORT N.V.

LG Smith Boulevard 51-53
Oranjestad, Aruba
Tel.: (297) 5827000
Fax: (297) 5834871

Casa Del Mar Beach Resort N.V.—(Continued)

E-Mail: cdmrs@setarnet.aw
Web Site: www.casadelmar-aruba.com
Emp.: 220
Business Description:
Resort & Hotel
S.I.C.: 7011
N.A.I.C.S.: 721110
Personnel:
Aisa van der Biezen *(Gen Mgr)*

CASA HOLDINGS LTD.

15 Kian Teck Crescent
Singapore, 628884, Singapore
Tel.: (65) 62680066
Fax: (65) 62668069
E-Mail: service@casa.com.sg
Web Site: www.casaholdings.com.sg
Year Founded: 1976
C04—(SES)
Sls.: $24,801,187
Assets: $49,650,277
Liabilities: $7,128,026
Net Worth: $42,522,251
Earnings: $7,562,350
Emp.: 559
Fiscal Year-end: 09/30/12
Business Description:
Holding Company; Household Appliances, Electronic Goods & Building Materials Distr
S.I.C.: 6719
N.A.I.C.S.: 551112
Personnel:
Soo Kong Lim *(Chm & CEO)*
Margaret Lee Hung Chak *(Co-Sec & Controller-Fin)*
Lotus Isabella Mei Hua Lim *(Co-Sec)*
Board of Directors:
Soo Kong Lim
Zhong Huai Hu
Stefan Matthieu Shing Yuan Lim
Yian Poh Lim
Seow Chay Low

CASABLANCA GROUP LIMITED

5/F Yan Hing Centre 9-13 Wong Chuk Yeung Steet
Fo Tan, Sha Tin, China (Hong Kong)
Tel.: (852) 2306 1699
Fax: (852) 2351 1933
E-Mail: info@casablanca.com.hk
Web Site: www.casablanca.com.hk
Year Founded: 1993
2223—(HKG)
Sales Range: $50-74.9 Million
Business Description:
Bedding Products Mfr & Distr
S.I.C.: 2399
N.A.I.C.S.: 314999
Personnel:
Sze Kin Cheng *(Chm)*
Sze Tsan Cheng *(Vice Chm)*
Shuk Ka Sung *(CEO)*
Board of Directors:
Sze Kin Cheng
Sze Tsan Cheng
Lin Cheong Leung
Kai Fat Li
Shuk Ka Sung
Yat Hong Tse
Pik Hung Wong

CASCADE BREWERY COMPANY

131 Cascade Road
South Hobart, Hobart, Tasmania, 7004, Australia
Tel.: (61) 362218300
Fax: (61) 362218379
E-Mail: ron.brady@fostersgroup.com
Web Site: www.cascade.com.au
Emp.: 130
Business Description:
Brewery
S.I.C.: 2082
N.A.I.C.S.: 312120
Personnel:
Ron Brady *(Mgr-Sls)*

CASCADE CORPORATION

(Acquired by Toyota Industries Corporation)

CASCADERO COPPER CORPORATION

590 Esat Kings Rd
North Vancouver, BC, V7N 1J3, Canada
Tel.: (604) 924-5504
Fax: (604) 924-5506
Web Site: www.cascadero.com
Year Founded: 2003
CCD—(TSXV)
Rev.: $191,207
Assets: $14,446,598
Liabilities: $446,574
Net Worth: $14,000,024
Earnings: ($1,316,879)
Fiscal Year-end: 11/30/12
Business Description:
Mineral Properties Exploration Services
S.I.C.: 1081
N.A.I.C.S.: 213114
Personnel:
Bill McWilliam *(Pres & CEO)*
Sharon Lewis *(CFO)*
Board of Directors:
Julio L. Carvalho
Brian F. Causey
Michael A. Denega
John G. Haag
Bill McWilliam
Juvenal Mesquita Filho
Legal Counsel:
Wilcox & Company Law Corporation
Suite 1910 777 Hornby Street
Vancouver, BC, Canada
Transfer Agent:
Computershare Trust Company
Suite 600 530 8th Avenue SW
Calgary, AB, Canada
Non-U.S. Subsidiary:

Salta Exploraciones S.A. (1)
Pasaje Franco Sosa 490
4400 Salta, Argentina
Tel.: (54) 387 4950717
Fax: (54) 387 4398785
Emp.: 9
Gold Mining Services
S.I.C.: 1041
N.A.I.C.S.: 212221
William James McWilliam *(Co-Founder & CEO)*

CASCADES INC.

404 Marie-Victorin Blvd
Kingsey Falls, QC, J0A 1B0, Canada
Tel.: (819) 363-5100
Fax: (819) 363-5155
E-Mail: info@cascades.com
Web Site: www.cascades.com
Year Founded: 1964
CAS—(TSX)
Sls.: $3,623,202,900
Assets: $3,671,909,880
Liabilities: $2,584,452,000
Net Worth: $1,087,457,880
Earnings: ($10,934,220)
Emp.: 12,000
Fiscal Year-end: 12/31/12
Business Description:
Boxboard, Fine Papers, Tissue Papers, Containerboard & Specialty Products Mfr
S.I.C.: 2653
N.A.I.C.S.: 322211
Personnel:
Alain Lemaire *(Chm)*
Laurent Lemaire *(Vice Chm)*
Mario Plourde *(Pres & CEO)*
Allan Hogg *(CFO & VP)*
Board of Directors:
Alain Lemaire
Paul R. Bannerman
Robert Chevrier
Andre Desaulniers
James B. C. Doak
Louis Garneau
Bernard Lemaire
Laurent Lemaire
Sylvie Lemaire
David McAusland
Martin P. Pelletier
Laurent Verreault
Transfer Agent:
Computershare Investor Services Inc.
1500 University St 7th Floor
Montreal, QC, Canada
Groups:

Cascades Boxboard Group Inc. (1)
1061 Tarent St
Saint-Bruno, QC, J3V 6R7, Canada (100%)
Tel.: (450) 461-8600
Fax: (450) 461-8636
E-Mail: info@norampac.com
Web Site: www.cascades.com
Emp.: 150
Boxboard Mfr
S.I.C.: 2631
N.A.I.C.S.: 322130
Yves Menard *(Gen Mgr-Eastern Canada)*

Subsidiary:

Norampac Inc. (2)
1061 rue Parent
Saint-Bruno, QC, J3V 6R7, Canada
Tel.: (450) 461-8600
Fax: (450) 461-8636
E-Mail: info@norampac.com
Web Site: www.cascades.com
Sales Range: $1-4.9 Billion
Emp.: 4,500
Packaging Materials Mfr
S.I.C.: 2657
N.A.I.C.S.: 322212
Marc-Andre Depin *(Pres & CEO)*
Charles Malo *(COO & VP)*

Plants:

Norampac Inc. - Drummondville (3)
600 Rue Janelle St
Drummondville, QC, J2C 5Z3, Canada
Tel.: (819) 475-4567
Fax: (819) 475-4579
E-Mail: maria-gorete_rodrigues@norampac.com
Web Site: www.norampac.com
Sales Range: $25-49.9 Million
Emp.: 180
Carton Box Mfr
S.I.C.: 2631
N.A.I.C.S.: 322130
Jean Denis Gravel *(Controller)*

Norampac Inc. - Newfoundland (3)
110 Clyde Ave Donovans Industrial Park
CP 8875
Saint John's, NL, A1B 3T2, Canada
Tel.: (709) 747-1200
Fax: (709) 747-6866
E-Mail: lana_littlejohn@norampac.com
Web Site: www.cascades.com
Emp.: 65
Corrugated Packaging Container Mfr
S.I.C.: 2653
N.A.I.C.S.: 322211
Lana LittleJohn *(Gen Mgr)*

Norampac Inc. - Vaudreuil (3)
400 Forbes St
Vaudreuil-Dorion, QC, J7V 6N8, Canada
Tel.: (450) 455-5731
Fax: (450) 455-7662
E-Mail: andre_therrien@norampac.com
Web Site: www.norampac.com
Sales Range: $150-199.9 Million
Emp.: 170
S.I.C.: 2631
N.A.I.C.S.: 322130
Francoif Goulet *(Dir-Sls)*

Norampac Inc. - Viau (3)
2755 Viau
Montreal, QC, H1V 3J4, Canada
Tel.: (514) 251-3800
Web Site: www.norampac.com
Emp.: 275
Corrugated Packaging Products Mfr
S.I.C.: 2653
N.A.I.C.S.: 322211

U.S. Subsidiaries:

Norampac Industries Inc. (3)
4001 Packard Rd
Niagara Falls, NY 14303 NY
Tel.: (716) 285-3681
Fax: (716) 285-3767
Web Site: www.norampac.com
Emp.: 200
Corrugated Medium Paper Mfr
S.I.C.: 2631
N.A.I.C.S.: 322130
Danick Lavoie *(Gen Mgr)*

Plant:

Norampac Industries Inc. - Lancaster (4)
4444 Walden Ave
Lancaster, NY 14086
Tel.: (716) 651-2000
Fax: (716) 651-4444
Toll Free: (800) 333-6525
Web Site: www.cascades.com
Emp.: 125
Corrugated Packaging Container Mfr
S.I.C.: 2653
N.A.I.C.S.: 322211

Norampac New England Inc. (3)
720 Thompson Rd CP 246
Thompson, CT 06277
Tel.: (860) 923-9563
Fax: (860) 923-3707
Web Site: www.cascades.com
Emp.: 75
Corrugated Packaging Container Mfr
S.I.C.: 2653
N.A.I.C.S.: 322211
Jason Corrigan *(Gen Mgr)*

Norampac New York City Inc. (3)
55-15 Grand Ave
Maspeth, NY 11378 NY
Tel.: (718) 386-3200
Fax: (718) 386-7370
Web Site: www.cascades.com
Emp.: 148
Corrugated Product Mfr
S.I.C.: 2653
N.A.I.C.S.: 322211

Norampac Schenectady Inc. (3)
Bldg 801 Corporation Park
Schenectady, NY 12302 NY
Tel.: (518) 346-6151
Fax: (518) 346-8504
Web Site: www.cascades.com
Emp.: 150
Corrugated Packaging Box Mfr
S.I.C.: 2653
N.A.I.C.S.: 322211
Craig Griffith *(Gen Mgr)*

Plants:

Cascades Boxboard Group Inc. - Cobourg (2)
Building 1E Northon Industrial Park
Cobourg, ON, K9A 4L1, Canada
Tel.: (905) 372-5199
Fax: (905) 372-4663
Web Site: www.cascades.com
Emp.: 85
Boxboard Container Mfr
S.I.C.: 2657
N.A.I.C.S.: 322212
Alain Levac *(Gen Mgr)*

Cascades Boxboard Group Inc. - East Angus (2)
2 Rue Angus Nord
CP 2001
East Angus, QC, Canada J0B 1R0
Tel.: (819) 832-5300
Fax: (819) 832-4756
Emp.: 84

Coated Boxboard Mfr
S.I.C.: 2631
N.A.I.C.S.: 322130

Cascades Boxboard Group Inc. - Lachute (2)
695 Cristini Blvd
Lachute, QC, J8H 4N6, Canada
Tel.: (450) 566-3200
Fax: (450) 566-3255
Emp.: 150
Paperboard & Box Mfr
S.I.C.: 2631
N.A.I.C.S.: 322130
Stephane Provost *(Plant Mgr)*

Cascades Boxboard Group Inc. - Mississauga (2)
7830 Tranmere Drive
Mississauga, ON, L5S 1L9, Canada
Tel.: (905) 678-8211
Fax: (905) 678-7462
Emp.: 200
Folding Carton Mfr
S.I.C.: 2631
N.A.I.C.S.: 322130

Cascades Boxboard Group Inc. - Winnipeg (2)
531 Golspie
Winnipeg, MB, R2K 2T9, Canada
Tel.: (204) 667-6600
Fax: (204) 663-1812
Toll Free: (877) 592-7696
Web Site: www.cascades.com
Emp.: 191
Folding Cartons Mfr
S.I.C.: 2657
N.A.I.C.S.: 322212
Herb Vielhaber *(Gen Mgr)*

Cascades Groupe Carton Plat Jonquiere (2)
4010 Chemim St Andre
Jonquiere, QC, G7S 5K5, Canada (100%)
Tel.: (418) 542-9544
Fax: (418) 542-5846
E-Mail: achats_jonquiere@cascades.com
Web Site: www.cascades.com
Emp.: 130
S.I.C.: 2631
N.A.I.C.S.: 322130
Nancy Servais *(Controller)*

Non-U.S. Subsidiary:

Cascades S.A.S. (2)
Avenue Maurice Franck
F-73110 Paris, France FR
Tel.: (33) 4 7965 3232 (100%)
Fax: (33) 4 7965 3235
E-Mail: info@cascades-europe.com
Emp.: 331
Cartons & Packaging Materials Mfr
S.I.C.: 2631
N.A.I.C.S.: 322130
Stephane Thiollier *(Pres/CEO-Careo)*

Non-U.S. Subsidiary:

Cascades Djupafors A.B. (3)
Haggatorpsvagen 45
PO Box 501
37225 Ronneby, Sweden
Tel.: (46) 457461700
Fax: (46) 457461774
E-Mail: sweden@cascades-europe.com
Web Site: www.cascades.com
Emp.: 150
Mfr. of Cartons & Packaging Materials
S.I.C.: 2657
N.A.I.C.S.: 322212
Lennart Larsson *(Mng Dir)*

Non-U.S. Holding:

Reno de Medici S.p.A. (3)
Via Durini 18
20122 Milan, Italy IT
Tel.: (39) 02 89966 111 (57.6%)
Fax: (39) 02 89966 200
E-Mail: info@rdmgroup.com
Web Site: www.renodemedici.it
RM—(ITA)
Rev.: $627,744,648
Assets: $558,888,053
Liabilities: $374,836,998
Net Worth: $184,051,055
Earnings: ($16,405,774)
Emp.: 1,430
Fiscal Year-end: 12/31/12
Cardboard Mfr
S.I.C.: 2679
N.A.I.C.S.: 322299
Robert Hall *(Chm)*
Giuseppe Garofano *(Deputy Chm)*
Ignazio Capuano *(CEO)*

Subsidiaries:

Careo S.r.l. (4)
Via Durini 18
IT-20122 Milan, Italy IT
Tel.: (39) 02 8996 6411 (70%)
Fax: (39) 02 8996 6401
E-Mail: contact@careo.biz
Web Site: www.careo.biz
Emp.: 2,400
Recycled Cartonboard & Folding Carton Mfr & Whslr
S.I.C.: 2657
N.A.I.C.S.: 322212
Stephane Thiollier *(Pres & CEO)*

Non-U.S. Subsidiaries:

Careo GmbH (5)
Uerdinger Strasse 99
47799 Krefeld, Germany De
Tel.: (49) 2151629390
Fax: (49) 2151629391O
E-Mail: info@careo.biz
Web Site: www.careo.biz
Emp.: 9
Cartons & Packaging Materials Mfr & Whslr
S.I.C.: 2657
N.A.I.C.S.: 322212
Holger Breuker *(Dir-Sls)*

Careo Kft (5)
Otvos Janos u 3
1119 Budapest, Hungary HU
Tel.: (36) 1 392 7259
Fax: (36) 1 392 7262
E-Mail: cascades@mail.kerszov.hu
Web Site: www.careo.biz
Emp.: 3
Cartons & Packaging Materials Whslr
S.I.C.: 5113
N.A.I.C.S.: 424130

Careo Limited (5)
Pacific Avenue Parkway
Wednesbury, W Midlands, WS10 7WS, United Kingdom UK
Tel.: (44) 121 505 9810
Fax: (44) 121 505 9811
E-Mail: sales@careo.biz
Web Site: www.careo.biz
Emp.: 35
Cartons & Packaging Materials Whslr
S.I.C.: 5113
N.A.I.C.S.: 424130
Brian Humphreys *(Mng Dir)*

Careo Sp. z o.o. (5)
Altowa 6
PL 02-386 Warsaw, Poland PL
Tel.: (48) 22 589 8700
Fax: (48) 22 867 5002
E-Mail:
Web Site: www.careo.biz
Emp.: 50
Cartons & Packaging Materials Whslr
S.I.C.: 5113
N.A.I.C.S.: 424130
Ewa Etmanowicz *(Mng Dir)*

Careo s.r.o. (5)
Jinonicka 80
CZ 15800 Prague, 5, Czech Republic CZ
Tel.: (420) 257290298
Fax: (420) 257290411
E-Mail:
Web Site: www.careo.biz
Emp.: 3
Cartons & Packaging Materials Whslr
S.I.C.: 5113
N.A.I.C.S.: 424130

Emmaus Pack S.r.L. (4)
via Rome 151
Marcallo Con Casone, 20010 Milan, Italy (51.39%)
Tel.: (39) 029760644
Fax: (39) 02 976 19 73
E-Mail: emmaus@renodemedici.it
Cardboard Mfr & Distr
S.I.C.: 2679
N.A.I.C.S.: 322299

Non-U.S. Subsidiary:

Reno de Medici Iberica S.L. (4)
Selvia No 2 floor 3 Office 1
08820 El Prat de Llobregat, Spain ES
Tel.: (34) 934759100 (100%)
Fax: (34) 934759152
E-Mail: renodemedici@careo.es
Web Site: www.careo.biz
Emp.: 9
Cardboard Distr
S.I.C.: 5113
N.A.I.C.S.: 424130
Roverto Novera *(Mgr-Fin)*

Cascades Specialty Products Group (1)
404 Marie-Victorin Boulevard
PO Box 30
Kingsey Falls, QC, J0A 1B0, Canada
Tel.: (819) 363-5100
Fax: (819) 363-5125
E-Mail: info@cascades.com
Emp.: 50
Industrial Packaging, Consumer Product Packaging, Specialty Papers & Recycled Paper & Plastic Products
S.I.C.: 2657
N.A.I.C.S.: 322212
Luc Langevin *(Pres & COO)*

Subsidiaries:

Cascades Conversion, Inc. (2)
457 Marie Victorin St
Kingsey Falls, QC, J0A 1B0, Canada (100%)
Tel.: (819) 363-5400
Fax: (819) 363-5455
E-Mail: reception_conversion@cascades.com
Emp.: 85
Headers & Cardboard Mfr
S.I.C.: 2631
N.A.I.C.S.: 322130

Cascades East Angus, Inc. (2)
248 Rue Wagner
East Angus, QC, J0B 1R0, Canada (100%)
Tel.: (819) 832-2451
Fax: (819) 832-3406
Web Site: www.cascade.com
Sales Range: $50-74.9 Million
Emp.: 300
Paper Board Mill
S.I.C.: 2631
N.A.I.C.S.: 322130
Paul Deraiche *(Pres)*

Cascades Enviropac Inc (2)
541 Melchers Street
Berthierville, QC, J0K 1A0, Canada
Tel.: (450) 836-1799
Fax: (450) 836-8235
Toll Free: (866) 836-1799
E-Mail: enviropac@cascades.com
Emp.: 46
Honeycomb Packaging Products Mfr
S.I.C.: 2671
N.A.I.C.S.: 322220

Plant:

Cascades Enviropac St-Cesaire (3)
1850 Avenue e l'union
Saint Cesaire, QC, J0L 1T0, Canada
Tel.: (450) 469-3389
Fax: (450) 469-1314
E-Mail: enviropac@cascades.com
Web Site: www.cascades.com
Emp.: 53
Paper & Pulp Mfr
S.I.C.: 2621
N.A.I.C.S.: 322121

Cascades Forma-Pak, Inc. (2)
406 Marie Victorin St
Kingsey Falls, QC, J0A 1B0, Canada (100%)
Tel.: (819) 363-5060
Fax: (819) 363-5066
E-Mail: nadia_cote@cascades.com
Web Site: www.cascades.com
Sales Range: $10-24.9 Million
Emp.: 35
S.I.C.: 2631
N.A.I.C.S.: 322130
Remi Fortin *(Gen Mgr)*

Cascades Inopak (2)
500 Rue Lauzon
Drummondville, QC, J2B 2Z3, Canada (100%)
Tel.: (819) 472-5757
Fax: (819) 475-4525
E-Mail: inopak@cascades.com
Sales Range: $1-9.9 Million
Emp.: 40
Plastic Containers & Coin Wrappers Mfr
S.I.C.: 2631
N.A.I.C.S.: 322130

Cascades Lupel, Inc. (2)
700 Notre Dame E St
PO Box 23
Trois Rivieres, QC, G9A 5E3, Canada (100%)
Tel.: (819) 373-4307
Fax: (819) 373-4379
E-Mail: lupel@cascades.com
Web Site: www.cascades.com
Emp.: 55
S.I.C.: 2631
N.A.I.C.S.: 322130
Martin Cote *(Mgr)*

Cascades Multi-Pro, Inc. (2)
495 Haggerty St
Drummondville, QC, J2C 3G5, Canada (100%)
Tel.: (819) 478-5903
Fax: (819) 475-4522
E-Mail: multi-procommercial@cascades.com
Web Site: www.cascades.com
Emp.: 50
Cartons Mfr
S.I.C.: 2631
N.A.I.C.S.: 322130
Eric Pare *(Plant Mgr)*

Cascades Papier Kingsey Falls (2)
408 Marie-Victorin Blvd
CP 150
Kingsey Falls, QC, J0A 1B0, Canada
Tel.: (819) 363-5200
Fax: (819) 363-5255
Emp.: 68
Uncoated Paperboard Mfr
S.I.C.: 2631
N.A.I.C.S.: 322130
Brian Bradley *(Mgr-Production)*

Cascades Recovery Inc. (2)
66 Shorncliffe Road
Toronto, ON, M8Z 5K1, Canada
Tel.: (416) 231-2525
Fax: (416) 232-6061
E-Mail: toronto@recoverycascades.com
Web Site: www.recoverycascades.com
Emp.: 40
Discarded Paper & Cardboard Collection & Transportation Services
S.I.C.: 4212
N.A.I.C.S.: 562119
Albino Metauro *(CEO)*
George Boothe *(CFO)*
Anthony Metauro *(COO)*

Plastiques Cascades, Inc. (2)
455 Rue Marie Victorin
PO Box 179
Kingsey Falls, QC, J0A 1B0, Canada (100%)
Tel.: (819) 363-5300
Fax: (819) 363-5355
E-Mail: csplastiques@cascades.com
Web Site: www.plastiquescascades.com
Emp.: 180
S.I.C.: 2631
N.A.I.C.S.: 322130
Marie-claude Nicole *(Dir-Mktg)*

Unit:

Cascades Fine Papers Group Inc. - Rolland Division (2)
455 Avenue Rolland
CP 850
Saint-Jerome, QC, J7Z 5S2, Canada
Tel.: (450) 569-3900
Fax: (450) 569-3937
Web Site: www.cascades.com
Emp.: 32
Paper Products Mfr
S.I.C.: 2671
N.A.I.C.S.: 322220

Cascades Inc.—(Continued)

U.S. Subsidiaries:

Cascades Auburn Fiber Inc. (2)
586 Lewiston Jct Rd
Auburn, ME 04210
Tel.: (207) 753-5300
Fax: (207) 753-5333
E-Mail: customerservice@cascades.com
Web Site: www.cascades.com
Emp.: 44
Bleached Kraft Pulp Deinking Services
S.I.C.: 2611
N.A.I.C.S.: 322110
Tony Newman *(Plant Mgr)*

Cascades Enviropac HPM LLC (2)
236 Stevens St Sw
Grand Rapids, MI 49507-1528
Tel.: (616) 243-4870
Fax: (616) 243-7519
Packaging Product Mfr
S.I.C.: 2671
N.A.I.C.S.: 322220

Cascades Moulded Pulp, Inc. (2)
112 Cascades Way
Rockingham, NC 28379
Mailing Address:
PO Box 609
Rockingham, NC 28380
Tel.: (910) 997-2775
Fax: (910) 997-2774
E-Mail: info@cascades.com
Web Site: www.cascades.com
Emp.: 24
Beverage Tray Mfr
S.I.C.: 2657
N.A.I.C.S.: 322212
Paul Landry *(Plant Mgr)*

Cascades Plastics Inc. (2)
7501 S Spoede Ln
Warrenton, MO 63383
Tel.: (636) 456-9576
Fax: (636) 456-6547
Emp.: 70
Mfr of Polystyrene Foam Containers for Packaging & Food Presentation
S.I.C.: 3086
N.A.I.C.S.: 326140
Peirre Renaud *(Gen Mgr)*

Cascades Recovery U.S., Inc. (2)
1845 Emerson St
Rochester, NY 14606
Tel.: (585) 527-8110
Fax: (585) 527-8125
E-Mail: rochester@recoverycascades.com
Web Site: www.cascades.com
Emp.: 100
Discarded Paper & Cardboards Collection & Transportation Services
S.I.C.: 4212
N.A.I.C.S.: 562119
Jeff Meyers *(Gen Mgr)*

U.S. Plant:

Cascades Sonoco, Inc. - Birmingham (2)
170 Cleage Dr
Birmingham, AL 35217
Tel.: (205) 854-8574
Fax: (205) 854-8308
Web Site: www.cascades.com
Emp.: 58
Paper Industry Machinery Mfr
S.I.C.: 3553
N.A.I.C.S.: 333243

Non-U.S. Subsidiaries:

Cascades Rollpack S.A.S (2)
496 Zone Industrielle de Neuilly
Chatenois, France 88170
Tel.: (33) 3 29 94 78 38
Fax: (33) 3 29 94 78 40
Web Site: www.cascades.com
Emp.: 38
Packaging Paper Products Mfr
S.I.C.: 2671
N.A.I.C.S.: 322220

Cascades Tissue Group (1)
75 boulevard Marie-Victorin
Candiac, QC, J5R 1C2, Canada
Tel.: (450) 444-6500
Fax: (450) 444-0518
E-Mail:
Web Site: www.afh.cascades.com
Emp.: 120
S.I.C.: 2631
N.A.I.C.S.: 322130
Suzanne Blanchet *(Pres & CEO)*

Subsidiary:

Papersource Converting Mill Corp. (2)
901 boul Industriel
Granby, QC, J2J 1A6, Canada (100%)
Tel.: (450) 375-0855
Fax: (450) 375-6458
Web Site: www.cascades.com
Rev.: $24,864,000
Emp.: 150
Tissue Papers Mfr
S.I.C.: 2679
N.A.I.C.S.: 322299
Domenic Sportello *(Mgr-Natl Sls)*

Plants:

Cascades Groupe Tissu - Agincourt & Scarborough (2)
45 Milliken Blvd
Toronto, ON, M1V 1V3, Canada
Tel.: (416) 329-5200
Fax: (416) 329-5236
Web Site: www.cascades.com
Emp.: 171
Tissue Paper Mfr
S.I.C.: 2621
N.A.I.C.S.: 322121
Stephane Deshaies *(Plant Mgr)*

Cascades Tissue Group - Kingsey Falls (2)
467 Marie Victorin St
Kingsey Falls, QC, J0A 1B0, Canada
Tel.: (819) 363-5600
Fax: (819) 363-5655
E-Mail: cgtks-iec@cascade.com
Web Site: www.cascade.com
Emp.: 200
Specialty Tissue Paper Mfr
S.I.C.: 2631
N.A.I.C.S.: 322130
Paule Lavigne *(Dir-Dev & Bus Optimization)*

Cascades Tissue Group - Lachute (2)
115 Rue Princesse
Lachute, QC, Canada J8H 4M3
Tel.: (450) 562-8585
Fax: (450) 562-1369
Web Site: www.cascades.com
Emp.: 155
Paper Hand Towel & Tissue Paper Mfr
S.I.C.: 2621
N.A.I.C.S.: 322121
Regis Arsenault *(Mgr)*

Cascades Tissue Group - Laval (2)
2345 Laurentides Highway
Laval, QC, H7S 1Z7, Canada
Tel.: (450) 688-1152
Fax: (450) 688-6245
Web Site: www.cascades.com
Emp.: 78
Napkin Mfr
S.I.C.: 2676
N.A.I.C.S.: 322291
Georg Berner *(Office Mgr)*

U.S. Subsidiaries:

Cascades Tissue Group - Arizona Inc. (2)
4625 Interstate Way
Kingman, AZ 86401 DE
Tel.: (928) 681-2600
Fax: (928) 681-2626
Web Site: www.cascades.com
Emp.: 65
Tissue Paper Converting Services
S.I.C.: 2679
N.A.I.C.S.: 322299
Luc Beaudoin *(Plant Mgr)*

Cascades Tissue Group - New York Inc. (2)
510 S Main St
Mechanicville, NY 12118 DE
Tel.: (518) 238-1900
Fax: (518) 238-1919
Web Site: www.cascades.com
Emp.: 42
Tissue Paper Mfr
S.I.C.: 2621
N.A.I.C.S.: 322121
Philip Bourassa *(Gen Mgr)*

Cascades Tissue Group - Oregon Inc. (2)
1300 Kaster Rd
Saint Helens, OR 97051
Tel.: (503) 397-9372
Fax: (503) 397-9440
Web Site: www.cascades.com
Emp.: 4
Tissue Papers Mfr
S.I.C.: 2621
N.A.I.C.S.: 322121

Cascades Tissue Group - Pennsylvania Inc. (Pittston) (2)
901 Sathers Dr CP 6000
Pittston, PA 18640 DE
Tel.: (570) 388-6161
Fax: (570) 883-0572
Web Site: www.cascades.com
Emp.: 186
Tissue Paper Mfr
S.I.C.: 2621
N.A.I.C.S.: 322121

Cascades Tissue Group - Pennsylvania Inc. (Ransom) (2)
1 Main St
Ransom, PA 18653 DE
Tel.: (570) 388-6161
Fax: (570) 883-4125
Emp.: 75
Tissue Paper Mfr
S.I.C.: 2621
N.A.I.C.S.: 322121

Cascades Tissue Group - Sales Inc. (2)
148 Hudson River Rd
Waterford, NY 12188 DE
Tel.: (518) 238-1900
Fax: (518) 238-0560
E-Mail: question@cascades.com
Web Site: www.cascades.com
Emp.: 92
Towel & Tissue Paper Mfr
S.I.C.: 2621
N.A.I.C.S.: 322121
Mandie Kolakowski *(Asst Controller)*

Cascades Tissue Group - Tennessee Inc. (2)
1535 Thomas St
Memphis, TN 38107 DE
Tel.: (901) 523-9118
Fax: (901) 522-0181
Web Site: www.cascades.com
Emp.: 53
Tissue Paper Mfr
S.I.C.: 2621
N.A.I.C.S.: 322121
Patrick Bernier *(Plant Mgr)*

IFC Disposables Inc. (2)
250 Kleervu Dr
Brownsville, TN 38012
Tel.: (731) 779-0959
Fax: (731) 772-2282
Toll Free: (800) 432-9473
Web Site: www.cascades.com
Emp.: 58
Disposable Wiping Cloth Products Mfr
S.I.C.: 2842
N.A.I.C.S.: 325612
Bob Briggs *(Pres)*

U.S. Plant:

Cascades Tissue Group - Rockingham (2)
PO Box 578
Rockingham, NC 28380-0578
Tel.: (910) 895-4033
Fax: (910) 895-9887
Web Site: www.cascades.com
Emp.: 150
Mfr. of Jumbo Rolls of Tissue Paper, Converted Tissue & Paper Towels
S.I.C.: 2676
N.A.I.C.S.: 322291

Subsidiaries:

Cascades Tenderco Inc. (1)
404 Marie-Victorin Blvd
Kingsey Falls, QC, J0A 1B0, Canada
Tel.: (819) 363-5100
Fax: (819) 363-5155
Paper & Pulp Mfr
S.I.C.: 2621
N.A.I.C.S.: 322121
Alain Lemaire *(CEO)*

Cascades Transport Inc. (1)
2 Parenteau Street
PO Box 300
Kingsey Falls, QC, J0A 1B0, Canada
Tel.: (819) 363-5800
Fax: (819) 363-5513
Emp.: 205
General Freight Trucking Services
S.I.C.: 4213
N.A.I.C.S.: 484121
Jean-Yves Delisle *(Gen Mgr)*

U.S. Subsidiary:

Cascades USA Inc. (1)
148 Hudson River Rd
Waterford, NY 12188
Tel.: (518) 880-3632
Packaging Product & Tissue Paper Mfr
S.I.C.: 2672
N.A.I.C.S.: 322220

Unit:

Cascades IFC (2)
250 Kleer Vu PO Box 469
Brownsville, TN 38012-0469
Tel.: (731) 779-0959
Fax: (731) 772-2282
Web Site: www.cascades.com
Emp.: 50
Supplier of Disposable Industrial & Food Service Fabrics & Wiping Products
S.I.C.: 2297
N.A.I.C.S.: 313230
Alain Lemaire *(CEO & Pres)*

CASCADIA CONSUMER ELECTRONICS CORP.

800 885 West Georgia Street
Vancouver, BC, V6C 3H1, Canada
Tel.: (604) 218-2100
Year Founded: 2011
CK—(CNSX)
Assets: $112,944
Liabilities: $49,130
Net Worth: $63,813
Earnings: ($305,034)
Fiscal Year-end: 01/31/13
Business Description:
Electronic Hardware & Software
S.I.C.: 3679
N.A.I.C.S.: 334419
Personnel:
Jin Zhang *(Acting CEO)*
William Wang *(Acting CFO)*

CASCADIA MOTIVATION INC

Suite 14 4646 Riverside Drive
Red Deer, AB, T4N 6Y5, Canada
Tel.: (403) 340-8687
Fax: (403) 346-6220
Toll Free: (800) 661-8360
E-Mail: mail@cascadiamotivation.com
Web Site: www.cascadiamotivation.com
Year Founded: 1984
Rev.: $13,506,303
Emp.: 40
Business Description:
Travel Agencies
S.I.C.: 3369
N.A.I.C.S.: 331529
Personnel:
Rob Thorsteinson *(Pres)*
Randy Thorsteinson *(COO)*

CASCADIA RESOURCES INC.

1530 715 - 5 Avenue SW
Calgary, AB, T2P 2X6, Canada
Tel.: (403) 262-9177
Fax: (403) 262-8284
E-Mail: info@cascadiaintl.com

Web Site: www.cascadiaintl.com
Year Founded: 1983
CCR—(TSXV)
Assets: $55,558
Liabilities: $107,796
Net Worth: ($52,239)
Earnings: ($170,075)
Fiscal Year-end: 07/31/13
Business Description:
Mineral Mining & Exploration Services
S.I.C.: 1099
N.A.I.C.S.: 212299
Personnel:
Gordon A. Bowerman *(CEO)*
Trish Olynyk *(CFO & VP-Bus Dev)*
Board of Directors:
Gordon A. Bowerman
James G. Evaskevich
Donald Poruchny
Legal Counsel:
Gowling Lafleur Henderson LLP
1400 700 2nd St SW
Calgary, AB, Canada

CASCO LTD.
Aviation Centre Star Industrial Estate
Partridge Green
Horsham, West Sussex, RH13 8RA, United Kingdom
Tel.: (44) 1403711444
Fax: (44) 1403711582
E-Mail: sales@casco.aero
Web Site: www.casco.co.uk
Year Founded: 1982
Rev.: $31,249,568
Emp.: 27
Business Description:
Aircraft Parts Distr
S.I.C.: 5088
N.A.I.C.S.: 423860
Personnel:
Barrie Roberts *(CEO)*

CASDON PLC
Cornford Road
Blackpool, Lancashire, FY4 4QQ, United Kingdom
Tel.: (44) 1253766411
Fax: (44) 1253691486
E-Mail: toys@casdon.co.uk
Web Site: www.casdon.co.uk
Year Founded: 1946
CDY—(AIM)
Sls.: $10,249,731
Assets: $7,082,178
Liabilities: $1,286,913
Net Worth: $5,795,265
Earnings: $658,915
Emp.: 13
Fiscal Year-end: 04/30/13
Business Description:
Toy Mfr
S.I.C.: 3944
N.A.I.C.S.: 339930
Personnel:
Paul M. Cassidy *(Chm & Co-Mng Dir)*
Peter C. Cassidy *(Co-Mng Dir)*
Philip T. Cassidy *(Co-Mng Dir)*
Stanley Wilkinson *(Sec & Dir-Fin)*
Board of Directors:
Paul M. Cassidy
Peter C. Cassidy
Philip T. Cassidy
Stanley Wilkinson
Legal Counsel:
Cuddy Woods and Cochrane
41 Springfield Road
Blackpool, FY1 1QE, United Kingdom

CASE 'N DRUM OIL LP
3462 White Oak Road
London, ON, N6E 2Z9, Canada
Tel.: (519) 681-3772
Fax: (519) 681-4680
Toll Free: (800) 265-7642
E-Mail: mailroom@cndoil.ca
Web Site: www.cndoil.ca
Year Founded: 1977
Rev.: $15,215,366
Emp.: 35
Business Description:
Lubricants Supplier
S.I.C.: 5172
N.A.I.C.S.: 424720
Personnel:
Suzanne Newington *(Dir-Credit & Admin)*

CASELLA WINES PTY. LTD.
Walkley Rd
PO Box 281
Yenda, NSW, 2681, Australia
Tel.: (61) 269613000
Fax: (61) 269613099
E-Mail: info@casellawines.com
Web Site: www.casellawines.com
Year Founded: 1965
Sales Range: $300-349.9 Million
Emp.: 450
Business Description:
Wine Mfr
S.I.C.: 2084
N.A.I.C.S.: 312130
Personnel:
John W. Casella *(Mng Dir)*

CASETEK HOLDINGS LIMITED
3F 37 Sec 2 Zhongyang S Rd
Beitou District, Taipei, 112, Taiwan
Tel.: (886) 2 5563 0588
Fax: (886) 2 2897 6673
E-Mail: ir@casetekholdings.com
Web Site: www.casetekholdings.com
5264—(TAI)
Sales Range: $600-649.9 Million
Business Description:
Dies, Molds & Electronic Products Mfr
S.I.C.: 3544
N.A.I.C.S.: 333511
Personnel:
T.H. Tung *(Chm)*
Jonathan Chang *(CFO)*

CASH CANADA GROUP LTD.
17316 107 Ave
Edmonton, AB, T5S 1E9, Canada
Tel.: (780) 424-1080
Fax: (780) 424-1242
Toll Free: (866) 696-9684
E-Mail: info@cashcanada.com
Web Site: www.cashcanada.com
Year Founded: 1988
Sales Range: $10-24.9 Million
Emp.: 100
Business Description:
Pawn Shop Owner & Operator; Loan Services
S.I.C.: 5399
N.A.I.C.S.: 452990
Personnel:
Tim Latimer *(CEO)*

CASH CONVERTERS INTERNATIONAL LIMITED
Level 18 37 St Georges Terrace
Perth, WA, 6000, Australia
Tel.: (61) 8 9221 9111
Fax: (61) 8 9221 9011
E-Mail: general.enquiries@cashconverters.com
Web Site: www.cashconverters.com
CCV—(ASX)
Rev.: $284,204,345
Assets: $361,582,775
Liabilities: $109,779,335
Net Worth: $251,803,440
Earnings: $34,253,798
Emp.: 929
Fiscal Year-end: 06/30/13
Business Description:
Second Hand Goods Purchasing & Reselling Services
S.I.C.: 5932
N.A.I.C.S.: 453310
Personnel:
Brian Cumins *(Founder)*
Peter Cumins *(Mng Dir)*
Ralph Groom *(CFO, Sec & Controller-Fin)*
Glen Fee *(CIO)*
David Patrick *(CEO-UK)*
Mike Osborne *(CFO/Sec-UK)*
Michael Cooke *(Legal Counsel)*
Board of Directors:
Reginald Webb
Joseph Beal
Peter Cumins
William Love
Legal Counsel:
Cooke & Co
50 Eora Creek Terrace, Dianelle
Perth, Australia

Computershare Investor Services Pty Ltd
Level 2 Reserve Bank Building 45 St Georges Terrace
Perth, Australia

Subsidiaries:

Cash Converters Pty Ltd (1)
37 St Georges Tce
Perth, Western Australia, WA 6000, Australia
Tel.: (61) 892219111
Fax: (61) 892219011
Financial & Broking Services
S.I.C.: 6159
N.A.I.C.S.: 522294
Ceter Cumins *(Mgr)*

Cash Converters (Stores) Pty Ltd (1)
182 Smith St
Collingwood, Victoria, VIC 3066, Australia
Tel.: (61) 394174620
Fax: (61) 394194673
Financial & Secondary Marketing Services
S.I.C.: 6159
N.A.I.C.S.: 522294

Safrock Finance Corporation (QLD) Pty Ltd (1)
Level 2 9 Mcinroy St
Taringa, Brisbane, Queensland, QLD 4068, Australia
Tel.: (61) 738769411
Fax: (61) 733050932
E-Mail: info@safrock.net
Web Site: www.safrock.net
Emp.: 50
Personal Loan Services
S.I.C.: 6141
N.A.I.C.S.: 522291
Peter Wessels *(Mng Dir)*

Non-U.S. Subsidiary:

Cash Converters UK Holdings PLC (1)
15-17 Gentlemens Field Westmill Rd
Ware, Hertfordshire, SG12 0EF, United Kingdom
Tel.: (44) 1920485696
Fax: (44) 1920485695
Web Site: www.cashconverters.co.uk
Emp.: 15
Financial & Broking Services
S.I.C.: 6159
N.A.I.C.S.: 522294
David Patrick *(CEO)*

CASH FINANCIAL SERVICES GROUP LIMITED
9/F Low Block Grand Millennium Plaza 181 Queen's Road
Central, China (Hong Kong)
Tel.: (852) 22878788
Fax: (852) 22878700
E-Mail: hotline@cashon-line.com
Web Site: www.cashon-line.com
0510—(HKG)
Rev.: $165,201,585
Assets: $397,477,672
Liabilities: $278,661,466
Net Worth: $118,816,206
Earnings: ($4,322,920)
Emp.: 1,184
Fiscal Year-end: 12/31/12
Business Description:
Investment Banking & Securities Dealing Services
S.I.C.: 6211
N.A.I.C.S.: 523110
Personnel:
Bankee Pak Hoo Kwan *(Chm)*
Benson Chi Ming Chan *(CEO)*
Bob Yau-ching Chan *(Deputy CEO-CASH)*
James Siu-pong Leung *(Deputy CEO-Pricerite)*
Bernard Ping Wah Law *(CFO)*
Raymond Pak Lau Yuen *(Deputy CFO)*
Majone Pui-lai Cheng *(COO)*
Horace Pak-leung Kwan *(Deputy COO)*
Derek Hin-sing Ng *(CEO-Pricerite)*
Hon-wo Shum *(Legal Counsel)*
Suzanne Wing Sheung Luke *(Sec)*
Board of Directors:
Bankee Pak Hoo Kwan
Benson Chi Ming Chan
Ben Man Pan Cheng
Majone Pui-lai Cheng
Raymond Shu Shing Cheng
Bernard Ping Wah Law
Charles Ming Chi Lo
John Kwok Hung Lo
Transfer Agent:
Tricor Standard Limited
26/F Tesbury Centre 28 Queens Road East
Hong Kong, China (Hong Kong)

Subsidiaries:

CASH Asset Management Limited (1)
21 F Low Block Grand Millennium Plz
181 Queens Rd, Central, China (Hong Kong)
Tel.: (852) 22878788
Fax: (852) 22878700
E-Mail: inquiry@cash.com.hk
Web Site: www.cash.com.hk
Asset Management Services
S.I.C.: 6282
N.A.I.C.S.: 523920

CASH E-Trade Limited (1)
21 F Low Block Grand Millennium Plz
181 Queens Rd, Central, China (Hong Kong)
Tel.: (852) 22878888
Fax: (852) 22878700
E-Mail: inquiry@cash.com.hk
Web Site: www.cash.com.hk
Administrative Management Services
S.I.C.: 8741
N.A.I.C.S.: 561110
Pen Cheng *(Mgr-Fin)*

CASH Frederick Taylor Limited (1)
21 F Low Block Grand Millennium Plz
181 Queen St, Central, China (Hong Kong)
Tel.: (852) 21392323
Fax: (852) 21392188
E-Mail: wendy.mak@cash.com.hk
Web Site: www.cash.com.hk
Financial Advisory Consultancy
S.I.C.: 8742
N.A.I.C.S.: 541611

Celestial Commodities Limited (1)
21 F Low Block Grand Millennium Plz
181 Queens Rd, Central, China (Hong Kong)
Tel.: (852) 22878888
Fax: (852) 22878700
E-Mail: inquiry@cash.com.hk
Web Site: www.cashon-line.com.hk
Electronic Trading Services
S.I.C.: 7389

CASH Financial Services Group Limited—(Continued)

N.A.I.C.S.: 425110
Carrie Law *(Mgr-HR)*

Celestial Securities Limited (1)
21 F Low Block Grand Millennium Plz
181 Queens Rd, Central, China (Hong Kong)
Tel.: (852) 22878788
Fax: (852) 28200660
E-Mail: inquiry@cash.com.hk
Web Site: www.cash.com.hk
Emp.: 450
Securities & Foreign Exchange Trading Services
S.I.C.: 6231
N.A.I.C.S.: 523210
Pankee Kwan *(Pres)*

THE CASH STORE AUSTRALIA HOLDINGS INC.

15511 123 Avenue
Edmonton, AB, T5V 0C3, Canada
Tel.: (780) 408-5110
Fax: (780) 408-5122
E-Mail: information@csfinancial.ca
Web Site: www.csfinancial.ca/ContactUs.aspx
AUC—(TSXV)
Business Description:
Pay Day Cash Advance Services
S.I.C.: 6099
N.A.I.C.S.: 522320
Personnel:
Gordon J. Reykdal *(Chm)*
Tom Denovan *(CEO)*
S. W. Johnson *(CFO)*
Board of Directors:
Gordon J. Reykdal
S. W. Johnson
Edward C. McClelland
Roopinder Mundi
Legal Counsel:
Cassels Brock & Blackwell, LLP
Toronto, ON, Canada

THE CASH STORE FINANCIAL SERVICES INC.

15511-123 Avenue
Edmonton, AB, T5V 0C3, Canada
Tel.: (780) 408-5110
Fax: (780) 408-5122
E-Mail: information@csfinancial.ca
Web Site: www.csfinancial.ca
Year Founded: 2001
CSF—(OTC TSX)
Rev.: $189,624,225
Assets: $163,600,782
Liabilities: $164,912,888
Net Worth: ($1,312,106)
Earnings: ($35,319,519)
Emp.: 1,856
Fiscal Year-end: 09/30/13
Business Description:
Payday Advance Lending Services
S.I.C.: 6141
N.A.I.C.S.: 522291
Personnel:
Eugene I. Davis *(Chm)*
Gordon J. Reykdal *(CEO)*
Craig Warnock *(CFO)*
Kevin Paetz *(Pres/COO-Ops-Canada)*
Barret J. Reykdal *(Pres/COO-Ops-UK)*
Michael J. L. Thompson *(Sec & Sr VP)*
Bill Johnson *(Sr Exec VP)*
Halldor Kristjansson *(Sr Exec VP-Strategic Plng & Fin)*
Bob Gloweski *(Sr VP-Mktg, Trng & Bus Dev)*
Cameron Schiffner *(Sr VP-Ops)*
Board of Directors:
Eugene I. Davis
Timothy J. Bernlohr
Donald C. Campion
Ron Chicoyne
Thomas L. Fairfield
Edward C. McClelland
Transfer Agent:
Computershare Investor Services Inc.
Montreal, QC, Canada
Divisions:

The Cash Store (1)
17631 103rd Ave
Edmonton, AB, T5S 1N8, Canada
Tel.: (780) 408-5110
Fax: (780) 408-5122
Toll Free: (877) 6004PAY
Web Site: www.cashstore.ca
Cash Advance Stores
S.I.C.: 6163
N.A.I.C.S.: 522310

Instaloans (1)
12405 107 Ave
Edmonton, AB, T5N 1Z2, Canada
Tel.: (780) 442-2233
Fax: (780) 451-9551
Web Site: www.instaloans.ca
Emp.: 200
Cash Advance Stores
S.I.C.: 6163
N.A.I.C.S.: 522310

CASHBUILD LIMITED

101 Northern Parkway cnr Crownwood Road
Ormonde, Johannesburg, 2091, South Africa
Tel.: (27) 112481500
Fax: (27) 86 6663291
Web Site: www.cashbuild.co.za
CSB—(JSE)
Rev.: $712,304,757
Assets: $231,107,300
Liabilities: $106,401,399
Net Worth: $124,705,901
Earnings: $27,763,147
Emp.: 4,552
Fiscal Year-end: 06/30/13
Business Description:
Building Materials Retailer
S.I.C.: 5251
N.A.I.C.S.: 444130
Personnel:
W. F. de Jager *(CEO)*
Board of Directors:
Donald Masson
W. F. de Jager
I. S. Fourie
H. H. Hickey
A. G. W. Knock
D. S. S. Lushaba
A. E. Prowse
Nomahlubi V. Simamane
Shane A. Thoresson
A. van Onselen
Transfer Agent:
Computershare Investor Services (Pty) Limited
Ground Floor 70 Marshall Street
Johannesburg, South Africa
Subsidiary:

Cashbuild Management Services (Pty) Ltd (1)
5 Aerodrome Rd
Aeroton, Johannesburg, Gauteng, 2013, South Africa
Tel.: (27) 11 248 1516
Fax: (27) 11 494 1108
E-Mail: agovender@Cashbuild.co.za
Management Services
S.I.C.: 8741
N.A.I.C.S.: 551114

Non-U.S. Subsidiary:

Cashbuild (Botswana) (Pty) Ltd (2)
PO Box 20227
Gaborone, Botswana
Tel.: (267) 3912991
Fax: (267) 3182032
Emp.: 12
Building Materials Retailer
S.I.C.: 5211
N.A.I.C.S.: 444190
Alex Mandeau *(Reg Mgr)*

CASH.LIFE AG

Zugspitzstrasse 3
82049 Pullach, Germany
Tel.: (49) 1802000393
Fax: (49) 89286953299
Web Site: www.cashlife.de
Year Founded: 1999
SGS—(DEU)
Sales Range: $200-249.9 Million
Business Description:
Life Insurance Services
S.I.C.: 6411
N.A.I.C.S.: 524210
Personnel:
Thomas Schmitt *(Chm-Supervisory Bd)*
Frank Alexander de Boer *(Chm-Mgmt Bd)*
Gunther Skrzypek *(Deputy Chm-Supervisory Bd)*
Supervisory Board of Directors:
Thomas Schmitt
Georg Mehl
Gunther Skrzypek

CASIL TELECOMMUNICATIONS HOLDINGS LIMITED

(d/b/a CASTEL)
Ste 4701 47th Fl Central Plz
Wanchai, China (Hong Kong)
Tel.: (852) 25861185
Fax: (852) 25310088
E-Mail: castel@castelecom.com
Web Site: www.castelecom.com
Sls.: $19,064,409
Emp.: 300
Business Description:
Holding Company; Electronic & Telecommunication Products Designer, Developer, Mfr, Marketer, System Integration & Professional System Services
S.I.C.: 6719
N.A.I.C.S.: 551112
Personnel:
Han Shuwang *(Vice Chm)*
Wang Xiaodong *(CEO)*
Steve Auyueng *(Sec)*
Board of Directors:
Yiu Ying Wai Alex
Tang Guohong
Wong Fai Philip
Zhu Shixiong
Han Shuwang
Wang Xiaodong
Moh Kwen Yung

CASINOS AUSTRIA AG

Renn Weg 44
Vienna, A-1038, Austria
Tel.: (43) 5077750
Fax: (43) 015344022222
E-Mail: info@casinos.at
Web Site: www.casinos.at
Sales Range: $1-4.9 Billion
Emp.: 9,642
Business Description:
Casino Management & Development Services
S.I.C.: 7999
N.A.I.C.S.: 713210
Personnel:
Walter Rothensteiner *(Chm-Supervisory Bd)*
Karl Stoss *(Chm-Mgmt Bd & Dir Gen)*
Maria Theresia Bablik *(Third Deputy Chm-Supervisory Bd)*
Wolfgang Duchatczek *(First Deputy Chm-Supervisory Bd)*
Gunter Geyer *(Second Deputy Chm-Supervisory Bd)*
Leo Wallner *(Fourth Deputy Chm-Supervisory Bd)*
Bettina Glatz-Kremsner *(Member-Mgmt Bd)*
Dietmar Hoscher *(Member-Mgmt Bd)*
Supervisory Board of Directors:
Walter Rothensteiner
Maria Theresia Bablik
Wolfgang Duchatczek
Gunter Geyer
Helmut Jonas
Konstantin Klien
Gerald Neuber
Thomas Schrofl
Gerhard Starsich
Leo Wallner
Peter Zollner
Subsidiaries:

Casinos Austria International GmbH (1)
Rennwet 44
Vienna, 1038, Austria
Tel.: (43) 1534400
Fax: (43) 153440515
E-Mail: office@casinos.at
Web Site: www.casinosaustriainternational.com
Emp.: 300
Casino Management & Development Services
S.I.C.: 7999
N.A.I.C.S.: 713210
Karl Stoss *(Chm)*

Casinos Austria International Holdings GmbH (1)
Rennweg 44
1038 Vienna, Austria
Tel.: (43) 5077750
Fax: (43) 15344022222
E-Mail: info@casinos.at
Web Site: www.casinos.com
Emp.: 45
Holding Company
S.I.C.: 6719
N.A.I.C.S.: 551112
Karl Stoss *(Mng Dir)*

CASIO COMPUTER CO., LTD.

6-2 Hon-machi 1-chome Shibuya-ku
Tokyo, 151-8543, Japan
Tel.: (81) 353344111
Fax: (81) 353344650
Web Site: www.casio.com
Year Founded: 1957
6952—(EUR NGO TKS)
Sls.: $3,275,393,000
Assets: $4,062,542,000
Liabilities: $2,258,894,000
Net Worth: $1,803,648,000
Earnings: $130,636,000
Emp.: 11,276
Fiscal Year-end: 03/31/13
Business Description:
Mfr. of Digital Watches & Calculators, Musical Instruments, Personal Computers, T.V.'s
Import Export
S.I.C.: 3571
N.A.I.C.S.: 334111
Personnel:
Kazuo Kashio *(Pres & CEO)*
Akira Kashio *(Sr Mng Dir)*
Fumitsune Murakami *(Sr Mng Dir)*
Hiroshi Nakamura *(Mng Dir)*
Akinori Takagi *(Mng Dir)*
Toshiyuki Iguchi *(Corp Officer)*
Nobuyuki Inada *(Corp Officer)*
Shigenori Itoh *(Corp Officer)*
Tetsuro Izumi *(Corp Officer)*
Takashi Kashio *(Corp Officer)*
Tetsuo Kashio *(Corp Officer)*
Nobuyuki Mochinaga *(Corp Officer)*

Koji Moriya *(Corp Officer)*
Jin Nakayama *(Corp Officer)*
Toshiharu Okimuro *(Corp Officer)*
Shin Takano *(Corp Officer)*
Masayuki Uehara *(Corp Officer)*
Atsushi Yazawa *(Corp Officer)*
Yukio Kashio *(Exec VP)*

Board of Directors:
Hirokazu Ishikawa
Akira Kashio
Kazuhiro Kashio
Kazuo Kashio
Yukio Kashio
Makoto Kobayashi
Makoto Kotani
Yuichi Masuda
Fumitsune Murakami
Hiroshi Nakamura
Akinori Takagi
Susumu Takashima
Toshiyuki Yamagishi

Subsidiaries:

Casio Electronic Manufacturing Co., Ltd. (1)
4084 Miyadera
Iruma, Saitama, 358-0014, Japan
Tel.: (81) 429348900
Electronic Component Mfr
S.I.C.: 3679
N.A.I.C.S.: 334419

Casio Information Systems Co., Ltd. (1)
3-3-5 Nihombashihongokucho
Nihombashitoku Bldg
Chuo-Ku, Tokyo, 103-0021, Japan
Tel.: (81) 352004730
Fax: (81) 352004901
Web Site: w3.cjnet.co.jp
Computer Peripheral Equipment Distr
S.I.C.: 5045
N.A.I.C.S.: 423430
Haruo Ohsawa *(Gen Mgr)*

Casio Micronics Co., Ltd. (1)
10-6 Imai 3-chome Ome City
Tokyo, 198-8555, Japan (75%)
Tel.: (81) 428321551
Fax: (81) 428321392
Web Site: www.casio-micronics.co.jp
Sales Range: $75-99.9 Million
Emp.: 345
Electronic Parts Developer, Mfr & Sales
S.I.C.: 3679
N.A.I.C.S.: 334419
Takeshi Wakabayashi *(Pres)*

Casio Techno Co., Ltd. (1)
33 Sakuma-cho 3-chome Kanda
Chiyoda-ku, Tokyo, 101-0025, Japan
Tel.: (81) 358217611
Fax: (81) 3 5821 7633
Web Site: www.casiotechno.co.jp
Electronic Device Distr
S.I.C.: 5065
N.A.I.C.S.: 423690

CXD NEXT Co., Ltd. (1)
1-46-3 Hatsudai Shimomoto Bldg 10 F
Shibuya-Ku, Tokyo, 151-0061, Japan
Tel.: (81) 3 5302 3760
Web Site: www.cxdnext.co.jp
Electronic Payment Services
S.I.C.: 5961
N.A.I.C.S.: 454111

Kofu Casio Co., Ltd. (1)
217 Ichouhata
Tokyo, Yamanashi, 409-3896, Japan
Tel.: (81) 55 273 3111
Web Site: www.kofu-casio.co.jp
Electronic Devices Mfr
S.I.C.: 3679
N.A.I.C.S.: 334419

Yamagata Casio Co., Ltd. (1)
5400-1 Higashine-ko
Higashine, Yamagata, 999-3701, Japan
Tel.: (81) 237435111
Fax: (81) 237432577
Web Site: www.yamagata-casio.co.jp
Electronic Devices Mfr & Distr
S.I.C.: 3679
N.A.I.C.S.: 334419

Masaki Isozaki *(Chm & CEO)*
Kohei Suzuki *(Mng Dir)*

U.S. Subsidiaries:

Casio America, Inc. (1)
570 Mount Pleasant Ave
Dover, NJ 07801-1631
Tel.: (973) 361-5400
Fax: (973) 537-8910
Web Site: www.world.casio.com
Emp.: 200
Electronic Musical Instruments Mfr
S.I.C.: 5044
N.A.I.C.S.: 423420
Shigenori Itoh *(Chm)*

Casio, Inc. (1)
570 Mount Pleasant Ave
Dover, NJ 07801-1620 NY
Mailing Address:
PO Box 7000
Dover, NJ 07802-7000
Tel.: (973) 361-5400
Fax: (973) 537-8926
Toll Free: (800) 836-8580
Web Site: www.casio.com
Sales Range: $450-499.9 Million
Emp.: 300
Consumer Electronics Mfr
Import
S.I.C.: 5044
N.A.I.C.S.: 423420
Larry Sampey *(Gen Mgr)*

Non-U.S. Subsidiaries:

Casio Benelux B.V. (1)
Prof WH Keesomlaan 6E
1183 DJ Amstelveen, Netherlands
Tel.: (31) 205451070
Fax: (31) 205451089
E-Mail: verkoop@casio.nl
Web Site: www.casio.nl
Emp.: 25
Calculators, Musical Instruments & Watches Mfr
S.I.C.: 5736
N.A.I.C.S.: 451140
Shigeru Watanabe *(Mng Dir)*

Casio Brasil Comercio De Produtos Eletronicos Ltda. (1)
Rua Leoncio de Carvalho 234
04003-010 Sao Paulo, Brazil
Tel.: (55) 1125392770
Fax: (55) 1132665221
Calculators, Musical Instruments & Watches Mfr
S.I.C.: 5736
N.A.I.C.S.: 451140

Casio Canada, Ltd. (1)
100 Commerce Valley Drive East
Thornhill, ON, L3T 7R1, Canada (100%)
Tel.: (905) 258-4400
Fax: (905) 882-6608
E-Mail: casio@casiocanada.com
Web Site: www.casio.com
Emp.: 25
Markets & Sales of Calculators, Musical Instruments & Watches
S.I.C.: 5736
N.A.I.C.S.: 451140
Carlisle Robertson *(Mgr-Key Acct & Bus Dev-Bus Products)*

Casio Computer (Hong Kong) Ltd. (1)
Unit 206 Two Harbourfront 22 Tak Fung Street Hunghom
22 TakFung St Hunghon, Kowloon, China (Hong Kong) HK
Tel.: (852) 23772288 (100%)
Fax: (852) 23184545
Web Site: www.casio.com
Emp.: 100
Mfr. of Electronic Calculators & Timepieces
S.I.C.: 5065
N.A.I.C.S.: 423690
Katsuyoshi Hosokawa *(Mng Dir)*

Casio Electronic Technology (Zhongshan) Co., Ltd. (1)
Avenue West 46 Torch Hi-Tech Industrial Development Zone
Zhongshan, Guangdong, 528437, China
Tel.: (86) 760 8858 0668
Web Site: www.casio.co.jp

Calculators, Musical Instruments & Watches Mfr
S.I.C.: 5736
N.A.I.C.S.: 451140

Casio Electronics Co., Ltd. (1)
Unit 6 1000 N Circular Rd
London, NW2 7JD, United Kingdom (100%)
Tel.: (44) 2084509131
Telex: 883446
Fax: (44) 2084526323
Web Site: www.casio.co.uk
Emp.: 150
Marketing of Computers
S.I.C.: 5734
N.A.I.C.S.: 443142
Akira Kashio *(Mng Dir)*
Hiroshi Nakamura *(Mng Dir)*
Akinori Takagi *(Mng Dir)*
Takatoshi Yamamoto *(Mng Dir)*

Casio Electronics (Guangzhou) Co., Ltd. (1)
6/F Lan Tian Lou Agriculture Building
Dongjiang Avenue, Guangzhou, 510730, China
Tel.: (86) 2082220488
Mfr of Timepieces
S.I.C.: 3829
N.A.I.C.S.: 334519
Minxing Dan *(Gen Mgr)*

Casio Electronics (Shenzhen) Co., Ltd. (1)
20 Shihua Road
Futian Free Trade Zone, Shenzhen, Guangdong, 518038, China
Tel.: (86) 75583590620
Fax: (86) 75583592047
Web Site: world.casio.com
Mfr of Electronics
S.I.C.: 3679
N.A.I.C.S.: 334419

Casio Espana, S.L. (1)
Torre Diagonal Litoral Josep Pla No 2
Edificio B2, Planta 12, 08019 Barcelona, Spain
Tel.: (34) 934858400
Fax: (34) 934858440
E-Mail: casio.spain@casio.es
Web Site: www.casio.es
Calculators, Musical Instruments & Watches Mfr
S.I.C.: 5736
N.A.I.C.S.: 451140

Casio Europe GmbH (1)
Kacaseon Paltc 1
22848 Norderstedt, Schleswig Holstein, Germany DE
Tel.: (49) 40528650 (60%)
Fax: (49) 4052865100
E-Mail: yamashita@casio.de
Web Site: www.casio-europe.com
Emp.: 378
Sales of Computers
S.I.C.: 5045
N.A.I.C.S.: 423430
Kazuyuki Yamashita *(Mng Dir)*

Casio France S.A. (1)
24 Rue Emile Baudot
91120 Palaiseau, France
Tel.: (33) 169192060
Fax: (33) 164470948
E-Mail: secretariatpalaiseau@casio.fr
Web Site: www.casio.com
Emp.: 70
Calculators, Musical Instruments & Watches Mfr
S.I.C.: 5736
N.A.I.C.S.: 451140

Casio India Company Private Ltd (1)
210 1st Floor Okhla Industrial Estate Phase III
New Delhi, 110020, India (100%)
Tel.: (91) 1141054321
Fax: (91) 1141054330
Web Site: www.casioindiacompany.com
Emp.: 60
Mfr. of Communications Equipment
S.I.C.: 3663
N.A.I.C.S.: 334220

Casio Italia S.r.l. (1)
Via Ludovico di Breme No.9
20156 Milan, Italy
Tel.: (39) 2 40708611

Calculators, Musical Instruments & Watches Mfr
S.I.C.: 5736
N.A.I.C.S.: 451140

Casio Korea Co., Ltd. (1)
654-4 Bongam-Dong
Masan, Kyung Sang Namdo, Korea (South) Ks
Tel.: (82) 552967111 (100%)
Mfr. of Electronic Timepieces
S.I.C.: 3829
N.A.I.C.S.: 334519

Casio Mexico Marketing, S. de R. L. de C.V. (1)
Montecito 38 Piso 42 Oficina 17
Delegacion Benito Juarez, Mexico, 03810, Mexico
Tel.: (52) 5590002071
E-Mail: aneve@casiomexio.mx
Web Site: www.casio-latin.com
Emp.: 20
Calculators, Musical Instruments & Watches Mfr
S.I.C.: 5736
N.A.I.C.S.: 451140

Casio Philippines Corporation (1)
First Cavite Industrial Estate Brgy
Langkaan, Dasmarinas, Cavite, Philippines
Tel.: (63) 402 0788
Mfr. of Pagers
S.I.C.: 3663
N.A.I.C.S.: 334220

Casio Scandinavia AS (1)
Hillerenveien 82
5174 Bergen, Norway
Tel.: (47) 55197990
E-Mail: info@casio.no
Web Site: www.casio.no
Calculators, Musical Instruments & Watches Mfr
S.I.C.: 5736
N.A.I.C.S.: 451140

Casio (Shanghai) Co., Ltd. (1)
Tower A 10/F 100Zunyi Road
Changning District, Shanghai, 200051, China
Tel.: (86) 2161974898
Web Site: www.casio.com.cn
Calculators, Musical Instruments & Watches Mfr
S.I.C.: 5736
N.A.I.C.S.: 451140

Casio Singapore Pte., Ltd. (1)
210 Middle Road
10-08 IOI Plaza, Singapore, 188994, Singapore
Tel.: (65) 64 81 8891
Calculators, Musical Instruments & Watches Mfr
S.I.C.: 5736
N.A.I.C.S.: 451140

Casio Taiwan Co., Ltd. (1)
7F No 21 Sec 6 Zhongxiao E Rd
Taipei, Nangang, Taiwan TW
Tel.: (886) 2 2653 2588 (100%)
E-Mail: service@casio.com.tw
Web Site: www.casio.com.tw
Emp.: 40
Mfr of Timepiece Cases & Electronic Calculators
S.I.C.: 3829
N.A.I.C.S.: 334519

Casio (Thailand) Co., Ltd. (1)
60/70 Moo 19
Nava Nakorn Industrial Estate, 12120
Pathumthani, Thailand
Tel.: (66) 252906114
Fax: (66) 25290615
Emp.: 880
Calculators, Musical Instruments & Watches Mfr
S.I.C.: 5736
N.A.I.C.S.: 451140
Nate-Napa Panyaboon *(Mgr-HR)*

Limited Liability Company Casio (1)
27 Suschevskaya Street Bld 1
127055 Moscow, Russia
Tel.: (7) 495 725 6466
Fax: (7) 495 725 6467
E-Mail: info@casio.ru
Web Site: www.casio.ru

Casio Computer Co., Ltd.—(Continued)

Emp.: 36
Electronic Component Mfr
S.I.C.: 3679
N.A.I.C.S.: 334419
Okuno Takayuki *(Gen Mgr)*

CASPIAN BEVERAGE HOLDING JSC

211 Gogol Street
050026 Almaty, Kazakhstan
Tel.: (7) 727 2421806
Web Site: www.zhigulevskoe.kz
CBH—(KAZ)
Sales Range: $10-24.9 Million
Business Description:
Beer Producer & Sales
S.I.C.: 2082
N.A.I.C.S.: 312120
Personnel:
Almas Akhmetov *(Pres)*

CASPIAN ENERGY INC.

410 396 11th Ave SW
Calgary, AB, T2R 0C5, Canada
Tel.: (403) 252-2462
Fax: (403) 252-1399
Web Site: www.caspianenergyinc.com
CEK—(TSX)
Rev.: $3,660,976
Assets: $40,668,340
Liabilities: $77,237,342
Net Worth: ($36,569,002)
Earnings: ($21,379,382)
Emp.: 2
Fiscal Year-end: 12/31/12
Business Description:
Oil & Gas Explorer
S.I.C.: 1389
N.A.I.C.S.: 213112
Personnel:
William A. G. Ramsay *(Pres & CEO)*
Brian D. Korney *(CFO)*
Charles J. Summers *(COO)*
Board of Directors:
Maurizio Barnaba
Gordon D. Harris
Brian D. Korney
Michael B. A. Nobbs
William A. G. Ramsay
Charles J. Summers
Legal Counsel:
Cassels, Brock & Blackwell LLP
2100 Scotia Plaza 40 King St W
Toronto, ON, M5H 3C2, Canada
Tel.: (416) 869-5300
Telex: 6-23415
Fax: (416) 360-8877
Transfer Agent:
Equity Transfer & Trust Company
200 University Avenue Ste 400
Toronto, ON, M5H 4H1, Canada
Tel.: (416) 361-0152
Fax: (416) 361-0470

CASPIAN HOLDINGS PLC

Suite E First Floor 9 Lion and Lamb Yard
Farnham, Surrey, GU9 7LL, United Kingdom
Tel.: (44) 1252821390
Fax: (44) 1252719232
Web Site: www.caspianoil.co.uk
CSH—(LSE)
Emp.: 4
Business Description:
Oil & Gas Exploration Services
S.I.C.: 1389
N.A.I.C.S.: 213112
Personnel:
Michael Masterman *(Chm)*
Board of Directors:
Michael Masterman
Michael Garland
Byron Pirola
Legal Counsel:
Kerman & Co LLP
No 7 Savoy Court Stand
London, United Kingdom

CASPIAN OIL & GAS LIMITED

(Name Changed to Equus Mining Limited)

CASSA DEPOSITI E PRESTITI SPA

(d/b/a CDP Group)
Via Goito 4
00185 Rome, Italy
Tel.: (39) 0642211
Fax: (39) 0642214026
Web Site: www.cassaddpp.it
Business Description:
Banking Services
S.I.C.: 6211
N.A.I.C.S.: 523110
Personnel:
Franco Bassanini *(Pres)*
Giovanni Gorno Tempini *(CEO)*

Non-U.S. Subsidiary:

Trans Austria Gasleitung GmbH **(1)**
Wiedner Hauptstrasse 120-124
A - 1050 Vienna, Austria De
Tel.: (43) 15975116 (89%)
Fax: (43) 1597511630
E-Mail: tag@taggmbh.at
Web Site: www.taggmbh.at
Emp.: 10
Gas Pipeline Services
S.I.C.: 4923
N.A.I.C.S.: 486210
Giuseppe Peluso *(Mng Dir)*

CASSA DI RISPARMIO DI ASTI S.P.A.

(d/b/a Banca C.R. Asti S.p.A.)
Piazza Liberta 23
14100 Asti, AT, Italy
Tel.: (39) 02 4540 3768 (Intl)
E-Mail: info@bancacrasti.it
Web Site: www.bancacrasti.it
Year Founded: 1842
Business Description:
Retail & Commercial Banking
S.I.C.: 6029
N.A.I.C.S.: 522110
Personnel:
Aldo Pia *(Chm)*
Gabriele Andreeta *(Vice Chm)*
Carlo Demartini *(Dir Gen)*
Board of Directors:
Aldo Pia
Gabriele Andreeta
Giansecondo Bossi
Pietro Cavallero
Giorgio Galvagno
Erminio Renato Goria
Pier Franco Marrandino
Secondo Scanavino
Maurizio Soave
Ercole Zuccaro

Subsidiary:

Cassa di Risparmio di Biella e Vercelli S.p.A. **(1)**
Via Carso 15
13900 Biella, BI, Italy IT
Tel.: (39) 01535081 (60.42%)
Fax: (39) 0153508370
E-Mail: bivebk@biverbanca.it
Web Site: www.biverbanca.it
Sales Range: $200-249.9 Million
Emp.: 747
Retail & Commercial Banking Services
S.I.C.: 6029
N.A.I.C.S.: 522110
Roberto De Battistini *(Deputy Chm)*

CASSIDY GOLD CORP.

1100 235 1st Avenue
Kamloops, BC, V2C 3J4, Canada
Tel.: (250) 372-8222
Fax: (250) 828-2269
E-Mail: info@cassidygold.com
Web Site: www.cassidygold.com
Year Founded: 1984
CDX—(TSXV)
Int. Income: $1,281
Assets: $27,906,813
Liabilities: $99,844
Net Worth: $27,806,969
Earnings: ($2,748,131)
Fiscal Year-end: 10/31/12
Business Description:
Mineral Exploration Services
S.I.C.: 1081
N.A.I.C.S.: 213114
Personnel:
James T. Gillis *(Pres)*
Marion Bush *(CEO)*
Marie Cupello *(CFO & Sec)*
Board of Directors:
Robert Barron
Marion Bush
James T. Gillis
Osvaldo Iadarola
Christopher J. Wild

CASSIDY VENTURES INC.

204 - 1110 Finch Ave West
Toronto, ON, M3J 3T6, Canada
Tel.: (613) 482-4886
Year Founded: 2009
CSVN—(OTC OTCB)
Liabilities: $102,693
Net Worth: ($102,693)
Earnings: ($125,677)
Fiscal Year-end: 06/30/13
Business Description:
Gold Mining Services
S.I.C.: 1041
N.A.I.C.S.: 212221
Personnel:
Keith Fredricks *(Pres)*
William Drury *(Treas & Sec)*
Board of Directors:
William Drury
Transfer Agent:
Empire Stock Transfer
1859 Whitney Mesa Dr
Henderson, NV 89014

CASSINI RESOURCES LIMITED

945 Wellington Street
West Perth, WA, 6005, Australia
Mailing Address:
PO Box 1263
West Perth, WA, 6872, Australia
Tel.: (61) 8 9322 7600
Fax: (61) 8 9322 7602
E-Mail: admin@cassiniresources.com.au
Web Site: www.cassiniresources.com.au
Year Founded: 2010
CZI—(ASX)
Business Description:
Metal Mining
S.I.C.: 1099
N.A.I.C.S.: 212299
Personnel:
Michael Young *(Chm)*
Richard Bevan *(Mng Dir & CEO)*
Steven Wood *(Sec)*
Board of Directors:
Michael Young
Richard Bevan
Greg Miles
Phil Warren
Legal Counsel:
Steinepreis Paganin
Level 4 The Read Buildings 16 Milligan Street
Perth, Australia

U.S. Subsidiary:

Lynx Resources (US) Inc. **(1)**
40 W Main St Ct Ste 250C
Alpine, UT 84004
Tel.: (801) 642-2254
Gold Exploration Services
S.I.C.: 1081
N.A.I.C.S.: 213114

CASSIUS VENTURES LTD.

3083 Three Bentall Centre 595 Burrard Street
Vancouver, BC, V7X 1L3, Canada
Tel.: (604) 558-1107
Fax: (604) 566-9081
E-Mail: darryl@k2kholdings.com
Web Site: www.cassiusventures.com
Year Founded: 2007
CZ.P—(TSXV)
Int. Income: $32,854
Assets: $5,278,441
Liabilities: $927,856
Net Worth: $4,350,585
Earnings: ($420,610)
Fiscal Year-end: 10/31/12
Business Description:
Investment Services
S.I.C.: 6211
N.A.I.C.S.: 523999
Personnel:
Steven Dean *(Chm)*
John Alan Thomas *(Pres & CEO)*
Irfan Shariff *(CFO & Sec)*
Board of Directors:
Steven Dean
Robert Atkinson
Jason Birmingham
John Alan Thomas
Transfer Agent:
Computershare Trust Company of Canada
Suite 200 510 Burrard Street
Vancouver, BC, Canada

CAST INDUSTRIES (PTY) LIMITED

38 Spanner Road
Clayville, Midrand, Gauteng, 1683, South Africa
Tel.: (27) 113162375
Fax: (27) 113162394
E-Mail: info@castindustries.co.za
Web Site: www.castindustries.co.za
Emp.: 90
Business Description:
Paving Bricks Mfr
S.I.C.: 3271
N.A.I.C.S.: 327331
Personnel:
Mariette Horton *(Mng Dir)*

CAST SA

3 rue Marcel Allegot
92190 Meudon, France
Tel.: (33) 146902100
Fax: (33) 146902101
E-Mail: info@castsoftware.com
Web Site: www.castsoftware.com
Year Founded: 1990
CAS—(EUR)
Sls.: $35,256,192
Earnings: ($5,223,140)
Fiscal Year-end: 12/31/12
Business Description:
Software Development Services
S.I.C.: 7371
N.A.I.C.S.: 541511
Personnel:
Vincent Delaroche *(Chm & CEO)*
Alexandre Rerolle *(CFO)*
Gregg Blatt *(Exec VP-Worldwide Sls & Field Ops)*
Gerard Karsenti *(Exec VP-Bus Dev-New Markets)*

Bill Curtis *(Sr VP)*
Ian Henderson *(Sr VP-Worldwide Field Ops)*

CASTEL FRERES SA

21 24 rue Georges Guynemer
33290 Blanquefort, France
Tel.: (33) 556955400
Fax: (33) 556955420
Web Site: www.groupe-castel.com
Year Founded: 1949
Sales Range: $1-4.9 Billion
Emp.: 500
Business Description:
Beverage Mfr
S.I.C.: 2084
N.A.I.C.S.: 312130
Personnel:
Pierre Castel *(Pres)*

CASTELAN LTD.

(d/b/a Castelan Group)
Alpha House
Sunnyside Road North, Weston-super-Mare, Somerset, BS23 3QY, United Kingdom
Tel.: (44) 870 320 3333
Fax: (44) 1934423422
Web Site: www.castelangroup.com
Business Description:
Retail Warranty Services
S.I.C.: 6411
N.A.I.C.S.: 524298
Personnel:
Martin John Napper *(Owner & Mng Dir)*

CASTELL HOWELL FOODS LTD.

Cross Hands Food Park
Carmarthen, Dyfed, SA14 6SX, United Kingdom
Tel.: (44) 1269846060
Fax: (44) 1269846070
E-Mail: enquiries@chfoods.co.uk
Web Site: www.castellhowellfoods.co.uk
Sales Range: $100-124.9 Million
Emp.: 280
Business Description:
General Grocery Whslr
S.I.C.: 5141
N.A.I.C.S.: 424410
Personnel:
David B Jones *(Mng Dir)*

CASTELLUM AB

Kaserntorget 5
PO Box 2269
403 14 Gothenburg, Sweden
Tel.: (46) 31607400
Fax: (46) 31131755
E-Mail: info@castellum.se
Web Site: www.castellum.se
CAST—(OMX)
Rev.: $475,700,400
Assets: $5,670,478,800
Liabilities: $3,802,816,800
Net Worth: $1,867,662,000
Earnings: $228,020,400
Emp.: 265
Fiscal Year-end: 12/31/12
Business Description:
Real Estate Services
S.I.C.: 6531
N.A.I.C.S.: 531390
Personnel:
Charlotte Stromberg *(Chm)*
Henrik Saxborn *(CEO)*
Board of Directors:
Charlotte Stromberg
Marianne Dicander Alexandersson
Per Berggren
Ulla-Britt Frajdin-Hellqvist
Christer Jacobson
Jan Ake Jonsson
Johan Skoglund

Ernst & Young
Gothenburg, Sweden

Subsidiaries:

Aspholmen Fastigheter AB **(1)**
Nasta Gratan 2
70277 Orebro, Sweden (100%)
Tel.: (46) 19276500
Fax: (46) 19276519
E-Mail: orebro@aspholmenfastigheter.se
Web Site: www.aspholmenfastigheter.se
Emp.: 33
Lessors of Other Real Estate Property
S.I.C.: 6519
N.A.I.C.S.: 531190
Claes Larsson *(Mng Dir)*

Eklandia Fastighets AB **(1)**
Ringogatan 12 8725
40275 Gothenburg, Sweden
Tel.: (46) 317440900
Fax: (46) 317440950
E-Mail: info@eklandia.se
Web Site: www.eklandia.se
Emp.: 35
Other Real Estate Property Lessors
S.I.C.: 6519
N.A.I.C.S.: 531190
Tage Christoffersson *(Mng Dir)*

Fastighets AB Briggen **(1)**
Fredriksbergsgatan 1
3158
20022 Malmo, Sweden (100%)
Tel.: (46) 40383720
Fax: (46) 40383737
E-Mail: fastighets.ab@briggen.se
Web Site: www.briggen.se
Emp.: 37
Other Holding Companies Offices
S.I.C.: 6719
N.A.I.C.S.: 551112
Gunnar Ostenson *(Mng Dir)*

Fastighets AB Brostaden **(1)**
Bolidenvagen 14
Johanneshov, 12105 Stockholm, Sweden (100%)
Tel.: (46) 86023300
Fax: (46) 86023330
E-Mail: info@brostaden.se
Web Site: www.brostaden.se
Emp.: 40
Other Real Estate Property Lessors
S.I.C.: 6519
N.A.I.C.S.: 531190
Anders Nilsson *(Mng Dir)*

Fastighets AB Corallen **(1)**
Jonkopingsvagen 41
33121 Varnamo, Sweden
Tel.: (46) 370694900
Fax: (46) 37047590
E-Mail: info@corallen.se
Web Site: www.corallen.se
Emp.: 35
Other Holding Companies Offices
S.I.C.: 6719
N.A.I.C.S.: 551112
Claes Juneselt *(Mng Dir)*

Harry Sjogren AB **(1)**
Kraketorpsgatan 20
43153 Molndal, Sweden (100%)
Tel.: (46) 317066500
Fax: (46) 317066529
E-Mail: info@harrysjogren.se
Web Site: www.harrysjogren.se
Emp.: 27
Other Real Estate Property Lessors
S.I.C.: 6519
N.A.I.C.S.: 531190
Christer Sundberg *(CEO & Mng Dir)*

CASTILLIAN RESOURCES CORP.

(Name Changed to Coastal Gold Corp.)

CASTILLO COPPER LIMITED

(Formerly Oakland Resources Limited)
Level 1 330 Churchill Avenue
Subiaco, WA, 6008, Australia
Mailing Address:
PO Box 540
Subiaco, WA, 6904, Australia
Tel.: (61) 8 9200 4491
Fax: (61) 8 9200 4469
E-Mail: info@castillocopper.com
Web Site: www.castillocopper.com
CCZ—(ASX)
Rev.: $21,647
Assets: $4,052,261
Liabilities: $747,568
Net Worth: $3,304,693
Earnings: ($643,035)
Fiscal Year-end: 06/30/13
Business Description:
Copper Mining Services
S.I.C.: 1021
N.A.I.C.S.: 212234
Personnel:
Brian McMaster *(Chm)*
Nicholas Lindsay *(Mng Dir)*
Scott Funston *(Sec)*
Board of Directors:
Brian McMaster
Daniel Crennan
Scott Funston
Nicholas Lindsay
Legal Counsel:
Steinepreis Paganin
Level 4 The Read Buildings 16 Milligan Street
6000 Perth, WA, Australia

CASTINGS PLC

Lichfield Road
Brownhills, West Midlands, WS8 6JZ, United Kingdom
Tel.: (44) 1543374341
Fax: (44) 1543377483
E-Mail: sales@castings.plc.uk
Web Site: www.castings.plc.uk
CGS—(LSE)
Rev.: $193,012,927
Assets: $204,979,208
Liabilities: $43,736,857
Net Worth: $161,242,350
Earnings: $23,351,382
Emp.: 1,052
Fiscal Year-end: 03/31/13
Business Description:
Iron Supplies
S.I.C.: 1011
N.A.I.C.S.: 212210
Personnel:
Brian J. Cooke *(Chm)*
David J. Gawthorpe *(CEO)*
Steve J. Mant *(Sec & Dir-Fin)*
Board of Directors:
Brian J. Cooke
Graham Cooper
David J. Gawthorpe
Alec N. Jones
C. Paul King
Mark A. Lewis
Steve J. Mant
Adam Vicary
Gerard B. Wainwright
Legal Counsel:
Pinsent Masons LLP
3 Colmore Circus
Birmingham, United Kingdom

Enoch Evans LLP
St Paul's Chambers 6/9 Hatherton Road
Walsall, West Midlands, WS1 1XS, United Kingdom

Subsidiaries:

CNC Speedwell Limited **(1)**
258-260 Lichfield Rd
Brownhills, West Midlands, WS8 6JZ, United Kingdom
Tel.: (44) 1543363880
Fax: (44) 1543363881
E-Mail: mail@cncspeedwell.co.uk
Web Site: www.cncspeedwell.co.uk
Emp.: 140
Ductile Iron Castings Mfr
S.I.C.: 3321
N.A.I.C.S.: 331511
Mark Lewis *(Mng Dir)*

William Lee Limited **(1)**
Callywhite Ln
Dronfield, Derbyshire, S18 2XU, United Kingdom
Tel.: (44) 1246416155
Fax: (44) 1246417165
E-Mail: sales@wmlee.co.uk
Web Site: www.wmlee.co.uk
Emp.: 400
Iron Castings Mfr
S.I.C.: 3322
N.A.I.C.S.: 331511
Graham Cooper *(Mng Dir)*

CASTLE ALTERNATIVE INVEST AG

Schutzenstrasse 6
8808 Pfaffikon, Switzerland
Tel.: (41) 554159487
Fax: (41) 554159488
E-Mail: lgt.cai@lgt.com
Web Site: www.castle.li
Year Founded: 1996
CASN—(SWX)
Rev.: $26,333,000
Assets: $407,151,000
Liabilities: $152,632,000
Net Worth: $254,519,000
Earnings: $18,496,000
Fiscal Year-end: 12/31/12
Business Description:
Investment Services
S.I.C.: 6211
N.A.I.C.S.: 523999
Personnel:
Tim Steel *(Chm)*
Konrad Bachinger *(Deputy Chm)*
Siva Sethuraman *(COO)*
Board of Directors:
Tim Steel
Konrad Bachinger
Reto Koller
Andre Lagger
Kevin Mathews

CASTLE FUELS INC.

1639 E Trans Canada Hwy
Kamloops, BC, V2C 3Z5, Canada
Tel.: (250) 372-5035
Fax: (250) 372-1383
Toll Free: (877) 372-5035
E-Mail: info@castlefuels.ca
Web Site: www.castlefuels.ca
Rev.: $21,375,238
Emp.: 25
Business Description:
Petroleum Products Whslr
S.I.C.: 2911
N.A.I.C.S.: 324110
Personnel:
Robert R. Vandriel *(Owner & Pres)*

CASTLE HILL RSL CLUB LTD.

77 Castle St
Castle Hill, New South Wales, 2154, Australia
Tel.: (61) 288584800
Fax: (61) 288584811
E-Mail: info@castlehillrsl.com.au
Web Site: www.castlehillrsl.com.au
Sales Range: $125-149.9 Million
Emp.: 208
Business Description:
Recreational Services
S.I.C.: 7032
N.A.I.C.S.: 721214
Personnel:
Warren E. Glenny *(Pres)*
Robbie B. Duncan *(Treas)*
Board of Directors:
Rick Cumming

Castle Hill RSL Club Ltd.—(Continued)

Merv W. Cummings
Robbie B. Duncan
Warren E. Glenny
Walter Hromow
Robert Hudson
Paul Lippman
Noel H. Simmons
Ron M. Smith
Bryan Stansfield
Don Tait
David B. Wood

CASTLE MINERALS LIMITED

Unit 6 1 Clive Street
West Perth, WA, 6005, Australia
Mailing Address:
PO Box 437
West Perth, WA, 6872, Australia
Tel.: (61) 893227018
Fax: (61) 8 9284 5413
E-Mail: info@castleminerals.com
Web Site: www.castleminerals.com
CDT—(ASX)
Rev.: $151,666
Assets: $2,415,155
Liabilities: $189,462
Net Worth: $2,225,693
Earnings: ($2,188,218)
Emp.: 4
Fiscal Year-end: 06/30/13
Business Description:
Gold Exploration & Mining Services
S.I.C.: 1041
N.A.I.C.S.: 212221
Personnel:
Michael Ivey *(CEO & Mng Dir)*
Desmond Kelly *(Sec)*
Board of Directors:
Michael Ashforth
Campbell Ansell
Michael Ivey
Legal Counsel:
Reindorf Chambers
20 Jones Nelson Road Adabraka
Accra, Ghana
Gilbert & Tobin
1202 Hay Street
West Perth, Australia

CASTLE MOUNTAIN MINING COMPANY LIMITED

(Formerly Foxpoint Capital Corp.)
83 Yonge Street Suite 200
Toronto, ON, M5C 1S8, Canada
Tel.: (416) 640-1930
Fax: (416) 640-1928
E-Mail: bmorales@83yonge.com
Web Site:
Year Founded: 2009
CMM—(TSXV)
Assets: $14,790,626
Liabilities: $4,641,373
Net Worth: $10,149,253
Earnings: ($5,742,798)
Fiscal Year-end: 12/31/12
Business Description:
Gold Mining Services
S.I.C.: 1041
N.A.I.C.S.: 212221
Personnel:
Gordon McCreary *(Pres & CEO)*
Brian Morales *(CFO)*
Transfer Agent:
Equity Financial Trust Company
200 University Avenue Suite 400
Toronto, ON, Canada

CASTLE PEAK HOLDINGS PUBLIC COMPANY LIMITED

CPH Tower 899 Petchkasem Road
Bangkae Sub-district
Khet Bangkae, Bangkok, 10160, Thailand
Tel.: (66) 24550300
Fax: (66) 24550358
Web Site: www.castlepeak.co.th
Year Founded: 1976
CPH—(THA)
Rev.: $40,062,813
Assets: $41,255,873
Liabilities: $12,276,548
Net Worth: $28,979,325
Earnings: ($1,490,610)
Emp.: 4,000
Fiscal Year-end: 12/31/12
Business Description:
Jacket & Apparel Mfr
S.I.C.: 2399
N.A.I.C.S.: 315990
Personnel:
Boonchoo Pongchaloem *(Chm & Pres)*
Henry Chor Ting Liu *(Vice Chm & Dir-Mktg)*
Aree Tempitayakom *(Vice Chm)*
Nophakoon Somboonviriya *(Sec & Dir-Fin & Acctg)*
Board of Directors:
Boonchoo Pongchaloem
Pailin Janyaniwat
Tipwan Kramsir
Henry Chor Ting Liu
Nophakoon Somboonviriya
Piyada Sooksai
Aree Tempitayakom
Songsak Wongsunkakorn
Man Fun Wu
Subsidiaries:

Castle Peak Real Estate Co., Ltd. **(1)**
393 Moo 4 th Floor CPS Tower Petkasem Road
Bangkhae, Bangkok, 10160, Thailand
Tel.: (66) 2 8011802
Fax: (66) 2 8011802
Real Estate Development Services
S.I.C.: 6531
N.A.I.C.S.: 531390

C.P.G. Garment Co., Ltd. **(1)**
2 Soi Petchakasem 50/2 Petchkasem Road Bangwah
Khet Pasricharoen, Bangkok, 10160, Thailand
Tel.: (66) 2 457 4142
Fax: (66) 2 457 3324
Garment Mfr
S.I.C.: 2259
N.A.I.C.S.: 315190

CASTLE PRIVATE EQUITY AG

Schutzenstrasse 6
8808 Pfaffikon, Switzerland
Tel.: (41) 55 415 9494
Fax: (41) 55 415 9497
Web Site: www.castlepe.com
Year Founded: 1997
CPENE—(SWX)
Rev.: $81,280,000
Assets: $694,807,000
Liabilities: $9,451,000
Net Worth: $685,356,000
Earnings: $58,600,000
Fiscal Year-end: 12/31/12
Business Description:
Investment Management Services
S.I.C.: 6211
N.A.I.C.S.: 523999
Personnel:
Gilbert Chalk *(Chm)*
Konrad Bachinger *(Deputy Chm)*
Siva Sethuraman *(COO)*
Board of Directors:
Gilbert Chalk
Thomas Amstutz
Konrad Bachinger
Marcel Erni
Robert Knapp
Heinz Nipp
James Pluhar

CASTLE RESOURCES INC.

20 Victoria Street 8th Floor
Toronto, ON, M5C 2N8, Canada
Tel.: (416) 366-4100
Fax: (416) 366-4101
E-Mail: info@castleresources.com
Web Site: www.castleresources.ca
Year Founded: 2004
CRI—(TSXV)
Int. Income: $36,452
Assets: $44,795,419
Liabilities: $4,882,442
Net Worth: $39,912,977
Earnings: ($5,154,567)
Fiscal Year-end: 09/30/13
Business Description:
Copper Mining
S.I.C.: 1021
N.A.I.C.S.: 212234
Personnel:
Stephen Shefsky *(Chm)*
Michel Sylvestre *(Pres & CEO)*
Eric Szustak *(CFO)*
Board of Directors:
Stephen Shefsky
Tony Croll
Lester Fernandez
Tim Mann
Tyler Mitchelson
Michel Sylvestre
Legal Counsel:
WeirFoulds LLP
Toronto, ON, Canada
Transfer Agent:
CST Trust Company
PO Box 721 Agnicourt
Toronto, ON, M1S 0A1, Canada

C.A.T. OIL AG

Kaerntner Ring 11-13
A-1010 Vienna, Austria
Tel.: (43) 153523200
Fax: (43) 1535232020
E-Mail: ir@catoilag.com
Web Site: www.catoilag.com
O2C—(DEU)
Rev.: $449,937,130
Assets: $492,445,140
Liabilities: $162,671,183
Net Worth: $329,773,957
Earnings: $28,313,994
Emp.: 2,522
Fiscal Year-end: 12/31/12
Business Description:
Oil & Gas Exploration Services
S.I.C.: 1389
N.A.I.C.S.: 213112
Personnel:
Gerhard Strate *(Chm-Supervisory Bd)*
Manfred Kastner *(Chm-Mgmt Bd & CEO)*
Manfred Zacher *(Deputy Chm-Supervisory Bd)*
Ronald Harder *(Vice Chm-Mgmt Bd & CFO)*
Anna Brinkmann *(COO & Member-Mgmt Bd)*
Leonid Mirzoyan *(Chief Corp Fin Officer & Member-Mgmt Bd)*
Supervisory Board of Directors:
Gerhard Strate
Walter Hoft
Mirco Schroeter
Manfred Zacher

CATACA RESOURCES, INC.

782 Ayala Avenue
Makati, 2130, Philippines
Tel.: (63) 917 234 0098
Year Founded: 2012
Business Description:
Gold Mining
S.I.C.: 1041
N.A.I.C.S.: 212221
Personnel:
Edward Barrios *(Pres)*
Maxwell Ramos *(Treas & Sec)*
Board of Directors:
Edward Barrios

CATALINA HOLDINGS (BERMUDA) LTD.

Cumberland House Victoria St
PO Box HM 3303
Hamilton, HM 22, Bermuda
Tel.: (441) 2946350
Fax: (441) 2946390
Web Site: www.catalinare.com
Business Description:
Acquirer & Manager of Non-Life Insurance & Reinsurance Companies in Run-Off
S.I.C.: 6411
N.A.I.C.S.: 524298
Personnel:
Chris Fagan *(CEO)*
Chris Fleming *(CFO)*
Peter Johnson *(COO)*
Peter Harnik *(Chief Investment Officer)*
Dean Dwonczyk *(Chief Actuarial Officer)*
Keith Lyon *(Gen Counsel)*
U.S. Subsidiary:

Quanta U.S. Holdings Inc. **(1)**
48 Wall St
New York, NY 10005 DE
Tel.: (212) 373-1800
Fax: (212) 373-1803
Emp.: 13
Insurance Services
S.I.C.: 6411
N.A.I.C.S.: 524210
Peter Johnson *(CEO)*

Non-U.S. Subsidiaries:

Catalina Holdings UK Limited **(1)**
18 Mansell 4th Floor
London, E1 8AA, United Kingdom
Tel.: (44) 2072655000
Fax: (44) 2072655001
Web Site: www.catalina.com
Insurance Related Activities
S.I.C.: 6411
N.A.I.C.S.: 524298

KX Reinsurance Company Limited **(1)**
The Isis Building
193 Marsh Wall, London, E14 9SG, United Kingdom
Tel.: (44) 2070688000
Fax: (44) 2070688001
E-Mail:
Emp.: 50
Reinsurance Products & Services
S.I.C.: 6399
N.A.I.C.S.: 524130
Colin Bird *(CEO)*

Subsidiaries:

OX Reinsurance Company Limited **(2)**
The Isis Building 193 Marsh Wall
London, E14 9SG, United Kingdom UK
Tel.: (44) 20 7068 8000
Fax: (44) 20 7068 8001
Reinsurance Services
S.I.C.: 6399
N.A.I.C.S.: 524130
Colin Bird *(CEO)*

CATALIS SE

Geldropseweg 26 28
5611 SJ Eindhoven, Netherlands
Tel.: (31) 402135930
Fax: (31) 402135604
E-Mail: info@catalisgroup.com
Web Site: www.catalisgroup.com
Year Founded: 2000
XAE—(DEU)

Rev.: $37,266,024
Assets: $33,456,363
Liabilities: $22,934,698
Net Worth: $10,521,665
Earnings: $141,348
Emp.: 349
Fiscal Year-end: 12/31/12
Business Description:
Digital Media & Entertainment Outsourcing Services
S.I.C.: 7819
N.A.I.C.S.: 512199
Personnel:
Dominic Wheatley *(CEO)*
Peter Biewald *(CFO)*
Nick Winks *(Chief Restructuring Officer)*
Board of Directors:
Jens Bodenkamp
Peter Biewald
Robert Kass
Dominic Wheatley
Nick Winks
U.S. Subsidiary:

Testronic Laboratories Inc. (1)
111 N First St Ste 204
Burbank, CA 91502
Tel.: (818) 845-3223
Fax: (818) 843-1433
Web Site: www.testroniclaboratories.com
Sales Range: $10-24.9 Million
Emp.: 52
Digital Media Quality Assurance Services
S.I.C.: 7389
N.A.I.C.S.: 561499
Seth Hallen *(Pres)*
Mike McGarvey *(CEO)*
Jason Gish *(Sr VP-Film & Television Svcs & Gen Mgr)*

Non-U.S. Subsidiaries:

Kuju Entertainment Ltd. (1)
Suite 2 River House
Broadford Business Park, Shalford, Surrey, GU4 8EP, United Kingdom
Tel.: (44) 1483409950
Fax: (44) 1483571662
E-Mail: admin@kuju.com
Web Site: www.kuju.com
Sales Range: $10-24.9 Million
Emp.: 238
Video Game Development Services
S.I.C.: 7372
N.A.I.C.S.: 511210
Ian Baverstock *(Co-Founder)*
Jonathan Newth *(Co-Founder)*
Dominic Wheatley *(Chm)*

Kuju Plc (1)
160 - 166 Borough High Street
London, SE1 1LB, United Kingdom
Tel.: (44) 20 7593 2230
Fax: (44) 1483571662
E-Mail: kuju@kuju.com
Web Site: www.kuju.com
Emp.: 70
Gaming Software Development Services
S.I.C.: 7371
N.A.I.C.S.: 541511
Dominic Wheatley *(CEO)*

Testronic Laboratories Ltd (1)
160-166 Borough High Street
London, SE1 1LB, United Kingdom
Tel.: (44) 207 253 7258
Fax: (44) 1753 654499
Web Site: www.testroniclabs.com
Product Testing Services
S.I.C.: 8734
N.A.I.C.S.: 541380
Seth Hallen *(CEO)*
Johan Craeybeckx *(CTO)*
David Hooker *(Sr VP-Sls & Mktg)*

Subsidiary:

Testline Ltd (2)
160-166 Borough High St
London, SE1 1LB, United Kingdom
Tel.: (44) 2072537258
Fax: (44) 2072537259
Web Site: www.testline.co.uk
Gaming Software Development Services
S.I.C.: 7371
N.A.I.C.S.: 541511

Testronic Laboratories N.V (1)
Wetenschapspark 7
Diepenbeek, Limburg, 3590, Belgium
Tel.: (32) 11303600
Fax: (32) 11303696
Emp.: 50
Product Testing Services
S.I.C.: 8734
N.A.I.C.S.: 541380
Johan Craeybeckx *(Mng Dir)*

CATALUNYA BANC, S.A.

(d/b/a CatalunyaCaixa Group)
Placa Antoni Maura 6
08003 Barcelona, Spain
Tel.: (34) 93 484 5000
Telex: 50722 CADC
Fax: (34) 934844958
E-Mail: info@catalunyacaixa.com
Web Site: www.catalunyacaixa.com
Year Founded: 1926
Sales Range: $1-4.9 Billion
Emp.: 7,200
Business Description:
Savings Bank
S.I.C.: 6036
N.A.I.C.S.: 522120
Personnel:
Jose Carlos Pla *(Chm)*
Jaume Masana Ribalta *(CEO)*
Joan Rafols Llach *(Sec)*
Board of Directors:
Jose Carlos Pla
Juan F. Corona Ramon
Jose Antonio Garcia Rico
Jose Garcia-Montalvo
Manuel Gari Eguillor
Helena Guardens Cambo
Juan M. Hernandez Andres
Jaume Masana Ribalta
Luis Conde Moller
Francisco Orenes Bo
Subsidiaries:

Ascat Corredoria d'Assequrances S.L. (1)
Napoles 249 Fl 2
08013 Barcelona, Spain (100%)
Tel.: (34) 902484484
Fax: (34) 934847355
Web Site: www.caixacat.es
Emp.: 11
Brokerage Insurance
S.I.C.: 6411
N.A.I.C.S.: 524210

Ascat Vida S.A. (1)
Provenca 398
08025 Barcelona, Spain ES
Tel.: (34) 901324324 (100%)
Fax: (34) 5934845371
Web Site: www.ascat.es
Emp.: 75
Life Insurance
S.I.C.: 6311
N.A.I.C.S.: 524113

Caixa Catalunya Consulting (1)
Fontanella 5 7
Barcelona, 8010, Spain ES
Tel.: (34) 934841111 (100%)
Fax: (34) 93 484 1101
Web Site: www.caixacatalunya-consulting.com
General Consulting Services
S.I.C.: 8742
N.A.I.C.S.: 541611

Caixa Catalunya Gestio (1)
Plza Antone Maura
08003 Barcelona, Spain (100%)
Tel.: (34) 934845000
Fax: (34) 934845381
E-Mail: info@caivacat.es
Web Site: www.caixacat.es
Emp.: 34
Investment Fund Management
S.I.C.: 6282
N.A.I.C.S.: 523920
Joseph Manuel *(Gen Mgr)*

Caixa Catalunya On-Line (1)
Pl Antoni Maura 6
8003 Barcelona, Spain ES
Tel.: (34) 902425542 (100%)
Fax: (34) 934799929
Web Site: www.caixacatalunya.com
Emp.: 25
On-Line Communications
S.I.C.: 6035
N.A.I.C.S.: 522120

Factorcat, Establecimiento Financiero de Credito, S.A. (1)
Fontanella 5 7
Barcelona, Spain, 8010, Spain (100%)
Tel.: (34) 934844349
Fax: (34) 934845290
Web Site: www.caixacat.com
Emp.: 27
Factoring
S.I.C.: 6159
N.A.I.C.S.: 522298

Gestio D'Actius Titulitzats, S.G.F.T.H. (1)
Fontanella 5 7
E 08010 Barcelona, Spain (100%)
Tel.: (34) 934847338
Fax: (34) 934847341
E-Mail: info@gat-sgft.com
Web Site: www.gat-sgft.info
Emp.: 5
Mortgage Backed Securitization & Asset Backed Securitization
S.I.C.: 6351
N.A.I.C.S.: 524126
Carlos Fruns *(CEO)*

Invercartera, S.A. (1)
Fontanella 5 7
E 08010 Barcelona, Spain (100%)
Tel.: (34) 934845329
Fax: (34) 934845352
E-Mail: invercartera@invercartera.com
Emp.: 20
Real Estate
S.I.C.: 6531
N.A.I.C.S.: 531210
Josep Fabrigit *(Mng Dir)*

Invercatalunya Tecnologia, SL (1)
Fontanella 5 7
E 08010 Barcelona, Spain (100%)
Tel.: (34) 934845329
Fax: (34) 934845352
E-Mail: invercartera@invercartera.com
Emp.: 14
S.I.C.: 6035
N.A.I.C.S.: 522120

Leasing Catalunya, Establecimiento Financiero de Credito S.A. (1)
Fontanella 5 7
E 08010 Barcelona, Spain (100%)
Tel.: (34) 934845483
E-Mail:
Web Site: www.catalunyacaixa.com
Emp.: 25
Leasing
S.I.C.: 6141
N.A.I.C.S.: 522220

Promotora Catalunya Mediterranea (1)
Passeig de Gracia 49 entresol 2a
08007 Barcelona, Spain (100%)
Tel.: (34) 934 961 680
Fax: (34) 934 879 836
E-Mail: procam@procam.net
Web Site: www.caixacatalunya.com
Emp.: 15
Real Estate Promotion
S.I.C.: 6531
N.A.I.C.S.: 531210

Sabel Serveis, S.A. (1)
Pl Espanya 6 8
E 08014 Barcelona, Spain (77.5%)
Tel.: (34) 934262600
Fax: (34) 9342604000
E-Mail: caixa@hoteles-catalunya.es
Emp.: 160
Provider of Hotel Services
S.I.C.: 7011
N.A.I.C.S.: 721110
Luther Sigja *(Office Mgr)*

THE CATALYST CAPITAL GROUP, INC.

T-D Centre Ste 3475
79 Wellington St W, Toronto, ON, M5K 1J3, Canada
Tel.: (416) 945-3000
Fax: (416) 945-3060
E-Mail: info@catcapital.com
Web Site: www.catcapital.com
Year Founded: 2002
Managed Assets: $942,664,000
Business Description:
Private Equity Firm
S.I.C.: 6211
N.A.I.C.S.: 523999
Personnel:
Newton Glassman *(Mng Partner)*
Subsidiaries:

Therapure Biopharma Inc. (1)
2585 Meadowpine Blvd
Mississauga, ON, L5N 8H9, Canada Ca
Tel.: (905) 286-6200
Fax: (905) 286-6300
E-Mail: info@therapurebio.com
Web Site: www.therapurebio.com
Sales Range: $25-49.9 Million
Global Contract Development & Manufacturing Therapeutics for Biopharmaceutical Companies
S.I.C.: 2836
N.A.I.C.S.: 325414
Nicholas Green *(Pres & CEO)*
Brian Fielding *(VP-Fin & CFO)*
David N. Bell *(VP-Drug Dev & Chief Scientific Officer)*

Planet Organic Health Corp. (1)
7915 104th Street Suite 230
Edmonton, AB, T6E 4E1, Canada AB
Tel.: (780) 433-7278
Fax: (780) 429-7133
E-Mail: info@planetorganic.ca
Web Site: www.planetorganichealthcorp.com
Sales Range: $75-99.9 Million
Natural Foods Supermarket Operator
S.I.C.: 5411
N.A.I.C.S.: 445110

Subsidiary:

Planet Organic Market Ltd. (2)
7917 - 104 Street
Edmonton, AB, T6E 4E1, Canada
Tel.: (708) 719-4667
Fax: (780) 429-7133
Web Site: www.planetorganic.ca
Natural Foods Supermarket Operator
S.I.C.: 5411
N.A.I.C.S.: 445110

U.S. Subsidiary:

Mrs. Green's Natural Markets (2)
780 White Plains Rd
Scarsdale, NY 10583 NY
Tel.: (914) 472-0111
Fax: (914) 472-0624
Web Site: www.mrsgreens.com
Emp.: 20
Natural Foods Supermarket Operator
S.I.C.: 5411
N.A.I.C.S.: 445110
Harold Hochberger *(Pres)*

CATALYST COPPER CORP.

Suite 555 - 999 Canada Place
Vancouver, BC, V6C 3E1, Canada
Tel.: (604) 638-5900
Fax: (604) 629-2572
E-Mail: info@catalystcopper.com
Web Site: www.catalystcopper.com
CCY—(OTC TSXV)
Assets: $15,538,297
Liabilities: $121,868
Net Worth: $15,416,429
Earnings: ($1,794,231)
Fiscal Year-end: 12/31/12
Business Description:
Metal Mining Exploration Service
S.I.C.: 1081

Catalyst Copper Corp.—(Continued)

N.A.I.C.S.: 213114
Personnel:
John W. Greenslade *(Pres & CEO)*
Denby Greenslade *(Interim CFO & Sec)*
Board of Directors:
John W. Greenslade
Terence W. Hodson
Gordon Keep
George W. Poling
John Douglas Reynolds

Non-U.S. Subsidiary:

Minera Hill 29, S.A de C.V. (1)
Sinaloa 106 Desp 302 Col Roma
6700 Mexico, Mexico
Tel.: (52) 5555250445
Emp.: 12
Mineral Mining Services
S.I.C.: 1481
N.A.I.C.S.: 213115

CATALYST INVESTMENT MANAGERS PTY. LIMITED

Level 9 151 153 Macquarie St
Sydney, NSW, 2000, Australia
Tel.: (61) 0292701200
Fax: (61) 0292701222
E-Mail: enquiries@catalystinvest.com.au
Web Site: www.catalystinvest.com.au
Emp.: 10
Business Description:
Private Equity Firm
S.I.C.: 6211
N.A.I.C.S.: 523999
Personnel:
Brian Gatfield *(Chm)*
Simon Dighton *(Mng Dir)*
Trent Peterson *(Mng Dir)*
John Story *(Mng Dir)*
Adrian Warner *(Mng Dir)*
Ishbel Sterrick *(CFO)*

Holding:

Cirrus Media Pty. Limited (1)
(Formerly Reed Business Information Pty. Limited)
Tower 2 475 Victoria Avenue
Locked Bag 2999
Chatswood, NSW, 2067, Australia AU
Tel.: (61) 294222999
Fax: (61) 294222922
E-Mail: hello@cirrusmedia.com.au
Web Site: www.cirrusmedia.com.au
Emp.: 300
Trade Journals Publisher & Information Services
S.I.C.: 2721
N.A.I.C.S.: 511120
Jeremy Knibbs *(CEO)*
Jeff Godwin *(CFO)*
Peter Smal *(COO)*
Phil Craig *(CTO)*
Ben Sole *(Chief Revenue Officer)*

Unit:

Catch (2)
Tower 1 L13 495 Victoria Ave
Locked Bag 2999
Chatswood, NSW, 2067, Australia
Tel.: (61) 294222999
Fax: (61) 294222922
E-Mail: enquiries@catch.com.au
Web Site: www.catch.com.au
Emp.: 150
Online Business Directory Publisher
S.I.C.: 2741
N.A.I.C.S.: 519130
Cameron Elliot *(Dir-Sls)*

CATALYST MEDIA GROUP PLC

4th Floor Roman House
296 Golders Green Road, London, NW11 9PY, United Kingdom
Tel.: (44) 2076378412
Fax: (44) 2084577810
E-Mail: info@cmg-plc.com
Web Site: www.cmg-plc.com
CMX—(AIM)
Sales Range: Less than $1 Million
Business Description:
Digital Multi-Media Content Distr
S.I.C.: 7379
N.A.I.C.S.: 541519
Personnel:
Michael Samuel Rosenberg *(Chm)*
Board of Directors:
Michael Samuel Rosenberg
Mark Hawtin
Melvin Lawson
Christopher Harwood Bernard Mills
Legal Counsel:
Lewis Silkin LLP
5 Chancery Lane Cliffords Inn
London, United Kingdom

CATALYST METALS LIMITED

Level 3 50 Colin Street
West Perth, WA, 6005, Australia
Tel.: (61) 893832825
Fax: (61) 892845426
E-Mail: admin@catalystmetals.com.au
Web Site: www.catalystmetals.com.au
CYL—(ASX)
Rev.: $58,301
Assets: $1,197,225
Liabilities: $282,801
Net Worth: $914,424
Earnings: ($1,049,792)
Emp.: 3
Fiscal Year-end: 06/30/13
Business Description:
Mineral Explorer
S.I.C.: 1481
N.A.I.C.S.: 213115
Personnel:
Frank Campagna *(Sec)*
Board of Directors:
Stephen Boston
Bruce Kay
Gary Schwab
Robin Scrimgeour

CATALYST PAPER CORPORATION

2nd Floor 3600 Lysander Lane
Richmond, BC, V7B 1C3, Canada
Tel.: (604) 247-4400
Fax: (604) 247-0512
E-Mail: contactus@catalystpaper.com
Web Site: www.catalystpaper.com
Year Founded: 1971
CYT—(TSX)
Sls.: $945,576,590
Assets: $629,634,935
Liabilities: $618,033,320
Net Worth: $11,601,615
Earnings: ($114,487,255)
Emp.: 1,550
Fiscal Year-end: 12/31/13
Business Description:
Paper & Pulp Products Mfr & Mill Operator
S.I.C.: 2621
N.A.I.C.S.: 322121
Personnel:
Leslie T. Lederer *(Chm)*
Joe Nemeth *(Pres & CEO)*
Brian Baarda *(CFO & VP-Fin)*
David Adderley *(Gen Counsel & VP)*
Alistair MacCallum *(Treas, VP & Controller)*
Steve Boniferro *(Sr VP-HR)*
Robert L. Stepusin *(Sr VP-Bus Improvement)*
Board of Directors:
John Raymond Brecker
John Charles
Todd Dillabough
Walter Jones
Jill Leversage
Transfer Agent:
CST Trust Company
Toronto, ON, Canada

CATCHA MEDIA BERHAD

45 7 The Boulevard Mid Valley City
59200 Kuala Lumpur, Malaysia
Tel.: (60) 3 22970999
Fax: (60) 3 22970888
E-Mail: publicrelations@catchamedia.com
Web Site: www.catchamedia.com
CATCHA—(KLS)
Rev.: $12,296,868
Assets: $13,514,207
Liabilities: $4,210,401
Net Worth: $9,303,806
Earnings: $1,503,771
Fiscal Year-end: 12/31/12
Business Description:
Online Media & Magazine Publishing
S.I.C.: 2741
N.A.I.C.S.: 519130
Personnel:
Patrick Y-Kin Grove *(CEO)*
Yit Chan Tai *(Co-Sec)*
Ai Ning Tan *(Co-Sec)*
Board of Directors:
Larry Nyap Liou Gan
Lucas Robert Elliott
Patrick Y-Kin Grove
Yin Chow Lim
Yong Sun Mah
Kensuke Tsurumaru

CATELLA GROUP

Birger Jarlsgatan 6
PO Box 5894
SE 102 40 Stockholm, Sweden
Tel.: (46) 84633310
Fax: (46) 8463393
E-Mail: info@catella.se
Web Site: www.catella.se
Sales Range: $100-124.9 Million
Emp.: 443
Business Description:
Asset Management & Financial Advisory Services
S.I.C.: 6211
N.A.I.C.S.: 523930
Personnel:
Johan Claesson *(Chm)*
Johan Ericsson *(CEO)*
Ando Wikstrom *(CFO)*
Johan Nordenfalk *(Chief Legal Officer)*
Board of Directors:
Johan Claesson
Stefan Carlsson
Bjorn Edgren
Niklas Johansson
Jan Roxendal

Non-U.S. Subsidiary:

Banque Invik S.A. (1)
2-4 Avenue Marie Gherese
2132 Luxembourg, Luxembourg
Tel.: (352) 27751101
Fax: (352) 27751272
E-Mail: contact@banqueinvik.lu
Web Site: www.banqueinvik.lu
Emp.: 108
Private Banking, Asset Management & Corporate Financial Services
S.I.C.: 6029
N.A.I.C.S.: 522110
Torben Madsen *(Pres)*

CATELLI HOLDING S.P.A.

(d/b/a Catelli Food Technology)
Via Paradigna 94/A
43122 Parma, Italy
Tel.: (39) 0521 277111
Fax: (39) 0521 798404
E-Mail: info@cft-group.com
Web Site: www.cft-group.com
Business Description:
Food Processing Equipment Mfr
S.I.C.: 3556
N.A.I.C.S.: 333241
Personnel:
Roberto Catelli *(Pres)*

Subsidiary:

Raytec Vision S.p.A. (1)
Via Maestri del Lavoro 1/3
Fraz Lemignano di Collecchio, 43044 Parma, Italy
Tel.: (39) 0521303427
Fax: (39) 0521339325
E-Mail: info@raytecvision.com
Web Site: www.raytecvision.com
Food Product Machinery Mfr
S.I.C.: 3556
N.A.I.C.S.: 333241
Raffaele Pezzoli *(Mng Dir)*

CATENON S.A.

Avda General Peron 38
28020 Madrid, Spain
Tel.: (34) 913096980
Fax: (34) 913096981
E-Mail: investors@catenon.com
Web Site: www.catenon.com
COM—(MAD)
Sales Range: $10-24.9 Million
Emp.: 90
Business Description:
Executive Search Services
S.I.C.: 8742
N.A.I.C.S.: 561312
Personnel:
Javier Ruiz de Azcarate Varela *(Pres)*

CATERING INTERNATIONAL & SERVICES S.A.

40 C avenue de Hambourg
13008 Marseille, France
Tel.: (33) 4 91 16 53 00
Fax: (33) 4 91 72 65 08
E-Mail: contact@cis-catering.com
Web Site: www.cis-catering.com
Year Founded: 1992
CTRG—(EUR)
Rev.: $424,844,521
Assets: $174,009,973
Liabilities: $94,647,867
Net Worth: $79,362,106
Earnings: $16,238,849
Emp.: 11,600
Fiscal Year-end: 12/31/12
Business Description:
Catering Services
S.I.C.: 5812
N.A.I.C.S.: 722320
Personnel:
Regis Arnoux *(Founder, Chm & CEO)*
Julian Salas *(Mng Dir)*
Board of Directors:
Regis Arnoux
Florence Arnoux
Monique Arnoux
Frederic Bedin
Christian Daumarie
Henri de Bodinat
Michel de Bonnecorse
Sonia de Demandolx
Pierre-Francois Forissier
Sophie Le Tanneur
Frederique Salamon

CATHAY FOREST PRODUCTS CORP.

30 Wertheim Court Suite 14
Richmond Hill, ON, L4B 1B9, Canada
Tel.: (416) 226-7269
Fax: (905) 731-7273
Web Site: www.cathayforest.com

Sales Range: $25-49.9 Million
Business Description:
Nursery & Tree Production Services
S.I.C.: 0181
N.A.I.C.S.: 111421
Personnel:
Anthony Ng *(Pres)*
Sean Vann *(Sr VP & Gen Mgr)*

CATHAY INDUSTRIAL BIOTECH LTD.

3F Building 5 1690 Cailun Road
Zhangjiang High-tech Park,
Shanghai, 201203, China
Tel.: (86) 2150801916
Fax: (86) 2150801386
E-Mail: info@cathaybiotech.com
Web Site: www.cathaybiotech.com
Sales Range: $100-124.9 Million
Emp.: 1,204
Business Description:
Chemical Intermediates Mfr
S.I.C.: 2899
N.A.I.C.S.: 325998
Personnel:
Xiucai Liu *(Chm & CEO)*
Paul J. Caswell *(Pres)*
Qixian Zhang *(Sr VP)*
Board of Directors:
Xiucai Liu
William Keller
Qixian Zhang

CATHAY INTERNATIONAL HOLDINGS LIMITED

Suites 1203 4 12 F Li Po Chun
Champers 189 Des Voeux Road
Central
Hong Kong, China (Hong Kong)
Tel.: (852) 28289289
Fax: (852) 25371338
Web Site: www.cathay-intl.com.hk
CTI—(LSE)
Rev.: $109,293,000
Assets: $391,505,000
Liabilities: $194,497,000
Net Worth: $197,008,000
Earnings: $76,000
Emp.: 2,003
Fiscal Year-end: 12/31/12
Business Description:
Pharmaceutical Products Mfr & Distr
S.I.C.: 2834
N.A.I.C.S.: 325412
Personnel:
Zhen Tao Wu *(Founder)*
Jin Yi Lee *(CEO)*
Rebecca Pui Ling Yip *(Sec)*
Board of Directors:
Soon Lim Sum
Stephen Burnau Hunt
Jin Yi Lee
Eric Ka Chi Siu
Patrick Sung
Kenneth Ken Kwok Toong
Zhen Tao Wu
Legal Counsel:
Stephenson Harwood LLP
1 Finsbury Circus
London, EC2M 7S, United Kingdom
Capita Registrars
The Registry 34 Beckenham Road
Beckenham, United Kingdom
Transfer Agent:
Capita Registrars
The Registry 34 Beckenham Road
Beckenham, United Kingdom
Non-U.S. Subsidiary:
Xi'an Haotian Bio-Engineering Technology Co. Limited **(1)**
Huahai 21 Tuanjienan Road Xi'an Hi-tech
Industries Development Zone
Xi'an, Shaanxi, 710075, China
Tel.: (86) 29 88324612
Fax: (86) 29 88327715
E-Mail: haotian@htinc.cn
Web Site: www.htinc.cn
Plant Extract & Chemical Intermediate Mfr
S.I.C.: 2899
N.A.I.C.S.: 325998
Peter Pubben *(Gen Mgr)*

CATHAY ORGANISATION HOLDINGS LTD

01-16 Unit The Cathay Bldg 2 handy
Road
229233 Singapore, Singapore
Tel.: (65) 63378181
Fax: (65) 67321944
E-Mail: corporate_services@cathay.com.sg
Web Site: www.cathay.com.sg
Year Founded: 1935
Sales Range: $25-49.9 Million
Emp.: 200
Business Description:
Entertainment, Leisure, Lifestyle & Property Management Services
S.I.C.: 7819
N.A.I.C.S.: 512199
Personnel:
Suhaimi Rafdi *(CEO)*
Evelyn Chua *(CFO)*
Board of Directors:
Hamish Alexander Christie
Sieh Kok Jiun
Kong Mun Kwong
Choo Meileen

CATHAY PACIFIC AIRWAYS LIMITED

Cathay Pacific City 8 Scenic Road
Hong Kong International Airport
Lantau, Hong Kong, China (Hong Kong)
Tel.: (852) 27471888
Fax: (852) 25601411
Toll Free: 800 233 2742
Web Site: www.cathaypacific.com
Year Founded: 1946
00293—(HKG)
Sls.: $12,814,535,200
Assets: $19,988,539,500
Liabilities: $12,598,930,800
Net Worth: $7,389,608,700
Earnings: $145,455,600
Emp.: 29,900
Fiscal Year-end: 12/31/12
Business Description:
Passenger & All-Freight Transportation Airline Services
S.I.C.: 4729
N.A.I.C.S.: 561599
Personnel:
John Robert Slosar *(Chm)*
Kwok Leung Ivan Chu *(CEO)*
David Yat Hung Fu *(Sec)*
Tom Owen *(Sr VP-Americas)*
Board of Directors:
John Robert Slosar
William Edward James Barrington
Jianjiang Cai
Kwok Leung Ivan Chu
Cheng Fan
James Wyndham John Hughes-Hallett
Peter Alan Kilgour
Irene Yun Lien Lee
Martin James Murray
Ian Sai Cheung Shiu
Jack Chak-Kwong So
Merlin Bingham Swire
Chee Chen Tung
Changshun Wang
Peter Tung Shun Wong
Xiaohang Zhao
Subsidiaries:
Cathay Pacific Catering Services (H.K.) Ltd. **(1)**
11 Catering Rd E Hong Kong Intl Airport
Lan Tau Island, China (Hong Kong)
Tel.: (852) 21162288
Fax: (852) 27657355
Web Site: www.cpcs.com.hk
Emp.: 1,644
Airline Catering Services
S.I.C.: 5812
N.A.I.C.S.: 722320

Hong Kong Airport Services Ltd. **(1)**
4th Floor South Tower 8 Scenic Road
Hong Kong Intl Airport, Lan Tau Island,
China (Hong Kong)
Tel.: (852) 29280100
Fax: (852) 2928 0141
Web Site: www.has.com.hk
Air Terminal Ramp Handling Services
S.I.C.: 7389
N.A.I.C.S.: 561499
Clement Lam *(Mng Dir)*

Hong Kong Dragon Airlines Limited **(1)**
Level 5 Dragonair House No 11 Tung Fai
Rd Hong Kong Intl Airport
Lan Tau Island, China (Hong Kong)
Tel.: (852) 31933193
Fax: (852) 31933194
Web Site: www.dragonair.com
Emp.: 1,500
Passenger & All-Freight Transportation Airline Services
S.I.C.: 4512
N.A.I.C.S.: 481111
James Tong *(CEO)*

Vogue Laundry Services Limited **(1)**
9/F East Asia Industrial Building 2 Ho Tin
Street
Tuen Mun, China (Hong Kong)
Tel.: (852) 2460 3506
Fax: (852) 2465 2135
E-Mail: cs@voguelaundry.com
Web Site: www.voguelaundry.com
Commercial Laundry Services
S.I.C.: 7218
N.A.I.C.S.: 812332

CATHEDRAL ENERGY SERVICES LTD.

6030 - 3rd Street SE
Calgary, AB, T2H 1K2, Canada
Tel.: (403) 265-2560
Fax: (403) 262-4682
Toll Free: (866) 276-8201
E-Mail: info@cathedralenergyservices.com
Web Site: www.cathedralenergyservices.com
Year Founded: 2009
CET—(TSX)
Rev.: $201,978,900
Assets: $222,740,002
Liabilities: $85,632,835
Net Worth: $137,107,167
Earnings: $14,708,514
Fiscal Year-end: 12/31/12
Business Description:
Oil & Natural Gas Extraction Services
S.I.C.: 1381
N.A.I.C.S.: 213111
Personnel:
Randal H. Pustanyk *(Founder, COO & Exec VP)*
Rod Maxwell *(Chm)*
P. Scott MacFarlane *(Pres, CEO & Interim CFO)*
Board of Directors:
Rod Maxwell
Ian S. Brown
Robert L. Chaisson
P. Scott MacFarlane
P. Daniel O'Neil
Scott Sarjeant
Jay Zammit
Legal Counsel:
Burstall Winger LLP
Calgary, AB, Canada
Transfer Agent:
Computershare Trust Company of Canada
Calgary, AB, Canada

CATHERWOOD TOWING LTD.

101 32885 Mission Way
Mission, BC, V2V 6E4, Canada
Tel.: (604) 826-9221
Fax: (604) 826-9223
E-Mail: dispatch@catherwoodtowing.com
Web Site: www.catherwoodtowing.com
Year Founded: 1971
Rev.: $10,868,119
Emp.: 75
Business Description:
Boat Mfr
S.I.C.: 3732
N.A.I.C.S.: 336612
Personnel:
Ernie Catherwood *(Owner)*

CATHOLIC CHURCH INSURANCE LIMITED

Level 8 485 La Trobe Street
Melbourne, VIC, 3000, Australia
Mailing Address:
GPO Box 180
Melbourne, VIC, 3001, Australia
Tel.: (61) 399343000
Fax: (61) 399343464
Toll Free: 800011028
E-Mail: info@ccinsurance.com.au
Web Site: www.ccinsurance.org.au
Rev.: $217,982,310
Assets: $1,052,930,545
Liabilities: $671,000,895
Net Worth: $381,929,650
Earnings: $66,343,212
Emp.: 241
Fiscal Year-end: 06/30/13
Business Description:
Insurance Services
S.I.C.: 6331
N.A.I.C.S.: 524126
Personnel:
Peter A. Rush *(CEO)*
D. Muscari *(CFO)*
Charlie Nettleton *(COO)*
Ian Smith *(Chief Investment Officer)*
Dominic P. Chila *(Sec)*
Board of Directors:
Paul A. Gallagher
Clare T. Condon
Julie Dawson
Richard M. Haddock
James Anthony Killen
Brian J. Lucas
Julie-Anne Schafer
Jane A. Tongs
Legal Counsel:
Gadens Lawyers
Level 25 Bourke Place 600 Bourke Street
Melbourne, Australia

CATHRX LTD

5 Parkview Drive
Homebush Bay, Sydney, NSW, 2127, Australia
Tel.: (61) 293975700
Fax: (61) 293975701
Web Site: www.cathrx.com
Business Description:
Cardiac Catheter Device Mfr
S.I.C.: 3845
N.A.I.C.S.: 334510
Personnel:
Denis Michael Hanley *(Chm & CEO)*
Gerard Wallace *(Pres)*
Cameron Billingsley *(Sec)*
Board of Directors:
Denis Michael Hanley
Colin McLean Adam
Elizabeth Wilson
Legal Counsel:
PFM Legal Pty Ltd
Level 12 117 York St
Sydney, Australia

CATLIN GROUP LIMITED
5th Floor Washington House 16 Church Street
Hamilton, HM 11, Bermuda
Tel.: (441) 2960060
Fax: (441) 2966016
E-Mail: catlininfo@catlin.com
Web Site: www.catlin.com
CGL—(LSE)
Rev.: $3,755,000,000
Assets: $14,041,000,000
Liabilities: $10,529,000,000
Net Worth: $3,512,000,000
Earnings: $349,000,000
Emp.: 2,077
Fiscal Year-end: 12/31/12

Business Description:
Property & Casualty Insurance
S.I.C.: 6331
N.A.I.C.S.: 524126

Personnel:
John Barton *(Chm)*
Stephen Catlin *(Deputy Chm & CEO)*
Benjamin Meuli *(CFO)*
Paul Jardine *(COO)*
Preben Prebensen *(Chief Investment Officer)*
Adrian Spieler *(Chief Admin Officer)*
Paul Brand *(Chief Underwriting Officer)*
Richard Clapham *(Chief Underwriting Officer-UK)*
Nick Greggains *(Chief Underwriting Officer-Insurance-US)*
Joseph Horan *(Chief Underwriting Officer-Reinsurance-US)*
Matthew Sage *(Chief Underwriting Officer-Bermuda)*
Richard S. Banas *(Chm-Asia Pacific & Canada)*
David Huebel *(CEO-Canada)*
Andrew McMellin *(CEO-US)*
Mark Newman *(CEO-Asia Pacific)*
Graham Pewter *(CEO-Bermuda)*
Peter Schmidt *(CEO-Reinsurance-Europe)*
Nick Sinfield *(CEO-UK & Syndicate)*
Ralf Tillenburg *(CEO-Direct-Europe)*
Daniel Primer *(Sec)*

Board of Directors:
John Barton
Bruce Carnegie-Brown
Stephen Catlin
Kenneth Goldstein
Robert Gowdy
Fiona E. Luck
Nicholas Stephen Leland Lyons
Benjamin Meuli

Transfer Agent:
Capita Registrars
The Registry 34 Beckenham Road
Beckenham, United Kingdom

Subsidiary:

Catlin Insurance Company Ltd. **(1)**
Washington House 5th Floor 16 Church Street
HM 11 Hamilton, Bermuda
Tel.: (441) 296 0060
Fax: (441) 296 6016
General Insurance Services
S.I.C.: 6331
N.A.I.C.S.: 524126

U.S. Subsidiaries:

Catlin Insurance Company Inc. **(1)**
3340 Peachtree Rd NE Ste 2950
Atlanta, GA 30326
Tel.: (404) 443-4910
Fax: (404) 443-4912
Web Site: www.catlin.com
Emp.: 100
General Insurance Services
S.I.C.: 6351
N.A.I.C.S.: 524126
Richard Banas *(Pres)*

Catlin Specialty Insurance Company **(1)**
4250 N Drinkwater Ste 300
Scottsdale, AZ 85251
Tel.: (480) 755-6700
Fax: (480) 755-6999
Toll Free: (877) 873-9742
General Insurance Services
S.I.C.: 6351
N.A.I.C.S.: 524126
Kelly Mace *(Mgr-Ops)*

Non-U.S. Subsidiaries:

Catlin Australia Pty Limited **(1)**
83 Clarence Street Suite 2 Level 19
Sydney, NSW, 2000, Australia
Tel.: (61) 282355100
Fax: (61) 2 8235 5110
General Insurance Services
S.I.C.: 6311
N.A.I.C.S.: 524113

Catlin Brasil Servicos Tecnicos Ltda **(1)**
Av Eng Luis Carlos Berrini 1511 12 Andar conj 122
Sao Paulo, 04571-011, Brazil
Tel.: (55) 1136275000
Fax: (55) 1136275001
Emp.: 5
Insurance Underwriting Services
S.I.C.: 6311
N.A.I.C.S.: 524113
Cid Andrade *(Gen Mgr)*

Catlin Canada Inc. **(1)**
36 Toronto St Ste 1210
Toronto, ON, M5C 2C5, Canada
Tel.: (416) 644-3312
Fax: (416) 644-3313
Web Site: www.catlincanada.com
Emp.: 60
General Insurance Services
S.I.C.: 6311
N.A.I.C.S.: 524113
David Huebel *(CEO)*
Greg Joyce *(Chief Underwriting Officer)*
April Savchuk *(Chief Risk & Compliance Officer)*
Greg Goff *(Sr VP-Eastern Canada)*

Catlin France SAS **(1)**
37 Rue de Caumartin
Paris, 75009, France
Tel.: (33) 158186655
Fax: (33) 158186656
E-Mail: info@catlin.com
Emp.: 21
General Insurance Services
S.I.C.: 6411
N.A.I.C.S.: 524210
Jean Pierre Baudet *(Gen Mgr)*

Catlin Guernsey Limited **(1)**
Butterfield House 9-11 The Grange
Saint Peter Port, GY1 2QL, Guernsey
Tel.: (44) 1481 720 003
Fax: (44) 1481 720 227
General Insurance Services
S.I.C.: 6311
N.A.I.C.S.: 524113

Catlin Hong Kong Limited **(1)**
Unit 1701 17th Floor Nexxus Building 41 Connaught Road
Central, China (Hong Kong)
Tel.: (852) 37194300
Fax: (852) 2169 3628
Insurance Underwriting Services
S.I.C.: 6311
N.A.I.C.S.: 524113

Catlin Iberia S.L **(1)**
Avenida Diagonal 416-12
Barcelona, Spain 08037
Tel.: (34) 93476340
Fax: (34) 93476377
Emp.: 6
General Insurance Services
S.I.C.: 6399
N.A.I.C.S.: 524130
Jose Nunez *(Gen Mgr)*

Catlin Innsbruck GmbH **(1)**
Herzog-Friedrich-Strasse 10
6020 Innsbruck, Austria
Tel.: (43) 5.1256375038e+012
E-Mail: innsbruck@catlin.com
Web Site: www.catlineurope.com
Emp.: 4
General Insurance Services
S.I.C.: 6351
N.A.I.C.S.: 524126
Herebert Haglauer *(Gen Mgr)*

Catlin Insurance Company (UK) Limited **(1)**
20 Gracechurch Street
London, EC3V 0BG, United Kingdom
Tel.: (44) 2076260486
Fax: (44) 2076239101
Emp.: 800
General Insurance Services
S.I.C.: 6351
N.A.I.C.S.: 524126
Michael Maran *(Chief Science Officer)*

Catlin Singapore Pte Ltd **(1)**
8 Marina View Asia Sq Tower 1 Ste 15-01
Singapore, 18960, Singapore
Tel.: (65) 6538 8718
Fax: (65) 57 0012
Web Site: www.catlin.com
Emp.: 70
General Insurance Services
S.I.C.: 6331
N.A.I.C.S.: 524126
Mark Newman *(CEO-Asia Pacific)*

Catlin **(1)**
6th fl 3 Minster mincinj line
London, EC3R 7C8, United Kingdom
Tel.: (44) 2073372000
Fax: (44) 2076239101
Emp.: 700
Insurance Underwriting Services
S.I.C.: 6399
N.A.I.C.S.: 524128
Benji Meuli *(CEO)*
Heather Thomas *(Gen Counsel & Sec)*

CATTLELAND FEEDYARDS LTD.
PO Box 2265
Strathmore, AB, T1P 1K2, Canada
Tel.: (403) 934-4030
Fax: (403) 934-4594
E-Mail: penny@cattleland.ca
Web Site: www.cattlelandfeedyards.com
Rev.: $17,910,660
Emp.: 30

Business Description:
Beef Cattle Feedlots
S.I.C.: 0211
N.A.I.C.S.: 112112

Personnel:
Karen Gregory *(Owner & CFO)*

CATTLES LIMITED
Kingston House Centre 27 Business Park
Woodhead Road Birstall, Batley, Yorkshire, WF17 9TD, United Kingdom
Tel.: (44) 1924444466
Fax: (44) 1924442255
E-Mail: info@cattles.co.uk
Web Site: www.cattles.co.uk
Sales Range: $750-799.9 Million
Emp.: 4,082

Business Description:
Financial Services for the Consumer Credit Market
S.I.C.: 6099
N.A.I.C.S.: 522320

Personnel:
Margaret Young *(Chm)*
Roland C. W. Todd *(Sec)*

Deloitte LLP
1 City Square
Leeds, United Kingdom

Legal Counsel:
Freshfields Bruckhaus Deringer LLP
65 Fleet Street
London, United Kingdom

Subsidiaries:

C L Finance Limited **(1)**
Lawrence House
Riverside Drive, Cleckheaton, BD19 4DH, United Kingdom (100%)
Tel.: (44) 1924444466
Fax: (44) 01275869933
E-Mail: info@lewisgroup.co.uk
Web Site: www.lewisgroup.co.uk
Emp.: 200
Financial Investment Activities
S.I.C.: 7322
N.A.I.C.S.: 561440
David Berry *(Mng Dir)*

Cattles Invoice Finance (Oxford) Limited **(1)**
Park House The Quadrant
Abingdon Science Park, Abingdon, Oxford, OX143YS, United Kingdom (100%)
Tel.: (44) 1235849999
Fax: (44) 1235554484
Emp.: 25
Financial Investment Activities
S.I.C.: 6211
N.A.I.C.S.: 523999
Adrian Chambers *(Mng Dir)*

Welcome Financial Services Limited **(1)**
Mere Way Ruddington Fields Business Park
Nottingham, NG11 6NZ, United Kingdom
Tel.: (44) 1159849200
Fax: (44) 08455438345
Web Site: www.wfs.co.uk
Emp.: 400
Financial Investment Activities
S.I.C.: 6211
N.A.I.C.S.: 523999
Robert D. East *(Mng Dir)*

CATTORINI HNOS. S.A.
Crisologo Larralde 1461
1870 Buenos Aires, Argentina
Tel.: (54) 1142042020
Fax: (54) 1142051644
E-Mail: info@cattorinihnos.com
Web Site: www.cattorinihnos.com
Year Founded: 1952
Emp.: 1,200

Business Description:
Glass Containers
S.I.C.: 3221
N.A.I.C.S.: 327213

Personnel:
Umberto Cattorini *(Pres)*

CATVISION LIMITED
E-14 &15 Sector-8
Noida, 201301, India
Tel.: (91) 120 4936750
Fax: (91) 120 4936776
E-Mail: catvision@catvisionindia.com
Web Site: www.catvisionindia.com
Year Founded: 1985
531158—(BOM)
Rev.: $5,347,439
Assets: $4,399,974
Liabilities: $2,226,940
Net Worth: $2,173,034
Earnings: $48,515
Emp.: 160
Fiscal Year-end: 03/31/13

Business Description:
Cable TV Products Mfr
S.I.C.: 5065
N.A.I.C.S.: 423690

Personnel:
S. A. Abbas *(Mng Dir)*
Vinod Rawat *(CFO)*
G. S. Butola *(Compliance Officer & Sec)*

Board of Directors:
S. A. Abbas
Sunil Anand
Sudhir Damodaran
Raman Rajiv Misra
Jagdish Prasad

Transfer Agent:
RCMC Share Registry Pvt. Ltd.
B-106 Sector-2
Noida, India

CAULDRON ENERGY LIMITED
32 Harrogate Street
Leederville, WA, 6007, Australia

Mailing Address:
PO Box 1385
Leederville, WA, 6901, Australia
Tel.: (61) 8 6181 9796
Fax: (61) 8 9380 9666
E-Mail: info@cauldronenergy.com.au
Web Site: www.cauldronenergy.com.au
CXU—(ASX OTC)
Rev.: $147,291
Assets: $11,006,553
Liabilities: $543,482
Net Worth: $10,463,071
Earnings: ($8,229,323)
Fiscal Year-end: 06/30/13
Business Description:
Uranium Mining & Exploration Services
S.I.C.: 1094
N.A.I.C.S.: 212291
Personnel:
Anthony Sage *(Chm)*
Lorena Fabris *(Legal Counsel-Argentina)*
Catherine Grant *(Sec)*
Board of Directors:
Anthony Sage
Derong Qiu
Brett Smith

Non-U.S. Subsidiary:

Jackson Global Ltd. (1)
Defensa 893 1st F
San Telmo, Buenos Aires, 1405, Argentina
Tel.: (54) 1143073512
Fax: (54) 1143073850
E-Mail: admin@jacksonglobal.com.ar
Web Site: www.jacksonglobal.com.ar
Emp.: 5
Gold Exploration Services
S.I.C.: 1041
N.A.I.C.S.: 212221

CAUVAL INDUSTRIES S.A.

8 allee des Palombes
Marne La Vallee, 77437 Lognes, France
Tel.: (33) 1 64 62 97 97
Fax: (33) 1 64 62 28 99
Sales Range: $500-549.9 Million
Emp.: 3,200
Business Description:
Mattress Mfr
S.I.C.: 2515
N.A.I.C.S.: 337910
Personnel:
Gilles Silberman *(CEO)*

Subsidiary:

Oniris S.A. (1)
61 Route de la Reine
Boulogne, 92100, France FR
Tel.: (33) 1 46 047587 (100%)
E-Mail: oniris.sa@wanadoo.fr
Web Site: www.oniris-sa.fr
Emp.: 35
Design & Manufacture of Bathrooms & Accessories
S.I.C.: 3999
N.A.I.C.S.: 327110

Non-U.S. Subsidiary:

Dunlopillo GmbH (2)
Brentanostrasse 7-8
63755 Alzenau, Germany DE
Tel.: (49) 6023 9680 0 (100%)
Fax: (49) 6023 9680 391
E-Mail: info@dunlopillo.de
Web Site: www.dunlopillo.de
Emp.: 100
Mattress Mfr & Distr
S.I.C.: 2515
N.A.I.C.S.: 337910
Gerald Malter *(Mng Dir)*
Gilles Silberman *(Mng Dir)*

CAVA RESOURCES INC.

65 Queen Street West Suite 510
Toronto, ON, M5H 2M5, Canada
Tel.: (416) 985-7810
Fax: (416) 863-4943
E-Mail: info@cavaresources.com
Web Site: www.cavaresources.com
CVA—(TSXV)
Assets: $475,169
Liabilities: $140,700
Net Worth: $334,470
Earnings: ($745,929)
Fiscal Year-end: 06/30/13
Business Description:
Mineral Exploration Services
S.I.C.: 1081
N.A.I.C.S.: 213114
Personnel:
John V. Hickey *(Pres & CEO)*
R. Brian Murray *(CFO)*
Board of Directors:
J. H. Decker
Alex Falconer
John V. Hickey
R. Brian Murray
Roger Peacock
Legal Counsel:
Fogler, Rubinoff LLP
95 Wellington Street West Suite 1200 Toronto-Dominion Centre
Toronto, ON, Canada
Transfer Agent:
Equity Transfer & Trust Company
200 University Avenue Ste 400
Toronto, ON, M5H 4H1, Canada
Tel.: (416) 361-0152
Fax: (416) 361-0470

CAVALCADE FORD LINCOLN SALES

420 Ecclestone Dr
Bracebridge, ON, P1L 1V9, Canada
Tel.: (705) 645-8731
Fax: (705) 645-6752
Toll Free: (800) 463-8731
Web Site: www.cavalcadeford.dealerconnection.com
Rev.: $17,635,033
Emp.: 40
Business Description:
New & Used Car Dealers
S.I.C.: 5511
N.A.I.C.S.: 441110
Personnel:
Larry Miller *(Pres)*

CAVALIER CORPORATION LIMITED

7 Grayson Ave
PO Box 97 040
Manukau, Auckland, 2241, New Zealand
Tel.: (64) 92776000
Fax: (64) 92787417
Web Site: www.cavcorp.co.nz
Year Founded: 1984
CAV—(NZE)
Rev.: $168,855,543
Assets: $164,585,169
Liabilities: $85,975,803
Net Worth: $78,609,366
Earnings: $2,536,110
Emp.: 745
Fiscal Year-end: 06/30/13
Business Description:
Carpet Mfr & Wool Processing Services
S.I.C.: 2273
N.A.I.C.S.: 314110
Personnel:
Colin A. McKenzie *(CEO & Mng Dir)*
Paul Alston *(CFO & Sec)*
Ron Cooper *(CEO-Elco Direct)*
Nigel Hales *(CEO-Cavalier Woolscourers)*
Dean Harriott *(CEO-Ontera Modular Carpets)*
Brent Wollaston *(CEO-Cavalier Bremworth & Norman Ellison Carpets)*
Board of Directors:
Alan M. James
Grant C. W. Biel
Graeme S. Hawkins
Sarah Haydon
Colin A. McKenzie
Keith L. Thorpe
Legal Counsel:
Minter Ellison Rudd Watts
Level 20 Lumley Centre 88 Shortland Street
PO Box 3798
Auckland, New Zealand
Tel.: (64) 9 353 9700
Fax: (64) 9 353 9701

Subsidiaries:

Cavalier Bremworth Limited (1)
7 Grayson Ave
PO Box 97040
2241 Auckland, New Zealand (100%)
Tel.: (64) 92776000
Fax: (64) 92787417
E-Mail: websales@cavbrem.co.nz
Web Site: www.cavbrem.co.nz
Emp.: 3,500
Carpet & Rug Mills
S.I.C.: 2273
N.A.I.C.S.: 314110
Colin McKenzie *(Mng Dir)*

Cavalier Spinners Limited (1)
Leamington St
4540 Wanganui, New Zealand (100%)
Tel.: (64) 63445116
Fax: (64) 63445190
Web Site: www.cavalierbrem.co.nz
Emp.: 180
Yarn Spinning Mills
S.I.C.: 2299
N.A.I.C.S.: 313110
Wayne Chung *(Mng Dir)*

Elco Direct Limited (1)
75 Victoria Road
PO Box 665
Cambridge, 3450, New Zealand
Tel.: (64) 78275084
Fax: (64) 78275056
E-Mail: elco@elcodirect.co.nz
Web Site: www.elcodirect.co.nz
Emp.: 10
Wool Products Distr
S.I.C.: 5159
N.A.I.C.S.: 424590
Ron Cooper *(Gen Mgr)*

Hawkes Bay Woolscourers Limited (1)
Waitangi Road Awatoto
4001 Napier, New Zealand (92.5%)
Tel.: (64) 68341421
Fax: (64) 68351237
E-Mail: office@hbws.co.nz
Emp.: 50
Sheep Farming
S.I.C.: 0214
N.A.I.C.S.: 112410
Nigel Halles *(Mng Dir)*

Knightsbridge Carpets Limited (1)
Unit 2 39 Apolloo Dr
Mairangi Bay, Auckland, 0745, New Zealand (100%)
Tel.: (64) 6494780123
Fax: (64) 94780145
E-Mail: bsmith@knightsbridgecarpets.co.nz
Web Site: www.knightsbridgecarpets.co.nz
Emp.: 6
Home Furnishing Whslr
S.I.C.: 5023
N.A.I.C.S.: 423220
Brent Smith *(Mgr)*

Norman Ellison Carpets Limited (1)
373 Neilson Street Onehunga
Onehunga, Auckland, New Zealand
Tel.: (64) 96229616
Fax: (64) 9 622 9617
E-Mail: sales@necarpet.co.nz
Web Site: www.normanellison.co.nz
Emp.: 260
Wool Carpet Mfr
S.I.C.: 2273
N.A.I.C.S.: 314110
Warren Drinkwater *(Gen Mgr)*

Ontera Modular Carpets Pty. Limited (1)
7 Grayson Avenue
1730 Papatoetoe, New Zealand
Tel.: (64) 92776000
Fax: (64) 92787417
E-Mail: websales@cavbram.co.nz
Web Site: www.cavalier.co.nz
Emp.: 300
Carpet & Rug Mills
S.I.C.: 2273
N.A.I.C.S.: 314110
Wayne Chung *(Mng Dir)*

Non-U.S. Subsidiaries:

Cavalier Bremworth (Australia) limited (1)
165-169 Gibbes Street
2067 Chatswood, NSW, Australia
Tel.: (61) 299322600
Fax: (61) 294177071
E-Mail: webausales@cavbrem.co.nz
Web Site: www.cavbrem.co.nz
Carpet & Rug Mills
S.I.C.: 2273
N.A.I.C.S.: 314110
Cathy Howitd *(Gen Mgr)*

Cavalier Bremworth Pty. Limited (1)
Unit 1 165-169 Gibbes Street
2067 Chatswood, Australia (100%)
Tel.: (61) 299322600
Fax: (61) 294177071
E-Mail: webausales@cavbrem.co.au
Web Site: www.cavbrem.com.au
Emp.: 40
Carpet & Rug Mills
S.I.C.: 2273
N.A.I.C.S.: 314110
Garyol Olchoway *(CFO)*

Kimberley Carpets Pty Limited (1)
Unit 1 165 169 Lower Gibbes Street
Chatswood, NSW, 2067, Australia
Tel.: (61) 299322660
Fax: (61) 2 9932 2655
Web Site: www.kimberleycarpets.com.au
Emp.: 50
Carpets Mfr
S.I.C.: 2273
N.A.I.C.S.: 314110

Norman Ellison Carpets Pty Limited (1)
13 Gassman Dr
Yatala, Gold Coast, QLD, Australia
Tel.: (61) 733820777
Fax: (61) 733820277
E-Mail: custserv@normanellisoncarpets.com
Web Site: www.normanellisoncarpets.com
Emp.: 15
Woolen Carpets Mfr
S.I.C.: 2273
N.A.I.C.S.: 314110
Mark Gannon *(Mgr-Natl Contracts)*

Ontera Modular Carpets Limited (1)
171 Briens Rd
Northmead, NSW, 2152, Australia
Tel.: (61) 288382500
Fax: (61) 296308531
E-Mail: ontera@ontera.com.au
Web Site: www.ontera.com.au
Emp.: 70
Carpet Tiles Mfr
S.I.C.: 3255
N.A.I.C.S.: 327120
Jeff Bee *(Mgr-Sls-Victoria State)*

CAVAN VENTURES INC.

Suite 1220 - 789 West Pender Street
Vancouver, BC, V6C 1H2, Canada
Tel.: (604) 683-3995
Fax: (604) 683-3988
Toll Free: (888) 945-4770
E-Mail: info@cavanventuresinc.com
Web Site: www.cavanventuresinc.com
Year Founded: 2006
CVN—(TSXV)

Cavan Ventures Inc.—(Continued)

Assets: $1,205,796
Liabilities: $222,064
Net Worth: $983,732
Earnings: ($679,200)
Fiscal Year-end: 02/28/13

Business Description:
Metal Mining Services
S.I.C.: 1099
N.A.I.C.S.: 212299

Personnel:
Peter P. Swistak *(Pres & CEO)*
Dave Cross *(CFO)*

Board of Directors:
Ernest Brisbane
Charles Desjardins
Andrew Mah
Lorne McCarthy
Peter P. Swistak

Transfer Agent:
Computershare Investor Services Inc.
3rd Floor 510 Burrard St
V6C 3B9 Vancouver, BC, Canada

CAVE INTERACTIVE CO., LTD.

87 Naitocho Shinjuku-ku
Tokyo, 160-8581, Japan
Tel.: (81) 3 5366 3310
Fax: (81) 3 5366 3159
Web Site: caveinteractive.com
Year Founded: 1994
3760—(JAS)

Business Description:
Mobile Entertainment Services
S.I.C.: 7389
N.A.I.C.S.: 711410

Personnel:
Kenichi Takano *(Chm)*
Ito Masahito *(Pres & CEO)*

Board of Directors:
Kenichi Takano
Ito Masahito
Toshihito Obi
Mikio Watanabe

CAVE SHEPHERD & CO., LTD.

1st Floor 24 Broad Street
Bridgetown, Barbados
Tel.: (246) 227 1330
Fax: (246) 431 0845
E-Mail: general@caveshepherd.com
Web Site: www.caveshepherd.com
Year Founded: 1906
CSP—(BARB)
Rev.: $7,634,428
Assets: $78,250,034
Liabilities: $23,770,454
Net Worth: $54,479,581
Earnings: $550,933
Emp.: 34
Fiscal Year-end: 12/31/12

Business Description:
Retail, Tourism & Financial Services
S.I.C.: 5999
N.A.I.C.S.: 453998

Personnel:
R. Geoffrey Cave *(Chm)*
John M. B. Williams *(CEO)*
Ian Gibson *(CFO)*
Peter Allan *(CEO-Duty Free Caribbean (Holdings) Ltd)*
Paul Ashby *(CEO-Signia Financial Group Inc)*

Board of Directors:
R. Geoffrey Cave
V. Eudine Barriteau
Roger M. Cave
Maureen D. Davis
Robert M. Harvey-Read
Edward Ince
Lyden L. Ramdhanny
Richard G. Simpson
M. Grantley Taylor
John M. B. Williams

Transfer Agent:
Barbados Central Securities Depository Inc.
8th Avenue, Belleville
Saint Michael, Barbados
Tel.: (246) 4295177

Joint Venture:

Duty Free Caribbean Holdings Ltd. **(1)**
24 Broad St
Bridgetown, Barbados
Tel.: (246) 227 1325
Web Site: www.dutyfreecaribbean.com
Holding Company; Duty Free Retail Stores Owner & Operator
S.I.C.: 6719
N.A.I.C.S.: 551112
Geoffrey Cave *(Chm)*
Peter Allan *(CEO)*
Ian Gibson *(CFO)*
Alan Huxtable *(COO)*
Maureen Davis *(Chief Dev Officer)*

CAVERION CORPORATION

Panuntie 11
00620 Helsinki, Finland
Mailing Address:
PO Box 59
00621 Helsinki, Finland
Tel.: (358) 10 4071
E-Mail: communications@caverion.com
Web Site: www.caverion.com
Year Founded: 2013
CAV1V—(HEL)
Rev.: $3,773,583,744
Earnings: $54,923,736
Emp.: 18,614
Fiscal Year-end: 12/31/12

Business Description:
Building Systems Design, Construction & Maintenance Services
S.I.C.: 1799
N.A.I.C.S.: 238990

Personnel:
Henrik Ehrnrooth *(Chm)*
Juhani Pitkakoski *(Chm-Mgmt Bd, Pres & CEO)*
Michael Rosenlaw *(Vice Chm)*
Antti Heinola *(CFO & Member-Mgmt Bd)*
Paivi Alakuijala *(Member-Mgmt Bd & VP-Mktg & Comm)*
Knut Gaaserud *(Member-Mgmt Bd-Norway)*
Jarno Hacklin *(Member-Mgmt Bd-Finland, Baltic Reg & Russia)*
Erkki Huusko *(Member-Mgmt Bd-Indus Svcs)*
Ulf Kareliusson *(Member-Mgmt Bd-Sweden)*
Ralf Lutz *(Member-Mgmt Bd-Germany)*
Matti Malmberg *(Member-Mgmt Bd-Building Svcs-Northern Europe & Svc Efficiency)*
Peter Rafn *(Member-Mgmt Bd-Denmark)*
Karl-Walter Schuster *(Member-Mgmt Bd-Building Svcs-Central Europe & Project Excellence)*
Manfred Simmet *(Member-Mgmt Bd-Austria)*
Sakari Toikkanen *(Member-Mgmt Bd-Bus Dev)*

Board of Directors:
Henrik Ehrnrooth
Anna Hyvonen
Ari Lehtoranta
Eva Lindqvist
Michael Rosenlaw

Non-U.S. Subsidiaries:

Caverion Asia Pte. Ltd. **(1)**
20 Science Park Rd No 02-27 Teletech Park
Singapore, 117674, Singapore SG
Tel.: (65) 67782093
Fax: (65) 67782090
Emp.: 15
Building Systems Design, Construction & Maintenance Services
S.I.C.: 1799
N.A.I.C.S.: 238990
Josef Klebert *(Mng Dir)*

Caverion Deutschland GmbH **(1)**
(Formerly YIT Germany GmbH)
Gstocketwiesenstrasse 9
Deggendorf, 94469, Germany De
Tel.: (49) 89 374288 500
Fax: (49) 89 374288 520
E-Mail: info@yit.de
Web Site: www.yit.de
Emp.: 500
Facility Management, Construction & Industrial Services
S.I.C.: 8744
N.A.I.C.S.: 561210
Johann Konig *(Dir-Tech)*

CAVICO CONSTRUCTION MANPOWER & SERVICES COMPANY JSC

5 Tuoi Tre Lane Hoang Quoc Viet Street
Tu Liem, Hanoi, Vietnam
Tel.: (84) 462690742
E-Mail: info@cavicocms.com
Web Site: www.cavicocms.com
Year Founded: 2007
CMS—(HNX)
Emp.: 600

Business Description:
Construction & Temporary Employment Services
S.I.C.: 1542
N.A.I.C.S.: 236220

Personnel:
Phuc Minh Pham *(Chm)*
Nhan Ngoc Kim *(Vice Chm)*

Board of Directors:
Phuc Minh Pham
The Dinh Chu
Toan Minh Dang
Nhan Ngoc Kim
Phong Duc Nguyen

CAVICO INDUSTRY AND MINERALS JOINT STOCK COMPANY

201 CT 1-2 Me Tri Ha Urban Zone Me Tri
Tu Liem, Hanoi, Vietnam
Tel.: (84) 437875441
Fax: (84) 437875440
E-Mail: info@cavicosm.com
Web Site: www.cavicosm.com
CMI—(HNX)
Emp.: 60

Business Description:
Petroleum Lubricating Oil & Grease Distr
S.I.C.: 5172
N.A.I.C.S.: 424720

Personnel:
Hai Thanh Tran *(Chm)*

CAVINKARE PVT. LTD.

Cavin Villa No 12
Cenotaph Road, Chennai, 600 018, India
Tel.: (91) 44 24317550
Fax: (91) 44 24362879
E-Mail: corpcomm@cavinkare.com
Web Site: www.cavinkare.com
Sales Range: $125-149.9 Million
Emp.: 1,000

Business Description:
Consumer Products Mfr
S.I.C.: 2841
N.A.I.C.S.: 325611

Personnel:
C. K. Ranganathan *(Founder & Chm)*

CAVOTEC SA

Via Sarafino Balestra 27
CH-6900 Lugano, Switzerland
Tel.: (41) 919114010
Fax: (41) 919225400
E-Mail: info@cavotec.com
Web Site: www.cavotec.com
CCC—(OMX)
Rev.: $296,254,324
Assets: $283,671,673
Liabilities: $139,861,678
Net Worth: $143,809,995
Earnings: $16,412,505
Emp.: 890
Fiscal Year-end: 12/31/12

Business Description:
Power Supply Equipment Design & Manufacturing Services
S.I.C.: 3568
N.A.I.C.S.: 333613

Personnel:
Stefan Widegren *(Chm)*
Ottonel Popesco *(CEO)*
Diego Fiorentini *(CFO)*
Giorgio Lingiardi *(CIO, VP & Reg Mgr-Southern Europe)*

Board of Directors:
Stefan Widegren
Fabio Cannavale
Leena Essen
Nicola Gerber
Christer Granskog
Lakshmi C. Khanna
Erik Lautmann
Joe Pope
Ottonel Popesco

Subsidiary:

Cavotec (Swiss) S.A. **(1)**
Via S Balestra 27
CH 6900 Lugano, Switzerland
Tel.: (41) 919114010
Fax: (41) 919225400
E-Mail: info@cavotec.com
Web Site: www.cavotec.com
Emp.: 14
Power Supply Equipment Design & Manufacturing Services
S.I.C.: 3568
N.A.I.C.S.: 333613
Stefan Widegren *(Chm)*
Christian Bernadotte *(Pres)*
Ottonel Popesco *(CEO)*
Peter Brandel *(CTO)*

U.S. Subsidiaries:

Cavotec Dabico US Inc. **(2)**
2995 Airway Ave
Costa Mesa, CA 92626
Tel.: (714) 545-7900
Fax: (714) 545-7676
E-Mail: gen.mail@dabico.com
Web Site: www.dabico.com
Sales Range: $10-24.9 Million
Emp.: 40
Aircraft Ground Support Equipment
S.I.C.: 3728
N.A.I.C.S.: 336413

Non-U.S. Subsidiary:

Cavotec Dabico UK Ltd. **(3)**
Unit 5A & 5B
Saint Annes Industrial Estate, Stockton-on-Tees, TS18 2LS, United Kingdom
Tel.: (44) 1642608245
Fax: (44) 1642608224
E-Mail: info.dabico@cavotec.com
Web Site: www.cavotec.com
Emp.: 25
Aircraft Ground Support Equipment
S.I.C.: 3728
N.A.I.C.S.: 336413
Gary Matthews *(Mng Dir)*

Cavotec US Holdings Inc **(2)**
2711 Cranlyn Rd
Shaker Heights, OH 44122
Tel.: (216) 464-5461
Fax: (216) 464-5406
Investment Management Services
S.I.C.: 6211

N.A.I.C.S.: 523999

Cavotec USA Inc. (2)
333 Oates Rd
Mooresville, NC 28117
Tel.: (704) 873-3009
Fax: (704) 873-3093
Web Site: www.cavotec.com
Emp.: 30
Power Supply Equipment Design & Manufacturing Services
S.I.C.: 3568
N.A.I.C.S.: 333613
Mike Larkin *(Pres)*

INET Airport Systems, Inc. (2)
4111 N Palm St
Fullerton, CA 92835
Tel.: (714) 888-2700
Fax: (714) 888-2727
Toll Free: (800) 777-4455
E-Mail: info@inetas.com
Web Site: www.inetas.com
Sales Range: $10-24.9 Million
Emp.: 50
Wholesale Aircraft Parts & Equipment Mfr & Sales
S.I.C.: 3728
N.A.I.C.S.: 336413
Gary Matthews *(Pres)*

Non-U.S. Subsidiaries:

Cavotec Alfo GmbH (2)
Am Aggerberg 5
51491 Overath, Germany
Tel.: (49) 220660950
Fax: (49) 2206609522
Web Site: www.cavotecalfo.com
Emp.: 60
Power Supply Equipment Design & Manufacturing Services
S.I.C.: 3568
N.A.I.C.S.: 333613
Joan Ibrahim *(Mng Dir)*

Cavotec Australia (2)
28 Mitchell Road
Cardiff, NSW, 2285, Australia
Tel.: (61) 249565788
Fax: (61) 249565823
E-Mail: info.au@cavotec.com
Web Site: www.cavotec.com.au
Emp.: 40
Power Supply Equipment Design & Manufacturing Services
S.I.C.: 3568
N.A.I.C.S.: 333613
Phillip Macridis *(Mng Dir)*

Cavotec Benelux B.V. (2)
PO Box 136
3440 AC Woerden, Netherlands
Tel.: (31) 786931200
Fax: (31) 348431703
E-Mail: info.nl@cavotec.com
Web Site: www.cavotec.com
Emp.: 4
Power Supply Equipment Design & Manufacturing Services
S.I.C.: 3568
N.A.I.C.S.: 333613

Cavotec Canada Inc. (2)
860 Denison St 6
Markham, ON, L3R 4H1, Canada
Tel.: (905) 415-2233
Fax: (905) 415-2238
E-Mail: info.ca@cavotec.com
Web Site: www.cavotec.com
Emp.: 6
Power Supply Equipment Design & Manufacturing Services
S.I.C.: 3568
N.A.I.C.S.: 333613
Marcelo Gonzalez *(Mng Dir)*

Cavotec Connectors AB (2)
Blockvagen 12
247 56 Lund, Sweden
Tel.: (46) 46202112
Fax: (46) 46 200 303
Web Site: www.cavotecconnectors.com
Power Supply Equipment Design & Manufacturing Services
S.I.C.: 3568
N.A.I.C.S.: 333613
Mats Tegner *(Mng Dir)*

Cavotec Danmark AS (2)
Rolundvej 19
5260 Odense, Denmark
Tel.: (45) 63131300
Fax: (45) 63131302
Emp.: 6
Power Supply Equipment Design & Manufacturing Services
S.I.C.: 3568
N.A.I.C.S.: 333613
Mikkel Falk *(Mng Dir)*

Cavotec Deutschland GmbH (2)
Ludwig Erhard Str 1a
65760 Eschborn, Germany
Tel.: (49) 6196509500
Fax: (49) 61965095022
E-Mail: info@cavotec.com
Web Site: www.cavotec.com
Emp.: 20
Power Supply Equipment Design & Manufacturing Services
S.I.C.: 3568
N.A.I.C.S.: 333613
Dreyer Thomas *(Mng Dir)*

Cavotec Deutschland Holdings GmbH (2)
Ludwig-Erhard-StraSSe 1a
65760 Eschborn, Germany
Tel.: (49) 6196509500
Fax: (49) 61965095022
E-Mail: info@cavotec.com
Web Site: www.cavotec.com
Emp.: 20
Power Supply Equipment Design & Manufacturing Services
S.I.C.: 3568
N.A.I.C.S.: 333613
Hans Winemar *(Mng Dir)*

Cavotec Finland Oy (2)
Olarinluoma 14 B
FI-02200 Espoo, Finland
Tel.: (358) 98870200
Fax: (358) 988702050
E-Mail: info@cavotec.com
Emp.: 8
Power Supply Equipment Design & Manufacturing Services
S.I.C.: 3568
N.A.I.C.S.: 333613
Benny Tornroos *(Mng Dir)*

Cavotec Fladung GmbH (2)
Heimbach 26
63776 Mombris, Germany
Tel.: (49) 602997100
Fax: (49) 60297464
E-Mail: info@fladung.com
Web Site: www.fladung.com
Emp.: 90
Power Supply Equipment Design & Manufacturing Services
S.I.C.: 3568
N.A.I.C.S.: 333613
Thomas Dreyer *(Mng Dir)*

Cavotec Hong Kong Ltd. (2)
1101 Golden Centre 188 Des Voeux Road
71-77 Wing Lok St, Central, China (Hong Kong)
Tel.: (852) 27916161
Fax: (852) 27911834
E-Mail: info.hongkong@cavotec.com
Web Site: www.cavotec.com
Emp.: 5
Power Supply Equipment Design & Manufacturing Services
S.I.C.: 3568
N.A.I.C.S.: 333613
John Rostagno *(Mng Dir)*

Cavotec Iberica S.L. (2)
Centro de Negocios de Alicante-Oficina 108
Muelle de Poniente s/n
Antigua Casa del Mar, 03001 Alicante, Spain
Tel.: (34) 966084054
Fax: (34) 965928616
E-Mail: info.es@cavotec.com
Emp.: 3
Marine Engineering Services
S.I.C.: 8711
N.A.I.C.S.: 541330
Jason Smith Hurtado *(Reg Mgr-Sls)*

Cavotec India Ltd. (2)
Phase - II Road
Hinjewadi
411057 Pune, Maharashtra, India
Tel.: (91) 2040224440
Fax: (91) 2040224443
E-Mail: info.in@cavotec.com
Emp.: 12
Power Supply Equipment Design & Manufacturing Services
S.I.C.: 3568
N.A.I.C.S.: 333613
Pihl Nicklas *(Mng Dir)*

Cavotec Latin America S.A. (2)
Bogota 1362
B1640DDL Buenos Aires, Argentina
Tel.: (54) 1148362726
Fax: (54) 1148362116
E-Mail: info@cavotec.com
Emp.: 5
Power Supply Equipment Design & Manufacturing Services
S.I.C.: 3568
N.A.I.C.S.: 333613
Andrea Della Bianca *(Mng Dir)*

Cavotec Meyerinck GmbH (2)
Gottlieb-Daimler-Str
DE-35463 Hessen, Germany
Tel.: (49) 64197250
Fax: (49) 6419725111
Power Supply Equipment Design & Manufacturing Services
S.I.C.: 3568
N.A.I.C.S.: 333613
Jochen Eberheim *(Mng Dir)*

Cavotec Micro-control as (2)
Wesselsv 2
Box 284
7501 Trondheim, Norway
Tel.: (47) 74839860
Fax: (47) 7483015
Emp.: 45
Power Supply Equipment Design & Manufacturing Services
S.I.C.: 3568
N.A.I.C.S.: 333613

Cavotec Micro-control GmbH (2)
Hoerlbacher Strasse 20
93326 Kelheim, Germany
Tel.: (49) 9443 92860 0
Fax: (49) 9443 92860 09
Power Supply Equipment Design & Manufacturing Services
S.I.C.: 3568
N.A.I.C.S.: 333613
Leo Schalk *(Mng Dir)*

Cavotec Middle East FZE (2)
Jebel Ali Free Zone
PO Box 61124
Dubai, United Arab Emirates
Tel.: (971) 48838350
Fax: (971) 48838352
E-Mail: info@cavotec.com
Emp.: 40
Power Supply Equipment Design & Manufacturing Services
S.I.C.: 3568
N.A.I.C.S.: 333613
Jurgen Strommer *(Mng Dir)*

Cavotec MoorMaster Ltd (2)
Level 1, Unit 9, Amuri Park
404 Barbadoes St
Christchurch, 8141, New Zealand
Tel.: (64) 33771226
Fax: (64) 33770553
Power Supply Equipment Design & Manufacturing Services
S.I.C.: 3568
N.A.I.C.S.: 333613
Dave Williams *(Gen Mgr)*

Cavotec Norge AS (2)
Strandveien 6
N-3050 Mjondalen, Norway
Tel.: (47) 32274300
Fax: (47) 32230077
E-Mail: info@cavotec.com
Emp.: 13
Power Supply Equipment Design & Manufacturing Services
S.I.C.: 3568
N.A.I.C.S.: 333613
Sofus Gedde-Dahl *(Mng Dir)*

Cavotec RMS SA (2)
ZI les Bethunes 16 Avenue du Fief
95310 Saint-Ouen-l'Aumone, France
Tel.: (33) 130379900
Fax: (33) 130379898
E-Mail: info@cavotec.com
Web Site: www.cavotec.com
Emp.: 10
Power Supply Equipment Design & Manufacturing Services
S.I.C.: 3568
N.A.I.C.S.: 333613
Guillaume Dormeuil *(Mng Dir)*

Cavotec Shanghai Ltd. (2)
Unit 3, 879 Shenfu Road
Xinzhuang Industrial Zone, Shanghai, Minhang District, 201108, China
Tel.: (86) 2154429778
Fax: (86) 34073498
E-Mail: infocn@cavotec.com
Emp.: 50
Power Supply Equipment Design & Manufacturing Services
S.I.C.: 3568
N.A.I.C.S.: 333613
Gustavo Miller *(Mng Dir)*

Cavotec Singapore PTE Ltd. (2)
30 Toh Guan Road #07-02
Singapore, 608840, Singapore
Tel.: (65) 68622545
Fax: (65) 68622548
Power Supply Equipment Design & Manufacturing Services
S.I.C.: 3568
N.A.I.C.S.: 333613
Denis Ong *(Mng Dir)*

Cavotec South Africa (Pty.) Ltd. (2)
PO Box 16897
Atlasville, 1465 Gauteng, South Africa
Tel.: (27) 119630015
Fax: (27) 119630064
Emp.: 5
Power Supply Equipment Design & Manufacturing Services
S.I.C.: 3568
N.A.I.C.S.: 333613
Johann Jankowitz *(Mng Dir)*

Cavotec Specimas S.p.A. (2)
Via Galvani 1
20054 Nova Milanese, Italy
Tel.: (39) 0362455101
Fax: (39) 036241233
Web Site: www.specimas.it
Emp.: 100
Power Supply Equipment Design & Manufacturing Services
S.I.C.: 3568
N.A.I.C.S.: 333613
Patrick Rosenwald *(Mng Dir)*

Cavotec Sverige AB (2)
Fagerstagatan 5
163 53 Spanga, Sweden
Tel.: (46) 855652200
Fax: (46) 855652222
Emp.: 16
Power Supply Equipment Design & Manufacturing Services
S.I.C.: 3568
N.A.I.C.S.: 333613
Erik Chilo *(Mng Dir)*

Non-U.S. Division:

Cavotec MSL Holdings Limited - Cavotec Italia Division (1)
Via Galvani 1
20834 Nova Milanese, Monza and Brianza, Italy
Tel.: (39) 0362 36 76 06
Fax: (39) 0362 36 75 88
E-Mail: info.it@cavotec.com
Emp.: 5
Marine Engineering Services
S.I.C.: 8711
N.A.I.C.S.: 541330
Mauro Gurioli *(Gen Mgr)*

Non-U.S. Subsidiaries:

Cavotec CIS Ltd. (1)
Of 206 84a Shkolnaya Str
Vidnoe, Moscow, 142703, Russia
Tel.: (7) 495 663 91 97
Fax: (7) 495 663 91 98
Emp.: 6
Engineering Services
S.I.C.: 8711
N.A.I.C.S.: 541330
Harry Giesbrecht *(Mng Dir)*
Andrei Bondar *(Deputy Mng Dir)*

Cavotec SA—(Continued)

Cavotec Engineering Services India Pvt. Ltd. (1)
The Business Plaza Unit No 901 9th Floor
36/3 Ghorpadi North Main Road
Koregoan Park, Pune, Maharashtra, 411001, India
Tel.: (91) 20 6725 5000
Fax: (91) 20 6725 5099
E-Mail: info.in@cavotec.com
Web Site: www.cavotec.com
Emp.: 21
Engineering Services
S.I.C.: 8711
N.A.I.C.S.: 541330
Nicklas Pihl *(Mng Dir)*

Cavotec Group Holdings NV (1)
Ohmweg 19
Alblasserdam, 2952 BD, Netherlands
Tel.: (31) 78 693 12 00
Fax: (31) 78 693 12 12
Crane & Gantries Machinery Mfr
S.I.C.: 3536
N.A.I.C.S.: 333923

Non-U.S. Subsidiaries:

Cavotec International Ltd (2)
Unit 5 Saint Annes Industrial Estate
Limeoak Way, Stockton-on-Tees, TS18 2LS, United Kingdom
Tel.: (44) 1642 608245
Fax: (44) 1642 608224
Web Site: www.cavotec.com
Emp.: 25
Lift Handling Equipment Mfr
S.I.C.: 3537
N.A.I.C.S.: 333924
Gary Matthews *(Gen Mgr)*

Cavotec Realty Italia Srl (2)
Via Luigi Galvani 1
Nova Milanese, Milan, 20054, Italy
Tel.: (39) 0362367606
Fax: (39) 0362367588
Aircraft Equipment Mfr
S.I.C.: 3728
N.A.I.C.S.: 336413

Cavotec Realty Norway AS (2)
Gevinglia 112
Hell, Stjordal, Nord-Trondelag, Norway
Tel.: (47) 74839860
Fax: (47) 74830151
Power Transmission Equipment Distr
S.I.C.: 5084
N.A.I.C.S.: 423830

Cavotec Korea Ltd (1)
5th Floor Gookto Building 160-7 Garak-dong
Song pa-gu, Seoul, Korea (South)
Tel.: (82) 5 663 91 97
Fax: (82) 2 444 0621
Automated Crane System Mfr
S.I.C.: 3536
N.A.I.C.S.: 333923

CAXTON AND CTP PUBLISHERS AND PRINTERS

Caxton House 368 Jan Smuts Avenue
Johannesburg, 2196, South Africa
Tel.: (27) 11 889 0600
Fax: (27) 118890600
Web Site: www.caxton.co.za
CAT—(JSE)
Sls.: $668,431,789
Assets: $745,702,386
Liabilities: $142,860,949
Net Worth: $602,841,437
Earnings: $56,163,654
Emp.: 6,205
Fiscal Year-end: 06/30/13
Business Description:
Printing, Publishing & Distribution
S.I.C.: 2759
N.A.I.C.S.: 323111
Personnel:
T. D. Moolman *(CEO)*
Gordon M. Utian *(Mng Dir)*
N. Sooka *(Sec)*
Board of Directors:
Paul M. Jenkins
Petrus G. Greyling
Timothy J. W. Holden
Andrew C. G. Molusi
T. D. Moolman
N. Albert Nemukula
T. Slabbert
Gordon M. Utian
Phillip Vallet
Legal Counsel:
Fluxmans Inc
11 Biermann Avenue
Rosebank, 2196, South Africa
Tel.: (27) 11 328 1700
Fax: (27) 11 880 2261
Transfer Agent:
Computershare Investor Services (Pty) Limited
70 Marshall Street
PO Box 61051
2107 Marshalltown, South Africa

CAYDEN RESOURCES INC.

700-1199 West Hastings Street
Vancouver, BC, V6E 3T5, Canada
Tel.: (778) 729-0600
Fax: (604) 683-8194
Toll Free: (800) 863-8655
E-Mail: info@caydenresources.com
Web Site: www.caydenresources.com
CYD—(OTC TSXV)
Rev.: $96,189
Assets: $46,553,626
Liabilities: $7,038,027
Net Worth: $39,515,599
Earnings: ($6,892,565)
Emp.: 60
Fiscal Year-end: 12/31/12
Business Description:
Silver & Gold Mining
S.I.C.: 1044
N.A.I.C.S.: 212222
Personnel:
Shawn Kristen Wallace *(Chm)*
Ivan James Bebek *(Pres & CEO)*
Peter Rees *(CFO & Sec)*
Russell Starr *(Sr VP)*
Board of Directors:
Shawn Kristen Wallace
Ivan James Bebek
Rene G. Carrier
Steven Mark Cook
David M. Jones
Daniel T. McCoy
Russell Starr
Legal Counsel:
McMillan LLP
Royal Centre 1055 West Georgia Street Suite 1500 PO Box 11117
Vancouver, BC, Canada
Transfer Agent:
Olympia Trust Company
Suite 1003 750 West Pender Street
Vancouver, BC, V6C 2T8, Canada

CAYENNE GOLD MINES LTD.

470 Granville St Ste 422
Vancouver, BC, V6C 1V5, Canada
Tel.: (604) 687-8623
Fax: (604) 687-8624
E-Mail: cayenne@telus.net
Web Site: www.cayennegoldmines.com
Year Founded: 2001
CYN—(CNSX)
Emp.: 10
Business Description:
Gold Mining & Exploration Services
S.I.C.: 1041
N.A.I.C.S.: 212221
Personnel:
H. Alexander Briden *(Pres & CEO)*
Aaron Henshaw *(CFO)*

CAYMAN AIRWAYS LTD.

181 Owen Roberts Dr
PO Box 10092
Georgetown, Grand Cayman, KY1-1001, Cayman Islands
Tel.: (345) 9498200
Fax: (345) 3459497607
Web Site: www.caymanairways.com
Year Founded: 1968
Emp.: 333
Business Description:
Airline
S.I.C.: 4512
N.A.I.C.S.: 481111
Personnel:
Fabian Whorms *(Pres & CEO)*
Paul Tibbetts *(CFO & Sr VP-Comml Affairs)*

CAYMAN ISLANDS MONETARY AUTHORITY

80e Shedden Road Elizabethan Square
PO Box 10052
KY1-1001 Georgetown, Grand Cayman, Cayman Islands
Tel.: (345) 9497089
Fax: (345) 9492532
E-Mail: j.miller@cimoney.com.ky
Web Site: www.cimoney.com.ky
Year Founded: 1996
Sales Range: $10-24.9 Million
Emp.: 103
Fiscal Year-end: 12/31/12
Business Description:
Banking Services
S.I.C.: 6011
N.A.I.C.S.: 521110
Personnel:
Carlyle McLaughlin, Jr. *(Chm)*
Cindy Scotland *(Mng Dir)*
Gilda Moxam-Murray *(CFO)*
Langston Sibblies *(Deputy Mng Dir & Gen Counsel-Legal Div)*
Patrick Bodden *(Deputy Mng Dir)*
Board of Directors:
Carlyle McLaughlin, Jr.
Bryan Bothwell
Warren Coats
William Gilmore
Richard W. Rahn
Christopher Rose
Cindy Scotland
Adriannie Webb

CAYMAN ISLANDS STOCK EXCHANGE LIMITED

4th Floor Elizabethan Square
PO Box 2408
KY1-1105 Georgetown, Cayman Islands
Tel.: (345) 9456060
Fax: (345) 3459456061
E-Mail: csx@csx.com.ky
Web Site: www.csx.ky
Emp.: 8
Business Description:
Stock Exchange Services
S.I.C.: 6231
N.A.I.C.S.: 523210
Personnel:
Anthony B. Travers *(Chm)*
Dax Basdeo *(Vice Chm)*
Valia Theodoraki *(CEO)*
Board of Directors:
Anthony B. Travers
Dax Basdeo
Valia Theodoraki

CAYMAN NATIONAL CORPORATION LTD.

Cayman National Building 200 Elgin Avenue 1st Fl
PO Box 1097
Georgetown, Grand Cayman, KY1-1102, Cayman Islands
Tel.: (345) 949 4655
Fax: (345) 949 7506
E-Mail: cnb@caymannational.com
Web Site: www.caymannational.com
Sales Range: $25-49.9 Million
Emp.: 260
Business Description:
Bank Holding Company
S.I.C.: 6712
N.A.I.C.S.: 551111
Personnel:
Truman Bodden *(Chm)*
Stuart Dack *(Pres & CEO)*
Board of Directors:
Truman Bodden
John C. Bierley
Sherri Bodden-Cowan
Stuart Dack
Clarence B. Flowers, Jr.
Bryan A. Hunter
Peter Adye Tomkins
Nigel Wardle

CAYMUS RESOURCES INC.

880 580 Hornby Street
Vancouver, BC, V6C 3B6, Canada
Tel.: (604) 806-0626
Fax: (604) 684-0642
E-Mail: arwconsulting@gmail.com
Year Founded: 2011
CJX.P—(TSXV)
Business Description:
Investment Services
S.I.C.: 6211
N.A.I.C.S.: 523999
Personnel:
David Sidoo *(Pres & CEO)*
Andrew Williams *(CFO)*
James Harris *(Sec)*
Board of Directors:
Nick DeMare
James Harris
James Hutton
David Sidoo
Andrew Williams
Transfer Agent:
Computershare Investor Services Inc.
3rd Floor 510 Burrard Street
Vancouver, BC, Canada

CAZA GOLD CORP.

301-700 West Pender Street
Vancouver, BC, V6C 1G8, Canada
Tel.: (604) 685-9750
Fax: (604) 685-9744
Toll Free: (877) 684-9700
E-Mail: info@cazagold.com
Web Site: www.cazagold.com
Year Founded: 2007
CZY—(DEU OTC TSXV)
Int. Income: $11,112
Assets: $7,302,900
Liabilities: $560,408
Net Worth: $6,742,492
Earnings: ($2,354,299)
Fiscal Year-end: 12/31/12
Business Description:
Gold Mining Services
S.I.C.: 1041
N.A.I.C.S.: 212221
Personnel:
Bradford James Cooke *(Chm)*
Greg Myers *(Pres & CEO)*
Philip Yee *(CFO & VP-Fin)*
Stewart Lockwood *(Legal Counsel & Sec)*
Board of Directors:
Bradford James Cooke
Anthony Grant Hawkshaw
Stewart Lockwood
Greg Myers
Philip Yee

Legal Counsel:
Vector Corporate Finance Lawyers
999 West Hastings Street Suite 1040
Vancouver, BC, V6C 2W2, Canada
Tel.: (604) 683-1102
Fax: (604) 683-2643

Transfer Agent:
Computershare Investor Services Inc.
3rd Floor 510 Burrard Street
Vancouver, BC, Canada

CAZALY RESOURCES LIMITED

Level 2 38 Richardson Street
West Perth, WA, 6005, Australia
Mailing Address:
PO Box 396
West Perth, WA, 6872, Australia
Tel.: (61) 893226283
Fax: (61) 893226398
E-Mail: admin@cazalyresources.com.au
Web Site: www.cazalyresources.com.au
CAZ—(ASX)
Rev.: $693,460
Assets: $31,826,201
Liabilities: $7,235,866
Net Worth: $24,590,335
Earnings: ($1,315,564)
Fiscal Year-end: 06/30/13
Business Description:
Mineral exploration
S.I.C.: 1481
N.A.I.C.S.: 213115
Personnel:
Clive Jones *(Co-Mng Dir)*
Nathan McMahon *(Co-Mng Dir)*
Mike Robbins *(Sec)*
Board of Directors:
Kent Hunter
Clive Jones
Nathan McMahon

Legal Counsel:
Price Seirakowski
Level 24 St Martins Tower 44 St Georges Terrace
6000 Perth, WA, Australia

CB AUSTRALIA LIMITED

Level 8 3 Spring Street
GPO Box 3510
Sydney, NSW, 2000, Australia
Mailing Address:
GPO Box 3510
Sydney, NSW, 2001, Australia
Tel.: (61) 292239223
Fax: (61) 292236666
E-Mail: info@cbal.com.au
Web Site: www.cbal.com.au
CBK—(ASX)
Sales Range: $1-9.9 Million
Emp.: 168
Business Description:
Real Estate Services
S.I.C.: 6531
N.A.I.C.S.: 531390
Personnel:
Alex Caraco *(Mng Dir)*
John Bell *(COO & Sec)*
Board of Directors:
Andrew Geddes
Alex Caraco
Kim Goodall

Legal Counsel:
Middletons
Level 26 52 Martin Place
Sydney, NSW, 2000, Australia
Tel.: (61) 2 9513 2300
Fax: (61) 2 9513 2399

Non-U.S. Subsidiary:

Admerex (Singapore) Pte Limited (1)
51 Goldhill Plz No 22-01
Goldhill Plz, Singapore, 308900, Singapore
Tel.: (65) 62582318
Fax: (65) 62586317
Software Development Services
S.I.C.: 7372
N.A.I.C.S.: 511210

CB ENGINEERING LTD

5040 - 12A Street SE
Calgary, AB, T2G 5K9, Canada
Tel.: (403) 259-6220
Fax: (403) 259-3377
Toll Free: (800) 992-2364
E-Mail: info@cbeng.com
Web Site: www.cbeng.com
Year Founded: 1974
Rev.: $12,520,073
Emp.: 45
Business Description:
Industrial Equipment Distr
S.I.C.: 5084
N.A.I.C.S.: 423830
Personnel:
Craig Bowyer *(Founder)*

CB GOLD INC.

Suite 907 1030 West Georgia St
Vancouver, BC, V6E 2Y3, Canada
Tel.: (604) 630-5870
Fax: (604) 630-5871
E-Mail: info@cbgoldinc.com
Web Site: www.cbgoldinc.com
Year Founded: 2005
CBJ—(TSXV)
Int. Income: $103,378
Assets: $28,620,818
Liabilities: $1,718,661
Net Worth: $26,902,157
Earnings: ($19,127,927)
Emp.: 60
Fiscal Year-end: 12/31/12
Business Description:
Gold, Copper, Precious Metals, Base Metals & Industrial Diamonds Mining & Exploration Services
S.I.C.: 1041
N.A.I.C.S.: 212221
Personnel:
Fabio Capponi *(Pres & CEO)*
Susan Rubin *(CFO)*
Dawn Wattie *(Sec)*
Board of Directors:
Peter Barnes
Fabio Capponi
Hernan Juan Jose Martinez Torres
Juan Manuel Pelaez

Legal Counsel:
Lawson Lundell LLP
1600 Cathedral Place 925 West Georgia Street
Vancouver, BC, V6C 3L2, Canada

Transfer Agent:
Computershare Investor Services Inc.
3rd Floor 510 Burrard St
V6C 3B9 Vancouver, BC, Canada

CB INDUSTRIAL PRODUCT HOLDING BERHAD

Lot 4 Jalan Waja 15 Kawasan Telok Panglima Garang
42500 Shah Alam, Selangor, Malaysia
Tel.: (60) 33122 7117
Fax: (60) 33122 1336
E-Mail: info@cbip.com.my
Web Site: www.cbip.com.my
CBIP—(KLS)
Rev.: $171,085,046
Assets: $218,825,935
Liabilities: $55,296,822
Net Worth: $163,529,113
Earnings: $80,650,284
Fiscal Year-end: 12/31/12
Business Description:
Palm Oil Mill Processing Equipment Trading Services
S.I.C.: 3556
N.A.I.C.S.: 333241
Personnel:
Chai Beng Lim *(Mng Dir)*
Chia Tyng Pang *(Co-Sec)*
Mee Hui Teo *(Co-Sec)*
Board of Directors:
Yusof Basiran
Ardy Esfandiari Abdul Hamid Shah Alhaj Shahbandar
Chai Beng Lim
Chai Huat Lim
Chee Meng Mak
Michael Sii Ching Ting
Chee Beng Wong

CB MOBIASBANCA S.A.

81A Stefan cel Mare si Sfant Avenue
Chisinau, 2012, Moldova
Tel.: (373) 22541974
Fax: (373) 22244182
E-Mail: office@mobiasbanca.md
Web Site: www.mobiasbanca.md
Year Founded: 1990
Sales Range: $1-9.9 Million
Emp.: 505
Business Description:
Banking Services
S.I.C.: 6029
N.A.I.C.S.: 522110
Personnel:
Nicolae Dorin *(Chm)*
Patrick Gelin *(Chm-Supervisory Bd)*
Jean-Francois Myard *(Pres)*
Danut Florsecu *(First Vice Chm-Mngmt Bd)*
Supervisory Board of Directors:
Patrick Gelin
Claudiu Cercel
Mihai Lisu
Lazari Todorov

C.BANNER INTERNATIONAL HOLDINGS LIMITED

(Formerly Hongguo International Holdings Limited)
31st Floor Nanjing International Trade Center
18 Zhongshan East Road, Nanjing, 210005, China
Tel.: (86) 25 84791598
Fax: (86) 25 84719691
E-Mail: info@cbanner.com.cn
Web Site: www.hongguo.com
1028—(HKG)
Rev.: $386,349,410
Assets: $359,137,611
Liabilities: $88,201,939
Net Worth: $270,935,672
Earnings: $51,461,681
Fiscal Year-end: 12/31/12
Business Description:
Women's Footwear Mfr & Retailer
S.I.C.: 2389
N.A.I.C.S.: 316210
Personnel:
Yixi Chen *(Chm)*
Wei Li *(Pres & CEO)*
Tingyu Xu *(CFO)*
Ming Wai Mok *(Sec)*
Board of Directors:
Yixi Chen
Chi Kit Ho
Li Huo
Wilson Wai Sun Kwong
Wei Li
Xindan Li
Xinhui Li
Bingwen Miao
Guangze Wu
Chengming Xu
Tingyu Xu
Zhiyong Zhang

Appleby Management (Bermuda) Limited
Argyle House 41A Cedar Avenue
Hamilton, Bermuda

Transfer Agent:
Appleby Management (Bermuda) Limited
Argyle House 41A Cedar Avenue
Hamilton, Bermuda

CBC CO., LTD.

2 15 13 Tsukishima
Chuo Ku, Tokyo, 104 0052, Japan
Tel.: (81) 335364500
Fax: (81) 335364780
E-Mail: hosogai@cbc.co.jp
Web Site: www.cbc.co.jp
Year Founded: 1925
Sales Range: $10-24.9 Million
Emp.: 397
Business Description:
Mfr., Importer, Exporter & Sales of Electronic Components, Processed Light Metals, Resin Products, Chemical Products, Industrial Machineries, Medical Products, Agricultural Chemicals, Foodstuffs & Clothing
Import Export
S.I.C.: 2821
N.A.I.C.S.: 325211
Personnel:
Koichi Morimoto *(Sr Mng Dir)*
Shoichi Takabatake *(Sr Mng Dir)*
Tsuyoshi Katakami *(Mng Dir)*
Takayasu Owada *(COO)*
Takashi Shimaoka *(Co-COO)*
Board of Directors:
Hidekazu Atarashi
Koichi Morimoto
Yutaka Sasaki
Takashi Shimaoka
Nobuyuki Sugita
Shoichi Takabatake
Norihiro Tanimura

U.S. Subsidiaries:

CBC America Co., Ltd. (1)
20521 Earl St
Torrance, CA 90503-3006
Tel.: (310) 793-1500
Fax: (310) 793-1506
Web Site: www.cbcamerica.com
Emp.: 12
Distributor of Security Camera Lenses, Tubes & Products
S.I.C.: 3663
N.A.I.C.S.: 334220
Jim Holihan *(VP)*

CBC America Co., Ltd. (1)
55 Mall Dr
Commack, NY 11725-5703 (100%)
Tel.: (631) 864-9700
Fax: (631) 864-9710
Web Site: www.cbcamerica.com
Emp.: 57
Distributor of Optical Lenses & Security Cameras
S.I.C.: 5043
N.A.I.C.S.: 423410

Non-U.S. Affiliates:

CBC Co (Milan) Ltd (1)
Via E Majorana 2
Nova, 20054 Milan, Italy IT
Tel.: (39) 362365079 (100%)
Fax: (39) 36241273
E-Mail: info@cbc.it
Web Site: www.cbc.it
Emp.: 21
Mfr. & Supplier of CCTV Equipment & Optical Lenses
S.I.C.: 3827
N.A.I.C.S.: 333314

CBC Co. (Paris) Ltd. (1)
1 Ave Des Marguerites Zone D Activites Des Petits Carreaux
94389 Bonneuil, France FR
Tel.: (33) 143990424 (100%)
Fax: (33) 143995906
Web Site: www.cbcfrance.com
Emp.: 12

CBC Co., Ltd.—(Continued)

Mfr. & Supplier of CCTV Equipment & Optical Lenses
S.I.C.: 3827
N.A.I.C.S.: 333314

CBC (Deutschland) GmbH (1)
Hansaallee 191
Dusseldorf, 40549, Germany De
Tel.: (49) 211530670 (100%)
Fax: (49) 21153067280
E-Mail: info@cbc-de.com
Web Site: www.cbc-de.com
Rev.: $42,810,576
Emp.: 40
Mfr. & Supplier of CCTV Equipment & Optical Lenses
S.I.C.: 3827
N.A.I.C.S.: 333314
Fumiya Sagawa *(Mng Dir)*

CBC (Europe) Ltd. (1)
7-8 Garrick Industrial Ctr Irving Way
London, NW9 6AQ, United Kingdom UK
Tel.: (44) 2087323333 (100%)
Fax: (44) 2082023387
E-Mail: info@cbcuk.com
Web Site: www.cbceurope.com
Emp.: 40
Mfr. & Supplier of CCTV Equipment & Optical Lenses
S.I.C.: 3827
N.A.I.C.S.: 333314
Ken Oti *(Mng Dir)*

CBC (H.K.) Co., Ltd. (1)
2101 21st Fl Tower 6 China Hong Kong City
33 Canton Rd Tsimshatsui, Kowloon, China (Hong Kong) HK
Tel.: (852) 28871326 (100%)
Fax: (852) 28872457
Web Site: www.cbc.co.hk
Emp.: 20
S.I.C.: 2821
N.A.I.C.S.: 325211
Kawai Shusaku *(Gen Mgr)*

CBC (H.K.) Co., Ltd. - Kwun Tong Branch (1)
423 China Hong Kong City
53 Canton Rd, Kowloon, China (Hong Kong) (100%)
Tel.: (852) 23458686
Fax: (852) 23422908
Web Site: www.cbc.co.hk
Emp.: 120
S.I.C.: 2821
N.A.I.C.S.: 325211

CBC (Poland) Sp.zo.o. (1)
UL G Morcinka 5 Paw 6
1496 Warsaw, Poland PL
Tel.: (48) 226384440 (100%)
Fax: (48) 226384541
E-Mail: info@cbcpoland.pl
Web Site: www.cbcpoland.pl
Emp.: 8
Mfr. & Supplier of CCTV Equipment & Optical Lenses
S.I.C.: 3827
N.A.I.C.S.: 333314
Cristhoper Ksowronski *(Mng Dir)*

CBC (Shanghai) Trading Co., Ltd. (1)
Room B-2703 Dawning Centre No 500 HongBaoShi Road
Shanghai, Changning District, China CN
Tel.: (86) 21 32092626
Fax: (86) 21 32092814
E-Mail: support@cbcsh.com.cn
Web Site: www.cbc-china.cn/en/company/related.html
Emp.: 40
Plastics Mfr & Distr
S.I.C.: 2821
N.A.I.C.S.: 325211
Shioda Osamu *(Gen Mgr)*

CBC (Thailand) Co., Ltd. (1)
21st Fl ITF Tower 140/48 Silom Rd
Bangkok, 10500, Thailand TH
Tel.: (66) 22316181 (100%)
Fax: (66) 22316180
Web Site: www.cbcthailand.com
Emp.: 15
S.I.C.: 2821
N.A.I.C.S.: 325211
Utaro Doi *(Pres)*
Naoyuki Takagi *(Mng Dir)*

CBC.S PTE Ltd. - Distribution Division (1)
15 Jalan Kilang Barat
#04-03 Front Tech Ctr, Singapore, 159357, Singapore SG
Tel.: (65) 62751221 (100%)
Fax: (65) 62750766
Web Site: www.cbcsingapore.com
Emp.: 20
S.I.C.: 2821
N.A.I.C.S.: 325211
Yuki Tsubota *(Gen Mgr)*

CBC.S PTE LTD - Trade Division (1)
15 Jalankilong Barat No 04 03
San Ctr, Singapore, 159357, Singapore SG
Tel.: (65) 62751221
Fax: (65) 62750766
Web Site: www.cbc.co.jp
Emp.: 20
Mfr. & Marketer of Plastics, Electronic Components, Clothing, Metals, Food & Other Products
S.I.C.: 3827
N.A.I.C.S.: 333314
N Ohta *(Mng Dir)*

T-CBC (Taiwan) Co., Ltd. (1)
Rm 1401 Chia Hsing Bldg 96 Chung Shan N Rd Sec 2
Taipei, 104, Taiwan TW
Tel.: (886) 225223901 (100%)
Fax: (886) 225213931
Web Site: www.cbc.co.jp
Emp.: 20
S.I.C.: 2821
N.A.I.C.S.: 325211
Osamu Shioda *(Gen Mgr)*

CBD ENERGY LIMITED

Level 2 Suite 2 53 Cross Street
Double Bay, NSW, 2028, Australia
Tel.: (61) 2 8069 7970
Fax: (61) 2 9363 9955
E-Mail: investor@cbdenergy.com.au
Web Site: www.cbdenergy.com.au
CBDNF—(OTC OTCB)
Rev.: $77,732,323
Assets: $45,026,015
Liabilities: $43,702,548
Net Worth: $1,323,467
Earnings: ($12,776,146)
Fiscal Year-end: 06/30/13

Business Description:
Energy & Mechanical Services
S.I.C.: 8999
N.A.I.C.S.: 541690

Personnel:
Gerry McGowan *(Chm & Mng Dir)*
Richard Pillinger *(CFO & Sec)*
Patrick Lennon *(COO)*
James Greer *(CEO-Intl Ops)*

Board of Directors:
Gerry McGowan
Todd Barlow
Carlo Botto
William C. Morro

Divisions:

CBD Energy Limited - CBD Solar Division (1)
Ste 2 Level 2 53 Cross St
Double Bay, NSW, 2028, Australia
Tel.: (61) 293639910
Fax: (61) 293639955
E-Mail: jwing@cbdenergy.com.au
Web Site: www.cbdenergy.com.au
Emp.: 12
Photovoltaic Devices Mfr
S.I.C.: 3568
N.A.I.C.S.: 333613
Gerry McGowan *(Mng Dir)*

CBD Energy Limited - CBD Wind Division (1)
Ste 2 Level 2 53 Cross St
Double Bay, New South Wales, 2028, Australia
Tel.: (61) 293630999
Fax: (61) 293639955
E-Mail: jwing@cbdenergy.com.au
Web Site: www.cbdenergy.com.au
Emp.: 12
Wind Power Structure Construction Services
S.I.C.: 1629
N.A.I.C.S.: 237130
Gerry McGowan *(Mng Dir)*

Subsidiaries:

Parmac Airconditioning & Mechanical Services Pty. Ltd. (1)
15 Terra Cotta Dr
Blackburn, VIC, 3130, Australia
Tel.: (61) 398532477
Fax: (61) 398532677
E-Mail: info@parmac.com.au
Web Site: www.parmac.com.au
Emp.: 45
Air Conditioning System Installation Services
S.I.C.: 3585
N.A.I.C.S.: 333415
Grant Hillman *(Mng Dir)*

Remote Area Power Systems Pty. Ltd. (1)
Ste 2 - Level 2 53 Cross St
Double Bay, 2028, Australia
Tel.: (61) 293639911
Fax: (61) 293639955
E-Mail: info@rapsystems.com.au
Web Site: www.rapsystems.com.au
Solar System Installation & Energy Storage Services
S.I.C.: 1623
N.A.I.C.S.: 237130

CBM ASIA DEVELOPMENT CORP.

404 - 815 Hornby Street
Vancouver, BC, V6Z 2E6, Canada
Tel.: (604) 684-2340
Fax: (604) 684-2474
E-Mail: info@cbmasia.ca
Web Site: www.cbmasia.ca
Year Founded: 2006
TCF—(TSXV)
Int. Income: $16,818
Assets: $3,306,481
Liabilities: $1,057,576
Net Worth: $2,248,906
Earnings: ($12,545,406)
Fiscal Year-end: 12/31/12

Business Description:
Oil & Gas Exploration Services
S.I.C.: 1389
N.A.I.C.S.: 213112

Personnel:
Charles W. Bloomquist *(Founder, Pres & CEO)*
Scott H. Stevens *(Chm)*
James Hurren *(CFO)*

Board of Directors:
Scott H. Stevens
Charles W. Bloomquist
James Charuk
Adam Clarke
James Friberg
Clint Sharples

Legal Counsel:
Gregory T Chu
650- 1188 West Georgia St
Vancouver, BC, Canada

Transfer Agent:
Computershare Limited
3rd Floor 510 Burrard St
Vancouver, BC, Canada

CBO TERRITORIA

Cours de l'Usine La Mare
BP 105
97438 Sainte-Marie-la-Blanche, France
Tel.: (33) 2 3220 3204
Fax: (33) 2 62542432
E-Mail: contact@cboterritoria.com
Web Site: www.cboterritoria.com
CBOT—(EUR)
Sls.: $147,405,615
Earnings: $21,807,954
Emp.: 75
Fiscal Year-end: 12/31/12

Business Description:
Real Estate Development & Management Services
S.I.C.: 6552
N.A.I.C.S.: 237210

Personnel:
Jerome Burgaud *(Dir Gen-Fin)*

C'BON COSMETICS CO., LTD.

7-18-12 Roppongi Minato-ku
Tokyo, 106-8556, Japan
Tel.: (81) 449791234
Fax: (81) 449792594
E-Mail: hh5103@cbon.co.jp
Web Site: www.cbon.co.jp
4926—(JAS TKS)
Sales Range: $125-149.9 Million
Emp.: 1,983

Business Description:
Cosmetics & Pharmaceutical Products Mfr & Sales
S.I.C.: 2844
N.A.I.C.S.: 325620

Personnel:
Masahiro Inuzuka *(Chm)*
Yasuyo Kaneko *(Pres)*
Shinichi Omori *(Corp Officer)*
Kazuko Shimizu *(Corp Officer)*

Board of Directors:
Masahiro Inuzuka
Reiko Akemine
Yasuyo Kaneko
Hideo Kubota
Yoshifumi Motomura
Kazuhiro Sakiyama
Takanori Susa
Ken Takahashi
Sumiko Tsukahara

CBR MANAGEMENT GMBH

Theatinerstrasse 7
80333 Munich, Germany
Tel.: (49) 892113777
Fax: (49) 8921137788
E-Mail: info@cbr-gmbh.de
Web Site: www.cbr-gmbh.de
Emp.: 7

Business Description:
Private Equity Firm
S.I.C.: 6211
N.A.I.C.S.: 523999

Personnel:
Wolfgang Behrens-Ramberg *(Co-Founder)*
Eberhard Crain *(Co-Founder)*

Subsidiary:

SELLNER Holding GmbH (1)
Windsbacher Str 40
91564 Neuendettelsau, Germany De
Tel.: (49) 98745050
Fax: (49) 9874505222
E-Mail: info@sellner.de
Web Site: www.sellner.de
Sales Range: $350-399.9 Million
Emp.: 2,100
Motor Vehicle Interior Surface Mfr
S.I.C.: 2396
N.A.I.C.S.: 336360
Werner Renzel *(Mng Dir)*
Jorn Trierweiler *(Mng Dir)*

CBS CONSTRUCTION LTD.

150 MacKay Crescent
Fort McMurray, AB, T9H 4W8, Canada
Tel.: (780) 743-1810
Fax: (780) 743-6264
Web Site: www.cbsconstruction.ca
Year Founded: 1978

Rev.: $61,480,757
Emp.: 380
Business Description:
Construction Services
S.I.C.: 1542
N.A.I.C.S.: 236220
Personnel:
Garry Fizzell *(Pres)*

CBZ HOLDINGS LIMITED
UNion House 60 Kwame Nkrumah Avenue
PO Box 3313
Harare, Zimbabwe
Tel.: (263) 4748050
Fax: (263) 4758077
E-Mail: info@cbz.co.zw
Web Site: www.cbz.co.zw
CBZH—(ZIM)
Int. Income: $156,861,775
Assets: $1,223,093,227
Liabilities: $1,062,415,992
Net Worth: $160,677,235
Earnings: $45,024,987
Emp.: 36
Fiscal Year-end: 12/31/12
Business Description:
Investment & Financial Management Services
S.I.C.: 6799
N.A.I.C.S.: 523920
Personnel:
John P. Mangudya *(CEO)*
Never Nyemudzo *(CFO)*
Board of Directors:
Luxon Zembe
Tinoziva Bere
Fouad M. Dernawi
Mohamed I. Ghali
Andrew Lowe
John P. Mangudya
Elliot Mugamu
David Mutambara
Mohammed Hanif Nanabawa
Roseline Nhamo
Never Nyemudzo
Rebecca Pasi
Givemore Taputaira
Richard Victor Wilde
Legal Counsel:
Mawere & Sibanda
3rd Floor Chiyedza House Cnr 1st Street/ Kwame Nkrumah Avenue
P O Box CY 1376
Causeway, Harare, Zimbabwe
Dube, Manikai & Hwacha
6th Floor Gold Bridge Eastgate Complex Robert Mugabe Road
Harare, Zimbabwe
Transfer Agent:
ZB Transfer Secretaries
ZB Centre, 1st Floor Cnr First Street/Kwame Nkrumah Avenue
P.O Box 2540
Harare, Zimbabwe
Subsidiaries:

CBZ Asset Management Company (Private) Limited (1)
1st Floor Cecil House 2 Central Avenue
Harare, Zimbabwe
Tel.: (263) 4702809
Fax: (263) 4700669
E-Mail: info@datvest.co.zw
Emp.: 40
Financial Marketing Services
S.I.C.: 6211
N.A.I.C.S.: 523999
J. Smith *(Mng Dir)*

CBZ Bank Limited (1)
Union House 60 Kwame Nkrumah Avenue
Harare, Zimbabwe
Tel.: (263) 4748050
Fax: (263) 4773783
E-Mail: info@cbz.co.zw
Web Site: www.cbzbank.co.zw
Commercial Banking Services
S.I.C.: 6029
N.A.I.C.S.: 522110
R. V. Wilde *(Chm)*
J. P. Mangudya *(CEO)*
N. Nyemudzo *(CFO)*
P. Zimunya *(COO)*
M. Mudondo *(Treas)*
R. A. Jakanani *(Sec)*

CBZ Properties (Pvt) Limited (1)
8th Floor Sapphire House Corner
PO Box 3313
Speke Avenue Angwa Street, Harare, Zimbabwe
Tel.: (263) 4759110
Fax: (263) 4 700538
E-Mail: cnazare@cbz.co.zw
Property Management Services
S.I.C.: 6531
N.A.I.C.S.: 531312
Chris Nazare *(Mgr)*

CC LAND HOLDINGS LIMITED
Rooms 3308-10 33/F China Resources Building 26 Harbour Road
Wanchai, China (Hong Kong)
Tel.: (852) 28207000
Fax: (852) 25980698
E-Mail: ccland@ccland.com.hk
Web Site: www.ccland.com.hk
1224—(HKG)
Rev.: $958,446,536
Assets: $5,361,081,292
Liabilities: $3,433,080,983
Net Worth: $1,928,000,309
Earnings: $86,686,122
Emp.: 1,620
Fiscal Year-end: 12/31/12
Business Description:
Investment Services; Land, Property & Manufacturing
S.I.C.: 6211
N.A.I.C.S.: 523999
Personnel:
Chung Kiu Cheung *(Chm)*
Peter How Mun Lam *(Deputy Chm & Mng Dir)*
Wai Choi Tsang *(Deputy Chm)*
Fung Yee Cheung *(Sec)*
Board of Directors:
Chung Kiu Cheung
Jeffrey Kin Fung Lam
Peter How Mun Lam
Chun Cheong Leung
Steven Yu Ming Leung
Wai Fai Leung
Wai Choi Tsang
Patrick Lung Tak Wong
Yat Fai Wong
HSBC Securities Services (Bermuda) Limited
6 Front Street
Hamilton, Bermuda
Transfer Agents:
Tricor Secretaries Limited
26th Floor Tesbury Centre 28 Queen's Road East
Wanchai, China (Hong Kong)
HSBC Securities Services (Bermuda) Limited
6 Front Street
Hamilton, Bermuda
Subsidiaries:

Hoi Tin Universal Limited (1)
Rm 607 Shui Hing Ctr 13 Sheung Yuet Rd
Kowloon Bay, Kowloon, China (Hong Kong)
Tel.: (852) 27540363
Fax: (852) 27547667
E-Mail: hoitin@hoitin.com.hk
Emp.: 17
Leather Products Mfr
S.I.C.: 3111
N.A.I.C.S.: 316110
Katy Kock *(Mng Dir)*

Qualipak International Holdings Limited (1)
7 F China United Ctr 28 Marble Rd
North Point, China (Hong Kong)
Tel.: (852) 25296196
Fax: (852) 25296632
E-Mail: qualipak@qualipakhk.com
Web Site: www.qualipakhk.com
1332—(HKG)
Sales Range: $500-549.9 Million
Emp.: 70
Leather & Wooden Products Mfr
S.I.C.: 3199
N.A.I.C.S.: 316998
How Mun Lam *(Chm)*

CC NAPRED JSC
115 Mihajla Pupina Street
11000 Belgrade, Serbia
Tel.: (381) 11 7113740
Fax: (381) 11 6135851
E-Mail: napred@napred.net
Web Site: www.napred.net
NPRD—(BEL)
Business Description:
Civil Engineering Services
S.I.C.: 1629
N.A.I.C.S.: 237990
Personnel:
Dobroslav Bojovic *(CEO)*

CCA INTERNATIONAL
77 Avenue de Segur
75015 Paris, France
Tel.: (33) 1 53 05 75 75
Fax: (33) 1 53 05 75 85
E-Mail: info@ccainternational.com
Web Site: www.ccainternational.com
CCA—(EUR)
Emp.: 3,580
Business Description:
Business Support Services
S.I.C.: 7389
N.A.I.C.S.: 561499
Personnel:
Eric Dadian *(Chm-Supervisory Bd)*
Patrick Dubreil *(Chm-Mgmt Bd)*
Sebastien Litou *(CFO)*
Supervisory Board of Directors:
Eric Dadian
Jerome Balladur
Gilles Etrillard
Olivier Lange
Erica Laptes
Dominique Laurent

CCI THERMAL TECHNOLOGIES, INC.
5918 Roper Rd
Edmonton, AB, T6B 3E1, Canada
Tel.: (780) 466-3178
Fax: (780) 468-5904
Toll Free: (800) 661-8529
E-Mail: info@ccithermal.com
Web Site: www.ccithermal.com
Emp.: 300
Business Description:
Heating & Filtration Services
S.I.C.: 5074
N.A.I.C.S.: 423720
Personnel:
Harold A. Roozen *(Chm & CEO)*
Bernard C. Moore *(Pres & COO)*

CCK CONSOLIDATED HOLDINGS BERHAD
Lot 999 Section 66 Jalan Keluli
Bintawa Industrial Estate
93450 Kuching, Sarawak, Malaysia
Tel.: (60) 82336520
Fax: (60) 82331479
Web Site: www.cck.com.my
CCK—(KLS)
Rev.: $137,055,530
Assets: $70,857,935
Liabilities: $23,465,760
Net Worth: $47,392,176
Earnings: $3,554,025
Emp.: 924
Fiscal Year-end: 06/30/13
Business Description:
Poultry Services
S.I.C.: 0254
N.A.I.C.S.: 112340
Personnel:
Shaw Fui Chong *(Vice Chm)*
Chiong Hiiung Tiong *(Mng Dir)*
Ting Leong Ling *(Co-Sec)*
Jan Moi Voon *(Co-Sec)*
Board of Directors:
Su Kouk Tiong
Pemanca Janggu Banyang
Wei Leong Bong
Shaw Fui Chong
Chung Peng Kueh
Liong Kii Lau
Ting Leong Ling
Putit Matzen
Chiong Hiiung Tiong
Chiong Soon Tiong
See Khong Wong

CCK FINANCIAL SOLUTIONS LIMITED
Level 3 12 St Georges Terrace
Perth, Western Australia, 6000, Australia
Tel.: (61) 892237600
Fax: (61) 892237699
Web Site: www.cck.com.au
Emp.: 20
Business Description:
Computer Software Provider
S.I.C.: 7372
N.A.I.C.S.: 511210
Personnel:
Joseph Wong *(Mng Dir)*
N. Gamage *(Sec)*
Board of Directors:
Michael E. Wright
Helen Glastras
Andrew Graeme Moffat
Joseph Wong
Subsidiary:

CCK Financial Solutions (Consulting) Pty. Ltd. (1)
L 3 12 St Georges Ter
Perth, WA, 6000, Australia
Tel.: (61) 892237600
Fax: (61) 892237699
E-Mail: florencep@cck.com.au
Web Site: www.cck.com.au/
Emp.: 21
Financial Software Consulting Services
S.I.C.: 7371
N.A.I.C.S.: 541511
Joseph Wong *(Mng Dir)*
Non-U.S. Subsidiary:

CCK Financial Solutions (Malaysia) Sdn. Bhd. (1)
Ste 13 08 13th Fl Wisma UOA II
21 Jalan Pinang, 50450 Kuala Lumpur, Malaysia
Tel.: (60) 321633529
Fax: (60) 321648591
E-Mail: cckss1@po.jaring.my
Web Site: www.cck.com.au
Emp.: 5
Treasury Management Services
S.I.C.: 8748
N.A.I.C.S.: 541618
Yin Shuey Tian *(Country Mgr)*

CCL INDUSTRIES INC.
105 Gordon Baker Road Suite 500
Willowdale, ON, M2H 3P8, Canada
Tel.: (416) 756-8500
Fax: (416) 756-8555
E-Mail: ccl@cclind.com
Web Site: www.cclind.com
Year Founded: 1951
CCL.B—(TSX)
Sls.: $1,300,725,865
Assets: $1,644,191,584
Liabilities: $762,309,962

CCL Industries Inc.—(Continued)

Net Worth: $881,881,622
Earnings: $96,907,010
Emp.: 6,600
Fiscal Year-end: 12/31/12

Business Description:
Labels, Aluminum Cans & Packaging & Plastic Tubes Mfr
S.I.C.: 7389
N.A.I.C.S.: 561910

Personnel:
Donald G. Lang *(Chm)*
Geoffrey T. Martin *(Pres & CEO)*
Sean Washchuk *(CFO & Sr VP)*
Bohdan I. Sirota *(Gen Counsel, Sec & Sr VP)*
Lalitha Vaidyanathan *(Sr VP-Fin, IT & Admin)*

Board of Directors:
Donald G. Lang
George Vail Bayly
Paul J. Block
Philip M. Gresh
Edward E. Guillet
Alan Douglas Horn
Stuart W. Lang
Geoffrey T. Martin
Douglas W. Muzyka
Thomas C. Peddie

Transfer Agent:
CIBC Mellon Trust Company
PO Box 700 Postal Station B
Montreal, QC, Canada

Subsidiaries:

CCL Container (1)
105 Gordon Baker Rd
Willowdale, ON, M2H 3P8, Canada (100%)
Tel.: (416) 756-8500
Web Site: www.cclcontainer.com
Emp.: 10
Recyclable Aluminum Aerosol Cans, Aluminum Bottles, Barrier Systems & Other Specialty Aluminum Packaging Mfr
S.I.C.: 3353
N.A.I.C.S.: 331315

U.S. Subsidiaries:

CCL Container (Hermitage), Inc. (2)
1 Llodio Dr
Hermitage, PA 16148-9015 (100%)
Tel.: (724) 981-4420
Fax: (724) 342-1116
Web Site: www.cclcontainer.com
Emp.: 250
Aluminum Cans & Packaging Mfr
S.I.C.: 3411
N.A.I.C.S.: 332431
Eric Frantz *(VP & Gen Mgr)*

CCL Label (1)
35 Mclachlan Dr
Etobicoke, ON, M9W 1E4, Canada (100%)
Tel.: (416) 675-3161
Fax: (416) 675-8831
E-Mail: info@cclind.com
Emp.: 200
S.I.C.: 2844
N.A.I.C.S.: 325620
Jim Sellor *(VP)*

Subsidiary:

CCL Label (2)
80 Paramount Rd
Winnipeg, MB, R2X 2W3, Canada (100%)
Tel.: (416) 756-8500
Fax: (204) 694-7125
Web Site: www.cclind.com
Emp.: 50
S.I.C.: 2844
N.A.I.C.S.: 325620

U.S. Subsidiary:

CCL Label Portland, Inc (2)
2511 Nw 30th Ave
Portland, OR 97210-2015
Tel.: (503) 274-9782
Beverage Products Packaging Services
S.I.C.: 7389
N.A.I.C.S.: 561910

Non-U.S. Subsidiaries:

CCL Label de Mexico S.A. de C.V. (2)
Av Michoacan 20 MD 21
Renouvacion Istapalapa, 09209 Mexico, Mexico MX
Tel.: (52) 5551485800 (100%)
Fax: (52) 55541970681
E-Mail: reception@cclmix.com.mx
Web Site: www.ccllabel.com
Emp.: 160
S.I.C.: 2841
N.A.I.C.S.: 325620
Ben Lilienthal *(Gen Mgr)*

Etiquetas CCL S.A. de C.V. (2)
Michoacan 20 Mod 21 Col Renovacion
9209 Mexico, Mexico
Tel.: (52) 55 5148 5800
E-Mail: recepcion@cclind.com
Web Site: www.ccllabel.com
Emp.: 20
Personal Care Products Labeling Services
S.I.C.: 7389
N.A.I.C.S.: 561910
Ernesto Montalvo *(Mgr-Mktg)*

U.S. Subsidiaries:

Avery Products Corporation (1)
(Formerly Avery Dennison Office Products Company)
50 Pointe Dr
Brea, CA 92821 NV
Tel.: (714) 674-8500
Fax: (714) 674-6929
Toll Free: (800) 462-8379
Web Site: www.avery.com
Sales Range: $750-799.9 Million
Emp.: 450
Self-Adhesive Labels, Binders & Sheet Protectors Mfr
S.I.C.: 2679
N.A.I.C.S.: 322299
Jim Sellors *(Pres-North America)*

Subsidiary:

AVERY OFFICE PRODUCTS PUERTO RICO L.L.C. (2)
Citibank Tower 250 Ponce de Leon Ave Ste 1002
San Juan, PR 00918
Tel.: (787) 753-3135
Fax: (787) 753-3144
Information Services
S.I.C.: 3291
N.A.I.C.S.: 327910

Non-U.S. Subsidiaries:

Avery Dennison Office Accessories U.K. Limited (2)
5/6 The Switchback Gardner Road
Maidenhead, Berks, SL6 7RJ, United Kingdom UK
Tel.: (44) 1628 764 000
Web Site: www.avery.co.uk
Label & Packaging Materials Mfr
S.I.C.: 3999
N.A.I.C.S.: 339999

Avery Office Products Pty. Ltd. (2)
(Formerly Avery Dennison Office Products Pty. Ltd.)
11 Carrington Road
Castle Hill, NSW, 2154, Australia AU
Mailing Address:
PO Box 396
Castle Hill, NSW, 1765, Australia
Tel.: (61) 2 9843 0777
Fax: (61) 2 9634 7018
E-Mail: consumerservice-au@avery.com
Web Site: www.averyproducts.com.au
Flexible Packaging Products Mfr
S.I.C.: 2671
N.A.I.C.S.: 322220

Avery TICO S.r.l. (2)
(Formerly Avery Dennison Office Products Italia S.r.l.)
Via Honduras 15
00040 Pomezia, RM, Italy IT
Tel.: (39) 06910461
Fax: (39) 0691046229
Web Site: www.avery.it
Labels & Office Products Whslr
S.I.C.: 5112
N.A.I.C.S.: 424120

CCL Industries Corp. (1)
161 Worcester Rd Ste 502
Boston, MA 01701
Tel.: (508) 872-4511
Web Site: www.cclind.com
Specialty Packaging Mfr
S.I.C.: 7389
N.A.I.C.S.: 561910
Geoffrey T. Martin *(CEO)*

Subsidiaries:

CCL Label, Inc. (2)
161 Worcester Rd Ste 502
Framingham, MA 01701 (100%)
Tel.: (508) 872-4511
Fax: (508) 872-7671
E-Mail: lvaidyanathan@cclind.com
Web Site: www.ccllabel.com
Emp.: 6
Business Services
S.I.C.: 2679
N.A.I.C.S.: 322299
Geoffrey Martin *(CEO)*
Bruce W. Bacon *(Sr VP-HR)*

Branches:

CCL Label/Auto-Sleeve (3)
2003 Case Pkwy S Unit 3
Twinsburg, OH 44240-2310
Tel.: (330) 487-2200
Toll Free: (800) 852-4571
Web Site: www.ccl-autosleeve.com
Sales Range: $1-9.9 Million
Emp.: 2
Stretch-Sleeve Labels Mfr
S.I.C.: 7389
N.A.I.C.S.: 561910

CCL Label (3)
576 College Commerce Way
Upland, CA 91786
Tel.: (909) 608-2260
Fax: (909) 981-5042
Web Site: www.ccllabel.com
Emp.: 75
Mfr of Pressure Sensitive Labels
S.I.C.: 2671
N.A.I.C.S.: 322220

CCL Label (3)
15 Controls Dr
Shelton, CT 06484-0511 (100%)
Tel.: (203) 926-1253
Fax: (203) 926-9324
Web Site: www.ccllabel.com
Emp.: 65
Mfr of Pressure Sensitive Labels
S.I.C.: 7389
N.A.I.C.S.: 561910
Jake Martin *(Gen Mgr)*

CCL Label (3)
1862 Suncast Ln
Batavia, IL 60510
Tel.: (630) 406-9147
Fax: (630) 406-9274
E-Mail: rryckman@cclind.com
Web Site: www.ccllabel.com
Sales Range: $10-24.9 Million
Emp.: 50
Label Printing Services
S.I.C.: 2759
N.A.I.C.S.: 323111
Michael Bergeron *(Mgr-Customer Svc)*

CCL Label (3)
1209 W Bailey
Sioux Falls, SD 57104
Tel.: (605) 336-7940
Fax: (605) 336-1462
Toll Free: (800) 225-4332
Web Site: www.ccllabel.com
Sls.: $70,100,000
Emp.: 280
Mfr of Pressure Sensitive Labels
S.I.C.: 2759
N.A.I.C.S.: 323111

Subsidiaries:

CCL Insertco de Puerto Rico, Inc (3)
Urb Industrial El Retiro Hwy 102 Km 33 2
San German, PR 00683
Tel.: (787) 892-1268
Fax: (787) 892-4112
Web Site: www.ccllabel.com
Emp.: 115
Healthcare Products Packaging Services
S.I.C.: 7389
N.A.I.C.S.: 561910
Luis Perez *(Plant Mgr)*

CCL Insertco, LLC (3)
1831-D Portal St
Baltimore, MD 21224
Tel.: (410) 633-6525
Fax: (410) 633-3864
Web Site: www.ccl-label.com
Healthcare Products Packaging Services
S.I.C.: 7389
N.A.I.C.S.: 561910

CCL Label de Puerto Rico, Inc (3)
Rd 171 KM 0 2 Zona Urbana
Cidra, PR 00739
Tel.: (787) 739-1044
Fax: (787) 739-3999
E-Mail: lvelacquecl@cclind.com
Web Site: www.ccl-label.com
Emp.: 40
Packaging Plastic Film Mfr
S.I.C.: 2672
N.A.I.C.S.: 322220
Eric Pagan *(Plant Mgr)*

CCL Label Sioux Falls, Inc (3)
1209 W Bailey St
Sioux Falls, SD 57104-1313
Tel.: (605) 336-7940
Fax: (605) 336-1462
Web Site: www.ccl-label.com
Emp.: 300
Food Products Packaging Services
S.I.C.: 7389
N.A.I.C.S.: 561910
Bill Goldsmith *(Gen Mgr)*

CCL Label (St. Louis), Inc (3)
208 Spring Dr
Saint Charles, MO 63303
Tel.: (636) 946-2439
Fax: (636) 724-4670
Web Site: www.ccl-label.com
Healthcare Products Packaging & Labeling Services
S.I.C.: 7389
N.A.I.C.S.: 561910
Stan Dultz *(Plant Mgr)*

CCL Tube, Inc. (2)
2250 E 220th St
Los Angeles, CA 90810
Tel.: (310) 635-4444
Fax: (310) 635-3877
Web Site: www.ccltube.com
Emp.: 200
Plastic Tube Packaging Mfr
S.I.C.: 3089
N.A.I.C.S.: 326199
Andy Iseli *(Gen Mgr)*

CCL Tube (Wilkes-Barre), Inc (1)
1 Lasley Ave
Wilkes Barre, PA 18706
Tel.: (570) 824-8485
Fax: (570) 824-8480
Health Care Products Labeling Services
S.I.C.: 7389
N.A.I.C.S.: 561910

Sancoa International (1)
92 Arch Rd
Lumberton, NJ 08048
Tel.: (856) 273-0700
Fax: (856) 273-2710
E-Mail: coswald@anchorconst.com
Web Site: www.sancoa.com
Sales Range: $75-99.9 Million
Emp.: 300
Provider of Commercial Printing Services
S.I.C.: 2759
N.A.I.C.S.: 323111
Joseph T. Sanski *(Pres)*
John Donbrewski *(CFO)*
Tom Mosca *(COO)*
William Tomasco *(COO)*

Non-U.S. Subsidiaries:

CCL Container Mexico (1)
Av De la Luz 85 Frac Industrial La Luz
Cuautitlan, Izcalli, 54730, Mexico
Tel.: (52) 5558726322
Fax: (52) 525526201596
E-Mail: lsanvicente@cclind.com
Web Site: www.cclind.com

Specialty Packaging Products
S.I.C.: 3221
N.A.I.C.S.: 327213

CCL Design GmbH (1)
Lindgesfeld 26
42653 Solingen, Germany
Tel.: (49) 212 3827 0
Fax: (49) 212 3827 156
E-Mail: designinfo@cclind.com
Web Site: www.ccl-design.de
Films & Aluminium Product Mfr
S.I.C.: 2672
N.A.I.C.S.: 322220
Peter Fleissner *(Gen Mgr)*

CCL Label A/S (1)
Nyager 11-13
2605 Brondby, Copenhagen, Denmark
Tel.: (45) 43 45 68 00
Fax: (45) 43 43 06 00
E-Mail: cphinfo@cclind.com
Web Site: www.ccllabel.dk
Emp.: 200
Label Distr
S.I.C.: 5131
N.A.I.C.S.: 424310
Lars Jensen *(Dir-Bus Dev)*

CCL Label (Ashford) Limited (1)
Foster Road Ashford Business Park
Sevington, Ashford, Kent, TN24 0SH, United Kingdom
Tel.: (44) 1233 503 333
Fax: (44) 1233 503 455
Adhesive Label Mfr
S.I.C.: 2671
N.A.I.C.S.: 322220

CCL Label do Brasil S/A (1)
Miguel Melhados Campos S N Km 79
Vinhedo, Sao Paulo, 13280 000, Brazil
Tel.: (55) 1938769300
Fax: (55) 1938764755
Web Site: www.ccllabel.com.br
Food Products Labeling Services
S.I.C.: 7389
N.A.I.C.S.: 561910
Armando Ubriaco de Oliveira *(Gen Mgr)*

CCL Label GmbH (1)
Industriestrasse 2
83607 Holzkirchen, Germany
Tel.: (49) 80 24 3 08 0
Fax: (49) 80 24 17 51
E-Mail: holinfo@cclind.com
Beverage Product Labeling Services
S.I.C.: 7389
N.A.I.C.S.: 561910
Wolfgang Zollner *(Gen Mgr)*

CCL Label (Guangzhou) Co., Ltd. (1)
No 8 Yongfeng Road Yonghe Zone
511356 Guangzhou, China
Tel.: (86) 20 8298 6800
Fax: (86) 20 8298 6803
Personal Care Product Labeling Services
S.I.C.: 7389
N.A.I.C.S.: 561910

CCL Label (Hefei) Co., Ltd (1)
Gengyun Road No 100 Hefei Economic & Technological Development Zone
230601 Hefei, Anhui, China
Tel.: (86) 551 385 1680
Fax: (86) 551 385 1630
Web Site: www.ccl-label.com
Beverage Product Labeling Services
S.I.C.: 7389
N.A.I.C.S.: 561910

CCL Label Limited (1)
Pioneer Way
Castleford, Wakefield, WF10 5QU, United Kingdom
Tel.: (44) 1977 711 111
Fax: (44) 1977 552 675
Web Site: www.ccllabel.co.uk
Emp.: 2
Adhesive Label Mfr
S.I.C.: 2671
N.A.I.C.S.: 322220
Calum Sharkey *(Mgr-Scotland)*

CCL Label Meerane GmbH (1)
Bruckenweg 5
08393 Meerane, Germany
Tel.: (49) 3764 5020
Fax: (49) 3764 4210
Web Site: www.ccl-label.com
Food Product Labeling Services
S.I.C.: 7389
N.A.I.C.S.: 561910

CCL Label S.A.S (1)
5 rue Rene Descartes
41350 Vineuil, France
Tel.: (33) 2 1854 8041
Fax: (33) 2 1854 8040
Web Site: www.ccllabel.com
Personal Care Products Packaging Services
S.I.C.: 7389
N.A.I.C.S.: 561910

CCL Label Sp z o.o (1)
ul Kierska 78 Kiekrz
62-090 Rokietnica, Poland
Tel.: (48) 61 896 0500
Fax: (48) 61 896 0520
Web Site: www.ccl-label.com
Emp.: 90
Personal Care Products Packaging Services
S.I.C.: 7389
N.A.I.C.S.: 561910
Marc Wuester *(Gen Mgr)*

CCL Label S.r.l. (1)
Via Commercio 2
20049 Concorezzo, Milan, Italy
Tel.: (39) 039 6043565
Fax: (39) 039 6042962
Web Site: www.ccl-label.com
Label Distr
S.I.C.: 5131
N.A.I.C.S.: 424310

CCL Label (Thai) Ltd. (1)
Wellgrow Industrial Estate KM 36 Bangna-Trad Highway 69 Moo5
Bangsamark Bangpakong, Chachoengsao, 24180, Thailand
Tel.: (66) 38 571 381
Fax: (66) 38 571 384
Web Site: www.ccl-label.com
Digital Printing & Labeling Services
S.I.C.: 7389
N.A.I.C.S.: 561910
Jim Anzai *(VP & Mng Dir-Asia)*

CCL Label (Vic) Pty. Ltd. (1)
120 Merrindale Drive
Croydon South, Melbourne, VIC, VIC, Australia
Tel.: (61) 3 9751 7107
Fax: (61) 3 9751 7158
Label Printing Services
S.I.C.: 2759
N.A.I.C.S.: 323111

CCL Label Vietnam Company Limited (1)
No 8 VSIP 2 Street No 6 Vietnam Hoa Phu Ward
Thu Dau Mot, Binh Duong, Vietnam
Tel.: (84) 650 3628130
Fax: (84) 650 3628125
Personal Care Products Labeling Services
S.I.C.: 7389
N.A.I.C.S.: 561910

CCL Package Label S.N.C (1)
20 Rue Arago
91385 Chilly-Mazarin, France
Tel.: (33) 1 6454 4141
Fax: (33) 1 6909 1009
E-Mail: packagelabel.france@cclind.com
Web Site: www.ccl-label.com
Healthcare Products Packaging Services
S.I.C.: 7389
N.A.I.C.S.: 561910

Continental Conveyor Ltd. (1)
West Key Rd
Quay Sunderland
Enterprise Park, Sunderland, Tyne and Wear, SR52TD, United Kingdom (100%)
Tel.: (44) 1915165353
Telex: 53368 HUWOOD G
Fax: (44) 1915165399
Web Site: www.continental-conveyor.co.uk
Emp.: 250
Mfr. of Mining Machinery
S.I.C.: 3532
N.A.I.C.S.: 333131
Clark Craft *(Mgr-Engrg)*

CCL PRODUCTS (INDIA) LIMITED

7-1-24 2 D Greendale
Ameerpet, Hyderabad, AP, 500 016, India
Tel.: (91) 40 23732455
Fax: (91) 40 23732499
E-Mail: info@cclproducts.com
Web Site: www.cclproducts.com
Year Founded: 1994
519600—(BOM)
Rev.: $120,994,617
Assets: $123,573,661
Liabilities: $71,961,675
Net Worth: $51,611,986
Earnings: $8,792,780
Fiscal Year-end: 03/31/13

Business Description:
Coffee Mfr
S.I.C.: 2095
N.A.I.C.S.: 311920

Personnel:
Challa Rajendra Prasad *(Chm & Mng Dir)*
K. V. L. N. Sarma *(CFO)*
Sridevi Dasari *(Compliance Officer & Sec)*

Board of Directors:
Challa Rajendra Prasad
K. Chandrahas
Jonathan T. Feuer
B. Mohan Krishna
J. Rambabu
I. J. Rao
Zafar Saifullah
K. K. Sarma
Vipin K. Singal
Challa Srishant

Transfer Agent:
Venture Capital & Corporate Investments Pvt. Limited
12-10-167 Bharat Nagar Colony
Hyderabad, 500018, India

CCM GROUP LIMITED

64 Woodlands Industrial Park E9
Singapore, 757833, Singapore
Tel.: (65) 6285 6565
Fax: (65) 6286 5656
E-Mail: admin@ccmgroup.sg
Web Site: www.ccmgroup.sg
5QZ—(CAT)
Rev.: $43,609,523
Assets: $30,748,063
Liabilities: $27,220,525
Net Worth: $3,527,538
Earnings: ($1,512,602)
Emp.: 188
Fiscal Year-end: 12/31/12

Business Description:
Residential & Commercial Construction Services
S.I.C.: 1522
N.A.I.C.S.: 236116

Personnel:
Sen Keong Liew *(Chm & CEO)*
Tuck Peng Goh *(CFO)*
Gn Jong Juh Gwendolyn *(Sec)*

Board of Directors:
Sen Keong Liew
Ambrose Heng Fai Chan
Basil Chan
Pui Yee Chan
Tien Chih Chan
Chin Yee Lai
Eng Khiam Tan
Yeoh Chi Tao
Aloysius Meng Seng Wee
Yee Leong Wong

Transfer Agent:
Boardroom Corporate & Advisory Services Pte. Ltd.
50 Raffles Place 32-01 Singapore Land Tower
Singapore, Singapore

Subsidiary:

CCM Industrial Pte. Ltd. (1)
64 Woodlands Industrial Park E9
Singapore, 757833, Singapore
Tel.: (65) 62856565
Fax: (65) 62865656
E-Mail: admin@ccmgroup.sg
Emp.: 200
Commercial Building Construction Support Services
S.I.C.: 1542
N.A.I.C.S.: 236220
Liew Sen Keong *(Chm & CEO)*

CCN-TECH PUBLIC COMPANY LIMITED

8/2 Soi Viphawadi Rangsit 44
Viphawadi Rangsit Rd
Ladyao
Chatuchak, Bangkok, 10900, Thailand
Tel.: (66) 2 941 3939
Fax: (66) 2 579 6242
Web Site: www.ccn-tech.co.th

Business Description:
Computer Systems Integration & IT Services
S.I.C.: 7373
N.A.I.C.S.: 541512

Personnel:
Surat Srinoi *(Chm)*

CCP AG

Berliner Strasse 17
63801 Kleinostheim, Germany
Tel.: (49) 6027 409 34 50
Fax: (49) 6027 409 34 60
E-Mail: info@ccp.ag
Web Site: www.ccp.ag
CC1—(DEU)

Business Description:
Vegetable Cultivation Services
S.I.C.: 2037
N.A.I.C.S.: 311411

Personnel:
Henry Schipper *(CEO)*

CCP HF

Grandagarour 8
101 Reykjavik, Iceland
Tel.: (354) 5409100
Fax: (354) 5409198
E-Mail: info@ccpgames.com
Web Site: www.ccpgames.com
Year Founded: 1997
Sls.: $65,000,000
Emp.: 600

Business Description:
Computer Game Software Publisher
S.I.C.: 7372
N.A.I.C.S.: 511210

Personnel:
Reynir Haroarson *(Founder & Dir-Creative)*
Hilmar Veigar Petursson *(CEO)*
Joseph Gallo *(CFO)*
Jon Horodal *(COO)*
Halldor Fannar Guojonsson *(CTO)*
Gabe Mahoney *(Sr VP-Engr)*

U.S. Subsidiary:

White Wolf Publishing, Inc. (1)
2075 W Pk Pl Blvd Ste G
Stone Mountain, GA 30087 GA
Tel.: (404) 292-1819
Fax: (678) 382-3883
Toll Free: (800) 454WOLF
E-Mail: retail@white-wolf.com
Web Site: www.white-wolf.com
Emp.: 55
Publisher of Games & Fiction
Export
S.I.C.: 2731
N.A.I.C.S.: 511130
Stewart Wieck *(Owner & Developer)*
Robert Goudie *(Chm)*

CCR S.A.
(d/b/a Grupo CCR)
Av Chedid Jafet 222 Bloco B 5 andar
CEP 04551-065 Sao Paulo, VI
Olimpia, Brazil
Tel.: (55) 11 3048 5900
Web Site: www.grupoccr.com.br
Year Founded: 1998
CCRO3—(BRAZ)
Sales Range: $1-4.9 Billion
Emp.: 9,600
Business Description:
Infrastructure Investment & Service Solutions
S.I.C.: 1611
N.A.I.C.S.: 237310
Personnel:
Renato Alves Vale *(CEO)*
Arthur Piotto Filho *(CFO & Officer-IR)*
Marcio Jose Batista *(Exec VP)*
Board of Directors:
Marcio Jose Batista
Antonio Linhares da Cunha
Eduardo Borges de Andrade
Marcus Rodrigo de Senna
Arthur Piotto Filho
Valdemar Jorge Martins Mendes
Ana Maria Marcondes Penido Sant'Anna
Luis Augusto Nesbitt Rebelo da SIlva
Italo Roppa
Renato Alves Vale
Leonardo Couto Vianna

CCR TECHNOLOGIES LIMITED
Suite 300 5 Richard Way SW
Calgary, AB, T3E 7M8, Canada
Tel.: (403) 543-6699
Fax: (403) 451-9906
Web Site: www.reclaim.com
Sales Range: $1-9.9 Million
Emp.: 16
Business Description:
Chemical Purification Technology
S.I.C.: 2899
N.A.I.C.S.: 325998
Personnel:
Michael J. Perkins *(Sec)*
Legal Counsel:
Armstrong Perkins Hudson LLP
530 Eighth Avenue Southwest, Suite 2300
Calgary, AB, T2P 2S8, Canada
U.S. Subsidiary:

CCR Technologies Ltd. (1)
1500 City West Blvd 550
Houston, TX 77042-2346
Tel.: (281) 988-5800
Fax: (281) 988-5858
E-Mail: info@reclaim.com
Web Site: www.reclaim.com
Emp.: 15
Provider of Chemical Purification Technology
S.I.C.: 4953
N.A.I.C.S.: 562211
Peter D. Graham *(Pres)*

CCS CORPORATION
(See Under Tervita Corporation)

CCS INC.
374 Okakuencho Shimodachiuri-agaru Karasuma-dori
Kamigyo-ku, Kyoto, 602 8011, Japan
Tel.: (81) 754158280
Fax: (81) 754158281
E-Mail: info@ccs-inc.co.jp
Web Site: www.ccs-inc.co.jp
Year Founded: 1992
6669—(JAS)
Sls.: $53,460,000
Assets: $63,008,000
Liabilities: $32,824,000
Net Worth: $30,184,000
Earnings: $4,983,000
Emp.: 205
Fiscal Year-end: 07/31/13
Business Description:
LED Lighting Developer, Mfr & Sales
S.I.C.: 3648
N.A.I.C.S.: 335129
Personnel:
Yoshiro Kagami *(Pres & CEO)*
Hironori Ishii *(Exec Officer)*
Norimasa Kaji *(Exec Officer)*
Yoshie Kajiwara *(Exec Officer)*
Hiroyuki Onishi *(Sr Exec Officer)*
Toshiyuki Toyofuku *(Exec Officer)*
Masanobu Yoshida *(Exec Officer)*
Shinji Matsumuro *(Sr VP)*
Board of Directors:
Akira Iwamoto
Yoshiro Kagami
Shinji Matsumuro
Mitsuo Nakagawa
Yasushi Sakemi
Yotaro Tokuo
U.S. Subsidiary:

CCS America Inc. (1)
5 Burlington Woods Ste 204
Burlington, MA 01803 (100%)
Tel.: (781) 272-6900
Fax: (781) 272-6902
E-Mail: info@ccsamerica.com
Web Site: www.ccsamerica.com
Emp.: 8
LED Lighting Developer, Mfr & Sales
S.I.C.: 3648
N.A.I.C.S.: 335129
Manny Lopez *(Pres)*
Non-U.S. Subsidiaries:

CCS Asia Pte Ltd. (1)
63 Hillview Avenue No 07-10
Lam Soon Industrial Bldg, Singapore, 669569, Singapore
Tel.: (65) 67691669
Fax: (65) 67693422
E-Mail: sales@ccs-asia.com.sg
Web Site: www.ccs-asia.com.sg/
Emp.: 15
LED Lighting Distr
S.I.C.: 3648
N.A.I.C.S.: 335129
Yukaiiko Itani *(Mng Dir)*

CCS Europe NV (1)
Bergensesteenweg 423 Bus 13
1600 Saint Pieters-Leeuw, Belgium (100%)
Tel.: (32) 23330080
Fax: (32) 23330081
E-Mail: info@ccseu.com
Web Site: www.ccs-grp.com
Emp.: 8
LED Lighting Sales for Machine Vision
S.I.C.: 3648
N.A.I.C.S.: 335129
Dirk Vermeersch *(Pres)*

CCS INFOTECH LIMITED
CCS Towers 14 Periyar Road T Nagar
Chennai, Tamil Nadu, 600 017, India
Tel.: (91) 44 2834 1121
Fax: (91) 44 2834 0784
E-Mail: hasan@ccsinfotech.com
Web Site: www.ccsinfotech.com
532405—(BOM)
Sales Range: $10-24.9 Million
Business Description:
Laptop Computers Export & Mfr
S.I.C.: 3571
N.A.I.C.S.: 334111
Personnel:
M.A. Hasan Abdul Kader *(Co-Founder, Chm & Mng Dir)*
Ratna Kumar *(Co-Founder)*
Board of Directors:
M.A. Hasan Abdul Kader
Ratna Kumar
Transfer Agent:
Venture Capital & Corporate Investment Limited
No-12-10-167 Bharat Nagar
Hyderabad, India
Non-U.S. Subsidiary:

CCS INFOTECH SINGAPORE PTE LTE (1)
11 - 06 Sim Lim Tower 10 Jalan Besar
Singapore, Singapore
Tel.: (65) 9069 2150
Fax: (65) 6296 5286
E-Mail: singapore@ccsinfotech.com
Emp.: 25
Computer Peripheral Equipment Mfr
S.I.C.: 3571
N.A.I.C.S.: 334111
Ramesh Balaraman, *(Head-Bus Ops)*

CCS SUPPLY CHAIN MANAGEMENT CO., LTD.
20/F HailianMasion No 20 Business Outer Ring Road
CBD Zhengdong New Area, Zhengzhou, 450000, China
Tel.: (86) 371 89988080
Fax: (86) 371 89988081
E-Mail: service@ccsoln.com
Web Site: www.ccsoln.com
Year Founded: 2000
600180—(SHG)
Business Description:
Coal Whslr
S.I.C.: 5052
N.A.I.C.S.: 423520
Personnel:
Yongxing Wan *(Pres)*

CCT CAPITAL LTD.
501 - 595 Howe Street
Vancouver, BC, V6C 2T5, Canada
Tel.: (604) 685-4655
Fax: (604) 685-4675
Year Founded: 2006
CCW—(TSXV)
Int. Income: $121
Assets: $21,630
Liabilities: $70,735
Net Worth: ($49,105)
Earnings: ($67,642)
Fiscal Year-end: 04/30/13
Business Description:
Mineral Exploration Services
S.I.C.: 1099
N.A.I.C.S.: 212299
Personnel:
Laurie Sadler *(Pres & CEO)*
Kim Evans *(CFO)*
Board of Directors:
Kim Evans
Jeffrey Lightfoot
Laurie Sadler

CCT TELECOM HOLDINGS LIMITED
31/F Fortis Tower 77-79 Gloucester Road
Hong Kong, China (Hong Kong)
Tel.: (852) 21028138
Fax: (852) 21028100
E-Mail: info@cct.com.hk
Web Site: www.cct.com.hk
Year Founded: 1980
0138—(HKG)
Rev.: $199,098,800
Assets: $484,207,250
Liabilities: $215,217,550
Net Worth: $268,989,700
Earnings: ($8,639,650)
Emp.: 5,971
Fiscal Year-end: 12/31/12
Business Description:
Holding Company; Cordless Telecommunication, Multimedia & Electronics Products
S.I.C.: 3663
N.A.I.C.S.: 334220
Personnel:
Clement Shiu Tong Mak *(Chm & CEO)*
Terry Ngai Hung Tam *(Deputy Chm, Sec & Dir-Fin)*
Kent Wah Shun Wong *(CEO-Mfg Ops)*
Henry Ho Yin Leung *(Gen Counsel)*
Board of Directors:
Clement Shiu Tong Mak
Li Chen
Flora Yuk Ching Cheng
Siu Ngor Chow
William Donald Putt
Kenny King Ching Tam
Terry Ngai Hung Tam
Transfer Agent:
Tricor Tengis Limited
26th Floor Tesbury Centre 28 Queen's Road East
Wanchai, China (Hong Kong)
Tel.: (852) 29801333
Fax: (852) 28108185
Subsidiaries:

CCT Marketing Limited (1)
18/f Cct Telecom Bldg 11 Wo Shing St Fotan
Sha Tin, New Territories, China (Hong Kong)
Tel.: (852) 26958333
Fax: (852) 26948660
Emp.: 100
Telecommunication Equipment Mfr
S.I.C.: 3699
N.A.I.C.S.: 335999

CCT Tech (HK) Limited (1)
18/f CCT Telecom Bldg 11 Wo Shing St
Sha Tin, New Territories, China (Hong Kong)
Tel.: (852) 26958333
Fax: (852) 26946140
Electronic Products Mfr
S.I.C.: 3679
N.A.I.C.S.: 334419

CCT Tech International Limited (1)
2208 22nd Floor St Georges Building
2 Ice House Street, Central, China (Hong Kong)
Tel.: (852) 21028138
Fax: (852) 21028100
Web Site: www.cct-tech.com.hk
Emp.: 20
Electronic Parts & Equipment Whslr
S.I.C.: 5065
N.A.I.C.S.: 423690
Feynman Man To Li *(Deputy Chm)*
Clement Shiu Tong Mak *(Chm & CEO)*

CCT Telecom (HK) Limited (1)
18th Fl CCT Telecom Bldg
Fotan, China (Hong Kong)
Tel.: (852) 26958333
Electronic Parts & Equipment Whslr
S.I.C.: 5065
N.A.I.C.S.: 423690
Flora Cheng *(Mng Dir)*

CCT Telecom Securities Limited (1)
Rm 2208 22/f St Georges Bldg 2 Ice House St
Central District, Hong Kong, China (Hong Kong)
Tel.: (852) 21028138
Fax: (852) 21028100
Securities Brokerage Services
S.I.C.: 6211
N.A.I.C.S.: 523120

Neptune Holding Limited (1)
18th Floor no 11 Wo Shing Street Cct Telecom Building
Fotan, China (Hong Kong) (100%)
Tel.: (852) 28873031
Fax: (852) 28873032
E-Mail: ckman@cct.com.hk
Web Site: www.cct.com.hk/eng/operation/plastic.php
Emp.: 100
Plastics Materials & Basic Forms & Shapes Whslr
S.I.C.: 5162
N.A.I.C.S.: 424610
Daniel Chin Keung Man *(Mng Dir)*

Rich Full International Industries Limited (1)
Rm 121 1/f Southorn Ctr 130 135 Hennessy Rd
Wan Chai, Hong Kong, China (Hong Kong)

Tel.: (852) 28922698
Electronic Component Mfr
S.I.C.: 3679
N.A.I.C.S.: 334419

Tradeeasy Holdings Limited (1)
20th-21st Floor Pan Asia Centre
Kwun Tong, Kowloon, China (Hong Kong)
Tel.: (852) 21620888
Fax: (852) 21620830
Web Site: www.tradeeasy.com
Internet Services
S.I.C.: 4899
N.A.I.C.S.: 517919
Danny Kwok Cheung Yip *(Mng Dir)*

Wiltec Industries Limited (1)
9th Floor Power Industrial Bldg
9-15 Wo Heung St, Fotan, China (Hong Kong)
Tel.: (852) 23754388
Fax: (852) 23753186
E-Mail: info@wiltechk.com
Web Site: www.wiltechk.com
Emp.: 40
Plastics Product Mfr
S.I.C.: 3089
N.A.I.C.S.: 326199

Non-U.S. Subsidiaries:

Huiyang CCT Plastic Products Co.,Ltd (1)
CC Telecom Tech Park Sanhe Economic Development Zone Huiyang
Huizhou, Guangdong, 516213, China
Tel.: (86) 7523500138
Fax: (86) 7523500984
Plastic Products Mfr
S.I.C.: 3089
N.A.I.C.S.: 326199

Huiyang CCT Telecommunications Products Co., Ltd (1)
Inside Zhongjian Technology Park Sanhe Economic Development Zone
Huizhou, Guangdong, 516213, China
Tel.: (86) 7523500138
Fax: (86) 7523500980
Telecommunication Products Mfr
S.I.C.: 3679
N.A.I.C.S.: 334419

CCV RISK SOLUTIONS LIMITED

(d/b/a Cullum Capital Ventures)
Towergate House Eclipse Park
Sittingbourne Road
Maidstone, Kent, ME14 3EN, United Kingdom
Tel.: (44) 1732 466402
Web Site: www.ccventures.co.uk
Year Founded: 2006
Emp.: 650

Business Description:
Insurance Intermediary
S.I.C.: 6411
N.A.I.C.S.: 524298

Personnel:
Peter Cullum *(Chm)*
Tim Johnson *(CEO)*
Keith Insch *(Reg Mng Dir)*
David Wrathall *(Reg Mng Dir)*
Sam Clark *(Sec)*

Subsidiary:

Protectagroup Acquisitions Ltd. (1)
Motaquote House
Dinas Isaf Industrial Estate
Williamstown, Wales, CF40 1NY, United Kingdom
Tel.: (44) 1443420700
Fax: (44) 1443420740
E-Mail: enquiries@protectagroup.co.uk
Web Site: www.protectagroup.co.uk
Emp.: 80
Acquisition Vehicle
S.I.C.: 6211
N.A.I.C.S.: 523999
Nigel Lombard *(Mng Dir)*

Subsidiary:

Culver Insurance Brokers Ltd. (2)
Llanmaes Michaelston Road
Saint Fagans, Cardiff, CF5 6DU, United Kingdom
Tel.: (44) 2920670067
Fax: (44) 2920576290
Web Site: ch.sitedesignlondon.co.uk/disclaimer/index.asp
Insurance Services
S.I.C.: 6331
N.A.I.C.S.: 524126

CDC GROUP PLC

80 Victoria St
London, SW1E5JL, United Kingdom
Tel.: (44) 2079634700
Fax: (44) 2079634750
E-Mail: enquiries@cdcgroup.com
Web Site: www.cdcgroup.com
Year Founded: 1948
Sales Range: $700-749.9 Million
Emp.: 50

Business Description:
Emerging Markets-Focused Investment Services
S.I.C.: 6211
N.A.I.C.S.: 523999

Personnel:
Richard Laing *(CEO)*
Godfrey Davies *(CFO)*
Mark Kenderdine Davies *(Gen Counsel & Chief Compliance Officer)*

Board of Directors:
Arnab Banerji
Richard Laing
Fields Wicker-Miurin
Andrew C. Williams

CDC S.P.A.

Via Calabria 1 Industrial Area of Gello
56025 Pontedera, Italy
Tel.: (39) 05872882
Fax: (39) 0587288640
E-Mail: investorrelations@cdcpoint.it
Web Site: www.cdc.it
Year Founded: 1986
CDC—(ITA)
Sales Range: $400-449.9 Million
Emp.: 394

Business Description:
Communication Technology Services
S.I.C.: 3575
N.A.I.C.S.: 334118

Personnel:
Giuseppe Diomelli *(Chm)*
Enrico Dell'Artino *(Mng Dir)*
S. Zecchi *(CFO & VP-Mktg & Sls)*

Board of Directors:
Giuseppe Diomelli
Enrico Barachini
Elena Cenderelli
Enrico Dell'Artino

Subsidiaries:

CD Cagliari S.r.l. (1)
Piazza della Repubblica 21
09125 Cagliari, Italy
Tel.: (39) 70306460
Communications Technology
S.I.C.: 5999
N.A.I.C.S.: 453998

CD Catania S.r.l. (1)
Viale Africa 120
Catania, Italy (100%)
Tel.: (39) 095533907
Emp.: 7
Computer & Software Stores
S.I.C.: 5731
N.A.I.C.S.: 443142

CD Firenze S.r.l. (1)
Viale Matteotti 9
50121 Florence, Italy
Tel.: (39) 555000101
Fax: (39) 055587765
E-Mail: info@cdfirenze.it
Web Site: www.cdfirenze.it
Emp.: 4
Computer & Software Stores
S.I.C.: 5731
N.A.I.C.S.: 443142
Luca Collu *(Mng Dir)*

CD Milano 5 S.r.l. (1)
Via Mazzini 74
20123 Pontedera, Italy
Tel.: (39) 028056911
Fax: (39) 390587288640
Computer & Software Stores
S.I.C.: 5734
N.A.I.C.S.: 443142

CD Milano 6 S.r.l. (1)
Viale Fulvio Testi 188
Cinisello Balsamo, Milan, Italy
Tel.: (39) 0226222880
Computer Products
S.I.C.: 5712
N.A.I.C.S.: 442110

CD Napoli 2 S.r.l. (1)
Via Cristoforo Colombo 55
Naples, Italy
Tel.: (39) 0815513075
Fax: (39) 0815528247
E-Mail: cdnapoli2@computerdiscount.it
Emp.: 4
Computer & Software Stores
S.I.C.: 5731
N.A.I.C.S.: 443142

CD Pisa S.r.l. (1)
P za Martiri della Liberta 25
56025 Pontedera, Italy
Tel.: (39) 58756738
Fax: (39) 058754813
E-Mail: cdpontedera@computerdiscount.it
Web Site: www.computerdiscount.it
Emp.: 3
Computer & Software Stores
S.I.C.: 5734
N.A.I.C.S.: 443142
Danilo Casalini *(Mng Dir)*

CDC Point S.p.A. (1)
Via Calabria
1 Industrial Area of Gello, 56025 Pontedera, Italy
Tel.: (39) 05872882
Fax: (39) 0587288640
Web Site: www.cdc.it/eng/
Computer & Software Stores
S.I.C.: 5734
N.A.I.C.S.: 443142

Soluzioni Informatiche Srl (1)
Via Massimo D Azeglio 1/ B Lumezzane
Brescia, Italy
Tel.: (39) 0308925378
Fax: (39) 0308248175
Emp.: 9
Computer & Software Stores
S.I.C.: 5731
N.A.I.C.S.: 443142
Paolo Grotto *(Gen Mgr)*

CDF INTERNATIONAL COOPERATIEF U.A.

Zwarteweg 149
1431 VL Aalsmeer, Netherlands
Tel.: (31) 302661111
Fax: (31) 302614428
E-Mail: info@cdfintl.com
Web Site: www.cdfintl.com
Year Founded: 2007
Sales Range: $350-399.9 Million

Business Description:
Holding Company; Tobacco Whslr
S.I.C.: 6719
N.A.I.C.S.: 551112

Personnel:
Tariq Rafique *(Chm)*
Gustav Stangl *(CEO)*
Douglas Conran *(CFO)*
Paul Taberer *(COO)*
Onno Molenaar *(Sr VP)*
Eric van der Linden *(Sr VP)*

CDG CO., LTD.

Herbis ENT 18F 2-2-22 Umeda Kita-ku
Osaka, 530-0001, Japan
Tel.: (81) 6 6133 5200
Fax: (81) 6 6133 5951
Web Site: www.cdg.co.jp
Year Founded: 1974
2487—(JAS)
Sls.: $101,629,000
Assets: $61,578,000
Liabilities: $22,836,000
Net Worth: $38,742,000
Earnings: $4,345,000
Fiscal Year-end: 03/31/13

Business Description:
Marketing & Promotion Consulting Services
S.I.C.: 8742
N.A.I.C.S.: 541613

Personnel:
Katsunoric Fujii *(CEO)*

Board of Directors:
Katsunoric Fujii
Satoshi Konishi
Jun Moriyama
Takashi Ohira
Ayako Ohta
Soumitsu Takehara
Tadashi Watanabe

CDG PACKAGING HOLDING AG

Promenadeplatz 12
80333 Munich, Germany
Tel.: (49) 89244118332
Fax: (49) 89244118310
E-Mail: info@cdgp-holding.com
Web Site: www.cdgp-holding.com
8PP—(DEU)

Business Description:
Eco-Friendly Paper Packaging Products
S.I.C.: 2672
N.A.I.C.S.: 322220

Personnel:
Zizu Wu *(Chm-Supervisory Bd)*
Zhixing Zhang *(Chm-Mgmt Bd)*

Supervisory Board of Directors:
Peng Jiang
Ying Wu
Zizu Wu

CDH CHINA HOLDINGS MANAGEMENT COMPANY LIMITED

(d/b/a CDH Investments)
Suite 418 Tower B Grand Pacific Trade Centre 8A Guanghua Road
Chaoyang District, Beijing, 100026, China
Tel.: (86) 10 6581 9299
Fax: (86) 10 6581 9969
E-Mail: cdhpe@cdhfund.com
Web Site: www.cdhfund.com
Year Founded: 2002

Business Description:
Private Equity Firm
S.I.C.: 6211
N.A.I.C.S.: 523999

Personnel:
Shangzhi Wu *(Chm)*

Non-U.S. Holding:

Sinomem Technology Limited (1)
10 Ang Mo Kio St 65 06-10 Techpoint
569059 Singapore, Singapore
Tel.: (65) 64816966
Fax: (65) 64816066
E-Mail: inquiry@sinomem.com
Web Site: www.sinomem.com
Emp.: 400
Water Purification Solutions
S.I.C.: 4971
N.A.I.C.S.: 221310
Ni Chen *(Co-Founder & Exec Dir)*
Weiguang Lan *(Co-Founder & Mngr Dir)*
Chung Wai Chan *(CFO)*

Subsidiaries:

Suntar Membrane Technology (Singapore) Pte Ltd (2)
10 Ang Mo Kio Street 65 06-10
Singapore, 569059, Singapore
Tel.: (65) 64816966

CDH China Holdings Management Company Limited—(Continued)

Fax: (65) 64816066
E-Mail: enquiry@sinomem.com
Web Site: www.sinomem.com
Emp.: 5
Polymer Membranes Mfr
S.I.C.: 3069
N.A.I.C.S.: 326299
Wei Guang Lan *(CEO)*

Non-U.S. Subsidiaries:

Microdyn-Nadir (Xiamen) Co., Ltd. **(2)**
No 66 Jinting N Rd
Xinglin, Xiamen, Fujian, 361022, China
Tel.: (86) 5926775500
Fax: (86) 5926775510
E-Mail: infochina@microdyn-nadir.cn
Web Site: www.microdyn-nadir.com
Emp.: 30
Membrane Materials Mfr
S.I.C.: 3069
N.A.I.C.S.: 326299
Walter Lamparter *(Mng Dir)*

SCT Suntar Ceramic Technology (Xiamen) Co., Ltd. **(2)**
Suntar Technological Park Zhongya Industry City
Xinglin, Xiamen, Fujian, China
Tel.: (86) 5926778100
Fax: (86) 5926778200
E-Mail: info@suntar.com
Web Site: www.suntar.com
Emp.: 200
Poly Membrane Products Mfr
S.I.C.: 3069
N.A.I.C.S.: 326299
Fulin Fang *(Gen Mgr)*

Siping Suntar Technology Co., Ltd. **(2)**
No 1 Xinzhou Road Wuping Industry Park
Wuping, Longyan, Fujian, China
Tel.: (86) 5974866980
Fax: (86) 5974866990
Waste Water Treatment Services
S.I.C.: 4952
N.A.I.C.S.: 221320

Suntar Environmental Engineering (Xiamen) Co., Ltd **(2)**
Suntar Technological Park Zhongya Industry City Xinglin
Xiamen, Fujian, 361022, China
Tel.: (86) 5925589900
Fax: (86) 592 6778200
E-Mail: info@suntar.com
Engineering Design & Software Development Services
S.I.C.: 8711
N.A.I.C.S.: 541330

Suntar Membrane Technology (Xiamen) Co., Ltd. **(2)**
Sanda Technology Park Zhongya Industrial City
Xinglin, Xiamen, Fujian, 361022, China
Tel.: (86) 5926778100
Fax: (86) 5926778200
E-Mail: info@suntar.com
Web Site: www.suntar.com
Emp.: 200
Polymer Membranes Mfr
S.I.C.: 3069
N.A.I.C.S.: 326299
Fang Fulin *(Mng Dir)*

Suntar Process Technology (Xiamen) Co., Ltd **(2)**
Suntar Technology Park Zhongyacheng Xinglin
Jimei District, Xiamen, Fujian, China
Tel.: (86) 5926778082
Fax: (86) 592677030
Emp.: 8
Polymer Membranes Mfr
S.I.C.: 3069
N.A.I.C.S.: 326299

CDL INVESTMENTS NEW ZEALAND LIMITED

Level 13 280 Queen Street Shortland Street
PO Box 3248
Auckland, 1140, New Zealand
Tel.: (64) 99138077
Fax: (64) 99138098
Web Site: www.cdlinvestments.co.nz
CDI—(NZE)
Rev.: $22,047,417
Assets: $90,421,110
Liabilities: $1,307,394
Net Worth: $89,113,716
Earnings: $7,786,611
Fiscal Year-end: 12/31/12
Business Description:
Property Investment, Development & Management Services
S.I.C.: 6799
N.A.I.C.S.: 523920
Personnel:
B. K. Chiu *(Mng Dir)*
Takeshi Ito *(Sec)*
Board of Directors:
Hong Ren Wong
Rob Challinor
B. K. Chiu
John Henderson
Vincent Yeo

CDMV INC.

2999 Choquette Blvd
PO Box 608
Saint-Hyacinthe, QC, J2S 7C2, Canada
Tel.: (450) 771-2368
Toll Free: (800) 668-2368
E-Mail: customer@cdmv.com
Web Site: www.cdmv.com
Year Founded: 1972
Rev.: $117,491,000
Emp.: 115
Business Description:
Pets Accessories Distr
S.I.C.: 5047
N.A.I.C.S.: 423450

CDN OILFIELD TECHNOLOGIES & SOLUTIONS CORP.

Suite 801 825 8th Avenue Southwest
Calgary, AB, T2P 2T3, Canada
Tel.: (403) 543-0060
Fax: (403) 543-0069
E-Mail: info@cotsoilfield.com
Web Site: www.cotsoilfield.com
OTS—(TSXV)
Sales Range: $1-9.9 Million
Emp.: 8
Business Description:
Oil, Gas, Utilities, Communications & Transportation Support Services
S.I.C.: 1389
N.A.I.C.S.: 213112
Personnel:
Scott Berry *(Chm)*
Phil D'Angelo *(Pres)*
Gordon Travis *(CFO)*
Board of Directors:
Scott Berry
Frank Antolovich
Phil D'Angelo
John MacMillan
Rene Spielman
Bob Tutty
Transfer Agent:
Computershare Trust Company of Canada
600 530 8th Avenue SW
Calgary, AB, T2P 3S8, Canada
Tel.: (403) 267-6555
Toll Free: (800) 558-0046

U.S. Subsidiaries:

CBM Pumps and Services, Inc. **(1)**
1451 Business Park Cir
Gillette, WY 82717
Tel.: (307) 682-0999
Fax: (307) 682-1999
Web Site: www.cotsoilfield.com
Emp.: 10
Electric Submersible Pumps Mfr
S.I.C.: 3561
N.A.I.C.S.: 333911
Justin Fultz *(Gen Mgr)*

ILI Technologies (2002) USA Corp. **(1)**
4900 Woodway Dr Ste 925
Houston, TX 77056
Mailing Address:
PO Box 2193
Gillette, WY 82717-2193
Tel.: (713) 960-0811
Fax: (713) 960-0856
Web Site: www.ilitech.com
Emp.: 1
Oil, Gas, Utilities, Communications & Transportation Support Services
S.I.C.: 1389
N.A.I.C.S.: 213112

CDON GROUP AB

Bergsgatan 20
PO Box 385
SE-201 23 Malmo, Sweden
Tel.: (46) 10 703 2000
Fax: (46) 10 703 2136
Web Site: www.cdongroup.com
CDON—(OMX)
Sls.: $690,671,160
Assets: $260,497,440
Liabilities: $219,258,720
Net Worth: $41,238,720
Earnings: ($23,483,160)
Emp.: 872
Fiscal Year-end: 12/31/12
Business Description:
E-Commerce Services
S.I.C.: 5961
N.A.I.C.S.: 454111
Personnel:
Lars-Johan Jarnheimer *(Chm)*
Paul Fischbein *(Pres & CEO)*
Nicolas Adlercreutz *(CFO)*
Christofer Gordon *(CTO)*
Therese Hillman *(CEO-Gymgrossisten.com & Bodystore.com & Head-Sports & Health)*
Magnus Mansson *(CEO-Nelly.com & och Members.com & Head-Fashion)*
Fredrik Palm *(CEO-Room21.com & Haed-Home & Garden)*
Ola Stromberg *(CEO-CDON.com & Tretti.se)*
Board of Directors:
Lars-Johan Jarnheimer
Patrick Andersen
Mengmeng Du
David Kelly
Jonas Kjellberg
Mia Brunell Livfors
Lars Nilsson

Subsidiary:

Gymgrossisten Nordic AB **(1)**
Ladugardsvagen 29
461 70 Trollhattan, Vastergotland, Sweden
Tel.: (46) 52089060
Fax: (46) 52 01 76 70
Web Site: www.gymgrossisten.com
Dietary Supplement Products Mfr
S.I.C.: 2023
N.A.I.C.S.: 311514

CDP-TRAVISSULLY LTD.

9 Lower John St
London, W1F 9DZ, United Kingdom
Tel.: (44) 207 437 4224
Fax: (44) 207 437 5445
E-Mail: mail@cdp-travissully.com
Web Site: www.cdp-travissully.com
Year Founded: 1960
Emp.: 25
Business Description:
Advertising Agency
S.I.C.: 7311
N.A.I.C.S.: 541810
Personnel:
Simon North *(CEO)*

CDS CO., LTD.

4F 1Goukan Nagoya Dia Building
3-16-22 Meieki Nakamura-ku
Nagoya, Aichi, 450-0002, Japan
Tel.: (81) 525875411
Fax: (81) 525875446
E-Mail: info@cds-japan.jp
Web Site: www.cds-japan.jp/english/index.htm
Year Founded: 1980
2169—(NGO TKS)
Sales Range: $50-74.9 Million
Emp.: 560
Business Description:
3D CAD Designer & Support Services
S.I.C.: 7379
N.A.I.C.S.: 541519
Personnel:
Akinori Shibazaki *(Pres & CEO)*

Subsidiaries:

BYNAS Co., Ltd **(1)**
41-1 Takashigehigashimachi
Inazawa, Aichi, 492-8424, Japan
Tel.: (81) 587248181
Fax: (81) 587248189
Web Site: www.bynas.com
Robot Systems Mfr
S.I.C.: 3559
N.A.I.C.S.: 333249

MCOR Co., Ltd. **(1)**
28-6 Kamegabuchi Kobari-Cho
Okazaki, Aichi, 444-0907, Japan
Tel.: (81) 564325480
Fax: (81) 564326966
Web Site: www.mcor.co.jp
Sls.: $33,415,200
Emp.: 277
Computer Aided Design Consultancy Services
S.I.C.: 7373
N.A.I.C.S.: 541512
Shinichi Oki *(Pres)*

Torindo Co., Ltd **(1)**
3F Kodama Printing Bldg 1-8 Shin-Ogawamachi
Shinju-Ku, Tokyo, 162-0814, Japan
Tel.: (81) 352066725
Fax: (81) 352066719
E-Mail: trans-info@torindo.ne.jp
Web Site: www.torindo.ne.jp
Translation & Localization Services
S.I.C.: 7389
N.A.I.C.S.: 541930
Akinori Shibazaki *(Chm)*
Shiro Watanabe *(Pres)*

CDU PLC

Gordon Mill
Barngate Street, Leek, Staffs, ST13 8AP, United Kingdom
Mailing Address:
PO Box 30
Leek, Staffs, ST13 8AR, United Kingdom
Tel.: (44) 1538 399141
Fax: (44) 1538 385438
E-Mail: plc@cduplc.com
Web Site: www.cduplc.com
SLM—(AIM)
Sales Range: $10-24.9 Million
Emp.: 91
Business Description:
Mfr, Marketer & Whslr of Ladieswear
S.I.C.: 2259
N.A.I.C.S.: 315190
Personnel:
Stephen James Thwaite *(CEO)*
A. Davies *(Sec)*
Board of Directors:
Christopher Graham Heath
Stephen James Thwaite

Legal Counsel:
HBJ Gateley Wareing LLP
One Eleven Edmund Street
Birmingham, United Kingdom

CDW HOLDING LTD.

Rm 6-10 11/F CCT Telecom Building
No 11 Wo Shing Street
Fotan, Shatin, China (Hong Kong)
Tel.: (852) 26882273
Fax: (852) 26903349
E-Mail: mail@cdw-holding.com.hk
Web Site: www.cdw-holding.com.hk
Year Founded: 2004
D38—(SES)
Rev.: $196,416,000
Assets: $118,825,000
Liabilities: $55,879,000
Net Worth: $62,946,000
Earnings: $11,423,000
Emp.: 2,556
Fiscal Year-end: 12/31/12

Business Description:
Holding Company
S.I.C.: 6719
N.A.I.C.S.: 551112

Personnel:
Koichi Urano *(Chm & CEO)*
Akihiro Kiyota *(COO)*
Robson Teck Leng Lee *(Legal Counsel)*
San-Ju Tan *(Sec)*

Board of Directors:
Koichi Urano
Pheng Chong
Philip Hua Cheung Dymo
Akihiro Kiyota
Edward Shi Hong Lai
Masatoshi Mitani
Wai Kee Ng
Shinichi Ochi

Transfer Agent:
Boardroom Corporate & Advisory Services Pte. Ltd.
50 Raffles Place 32-01 Singapore Land Tower
Singapore, Singapore

Subsidiary:

Tomoike Industrial (H.K.) Limited **(1)**
Room 6-10 11th Floor Telecom Building
11 Wo Shing St Fo Tan, Sha Tin, China (Hong Kong) (100%)
Tel.: (852) 26885223
Fax: (852) 26886170
Web Site: www.hktomoike.com.hk
Emp.: 110
Other Electronic Parts & Equipment Whslr
S.I.C.: 5065
N.A.I.C.S.: 423690

Non-U.S. Subsidiaries:

Tomoike Electronics (Shanghai) Co., Limited **(2)**
3-4F Yong Fu Building 85 Tai Gu Road Wai Gao Qiao FTZ
Pudong New Area, Shanghai, 200131, China
Tel.: (86) 2158682105
Fax: (86) 21 5868 2106
Web Site: www.hktomoike.com.hk/english/fac_electronics.html
Emp.: 93
Flat Panel Display Component Mfr & Distr
S.I.C.: 3679
N.A.I.C.S.: 334419

Tomoike Industrial Co., Ltd. **(2)**
12F Kintetsu Nanba Building 1-4-38 Minato-machi
Naniwa-ku, Osaka, 556-0017, Japan
Tel.: (81) 676687666
Fax: (81) 676687667
Web Site: www.tomoike.co.jp
Precision Products Mfr & Distr
S.I.C.: 3423
N.A.I.C.S.: 332216

Tomoike Precision Machinery (Shanghai) Co., Limited **(2)**
Chenbao Road 58 Malu Ind City
Jiading District, Shanghai, 201801, China
Tel.: (86) 2169154464
Web Site: www.cdw-holding.com.hk/product/facilities.html
Office Automation Machinery Parts Mfr & Distr
S.I.C.: 3559
N.A.I.C.S.: 333249

CEAPRO INC.

Suite 4174 Enterprise Square 10230 Jasper Avenue
Edmonton, AB, T5J 4P6, Canada
Tel.: (780) 421-4555
Fax: (780) 421-1320
E-Mail: info@ceapro.com
Web Site: www.ceapro.com
Year Founded: 1987
CZO—(TSXV)
Rev.: $5,134,388
Assets: $3,862,730
Liabilities: $3,849,247
Net Worth: $13,483
Earnings: ($535,134)
Emp.: 17
Fiscal Year-end: 12/31/12

Business Description:
Biotechnology & Pharmaceutical Products Mfr
S.I.C.: 2834
N.A.I.C.S.: 325412

Personnel:
Edward A. Taylor *(Chm)*
Gilles R. Gagnon *(Pres & CEO)*
Branko Jankovic *(CFO & VP-Fin)*

Board of Directors:
Edward A. Taylor
Gilles R. Gagnon
Donald Oborowsky
Glenn Rourke
John Zupancic

Legal Counsel:
Bryan & Company
2600 Manulife Place 10180 101 Street NW
Edmonton, AB, Canada

Transfer Agent:
Olympia Trust Company
2300 Palliser Square 125 9 Avenue SE
Calgary, AB, Canada

CEAT LTD.

RPG House 463 Dr Annie Besant Road Worli
Mumbai, 400 030, India
Tel.: (91) 2224930621
Fax: (91) 2224975798
Web Site: www.ceat.in
CEATLTD—(NSE)
Rev.: $1,023,508,116
Assets: $583,453,559
Liabilities: $437,813,127
Net Worth: $145,640,432
Earnings: $22,283,207
Emp.: 5,322
Fiscal Year-end: 03/31/13

Business Description:
Tyre Mfr
S.I.C.: 3999
N.A.I.C.S.: 339999

Personnel:
Anant Vardhan Goenka *(Mng Dir)*
H. N. Singh Rajpoot *(Compliance Officer & Sec)*

Board of Directors:
H. V. Goenka
Arnab Banerjee
Vinay Bansal
Atul C. Choksey
Paras K. Chowdhary
S. Doreswamy
Anant Vardhan Goenka
Mahesh S. Gupta
Haigreve Khaitan
Bansi S. Mehta
Hari L. Mundra
Kantikumar R. Podar

Transfer Agent:
TSR Darashaw Limited
6-10 First F Haji Moosa Patrawala Industrial Estate
20 Dr. E Moses Road, Mumbai, India

CEBU PROPERTY VENTURES AND DEVELOPMENT CORPORATION

7/F Cebu Holdings Center Cardinal Rosales Avenue
Cebu Business Park, Cebu, 6000, Philippines
Tel.: (63) 322315301
Fax: (63) 322315300
E-Mail: customer_care@cpvdc.com
Web Site: www.cpvdc.com
CPV—(PHI)
Rev.: $5,930,482
Assets: $38,369,867
Liabilities: $4,610,735
Net Worth: $33,759,132
Earnings: $3,234,803
Emp.: 4
Fiscal Year-end: 12/31/12

Business Description:
Property Management & Development Services
S.I.C.: 6531
N.A.I.C.S.: 531311

Personnel:
Antonino T. Aquino *(Chm)*
Francis O. Monera *(Pres)*
Enrique B. Manuel, Jr. *(CFO & Compliance Officer)*
Ma. Theresa M. Javier *(Treas)*
Sheila Marie U. Tan *(Sec)*

Board of Directors:
Antonino T. Aquino
Ma. Theresa M. Javier
Francis O. Monera
Anastacio T. Muntuerto Jr.
Armando O. Samia
Rory Jon Q. Sepulveda
Emilio J. Tumbocon

CEC INTERNATIONAL HOLDINGS LIMITED

2/F Hing Win Factory Building 110 How Ming Street
Kwun Tong, Kowloon, China (Hong Kong)
Tel.: (852) 23415539
Fax: (852) 2343 5082
E-Mail: info@ceccoils.com
Web Site: www.ceccoils.com
0759—(HKG)
Rev.: $165,017,444
Assets: $132,781,491
Liabilities: $68,055,555
Net Worth: $64,725,937
Earnings: $2,598,343
Emp.: 3,500
Fiscal Year-end: 04/30/13

Business Description:
Holding Company; Coils, Ferrite Materials, Inductors, Transformers, Line Filters & Capacitors Designer & Mfr
S.I.C.: 3675
N.A.I.C.S.: 334416

Personnel:
Wai Chun Lam *(Chm & Mng Dir)*
Wing Yi Ho *(Sec & Head-Acctg)*

Board of Directors:
Wai Chun Lam
Son Yiu Au
Gen Cheung Goh
Man Lee Ho
Hong Li
Fung Kwan Tang
Tin Sek Tang
Yuhe Zhu

Butterfield Fulcrum Group (Bermuda) Limited
26 Burnaby Street
Hamilton, HM 11, Bermuda

Transfer Agents:
Computershare Hong Kong Investor Services Limited
Shops 1712-1716 17th Floor Hopewell Centre
183 Queens Road East
Wanchai, China (Hong Kong)

Butterfield Fulcrum Group (Bermuda) Limited
26 Burnaby Street
Hamilton, HM 11, Bermuda

Subsidiary:

Coils Electronic Co., Limited **(1)**
2 F Hing Win Factory Building 110 How Ming Street
Kwun Tong, Hong Kong, China (Hong Kong) HK (100%)
Tel.: (852) 23415539
Fax: (852) 23435082
E-Mail: info@ceccoils.com
Web Site: www.ceccoils.com
Emp.: 150
Coils, Ferrite Materials, Inductors, Transformers, Line Filters & Capacitors Designer & Mfr
S.I.C.: 3676
N.A.I.C.S.: 334416
Wai Chun Lam *(Chm)*

Non-U.S. Subsidiaries:

CEC-Coils Singapore Pte Ltd. **(1)**
69 Ubi Cresent Ste 04-07 CES Bldg
Singapore, 408561, Singapore SG (100%)
Tel.: (65) 62223321
Fax: (65) 62266223
E-Mail: info@ceccoils.com
Emp.: 6
Coils & Other Electronic Components Mfr & Sales
S.I.C.: 3676
N.A.I.C.S.: 334416
Po Leng Poh *(Asst Gen Mgr)*

Coils Electronic (Zhongshan) Co., Ltd. **(1)**
Li Xin Jie Yong An Lu
Dong Feng Zhen, Zhongshan, Guangdong, 528425, China CN (100%)
Tel.: (86) 7602601608
Fax: (86) 7602602810
Web Site: www.ceccoils.com
Coils, Ferrite Materials, Inductors, Transformers, Line Filters & Capacitors Designer & Mfr
S.I.C.: 3676
N.A.I.C.S.: 334416
Shaobing Huang *(Head-Bus)*

Dongguan Coils Electronic Co. Ltd. **(1)**
Bei An Guan Li Au
Huang Jiang Zhen
Dongguan, Guangdong, 523759, China CN (100%)
Tel.: (86) 769 362 2565
Fax: (86) 769 362 2569
Coils & Other Electronic Components Mfr & Sales
S.I.C.: 3676
N.A.I.C.S.: 334416

Nanjing Guo Zhong Magnetic Material Co., Ltd. **(1)**
357 Yao Xin Road Nanjing Economic & Technical
Development Zone
Nanjing, 210038, China CN (100%)
Tel.: (86) 2585804419
Fax: (86) 25 8580 4420
Web Site: www.ceccoils.com
Ferrite Powder Mfr & Sales
S.I.C.: 2899
N.A.I.C.S.: 325998

Tonichi Ferrite Co., Ltd. **(1)**
Lin Jin Xie 71 Yong An Lu
Dong Feng Zhen, Zhongshan, Guangdong, 528425, China CN (100%)
Tel.: (86) 76022601608
Fax: (86) 76022602810

CEC International Holdings Limited—(Continued)

E-Mail: info@ceccoils.com
Web Site: www.ceccoils.com
Emp.: 4,000
Coils & Other Electronic Components Mfr & Sales
S.I.C.: 3677
N.A.I.C.S.: 334416

CECCON FRERES SA

Ave Des Iles Prolongee
74000 Annecy, Haute Savoie, France
Tel.: (33) 450571156
Fax: (33) 450572489
E-Mail: accuail@ceccon-freres.fr
Web Site: www.ceccon-freres.fr
Sales Range: $25-49.9 Million
Emp.: 226

Business Description:
Constructopn Services
S.I.C.: 1541
N.A.I.C.S.: 236210
Personnel:
Thierry Ceccon *(CEO)*

CECEP COSTIN NEW MATERIALS GROUP LIMITED

(Formerly COSTIN New Materials Group Limited)
Unit 2703-04 27/F Tower 6 The Gateway 9 Canton Road
Tsimshatsui, Kowloon, China (Hong Kong)
Tel.: (852) 35280390
Fax: (852) 35280391
E-Mail: info@costin99.com
Web Site: www.costingroup.com
Year Founded: 1999
2228—(HKG)
Sls.: $247,678,920
Earnings: $39,013,560
Emp.: 796
Fiscal Year-end: 12/31/12

Business Description:
Holding Company; Nonwoven Fabrics Mfr & Whslr
S.I.C.: 6719
N.A.I.C.S.: 551112
Personnel:
Wai Kong Chim *(Co-Chm)*
Heping Yu *(Co-Chm)*
Jackson Wai Shing Chim *(CEO)*
Hui Chen *(Deputy CEO & Fin Controller)*
Min Tsung Chen *(Deputy CEO-HR)*
Yu Sheng Tian *(Deputy CEO-Production)*
Hong Hai Wang *(Deputy CEO-Supply Chain Mgmt)*
Elvis Kwok Yuen Chan *(CFO & Sec)*
Li Quan Ji *(COO)*
Kai Lam Wong *(Internal Control Officer)*
Board of Directors:
Wai Kong Chim
Heping Yu
Bo Chen
Jackson Wai Shing Chim
Xue Ben Feng
Yun Ma
Tingxuan Pan
Pingji Qu
Yangzu Wang
Siu Hong Wong
Xiaoqing Wu
Ying Xiong
Mangmang Xue
Xiangdong Zhao
Min Ru Zhu

Appleby Trust (Cayman) Ltd.
Clifton House 75 Fort Street
PO Box 1350
Grand Cayman, Cayman Islands

Transfer Agents:
Computershare Hong Kong Investor Services Limited
Shops 1712-1716 17th Floor Hopewell Centre
183 Queens Road East
Wanchai, China (Hong Kong)

Appleby Trust (Cayman) Ltd.
Clifton House 75 Fort Street
PO Box 1350
Grand Cayman, Cayman Islands

CECURITY.COM SA

75 Rue Saint Lazare
75009 Paris, France
Tel.: (33) 156433737
Fax: (33) 156433740
E-Mail: contact@cecurity.com
Web Site: www.cecurity.com
MLCEC—(EUR)
Sales Range: $1-9.9 Million
Emp.: 10

Business Description:
Data Protection, Legal Archiving & Traceability Software Products
S.I.C.: 7372
N.A.I.C.S.: 511210
Personnel:
Alain Borghesi *(Chm & Mng Dir)*

CEDAR CREEK MINES LTD.

4170 Still Creek Drive Suite 200
Burnaby, BC, V5C 6C6, Canada
Tel.: (604) 320-7877
Fax: (604) 299-4511
E-Mail: info@cedarcreekmines.com
Web Site: www.cedarcreekmines.com
Year Founded: 2008
CEDA—(OTC)

Business Description:
Gold Exploration & Mining Services
S.I.C.: 1041
N.A.I.C.S.: 212221
Personnel:
Guy Brusciano *(Pres, CEO, CFO, Chief Acctg Officer & Treas)*
Board of Directors:
Guy Brusciano
Anthony William Howland-Rose

Transfer Agent:
Island Stock Transfer
100 2nd Ave S Ste 7055
Saint Petersburg, FL 33701

CEDAR SHAKE & SHINGLE BUREAU

No 2 7101 Horne St
Mission, BC, V2V 7A2, Canada
Tel.: (604) 820-7700
Fax: (604) 820-0266
E-Mail: info@cedarbureau.com
Web Site: www.cedarbureau.org
Year Founded: 1915
Sales Range: $10-24.9 Million
Emp.: 10

Business Description:
Certi-Label Cedar Roofing & Sidewall Products
S.I.C.: 2499
N.A.I.C.S.: 321999
Personnel:
Lynne Christensen *(Dir-Ops)*

CEDAR WOODS PROPERTIES LIMITED

Ground Floor 50 Colin Street
West Perth, WA, 6005, Australia
Mailing Address:
PO Box 788
West Perth, WA, 6872, Australia
Tel.: (61) 894801500
Fax: (61) 894801599
E-Mail: email@cedarwoods.com.au
Web Site: www.cedarwoods.com.au
CWP—(ASX)
Rev.: $180,023,817
Assets: $313,697,110
Liabilities: $97,207,088
Net Worth: $216,490,022
Earnings: $37,866,788
Emp.: 54
Fiscal Year-end: 06/30/13

Business Description:
Residential, commercial & Industries Construction
S.I.C.: 1531
N.A.I.C.S.: 236117
Personnel:
Paul Stephen Sadleir *(Mng Dir)*
Paul Samuel Freedman *(CFO & Sec)*
Board of Directors:
William George Hames
Robert Stanley Brown
Ronald Packer
Paul Stephen Sadleir

Subsidiaries:

Esplanade (Mandurah) Pty. Ltd. **(1)**
66 King Park Rd
West Perth, Western Australia, 6005, Australia
Tel.: (61) 893213777
Fax: (61) 894801599
E-Mail: email@cedarwoods.com.au
Web Site: www.cedarwoods.com.au
Emp.: 30
Property Management & Development Services
S.I.C.: 6531
N.A.I.C.S.: 531312

Lonnegal Property Pty. Ltd. **(1)**
50 Colin Street
West Perth, WA, 6005, Australia
Tel.: (61) 894801500
Fax: (61) 894801599
E-Mail: email@cedarwoods.com.au
Web Site: www.cedarwoodsproperty.com.au
Emp.: 20
Real Estate Agency
S.I.C.: 6531
N.A.I.C.S.: 531210
Paul Sadleir *(Mng Dir)*

CEDARBRAE VOLKSWAGEN LTD

666 Markham Rd
Scarborough, ON, M1H 2A7, Canada
Tel.: (416) 438-1900
Fax: (416) 438-2515
Rev.: $21,168,197
Emp.: 46

Business Description:
New & Used Car Dealers
S.I.C.: 5511
N.A.I.C.S.: 441110

THE CEDARGLEN GROUP INC

(d/b/a Cedarglen Homes)
Suite 140 550 71 Avenue SE
Calgary, AB, T2H 0S6, Canada
Tel.: (403) 255-2000
Fax: (403) 258-1120
E-Mail: info@cedarglenhomes.com
Web Site: www.cedarglenhomes.com
Year Founded: 1981
Rev.: $16,739,464
Emp.: 75

Business Description:
Construction Services
S.I.C.: 1521
N.A.I.C.S.: 236115
Personnel:
Scott Haggins *(Pres)*

CEDIMA GMBH

Larchenweg 3
Celle, 29227, Germany
Tel.: (49) 514188540
Fax: (49) 514186427
E-Mail: info@cedima.com
Web Site: www.cedima.com
Year Founded: 1984
Emp.: 100

Business Description:
Diamond Tools & Construction Industry Machinery Development & Sales
S.I.C.: 3545
N.A.I.C.S.: 333515

CEEREF S.A.

42 rue de la Vallee
L-2661 Luxembourg, Luxembourg
Tel.: (352) 262 626 67
Fax: (352) 262 626 77
E-Mail: info@ceeref.com
Web Site: www.ceeref.com
Year Founded: 2006
CRF—(VIE)

Business Description:
Real Estate Investment & Development
S.I.C.: 6211
N.A.I.C.S.: 523999
Personnel:
Cedric Jauquet *(Member-Mgmt Bd)*
Nathalie Lett *(Member-Mgmt Bd)*
Matjaz Martincic *(Member-Mgmt Bd)*
Tanja Petrocnik *(Member-Mgmt Bd)*

CEESEG AG

(d/b/a CEE Stock Exchange Group)
Wallnerstrasse 8
Vienna, 1014, Austria
Tel.: (43) 1531650
Fax: (43) 15329740
E-Mail: info@wienerporse.at
Web Site: www.ceeseg.com
Year Founded: 2009
Emp.: 110

Business Description:
Stock Exchange Operator
S.I.C.: 6231
N.A.I.C.S.: 523210
Personnel:
Michael Buhl *(Co-CEO)*
Supervisory Board of Directors:
Johannes Attems
Patrick Butler
David C. Davies
Franz Gasselsberger
Franz Glatzer
Rudolf Gruber
Hans-Peter Hagen
Franz Hochstrasser
Erwin Hof
Friedrich Kadrnoska
Konstantin Klien
Ulrike Mulleder
Claus J. Raidl
Christoph Raninger
Wolfgang Reithofer
Gerhard Schwediauer
Margit Scozzari

Subsidiary:

Wiener Boerse AG **(1)**
Wallnerstrasse 8
A 1014 Vienna, Austria (100%)
Tel.: (43) 1531650
Fax: (43) 15329740
E-Mail: info@wienerborse.at
Web Site: www.wienerborse.at
Sales Range: $100-149.9 Billion
Emp.: 100
Stock Exchange Services
S.I.C.: 6231
N.A.I.C.S.: 523210
Michael Buhl *(Co-CEO)*

Joint Venture:

CCP Austria Abwicklungsstelle fur Borsengeschafte GmbH **(2)**
Strauchgasse 1-3
A-1010 Vienna, Austria
Tel.: (43) 5332244
Fax: (43) 53322442880

E-Mail: office@ccpa.at
Web Site: www.ccpa.at
Banking Services; Owned 50% by Oesterreichische Kontrollbank AG, 50% by Wiener Boerse AG
S.I.C.: 6029
N.A.I.C.S.: 522110
Wolfgang Aubrunner *(Mng Dir)*
Ludwig Niessen *(Mng Dir)*

Non-U.S. Subsidiaries:

Budapesti Ertektozsde Zrt. **(1)**
Pf 24
H-1364 Budapest, Hungary (50.45%)
Tel.: (36) 14296700
Fax: (36) 14296800
E-Mail: info@bse.hu
Web Site: www.bse.hu
Rev.: $10,835,452
Assets: $29,389,402
Liabilities: $4,688,149
Net Worth: $24,701,253
Earnings: $2,605,500
Emp.: 56
Fiscal Year-end: 12/31/12
Stock Exchange
S.I.C.: 6231
N.A.I.C.S.: 523210
Michael Buhl *(Chm)*
Attila Dezso *(Chm-Supervisory Bd)*
Balint Szecsenyi *(Vice Chm)*
Johannes Attems *(Vice Chm-Supervisory Bd)*
Zsolt Katona *(CEO)*
Ferenc Pittner *(Deputy CEO-IT)*
Attila Toth *(Gen Deputy CEO)*
Attila Vass *(CIO-IT Div)*

Burza cennych papiru Praha, a.s. **(1)**
Rybna 14
1 Prague, 110 05, Czech Republic(92.74%)
Tel.: (420) 221831111
Fax: (420) 221833040
E-Mail: info@pse.cz
Web Site: www.pse.cz
Sls.: $6,516,111
Emp.: 50
Stock Exchange Services
S.I.C.: 6231
N.A.I.C.S.: 523210
Petr Koblic *(Chm & Gen Dir)*

Ljubljanska borza, d.d. **(1)**
Slovenska 56
1000 Ljubljana, Slovenia (81.01%)
Tel.: (386) 14710211
Fax: (386) 014710213
E-Mail: info@ljse.si
Web Site: www.ljse.si
Sales Range: $1-9.9 Million
Emp.: 29
Stock Exchange Services
S.I.C.: 6231
N.A.I.C.S.: 523210
Andrej Sketa *(Pres)*
Mojca Mele *(Head, Mgmt Board-Cabinet & PR)*
Polona Peterle *(Member-Mgmt Bd)*

Non-U.S. Affiliates:

Banjaluka berza hartija od vrijednosti AD **(2)**
Petra Kocica B B
78000 Banja Luka, Bosnia & Herzegovina BA
Tel.: (387) 51326041
Fax: (387) 51326056
E-Mail: office@blberza.com
Web Site: www.blberza.com
Stock Exchange Services
S.I.C.: 6231
N.A.I.C.S.: 523210
Gordana Vuckovic *(Chm-Supervisory Bd)*
Bratoljub Radulovic *(Chm-Mgmt Bd)*
Milan Bozic *(CEO)*
Vesna Frozdanic *(Member-Mgmt Bd)*
Smilja Jokic *(Member-Mgmt Bd)*
Dobrivoje Tukic *(Member-Mgmt Bd)*

Beogradska Berza a.d. **(2)**
Omladinskih brigada 1
PO Box 50
11070 Belgrade, Serbia
Tel.: (381) 113117297
Fax: (381) 112138242
E-Mail: info@belex.rs
Web Site: www.belex.rs
Emp.: 40
Stock Exchange
S.I.C.: 6231
N.A.I.C.S.: 523210
Gordana Dostanic *(CEO)*

Macedonian Stock Exchange, Inc. **(2)**
Orce Nikolov 75
Skopje, Macedonia
Tel.: (389) 23122055
Fax: (389) 23122069
E-Mail: mse@mse.org.mk
Web Site: www.mse.com.mk
Emp.: 15
Stock Exchange Services
S.I.C.: 6231
N.A.I.C.S.: 523210

The Sarajevo Stock Exchange **(2)**
Doke Mazalic'a 4
71000 Sarajevo, Bosnia & Herzegovina
Tel.: (387) 33251462
Fax: (387) 33559460
E-Mail: contact@sase.ba
Web Site: www.sase.ba
Stock Exchange Services
S.I.C.: 6231
N.A.I.C.S.: 523210
Muris Cicic *(Chm-Supervisory Bd)*

CEETA INDUSTRIES LIMITED

240B A J C Bose Road
Kolkata, 700020, India
Tel.: (91) 33 22832925
Fax: (91) 33 22832927
E-Mail: info@ceeta.com
Web Site: www.ceeta.com
514171—(BOM)
Rev.: $1,713,077
Assets: $3,257,250
Liabilities: $134,817
Net Worth: $3,122,433
Earnings: $206,050
Emp.: 60
Fiscal Year-end: 03/31/13
Business Description:
Granite Slab Mfr
S.I.C.: 3281
N.A.I.C.S.: 327991
Personnel:
Vaibhav Poddar *(CEO)*
K. M. Poddar *(Mng Dir)*
Vikas Kedia *(Compliance Officer & Mgr-Comml)*
Board of Directors:
S. K. Chhawchharia
A. De
O. P. Kedia
K. M. Poddar
S. L. Singhania
Transfer Agent:
Niche Technologies Private Limited
D-511 Bagree Market 71 B. R. B. Basu Road
Kolkata, India

CEF (SOC) LIMITED

(d/b/a CEF Group of Companies)
CEF House Block C Upper Grayston Office Park
152 Ann Crescent Strathavon, Sandton, 2031, South Africa
Mailing Address:
PO Box 786141
Sandton, 2146, South Africa
Tel.: (27) 10 201 4700
Fax: (27) 10 201 4820
E-Mail: webmaster@cefgroup.co.za
Web Site: www.cefgroup.co.za
Sales Range: $1-4.9 Billion
Emp.: 2,100
Business Description:
Energy Holding Company
S.I.C.: 6719
N.A.I.C.S.: 551112
Personnel:
Busi Mabuza *(CEO)*
A. Haffejee *(Sec)*
Board of Directors:
S. Mthembi-Mahanyele
O. Aphane
R. Jawoodeen
Busi Mabuza
Linda Makatini
T. Maqubela
T. Ramuedzisi
Yekani R. Tenza
Subsidiary:

The Petroleum Oil & Gas Corporation of South Africa (SOC) Limited **(1)**
151 Frans Conradie Drive
Parow, 7500, South Africa ZA
Mailing Address:
Private Bag X5
Parow, 7499, South Africa
Tel.: (27) 21 929 3000
Fax: (27) 21 929 3144
E-Mail: petrosa@petrosa.co.za
Web Site: www.petrosa.com
Rev.: $2,197,866,390
Assets: $3,823,876,142
Liabilities: $1,734,856,375
Net Worth: $2,089,019,767
Earnings: $66,288,588
Emp.: 1,616
Fiscal Year-end: 03/31/13
Oil & Natural Gas Exploration & Production Services
S.I.C.: 1311
N.A.I.C.S.: 211111
Nosizwe Nokwe-Macamo *(Pres & CEO)*
Webster Fanadzo *(Acting CFO)*
Gustav Griessel *(COO)*

CEFLA S.C.

via Bicocca 14/C
40026 Imola, Italy
Tel.: (39) 0542 653441
Fax: (39) 0542 653444
Web Site: www.cefla.com
Sales Range: $450-499.9 Million
Emp.: 1,700
Business Description:
Holding Company
S.I.C.: 6719
N.A.I.C.S.: 551112
Personnel:
Giovanni Antonelli *(Pres)*
Units:

Cefla Arredamenti Group **(1)**
Via Selice Provinciale 23/A
40026 Imola, Italy
Tel.: (39) 0542 653111
Fax: (39) 0542 653444
Shelving, Rack & Point-of-Purchase Display Mfr
S.I.C.: 2599
N.A.I.C.S.: 337215
James Cowell *(Mgr-Export Sls)*

Cefla Dental Group **(1)**
Via Selice Provinciale 23/A
40026 Imola, Italy
Tel.: (39) 0542 653111
Fax: (39) 0542 653444
Dental Equipment & Supplies Mfr
S.I.C.: 3843
N.A.I.C.S.: 339114
Andrea Albertini *(Mng Dir)*

Cefla Finishing Group **(1)**
Via Bicocca 14/C
40026 Imola, Italy
Tel.: (39) 0542 653441
Fax: (39) 0542 653444
E-Mail: cefla.finishing@cefla.it
Finishing Equipment Mfr
S.I.C.: 3559
N.A.I.C.S.: 333249
Riccardo Quattrini *(Mng Dir)*

U.S. Subsidiary:

Cefla North America Inc. **(2)**
6125 Harris Technology Blvd
Charlotte, NC 28269
Tel.: (704) 598-0020
Fax: (704) 598-3950
E-Mail: info@ceflaamerica.com
Finishing Equipment Mfr
S.I.C.: 3559
N.A.I.C.S.: 333249
Massimo Di Russo *(VP)*

Subsidiaries:

Delle Vedove USA, Inc. **(3)**
6125 Harris Technology Blvd
Charlotte, NC 28269
Tel.: (704) 598-0020
Emp.: 20
Sawmill & Woodworking Machinery Mfr
S.I.C.: 3554
N.A.I.C.S.: 333243
Walter Scala *(Mng Dir)*

Cefla Impianti Group **(1)**
Via Selice Provinciale 23/A
40026 Imola, Italy
Tel.: (39) 0542 653111
Fax: (39) 0542 653129
E-Mail: ceflaimpianti@cefla.it
Civil & Industrial Engineering Services
S.I.C.: 1629
N.A.I.C.S.: 237990

CEGEDIM S.A.

127-137 rue d'Aguesseau
92100 Boulogne-Billancourt, France
Tel.: (33) 149092200
Fax: (33) 146034595
E-Mail: communication@cefedim.fr
Web Site: www.cegedim.fr
Year Founded: 1969
CGM—(EUR)
Rev.: $1,240,863,159
Assets: $1,734,266,772
Liabilities: $1,161,790,480
Net Worth: $572,476,293
Earnings: ($114,777,147)
Emp.: 8,118
Fiscal Year-end: 12/31/12
Business Description:
Market Research & Technology Services for the Healthcare & Pharmaceutical Industry
S.I.C.: 8742
N.A.I.C.S.: 541611
Personnel:
Jean-Claude Labrune *(Chm & CEO)*
Pierre Marucchi *(Mng Dir)*
Jan Eryk Umiastowski *(Chief IR Officer & Chief Investment Officer)*
Karl Guenault *(Chief Operational Excellence Officer)*
Board of Directors:
Jean-Claude Labrune
Jean-Pierre Cassan
Laurent Labrune
Aude Labrune-Marysse
Nicolas Manardo
Pierre Marucchi
Jean-Louis Mery
Valerie Raoul-Desprez
Anthony Roberts
Philippe Tcheng

Grant Thornton
100 rue de Courcelles
75017 Paris, France
Group:

Cededim Relationship Management **(1)**
127-137 Rue d'Aguesseau
92641 Boulogne-Billancourt, France NJ
Tel.: (33) 149092200
Fax: (33) 146034595
Web Site: www.cegedimdendrite.com
Sales Range: $400-449.9 Million
Emp.: 2,793
Customer Management Systems & Support Services for Pharmaceutical & Consumer Packaged Goods Industries
S.I.C.: 3652
N.A.I.C.S.: 334614
Laurent Labrune *(CEO)*

Subsidiary:

SK&A Information Services, Inc. **(2)**
2601 Main St Ste 650
Irvine, CA 92614

Cegedim S.A.—(Continued)

Tel.: (949) 476-2051
Fax: (949) 476-2168
Toll Free: (800) 258-9479
E-Mail: customerservice@skainfo.com
Web Site: www.skainfo.com
Sls.: $15,000,000
Emp.: 100
Health Care Marketing Information Services
S.I.C.: 8732
N.A.I.C.S.: 541910
Albert Chang *(Mng Dir)*

Non-U.S. Subsidiaries:

Cegedim Dendrite (China) Co. Ltd. (2)
9th Fl Asia Mansion
No 650 Hankou Rd, Shanghai, 200001, China CN
Tel.: (86) 2161350011 (100%)
Fax: (86) 2161220300
Web Site: www.crm.cegedim.com
Customer Management Systems & Support Services for Pharmaceutical & Consumer Packaged Goods Industries
S.I.C.: 7371
N.A.I.C.S.: 541511
Yan Tang *(Gen Mgr)*

Cegedim Dendrite Colombia Ltda. (2)
Calle 97 23-60 Edificio Logic
Piso 9, Bogota, Colombia Co
Tel.: (57) 16382727
Fax: (57) 576224132
E-Mail: jabier.moreno@cegedim.com
Web Site: www.cegedimdrte.com
Emp.: 65
Hardware & Asset Management Services
S.I.C.: 7376
N.A.I.C.S.: 541513
Ramiro Aviles *(Mng Dir)*

Cegedim Dendrite Hellas S.A. (2)
68 Alimou Ave
Alimos Athens, 174 55, Greece GR
Tel.: (30) 2109850400
Fax: (30) 2109850866
Mobile Intelligence, Data Warehousing & Sales Force Optimization Services
S.I.C.: 7379
N.A.I.C.S.: 518210

Cegedim Dendrite Italia srl (2)
Piazza I Montanelli 20 Sesto San Giovanni
20099 Milan, Italy IT
Tel.: (39) 02243431
Fax: (39) 0269553299
E-Mail: valaria.debafquale@cegedimdendrite.com
Web Site: www.cegedim.com
Emp.: 140
Analytical Data Warehousing & Mobile Services
S.I.C.: 7374
N.A.I.C.S.: 518210
Emeleano Gummate *(Mng Dir)*
Francesco Di Liscia *(Mng Dir)*

Cegedim Dendrite Netherland B.V. (2)
AB Naarden Gooimeer 1E
PO Box 1410
1411 DC Naarden, Netherlands NL
Tel.: (31) 356955300 (100%)
Fax: (31) 356945089
E-Mail: reception@cegedim.com
Web Site: www.cegedim.com
Emp.: 50
Customer Management Systems & Support Services for Pharmaceutical & Consumer Packaged Goods Industries
S.I.C.: 7371
N.A.I.C.S.: 541511
Hanno Luteijn *(Head-Ops)*

Cegedim Dendrite UK Ltd. (2)
Unit SA Charnwood Buillding Holywell Park
Ashby Rd
Rectory Place, Loughborough, LE11 1TW, United Kingdom UK
Tel.: (44) 1509224700
Fax: (44) 1509233673
Web Site: www.drte.com
Emp.: 40
Mobile Intelligence & Direct Mail Services
S.I.C.: 7331
N.A.I.C.S.: 541860
David Round *(Mng Dir)*

Cegedim Relationship Management (2)
20 McCallum St #04-01
Tokio Marine Center, Singapore, 069046, Singapore SG
Tel.: (65) 63725200 (100%)
Fax: (65) 6372 5201
Web Site: www.cegedim.com
Emp.: 30
Customer Relationship Management & Support Services for Pharmaceutical & Consumer Packaged Goods Industries
S.I.C.: 7371
N.A.I.C.S.: 541511
Franck Levassort *(Pres-Asia Pacific)*

Dendrite Australia Pty. Ltd. (2)
14-16 Suikin St
Pymble, NSW, 2073, Australia AU
Tel.: (61) 298557900 (100%)
Fax: (61) 298557999
Web Site: www.cegedim.com
Emp.: 35
Customer Management Systems & Support Services for Pharmaceutical & Consumer Packaged Goods Industries
S.I.C.: 7371
N.A.I.C.S.: 541511
Sinjay Reahy *(Head-Sls Solutions)*

Dendrite Brasil Ltda. (2)
Rua Helena 235 - 11 andar
Vila Olimpia, SP Sao Paulo, Brazil BR
Tel.: (55) 1131030457 (100%)
Fax: (55) 1131030470
E-Mail: marta.luivaf@ilvacagadim.com
Web Site: www.cagadim.com
Emp.: 97
Mobile Intelligence, Data Warehousing & Sales Force Optimization Services
S.I.C.: 7379
N.A.I.C.S.: 518210
Mareo Martinz *(Gen Mgr)*

Dendrite New Zealand Ltd. (2)
Unit H Paul Matthews Office Park
43 Omega Street
PO Box 302-566, North Harbour Auckland, New Zealand NZ
Tel.: (64) 93076647 (100%)
Fax: (64) 9 307 6650
Mobile Intelligence, Data Warehousing & Sales Force Optimization Services
S.I.C.: 7389
N.A.I.C.S.: 561499
Steve Holohan *(Mgr-Sls)*

Dendrite Software India Pte. Ltd. (2)
Maruthi Infotech Centre
11-1 12-1 Koramangala
Inner Ring Road, Bengaluru, 560 071, India
Tel.: (91) 80 66231500
Fax: (91) 80 66231800
Pharmaceutical Software Products Mfr
S.I.C.: 7372
N.A.I.C.S.: 511210

Medical Data Management (2)
2 Solomenskaya Sq Ofc 506
03035 Kiev, Ukraine UA
Tel.: (380) 444960430
Fax: (380) 444960431
E-Mail: hq.ukraine@mdmworld.com
Web Site: www.mdmworld.com
Emp.: 50
Web & Mobile Telecommunications & Telemarketing Services
S.I.C.: 7389
N.A.I.C.S.: 561422
Nadya Vorushylo *(Mng Dir)*

Schwarzeck-Verlag GmbH (2)
Stefan-George-Ring 19
81929 Munich, Germany De
Mailing Address:
Postfach 1391
85505 Ottobrunn, Germany
Tel.: (49) 89608040
Fax: (49) 8960804400
E-Mail: info@schwarzeck.de
Web Site: www.schwarzeck.de
Emp.: 25
Global Optimization Marketing & Sales Performances of Pharmaceutical Companies
S.I.C.: 8742
N.A.I.C.S.: 541613
Arnem Kost *(Mng Dir)*

Subsidiaries:

3S/Tracere (1)
131 137 rue d'Aguesseau
Boulogne-Billancourt, 92641, France
Tel.: (33) 149092494
Fax: (33) 1 4712 9095
Web Site: www.cegedim.com
Sample Management Systems
S.I.C.: 8742
N.A.I.C.S.: 541611

Pharmastock (1)
326 rue du Gros Moulin
Amilly, Paris, 45200, France
Tel.: (33) 238876081
Fax: (33) 238876098
E-Mail: gocelyne.ramond@cejedim.fr
Emp.: 20
Sample Management Systems
S.I.C.: 8742
N.A.I.C.S.: 541611

RESIP (1)
56 rue Ferdinand Buisson
Boulogne-sur-Mer, 62200, France
Tel.: (33) 321103400
Fax: (33) 321103409
E-Mail: bcb@resip.fr
Web Site: www.resip.fr
Scientific Database Management Services
S.I.C.: 8742
N.A.I.C.S.: 541611

CEGEKA NV

Universiteitslaan 9
Hasselt, 3500, Belgium
Tel.: (32) 11 24 02 34
Fax: (32) 11 23 34 25
E-Mail: info@cegeka.be
Web Site: www.cegeka.be
Sales Range: $250-299.9 Million
Emp.: 1,650
Business Description:
IT Services
S.I.C.: 7373
N.A.I.C.S.: 541512
Personnel:
Andre Knaepen *(Chm, Pres & CEO)*
Stephan Daems *(CFO)*
Board of Directors:
Andre Knaepen
Hendrik Bergmans
Stijn Bijnens
Robert Ceuppens
Stephan Daems
Sonja Nouwen
Jef Roos
Guy Schiepers
Marc Van den Abeelen

CEGID GROUP SA

52 quai Paul Sedallian
69279 Lyon, Cedex 09, France
Tel.: (33) 811884888
Fax: (33) 4 26 29 50 50
E-Mail: cegid@cegid.fr
Web Site: www.cegid.com
CGD—(EUR)
Sls.: $347,455,900
Assets: $493,095,340
Liabilities: $248,830,101
Net Worth: $244,265,239
Earnings: $16,971,165
Emp.: 2,140
Fiscal Year-end: 12/31/12
Business Description:
Management Software Developer
S.I.C.: 7372
N.A.I.C.S.: 511210
Personnel:
Jean-Michel Aulas *(Chm)*
Patrick Bertrand *(CEO)*
Thierry Luthi *(CFO)*
Board of Directors:
Jean-Michel Aulas
Valerie Irene Amelie Monique Bernis
Patrick Bertrand
Philippe Delerive
Franklin Devaux
Lucien Deveaux
Jean-Luc Lenart
Quitterie Lenoir
Jacques Matagrin
Nicolas Michel-Vernet
Astrid Panosyan
Florence Poivey
Michel Reybier

Grant Thornton
42 Avenue Georges Pompidou
69442 Lyon, Cedex, France

Non-U.S. Subsidiary:

CEGID LTD (1)
1 Copperhouse Court
Caldecotte, Milton Keynes, MK7 8NL, United Kingdom
Tel.: (44) 1908272420
Fax: (44) 1908272438
E-Mail: cegiduk@cegid.com
Web Site: www.cegid.co.uk
Emp.: 10
Retail Software Solutions
S.I.C.: 7372
N.A.I.C.S.: 511210
Lyndsey Sparnon *(Mgr-Mktg)*

U.S. Subsidiary:

CEGID CORPORATION (1)
130 West 57th St
New York, NY 10019
Tel.: (212) 757-9038
Fax: (212) 757-9051
Web Site: www.cegid.us/
Computer Software Services
S.I.C.: 7371
N.A.I.C.S.: 541511
Arnaud Coste *(Mgr)*

Subsidiary:

COMPTANOO SAS (1)
52 Quai Paul Sedallian
69009 Lyon, France
Tel.: (33) 223455570
Fax: (33) 299839786
E-Mail: info@comptanoo.com
Web Site: www.comptanoo.com
Emp.: 14
Computer Software Services
S.I.C.: 7371
N.A.I.C.S.: 541511
Patrick Lefevre *(Mng Dir)*

CEI CONTRACT MANUFACTURING LTD

No 2 Ang Mo Kio Ave 12
Singapore, 569707, Singapore
Tel.: (65) 64811882
Fax: (65) 64813293
E-Mail: limph@cei.com.sg
Web Site: www.cei.com.sg
C11—(SES)
Rev.: $86,254,996
Assets: $52,031,722
Liabilities: $26,667,819
Net Worth: $25,363,903
Earnings: $2,885,401
Emp.: 616
Fiscal Year-end: 12/31/12
Business Description:
Printed Circuit Board Assemblies
S.I.C.: 3575
N.A.I.C.S.: 334118
Personnel:
Sing Cheong Tien *(Chm)*
Ka Huat Tan *(Mng Dir)*
Chee Hoe Sia *(CFO)*
Susie Geok Eng Low *(Co-Sec)*
Soon Hock Teo *(Co-Sec)*
Board of Directors:
Sing Cheong Tien
Chee Yen Gan
Colin Teck Sim Ng
Bien Chuan Tan
Ka Huat Tan
Martin Yue Nien Tang

Legal Counsel:
Colin Ng & Partners
36 Carpenter Street
Singapore, Singapore
Transfer Agent:
Boardroom Corporate & Advisory Services Pte. Ltd.
50 Raffles Place 32-01 Singapore Land Tower
Singapore, Singapore

CELADOR PRODUCTIONS LTD.
38 Long Acre
London, WC2E 9JT, United Kingdom
Tel.: (44) 2072408101
Fax: (44) 2078369633
E-Mail: info@cplproductions.co.uk
Web Site: www.cplproductions.co.uk
Year Founded: 1983
Sales Range: $25-49.9 Million
Emp.: 100
Business Description:
Television Production Company
S.I.C.: 4833
N.A.I.C.S.: 515120
Personnel:
Danielle S. Lux *(Mng Dir)*

CELAMIN HOLDINGS NL
Suite 304 22 St Kilda Road
Saint Kilda, VIC, 3182, Australia
Tel.: (61) 3 9692 7222
Fax: (61) 3 9529 8057
Web Site: www.victoriangoldmines.com.au
CNL—(ASX)
Business Description:
Gold Mining Services
S.I.C.: 1041
N.A.I.C.S.: 212221
Personnel:
Andrew Thomson *(Chm)*
Melanie Leydin *(Sec)*
Board of Directors:
Andrew Thomson
Peter Avery
Russell Luxford
David Regan
Gary Scanlan
Legal Counsel:
Hemming+Hart Lawyers
2nd Floor 307 Queen Street
Brisbane, QLD, 4000, Australia
Tel.: (61) 7 30028700

CELARTEM TECHNOLOGY INC.
5th Floor Sumitomo Higashi-Shimbashi Bldg 5
2-11-7 Higashi-Shimbashi
Minato-ku, Tokyo, 105-0021, Japan
Tel.: (81) 3 5574 7231
Web Site: www.celartem.com
Year Founded: 1996
4330—(TKS)
Sales Range: $25-49.9 Million
Emp.: 103
Business Description:
Digital Contents Supply Chain Software & Technology Applications
S.I.C.: 7373
N.A.I.C.S.: 541512
Personnel:
Osamu Ikeda *(Pres & CEO)*
Hiroaki Miyanaga *(CFO)*
Board of Directors:
Syuichi Fujimoto
Hiroaki Miyanaga
U.S. Subsidiary:

Lizardtech (1)
1008 Western Ave Ste 200
Seattle, WA 98104
Tel.: (206) 652-5211
Fax: (206) 652-0880
E-Mail: info@lizardtech.com
Web Site: www.lizardtech.com
Emp.: 151
Software Publishing & Application Services
S.I.C.: 7372
N.A.I.C.S.: 511210
Nahhe Nomie *(CFO)*

CELEBI HOLDING A.S.
Nispetiye Caddesi Akmerkez B3 Blok Kat 12
Etiler, 34337 Istanbul, Turkey
Tel.: (90) 2123394039
Fax: (90) 2122821383
Web Site: www.celebi.com
Emp.: 2,500
Business Description:
Holding Company
S.I.C.: 6719
N.A.I.C.S.: 551112
Personnel:
A. Cemil Erman *(Dir Gen)*

CELEBRITY FASHIONS LIMITED
SDF-IV 3rd Main Road MEPZ SE
Tambaram, Chennai, Tamil Nadu, 600 045, India
Tel.: (91) 4443432000
Fax: (91) 4422622897
E-Mail: admin@celebritygroup.com
Web Site: www.celebritygroup.com
CELEBRITY—(NSE)
Rev.: $35,101,782
Assets: $25,210,692
Liabilities: $33,557,400
Net Worth: ($8,346,708)
Earnings: ($867,672)
Emp.: 4,000
Fiscal Year-end: 03/31/13
Business Description:
Garments Mfr & Distr
S.I.C.: 2389
N.A.I.C.S.: 315280
Personnel:
Venkatesh Rajagopal *(Chm)*
Charath Ram Narsimhan *(Mng Dir)*
Senthil Kumar K *(Sec)*
Board of Directors:
Venkatesh Rajagopal
Charath Ram Narsimhan
Rama Rajagopal
P. S. Raman
N. K. Ranganath
Nidhi Reddy
Ramji Sinha
Anil Nair & Associates
Egmore, Chennai, India
Transfer Agent:
Link Intime India Private Limited
C-13 Pannalal Silk Mills Compound L.B.S. Marg Bhandup
Mumbai, India

CELEST PAPER KLIPPAN AB
Fabriksvagen 2
264 39 Klippan, Sweden
Tel.: (46) 43514040
Fax: (46) 43515455
E-Mail: admin@celestpaper.se
Web Site: www.celestpaper.se
Sales Range: $10-24.9 Million
Emp.: 40
Business Description:
Paper Mill
S.I.C.: 2621
N.A.I.C.S.: 322122
Personnel:
Ronny Andersson *(Mng Dir)*
Subsidiary:

Klippan AB (1)
Kvarnbygatan 8
PO Box 213
431 23 Molndal, Sweden (100%)
Tel.: (46) 31675000
Fax: (46) 4352929
Web Site: www.klippan.com
Emp.: 400
Newsprint Mills
S.I.C.: 2621
N.A.I.C.S.: 322122
Thomas Billing *(Mng Dir)*

CELESTE COPPER CORPORATION
(Name Changed to Celeste Mining Corporation)

CELESTE MINING CORPORATION
(Formerly Celeste Copper Corporation)
c/o Sunnyfield 11 Millford Road
Sidmouth, Devon, EX10 8DR, United Kingdom
Tel.: (44) 1209 715777
Fax: (44) 1209 7166777
E-Mail: info@celestecopper.com
Web Site: www.celestecopper.com
Year Founded: 2007
C—(TSXV)
Assets: $7,544,487
Liabilities: $196,366
Net Worth: $7,348,121
Earnings: ($2,242,020)
Fiscal Year-end: 11/30/12
Business Description:
Copper Mining Services
S.I.C.: 1021
N.A.I.C.S.: 212234
Personnel:
Farhad Abasov *(Chm)*
Richard A. Kelertas *(Interim CEO)*
Max Missiouk *(CFO)*
Chris Davie *(COO)*
Board of Directors:
Farhad Abasov
Richard A. Kelertas
Diana Walters

CELESTIAL ASIA SECURITIES HOLDINGS LIMITED
(Formerly Net2Gather (China) Holdings Ltd.)
(d/b/a CASH Group)
28th Floor Manhattan Place
23 Wang Tai Road, Kowloon, China (Hong Kong)
Tel.: (852) 2287 8888
Fax: (852) 2287 8000
Web Site: www.cash.com.hk
1049—(HKG)
Rev.: $166,385,990
Assets: $391,142,359
Liabilities: $293,719,602
Net Worth: $97,422,757
Earnings: ($32,554,201)
Emp.: 350
Fiscal Year-end: 12/31/12
Business Description:
Investment Services
S.I.C.: 6211
N.A.I.C.S.: 523999
Personnel:
Bankee Pak Hoo Kwan *(Chm & CEO)*
Sammy Wing Cheong Tsui *(Deputy CEO)*
Bernard Ping Wah Law *(CFO)*
Raymond Pak-Lau Yuen *(Deputy CFO)*
Jack Ho *(Deputy COO)*
Raymond Kung Chit Ng *(COO)*
Suzanne Wing Sheung Luke *(Sec)*
Board of Directors:
Bankee Pak Hoo Kwan
Hak-sin Chan
Bernard Ping Wah Law
Johnny Ka Kui Leung
Derek Hin-sing Ng
Raymond Kung Chit Ng
Sammy Wing Cheong Tsui
Chuk-yan Wong
Legal Counsel:
Sidley Austin
Level 39, Two International Finance Centre 8 Finance Street
Central, China (Hong Kong)
Transfer Agent:
Tricor Standard Limited
26/F Tesbury Centre 28 Queen's Road East
Wanchai, China (Hong Kong)
Tel.: (852) 2980 1333
Fax: (852) 2810 8185
Non-U.S. Subsidiary:

Moli Group Limited (1)
6F The Point-Jing An No 555 Anyuan Rd
Shanghai, 200040, China
Tel.: (86) 2132279868
Fax: (86) 2132212655
Web Site: ir.moliyo.com
Emp.: 300
Online Game Development Services
S.I.C.: 2741
N.A.I.C.S.: 519130
Bankee Kwan *(Chm & CEO)*

CELESTIAL BIOLABS LIMITED
Plot No 231/A MLA Colony
Road No 12 Banjara Hills
500034 Hyderabad, Andhra Pradesh, India
Tel.: (91) 40 2354 0008
Fax: (91) 40 2354 2844
E-Mail: investors@celestialbiolabs.com
Web Site: www.celestiabiolabs.com
CELESTIAL—(NSE)
Business Description:
Research & Development, Commercial Production & Marketing of Chemical Enzymes
S.I.C.: 2833
N.A.I.C.S.: 325411
Personnel:
Aditya Narayan Singh *(Chm & Mng Dir)*
Board of Directors:
Aditya Narayan Singh
Jeetainder Roy Gour
B. Silva Kumar
Deverakonda Chidvilasa Sastry
Padma Singh
Transfer Agent:
Karvy Computershare Private Limited
46 Avenue 4 Street No 1 Banjara Hills
Hyderabad, 500 034, India
Tel.: (91) 40 23320666
Fax: (91) 40 23323058

CELESTIAL GREEN VENTURES PLC
93 St Stephens Green
Dublin, 2, Ireland
Tel.: (353) 1 428 3404
E-Mail: info@celestialgreen.eu
Web Site: www.celestialgreenventures.com
9CG—(DEU)
Business Description:
Carbon Mfr
S.I.C.: 2819
N.A.I.C.S.: 325180
Personnel:
Dieter Huhne *(Co-Founder)*
Ciaran Kelly *(Co-Founder)*
Subsidiary:

Carbon Assessment Project (1)
93 St Stephens Green
Dublin, Ireland
Tel.: (353) 1 428 3410
E-Mail: info@carbonassessmentproject.com
Web Site: www.carbonassessmentproject.ie
Emp.: 5
Accounting Software Development Services
S.I.C.: 7371

Celestial Green Ventures PLC—(Continued)

N.A.I.C.S.: 541511

CELESTIAL NUTRIFOODS LIMITED

15/F International Metro Center First
3 Shilpu
Chao Yang District, Beijing, 100025, China
Tel.: (86) 1065561809
Fax: (86) 1065575240
E-Mail: info@celestialsms.com
Web Site: www.celestialnutrifoods.com
Year Founded: 1997
C56—(SES)
Sales Range: $200-249.9 Million
Business Description:
Soy Protein-Based Food & Beverage Mfr
S.I.C.: 2099
N.A.I.C.S.: 311999
Personnel:
Dequan Ming *(Chm & CEO)*
Shunfu Liu *(COO)*
Ping Ping Tan *(Sec)*
Board of Directors:
Dequan Ming
Seng Kwoon Lai
Choon Chiaw Loo
Bryan Win Yun Ma
Chaunnong Zhou

CELL-LOC LOCATION TECHNOLOGIES INC.

1600 37St SW
Calgary, AB, T3C 3P1, Canada
Tel.: (403) 569-5700
Fax: (403) 569-5701
E-Mail: investors@cell-loc.com
Web Site: www.cell-loc.com
Year Founded: 1995
XCT—(TSXV)
Sales Range: $1-9.9 Million
Emp.: 12
Business Description:
Wireless Location Solutions
S.I.C.: 4813
N.A.I.C.S.: 517110
Personnel:
Alvaro Schocair *(Chm)*
Keith J. Bohn *(CEO & Pres)*
Dave Guebert *(CFO & VP-Fin)*
Board of Directors:
Alvaro Schocair
Ariovaldo Aprikian
Keith J. Bohn
Michel Fattouche
Robert Henschel
Roberto Junqueira
Dick Tchairdjian
Legal Counsel:
Burnet, Duckworth & Palmer LLP
Suite 1400 350 7th Avenue Southwest
Calgary, AB, T2P 3N9, Canada
Tel.: (403) 263-3050
Transfer Agent:
Computershare Trust Company of Canada
Ste 600 530 8th Ave SW
Calgary, AB, Canada T2P 3S8
Tel.: (800) 558-0046

CELLARMASTER WINES PTY LIMITED

Level 2 26 Waterloo St cnr of Waterloo & Cooper Streets
Surry Hills, NSW, 2010, Australia
Tel.: (61) 293338008
Fax: (61) 293338099
E-Mail: orders@cellarmasters.com.au
Web Site: www.cellarmasters.com.au
Sales Range: $1-4.9 Billion
Emp.: 900
Business Description:
Wine Retailer
S.I.C.: 2084
N.A.I.C.S.: 312130
Personnel:
Kate Langford *(Dir-Cellar)*

CELLAVISION AB

Ideon Science Park
SE-223 70 Lund, Sweden
Tel.: (46) 46 286 44 00
Fax: (46) 46 286 44 70
E-Mail: info@cellavision.com
Web Site: www.cellavision.com
Year Founded: 1994
CEVI—(OMX)
Sls.: $26,240,458
Assets: $27,640,469
Liabilities: $8,304,091
Net Worth: $19,336,378
Earnings: $998,615
Emp.: 65
Fiscal Year-end: 12/31/12
Business Description:
Digital Image Analysis, Artificial Intelligence & Automated Microscopy Products Mfr
S.I.C.: 3841
N.A.I.C.S.: 339112
Personnel:
Christer Fahraeus *(Founder)*
Lars Gatenbeck *(Chm)*
Yvonne Martensson *(CEO)*
Magnus Blixt *(CFO)*
Stefan Bengtsson *(COO)*
Peter Wilson *(Pres-CellaVision Canada Inc)*
Board of Directors:
Lars Gatenbeck
Anna Malm Bernsten
Christer Fahraeus
Sven-Ake Henningsson
Lars Henriksson
Roger Johanson
Torbjorn Kronander
U.S. Subsidiary:

CellaVision Inc. (1)
4107 Burns Rd
Palm Beach Gardens, FL 33410
Tel.: (561) 741-3003
Fax: (561) 741-3823
Toll Free: (800) 390-1374
E-Mail: us.info@cellavision.com
Web Site: www.cellavision.com
Electronic Diagnostic Instruments Distr
S.I.C.: 5047
N.A.I.C.S.: 423450

Non-U.S. Subsidiaries:

CellaVision Canada Inc. (1)
2 Bloor St W Ste 2120
Toronto, ON, M4W 3E2, Canada
Tel.: (561) 741-3003
Fax: (919) 960-8386
E-Mail: ca.info@cellavision.com
Web Site: www.cellavision.com
Electronic Diagnostic Instruments Distr
S.I.C.: 5047
N.A.I.C.S.: 423450

CellaVision Japan K.K. (1)
20 F Yokohama LandMark Tower 2-2-1 Minatomirai
Nishi-ku, Yokohama, Kanagawa, 220-8120, Japan
Tel.: (81) 456707110
Fax: (81) 456707001
E-Mail: jp.info@cellavision.com
Web Site: www.cellavision.com
Emp.: 3
Electronic Diagnostic Instruments Distr
S.I.C.: 5047
N.A.I.C.S.: 423450
Naofumi Ohizumi *(Mgr-Customer Support)*

CELLCAST PLC

150 Great Portland Street
London, W1W 6QD, United Kingdom
Tel.: (44) 203 376 9420
Fax: (44) 203 376 9421
E-Mail: web@cellcast.tv
Web Site: www.cellcast.tv
CLTV—(AIM)
Rev.: $30,263,836
Assets: $7,381,884
Liabilities: $6,221,506
Net Worth: $1,160,379
Earnings: ($87,295)
Emp.: 22
Fiscal Year-end: 12/31/12
Business Description:
Participatory Television Programming & Interactive Telephony Technology
S.I.C.: 4899
N.A.I.C.S.: 517919
Personnel:
Andrew Wilson *(CEO)*
Emmanuelle Guicharnaud *(CFO, Sec & Dir-Fin)*
Bertrand Folliet *(COO)*
Board of Directors:
Michael Neville
Bertrand Folliet
Emmanuelle Guicharnaud
Andrew Wilson
Legal Counsel:
Memery Crystal
44 Southampton Buildings
WC2A 1AP London, United Kingdom
Non-U.S. Subsidiary:

Cellcast Middle East (1)
2nd Fl New Starco Bldg Omar Daouk St
Minet El Hosn, Beirut, 1107-2210, Lebanon
Tel.: (961) 1377520
Fax: (961) 1377523
E-Mail: contact@cellcastme.com
Web Site: www.cellcastme.com
Mobile Marketing Services
S.I.C.: 7389
N.A.I.C.S.: 561422
Pascal Dufour *(VP)*

CELLCURA ASA

Unionsgata 18
3732 Skien, Norway
Tel.: (47) 35 12 26 10
E-Mail: post@cellcura.com
Web Site: www.cellcura.com
CELL—(OSL)
Rev.: $516,726
Assets: $5,517,299
Liabilities: $6,709,299
Net Worth: ($1,192,000)
Earnings: ($5,711,320)
Emp.: 4
Fiscal Year-end: 12/31/12
Business Description:
Assisted Reproductive Technology & Stem Cell Research Equipment Developer
S.I.C.: 3841
N.A.I.C.S.: 339112
Personnel:
Lesley Hutchins *(Co-Founder & CEO-CellCura Inc)*
Dag Dvergsten *(Chm)*
Tore Kvam *(CEO)*
Bent Nordbo *(COO)*
Board of Directors:
Dag Dvergsten
Cornelia Horn
Christina Hugosson
Kristine Landmark
Lars Ronn
U.S. Subsidiary:

CellCura, Inc. (1)
505 S Rosa Rd Ste 115
Madison, WI 53719
Tel.: (608) 441-8075
Fax: (608) 441-8076
E-Mail: info@cellcura.com
Web Site: www.cellcura.com
Emp.: 5
Medical Diagnostic Equipments Distr
S.I.C.: 5047
N.A.I.C.S.: 423450
Lesley Hutchins *(Mgr)*

Non-U.S. Subsidiary:

IHMedical A/S (1)
Symbion Science Park Fruebjergvej 3
2100 Copenhagen, Denmark
Tel.: (45) 70206750
Fax: (45) 70206751
E-Mail: info@ihmedical.com
Web Site: www.ihmedical.com
Emp.: 15
Medical Diagnostic Equipments Distr
S.I.C.: 5047
N.A.I.C.S.: 423450
Morten Raaschou-Jensen *(Mng Dir)*

CELLECTIS S.A.

8 rue de la Croix Jarry
75013 Paris, France
Tel.: (33) 181691600
Fax: (33) 141839903
E-Mail: mail@cellectis.com
Web Site: www.cellectis.com
ALCLS—(EUR)
Rev.: $28,312,647
Assets: $117,165,252
Liabilities: $34,017,716
Net Worth: $83,147,536
Earnings: ($29,979,206)
Emp.: 214
Fiscal Year-end: 12/31/12
Business Description:
Genome Research & Development Services
S.I.C.: 8731
N.A.I.C.S.: 541712
Personnel:
Andre Choulika *(Chm & CEO)*
Xavier Champavere *(Deputy CEO-Cellectis Bioresearch)*
Jean-Charles Epinat *(Deputy CEO-Cellectis Bioresearch)*
Pierre Schwich *(CFO)*
Delphine Jay *(Chief Admin Officer & Chief HR Officer)*
Philippe Duchateau *(Chief Scientific Officer)*
Luc Mathis *(CEO-Cellectis Plant Sciences)*
Philippe Valachs *(Sec)*
David J. D. Sourdive *(Exec VP-Corp Dev)*
Sylvie Delassus *(Sr VP-Corp Comm)*
Board of Directors:
Andre Choulika
Laurent Arthaud
Pierre Bastid
Alain Godard
Roger J. Hajjar
Annick Schwebig
David J. D. Sourdive
Subsidiaries:

Cellectis Bioresearch (1)
102 Avenue Gaston Roussel
93230 Romainville, France
Tel.: (33) 1 41 83 99 00
Fax: (33) 1 41 83 99 03
Web Site: www.cellectis-bioresearch.com
Cell Biology & Analytical Services
S.I.C.: 8731
N.A.I.C.S.: 541711
Jean-Pierre Cabaniols *(COO)*
Christophe Delenda *(Chief Scientific Officer)*

Cellectis therapeutics (1)
102 Avenue Gaston Roussel
93230 Romainville, France
Tel.: (33) 1 41 83 99 00
Fax: (33) 1 41 83 99 03
Health Care Services
S.I.C.: 8099
N.A.I.C.S.: 621999

Ectycell SASU (1)
4 Rue Pierre Fontaine
91058 Evry, France

Tel.: (33) 1 41 83 99 00
Fax: (33) 1 41 83 99 03
Pluripotent Stem Cells Mfr
S.I.C.: 2834
N.A.I.C.S.: 325412

CELLMARK AB

Lilla Bommen 3C
PO Box 11927
SE-404 39 Gothenburg, Sweden
Tel.: (46) 31100300
Fax: (46) 31136421
Web Site: www.cellmark.com
Year Founded: 1984
Sales Range: $1-4.9 Billion
Emp.: 700
Business Description:
Pulp, Paper, Chemicals & Metals Supply Chain Services
S.I.C.: 4731
N.A.I.C.S.: 541614
Personnel:
Adrian Montague *(Chm)*
Hans Kling *(Pres, CEO & Sr VP-Metals Div)*
Ulf Eggefors *(CFO)*
Kerstin Ajax *(Chief Acctg Officer)*
Fredrik Anderson *(Sr VP-Pulp Div)*
Paul Busnardo *(Sr VP-Packaging Div)*
Hugo Galletta *(Sr VP-Chemicals Div)*
Joe Hoffman *(Sr VP-Paper Div)*
Vic Rice *(Sr VP-Recycling Div)*
Board of Directors:
Adrian Montague
Jay Hambro
Hans Kling
Philippe Lietard
Vic Rice
U.S. Subsidiaries:

Cellmark Inc. (1)
22 Pelican Way
San Rafael, CA 94901
Tel.: (415) 927-1700
Fax: (415) 381-4358
Web Site: www.cellmark.com
Emp.: 60
Paper & Wood Pulp Whslr
S.I.C.: 5111
N.A.I.C.S.: 424110
Victor E. Rice *(Sr VP)*

Cellmark Inc. (1)
80 Washington St
Norwalk, CT 06854
Tel.: (203) 838-2600
Web Site: www.cellmark.com
Emp.: 15
Paper Product Whslr
S.I.C.: 5093
N.A.I.C.S.: 423930
James Derrico *(VP)*

CellMark USA, LLC (1)
333 Ludlow St 8th Fl
Stamford, CT 06902
Tel.: (203) 541-9000
Fax: (203) 541-9395
E-Mail:
Emp.: 40
Chemical, Mineral, Raw Material & Industrial Product Wholesale Trade Agency
S.I.C.: 7389
N.A.I.C.S.: 425120
Hugo Galletta *(Pres)*
Tom Sliker *(Exec VP)*

Non-U.S. Subsidiaries:

CellMark Papier SAS (1)
1 Avenue Sonia Delaunay
94506 Champigny-sur-Marne, France
Tel.: (33) 148810058
Fax: (33) 1 4881 1297
Emp.: 15
Paper Product Whslr
S.I.C.: 5111
N.A.I.C.S.: 424110
Raoul Gil Turu *(Pres)*

Cellmark AB (Shanghai) (1)
Room 2007 Rui Jin Building
205 South Mao Ming Road, Shanghai, 200020, China
Tel.: (86) 2164730266
Fax: (86) 22164730030
Web Site: www.cellmark.com
Emp.: 14
Books, Periodicals & Newspapers
S.I.C.: 5192
N.A.I.C.S.: 424920
Henry Peng *(Mgr-Pulp)*

CellMark Belgium NV (1)
Verlorenbroodstraat 63b
B 9820 Merelbeke, Belgium
Tel.: (32) 9 218 7180
Fax: (32) 9 233 0831
E-Mail:
Emp.: 10
Chemical, Mineral, Raw Material & Industrial Product Wholesale Trade Agency
S.I.C.: 7389
N.A.I.C.S.: 425120
Luc Vereecken *(Mng Dir)*

CellMark Chemicals Ltd. (1)
Regal Ct 42-44 High St
Slough, Berks, SL1 1EL, United Kingdom
Tel.: (44) 1753 245 530
Fax: (44) 1753 245531
E-Mail:
Emp.: 75
Chemical, Mineral, Raw Material & Industrial Product Wholesale Trade Agency
S.I.C.: 7389
N.A.I.C.S.: 425120

CellMark Chemicals Singapore Pte Ltd. (1)
175A Bencoolen Street 05-11 Burlington Square
Singapore, 189650, Singapore
Tel.: (65) 6603 1288
Fax: (65) 6238 8078
E-Mail: chemicals-asia@cellmark.com
Emp.: 11
Chemical, Mineral, Raw Material & Industrial Product Wholesale Trade Agency
S.I.C.: 7389
N.A.I.C.S.: 425120

CellMark Espana SA (1)
C/Pere i Pons n 9-11 floor 12 P 3
ES-080034 Barcelona, Spain ES
Tel.: (34) 93 494 9900
Fax: (34) 93 419 9280
E-Mail:
Emp.: 20
Chemical, Mineral, Raw Material & Industrial Product Wholesale Trade Agency
S.I.C.: 7389
N.A.I.C.S.: 425120

CellMark Japan (1)
7F Shinjuku i-Land Tower 6-5-1 Nishi-Shinjuku
Shinjuku-ku, Shinjuku, 163-1307, Japan (100%)
Tel.: (81) 333496600
Fax: (81) 333444392
E-Mail:
Emp.: 20
Chemical, Mineral, Raw Material & Industrial Product Wholesale Trade Agency
S.I.C.: 7389
N.A.I.C.S.: 425120
Masaru Sakamoto *(Pres)*

Singapore Pulp (Pte) Ltd. (1)
271 Bukit timach Rd 03/13 Balmoral Plz
259008 Singapore, Singapore
Tel.: (65) 67378830
Fax: (65) 67378680
Sales Range: $125-149.9 Million
Emp.: 20
Acacia Pulp Marketer
S.I.C.: 2611
N.A.I.C.S.: 322110

CELLMID LIMITED

Suite 1802 Level 18 15 Castlereagh Street
Sydney, NSW, 2000, Australia
Tel.: (61) 2 9221 6830
Fax: (61) 2 9221 8535
E-Mail: info@cellmid.com.au
Web Site: www.cellmid.com.au
CDY—(ASX)
Rev.: $793,338
Assets: $6,246,055
Liabilities: $717,550
Net Worth: $5,528,504
Earnings: ($1,606,196)
Fiscal Year-end: 06/30/13
Business Description:
Biotechnology Research Services
S.I.C.: 8731
N.A.I.C.S.: 541711
Personnel:
Maria Halasz *(CEO & Mng Dir)*
Jillian McGregor *(Gen Counsel & Co-Sec)*
Nicholas Falzon *(Co-Sec & Controller-Fin)*
Board of Directors:
David King
Maria Halasz
Graeme Roy Kaufman
Martin Rogers
Legal Counsel:
Piper Alderman
Governor Macquarie Tower 1 Farrer Place
Sydney, Australia

CELLNET GROUP LIMITED

59-61 Qantas Drive
Eagle Farm, QLD, 4009, Australia
Tel.: (61) 738535555
Fax: (61) 738535600
E-Mail: info@cellnet.com.au
Web Site: www.cellnet.com.au
Year Founded: 1992
CLT—(ASX)
Rev.: $79,690,429
Assets: $28,064,795
Liabilities: $12,441,632
Net Worth: $15,623,163
Earnings: $1,002,500
Emp.: 89
Fiscal Year-end: 06/30/13
Business Description:
Telecommunications, Audio Visual & Information Technology Products Distr
S.I.C.: 5064
N.A.I.C.S.: 423620
Personnel:
Chris Barnes *(Sec & Gen Mgr)*
Board of Directors:
Alexander Damien Harry Beard
Mel Brookman
Elliot Kaplan
Legal Counsel:
Thomsons Lawyers
Level 16 Waterfront Place 1 Eagle Street
Brisbane, Australia
Subsidiary:

VME Systems Pty Ltd (1)
59-61 Qantas Dr
4009 Eagle Farm, Australia
Tel.: (61) 738535555
Fax: (61) 738535600
E-Mail: reception@cellnet.com.au
Mobile Accessories Whslr
S.I.C.: 5065
N.A.I.C.S.: 423690
Stuart Smith *(CEO)*

Non-U.S. Subsidiary:

Cellnet Limited (1)
10A Orbit Dr
Albany, 0632 Auckland, New Zealand
Tel.: (64) 94154747
Fax: (64) 99293021
E-Mail: sales@cellnet.co.nz
Web Site: www.webcell.co.nz
Emp.: 25
Telecommunications, Audio Visual & Information Technology Products Distr
S.I.C.: 5064
N.A.I.C.S.: 423620
Dave Clark *(Country Mgr)*

CELLO ELECTRONICS (UK) LTD.

Tumbledown
Wensley, Leyburn, North Yorkshire, DL8 4HL, United Kingdom
Tel.: (44) 7931263565
Web Site: www.celloelectronics.com
Year Founded: 1996
Sales Range: $50-74.9 Million
Business Description:
Television Mfr
S.I.C.: 3663
N.A.I.C.S.: 334220
Personnel:
Brian Palmer *(CEO)*

CELLO GROUP PLC

11-13 Charterhouse Bldg
London, EC1M 7AP, United Kingdom
Tel.: (44) 20 7812 8460
Fax: (44) 20 7253 5376
E-Mail: info@cellogroup.co.uk
Web Site: www.cellogroup.co.uk
Year Founded: 2004
CLL—(LSE)
Rev.: $213,426,830
Assets: $173,173,886
Liabilities: $69,578,780
Net Worth: $103,595,107
Earnings: ($568,544)
Emp.: 762
Fiscal Year-end: 12/31/12
Business Description:
Advertising Agency
S.I.C.: 7311
N.A.I.C.S.: 541810
Personnel:
Mark Scott *(CEO)*
Tim Blandford *(Mng Partner)*
Nicola Cowland *(Mng Partner)*
Doug Edmonds *(Mng Partner)*
Peter Frings *(Mng Partner)*
Richard Marsham *(Mng Partner)*
Andrew Needham *(Mng Partner)*
Vincent Nolan *(Mng Partner)*
Julia Ralston *(Mng Partner)*
John Rowley *(Mng Partner)*
Jane Shirley *(Mng Partner)*
Owen Williams *(Mng Partner)*
Avanti Ananthram *(Partner)*
Bryan Atkin *(Partner)*
Jane Ayton *(Partner)*
Jon Bircher *(Partner)*
Ed Brooke *(Partner)*
Andy Brown *(Partner)*
Pete Burns *(Partner)*
Jessica Cunningham *(Partner)*
Alison Drake *(Partner)*
Paul Handley *(Partner)*
Barney Hosey *(Partner)*
Minh Huynh *(Partner)*
Gillian James *(Partner)*
Giles Lury *(Partner)*
Job Muscroft *(Partner)*
Alex Nketiah *(Partner)*
Richard Oldham *(Partner)*
Ian Robertson *(Partner)*
Juliet Simpson *(Partner)*
Chris Stead *(Partner)*
Paul Stuart-Kregor *(Partner)*
Phil Stubington *(Partner)*
Karen Trickett *(Partner)*
Roger Viola *(Partner)*
Alex Waters *(Partner)*
Larry Wright *(Partner)*
Mark Bentley *(Sec & Dir-Fin)*
Board of Directors:
Allan Rich
Mark Bentley
Will David
Paul Hamilton
Stephen Highley
Mark Scott
Legal Counsel:
Marriott Harrison
Staple Court 11 Staple Inn Buildings
London, United Kingdom

Cello Group plc—(Continued)

U.S. Subsidiary:

MedErgy HealthGroup Inc. (1)
790 Township Line Rd Ste 200
Yardley, PA 19067-4261
Tel.: (215) 504-5082
Fax: (215) 504-2916
Web Site: www.medergygroup.com
Emp.: 30
Advertising Agency
S.I.C.: 7389
N.A.I.C.S.: 519190
Julia Ralston *(Pres & CEO)*
Roger Viola *(Sr VP-Strategic Client Partnerships)*

CELLO PRODUCTS INC.

210 Avenue Road
PO Box 37
Cambridge, ON, N1R 5S9, Canada
Tel.: (519) 621-9150
Fax: (519) 621-4108
Toll Free: (800) 265-7882
E-Mail: cello@cello.on.ca
Web Site: www.cello.on.ca
Year Founded: 1946
Rev.: $19,775,000
Emp.: 70
Business Description:
Copper Solder & Cast Brass Fittings Mfr
S.I.C.: 3432
N.A.I.C.S.: 332913
Personnel:
Harry Lee *(Founder)*

CELLSCREEN DIRECT LIMITED

Suite 39-40 112 McEvoy Street
Alexandria, NSW, 2015, Australia
Tel.: (61) 2 9009 6606
Web Site: www.cellscreendirect.com
Sales Range: Less than $1 Million
Business Description:
Molecular Diagnostic Testing & Sample Processing Services
S.I.C.: 2835
N.A.I.C.S.: 325413
Personnel:
Alison Coutts *(Chm)*
Peter Hughes *(Mng Dir)*
Nick Geddes *(Sec)*
Board of Directors:
Alison Coutts
Adrian Cachia
Warwick Doughty
Peter Hughes
Russell Tate
Michael Wooldridge

CELLSEED INC.

R-Bldg Shinjuku 1F 33-8 Wakamatsu-cho
Shinjuku-ku, Tokyo, 162-0056, Japan
Tel.: (81) 352866231
Fax: (81) 352866233
E-Mail: staff@cellseed.com
Web Site: www.cellseed.com
Year Founded: 2001
7776—(JAS)
Sales Range: $1-9.9 Million
Emp.: 50
Business Description:
Novel Surface & Cell Culture Products Researcher, Developer & Mfr
S.I.C.: 2835
N.A.I.C.S.: 325413
Personnel:
Yukio Hasegawa *(Pres & CEO)*
Board of Directors:
Yasushi Hosono
Hiromichi Kimura
Teruo Okano
Tadakazu Shimizu

CELLSTAR (ASIA) CORPORATION LIMITED

509 510 5 Fl Block B Sing Tao Bldg
1 Wang Kwong Rd, Kowloon, China (Hong Kong)
Tel.: (852) 27570998
Fax: (852) 27595255
E-Mail: info_hk@cellstar.com
Business Description:
Wireless Communications Products & Solutions
S.I.C.: 3663
N.A.I.C.S.: 334220

CELLSTAR CHILE, S.A.

Adva Pdte. Eduardo Frie
Montalva 4251
Communa de Conchali, Santiago, Chile
Tel.: (56) 2 550 1700
Fax: (56) 2 550 1716
E-Mail: info_cl@cellstar.com
Web Site: cl.cellstar.com
Sales Range: $1-9.9 Million
Emp.: 147
Business Description:
Wireless Communications Products & Solutions
S.I.C.: 3663
N.A.I.C.S.: 334220

CELLTRION, INC.

13-6 Songdo-dong
Yeonsu-gu, Incheon, Korea (South) 406-840
Tel.: (82) 32 850 5000
Fax: (82) 32 850 5057
E-Mail: contact@celltrion.com
Web Site: www.celltrion.com
Year Founded: 2002
068270—(KRS)
Rev.: $325,682,280
Assets: $1,611,610,020
Liabilities: $634,971,450
Net Worth: $976,638,570
Earnings: $162,220,830
Emp.: 809
Fiscal Year-end: 12/31/12
Business Description:
Biopharmaceutical Product Mfr
S.I.C.: 2836
N.A.I.C.S.: 325414
Personnel:
Seung Seo Hong *(Pres)*

CELLTRION PHARM. INC.

17 floor LG dacom bldg 706-1
Yeoksam 2 dong
Kangnamgu, Seoul, Korea (South)
Tel.: (82) 2 2216 3611
Fax: (82) 2 2216 0355
Web Site: www.celltrionph.com
Year Founded: 1976
068760—(KRS)
Business Description:
Pharmaceutical Preparation Mfr
S.I.C.: 2834
N.A.I.C.S.: 325412
Personnel:
Jung Jin Seo *(Chm & CEO)*

CELLULAC LIMITED

Second Floor Unit 14 Galway Technology Park
Parkmore, Galway, Ireland
Tel.: (353) 91 766 582
Fax: (353) 91 763 690
E-Mail: info@cellulac.co.uk
Web Site: www.cellulac.co.uk
Year Founded: 2009
Business Description:
Industrial Biochemical Equipment Designer & Mfr
S.I.C.: 3559
N.A.I.C.S.: 333249
Personnel:
Patrick J. Walsh *(Founder & Chief Scientific Officer)*
Gerard Brandon *(CEO)*
Camillus Glover *(CFO)*
Board of Directors:
Howard Prince-Wright
Patrick J. Walsh

CELLULAR ONE, INC.

9280 Boul De L Acadie
Montreal, QC, H4N 3C5, Canada
Tel.: (514) 385-0770
Fax: (514) 385-4526
Rev.: $13,639,375
Emp.: 90
Business Description:
Mobile Telephone Equipment Whslr
S.I.C.: 4812
N.A.I.C.S.: 517210
Personnel:
Peter Laschuck *(Pres)*

CELOXICA HOLDINGS PLC

66 Milton Park
Abingdon, oxon, OX14 4RX, United Kingdom
Tel.: (44) 1235 863656
Fax: (44) 1235 863648
E-Mail: info@celoxica.com
Web Site: www.celoxica.com
Emp.: 37
Business Description:
Accelerated Computing & Electronic System-Level (ESL) Designer & Services
S.I.C.: 7373
N.A.I.C.S.: 541512
Personnel:
Jean-Marc Bouhelier *(Chm)*
John Oddie *(CEO)*
Antoine Rescourio *(COO & Sec)*
Gilles Herfeld *(CTO)*
Board of Directors:
Jean-Marc Bouhelier
John Oddie

Subsidiary:

Celoxica Ltd (1)
34 Porchester Road
London, W2 6ES, United Kingdom (100%)
Tel.: (44) 2073133180
E-Mail: support@celoxica.com
Web Site: www.celoxica.com
Emp.: 35
Electronic System Level Design Technology
S.I.C.: 7372
N.A.I.C.S.: 511210
Ken Tregidgo *(Dir-Bus Dev)*

U.S. Subsidiary:

Celoxica Inc. (1)
Ste 185 Lakeview Plaza 4516 Seton Ctr Pkwy
Austin, TX 78759 (100%)
Tel.: (512) 795-8170
Fax: (512) 795-8167
Toll Free: (800) 570-7004
E-Mail: support@celoxica.com
Electronic System Level Design Technology
S.I.C.: 7372
N.A.I.C.S.: 511210

CELSA GROUP

Poligono Industrial San Vicente S N
08755 Castellbisbal, Barcelona, Spain
Tel.: (34) 937730400
Fax: (34) 937720276
E-Mail: info@gcelsa.com
Web Site: www.gcelsa.com
Sales Range: $5-14.9 Billion
Emp.: 7,525
Business Description:
Steel Production
S.I.C.: 3312
N.A.I.C.S.: 331110
Personnel:
Joan Puiggali *(Mgr)*

Non-U.S. Subsidiary:

Celsa Steel (UK) Ltd. (1)
Building 58 Castle Works
East Moors Road, Cardiff, CF24 5NN, United Kingdom
Tel.: (44) 2920351800
Fax: (44) 2920351801
Web Site: www.celsauk.com
Emp.: 100
Steel Mfr
S.I.C.: 3312
N.A.I.C.S.: 331110
Luis Sanz *(Mng Dir)*

Subsidiaries:

ROM Group Limited (2)
Eastern Avenue Trent Valley
Lichfield, WS13 6RN, United Kingdom UK
Tel.: (44) 1543 414 111
Fax: (44) 1543 421 657
E-Mail: info@rom.co.uk
Web Site: www.rom.co.uk
Sales Range: $50-74.9 Million
Emp.: 300
Reinforcements, Wire & Fencing Mfr
S.I.C.: 3496
N.A.I.C.S.: 332618

Subsidiary:

RFA-Tech Ltd. (3)
South Yorkshire Industrial Estate Whaley Road
Barugh, Barnsley, S75 1HT, United Kingdom UK
Tel.: (44) 870 011 2881
Fax: (44) 870 011 2882
E-Mail: sales@rfa-tech.co.uk
Web Site: www.rfa-tech.co.uk
Construction Products Mfr
S.I.C.: 3496
N.A.I.C.S.: 332618
Shane Hobson *(Sls Mgr)*

Express Reinforcements Ltd. (2)
Eaglesbush Works
Milland Road, Neath, SA11 1NJ, United Kingdom
Tel.: (44) 1639645555
Fax: (44) 16396455588
E-Mail: commercial@expressreinforcements.co.uk
Web Site: www.expressreinforcements.co.uk
Emp.: 80
Steel Reinforcing Product Mfr
S.I.C.: 3312
N.A.I.C.S.: 331110
Andrew Lodge *(Mng Dir)*

CELSIUS COAL LIMITED

Level 1 12 Kings Park Road
West Perth, WA, 6005, Australia
Mailing Address:
PO Box 44
West Perth, WA, 6872, Australia
Tel.: (61) 8 9226 4500
Fax: (61) 8 9226 4300
E-Mail: info@celsiuscoal.com.au
Web Site: www.celsiuscoal.com.au
FX8—(ASX DEU)
Rev.: $135,112
Assets: $21,888,615
Liabilities: $823,810
Net Worth: $21,064,805
Earnings: ($7,184,488)
Emp.: 4
Fiscal Year-end: 06/30/13
Business Description:
Thermal Coal Mining Services
S.I.C.: 1221
N.A.I.C.S.: 212111
Personnel:
Alexander Alan Molyneux *(Chm)*

Berenaliev Adylbek Jumabekovich *(Dir Gen-Pandj Sher ANK Ltd)*
Baisakov Narynbek Sadybakasovich *(Deputy Dir Gen-NUR Telecom LLC)*
Matthew O'Kane *(CFO)*
Ranko Matic *(Sec)*
Board of Directors:
Alexander Alan Molyneux
Ranko Matic
Alistair Muir
William Oliver
Legal Counsel:
Steinepreis Paganin
Level 4 The Read Buildings 16 Milligan Street
6000 Perth, WA, Australia

CELSUS THERAPEUTICS PLC

(Formerly Morria Biopharmaceuticals PLC)
53 Davies Street
London, W1K 5JH, United Kingdom
Tel.: (44) 203 322 1321
Fax: (44) 207 152 6342
E-Mail: info@celsustx.com
Web Site: www.celsustx.com
Year Founded: 2004
CLTX—(NASDAQ)
Assets: $1,120,000
Liabilities: $4,480,000
Net Worth: ($3,360,000)
Earnings: ($4,268,000)
Emp.: 4
Fiscal Year-end: 12/31/12
Business Description:
Biopharmaceutical Mfr
S.I.C.: 2834
N.A.I.C.S.: 325412
Personnel:
Mark S. Cohen *(Chm)*
Yuval Cohen *(Pres)*
Gur Roshwalb *(CEO)*
Dov Elefant *(CFO)*
Pablo Jimenez *(Chief Medical Officer)*
Saul Yedgar *(Chief Scientific Officer)*
Board of Directors:
Mark S. Cohen
Yuval Cohen
Amos Eiran
Johnson Yiu-Nam Lau
Gilead Raday
David Sidransky
Saul Yedgar

CELTIC MINERALS LTD.

311 Beckley Ave
Victoria, BC, V8V 1J6, Canada
Tel.: (250) 590-7064
Fax: (888) 678-7396
E-Mail: info@celticminerals.com
Web Site: www.celticminerals.com
CWE—(CNSX)
Assets: $191,560
Liabilities: $1,013,243
Net Worth: ($821,684)
Earnings: ($409,472)
Fiscal Year-end: 12/31/12
Business Description:
Gold & Base Metal Mining Services
S.I.C.: 1041
N.A.I.C.S.: 212221
Personnel:
David Grand *(Pres & CEO)*
Ken Johnston *(CFO)*
Board of Directors:
Wayne Ewert
David Grand
Ken Johnston
Legal Counsel:
Borden Ladner & Gervais LLP
Calgary, AB, Canada
Transfer Agent:
Computershare Trust Company
Calgary, AB, Canada

CELTIC PHARMA LIMITED

Cumberland House
1 Victoria Street 4th Floor, Hamilton, HM 11, Bermuda
Tel.: (441) 299-7440
Fax: (441) 299-7441
E-Mail: info@celticpharma.com
Web Site: www.celticpharma.com
Business Description:
Pharmaceutical Development Services
S.I.C.: 2834
N.A.I.C.S.: 325412
Personnel:
Stephen B. Parker *(Partner)*
Non-U.S. Subsidiary:

Celtic Pharma Development UK plc (1)
Liverton House
13 Bedford Square, London, WC1B 3RA, United Kingdom
Tel.: (44) 2072915400
Web Site: www.celticpharma.com
Emp.: 20
Financial Management Services
S.I.C.: 6211
N.A.I.C.S.: 523999
John Mayo *(Mng Dir)*

CELTIC PROPERTY DEVELOPMENTS S.A.

ul Cybernetyki 7b
02 677 Warsaw, Poland
Tel.: (48) 22 321 05 00
Fax: (48) 22 321 05 01
E-Mail: info@celtic.pl
Web Site: www.celtic.pl
CPD—(WAR)
Rev.: $5,304,951
Assets: $165,494,608
Liabilities: $43,836,880
Net Worth: $121,657,728
Earnings: ($51,642,718)
Emp.: 40
Fiscal Year-end: 12/31/12
Business Description:
Property Investor & Developer
S.I.C.: 1531
N.A.I.C.S.: 236117
Personnel:
Marzena Bielecka *(Chm-Supervisory Bd)*
Elzbieta Wiczkowska *(Chm-Mgmt Bd)*
Wieslaw Oles *(Vice Chm-Supervisory Bd)*
Iwona Makarewicz *(Member-Mgmt Bd)*
Piotr Turchonski *(Member-Mgmt Bd)*
Supervisory Board of Directors:
Marzena Bielecka
Miroslaw Gronicki
Colin Kingsnorth
Wieslaw Oles
Wieslaw Rozlucki
Subsidiaries:

Celtic Asset Management Sp. z o.o. (1)
Rondo ONZ 1
00-124 Warsaw, Poland
Tel.: (48) 225448100
Asset Management Services
S.I.C.: 6282
N.A.I.C.S.: 523920

Challange Eighteen Sp. z o.o. (1)
Rondo ONZ 1
00-124 Warsaw, Poland
Tel.: (48) 22 544 81 00
Fax: (48) 22 544 8101
Investment Management Services
S.I.C.: 6211
N.A.I.C.S.: 523999

Elara Investments Sp. z o.o. (1)
Al Jerozolimskie 56 c
00-803 Warsaw, Poland
Tel.: (48) 22 379 94 40
Real Estate Development Services
S.I.C.: 6531
N.A.I.C.S.: 531390

Gaston Investments Sp. z o.o. (1)
Rondo ONZ 1 00-124
Warsaw, Poland
Tel.: (48) 22 544 81 00
Fax: (48) 22 379 94 40
Investment Management Services
S.I.C.: 6211
N.A.I.C.S.: 523999

Non-U.S. Subsidiary:

Celtic Italy SRL (1)
Piazza Cavour 2
20121 Milan, Italy
Tel.: (39) 02 76 20 17
Fax: (39) 02 76 02 06 86
E-Mail: info@celticitaly.it
Web Site: www.celticitaly.it
Property Management Services
S.I.C.: 6531
N.A.I.C.S.: 531311

CELTIC PLC

Celtic Park
Glasgow, G40 3RE, United Kingdom
Tel.: (44) 8712261888
Fax: (44) 141 551 8106
E-Mail: superstore@celticfc.net
Web Site: www.celticfc.net
CCP—(LSE)
Rev.: $119,735,451
Assets: $129,928,188
Liabilities: $62,718,344
Net Worth: $67,209,845
Earnings: $15,380,705
Emp.: 455
Fiscal Year-end: 06/30/13
Business Description:
Football & Soccer Team Operator
S.I.C.: 7941
N.A.I.C.S.: 711211
Personnel:
Peter T. Lawwell *(CEO)*
Michael Nicholson *(Sec)*
Board of Directors:
Ian P. Bankier
Thomas E. Allison
Dermot F. Desmond
Brian Duffy
Peter T. Lawwell
Ian Livingston
Eric J. Riley
Brian D. H. Wilson
Legal Counsel:
Pinsent Masons LLP
141 Bothwell Street
Glasgow, G2 7EQ, United Kingdom
Subsidiary:

Celtic F.C. (1)
Celtic Pk
Glasgow, G40 3RE, United Kingdom
Tel.: (44) 8712261888
Fax: (44) 1415518106
Web Site: www.celticfc.net
Emp.: 100
Football Club & Support Services
S.I.C.: 7941
N.A.I.C.S.: 711211
Peter Lawwell *(CEO)*

CELULOSE IRANI S.A.

Rua General Joao Manoel 157
90010 030 Porto Alegre, Brazil
Tel.: (55) 4935275100
Fax: (55) 4935275185
Web Site: www.irani.com.br
RANI3—(BRAZ)
Sales Range: $250-299.9 Million
Emp.: 1,760
Business Description:
Cellulose Paper, Corrugated Cardboard Sheets, Resins & Furniture Mfr
S.I.C.: 2653
N.A.I.C.S.: 322211
Personnel:
Pericles de Freitas Druck *(Pres & CEO)*
Pericles Pereira Druck *(Mng Dir & Dir-Forest Bus)*
Board of Directors:
Pericles de Freitas Druck
Ernani Medaglia Muniz Tavares
Jorge Juerecy Oliveira da Cunha
Pericles Pereira Druck
Paulo Antonio Schmidt
Paulo Sergio Viana Mallmann
Divisions:

Celulose Irani S.A. - Forest Factory Division (1)
Vila Campina da Alegria
Vargem Bonita, Santa Catarina, Brazil 89600-000
Tel.: (55) 49 3548 9156
Fax: (55) 49 3548 9242
E-Mail: comercialpapel@irani.com.br
Kraft Paper Mfr
S.I.C.: 2621
N.A.I.C.S.: 322121
Denis Baialuna *(Mgr)*

Celulose Irani S.A. - Furniture Commercial and Factory Division (1)
Vila Nova
Rio Negrinho, Santa Catarina, Brazil 89295-000
Tel.: (55) 47 3203 4500
Fax: (55) 47 3203 4512
E-Mail: comercialmoveis@irani.com.br
Kraft Paper Mfr
S.I.C.: 2621
N.A.I.C.S.: 322121

Celulose Irani S.A. - Packaging Commercial Division (1)
Rodovia Engenheiro Erminio de Oliveira Penteado
Caldeira Indaiatuba, Sao Paulo, Brazil
Tel.: (55) 19 2107 7148
Fax: (55) 11 4154 8218
E-Mail: comercialchapas@irani.com.br
Packaging Services
S.I.C.: 7389
N.A.I.C.S.: 561910

Celulose Irani S.A. - Packaging Factory Division (1)
Rodovia Engenheiro Erminio de Oliveira Penteado
Caldeira Indaiatuba, Sao Paulo, 13347-600, Brazil
Tel.: (55) 19 2107 00
Fax: (55) 11 4154 8202
Packaging Services
S.I.C.: 7389
N.A.I.C.S.: 561910

Celulose Irani S.A. - Paper Commercial Division (1)
St Geraldo Flausino Gomes
Sao Paulo, Brazil
Tel.: (55) 1155024100
Fax: (55) 1155024120
E-Mail: comercialpapel@irani.com.br
Emp.: 7
Kraft Paper Mfr
S.I.C.: 2621
N.A.I.C.S.: 322121
Henrique Zugman *(Mgr)*

Celulose Irani S.A. - Paper Factory Division (1)
Campina da Alegria
PO Box 87
Vargem Bonita, Santa Catarina, Brazil 89600-000
Tel.: (55) 49 3548 9000
Fax: (55) 49 3548 9000
E-Mail: comercialpapel@irani.com.br
Kraft Paper Mfr
S.I.C.: 2621
N.A.I.C.S.: 322121
Agostinho Deon *(Mgr)*

Celulose Irani S.A. - Resins Commercial Division (1)
St Geraldo Flausino Gomes
Sao Paulo, Brazil 04575-060
Tel.: (55) 11 5502 4128
Fax: (55) 11 5502 4120

Celulose Irani S.A.—(Continued)

E-Mail: export@irani.com.br
Kraft Paper Mfr
S.I.C.: 2621
N.A.I.C.S.: 322121

Celulose Irani S.A. - Resins Factory Division (1)
Rodovia
Balneario Pinhal, Rio Grande, Brazil
Tel.: (55) 5136820100
Fax: (55) 51 3682 0101
Resins & Paper Mfr
S.I.C.: 2821
N.A.I.C.S.: 325211

Subsidiary:

Habitasul Florestal S.A. (1)
Rua General Joao Manoel 157
Centro, Porto Alegre, 9001 0030, Brazil
Tel.: (55) 5132203535
Fax: (55) 5132203757
E-Mail: henriquezugman@habitasul.com.br
Web Site: www.habitasul.com.br
Emp.: 25
Kraft Paper Mfr
S.I.C.: 2621
N.A.I.C.S.: 322121

CEMACON S.A.

Cladirea Silver Business Center Etaj 1
Cluj-Napoca, Romania
Tel.: (40) 364 711030
Fax: (40) 360 816083
E-Mail: office@cemacon.ro
Web Site: www.cemacon.ro
Year Founded: 1969
CEON—(BUC)
Rev.: $13,993,806
Emp.: 100
Fiscal Year-end: 12/31/12
Business Description:
Ceramic Block Mfr
S.I.C.: 3999
N.A.I.C.S.: 327110
Personnel:
Liviu Ionel Stoleru *(Pres & Gen Mgr)*

CEMATRIX CORPORATION

5440 - 53 Street SE
Calgary, AB, T2C 4B6, Canada
Tel.: (403) 219-0484
Fax: (403) 243-9839
E-Mail: sales@cematrix.com
Web Site: www.cematrix.com
Year Founded: 1998
CVX—(TSXV)
Rev.: $8,498,026
Assets: $5,986,097
Liabilities: $2,084,703
Net Worth: $3,901,393
Earnings: $851,173
Fiscal Year-end: 12/31/12
Business Description:
Concrete Product Mfr & Distr
S.I.C.: 3272
N.A.I.C.S.: 327390
Personnel:
Jeffrey Kendrick *(Pres & CEO)*
Bruce McNaught *(CFO)*
Board of Directors:
Robert L. Benson
Steve Bjornson
Rick Breen
Jeffrey Kendrick
Dan Koyich
Minaz H. Lalani

Subsidiary:

CEMATRIX (Canada) Inc. (1)
5440-53 Street SE
Calgary, AB, T2C 4B6, Canada
Tel.: (403) 219-0484
Fax: (403) 243-9839
E-Mail: sales@cematrix.com
Concrete Products Mfr & Distr
S.I.C.: 3272
N.A.I.C.S.: 327390
Steve Bent *(VP)*

Subsidiary:

CEMATRIX (Calgary) Ltd. (2)
5440 53 St SE
Calgary, AB, T2C 4B6, Canada
Tel.: (403) 219-0484
Fax: (403) 243-9839
Construction Materials Distr
S.I.C.: 5039
N.A.I.C.S.: 423390

U.S. Subsidiary:

CEMATRIX (USA) Inc. (2)
28 Larkspur Ln
Bristol, IL 60512
Tel.: (630) 917-2376
Emp.: 1
Concrete Products Mfr
S.I.C.: 3272
N.A.I.C.S.: 327390
Steve La Vallee *(Gen Mgr)*

CEMBRA MONEY BANK AG

Bandliweg 20
8048 Zurich, Switzerland
Tel.: (41) 44 439 40 20
E-Mail: investor.relations@cembra.ch
Web Site: www.cembra.ch
Year Founded: 2009
CMBN—(SWX)
Emp.: 700
Business Description:
Banking, Sales Financing, Consumer Lending, Credit Card Issuing & Insurance Brokerage Services
S.I.C.: 6029
N.A.I.C.S.: 522110
Personnel:
Felix Weber *(Chm)*
Robert Oudmayer *(CEO)*
Antoine Boublil *(CFO)*
Michael Marek *(COO)*
Roland Luthi-Oetterli *(CIO)*
Emanuel Hofacker *(Chief Compliance Officer)*
Volker Gloe *(Chief Risk Officer)*
Alain Rothlisberger *(Gen Counsel)*
Board of Directors:
Felix Weber
Chris Chambers
Denis Hall
Richard Laxer

CEMBRE S.P.A.

via Serenissima 9
25135 Brescia, Italy
Tel.: (39) 03036921
Fax: (39) 0303365766
E-Mail: info@cembre.com
Web Site: www.cembre.com
Year Founded: 1969
CMB—(ITA)
Rev.: $140,834,959
Assets: $178,660,990
Liabilities: $41,276,265
Net Worth: $137,384,726
Earnings: $15,533,456
Emp.: 606
Fiscal Year-end: 12/31/12
Business Description:
Electrical Connectors & Tools Mfr
S.I.C.: 3643
N.A.I.C.S.: 335931
Personnel:
Giovanni Rosani *(Chm & Mng Dir)*
Anna Maria Onofri *(Vice Chm)*
Giorgio Rota *(Sec)*
Board of Directors:
Giovanni Rosani
Aldo Bottini Bongrani
Giovanni De Vecchi
Fabio Fada
Giancarlo Maccarini
Anna Maria Onofri
Sara Rosani
Renzo Torchiani

Subsidiary:

General Marketing srl (1)
Via Serenissima 9
25135 Brescia, Italy (100%)
Tel.: (39) 03036921
Fax: (39) 0303365766
E-Mail: info@cembre.com
Emp.: 350
Electrical Connectors & Tools
S.I.C.: 7389
N.A.I.C.S.: 561499

U.S. Subsidiary:

CEMBRE Inc. (1)
181 Field Crest Ave
Edison, NJ 08837 (100%)
Tel.: (732) 225-7415
Fax: (732) 225-7414
E-Mail: info@cembre.com
Web Site: www.cembre.com
Emp.: 20
Electrical Connectors & Tools
S.I.C.: 3643
N.A.I.C.S.: 335931
Pierpaolo Desi *(VP)*

Non-U.S. Subsidiaries:

CEMBRE AS (1)
Fossnes Senter
3160 Stokke, Norway (100%)
Tel.: (47) 33361765
Fax: (47) 33361766
E-Mail: cembre@cembre.no
Web Site: www.cembre.com
Emp.: 2
Electrical Connectors & Tools
S.I.C.: 3643
N.A.I.C.S.: 335931

CEMBRE Espana SL (1)
Calle Verano 6 & 8
28850 Torrejon de Ardoz, Madrid, Spain (100%)
Tel.: (34) 914852580
Fax: (34) 914852581
E-Mail: enso@cembre.es
Emp.: 50
Electrical Connectors & Tools
S.I.C.: 3643
N.A.I.C.S.: 335931
Berrocal Lafael *(Gen Mgr)*

CEMBRE GmbH (1)
Taunustrasse 23
80807 Munich, Germany (100%)
Tel.: (49) 893580676
Fax: (49) 8935806777
E-Mail: info@cembre.de
Web Site: www.cembre.de
Emp.: 12
Electrical Connectors & Tools
S.I.C.: 3643
N.A.I.C.S.: 335931
Vitor Tornvald *(Mng Dir)*

CEMBRE Ltd. (1)
Dunton Park Kingsbury Road
Curdworth, Sutton Coldfield, W Midlands, B76 9EB, United Kingdom (100%)
Tel.: (44) 1675470440
Fax: (44) 1675470220
E-Mail: sales@cembre.co.uk
Web Site: www.cembre.co.uk
Emp.: 80
Electrical Connectors & Tools Mfr
S.I.C.: 3643
N.A.I.C.S.: 335931
Benjamin Thomas Davies *(Mng Dir)*

CEMBRE Sarl (1)
Avenue Gerdinand de Lesseps 22
91420 Morangis, France (100%)
Tel.: (33) 160491190
Fax: (33) 160492910
E-Mail: enso@cembre.com
Web Site: www.cembre.com
Emp.: 25
Electrical Connectors & Tools Mfr
S.I.C.: 3643
N.A.I.C.S.: 335931
Philippe Barrier *(Dir-Mktg & Comml)*

CEMEDINE CO., LTD.

Gate City Ohsaki East Tower 1-11-2 Osaki
Shinagawa-ku, Tokyo, 141-8620, Japan
Tel.: (81) 3 6421 7411
Fax: (81) 3 6421 7415
Web Site: www.cemedine.co.jp
Year Founded: 1923
4999—(TKS)
Emp.: 263
Business Description:
Adhesive Mfr
S.I.C.: 2891
N.A.I.C.S.: 325520
Personnel:
Yasuo Kurokawa *(Chm)*

CEMENTIR HOLDING S.P.A.

Corso Di Francia 200
00191 Rome, Italy
Tel.: (39) 06324931
Fax: (39) 0632493259
E-Mail: invrel@cementirholding.it
Web Site: www.cementir.it
CEM—(ITA)
Rev.: $1,342,529,956
Assets: $2,658,902,483
Liabilities: $1,159,103,524
Net Worth: $1,499,798,959
Earnings: $32,367,311
Emp.: 3,311
Fiscal Year-end: 12/31/12
Business Description:
Holding Company; Cement & Cement Products Mfr
S.I.C.: 6719
N.A.I.C.S.: 551112
Personnel:
Francesco Caltagirone, Jr. *(Chm & CEO)*
Carlo Carlevaris *(Deputy Chm)*
Massimo Sala *(CFO, Head-IR & Mgr-Fin Reporting)*
Riccardo Nicolini *(COO)*
Alessandro Galaverna *(CIO)*
Claus Bech *(CTO)*
Mario De Gennaro *(Chief HR Officer)*
Pasquale Vetrano *(Chief Strategic Sourcing Officer)*
Mario Ciliberto *(Chm-Italy)*
Walter Montevecchi *(Chm-Cimentas Grp)*
Soren Vinther *(Chm-Aalborg Portland Grp)*
Board of Directors:
Francesco Caltagirone, Jr.
Carlo Carlevaris
Alessandro Caltagirone
Azzurra Caltagirone
Edoardo Caltagirone
Saverio Caltagirone
Flavio Cattaneo
Mario Ciliberto
Fabio Corsico
Mario Delfini
Paolo Di Bendetto
Alfio Marchini
Riccardo Nicolini
Subsidiaries:

Aalborg White Italia Srl (1)
Via del Bragozzo 11
48100 Ravenna, Italy
Tel.: (39) 0544430319
Fax: (39) 0544430131
Concrete Contractors
S.I.C.: 1771
N.A.I.C.S.: 238110
Maurizio del Console *(Mgr-Sls)*

Cementir Delta S.p.A. (1)
Corso Di Francia 200
Rome, Italy
Tel.: (39) 0636308082
Web Site: www.cementirholding.it/italy.php
New Single-Family Housing Construction

S.I.C.: 1521
N.A.I.C.S.: 236115
Vincenzo Cremonini *(CEO)*

Non-U.S. Subsidiaries:

Aalborg Portland A/S (1)
Rordalsvej 44
PO Box 165
DK 9100 Aalborg, Denmark DK
Tel.: (45) 98167777
Fax: (45) 98777675
Web Site: www.aalborg-portland.dk
Sls.: $297,990,000
Emp.: 300
Grey & White Cement Mfr
S.I.C.: 3255
N.A.I.C.S.: 327120
Flands Erex *(Gen Mgr)*

Unicon A/S (1)
Kogevej 172
DK 4000 Roskilde, Denmark
Tel.: (45) 46346000
Fax: (45) 46346099
E-Mail: unicon@data.fls.dk
Web Site: www.unicon.dk
Sls.: $113,127,700
Emp.: 3,000
Produces and Markets Ready-Mix Concrete, Precast Concrete Products & Related Services in Denmark, Sweden, USA, Spain & Portugal
S.I.C.: 3272
N.A.I.C.S.: 327332

CEMENTOS MOLINS S.A.

Ctra N 340 km 1242 300
Barcelona, Spain
Tel.: (34) 936806000
Fax: (34) 936569930
Web Site: www.cemolins.es
CMTM—(BAR)
Sales Range: $1-4.9 Billion
Emp.: 3,500
Business Description:
Cement Supplier & Mfr
S.I.C.: 3241
N.A.I.C.S.: 327310
Personnel:
Casimiro Molins Ribot *(Chm)*
Juan Molins Amat *(First Deputy Chm & Mng Dir)*
Joaquin Molins Gil *(Second Deputy Chm)*
Jorge Molins Amat *(Sec)*
Board of Directors:
Casimiro Molins Ribot
Miguel del Campo Rodriguez
Emilio Gutierrez Fernandez de Liencres
Joaquim Molins Amat
Juan Molins Amat
Pablo Molins Amat
Joaquin Molins Gil
Ana Maria Molins Lopez-Rodo
Joaquin M. Molins Lopez-Rodo
Maria Regina Molins Lopez-Rodo
Jose Antonio Pujante Consea
Roser Fafols Vives

Subsidiary:

Promsa (1)
Carretera Nacional 340 KM 242-300
Santo Vincenco dels Horts, 08620
Barcelona, Spain
Tel.: (34) 936806023
Fax: (34) 936569936
Web Site: www.cemolins.es/portal/page?_pageid=353,41820&_dad=portal&_schema=PORTAL
Emp.: 2,000
Concrete Distributor & Mfr
S.I.C.: 3241
N.A.I.C.S.: 327310
Carlos Raich *(Gen Mgr)*

Non-U.S. Joint Venture:

Surma Holdings B.V. (1)
Leliegracht 10
1015 DE Amsterdam, Netherlands
Tel.: (31) 2052 16344
Holding Company
S.I.C.: 6719
N.A.I.C.S.: 551112

Non-U.S. Holding:

Lafarge Surma Cement Limited (2)
Suvastu Imam Square 3rd Floor 65
Gulshan Avenue Gulshan-1
Dhaka, 1212, Bangladesh
Tel.: (880) 2 8854847
Fax: (880) 2 8825413
E-Mail: info@bd.lafarge.com
Web Site: www.lafarge-bd.com
LAFSURCEML—(DHA)
Sales Range: $50-74.9 Million
Cement Mfr
S.I.C.: 3241
N.A.I.C.S.: 327310
Martin Kriegner *(Chm)*
Michael Andrew Cowell *(Mng Dir)*
Asim Chattopadhyay *(Sr Vp-Ops)*

CEMENTOS PACASMAYO S.A.A.

Calle La Colonia 150 Urbanizacion El Vivero Surco
Lima, Peru
Tel.: (51) 13176000
Fax: (51) 14375009
Web Site: www.pacasmayo.com.pe
CPAC—(LIM NYSE)
Sls.: $448,586,274
Assets: $913,933,254
Liabilities: $187,596,975
Net Worth: $726,336,279
Earnings: $59,667,932
Emp.: 1,734
Fiscal Year-end: 12/31/12
Business Description:
Cement, Lime & Concrete Mfr & Distr
S.I.C.: 3241
N.A.I.C.S.: 327310
Personnel:
Eduardo Hochschild Beeck *(Chm)*
Lino Alfredo Abram Caballerino *(Vice Chm)*
Roberto Enrique Danino Zapata *(Vice Chm)*
Board of Directors:
Eduardo Hochschild Beeck
Lino Alfredo Abram Caballerino
Gianfranco Maximo Dante Castanola Zuniga
Roberto Enrique Danino Zapata
Juan Victoriano Inchaustegui Vargas
Jose Raimundo Morales Dasso
Humberto Reynaldo Nadal del Carpio
Dionisio Romero Paoletti

Non-U.S. Subsidiary:

Suzorite Mica Products, Inc. (1)
1475 Graham Bell St
Boucherville, QC, J4B 6A1, Canada QC
Tel.: (450) 655-2450 (100%)
Fax: (450) 655-9942
Sales Range: $1-9.9 Million
Emp.: 29
Supplier of Phlogopite Mica
S.I.C.: 1499
N.A.I.C.S.: 212399
Joel Ventura *(Plant Mgr)*

CEMEX, S.A.B. DE C.V.

Avenida Ricardo Margain Zozaya 325
Colonia Valle del Campestre
Garza Garcia, Monterrey, NL, Mexico 66265
Tel.: (52) 81 8888 8888
Fax: (52) 81 8888 4417
E-Mail: ir@cemex.com
Web Site: www.cemex.com
Year Founded: 1906
CX—(CAR MEX NYSE)
Sls.: $15,502,792,480
Assets: $37,669,623,600
Liabilities: $25,427,015,600
Net Worth: $12,242,608,000
Earnings: ($882,710,920)
Emp.: 43,905
Fiscal Year-end: 12/31/12
Business Description:
Holding Company; Ready-Mix Concrete & Concrete Products Mfr & Distr
S.I.C.: 6719
N.A.I.C.S.: 551112
Personnel:
Lorenzo H. Zambrano Trevino *(Chm & CEO)*
Francisco Garza *(Chm-Latin America)*
Jaime Elizondo *(Pres-South & Central America & Caribbean)*
Ignacio Madridejos *(Pres-Northern Europe)*
Juan Romero *(Pres-Mexico)*
Karl Watson, Jr. *(Pres-USA)*
Ramiro Gerardo Villarreal Morales *(Gen Counsel & Sec)*
Fernando A. Gonzalez *(Exec VP-Fin & Admin)*
Luis Hernandez *(Exec VP-Org & HR)*
Victor M. Romo *(Exec VP-Admin)*
Board of Directors:
Lorenzo H. Zambrano Trevino
Rodolfo Garcia Muriel
Armando J. Garcia Segovia
Dionisio Garza Medina
Bernardo Quintana Isaac
Jose Manuel Rincon Gallardo
Tomas Milmo Santos
Rogelio Zambrano Lozano
Mauricio Zambrano Villarreal
Roberto Zambrano Villarreal

Subsidiaries:

CEMEX Mexico, S.A. de C.V. (1)
Av Ricardo Margain Zozaya 325
Garza Garcia, Nuevo Leon, 66265, Mexico MX
Tel.: (52) 81 8888 8888
Web Site: www.cemex.com
Cement & Ready Mix Concrete Mfr
S.I.C.: 3241
N.A.I.C.S.: 327310
Juan Romero Torres *(Pres)*

U.S. Subsidiaries:

CEMEX de Puerto Rico Inc. (1)
Km 2 7 Carretera Zona Industrial Amelia
Guaynabo, PR 00968 PR
Mailing Address: (100%)
PO Box 364487
San Juan, PR 00936-4487
Tel.: (787) 783-3000
Fax: (787) 781-8850
Web Site: www.cemexpuertorico.com
Cement, Concrete & Other Construction Materials Mfr
Export
S.I.C.: 3241
N.A.I.C.S.: 327310
Carlos Jacks *(Pres)*
Pedro M. Mena *(CFO)*

Divisions:

CEMEX de Puerto Rico Inc. - Lime Division (2)
State Rd 123 Km 8
Ponce, PR 00731
Tel.: (787) 842-3000
Fax: (787) 842-9582
Toll Free: (800) 981-2388
Web Site: www.cemexpuertorico.com
Sales Range: $1-9.9 Million
Emp.: 37
Hydrated Lime Mfr
S.I.C.: 3274
N.A.I.C.S.: 327410

Subsidiaries:

Desarrollos Multiples Insulares, Inc. (2)
PO Box 364487
San Juan, PR 00936 PR
Tel.: (787) 783-3000 (100%)
Fax: (787) 300-6557
Toll Free: (800) 981-0918
E-Mail: cxt.puertorico@cemex.com
Web Site: www.prcements.com
Sls.: $119,634
Emp.: 2
Real Estate Sales
S.I.C.: 6531
N.A.I.C.S.: 531210

Ready Mix Concrete, Inc. (2)
PO Box 364487
San Juan, PR 00936-4487 (100%)
Tel.: (787) 783-3000
Fax: (787) 781-8850
Web Site: www.cemexpuertorico.com
Pre-Mixed Concrete Production
S.I.C.: 3273
N.A.I.C.S.: 327320
Leopoldo Navarro *(Pres)*

CEMEX, Inc. (1)
929 Gessner Rd Ste 1900
Houston, TX 77024 LA
Tel.: (713) 650-6200
Fax: (713) 653-6815
E-Mail: hrsc@cemexusa.com
Web Site: www.cemexusa.com
Emp.: 4,100
Cement, Concrete Products, Construction Aggregates & Specialty Minerals Mfr
S.I.C.: 3273
N.A.I.C.S.: 327320
Karl Watson *(Pres-Ops-CEMEX-US)*
Leslie S. White *(Gen Counsel & Exec VP)*
Robert Craddock *(Exec VP-Comml)*

Subsidiaries:

American Transit Mix Cemex (2)
2638 Nathan Ave
Modesto, CA 95354-4025 CA
Tel.: (209) 529-4115
Fax: (209) 521-8546
E-Mail: info@americantransitmix.com
Web Site: www.americantransitmix.com
Sls.: $140,000,000
Emp.: 330
Ready Mixed Concrete Mfr
Import Export
S.I.C.: 3273
N.A.I.C.S.: 327320

CEMEX Construction Materials Florida, LLC (2)
1501 Belvedere Rd
West Palm Beach, FL 33406-1501 DE
Tel.: (561) 833-5555
Fax: (561) 820-8309
Toll Free: (800) 226-5521
E-Mail: info@cemex.com
Web Site: www.cemexusa.com
Sales Range: $1-4.9 Billion
Concrete Block, Pipe, Aggregate, Ready Mixed Concrete & Cement Mfr
S.I.C.: 3271
N.A.I.C.S.: 327331
Karl Watson, Jr. *(Pres)*
Gonzalo Galindo *(Pres-Florida & Carolinas Reg)*
Frank Angelle *(Exec VP-HR & Comm)*

Divisions:

Rinker Materials-Engineering (3)
6560 Langfield Rd Bldg 3
Houston, TX 77092-1008
Tel.: (832) 590-5300
Fax: (832) 590-5499
Web Site: www.rinkerstormceptor.com
Concrete Pipe, Plastic Pipe, Pre-Stressed Concrete Products, Concrete Block, Quarry Products, Sand, Pre-Mixed Concrete & Asphalt
S.I.C.: 3272
N.A.I.C.S.: 327390

Units:

Rinker Materials-Concrete Pipe & Stormwater Treatment (4)
800 Industrial Dr
Middletown, DE 19709
Tel.: (302) 378-8920
Fax: (302) 378-8923
Web Site: www.rinkerpipe.com
Emp.: 50
Concrete Block & Brick Mfr
S.I.C.: 3272
N.A.I.C.S.: 327332
Tim Meyer *(Gen Mgr)*

Rinker Materials-Harrisburg (4)
5601 Pharr Mill Rd
Harrisburg, NC 28075-7597

CEMEX, S.A.B. de C.V.—(Continued)

Tel.: (704) 455-1100
Fax: (704) 455-1105
Web Site: www.cemexusa.com
Emp.: 30
Concrete Products Mfr
S.I.C.: 3272
N.A.I.C.S.: 327332
Rick Santiago *(Mgr-Sls)*

Rinker Materials West, LLC (3)
7150 Pollock Dr
Las Vegas, NV 89119
Tel.: (702) 260-9900
Fax: (702) 260-9901
Web Site: www.rinkerpipe.com
Emp.: 600
Concrete Pipe Mfr
S.I.C.: 3272
N.A.I.C.S.: 327332

Subsidiaries:

Guernsey Stone Company (3)
49 Quarry Rd
Guernsey, WY 82214 (100%)
Mailing Address:
PO Box 339
Guernsey, WY 82214
Tel.: (307) 836-2514
Fax: (307) 836-2249
Emp.: 20
Crushed & Broken Granite Mining & Quarrying
S.I.C.: 1423
N.A.I.C.S.: 212313

Steel Construction Systems (3)
11250 Astronaut Blvd
Orlando, FL 32837-9204 (55%)
Tel.: (407) 438-1664
Fax: (407) 438-1667
Toll Free: (800) 548-8499
E-Mail: info@steelconsystems.com
Web Site: www.steelconsystems.com
Sales Range: $10-24.9 Million
Emp.: 40
Metal Building Components Mfr
S.I.C.: 3448
N.A.I.C.S.: 332311
Dan Dry *(Gen Mgr)*

Units:

Rinker Materials-Environmental Services (3)
1200 NW 137th Ave
Miami, FL 33182-1803
Tel.: (305) 790-6648
Fax: (305) 386-0105
Web Site: www.cemexusa.com
Emp.: 100
Non-Clay Refractories & Hydraulic Cement Mfr
S.I.C.: 3271
N.A.I.C.S.: 327331

Rinker Materials-Twin Mountain (3)
3700 Hwy 528
Bernalillo, NM 87004-6600 NM
Tel.: (505) 867-2394
Fax: (505) 867-2563
Web Site: www.cemexusa.com
Emp.: 30
Crushed & Broken Granite Mfr
S.I.C.: 1423
N.A.I.C.S.: 212313
Bruce Spatz *(Gen Mgr)*

CEMEX Corp. (2)
929 Gessner Rd Ste 1900
Houston, TX 77024
Tel.: (713) 650-6200
Fax: (918) 401-2129
Cement Mfr & Distr
S.I.C.: 3241
N.A.I.C.S.: 327310

CEMEX Materials LLC (2)
1501 Belvedere Rd
West Palm Beach, FL 33406-1501
Tel.: (561) 833-5555
Concrete Products Mfr
S.I.C.: 3271
N.A.I.C.S.: 327331

Units:

CEMEX Canada (2)
3990 E Concourse St Ste 200
Ontario, CA 91764-5456
Tel.: (909) 974-5500
Fax: (909) 974-5536
E-Mail: info@cemex.com
Sls.: $90,000,000
Emp.: 500
Mfr. of Ready-Mixed Concrete
S.I.C.: 3299
N.A.I.C.S.: 327332
Linda Robinson *(Controller)*

CEMEX Concrete Products (2)
929 Gessner Rd Ste 2100
Houston, TX 77024
Tel.: (713) 650-6200
Fax: (713) 722-5105
E-Mail: HRSC@cemexusa.com
Web Site: www.cemexusa.com
Emp.: 100
Concrete Products
S.I.C.: 3271
N.A.I.C.S.: 327331
Gilberto Perez *(Pres)*

CEMEX, Inc. - East Tennessee (2)
2209 Blount Ave
Knoxville, TN 37920-1956
Tel.: (865) 573-4501
Fax: (865) 573-3327
Web Site: www.cemexusa.com
Concrete & Limestone Mfr
S.I.C.: 1422
N.A.I.C.S.: 212312
Harvey Johnston *(Gen Mgr)*

CEMEX, Inc. - Lakeland (2)
PO Box 3858
Lakeland, FL 33802
Tel.: (863) 688-5787
Fax: (863) 686-4085
Emp.: 700
Ready-Mixed Concrete Mfr
S.I.C.: 3273
N.A.I.C.S.: 327320
Dave Sligh *(Territory Mgr)*

CEMEX, Inc. - McKellington Canyon (2)
1 McKelligon Canyon Rd
El Paso, TX 79930
Tel.: (915) 565-4681
Fax: (915) 562-6218
Web Site: www.cemexusa.com
Emp.: 500
Ready-Mixed Concrete Mfr
S.I.C.: 3273
N.A.I.C.S.: 327320

CEMEX, Inc. - Mesa (2)
4646 E Van Buren Ste 250
Mesa, AZ 85008
Tel.: (602) 416-2600
Fax: (602) 495-1672
E-Mail: info@chandlerreadymix.com
Emp.: 90
Ready-Mixed Concrete Mfr
S.I.C.: 3273
N.A.I.C.S.: 327320
Rob Cutter *(VP & Gen Mgr)*

CEMEX, Inc. - Naples (2)
1425 E Wiggins Pass Rd
Naples, FL 34110
Tel.: (239) 597-3162
Fax: (239) 597-3060
Toll Free: (800) 226-3162
Web Site: www.cemex.com
Emp.: 60
Ready Mixed Concrete Mfr
S.I.C.: 3273
N.A.I.C.S.: 327320
Gilberto Perez *(Pres)*

CEMEX, Inc. - Spartanburg (2)
475 Simuel Rd
Spartanburg, SC 29303
Tel.: (864) 594-4000
Fax: (864) 594-4009
E-Mail: info@metromontmaterials.com
Web Site: www.metromontmaterials.com
Emp.: 1,000
Ready Mixed Concrete Mfr
S.I.C.: 3272
N.A.I.C.S.: 327390
Randy Shore *(Mgr-HR)*

Non-U.S. Subsidiaries:

APO Cement Corporation (1)
8 F Petron Mega Plaza 358 Sen Gil J Puyat Avenue
Makati, 1200, Philippines
Tel.: (63) 28493600
Fax: (63) 28493639
Web Site: www.cemex.com.ph
Emp.: 232
Cement Mfr
S.I.C.: 3241
N.A.I.C.S.: 327310
Roman Azanza *(Dir-Treas)*

CEMEX Argentina s.a (1)
Julio Troxler 3275
Buenos Aires, Argentina Ar
Tel.: (54) 11 49180106
Fax: (54) 11 49180106 120
Web Site: www.cemex.com
Emp.: 75
Ready Mix Concrete Mfr
S.I.C.: 3273
N.A.I.C.S.: 327320
Marcelo Oscar Paredes *(Pres)*

Subsidiary:

Readymix Argentina, S.A. (2)
Pasaje Julio Troxler 3275 Ciudad de 1437
Buenos Aires, 1437, Argentina
Tel.: (54) 1149180106
Emp.: 75
Ready Mix Concrete Mfr
S.I.C.: 3273
N.A.I.C.S.: 327320
Marcelo Oscar Paredes *(CEO)*

CEMEX AS (1)
Meierisvingen 2 C
1383 Asker, Norway
Tel.: (47) 22 92 43 70
Fax: (47) 66 78 49 08
Web Site: www.cemex.no
Cement Mfr & Distr
S.I.C.: 3241
N.A.I.C.S.: 327310

CEMEX Asia Holdings Ltd. (1)
3 Temasek Avenue
22-01 Centennial Tower, Singapore, 039190, Singapore
Tel.: (65) 63338010
Fax: (65) 6 433 0781
Web Site: www.cemex.com
Emp.: 20
Holding Company
S.I.C.: 6719
N.A.I.C.S.: 551112

Non-U.S. Subsidiaries:

CEMEX (Thailand) Co. Ltd. (2)
1910 Electrolux Bldg 12th Floor New Petchburi Road Huaykwang
Bangkapi, Bangkok, 10310, Thailand
Tel.: (66) 2 3659510
Fax: (66) 2 718 0250
E-Mail: thailand@cemex.com
Web Site: www.cemexthailand.com
Cement Mfr
S.I.C.: 3241
N.A.I.C.S.: 327310
Bank Asapaporn *(Dir-Plng & Admin)*

Solid Cement Corp. (2)
Solid Cement Plant Sitio Tagbac Barangay Jose
Antipolo, 1870, Philippines
Tel.: (63) 28493585
Fax: (63) 28493649
Cement Mfr
S.I.C.: 3241
N.A.I.C.S.: 327310
Louie Anain *(Superintendent-Mechanical Maintenance)*

CEMEX Austria AG (1)
Lagerstrasse 1-5
Langenzersdorf, 2103, Austria
Tel.: (43) 50543 0
Web Site: www.cemex.at
Ready Mix Concrete Distr
S.I.C.: 5032
N.A.I.C.S.: 423320

CEMEX Brazil (1)
Rua Desembargador Cesar Do Rego No 2
Colonia Antonio Aleixo
Manaus, Brazil
Tel.: (55) 92 2125 5150
Cement Mfr
S.I.C.: 3241
N.A.I.C.S.: 327310

Subsidiary:

Cimentos Vencemos do Amazonas, Ltda. (2)
Rua des Cezar do Rego 2
Manaus, 69083-200, Brazil
Tel.: (55) 9221255150
Cement Mfr
S.I.C.: 3241
N.A.I.C.S.: 327310

CEMEX Colombia, S.A. (1)
Calle 99 No 9A-54 Piso 7
Bogota, Colombia (98%)
Tel.: (57) 16039000
Fax: (57) 16469000
E-Mail: contactanos@cemexcolombia.com
Web Site: www.cemexcolombia.com
Emp.: 950
Cement Mfr
S.I.C.: 3241
N.A.I.C.S.: 327310
Lorenzo H. Zambrano Trevio *(Pres)*

CEMEX Costa Rica S.A. (1)
45 Km al sur de Iglesia
San Antonio de Desamparados, San Jose, Costa Rica (98%)
Tel.: (506) 22012000
Web Site: www.cemexcostarica.com
Emp.: 220
Cement Mfr
S.I.C.: 3241
N.A.I.C.S.: 327310
Alejandro Cableron *(Head-Comml)*

CEMEX Czech Republic k.s. (1)
Oregon House Revnika 170/4
155 21 Prague, Trebonice, Czech Republic
Tel.: (420) 257257400
Fax: (420) 272704360
E-Mail: info.malesice@cemez.cz
Ready Mixed Concrete Mfr
S.I.C.: 3273
N.A.I.C.S.: 327320
Peter Dajko *(VP-Matls-Czech Republic & Dir-Strategic Plng)*

CEMEX Deutschland AG (1)
Theodorstrasse 178
40472 Dusseldorf, Germany De
Tel.: (49) 211 4470 0
Fax: (49) 211 4470 1601
E-Mail: kundenservice.de@cemex.com
Web Site: www.cemex.de
Holding Company, Building Materials
S.I.C.: 6719
N.A.I.C.S.: 551112
Eric Wittmann *(Chm-Mgmt Bd & Pres-Germany)*
Jurgen Winkelmann *(Member-Mgmt Bd & VP-HR-Germany)*

CEMEX Dominicana, S.A. (1)
Torre Acropolis Piso 20 Av Winston Churchill 67
Ensanche Piantini, Santo Domingo, Dominican Republic
Tel.: (809) 6834901
Fax: (809) 683 4949
Web Site: www.cemexdominicana.com
Emp.: 457
Cement Mfr
S.I.C.: 3241
N.A.I.C.S.: 327310
Carlos Jacks *(Pres)*

CEMEX Egypt (1)
3 Abbas El Akkad Street Nasr City
Cairo, Egypt
Tel.: (20) 22407 8600
Fax: (20) 2260 3325
Web Site: www.cemex.com.eg
Cement & Concrete Mfr
S.I.C.: 3241
N.A.I.C.S.: 327310

Subsidiary:

Assiut Cement Company (2)
3 Abbas El Akad Street
Nasr City, Cairo, Egypt (96%)
Tel.: (20) 2 242 4302
Fax: (20) 2 236 1592
Web Site: www.cemex.com.eg
Emp.: 1,100
Cement Mfr
S.I.C.: 3241
N.A.I.C.S.: 327310
Jesus Caviedes Mondragon *(VP-Comml)*

CEMEX el Salvador S.A. de C.V. (1)
Avenida Albert Einstein Edificio
Construmark 3 nivel No 4 Antiguo
Cuscatlan, San Salvador, El Salvador SV
Tel.: (503) 25298300
Cement Mfr
S.I.C.: 3241
N.A.I.C.S.: 327310

CEMEX Espana S.A. (1)
Hernandez de Tejada 1
28027 Madrid, Spain
Tel.: (34) 913779200
Fax: (34) 913779203
Web Site: www.cemex.es
Sales Range: $1-4.9 Billion
Emp.: 200
Cement Mfr
S.I.C.: 3241
N.A.I.C.S.: 327310
Ignacio Madridejos Fernandez *(Mng Dir)*

CEMEX Finland (1)
Fiskarsinkatu 7 A 2 Kerros
20750 Turku, Finland
Tel.: (358) 207 121434
Fax: (358) 207 121431
Web Site: www.cemexfinland.fi
Cement Distr
S.I.C.: 5032
N.A.I.C.S.: 423320

CEMEX France S.A. (1)
2 Rue Du Verseau
Silic 423, 94583 Rungis, Cedex,
France FR
Tel.: (33) 0149794444
Fax: (33) 146875082
E-Mail: info@cemex.com
Web Site: www.cemex.fr
Emp.: 2,100
Production, Distribution, Marketing & Sale of Cement, Ready-Mix Concrete, Aggregates & Clinker
S.I.C.: 3241
N.A.I.C.S.: 327310
Pieaae Laplange *(Pres)*

Subsidiary:

CEMEX France Gestion (S.A.S.) (2)
2 Rue du Verseau SILIC 423
Rungis, Ile-de-France, 94583, France
Tel.: (33) 149794444
E-Mail: fr-webcontact@cemex.com
Web Site: www.cemex.fr
Concrete Product Mfr & Distr
S.I.C.: 3272
N.A.I.C.S.: 327390

CEMEX Guatemala (1)
3era Avenida 13-78 Zona 10 Torre Citibank
Nivel 7 Oficina 702
Guatemala, Guatemala
Tel.: (502) 2204 5600
Web Site: www.cemex.com
Cement Mfr
S.I.C.: 3241
N.A.I.C.S.: 327310

CEMEX Holdings (Israel) Limited (1)
155 Bialik
Ramat Gan, 52523, Israel
Tel.: (972) 3 7519464
Fax: (972) 3 7510201
Investment Management Services
S.I.C.: 6282
N.A.I.C.S.: 523920

Subsidiary:

Readymix Industries (Israel) Limited (2)
155 Bialik St
Ramat Gan, 52523, Israel IL
Tel.: (972) 37519464
Fax: (972) 37510201
E-Mail: infocenter@readymix.co.il
Web Site: www.readymix.co.il
Emp.: 110
Ready Mixed Concrete Mfr
S.I.C.: 3273
N.A.I.C.S.: 327320
Y. Dejarano *(Mng Dir)*

Division:

Concrete Industry Div (3)
155 Bialik St
Ramat Gan, 52523, Israel II
Tel.: (972) 36129240
Fax: (972) 37510201
E-Mail: infocenter@readymix.co.il
Web Site: www.readymix.co.il
Emp.: 800
Ready Mixed Concrete Mfr
S.I.C.: 3273
N.A.I.C.S.: 327320
Isaac Bejerano *(Gen Mgr)*

Subsidiaries:

Lime & Stone Production Co Ltd (3)
155 Bialik Street
Ramat Gan, Israel II
Tel.: (972) 3 755 4777
Web Site: www.readymix.co.il
Concrete Blocks Mfr
S.I.C.: 3271
N.A.I.C.S.: 327331

Readymix Concrete Products (Israel) Ltd (3)
Ad Halom Industrial Zone
Ashdod, Israel II
Tel.: (972) 88548888
Fax: (972) 88548890
E-Mail: infocenter@readymix.co.il
Web Site: www.readymix.co.il
Concrete Pipe Mfr
S.I.C.: 3272
N.A.I.C.S.: 327332
Yoram Dlear *(Mng Dir)*

CEMEX Hrvatska d.d. (1)
F Tudmana 45
21212 Kastel Sucurac, Croatia
Tel.: (385) 21 201 111
Fax: (385) 21 211 255
Web Site: www.cemex.hr
Concrete Product Mfr
S.I.C.: 3272
N.A.I.C.S.: 327390

CEMEX Hungaria Kft. (1)
Hajoallomas U 1
1095 Budapest, Hungary HU
Tel.: (36) 12150874
Fax: (36) 12156317
E-Mail: clara.lepp@cemex.com
Web Site: www.cemex.hu
Emp.: 280
Ready Mixed Concrete Mfr
S.I.C.: 3273
N.A.I.C.S.: 327320
Elsokent Renars Griskevics *(Mng Dir)*

CEMEX Netherlands B.V. (1)
Riverstate Building Amsteldijk 166
Amsterdam, North Holland, 1079 LH,
Netherlands NL
Tel.: (31) 20 642 4288
Web Site: www.cemex.nd
Cement & Ready Mix Concrete Mfr
S.I.C.: 3241
N.A.I.C.S.: 327310
Peter Andriessen *(Engr-Concrete)*

Subsidiaries:

Neoris N.V. (2)
Amsteldijk 166
Box 42
1079 LH Amsterdam, Netherlands
Tel.: (31) 206444558
Information Technology Consulting Services
S.I.C.: 7373
N.A.I.C.S.: 541512

New Sunward Holding B.V. (2)
Amsteldijk 166
1079 LH Amsterdam, Netherlands
Tel.: (31) 206422048
Fax: (31) 206444095
Investment Management Services
S.I.C.: 6282
N.A.I.C.S.: 523920

New Sunward Holding Financial Ventures B.V. (2)
Amsteldijk 166
1079LH Amsterdam, Noord-Holland,
Netherlands
Tel.: (31) 20 6422048
Investment Management Services
S.I.C.: 6282
N.A.I.C.S.: 523920

CEMEX Norway (1)
Dairy Svingen 2 C N-1383
Asker, 1383, Norway
Tel.: (47) 48264390
Fax: (47) 66 78 49 08
Web Site: www.cemex.no
Cement Mfr & Distr
S.I.C.: 3241
N.A.I.C.S.: 327310

CEMEX Polska Sp.z.o.o. (1)
Aleje Jerozolimskie 212a
PL 02 486 Warsaw, Poland
Tel.: (48) 225714100
Fax: (48) 225714101
E-Mail: cemextolaska@cemex.com
Web Site: www.cemex.pl
Emp.: 130
Cement Mfr
S.I.C.: 3241
N.A.I.C.S.: 327310
Ruediger Tuhn *(Pres)*

CEMEX SIA (1)
Lielirbes liela 17a - 28
Riga, 1046, Latvia
Tel.: (371) 67033400
Fax: (371) 67033414
E-Mail: informacija@cemex.com
Web Site: www.cemex.lv
Cement & Concrete Product Mfr
S.I.C.: 3241
N.A.I.C.S.: 327310
Maris Gruznins *(Dir-Comml & Logistics)*

CEMEX Sweden (1)
Jorgen Kocksgatan 4
211 20 Malmo, Sweden
Tel.: (46) 40 31 75 50
Fax: (46) 40 94 77 25
Web Site: www.cemex.se
Concrete Distr
S.I.C.: 5032
N.A.I.C.S.: 423320

CEMEX UK (1)
CEMEX House Coldharbour Lane
Egham, Surrey, TW20 8TD, United
Kingdom UK
Tel.: (44) 1932568833
Fax: (44) 1932568933
E-Mail: info@cemex.uk
Web Site: www.cemex.co.uk
Sls.: $7,293,579,776
Emp.: 350
Materials & Services to the Construction Industry & Maintenance of the Environment; Cement Mfr
S.I.C.: 3241
N.A.I.C.S.: 327310
Jesus Gonzalez *(Pres)*

Subsidiaries:

CEMEX Specialist Products (2)
Waldorf Way Denby Dale Rd
Wakefield, W Yorkshire, WF2 8DH, United
Kingdom
Tel.: (44) 924362081
Fax: (44) 924290126
Web Site: www.thermabate.co.uk
Emp.: 20
Mfr. of Insulated Cavity Closer, Dry Cavity Wall Insulation, Thermal & Acoustic Insulation for Roofs & Walls, Fire Protection, Surfacing Texturing Material for Walls & Ceilings, & Plasterboard Jointing Strip
S.I.C.: 3086
N.A.I.C.S.: 326140

CEMEX UK Construction Services Ltd (2)
Cemex House Savile Street
Sheffield, S4 7UL, United Kingdom UK
Tel.: (44) 1142418282
Fax: (44) 1142418283
E-Mail: info@cemex.com
Web Site: www.cemex.co.uk
Emp.: 240
Cement Mfr & Road Surfacing Services
S.I.C.: 4789
N.A.I.C.S.: 488490

Subsidiaries:

Readymix NI Ltd (3)
6 Channel Wharf
21 Old Channel Road, Belfast, BT39 DA,
United Kingdom
Tel.: (44) 2890616611
Fax: (44) 2890619969
E-Mail: general@cemex.com
Web Site: www.cemexni.com
Emp.: 200
Road Surfacing Contractor
S.I.C.: 1611
N.A.I.C.S.: 237310
John McCambridge *(Treas)*

CEMEX UK Marine Ltd. (2)
Baltic Wharf Elm St Marine Parade
Southampton, Hamps, SO14 5JF, United
Kingdom UK
Tel.: (44) 2380720200
Telex: 47244 SANDCO G
Fax: (44) 2380334528
Web Site: www.cemex.co.uk
Emp.: 25
Freight Transportation Services
S.I.C.: 4424
N.A.I.C.S.: 483113
John Miller *(Gen Mgr)*

Chesterfield Macadam (2)
49 Birmington Rd N
Chesterfield, Derbys, S41 9BE, United
Kingdom UK
Tel.: (44) 246261400
Fax: (44) 01246455601
Emp.: 4
Supplier of Coated Stone
S.I.C.: 3281
N.A.I.C.S.: 327991
Steve Taylor *(Gen Mgr)*

Nottingham Coated Stone (2)
Private Rd 4 Colwick Industrial Estate
Netherfield, Nottinghamshire, NG4 2JT,
United Kingdom
Tel.: (44) 1159400171
Fax: (44) 1159404076
E-Mail: info@cemex.com
Emp.: 4
Suppliers of Coated Stone
S.I.C.: 1429
N.A.I.C.S.: 212319
Colin Burdett *(Branch Mgr)*

RMC Materials Ltd. (2)
Cemex House
Rugby, Warwickshire, CV21 2DT, United
Kingdom UK
Tel.: (44) 1788542111
Fax: (44) 1788517009
Emp.: 260
Holding Company
S.I.C.: 6719
N.A.I.C.S.: 551112

Subsidiaries:

CEMEX Ready Mixed Concrete (East Midlands) Ltd. (3)
RMC House Long Ln
Attenborough, Nottingham, Notts, NG9 6BL,
United Kingdom UK
Tel.: (44) 59220660
Fax: (44) 1159222827
Emp.: 50
Ready Mixed Concrete Mfr
S.I.C.: 3273
N.A.I.C.S.: 327320

Sheffield Coated Stone (2)
Stephenson Rd
Attercliffe, Sheffield, S Yorkshire, S9 3XG,
United Kingdom UK
Tel.: (44) 42560497
Fax: (44) 42424128
Web Site: www.cemex.com
Emp.: 6
Suppliers of Coated Stone
S.I.C.: 1429
N.A.I.C.S.: 212319

Wondertex Ltd. (2)
Birch Coppice Danny Morson Way
Tamworth, West Sussex, B78 1SE, United
Kingdom UK
Tel.: (44) 1903725221
Fax: (44) 1903717508
E-Mail: info@cemex.com
Web Site: www.wondertex.co.uk/
Emp.: 180
Texture Plasters for Decorative Ceilings & Wall Finishes Mfr
S.I.C.: 3275
N.A.I.C.S.: 327420
Gary Pierca *(Mng Dir)*

Non-U.S. Subsidiary:

Island Aggregates Limited (2)
Island House Isleosnan Business Park
Douglas, IM2 2QZ, Isle of Man

CEMEX, S.A.B. de C.V.—(Continued)

Tel.: (44) 1624624461
Fax: (44) 01624620912
Emp.: 60
Sand, Gravel & Ready-Mixed Concrete
S.I.C.: 1442
N.A.I.C.S.: 212321
Mike Shaw *(Mng Dir)*

CEMEX Venezuela, S.A.C.A. **(1)**
Calle Londres entre c/Nueva York y Trinidad
Torre CEMEX Venezuela
Urbanizacion Las Mercedes, Caracas,
1060, Venezuela (76%)
Tel.: (58) 2129997000
Fax: (58) 2129997302
E-Mail: contactanos@cemexvenezuela.com
Web Site: www.cemexvenezuela.com
Emp.: 6,000
Concrete & Cement Mfr
S.I.C.: 3241
N.A.I.C.S.: 327310
Eduardo Horowitz *(Mng Dir)*

Dalmacijacement d.d. **(1)**
Cesta Dr Franje Tudjmana bb
21212 Kastel Sucurac, Croatia
Tel.: (385) 21201111
Fax: (385) 21211255
E-Mail: trpimir.renic@cemex.com
Web Site: www.dalmacijacement.hr
Emp.: 730
Cement Mfr
S.I.C.: 3241
N.A.I.C.S.: 327310
Trpimir Renic *(Pres)*

Readymix Limited **(1)**
Killeen Road
Dublin, 12, Ireland IE
Tel.: (353) 18658700 (61.2%)
Telex: 30128
Fax: (353) 18556595
E-Mail:
Sales Range: $75-99.9 Million
Emp.: 355
Ready Mixed Concrete Mfr
S.I.C.: 3273
N.A.I.C.S.: 327320
Adrian Auer *(Chm)*
Roger Gonzalez *(Mng Dir)*

Units:

Readymix (ROI) Ltd **(2)**
Arden
Tullamore, Offaly, Ireland
Tel.: (353) 50621485
Fax: (353) 50661182
Web Site: www.readymix.ie
Emp.: 50
Ready Mixed Concrete Mfr
S.I.C.: 3273
N.A.I.C.S.: 327320

Readymix **(2)**
Maudlins
Naas, Kildare, Ireland IE
Tel.: (353) 145879355
Fax: (353) 145875202
Emp.: 60
Concrete Pipes Mfr
S.I.C.: 3272
N.A.I.C.S.: 327332

CEMTAS CELIK MAKINA SANAYI VE TICARET A.S.

Organize Sanayi Bolgesi Ali Osman Sonmez
Bulvari 3, 16159 Bursa, Turkey
Tel.: (90) 2242431230
Fax: (90) 2242431318
E-Mail: info@cemtas.com.tr
Web Site: www.cemtas.com.tr
CEMTS—(IST)
Sales Range: $100-124.9 Million
Emp.: 289
Business Description:
Steel & Steel Products Mfr & Marketer
S.I.C.: 3325
N.A.I.C.S.: 331513
Personnel:
Ergun Kagitcibasi *(Chm)*
Board of Directors:
Ergun Kagitcibasi
S. Feyha Duraner
Burhan Evcil
M. Celal Gokcen
M. Cuneyt Pekman
Erdem Saker

CENCORP OYJ

Insinoorinkatu 8
FI 50100 Mikkeli, Finland
Tel.: (358) 20 7747 788
Fax: (358) 20 7747 770
E-Mail: info@cencorp.com
Web Site: www.cencorp.com
CNC1V—(HEL)
Sls.: $20,786,211
Assets: $25,176,071
Liabilities: $18,846,380
Net Worth: $6,329,691
Earnings: ($17,979,447)
Emp.: 336
Fiscal Year-end: 12/31/12
Business Description:
Automation Equipment Mfr
S.I.C.: 3559
N.A.I.C.S.: 333249
Personnel:
Hannu Savisalo *(Chm)*
Marjukka Karttunen *(Vice Chm)*
Iikka Savisalo *(Pres & CEO)*
Seija Kurki *(CFO)*
Board of Directors:
Hannu Savisalo
Marjukka Karttunen
Iikka Savisalo

Non-U.S. Subsidiaries:

Cencorp AS **(1)**
Mustamaee tee 44
Tallinn, 10621, Estonia
Tel.: (372) 6671710
Industrial Automation Equipment Distr
S.I.C.: 5084
N.A.I.C.S.: 423830

Savcor Face (Beijing) Technologies Co., Ltd. **(1)**
No 18 Jinxiu Road Beijing Economic & Technological Development Area
Beijing, 100176, China
Tel.: (86) 10 6787 0011
Fax: (86) 10 6787 8450
Electromagnetic Shielding Mfr
S.I.C.: 3679
N.A.I.C.S.: 334419

Savcor Face (Guangzhou) Technologies Co., Ltd. **(1)**
No 18 Jungong Road Eastern Section GETDD
Guangzhou, 510530, China
Tel.: (86) 20 8226 6811
Fax: (86) 20 8226 7864
Web Site: www.cencorp.com
Film Coating Mfr
S.I.C.: 2672
N.A.I.C.S.: 322220

CENCOSUD S.A.

Av Kennedy 9001 Piso 6
Las Condes, Santiago, Chile
Tel.: (56) 29590000
Fax: (56) 29590040
E-Mail: contacto@cencosud.cl
Web Site: www.cencosud.cl
CNCO—(NYSE SGO)
Rev.: $19,396,043,467
Assets: $20,508,879,137
Liabilities: $13,304,670,240
Net Worth: $7,204,208,897
Earnings: $535,955,356
Emp.: 157,967
Fiscal Year-end: 12/31/12
Business Description:
Supermarkets, Homecenters & Malls Owner & Operator
S.I.C.: 5411
N.A.I.C.S.: 445110
Personnel:
Horst Paulmann Kemna *(Chm)*
Daniel Rodriguez *(CEO)*
Juan Manuel Parada *(CFO)*
Board of Directors:
Horst Paulmann Kemna
Cristian Eyzaguirre Johnston
Peter Paulmann Koepfer
Julio Neto Moura
David Gallagher Patrickson
Heike Paulmann Koepfer
Roberto Oscar Philipps
Sven Von Appen Behrmann
Erasmo Lu Wong
Subsidiaries:

Banco Paris S.A. **(1)**
Morande 115 Piso 4
Santiago, Chile
Tel.: (56) 2 410 11 00
E-Mail: contacto@paris.cl
Web Site: www.bancoparis.cl
Financial Management Services
S.I.C.: 6211
N.A.I.C.S.: 523999

Subsidiaries:

Administradora de Servicios Paris Ltda. **(2)**
Piso 7 9001 Av Kennedy
Santiago, Chile CL
Tel.: (56) 2 959 0700
Fax: (56) 2 959 0040
Supermarket Operator
S.I.C.: 5411
N.A.I.C.S.: 445110

Viajes Paris S.A. **(2)**
Coyancura 2270
Santiago, Chile CL
Tel.: (56) 23367015
E-Mail: info@viajesparis.cl
Web Site: www.viajesparis.cl
Travel Agency Services
S.I.C.: 4724
N.A.I.C.S.: 561510

Cencosud Retail S.A. **(1)**
Av Kennedy 9001 Piso 7
Las Condes, Santiago, Chile CL
Tel.: (56) 2 959 0700 959
Fax: (56) 23367171
Supermarket Operator
S.I.C.: 5411
N.A.I.C.S.: 445110
Javiera Espina Ross *(Product Mgr)*

Cencosud Shopping Center S.A. **(1)**
Avenida Presidente Kennedy 9001 Piso 4-5
Las Condes, Santiago, Chile CL
Tel.: (56) 2 9590000
Fax: (56) 2 2121469
E-Mail: oficinas@cencosud.cl
Web Site: www.cencosudshopping.cl
Shopping Mall Operator
S.I.C.: 6512
N.A.I.C.S.: 531120
Horst Paulmann *(Mng Dir)*

EUROFASHION Ltda **(1)**
San Ignacio 700
Quilicura, Santiago, Chile
Tel.: (56) 2 677 9010
Fax: (56) 2 738 6433
Web Site: www.eurofashion.cl
Supermarket Operator
S.I.C.: 5411
N.A.I.C.S.: 445110

Johnsons Mega San Bernardo S.A. **(1)**
Nuble 1034
Santiago, Chile CL
Tel.: (56) 2 3872100
Supermarket Operator
S.I.C.: 5411
N.A.I.C.S.: 445110

Mega Johnsons Vina del Mar S.A. **(1)**
Avenida Benidorm 961 Loc 253
Vina del Mar, Chile
Tel.: (56) 32 2384700
Departmental Store Operator
S.I.C.: 5411
N.A.I.C.S.: 445110

RETAIL S.A. **(1)**
Nueva Lyon 72 Piso 6
Santiago, Chile
Tel.: (56) 2 898 3002
Supermarket Operator
S.I.C.: 5411
N.A.I.C.S.: 445110

Santa Isabel S.A. **(1)**
Avenida Kennedy 9001 4th Floor
Las Condes, Santiago, Chile
Tel.: (56) 29590000
Fax: (56) 29590490
Web Site: www.santaisabel.cl
Emp.: 5,000
Supermarket Operator
S.I.C.: 5411
N.A.I.C.S.: 445110
Horst Paulmann Kemna *(Pres)*

Non-U.S. Subsidiaries:

Cencosud Peru S.A. **(1)**
Cal Augusto Angulo Nro 130
Miraflores, Lima, Peru PE
Tel.: (51) 1 626 0000
Fax: (51) 1 626 0155
Supermarket Operator
S.I.C.: 5411
N.A.I.C.S.: 445110

Subsidiaries:

Banco Cencosud S.A. **(2)**
Av Benavides No 1555 Urbanizacion
San Antonio, Lima, Peru PE
Tel.: (51) 1 626 0000
Fax: (51) 1 626 0082
Supermarket Operator
S.I.C.: 5411
N.A.I.C.S.: 445110

E.Wong S.A. **(2)**
Calle Augusto Angulo Suite 130
San Antonio, Miraflores, Peru PE
Tel.: (51) 1 6138888
Fax: (51) 1 6138889
E-Mail: ventas.corporativas@ewong.com
Web Site: www.ewong.com
Supermarket Operator
S.I.C.: 5411
N.A.I.C.S.: 445110

Travel Internacional Partners Peru S.A.C. **(2)**
Cal Monte Grande Nro 129
Santiago de Surco, Lima, Peru PE
Tel.: (51) 1 6179797
Travel & Tour Operator
S.I.C.: 4724
N.A.I.C.S.: 561510

Cencosud S.A. **(1)**
Parana 3617
Martinez, Buenos Aires, 1640, Argentina Ar
Tel.: (54) 1147331400
Fax: (54) 11 47175210
Web Site: www.easy.com.ar
Emp.: 640
Supermarket Operator
S.I.C.: 5411
N.A.I.C.S.: 445110
Horst Paulmann *(Pres)*

Subsidiaries:

Blaisten SA **(2)**
Avenida Juan Bautista Alberdi 3922/2
Buenos Aires, C1407GZS, Argentina
Tel.: (54) 1146362000
Fax: (54) 1147331000
E-Mail: info@blaisten.com.ar
Web Site: www.blaisten.com.ar
Construction Materials Retailer
S.I.C.: 5032
N.A.I.C.S.: 423320
Roberto Devoto *(CEO)*

Cencosud Viajes Argentina S.A. **(2)**
Parana 3617
Martinez, Buenos Aires, 1640, Argentina Ar
Tel.: (54) 1147331000
Retail Store Operator
S.I.C.: 5999
N.A.I.C.S.: 453998

Disco S.A. **(2)**
Larrea 833
Buenos Aires, Argentina

Tel.: (54) 49 611952
E-Mail: discoplus@disco.com.ar
Web Site: www.disco.com.ar
Sales Range: $500-549.9 Million
Emp.: 12,000
Supermarket Operations
S.I.C.: 5411
N.A.I.C.S.: 445110

Jumbo Retail Argentina S.A. (2)
1111 Suipacha Street 18th Floor
Buenos Aires, 1640, Argentina
Tel.: (54) 810 999 58626
E-Mail: jumbomas@cencosud.com.ar
Web Site: www.jumbo.com.ar
Emp.: 20,000
Supermarkets Operator
S.I.C.: 5411
N.A.I.C.S.: 445110

Supermercados Davi S.A. (2)
Larrea 847 11 12 Ciudad de 1117
Buenos Aires, Argentina Ar
Tel.: (54) 1146681713
Supermarket Operator
S.I.C.: 5411
N.A.I.C.S.: 445110

Unicenter S.A. (2)
Parana 3745
Martinez, Buenos Aires, B1640FRE,
Argentina Ar
Tel.: (54) 11 4733 1111
Fax: (54) 47331165
E-Mail: info@unicenter.com.ar
Web Site: www.unicenter.com.ar
Shopping Mall Operator
S.I.C.: 5411
N.A.I.C.S.: 445110

East Colombia S.A. (1)
Nit 900 155 107 1 Calle 175 No 22 13
Mezanine, Bogota, Colombia Co
Tel.: (57) 1 742 9800
Fax: (57) 1 742 9805
E-Mail: clientes@easy.com.co
Web Site: www.easy.com.co
Home Improvement Store Operator
S.I.C.: 5211
N.A.I.C.S.: 444110

Perini Comercial de Alimentos Ltda. (1)
Av Vasco da Gama 3051
Salvador, 40230-731, Brazil BR
Tel.: (55) 71 3203 0062
E-Mail: contatoperini@perini.com.br
Web Site: www.perini.com.br
Emp.: 750
Food Products Mfr & Distr
S.I.C.: 5142
N.A.I.C.S.: 424420

CENCOTECH INC.

141 Adelaide Street West Suite 1470
Toronto, ON, M5H 3L5, Canada
Tel.: (416) 861-1474
Fax: (416) 861-1478
Web Site: www.cencotech.com
CTZ—(TSXV)
Rev.: $1,005,226
Assets: $221,099
Liabilities: $1,898,174
Net Worth: ($1,677,075)
Earnings: ($142,294)
Emp.: 12
Fiscal Year-end: 10/31/12
Business Description:
Financial Technology Services
S.I.C.: 7371
N.A.I.C.S.: 541511
Personnel:
E. Christopher Stait-Gardner *(Chm)*
K. Barry Sparks *(Pres & CEO)*
Christopher J. Adams *(CFO)*
Leslie T. Gord *(Sec)*
Board of Directors:
E. Christopher Stait-Gardner
Derek H. L. Buntain
Leslie T. Gord
G. James Johnson
K. Barry Sparks

Subsidiary:

NamSys Inc. (1)
5 Loring Dr
Bolton, ON, L7E 1Y1, Canada
Tel.: (905) 857-9500
Fax: (905) 857-9499
E-Mail: sales@namsys.com
Web Site: www.namsys.com
Emp.: 10
Currency Handling & Cash Management Technology Services
S.I.C.: 7389
N.A.I.C.S.: 561499
E. Christopher Strait-Gardner *(Chm)*

CENERIC (HOLDINGS) LIMITED

(Formerly Morning Star Resources Limited)
28/F LHT Tower 31 Queen's Road
Central, China (Hong Kong)
Tel.: (852) 27230111
Fax: (852) 27235111
E-Mail: info@muihk.com
Web Site: www.cenericholdings.com
0542—(HKG)
Rev.: $1,128,828
Assets: $87,885,357
Liabilities: $8,958,285
Net Worth: $78,927,071
Earnings: $47,583
Fiscal Year-end: 12/31/12
Business Description:
Real Estate Development Services
S.I.C.: 6531
N.A.I.C.S.: 531390
Personnel:
Kenneth Chi Hung Chi *(CEO)*
Candy Lai Seung Leung *(Sec)*
Board of Directors:
Hoi Ling Chan
Kenneth Chi Hung Chi
Matthew Tak Pong Ho
Zhenda Huang
Kuang Yeu Lee
Wai Lam So
Yat Chun Sung
Kwok Leung Yeung

CENIT AG

Industriestrasse 52-54
D-70565 Stuttgart, Germany
Tel.: (49) 711782530
Fax: (49) 71178254000
E-Mail: info@cenit.de
Web Site: www.cenit.de
CSH—(DEU)
Rev.: $159,997,689
Assets: $79,424,030
Liabilities: $32,781,932
Net Worth: $46,642,098
Earnings: $7,294,895
Emp.: 675
Fiscal Year-end: 12/31/12
Business Description:
Software & Consultancy Solutions
S.I.C.: 7373
N.A.I.C.S.: 541512
Personnel:
Andreas Schmidt *(Chm-Supervisory Bd)*
Hubert Leypoldt *(Deputy Chm-Supervisory Bd)*
Kurt Bengel *(Member-Exec Bd-Mktg, IR & Bus Ops-Worldwide)*
Matthias Schmidt *(Member-Exec Bd-Fin, Controlling & HR)*
Supervisory Board of Directors:
Andreas Schmidt
Andreas Karrer
Hubert Leypoldt

U.S. Subsidiary:

CENIT North America Inc. (1)
691 N Squirrel Rd Ste 275
Auburn Hills, MI 48326
Tel.: (248) 276-8540
Fax: (248) 856-2478
E-Mail: info@cenit-group.com
Web Site: www.cenit.us
Information Technology Consulting Services
S.I.C.: 7373
N.A.I.C.S.: 541512
Pat Hamel *(Sec & Sr Mgr-HR)*

Non-U.S. Subsidiaries:

CENIT France SARL (1)
15 Chemin de la Crabe
31300 Toulouse, France
Tel.: (33) 56 7310220
Fax: (33) 56 1158805
E-Mail: info@cenit.de
Web Site: www.cenit.fr
Emp.: 680
Information Technology Consulting Services
S.I.C.: 7373
N.A.I.C.S.: 541512

CENIT Japan K. K. (1)
Teiken Tokyo BLDG 8F 2-17-13 Takanawa
Minato-ku, Tokyo, 108-0074, Japan
Tel.: (81) 3 5422 6691
Fax: (81) 3 5422 6692
E-Mail: info@cenit.de
Web Site: www.cenit.jp
Information Technology Consulting Services
S.I.C.: 7373
N.A.I.C.S.: 541512
Kurt Bengel, *(Gen Mgr)*

CENIT Schweiz AG (1)
Im Langhag 11
8307 Effretikon, Switzerland
Tel.: (41) 52 3541010
Fax: (41) 52 3541011
E-Mail: info@cenit.de
Web Site: www.cenit-ag.ch
Information Technology Consulting Services
S.I.C.: 7373
N.A.I.C.S.: 541512
Alfonso Panichella *(Mng Dir)*

CENIT S.R.L. (1)
Str Calea Chisinaului 104-106bis
700180 Iasi, Romania
Tel.: (40) 33 2430 574
Fax: (40) 33 2430 572
E-Mail: info@cenit.de
Web Site: www.cenit.ro
Information Technology Consulting Services
S.I.C.: 7373
N.A.I.C.S.: 541512

CENKOS CHANNEL ISLAND LIMITED

(Name Changed to Ravenscroft Limited)

CENKOS SECURITIES PLC

6 7 8 Tokenhouse Yard
London, EC2R 7AS, United Kingdom
Tel.: (44) 2073978900
Fax: (44) 2073978901
E-Mail: info@cenkos.com
Web Site: www.cenkos.com
CNKS—(AIM)
Rev.: $68,154,260
Assets: $78,037,457
Liabilities: $42,931,419
Net Worth: $35,106,037
Earnings: $13,392,379
Emp.: 108
Fiscal Year-end: 12/31/12
Business Description:
Securities Dealing & Investment Banking
S.I.C.: 6211
N.A.I.C.S.: 523110
Personnel:
Jim Durkin *(CEO)*
Stephen Doherty *(Sec)*
Board of Directors:
Gerry Aherne
Jeremy Warner Allen
Mike Chilton
Jim Durkin
Jeff Hewitt
Paul Hodges
Anthony Hotson
Joe Nally
Legal Counsel:
Travers Smith
10 Snow Hill
London, EC1A 2AL, United Kingdom
Tel.: (44) 171 248 9133
Telex: 887117 Traver G
Fax: (44) 171 236 3728

CENLUB INDUSTRIES LTD.

35 DLF Industrial Estate - 1
Faridabad, Haryana, 121003, India
Tel.: (91) 129 4113701
Fax: (91) 129 2260524
E-Mail: cenlub@cenlub.in
Web Site: www.cenlub.in
522251—(BOM)
Rev.: $6,243,056
Assets: $5,932,447
Liabilities: $3,420,016
Net Worth: $2,512,431
Earnings: $411,387
Fiscal Year-end: 03/31/13
Business Description:
Lubrication Systems Mfr
S.I.C.: 7549
N.A.I.C.S.: 811191
Personnel:
Vijendra Kumar Mittal *(Chm & Mng Dir)*
Virendra Kumar Gupta *(CFO & Compliance Officer)*
Board of Directors:
Vijendra Kumar Mittal
Ashok Kumar Agarwal
Ankur Garg
Virendra Kumar Gupta
Dinesh Kaushal
Aman Mittal
Ansh Mittal
Madhu Mittal
Hakikat Singh
Omprakash Verma
Transfer Agent:
Beetal Financial & Computer Services Pvt. Ltd
Beetal House 3rd Floor 99 Madangir Behind Local Shopping Centre
New Delhi, India

Plant:

Cenlub Industries Ltd. - Faridabad Plant - I (1)
35 DLF Industrial Estate-I
Faridabad, Haryana, 121 003, India
Tel.: (91) 129 2275483
Fax: (91) 129 2260524
E-Mail: cenlub@cenlub.in
Lubrication System Mfr
S.I.C.: 3561
N.A.I.C.S.: 333911

CENOVUS ENERGY INC.

2600 500 Centre Street SE
Calgary, AB, T2G 1A6, Canada
Tel.: (403) 766-2000
Fax: (403) 766-7600
Web Site: www.cenovus.com
CVE—(NYSE TSX)
Sls.: $17,081,354,550
Assets: $22,685,204,400
Liabilities: $13,740,269,300
Net Worth: $8,944,935,100
Earnings: $595,369,700
Emp.: 3,544
Fiscal Year-end: 12/31/13
Business Description:
Oil & Gas Exploration & Production Services
S.I.C.: 1311
N.A.I.C.S.: 211111
Personnel:
Michael A. Grandin *(Chm)*
Brian C. Ferguson *(Pres & CEO)*
Ivor Melvin Ruste *(CFO & Exec VP)*
John K. Brannan *(Exec VP & COO)*

CENOVUS ENERGY INC.—(Continued)

Harbir S. Chhina *(Exec VP-Enhanced Oil Dev & New Resource Plays)*
Kerry D. Dyte *(Exec VP-Legal, Secretarial & Internal Audit)*
Judy A. Fairburn *(Exec VP-Environment & Strategic Plng)*
Sheila M. McIntosh *(Exec VP-Comm & Stakeholder Rels)*
Donald T. Swystun *(Exec VP-Refining, Mktg, Transportation & Dev)*
Hayward J. Walls *(Exec VP-Org & Workplace Dev)*
Board of Directors:
Michael A. Grandin
Ralph S. Cunningham
Patrick Donald Daniel
Ian W. Delaney
Brian C. Ferguson
Valerie A.A. Nielsen
Charles M. Rampacek
Colin Taylor
Wayne G. Thomson

Computershare Investor Services, Inc.
250 Royall St
Canton, MA 02021
Tel.: (781) 575-2000
Toll Free: (800) 317-4445

Transfer Agents:
Computershare Investor Services, Inc.
250 Royall St
Canton, MA 02021
Tel.: (781) 575-2000
Toll Free: (800) 317-4445

Computershare Investor Services Inc
100 University Avenue 9th Floor North Tower
Toronto, ON, Canada

CENSOF HOLDINGS BERHAD

A-8 Block A Level 8 Sunway PJ51A
Jalan SS9A/19
Seri Setia, 47300 Petaling Jaya, Selangor Darul Ehsa, Malaysia
Tel.: (60) 3 79627888
Fax: (60) 3 79627800
Web Site: www.censof.com.my
CENSOF—(KLS)
Rev.: $14,679,533
Assets: $26,948,733
Liabilities: $5,469,814
Net Worth: $21,478,919
Earnings: $3,098,789
Fiscal Year-end: 12/31/12
Business Description:
Financial Management Software
S.I.C.: 7372
N.A.I.C.S.: 511210
Personnel:
Samsul Husin *(Mng Dir)*
Mark John Rees *(CTO)*
Ameer Mydin *(CEO-T-Melmax Sdn Bhd)*
Tamil Selvan *(CEO-Century Software (Malaysia) Sdn Bhd)*
M. Chandrasegaran *(Co-Sec)*
Seck Wah Lim *(Co-Sec)*
Board of Directors:
Mohd Ibrahim Mohd Zain
Hsin Hsien Ang
Tak Kong Boey
Abdul Mushir Che Chik
Abdul Gani Haron
Samsul Husin
Ameer Mydin
Tamil Selvan

CENTAMIN PLC

14 Berkeley Street
London, W1J 8DX, United Kingdom
Tel.: (44) 20 7569 1670
Fax: (44) 20 4709 1342
E-Mail: info@centamin.co.uk
Web Site: www.centamin.com
CEY—(LSE TSX)
Rev.: $426,133,000
Assets: $1,084,956,000
Liabilities: $65,112,000
Net Worth: $1,019,844,000
Earnings: $199,038,000
Emp.: 1,000
Fiscal Year-end: 12/31/12
Business Description:
Holding Company; Gold Exploration & Mining
S.I.C.: 6719
N.A.I.C.S.: 551112
Personnel:
Josef El-Raghy *(Chm & CEO)*
Pierre Louw *(CFO)*
Andrew Pardey *(COO)*
Christopher Aujard *(Gen Counsel & Sec)*
Board of Directors:
Josef El-Raghy
Mark Arnesen
Mark Bankes
G. Robert Bowker
Gordon Edward Haslam
Trevor Schultz
Kevin Michael Tomlinson

Computershare
100 University Avenue 8th Floor
Toronto, ON, Canada

Non-U.S. Subsidiary:

Centamin Egypt Limited (1)
57 Kishorn Road
Mount Pleasant, WA, 6153, Australia AU
Tel.: (61) 8 9316 2640
Fax: (61) 8 9316 2650
Web Site: www.centamin.com
Holding Company
S.I.C.: 6719
N.A.I.C.S.: 551112
Andrew Pardey *(Grp COO)*

Subsidiary:

Pharaoh Gold Mines NL (2)
57 Kishorn Road
Mount Pleasant, WA, 6153, Australia
Tel.: (61) 893162640
Fax: (61) 893162650
E-Mail: centamin@centamin.com.au
Emp.: 1
Gold Ore Mining
S.I.C.: 1041
N.A.I.C.S.: 212221

CENTAUR IMPORT MOTORS (1977) LTD.

(d/b/a Centaur Subaru)
3819 MacLeod Trail SW
Calgary, AB, T2G 2R3, Canada
Tel.: (403) 287-2544
Fax: (403) 243-1277
Toll Free: (800) 668-3128
E-Mail: admin@centaursubaru.ca
Web Site: www.centaursubaru.ca
Year Founded: 1977
Rev.: $10,286,554
Emp.: 23
Business Description:
New & Used Car Dealers
S.I.C.: 5511
N.A.I.C.S.: 441110
Personnel:
Paul Williams *(VP & Gen Mgr-Sls)*

CENTAUR MEDIA PLC

79 Wells Street
London, W1T 3QN, United Kingdom
Tel.: (44) 2079704000
Web Site: www.centaur.co.uk
Year Founded: 1982
CAU—(LSE)
Rev.: $113,708,880
Assets: $233,103,204
Liabilities: $104,233,140
Net Worth: $128,870,064
Earnings: ($60,644,736)
Emp.: 593
Fiscal Year-end: 06/30/13
Business Description:
Holding Company; Business Publishing, Information, & Exhibition Services
S.I.C.: 6719
N.A.I.C.S.: 551112
Personnel:
Andria Vidler *(CEO)*
Stephen Farish *(Interim Mng Dir-Bus Publ)*
Peter Harris *(Interim CFO)*
Claire V. Baty *(Sec)*
Board of Directors:
J. Patrick E. Taylor
Robert W. Boyle
Mark Kerswell
Rebecca S. Miskin
Colin Morrison
Christopher Satterthwaite
Legal Counsel:
Travers Smith LLP
10 Snow Hill
EC1A 2AL London, United Kingdom

Macfarlanes LLP
10 Norwich Street
EC4A 1BD London, United Kingdom

Subsidiaries:

Ascent Publishing Ltd (1)
Unit 2 Sugarbrook Court
Bromsgrove, B60 3EX, United Kingdom
Tel.: (44) 1527836600
Fax: (44) 01527579450
E-Mail: ascent@centaur.co.uk
Web Site: www.moveorimprove.co.uk
Magazine Publishing
S.I.C.: 2721
N.A.I.C.S.: 511120

Perfect Information Ltd (1)
Michael House
35 Chiswell Street, London, EC1Y 4SE, United Kingdom
Tel.: (44) 2078924200
Fax: (44) 2078924201
E-Mail: support@perfectinfo.com
Web Site: www.perfectinfo.com
Emp.: 50
Publishes Online Database of Corporate Financial Information
S.I.C.: 2741
N.A.I.C.S.: 519130
Greg Simidian *(CEO)*

The Profile Group (UK) Limited (1)
79 Wells Street
London, W1T 3QN, United Kingdom UK
Tel.: (44) 20 7970 4299
E-Mail: info@profilegroup.co.uk
Web Site: www.profilegroup.co.uk
Sales Range: $1-9.9 Million
Emp.: 50
Forward Planning & Industry Contact Information Services
S.I.C.: 7389
N.A.I.C.S.: 519190

Taxbriefs Limited (1)
Street Giles House 50 Poland Street
London, W1F 7AX, United Kingdom
Tel.: (44) 2072500967
Fax: (44) 2072518867
E-Mail: info@taxbriefs.co.uk
Web Site: www.taxbriefs.co.uk
Emp.: 15
Financial Books Publishing Services
S.I.C.: 2731
N.A.I.C.S.: 511130
Helen MacDonald *(Gen Mgr)*

CENTAURUS METALS LIMITED

Level 1 16 Ord Street
West Perth, WA, 6005, Australia
Tel.: (61) 8 9420 4000
Fax: (61) 8 9420 4040
E-Mail: office@centaurus.com.au
Web Site: www.centaurus.com.au
CTM—(ASX)
Sales Range: Less than $1 Million
Business Description:
Exploration For Base Metals, Gold & Other Mineral Resources
S.I.C.: 1081
N.A.I.C.S.: 213114
Personnel:
Darren P. Gordon *(Mng Dir)*
John Westdorp *(CFO)*
Luiz Carlos Noronha *(Legal Counsel)*
Geoffrey A. James *(Sec)*
Board of Directors:
Didier Marcel Murcia
Peter E. Freund
Darren P. Gordon
Mark D. Hancock
Richard G. Hill
Steven Zaninovich
Legal Counsel:
Murcia Pestell Hillard
MPH Building 23 Barrack Street
Perth, Australia

CENTENARI E ZINELLI SPA

Corso Italia 62
20025 Legnano, MI, Italy
Tel.: (39) 0331453968
Fax: (39) 0331549991
E-Mail: info@zinelli.it
Web Site: www.zinelli.it
Year Founded: 1872
Emp.: 404
Business Description:
Yarns & Textiles
S.I.C.: 2299
N.A.I.C.S.: 313110

CENTENNIAL BUICK GMC

(See Under O'Leary Buick GMC (Saint John) Ltd.)

CENTENNIAL OPTICAL LTD.

158 Norfinch Dr
Toronto, ON, M3N 1X6, Canada
Tel.: (416) 739-8539
Fax: (416) 739-8234
Web Site: www.centennialoptical.com
Year Founded: 1967
Emp.: 125
Business Description:
Eyeglass Lens Distr
S.I.C.: 3827
N.A.I.C.S.: 333314
Personnel:
Shraga Bellon *(Gen Mgr)*

CENTENNIAL PLYMOUTH CHRYSLER (1973) LTD

(d/b/a Centennial Chrysler)
395 Dunlop Street West
Barrie, ON, L4N 1C3, Canada
Tel.: (705) 726-0393
Fax: (705) 739-7034
Toll Free: (800) 337-1007
E-Mail: sales@centennialchrysler.ca
Web Site: www.centennialchrysler.ca
Year Founded: 1973
Rev.: $56,179,200
Emp.: 110
Business Description:
New & Used Car Dealers
S.I.C.: 5511
N.A.I.C.S.: 441110
Personnel:
Ray Billett *(Mgr-Parts)*

CENTENNIAL WINDOWS LTD.

687 Sovereign Road
London, ON, N5V 4K8, Canada
Tel.: (519) 451-0508
Fax: (519) 451-8582
Toll Free: (800) 367-7543
E-Mail: service@centennialwindows.com

Web Site: www.centennialwindows.com
Year Founded: 1991
Rev.: $15,041,476
Emp.: 130
Business Description:
Windows & Doors Mfr
S.I.C.: 3442
N.A.I.C.S.: 332321
Personnel:
George Warren *(Pres)*

CENTER NALOZBE D.D.

Ulica Vita Kraigherja 1
2000 Maribor, Slovenia
Tel.: (386) 2 2522802
Fax: (386) 2 2522053
E-Mail: info@center-nalozbe.si
Web Site: www.center-nalozbe.si
IFHR—(LJU)
Sales Range: $100-124.9 Million
Business Description:
Investment Management Services
S.I.C.: 6211
N.A.I.C.S.: 523999
Personnel:
Sasa Fajs *(Chm-Mgmt Bd)*

CENTERPULSE AUSTRALIA PTY LTD

Level 5, 384 Eastern Valley Way
Chatswood, Sydney, 2067, Australia
Tel.: (61) 2 94177922
Fax: (61) 2 94174722
Sales Range: $25-49.9 Million
Emp.: 40
Business Description:
Medical & Hospital Equipment Mfr
S.I.C.: 5047
N.A.I.C.S.: 423450

CENTERRA GOLD INC.

1 University Avenue Suite 1500
Toronto, ON, M5J 2P1, Canada
Tel.: (416) 204-1953
Fax: (416) 204-1954
E-Mail: info@centerragold.com
Web Site: www.centerragold.com
CG—(TSX)
Rev.: $660,737,000
Assets: $1,554,131,000
Liabilities: $225,305,000
Net Worth: $1,328,826,000
Earnings: ($183,998,000)
Emp.: 3,159
Fiscal Year-end: 12/31/12
Business Description:
Gold Mining Services
S.I.C.: 1041
N.A.I.C.S.: 212221
Personnel:
Stephen A. Lang *(Chm)*
Bruce V. Walter *(Vice Chm)*
Ian Atkinson *(Pres & CEO)*
Jeffrey S. Parr *(CFO & VP)*
Gordon D. Reid *(COO & VP)*
Frank H. Herbert *(Gen Counsel & Sec)*
Board of Directors:
Stephen A. Lang
Ian Atkinson
Richard W. Connor
Raphael A. Girard
Karybek Ibraev
John W. Lill
Amandgeldy Muraliev
Sheryl K. Pressler
Bruce V. Walter
Legal Counsel:
Torys LLP
Toronto, ON, Canada
Transfer Agent:
CIBC Mellon Trust Company
320 Bay Street
PO Box 1
Toronto, ON, M5H 2A6, Canada
Tel.: (416) 643-5500
Fax: (416) 643-5570
Toll Free: (800) 387-0825

CENTIUS GOLD LIMITED

Level 3 32 Walker Street
North Sydney, NSW, 2060, Australia
Tel.: (61) 2 8958 2226
Fax: (61) 2 9954 6408
E-Mail: admin@centiusgold.com
Web Site: www.centiusgold.com
Year Founded: 2009
CNS—(ASX)
Rev.: $94,257
Assets: $2,146,875
Liabilities: $157,449
Net Worth: $1,989,426
Earnings: ($3,332,433)
Fiscal Year-end: 12/31/12
Business Description:
Gold Mining Services
S.I.C.: 1041
N.A.I.C.S.: 212221
Personnel:
Pipvide Tang *(Sec)*
Board of Directors:
Scott Brown
Robert McLennan
John Robson
Chiong Ee Tiong
Legal Counsel:
Websters
Level 11 37 Bligh St
Sydney, NSW, 2000, Australia

CENTRAIS ELETRICAS BRASILEIRAS S.A.

(d/b/a Eletrobras)
Avenida Presidente Vargas 409 9th Floor Edificio Herm Stoltz Centro
20071-003 Rio de Janeiro, Brazil
Tel.: (55) 21 2514 6331
Fax: (55) 25146479
E-Mail: rachel.rocha@eletrobras.com
Web Site: www.eletrobras.com
Year Founded: 1962
EBR—(BRAZ NYSE)
Rev.: $16,755,975,592
Assets: $84,701,282,862
Liabilities: $51,606,631,972
Net Worth: $33,094,650,891
Earnings: ($3,406,658,962)
Emp.: 27,940
Fiscal Year-end: 12/31/12
Business Description:
Holding Company; Electric Power Distr
S.I.C.: 6719
N.A.I.C.S.: 551112
Personnel:
Marcio Pereira Zimmermann *(Chm)*
Jose da Costa Carvalho Neto *(CEO)*
Armando Casado de Araujo *(CFO, Chief IR Officer)*
Miguel Colasuonno *(Chief Admin Officer)*
Valter Luiz Cardeal de Souza *(Chief Generation Officer)*
Marcos Aurelio Madureira da Silva *(Chief Distr Officer)*
Jose Antonio Muniz Lopes *(Chief Transmission Officer)*
Board of Directors:
Marcio Pereira Zimmermann
Mauricio Muniz Barreto de Carvalho
Wagner Bittencourt de Oliveira
Jose da Costa Carvalho Neto
Jose Antonio Correa Coimbra
Lindemberg de Lima Bezerra

Subsidiaries:

Boa Vista Energia S.A. (1)
Av Capitao Julio Bezerra Forest
Rio de Janeiro, Brazil
Tel.: (55) 32125700
Web Site: www.boavistaenergia.gov.br
Electric Company
S.I.C.: 9631
N.A.I.C.S.: 926130

Centrais Eletricas do Norte do Brasil SA (1)
SCN-Qd 06-Conj A Bloco B Asa Norte
Brasilia, 70 718-900, Brazil
Tel.: (55) 6134295151
Fax: (55) 6133281463
E-Mail: ouvidoria@eletronorte.gov.br
Web Site: www.eletronorte.gov.br
Emp.: 2,213
Energy Generation & Transmission Services
S.I.C.: 4939
N.A.I.C.S.: 221111
Astrogildo F. Quental *(Dir-Fin)*

Subsidiary:

Manaus Energia SA (2)
Av Sete de Setembro 50 Centro
Manaus, 69005-140, Brazil
Tel.: (55) 9236211110
Fax: (55) 3633332406
E-Mail: marcus.aurlye@elecrobras.com
Web Site: www.manausenergia.com.br
Emp.: 429
Power Generation & Transmission Services
S.I.C.: 4931
N.A.I.C.S.: 221122
Marcus Aurelius *(Pres)*

Centro de Pesquisas de Energia Eletrica (1)
Av Um sn - Cidade Universitaria
Rio de Janeiro, 21941-590, Brazil
Tel.: (55) 2125986000
Fax: (55) 2122601340
Web Site: www.cepel.br
Research Center
S.I.C.: 8731
N.A.I.C.S.: 541712

CEPISA-Companhia Energetica do Piaui (1)
Ave Maranhao 759 Sul
Sao Miguel, Brazil
Tel.: (55) 8632288000
Fax: (55) 8632216679
Web Site: www.cepisa.com.br
Electric Company
S.I.C.: 9631
N.A.I.C.S.: 926130

Companhia de Geracao Termica de Energia Eletrica (1)
Rua Sete de Setembro 539
90010-190 Porto Alegre, Brazil
Tel.: (55) 5132871500
Fax: (55) 5132871566
E-Mail: pr@cgtee.gov.br
Web Site: www.cgtee.gov.br
Emp.: 500
Energy Generation Services
S.I.C.: 4939
N.A.I.C.S.: 221118
Sereno Chaise *(Chm)*
Eduardo Antonio Peters *(Mng Dir)*

Companhia Energetica de Alagoas (1)
Av Fernandes Lima 3349 Gruta de Lourdes
57057-900 Maceio, Alagoas, Brazil
Tel.: (55) 82 2126 9300
Fax: (55) 82 218 9300
Web Site: www.ceal.com.br
Electric Power Generation & Distribution Services
S.I.C.: 4931
N.A.I.C.S.: 221118

Companhia Energetica de Roraima (1)
Av Presidente Castelo Branco 1163 Calunga
Boa Vista, Roraima, Brazil
Tel.: (55) 95 4009 1500
Fax: (55) 95 3623 1350
Web Site: www.cerr.rr.gov.br
Electric Power Generation & Distribution Services
S.I.C.: 4939
N.A.I.C.S.: 221118

Companhia Hidreletrica do Sao Francisco (1)
Rua Delmiro Gouveia 333
San Martin, Recife, Pernambuco, 50761-901, Brazil
Tel.: (55) 81 3229 2000
Fax: (55) 81 3229 3288
Web Site: www.chesf.gov.br
Electric Power Generation & Distribution Services
S.I.C.: 4939
N.A.I.C.S.: 221118

Companhia Hidro Eletrica do Sao Francisco SA (1)
Rua Delmiro Gouveia 333 - Bongi
Recife, Pernambuco, 50761-901, Brazil
Tel.: (55) 8132292000
E-Mail: chesf@chesf.gov.br
Web Site: www.chesf.gov.br
Emp.: 5,625
Energy Generation & Transmission Services
S.I.C.: 4931
N.A.I.C.S.: 221122

Eletrobras Eletronorte (1)
SCN Quadra 06 Conj A Blocos B e C
Entrada Norte 2
Asa Norte, 70716-901, Brazil
Tel.: (55) 61 3429 5151
Electric Power Generation & Distribution Services
S.I.C.: 4939
N.A.I.C.S.: 221118

Eletrobras Termonuclear SA (1)
Rua da Candelaria 65 Centro
Rio de Janeiro, 20091-020, Brazil
Tel.: (55) 2125887000
Fax: (55) 2125887200
E-Mail: aregina@eletronuclear.gov.br
Web Site: www.eletronuclear.gov.br
Emp.: 2,000
Nuclear Power Generation
S.I.C.: 4911
N.A.I.C.S.: 221113
Othon Luiz Pinheiro da Silva *(Chm & Pres)*

Eletrosul Centrais Eletricas SA (1)
Deputado Antonio Edu Vieira 999
88040-901 Florianopolis, Santa Catarina, Brazil
Tel.: (55) 4832317262
Fax: (55) 482344040
E-Mail: webmaster@eletrosul.gov.br
Web Site: www.eletrosul.gov.br
Electric Power Transmission Services
S.I.C.: 4931
N.A.I.C.S.: 221121
Ronaldo dos Santos Custodio *(Dir-Ops)*

Subsidiary:

Porto Velho Transmissora de Energia S.A. (2)
Rua Deputado Antonio Edu Vieira 999
Salao Terreo - Pantanal
Florianopolis, Santa Catarina, 88040-901, Brazil
Tel.: (55) 48 3231 7277
Fax: (55) 48 3234 2608
Emp.: 1,000
Electric Power Transmission Services
S.I.C.: 4911
N.A.I.C.S.: 221121

FURNAS Centrais Eletricas SA (1)
Rua Real Grandeza 219
Rio de Janeiro, 22283-900, Brazil
Tel.: (55) 2125283112
Fax: (55) 21 2528 5858
E-Mail: webfurnas@furnas.com.br
Web Site: www.furnas.com.br
Emp.: 5,545
Energy Production Services
S.I.C.: 4939
N.A.I.C.S.: 221111

CENTRAIS ELETRICAS DE SANTA CATARINA S.A. - CELESC

Av Itamarati 160
88034900 Florianopolis, SC, Brazil
Tel.: (55) 48 3231 5021
Fax: (55) 48 3231 6019
E-Mail: ri@celesc.com.br
Web Site: www.celesc.com.br
Year Founded: 1955
CLSC3—(BRAZ)
Sales Range: $1-4.9 Billion
Emp.: 2,964

Centrais Eletricas de Santa Catarina S.A. - Celesc—(Continued)

Business Description:
Investment Management Services
S.I.C.: 6282
N.A.I.C.S.: 523920
Personnel:
Jose Carlos Oneda *(Dir-IR)*

CENTRAL AREA ELECTRICAL MECHANICAL JOINT STOCK COMPANY

Street No 3 Hoa Cam Industrial Zone
Cam le District, Da Nang, Vietnam
Tel.: (84) 511 2218455
Fax: (84) 511 3846224
E-Mail: codien@cemc.com.vn
Web Site: www.cemc.com.vn
CJC—(HNX)
Business Description:
Mechanical & Electrical Equipment Mfr
S.I.C.: 3568
N.A.I.C.S.: 333613
Personnel:
Viet Hai Ngo *(Chm-Mgmt Bd)*
Minh Chau Hoang *(Gen Dir)*
Cung Thac Nguyen *(Member-Mgmt Bd)*
Nhu Khai Tran *(Member-Mgmt Bd)*

CENTRAL ASIA DEVELOPMENT GROUP, INC.

350 Orchard Road #16-09/10
Singapore, 238868, Singapore
Tel.: (65) 68872234
Fax: (65) 63336621
E-Mail: admin@central-asia.net
Web Site: www.central-asia.net
Emp.: 100
Business Description:
Engineering, Logistics, Aid Management & Development Services
S.I.C.: 7389
N.A.I.C.S.: 561990
Personnel:
Raju K. Shaulis *(Pres)*
Michael Lambert *(CFO)*
Marijohn Sampson *(Chief Strategic Bus Dev Officer)*

CENTRAL ASIA METALS PLC

Masters House 107 Hammersmith Road
London, W14 0QH, United Kingdom
Tel.: (44) 207 603 1515
Fax: (44) 207 603 8448
Web Site: www.centralasiametals.com
CAML—(AIM)
Rev.: $30,656,304
Assets: $91,572,529
Liabilities: $20,543,681
Net Worth: $71,028,848
Earnings: $9,794,292
Emp.: 259
Fiscal Year-end: 12/31/12
Business Description:
Copper, Gold & Molybdenum Mining & Exploration Services
S.I.C.: 1021
N.A.I.C.S.: 212234
Personnel:
Nick Clarke *(CEO)*
Nigel Robinson *(CFO)*
Saken Ashirbekova *(Gen Dir-Kounrad Copper Company)*
Yerken Magad *(Gen Dir-New CAML Mongolia)*
Pavel Semenchenko *(Gen Dir-Sary Kazna)*
Tony Hunter *(Sec)*
Board of Directors:
Christopher Nigel Hurst-Brown
Robert Cathery
Nick Clarke
Howard Nicholson
Michael Price
Kenges Rakishev
Nigel Robinson
Nurlan Zhakupov
Legal Counsel:
White & Case Kazakhstan LLP
77 Kunayev Street 8th Floor Park View Office Tower
Almaty, Kazakhstan
Tsets
Suite 409 Bridge Group Bld. Enhtaivni Avenue
Ulaanbaatar, Mongolia
Ashurst LLP
Broadwalk House 5 Appold Street
London, EC2A 2HA, United Kingdom

CENTRAL ASIA RESOURCES LIMITED

283 Rokeby Road
Subiaco, WA, 6008, Australia
Tel.: (61) 863140500
Fax: (61) 894811947
Web Site: www.centralasia.com.au
CVR—(ASX)
Rev.: $4,211,509
Assets: $24,015,199
Liabilities: $5,424,218
Net Worth: $18,590,981
Earnings: ($6,709,173)
Emp.: 46
Fiscal Year-end: 12/31/12
Business Description:
Gold Explorer
S.I.C.: 1041
N.A.I.C.S.: 212221
Personnel:
Peter Robert Thompson *(CEO)*
Robin Gill *(Mng Dir)*
Duncan Greenaway *(COO)*
Harry Spindler *(Sec)*
Board of Directors:
Alan Hopkins
Robin Gill
Erulan Kanapyanov
Philippe Reiser
Legal Counsel:
Gilbert Tobin
1202 Hay Street
West Perth, Australia
Subsidiary:

Moonstone Holdings Ltd. **(1)**
Cockburn Rd
Hamilton Hill, Perth, Western Australia, 6163, Australia
Tel.: (61) 893362807
Gold Ore Mining & Exploration Services
S.I.C.: 1041
N.A.I.C.S.: 212221

CENTRAL-ASIAN FUEL ENERGY COMPANY

Karasay Batyr St 89
050012 Almaty, Kazakhstan
Tel.: (7) 7272584941
Fax: (7) 7272584942
E-Mail: info@energy.kz
Web Site: www.capec.kz
CTECB1—(KAZ)
Sales Range: $400-449.9 Million
Emp.: 8,970
Business Description:
Electricity Generation Services
S.I.C.: 1623
N.A.I.C.S.: 237130
Personnel:
Aleksandr Yakovlevich Klebanov *(Chm)*
Gulnara Artambayeva Dzhumagalievna *(Pres)*
Board of Directors:
Aleksandr Yakovlevich Klebanov
Yerkyn Adamiyanovich Amirkhanov
Gennadiy Ivanovich Andreyev
Gulnara Artambayeva Dzhumagalievna
Sergey Vladimirovich Kan
Valeriya Viktorovna Kim
Subsidiary:

Eximbank Kazakhstan JSC **(1)**
80 Bogenbai Batyr Str
010010 Almaty, Kazakhstan
Tel.: (7) 272663093
Fax: (7) 27 266 39 10
E-Mail: info@eximbank.kz
Web Site: www.eximbank.kz
Emp.: 43
Banking Services
S.I.C.: 6029
N.A.I.C.S.: 522110
Dmitriy A. Prikhozhan *(Chm-Mgmt Bd)*
Nataliya G. Rimer *(Deputy Chm-Mgmt Bd)*
Dzhaksymbetova K. Altynai *(Mng Dir-Mgmt Bd)*
Baurzhan B. Dyussebayev *(Mng Dir-Mgmt Bd)*
Alma M. Kazova *(Mng Dir-Mgmt Bd)*
Yakov A. Klebanov *(Mng Dir-Mgmt Bd)*

CENTRAL ASIAN MINERALS & RESOURCES PLC

34 North Quay
Douglas, IM1 4LB, Isle of Man
Tel.: (44) 1624 679 000
Web Site: www.camarplc.com
CMRP—(ISDX)
Business Description:
Investment Services
S.I.C.: 6211
N.A.I.C.S.: 523999
Personnel:
David Russell *(CEO)*
Board of Directors:
A. M. Ehlers
M. C. Melian
Richard Fredrick Nanna
David Russell

CENTRAL AUTOMOTIVE PRODUCTS LTD.

(d/b/a CAPCO)
2-30 4-Chome Nakanoshima
Osaka, 530-0005, Japan
Tel.: (81) 664435182
Telex: 63297
Fax: (81) 64436654
E-Mail: autocent@central-auto.co.jp
Web Site: www.central-auto.co.jp
Year Founded: 1943
8117—(TKS)
Sales Range: $150-199.9 Million
Emp.: 268
Business Description:
Automotive Parts & Accessories & Air Conditioner Parts Development, Mfr & Sales; New & Used Car Sales Import Export
S.I.C.: 3714
N.A.I.C.S.: 336390
Personnel:
Michio Fukutsuji *(Pres)*
U.S. Subsidiary:

CAPCO U.S.A., Inc. **(1)**
2300 E Higgins Rd Ste 205 A
Elk Grove Village, IL 60007-2632 (100%)
Tel.: (847) 364-0888
Fax: (847) 364-4518
Emp.: 1
Distribution of Automotive Products
S.I.C.: 4731
N.A.I.C.S.: 488510
Taka Kinoshita *(VP)*
Non-U.S. Subsidiary:

CAPCO Private Ltd. **(1)**
371 Beach Rd
Unit 1501, 199597 Singapore, Singapore SG
Tel.: (65) 62941915
Fax: (65) 62965173
E-Mail: autocent@singnet.com.sg
Emp.: 4
Business Support Services
S.I.C.: 7389
N.A.I.C.S.: 561499

CENTRAL AZUCARERA DE TARLAC, INC.

Jose Cojuangco Sons Bldg 119 de la Rosa St Legaspi Village
Makati, 1200, Philippines
Tel.: (63) 28183911
Fax: (63) 28179309
E-Mail: info@luisitasugar.com
Web Site: www.luisitasugar.com
Year Founded: 1927
CAT—(PHI)
Sales Range: $10-24.9 Million
Emp.: 749
Business Description:
Raw Sugar Mfr
S.I.C.: 2061
N.A.I.C.S.: 311314
Personnel:
Pedro Cojuangco *(Chm & Pres)*
Jose Cojuangco Jr. *(Pres)*
Fernando C. Cojuangco *(COO)*
Josephine C. Reyes *(Treas & VP)*
Arcadio M. Lopez *(Sec)*
Board of Directors:
Pedro Cojuangco
Jose Cojuangco Jr.
Fulgenico S. Factoran Jr.
Jose Manuel C. Lopa
Josephine C. Reyes
Ernesto G. Teopaco
Georg Weber-Hoehl

CENTRAL BANK & FINANCIAL SERVICES AUTHORITY OF IRELAND

Dame Street
PO Box 559
Dublin, 2, Ireland
Tel.: (353) 14344000
Fax: (353) 16716561
Web Site: www.centralbank.ie
Sales Range: $800-899.9 Million
Emp.: 963
Business Description:
Central Bank
S.I.C.: 6011
N.A.I.C.S.: 521110
Personnel:
John Hurley *(Governor)*
Tom O'Connell *(Asst Gen Dir-Economic Analysis/Res & Publications)*
Brian Halpin *(Sec)*
Board of Directors:
David Begg
Gerard Danaher
Roy Donovan
David Doyle
John Dunne
Alan Gray
Brian Halpin
John Hurley
Patrick Neary
Martin O'Donoghue
Brian Patterson
Deirdre Purcell

CENTRAL BANK OF ARMENIA

Vazgen Sargsyan Str 6
375010 Yerevan, Benin
Tel.: (229) 10583841
Fax: (229) 10523852
E-Mail: Chairman@cba.am
Web Site: www.cba.am
Sales Range: $100-124.9 Million
Emp.: 531

Business Description:
Central Bank
S.I.C.: 6029
N.A.I.C.S.: 522110
Personnel:
Artur Javadyan *(Chm)*
Vache Gabrielyan *(Deputy Chm)*
Board of Directors:
Artur Javadyan
Vache Gabrielyan
Karine Minasyan
Vardan Movsesyan
Andranik Norekyan
Amalya Saribekyan
Hrant Suvaryan

CENTRAL BANK OF BAHRAIN
PO Box 27
Manama, Bahrain
Tel.: (973) 17547777
Fax: (973) 17530399
E-Mail: info@cbb.gov.bh
Web Site: www.cbb.gov.bh
Sales Range: $125-149.9 Million
Emp.: 303
Business Description:
Central Bank
S.I.C.: 6011
N.A.I.C.S.: 521110
Personnel:
Rasheed Mohammed Al Maraj *(Governor)*

CENTRAL BANK OF BARBADOS
Tom Adams Financial Centre
Spry Street, Bridgetown, Barbados
Mailing Address:
PO Box 1016
Bridgetown, Barbados
Tel.: (246) 4366870
Fax: (246) 4279559
E-Mail: cbb.libr@caribsurf.com
Web Site: www.centralbank.org.bb
Emp.: 300
Business Description:
Central Bank
S.I.C.: 6011
N.A.I.C.S.: 521110
Personnel:
Marion Williams *(Chm & Governor)*
Board of Directors:
Marion Williams
Cicely P. Chase
Michael G. Howard
Parick J. Mayers
Grantley Smith
Patrick B. Toppin

CENTRAL BANK OF BELIZE
Gabourel Ln
PO Box 852
Belize, Belize
Tel.: (501) 2236194
Fax: (501) 2236226
E-Mail: cbbhrd@bcl.net
Web Site: www.centralbank.org.bz
Emp.: 109
Business Description:
Central Bank
S.I.C.: 6011
N.A.I.C.S.: 521110
Board of Directors:
Kerry Belisle
Jaime Briceno
Michel Chebat

CENTRAL BANK OF EGYPT
54 Elgomhoreya Street
11511 Cairo, Egypt
Tel.: (20) 27702770
E-Mail: info@cbe.org.eg
Web Site: www.cbe.org.eg
Year Founded: 1961
Business Description:
Central Bank
S.I.C.: 6011
N.A.I.C.S.: 521110
Personnel:
Farouk Abd El Baky El Okdah *(Chm & Governor)*
Tarek Hassan Aly Amer *(Deputy Governor)*
Board of Directors:
Farouk Abd El Baky El Okdah
Hasan El Sayed Abdalla
Tarek Hassan Aly Amer
Mohamed Kamal El-Din Barakat
Abd El Salam Mostafa El Anwar
Ziyad Ahmed Bahaa El Din
Moawad Hassan El Habashi
Hatem Abdel Galil El Karnashawy
Hani Salah Mohammed Serry El-Dine
Momtaz Mohamed El-Said
Hazem Zaki Hassan
Mahmoud Abd El Fadeel Hussein
Mohamed Saleh Younes
Mona Zulficar

CENTRAL BANK OF INDIA LIMITED
Chander Mukhi Nariman Point
Central Office, Mumbai, 400 021, India
Tel.: (91) 2266387777
Fax: (91) 22044336
Web Site: www.centralbankofindia.co.in
Year Founded: 1911
532885—(BOM NSE)
Rev.: $4,370,513,384
Assets: $49,813,588,886
Liabilities: $46,927,731,151
Net Worth: $2,885,857,735
Earnings: $190,983,581
Emp.: 37,113
Fiscal Year-end: 03/31/13
Business Description:
Central Bank
S.I.C.: 6029
N.A.I.C.S.: 522110
Personnel:
Rajeev Rishi *(Chm & Mng Dir)*
Anand Kumar Das *(Compliance Officer, Sec & Asst Gen Mgr-MBD)*
Board of Directors:
Rajeev Rishi
N. Balakrishnan
Animesh Chauhan
Salim Gangadharan
Raj Kumar Goyal
Gurbax Kumar Joshi
K. P. Krishnan
S. B. Rode
Krishan Sethi
M. P. Shorawala
Guman Singh

P K Subramaniam & Co
11-5-23 Karthik Complex Above Vijaya Bank Bresthwarpet
Raichur, 584101, India

Kumar Chopra & Associates
B-12 Ground Floor Kalindi Colony
New Delhi, 110065, India

K. S. Aiyar & Co
H F-7 Laxmi Mills Shakti Mills Lane Off Dr E Moses Road
Mahalaxmi, 400011 Mumbai, India

Ghiya & Co
E-68 Ghiya Hospital Complex Sector 12
Malviya Nagar
Jaipur, 302017, India

D. Rangaswamy & Co
R C Towers II Floor New 82 Old No 27 Josier Street
Nungambakkam, Chennai, 600034, India

Transfer Agent:
Link Intime India Pvt. Ltd.
C-13 Pannalal Silk Mills Compound
LBS Marg
Bhandup, Mumbai, 400 078, India
Tel.: (91) 22 2596 3838
Fax: (91) 22 2594 6969

CENTRAL BANK OF IRAQ
Al-Rasheed Street
Baghdad, Iraq
Tel.: (964) 1 8165170
Fax: (964) 1 8166802
E-Mail: cbi@cbiraq.org
Web Site: www.cbiraq.org
Business Description:
Central Bank
S.I.C.: 6011
N.A.I.C.S.: 521110

CENTRAL BANK OF JORDAN
PO Box 37
Amman, 11118, Jordan
Tel.: (962) 64630301
Fax: (962) 64638889
E-Mail: info@cbj.gov.jo
Web Site: www.cbj.gov.jo
Sales Range: $200-249.9 Million
Emp.: 578
Business Description:
Banking Services
S.I.C.: 6029
N.A.I.C.S.: 522110
Personnel:
Umayya Salah Toukan *(Chm)*
Mohammad Said Shahin *(Vice Chm)*
Faris A. Sharaf *(Vice Chm)*
Board of Directors:
Umayya Salah Toukan
Mufleh Akel
Ibrahim Izz Al-Din
Adel Al-Kodah
Saeed Darwazeh
Najib Qubain
Mohammad Said Shahin
Faris A. Sharaf

CENTRAL BANK OF KENYA
Haile Salassie Avenue
PO Box 60000
00200 Nairobi, Kenya
Tel.: (254) 202860000
Fax: (254) 202340192
E-Mail: info@centralbank.go.ke
Web Site: www.centralbank.go.ke
Int. Income: $66,301,920
Assets: $6,630,068,470
Liabilities: $6,035,788,100
Net Worth: $594,280,370
Earnings: $41,011,960
Fiscal Year-end: 06/30/13
Business Description:
Central Bank
S.I.C.: 6011
N.A.I.C.S.: 521110
Personnel:
Mbui Wagacha *(Chm)*
Board of Directors:
Mbui Wagacha
Vivienne A. Y. Apopo
John G. Msafari
Florence K. Muindi
Njuguna S. Ndung'u
William Otiende Ogara
Legal Counsel:
Oraro & Co Advocates
ACK Garden House 1st Ngong Avenue
P.O Box 51236
Nairobi, Kenya

CENTRAL BANK OF KUWAIT
PO Box 526
Safat, Kuwait, 13006, Kuwait
Tel.: (965) 2240 3257
Fax: (965) 2244 0887
E-Mail: cbk@cbk.gov.kw
Web Site: www.cbk.gov.kw
Int. Income: $291,462,280
Assets: $28,567,769,199
Liabilities: $1,212,608,415
Net Worth: $27,355,160,784
Earnings: $56,299,654
Emp.: 1,011
Fiscal Year-end: 03/31/13
Business Description:
Central Bank
S.I.C.: 6011
N.A.I.C.S.: 521110
Personnel:
Mohammed Y. Al-Hashel *(Chm & Governor)*
Board of Directors:
Mohammed Y. Al-Hashel
Abdul Rasoul Yousef Abulhassan
Mohammed Ali Al-Kadi
Osamah M. Y. Al-Nisf
Abdulaziz M. Alkhaldi
Yousef J. Alobaid
Nasser Abdullah Mishari Alroudan
Khalifa M. Hamada

Ernst & Young Al Aiban Al Osaimi & Partners
Kuwait, Kuwait

CENTRAL BANK OF LESOTHO
Corner Airport and Moshoeshoe Roads
PO Box 1184
Maseru, 100, Lesotho
Tel.: (266) 22314281
Fax: (266) 22310051
E-Mail: cbl@centralbank.org.ls
Web Site: www.centralbank.org.ls
Year Founded: 1978
Sales Range: $25-49.9 Million
Emp.: 200
Business Description:
Central Bank
S.I.C.: 6011
N.A.I.C.S.: 521110
Personnel:
R.A. Matlanyane *(Chm)*
M.G. Makenete *(Co-Deputy Chm)*
M. P. Makhetha *(Co-Deputy Chm)*
Board of Directors:
R.A. Matlanyane
O. Letebele
M.G. Makenete
M. P. Makhetha
S. Malebanye
M.P. Mangoaela
M. Posholi
M. Rapapa

CENTRAL BANK OF LIBYA
PO Box 1103
Tripoli, Libya
Tel.: (218) 213333591
Fax: (218) 442471
E-Mail: info@cbl.gov.ly
Web Site: www.cbl.gov.ly
Business Description:
Central Bank
S.I.C.: 6011
N.A.I.C.S.: 521110
Personnel:
Farhat O. Bengdara *(Chm & Governor)*
Mohammed A. Shukri *(Vice Chm & Deputy Governor)*
Board of Directors:
Farhat O. Bengdara
Idrss Abd-Aslam Eshteiwi
Omar Ibrahim Hussein
Mohammed A. Shukri
Bilgasim Omar Tbouli
Ashur Kahlifa Triable
Bashir Ali Tweirgui

CENTRAL BANK OF NIGERIA
33 Abubakar Tafawa Balewa Way
Central Business Dist
PMB 0187
Cadastral Zone, Abuja, Nigeria

Central Bank of Nigeria—(Continued)

Tel.: (234) 946236011
Fax: (234) 946236012
E-Mail: info@cenbank.org
Web Site: www.cenbank.org
Sales Range: $550-599.9 Million
Emp.: 4,862
Business Description:
Central Bank
S.I.C.: 6011
N.A.I.C.S.: 521110
Personnel:
Chukwuma C. Soludo *(Chm & Governor)*
Sarah Alade *(Deputy Chm-Economic Policy)*
Tunde Lemo *(Deputy Chm)*
Ernest C. Ebi *(Chm-Corp Svcs)*
Alhaji Umaru Bello Girei *(Sec)*
Board of Directors:
Ernest C. Ebi
Chukwuma C. Soludo
Sarah Alade
Akpan H. Ekpo
Alhaji Umaru Bello Girei
Danladi Kifasi
Tunde Lemo
Mallam Dahiru Muhammad
Samuel O. Olofin
Joshua O. Omuya

CENTRAL BANK OF OMAN
PO Box 1161
Ruwi, 112, Oman
Tel.: (968) 24777777
Fax: (968) 24777728
Web Site: www.cbo-oman.org
Sales Range: $125-149.9 Million
Emp.: 600
Business Description:
Central Bank
S.I.C.: 6011
N.A.I.C.S.: 521110
Personnel:
Hamood Sangour Al-Zadjali *(Pres & CEO)*
Board of Directors:
Salem Bin Hilal Al Khalili
Salim Bin Abdulla Bin Said Al Rawas
Mohammed Bin Nasser Al-Khuseiby
Hamood Sangour Al-Zadjali
Ali Mohammed Moosa
Yahya Bin Mohamed Naseeb

CENTRAL BANK OF SAMOA
PO Box Private Bag
Apia, Samoa (Western)
Tel.: (685) 34100
Fax: (685) 24019
E-Mail: centralbank@cbs.gov.ws
Web Site: www.cbs.gov.ws
Sales Range: $25-49.9 Million
Emp.: 100
Business Description:
Central Bank
S.I.C.: 6011
N.A.I.C.S.: 521110
Personnel:
Leasi Papali'i T. Scanlan *(CEO)*
Mary Fidow *(Chief Publications Officer)*
Board of Directors:
Tootoovao Sanele Afoa
Muliagatele L. MacDonald
Lealiie'e R. Ott
Hinauri Petana
Malaeoali'i So'otala Pua
Leasi Papali'i T. Scanlan

CENTRAL BANK OF SEYCHELLES
Independence Avenue
PO Box 701
Victoria, Mahe, Seychelles
Tel.: (248) 4282000
Fax: (248) 4226104
E-Mail: enquiries@cbs.sc
Web Site: www.cbs.sc
Emp.: 135
Business Description:
Central Bank
S.I.C.: 6011
N.A.I.C.S.: 521110
Personnel:
Caroline Abel *(First Deputy Governor)*
Naadir Hassan *(Dir & Supvr-Banking & Foreign Exchange)*
Terry Adrienne *(Officer-Banking Payment Sys)*
Martine Faure *(Legal Officer)*
Levina Francoise *(Officer-HR)*
Shannon Jolicoeur *(Legal Officer)*
Jeannette Payet *(Officer-Banking)*
Board of Directors:
Errol Dias
Wilfred Jackson

CENTRAL BANK OF SOLOMON ISLANDS
PO Box 634
Honiara, Solomon Islands
Tel.: (677) 21791
Fax: (677) 23513
E-Mail: info@cbsi.com.sb
Web Site: www.cbsi.com.sb
Year Founded: 1983
Sales Range: $1-9.9 Million
Emp.: 73
Business Description:
Central Bank
S.I.C.: 6011
N.A.I.C.S.: 521110
Personnel:
Rick N. Hounipwela *(Chm)*
Denton H. Rarawa *(Deputy Governor)*
Bella Simiha *(Sec)*
Board of Directors:
Rick N. Hounipwela
Val Beniuk
Michael Brown
Tony Hughes
Jack Kairi
George Kejoa
George Kiriau
Moses Pelomo
Yoshi Yuki Sato
Bella Simiha

CENTRAL BANK OF SRI LANKA
30 Janadhipathi Mawatha
PO Box 590
Colombo, 00100, Sri Lanka
Tel.: (94) 112477000
Fax: (94) 2477721
E-Mail: cbslgen@cbsl.gov.lk
Web Site: www.cbsl.gov.lk
Sales Range: $100-124.9 Million
Emp.: 1,300
Fiscal Year-end: 12/31/12
Business Description:
Central Bank
S.I.C.: 6011
N.A.I.C.S.: 521110
Personnel:
M. I. Sufiyan *(Dir-Mgmt Audit)*

CENTRAL BANK OF SWAZILAND
Umntsholi Building Warner Street
PO Box 546
H100 Mbabane, Swaziland
Tel.: (268) 4082000
Fax: (268) 4040013
E-Mail: info@centralbank.org.sz
Web Site: www.centralbank.org.sz
Year Founded: 1974
Emp.: 300
Business Description:
Central Bank
S.I.C.: 6011
N.A.I.C.S.: 521110
Personnel:
M. G. Dlamini *(Chm)*
Board of Directors:
M. G. Dlamini
P. N. Joubert
S. M. Khumalo
D. E. Masilela
D. J. Matse
S. G. Mdluli
V. M. Mhlanga
M. Simelane
T. Vilakati-Jele

THE CENTRAL BANK OF THE BAHAMAS
PO Box N-4868
Nassau, Bahamas
Tel.: (242) 3222193
Fax: (242) 3029806
E-Mail: deveaux@centralbankbahamas.com
Web Site: www.centralbankbahamas.com
Sales Range: $25-49.9 Million
Emp.: 300
Fiscal Year-end: 12/31/12
Business Description:
Central Bank
S.I.C.: 6011
N.A.I.C.S.: 521110
Personnel:
Wendy M. Craigg *(Chm)*
Board of Directors:
Wendy M. Craigg
Wayne Aranha

CENTRAL BANK OF THE RUSSIAN FEDERATION
12 Neglinnaya Street
107016 Moscow, Russia
Tel.: (7) 495 7719100
Fax: (7) 495 6216465
E-Mail: webmaster@cbr.ru
Web Site: www.cbr.ru
Emp.: 4,417
Business Description:
Central Bank
S.I.C.: 6011
N.A.I.C.S.: 521110
Personnel:
Sergey M. Ignatiev *(Chm)*
Konstantin N. Korischenko *(Deputy Chm)*
Georgy I. Luntovsky *(Deputy Chm)*
Gennady G. Melikyan *(Deputy Chm)*
Viktor N. Melnikov *(Deputy Chm)*
Alexey Valentinovitch Ulyukaev *(First Deputy Chm)*
Board of Directors:
Sergey M. Ignatiev
Lyudmila I. Gudenko
Nadezhda Yu. Ivanova
Konstantin N. Korischenko
Georgy I. Luntovsky
Gennady G. Melikyan
Viktor N. Melnikov
Nadezhda A. Savinskaya
Konstantin B. Shor
Alexey Y. Simanovsky
Mikhail I. Sukhov
Alexey Valentinovitch Ulyukaev

CENTRAL BANK OF THE UNITED ARAB EMIRATES
PO Box 854
Abu Dhabi, United Arab Emirates
Tel.: (971) 26652220
Fax: (971) 26652504
E-Mail: uaecbpr@cbuae.gov.ae
Web Site: www.centralbank.ae
Sales Range: $400-449.9 Million
Business Description:
Central Bank
S.I.C.: 6011
N.A.I.C.S.: 521110
Personnel:
Khalil Mohammed Sharif Foulathi *(Chm)*
Omar Mohammed Ahmed Bin Sulaiman *(Vice Chm)*
Sultan Bin Nasser Al Suwaidi *(Governor)*
Board of Directors:
Khalil Mohammed Sharif Foulathi
Ali Al Sayed Abdulla
Saeed Rashid Al Yateem Al Muhairy
Sultan Bin Nasser Al Suwaidi
Omar Mohammed Ahmed Bin Sulaiman
Khalifa Nasser Bin Huwaileel
Jamal Nasser Lootah

CENTRAL BANK OF THE UNITED REPUBLIC OF TANZANIA
(d/b/a Bank of Tanzania)
Mirambo Street No 10
PO Box 2939
Dar es Salaam, Tanzania
Tel.: (255) 22 2233000
Fax: (255) 22 223 4075
E-Mail: info@hq.bot-tz.org
Web Site: www.bot-tz.org
Sales Range: $75-99.9 Million
Emp.: 100
Business Description:
Central Bank
S.I.C.: 6011
N.A.I.C.S.: 521110
Personnel:
Benno Ndulu *(Governor & Chm)*
Natu E. Mwamba *(Deputy Governor-Economics & Fin)*
Juma H. Reli *(Deputy Governor)*
Board of Directors:
Benno Ndulu
Natu E. Mwamba
K. M. Omar
Juma H. Reli

CENTRAL BANK OF TRINIDAD & TOBAGO
Eric Williams Plaza Independence Square
PO Box 1250
Port of Spain, Trinidad & Tobago
Tel.: (868) 6254835
Fax: (868) 6274696
E-Mail: info@central-bank.org.tt
Web Site: www.central-bank.org.tt
Year Founded: 1964
Business Description:
Central Bank
S.I.C.: 6011
N.A.I.C.S.: 521110
Personnel:
Ewart S. Williams *(Chm)*
Joan John *(Deputy Governor-Ops)*
Shelton Nicholls *(Deputy Governor-Res & Policy)*
Marie Borely *(CFO)*
Norris Campbell *(Sec)*
Board of Directors:
Ewart S. Williams
Norris Campbell
Amelia Carrington
Barbara Chatoor
Selwyn Cudjoe
Carlyle Greaves
Joan John
Alison Lewis
Shelton Nicholls

CENTRAL BANK OF WEST AFRICAN STATES
(See Under Banque Centrale des Etats de l'Afrique de l'Ouest)

CENTRAL CHINA REAL ESTATE LIMITED
No 88 Jianye City Garden Jianye Road
Zhengzhou, Henan, China
Tel.: (86) 371 66516000
Fax: (86) 371 66515003
E-Mail: ir@centralchina.com
Web Site: www.centralchina.com
Year Founded: 1992
AJ5—(DEU)
Sls.: $1,007,986,964
Assets: $3,867,721,736
Liabilities: $2,974,474,828
Net Worth: $893,246,909
Earnings: $138,166,777
Emp.: 1,489
Fiscal Year-end: 12/31/12
Business Description:
Real Estate Development Services
S.I.C.: 6531
N.A.I.C.S.: 531390
Personnel:
Po Sum Wu *(Founder & Chm)*
Jianye Chen *(CEO)*
Bing Hu *(CFO)*
Tak Chun Wong *(Sec)*
Board of Directors:
Po Sum Wu
Jianye Chen
Shek Lun Cheung
Yongmin Hu
Jason Juan Thong Leow
Ming Yan Lim
Wu Wallis
Shi Wang
Luo Lin Xin
Yingchun Yan
Computershare Hong Kong Investor Services Limited
Shops 1712-1716 17th Floor Hopewell Centre
183 Queens Road East
Wanchai, China (Hong Kong)
Transfer Agents:
Royal Bank of Canada Trust Company (Cayman) Limited
4th Floor Royal Bank House 24 Shedden Road
Georgetown, Cayman Islands
Computershare Hong Kong Investor Services Limited
Shops 1712-1716 17th Floor Hopewell Centre
183 Queens Road East
Wanchai, China (Hong Kong)

THE CENTRAL COAST LEAGUES CLUB LTD.
Dane Drive
Locked Bag 10
Gosford, NSW, 2250, Australia
Tel.: (61) 243259888
Fax: (61) 243259810
E-Mail: reception@cclc.com.au
Web Site: www.cclc.com.au
Rev.: $29,764,800
Assets: $39,821,535
Liabilities: $13,130,191
Net Worth: $26,691,344
Earnings: $770,906
Emp.: 300
Fiscal Year-end: 06/30/13
Business Description:
Entertainment Services
S.I.C.: 7999
N.A.I.C.S.: 713910
Personnel:
J. M. Ryan *(Chm)*
Trevor Owen Andrews *(Asst Deputy Chm)*
E. Johnson *(Deputy Chm)*
Board of Directors:
J. M. Ryan
Trevor Owen Andrews
M. J. Bell
Robert Peter Clark
P. D. James
E. Johnson
M. Love
G. G. Needham
K. J. Ruffels

CENTRAL EQUITY LIMITED
Level 4 32 Power St
Southbank, VIC, 3006, Australia
Tel.: (61) 396001111
Fax: (61) 92788800
Web Site: www.centralequity.com.au
Sales Range: $150-199.9 Million
Emp.: 200
Business Description:
Property Development & Management Services
S.I.C.: 6531
N.A.I.C.S.: 531311
Personnel:
John Bourke *(Mng Dir)*
Dennis Wilson *(Mng Dir)*

CENTRAL FINANCE COMPANY PLC
84 Raja Vidiya
Kandy, Sri Lanka
Tel.: (94) 81 222 7000
Fax: (94) 81 223 2047
E-Mail: cenfin@cf.lk
Web Site: www.cf.lk
Year Founded: 1957
CFIN—(COL)
Rev.: $88,852,376
Assets: $443,975,127
Liabilities: $306,434,602
Net Worth: $137,540,525
Earnings: $25,785,028
Emp.: 1,450
Fiscal Year-end: 03/31/13
Business Description:
Financial Services Holding Company
S.I.C.: 6712
N.A.I.C.S.: 551111
Personnel:
Eranjith Harendra Wijenaike *(Mng Dir)*
Board of Directors:
Jayampathi Divale Bandaranayake
Dhammika Prasanna de Silva
Anthony Nirmal Fernando
Arjuna Kapila Gunaratne
Chandima Lalith Kumar Perera Jayasuriya
Faiz Mohideen
Gerard Shamil Niranjan Peiris
Ravindra Erle Rambukwelle
Sunil Chandra Sillapana Wickramasinghe
Eranjith Harendra Wijenaike
Legal Counsel:
F.J. & G. De Saram
P.O.Box 212
Colombo, Sri Lanka
Co-Headquarters:

Central Finance Company PLC - City Office **(1)**
270 Vauxhall St
Colombo, 02, Sri Lanka
Tel.: (94) 112300555
Fax: (94) 112300441
E-Mail: cenfin@cf.lk
Web Site: www.cf.lk
Corporate Office
S.I.C.: 8741
N.A.I.C.S.: 551114
Eranjith Harendra Wijenaike *(Mng Dir)*

Holding:

Central Industries PLC **(2)**
312 Nawala Road
Rajagiriya, Sri Lanka LK
Tel.: (94) 112806623 (49.98%)
Fax: (94) 112806622
E-Mail: info@nationalpvc.com
Web Site: www.nationalpvc.com
CIND—(COL)
Rev.: $13,518,799
Assets: $9,117,681
Liabilities: $1,719,346
Net Worth: $7,398,335
Earnings: $755,751
Emp.: 304
Fiscal Year-end: 03/31/13
Water Supply Pipes & Pipe Fittings Mfr
S.I.C.: 3084
N.A.I.C.S.: 326122
Stanley V. Wanigasekera *(Chm)*
A. Newton P. Wickramasuriya *(CEO)*

Subsidiary:

Kandy Private Hospitals Ltd **(1)**
255/08 Katugastota Road
Kandy, Central Province, Sri Lanka LK
Tel.: (94) 812225474
Fax: (94) 814493492
Emp.: 105
General Medical Services
S.I.C.: 8062
N.A.I.C.S.: 622110
Sarath Jayasingha *(Gen Mgr)*

CENTRAL FOOD RETAIL COMPANY LIMITED
(d/b/a Tops Supermarket)
6th-7th Floors Central Plz Ofc Tower
1693 Phaholyothin Road
Lardyao Jatujak, Bangkok, 10900, Thailand
Tel.: (66) 29371700
Fax: (66) 2 937 1713
Web Site: www.tops.co.th
Year Founded: 1996
Sales Range: $400-449.9 Million
Emp.: 5,500
Business Description:
Grocery Retail
S.I.C.: 5411
N.A.I.C.S.: 445110
Personnel:
Alisa Taylor *(Pres)*
Chiranun Poopat *(Sr VP-Buying, Mdsg & Mktg)*

Subsidiary:

Central Retail Corporation (CRC) CO. Limited **(1)**
Central World Bldg 8th Floor
999/9 Rama1 Rd Pathumwan, 10330
Bangkok, Thailand
Tel.: (66) 2309507175
Fax: (66) 230950056
Web Site: www.central.co.th
Grocery Products Whslr
S.I.C.: 5149
N.A.I.C.S.: 424490
Tos Chirathivat *(CEO)*

CENTRAL FUND OF CANADA LIMITED
Hallmark Estates 805 1323-15th Avenue SW
Calgary, AB, T3C 0X8, Canada
Tel.: (403) 228-5861
Fax: (403) 228-2222
E-Mail: info@centralfund.com
Web Site: www.centralfund.com
Year Founded: 1961
CEF—(NYSEMKT TSX)
Int. Income: $114,300
Assets: $3,989,111,896
Liabilities: $4,536,465
Net Worth: $3,984,575,431
Earnings: ($1,459,301,882)
Fiscal Year-end: 10/31/13
Business Description:
Closed-End Investment Fund
S.I.C.: 6726
N.A.I.C.S.: 525990
Personnel:
Philip M. Spicer *(Chm)*
Dale R. Spackman *(Vice Chm)*
J. C. Stefan Spicer *(Pres & CEO)*
Catherine A. Spackman *(CFO & Treas)*
John S. Elder *(Sec)*
Board of Directors:
Philip M. Spicer
Brian E. Felske
Bruce D. Heagle
Ian M. T. McAvity
Michael A. Parente
Dale R. Spackman
J. C. Stefan Spicer
Legal Counsel:
Parlee McLaws LLP
Calgary, AB, Canada
Fraser Milner Casgrain LLP
Toronto, ON, Canada
Dorsey & Whitney LLP
Seattle, WA 98104
American Stock Transfer & Trust Company LLC
New York, NY 10021
Transfer Agents:
CST Trust Company
Calgary, AB, Canada
American Stock Transfer & Trust Company LLC
New York, NY 10021

CENTRAL GLASS CO LTD
Kowa-Hitotsubashi Building 7-1
Kanda-Nishikicho 3-chome Chiyoda-ku
Tokyo, 101-0054, Japan
Tel.: (81) 332597111
Web Site: www.cgco.co.jp
4044—(TKS)
Sls.: $1,908,973,000
Assets: $2,611,202,000
Liabilities: $1,231,615,000
Net Worth: $1,379,587,000
Earnings: $53,460,000
Emp.: 5,009
Fiscal Year-end: 03/31/13
Business Description:
Glass & Chemicals Mfr & Sales
S.I.C.: 3211
N.A.I.C.S.: 327211
Personnel:
Shuichi Sarasawa *(Pres & CEO)*
Shigeyuki Aoki *(Exec Officer)*
Takao Ayama *(Exec Mng Officer)*
Shigetoshi Iwasaki *(Exec Officer)*
Makoto Kikuchi *(Exec Mng Officer)*
Takeo Komata *(Exec Officer)*
Masamichi Maruta *(Sr Exec Mng Officer)*
Shigeki Murata *(Exec Officer)*
Takashi Nagahama *(Exec Mng Officer)*
Hajime Nakai *(Sr Exec Mng Officer)*
Tadashi Shimizu *(Exec Mng Officer)*
Kazuyoshi Takagi *(Exec Mng Officer)*
Satoshi Takayama *(Exec Officer)*
Board of Directors:
Masuo Aizawa
Takao Ayama
Makoto Kikuchi
Masamichi Maruta
Takashi Nagahama
Hajime Nakai
Shuichi Sarasawa
Tadashi Shimizu
Kazuyoshi Takagi
Teiichi Yamamoto

Subsidiaries:

Central Glass Chubu Co., Ltd. **(1)**
3773 Dotsubo Sennonji Tomida-cho
Nakagawa-ku, Nagoya, Aichi, 454-0971, Japan
Tel.: (81) 524317532
Fax: (81) 0524317421
Web Site: www.cgchubu.co.jp

Central Glass Co Ltd—(Continued)

Emp.: 30
Architectural Glass Mfr & Whslr
S.I.C.: 3211
N.A.I.C.S.: 327211
Kobayashi Syuichi *(Pres)*

Central Glass Engineering Co., Ltd. **(1)**
7 21 Izumi 2 Chome Suginami-ku
Tokyo, 168-0063, Japan
Tel.: (81) 353013210
Fax: (81) 353013208
Web Site: www.cgc-jp.com
Emp.: 40
Architectural Glass Contracting Works & Construction
S.I.C.: 1793
N.A.I.C.S.: 238150
Yoshatugu Yamashita *(Pres)*

Central Glass Fiber Co., Ltd. **(1)**
926 Okuchi-cho
Matsusaka, Mie, 515-0001, Japan
Tel.: (81) 598511611
Fax: (81) 598515771
Web Site: www.cgc-jp.com
Emp.: 250
Glass Fiber Mfr
S.I.C.: 3229
N.A.I.C.S.: 327212

Central Glass Hokkaido Co., Ltd. **(1)**
Nangodouri 8 Chome Kita
Shiraishi-ku, Sapporo, Hokkaido, 983-0034, Japan
Tel.: (81) 118664960
Fax: (81) 118664962
Web Site: www.cgco.co.jp
Architectural Glass Mfr & Supplier
S.I.C.: 3211
N.A.I.C.S.: 327211

Central Glass Kansai Co., Ltd. **(1)**
6 Minami-machi Chikkou Sakai-ku
Sakai, Osaka, 590-0987, Japan
Tel.: (81) 722248460
Fax: (81) 722248474
Web Site: www.cgc-jp.com
Architectural Glass Mfr & Whslr
S.I.C.: 3211
N.A.I.C.S.: 327211

Central Glass Kyushu Co., Ltd. **(1)**
127-4 Ishibashi Yusu Kasuyamachi
Kasuya-gun, Fukuoka, 811-2305, Japan
Tel.: (81) 92 624 2810
Fax: (81) 92 624 2808
Web Site: www.cgc-jp.com
Architectural Glass Mfr & Whslr
S.I.C.: 3211
N.A.I.C.S.: 327211
Shuichi Sarasawa *(Pres)*

Central Glass Module Co., Ltd. **(1)**
2333 Suoduka Shimokoyama
Tochigi, 329-0502, Japan
Tel.: (81) 285534251
Fax: (81) 285534316
Web Site: www.cgco.co.jp
Emp.: 50
Automotive Parts Mfr & Sales
S.I.C.: 5013
N.A.I.C.S.: 441310

Central Glass Tohoku Co., Ltd. **(1)**
11-5 Oogimachi 3-Chome
Miyagino-ku, Sendai, Miyagi, 983-0034, Japan
Tel.: (81) 222399122
Fax: (81) 22 239 9130
Web Site: www.cgco.co.jp/english/about/network/kanren.html
Architectural Glass Mfr & Suppliers
S.I.C.: 3211
N.A.I.C.S.: 327211

Central Glass Tokyo Co., Ltd. **(1)**
14-5 Yagumo-Dai 2-chome
Chofu-Shi, Tokyo, 182-0015, Japan
Tel.: (81) 424857662
Fax: (81) 424991460
Web Site: www.cgtokyo.co.jp
Emp.: 220
Glass Mfr & Whslr
S.I.C.: 3211
N.A.I.C.S.: 327211
Yamataka Akira *(Pres)*
Bear Tani Kaoru *(Mng Dir)*

Central Glass Wool Co., Ltd. **(1)**
4387-1 Aza Komeno
Takakicho, Kasugai, Aichi, 486-0804, Japan
Tel.: (81) 568811361
Fax: (81) 568838763
Web Site: www.cgc-jp.com
Emp.: 70
Glass Wool Mfr
S.I.C.: 3231
N.A.I.C.S.: 327215

Central Godo Fertilizer Co., Ltd. **(1)**
Kowa Hitotsubashi Bldg 7-1 Kanda-Nishikicho 3 chome
Chiyoda-ku, Tokyo, 101-0054, Japan
Tel.: (81) 332592400
Fax: (81) 332592426
E-Mail: kyokonoto@cgco.co.jp
Web Site: www.cgco.co.jp
Emp.: 80
Ammonium Chloride Fertilizers Whslr
S.I.C.: 2875
N.A.I.C.S.: 325314
Nobuyuki Yagi *(Gen Mgr)*

Central Insulation Co., Ltd. **(1)**
4387-1 Aza Komeno
Takakicho, Kasugai, Aichi, 486-0804, Japan
Tel.: (81) 568 87 7716
Fax: (81) 568 87 7718
Web Site: www.cgc-jp.com
Glass Wool Mfr
S.I.C.: 3231
N.A.I.C.S.: 327215

Central Kasei Chemical Co., Ltd. **(1)**
5254-7 Okiube
Ube, Yamaguchi, 755-0001, Japan
Tel.: (81) 836345848
Fax: (81) 836217455
Compound Fertilizers Mfr
S.I.C.: 2875
N.A.I.C.S.: 325314

Central Saint-Gobain Co., Ltd. **(1)**
Kowa Hitotsubashi Bldg 2F 7-1 Kanda-Nishikicho 3-Chome
Chiyoda-ku, Tokyo, 101-0054, Japan
Tel.: (81) 332597694
Fax: (81) 332597667
Web Site: www.saint-gobain.co.jp
Emp.: 40
Automotive Glass Sales
S.I.C.: 7536
N.A.I.C.S.: 811122
Koshinori Nakayama *(Pres)*

Japan Tempered & Laminated Glass Co., Ltd. **(1)**
401 Kawahara Hataosa Hirata-cho
Kaidu, Gifu, 503-0304, Japan
Tel.: (81) 584673888
Fax: (81) 584673219
Web Site: www.cgco.co.jp
Glass Mfr
S.I.C.: 3211
N.A.I.C.S.: 327211

Mie Glass Industry Co., Ltd. **(1)**
1565 1 Azashinchi Okuchi-cho
Matsusaka, Mie, 515-0001, Japan
Tel.: (81) 598533400
Fax: (81) 598533406
E-Mail: mie-glass@cgco.co.jp
Web Site: www.mie-glass.co.jp
Glass Mfr
S.I.C.: 3229
N.A.I.C.S.: 327212

Niigata Yoshino Gypsum Co., Ltd. **(1)**
901 1 Tarodai
Niigata, 950-3101, Japan
Tel.: (81) 252552521
Fax: (81) 252552578
E-Mail: pl@ny-gypsum.com
Gypsum Plasters Mfr
S.I.C.: 3275
N.A.I.C.S.: 327420

SunGreen Co., Ltd. **(1)**
Kanda-Nishikicho 3 7 1
Chiyoda-ku, Tokyo, 101-0054, Japan
Tel.: (81) 332592407
Fax: (81) 3325292426
E-Mail: span@sgco.co.jp
Web Site: www.sgco.co.jp
Emp.: 300
Fertilizers Mfr & Whslr
S.I.C.: 2875
N.A.I.C.S.: 325314
Nakamura Shinji *(Pres)*

Tokai Processing Center Co., Ltd. **(1)**
1624 3 Azashinchi Okuchi-choi
Matsusaka, Mie, 515-0001, Japan
Tel.: (81) 598533421
Fax: (81) 598533420
Web Site: www.cgc-jp.com
Crates & Pallets Mfr
S.I.C.: 2449
N.A.I.C.S.: 321920

Ube Yoshino Gypsum Co., Ltd. **(1)**
5254-11 Okiube
Ube, Yamaguchi, 755-0001, Japan
Tel.: (81) 836216158
Fax: (81) 836 21 3332
Web Site: www.cgco.co.jp/english/about/network/kanren.html
Gypsum Plaster Mfr
S.I.C.: 3275
N.A.I.C.S.: 327420

U.S. Subsidiaries:

Carlex Glass Company **(1)**
77 Excellence Way
Vonore, TN 37885
Tel.: (423) 884-1105
Fax: (423) 884-1041
E-Mail: autgls@carlex.com
Web Site: www.carlex.com
Automotive Glass Mfr
S.I.C.: 3211
N.A.I.C.S.: 327211
Charles Doerr *(Mgr)*

Central Glass International Inc. **(1)**
PO Box 789
Alachua, FL 32616-0789
Tel.: (386) 462-0588
Fax: (386) 462-0425
Web Site: www.cgco.co.jp
Emp.: 2
Investigation Services
S.I.C.: 7381
N.A.I.C.S.: 561611
Yokusu Kuriyama *(Mgr)*

Northwestern Industries Inc. **(1)**
2500 W Jameson St
Seattle, WA 98199
Tel.: (206) 285-3140
Fax: (206) 285-3603
Toll Free: (800) 426-2771
E-Mail: rickn@nwiglass.com
Web Site: www.nwiglass.com
Emp.: 260
Glass Mfr
S.I.C.: 3211
N.A.I.C.S.: 327211
Darrell Aldrich *(VP & Gen Mgr)*

Synquest Laboratories, Inc. **(1)**
PO Box 309
Alachua, FL 32616-0789 FL
Tel.: (386) 462-0788
Fax: (386) 462-7097
Toll Free: (877) 435-8676
E-Mail: info@synquestlabs.com
Web Site: www.synquestlabs.com
Emp.: 20
Fluorine Chemicals Mfr & Sales
S.I.C.: 2819
N.A.I.C.S.: 325180
Rick D. Boisson *(Pres)*

Non-U.S. Subsidiaries:

Apollo Scientific Limited **(1)**
Whitefield Rd
Bredbury, Stockport, Cheshire, SK6 2QR, United Kingdom
Tel.: (44) 1614060505
Fax: (44) 1614060506
E-Mail: sales@apolloscientific.co.uk
Web Site: www.apolloscientific.co.uk
Emp.: 25
Fluorine Chemicals Mfr & Sales
S.I.C.: 2819
N.A.I.C.S.: 325180
Neil Hamilton *(Mng Dir)*

Central Glass Europe Limited **(1)**
Whitefield Rd
Bredbury, Stockport, Cheshire, SK6 2QR, United Kingdom
Tel.: (44) 1614060888
Fax: (44) 1614060999
E-Mail: cge.uk@fluoroquest.com
Emp.: 2
Investigation & Information Services
S.I.C.: 7381
N.A.I.C.S.: 561611
Neil Hamilton *(Mng Dir)*

Central Glass Germany GmbH **(1)**
Kantstr 2
33790 Halle, Germany
Tel.: (49) 520166130
Fax: (49) 52016613118
E-Mail: marketing@cg-germany.com
Web Site: www.cg-germany.com
Emp.: 60
Glass Mfr & Suppliers
S.I.C.: 3211
N.A.I.C.S.: 327211
Hans Hiller *(Mgr)*

Taiwan Central Glass Co., Ltd. **(1)**
40-21 Po-Kung Keng Hsi-Hu Tsun Sanyi Hsiang
Miao-li, 36705, Taiwan
Tel.: (886) 37876586
Fax: (886) 37876448
E-Mail: service@tcgco.com.tw
Emp.: 100
Glass Mfr & Suppliers
S.I.C.: 3229
N.A.I.C.S.: 327212
Yukihiko Ueno *(Gen Mgr)*

CENTRAL GLOBAL CARGO GMBH

Langer Kornweg 34 D
65451 Kelsterbach, Germany
Tel.: (49) 610790480
Fax: (49) 6107904811
E-Mail: admin@central-global.aero
Web Site: www.central-global.de
Year Founded: 1993
Rev.: $10,014,846
Emp.: 33

Business Description:
Logistic Services
S.I.C.: 4499
N.A.I.C.S.: 488390

Personnel:
Werner Eyhorn *(Founder & Mng Dir)*
Dieter Eyhorn *(Founder)*
Roland Eyhorn *(Founder)*

CENTRAL GOLDTRUST

55 Broad Leaf Crescent
Ancaster, ON, L9G 3P2, Canada
Tel.: (905) 304-4653
Fax: (905) 648-4196
E-Mail: info@gold-trust.com
Web Site: www.gold-trust.com
Year Founded: 2003
GTU—(NYSEMKT TSX)
Int. Income: $44,481
Assets: $860,608,672
Liabilities: $485,491
Net Worth: $860,123,181
Earnings: ($329,451,078)
Fiscal Year-end: 12/31/13

Business Description:
Gold Investment Services
S.I.C.: 6211
N.A.I.C.S.: 523999

Personnel:
Philip M. Spicer *(Chm)*
J. C. Stefan Spicer *(Pres & CEO)*
William L. Trench *(CFO)*
Krystyna S. Bylinowski *(Treas)*
John S. Elder *(Sec)*

American Stock Transfer & Trust Company LLC
New York, NY 10021

Transfer Agents:
CST Trust Company
Toronto, ON, Canada

American Stock Transfer & Trust Company LLC
New York, NY 10021

CENTRAL IRON ORE LIMITED

Suite 1 Level 2 49-51 York Street
Sydney, NSW, 2000, Australia
Tel.: (61) 293977500
Fax: (61) 293977575
E-Mail: info@centralironorelimited.com
Web Site: www.centralironorelimited.com
CIO—(TSXV)
Rev.: $113,025
Assets: $4,048,483
Liabilities: $252,730
Net Worth: $3,795,753
Earnings: ($1,519,521)
Fiscal Year-end: 06/30/13

Business Description:
Iron Mining Services
S.I.C.: 1011
N.A.I.C.S.: 212210

Personnel:
Richard Homsany *(Chm)*
Brett Hodgins *(Pres & CEO)*
David Deitz *(CFO)*
Hugh Pinniger *(COO)*
Katherine Garvey *(Sec)*

Board of Directors:
Richard Homsany
Brett Hodgins
Anthony Howland-Rose

Computershare Investor Services Inc.
401 510 Burrard Street
Vancouver, BC, Canada

CENTRAL JAPAN RAILWAY COMPANY

(d/b/a JR Central)
JR Central Towers 1-1-4 Meieki
Nakamura-ku
Nagoya, Aichi, 450-6101, Japan
Tel.: (81) 52 564 2413
Fax: (81) 52 587 1300
Web Site: www.jr-central.co.jp
Year Founded: 1987
9022—(TKS)
Rev.: $17,438,509,000
Assets: $57,542,144,000
Liabilities: $40,404,452,000
Net Worth: $17,137,692,000
Earnings: $2,199,681,000
Emp.: 28,348
Fiscal Year-end: 03/31/13

Business Description:
Passenger Rail Transportation Services
S.I.C.: 4111
N.A.I.C.S.: 485112

Personnel:
Yoshiyuki Kasai *(Chm)*
Yoshiomi Yamada *(Pres)*
Sumio Atsuchi *(Corp Exec Officer)*
Makoto Baba *(Corp Exec Officer)*
Yasukazu Endo *(Corp Officer)*
Hidenori Fujii *(Corp Exec Officer)*
Kenji Hamada *(Corp Officer)*
Kazuhiro Igarashi *(Corp Officer)*
Hiroyuki Kawarasaki *(Corp Officer)*
Shun-ichi Kosuge *(Corp Exec Officer)*
Sumio Kudo *(Sr Corp Exec Officer)*
Tokuji Matsuno *(Corp Officer)*
Katsumi Miyazawa *(Sr Corp Exec Officer)*
Takanori Mizuno *(Corp Officer)*
Yutaka Osada *(Sr Corp Exec Officer)*
Masaki Seki *(Sr Corp Exec Officer)*
Noriyuki Shirakuni *(Sr Corp Exec Officer)*
Hideyuki Shoji *(Corp Exec Officer)*
Yoshiki Suyama *(Corp Exec Officer)*
Shuichi Takashima *(Corp Officer)*
Kimiaki Tanaka *(Corp Exec Officer)*
Motoaki Terai *(Corp Officer)*
Yoshito Tsubouchi *(Corp Exec Officer)*
Mamoru Uno *(Corp Exec Officer)*
Kiyoshi Watanabe *(Corp Exec Officer)*
Yoshihisa Yamaguchi *(Corp Officer)*
Yoshihiro Yamamoto *(Corp Officer)*
Shin Kaneko *(Exec VP)*
Tsutomu Morimura *(Exec VP)*
Koei Tsuge *(Exec VP)*
Naotoshi Yoshikawa *(Exec VP)*

Board of Directors:
Yoshiyuki Kasai
Fujio Cho
Shin Kaneko
Kenji Koroyasu
Sumio Kudo
Katsumi Miyazawa
Tsutomu Morimura
Yutaka Osada
Takashi Saeki
Masaki Seki
Kimiaki Tanaka
Koei Tsuge
Yoshiomi Yamada
Naotoshi Yoshikawa

Subsidiaries:

Hamamatsu Terminal Development Co., Ltd. **(1)**
6-1 Sunayamacho
Naka-Ku, Hamamatsu, Shizuoka, 430-0926, Japan
Tel.: (81) 534574000
Real Estate Leasing Services
S.I.C.: 6519
N.A.I.C.S.: 531190

JR Central Building Co Ltd **(1)**
JR Sentorarutawazu 20F 1 1 4 Meiki
Nakamura ku, Nagoya, Aichi, 450 6020, Japan
Tel.: (81) 525868760
Fax: (81) 52 586 8703
Web Site: www.towers.co.jp
Real Estate Leasing Services
S.I.C.: 6531
N.A.I.C.S.: 531390
Amaya Akihiro *(Pres)*

JR Central Passengers Co Ltd **(1)**
8F Nihombashi hirose bldg
Tokyo, Tokyo, Japan
Tel.: (81) 332732941
Fax: (81) 332813503
Web Site: www.jr-cp.com
Emp.: 3,024
Food & Beverage Stores
S.I.C.: 5499
N.A.I.C.S.: 445299
Watanabe Kazutoshi *(Pres)*

JR Development and Management Corporation of Shizuoka **(1)**
Shizuoka 29 St
Niello Aoi Ward, Shizuoka, Shizuoka, 420 0851, Japan
Tel.: (81) 542825896
Web Site: www.asty-shizuoka.co.jp
Real Estate Leasing Services
S.I.C.: 6531
N.A.I.C.S.: 531390
Taro Takahashi *(Pres & CEO)*

JR Tokai Agency Co., Ltd. **(1)**
2-1-95 Konan Jrtokaishinagawa Bldg Bto7f
Minato-Ku, Tokyo, 108-0075, Japan
Tel.: (81) 366884288
Web Site: www.jrta.co.jp
Advertising Agency Services
S.I.C.: 7311
N.A.I.C.S.: 541810

JR Tokai Bus Company **(1)**
3-103 Komoto
Nakagawa-Ku, Nagoya, Aichi, 454-0828, Japan
Tel.: (81) 523527800
Web Site: www.jrtbinm.co.jp
Passenger Bus Transportation Services
S.I.C.: 4119
N.A.I.C.S.: 485999

JR Tokai Construction Co., Ltd. **(1)**
JR Central Towers Meieki 1-1-4
Nakamura-ku, Nagoya, Aichi, 453-0014, Japan
Tel.: (81) 524532525
Fax: (81) 524532529
Web Site: www.jken.co.jp
Emp.: 412
Civil Engineering & Construction Services
S.I.C.: 1629
N.A.I.C.S.: 237990
Honda Takashi *(Pres)*

JR Tokai Corporation **(1)**
Meieki 1 Chome No 4 JR Sentorarutawazu
Nakamura ku, Nagoya, Aichi, 450 6032, Japan
Tel.: (81) 523882131
Fax: (81) 523882141
E-Mail: y-sato@jrtc.co.jp
Web Site: www.jrtc.co.jp
Emp.: 50
Building Materials Distr
S.I.C.: 5039
N.A.I.C.S.: 423390
Okio Shozawa *(Pres)*

JR Tokai Food Service Co Ltd **(1)**
Nagoya Meiekiminami 18 Neo 15 Building 6F No Sasajima
1 chome Nakamura ku, Nagoya, Aichi, 450-0003, Japan
Tel.: (81) 525871752
Fax: (81) 525871480
E-Mail: misso@jrt-food-service.co.jp
Web Site: www.jrt-food-service.co.jp
Emp.: 140
Food & Beverage Stores
S.I.C.: 5499
N.A.I.C.S.: 445299
Honda Kiyono *(Mgr)*

JR Tokai Hotels Co Ltd **(1)**
Meieki Nakamura
Nagoya, Aichi, 450 6002, Japan
Tel.: (81) 525841215
Fax: (81) 525841219
E-Mail: nagano@associa.co.jp
Web Site: www.associa.com
Emp.: 1,000
Hotel Management Services
S.I.C.: 7011
N.A.I.C.S.: 721110
Takao Inami *(Pres)*

JR Tokai Information Systems Company **(1)**
Higashi ku No 46-30
Higashi Ozone-Cho, Nagoya, Aichi, 461 0022, Japan
Tel.: (81) 529303301
Fax: (81) 529300340
E-Mail: n-hariyama@jtis.co.jp
Web Site: www.jtis.co.jp
Sls.: $3,070,736,000
Emp.: 350
System Development & Maintenance Services
S.I.C.: 7376
N.A.I.C.S.: 541513
Takatoshi Yoshida *(CEO & Pres)*
Tsuruta Akira *(Sr Mng Dir)*

JR Tokai Logistics Company **(1)**
Meieki 1 Chome No 13
Nakamura ku, Nagoya, Aichi, 453 0002, Japan
Tel.: (81) 525336811
Fax: (81) 52 533 6812
Web Site: www.jrtl.co.jp
Freight Handling & Logistics Services
S.I.C.: 4522
N.A.I.C.S.: 481212
Ishimaru Hiroshi *(Pres)*

JR Tokai Real Estate Co., Ltd. **(1)**
2 1 95 Shinagawa JR Tokai Bldg 5 Floor Bldg B
Kounan Minato Ward, Tokyo, 108 0075, Japan
Tel.: (81) 367167221
Fax: (81) 367119486
Web Site: www.jr-estate.com
Emp.: 300
Real Estate Leasing Services
S.I.C.: 6531
N.A.I.C.S.: 531390
Sugou Kunitaka *(Pres)*

JR Tokai Takashimaya Co., Ltd. **(1)**
1-1-4 Meieki
Nakamura-Ku, Nagoya, Aichi, 450-0002, Japan
Tel.: (81) 525661101
Web Site: www.jr-takashimaya.co.jp
Departmental Stores Operating Services
S.I.C.: 5311
N.A.I.C.S.: 452111

JR Tokai Tours **(1)**
3rd Floor Kyobashi TD Bldg
Bldg1-2-5 Kyobashi Chuo-ku
Tokyo, 104 0031, Japan
Tel.: (81) 332749774
Fax: (81) 332749790
Web Site: www.jrtours.co.jp
Emp.: 35
Travel Agency Services
S.I.C.: 4724
N.A.I.C.S.: 561510
Yoshida Osamu *(Pres)*

Nagoya Station Area Development Corporation **(1)**
15-12 Takebashicho Nsk Bldg
Nakamura-Ku, Nagoya, Aichi, 453-0016, Japan
Tel.: (81) 524535937
Railway Transportation Services
S.I.C.: 4789
N.A.I.C.S.: 488210

Shin Yokohama Station Development Co Ltd **(1)**
Shin-Yokohama Bldg 5F W
Kohoku, Yokohama, Kanagawa, 222-0033, Japan
Tel.: (81) 454782722
Web Site: www.cubicplaza.com
Emp.: 55
Real Estate Leasing Services
S.I.C.: 6531
N.A.I.C.S.: 531390
Takashi Sugou Kuni *(Pres)*

Tokai Kiosk Company **(1)**
Meieki 3 chome
Nakamura ku, 450 0002 Nagoya, Aichi, Japan
Tel.: (81) 525626011
Fax: (81) 525626055
Web Site: www.kiosk.co.jp
Grocery Retail Stores
S.I.C.: 5411
N.A.I.C.S.: 445110
Takeshi Mori Hard *(Pres)*

Tokai Rolling Stock & Machinery Co., Ltd. **(1)**
Nagoya Building 1 23 27 Shin Sasazima
Meiekiminami Nakamura ku, Nagoya, Aichi, 450 0003, Japan
Tel.: (81) 525662081
Web Site: www.t-ckk.co.jp
Industrial Machinery Maintenance Services
S.I.C.: 7699
N.A.I.C.S.: 811310
Sano Morihiko *(Pres)*

Tokai Transport Service Company **(1)**
8 1 Yasujicho
Nishi ku, Nagoya, Aichi, 452 0815, Japan
Tel.: (81) 525043051
Fax: (81) 525043046
Web Site: www.tkj-i.co.jp
Travel Related Services
S.I.C.: 4729
N.A.I.C.S.: 561599

Tokyo Station Development Co Ltd **(1)**
Marunouchi 1-9-1 Marunouchi Bldg 11th Fl Central 1st St
Tokyo, Tokyo, 100-0005, Japan
Tel.: (81) 332100077
Web Site: www.tokyoeki-1bangai.co.jp
Real Estate Leasing Services
S.I.C.: 6531
N.A.I.C.S.: 531390
Akashi Hirokazu *(Pres & CEO)*
Akashi Youici *(Pres & CEO)*

Toyohashi Station Building Co., Ltd. **(1)**
Kalmia Toyohashi Station Bldg
Nagoya, Aichi, 440 0075, Japan
Tel.: (81) 532552711
Fax: (81) 53 256 0511
Web Site: www.toyohashi-kalmia.jp
Real Estate Leasing Services
S.I.C.: 6531
N.A.I.C.S.: 531390

CENTRAL MACHINE & MARINE INC.

649 McGregor Rd
Sarnia, ON, N7T 7H5, Canada
Tel.: (519) 337-3722
Fax: (519) 337-4239
E-Mail: shop@centralmm.ca
Web Site: www.centralmm.ca
Year Founded: 1973
Rev.: $17,082,174
Emp.: 75
Business Description:
Industrial Machinery Mfr
S.I.C.: 3559
N.A.I.C.S.: 333249
Personnel:
Marten VandenBroek *(Pres)*

CENTRAL MOUNTAIN AIR LTD.

6431 Airport Rd
PO Box 998
Smithers, BC, VOJ 2NO, Canada
Tel.: (250) 877-5000
Fax: (250) 847-3744
E-Mail: info@flycma.com
Web Site: www.cmair.bc.ca
Year Founded: 1987
Emp.: 300
Business Description:
Air Transportation Services
S.I.C.: 4512
N.A.I.C.S.: 481111
Personnel:
Doug McCrea *(Pres)*

CENTRAL PATTANA PUBLIC COMPANY LIMITED

31st Floor The Offices at Centralworld 999/9 Rama I Road
Patumwan, Bangkok, 10330, Thailand
Tel.: (66) 26675555
Fax: (66) 22645575
Web Site: www1.cpn.co.th
Year Founded: 1980
CPN—(THA)
Rev.: $647,392,122
Assets: $2,328,502,922
Liabilities: $1,470,436,776
Net Worth: $858,066,147
Earnings: $207,123,828
Fiscal Year-end: 12/31/12
Business Description:
Construction Services
S.I.C.: 1541
N.A.I.C.S.: 236210
Personnel:
Suthichai Chirathivat *(Chm)*
Kobchai Chirathivat *(Pres & CEO)*
Somchart Baramichai *(Sr Exec VP-Ops)*
Naris Cheyklin *(Sr Exec VP-Fin, Acctg & Risk Mgmt)*
Sudthidej Chirathivat *(Sr Exec VP)*
Wallaya Chirathivat *(Sr Exec VP-Bus Dev & Project Construction Mgmt)*
Narttaya Chirathivat *(Exec VP)*
Suthipak Chirathivat *(Exec VP)*
Terachart Numanit *(Exec VP-Project Construction)*
Narit Ratanaphichetchai *(Exec VP-Dev)*
Panida Sooksridakul *(Exec VP-Property Mgmt)*
Naparat Sriwanvit *(Exec VP-Fin & IT)*
Nattakit Tangpoonsinthana *(Exec VP-Mktg)*
Board of Directors:
Suthichai Chirathivat
Kanchit Bunajinda
Kobchai Chirathivat
Prin Chirathivat
Sudhisak Chirathivat
Sudhitham Chirathivat
Suthichart Chirathivat
Suthikiati Chirathivat
Karun Kittisataporn
Chackchai Panichapat
Paitoon Taveebhol
Sunandha Tulayadhan

CENTRAL PETROLEUM LIMITED

56-58 Jephson Street
PO Box 1571
Toowong, QLD, 4066, Australia
Tel.: (61) 7 3181 3800
Fax: (61) 7 3181 3855
E-Mail: johnheugh@centralpetroleum.com.au
Web Site: www.centralpetroleum.com.au
CTP—(ASX)
Rev.: $9,669,624
Assets: $30,314,529
Liabilities: $4,631,011
Net Worth: $25,683,517
Earnings: ($9,674,224)
Emp.: 26
Fiscal Year-end: 06/30/13
Business Description:
Petroleum Exploration & Mining Services
S.I.C.: 1311
N.A.I.C.S.: 211111
Personnel:
Richard Cottee *(CEO & Mng Dir)*
Bruce William Elsholz *(CFO & Co-Sec)*
Michael R. Herrington *(COO)*
Leon Devaney *(Chief Comml Officer)*
Daniel C. M. White *(Gen Counsel & Co-Sec)*
Board of Directors:
Andrew Philip Whittle
Richard Cottee
William J. Dunmore
Wrix Frank Gasteen
Michael R. Herrington
Robert Hubbard

CENTRAL PLAZA HOTEL PUBLIC COMPANY LIMITED

(d/b/a CENTEL)
1695 Phaholyothin Road
Chatuchak, Bangkok, 10900, Thailand
Tel.: (66) 25411234
Fax: (66) 25411087
E-Mail: centara@chr.co.th
Web Site: www.centralhotelsresorts.com
Year Founded: 1980
CENTEL—(THA)
Rev.: $509,552,717
Assets: $919,595,448
Liabilities: $586,346,657
Net Worth: $333,248,791
Earnings: $53,793,393
Emp.: 9,500
Fiscal Year-end: 12/31/12
Business Description:
Holding Company; Hotel & Resort Owner & Operator; Fast Food Franchises Owner & Operator
S.I.C.: 6719
N.A.I.C.S.: 551112
Personnel:
Suthikiati Chirathivat *(Chm)*
Suthichai Chirathivat *(Vice Chm)*
Thirayuth Chirathivat *(CEO)*
Kevin Wallace *(Chief Dev Offier-Centara Intl Mgmt)*
Thiradej Chirathivat *(CEO-Central Restaurant Grp)*
Ronnachit Mahattanapreut *(Sec & Sr VP-Fin & Admin)*
Christopher Bailey *(Sr VP-Sls & Mktg)*
Supatra Chirathivat *(Sr VP-Corp Affairs & Social Responsibilities)*
Board of Directors:
Suthikiati Chirathivat
Kanchit Bunajinda
Prin Chirathivat
Sudhisak Chirathivat
Sudhitham Chirathivat
Suthichai Chirathivat
Suthichart Chirathivat
Thirayuth Chirathivat
Bhisit Kuslasayanon
Chanvitaya Suvarnapunya
Vichien Tejapaibul
Legal Counsel:
Weerawong, Chinnavat & Peangpanor Ltd
22nd floor Mercury Tower 540 Ploenchit Road
Lumpini
Bangkok, Thailand

Business Advisory (Thailand) Ltd
15th Floor, Maneeya Center Building, 518/5 Ploenchit Road
Pathumwan, Bangkok, 10330, Thailand
Tel.: (66) 22558977
Fax: (66) 22544576

Subsidiaries:

Centara Villas Phuket (1)
701 Patak Road Karon Beach
Muang, Phuket, 83100, Thailand
Tel.: (66) 7628 6300
Fax: (66) 7628 6316
E-Mail: cvp@chr.co.th
Web Site: www.centarahotelsresorts.com
Emp.: 100
Hotel Management Services
S.I.C.: 7011
N.A.I.C.S.: 721110
Darren Shaw *(Gen Mgr)*

Central Krabi Bay Resort (1)
334 Moo 2 Ao Nang
Muang, Krabi, 81000, Thailand
Tel.: (66) 75637789
Fax: (66) 75637800
E-Mail: ckbr@chr.co.th
Web Site: www.tentaiahotelsresorts.com
Emp.: 250
Hotel & Resort
S.I.C.: 7011
N.A.I.C.S.: 721110
Prapaijit Thongma *(Exec Asst Mgr)*

Central Mae Sot Hill Hotel Co Ltd (1)
100 Asia Rd
Mae Sot, 63110 Bangkok, Thailand
Tel.: (66) 55532601
Fax: (66) 55532600
Web Site: www.centralhotelsresorts.com
Hotels & Motels
S.I.C.: 7011
N.A.I.C.S.: 721110
Sonsak Saisa *(Gen Mgr)*

Central Restaurants Group Co., Ltd (1)
306 Silom Road
Bangrak, Bangkok, 10500, Thailand
Tel.: (66) 26357930
Fax: (66) 26357940
Web Site: www.cpn.co.ch
Hotel Management Services
S.I.C.: 7011
N.A.I.C.S.: 721110
Nathapor Montolsopon *(VP-Bus Dev)*

Central Samui Beach Resort Co., Ltd. (1)
38/2 Moo 3 Borpud Chaweng Beach Koh Samui
Surat Thani, 84320, Thailand
Tel.: (66) 7723 0500
Fax: (66) 7742 2385
E-Mail: csbr@chr.co.th
Emp.: 335
Hotel Management Services
S.I.C.: 7011
N.A.I.C.S.: 721110
Martin Heiniter *(Gen Mgr)*

Central Samui Village Co., Ltd. (1)
111 Moo 2
Ko Samui, Surat Thani, 84310, Thailand
Tel.: (66) 77424020
Fax: (66) 77424022
E-Mail: csv@chr.co.th
Hotel Management Services
S.I.C.: 7011
N.A.I.C.S.: 721110
Scott Bowen *(Gen Mgr)*

Central World Hotel Co., Ltd. (1)
999/99 Rama 1 Road Pathumwan
Bangkok, 10330, Thailand
Tel.: (66) 21001234
Fax: (66) 21001235
E-Mail: cgcw@chr.co.th
Web Site: www.centarahotelsresorts.com
Emp.: 870
Hotel Management Services
S.I.C.: 7011
N.A.I.C.S.: 721110
Robert Maurer-Loeffler *(Gen Mgr)*

Sofitel Central Hua Hin Resort (1)
1 Damnernkasem Road
Hua Hin, Prachuab-Khirikhan, 77110, Thailand
Tel.: (66) 32512021
Fax: (66) 32511014
E-Mail: sofitel@sofitel.co.th
Web Site: www.accorhotels-asia.com
Hotel Services
S.I.C.: 7011
N.A.I.C.S.: 721110
Jacques Mury *(Gen Mgr)*

CENTRAL RAND GOLD LIMITED

CRG Slot 8 10 Spencer Road
Robertville
Roodepoort, 1709, South Africa
Tel.: (27) 112466600
Fax: (27) 112466650
E-Mail: info@centralrandgold.com
Web Site: www.centralrandgold.com
CRD—(AIM JSE)
Rev.: $1,331,000
Assets: $28,968,000
Liabilities: $21,974,000
Net Worth: $6,994,000
Earnings: ($4,507,000)
Emp.: 92
Fiscal Year-end: 12/31/12
Business Description:
Gold Ore Mining
S.I.C.: 1041
N.A.I.C.S.: 212221
Personnel:
Sarel Johan du Toit *(CEO)*
Ronelle Kleyn *(Sec)*
Board of Directors:
John Michael McMahon
Sarel Johan du Toit
Jason Hou
Patrick Malaza
Miklos Salamon
Nathan Taylor
Legal Counsel:
Rudolph Bernstein & Associates
Block A 7 Eton Road Sandhurst
Sandton, South Africa

K&L Gates LLP
One New Change
London, United Kingdom

Carey Olsen
7 New Street
Saint Peter Port, Guernsey Channel Islands
Transfer Agents:
Computershare Investor Services (Pty) Ltd
70 Marshall Street
Johannesburg, South Africa

Computershare Investor Services (Channel Islands) Limited
Ordnance House 31 Pier Road
PO Box 83
JE4 8PW Saint Helier, Jersey
Non-U.S. Subsidiary:

Central Rand Gold South Africa (Proprietary) Limited (1)
6 10 Riviera Rd
Houghton, Johannesburg, Gauteng, 2198, South Africa

Tel.: (27) 11 551 4000
Emp.: 300
Gold Ore Mining Services
S.I.C.: 1041
N.A.I.C.S.: 212221
Johan du Toit *(Mng Dir)*

CENTRAL REFRIGERATION AND AIR CONDITIONING LTD.

28 Chicago St
Alexandra, 9320, New Zealand
Tel.: (64) 34487600
Fax: (64) 34487900
E-Mail: sales@heatpumpcentral.co.nz
Web Site: www.heatpumpcentral.co.nz
Emp.: 10
Business Description:
Heating & Air-Conditioning Contractor
S.I.C.: 1711
N.A.I.C.S.: 238220
Personnel:
Bruce Blackman *(Co-Founder)*
Bob Johnston *(Co-Founder)*

CENTRAL REINSURANCE CORPORATION

12F 53 Nanking East Road Section 2
Taipei, 10457, Taiwan
Tel.: (886) 225115211
Fax: (886) 225629683
E-Mail: centralre@centralre.com
Web Site: www.centralre.com
2851—(TAI)
Premiums: $486,663,398
Assets: $1,087,192,385
Liabilities: $816,456,570
Net Worth: $270,735,814
Earnings: $23,010,194
Emp.: 123
Fiscal Year-end: 12/31/12
Business Description:
Reinsurance Services
S.I.C.: 6399
N.A.I.C.S.: 524130
Personnel:
Cheng-Tui Yang *(Chm)*
Kuo-Cheng Chang *(Vice Chm)*
Chong-Tsang Juang *(Pres)*
Shyh-Laang Lin *(Dir Gen)*
Yi-Fen Lee *(Sr Exec Officer)*
Caroline Cheng *(Exec VP-Fin Div)*
Nancy Ko *(Sr VP-Life & Health Div)*
David Lin *(Sr VP-Property & Casualty Div)*
Board of Directors:
Cheng-Tui Yang
Kuo-Cheng Chang
Chong-Tsang Juang
Yi-Fen Lee
Shyh-Laang Lin
Chin-Shun Wu
Sea-Wain Yau
Supervisory Board of Directors:
Mei-Hsueh Ku Lai
Shuh-Yuan Liao
Kuang-Hui Wu

CENTRAL RESOURCES CORP.

510-1199 West Pender Street
Vancouver, BC, V6E 2R1, Canada
Tel.: (604) 630-3730
E-Mail: info@centralres.ca
Web Site: www.centralres.ca
Year Founded: 2007
CBC—(TSXV)
Int. Income: $229
Assets: $777,493
Liabilities: $316,098
Net Worth: $461,394
Earnings: ($627,356)
Fiscal Year-end: 03/31/13
Business Description:
Metal Exploration Services
S.I.C.: 1081
N.A.I.C.S.: 213114
Personnel:
Paul Reynolds *(Pres & CEO)*
Tim McNulty *(CFO & Sec)*
Board of Directors:
Ken Carter
Stephen Patrick Kenwood
Tim McNulty
Paul Reynolds
Legal Counsel:
Lang Michener LLP
Suite 1500 1055 West Georgia Street
Vancouver, BC, Canada
Transfer Agent:
Equity Transfer & Trust
Suite 1620 1185 West Georgia Street
Vancouver, BC, Canada

CENTRAL SPORTS CO., LTD

Kayabacho Tower
1-21-2 Shinkawa, Tokyo, Chuo-Ku, Japan
Tel.: (81) 2 5543 1800
Fax: (81) 3 5543 1850
Web Site: www.central.co.jp/
4801—(TKS)
Rev.: $516,285,000
Assets: $442,343,000
Liabilities: $278,069,000
Net Worth: $164,274,000
Earnings: $24,541,000
Emp.: 1,026
Fiscal Year-end: 03/31/13
Business Description:
Fitness Clubs
S.I.C.: 7999
N.A.I.C.S.: 713940
Personnel:
Takashi Tadaharu *(Pres)*
Yukio Yamazaki *(Sr Mng Dir)*
Yoji Suzuki *(Mng Dir)*
Moriki Goto *(Exec VP)*
Seiji Goto *(Exec VP)*
Yoshitaka Murai *(Exec VP)*
Shinetsu Nakazawa *(Exec VP)*
Board of Directors:
Moriki Goto
Seiji Goto
Hiro Hamada
Takashi Imoto
Nobuhiko Kawamura
Yoshitaka Murai
Shinetsu Nakazawa
Toki Sasaki
Takashi Tadaharu
Seishi Tone
Kyoichi Yada

CENTRAL TANSHI CO., LTD.

3-3-14 Nihonbashi-cho
Tokyo, 103-0021, Japan
Tel.: (81) 3242 6611
Web Site: www.central-tanshi.com
Business Description:
Loan, Security & Financial Brokerage Services
S.I.C.: 6211
N.A.I.C.S.: 523120
Personnel:
Onishi Yoshihisa *(Chm, Pres & CEO)*

Subsidiary:

ICAP Totan Securities Co., Ltd. **(1)**
8 Fl Totan Muromachi Bldg 4-4-10
Nihonbashi-Muromachi
Chuo-ku, Tokyo, 103-0022, Japan JP
Tel.: (81) 352008300 (60%)
Fax: (81) 352038340
Web Site: www.icap.com
Emp.: 25
Equity Derivatives Brokerage & Dealing Services
S.I.C.: 6211
N.A.I.C.S.: 523120
Toby Hunn *(CEO)*

CENTRAL VIETNAM METAL CORPORATION

(d/b/a CEVIMETAL)
16 Thai Phien St
Hai Chau District, Da Nang, Vietnam
Tel.: (84) 5113822450
Fax: (84) 5113823306
E-Mail: cevimetal@dng.vnn.vn
Web Site: www.cevimetal.com.vn
KMT—(HNX)
Sales Range: $25-49.9 Million
Business Description:
Steel Products Distr & Mfr
S.I.C.: 5051
N.A.I.C.S.: 423510
Personnel:
Que Tan Huynh *(Chm)*

CENTRAL WEST GOLD N.L.

C/- Investorlink Corporate Limited
Level 26 56 Pitt Street
Sydney, NSW, 2000, Australia
Tel.: (61) 2 9247 9555
Fax: (61) 2 9247 9977
E-Mail: admin@centralwestgold.com.au
Web Site: www.centralwestgold.com.au
CWG—(ASX)
Rev.: $1,191
Assets: $801,282
Liabilities: $33,513
Net Worth: $767,769
Earnings: ($566,372)
Fiscal Year-end: 06/30/13
Business Description:
Mineral Exploration Services
S.I.C.: 1099
N.A.I.C.S.: 212299
Personnel:
Maxwell James Davis *(Sec)*
Board of Directors:
Christopher John Ryan
Maxwell James Davis
Jun Feng Liao
Grant John Williams

CENTRAL WIRE INDUSTRIES LTD

1 N St
Perth, ON, K7H 2S2, Canada
Tel.: (613) 267-3752
Fax: (613) 267-3929
Web Site: www.centralwire.com
Emp.: 400
Business Description:
Stainless Steel & High Nickel Alloy Wire Mfr
S.I.C.: 3496
N.A.I.C.S.: 332618
Personnel:
Chris Charron *(Pres & CEO)*

CENTRALAND LIMITED

21st Fl No 12 CBD ShangWu Wai Huan Rd
Zhengdongxin District
450016 Zhengzhou, Henan, China
Tel.: (86) 63890406
Fax: (86) 63890345
Web Site: www.centralandltd.com
E3S—(SES)
Sales Range: $25-49.9 Million
Business Description:
Property Development Services
S.I.C.: 6531
N.A.I.C.S.: 531312
Personnel:
Tao Yan *(CEO)*
Jian Wang *(COO)*
Timothy Ding *(Chief HR Officer & Chief Admin Officer)*
Yudong Cui *(Chief Project Plng Officer & Chief Dev Officer)*
Xiaowei Li *(Chief Architectural & Engrg Officer)*
Raymond Ho *(Co-Sec & Controller-Fin)*
Abdul Jabbar Karam Din *(Co-Sec)*
Board of Directors:
Wei Li
Danny Fui Lung Li
Carol Xuemei Liu
Siok Sing Tan
Jian Wang
Wayne Zhimin Wang
Tao Yan

CENTRALE BANK VAN ARUBA

JE Irausquin Blvd 8
PO Box 18
Oranjestad, Aruba
Tel.: (297) 5252100
Fax: (297) 5252101
Web Site: www.cbaruba.org
Sales Range: $50-74.9 Million
Emp.: 90
Business Description:
Central Bank
S.I.C.: 6011
N.A.I.C.S.: 521110
Personnel:
A.J. Swaen *(Chm-Supervisory Bd)*
J. R. Semeleer *(Pres)*
Supervisory Board of Directors:
A.J. Swaen
M.R. Croes
G.G. Oduber
H.O. Van Trikt

CENTRALE BANK VAN SURINAME

Waterkant 16-20
Paramaribo, Suriname
Tel.: (597) 473741
Fax: (597) 476444
E-Mail: info@cbvs.sr
Web Site: www.cbvs.sr
Year Founded: 1957
Emp.: 330
Business Description:
Central Bank
S.I.C.: 6011
N.A.I.C.S.: 521110
Personnel:
Gilmorel Hoefdroed *(Pres)*

CENTRALE DEL LATTE DI TORINO & C. S.P.A.

Via Filadelfia 220
10137 Turin, Italy
Tel.: (39) 0113240200
Fax: (39) 0113240300
E-Mail: posta@centralelatte.torino.it
Web Site: www.centralelatte.torino.it
Year Founded: 1950
CLT—(ITA)
Rev.: $140,104,315
Assets: $141,304,515
Liabilities: $88,309,654
Net Worth: $52,994,862
Earnings: ($1,479,363)
Emp.: 278
Fiscal Year-end: 12/31/12
Business Description:
Milk & Dairy Products Producer & Marketer
S.I.C.: 2023
N.A.I.C.S.: 311514
Personnel:
Luigi Luzzati *(Chm)*
Riccardo Pozzoli *(Vice Chm & Co-CEO)*
Nicola Codispoti *(Co-CEO)*
Board of Directors:
Luigi Luzzati
Adele Artom

Centrale del Latte di Torino & C. S.p.A.—(Continued)

Guido Artom
Nicola Codispoti
Benedetto De Denedetti
Antonella Forchino
Maurizio Macchiavello
Riccardo Pozzoli
Luciano Roasio
Alberto Tazzetti
Germano Turinetto

Subsidiaries:

Centrale del Latte di Vicenza S.p.A. (1)
Via G Medici 98
36100 Vicenza, Italy
Tel.: (39) 0444922066
Emp.: 65
Creamery Butter Producer
S.I.C.: 2021
N.A.I.C.S.: 311512

Centrale Latte Rapallo S.p.A. (1)
Via Santa Maria del Campo 175
16035 Rapallo, Italy
Tel.: (39) 0185260101
Fax: (39) 0185262367
E-Mail: info@lattetigullio.it
Web Site: www.lattetigullio.it
Emp.: 35
Fluid Milk Producer
S.I.C.: 2026
N.A.I.C.S.: 311511

Frascheri S.p.A. (1)
Centrale del Latte
Via Cesare Battisti 29 Bardine, 17057
Savona, Italy
Tel.: (39) 0197908005
Fax: (39) 0197908042
E-Mail: info@frascheri.com
Web Site: www.frascheri.com
Emp.: 50
Dry Condensed & Evaporated Dairy Product Mfr
S.I.C.: 2023
N.A.I.C.S.: 311514
Fiorenzo Fiorenzo *(Gen Mgr)*

Salads & Fruits Srl (1)
Via Rossini 10
27045 Casteggio, Italy
Tel.: (39) 038383740
Fax: (39) 0383805711
Fruit & Vegetable Canning
S.I.C.: 2033
N.A.I.C.S.: 311421

CENTRALE TECHNIQUE D'APPROVISIONNEMENT INDUSTRIEL

11 Rue Louis Armand
92600 Asnieres, France
Tel.: (33) 141115500
Fax: (33) 140865533
E-Mail: com@cta-france.com
Web Site: www.cta-france.com
Sls.: $21,700,000
Emp.: 18
Business Description:
Motor Vehicle Supplies & New Parts
S.I.C.: 5013
N.A.I.C.S.: 423120
Personnel:
Eric Courtiol *(Mgr-Personnel)*
Board of Directors:
Christian Legall

CENTRALNIC GROUP PLC

35-39 Moorgate
London, EC2R 6AR, United Kingdom
Tel.: (44) 20 33 88 0600
Fax: (44) 20 33 88 0601
E-Mail: info@centralnic.com
Web Site: www.centralnic.com
CNIC—(AIM)
Business Description:
Domain Name Registry Services
S.I.C.: 7379
N.A.I.C.S.: 518210
Personnel:
John Swingewood *(Chm)*
Benjamin Crawford *(CEO)*
Glenn Hayward *(CFO)*
Gavin Brown *(CTO)*
Board of Directors:
John Swingewood
Benjamin Crawford
Samuel Dayani
Glenn Hayward
Robert Pooke
Thomas Pridmore
Thomas Rickert

CENTRE BRETAGNE MOTOCULTURE

21 Boulevard Nominoe
35740 Pace, Ille Et Vilaine, France
Tel.: (33) 299606192
Web Site: www.cbm-jd.com
Sls.: $30,300,000
Emp.: 50
Business Description:
Garden Machinery Mfr
S.I.C.: 5083
N.A.I.C.S.: 423820
Personnel:
Christian Clouard *(Pres)*

CENTRE TESTING INTERNATIONAL CORPORATION

Building C Hongwei Industrial Zone
Baoan 70
Shenzhen, China
Tel.: (86) 75533683668
Fax: (86) 75533683385
E-Mail: info@cti-cert.com
Web Site: www.cti-cert.com
300012—(CHIN)
Sales Range: $50-74.9 Million
Emp.: 1,789
Business Description:
Product Testing & Consulting Services
S.I.C.: 8734
N.A.I.C.S.: 541380
Personnel:
Feng Wan *(CEO)*

CENTRE VEHICULES INDUSTRIELS

33 Avenue Du Grand Sud
37170 Chambray les Tours, Indre-et-Loire, France
Tel.: (33) 247807510
Fax: (33) 247807501
E-Mail: info@cevi.fr
Web Site:
Sls.: $24,200,000
Emp.: 48
Business Description:
New & Used Car Dealers
S.I.C.: 5511
N.A.I.C.S.: 441110
Personnel:
Mohamed Boudali *(Pres)*

CENTRELEC

2 Avenue du Canal de Berry
BP 2230
03101 Montlucon, Cedex, France
Tel.: (33) 4 70022136
Fax: (33) 4 70022185
E-Mail: sofilec@sofilec23.fr
Web Site:
Year Founded: 1995
Rev.: $11,000,000
Emp.: 77
Business Description:
Electrical Contracting Services
S.I.C.: 1731
N.A.I.C.S.: 238210
Personnel:
Jean-Yves Martin *(Mng Dir)*

CENTREPOINT ALLIANCE LIMITED

Level 6 2 Elizabeth Plaza
North Sydney, NSW, 2060, Australia
Tel.: (61) 29921 6900
Fax: (61) 1300737660
E-Mail: info@centrepointalliance.com.au
Web Site: www.cpal.com.au
CAF—(ASX)
Rev.: $133,402,347
Assets: $156,547,388
Liabilities: $138,583,669
Net Worth: $17,963,720
Earnings: ($7,594,825)
Emp.: 187
Fiscal Year-end: 06/30/13
Business Description:
Insurance Company
S.I.C.: 6351
N.A.I.C.S.: 524126
Personnel:
John M. de Zwart *(CEO & Mng Dir)*
Glenn Toohey *(CFO & Co-Sec)*
Robert M. Dodd *(CEO-Insurance Premium Funding)*
Debra Anderson *(Co-Sec & Mgr-Legal)*
Board of Directors:
Richard John Nelson
John M. de Zwart
Noel J. Griffin
Matthew Kidman
Stephen J. Maitland

CENTREX METALS LIMITED

Unit 1102 147 Pirie Street
Adelaide, SA, 5000, Australia
Tel.: (61) 8 8100 2200
Fax: (61) 882320500
E-Mail: reception@centrexmetals.com.au
Web Site: www.centrexmetals.com.au
CXM—(ASX)
Rev.: $5,437,124
Assets: $79,261,462
Liabilities: $6,135,953
Net Worth: $73,125,510
Earnings: $1,046,856
Emp.: 25
Fiscal Year-end: 06/30/13
Business Description:
Iron Ore Exploration
S.I.C.: 1011
N.A.I.C.S.: 212210
Personnel:
Ben Hammond *(CEO)*
Gavin Mathew Bosch *(CFO & Co-Sec)*
Angela Webb *(Co-Sec)*
Board of Directors:
David Klingberg
Graham Chrisp
John den Dryver
Jim Hazel
Bingqiang Lu
Kiat Poh

CENTRIA INC.

3131 St-martin W 500
Laval, QC, H7T 2Z5, Canada
Tel.: (514) 849-8000
Fax: (514) 849-8949
E-Mail: lbourcier@centria.ca
Web Site: www.centria.ca
Emp.: 6
Business Description:
Investments
S.I.C.: 6722
N.A.I.C.S.: 525910
Personnel:
Jean-Guy Desjardins *(Chm & CEO)*
Board of Directors:
Jean-Guy Desjardins
Jean C. Monty
Subsidiaries:

Centria Capital (1)
1501 McGill College Avenue Office 800
Montreal, QC, H3A 3M8, Canada
Tel.: (514) 849-8000
Fax: (514) 849-8949
Web Site: www.centria.com
Emp.: 125
Financial Investment Services
S.I.C.: 6722
N.A.I.C.S.: 525910
Geam-Guy Dsgerdims *(Pres)*

Centria Commerce (1)
3131 St-Martin Blvd West Ste 500
Laval, QC, H7T 2Z5, Canada
Tel.: (514) 874-0122
Fax: (514) 874-9150
E-Mail: info@centria.ca
Web Site: www.centriacommerce.com
Emp.: 50
Electronic Commerce Specializing in Integrated Management Solutions for Construction Projects
S.I.C.: 6726
N.A.I.C.S.: 525990
Gilbert Doyon *(VP-Fin & Admin)*

CENTRIC HEALTH CORPORATION

20 Eglinton Avenue West Suite 2100
Toronto, ON, M4R 1K8, Canada
Tel.: (416) 927-8400
Fax: (416) 927-8405
Toll Free: (800) 265-9197
E-Mail: info@centrichealth.ca
Web Site: www.centrichealth.ca
Year Founded: 2001
CHH—(TSX)
Rev.: $434,039,827
Assets: $483,080,798
Liabilities: $389,303,957
Net Worth: $93,776,841
Earnings: ($7,045,614)
Emp.: 320
Fiscal Year-end: 12/31/12
Business Description:
Healthcare Services Including Surgical Procedures, Disability Management, Third-Party Medical Assessments & Drug Trial Administration Support
S.I.C.: 8062
N.A.I.C.S.: 622110
Personnel:
Jack Shevel *(Chm)*
David Cutler *(Pres & CEO)*
Daniel Gagnon *(CFO)*
Chris Dennis *(COO & Interim Pres-Retail & Home Medical Equipment Segment)*
Jim Black *(CIO)*
Diane Mason *(Chief HR Officer)*
Moe Green *(CEO-Classic Care)*
Shari Cohen *(Sr VP-Bus Dev, Mergers & Acq)*
Board of Directors:
Jack Shevel
Yazdi J. Bharucha
David Cutler
Ingrid Davis
Paul Gamble
Craig Gattinger
Tom Magyarody
Darren Youngleson
Transfer Agent:
Equity Financial Trust Company
Toronto, ON, Canada
Subsidiaries:

Don Mills Surgical Unit Ltd. (1)
20 Wynford Dr Ste 208
Don Mills, Toronto, ON, M3C 1J4, Canada

Tel.: (416) 441-2111
Fax: (416) 441-2114
Toll Free: (888) 857-6069
E-Mail: info@dmsu.com
Web Site: www.dmsu.com
Emp.: 10
Rehabilitation Services
S.I.C.: 8331
N.A.I.C.S.: 624310
Debra Forrest *(Gen Mgr)*

LifeMark Health (1)
1 Eglinton Avenue East Suite 202
Toronto, ON, M4P 3A1, Canada
Fax: (416) 485-1692
Toll Free: (800) 265-9197
E-Mail: info@lifemark.ca
Web Site: www.lifemark.ca
Sales Range: $50-74.9 Million
Emp.: 750
Health Rehabilitation Services
S.I.C.: 8082
N.A.I.C.S.: 621610
Ron Lowe *(Pres)*
Craig Gattinger *(CEO)*
Daniel McCrimmon *(CFO)*

Work Able Centres Inc. (1)
36 George St
Barrie, ON, L4N 5N3, Canada
Tel.: (705) 727-1688
Fax: (705) 727-1672
Toll Free: (800) 771-3955
Web Site: www.workable.ca
Emp.: 10
Rehabilitation Services
S.I.C.: 8331
N.A.I.C.S.: 624310
Amanda Basant *(Gen Mgr)*

Work Able Centres North York Inc. (1)
4 Lansing Sq
North York, ON, M2J5A2, Canada
Tel.: (416) 490-8484
Fax: (416) 490-0506
Toll Free: (866) 490-8484
E-Mail: nishalalsingh@centrichealth.ca
Web Site: www.workable.ca
Emp.: 25
Rehabilitation Services
S.I.C.: 8331
N.A.I.C.S.: 624310

CENTRIC HOLDING B.V.

Antwerpseweg 8
2800 PB Gouda, Netherlands
Tel.: (31) 182 64 80 00
Fax: (31) 182 64 80 01
E-Mail: info@centric.eu
Web Site: www.centric.eu
Year Founded: 1992
Rev.: $720,558,567
Assets: $395,953,274
Liabilities: $181,376,434
Net Worth: $214,576,840
Earnings: $16,639,347
Emp.: 4,959
Fiscal Year-end: 12/31/12

Business Description:
Holding Company; IT & Software Solutions
S.I.C.: 6719
N.A.I.C.S.: 551112

Personnel:
Gerard P. Sanderink *(CEO)*

Subsidiaries:

Centric Financial Professionals B.V. (1)
Van der Hooplaan 241
1185 LN Amstelveen, Netherlands NL
Tel.: (31) 20 3113800 (100%)
Fax: (31) 20 3113809
E-Mail:
Web Site: www.centric.eu/NL/Default/Staffing-Services/Financial-professionals
Financial Process Technical Support Services
S.I.C.: 7373
N.A.I.C.S.: 541512

Centric Netherlands Holding B.V. (1)
Antwerpseweg 8
2803 PB Gouda, Netherlands NL
Tel.: (31) 182 64 80 00
Fax: (31) 182 64 80 01
Web Site: www.centric.eu
Holding Company
S.I.C.: 6719
N.A.I.C.S.: 551112

Oranjewoud N.V. (1)
Antwerpseweg 8
2800 AH Gouda, Netherlands (79.2%)
Mailing Address:
PO Box 24
8440 AA Heerenveen, Netherlands
Tel.: (31) 182648000
Fax: (31) 182648001
E-Mail: info@oranjewoud.nl
Web Site: www.oranjewoud.nl
ORANW—(EUR)
Rev.: $2,384,540,922
Assets: $1,505,229,409
Liabilities: $1,154,401,353
Net Worth: $350,828,056
Earnings: $31,602,687
Emp.: 9,819
Fiscal Year-end: 12/31/12
Engineering Consulting Services
S.I.C.: 8711
N.A.I.C.S.: 541330
Herman G. B. Spenkelink *(Chm-Supervisory Bd)*
Pieter G. Pijper *(CFO & Member-Mgmt Bd)*
Gerard P. Sanderink *(Member-Mgmt Bd)*

Subsidiary:

Strukton Groep N.V. (2)
Westkanaaldijk 2
3542 DA Utrecht, Netherlands
Tel.: (31) 302486911
Fax: (31) 302486466
E-Mail: info@strukton.com
Web Site: www.strukton.com
Rev.: $1,823,108,608
Assets: $1,152,015,939
Liabilities: $875,155,886
Net Worth: $276,860,053
Earnings: $24,516,448
Emp.: 5,873
Fiscal Year-end: 12/31/12
Supply, Management, Engineering & Construction Services
S.I.C.: 1629
N.A.I.C.S.: 236210
Gerard P. Sanderink *(Chm-Mgmt Bd)*

Subsidiaries:

Strukton Bouw B.V. (3)
Westkanaaldijk 2
3542 DA Utrecht, Netherlands
Tel.: (31) 30 248 69 11
Fax: (31) 30 2486700
Web Site: www.strukton.com
Sales Range: $250-299.9 Million
Emp.: 40
Property Development Services
S.I.C.: 1542
N.A.I.C.S.: 236220
Gert Jan Vos *(Chm-Mgmt Bd)*

Strukton Civiel B.V. (3)
Westkanaaldijk 2
3542 DA Utrecht, Netherlands
Tel.: (31) 30 248 69 11
Fax: (31) 30 248 67 00
E-Mail: info@struktonciviel.com
Web Site: www.struktonciviel.com
Sales Range: $500-549.9 Million
Emp.: 100
Civil Engineering Services
S.I.C.: 1629
N.A.I.C.S.: 237990
Jos J. Hegeman *(Chm-Mgmt Bd)*

Strukton Integrale Projecten B.V. (3)
Westkanaaldijk 2
3542 DA Utrecht, Netherlands
Tel.: (31) 30 248 69 11
Fax: (31) 30 240 78 99
E-Mail: info@struktonpps.com
Web Site: www.struktonpps.com
Engineering Services
S.I.C.: 8711
N.A.I.C.S.: 541330
Erik A. Hermsen *(CEO)*

Strukton Railinfra N.V. (3)
Westkanaaldijk 2
3542 DA Utrecht, Netherlands
Mailing Address:
PO Box 1025
3600 BA Maarssen, Netherlands
Tel.: (31) 302407200
Fax: (31) 302407960
E-Mail: info@struktonrail.com
Web Site: www.struktonrail.com
Sales Range: $800-899.9 Million
Emp.: 3,200
Rail Infrastructure & Information Systems
S.I.C.: 4111
N.A.I.C.S.: 485112
Aike Schoots *(Chm-Mgmt Bd & CEO)*
Diederik Schonebaum *(COO)*
Hijlke Huijzer *(Member-Mgmt Bd)*

Strukton Systems B.V. (3)
Welbergweg 60
PO Box 258
7550 AG Hengelo, Netherlands
Tel.: (31) 742558800
Fax: (31) 742558801
Web Site: www.struktonsystems.com
Emp.: 80
Electrical Engineering Services
S.I.C.: 8711
N.A.I.C.S.: 541330
Lex Sezenter *(Gen Dir)*

Strukton Worksphere B.V. (3)
Planetenbaan 1
PO Box 1830
3600 BV Maarssen, Netherlands
Mailing Address:
Postbus 225
3454 ZL De Meern, Netherlands
Tel.: (31) 346588888
Fax: (31) 302730394
E-Mail: utrecht@worksphere.nl
Web Site: www.worksphere.nl
Sales Range: $300-349.9 Million
Emp.: 1,500
Engineering Services
S.I.C.: 8711
N.A.I.C.S.: 541330

U.S. Subsidiary:

Antea USA, Inc. (2)
5910 Rice Creek Pkwy Ste 100
Saint Paul, MN 55126-5023 MN
Tel.: (651) 639-9449
Fax: (651) 639-9473
Toll Free: (800) 477-7411
E-Mail: info.us@anteagroup.com
Web Site: www.anteagroup.com
Sales Range: $50-74.9 Million
Emp.: 600
Engineering & Environmental Consulting Services
Import Export
S.I.C.: 8999
N.A.I.C.S.: 541620
Gary Wisniewski *(CEO)*

Non-U.S. Subsidiaries:

Antea Belgium N.V. (2)
Posthofbrug 10
2600 Antwerp, Belgium
Tel.: (32) 3 221 55 00
Fax: (32) 3 221 55 01
E-Mail: info.be@anteagroup.com
Web Site: www.anteagroup.com
Emp.: 23
Engineering & Environmental Consulting Services
S.I.C.: 8999
N.A.I.C.S.: 541620
Kris Van Malderen *(CEO)*

Antea S.A.S. (2)
11 rue de la Vanne
92120 Montrouge, France
Tel.: (33) 1 57 63 14 00
Fax: (33) 1 57 63 14 01
Web Site: www.anteagroup.com
Engineering & Environmental Consulting Services
S.I.C.: 8999
N.A.I.C.S.: 541620
Jean-Philippe Loiseau *(CEO)*

GeoIngenierla S.A. (2)
Calle 35 No 7 25 Piso 12
Bogota, Colombia
Tel.: (57) 1 327 63 00
Fax: (57) 1 327 63 02
Web Site: www.geoingenieria.com
Emp.: 400
Engineering & Environmental Consulting Services
S.I.C.: 8999
N.A.I.C.S.: 541620

CENTRIC HOLDINGS S.A.

20 Makrigianni St
18344 Moschato, Greece
Tel.: (30) 210 9480000
Fax: (30) 210 9402163
E-Mail: marbaniti@centric.gr
Web Site: www.centric.gr
CENTR—(ATH)
Sls.: $678,507,627
Assets: $67,646,858
Liabilities: $6,030,541
Net Worth: $61,616,317
Earnings: $4,693,606
Emp.: 14
Fiscal Year-end: 12/31/12

Business Description:
Electronic Games & Computer Peripheral Products Whslr
S.I.C.: 5092
N.A.I.C.S.: 423920

Personnel:
Rodolfo F. Odoni *(Founder, Chm & Mng Dir)*
Ioannis G. Capodistrias *(Vice Chm)*
Maria Arvaniti *(CFO)*
Eleftherios Kostakis *(Internal Audit Officer)*

Board of Directors:
Rodolfo F. Odoni
Ioannis G. Capodistrias
Kalypso Kontogianni
Foteini Sarantakou
George Tsagklis
Emmanouil P. Vlasseros

CENTRICA PLC

Millstream Maidenhead Road
Windsor, Berks, SL4 5GD, United Kingdom
Tel.: (44) 1753494000
Fax: (44) 1753494001
Web Site: www.centrica.com
Year Founded: 1997
CNA—(LSE)
Rev.: $37,811,361,180
Assets: $34,668,574,080
Liabilities: $25,308,122,250
Net Worth: $9,360,451,830
Earnings: $2,010,436,170
Emp.: 38,642
Fiscal Year-end: 12/31/12

Business Description:
Holding Company; Gas Distr; Electricity Supplier; Security Services; Financial Services
Export
S.I.C.: 6719
N.A.I.C.S.: 551112

Personnel:
Roger Carr *(Chm)*
William Samuel Hugh Laidlaw *(CEO)*
Grant Dawson *(Gen Counsel & Sec)*

Board of Directors:
Roger Carr
Richard N. Haythornthwaite
Mary E. Francis
Mark Hanafin
Lesley M. S. Knox
William Samuel Hugh Laidlaw
Nicholas L. Luff
Ian K. Meakins
Paul Ashley Rayner
Margherita Della Valle

Subsidiaries:

Accord Energy Ltd. (1)
Charter Court
50 Windsor Road, Slough, Berkshire, SL1 2HA, United Kingdom (100%)
Tel.: (44) 1753758058
Fax: (44) 1753758010

Centrica plc—(Continued)

Emp.: 50
Natural Gas Distr to Worldwide Market
S.I.C.: 1311
N.A.I.C.S.: 211111

British Gas Services Limited (1)
Lakeside House 30 The Causeway
Staines-upon-Thames, TW18 3BY, United Kingdom UK
Tel.: (44) 1784874000 (100%)
Fax: (44) 1784874201
E-Mail: info@centrica.com
Web Site: www.britishgas.co.uk
Emp.: 1,100
Gas Energy & Services for Homes & Businesses
S.I.C.: 4924
N.A.I.C.S.: 221210
Chris Weston *(CEO)*
Phil Bentley *(Mng Dir)*
Melanie Rowlands *(Gen Counsel)*

Caythorpe Gas Storage Limited (1)
119-123 Marfleet Lane
Hull, East Yorkshire, HU9 5RN, United Kingdom
Tel.: (44) 7881 816369
Web Site: www.caythorpegasstorage.com
Gas Storage Facilities Management Services
S.I.C.: 4226
N.A.I.C.S.: 493190

Centrica Brigg Limited (1)
Scawby Brook
Brigg, North Lincolnshire, DN20 9LT, United Kingdom
Tel.: (44) 1652650011
Fax: (44) 1652600001
Emp.: 35
Electric Power Generation Services
S.I.C.: 4911
N.A.I.C.S.: 221118
Paul Dalton *(Mgr-Station)*

Centrica Energy Limited (1)
Sully Moors Road Penarth South Glamorgan
Slough, Berkshire, CF64 5YU, United Kingdom
Tel.: (44) 1446720220
Fax: (44) 1446744957
Emp.: 35
Electric Power Generation Services
S.I.C.: 4931
N.A.I.C.S.: 221118
Corin Taylor *(Head-Comm Res)*

The Centrica Gas Production LP (1)
Millstream Maidenhead Road
Windsor, SL4 5GD, United Kingdom
Tel.: (44) 1753494000
Natural Gas Extraction Services
S.I.C.: 1311
N.A.I.C.S.: 211111

Centrica RPS Limited (1)
Roosecote Power Station Roose
Barrow-in-Furness, Cumbria, LA13 0PQ, United Kingdom
Tel.: (44) 1229845630
Fax: (44) 1229813808
Emp.: 32
Electric Power Distr
S.I.C.: 4911
N.A.I.C.S.: 221122
Dave Priestley *(Gen Mgr)*

Centrica SHB Limited (1)
South Marsh Rd Stallingborough South Humber Bank Powerstation
Stallingborough, South Humberside, DN41 8BZ, United Kingdom
Tel.: (44) 1469577236
Emp.: 60
Electric Power Transmission Services
S.I.C.: 4911
N.A.I.C.S.: 221121

Centrica Storage Limited (1)
Venture House 42-54 London Road
Staines-upon-Thames, TW18 4HF, United Kingdom
Tel.: (44) 1784415300
Fax: (44) 1784415318
E-Mail: salesandmarketing@centrica-sl.co.uk
Web Site: www.centrica-sl.co.uk
Emp.: 70
Oil & Gas Field Services
S.I.C.: 1389
N.A.I.C.S.: 213112
Simon Wills *(Mng Dir)*

Centrica Telecommunications Ltd. (1)
Onetel Chiswick Park Bldg 1 3rd Fl
566 Chiswick High Rd, London, W4 5BY, United Kingdom (100%)
Tel.: (44) 8458188000
Fax: (44) 2071819972
Toll Free: 800 957 0700
E-Mail: customerservice@onetel.co.uk
Web Site: www.onetel.co.uk
Emp.: 150
Telephone & Internet Service Provider
S.I.C.: 4812
N.A.I.C.S.: 517110
Justin Henderson *(Mktg Dir-Services)*

Venture North Sea Gas Limited (1)
Kings Close 62 Huntly Street
Aberdeen, Aberdeenshire, AB10 1RS, United Kingdom
Tel.: (44) 1224 619000
Fax: (44) 1224 658151
Oil & Natural Gas Extraction Services
S.I.C.: 1389
N.A.I.C.S.: 213112

Venture North Sea Oil Limited (1)
15 Justice Mill Lane
Aberdeen, Aberdeenshire, AB11 6EQ, United Kingdom
Tel.: (44) 1224 619000
Fax: (44) 1224 64150
Web Site: www.centrica.com
Emp.: 400
Oil & Gas Extraction Services
S.I.C.: 1389
N.A.I.C.S.: 213112
Jonathan Roger *(Mng Dir)*

U.S. Subsidiary:

Direct Energy, LP (1)
12 Greenway Plz Ste 250
Houston, TX 77046-0813 TX
Tel.: (713) 877-3500
Web Site: www.directenergy.com
Holding Company; Natural Gas & Electrical Power Products & Services
S.I.C.: 6719
N.A.I.C.S.: 551112
Badar Khan *(Pres & CEO)*
Andrew Sunderman *(CFO)*
Steven Murray *(COO)*
Jerry Brace *(CIO)*
Manu Asthana *(Pres-Residential)*
Scott Boose *(Pres-Svcs)*
Maura J. Clark *(Pres-Bus)*
Carol Graebner *(Exec VP-Legal, Govt & Regulatory Affairs, Compliance & External)*
Melinda Guerra Reeves *(Exec VP-HR)*

Subsidiaries:

Bounce Energy, Inc. (2)
2802 Albany St
Houston, TX 77006
Mailing Address:
PO Box 8387
Houston, TX 77288
Tel.: (281) 745-9020
Toll Free: (888) 452-6862
E-Mail: CustomerCare@BounceEnergy.com
Web Site: www.bounceenergy.com
Electric Power Distr
S.I.C.: 4939
N.A.I.C.S.: 221122
Robbie Wright *(CEO)*
Karl Trollinger *(CIO)*
Paul Colgin *(CMO)*
James Moskosky *(Exec VP)*
Sabrina Colgin *(Sr VP-Ops)*
Elizabeth Maberry *(Sr VP-Bus Dev)*

Direct Energy Business, LLC (2)
1001 Liberty Ave Ste 1200
Pittsburgh, PA 15222 DE
Tel.: (412) 667-5100
Fax: (412) 394-6677
Toll Free: (800) 830-5923
E-Mail: businessinfo@directenergy.com
Web Site: www.business.directenergy.com
Emp.: 230
Commercial Electric & Natural Gas Distr
S.I.C.: 4939
N.A.I.C.S.: 221122
Maura J. Clark *(Pres)*
Paul Dobson *(Sr VP-Pricing & Ops)*

Subsidiary:

Hess Energy Marketing, LLC (3)
1 Hess Plz
Woodbridge, NJ 07095-1229 DE
Tel.: (732) 750-6000
Fax: (732) 750-7126
E-Mail:
Web Site: www.hessenergy.com
Sales Range: $5-14.9 Billion
Natural Gas & Electric Power Marketer & Distr
S.I.C.: 4924
N.A.I.C.S.: 221210

Branch:

Hess Energy Marketing, LLC - Southeast Region (4)
13850 Ballantyne Corporate Pl Ste 425
Charlotte, NC 28277
Tel.: (704) 544-6655
Fax: (704) 544-2656
Web Site: www.hessenergy.com
Natural Gas & Electric Power Marketer & Distr
S.I.C.: 4924
N.A.I.C.S.: 221210

Subsidiary:

Hess Energy New York Corporation (4)
115 Solar St Ste 102
Syracuse, NY 13204 DE
Tel.: (315) 234-5300
Web Site: www.hessenergy.com
Natural Gas & Electric Power Marketer & Distr
S.I.C.: 4924
N.A.I.C.S.: 221210
Richard Cohen *(Sr VP)*

Direct Energy Services, LLC (2)
12 Greenway Plz Ste 600
Houston, TX 77046 DE
Tel.: (412) 667-5100
Holding Company; Heating, Ventilation, Air Conditioning & Plumbing Contractor & Energy Management Consulting Services
S.I.C.: 6719
N.A.I.C.S.: 551112
Scott Boose *(Pres)*

Subsidiary:

Direct Energy US Home Services, Inc. (3)
583 S Riverview Ave
Miamisburg, OH 45342-3027 DE
Tel.: (937) 898-0826
Toll Free: (800) 488-6983
Residential Heating, Ventilation, Air Conditioning & Plumbing Contractor Services
S.I.C.: 1711
N.A.I.C.S.: 238220
Eric Salzer *(Sr VP)*

Subsidiaries:

Clockwork, Inc. (4)
Plaza Five Points 50 Central Ave Ste 920
Sarasota, FL 34236 DE
Tel.: (941) 366-9692
Fax: (941) 366-9592
Toll Free: (866) 574-7431
E-Mail: kmiller@clockworkhomeservices.com
Web Site: www.clockworkhomeservices.com
Sales Range: $1-9.9 Million
Emp.: 1,500
Home Services Franchisor for Plumbing, HVAC & Electrical Industries
S.I.C.: 6794
N.A.I.C.S.: 533110
James D. Abrams *(Founder)*
John Young *(CMO)*
Scott Boose *(Pres-Direct Energy Home Svcs)*
Rebecca Cassel *(Pres-CSG)*

Home Warranty of America, Inc. (4)
1371 Abbott Ct Ste A
Buffalo Grove, IL 60089 IL
Tel.: (847) 325-5143
Fax: (847) 634-7506
Toll Free: (888) 492-7359
E-Mail: info@hwahomewarranty.com
Web Site: www.hwahomewarranty.com
Sales Range: $25-49.9 Million
Emp.: 123
Home Warranty Coverage
S.I.C.: 6399
N.A.I.C.S.: 524128
Rob Sobel *(Dir-Ops)*

Energetix, Inc. (2)
50 Methodist Hill Dr St 1500
Rochester, NY 14623
Tel.: (585) 487-3600
Fax: (877) 224-7812
Toll Free: (800) 544-0182
E-Mail: marketing@energetix.net
Web Site: www.energetix.net
Emp.: 35
Energy Products & Services; Natural Gas, Electricity, Fuel Oil
S.I.C.: 4931
N.A.I.C.S.: 221122
Mark Beaudoin *(Pres)*

First Choice Power, L.P. (2)
225 E John Carpenter Fwy Ste 1500
Fort Worth, TX 76109 TX
Mailing Address:
PO Box 659603
San Antonio, TX 78265-9603
Tel.: (817) 731-0099
Fax: (817) 735-5731
Toll Free: (866) 469-2464
E-Mail: CustomerService@FirstChoicePower.com
Web Site: www.firstchoicepower.com
Sales Range: $200-249.9 Million
Electrical Utility Services
S.I.C.: 4911
N.A.I.C.S.: 221118
Brian Hayduk *(Pres)*

Frontera Generation LP (2)
320 S Goodwin Rd
Mission, TX 78572
Tel.: (956) 519-7728
Fax: (956) 580-6203
Electric Power Generation Services
S.I.C.: 4931
N.A.I.C.S.: 221118
Michael Taylor *(Gen Mgr)*

NYSEG Solutions, Inc. (2)
31 Lewis St Ste 401
Binghamton, NY 13901-3058 NY
Tel.: (607) 721-1700
Fax: (607) 721-1717
Toll Free: (800) 567-6520
Web Site: www.nysegsolutions.com
Emp.: 7
Electricity & Natural Gas Distr
S.I.C.: 4939
N.A.I.C.S.: 221122

WTU Retail Energy LP (2)
12 Greenway Plz Ste 600
Houston, TX 77046
Tel.: (866) 322-5563
Fax: (800) 666-8867
Toll Free: (866) 223-8508
E-Mail: customercare@WTUretailenergy.com
Web Site: www.wturetailenergy.com
Electric Power Distribution Services
S.I.C.: 4939
N.A.I.C.S.: 221122
Claire Monaghan *(Sr Mgr-PR)*

Non-U.S. Subsidiaries:

Direct Energy Marketing Limited (2)
2225 Sheppard Avenue East Ste 1500
Toronto, ON, M2J 5C2, Canada (100%)
Tel.: (416) 221-4441
E-Mail: customerservice@directenergy.com
Web Site: www.directenergy.com
Sales Range: $5-14.9 Billion
Emp.: 4,800
Holding Company; Electric Power & Natural Gas Products Distr & Support Services
S.I.C.: 6719
N.A.I.C.S.: 551112
Andy Hunt *(VP & Gen Mgr-Bus Svcs)*

Division:

Direct Energy Marketing Ltd. - Canada Home Services (3)
80 Allstate Parkway 3rd Floor
Markham, ON, L3R 6H3, Canada

Tel.: (905) 944-9944
Web Site: www.directenergy.com
Residential Heating, Ventilation, Air Conditioning & Plumbing Contractor Services
S.I.C.: 1711
N.A.I.C.S.: 238220

Direct Energy Resources Partnership (2)
111 5th Avenue South West Suite 1000
Calgary, AB, T2P 3T6, Canada
Tel.: (403) 538-5000
Web Site: www.directenergy.com
Natural Gas Extraction & Distr
S.I.C.: 1311
N.A.I.C.S.: 211111
Badar Khan *(Pres)*

CENTRO ESCOLAR UNIVERSITY

9 Mendiola St San Miguel
Manila, 1005, Philippines
Tel.: (63) 27356861
Fax: (63) 27355991
E-Mail: ceuadmission@ceu.edu.ph
Web Site: www.ceu.edu.ph
CEU—(PHI)
Rev.: $36,277,656
Assets: $78,927,461
Liabilities: $19,398,467
Net Worth: $59,528,995
Earnings: $7,228,109
Emp.: 1,183
Fiscal Year-end: 03/31/13

Business Description:
Educational Services
S.I.C.: 8221
N.A.I.C.S.: 611310

Personnel:
Emilio T. Yap *(Chm)*
Ma. Cristina D. Padolina *(Pres & Chief Academic Officer)*
Sergio F. Apostol *(Compliance Officer & Sec)*
Cesar F. Tan *(Treas & Asst Sec)*
Ricardo F. de Leon *(Exec VP)*

Board of Directors:
Emilio T. Yap
Angel C. Alcala
Ricardo F. de Leon
Alejandro C. Dizon
Emil Q. Javier
Ma. Cristina D. Padolina
Corazon M. Tiongco
Emilio C. Yap, III
Johnny C. Yap

CENTRO RETAIL GROUP

(See Under Federation Limited)

CENTRON TELECOM INTERNATIONAL HOLDING LTD

Unit 2001 20/F Grandtech Centre 8 On Ping Street
Sha Tin, NT, China (Hong Kong)
Tel.: (852) 2648 2811
Fax: (852) 2648 2833
E-Mail: wk@centron.com.hk
Web Site: www.centron.com.hk
1155—(HKG)
Rev.: $234,898,326
Assets: $345,197,570
Liabilities: $98,392,166
Net Worth: $246,805,404
Earnings: $9,558,005
Emp.: 2,000
Fiscal Year-end: 12/31/12

Business Description:
Wireless Telecommunication Equipment Mfr & Sales
S.I.C.: 7359
N.A.I.C.S.: 532490

Personnel:
Guoliang Dai *(Chm & CEO)*
Zeli Guo *(Vice Chm)*
Wan Sze Lee *(CFO)*
Wai-kee Ng *(Sec)*

Board of Directors:
Guoliang Dai
Guoyu Dai
Zeli Guo
Ee Tek Hung
Hongbin Li
Yuanfang Lin
Wai-kee Ng
Zhangtao Yi

Transfer Agent:
Computershare Hong Kong Investor Services Limited
17M Floor Hopewell Centre 183 Queens Road East
Hong Kong, China (Hong Kong)

Non-U.S. Subsidiary:

Centron Communication System (xiamen) Co., LTD (1)
207 No 26 Guan Ri Rd Software Park II
Xiamen, Fujian, China
Tel.: (86) 592 5630388
Fax: (86) 592 5751288
Web Site: www.centroncom.cn
Television Broadcasting Equipments Mfr
S.I.C.: 3663
N.A.I.C.S.: 334220

CENTROPROIZVOD A.D.

(See Under Nestle S.A.)

CENTROSOLAR GROUP AG

Walter-Gropius Strasse 15
80807 Munich, Germany
Tel.: (49) 89201800
Fax: (49) 8920180555
E-Mail: info@centrosolar.com
Web Site: www.centrosolar-group.de
C3O—(DEU)
Rev.: $254,348,052
Assets: $206,390,746
Liabilities: $195,959,275
Net Worth: $10,431,471
Earnings: ($96,877,124)
Emp.: 761
Fiscal Year-end: 12/31/12

Business Description:
Photovoltaic Cell Mfr
S.I.C.: 4911
N.A.I.C.S.: 221118

Personnel:
Guido A. Krass *(Chm-Supervisory Bd)*
Alexander Kirsch *(Chm-Mgmt Bd, CEO & CFO)*
Bernhard Heiss *(Deputy Chm-Supervisory Bd)*
Thomas Guntzer *(Member-Mgmt Bd)*
Axel Muller-Groeling *(Member-Mgmt Bd)*

Supervisory Board of Directors:
Guido A. Krass
Martinus Brandal
Bernhard Heiss

Subsidiaries:

Centroplan GmbH (1)
Am Pannhaus 2-10
Geilenkirchen, 52511 Heinsberg, Germany
Tel.: (49) 245162030
Fax: (49) 2451620339
E-Mail: info@centroplan.de
Web Site: www.centroplan.de
Emp.: 25
Thin Film Modules Installation Services
S.I.C.: 3679
N.A.I.C.S.: 334419
Klaus Reinartz *(Mng Dir)*

Centrosolar AG (1)
Stresemannstrasse 163
22769 Hamburg, Germany
Tel.: (49) 403910650
Fax: (49) 4039106599
E-Mail: hamburg@centrosolar.com
Web Site: www.centrosolar.ag
Emp.: 40
Photovoltic Modules Mfr
S.I.C.: 3674
N.A.I.C.S.: 334413
Josef Wrobel *(Mng Dir)*
Bernhard Pawlik *(Member-Mgmt Bd)*
Gunther Wuhr *(Member-Mgmt Bd)*

Centrosolar Cell GmbH (1)
Walter Gropius Str 15
80807 Munich, Germany
Tel.: (49) 89201800
Fax: (49) 8920180555
E-Mail: info@centrosolar.com
Web Site: www.centrosolar-group.com
Emp.: 20
Solar Modules Mfr
S.I.C.: 3674
N.A.I.C.S.: 334413

Centrosolar Glas Holding GmbH (1)
Walter Gropius Str 15
80807 Munich, Germany
Tel.: (49) 89201800
Fax: (49) 8920180555
E-Mail: info@centrosolar.com
Web Site: www.centrosolar.de
Emp.: 20
Solar Cells & Modules Mfr
S.I.C.: 3674
N.A.I.C.S.: 334413
Alexander Kirsch *(CEO)*

Centrosolar Glas Verwaltungs GmbH (1)
Walter Gropius Str 15
80807 Munich, Germany
Tel.: (49) 89201800
Fax: (49) 8920180555
E-Mail: info@centrosolar.com
Web Site: www.centrosolar.com
Emp.: 20
Solar Cells & Modules Mfr
S.I.C.: 3674
N.A.I.C.S.: 334413
Alexander Kirsch *(CEO)*

Renusol GmbH (1)
Piccoloministr 2
D 51063 Cologne, Germany
Tel.: (49) 2217887070
Fax: (49) 22178870799
E-Mail: info@renusol.com
Web Site: www.renusol.com
Emp.: 80
Solar Modules Whslr
S.I.C.: 5065
N.A.I.C.S.: 423690
Wim Coopens *(Co-Mng Dir)*
Michael Kubsch *(Co-Mng Dir)*
Geerling Loois *(Mng Dir)*

Non-U.S. Subsidiaries:

Centrosolar Fotovoltaico Espana S.L. (1)
World Trade Ctr Moll de Barcelona s/n
Edificio Nord 7A planta, 08039 Barcelona, Spain
Tel.: (34) 933435048
Fax: (34) 933023846
E-Mail: info.espana@centrosolar.com
Web Site: www.centrosolar.es
Emp.: 7
Photovoltic Devices Mfr
S.I.C.: 3674
N.A.I.C.S.: 334413
Nina Schubert *(Mgr)*

Centrosolar Hellas MEPE (1)
Adio Alexandrou 57 59
GR-17561 Palaion Faliron, Greece
Tel.: (30) 2106228791
Fax: (30) 2108131988
E-Mail: info.hellas@centrosolar.com
Web Site: www.energyindie.com
Emp.: 2
Solar Modules Mfr
S.I.C.: 3674
N.A.I.C.S.: 334413
Panos Kilimis *(Mng Dir)*

Centrosolar Italia S.r.l. (1)
Viale del Lavoro 33
S Martino B A, 37036 Verona, Italy
Tel.: (39) 045 8781225
Fax: (39) 045 8798589
E-Mail: info.italia@centrosolar.com
Web Site: www.centrosolar.it
Emp.: 20
Photovoltic Devices Sales
S.I.C.: 5065
N.A.I.C.S.: 423690
Wojciech Swietochowski *(Mng Dir)*

Solarsquare AG (1)
Thunstrasse 162
3074 Muri, Switzerland
Tel.: (41) 319526066
Fax: (41) 319526067
Web Site: www.centrosolar.de
Emp.: 2
Solar Cells & Modules Mfr
S.I.C.: 3674
N.A.I.C.S.: 334413

CENTROTEC SUSTAINABLE AG

Am Patbergschen Dorn 9
59929 Brilon, Germany
Tel.: (49) 296196631111
Fax: (49) 296196631000
E-Mail: info@centrotec.de
Web Site: www.centrotec.de
CEV—(DEU)
Rev.: $718,559,969
Assets: $562,923,870
Liabilities: $323,212,725
Net Worth: $239,711,146
Earnings: $30,008,822
Emp.: 2,937
Fiscal Year-end: 12/31/12

Business Description:
Energy Savings Systems & Engineering Plastics
S.I.C.: 8731
N.A.I.C.S.: 541712

Personnel:
Guido A. Krass *(Chm-Supervisory Bd)*
Gert-Jan Huisman *(Chm-Mgmt Bd & CEO)*
Anton Hans *(CFO & Member-Mgmt Bd)*
Christoph Traxler *(Member-Mgmt Bd)*

Supervisory Board of Directors:
Guido A. Krass
Bernhard Heiss
Christian C. Pochtler

Subsidiaries:

Brink-Innosource GmbH (1)
Vidda Strassa 22
48683 Ahaus, Nordrhein-Westfalen, Germany
Tel.: (49) 2734435506
Fax: (49) 2734435507
E-Mail: info@brinkclimatesystems.de
Web Site: www.brinkclimatesystems.de
Emp.: 12
Ventilation Equipments Distr
S.I.C.: 5075
N.A.I.C.S.: 423730
Martin Klein-Reesink *(Mng Dir)*

CENTROTEC Composites GmbH (1)
Am Patbergschen Dorn 9
59929 Brilon, Nordrhein-Westfalen, Germany
Tel.: (49) 2961966320
Fax: (49) 296196632400
E-Mail: composites@centrotec.com
Web Site: www.centrotec-composites.de
Emp.: 5
Roofing Materials & Photovoltaic System Mfr
S.I.C.: 2899
N.A.I.C.S.: 325998
Frank Sager *(Gen Mgr)*

CENTROTEC International GmbH (1)
Am Patbergschen Dorn 9
59929 Brilon, Nordrhein-Westfalen, Germany
Tel.: (49) 2961966320
Fax: (49) 296196632400
E-Mail: info@centrotec.de
Web Site: www.centrotec.de/en/company/subsidiaries.html

CENTROTEC Sustainable AG—(Continued)

Emp.: 150
Plastic Gas Fuel Systems Mfr
S.I.C.: 3082
N.A.I.C.S.: 326121

CENTROTHERM Systemtechnik GmbH (1)
Am Patbergschen Dorn 9
59929 Brilon, Nordrhein-Westfalen, Germany
Tel.: (49) 2961 96 700
Fax: (49) 2961 96 7020
E-Mail: info@centrotherm.com
Web Site: www.centrotherm.com
Emp.: 300
Plastic Gas Flue Systems Mfr
S.I.C.: 3089
N.A.I.C.S.: 326199
Norbert Wuelbeck *(Mng Dir)*

U.S. Subsidiary:

CENTROTHERM Eco Systems, LLC (2)
75 Champlain St
Albany, NY 12204
Tel.: (518) 434-3400
Fax: (518) 618-3166
Toll Free: (877) 434-3432
E-Mail: info@centrotherm.us.com
Web Site: www.centrotherm.us.com
Emp.: 8
Polypropylene Flue Gas Systems Mfr & Distr
S.I.C.: 3082
N.A.I.C.S.: 326121
Joel Dzekciorius *(Mgr-Ops)*

EnEV-Air GmbH (1)
Ridderstrasse 22
48683 Ahaus, Nordrhein-Westfalen, Germany
Tel.: (49) 256198450
Fax: (49) 25 61 98 45 45
E-Mail: info@enev-air.de
Web Site: www.enev-air.de
Ventilation Equipments Mfr & Distr
S.I.C.: 3999
N.A.I.C.S.: 335210
Martin Klein-Reesink *(Mng Dir)*

Kuntschar u. Schluter GmbH (1)
Unterm Dorfe 8
Ippingh, 34466 Wolfhagen, Hesse, Germany
Tel.: (49) 569298800
Fax: (49) 5692988020
E-Mail: info@kuntschar-schlueter.de
Emp.: 65
Plumbing & Electrical Engineering Services
S.I.C.: 1711
N.A.I.C.S.: 238220
Hans Schluter *(Gen Mgr)*

medimondi AG (1)
Wasserkuppenstrasse 29-31
36043 Fulda, Hessen, Germany
Tel.: (49) 661941950
Fax: (49) 6619419590
E-Mail: info@medimondi.com
Web Site: www.medimondi.com
Emp.: 190
Medical Products Mfr
S.I.C.: 3082
N.A.I.C.S.: 326121
Peter Schremp *(CEO)*

Subsidiary:

CENTROPLAST Engineering Plastics GmbH (2)
Unterm Ohmberg 1
34431 Marsberg, Nordrhein-Westfalen, Germany
Tel.: (49) 299297040
Fax: (49) 2992970430
E-Mail: info@centroplast.de
Web Site: www.centroplast.de
Emp.: 80
Extruded Plastic Products Mfr
S.I.C.: 2821
N.A.I.C.S.: 325211
Ulrich Terbrueggen *(Mng Dir)*

Moller Medical GmbH (1)
Wasserkuppenstrasse 29-31
36043 Fulda, Hessen, Germany
Tel.: (49) 661941950
Fax: (49) 6619419590
E-Mail: info@moeller-medical.com
Web Site: www.moeller-medical.com
Emp.: 190
Medical Devices Mfr
S.I.C.: 3841
N.A.I.C.S.: 339112
Berthold Mollenhauer *(Head-Dev)*

Wolf GmbH (1)
Industriestrasse 1
D 84048 Mainburg, Germany DE
Mailing Address:
Postfach 1380
84048 Mainburg, Germany
Tel.: (49) 8751740
Fax: (49) 8751741600
E-Mail: info@wolf-heiztechnik.de
Web Site: www.wolf-heiztechnik.de
Rev.: $242,726,400
Emp.: 1,230
Heating Boilers & Air-Conditioning Units Mfr.
S.I.C.: 3433
N.A.I.C.S.: 333414
Bernhard Steppe *(Mng Dir)*

Wolf Holding GmbH (1)
Industriestr 1
84048 Mainburg, Bayern, Germany
Tel.: (49) 8751740
Fax: (49) 8751741600
Web Site: www.wolf-hitecknik.de
Emp.: 1,500
Management Services
S.I.C.: 8741
N.A.I.C.S.: 551114
Alfred Gaffal *(Mng Dir)*

Non-U.S. Subsidiaries:

Wolf Iberica S.A. (2)
Avenida de la Astronomia 2
28830 San Fernando de Henares, Madrid, Spain
Tel.: (34) 916611853
Fax: (34) 916610398
Web Site: www.wolf-iberica.es
Emp.: 25
Heating & Ventilation Equipments Distr
S.I.C.: 5075
N.A.I.C.S.: 423730
Miguel Testera Verano *(Dir Gen)*

Wolf Klimaattechniek B.V. (2)
Eckertstraat 18 A
8263 CB Kampen, Overijssel, Netherlands
Tel.: (31) 383336801
Fax: (31) 383336802
E-Mail: info@wolf-klimaattechniek.nl
Web Site: www.wolf-klimaattechniek.nl
Emp.: 10
Heating & Ventilation Equipments Distr
S.I.C.: 5075
N.A.I.C.S.: 423730
Martin Wendels *(Mng Dir)*
Alfred Gaffal *(Principal)*

Wolf - Technika Grzewcza Sp. z o.o. (2)
ul Sokolowska 36
Komorow, 05-806 Warsaw, Poland
Tel.: (48) 227206901
Fax: (48) 227206902
E-Mail: wolf@wolf-polska.pl
Web Site: www.wolf-polska.pl
Heating & Ventilation Equipments Distr
S.I.C.: 5075
N.A.I.C.S.: 423730

Non-U.S. Subsidiaries:

Bricon AG (1)
Silbernstrasse 10
8953 Dietikon, Zurich, Switzerland
Tel.: (41) 43 455 48 50
Fax: (41) 43 455 48 51
E-Mail: verkauf@bricon.ch
Web Site: www.bricon.ch
Spine Implants Mfr
S.I.C.: 3842
N.A.I.C.S.: 339113
Franco Merli *(Dir-Dev)*

Brink Climate Systems B.V. (1)
RD Bugelstraat 3
7951 DA Staphorst, Overijssel, Netherlands
Tel.: (31) 522469944
Fax: (31) 522 46 94 00
E-Mail: info@brinkclimatesystems.nl
Web Site: www.brinkclimatesystems.nl
Emp.: 150
Air Conditioning & Heating Units Mfr
S.I.C.: 3585
N.A.I.C.S.: 333415
Johan van Renselaar *(Mng Dir)*

Centrotec Energy Solutions B.V. (1)
RD Bugelstraat 3
7951 DA Staphorst, Overijssel, Netherlands
Tel.: (31) 522469900
Fax: (31) 522469406
Air Conditioning & Heating Units Mfr
S.I.C.: 3585
N.A.I.C.S.: 333415

CENTROTEC J I Asia Pte. Ltd. (1)
18 Kaki Bukit Road 3 03-16 Entrepreneur Business Centre
Singapore, 415978, Singapore
Tel.: (65) 67442242
Fax: (65) 67457747
E-Mail: jitpl@pacific.net.sg
Web Site: www.centrotec.com.sg
Emp.: 2
Roofing Materials Mfr & Distr
S.I.C.: 2439
N.A.I.C.S.: 321214
Lan Lim *(Mng Dir)*

Deveko Klimaatbeheersing B.V. (1)
Elbingstraat 8
Postbus 579
7400 AN Deventer, Overijssel, Netherlands
Tel.: (31) 570625959
Fax: (31) 570633382
E-Mail: info@deveko.nl
Web Site: www.deveko.nl
Emp.: 25
Plumbing & Electrical Engineering Services
S.I.C.: 1711
N.A.I.C.S.: 238220
Tom Geluk *(Gen Mgr)*

Golu Klimaatbeheersing B.V. (1)
Nieuwegracht 25
3763 LP Soest, Utrecht, Netherlands
Tel.: (31) 35 60 21 084
Fax: (31) 522469497
E-Mail: info@golu.nl
Web Site: www.golu.nl
Emp.: 15
Plumbing & Electrical Engineering Services
S.I.C.: 1711
N.A.I.C.S.: 238220
Peter Vries *(Mgr)*

Kempair Klimaatbeheersing B.V. (1)
Hastelweg 274
5652 CN Eindhoven, Noord-Brabant, Netherlands
Tel.: (31) 402511431
Fax: (31) 402513869
E-Mail: info@kempair.nl
Web Site: www.kempair.nl
Emp.: 19
Plumbing & Electrical Engineering Services
S.I.C.: 1711
N.A.I.C.S.: 238220
Peter Vennix *(Mgr)*

Ned Air B.V. (1)
Constructieweg 49
8263 BC Kampen, Overijssel, Netherlands
Tel.: (31) 383370833
Fax: (31) 383322750
E-Mail: info@nedair.nl
Web Site: www.ned-air.nl
Emp.: 80
Air Conditioning & Heating Units Mfr
S.I.C.: 3585
N.A.I.C.S.: 333415
Tom Hoogeveen *(Controller)*

Ned Air Holding B.V. (1)
Constructieweg 49
8263 BC Kampen, Overijssel, Netherlands
Tel.: (31) 383370833
Fax: (31) 383322750
Web Site: www.nedair.nl
Emp.: 60
Management Services
S.I.C.: 8741
N.A.I.C.S.: 551114

Non-U.S. Subsidiaries:

Ned Air Polska Sp.z.o.o (2)
ul Rozdzienskiego 188
40-203 Katowice, Silesian, Poland
Tel.: (48) 322042125
Fax: (48) 322041318
E-Mail: info@ned-air.pl
Web Site: www.ned-air.pl
Emp.: 4
Ventilation Equipments Distr
S.I.C.: 5075
N.A.I.C.S.: 423730
Ingrid Veenstra *(Gen Mgr)*

Ned Air UK Ltd. (2)
84 Lower Ham Road
Kingston upon Thames, Surrey, KT2 5BB, United Kingdom
Tel.: (44) 770 100 98 76
E-Mail: sales@ned-air.co.uk
Web Site: www.ned-air.co.uk
Ventilation Equipments Distr
S.I.C.: 5075
N.A.I.C.S.: 423730
Jeroen Stoel *(Gen Mgr)*

Rolf Schmidt Industri Plast A/S (1)
Jernet 4H
6000 Kolding, Denmark
Tel.: (45) 75534166
Fax: (45) 75 50 47 15
E-Mail: rsip@rsip.com
Web Site: www.rsip.com
Emp.: 50
Extruded Plastic Products Mfr & Conveyor Belts Distr
S.I.C.: 2821
N.A.I.C.S.: 325211
Flemming Andreassen *(CEO & CFO)*
Ken Andresen *(Officer-Cam)*

Ubbink B.V. (1)
Verhuellweg 9
6984 AA Doesburg, Gelderland, Netherlands
Tel.: (31) 313480200
Fax: (31) 313473859
E-Mail: info@ubbink.nl
Web Site: www.ubbink.nl
Emp.: 250
Environmental Engineering Services
S.I.C.: 1623
N.A.I.C.S.: 237130

Non-U.S. Subsidiary:

Ubbink (UK) Ltd. (2)
Unit 33 Liliput Road
Brackmills Industrial Estate, Northampton, Northants, NN4 7DT, United Kingdom UK
Tel.: (44) 1280700211
Fax: (44) 1604433001
E-Mail: info@ubbink.co.uk
Web Site: www.ubbink.co.uk
Emp.: 30
Environmental Engineering Services
S.I.C.: 1623
N.A.I.C.S.: 237130

Ubbink France S.A.S. (1)
13 rue de Bretagne ZA Malabry
BP 4301
44 243 La Chapelle-sur-Erdre, Loire-Atlantique, France
Tel.: (33) 251134646
Fax: (33) 251134546
E-Mail: ubbink@ubbink.fr
Web Site: www.ubbink-france.fr
Emp.: 70
Environmental Engineering Services
S.I.C.: 1629
N.A.I.C.S.: 237130

Ubbink NV (1)
Jan Samijnstraat 9
Gentbrugge, 9050 Gent, East Flanders, Belgium
Tel.: (32) 92371100
Fax: (32) 92371129
E-Mail: info.bouw@ubbink.be
Web Site: www.ubbink.be
Emp.: 25
Environmental Engineering Services
S.I.C.: 1623
N.A.I.C.S.: 237130

Wolf France S.A.S. (1)
Parc Galvani 4 rue Galvani
91349 Massy, Essonne, France
Tel.: (33) 160136470
Fax: (33) 160136473
Web Site: www.wolf-heiztechnik.fr/fr/pkp/acoucil.html
Emp.: 20
Heating & Ventilation Equipments Distr

S.I.C.: 5075
N.A.I.C.S.: 423730
Franck Stocker *(Mgr-Export)*

CENTROTEXTIL A.D.
Knez Mihailova 1-3
11000 Belgrade, Serbia
Tel.: (381) 11 218 36 41
E-Mail: office@centrotextil.co.rs
Web Site: www.centrotextil.co.rs
Year Founded: 1946
CNTX—(BEL)
Business Description:
Textile Import & Export Services
S.I.C.: 2399
N.A.I.C.S.: 314999
Personnel:
Mirko Rasic *(Gen Dir)*

CENTROTHERM PHOTOVOLTAICS AG
Johannes Schmid Strasse
89143 Blaubeuren, Germany
Tel.: (49) 7344 9180
Fax: (49) 7344 9188388
E-Mail: info@centrotherm-pv.de
Web Site: www.centrotherm-pv.de
Sales Range: $800-899.9 Million
Emp.: 1,928
Business Description:
Solar Cell & Silicon Production Equipment Mfr
S.I.C.: 3559
N.A.I.C.S.: 333249
Personnel:
Brigitte Zurn *(Chm-Supervisory Bd)*
Jan von Schuckmann *(Chm-Mgmt Bd & CEO)*
Robert M. Hartung *(Deputy Chm-Supervisory Bd)*
Peter Augustin *(COO & Member-Mgmt Bd)*
Hans Autenrieth *(CMO, Chief Sls Officer & Member-Mgmt Bd)*
Tobias Hoefer *(Chief Restructuring Officer & Member-Mgmt Bd)*
Supervisory Board of Directors:
Brigitte Zurn
Rolf Breyer
Robert M. Hartung
Subsidiaries:

Centrotherm Photovoltaics Technology GmbH **(1)**
Johannes Schmid Strasse 8
89143 Blaubeuren, Germany
Tel.: (49) 734491880
Fax: (49) 73449188388
E-Mail: info@centrotherm.de
Web Site: www.centrotherm.de
Emp.: 900
Photovoltaic Systems Mfr
S.I.C.: 3674
N.A.I.C.S.: 334413
Josef Haase *(Mgr-Sls)*

Centrotherm SiTec GmbH **(1)**
Johannes Schmid Strasse 8
89143 Blaubeuren, Germany
Tel.: (49) 73449187849
Fax: (49) 73449187882
E-Mail: info@centrotherm-sitec.de
Web Site: www.sitec.centrotherm.de
Emp.: 1,400
Semiconductor Machinery Mfr
S.I.C.: 3559
N.A.I.C.S.: 333242
Dirk Stenkamp *(CEO)*

Centrotherm Thermal Solution GmbH & Co.KG **(1)**
Johannes-Schmid-Strasse 8
89143 Blaubeuren, Germany
Tel.: (49) 734491860
Fax: (49) 73449186387
E-Mail: info@centrotherm-ts.de
Web Site: www.centrotherm-ts.de
Furnace Mfr
S.I.C.: 3567
N.A.I.C.S.: 333994

Non-U.S. Subsidiary:

Centrotherm Sud Europe SAS **(2)**
1Ter Bd Aristide Briand
31600 Muret, France
Tel.: (33) 561439005
Fax: (33) 561439978
E-Mail: thierry.barbe@centrotherm.fr
Web Site: www.centrotherm-ts.com
Emp.: 6
Furnace Mfr
S.I.C.: 3567
N.A.I.C.S.: 333994

FHR Anlagenbau GmbH **(1)**
Am Hugel 2
Ottendorf-Okrilla, 01458 Bautzen, Saxony, Germany
Tel.: (49) 352055200
Fax: (49) 35205 52040
E-Mail: postbox@fhr.de
Web Site: www.fhr.de
Thin Film Equipment Mfr
S.I.C.: 3674
N.A.I.C.S.: 334413

GP Solar GmbH **(1)**
Turmstrasse 22
78467 Konstanz, Germany
Tel.: (49) 753128248400
Fax: (49) 753128248410
E-Mail: info@gpsolar.de
Web Site: www.gpsolar.de
Emp.: 120
Solar Cells Mfr
S.I.C.: 3674
N.A.I.C.S.: 334413
Petra Hoffmann *(Mng Dir)*
Eric Ruland *(Mng Dir)*
Jennifer Reuter *(Asst Mng Dir)*

Subsidiary:

GP Inspect GmbH **(2)**
Fraunhoferstrasse 15
82152 Martinsried, Germany
Tel.: (49) 8918904680
Fax: (49) 89189046810
E-Mail: info@gp-inspect.de
Web Site: www.gpsolar.de
Emp.: 30
Research & Develpoment Services
S.I.C.: 8731
N.A.I.C.S.: 541712
Christian Propst *(Mng Dir)*

U.S. Subsidiary:

Centrotherm Photovoltaics USA Inc. **(1)**
100 Cummings Ctr Ste 325k
Beverly, MA 01915-6119
Tel.: (978) 922-1997
Fax: (978) 922-1993
Emp.: 5
Solar Cells Whslr
S.I.C.: 5065
N.A.I.C.S.: 423690

Non-U.S. Subsidiaries:

Centrotherm Photovoltaics Italia S.R.L. **(1)**
Via Giorgione 46
31100 Treviso, Italy
Tel.: (39) 0422590451
Fax: (39) 0422574806
Web Site: www.centrotherm.de
Emp.: 3
Solar Cells Whslr
S.I.C.: 5065
N.A.I.C.S.: 423690
Mario Poletti *(Gen Mgr)*

Centrotherm Photovoltaics Technology Shanghai Co. Ltd. **(1)**
1st Fl Bldg 13 27 Xin Jin Qiao Rd
Pudong, 201206 Shanghai, China
Tel.: (86) 2150301089
Fax: (86) 2150301019
E-Mail: info@centrotherm.com
Web Site: www.centrotherm-pv.com
Emp.: 20
Solar Cells Mfr
S.I.C.: 3674
N.A.I.C.S.: 334413
Renjun Wan *(Gen Mgr)*

CENTRUM CAPITAL LTD.
Centrum House CST Road Vidya Nagari Marg Kalina
Santa Cruz East, Mumbai, 400 098, India
Tel.: (91) 2242159000
E-Mail: info@centrum.co.in
Web Site: www.centrum.co.in
501150—(BOM)
Rev.: $527,142,456
Assets: $99,445,714
Liabilities: $56,091,847
Net Worth: $43,353,867
Earnings: $2,659,720
Emp.: 874
Fiscal Year-end: 06/30/13
Business Description:
Investment Banking Services
S.I.C.: 6211
N.A.I.C.S.: 523110
Personnel:
Khushrooh Byramjee *(Co-Founder)*
Chandir Gidwani *(Co-Founder)*
P. R. Kalyanaraman *(Mng Dir)*
Alpesh Shah *(Compliance Officer & Sec)*
Rajnish Bahl *(CEO/Mng Dir-Grp Retail Fin Svcs)*
K. Sandeep Nayak *(CEO-Broking)*
Board of Directors:
Chandir Gidwani
Ibrahim S. Belselah
Subimal Bhattacharjee
Mahakhurshid Byramjee
Rishad Byramjee
Dhanpal Jhaveri
P. R. Kalyanaraman
Rashid Kidwai
Ameet Naik
Rajesh Nanavaty
R. S. Reddy
Manmohan Shetty
Transfer Agent:
Link Intime India Pvt. Ltd
C-13 Pannalal Silk Mills Compound LBS Marg
Bhandup (West)
Mumbai, India
Subsidiary:

Club 7 Holidays Limited **(1)**
10 Lansdowne Terrace
Kolkata, 700 026, India
Tel.: (91) 33 4013 1111
Fax: (91) 33 2463 0971
E-Mail: club7sales@club7holidays.co.in
Web Site: www.club7holidays.co.in
Emp.: 80
Travel & Tour Operator
S.I.C.: 4725
N.A.I.C.S.: 561520
Barun Bhattacharya *(Asst Mgr)*

CENTRUM KLIMA S.A.
Wieruchow Sochaczewska 144 Street
05-850 Ozarow Mazowiecki, Poland
Tel.: (48) 222505050
Fax: (48) 222505060
E-Mail: office@centrumklima.pl
Web Site: www.centrumklima.pl
Sales Range: $25-49.9 Million
Business Description:
Heating, Ventilation & Air Conditioning Materials Whslr & Mfr
S.I.C.: 5075
N.A.I.C.S.: 423730
Personnel:
Pascal Gelugne *(Mng Dir)*
Wojciech Jakrzewski *(Vice Mng Dir)*
Iwona Gorska *(Sec)*
Legal Counsel:
Kurek Kosciolek Wojcik
Kancelaria Radcow Prawnych
Krakow, Poland

Euler Hermes, Mierzejewska Kancelaria S.p.k
ul. Domaniewska 50B
02-672 Warsaw, Poland

CENTRUM MEDYCZNE ENEL-MED S.A.
(d/b/a ENEL-MED)
Ul Slominskiego 19
00-195 Warsaw, Poland
Tel.: (48) 22 4317701
Fax: (48) 22 4317703
E-Mail: enel@enel.pl
Web Site: www.enel.pl
Year Founded: 1993
ENEA—(WAR)
Sales Range: $25-49.9 Million
Emp.: 1,100
Business Description:
Hospital Management & Other Medical Related Services
S.I.C.: 8062
N.A.I.C.S.: 622110
Personnel:
Anna Rozwadowska *(Chm-Supervisory Bd)*
Adam Rozwadowski *(Chm-Mgmt Bd & CEO)*
Jacek Rozwadowski *(Mng Dir & VP)*
Supervisory Board of Directors:
Anna Rozwadowska
Adam Ciuhak
Janusz Jakubowski
Zbigniew Okonski
Anna Piszcz

CENTUM ELECTRONICS LTD.
44 KHB Industrial Area Yelahanka New Town
Bengaluru, 560 106, India
Tel.: (91) 8041436000
Fax: (91) 8030046005
E-Mail: sales@centumelectronics.com
Web Site: www.centumindia.com
517544—(BOM)
Rev.: $53,056,511
Assets: $48,881,417
Liabilities: $25,988,312
Net Worth: $22,893,104
Earnings: $1,719,857
Emp.: 700
Fiscal Year-end: 03/31/13
Business Description:
Electronic Component Mfr
S.I.C.: 3674
N.A.I.C.S.: 334413
Personnel:
Apparao V. Mallavarapu *(Chm & Mng Dir)*
K. S. Desikan *(CFO)*
Ramu Akkili *(Compliance Officer & Sec)*
Board of Directors:
Apparao V. Mallavarapu
S. Krishnan
Rajiv C. Mody
Manoj Nagrath
Pranav Kumar Patel
P. Rama Rao
Transfer Agent:
Karvy Computershare Private Limited
Plot No 17-24 Vittal Rao Nagar Madhapur
Hyderabad, 500 081, India
Tel.: (91) 40 2342 0818

CENTURIA CAPITAL LIMITED
Level 23 111 Pacific Highway
PO Box 6274
North Sydney, NSW, 2060, Australia
Tel.: (61) 2 8923 8923
Fax: (61) 2 9460 2960
E-Mail: contactus@centuria.com.au
Web Site: www.centuria.com.au
Year Founded: 1991
CNI—(ASX)
Rev.: $48,701,501
Assets: $747,223,216
Liabilities: $647,796,455
Net Worth: $99,426,761

Centuria Capital Limited—(Continued)

Earnings: $7,646,930
Fiscal Year-end: 06/30/13
Business Description:
Investment Management Services
S.I.C.: 6211
N.A.I.C.S.: 523999
Personnel:
John E. McBain *(CEO)*
Matthew J. Coy *(CFO & Co-Sec)*
Nicholas Collishaw *(CEO-Listed Property Funds)*
Jason C. Huljich *(CEO-Unlisted Property Funds)*
Terry D. Reid *(Co-Sec & Gen Mgr-Friendly Societies)*
Board of Directors:
Roger William Dobson
Peter John Done
Jason C. Huljich
John E. McBain
John Slater

Subsidiaries:

Centuria Property Funds Limited (1)
Level 23 111 Pacific Highway
North Sydney, Sydney, NSW, 2060, Australia
Tel.: (61) 289238923
Fax: (61) 294602960
E-Mail: contactus@centuria.com.au
Web Site: www.centuria.com.au
Emp.: 5
Property Fund Management Services
S.I.C.: 6722
N.A.I.C.S.: 525910
Jason C. Huljich *(CEO)*

Over Fifty Funds Management Pty Ltd (1)
L 30 367 Collins St
Melbourne, VIC, 3000, Australia
Tel.: (61) 1300505050
Fax: (61) 396293397
Emp.: 5
Financial Management Services
S.I.C.: 6211
N.A.I.C.S.: 523999
Terry Reid *(Gen Mgr)*

Over Fifty Insurance Pty Ltd (1)
Se 301 L 23 110 Pacific Hwy
North Sydney, Sydney, NSW, 2055, Australia
Tel.: (61) 1300505050
Web Site: www.over50insurance.com
General Insurance Services
S.I.C.: 6411
N.A.I.C.S.: 524298

CENTURION CORPORATION LIMITED

45 Ubi Road 1 Summit Building
Singapore, 408696, Singapore
Tel.: (65) 67453288
Fax: (65) 67489612
E-Mail: co@centurioncorp.com.sg
Web Site: www.centurioncorp.com.sg
OU8—(SES)
Sls.: $52,816,236
Assets: $181,117,319
Liabilities: $49,108,969
Net Worth: $89,002,455
Earnings: $7,688,721
Fiscal Year-end: 12/31/12
Business Description:
Holding Company; Dormitory Management Services; Optical Storage Media Mfr
S.I.C.: 6719
N.A.I.C.S.: 551112
Personnel:
Kok Hoe Wong *(Chm)*
Chee Min Kong *(CEO)*
Ai Huey Foo *(CFO)*
Hazel Luang Chew Chia *(Co-Sec)*
Juliana Beng Hwee Tan *(Co-Sec)*
Board of Directors:
Kok Hoe Wong
Tony Hee Din Bin
Hiang Meng Gn
Chee Min Kong
Kerk Chong Lee
Chandra Mohan

Subsidiaries:

Centurion Dormitories Pte Ltd. (1)
45 Ubi Road 1 Summit Building
Singapore, 408696, Singapore
Tel.: (65) 6745 3288
Fax: (65) 6743 5818
Dormitory Building & Management Services
S.I.C.: 6531
N.A.I.C.S.: 531311

Non-U.S. Subsidiary:

Centurion Dormitories Sdn Bhd (2)
PLO 250 Jalan Firma 2
Kawasan Perindustrian
Tebrau IV, 81100 Johor Bahru, Johor, Malaysia
Tel.: (60) 351 5201
Fax: (60) 351 5202
Dormitory Management Services
S.I.C.: 6531
N.A.I.C.S.: 531311

Centurion Dormitory (Westlite) Pte Ltd. (1)
18 Toh Guan Road East #02-01
Westlite Dormitory, Singapore, 608591, Singapore
Tel.: (65) 6316 3018
Fax: (65) 6316 3020
Dormitory Building & Management Services
S.I.C.: 6531
N.A.I.C.S.: 531311

SM Summit Holdings Pte Ltd. (1)
45 Ubi Road 1 Summit Building
Singapore, 408696, Singapore
Tel.: (65) 6745 3288
Fax: (65) 6748 9612
Holding Company
S.I.C.: 6719
N.A.I.C.S.: 551112

Subsidiary:

Summit CD Manufacture Pte Ltd (2)
45 Ubi Road 1 Summit Building
Singapore, 408696, Singapore
Tel.: (65) 67453288
Fax: (65) 67489612
E-Mail: sales@smsummit.com.sg
Web Site: www.smsummit.com.sg/contact_us.htm
Emp.: 100
Compact Discs Mfr
S.I.C.: 3695
N.A.I.C.S.: 334613
Janice Lee *(Mgr-HR)*

SM Summit Investment Pte. Ltd. (1)
45 Ubi Road 1 Summit Building
Singapore, Singapore
Tel.: (65) 67453288
Fax: (65) 67489612
Investment Management Services
S.I.C.: 6211
N.A.I.C.S.: 523999

Summit Hi-Tech Pte Ltd (1)
45 Ubi Road 1 Summit Building
Singapore, Singapore
Tel.: (65) 67453288
Fax: (65) 67489612
E-Mail: co@smsummit.com.sg
Web Site: www.smsummit.com.sg/contact_us.htm
Compact Discs Mfr
S.I.C.: 3695
N.A.I.C.S.: 334613

WOW Vision Pte Ltd (1)
45 Ubi Rd 1 05-03 Summit Bldg
Singapore, Singapore
Tel.: (65) 67457798
E-Mail: info@wow-vision.com
Web Site: www.wow-vision.com
Emp.: 5
Audio Visual Equipments Distr
S.I.C.: 5045
N.A.I.C.S.: 423430
Dinesh Tripathi *(CEO)*

Non-U.S. Subsidiaries:

PT Digital Media Technology (1)
MM2100 Industrial Town
Jl Bali H1-1 Cibitung
Bekasi, 17520, Indonesia
Tel.: (62) 21 8998 3333
Fax: (62) 21 8998 3939
E-Mail: marketing@dmtech.web.id
Web Site: www.dmtech.web.id
Emp.: 120
Compact Discs & Digital Video Discs Mfr
S.I.C.: 3695
N.A.I.C.S.: 334613
Sony Tan *(CEO)*

Summit Technology Australia Pty Ltd (1)
Unit 28 Slough Avenue Slough Business Park
Locked Bag 122
Silverwater, NSW, 2128, Australia
Tel.: (61) 2 8756 4488
Fax: (61) 2 8756 4483
E-Mail: sales@summittech.com.au
Web Site: www.summittechnology.com.au
Compact & Digital Versatile Discs Mfr
S.I.C.: 3695
N.A.I.C.S.: 334613
Francis Sek *(CEO)*

Subsidiary:

Summit Printing (Australia) Pty Limited (2)
Unit 51 Slough Avenue Slough Business Park
Silverwater, NSW, 2128, Australia
Tel.: (61) 2 8756 4488
Fax: (61) 2 8756 4468
E-Mail: sales@summitprinting.com.au
Web Site: www.summitprinting.com.au
Emp.: 50
Optical Discs Processing & Printing Serivces
S.I.C.: 2759
N.A.I.C.S.: 323111
Clifton Tan *(Gen Mgr)*

CENTURION MINERALS LTD.

Suite 322 470 Granville St
Vancouver, BC, V6C 1V5, Canada
Tel.: (604) 484-2161
Fax: (604) 683-8544
Toll Free: (877) 784-2161
E-Mail: info@centurionminerals.com
Web Site: www.centurionminerals.com
Year Founded: 2005
CTN—(TSXV)
Assets: $1,913,934
Liabilities: $1,054,626
Net Worth: $859,307
Earnings: ($969,439)
Fiscal Year-end: 07/31/13
Business Description:
Mineral Properties Exploration Services
S.I.C.: 1081
N.A.I.C.S.: 213114
Personnel:
Alfred Lenarciak *(Chm)*
David Tafel *(Pres & CEO)*
Ken Cawkell *(Interim CFO)*
Board of Directors:
Alfred Lenarciak
Ken Cawkell
Joseph Del Campo
David Tafel
Stephen Wilkinson
Legal Counsel:
Cawkell, Brodie & Glaister LLP
439 Helmcken Street
Vancouver, BC, V6B 2E6, Canada
Transfer Agent:
Computershare Investor Services
510 Burrard St
Vancouver, BC, Canada

CENTURION SAFETY PRODUCTS LIMITED

Howlett Way
Thetford, Thetford, IP24 1HZ, United Kingdom
Tel.: (44) 1842754266
Fax: (44) 1842765590
E-Mail: sales@centurionsafety.co.uk
Web Site: www.centurionsafety.co.uk
Year Founded: 1879
Rev.: $18,975,851
Emp.: 119
Business Description:
Safety Products Distr
S.I.C.: 5085
N.A.I.C.S.: 423840
Personnel:
David Holdham *(CEO)*

CENTURY AUSTRALIA INVESTMENTS LIMITED

Level 3 99 Bathurst Street
Sydney, NSW, 2000, Australia
Tel.: (61) 2 8262 2800
Fax: (61) 2 9221 1194
E-Mail: century@whiteoutsourcing.com.au
Web Site: www.centuryaustralia.com.au
CYA—(ASX)
Rev.: $3,071,069
Assets: $72,203,983
Liabilities: $1,913,296
Net Worth: $70,290,687
Earnings: $2,367,651
Fiscal Year-end: 06/30/13
Business Description:
Telecommunications Services
S.I.C.: 4813
N.A.I.C.S.: 517110
Personnel:
Peter A. Roberts *(Sec)*
Board of Directors:
Robert J. Turner
Ross J. Finley
Stephen J. Menzies

CENTURY BOND BHD.

Suite 5 11 & 5 12 5th Floor Menara TJB
No 9 Jalan Syed Mohd Mufti, 80000 Johor Bahru, Malaysia
Tel.: (60) 72242823
Fax: (60) 72230229
E-Mail: enquiry@centurybond.com
Web Site: www.centurybond.com
CENBOND—(KLS)
Rev.: $61,268,819
Assets: $64,481,672
Liabilities: $13,115,550
Net Worth: $51,366,122
Earnings: $6,740,932
Fiscal Year-end: 03/31/13
Business Description:
Industrial Packaging Tapes Mfr
S.I.C.: 2672
N.A.I.C.S.: 322220
Personnel:
Siew Kim Tan *(Mng Dir)*
Pow Juliet *(Co-Sec)*
Wee Hee Lee *(Co-Sec)*
Board of Directors:
Poh Fye Lai
Saw Leong Ho
Hai Ngon Kuan
Kai Siang Lim
Boon Leng Tan
Seok Kim Tan
Sew Kee Tan
Siew Kim Tan
Sui Moi Tan
How Kiat Yoong

CENTURY CIRCUITS INC.
3241 Kennedy Road
Scarborough, ON, Canada M1V 2J8
Tel.: (416) 298-9974
Fax: (416) 298-0458
E-Mail: info@centurycan.com
Web Site: www.centurycan.com
Rev.: $13,041,743
Emp.: 125
Business Description:
Printed Circuit Boards Mfr
S.I.C.: 3679
N.A.I.C.S.: 334418
Personnel:
Frank Durigon *(Pres)*
Stanley Sugar *(COO)*

CENTURY CITY INTERNATIONAL HOLDINGS LTD
11th Fl 68 Yee Wo St
Causeway Bay, China (Hong Kong)
Tel.: (852) 28947888
Fax: (852) 28901697
Web Site: www.centurycity.com.hk
0355—(HKG)
Sales Range: $10-24.9 Million
Emp.: 2,130
Business Description:
Building Construction
S.I.C.: 1542
N.A.I.C.S.: 236220
Personnel:
Yuk Sui Lo *(Chm & CEO)*
Kenneth Kwai Kai Ng *(COO)*
Eliza Sau Fun Lam *(Sec)*
Board of Directors:
Yuk Sui Lo
Anthony Chuang
Donald Tung Fan
Kelvin So Po Leung
Jimmy Chun To Lo
Po Man Lo
Kenneth Kwai Kai Ng
Siu Chan Ng
Chi Keung Wong
Butterfield Fulcrum Group (Bermuda) Limited
Rosebank Centre 11 Bermudiana Road
Pembroke, Bermuda

CENTURY EXTRUSIONS LIMITED
113 Park Street N Block 2nd Floor
Kolkata, 700 016, India
Tel.: (91) 3322291012
Fax: (91) 3322261110
E-Mail: century@centuryextrusions.com
Web Site: www.centuryextrusions.com
CENTEXT—(NSE)
Rev.: $33,781,734
Assets: $18,717,984
Liabilities: $11,986,110
Net Worth: $6,731,874
Earnings: ($3,708)
Fiscal Year-end: 03/31/13
Business Description:
Aluminum Extruded Products Mfr
S.I.C.: 3354
N.A.I.C.S.: 331318
Personnel:
M. P. Jhunjhunwala *(Chm & Mng Dir)*
J. K. Malpani *(Pres)*
Sumana Raychaudhuri *(Compliance Officer & Sec)*
Board of Directors:
M. P. Jhunjhunwala
A. K. Hajra
Vikram Jhunjhunwala
V. K. Musharan
R. K. Sharma
M. G. Todi
Transfer Agent:
CB Management Services (P) Limited
P22 Bondel Road
Kolkata, India

CENTURY IRON MINES CORPORATION
200 University Avenue Suite 1301
Toronto, ON, M5H 3C6, Canada
Tel.: (416) 977-3188
Fax: (416) 977-8002
E-Mail: info@centuryiron.com
Web Site: www.centuryiron.com
FER—(TSX)
Sales Range: Less than $1 Million
Emp.: 52
Business Description:
Iron Mining Services
S.I.C.: 1011
N.A.I.C.S.: 212210
Personnel:
M. Marcel Aubut *(Chm)*
Sandy C. K. Chim *(Pres & CEO)*
Rebecca Ng *(CFO)*
Michael R. Skutezky *(Gen Counsel & Sec)*
Peter R. Jones *(Exec VP)*
Ivan Chun Wa Wong *(Sr VP-Corp Fin & Project Dev)*
Board of Directors:
M. Marcel Aubut
Hua Bai
Howard Bernier
Sandy C. K. Chim
Jacques Gauthier
Zhong Xiang Kuang
Paul J. Murphy
Wei Ke Peng
Maurice Strong
Jionghui Wang
David Ben Koon Wong
Jun Kuang Yi
Transfer Agent:
Equity Financial Trust Company
Toronto, ON, Canada

CENTURY LEGEND HOLDINGS LTD
Unit 906 9th Floor AXA Centre 151 Gloucester Road
Wanchai, China (Hong Kong)
Tel.: (852) 28489300
Fax: (852) 28489482
E-Mail: info@clh.com.hk
Web Site: www.clh.com.hk
0079—(HKG)
Rev.: $3,694,031
Assets: $56,692,094
Liabilities: $9,890,594
Net Worth: $46,801,500
Earnings: $1,520,192
Emp.: 40
Fiscal Year-end: 12/31/12
Business Description:
Travel & Gaming Business
S.I.C.: 2015
N.A.I.C.S.: 311615
Personnel:
Samuel Chiu Mo Tsang *(Chm)*
Chiu Ching Tsang *(Deputy Chm)*
Tak On Sze *(Sec & Controller-Fin)*
Board of Directors:
Samuel Chiu Mo Tsang
Edward Chi Wai Au
Evans Tania Ming Tak Chu
Yan Kit Hui
Chiu Ching Tsang
Sylvia Chiu Yuen Tsang
Gary Tak Ming Wong
Boardroom Share Registrars (HK) Limited
12th Floor The Lee Gardens 33 Hysan Avenue
Causeway Bay, China (Hong Kong)
Transfer Agent:
Boardroom Share Registrars (HK) Limited
12th Floor The Lee Gardens 33 Hysan Avenue
Causeway Bay, China (Hong Kong)
Subsidiaries:

Century Legend Finance Limited **(1)**
Rm 3403-4 34 F W Tower Shun Tak Ctr
168-200 Connaught Rd
Central, China (Hong Kong)
Tel.: (852) 25252669
Fax: (852) 29710333
E-Mail: info@clh.com.hk
Emp.: 25
Commercial & Personal Loan Lending Services
S.I.C.: 6163
N.A.I.C.S.: 522310
Amy Wong *(Mgr-HR)*

Century Legend Management Limited **(1)**
Rm 03-04 34 F Shun Tak Ctr W Tower 168-200 Connaught Rd
Central, China (Hong Kong)
Tel.: (852) 25252669
Fax: (852) 29710333
Property Management Services
S.I.C.: 6531
N.A.I.C.S.: 531311

Century Legend Securities Limited **(1)**
Rm 3403-3404 34 F W Tower Shun Tak Ctr
168-200 Connaught Rd
Central, China (Hong Kong)
Tel.: (852) 28489333
Fax: (852) 28489433
Web Site: www.clh.com.hk
Emp.: 20
Stock Broking Services
S.I.C.: 6211
N.A.I.C.S.: 523120
David Chan *(Mng Dir)*

Headquarters Limited **(1)**
11 F Pacific House 20 Queens Rd
Central, China (Hong Kong)
Tel.: (852) 28689092
Fax: (852) 25301237
Hair Salon Operation Services
S.I.C.: 7231
N.A.I.C.S.: 812112

CENTURY LOGISTICS HOLDINGS BERHAD
Lot 8 Lingkaran Sultan Mohamed 1
Bandar Sultan Suleiman
PO Box 93
42008 Port Klang, Selangor Darul Ehsan, Malaysia
Tel.: (60) 333755888
Fax: (60) 333755969
E-Mail: info@century.com.my
Web Site: www.century.com.my
CENTURY—(KLS)
Rev.: $84,227,236
Assets: $121,787,848
Liabilities: $49,331,629
Net Worth: $72,456,219
Earnings: $5,373,297
Emp.: 700
Fiscal Year-end: 12/31/12
Business Description:
Freight Forwarding, Transportation & Warehousing Services
S.I.C.: 4225
N.A.I.C.S.: 493110
Personnel:
Sin Mo Phua *(Chm)*
Choo Hing Teow *(Mng Dir)*
Edwin Khoo Soon Yeap *(CFO)*
Mohamed Amin Mohd Kassim *(Deputy Mng Dir)*
Siew Chuan Chua *(Sec)*
Board of Directors:
Sin Mo Phua
Samad Kassim
Mohamed Amin Mohd Kassim
Chee Keong Soong
Choo Chuan Teow
Choo Hing Teow
Edwin Khoo Soon Yeap
Seng Yeow Yong

CENTURY PAPER & BOARD MILLS LIMITED
Lakson Square Building No 2 Sarwar Shaheed Road
Karachi, 74240, Pakistan
Tel.: (92) 2135698000
Fax: (92) 2135681163
E-Mail: info@centurypaper.com.pk
Web Site: www.centurypaper.com.pk
Year Founded: 1984
CEPB—(KAR)
Sls.: $144,206,841
Assets: $134,476,672
Liabilities: $75,333,305
Net Worth: $59,143,367
Earnings: $9,402,322
Emp.: 1,643
Fiscal Year-end: 06/30/13
Business Description:
Paper Mfr
S.I.C.: 2621
N.A.I.C.S.: 322121
Personnel:
Aftab Ahmad *(CEO)*
Ahmad Ashraf *(CFO)*
Mansoor Ahmed *(Sec)*
Board of Directors:
Iqbal Ali Lakhani
Tasleemuddin Ahmed Batley
Shahid Ahmed Khan
Amin Mohammed Lakhani
Zulfiqar Ali Lakhani
Muhammad Imran Rafiq
Kemal Shoaib

CENTURY PEAK METALS HOLDINGS CORP.
1403-1404 Equitable Twr
8751 Paseoe De Roxas, Makati, 1226, Philippines
Tel.: (63) 28560999
Fax: (63) 28564844
E-Mail: info@centurypeakmetals.com
Web Site: www.centurypeakmetals.com
CPM—(PHI)
Sales Range: $1-9.9 Million
Emp.: 150
Business Description:
Metal Mining Services
S.I.C.: 1099
N.A.I.C.S.: 212299
Personnel:
Wilfredo D. Keng *(Chm, Pres & CEO)*
Luis T. Banson *(CFO)*
David L. Wuson *(CIO)*
Josephine Joy D. Caneba *(Corp Officer)*
Board of Directors:
Wilfredo D. Keng
Luis T. Banson
Ernesto Herrera
Guanghuo Liu
Benito Ong
Melito S. Salazar, Jr.
Venancio Sambar
Emilio Tiu
David L. Wuson

CENTURY PLYBOARDS (I) LTD.
6 Lyons Range
Kolkata, 700 001, India
Tel.: (91) 33 3940 3950
Fax: (91) 33 2248 3539
E-Mail: kolkata@centuryply.com
Web Site: www.centuryply.com
532548—(BOM)

Century Plyboards (I) Ltd.—(Continued)

Rev.: $237,452,144
Assets: $173,467,100
Liabilities: $124,446,691
Net Worth: $49,020,409
Earnings: $10,691,499
Emp.: 4,752
Fiscal Year-end: 03/31/13

Business Description:
Plywood Mfr
S.I.C.: 2435
N.A.I.C.S.: 321211

Personnel:
Sajjan Bhajanka *(Chm)*
Hari Prasad Agarwal *(Vice Chm)*
Sanjay Agarwal *(CEO & Co-Mng Dir)*
Prem Kumar Bhajanka *(Co-Mng Dir)*
Vishnu Khemani *(Co-Mng Dir)*
Arun Kumar Julasaria *(CFO)*
Sundeep Jhunjhunwala *(Sec)*

Board of Directors:
Sajjan Bhajanka
Hari Prasad Agarwal
Sanjay Agarwal
Ajay Baldawa
Manindra Nath Banerjee
Sajan Kumar Bansal
Prem Kumar Bhajanka
Mangi Lal Jain
Vishnu Khemani
Samrendra Mitra
Asit Pal
Santanu Roy

Transfer Agent:
Maheswari Datamatics Private Limited
6 Mangoe Lane 2nd Floor
Kolkata, India

Subsidiaries:

Aegis Business Ltd. (1)
36-A Shakespeare Sarani
Kolkata, West Bengal, 700 017, India
Tel.: (91) 98300 45600
Fax: (91) 98300 95600
E-Mail: info@aegisbusiness.net
Web Site: www.aegisbusiness.net
Welding & Refractory Product Mfr
S.I.C.: 3548
N.A.I.C.S.: 333992
Vineet Rathi *(Mgr-Comml)*

Cement Manufacturing Co. Ltd (1)
Satyam Towers 3 Alipore Road 1st Floor Unit No 9B
Kolkata, 700 027, India
Tel.: (91) 33 24484169
Fax: (91) 33 24484168
E-Mail: kolkata@cmcl.co.in
Web Site: www.cmcl.co.in
Emp.: 100
Cement Mfr
S.I.C.: 3241
N.A.I.C.S.: 327310
Sajjan Bhajanka *(Chm)*

CENTURY PROPERTIES GROUP, INC.

21st Floor Pacific Star Building
Sen Gil Puyat c/r Makati Ave, Makati, Philippines
Tel.: (63) 2 793 5500
Fax: (63) 2 893 6806
E-Mail: ask@century-properties.com
Web Site: www.century-properties.com
CPG—(PHI)
Sales Range: $75-99.9 Million

Business Description:
Real Estate Development Services
S.I.C.: 6531
N.A.I.C.S.: 531390

Personnel:
Jose E.B. Antonio *(Chm, Pres & CEO)*
Neko Lyree Uson-Cruz *(CIO & Compliance Officer)*
Brigida S. Aldeguer *(Sec)*
Jose Roberto R. Antonio *(Exec VP & Head-Bus Dev)*
John Victor R. Antonio *(Exec VP-Sls & Dev)*
Jose Carlo R. Antonio *(Exec VP-Corp Plng & Control)*
Jose Marco R. Antonio *(Exec VP-Sls & Dev)*
Domie S. Eduvane *(Sr VP-Legal & Corp Affairs)*

Board of Directors:
Jose E.B. Antonio
John Victor R. Antonio
Jose Carlo R. Antonio
Jose Marco R. Antonio
Jose Roberto R. Antonio
Ricardo P. Cuerva
Monico V. Jacob
Washington Z. SyCip, Jr.
Rafael G. Yaptinchay

CENTURY REAL ESTATE HOLDINGS PVT. LTD.

No 74 4th Floor Prestige Feroze Cunningham Road
Bengaluru, 560052, India
Tel.: (91) 80 4045 3453
Fax: (91) 80 4045 3409
E-Mail: sales@centuryrealestate.in
Web Site: www.centuryrealestate.in
Year Founded: 1973
947121—(BOM)

Business Description:
Real Estate Development Services
S.I.C.: 6531
N.A.I.C.S.: 531390

Personnel:
P. Dayananda Pai *(Co-Founder)*
P. Satish Pai *(Co-Founder)*
Ravindra Pai *(Mng Dir)*

Board of Directors:
Ashwin Pai
Ravindra Pai
Dev Patel
Mahesh Prabhu

CENTURY SUNSHINE GROUP HOLDINGS LIMITED

Unit 2605 26/F Harbour Centre 25 Harbour Road
Wanchai, China (Hong Kong)
Tel.: (852) 2802 2165
Fax: (852) 2802 2697
E-Mail: cs@centurysunshine.com.hk
Web Site: www.centurysunshine.com.hk
0509—(HKG)
Rev.: $160,275,824
Assets: $304,765,330
Liabilities: $76,586,500
Net Worth: $228,178,830
Earnings: $21,738,907
Emp.: 910
Fiscal Year-end: 12/31/12

Business Description:
Holding Company; Agricultural Products
S.I.C.: 2875
N.A.I.C.S.: 325314

Personnel:
Wen Fu Chi *(Chm & CEO)*
Simon Sai Wai Luk *(CFO & Sec)*
Sai Chit Shum *(COO)*
Yuchuan Yang *(CEO-Sunshine Partners Fin Grp)*

Board of Directors:
Wen Fu Chi
Bi Fen Chi
Mengyong Guo
Ping Man Kwong
Hoi Keung Liu
Hong Sheng
Sai Chit Shum

Royal Bank of Canada Trust Company (Cayman) Limited
4th Floor Royal Bank House 24 Shedden Road
Georgetown, Cayman Islands

Transfer Agents:
Tricor Investor Services Limited
26/F Tesbury Centre 28 Queen's Road East
Hong Kong, China (Hong Kong)

Royal Bank of Canada Trust Company (Cayman) Limited
4th Floor Royal Bank House 24 Shedden Road
Georgetown, Cayman Islands

CENTURY TEXTILES AND INDUSTRIES LIMITED

Century Bhavan Dr Annie Besant Road Worli
Mumbai, 400030, India
Tel.: (91) 2224957000
Fax: (91) 2224309491
E-Mail: centextho@centurytext.com
Web Site: www.centurytextind.com
Year Founded: 1897
CENTURYTEX—(NSE)
Rev.: $1,108,018,998
Assets: $1,531,481,868
Liabilities: $1,196,844,138
Net Worth: $334,637,730
Earnings: ($6,394,446)
Emp.: 12,972
Fiscal Year-end: 03/31/13

Business Description:
Textile, Pulp Paper Products & Cement Mfr
S.I.C.: 2399
N.A.I.C.S.: 314999

Personnel:
B. K. Birla *(Chm)*
D. K. Agrawal *(Compliance Officer, Pres-Corp Fin-Birla Century & Sec)*
Pawan Mehra *(Chief Sourcing Officer-Century Pulp & Paper)*
P. S. Bakshi *(Pres-Works-Manikgarh Cement Unit I)*
O. R. Chitlange *(Sr Pres-Century Rayon, Tyrecord & Chemicals)*
R. K. Dalmia *(Sr Pres-Birla Century, Century Yarn & Century Denim)*
R. S. Doshi *(Pres-Comml-Maihar Cement Unit II)*
U. G. Garg *(Pres-Pur & Projects-Birla Century, Century Yarn & Century Denim)*
Arun Gaur *(Pres-Fin-Century Cement & Sonar Bangla Cement)*
B. L. Jain *(Sr Pres-Century, Maihar, Manikgarh & Sonar Bangla Cements)*
Kamal Kishore *(Pres-Co-ordination-Century, Maihar, Manikgarh & Sonar Bangla Ce)*
R. Lalwani *(Pres-Comml-Century Rayon, Tyrecord & Chemicals)*
A. K. Panja *(Pres-Comml-Century Cement & Sonar Bangla Cement)*
Alok Patni *(Pres-Works-Century Cement & Sonar Bangla Cement)*
Ashwani Kumar Sharma *(Sr Pres-Century Pulp & Paper)*
R. K. Vaishnavi *(Pres-Works-Maihar Cement Unit I)*
Bipin Lal *(CEO-Century Pulp & Paper)*
J. L. Tiwari *(Sr Exec VP-Plant-Manikgarh Cement Unit II)*
Subodh Dave *(Sr VP-Personnel & Admin-Century Rayon, Tyrecord & Chemicals)*
Apurva Gupta *(Sr VP-Rayon-Century Rayon, Tyrecord & Chemicals)*
N. D. Hemke *(Sr VP-Mechanical-Manikgarh Cement Unit II)*
M. K. Jain *(Sr VP-Pur-Century Cement & Sonar Bangla Cement)*
O. P. Moondra *(Sr VP-Electrical & Instrumentation-Maihar Cement Unit III)*

Board of Directors:
B. K. Birla
Kumar Mangalam Birla
Pradip Kumar Daga
Arvind C. Dalal
Amal Ganguli
B. L. Jain

Transfer Agent:
Link Intime India Pvt. Ltd
C-13 Pannalal Silk Mills Compound LBS Marg
Bhandup (West)
Mumbai, India

Divisions:

Century Textiles and Industries Limited - Birla Century Division (1)
Century Bhavan Dr Annie Besant Road
Worli, Mumbai, 400 030, India
Tel.: (91) 22 2495 7000
Fax: (91) 22 2430 9491
E-Mail: info@birlacentury.com
Web Site: www.birlacentury.com
Textile Products Mfr
S.I.C.: 2299
N.A.I.C.S.: 314999
B. K. Birla *(Chm)*

Century Textiles and Industries Limited - Century Cement Division (1)
Industry House 159 Churchgate Reclammation
Mumbai, 400 020, India
Tel.: (91) 22 22023936
Fax: (91) 22 22853085
E-Mail: headoffice@maiharcement.co.in
Web Site: www.centurycement.co.in
Emp.: 29
Cement Mfr
S.I.C.: 3241
N.A.I.C.S.: 327310
B. L. Jain *(Sr Pres)*
Alok Patni *(Pres-Works)*
Arun Gaur *(Sr VP-Fin)*
Satish Gurtoo *(Sr VP-Electrical & Instrumentation)*
M. K. Jain *(Sr VP-Pur)*
A. K. Panja *(Sr VP-Comml)*

Century Textiles and Industries Limited - Century Denim Division (1)
Century Bhavan Dr Annie Besant Road
Worli, Mumbai, 400030, India
Tel.: (91) 22 2495 7000
Fax: (91) 7285255305
E-Mail: centextho@centurytext.com
Web Site: www.centurydenim.com
Emp.: 75
Denim Fabric Mfr
S.I.C.: 2299
N.A.I.C.S.: 313210

Plant:

Century Textiles and Industries Limited - Century Denim Works (2)
Village & Post Satrati Tehsil - Kasrawad
Tehsil - Kasrawad, Khargone, Madhya Pradesh, 451 660, India
Tel.: (91) 7285 255277
Fax: (91) 7285 255305
E-Mail: cendenim@centurytext.com
Web Site: www.centurydenim.com
Denim Fabric Mfr
S.I.C.: 2299
N.A.I.C.S.: 313210

Century Textiles and Industries Limited - Century Pulp and Paper Division (1)
Ghanshyamdham
Nainital, Lalkuan, Uttranchal, 262402, India
Tel.: (91) 5945 268044
Fax: (91) 5945 268047
E-Mail: adm@centurypaper.org.in
Web Site: www.centurypaperindia.com
Pulp & Paper Mfr
S.I.C.: 2611
N.A.I.C.S.: 322110

Century Textiles and Industries Limited - Century Rayon Division (1)
Industry House 159 Churchgate Reclammation
Mumbai, Maharashtra, 400 020, India

Tel.: (91) 22 22027570
Fax: (91) 22 22025109
E-Mail: admnho@cenrayon.com
Web Site: www.centuryrayon.co.in
Emp.: 70
Rayon Yarn Mfr
S.I.C.: 2299
N.A.I.C.S.: 313110
O. R. Chitlange *(Sr Pres)*
S. M. Sanklecha *(Co-Pres-Pur)*
R. Lalwani *(Pres-Comml)*
Subodh Dave *(Sr VP-Personnel & Admin)*
Apurva Gupta *(Sr VP-Rayon)*
V. K. Jhingon *(Sr VP-Tyre Cord, CSY & TQM)*
S. A. Luthra *(Sr VP-Chemicals & Safety)*

Plant:

Century Textiles and Industries Limited - Century Rayon Plant (2)
Murbad Road
PO Box No 22
Shahad, 421 103 Thane, Maharashtra, India
Tel.: (91) 251 2733670
Fax: (91) 251 2730064
E-Mail: cenray@cenrayon.com
Rayon Yarn Mfr
S.I.C.: 2299
N.A.I.C.S.: 313110

Century Textiles and Industries Limited - Century Yarn Division (1)
Century Bhavan Dr Annie Besant Road
Worli, Mumbai, 400 030, India
Tel.: (91) 22 2495 7000
Fax: (91) 22 2430 9192
E-Mail: centextho@centurytext.com
Web Site: www.centuryyarn.com
Cotton Yarn Mfr
S.I.C.: 2299
N.A.I.C.S.: 313110

Plant:

Century Textiles and Industries Limited - Century Yarn Works (2)
Village and Post Satrati
Tehsil - Kasrawad, Khargone, Madhya Pradesh, 451 660, India
Tel.: (91) 7285 255277
Fax: (91) 7285 255305
E-Mail: centextho@centurytext.com
Web Site: www.centurytext.com
Emp.: 70
Cotton Yarn Mfr
S.I.C.: 2299
N.A.I.C.S.: 313110
Vinod Gupta *(Gen Mgr-Mktg)*

Century Textiles and Industries Limited - Cottons by Century Division (1)
Bhavan Dr Annie Besant Road
Worli, Mumbai, 400 030, India
Tel.: (91) 22 2495 7000
Fax: (91) 22 2430 5757
Web Site: www.cottonsbycentury.com
Emp.: 30
Textile Products Mfr
S.I.C.: 2399
N.A.I.C.S.: 314999
B. K. Birla *(Chm)*

Century Textiles and Industries Limited - Maihar Cement Division (1)
Industry House 159 Churchgate Reclammation
Mumbai, 400 020, India
Tel.: (91) 22 22023936
Fax: (91) 22 22853085
E-Mail: headoffice@maniharcement.co.in
Web Site: www.maiharcement.co.in
Emp.: 25
Cement Mfr
S.I.C.: 3241
N.A.I.C.S.: 327310
B. L. Jain *(Sr Pres)*
R. S. Doshi *(Pres-Comml)*
P. M. Intodia *(Pres-Mktg)*
P. K. Agrawal *(Sr VP-Pur)*
Manoj Gupta *(Sr VP-Fin)*

Plant:

Century Textiles and Industries Limited - Maihar Cement Works (2)
P O Sarlanagar
Satna, Madhya Pradesh, 485 772, India
Tel.: (91) 7674 277067
Fax: (91) 7674 277846
E-Mail:
Web Site: www.maiharcement.co.in
Emp.: 500
Cement Mfr
S.I.C.: 3241
N.A.I.C.S.: 327310

Century Textiles and Industries Limited - Manikgarh Cement Division (1)
Industry House 159 Churchgate Reclammation
Mumbai, 400 020, India
Tel.: (91) 22 22023936
Fax: (91) 22 22853085
E-Mail: headoffice@manikgarhcement.com
Web Site: www.manikgarhcement.com
Emp.: 26
Cement Mfr
S.I.C.: 3241
N.A.I.C.S.: 327310
B. L. Jain *(Sr Pres)*
A. D. Karwa *(Pres-Fin & Mktg)*
S. K. Mandelia *(Pres-Comml)*
A. K. Jain *(Sr VP-Mechanical)*
M. P. Joshi *(Sr VP-Electrical & Instrumentation)*
R. K. Udge *(Sr VP-Mines)*

CENTURY TOKYO LEASING CORPORATION

FUJISOFT Bldg 3 Kanda-neribeicho
Chiyoda-ku
Tokyo, 101-0022, Japan
Tel.: (81) 352097055
Fax: (81) 352960230
E-Mail: ir@cls-jp.co.jp
Web Site: www.ctl.co.jp
Year Founded: 1969
8439—(TKS)
Rev.: $7,602,408,000
Assets: $27,123,987,000
Liabilities: $24,553,639,000
Net Worth: $2,570,348,000
Earnings: $318,274,000
Emp.: 1,722
Fiscal Year-end: 03/31/13

Business Description:
Diversified Leasing Services
S.I.C.: 6211
N.A.I.C.S.: 523999

Personnel:
Toshihito Tamba *(Chm & Co-CEO)*
Shunichi Asada *(Pres & Co-CEO)*
Koichi Nakajima *(Deputy Pres)*
Makoto Nogami *(Deputy Pres)*
Noboru Akatsuka *(Mng Exec Officer)*
Yuzuru Asaba *(Exec Officer)*
Mahoko Hara *(Exec Officer)*
Takeshi Honda *(Sr Mng Exec Officer)*
Yuichiro Ikeda *(Sr Mng Exec Officer)*
Takashi Ito *(Mng Exec Officer)*
Atsuhiko Iwatake *(Mng Exec Officer)*
Koichiro Izutsu *(Exec Officer)*
Takashi Kamite *(Exec Officer)*
Ryoji Kawaguchi *(Exec Officer)*
Osamu Miyata *(Exec Officer)*
Masao Mizuno *(Mng Exec Officer)*
Yasuo Mori *(Mng Exec Officer)*
Kenji Murai *(Mng Exec Officer)*
Takashi Muramatsu *(Mng Exec Officer)*
Yoichiro Nakai *(Mng Exec Officer)*
Akihiro Naruse *(Exec Officer)*
Yoshio Nomura *(Exec Officer)*
Shogo Ozaki *(Exec Officer)*
Masahiko Shishido *(Exec Officer)*
Akira Sugimoto *(Exec Officer)*
Masuo Suzuki *(Mng Exec Officer)*
Osamu Tamano *(Exec Officer)*
Yukio Tanaka *(Exec Officer)*
Yasushi Yoshino *(Mng Exec Officer)*
Masataka Yukiya *(Mng Exec Officer)*

Board of Directors:
Toshihito Tamba
Shunichi Asada
Hideo Kondou
Masao Mizuno
Koichi Nakajima
Makoto Nogami
Yoshinori Shimizu
Masuo Suzuki
Masataka Yukiya

Transfer Agent:
Mizuho Trust & Banking Co., Ltd.
2-1 Yaesu 1-Chome Chuo-ku
Tokyo, 103 8670, Japan
Tel.: (81) 332788111
Fax: (81) 332816947

Subsidiaries:

Fujitsu Leasing Co., Ltd. (1)
Fujisoft Building 3 Kanda-neribeicho
Chiyoda-ku, Tokyo, 101-0022, Japan JP
Tel.: (81) 358436301
Fax: (81) 352984125
Web Site: www.jp.fujitsu.com
Emp.: 170
Computer Leasing Services
S.I.C.: 7379
N.A.I.C.S.: 541519
Isao Kato *(Pres)*

IHI Finance Support Corporation (1)
1-8-17 Yaesu
Chuo-ku, Tokyo, 103-0028, Japan JP
Tel.: (81) 332753721
Fax: (81) 332753655
Web Site: www.ctl.co.jp/english/network/related.html#link14
Emp.: 20
Finance & Leasing Services
S.I.C.: 6159
N.A.I.C.S.: 522220
Haruo Sakurai *(Pres)*

ITEC Leasing Co., Ltd. (1)
Kyodo Building 7 1-4-1 Jinnan
Shibuya-ku, Tokyo, 150-0041, Japan JP
Tel.: (81) 3 5456 4760
Broadcasting Equipment Leasing Services
S.I.C.: 7359
N.A.I.C.S.: 532490

Nippon Car Solutions Co., Ltd. (1)
Seavans N Bldg 1-2-1 Shibaura
Minato-ku, Tokyo, 105-0023, Japan
Tel.: (81) 364361190
Fax: (81) 364369809
Web Site: www.ncsol.co.jp
Automobile Leasing Services
S.I.C.: 7515
N.A.I.C.S.: 532112

S.D.L. Co., Ltd. (1)
Mitoku Shimbashi 5-13-1
Tokyo, 104-0061, Japan JP
Tel.: (81) 332892028
Web Site: www.ctl.co.jp/english/network/related.html#link04
Automobile Leasing Services
S.I.C.: 7515
N.A.I.C.S.: 532112

TC Agency Corporation (1)
Nittochi Okachimachi Building 27-5 Taito 2-chome
Taito-ku, Tokyo, 110-0016, Japan JP
Tel.: (81) 358188370
Web Site: www.ctl.co.jp/english/network/related.html#link12
Casualty Insurance & Financial Support Services
S.I.C.: 6141
N.A.I.C.S.: 522291

TC Business Experts Corporation (1)
Nittochi Okachimachi Building 2-27-5 Taito Taito-ku
Tokyo, 110-0016, Japan JP
Tel.: (81) 3 5818 8501
Web Site: www.ctl.co.jp/english/network/related.html#link13
Business Inspection Services
S.I.C.: 8611
N.A.I.C.S.: 813910

TC Business Service Corporation (1)
Kodenma-cho Building 1-4 Nihonbashi-Kodenmacho
Chuo- ku, Tokyo, 103-0001, Japan JP
Tel.: (81) 358188076
Business Processing Service
S.I.C.: 7389
N.A.I.C.S.: 561439

Tokyo Auto Leasing Co., Ltd. (1)
Nittochi Okachimachi Building 27-5 Taito 2-chome
Taito-ku, Tokyo, 110-0016, Japan JP
Tel.: (81) 3 6367 5566 (100%)
Web Site: www.tokyo-autoleasing.co.jp
Emp.: 221
Auto Leasing Services
S.I.C.: 7514
N.A.I.C.S.: 532111

TRY, Inc. (1)
World Trade Ctr Bldg 4-1 Hamamatsu-cho 2-chome
Minato-ku, Tokyo, 105-6110, Japan JP
Tel.: (81) 334354481
Web Site: www.ctl.co.jp/english/network/related.html#link06
Data Deletion & Computer Recycling Services
S.I.C.: 7379
N.A.I.C.S.: 518210

U.S. Subsidiary:

Tokyo Leasing (U.S.A.), Inc. (1)
3020 Westchester Ave Ste 202
Purchase, NY 10577
Tel.: (914) 697-9030
Fax: (914) 697-9034
E-Mail: inquiry@ctleasingusa.com
Web Site: www.ctl.co.jp/english/network/usa.html
Emp.: 25
Leasing Services
S.I.C.: 7359
N.A.I.C.S.: 532210
Hosoya Kohei *(Pres)*

Non-U.S. Subsidiaries:

Century Tokyo Capital (Malaysia) Sdn. Bhd. (1)
Suite 11 2 Level 11 Menara Weld No 76 Jalan Raja Chulan
50200 Kuala Lumpur, Malaysia
Tel.: (60) 320702633
Fax: (60) 320705633
Emp.: 8
General Leasing Services
S.I.C.: 7389
N.A.I.C.S.: 561990
Siang Seng Foo *(Mng Dir)*

Century Tokyo Leasing China Corporation (1)
A2501-02 14 City Ctr Shanghai 100 Zunyi Rd
Changning District, Shanghai, 200051, China
Tel.: (86) 2162370066
Fax: (86) 2162370105
Web Site: www.ctl.co.jp/english/network/tozui.html
Emp.: 27
Financial Services
S.I.C.: 6211
N.A.I.C.S.: 523999
Shuya Sugawara *(Chm)*

Tokyo Leasing (Hong Kong) Ltd. (1)
Room 301 3rd Floor Sun Hung Kai Centre 30 Harbour Road
Wan Chai, Hong Kong, China (Hong Kong) (100%)
Tel.: (852) 25214373
Fax: (852) 28681515
Web Site: www.ctl.co.jp/english/network/hk.html
Emp.: 50
Leasing Services
S.I.C.: 7359
N.A.I.C.S.: 532210
Yukio Matsumoto *(Mng Dir)*

Tokyo Leasing (Singapore) Pte., Ltd. (1)
138 Robinson Road The Corporate Office #12-01
Singapore, 068906, Singapore
Tel.: (65) 32 3436
Fax: (65) 33 0117
Leasing Services
S.I.C.: 7359
N.A.I.C.S.: 532210
Foo Siang Seng *(Mng Dir)*

Century Tokyo Leasing Corporation—(Continued)

Tokyo Leasing (UK) PLC (1)
1st Floor Kingsbridge House
Pinner, Mddx, HA5 5LX, United Kingdom
Tel.: (44) 20 8429 1963
Web Site: www.ctl.co.jp/english/network/uk.html
Real Estate & Financial Leasing Services
S.I.C.: 6531
N.A.I.C.S.: 531390
Masafumi Kitagawa *(Mng Dir)*

CENTURY21 REAL ESTATE OF JAPAN LTD.

7F Kita-Aoyama YOSHIKAWA
Building 2-12-16 Kita-Aoyama
Minato-ku
107-0071 Osaka, Japan
Tel.: (81) 3 3497 0954
Fax: (81) 3 3497 0071
Web Site: www.century21japan.co.jp
Year Founded: 1971
8898—(JAS)

Business Description:
Real Estate Sales & Services
S.I.C.: 6531
N.A.I.C.S.: 531210

Personnel:
Kazunari Mitsukawa *(Pres & CEO)*

CENTURYTOUCH LTD, INC.

Stanton House 31 Westgate
Grantham, NG31 6LX, United Kingdom
Tel.: (44) 1476 591111
E-Mail: info@centurytouch.com
Web Site: www.centurytouch.com
Year Founded: 2010
Rev.: $238,765
Assets: $4,092,014
Liabilities: $4,422,747
Net Worth: ($330,733)
Earnings: ($379,688)
Fiscal Year-end: 06/30/13

Business Description:
Property Development & Hotel Management Services
S.I.C.: 6552
N.A.I.C.S.: 237210

Personnel:
Eric Y.K. Wong *(Chm, CEO, CFO & Treas)*
Edmund Wong *(COO)*

Board of Directors:
Eric Y.K. Wong

CEOTRONICS AG

Adam-Opel-Str 6
63322 Rodermark, Germany
Tel.: (49) 607487510
Fax: (49) 60748751265
E-Mail: chairman@ceotronics.com
Web Site: www.ceotronics.com
CEK—(DEU)
Sls.: $26,183,007
Assets: $24,769,528
Liabilities: $9,288,573
Net Worth: $15,480,955
Earnings: $498,083
Emp.: 158
Fiscal Year-end: 05/31/13

Business Description:
Data Communication Equipment Mfr
S.I.C.: 3669
N.A.I.C.S.: 334290

Personnel:
Matthias Low *(Chm-Supervisory Bd)*
Thomas H. Gunther *(Chm-Mgmt Bd & CEO)*
Horst Schoppner *(Deputy Chm-Supervisory Bd)*
Berthold Hemer *(Deputy Chm-Mgmt Bd & CTO)*
Gunther Thoma *(COO & Member-Mgmt Bd)*

Supervisory Board of Directors:
Matthias Low
Hans-Dieter Gunther
Horst Schoppner

Non-U.S. Subsidiaries:

CeoTronics (Schweiz) AG (1)
Grundstr 16
6343 Rotkreuz, Switzerland
Tel.: (41) 417905838
Fax: (41) 417905839
E-Mail: info@ceotronics.ch
Web Site: www.ceotronics.ch
Emp.: 2
Radio Communication Devices Mfr
S.I.C.: 3663
N.A.I.C.S.: 334220
Thomas H. Guenther *(Gen Mgr)*

CeoTronics S.a.r.l. (1)
Bat Delta T ZA du Tuboeuf Allee des Pleus
77170 Brie-Comte-Robert, France
Tel.: (33) 160183300
Fax: (33) 160286060
E-Mail: ventes@ceotronics.fr
Web Site: www.ceotronics.fr
Emp.: 2
Communications Equipment Distr
S.I.C.: 5065
N.A.I.C.S.: 423690
Gunther Thomas *(Mgr)*

Subsidiary:

CT-Video GmbH (1)
Gewerbegebiet Rothenschirmbach 9
06295 Eisleben, Saxony-Anhalt, Germany
Tel.: (49) 3477661490
Fax: (49) 34776614911
E-Mail: ctv.info@ceotronics.com
Web Site: www.ct-video.com
Emp.: 40
Surveillance Equipments Mfr
S.I.C.: 3812
N.A.I.C.S.: 334511
Rolf-Dieter Glasel *(Dir-Sls)*

U.S. Subsidiary:

CeoTronics, Inc. (1)
512 S Lynnhaven Rd Ste 104
Virginia Beach, VA 23452-6664
Tel.: (757) 549-6220
Fax: (757) 549-6240
E-Mail: sales@ceotronicsusa.com
Web Site: www.ceotronicsusa.com
Emp.: 25
Communication Equipment Mfr
S.I.C.: 3663
N.A.I.C.S.: 334220
Jack Darden *(Mgr-Sls)*

CEP COMMUNICATIONS SARL

31 rue du Colisee
Paris, 75008, France
Tel.: (33) 153533000
Fax: (33) 4495 5656

Business Description:
Publishing Services
S.I.C.: 2741
N.A.I.C.S.: 511199

Joint Venture:

Hoche Friedland (1)
20 Avenue Hoche
75008 Paris, France (50%)
Tel.: (33) 142250598
Holding Company
S.I.C.: 6719
N.A.I.C.S.: 551112

Subsidiary:

Editions Privat SA (2)
10 rue des Arts
BP 38028
F-31080 Toulouse, Cedex 6, France
Tel.: (33) 5 61 33 7700
Telex: 521001 F
Fax: (33) 5 34 31 64 44
E-Mail: info@editions-privat.com
Web Site: www.editions-privat.com
Publisher of Books on French Regional History & Culture; Educational & Professional Books
S.I.C.: 2731
N.A.I.C.S.: 511130
Pierre-Yves Revol *(Pres)*
Philippe Terrancle *(Deputy Dir)*

CEPATWAWASAN GROUP BERHAD

Lot 70 Block 6 Prima Square Mile 4
North Road
90000 Sandakan, Sabah, Malaysia
Tel.: (60) 89272773
Fax: (60) 89272772
E-Mail: pa@cepatgroup.com
Web Site: www.cepatgroup.com
CEPAT—(KLS)
Rev.: $71,825,629
Assets: $190,160,808
Liabilities: $51,882,519
Net Worth: $138,278,289
Earnings: $7,409,352
Fiscal Year-end: 12/31/12

Business Description:
Oil Palm Cultivation Services
S.I.C.: 2079
N.A.I.C.S.: 311225

Personnel:
King Thian Mah *(Chm)*
King Seng Mah *(Mng Dir)*
Shew Meng Kang *(Co-Sec)*
Fei San Seow *(Co-Sec)*

Board of Directors:
King Thian Mah
Kam Leong Chan
Pak Wan Choong
Kim Yin Chua
King Seng Mah
Ah Seng Tan

CEPD N.V.

WTC Amsterdam Tower A-7
Strawinskylaan 709, 1077 XX
Amsterdam, Netherlands
Tel.: (31) 20 670 1316
Fax: (31) 20 670 4428
E-Mail: office@cepd.nl
Web Site: www.cepd.nl

Business Description:
Pharmaceutical Products Sales
S.I.C.: 5912
N.A.I.C.S.: 446110

Personnel:
Jacek Szwajcowski *(Vice Chm-Supervisory Bd)*
Roni Drori *(Pres & CEO)*
Michael Perlil *(CFO & Bus Dev Officer)*

Supervisory Board of Directors:
Jack Dauenhauer
Zbigniew Molenda
Sylwia Pyskiewicz
Mark Schneiders
Jacek Szwajcowski

Non-U.S. Subsidiaries:

Bez Recepty Sp. z o.o. (1)
Ul Zbaszynska 3
91-342 Lodz, Poland
Tel.: (48) 42 200 7289
Fax: (48) 42 200 7268
Web Site: www.bez-recepty.pgf.com.pl
Pharmaceutical Services
S.I.C.: 2834
N.A.I.C.S.: 325412

Business Support Solution S.A. (1)
Ul Pojezierska 90 A
93 341 Lodz, Poland
Tel.: (48) 42 200 7000
Fax: (48) 42 200 7432
E-Mail: bss@bssce.com
Web Site: www.bssce.com
Pharmaceutical Support Services
S.I.C.: 2834
N.A.I.C.S.: 325412

CEPD Management Sp. z o.o. (1)
Ul 17 Stycznia 45B
02-146 Warsaw, Poland
Tel.: (48) 22 329 6400
Fax: (48) 22 329 6401
Web Site: www.cepd.nl
Emp.: 1
Pharmacy Management Services
S.I.C.: 5912
N.A.I.C.S.: 446110
Andrew Benson *(Gen Mgr)*

DOZ S.A. (1)
Ul 17 Stycnia 45 B
02-146 Warsaw, Poland
Tel.: (48) 22 329 6500
Fax: (48) 22 329 6401
E-Mail: bzarzad@doz.pl
Web Site: www.doz.pl
Online Medical Information
S.I.C.: 2741
N.A.I.C.S.: 519130

ePRUF S.A. (1)
Ul Zbaszynska 3
91 342 Lodz, Poland
Tel.: (48) 42 200 7568
Fax: (48) 42 200 7899
E-Mail: kontakt@epruf.pl
Web Site: www.epruf.pl
Pharmaceutical Services
S.I.C.: 2834
N.A.I.C.S.: 325412

Eubioco S.A. (1)
Ul Pojezierska 90-A
91-341 Lodz, Poland
Tel.: (48) 42 200 7930
Fax: (48) 42 200 7929
E-Mail: eubioco@eubioco.eu
Web Site: www.eubioco.eu
Emp.: 4
Pharmaceutical Services
S.I.C.: 2834
N.A.I.C.S.: 325412
Oliver Brown *(Gen Mgr)*

Farm-Serwis Sp. z o.o. (1)
Ul Zbaszynska 3
91 342 Lodz, Poland
Tel.: (48) 42 200 7176
Fax: (48) 42 200 7180
E-Mail: fs@farm-serwis.pl
Pharmaceutical Support Services
S.I.C.: 2834
N.A.I.C.S.: 325412

PGF Urtica Sp. z o.o. (1)
Ul Krzemienecka 120
54-613 Wroclaw, Poland
Tel.: (48) 71 782 6601
Fax: (48) 71 782 6609
E-Mail: sekretariat@urtica.pgr.com.pl
Web Site: www.urtica.com.pl
Hospital Supplies Sales
S.I.C.: 5047
N.A.I.C.S.: 423450

Pharmalink Sp. z o.o. (1)
Ul Zbaszynska 3
91 342 Lodz, Poland
Tel.: (48) 42 200 7555
Fax: (48) 42 200 7433
E-Mail: logystyka@pharmalink.pl
Web Site: www.pharmalink.pl
Pharmaceutical Support Services
S.I.C.: 2834
N.A.I.C.S.: 325412

Pharmena S.A. (1)
Ul Wolczanska 178
90-530 Lodz, Poland
Tel.: (48) 42 291 3370
Fax: (48) 42 291 3871
E-Mail: biuro@pharmena.com.pl
Web Site: www.pharmena.pl
Emp.: 15
Pharmaceutical Services
S.I.C.: 2834
N.A.I.C.S.: 325412
John Kim *(Gen Mgr)*

UAB NFG (1)
Gedimino str 13
LT-44318 Kaunas, Lithuania
Tel.: (370) 37 321199
Fax: (370) 37 320220
E-Mail: limedika@limedika.lt
Web Site: www.limedika.lt
Pharmaceutical Products Sales
S.I.C.: 5912
N.A.I.C.S.: 446110

Unit:

UAB Limedika (2)
Gedimino Str 13
LT-44318 Kaunas, Lithuania (50.1%)
Tel.: (370) 37321199
Fax: (370) 37320220
E-Mail: limedika@limedika.lt
Web Site: www.limedika.lt
Emp.: 150
Pharmaceutical Whslr
S.I.C.: 5047
N.A.I.C.S.: 423450
Asta Dcitaite *(Mgr-Fin)*

CEPOVETT

150 Ancienne Route De Beaujeu
Gleize, 69400 Villefranche-sur-Saone, France
Tel.: (33) 474624700
Fax: (33) 474624999
E-Mail: bereau@cepovett.com
Web Site: www.cepovett.com
Rev.: $22,500,000
Emp.: 200
Business Description:
Mens & Boys Work Clothing
S.I.C.: 2329
N.A.I.C.S.: 315220
Personnel:
Michel Sandjian *(Pres)*

CEPROCIM S.A.

6 Preciziei Blvd Sector 6
Bucharest, 062203, Romania
Tel.: (40) 213188884
Fax: (40) 213188876
E-Mail: office@ceprocim.ro
Web Site: www.ceprocim.ro
CEPO—(BUC)
Rev.: $2,115,999
Assets: $4,639,927
Liabilities: $359,179
Net Worth: $4,280,748
Earnings: $3,334
Emp.: 75
Fiscal Year-end: 12/31/12
Business Description:
Natural Sciences & Engineering Research Development
S.I.C.: 8731
N.A.I.C.S.: 541712
Personnel:
Hariton George Predescu *(Pres & Gen Dir)*
Madalina Niculescu *(Sec)*
Board of Directors:
Dumitru Balan
Constantin Ignat
Hariton George Predescu
Doru Vladimir Puscasu

CEPS PLC

12b George Street
Bath, BA1 2EH, United Kingdom
Tel.: (44) 1225483030
E-Mail: ceps@cepsplc.com
Web Site: www.cepsplc.com
CEPS—(LSE)
Rev.: $23,796,742
Assets: $13,483,978
Liabilities: $7,460,566
Net Worth: $6,023,412
Earnings: ($3,918,218)
Emp.: 178
Fiscal Year-end: 12/31/12
Business Description:
Investment Holding Company
S.I.C.: 6719
N.A.I.C.S.: 551112
Personnel:
Peter G. Cook *(Mng Dir)*
Vivien E. Langford *(Fin Dir & Sec)*
Board of Directors:
Richard T. Organ
Peter G. Cook
David A. Horner
Vivien E. Langford
Geoff C. Martin
Legal Counsel:
Berwin Leighton Paisner LLP
Adelaide House London Bridge
London, United Kingdom
Transfer Agent:
Share Registrars Limited
Suite E First Floor 9 Lion and Lamb Yard
Farnham, United Kingdom
Holdings:

Davies Odell Ltd. (1)
Davies Odell Ltd
Rushden, Northamptonshire, NN10 0DJ, United Kingdom UK
Tel.: (44) 1933410818
Fax: (44) 1933315976
E-Mail: info@daviesodell.co.uk
Web Site: www.daviesodell.com
Emp.: 25
Body Armour & Matting & Footwear Products Mfr & Distr
S.I.C.: 2389
N.A.I.C.S.: 316210
Andy Gregory *(Mng Dir)*

Friedman's Ltd. (1)
Sunaco House Unit 2 Bletchley Rd Heaton Mersey Indus Estate
Heaton Mersey, Stockport, Greater Manchester, SK4 3EF, United Kingdom UK
Tel.: (44) 1619759002
Fax: (44) 1619759003
E-Mail: sales@friedmans.co.uk
Web Site: www.friedmans.co.uk
Emp.: 7
Fabrics Mfr
S.I.C.: 2259
N.A.I.C.S.: 313240

Sunline Direct Mail Ltd. (1)
Cotton Way Weldon Rd Indus Est
Loughborough, Leicestershire, LE11 5FJ, United Kingdom UK
Tel.: (44) 1509263434
Fax: (44) 1509264225
E-Mail: sales@sunlinedirect.co.uk
Web Site: www.sunlinedirect.co.uk
Emp.: 150
Polywrapping & Mailing Services
S.I.C.: 7389
N.A.I.C.S.: 561431
Nigel Maybury *(Mng Dir)*

Division:

Sunline Direct Mail Ltd. - Sunline Solutions (2)
49 Heming Rd
Washford, Redditch, Worcestershire, B98 0EA, United Kingdom
Tel.: (44) 1527510444
Fax: (44) 1527510006
E-Mail: sales@sunlinesolutions.com
Web Site: www.sunlinesolutions.com
Emp.: 50
Data Processing Services
S.I.C.: 7374
N.A.I.C.S.: 518210
Nigel Maybury *(Mng Dir)*

CEQUENCE ENERGY LTD.

Suite 3100 525 8th Avenue SW
Calgary, AB, T2P 1G1, Canada
Tel.: (403) 229-3050
Fax: (403) 229-0603
Toll Free: (866) 764-4569
E-Mail: info@cequence-energy.com
Web Site: www.cequence-energy.com
Year Founded: 2006
CQE—(OTC TSX)
Rev.: $71,216,563
Assets: $516,218,442
Liabilities: $102,283,664
Net Worth: $413,934,779
Earnings: ($17,567,315)
Emp.: 28
Fiscal Year-end: 12/31/12
Business Description:
Oil & Gas Exploration Services
S.I.C.: 1311
N.A.I.C.S.: 211111
Personnel:
Don Archibald *(Chm)*
Paul Wanklyn *(Pres & CEO)*
David Gillis *(CFO & VP-Fin)*
Howard James Crone *(COO & Exec VP)*
Kirk Litvenenko *(Sec)*
Board of Directors:
Don Archibald
Peter Bannister
Robert C. Cook
Howard James Crone
Brian Felesky
Daryl Harvey Gilbert
Francesco G. Mele
Paul Wanklyn
Transfer Agent:
Valiant Trust Company
Calgary, AB, Canada

CERA SANITARYWARE LTD.

9 GIDC Industrial Estate Mehsana
Kadi, Gujarat, 382715, India
Tel.: (91) 2764242329
Fax: (91) 2764242465
E-Mail: kadi@cera-india.com
Web Site: www.cera-india.com
CERA—(NSE)
Rev.: $92,117,986
Assets: $70,389,146
Liabilities: $37,109,168
Net Worth: $33,279,978
Earnings: $8,566,572
Emp.: 2,099
Fiscal Year-end: 03/31/13
Business Description:
Sanitary Ware Mfr & Distr
S.I.C.: 3499
N.A.I.C.S.: 332999
Personnel:
Vikram Somany *(Chm & Mng Dir)*
Narendra N. Patel *(Pres & Sec)*
S. C. Kothari *(CEO)*
Rajesh B. Shah *(CFO & COO-Fin & Comm)*
Atul Sanghvi *(COO)*
Board of Directors:
Vikram Somany
Mahendra Kumar Bhandari
Lalit Kumar Bohania
Ashok Chhajed
K. N. Maiti
Sajan Kumar Pasari
Govindbhai P. Patel
Transfer Agent:
MCS Limited
101 Shatdal Complex 1st Floor Opp Bata Show Room Ashram Road
Ahmedabad, India

CERA SCRL

Philipssite 5 Boite 10
Leuven, Belgium
Tel.: (32) 70695242
Fax: (32) 70695241
E-Mail: info@cera.be
Web Site: www.cera.be
Emp.: 43
Business Description:
Holding Company
S.I.C.: 6719
N.A.I.C.S.: 551112
Personnel:
Franky Depickere *(Mng Dir)*

Subsidiary:

KBC Ancora SCA (1)
Mgr Ladeuzeplein 15
3000 Leuven, Belgium
Tel.: (32) 16279672
Fax: (32) 16279694
Web Site: www.almancora.be
KBCA—(EUR)
Rev.: $68,385,913
Assets: $3,486,342,530
Liabilities: $777,064,242
Net Worth: $2,709,278,288
Earnings: ($12,504,191)
Fiscal Year-end: 06/30/13
Investment Management Services; Owned 63% by Cera SCRL
S.I.C.: 6211
N.A.I.C.S.: 523999
Franky Depickere *(Co-Mng Dir)*
Luc Discry *(Co-Mng Dir)*

CERAGON NETWORKS LTD.

24 Raoul Wallenberg Street
Tel Aviv, 69719, Israel
Tel.: (972) 35431000
Fax: (972) 36455499
E-Mail: info@ceragon.com
Web Site: www.ceragon.com
Year Founded: 1996
CRNT—(NASDAQ TAE)
Rev.: $446,651,000
Assets: $393,596,000
Liabilities: $249,887,000
Net Worth: $143,709,000
Earnings: ($23,391,000)
Emp.: 1,117
Fiscal Year-end: 12/31/12
Business Description:
Point-to-Point Wireless Backhaul Telecommunications Products & Services Designer, Developer, Mfr & Whslr
S.I.C.: 3663
N.A.I.C.S.: 334220
Personnel:
Zohar Zisapel *(Chm)*
Ira Palti *(Pres & CEO)*
Aviram Steinhart *(CFO & Exec VP)*
John Earley *(Pres-Africa)*
Trevor Gordon *(Pres-Key Accts & Strategic Partners)*
Thomas Knudsson *(Pres-Europe)*
Donna Gershowitz *(Gen Counsel & VP)*
Eyal Assa *(Exec VP & Gen Mgr-Long Haul Bus Unit)*
Sharon Ganot *(Exec VP-HR-Global)*
Udi Gordon *(Exec VP-Corp Mktg & Bus Dev)*
Gil Solovey *(Exec VP-Global Ops)*
Hagai Zyss *(Exec VP-Global Products)*
Board of Directors:
Zohar Zisapel
Joseph Atsmon
Yael Langer
Yair E. Orgler
Avshalom Patir

U.S. Subsidiaries:

Ceragon Networks, Inc. (1)
10 Forest Ave Ste 120
Paramus, NJ 07652
Tel.: (201) 845-6955
Fax: (201) 845-5665
E-Mail: infoNA@ceragon.com
Web Site: www.ceragon.com
Point-to-Point Wireless Backhaul Telecommunications Products & Services Designer, Developer, Mfr & Whslr
S.I.C.: 3663
N.A.I.C.S.: 334220
S. Jayne Leighton *(Pres)*

Ceragon USA (1)
1303 E Arapaho Rd Ste 202
Richardson, TX 75081
Tel.: (972) 265-8118
Fax: (972) 265-8130
E-Mail: infoNA@ceragon.com
Web Site: www.ceragon.com
Emp.: 20
Telecommunication Equipment Sales
S.I.C.: 4899
N.A.I.C.S.: 517919
Billy Cain *(Chief Sls Officer)*

Ceragon Networks Ltd.—(Continued)

Non-U.S. Subsidiaries:

Ceragon Italy (1)
Centro Direzionale Colombirolo Edificio A
Via Roma 74
Cassina de Pecchi, 20060 Cassina de' Pecchi, Italy
Tel.: (39) 0295299348
Fax: (39) 029522752
E-Mail: infoeurope@ceragon.com
Emp.: 4
Telecommunication Services
S.I.C.: 3663
N.A.I.C.S.: 334220
Jorge Rachcovsky *(Gen Mgr)*

Ceragon Moscow (1)
Armyanskiy Pereulok 9/1/1 Bldg 1 Office 502
Moscow, 101990, Russia
Tel.: (7) 4957893597
E-Mail: infoeurope@ceragon.com
Web Site: www.ceragon.com
Telecommunication Services
S.I.C.: 3663
N.A.I.C.S.: 334220

Ceragon Networks APAC (S) Pte Ltd (1)
100 Beach Road 27-01/03 Shaw Towers
Singapore, 189702, Singapore
Tel.: (65) 6572 4170
Fax: (65) 72 4199
E-Mail: infoAPAC@ceragon.com
Web Site: www.ceragon.com
Point-to-Point Wireless Backhaul Telecommunications Products & Services Whslr
S.I.C.: 4899
N.A.I.C.S.: 517919
Peter Humphreys *(Pres)*

Ceragon Networks AS (1)
Kokstadveien 23
5257 Kokstad, Norway NO
Mailing Address:
PO Box 7090
5020 Bergen, Norway
Tel.: (47) 55225100
Fax: (47) 55225299
E-Mail: infoeurope@ceragon.com
Web Site: www.ceragon.com
Sales Range: $350-399.9 Million
Emp.: 200
Telecommunication Services
S.I.C.: 4812
N.A.I.C.S.: 517210
Thomas Knudsson *(Pres-Europe)*

Ceragon Networks Australia Pty Ltd (1)
Suite 6 Level 6 144-148 Pacific Highway
North Sydney, NSW, 2060, Australia
Tel.: (61) 289074000
Fax: (61) 289074099
E-Mail: infoAPAC@ceragon.com
Point-to-Point Wireless Backhaul Telecommunications Products & Services Whslr
S.I.C.: 4899
N.A.I.C.S.: 517919
Peter Humphreys *(Pres)*

Ceragon Networks do Brasil Ltda (1)
Avenida Aruana 1050 Tambore
Barueri, Sao Paulo, SP, 06460 010, Brazil
Tel.: (55) 1146894800
Fax: (55) 1146894801
E-Mail: infobrasil@ceragon.com
Web Site: www.ceragon.com
Sales Range: $1-9.9 Million
Emp.: 40
Telecommunication Services
S.I.C.: 4899
N.A.I.C.S.: 517919
Billy Cain *(Pres-Latin America)*

Non-U.S. Branch:

Ceragon Colombia (2)
Carrera 47 No 91-67
Bogota, DC, Colombia
Tel.: (57) 1 257 1999
Fax: (57) 1 257 6241
Web Site: www.ceragon.com
Emp.: 75
Telecommunication Services
S.I.C.: 4899
N.A.I.C.S.: 517919
Billy Cain *(Pres-Latin America)*

Ceragon Networks Hellas S.A. (1)
Sorou 12
15125 Maroussi, Greece
Tel.: (30) 2106108998
Fax: (30) 210 6179107
E-Mail: infoeurope@ceragon.com
Point-to-Point Wireless Backhaul Telecommunications Products & Services Whslr
S.I.C.: 4899
N.A.I.C.S.: 517919
Thomas Knudsson *(Pres-Europe)*

Ceragon Networks (HK) Ltd. (1)
Rm 308B Tower B Grand Pacific Bldg 8A Guanghua Rd
Chaoyang District, Beijing, 100026, China
Tel.: (86) 1065815798
Fax: (86) 1065815786
E-Mail: infoAPAC@ceragon.com
Web Site: www.ceragon.com
Telecommunication Services
S.I.C.: 4899
N.A.I.C.S.: 517919
Peter Humphreys *(Pres-APAC)*

Ceragon Networks (India) Private Limited (1)
The Genesis A-32 Mohan Cooperative Industrial Estate
Mathura Road, New Delhi, 110044, India
Tel.: (91) 1166244700
Fax: (91) 1166244704
E-Mail: infoindia@ceragon.com
Emp.: 50
Telecommunication Services
S.I.C.: 3663
N.A.I.C.S.: 334220
Ram Prakash Tripathi *(Pres & Mng Dir)*

Ceragon Networks (Nigeria) Limited (1)
Africa Reinsurance Building Plot 1679 Karimu Ikotun Street
Victoria Island, Lagos, Nigeria
Tel.: (234) 808 718 0961
Fax: (234) 805 700 4548
E-Mail: infoafrica@ceragon.com
Web Site: www.ceragon.com
Point-to-Point Wireless Backhaul Telecommunications Products & Services Whslr
S.I.C.: 4899
N.A.I.C.S.: 517919
John Earley *(Pres)*

Ceragon Networks Philippines, Inc. (1)
Unit 2A Country Space 1 Bldg No 133 Sen Gil Puyat Ave
Salcedo Village, Makati, 1500, Philippines
Tel.: (63) 28933659
Fax: (63) 28941025
E-Mail: infoAPAC@ceragon.com
Web Site: www.ceragon.com
Point-to-Point Wireless Backhaul Telecommunications Products & Services Designer, Developer, Mfr & Whslr
S.I.C.: 3661
N.A.I.C.S.: 334210
Peter Humphreys *(Pres)*

Ceragon Networks S.A. de C.V. (1)
Lago Iseo 77 Colonia Anahuac Delegacion Miguel Hidalgo
Mexico, DF, CP 11320, Mexico
Tel.: (52) 5591718560
Fax: (52) 5591718561
E-Mail: infola@ceragon.com
Emp.: 25
Telecommunication Services
S.I.C.: 3663
N.A.I.C.S.: 334220
Billy Cain *(Pres)*

Ceragon Networks SARL (1)
6 Place du Village
ZAC Barbanniers, 92330 Gennevilliers, France
Tel.: (33) 140867002
Fax: (33) 140860189
E-Mail: infoeurope@ceragon.com
Web Site: www.ceragon.com
Point-to-Point Wireless Backhaul Telecommunications Products & Services Whslr
S.I.C.: 4899
N.A.I.C.S.: 517919
Thomas Knudsson *(Pres-Europe)*

Ceragon Networks (UK) Limited (1)
4 Oak Tree Park Burnt Meadow Road
North Moons Moat, Redditch, Worcestershire, B98 9NW, United Kingdom
Tel.: (44) 1527591900
Fax: (44) 1527591903
E-Mail: infoeurope@ceragon.com
Web Site: www.ceragon.com
Emp.: 6
Telecommunication Services
S.I.C.: 3663
N.A.I.C.S.: 334220
Thomas Knudsson *(Pres-Europe)*

Ceragon Poland (1)
Ul Smolenskiego 4/6
01 698 Warsaw, Poland
Tel.: (48) 226393505
Fax: (48) 226393506
E-Mail: infoeurope@ceragon.com
Web Site: www.ceragon.com
Emp.: 10
Telecommunication Services
S.I.C.: 3663
N.A.I.C.S.: 334220

Ceragon Thailand (1)
Level 32 Interchange 21 No 399 Sukhumvit Road North
Klongtoey Wattana, Bangkok, 10110, Thailand
Tel.: (66) 2 660 3699
Fax: (66) 2 660 3881
E-Mail:
Point-to-Point Wireless Backhaul Telecommunications Products & Services Whslr
S.I.C.: 4899
N.A.I.C.S.: 517919

CERAM RESEARCH, LTD.

Queens Road Penkhull
Stoke-on-Trent, ST4 7LQ, United Kingdom
Tel.: (44) 1782 764428
Fax: (44) 1782 412331
E-Mail: enquiries@ceram.com
Web Site: www.ceram.com

Business Description:
Materials Testing Services
S.I.C.: 8734
N.A.I.C.S.: 541380

Personnel:
Tony Kinsella *(CEO)*

U.S. Subsidiary:

The M&P Lab, Inc. (1)
2210 Technology Dr
Schenectady, NY 12308 NY
Tel.: (518) 382-0082
E-Mail: info@mandplabs.com
Web Site: www.mandplabs.com
Emp.: 30
Testing Laboratories
S.I.C.: 8734
N.A.I.C.S.: 541380
Frank E. Anderson *(Pres)*

CERAMAX INC.

8200 Decarie Blvd Ste 155
H4P 2P5 Montreal, QC, Canada
Tel.: (514) 336-8155
Fax: (514) 336-7326
Emp.: 20

Business Description:
Ceramic Wall & Floor Tile Mfr
S.I.C.: 3255
N.A.I.C.S.: 327120

Personnel:
Maxime Giordanengo *(Pres)*

CERAMIC FUEL CELLS LIMITED

170 Browns Road
Noble Park, Melbourne, VIC, 3174, Australia
Tel.: (61) 3 9554 2300
Fax: (61) 3 9790 5600
E-Mail: info@cfcl.com.au
Web Site: www.cfcl.com.au
CFU—(AIM ASX OTC)
Rev.: $4,445,276
Assets: $34,728,995
Liabilities: $18,319,753
Net Worth: $16,409,242
Earnings: ($20,610,254)
Emp.: 135
Fiscal Year-end: 06/30/13

Business Description:
Solid Oxide Fuel Cell Development
S.I.C.: 1311
N.A.I.C.S.: 211111

Personnel:
Robert J. Kennett *(CEO)*
Clifford Ashby *(CFO)*
Richard J. Payne *(COO)*
Karl Foger *(CTO)*
Glenn Raines *(Sec)*

Board of Directors:
Alasdair James D. Locke
Clifford Ashby
Roman Dudenhausen
Robert J. Kennett

Computershare Investor Services Pty Ltd
GPO Box 2975
Melbourne, VIC, Australia VIC

Plant:

Ceramic Fuel Cells Limited - Manufacturing Plant (Melbourne) (1)
170 Browns Rd
Noble Park, VIC, 3174, Australia
Tel.: (61) 395542300
Fax: (61) 397905600
E-Mail: enquiries@cfcl.com.au
Web Site: www.cfcl.com.au
Emp.: 50
Fuel Cell Mfr
S.I.C.: 3699
N.A.I.C.S.: 335999
Brendan Dow *(CEO)*

Non-U.S. Subsidiaries:

Ceramic Fuel Cells (Europe) Limited (1)
Unit 8 Candy Park
Hardknott Rd, Bromborough, Wirral, CH62 3QB, United Kingdom
Tel.: (44) 151 334 8880
Fax: (44) 151 334 8804
E-Mail: europe@cfcl.com.au
Web Site: www.cfcl.com.au
Emp.: 4
Fuel Cell Mfr
S.I.C.: 3699
N.A.I.C.S.: 335999

Ceramic Fuel Cells GmbH (1)
Industriepark Oberbruch
Boos Fremery Str 62, 52525 Heinsberg, Nordrhein-Westfalen, Germany
Tel.: (49) 2452153752
Fax: (49) 245215
E-Mail: germany@cfcl.com.au
Web Site: www.cfcl.com.au
Emp.: 10
Fuel Cell Mfr
S.I.C.: 3699
N.A.I.C.S.: 335999
Frank Obernitz *(Gen Mgr-Bus Dev)*

Ceramic Fuel Cells (Powder) Limited (1)
Unit 8 Candy Park
Hardknott Rd, Bromborough, Wirral, CH62 3QB, United Kingdom
Tel.: (44) 1513348880
Fax: (44) 1513348804
E-Mail: europe@cfcl.com.au
Web Site: www.cfcl.com.au
Emp.: 4
Powder & Ceramic Production Services
S.I.C.: 1459
N.A.I.C.S.: 212325
Alan Chapman *(Mgr-Tech)*

CERAMIC INDUSTRIES LIMITED

Farm 2 Old Potchefstroom Road
1939 Vereeniging, South Africa

Tel.: (27) 169303600
Fax: (27) 169303803
E-Mail: info@ceramic.co.za
Web Site: www.ceramic.co.za
Emp.: 452
Business Description:
Tiles, Sanitary Ware & Bathroom Ware Mfr
S.I.C.: 3269
N.A.I.C.S.: 327110
Personnel:
Nicholas Booth *(CEO)*
David R. Alston *(CFO)*
E. J. Willis *(Sec)*
Board of Directors:
Giovanni A.M. Ravazzotti
David R. Alston
Nicholas Booth
Sean D. Jagoe
E. M. Mafuna
Nkhumeleni S. Nematswerani
N. D. Orleyn
L. E. V. Ravazzotti
Klaus M. Schultz
G. Zannoni

CERAMICA CHIARELLI S.A.
R Domingos Brunelli 180
13840020 Mogi-Guacu, SP, Brazil
Tel.: (55) 19 3861 0642
Fax: (55) 19 3861 0842
Year Founded: 1936
CCHI3—(BRAZ)
Business Description:
Ceramic Tile Mfr & Whslr
S.I.C.: 3297
N.A.I.C.S.: 327120
Personnel:
Caio Albino de Souza *(Dir-IR)*

CERAMICA LIMA S.A.
Av Alfredo Mendiola 1465
Lima, 31, Peru
Tel.: (51) 15342313
Fax: (51) 16377316
E-Mail: info@celima-trebol.com.be
Web Site: www.celima-trebol.com
Sales Range: $10-24.9 Million
Emp.: 1,000
Business Description:
Mfr. of Plumbing Fixtures
S.I.C.: 3269
N.A.I.C.S.: 327110
U.S. Subsidiary:

Briggs Industries, Inc. **(1)**
300 Eagle Rd
Goose Creek, SC 29445-6024 MI
Mailing Address:
PO Box 1728
Goose Creek, SC 29445-1728
Tel.: (843) 569-7887
Fax: (843) 569-2091
Toll Free: (800) 888-4458
E-Mail: webmaster@briggsplumbing.com
Web Site: www.briggsplumbing.com
Emp.: 50
Distributor of Porcelain-on-Steel & Vitreous China Plumbing Fixtures & Brassware Import Export
S.I.C.: 3269
N.A.I.C.S.: 327110
Nick Quattro *(Controller-US Ops)*

CERCLE ENTREPRISE
Parc d'activites des charmes
BP 12033
71601 Paray-le-Monial, Cedex, France
Tel.: (33) 385816008
Fax: (33) 385888177
Web Site: www.cercle-entreprise.fr
Sales Range: $10-24.9 Million
Emp.: 30
Business Description:
Engineering Services
S.I.C.: 8711
N.A.I.C.S.: 541330
Personnel:
Jean-Claude Fulchiron *(Dir-Sls)*

CEREBRA INTEGRATED TECHNOLOGIES LTD.
S-5 Off 3rd Cross Peenya Industrial Area
Peenya 1st Stage, Bengaluru, 560 058, India
Tel.: (91) 8028370282
Fax: (91) 8028372609
E-Mail: info@cerebracomputers.com
Web Site: www.cerebracomputers.com
532413—(BOM)
Rev.: $37,453,046
Assets: $21,164,928
Liabilities: $5,628,230
Net Worth: $15,536,698
Earnings: $865,617
Fiscal Year-end: 09/30/13
Business Description:
Information Technology Services
S.I.C.: 7389
N.A.I.C.S.: 519190
Personnel:
Asit Ahuja *(CEO-Cerebra Middle East FZCO)*
V. Ranganathan *(Mng Dir)*
Shridhar S. Hegde *(Compliance Officer)*
Sudhakar Sarvepalli *(CEO-Software Div)*
Vijayakrishna K. T. *(Sec)*
Board of Directors:
S. Gopalakrishnan
Shridhar S. Hegde
P. E. Krishnan
T. S. Suresh Kumar
V. Ranganathan
Gururaja K. Upadhya
P. Vishwamurthy
Transfer Agent:
Karvy Computershare Private Limited
17-24 Vittal Rao Nagar Madhapur
Hyderabad, India
Subsidiaries:

Cerebra LPO India Limited. **(1)**
26/4 2nd Floor A Block Industrial Suburb
Rajajinagar, Bengaluru, 560 055, India
Tel.: (91) 80 2204 6969
Fax: (91) 80 2204 6980
E-Mail: info@cerebralpo.com
Web Site: www.cerebralpo.com
Emp.: 200
Legal Process Outsourcing Services
S.I.C.: 7389
N.A.I.C.S.: 541199
Shobha Srinivas *(CEO)*
V. Ranganathan, *(Mng Dir)*

Geeta Monitors Private Limited. **(1)**
381/1 N S Iyengar street
Seshadripuram, Bengaluru, 560 020, India
Tel.: (91) 80 23466365
Fax: (91) 80 23564904
E-Mail: sales@geetaelectronics.in
Web Site: www.geetaelectronics.in
Emp.: 15
Computer Hardware & Software Distr
S.I.C.: 5045
N.A.I.C.S.: 423430

CEREP S.A.
Le bois l'Eveque
86600 Celle l'Evescault, France
Tel.: (33) 5 49 89 30 00
Fax: (33) 5 49 43 21 70
E-Mail: sales@cerep.com
Web Site: www.cerep.fr
Year Founded: 1989
ALCER—(EUR)
Sales Range: $25-49.9 Million
Emp.: 243
Business Description:
Pharmaceuticals Mfr & Researcher
S.I.C.: 2834
N.A.I.C.S.: 325412
Personnel:
Thierry Jean *(Chm & CEO)*
Sophie Macault *(Gen Counsel & Sec)*
Board of Directors:
Thierry Jean
Pierre Bart
Jean-Paul Boulan
Monique Capron
Sandrine Dufour
Frederic Revah
U.S. Subsidiary:

Cerep, Inc. **(1)**
15318 NE 95th St
Redmond, WA 98052
Tel.: (425) 895-8666
Fax: (425) 895-8668
Web Site: www.cerep.com
Sales Range: $1-9.9 Million
Emp.: 36
Pharmaceuticals Developer
S.I.C.: 2834
N.A.I.C.S.: 325412
Cheryl Wu *(Gen Mgr)*

Non-U.S. Subsidiary:

Cerep Ltd. **(1)**
326 Aidisheng Road B 302-1
Zhangjiang High-Tech Park, Shanghai, 201203, China
Tel.: (86) 21 5132 0568
Fax: (86) 21 5132 0569
Pharmaceutical Research Services
S.I.C.: 2834
N.A.I.C.S.: 325412

CERERIA SGARBI S.P.A.
Strada Quaglia 26
Santena, TO, 10026, Italy
Tel.: (39) 0341266611
Fax: (39) 0341579205
E-Mail: info.sgarbi@sgarbi.it
Web Site: www.sgarbi.it
Emp.: 100
Business Description:
Candle Mfr
S.I.C.: 3999
N.A.I.C.S.: 339999
Non-U.S. Subsidiary:

Price's Patent Candle Ltd. **(1)**
16 Hudson Road
Bedford, MK41 0LZ, United Kingdom UK
Tel.: (44) 1234264500
Fax: (44) 1234264561
E-Mail: sales@prices-candles.co.uk
Web Site: www.prices-candles.co.uk
Emp.: 20
Candle Mfr
S.I.C.: 3999
N.A.I.C.S.: 339999
Piergiorgio Ambroggio *(Mgr)*

CERES GLOBAL AG CORP.
33 Yonge Street Suite 600
Toronto, ON, M5E 1G4, Canada
Tel.: (416) 915-2426
Fax: (416) 364-8893
Toll Free: (800) 513-2832
Web Site: www.ceresglobalagcorp.com
Year Founded: 2007
CRP—(TSX)
Rev.: $221,745,901
Assets: $294,478,120
Liabilities: $150,463,994
Net Worth: $144,014,126
Earnings: ($11,416,445)
Fiscal Year-end: 03/31/13
Business Description:
Asset Management Services
S.I.C.: 6282
N.A.I.C.S.: 523920
Personnel:
Gary P. Selke *(Chm & CEO)*
Michael E. Detlefsen *(Pres)*
Jason C. Gould *(CFO)*
Thomas P. Muir *(Chief Transaction Officer)*
Board of Directors:
Gary P. Selke
R. John Heimbecker
W. Brian Little
Thomas P. Muir
Mary F. Parniak
Legal Counsel:
Blake, Cassels & Graydon LLP
199 Bay Street Suite 4000 Commerce Court West
Toronto, ON, M5L 1A9, Canada
Transfer Agent:
Canadian Stock Transfer
320 Bay Street
P.O. Box 1
Toronto, ON, Canada

CERES MEDIA INTERNATIONAL PLC
81 Rivington Street
London, EC2A 3AY, United Kingdom
Tel.: (44) 20 3178 5618
Fax: (44) 20 3178 5619
E-Mail: info@ceresmediaplc.com
Web Site: www.ceresmediaplc.com
CMI—(AIM)
Business Description:
Holding Company; Advertising Related Services
S.I.C.: 6719
N.A.I.C.S.: 551112
Personnel:
Norman Fetterman *(Chm)*
Alexander Stuart Dowdeswell *(CEO)*
Matthew James Howes *(CFO)*
Board of Directors:
Norman Fetterman
Leslie Christopher Barber
Clive Richard Garston
Subsidiary:

Natural AdCampaign Limited **(1)**
81 Rivington Street
London, EC2A 3AY, United Kingdom
Tel.: (44) 20 3178 5618
Fax: (44) 20 3178 5619
E-Mail: info@NaturalAdCampaign.com
Web Site: www.naturaladcampaign.com
Emp.: 20
Print Media Mfr & Distr
S.I.C.: 3861
N.A.I.C.S.: 325992
Kaori Okano *(Office Mgr)*

CERES POWER HOLDINGS PLC
Viking House Foundry Lane
Horsham, W Sussex, RH13 5PX, United Kingdom
Tel.: (44) 1403 273463
Fax: (44) 1403 327860
E-Mail: info@cerespower.com
Web Site: www.cerespower.com
CWR—(LSE)
Rev.: $825,969
Assets: $30,273,410
Liabilities: $7,203,142
Net Worth: $23,070,268
Earnings: ($17,964,424)
Emp.: 76
Fiscal Year-end: 06/30/13
Business Description:
Development & Commercial Exploitation Of Microgeneration Products
S.I.C.: 2048
N.A.I.C.S.: 311119
Personnel:
Philip Caldwell *(CEO)*
Bruce Girvan *(Sec)*
Board of Directors:
Alan Aubrey

Ceres Power Holdings plc—(Continued)

Philip Caldwell
Steve Callaghan
Mike Lloyd
Richard Preston
Robert Trezona
Legal Counsel:
DAC Beachcroft LLP
Portwall Place Portwall Lane
Bristol, BS99 7UD, United Kingdom

Subsidiary:

Ceres Power Limited (1)
Viking House Foundry Lane
Horsham, West Sussex, RH13 5PX, United Kingdom
Tel.: (44) 1293400404
Fax: (44) 1403327860
E-Mail: info@cerespower.com
Web Site: www.cerespower.com
Emp.: 40
Fuel Cells Mfr
S.I.C.: 3699
N.A.I.C.S.: 335999
Philip Caldwell *(CEO)*

CERESCO

166 chemin de la Grande Ligne
Saint-Urbain-Premier, QC, Canada
J0S 1Y0
Tel.: (450) 427-3831
Fax: (450) 427-2067
Toll Free: (888) 427-7692
E-Mail: info@sgceresco.com
Web Site: www.sgceresco.com
Rev.: $40,386,207
Emp.: 40
Business Description:
Agriculture Services
S.I.C.: 9641
N.A.I.C.S.: 926140
Personnel:
Thierry Gripon *(Co-Owner & VP-Sls & Procurement)*
Mireille Raymond *(Co-Owner & VP-Ops, HR & Fin)*
Hidetsugu Ochiai *(Pres-Mktg)*

CERF INCORPORATED

8430-24 Street
Edmonton, AB, T6P 1X8, Canada
Tel.: (780) 410-2998
Fax: (780) 417-4929
E-Mail: info@cerfcorp.com
Web Site: www.cerfcorp.com
Year Founded: 2005
CFL—(TSXV)
Rev.: $33,567,916
Assets: $56,894,778
Liabilities: $38,958,268
Net Worth: $17,936,510
Earnings: $260,302
Emp.: 165
Fiscal Year-end: 12/31/12
Business Description:
Waste Management Services
S.I.C.: 4959
N.A.I.C.S.: 562998
Personnel:
Wayne Wadley *(Pres & CEO)*
Ken Stephens *(CFO & VP-Fin)*
David Kerr *(COO)*
William Guinan *(Sec)*
Board of Directors:
William Guinan
John Koop
Gary Layden
David W. Maplethorpe
Ken Stephens
Wayne Wadley
Legal Counsel:
Bordner Ladner Gervais LLP
1900, 520-3rd Avenue SW
Calgary, AB, T2P 0R3, Canada
Transfer Agent:
Valiant Trust Company
Calgary, AB, Canada

Subsidiaries:

4-Way Equipment Rentals Corp. (1)
8430 - 24th Street
Edmonton, AB, T6P 1X8, Canada
Tel.: (780) 464-4929
Fax: (780) 417-4929
E-Mail: info@4-way.com
Web Site: www.4-way.com
Construction & Industrial Equipment Rental Services
S.I.C.: 7353
N.A.I.C.S.: 532412
Wayne Wadley *(Pres & CEO)*
Marc Mandin *(COO)*

MCL Waste Systems & Environmental Inc. (1)
4802-40 Avenue
Wetaskiwin, AB, T9A 0A2, Canada
Tel.: (780) 352-2625
Fax: (780) 352-3584
E-Mail: reception@mclwaste.ca
Web Site: www.mclwaste.ca
Landfill Waste Management Services
S.I.C.: 4959
N.A.I.C.S.: 562998

Plant:

MCL Waste Systems & Environmental Inc. - Aspen Waste Management Facility (2)
4802 - 40 Avenue
Wetaskiwin, AB, T9A 0A2, Canada
Tel.: (780) 542-5919
Fax: (780) 352-3584
E-Mail: reception@mclwaste.ca
Web Site: www.aspenwastemanagement.ca
Waste Management Services
S.I.C.: 4959
N.A.I.C.S.: 562998
Skip Kerr *(COO)*

The Smart-Way Disposal & Recycling Company Ltd. (1)
8430 24 Street Northwest
Edmonton, AB, T6P 1X8, Canada
Tel.: (780) 465-4888
Fax: (780) 410-2999
Toll Free: (855) 539-2247
Web Site: www.smartwaydisposal.com
Emp.: 12
Waste Disposal & Recycling Services
S.I.C.: 4953
N.A.I.C.S.: 562219
Matthew Horvath *(Gen Mgr)*

CERIC TECHNOLOGIES

42 rue de Paradis
F-75010 Paris, France
Tel.: (33) 153055500
Fax: (33) 143129230
E-Mail: info@ceric.fr
Web Site: www.ceric.fr
Year Founded: 1960
Sales Range: $25-49.9 Million
Emp.: 85
Business Description:
Building Material Industrial Plant & Manufacturing Equipment Design, Construction & Installation Services
S.I.C.: 1541
N.A.I.C.S.: 236210
Personnel:
Patrick Hebrard *(CEO)*

CERMAK A HRACHOVEC SPOL S.R.O.

Smichovska 31
Prague, 155000, Czech Republic
Tel.: (420) 251091311
Web Site: www.cerhra.cz
Business Description:
Sewerage Pipe Construction
S.I.C.: 1623
N.A.I.C.S.: 237120
Personnel:
Milos Hrachovec *(Vice Chm)*
Board of Directors:
Vlastimil Cermak
Tomas Farka
Milos Hrachovec

CERMAQ ASA

Grev Wedels Plass 5
PO Box 144
Sentrum, N 0102 Oslo, Norway
Tel.: (47) 23685000
Fax: (47) 23685099
E-Mail: cermaq@cermaq.com
Web Site: www.cermaq.com
CEQ—(OSL)
Rev.: $2,132,409,882
Assets: $2,186,570,958
Liabilities: $1,305,349,290
Net Worth: $881,221,668
Earnings: $43,500,404
Emp.: 4,263
Fiscal Year-end: 12/31/12
Business Description:
Holding Company; Fish Farming & Fish Feed Mfr
S.I.C.: 6719
N.A.I.C.S.: 551112
Personnel:
Bard Mikkelsen *(Chm)*
Rebekka Glasser Herlofsen *(Deputy Chm)*
Jon Hindar *(CEO)*
Tore Valderhaug *(CFO)*
Board of Directors:
Bard Mikkelsen
Jan Helge Forde
Rebekka Glasser Herlofsen
Ase Aulie Michelet
Helge Midttun
Lise Caroline Mortensen
Jan Robert Roli-Gjervik

Subsidiaries:

Mainstream Norway AS (1)
8286 Nordfold
Steigen, Norway NO
Tel.: (47) 2368 5500
Fax: (47) 2368 5599
E-Mail: post@mainstream.no
Web Site: www.mainstream.no
Emp.: 200
Fish Farming & Fish Whslr
S.I.C.: 0921
N.A.I.C.S.: 112511
Snorre Jonassen *(Mng Dir)*

Norgrain AS (1)
Kjelvene
PO Box 1569
4093 Stavanger, Norway NO
Tel.: (47) 51891045 (72.48%)
Fax: (47) 51 89 04 40
Web Site: www.norgrain.no
Rev.: $52,569,000
Emp.: 5
Grain Storage & Whslr
S.I.C.: 4221
N.A.I.C.S.: 493130
Are Paulsen *(Gen Mgr)*

CERMED INTERNATIONAL INC.

Schubertstr 10
Munich, 80336, Germany
Tel.: (49) 89 210 228 20
Web Site: www.cermedint.com
CRX—(DEU)
Business Description:
Medical Products Mfr
S.I.C.: 5122
N.A.I.C.S.: 424210
Personnel:
Peter Gombrich *(Chm & CEO)*
Drew Hofmann *(COO & Exec VP)*
Paul Vichi *(CTO)*
Board of Directors:
Peter Gombrich
Lynne Golding
Kenneth W. Holbrook
Jimmy Lee
J. R. Parrish
Irene Podolak
Blaine Rieke
Mary Ruberry

CEROS HOLDING AG

Pilatusstrasse 38
6002 Lucerne, Switzerland
Tel.: (41) 410 4470
Fax: (41) 410 4475
Web Site: www.ceros.de/
CKH—(DEU)
Business Description:
Holding Company; Private Equity Firm
S.I.C.: 6719
N.A.I.C.S.: 551112
Personnel:
Bruno Hofstetter *(Pres)*

U.S. Subsidiary:

CEROS Financial Services, Inc. (1)
1445 Research Blvd Ste 530
Rockville, MD 20850
Tel.: (866) 842-3356
Toll Free: (866) 842-3356
Web Site: www.cerosfs.com
Investment Management Brokering Services
S.I.C.: 6211
N.A.I.C.S.: 523999
Mark Hausman *(Pres)*

Non-U.S. Subsidiary:

CEROS Vermogensverwaltung AG (1)
Bockenheimer Landstrasse 61
60325 Frankfurt, Germany De
Tel.: (49) 699757070
Fax: (49) 69740550
E-Mail: jg@ceros.de
Web Site: www.ceros.de
Asset Management
S.I.C.: 6211
N.A.I.C.S.: 523999
Franz Winklbauer *(Chm-Supervisory Bd)*
Mark Ross *(Member-Exec Bd)*
Stefan Graf von Montgelas *(Member-Exec Bd)*

CERRO GRANDE MINING CORPORATION

TD Waterhouse Tower 79 Wellington Street West Suite 2300
P O Box 128
Toronto, ON, M5K 1H1, Canada
Tel.: (902) 420-3200
E-Mail: ceg@cegmining.com
Web Site: www.cegmining.com
Year Founded: 1996
CEG—(OTC TSX)
Rev.: $27,445,000
Assets: $26,808,000
Liabilities: $9,499,000
Net Worth: $17,309,000
Earnings: ($3,712,000)
Emp.: 310
Fiscal Year-end: 09/30/12
Business Description:
Mineral Properties Exploration & Development
S.I.C.: 1481
N.A.I.C.S.: 213115
Personnel:
Stephen W. Houghton *(Founder & CEO)*
Paul James DesLauriers *(Chm)*
Peter W. Hogg *(CFO)*
Richard J. Lachcik *(Sec)*
Mario A. Hernandez *(Exec VP-Claims & Land Mgmt)*
David R. S. Thomson *(Exec VP-Exploration)*
Board of Directors:
Paul James DesLauriers
Mario A. Hernandez
William Hill
Stephen W. Houghton
Richard J. Lachcik

Fernando Saenz Poch
Juan A. Proano
Frederick D. Seeley
David R. S. Thomson
Legal Counsel:
Norton Rose LLP
Toronto, ON, Canada
Transfer Agent:
Computershare Investor Services
Toronto, ON, Canada

Non-U.S. Subsidiary:

Cerro Grande Mining Corporation **(1)**
La Concepcion 266 Office 704
Providencia, Santiago, Chile (100%)
Tel.: (56) 2 264 2295
Fax: (56) 2 264 2309
E-Mail: ceg@cegmining.com
Web Site: www.cegmining.com
Explorer & Developer of Mining Properties
S.I.C.: 1481
N.A.I.C.S.: 213115
Mario Hernandez *(Exec VP & Dir-Claims & Land Mgmt)*
David R.S. Thompson *(Exec VP & Dir-Exploration)*

CERRO MINING CORP.

1980-1075 West Georgia Street
Vancouver, BC, V6E 3C9, Canada
Tel.: (604) 888-9588
Fax: (778) 329-9361
Web Site:
Year Founded: 1987
CRX—(TSXV)
Assets: $5,234,549
Liabilities: $507,667
Net Worth: $4,726,882
Earnings: ($5,918,541)
Fiscal Year-end: 01/31/13
Business Description:
Mineral Properties Exploration Services
S.I.C.: 1081
N.A.I.C.S.: 213114
Personnel:
Jason Birmingham *(Pres & CEO)*
Sharon Lewis *(CFO)*
Board of Directors:
Jason Birmingham
Sean Farrell
Sharon Lewis
Alexander Polevoy
Transfer Agent:
Computershare Trust Company of Canada
9th Floor 100 University Avenue
Toronto, ON, Canada

CERRO RESOURCES NL

(Acquired & Absorbed by Primero Mining Corp.)

CERSANIT S.A.

Aleja Solidarnosci 36
25-323 Kielce, Poland
Tel.: (48) 413158003
Fax: (48) 413158006
E-Mail: ir@cersanit.com.pl
CST—(WAR)
Sales Range: $500-549.9 Million
Business Description:
Bathroom Furnishings Mfr
S.I.C.: 3499
N.A.I.C.S.: 332999
Personnel:
Artur Kloczko *(Chm-Supervisory Bd)*
Miroslaw Wladyslaw Jedrzejczyk *(Chm-Mgmt Bd)*
Grzegorz Mironski *(Deputy Chm-Supervisory Bd)*
Ireneusz Kazimierski *(Member-Mgmt Bd)*
Piotr Mrowiec *(Member-Mgmt Bd)*
Marcin Rybarczyk *(Member-Mgmt Bd)*
Grzegorz Saniawa *(Member-Mgmt Bd)*
Supervisory Board of Directors:
Artur Kloczko
Grzegorz Mironski
Robert Oskard
Jacek Tucharz
Mariusz Waniolka

CERTECO LIMITED

25 Watling Street
London, EC4M 9BR, United Kingdom
Tel.: (44) 207 099 0803
Fax: (44) 207 183 7780
E-Mail: info@certeco.co.uk
Web Site: www.certeco.co.uk
Sales Range: $10-24.9 Million
Emp.: 120
Business Description:
IT Services
S.I.C.: 7373
N.A.I.C.S.: 541512
Personnel:
Gary Davies *(Mng Dir)*

CERTINA HOLDING AG

Tumblinger str 23
80337 Munich, Bayern, Germany
Tel.: (49) 00892108960
Fax: (49) 8921089650
E-Mail: info@certina.de
Web Site: www.certina.de
Sales Range: $150-199.9 Million
Emp.: 1,100
Business Description:
Holding Company
S.I.C.: 6719
N.A.I.C.S.: 551112
Personnel:
Klaus Wehrmann *(CEO)*

Subsidiary:

Eiffel Deutschland Stahltechnologie GmbH **(1)**
Hackethalstrasse 4
30179 Hannover, Germany
Mailing Address:
Postfach 3507
D-30035 Hannover, Germany
Tel.: (49) 51167990
Fax: (49) 5116799199
E-Mail: info@eiffel.eiffage.de
Web Site: www.eiffel.de
Emp.: 100
Steel Mfr.
S.I.C.: 3325
N.A.I.C.S.: 331513
Michael Pfeiffer *(Mng Dir)*
Uwe Heiland *(Mng Dir)*

Subsidiary:

Eiffel Deutschland Stahltechnologie GmbH - Duisburg **(2)**
Friedrich Ebert Strasse 134
47229 Duisburg, Germany
Tel.: (49) 2065823010
Fax: (49) 2065823090
E-Mail: tstihl@eiffel.eiffage.de
Web Site: www.eiffel.de
Emp.: 200
Steel Mfr.
S.I.C.: 3325
N.A.I.C.S.: 331513
Thomas Stihl *(Project Mgr)*

CERVANTES CORPORATION LIMITED

Shop 11 South Shore Piazza 85
South Perth Esplanade
South Perth, WA, 6151, Australia
Mailing Address:
PO Box 1196
South Perth, WA, 6951, Australia
Tel.: (61) 8 6436 2300
Fax: (61) 8 9367 2450
E-Mail: admin@cervantescorp.com.au
Web Site: www.cervantescorp.com.au
CVS—(ASX)
Rev.: $26,162
Assets: $335,416
Liabilities: $554,970
Net Worth: ($219,555)
Earnings: ($473,008)
Emp.: 1
Fiscal Year-end: 06/30/13
Business Description:
Seafood Mfr & Whslr
S.I.C.: 2092
N.A.I.C.S.: 311710
Personnel:
Collin Vost *(Chm & Mng Dir)*
Patrick J. O'Neill *(Sec)*
Board of Directors:
Collin Vost
Timothy Clark
Justin Vost
Legal Counsel:
Steinepreis Paganin
GPO Box 2799
Perth, Australia

CERVUS EQUIPMENT CORPORATION

Harvest Hills Bus Park 5201-333 96 Avenue NE
Calgary, AB, T3K 0S3, Canada
Tel.: (403) 567-0339
Fax: (403) 567-0309
E-Mail: placey@cervuscorp.com
Web Site: www.cervuscorp.com
Year Founded: 2003
CVL—(TSX)
Rev.: $729,854,215
Assets: $399,553,297
Liabilities: $197,980,951
Net Worth: $201,572,346
Earnings: $24,435,000
Emp.: 1,115
Fiscal Year-end: 12/31/12
Business Description:
Tractors & Farming Machinery & Equipment Dealer
S.I.C.: 5083
N.A.I.C.S.: 423820
Personnel:
Peter Alan Lacey *(Chm)*
Graham Drake *(Pres & CEO)*
Randall Muth *(CFO)*
Board of Directors:
Peter Alan Lacey
Don Bell
Larry Benke
Steven M. Collicutt
Graham Drake
Gary Wayne Harris
Angela Lekatsas
Legal Counsel:
Shea Nerland Calnan
Calgary, AB, Canada
Transfer Agent:
Computershare Trust Company of Canada
600 530 8th Avenue SW
Calgary, AB, T2P 3S8, Canada
Tel.: (403) 267-6555
Toll Free: (800) 558-0046

Subsidiary:

Contractors Equipment LP **(1)**
333 96 Ave Ne Ste 5201
Calgary, AB, T3K 0S3, Canada
Tel.: (403) 567-0339
Fax: (403) 567-0392
Web Site: www.cervusequipment.com
Emp.: 100
Construction Equipments Whslr
S.I.C.: 5082
N.A.I.C.S.: 423810
Graham Drake *(Pres)*
Peter Alan Lacey *(Pres)*

CESAR SA

19 rue des Bretons
93210 Saint Denis, France
Tel.: (33) 1 49 98 16 10
Fax: (33) 1 49 98 38 60
E-Mail: contact@cesar-group.com
Web Site: www.cesar-group.com
ALCES—(EUR)
Sales Range: $50-74.9 Million
Business Description:
Party Items Mfr
S.I.C.: 3942
N.A.I.C.S.: 339930
Personnel:
Daniel Velasco *(Chm-Exec Bd)*

CESARE PACIOTTI S.P.A.

Via Sant Andrea 8
Milan, 20121, Italy
Tel.: (39) 276013887
Fax: (39) 0276003560
E-Mail: info@cesare-paciotti.com
Web Site: www.cesare-paciotti.com
Year Founded: 1948
Sales Range: $1-9.9 Million
Emp.: 200
Business Description:
Footwear Designer & Mfr
S.I.C.: 2389
N.A.I.C.S.: 316210
Personnel:
Maximiliano Bennettin *(Mng Dir)*

CESC LIMITED

CESC House Chowringhee Square
Kolkata, 700 001, India
Tel.: (91) 3322256040
Fax: (91) 3322555155
E-Mail: cesc@cesc.co.in
Web Site: www.cesc.co.in
Year Founded: 1897
500084—(BOM)
Rev.: $1,427,650,452
Assets: $3,879,244,710
Liabilities: $2,787,967,332
Net Worth: $1,091,277,378
Earnings: $85,169,052
Fiscal Year-end: 03/31/13
Business Description:
Electric Utility Services
S.I.C.: 4931
N.A.I.C.S.: 221122
Personnel:
Aniruddha Basu *(Mng Dir)*
Subhasis Mitra *(Compliance Officer & Sec)*
Board of Directors:
Sanjiv Goenka
Aniruddha Basu
Chandra Kumar Dhanuka
Brij Mohan Khaitan
Pradip Kumar Khaitan
Srikandath Narayan Menon
Sanjay Kumar Pal
Legal Counsel:
Khaitan & Co.
9 Old Post Office St
Kolkata, India
Computershare Investor Services plc
The Pavilions Bridgewater Road
PO Box 859
BS99 1XZ Bristol, United Kingdom
Transfer Agent:
Link Intime India Pvt. Ltd.
59-C Chowringhee Road 3rd Floor
Kolkata, 700 020, India
Tel.: (91) 33 2289 0540
Fax: (91) 33 2289 0539

Subsidiaries:

Au Bon Pain Cafe India Limited **(1)**
57 Industrial Suburb
Yeshwanthpur, Bengaluru, 560057, India
Tel.: (91) 96 8652 9049
Retail Chain Operators
S.I.C.: 5999

CESC Limited—(Continued)

N.A.I.C.S.: 453998

CESC Properties Limited (1)
CESC House Chowringhee Sq
Kolkata, 700 001, India
Tel.: (91) 3322256040
Fax: (91) 3322255155
Property Development Services
S.I.C.: 6531
N.A.I.C.S.: 531311

Music World Retail Limited (1)
2 St George Gate Road 7th Floor Hastings
Kolkata, West Bengal, 700022, India
Tel.: (91) 33 222 36 337
Fax: (91) 33 2223 6339
E-Mail: contactus@musicworld.in
Web Site: www.musicworld.in
Music Publishing Services
S.I.C.: 2741
N.A.I.C.S.: 512230

Nalanda Power Company Limited (1)
Regd Clfice 6 Church Lane 1st Floor
Kolkata, 700 001, India
Tel.: (91) 3322109358
Fax: (91) 3322109356
Electric Power Generation
S.I.C.: 4931
N.A.I.C.S.: 221118

Spencer's Retail Limited (1)
Shakuntala Sarkar 7th Floor 5 Clive Row
700 001 Kolkata, India
Tel.: (91) 33 6625 7800
Fax: (91) 97487 73132
Web Site: www.spencersretail.com
Emp.: 7,000
Supermarket & Grocery Stores
S.I.C.: 5411
N.A.I.C.S.: 445110
Vineet Kapila *(Pres)*

CESP - COMPANHIA ENERGETICA DE SAO PAULO

Avenida Nossa Senhora do Sabara
No 5 312 Escritorio 17
Bairro Pedreira, Sao Paulo, 04447-011, Brazil
Tel.: (55) 1156132100
Fax: (55) 1156126814
E-Mail: ricesp@cesp.com.br
Web Site: www.cesp.com.br
CESP6—(BRAZ)
Sales Range: $50-74.9 Million
Emp.: 1,321

Business Description:
Electric Power Generation & Distribution
S.I.C.: 4939
N.A.I.C.S.: 221118

Personnel:
Dilma Seli Pena *(Chm)*
Mauro Guilherme Jardim Arce *(CEO, Member-Exec Bd & Dir-Engrg & Construction)*
Vicente K. Okazaki *(CFO, Member-Exec Bd & Dir-IR)*
Mituo Hirota *(Dir-Production & Member-Exec Bd)*
Armando Shalders Neto *(Dir-Admin & Member-Exec Bd)*

Board of Directors:
Dilma Seli Pena
Fernando Carvalho Braga
Paulo Renato Costa de Souza
Isabel da Silva Ramos Kemmelmeier
Marcos Antonio de Albuquerque
Andre Luiz de Lacerda Sousa
Gesner Jose de Oliveira Filho
Carlos Pedro Jens
Antonio Mardevanio Goncalves da Rocha
Andrea Sandro Calabi
Francisco Vidal Luna
Nelson Vieira Barreira

CESSOT DECORATION SARL

14 rue Croix la Comtesse
Nogent le Rotrou, 28400 Le Mans, France
Tel.: (33) 237534200
Fax: (33) 237522423
E-Mail: cessot@cessot-decoration.com
Web Site: www.cessot-decoration.fr/
Sls.: $21,800,000
Emp.: 105

Business Description:
Hardware
S.I.C.: 3429
N.A.I.C.S.: 332510

Personnel:
Claude Tournier *(Mng Partner)*

Board of Directors:
Yohan Harduin

CETIP S.A.

Av Republica do Chile 230 - 11 andar Centro
20031-919 Rio de Janeiro, Brazil
Tel.: (55) 2122767474
Fax: (55) 2122767435
Web Site: www.cetip.com.br
CTIP3—(BRAZ)
Rev.: $389,044,655
Assets: $1,295,532,012
Liabilities: $593,072,757
Net Worth: $702,459,255
Earnings: $135,464,047
Fiscal Year-end: 12/31/12

Business Description:
Commodity Contracts Brokerage Services
S.I.C.: 6221
N.A.I.C.S.: 523140

Personnel:
Edgar da Silva Ramos *(Chm)*
David Scott Goone *(Vice Chm)*
Gilson Finkelsztain *(CEO)*
Roberto Dagnoni *(Exec Officer-Financing Unit & New Bus & VP)*
Wagner Anacleto *(Exec Officer-Ops-Securities Unit)*
Giovanni de Mello Viotti *(Exec Officer-Institutional Rels-GRV Bus Unit)*
Reinaldo Rabelo de Morais Filho *(Exec Officer-Legal & Standards-Financing Unit)*
Mauricio Reboucas Freire dos Santos *(Exec Officer-Tech-Securities Unit)*
Carlos Cesar Menezes *(Exec Officer-Self Regulation)*
Mauro Negrete *(Exec Officer-Ops & Tech-Financing Unit)*
Carlos Eduardo Ratto Pereira *(Exec Officer-Comml, Products & Mktg-Securities Unit)*

Board of Directors:
Edgar da Silva Ramos
Roberto de Jesus Paris
Ary Oswaldo Mattos Filho
David Scott Goone
Alexsandro Broedel Lopes
Alkimar Ribeiro Moura
Pedro Paulo Mollo Neto
Joao Carlos Ribeiro
Robert Taitt Slaymaker

CETIS, D.D.

Copova ulica 24
3000 Celje, Slovenia
Tel.: (386) 34278500
Fax: (386) 34278817
E-Mail: info@cetis.si
Web Site: www.cetis.si
CETG—(LJU)
Sales Range: $25-49.9 Million
Emp.: 344

Business Description:
Documents, Cards, Forms, Labels & Flexible Packaging
S.I.C.: 2759
N.A.I.C.S.: 323111

Personnel:
Ljubo Pece *(Chm-Supervisory Bd)*
Franc Jesovnik *(Deputy Chm-Supervisory Bd)*
Simona Potocnik *(Gen Dir)*

Supervisory Board of Directors:
Ljubo Pece
Borut Bizaj
Franc Jesovnik
Bernard Gregl
Marko Melik
Dusan Mikus

Non-U.S. Subsidiary:

Cetis-ZG d.o.o., (1)
Industrijska Ulica 11
10431 Sveta Nedelja, Croatia
Tel.: (385) 13335000
Fax: (385) 13335001
E-Mail: cetis@cetis.hr
Web Site: www.cetis.hr
Emp.: 20
Security Printing Services
S.I.C.: 2759
N.A.I.C.S.: 323111
Matej Polutnik *(Gen Mgr)*

Subsidiary:

Amba Co., proizvodnja in trgovina d.o.o., Ljubljana (1)
Leskoskova 11
1000 Ljubljana, Slovenia
Tel.: (386) 15874300
Fax: (386) 15874305
E-Mail: info@ambatc.si
Web Site: www.amba-tc.si
Emp.: 40
Flexo Printing Technology Services
S.I.C.: 2759
N.A.I.C.S.: 323111

CETSI

(See Under Conseils et Systemes Informatiques)

CEVITAL S.P.A.

Ilot D No 6 ZHUN Garidi II
Kouba, 16005 Algiers, Algeria
Tel.: (213) 2356 3802
Fax: (213) 2356 3814
E-Mail: contact@cevital.com
Web Site: www.cevital.com
Year Founded: 2007
Sales Range: $1-4.9 Billion
Emp.: 13,000

Business Description:
Investment Holding Company
S.I.C.: 6719
N.A.I.C.S.: 551112

Personnel:
Issad Rebrab *(Founder & Chm)*
Louis L. Roquet *(Mng Dir)*

Board of Directors:
Issad Rebrab
Mohamed Ahmed El-Antri Tibaoui
Lynda Rebrab
Malik Rebrab
Omar Rebrab
Salim Rebrab
Yassine Rebrab
Louis L. Roquet
Ahmed Sadoudi
Smail Seghir

Non-U.S. Subsidiary:

Oxxo SA (1)
3 Route de Jalogny
BP 23
71250 Cluny, France FR
Tel.: (33) 385595566
Fax: (33) 385595550
Web Site: www.oxxo.fr
Emp.: 288
PVC Window Frames Mfr
S.I.C.: 3089
N.A.I.C.S.: 326199

CEWE COLOR HOLDING AG

Meerweg 30-32
D-26133 Oldenburg, Germany
Tel.: (49) 4414040
Fax: (49) 441404421
E-Mail: info@cewecolor.de
Web Site: www.cewecolor.de
CWC—(DEU)
Rev.: $677,589,285
Assets: $433,298,469
Liabilities: $252,005,716
Net Worth: $181,292,752
Earnings: $25,341,650
Emp.: 3,192
Fiscal Year-end: 12/31/12

Business Description:
Photofinishing Services
S.I.C.: 4813
N.A.I.C.S.: 517110

Personnel:
Otto Korte *(Chm-Supervisory Bd)*
Rolf Hollander *(Chm-Mgmt Bd)*
Hans-Jurgen Appelrath *(Deputy Chm-Supervisory Bd)*
Reiner Fageth *(Member-Mgmt Bd)*
Andreas F. L. Heydemann *(Member-Mgmt Bd)*
Olaf Holzkamper *(Member-Mgmt Bd)*

Supervisory Board of Directors:
Otto Korte
Hans-Jurgen Appelrath
Christiane Hipp
Corinna Linner
Michael Paetsch
Hans-Henning Wiegmann

Subsidiary:

Cewe Color AG & Co. OHG (1)
Meerweg 30 32
D 26133 Oldenburg, Germany
Tel.: (49) 4414040
Fax: (49) 441404421
E-Mail: info@pohoprintigph.de
Web Site: www.cewe.de
Photofinishing Services
S.I.C.: 7384
N.A.I.C.S.: 812921

Subsidiaries:

Diginet Gmbh & Co. KG (2)
161 Industriestrasse
D 50999 Cologne, Nordhein-Westfalen, Germany
Tel.: (49) 221 2236 886 0
Fax: (49) 221 65 00 40 99
E-Mail: info@pixum.com
Web Site: www.pixum.de
Photofinishing Services
S.I.C.: 7384
N.A.I.C.S.: 812921
Daniel Attallah *(CEO & Founder)*
Marc Rendel *(CTO)*

diron Wirtschaftsinformatik GmbH & Co. KG (2)
Otto-Hahn-Str 21
48161 Munster, Nordrhein-Westfalen, Germany
Tel.: (49) 251979200
Fax: (49) 2519792020
E-Mail: info@diron.de
Web Site: www.diron.de
Emp.: 40
Photofinishing Services
S.I.C.: 7384
N.A.I.C.S.: 812921
Michael Fries *(Mng Dir)*

Fotocolor GmbH (2)
Freiburger Str 20
79427 Eschbach, Baden-Wurttemberg, Germany
Tel.: (49) 76345050
Fax: (49) 7634505250
Photofinishing Services
S.I.C.: 7384
N.A.I.C.S.: 812921

Non-U.S. Subsidiaries:

CeWe Color, a.s. (2)
Kloknerova 2278 24
148 00 Prague, 4, Czech Republic
Tel.: (420) 272071200
E-Mail: fotolabcz@cewecolor.cz
Web Site: www.fotolab.cz
Emp.: 80
Photofinishing Services
S.I.C.: 7384
N.A.I.C.S.: 812921
Petr Turecek *(Mgr-Mktg)*

CEWE COLOR Belgium S.A. (2)
Blauwesteenstraat 87
2550 Kontich, Belgium
Tel.: (32) 3 4 51 92 00
Fax: (32) 3 4 58 06 17
Photofinishing Services
S.I.C.: 7384
N.A.I.C.S.: 812921

CEWE COLOR Danmark A.S. (2)
Segaltvej 16
8541 Skodstrup, Denmark
Tel.: (45) 86991422
Fax: (45) 86 99 24 33
Photofinishing Services
S.I.C.: 7384
N.A.I.C.S.: 812921

CEWE COLOR Limited (2)
Unit 4 Spartan Close Titan Bus Ctr
Tachbrook Park
Warwick, Warwickshire, CV34 6RR, United Kingdom
Tel.: (44) 1926463107
Fax: (44) 1926463101
E-Mail: photoworld@cewecolor.co.uk
Web Site: www.cewe-photoworld.co.uk
Emp.: 80
Photofinishing Services
S.I.C.: 7384
N.A.I.C.S.: 812921
Duncan Midwood *(Mng Dir)*

CEWE COLOR Magyarorszag Kft (2)
Beke ut 21-29
1135 Budapest, Hungary
Tel.: (36) 14511088
Fax: (36) 12380709
E-Mail: digital@cewecolor.hu
Web Site: www.cewe-fotokonyv.hu
Emp.: 60
Photofinishing Services
S.I.C.: 7384
N.A.I.C.S.: 812921
Zoltan Zoboki *(Mng Dir)*

CEWE COLOR Nederland B.V. (2)
Industrieweg 73
8071 CS Nunspeet, Netherlands
Tel.: (31) 341255355
Fax: (31) 341255333
E-Mail: cewenederland@cewecolor.de
Web Site: www.cewe-fotoboek.nl
Emp.: 35
Photofinishing Services
S.I.C.: 7384
N.A.I.C.S.: 812921

CEWE COLOR S.A.S (2)
189 rue d Aubervilliers
75886 Paris, Cedex, 18, France
Tel.: (33) 153266666
Fax: (33) 153266638
Photofinishing Services
S.I.C.: 7384
N.A.I.C.S.: 812921

CEWE COLOR Sp. z o. o (2)
Ul Strzelecka 11
47230 Kedzierzyn-Kozle, Opole, Poland
Tel.: (48) 774063000
Fax: (48) 774063025
E-Mail: info@cewecolor.pl
Web Site: www.cewecolor.pl
Emp.: 60
Photofinishing Services
S.I.C.: 7384
N.A.I.C.S.: 812921
Michal Szendzielorz *(Mng Dir)*

Fotojoker Sp. z o. o. (2)
Ul Strzelecka 11
47230 Kedzierzyn-Kozle, Opole, Poland
Tel.: (48) 774063200
Fax: (48) 774063201
E-Mail: info@fotojoker.pl
Web Site: www.fotojoker.pl
Emp.: 50
Camera & Photofinishing Equipment Sales
S.I.C.: 5043
N.A.I.C.S.: 423410
Michal Szendzielorz *(Mgr)*

Japan Photo Holding Norge AS (2)
Flatestadveien 3
1416 Oppegard, Norway
Tel.: (47) 66822660
Fax: (47) 66 82 26 70
E-Mail: kundeservice@japanphoto.com
Web Site: www.japanphoto.no
Emp.: 300
Photofinishing Services
S.I.C.: 7384
N.A.I.C.S.: 812921
Stephan Stein *(Pres)*

CEYLON & FOREIGN TRADES PLC

No 414/18 K Cyril C Perera Mawatha
Colombo, 13, Sri Lanka
Tel.: (94) 117608500
Fax: (94) 112447886
E-Mail: cft@cft.lk
Web Site: www.cft.lk
CFT—(COL)
Rev.: $1,895,331
Assets: $9,056,015
Liabilities: $2,095,589
Net Worth: $6,960,427
Earnings: $99,573
Fiscal Year-end: 03/31/13

Business Description:
Consumer Goods Export Services
S.I.C.: 6159
N.A.I.C.S.: 522293

Personnel:
Shabbir Abbas Gulamhusein *(Chm)*

Board of Directors:
Shabbir Abbas Gulamhusein
Taher Abbas Gulamhusein
Darindranath Charith Gunasekera
Loolbadda Waduge Waruna Priyankara
Aliasger A. Shabbir
Idris Shabbir
Aliasghar Yusuf Tyebkhan
Imran Zahir

CEYONIQ TECHNOLOGY GMBH

Boulevard 9
33613 Bielefeld, Germany
Tel.: (49) 52193181000
Fax: (49) 52193181111
E-Mail: info@ceyoniq.com
Web Site: www.ceyoniq.com
Rev.: $19,422,000
Emp.: 98

Business Description:
Software Development Services
S.I.C.: 7371
N.A.I.C.S.: 541511

Personnel:
Andreas Ahmann *(Head-R&D)*

CEZ, A.S.

(d/b/a CEZ Group)
Duhova 2/1444
140 53 Prague, 4, Czech Republic
Tel.: (420) 211041111
Fax: (420) 211042001
E-Mail: cez@cez.cz
Web Site: www.cez.cz
Year Founded: 1992
CEZ—(DEU PRA)
Rev.: $11,307,544,150
Assets: $33,438,199,900
Liabilities: $20,073,907,070
Net Worth: $13,364,292,830
Earnings: $2,110,843,210
Emp.: 31,308
Fiscal Year-end: 12/31/12

Business Description:
Electrical & Energy Power Services & Distr
S.I.C.: 4911
N.A.I.C.S.: 221122

Personnel:
Daniel Benes *(Chm & CEO)*
Martin Roman *(Chm-Supervisory Bd)*
Martin Novak *(Vice Chm & CFO)*
Vladimir Hronek *(Vice Chm-Supervisory Bd)*
Vaclav Paces *(Vice Chm-Supervisory Bd)*
Alan Svoboda *(Chief Sls Officer)*
Peter Bodnar *(Chief Investment Officer)*
Pavel Cyrani *(Chief Strategy Officer)*
Hana Krbcova *(Chief HR Officer)*
Ladislav Kriz *(Press Officer & Dir-Media Dept)*
Martin Sobotka *(Press Officer & Mgr-Comm-Central Bohemia)*
Michaela Chaloupkova *(Chief Pur Officer)*
Jan Pavlu *(Press Officer)*
Tomas Pleskac *(Distr & Foreign Countries Officer)*
Barbora Pulpanova *(Press Officer)*
Martin Schreier *(Press Officer-Renewable Sources)*
Petr Spilka *(Press Officer-Dukovany Nuclear Power Plant)*
Ladislav Stepanek *(Acting Chief Production Officer)*
Marek Svitak *(Press Officer-Temelin Nuclear Power Plant)*

Board of Directors:
Daniel Benes
Peter Bodnar
Michaela Chaloupkova
Pavel Cyrani
Martin Novak
Tomas Pleskac
Ladislav Stepanek

Supervisory Board of Directors:
Martin Roman
Milan Bajgar
Vladimir Hronek
Jiri Kadrnka
Radek Mucha
Jiri Novotny
Vaclav Paces
Lubomir Poul
Vladimir Riha
Drahoslav Simek
Jiri Volf

Subsidiaries:

CEZ Bohunice a.s. (1)
Duhova 2/1444
Prague, 140 53, Czech Republic
Tel.: (420) 211 041 111
Fax: (420) 211 042 001
E-Mail: cez@cez.cz
Electric Power Generation Services
S.I.C.: 4911
N.A.I.C.S.: 221118
Daniel Benes *(Gen Dir)*

CEZ Distribuce, a. s. (1)
Teplicka 874/8
405 02 Decin, Czech Republic
Tel.: (420) 840 840 840
E-Mail: info@cezdistribuce.cz
Web Site: www.cezdistribuce.cz
Electric Power Distribution Services
S.I.C.: 4939
N.A.I.C.S.: 221122
Tomas Pleskac *(Co-Chm-Supervisory Bd)*
Richard Vidlicka *(Co-Chm-Supervisory Bd)*
Petra Holomkova *(Vice Chm-Supervisory Bd)*
Jaroslav Janda *(Vice Chm-Supervisory Bd)*

CEZ Energeticke produkty, s.r.o. (1)
Komenskeho 534
Hostivice, 253 01, Czech Republic
Tel.: (420) 211 046 504
Fax: (420) 211 022 505
E-Mail: info@cezep.cz
Web Site: www.cezep.cz
Emp.: 32
Electric Power Generation & Distribution Services
S.I.C.: 4931
N.A.I.C.S.: 221118
Vladimir Hlavinka *(Chm-Supervisory Bd)*
Paul Sokol *(CEO)*

CEZ Energoservis Spol, s.r.o. (1)
Brafova 16
674 01 Trebic, Czech Republic CZ
Tel.: (420) 568815013 (100%)
Fax: (420) 568866343
E-Mail: obchod@cezenergoservis.cz
Web Site: www.cezenergoservis.cz
Emp.: 270
Machinery Maintenance Services
S.I.C.: 7699
N.A.I.C.S.: 811310

CEZ Logistika, s.r.o. (1)
28 Rijna 568 147
709 02 Prague, Ostrava, Czech Republic CZ
Tel.: (420) 591 113 839 (100%)
Fax: (420) 591 114 680
E-Mail: infoclg@cez.cz
Emp.: 160
Electrical Fitting Whslr
S.I.C.: 5063
N.A.I.C.S.: 423610

CEZ Sprava majetku, s.r.o. (1)
Teplicka 874/8
Decin, 405 49, Czech Republic
Tel.: (420) 840 840 840
Fax: (420) 371 102 008
Property Management Services
S.I.C.: 6531
N.A.I.C.S.: 531312

CEZData, s.r.o. (1)
Guldenerova 2577 19
303 28 Plzen, Czech Republic CZ
Tel.: (420) 37 800 2931 (100%)
Fax: (420) 37 800 2992
E-Mail: info@cezdata.cz
Web Site: www.cezdata.cz
Emp.: 70
Information Systems & Technology Services
S.I.C.: 7379
N.A.I.C.S.: 541519

CEZnet, a.s. (1)
Fugnerovo Nam 1866 5
12000 Prague, Czech Republic CZ
Tel.: (420) 0211046312 (100%)
Fax: (420) 211046310
E-Mail: office@cez.cz
Web Site: www.ceznet.cz
Emp.: 256
Telecommunication & Data Services
S.I.C.: 4899
N.A.I.C.S.: 517919
Milan Dorko *(Dir-Comml)*

CEZTel, a.s. (1)
Fugnerovo Nam 1866 5
Prague, 2, Czech Republic CZ
Tel.: (420) 224086301 (100%)
Fax: (420) 224086310
Web Site: www.cez.cz
Emp.: 80
Telecommunication Services
S.I.C.: 4899
N.A.I.C.S.: 517919

Energeticke centrum s.r.o. (1)
Otin 3
377 01 Jindrichuv Hradec, Czech Republic
Tel.: (420) 384 322 701
Fax: (420) 384 322 704
Web Site: www.ecjh.cz
Emp.: 47
Electric Power Generation & Distribution Services
S.I.C.: 4931
N.A.I.C.S.: 221118
Radek Kozak *(Mng Dir)*

Energeticke Opravny, a.s. (1)
Prunerov C 375
432 01 Kadan, Czech Republic CZ
Tel.: (420) 471 105 067 (100%)
Fax: (420) 471 105 088
E-Mail: info@eopru.cz
Web Site: www.eopru.cz
Emp.: 415
Power Equipment Repair Services

CEZ, a.s.—(Continued)

S.I.C.: 7629
N.A.I.C.S.: 811219

Kotouc Stramberk Spol, s.r.o. (1)
Stramberk 500
742 67 Zenklava, Czech Republic CZ
Tel.: (420) 556813174 (64.87%)
Fax: (420) 556852711
E-Mail: kotouc@kotouc.cz
Web Site: www.kotouc.cz
Emp.: 430
Limestone Miner
S.I.C.: 1422
N.A.I.C.S.: 212312

Lomy Morina Spol, s.r.o. (1)
Morina
267 17 Beroun, Czech Republic CZ
Tel.: (420) 311702111 (52.46%)
Fax: (420) 311702314
E-Mail: info@lomy-morina.cz
Web Site: www.lomy-morina.cz
Emp.: 170
Limestone Miner
S.I.C.: 1422
N.A.I.C.S.: 212312

MARTIA a.s. (1)
Mezni 2854/4
400 11 Usti nad Labem, Czech Republic
Tel.: (420) 475 650 111
Fax: (420) 475 650 999
E-Mail: martia@martia.cz
Technical Consulting Services
S.I.C.: 8999
N.A.I.C.S.: 541690

OSC, a.s. (1)
Stankova 18A
612 00 Brno, Czech Republic CZ
Tel.: (420) 541643111 (66.67%)
Fax: (420) 541643109
E-Mail: osc@osc.cz
Web Site: www.osc.cz
Emp.: 70
Electrical Machinery & Instruments Mfr; Engineering Services
S.I.C.: 3699
N.A.I.C.S.: 335999

SD - KOMES, a.s. (1)
Moskevska 14/1
434 01 Most, Czech Republic
Tel.: (420) 476 146 000
Fax: (420) 476 146 055
Rubber Belt & Petroleum Products Whslr
S.I.C.: 5085
N.A.I.C.S.: 423840

SD - Rekultivace, a.s. (1)
Tusimice 7
Kadan, 432 01, Czech Republic
Tel.: (420) 474 60 4001
Fax: (420) 474 60 2444
E-Mail: info@sd-rekultivace.cz
Emp.: 60
Agricultural Reclamation Services
S.I.C.: 1799
N.A.I.C.S.: 562910

Severoceska Energetika, a.s. (1)
Teplicka 874 8
Decin, IV, Czech Republic CZ
Tel.: (420) 412441111 (56.93%)
Fax: (420) 412572977
Web Site: www.cez.cz
Emp.: 1,490
Power Distr
S.I.C.: 4911
N.A.I.C.S.: 221122

Severoceske doly a.s. (1)
Bozeny Nemcove 5359
CZ-430 01 Chomutov, Czech Republic CZ
Tel.: (420) 474 602 111 (100%)
Fax: (420) 474 652 264
Web Site: www.sdas.cz
Sales Range: $600-649.9 Million
Coal Mining
S.I.C.: 1221
N.A.I.C.S.: 212111
Jan Demjanovic *(Chm & CEO)*
Daniel Benes *(Chm-Supervisory Bd)*
Jiri Zahradnik *(Vice Chm & Fin Dir)*
Tomas Dzik *(Vice Chm-Supervisory Bd)*
Pavel Stehlik *(Vice Chm-Supervisory Bd)*

Non-U.S. Joint Venture:

Mitteldeutsche Braunkohlengesellschaft mbH (2)
Glueck-Auf-Strasse 1
Zeitz, 06711, Germany De
Tel.: (49) 34416840
Fax: (49) 3441684425
Web Site: www.mibrag.de
Sales Range: $500-549.9 Million
Emp.: 2,000
Coal Mining
S.I.C.: 1221
N.A.I.C.S.: 212111
Wilhelm Hans Beermann *(Chm-Supervisory Bd)*
Joachim Geisler *(Chm-Mgmt Bd & CEO)*
Ralf Bartels *(Deputy Chm-Supervisory Bd)*
Heinz Junge *(Mng Dir-HR & Member-Mgmt Bd)*
Horst Schmidt *(Mng Dir-Technical & Member-Mgmt Bd)*

Severomoravska Energetika, a.s. (1)
28 Rijna 3123 152
709 02 Ostrava, Moravska, Czech Republic CZ
Tel.: (420) 840840840 (99.13%)
Fax: (420) 378002008
Web Site: www.cez.cz
Sales Range: $600-649.9 Million
Emp.: 1,555
Electricity Distr & Supplier
S.I.C.: 4931
N.A.I.C.S.: 221122

Subsidiaries:

Energetika Vitkovice, a.s. (2)
Vystavni 1144 103
706 02 Ostrava, Vitkovice, Czech Republic CZ
Tel.: (420) 597015300 (100%)
Fax: (420) 597015309
Web Site: www.evias.cz
Emp.: 560
Electricity Distr
S.I.C.: 4931
N.A.I.C.S.: 221122

ePRIM, a.s. (2)
28 Rijna 568 147
709 02 Ostrava, Moravska, Czech Republic CZ
Tel.: (420) 596673839 (100%)
Fax: (420) 596611527
Web Site: www.eprim.cz
Emp.: 50
Wiring Materials Whslr
S.I.C.: 5063
N.A.I.C.S.: 423610

Sinit, a.s. (2)
Emila Filly 296 13
709 00 Ostrava, Marianske Hory, Czech Republic (100%)
Tel.: (420) 596 673 110
Fax: (420) 596 673 150
Web Site: www.sinit.cz
Emp.: 30
Electrical Equipment & Wiring Whslr
S.I.C.: 5063
N.A.I.C.S.: 423610

Stmem, a.s. (2)
Trzni 8
750 02 Prerov, Czech Republic (100%)
Tel.: (420) 581281111
Fax: (420) 581225478
Web Site: www.sme.cz
Emp.: 60
Electrical Machinery & Instruments Mfr & Repair Services
S.I.C.: 3699
N.A.I.C.S.: 335999

Sigma Energo, s.r.o. (1)
Na Nivkach 299
674 01 Trebic, Czech Republic CZ
Tel.: (420) 568822160 (51%)
Fax: (420) 568824749
Web Site: www.sigma-energo.cz
Emp.: 90
Pumps & Compressors Maintenance & Refurbishment Services
S.I.C.: 7699
N.A.I.C.S.: 811219

Skoda Praha, a.s. (1)
Duhova 2/1444
160 41 Prague, 6, Czech Republic CZ
Tel.: (420) 224396444 (100%)
E-Mail: info@skodapraha.cz
Web Site: www.skodapraha.cz
Emp.: 340
Energy Designer & Engineering Services
S.I.C.: 8711
N.A.I.C.S.: 541330

SKODA PRAHA Invest s.r.o. (1)
Duhova 2/1444
Prague, 140 74, Czech Republic
Tel.: (420) 211 045 300
Fax: (420) 211 045 050
E-Mail: info@spinvest.cz
Web Site: www.spinvest.cz
Power Plant Construction Services
S.I.C.: 1629
N.A.I.C.S.: 237130
Milos Mostecky *(Dir-Comml)*

Stredoceska Energeticka, a.s. (1)
Vinohradska 325 8
120 21 Prague, Czech Republic CZ
Tel.: (420) 222 031 111 (97.72%)
Fax: (420) 222 032 555
Web Site: www.cez.cz
Emp.: 1,548
Electricity Distr
S.I.C.: 4931
N.A.I.C.S.: 221122

Subsidiaries:

Eltraf, a.s. (2)
Kralice 49
285 04 Uhlirske Janovica, Czech Republic (51%)
Tel.: (420) 327543617
Fax: (420) 327543637
E-Mail: eltraf@eltraf.cz
Web Site: www.eltraf.cz
Emp.: 30
Electrical Equipment Mfr
S.I.C.: 3699
N.A.I.C.S.: 335999

STE Obchodni Sluzby Spol, s r.o. (2)
Vinohradska 8
Prague, 2, Czech Republic CZ
Tel.: (420) 222032518 (74.42%)
Fax: (420) 222240157
Web Site: www.cez.cz
Emp.: 65
Material & Technical Supplies Whslr
S.I.C.: 5063
N.A.I.C.S.: 423610

Teplarna Trmice, a.s. (1)
Edisonova 453
Trmice, 400 04, Czech Republic
Tel.: (420) 475 256 111
Fax: (420) 475 620 579
E-Mail: info@tetr.cz
Emp.: 345
Electric Power Generation & Distribution Services
S.I.C.: 4931
N.A.I.C.S.: 221118
Petr Kreissl *(Chm)*

Subsidiary:

ULITEP, spol. s r.o. (2)
Spitalske Nam 11
400 01 Usti nad Labem, Czech Republic
Tel.: (420) 475 214 481
Fax: (420) 475 221 693
E-Mail: ulitep@ulitep.cz
Monitoring & Testing Equipment Mfr
S.I.C.: 3812
N.A.I.C.S.: 334511

Ustav Jaderneho Vyzkumu Rez, a.s. (1)
Husinec Rez 130
250 68 Rez, Czech Republic CZ
Tel.: (420) 266172000 (52.46%)
Fax: (420) 220940840
Web Site: www.nri.cz
Sales Range: $25-49.9 Million
Emp.: 858
Nuclear Technology Research & Development Services
S.I.C.: 4931
N.A.I.C.S.: 221113
Alex Johan *(Gen Mgr)*

Subsidiaries:

Centrum vyzkumu Rez s.r.o. (2)
Husinec-Rez Cp 130
250 68 Rez, Czech Republic
Tel.: (420) 266 173 181
Fax: (420) 266 173 505
E-Mail: cvrez@cvrez.cz
Web Site: www.cvrez.cz
Emp.: 200
Nuclear Power Research & Development Services
S.I.C.: 8731
N.A.I.C.S.: 541712
Jiri Zaborsky *(Head-Jules Horowitz Reactor Section)*

EGP INVEST, spol. s r.o. (2)
Antonina Dvoraka 1707
688 01 Uhersky Brod, Czech Republic
Tel.: (420) 572 610 311
Fax: (420) 572 633 725
E-Mail: egpi@egpi.cz
Web Site: www.egpi.cz
Emp.: 11
Nuclear Energy Consulting Services
S.I.C.: 8999
N.A.I.C.S.: 541690

LACOMED, spol. s r.o. (2)
Husinec - Rez No 130
250 68 Rez, Czech Republic
Tel.: (420) 220 941 165
Fax: (420) 220940162
E-Mail: lacomed@lacomed.cz
Web Site: www.lacomed.cz
Medicinal Product Distr
S.I.C.: 5122
N.A.I.C.S.: 424210
Michael Bauer *(CEO)*

Ustav aplikovane mechaniky Brno, s.r.o. (2)
Resslova 972
611 00 Brno, Czech Republic
Tel.: (420) 541 321 291
Fax: (420) 541 211 189
E-Mail: uam@uam.cz
Web Site: www.uam.cz
Emp.: 3
Technical Consulting Services
S.I.C.: 8999
N.A.I.C.S.: 541690
Lubomir Junek *(Mng Dir)*
Libor Vlcek *(Sec)*

Vychodoceska Energetika, a.s. (1)
Sladkovskeho 215
501 03 Hradec Kralove, Czech Republic CZ
Tel.: (420) 495841111 (98.83%)
Fax: (420) 495842198
Web Site: www.cez.cz
Emp.: 1,600
Electrical Energy Distr
S.I.C.: 4931
N.A.I.C.S.: 221122

Subsidiaries:

VCE Elektrarny, s.r.o. (2)
Krizikova 788
500 03 Hradec Kralove, Czech Republic CZ
Tel.: (420) 495842218 (98.83%)
Fax: (420) 495842708
Web Site: www.vceelektrarny.cz
Emp.: 485
Hydraulic Power Plant Operator
S.I.C.: 4911
N.A.I.C.S.: 221118

VCE Montaze, a.s. (2)
Arnosta Z Pardubic 2082
531 17 Pardubice, Czech Republic CZ
Tel.: (420) 466871111 (98.83%)
Fax: (420) 466872708
Web Site: www.vcemontaze.cz
Electrical Equipment Repair & Maintenance Services
S.I.C.: 7539
N.A.I.C.S.: 811118

VCE Transformatory, s.r.o. (2)
Koutnikova 208
503 01 Hradec Kralove, 16, Czech Republic (100%)
Tel.: (420) 495842164
Fax: (420) 495842762
E-Mail: vce.transformatory@vce.cz
Web Site: www.vcetransformatory.cz
Emp.: 40
Transformers Mfr & Repair Services
S.I.C.: 3676
N.A.I.C.S.: 334416

Zapadoceska Energetika, a.s. (1)
Guldenerova 19
303 28 Plzen, Czech Republic CZ
Tel.: (420) 37 800 1111 (99.13%)
Fax: (420) 37 800 2008
Web Site: www.cez.cz
Emp.: 1,330
Electrical Devices Designer, Mfr & Repair Services
S.I.C.: 7539
N.A.I.C.S.: 811118

Subsidiary:

Lidrone Spol, s.r.o. (2)
Zeleznicni 34
326 00 Plzen, Czech Republic (100%)
Mailing Address:
PO Box 238
306 38 Plzen, Czech Republic
Tel.: (420) 378003832
Fax: (420) 378003833
E-Mail: info@lidrone.cz
Web Site: www.lidrone.cz
Waste Processing Services
S.I.C.: 4959
N.A.I.C.S.: 562998

Plants:

CEZ, a.s. - Dukovany Nuclear Power Station (1)
Jaderna Elektrarna Dukovany
675 50 Dukovany, Czech Republic
Tel.: (420) 561 101 111
Fax: (420) 561 104 980
Electric Power Generation & Distribution Services
S.I.C.: 4931
N.A.I.C.S.: 221118

CEZ, a.s. - Hodonin Power Plant (1)
Elektrarna Hodonin U Elektrarny 1
695 23 Hodonin, Czech Republic
Tel.: (420) 511 100 111
Fax: (420) 511 100 411
Web Site: www.cez.cz/en/contacts/power-plants.html
Electric Power Generation Services
S.I.C.: 4939
N.A.I.C.S.: 221118

CEZ, a.s. - Hydro Power Plant (1)
Vodni Elektrarny
252 07 Stechovice, Czech Republic
Tel.: (420) 211 026 111
Fax: (420) 211 026 577
E-Mail: info@cez.cz
Electric Power Generation Services
S.I.C.: 4939
N.A.I.C.S.: 221118
Zdenek Saturka *(Dir-Hydro Power Plant)*

CEZ, a.s. - Ledvice Power Station (1)
Elektrarna Ledvice
418 48 Bilina, Czech Republic
Tel.: (420) 411 101 111
Fax: (420) 411 101 501
Electric Power Generation & Distribution Services
S.I.C.: 4939
N.A.I.C.S.: 221118

CEZ, a.s. - Melnik Power Station (1)
Elektrarna Melnik
277 03 Horni Pocaply, Czech Republic
Tel.: (420) 311 101 111
Fax: (420) 311 102 102
E-Mail: cez@cez.cz
Emp.: 50
Electric Power Generation Services
S.I.C.: 4911
N.A.I.C.S.: 221118
Andreas Geyr *(Gen Mgr)*

CEZ, a.s. - Porici Power Stations (1)
Elektrarny Porici
541 37 Trutnov, Czech Republic
Tel.: (420) 492 102 111
Fax: (420) 492 102 199
Electric Power Generation Services
S.I.C.: 4939
N.A.I.C.S.: 221118

CEZ, a.s. - Prunerov Power Stations (1)
Elektrarny Prunerov
432 01 Kadan, Czech Republic
Tel.: (420) 471 101 111
Fax: (420) 471 102 697
Web Site: www.cez.cz/en/contacts/power-plants.html
Electric Power Generation & Distribution Services
S.I.C.: 4939
N.A.I.C.S.: 221118

CEZ, a.s. - Temelin Nuclear Power Station (1)
Jaderna Elektrarna Temelin
373 05 Temelin, Czech Republic
Tel.: (420) 381 101 111
Fax: (420) 381 102 298
Emp.: 146
Electric Power Generation & Distribution Services
S.I.C.: 4911
N.A.I.C.S.: 221118
Milos Stepanovsky *(Gen Mgr)*

CEZ, a.s. - Tisova Power Plant (1)
Elektrarna Tisova Postovni Prihradka 98
356 69 Sokolov, Czech Republic
Tel.: (420) 351 101 111
Fax: (420) 351 101 129
Electric Power Generation Services
S.I.C.: 4931
N.A.I.C.S.: 221118

CEZ, a.s.- Tusimice Power Stations (1)
Elektrarny Tusimice
432 01 Kadan, Czech Republic
Tel.: (420) 471 111 111
Fax: (420) 471 113 880
E-Mail: cez@cez.cz
Emp.: 2,000
Electric Power Generation Services
S.I.C.: 4911
N.A.I.C.S.: 221118
Rita Ferreira *(Gen Mgr)*

Non-U.S. Subsidiaries:

Astellas Pharma d.o.o. (1)
Rezidenca 3rd Floor Smartinska Cesta 53
1000 Ljubljana, Slovenia
Tel.: (386) 1 401 1400
Fax: (386) 1 401 1401
E-Mail: info@si.astellas.com
Pharmaceutical Product Whslr
S.I.C.: 5122
N.A.I.C.S.: 424210
Adam Pearson *(Gen Mgr)*

CEZ Bulgaria EAD (1)
140 G S Rakovski Str
Sofia, 1000, Bulgaria BG
Tel.: (359) 700 10 010
Fax: (359) 2 8959 667
E-Mail: zaklienta@cez.bg
Web Site: www.cez.bg/en/about-us/cez-group-companies/cez-bulgaria.html
Electric Power Generation Services
S.I.C.: 4911
N.A.I.C.S.: 221118
Tomas Pleskac *(Chm-Supervisory Bd)*
Petr Dokladal *(Chm-Mgmt Bd & CEO)*
Martin Pacovski *(Vice Chm-Supervisory Bd)*
Petr Baran *(Vice Chm-Mgmt Bd & COO)*
Marcel Mitosinka *(CFO & Member-Mgmt Bd)*
Vladimir Marek *(Member-Mgmt Bd)*
Georgi Petrov Rissin *(Member-Mgmt Bd)*

CEZ Chorzow B.V. (1)
Hogehilweg 5d
Amsterdam, 1101 CA, Netherlands
Tel.: (31) 207586694
Electric Power Distribution Services
S.I.C.: 4911
N.A.I.C.S.: 221122

Non-U.S. Subsidiary:

Elektrocieplownia Chorzow ELCHO sp. z.o.o. (2)
M Sklodowskiej-Curie 30
41-503 Chorzow, Poland
Tel.: (48) 32 771 40 01
Fax: (48) 32 771 40 20
E-Mail: elcho@cezpolska.pl
Emp.: 20
Power Plant Construction Services
S.I.C.: 1623
N.A.I.C.S.: 237130
Jan Mikulka *(Chm & Dir Gen)*

CEZ Elektro Bulgaria AD (1)
140 G S Rakovski Str
Sofia, 1000, Bulgaria
Tel.: (359) 700 10 010
Fax: (359) 28959667
E-Mail: zaklienta@cez.bg
Web Site: www.cez.bg/en/about-us/cez-group-companies/cez-electro-bulgaria.html
Electric Power Distribution Services
S.I.C.: 4931
N.A.I.C.S.: 221122
Karel Klusak *(Co-Chm-Supervisory Bd)*
Kremena Stoyanova *(Co-Chm-Supervisory Bd)*
Petr Baran *(Deputy Chm-Supervisory Bd)*

CEZ Finance B.V. (1)
Hogehilweg 5d
Amsterdam, 1101 CA, Netherlands
Tel.: (31) 207586694
Fax: (31) 204527661
Financial Management Services
S.I.C.: 6211
N.A.I.C.S.: 523999
Jiri Postolka *(Mng Dir)*

CEZ Hungary Ltd. (1)
Retkoz Utca 5
1118 Budapest, Hungary
Tel.: (36) 1 266 9324
Fax: (36) 1 266 9331
E-Mail: hungary@cez.hu
Web Site: www.cez.hu
Electric Power Distribution Services
S.I.C.: 4911
N.A.I.C.S.: 221122
Tibor Bereczki *(Acct Mgr)*

CEZ MH B.V. (1)
Hogehilweg 5d
Amsterdam, 1101 CA, Netherlands
Tel.: (31) 207586694
Fax: (31) 204526695
Electric Power Generation & Distribution Services
S.I.C.: 4931
N.A.I.C.S.: 221122
Jiri Postolka *(Mng Dir)*

CEZ Poland Distribution B.V. (1)
Hogehilweg 5d
Amsterdam, 1101 CA, Netherlands
Tel.: (31) 207586694
Fax: (31) 204526695
Electric Power Distribution Services
S.I.C.: 4911
N.A.I.C.S.: 221122

Non-U.S. Subsidiaries:

Eco-Wind Construction S.A. (2)
Ul Marynarska 11
02-674 Warsaw, Poland
Tel.: (48) 22 444 08 81
Fax: (48) 22 444 07 24
E-Mail: biuro@ecowind.pl
Emp.: 15
Wind Farm Development Services
S.I.C.: 1629
N.A.I.C.S.: 237130
Piotr Beaupre *(Pres)*

Elektrownia Skawina S.A. (2)
Pilsudskiego 10
32-050 Skawina, Poland
Tel.: (48) 12 276 20 00
Fax: (48) 12 276 59 30
E-Mail: sekretariat.skawina@cezpolska.pl
Web Site: www.cezpolska.pl/en/cez-in-poland/elektrownia-skawina-s-a.html
Emp.: 421
Electric Power Generation & Distribution Services
S.I.C.: 4911
N.A.I.C.S.: 221118
Martin Hancar *(Pres & Dir-Strategic)*
Ryszard Mlodzianowski *(Dir Gen)*

CEZ Polska sp. z.o.o. (1)
Rondo ONZ 1
00-124 Warsaw, Poland
Tel.: (48) 22 544 94 80
Fax: (48) 22 544 94 85
E-Mail: info@cezpolska.pl
Web Site: www.cezpolska.pl/en/cez-in-poland/cez-polska-sp-z-o-o.html
Emp.: 10
Electric Power Generation & Distribution Services
S.I.C.: 4931
N.A.I.C.S.: 221122
Petr Ivanek *(Mng Dir)*

CEZ Produkty Energetyczne Polska sp. z.o.o. (1)
Ul M Sklodowskiej - Curie 30
41-503 Chorzow, Poland
Tel.: (48) 32 770 42 51
Fax: (48) 32 771 40 15
E-Mail: biuro@cezep.pl
Web Site: www.cezpolska.pl/en/cez-in-poland/cez-produkty-energetyczne-polska.html
Electric Power Generation Services
S.I.C.: 4911
N.A.I.C.S.: 221118
Pavel Sokol *(Dir Gen)*
Jaroslav Pjecha *(Member-Mgmt Bd)*
Daniel Prymus *(Member-Mgmt Bd)*

CEZ Razpredelenie Bulgaria AD (1)
330 Tzar Simeon Str
Sofia, 1309, Bulgaria
Tel.: (359) 700 10 010
Fax: (359) 2 8959 667
E-Mail: zaklienta@cez.bg
Web Site: www.cez-rp.bg/en/about-us.html
Electric Power Distribution Services
S.I.C.: 4911
N.A.I.C.S.: 221122
Irena Truneckova *(Chm-Supervisory Bd)*
Ales Damm *(Chm-Mgmt Bd)*
Marcel Mitosinka *(Vice Chm-Mgmt Bd)*
Vladimir Marek *(Member-Mgmt Bd)*

CEZ Shperndarje Sh.A. (1)
Egt Tower 12 1 Abdyl Frasheri
Tirana, 1000, Albania
Tel.: (355) 42421480
Fax: (355) 42421480
Web Site: www.cez.al
Electric Power Distribution Services
S.I.C.: 4931
N.A.I.C.S.: 221122

CEZ Srbija d.o.o. (1)
6 Bulevar Mihajla Pupina
Novi Beograd, Belgrade, 11070, Serbia
Tel.: (381) 112200701
Fax: (381) 112200704
Emp.: 2
Electric Power Distr
S.I.C.: 4911
N.A.I.C.S.: 221122
Ljubin Popovski *(Mng Dir)*

CEZ Trade Albania Sh.P.K. (1)
EGT Tower 12/1 2nd Floor Rr Abdyl Frasheri
Tirana, Albania
Tel.: (355) 4 242 1480
Web Site: www.cez.al/en/about-us/cez-trade-albania.html
Electric Power Generation & Distribution Services
S.I.C.: 4911
N.A.I.C.S.: 221118
Zsolt Bojtos *(Head-Portfolio-South Eastern Europe)*

CEZ Trade Polska sp. z o.o. (1)
Rondo ONZ 1
00-124 Warsaw, Poland
Tel.: (48) 22 544 94 60
Fax: (48) 22 544 94 65
E-Mail: trade@cezpolska.pl
Web Site: www.cezpolska.pl/en/cez-in-poland/cez-trade-polska-sp-z-o-o.html
Emp.: 10
Electric Power Generation Services
S.I.C.: 4911
N.A.I.C.S.: 221118
Witold Pawlowski *(Mng Dir)*

Elektrownie Wiatrowe Lubiechovo sp. z.o.o. (1)
Chobolanska 29
Szczecin, 71-023, Poland
Tel.: (48) 914315485
Fax: (48) 914315486
Electric Power Generation & Distribution Services
S.I.C.: 4931
N.A.I.C.S.: 221118

RPG Energiehandel GmbH (1)
Karl Theodor Str 69
D-80803 Munich, Germany De
Tel.: (49) 8918943850 (100%)
Fax: (49) 8918943848
Web Site: www.rpg-energie.de
Emp.: 2

CEZ, a.s.—(Continued)

Energy Exchange Services
S.I.C.: 7389
N.A.I.C.S.: 541990

C.F. GOMMA S.P.A.

Sede Legale e Stabilimento Via S Antonio 59
Passirano, 25050 Brescia, Italy
Tel.: (39) 03068551
Fax: (39) 0306855443
E-Mail: info@cfgomma.com
Web Site: www.cfgomma.com
Sales Range: $500-549.9 Million
Emp.: 5,018
Business Description:
Automotive & Industrial Components Supplier
S.I.C.: 5013
N.A.I.C.S.: 441310
Personnel:
Mario Cancarini *(Pres)*

CF ITALIA SRL

Corso Columbo 46
21013 Gallarate, Italy
Tel.: (39) 033175071
Fax: (39) 0331776118
E-Mail: info@cfrimoldi.com
Web Site: www.cfitalia.it
Business Description:
Industrial Sewing Machine Producer
S.I.C.: 2499
N.A.I.C.S.: 321999

Subsidiary:

Necchi S.p.A. (1)
Via Primo Levi 6 - Zone Industriale
27049 Pavia, Stradella, Italy IT
Tel.: (39) 03825141
Fax: (39) 0382514340
E-Mail: info@necchi.it
Web Site: www.necchi.it
Sales Range: $50-74.9 Million
Emp.: 424
Mfr. of Industrial Sewing Machines Export
S.I.C.: 3589
N.A.I.C.S.: 333318

U.S. Subsidiary:

Rimoldi of America Inc. (1)
2315 NW 107th Ave Ste M 43 Box 85
Miami, FL 33172-2116
Tel.: (305) 477-9943
Fax: (305) 477-9950
E-Mail: lmelocci@rimoldiusa.com
Web Site: www.cfrimoldi.com
Emp.: 7
Mfr. of Industrial Sewing Machines
S.I.C.: 5084
N.A.I.C.S.: 423830
Efren Gutierrez *(Office Mgr & Mgr-Opers)*

Non-U.S. Subsidiaries:

Rimoldi da Amazonia Ind. e Com. Ltda. (1)
Maestro Gabriel Migliori 237
Baillo do Limao
CEP 02712 Sao Paulo, SP, Brazil
Tel.: (55) 8577433
Mfr. of Industrial Sewing Machines
S.I.C.: 3589
N.A.I.C.S.: 333318

Euromac Sistemas de Confeccion, S.A. (1)
(Formerly Rimoldi Espana S.A.)
c/Felix Campllonch 4-6
08301 Barcelona, Mataro, Spain
Tel.: (34) 93 775 7969
Fax: (34) 93 778 5671
E-Mail: euromac@euromac.es
Web Site: www.euromac.es
Marketing of Industrial Sewing Machines
S.I.C.: 5084
N.A.I.C.S.: 423830

CFAO S.A.

(Acquired by Toyota Tsusho Corporation)

CFC GROUP PTY. LTD.

HighwayLevel 1 1300 Abernethy Road
Hazelmere, Perth, WA, 6055, Australia
Tel.: (61) 8 9270 5150
Fax: (61) 8 9270 5159
E-Mail: contact@cfc.com.au
Web Site: www.cfc.com.au
Emp.: 1,100
Business Description:
Holding Company; Agricultural & Construction Equipment Distr
S.I.C.: 6719
N.A.I.C.S.: 551112
Personnel:
Philip Cardaci *(Exec Chm)*
Marc Cardaci *(CEO)*
Chris J. Mallios *(CFO)*

Subsidiaries:

Cape Crushing & Earthmoving Contractors Pty. Ltd. (1)
16 Kalamunda Road
South Guilford, Perth, WA, 6055, Australia AU
Tel.: (61) 8 9379 6800
Fax: (61) 8 9379 6855
E-Mail: office@capecrushing.com.au
Web Site: www.capecrushing.com.au
Emp.: 275
Crushing & Earthmoving Contractors; Mining Services
S.I.C.: 1799
N.A.I.C.S.: 238910
Leanne Heddon *(Co-Founder)*
Mike Heddon *(Co-Founder)*

Centurion Transport Co. Pty Ltd (1)
Yagine Close Lot 1300 Abernethy Road
Hazelmere, Perth, WA, 6055, Australia AU
Tel.: (61) 8 9278 3000
Fax: (61) 8 9278 3080
E-Mail: customerserviceteam@centurion.net.au
Web Site: www.centurion.net.au
Logistics Services to the Resources, Energy & Retail Sectors
S.I.C.: 4731
N.A.I.C.S.: 541614
Mark Doig *(Exec Gen Mgr)*

JCB Construction Equipment Australia (1)
434-442 South Gippsland Hwy
Dandenong, VIC, 3175, Australia
Tel.: (61) 3 9797 3444
Fax: (61) 3 9797 3497
E-Mail: melbourne@cea.net.au
Web Site: www.cea.net.au
Construction & Agricultural Equipment Distr
S.I.C.: 5082
N.A.I.C.S.: 423810
Anthony Whelan *(Exec Gen Mgr)*

Underground Services Australia Pty Ltd (1)
1 Eyre Street
Rivervale, Perth, WA, 6103, Australia
Tel.: (61) 8 9272 0100
Fax: (61) 8 9272 0199
E-Mail: info@usa.com.au
Web Site: www.undergroundservices.com.au
Emp.: 200
Utility Infrastructure Installation & Maintenance Services
S.I.C.: 1629
N.A.I.C.S.: 237130
Tim Abrahams *(Exec Gen Mgr)*

CFC INDUSTRIEBETEILIGUNGEN AG

(Name Changed to UET United Electronic Technology AG)

CFI-COMPAGNIE FONCIERE INTERNATIONALE

72 rue du Faubourg Saint-Honore
75008 Paris, France
Tel.: (33) 140078103
Fax: (33) 140078512
Web Site: www.cfi-france.com
CFI—(EUR)
Sales Range: $50-74.9 Million
Emp.: 1
Business Description:
Real Estate Investment Services
S.I.C.: 6531
N.A.I.C.S.: 531390
Personnel:
Alain Benon *(CEO)*
Board of Directors:
Alain Benon
Daniel Rigny
Emmanuel Rodocanachi
Vincent Rouget
Catherine Sejournant

Auditeurs Et Conseils D'Entreprise
5 Avenue Franklin-Roosevelt
Paris, France

CFM HOLDINGS LIMITED

14 New Industrial Road 07-02A
Hudson Industrial Building
Singapore, 536203, Singapore
Tel.: (65) 64812888
Fax: (65) 64811122
E-Mail: irc@cfmholdings.com
Web Site: www.cfmholdings.com
5EB—(SES)
Rev.: $34,685,072
Assets: $24,060,451
Liabilities: $9,320,226
Net Worth: $14,740,224
Earnings: ($2,667,896)
Fiscal Year-end: 06/30/13
Business Description:
Die Design Services
S.I.C.: 1799
N.A.I.C.S.: 238390
Personnel:
Kwok Wing Ip *(Chm)*
Janet Fong Li Lim *(CEO)*
Chris Chee Keong Chong *(Co-Sec)*
Benny Heng Chong Lim *(Co-Sec)*
Board of Directors:
Kwok Wing Ip
Peter Hock Meng Lai
Janet Fong Li Lim
Er Kwong Wah
Kok Hoe Wong

Subsidiary:

Cheong Fatt Metal Factory Pte Ltd (1)
14 New Industrial Road Unit 06-01 Hudson Industrial Building
Singapore, 536203, Singapore
Tel.: (65) 6481 2888
Fax: (65) 6481 1122
E-Mail: sales-sg@cfmholdings.com
Web Site: www.cfmholdings.com
Emp.: 15
Metal Stamping Mfr
S.I.C.: 3466
N.A.I.C.S.: 332119

Non-U.S. Subsidiaries:

CFM Slovakia s.r.o. (1)
Radlinskeho 17
052 01 Spisska Nova Ves, Kosice, Slovakia
Tel.: (421) 534188888
Fax: (421) 00421534466888
E-Mail: sales-sk@cfmholdings.com
Web Site: www.cfmsk.sk
Emp.: 200
Metal Stamping Mfr
S.I.C.: 3466
N.A.I.C.S.: 332119
Maros Stanco *(Head-Sls)*

Han Tong Precision Engineering Sdn Bhd (1)
No 4 Jalan Haji Saat Sungai Tiram
81800 Ulu Tiram, Johor, Malaysia
Tel.: (60) 78616666
Fax: (60) 78619999
E-Mail: sales-jb@cfmholdings.com
Web Site: www.cfmholdings.com
Emp.: 140
Metal Stampings Mfr
S.I.C.: 3466
N.A.I.C.S.: 332119
Ip Kwok Wing *(Chm)*

Hantong Metal Component (KL) Sdn Bhd (1)
Lot 1911-A Kawasan Perindustrian
Kampung Baru Balakong, 43300 Seri Kembangan, Selangor, Malaysia
Tel.: (60) 389618882
Fax: (60) 389611882
E-Mail: sales-kl@cfmholdings.com
Web Site: www.cfmholdings.com
Emp.: 57
Metal Stampings Mfr
S.I.C.: 3466
N.A.I.C.S.: 332119
Kin Man Mak *(Mng Dir)*

Hantong Metal Component (Penang) Sdn. Bhd. (1)
Plot 155 Jalan Pknk Utama Kawasan
Perusahaan Lpk Taman Ria Jaya
08000 Sungai Petani, Kedah, Malaysia
Tel.: (60) 44411333
Fax: (60) 44422333
E-Mail: sales-pg@cfmholdings.com
Web Site: www.cfmholdings.com
Emp.: 160
Metal Stampings Mfr
S.I.C.: 3466
N.A.I.C.S.: 332119
Kenneth Yew Wa Ip *(Gen Mgr)*

Hantong Metal Component Sdn Bhd (1)
No 4 Jalan Haji Saat Sungai Tiram
81800 Ulu Tiram, Johor, Malaysia
Tel.: (60) 78616666
Fax: (60) 78619999
E-Mail: sales-jb@cfmholdings.com
Metal Stampings Mfr
S.I.C.: 3466
N.A.I.C.S.: 332119

PT Hantong Precision Manufacturing Batam (1)
Komplek Citra Buana Centre Park 2
Kelurahan Kampung Seraya
Kecamatan Batu Ampar, Batam, Riau Islands, 29432, Indonesia
Tel.: (62) 778428222
Fax: (62) 778429111
E-Mail: sales-bt@cfmholdings.com
Emp.: 115
Metal Stampings Mfr
S.I.C.: 3466
N.A.I.C.S.: 332119
Soh Thomas *(Gen Mgr)*

CFN PRECISION LTD.

1000 Creditstone Road
Concord, ON, L4K 4P8, Canada
Tel.: (905) 669-8191
Fax: (905) 669-8684
Web Site: www.cfn-inc.com
Year Founded: 1981
Rev.: $10,302,885
Emp.: 95
Business Description:
Aircraft Parts & Auxiliary Equipment Mfr
S.I.C.: 3728
N.A.I.C.S.: 336413
Personnel:
Tony Karadimas *(Dir-Sls)*

CFR PHARMACEUTICALS SA

Avenida Pedro de Valdivia 295
Providencia, Santiago, Chile
Tel.: (56) 2 350 52 14
Fax: (56) 2 350 52 12
Year Founded: 1922
CFR—(SGO)
Rev.: $570,832,000
Assets: $1,484,561,000
Liabilities: $765,150,000
Net Worth: $719,411,000
Earnings: $79,566,000
Emp.: 7,254

Fiscal Year-end: 12/31/12
Business Description:
Pharmaceutical Mfr
S.I.C.: 2834
N.A.I.C.S.: 325412
Personnel:
Alejandro Weinstein Crenovich *(Chm)*
Alejandro Weinstein Manieu *(CEO & Exec VP-Specialty Pharma)*
Patricio Vargas Munoz *(CFO)*
Agustin Eguiguren Correa *(Chief Legal Officer & Sec)*
Victor Chunco Orlandi *(Pres-Specialty Pharma-North Latam)*
Eduardo Trenova Celedon *(Pres-Specialty Pharma-South East Asia)*
Daniel Salvadori *(Exec VP-Complex Therapeutics)*
Board of Directors:
Alejandro Weinstein Crenovich
Alberto Eguiguren Correa
Juan Antonio Guzman Molinari
Juan Bilbao Hormaeche
Eliahu Shohet
Guillermo Tagle Quiroz
Nicolas Weinstein Manieu

CFS GROUP, INC.
103 The East Mall
Etobicoke, ON, M8Z 5X9, Canada
Tel.: (416) 237-1234
Fax: (416) 237-1227
E-Mail: info@ifscos.com
Web Site: www.ifscos.com
Year Founded: 1892
Sales Range: $75-99.9 Million
Emp.: 255
Business Description:
Producer of Industrial Products, Coatings, Chemicals & Fertilizers
S.I.C.: 1479
N.A.I.C.S.: 212393
Personnel:
Michael Kawaja *(Pres)*
Domenic Scozzafava *(CFO & Sec)*
Legal Counsel:
Torys LLP
Toronto, ON, Canada
Transfer Agent:
Computershare Trust Company of Canada
1800 McGill College Ave 6th Fl
Montreal, QC, H3A 3K9, Canada
Tel.: (514) 982-7888
Subsidiaries:

Duquesne Refractories Limited (1)
550 Marshall Ave
Dorval, QC, H9P 1C9, Canada (100%)
Tel.: (514) 937-3965
Fax: (514) 636-3789
Web Site: www.ifscos.com
Emp.: 20
Producer of Industrial Products, Chemicals & Fertilizers
S.I.C.: 1479
N.A.I.C.S.: 212393
Mike Casey *(Pres)*

Multibond, Inc. (1)
550 Marshall Ave
Dorval, QC, H9P 1C9, Canada (100%)
Tel.: (514) 937-3965
Fax: (514) 631-7737
E-Mail: dural@ifscos.com
Web Site: www.ifscos.com
Emp.: 40
Producer of Industrial Products, Chemicals & Fertilizers
S.I.C.: 1479
N.A.I.C.S.: 212393

Multibond, Inc. (1)
103 The East Mall
Etobicoke, ON, M8Z 5X9, Canada (100%)
Tel.: (416) 237-1234
Fax: (416) 237-1227
Emp.: 12
Producer of Industrial Products, Chemicals & Fertilizers
S.I.C.: 1479
N.A.I.C.S.: 212393
Michael Sales *(COO)*

U.S. Subsidiaries:

Castec, Inc. & Ona Corporation (1)
400 Orrton Ave
Reading, PA 19611
Tel.: (610) 378-1381
Fax: (610) 378-5080
Web Site: www.ifscof.com
Emp.: 50
Producer of Industrial Products, Chemicals & Fertilizers
S.I.C.: 3259
N.A.I.C.S.: 327120

IFS Coatings, Inc. (1)
3601 N Interstate 35
Gainesville, TX 76240
Mailing Address:
3601 N Interstate 35
Gainesville, TX 76240-1939
Tel.: (940) 668-1062
Fax: (940) 668-1061
E-Mail: gmason@ifscos.com
Web Site: www.ifscoatings.com
Emp.: 30
Powdered Coatings Mfr
S.I.C.: 2851
N.A.I.C.S.: 325510
Glen Nathan *(Pres)*

IFS Industries, Inc. (1)
400 Orrton Ave
Reading, PA 19611 (100%)
Mailing Address:
PO Box 1053
Reading, PA 19603
Tel.: (610) 378-1381
Fax: (610) 378-5080
Toll Free: (800) 537-4502
Web Site: www.ifscos.com
Emp.: 98
Adhesives, Coatings & Polymers Mfr
S.I.C.: 2891
N.A.I.C.S.: 325520
Patrick Donahue *(Pres)*
Richard Tomlin *(Mng Dir)*

IFS Industries, Inc. (1)
2222 Lonnecker Dr
Garland, TX 75041
Tel.: (972) 864-2202
Fax: (972) 278-5595
E-Mail: info@ifscos.com
Web Site: www.ifscos.com
Emp.: 15
Producer of Industrial Products, Chemicals & Fertilizers
S.I.C.: 3255
N.A.I.C.S.: 327120
Eric Delong *(VP-Sls)*

Refractory Sales & Service Co., Incorporated (1)
1750 Hwy 150
Bessemer, AL 35022-4044 (100%)
Tel.: (205) 424-3980
Fax: (205) 426-4303
Web Site: www.rssdixie.com
Producer of Industrial Products, Chemicals & Fertilizers
S.I.C.: 3259
N.A.I.C.S.: 327120

Non-U.S. Subsidiary:

R.C. Multibond Dural S.R.L. (1)
Str Abatorulvi NR3
Craiova, Jud Dolj, COD 1156, Romania
Tel.: (40) 51 264 448
S.I.C.: 2869
N.A.I.C.S.: 325110

CFT CONSULTING GMBH
Edisonstrasse 22a
86399 Bobingen, Germany
Tel.: (49) 8234 9669 0
Fax: (49) 8234 9669 99
E-Mail: info@cft.de
Web Site: www.cft.de
Year Founded: 1994
Sales Range: $10-24.9 Million
Business Description:
Document & Content Management Custom Software Developer
S.I.C.: 7371
N.A.I.C.S.: 541511
Personnel:
Gert Lorenz *(Mng Dir)*

CFT ENERGY LIMITED
Level 1 1 Queens Road
Melbourne, VIC, Australia 3002
Tel.: (61) 3 9863 7739
Web Site: www.cftenergy.com.au
CFY—(ASX)
Sales Range: $10-24.9 Million
Business Description:
Gas Extraction Services
S.I.C.: 1389
N.A.I.C.S.: 213112
Personnel:
Robert Pertich *(Sec)*
Board of Directors:
Chris Burrell
Harry Fung
Robert Pertich
Andrew Roach

CFT GMBH
Beisenstrasse 39-41
45964 Gladbeck, Germany
Tel.: (49) 204348110
Fax: (49) 2043481120
E-Mail: mail@cft-gmbh.de
Web Site: www.cft-gmbh.com
Rev.: $35,530,447
Emp.: 66
Business Description:
Dedusting Systems Mfr
S.I.C.: 3569
N.A.I.C.S.: 333999
Personnel:
Reinhold Both *(Mng Dir)*

THE CG&B GROUP INC.
120 South Town Centre Blvd
Markham, ON, L6G 1C3, Canada
Tel.: (905) 479-6670
Fax: (905) 479-9164
Toll Free: (800) 267-6670
Web Site: www.cgbgroup.com
Year Founded: 1972
Rev.: $21,700,000
Emp.: 160
Business Description:
Insurance Agencies
S.I.C.: 6411
N.A.I.C.S.: 524210
Personnel:
H. Larry Later *(Pres & CEO)*
Ross H. Sykes *(CFO)*
Adam Nowak *(Pres-Sls-Mississauga)*
Jamie Robertson *(Pres-Investment Svcs)*
Kevin A.G. Goranson *(Exec VP-Sls-Comml Lines)*
Hugh Fardy *(Sr VP-Pro Liability)*
Len Notaro *(Sr VP-Marine)*
Darryl D. Ticknor *(Sr VP-Marine & Intl)*
David J.R. Yeates *(Sr VP-IBAO Program)*

C.G. HACKING & SONS LIMITED
Calverts Buildings 50 Borough High Street
London, SE1 1XW, United Kingdom
Tel.: (44) 2074076451
Fax: (44) 2074073001
Web Site: www.cghacking.com
Year Founded: 1972
Rev.: $55,700,000
Emp.: 10
Business Description:
Nuts Distr
S.I.C.: 0179
N.A.I.C.S.: 111336
Personnel:
Christopher Hacking *(Chm)*
Giles Hacking *(Mng Dir)*
Nikki Shaw *(Sec)*

CG-VAK SOFTWARE & EXPORTS LTD.
171 Mettupalayam Road
Coimbatore, 641 043, India
Tel.: (91) 422 2434491
Fax: (91) 422 2440679
Web Site: www.cgvak.com
Year Founded: 1995
531489—(BOM)
Rev.: $4,306,668
Assets: $2,724,224
Liabilities: $708,503
Net Worth: $2,015,721
Earnings: $233,574
Emp.: 163
Fiscal Year-end: 03/31/13
Business Description:
Computer Software Development Services
S.I.C.: 7371
N.A.I.C.S.: 541511
Personnel:
C. Ganapathy *(Chm)*
G. Suresh *(CEO & Mng Dir)*
P. S. Subramanian *(CFO)*
Vijay Sasidar *(CTO)*
Shainshad Aduvanni *(Compliance Officer & Sec)*
Board of Directors:
C. Ganapathy
M. Durairaj
S. Mohan
S. Muthukumar
A. Sankar
G. Suresh
Transfer Agent:
SKDC Consultants Ltd
Kanapathy Towers 3rd Floor 1391 A-1 Sathy Road Ganapathy Post
614008 Coimbatore, India
U.S. Subsidiary:

CG-VAK Software USA Inc. (1)
1661 Tice Valley Blvd Ste 101
Walnut Creek, CA 94595
Tel.: (925) 262-8211
E-Mail: info@cgvakusa.com
Web Site: www.cgvakusa.com
Software Development Services
S.I.C.: 7371
N.A.I.C.S.: 541511

CGE CONTINENTAL GLASS ENGINEERING GMBH
Kattrepel 2 Montanhof
20095 Hamburg, Germany
Tel.: (49) 405701020
Fax: (49) 4057010299
E-Mail: info@continental-glass.com
Web Site: www.continental-glass.com
Year Founded: 1960
Rev.: $19,035,720
Emp.: 10
Business Description:
Glass Manufacturing Equipment Supply Services
S.I.C.: 5084
N.A.I.C.S.: 423830
Personnel:
Ulrich Steffes *(Mng Dir)*

CGE MINAS INDUSTRIA E COMERCIO DE ARTEFATOS PLASTICOS LTDA.
Rod MG 050 S N Km 29
Mateus Leme, MG, 35670 000, Brazil
Tel.: (55) 3135351833
Fax: (55) 3135351833
E-Mail: tgemg@tgemg.com.br
Web Site: www.tgemg.com.br

CGE Minas Industria E Comercio de Artefatos Plasticos Ltda.—(Continued)

Emp.: 1,000

Business Description:
Mfr. of Motor Vehicle Plastic Parts & Accessories
S.I.C.: 3714
N.A.I.C.S.: 336340

Subsidiary:

CGE Sociedade Fabricadora de Pecas Plasticas Ltda. **(1)**
Rua Gen Castilho De Lima 150
09371 340 Maua, SP, Brazil BR
Tel.: (55) 45126600 (100%)
Telex: 1146462cfde br
Fax: (55) 1145126609
E-Mail: dis.cge@cge.ind.br
Web Site: www.cge.ind.br
Sales Range: $10-24.9 Million
Emp.: 300
Mfr. of Motor Vehicle Plastic Parts & Accessories
S.I.C.: 3714
N.A.I.C.S.: 336340

CGG

(Formerly Compagnie Generale de Geophysique-Veritas)
Tour Maine-Montparnasse 33 avenue du Maine
75015 Paris, Cedex 15, France
Tel.: (33) 1 6447 4500
Fax: (33) 1 6447 3429
Web Site: www.cgg.com
Year Founded: 1931
CGG—(EUR NYSE)
Rev.: $3,414,100,000
Assets: $8,332,800,000
Liabilities: $3,740,900,000
Net Worth: $4,591,900,000
Earnings: $91,400,000
Emp.: 7,560
Fiscal Year-end: 12/31/12

Business Description:
Holding Company; Oil & Gas Field Geophysical Surveying Services & Geophysical Equipment Mfr
S.I.C.: 6719
N.A.I.C.S.: 551112

Personnel:
Robert Brunck *(Chm)*
Jean-Georges Malcor *(CEO)*
Stephane-Paul Frydman *(CFO & Sr Exec VP-Fin)*
Pascal Rouiller *(CEO-Sercel & Sr Exec VP-Equipment)*
Beatrice Place-Faget *(Gen Counsel, Gen Sec & Sr VP)*
Michel Ponthus *(Sec)*
Benoit Ribadeau-Dumas *(Sr Exec VP-Acq Div & Marine Bus Line)*
Sophie Zurquiyah *(Sr Exec VP-Geology, Geophysics & Reservoir)*
Thierry Brizard *(Exec VP-Tech)*
David Dragone *(Exec VP-HR)*
Raoul Jacquand *(Exec VP-Geomarkets Sls & Mktg)*
Thierry Le Roux *(Exec VP-Bus Dev)*
Lionel Lhommet *(Exec VP-Geomarkets & Global Mktg)*
Stephan Midenet *(Exec VP-Land Div)*
Colin Murdoch *(Exec VP-Processing, Imaging & Reservoir Div)*
Dominique Robert *(Exec VP-Global Operational Excellence)*
Eva Rudin *(Exec VP-Global Operational Excellence)*
Luc Schlumberger *(Exec VP-Multi Client & New Ventures Div)*

Board of Directors:
Robert Brunck
Olivier Appert
Loren K. Carroll
Remi Dorval
Jean Dunand
Agnes Lemarchand
Gilberte Lombard
Jean-Georges Malcor
Hilde Myrberg
Robert F. Semmens
Kathleen E. Sendall
Daniel L. Valot
Terence Young

Ernst & Young
1-2 place des Saisons Paris La Defense 1
92400 Courbevoie, France

Subsidiaries:

CGG Services S.A. **(1)**
(Formerly CGGVeritas Services S.A.)
27 Avenue Carnot
91341 Massy, Cedex, France FR
Tel.: (33) 1 6447 3000
Telex: 602442F CGGEC
Fax: (33) 1 6447 3970
E-Mail: invrel@cggveritas.com
Web Site: www.cgg.com
Emp.: 100
Oil & Gas Field Geophysical Surveying Services
S.I.C.: 1389
N.A.I.C.S.: 213112
Robert Brunck *(Chm & CEO)*
Thierry Le Roux *(Pres & COO)*
Guillaume Cambois *(CTO & Head-Data Processing Products)*
Luc Benoit-Cattin *(Pres-Eastern Hemisphere)*
Christophe Pettenati-Auziere *(Pres-Svcs)*
Tim L. Wells *(Pres-Western Hemisphere)*
Pascal Rouiller *(CEO-Sercel)*
Stephan Midenet *(Exec VP-Land Div)*
C.Richard Price *(Exec VP-Marine Acq Product Line)*
Dominique Robert *(Exec VP-Land SBU)*
Luc Schlumberger *(Exec VP-Latin America)*

Subsidiaries:

CGG Explo SARL **(2)**
1 Rue Leon Migaux
Massy, France (100%)
Tel.: (33) 164473000
Fax: (33) 161473970
Web Site: www.cggveritas.com
Emp.: 300
Engineering Services
S.I.C.: 8711
N.A.I.C.S.: 541330

CGG I SA **(2)**
1 Rue Leon Migaux
91341 Massy, France (100%)
Tel.: (33) 164473000
Fax: (33) 161473970
Emp.: 200
Engineering Services
S.I.C.: 8711
N.A.I.C.S.: 541330

U.S. Subsidiary:

CGG Services (U.S.) Inc. **(2)**
(Formerly CGGVeritas Services (U.S.) Inc.)
10300 Town Park Dr
Houston, TX 77072-5236 DE
Tel.: (832) 351-8300
Fax: (832) 351-8701
Web Site: www.cgg.com
Emp.: 1,000
Oil & Gas Geophysical Services
S.I.C.: 1389
N.A.I.C.S.: 213112
Dennis S. Baldwin *(CFO, Treas & Exec VP)*
Stephane-Paul Frydman *(Exec VP-Fin & Strategy)*
Thierry Le Roux *(Exec VP-Bus Dev)*
Colin Murdoch *(Exec VP-Processing, Imaging & Reservoir Div)*
Scott Smith *(Sr VP-HR)*
Vincent M. Thielen *(Sr VP)*

Subsidiary:

Geophysical Research Company, LLC **(3)**
6540 E Apache St
Tulsa, OK 74115 OK
Tel.: (918) 834-9600
Web Site: www.grcamerada.com
Sales Range: $10-24.9 Million
Emp.: 120
Designer & Mfr of Downhole Sensors & Temperature Gauges for Oil & Gas Industry
S.I.C.: 3823
N.A.I.C.S.: 334513
Bob Laird *(CEO)*

Non-U.S. Subsidiaries:

CGG Services (Australia) Pty. Ltd. **(2)**
(Formerly CGGVeritas Services (Australia) Pty. Ltd.)
CGGVeritas Centre 38 Ord Street
West Perth, WA, 6005, Australia AU
Mailing Address:
PO Box 1802
West Perth, 6872, Australia
Tel.: (61) 892146200
Fax: (61) 892146222
E-Mail: info@cggveritas.com
Web Site: www.cggveritas.com
Emp.: 60
Geophysical Surveying Services
S.I.C.: 8713
N.A.I.C.S.: 541360

CGG Services (Canada) Inc. **(2)**
(Formerly CGGVeritas Services (Canada) Inc.)
715-5th Avenue S W Suite 2200
Calgary, AB, T2P 5A2, Canada AB
Tel.: (403) 205-6000
Fax: (403) 205-6400
Emp.: 20
Oil & Gas Field Geophysical Information Services
S.I.C.: 8713
N.A.I.C.S.: 541360

CGG Services de Mexico SA de CV **(2)**
(Formerly CGGVeritas Services de Mexico SA de CV)
Lago Victoria No 74 Piso 11 Granada
Miguel Hidalgo, Mexico, 11520, Mexico MX
Tel.: (52) 5591527400
Fax: (52) 5591527414
Emp.: 21
Geophysical Surveying Services
S.I.C.: 8713
N.A.I.C.S.: 541360
Gehant Dominique *(Mng Dir)*

CGG Services Holding B.V. **(2)**
(Formerly CGGVeritas Services Holding B.V.)
Schiphol Boulevard 299
Luchthaven Schiphol, Amsterdam, 1118 BH, Netherlands NL
Tel.: (31) 202065970
Fax: (31) 202065974
Web Site: www.cggveritas.com
Emp.: 11
Holding Company
S.I.C.: 6719
N.A.I.C.S.: 551112
Christian Klemt *(Mng Dir)*

CGG Services Holding (Latin America) B.V. **(2)**
(Formerly CGGVeritas Services Holding (Latin America) B.V.)
Schiphol Boulevard 299
Luchthaven Schiphol, Amsterdam, 1118 BH, Netherlands NL
Tel.: (31) 202065970
Fax: (31) 206429005
Holding Company
S.I.C.: 6719
N.A.I.C.S.: 551112

CGG Services India Private Ltd. **(2)**
(Formerly CGGVeritas Services India Private Ltd.)
504-B Delphi Building Hiranandani Business Park Orchard Avenue Road
Powai, Mumbai, 400076, India In
Tel.: (91) 22 6703 1213, ext. 221
Fax: (91) 22 6703 1220
E-Mail: supporthrs.apac@cggveritas.com
Emp.: 35
Geographical Software Development Services
S.I.C.: 7371
N.A.I.C.S.: 541511
Lam Pham *(Mng Dir)*

CGG Services (Norway) AS **(2)**
(Formerly CGGVeritas Services (Norway) AS)
Carlkonowsgt 34
5162 Laksevag, Norway NO
Tel.: (47) 56113100 (100%)
Fax: (47) 56113101
E-Mail: reception@cggveritas.com
Emp.: 120
Marine Seismic Services
S.I.C.: 8713
N.A.I.C.S.: 541360
Cato Bolstad *(Mng Dir)*

Subsidiaries:

Exploration Investment Resources II AS **(3)**
Carl Konows Gate 34
5162 Laksevag, Norway (100%)
Tel.: (47) 56113100
Fax: (47) 56113101
E-Mail: reception.burgan@cgg.com
Web Site: www.cgg.com
Emp.: 90
Architectural Services
S.I.C.: 8712
N.A.I.C.S.: 541310
Marianne Lefdal *(Mng Dir)*

Exploration Vessel Resources AS **(3)**
Carl Konows gate 34
5162 Laksevag, Norway (100%)
Tel.: (47) 56113100
Fax: (47) 56113101
E-Mail: bargen.reception@cgg.com
Web Site: www.cgg.com
Emp.: 100
Water Transportation Services
S.I.C.: 4499
N.A.I.C.S.: 488390
Cato Bolstad *(Mng Dir)*

Multiwave Geophysical Company AS **(3)**
Damsgardsveien 125
5162 Laksevag, Norway (100%)
Tel.: (47) 56113100
Fax: (47) 56113101
Web Site: www.cggveritas.com
Emp.: 60
Architectural Services
S.I.C.: 8712
N.A.I.C.S.: 541310
Cato Bolstad *(Mng Dir)*

CGG Services (Singapore) Pte. Ltd. **(2)**
(Formerly CGGVeritas Services (Singapore) Pte. Ltd.)
9 Serangoon North Avenue 5
Singapore, 554531, Singapore SG
Tel.: (65) 67235500
Fax: (65) 67235550
Oil & Gas Exploration Services
S.I.C.: 1389
N.A.I.C.S.: 213112

CGG Services (UK) Ltd. **(2)**
(Formerly CGGVeritas Services (UK) Ltd.)
Digicon Centre Crompton Way
Crawley, RH10 9QN, United Kingdom UK
Tel.: (44) 12 9368 3000
Fax: (44) 12 9368 3010
Oil & Gas Exploration Equipment Mfr
S.I.C.: 3533
N.A.I.C.S.: 333132

CGG Technology Services (Beijing) Co. Ltd. **(2)**
(Formerly CGGVeritas Technology Services (Beijing) Co. Ltd.)
Room 331 Lido Commercial Building
Beijing, 100004, China CN
Tel.: (86) 10 6437 4330
Fax: (86) 10 6437 4515
E-Mail:
Web Site: www.cgg.com
Technical Software Training Services
S.I.C.: 8299
N.A.I.C.S.: 611430

Sercel Holding SA **(1)**
Z I De Nantes Ca
Carquefou, France
Tel.: (33) 240301181
Fax: (33) 240301948
Web Site: www.sercel.com
Holding Company
S.I.C.: 6719
N.A.I.C.S.: 551112

Arnaud Surpas *(Exec VP-Global Ops-Equipment Div-Nantes)*

Subsidiary:

Sercel S.A (2)
16 rue de Bel Air
BP 30439
44474 Carquefou, France
Tel.: (33) 2 40 30 11 81
Fax: (33) 2 40 30 19 48
E-Mail: customersupport.land@sercel.com
Web Site: www.sercel.com
High Tech Integrated Equipment Mfr
S.I.C.: 3559
N.A.I.C.S.: 333249
Pascal Rouiller *(CEO)*
Laurent Dollon *(Sr VP-Ops)*

Branch:

Sercel - Les Ulis (3)
Mini Parc du Verger Batiment E Zone de Cortaboeuf
1 Rue de Terre Neuve, 91940 Les Ulis, France
Tel.: (33) 0169938360
Fax: (33) 169817809
E Mail: info@sercel.com
Web Site: www.sercel.com
Emp.: 30
Geophysical Services & Manufacturer of Geophysical Equipment
S.I.C.: 8713
N.A.I.C.S.: 541360
Jean-Eric Negre *(CEO)*
Pascal Rouiller *(CEO)*

U.S. Subsidiary:

Sercel, Inc. (2)
17200 Park Row
Houston, TX 77084-4925 OK
Tel.: (281) 492-6688
Fax: (281) 579-6555
Web Site: www.sercel.com
Measuring & Controlling Device Mfr
S.I.C.: 3829
N.A.I.C.S.: 334519
Bill Demko *(Controller)*

Non-U.S. Subsidiaries:

Hebei Sercel-JunFeng Geophysical Prospecting Equipment Co., Ltd. (2)
PO Box 121-7
Xushui, Hebei, 072550, China CN
Tel.: (86) 312 864 8351 (51%)
Fax: (86) 312 864 8441
Navigational Services to Shipping
S.I.C.: 4499
N.A.I.C.S.: 488330
Thierry Le Roux *(Chm)*

Sercel Beijing Technological Services Co Ltd. (2)
Room 703 Lido Commercial Building
Beijing, 100004, China
Tel.: (86) 106 43 76 710
Fax: (86) 106 43 76 305
E-Mail: support.china@geo-mail.com
Information Technology Consulting Services
S.I.C.: 7373
N.A.I.C.S.: 541512

Sercel Canada Ltd (2)
1108-55th Ave NE
T2E6Y4 Calgary, AB, Canada (100%)
Tel.: (403) 275-3544
Fax: (403) 295-1805
Web Site: www.sercel.com
Emp.: 7
Measuring & Controlling Device Mfr
S.I.C.: 3829
N.A.I.C.S.: 334519
Vickie Dafoar *(Asst Controller)*

Sercel England Ltd (2)
Birchwood Way Cotes Park Industrial Estate
Alfreton, DE554QQ, United Kingdom
Tel.: (44) 1773605078
Fax: (44) 1773541778
E-Mail: info@sercel.com
Web Site: www.sercel.com
Emp.: 70
Measuring & Controlling Device Mfr
S.I.C.: 3829
N.A.I.C.S.: 334519
Doug McConnachie *(Mng Dir)*

Sercel Singapore Pte Ltd (2)
68 Loyang Way
508758 Singapore, Singapore (100%)
Tel.: (65) 65450411
Fax: (65) 65451418
Web Site: www.sercel.com
Emp.: 45
Motor Vehicle Electrical & Electronic Equipment Mfr
S.I.C.: 3714
N.A.I.C.S.: 336320
Martyn Towle *(Mng Dir)*

U.S. Subsidiary:

CGG Americas Inc. (1)
10300 Town Park Dr
Houston, TX 77072 DE
Tel.: (832) 351-8300
Fax: (832) 351-8701
Web Site: www.cgg.com
Emp.: 300
Holding Company; Regional Managing Office; Oil & Gas Geophysical Products & Services
S.I.C.: 6719
N.A.I.C.S.: 551112
Sophie Zurquiyah *(Sr Exec VP-Geology, Geophysics & Reservoir)*
Colin Murdoch *(Exec VP)*

Subsidiary:

CGG Holding (U.S.) Inc. (2)
(Formerly CGGVeritas Services Holding (U.S.) Inc.)
10300 Town Park Dr
Houston, TX 77072 DE
Tel.: (832) 351-8300
Fax: (832) 351-8701
Investment Management Services
S.I.C.: 6211
N.A.I.C.S.: 523999

Unit:

CGG Marine USA (3)
(Formerly Fugro Geoteam, Inc.)
6100 Hillcroft
Houston, TX 77081
Tel.: (713) 369-5600
Fax: (713) 346-4054
E-Mail:
Marine Broadband & Seismic Surveying Services
S.I.C.: 1389
N.A.I.C.S.: 213112

Non-U.S. Group:

CGG Canada (2)
(Formerly CGGVeritas Canada)
715 5th Ave SW Ste 2200
Calgary, AB, T2P 5A2, Canada
Tel.: (403) 205-6000
Fax: (403) 205-6400
E-Mail:
Web Site: www.cgg.com
Sales Range: $1-9.9 Million
Emp.: 325
Data Services
S.I.C.: 7379
N.A.I.C.S.: 518210

Subsidiaries:

CGG Geophysical (Canada) Corporation (3)
(Formerly Veritas Geophysical (Canada) Corporation)
715 5 Ave SW Ste 2200
Calgary, AB, T2P 5A2, Canada NS
Tel.: (403) 205-6000
Fax: (403) 205-6400
Web Site: www.cgg.com
Emp.: 200
Geophysical Exploration Services
S.I.C.: 8713
N.A.I.C.S.: 541360

Hampson Russel Limited Partnership (3)
715 5 Ave SW Ste 510
Calgary, AB, T2P 2X6, Canada
Tel.: (403) 266-3225
Fax: (403) 265-6651
Emp.: 50
Software Development Services
S.I.C.: 7371
N.A.I.C.S.: 541511
Dan Hampson *(Gen Mgr)*

Subsidiary:

Hampson-Russell Software Services LP (4)
715 5th Ave SW Ste 510
Calgary, AB, T2P 2X6, Canada
Tel.: (403) 266-3225
Fax: (403) 265-6651
E-Mail: infohrs_calgary@cggveritas.com
Emp.: 49
Geophysical Software & Services
S.I.C.: 7371
N.A.I.C.S.: 541511
Daniel Hampson *(Pres)*

Non-U.S. Subsidiaries:

CGG do Brasil Ltda. (2)
(Formerly Veritas do Brasil Ltda.)
Av Presidente Wilson 231 1703
20030-021 Rio de Janeiro, Brazil BR
Tel.: (55) 2121361650
Fax: (55) 2121361651
E-Mail: info@cggveritas.com
Web Site: www.cgg.com
Emp.: 40
Geophysical Software & Services
S.I.C.: 8713
N.A.I.C.S.: 541360
Patrick Postal *(Mng Dir)*

CGG Geophysical (Chile) SA (2)
(Formerly Veritas Geophysical (Chile) SA)
Avda Nueva Tajamar 481 Torre Norte Piso 21
Las Condes, Santiago, Chile CL
Tel.: (56) 23471000
Web Site: www.cgg.com
Geophysical Surveying Services
S.I.C.: 8713
N.A.I.C.S.: 541360

Non-U.S. Representative Offices:

CGG - Argentina (2)
Maipu 757 9th Floor
Buenos Aires, 1047, Argentina
Tel.: (54) 11 4325 0275
Fax: (54) 11 4325 0271
E-Mail:
Web Site: www.cgg.com
Emp.: 24
Geophysical Services
S.I.C.: 8713
N.A.I.C.S.: 541360
David Amaya *(Gen Mgr)*

CGG - Peru (2)
Calle Las Golondrinas
193 San Isidro, Lima, Peru
Tel.: (51) 12224585
Fax: (51) 12224586
Web Site: www.cgg.com
Emp.: 5
Seismic & Geological Services
S.I.C.: 8713
N.A.I.C.S.: 541360
Dominique Uzu *(Gen Mgr)*

Non-U.S. Subsidiaries:

Ardiseis FZCO (1)
Jebel Ali Free Zone
PO Box 261159
Dubai, United Arab Emirates
Tel.: (971) 4 883 9464
Fax: (971) 3 883 9465
E-Mail: cgg1@emirates.net.ae
Emp.: 10
Oil & Gas Exploration Equipment Distr
S.I.C.: 5084
N.A.I.C.S.: 423830
Danielle Maillet *(Gen Mgr)*

CGG Data Management (UK) Ltd. (1)
(Formerly Fugro Data Solutions Ltd.)
Maelgwn House Parc Caer Seion
Conwy, Conway, LL32 8FA, United Kingdom UK
Tel.: (44) 14 9256 4500
Fax: (44) 14 9256 4545
E-Mail: training@fugro-data.com
Web Site: www.fugro-data.com
Emp.: 10
Data Management & Consulting Services
S.I.C.: 7379
N.A.I.C.S.: 518210
Luke Durcan *(Gen Mgr)*

U.S. Unit:

CGG Data Management U.S. (2)
(Formerly Fugro Data Solutions, Inc.)
6100 Hilcroft 5th Fl
Houston, TX 77081
Tel.: (713) 369-6100
Fax: (713) 369-6110
Web Site: data.cgg.com
Data Management & Consulting Services
S.I.C.: 7374
N.A.I.C.S.: 518210

Non-U.S. Subsidiary:

CGG Data Solutions (Canada) Inc. (2)
(Formerly Fugro Data Solutions (Canada) Inc.)
3675 63rd Avenue NE
Calgary, AB, T3J 5K1, Canada Ca
Tel.: (403) 250-1119
Fax: (403) 291-2921
Toll Free: (877) 248-7890
E-Mail:
Web Site: data.cgg.com
Emp.: 50
Data Management & Consulting Services
S.I.C.: 7379
N.A.I.C.S.: 518210

CGG Data Services AG (1)
(Formerly Fugro Data Services AG)
Bahnhofstrasse 29
6300 Zug, Switzerland CH
Tel.: (41) 417280808
Fax: (41) 417280800
E-Mail:
Holding Company; Geophysical Software & Services
S.I.C.: 6719
N.A.I.C.S.: 551112

U.S. Subsidiary:

CGG Jason (U.S.) Inc. (2)
(Formerly Fugro-Jason, Inc.)
6671 SW Freeway Ste 500
Houston, TX 77074 DE
Tel.: (713) 369-6900
Fax: (713) 369-6936
Web Site: jason.cgg.com
Emp.: 100
Seismic Inversion & Reservoir Characterization Software & Services
S.I.C.: 7372
N.A.I.C.S.: 511210
H. Beverly Taylor *(Reg Mgr-Sls)*

Non-U.S. Subsidiaries:

CGG Jason (Australia) Pty. Ltd. (2)
(Formerly Fugro-Jason Australia Pty. Ltd.)
69 Outram St
West Perth, Perth, WA, 6005, Australia AU
Tel.: (61) 8 9420 6057
Fax: (61) 8 9420 6060
E-Mail: hsidi@fugro-jason.com
Web Site: jason.cgg.com
Seismic Inversion & Reservoir Characterization Software & Services
S.I.C.: 5045
N.A.I.C.S.: 423430
Pieter Gabriels *(Bus Mgr)*

CGG Jason (Netherlands) B.V. (2)
(Formerly Fugro-Jason Netherlands B.V.)
Veurse Achterweg 10
Leidschendam, 2264 SG, Netherlands NL
Tel.: (31) 703 170 515
Fax: (31) 703 170 511
E-Mail: info@fugro-jason.com
Seismic Inversion & Reservoir Characterization Software & Services
S.I.C.: 5045
N.A.I.C.S.: 423430
Rene Admiraal *(Bus Mgr)*

CGG Jason (UK) Ltd. (2)
(Formerly Fugro-Jason (UK) Ltd.)
Survey House Denmore Roadt
Bridge of Don, Aberdeen, AB23 8JW, United Kingdom UK
Tel.: (44) 1224 257 500
E-Mail:
Web Site: jason.cgg.com
Emp.: 5

CGG—(Continued)

Seismic Inversion & Reservoir Characterization Software & Services
S.I.C.: 5045
N.A.I.C.S.: 423430
Peter Redpath *(Bus Mgr)*

CGG Marine (Australia) Pty. Ltd. **(1)**
(Formerly Fugro-Geoteam Pty. Ltd.)
69 Outram Street
West Perth, Perth, WA, 6005, Australia AU
Tel.: (61) 8 9481 2043
Fax: (61) 8 9486 8675
E-Mail: geoteam@fugro.com
Emp.: 23
Marine Broadband & Seismic Surveying Services
S.I.C.: 1389
N.A.I.C.S.: 213112

CGG Marine (Norway) AS **(1)**
(Formerly Fugro-Geoteam AS)
Hoffsveien 1c
Oslo, 275, Norway NO
Tel.: (47) 22134600
Fax: (47) 22134646
E-Mail: geoteam@fugro.no
Web Site: www.fugro.geoteam.no
Marine Broadband & Seismic Surveying Services
S.I.C.: 1389
N.A.I.C.S.: 213112

CGG Marine Resources Norge AS **(1)**
O H Bangs Vei 70
1322 Hovik, Norway NO
Tel.: (47) 6711 6500 (100%)
Fax: (47) 6711 6501
Emp.: 4
Marine Engineering Services
S.I.C.: 8711
N.A.I.C.S.: 541330

CGG Seismic Imaging (Australia) Pty. Ltd. **(1)**
(Formerly Fugro Seismic Imaging Pty. Ltd.)
69 Outram Street
West Perth, WA, 6005, Australia AU
Tel.: (61) 8 9322 2490
Fax: (61) 8 9481 6721
E-Mail:
Subsurface Seismic Geophysical Data Acquisition, Processing & Analysis Services
S.I.C.: 7374
N.A.I.C.S.: 518210

CGG Seismic Imaging (Norway) AS **(1)**
(Formerly Fugro Seismic Imaging AS)
Hoffsveien 1C
0213 Oslo, Norway NO
Tel.: (47) 2213 4600
Fax: (47) 2213 4646
E-Mail:
Subsurface Seismic Geophysical Data Acquisition, Processing & Analysis Services
S.I.C.: 7374
N.A.I.C.S.: 518210

CGG Seismic Imaging (UK) Limited **(1)**
(Formerly Fugro Seismic Imaging Ltd.)
Horizon House Azalea Drive
Swanley, Kent, BR8 8JR, United Kingdom UK
Tel.: (44) 13 2266 8011 (100%)
Fax: (44) 13 2261 3650
E-Mail:
Emp.: 70
Subsurface Seismic Geophysical Data Acquisition, Processing & Analysis Services
S.I.C.: 7374
N.A.I.C.S.: 518210

Exgeo CA **(1)**
Av Fco De Miranda Edificio Parque Cristal Urbanizacion
Los Palos Grandes, Caracas, Venezuela
Tel.: (58) 212 2855334
Fax: (58) 212 2835601
Web Site: www.exgeo.com
Emp.: 25
Oil & Gas Exploration Services
S.I.C.: 1389
N.A.I.C.S.: 213112
Marco Antonio Suarez *(Gen Mgr)*

Geoscience (Beijing) Ltd. **(1)**
(Formerly Fugro Geoscience (Beijing) Ltd.)
A 1206-1209 Ocean International Center No 56 East 4th Ring Road
Chaoyang District, Beijing, 100025, China CN
Tel.: (86) 10 5908 1801
Fax: (86) 10 5908 1802
E-Mail:
Geophysical Software Products & Services
S.I.C.: 5045
N.A.I.C.S.: 423430

Multifield Geophysics AS **(1)**
Carl Konows Gate 34
Laksevag, 5162, Norway
Tel.: (47) 56114800
Fax: (47) 56114801
E-Mail: enquiries@multifield-geophysics.com
Web Site: www.multifield-geophysics.com
Emp.: 120
Geophysical Surveying Services
S.I.C.: 8713
N.A.I.C.S.: 541360
Leif Olav Saetenes *(Gen Mgr)*

Optoplan AS **(1)**
Vestre Rosten 77
PO Box 1963
7448 Trondheim, Norway
Tel.: (47) 73820500
Fax: (47) 73820599
Web Site: www.sercel.com
Hydrocarbon Exploration Equipment Mfr
S.I.C.: 3559
N.A.I.C.S.: 333249

PT Veritas DGC Mega Pratama **(1)**
Graha Paramita Bldg 6th Floor Jalan Denpasar Blok D-2
Kuningan Jakarta, 12940, Indonesia Id
Tel.: (62) 212522240
Fax: (62) 212522245
E-Mail: dinni.prihandayani@cgcveritas.com
Web Site: www.cgcveritas.com
Emp.: 100
P T Veritas DGC Mega Pratama
S.I.C.: 7379
N.A.I.C.S.: 518210
John Coffin *(Gen Mgr)*

Robertson (UK) Limited **(1)**
(Formerly Fugro Robertson Limited)
Tyn-y-Coed Pentywyn Road
Llandudno, LL30 1SA, United Kingdom UK
Tel.: (44) 1492 581 811
Telex: 61216
Fax: (44) 1492 583 416
E-Mail:
Web Site: www.robertson-cgg.com
Emp.: 250
Geophysical & Geological Software & Services
S.I.C.: 7372
N.A.I.C.S.: 511210
Chris Burgess *(Mng Dir)*

U.S. Subsidiary:

Robertson (USA) Inc. **(2)**
(Formerly Fugro Robertson Inc.)
6100 Hillcroft 5th Fl
Houston, TX 77081 DE
Tel.: (713) 369-6100
Fax: (713) 369-6110
E-Mail: infoFR@fugro-robertson.com
Web Site: www.robertson-cgg.com
Emp.: 100
Geophysical & Geological Software & Services
S.I.C.: 5045
N.A.I.C.S.: 423430
Guy M. Oliver *(Pres)*

Seismic Support Services **(1)**
Bldg 1 4 Tessinsky Lane
109028 Moscow, Russia
Tel.: (7) 495 644 08 05
Fax: (7) 495 644 08 04
E-Mail: support.cis@geo-mail.org
Oil & Gas Exploration Services
S.I.C.: 1389
N.A.I.C.S.: 213112

Veritas DGC Limited **(1)**
Crompton Way
Manor Royal Estate, Crawley, W Sussex, RH10 9QN, United Kingdom UK
Tel.: (44) 12 9368 3000
Fax: (44) 12 9368 3010
E-Mail: info@veritasdgc.com
Web Site: www.veritasdgc.com
Emp.: 100
Data Processing Services
S.I.C.: 7374
N.A.I.C.S.: 518210

Branch:

Veritas DGC Ltd. - Aberdeen **(2)**
Davidson House Campus 1 Aberdeen Energy & Innovation Park Balgownie Rd
Bridge of Don, Aberdeen, AB22 8GT, United Kingdom
Tel.: (44) 12 2433 8310
Fax: (44) 12 2433 8311
Web Site: www.veritasdgc.com
Emp.: 5
Data Processing Services
S.I.C.: 7374
N.A.I.C.S.: 518210

Veritas DGC (Malaysia) Sdn. Bhd. **(1)**
Level 56 Tower 2 Petronas Twin Towers
Kuala Lumpur, 50888, Malaysia MY
Tel.: (60) 323821100
Fax: (60) 323821122
E-Mail: info@cggveritas.com
Emp.: 23
Processing Seismic Data
S.I.C.: 7379
N.A.I.C.S.: 518210
K. Pong *(Gen Mgr)*

CGI GROUP INC.

1350 Rene-Levesque Boulevard West 15th Floor
Montreal, QC, H3G 1T4, Canada
Tel.: (514) 841-3200
Fax: (514) 841-3299
Web Site: www.cgi.com
Year Founded: 1981
GIB—(NYSE TSX)
Rev.: $10,024,317,948
Assets: $10,814,213,953
Liabilities: $6,782,770,022
Net Worth: $4,031,443,932
Earnings: $453,094,196
Emp.: 68,000
Fiscal Year-end: 09/30/13

Business Description:
Information Technology & Business Process Services; Consulting Services
S.I.C.: 8999
N.A.I.C.S.: 541690

Personnel:
Serge Godin *(Co-Founder & Chm)*
Andre Imbeau *(Co-Founder, Vice Chm & Sec)*
Michael E. Roach *(Pres & CEO)*
R. David Anderson *(CFO & Exec VP)*
Eva Maglis *(CIO & Exec VP)*
Jame Cofran *(CMO & Sr VP)*
Benoit Dube *(Chief Legal Officer & Exec VP)*
Joao Baptista *(Pres-Nordics, Southern Europe & South America)*
Jean-Michel Baticle *(Pres-France)*
Serge Dubrana *(Pres-Ops-Central & Eastern Europe)*
Timothy Gregory *(Pres-United Kingdom)*
Colin Holgate *(Pres-Asia Pacific)*
George D. Schindler *(Pres-US & Canada)*
Julie Godin *(Exec VP-Global HR & Strategic Plng)*
Douglas McCuaig *(Exec VP-Global Client Transformation Svcs)*
Luc Pinard *(Exec VP-Corp Performance)*
Daniel Rocheleau *(Chief Bus Engrg Officer & Exec VP)*
S. Chandramouli *(Mng Dir-India & Sr VP)*
Pete Ihrig *(Sr VP/Gen Mgr-Enterprise Markets-US)*
Rejean Bernard *(Sr VP-Global Infrastructure Svcs-Canada)*
Alain Bouchard *(Sr VP-Quebec City Bus Unit)*
Mark Boyajian *(Sr VP-Mid-Atlantic-US)*
Dave Delgado *(Sr VP- West-US)*
Shawn Derby *(Sr VP-Western Canada)*
Michael Godin *(Sr VP-Natl Capital Reg-Canada)*
Lorne Gorber *(Sr VP-Global Comm & IR)*
Dave Henderson *(Sr VP-Central-South-US)*
Jamie Holland *(Sr VP-Canadian IP Solutions)*
Roy Hudson *(Sr VP-Comm Svcs Bus)*
Christopher Earl James *(Sr VP-IP Solutions & Onshore Delivery)*
Marie T. Macdonald *(Sr VP-Greater Toronto Area)*
Jay MacIsaac *(Sr VP-Atlantic Canada)*
Gregg Thomas Mossburg *(Sr VP-Northeast-US)*
Claude Seguin *(Sr VP-Corp Dev & Strategic Investments)*
Guy Vigeant *(Sr VP-Greater Montreal)*

Board of Directors:
Serge Godin
Alain Bouchard
Bernard A. J. Bourigeaud
Jean Brassard
Robert Chevrier
Dominic D'Alessandro
Thomas P. d'Aquino
Paule Dore
Richard B. Evans
Julie Godin
Andre Imbeau
Gilles Labbe
Michael E. Roach
Joakim Westh

Computershare Investor Services Inc.
Toronto, ON, Canada

Computershare
Montreal, QC, Canada

Transfer Agents:
Computershare Trust Company, N.A.
Golden, CO 80401

Computershare Investor Services Inc.
Toronto, ON, Canada

Computershare
Montreal, QC, Canada

Subsidiaries:

CGI Information Systems & Management Consultants Inc. **(1)**
1130 Sherbrooke St West 7th Fl
Montreal, QC, H3A 2M8, Canada (100%)
Tel.: (514) 841-3200
Fax: (514) 841-3299
Web Site: www.cgi.ca
Emp.: 2,000
Computer Consulting & Systems Integration Services
S.I.C.: 7373
N.A.I.C.S.: 541512
Michael Roach *(Pres & CEO)*

Branches:

CGI Inc. **(2)**
930 Jacques Cartier East 3rd Fl
Chicoutimi, QC, G7H 7K9, Canada (100%)
Tel.: (418) 696-6789
Fax: (418) 696-6795
E-Mail: info@cgi.com
Web Site: www.cgi.com
Emp.: 430
Information Technology Consulting Services
S.I.C.: 8742
N.A.I.C.S.: 541611
Daniel Bouchard *(VP)*

CGI Information Systems **(2)**
275 Slater St 14th Fl
Ottawa, ON, K1P 5H9, Canada

Tel.: (613) 234-2155
Fax: (613) 234-6934
Web Site: www.cgi.ca
Emp.: 700
Systems Integration & Consulting Services
S.I.C.: 7373
N.A.I.C.S.: 541512
Michael E. Roach *(Pres & CEO)*

CGI Information Systems (2)
800 5th Ave SW Ste 900
Calgary, AB, T2P 3T6, Canada (100%)
Tel.: (403) 218-8300
Fax: (403) 213-8488
Toll Free: (888) 5DBCORP
E-Mail: info@cgi.com
Web Site: www.cgi.com
Emp.: 250
Remote Database Administration
S.I.C.: 7373
N.A.I.C.S.: 541512
Shawn Derby *(Sr VP--Western Canada)*

CGI (2)
1350 Rene-Levesque Blvd West 15th Floor
Montreal, QC, H3G 1T4, Canada (100%)
Tel.: (514) 841-3200
Fax: (514) 841-3299
Web Site: www.cgi.com
Emp.: 1,000
Research and Development in Technology Solutions & Performance Platforms
S.I.C.: 7371
N.A.I.C.S.: 541511
Michael D. Schindler *(Pres-U.S. & Canada)*
Claude Marcoux *(COO)*
Alain Bouchard *(Sr VP-Quebec Bus Unit)*
Guy Vigeant *(Sr VP-Greater Montreal)*

Conseillers en gestion et informatique CGI Inc. (1)
1130 Sherbrooke St W 7 Fl
Montreal, QC, H3A 2M8, Canada
Tel.: (514) 841-3200
Fax: (514) 841-3299
Information Technology Consulting Services
S.I.C.: 7371
N.A.I.C.S.: 541511

U.S. Subsidiaries:

CGI Federal, Inc. (1)
12601 Fair Lakes Cir
Fairfax, VA 22030
Tel.: (703) 227-6000
Fax: (703) 267-8000
E-Mail: info@cgifederal.com
Web Site: www.cgifederal.com
Emp.: 1,000
Information Technology Services for US Government
S.I.C.: 8999
N.A.I.C.S.: 541690
James Peake *(Pres)*
Toni Townes-Whitley *(COO)*
Michelle Hertz *(Gen Counsel)*
Cheryl Campbell *(Sr VP)*

CGI Information Systems & Management Consultants, Inc. (1)
12 Corporate Woods Blvd
Albany, NY 12211
Tel.: (518) 436-0772
Web Site: www.cgi.com
Sales Range: $1-9.9 Million
Emp.: 60
Computer Integrated Systems Design Services
S.I.C.: 7373
N.A.I.C.S.: 541512
Jo Raquel *(Sr VP-Admin)*

CGI Technologies & Solutions Inc. (1)
1130 Random Hills
Fairfax, VA 22033 DE
Tel.: (703) 267-8679 (100%)
Fax: (703) 267-5073
E-Mail: info@cgi.com
Web Site: www.cgi.com
Sales Range: $900-999.9 Million
Emp.: 6,500
Systems Integration & Consulting Services
S.I.C.: 7373
N.A.I.C.S.: 541512

Non-U.S. Group:

Logica Limited (1)
250 Brook Drive
Green Park, Reading, RG2 6UA, United Kingdom UK
Tel.: (44) 2076379111
Fax: (44) 2074687006
E-Mail: info.eu@cgi.com
Web Site: www.cgi.com
Emp.: 41,784
Holding Company; Computer Consultancy, Systems Integration, Project Management, Products & Outsourcing Services
S.I.C.: 6719
N.A.I.C.S.: 551112
Jean-Marc Lazzari *(Pres/Chief Client Officer-France)*
Gary Bullard *(Pres-UK)*

Subsidiaries:

Logica IT Services UK Limited (2)
20 Kingston Road
Staines-upon-Thames, TW18 4LG, United Kingdom
Tel.: (44) 1784 416000
Fax: (44) 1784 416008
Emp.: 15
Software Development Services
S.I.C.: 7371
N.A.I.C.S.: 541511

Logica UK Ltd. (2)
250 Brook Dr
Green Park, Reading, RG2 6UA, United Kingdom UK
Tel.: (44) 2076379111 (100%)
Fax: (44) 2074687006
E-Mail: enqueries.uk@logica.com
Emp.: 100
Computer Consulting Services
S.I.C.: 7373
N.A.I.C.S.: 541512

Branches:

Logica UK Ltd. - Aberdeen (3)
Seafield House Floor 3C Hill of Rubislaw
Aberdeen, AB15 6BL, United Kingdom
Tel.: (44) 1224 388988
Web Site: www.logica.co.uk
Emp.: 100
Computer Consulting Services
S.I.C.: 7373
N.A.I.C.S.: 541512

Logica UK Ltd. - Bridgend (3)
Technology Dr Science Pk
Bridgend, Midgomargan, CF31 3NA, United Kingdom
Tel.: (44) 656765000
Fax: (44) 656765987
Web Site: www.Logica.com
Emp.: 100
Computer Consulting Services
S.I.C.: 7373
N.A.I.C.S.: 541512

Logica UK Ltd. - Bristol (3)
400 Park Ave Aztec W
Almondsbury, Bristol, BS32 4TR, United Kingdom
Tel.: (44) 454614455
Fax: (44) 1454620527
Web Site: www.logicacmg.com
Emp.: 200
Computer Consulting Services
S.I.C.: 7373
N.A.I.C.S.: 541512

Logica UK Ltd. - Cardiff (3)
Newport Rd
St Mellons Cardiff, CF3 5WW, United Kingdom
Tel.: (44) 29-2072-1111
Fax: (44) 29-2077-3063
Computer Consulting Services
S.I.C.: 7373
N.A.I.C.S.: 541512

Logica UK Ltd. - Edinburgh (3)
81 George St
EH129Dj
Edinburgh, Scotland, United Kingdom
Tel.: (44) 315278500
Fax: (44) 315278000
Web Site: www.logicacmg.com
Emp.: 1,750
Computer Consulting Services
S.I.C.: 7373
N.A.I.C.S.: 541512

Logica UK Ltd. - Leatherhead (3)
Chaucer House & Keats House The Office Park
Springfield Dr, Leatherhead, Surrey, KT22 7LP, United Kingdom
Tel.: (44) 1372369576
Web Site: www.logica.co.uk
Emp.: 450
Computer Consulting Services
S.I.C.: 7373
N.A.I.C.S.: 541512

Logica UK Ltd. - Manchester (3)
Kingston House Towers Business Pk
Wilmslow Rd, Manchester, Didsbury, M20 2LX, United Kingdom
Tel.: (44) 1614388000
Fax: (44) 1614388100
Web Site: www.logica.com
Emp.: 185
Computer Consulting Services
S.I.C.: 7373
N.A.I.C.S.: 541512

U.S. Subsidiary:

Logica North America Inc. (2)
Westchase Park 3700 W Sam Houston Pkwy S Ste 500
Houston, TX 77042 (100%)
Tel.: (713) 954-7000
Fax: (713) 954-7380
Web Site: www.logica.us
Emp.: 450
IT Consulting Services
S.I.C.: 8999
N.A.I.C.S.: 541690
Josh Strasner *(CEO)*
Bryan Wall *(CFO)*
Mike Lewsley *(COO)*
Joe Perino *(Sr VP-Oil & Gas Sector)*
Jeremy Schutte *(Sr VP-Fin Svcs, Energy & Utilities)*

Non-U.S. Subsidiaries:

Logica AB (2)
Augustendalsvagen 21, Nacka Strand
131 85 Stockholm, Sweden
Tel.: (46) 86702000
Fax: (46) 86702001
Web Site: www.logica.se
Emp.: 9,000
IT Consulting Services
S.I.C.: 8999
N.A.I.C.S.: 541690
Stefan Gardefjord *(Pres)*
Charles Gill *(CFO)*

Logica America do Sul Solucoes de Technologica Ltda. (2)
Av Das Nacoes Unidas N 11541 8 Andar
Brooklin Novo, 04578 000 Sao Paulo, SP, Brazil BR
Tel.: (55) 1121653000 (100%)
Fax: (55) 1121653080
E-Mail: info@logica.com
Web Site: www.logica.com.br
Emp.: 80
IT Consulting Services
S.I.C.: 8999
N.A.I.C.S.: 541690
Edson F. Leite *(CEO)*

Logica Australia Pty Ltd. (2)
13th Floor 100 Pacific Hwy
North Sydney, NSW, 2060, Australia AU
Tel.: (61) 2 8062 3000 (100%)
Fax: (61) 2 9021 7000
Web Site: www.logica.com.au
Emp.: 150
IT Consulting Services
S.I.C.: 8999
N.A.I.C.S.: 541690

Branch:

Logica Australia Pty Ltd. (3)
Ground Fl 436 Elgar Rd
Box Hill, VIC, 3128, Australia AU
Tel.: (61) 398430600 (100%)
Telex: 22632
Fax: (61) 398986270
Web Site: www.logica.com.au
Emp.: 25
IT Consulting Services
S.I.C.: 8999
N.A.I.C.S.: 541690
Bill Richards *(Chief Client Officer)*

Logica Belgium NV/SA (2)
Logica House Woluwedal
Blvd De La Woluwe 106, B 1200 Brussels, Belgium (100%)
Tel.: (32) 27086100
Fax: (32) 27055193
Web Site: www.logica.be
Emp.: 400
IT Consulting Services
S.I.C.: 8999
N.A.I.C.S.: 541690
Hans Zets *(Pres)*

Logica Business Process Outsourcing BV (2)
Prof W H Keesomlaan 14
Amstelveen, Noord-Holland, 1183 DJ, Netherlands
Tel.: (31) 885640000
Business Process Outsourcing Services
S.I.C.: 7389
N.A.I.C.S.: 561499

Logica Czech Republic Sro (2)
Na Okraju 335 42
16200 Prague, 6, Czech Republic CZ
Tel.: (420) 284020111
Fax: (420) 284020112
Web Site: www.logica.cz
Emp.: 300
IT Consulting Services
S.I.C.: 8999
N.A.I.C.S.: 541690
Stefan Szabo *(Gen Mgr)*

Logica Danmark AS (2)
Strommen 6
9400 Norresundby, Denmark
Tel.: (45) 44 78 40 00
Fax: (45) 44 78 40 01
Web Site: www.logica.dk
IT Consulting Services
S.I.C.: 8999
N.A.I.C.S.: 541690
Jesper Scharff *(CEO)*

Logica Deutschland GmbH & Co. KG (2)
Leinfelder Strasse 60
70771 Leinfelden-Echterdingen, Germany De
Tel.: (49) 711728460
Fax: (49) 711 72846 846
Web Site: www.logica.de
Emp.: 100
Management Consulting Services
S.I.C.: 8742
N.A.I.C.S.: 541611
Torsten Strass *(CEO)*

Logica France S.A.S. (2)
Immeuble CB 16
17 place des Reflets, 92097 Paris, Cedex, France FR
Tel.: (33) 157874000 (100%)
Fax: (33) 157874080
Web Site: www.logica.fr
Emp.: 12
Computer Consulting Services
S.I.C.: 7371
N.A.I.C.S.: 541511
Jean-Marc Lazzari *(CEO)*

Branches:

Logica France S.A.S. - Aix-en-Provence (3)
1330 rue Guillibert de la Lauziere
Europarc de Pichaury - Bat B1, 13856 Aix-en-Provence, Cedex 3, France
Tel.: (33) 442972220
Fax: (33) 442972222
E-Mail: info@logica.com
Web Site: www.logica.com
Emp.: 110
Computer Consulting Services
S.I.C.: 7371
N.A.I.C.S.: 541511
Eric Llano *(CEO)*

Logica France S.A.S. - Bordeaux (3)
Parc d Activites Kennedy 3
1 Avenue Neil Armstrong, 33700 Merignac, Bordeaux, France
Tel.: (33) 557929500
Fax: (33) 557929501
Emp.: 1,000
Computer Consulting Services
S.I.C.: 7371
N.A.I.C.S.: 541511
Andy Green *(Pres)*

Logica France S.A.S. - Brest (3)
Immeuble Grand Large
Quai de la Douane, 29200 Brest, France

CGI Group Inc.—(Continued)

Tel.: (33) 2 98 80 98 80
Fax: (33) 2 98 80 39 58
Web Site: www.logica.fr/brest/400005753
Emp.: 27
S.I.C.: 7371
N.A.I.C.S.: 541511

Logica France S.A.S. - Lille (3)
8 rue Anatole France
59043 Lille, France
Tel.: (33) 320438840
Fax: (33) 362599399
E-Mail: info@logica.com
Web Site: www.logica.com
Emp.: 400
Computer Consulting Services
S.I.C.: 7371
N.A.I.C.S.: 541511

Logica France S.A.S. - Lyon (3)
Bat Docksite 47-49 rue des Docks
CS 20 218
69336 Lyon, Cedex, France
Tel.: (33) 469646000
Fax: (33) 469646001
E-Mail: acuueil.lyon@logica.com
Emp.: 100
Computer Consulting Services
S.I.C.: 7371
N.A.I.C.S.: 541511
Debu Sabien *(Gen Mgr)*

Logica France S.A.S. - Montpellier (3)
Parc Euromedecine
61/67 rue Guillaume Dupuytren, 34196
Montpellier, Cedex, France
Tel.: (33) 467637110
Fax: (33) 467637111
Web Site: www.logica.com
Emp.: 20
Computer Consulting Services
S.I.C.: 7371
N.A.I.C.S.: 541511

Logica France S.A.S. - Nantes (3)
9 Boulevard Ampere
BP 10727
44481 Carquefou, Cedex, France
Tel.: (33) 228015470
Fax: (33) 228015924
Web Site: www.cgi.com
Emp.: 500
Computer Consulting Services
S.I.C.: 7371
N.A.I.C.S.: 541511

Logica France S.A.S. - Niort (3)
141 avenue Salvador Allende
79000 Niort, France
Tel.: (33) 549260707
Fax: (33) 549248220
Emp.: 75
Computer Consulting Services
S.I.C.: 7371
N.A.I.C.S.: 541511

Logica France S.A.S. - Pau (3)
37 Rte de Tarbes
Idron, 64320 Pau, France
Tel.: (33) 559806170
Fax: (33) 559806180
E-Mail: annie.falanchere@logica.com
Emp.: 25
Computer Consulting Services
S.I.C.: 7371
N.A.I.C.S.: 541511
Annie Falanchere *(Project Mgr)*

Logica France S.A.S. - Rennes (3)
Espace Sivigni
ZA La Rigourdihre, 35510 Cesson Sevigne, France
Tel.: (33) 299837388
Fax: (33) 29-983-7416
Web Site: www.logicacmg.com
Emp.: 60
Computer Consulting Services
S.I.C.: 7371
N.A.I.C.S.: 541511

Logica France S.A.S. - Strasbourg (3)
9 B Rue Du Parc
Valparc Oberhausbergen, 67088
Strasbourg, Cedex, France
Tel.: (33) 388568787
Fax: (33) 38 85 64777
Web Site: www.logicacmg.com
Emp.: 28
Computer Consulting Services
S.I.C.: 7371
N.A.I.C.S.: 541511

Logica France S.A.S. - Toulouse (3)
Le parc du Millenaire Bat C2 Avenue
Escadrille Normandie-Niemen
31700 Blagnac, Colomiers, France
Tel.: (33) 567692222
Fax: (33) 567692221
E-Mail: toulouse.actueil@cgi.com
Web Site: www.cgi.com
Emp.: 42
Computer Consulting Services
S.I.C.: 7371
N.A.I.C.S.: 541511
Sylvain Laduree *(Gen Mgr)*

Logica Luxembourg S.A.. (2)
7 Zone d'activites Bourmicht
L 8070 Bertrange, Luxembourg LU
Tel.: (352) 4852221 (100%)
Fax: (352) 26514740
E-Mail: compact.lu@logica.com
Web Site: www.logica.com
Emp.: 150
IT Consulting Services
S.I.C.: 8999
N.A.I.C.S.: 541690
Genesca Sebasgien *(Mng Dir)*

Logica Malaysia Sdn. Bhd. (2)
601 Level 6 Uptown 1
1 Jalan SS21 58 Damansara Upto, 47400
Petaling Jaya, Selangor Darul Ehsan, Malaysia (100%)
Tel.: (60) 377256890
Fax: (60) 377256940
Web Site: www.logica.com
Emp.: 100
IT Consulting Services
S.I.C.: 8999
N.A.I.C.S.: 541690

Logica Nederland B.V. (2)
Prof W H Keesomlaan 14
1183 DJ Amstelveen, Netherlands NL
Mailing Address: (100%)
Postbus 91
1180 AB Amstelveen, Zuidoost, Netherlands
Tel.: (31) 205033000
Fax: (31) 205033018
E-Mail: infol@logica.com
Web Site: www.logica.nl
Emp.: 400
Prepackaged Software Services
S.I.C.: 3652
N.A.I.C.S.: 334614
Seamus Keating *(CEO)*

Branches:

Logica Nederland B.V. - Arnhem (3)
Meander 901
6825 MH Arnhem, Netherlands
Mailing Address:
Postbus 7015
6801 HA Arnhem, Netherlands
Tel.: (31) 263765000
Fax: (31) 263765010
E-Mail: info@logica.com
Web Site: www.logica.com
Emp.: 300
Prepackaged Software Services
S.I.C.: 3652
N.A.I.C.S.: 334614

Logica Nederland B.V. - Groningen (3)
Eemsgolaan 1
9727 DW Groningen, Netherlands
Mailing Address:
PO Box 70237
Groningen, 9704 AE, Netherlands
Tel.: (31) 505219500
Fax: (31) 505219501
Web Site: www.logica.com
Emp.: 350
Prepackaged Software Services
S.I.C.: 7371
N.A.I.C.S.: 541511
Seamus Keating *(CEO)*

Logica Nederland B.V. - Maastricht (3)
Prof. W.H. Keesomlaan 14 Amstelveen
PO Box 159
1180AD Amstelveen, 1183 DJ, Netherlands
Mailing Address:
PO Box 1893
6201 BW Maastricht, Netherlands
Tel.: (31) 433524200
Fax: (31) 433524222
E-Mail: info.nl@logica.com
Emp.: 230
Prepackaged Software Services
S.I.C.: 3652
N.A.I.C.S.: 334614

Logica Norge AS (2)
Grenseveien 86
0605 Oslo, Norway
Tel.: (47) 22 57 70 00
Fax: (47) 22 57 70 70
Web Site: www.logica.no
IT Consulting Services
S.I.C.: 8999
N.A.I.C.S.: 541690

Logica Private Limited (2)
Divyasree Technopolis 124 125 Yemlur PO
Off Airport Rd
Bengaluru, 560037, India
Tel.: (91) 8041940000
Fax: (91) 8041943666
Web Site: www.logica.co.in
Emp.: 4,100
Management Consulting Services
S.I.C.: 8742
N.A.I.C.S.: 541611
Abhay Gupte *(CEO)*

Logica S.r.l. (2)
Piazzale Biancamano 8
20121 Milan, Italy IT
Tel.: (39) 0262032189 (100%)
Fax: (39) 0262034033
Emp.: 20
IT Consulting Services
S.I.C.: 8999
N.A.I.C.S.: 541690

Logica Suomi Oy (2)
Karvaamokuja 2 PL 38
00381 Helsinki, Finland
Tel.: (358) 10 302 010
Fax: (358) 10 302 011
Web Site: www.logica.fi
IT Consulting Services
S.I.C.: 8999
N.A.I.C.S.: 541690
Heikki Nikku *(CEO)*

Logica Sverige AB (2)
Augustendalsvagen 21
Nacka Strand, Stockholm, Sweden
Tel.: (46) 8 6702000
Fax: (46) 8 6702001
Web Site: www.logica.se
Information Technology Consulting Services
S.I.C.: 7373
N.A.I.C.S.: 541512

Subsidiary:

Logica Sverige Infrastructure Management AB (3)
Augustendalsvagen 21
Nacka Strand, Stockholm, 131 52, Sweden
Tel.: (46) 86702000
Information Technology Consulting Services
S.I.C.: 7373
N.A.I.C.S.: 541512

LogicaTI Portugal SA (2)
Av Jose Malhoa 16
1079 159 Lisbon, Portugal
Tel.: (351) 210 018 000
Fax: (351) 210 007 010
Web Site: www.logica.pt
IT Consulting Services
S.I.C.: 8999
N.A.I.C.S.: 541690
Jose Carlos Goncalves *(CEO)*

Non-U.S. Units:

Logica-Dubai (2)
Dubai Internet City Bldg 4 301 Fl
PO Box 26379
Dubai, 26379, United Arab Emirates
Tel.: (971) 43916200
Fax: (971) 43918800
E-Mail: leianne.dicolen@cgi.com
Web Site: www.logica.com
Emp.: 80
IT Consulting Services
S.I.C.: 8999
N.A.I.C.S.: 541690
Raymond McMann *(CEO)*

Non-U.S. Subsidiaries:

CGI Information Systems & Management Consultants Australia Pty Ltd (1)
Suite 2 Level 20 1 Market Street
Sydney, NSW, 2000, Australia (100%)
Tel.: (61) 292341300
Fax: (61) 292341333
E-Mail: cgi_australia.aus@cgi.com
Web Site: www.cgi.com
Emp.: 100
Systems Integration & Consulting Services
S.I.C.: 7373
N.A.I.C.S.: 541512
Dave Hudson *(Mng Dir)*

CGI Information Systems & Management Consultants Deutschland GmbH (1)
Heerdter Lohweg 35
40549 Dusseldorf, NRW, Germany (100%)
Tel.: (49) 21153550
Fax: (49) 2115355155
E-Mail: info@cgi.com
Web Site: www.cgi.com
Emp.: 287
Systems Integration & Consulting Services
S.I.C.: 7373
N.A.I.C.S.: 541512
Klaus Elix *(VP)*

CGI Information Systems & Management Consultants Espana S.A. (1)
Avenida Manoteras 32 Parque Empresarial
La Moraleja
Alcobendas, 28108 Madrid, Spain ES
Tel.: (34) 916578100 (100%)
Fax: (34) 916578151
Web Site: www.cgi.com
Emp.: 200
Systems Integration & Consulting Services
S.I.C.: 7373
N.A.I.C.S.: 541512

CGI Information Systems & Management Consultants Netherlands B.V. (1)
Prinses Beatrixlaan 614
2595 BM Hague, Netherlands NL
Tel.: (31) 703787000 (100%)
Fax: (31) 703787100
Web Site: www.cgi.com
Emp.: 30
Systems Integration & Consulting Services
S.I.C.: 7373
N.A.I.C.S.: 541512

CGI Information Systems & Management Consultants Polska (1)
Warsaw Towers 1st Floor
Ul Sienna 39, 00 121 Warsaw, Poland
Tel.: (48) 225265700
Fax: (48) 225265701
E-Mail: poland.reception@cgi.com
Web Site: www.cgi.com
Emp.: 100
Systems Integration & Consulting Services
S.I.C.: 7371
N.A.I.C.S.: 541511
Dariusz Gorzen *(Mng Dir)*

CGI Information Systems & Management Consultants Portugal (1)
Rua Tomas da Fonseca
Torresde Lisboa Torre G12 Fl D, 1600-209
Lisbon, Portugal (100%)
Tel.: (351) 217219000
Fax: (351) 217219100
E-Mail: taniaisabel.gomes@cgi.com
Web Site: www.cgi.com
Emp.: 50
Systems Integration & Consulting Services
S.I.C.: 7373
N.A.I.C.S.: 541512
Jose Pratas *(Mng Dir)*

CGI Information Systems & Management Consultants SA/NV (1)
Avenue du Boulevard/Bolwerklaan 21 b26
1210 Brussels, Belgium (100%)
Tel.: (32) 22089111
Fax: (32) 22089112

Web Site: www.cgi.com
Emp.: 20
Systems Integration & Consulting Services
S.I.C.: 7373
N.A.I.C.S.: 541512
Zan Ainatten *(Mng Dir)*

CGI Information Systems & Management Consultants (Sverige) AB (1)
Hammarby Fabrik Vagen 23
12033 Stockholm, Solna, Sweden SE
Tel.: (46) 852802000 (100%)
Fax: (46) 86675117
Web Site: www.cgi.com
Emp.: 35
Systems Integration & Consulting Services
S.I.C.: 7373
N.A.I.C.S.: 541512

CGI Information Systems & Management Consultants Switzerland SA (1)
Weltpoststrasse 20
Postflach 263
CH 3000 Bern, 15, Switzerland CH
Tel.: (41) 313564444 (100%)
Fax: (41) 31 356 4455
Web Site: www.cgi.com
Emp.: 30
Systems Integration & Consulting Services
S.I.C.: 7373
N.A.I.C.S.: 541512

CGI Information Systems & Management Consultants UK Ltd. (1)
Broadlands House
Primett Road, Stevenage, Hertfordshire, SG1 3EE, United Kingdom UK
Tel.: (44) 1438317966
Fax: (44) 1438314368
Web Site: www.cgi.com
Emp.: 360
Systems Integration & Consulting Services
S.I.C.: 7373
N.A.I.C.S.: 541512

CGS MANAGEMENT AG

Huobstrasse 14
Po Box 355
CH-8808 Pfaffikon, Switzerland
Tel.: (41) 554161640
Fax: (41) 554161641
E-Mail: info@cgs-management.com
Web Site: www.cgs-management.com
Emp.: 8

Business Description:
Private Equity Firm
S.I.C.: 6211
N.A.I.C.S.: 523999

Personnel:
Peter Giesinger *(Mng Partner)*
Peter F. Gloor *(Mng Partner)*
Rolf Lanz *(Mng Partner)*

CGX ENERGY INC.

333 Bay Street Suite 1100
Toronto, ON, M5H 2R2, Canada
Tel.: (416) 364-5569
Fax: (416) 364-5400
E-Mail: info@cgxenergy.com
Web Site: www.cgxenergy.ca
OYL—(OTC TSXV)
Int. Income: $145,213
Assets: $46,568,125
Liabilities: $18,396,602
Net Worth: $28,171,523
Earnings: ($152,224,578)
Emp.: 15
Fiscal Year-end: 12/31/12

Business Description:
Oil & Gas Exploration & Production Services
S.I.C.: 1311
N.A.I.C.S.: 211111

Personnel:
Serafino Iacono *(Co-Chm)*
Suresh Narine *(Co-Chm)*
Dewi Jones *(CEO)*
Tralisa Maraj *(CFO)*
Michael Galego *(Gen Counsel & Sec)*
Charlotte M. May *(Sec & Mgr-Comm)*

Board of Directors:
Serafino Iacono
Suresh Narine
Jose Francisco Arata
John R. Cullen
Dennis J. Mills
Marino Ostos
Ronald F. Pantin
Dennis A. Pieters

Legal Counsel:
Cassels, Brock & Blackwell LLP
2100 Scotia Plaza 40 King St W
Toronto, ON, M5H 3C2, Canada
Tel.: (416) 869-5300
Telex: 6-23415
Fax: (416) 360-8877

Transfer Agent:
Equity Financial Trust Company
200 University Avenue Suite 400
Toronto, ON, Canada

Subsidiaries:

CGX Resources Inc. (1)
120 Adelaide Street West Suite 512
Toronto, ON, M5H 1T1, Canada BS
Tel.: (416) 364-6653 (100%)
Natural Gas Exploration Services
S.I.C.: 1311
N.A.I.C.S.: 211111

ON Energy Inc. (1)
130 Adelaide St W Ste 2700
Toronto, ON, M5H 1T5, Canada GY
Tel.: (416) 364-5569 (85.5%)
Energy Exploration Services
S.I.C.: 8713
N.A.I.C.S.: 541360

C.H. BAILEY PLC

Alexandra Dock
Newport, S Wales, NP20 2NP, United Kingdom
Tel.: (44) 1633262961
Fax: (44) 1633246342
E-Mail: info@chbaileyplc.co.uk
Web Site: www.chbaileyplc.co.uk
BLEY—(LSE)
Rev.: $8,827,168
Assets: $37,437,502
Liabilities: $15,478,153
Net Worth: $21,959,349
Earnings: ($348,283)
Emp.: 39
Fiscal Year-end: 03/31/13

Business Description:
Engineering & Electrical Services
S.I.C.: 8711
N.A.I.C.S.: 541330

Personnel:
Charles H. Bailey *(Chm & Mng Dir)*
Bryan J. Warren *(Sec)*

Board of Directors:
Charles H. Bailey
Sarah A. Bailey
William McAlpine
David C. Orchard
Rod Michael Reynolds

Legal Counsel:
Squire, Sanders & Dempsey (UK) LLP
Rutland House 148 Rutland Street
Birmingham, B3 2JR, United Kingdom

Transfer Agent:
Computershare Investor Services PLC
PO Box 82 The Pavilions
Bridgwater Road, Bristol, B599 7NH, United Kingdom
Tel.: (44) 870 702 0001

C.H. BOEHRINGER SOHN AG & CO. KG

Binger Strasse 173
DE-55216 Ingelheim, Germany
Tel.: (49) 6132770
Fax: (49) 6132720
E-Mail: info@boehringer-ingelheim.com
Web Site: www.boehringer-ingelheim.com
Emp.: 120

Business Description:
Holding Company
S.I.C.: 6719
N.A.I.C.S.: 551112

Personnel:
Andreas Barner *(Chm-Mgmt Bd)*

Subsidiary:

Boehringer Ingelheim GmbH (1)
Binger Strasse 173
55216 Ingelheim, Germany DE
Tel.: (49) 6132770
Telex: 4187 910 bi d
Fax: (49) 6132720
E-Mail: webmaster@boehringer-ingelheim.com
Web Site: www.boehringer-ingelheim.com
Rev.: $21,834,877,400
Assets: $23,275,279,300
Liabilities: $14,958,641,040
Net Worth: $8,316,638,260
Earnings: $1,665,212,290
Emp.: 44,094
Fiscal Year-end: 12/31/12
Holding Company; Human & Veterinary Pharmaceuticals Researcher, Developer, Mfr & Marketer
S.I.C.: 6719
N.A.I.C.S.: 551112
Andreas Barner *(Chm)*

Subsidiaries:

Boehringer Ingelheim microParts GmbH (2)
Hauert 7
44227 Dortmund, Germany
Tel.: (49) 23197990
Fax: (49) 231979999009
E-Mail: service@microparts.de
Web Site: www.boehringer-ingelheim.de
Pharmaceutical Preparation Mfr
S.I.C.: 2834
N.A.I.C.S.: 325412

Boehringer Ingelheim Pharma GmbH & Co. KG (2)
Binger Strasse 173
D 55216 Ingelheim, Germany De
Tel.: (49) 6132770
Fax: (49) 6132720
Web Site: www.boehringeringelheim.com
Emp.: 6,000
Pharmaceutical Products Developer & Mfr
S.I.C.: 2834
N.A.I.C.S.: 325412
Engelbert Gunster *(Pres)*

Boehringer Ingelheim Vetmedica GmbH (2)
Binger Strasse 173
D 55216 Ingelheim, Germany DE
Tel.: (49) 6132778219
Fax: (49) 6132772431
E-Mail: vetservice@ing.boehringeringelheim.com
Web Site: www.boehringeringelheim.de
Emp.: 165
Animal Health Veterinary Pharmaceuticals Mfr
S.I.C.: 2834
N.A.I.C.S.: 325412

U.S. Subsidiary:

Boehringer Ingelheim Corp. (2)
900 Ridgebury Rd
Ridgefield, CT 06877-1058
Mailing Address:
PO Box 368
Ridgefield, CT 06877-0368
Tel.: (203) 798-9988
E-Mail: webmaster@rdg.boehringer-ingelheim.com
Web Site: us.boehringer-ingelheim.com
Sls.: $3,167,427,500
Emp.: 6,493
Holding Company; Pharmaceutical Products & Chemical Drug Materials Developer & Mfr
S.I.C.: 6719
N.A.I.C.S.: 551112
Paul Fonteyne *(Pres & CEO)*

Subsidiaries:

Boehringer Ingelheim Chemicals, Inc. (3)
2820 N Normandy Dr
Petersburg, VA 23805-9372
Tel.: (804) 504-8600
Fax: (804) 504-8637
E-Mail: solutions@bichemicals.com
Web Site: www.boehringeringelheim.com
Emp.: 375
Pharmaceutical Intermediates & Chemical Substances Mfr
S.I.C.: 2899
N.A.I.C.S.: 325998
Ken Glaize *(Assoc Dir-Maintenance & Facilities Ops)*

Boehringer Ingelheim Fremont, Inc. (3)
6701 Kaiser Dr
Fremont, CA 94555-3616 DE
Tel.: (510) 608-6500
E-Mail: webmaster@rdg.boehringer-ingelheim.com
Web Site: us.boehringer-ingelheim.com
Emp.: 300
Biopharmaceuticals Mfr
S.I.C.: 2836
N.A.I.C.S.: 325414
Anurag Khetan *(Dir-Cell Culture-Process Sciences)*

Boehringer Ingelheim Pharmaceuticals, Inc. (3)
900 Ridgebury Rd
Ridgefield, CT 06877
Mailing Address:
PO Box 368
Ridgefield, CT 06877-0368
Tel.: (203) 798-9988
Fax: (203) 791-6234
E-Mail: webmaster@rdg.boehringer-ingelheim.com
Web Site: www.boehringer-ingelheim.com
Emp.: 100
Drugs Acting On The Cardiovascular System Except Diagnostic
S.I.C.: 2834
N.A.I.C.S.: 325412
Ross Ullman *(Exec Dir-Mktg-Consumer Healthcare)*

Boehringer Ingelheim Vetmedica, Inc. (3)
2621 N Belt Hwy
Saint Joseph, MO 64506
Tel.: (816) 233-2571
Fax: (816) 236-2735
Toll Free: (800) 821-7467
Web Site: www.bi-vetmedica.com
Emp.: 593
Veterinary Serums, Biologics, Pharmaceuticals, Insecticides & Efficiency Enhancers Mfr
Export
S.I.C.: 2836
N.A.I.C.S.: 325414
Albrecht Kissel *(Pres & CEO)*

Roxane Laboratories, Inc. (3)
1809 Wilson Rd
Columbus, OH 43228 DE
Mailing Address:
PO Box 16532
Columbus, OH 43216-6532
Tel.: (614) 276-4000
Fax: (614) 308-3540
Toll Free: (800) 962-8364
Web Site: www.roxane.com
Emp.: 1,029
Ethical Pharmaceuticals Mfr
Export
S.I.C.: 2834
N.A.I.C.S.: 325412
Rex VanHorn *(Principal & EngrSoftware)*

Affiliate:

Ben Venue Laboratories Incorporated (3)
300 Northfield Rd
Bedford, OH 44146-4650
Mailing Address:
PO Box 46568
Cleveland, OH 44146-0568

C.H. Boehringer Sohn AG & Co. KG—(Continued)

Tel.: (440) 232-3320
Fax: (440) 439-6398
Web Site: www.benvenue.com
Emp.: 1,000
Pharmaceutical Preparations
S.I.C.: 2834
N.A.I.C.S.: 325412
Tom Mercy *(Pres)*

Non-U.S. Subsidiaries:

Boehringer Ingelheim AB (2)
Liljeholmsstranden 3
PO Box 47608
SE 117 94 Stockholm, Sweden SE
Mailing Address:
Box 44
SE-127 21 Skarholmen, Sweden
Tel.: (46) 87212100
Fax: (46) 87109884
E-Mail: boehringeringelheim@boerhingeringelheim.com
Web Site: www.boehringeringelheim.se
Rev.: $30,000,000
Emp.: 100
Provider of Pharmaceuticals
S.I.C.: 2834
N.A.I.C.S.: 325412
Andreas Kruger *(Mng Dir)*

Boehringer Ingelheim Austria GmbH (2)
Dr Boehringer Gasse 5-11
AT-1121 Vienna, Austria AT
Tel.: (43) 1801050
Fax: (43) 18040823
E-Mail: info@boehringer-ingelheim.at
Web Site: www.boehringer-ingelheim.at
Emp.: 1,350
Researcher & Developer of Oncology Products & Manufacturer of Biopharmaceuticals
S.I.C.: 2834
N.A.I.C.S.: 325412
Christian Sehilling *(Exec Dir)*

Subsidiary:

Boehringer Ingelheim Pharma Ges.m.b.H. (3)
Dr Boehringer Gasse 5-11
A 1121 Vienna, Austria AT
Tel.: (43) 1801050
Fax: (43) 18040823
E-Mail: info@boehringer-ingelheim.at
Web Site: www.boehringeringelheim.at
Emp.: 1,200
Pharmaceuticals Mfr & Marketer
S.I.C.: 2834
N.A.I.C.S.: 325412
Christian Schilling *(Gen Mgr)*

Unit:

I.M.P. Research Institute of Molecular Pathology (3)
Dr Bohr Gasse 7
1030 Vienna, Austria
Tel.: (43) 179730
Fax: (43) 17987153
E-Mail: office@imp.univie.ac.at
Web Site: www.imp.univie.ac.at
Emp.: 250
Research Services
S.I.C.: 8731
N.A.I.C.S.: 541712

Boehringer Ingelheim B.V. (2)
Comenius Straase 6
1817MS Alkmaar, Holland, Netherlands
Tel.: (31) 725662424
Fax: (31) 725641934
E-Mail: onno.wisman@boehringer-ingelheim.com
Web Site: www.boehringer-ingelheim.com
Emp.: 250
Pharmaceuticals & Animal Health Products Mfr
S.I.C.: 2834
N.A.I.C.S.: 325412
Mark Connolly *(Mng Dir)*

Boehringer Ingelheim C.A. (2)
Av La Estancia Torre B piso 3 Centro Banaven
Chuao, Caracas, 64745, Venezuela
Tel.: (58) 212 950 01 11
Fax: (58) 212 959 14 56
E-Mail: webmaster@boehringer-ingelheim.com
Web Site: www.sudamerica.boehringer-ingelheim.com
Emp.: 197
Pharmaceuticals Distr
S.I.C.: 5122
N.A.I.C.S.: 424210

Boehringer Ingelheim (Canada) Ltd. (2)
5180 South Service Rd
Burlington, ON, L7L 5H4, Canada
Tel.: (905) 639-0333
Fax: (905) 639-3769
E-Mail: webmaster@bur.boehringer-ingelheim.com
Web Site: www.boehringer-ingelheim.ca
Emp.: 700
Pharmaceuticals Research & Development; Human Prescription Pharmaceuticals & Animal Health Products Sales & Marketing
S.I.C.: 5122
N.A.I.C.S.: 424210
Theodore J. Witek, Jr. *(Pres & CEO)*

Boehringer Ingelheim Danmark A/S (2)
Strodamvaj 52
2100 Copenhagen, Denmark DK
Tel.: (45) 39158888
Fax: (45) 39158989
E-Mail: Info@cop.boehringer-ingelheim.com
Web Site: www.boehringer-ingelheim.dk
Emp.: 125
Pharmaceuticals & Animal Health Products Mfr & Marketer
S.I.C.: 2834
N.A.I.C.S.: 325412
Timmo Andersen *(Mng Dir)*

Boehringer Ingelheim del Ecuador Cia. Ltda. (2)
Avenida de los Shyris No 37 313 y El Telegrafo
Quito, Ecuador
Tel.: (593) 2 226 4308
Fax: (593) 22264571
E-Mail: info@qto.boehringeringelheim.com
Web Site: www.qto.boehringer-ingelheim.com
Sales Range: $1-9.9 Million
Emp.: 100
Pharmaceuticals Distr
S.I.C.: 5122
N.A.I.C.S.: 424210

Boehringer Ingelheim do Brasil Quimica e Farmaceutica Ltda. (2)
Rochavera Corporate Towers Av das Nacoes Unidas 14.171 Torre Marble 18 andar
Santo Amaro, Sao Paulo, SP, CEP 04794 000, Brazil
Tel.: (55) 11 4949 4700
E-Mail: sac@sao.boehringer-ingelheim.com
Web Site: www.boehringer-ingelheim.com.br
Sales Range: $125-149.9 Million
Emp.: 1,107
Pharmaceuticals & Animal Health Products Mfr & Marketer
S.I.C.: 2834
N.A.I.C.S.: 325412

Subsidiary:

Solana Agro Pecuaria Ltda. (3)
Fazendo Nossa Senhora Iparecida
Zona Rural, CEP 86700-970 Arapongas, Brazil
Medicinal Plants Production
S.I.C.: 2834
N.A.I.C.S.: 325412

Boehringer Ingelheim Ellas AE (2)
Ellinikou 2
Elliniko, 16777 Athens, Greece GR
Tel.: (30) 2108906300
Fax: (30) 2108983207
Emp.: 299
Pharmaceuticals, Consumer Health Products & Animal Health Products Mfr & Distr
S.I.C.: 2834
N.A.I.C.S.: 325412

Boehringer Ingelheim Espana, S.A. (2)
Prat de la Riba s/n
San Cugat del Valles, 08173 Barcelona, Spain
Tel.: (34) 934045100
Fax: (34) 934045484
E-Mail: webmaster@boehringer-ingelheim.es
Web Site: www.boehringer-ingelheim.es
Emp.: 1,515
Pharmaceuticals Mfr & Marketer
S.I.C.: 2834
N.A.I.C.S.: 325412
Luis Llubia Maristany *(Pres)*
Hector Ornaque Font *(Sec)*

Boehringer Ingelheim Finland Ky (2)
Tammasaarenkatu 5
00180 Helsinki, Finland
Tel.: (358) 103102800
Fax: (358) 103102999
E-Mail: info@hel.boehringer-ingelheim.com
Web Site: www.boehringer-ingelheim.fi
Sales Range: $50-74.9 Million
Emp.: 86
Pharmaceuticals Sales, Marketing & Clinical Trials
S.I.C.: 5122
N.A.I.C.S.: 424210
Amos Gyllenbogel *(Mng Dir)*

Boehringer Ingelheim France S.A.S. (2)
12 rue Andre Huet
51721 Reims, Cedex, France
Mailing Address:
BP 292
51060 Reims, Cedex, France
Tel.: (33) 326504533
Fax: (33) 326504511
Web Site: www.boehringer-ingelheim.fr
Emp.: 1,282
Pharmaceuticals, Chemicals & Animal Health Products
S.I.C.: 2834
N.A.I.C.S.: 325412

Subsidiary:

LABSO Chimie Fine S.A.R.L. (3)
20 Rue Jean Duvert
33290 Blanquefort, France FR
Mailing Address:
PO Box 7
33291 Blanquefort, France
Tel.: (33) 5 5635 5050
Fax: (33) 5 5695 2604
E-Mail:
Sales Range: $1-9.9 Million
Emp.: 12
Mfr. of Chemical Products
S.I.C.: 2899
N.A.I.C.S.: 325998
Thomas Roulet *(Pres)*

Boehringer Ingelheim Ilac Ticaret A.S. (2)
Eski Buyukdere Caddesi Uso Center 245
Maslak, 34398 Istanbul, Turkey
Tel.: (90) 2123291100
Fax: (90) 2123291101
E-Mail: info@ist.boehringer-ingelheim.com
Web Site: www.boehringer-ingelheim.com
Emp.: 400
Pharmaceutical Preparation Mfr
S.I.C.: 2834
N.A.I.C.S.: 325412
Roland Stehlin *(Mng Dir)*

Boehringer Ingelheim International Trading (Shanghai) Co. Ltd. (2)
29/F Park Pl 1601 W Nanjing Rd
Jing An Dist, Shanghai, 200040, China
Tel.: (86) 2158882200
Fax: (86) 2158780088
Web Site: www.boehringer-ingelheim.com.cn
Pharmaceuticals Sales & Marketing
S.I.C.: 5122
N.A.I.C.S.: 424210

Boehringer Ingelheim Italia S.p.A. (2)
Via Lorenzini 8
20139 Milan, Italy IT
Mailing Address:
Casella Postale n13059
Milan, 20130, Italy
Tel.: (39) 0253551
Fax: (39) 025355222
E-Mail: info@boehringeringelheim.it
Web Site: www.boehringer-ingelheim.it
Emp.: 900
Prescription & Over-the-Counter Pharmaceuticals Mfr
S.I.C.: 2834
N.A.I.C.S.: 325412
Sergio Diniotti *(Mng Dir)*

Subsidiary:

Bidachem S.p.A. (3)
Strada Statale 11 Padana Sup N 8
24040 Bergamo, Fornovo San Giovanni, Italy IT
Tel.: (39) 036335521
Fax: (39) 0363351020
E-Mail: bidachem@ctrade.it
Web Site: www.bidachem.it
Emp.: 110
Provider of Chemical Products
S.I.C.: 2899
N.A.I.C.S.: 325998
Ambrosini Leonardo *(Mng Dir)*

Boehringer Ingelheim Korea Ltd. (2)
Yonsei Severance Bldg
84-11 Nambae Munro 5 KA, Seoul, 100753, Korea (South) Ks
Tel.: (82) 27090013
Fax: (82) 7950047
Web Site: www.boehringeringelheim.co.kr
Emp.: 270
Provider of Pharmaceuticals & Animal Health Products
S.I.C.: 2834
N.A.I.C.S.: 325412

Subsidiary:

Boehringer Ingelheim Vetmedica Korea Ltd. (3)
Hanganglo 3 Ga 40 883 Young Santu
Kolea, Seoul, Korea (South) Ks
Tel.: (82) 27090114
Fax: (82) 25163405
Web Site: www.bivkorea.com
Emp.: 30
Provider of Animal Health Products
S.I.C.: 0291
N.A.I.C.S.: 112990

Boehringer Ingelheim Ltda. (2)
Av badua11
1800-294 Lisbon, Portugal PT
Tel.: (351) 213135300
Fax: (351) 213135303
E-Mail: webmaster@lis.boehringeringelheim.com
Web Site: www.boehringeringelheim.com
Sales Range: $25-49.9 Million
Emp.: 204
Provider of Pharmaceuticals
S.I.C.: 2834
N.A.I.C.S.: 325412
Sabena Nicolas *(Gen Mgr)*

Subsidiary:

Unilfarma-Uniao Internacional de Laboratorios Farmaceuticos, Lda. (3)
Av de Padua 11
1800-294 Lisbon, Portugal PT
Tel.: (351) 213135300
Fax: (351) 213135303
Web Site: www.boehringer-ingelheim.com
Sales Range: $25-49.9 Million
Emp.: 210
Pharmaceuticals Distr
S.I.C.: 5122
N.A.I.C.S.: 424210

Boehringer Ingelheim Ltda. (2)
General del Canto 421 Piso 6
Providencia, Santiago, Chile
Tel.: (56) 22640000
Fax: (56) 2 264 00 10
E-Mail: webmaster@scl.boehringer-ingelheim.com
Web Site: www.boehringer-ingelheim.com
Emp.: 80
Pharmaceuticals Distr
S.I.C.: 5122
N.A.I.C.S.: 424210
Francisco Gonzales *(Gen Mgr)*

Boehringer Ingelheim Ltd. (2)
Ellesfield Ave
Bracknell, Berks, RG12 8YS, United Kingdom UK
Tel.: (44) 1344424600
Fax: (44) 1344741444

Web Site: www.boehringer-ingelheim.com
Sales Range: $200-249.9 Million
Emp.: 700
Provider of Pharmaceuticals & Animal Health Products
S.I.C.: 2834
N.A.I.C.S.: 325412
Zinta Krumins *(Mng Dir-UK & Ireland)*

Boehringer Ingelheim Norway KS (2)
Drengsrudbekken 8
1373 Asker, Norway
Mailing Address:
Postboks 405
1373 Asker, Norway
Tel.: (47) 66761300
Fax: (47) 66902533
E-Mail: webmaster@osl.boehringer-ingelheim.com
Web Site: www.boehringer-ingelheim.no
Emp.: 300
Pharmaceuticals Sales & Marketing
S.I.C.: 5122
N.A.I.C.S.: 424210
Harald H. Hauge *(Mng Dir)*

Boehringer Ingelheim (N.Z.) Limited (2)
42 Ormiston Rd East Tamaki
Manukau City, Auckland, New Zealand
Tel.: (64) 92748664
Fax: (64) 92710629
E-Mail: frontdesk@syd.boehringer-ingelheim.com
Emp.: 20
Pharmaceuticals Sales & Marketing
S.I.C.: 5122
N.A.I.C.S.: 424210
Dascy Downey *(Gen Mgr)*

Boehringer Ingelheim (Philippines) Inc. (2)
23rd Fl Citibank Tower Citibank Plz
Salcedo Village, Makati, Metro Menila, 1227, Philippines
Tel.: (63) 28670800
Fax: (63) 28480506
Web Site: www.boehringeringelheim.com
Sales Range: $25-49.9 Million
Emp.: 300
Provider of Pharmaceuticals & Animal Health Products
S.I.C.: 2834
N.A.I.C.S.: 325412
Erik Musalem *(Mng Dir)*

Boehringer Ingelheim Promeco, S.A. de C.V. (2)
Maiz Numero 49
Xaltocan, 16090 Xochimilco, Mexico MX
Tel.: (52) 5556298300
Fax: (52) 5556535147
E-Mail: webmaster@mex.boehringer-ingelheim.com
Web Site: www.boehringer-ingelheim.com.mx
Sales Range: $200-249.9 Million
Emp.: 1,212
Mfr. of Pharmaceuticals
S.I.C.: 2834
N.A.I.C.S.: 325412
Miguel Salazar *(Gen Mgr)*

Boehringer Ingelheim (Pty.) Ltd. (2)
PO Box 3032
Randburg, 2125, South Africa
Tel.: (27) 113482400
Fax: (27) 118863205
Web Site: www.boehringer-ingelheim.com
Emp.: 226
Holding Company; Pharmaceutical Products Mfr
S.I.C.: 6719
N.A.I.C.S.: 551112
Paul Stewart *(CEO)*

Subsidiary:

Ingelheim Pharmaceuticals (Pty.) Ltd. (3)
404 Main Avenue
Private Bag X 3032
Randburg, 2194, South Africa
Tel.: (27) 113482400
Fax: (27) 117873766
E-Mail: information@jnb.boehringeringelheim.com
Web Site: www.boehringeringelheim.com
Sales Range: $50-74.9 Million
Emp.: 200
Provider of Pharmaceuticals
S.I.C.: 2834
N.A.I.C.S.: 325412
Mark Russell *(Dir-HR)*

Boehringer Ingelheim Pty. Ltd. (2)
78 Waterloo Rd
North Ryde, NSW, 2113, Australia
Tel.: (61) 288758800
Fax: (61) 288758801
E-Mail: frontdesk@syd.boehringeringelheim.com
Web Site: www.boehringeringelhiem.com
Emp.: 300
Mfr. & Sales of Pharmaceuticals, Chemicals & Animal Health Products
S.I.C.: 2834
N.A.I.C.S.: 325412
Wes Cook *(Mng Dir)*

Boehringer Ingelheim s.a./n.v. (2)
16 Ave Ariane
B 1200 Brussels, Belgium BE
Tel.: (32) 27733311
Fax: (32) 27733300
E-Mail: external@bru.boehringeringelheim.com
Web Site: www.boehringeringelheim.com
Emp.: 201
Provider of Pharmaceuticals & Animal Health Products
S.I.C.: 2834
N.A.I.C.S.: 325412
Mark Connollo *(Gen Mgr)*

Boehringer Ingelheim S.A. (2)
Complejo Empresarial Urbana Cazadores de Coquimbo 2841 Piso 2
B1605AZE Munro, Buenos Aires, Argentina
Tel.: (54) 11 47048600
Fax: (54) 11 47048690
E-Mail: info@bai.boehringer-ingelheim.com
Web Site: www.sudamerica.boehringer-ingelheim.com
Sales Range: $25-49.9 Million
Emp.: 402
Mfr & Distr of Prescription Medicines, Consumer Health Care Products & Animal Health Products
S.I.C.: 2834
N.A.I.C.S.: 325412
Andreas Barner *(Head-Pharma Res)*

Boehringer Ingelheim S.A. (2)
Carrrera 11 N 84-09 Floor 5th Apartado Aereo No 4028
Santa Fe de Bogota, Bogota, DC, Colombia
Tel.: (57) 13199100
Fax: (57) 14238001
E-Mail: webmaster@boehringer-ingelheim.com
Web Site: www.boehringer-ingelheim.com
Sales Range: $25-49.9 Million
Emp.: 348
Provider of Pharmaceuticals & Animal Health Products
S.I.C.: 2834
N.A.I.C.S.: 325412

Boehringer Ingelheim (Schweiz) GmbH (2)
Dufour Strasse 54
CH 4002 Basel, Switzerland
Tel.: (41) 612952525
Fax: (41) 612952501
E-Mail: gregor.brunner@bas.boehr-ingeringelheim.com
Web Site: www.boehringer-ingelheim.ch
Sales Range: $50-74.9 Million
Provider of Pharmaceuticals, Animal Health Products & Nature-Based Consumer Health Care Products
S.I.C.: 2834
N.A.I.C.S.: 325412
Markus Hammer *(Gen Mgr)*

Subsidiary:

Pharmaton S.A. (3)
Veaumureni
CH 6934 Bioggio, Switzerland
Tel.: (41) 916103111
Fax: (41) 916103209
E-Mail: webmasterselfmedication@boehringeringelheim.com
Web Site: www.pharmaton.com
Emp.: 200
Developer of Pharmaceuticals
S.I.C.: 2834
N.A.I.C.S.: 325412
Genovesi Michele *(Gen Mgr)*

Boehringer Ingelheim Shanghai Pharmaceuticals Co., Ltd. (2)
22F No 138 Pudong Avenue
Shanghai, 200120, China
Tel.: (86) 2158882200
Fax: (86) 2158780088
E-Mail: webmaster@sha.boehringer-ingelheim.com
Web Site: www.boehringer-ingelheim.com
Pharmaceuticals Mfr
S.I.C.: 2834
N.A.I.C.S.: 325412

Boehringer Ingelheim Sp. z o.o. (2)
Mokotow Business Park, Taurus
ul Domaniewska 41, 02-672 Warsaw, Poland PL
Tel.: (48) 226425822
Fax: (48) 226990698
E-Mail: webmaster@waw.boehringer-ingelheim.com
Web Site: www.boehringer-ingelheim.com
Sales Range: $25-49.9 Million
Emp.: 140
Sales of Pharmaceuticals
S.I.C.: 5122
N.A.I.C.S.: 446191

Boehringer Ingelheim s.r.o. (2)
Na Porici 1079/3a
110 00 Prague, Czech Republic
Tel.: (420) 234655111
Fax: (420) 234655112
E-Mail: info@boehringer-ingelheim.cz
Web Site: www.boehringer-ingelheim.cz
Rev.: $23,350,000
Emp.: 86
Provider of Pharmaceuticals
S.I.C.: 2834
N.A.I.C.S.: 325412
Heribert Johann *(Chm)*

Boehringer Ingelheim Taiwan Ltd. (2)
12th Fl Min Sheng Commercial Bldg
Section 3, Taipei, 104, Taiwan TW
Tel.: (886) 225032636
Fax: (886) 225051041
E-Mail: bitw@tpe.boehringeringelheim.com
Web Site: www.boehringeringelheim.com
Emp.: 250
Provider of Pharmaceuticals
S.I.C.: 2834
N.A.I.C.S.: 325412
Timm Pfannenschmidt *(Pres)*

Boehringer Ingelheim (Thai) Ltd. (2)
2922207 208 12th Fl Charn Issara Tower II
New Petchburi Rd
Bangkapi Huaykwang, Bangkok, 10320, Thailand
Tel.: (66) 23082100
Fax: (66) 230821178
E-Mail: webmaster@bkk.boehringer-ingelheim.com
Web Site: www.boehringer-ingelheim.com
Sales Range: $10-24.9 Million
Emp.: 132
Provider of Pharmaceuticals
S.I.C.: 2834
N.A.I.C.S.: 325412

Boehringer Ingelheim Vetmedica S.A. de C.V. (2)
Calle 30 No 2614 Zona Industrial
CP 44940 Guadalajara, Jalisco, Mexico
Tel.: (52) 36688000
Fax: (52) 36688030
E-Mail: webmaster@mex.boehringer-ingelheim.com
Web Site: www.bi-vetmedica.com.mx
Emp.: 100
Human Pharmaceuticals & Animal Health
S.I.C.: 2834
N.A.I.C.S.: 325412

Nippon Boehringer Ingelheim Co. Ltd. (2)
ThinkPark Tower 2-1-1 Osaki Shinagawa-ku
Shinagawa-ku, Tokyo, 141-6017, Japan JP
Tel.: (81) 364172200
Fax: (81) 354352920
Web Site: www.boehringer-ingelheim.com
Emp.: 1,500
Holding Company; Pharmaceutical Products Mfr
S.I.C.: 6719
N.A.I.C.S.: 551112
Yoshiaki Aono *(Gen Mgr)*

Subsidiaries:

Boehringer Ingelheim Seiyaku Co., Ltd. (3)
5353 1 Higashine Kou
Higashine Shi, Yamagata, 999 3701, Japan JP
Tel.: (81) 237421193
Fax: (81) 237411013
Web Site: www.boehringeringelheim.co.jp
Emp.: 50
Provider of Pharmaceuticals
S.I.C.: 2834
N.A.I.C.S.: 325412
Yasuko Suzuki *(Mgr-HR)*

Boehringer Ingelheim Vetmedica Japan (3)
2 8 8 Sarugaku Cho
Chiyoda-ku, Tokyo, 102-0073, Japan
Tel.: (81) 352807200
Fax: (81) 332341894
E-Mail: webmaster@boehringer-ingelheim.co.jp
Web Site: www.boehringer-ingelheim.co.jp
Provider of Animal Health Products
S.I.C.: 2834
N.A.I.C.S.: 325412

PT Boehringer Ingelheim Indonesia (2)
6/F North Tower Sampoerna Strategic Square
Jln Jend Sudirman Kav 45-46, Jakarta, 12930, Indonesia
Tel.: (62) 215732375
Fax: (62) 215732383
E-Mail: info@jak.boehringer-ingelheim.com
Web Site: www.boehringer-ingelheim.com
Emp.: 390
Pharmaceutical Preparation Mfr & Marketer
S.I.C.: 2834
N.A.I.C.S.: 325412
Andrew Eve *(Pres)*

CH ENERGY GROUP, INC.

(Acquired by Fortis Inc.)

CH. KARNCHANG PUBLIC COMPANY LIMITED

587 Viriyathavorn Building
Sutthisarvinitchai Road
Dindaeng District, Bangkok, 10400, Thailand
Tel.: (66) 22770460
Fax: (66) 22757029
E-Mail: webmaster@ch-karnchang.co.th
Web Site: www.ch-karnchang.co.th
Year Founded: 1972
CK—(THA)
Rev.: $731,986,229
Assets: $1,695,753,618
Liabilities: $1,402,209,465
Net Worth: $293,544,153
Earnings: $19,903,084
Fiscal Year-end: 12/31/12

Business Description:
General Contractor
S.I.C.: 1542
N.A.I.C.S.: 236220

Personnel:
Aswin Kongsiri *(Chm)*
Plew Trivisvavet *(Chm-Mgmt Bd & CEO)*
Prasert Marittanaporn *(Member-Mgmt Bd & Sr Exec VP-Admin)*
Narong Sangsuriya *(Member-Mgmt Bd & Sr Exec VP-Ops)*
Viboon Mongkolpiyathana *(Member-Mgmt Bd & Exec VP-Construction 2)*
Watchara Sanghattawattana *(Member-Mgmt Bd & Exec VP-Engrg)*
Ratn Santaannop *(Member-Mgmt Bd & Exec VP-Construction 1)*

CH. Karnchang Public Company Limited—(Continued)

Phongsarit Tantisuvanitchkul *(Member-Mgmt Bd & Exec VP-Bus Dev)*
Sittidej Trivisvavet *(Member-Mgmt Bd & Exec VP-Pur)*
Supamas Trivisvavet *(Member-Mgmt Bd & Exec VP-Pres Office)*
Anukool Tuntimas *(Member-Mgmt Bd & Exec VP-HR & Gen Admin)*
Vorapote Uchpaiboonvong *(Member-Mgmt Bd & Exec VP-Acctg & Fin)*
Board of Directors:
Aswin Kongsiri
Sombat Kitjalaksana
Prasert Marittanaporn
Don Pramudwinai
Narong Sangsuriya
Ratn Santaannop
Thawansak Sukhawun
Vitoon Tejatussanasoontorn
Pavich Thangroach
Kamthorn Trivisvavet
Plew Trivisvavet
Anukool Tuntimas
Subsidiaries:

Bangkok Expressway Public Company Limited (1)
238/7 Asoke-dindaeng Road Bangkapi
Subdistrict Huaykwang District
Bangkok, 10310, Thailand
Tel.: (66) 26414611
Fax: (66) 26414610
E-Mail: webmaster@becl.co.th
Web Site: www.becl.co.th
BECL—(BAK)
Rev.: $305,601,669
Assets: $1,368,829,326
Liabilities: $653,192,309
Net Worth: $715,637,017
Earnings: $74,379,083
Emp.: 630
Fiscal Year-end: 12/31/12
Highway, Street & Bridge Construction Services
S.I.C.: 1611
N.A.I.C.S.: 237310
Virabongsa Ramangkura *(Chm)*
Plew Trivisvavet *(Chm-Exec Bd)*
Supong Chayutsahakij *(Vice Chm-Exec Bd)*
Payao Marittanaporn *(Mng Dir & Member-Exec Bd)*
Phakpoom Thaweewittayarut *(Asst Mng Dir-Admin & Sec)*
Ngamnit Kanokgarnjanar *(Asst Mng Dir-Compliance Unit)*
Sanguan Kunatinun *(Asst Mng Dir-Engrg)*
Sudruthai Prommart *(Asst Mng Dir-Ops)*
Panan Tosuwanthaworn *(Asst Mng Dir-Fin)*
Vallapa Assakul *(Member-Exec Bd)*
M. L. Prasobchai Kasemsant *(Member-Exec Bd)*

Bangkok Metro Public Company Limited (1)
189 Rama LX Road
Huai Khwang District, Bangkok, Thailand
Tel.: (66) 23542000
Fax: (66) 23542020
Web Site: www.bangkokmetro.co.th
Commercial & Institutional Building Construction
S.I.C.: 1542
N.A.I.C.S.: 236220

CH. Karnchang Real Estate Co., Ltd. (1)
587 Sutthisarn Road
Dindaeng District, Bangkok, Thailand (99%)
Tel.: (66) 22750026
Fax: (66) 22757029
Web Site: www.ch-karnchang.co.th
Residential Property Managers
S.I.C.: 6531
N.A.I.C.S.: 531311
Plew Trivisvavet *(Mng Dir)*

CH. Karnchang - Tokyu Construction Co Ltd (1)
587 Sutthisarn Road
Dindaeng District, Bangkok, Thailand (55%)
Tel.: (66) 227536515
Fax: (66) 22753657
Special Trade Contractors
S.I.C.: 1799
N.A.I.C.S.: 238990
Miyakawa Hideo *(Mng Dir)*

Construction Material Supply Co., Ltd. (1)
587 Sutthisarn Road 17th Floor
Viriyathavorn Building
Dindaeng District, Bangkok, 10400, Thailand CN
Tel.: (66) 22749801 (99.99%)
Fax: (66) 22757029
Construction Material Whslr
S.I.C.: 5039
N.A.I.C.S.: 423390

SouthEast Asia Energy Limited (1)
587 Viriyathavorn Bldg 20th Fl
Suthisarn Rd Dindaeng, Bangkok, 10400, Thailand (28.5%)
Tel.: (66) 22754873
Fax: (66) 26918307
E-Mail: webmaster@sean.co.th
Web Site: www.sean.co.th/
Hydroelectric Power Operations
S.I.C.: 4911
N.A.I.C.S.: 221111

Joint Venture:

Bangpa-in Cogeneration Limited (1)
No 587 Sutthisarnvinijchai Road
Dindaeng District, Bangkok, Thailand TH
Tel.: (66) 2 275 0026
Fax: (66) 2 275 7029
Electric Power & Steam Generation & Distribution Services
S.I.C.: 4939
N.A.I.C.S.: 221118

Non-U.S. Subsidiary:

CH. Karnchang (Lao) Co., Ltd (1)
10 Thadeua Road Thaphalansay
Vientiane, Laos
Tel.: (856) 21 35 3390
Fax: (856) 21 35 3396
Construction Materials Distr
S.I.C.: 5032
N.A.I.C.S.: 423320

CH OFFSHORE LTD

388 Jalan Ahmad Ibrahim
Singapore, 629157, Singapore
Tel.: (65) 68611711
Fax: (65) 68622336
E-Mail: investor@choffshore.com.sg
Web Site: www.choffshore.com.sg
Year Founded: 1976
C13—(SES)
Rev.: $47,819,000
Assets: $245,852,000
Liabilities: $19,862,000
Net Worth: $225,990,000
Earnings: ($7,108,000)
Fiscal Year-end: 06/30/13
Business Description:
Offshore Oil & Gas Marine Services
S.I.C.: 1389
N.A.I.C.S.: 213112
Personnel:
Kok Leong Koh *(CEO)*
Peck Bee Teo *(CFO)*
Valerie May Wei Tan *(Sec)*
Board of Directors:
Pong Tyea Tan
John Boon Heng Cheak
Wah Kwang Gan
Boon Kiat Goh
Kwee Chim Peh
Joanna Sau Kwan Young

Subsidiary:

Chuan Hup Agencies (Private) Limited (1)
388 Jalan Ahmed Ibrahim
Singapore, 629157, Singapore
Tel.: (65) 68611711
Fax: (65) 68622336
E-Mail: operations@choffshore.com.sg
Web Site: www.choffshore.com.sg
Emp.: 30
Boat Charter Rental & Leasing Services
S.I.C.: 5551
N.A.I.C.S.: 441222
Gary Koh *(CEO)*

CHA BIO&DISOTECH CO., LTD.

Vision building 606-16 Yoksam-dong
Gangnam-Gu, Seoul, Korea (South)
Tel.: (82) 2 3468 3589
Fax: (82) 2 3468 3592
E-Mail: chabio@chamc.co.kr
Web Site: www.chabio.com
Year Founded: 2000
085660—(KRS)
Business Description:
Pharmaceutical Product Mfr
S.I.C.: 2834
N.A.I.C.S.: 325412
Personnel:
Won S. Yang *(CEO)*

CHAARAT GOLD HOLDINGS LIMITED

6 Conduit Street
London, W1S 2XE, United Kingdom
Tel.: (44) 2074992612
Fax: (44) 5601264433
E-Mail: info@chaarat.com
Web Site: www.chaarat.com
CGH—(LSE)
Rev.: $1,075,948
Assets: $80,034,302
Liabilities: $2,979,510
Net Worth: $77,054,792
Earnings: ($12,368,049)
Emp.: 471
Fiscal Year-end: 12/31/12
Business Description:
Gold Exploration & Mining Services
S.I.C.: 1041
N.A.I.C.S.: 212221
Personnel:
Dekel Golan *(CEO)*
Linda Naylor *(Fin Dir & Sec)*
David McNee *(COO)*
Board of Directors:
Christopher Palmer-Tomkinson
Marcel DeGuire
Dekel Golan
Linda Naylor
Alexander Novak
Richard Anthony Rae
Robert Weinberg
Legal Counsel:
Watson, Farley & Williams
15 Appold Street
London, EC2A 2HB, United Kingdom

Maclay Murray & Spens
One London Wall
London, EC2Y 5AB, United Kingdom

Kalikova & Associates
71 Erkindik Boulevard
Bishkek, Kyrgyzstan

Non-U.S. Subsidiary:

Chaarat Operating Company GmbH (1)
19 Razzakov Street Business Centre
Rossiya 15th Floor
720040 Bishkek, Kyrgyzstan
Tel.: (996) 312 398 039
Gold Ore Mining Services
S.I.C.: 1041
N.A.I.C.S.: 212221

CHAGALA GROUP LIMITED

23 Baisheshek str
Almaty, 050040, Kazakhstan
Tel.: (7) 7272980131
Fax: (7) 7272632823
E-Mail: reservation.almaty@chagalagroup.kz
Web Site: www.chagalagroup.com
Year Founded: 1994
CHGG—(LSE)
Rev.: $31,996,000
Assets: $154,974,000
Liabilities: $44,887,000
Net Worth: $110,087,000
Earnings: ($25,178,000)
Emp.: 650
Fiscal Year-end: 12/31/12
Business Description:
Commercial Properties Development Services
S.I.C.: 6531
N.A.I.C.S.: 531390
Personnel:
Timothy Laird Abson *(Chm)*
Francisco Parrilla *(CEO)*
Margarita Kapustyanskaya *(CFO)*
Board of Directors:
Timothy Laird Abson
Javier del Ser
Baltabek Kuandykov
Edmund Limerick
Mark Lockwood
Francisco Parrilla

Subsidiary:

Chagala Management LLP (1)
23 Baishehek Str
Almaty, 050040, Kazakhstan
Tel.: (7) 7272980131
Fax: (7) 7272632823
Web Site: www.chagalagroup.com
Shopping Mall Management Services
S.I.C.: 6512
N.A.I.C.S.: 531120

Non-U.S. Subsidiaries:

Chagala Cooperatief U.A. (1)
Johannes Vermeerplein 11
1071 DV Amsterdam, Netherlands
Tel.: (31) 20 6717452
Oil & Gas Exploration Services
S.I.C.: 1389
N.A.I.C.S.: 213112

Chagala International Holding B.V. (1)
Johannes Vermeerplein 11
1071 DV Amsterdam, Netherlands
Tel.: (31) 206717452
Investment Management Services
S.I.C.: 6211
N.A.I.C.S.: 523999

CHAI CHA NA MINING INC.

3045 Southcreek Road Unit 11
Mississauga, ON, L4X 2E9, Canada
Tel.: (905) 624-2266
Fax: (905) 624-2267
E-Mail: info@chaichanamining.com
Web Site: www.chaichanamining.com
Year Founded: 2007
CNN—(CNSX)
Sales Range: Less than $1 Million
Business Description:
Gold Mining Services
S.I.C.: 1041
N.A.I.C.S.: 212221
Personnel:
Frederick Fisher *(Pres & CEO)*
Thomas Murdoch *(CFO)*
Board of Directors:
Isabel Alves
Peter Ball
Frederick Fisher
Thomas Murdoch

CHAI WATANA TANNERY GROUP PUBLIC COMPANY LIMITED

176 1 1480 MOO 1 Sukhumvit Road
KM 30 Taiban Muang
Samut Prakan, 10280, Thailand
Tel.: (66) 23892510
Fax: (66) 23892519
Web Site: www.cwt.co.th

Year Founded: 1972
CWT—(THA)
Rev.: $44,543,948
Assets: $53,759,720
Liabilities: $27,465,433
Net Worth: $26,294,287
Earnings: $2,847,524
Fiscal Year-end: 12/31/12
Business Description:
Leather Mfr
S.I.C.: 3199
N.A.I.C.S.: 316998
Personnel:
Boonchai Chaiteerath *(Chm)*

CHAILEASE HOLDING COMPANY LIMITED

No 362 Rueiguang Rd
Neihu District, Taipei, Taiwan
Tel.: (886) 2 8752 6388
Fax: (886) 2 8752 6280
E-Mail: prd@chailease.com.tw
Web Site: www.chaileaseholding.com
5871—(TAI)
Business Description:
Financial Services
S.I.C.: 6159
N.A.I.C.S.: 522294
Personnel:
Andre J.L. Koo *(Exec Chm)*
Subsidiaries:

Chailease Finance Co., Ltd. **(1)**
8-12th Floor 362 Rueiguang Road Neihu Dist
Nei-Hu District, Taipei, 11492, Taiwan TW
Tel.: (886) 287526388
Fax: (886) 287526286
E-Mail: service@chailease.com.tw
Web Site: www.chailease.com.tw
Emp.: 600
Financial Support Services
S.I.C.: 6159
N.A.I.C.S.: 522298
Albert F.L. Chen *(Chm)*
Simon Hou *(Pres)*
Tiffany Jeng *(CFO)*
Janny Cheng *(Chief HR Officer)*
Ron Lee *(Chief Risk Officer)*

Fina Finance & Trading Co., Ltd. **(1)**
5F No 362 Ruiguang Road
Neihu District, Taipei, Taiwan
Tel.: (886) 2 8797 6168
Fax: (886) 2 2799 6828
E-Mail: finatrade@chailease.com.tw
Web Site: www.finatrade.com.tw
Emp.: 100
Equipment & Machinery Leasing Services
S.I.C.: 7359
N.A.I.C.S.: 532420
Albert Chen *(Pres)*

U.S. Subsidiary:

Grand Pacific Financial Corp. **(1)**
141-07 20th Ave Ste 401
Whitestone, NY 11357
Tel.: (718) 717-7000
Fax: (718) 717-7007
Web Site: www.gpusa.com
Investment Banking Services
S.I.C.: 6211
N.A.I.C.S.: 523110

Non-U.S. Subsidiaries:

Chailease Finance (B.V.I.) Company, Ltd **(1)**
Palm Grove House
Road Town, Tortola, Virgin Islands (British)
Tel.: (284) 494 2616
Fax: (284) 494 2704
Financial Leasing Services
S.I.C.: 6211
N.A.I.C.S.: 523999

Chailease International Finance Corporation **(1)**
No 8 Xingyi Road
Changning District, Shanghai, 200336, China
Tel.: (86) 2152080101
Fax: (86) 2152081838
Web Site: www.chailease.com.cn
Equipment Leasing Services
S.I.C.: 6141
N.A.I.C.S.: 522220
Ken Chen *(Pres)*

CHAIN REACTION CYCLES LTD.

Kilbride Road Doagh
Ballyclare, BT39 0QA, United Kingdom
Tel.: (44) 28 9335 2976
Fax: (44) 28 9334 9461
Web Site: www.chainreactioncycles.com
Year Founded: 1985
Sales Range: $200-249.9 Million
Emp.: 365
Business Description:
Electronic Shopping Services
S.I.C.: 5961
N.A.I.C.S.: 454111
Personnel:
Chris Watson *(Mng Dir)*

CHAIRMAN'S BRANDS CORPORATION

77 Progress Ave
Toronto, ON, M1P 2Y7, Canada
Tel.: (416) 288-8515
Fax: (416) 288-8895
E-Mail: info@chairmansbrands.com
Web Site: www.chairmansbrands.com
Year Founded: 1982
Emp.: 75
Business Description:
Fastfood Restaurant Services
S.I.C.: 5812
N.A.I.C.S.: 722513
Personnel:
Tom Michalopoulos *(Pres & CEO)*
Subsidiaries:

241 Pizza (2006) Ltd. **(1)**
77 Progress Avenue
Toronto, ON, M1P 2Y7, Canada
Tel.: (416) 646-0987
Fax: (416) 646-2204
Toll Free: (877) 241-0241
E-Mail: info@coffeetime.ca
Web Site: www.241pizza.com
Emp.: 50
Fastfood Restaurant Services
S.I.C.: 5812
N.A.I.C.S.: 722513
Tom Michalopoulos *(Pres)*

Coffee Time Donuts Incorporated **(1)**
77 Progress Avenue
Toronto, ON, M1P 2Y7, Canada
Tel.: (416) 288-8515
Fax: (416) 288-8895
E-Mail: info@coffeetime.ca
Web Site: www.coffeetime.ca
Emp.: 40
Fastfood Restaurant Services
S.I.C.: 5812
N.A.I.C.S.: 722513
Dan Lepidas *(Exec VP)*

Robins Donuts **(1)**
77 Progress Avenue
Toronto, ON, M1P 2Y7, Canada
Tel.: (416) 646-0987
Fax: (416) 646-2204
E-Mail: info@coffeetime.ca
Web Site: www.robinsdonuts.com
Fastfood Restaurant Services
S.I.C.: 5812
N.A.I.C.S.: 722513
Dan Lepidas *(VP)*

CHALICE GOLD MINES LIMITED

Level 2 1292 Hay Street
West Perth, WA, 6005, Australia
Mailing Address:
GPO Box 2890
Perth, WA, 6001, Australia
Tel.: (61) 893223960
Fax: (61) 893225800
E-Mail: info@chalicegold.com
Web Site: www.chalicegold.com
CHN—(ASX)
Sales Range: Less than $1 Million
Emp.: 39
Business Description:
Mineral Exploration
S.I.C.: 1481
N.A.I.C.S.: 213115
Personnel:
Timothy Rupert Barr Goyder *(Chm)*
William B. Bent *(Mng Dir)*
Richard K. Hacker *(CFO & Co-Sec)*
Leanne Forgione *(Co-Sec & Mgr-Fin)*
Board of Directors:
Timothy Rupert Barr Goyder
William B. Bent
Douglas Alan Jones
Anthony W. Kiernan
Stephen Paul Quin

Computershare Investor Services
100 University Avenue 9th Floor
Toronto, ON, Canada

CHALLAND PIPELINE LTD

Highway 11 South
PO Box 1807
Rocky Mountain House, AB, T4T 1B4, Canada
Tel.: (403) 845-2469
Fax: (403) 845-4844
E-Mail: info@challand.ca
Web Site: www.challand.ca
Year Founded: 1974
Rev.: $39,610,513
Emp.: 250
Business Description:
Pipeline Construction
S.I.C.: 1629
N.A.I.C.S.: 237120
Personnel:
Clint Challand *(Mgr-HR)*

CHALLENGER DEEP RESOURCES CORP.

1321 Frontanac Avenue SW
Calgary, AB, T2T 1C1, Canada
Tel.: (403) 537-0067
Year Founded: 2007
CDE—(TSXV)
Int. Income: $2,503
Assets: $2,443,999
Liabilities: $121,594
Net Worth: $2,322,405
Earnings: ($1,802,458)
Fiscal Year-end: 12/31/12
Business Description:
Coal Exploration Services
S.I.C.: 1241
N.A.I.C.S.: 213113
Personnel:
Ranjeet Sundher *(Pres & CEO)*
Darold H. Parken *(CFO)*
Board of Directors:
J. Garry Clark
Leo R. Kelly
Paul McKenzie
Darold H. Parken
Terence K. Shaunessy
Ranjeet Sundher
Transfer Agent:
Olympia Trust Company
Suite 1003-750 West Pender Street
Vancouver, BC, Canada

CHALLENGER DEVELOPMENT CORP.

3467 Commercial St
Vancouver, BC, Canada V5N 4E8
Tel.: (604) 668-5972
Fax: (604) 871-9926
E-Mail: info@challenger-development.com
Web Site: www.challenger-development.com
Year Founded: 1990
CDQ—(TSXV)
Business Description:
Mineral Exploration Services
S.I.C.: 1081
N.A.I.C.S.: 213114
Personnel:
Simon Tam *(Pres & CEO)*
Simon Ma *(CFO)*
Board of Directors:
Tai Chen
Simon Tam
Craig Walker
Legal Counsel:
Fang & Associates
3rd Floor 578 Seymour Street
Vancouver, BC, Canada V6B 3K1
Transfer Agent:
Computershare Investor Services Inc.
100 University Ave 9th Floor
Toronto, ON, Canada

CHALLENGER DIVERSIFIED PROPERTY GROUP

(See Under Challenger Limited)

CHALLENGER ENERGY LIMITED

Level 17 500 Collins Street
Melbourne, VIC, 3000, Australia
Tel.: (61) 3 9614 0600
Fax: (61) 3 9614 0550
E-Mail: admin@challengerenergy.com.au
Web Site: www.challengerenergy.com.au
CEL—(ASX)
Rev.: $92,585
Assets: $5,485,063
Liabilities: $235,547
Net Worth: $5,249,516
Earnings: ($8,501,558)
Emp.: 1
Fiscal Year-end: 06/30/13
Business Description:
Oil & Gas Exploration Services
S.I.C.: 1311
N.A.I.C.S.: 211111
Personnel:
Robert A. Willes *(Mng Dir)*
Adrien Wing *(Sec)*
Board of Directors:
Michael John Fry
Paul Bilston
Bill Bloking
Robert A. Willes

CHALLENGER GEOMATICS LTD.

Suite 200 9945 50th Street
Edmonton, AB, T6A 0L4, Canada
Tel.: (780) 424-5511
Fax: (780) 424-3837
Toll Free: (888) 424-5512
E-Mail: edmonton@challengergeomatics.com
Web Site: www.challengergeomatics.com
Year Founded: 1984
Rev.: $14,432,862
Emp.: 180
Business Description:
Oil & Gas Pipeline Construction Services
S.I.C.: 1623
N.A.I.C.S.: 237120

Challenger Geomatics Ltd.—(Continued)

Personnel:
David R. Thomson *(Pres)*

CHALLENGER LIMITED
Level 15 255 Pitt Street
Sydney, NSW, 2000, Australia
Tel.: (61) 299947000
Fax: (61) 299947777
Web Site: www.challenger.com.au
CGF—(ASX)
Rev.: $1,665,692,640
Assets: $18,533,540,080
Liabilities: $16,142,754,260
Net Worth: $2,390,785,820
Earnings: $480,720,730
Emp.: 487
Fiscal Year-end: 06/30/13
Business Description:
Financial & Insurance Services
S.I.C.: 6726
N.A.I.C.S.: 525990
Personnel:
Peter L. Polson *(Chm)*
Brian Benari *(CEO & Mng Dir)*
Andrew Tobin *(CFO)*
Richard Willis *(Chief Risk Officer)*
Richard Howes *(CEO-Life)*
Paul Rogan *(CEO-Distr, Product & Mktg)*
Robert Woods *(CEO-Funds Mgmt)*
Michael Vardanega *(Gen Counsel & Co-Sec)*
Andrew Brown *(Co-Sec)*
Board of Directors:
Peter L. Polson
Brian Benari
Graham A. Cubbin
Steven Gregg
Jonathan H. Grunzweig
Russell R. Hooper
Brenda M. Shanahan
JoAnne Stephenson
Leon Zwier

Subsidiaries:

Challenger Group Holdings Limited **(1)**
255 Pitt Level 15
Sydney, NSW, Australia (100%)
Tel.: (61) 299947000
Fax: (61) 299947777
E-Mail: info@challenger.com.au
Web Site: www.challengergroup.com
Emp.: 500
Miscellaneous Financial Investment Activities
S.I.C.: 6211
N.A.I.C.S.: 523999
Brian Benari *(CEO)*

Challenger Group Services Pty Ltd **(1)**
Level 15 255 Pitt Street
Sydney, NSW, Australia (100%)
Tel.: (61) 299947000
Fax: (61) 299947777
E-Mail: reception1@challenger.com.au
Web Site: www.challengergroup.com
Emp.: 450
Other Management Consulting Services
S.I.C.: 8748
N.A.I.C.S.: 541618
Dominic Stevens *(CEO)*
Brian Benari *(CFO)*

Challenger International Nominees Ltd **(1)**
255 Pitt Level 15
Sydney, NSW, 2001, Australia (100%)
Tel.: (61) 299947000
Fax: (61) 299947777
E-Mail: info@challengergroup.au
Web Site: www.challengergroup.au
Emp.: 475
Other Management Consulting Services
S.I.C.: 8748
N.A.I.C.S.: 541618
Dominic Stevens *(CEO)*

Challenger Life Holdings Pty Limited **(1)**
255 Pitt Level 15
Sydney, NSW, 2001, Australia (100%)
Tel.: (61) 299947000
Fax: (61) 299947777
E-Mail: info@challenger.com.au
Web Site: www.challenger.com.au
Emp.: 500
Other Holding Companies Offices
S.I.C.: 6719
N.A.I.C.S.: 551112
Brian Benari *(CEO)*

Challenger Managed Investments Ltd **(1)**
255 Pitt Level 15
2000 Sydney, NSW, Australia (100%)
Tel.: (61) 299947000
Fax: (61) 299947777
E-Mail: info@challenger.com.au
Web Site: www.challenger.com.au/about/OtherOffices.asp
Emp.: 35
Miscellaneous Financial Investment Activities
S.I.C.: 6211
N.A.I.C.S.: 523999
Golinic Spevens *(CEO)*

Challenger Management Services Limited **(1)**
255 Pitt Level 15
Sydney, NSW, Australia (100%)
Tel.: (61) 299947000
Fax: (61) 299947777
E-Mail: insi@challenger.com.au
Web Site: www.challenger.com.au/about/ContactUs.asp
Emp.: 400
Miscellaneous Financial Investment Activities
S.I.C.: 6211
N.A.I.C.S.: 523999
Steven Dominics *(CEO)*

Challenger Portfolio Management Limited **(1)**
255 Pitt Level 15
Sydney, NSW, 2000, Australia (100%)
Tel.: (61) 299947000
Fax: (61) 299947777
E-Mail: info@challenger.com.au
Web Site: www.challenger.com.au
Emp.: 500
Other Management Consulting Services
S.I.C.: 8748
N.A.I.C.S.: 541618
Brian Benari *(CEO)*

Challenger Property Asset Management Pty Limited **(1)**
255 Pitt Level 15
Sydney, NSW, Australia (100%)
Tel.: (61) 299947000
Fax: (61) 299947777
E-Mail: reception1@challenger.com.au
Web Site: www.challengergroup.com
Emp.: 60
Management Services
S.I.C.: 4959
N.A.I.C.S.: 562998
Dominic Steven *(CEO)*
Trevor Hardie *(Mng Dir)*

Endowment Warrants Limited **(1)**
255 Pitt Level 15
Sydney, NSW, 2000, Australia (100%)
Tel.: (61) 299947000
Fax: (61) 299947777
E-Mail: info@challenger.com
Business Consulting Services
S.I.C.: 7389
N.A.I.C.S.: 561499
Mominic Stevens *(CEO)*

Affiliate:

Challenger Diversified Property Group **(1)**
Level 15 255 Pitt Street
Sydney, NSW, 2000, Australia
Tel.: (61) 299947000
Fax: (61) 299947777
E-Mail:
Web Site: www.challenger.com.au/listed/cdi/CDI.asp
CDI—(ASX)
Sales Range: $50-74.9 Million
Emp.: 837
Retail & Industrial Real Estate Investment Trust
S.I.C.: 6726
N.A.I.C.S.: 525990
Michael Cole *(Chm)*
Robert Woods *(CEO-Funds Mgmt)*

Non-U.S. Subsidiary:

Challenger Limited **(1)**
Level 19 Heron Tower 110 Bishopsgate
London, EC2N 4AY, United Kingdom (100%)
Tel.: (44) 207 976 3300
Fax: (44) 207 976 3301
Web Site: www.challenger.com.au
Emp.: 15
Business Services
S.I.C.: 7389
N.A.I.C.S.: 561499

CHALLENGER MOTOR FREIGHT INC.
300 Maple Grove Rd
Cambridge, ON, N3E 1B7, Canada
Tel.: (519) 653-6226
Fax: (519) 653-9810
Toll Free: (800) 265-6358
E-Mail: info1@challenger.com
Web Site: www.challenger.com
Year Founded: 1975
Sales Range: $150-199.9 Million
Emp.: 1,300
Business Description:
Trucking Operator
S.I.C.: 4212
N.A.I.C.S.: 484110
Personnel:
Daniel Einwechter *(Founder, Chm, Pres & CEO)*
Enno Jakobson *(Exec VP)*

CHALLENGER TECHNOLOGIES LTD.
1 Ubi Link Challenger TecHub
Singapore, 408553, Singapore
Tel.: (65) 6318 9800
Fax: (65) 63189801
E-Mail: ir@challenger.sg
Web Site: www.challengerasia.com
Year Founded: 1984
573—(SES)
Rev.: $273,071,057
Assets: $73,082,526
Liabilities: $31,443,923
Net Worth: $41,638,604
Earnings: $13,247,984
Emp.: 400,000
Fiscal Year-end: 12/31/12
Business Description:
IT Products Retailer
S.I.C.: 5946
N.A.I.C.S.: 443142
Personnel:
Leong Thye Loo *(CEO)*
Tan Wee Ko *(CFO)*
Huat Ben Tan *(COO)*
Yoon Siong Woon *(CIO)*
Foon Yeow Chia *(Sec)*
Board of Directors:
Wilson Boon Chuan Ho
Leong Thye Loo
Kian Teck Ng
Max Chee Weng Ng
Chay Boon Tan
Han Beng Tan
Transfer Agent:
Boardroom Corporate & Advisory Services Pte. Ltd.
50 Raffles Place 32-01 Singapore Land Tower
Singapore, Singapore

Subsidiary:

CBD eVision Pte Ltd **(1)**
1 Ubi Link 03-00
Singapore, 408553, Singapore
Tel.: (65) 62888233
Fax: (65) 62832828
E-Mail: johnny@cbd-evision.com
Web Site: www.cbd-evision.com
Emp.: 6
LED Technology Mfr
S.I.C.: 3674
N.A.I.C.S.: 334413
Kang Whye Chia *(Gen Mgr)*

Non-U.S. Subsidiary:

Challenger Technologies (M) Sdn Bhd **(1)**
L4 16 4th Fl Mines Shopping Fair Jalan Dulang Mines Resort City
Mines Resort City, Seri Kembangan, 43300, Malaysia
Tel.: (60) 389469000
Fax: (60) 389469009
E-Mail: enquiry@challenger.my
Web Site: www.challenger.my
Emp.: 50
Software Services
S.I.C.: 7372
N.A.I.C.S.: 511210
Ng Gak Seng *(Gen Mgr)*

CHALMERS LIMITED
20-28 Cawley Road
PO Box 50
Yarraville, VIC, 3013, Australia
Tel.: (61) 3 9316 2011
Fax: (61) 3 9316 2066
E-Mail: enquiries@vic.chalmers.net.au
Web Site: www.chalmers.net.au
Year Founded: 1882
CHR—(ASX)
Rev.: $62,809,503
Assets: $54,457,800
Liabilities: $19,345,157
Net Worth: $35,112,643
Earnings: $1,759,734
Emp.: 176
Fiscal Year-end: 06/30/13
Business Description:
Container Handling, Warehousing, Distribution & Transport Services
S.I.C.: 4225
N.A.I.C.S.: 493110
Personnel:
Graeme F. Birch *(CEO)*
John P. Fedorko *(CFO & Sec)*
Board of Directors:
Andrew J. Murrowood
Graeme F. Birch
John Carew
Gary W. Chalmers
Graham D. Mulligan
John Wilson

Subsidiaries:

Chalmers (Australia) Pty. Ltd **(1)**
20-28 Cawley Rd
Yarraville, VIC, 3013, Australia
Tel.: (61) 393162011
Fax: (61) 93162066
E-Mail: admin@vic.chalmers.net.au
Web Site: www.chalmers.net.au
Emp.: 20
Transport & Logistics Services
S.I.C.: 4412
N.A.I.C.S.: 483111
Martin Filmer *(Mgr)*

Chalmers Industries (Brisbane) Pty. Ltd **(1)**
Whimbrel St
Brisbane, 4178, Australia
Tel.: (61) 738956000
Fax: (61) 738956060
E-Mail: reception@qld.chalmers.net.au
Emp.: 150
Water Transportation Services
S.I.C.: 4449
N.A.I.C.S.: 483211
John Cirew *(Gen Mgr)*

Chalmers Industries Pty. Ltd **(1)**
20-28 Cawley Rd
Yarraville, 3013, Australia
Tel.: (61) 393162011

Fax: (61) 393162066
Web Site: www.chalmers.net.au/
Water Transportation Services
S.I.C.: 4449
N.A.I.C.S.: 483211

CHALODIS SAS

Espace Layon 3 rue Laffon de Ladebat
49290 Chalonnes-sur-Loire, France
Tel.: (33) 241741941
Year Founded: 1986
Sales Range: $10-24.9 Million
Emp.: 49
Business Description:
Grocery Stores
S.I.C.: 5411
N.A.I.C.S.: 445110
Personnel:
Dominique Biron *(Pres)*

CHAM PAPER GROUP HOLDING AG

Fabrikstrasse
6330 Cham, Switzerland
Tel.: (41) 41 7853333
Fax: (41) 41 7853150
E-Mail: mail.cham@cham-group.com
Web Site: www.cham-group.com
CPGN—(SWX)
Rev.: $301,925,739
Assets: $267,678,915
Liabilities: $158,833,811
Net Worth: $108,845,105
Earnings: ($1,331,881)
Emp.: 545
Fiscal Year-end: 12/31/12
Business Description:
Holding Company; Specialty Coated Papers Developer, Mfr & Distr
S.I.C.: 6719
N.A.I.C.S.: 551112
Personnel:
Philipp Buhofer *(Chm)*
Felix A. Thoni *(Vice Chm)*
Board of Directors:
Philipp Buhofer
Niklaus Peter Nuesch
Peter J. Schmid
Felix A. Thoni
Urs Ziegler

Subsidiary:

Cham Paper Group AG (1)
Fabrikstrasse
CH-6330 Cham, Switzerland CH
Tel.: (41) 41 785 3333 (100%)
Fax: (41) 41 785 3150
E-Mail: mail.cham@cham-group.com
Web Site: www.cham-group.com
Holding Company
S.I.C.: 6719
N.A.I.C.S.: 551112

Subsidiaries:

Cham Paper Group Immobilien AG (2)
Fabrikstrasse
CH-6330 Cham, Switzerland CH
Tel.: (41) 41 785 3333 (100%)
Fax: (41) 41 785 3150
E-Mail: mail.cham@cham-group.com
Web Site: www.champaper.ch
Industrial Real Estate Investment & Development
S.I.C.: 6531
N.A.I.C.S.: 531390

Cham Paper Group Management AG (2)
Fabrikstrasse
Cham, 6330, Switzerland CH
Tel.: (41) 41 785 3333 (100%)
Fax: (41) 7853150
E-Mail: champaper.info@cham-group.com
Web Site: www.homeepaper.com
Emp.: 360
Product Logistics & Technical Support Services
S.I.C.: 7389
N.A.I.C.S.: 541990
Peter Muller *(Mng Dir)*

Cham Paper Group Schweiz AG (2)
Fabrikstrasse
CH-6330 Cham, Switzerland CH
Tel.: (41) 41 785 3333 (100%)
Fax: (41) 41 785 3150
E-Mail: mail.cham@cham-group.com
Web Site: www.champaper.ch
Emp.: 360
Coated Specialty Papers Mfr & Distr
S.I.C.: 2621
N.A.I.C.S.: 322121
Peter Muller *(Mng Dir)*

Industrieverwaltungsgesellschaft Cham AG (2)
Fabrikstrasse
Cham, ZG, 6330, Switzerland CH
Tel.: (41) 417 853333
Fax: (41) 417 853150
E-Mail: mail.cham@cham-group.com
Emp.: 35
Intellectual Property Administrative Services
S.I.C.: 6794
N.A.I.C.S.: 533110
Peter Muller *(Mng Dir)*

Non-U.S. Subsidiaries:

Cham Paper Group Italia S.p.A. (2)
Via Roma 67
Carmignano Di Brenta Padova, Padua, 35010, Italy IT
Tel.: (39) 049 9423 600 (100%)
Fax: (39) 049 9423 700
E-Mail: info@cham-group.com
Web Site: www.champaper.com
Sales Range: $200-249.9 Million
Emp.: 300
Specialty Coated Paper Mfr & Distr
S.I.C.: 2671
N.A.I.C.S.: 322220
Marcello Di Giacomo *(Mng Dir)*

Plant:

Cham Paper Group Italia S.p.A. - Condino Mill (3)
Via Roma 153
38083 Condino, TN, Italy
Tel.: (39) 0465 622 511
Fax: (39) 0465 622 540
E-Mail: mail.condino@cham-group.com
Web Site: www.champaper.ch
Specialty Coated Paper Mill
S.I.C.: 2621
N.A.I.C.S.: 322121
Gerold Zuegg *(Plant Mgr)*

CHAMAN LAL SETIA EXPORT LTD.

408 Krishna Apra Business Square
Netaji Subhash Place Pitampura
Delhi, 110034, India
Tel.: (91) 11 47041408
Fax: (91) 11 47041409
E-Mail: maharanirice@airtelmail.in
Web Site: www.maharanirice.com
530307—(BOM)
Sales Range: $10-24.9 Million
Business Description:
Basmati Rice Mfr & Distr
S.I.C.: 2044
N.A.I.C.S.: 311212
Personnel:
Chaman Lal Setia *(Chm & Mng Dir)*
Sankesh Setia *(CEO-Sls & Mktg)*
Board of Directors:
Chaman Lal Setia
Rajeev Setia
Vijay Setia

CHAMARRE SCA

1 rue Mehul
75002 Paris, France
Tel.: (33) 140200470
Fax: (33) 140200471
E-Mail: info@chamarre.com
Web Site: www.chamarre.com
MLCHA—(EUR)
Sales Range: $10-24.9 Million
Emp.: 10
Business Description:
Wine Producer & Marketer
S.I.C.: 2084
N.A.I.C.S.: 312130
Personnel:
Pascal Renaudat *(Pres)*
Paul Bougnoux *(CFO)*

CHAMBAL BREWERIES & DISTILLERIES LIMITED

A/7 Shopping Centre
Kota, Rajasthan, India
Tel.: (91) 744 2362346
E-Mail: chambalbreweries@gmail.com
Web Site: www.chambalkota.in
Year Founded: 1985
512301—(BOM)
Rev.: $838,231
Assets: $2,736,973
Liabilities: $3,907
Net Worth: $2,733,066
Earnings: $2,062
Fiscal Year-end: 03/31/13
Business Description:
Beer & Liquor Whslr
S.I.C.: 5181
N.A.I.C.S.: 424810
Personnel:
Parasram Jhamnani *(CEO, Mng Dir & Compliance Officer)*
Vinod Jhamnani *(CFO)*
Board of Directors:
Parasram Jhamnani
Anupam Garg
Raj Kumar Jain
Gajraj Singh
Transfer Agent:
Adroit Corporate Services Pvt. Ltd
19/20 Jaferbhoy Industrial Estate 1st Floor
Makwana Road Marol Naka
Andheri East, Mumbai, 400 059, India

CHAMBERLIN PLC

Chuckery Road
Walsall, W Midlands, WS1 2DU, United Kingdom
Tel.: (44) 1922707100
Fax: (44) 1922638370
E-Mail: plc@chamberlin.co.uk
Web Site: www.chamberlin.co.uk
Year Founded: 1890
CMH—(LSE)
Rev.: $66,641,300
Assets: $33,765,220
Liabilities: $20,668,168
Net Worth: $13,097,052
Earnings: $1,252,377
Emp.: 441
Fiscal Year-end: 03/31/13
Business Description:
Holding Company; Metal Castings & Engineered Products Mfr
S.I.C.: 6719
N.A.I.C.S.: 551112
Personnel:
Kevin Nolan *(CEO)*
Board of Directors:
Keith Butler-Wheelhouse
Alan Howarth
Keith Jackson
Legal Counsel:
DLA Piper
Birmingham, United Kingdom
Subsidiaries:

Chamberlin & Hill Castings Limited (1)
Chuckery Road
Walsall, W Midlands, WS1 2DU, United Kingdom UK
Tel.: (44) 1922 721 411
Fax: (44) 1922 638 370
Web Site: www.chcastings.co.uk
Non-Ferrous Die Castings Foundry
S.I.C.: 3364
N.A.I.C.S.: 331523

Exidor Limited (1)
Progress Drive
Cannock, Staffs, WS11 0JE, United Kingdom UK
Tel.: (44) 1543 578 661 (100%)
Fax: (44) 1543 570 050
E-Mail: info@exidor.co.uk
Web Site: www.exidor.co.uk
Sales Range: $10-24.9 Million
Emp.: 40
Emergency Exit Hardware Mfr & Distr
S.I.C.: 3429
N.A.I.C.S.: 332510

Petrel Limited (1)
Fortnum Close
Mackadown Lane, Birmingham, B33 OLB, United Kingdom UK
Tel.: (44) 121 783 7161 (100%)
Fax: (44) 121 783 5717
E-Mail: webenquiries@petrel-ex.co.uk
Web Site: www.petrel-ex.co.uk
Hazardous Area Lighting & Control Equipment Mfr & Distr
S.I.C.: 3646
N.A.I.C.S.: 335122
Peter D. Maclean *(Mng Dir)*

Russell Ductile Castings Limited (1)
Dawes Lane
Scunthorpe, DN1 56UW, United Kingdom UK
Tel.: (44) 1724862152 (100%)
Fax: (44) 1724280461
E-Mail: general@russellcastings.co.uk
Web Site: www.iron-foundries.co.uk
Emp.: 100
Ductile & Gray Iron Castings Foundry
S.I.C.: 3321
N.A.I.C.S.: 331511
John Harwood *(Gen Mgr)*

CHAMBERS & COOK FREIGHT LTD.

European House Perrywell Road
Witton, Birmingham, B6 7AT, United Kingdom
Tel.: (44) 1213561441
Fax: (44) 1213567880
E-Mail: info@ccfreight.com
Web Site: www.ccfreight.com
Year Founded: 1925
Sales Range: $10-24.9 Million
Emp.: 89
Fiscal Year-end: 09/30/12
Business Description:
Freight Transportation & Logistics Services
S.I.C.: 4214
N.A.I.C.S.: 484110
Personnel:
Chris Blackburn *(Dir-Ops)*

CHAMBERS & PARTNERS MEDIA LTD.

39-41 Parker Street
London, WC2B 5PQ, United Kingdom
Tel.: (44) 20 7606 8844
Fax: (44) 20 7831 5662
E-Mail: postmaster@chambersandpartners.co.uk
Web Site: www.chambersandpartners.co.uk
Emp.: 140
Business Description:
Legal Guides Publisher & Researcher
S.I.C.: 2741
N.A.I.C.S.: 511140
Personnel:
Michael Chambers *(Pres & Publr)*

CHAMP PRIVATE EQUITY PTY. LTD.

Level 4 Customs House 31 Alfred Street
Sydney, NSW, 2000, Australia

CHAMP Private Equity Pty. Ltd.—(Continued)

Tel.: (61) 282488888
Fax: (61) 282488877
E-Mail: champ@champequity.com.au
Web Site: www.champequity.com.au
Year Founded: 2000

Business Description:
Private Equity Firm
S.I.C.: 6211
N.A.I.C.S.: 523999

Personnel:
John Haddock *(CEO & Mng Dir)*
Bill Ferris *(Partner)*
Joe Skrzynski *(Partner)*
Cam Buchanan *(Mng Dir)*
Nat Childres *(Mng Dir)*
Ben Sebel *(Mng Dir)*

Holdings:

Accolade Wines Australia Limited (1)
Reynell Road
Reynella, Adelaide, SA, 5161, Australia AU
Tel.: (61) 883922222 (80%)
Fax: (61) 883922122
E-Mail: corporate@accolade-wines.com
Web Site: www.accolade-wines.com
Sales Range: $250-299.9 Million
Emp.: 600
Producer, Marketer & Exporter of Wines
S.I.C.: 2084
N.A.I.C.S.: 312130
Gavin Brockett *(CFO)*
David Cunningham *(CMO)*
Neil Truelove *(CTO)*
Tim Sinclair *(Chief HR Officer)*
Simon Williams *(Chief Supply Chain Officer)*
Jeremy Stevenson *(Gen Counsel)*

Branches:

Accolade Wines Australia Ltd. - Botany (2)
Bldg E Level 2 40 Lord St
Botany, NSW, 2019, Australia
Tel.: (61) 296665855
Fax: (61) 0283368233
Web Site: www.accolade-wines.com
Sales Range: $25-49.9 Million
Emp.: 60
Mfr. of Wine
S.I.C.: 2084
N.A.I.C.S.: 312130
Michael East *(Gen Mgr)*

Accolade Wines Australia Ltd. - Bowen Hills (2)
43 Murray Street
Bowen Hills, QLD, 4006, Australia
Tel.: (61) 732527933
Fax: (61) 732525619
E-Mail:
Web Site: www.accolade-wines.com
Sales Range: $25-49.9 Million
Emp.: 30
Mfr. of Wine
S.I.C.: 2084
N.A.I.C.S.: 312130
Mark Craig *(Mng Dir)*

Accolade Wines Australia Ltd. - Mount Waverley (2)
Unit 4 19 Ketty St
Mount Waverley, VIC, 3170, Australia
Tel.: (61) 395588322
Fax: (61) 395588646
Web Site: www.accolade-wines.com
Sales Range: $1-9.9 Million
Emp.: 20
Mfr. of Wine
S.I.C.: 2084
N.A.I.C.S.: 312130
David Hounsome *(Mgr)*

Units:

Houghton Wines (2)
Dale Rd
Middle Swan, Perth, WA, 6056, Australia
Tel.: (61) 892749540
Fax: (61) 892745372
E-Mail: info@houghton-wines.com.au
Web Site: www.houghton-wines.com.au
Sales Range: $250-299.9 Million
Wine Mfr & Seller
S.I.C.: 2084
N.A.I.C.S.: 312130

Stanley Wine Company (2)
Silver City Hwy
Buronga, NSW, 2739, Australia (100%)
Tel.: (61) 350234341
Fax: (61) 350234344
Web Site: www.stanleywines.com.au
Sales Range: $25-49.9 Million
Emp.: 50
Winery
S.I.C.: 2084
N.A.I.C.S.: 312130
Tony Allen *(Gen Mgr)*

Tintara Winery (2)
Main Rd
McLaren Vale, SA, 5171, Australia (100%)
Tel.: (61) 883294110
Fax: (61) 883294100
Web Site: www.tintara.com.au
Sales Range: $25-49.9 Million
Emp.: 15
Winery
S.I.C.: 2084
N.A.I.C.S.: 312130
Neville Rowe *(Mgr)*

Non-U.S. Subsidiaries:

Accolade Wines Limited (2)
Accolade House The Guildway
Old Portsmouth Road, Guildford, Surrey, GU3 1LR, United Kingdom (100%)
Tel.: (44) 1483 690000
Fax: (44) 1483 690100
Sales Range: $50-74.9 Million
Emp.: 150
Wine Production
S.I.C.: 2084
N.A.I.C.S.: 312130
Troy Christensen *(Pres)*
David Klein *(Sr VP & Treas)*

Affiliate:

Matthew Clark Brands Ltd. (3)
Constellation House The Guildway
Old Portsmouth Road, Guildford, Surrey, GU3 1LR, United Kingdom (50%)
Tel.: (44) 1483690000
Telex: 445565
Fax: (44) 1483690140
Web Site: www.matthewclark.co.uk
Sales Range: $1-4.9 Billion
Emp.: 1,900
Ciders, Perries, Cream Liqueurs, Wines, Mineral Water & Fortified British Wine Mfr Import Export
S.I.C.: 2084
N.A.I.C.S.: 312130
Steve Thompson *(Mng Dir)*

Gerard Lighting Group Limited (1)
142-144 Fullarton Road
PO Box 2369
Rose Park, SA, 5071, Australia
Mailing Address:
PO Box 186
Enfield Plaza, Adelaide, SA, 5085, Australia
Tel.: (61) 8 8122 2300
Fax: (61) 881397325
E-Mail: administration@gerardlighting.com.au
Web Site: www.gerardlighting.com.au
Emp.: 1,045
Lighting Products Mfr
S.I.C.: 3645
N.A.I.C.S.: 335121
Simon Gerard *(CEO & Mng Dir)*
Graham Ellis *(CFO)*
Mark Pearson *(Co-Sec)*
Gary Savage *(Co-Sec)*

Subsidiaries:

Austube Pty Limited (2)
23 Foundry Road
Seven Hills, NSW, 2147, Australia
Tel.: (61) 296749122
Fax: (61) 296749133
E-Mail: sales@austube.com.au
Web Site: www.austube.com.au
Tubular Lighting Systems Mfr
S.I.C.: 3646
N.A.I.C.S.: 335122
Santina Cominguez *(Mgr)*

Crompton Lighting Pty Limited (2)
96-112 Gow St
Padstow, NSW, 2211, Australia
Tel.: (61) 2 9794 9393
Fax: (61) 2 9796 4812
E-Mail: clfeedback@crompton.com.au
Web Site: www.crompton.com.au
Sales Range: $50-74.9 Million
Emp.: 40
Lamps & Light Fittings Distr
S.I.C.: 5065
N.A.I.C.S.: 423690
Margaret Gao *(Mgr-Pur)*

Inlite Pty Limited (2)
44-46 Chippen Street
Chippendale, NSW, 2008, Australia
Tel.: (61) 2 9699 3900
Fax: (61) 2 9699 3800
E-Mail: nsw@inlite.com.au
Web Site: www.inlite.com.au
Emp.: 15
Lighting System Installation & Distr
S.I.C.: 1731
N.A.I.C.S.: 238210
Jarrod Huxtable *(Mgr)*

Lighting Corporation Pty Ltd (2)
12/37 O'Riordan Street
PO Box 7424
Alexandria, NSW, 2015, Australia AU
Tel.: (61) 283060900
Fax: (61) 283060911
Sales Range: $150-199.9 Million
Lighting Fixture Marketer & Distr
S.I.C.: 3645
N.A.I.C.S.: 335121

Moonlighting Pty Limited (2)
351 King Street
Melbourne, VIC, 3003, Australia
Tel.: (61) 392352400
Fax: (61) 392352499
E-Mail: sales@moonlighting.com.au
Web Site: www.moonlighting.com.au
Emp.: 10
Lighting Fixtures Mfr & Distr
S.I.C.: 3645
N.A.I.C.S.: 335121

Pierlite Australia Pty Limited (2)
96-112 Gow Street
PO Box 314
Padstow, NSW, 2211, Australia
Tel.: (61) 297949300
Fax: (61) 297964010
E-Mail: lighting@pierlite.com.au
Web Site: www.pierlite.com.au
Emp.: 500
Lighting Systems Mfr & Distr
S.I.C.: 3645
N.A.I.C.S.: 335121
Geoff Daniow *(Mgr-Bus Dev)*

Sylvania Lighting Australasia Pty Limited (2)
Sylvania Way
Lisarow, NSW, 2250, Australia
Tel.: (61) 243280600
Fax: (61) 243282605
E-Mail: sylvania@sla.net.au
Web Site: www.sla.net.au
Emp.: 100
Lighting Systems Mfr & Distr
S.I.C.: 3645
N.A.I.C.S.: 335121
Sebastian Beier *(Product Mgr)*

Non-U.S. Subsidiary:

Gerard Lighting (NZ) Limited (2)
59 Montgomerie Road
Airport Oaks, Auckland, 2022, New Zealand
Tel.: (64) 9 255 0006
Fax: (64) 508 743 755
E-Mail: sales@gerardlighting.co.nz
Web Site: www.gerardlighting.co.nz
Emp.: 15
Lighting Products Mfr
S.I.C.: 3645
N.A.I.C.S.: 335121

oOh!media Group Limited (1)
Level 2 76 Berry Street
North Sydney, NSW, 2060, Australia AU
Tel.: (61) 299275555
Fax: (61) 299275599
Web Site: www.oohmedia.com.au
Emp.: 129
Holding Company; Out-of-Home Advertising Services
S.I.C.: 6719
N.A.I.C.S.: 551112
John C. Porter *(Chm)*
Brendon Cook *(CEO & Mng Dir)*

Subsidiaries:

oOh!media Pty. Ltd. (2)
Level 2 76 Berry Street
North Sydney, NSW, 2060, Australia AU
Tel.: (61) 2 9927 5555 (100%)
Web Site: www.oohmedia.com.au
Out-of-Home Advertising Services
S.I.C.: 7312
N.A.I.C.S.: 541850
Brendon Cook *(CEO & Mng Dir)*

Sports & Outdoor Media Pty Limited (2)
Level 2 76 Berry St
North Sydney, New South Wales, 2060, Australia
Tel.: (61) 294500945
Fax: (61) 299275599
E-Mail: reception@oohmedia.com.au
Web Site: www.sportsandoutdoor.com.au
Emp.: 1
Billboard Advertising Services
S.I.C.: 7311
N.A.I.C.S.: 541810
Brendon Cook *(CEO)*

Non-U.S. Holdings:

Blue Star Print Group Limited (1)
30 Constellation Drive Mairangi Bay
Auckland, New Zealand (84%)
Tel.: (64) 94770400
Fax: (64) 94770401
E-Mail: enquiries@bluestargroup.co.nz
Web Site: www.bluestargroup.com.au
Sales Range: $400-449.9 Million
Emp.: 12
Printing Services
S.I.C.: 2759
N.A.I.C.S.: 323111
Greg Howell *(CEO)*

Miclyn Express Offshore Limited (1)
3 Harbour Front Place 11-01/04
HarbourFront Tower 2
Singapore, 099254, Singapore (50%)
Tel.: (65) 65456211
Fax: (65) 62756212
E-Mail: corporate@miclynexpressoffshore.com
Web Site: www.miclynexpressoffshore.com
Rev.: $245,338,000
Assets: $672,996,000
Liabilities: $289,571,000
Net Worth: $383,425,000
Earnings: $47,539,000
Emp.: 1,431
Fiscal Year-end: 06/30/13
Offshore Support Vessels
S.I.C.: 4499
N.A.I.C.S.: 488390
Diederik de Boer *(CEO)*
Derek Koh *(CFO)*
Darren Ang *(COO)*
Lawrence Chan *(Sec)*

CHAMPADOR

Avenue Jean Ducourtieux
24530 Champagnac-de-Belair, Dordogne, France
Tel.: (33) 553026363
Fax: (33) 53542093
E-Mail: contact@champador.fr
Web Site: www.champador.com
Sls.: $21,800,000
Emp.: 220

Business Description:
Cookies & Crackers
S.I.C.: 2052
N.A.I.C.S.: 311821

Personnel:
Alain Teot *(Pres)*

CHAMPAGNE ALAIN THIENOT S.A.S.

14 Rue Des Moissons
Reims, 51100, France

Tel.: (33) 326775010
Fax: (33) 326775019
E-Mail: info@thienot.com
Web Site: www.thienot.com
Sales Range: $100-124.9 Million

Business Description:
Winery Services
S.I.C.: 2084
N.A.I.C.S.: 312130

Personnel:
Alain Thienot *(Founder & Pres)*

Subsidiary:

Champagne Canard-Duchene S.A. (1)
1 Rue Edmond Canard
51500 Ludes, France (100%)
Tel.: (33) 326610998
Fax: (33) 326611390
E-Mail: export1@distribucion.com
Web Site: www.canard-duchene.fr
Emp.: 15
Champagne Mfr
S.I.C.: 2084
N.A.I.C.S.: 312130
Alexis Petit Gats *(Mgr)*

CHAMPAGNE HENRIOT

81 Rue Coquebert
51100 Reims, Marne, France
Tel.: (33) 326895300
Fax: (33) 326895310
E-Mail: contact@champagne-henriot.com
Web Site: www.champagne-henriot.com
Sls.: $20,700,000
Emp.: 27

Business Description:
Wines, Brandy & Brandy Spirits
S.I.C.: 2084
N.A.I.C.S.: 312130

Personnel:
Viviane Fastenackels *(Mgr-Personnel)*

Board of Directors:
Genevieve Pelleter

CHAMPAGNE LAURENT-PERRIER

Domaine Laurent Perrier
51150 Tours-sur-Marne, France
Tel.: (33) 326589122
Fax: (33) 326587729
E-Mail: katrin.binje@laurent-perrier.fr
Web Site: www.laurent-perrier.fr
Year Founded: 1812
Sales Range: $250-299.9 Million
Emp.: 200

Business Description:
Champagne Producer
S.I.C.: 2084
N.A.I.C.S.: 312130

Personnel:
Michel Boulaire *(Chm)*

Non-U.S. Subsidiary:

Laurent-Perrier UK Ltd. (1)
66-68 Chapel Street
Marlow, Bucks, SL7 1DE, United Kingdom (100%)
Tel.: (44) 1628475404
Telex: 91750
Fax: (44) 1628471891
E-Mail: enquiries@laurent-perrier.co.uk
Web Site: www.laurent-perrier.co.uk
Emp.: 20
Importer & Exporter of Champagne
S.I.C.: 5182
N.A.I.C.S.: 424820
David Hesketh *(Mng Dir)*

CHAMPAGNE POL ROGER

1 Rue Henri Winston Churchill
BP 199
51206 Epernay, France
Tel.: (33) 326595800
Fax: (33) 326552570
E-Mail: polroger@polroger.fr
Web Site: www.polroger.com
Sls.: $28,100,000
Emp.: 52

Business Description:
Wines, Brandy & Brandy Spirits
S.I.C.: 2084
N.A.I.C.S.: 312130

Personnel:
Patrice Noyelle *(Pres & CEO)*

CHAMPION BEAR RESOURCES LTD.

2005 - 9th Street SW
Calgary, AB, T2T 3C4, Canada
Tel.: (403) 229-9522
Fax: (403) 229-9518
Web Site: www.championbear.com
Year Founded: 1987
CBA—(TSXV)

Business Description:
Mineral Exploration Services
S.I.C.: 1081
N.A.I.C.S.: 213114

Personnel:
Richard D. Kantor *(Chm & Pres)*
Audrey Och *(CFO)*

Board of Directors:
Richard D. Kantor
Rob Foy
David R. Haigh
Marc J. Stachiw

CHAMPION IRON MINES LIMITED

20 Adelaide Street East Suite 301
Toronto, ON, M5C 2T6, Canada
Tel.: (416) 866-2200
Fax: (416) 361-1333
Toll Free: (877) 448-2201
E-Mail: info@championironmines.com
Web Site: www.championironmines.com
Year Founded: 1985
CHM—(OTC TSX)
Rev.: $361,435
Assets: $98,781,324
Liabilities: $2,904,006
Net Worth: $95,877,318
Earnings: ($7,857,065)
Emp.: 5
Fiscal Year-end: 03/31/13

Business Description:
Iron Ore Mining Services
S.I.C.: 1011
N.A.I.C.S.: 212210

Personnel:
Thomas G. Larsen *(Chm, Pres & CEO)*
Miles Nagamatsu *(CFO)*
Jorge Estepa *(Treas, Sec & VP)*
Martin Bourgoin *(Exec VP-Ops)*
Alexander S. Horvath *(Exec VP-Exploration & Project Dev)*
Beat Frei *(Sr VP-Project Fin)*
Jeff Hussey *(Sr VP-Corp Dev)*

Board of Directors:
Thomas G. Larsen
Paul Ankcorn
Harry Burgess
William J. Harding
Alexander S. Horvath
Francis Sauve
Donald A. Sheldon
James Wang

Legal Counsel:
Stikeman Elliott LLP
5300 Commerce Court West 199 Bay Street
Toronto, ON, Canada

Sheldon Huxtable Professional Corporation
180 Dundas Street West Suite1801
Toronto, ON, Canada

McCarthy Tetrault LLP
Suite 2500 1000 De La Gauchetiere Street West
Montreal, QC, Canada

Transfer Agent:
Equity Financial Trust Company
200 University Avenue Suite 400
Toronto, ON, Canada

CHAMPION MICROELECTRONIC CORP.

No 11 YuanQu Road East District
Hsin-chu, 300, Taiwan
Tel.: (886) 3 5679979
Fax: (886) 3 5670701
E-Mail: invest@championmicro.com.tw
Web Site: www.championmicro.com.tw
Year Founded: 1999
3257—(TAI)
Sales Range: $10-24.9 Million
Emp.: 60

Business Description:
Semiconductor Device Mfr
S.I.C.: 3674
N.A.I.C.S.: 334413

Personnel:
David Liu *(Chm)*

U.S. Subsidiary:

Champion Microelectronic (1)
960 Saratoga Ave
San Jose, CA 95129
Tel.: (408) 985-1898
Fax: (408) 985-1683
Web Site: www.champion-micro.com
Emp.: 6
Semiconductor & Related Device Mfr
S.I.C.: 3674
N.A.I.C.S.: 334413
Jeffrey Hwang *(VP-R&D)*

CHAMPION MINERALS INC.

(See Under Champion Iron Mines Limited)

CHAMPION REAL ESTATE INVESTMENT TRUST

Suite 3008 30th Floor Great Eagle Centre 23 Harbour Road
Wanchai, China (Hong Kong)
Tel.: (852) 28791288
Fax: (852) 28271338
E-Mail: info@eam.com.hk
Web Site: www.championreit.com
2778—(HKG OTC)
Sales Range: $250-299.9 Million
Emp.: 643

Business Description:
Real Estate Investment Trust
S.I.C.: 6726
N.A.I.C.S.: 525990

Personnel:
Adrian Ching Ming Lee *(CEO)*
Chi Kwong Kwong *(COO)*
Patrick Choo *(Chief Investment Officer)*

Board of Directors:
Ka Shui Lo
Payson Mou Sing Cha
Christopher Wai Chee Cheng
Shut Kan Ho
Albert Yuk Keung Ip
Adrian Ching Ming Lee
Kai Shui Lo
Abraham Lai Him Shek

Legal Counsel:
Baker & McKenzie
Hong Kong, China (Hong Kong)

Transfer Agent:
Computershare Hong Kong Investor Services Limited
Shops 1712-1716 17th Floor Hopewell Centre
183 Queens Road East
Wanchai, China (Hong Kong)

CHAMPION TECHNOLOGY HOLDINGS LTD

3/F Kantone Centre 1 Ning Foo Street
Chai Wan, China (Hong Kong)
Tel.: (852) 28971111
Fax: (852) 2558 3333
E-Mail: info@kantone.com
Web Site: www.championtechnology.com
0092—(HKG OTC)
Sls.: $574,167,412
Assets: $1,213,339,680
Liabilities: $52,147,122
Net Worth: $1,161,192,558
Earnings: $12,886,489
Emp.: 1,200
Fiscal Year-end: 06/30/13

Business Description:
Software Develpoment
S.I.C.: 7372
N.A.I.C.S.: 511210

Personnel:
Paul Man Lok Kan *(Founder & Chm)*
Leo Kin Leung Kan *(CEO)*
Yat Kwong Lai *(CFO)*
Stephen Gentry *(CEO-Multitone Electronics Plc & Head-Intl Bus-Kantone)*
Jennifer Mei Ha Cheung *(Sec)*
Francis Kan *(Exec VP-Sys Dev)*
Kin Leoung Fung *(Sr VP-Microelectronics)*
Iris Kin Hing Koo *(Sr VP-Fin)*

Board of Directors:
Paul Man Lok Kan
Frank Bleackley
Shirley Suk Ling Ha
Leo Kin Leung Kan
Francis Gilbert Knight
Yat Kwong Lai
Chi Wah Lee
Terry John Miller

Butterfield Fulcrum Group (Bermuda) Limited
26 Burnaby Street
Hamilton, HM 11, Bermuda

Transfer Agents:
Tricor Secretaries Limited
26th Floor Tesbury Centre 28 Queen's Road East
Wanchai, China (Hong Kong)

Butterfield Fulcrum Group (Bermuda) Limited
26 Burnaby Street
Hamilton, HM 11, Bermuda

Subsidiaries:

Hong Kong IT Alliance Limited (1)
No 1 Ning Foo St
Chai Wan, China (Hong Kong)
Tel.: (852) 28968838
Fax: (852) 28969378
E-Mail: info@italliance.com.hk
Web Site: www.italliance.com.hk
Information Technology Development Services
S.I.C.: 7373
N.A.I.C.S.: 541512
Paul Kan Man-Lok *(Chm)*

Kannet Limited (1)
3 F Kantone Ctr 1 Ning Foo St
Chai Wan, China (Hong Kong)
Tel.: (852) 28971111
Fax: (852) 25583111
E-Mail: info@championtechnology.com
Web Site: www.kannethk.com
News & Entertainment Website Portals

Champion Technology Holdings Ltd—(Continued)

S.I.C.: 2741
N.A.I.C.S.: 519130
Walter Wellington *(Pres)*

Kantone Paging Company Limited (1)
3 F Kantone Ctr No 1 Ning Foo St
Chai Wan, China (Hong Kong)
Tel.: (852) 28969399
Fax: (852) 25583103
E-Mail: info@championtechnology.com
Emp.: 100
Pagers Sales & Paging Services
S.I.C.: 5946
N.A.I.C.S.: 443142

New Telecomm Company Limited (1)
9 F Kantone Ctr 1 Ning Foo St
Chai Wan, China (Hong Kong)
Tel.: (852) 28971111
Fax: (852) 25583111
E-Mail: info@championtechnology.com
Web Site: www.championtechnology.com
Emp.: 200
Telecommunications Equipment Sales
S.I.C.: 7359
N.A.I.C.S.: 532490

Y28.COM Limited (1)
3 F Kantone Ctr 1 Ning Foo St
Chai Wan, China (Hong Kong)
Tel.: (852) 28986668
Fax: (852) 28986268
Web Site: www.y28.com
News & Entertainment Website Portals
S.I.C.: 2741
N.A.I.C.S.: 519130
Paul Kan *(Chm)*
Raymond Chung *(Exec Dir & Chief Portal Officer)*

CHAMPIONS (UK) PLC.

Barrington House Leake Road
Costock
Loughborough, Leicestershire, LE12 6XA, United Kingdom
Tel.: (44) 1509 85 29 27
E-Mail: info@championsukplc.com
Web Site: www.championsukplc.com
Year Founded: 2003
Sales Range: $10-24.9 Million
Emp.: 36
Business Description:
Brand Management Agency Services
S.I.C.: 9651
N.A.I.C.S.: 926150
Personnel:
Matthew Hayes *(Mng Dir)*

CHAMPLAIN MOTORS LTD.

1810 Main St W
Moncton, NB, E1E 4S7, Canada
Tel.: (506) 857-1800
Fax: (506) 857-0768
Web Site: www.champlain.nissan.ca
Year Founded: 1971
Rev.: $12,346,183
Emp.: 30
Business Description:
New & Used Car Dealers
S.I.C.: 5511
N.A.I.C.S.: 441110
Personnel:
Terry Gibson *(Gen Mgr)*

CHAMVYLE SA

Avenue De La Gare
64800 Coarraze, Pyrenees Atlantiques, France
Tel.: (33) 559612264
Fax: (33) 559612593
Sls.: $21,700,000
Emp.: 45
Business Description:
Grocery Stores
S.I.C.: 5411
N.A.I.C.S.: 445110
Personnel:
Evelyne Barrau *(Gen Mgr)*

CHANCERY RESOURCES, INC.

1040 South Service Road
Stoney Creek, ON, L8E 6G3, Canada
Tel.: (289) 656-1264
Web Site:
Year Founded: 2006
CCRY—(OTC)
Emp.: 2
Business Description:
Gold Mining & Exploration Services
S.I.C.: 1041
N.A.I.C.S.: 212221
Personnel:
James Cairns *(Pres)*
Juan Restrepo Gutierrez *(COO & Sec)*
Board of Directors:
James Cairns
Jeffrey Fanning
Juan Restrepo Gutierrez
Vincent Higgins
Transfer Agent:
Empire Stock Transfer Inc.
7251 W Lake Mead Blvd Ste 300
Las Vegas, NV 89128

CHANCETON FINANCIAL GROUP LIMITED

Units A 23/F CMA Building 64-66 Connaught Road
Central, China (Hong Kong)
Tel.: (852) 2158 9999
Fax: (852) 2543 9311
Web Site: www.chanceton.com
8020—(HKG)
Rev.: $1,099,428
Assets: $43,144,865
Liabilities: $18,118,893
Net Worth: $25,025,971
Earnings: ($1,182,214)
Emp.: 16
Fiscal Year-end: 03/31/13
Business Description:
Corporate Finance Advisory Services
S.I.C.: 6282
N.A.I.C.S.: 523930
Personnel:
Kam Wah Wong *(Chm, CEO & Compliance Officer)*
Victor Chor Keung Cheung *(Pres)*
Wing Yan Ho *(Sec)*
Board of Directors:
Kam Wah Wong
Chi Kong Chiu
Ling Tak Lau
Man Kit Leung
William Robert Majcher
Ginny Wing Yee Man
Raymond Yan Ming Yau
Transfer Agent:
Union Registrars Limited
18/F Fook Lee Commercial Centre Town Place
33 Lockhart Road
Wanchai, China (Hong Kong)

Subsidiary:

Chanceton Capital Partners Limited (1)
Units A 23/F CMA Building 64-66
Connaught Road
Central, China (Hong Kong)
Tel.: (852) 2158 9999
Fax: (852) 2543 9311
E-Mail: admin@chanceton.com
Web Site: www.chanceton.com
Corporate Financial Advisory Services
S.I.C.: 6282
N.A.I.C.S.: 523930
Kam Wah Wong *(Chm)*

CHANCO INTERNATIONAL GROUP LIMITED

3/F Victory Industrial Building 151-157 Wo Yi Hop Road
Kwai Chung, New Territories, China (Hong Kong)
Tel.: (852) 2424 0392
Fax: (852) 2420 8510
E-Mail: info@chancogroup.com
Web Site: www.chancogroup.com
264—(HKG)
Sls.: $24,185,991
Assets: $39,839,360
Liabilities: $2,645,409
Net Worth: $37,193,951
Earnings: ($331,273)
Emp.: 122
Fiscal Year-end: 03/31/13
Business Description:
Leather Product Mfr & Whslr
S.I.C.: 2399
N.A.I.C.S.: 315990
Personnel:
Edwin King Hong Chan *(Chm & CEO)*
Stanley King Yuen Chan *(Vice Chm)*
Wai Hung Lau *(Sec & Controller-Fin)*
Board of Directors:
Edwin King Hong Chan
Rebecca Wai Po Chan
Stanley King Yuen Chan
Cynthia Sin Ha Chau
David Pui Sheung Fong
Janson Kam Chung Or

Computershare Hong Kong Investor Services Limited
Shops 1712-1716 17th Floor Hopewell Centre
183 Queen's Road East
Hong Kong, China (Hong Kong)

Transfer Agents:
Royal Bank of Canada Trust Company (Cayman) Limited
4th Floor Royal Bank House 24 Shedden Road
Georgetown, Cayman Islands

Computershare Hong Kong Investor Services Limited
Shops 1712-1716 17th Floor Hopewell Centre
183 Queen's Road East
Hong Kong, China (Hong Kong)

CHANDIS

Centre Du Grand Pin
72560 Change, Sarthe, France
Tel.: (33) 243783010
Sls.: $20,900,000
Emp.: 66
Business Description:
Grocery Stores
S.I.C.: 5411
N.A.I.C.S.: 445110
Personnel:
Samuel Chevallier *(Pres)*

CHANDLER CORPORATION

(Formerly Richard Chandler Corporation)
Level 46 UOB Plaza 1 80 Raffles Place
Singapore, 048624, Singapore
Tel.: (65) 6210 5555
Fax: (65) 6210 5556
E-Mail: info@chandlergroup.com
Web Site: www.chandlergroup.com
Year Founded: 1986
Business Description:
Investment Holding Company
S.I.C.: 6719
N.A.I.C.S.: 551112
Personnel:
Richard F. Chandler *(Founder & Chm)*
David Walker *(CEO)*

CHANDLER MACLEOD GROUP LIMITED

Level 8 32 Walker Street
Sydney, NSW, 2060, Australia
Tel.: (61) 289137777
Fax: (61) 289137001
Web Site: www.chandlermacleod.com
Year Founded: 1959
CMG—(ASX)
Rev.: $1,567,223,569
Assets: $392,689,333
Liabilities: $229,253,663
Net Worth: $163,435,669
Earnings: $11,541,258
Emp.: 23,000
Fiscal Year-end: 06/30/13
Business Description:
Human Resources Outsourcing & Recruitment Services
S.I.C.: 8999
N.A.I.C.S.: 541612
Personnel:
Cameron J. C. Judson *(CEO & Mng Dir)*
Owen J. Wilson *(CFO & Co-Sec)*
Morgan H. Sloper *(Chief Legal Officer, Chief Risk Officer & Co-Sec)*
Phil Gray *(CTO & Chief Transformation Officer)*
Anne Simic *(Chief People Officer)*
Greg J. Coolahan *(Legal Counsel & Co-Sec)*
Board of Directors:
Richard A. F. England
Mark H. Carnegie
Jack J. Cowin
Elizabeth A. Crouch
Cameron J. C. Judson
John C. Plummer

Division:

Forstaff Avalon Pty Limited (1)
Bldg 15 Avalon Airport Avalon
Geelong, VIC, 3212, Australia
Tel.: (61) 352279164
Fax: (61) 352279388
E-Mail: enquiries@forstaffaviation.com
Web Site: www.forstaffaviation.com
Emp.: 800
Aviation Personnel Recruitment Services
S.I.C.: 7361
N.A.I.C.S.: 561311
Simon Thorne *(Gen Mgr)*

Subsidiaries:

A.C.N. 112 228 716 Pty Limited (1)
Shop 2 98-100 Henry St
Penrith, New South Wales, 2747, Australia
Tel.: (61) 2 4722 9400
E-Mail: 1252@52.msn.com
Emp.: 4
Employment Placement Services
S.I.C.: 7361
N.A.I.C.S.: 561311
Lisa Malviser *(Mng Dir)*

Chandler Macleod Consultants Pty Limited (1)
Level 8 32 Walker St
Sydney, NSW, 2000, Australia
Tel.: (61) 289137777
Fax: (61) 292902541
Web Site: www.chandlermacleod.com
Emp.: 100
Professional & Management Services
S.I.C.: 8748
N.A.I.C.S.: 541618
Cameron Jusson *(Gen Mgr)*

Chandler Macleod Health Pty Limited (1)
18-363 George St
Sydney, NSW, 2000, Australia
Tel.: (61) 292698647
Fax: (61) 292698877
Web Site: www.chandlermacleod.com
Emp.: 25
Medical Health Care Services
S.I.C.: 8099
N.A.I.C.S.: 621999

Chandler Macleod Medical Pty Ltd (1)
Level 12 2 Park St
Sydney, New South Wales, 2000, Australia
Tel.: (61) 292698729
Fax: (61) 292698877
E-Mail: info@cmmedical.com.au
Web Site: www.cmmedical.com.au
Medical Employment Agency Services
S.I.C.: 7361
N.A.I.C.S.: 561311

Chandler Macleod Services Pty Limited (1)
Level 8 32 Walker St
Sydney, New South Wales, 2060, Australia
Tel.: (61) 289137777
Fax: (61) 289137001
Web Site: www.chandlermacleod.com
Emp.: 100
Recruitment Services
S.I.C.: 7361
N.A.I.C.S.: 561311
E. N. Basser *(Mng Dir)*

Chandler Macleod Technical and Engineering Pty Limited (1)
Level 8 32 Walker St
North Sydney, NSW, 2060, Australia
Tel.: (61) 289137777
Fax: (61) 289137001
Web Site: www.chandlermacleod.com
Emp.: 100
Engineering Services
S.I.C.: 8711
N.A.I.C.S.: 541330
Cameron Judson *(CEO)*

CMHR Pty Limited (1)
Level 12 2 Park St
Sydney, New South Wales, 2000, Australia
Tel.: (61) 292698666
Fax: (61) 292698700
Web Site: www.cmhr.com.au
Emp.: 4
Recruitment Services
S.I.C.: 7361
N.A.I.C.S.: 561311

Diversiti Pty Limited (1)
Level 12 2 Park St
Sydney, New South Wales, 2000, Australia
Tel.: (61) 292698855
Fax: (61) 292698700
Web Site: www.diversiti.com.au
Recruitment Services
S.I.C.: 7361
N.A.I.C.S.: 561311

Human Capital Solutions Pty Limited (1)
Level 6 77 Pacific Hwy
Sydney, NSW, 2060, Australia
Tel.: (61) 299238000
Fax: (61) 1300880289
E-Mail: reception@comots.com.au
Web Site: www.hcsgroup.com.au
Emp.: 2
Consultancy Services
S.I.C.: 8999
N.A.I.C.S.: 541612

Mettle Group Pty Limited (1)
Level 12 2 Park St
Sydney, New South Wales, 2000, Australia
Tel.: (61) 299649511
Fax: (61) 2 9269 8694
E-Mail: sydney@mettle.com.au
Web Site: www.mettle.biz
Emp.: 6
Business Management Consulting Services
S.I.C.: 8748
N.A.I.C.S.: 541618
Ian Richard Basser *(CEO)*
Jeremy Nichols *(Mng Dir)*

Ready Workforce (Parramatta) Pty Limited (1)
Level 1 75 George St
Parramatta, NSW, 2150, Australia
Tel.: (61) 97945888
Fax: (61) 2 9633 8691
Emp.: 10
Recruitment Services
S.I.C.: 7361
N.A.I.C.S.: 561311
Darren Parrott *(Office Mgr)*

Ready Workforce Pty Limited (1)
Level 8 32 Walker St
Sydney, New South Wales, 2060, Australia
Tel.: (61) 289137777
Fax: (61) 89137852
Web Site: www.chandlermacleod.com
Emp.: 300
Recruitment Services
S.I.C.: 7361
N.A.I.C.S.: 561311
Ian Basser *(Mng Dir)*

Recruitment Solutions Limited (1)
Level 13 307 Queen St
Brisbane, Queensland, 4000, Australia
Tel.: (61) 730037755
Fax: (61) 730037789
Web Site: www.chandlermacleod.com
Recruitment Services
S.I.C.: 7361
N.A.I.C.S.: 561311

Recruitment Solutions Pty Limited (1)
Level 8 32 Walker St
Sydney, NSW, 2060, Australia
Tel.: (61) 289137777
Fax: (61) 289137001
Web Site: www.chandlermacleod.com
Emp.: 50
Recruiting Services
S.I.C.: 7361
N.A.I.C.S.: 561311
Jason MacArthur *(Chief Risk Officer)*

Ross Human Directions Limited (1)
Level 11 133 Castlereagh Street
Sydney, NSW, 2000, Australia
Tel.: (61) 282674600
Fax: (61) 282674666
E-Mail: sydney@rossjuliaross.com
Web Site: www.rosshumandirections.com
Sales Range: $300-349.9 Million
Employment Services, Human Resources Management & Consulting Services
S.I.C.: 7361
N.A.I.C.S.: 561311
Fergus Allan McDonald *(Chm)*
Julia Mary Ross *(Deputy Chm & Mng Dir)*
David Andrew Marshall *(CFO & Co-Sec)*
Gregory Joseph Coolahan *(Co-Sec)*

Subsidiaries:

Aurion Corporation Pty Limited (2)
Level 2
555 Coronation Dr, Toowong, Queensland, 4066, Australia AU
Mailing Address:
PO Box 323
Toowong, QLD, Australia
Tel.: (61) 733689644
Fax: (61) 737208455
E-Mail: info@aurion.com.au
Web Site: www.aurion.com.au
Emp.: 40
Payroll & Human Resources Services
S.I.C.: 7372
N.A.I.C.S.: 511210
Silvano Basso *(Mng Dir)*

Julia Ross Call Centre Solutions Pty Limited (2)
Level 2 80 King William St
Adelaide, SA, 5000, Australia AU
Tel.: (61) 882129522
Fax: (61) 882129511
E-Mail: adelaide@juliaross.com
Web Site: www.juliaross.com
Emp.: 6
Business Process Outsourcing Services
S.I.C.: 7389
N.A.I.C.S.: 561422
Hamish Jackson *(Gen Mgr)*

Julia Ross Personnel Pty Limited (2)
Level 4
182 Saint George Ter, Perth, Western Australia, 6000, Australia AU
Tel.: (61) 894869600
Fax: (61) 894869966
E-Mail: jrperth@juliaross.com
Web Site: www.rossjuliaross.com
Emp.: 10
Employment Agencies
S.I.C.: 7361
N.A.I.C.S.: 561311
Susan Lawrance *(Gen Mgr)*

Ross Human Directions Group Limited (2)
Level 8. 32 Walker St
Sydney, New South Wales, 2060, Australia AU
Tel.: (61) 282674600
Fax: (61) 282674666
Web Site: www.rossjuliaross.com
Emp.: 100
Employment Agencies
S.I.C.: 7361
N.A.I.C.S.: 561311
Cameron Judson *(CEO)*

Ross Logic Outsourcing Pty Limited (2)
Level 18 363 George St
Sydney, NSW, 2000, Australia AU
Tel.: (61) 282674600
Fax: (61) 282674666
Web Site: www.chandlermacleod.com
Emp.: 16
Business Management Consulting Services
S.I.C.: 8748
N.A.I.C.S.: 541618

Non-U.S. Subsidiaries:

Ross Human Directions Limited (2)
Level 3
100 Cannon St, London, EC4N 6EU, United Kingdom UK
Tel.: (44) 2079291199
Fax: (44) 2079297196
E-Mail: london@juliaross.co.uk
Web Site: www.juliaross.com
Emp.: 15
Employment Agencies
S.I.C.: 7361
N.A.I.C.S.: 561311
Esther Marsden *(Branch Mgr)*

Ross Recruitment (S) Pte Limited (2)
Level 27 Prudential Tower
30 Cecil St, Singapore, 049712, Singapore SG
Tel.: (65) 62255077
Fax: (65) 68248399
E-Mail: singapore@juliaross.com
Web Site: www.rossjuliaross.com
Emp.: 15
Employment Agencies
S.I.C.: 7361
N.A.I.C.S.: 561311
May Chan *(Mgr-Fin)*

Non-U.S. Subsidiaries:

Pinnacle Recruitment Limited (1)
29 Customs St W Level 8
AMP Bldg, Auckland, 1141, New Zealand
Tel.: (64) 93075515
Fax: (64) 93074571
E-Mail: info@pinnaclerecruit.co.nz
Web Site: www.pinnaclerecruit.co.nz
Emp.: 5
Placement Services
S.I.C.: 7361
N.A.I.C.S.: 561311

The Recruitment Advertising Bureau Limited (1)
Ste 5 Level 3 30 St Benedicts St
Newton, New Zealand
Tel.: (64) 93771844
Fax: (64) 93777670
E-Mail: giselle@trab.co.nz
Web Site: www.trab.co.nz
Emp.: 12
Advertising Agency
S.I.C.: 7311
N.A.I.C.S.: 541810
Ron Sneddon *(Gen Mgr)*

CHANDNI TEXTILES ENGINEERING INDUSTRIES LIMITED

110 TV Industrial Estate 52 SK Ahire Marg
Worli, Mumbai, 400 030, India
Tel.: (91) 22 24937033
Fax: (91) 22 24950328
Web Site: www.cteil.com
522292—(BOM)
Sales Range: $1-9.9 Million
Business Description:
Yarn Mfr
S.I.C.: 2299
N.A.I.C.S.: 313110
Personnel:
Jayesh R. Mehta *(Chm & Mng Dir)*
Board of Directors:
Jayesh R. Mehta
Bharat Bhatia
R. C. Garg
V. G. Joshi
Amita J. Mehta

CHANDRA PRABHU INTERNATIONAL LTD.

14 Rani Jhansi Road
New Delhi, 110055, India
Tel.: (91) 11 23516567
Fax: (91) 11 23553698
E-Mail: info@cpil.com
Web Site: www.cpil.com
530309—(BOM)
Rev.: $16,382,006
Assets: $6,857,458
Liabilities: $5,019,067
Net Worth: $1,838,391
Earnings: $348,295
Fiscal Year-end: 03/31/13
Business Description:
Petrochemical Products Mfr
S.I.C.: 2869
N.A.I.C.S.: 325110
Personnel:
Akash Jain *(Chm, Mng Dir & Compliance Officer)*
Board of Directors:
Akash Jain
Sanjay Goel
Nishant Goyal
Prakash Goyal
Transfer Agent:
Alankit Assignments Limited
Alankit House 2E/21 Jhandewalan Extension
New Delhi, India

CHANEL S.A.

135 Ave Charles De Gaulle
92521 Neuilly-sur-Seine, Cedex, France
Tel.: (33) 146434000
Fax: (33) 0158374000
Web Site: www.chanel.com
Emp.: 2,000
Business Description:
Cosmetics, Fragrances & Clothing Mfr
S.I.C.: 2389
N.A.I.C.S.: 315210
Personnel:
Arie Kopelman *(Vice Chm & COO)*

U.S. Subsidiary:

Chanel, Inc. (1)
9 W 57th St Fl 44
New York, NY 10019-2701
Tel.: (212) 688-5055
Fax: (212) 752-1851
Toll Free: (800) 550-0005
E-Mail: info@chanel.com
Web Site: www.chanel.com
Sales Range: $200-249.9 Million
Emp.: 300
Fragrances, Cosmetics & Mens & Womens Accessories Mfr
S.I.C.: 2844
N.A.I.C.S.: 325620
Lynn Kopper *(Dir-Mktg)*

Subsidiary:

Fragrances Exclusive Inc. (2)
600 Madison Ave
New York, NY 10022-1615 (100%)
Tel.: (212) 891-5100
Fax: (212) 891-5190
Emp.: 12
Distributor of Fragrances
S.I.C.: 5122
N.A.I.C.S.: 424210

Non-U.S. Subsidiary:

Barrie Knitwear Ltd. (1)
Burnfoot Indust Est
Hawick, Scotland, TD9 8RJ, United

Chanel S.A.—(Continued)

Kingdom UK
Tel.: (44) 1450365500 (100%)
Fax: (44) 1450365508
E-Mail: enquiries@barrie.co.uk
Web Site: www.barrie.co.uk
Emp.: 150
Cashmere Knitwear & Apparel Designer, Mfr & Distr
S.I.C.: 2389
N.A.I.C.S.: 315990
Clive Brown *(Dir-Sls)*

CHANG HWA COMMERCIAL BANK LTD.

38 Tsuyu Road Sec 2
Taichung, 40045, Taiwan
Tel.: (886) 4 2222 2001
E-Mail: customer@ms1.chb.com.tw
Web Site: www.chb.com.tw
2801—(TAI)
Int. Income: $910,138,789
Assets: $54,517,624,757
Liabilities: $51,001,617,145
Net Worth: $3,516,007,612
Earnings: $286,904,303
Emp.: 6,323
Fiscal Year-end: 12/31/12

Business Description:
Commercial Bank
S.I.C.: 6029
N.A.I.C.S.: 522110

Personnel:
Julius Chen *(Chm)*
Henry C. S. Kao *(Chm-Supervisory Bd)*
Chu-Lieh Tarng *(Pres)*
Kuo-Yuan Liang *(Mng Dir)*
Cheng Ching Wu *(Mng Dir)*
Chin-Ying Chen *(Exec VP)*
Paul H. C. Huang *(Exec VP)*
Carol Lai *(Exec VP)*
Diao-Li Lin *(Exec VP)*
James Shih *(Exec VP)*
Shiou-Yu Chang *(Sr VP & Head-Secretariat)*
Chen-Yu Chen *(Sr VP & Head-Intl Banking)*
Fu-Lung Chen *(Sr VP & Head-Trust)*
George M. Chen *(Sr VP & Head-Comml Reg Center 3)*
Shyi-Nang Chen *(Sr VP & Head-Loan Asset Mgmt)*
Kuo-Fang Chi *(Sr VP & Head-Gen Affairs)*
Guo Liang Huang *(Sr VP & Head-Comml Reg Center)*
Gwo-Chen Huang *(Sr VP & Head-Domestic Banking)*
John-Shien Jean *(Sr VP & Head-Comml Reg Center 1)*
Tsaifeng Lin *(Sr VP & Head-Fin Mgmt)*
Ya-Ling Lin *(Sr VP & Head-Credit Mgmt Div)*
Yao-Huei Lin *(Sr VP & Head-Internal Auditing)*
Ping-Chen Lo *(Sr VP & Head-Treasury)*
Mei-Tung Lou *(Sr VP & Head-E Bus Div)*
Wen-Hsiang Lu *(Sr VP & Head-Comml Reg Center 4)*
Yin-Che Teng *(Sr VP & Head-Comml Reg Center)*
Nell H. Tseng *(Sr VP & Head-Risk Mgmt)*
Horng-Yao Tu *(Sr VP & Head-Domestic Banking)*
Fangming Tzeng *(Sr VP & Head-IT)*
Hom-Gang Wang *(Sr VP & Head-Product Mgmt Div)*
Sheng-Chao Wang *(Sr VP & Head-Ops)*
Jih-Cheng Yang *(Sr VP & Head-HR)*

Board of Directors:
Julius Chen
Deng-Shan Chen
Shang-Chen Chen
Chia-Chung Cheng
Hwai-Hsin Liang
Kuo-Yuan Liang
Cheng-Hsien Lin
Chu-Lieh Tarng
Cheng Ching Wu

Supervisory Board of Directors:
Henry C. S. Kao
Ching-Hwa Juan
Charles W. Y. Wang

Divisions:

Chang Hwa Bank (Taichung) **(1)**
2 Tsu Yu Rd
Taichung, 40045, Taiwan
Tel.: (886) 422230001
Fax: (886) 422231170
Commercial Banking Services
S.I.C.: 6029
N.A.I.C.S.: 522110

Chang Hwa Bank (Taipei) **(1)**
Sec 2 Chung Shan North Road 57
Taipei, 10412, Taiwan
Tel.: (886) 225362951
Fax: (886) 225114735
E-Mail: fi@chb.com.tw
Web Site: www.chb.com.tw
Emp.: 800
Commercial Banking Services
S.I.C.: 6029
N.A.I.C.S.: 522110
Daniel Tarng *(Pres)*

Chang Hwa International Banking **(1)**
7th Fl No 57 Sec 2 Chung Shan N Rd
Taipei, 10412, Taiwan
Tel.: (886) 225621919
Fax: (886) 225114735
Commercial Banking
S.I.C.: 6029
N.A.I.C.S.: 522110
James Chen *(Gen Mgr)*

Subsidiaries:

CHB Insurance Brokerage Company, Ltd. **(1)**
6th Floor 57 Sec 2
Chung Shan N Road, Taipei, 104, Taiwan
Tel.: (886) 225362951
Fax: (886) 225114735
E-Mail: fi@ms1.chb.com.tw
Emp.: 6,000
Insurance Agencies & Brokerages
S.I.C.: 6411
N.A.I.C.S.: 524210
Julis Chen *(Chm)*
Frank Chen *(Pres)*

CHB Life Insurance Agency Company, Ltd. **(1)**
6th Floor 57 Sec 2
Chung Shan N Road, Taipei, Taiwan
Tel.: (886) 225362951
Fax: (886) 225114735
E-Mail: fi@ms1.chb.com.tw
Web Site: www.chb.com.tw
Sales Range: $10-24.9 Million
Insurance Agencies & Brokerages
S.I.C.: 6411
N.A.I.C.S.: 524210
Walter W.T. Yeh *(Chm)*
William Lin *(Pres)*

U.S. Branch:

Chang Hwa Commercial Bank - New York Branch **(1)**
685 3rd Ave 29th Fl
New York, NY 10017
Tel.: (212) 651-9769
Fax: (212) 651-9785
E-Mail: chbny@worldnet.att.net
Rev.: $6,923,000
Emp.: 23
Commercial Banking
S.I.C.: 6029
N.A.I.C.S.: 522110
Eric Tsai *(Gen Mgr)*

CHANG-ON INTERNATIONAL, INC.

514 No 18 Building High New Technology Department
Harbin, Heilongjiang, China
Tel.: (86) 45182695010
Web Site: www.changon.com
Year Founded: 1972
CAON—(OTC OTCB)
Assets: $3,984
Liabilities: $620,554
Net Worth: ($616,570)
Earnings: ($110,580)
Emp.: 6
Fiscal Year-end: 12/31/12

Business Description:
Recycled Plastic Construction Materials Mfr
Import Export
S.I.C.: 3089
N.A.I.C.S.: 326199

Personnel:
Bing Xiao *(Pres, CEO & CFO)*

Board of Directors:
Chao Lin
Bing Xiao
Ming Zhao

Transfer Agent:
Island Stock Transfer Inc.
Roosevelt Office Center 15500 Roosevelt Blvd Ste 301
Clearwater, FL 33760
Tel.: (727) 289-0010
Fax: (727) 289-0069

CHANGAN MINSHENG APLL LOGISTICS CO., LTD.

561 Hongjin Avenue
Yubei District, Chongqing, 401121, China
Tel.: (86) 23 8918 2222
Web Site: www.camsl.com
Year Founded: 2001
1292—(HKG)
Rev.: $576,898,563
Assets: $374,164,344
Liabilities: $176,729,838
Net Worth: $197,434,506
Earnings: $37,083,533
Emp.: 7,899
Fiscal Year-end: 12/31/12

Business Description:
Motor Vehicle Parts Distr
S.I.C.: 5013
N.A.I.C.S.: 423120

Personnel:
Lungang Zhang *(Chm)*
Guoji Lu *(Vice Chm)*

Board of Directors:
Lungang Zhang
Teck Sin Chong
Peizheng Gao
Chan Peng Goh
Danny Yan Nan Goh
Jing Jie
Ming Li
Guoji Lu
Xiaozhong Lu
Qifa Peng
Chiu Kwok Poon
William K. Villalon
Xiaohua Wu
Yun Zhang
Zhengli Zhou
Minghui Zhu

CHANGCHUN GROUP

301 Songkiang Rd
7th Fl, Taipei, 104, Taiwan
Tel.: (886) 225038131
Fax: (886) 25018317
Web Site: www.ccp.com.tw
Emp.: 1,200

Business Description:
Holding Company
S.I.C.: 6719
N.A.I.C.S.: 551112

Personnel:
Su Hung Lin *(Pres)*

Subsidiaries:

Chang Chun Plastics Co., LTD. **(1)**
301 Songkiang Rd 7th Fl
Taipei, 104, Taiwan
Tel.: (886) 225038131
Fax: (886) 225018317
Web Site: www.ccp.com
Emp.: 200
Plastics Products
S.I.C.: 3089
N.A.I.C.S.: 326199
Shu Ho Lin *(Pres)*

ChangChun PetroChemical Co., LTD. **(1)**
301 Song Jiang Rd 7th Fl
Taipei, 104, Taiwan
Tel.: (886) 225038131
Fax: (886) 225018317
Web Site: www.ccp.com
Emp.: 300
Hydrogen Peroxide
S.I.C.: 2819
N.A.I.C.S.: 325180
Su Hon Lin *(Gen Mgr)*

Tsu-Kong Co., LTD. **(1)**
301 Songkiang Rd 8th Fl
Taipei, 104, Taiwan
Tel.: (886) 225020221
Fax: (886) 225042977
Epoxy Moulding Compounds
S.I.C.: 2821
N.A.I.C.S.: 325211

Joint Ventures:

Chang Chiang Chemical Co., Ltd. **(1)**
301 Songkiang Rd 8th Fl
Taipei, 104, Taiwan
Tel.: (886) 225097431
Fax: (886) 225097433
E-Mail: tjlin@ccp.com.tw
Emp.: 10
Antioxidants & PVC Products
S.I.C.: 2821
N.A.I.C.S.: 325211
Toru Yamada *(VP)*

Dairen Chemical Corporation **(1)**
9th Fl 301 Song Kiang Rd
Taipei, 104, Taiwan (60%)
Tel.: (886) 225020238
Fax: (886) 225099619
E-Mail: info@dcc.com.tw
Web Site: www.dcc.com.tw
Emp.: 90
Chemical Products
S.I.C.: 2899
N.A.I.C.S.: 325998
Suhon Lin *(Chm)*

Non-U.S. Subsidiaries:

Dairen Chemical (Jiangsu) Co. Ltd. **(2)**
1 Dalian Rd
Chemical Industry Park, Yangzhou, Jiangsu, 211900, China (100%)
Tel.: (86) 51483268888
Fax: (86) 51483298855
E-Mail: service@dcc.com.cn
Web Site: www.dcc.com
Emp.: 127
Chemical Mfr
S.I.C.: 2899
N.A.I.C.S.: 325998

Dairen Chemical (M) Sdn. Bhd. **(2)**
Plo 18 Tanjung Langsat Industrial Est
Mukim Sungai Tiram Pasir Gudan, Johor, 81700, Malaysia (100%)
Tel.: (60) 72565800
Fax: (60) 72565799
E-Mail: myservice@ms.dcc.com.my
Web Site: www.dcc.com.tw
Emp.: 70
Chemical Mfr
S.I.C.: 2899
N.A.I.C.S.: 325998
Jong Yuh Lih *(Mng Dir)*

RCCT Technology Co., Ltd. **(1)**
301 SongKiang Rd 7th Fl
Taipei, 104, Taiwan

Tel.: (886) 225001767
Fax: (886) 225187929
E-Mail: nenewang@rogerscorporation.com
Web Site: www.rcct.com.tw
Sales Range: $125-149.9 Million
Flexible Copper Clad Laminate; Joint Venture of Chang Chun Corporation & Rogers Corporation
S.I.C.: 3083
N.A.I.C.S.: 326130
Grant Wang *(Gen Mgr)*

Sumitomo Bakelite (Taiwan) Corporation Limited (1)
No 1 Hwa Syi Road
Ta Fa Industries District
Ta Liao, Kaohsiung, Taiwan
Tel.: (886) 77871285
Fax: (886) 225042977
Web Site: www.sumibe.co.jp
Epoxy Moulding Compound; Owned by ChangChun Group & Sumitomo Bakelite Co., Ltd.
S.I.C.: 2821
N.A.I.C.S.: 325211

Tai Hong Circuit Ind. Co., LTD. (1)
1 Chung-Chun Lane Min-Sheng N Rd
Taoyuan, 333, Taiwan
Tel.: (886) 33527960
Fax: (886) 33527980
Web Site: www.taihong.com.tw
Emp.: 430
Circuit Printing Board; Owned by ChangChun Group, Mitsubishi Gas Chemical Company, Inc. & Japan Printed Circuit Ind.Co.
S.I.C.: 3672
N.A.I.C.S.: 334412

TOK Taiwan Co., Ltd. (1)
10 Fl 675 Jing Guo Rd Sec 1
Hsin-chu, 300, Taiwan
Tel.: (886) 35345953
Fax: (886) 35350178
E-Mail: info@tok.co.jp
Web Site: www.tok.co.in
Emp.: 40
Photolithography Materials Mfr & Supplier; Owned by ChangChung Group & Tokyo Ohka Kogyo Co., Ltd.
S.I.C.: 7389
N.A.I.C.S.: 425110
Yoshio Nishina *(Gen Mgr)*

Non-U.S. Subsidiary:

PT. Chang Chun DPN Chemical Industry (1)
Cikarang Industrial Estate
Jl Jababeka XI BLOK G18-G23
Cikarang Bekasi, Jakarta, 17530, Indonesia Id
Tel.: (62) 218934205
Fax: (62) 218934203
Emp.: 150
Resins
S.I.C.: 2821
N.A.I.C.S.: 325211
Chen Leeng Ye *(Gen Mgr)*

CHANGCHUN UP OPTOTECH CO., LTD.

18 YingKou Road Changchun Economic Technology Development Zone
Changchun, 130031, China
Tel.: (86) 431 86176388
Fax: (86) 431 86176711
E-Mail: market@up-china.com
Web Site: www.up-china.com
Year Founded: 2001
002338—(SSE)
Emp.: 800
Business Description:
Photoelectric Measurement & Control Equipment Mfr
S.I.C.: 3827
N.A.I.C.S.: 333314
Personnel:
Ming Xuan *(Chm)*

CHANGCHUN YIDONG CLUTCH CO., LTD.

No 2555 ChaoRan Street Hi tech Development Zone
Changchun, China
Tel.: (86) 431 85158488
Fax: (86) 431 85174234
E-Mail: 600148@ccyd.com.cn
Web Site: www.ccyd.com.cn
Year Founded: 1992
600148—(SHG)
Emp.: 1,217
Business Description:
Automobile Clutch Mfr
S.I.C.: 3714
N.A.I.C.S.: 336350
Personnel:
Jerry Lu *(Vice Gen Mgr)*

CHANGDA INTERNATIONAL HOLDINGS, INC.

10th Floor Chenhong Bldg No 301East Dong Feng St
Weifang, China
Tel.: (86) 536 8513228
Fax: (86) 536 8513232
E-Mail: office@changdaint.com
Web Site: www.changdastock.com
CIHD—(OTCB)
Sales Range: $75-99.9 Million
Emp.: 190
Business Description:
Holding Company; Chemical & Microbial Organic-Inorganic Compound Fertilizers Mfr
S.I.C.: 2879
N.A.I.C.S.: 325320
Personnel:
QingRan Zhu *(Chm & CEO)*
Leodegario Quinto Camacho *(CFO)*
Jan Panneman *(Exec VP)*
Board of Directors:
QingRan Zhu
David Cohen
HuaRan Zhu

CHANGE CAPITAL PARTNERS LLP

2nd Floor College House
272 Kings Road, London, SW3 5AW, United Kingdom
Tel.: (44) 2078089110
Fax: (44) 02078089111
E-Mail: info@changecapitalpartners.com
Web Site: www.changecapitalpartners.com
Emp.: 15
Business Description:
Private Equity Firm
S.I.C.: 6211
N.A.I.C.S.: 523999
Personnel:
Roger Holmes *(Mng Dir)*
Stephan Lobmeyr *(Mng Dir)*
Steven Petrow *(Mng Dir)*
Luc Vandevelde *(Mng Dir)*
Andrew Wood *(CFO & Chief Compliance Officer)*

THE CHANGE GROUP CORPORATION LTD.

4th Floor 1 Ely Place
London, EC1N 6RY, United Kingdom
Tel.: (44) 2036758200
Web Site: www.changegroup.com
Year Founded: 1992
Sales Range: $600-649.9 Million
Emp.: 526
Business Description:
Foreign Currency Exchange Services
S.I.C.: 6221
N.A.I.C.S.: 523130
Personnel:
Zackariya Marikar *(Chm)*
Sacha Alexander Zackariya *(CEO)*
Theodore Nussbaum *(Co-Sec & Gen Counsel-New York)*
Chris Mason *(Co-Sec)*
Board of Directors:
Zackariya Marikar
Norbert Lill
Chris Mason
Paul Meehan
Theodore Nussbaum
Bette Zackariya
Sacha Alexander Zackariya

THE CHANGE ORGANISATION LTD.

92-93 John Wilson Business Park
Whitstable, Kent, CT5 3QT, United Kingdom
Tel.: (44) 1227 779000
Web Site: www.thechange.co.uk
Year Founded: 1992
Sales Range: $25-49.9 Million
Emp.: 46
Business Description:
Computer Distrubution Services
S.I.C.: 5045
N.A.I.C.S.: 423430
Personnel:
Graham Burns *(Chm)*
Tim Scholfield *(Mng Dir)*

CHANGFENG AXLE (CHINA) COMPANY LIMITED

Longyan Economic Zone
Longyan, Fujian, China 364028
Tel.: (86) 5972791939
Fax: (86) 5972799019
E-Mail: ir@changfengaxle.com
Web Site: www.changfengaxle.com
Year Founded: 2001
1039—(HKG)
Rev.: $80,035,143
Assets: $280,349,758
Liabilities: $105,580,606
Net Worth: $174,769,153
Earnings: ($73,188,231)
Emp.: 1,837
Fiscal Year-end: 12/31/12
Business Description:
Axle Mfr
S.I.C.: 3714
N.A.I.C.S.: 336390
Personnel:
Kwai Mo Wong *(Chm)*
Fengcai Lai *(CEO)*
Wai Shing Chan *(CFO & Sec)*
Board of Directors:
Kwai Mo Wong
Ching Hei Chong
Dorothy Ying Dong
Fengcai Lai
Xiuqing Li
Ching Wu
Weizhou Zhu

Computershare Hong Kong Investor Services Limited
Shops 1712-1716 17th Floor Hopewell Centre
183 Queens Road East
Wanchai, China (Hong Kong)

Transfer Agent:
Royal Bank of Canada Trust Company (Cayman) Limited
4th Floor Royal Bank House 24 Shedden Road
Georgetown, Cayman Islands

CHANGFENG ENERGY INC.

25 Adelaide Street East Suite 1612
Toronto, ON, M5C 3A1, Canada
Tel.: (416) 362-5032
Fax: (416) 362-2393
E-Mail: info@changfengenergy.com
Web Site: www.changfengenergy.com
Year Founded: 2006
CFY—(TSXV)
Rev.: $33,073,710
Assets: $60,833,559
Liabilities: $44,861,664
Net Worth: $15,971,894
Earnings: $2,463,589
Emp.: 150
Fiscal Year-end: 12/31/12
Business Description:
Oil & Gas Exploration Services
S.I.C.: 1311
N.A.I.C.S.: 211111
Personnel:
Huajun Lin *(Founder, Chm, Pres & CEO)*
Zhao Yan *(CFO)*
Ann Siyin Lin *(Sec & VP-Corp Dev)*
Daniel S.W. Chan *(Sr VP-Sanya Changfeng New Energy Investment Co Ltd)*
Board of Directors:
Huajun Lin
Hui Cai
John Kutkevicius
Dan Liu
Graham C. Warren
Wencheng Zhang
Transfer Agent:
Olympia Transfer Service Inc
Suite 920 120 Adelaide Street West
Toronto, ON, Canada

CHANGFENG (GROUP) CO., LTD.

19/F Hualing Mansion No 111 Er Road Furong Middle Road
Changsha, Hunan, 410011, China
Tel.: (86) 7462881664
Web Site:
Year Founded: 1950
Emp.: 3,600
Business Description:
Holding Company; Automobile Mfr
S.I.C.: 6719
N.A.I.C.S.: 551112
Personnel:
Jianxin Li *(Chm)*

Subsidiary:

Anhui Changfeng Yangzi Automobile Manufacturing Co., Ltd, (1)
Yangzi Industrial Zone
Chuzhou, Anhui, China
Tel.: (86) 550 3160498
Fax: (86) 550 3169199
E-Mail: export@cfyzmotor.com
Web Site: www.cfyzmotor.com
Emp.: 900
Automobile Mfr
S.I.C.: 3711
N.A.I.C.S.: 336111
Junxian Tan *(Gen Mgr)*

CHANGHAE ENERGEERING CO., LTD.

904 Owner's Tower 16-5 Sunae-Dong
Bundang-Gu, Seongnam, Kyunggi-Do, 463-825, Korea (South)
Tel.: (82) 31 698 2207
Fax: (82) 31 718 3016
E-Mail: contact@chenergeering.com
Web Site: www.chenergeering.com
074150—(KRS)
Business Description:
Ethanol Product Mfr
S.I.C.: 2869
N.A.I.C.S.: 325193
Personnel:
Hyo Seop Yim *(Pres)*

CHANGHUAT CORPORATION BERHAD

Ste 3 6 Level 3 Menara Pelangi No 2
Jalan Kuning
Taman Pelangi
80400 Johor Bahru, Malaysia

Changhuat Corporation Berhad—(Continued)

Tel.: (60) 73341750
Fax: (60) 73318617
E-Mail: investor@changhuat.com.my
Web Site: www.changhuat.com.my
CHANG—(KLS)
Sales Range: $10-24.9 Million
Business Description:
Plastic Injection Components Mfr
S.I.C.: 8011
N.A.I.C.S.: 621111
Personnel:
See Khai Lim *(Chm)*
Lai Huat Lim *(Grp Mng Dir)*
Sujata Menon *(Sec)*
Board of Directors:
See Khai Lim
Baharudin Abd Kadir
Lai Huat Lim
Thean Hong P'Ng
Kee Yen Siow
Kian Huat Ti
Winston Paul Chi-Huang Wong
Choong Cheong Yu

CHANGLIN COMPANY LIMITED

No 898 West Huang He Road
Changzhou, Jiangsu, China 213136
Tel.: (86) 519 86781288
Fax: (86) 519 86781387
E-Mail: sales@changlin.com.cn
Web Site: www.changlin.com.cn
Year Founded: 1961
600710—(SHG)
Business Description:
Construction Machinery Mfr & Whslr
S.I.C.: 3531
N.A.I.C.S.: 333120
Personnel:
Peiguo Wu *(Chm)*

CHANGMAO BIOCHEMICAL ENGINEERING COMPANY LIMITED

1228 North Changjiang Road
Xinbei District, Changzhou, Jiangsu, 213034, China
Tel.: (86) 519 86850125
Fax: (86) 519 86892161
E-Mail: chk@cmbec.cn
Web Site: www.cmbec.cn
Year Founded: 1992
954—(HKG)
Sales Range: $100-124.9 Million
Emp.: 550
Business Description:
Organic Acids Mfr
S.I.C.: 2899
N.A.I.C.S.: 325998
Personnel:
Xin Sheng Rui *(Chm & CEO)*

CHANGO INC.

488 Wellington Street West Suite 202
Toronto, ON, M5V 1E3, Canada
Tel.: (800) 385-0607
Web Site: www.chango.com
Sales Range: $1-9.9 Million
Emp.: 40
Business Description:
Advertising Services
S.I.C.: 7319
N.A.I.C.S.: 541890
Personnel:
Chris Sukornyk *(CEO)*
Dax Hamman *(Chief Strategy Officer & Chief Revenue Officer)*
Mazdak Rezvani *(CTO)*
Board of Directors:
Roger Chabra
John Elton
Lewis Gersh
Duncan Hill
Chris Sukornyk
Lynn Wunderman

CHANGSHA KAIYUAN INSTRUMENTS CO., LTD.

172 Kaiyuan Road Changsha Econ & Tech Dev Zone
Changsha, 410100, China
Tel.: (86) 731 84012074
E-Mail: susanky@chs5e.com
Web Site: www.ckic.net
Year Founded: 1992
300338—(CHIN)
Sales Range: $25-49.9 Million
Emp.: 850
Business Description:
Coal Quality Testing & Analysis Instruments & Equipment Mfr
S.I.C.: 3823
N.A.I.C.S.: 334513
Personnel:
Jianwen Luo *(Chm)*

CHANGSHA SINOCARE CO., LTD.

28 Jixian Road High-Tech Industrial Zone
Changsha, 410013, China
Tel.: (86) 731 84164629
Fax: (86) 731 88905123
Web Site: www.sinocare.com.cn
300298—(CHIN)
Sales Range: $25-49.9 Million
Emp.: 630
Business Description:
Medical Device Mfr
S.I.C.: 3841
N.A.I.C.S.: 339112
Personnel:
Shaobo Li *(Chm)*

CHANGSHENG CHINA PROPERTY COMPANY LIMITED

Unit D 10th Floor China Overseas Building 139 Hennessy Road
1 Harbour Road, Wanchai, China (Hong Kong)
Tel.: (852) 28322910
Fax: (852) 28935930
Web Site: www.cschina.com.hk
Emp.: 170
Business Description:
Real Estate Developer
S.I.C.: 1542
N.A.I.C.S.: 236220
Personnel:
Shek Cheong Chau *(Chm)*
Yan Tung *(CEO)*
Sui Kay Chan *(CFO)*
Board of Directors:
Shek Cheong Chau
Sui Kay Chan
Sye Sye Chan
Shun Cheong Chau
Yan Tung

CHANGSHU FENGFAN POWER EQUIPMENT CO., LTD.

No 8 South Renmin Road Shanghu Town
Changshu, China 215551
Tel.: (86) 51252122998
Fax: (86) 51252401600
E-Mail: cstower@126.com
Web Site: www.cstower.cn
Year Founded: 1993
601700—(SHG)
Sales Range: $150-199.9 Million
Emp.: 1,694
Business Description:
Steel Tower Mfr
S.I.C.: 3399
N.A.I.C.S.: 331110
Personnel:
Jiangang Fang *(Pres)*

CHANGSHU TIANYIN ELECTROMECHANICAL CO., LTD.

8 Yingbin Road Bixi New Zone
Changshu, Suzhou, 215513, China
Tel.: (86) 512 52690818
Fax: (86) 512 52691888
Web Site: www.tyjd.cc
300342—(CHIN)
Sales Range: $50-74.9 Million
Emp.: 360
Business Description:
Refrigerator Compressor Parts & Components Mfr
S.I.C.: 3585
N.A.I.C.S.: 333415
Personnel:
Xiaodong Zhao *(Chm)*

CHANGTIAN PLASTIC & CHEMICAL LIMITED

18 Xinsheng Road Xinyang Industrial Zone Haicang District
Xiamen, Fujian, China 361026
Tel.: (86) 5926517000
Fax: (86) 5926519700
Web Site: www.changtian.com.sg
D2V—(SES)
Rev.: $32,304,213
Assets: $176,377,032
Liabilities: $4,597,596
Net Worth: $171,779,437
Earnings: ($988,524)
Fiscal Year-end: 12/31/12
Business Description:
Adhesive Tapes Mfr
S.I.C.: 2891
N.A.I.C.S.: 325520
Personnel:
Qingjin Yang *(Chm & CEO)*
Yongfu Chen *(Deputy Chm)*
Pak Kin Ken Chan *(Sec & Controller-Fin)*
Board of Directors:
Qingjin Yang
David Yin Chan
Yongfu Chen
Quanwen Liao
Siok Sing Tan
Qiu Cai Wei
Junqing Yang

BDO Limited
25th Floor Wing On Centre 111 Connaught Road
Hong Kong, China (Hong Kong)

Legal Counsel:
Rajah & Tann LLP
9 Battery Road 25-01 Straits Trading Building
049910 Singapore, Singapore

Boardroom Corporate & Advisory Services Pte. Ltd.
50 Raffles Place 32-01 Singapore Land Tower
Singapore, Singapore

Transfer Agents:
HSBC Securities Services (Bermuda) Limited
Bank of Bermuda Building 6 Front Street
Hamilton, Bermuda

Boardroom Corporate & Advisory Services Pte. Ltd.
50 Raffles Place 32-01 Singapore Land Tower
Singapore, Singapore

Subsidiary:

Xiamen Changtian Enterprise Co., Ltd. **(1)**
No 18 Xinsheng Road Xinyang Industrial Zone
Haicang District, Xiamen, Fujian, 361026, China
Tel.: (86) 5926807002
Fax: (86) 5926515199
E-Mail: changtian@chang-tian.com.cn
Web Site: www.chang-tian.com.cn
Chemical Products Mfr & Sales
S.I.C.: 3089
N.A.I.C.S.: 326199

CHANGYUAN GROUP LTD.

5th Floor Block F Changyuan New Material Port Keyuan Middle Road
518057 Shenzhen, China
Tel.: (86) 75526719476
Fax: (86) 75526739900
Web Site: www.cyg.com
Year Founded: 1986
600525—(SHG)
Sales Range: $200-249.9 Million
Emp.: 1,200
Business Description:
Electronic Components Mfr & Distr
S.I.C.: 3679
N.A.I.C.S.: 334419
Personnel:
Steven Xu *(Chm & CEO)*
Kenneth Yang *(CFO)*
Zhongwei Xie *(CTO)*
Erbin Lu *(Exec VP)*

Subsidiaries:

Changyuan Electronics (Shenzhen) Co., Ltd. **(1)**
A/ F6 Changyuan New Material Port Keyuan Road
Shenzhen, China
Tel.: (86) 755 26549490
Fax: (86) 755 26553707
Web Site: www.heat-shrink-manufacturer.com
Heat Shrink Tube Mfr
S.I.C.: 2652
N.A.I.C.S.: 322219

Dongguan Salipt Co., Ltd. **(1)**
Sanlian Technological Park Jingxiang Village Liaobu Town
Dongguan, Guangdong, China
Tel.: (86) 769 81120150
Fax: (86) 769 83219706
E-Mail: salipt@salipt.com
Web Site: www.salipt.com
Emp.: 20
Polyolefin Fiber Mfr
S.I.C.: 2823
N.A.I.C.S.: 325220
Cherry Huang *(Gen Mgr)*

CHANGZHOU ALMADEN STOCK CO., LTD.

639 Qinglong East Road
Changzhou, China
Tel.: (86) 51988880015
Fax: (86) 51988880017
E-Mail: amd@czamd.com
Web Site: www.czamd.com
002623—(SSE)
Sales Range: $25-49.9 Million
Business Description:
Glass Coating Mfr
S.I.C.: 3211
N.A.I.C.S.: 327211
Personnel:
Jinxi Lin *(Chm)*

CHANGZHOU QIANHONG BIO-PHARMA CO., LTD.

90 Changjiang Middle Road
Xinbei Distract, Changzhou, Jiangsu, 213022, China
Tel.: (86) 519 5156026
Fax: (86) 519 5156028
E-Mail: shqhzy@public.cz.js.cn
Web Site: www.qhsh.com.cn
Year Founded: 1971
002550—(SSE)
Sales Range: $50-74.9 Million

Business Description:
Biopharmaceutical Products Mfr, Distr, Importer & Exporter
S.I.C.: 2834
N.A.I.C.S.: 325412
Personnel:
Yaofang Wang *(Chm)*

CHANGZHOU TIANSHENG NEW MATERIALS CO., LTD.

No 985 Zhongwu Road
Changzhou, China 213000
Tel.: (86) 51989826671
Fax: (86) 51988859188
E-Mail: xxb@tschina.com
Web Site: www.tschina.com
Year Founded: 1998
300169—(CHIN)
Sales Range: $350-399.9 Million
Emp.: 661
Business Description:
Macromolecule Foam Materials Mfr & Distr
S.I.C.: 2515
N.A.I.C.S.: 337910
Personnel:
Ze Wei Lu *(CEO)*

CHANNEL FOUR TELEVISION CORPORATION

124 Horseferry Road
London, SW1P 2TX, United Kingdom
Tel.: (44) 2073964444
Fax: (44) 2073068697
Web Site: www.channel4.com
Rev.: $1,460,843,250
Assets: $1,227,108,330
Liabilities: $494,317,770
Net Worth: $732,790,560
Earnings: ($42,640,830)
Emp.: 795
Fiscal Year-end: 12/31/12
Business Description:
Public Television Broadcasting Network
S.I.C.: 4833
N.A.I.C.S.: 515120
Personnel:
Terry Burns *(Chm)*
Mark Price *(Deputy Chm)*
Jane Fletcher *(Head-Pres)*
David Abraham *(CEO)*
Jay Hunt *(Chief Creative Officer)*
Board of Directors:
Terry Burns
David Abraham
Jonathan Allan
Dan Brooke
Monica Burch
Jay Hunt
Alicja Lesniak
Paul Potts
Mark Price
Mary Teresa Rainey
Richard Rivers
Josie Rourke
Joint Venture:

Box Television Ltd. **(1)**
Mappin House 4
Winsley Street, London, W1W 8HF, United Kingdom
Tel.: (44) 2071828000
Fax: (44) 2073761313
Web Site: www.thebox.co.uk
Emp.: 60
Cable Television Broadcasting; Owned 50% by Heinrich Bauer Verlag KG & 50% by Channel Four Television Corporation
S.I.C.: 4841
N.A.I.C.S.: 515210
Matt Rennie *(Mng Dir)*

CHANNEL ISLANDS STOCK EXCHANGE

One Lefebvre Street
PO Box 623
Saint Peter Port, GY1 4PJ, Guernsey
Tel.: (44) 481713831
Fax: (44) 481714856
Web Site: www.cisx.com
Business Description:
Stock Exchange Services
S.I.C.: 6231
N.A.I.C.S.: 523210
Personnel:
Jon Moulton *(Chm)*
Board of Directors:
Jon Moulton
Robert Christensen
Graham A. Hall
Peter A. Harwood
Timothy Herbert
Mark N. Huntley
Stephen Lansdown
Shane Le Provost
Mark Thistlethwayte

CHANNEL NINE ENTERTAINMENT LTD

Asaf Ali Road 3/12 Ground Floor
New Delhi, 110002, India
Tel.: (91) 11 32315575
E-Mail: info@channelnineentertainment.com
Web Site: www.channelnineentertainment.com
Year Founded: 2002
Business Description:
Television, Films & Video Game Production & Distribution
S.I.C.: 7812
N.A.I.C.S.: 512110
Personnel:
Gagan Goel *(Sec)*
Board of Directors:
Dinesh Kumar Jindal
Gaj Raj Singh
Neena Sood

CHANNEL RESOURCES LTD.

(Acquired by West African Resources Limited)

CHANT SINCERE CO., LTD.

7F-2 No 188 Sec 3 Ta Tung Rd
Hsi-chieh, Taipei, Taiwan
Tel.: (886) 286471251
Fax: (886) 286471842
E-Mail: service@coxoc.com.tw
Web Site: www.coxoc.com.tw
6205—(TAI)
Sales Range: $25-49.9 Million
Emp.: 1,445
Business Description:
Electronic Components Mfr
S.I.C.: 3675
N.A.I.C.S.: 334416
Personnel:
Jung-Chun Wu *(Chm)*

CHANTIER CATANA

Zone Technique Du Port
66140 Canet, Pyrenees Orientales, France
Tel.: (33) 468801313
Fax: (33) 468801312
E-Mail: info@catana.com
Web Site: www.catana.com
Rev.: $24,200,000
Emp.: 130
Business Description:
Boatbuilding & Repairing
S.I.C.: 3732
N.A.I.C.S.: 336612
Personnel:
Olivier Poncin *(Pres)*
Board of Directors:
Christian Castanie

CHAODA MODERN AGRICULTURE HOLDINGS LIMITED

No 29 Tongpan Road
Fuzhou, Fujian, 350003, China
Tel.: (86) 591 2837 8888
Fax: (86) 591 2802 3860
E-Mail: investor@chaoda.com.hk
Web Site: www.chaoda.com.hk
Sales Range: $1-4.9 Billion
Emp.: 23,236
Business Description:
Agricultural Products Producer
S.I.C.: 0191
N.A.I.C.S.: 111998
Personnel:
Ho Kwok *(Chm)*
Andy Chi Po Chan *(CFO)*
David Alfred Sealey *(Deputy COO)*
Board of Directors:
Ho Kwok
Andy Chi Po Chan
Jun Hua Chen
Chi Kin Fung
Xie Ying Huang
Chi Ming Ip
Qiao Kuang
Yan Li
Shun Quan Lin
Yue Wen Luan
Ching Ho Tam
Transfer Agent:
Tricor Abacus Limited
26/F Tesbury Centre 28 Queen's Road East
Hong Kong, China (Hong Kong)
Non-U.S. Subsidiary:

Chaoda Vegetable & Fruits Limited **(1)**
Rm 2705 27 F China Resources Bldg 26 Harbour Rd
Wanchai, China (Hong Kong)
Tel.: (852) 28450168
Fax: (852) 28270278
E-Mail: info@chaodo.com.hk
Web Site: www.chaodo.com.hk
Emp.: 20
Fruit & Vegetable Farming Services
S.I.C.: 0182
N.A.I.C.S.: 111419
Andy Chan *(CFO)*

CHAOWEI POWER HOLDINGS LIMITED

No 12 Zhizhou Road Xinxing Industrial Park
Zhicheng, Changxing, Zhejiang, 313100, China
Tel.: (86) 572 6562868
Fax: (86) 572 6762999
E-Mail: ir@chaowei.com.hk
Web Site: www.chaowei.com.hk
Year Founded: 1998
951—(HKG)
Rev.: $1,518,516,885
Assets: $1,130,680,321
Liabilities: $713,510,357
Net Worth: $417,169,964
Earnings: $98,476,516
Emp.: 18,696
Fiscal Year-end: 12/31/12
Business Description:
Motive Battery Mfr
S.I.C.: 3692
N.A.I.C.S.: 335912
Personnel:
Mingming Zhou *(Founder, Chm & CEO)*
Wai Yip Leung *(CFO & Sec)*
Board of Directors:
Mingming Zhou
Xihong Deng
Conway Kong Wai Lee
Chi Kit Ng
Minggao Ouyang
Jiqiang Wang
Xinxin Yang
Yunfei Yang
Longrui Zhou

Computershare Hong Kong Investor Services Limited
Shops 1712-16 17th Floor Hopewell Centre 183 Queen's Road East
Hong Kong, China (Hong Kong)
Transfer Agent:
Royal Bank of Canada Trust Company (Cayman) Limited
4th Floor Royal Bank House 24 Shedden Road
Georgetown, Cayman Islands

CHAPMAN FREEBORN AIRCHARTERING LTD.

3 City Place Beehive Ring Road
Gatwick
London, West Sussex, RH6 0PA, United Kingdom
Tel.: (44) 1293572872
Fax: (44) 1293572873
Web Site: www.chapman-freeborn.com
Year Founded: 1973
Sales Range: $700-749.9 Million
Emp.: 365
Business Description:
Aircraft Charter Services
S.I.C.: 4522
N.A.I.C.S.: 481219
Personnel:
Dmitri Kourenkov *(Dir-Ops)*

CHAPMANS LIMITED

9th Floor 82 Elizabeth Street
Sydney, NSW, 2000, Australia
Mailing Address:
GPO Box 4246
Sydney, NSW, 2001, Australia
Tel.: (61) 2 9233 6022
Fax: (61) 2 9233 6475
E-Mail: chp@chapmansltd.com
Web Site: www.chapmansltd.com
Year Founded: 1922
CHP—(ASX)
Rev.: $30,341
Assets: $1,073,159
Liabilities: $310,198
Net Worth: $762,961
Earnings: ($3,393,640)
Fiscal Year-end: 12/31/12
Business Description:
Investment Services
S.I.C.: 6211
N.A.I.C.S.: 523999
Personnel:
Peter Dykes *(Chm)*
Bruce David Burrell *(Sec)*
Board of Directors:
Peter Dykes
Bruce David Burrell
Anthony Dunlop
John Houston
K. Skelton

CHAPUS PRODUITS PETROLIERS

Z D"activite Le Puy De Ceaux 12
Route De Joue
Ceaux En Loudun, 86200 Bressuire, France
Tel.: (33) 549223547
Sls.: $22,400,000
Emp.: 9
Business Description:
Coal & Other Minerals & Ores
S.I.C.: 5052
N.A.I.C.S.: 423520
Personnel:
Francis Amand *(Pres)*

THE CHARACTER GROUP PLC
2nd Floor 86-88 Coombe Road
New Malden, Surrey, KT3 4QS, United Kingdom
Tel.: (44) 2089495898
Fax: (44) 2083362585
E-Mail: info@charactergroup.plc.co.uk
Web Site: www.thecharacter.com
CCT—(LSE)
Rev.: $106,109,337
Assets: $66,559,177
Liabilities: $52,396,104
Net Worth: $14,163,073
Earnings: $1,078,655
Emp.: 177
Fiscal Year-end: 08/31/13
Business Description:
Toys, Games & Gifts Mfr & Distr
S.I.C.: 3944
N.A.I.C.S.: 339930
Personnel:
Richard King *(Chm)*
Jonathan James Diver *(Co-Mng Dir & Dir-Mktg)*
Kirankumar Premchand Shah *(Co-Mng Dir & Dir-Fin)*
Board of Directors:
Richard King
Lord Birdwood
Jonathan James Diver
David Harris
Michael Spencer Hyde
Joseph John Patrick Kissane
Kirankumar Premchand Shah
Legal Counsel:
Duane Morris
2nd Floor 10 Chiswell Street
London, United Kingdom
Subsidiaries:

Character Games Limited (1)
86 88 Coombe Rd
New Malden, Surrey, KT3 4QS, United Kingdom
Tel.: (44) 2089495898
Fax: (44) 2083362585
E-Mail: characterg@aol.com
Web Site: www.character-online.com
Emp.: 12
Toys & Electronic Goods Mfr
S.I.C.: 3944
N.A.I.C.S.: 339930
Jon Diver *(Dir-Mktg)*

Character Gifts Limited (1)
86 88 Coombe Rd
New Malden, Surrey, KT3 4QS, United Kingdom
Tel.: (44) 2089495898
Fax: (44) 2083293384
E-Mail: info@charactergroup.plc.uk
Web Site: www.Character-online.co.uk
Emp.: 20
Toys & Collectibles Whslr
S.I.C.: 5092
N.A.I.C.S.: 423920
Jon Diver *(Mng Dir)*

Character Options Limited (1)
Lees Brook Mill Lees Rd
Oldham, OL4 5JL, United Kingdom
Tel.: (44) 1616339800
Fax: (44) 1616339840
Web Site: www.character-online.com
Emp.: 100
Toys & Electronic Goods Mfr
S.I.C.: 3944
N.A.I.C.S.: 339930
Joe Kissane *(Mng Dir)*

Non-U.S. Subsidiary:

Toy Options (Far East) Limited (1)
Room 1005-1007A 10 Fl
Empire Centre 68 Mody Rd E, Kowloon, Tsim Sha Tsui, 808 811, China (Hong Kong)
Tel.: (852) 21766380
Fax: (852) 21766330
Toys & Electronic Goods Mfr
S.I.C.: 3944
N.A.I.C.S.: 339930

CHARCO SAS
197/199 Avenue Carnot
Centre Commercial Mohon, 08000
Charleville-Mezieres, France
Tel.: (33) 324374611
Fax: (33) 324379078
Web Site: www.intermarche.com
Sls.: $23,500,000
Emp.: 49
Business Description:
Franchise Supermarket Owner & Operator
S.I.C.: 5411
N.A.I.C.S.: 445110
Personnel:
Marc Jaloux *(Pres)*

CHARCOL LIMITED
(d/b/a John Charcol)
5th Floor Cutlers Exchange 123 Houndsditch
London, EC3A 7BU, United Kingdom
Tel.: (44) 2076117000
Fax: (44) 8454131101
Web Site: www.johncharcol.co.uk
Sales Range: $10-24.9 Million
Emp.: 150
Business Description:
Mortgage Services
S.I.C.: 6163
N.A.I.C.S.: 522310
Personnel:
Walter Avrili *(Mng Dir)*
Alan Mudd *(Mng Dir)*

CHARCUTERIES CUISINEES DE PLELAN
Rue De La Pointe
35380 Rennes, France
Tel.: (33) 299618400
Fax: (33) 299618401
Sls.: $23,200,000
Emp.: 99
Business Description:
Sausages & Other Prepared Meats
S.I.C.: 5147
N.A.I.C.S.: 311612
Personnel:
Raymond Doizon *(Pres)*
Board of Directors:
Jean-Daniel Decroocq

CHARDAN METROPOL ACQUISITION CORP.
13 Donskaya Ulitsa
119049 Moscow, Russia
Tel.: (7) 495 933 3310
Year Founded: 2011
Business Description:
Investment Services
S.I.C.: 6211
N.A.I.C.S.: 523999
Personnel:
Kerry S. Propper *(Co-Chm & CEO)*
Alexis O. Rodzianko *(Co-Chm & CFO)*
Board of Directors:
Kerry S. Propper
Alexis O. Rodzianko
George Kaufman
Grigoriy Leshchenko
Sergey A. Solousov
Mark Xue

CHARGEMASTER PLC
Mulberry House 750 Capability Green
Luton, LU1 3LU, United Kingdom
Tel.: (44) 1582 400331
Web Site: www.chargemasterplc.com
Sales Range: $1-9.9 Million
Business Description:
Electric Vehicle Charging Solutions
S.I.C.: 3621
N.A.I.C.S.: 335312
Personnel:
John Miles *(Chm)*
David Martell *(CEO)*
Board of Directors:
John Miles
Michael Brooks
David Martell
Jeff Solomon
Ian Williams

CHARGEURS SA
112 avenue Kleber
75016 Paris, France
Tel.: (33) 147041340
Fax: (33) 147044027
Web Site: www.chargeurs.fr
CRI—(EUR)
Rev.: $706,200,782
Assets: $611,834,265
Liabilities: $378,677,621
Net Worth: $233,156,644
Earnings: ($21,269,486)
Emp.: 1,811
Fiscal Year-end: 12/31/12
Business Description:
Wool, Textiles & Protective Surfacing Mfr
Export
S.I.C.: 2399
N.A.I.C.S.: 314999
Personnel:
Eduardo Malone *(Chm & CEO)*
Laurent Derolez *(Mng Dir-Protective Films)*
Bernard Vossart *(Mng Dir)*
Martine Odillard *(COO)*
Board of Directors:
Eduardo Malone
Martine Odillard
Giuseppe Pirola
Georges Ralli
Jerome Seydoux
PricewaterhouseCoopers Audit SA
63, rue de Villiers
Neuilly-sur-Seine, France
Subsidiaries:

Chargeurs Fabrics (1)
38 rue Marbeuf
09301 Paris, Cedex 1, France (100%)
Tel.: (33) 149531000
Fax: (33) 149531001
E-Mail: chargeurs@chargeurs.fr
Web Site: www.chargeurs.fr
Garment Fabric Mfr
S.I.C.: 2295
N.A.I.C.S.: 313320
Christian Laffont *(Mng Dir)*

Subsidiaries:

Avelana (2)
Saint Nestor
PO Box 105
9301 Villeneuve d'Olmes, Lavelanet, France (100%)
Tel.: (33) 561032222
Fax: (33) 561032200
E-Mail: avelana@avelana.com
Web Site: www.avelana.com
Emp.: 250
Wool-Lycra Blend Fabric Mfr
S.I.C.: 2389
N.A.I.C.S.: 315990
Lasfont Ghristeran *(Mng Dir)*

Lepoutre Ternynck (2)
Zi De La Martinoire 1 Rue Jacquard
BP 40039
59392 Wattrelos, Cedex, France
Tel.: (33) 320233030
Fax: (33) 320233030
E-Mail: lepoutre@lepoutre.fr
Web Site: www.lepoutre.fr
Emp.: 12
Stretch Fabric Mfr
S.I.C.: 2399
N.A.I.C.S.: 315990

Roudiere SA (2)
1 Bis Chemin De La Coume
PO Box 38
9300 Lavelanet, France (100%)
Tel.: (33) 561032000
Fax: (33) 561032011
E-Mail: roudiere@roudiere.com
Web Site: www.roudiere.com
Woolen Fabric Mfr
S.I.C.: 2399
N.A.I.C.S.: 315990

Chargeurs Interlining (1)
BP 89
Buires Courcelles, 80202 Peronne, Cedex, France (100%)
Tel.: (33) 322734000
Fax: (33) 322734001
Web Site: www.chargeurs.fr
Emp.: 300
Garment Interlinings Mfr
S.I.C.: 2295
N.A.I.C.S.: 313320

Subsidiaries:

Chargeurs Interlining (2)
BP 89
Buires Courcelles, 80202 Peronne, Cedex, France (100%)
Tel.: (33) 322734000
Fax: (33) 322838399
E-Mail: contact@chargeurs-interlining.com
Web Site: www.chargeurs-interlining.com
Emp.: 200
Fabric Mfr
S.I.C.: 2269
N.A.I.C.S.: 313310
Rigaut Stephane *(Mgr)*

DHJ International (2)
4 Rue Frederic
Meyer, 67600 Selestat, France (100%)
Tel.: (33) 388850777
Fax: (33) 388822821
Web Site: www.dhjinternational.com
Emp.: 250
Garment Interlining & Technical Fabric Mfr
S.I.C.: 2399
N.A.I.C.S.: 315990

Interlana S.r.o (2)
Svermova 21
460 10 Liberec, 10, Czech Republic
Tel.: (420) 488055555
Fax: (420) 488055562
Web Site: www.chargeurs-interlining.com
Garment Interlining Mfr
S.I.C.: 2399
N.A.I.C.S.: 315990

Lainiere de Picardie BC (2)
BP 89
80202 Peronne, Cedex, France (100%)
Tel.: (33) 322838383
Fax: (33) 322838360
E-Mail: lain@scarguarsinterlining.com
Web Site: www.lainieredepicardie.com
Emp.: 300
Garment Interlining Mfr
S.I.C.: 2389
N.A.I.C.S.: 315990
Sebastien Paillet *(Dir-Mktg)*

Subsidiaries:

Lainiere de Picardie Argentina S.A. (3)
Avda Brasil 2543
1260 Buenos Aires, Argentina (100%)
Tel.: (54) 43080096
Fax: (54) 11497202
Web Site: www.entamer.com.ar
Emp.: 50
Garment Interlining Mfr
S.I.C.: 2399
N.A.I.C.S.: 315990

Lainiere de Picardie Golaplast Brazil Textil Ltda (3)
450 Rua Urbano Santos Cumbica
Sao Paulo, Cumbica Garhulhos, CEP 07183-280, Brazil (100%)
Tel.: (55) 11 64 32 50 08
Fax: (55) 11 64 32 53 85
Web Site. www.lainieredepicardie.com
Emp.: 44
Garment Interlining Mfr

S.I.C.: 2399
N.A.I.C.S.: 315990
Rafael Soler *(Mgr)*

Lainiere de Picardie Deutschland GmbH (3)
Rossdorfer Strasse 48
Messel, D 64409 Darmstadt, Germany (100%)
Tel.: (49) 61599173
Fax: (49) 6159917420
Web Site: www.lainieredepicardie.com
Garment Interlining Mfr
S.I.C.: 2399
N.A.I.C.S.: 315990

Lainiere de Picardie Hispana S.A. (3)
Avenida Conde De Torroja 16
28022 Madrid, Spain (100%)
Tel.: (34) 917474999
Fax: (34) 91329481
E-Mail: lpespana@administrator.com
Web Site: www.lainieredepicardie.com
Emp.: 7
Garment Interlining Mfr
S.I.C.: 2399
N.A.I.C.S.: 315990
Antonio Martins *(Mgr)*

Lainiere de Picardie, Inc. (3)
835 Wheeler Way Ste A
Langhorne, PA 19047
Tel.: (215) 702-9090
Fax: (215) 702-9040
Web Site: www.lainieredepicardie.com
Emp.: 70
Garment Interlining Mfr
S.I.C.: 5199
N.A.I.C.S.: 424310
John Suhuss *(Gen Mgr)*

Lainiere de Picardie UK Ltd (3)
5 Danbury Ct
Linford Wood, Milton Keynes, Buckinghamshire, MK14 6PQ, United Kingdom (100%)
Tel.: (44) 8701213160
Fax: (44) 8701213161
E-Mail: lpup@georgiainterlining.com
Web Site: www.lainieredepicardie.com
Emp.: 4
Garment Interlining Mfr
S.I.C.: 2399
N.A.I.C.S.: 315990

Lainiere de Picardie Uruguay S.A. (3)
Lainiere De Picadie Argentina S A
Avda Brasil 2543, 1260 Buenos Aires, Argentina (100%)
Tel.: (54) 43080096
Fax: (54) 49417202
Web Site: www.lainieredepicardie.com
Garment Interlining Mfr
S.I.C.: 2389
N.A.I.C.S.: 315990

Stroud Riley (Pty) Ltd (2)
12 Lindsay Rd
Korsten, Port Elizabeth, Eastern Cape, 6001, South Africa (100%)
Tel.: (27) 414531990
Fax: (27) 414535798
E-Mail: sr@chargeurs-interlining.com
Web Site: www.chargeurs-interlining.com
Emp.: 11
Garment Interlining Mfr
S.I.C.: 2399
N.A.I.C.S.: 315990
Anthony Allen *(Mng Dir)*

Chargeurs Protective Films (1)
27 Rue Du Dr Emile Bataille
PO Box 4
Deville les Rouen, 76250 Rouen, France (100%)
Tel.: (33) 232827232
Fax: (33) 235754724
E-Mail: info@chargeurs.com
Web Site: www.chargeurs-protective.com
Emp.: 250
Mfr of Temporary Protective Films
S.I.C.: 2672
N.A.I.C.S.: 322220

U.S. Subsidiaries:

Novacel, Inc. (2)
21 3rd St
Palmer, MA 01069-1542
Tel.: (413) 283-3468
Web Site: www.novacel.com
Emp.: 200
Mfr. of Protective Coatings
S.I.C.: 2671
N.A.I.C.S.: 322220
Mike Desjardins *(Mgr-Logistic)*

Unit:

Troy Laminating & Coating, Inc. (3)
421 S Union St
Troy, OH 45373-4151
Tel.: (937) 335-5611
Fax: (937) 339-9223
E-Mail: tlc@chargeurs-protective.com
Web Site: www.troylaminatingandcoating.com
Emp.: 100
Mfr. of Coated & Laminated Products
S.I.C.: 2621
N.A.I.C.S.: 322121
Dave Bullard *(Mng Dir)*

Subsidiaries:

Boston Tapes S.p.A (2)
Via G Sitori 45
Passirana di Rho, 20017 Milan, Italy(100%)
Tel.: (39) 2937521
Fax: (39) 29301605, ext. 23933704
E-Mail: csom@bostontapes.it
Web Site: www.bostontapes.it
Mfr of Protective Coatings
S.I.C.: 2851
N.A.I.C.S.: 325510

Novacel GmbH (2)
Normandie Strasse 3
50259 Pulheim, Germany (100%)
Tel.: (49) 223498740
Fax: (49) 2234987475
E-Mail: novacel_germany@chargeursprotective.com
Web Site: www.novacel.de
Sls.: $30,045,116
Emp.: 20
Mfr of Protective Coatings
S.I.C.: 2851
N.A.I.C.S.: 325510
Karl Frideric Boehle *(Mng Dir)*

Novacel Iberica S.p.A. (2)
Poligono Industrial Pla d'En Coll Calle del Mig No 23 esq c Segre sn
Montcada i Reixac, 08110 Barcelona, Spain
Tel.: (34) 935752252
Fax: (34) 935751987
E-Mail: novaceliberica@chargeurs-protective.com
Web Site: www.chargeurs-protective.com
Mfr of Protective Coatings
S.I.C.: 2851
N.A.I.C.S.: 325510

Novacel Italia S.R.L (2)
Via Machiavelli 6/8
20028 Legnano, MI, Italy
Tel.: (39) 00293990001
Fax: (39) 00293500580
E-Mail: novacel_italy@chargeurs-protective.com
Web Site: www.chargeurs-protective.com
Mfr of Protective Coatings
S.I.C.: 2851
N.A.I.C.S.: 325510

Novacel Shanghai (2)
159 5 Jiugan Rd Sijing Indus Pk Sec 2
Shanghai, 201601, China (100%)
Tel.: (86) 157617568
Fax: (86) 157617445
E-Mail: liu@chargeursprotective.com
Web Site: www.chargeursprotective.com
Emp.: 17
Mfr of Protective Coatings
S.I.C.: 2851
N.A.I.C.S.: 325510

Novacel UK Ltd (2)
Unit 6 Sundon Bus Pk
Dencorra Way, Luton, Bedfordshire, LU3 3HP, United Kingdom (100%)
Tel.: (44) 582490945
Fax: (44) 582490946
E-Mail: novacel_uk@chargeursprotective.com
Web Site: www.novacel.be/modules.php?name=Content&pa=showpage&pid=17
Emp.: 20
Mfr of Protective Coatings
S.I.C.: 2851
N.A.I.C.S.: 325510

Novacel (2)
27 Rue Du Docteur Emille Bataille
PO Box 4
Deville Les Rouen, 76250 Rouen, France (100%)
Tel.: (33) 232827222
Fax: (33) 232827252
E-Mail: novacel@chargeurs-protective.com
Web Site: www.novacel.fr
Emp.: 200
Mfr of Protective Coatings
S.I.C.: 2851
N.A.I.C.S.: 325510
Guroluz Lauaunt *(Mng Dir)*

S.A Novacel Belgium NV (2)
Doornveld 21
1730 Zellik, Belgium
Tel.: (32) 24665247
Fax: (32) 24669453
E-Mail: novacel_belgium@chargeurs-protective.com
Web Site: www.chargeurs-protective.com
Mfr of Protective Coatings
S.I.C.: 2851
N.A.I.C.S.: 325510

Chargeurs Wool (1)
159 Ave Delamarne Parc De La Marcqren Baroeul
59700 Wattrelos, France (100%)
Tel.: (33) 320996868
Fax: (33) 320996881
E-Mail: chargeurs@chargeurs.fr
Web Site: www.chargeurs.fr
Emp.: 10
Wool Tops Mfr
S.I.C.: 2269
N.A.I.C.S.: 313310
Edourado Malone *(Mng Dir)*

U.S. Subsidiary:

Chargeurs Wool (USA) Inc. (2)
178 Wool Rd
Jamestown, SC 29453
Tel.: (843) 257-2212
Protective Fabric Mfr
S.I.C.: 2299
N.A.I.C.S.: 313210
Martin Doldan *(Controller)*

Subsidiary:

Chargeurs Wool (Argentina) SA (2)
Avenida De Mayo 605 Piso 11
C1084 AAB Buenos Aires, Argentina (100%)
Tel.: (54) 143457983
Fax: (54) 143420631
E-Mail: cwarg@cwarg.com.ar
Web Site: www.chargeurs.fr
Wool Tops Mfr
S.I.C.: 2299
N.A.I.C.S.: 313310
Richard von Gerstenberg *(Mng Dir)*

Intissel SAS (1)
Rue Jacquard - ZI de la Martinoire
BP 107
59393 Wattrelos, France
Tel.: (33) 320116050
Fax: (33) 320116092
Web Site: www.intissel.com
Textile Non Woven Fabric Mfr
S.I.C.: 2297
N.A.I.C.S.: 313230
Philippe Marem *(Mgr)*

Non-U.S. Subsidiaries:

Chargeurs Entretelas (Portugal) Ltd (1)
Rua de Sangemil 175
Aguas Santas, 4425-692 Maia, Portugal
Tel.: (351) 229783140
Fax: (351) 229720197
Textile Products Mfr
S.I.C.: 2299
N.A.I.C.S.: 314999
Antonio Martins *(Gen Mgr)*

Chargeurs Interfodere Italia S.p.A. (1)
Via Oratorio 48
20016 Pero, Milan, Italy
Tel.: (39) 023537121
Fax: (39) 023561430
Web Site: www.chargeurs-interfodere.com
Emp.: 3
Textile Interlining Mfr
S.I.C.: 2299
N.A.I.C.S.: 314999
Fabio Sgattoni *(Mng Dir)*

Chargeurs Interlining (HK) Limited (1)
Unit 1501 COL Tower Wharf T & T Square
123 Hoi Bun Road
Kwun Tong, Kowloon, China (Hong Kong)
Tel.: (852) 27556788
Fax: (852) 27559873
Textile Products Mfr
S.I.C.: 2389
N.A.I.C.S.: 314999

Chargeurs Wool Sales (Europe) SRL (1)
Via Candelo 60
13900 Biella, Italy
Tel.: (39) 0152528400
Fax: (39) 0152528450
Textile Products Mfr
S.I.C.: 2299
N.A.I.C.S.: 314999

Chargeurs Wool (South Africa) (Pty) Ltd (1)
163 Main Road Warmer
Port Elizabeth, Eastern Cape, 6070, South Africa
Tel.: (27) 415810081
Fax: (27) 415810212
Emp.: 2
Textile Wool Distr
S.I.C.: 5137
N.A.I.C.S.: 424330

DHJ Interlining Limited (1)
No 2680 Zhulu West Rd
Qingpu Xujing, Shanghai, China
Tel.: (86) 2169762683
Fax: (86) 2169762693
Emp.: 20
Textile Products Mfr
S.I.C.: 2399
N.A.I.C.S.: 314999
Chuck Lai *(Gen Mgr)*

DHJ (Malaysia) Sdn Bhd (1)
27 Lebuh Perusahaan Kelebang 11
Perak Darul Ridzuan, Chemor, 31200, Malaysia
Tel.: (60) 52912345
Fax: (60) 52915185
Textile Products Mfr
S.I.C.: 2389
N.A.I.C.S.: 314999
Fred Chi Siong Lau *(Mng Dir)*

Lainiere de Picardie Korea Co. Ltd (1)
4 F Sebang Bldg 935-40 Bangbae-dong
Seocho-ku, Seoul, Korea (South)
Tel.: (82) 25847311
Fax: (82) 25861367
E-Mail: chloe@picardie.co.kr
Emp.: 22
Textile Products Mfr
S.I.C.: 2299
N.A.I.C.S.: 314999
Ko Yoong-Sik *(Mgr)*

Lanas Trinidad SA (1)
Miami Street 2047
11500 Montevideo, Uruguay
Tel.: (598) 26010024
Fax: (598) 26060032
E-Mail: cwuruguay@wtp.com.uy
Web Site: www.lanastrinidad.com
Sls.: $50,000,000
Wool Tops Mfr & Distr
S.I.C.: 2269
N.A.I.C.S.: 313310
Pedro Otegui *(Gen Mgr)*

Ningbo Chargeurs Yak Textile Trading Co. Ltd (1)
No 501 Yayuan S Rd Shigan St
Yinzhou Dist, Ningbo, 315153, China
Tel.: (86) 57488251123
Fax: (86) 57488253567
Emp.: 800
Textile Products Mfr
S.I.C.: 2299

Chargeurs SA—(Continued)

N.A.I.C.S.: 314999
Chuck Lai *(Gen Mgr)*

Yangtse Wool Combing Co. Ltd **(1)**
European Industrial Park Tangshi
Yangshe Town, Zhangjiagang, China
Tel.: (86) 51258592144
Fax: (86) 51258592302
Textile Products Mfr
S.I.C.: 2399
N.A.I.C.S.: 314999

CHARILAOS APOSTOLIDES PUBLIC LTD.

75 Athalassa Avenue 1st Floor Chapo Tower
Strovolos, 2012 Nicosia, Cyprus
Mailing Address:
PO Box 24819
1304 Nicosia, Cyprus
Tel.: (357) 22312000
Fax: (357) 22496795
E-Mail: chapoinfo@chapogroup.com
Web Site: www.chapogroup.com
Year Founded: 1949
CHAP—(CYP)
Sales Range: $75-99.9 Million
Emp.: 583
Business Description:
Building & Civil Engineering Services
S.I.C.: 8711
N.A.I.C.S.: 541330
Personnel:
George Photiou *(Mng Dir)*
Chris Matthew *(Sec & Dir-Dev)*
Board of Directors:
Mikis A. Ioannou
Christos Papastavrou
Lambros Pelekanos
Nicolaos Philippou
George Photiou
Harris G. Photiou

Subsidiaries:

Chapomed Ltd **(1)**
75 Athalassis Ave Chapo Bldg
PO Box 24765
1303 Nicosia, Cyprus (100%)
Tel.: (357) 22497874
Fax: (357) 22497924
E-Mail: chapomed@chapomed.com
Web Site: www.chapogroup.com
Emp.: 40
Engineering Services
S.I.C.: 8711
N.A.I.C.S.: 541330
Costas Assiotis *(Mng Dir)*

Getian General Services Ltd **(1)**
Tseriou Avenue
Strovolos Municipality, Nicosia, Cyprus (100%)
Tel.: (357) 22323533
Fax: (357) 22323421
E-Mail: info@ggs.com.cy
Web Site: www.ggs.com.cy
Emp.: 50
Concrete Contractors
S.I.C.: 1771
N.A.I.C.S.: 238110
Andreas Phociou *(Gen Mgr)*

CHARIOT CARRIERS INC.

105 5760 9th Street SE
Calgary, AB, T2H 1Z9, Canada
Tel.: (403) 640-0822
Fax: (403) 640-0759
E-Mail: ask.us@chariotcarriers.com
Web Site: www.chariotcarriers.com
Year Founded: 1992
Rev.: $32,054,292
Emp.: 180
Business Description:
Child Carrier Products Mfr
S.I.C.: 3944
N.A.I.C.S.: 339930

CHARIOT OIL & GAS LIMITED

Regency Court Glategny Esplanade
PO Box 282
Saint Peter Port, Guernsey GY1 3RH
Tel.: (44) 2073180450
Fax: (44) 2074092169
Web Site: www.chariotoilandgas.com
CHAR—(AIM)
Rev.: $1,561,000
Assets: $215,853,000
Liabilities: $19,207,000
Net Worth: $196,646,000
Earnings: ($88,561,000)
Emp.: 20
Fiscal Year-end: 12/31/12
Business Description:
Oil & Gas Exploration Services
S.I.C.: 1311
N.A.I.C.S.: 211111
Personnel:
Adonis Pouroulis *(Founder)*
Larry Anthony Bottomley *(CEO)*
Mark Reid *(CFO)*
Board of Directors:
George Frances Canjar
David Hamilton Bodecott
Larry Anthony Bottomley
Heindrich Steven Ndume
Adonis Pouroulis
Mark Reid
Robert Archibald Gilchrist Sinclair
Matthew Taylor
William Roger Trojan
Legal Counsel:
Memery Crystal LLP
44 Southampton Buildings
London, United Kingdom

Lorentz Angula Inc.
Windhoek 3rd floor LA Chambers Ausspann Plaza
Windhoek, Namibia

Babbe
1820 Smith Street
PO Box 69
Saint Peter Port, Guernsey GY1 3EL

Allen & Overy
Twin Center Tour A 7th floor Corner of Boulevard Zerktouni
Massira Al Khadra, Casablanca, 20000, Morocco

CHARKHESHGAR CO.

No 172 Shahid Vahid Dastgerdi Zafar St
Tehran, Iran
Tel.: (98) 21 2276773
Fax: (98) 21 2276710
E-Mail: info@charkheshgar.com
Web Site: www.charkheshgar.com
Year Founded: 1969
CHAR—(THE)
Business Description:
Transmission & Steering Mfr
S.I.C.: 3714
N.A.I.C.S.: 336350
Personnel:
Vali Maleki *(Chm)*
Davoud Yaghoubi *(Mng Dir)*
Nasser Shahlaei Motlagh *(Exec VP)*
Board of Directors:
Vali Maleki
Naser Baghinejad
Seyed Majid Bakhtiari
Ewald Schnepp
Davoud Yaghoubi

CHARLEMAGNE CAPITAL (UK) LIMITED

39 St James's Street
London, SW1A 1JD, United Kingdom
Tel.: (44) 2075182100
Fax: (44) 2075182199
E-Mail: marketing@charlemagnecapital.com
Web Site: www.charlemagnecapital.com
Year Founded: 2000
CCAP—(LSE)
Rev.: $30,708,000
Assets: $43,976,000
Liabilities: $12,940,000
Net Worth: $31,036,000
Earnings: $5,107,000
Emp.: 61
Fiscal Year-end: 12/31/12
Business Description:
Investment Management Services
S.I.C.: 6211
N.A.I.C.S.: 523999
Personnel:
Jayne Sutcliffe *(CEO)*
Jane McAndry *(Sec)*
Board of Directors:
Michael Baer
Adrian Jones
Huw Lloyd Jones
Ian Bruce Lang
Jane McAndry
James Mellon
Jayne Sutcliffe
Jacob Johan van Duijn
Legal Counsel:
Stephenson Harwood
1 Finsbury Circus
London, United Kingdom

Non-U.S. Subsidiary:

Charlemagne Capital (IOM) Limited **(1)**
Saint Mary's Court 20 Hill Street
Douglas, IM1 1EU, Isle of Man
Tel.: (44) 1624640200
Fax: (44) 1624614475
E-Mail: marketing@charlemagnecapital.com
Emp.: 34
Investment Management Services
S.I.C.: 6799
N.A.I.C.S.: 523920
Andrea Matthews *(Office Mgr)*

CHARLES ENGLISH MOTOR CARS LTD.

(d/b/a Jaguar Calgary)
1100 Meridian Rd NE
Calgary, AB, T2A 2N9, Canada
Tel.: (403) 571-3077
Fax: (403) 571-3070
Toll Free: (866) 641-7972
Web Site: www.jaguarcalgary.com
Year Founded: 1950
Rev.: $26,844,000
Emp.: 33
Business Description:
New & Used Car Dealers
S.I.C.: 5511
N.A.I.C.S.: 441110
Personnel:
Tom Glen *(Owner & Pres)*

CHARLES STANLEY GROUP PLC

25 Luke Street
London, EC2A 4AR, United Kingdom
Tel.: (44) 2077398200
Fax: (44) 2077397798
E-Mail: info@charles-stanley.co.uk
Web Site: www.charles-stanley.co.uk
CAY—(LSE)
Rev.: $201,465,287
Assets: $556,458,094
Liabilities: $426,927,886
Net Worth: $129,530,207
Earnings: $10,664,945
Emp.: 827
Fiscal Year-end: 03/31/13
Business Description:
Stockbroking Services
S.I.C.: 6799
N.A.I.C.S.: 523920
Personnel:
David Howard *(Chm & Mng Dir)*
Gary Teper *(Sec)*
Board of Directors:
David Howard
E. Michael Clark
Bridget Guerin
Michael R. I. Lilwall
David Pusinelli
James Rawlingson
Gary Teper

Subsidiaries:

Charles Stanley & Co Ltd **(1)**
25 Luke St
London, EC2A 4AR, United Kingdom
Tel.: (44) 2077398200
Fax: (44) 2077397798
E-Mail: stephan.king@charles-stanley.co.uk
Emp.: 800
Brokerage Services, Investment Advice & Asset Management
S.I.C.: 6282
N.A.I.C.S.: 523930
David Howard *(Chm)*

Subsidiary:

Rock (Nominees) Limited **(2)**
25 Luke Street
London, United Kingdom
Tel.: (44) 2071496000
Fax: (44) 2077397798
Web Site: charlesstanley.co.uk
Emp.: 850
Securities Brokerage Services
S.I.C.: 6211
N.A.I.C.S.: 523120
David Howard *(Mng Dir)*

EBS (Management) Plc **(1)**
25 Luke Street
London, EC2A 4AR, United Kingdom
Tel.: (44) 2077398200
Fax: (44) 74196960
E-Mail: info@ebsmanagement.co.uk
Web Site: www.ebsmanagement.co.uk
Emp.: 20
Pension Fund Management
S.I.C.: 6371
N.A.I.C.S.: 524292
David Howard *(Chm)*

EBS Pensioneer Trustees Limited **(1)**
25 Luke Street
London, EC2A4AR, United Kingdom
Tel.: (44) 2079532560
Fax: (44) 2079532152
E-Mail: enquries@charles-stanley.co.uk
Web Site: www.ebsmanagement.co.uk
Emp.: 18
Pension Funds
S.I.C.: 6371
N.A.I.C.S.: 525110

Garrison Investment Analysis Limited **(1)**
5-7 Landress Lane
Beverley, East Yorkshire, HU17 8HA, United Kingdom
Tel.: (44) 1482861455
Fax: (44) 1482889828
E-Mail: admin@fundchoice.co.uk
Web Site: www.fundchoice.co.uk
Emp.: 12
Financial Management Consulting Services
S.I.C.: 8742
N.A.I.C.S.: 541611
John Shires *(Mng Dir)*

EBS Self-Administered Personal Pension Plan Trustees Limited **(1)**
25 Luke Street
London, EC2A4AR, United Kingdom
Tel.: (44) 2079532560
Fax: (44) 2071496960
E-Mail: info@ebsmanagement.co.uk
Web Site: www.ebsmanagement.co.uk
Emp.: 800
Pension Funds
S.I.C.: 6371
N.A.I.C.S.: 525110
Kate Rignauth *(Dir)*

CHARLES TAYLOR PLC

Standard House 12 13 Essex Street
London, WC2R 3AA, United Kingdom
Tel.: (44) 2033208888

Fax: (44) 2033208800
E-Mail: headoffice@ctcplc.com
Web Site: www.charlestaylorconsulting.com
CTR—(LSE)
Rev.: $170,883,916
Assets: $809,504,572
Liabilities: $720,099,386
Net Worth: $89,405,186
Earnings: $8,487,104
Emp.: 929
Fiscal Year-end: 12/31/12
Business Description:
Consulting & Management Services
S.I.C.: 8742
N.A.I.C.S.: 541611
Personnel:
David Gideon Marock *(Grp CEO)*
Tito Marzio Soso *(Grp CFO)*
Thomas Damian Ely *(COO)*
Michael Edwin Peachey *(Chief Risk Officer)*
Stephen Williams *(Compliance Officer)*
Richard Cornah *(Chm-RHL)*
Joe McMahon *(Chm-Adjusting)*
Stephen Card *(CEO-CTIS)*
Arthur Clarke *(CEO-Adjusting)*
Martin Fone *(CEO-Specialty Risk Dept)*
Jeffrey More *(CEO-LCL Isle of Man)*
Ivan Keane *(Gen Counsel & Sec)*
David Lanchester *(Deputy Sec)*
Board of Directors:
Rupert Hugo Wynne Robson
Charles Julian Cazalet
Edward Creasy
Thomas Damian Ely
David Gideon Marock
Gill Rider
Joseph Garland Roach, III
Tito Marzio Soso
David Watson
Subsidiaries:

Axiom Broker Services Ltd (1)
Lloyds Chambers 1 Portsoken Street
London, E1 8BT, United Kingdom
Tel.: (44) 20 7767 2700
Fax: (44) 20 7767 2704
Emp.: 100
General Insurance Services
S.I.C.: 6311
N.A.I.C.S.: 524113
Stephen Card *(CEO)*

Bestpark International Limited (1)
Lloyds Chambers 1 Portsoken St
E1 8BT London, United Kingdom (100%)
Tel.: (44) 2077672700
Fax: (44) 2076234352
Emp.: 20
Insurance Agencies & Brokerages
S.I.C.: 6411
N.A.I.C.S.: 524210
Andrew Brinnon *(Chm)*

Charles Taylor Adjusting Limited (1)
88 Leadenhall Street
London, EC3A 3BA, United Kingdom
Tel.: (44) 2076231819
Fax: (44) 20 7702 3987
E-Mail: headoffice@stplc.com
Web Site: www.charlestayloradj.com
Emp.: 200
General Insurance Services
S.I.C.: 6411
N.A.I.C.S.: 524210
Arthur Clarke *(CEO)*

Subsidiary:

Charles Taylor Aviation (Asset Management) Limited. (2)
Second Floor Office Suite New House
Market Place
Ringwood, Hampshire, PH24 1EN, United Kingdom
Tel.: (44) 1725 511144
Web Site: www.ctaam.com
Emp.: 8
Aviation Consulting Services
S.I.C.: 8748
N.A.I.C.S.: 541618
Jeff Solomon *(Mng Dir)*

Charles Taylor Administration Services Limited (1)
5th Floor Cathedral Buildings Dean Street
Newcastle upon Tyne, Tyne and Wear, NE1 1PG, United Kingdom
Tel.: (44) 1912322745
Emp.: 5
Secretarial Services
S.I.C.: 7389
N.A.I.C.S.: 561410
Susan Green *(Mng Dir)*

Charles Taylor & Co Ltd (1)
Standard House 12-13 Essex Street
London, WC2R 3AA, United Kingdom
Tel.: (44) 2074883494
Fax: (44) 203 3208800
E-Mail: headoffice@ctplc.com
Web Site: www.charlestaylorconsulting.com
Emp.: 200
Employee Benifit Services
S.I.C.: 6371
N.A.I.C.S.: 525110
David Marock *(Mng Dir)*

Charles Taylor Insurance Services Limited (1)
Lloyds Chambers 1 Portsoken Street
London, E1 8BT, United Kingdom
Tel.: (44) 2077672700
Fax: (44) 20 7767 2999
E-Mail: enquiries@ctinsuranceservices.co.uk
Web Site: www.ctinsuranceservices.co.uk
General Insurance Services
S.I.C.: 6411
N.A.I.C.S.: 524210
Stephen Card *(CEO)*

Charles Taylor Investment Management Company Limited (1)
Standard House 12-13 Essex St
London, WC2R 3AA, United Kingdom
Tel.: (44) 20 7488 3494
Fax: (44) 20 3320 8800
E-Mail: headoffice@ctplc.com
Web Site: www.charlestaylorconsulting.com
Emp.: 200
Investment Management Services
S.I.C.: 6211
N.A.I.C.S.: 523999

LCL Acquisitions Limited (1)
Lloyds Chambers 1 Portsoken Street
London, E1 8BT, United Kingdom
Tel.: (44) 20 7767 2700
Fax: (44) 20 7767 2999
E-Mail: enquiries@lcl-group.com
Web Site: www.lcl-group.com
Reinsurance Services
S.I.C.: 6399
N.A.I.C.S.: 524130
Andrew Holland *(COO)*

LCL Group Limited (1)
Lloyds Chambers 1 Portsoken St
E1 8BT London, United Kingdom (100%)
Tel.: (44) 2077672700
Fax: (44) 2077672700
Web Site: www.lcl-group.com
Emp.: 8
Reinsurance Carriers
S.I.C.: 6399
N.A.I.C.S.: 524130

The Richards Hogg Lindley Group Limited (1)
88 Leadenhall St
EC3A3BA London, United Kingdom (100%)
Tel.: (44) 2076231819
Fax: (44) 2070152091
Web Site: www.charlestaylor.com
Emp.: 150
Insurance Agencies & Brokerages
S.I.C.: 6411
N.A.I.C.S.: 524210
Andrew Patin *(Mng Dir)*

Non-U.S. Subsidiaries:

Charles Taylor Adjusting (Australia) Pty Ltd (1)
Ground Fl 1 Havelock St
Perth, WA, 6005, Australia
Tel.: (61) 893212022
Web Site: www.charlestayloradj.com.au
Insurance Claims Adjusting Services
S.I.C.: 6411
N.A.I.C.S.: 524291

Charles Taylor Consulting (Australia) Pty Ltd (1)
1 Havelock St
Perth, WA, 6005, Australia
Tel.: (61) 893212022
Fax: (61) 292529070
General Insurance Services
S.I.C.: 6411
N.A.I.C.S.: 524210

Charles Taylor Consulting (Canada) Inc (1)
321 6 Ave Southwest Ste 910
Calgary, AB, T2P 3H3, Canada
Tel.: (403) 266-3336
Fax: (403) 266-3337
Web Site: www.charlestaylorconsulting.com
Emp.: 25
Insurance Management Consulting Services
S.I.C.: 6411
N.A.I.C.S.: 524298
Bob Moore *(Exec VP)*

Charles Taylor Consulting (Japan) Limited (1)
2-10-12 Kandatsukasamachi Park Side 7 Building 3f
Chiyoda-Ku, Tokyo, 101-0048, Japan
Tel.: (81) 332558640
Fax: (81) 352974701
Web Site: www.rhlg.com
General Insurance Services
S.I.C.: 6411
N.A.I.C.S.: 524210

Charles Taylor (Hamilton) Ltd (1)
PO Box HM1743
Hamilton, HMGX, Bermuda (100%)
Tel.: (441) 292 9157
Fax: (441) 292 8992
Emp.: 11
Other Management Consulting Services
S.I.C.: 8748
N.A.I.C.S.: 541618
John Rowe *(CEO)*

CTC Services (Malaysia) SDN Bhd (1)
602/6 Menara Mutiara Majestic 15 Jalan Othman
46000 Petaling Jaya, Selangor, Malaysia
Tel.: (60) 377812260
Fax: (60) 377812261
Emp.: 3
Marine Surveying Services
S.I.C.: 4499
N.A.I.C.S.: 488390

LCL Services (IOM) Limited (1)
St Georges Court Upper Church Street
Douglas, IM1 1EE, Isle of Man
Tel.: (44) 1624683699
Fax: (44) 1624683799
E-Mail: enquiries@lcl.co.im
Web Site: www.lcl.co.im
Emp.: 20
General Insurance Services
S.I.C.: 6411
N.A.I.C.S.: 524210
Jeffrey More *(CEO)*
Stuart Fairclough *(Chm-Ops-Life Insurance Div)*
Peter Craddock *(Sec & Dir-Fin)*

LCL Services (Ireland) Limited (1)
10 Herbert Street
Dublin, 2, Ireland
Tel.: (353) 1 6766620
Fax: (353) 1 6624289
E-Mail: enquiries@lcl-group.com
Web Site: www.lcl-group.ie
Emp.: 2
General Insurance Services
S.I.C.: 6411
N.A.I.C.S.: 524210
Gavin MacDonagh *(Controller-Fin)*

Overseas Adjusters and Surveyors Co (1)
1205-7 12 F 237 Fu Hsing South Road Section 2
Taipei, 106, Taiwan
Tel.: (886) 2 2706 6509
Fax: (886) 2 2700 1441
Marine Consulting Services
S.I.C.: 8748
N.A.I.C.S.: 541618

PT Radita Hutama Internusa (1)
Kawasan Niaga dan Hunian Terpadu
Sudirman JL Jend Sudirman Kav 52-53
Jakarta, 12190, Indonesia
Tel.: (62) 215152084
Fax: (62) 215152085
Emp.: 40
General Insurance Services
S.I.C.: 6411
N.A.I.C.S.: 524210
Guntur Tampubolon *(Mng Dir)*

Richards Hogg Lindley (Hellas) Ltd. (1)
85 Akti Miaouli Str
185 38 Piraeus, Greece
Tel.: (30) 210 4291 300
Fax: (30) 210 4291 236
Web Site: www.rhlg.com
Emp.: 5
Marine Insurance Services
S.I.C.: 6411
N.A.I.C.S.: 524298
James Greene *(Mgr)*

Richards Hogg Lindley (India) Ltd (1)
319 Maker Chambers V 221 Nariman Point
Mumbai, Maharashtra, 400021, India
Tel.: (91) 22 2283 5851
Fax: (91) 22 2283 5951
Web Site: www.rhlg.com
Emp.: 2
General Insurance Services
S.I.C.: 6411
N.A.I.C.S.: 524210
Alex Pinto *(Mgr)*

CHARLES TYRWHITT LLP.

13 Silver Road
London, W12 7RR, United Kingdom
Tel.: (44) 20 7839 6060
Fax: (44) 20 7839 7272
E-Mail: info@ctshirts.co.uk
Web Site: www.ctshirts.co.uk
Year Founded: 1986
Sales Range: $150-199.9 Million
Emp.: 480
Business Description:
Men Apparel Mfr
S.I.C.: 5699
N.A.I.C.S.: 315220
Personnel:
Nick Wheeler *(Owner)*

CHARLES VOGELE HOLDING AG

Gwattstrasse 15
8808 Pfaffikon, Switzerland
Tel.: (41) 554167111
Fax: (41) 554167171
E-Mail: investor-relations@charles-voegele.com
Web Site: www.charles-voegele.com
VCH—(SWX)
Sls.: $1,048,918,794
Assets: $660,296,676
Liabilities: $407,306,226
Net Worth: $252,990,449
Earnings: ($118,124,019)
Emp.: 6,743
Fiscal Year-end: 12/31/12
Business Description:
Holding Company; Clothing Retailer
S.I.C.: 6719
N.A.I.C.S.: 551112
Personnel:
Hans Ziegler *(Chm-Supervisory Bd)*
Max E. Katz *(Vice Chm-Supervisory Bd)*
Markus Voegeli *(Interim CEO & CFO)*
Matthias Freise *(Interim Chief Pur Officer)*
Supervisory Board of Directors:
Hans Ziegler
Ulla Ertelt

Charles Vogele Holding AG—(Continued)

Matthias Freise
Max E. Katz

Non-U.S. Subsidiary:

Charles Vogele (Netherlands) BV **(1)**
Hyperonenweg 4
3542 AG Utrecht, Netherlands
Tel.: (31) 302405111
Fax: (31) 02405171
Web Site: www.charles-vogele.nl
Emp.: 750
Inexpensive Apparel Stores
S.I.C.: 5699
N.A.I.C.S.: 448150
Richard Turk *(Mng Dir)*

CHARLESGLEN LTD.

(d/b/a Charlesglen Toyota)
21 Crowfoot Circle NW
Calgary, AB, T3G 3J8, Canada
Tel.: (403) 241-0888
Fax: (403) 241-0678
Toll Free: (888) 306-3770
E-Mail: info@charlesglentoyota.com
Web Site: www.charlesglentoyota.com
Year Founded: 1987
Rev.: $90,976,282
Emp.: 90
Business Description:
New & Used Car Dealers
S.I.C.: 5511
N.A.I.C.S.: 441110
Personnel:
Tim Beach *(Gen Mgr-Sls)*

CHARLOTTE RESOURCES LTD.

1500 885 West Georgia Street
Vancouver, BC, V6C 2T8, Canada
Tel.: (604) 696-9020
Fax: (416) 488-0319
E-Mail: eau@jproust.ca
CHT—(CNSX)
Business Description:
Mineral Exploration Services
S.I.C.: 1499
N.A.I.C.S.: 212399
Personnel:
John Graham Proust *(Pres & CEO)*

CHARLWOOD PACIFIC GROUP

1199 West Pender Street Suite 900
Vancouver, BC, V6E 2R1, Canada
Tel.: (604) 718-2600
Fax: (604) 718-2678
Web Site: www.charlwoodpacificgroup.com
Business Description:
Holding Company; Travel, Real Estate & Mortgage Brokerage Franchisor
S.I.C.: 6719
N.A.I.C.S.: 551112
Personnel:
U. Gary Charlwood *(Founder & Chm)*
Christopher Charlwood *(Partner)*
Martin Charlwood *(CEO-Real Estate)*

Subsidiaries:

Centum Financial Group Inc. **(1)**
1199 West Pender Street Suite 700
Vancouver, BC, V6E 2R1, Canada Ca
Tel.: (604) 257-3940
Fax: (604) 257-3949
E-Mail: mail@centum.ca
Web Site: www.centum.ca
Mortgage Brokerage Agency Franchisor
S.I.C.: 6794
N.A.I.C.S.: 533110
U. Gary Charlwood *(Chm & CEO)*
Don Lawby *(Pres)*

Century 21 Canada Limited Partnership **(1)**
1199 West Pender Street Suite 700
Vancouver, BC, V6E 2R1, Canada BC
Tel.: (604) 606-2100
Fax: (604) 606-2125
E-Mail: info@century21.ca
Web Site: www.century21.ca
Real Estate Agency Franchisor
S.I.C.: 6794
N.A.I.C.S.: 533110
U. Gary Charlwood *(Chm & CEO)*
C. Brian Rushton *(Exec VP)*

UNIGLOBE Travel International Limited Partnership **(1)**
1199 West Pender Street Suite 900
Vancouver, BC, V6E 2R1, Canada BC
Tel.: (604) 718-2600
Fax: (604) 718-2678
E-Mail: info@uniglobetravel.com
Web Site: www.uniglobetravel.com
Travel Agency Franchisor
S.I.C.: 6794
N.A.I.C.S.: 533110
U. Gary Charlwood *(Founder, Chm & CEO)*
Martin H. Charlwood *(Pres & COO)*
Tracy Bartram *(CFO & Exec VP)*
John L. Henry *(Sr VP-Dev-Global)*

CHARM CARE CORPORATION K.K.

3-3-3 Nakanoshima Kita-ku
Nakanoshimamitsui Bldg 401
Osaka, 530-0005, Japan
Tel.: (81) 6 6445 3389
Web Site: www.charmcc.jp
Year Founded: 1984
6062—(JAS)
Sales Range: $50-74.9 Million
Emp.: 254
Business Description:
Residential Care Services
S.I.C.: 8361
N.A.I.C.S.: 623990
Personnel:
Takahiko Shimomura *(Pres)*

CHARM COMMUNICATIONS INC.

Legend Town CN01 Floor 4 No 1 Ba Li Zhuang Dong Li
Chaoyang District, Beijing, 100025, China
Tel.: (86) 10 6581 1111
Fax: (86) 10 6583 0100
Web Site: www.charmgroup.cn
CHRM—(NASDAQ)
Rev.: $165,498,000
Assets: $358,630,000
Liabilities: $136,688,000
Net Worth: $221,942,000
Earnings: ($2,476,000)
Emp.: 813
Fiscal Year-end: 12/31/12
Business Description:
Television Advertising Services
S.I.C.: 7311
N.A.I.C.S.: 541810
Personnel:
He Dang *(Founder, Chm & CEO)*
Tony Yu *(CTO)*
Cathy Chen *(Pres-Agency Bus)*
Board of Directors:
He Dang
Andrew J. Rickards
Zhan Wang
Nick Waters

CHARM ENGINEERING CO., LTD.

374-1 Gajang-dong
Osan, Gyeonggi-do, Korea (South)
Tel.: (82) 313700500
Fax: (82) 313700500
E-Mail: irteam@charmeng.com
Web Site: www.charmnci.com
Year Founded: 1973
009310—(KRS)
Business Description:
Semiconductor Products Mfr
S.I.C.: 3674
N.A.I.C.S.: 334413
Personnel:
In-Soo Han *(CEO)*

CHARMS INDUSTRIES LTD.

108-B/109 Sampada Building
Mithakhali Six Roads
Opp-Hare Krishna Complex B/H A K Patel House, Ahmedabad, 380009, India
Tel.: (91) 79 26440404
Fax: (91) 79 26422081
E-Mail: charmsltd@yahoo.com
Web Site: www.charmsindustries.in
531327—(BOM)
Rev.: $664,199
Assets: $412,189
Liabilities: $31,530
Net Worth: $380,659
Earnings: $9,407
Fiscal Year-end: 03/31/13
Business Description:
Foreign Currency Trading Services
S.I.C.: 6221
N.A.I.C.S.: 523130
Personnel:
Shivkumar Chauhan Raghunandan *(Chm, Co-Mng Dir & Compliance Officer)*
Ketan Nalinkant Shah *(Co-Mng Dir)*
Board of Directors:
Shivkumar Chauhan Raghunandan
Harsad Shantilal Gandhi
Ashokkumar Ramanlal Patel
Nishit Madhavbhai Rupapara
Dahyabhai Bhavanjibhai Sachania
Ketan Nalinkant Shah
Nayan Champakdal Shah
Sandip Rajnikant Shah
Transfer Agent:
Sharepro Services (India) Pvt. Ltd.
416-420 4th Floor Devnandan Mall Opp. Sanyash Ashram Ellisbridge
Ahmedabad, India

CHARMWELL HOLDINGS LTD.

9/F Surson Coml Bldg 140-142 Austin Rd
Tsim Sha Tsui, Kowloon, China (Hong Kong)
Tel.: (852) 2314 3668
Fax: (852) 2199 7822
Business Description:
Holding Company
S.I.C.: 6719
N.A.I.C.S.: 551112

U.S. Subsidiary:

Woodland Pulp, LLC **(1)**
144 Main St
Baileyville, ME 04694 (100%)
Tel.: (207) 427-3311
Fax: (207) 427-4102
Web Site: woodlandpulp.com
Emp.: 300
Pulp Mill
S.I.C.: 2611
N.A.I.C.S.: 322110
Scott Beal *(Mgr-Comm)*

CHARN ISSARA DEVELOPMENT PUBLIC COMPANY LIMITED

2922/200 10th Floor Charn Issara Tower II New Petch buri Road
Bangkapi
Huay Kwang, Bangkok, 10320, Thailand
Tel.: (66) 23082020
Fax: (66) 23082990
Web Site: www.charnissara.co.th
Year Founded: 1989
CI—(THA)
Rev.: $70,643,201
Assets: $122,366,907
Liabilities: $78,651,191
Net Worth: $43,715,716
Earnings: $7,069,133
Fiscal Year-end: 12/31/12
Business Description:
Real Estate Development Services
S.I.C.: 6531
N.A.I.C.S.: 531390
Personnel:
Srivara Issara *(Chm)*
Songkran Issara *(Mng Dir)*
Board of Directors:
Srivara Issara
Phisud Dajakaisaya
Songkran Issara
Niti Osathanugrah
Linda Prasertsom
Pinit Puapan
Witit Rachatatanun
Pravesvudhi Raiva
Teeraporn Srijaroenwong

Subsidiary:

Charn Issara Viphapol Company Limited **(1)**
2922/181 New Phetchaburi Road
Huai Khwang, Bangkok, 10310, Thailand
Tel.: (66) 2 308 2016
Real Estate Development Services
S.I.C.: 6531
N.A.I.C.S.: 531390

CHAROEN AKSORN HOLDING GROUP CO. LTD.

1 Charoenrat Road Thung Wat Don Sathon
Bangkok, 10120, Thailand
Tel.: (66) 2210 8888
Fax: (66) 2210 8811
E-Mail: webmaster_group@cas-group.com
Web Site: www.cas-group.com
Sales Range: $75-99.9 Million
Business Description:
Printing Supplies & Equipment Distr
S.I.C.: 5111
N.A.I.C.S.: 424110
Personnel:
Surapol D araratanaroj *(CEO)*

Subsidiary:

Norske Skog (Thailand) Company Ltd. **(1)**
10th Floor Vibulthani Tower I 3195/15 Rama IV Road Klongton
Klongtoey District, Bangkok, 10110, Thailand
Tel.: (66) 2 661 3486
Fax: (66) 2 661 3012
Emp.: 30
Newsprint Mfr
S.I.C.: 2621
N.A.I.C.S.: 322122
Torpong Thongcharoen *(Gen Mgr)*

Unit:

Norske Skog (Thailand) Company Ltd. - Sing Buri **(2)**
64/3 Moo 3 Asian Highway T Phokruam
A Muang, Sing Buri, 16000, Thailand
Tel.: (66) 36 531 111
Fax: (66) 36 531 100
Web Site: www.norskeskog.com
Paper Products Mfr
S.I.C.: 2621
N.A.I.C.S.: 322121
Torpong Thongcharoen *(Gen Mgr)*

CHAROEN POKPHAND FOODS PUBLIC COMPANY LIMITED

CP Tower 313 Silom Road
Bangrak, Bangkok, 10500, Thailand

Tel.: (66) 26258000
Fax: (66) 26257192
E-Mail: consumercenter@cpf.co.th
Web Site: www.cpfworldwide.com
CPF—(THA)
Rev.: $12,418,875,616
Assets: $10,288,331,400
Liabilities: $6,286,863,496
Net Worth: $4,001,467,904
Earnings: $696,360,232
Emp.: 97,942
Fiscal Year-end: 12/31/12

Business Description:
Holding Company; Animal Feed Mfr, Animal Farming & Meat Processing Services
S.I.C.: 6719
N.A.I.C.S.: 551112

Personnel:
Dhanin Chearavanont *(Chm)*
Min Tieanworn *(Vice Chm, Pres, CEO & Acting COO-Food Bus)*
Chingchai Lohawatanakul *(Vice Chm)*
Prasert Poongkumarn *(Vice Chm)*
Pow Sarasin *(Vice Chm)*
Adirek Sripratak *(Vice Chm)*
Paisan Chirakitcharern *(CFO)*
Virachai Ratanabanchuen *(COO-Livestock Bus & Acting Exec VP-Livestock Feed Unit)*
Teerasak Urunanon *(COO-Domestic Trading & Exec VP-Livestock Food Processing Unit)*
Patchara Chartbunchachai *(Sec)*
Anek Boonnoon *(Exec VP-Livestock Farming Unit)*
Somkuan Choowatanapakorn *(Exec VP-Swine Breeding & Farming R&D Unit)*
Praderm Chotsuparach *(Exec VP-IT & Application Unit)*
Sukhawat Dansermsuk *(Exec VP-Ready Meal Unit)*
Voravit Janthanakul *(Exec VP-Gen Admin Unit)*
Vitit Pootanasap *(Exec VP-Aquatic Feed Unit)*
Tinakorn Ruenthip *(Exec VP-HR Unit)*
Sommai Tachasirinugune *(Exec VP-Aquatic Food Processing Unit)*
Vittavat Tantivess *(Exec VP-Mktg Unit)*
Sujint Thammasart *(Exec VP-Aquatic Farming Unit & Aquatic Breeding & Farming R&D)*
Prajit Udnoon *(Exec VP-Poultry Breeding & Farming R&D Unit)*

Board of Directors:
Dhanin Chearavanont
Sunthorn Arunanondchain
Phongthep Chiaravanont
Veeravat Kanchanadul
Chingchai Lohawatanakul
Prasert Poongkumarn
Supapun Ruttanaporn
Arsa Sarasin
Pow Sarasin
Adirek Sripratak
Min Tieanworn
Athasit Vejjajiva
Pong Visedpaitoon
Arunee Watcharananan
Chaiyawat Wibulsawasdi

BNY Mellon Shareowner Services
PO Box 358516
Pittsburgh, PA 15252-8516

Subsidiaries:

Bangkok Agro-Industrial Products Public Company Limited **(1)**
64 Navathani Village Soi 3 Sukhaphiban 2 Khwang
Khlong Kum Khet Buengkum, Bangkok, Thailand
Tel.: (66) 26804500
Fax: (66) 2680 4692
Animal Feed Mfr
S.I.C.: 2047
N.A.I.C.S.: 311111

Bangkok Food Products Co., Ltd. **(1)**
Ramkhamhaeng 24 Rd Hua Mak
Bang Kapi, Bangkok, 10240, Thailand
Tel.: (66) 26759859
Fax: (66) 2675 9791
Animal Feed Mfr
S.I.C.: 2047
N.A.I.C.S.: 311111

Bangkok Produce Merchandising Public Company Limited **(1)**
313 Silom Road
Bang Rak, Bangkok, Thailand
Tel.: (66) 26258000
Fax: (66) 2631 0989
Animal Feeds Distr
S.I.C.: 5191
N.A.I.C.S.: 424910

B.P. Food Products Co., Ltd. **(1)**
57 Moo 5 Pahonyothin Road Nongkhainam
Nongkae, Saraburi, Thailand
Tel.: (66) 3637 1885
Fax: (66) 3637 6578
Livestock & Animal Feed Mfr
S.I.C.: 2048
N.A.I.C.S.: 311119

Charoen Pokphand Northeastern Public Company Limited **(1)**
Bangkok 313 C P Tower 15th Floor Silom Road
Bangrak, 10500 Bangkok, Thailand
Tel.: (66) 26804500
Fax: (66) 2680 4692
Livestock & Animal Feed Mfr
S.I.C.: 2047
N.A.I.C.S.: 311111

C.P. Agro-Industry Co., Ltd. **(1)**
442/302 Taladmai Road Tambon Talad
Amphoe Muang, Surat Thani, 84000, Thailand
Tel.: (66) 77282229
Fax: (66) 7728 2230
Livestock Farming Services
S.I.C.: 0219
N.A.I.C.S.: 112990

C.P. Food Products Co., Ltd. **(1)**
1 CP Tower II 18th Floor Ratchadapisek Road
Dindaeng, 10320 Bangkok, Thailand
Tel.: (66) 2641 1333
Fax: (66) 2641 0333
Restaurant Management Services
S.I.C.: 5812
N.A.I.C.S.: 722511

C.P. Merchandising Co., Ltd. **(1)**
313 18th Floor CP Tower
Silom, 10500 Bangkok, Thailand
Tel.: (66) 26258000
Fax: (66) 26382749
E-Mail: cpm3@cpf.co.th
Web Site: www.cpmerchandising.com
Emp.: 100
Animal Feed Mfr
S.I.C.: 2048
N.A.I.C.S.: 311119
Tony Lovell *(Asst VP)*

CPF Food Products Co., Ltd. **(1)**
252/129-132 Muang Thai-Phatra Office Tower 2 29-3
10310 Bangkok, Thailand
Tel.: (66) 2 6944466
Fax: (66) 2 6944477
E-Mail: consumercenter@cpf.co.th
Emp.: 100
Processed Meats Mfr
S.I.C.: 5147
N.A.I.C.S.: 311612
Peerapong Saiyud *(VP)*

CPF IT Center Co., Ltd. **(1)**
313 CP Tower 16 Fl
Silom, 10500 Bangkok, Thailand
Tel.: (66) 26258000
Fax: (66) 26382300
Information Technology Services
S.I.C.: 7371
N.A.I.C.S.: 541511

CPF Logistics Co., Ltd. **(1)**
38 Q-House Tower Convent 5 AB 5th Floor
Convent Road
Silom, Bangkok, Thailand
Tel.: (66) 27845713
Fax: (66) 27845799
Logistics Services
S.I.C.: 4731
N.A.I.C.S.: 541614

CPF Premium Foods Co., Ltd **(1)**
26/3 Moo 7 Suwinthawong Road Tambol Klongnakornnueng
24000 Chachoengsao, Thailand
Tel.: (66) 38593046
Fax: (66) 3859 3587
Food Processing Services
S.I.C.: 2092
N.A.I.C.S.: 311710

CPF Trading Co., Ltd. **(1)**
28/F Muang Thai-Phatra Office Tower 2
252/115-116
Huaykwang, Bangkok, 10310, Thailand
Tel.: (66) 26930583
Fax: (66) 26930584
Animal Food Products Whslr
S.I.C.: 5149
N.A.I.C.S.: 424490

International Pet Food Co., Ltd. **(1)**
37-57 Soi Chan 18/7 Saint Louis Square Building 5th Floor
Toungwatdorn, Sathorn, Thailand
Tel.: (66) 26733146
Fax: (66) 26731363
Web Site: www.jerhigh.com
Emp.: 40
Pet Food Mfr & Distr
S.I.C.: 2048
N.A.I.C.S.: 311119
Kiattirat Thanarojphakorn *(Mgr)*

Klang Co., Ltd. **(1)**
313 CP Tower Silom Road Bangrak
Bangkok, 10500, Thailand
Tel.: (66) 26258000
Fax: (66) 26382280
Web Site: www.cpfworldwide.com
Shrimp Processing Services
S.I.C.: 0273
N.A.I.C.S.: 112512
Adirak Pratak *(Mgr)*

Rajburi Foods Co., Ltd. **(1)**
80/3 Moo 8 Donkrabueng
Banpong, Ratchaburi, 70110, Thailand
Tel.: (66) 3236 8181
Fax: (66) 3236 8189
Animal Feeds Mfr
S.I.C.: 2048
N.A.I.C.S.: 311119

Seafoods Enterprise Co., Ltd **(1)**
82/12-13 Moo 4 Thonburi-Paktor Road
Bangkok, Thailand
Tel.: (66) 26258000
Fax: (66) 2631 0776
Shrimp Mfr
S.I.C.: 0273
N.A.I.C.S.: 112512

Non-U.S. Subsidiaries:

Asia Aquaculture (M) Sdn. Bhd. **(1)**
Batu 22 Kg Sg Hj Muhammad
36200 Selekoh, Perak, Malaysia
Tel.: (60) 56486481
Fax: (60) 56486481
Web Site: www.cp-malaysia.com
Emp.: 29
Shrimp Farming Services
S.I.C.: 0273
N.A.I.C.S.: 112512
Wichit Kongkheaw *(CEO)*

Calibre Nature (M) Sdn. Bhd. **(1)**
Unit 06-01 6th Floor Lee Kay Huan Lot 14408 Jalan Genting Kelang
Setapak, 53200 Kuala Lumpur, Malaysia
Tel.: (60) 3 4027 1800
Fax: (60) 3 4027 1900
Aquaculture Integration Services
S.I.C.: 0919
N.A.I.C.S.: 112519
Hiew Wei *(Mgr-Mktg)*

Charoen Pokphand Enterprise (Taiwan) Co., Ltd. **(1)**
17th Floor No 87 Sung Chiang Road
10486 Taipei, Taiwan
Tel.: (886) 225077071
Fax: (886) 225064137
E-Mail: service@cptwn.com.tw
Web Site: www.cptwn.com.tw
Emp.: 100
Chicken Poultry Farming Services
S.I.C.: 2015
N.A.I.C.S.: 311615
Cheng Wu Yueh *(Pres)*

Charoen Pokphand Foods (Overseas) LLC **(1)**
Moscow Per Vasnetsova 9/1
Moscow, 129090, Russia
Tel.: (7) 4956847466
Fax: (7) 4956847466
E-Mail: sales@cpfoods.ru
Web Site: www.cpfoods.ru
Emp.: 3
Convenience Foods Mfr
S.I.C.: 2092
N.A.I.C.S.: 311710
Sergey Tishin *(Gen Mgr)*

Charoen Pokphand Foods Philippines Corporation **(1)**
Unit 1C-1D LSC Building Lazatin Boulevard
Dolores Homesite Exit 2, San Fernando, Pampanga, 2000, Philippines
Tel.: (63) 344320994
Fax: (63) 344320994
E-Mail: ekewit.sr@gmail.com
Emp.: 55
Shrimp Hatching Services
S.I.C.: 0273
N.A.I.C.S.: 112512
Wichet Kaewpa *(Asst VP)*

Charoen Pokphand (India) Private Limited **(1)**
47/D-3 Gandhi Mandapam Road
Kotturpuram, Chennai, Tamil Nadu, 600085, India
Tel.: (91) 4424470790
Fax: (91) 4424472880
Web Site: www.mycpindia.com
Emp.: 6
Livestock Feeds Mfr
S.I.C.: 5154
N.A.I.C.S.: 424520
K. Vitoon *(VP)*

Charoen Pokphand (Taiwan) Co., Ltd. **(1)**
17 Floor 87 Sung Chiang Road
10466 Taipei, Taiwan
Tel.: (886) 2 25060567
Fax: (886) 2 25064137
Vaccines Whslr
S.I.C.: 5122
N.A.I.C.S.: 424210

C.P. Aquaculture (Beihai) Co., Ltd. **(1)**
Hong Kong Road Bei Hai Industrial Zone
Beihai, Guangxi, 536005, China
Tel.: (86) 7792084362
Fax: (86) 7792083950
Aquatic Feeds Mfr & Distr
S.I.C.: 2048
N.A.I.C.S.: 311119

C.P. Aquaculture (Dongfang) Co., Ltd. **(1)**
Laocheng Development Zone
Chengmai, Haikou, Hainan, 570125, China
Tel.: (86) 898 3696 3928
Fax: (86) 898 3696 5688
Shrimp Hatching Services
S.I.C.: 0273
N.A.I.C.S.: 112512

CP Foods (UK) Limited **(1)**
Avon House Hartlebury Trading Estate
Hartlebury, Kidderminster, Worcs, DY10 4JB, United Kingdom UK
Tel.: (44) 1299253131 (52%)
Fax: (44) 299253232
E-Mail: help@cpfoods.co.uk
Web Site: www.cpfoods.co.uk
Emp.: 50
Processed Meat & Food Products Importer & Distr
S.I.C.: 5147
N.A.I.C.S.: 424470
Bob Miller *(Mng Dir)*

C.P. Laos Co., Ltd. **(1)**
363/4-5 34 Kamphengmeuang St
PhonthanNeua
Vientiane, Laos
Tel.: (856) 21453508

Charoen Pokphand Foods Public Company Limited—(Continued)

Fax: (856) 21453507
Livestock Farming & Animal Feeds Mfr
S.I.C.: 0752
N.A.I.C.S.: 115210

C.P. Pokphand Co. Ltd. (1)
21/F Far East Finance Centre 16 Harcourt Road
Central, China (Hong Kong) BM
Tel.: (852) 25201601 (74%)
Fax: (852) 28612514
E-Mail: contact@charoenpokphand.com
Web Site: www.cpp.hk
0043—(HKG)
Rev.: $4,959,059,000
Assets: $2,116,880,000
Liabilities: $1,024,325,000
Net Worth: $1,092,555,000
Earnings: $235,507,000
Emp.: 35,000
Fiscal Year-end: 12/31/12
Investment Holding Company
S.I.C.: 6719
N.A.I.C.S.: 551112
Dhanin Chearavanont *(Chm)*
Thanakorn Seriburi *(Vice Chm & CEO-Indus Div)*
Soopakij Chearavanont *(Vice Chm)*
Adirek Sripratak *(Vice Chm)*
Bobby Bo Wai Chang *(CFO)*
Sooksunt Jiumjaiswanglerg *(CEO-Vietnam)*
Bai Shanlin *(CEO-China)*
Wing Yuen Lau *(Sec & Controller-Fin)*

Non-U.S. Subsidiary:

Pucheng Chia Tai Biochemistry Co., Ltd. (2)
305 Chia Tai Rd
Pucheng, Nanping, Fujian, 353400, China (69.5%)
Tel.: (86) 5992822604
Fax: (86) 5992827002
E-Mail: pcsal@ct-bio.com
Web Site: www.cpp.hk/en/pucheng_chia_tai.jsp
Emp.: 600
Antibiotics Mfr & Marketer
S.I.C.: 2833
N.A.I.C.S.: 325411

C.P. Standart Gida Sanayi ve Ticaret A.S. (1)
Buyukdere Cad Akinci Bayiri Sok No 6
34394 Istanbul, Turkey
Tel.: (90) 2122748536
Fax: (90) 212 273 2528
E-Mail: info@cpturkiye.com
Web Site: www.cpturkeia.com
Poultry & Cattle Feeds Mfr
S.I.C.: 2048
N.A.I.C.S.: 311119
Nezih Gencer *(Mng Dir-Sls)*

CPF Denmark A/S (1)
Tomrervej 10A
6800 Varde, Denmark DK
Tel.: (45) 75261330 (52%)
Fax: (45) 75261336
Web Site: www.cpf.co.th
Processed Meat & Food Products Importer & Distr
S.I.C.: 5147
N.A.I.C.S.: 424470

CPF Europe S.A. (1)
Avenue Belle Vue 17
1410 Waterloo, Belgium BE
Tel.: (32) 23575380 (99.99%)
Fax: (32) 23575398
E-Mail: contact@cpfeurope.be
Web Site: www.cpfeurope.com
Emp.: 13
Processed Meat & Food Products Importer & Distr
S.I.C.: 5147
N.A.I.C.S.: 424470

CPF Tokyo Co., Ltd. (1)
No 9-1 Shibadanishii Building Shiba 4-Chome Klangu
Minato-Ku Klangu, Tokyo, 108 0014, Japan
Tel.: (81) 354012231
Fax: (81) 354012236
E-Mail: adachi@su-cpi.co.jp
Web Site: www.su-cpi.co.jp
Emp.: 11
Processed Meats Distr
S.I.C.: 5147
N.A.I.C.S.: 424470
Kittiya Kongmanmana *(Asst VP)*

Lianyungang Chia Tai Feed Co., Ltd. (1)
Lianyungang Development Zone
Lianyungang, Jiangsu, China
Tel.: (86) 51882342558
Fax: (86) 51882340802
E-Mail: ctlyg@pub.lyg.jsinfo.net
Animal Feeds Mfr
S.I.C.: 2048
N.A.I.C.S.: 311119

Star Feedmills (M) Sdn. Bhd. (1)
No PT 12007 Jalan Perindustrian Mahkota 2
43700 Beranang, Selangor, Malaysia
Tel.: (60) 389218299
Fax: (60) 389218299
E-Mail: aquatic.seed@cp-malaysia.com
Web Site: www.cp-malaysia.com
Emp.: 200
Aquatic Feeds Mfr & Distr
S.I.C.: 2048
N.A.I.C.S.: 311119
Suphot Laotanan *(Gen Mgr)*

CHAROEN POKPHAND GROUP CO., LTD.

CP Tower 12th Fl 313 Silom Rd
Bangrak, Bangkok, 10500, Thailand
Tel.: (66) 26258000
Fax: (66) 26382741
E-Mail: pr@cpthailand.com
Web Site: www.cpthailand.com
Year Founded: 1921
Emp.: 100,000

Business Description:
Diversified Holding Company
S.I.C.: 6719
N.A.I.C.S.: 551112

Personnel:
Dhanin Chearavanont *(Chm & CEO)*
Prasit Damrongchitanon *(CEO-Trading Bus-Intl & Co-CEO-Crop Integration Bus)*
Pong Visedpaitoon *(CEO-Aqua Culture Bus Grp)*
Korsak Chairasmisak *(Chm/CEO-Mktg & Distr Bus Grp)*
Sunthorn Arunanondchai *(Chm-Real Estate & Land Dev Bus Grp)*
Pongthep Chearavanont *(Chm-Petfood Bus Grp)*
Chingchai Lohawatanakul *(Chm-Agro-Indus & Food Bus)*
Eam Ngamdamronk *(Chm-Crop Integration Bus)*
Prasert Poongkumarn *(Chm-Agro-Indus & Food Bus)*
Thanakorn Seriburi *(Chm-Automotive Indus Products & Fin Bus Grp)*
Suphachai Chearavanont *(Pres/CEO-Telecom Bus)*
Manu Chiaravanond *(Pres-Seeds, Fertilizers & Plant Protection Bus Grp)*
Montri Congtrakultien *(CEO-Crop Integration Bus)*
Adirek Sripratak *(CEO-Agro-Indus & Food Bus)*

Subsidiaries:

CPPC Public Company Limited (1)
313 CP Tower 18th Floor Silom Road
Bangrak, 10500, Thailand
Tel.: (66) 2 6258075
E-Mail: Customercare@cppcnet.com
Web Site: www.cppcnet.com
Plastics & Packaging Mfr
S.I.C.: 3089
N.A.I.C.S.: 326199
Prasert Poongkumarn *(Chm, Pres & CEO)*

True Corporation Public Company Limited (1)
18 True Tower Ratchadapisek Road
Huai Khwang, Bangkok, 10310, Thailand
Tel.: (66) 26431111
Fax: (66) 26431651
Web Site: www.truecorp.co.th
TRUE—(THA)
Rev.: $2,961,222,826
Assets: $5,975,438,439
Liabilities: $5,511,473,406
Net Worth: $463,965,033
Earnings: ($246,742,202)
Emp.: 15,021
Fiscal Year-end: 12/31/12
Cable Television, Internet & Mobile Services
S.I.C.: 4833
N.A.I.C.S.: 515120
Dhanin Chearavanont *(Chm)*
Athueck Asvanund *(Vice Chm & Gen Counsel)*
Ajva Taulananda *(Vice Chm)*
Suphachai Chearavanont *(Pres & CEO)*
Noppadol Dej-Udom *(CFO)*
Papon Ratanachaikanont *(Chief Comml Officer-Sls & Retail)*
Carl Goodier *(Chief Customer Svc Officer)*
Rangsinee Sujaritsunchai *(Sec)*

Subsidiaries:

Cineplex Company Limited (2)
Tipco Tower 118/1 Rama VI Road
Samsennai Phyathai, Bangkok, 10400, Thailand (99.99%)
Tel.: (66) 26159000
Fax: (66) 26159388
Emp.: 12
Motion Picture & Video Producer
S.I.C.: 7812
N.A.I.C.S.: 512110

UBC Cable Network Public Company Limited (2)
Tipco Tower 118/Rama VI Road
Samsennai Phyathai, Bangkok, 10400, Thailand (99.02%)
Tel.: (66) 26159000
Fax: (66) 26159900
Emp.: 1,016
Cable Television Broadcasting Services
S.I.C.: 4833
N.A.I.C.S.: 515120

Joint Ventures:

Allianz C.P. General Insurance Co., Ltd. (1)
CP Twr 19 Fl 313 Silom Rd Bangrak
Bangkok, 10500, Thailand
Tel.: (66) 26389000
Fax: (66) 26389020
E-Mail: contact@allianzcp.com
Web Site: www.allianzcp.com
Emp.: 100
Insurance Services; Owned by Allianz AG & by Charoen Pokphang Group
S.I.C.: 6411
N.A.I.C.S.: 524298
Pakit Iamopus *(Pres & CEO)*
Ampai Bumrungsaksilp *(CFO)*

Ayudhya Allianz C.P. Life Pcl. (1)
Ground Floor Ploenchit Tower
898 Ploenchit Road, Bangkok, 10330, Thailand TH
Tel.: (66) 23057000
Fax: (66) 23057999
E-Mail: customercare@aacp.co.th
Web Site: www.aacp.co.th
Life Insurance Products & Services
S.I.C.: 6311
N.A.I.C.S.: 524113
Bryan Smith *(Pres & CEO)*
Ulf Lange *(CFO)*
Robert Paul Gray *(COO)*
Surajak Kotikula *(Chief Investment Officer)*
Patchara Taveechaiwattana *(Chief Market Mgmt Officer & Chief HR Officer)*
Sunchai Larpsumphunchai *(Chief Agency Officer)*
Hadil Tjeng *(Chief IT Officer)*
Sugunya Tongchenchitt *(Chief Regulatory Affairs Officer)*
Kavita Boonpochanasoontorn *(Sr VP-Legal, Compliance & Internal Audit)*

Non-U.S. Subsidiaries:

C.P. Lotus Corporation (1)
21st Floor Far East Finance Centre
16 Harcourt Road, Hong Kong, China (Hong Kong) Ky
Tel.: (852) 2520 1601
Fax: (852) 2868 2860
E-Mail: contact@cplotuscorp.com
Web Site: www.cplotuscorp.com
121—(HKG OTC)
Rev.: $1,696,108,961
Assets: $861,942,180
Liabilities: $532,687,431
Net Worth: $329,254,749
Earnings: ($62,211,855)
Emp.: 16,600
Fiscal Year-end: 12/31/12
Grocery Stores
S.I.C.: 5411
N.A.I.C.S.: 445110
Soopakij Chearavanont *(Chm)*
Ed Yiu-Cheong Chan *(Vice Chm)*
Narong Chearavanont *(Vice Chm)*
Wen Hai Li *(Vice Chm)*
Michael Ross *(Vice Chm)*
Xiaoping Yang *(Vice Chm)*
Yi Mei Choi *(Sec)*

EK Chor China Motorcycle Co., Ltd. (1)
21st Fl Far E Finance Ctr
16 Harcourt Rd, Hong Kong, China (Hong Kong) BM
Tel.: (852) 25201601 (68%)
Fax: (852) 28612514
Web Site: www.ekchor-china.com
Emp.: 3,000
Holding Company; Motorcycle Mfr
S.I.C.: 6719
N.A.I.C.S.: 551112
Thanakorn Seriburi *(Chm, Pres & CEO)*
Robert Ping-Hsien Ho *(Vice Chm)*
Edward Chen *(CFO, Sr VP & Chief Fin & Acctg Officer)*

CHAROONG THAI WIRE & CABLE PUBLIC COMPANY LIMITED

589/71 Central City Tower Floor 12A
Bangna Trad Road
Bangna District, Bangkok, 10260, Thailand
Tel.: (66) 27456118
Fax: (66) 27456131
E-Mail: sales@ctw.co.th
Web Site: www.ctw.co.th
Year Founded: 1967
CTW—(BAK)
Rev.: $249,701,689
Assets: $205,594,626
Liabilities: $60,450,485
Net Worth: $145,144,141
Earnings: $17,829,950
Emp.: 1,186
Fiscal Year-end: 12/31/12

Business Description:
Electric Wire, Cable & Telephone Cable Mfr
S.I.C.: 3357
N.A.I.C.S.: 335929

Personnel:
Chai Sophonpanich *(Chm)*
Premchai Karnasuta *(Vice Chm)*
Tao-Heng Sun *(Mng Dir)*
Tanasit Aungkasit *(Asst Mng Dir-Sls & Mktg)*
Hsiao-Chun Chang *(Asst Mng Dir-Mng Dir Office)*
Ponrawat Charoensukpaisarn *(Asst Mng Dir-Personnel & Gen Affair)*
Chih-Chung Kuei *(Asst Mng Dir-Plng)*
Sununtha Phaengsook *(Asst Mng Dir-Fin)*
Sathit Tabpech *(Asst Mng Dir-Quality Assurance)*
Suvit Veerapong *(Asst Mng Dir-Production & Engrg)*

Board of Directors:
Chai Sophonpanich
Nijaporn Charanachitta
Premchai Karnasuta
Kasem Kularbkeo
Michael Chao Chun Lee
Sununtha Phaengsook
Simon Wah Suen Sai

Pornwut Sarasin
Surachai Sirivallop
Steven Ku Suey
Tao-Heng Sun
Chun-Tang Yuan
Legal Counsel:
Suriyatham Law Office
423 Nakornsawan Road Wat Sommanut
Pomprabsattrupai
Bangkok, Thailand

CHARRIER SA

53 rue de la Jominere
49300 Cholet, Maine Et Loire, France
Tel.: (33) 241710485
Web Site: www.charriersa.com
Sls.: $26,200,000
Emp.: 21
Business Description:
New & Used Car Dealers
S.I.C.: 5511
N.A.I.C.S.: 441110
Personnel:
Alain Charrier *(Mng Dir)*

CHARTER HALL GROUP

Level 11 333 George Street
Sydney, NSW, 2000, Australia
Mailing Address:
GPO Box 2704
Sydney, NSW, 2001, Australia
Tel.: (61) 2 8908 4000
Fax: (61) 2 8908 4040
E-Mail: reits@charterhall.com.au
Web Site: www.charterhall.com.au
Year Founded: 1991
CHC—(ASX)
Rev.: $165,420,870
Assets: $853,305,869
Liabilities: $81,845,492
Net Worth: $771,460,377
Earnings: $56,680,861
Emp.: 270
Fiscal Year-end: 06/30/13
Business Description:
Real Estate Investment Trust
S.I.C.: 6726
N.A.I.C.S.: 525990
Personnel:
David Southon *(Co-Founder & Co-Mng Dir)*
Cedric Fuchs *(Co-Founder)*
David Harrison *(Co-Mng Dir)*
Paul Altschwager *(CFO)*
Tracey Jordan *(Gen Counsel & Sec)*
Board of Directors:
Kerry Roxburgh
Anne Brennan
David Deverall
Philip Garling
David Harrison
Peter Kahan
Colin McGowan
David Southon
Legal Counsel:
Allens Linklaters
Level 28 Deutsche Bank Place Cnr of Hunter & Phillip Streets
Sydney, NSW, 2000, Australia

CHARTER PACIFIC CORPORATION LIMITED

Level 18 50 Cavill Avenue
PO Box 40
Surfers Paradise, QLD, 4217, Australia
Tel.: (61) 755382558
Fax: (61) 755268922
E-Mail: charpac@charpac.com.au
Web Site: www.charpac.com.au
CHF—(ASX)
Rev.: $48,234
Assets: $3,147,259
Liabilities: $2,921,705
Net Worth: $225,554
Earnings: ($4,678,295)
Emp.: 20
Fiscal Year-end: 06/30/13
Business Description:
Financial Services
S.I.C.: 6282
N.A.I.C.S.: 523930
Personnel:
Kevin John Dart *(Mng Dir)*
Steven Allan Cole *(Sec)*
Board of Directors:
Brian Victor Sprod
Peter John Bradfield
Kevin John Dart
David Selfe

CHARTERED CAPITAL & INVESTMENT LTD.

711 Mahakant Opp VS Hospital
Ellisbridge, Ahmedabad, 380 006, India
Tel.: (91) 79 2657 7571
Fax: (91) 79 2657 5731
E-Mail: info@charteredcapital.net
Web Site: www.charteredcapital.net
511696—(BOM)
Rev.: $273,613
Assets: $4,589,180
Liabilities: $748,152
Net Worth: $3,841,028
Earnings: $38,572
Emp.: 9
Fiscal Year-end: 03/31/13
Business Description:
Financial Investment Services
S.I.C.: 6211
N.A.I.C.S.: 523999
Personnel:
Mohib N. Khericha *(Mng Dir)*
Manoj Kumar Ramrakhyani *(Compliance Officer & Sec)*
Board of Directors:
Sanatan N. Munsif
Ashok Kavdia
Mohib N. Khericha
A. L. Sanghvi
Deepak P. Singhvi
Transfer Agent:
Link Intime India Private Limited
C-13 Pannalal Silk Mills Compound L.B.S. Marg
Bhandup
Mumbai, India

CHARTERED LOGISTICS LTD.

C-1 Jay Tower 4th Floor Ankur Road
Naranpura
Ahmedabad, 380013, India
Tel.: (91) 79 27478614
Fax: (91) 79 27478614
E-Mail: city@chartered.co.in
Web Site: www.chartered.co.in
531977—(BOM)
Sls.: $46,372,155
Assets: $25,765,798
Liabilities: $20,133,439
Net Worth: $5,632,359
Earnings: $522,624
Fiscal Year-end: 03/31/13
Business Description:
Road Transportation Services
S.I.C.: 4789
N.A.I.C.S.: 488490
Personnel:
Lalitkumar Gandhi *(Mng Dir)*
Bhanwar Rawal *(CFO)*
Anamika Jajoo *(Sec)*
Board of Directors:
Mohib N. Khericha
Mangilal Bohra
Kishore Kumar Gandhi
Lalitkumar Gandhi
Nisha Kalyan
Ajay Chinubhai Shah
Sandeep Motilal Shah
Transfer Agent:
Sharepro Services (India) Private Limited
13 AB Samhita Warehousing Complex II Floor
Sakinaka Telephone Lane
Off Andheri Kurla Rd Sakinaka, Mumbai, India
Subsidiary:

Chartered Motors Pvt Ltd **(1)**
Opposite Viraj Farm Navagam Rajkot Highway
Vartej, Bhavnagar, 364 060, India
Tel.: (91) 278 2541101
Fax: (91) 278 2541102
Emp.: 35
Motor Vehicle Whslr
S.I.C.: 5012
N.A.I.C.S.: 423110
Nirav Dave, *(Gen Mgr)*

CHARTERHOUSE CAPITAL PARTNERS LLP

Warwick Court 7th Floor
Paternoster Square, London, EC4M 7DX, United Kingdom
Tel.: (44) 2073345300
Fax: (44) 2073345333
E-Mail: reception@charterhouse.co.uk
Web Site: www.charterhouse.co.uk
Year Founded: 1982
Emp.: 40
Business Description:
Private Equity Firm
S.I.C.: 6211
N.A.I.C.S.: 523999
Personnel:
Stuart Simpson *(Founder)*
J. Gordon Bonnyman *(CEO)*
Duncan Aldred *(Partner)*
Malcolm I. Offord *(Partner)*
Vincent Pautet *(Partner)*
James S.E. Arnell *(Principal)*
Graeme Coulthard *(Principal)*
Stephane Etroy *(Principal)*
Christian Fehling *(Principal)*
Fabrice Georget *(Principal)*
Lionel Giacomotto *(Principal)*
Stephan Morgan *(Principal)*
Arthur Mornington *(Principal)*
Roger Pilgrim *(Principal)*
Giuseppe Prestia *(Principal)*
Frank van den Bosch *(Principal)*
Holding:

Environmental Resources Management Limited **(1)**
2nd Floor Exchequer Court 33 St Mary Axe
London, EC3A 8AA, United Kingdom (55%)
Tel.: (44) 20 3206 5200
Fax: (44) 20 3206 5440
Web Site: www.erm.com
Sales Range: $450-499.9 Million
Emp.: 400
Environmental Consulting Services
S.I.C.: 8999
N.A.I.C.S.: 541620
John Alexander *(CEO)*

U.S. Subsidiary:

ERM Group, Inc. **(2)**
350 Eagleview Blvd
Exton, PA 19341-2843 PA
Tel.: (610) 524-3500
Fax: (610) 524-7335
E-Mail: mkt-info@erm.com
Web Site: www.erm.com
Emp.: 100
Environmental Engineering & Consulting Services
S.I.C.: 8999
N.A.I.C.S.: 541620
Joe Tarsavage *(Partner)*

Branches:

ERM - Alaska **(3)**
(Formerly Oasis Environmental, Inc.)
825 W 8th Ave Ste 200
Anchorage, AK 99501
Tel.: (907) 258-4880
Fax: (907) 258-4033
Emp.: 100
Environmental Consulting Services
S.I.C.: 8999
N.A.I.C.S.: 541620
Brad Authier *(VP)*

Subsidiaries:

ERM NC, P.C. **(3)**
8000 Corp Ctr Dr
Charlotte, NC 28226
Tel.: (704) 541-8345
Web Site: www.erm.com
Emp.: 18
Environmental Consulting Services
S.I.C.: 8999
N.A.I.C.S.: 541620
Tom Wilson *(Pres)*

Joint Venture:

Acromas Holdings Ltd. **(1)**
Enbrook Park
Folkestone, Kent, CT20 3SE, United Kingdom UK
Tel.: (44) 1303771111
Web Site: www.acromas.com
Sls.: $3,551,507,352
Assets: $10,715,166,792
Liabilities: $16,122,497,823
Net Worth: ($5,407,331,031)
Earnings: ($1,001,427,789)
Emp.: 31,302
Fiscal Year-end: 01/31/13
Holding Company; Financial, Insurance, Travel, Healthcare & Lifestyle Products & Services
S.I.C.: 6719
N.A.I.C.S.: 551112
J. Andrew Goodsell *(CEO)*
Stuart M. Howard *(CFO)*
A. P. Stringer *(Sec)*

Subsidiaries:

The Automobile Association Limited **(2)**
Fanum House Basingview
Basingstoke, Hants, RG21 4EA, United Kingdom UK
Tel.: (44) 8705448866
E-Mail: hr.operations@theaa.com
Web Site: www.theaa.com
Emp.: 1,000
Motoring Assistance; Financial Services; Owned by Permira Advisers Limited & CVC Capital Partners Limited
S.I.C.: 6153
N.A.I.C.S.: 522220
Andrew Strong *(CEO)*

Saga Group Limited **(2)**
Enbrook Park
Middleburg Square, Folkestone, Kent, CT20 3SE, United Kingdom UK
Tel.: (44) 1303771111
E-Mail: sagazone@saga.co.uk
Web Site: www.saga.co.uk
Emp.: 300
Holding Company; Insurance, Travel, Financial & Lifestyle Products & Services
S.I.C.: 6719
N.A.I.C.S.: 551112
Ros Altmann *(Dir Gen)*
Susan Hooper *(CEO-Saga Holidays)*
Roger Ramsden *(CEO-Saga Svcs)*
Robin Shaw *(CEO-Saga Shipping)*

Subsidiaries:

Acromas Holidays Limited **(3)**
Enbrook Park
Middleburg Square, Folkestone, Kent, CT20 3SE, United Kingdom UK
Tel.: (44) 1303 771 111 (Switchboard)
E-Mail: reservations@saga.co.uk
Web Site: travel.saga.co.uk
Vacation & Tour Travel Agency
S.I.C.: 4724
N.A.I.C.S.: 561510
Susan Hooper *(CEO)*

Acromas Shipping Limited **(3)**
Enbrook Park
Middleburg Square, Folkestone, Kent, CT20 1AZ, United Kingdom UK
Tel.: (44) 1303 771 111 (Switchboard)
Web Site: travel.saga.co.uk

Charterhouse Capital Partners LLP—(Continued)

Cruise Vacation Travel Agency
S.I.C.: 4724
N.A.I.C.S.: 561510
Robin Shaw *(CEO)*

Nestor Healthcare Group Limited (3)
Beaconsfield Court Beaconsfield Road
Hatfield, Herts, AL10 8HU, United Kingdom UK
Tel.: (44) 8458501435
Fax: (44) 8458501433
E-Mail: homecare.services@saga.co.uk
Web Site: www.saga.co.uk
Sales Range: $200-249.9 Million
Emp.: 991
Holding Company; Health & Social Care Staffing
S.I.C.: 6719
N.A.I.C.S.: 551112
John Rennocks *(Chm)*
John Ivers *(CEO)*

Subsidiary:

Nestor Primecare Services Ltd. (4)
Beaconfields Court Beaconsfield Road
Hatfield, Herts, AL10 8HU, United Kingdom
Tel.: (44) 1707 286800
Fax: (44) 845 850 1433
Web Site: www.nestor-healthcare.co.uk/
Emp.: 200
Health Care Services
S.I.C.: 8099
N.A.I.C.S.: 621999
David Collison *(Controller)*

Saga Services Limited (3)
Enbrook Park
Middleburg Square, Folkestone, Kent, CT20 1AZ, United Kingdom UK
Tel.: (44) 1303771111
Web Site: www.saga.co.uk
Emp.: 3,000
Financial Information & Advisory Services
S.I.C.: 6726
N.A.I.C.S.: 525990
Andrew Goodsell *(CEO)*

U.S. Subsidiary:

Allied Healthcare International Inc. (3)
245 Park Ave 39th Fl
New York, NY 10167 NY
Tel.: (212) 750-0064
Fax: (212) 750-7221
Web Site: www.alliedhealthcare.com
Sales Range: $250-299.9 Million
Emp.: 1,160
Holding Company; Healthcare Staffing
S.I.C.: 7363
N.A.I.C.S.: 561320
Leslie J. Levinson *(Sec)*

Non-U.S. Subsidiary:

Allied Healthcare Group Holdings Limited (4)
Stone Business Park
Brooms Road, Stone, Staffs, ST15 0TL, United Kingdom UK
Tel.: (44) 1785810600
Fax: (44) 1785818200
E-Mail: info@alliedhealthcare.com
Web Site: www.alliedhealthcare.co.uk
Holding Company
S.I.C.: 6719
N.A.I.C.S.: 551112
Lisa Mclean *(Dir-Care Delivery)*

Subsidiary:

Allied Healthcare Holdings Limited (5)
Stone Business Park
Brooms Road, Stone, Staffs, ST15 0TL, United Kingdom UK
Tel.: (44) 1785810600
Fax: (44) 1785818200
E-Mail: info@alliedhealthcare.com
Web Site: www.alliedhealthcare.co.uk
Sales Range: $150-199.9 Million
Emp.: 200
Holding Company; Healthcare Staffing Services
S.I.C.: 6719
N.A.I.C.S.: 551112

Subsidiary:

Allied Healthcare Group Limited (6)
Stone Business Park
Brooms Road, Stone, Staffordshire, ST15 0TL, United Kingdom UK
Tel.: (44) 1785810600
Fax: (44) 1785288849
Web Site: www.alliedhealthcare.co.uk
Sales Range: $25-49.9 Million
Nursing & Healthcare Services
S.I.C.: 8082
N.A.I.C.S.: 621610

Non-U.S. Holdings:

Holding Bercy Investissement SCA (1)
61/69 rue de Bercy
75589 Paris, Cedex 12, France FR
Tel.: (33) 140195000 (c/o Elior)
Fax: (33) 133414276
Holding Company
S.I.C.: 6719
N.A.I.C.S.: 551112
Robert Zolade *(Chm-Supervisory Bd)*

Holding:

Elior SCA (2)
61-69 rue de Bercy
75589 Paris, France FR
Tel.: (33) 140195000
Fax: (33) 143414236
E-Mail: contact@elior.com
Web Site: www.elior.com
Sales Range: $5-14.9 Billion
Emp.: 84,000
Food Catering & Contract Services
S.I.C.: 5812
N.A.I.C.S.: 722320
Robert Zolade *(Chm)*
Philippe Chevallier *(CFO)*
Jaques Suart *(Chief Comm Officer)*

U.S. Subsidiary:

TrustHouse Services Group, Inc. (3)
2201 Water Ridge Pkwy Ste 320
Charlotte, NC 28217 DE
Tel.: (704) 424-1071
Fax: (704) 424-1074
Web Site: www.trusthouseservices.com
Sales Range: $450-499.9 Million
Emp.: 2,500
Holding Company; Food Management Outsourcing Services
S.I.C.: 6719
N.A.I.C.S.: 551112
Michael Bailey *(Chm, Pres & CEO)*
Hugh F. Totman *(CFO, Treas & Asst Sec)*

Subsidiaries:

Aladdin Food Management Services, LLC (4)
21 Armory Dr
Wheeling, WV 26003 WV
Tel.: (304) 242-6200
Fax: (304) 242-1439
E-Mail: headquarters@aladdinfood.com
Web Site: www.aladdinfood.com
Sales Range: $75-99.9 Million
Emp.: 1,400
Contract Food Services
S.I.C.: 5812
N.A.I.C.S.: 722310
Wayne F. Burke *(Pres & CEO)*

Subsidiaries:

AmeriServe Food Management Services (5)
200 E Walnut St
Columbia, MO 65203
Tel.: (573) 499-1500
Fax: (573) 499-1502
Toll Free: (866) 274-3663
E-Mail: asi@ameriservefood.com
Web Site: www.ameriservefood.com
Sales Range: $10-24.9 Million
Emp.: 300
Contract Food Services
S.I.C.: 5812
N.A.I.C.S.: 722310
Richard Liebman *(Founder)*
Terry Orf *(Pres)*

Dowling Food Service Management, Inc. (5)
PO Box 154
Layton, NJ 07851 NJ
Tel.: (973) 948-2006
Fax: (888) 761-8790
E-Mail: dowling@aladdinfood.com
Web Site: www.dowlingfood.com
Contract Food Services
S.I.C.: 5812
N.A.I.C.S.: 722310

A'viands, LLC (4)
1751 County Rd B W Ste 300
Roseville, MN 55113 MN
Tel.: (651) 631-0940
Fax: (651) 631-0941
Toll Free: (888) 872-3788
Web Site: www.aviands.com
Sales Range: $75-99.9 Million
Food Service Management Contractor
S.I.C.: 5812
N.A.I.C.S.: 722310
William J. Benzick *(Founder & Chm)*
Perry Rynders *(CEO)*
Mitch Speicher *(CFO)*
Ron Villani *(COO)*

Fitz, Vogt & Associates, Ltd. (4)
28 Main St
Walpole, NH 03608 VT
Mailing Address:
PO Box 819
Walpole, NH 03608
Tel.: (603) 756-4578
Fax: (603) 756-9248
E-Mail: info@fitzvogt.com
Web Site: www.fitzvogt.com
Sales Range: $25-49.9 Million
Emp.: 300
Contract Food Services
S.I.C.: 5812
N.A.I.C.S.: 722310
Mark Fortino *(Pres)*
Charles M. Swart, III *(CFO)*

Lindley Food Service Corporation (4)
201 Wallace St
New Haven, CT 06511
Tel.: (203) 777-3598
Fax: (203) 776-1941
E-Mail: grossomando@lindleyfoodservice.com
Web Site: www.lindleyfoodservice.com
Sales Range: $10-24.9 Million
Emp.: 225
Contract Food Services
S.I.C.: 5812
N.A.I.C.S.: 722310
Gilbert Rossomando *(Pres)*
Mark Cerreta *(Exec VP)*

Valley Services, Inc. (4)
4400 Mangum Dr
Flowood, MS 39232-2113 MS
Mailing Address: (100%)
PO Box 5454
Jackson, MS 39288-5454
Tel.: (601) 664-3100
Fax: (601) 664-3399
Toll Free: (800) 541-3805
E-Mail: sales@valleyservicesi.com
Web Site: www.valleyinc.com
Emp.: 2,750
Food Contracting Services
S.I.C.: 5812
N.A.I.C.S.: 722310
Jim Walt *(Pres & CEO)*
George M. Ardelean *(Exec VP-Dining & Health Svcs)*
Scott Ball *(Exec VP-Bus Dev)*
John Covert *(Exec VP-Sr & Correction Svcs)*

Non-U.S. Subsidiary:

Avenance Italia S.p.A (3)
Via Venezia Giulia 5/A
Milan, 20157, Italy
Tel.: (39) 02 39039630
Fax: (39) 02 93661297
Catering Services
S.I.C.: 5812
N.A.I.C.S.: 722320
Damiano Baccelloni *(Mgr-HR)*

Subsidiaries:

Gemeaz Cusin S.p.A. (4)
Via Privata Venezia Giulia 5/a
20157 Milan, Italy
Tel.: (39) 02 390391
Fax: (39) 02 39000041
E-Mail: infogemeaz@gemeaz.it
Web Site: www.gemeaz.it
Sales Range: $400-449.9 Million
Emp.: 6,000
Catering Services
S.I.C.: 5812
N.A.I.C.S.: 722320
Grazziella Gaeezzotti *(Founder)*

Subsidiaries:

Scapa Italia Srl (5)
SP 128 KM 2
27010 Marzano, PV, Italy
Tel.: (39) 0382 945111
Fax: (39) 0382 945500
E-Mail:
Web Site: www.scapaitalia.it
Products & Services for Catering Industry
S.I.C.: 2099
N.A.I.C.S.: 311999

ista International GmbH (1)
Grugaplatz 2
D-45131 Essen, Germany De
Tel.: (49) 2014593333
Fax: (49) 2014593179
E-Mail: info@ista.com
Web Site: www.ista.com
Emp.: 4,556
Holding Company; Consumption-Dependent Energy, Water & Ancillary Costs Billing & Meter Installation Services
S.I.C.: 6719
N.A.I.C.S.: 551112
Walter Schmidt *(CEO & Chm-Mgmt Bd)*
Christian Leu *(CFO & Member-Mgmt Bd)*

Division:

ista Deutschland GmbH (2)
Grugplatz 2
D-45131 Essen, Germany De
Tel.: (49) 20145902 (100%)
Fax: (49) 2014593630
E-Mail: info@ista.de
Web Site: www.ista.de
Sales Range: $450-499.9 Million
Emp.: 1,044
Consumption-Dependent Energy, Water & Ancillary Costs Billing & Meter Installation Services
S.I.C.: 7389
N.A.I.C.S.: 561499
Walter Schmidt *(CEO & Chm-Mgmt Bd)*
Dieter Hackenberg *(CFO)*
Jochen Schein *(COO)*
Peter Ruwe *(Chief Sls Officer)*

U.S. Subsidiaries:

ista North America Inc. (2)
3655 Northpoint Pkwy Ste 150
Alpharetta, GA 30005-2025 (100%)
Tel.: (678) 336-2200
E-Mail: info@ista-na.com
Web Site: www.ista-na.com
Consumption-Dependent Energy, Water & Ancillary Costs Billing & Meter Installation Services
S.I.C.: 7389
N.A.I.C.S.: 561499
Mark Ianni *(CEO)*
Thomas Lemper *(CFO)*
Jim Crysdale *(CIO)*
Ruediger Neubauer *(Sr VP-Electronic Data Interchange & Customer Info Sys)*

Non-U.S. Joint Venture:

TDF S.A.S. (1)
106 avenue Marx Dormoy
92541 Montrouge, France
Tel.: (33) 155951000
Web Site: www.tdf-group.com
Sales Range: $1-4.9 Billion
Emp.: 4,500
Television, Radio, Telecommunications & Satellite Communications Infrastructure Operator
S.I.C.: 4833
N.A.I.C.S.: 515120
Olivier Huart *(CEO)*

CHARTERIS PLC

Napier House 24 High Holborn
London, WC1V 6AZ, United Kingdom
Tel.: (44) 2076009199
Fax: (44) 2076009212

E-Mail: info@charteris.com
Web Site: www.charteris.com
CAE—(AIM)
Emp.: 73

Business Description:
Systems Integration Services & Other Consulting Services
S.I.C.: 7389
N.A.I.C.S.: 561499

Personnel:
Allan Barr *(CEO)*
Julie Merry *(Fin Dir & Sec)*
Alan Woodward *(CTO & Dir-Comml)*

Board of Directors:
Stephen Vaughan
Allan Barr
David W. Mann
L. D. Chris Rees

Legal Counsel:
Pinsent Masons LLP
30 Crown Place
London, EC2A 4ES, United Kingdom

CHARTRAND FORD
1610 boul Saint Martin Est
Laval, QC, H7G 4W6, Canada
Tel.: (450) 669-6110
Fax: (450) 669-8196
E-Mail: info@chartrandford.com
Web Site: www.chartrandford.com
Rev.: $74,366,650
Emp.: 95

Business Description:
New & Used Car Dealers
S.I.C.: 5511
N.A.I.C.S.: 441110

Personnel:
Josiane Boivin *(Mgr-Fin Svcs)*

CHARTRES POIDS LOURDS (LECHEVALIER-DOURS) S.A.
ZI 3 av Laennec Rocade Sud 19 rue Rene Cassin
28000 Chartres, France
Tel.: (33) 237910931
Sales Range: $10-24.9 Million
Emp.: 62

Business Description:
New & Used Car Sales
S.I.C.: 5511
N.A.I.C.S.: 441110

Personnel:
Christian Dours *(Pres)*

CHARTWELL GROUP LIMITED
(See Under Close Brothers Group plc)

CHARTWELL RETIREMENT RESIDENCES
100 Milverton Drive Suite 700
Mississauga, ON, L5R 4H1, Canada
Tel.: (905) 501-9219
Fax: (905) 501-0813
Toll Free: (888) 584-2386
E-Mail: info@chartwell.com
Web Site: www.chartwell.com
Year Founded: 2003
CSH.DB.B—(TSX)
Rev.: $878,436,348
Assets: $2,987,316
Liabilities: $2,436,505
Net Worth: $550,811
Earnings: ($138,509)
Emp.: 13,500
Fiscal Year-end: 12/31/12

Business Description:
Real Estate Investment Services
S.I.C.: 6211
N.A.I.C.S.: 523999

Personnel:
Michael D. Harris *(Chm)*
W. Brent Binions *(Pres & CEO)*
Vlad Volodarski *(CFO)*
Karen Sullivan *(COO)*
Sheri Annable *(Chief Admin Officer)*
Jonathan M. Boulakia *(Gen Counsel & Exec VP)*
Phil McKenzie *(Exec VP-Sls & Mktg)*

Board of Directors:
Michael D. Harris
Lise Bastarache
W. Brent Binions
Andre R. Kuzmicki
Sidney P. H. Robinson
Sharon Sallows
Thomas Schwartz
J. Huw Thomas

Legal Counsel:
Osler, Hoskin & Harcourt LLP
Toronto, ON, Canada

Transfer Agent:
Computershare Investor Services Inc
100 University Avenue 9 Floor North Tower
Toronto, ON, M5J 2Y1, Canada

CHASE BRIGHT STEEL LTD.
R-237 T T C Industrial Area MIDC
Thane Belapur Road
Rabale, Navi Mumbai, Maharashtra, 400 701, India
Tel.: (91) 22 2760 6679
Fax: (91) 22 2769 0627
Web Site: www.chasebright.com
504671—(BOM)
Rev.: $8,402,335
Assets: $3,919,354
Liabilities: $3,595,931
Net Worth: $323,424
Earnings: $88,208
Fiscal Year-end: 03/31/13

Business Description:
Steel Bars Mfr & Distr
S.I.C.: 3312
N.A.I.C.S.: 331110

Personnel:
Avinash Jajodia *(Chm & Mng Dir)*
Kishor Gupta *(Sr Exec-Mark)*
Rajendar Rathore *(Exec-Exports)*

Board of Directors:
Avinash Jajodia
P. L. Dabral
Manju Devi Jajodia
N. G. Khaitan
K. S. Shikari

CHASEN HOLDINGS LIMITED
18 Jalan Besut
Singapore, 619571, Singapore
Tel.: (65) 62665978
Fax: (65) 62624286
E-Mail: shareholdings@chasen-logistics.com
Web Site: www.chasen.com.sg
5NV—(SES)
Rev.: $64,302,357
Assets: $79,011,813
Liabilities: $34,602,484
Net Worth: $44,409,329
Earnings: ($5,920,380)
Emp.: 1,200
Fiscal Year-end: 03/31/13

Business Description:
Logistics Services
S.I.C.: 4731
N.A.I.C.S.: 541614

Personnel:
Weng Fatt Low *(CEO & Mng Dir)*
Choy Seng Chew *(CFO)*
Kok Liang Chew *(Sec)*

Board of Directors:
Weng Fatt Low
Jwee Phuan Ng
Boon Hock Siah
Dennis Sin Huat Tan
Koon Bee Yap

Transfer Agent:
Boardroom Corporate & Advisory Services Pte. Ltd.
50 Raffles Place 32-01 Singapore Land Tower
Singapore, Singapore

Subsidiaries:

Chasen Logistics Services Limited **(1)**
18 Jalan Besut
Singapore, 619571, Singapore
Tel.: (65) 62665978
Fax: (65) 62624286
E-Mail: sales-admin@chasen-logistics.com
Web Site: www.chasen.com.sg/contact_subsidiaries.asp
Emp.: 150
Warehousing & Logistics Services
S.I.C.: 4225
N.A.I.C.S.: 493110
Chuan Jee *(Mgr-Fin)*

DNKH Logistics Pte Ltd **(1)**
8 Tuas Avenue 20
Singapore, 638822, Singapore
Tel.: (65) 6846 8485
Fax: (65) 64170774
E-Mail: sales@dnkh-logistics.com
Web Site: www.dnkh-logistics.com
Emp.: 130
Logistics & Warehousing Services
S.I.C.: 4731
N.A.I.C.S.: 541614
Yorky Lim *(Mgr-Sls & Mktg)*

Goh Kwang Heng Pte Ltd **(1)**
No 31 Jurong Port Road 07-32 Jurong Logistics Hub
Singapore, 619115, Singapore
Tel.: (65) 68937797
Fax: (65) 68930667
E-Mail: info@gkh.com.sg
Web Site: www.gkh.com.sg
Emp.: 100
Scaffolding Services
S.I.C.: 1799
N.A.I.C.S.: 238190
Lim Jit Sing Jackson *(Exec Dir)*

Hup Lian Engineering Pte Ltd **(1)**
No 56 Senoko Road Woodlands East Industrial Estate
Singapore, Singapore
Tel.: (65) 63822180
Fax: (65) 63825708
E-Mail: huplian@singnet.com.sg
Web Site: www.1991huplian.com
Steel Fabrication Services
S.I.C.: 3399
N.A.I.C.S.: 331110

Liten Logistics Services Pte Ltd **(1)**
6 Tuas Ave 20
Singapore, Singapore
Tel.: (65) 68973551
Fax: (65) 68970026
E-Mail: sales@liten-log.com
Web Site: www.liten-log.com
Emp.: 50
General Warehouse & Logistics Management Services
S.I.C.: 4225
N.A.I.C.S.: 493110

REI Promax Technologies Pte Ltd **(1)**
Blk 11 Kallang Place 02-09 Kallang Basin Industrial Estate
Singapore, Singapore
Tel.: (65) 62995758
Fax: (65) 62993202
E-Mail: enquiry@reitech.com.sg
Web Site: www.chasen.com.sg/contact_subsidiaries.asp
Emp.: 40
Precision Moldings & Assemblies Mfr
S.I.C.: 3544
N.A.I.C.S.: 333511
Long Hein Ke *(Mng Dir)*

REI Technologies Pte Ltd **(1)**
8 Tuas Ave 20
Singapore, 638821, Singapore
Tel.: (65) 6268 5700
Fax: (65) 6268 0780
E-Mail: enquiry@reitech.com.sg
Web Site: www.reitech.com.sg
Emp.: 50
Industrial Engineering Services
S.I.C.: 8711
N.A.I.C.S.: 541330
Alvin Chiang *(Gen Mgr)*

Non-U.S. Subsidiary:

REI Hi-Tech Sdn Bhd **(2)**
30 Lorong Nagasari 11 Taman Nagasari
13600 Prai, Penang, Malaysia
Tel.: (60) 4 399 8425
Fax: (60) 4 399 2425
Web Site: www.reitech.com.sg/page010.html
Industrial Engineering Services
S.I.C.: 8711
N.A.I.C.S.: 541330
Liew Yit Shin *(Mng Dir & Mgr)*

Non-U.S. Subsidiaries:

Chasen Logistics Sdn Bhd **(1)**
Block 5 Lot 247 Lorong Perusahaan 10 Prai Industrial Estate
13600 Prai, Penang, Malaysia
Tel.: (60) 4 380 0600
Fax: (60) 4 380 0606
E-Mail: thh.enquiry@chasen-logistics.com
Emp.: 100
Warehousing & Logistics Services
S.I.C.: 4225
N.A.I.C.S.: 493110
Alvin Lau *(Mgr)*

Chasen (Shanghai) Hi Tech Machinery Services Pte Ltd **(1)**
Unit 98 7155 BeiSongGongLu CheDun Town
SongJiang District, Shanghai, 201600, China
Tel.: (86) 2157775421
Fax: (86) 2157774829
E-Mail: sales-admin@chasen.com.cn
Web Site: www.chasen.com.cn
Machinery & Equipment Transportation Services
S.I.C.: 4212
N.A.I.C.S.: 484210

Chasen Sino-Sin (Beijing) Hi Tech Services Pte Ltd **(1)**
JingMengGaoKe Plaza A 407 ShangDi East Road
HaiDian District, Beijing, 100085, China
Tel.: (86) 2157775422
Fax: (86) 2157774829
E-Mail: sales-admin@chasen.com.cn
Web Site: www.chasen.com.sg/contact_subsidiaries.asp?id=3
Machinery & Equipment Transportation Services
S.I.C.: 4449
N.A.I.C.S.: 483211

City Zone Express Sdn. Bhd. **(1)**
Block 5 Lot 247 Lorong Perusahaan 10 Prai Industrial Estate
13600 Perai, Penang, Malaysia (73.2%)
Tel.: (60) 43800600
Fax: (60) 43800601
E-Mail: sales@czone.com.my
Web Site: www.czone.com.my
Warehousing & Transportation Services
S.I.C.: 4212
N.A.I.C.S.: 484110
Cheong Chin Ghee *(Mgr-IT)*

CHASHMA SUGAR MILLS LIMITED
Kings Arcade 20 A Markaz F7
Islamabad, Pakistan
Tel.: (92) 51 2650805
Fax: (92) 51 2651285
Web Site: www.premiergrouppk.com
Year Founded: 1991
CHAS—(ISL)
Sls.: $64,337,801
Assets: $64,189,873
Liabilities: $48,817,769
Net Worth: $15,372,104
Earnings: ($2,408,681)
Fiscal Year-end: 09/30/12

Business Description:
Sugar Mfr
S.I.C.: 2063
N.A.I.C.S.: 311313

CHASHMA SUGAR MILLS LIMITED—(Continued)

Personnel:
Khan Aziz Sarfaraz Khan *(Chm & CEO)*
Rizwan Ullah Khan *(CFO)*
Mujahid Bashir *(Sec)*
Board of Directors:
Khan Aziz Sarfaraz Khan
Abbas Sarfaraz Khan
Babar Ali Khan
Iskander M. Khan
Abdul Qadar Khattak
Begum Laila Sarfaraz
Najda Sarfaraz
Zarmine Sarfaraz

CHASSAY AUTOMOBILES SAS

11 Boulevard Abel Gance
37 100 Tours, Indre-et-Loire, France
Tel.: (33) 247406060
E-Mail: chassay@chassay.fr
Web Site: www.chassay.fr
Sales Range: $10-24.9 Million
Business Description:
New & Used Car Dealers
S.I.C.: 5511
N.A.I.C.S.: 441110
Personnel:
Christian Chassay *(Pres)*

CHASWOOD RESOURCES HOLDINGS LTD.

Lot 242 2nd Floor The Curve No 6 Jalan PJU 7/13
Mutiara Damansara, Petaling Jaya, Selangor, 47800, Malaysia
Tel.: (60) 3 7727 2257
Fax: (60) 3 7727 2267
E-Mail: info@chaswood.com.my
Web Site: www.chaswood.com.my
5TW—(SES)
Emp.: 1,200
Business Description:
Holding Company; Casual Dining Restaurant Operator
S.I.C.: 6719
N.A.I.C.S.: 551112
Personnel:
Andrew Roach Reddy *(Mng Dir)*
Poh Hean Kek *(Grp CFO)*
Cheng Seong Lim *(CFO)*
Joannis Martin Beins *(COO)*
Elaine Pur-Lin Beh *(Co-Sec)*
Siew Tian Low *(Co-Sec)*
Board of Directors:
Mohammed Azlan Hashim
Jared Chih Li Lim
Christopher John McAuliffe
Colin Teck Sim Ng
Teck Wah Ng
Andrew Roach Reddy

CHASYS CO., LTD

411-3 Danggok-Ri Jillyang-Eup
Gyeongsan, Gyeongbuk, Korea (South) 712-832
Tel.: (82) 53 851 8511
Fax: (82) 53 851 8519
Web Site: www.chasys.com
Year Founded: 1989
033250—(KRS)
Business Description:
Automobile Parts Mfr
S.I.C.: 3714
N.A.I.C.S.: 336390
Personnel:
Myeong-Gon Lee *(Chm & CEO)*

CHATEAU INTERNATIONAL DEVELOPMENT CO., LTD.

15 Aly 2 Ln 40 Shengbei Rd
Hengchun Township, Ping-tung, 946, Taiwan
Tel.: (886) 8 8862377
Fax: (886) 8 8862482
Web Site: www.ktchateau.com.tw
2722—(TAI)
Sales Range: $10-24.9 Million
Emp.: 290
Business Description:
Hotels, Amusement Parks & Restaurant Owner & Operator
S.I.C.: 7011
N.A.I.C.S.: 721110
Personnel:
Hsi-chun Chen *(Chm)*

CHATTER BOX CALL CENTER LTD

Flat E 16/F Block One Kin Ho Ind Bldg
14-24 Au Pui Wan Street, Sha Tin, China (Hong Kong)
Tel.: (852) 2414 1831
E-Mail: info@chatterboxcallcenter.com
Web Site: www.chatterboxcallcenter.com
CXLL—(OTC OTCB)
Business Description:
Call Center Operations
S.I.C.: 7389
N.A.I.C.S.: 561421
Personnel:
Roger Kwok Wing Fan *(Chm, Pres & CEO)*
Gene Thompson *(Interim CFO)*
Mei Ling Szeto *(Sec & Sr VP)*
Board of Directors:
Roger Kwok Wing Fan
Hung Man To

CHAUDRONNERIE DE L EST

Zi Rue De L Avenir
52200 Langres, France
Tel.: (33) 325875587
Fax: (33) 0325844747
Web Site: www.cbeual
Sls.: $22,700,000
Emp.: 111
Business Description:
Fabricated Plate Work
S.I.C.: 3443
N.A.I.C.S.: 332313
Personnel:
Frederec Legros *(Gen Mgr)*

CHAUX ET ENDUITS DE SAINT ASTIER

Lieu Dit La Jarthe
24110 Perigueux, Saint-Astier, France
Tel.: (33) 553540660
Fax: (33) 553046791
E-Mail: cesa@c-e-s-a.fr
Web Site: www.c-e-s-a.fr
Sls.: $23,900,000
Emp.: 120
Business Description:
Plumbing Fixtures, Equipment & Supplies
S.I.C.: 5074
N.A.I.C.S.: 423720
Personnel:
Alain Stipal *(Pres)*

CHC HEALTHCARE GROUP

5F 380 Chang Chun Road
Taipei, Taiwan
Tel.: (886) 2 6608 1999
Fax: (886) 2 6608 0707
Web Site: www.chengyeh.com
4164—(TAI)
Sls.: $23,671,438
Emp.: 160
Fiscal Year-end: 12/31/12
Business Description:
Medical Products Distr
S.I.C.: 5047
N.A.I.C.S.: 423450
Personnel:
Pei-Lin Lee *(Chm)*

CHC REALTY CAPITAL CORP.

166 Pearl Street Suite 300
Toronto, ON, M5H 1L3, Canada
Tel.: (416) 863-1085
E-Mail: mhansen@chcrealty.ca
Year Founded: 2013
CHC.P—(TSXV)
Business Description:
Investment Services
S.I.C.: 6211
N.A.I.C.S.: 523999
Personnel:
Mark Hansen *(Pres & CEO)*
Robert Waxman *(CFO)*
Vaughan MacLellan *(Sec)*
Board of Directors:
Mark Hansen
Vaughan MacLellan
Thomas Murphy
Craig Smith
Transfer Agent:
TMX Equity Transfer Services
200 University Avenue Suite 400
Toronto, ON, M5H 4H1, Canada

CHD DEVELOPERS LTD

SF-16-17 1st Floor Madame Bhikaji Cama Bhawan
11 Bhikaji Cama Place, New Delhi, 110066, India
Tel.: (91) 1140100100
Fax: (91) 1140100190
E-Mail: info@chddevelopers.com
Web Site: www.chddevelopers.com
526917—(BOM)
Rev.: $50,323,407
Assets: $79,534,133
Liabilities: $62,392,849
Net Worth: $17,141,284
Earnings: $2,578,783
Emp.: 211
Fiscal Year-end: 03/31/13
Business Description:
Real estate services
S.I.C.: 1542
N.A.I.C.S.: 236220
Personnel:
R. K. Mittal *(Chm)*
Gaurav Mittal *(Mng Dir)*
Sunil Jindal *(CFO)*
Ritu Goyal *(Compliance Officer & Sec)*
Board of Directors:
R. K. Mittal
M. P. Goel
M. S. Kapur
Gaurav Mittal
Pran Nath
Transfer Agent:
Skyline Financial Services Pvt Ltd.
D 153A 1st Floor Okhla Industrial Area Phase 1
New Delhi, India

CHEAPFLIGHTS MEDIA LTD.

One Alfred Place
London, WC1E 7E, United Kingdom
Tel.: (44) 2032197602
E-Mail: corporate-pr@cheapflights.com
Web Site: www.cheapflights.co.uk
Year Founded: 1996
Sales Range: $25-49.9 Million
Emp.: 102
Business Description:
Airfare Comparison Website
S.I.C.: 2741
N.A.I.C.S.: 519130
Personnel:
Hugo Burge *(Chm & CEO)*
Alan Martin *(Interim CFO)*
Christopher Martin *(CTO)*
Board of Directors:
Hugo Burge
Mohini Bulbrook
Richard K. Medlock
David Soskin

CHEBUCTO FORD SALES

(See Under MacPhee Ford Sales)

CHECK POINT SOFTWARE TECHNOLOGIES LTD.

5 Ha'Solelim Street
Tel Aviv, 67897, Israel
Tel.: (972) 3 753 4555
Fax: (972) 3 573 9256
E-Mail: info@checkpoint.com
Web Site: www.checkpoint.com
Year Founded: 1993
CHKP—(NASDAQ)
Rev.: $1,342,695,000
Assets: $4,552,393,000
Liabilities: $1,206,084,000
Net Worth: $3,346,309,000
Earnings: $620,000,000
Emp.: 2,706
Fiscal Year-end: 12/31/12
Business Description:
Internet Security Solutions Including VPN & Firewall
S.I.C.: 7372
N.A.I.C.S.: 511210
Personnel:
Gil Shwed *(Co-Founder, Chm & CEO)*
Marius Nacht *(Co-Founder & Vice Chm)*
Jerry Ungerman *(Vice Chm)*
Amnon Bar-Lev *(Pres)*
Tal Payne *(CFO)*
Board of Directors:
Gil Shwed
Yoav Chelouche
Irwin B. Federman
Guy Gecht
Marius Nacht
Dan Propper
Ray A. Rothrock
Tibnor David Rubner
Tal Shavit
Jerry Ungerman
Transfer Agent:
American Stock Transfer & Trust Company
59 Maiden Ln Plz Level
New York, NY 10038
Tel.: (212) 936-5100
Toll Free: (800) 937-5449

Co-Headquarters:

Check Point Software Technologies, Inc. **(1)**
800 Bridge Pkwy
Redwood City, CA 94065 DE
Tel.: (650) 628-2000 (100%)
Fax: (650) 628-2180
Toll Free: (800) 429-4391
E-Mail: sales@checkpoint.com
Web Site: www.checkpoint.com
Emp.: 200
Develops, Markets & Supports Network Security Software Products Which Enable Connectivity with Security & Manageability
S.I.C.: 7372
N.A.I.C.S.: 511210
Marius Nacht *(Vice Chm)*
Jerry Ungerman *(Vice Chm)*
Gil Shwed *(CEO)*

Subsidiary:

Zone Labs LLC **(2)**
800 Bridge Pkwy
Redwood City, CA 94065 CA
Tel.: (650) 628-2000

Fax: (650) 628-2180
E-Mail: info@zonelabs.com
Web Site: www.zonelabs.com
Emp.: 160
Security Software Mfr
S.I.C.: 7371
N.A.I.C.S.: 541511

Non-U.S. Subsidiaries:

Check Point Holding AB (2)
Luntmakargatan 22
Stockholm, 111 37, Sweden
Tel.: (46) 8 459 54 00
Fax: (46) 8 459 54 10
Emp.: 25
Investment Management Services
S.I.C.: 6211
N.A.I.C.S.: 523999
Lars Berggren *(Mgr-Sls)*

Check Point Holding (Singapore) PTE Ltd. (2)
100 Beach Rd 20-04 Shaw Tower
Singapore, 189702, Singapore
Tel.: (65) 6435 1318
Fax: (65) 6532 1317
E-Mail: info_sg@checkpoint.com
Emp.: 15
Information Technology Consulting Services
S.I.C.: 7373
N.A.I.C.S.: 541512
S. Raj *(Gen Mgr)*

Check Point Software Technologies Australia Pty Ltd (2)
202 657 Pacific Highway
Saint Leonards, NSW, 2065, Australia (100%)
Tel.: (61) 294936000
Fax: (61) 294608102
E-Mail: inz@checkpoint.com
Web Site: www.checkpoint.com.au
Emp.: 20
S.I.C.: 5946
N.A.I.C.S.: 443142
Scott McKinnel *(Reg Dir)*

Check Point Software Technologies (Austria) GmbH (2)
Vienna Twin Tower A1504
Wienerbergstrasse 11
Vienna, 1100, Austria
Tel.: (43) 1 99460 6701
Fax: (43) 1 99460 5000
Web Site: www.checkpoint.com
Computer Software Development Services
S.I.C.: 7373
N.A.I.C.S.: 541512

Check Point Software Technologies (Belgium) S.A. (2)
Imperiastraat 10 - Bus 4
1930 Zaventem, Belgium
Tel.: (32) 2 416 27 80
Fax: (32) 2 416 27 81
E-Mail: info_benelux@checkpoint.com
Web Site: www.checkpoint.com
Emp.: 10
Security Software Development Services
S.I.C.: 7371
N.A.I.C.S.: 541511
Xavier Duyck *(Gen Mgr)*

Check Point Software Technologies (Brazil) LTDA (2)
Rua Samuel Morce 120
04576-060 Sao Paulo, Brazil
Tel.: (55) 11 5501 2040
Fax: (55) 11 5501 2040
E-Mail: info-br@la.checkpoint.com
Web Site: www.checkpoint.com
Security Software Development Services
S.I.C.: 7371
N.A.I.C.S.: 541511

Check Point Software Technologies B.V. (2)
Hoofdveste 7A
3992 DH Houten, Netherlands
Tel.: (31) 30 5112110
E-Mail: info_benelux@checkpoint.com
Web Site: www.checkpoint.com
Computer Software Whslr
S.I.C.: 5045
N.A.I.C.S.: 423430

Check Point Software Technologies (Czech Republic) s.r.o. (2)
IBC Building Pobrezni 3/620
186 00 Prague, Czech Republic
Tel.: (420) 222 311 495
E-Mail: info_ee@checkpoint.com
Web Site: www.checkpoint.com
Emp.: 6
Software Development Services
S.I.C.: 7371
N.A.I.C.S.: 541511
Daniel Safar *(Country Mgr)*

Check Point Software Technologies (Denmark) ApS (2)
Ragnagade 7
2100 Copenhagen, Denmark
Tel.: (45) 70 219 219
E-Mail: Denmark@checkpoint.com
Web Site: www.checkpoint.com
Computer Software Whslr
S.I.C.: 5045
N.A.I.C.S.: 423430

Check Point Software Technologies (Finland) Oy (2)
Innopoli 2 Tekniikantie 14
02150 Espoo, Finland
Tel.: (358) 46 7121390
Fax: (358) 9 5657 6710
E-Mail: finland@checkpoint.com
Web Site: www.checkpoint.com
Emp.: 11
Information Technology Consulting Services
S.I.C.: 7373
N.A.I.C.S.: 541512
Petra Nyman *(Acct Mgr)*

Check Point Software Technologies GmbH (2)
Fraunhofer Strasse 7
D 85737 Ismaning, Germany (100%)
Tel.: (49) 899998190
Fax: (49) 89999819499
E-Mail: info@checkpoint.com
Web Site: www.checkpoint.com
Emp.: 30
Security System Sales
S.I.C.: 5946
N.A.I.C.S.: 443142
Jorg Kurowski *(Gen Mgr)*

Check Point Software Technologies (Hong Kong) Ltd. (2)
Suite 1813 Tower 1 Time Square 1
Matheson Street
Causeway Bay, China (Hong Kong)
Tel.: (852) 2108 7228
Fax: (852) 2892 2210
E-Mail: info_ap@checkpoint.com
Emp.: 10
Computer Software Development Services
S.I.C.: 7371
N.A.I.C.S.: 541511
Calvin Ng *(Country Mgr)*

Check Point Software Technologies (India) Private Limited (2)
33/1 4th Floor Vittal Mallya Road
Bengaluru, 560 001, India
Tel.: (91) 80 3079 1400
E-Mail: indiasales@checkpoint.com
Web Site: www.checkpoint.com
Computer Software Development Services
S.I.C.: 7373
N.A.I.C.S.: 541512

Check Point Software Technologies (Italia) Srl (2)
Via M Vigano De Vizzi 93/95
20092 Cinisello Balsamo, Milan, Italy
Tel.: (39) 02 6659981
Fax: (39) 02 66599899
E-Mail: info_it@checkpoint.com
Web Site: www.checkpoint.com
Software Publishing Services
S.I.C.: 7372
N.A.I.C.S.: 511210
Ciro Valerio Del Nobile *(Engr-Security)*

Check Point Software Technologies (Japan) Ltd. (2)
6F Kensei Shinjuku Bldg 5-5-3 Shinjuku
Shinjuku Ku, Tokyo, 160 0022, Japan (100%)
Tel.: (81) 353672500
Fax: (81) 353672501
E-Mail: info_jp@checkpoint.com
Web Site: www.checkpoint.co.jp
Emp.: 15
S.I.C.: 5731
N.A.I.C.S.: 443142
Gil Shwedi *(Chm)*

Check Point Software Technologies (Korea) Ltd. (2)
22f Hanhwa B/D 23-5 Youido-Dong
Youngdeungpo-Ku, Seoul, 150-717, Korea (South)
Tel.: (82) 2 786 2320
Fax: (82) 2 786 2316
Web Site: www.checkpoint.com
Emp.: 6
Security Software Development Services
S.I.C.: 7371
N.A.I.C.S.: 541511

Check Point Software Technologies Ltd. (2)
Coudezome 1 Plz Dlaze Zictol Hugo
92411 Puteaux, France (100%)
Tel.: (33) 155491200
Fax: (33) 155491201
E-Mail: info_fr@checkpoint.com
Web Site: www.checkpoint.com
Emp.: 30
Security Solutions Sales
S.I.C.: 5731
N.A.I.C.S.: 443142
David Darmon *(Mgr)*

Check Point Software Technologies Ltd. (2)
Luntmakargatan 22
PO Box 5376
102 49 Stockholm, Sweden
Tel.: (46) 84595400
Fax: (46) 84595410
E-Mail: sales@pointsec.com
Web Site: www.checkpoint.com
Sales Range: $25-49.9 Million
Emp.: 60
Security Technology Services
S.I.C.: 7382
N.A.I.C.S.: 561621
Orjan Westman *(Dir-Sls)*

Non-U.S. Subsidiaries:

Check Point Software Technologies (UK) Ltd. (3)
No 2 Finch Lane
London, EC3V 3NA, United Kingdom
Tel.: (44) 207 7636970
Fax: (44) 207 7636973
E-Mail: ukinfo@checkpoint.com
Web Site: www.checkpoint.com
Mobile Technology Mfr
S.I.C.: 4899
N.A.I.C.S.: 517919

Check Point Software Technologies Mexico S.A. de C.V. (2)
Paseo de Tamarindos N 400 Torre A 5 Piso
Colonia Bosque de las Lomas
Mexico, 05120, Mexico
Tel.: (52) 55 15178736
Fax: (52) 55 15179078
Software Development Services
S.I.C.: 7371
N.A.I.C.S.: 541511

Check Point Software Technologies Norway A.S. (2)
St Olavs Plass 2
0165 Oslo, Norway
Tel.: (47) 23 30 80 50
E-Mail: norway@checkpoint.com
Web Site: www.checkpoint.com
Computer Software Development Services
S.I.C.: 7371
N.A.I.C.S.: 541511

Check Point Software Technologies (Poland) Sp. z o. o. (2)
Bagno 2/221
00-112 Warsaw, Poland
Tel.: (48) 22 403 30 93
Fax: (48) 22 401 71 54
E-Mail: info_pl@checkpoint.com
Web Site: www.checkpoint.pl
Emp.: 10
Security Software Development Services
S.I.C.: 7371
N.A.I.C.S.: 541511
Pawel Pietrzak *(Engr-Security)*

Check Point Software Technologies (RMN) SRL. (2)
Str Burdujeni 1 Bucharest Sector 3
Bucharest, Romania
Tel.: (40) 721 275492
Software Development Services
S.I.C.: 7371
N.A.I.C.S.: 541511

Check Point Software Technologies (Russia) OOO (2)
Nikoloyamskaya St 13 bld 17
Moscow, 108249, Russia
Tel.: (7) 495 967 7444
Fax: (7) 495 967 7444
Web Site: www.checkpoint.com
Retail Software Publisher
S.I.C.: 5045
N.A.I.C.S.: 423430

Check Point Software Technologies (Singapore) Ltd. (2)
100 Beach Rd Unit 2004 Shaw Tower
Singapore, 189702, Singapore (100%)
Tel.: (65) 64351318
Fax: (65) 65321317
E-Mail: info_sg@checkpoint.com
Emp.: 15
S.I.C.: 5734
N.A.I.C.S.: 443142
S. Raj *(Reg Dir)*

Check Point Software Technologies (Switzerland) A.G. (2)
Otto Schutz-Weg 9
8050 Zurich, Switzerland
Tel.: (41) 44 316 64 44
Fax: (41) 44 316 64 45
Web Site: www.checkpoint.com
Network Security Software Development Services
S.I.C.: 7382
N.A.I.C.S.: 561621

Check Point Software Technologies (UK) Ltd. (2)
St Johns Innovation Centre
Cowley Rd, Cambridge, CB4 4WS, United Kingdom (100%)
Tel.: (44) 1223 421338
Fax: (44) 1223 421391
E-Mail: ukinfo@checkpoint.com
Web Site: www.checkpoint.com
Emp.: 27
Software Mfr
S.I.C.: 5731
N.A.I.C.S.: 443142

CHEE WAH CORPORATION BERHAD

6428 Lorong Mak Mandin Tiga Mak Mandin Indus Estate
Butterworth, Pulau Pinang, 13400, Malaysia
Tel.: (60) 43329299
Fax: (60) 43332299
E-Mail: enquiry@cicm.com.my
Web Site: www.campap.com
CHEEWAH—(KLS)

Business Description:
Stationery & Printing Material Mfr
S.I.C.: 3269
N.A.I.C.S.: 327110

Personnel:
Say Kai Khor *(Chm)*
Say Beng Khor *(Mng Dir)*
Joo Seong Ang *(Co-Sec)*
Lee Nee Khor *(Co-Sec)*

Board of Directors:
Say Kai Khor
Say Beng Khor
Wan Keong Khor
Wan Tat Khor
Kah Kheng Koay
Eng Sheng Lee
Mohd. Junid Mohd. Noor
Tet Siem Teh
Hoong Sam Wong

Legal Counsel:
Hong, Cheah & Co.
Suite 7.05 Sri Weld 3A Pengkalan Weld
Penang, Malaysia

CHEER TIME ENTERPRISES CO., LTD.

2 Lane 305 Chyong Lin South Rd
Hsin Chuang, Taipei, Taiwan
Tel.: (886) 222052032

Cheer Time Enterprises Co., Ltd.—(Continued)

Fax: (886) 222053346
E-Mail: sales@cheer-time.com.tw
Web Site: www.cheer-time.com
Year Founded: 1987
3229—(TAI)
Sales Range: $25-49.9 Million
Emp.: 500

Business Description:
Single, Double & Multi-Layer Printed Circuit Boards Mfr
S.I.C.: 3672
N.A.I.C.S.: 334412

Personnel:
Bingjie Jiang *(Chm)*

Plant:

Cheer Time Enterprises Co., Ltd - Kuei-Shan Plant (1)
No 8 Cha Juan Rd Gueishan Shiang
Taoyuan, 333, Taiwan
Tel.: (886) 3350 9199
Fax: (886) 3329 6188
Printed Circuit Boards Mfr
S.I.C.: 3672
N.A.I.C.S.: 334412

CHEETAH HOLDINGS BERHAD

Suite 11 1 A Level 11 Menara Weld
76 Jalan Raja Chulan
50200 Kuala Lumpur, Malaysia
Tel.: (60) 3 2031 1988
Fax: (60) 3 2031 9788
E-Mail: cheetah@cheetah.com.my
Web Site: www.cheetah.com.my
CHEETAH—(KLS)
Rev.: $41,756,857
Assets: $53,054,128
Liabilities: $12,506,530
Net Worth: $40,547,598
Earnings: $3,120,840
Fiscal Year-end: 06/30/13

Business Description:
Sports Apparel Retailer
S.I.C.: 2389
N.A.I.C.S.: 315210

Personnel:
Kee Foo Chia *(Chm & Mng Dir)*
Rebecca Siew Kwan Leong *(Sec)*

Board of Directors:
Kee Foo Chia
Kee Kwei Chia
Kee Yew Chia
Jock Peng Chong
Wooi Teik Gong
Ah Kuan Hor
Chong Keat Yeoh

CHEIL GRINDING WHEEL IND. CO., LTD.

JangHeung-dong 34 DaeSong-ro 101beon-gil
Nam-Gu, Pohang, GyeongBuk, Korea (South)
Tel.: (82) 54 285 8401
Fax: (82) 54 285 5780
E-Mail: kprix@grinding.co.kr
Web Site: www.grinding.co.kr
Year Founded: 1955
001560—(KRS)

Business Description:
Grinding Wheel Product Mfr
S.I.C.: 3291
N.A.I.C.S.: 327910

Personnel:
Yu Yin Oh *(CEO)*

CHEIL WORLDWIDE INC.

736 1 Hannam 2 dong
Yongsan gu, Seoul, 140-739, Korea (South)
Tel.: (82) 2 3780 2114
Fax: (82) 2 3780 2730
E-Mail: webmaster@cheil.co.kr
Web Site: www.cheil.com
Year Founded: 1973
030000—(KRS)
Sls.: $2,198,985,000
Earnings: $90,675,000
Emp.: 1,074
Fiscal Year-end: 12/31/12

Business Description:
Advertising Agency
S.I.C.: 7311
N.A.I.C.S.: 541810

Personnel:
Dai-ki Lim *(Pres & CEO)*
Jason Zhao *(COO & Exec Creative Dir-China)*
Michael Cheonsoo Kim *(Global COO)*
Chris Chalk *(Pres/Chief Strategy Officer-Europe)*
Atishi Pradhan *(Chief Strategy Officer-Southwest Asia)*
Buz Sawyer *(Pres/CEO-North America)*
Matt Cammaert *(Pres-Canada)*
Simon Hathaway *(Pres-Shopper Mktg & Retail Ops-Europe)*
Chanhyoung S. Park *(Pres-Southeast Asia)*
Keesoo Kim *(CEO-Middle East & North Africa)*
Mark Kronenberg *(VP & Deputy Mng Dir-South Africa)*
Keun Ho Kim *(Deputy Mng Dir-Singapore)*
Wiwat Taksinwarajan *(Deputy Mng Dir-Thailand)*
Volker Selle *(COO-Germany & Sr VP)*
Rajesh Bhatia *(Sr VP & Head-Digital Svcs)*
Mark Francolini *(Sr VP & Exec Dir-Creative-Canada)*

Board of Directors:
Ina Choi
Seong-Soo Hyun
Yun Keun Jung
Byung-do Kim
Michael Cheonsoo Kim
Chanhyoung S. Park

U.S. Division:

Cheil Americas (1)
11 Beach St 9th Fl
New York, NY 10013
Tel.: (646) 597-4698
Fax: (646) 380-5809
Web Site: www.cheil.com
Emp.: 250
Advertising Agency
S.I.C.: 7311
N.A.I.C.S.: 541810
Alex Van Gestel *(Pres & CEO)*
Henry Dosch *(CFO)*

Subsidiary:

Cheil USA Inc. (2)
11 Beach St 9th Fl
New York, NY 10013 DE
Tel.: (646) 380-5815
Fax: (646) 380-5809
E-Mail:
Web Site: www.cheilusa.com
Billings: $70,000,000
Emp.: 8
Communications, Consumer Marketing, Information Technology
S.I.C.: 7311
N.A.I.C.S.: 541810
Ian Baer *(Chief Strategy Officer)*

Subsidiaries:

The Barbarian Group, LLC (3)
129 S St 2nd Fl
Boston, MA 02111 MA
Tel.: (617) 424-8887
Fax: (617) 437-9499
E-Mail: info@barbariangroup.com
Web Site: www.barbariangroup.com
Rev.: $9,000,000
Emp.: 16
Digital Advertising Agency
S.I.C.: 7311
N.A.I.C.S.: 541810
Benjamin Palmer *(Co-Founder & Chm)*
Keith Butters *(Co-Founder & Chief Experience Officer)*
Sophie Kelly *(CEO)*

Branch:

The Barbarian Group (4)
11 Beach St 10th Fl
New York, NY 10013
Tel.: (212) 343-4215
Fax: (212) 343-4216
E-Mail: info@barbariangroup.com
Web Site: www.barbariangroup.com
Emp.: 70
S.I.C.: 7311
N.A.I.C.S.: 541810
Colin Nagy *(Exec Dir-Earned Media)*

McKinney & Silver LLC (3)
318 Blackwell St
Durham, NC 27701 DE
Tel.: (919) 313-0802
Fax: (919) 313-0805
E-Mail: ssumner@mckinney.com
Web Site: www.mckinney.com
Sales Range: $75-99.9 Million
Emp.: 200
Advertising Agency
S.I.C.: 7311
N.A.I.C.S.: 541810
Brad Brinegar *(Chm, Partner & CEO)*
John Newall *(Partner & Pres)*
Tim Jones *(Partner & CFO)*
Joni Madison *(Partner & COO)*
Jonathan Cude *(Chief Creative Officer & Partner)*
Ellen Steinberg *(Partner & Grp Creative Dir)*
Janet Northen *(Partner & Dir-Agency Comm)*
Jim Russell *(Chief Innovation Officer & Partner)*
Jim Reath *(Exec VP & Dir-Retail & Shopper Mktg)*
Lisa Hughes *(Exec VP)*
Philip Marchington *(Exec VP)*

Non-U.S. Subsidiary:

Cheil Mexico Inc. S.A. de C.V. (2)
Av Presidente Masaryk No 111 int 701 Col Chapultepec Morales
Del Miguel Hidalgo, Mexico, 11570, Mexico
Tel.: (52) 55 5 747 5100
Fax: (52) 55 5 747 5211
E-Mail: cd.sandoval@samsung.com
Web Site: www.cheilusa.com
Emp.: 14
Communications, Consumer Marketing, Information Technology
S.I.C.: 7311
N.A.I.C.S.: 541810
Fernando Kim *(Pres)*

CHELLARAMS PLC

2 Goriola Street off Adeola Odeku Street
Victoria Island, Lagos, Nigeria
Tel.: (234) 12627880
Fax: (234) 12622458
E-Mail: head.office@chellaramsplc.com
Web Site: www.chellaramsplc.com
Year Founded: 1923
CHELLARAM—(NIGE)
Sales Range: $125-149.9 Million
Emp.: 5,500

Business Description:
Diversified Trading Services
S.I.C.: 7389
N.A.I.C.S.: 425120

Personnel:
Solomon Kayode Onafowokan *(Chm)*
Suresh M. Chellaram *(Mng Dir)*

Board of Directors:
Solomon Kayode Onafowokan
Richard Adeniyi Adebayo
Kishore Bhambhani
Aditya S. Chellaram
Suresh M. Chellaram
Suhas S. Kulkarni

Transfer Agent:
Union Registrars Limited
2 Burma Road Apapa
Lagos, Nigeria

CHELSEA ACQUISITION CORPORATION

1600 333 7th Avenue SW
Calgary, AB, T2P 2Z1, Canada
Tel.: (403) 234-3337
Fax: (403) 265-8565
E-Mail: dstuve@burstall.com
Year Founded: 2011
CAV.P—(TSXV)

Business Description:
Investment Services
S.I.C.: 6211
N.A.I.C.S.: 523999

Personnel:
Greg Chamandy *(Pres, CEO, CFO & Sec)*

Board of Directors:
Greg Chamandy
Darren Stark
Douglas Murray Stuve

Transfer Agent:
CIBC Mellon Trust Company
Ste 600 333 7th Ave SW
Calgary, AB, T2P 2Z1, Canada
Tel.: (403) 232-2400
Fax: (403) 264-2100
Toll Free: (800) 387-0825

CHELSEA FC PLC

Stamford Bridge Fulham Road
London, SW6 1HS, United Kingdom
Tel.: (44) 20 7386 9373
E-Mail: info@chelseafc.com
Web Site: www.chelseafc.com

Business Description:
Holding Company; Professional Soccer Club & Sports Arena Operator
S.I.C.: 6719
N.A.I.C.S.: 551112

Personnel:
Bruce Buck *(Chm)*
Ron Gourlay *(CEO)*
Alan Shaw *(Sec)*

Board of Directors:
Bruce Buck
Ron Gourlay
Marina Granovskaia
Eugene Tenenbaum

Subsidiary:

Chelsea Football Club Limited (1)
Stamford Bridge Fulham Road
London, SW6 1HS, United Kingdom UK
Tel.: (44) 2073869373
Fax: (44) 2073814831
E-Mail: info@chelseafc.com
Web Site: www.chelseafc.com
Professional Soccer Club
S.I.C.: 7941
N.A.I.C.S.: 711211
Bruce Buck *(Chm)*
Ron Gourlay *(CEO)*
David Barnard *(Sec & Dir-Admin-Football Dept)*

CHELSFIELD PARTNERS LLP

67 Brook Street
London, W1K 4NJ, United Kingdom
Tel.: (44) 20 7290 2388
E-Mail: enquiries@chelsfield.com
Web Site: www.chelsfield.com
Emp.: 25

Business Description:
Real Estate Investment & Development Services
S.I.C.: 6531
N.A.I.C.S.: 531390

Personnel:
Elliott Bernerd *(Co-Founder & Chm)*
Robert Burrow *(CEO)*

CHEM-DRY FRANCHISING LIMITED
Belprin Rd E Yorkshire
Beverley, Yorkshire, HU17 0LP, United Kingdom
Tel.: (44) 1482888195
Fax: (44) 1 482 888 193
E-Mail: sales@chemdry.co.uk
Web Site: www.chemdry.co.uk
Emp.: 200
Business Description:
Polish & Sanitation Good Mfr
S.I.C.: 2842
N.A.I.C.S.: 325612
Personnel:
Ken Hills *(Chm)*
Andrew Lloyd-Jones *(Mng Dir)*
Subsidiary:

Chem-Dry UK Limited (1)
Colonial House
Swinemoor Lane, Beverley, Yorkshire, HU170LS, United Kingdom (100%)
Tel.: (44) 1482872770
Fax: (44) 1482872244
E-Mail: info@chemdry.co.uk
Web Site: www.chemdry.co.uk
Piece Goods Notions & Dry Goods Whslr
S.I.C.: 5131
N.A.I.C.S.: 424310

CHEMAPHOR INC.
(Name Changed to Avivagen Inc.)

CHEMBOND CHEMICALS LTD
Chembond Centre EL-71 MIDC Mahape
Navi Mumbai, Maharastra, 400 710, India
Tel.: (91) 22 39213000
Fax: (91) 22 39213100
E-Mail: info@chembondindia.com
Web Site: www.chembondindia.com
530871—(BOM)
Rev.: $49,551,784
Assets: $33,954,119
Liabilities: $17,060,267
Net Worth: $16,893,852
Earnings: $1,465,012
Emp.: 307
Fiscal Year-end: 03/31/13
Business Description:
Chemicals
S.I.C.: 2833
N.A.I.C.S.: 325411
Personnel:
Sameer V. Shah *(Chm & Mng Dir)*
Nirmal V. Shah *(Vice Chm & Mng Dir)*
Akshay Shah *(CEO-Water Equipments)*
Omkar Mhamunkar *(Sec)*
Board of Directors:
Sameer V. Shah
Perviz H. Dastur
Mahendra K. Ghelani
Sushil U. Lakhani
O. P. Malhotra
Jawahar I. Mehta
Ashwin R. Nagarwadia
Nirmal V. Shah
Jayantilal S. Vasani
Transfer Agent:
TSR Darashaw Limited
6-10 Haji Moosa Patrawala Industrial Estate 20 Dr. E Moses Road
Near Famous Studio Mahalaxmi, Mumbai, India
Divisions:

Chembond Chemicals Ltd - Construction Chemical Division (1)
Chembond Centre EL-71 MIDC
Mahape, Navi Mumbai, 400701, India
Tel.: (91) 2266143000
Fax: (91) 2227681294
E-Mail: info@chembondconschem.com
Web Site: www.chembondconschem.com
Emp.: 900
Construction Chemical Mfr & Whslr
S.I.C.: 5169
N.A.I.C.S.: 424690
Samir Shah *(Mng Dir)*

Chembond Chemicals Ltd - Manufacturing Plant (1)
Khasra No 177 2 Vlg Theda PO Lodhimajra Tehsil Nalagarh Baddi Dist, Solan, Himachal Pradesh, 174101, India
Tel.: (91) 9218444550
Fax: (91) 1795236023
Web Site: www.chembondindia.com
Emp.: 6
Construction Chemical Mfr & Whslr
S.I.C.: 5169
N.A.I.C.S.: 424690
D. N. Sharma *(Plant Mgr)*

Plants:

Chembond Chemicals Ltd - BADDI Plant (1)
Khasra No 77/2 Village Theda Lodhimajra Tehsil Nalagarh
Baddi, Solan, Himachal Pradesh, 174101, India
Tel.: (91) 92184 44550
Fax: (91) 921795236023
Emp.: 25
Chemical Mfr
S.I.C.: 2891
N.A.I.C.S.: 325520
D. N. Sharma *(Plant Mgr)*

Chembond Chemicals Ltd - BALASORE Plant (1)
Near Ramuna Golai Opp Gurudwara Gati Courier Office
Beside Rajesh Chemicals, Baleshwar, Orissa, 756019, India
Tel.: (91) 93380 13422
Web Site: www.chembondindia.com
Emp.: 3
Chemical Mfr
S.I.C.: 2899
N.A.I.C.S.: 325998
Nirmal V. Shah *(Mgr-Factory)*

Chembond Chemicals Ltd - CHENNAI Plant (1)
S F No 5/5 6 Avadi Road Sennerkuppam Poonamallee, Chennai, Tamil Nadu, 600056, India
Tel.: (91) 4426801331
Fax: (91) 44 6455 2655
Emp.: 11
Chemical Mfr
S.I.C.: 2891
N.A.I.C.S.: 325520
Nirmal V. Shah *(Mng Dir)*

Chembond Chemicals Ltd - DUDHWADA Plant (1)
404/B/P 1 Village Dudhawada ECP Road Vadodara, Padra, Gujarat, 391450, India
Tel.: (91) 2662 273778
Fax: (91) 2662 273781
Web Site: www.chembondindia.com
Construction Chemical Mfr
S.I.C.: 2899
N.A.I.C.S.: 325998

Chembond Chemicals Ltd - Manufacturing Plant (1)
Opp Gurudwara Gati Courier Ofc
Beside Rajesh Chem, Baleshwar, Orissa, 756019, India
Tel.: (91) 9338013422
Fax: (91) 2227681294
E-Mail: chembond@bsnl.com
Web Site: www.chembondbsnl.com
Emp.: 100
Industrial Chemical Mfr & Whslr
S.I.C.: 5169
N.A.I.C.S.: 424690
Nirmal Shah *(Mng Dir)*
Sameer Shah *(Mng Dir)*

Chembond Chemicals Ltd - TARAPUR Plant (1)
E 6/4 MIDC Tarapur
Thane, Maharashtra, 401506, India
Tel.: (91) 2525 272615
Fax: (91) 2525 271172
Web Site: www.chembondindia.com
Chemical Mfr
S.I.C.: 2891
N.A.I.C.S.: 325520

CHEMCEL BIO-TECH LIMITED
16-130/12 JRD Tata Industrial Estate Kanuru
Vijayawada, Andhra Pradesh, 520007, India
Tel.: (91) 8662544996
Fax: (91) 8662541175
E-Mail: ipo@chemcelbiotechltd.com
Web Site: www.chemcelbiotechltd.com
Year Founded: 1995
533026—(BOM)
Sales Range: $10-24.9 Million
Business Description:
Agrochemicals Mfr
S.I.C.: 2879
N.A.I.C.S.: 325320
Personnel:
Kanuparthi Trinatha Vijay Kumar *(Mng Dir)*
S. Rahmatullah *(Sec)*
Board of Directors:
Kanuparthi Balakrishna Rao
Kanuparthi Trinatha Vijay Kumar
Polamraju Narasimha Murthy
Kanuparthi Chandra Shekhar Prasad
Koka Shri Hari Rao
V. Vara Prasad Rao
Transfer Agent:
Bigshare Services Pvt. Ltd.
E-2/3 Ansa Industrial Estate Sakivihar Road Saki Naka Andheri E
Mumbai, India

CHEMCO ELECTRICAL CONTRACTORS LTD.
9220 39th Ave
Edmonton, AB, T6E 5T9, Canada
Tel.: (780) 436-9570
Fax: (780) 434-0811
E-Mail: mail@chemco-elec.com
Web Site: www.chemco-elec.com
Year Founded: 1963
Sales Range: $150-199.9 Million
Emp.: 1,300
Business Description:
Electrical Contractor
S.I.C.: 1731
N.A.I.C.S.: 238210
Personnel:
Brian Halina *(Pres)*
Len Shankowsky *(Sec & Gen Mgr)*

CHEMFAB ALKALIS LIMITED
Team House GST Salai Vandalur
Chennai, 600 048, India
Tel.: (91) 4466799595
Fax: (91) 4422750771
E-Mail: chemfabalkalis@drraoholdings.com
Web Site: www.chemfabalkalis.com
CHEMFALKAL—(NSE)
Rev.: $24,020,124
Assets: $25,142,433
Liabilities: $5,487,989
Net Worth: $19,654,444
Earnings: $4,353,636
Emp.: 172
Fiscal Year-end: 03/31/13
Business Description:
Speciality Chemicals Mfr
S.I.C.: 2819
N.A.I.C.S.: 325180
Personnel:
Nitin S. Cowlagi *(VP-Fin)*
Board of Directors:
Suresh Krishnamurthi Rao
N. Ganga Ram
T. Ramabadran
C. S. Ramesh
J. Venkataraman
Transfer Agent:
Cameo Corporate Services Limited
Subramanian Building No 1 Club House Road 5th Floor
Chennai, India

CHEMFAB INDUSTRIES INC.
466 Polymoore Drive
PO Box 3200
Corunna, ON, N0N 1G0, Canada
Tel.: (519) 862-1433
Fax: (519) 862-3513
E-Mail: generalinfo@cii-chemfab.com
Web Site: www.cii-chemfab.com
Year Founded: 1980
Rev.: $40,891,176
Emp.: 300
Business Description:
Mechanical Contractors
S.I.C.: 1711
N.A.I.C.S.: 238220
Personnel:
Jeff Devlugt *(VP-Project Mgmt)*

CHEMICAL COMPANY OF MALAYSIA BERHAD
13th Floor Menara PNB 20-A Jalan Tun Razak
50400 Kuala Lumpur, Malaysia
Tel.: (60) 326123888
Fax: (60) 326123999
Web Site: www.ccm.com.my
Year Founded: 1930
CCM—(KLS)
Rev.: $496,480,718
Assets: $672,951,521
Liabilities: $355,540,045
Net Worth: $317,411,476
Earnings: $17,713,910
Emp.: 1,977
Fiscal Year-end: 12/31/12
Business Description:
Mfr of Fertilizers, Chlor-Alkali Chemicals, Agrochemicals & Paints
S.I.C.: 1479
N.A.I.C.S.: 212393
Personnel:
Amirul Feisal Zahir *(Mng Dir)*
Ibrahim Hussin Salleh *(Co-Sec & Gen Mgr-Legal)*
Noor Azwah Samsudin *(Co-Sec)*
Board of Directors:
Hamad Kama Piah Othman
Kartini Abdul Manaf
Chik Weng Leong
Azmi Mohd Ali
Karunakaran Ramasamy
Khalid Sufat
Zaini Ujang
Amirul Feisal Zahir
Legal Counsel:
Salleh & Co
B4-3-1 to 5 Solaris Dutamas No 1 Jalan Dutamas 1
Kuala Lumpur, Malaysia
Raja Darryl & Loh
18th Floor Wisma Sime Darby Jalan Raja Laut
Kuala Lumpur, Malaysia
Subsidiaries:

CCM Agri-Max Sdn Bhd (1)
Lot PT 200 Persiaran Selangor
Shah Alam, Selangor Darul Ehsan, 40000, Malaysia
Tel.: (60) 351632288
Fax: (60) 355428088
E-Mail: sales@ccmfertilizers.com.my
Web Site: www.ccmfertilizers.com.my
Emp.: 400
Fertilizers Mfr
S.I.C.: 2873
N.A.I.C.S.: 325311
Azmal Rais *(Gen Mgr)*

CCM Agriculture Sdn Bhd (1)
No 126 Lot 3412 ParkCity Comml Sq
97000 Bintulu, Sarawak, Malaysia
Tel.: (60) 86335418

Chemical Company of Malaysia Berhad—(Continued)

Fax: (60) 86336418
E-Mail: sales@ccmfertilizers.com.my
Web Site: www.ccmfertilizers.com.my
Emp.: 60
Fertilizers Mfr
S.I.C.: 2873
N.A.I.C.S.: 325311
Lai Seow Pheng *(Gen Mgr)*

CCM Water Systems Sdn Bhd (1)
Jalan Kemajuan Satu 16 17A Lot 4 & 6
40000 Shah Alam, Selangor Darul Ehsan, Malaysia
Tel.: (60) 355196666
Fax: (60) 355193666
E-Mail: Karim@ccmberhad.com
Web Site: www.ccm.com.my
Emp.: 10
Water Treatment Services
S.I.C.: 4941
N.A.I.C.S.: 221310
Abdul Karim *(Mgr-Indus)*

Sentosa Pharmacy Sdn Bhd (1)
No 64 Jln Permas 9 13 Taman Permas Jaya
Johor, Masai, 81750, Malaysia
Tel.: (60) 73887328
Fax: (60) 3887330
E-Mail: sentosa@ccnpharmaceuticals.com
Emp.: 9
Pharmaceutical Products Mfr
S.I.C.: 2834
N.A.I.C.S.: 325412
Chong Choo *(Bus Mgr)*

Unique Pharmacy (Ipoh) Sdn Bhd (1)
No 81
Jln Yang Kalsom, Ipoh, Perak, 30250, Malaysia
Tel.: (60) 52557662
Fax: (60) 52557663
Pharmaceutical & Healthcare Products Mfr
S.I.C.: 2834
N.A.I.C.S.: 325412

Non-U.S. Subsidiaries:

CCM International (Philippines), Inc (1)
Unit 803 The Taipan Place F The Taipan Place F Ortigas Jr Ave
Ortigas, Pasig, 1600, Philippines
Tel.: (63) 26387805
Fax: (63) 26389227
Web Site: www.ccm.com.my/contact.asp
Emp.: 10
Pharmaceuticals & Chemicals & Fertilizers Product Whslr
S.I.C.: 2834
N.A.I.C.S.: 325412
Idris Ashraf *(Bus Mgr)*

P.T. CCM AgriPharma (1)
Plaza DM 8th Fl Ste 805 JL Jend Sudirman Kav 25, Jakarta, 12920, Indonesia
Tel.: (62) 215221961
Fax: (62) 215221960
E-Mail: nita@ccmindonesia.co.id
Web Site: www.ccmfertilizers.com.my/contact_us/contactUs.asp
Emp.: 50
Fertilizers & Pharmaceutical Products Distr
S.I.C.: 5122
N.A.I.C.S.: 424210
Buyung Wijaya *(Mgr)*

CHEMICAL INDUSTRIES (FAR EAST) LTD.

3 Jalan Samulun
Singapore, 629127, Singapore
Tel.: (65) 62650411
Fax: (65) 62656690
E-Mail: chemical.ind@cifel.com.sg
Year Founded: 1962
CO5—(SES)
Rev.: $90,555,421
Assets: $116,647,359
Liabilities: $51,006,601
Net Worth: $65,640,758
Earnings: $1,347,308
Emp.: 152
Fiscal Year-end: 03/31/13

Business Description:
Holding Company; Chemical Mfr & Distr; Real Estate Services
S.I.C.: 2899
N.A.I.C.S.: 325998

Personnel:
Soo Peng Lim *(Founder, Chm & Mng Dir)*

Board of Directors:
Soo Peng Lim
Sui Leng Chua
Eric Yew Tou Lim
Valerie Choo Lin Ong
Kah Chye Tay
Soon Bee Wan

CHEMICAL INDUSTRIES HOLDING COMPANY

(d/b/a CIHC)
5 Tolombat St
Garden City, Cairo, Egypt
Tel.: (20) 27954006
Fax: (20) 27957475
E-Mail: chairman@cihc-eg.com
Web Site: www.cihc-eg.com
Sales Range: $100-124.9 Million

Business Description:
Nitogenous Fertilizers, Paper, Chemicals, Plastics, Leathers, Cement, Cigarettes & Tobacco Mfr
S.I.C.: 2899
N.A.I.C.S.: 325998

Personnel:
Mohamed Adel El Mouzi *(Chm)*

Subsidiaries:

Egyptian Chemical Industries Co. (Kima) (1)
12 Talaat Harb St
Cairo, Egypt EG
Mailing Address:
PO Box 81514
Aswan, Egypt
Tel.: (20) 25740774
Fax: (20) 25771239
Web Site: www.kimaegypt.com
EGCH—(EGX)
Sales Range: $200-249.9 Million
Emp.: 2,400
Chemicals Mfr
S.I.C.: 2816
N.A.I.C.S.: 325130
Yahya Mashaly *(Chm)*

El-Delta Company (1)
PO Box 35691
Talkha, Dakahlia, Egypt EG
Tel.: (20) 502525834
Fax: (20) 502522279
E-Mail: delta@deltafert.com.eg
Web Site: www.el-deltafert.com.eg
Producer of Nitrogen Fertilizers
S.I.C.: 2873
N.A.I.C.S.: 325311
Aly Maher Ghoneim *(Mng Dir)*

General Trading & Chemicals Co. (1)
Immobilia Bldg 26 Sherif St
Cairo, Egypt EG
Tel.: (20) 23933347 (100%)
Telex: 92246 genco un
Fax: (20) 23923316
E-Mail: cihc@genco.com
Web Site: www.genco.com
Import & Export of Chemicals
S.I.C.: 2899
N.A.I.C.S.: 325998
Samir Sultan *(Chm & Mng Dir)*

National Plastics Company (1)
72 Gameat El Dowel Al Arabia St
Mohandessen, Giza, Egypt EG
Tel.: (20) 3389151
Mfr. of Lead Acid Batteries; Urea Trays; Melamine Sets; Toilet Seats
S.I.C.: 3691
N.A.I.C.S.: 335911
Venice K. Gouda *(Pres)*

CHEMICAL INDUSTRIES OF THE PHILIPPINES, INC.

Chemphil Building 851 Antonia S Arnaiz Avenue Legaspi Village
Makati, Philippines
Tel.: (63) 28188711
Fax: (63) 28174803
E-Mail: chemphilgroup@chemphil.com.ph
Web Site: www.chemphil.com.ph
CIP—(PHI)
Rev.: $5,399,408
Assets: $33,833,676
Liabilities: $8,796,875
Net Worth: $25,036,801
Earnings: ($961,881)
Emp.: 78
Fiscal Year-end: 12/31/12

Business Description:
Industrial Chemicals Mfr
S.I.C.: 2819
N.A.I.C.S.: 325180

Personnel:
Antonio M. Garcia *(Chm)*
Ana Maria G. Ordoveza *(Pres & CEO)*
Alexandra G. Garcia *(COO)*
Jose Ricardo C. Garcia *(Treas)*
Luis A. Vera Cruz *(Sec)*

Board of Directors:
Antonio M. Garcia
Jesus N. Alcordo
Paulino C. Alvaro
Manuel M. Gamboa
Ramon M. Garcia
Augusto P. Nilo

Subsidiary:

CAWC, Inc (1)
Chemphil Building 851 Antonio S Arnaiz Avenue
Legaspi Village, Makati, 1229, Philippines
Tel.: (63) 28188711
Fax: (63) 28174803
E-Mail: chemphilgroup@chemphil.com.ph
Emp.: 30
Sodium Polyphosphate Mfr
S.I.C.: 2819
N.A.I.C.S.: 325180
Ana Maria G. Ordoveza *(Pres & CEO)*
Alexandra G. Garcia *(COO)*
Jose Ricardo C. Garcia *(Treas)*
Erwin Temprosa *(Sec)*

THE CHEMICAL SOCIETY ALKIMIA

11 Rue des Lilas
Mahrajene, 1082 Tunis, Tunisia
Tel.: (216) 71 792 564
Fax: (216) 71 787 283
E-Mail: head.office@alkimia.com.tn
Web Site: www.alkimia.tn
Year Founded: 1972
ALKIM—(BVT)
Emp.: 302

Business Description:
Chemical Products Mfr
S.I.C.: 2899
N.A.I.C.S.: 325998

Personnel:
Ali Mhiri *(CEO)*

Subsidiary:

ALKIMIA-Packaging SA (1)
11 rue des lilas
1082 Tunis, Tunisia
Tel.: (216) 71 846 052
Fax: (216) 71 787 283
E-Mail: head.office@alkimia.com.tn
Chemical Product Mfr
S.I.C.: 2899
N.A.I.C.S.: 325998
Monsieur Ali Mhiri, *(CEO & Mng Dir)*

CHEMICAL SPECIALTIES LTD.

2029 Old Mill Road
Canelands, Verulam, Kwa-Zulu Natal, South Africa
Tel.: (27) 32 541 8600
Fax: (27) 32 541 8648
E-Mail: enquiries@chemspecpaint.com
Web Site: www.chemspec.co.za
Year Founded: 1957
Rev.: $52,604,557
Assets: $75,617,102
Liabilities: $34,644,202
Net Worth: $40,972,900
Earnings: ($3,452,312)
Emp.: 683
Fiscal Year-end: 03/31/13

Business Description:
Paint Mfr & Whslr
S.I.C.: 2851
N.A.I.C.S.: 325510

Personnel:
Ivan Arthur James Clark *(Chm)*
Baron Christopher Schreuder *(CEO)*
Bruce Robert Mackinnon *(COO)*

Board of Directors:
Ivan Arthur James Clark
Iain Bruce Brereton Buchan
Darryn John Coyle-Dowling
John Gifford Jones
Bruce Robert Mackinnon
Jonathan Grant Maehler
Gerard Metzer
Neil Anthony Page
Baron Christopher Schreuder
Namhla Thina Yvonne Siwendu
Sipho Eric Sono

CHEMIE TECHNIK GMBH

Robert Bosch Strasse 19
72189 Vohringen, Germany
Tel.: (49) 745496520
Fax: (49) 7454965235
E-Mail: elkalub@chemietechnik.com
Web Site: www.chemietechnik.com
Year Founded: 1956
Rev.: $10,026,859
Emp.: 30

Business Description:
Automotive Lubricants Mfr
S.I.C.: 2992
N.A.I.C.S.: 324191

Personnel:
Elisabeth Hof *(Co-CEO)*
Joachim Hof *(Co-CEO)*

CHEMIPLASTICA S.P.A.

Via A Cechov 50
20151 Milan, Italy
Tel.: (39) 023342101
Fax: (39) 02 33400793
Web Site: www.chemiplastica.com
Sales Range: $100-124.9 Million
Emp.: 200

Business Description:
Chemical Mfr
S.I.C.: 2899
N.A.I.C.S.: 325998

Personnel:
Claudio Colombo *(Chm & CEO)*

U.S. Subsidiary:

Chemiplastica Inc. (1)
238 Nonotuck St
Florence, MA 01062-2671
Tel.: (413) 584-2472
Fax: (413) 586-4089
Web Site: www.thermosets.com
Emp.: 28
Amino Polymers Engineering Materials Mfr
S.I.C.: 3089
N.A.I.C.S.: 326199
Scott Chisholm *(Gen Mgr)*

Non-U.S. Subsidiary:

Chemiplastica AB (1)
Perstorp Industrial Park
SE-284 80 Perstorp, Sweden
Tel.: (46) 43538000
Fax: (46) 43538805

Emp.: 110
Amino Polymers Engineering Materials Mfr
S.I.C.: 3089
N.A.I.C.S.: 326199
Gabriel Munck *(Gen Mgr)*

CHEMISOL ITALIA S.R.L.

Corso Sempione 13
I-21053 Castellanza, VA, Italy
Tel.: (39) 0331523111
Fax: (39) 0331523443
E-Mail: agrolinz.mail@agrolinz.it
Web Site: www.agrolinz.com
Rev.: $42,140,080
Emp.: 280
Business Description:
Marketer of Plant Protectives
S.I.C.: 1389
N.A.I.C.S.: 213112
Personnel:
Gianluca Bagatti *(Mgr)*

CHEMITALIC DENMARK A/S

Egebjergvej 128
8700 Horsens, Denmark
Tel.: (45) 2496 1350
E-Mail: info@chemitalic.com
Web Site: www.chemitalic.com
Emp.: 120
Business Description:
Printed Circuit Board Mfr
S.I.C.: 3672
N.A.I.C.S.: 334412
Personnel:
Palle Morthorst *(Dir-Sls)*
Non-U.S. Subsidiary:

Chemitalic Suzhou Ltd. **(1)**
Unit 3 Genway Ready Build Factory
SIP Export Processing Zone Dis, 215021
Suzhou, Jiangsu, China
Tel.: (86) 51262823088
Fax: (86) 51262823079
Bare Printed Circuit Board Mfr
S.I.C.: 3672
N.A.I.C.S.: 334412
John Lee *(Gen Mgr)*

CHEMO IBERICA SA

Edificio Nectar c Quintanapalla 2 4th Floor
28050 Madrid, Spain
Tel.: (34) 91 302 15 60
Fax: (34) 91 766 89 63
Web Site: www.chemogroup.com
Emp.: 3,000
Business Description:
Pharmaceutical Mfr
S.I.C.: 2834
N.A.I.C.S.: 325412
Personnel:
Leandro Sigman *(Mng Dir)*
U.S. Subsidiary:

Everett Laboratories, Inc. **(1)**
29 Spring St
West Orange, NJ 07052 NJ
Tel.: (973) 324-0200
Fax: (973) 324-0795
Web Site: www.everettlabs.com
Sales Range: $10-24.9 Million
Emp.: 60
Pharmaceutical Preparations
S.I.C.: 2834
N.A.I.C.S.: 325412
Everett Felper *(Pres)*

Subsidiary:

Quinnova Pharmaceuticals, Inc. **(2)**
2500 York Rd Ste 200
Jamison, PA 18929
Tel.: (215) 860-6263
Fax: (215) 860-6265
Toll Free: (877) 660-6263
E-Mail: info@quinnova.com
Web Site: www.quinnova.com
Rev.: $2,600,000
Emp.: 30
Pharmaceutical Preparation Mfr
S.I.C.: 2834
N.A.I.C.S.: 325412
Jeffrey Day *(Pres)*

CHEMO PHARMA LABORATORIES LTD

Empire House 3rd Floor 214 D N Road
Fort, Mumbai, 400 001, India
Tel.: (91) 22 22078381
Fax: (91) 22 22074294
E-Mail: contact@thechemopharmalaboratoriesltd.com
Web Site: www.thechemopharmalaboratoriesltd.com
Year Founded: 1942
506365—(BOM)
Rev.: $50,028
Assets: $904,573
Liabilities: $50,005
Net Worth: $854,567
Earnings: $26,556
Fiscal Year-end: 03/31/13
Business Description:
Pharmaceutical Product Mfr
S.I.C.: 2834
N.A.I.C.S.: 325412
Personnel:
Balkishan Devkaran Lohia *(CFO)*
Board of Directors:
Ashok Kumar Joshi
Ghanshyam K. Joshi
Balkishan Devkaran Lohia
Ashok Somani
Transfer Agent:
Sharex Dynamic (India) Pvt. Ltd
Unit 1 Luthra Indus Premises Andheri Kurla Road Safed Pool Andheri E
Mumbai, India

CHEMOFORM AG

Heinrich Otto Str 28
D-73240 Wendlingen am Neckar, Germany
Tel.: (49) 702440480
Fax: (49) 702440482800
E-Mail: nfo@chemoform.com
Web Site: www.chemoform.com
Year Founded: 1962
Rev.: $11,862,840
Emp.: 25
Business Description:
Chemical Products Mfr
S.I.C.: 2899
N.A.I.C.S.: 325998
Personnel:
Gerhard Mayer-Klenk *(Founder)*

CHEMOPROJEKT, A.S.

Trebohosticka 14
100 31 Prague, Czech Republic
Tel.: (420) 261305200
E-Mail: info@chemoprojekt.cz
Web Site: www.chemoprojekt.cz
Year Founded: 1950
Sales Range: $25-49.9 Million
Emp.: 200
Business Description:
Engineering & Procurement Services
S.I.C.: 8711
N.A.I.C.S.: 541330
Personnel:
Tomas Plachy *(Chm & CEO)*
Tomas Jendrejcik *(Dir-Design Section)*
Board of Directors:
Tomas Plachy
Jan Mengler
Zdenka Wittlingerova

CHEMOSERVIS-DWORY S.A.

ul Chemikow 1
32-600 Oswiecim, Poland
Tel.: (48) 334802000
Fax: (48) 334446059
E-Mail: sekretariat@chemoservis.pl
Web Site: en.chemoservis.pl
CHS—(WAR)
Rev.: $14,199,496
Assets: $24,123,445
Liabilities: $4,614,242
Net Worth: $19,509,203
Earnings: $142,391
Emp.: 338
Fiscal Year-end: 12/31/12
Business Description:
Industrial Maintenance & Repair Services
S.I.C.: 4581
N.A.I.C.S.: 488190
Personnel:
Andrzej Rusek *(Chm-Supervisory Bd)*
Andrzej Gastolek *(Vice Chm-Supervisory Bd)*
Wojciech Mazur *(CEO & Member-Mgmt Bd)*
Mariusz Wandor *(Member-Mgmt Bd)*
Supervisory Board of Directors:
Andrzej Rusek
Andrzej Gastolek
Tomasz Mazur
Edward Sosnowski
Marek Wroblewski

CHEMOXY INTERNATIONAL LIMITED

All Saints Refinery Cargo Fleet Road
Middlesbrough, Cleveland, TS3 6AF, United Kingdom
Tel.: (44) 1642 248 555
Fax: (44) 1642 244 340
Web Site: www.chemoxy.com
Year Founded: 1939
Sales Range: $50-74.9 Million
Emp.: 85
Business Description:
Solvents & Specialty Chemicals Mfr
S.I.C.: 2899
N.A.I.C.S.: 325998
Personnel:
Ian Stark *(CEO)*
Martyn Bainbridge *(COO)*

CHEMRING GROUP PLC

Chemring House 1500 Parkway Whiteley
Fareham, Hampshire, PO15 7AF, United Kingdom
Tel.: (44) 1489881880
Fax: (44) 1489881880
E-Mail: info@chemring.co.uk
Web Site: www.chemring.co.uk
CHG—(LSE)
Rev.: $1,169,148,387
Assets: $1,698,210,537
Liabilities: $1,013,588,322
Net Worth: $684,622,215
Earnings: $24,163,137
Emp.: 4,193
Fiscal Year-end: 10/31/12
Business Description:
Design & Mfr of Electronic, Engineering & Chemical Products for Military & Marine Safety
S.I.C.: 2899
N.A.I.C.S.: 325998
Personnel:
Mark Papworth *(Grp CEO)*
Sarah Ellard *(Sec & Dir-Legal)*
Board of Directors:
Peter C. F. Hickson
Steve Bowers
Sarah Ellard
Andy Hamment
Ian F. R. Much
Vanda Murray
Mark Papworth
Nigel Young
Legal Counsel:
Seyfarth Shaw
Washington, DC 20006
Ashurst
London, United Kingdom
Subsidiaries:

Chemring Countermeasures Ltd **(1)**
High Post Wiltshire
Salisbury, SP4 6AS, United Kingdom (100%)
Tel.: (44) 1722411611
Fax: (44) 1722428792
E-Mail: info@chemringcm.com
Web Site: www.chemringcm.com
Emp.: 450
Small Arms Ammunition Mfr
S.I.C.: 3482
N.A.I.C.S.: 332992
Philippa Walker *(Dir-HR)*

Chemring Defence UK Ltd **(1)**
Wilne Mill Draycott
Derby, DE72 3QJ, United Kingdom (100%)
Tel.: (44) 1332871100
Fax: (44) 1332873046
E-Mail: Info@chemringdefence.com
Web Site: www.chemringdefence.com
Emp.: 200
Chemical Product & Preparation Mfr
S.I.C.: 2899
N.A.I.C.S.: 325998

Chemring Energetics UK Limited **(1)**
Leafield Way Wiltshire
Corsham, SN139SS, United Kingdom (100%)
Tel.: (44) 1225810771
Fax: (44) 1225810614
Web Site: www.chemringenergetics.co.uk
Emp.: 70
Engineering Services
S.I.C.: 8711
N.A.I.C.S.: 541330
Stewert Cameron *(Mng Dir)*

U.S. Subsidiaries:

Chemring Military Products, Inc. **(2)**
7400 Regency Rd
Marshall, TX 75672
Tel.: (903) 934-9200
Fax: (903) 934-9202
E-Mail: sales@chemringmp.com
Web Site: www.chemringmp.com
Ammunition Mfr
S.I.C.: 3483
N.A.I.C.S.: 332993

Non-Intrusive Inspection Technology, Inc. **(2)**
23031 Ladbrook Dr
Dulles, VA 20166
Tel.: (703) 661-0283
Fax: (703) 661-0284
Web Site: www.niitek.com
Emp.: 500
Landmine Detection System Mfr
S.I.C.: 3812
N.A.I.C.S.: 334511
Juan Navarro *(Pres)*

Plant:

Non-Intrusive Inspection Technology, Inc. - Charlottesville Facility **(3)**
1725 Discovery Dr
Charlottesville, VA 22911
Tel.: (434) 964-4800
Fax: (434) 973-3430
Web Site: www.niitek.com
Landmine Detection System Mfr
S.I.C.: 3812
N.A.I.C.S.: 334511
Thomas Thebes *(Gen Mgr)*

Non-U.S. Subsidiaries:

Chemring Defence Spain S.L. **(2)**
Carretera Mendi S/N
Galar, Navarra, 31191, Spain
Tel.: (34) 948317862
Fax: (34) 948317928
Emp.: 25
Explosive Mfr
S.I.C.: 2892
N.A.I.C.S.: 325920
Maitane Arana *(Gen Mgr)*

Chemring Group plc—(Continued)

Chemring Nobel AS (2)
Engeneveien 7
3475 Saetre, Norway
Tel.: (47) 32 27 8600
Fax: (47) 32 27 8610
E-Mail: sales@chemringnobel.no
Web Site: www.chemringnobel.no
Emp.: 80
Explosives Mfr
S.I.C.: 2892
N.A.I.C.S.: 325920
Erland Skjold *(Gen Mgr)*

Mecar S.A. (2)
Rue Grinfaux 50
Petit-Roeulx-lez-Nivelles, 7181 Nivelles, Belgium
Tel.: (32) 67 876 411
Fax: (32) 67 211 823
E-Mail: marketing@mecar.be
Web Site: www.mecar.be
Weapon System & Ammunitions Mfr
S.I.C.: 3483
N.A.I.C.S.: 332993

Chemring EOD Limited (1)
Ordnance House Blackhill Rd
Holton Heath Poole, Dorset, BH16 6LW, United Kingdom (100%)
Tel.: (44) 1202628155
Fax: (44) 1202620182
E-Mail: sales@chemringeod.com
Web Site: www.chemringeod.com
Emp.: 49
Semiconductor & Related Device Mfr
S.I.C.: 3674
N.A.I.C.S.: 334413
David McDonald *(Mng Dir)*

Richmond Eei Ltd (1)
Thetford Armtec Estate North Lopham
Norfolk, IP222LR, United Kingdom (100%)
Tel.: (44) 1379686800
Fax: (44) 1379686888
E-Mail: info@richmondeei.co.uk
Emp.: 30
Electrical Equipment & Component Mfr
S.I.C.: 3699
N.A.I.C.S.: 335999
Robert Gilbert *(Mng Dir)*

Roke Manor Research Ltd (1)
Old Salisbury Lane
Romsey, Hampshire, SO51 0ZN, United Kingdom
Tel.: (44) 1794 833000
Fax: (44) 1794 833433
E-Mail: info@chemringts.com
Web Site: www.chemringts.com
Technology Consulting Services
S.I.C.: 8999
N.A.I.C.S.: 541690
David McDonald *(Mng Dir)*

U.S. Subsidiaries:

Alloy Surfaces Company, Inc. (1)
121 N Commerce Dr
Chester, PA 19014 (100%)
Tel.: (610) 497-7979
Fax: (610) 494-7259
E-Mail: sales@alloySurfaces.com
Emp.: 100
Ordnance & Accessories Mfr
S.I.C.: 3489
N.A.I.C.S.: 332994
John Lafemina *(Pres)*

Hi-Shear Technology Corporation (1)
24225 Garnier St
Torrance, CA 90505-5323 DE
Tel.: (310) 784-2100
Fax: (310) 325-5354
E-Mail: info@hstc.com
Web Site: www.hstc.com
Sales Range: $25-49.9 Million
Emp.: 86
Pyrotechnic, Mechanical & Electronic Products Mfr
S.I.C.: 3769
N.A.I.C.S.: 336419
Jan Hauhe *(CFO)*
Linda A. Nespole *(Sec & Dir-HR)*

Kilgore Flares (1)
155 Kilgore Rd
Toone, TN 38381-7850
Tel.: (731) 658-5231
Telex: 53-4446
Fax: (731) 658-4173
E-Mail: info@kilgoreflares.com
Web Site: www.kilgoreflares.com
Emp.: 300
Mfr of Military & Commercial Flares & Pyrotechnics
Import Export
S.I.C.: 3728
N.A.I.C.S.: 336413
Chris Watt *(Pres)*

Chemring Ordnance, Inc. (1)
10625 Puckett Rd
Perry, FL 32348 DE
Tel.: (850) 584-2634
Fax: (850) 584-2044
E-Mail: CORContacts@ChemringOrdnance.com
Web Site: www.chemringordnance.com
Emp.: 250
Ammunition & Pyrotechnic Products Mfr
Export
S.I.C.: 3489
N.A.I.C.S.: 332994
Michael Quesenberry *(Pres)*

Non-U.S. Subsidiaries:

Chemring Australia Pty Ltd (1)
230 Staceys Road
3212 Lara, VIC, Australia (100%)
Mailing Address:
PO Box 96
Lara, VIC, 3212, Australia
Tel.: (61) 3 5220 8500
Fax: (61) 3 5282 3545
E-Mail: info@chemring.com.au
Web Site: www.chemring.com.au
Emp.: 20
Navigational Services to Shipping
S.I.C.: 4499
N.A.I.C.S.: 488330
Michael Flowers *(Mng Dir)*

Chemring Defence Germany GmbH (1)
Vielander Weg 147
27574 Bremerhaven, Germany (100%)
Tel.: (49) 4713930
Fax: (49) 47139394
E-Mail: info@chemringdefence.com
Semiconductor & Related Device Mfr
S.I.C.: 3674
N.A.I.C.S.: 334413
Michael Helme *(Mng Dir)*

Simmel Difesa S.p.A. (1)
Via Ariana Km 5 2
00034 Colleferro, Italy
Tel.: (39) 0697092400
Fax: (39) 0697092476
E-Mail: info@simmeldifesa.com
Web Site: www.simmeldifesa.com
Emp.: 250
Small Arms Ammunition Mfr
S.I.C.: 3482
N.A.I.C.S.: 332992
Antonio Pompili *(Gen Mgr)*

CHEMSPEC INTERNATIONAL LIMITED

No 200 Wu Wei Road
Shanghai, 200331, China
Tel.: (86) 2163639090
Fax: (86) 00862163636993
E-Mail: sales@chemspec.com.cn
Web Site: www.chemspec.com.cn
Sales Range: $150-199.9 Million
Emp.: 1,794

Business Description:
Specialty Chemical Mfr
S.I.C.: 2899
N.A.I.C.S.: 325998

Personnel:
Jianhua Yang *(Chm & CEO)*

Board of Directors:
Jianhua Yang
Hai Mi
Zixin Wang
Kevin Wu
Zuowei Xie
Qian Zhao

CHEMTECH INDUSTRIAL VALVES LIMITED

105 Hiranandani Industrial Estate
Opp Kanjurmarg Railway Station
Kanjurmarg West, Mumbai, 400 078, India
Tel.: (91) 22 2577 3308
Fax: (91) 22 2579 4128
E-Mail: investors@chemtechvalves.com
Web Site: www.chemtechvalves.com
Year Founded: 1997
537326—(BOM)
Rev.: $4,215,565
Emp.: 97
Fiscal Year-end: 03/31/13

Business Description:
Industrial Valve Mfr
S.I.C.: 3491
N.A.I.C.S.: 332911

Personnel:
Pradeep Shikharchand Badkur *(Chm)*
Harsh Pradeep Badkur *(Mng Dir)*
Mohammed Abdullah Slatewala *(Compliance Officer & Sec)*

Board of Directors:
Pradeep Shikharchand Badkur
Harsh Pradeep Badkur
Namrata Pradeep Badkur
Niranjay Amritlal Choudhary
Ignatious Chittatukaraka Inasu
Amit Kumar Jain
Amitabh Rameshchand Luhadia
Rajnikant Hemchandra Panday

CHEMTRADE LOGISTICS INCOME FUND

155 Gordon Baker Road Suite 300
Toronto, ON, M2H 3N5, Canada
Tel.: (416) 496-5856
Fax: (416) 496-9942
E-Mail: investor-relations@chemtradelogistics.com
Web Site: www.chemtradelogistics.com
Year Founded: 2001
CHE.UN—(TSX)
Rev.: $913,869,185
Assets: $967,769,920
Liabilities: $648,261,077
Net Worth: $319,508,843
Earnings: $38,793,619
Emp.: 685
Fiscal Year-end: 12/31/12

Business Description:
Holding Company
S.I.C.: 6719
N.A.I.C.S.: 551112

Personnel:
Mark Davis *(Pres & CEO)*
Rohit Bhardwaj *(CFO & VP-Fin)*
Beat Heller *(Pres-Chemtrade Aglobis)*
Susan Pare *(Sec)*

Transfer Agent:
Valiant Trust Company
Suite 710 130 King Street West
P.O. Box 34
Toronto, ON, Canada

Subsidiaries:

Chemtrade Logistics, Inc. (1)
155 Gordon Baker Rd Ste 300
Toronto, ON, M2H 3N5, Canada (100%)
Tel.: (416) 496-5856
Fax: (416) 496-9942
Web Site: www.chemtradelogistics.com
Sales Range: $450-499.9 Million
Emp.: 1,500
Supplier of Sulphuric Acid, Liquid Sulphur Dioxide & Sodium Hydrosulphite: Spent Acid Processing Services
S.I.C.: 2899
N.A.I.C.S.: 325998
Mark Davis *(Pres & CEO)*
Rohit Bhardwaj *(CFO & VP-Fin)*

Chemtrade Pulp Chemicals Trust (1)
111 Gordon Baker Rd
Toronto, ON, M2H 3R1, Canada
Tel.: (416) 496-5856
Fax: (416) 496-9414
Investment Management Services
S.I.C.: 6211
N.A.I.C.S.: 523999

U.S. Subsidiaries:

Chemtrade Logistics (US), Inc. (1)
7680 Ottawa Rd
Elida, OH 45820
Tel.: (419) 641-4151
Fax: (419) 641-6291
Chemical Products Mfr
S.I.C.: 2899
N.A.I.C.S.: 325998

Chemtrade Performance Chemicals US, LLC (1)
814 Tyvola Rd Ste 126
Charlotte, NC 28217-3539
Tel.: (704) 369-2489
Fax: (704) 523-7764
Chemical Products Mfr
S.I.C.: 2899
N.A.I.C.S.: 325998

Chemtrade Phosphorous Specialties L.L.C. (1)
440 N 9th St
Lawrence, KS 66044-5424
Tel.: (785) 843-2290
Fax: (785) 843-2296
Industrial Chemicals Whslr
S.I.C.: 5169
N.A.I.C.S.: 424690

Chemtrade Refinery Services Inc. (1)
140 Goes In Lodge Rd
Riverton, WY 82501-9100
Tel.: (307) 856-9217
Fax: (307) 856-7842
Chemical Products Mfr & Distr
S.I.C.: 2819
N.A.I.C.S.: 325180

Non-U.S. Subsidiaries:

Chemtrade Aglobis AG (1)
Grienbachstrasse 17
6300 Zug, Switzerland
Tel.: (41) 417683700
Fax: (41) 41 768 37 47
E-Mail: switzerland@chemtradelogistics.com
Emp.: 16
Chemical Products Distr
S.I.C.: 5169
N.A.I.C.S.: 424690
Beat Heller *(CEO)*

Chemtrade Aglobis GmbH (1)
Alfredstrasse 61
45130 Essen, Germany
Tel.: (49) 20180987100
Fax: (49) 201800987193
E-Mail: info@chemtradelogistics.com
Web Site: www.chemtradelogistics.com
Emp.: 16
Chemical Products Mfr & Sales
S.I.C.: 2819
N.A.I.C.S.: 325180
Beat Heller *(Pres)*

CHEMTRONICS CO., LTD.

3th Fl DTC Tower 49
Daewangpangyo-ro 644beon-gil
Bundang-gu, Seongnam, Gyeonggi-do, Korea (South)
Tel.: (82) 31 776 7690
Fax: (82) 31 776 7691
Web Site: www.chemtronics.co.kr
Year Founded: 1997
089010—(KRS)

Business Description:
Sensor Product Mfr
S.I.C.: 3674
N.A.I.C.S.: 334413

Personnel:
Bo Kyun Kim *(Pres & CEO)*

CHEN HSONG HOLDINGS LTD.

13-15 Dai Wang St Tai Po Industrial Estate
Tai Po, China (Hong Kong)
Tel.: (852) 26653222
Fax: (852) 26648202
E-Mail: comm@chensong.com.hk
Web Site: www.chenhsong.com.hk
Year Founded: 1958
0057—(HKG)
Rev.: $231,278,530
Assets: $490,636,955
Liabilities: $119,155,990
Net Worth: $371,480,965
Earnings: $13,515,250
Emp.: 2,700
Fiscal Year-end: 03/31/13

Business Description:
Holding Company; Manufacturer of Injection Moulding Machines
S.I.C.: 6719
N.A.I.C.S.: 551112

Personnel:
Chen Chiang *(Chm)*
Lai Yuen Chiang *(CEO)*
Alice Sin Ping Lip *(Sec)*

Board of Directors:
Chen Chiang
Bernard Charnwut Chan
Chi Kin Chiang
Lai Yuen Chiang
Stephen Hau Leung Chung
Anish Lalvani
Michael Tze Hau Lee
Sam Hon Wah Ng
Johnson Chin Kwang Tan

Legal Counsel:
Mayer Brown JSM
17th Floor Prince's Building 10 Chater Road
Hong Kong, China (Hong Kong)
Tel.: (852) 28432211

Appleby Spurling & Kempe
Cedar House
P O Box HM 1179
41 Cedar Ave, Hamilton, HM EX, Bermuda

Butterfield Fulcrum Group (Bermuda) Limited
26 Burnaby Street
Hamilton, HM 11, Bermuda

Subsidiaries:

Chen Hsong Industrial Trading Co. Ltd. (1)
13-15 Dai Wang St Tai Po Industrial Estate
Tai Po, China (Hong Kong) HK
Tel.: (852) 26653222 (100%)
Fax: (852) 26641115
E-Mail: marketing@chenhsong.com.hk
Web Site: www.chenhsong.com.hk
Emp.: 150
Trading of Machinery Parts
S.I.C.: 5084
N.A.I.C.S.: 423830
Chen Chiang *(Chm)*
L. Y. Chiang *(CEO)*

Chen Hsong Logistics Services Co. Ltd. (1)
13-15 Dai Want St
Tai Po Industrial Estate, Tai Po, China (Hong Kong) HK
Tel.: (852) 26653883 (100%)
Fax: (852) 26665968
E-Mail: pm@chenhsong.com.hk
Web Site: www.chlogistics.com
Emp.: 150
Provider of Logistics Solutions Including Warehousing, Inventory Management, Repacking & Distribution
S.I.C.: 4731
N.A.I.C.S.: 541614

Chen Hsong Machinery Co. Ltd. (1)
13-15 Dai Wang St
Tai Po Industrial Estate, Tai Po, China (Hong Kong) HK
Tel.: (852) 26653222 (100%)
Fax: (852) 26641115
E-Mail: marketing@chenhsong.com.hk
Web Site: www.chenhsong-machinery.com.hk
Emp.: 100
Mfr. of Plastic Injection Moulding Machines
S.I.C.: 3559
N.A.I.C.S.: 333249
Chen Chiang *(Chm)*

Chen Hsong Precision Mould Co., Ltd. (1)
13-15 Dai Want St
Tai Po Indus Estate, Tai Po, China (Hong Kong) HK
Tel.: (852) 26653888 (100%)
Fax: (852) 26641115
E-Mail: pm@chenhsong.com.hk
Web Site: www.chenhsong.com.hk
Emp.: 100
Mfr. & Sales of Moulds & Dies
S.I.C.: 3544
N.A.I.C.S.: 333514
Chen Chiang *(Chm)*

Productive Heat Treatment Co. Ltd. (1)
13-15 Dai Wang St
Tai Po Industrial Estate, Tai Po, China (Hong Kong) HK
Tel.: (852) 24238433 (100%)
Fax: (852) 26648202
E-Mail:
Emp.: 100
Heating Equipment
S.I.C.: 3433
N.A.I.C.S.: 333414
Chen Chiang *(Chm)*

Non-U.S. Subsidiaries:

Asian Plastic Machinery Co. Ltd. (1)
1 Sung Chiang Rd N
Chung Li Industrial District, Chung-li, Tao Yuan, 320, Taiwan TW
Tel.: (886) 34522288 (100%)
Fax: (886) 34520261
E-Mail: asian@asianplastic.com.tw
Web Site: www.asianplastic.com.tw
Emp.: 200
Trading of Plastic Injection Moulding Machines
S.I.C.: 3559
N.A.I.C.S.: 333249
Chen Chiang *(Chm)*

Chen Hsong Machinery Taiwan Co. Ltd. (1)
1 Sung Chiang N Rd
Chung Li Industrial District, Chung-li, Tao Yuan, Taiwan TW
Tel.: (886) 34522288 (100%)
Fax: (886) 34520261
E-Mail: asian@asianplastic.com.tw
Web Site: www.asianplastic.com.tw
Emp.: 300
Mfr. & Sales of Plastic Injection Moulding Machines
S.I.C.: 3559
N.A.I.C.S.: 333249
Chen Chiang *(Chm)*

Shenzhen Chen Hsong Machinery Co. Ltd. (1)
Chen Hsong Industrial Park Kengzi Town
Longgang, Shenzhen, Guangdong, 518122, China HK
Tel.: (86) 75584139999 (100%)
Fax: (86) 75584137875
Web Site: www.chenhsong.com.hk
Emp.: 2,500
Mfr. & Sales of Plastic Injection Moulding Machines & Related Components
S.I.C.: 3559
N.A.I.C.S.: 333249
Chiang Chen *(Founder & Chm)*

Non-U.S. Joint Venture:

B+C Extrusion Systems (Foshan) Ltd. (1)
2 Jinxiang Rd Daliang
Foshan, 528300, China CN
Tel.: (86) 75722380110
Fax: (86) 75722211801
Web Site: www.bcc-battenfeld.com
Emp.: 600
Plastics Extrusion Machinery & Extrusion Lines Mfr; Owned 60% by Battenfeld GmbH & 40% by Chen Hsong Holdings Ltd.
S.I.C.: 3089
N.A.I.C.S.: 326199
Jian Peng *(Mng Dir)*

CHENAB LIMITED

Nishatabad
Faisalabad, Pakistan
Tel.: (92) 418754472
Fax: (92) 418752400
E-Mail: info@chenabgroup.com
Web Site: www.chenabgroup.com
CHBL—(KAR)
Sls.: $21,999,578
Assets: $152,412,630
Liabilities: $145,381,758
Net Worth: $7,030,873
Earnings: ($5,002,182)
Fiscal Year-end: 06/30/13

Business Description:
Textile & Garments Mfr
S.I.C.: 2299
N.A.I.C.S.: 313210

Personnel:
Muhammad Latif *(CEO)*
Muhammad Arshad *(CFO & Sec)*

Board of Directors:
Muhammad Javaid Iqbal
Muhammad Latif
Muhammad Faisal Latif
Muhammad Farhan Latif
Muhammad Zeeshan Latif
Shahnaz Latif
Muhammad Naeem

Subsidiaries:

ChenOne Stores Limited. (1)
Park Tower
Clifton, Karachi, Sindh, Pakistan
Tel.: (92) 418754472
Fax: (92) 418751907
E-Mail: chenone@chenabgroup.com
Web Site: www.chenone.com.pk
Emp.: 1,500
Apparel Retail Stores Operation Services
S.I.C.: 5699
N.A.I.C.S.: 448150
Masood Akhtar Bajwa *(Gen Mgr)*

ChenSoft Private Limited (1)
Nishatabad
Faisalabad, Punjab, Pakistan
Tel.: (92) 418754472
Fax: (92) 418752400
Web Site: www.chensoft.com.pk
Emp.: 13
Document Processing Services
S.I.C.: 7389
N.A.I.C.S.: 561410
Akbar Hussain *(Mgr-IT)*

U.S. Subsidiary:

Chenab USA Inc (1)
261 5th Ave Ste 301
New York, NY 10016-7706
Tel.: (212) 686-0955
Fax: (212) 686-0957
E-Mail: info@chenabusa.com
Web Site: www.chenabusa.com
Emp.: 11
Home Furnishings Whslr
S.I.C.: 5023
N.A.I.C.S.: 423220
Jud Lusk *(Sr VP-Ops)*

Non-U.S. Subsidiary:

CGI Limited (1)
Office S-20204 South Zone
PO Box 72629
Jebel Ali Free Zone Authority, Dubai, United Arab Emirates
Tel.: (971) 48861445
Fax: (971) 4 8861447
E-Mail: info@cgiuae.com
Web Site: www.cgiuae.com
Textile Products Mfr & Distr
S.I.C.: 2299
N.A.I.C.S.: 313210
Muhammad Rizuan Ladif *(Mgr)*

CHENBRO MICOM CO., LTD.

15 Fl 150 Jian Yi Road
Zhonghe District, Taipei, Taiwan
Tel.: (886) 282265500
Fax: (886) 282265395
E-Mail: joycechih@chenbro.com.tw
Web Site: www.chenbro.com.tw
8210—(TAI)
Sales Range: $125-149.9 Million

Business Description:
Computer Related Products Mfr
S.I.C.: 3577
N.A.I.C.S.: 334118

Personnel:
Maggi Chen *(Chm & Gen Mgr)*

U.S. Subsidiary:

Chenbro Micom (USA) Inc. (1)
2888 E Spruce St
Ontario, CA 91761
Tel.: (909) 947-3200
Fax: (909) 947-4300
E-Mail: info@chenbro.com
Computer Terminal Mfr
S.I.C.: 3575
N.A.I.C.S.: 334118
Bronson Peng *(Project Mgr)*

Non-U.S. Subsidiaries:

Chenbro Europe B.V. (1)
Avignonlaan 35
5627 GA Eindhoven, Netherlands
Tel.: (31) 40 295 2045
Fax: (31) 40 295 2044
E-Mail: info@chenbro.nl
Web Site: www.chenbro.eu
Emp.: 10
Chassis Product Mfr
S.I.C.: 3711
N.A.I.C.S.: 336111
Ernst Jan Dijk *(Reg Mgr-Sls)*

Chenbro Micom (Shenzhen) Co., Ltd. (1)
Room 2109 Hua Rong Building 178 Mintian Road
Futian CBD, Shenzhen, 518048, China
Tel.: (86) 755 2382 4355
Fax: (86) 755 2382 4356
E-Mail: cninfo@chenbro.com
Chassis Product Mfr
S.I.C.: 3711
N.A.I.C.S.: 336111

Chenbro UK Ltd. (1)
Crossford Court Dane Road
Sale, Manchester, M33 7BZ, United Kingdom
Tel.: (44) 1614255341
E-Mail: ukinfo@chenbro.com.tw
Computer Peripheral Equipment Whslr
S.I.C.: 5045
N.A.I.C.S.: 423430

CHENG EUI PRECISION INDUSTRY CO., LTD.

(d/b/a Foxlink Image Technology)
No 49 Sec 4 Zhongyang Road
Tucheng, 236, Taiwan
Tel.: (886) 222699888
Fax: (886) 222681240
E-Mail: alvin_yu@foxlink.com
Web Site: www.foxlink.com.tw
6298—(TAI)
Sales Range: $25-49.9 Million
Emp.: 10,000

Business Description:
Mfr. of Networking Products, Communications Connectors & Cablings
S.I.C.: 3678
N.A.I.C.S.: 334417

Personnel:
Tai Chiang Gou *(Chm)*

U.S. Subsidiary:

Foxlink International Inc (1)
925 W Lambert Rd Ste C
Brea, CA 92821-2943 CA
Tel.: (714) 256-1777
Fax: (714) 256-1700
E-Mail: info@foxlink.com
Web Site: www.foxlink.com
Sls.: $38,164,520
Emp.: 45
Communications Connectors Import Export

Cheng Eui Precision Industry Co., Ltd.—(Continued)

S.I.C.: 3643
N.A.I.C.S.: 335931
James Lee *(Pres)*

CHENG LOONG CORP.

No 1 Section 1 Ming Shen Rd
Panchiao, Taipei, Taiwan
Tel.: (886) 222225131
Fax: (886) 222226110
E-Mail: clc@mail.clc.com.tw
Web Site: www.clc.com.tw
1904—(TAI)
Sales Range: $200-249.9 Million
Business Description:
Corrugated Paper Box Mfr
S.I.C.: 2653
N.A.I.C.S.: 322211
Personnel:
Suanne Cheng *(Chm)*
Frank Cheng *(Vice Chm)*
Tong-Ho Tsai *(Pres)*
Board of Directors:
Suanne Cheng
Frank Cheng

CHENG SHIN RUBBER (XIAMEN) IND., LTD.

15 Xibin Rd
Xinglin District, Xiamen, 361022, China
Tel.: (86) 5926211606
Fax: (86) 5926214649
Web Site: www.csttires.com
Year Founded: 1989
Sales Range: $100-124.9 Million
Emp.: 3,500
Business Description:
Tires & Tubes Distr
S.I.C.: 5014
N.A.I.C.S.: 441320
Personnel:
Marx Lee *(Mgr-Sls)*
Non-U.S. Joint Ventures:

New Pacific Industry Co., Ltd. **(1)**
44 Sec 1 Chung Shan Rd
Chung Chuang Vlg Hua Tan, Chang-Hua, Taiwan TW
Tel.: (886) 47869711
Fax: (886) 47863284
Web Site: www.newpacific.com.tw
Emp.: 120
Mfr. of Automotive Parts
S.I.C.: 3714
N.A.I.C.S.: 336340
Kato Toshiaki *(Gen Mgr)*

CHENGDU DR. PENG TELECOM & MEDIA GROUP CO., LTD.

(d/b/a Dr. Peng Telecom & Media Group)
5/F Shun Cheng Bldg No 229 Shun Cheng Avenue
Chengdu, 610015, China
Tel.: (86) 28 8675 1933
Fax: (86) 28 8662 2006
Web Site: www.drpeng.com.cn
Year Founded: 1985
600804—(SHG)
Business Description:
Holding Company;
Telecommunications & Internet Services
S.I.C.: 6719
N.A.I.C.S.: 551112
Personnel:
Xueping Yang *(Chm)*
Guoliang Yang *(Vice Chm)*
Weimin Qiu *(Gen Mgr)*
Jinkun Li *(CFO)*
Chunxiao Ren *(Sec & Deputy Gen Mgr)*
Board of Directors:
Xueping Yang
Youzhong Bai
Nan Lin
Weimin Qiu
Chunxiao Ren
Guoliang Yang
Guangjian Zhang
Joint Venture:

Great Wall Broadband Network Service Co., Ltd. **(1)**
68 ZijinBuilding Floor 17th Wanquan Road
Haidian District, Beijing, 100086, China CN
Tel.: (86) 1082659931
Fax: (86) 1082659790
Sales Range: $1-4.9 Billion
Computer Storage Technology Mfr
S.I.C.: 3572
N.A.I.C.S.: 334112

CHENGDU GALAXY MAGNET CO., LTD.

(d/b/a Galaxy Magnets)
Chengdu High-Tech Development Zone Road 6 Western Herbs
Chengdu, Sichuan, 611731, China
Tel.: (86) 28 87823555
Fax: (86) 28 87824018
E-Mail: sales@galaxymagnets.com
Web Site: www.galaxymagnets.com
Year Founded: 1993
300127—(CHIN)
Emp.: 1,200
Business Description:
Magnetic Components Mfr
S.I.C.: 3695
N.A.I.C.S.: 334613
Personnel:
Yan Dai *(Chm)*

CHENGDU GEEYA TECHNOLOGY CO., LTD

No 50 Shuhan Road West
Chengdu, China 610091
Tel.: (86) 2868232103
Fax: (86) 2868232100
E-Mail: stocks@geeya.cn
Web Site: www.geeya.cn
Year Founded: 1999
300028—(CHIN)
Sales Range: $75-99.9 Million
Emp.: 650
Business Description:
Digital Television Equipment Mfr & Distr
S.I.C.: 3663
N.A.I.C.S.: 334220
Personnel:
Xuhui Zhou *(Chm)*
Miao He *(CEO)*
Yu Qiao *(CFO)*
Yong You *(CMO)*
Board of Directors:
Xuhui Zhou
Chun Cai
Xiaodong He
Weili Lei
Daiwei Li
Hailong Wang
Liangchao Zhou
Supervisory Board of Directors:
Dahua Yang
Xingyong Zeng
Shijie Zhang

CHENGDU GOLDTEL ELECTRONICAL TECHNOLOGY CO., LTD.

3 Xixin Avenue Hi-Tech West Zone
Chengdu, 611731, China
Tel.: (86) 2865557543
Fax: (86) 2865557540
Web Site: www.gotecom.com
300101—(CHIN)
Emp.: 120
Business Description:
Electronic Component & Equipment Mfr
S.I.C.: 3679
N.A.I.C.S.: 334419
Personnel:
Jun Xie *(CEO)*

CHENGDU HONGQI CHAIN CO., LTD.

7 Dikang Avenue
West District, Chengdu, 611731, China
Tel.: (86) 28 8787 7333
Fax: (86) 28 8787 7388
E-Mail: xcb@hqls.com.cn
Web Site: www.hqls.com.cn
002697—(SSE)
Sales Range: $600-649.9 Million
Emp.: 13,230
Business Description:
Convenience Store Owner & Operator
S.I.C.: 5411
N.A.I.C.S.: 445120
Personnel:
Shiru Cao *(Chm)*

CHENGDU ROAD & BRIDGE ENGINEERING CO., LTD.

11 Wukedongsi Road
Wuhou District, Chengdu, 610045, China
Tel.: (86) 2885003688
Fax: (86) 2885003588
E-Mail: zqb@cdlq.com
Web Site: www.cdlq.com
Year Founded: 1988
002628—(SSE)
Emp.: 360
Business Description:
Road & Bridge Construction & Engineering
S.I.C.: 1611
N.A.I.C.S.: 237310
Personnel:
Yuli Zheng *(Chm)*
Xuan Luo *(Vice Chm)*
Xiaoling Qiu *(CFO & VP)*
Han Hu *(Sec)*
Board of Directors:
Yuli Zheng
Han Hu
Xuan Luo
Xiaoling Qiu
Jiwei Wang
Weigang Zhou

CHENGDU SANTAI ELECTRONICS INDUSTRY CO., LTD.

42 Shuxi Road Hi-Tech Industry Zone
Jinniu District, Chengdu, 610091, China
Tel.: (86) 2887506876
Fax: (86) 2887506980
E-Mail: office@isantai.com
Web Site: www.isantai.com
002312—(SSE)
Emp.: 670
Business Description:
Electronic Receipt, Automatic Teller Machine (ATM) Monitoring & Digital Bank Network Security Monitoring Systems Mfr & Distr
S.I.C.: 3679
N.A.I.C.S.: 334419
Personnel:
Jian Bu *(Chm)*

CHENGDU TIANQI INDUSTRY (GROUP) CO., LTD.

(d/b/a Tianqi Group)
No 10 East Gaopeng Road
Hi-Tech Development Zone,
Chengdu, Sichuan, 610041, China
Tel.: (86) 28 8514 0380
Fax: (86) 28 8518 5662
E-Mail: tianqixz@tianqigroup.cn
Web Site: www.tianqigroup.cn
Year Founded: 1997
Business Description:
Holding Company
Import Export
S.I.C.: 6719
N.A.I.C.S.: 551112
Subsidiary:

Chengdu Tianqi Machinery, Metals & Minerals Import & Export Co., Ltd. **(1)**
No 10 East Gaopeng Road
Hi-Tech Development Zone, Chengdu, Sichuan, China CN
Tel.: (86) 28 8515 9223
Fax: (86) 28 8515 6117
E-Mail: tianqi@tqmmm.com.cn
Web Site: www.tqmmm.com.cn
Resource Minerals & Large-Scale Machinery Wholesale Trade Distr
Import Export
S.I.C.: 7389
N.A.I.C.S.: 425120
Non-U.S. Subsidiary:

Talison Lithium Limited **(1)**
Level 4 37 St Georges Terrace
Perth, WA, 6000, Australia AU
Mailing Address:
Locked Bag 40
Cloisters Square, Perth, WA, 6850, Australia
Tel.: (61) 8 9263 5555
Fax: (61) 8 9202 1144
E-Mail: perth@talisonlithium.com
Web Site: www.talisonlithium.com
Sales Range: $125-149.9 Million
Emp.: 140
Lithium Mining
S.I.C.: 1099
N.A.I.C.S.: 212299
Peter Oliver *(CEO & Mng Dir)*
Lorry Mignacca *(CFO & Sec)*

CHENGDU XINZHU ROAD & BRIDGE MACHINERY CO., LTD.

Sichuan Xinjin Industrial Park
Xinjin, Chengdu, Sichuan, 611430, China
Tel.: (86) 28 82556968
E-Mail: vendition@xinzhu.com
Web Site: www.xinzhu.com
Year Founded: 2001
002480—(SSE)
Business Description:
Road & Bridge Machinery Mfr
S.I.C.: 3531
N.A.I.C.S.: 333120
Personnel:
Zhiming Huang *(Chm)*

CHENGUANG BIOTECH GROUP CO., LTD.

1 Chenguang Road
Quzhou, Hebei, 057250, China
Tel.: (86) 310 8851999
Fax: (86) 310 8851339
E-Mail: sesu@hdchenguang.com
Web Site: www.cn-cg.com
300138—(CHIN)
Sales Range: $25-49.9 Million
Emp.: 400
Business Description:
Flavoring Syrups & Food Extracts Mfr
S.I.C.: 2087
N.A.I.C.S.: 311930
Personnel:
Qingguo Lu *(Chm)*

Subsidiaries:

Handan Chenguang Precious Oil Co., Ltd **(1)**
No 1 Kaifa Road
Quzhou County, Handan, 057250, China
Tel.: (86) 310 8852088
Fax: (86) 310 8852066
E-Mail: silu@hdcgzp.com
Web Site: www.hdcgzp.com
Edible Oil Mfr
S.I.C.: 2079
N.A.I.C.S.: 311225

Yingkou Chenguang Foods Co Ltd **(1)**
Qinglongshan St
Bayuquan District, Yingkou, Liaoning, 115007, China
Tel.: (86) 417 6237628
Edible Oils Mfr
S.I.C.: 2079
N.A.I.C.S.: 311225

CHENMING MOLD IND. CORP.

2-6F No 27 Sec 6 Mincyuan E Rd
Neihu District
114 Taipei, Taiwan
Tel.: (886) 227973999
Fax: (886) 227973699
E-Mail: service@tw.uneec.com
Web Site: www.uneec.com
3013—(TAI)
Sales Range: $75-99.9 Million

Business Description:
Computer Equipment Mfr
S.I.C.: 7374
N.A.I.C.S.: 518210

Personnel:
Mu-Ho Lin *(Chm)*

Subsidiary:

Chenming Mold Ind. Corp. - Keelung Plant **(1)**
23 Wu Shuin Street
Keelung, Taiwan
Tel.: (886) 2 2432 4032
Fax: (886) 2 2431 0103
E-Mail: service@tw.uneec.com
Web Site: www.uneec.com
Emp.: 40
Metal Stampings Mfr
S.I.C.: 3466
N.A.I.C.S.: 332119

U.S. Subsidiary:

Chenming USA Inc. **(1)**
30631 San Antonio St
Hayward, CA 94544
Tel.: (510) 429-3882
Fax: (510) 429-3883
E-Mail: info@chenmingusa.com
Web Site: www.chenmingusa.com
Emp.: 9
Computer Peripheral Equipments Distr
S.I.C.: 5045
N.A.I.C.S.: 423430
Walter Yeung *(Exec VP)*

Non-U.S. Subsidiary:

Chenming Electronic (Dongguan) Co., Ltd. **(1)**
4th Industrial District Hsiakang
Changan Chen, Dongguan, Guangdong, 523710, China
Tel.: (86) 76985419999
Fax: (86) 76985411688
Web Site: www.uneec.com
Electronics Metal Parts Mfr
S.I.C.: 3679
N.A.I.C.S.: 334419

CHENNAI MEENAKSHI MULTISPECIALITY HOSPITAL LIMITED

New No 72 Old No 148 Luz Church Road
Mylapore, Chennai, Tamil Nadu, 600 004, India
Tel.: (91) 4442938938
Fax: (91) 4424993282
E-Mail: cmmhospitals@gmail.com
Web Site: www.cmmh.in
523489—(BOM)
Rev.: $3,007,492
Assets: $3,205,244
Liabilities: $4,122,618
Net Worth: ($917,374)
Earnings: $127,369
Fiscal Year-end: 03/31/13

Business Description:
Hospital Management Services
S.I.C.: 8069
N.A.I.C.S.: 622310

Personnel:
A. N. Radhakrishnan *(Chm & Mng Dir)*
V. Krishnamurthy *(CEO)*
M. T. Jeya Pragasam *(Compliance Officer & Sec)*

Board of Directors:
A. N. Radhakrishnan
S. Kameswaran
Premalatha Kanikannan
G. R. Navin Rakesh
B. Ramachandran
R. Venkataswami

Legal Counsel:
A.K. Mylsamy
61 TTK Road
Chennai, 600 004, India

Transfer Agent:
Cameo Corporate Services Limited
Subramanian Bldg No 1 Club House Road
Chennai, 600 002, India
Tel.: (91) 44 2846 0390
Fax: (91) 44 2846 0129

CHEONG MING INVESTMENTS LIMITED

4/F Mai Sik Industrial Building 1-11 Kwai Ting Road
Kwai Chung, Hong Kong, New Territories, China (Hong Kong)
Tel.: (852) 24282721
Fax: (852) 24805997
E-Mail: info@cheongming.com
Web Site: www.cheongming.com
1196—(HKG)
Rev.: $55,409,944
Assets: $87,570,977
Liabilities: $20,169,972
Net Worth: $67,401,004
Earnings: $2,296,986
Emp.: 1,175
Fiscal Year-end: 03/31/13

Business Description:
Paper Cartons Books Mfr & Sales
S.I.C.: 5113
N.A.I.C.S.: 424130

Personnel:
Brian Shing Ming Lui *(Chm)*
Shing Cheong Lui *(Mng Dir)*
Chin Pang Tsang *(CFO & Sec)*

Board of Directors:
Brian Shing Ming Lui
Chun Kong Lam
Wing Man Lo
Shing Cheong Lui
Victor Shing Chung Lui
Carmen Lai Man Ng

Butterfield Fulcrum Group (Bermuda) Limited
26 Burnaby Street
Hamilton, HM 11, Bermuda

Transfer Agents:
Tricor Tengis Limited
26th Floor Tesbury Centre 28 Queen's Road East
Wanchai, China (Hong Kong)
Tel.: (852) 29801333
Fax: (852) 28108185

Butterfield Fulcrum Group (Bermuda) Limited
26 Burnaby Street
Hamilton, HM 11, Bermuda

CHEOPS TECHNOLOGY FRANCE SA

37 Rue Thomas Edison
33610 Merignac, France
Tel.: (33) 556188383
Fax: (33) 556188384
E-Mail: cheops@cheops.fr
Web Site: www.cheops.fr
MLCHE—(EUR)
Sales Range: $10-24.9 Million
Emp.: 300

Business Description:
Computer Services
S.I.C.: 7379
N.A.I.C.S.: 541519

Personnel:
Nicholas Leroy-Fleuriot *(Pres)*

CHEOUM & C CO., LTD.

3F KT Int-l Telephone Office Bldg 1-2 Wonhyoro-3Ga
Yongsan-Gu, Seoul, 140-718, Korea (South)
Tel.: (82) 27157760
Fax: (82) 27142808
E-Mail: secret34@mp1.co.kr
Web Site: www.mp1.co.kr
111820—(KRS)

Business Description:
Business Management Services
S.I.C.: 8741
N.A.I.C.S.: 561110

Personnel:
Jaewoo Jeong *(Gen Mgr)*

CHEPRI HOLDING B.V.

Karolusguldenstraat 6
's-Hertogenbosch, Netherlands
Tel.: (31) 736400715
Fax: (31) 736400717
Web Site: www.chepriplant.nl

Business Description:
Investment Company
S.I.C.: 6282
N.A.I.C.S.: 523930

Subsidiary:

ECF Group B.V. **(1)**
Hooge Zijde 32
PO Box 8565
Eindhoven, 5605, Netherlands
Tel.: (31) 402380480
Fax: (31) 402380465
Web Site: www.ecfgroup.com
Emp.: 150
Investment Company
S.I.C.: 6282
N.A.I.C.S.: 523930

Subsidiaries:

Bakker Continental B.V. **(2)**
Marinus Van Meelweg 19
5657 EN Eindhoven, Hooge Zegde, Netherlands (100%)
Tel.: (31) 402380482
Fax: (31) 402380465
E-Mail: info@bakkercontinental.com
Web Site: www.bakkercontinental.com
Emp.: 70
Direct Marketing & Sales Promotion Services
S.I.C.: 5963
N.A.I.C.S.: 454390

MediaMotion **(2)**
10 Fortranweg
3802 RE Amersfoort, Netherlands (100%)
Tel.: (31) 334502811
Fax: (31) 334602871
Web Site: www.media-motion.nl
Emp.: 150
S.I.C.: 7812
N.A.I.C.S.: 512110

CHEQUERS CAPITAL

48 Avenue Montaigne
75008 Paris, France
Tel.: (33) 153576100
Fax: (33) 153576111
E-Mail: mail@chequerscapital.com
Web Site: www.chequerscapital.com
Emp.: 20

Business Description:
Brokerage, Investment & Management Consulting Services
S.I.C.: 6221
N.A.I.C.S.: 523130

CHERAT CEMENT COMPANY LIMITED

Modern Motors House Beaumont Road
Karachi, 75530, Pakistan
Tel.: (92) 21111000009
Fax: (92) 2135683425
E-Mail: cherat@gfg.com.pk
Web Site: www.gfg.com.pk
CHCC—(KAR)
Sls.: $63,762,029
Assets: $51,303,395
Liabilities: $13,735,946
Net Worth: $37,567,449
Earnings: $12,401,288
Emp.: 508
Fiscal Year-end: 06/30/13

Business Description:
Cement Mfr
S.I.C.: 2891
N.A.I.C.S.: 325520

Personnel:
Azam Faruque *(CEO)*
Yasir Masood *(CFO)*
Abid A. Vazir *(Sec)*

Board of Directors:
Mohammed Faruque
Aamir Amin
Javaid Anwar
Azam Faruque
Shehryar Faruque
Tariq Faruque
Akbarali Pesnani
Saquib H. Shirazi

CHERAT PACKAGING LIMITED

1st Floor Betani Arcade Jumrud Road
Peshawar, Pakistan
Tel.: (92) 21 35683566
Fax: (92) 21 35683425
E-Mail: cherat@gfg.com.pk
Web Site: www.gfg.com.pk/cheratpaper/
CPPL—(KAR LAH)
Sls.: $41,830,153
Assets: $36,077,732
Liabilities: $23,801,752
Net Worth: $12,275,980
Earnings: $1,201,104
Emp.: 68
Fiscal Year-end: 06/30/13

Business Description:
Packaging Mfr
S.I.C.: 2679
N.A.I.C.S.: 322299

Personnel:
Amer Faruque *(CEO)*
Yasir Masood *(CFO)*
Abid A. Vazir *(Sec)*

Board of Directors:
Mohammed Faruque
Amer Faruque
Arif Faruque
Aslam Faruque
Mahmood Faruque
Shehryar Faruque
Tariq Faruque
Abrar Hasan
Akbarali Pesnani

Subsidiary:

Greaves Airconditioning (Pvt.) Ltd **(1)**
3rd Floor Modern Motors House Beaumont Road
Karachi, Pakistan

Cherat Packaging Limited—(Continued)

Tel.: (92) 21 35682 565
Fax: (92) 21 35682 839
Airconditioning & Refrigeration Parts Distr
S.I.C.: 5078
N.A.I.C.S.: 423740

CHERRY OPTICAL, INC.

(Acquired by Essilor International, S.A.)

CHERY AUTOMOBILE CO., LTD.

8 Changchun Rd Economic & Technological Development Zone
Wuhu, 241009, China
Tel.: (86) 5535922993
Fax: (86) 5535923205
Web Site: www.cheryinternational.com
Year Founded: 1997
Sales Range: $1-4.9 Billion
Emp.: 20,000
Fiscal Year-end: 12/31/12
Business Description:
Motor Vehicles Mfr
S.I.C.: 3711
N.A.I.C.S.: 336111
Personnel:
Tongyao Yin *(Chm)*

CHERYONG INDUSTRIAL CO LTD

339 1 Kwangjang Dong
Kwangjin Gu
143811 Seoul, Korea (South)
Tel.: (82) 82222046300
Fax: (82) 82222046388
Web Site: www.cheryong.co.kr
33100—(KRS)
Sales Range: $50-74.9 Million
Emp.: 155
Business Description:
Power Transmission Products Mfr
S.I.C.: 4939
N.A.I.C.S.: 221121
Personnel:
Jong Tae Park *(CEO)*

Plants:

Cheryong Industrial Co Ltd - Cheongsan Factory (1)
No 494-6 Pansu-ri Cheongsan-myon
Okcheon, North Chungcheong, Korea (South)
Tel.: (82) 437302200
Fax: (82) 437335964
E-Mail: Cheryong260@Cheryong.co.kr
Power Transmission Equipments Whslr
S.I.C.: 5085
N.A.I.C.S.: 423840

Cheryong Industrial Co Ltd - Daejeon Factory (1)
1686-2 Sinil-dong
Daedeok-gu, Daejeon, Chungcheong, Korea (South)
Tel.: (82) 429303000
Fax: (82) 429303099
E-Mail: cheryong@cheryong.co.kr
Web Site: www.cheryongelec.com
Power Transmission Equipments Whslr
S.I.C.: 5085
N.A.I.C.S.: 423840

CHESAPEAKE GOLD CORPORATION

Suite 201 - 1512 Yew Street
Vancouver, BC, V6K 3E4, Canada
Tel.: (604) 731-1094
Fax: (604) 731-0209
E-Mail: chesapeake@shaw.ca
Web Site: www.chesapeakegold.com
Year Founded: 2002
CKG—(OTC TSXV)
Rev.: $450,192
Assets: $104,382,040
Liabilities: $8,204,740
Net Worth: $96,177,300
Earnings: ($9,388,121)
Emp.: 2
Fiscal Year-end: 12/31/12
Business Description:
Gold & Silver Mining Services
S.I.C.: 1041
N.A.I.C.S.: 212221
Personnel:
P. Randy Reifel *(Pres)*
Sam Wong *(CFO)*
Bernard G. Poznanski *(Sec)*
Gerald L. Sneddon *(Exec VP-Ops)*
Board of Directors:
Chris K. Falck
Daniel J. Kunz
Peter F. Palmedo
John Perston
P. Randy Reifel
Gerald L. Sneddon
Legal Counsel:
Koffman Kalef
Vancouver, BC, Canada
Transfer Agent:
Computershare Trust Company of Canada
100 University Avenue 11th Floor
Toronto, ON, M5J 2Y1, Canada
Tel.: (416) 891-9633
Toll Free: (800) 663-9097

CHESHER EQUIPMENT LTD.

6599 Kitimat Rd Unit 2
Mississauga, ON, L5N 4J4, Canada
Tel.: (905) 363-0309
Fax: (905) 363-0426
Toll Free: (800) 668-8765
E-Mail: sales@chesher.com
Web Site: www.chesher.com
Year Founded: 1967
Sales Range: Less than $1 Million
Emp.: 6
Business Description:
Food Machinery & Equipment Distr Import
S.I.C.: 5087
N.A.I.C.S.: 423850
Personnel:
Michaela Chesher *(Mgr-Ops)*

CHESLIND TEXTILES LTD.

B Muduganapalli Hosur
Krishnagiri District
635103 Bengaluru, Tamil Nadu, India
Tel.: (91) 4344254184
Fax: (91) 4344254276
E-Mail: cheslind@cheslind.com
Web Site: www.cheslind.co.in
521056—(BOM)
Sales Range: $25-49.9 Million
Emp.: 1,000
Business Description:
Yarn Mfr
S.I.C.: 2299
N.A.I.C.S.: 313110
Personnel:
Ravi Jhunjhunwala *(Chm)*
Vinod Mehta *(Pres)*
Ananta R. Deshpande *(Sec)*
Kamal Kishore Mittal *(Sr VP-Mktg)*
Board of Directors:
Ravi Jhunjhunwala
T. K. Arun
G. B. Bagrodia
Riju Jhunjhunwala
Prakash Maheshwari
A. Murali
S. C. Parasrampuria
K P RAO & CO
25 State Bank Road
Bengaluru, India
Transfer Agent:
Karvy Computershare Private Limited
Plot No 17 to 24 Vittalrao Nagar Madhapur
Hyderabad, India

CHESNARA PLC

Harbour House Portway
Preston, Lancashire, PR2 2PR, United Kingdom
Tel.: (44) 1772840000
Fax: (44) 1772840010
E-Mail: info@chesnara.co.uk
Web Site: www.chesnara.co.uk
CSN—(LSE)
Rev.: $787,339,237
Assets: $7,344,679,239
Liabilities: $6,999,847,585
Net Worth: $344,831,654
Earnings: $44,126,942
Emp.: 148
Fiscal Year-end: 12/31/12
Business Description:
Holding Company; Life Insurance
S.I.C.: 6719
N.A.I.C.S.: 551112
Personnel:
Graham Kettleborough *(CEO)*
Mary Fishwick *(Sec)*
Board of Directors:
Peter Edward Mason
David Brand
Mike Evans
Veronica France
Frank Hughes
Graham Kettleborough
David Rimmington
Peter Wright
Legal Counsel:
Ashurst LLP
5 Appold St
London, EC2A 2HA, United Kingdom
Addleshaw Goddard LLP
100 Barbirolli Square
Manchester, United Kingdom

Subsidiary:

Countrywide Assured Plc (1)
83 School Road
Sale, Chester, Cheshire, M33 7XA, United Kingdom (100%)
Tel.: (44) 1619736248
Fax: (44) 1619626085
Emp.: 4
Financial Investment Activities
S.I.C.: 6211
N.A.I.C.S.: 523999
Paul Smith *(Mng Dir)*

Holding:

City of Westminster Assurance Company Limited (1)
Arndale House Arndale Ctr
P O Box 1023
LU12TG Luton, United Kingdom
Tel.: (44) 1582742800
Fax: (44) 1582 742899
Life Insurance Services
S.I.C.: 6311
N.A.I.C.S.: 524113

Non-U.S. Subsidiary:

Moderna Forsakringar Liv AB (1)
Sveavagen 167
PO Box 7830
103 98 Stockholm, Sweden
Tel.: (46) 856200600
Fax: (46) 856200688
Web Site: www.modernaforsakringar.se
Sales Range: $10-24.9 Million
Emp.: 30
Life Insurance Services
S.I.C.: 6411
N.A.I.C.S.: 524210
Mikael Claesson *(CEO)*
Lars Nordstrand *(Mng Dir)*
Anna Salesjo *(CFO)*

Subsidiary:

Movestic Kapitalforvaltning AB (2)
Tulegatan 2
PO Box 7853
103 99 Stockholm, Sweden
Tel.: (46) 812039200
Fax: (46) 8 120 39 310
E-Mail: order@movestickapital.se
Web Site: www.movestickapital.se
General Insurance Services
S.I.C.: 6411
N.A.I.C.S.: 524210

CHESSER RESOURCES LIMITED

96 Stephens Road
Brisbane, QLD, 4101, Australia
Tel.: (61) 7 3844 0613
Fax: (61) 7 3844 0154
E-Mail: info@chesserresources.com.au
Web Site: www.chesserresources.com.au
CHZ—(ASX)
Rev.: $369,669
Assets: $31,401,812
Liabilities: $446,634
Net Worth: $30,955,178
Earnings: ($4,379,638)
Fiscal Year-end: 06/30/13
Business Description:
Mineral Exploration
S.I.C.: 1481
N.A.I.C.S.: 213115
Personnel:
Richard Valenta *(Mng Dir)*
Stephen Kelly *(CFO & Sec)*
Board of Directors:
Robert Gordon Reynolds
Morrice Cordiner
Peter Lester
Simon O'Loughlin
Simon Taylor
Richard Valenta
Legal Counsel:
O'Loughlins Lawyers
Level 2 99 Frome Street
Adelaide, Australia

Non-U.S. Subsidiary:

Chesser Arama ve Madencilik Limited Sirketi (1)
Sehit Ersan Cad No 4/17
Cankaya, Ankara, Turkey
Tel.: (90) 3124666042
Fax: (90) 3124666043
E-Mail: Cdaghnhlp@chesserresources.com
Web Site: www.chesserresources.com
Emp.: 6
Copper Ore Mining Services
S.I.C.: 1021
N.A.I.C.S.: 212234
Cemyuceer Ujr *(Mgr)*

CHESSWOOD GROUP LIMITED

4077 Chesswood Drive
Toronto, ON, M3J 2R8, Canada
Tel.: (416) 386-3099
Fax: (416) 386-3085
E-Mail: info@chesswoodgroup.com
Web Site: www.chesswoodgroup.com
Year Founded: 2006
CHW—(TSX)
Rev.: $35,733,031
Assets: $160,429,858
Liabilities: $100,236,977
Net Worth: $60,192,881
Earnings: $8,935,246
Emp.: 38
Fiscal Year-end: 12/31/12
Business Description:
Investment Management Services
S.I.C.: 6211
N.A.I.C.S.: 523999
Personnel:
Frederick Steiner *(Chm)*
Barry Shafran *(Pres & CEO)*
Lisa Stevenson *(CFO & Dir-Fin)*
Board of Directors:
Frederick Steiner

Clare R. Copeland
Robert J. Day
Samuel L. Leeper
David Obront
Barry Shafran
Jeffrey Wortsman

Legal Counsel:
McCarthy Tetrault
Suite 5300T TD Bank Tower Toronto Dominion Centre 66 Wellington Street
Toronto, ON, Canada

Transfer Agent:
Equity Financial Trust Company
200 University Avenue Suite 400
Toronto, ON, Canada

Subsidiaries:

Acura Sherway (1)
2000 The Queensway
Toronto, ON, M9C 5H5, Canada
Tel.: (416) 620-1987
Fax: (416) 620-5254
Toll Free: (800) 864-4266
Web Site: www.acurasherway.com
Automobile Dealership
S.I.C.: 5511
N.A.I.C.S.: 441110
Ameer Khan *(Gen Mgr)*

cars4u Ltd. (1)
4077 Chesswood Dr
Toronto, ON, M3J 2R8, Canada ON
Tel.: (416) 385-8055
Fax: (416) 385-8805
Toll Free: (877) 622-7748
E-Mail: info@cars4u.com
Web Site: www.cars4ultd.com
Sales Range: $50-74.9 Million
Automobile Dealer
S.I.C.: 5012
N.A.I.C.S.: 423110
Edward Sonshine *(Chm)*
Barry Shafran *(Pres & CEO)*

Chesswood GP Limited (1)
4077 Chesswood Drive
Toronto, ON, M3J 2R8, Canada
Tel.: (416) 386-3099
Fax: (416) 398-2282
Web Site: www.chesswoodfund.com
Financial Management & Investment Services
S.I.C.: 6211
N.A.I.C.S.: 523999
Barry Shafran *(Pres & CEO)*

Lease-Win Limited (1)
4077 Chesswood Dr
Toronto, ON, M3J 2R8, Canada
Tel.: (416) 398-2277
Fax: (416) 398-2282
Web Site: www.leasewin.com
Automobile Leasing Services
S.I.C.: 7515
N.A.I.C.S.: 532112

U.S. Subsidiary:

Pawnee Leasing Corporation (1)
700 Centre Ave
Fort Collins, CO 80526
Tel.: (970) 482-2556
Fax: (970) 482-2666
Web Site: www.pawneeleasing.com
Equipment Leasing Services
S.I.C.: 7359
N.A.I.C.S.: 532490
Rob Day *(Chm)*
Gary Souverein *(Pres & COO)*
Mike Prenzlow *(CFO & Exec VP)*
Jerry Reeves *(Exec VP & Credit Mgr)*

CHESTER CARTAGE LTD.

1995 Markham Rd
Toronto, ON, M1B 2W3, Canada
Tel.: (416) 754-7720
Fax: (416) 754-4259
Toll Free: (888) 754-7716
Web Site: www.chestercartage.com
Year Founded: 1945
Rev.: $11,734,560
Emp.: 130

Business Description:
Transportation & Warehousing Services
S.I.C.: 4225
N.A.I.C.S.: 493110

Personnel:
Bill Beighton *(Mgr-Ops)*

CHETTINAD GROUP OF COMPANIES

Rani Seethai Hall 5th Floor #603
Anna Salai, Chennai, 600 006, India
Tel.: (91) 44 2829 2727
Fax: (91) 44 2829 1258
Web Site: www.chettinda.com
Year Founded: 1962

Business Description:
Holding Company
S.I.C.: 6719
N.A.I.C.S.: 551112

Personnel:
M.A.M. Ramaswamy *(Chm)*
M.A.M.R. Muthiah *(Vice Chm & Mng Dir)*

Subsidiary:

Chettinad Cements Corporation Limited (1)
Rani Seethai Hall 5th Floor 603 Anna Salai
Chennai, 600 006, India In
Tel.: (91) 4428292727
Fax: (91) 4428291258
E-Mail: info@chettinadcement.com
Web Site: www.chettinad.com
Rev.: $455,574,150
Assets: $489,969,558
Liabilities: $268,305,318
Net Worth: $221,664,240
Earnings: $25,499,916
Emp.: 1,582
Fiscal Year-end: 03/31/13
Cement & Construction Materials Mfr
S.I.C.: 3241
N.A.I.C.S.: 327310
M.A.M.R. Muthiah *(Mng Dir)*
S. Hariharan *(Sec)*

Plants:

Chettinad Cements Corp. Ltd. - Karikkali Plant (2)
Rani Meyyammai Nagar Vedasandur Taluk
Karikkali Post, Vedasandur, Tamil Nadu, 624 703, India
Tel.: (91) 4551 234441
Fax: (91) 4551 234440
E-Mail:
Web Site: www.chettinad.com
Emp.: 25
Cement Mfr
S.I.C.: 3241
N.A.I.C.S.: 327310
Alex West *(Sr VP)*

Chettinad Cements Corp. Ltd. - Puliyur Plant (2)
Kumara Rajah Muthiah Nagar Puliyur CF Post
Karur, Tamil Nadu, 639 114, India
Tel.: (91) 4324 251354
Fax: (91) 4324 251320
E-Mail:
Web Site: www.chettinad.com
Cement Mfr
S.I.C.: 3241
N.A.I.C.S.: 327310

CHEUK NANG HOLDINGS LIMITED

30th 35th Fl Cheuk Nang Plz
250 Hennessy Rd
Wanchai, China (Hong Kong)
Tel.: (852) 25267799
Fax: (852) 25217728
E-Mail: cheuknang@hknet.com
Web Site: www.cheuknang.com.hk
0131—(HKG)
Sales Range: $1-9.9 Million
Emp.: 43

Business Description:
Property Management Services
S.I.C.: 6552
N.A.I.C.S.: 237210

Personnel:
Cecil Sze-Tsung Chao *(Chm)*
Connie Sau-Fun Ho *(Sec)*

Board of Directors:
Cecil Sze-Tsung Chao
Howard Chao
Connie Sau-Fun Ho
Graham Ka Wai Lam
Joseph Ding Yue Lee
Joseph Wing Kong Leung
Samson Ping Hsu Sun
Philip Yung

Transfer Agent:
Computershare Hong Kong Investor Services Limited
46th Floor Hopewell Centre 183 Queen's Road East
Hong Kong, China (Hong Kong)

Subsidiaries:

Cheuk Nang Property Management Company (1)
31-32 F Cheuk Nang 21 Century Plaza 250 Hennessy Road
Wanchai, China (Hong Kong)
Tel.: (852) 25267799
Fax: (852) 25217728
Property Development Services
S.I.C.: 6519
N.A.I.C.S.: 531190

Lo & Son Land Investment Company Limited (1)
30-32 F Cheuk Nang 21st Century Plz
Wanchai, China (Hong Kong)
Tel.: (852) 25267799
Property Management Services
S.I.C.: 6531
N.A.I.C.S.: 531312

Yorksbon Development Limited (1)
30-33 F Cheuk Nang Plz 250 Hennessy Rd
Wanchai, China (Hong Kong)
Tel.: (852) 25267799
Fax: (852) 25217728
E-Mail: hknang@cheuknang.com
Property Investment & Development Services
S.I.C.: 6531
N.A.I.C.S.: 531312
Howald Cho *(Mgr-Mktg)*

Non-U.S. Subsidiary:

Martego Sdn Bhd (1)
Lot 690 Sect 57 Lorong Perak
Jalan P Ramlee, Kuala Lumpur, Malaysia
Tel.: (60) 321433135
Fax: (60) 321483917
E-Mail: martego@streamyx.com
Emp.: 10
Property Investment & Development Services
S.I.C.: 6531
N.A.I.C.S.: 531312
Karen Haw *(Exec Sec)*

CHEUNG KONG (HOLDINGS) LIMITED

Cheung Kong Center 7th Floor
2 Queen's Road, Central, China (Hong Kong)
Tel.: (852) 21288888
Fax: (852) 28452940
E-Mail: contactckh@ckh.com.hk
Web Site: www.ckh.com.hk
Year Founded: 1971
0001—(HKG OTC)
Sales Range: $1-4.9 Billion
Emp.: 9,500

Business Description:
Holding Company; Property Development & Investment Services
S.I.C.: 6719
N.A.I.C.S.: 551112

Personnel:
Ka-Shing Li *(Chm)*
Victor Tzar Kuoi Li *(Deputy Chm & Mng Dir)*
Andrew John Hunter *(CFO)*
Wendy Barnes Wai Che Tong *(Chief Corp Affairs Officer)*
Edmond Tak Chuen Ip *(Deputy Mng Dir)*
Hing Lam Kam *(Deputy Mng Dir)*
Eirene Yeung *(Sec)*

Board of Directors:
Ka-Shing Li
Henry Ying Chew Cheong
Justin Kwok Hung Chiu
Albert Nin Mow Chow
Roland Kun Chee Chow
Davy Sun Keung Chung
Canning Kin Ning Fok
Katherine Siu-lin Hung
Edmond Tak Chuen Ip
Hing Lam Kam
Stanley Tun-Li Kwok
Charles Yeh Kwong Lee
Siu Hon Leung
Victor Tzar Kuoi Li
George Colin Magnus
Ezra Yee Wan Pau
Frank John Sixt
Rosanna Yick Ming Wong
Grace Chia Ching Woo
Anthony Yuan Chang Yeh

Transfer Agent:
Computershare Hong Kong Investor Services Limited
Rooms 1712-1716 17/F Hopewell Centre 183 Queen's Road East
Wanchai, China (Hong Kong)
Tel.: (852) 2862 8628
Fax: (852) 2865 0990

Subsidiaries:

Citybase Property Management Limited (1)
Unit No 1 5/f Hampton Loft 11 Hoi Fan Road
Tai Kok Tsui, Kowloon, China (Hong Kong)
Tel.: (852) 2388 7786
Fax: (852) 2710 8887
E-Mail: public.relations@citybaseltd.com
Web Site: www.citybaseltd.com
Emp.: 2,000
Property Management Services
S.I.C.: 6531
N.A.I.C.S.: 531311

Goodwell Property Management Limited (1)
2/F New Treasure Centre 10 Ng Fong Street
San Po Kong, Kowloon, China (Hong Kong)
Tel.: (852) 2960 0982
Fax: (852) 2960 0082
E-Mail: info@goodwell.com.hk
Web Site: www.goodwell.com.hk
Emp.: 2,000
Property Management Services
S.I.C.: 6531
N.A.I.C.S.: 531311
Dicto Leung *(Gen Mgr)*

Harbour Plaza 8 Degrees Limited (1)
199 Kowloon City Road
Tokwawan, Kowloon, China (Hong Kong)
Tel.: (852) 21261988
Fax: (852) 21261900
E-Mail: enquiry.hp8d@harbour-plaza.com
Web Site: www.harbour-plaza.com
Emp.: 200
Hotel Management Services
S.I.C.: 7011
N.A.I.C.S.: 721110
Christina Cheng *(Gen Mgr)*

iMarkets Limited (1)
Unit 2808 28/F The Center 99 Queens Road Central
Hong Kong, China (Hong Kong)
Tel.: (852) 3520 3028
Fax: (852) 3520 3038
E-Mail: imarkets@ckh.com.hk
Web Site: www.imarkets.com.hk
Electronic Platform Financial Investment Services
S.I.C.: 6211
N.A.I.C.S.: 523999
Patrick Wong *(Co-Founder)*
James Yip *(Co-Founder)*
Edmond Tak Chuen Ip *(Chm)*

Cheung Kong (Holdings) Limited—(Continued)

Winchesto Finance Company Limited (1)
7-12/F Cheung Kong Ctr 2 Queens Rd C
Central District, Hong Kong, China (Hong Kong)
Tel.: (852) 25266911
Fax: (852) 28451641
Financial Management Services
S.I.C.: 6211
N.A.I.C.S.: 523999

Holdings:

CK Life Sciences International, (Holdings) Inc. (1)
2 Dai Fu Street Tai Po Industrial Estate
Tai Po, China (Hong Kong) Ky
Tel.: (852) 21261212
Fax: (852) 21261211
E-Mail: info@ck-lifesciences.com
Web Site: www.ck-lifesciences.com
0775—(HKG)
Sls.: $586,080,587
Assets: $1,199,230,229
Liabilities: $461,159,372
Net Worth: $738,070,857
Earnings: $25,536,484
Emp.: 1,278
Fiscal Year-end: 12/31/12
Holding Company
S.I.C.: 6719
N.A.I.C.S.: 551112
Victor Tzar Kuoi Li *(Chm)*
Hing Lam Kam *(Pres & CEO)*
Alan Abel Ying Choi Yu *(COO, Compliance Officer & VP)*
Edmond Tak Chuen Ip *(Chief Investment Officer & Sr VP)*
Kee Hung Chu *(Chief Scientific Officer & VP)*
Wendy Wai Che Tong Barnes *(Chief Corp Affairs Officer)*
John Chiplin *(CEO-Polynoma LLC)*
Dean Corbett *(CEO-Accensi Pty Ltd)*
Keith Frankel *(CEO-Vitaquest International LLC)*
Nick Gill *(CEO-Belvino Investments Pty Ltd)*
Bob Opacic *(CEO-Amgrow Pty Ltd)*
Dusko Pejnovic *(CEO-Lipa Pharmaceuticals Ltd)*
Dennis King Sang Hon *(Legal Counsel)*
Eirene Yeung *(Sec)*

Non-U.S. Subsidiaries:

Cheetham Salt Limited (2)
Collins Street West
PO BOX 1618
Melbourne, VIC, 8007, Australia AU
Tel.: (61) 352758000 (100%)
Fax: (61) 386246505
E-Mail: enquiries@cheethamsalt.com.au
Web Site: www.cheethamsalt.com.au
Salt Products Mfr
S.I.C.: 3299
N.A.I.C.S.: 327999
Andrew Speed *(CEO)*

Non-U.S. Subsidiary:

PT Cheetham Garam Indonesia (3)
Krakatau Industrial Estate Jl Australia I Kav D13/1
Cilegon, Banten, 42443, Indonesia
Tel.: (62) 254 310 887
Fax: (62) 254 387 023
E-Mail: info@cheetham.co.id
Web Site: www.cheethamindonesia.com
Emp.: 40
Salt Products Mfr
S.I.C.: 2899
N.A.I.C.S.: 325998
Arthur Tanudaja *(Pres)*

Lipa Pharmaceuticals Limited (2)
21 Reaghs Farm Road
Minto, NSW, Australia
Tel.: (61) 287961400
Fax: (61) 287961440
E-Mail: info@lipa.com.au
Web Site: www.lipa.com.au
Sales Range: $75-99.9 Million
Emp.: 350
Vitamin & Nutritional Pharmaceutical Mfr
S.I.C.: 2834
N.A.I.C.S.: 325412
Dusko Pejnovic *(CEO)*

WEX Pharmaceuticals Inc. (2)
Ste 1601 700 W Pender Street
Vancouver, BC, V6C 1G8, Canada
Tel.: (604) 683-8880
Fax: (604) 683-8868
Toll Free: (800) 722-7549
E-Mail: wex@wexpharma.com
Web Site: www.wexpharma.com
Sales Range: Less than $1 Million
Emp.: 26
Pharmaceutical Development Services
S.I.C.: 8731
N.A.I.C.S.: 541712
Peter H. Stafford *(Sec)*

Hutchison Whampoa Limited (1)
22 Floor Hutchison House 10 Harcourt Road
Hong Kong, China (Hong Kong)
Tel.: (852) 21281188
Fax: (852) 21281705
E-Mail: info@hwl.com.hk
Web Site: www.hutchison-whampoa.com
0013—(HKG OTC)
Rev.: $31,346,326,550
Assets: $103,660,454,950
Liabilities: $47,104,016,550
Net Worth: $56,556,438,400
Earnings: $4,172,822,000
Emp.: 250,000
Fiscal Year-end: 12/31/12
Property Development & Investment Services
S.I.C.: 6531
N.A.I.C.S.: 531210
Ka-Shing Li *(Chm)*
Victor Tzar Kuoi Li *(Deputy Chm)*
Canning Kin Ning Fok *(Mng Dir)*
Susan Mo Fong Chow Woo *(Deputy Mng Dir)*
Edith Shih *(Sec)*

Subsidiaries:

Hutchison China Meditech Limited (2)
22nd Floor Hutchison House 10 Harcourt Road
Hong Kong, China (Hong Kong) (71.6%)
Tel.: (852) 2128 1188
Fax: (852) 2128 1778
E-Mail: info@chi-med.com
Web Site: www.chi-med.com
HCM—(AIM)
Rev.: $195,392,000
Assets: $209,465,000
Liabilities: $125,817,000
Net Worth: $83,648,000
Earnings: $3,540,000
Emp.: 4,000
Fiscal Year-end: 12/31/12
Holding Company; Pharmaceutical Mfr
S.I.C.: 6719
N.A.I.C.S.: 551112
Simon To *(Chm)*
Christian Hogg *(CEO)*
Johnny Chig Fung Cheng *(CFO)*
Edith Shih *(Sec)*

Hutchison Harbour Ring Limited (2)
22nd Floor Hutchison House 10 Harcourt Road
Hong Kong, China (Hong Kong) BM
Tel.: (852) 2128 1188
Fax: (852) 2128 1778
Web Site: www.hutchisonharbourring.com
715—(HKG)
Rev.: $32,081,728
Assets: $852,642,158
Liabilities: $43,425,588
Net Worth: $809,216,570
Earnings: $24,707,465
Emp.: 49
Fiscal Year-end: 12/31/12
Investment Management Services
S.I.C.: 6799
N.A.I.C.S.: 523920
Canning Kin Ning Fok *(Chm)*
Dominic Kai Ming Lai *(Deputy Chm)*
Tony Kin Tung Tsui *(Mng Dir)*
Edith Shih *(Sec)*

Hutchison Port Holdings Limited (2)
Terminal 4
Container Port Rd S, Kwai Chung, NT, China (Hong Kong)
Tel.: (852) 26197888
Fax: (852) 24804765
E-Mail: gca@hph.com
Web Site: www.hph.com.hk
Emp.: 30,000
Operator of Ports & Terminals
S.I.C.: 4491
N.A.I.C.S.: 488310
John E. Meredith *(Grp Mng Dir)*
James S. Tsien *(CFO)*

Non-U.S. Subsidiary:

Europe Containers Terminals B.V. (3)
Reeweg 25
3199 LJ Rotterdam, Netherlands (100%)
Mailing Address:
PO Box 2755
3000 CT Rotterdam, Netherlands
Tel.: (31) 104916911
Telex: 28010 (Oper.)
Fax: (31) 104280380
E-Mail: info@ect.nl
Web Site: www.ect.nl
Emp.: 1,000
Container Terminal Operator
S.I.C.: 4491
N.A.I.C.S.: 488320
Jan Westerhoud *(Pres)*

Hutchison Telecommunications International Ltd. (2)
20/F Hutchison Telecom Tower 99 Cheung Fai Rd
Tsing Yi, China (Hong Kong) Ky
Tel.: (852) 21283222
Fax: (852) 2827 1371
E-Mail: adayeung@htil.com.hk
Web Site: www.htil.com
Sales Range: $200-249.9 Million
Emp.: 2,200
Telecommunications Services
S.I.C.: 4813
N.A.I.C.S.: 517110
Canning Kin Ning Fok *(Chm)*
Dennis Pok Man Lui *(CEO)*
Thirukumar Nadarasa *(CEO-Sri Lanka)*

Subsidiary:

Hutchison Telecommunications Hong Kong Holdings Limited (3)
22/F Hutchison House 10 Harcourt Road
Hong Kong, China (Hong Kong) (100%)
Tel.: (852) 21281188
Fax: (852) 2128 1778
E-Mail: pr@htil.com.hk
Web Site: www.hthkh.com
0215—(HKG OTC)
Sls.: $2,003,367,200
Assets: $2,695,055,000
Liabilities: $1,264,870,550
Net Worth: $1,430,184,450
Earnings: $196,906,650
Emp.: 1,920
Fiscal Year-end: 12/31/12
Telecommunications Services
S.I.C.: 4812
N.A.I.C.S.: 517210
Peter King Fai Wong *(CEO & Mng Dir)*
Suzanne Wai Sin Cheng *(CFO)*
Daniel Yiu Man Chung *(CTO-Mobile)*
Wai Ming Ho *(CEO-Mobile-Macau)*
Winnie Yuen Wah Ma *(Gen Counsel-Legal & Regulatory)*
Edith Shih *(Sec)*

Non-U.S. Joint Venture:

Hutchison Essar Limited (3)
Hutch House Peninsula Corporate Park
Ganpatrao Kdam Marg
Lower Parel, Mumbai, 400 013, India
Tel.: (91) 2256661200
Wireless Telecommunications Services; Owned by Cheung Kong (Holdings) Limited & Essar Group
S.I.C.: 4812
N.A.I.C.S.: 517210
Naveen Chopra *(VP-Corp Mktg)*

Holdings:

A.S. Watson & Co. Ltd. (2)
Watson House 1 5
Wo Liu Hang Rd Fotan, Hong Kong, China (Hong Kong) (100%)
Tel.: (852) 26068833
E-Mail: grouppr@aswatson.com
Web Site: www.aswatson.com
Holding Company
S.I.C.: 6719
N.A.I.C.S.: 551112
Martin So *(CEO-Health & Beauty-Asia)*

Non-U.S. Subsidiaries:

Kruidvat Retail BV (3)
Nijborg 17
3927 DA Renswoude, Netherlands
Tel.: (31) 318579111
Web Site: www.kruidvat.nl
Emp.: 3,900
Health & Beauty Supplies
S.I.C.: 5122
N.A.I.C.S.: 446120
Kam M.D. Lai *(CEO)*

The Perfume Shop Limited (3)
Cypress House The Gateway Centre
Coronation Rd
Cressex Business Park, High Wycombe, HP12 3SU, United Kingdom
Tel.: (44) 1494539900
Fax: (44) 494894093
E-Mail: admin@the-perfume-shop.com
Web Site: www.theperfumeshop.com
Sales Range: $125-149.9 Million
Emp.: 2,000
Perfume Store Operator
S.I.C.: 5999
N.A.I.C.S.: 446199
Jo Walker *(Mng Dir)*

Superdrug Stores PLC (3)
118 Beddington Ln
Croydon, Surrey, CR0 4TB, United Kingdom UK
Tel.: (44) 845 6710709
E-Mail: Sally.chandler.uk@iswatson.com
Web Site: www.superdrug.com
Sls.: $1,497,400,064
Emp.: 300
Retail Drugs & Sundries
Import
S.I.C.: 5912
N.A.I.C.S.: 446110
Duam Sutherland *(CEO)*
Sally Chandler *(Sec)*

Cheung Kong Infrastructure Holdings Limited (2)
12 F Cheung Kong Ctr
2 Queens Road, Central, China (Hong Kong) (100%)
Tel.: (852) 21223133
Fax: (852) 25014550
E-Mail: contact@cki.com.hk
Web Site: www.cki.com.hk
1038—(HKG OTC)
Sales Range: $750-799.9 Million
Emp.: 1,045
Developer & Investor
S.I.C.: 6221
N.A.I.C.S.: 523130
Victor Tzar Kuoi Li *(Chm)*
Canning Kin Ning Fok *(Deputy Chm)*
Edmond Tak Chuen Ip *(Deputy Chm)*
Lambert Ying Wah Leung *(CEO)*
Hing Lam Kam *(Mng Dir)*
Dominic Loi Shun Chan *(CFO)*
Ivan Kee Ham Chan *(Chief Plng Officer & Chief Investment Officer)*
Wendy Barnes Wai Che Tong *(Chief Corp Affairs Officer)*
Andrew John Hunter *(Deputy Mng Dir)*
Victor Sai Hong Luk *(Gen Counsel)*
Irene Yeung *(Sec)*

Joint Venture:

Alliance Construction Materials Ltd. (3)
1901A 19/F One Harbourfront
18 Tak Fung Street Hung Horn, Kowloon, China (Hong Kong) HK
Tel.: (852) 28622200
Fax: (852) 25291035
E-Mail: enquiry@concrete.hk
Web Site: www.acm-hk.biz
Emp.: 240
Construction Materials Mfr & Distr; Owned 50% by Hanson Limited & 50% by Cheung Kong Infrastructure Holdings
S.I.C.: 1771
N.A.I.C.S.: 238110
Lambert Leung Ying Wah *(Chm)*
David Hogan *(CEO)*

Non-U.S. Subsidiaries:

Northumbrian Water Group Plc (3)
Northumbria House Abbey Road
Pity Me, Durham, DH1 5FJ, United Kingdom
Tel.: (44) 8706084820
E-Mail: billingcentre@nwl.co.uk
Web Site: www.nwl.co.uk
Sales Range: $1-4.9 Billion
Emp.: 3,031
Water Supply & Waste Water Services
S.I.C.: 9511
N.A.I.C.S.: 924110
Heidi Mottram *(CEO)*
Martin Parker *(Sec & Gen Counsel)*

Subsidiaries:

Ayr Environmental Services Limited (4)
Meadowhead Road Works & Sludge Treatment Centre
Irvine, KA11 5AY, United Kingdom (75%)
Tel.: (44) 1913016836
Fax: (44) 1913016711
Emp.: 20
Waste Water Treatment Services
S.I.C.: 4959
N.A.I.C.S.: 562998
Mick McGreevy *(Mng Dir)*

Ayr Environmental Services Operations Limited (4)
Meadowhead Road Works & Sludge Treatment Centre
Irvine, Ayrshire, KA11 5AY, United Kingdom
Tel.: (44) 1294278871
Fax: (44) 1294279382
Water Treatment Services
S.I.C.: 4953
N.A.I.C.S.: 562219

Northumbrian Services Limited (4)
Northumbria House Abbey Road
Pity Me, Durham, DH1 5FJ, United Kingdom UK
Tel.: (44) 8706084820 (100%)
E-Mail: northumbrian@pelhampr.com
Web Site: www.nwl.co.uk/Contacts.aspx
Emp.: 1,000
Water Supply Services
S.I.C.: 4941
N.A.I.C.S.: 221310
Heidi Mottram *(CEO)*

Northumbrian Water Limited (4)
Northumbria House
Abbey Road Pity Me, DH15FJ Durham, United Kingdom UK
Tel.: (44) 8706084820 (100%)
Fax: (44) 1912766612
Web Site: www.nwl.co.uk
Emp.: 600
Water Supply & Irrigation Systems
S.I.C.: 4941
N.A.I.C.S.: 221310
Heidi Mottram *(Mng Dir)*

Division:

Northumbrian Water Scientific Services (NWSS) (5)
Northumberland Dock Road
Wallsend, Newcastle upon Tyne, NE28 0QD, United Kingdom (100%)
Tel.: (44) 870 320 4567
Fax: (44) 191 296 8560
E-Mail: enquiry-nwss@nwl.co.uk
Web Site: www.nw-ss.co.uk
Emp.: 170
Analysis & Sampling of Waters, Air Emissions & Soils
S.I.C.: 8734
N.A.I.C.S.: 541380
Graham Neave *(Dir-Ops)*

Subsidiary:

Essex & Suffolk Water Ltd (5)
PO Box 292
Durham, DH1 9TX, United Kingdom
Tel.: (44) 8457820999
Fax: (44) 08456047468
Water Treatment Services
S.I.C.: 4971
N.A.I.C.S.: 221310
Heidi Mottram *(CEO)*

Northumbrian Water Projects Limited (4)
Tower Knowe Falstone
Hexham, Northumberland, NE48 1BX, United Kingdom
Tel.: (44) 1434240436
Web Site: www.nwg.co.uk/Aboutus.aspx
Operation & Maintenance of Waste Water Treatment Assets
S.I.C.: 4959
N.A.I.C.S.: 562998

Non-U.S. Subsidiary:

AquaGib Limited (4)
Suite 10B Leanse Place
50 Town Range, Gibraltar, Gibraltar (66.67%)
Tel.: (350) 20040880
Fax: (350) 20040881
E-Mail: main.office@aquagib.gi
Web Site: www.aquagib.gi
Emp.: 28
Water Supply Services
S.I.C.: 4971
N.A.I.C.S.: 221310
Peter Latin *(Mng Dir)*

TransAlta Power, L.P. (3)
110 12th Ave SW
Calgary, AB, T2P 2M, Canada (100%)
Tel.: (403) 267-2520
Fax: (403) 267-2590
Toll Free: (800) 387-3598
E-Mail: info@transaltapower.com
Web Site: www.transaltapower.com
Emp.: 2,470
Electric Power Generation & Distr
S.I.C.: 4939
N.A.I.C.S.: 221122
Brian Burden *(Pres & CFO)*

Non-U.S. Joint Ventures:

CitiPower (3)
Locked Bag 14031
Melbourne, VIC, 8001, Australia
Tel.: (61) 01300301101
Fax: (61) 01300301102
E-Mail: info@citipower.com.au
Web Site: www.citipower.com.au
Sales Range: $650-699.9 Million
Emp.: 1,500
Electric Power Distr
S.I.C.: 4931
N.A.I.C.S.: 221122
Shane Breheny *(CEO)*
Julie Williams *(CFO)*
Simon Lucas *(Sec & Gen Mgr-Legal Svcs)*

ETSA Utilities (3)
1 ANZAC Highway
Keswick, SA, 5035, Australia
Mailing Address:
GPO Box 77
Adelaide, SA, 5001, Australia
Tel.: (61) 884045667
Fax: (61) 884045668
E-Mail:
Web Site: www.sapowernetworks.com.au
Rev.: $564,627,200
Emp.: 1,300
Electricity Distr
S.I.C.: 4931
N.A.I.C.S.: 221122
Peter Tulloch *(Chm)*
Bob Stobbe *(CEO)*
Rob Stevens *(CFO)*

Powercor Australia Limited (3)
40 Market St
Melbourne, VIC, 3000, Australia AU
Mailing Address: (100%)
Locked Bag 14090
Melbourne, VIC, 8001, Australia
Tel.: (61) 396834444
Fax: (61) 396834499
E-Mail: info@powercor.com.au
Web Site: www.powercor.com.au
Emp.: 80
Electric Power Distr
S.I.C.: 4911
N.A.I.C.S.: 221122
Tim Rourke *(CEO)*

Joint Venture:

HUD Group (2)
TYTL 108 RP Sai Tso Wan Road
Tsing Yi, New Territories, China (Hong Kong)
Tel.: (852) 24312828
Fax: (852) 24330180
E-Mail: shiprepair@hud.com.hk
Web Site: www.hud.com.hk
Emp.: 600
Dry Dock Services & Repair; Joint Venture Between Hutchison Whampoa Limited
S.I.C.: 3731
N.A.I.C.S.: 336611
David Murphy *(CEO)*

Subsidiary:

HongKong Salvage & Towage (3)
2 F HUD Administration Building
Sai Tso Wan Road, Tsing Yi, NT, China (Hong Kong)
Tel.: (852) 24277477
Fax: (852) 24805894
E-Mail: hkst@hktug.com
Web Site: www.hud.com.hk
Emp.: 50
Shipbuilding & Repair Services
S.I.C.: 3731
N.A.I.C.S.: 336611
David Murphy *(Mng Dir)*

Non-U.S. Subsidiaries:

Hutchison 3G Austria GmbH (2)
Brunner Strasse 52
1210 Vienna, Austria AT
Tel.: (43) 1 27728 0
Fax: (43) 660 303031
Web Site: www.drei.at
Mobile Telecommunications Services
S.I.C.: 4812
N.A.I.C.S.: 517210
Jan Trionow, *(CEO)*
Sabine Hogl *(CFO)*
Matthias Baldermann *(CTO)*
Rudolf Schrefl *(Chief Compliance Officer)*
Simone Keglovics *(Gen Counsel & Sr Head-Wholesale & Regulatory)*

Subsidiary:

Orange Austria Telecommunication GmbH (3)
Brunner Strasse 52
1210 Vienna, Austria (100%)
Tel.: (43) 1 27728 0
Fax: (43) 699 70770
E-Mail: info@orange.co.at
Web Site: www.orange.at
Sales Range: $650-699.9 Million
Emp.: 800
Mobile Telecommunications Services
S.I.C.: 4812
N.A.I.C.S.: 517210
Elmar Grasser *(CIO)*
Sabine Bauer *(Chief Sls Officer)*

Hutchison Telecommunications (Australia) Limited (2)
Level 7 40 Mount Street
North Sydney, NSW, 2060, Australia (87.87%)
Tel.: (61) 299644646
Fax: (61) 289040457
E-Mail: investors@hutchison.com.au
Web Site: www.hutchison.com.au
HTA—(ASX)
Rev.: $19,831,163
Assets: $1,552,703,990
Liabilities: $631,117,644
Net Worth: $921,586,346
Earnings: ($410,073,645)
Emp.: 4,500
Fiscal Year-end: 12/31/12
Telecommunications Services
S.I.C.: 4812
N.A.I.C.S.: 517210
Barry Roberts-Thomson *(Deputy Chm)*
Nigel Dews *(CEO)*
Dave Boorman *(CFO)*
Michael Young *(CTO)*
Louise Sexton *(Gen Counsel & Co-Sec)*
Edith Shih *(Co-Sec)*

Joint Venture:

Vodafone Hutchison Australia Pty. Limited (3)
207 Pacific Hwy Building A
Saint Leonards, NSW, 2065, Australia
Tel.: (61) 299644646
Fax: (61) 299644668
Web Site: www.vodafone.com.au
Emp.: 4,000
Mobile Telecommunications Services; Joint Venture of Hutchison Telecommunications (Australia) Limited (50%) & Vodafone Group plc (50%)
S.I.C.: 4812
N.A.I.C.S.: 517210
Inaki Berroeta *(CEO)*

TOM Group Limited (1)
48/Fl The Center 99 Queen's Road
Central, China (Hong Kong)
Tel.: (852) 21217838
Fax: (852) 21867711
E-Mail: ir@tomgroup.com
Web Site: www.tomgroup.com
2383—(HKG)
Rev.: $284,452,868
Assets: $576,646,605
Liabilities: $432,011,772
Net Worth: $144,634,833
Earnings: ($44,375,048)
Emp.: 2,900
Fiscal Year-end: 12/31/12
News & Reference Web Sites, Advertising & Marketing Services & Magazine Publisher
S.I.C.: 7319
N.A.I.C.S.: 541890
Kwok Mung Yeung *(CEO)*
Angela Soek Fun Mak *(CFO & Sec)*

Non-U.S. Subsidiary:

TOM Online, Inc. (2)
8th Fl Tower W3 Oriental Plz
No 1 Dong Chang An Ave, Beijing, 100738, China Ky
Tel.: (86) 1065283399 (65.9%)
Fax: (86) 1085182929
E-Mail: tominfo@tomonline-inc.com
Web Site: www.tom.com
Wireless Internet Services; Website Operator
S.I.C.: 3577
N.A.I.C.S.: 334118
Frank John Sixt *(Chm)*
Tommei Tong Mei Kuen *(Vice Chm)*
Angela Soek Fun Mak *(Gen Counsel)*
Yu Pessy Patricia Dawn *(Sec)*
Feng Jue Elaine *(Exec VP)*
Elaine Jue Feng *(Exec VP)*
Bing Hai Liu *(Exec VP-Wireless Internet)*
Ying Qi Su *(Exec VP-Portal Ops)*

Non-U.S. Subsidiary:

Beijing Net-Infinity Technology Development Co. Ltd. (1)
Room 708 Tower W3 The Towers Oriental Plaza No 1 East Chang An Avenue
Dong Cheng District, Beijing, 100738, China
Tel.: (86) 10 5815 0088
Fax: (86) 10 5815 0099
E-Mail: info@net-infinity.net
Web Site: www.net-infinity.net
Internet Access Services
S.I.C.: 4899
N.A.I.C.S.: 517919

CHEUNG WING BIOTECHNOLOGY COMPANY LIMITED

Flat 11 6/F Block B Merit Industrial Centre 94 To Kwa Wan Road
Kowloon, China (Hong Kong)
Tel.: (852) 63876337
E-Mail: info@cheungwingbiotech.com
Web Site: cheungwingbiotech.com
Year Founded: 2006
53W—(DEU)

Business Description:
Bamboo Extracts Mfr
S.I.C.: 2834
N.A.I.C.S.: 325412

Personnel:
May Cheung *(Chm, Pres & CEO)*

CHEUNG WOH TECHNOLOGIES LTD.

23 Tuas South Street 1
Singapore, 638033, Singapore
Tel.: (65) 68618036
Fax: (65) 6568615784
E-Mail: ir@cheungwoh.com.sg
Web Site: www.cheungwoh.com.sg

Cheung Woh Technologies Ltd.—(Continued)

Year Founded: 1972
C50—(SES)
Sls.: $49,145,957
Assets: $85,643,902
Liabilities: $14,136,203
Net Worth: $71,507,699
Earnings: ($1,204,804)
Emp.: 1,800
Fiscal Year-end: 02/28/13

Business Description:
Computer Component Mfr
S.I.C.: 3575
N.A.I.C.S.: 334118

Personnel:
Kung Ying Law *(Chm & Mng Dir)*
Yu Chui Law *(Fin Dir, Co-Sec & Dir-Admin)*
Lai Yin Chan *(Co-Sec)*

Board of Directors:
Kung Ying Law
Yuk Fu Chen
Kung Ming Law
Yu Chui Law
Leonard Kian Wee Lim
Kuang Hua Ngu
Poh Hong Teo

Non-U.S. Subsidiaries:

Cheung Woh Precision (Zhuhai) Co., Ltd (1)
163 Zhu Feng Way Xin Qing Science & Technology Park
Doumen, Zhuhai, 519180, China
Tel.: (86) 7565213425
Fax: (86) 7565212658
Web Site: www.cheungwoh.com
Precision Tools & Die Mfr
S.I.C.: 3425
N.A.I.C.S.: 332216

Cheung Woh Technologies (Zhuhai) Co., Ltd (1)
163 Zhu Feng Way Xin Qing Science & Technology Park
Doumen, Zhuhai, 519180, China
Tel.: (86) 7565213425
Fax: (86) 7565212966
E-Mail: hysun@cheungwohch.com
Web Site: www.cheungwoh.com.sg/contact.asp
Emp.: 1,000
Precision Tools & Die Mfr
S.I.C.: 3425
N.A.I.C.S.: 332216
Teo Pohong *(Gen Mgr)*

CHEVAL QUANCARD

La Mouline 4 Rue Du Carbouney
Carbon Blanc, 33560 Bordeaux, France
Tel.: (33) 557778888
Web Site: www.chevalquancard.com
Sls.: $21,200,000
Emp.: 43

Business Description:
Wine & Distilled Beverages
S.I.C.: 5182
N.A.I.C.S.: 424820

Personnel:
Rolland Quancard *(Mgr-Export Sls & Chm)*
Christiane Quancard *(Deputy Chm-Supervisory Bd)*

Board of Directors:
Aris Quancard

Supervisory Board of Directors:
Christiane Quancard

CHEVALIER INTERNATIONAL HOLDINGS LIMITED

22/F Chevalier Commercial Centre 8 Wang Hoi Road
Kowloon, China (Hong Kong)
Tel.: (852) 23181818
Fax: (852) 27575138
E-Mail: enquiry@chevalier.com
Web Site: www.chevalier.com
0025—(HKG)
Rev.: $540,204,819
Assets: $1,650,015,702
Liabilities: $849,101,836
Net Worth: $800,913,866
Earnings: $139,689,730
Emp.: 3,400
Fiscal Year-end: 03/31/13

Business Description:
Holding Company; Coffee & Other Beverage Products Mfr & Distr
S.I.C.: 6719
N.A.I.C.S.: 551112

Personnel:
Yei Ching Chow *(Chm)*
Hoi Sang Kuok *(Vice Chm & Mng Dir)*
Kwok Wing Tam *(Deputy Mng Dir)*
Chin Leung Mui *(Sec)*

Board of Directors:
Yei Ching Chow
Joseph Ming Kuen Chow
Lily Chow
Oscar Vee Tsung Chow
Chung Leung Ho
William Chan Gock Ko
Hoi Sang Kuok
Chi Wing Ma
Chung Kwong Poon
George Kai Dah Sun
Kwok Wing Tam
Charles Chuen Liang Yang

Butterfield Fulcrum Group (Bermuda) Limited
26 Burnaby Street
Hamilton, HM 11, Bermuda

Transfer Agent:
Tricor Standard Limited
26/F Tesbury Centre 28 Queen's Road East
Wanchai, China (Hong Kong)
Tel.: (852) 2980 1333
Fax: (852) 2810 8185

U.S. Subsidiary:

Chevalier International (USA), Inc. (1)
430 E Grand Ave
South San Francisco, CA 94080 CA
Tel.: (650) 877-8118
Fax: (650) 877-8283
Web Site: www.chevalier.com
Sales Range: $10-24.9 Million
Groceries, General Line
S.I.C.: 5141
N.A.I.C.S.: 424410
Chow Yei Ching *(Founder & Chm)*
Yei Chow *(Pres)*

CHEVALLIER SUD

2 Boulevard De Sarrians
84170 Monteux, Vaucluse, France
Tel.: (33) 490662014
Sales Range: $10-24.9 Million
Emp.: 29

Business Description:
Local Trucking, Without Storage
S.I.C.: 4212
N.A.I.C.S.: 484110

Personnel:
Dominique Chevallier *(Mng Dir)*

Board of Directors:
Dominique Chevallier

CHEVIOT BRIDGE LIMITED

Level 9 564 St Kilda Rd
Melbourne, VIC, 3000, Australia
Tel.: (61) 386567000
Fax: (61) 395103277
E-Mail: info@cheviotbridge.com.au
Web Site: www.cheviotbridge.com.au
Sales Range: $10-24.9 Million
Emp.: 28

Business Description:
Wine Mfr & Sales
S.I.C.: 2084
N.A.I.C.S.: 312130

Personnel:
Maurice Dean *(Mng Dir)*

Subsidiaries:

Kirribilly Vineyards Pty Limited (1)
318 Main N Rd
PO Box 771
Clare, South Australia, 5453, Australia
Tel.: (61) 8 88421849
Fax: (61) 8 88421131
E-Mail: admin@kirribilly.com.au
Web Site: www.kirribillyviticulture.com.au
Vineyards & Wineries Services
S.I.C.: 2084
N.A.I.C.S.: 312130
Robert Ian Stanway *(Mng Dir)*

Kirribilly Viticulture Pty Limited (1)
318 Main N Rd
PO Box 771
Clare, South Australia, 5453, Australia
Tel.: (61) 888421122
Fax: (61) 888421131
E-Mail: admin@kirribilly.com.au
Web Site: www.kirribillyviticulture.com.au
Emp.: 35
Vineyard Cultivation Services
S.I.C.: 0172
N.A.I.C.S.: 111332
Rob Stanway *(Mgr)*

CHEVIOT COMPANY LIMITED

24 Park Street Magma House 9th Floor
Kolkata, West Bengal, 700 016, India
Tel.: (91) 33 3291 9624
Fax: (91) 33 2249 7269
E-Mail: cheviot@chevjute.com
Web Site: www.groupcheviot.net
526817—(BOM)
Rev.: $55,260,454
Assets: $65,993,760
Liabilities: $7,751,741
Net Worth: $58,242,020
Earnings: $5,694,413
Emp.: 4,301
Fiscal Year-end: 03/31/13

Business Description:
Jute Products Mfr
S.I.C.: 2299
N.A.I.C.S.: 313210

Personnel:
Harsh Vardhan Kanoria *(Chm, CEO & Mng Dir)*
Deo Kishan Mohta *(Pres-Corp Affairs, CFO, Compliance Officer & Sec)*

Board of Directors:
Harsh Vardhan Kanoria
Parag Keshar Bhattacharjee
Sushil Dhandhania
Nawal Kishore Kejriwal
Padam Kumar Khaitan
Navin Nayar

Transfer Agent:
Maheshwari Datamatics Pvt. Ltd.
6 Mangoe Lane 2nd Fl
Kolkata, 700 001, India
Tel.: (91) 33 22435029
Fax: (91) 913322484787

CHEVITA GMBH

Raiffeisenstrasse 2
D-85266 Pfaffenhofen, Germany
Tel.: (49) 84418530
Fax: (49) 844185351
E-Mail: chevita@chevita.de
Web Site: www.chevita.com
Year Founded: 1968
Rev.: $12,402,130
Emp.: 40

Business Description:
Animal Health Products Mfr
S.I.C.: 2048
N.A.I.C.S.: 311119

Personnel:
Ludwig Schrag *(Mng Dir)*

CHEVRILLON PHILIPPE INDUSTRIE

(d/b/a CPI Group)
23 Bis Rue Danjou
92100 Boulogne-Billancourt, France
Tel.: (33) 155389494
Fax: (33) 155389480
E-Mail: contact@cpibooks.com
Web Site: www.cpibooks.com
Year Founded: 1996
Sales Range: $500-549.9 Million
Emp.: 3,700

Business Description:
Monochrome Book Mfr; Owned by CVC Capital Partners & by Cognetas LLP
S.I.C.: 2732
N.A.I.C.S.: 323117

Personnel:
Pierre-Francois Catte *(Mng Dir)*

Non-U.S. Subsidiaries:

Clausen & Bosse GmbH (1)
Birkstrasse 10
25917 Leck, Germany De
Mailing Address:
Postfach 1260
25917 Leck, Germany
Tel.: (49) 4662830
Telex: 221417
Fax: (49) 466283129
E-Mail: info@clausenbosse.de
Web Site: www.clausenbosse.de
Emp.: 600
Book Printing
S.I.C.: 2731
N.A.I.C.S.: 511130
Ingo Rudolf Scholz *(CEO)*

Fulmar Colour Printing Company Ltd (1)
108 Beddington Ln The Orion Centre
Croydon, Surrey, CR0 4YY, United Kingdom
Tel.: (44) 2086887500
Fax: (44) 2086889500
E-Mail: info@fulmarcolour.com
Web Site: www.fulmarcolour.com
Sales Range: $550-599.9 Million
Emp.: 416
Printing Services
S.I.C.: 2759
N.A.I.C.S.: 323111
Francois Golicheff *(CEO)*
Keith Marley *(Mng Dir)*
Derek J. Harris *(Sec & Dir-Fin)*

Subsidiaries:

Bookmarque (2)
110 Beddington Lane
Croydon, Surrey, CR0 4TD, United Kingdom
Tel.: (44) 2086123400
Fax: (44) 2086123401
Web Site: www.fulmar.com
Emp.: 80
Paperback Book Printing
S.I.C.: 2732
N.A.I.C.S.: 323117
Fraincois Tollicheffe *(CEO)*
Keith Marley *(Mng Dir)*

CPI Colour (2)
(Formerly Pegasus Colourprint)
108-110 Beddington Lane
Croydon, Surrey, CR0 4YY, United Kingdom
Tel.: (44) 20 8612 3400
Web Site: cpibooks.com
Book Publishers
S.I.C.: 2731
N.A.I.C.S.: 511130

Quadracolor Limited (2)
Units 2-3 Kangley Bridge Rd
Lower Sydenham, London, SE26 5AQ, United Kingdom
Tel.: (44) 2086766700
Fax: (44) 2086591869
E-Mail: quad@quadracolor.co.uk
Web Site: www.quadracolor.co.uk
Emp.: 40
Commercial/Point of Sale Printing
S.I.C.: 2759
N.A.I.C.S.: 323111
John Grima *(Mng Dir)*

Royle Corporate Print Ltd. (2)
Royle House
110 Beddington Lane, Croydon, Surrey, CR0 4TD, United Kingdom
Tel.: (44) 2086882300
Fax: (44) 2082530300
E-Mail: printing@fulmar.com
Web Site: www.royle-print.co.uk
Emp.: 100
Printing of Corporate & Marketing Literature
S.I.C.: 2759
N.A.I.C.S.: 323111
Mike Taylor *(CEO)*

Royle Design Associates Limited (2)
Gate House
1 St Johns Square, London, EC1M 4DH, United Kingdom
Tel.: (44) 2075533550
Fax: (44) 20 7553 3555
E-Mail: rda@royle-design.co.uk
Web Site: www.royle-design.co.uk
Emp.: 25
Domestic & International Corporate Finance Printing Services
S.I.C.: 2759
N.A.I.C.S.: 323111

Roylc Financial Print Ltd (2)
Gate House
1-3 St Johns Square, London, EC1M 4DH, United Kingdom
Tel.: (44) 2075533500
Fax: (44) 2075533555
E-Mail: comms@roylefinancial.com
Web Site: www.roylefinancial.com
Emp.: 30
Domestic & International Corporate Finance Printing
S.I.C.: 2759
N.A.I.C.S.: 323111
John Cullender *(Mng Dir)*

The White Quill Press (2)
The Orion Centre
108 Beddington Lane, Croydon, Surrey, CR0 4YY, United Kingdom
Tel.: (44) 2086888300
Fax: (44) 2087746800
Emp.: 300
Book Jacket Mfr
S.I.C.: 2759
N.A.I.C.S.: 323111

CHEW'S GROUP LIMITED

20 Murai Farmway
Singapore, 709153, Singapore
Tel.: (65) 6793 7674
Fax: (65) 6793 7675
E-Mail: chewsegg@singnet.com.sg
Web Site: www.chewsegg.com
5SY—(CAT)
Rev.: $19,304,265
Assets: $20,831,075
Liabilities: $5,507,074
Net Worth: $15,324,001
Earnings: $1,682,339
Emp.: 114
Fiscal Year-end: 12/31/12
Business Description:
Egg Producer
S.I.C.: 0252
N.A.I.C.S.: 112310
Personnel:
Chee Bin Chew *(Chm)*
Eng Hoe Chew *(Mng Dir)*
Dorriz Bee Gek Tay *(CFO & Co-Sec)*
Janet Tan *(Co-Sec)*
Board of Directors:
Chee Bin Chew
Chee Keong Chew
Eng Hoe Chew
Chin Fan Chong
Boon Seng Choo
Sou Wai Yuen
Subsidiary:

Chew s Agriculture Pte Ltd (1)
M26 Murai Farmway
Singapore, 700000, Singapore
Tel.: (65) 67937674
Fax: (65) 6793 7675
Fresh Egg Mfr
S.I.C.: 0252
N.A.I.C.S.: 112310

CHEYNET S.A.S

(d/b/a Groupe Cheynet)
47 Rue Servient
69003 Lyon, France
Tel.: (33) 477356043
Fax: (33) 477350988
E-Mail: info@cheynet.com
Web Site: www.cheynet.fr
Emp.: 900
Business Description:
Fabric Mfr
S.I.C.: 6719
N.A.I.C.S.: 551112
Personnel:
Gregoire Giraud *(Chm)*
Subsidiary:

Bertheas & Cie (1)
Parc d Activites de Stelytec
BP 28
42401 Saint-Chamond, Cedex, France
Tel.: (33) 477 29 33 33
Fax: (33) 477 29 33 39
E-Mail: info@bertheas.com
Web Site: www.bertheas.com
Elastic Bandage Mfr
N.A.I.C.S.: 339113
U.S. Holding:

Narrow Fabric Industries Corp. (1)
701 W Reading Ave
Reading, PA 19611
Mailing Address:
701 Reading Ave
Reading, PA 19611-1013
Tel.: (610) 376-2891
Fax: (610) 376-2869
Toll Free: (800))523-8118
E-Mail: cmiller@narrowfabric.com
Web Site: www.narrowfabric.com
Emp.: 100
Mfr. of Narrow Elastics for Use in Lingerie & Foundation Trades
S.I.C.: 2241
N.A.I.C.S.: 313220
Gregoire Giraud *(Chm)*
Charles Miller *(Pres & COO)*
Non-U.S. Subsidiary:

Cheynet Asia (Co.) Ltd. (1)
304 Industrial Park 324 Moo 7 Tambol Tha Toom
Amphur, Prachin Buri, 25140, Thailand
Tel.: (66) 837 414 101
Fax: (66) 837 414 103
Apparel Mfr
N.A.I.C.S.: 315240
Florian Peignard *(Mng Dir)*

CHEZE S.A.

38 Voie Des Jumeaux
91320 Wissous, Essonne, France
Tel.: (33) 146861955
Web Site: www.cheze-sa.com
Sls.: $21,700,000
Emp.: 28
Business Description:
Construction Sand & Gravel
S.I.C.: 1442
N.A.I.C.S.: 212321
Personnel:
Roland Haby *(Pres)*

CHI & PARTNERS LIMITED

7 Rathbone St
London, W1T 1LY, United Kingdom
Tel.: (44) 20 7462 8500
Fax: (44) 20 7462 8501
E-Mail: info@chiandpartners.com
Web Site: www.chiandpartners.com
Year Founded: 2001
Emp.: 200
Business Description:
Advertising Agency
S.I.C.: 7311
N.A.I.C.S.: 541810
Personnel:
Charles Inge *(Founding Partner & Dir-Creative)*
Simon Clemmow *(Founding Partner)*
Warren Moore *(Founding Partner)*
Johnny Hornby *(Chm)*
Tim Allnutt *(Mng Partner-MCHI)*
Jonathan Burley *(Mng Partner)*
Sarah Gold *(Mng Partner)*
Neil Goodlad *(Mng Partner)*
Nick Howarth *(Mng Partner)*
Mark Leversedge *(Mng Partner)*
Peter Walker *(Mng Partner)*
Danny Josephs *(Partner)*
Enyi Nwosu *(Partner)*
Subsidiaries:

Halpern Ltd. (1)
250 A Kings Rd
London, SW3 5UE, United Kingdom UK (50.1%)
Tel.: (44) 20 7351 2888
Fax: (44) 20 7351 2444
E-Mail: info@halpern.co.uk
Web Sitc: www.halpern.co.uk
Emp.: 20
Public Relations Agency
S.I.C.: 8743
N.A.I.C.S.: 541820
Jenny Halpern Prince *(Founder & CEO)*

Rapier Communications Limited (1)
The Network Bldg 97 Tottenham Court Rd
London, WIT 4TP, United Kingdom UK
Tel.: (44) 2073698000
Fax: (44) 2073698013
E-Mail: info@rapieruk.com
Web Site: www.rapieruk.com
Billings: $269,407,050
Emp.: 9
Advertising Agency
S.I.C.: 7311
N.A.I.C.S.: 541810
Jonathan Stead *(Founder & CEO)*
Bill Griffin *(Partner-Strategy)*
Ed Morris *(Partner-Creative)*
Alex Naylor *(Partner-Strategy)*
John Shaw *(Partner-Strategy & Plng)*

CHI CHEUNG INVESTMENT CO., LTD.

(Name Changed to LT Holdings Limited)

CHI MEI GROUP

59-1 San Chia Tsun Jen Te
T'ainan, Hsien, 71710, Taiwan
Tel.: (886) 62663000
Fax: (886) 2667983
Web Site: www.chimeicorp.com
Year Founded: 1960
Sales Range: $5-14.9 Billion
Emp.: 36,000
Business Description:
Holding Company
S.I.C.: 6719
N.A.I.C.S.: 551112
Personnel:
Chiang Siang Liao *(Chm)*
Holding:

Chi Mei Corporation (1)
No 59-1 San Chia Jen Te
T'ainan, Hsien, 71702, Taiwan
Tel.: (886) 62663000
Fax: (886) 62665555
E-Mail: service@mail.chimei.com.tw
Web Site: www.chimeicorp.com
Plastic Processing Services
S.I.C.: 3089
N.A.I.C.S.: 326199
Chiang Siang Liao *(Chm)*
J. Y. Ho *(Pres)*
Zhi Xiang Chen *(Sr VP-Tech)*
Chun Hua *(Sr VP-Sls)*

CHI MEI MATERIALS TECHNOLOGY CORPORATION

13 Mujhangang West Rd
Shanhua Town, T'ainan, 74148, Taiwan
Tel.: (886) 6 5889988
Fax: (886) 6 5091005
E-Mail: cmmt_ir@cmmt.com.tw
Web Site: www.cmmt.com.tw
4960—(TAI)
Sales Range: $550-599.9 Million
Emp.: 2,100
Business Description:
Optoelectronics
S.I.C.: 3679
N.A.I.C.S.: 334419
Personnel:
Chin-Hsiang Liao *(Chm)*
Jack Tseng *(CFO)*

CHIA CHANG CO., LTD.

45 Lane 205 Section 2 Nanshan Road
Luchi Hsiang, Taoyuan, Taiwan
Tel.: (886) 3 3228175
Fax: (886) 3 3222662
E-Mail: services@chiachang.com
Web Site: www.chiachang.com
Year Founded: 1985
4942—(TAI)
Sales Range: $250-299.9 Million
Emp.: 4,430
Business Description:
Metal Stamping & Injection Molds
S.I.C.: 3469
N.A.I.C.S.: 332119
Personnel:
Kuei Hsiu Sung *(Chm)*

CHIANGMAI FROZEN FOODS PUBLIC COMPANY LIMITED

149/34 Soi Anglo Plaza Surawongse Road Bangrak
Bangkok, 10500, Thailand
Tel.: (66) 26340061
Fax: (66) 22384090
Web Site: www.cmfrozen.com
Year Founded: 1988
CM—(THA)
Sls.: $49,414,346
Assets: $47,532,861
Liabilities: $4,740,473
Net Worth: $42,792,388
Earnings: $5,789,078
Emp.: 1,774
Fiscal Year-end: 12/31/12
Business Description:
Frozen Vegetables & Fruits Processing & Export Services
S.I.C.: 2037
N.A.I.C.S.: 311411
Personnel:
Prayoon Pholpipattanaphong *(Chm)*
Prapas Pholpipattanaphong *(Mng Dir)*
Ankoon Pholpipattanaphong *(Asst Mng Dir)*
Board of Directors:
Prayoon Pholpipattanaphong
Mu-Chiou Lan
Ankoon Pholpipattanaphong
Prapas Pholpipattanaphong
Prayuth Pholpipattanaphong
Suwat Phongphasura
Ampon Ruayfupant
Santichai Suakanonth
Kenichi Tai
Phusit Wonglorsaichon
Amnuay Yossuk
Legal Counsel:
Wisal & Associates Law Co.,Ltd
83-85 Soi Anuman Rajathon Dejo Rd Khet Bangrak
Bangkok, 10500, Thailand
Tel.: (66) 2 266 8217

THE CHIBA BANK, LTD.

1-2 Chiba-minato Chuo-ku
Chiba City, Chiba, 260-8720, Japan
Tel.: (81) 432451111
Fax: (81) 432429121

The Chiba Bank, Ltd.—(Continued)

E-Mail: investor@chibabank.co.jp
Web Site: www.chibabank.co.jp
Year Founded: 1943
8331—(TKS)
Rev.: $2,450,041,000
Assets: $125,111,151,000
Liabilities: $117,089,478,000
Net Worth: $8,021,673,000
Earnings: $485,672,000
Emp.: 4,282
Fiscal Year-end: 03/31/13
Business Description:
Banking Services
S.I.C.: 6029
N.A.I.C.S.: 522110
Personnel:
Hidetoshi Sakuma *(Pres)*
Takeshi Kubo *(Mng Exec Officer-Corp Admin, HR & Sec)*
Kyoichi Hanashima *(Sr Exec Officer & Head-Credit Unit)*
Tetsuya Koike *(Sr Exec Officer & Head-Bus Promotion Unit)*
Shoichi Hatano *(Mng Exec Officer-Bus Plng, Branch Support, Corp Bus & Asset Mgmt)*
Osamu Kimura *(Mng Exec Officer-Treasury)*
Masao Morimoto *(Mng Exec Officer-Ops Plng, EDP Sys, IT Stategy & Bus Ops)*
Toru Nomura *(Mng Exec Officer-Risk Mgmt & Compliance)*
Toshikazu Okubo *(Sr Exec Officer-Corp Plng & Admin Unit)*
Board of Directors:
Kyoichi Hanashima
Shoichi Hatano
Osamu Kimura
Tetsuya Koike
Takeshi Kubo
Masao Morimoto
Toru Nomura
Toshikazu Okubo
Hidetoshi Sakuma
Toyokuni Yazaki
Transfer Agent:
Japan Securities Agents, Ltd
1-2-4, Nihombashi Kayabacho Chuo-ku
Tokyo, Japan

Branch:

The Chiba Bank Ltd. **(1)**
8-1 Nihonbashi Chome Nuromahi Chuo Ku
Tokyo, 1030022, Japan (100%)
Tel.: (81) 332708351
Fax: (81) 332421736
E-Mail: kikaku@chibabank.co.jp
Web Site: www.chibabank.co.jp/
Emp.: 319
Provider of Securities Services
S.I.C.: 6211
N.A.I.C.S.: 523999
Hidetoshi Sakuma *(Pres)*

Divisions:

The Chiba Bank, Ltd.-Treasury Division **(1)**
5-3 Nihonbashi Muromachi 1 Chome
Tokyo, Chuo Ku, 103 0022, Japan (100%)
Tel.: (81) 332708351
Telex: J23671
Fax: (81) 332421736
E-Mail: kikaku@chibabank.co.jp
Web Site: ir.chibabank.co.jp/english/Profile/main.html
Emp.: 30
S.I.C.: 6141
N.A.I.C.S.: 522210
Ikeda Tomo *(Gen Mgr)*

The Chiba Bank, Ltd. - Treasury Operation Division **(1)**
2-2-1 Nihombashi Muromachi
Chuo-ku, Tokyo, 103-0022, Japan
Tel.: (81) 332708459
Fax: (81) 332421735
E-Mail: int@chibabank.co.jp
Financial Management Consulting Services
S.I.C.: 8742
N.A.I.C.S.: 541611

U.S. Subsidiary:

Chiba Bank Ltd. **(1)**
1133 Ave Of The Americas #1516
New York, NY 10036
Tel.: (212) 354-7777
Fax: (212) 354-8575
Emp.: 10
Banking Services
S.I.C.: 6029
N.A.I.C.S.: 522110
Morio Tsumita *(Mgr)*

Subsidiaries:

Chiba Servicer Co.,Ltd. **(1)**
Toho Kogyo Building 4 F
Chiba, 260-0016, Japan
Tel.: (81) 432256375
Nondepository Credit Intermediation Services
S.I.C.: 6159
N.A.I.C.S.: 522298

Chibagin Accounting Service Co., Ltd. **(1)**
1-2 Chiba Minato Chuo-ku
Chiba, 260-8720, Japan
Tel.: (81) 432451111
Fax: (81) 0430429121
Web Site: ir.chibabank.co.jp
Emp.: 3,500
Provider of Accounting, Staffing & Administration Services
S.I.C.: 8721
N.A.I.C.S.: 541211
Hidetoshi sakuma *(Mgr)*

Chibagin Asset Management Co., Ltd. **(1)**
5-3 Nihombashi Muromachi 1 Chome
Chuo Ku, Tokyo, 103022, Japan (100%)
Tel.: (81) 332708351
Fax: (81) 332421736
Emp.: 40
S.I.C.: 6141
N.A.I.C.S.: 522210

Chibagin Capital Co., Ltd. **(1)**
1-2 Chiba Minato
Chuo-ku, Chiba, 260-8720, Japan (25%)
Tel.: (81) 432451111
Fax: (81) 432429121
Emp.: 4,000
Consulting Services
S.I.C.: 6799
N.A.I.C.S.: 523910
Hidetoshi Sakuma *(Pres)*

Chibagin Cash Business Co., Ltd. **(1)**
1-2 Chiba Minato Chukou
Chiba, Tokyo, 2600026, Japan (100%)
Tel.: (81) 432451111
Fax: (81) 432438232
E-Mail: investor@chibabank.co.jp
Web Site: www.chibabank.co.jp
Emp.: 197
Collection Services
S.I.C.: 7322
N.A.I.C.S.: 561440

Chibagin Computer Service Co., Ltd. **(1)**
6-12 Oyuminochuo
Midori-ku, Chiba, 266-0032, Japan (4%)
Tel.: (81) 432928881
Computer Systems Development & Commissioned Computation Tasks
S.I.C.: 7371
N.A.I.C.S.: 541511

Chibagin DC Card Co.,Ltd. **(1)**
2-15-11 Foujimi Ghyoku
Chiba, 260-0015, Japan
Tel.: (81) 432258411
Web Site: www.chibagindc.co.jp
Credit Card Processing Services
S.I.C.: 6099
N.A.I.C.S.: 522320

Chibagin Guarantee Company Ltd. **(1)**
1-2 Chiba-minato
Chuo-ku, Chiba, 260-8720, Japan (100%)
Tel.: (81) 432451111
Fax: (81) 432389804
Web Site: ir.chibabank.co.jp/english/Profile/main.html
Emp.: 84
Housing-Loan Guarantees & Fee Collection Services
S.I.C.: 6531
N.A.I.C.S.: 531390
Hidetoshi Sakuma *(Pres)*

Chibagin Heartful Co.,Ltd. **(1)**
4-1-10 Masago
Mihama-ku, Chiba, 261-0011, Japan
Tel.: (81) 432707341
Web Site: www.chibagin-heartful.co.jp
Business Management Consulting Services
S.I.C.: 8748
N.A.I.C.S.: 541618

Chibagin JCB Card Co.,Ltd. **(1)**
1-14-11 Fujimi
Chuo-ku, Chiba, 260-0015, Japan
Tel.: (81) 432252611
Web Site: www.chibaginjcb.co.jp
Credit Card Processing Services
S.I.C.: 6099
N.A.I.C.S.: 522320

Chibagin Lease Co., Ltd. **(1)**
2-1-22 Hanazono
Hanamigawa Ku, Chiba, 2620025, Japan (5%)
Tel.: (81) 432758001
Fax: (81) 433502951
Emp.: 71
Leasing & Loans
S.I.C.: 6159
N.A.I.C.S.: 522298

Chibagin Leasing Co., Ltd. **(1)**
2-1-22 Hanazono
Hanamigawa-ku, Chiba, 262-0025, Japan
Tel.: (81) 432758001
Fax: (81) 4323502951
Web Site: www.chibabank.co.jp
Leasing Services
S.I.C.: 6726
N.A.I.C.S.: 525990
Takeshi Kubo *(Mng Exec Officer & Dir)*

Chibagin Research Institute Co.,Ltd. **(1)**
2-3-12 Konakadai
Inage-ku, Chiba, 263-0043, Japan
Tel.: (81) 432451111
Fax: (81) 432070731
Computer Systems Consulting Services
S.I.C.: 7371
N.A.I.C.S.: 541511

Chibagin Securities Co.,Ltd. **(1)**
2-5-1 Chuo
Chuo-ku, Chiba, 260-0801, Japan
Tel.: (81) 432221141
Securities Dealing Services
S.I.C.: 6211
N.A.I.C.S.: 523110

Sobu Co., Ltd. **(1)**
61-4 Noda
Katori-gun, Chiba, 289-0314, Japan
Tel.: (81) 478833350
Fax: (81) 478832580
Commercial Buildings Rental & Maintenance Services
S.I.C.: 6512
N.A.I.C.S.: 531120

THE CHIBA KOGYO BANK, LTD.

1-2 Saiwaicho 2-chome Mihama-ku
Chiba, 261-0001, Japan
Tel.: (81) 432432111
Fax: (81) 432430235
E-Mail: reiko_yamada@chibakogyo-bank.co.jp
Web Site: www.chibakogyo-bank.co.jp
Year Founded: 1952
8337—(TKS)
Rev.: $593,890,000
Assets: $26,463,943,000
Liabilities: $24,464,792,000
Net Worth: $1,999,151,000
Earnings: $95,425,000
Emp.: 1,239
Fiscal Year-end: 03/31/13
Business Description:
Commercial Banking Services
S.I.C.: 6029
N.A.I.C.S.: 522110
Personnel:
Shunichi Aoyagi *(Pres & CEO)*
Seiji Umemura *(COO & Deputy Pres)*
Satoshi Hoshino *(Mng Dir)*
Hiroshi Tanaka *(Mng Dir)*
Yasumi Inaba *(Exec Officer)*
Hironari Itoh *(Exec Officer)*
Masatoshi Itohiya *(Exec Officer)*
Shigeto Katoh *(Mng Exec Officer)*
Kazuto Matsui *(Exec Officer)*
Ryu-ichiro Ochi *(Exec Officer)*
Masakazu Ohba *(Exec Officer)*
Shigeo Okamoto *(Mng Exec Officer)*
Yoshiaki Tateno *(Mng Exec Officer)*
Yasuo Toda *(Exec Officer)*
Board of Directors:
Shunichi Aoyagi
Satoshi Hoshino
Shigeto Katoh
Shigeo Okamoto
Hiroshi Tanaka
Yoshiaki Tateno
Seiji Umemura

Division:

Chiba Kogyo Bank-Financial Market Div **(1)**
3-10 Higashi-Kamba
2-chome
Chiyoda-ku, Tokyo, Japan
Tel.: (81) 3 3561 5031
Fax: (81) 3 3564 5064
S.I.C.: 6159
N.A.I.C.S.: 522298

Subsidiaries:

Chiba General Lease Co., Ltd. **(1)**
1-17 Fujimi 1 Chome Chuo-ku 3rd Floor
Chiba Kogyo Bank
Chibaekimae Branch Bldg, Chiba, 260 0015, Japan (26%)
Tel.: (81) 43 227 9361
Fax: (81) 43 227 4986
Web Site: www.chiba-general-lease.co.jp
Emp.: 40
General Insurance Services
S.I.C.: 6311
N.A.I.C.S.: 524113

Chiba Kogin Business Service Co., Ltd. **(1)**
1-2 Saiwaicho 2 Chome
Mihama Ku, Chiba, 261 0001, Japan (100%)
Tel.: (81) 432432111
Fax: (81) 432449203
Emp.: 300
S.I.C.: 6159
N.A.I.C.S.: 522298
Shunichi Aoyagi *(Pres)*
Toru Kipao *(Mng Dir)*

Chiba Kogin Card Service Co., Ltd. **(1)**
4-5 Honchibacho Chibakoginchibashiten 5f
Chuo-Ku, Chiba, 260-0014, Japan
Tel.: (81) 432247811
Fax: (81) 432272284
Credit Card Processing Services
S.I.C.: 6099
N.A.I.C.S.: 522320

Chiba Kogin Computer Soft Co., Ltd. **(1)**
1-2 Saiwaicho 2 Chome
Mihama Ku, Chiba, Japan
Tel.: (81) 432426346
Web Site: www.chibakogin-cs.co.jp/
S.I.C.: 6159
N.A.I.C.S.: 522298

Affiliates:

Chiba Kogin Finance Co., Ltd. **(1)**
1-17 Fujimi 1 Chome
Chuo Ku, Chiba, 600015, Japan
Tel.: (81) 432272821
S.I.C.: 6159

N.A.I.C.S.: 522298

Chiba Kogin Staff Services Co., Ltd. (1)
1-2 Saiwaicho 2 Chome
Mihama Ku, Chiba, Japan
Tel.: (81) 432436161
S.I.C.: 6159
N.A.I.C.S.: 522298

Chiba Kogin UC Card Co., Ltd. (1)
No 17 3rd Floor Sodegaura Building
4-chome Chiba Chuo
Chiba, 260 0013, Japan (98%)
Tel.: (81) 43 224 0821
Fax: (81) 432240940
Web Site: www.cuccard.co.jp
Emp.: 30
Banking & Credit Card Issuance Services
S.I.C.: 6141
N.A.I.C.S.: 522210

CHIBOUGAMAU DRILLING LTD

527 Road 167 CP 4
Chibougamau, QC, G8P 2K5, Canada
Tel.: (418) 748-3977
Fax: (418) 748-4249
Web Site: www.chibougamaudrilling.ca
Year Founded: 1968
Rev.: $12,520,073
Emp.: 180
Business Description:
Diamond Drilling Services
S.I.C.: 3914
N.A.I.C.S.: 339910
Personnel:
M. Serge Larouche *(Pres-Admin)*

CHIBOUGAMAU INDEPENDENT MINES INC.

86 14e Rue
Rouyn-Noranda, QC, J9X 2J1, Canada
Tel.: (819) 797-5242
Fax: (819) 797-1470
CBG—(TSXV)
Business Description:
Metal Mining
S.I.C.: 1099
N.A.I.C.S.: 212299
Personnel:
Jack Stoch *(Pres & CEO)*

CHICAGO BRIDGE & IRON COMPANY N.V.

(d/b/a CB&I Group)
Oostduinlaan 75
NL-2596 JJ Hague, Netherlands
Tel.: (31) 70 373 2010
Fax: (31) 70 373 2750
E-Mail: info@cbi.com
Web Site: www.cbi.com
Year Founded: 1889
CBI—(NYSE)
Rev.: $11,094,527,000
Assets: $9,389,593,000
Liabilities: $6,882,155,000
Net Worth: $2,507,438,000
Earnings: $512,590,000
Emp.: 55,900
Fiscal Year-end: 12/31/13
Business Description:
Holding Company; Process Technology Licensing, Specialty Engineering & Construction Services
S.I.C.: 6719
N.A.I.C.S.: 551112
Personnel:
Philip K. Asherman *(Pres & CEO)*
Ronald A. Ballschmiede *(CFO & Exec VP)*
Patrick K. Mullen *(Pres-Engrg, Construction & Maintenance-Operating Grp & Exec VP)*
Daniel M. McCarthy *(Exec VP & Grp Pres-Tech)*
Edgar Chip Ray *(Exec VP & Grp Pres-Govt Solutions)*
James Sabin *(Exec VP-Global Sys)*
Supervisory Board of Directors:
L. Richard Flury
Philip K. Asherman
James R. Bolch
Deborah M. Fretz
W. Craig Kissel
Larry D. McVay
Michael L. Underwood
Marsha C. Williams
Transfer Agent:
The Bank of New York
PO Box 11258 Church St Sta
New York, NY 10286-1258
Tel.: (800) 524-4458

Subsidiaries:

CB&I Holdings B.V. (1)
Oostduinlaan 75
Hague, 2596 JJ, Netherlands
Tel.: (31) 703732010
Investment Management Services
S.I.C.: 6211
N.A.I.C.S.: 523999

Chicago Bridge & Iron Company B.V. (1)
Oostduinlaan 75
NL-2596 JJ Hague, Netherlands NL (100%)
Tel.: (31) 70 373 2010
Fax: (31) 70 373 2750
E-Mail: info@cbiepc.com
Web Site: www.cbiepc.com
Emp.: 900
Process Technology Licensing, Specialty Engineering & Construction Services
S.I.C.: 8711
N.A.I.C.S.: 541330
Philip K. Asherman *(Mng Dir)*

Subsidiaries:

CB&I Lummus B.V. (2)
Oostduinlaan 75
2596 JJ Hague, Netherlands
Tel.: (31) 703732722
Fax: (31) 703732750
Web Site: www.cbi.com
Emp.: 700
Engineering Services
S.I.C.: 8711
N.A.I.C.S.: 541330

CB&I Oil & Gas Europe B.V. (2)
Oostduinlaan 75
Hague, 2596 JJ, Netherlands
Tel.: (31) 703732010
Oil & Gas Exploration Services
S.I.C.: 1389
N.A.I.C.S.: 213112

Subsidiary:

Lummus Technology Heat Transfer B.V. (3)
Oostduinlaan 75
Hague, 2596 JJ, Netherlands
Tel.: (31) 703733010
Fax: (31) 703732750
Heat Transfer Equipment Distr
S.I.C.: 5074
N.A.I.C.S.: 423720

Non-U.S. Subsidiary:

CB&I Lummus s.r.o. (3)
Holandska 8
656 80 Brno, Czech Republic
Tel.: (420) 5 45 517 111
Fax: (420) 5 45 517 444
Construction Engineering Services
S.I.C.: 8711
N.A.I.C.S.: 541330

CMP Holdings B.V. (2)
Oostduinlaan 75
Hague, 2596 JJ, Netherlands
Tel.: (31) 703732010
Fax: (31) 703732750
Investment Management Services
S.I.C.: 6211
N.A.I.C.S.: 523999

Subsidiary:

CB&I Europe B.V. (3)
Oostduinlaan 75
2596 JJ Hague, Netherlands
Tel.: (31) 70 373 20 10
Fax: (31) 70 373 27 50
Oil & Gas Exploration Services
S.I.C.: 1389
N.A.I.C.S.: 213112

Non-U.S. Branch:

CBI Constructors, Ltd. (London) (2)
20 Eastbourne Terrace
Staines-upon-Thames, TW18 4AX, United Kingdom
Tel.: (44) 2079573388
Fax: (44) 2079573443
Web Site: www.cbi.com
Mfr of Metal Structures & Parts of Structures
S.I.C.: 3441
N.A.I.C.S.: 332312

Non-U.S. Subsidiaries:

Arabian CBI Ltd. (2)
6th Floor Al Fadhl Building Junction of King Saud & 2nd
PO Box 1218
Dammam, 31431, Saudi Arabia (75%)
Tel.: (966) 38330990
Fax: (966) 38335836
E-Mail: acbi@chicagobridge.com
Web Site: www.chicagobridge.com
Sales Range: $25-49.9 Million
Emp.: 1,000
S.I.C.: 1799
N.A.I.C.S.: 562910
Ahmed Ezzie *(Mgr-Ops)*

CB&I Lummus GmbH (2)
Lorenz-Schott Strasse 4
55252 Mainz, Kastel, Germany De
Tel.: (49) 61347120
Fax: (49) 6134712387
E-Mail: CWiedel@cbi.com
Web Site: www.lummusonline.com
Engineering Services
S.I.C.: 8711
N.A.I.C.S.: 541330

Subsidiary:

Lummus Novolen Technology GmbH (3)
Gottlieb Daimler Str 8
68165 Mannheim, Germany
Tel.: (49) 62149494011
Telex: 4186731
Fax: (49) 62149494002
E-Mail: novolen@cbi.com
Web Site: www.cbi.com
Emp.: 28
Engineering & Construction Services
S.I.C.: 8711
N.A.I.C.S.: 541330

CB&I UK Limited (2)
40 Eastbourne Terrace
London, W2 6LG, United Kingdom
Tel.: (44) 20 7053 3000
Fax: (44) 20 7053 3001
Civil Engineering Construction Services
S.I.C.: 1629
N.A.I.C.S.: 237990

CB&I (2)
20th Floor Equitable Bank Tower 8751 Paseo de Roxas Ave
Makati, 1226 Manila, Philippines
Mailing Address:
PO Box 3866
Manila, Makati, 1299, Philippines
Tel.: (63) 22386911
Fax: (63) 28860552
Web Site: www.cbi.com
Emp.: 77
Engineering & Construction Services
S.I.C.: 1799
N.A.I.C.S.: 562910
Orlanda Badang *(Mgr-Fin)*

CBI Construcciones S.A. (2)
Arenales 1123, Piso 6
Cuidad Autonoma, 1010 Buenos Aires, Argentina
Tel.: (54) 1148127887
Fax: (54) 11 4816 7455
Industrial Buildings & Warehouses
S.I.C.: 1542
N.A.I.C.S.: 236220

CBI Constructors Pty. Ltd (2)
Tenancy 8B Level 8 120 Edward St
Brisbane, QLD, 2000, Australia (100%)
Tel.: (61) 730145500
Fax: (61) 730145507
Web Site: www.cbi.com
Emp.: 16
Engineering Services
S.I.C.: 8711
N.A.I.C.S.: 541330
William Callijeros *(Gen Mgr)*

Branch:

CBI Constructors Pty. Ltd. (Perth) (3)
Level 13 197 St George's Terrace
Perth, WA, 6000, Australia (100%)
Tel.: (61) 893245555
Fax: (61) 893228205
E-Mail: info@cbi.com
Web Site: www.cbi.com
Emp.: 100
Engineering Services
S.I.C.: 8711
N.A.I.C.S.: 541330
Peter Bennett *(Gen Mgr)*

CBI Montajes de Chile Limitada (2)
Cam to Loncura S / N Vina del Mar
Santiago, Chile
Tel.: (56) 322449534
Civil Engineering Construction Services
S.I.C.: 1629
N.A.I.C.S.: 237990

CBI Peruana S.A.C. (2)
Avenida Camino Real No 390 Torre Central Pico 12 Oficina 1202
San Isidro, Lima, 27, Peru
Tel.: (51) 1 7059100
Fax: (51) 1 707 9140
Web Site: www.cbi.com
Emp.: 12
Construction Engineering Services
S.I.C.: 8711
N.A.I.C.S.: 541330
Gonzalo Crosby *(Country Mgr)*

CBI Venezolana, S.A. (2)
2 Da Av De Campo Alegre Torre Credival Piso 9
1010 Caracas, Venezuela (100%)
Tel.: (58) 2122634011
Fax: (58) 2122630309
E-Mail: cbivenensa@movistlr.net
Web Site: www.cbi.com
Emp.: 200
S.I.C.: 1799
N.A.I.C.S.: 562910
Martin Galena *(Gen Mgr)*

Chicago Bridge & Iron Company (Egypt) LLC (2)
Intersection of Makram Ebeid & Abdel Razzak Al Sanhoury Streets
Nasr, Cairo, 11762, Egypt
Tel.: (20) 222768000
Fax: (20) 222768099
Engineering & Construction Services
S.I.C.: 1629
N.A.I.C.S.: 237990

Horton CBI, Limited (2)
03 Lower Level 9816 Hardin Street
Fort McMurray, AB, T9H 4K3, Canada
Tel.: (780) 743-0114
Fax: (780) 743-0155
Web Site: www.cbiepc.com
Construction, Repair & Maintenance of Engineered Plate Metal Structures
S.I.C.: 1629
N.A.I.C.S.: 237990

Branches:

Horton CBI, Limited (3)
Ste 600 205 5th Ave Southwest
Bow Valley Sq 2, Calgary, AB, T2P 2V7, Canada (100%)
Tel.: (403) 264-1333
Fax: (403) 266-2453
Web Site: www.hortoncbi.com
Emp.: 6
Construction, Repair & Maintenance of Engineered Plate Metal Structures

Chicago Bridge & Iron Company N.V.—(Continued)

S.I.C.: 1629
N.A.I.C.S.: 237990

Horton CBI, Limited (3)
4342 Queen St Fl 3
Niagara Falls, ON, L2E 7J7, Canada (100%)
Tel.: (905) 371-1500
Fax: (905) 371-3930
Web Site: www.hortoncbi.com
Emp.: 50
Structural Steel Erection
S.I.C.: 1629
N.A.I.C.S.: 237990

Horton CBI, Limited (3)
825 Sturgeon Industrial Pk
PO Box 3534
Fort Saskatchewan, AB, T8L 2T4, Canada (100%)
Tel.: (780) 998-2800
Fax: (780) 998-2841
E-Mail: mbeauregard@cbi.com
Web Site: www.cbi.com
Sales Range: $50-74.9 Million
Emp.: 36
Construction, Repair & Maintenance of Engineered Plate Metal Structures
S.I.C.: 1629
N.A.I.C.S.: 237990
Philip K. Asherman *(Pres)*

Non-U.S. Affiliate:

P.T. Chicago Bridge & Iron (2)
Jl Sugiyopranoto Alley III No 1
Bontang, 37431, Indonesia Id
Tel.: (62) 272321077
Fax: (62) 272321356
E-Mail: clusa@cbi.id
Emp.: 15
Blast Furnace & Steel Mills
S.I.C.: 3312
N.A.I.C.S.: 331110
Samuel Filiaci *(Mng Dir)*

U.S. Subsidiary:

Chicago Bridge & Iron Company (1)
2103 Research Forest Dr
The Woodlands, TX 77380-1123
Tel.: (832) 513-1600
Fax: (832) 513-1605
E-Mail: media-relations@cbi.com
Web Site: www.cbi.com
Sales Range: $1-4.9 Billion
Emp.: 300
Holding Company; Corporate Administrative Office
S.I.C.: 6719
N.A.I.C.S.: 551112
Mark Coscio *(VP-Corp Plng)*

Subsidiaries:

CB&I Inc. (2)
2103 Research Forrest Dr
The Woodlands, TX 77380 TX
Tel.: (832) 513-1600
Fax: (832) 513-1605
Web Site: www.cbi.com
Construction of Plate Steel Structures
S.I.C.: 1791
N.A.I.C.S.: 238120
Philip K. Asherman *(Pres & CEO)*
Lasse Petterson *(COO & Exec VP-Engrg, Construction & Maintenance Operating Grp)*
Jeffrey J. Lyash *(Pres-Power Bus Unit-Charlotte)*
Luke V. Scorsone *(Pres-Fabrication Svcs)*
Patrick K. Mullen *(Exec VP-Corp Dev)*

Branches:

CB&I - Alpharetta (3)
3600 Mansell Rd Ste 230
Alpharetta, GA 30022 (100%)
Tel.: (678) 935-3650
Fax: (678) 935-3659
E-Mail: donald.nason@cbi.com
Web Site: www.cbi.com
Emp.: 6
Structural Steel Erectors
S.I.C.: 3443
N.A.I.C.S.: 332410

CB&I - Beaumont (3)
350 Pine St
Beaumont, TX 77701
Tel.: (409) 981-6700
Fax: (409) 980-5793
Web Site: www.cbi.com
Emp.: 450
Consulting Engineers & Contractor of Industrial Facilities
S.I.C.: 8711
N.A.I.C.S.: 541330

CB&I - Clive (3)
9550 Hickman Rd
Clive, IA 50325-5316
Tel.: (515) 254-9228
Fax: (515) 254-9511
Web Site: www.cbi.com
Emp.: 40
S.I.C.: 3441
N.A.I.C.S.: 332312
Greg Larson *(VP & Engr)*

CB&I - Los Angeles (3)
250 W 1st St 210
Claremont, CA 91711-4736
Tel.: (909) 624-4000
Fax: (909) 624-4080
E-Mail: stomco@cbi.com
Emp.: 7
Construction Services
S.I.C.: 1791
N.A.I.C.S.: 238120

CBI Americas Ltd. (2)
6001 Rogerdale Rd
Houston, TX 77072
Tel.: (713) 485-1000
Fax: (713) 485-1005
Web Site: www.cbi.com
Construction Engineering Services
S.I.C.: 8711
N.A.I.C.S.: 541330

CBI Company Ltd. (2)
2103 Research Forest Dr
The Woodlands, TX 77380-2624
Tel.: (832) 513-1000
Fax: (832) 513-1005
Construction Engineering Services
S.I.C.: 8711
N.A.I.C.S.: 541330

CBI Services, Inc. (New Castle) (2)
24 Reads Way
New Castle, DE 19720-1649 (100%)
Tel.: (302) 325-8400
Fax: (302) 323-0788
E-Mail: info@cbi.com
Web Site: www.cbi.com
Emp.: 15
Steel Construction
S.I.C.: 1541
N.A.I.C.S.: 236210
Philip K. Asherman *(Pres)*

CBI Services, Inc. (2)
1000 Remington Blvd Ste 105A
Bolingbrook, IL 60440
Mailing Address:
PO Box 9
Plainfield, IL 60544-0009
Tel.: (815) 439-6668
Fax: (630) 378-7701
Web Site: www.cbi.com
Emp.: 50
Steel Plates Contractor
S.I.C.: 1629
N.A.I.C.S.: 236210
James E. Bollweg *(Pres)*

CSA Trading Company, Ltd (2)
2103 Research Forest Dr
The Woodlands, TX 77380-2624
Tel.: (832) 513-1000
Fax: (832) 513-1005
Civil Engineering Construction Services
S.I.C.: 1629
N.A.I.C.S.: 237990

Lummus Technology, Inc. (2)
1515 Broad St
Bloomfield, NJ 07003-3096 DE
Tel.: (973) 893-1515
Fax: (973) 893-2000
Web Site: www.cvi.com
Sales Range: $1-4.9 Billion
Emp.: 400
Process Technology, Engineering & Industrial Construction Services
S.I.C.: 8711
N.A.I.C.S.: 541330
Daniel M. McCarthy *(Exec VP)*

Divisions:

Lummus Technology - Heat Transfer (3)
1515 Broad St
Bloomfield, NJ 07003-3002
Tel.: (973) 893-3000
Fax: (973) 893-2106
Web Site: www.cbi.us
Emp.: 70
Heat Transfer Equipment Supplier & Mfr
S.I.C.: 8742
N.A.I.C.S.: 541611

Lummus Technology - Randall (3)
3010 Briarpark Dr
Houston, TX 77042-6052
Tel.: (713) 821-4100
Fax: (713) 821-3589
E-Mail: info@cbi.com
Web Site: www.cbi.com
Emp.: 30
Chemical Engineering Services
S.I.C.: 3612
N.A.I.C.S.: 335311
Robert R. Huebel *(Gen Mgr)*

Non-U.S. Subsidiaries:

CB&I Lummus Pte. Ltd. (3)
3A International Business Park Icon@IBP #09-01/09
Singapore, 609935, Singapore
Tel.: (65) 67738638
Telex: 33775
Fax: (65) 66863507
E-Mail: sglum@sg.cbi.com
Web Site: www.cbi.com.sg
Emp.: 150
Engineering Services
S.I.C.: 8711
N.A.I.C.S.: 541330
James Mathieson *(Gen Mgr)*

Lummus Alireza Ltd. Co. (3)
3rd Fl Sadat Tower Bldg
Al Khobar, Saudi Arabia
Tel.: (966) 38821111
Telex: 202012
Fax: (966) 38877711
E-Mail: ybuella@cbi.com
Web Site: www.lummusonline.com
Emp.: 150
Engineering Services
S.I.C.: 8711
N.A.I.C.S.: 541330
Tareq Kawash *(Gen Mgr)*

The Shaw Group Inc. (2)
4171 Essen Ln
Baton Rouge, LA 70809 LA
Tel.: (225) 932-2500
Fax: (225) 932-2661
Toll Free: (800) 747-3322
E-Mail: webmaster@shawgrp.com
Web Site: www.shawgrp.com
Emp.: 25,000
Prefab Piping Systems Mfr; Bending & Shaping Steel Pipe; Specialty Pipe Fittings; Design & Engineering Services; Industrial Building Construction
S.I.C.: 3084
N.A.I.C.S.: 326122
James C. Wilems *(Chief Acctg Officer & Interim VP)*
James Glass *(Pres-Energy & Chemicals Grp)*
Timothy J. Poche *(CFO-Power Grp & Sr VP)*
Jeffrey S. Merrifield *(Sr VP-Bus Dev-Power Grp)*

Subsidiaries:

B.F. Shaw, Inc. (3)
366 Old Airport Rd
Laurens, SC 29360
Tel.: (864) 682-4000
Fax: (864) 683-4771
Sales Range: $100-124.9 Million
Emp.: 350
Welder & Fabricator of Piping Systems
S.I.C.: 3498
N.A.I.C.S.: 332996

Field Services, Inc. (3)
135 Palm St
Canton, GA 30115
Tel.: (770) 345-9277
Fax: (800) 655-5055
Toll Free: (800) 864-0523
E-Mail: info@fieldservices.com
Web Site: www.fieldservices.com
Testing Laboratories
S.I.C.: 8734
N.A.I.C.S.: 541380

KB Home/Shaw Louisiana LLC (3)
10990 Wilshire Blvd Fl 7
Los Angeles, CA 90024-3907
Tel.: (310) 231-4000
Testing Laboratories
S.I.C.: 8734
N.A.I.C.S.: 541380

The LandBank Group, Inc. (3)
9201 E Dry Creek Rd
Centennial, CO 80112
Tel.: (303) 763-8500
Fax: (303) 763-5700
Web Site: www.landbank.net
Sales Range: $1-9.9 Million
Emp.: 5
Distressed Land, Buildings & Operating Facilities Acquirer, Restorer & Redeveloper
S.I.C.: 8711
N.A.I.C.S.: 541330
Corrie Symons *(Controller-The Shaw Grp)*

LandBank Properties, L.L.C. (3)
10540 Lansing St Ste 1
Mendocino, CA 95460
Tel.: (707) 937-4523
Testing Laboratories
S.I.C.: 8734
N.A.I.C.S.: 541380

Shaw Alloy Piping Products, Inc. (3)
740 N Market St
Shreveport, LA 71137
Tel.: (318) 674-9860
Fax: (318) 674-9801
Web Site: www.theshawgrp.com
Sales Range: $25-49.9 Million
Emp.: 50
Mfr of Stainless, Alloy, Carbon, High Yield & Chrome Steel Fittings for the Power & Process Industries
S.I.C.: 3498
N.A.I.C.S.: 332996
Ben Arnold *(Mgr)*

Shaw APP Tubeline, Inc. (3)
475 Jersey Ave
New Brunswick, NJ 08901
Tel.: (732) 435-0777
Fax: (732) 435-0888
Testing Laboratories
S.I.C.: 8734
N.A.I.C.S.: 541380
Robert Shelton *(VP)*

Shaw Connex, Inc. (3)
1 Connex Way
Troutville, VA 24175
Tel.: (540) 992-1600
Sales Range: $100-124.9 Million
Pipe Fittings Mfr
S.I.C.: 3498
N.A.I.C.S.: 332996

Shaw Constructors, Inc. (3)
4809 E Napoleon
Sulphur, LA 70663
Tel.: (337) 626-7429
Fax: (337) 626-7428
Web Site: www.shawgrp.com
Sales Range: $10-24.9 Million
Emp.: 6
Construction Services for the Refining, Petrochemical, Pipeline, Pulp & Paper & Electric Power Industries
S.I.C.: 1799
N.A.I.C.S.: 238990
Allen Mccall *(Office Mgr)*

Shaw Consultants International, Inc. (3)
4171 Essen Ln
Baton Rouge, LA 70809 LA
Tel.: (225) 932-2500
Energy & Chemical Technical Consulting Services
S.I.C.: 8999
N.A.I.C.S.: 541690

Non-U.S. Subsidiary:

Shaw Consultants International Limited (4)
Witan Gate House 500-600 Witan Gate West

Milton Keynes, MK9 1BA, United Kingdom UK
Tel.: (44) 1908 6688664
Fax: (44) 1908 602211
Sales Range: $10-24.9 Million
Emp.: 30
Management Consulting Services Specializing in Power & Processing Regulation & Utility Privitization
S.I.C.: 8742
N.A.I.C.S.: 541611
Pierre Hibble *(Dir)*

Shaw Environmental & Infrastructure, Inc. (3)
1 Muldoon Ave
Staten Island, NY 10312
Tel.: (718) 605-2669
Testing Laboratories
S.I.C.: 8734
N.A.I.C.S.: 541380
Nikolay Mikhalchuk *(Mgr-Construction & Engrg Field-I)*

Shaw Environmental (3)
13 British American Blvd
Latham, NY 12110
Tel.: (518) 783-1996
Fax: (518) 783-8397
E-Mail: environmental@shawgrp.com
Sales Range: $75-99.9 Million
Integrated Solid Waste Services
S.I.C.: 8999
N.A.I.C.S.: 541690
Cornelius Murphy *(Sr VP-Federal Div)*

Subsidiaries:

American Plastic Pipe and Supply, L.L.C. (4)
725 Friendship Dr
New Concord, OH 43762 (100%)
Tel.: (740) 826-7683
Fax: (740) 826-9047
E-Mail: Firstname.lastname@shawgrp.com
Web Site: www.shawgrp.com
Sales Range: $150-199.9 Million
Emp.: 20
Supplier of Pipe, Valves, Fittings, Specialty Items, Pumps & Pre-Fabricated Geomembrane Liners to the Landfill Industry
S.I.C.: 5051
N.A.I.C.S.: 423510

LFG Specialties, L.L.C. (4)
16406 Rte 224 E
Findlay, OH 45840 (100%)
Tel.: (419) 424-4999
Fax: (419) 424-4997
Web Site: www.lfgspecialties.com
Sales Range: $75-99.9 Million
Emp.: 250
Gas Management Equipment Designer & Mfr
S.I.C.: 2899
N.A.I.C.S.: 325998

Shaw Fronek Company (FCI), Inc. (3)
Ste 2D 105 Fieldcrest Ave
Edison, NJ 08837-3635
Tel.: (201) 569-8111
Fax: (201) 569-9766
Sales Range: $75-99.9 Million
Designer & Mfr of Piping Hangers & Support Systems
S.I.C.: 8711
N.A.I.C.S.: 541330

Shaw FVF, Inc. (3)
15650 Industrial Way
Walker, LA 70785
Tel.: (225) 756-5577
Fax: (225) 751-2277
Web Site: app.shawgrp.com
Sales Range: $25-49.9 Million
Emp.: 22
Carbon Steel Fittings & Flanges Mfr
S.I.C.: 5074
N.A.I.C.S.: 423720
Brad Fourrier *(Gen Mgr)*

Shaw GBB, LLC (3)
3600 Springhill Business Park Ste 200
Mobile, AL 36608-1203 AL
Tel.: (251) 344-1913
Fax: (251) 342-3229
Engineering Services
S.I.C.: 8711
N.A.I.C.S.: 541330
Jeffrey Boos *(Principal)*
Paul Bridges *(Principal)*
William Hess *(Principal)*
James LaRose *(Principal)*

Shaw Maintenance, Inc. (3)
1241 Underwood Rd
La Porte, TX 77571
Tel.: (281) 842-6400
Fax: (281) 842-6401
Web Site: www.shawgrp.com
Sales Range: $150-199.9 Million
Emp.: 60
Maintenance Services for the Chemical, Petrochemical, Refining, Grain, Pulp, Paper & Power Industries
S.I.C.: 1541
N.A.I.C.S.: 236210
Marcus Deal *(Mgr-Maintenance)*

Shaw NAPTech, Inc. (3)
210 E 700 S
Clearfield, UT 84015
Tel.: (801) 773-7300
Fax: (801) 773-6185
Web Site: www.shawgroup.com
Sales Range: $75-99.9 Million
Emp.: 200
Fabricator of Industrial Piping Systems & Engineered Piping Modules
S.I.C.: 3443
N.A.I.C.S.: 332313
Frank Corgiat *(Gen Mgr)*

Shaw Process Fabricators, Inc. (3)
4150 S Sherwood Forest Blvd Ste 210
Baton Rouge, LA 70816-4605
Tel.: (318) 387-0212
Fax: (318) 387-9011
Web Site: www.shawgrp.com
Sales Range: $100-124.9 Million
Pipe Fabricator & Cold Bending Machine Mfr
S.I.C.: 3498
N.A.I.C.S.: 332996

Shaw Services, L.L.C (3)
107 Wapikiya Dr
Missoula, MT 59803
Tel.: (406) 544-3844
Testing Laboratories
S.I.C.: 8734
N.A.I.C.S.: 541380

Shaw SSS Fabricators, Inc. (3)
7012 Hwy 1 S
Addis, LA 70710
Tel.: (225) 749-3165
Fax: (225) 749-2466
Web Site: www.shawgrp.com
Sales Range: $150-199.9 Million
Structural Steel Fabricator
S.I.C.: 3441
N.A.I.C.S.: 332312
Zach Boudreau *(Gen Mgr)*

Shaw Sunland Fabricators, Inc. (3)
30103 Sunland Dr
Walker, LA 70785
Tel.: (225) 667-1000
Fax: (225) 664-6390
Web Site: www.cbi.com
Sales Range: $75-99.9 Million
Emp.: 400
Mfr of Pipe Induction & Cold Bending Machines
S.I.C.: 3498
N.A.I.C.S.: 332996
T. J. Dicky *(Gen Mgr)*

Non-U.S. Subsidiaries:

Cojafex B.V. (3)
Blaak 22
3011TA Rotterdam, Netherlands NL
Tel.: (31) 2068080 (100%)
Fax: (31) 104122494
E-Mail: mail@cojafex.com
Web Site: www.cojafex.com
Sales Range: $125-149.9 Million
Mfr & Supplier of Induction Pipe Bending Equipment & Induction Structural Shape Bending Machines
S.I.C.: 3542
N.A.I.C.S.: 333517

Manufacturas Shaw South America, C.A. (3)
Avda Principal Zona Industrial
Maracaibo, Venezuela
Tel.: (58) 2617360153
Fax: (58) 2617360160
E-Mail: nelson.fanchez@mssa.com.ve
Web Site: www.shahgroup.com
Sales Range: $10-24.9 Million
Emp.: 32
Engineering Services
S.I.C.: 8711
N.A.I.C.S.: 541330
Giamfranco Occupati *(Gen Mgr)*

Pluritec Ltd (3)
1100 du Technoparc Place Office 200
Trois Rivieres, QC, G9A2G7, Canada (100%)
Tel.: (819) 379-8010
Fax: (819) 379-8092
E-Mail: pluritec@pluritec.qc.ca
Web Site: www.pluerítec.qc.ca
Sales Range: $25-49.9 Million
Emp.: 100
Engineering Services
S.I.C.: 8711
N.A.I.C.S.: 541330
Jonathan Dugay *(Pres)*

Roche Ltd., Consulting Group (3)
3075 Ch des Quatre Bourgeois Ste 300
Sainte-Foy, QC, G1W4Y4, Canada Ca
Tel.: (418) 654-9600 (100%)
Fax: (418) 654-9699
E-Mail: reception@roche.ca
Web Site: www.roche.ca
Sales Range: $200-249.9 Million
Emp.: 1,400
Engineering & Construction Services
S.I.C.: 8711
N.A.I.C.S.: 541330
Elizabeth Tessier *(Dir-Comm & Mktg)*

Branch:

Roche Consulting Group (4)
630 Rene Levesque Blvd W Ste 1500
Montreal, QC, H3B 1S6, Canada (100%)
Tel.: (514) 393-3363
Fax: (514) 393-1511
E-Mail: marketing@roche.ca
Web Site: www.roche.ca
Sales Range: $10-24.9 Million
Emp.: 80
Transport & Traffic Studies for Canada
S.I.C.: 7389
N.A.I.C.S.: 561499
Martin Choiniere *(Gen Mgr)*

Divisions:

Roche International Inc. (4)
3075 Champagne des Quatre Bourgeois Ste 300
Quebec, QC, G1W4Y4, Canada (100%)
Tel.: (418) 654-9600
Fax: (418) 654-9699
E-Mail: reception@roche.ca
Web Site: www.roche.ca
Sales Range: $150-199.9 Million
Emp.: 1,800
Construction & Engineering Services
S.I.C.: 8711
N.A.I.C.S.: 541330
Elizabeth Tessier *(Mgr-Mktg)*

Roche Ltd. Consulting Group (Construction Division) (4)
30375 Ch Des Quatre Bourgeois Ste 300
Quebec, QC, G1W 4Y4, Canada (100%)
Tel.: (418) 654-9600
Fax: (418) 654-9699
E-Mail: info@roche.ca
Web Site: www.roche.ca
Sales Range: $150-199.9 Million
Emp.: 1,000
Construction Services
S.I.C.: 8711
N.A.I.C.S.: 541330
Mario Martel *(CEO & Pres)*

Roche Ltd. Consulting Group (Evimbec Ltd. Division) (4)
3075 Chemaie dea Quatre Bourgeois Ste 300
Sainte-Foy, QC, G1W 4Y4, Canada Ca
Tel.: (418) 654-9622 (100%)
Fax: (418) 654-9699
E-Mail: reception@roche.ca
Web Site: www.roche.ca
Sales Range: $200-249.9 Million
Emp.: 1,400
Engineering Services
S.I.C.: 8711
N.A.I.C.S.: 541330
Mario Martel *(Pres)*

Roche Ltd. Consulting Group (Soderoc Developpement Ltee Division) (4)
3075 Ch des Quatre Bourgeois Ste 300
Sainte-Foy, QC, G1W 4Y4, Canada (100%)
Tel.: (418) 654-9600
Fax: (418) 654-9699
Web Site: www.roche.ca
Sales Range: $1-4.9 Billion
Emp.: 1,800
Real Estate Manager
S.I.C.: 6531
N.A.I.C.S.: 531210
Mario Martel *(Pres)*

Shaw Group UK Limited (3)
Stores Rd
Derby, Derbyshire, DE214BG, United Kingdom (100%)
Tel.: (44) 332291122
Fax: (44) 01332291123
Web Site: www.shawgrp.com
Sales Range: $50-74.9 Million
Emp.: 100
Pipework Systems & Repair & Maintenance Services Supplier
S.I.C.: 3498
N.A.I.C.S.: 332996
Derek Hunter *(Mng Dir)*
Ronald W. Oakley *(Mng Dir)*

Subsidiaries:

Shaw Energy & Chemicals Ltd. (4)
Witan Gate House 500-600 Witan Gate West
Milton Keynes, MK9 1BA, United Kingdom (100%)
Tel.: (44) 1908668844
Fax: (44) 1908602211
Sales Range: $75-99.9 Million
Emp.: 300
Engineering, Design, Construction & Consulting Services for Power, Industrial & Civil Works Projects, Oil & Gas Exploration & Production
S.I.C.: 8711
N.A.I.C.S.: 541330
James Glass *(Pres)*

The Shaw Group UK Pension Plan Limited (4)
Stores Rd
Derby, DE21 4BG, United Kingdom
Tel.: (44) 1332291122
Testing Laboratories
S.I.C.: 8734
N.A.I.C.S.: 541380

Shaw Lancas, C.A. (3)
Avenida Intercomunal
Ali Primera, Judibana, Estado Falcon, Venezuela
Tel.: (58) 2692460584
Fax: (58) 26924 61487
Sales Range: $75-99.9 Million
Engineering Services
S.I.C.: 8711
N.A.I.C.S.: 541330

Shaw Nass Middle East, W.L.L. (3)
1242 S Alba Industrial Area
Asker, Bahrain
Tel.: (973) 017830988
Fax: (973) 017830939
E-Mail: mazen.azizieh@shawgrp.com
Web Site: www.shawgrp.com
Sales Range: $150-199.9 Million
Emp.: 750
Fabricator of Pipe & Pipe Fittings
S.I.C.: 3498
N.A.I.C.S.: 332996
Majan Azizieg *(Gen Mgr)*

Non-U.S. Subsidiaries:

CB&I London (2)
40 Eastbourne Terrace
London, W2 6LG, United Kingdom
Tel.: (44) 20 7053 3000
Fax: (44) 20 7053 3001
Oil & Gas Pipeline Construction Services
S.I.C.: 1629
N.A.I.C.S.: 237120

Chicago Bridge & Iron Company N.V.—(Continued)

U.S. Subsidiary:

CB&I Woodlands L.L.C. (3)
1 CB&I Plz 2103 Research Forest Dr
The Woodlands, TX 77380
Tel.: (832) 513-1000
Fax: (832) 513-1005
Construction Engineering Services
S.I.C.: 8711
N.A.I.C.S.: 541330

CB&I Paddington Limited (2)
C B & I House
London, W2 6LG, United Kingdom
Tel.: (44) 20 7053 3000
Fax: (44) 20 7053 3001
Oil & Gas Pipeline Construction Services
S.I.C.: 1629
N.A.I.C.S.: 237120

Non-U.S. Subsidiaries:

CBI Eastern Anstalt (1)
Acico business park portsaeed
PO box 2750
Dubai, United Arab Emirates (100%)
Mailing Address:
PO Box 2750
Dubai, United Arab Emirates
Tel.: (971) 42609111
Fax: (971) 42942989
E-Mail: lwallace@cbi.com
Web Site: www.cbi.com
Emp.: 120
S.I.C.: 1799
N.A.I.C.S.: 562910
Tom Boshoff *(Mng Dir)*

CBI Overseas, LLC (1)
3A Internation Business Park Unit 09/01/09
Icon IBP Tower A
Singapore, 609935, Singapore (100%)
Tel.: (65) 64417800
Fax: (65) 65727100
E-Mail: info@cbi.com
Web Site: www.cbi.com
Sales Range: Less than $1 Million
Emp.: 13
Structural Steel Erection
S.I.C.: 3441
N.A.I.C.S.: 332312
Jeremy Taylor *(Gen Mgr)*

CHICAGO METALLIC CORPORATION

(Acquired by Rockwool International A/S)

CHICONY ELECTRONICS CO., LTD.

No 25 Wugong 6th Rd Wugu Dist
Taipei, 248, Taiwan
Tel.: (886) 222988120
Fax: (886) 222988442
Web Site: www.chicony.com.tw
Year Founded: 1983
2385—(TAI)
Sales Range: $400-449.9 Million
Emp.: 600

Business Description:
Input Devices (Keyboards), Power Supplies & Digital Image Products Mfr & Marketer
S.I.C.: 3577
N.A.I.C.S.: 334118

Personnel:
Kent Kun Tai Xu *(Chm)*
Maogui Lin *(Vice Chm & Gen Mgr)*
Yuling Lin *(CFO)*

Board of Directors:
Kent Kun Tai Xu
Maogui Lin

U.S. Subsidiary:

Chicony America Inc. (1)
53 Parker
Irvine, CA 92618
Tel.: (949) 380-0928
Fax: (949) 380-8201
Web Site: www.chicony.com.tw/aboutchicony.htm
Input Devices (keyboards), Power Supplies, & Digital Image Products Mfr & Marketer
S.I.C.: 3577
N.A.I.C.S.: 334118
Yaoqing Zhang *(Gen Mgr)*

Non-U.S. Subsidiaries:

CHICONY ELECTRONICS CEZ S.R.O (1)
1553 Tovarni
535 01 Prelouc, Czech Republic
Tel.: (420) 469775555
Fax: (420) 469775578
Web Site: www.chicony.com.tw/test10-2.htm#contactchicony
Emp.: 55
Computer Peripheral Mfr
S.I.C.: 3575
N.A.I.C.S.: 334118
Eric Wang *(Mng Dir)*

Chicony Electronics GmbH (1)
Borsteler Chaussee
85-99A Hamburg, Germany
Tel.: (49) 405144000
Fax: (49) 40512932
E-Mail: tang@chicony.de
Web Site: www.chicony.de
Emp.: 20
Input Devices, Power Supplies, & Digital Image Products Mfr & Marketer
S.I.C.: 3575
N.A.I.C.S.: 334118
Shaolong Chen *(Gen Mgr)*

Chicony Electronics Japan Co., Ltd. (1)
4B Iwasaki Building 3-11-15 Mizonokuchi
Takatsu-ku, Kawasaki, Kanagawa, 213-0001, Japan
Tel.: (81) 448508808
Fax: (81) 44 850 8830
Web Site: www.chicony.com.tw/test10-2.htm
Emp.: 7
Computer Peripheral Equipments Distr
S.I.C.: 5045
N.A.I.C.S.: 423430

Chicony Electronics (Mainland China II) Co., Ltd. (1)
San Zhong Gong Ye Qu
Qingxi, Dongguan, China
Tel.: (86) 769 7311688
Fax: (86) 769 7312680
Web Site: www.chicony.com.tw/aboutchicony.htm
Input Devices, Power Supplies, & Digital Image Products Mfr & Marketer
S.I.C.: 3575
N.A.I.C.S.: 334118
Jingguan Tong *(Gen Mgr)*

Chicony Electronics (SU Zou, Mainland China III) Co., Ltd. (1)
No 2379 Zhongshan North Road Songling Town
Wujiang, Jiangsu, China
Tel.: (86) 51263408988
Fax: (86) 51263409388
Web Site: www.chicony.com.tw/test10-2.htm#contactchicony
Computer Peripheral Equipment Distr
S.I.C.: 5045
N.A.I.C.S.: 423430

CHICONY POWER TECHNOLOGY CO., LTD.

No 2 Wuquan 5th Road Wu-Ku Industrial Park
Taipei, Hsien, Taiwan
Tel.: (886) 2 22995636
Fax: (886) 2 22995635
Web Site: www.chiconypower.com.tw
6412—(TAI)
Sls.: $811,533,634
Fiscal Year-end: 12/31/12

Business Description:
Electronic & Computer Parts & Components Mfr
S.I.C.: 3679
N.A.I.C.S.: 334419

Personnel:
Kent Hsu *(Chm)*

CHIEFTAIN METALS INC.

2 Bloor Street West Suite 2000
Toronto, ON, M4W 3E2, Canada
Tel.: (416) 479-5410
Fax: (416) 479-5420
E-Mail: info@chieftainmetals.com
Web Site: www.chieftainmetals.com
Year Founded: 2009
CFB—(TSX)
Int. Income: $38,385
Assets: $28,045,493
Liabilities: $19,365,355
Net Worth: $8,680,139
Earnings: ($8,515,247)
Fiscal Year-end: 09/30/13

Business Description:
Zinc, Copper, Lead, Gold & Silver Mining Services
S.I.C.: 1099
N.A.I.C.S.: 212299

Personnel:
Victor P. Wyprysky *(Founder, Chm, Pres & CEO)*
Pompeyo Gallardo *(CFO)*
Keith Boyle *(COO)*
Peter F. Chodos *(Exec VP-Corp Dev)*

Board of Directors:
Victor P. Wyprysky
Larry Philip Fontaine
Raymond Mah
James R. Pickell
Patrick Raleigh
Kenneth Sangster
Richard S. Sutin
Edward Alfred Yurkowski

Transfer Agent:
Equity Financial Trust Company
200 University Avenue Suite 400
Toronto, ON, Canada

CHIEN SHING STAINLESS STEEL CO., LTD.

No 222 Industry Rd Hsiao Pyi Li
Madou, Tainan, Taiwan
Tel.: (886) 65703271
Fax: (886) 65700296
E-Mail: service@msa.csss.com.tw
Web Site: www.csssc.com.tw
2025—(TAI)
Sales Range: $75-99.9 Million

Business Description:
Stainless Steel Mfr
S.I.C.: 3312
N.A.I.C.S.: 331110

Personnel:
Shih-Tang Yeh *(Chm & Gen Mgr)*

CHIESI FARMACEUTICI SPA

Via Palermo 26/A
43122 Parma, Italy
Tel.: (39) 5212791
Fax: (39) 0521774468
E-Mail: info@chiesigroup.com
Web Site: www.chiesigroup.com
Year Founded: 1935
Sales Range: $1-4.9 Billion
Emp.: 3,737

Business Description:
Pharmaceutical Mfr
S.I.C.: 2834
N.A.I.C.S.: 325412

Personnel:
Alberto Chiesi *(Pres & CEO)*

Division:

Chiesi Farmaceutical Italia (1)
Via Palermo 26/A
43122 Parnell, Italy
Tel.: (39) 05212791
E-Mail: info@chiesigroup.com
Pharmaceutical Mfr
S.I.C.: 2834
N.A.I.C.S.: 325412

U.S. Subsidiaries:

Chiesi Pharmaceuticals Inc. (1)
9605 Metical Central Dr
Rockville, MD 20850
Tel.: (301) 424-2661
Fax: (301) 424-2924
E-Mail: info@chiesiusa.com
Web Site: www.chiesi.com
Emp.: 10
Pharmaceutical Mfr
S.I.C.: 2834
N.A.I.C.S.: 325412
Erika Panico *(Mng Dir)*

Cornerstone Therapeutics, Inc. (1)
1255 Crescent Green Dr Ste 250
Cary, NC 27518 DE
Tel.: (919) 678-6611
Fax: (919) 678-6599
E-Mail: investor.relations@crtx.com
Web Site: www.crtx.com
Rev.: $116,084,000
Assets: $369,375,000
Liabilities: $203,202,000
Net Worth: $166,173,000
Earnings: ($11,888,000)
Emp.: 105
Fiscal Year-end: 12/31/12
Asthma Prevention & Therapeutic Products Mfr
S.I.C.: 2834
N.A.I.C.S.: 325412
Kenneth McBean *(Pres)*
Craig A. Collard *(CEO)*
Alastair S. McEwan *(CFO & Treas)*

Subsidiaries:

Cornerstone BioPharma, Inc. (2)
1255 Crescent Green Dr Ste 250
Cary, NC 27518-8123
Tel.: (919) 678-6507
Fax: (888) 466-6503
Pharmaceutical Products Mfr
S.I.C.: 2834
N.A.I.C.S.: 325412
Craig A. Collard *(Pres & CEO)*

Non-U.S. Subsidiaries:

Asche Chiesi GmbH (1)
Gasstrasse 6
22761 Hamburg, Germany DE
Tel.: (49) 40897240
Fax: (49) 4089724212
E-Mail: info@chiese.de
Web Site: www.asche-chiesi.de
Emp.: 392
Mfr. of Pharmaceuticals
S.I.C.: 2834
N.A.I.C.S.: 325412

Chiesi Espana S.A. (1)
Berlin 38-48 7a Planta
08029 Barcelona, Spain
Tel.: (34) 93494800
Fax: (34) 934948030
Web Site: www.chiesigroup.com
Pharmaceutical Mfr
S.I.C.: 2834
N.A.I.C.S.: 325412

Chiesi Pharmaceuticals (Pvt) Limited (1)
57-A Block G Gulberg III
Lahore, Pakistan
Tel.: (92) 425838174
Fax: (92) 425836786
Web Site: www.chiesigroup.com
Pharmaceutical Mfr
S.I.C.: 2834
N.A.I.C.S.: 325412

Chiesi S.A. (1)
Immeuble le Doublon
11 Ave Dubonnet, 92400 Courbevoie, France
Tel.: (33) 147688899
Fax: (33) 143340279
E-Mail: courbevoie@chiesifrance.com
Web Site: www.chiesifrance.com
Emp.: 150
Pharmaceutical Mfr
S.I.C.: 2834
N.A.I.C.S.: 325412
Eric Setalot *(Mng Dir)*

Farmalab Industrias Quiimicas e Farmaceuticas Ltda (1)
Alexandre Dumas 1658 1213 floor
Chacara Santo Antonio, 04717-004 Sao Paulo, Brazil

Tel.: (55) 01130952300
Fax: (55) 1130952350
Web Site: www.farmalabchiesi.com.br
Pharmaceutical Mfr
S.I.C.: 2834
N.A.I.C.S.: 325412

Torrex Chiesi Pharma GmbH (1)
Gonzagagasse 16/16
10101 Vienna, Austria
Tel.: (43) 140739190
Fax: (43) 14073919999
E-Mail: office.at@chiesi.com
Web Site: www.chiesi-cee.com
Emp.: 80
Pharmaceutical Mfr
S.I.C.: 2834
N.A.I.C.S.: 325412
Hrrer Wolftang *(Gen Mgr)*

Trinity-Chiesi Pharmaceuticals Ltd. (1)
Cheadle Royal Business Park
Highfield, Cheadle, SK8 3GY, United Kingdom UK
Tel.: (44) 1614885555
Fax: (44) 1614885566
Web Site: www.chiesi.uk.com
Pharmaceutical Mfr
S.I.C.: 2834
N.A.I.C.S.: 325412

CHIGO HOLDING LIMITED

Shengli Industrial Park Lishui Town
Foshan, Guangdong, China 528244
Tel.: (86) 75785668114
Fax: (86) 75785682389
E-Mail: sale@chigogroup.com
Web Site: www.chigogroup.com
449—(HKG)
Sls.: $1,398,168,154
Assets: $1,651,359,645
Liabilities: $1,216,711,575
Net Worth: $434,648,070
Earnings: $15,639,418
Emp.: 14,066
Fiscal Year-end: 12/31/12

Business Description:
Air Conditioner Mfr
S.I.C.: 3585
N.A.I.C.S.: 333415

Personnel:
Xinghao Li *(Founder, Chm & CEO)*
Hon Man Leung *(Sec)*

Board of Directors:
Xinghao Li
Xiaojiang Ding
Xiaosi Fu
Xingke Huang
Junchu Wan
Xiaoming Zhang
Zuyi Zheng

Royal Bank of Canada Trust Company (Cayman) Limited
4th Floor Royal Bank House 24 Shedden Road
PO Box 1586
Georgetown, Cayman Islands

CHIH LIEN INDUSTRIAL CO., LTD.

No 480 Chung Shing Road
327 Shin Wu Hsiang, Taoyuan, Taiwan
Tel.: (886) 34772797
Fax: (886) 34870042
E-Mail: sales@mail.chihlien.com.tw
Web Site: www.chihlien.com.tw
2024—(TAI)
Sales Range: $75-99.9 Million
Emp.: 251

Business Description:
Steel Wire & Steel Bar Mfr
S.I.C.: 3312
N.A.I.C.S.: 331110

Personnel:
Chun Xing Liu *(Pres & Gen Mgr)*

Plant:

Chih Lien Industrial Co., Ltd. - Shin Wu Factory (1)
No 480 Chung Shing Road
Shin Wu Hsiang, Taoyuan, 327, Taiwan
Tel.: (886) 34772797
Fax: (886) 34870042
Emp.: 155
Steel Wire & Bar Mfr
S.I.C.: 3399
N.A.I.C.S.: 331110
Chun Shin Liu *(Gen Mgr)*

Non-U.S. Plant:

Chih Lien Industrial Co., Ltd. - Dong Guan Factory (1)
Chih Lien Industrial Zone Wu Sha Sec
Zhen An Road
Chang An Town, Dongguan, Guangdong, China
Tel.: (86) 76985312723
Fax: (86) 76985416259
Emp.: 96
Steel Wire & Bar Mfr
S.I.C.: 3399
N.A.I.C.S.: 331110

CHIHO-TIANDE GROUP LTD

48 Wang Lok Street
Yuen Long Industrial Estate, Hong Kong, China (Hong Kong)
Tel.: (852) 2587 7700
Fax: (852) 2587 7799
E-Mail: info@chiho-tiande.com
Web Site: www.chiho-tiande.com
976—(HKG)
Rev.: $1,057,738,423
Assets: $670,795,192
Liabilities: $403,411,951
Net Worth: $267,383,241
Earnings: $5,074,311
Emp.: 274
Fiscal Year-end: 12/31/12

Business Description:
Metal Scrap Recycling Services
S.I.C.: 5051
N.A.I.C.S.: 423510

Personnel:
Ankong Fang *(Chm & CEO)*
Paul Wan Hoi Chow *(CFO)*
Miu Cheung Yu *(Sec)*
Guopei Ding *(Sr VP-Mgmt & Admin)*

Board of Directors:
Ankong Fang
Liyong Gu
Xikui Li
Michael Charles Lion
Yu Loke
Stephanus Maria van Ooijen
Jingdong Zhang

Legal Counsel:
Zhong Lun Law Firm
36-37/F SK Tower 6A Jianguomenwai Avenue
Chaoyang District
Beijing, China

Stephenson Harwood
35th Floor Bank of China Tower 1 Garden Road
Central, China (Hong Kong)

Conyers Dill & Pearman
Cricket Square, Hutchins Drive P.O. Box 2681
KY1-1111 Georgetown, Cayman Islands

Codan Trust Company (Cayman) Limited
Cricket Square Hutchins Drive
PO Box 2681
Georgetown, Grand Cayman, Cayman Islands

Transfer Agents:
Computershare Hong Kong Investor Services Limited
Rooms 1712-1716 17/F Hopewell Centre 183
Queen's Road East
Wanchai, China (Hong Kong)
Tel.: (852) 2862 8628
Fax: (852) 2865 0990

Codan Trust Company (Cayman) Limited
Cricket Square Hutchins Drive
PO Box 2681
Georgetown, Grand Cayman, Cayman Islands

CHIIKISHINBUNSHA CO., LTD.

678-2 Takazu Yachiyo-shi
Chiba, 276-0036, Japan
Tel.: (81) 474803377
Fax: (81) 47 4803399
E-Mail: info@chiikinews.co.jp
Web Site: www.chiikinews.co.jp/
Year Founded: 1984
2164—(TKS)
Sales Range: $10-24.9 Million
Emp.: 120

Business Description:
Newspaper Publisher; Advertising Services
S.I.C.: 2711
N.A.I.C.S.: 511110

Personnel:
Yukifumi Chikama *(Pres)*

CHILE MINING TECHNOLOGIES INC.

Jorge Canning 1410
Nunoa, Santiago, Chile
Tel.: (56) 2 8131087
LVEN—(OTC OTCB)
Sls.: $261,089
Assets: $7,717,564
Liabilities: $11,824,890
Net Worth: ($4,107,326)
Earnings: ($4,385,310)
Emp.: 31
Fiscal Year-end: 03/31/13

Business Description:
Copper Mining Services
S.I.C.: 1021
N.A.I.C.S.: 212234

Personnel:
James Groh *(Chm)*
Jorge Osvaldo Orellana *(Pres, CEO & Sec)*
Gerard Pascale *(CFO & Treas)*

Board of Directors:
James Groh
Pierre Galoppi
Jorge Fernando Pizarro Arriagada
William E. Thomson

CHILIME HYDROPOWER COMPANY LIMITED

Lazimpat
PO Box 25210
Kathmandu, Nepal
Tel.: (977) 1 4439163
Fax: (977) 1 4443077
E-Mail: chpcl@wlink.com.np
Web Site: www.chilime.com.np
Year Founded: 1996
CHCL—(NEP)

Business Description:
Hydropower Generation Services
S.I.C.: 4911
N.A.I.C.S.: 221111

Personnel:
B. C. Teeka Ram *(Chm)*
Kul Man Ghising *(Mng Dir)*
Narayan Prasad Achrya *(Acct Officer)*
Shree Raj Bajracharya *(Asst Computer Officer)*
Deepak Raj Panta *(Admin Officer)*
Bidur Bahadur Dhungana *(Sec)*

Board of Directors:
B. C. Teeka Ram
Lila Nath Bhattrai
Tulasi Ram Dhakal
Bidur Bahadur Dhungana
Kul Man Ghising
Badri Nath Roka
Jayandra Shrestha
Mahendra Lal Shrestha
Yam Kumar Shrestha
Phrupu Tenjen Tamang

CHILISIN ELECTRONICS CORP.

No 29 Ln 301 Dexing Rd Hukou Township
Hsin-chu, 303, Taiwan
Tel.: (886) 35992646
Fax: (886) 35999176
E-Mail: sales@chilisin.com.tw
Web Site: www.chilisin.com.tw
2456—(TAI)
Sls.: $122,052,950
Assets: $194,626,402
Liabilities: $95,806,003
Net Worth: $98,820,399
Earnings: $8,790,721
Fiscal Year-end: 12/31/12

Business Description:
Magnetic Materials & Inductors Mfr
S.I.C.: 3677
N.A.I.C.S.: 334416

Personnel:
Pierre Chen *(Chm & Pres)*
Yuan-Ho Lai *(Vice Chm)*
Hweijan Lee *(Vice Chm)*
Hellen Chou *(CFO)*

Board of Directors:
Pierre Chen
David Chang
Yuan-Ho Lai
Hweijan Lee
Victor C. Wang

Supervisory Board of Directors:
Dora Chang
Yung-Tu Wei

Transfer Agent:
MasterLink Securities Corporation
6F 97 Section 2 Tun Hua South Road
Taipei, Taiwan

Non-U.S. Subsidiaries:

Chilisin Asia Investment Limited (1)
Dongyang Trebellepark 903ho 1598-1
Kwanyang-dong
Dongan-gu, Anyang, Kyunggi-do, 430-010, Korea (South)
Tel.: (82) 313848433
Fax: (82) 31 436 9391
Electronic Components Distr
S.I.C.: 5065
N.A.I.C.S.: 423690

Chilisin Electronics Singapore Pte. Ltd. (1)
19 Woodlands Industrial Park E1 03-07
Singapore, Singapore SG
Tel.: (65) 68921191
Fax: (65) 67606760
E-Mail: sales@chilisin.com
Web Site: www.chilisin.com.sg
Electronic Components Mfr
S.I.C.: 3676
N.A.I.C.S.: 334416

Chilisin International Ltd. (1)
Units 1-3 7-10 8F Prosperity Centre 25
Chong Yip Street
Kwun Tong, Kowloon, China (Hong Kong)
Tel.: (852) 26871975
Fax: (852) 2687 1978
E-Mail: mon8@chilisin.biz.com.hk
Web Site: www.chilisin.com.tw/index.php?_Page=msg&md=news&id=49&_lang=E
Electronic Components Mfr
S.I.C.: 3676
N.A.I.C.S.: 334416

Dongguan Chilisin Electronics Co., Ltd. (1)
Yuliangwei Administration Area
Qingzi Town, Dongguan, Guangdong, 523000, China
Tel.: (86) 76987730251
Fax: (86) 76987730232
E-Mail: cect@chilisin.com.tw
Inductors Mfr
S.I.C.: 3675
N.A.I.C.S.: 334416

CHILTERN INTERNATIONAL LIMITED
171 Bath Rd
Slough, Berks, SL1 4AA, United Kingdom
Tel.: (44) 1753512000
Fax: (44) 1753511116
E-Mail: info@chiltern.com
Web Site: www.chiltern.com
Year Founded: 1982
Emp.: 150
Business Description:
Data Management, Medical Writing & Clinical Research
S.I.C.: 8731
N.A.I.C.S.: 541712
Personnel:
Jim Esinhart *(CEO)*
Aize Smink *(COO)*
Tim Burrows *(Sr Officer-Regulatory Affairs)*
Sharon Moore *(Exec VP-Global Medical & Regulatory Affairs)*

CHIMATA GOLD CORP.
1250 West Hastings Street
Vancouver, BC, V6E 2M4, Canada
Tel.: (604) 687-0879
Fax: (604) 408-9301
Year Founded: 2010
CAT—(TSXV)
Business Description:
Gold Mining
S.I.C.: 1041
N.A.I.C.S.: 212221
Personnel:
Thomas Robert Tough *(Pres & CEO)*
Larry Tsang *(CFO)*
Board of Directors:
Sonny Janda
Gurdeep Johal
Thomas Robert Tough

CHIMCOMPLEX S.A. BORZESTI
3 Industriilor St
Onesti
601124 Bacau, Romania
Tel.: (40) 234302006
Fax: (40) 234302102
E-Mail: marketing@chimcomplex.ro
Web Site: www.chimcomplex.ro
CHOB—(BUC)
Sales Range: $50-74.9 Million
Business Description:
Organic Products & Chemical Producer
S.I.C.: 2911
N.A.I.C.S.: 324110
Personnel:
Virgiliu Bancila *(Pres-Admin)*

CHIME COMMUNICATIONS PLC
Southside 6th Floor 105 Victoria Street
Victoria, London, SW1E 6QT, United Kingdom
Tel.: (44) 20 7096 5888
Fax: (44) 20 7096 5889
Web Site: www.chime.plc.uk
CHW—(LSE)
Rev.: $543,645,314
Assets: $439,224,238
Liabilities: $191,913,741
Net Worth: $247,310,497
Earnings: $211,625
Emp.: 1,732
Fiscal Year-end: 12/31/12
Business Description:
Holding Company; Advertising Agencies
S.I.C.: 6719
N.A.I.C.S.: 551112
Personnel:
Mervyn Davies *(Chm)*
Christopher Satterthwaite *(CEO)*
Mark Smith *(COO & Fin Dir)*
Nick Lamb *(Chm-Chime Insight & Engagement)*
Kevin Murray *(Chm-The Good Relations Group)*
Crispin Beale *(CEO-CIE)*
Adrian Coleman *(CEO-VCCP Partnership)*
Jim Glover *(CEO-CSM Sports & Entertainment)*
Joanne Parker *(CEO-Teamspirit)*
David Rowley *(CEO-Open Health)*
Robert Davison *(Sec)*
Board of Directors:
Mervyn Davies
Richard Alston
Martin Glenn
Rodger Hughes
Vin Murria
Paul Richardson
Christopher Satterthwaite
Mark Smith
Chris Sweetland
Legal Counsel:
Slaughter & May
One Bunhill Row
London, EC1Y 8YY, United Kingdom
Tel.: (44) 20 7600 1200
Fax: (44) 20 7600 0289

Subsidiaries:

BMT **(1)**
4th Floor Holborn Gate 330 High Holborn
London, WC1V 7QG, United Kingdom UK
Tel.: (44) 20 7861 3165
E-Mail: info@bmt.uk.com
Web Site: www.bmt.uk.com
Emp.: 22
Advertising Agency
S.I.C.: 7311
N.A.I.C.S.: 541810
Simon Melville *(Mng Dir)*

Bullnose Limited **(1)**
Duval House High Street
Harmondsworth, UB7 0BT, United Kingdom
Tel.: (44) 20 8754 8706
Fax: (44) 20 8759 5395
Web Site: www.bullnose.co.uk
Emp.: 5
Graphic Design Services
S.I.C.: 7336
N.A.I.C.S.: 541430

Chime Insight & Engagement Limited **(1)**
4th Floor Holborn Gate 26 Southampton Buildings
London, WC2A 1AH, United Kingdom UK
Tel.: (44) 20 7861 2540
Fax: (44) 20 7861 3081
E-Mail: enquiries@cie.uk.com
Web Site: www.cie.uk.com
Emp.: 18
Methodology Neutral Research Services
S.I.C.: 8731
N.A.I.C.S.: 541712
Nick Lamb *(Chm)*
Crispin Beale *(CEO)*
Cory Inglis *(Partner)*

Corporate Citizenship Limited **(1)**
5th Floor Holborn Gate 330 High Holborn
London, WC1V 7QG, United Kingdom
Tel.: (44) 20 7861 1616
Fax: (44) 20 7861 3908
Web Site: www.corporate-citizenship.com
Emp.: 3
Public Relation Agency Services
S.I.C.: 8742
N.A.I.C.S.: 541611
Amanda Jordan *(Dir-Chair & Founding)*

De Facto Communications Ltd. **(1)**
330 High Holborn
London, WC1V 7QD, United Kingdom UK
Tel.: (44) 20 7861 3838
Fax: (44) 20 7861 3839
E-Mail: info@defacto.com
Web Site: www.defacto.com
Advertising Agency
S.I.C.: 7311
N.A.I.C.S.: 541810
Kevin Payne *(Co-Founder & Dir-Healthcare)*
Richard Anderson *(CEO-De Facto Comm)*

Essentially Sports Marketing Limited **(1)**
Southside 6th Floor 105 Victoria Street
London, SW1E 6QT, United Kingdom UK
Tel.: (44) 20 7820 7000
Fax: (44) 20 7820 7001
E-Mail: enquiries@essentiallygroup.com
Web Site: www.essentiallygroup.com
Sales Range: $10-24.9 Million
Emp.: 86
Sports Marketing Management
S.I.C.: 7311
N.A.I.C.S.: 541810
Bart Campbell *(CEO)*
Matthew Vandrau *(Mng Dir)*
Dwight Mighty *(COO)*

Non-U.S. Subsidiaries:

Essentially Athlete Management (Rugby and Cricket) Limited **(2)**
Level 2 2 Heather Street
Parnell, Auckland, 1052, New Zealand
Tel.: (64) 99214251
Fax: (64) 3576800
Athlete Management Consulting Services
S.I.C.: 8748
N.A.I.C.S.: 541618

Essentially Australia **(2)**
Ste 231, Fox Studios Australia, Driver Ave
Sydney, NSW, 2021, Australia
Tel.: (61) 2 8235 2796
Fax: (61) 2 8235 2763
E-Mail: craig.nettelbeck@essentiallygroup.com
Web Site: www.essentiallygroup.com
Advertising Agency
S.I.C.: 7311
N.A.I.C.S.: 541810
Craig Nettlebeck *(Gen Mgr)*

Frontiers Group-China **(2)**
169 Mount Rd Unit 2 Room 105
Shanghai, 200031, China
Tel.: (86) 21 6218 1212
Fax: (86) 21 5298 5037
Web Site: www.frontiersgroup.com
Emp.: 10
Advertising Agency
S.I.C.: 7311
N.A.I.C.S.: 541810
Louise Ardagh *(CEO)*

Frontiers Group-India **(2)**
3321 12th A Main 7th Cross HAL II Stage
Indiranagar, Bengaluru, 560 008, India
Tel.: (91) 80 5115 4932
Fax: (91) 80 5115 4933
E-Mail: info@sportingfrontiersindia.com
Web Site: www.frontiersgroupindia.com
Emp.: 10
Advertising Agency
S.I.C.: 7311
N.A.I.C.S.: 541810
Abhay Mehta *(CEO)*
Patrick Smith *(CEO)*
Martin Thomas *(CFO)*

Kaelo Worldwide Media **(2)**
Ground Fl Unit 9 Pinewood Office Park
Riley Rd
Woodmead, 2128 Johannesburg, South Africa
Tel.: (27) 11 234 1195
Fax: (27) 11 234 1204
E-Mail: kelvin@kaelowm.com
Web Site: www.kaelowm.com
Advertising Agency
S.I.C.: 7311
N.A.I.C.S.: 541810
Sandile Koza *(Mng Dir)*

Fast Track Events Limited **(1)**
Fast Track Southside 6th Floor 105 Victoria Street
London, SW1E 6QT, United Kingdom
Tel.: (44) 207 593 5200
Fax: (44) 207 593 5201
Web Site: www.fast-track-events.com
Emp.: 17
Event Management Services
S.I.C.: 7999
N.A.I.C.S.: 711310
Andy Westlake *(CEO)*
Michelle Dite *(Mng Partner)*
Steve Chisholm *(Partner)*
Jon Ridgeon *(Partner)*

Fast Track Sailing Limited **(1)**
One Brewers Green Buckingham Gate
London, SW1H 0RH, United Kingdom
Tel.: (44) 207 593 5200
E-Mail: info@fasttracksailing.com
Web Site: www.fasttracksailing.com
Emp.: 250
Sports Marketing Consultancy Services
S.I.C.: 8742
N.A.I.C.S.: 541613

FIL Market Research Limited **(1)**
Facts International Unit 3
Ashford, Kent, TN24 8FL, United Kingdom
Tel.: (44) 1233 637000
Fax: (44) 1233 626950
Management Consulting Services
S.I.C.: 8748
N.A.I.C.S.: 541618
Crispin Beale *(CEO)*

Good Relations **(1)**
Holborn Gate 26 Southampton Bldg
London, WC2A 1PQ, United Kingdom
Tel.: (44) 20 7861 3030
Fax: (44) 20 7861 3131
E-Mail: afossey@goodrelations.co.uk
Web Site: www.goodrelations.co.uk
S.I.C.: 8743
N.A.I.C.S.: 541820
Theresa-Ann Dunleavy *(CEO)*

Insight Marketing & Communications Limited **(1)**
Pinewood Court Larkwood Way
Macclesfield, Cheshire, SK10 2XR, United Kingdom
Tel.: (44) 1625 500 800
Fax: (44) 1625 500 900
E-Mail: info@insightmkt.com
Web Site: www.insightmkt.com
Emp.: 45
Advertising Agency Services
S.I.C.: 7311
N.A.I.C.S.: 541810
Chris Warham *(Mng Dir)*

Opinion Leader Research Limited **(1)**
4th Floor Holborn Gate 26 Southampton Buildings
London, WC2A 1AH, United Kingdom
Tel.: (44) 20 7861 3080
Fax: (44) 20 7861 3081
E-Mail: enquiries@opinionleader.co.uk
Web Site: www.opinionleader.co.uk
Emp.: 5
Marketing Research Services
S.I.C.: 8732
N.A.I.C.S.: 541910
Crispin Beale *(CEO)*
Mark Squires *(Grp Dir-Ops)*

PMP Legacy Limited **(1)**
Southside 105 Victoria Street
London, SW1E 6QT, United Kingdom
Tel.: (44) 7887 546495
E-Mail: info@pmplegacy.com
Web Site: www.pmplegacy.com
Sports Management Consulting Services
S.I.C.: 8748
N.A.I.C.S.: 541618
Cathy Livock *(Dir-Consulting)*

Pure Media Limited **(1)**
78 Cowcross Street
London, EC1M 6HE, United Kingdom UK
Tel.: (44) 207 438 9429
Fax: (44) 207 836 9289
E-Mail: info@puremedia.co.uk
Web Site: www.puremedia.co.uk
Sales Range: Less than $1 Million
Emp.: 7
Media Buying Services
S.I.C.: 7319
N.A.I.C.S.: 541830
Hugh Walker *(Dir-Media)*

Rare Corporate Design **(1)**
16-24 Underwood St
London, WC1V 7QD, United Kingdom
Tel.: (44) 84522683
Fax: (44) 207 861 2472
E-Mail: info@rarecorporate.co.uk
Web Site: www.rarecorporate.co.uk

Emp.: 15
S.I.C.: 7311
N.A.I.C.S.: 541810
Peter Higgins *(Mng Dir)*

Resonate (1)
Holborn Gates 5th Floor 330 High Holborn
London, WC1V 7QG, United Kingdom
Tel.: (44) 207 861 2525
Fax: (44) 207 861 2526
E-Mail: noise@resonate.uk.com
Web Site: www.resonate.uk.com
Sales Range: $10-24.9 Million
Emp.: 18
S.I.C.: 8743
N.A.I.C.S.: 541820
Michael Frohlich *(Mng Dir)*

The Sports Business Limited (1)
3rd Flr 231 St Vincent Street
Glasgow, G2 5QY, United Kingdom
Tel.: (44) 141 332 9003
Fax: (44) 141 332 9006
E-Mail:
Web Site: www.fasttrackagency.com
Emp.: 4
Sports Marketing Consulting Services
S.I.C.: 8742
N.A.I.C.S.: 541613
Alan Ferguson *(Mng Dir)*

Stuart Higgins Communications Limited (1)
Southside 6th Floor 105 Victoria Street
London, SW1E 6QT, United Kingdom
Tel.: (44) 207 096 5814
E-Mail: stuart@stuart-higgins.com
Web Site: www.stuart-higgins.com
Public Relations Agency Services
S.I.C.: 8743
N.A.I.C.S.: 541820
Stuart Higgins *(Mng Dir)*

Sunesis (1)
Harvard House Summerhouse Ln
Harmondsworth, Middlesex, UB7 0AW, United Kingdom
Tel.: (44) 20 8564 6398
Fax: (44) 20 8564 6354
E-Mail: info@sunesis-global.com
Web Site: www.sunesis-global.com
Emp.: 30
S.I.C.: 8743
N.A.I.C.S.: 541820
David Rossiter *(Mng Partner)*

Teamspirit Limited (1)
78 Cowcross St
Farringdon, London, EC1M 6HE, United Kingdom UK
Tel.: (44) 20 7438 9400
Fax: (44) 20 7438 9420
E-Mail: info@teamspirit.uk.com
Web Site: www.teamspirit.uk.com
Emp.: 50
Advertising Agency
S.I.C.: 7311
N.A.I.C.S.: 541810
Joanne Parker *(CEO)*

Subsidiary:

Teamspirit Brand Limited (2)
78 Cowcross Street
Farringdon, London, EC1M 6HE, United Kingdom
Tel.: (44) 20 7364 4100
Fax: (44) 20 7360 7833
E-Mail: nportet@teamspiritbrand.co.uk
Web Site: www.teamspiritbrand.co.uk
Emp.: 60
Financial Management Services
S.I.C.: 6211
N.A.I.C.S.: 523999

Tree (London) Limited (1)
4th Floor Holborn Gate 26 Southampton Buildings
London, WC2A 1AH, United Kingdom
Tel.: (44) 2078612828
Fax: (44) 2078613991
E-Mail: info@treelondon.com
Web Site: www.treelondon.com
Market Research & Data Analysis
S.I.C.: 8732
N.A.I.C.S.: 541910
Matthew Bayfield *(Mng Partner)*
Steve Mattey *(Mng Partner)*
Sharon Last *(Mng Dir)*

TTA Public Relations Ltd. (1)
26 Southampton Buildings
London, W1J7RH, United Kingdom
Tel.: (44) 207 886 0300
Fax: (44) 207 351 7733
E-Mail: info@ttagroup.co.uk
Web Site: www.ttagroup.co.uk
Emp.: 45
S.I.C.: 8743
N.A.I.C.S.: 541820
Tim Reed *(Dir-PR)*

VCCP Limited (1)
Greencoat House Francis Street Victoria
London, SW1P 1DH, United Kingdom UK
Tel.: (44) 20 7592 9831
Fax: (44) 20 7592 7465
E-Mail: info@vccp.com
Web Site: www.vccp.com
Emp.: 350
Advertising Agency
S.I.C.: 7311
N.A.I.C.S.: 541810
Charles Vallance *(Chm & Partner)*
Adrian Coleman *(Partner & Grp CEO)*
Rooney Carruthers *(Founding Partner)*
Ian Priest *(Founding Partner)*
Julian Douglas *(Vice Chm)*
Michael Sugden *(CEO)*
David Boscawen *(Grp Mng Dir)*
Andrew Peake *(Mng Dir)*
Maggie Frost *(CFO)*

Subsidiaries:

VCCP Blue Limited (2)
5th Floor Greencoat House Francis Street
London, SW1P 1DH, United Kingdom
Tel.: (44) 20 7592 7538
Fax: (44) 20 7592 7465
E-Mail: cliffh@vccpblue.com
Web Site: www.vccpblue.com
Advertising Agency Services
S.I.C.: 7311
N.A.I.C.S.: 541810

VCCP Digital Limited (2)
Greencoat House Francis Street
London, SW1P 1DH, United Kingdom
Tel.: (44) 2075929331
Fax: (44) 2075927465
Web Site: www.vccpdigital.co.uk
Digital Advertising Services
S.I.C.: 7319
N.A.I.C.S.: 541890
Adrian Coleman *(Gen Mgr)*

VCCP Health Limited (2)
Greencoat House Francis Street
Victoria, London, SW1P 1DH, United Kingdom
Tel.: (44) 20 7592 9331
Fax: (44) 20 7592 7465
E-Mail: info@vccp.com
Web Site: www.vccphealth.com
Pharmaceutical Advertising Agency Services
S.I.C.: 7311
N.A.I.C.S.: 541810
Paul Phillips *(Mng Dir)*

VCCP Search Limited (2)
Greencoat House Francis Street
Victoria, London, SW1P 1DH, United Kingdom
Tel.: (44) 207 592 2992
Fax: (44) 207 592 7465
E-Mail: hello@vccpsearch.com
Web Site: www.vccpsearch.com
Emp.: 50
Advertising Agency Services
S.I.C.: 7311
N.A.I.C.S.: 541810
Paul Wolferstan *(Partner & Head-SEO)*
Kirsten Pistor *(Partner & Dir-Client Svcs)*
Paul Mead *(Mng Dir)*
David Midgley *(CTO)*

Non-U.S. Subsidiaries:

VCCP GmbH (2)
Swinemunder Strasse 121
10435 Berlin, Germany
Tel.: (49) 30 284897 27
Fax: (49) 30 284 897 95
E-Mail: berlin@vccp.com
Web Site: www.vccp.de
Emp.: 55
Advertising Agency Services
S.I.C.: 7311
N.A.I.C.S.: 541810
Markus Wieser *(Mng Dir)*

VCCP s.r.o. (2)
Ostrovni 30
110 00 Prague, Czech Republic
Tel.: (420) 234 648 801
Web Site: www.vccp.com
Emp.: 7
Advertising Agency Services
S.I.C.: 7311
N.A.I.C.S.: 541810
Helena de la Barre *(Mng Dir)*

U.S. Subsidiary:

Just Marketing, Inc. (1)
10960 Bennett Pkwy
Zionsville, IN 46077 DE
Tel.: (317) 344-1900
Fax: (317) 344-1901
E-Mail: info@justmarketing.com
Web Site: www.justmarketing.com
Sales Range: $10-24.9 Million
Emp.: 120
Motor Sports Industry Corporate Marketing Services
S.I.C.: 7999
N.A.I.C.S.: 711320
Zak Brown *(Founder & CEO)*

Non-U.S. Subsidiary:

Just Marketing International Ltd. (2)
Second Floor 171 175 Brompton Road
Knightsbridge, London, SW3 1NF, United Kingdom
Tel.: (44) 2075905850
Fax: (44) 2075843686
Web Site: www.justmarketing.com
Motor Sports Marketing & Promotional Services
S.I.C.: 7999
N.A.I.C.S.: 711310

Non-U.S. Subsidiary:

MMK Markt- & Medien-Kommunikation GmbH (1)
An der Alster 47
20099 Hamburg, Germany De
Tel.: (49) 40 31 80 4 0
Fax: (49) 4031804199
E-Mail: mmk@mmk-pr.de
Web Site: www.mmk-pr.de
Emp.: 15
Public Relations Agency
S.I.C.: 8743
N.A.I.C.S.: 541820
Lars Burmeister *(Mng Dir)*

CHIMEI INNOLUX CORPORATION

(See Under Innolux Corporation)

CHIMIMPORT AD

2 Stefan Karadja Str
Sofia, 1000, Bulgaria
Tel.: (359) 2 9817420
E-Mail: info@chimimport.bg
Web Site: www.chimimport.bg
6C4—(BUL)
Rev.: $331,669,742
Assets: $4,099,671,276
Liabilities: $2,977,183,832
Net Worth: $1,122,487,444
Earnings: $78,578,578
Emp.: 6,207
Fiscal Year-end: 12/31/12

Business Description:
Investment Holding Company
S.I.C.: 6719
N.A.I.C.S.: 551112

Personnel:
Tsvetan Botev *(Chm-Mgmt Bd)*
Alexander Kerezov *(Deputy Chm-Mgmt Bd)*
Ivo Kamenov Georgiev *(Member-Mgmt Bd & Exec Dir)*
Marin Mitev *(Member-Mgmt Bd & Exec Dir)*
Miroliub Panchev Ivanov *(Member-Mgmt Bd)*
Nicola Mishev *(Member-Mgmt Bd)*

Supervisory Board of Directors:
Mariana Angelova Bazhdarova
Miroliub Panchev Ivanov
Marin Mitev

Subsidiaries:

Bulgaria Air AD (1)
1 Brussels Blvd Sofia Airport
Sofia, 1540, Bulgaria BG
Tel.: (359) 29373254
E-Mail: callfb@air.bg
Web Site: www.air.bg
Air Transportation Services
S.I.C.: 4512
N.A.I.C.S.: 481111
Nedyalko Delchinov *(Co-CEO)*
Yanko Georgiev *(Co-CEO)*

CCB Group EAD (1)
103 GS Rakovski Str
1086 Sofia, Bulgaria BG
Tel.: (359) 2 926 6107 (100%)
Bank Holding Company; Banking & Insurance Products & Services
S.I.C.: 6712
N.A.I.C.S.: 551111

Subsidiary:

Central Cooperative Bank Plc (2)
103 GS Rakovski Str
1086 Sofia, Bulgaria BG
Tel.: (359) 2 926 6107 (68.56%)
E-Mail: office@ccbank.bg
Web Site: www.ccbank.bg
4CF—(BUL)
Sales Range: $100-124.9 Million
Retail & Commercial Banking
S.I.C.: 6029
N.A.I.C.S.: 522110
Ivo Kamenov *(Chm-Supervisory Bd)*
Aleksander Vodenicharov *(Chm-Mgmt Bd)*
Tsvetan Botev *(Deputy Chm-Mgmt Bd)*
Ivaylo Donchev *(Member-Mgmt Bd & Exec Dir)*
Georgi Konstantinov *(Member-Mgmt Bd & Exec Dir)*
Sava Stoynov *(Member-Mgmt Bd & Exec Dir)*
Aleksander Kerezov *(Member-Mgmt Bd)*
Tsvetanka Krumova *(Member-Mgmt Bd)*
Biser Slavkov *(Member-Mgmt Bd)*

Non-U.S. Subsidiary:

TatInvestBank ZAO (3)
ul Vishnevskogo 24
Tatarstan Republic
420043 Kazan, Russia RU
Tel.: (7) 843 238 0339 (55.91%)
Fax: (7) 843 238 0756
E-Mail: tib@tib.ru
Web Site: www.tib.ru
Retail, Commercial & Investment Banking
S.I.C.: 6029
N.A.I.C.S.: 522110
Stoyanov Deltcho Kolev *(Chm)*

CHIMIREC

5 Rue De L Extension
93440 Saint Denis, France
Tel.: (33) 149929765
Fax: (33) 149922309
E-Mail: info@chimirec.fr
Web Site: www.chimirec.fr
Sls.: $20,200,000
Emp.: 70

Business Description:
Scrap & Waste Mats
S.I.C.: 5093
N.A.I.C.S.: 423930

Personnel:
Jean Fixot *(Pres)*

CHIMPHARM JSC

(d/b/a SANTO)
Rashidova Street
160019 Shymkent, Kazakhstan
Tel.: (7) 7252560722
Fax: (7) 7252560533
E-Mail: santo@santo.kz
Web Site: www.santo.kz
CHFM—(KAZ)

Chimpharm JSC—(Continued)

Emp.: 1,000
Business Description:
Pharmaceutical Mfr
S.I.C.: 2834
N.A.I.C.S.: 325412
Personnel:
Omarov Kairat Ersentayevich *(Chm)*
Baigarin Rustam Shamilyevich *(Dir Gen)*
Board of Directors:
Omarov Kairat Ersentayevich
Baigarin Rustam Shamilyevich
Sharmanov Turegeldy Sharmanovich

CHIN POON INDUSTRIAL CO., LTD.

No 46 Nei-Tsuoh Street 3rd Lin
Nei-Tsuoh Village Lu-Chu, Taoyuan, Hsien, Taiwan 338
Tel.: (886) 3 322 2226
Fax: (886) 3 352 6641
E-Mail: sales@chinpoon.com.tw
Web Site: www.cppcb.com.tw
2355—(TAI)
Sls.: $605,014,967
Assets: $683,797,230
Liabilities: $253,274,746
Net Worth: $430,522,484
Earnings: $52,542,802
Fiscal Year-end: 12/31/12
Business Description:
Printed Circuit Boards Mfr
S.I.C.: 3672
N.A.I.C.S.: 334412
Personnel:
Vincent Huang *(Chm)*

CHIN TECK PLANTATIONS BERHAD

Suite 2B-3A-2 Block 2B Level 3A
Plaza Sentral Jalan Stesen Sentral 5
Kuala Lumpur Sentral, 50470 Kuala Lumpur, Malaysia
Tel.: (60) 322614633
Fax: (60) 322614733
E-Mail: enquiry@chinteck.com.my
Web Site: www.chinteck.com.my
CHINTEK—(KLS)
Rev.: $31,093,881
Assets: $193,283,988
Liabilities: $4,795,452
Net Worth: $188,488,536
Earnings: $7,556,238
Fiscal Year-end: 08/31/13
Business Description:
Oil Palms Cultivation & Palm Oil Mfr
S.I.C.: 0761
N.A.I.C.S.: 115115
Personnel:
Eng Chew Goh *(Chm)*
Kok Tiong Gan *(Sec)*
Board of Directors:
Eng Chew Goh
Kim Leng Gan
Lian Chin Gho
Beng Hwa Goh
Pock Ai Goh
Tju Kiang Goh
Wei Lei Goh
Yeok Beng Goh
Choon Keat Keong
Sit Po Sio
Aun Phui Wong

CHIN WELL HOLDINGS BERHAD

51-21-A Menara BHL Bank Jalan
Sultan Ahmad Shah
10050 Penang, Malaysia
Tel.: (60) 42108833
Fax: (60) 42108831
E-Mail: chinwell@chinwell.com.my
Web Site: www.chinwell.com.my
CHINWEL—(KLS)
Rev.: $151,462,739
Assets: $180,111,081
Liabilities: $47,308,886
Net Worth: $132,802,195
Earnings: $8,772,982
Fiscal Year-end: 06/30/13
Business Description:
Fasteners Mfr
S.I.C.: 3965
N.A.I.C.S.: 339993
Personnel:
Yung Chuan Tsai *(Mng Dir)*
Peng Loon Lee *(Co-Sec)*
Chiew Keem P'ng *(Co-Sec)*
Board of Directors:
Chien Ch'eng Lim
Onn Hafiz Ghazi
Eng Choon Ong
Chang Hsiu-Hsiang Tsai
Chia Ling Tsai
Yung Chuan Tsai
Peng Joo Ung

CHINA 3C GROUP

(Name Changed to YOSEN GROUP, INC.)

CHINA 3D DIGITAL ENTERTAINMENT LIMITED

7/F Zung Fu Industrial Building 1067
King's Road Quarry Bay
Hong Kong, China (Hong Kong)
Tel.: (852) 2892 7859
Fax: (852) 2898 8553
E-Mail: info@china3d8078.com
Web Site: www.china3d8078.com
8078—(DEU HKG)
Sls.: $9,028,821
Assets: $36,540,562
Liabilities: $5,179,406
Net Worth: $31,361,156
Earnings: ($2,700,600)
Emp.: 28
Fiscal Year-end: 06/30/13
Business Description:
Film Production Services
S.I.C.: 7812
N.A.I.C.S.: 512110
Personnel:
Stephen Shiu, Jr. *(Chm & CEO)*
Albert Wing Ho Lee *(Compliance Officer)*
Sophie Suk Fan Mak *(Sec)*
Board of Directors:
Stephen Shiu, Jr.
Chi Ho Chan
Tik Lun Kam
Albert Wing Ho Lee
Christopher Lap Key Sun
Banny Kwok Ming Tam

Butterfield Fulcrum Group (Bermuda) Limited
26 Burnaby Street
Hamilton, HM 11, Bermuda

Subsidiary:

China 3D Digital Distribution Limited (1)
1/F Morrison Plaza 9 Morrison Hill Road
Wanchai, China (Hong Kong)
Tel.: (852) 2882 1816
Fax: (852) 2882 3199
Motion Picture Distr
S.I.C.: 7829
N.A.I.C.S.: 512120

CHINA 9D CONSTRUCTION GROUP, INC.

4F Jia De Plaza 118 Qing Chun Road
Hangzhou, Zhejiang, 310000, China
Tel.: (86) 571 8722 0222
CNAG—(OTC)
Sales Range: $50-74.9 Million
Business Description:
Architectural & Construction Services
S.I.C.: 8712
N.A.I.C.S.: 541310
Personnel:
Zheng Ying *(Chm & CEO)*
Yanbin Wang *(CFO)*
Board of Directors:
Zheng Ying
Song Cai
Jingsong Li
Ying Luo
Yufei Yu

CHINA ADVANCED CONSTRUCTION MATERIALS GROUP, INC.

9 North West Fourth Ring Road
Yingu Mansion Suite 1708
Haidian District, Beijing, China 100190
Tel.: (86) 1082525361
Web Site: www.china-acm.com
CADC—(NASDAQ)
Rev.: $74,486,972
Assets: $145,773,796
Liabilities: $89,081,697
Net Worth: $56,692,099
Earnings: ($23,598,379)
Emp.: 453
Fiscal Year-end: 06/30/13
Business Description:
Ready Mix Concrete Materials Mfr
S.I.C.: 3273
N.A.I.C.S.: 327320
Personnel:
Xianfu Han *(Chm & CEO)*
Weili He *(Vice Chm & COO)*
Yanwei He *(Interim CFO)*
Board of Directors:
Xianfu Han
Xinyong Gao
Weili He
Tao Jin
Ken Ren

CHINA AEROSPACE INTERNATIONAL HOLDINGS LIMITED

Room 1103-1107A 11/F One
Harbourfront 18 Tak Fung Street
Hunghom, Kowloon, China (Hong Kong)
Tel.: (852) 2193 8888
Fax: (852) 2193 8899
E-Mail: public@casil-group.com
Web Site: www.casil-group.com
31—(HKG)
Sls.: $337,217,274
Assets: $855,629,543
Liabilities: $231,422,439
Net Worth: $624,207,104
Earnings: $38,428,518
Emp.: 6,500
Fiscal Year-end: 12/31/12
Business Description:
Aerospace Equipment Mfr
S.I.C.: 3812
N.A.I.C.S.: 334511
Personnel:
Honqjun Li *(Pres)*
Ken Ka Kin Chan *(Sec)*
Xuesheng Jin *(Exec VP)*
Board of Directors:
Jianheng Zhang
Xuechuan Chen
Xuesheng Jin
Sylvia Sau Fan Leung
Honqjun Li
Zhenbang Luo
Weiguo Shi
Junyan Wang
Zhuo Wu

CHINA AFRICA RESOURCES PLC

180 Piccadilly
London, W1J 9HF, United Kingdom
Tel.: (44) 207 917 9917
Fax: (44) 207 439 0262
E-Mail: info@weatherlyplc.com
Web Site: www.chinaafricares.com
Year Founded: 2010
CAF—(AIM)
Rev.: $192,000
Assets: $9,683,000
Liabilities: $214,000
Net Worth: $9,469,000
Earnings: ($495,000)
Emp.: 8
Fiscal Year-end: 12/31/12
Business Description:
Metal Mining
S.I.C.: 1099
N.A.I.C.S.: 212299
Personnel:
Roderick Webster *(CEO)*
Max Herbert *(Sec)*
Board of Directors:
Jianrong Xu
John Bryant
Frank Lewis
Shasha Lu
James Richards
Jingbin Tian
Roderick Webster
Xingnan Xie
Legal Counsel:
Morrison & Foerster (UK) LLP
CityPoint One Ropemaker Street
London, United Kingdom

CHINA AGRI-BUSINESS, INC.

Building 2 Unit 1 15th Floor Ling Xian
Xin Cheng
86 Gaoxin Road
Hi-Tech Industrial Devel Zone, Xi'an, Shaanxi, 710065, China
Tel.: (86) 29 6859 6556
Web Site: www.chinaagri-business.com
CHBU—(OTC)
Sales Range: $10-24.9 Million
Emp.: 138
Business Description:
Biochemical Agricultural Products Developer & Mfr
S.I.C.: 2879
N.A.I.C.S.: 325320
Personnel:
Limin Deng *(Chm)*
Liping Deng *(Pres & CEO)*
Xiaolong Zhou *(CFO & Principal Acctg Officer)*
Jianhua Wang *(Sec)*
Board of Directors:
Limin Deng
Liping Deng
Michael Segal
Transfer Agent:
Securities Transfer Corporation
2591 Dallas Pkwy Ste 102
Frisco, TX 75034
Tel.: (469) 633-0101
Fax: (469) 633-0088

CHINA AGRI PRODUCTS EXCHANGE LIMITED

5th Floor Wai Yuen Tong Medicine
Building 9 Wang Kwong Road
Kowloon Bay, Kowloon, China (Hong Kong)
Tel.: (852) 35273621
Fax: (852) 35273620
E-Mail: anitamak@wangon.com
Web Site: www.cnagri-products.com
0149—(HKG)
Sls.: $37,070,804
Assets: $558,598,247
Liabilities: $395,153,348

Net Worth: $163,444,899
Earnings: $27,915,612
Emp.: 942
Fiscal Year-end: 12/31/12

Business Description:
Agricultural Products Development
S.I.C.: 4214
N.A.I.C.S.: 484220

Personnel:
Thomas Chun Hong Chan *(Chm & CEO)*
Lawrence Koon Kui Wong *(Mng Dir)*
Raymond Sui Wah Leung *(CFO)*
Angus Chin Wa Cheung *(Sec)*

Board of Directors:
Thomas Chun Hong Chan
Katherine Ka Jen Lam
King Lung Lau
Raymond Sui Wah Leung
Yat Cheung Ng
Lawrence Koon Kui Wong
Yuk Shing Yau

Butterfield Fulcrum Group (Bermuda) Limited
26 Burnaby Street
Hamilton, HM 11, Bermuda

Transfer Agents:
Tricor Investor Services Limited
26th Floor Tesbury Centre 28 Queens Road East
Wanchai, China (Hong Kong)

Butterfield Fulcrum Group (Bermuda) Limited
26 Burnaby Street
Hamilton, HM 11, Bermuda

CHINA AGRITECH, INC.

Room 3F No 11 Building Zhonghong Intl Business Garden
Future Business Center
Chaoyang North Road, Chaoyang
Beijing, 100024, China
Tel.: (86) 10 5962 1278
Web Site: www.chinaagritechinc.com
CAGC—(OTC)
Sales Range: $75-99.9 Million
Emp.: 305

Business Description:
Holding Company; Organic Liquid Compound Fertilizers & Related Agricultural Products Mfr & Sales
S.I.C.: 3269
N.A.I.C.S.: 327110

Personnel:
Yu Chang *(Chm, Pres, CEO & Sec)*
Ge Wen *(Interim CFO)*

CHINA AIRLINES LTD.

131 Sec 3 Nanjing East Road
Taipei, 104, Taiwan
Tel.: (886) 227152233
Telex: 11346
Fax: (886) 225146004
E-Mail: cal@china-airlines.com
Web Site: www.china-airlines.com
Year Founded: 1959
2610—(TAI)
Rev.: $4,491,461,106
Assets: $6,446,301,450
Liabilities: $4,680,277,956
Net Worth: $1,766,023,494
Earnings: $1,991,691
Emp.: 10,693
Fiscal Year-end: 12/31/12

Business Description:
Passenger & Cargo Air Transportation Services
S.I.C.: 4512
N.A.I.C.S.: 481111

Personnel:
Huang-Hsiang Sun *(Chm)*

Board of Directors:
Huang-Hsiang Sun
Charles Chih-Yuan Chen
Lo-Min Chung
Hsiu-Gu Huang
Tso-Liang Ko
Ching-Chyi Lai
Cho-Ping Lee
Su-Ming Lin
Shao-Liang Liu
Hsiao-Hsien Luo
Hong-Lei Sung
Kwang-Hung Ting

Transfer Agent:
Chinatrust Commercial Bank Transfer Agency Department
5F 83 Sec 1 Chung Ching S Rd
Taipei, Taiwan

Subsidiaries:

Abacus Distribution Systems Taiwan Ltd. **(1)**
15th Floor No 57 Fu-Hsin North Road
Taipei, Taiwan (93.93%)
Tel.: (886) 227516988
Fax: (886) 227516398
E-Mail: service@abacus.com.tw
Web Site: www.abacus.com.tw
Emp.: 110
Computer Systems Design Services
S.I.C.: 7373
N.A.I.C.S.: 541512
David Chen *(Gen Mgr)*

China Pacific Catering Services Ltd. **(1)**
22 Lane 156 Sec 2 Hai-Shan Road
Lu Chu Township, 338 Taoyuan, Taiwan (51%)
Tel.: (886) 33541000
Fax: (886) 33543405
E-Mail: webservice@cpcs.com.tw
Web Site: www.cpcs.com.tw
Emp.: 800
Airline Kitchen Services; Catering Services
S.I.C.: 5963
N.A.I.C.S.: 722330
Cheng-Kang Chou *(Gen Mgr)*

Hwa Hsia Company Ltd. **(1)**
HangZhan S Rd Dayuan Township
Taoyuan, 33758, Taiwan TW (100%)
Tel.: (886) 33833242
Fax: (886) 33834222
Web Site: www.hh-cal.com.tw
Emp.: 425
Airport Terminal Ground Service-Airline Cabin Cleaning, Cargo Container Maintenance & Aircraft Accessory Cleaning
S.I.C.: 4581
N.A.I.C.S.: 488190
K. S. Yang Jerry *(Gen Mgr)*

Mandarin Airlines **(1)**
13F 134 Sec 3 Minsheng E Rd
Taipei, Taiwan TW (93.99%)
Tel.: (886) 227171230
Fax: (886) 225451812
Web Site: www.mandarin-airlines.com
Emp.: 300
Scheduled Passenger Air Transportation
S.I.C.: 4512
N.A.I.C.S.: 481111
Harris H. Y. Wang *(Chm)*
Min Tang Chen *(Pres)*

Taiwan Air Cargo Terminal Ltd. **(1)**
No 10-1 Hangchin N Road
Taoyuan International Airport, Taoyuan, 33758, Taiwan TW (54%)
Tel.: (886) 33987877
Fax: (886) 33987971
E-Mail: service@tactlo.com
Web Site: www.tactlo.com
Emp.: 600
Aviation Cargo Transportation Services
S.I.C.: 4581
N.A.I.C.S.: 488190
Bobby Yu *(CEO)*

U.S. Branch:

China Airlines Ltd. **(1)**
200 Continental Blvd
El Segundo, CA 90245
Tel.: (310) 322-2888
Fax: (310) 322-3888
Toll Free: (800) 227-5118
Web Site: www.china-airlines.com
Emp.: 75
Airline Service
S.I.C.: 4512
N.A.I.C.S.: 481112

U.S. Subsidiaries:

CAL-Dynasty International, Inc. **(1)**
200 N Continental Blvd
El Segundo, CA 90245 (100%)
Tel.: (310) 322-2888
Fax: (310) 322-3888
Toll Free: (800) 227-5118
Web Site: www.china-airlines.com
Scheduled Passenger Air Transportation & Various Travel Services
S.I.C.: 4512
N.A.I.C.S.: 481111
Hsing-Hsiung Wei *(Chm)*

Subsidiaries:

Dynasty Hotel of Hawaii, Inc **(2)**
1830 Ala Moana Blvd
Honolulu, HI 96815-1602
Tel.: (808) 955-1111
Fax: (808) 947-1799
Web Site: www.ramadaplazawaikiki.com
Hotel Management Services
S.I.C.: 7011
N.A.I.C.S.: 721110
Roger Chang *(Gen Mgr)*

Dynasty Properties Co., Ltd. **(2)**
750 N 43rd St Apt 47
Grand Forks, ND 58203-1903 (100%)
Tel.: (701) 741-2574
Real Estate Agent
S.I.C.: 6531
N.A.I.C.S.: 531210
Ringo Chao *(Chm & Pres)*

Ramada Waikiki **(2)**
1830 Ala Moana Blvd
Honolulu, HI 96815-1602 (100%)
Tel.: (808) 955-1111
Fax: (808) 947-1799
Web Site: www.ramadawaikiki.com
Emp.: 50
Hotel
S.I.C.: 7011
N.A.I.C.S.: 721110
Pony Tung *(Gen Mgr)*

Cal Hotel Co. Ltd. **(1)**
2008 Shattuck Ave
Berkeley, CA 94704-1117 (100%)
Tel.: (510) 849-9479
Emp.: 1
Hotels & Motels
S.I.C.: 7011
N.A.I.C.S.: 721110
Albert Ho *(Gen Mgr)*

Non-U.S. Subsidiary:

Dynasty Holidays, Inc. **(1)**
You Ginza Dai Ni Bldg 5Fl 197
Chuo-ku, Tokyo, 104 0061, Japan (51%)
Tel.: (81) 355240880
Fax: (81) 355240887
E-Mail: welcome@dynasty-holidays.com
Web Site: www.dynasty-holidays.com
Emp.: 30
Travel Agencies
S.I.C.: 4724
N.A.I.C.S.: 561510
Masaru Kunihiro *(Pres)*

CHINA ALL ACCESS (HOLDINGS) LIMITED

Room 805 Greenfield Tower
Concordia Plaza 1 Science Museum Road TST
Kowloon, China (Hong Kong)
Tel.: (852) 3579 2368
Fax: (852) 3579 2328
Web Site: www.chinaallaccess.com
Year Founded: 2003
0633—(HKG)
Rev.: $96,410,195
Assets: $953,266,634
Liabilities: $602,755,690
Net Worth: $350,510,944
Earnings: $27,024,674
Emp.: 5,010
Fiscal Year-end: 12/31/12

Business Description:
Integrated Information Communication Application Solutions Designer & Developer
S.I.C.: 3669
N.A.I.C.S.: 334290

Personnel:
Yuen Ming Chan *(Chm)*
Kwok Keung Shao *(CEO)*
Qing An Zhao *(CTO)*
Ki Lun Au *(Sec & Head-Risk Control Dept)*

Board of Directors:
Yuen Ming Chan
Patrick Kin Hung Lam
Yan Chak Pun
Kwok Keung Shao
Eddy Che Man Wong
Zhi Bao Xiu
Qing An Zhao

Legal Counsel:
Chiu & Partners
40th Fl Jardine House 1 Connaught Place
Central, China (Hong Kong)

Royal Bank of Canada Trust Company (Cayman) Limited
4th Floor Royal Bank House 24 Shedden Road
Georgetown, Cayman Islands

Transfer Agents:
Union Registrars Limited
Rooms 1901-02 Fook Lee Commercial Centre
Town Place 33 Lockhart Road
Wanchai, China (Hong Kong)

Royal Bank of Canada Trust Company (Cayman) Limited
4th Floor Royal Bank House 24 Shedden Road
Georgetown, Cayman Islands

CHINA ALUMINUM CANS HOLDINGS LIMITED

Flat G 20/F Golden Sun Centre 59/67 Bonham Strand West
Sheung Wan, China (Hong Kong)
Tel.: (852) 25482780
Fax: (852) 25599036
Web Site: www.euroasia-p.com
6898—(HKG)
Sales Range: $25-49.9 Million
Emp.: 390

Business Description:
Aluminum Aerosol Cans Mfr
S.I.C.: 3411
N.A.I.C.S.: 332431

Personnel:
Wan Tsang Lin *(Chm & Gen Mgr)*

Board of Directors:
Wan Tsang Lin
Yi To Chung
Yang Guo
Sau Mee Ko
Tak Wang Kwok
Man Fai Leung
Tat Pang Lin
Chamlong Wachakorn

CHINA ALUMINUM INTERNATIONAL ENGINEERING CORPORATION LIMITED

(d/b/a Chalieco)
Building C 99 Xingshikou Road
Haidian District, Beijing, 100093, China
Tel.: (86) 10 82406888
Fax: (86) 10 82406666
E-Mail: marketing@chalieco.com.cn
Web Site: www.chalieco.com.cn
Year Founded: 2003
2068—(HKG)
Sales Range: $1-4.9 Billion
Emp.: 10,000

Business Description:
Nonferrous Metals
S.I.C.: 3369
N.A.I.C.S.: 331529

China Aluminum International Engineering Corporation Limited—(Continued)

Personnel:
Chengzhong Zhang *(Chm)*
Zhihui He *(Pres)*
Jun Wang *(CFO)*
Chaosheng Long *(Sec)*
Board of Directors:
Chengzhong Zhang
Zhihui He
Ning Ma
Jun Wang
Yuewu Wu

CHINA ANIMAL HEALTHCARE LTD.

6 Kangding Street Beijing Economic-Technological Development Area
Beijing, 100176, China
Tel.: (86) 10 51571908
Fax: (86) 10 51571909
Web Site: www.chinanimalhealthcare.com
EP4—(HKG SES)
Rev.: $137,044,502
Assets: $322,143,988
Liabilities: $102,713,363
Net Worth: $219,430,625
Earnings: $20,332,006
Emp.: 2,600
Fiscal Year-end: 12/31/12
Business Description:
Animal Drug Mfr
S.I.C.: 2834
N.A.I.C.S.: 325412
Personnel:
Yangang Wang *(Chm & CEO)*
Jun Li *(Deputy CEO)*
Guimin Lin *(Asst CEO)*
Yanmei Song *(Asst CEO)*
Jinguo Sun *(Deputy CEO)*
Edwin Kay Seng Goh *(CFO & Co-Sec)*
Kit Fong Ngai *(Co-Sec)*
Sharon Kar Choo Yeoh *(Co-Sec)*
Board of Directors:
Yangang Wang
Jinglan Feng
Shan Fu
Steven Yan Qing Ma
Joshua Kian Guan Ong
Jinguo Sun
Gang Wong
HSBC Bank Bermuda Limited
Bank of Bermuda Building, 6 Front Street
Hamilton, Bermuda
Transfer Agent:
M & C Services Private Limited
112 Robinson Road 05-01
Singapore, Singapore

CHINA AOYUAN PROPERTY GROUP LIMITED

AoYuan Mansion No 108 HuangPu Avenue West
Tianhe District, Guangzhou, China 510620
Tel.: (86) 20 3868 6666
Fax: (86) 20 3868 6688
E-Mail: aoyuanclub@aoyuan.net
Web Site: www.aoyuan.com.cn
Year Founded: 2007
47C—(DEU)
Rev.: $626,378,114
Assets: $3,306,151,563
Liabilities: $2,177,731,201
Net Worth: $1,128,420,362
Earnings: $148,150,499
Emp.: 1,972
Fiscal Year-end: 12/31/12
Business Description:
Real Estate Development Services
S.I.C.: 6531
N.A.I.C.S.: 531390
Personnel:
Zi Wen Guo *(Chm)*
Zi Ning Guo *(Vice Chm & CEO)*
Zhong Ping *(CFO)*
Zhong Yang *(COO)*
Joyce Kar-yan Ho *(Sec)*
Zhu Xin *(Exec VP)*
Board of Directors:
Zi Wen Guo
Kwok Keung Cheung
Zi Ning Guo
Kwai Yuen Ma
Xian Zhong Song
King Fai Tsui
Paul Steven Wolansky
Jie Si Wu
Zhu Xin
Zhong Yang
Computershare Hong Kong Investor Services Limited
17M Floor Hopewell Centre 183 Queen's Road East
Wanchai, China (Hong Kong)
Transfer Agents:
Royal Bank of Canada Trust Company (Cayman) Limited
4th Floor Royal Bank House 24 Shedden Road
Georgetown, Cayman Islands
Computershare Hong Kong Investor Services Limited
17M Floor Hopewell Centre 183 Queen's Road East
Wanchai, China (Hong Kong)

CHINA ARCHITECTURE DESIGN & RESEARCH GROUP

No 19 Chegongzhuang Street
100044 Beijing, China
Tel.: (86) 10 68302001
Fax: (86) 10 68348832
Web Site: en.cadreg.com
Business Description:
Engineering Project Consultation, Planning, Design, Project Management & Surveying
S.I.C.: 8712
N.A.I.C.S.: 541310
Personnel:
Xiu Long *(Pres)*
Non-U.S. Subsidiary:

CPG Corporation Pte Ltd. (1)
238B Thomson Rd 18-00
Tower B Novena Square, 307685
Singapore, Singapore (100%)
Tel.: (65) 63574888
Fax: (65) 63574188
E-Mail: cpgcorp@cpgcorp.com.sg
Web Site: www.cpgcorp.com.sg
Emp.: 2,000
Engineering Services
S.I.C.: 8711
N.A.I.C.S.: 541330
Sin Khoon Khew *(Pres & CEO)*

Subsidiaries:

CPG Consultants Pte Ltd. (2)
238B Thomson Road 18-00
Tower B Novena Square, Singapore, 307685, Singapore (100%)
Tel.: (65) 63574888
Fax: (65) 63574188
E-Mail: cpgcorp@cpgcorp.com.sg
Web Site: www.cpgcorp.com.sg
Emp.: 1,500
Engineering Services
S.I.C.: 8711
N.A.I.C.S.: 541330

CPG Facilities Management Pte Ltd. (2)
37 Jalan Pemimpin Unit 02-05 Block B Clarus Ctr
577177 Singapore, Singapore (100%)
Tel.: (65) 63258880
Fax: (65) 63258881
E-Mail: contactus@cpgfm.com.sg
Web Site: www.cpgfm.com.sg/
Emp.: 100
Services to Buildings & Dwellings
S.I.C.: 7349
N.A.I.C.S.: 561790
Pang Poh Yong *(Mng Dir)*

CPG Investments Pte Ltd. (2)
238B Thomson Road #18-00
Tower B Novena Square, 307685
Singapore, Singapore
Tel.: (65) 63574888
Fax: (65) 63574188
E-Mail: cpgcorp@cpgcorp.com.sg
Web Site: www.cpgcorp.com.sg
Emp.: 1,007
Financial Investment Activities
S.I.C.: 6211
N.A.I.C.S.: 523999
Kok Kingmin *(Mng Dir)*

PM Link Pte Ltd (2)
70 Bendemeer Road 03-01 Luzerne
Singapore, 339940, Singapore
Tel.: (65) 6391 7088
Fax: (65) 6391 7033
E-Mail: enquiry@pmlink.com.sg
Web Site: www.pmlink.com.sg
Project Management Services
S.I.C.: 8748
N.A.I.C.S.: 541618
Annie Lai *(Mgr-Admin)*

Non-U.S. Subsidiaries:

CPG Advisory (Shanghai) Co. Ltd. (2)
9th Fl Golden Bridge Plz No 585 Xi Zang Rd
200003 Shanghai, China (100%)
Tel.: (86) 2163517888
Fax: (86) 2163519888
E-Mail: cpg.advisory@cpgcorp.com.sg
Web Site: www.cpgcorp.com.sg/contact/contactintl.asp
Emp.: 70
Engineering Services
S.I.C.: 8711
N.A.I.C.S.: 541330

CPG Consultants India Pvt Ltd (2)
21/30 Prestige Craig House Craig Park Layout Mahatma Gandhi Road
Bengaluru, 560 001, India
Tel.: (91) 80 2559 0281
Fax: (91) 80 2559 0285
E-Mail: cpgcorp.india@cpgcorp.com.sg
Web Site: www.cpgindia.com
Emp.: 85
Engineering Design Services
S.I.C.: 7389
N.A.I.C.S.: 541490
Raimi Rahim *(Mng Dir)*

CPG Vietnam Co Ltd (2)
Floor 16th No 2A-4A Ton Duc Thang Street District 1, Ho Chi Minh City, Vietnam
Tel.: (84) 8 3821 7000
Fax: (84) 8 3914 3815
E-Mail: cpgvietnam@cpgcorp.com.sg
Web Site: www.cpgcorp.com.sg/contact/contactintl.asp
Emp.: 130
Consulting Engineering Services
S.I.C.: 8711
N.A.I.C.S.: 541330
Jimmy Tsen *(Gen Dir)*

CHINA-ASEAN CAPITAL ADVISORY COMPANY

67/F Two International Finance Centre 8 Finance Street
Central, China (Hong Kong)
Tel.: (852) 6297 5019
E-Mail: information@china-asean-fund.com
Web Site: www.china-asean-fund.com
Personnel:
Yao Li *(CEO)*
Geoffrey Seeto *(Mng Dir)*

CHINA ASEAN RESOURCES LIMITED

8th Floor Teda Building 87 Wing Lok Street
Hong Kong, China (Hong Kong)
Tel.: (852) 2543 8223
Fax: (852) 2854 1121
E-Mail: info@chinaaseanresources.com
Web Site: www.chinaaseanresources.com
MJD1—(DEU)
Sales Range: Less than $1 Million
Business Description:
Natural Resource Preservation & Rubber Plantation Services
S.I.C.: 8399
N.A.I.C.S.: 813312
Personnel:
Xiao Min Yu *(Chm)*
Zhenzhong Zhang *(CEO)*
Board of Directors:
Xiao Min Yu
Gankhuyag Chultemsuren
Ting Gong
Bing Xian Hong
Alan Sze Yuan Leung
Huiying Wen
Lingchen Zeng
Ying Zhang

CHINA ASSET MANAGEMENT CO., LTD.

12/F Building B Tongtai Plaza No 33 Jinrong Street
Xicheng District, Beijing, 100033, China
Tel.: (86) 10 8806 6688
Fax: (86) 10 8806 6508
E-Mail: service@chinaamc.com
Web Site: www.chinaamc.com
Year Founded: 1998
Managed Assets: $50,600,000,000
Business Description:
Investment Management & Advisory Services
S.I.C.: 6799
N.A.I.C.S.: 523920
Personnel:
Tianming Teng *(Exec VP)*
Non-U.S. Subsidiary:

China Asset Management (Hong Kong) Limited (1)
37/F Bank of China Tower 1 Garden Road
Hong Kong, China (Hong Kong) HK
Tel.: (852) 3406 8688 (100%)
Fax: (852) 3406 8500
E-Mail: hkservice@chinaamc.com
Web Site: www.chinaamc.com.hk
Investment Management & Advisory Services
S.I.C.: 6799
N.A.I.C.S.: 523920
Iris Chen *(CEO)*
Freddie Chen *(Mng Dir)*

CHINA ASSETS (HOLDINGS) LIMITED

19/F Wing On House 71 Des Voeux Road
Central, China (Hong Kong)
Tel.: (852) 25219888
Fax: (852) 25268781
E-Mail: info@chinaassets.com
Web Site: www.chinaassets.com
Year Founded: 1978
0170—(HKG)
Rev.: $845,377
Assets: $146,572,471
Liabilities: $5,062,997
Net Worth: $141,509,474
Earnings: ($20,815,260)
Fiscal Year-end: 12/31/12
Business Description:
Financial Investment Services
S.I.C.: 6211
N.A.I.C.S.: 523999
Personnel:
Yuen Yat Lo *(Chm)*
Sai Wai Cheng *(Sec)*
Board of Directors:

Yuen Yat Lo
Jia Yan Fan
Wei Jiang
Yuan Yuan Lao
David William Maguire
Ming Yu Wu
Wai Kin Yeung
Yu Qiao Zhao

CHINA ASSURANCE FINANCE GROUP LIMITED

Unit 03-05 17/F K Wah Centre 191 Java Road
North Point, China (Hong Kong)
Tel.: (852) 3157 0001
Fax: (852) 3157 0002
E-Mail: info@cafgroup.hk
Web Site: www.cafgroup.hk
8090—(HKG)

Business Description:
Corporate Credit Financial Services
S.I.C.: 6099
N.A.I.C.S.: 522390

Personnel:
Xi Min Chang *(Chm)*
Nixon Man Kin Pang *(Vice Chm)*
Hoi Nam Chang *(CEO)*
Gao Sen Xu *(CFO)*
Xiang Bai Li *(Chief Risk Control Officer)*
Xiao Li Chen *(Compliance Officer)*
Lavender Tsz Sai Man *(Sec)*

Board of Directors:
Xi Min Chang
Kai Wing Chan
Hoi Nam Chang
Xiao Li Chen
Shiu Ki Chow
Raymond Shiu Cheung Lam
Nixon Man Kin Pang

Non-U.S. Divisions:

China Assurance Finance Group Limited **(1)**
23/F Office Tower Zhongxin Huiyang Building 59 Hubin Road North
Siming District, Xiamen, China
Tel.: (86) 592 5360307
Fax: (86) 592 5360302
Corporate Credit Financial Services
S.I.C.: 6099
N.A.I.C.S.: 522390

China Assurance Finance Group Limited **(1)**
13/F Liaohai International Building 6 Wei San Road
Zhangjiakou, Hebei, China
Tel.: (86) 313 5911313
Corporate Credit Financial Services
S.I.C.: 6099
N.A.I.C.S.: 522390

CHINA AUTO CORPORATION LTD

17 Jurong Port Road
Singapore, 619092, Singapore
Tel.: (65) 62687733
Fax: (65) 62683338
Web Site: www.china-auto-corporation.com
A01—(SES)
Rev.: $43,924,330
Assets: $109,816,089
Liabilities: $27,623,853
Net Worth: $82,192,236
Earnings: ($6,034,545)
Fiscal Year-end: 12/31/12

Business Description:
Plastic Interior Parts Mfr
S.I.C.: 3089
N.A.I.C.S.: 326199

Personnel:
Sim Pin Queck *(Chm)*
Kong Seng Chou *(CFO)*
Rajen Rai *(COO)*
Keloth Raj Kumar *(Sec)*

Board of Directors:
Sim Pin Queck
Victor Levin
Robert Mui Kiat Low
Seow Chye Low
Keng Lin Tan

Subsidiary:

Ray Tech Acot Singapore Pte. Ltd. **(1)**
17 Jurong Port Road
Singapore, Singapore
Tel.: (65) 62619168
Fax: (65) 62619290
Web Site: www.acotgroup.com
Emp.: 4
Steel Molds Distr
S.I.C.: 5051
N.A.I.C.S.: 423510

Non-U.S. Subsidiaries:

Acot Plastics (Xiamen) Co., Ltd. **(1)**
No 2 Factory Building Malong Development District
Huli District, Xiamen, Fujian, 361006, China
Tel.: (86) 5925719303
Fax: (86) 5925719319
Web Site: www.acotgroup.cn/ContactUs.asp
Emp.: 400
Molded Goods Mfr
S.I.C.: 3061
N.A.I.C.S.: 326291
Eddie Low *(Mgr)*

Acot Tooling Xiamen Ltd. **(1)**
No 3 Factory Building Malong Development District
Huli, Xiamen, Fujian, 361006, China
Tel.: (86) 592 5705753
Fax: (86) 592 5705780
Emp.: 200
Machine Tools Mfr
S.I.C.: 3541
N.A.I.C.S.: 333517

CHINA AUTO ELECTRONICS GROUP LIMITED

215 East Part Qibin Rd
Qibin District, Hebi, Henan, China 458030
Tel.: (86) 3923314522
Fax: (86) 3923362298
E-Mail: sale@thb.com.cn
Web Site: www.thb.com.cn
T42—(SES)
Rev.: $247,575,350
Assets: $283,169,981
Liabilities: $200,448,526
Net Worth: $82,721,455
Earnings: $665,899
Emp.: 10,000
Fiscal Year-end: 12/31/12

Business Description:
Electrical & Electronics Systems Mfr
S.I.C.: 3825
N.A.I.C.S.: 334515

Personnel:
Jingtang Zhang *(Chm)*
Ying Zhang *(CEO)*
Hong Qin *(Deputy CEO)*
Ping Zhou *(Deputy CEO)*
Peter How Onn Cheong *(CFO & Sec)*

Board of Directors:
Jingtang Zhang
Ker Chern Ho
Delin Li
Zhifu Shen
Hong Boon Sim
Laisheng Wang
Shulin Zhang

Appleby Management (Bermuda) Limited
Argyle House 41A Cedar Avenue
Hamilton, Bermuda

Transfer Agent:
B.A.C.S. Private Limited
63 Cantonment Road
Singapore, 089758, Singapore
Tel.: (65) 3236 2000

Subsidiary:

Hebi Haichang Special Equipment Co Ltd **(1)**
215 Qibin Road
Qibin District, Hebi, Henan, 458030, China
Tel.: (86) 3923357155
Fax: (86) 39 2331 3264
E-Mail: hmsales@thb.com.cn
Web Site: www.thbhc.com.cn
Industrial Machinery Mfr
S.I.C.: 3545
N.A.I.C.S.: 333515

CHINA AUTO LOGISTICS INC.

Floor 1 FTZ International Auto Mall
86 Tianbao Avenue Free Trade Zone
Tianjin, China 300461
Tel.: (86) 22 25762771
Web Site: www.chinaautologisticsinc.com
Year Founded: 2005
CALI—(NASDAQ)
Rev.: $591,315,104
Assets: $166,195,716
Liabilities: $106,695,595
Net Worth: $59,500,121
Earnings: $2,580,526
Emp.: 73
Fiscal Year-end: 12/31/12

Business Description:
Automobile Retailer
S.I.C.: 5012
N.A.I.C.S.: 423110

Personnel:
Shiping Tong *(Chm, Pres & CEO)*
Xinwei Wang *(CFO, Treas & VP)*
Yan Jin *(COO)*
Weihong Cheng *(Sec, Sr VP & Head-HR & Gen Admin)*

Board of Directors:
Shiping Tong
Howard S. Barth
Weihong Cheng
Wei Wang
Xinwei Wang
Lili Yang
Baoying Zou

Transfer Agent:
Corporate Stock Transfer
3200 Cherry Creek Dr S Ste 430
Denver, CO 80209

CHINA AUTO RENTAL HOLDINGS INC.

2F Lead International Bldg 2A
Zhonghuan South Road
Wanging Chaoyang District, Beijing, 100102, China
Tel.: (86) 10 5820 9999
Fax: (86) 10 5820 9966
Sales Range: $10-24.9 Million
Emp.: 3,384

Business Description:
Car Rental & Leasing Services
S.I.C.: 7514
N.A.I.C.S.: 532111

Personnel:
Charles Zhengyao Lu *(Chm & CEO)*
Robert Yong Sha *(CFO)*
Jenny Zhiya Qian *(Exec VP-Ops)*
Kevin Junhong Yao *(Exec VP-Sls & Mktg)*

Board of Directors:
Charles Zhengyao Lu
Erhai Liu
Linan Zhu

CHINA AUTO SYSTEM TECHNOLOGIES LIMITED

Room 1613 16/F Leighton Centre
77 Leighton Road, Causeway Bay, China (Hong Kong)
Tel.: (852) 2881 5300
Fax: (852) 2881 5336
Web Site: www.chinaautosystem.com
Sales Range: $150-199.9 Million
Emp.: 300

Business Description:
Automobile Air-Conditioning Compressors Mfr
S.I.C.: 3714
N.A.I.C.S.: 336390

Personnel:
Yichen Zhang *(Chm)*
Yonggui Qian *(CEO)*

Board of Directors:
Yichen Zhang
Kenneth Fang
Xiaoping Liu
Yonggui Qian
Zhenyu Wang

CHINA AUTOMATION GROUP LIMITED

Unit 3205B 3206 32/F Office Tower
Convention Plaza 1 Harbour Road
Wanchai, China (Hong Kong)
Tel.: (852) 25980088
Fax: (852) 25986633
Web Site: www.cag.com.hk
0569—(HKG)
Rev.: $351,178,273
Assets: $742,881,564
Liabilities: $413,211,581
Net Worth: $329,669,983
Earnings: $20,398,246
Emp.: 3,082
Fiscal Year-end: 12/31/12

Business Description:
Engineering Services
S.I.C.: 8711
N.A.I.C.S.: 541330

Personnel:
Rui Guo Xuan *(Chm)*
Jian Ping Kuang *(CEO)*
Da Chao Cui *(CFO)*
Benson Chiu Chi Chow *(Sec & Controller-Fin)*
Wen Hui Wang *(Sr VP)*
Zheng Qiang Zhou *(Sr VP)*

Board of Directors:
Rui Guo Xuan
Zhi Yong Huang
Jian Ping Kuang
Wing Fai Ng
Yong Bin Sui
Tai Wen Wang

Legal Counsel:
Woo, Kwan, Lee & Lo
26th Floor Jardine House
Central, China (Hong Kong)

Conyers Dill & Pearman
Georgetown, Grand Cayman, Cayman Islands

Commerce & Finance Law Offices
6F NCI Tower A12 Jianguomenwai Avenue
Beijing, China

Transfer Agent:
Tricor Services Limited
Level 28 Three Pacific Place 1 Queen's Road East
Hong Kong, China (Hong Kong)

CHINA AUTOMOBILE PARTS HOLDINGS LIMITED

Suite 13.03 13th Floor Menara Tan & Tan
207 Jalan Tun Razak, Kuala Lumpur, 50400, Malaysia
Tel.: (60) 3 2164 0206
Fax: (60) 3 2164 0207
Web Site: www.china-autoparts.biz
5229—(KLS)

Business Description:
Holding Company; Motor Vehicle Chassis Components & Other Motor Vehicle Parts Mfr
S.I.C.: 6719
N.A.I.C.S.: 551112

Personnel:
Jalaluddin Abdul Rahim *(Chm)*

China Automobile Parts Holdings Limited—(Continued)

Juan Tee Ong *(Vice Chm)*
Guo Qing Li *(Mng Dir)*
Wai Teck Chai *(CFO)*
Board of Directors:
Jalaluddin Abdul Rahim
Boon Heow Chen
Wai Choong Chung
Guo Qing Li
Kock Hooi Lim
Juan Tee Ong
Yu-Yun Wang

CHINA AUTOMOBILE TRADING CO., LTD.

F 22 23 Millennium Plaza Tower A No 72 North Xisanhuan Road
Haidian District, Beijing, China
Tel.: (86) 10 88422222
Fax: (86) 10 68488202
Web Site: www.ctcai.com
Year Founded: 1993
Business Description:
Motor Vehicle Importing
S.I.C.: 5012
N.A.I.C.S.: 423110
Personnel:
Hongxiang Ding *(Pres)*
Joint Venture:

Spyker of China Ltd. (1)
West Third Ring North Road
Beijing Economic & Trade Build, Beijing, Haidian, China
Tel.: (86) 1068484266
Fax: (86) 1068489488
Automobile Mfr; Sportscars
S.I.C.: 3711
N.A.I.C.S.: 336111
Martyn Schilte *(Mng Dir)*

CHINA AUTOMOTIVE ENGINEERING RESEARCH INSTITUTE CO., LTD.

No 101 Chaotiancun Chenjiaping
Jiulongpo District, Chongqing, 400039, China
Tel.: (86) 23 68824060
Fax: (86) 23 68821361
E-Mail: office@caeri.com.cn
Web Site: www.caeri.com.cn
Year Founded: 1965
601965—(SHG)
Business Description:
Technical Consulting Services
S.I.C.: 8999
N.A.I.C.S.: 541690
Personnel:
Ning Song *(Chm)*
Xiaochang Ren *(Pres)*

CHINA AUTOMOTIVE INTERIOR DECORATION HOLDINGS LIMITED

(d/b/a Joystar)
28 Xinfeng Road Fangqian Town
Wuxi, Jiangsu, 214111, China
Tel.: (86) 510 88278561
Fax: (86) 510 88278571
Web Site: www.joystar.com.hk
Year Founded: 2003
8321—(HKG)
Rev.: $26,513,018
Assets: $38,259,976
Liabilities: $8,397,129
Net Worth: $29,862,847
Earnings: $1,715,262
Emp.: 184
Fiscal Year-end: 12/31/12
Business Description:
Automotive Interior Mfr
S.I.C.: 2396
N.A.I.C.S.: 336360
Personnel:
Yuejin Zhuang *(Chm & CEO)*
Ho Yin Wong *(Sec)*
Board of Directors:
Yuejin Zhuang
Xueben Feng
Wai Ho Mak
Ping Pak
Bixia Ruan
Yanfei Tang
Ho Yin Wong

Codan Trust Company (Cayman) Limited
Cricket Square Hutchins Drive
PO Box 2681
Georgetown, Grand Cayman, Cayman Islands
Transfer Agents:
Tricor Investor Services Limited
26th Floor Tesbury Centre 28 Queens Road East
Wanchai, China (Hong Kong)

Codan Trust Company (Cayman) Limited
Cricket Square Hutchins Drive
PO Box 2681
Georgetown, Grand Cayman, Cayman Islands

CHINA AUTOMOTIVE SYSTEMS, INC.

1 Henglong Road Yu Qiao Development Zone Shashi District
Jingzhou, Hubei, China 434000
Tel.: (86) 7168329196
Fax: (86) 2759808808
E-Mail: richard@chl.com.cn
Web Site: www.caasauto.com
Year Founded: 1999
CAAS—(NASDAQ)
Rev.: $336,005,000
Assets: $485,825,000
Liabilities: $253,425,000
Net Worth: $232,400,000
Earnings: $25,486,000
Emp.: 3,617
Fiscal Year-end: 12/31/12
Business Description:
Power Steering Systems & Components Mfr
S.I.C.: 3711
N.A.I.C.S.: 336211
Personnel:
Hanlin Chen *(Chm)*
Qizhou Wu *(CEO)*
Jie Li *(CFO)*
Daming Hu *(Chief Acctg Officer)*
Andy Yiu Wong Tse *(Sr VP)*
Shaobo Wang *(Sr VP)*
Shengbin Yu *(Sr VP)*
Board of Directors:
Hanlin Chen
Robert Tung
Arthur Wong
Qizhou Wu
Guangxun Xu
Transfer Agent:
Securities Transfer Corporation
Frisco, TX 75034
Subsidiaries:

Jingzhou Henglong Automotive Parts Co., Ltd. (1)
No 1 Henglong Road Yuqiao Development Zone
Jingzhou, 434000, China
Tel.: (86) 7168327809
Fax: (86) 7168327827
Automobile Parts Mfr
S.I.C.: 3711
N.A.I.C.S.: 336111

Jingzhou Hengsheng Automotive System Co., Ltd. (1)
Cross Of Shacen Road Dongfang Ave Development Zone
Jingzhou, Hubei, 434000, China
Tel.: (86) 7168304756
Fax: (86) 7168304739
Emp.: 22
Auto Steering System Mfr & Distr
S.I.C.: 3714
N.A.I.C.S.: 336330

Shashi Jiulong Power Steering Gears Co., Ltd. (1)
1 Henglong Road
Yu Qiao Development Zone
Shashi District, Jinzhou, Hubei, 434000, China (81%)
Tel.: (86) 7168327777
E-Mail: jiulong@chl.com.cn
Emp.: 700
Power Steering Components Mfr
S.I.C.: 3714
N.A.I.C.S.: 336330
Y. Xie *(Gen Mgr)*

Joint Ventures:

Shenyang Jinbei Henglong Automotive Steering System Co. , Ltd. (1)
No 15 Yunhai Road
Development Zone, 110141 Shenyang, Liaoning, China (70%)
Tel.: (86) 2425377031
Fax: (86) 2425815649
E-Mail: jinbeihenglong@163.com
Web Site: www.chl.com.cn/english/car/jinbeihl1.htm
Motor Vehicle Parts Mfr
S.I.C.: 3714
N.A.I.C.S.: 336390

Universal Sensors, Inc. (1)
Henglong Group Building No 1 Guan Shan 1 Road
East Lake Hi-Tech Zone, Wuhan, Hubei, 430073, China (60%)
Tel.: (86) 13476067938
Fax: (86) 2759818575
E-Mail: sales@usisensor.com
Web Site: www.usisensor.com
Measuring & Controlling Device Mfr
S.I.C.: 3829
N.A.I.C.S.: 334519

U.S. Subsidiary:

Henglong USA Corporation (1)
1166 E Big Beaver Rd
Troy, MI 48083
Tel.: (248) 689-2227
Fax: (248) 689-2226
E-Mail: info@caas-usa.com
Web Site: www.caas-usa.com
Automobile Parts Mfr
S.I.C.: 3714
N.A.I.C.S.: 336390

CHINA AVIATION OIL SINGAPORE CORPORATION LIMITED

(See Under China National Aviation Fuel Group Corporation)

CHINA BAK BATTERY INC.

BAK Industrial Park No 1 BAK Street
Kuichong Town
Longgang District, Shenzhen, 518119, China
Tel.: (86) 755 61886818
Fax: (86) 755 89770014
Web Site: www.bak.com.cn
CBAK—(NASDAQ)
Rev.: $185,552,560
Assets: $340,605,180
Liabilities: $383,877,345
Net Worth: ($43,272,165)
Earnings: ($116,029,079)
Emp.: 3,400
Fiscal Year-end: 09/30/13
Business Description:
Rechargeable Batteries
S.I.C.: 3691
N.A.I.C.S.: 335911
Personnel:
Xiangqian Li *(Chm, Pres & CEO)*
Board of Directors:
Xiangqian Li
Martha C. Agee
Jianjun He
Huanyu Mao
Chunzhi Zhang
Subsidiaries:

BAK Battery Ltd. (1)
BAK Industrial Park
1 BAK Street Kuichong, Shenzhen, 518119, China
Tel.: (86) 75589770060
Web Site: www.bak.com.cn/contact.asp
Rechargeable Battery
S.I.C.: 3692
N.A.I.C.S.: 335912
Xiangqian Li *(Gen Mgr)*

BAK International Ltd. (1)
BAK Industrial Park Kuichong Town
Lonngang District, Shenzhen, 518119, China
Tel.: (86) 75589770088
E-Mail: info@bak.com.cn
Emp.: 7,000
Rechargeable Batteries
S.I.C.: 3692
N.A.I.C.S.: 335912
Xiangqian Li *(Gen Mgr)*

Non-U.S. Subsidiaries:

BAK Battery Canada Ltd. (1)
1750 Coast Meridian Road
Port Coquitlam, BC, V3C 6R8, Canada
Tel.: (604) 464-5221
Battery Mfr
S.I.C.: 3691
N.A.I.C.S.: 335911

BAK Europe GmbH (1)
Max Nonne Str 45
22419 Hamburg, Germany
Tel.: (49) 40 533 27 36 88
E-Mail: info@bak-europe.de
Web Site: www.bak-europe.de
Telecommunication Equipment Mfr & Distr
S.I.C.: 3669
N.A.I.C.S.: 334290

CHINA BANKING CORPORATION

8745 Paseo de Roxas Corner Villar St
Makati, 1226, Philippines
Tel.: (63) 8855555
Fax: (63) 8920220
E-Mail: online@chinabank.ph
Web Site: www.chinabank.ph
Year Founded: 1920
CHIB—(PHI)
Int. Income: $322,064,798
Assets: $7,926,077,423
Liabilities: $6,890,361,174
Net Worth: $1,035,716,250
Earnings: $123,281,370
Emp.: 5,198
Fiscal Year-end: 12/31/12
Business Description:
International & Commercial Banking Services
S.I.C.: 6029
N.A.I.C.S.: 522110
Personnel:
Hans T. Sy *(Chm)*
Gilbert U. Dee *(Vice Chm)*
Peter S. Dee *(Pres & CEO)*
Ricardo R. Chua *(COO & Sr Exec VP)*
Ananias S. Cornelio, III *(Chief Risk Officer & First VP)*
Corazon I. Morando *(Sec & VP)*
Samuel L. Chiong *(Sr VP & Deputy Head-Branch Banking Grp)*
Alexander C. Escucha *(Sr VP & Head-Corp Plng Div & IR Office)*
Antonio S. Espedido, Jr. *(Sr VP & Head-Treasury)*
Rene J. Sarmiento *(Sr VP & Head-Trust Grp)*
William C. Whang *(Sr VP & Head-Institutional Banking Grp)*
Nancy D. Yang *(Sr VP & Head-Branch Banking Grp & Binondo Bus Center)*

Ramon R. Zamora *(Sr VP & Head-Centralized Ops & Remittance Bus Div)*
Alberto Emilio V. Ramos *(Sr VP)*
Board of Directors:
Hans T. Sy
Ricardo R. Chua
Gilbert U. Dee
Joaquin T. Dee
Peter S. Dee
Robert F. Kuan
Jose T. Sio
Harley T. Sy
Herbert T. Sy
Dy Tiong
Alberto S. Yao
Transfer Agent:
Stock Transfer Service Inc
Unit 34-D Rufino Pacific Tower 6784 Ayala Avenue
Makati, Philippines

CHINA BCT PHARMACY GROUP, INC.

No 102 Chengzhan Road
Liuzhou, Guangxi, China 545007
Tel.: (86) 7723638318
Web Site: www.china-bct.com
Year Founded: 2006
CNBI—(OTC)
Rev.: $241,869,347
Assets: $244,972,562
Liabilities: $110,707,374
Net Worth: $134,265,188
Earnings: $21,050,927
Emp.: 1,677
Fiscal Year-end: 12/31/12
Business Description:
Pharmaceuticals & Medicines Mfr & Retailer
S.I.C.: 2834
N.A.I.C.S.: 325412
Personnel:
Huitian Tang *(Chm & CEO)*
Xiaoyan Zhang *(CFO)*
Jing Hua Li *(COO)*
Board of Directors:
Huitian Tang
Kam-Cheung Chin
Manwai Chiu
Simon Choi
Yunli Lou
Xiaoyan Zhang
Legal Counsel:
Loeb & Loeb
345 Park Ave.
New York, NY 10154
Tel.: (212) 408-4800
Transfer Agent:
Empire Stock Transfer, Inc.
1859 Whitney Mesa Dr
Henderson, NV 89009

CHINA BEARING (SINGAPORE) LTD.

161A Thomson Road Goldhill Centre
Singapore, 307614, Singapore
Tel.: (65) 62873059
Fax: (65) 62344402
Web Site: www.ym-bearing.cn
AD7—(SES)
Rev.: $16,955,712
Assets: $37,507,496
Liabilities: $11,617,144
Net Worth: $25,890,352
Earnings: ($573,545)
Fiscal Year-end: 12/31/12
Business Description:
Bearing Products Mfr
S.I.C.: 3568
N.A.I.C.S.: 333613
Personnel:
Anxi Zhang *(CEO & Mng Dir)*
Kok Liang Chew *(Co-Sec)*
Shirley Sey Liy Tan *(Co-Sec)*
Board of Directors:
Yuankai Zhang
David Yew Choong Chin
Ruicheng Du
William Choon Kow Teo
Yihe Xu
Kian Peng Yap
Anxi Zhang
Transfer Agent:
Tricor Barbinder Share Registration Services
80 Robinson Road 02-00
Singapore, Singapore

Non-U.S. Subsidiary:

Linyi Kaiyuan Bearing Co., Ltd. **(1)**
Yinan Economic Development Zone
Yinan, Linyi, Shandong, 276000, China
Tel.: (86) 5393641049
Fax: (86) 5393223179
E-Mail: sales@ym-bearing.cn
Web Site: www.ym-bearing.cn
Emp.: 1,182
Bearings Mfr
S.I.C.: 3562
N.A.I.C.S.: 332991
Zhang Anxi *(Pres)*

CHINA BEST GROUP HOLDING LIMITED

Room 3405 Bank of America Tower
12 Harcourt Road
Central, China (Hong Kong)
Tel.: (852) 28778838
Fax: (852) 27231154
E-Mail: info@cbgroup.com.hk
Web Site: www.cbgroup.com.hk
0370—(HKG)
Sls.: $19,516,969
Assets: $57,739,297
Liabilities: $11,727,874
Net Worth: $46,011,423
Earnings: $329,725
Emp.: 92
Fiscal Year-end: 12/31/12
Business Description:
Coke Mfr & Sales
S.I.C.: 5052
N.A.I.C.S.: 423520
Personnel:
Boqi Huang *(Chm)*
Chunyu Du *(Deputy Chm)*
Yu Ho *(CFO & Sec)*
Board of Directors:
Boqi Huang
Chunyu Du
Angel Yan Ki Wong
Liang Zhang
Mingchi Zhou
Butterfield Fulcrum Group (Bermuda) Limited
26 Burnaby Street
Hamilton, HM 11, Bermuda
Transfer Agents:
Tricor Tengis Limited
26th Floor Tesbury Centre 28 Queen's Road East
Wanchai, China (Hong Kong)
Tel.: (852) 29801333
Fax: (852) 28108185
Butterfield Fulcrum Group (Bermuda) Limited
26 Burnaby Street
Hamilton, HM 11, Bermuda

U.S. Subsidiary:

Jet Dispatch Limited **(1)**
15615 146th Ave Ste 213
Jamaica, NY 11434-4211
Tel.: (718) 949-8325
Fax: (718) 528-7713
Freight Forwarding Services
S.I.C.: 4731
N.A.I.C.S.: 488510

Non-U.S. Subsidiary:

Jet Air (Singapore) Private Limited **(1)**
02-222 Air freight terminal 2 95 Airport Cargo Rd
Singapore, Singapore
Tel.: (65) 65427966
Fax: (65) 65423083
E-Mail: jasin@pacific.net.sg
Emp.: 3
Air Freight Forwarding Services
S.I.C.: 4522
N.A.I.C.S.: 481212
Katherine Sim *(Mgr-Admin)*

CHINA BILINGUAL TECHNOLOGY & EDUCATION GROUP INC.

No 2 Longbao Street Xiaodian zone
Taiyuan, Shanxi, 030031, China
Tel.: (86) 3517963988
Web Site: www.chinabilingualedu.com
Year Founded: 2009
CBLY—(OTC)
Emp.: 1,876
Business Description:
Educational Services
S.I.C.: 8299
N.A.I.C.S.: 611710
Personnel:
Zhiqing Ren *(Chm & CEO)*
Zhao Hegui *(Exec VP)*
Mingxiao Pan *(Exec VP)*
Board of Directors:
Zhiqing Ren
Dora Dong
Ying Fengmei
Mingxiao Pan
Jun Zhang
Transfer Agent:
Island Stock Transfer
15500 Roosevelt Blvd Ste 301
Clearwater, FL 33760

CHINA BILLION RESOURCES LIMITED

China Merchants Tower Room 2811 28th Floor No 168-200 Connaught Road
Central, China (Hong Kong)
Tel.: (852) 22014555
Fax: (852) 28512990
E-Mail: contact@chinabillion.net
Web Site: www.chinabillion.net
0274—(HKG)
Sales Range: $10-24.9 Million
Business Description:
Home & Personal Care Products Mfr
S.I.C.: 2844
N.A.I.C.S.: 325620
Personnel:
Xiaobo Long *(Chm)*
Weiqi Zuo *(CEO)*
Cheung Yuk Chuen *(Sec)*
Board of Directors:
Xiaobo Long
Yi Chung Chen
Tsung-Nien Chiang
Shunxing Jin
Jing Zhu
Weiqi Zuo
Legal Counsel:
Leung & Lau
13/F Public Bank Centre 120 Des Voeux Road
Central, China (Hong Kong)
Conyers Dill & Pearman
Cricket Square, Hutchins Drive P.O. Box 2681
KY1-1111 Georgetown, Cayman Islands
Cheng Wong Lam & Partners
50th Floor Bank of China Tower 1 Garden Road
Central, China (Hong Kong)
Bank of Butterfield International (Cayman) Ltd
Butterfield House Fort Street PO Box 705
Georgetown, Cayman Islands
Transfer Agents:
Tricor Tengis Limited
26/F Tesbury Centre, 28 Queens Road East
Hong Kong, China (Hong Kong)
Bank of Butterfield International (Cayman) Ltd
Butterfield House Fort Street PO Box 705
Georgetown, Cayman Islands

Subsidiaries:

Cristal Marketing Management Company Limited **(1)**
68 Mody Road Empire Centre Level 3 Room 305-307
Hong Kong, China (Hong Kong)
Tel.: (852) 24109866
Fax: (852) 29732033
Beauty Treatment Services & Cosmetics Retailer
S.I.C.: 5122
N.A.I.C.S.: 424210

Global Idea (Intl) Company Limited **(1)**
Rm 3402-08 34 F Convention Plz Ofc Twr 1 Harbour Rd
Wanchai, China (Hong Kong)
Tel.: (852) 25222811
Fax: (852) 29730033
E-Mail: sales@global-idea.com.hk
Web Site: www.global-idea.com.hk
Personal Care Products Mfr
S.I.C.: 2844
N.A.I.C.S.: 325620
David Yip *(CEO)*

CHINA BIO-ENERGY CORP.

Pudong Building 2nd Floor Jiulong Avenue
Longwen Districe, Zhangzhou, Fujian, China
Tel.: (86) 596 296 7018
Year Founded: 1988
CHIOD—(OTC)
Emp.: 7
Business Description:
Biodiesel Fuels Producer & Distr
S.I.C.: 5989
N.A.I.C.S.: 454310
Personnel:
PokKam Li *(CEO)*
Ming Yi *(CFO)*
Yujia Gao *(Sec)*
Board of Directors:
Yujia Gao
PokKam Li
Cherrie Liu
Ming Yi
Transfer Agent:
Corporate Stock Transfer, Inc.
3200 Cherry Creek Dr S Ste 430
Denver, CO 80209
Tel.: (303) 282-4800
Fax: (303) 282-5800

CHINA BIOLOGIC PRODUCTS, INC.

18th Floor Jialong International Building
19 Chaoyang Park Road
Chaoyang District, Beijing, 100125, China
Tel.: (86) 10 6598 3111
Fax: (86) 10 6598 3222
E-Mail: ir@chinabiologic.com
Web Site: www.chinabiologic.com
CBPO—(NASDAQ)
Sls.: $203,356,856
Assets: $403,781,207
Liabilities: $99,811,598
Net Worth: $303,969,609
Earnings: $76,861,064
Emp.: 1,533
Fiscal Year-end: 12/31/13
Business Description:
Biological Products Mfr
S.I.C.: 2836
N.A.I.C.S.: 325414

China Biologic Products, Inc.—(Continued)

Personnel:
David Xiaoying Gao *(Chm, Pres & CEO)*
Ming Yang *(CFO, Treas & VP-Fin & Compliance)*
Board of Directors:
David Xiaoying Gao
Bing Li
David Li
Wenfang Liu
Yungang Lu
Sean S. Shao
Zhijun Tong
Albert Yeung
Charles Zhang

Subsidiary:

Shandong Taibang Biological Products Co. Ltd. **(1)**
No 14 Hushan E Rd
Taishan District, 271000 Taishan, Shandong, China
Tel.: (86) 5386203897
Fax: (86) 5386203897
Biopharmaceutical Whslr
S.I.C.: 5912
N.A.I.C.S.: 446110

CHINA-BIOTICS, INC.

No 26 Orient Global Headquarter Lane 118 Yonghe Road
Zhabei District, Shanghai, 200072, China
Tel.: (86) 21 58349748
E-Mail: ir@chn-biotics.com
Web Site: www.chn-biotics.com
CHBT—(OTC)
Sls.: $75,716,189
Assets: $278,011,788
Liabilities: $56,982,665
Net Worth: $221,029,123
Earnings: $15,383,815
Emp.: 341
Fiscal Year-end: 03/31/13
Business Description:
Probiotic Products Developer for Dietary Supplements & Food Additives
S.I.C.: 2836
N.A.I.C.S.: 325414
Personnel:
Jinan Song *(Chm, Pres, CEO, Treas & Sec)*
Yihan Yan *(Interim CFO)*
Board of Directors:
Jinan Song
Ji Wei Chin
Ivan Siu-Lun Chu
Wen Min Du

CHINA BLUECHEMICAL LTD.

65/F Bank of China Tower 1 Garden Road
Central, China (Hong Kong)
Tel.: (852) 22132502
Fax: (852) 25259322
Web Site: www.chinabluechem.com.cn
3983—(HKG OTC)
Rev.: $1,705,923,667
Assets: $2,721,340,364
Liabilities: $397,893,357
Net Worth: $2,323,447,006
Earnings: $315,098,037
Emp.: 5,935
Fiscal Year-end: 12/31/12
Business Description:
Natural Gas Mfr & Sales
S.I.C.: 1311
N.A.I.C.S.: 211111
Personnel:
Hui Li *(Chm)*
Kewen Qiu *(Chm-Supervisory Bd)*
Yexin Yang *(Pres & CEO)*
Changsheng Quan *(CFO, Sec & VP)*
Kai Chen *(Exec VP)*
Yong Fang *(Exec VP)*
Fan Zhou *(Exec VP)*
Board of Directors:
Hui Li
Zongqin Gu
Eddie Kwan Hung Lee
Karen Kit Ying Lee
Shubo Yang
Yexin Yang
Lei Zhu
Supervisory Board of Directors:
Kewen Qiu
Jinggui Huang
Lijie Liu
Legal Counsel:
Jun He Law Offices
China Resources Building 20th Floor 8 Jianguomenbei Avenue
Beijing, China
Freshfields Bruckhaus Deringer
11F Two Exchange Square
Central, China (Hong Kong)
Transfer Agent:
Computershare Hong Kong Investor Services Limited
Shops 1712-1716 17th Floor Hopewell Centre
183 Queens Road East
Wanchai, China (Hong Kong)

CHINA BOON HOLDINGS LTD

Room 2118 Leighton Centre 77 Leighton Road
Causeway Bay, China (Hong Kong)
Tel.: (852) 31152128
Fax: (852) 28080791
Web Site: www.china-boon.com
922—(HKG)
Rev.: $16,428,875
Assets: $102,587,849
Liabilities: $45,809,745
Net Worth: $56,778,103
Earnings: ($564,672)
Emp.: 13
Fiscal Year-end: 03/31/13
Business Description:
Holding Company; Consumer Electronics; Scrap Metal; Leather; Cemetery Services
S.I.C.: 6719
N.A.I.C.S.: 551112
Personnel:
Hua Shi *(Chm & CEO)*
Fei Shing Law *(Sec)*
Board of Directors:
Hua Shi
Xiao Dong Fu
Siu Ngor Lau
Fei Shing Law
Xing Gang Qi
Mingzhen Shen
Jun Shi
Yan Tang
Ping Yu
Butterfield Fulcrum Group (Bermuda) Limited
Rosebank Centre 11 Bermudiana Rd
Pembroke, Bermuda
Transfer Agents:
Tricor Abacus Limited
Tesbury Centre 28 Queen's Road East
Hong Kong, China (Hong Kong)
Butterfield Fulcrum Group (Bermuda) Limited
Rosebank Centre 11 Bermudiana Rd
Pembroke, Bermuda

CHINA BOTANIC PHARMACEUTICAL INC.

Level 11 Changjiang International Building
No 28 Changjiang Road Nangang District, Harbin, Heilongjiang, 150090, China
Tel.: (86) 451 5762 0378
E-Mail: ir@renhuang.com
Web Site: www.renhuang.com
Year Founded: 1988
Sales Range: $50-74.9 Million
Emp.: 83
Business Description:
Pharmaceutical Mfr
S.I.C.: 2834
N.A.I.C.S.: 325412
Personnel:
Shaoming Li *(Chm, Pres & CEO)*
Weiqiu Dong *(CFO)*
Jingwang Lou *(CMO & Chief Sls Officer)*
Board of Directors:
Shaoming Li
Dianjun Pi
Changxiong Sun
Bingchun Wu
Jack Zhao

CHINA BPIC SURVEYING INSTRUMENTS AG

Room 413 Long Guanzhiye Building Hui Longguan
Chang Ping District, Beijing, China
Tel.: (86) 10 5981 2259
E-Mail: bpic@bpicsurvey.com
Web Site: www.bpicsurvey.com
Year Founded: 2012
CSY—(DEU)
Business Description:
Holding Company; Surveying Instruments Mfr
S.I.C.: 6719
N.A.I.C.S.: 551112
Personnel:
Matthias Schroeder *(Chm-Supervisory Bd)*
Wei Xie *(Mng Dir & Chm-Mgmt Bd)*
Took Jwee Ngoh *(CFO & Member-Mgmt Bd)*
Yan Zhao *(Member-Mgmt Bd)*
Supervisory Board of Directors:
Matthias Schroeder
Jie Luo
Moll Xiaoping Zhao

Subsidiary:

Beijing Precise Instruments Co., Ltd. **(1)**
Room 313 Unit 2 Building 3 ZhuJiangmoer International
ChangPing District, Beijing, China CN
Tel.: (86) 10 5722 7983
E-Mail: bpic@bpicsurvey.com
Web Site: www.bpicsurvey.com
Surveying Instruments Mfr
S.I.C.: 3829
N.A.I.C.S.: 334519
Wei Xie *(Mng Dir)*

CHINA BRIGHT STONE INVESTMENT MANAGEMENT GROUP

Unit 2209 22/F Wu Chung House 213 Queens Road East
Wanchai, China (Hong Kong)
Tel.: (852) 39737725
Web Site: www.chinabrightstone.com
Business Description:
Investment Management Services
S.I.C.: 6211
N.A.I.C.S.: 523999
Personnel:
Feng Gao *(Chm)*

CHINA CABLECOM HOLDINGS, LTD.

Room 458 North Building Wenjiao Plaza
No 1 Qingnian Dong Road, Jinan, 250001, China
Tel.: (86) 21 6207 9731
Year Founded: 2006
CABLF—(OTC)
Int. Income: $144,022
Assets: $11,728,116
Liabilities: $5,770,473
Net Worth: $5,957,643
Earnings: ($5,988,844)
Emp.: 11
Fiscal Year-end: 12/31/12
Business Description:
Cable Television Network Services
S.I.C.: 4841
N.A.I.C.S.: 515210
Personnel:
Clive Ng *(Chm)*
Yue Pu *(CEO)*
Sikan Tong *(CFO)*
Board of Directors:
Clive Ng
Mark A. Nordlicht
Kerry S. Propper

CHINA CARBON GRAPHITE GROUP, INC.

787 Xicheng Wai
Chengguantown, Xinghe, Inner Mongolia, China
Tel.: (86) 4747209723
E-Mail: ir@chinacarboninc.com
Web Site: www.chinacarboninc.com
CHGI.OB—(OTCB)
Sls.: $31,482,852
Assets: $141,375,680
Liabilities: $94,084,122
Net Worth: $47,291,558
Earnings: ($3,561,515)
Emp.: 560
Fiscal Year-end: 12/31/12
Business Description:
Carbon Graphite Product Mfr
S.I.C.: 3624
N.A.I.C.S.: 335991
Personnel:
Donghai Yu *(CEO)*
Zhenfang Yang *(Interim CFO)*
Board of Directors:
John Chen
Dong Jin
Hongbo Liu
Donghai Yu
Philip Yizhao Zhang
Transfer Agent:
Empire Stock Transfer Inc
2470 St Rose Pkwy Ste 304
Henderson, NV 89014

Subsidiary:

Xinghe Yongle Carbon Co., Ltd. **(1)**
787 Xicheng Wai
Chengguan, Xinghe, Inner Mongolia, 013650, China
Tel.: (86) 4747209723
Fax: (86) 4747209799
Graphite Products Mfr
S.I.C.: 3624
N.A.I.C.S.: 335991

CHINA CEETOP.COM, INC.

A2803 Lianhe Guangchang 5022 Binhe Dadao
Futian District, Shenzhen, China 518026
Tel.: (86) 755 3336 6628
Year Founded: 2003
CTOP—(OTCB)
Sls.: $4,774,156
Assets: $553,629
Liabilities: $697,546
Net Worth: ($143,917)
Earnings: ($1,393,388)
Emp.: 21
Fiscal Year-end: 12/31/12
Business Description:
Online Shopping Services
S.I.C.: 5961
N.A.I.C.S.: 454111

Personnel:
Weiliang Liu *(Chm, Pres, CEO & Sec)*
Jia Shengming *(CFO)*

CHINA CENTURY DRAGON MEDIA, INC.

Room 801 7 Wenchanger Road
Jiangbei, Huizhou, Guangdong, China
Tel.: (86) 752 3138789
CCDM—(OTC)
Sales Range: $50-74.9 Million
Emp.: 98
Business Description:
Television Advertising Services
S.I.C.: 7319
N.A.I.C.S.: 541890
Personnel:
HuiHua Li *(Chm)*
HaiMing Fu *(CEO)*
Dapeng Duan *(CFO & Sec)*
Board of Directors:
HuiHua Li
Yue Lu
ZhiFeng Yan
Fang Yuan

CHINA CERAMICS CO., LTD.

Junbing Industrial Zone Anhai
Jingjiang, Fujian, China
Tel.: (86) 595 8576 5053
Fax: (86) 595 8576 5053
Web Site: www.cceramics.com
Year Founded: 2007
CCCL—(NASDAQ)
Rev.: $229,520,935
Assets: $265,502,367
Liabilities: $36,251,635
Net Worth: $229,250,732
Earnings: $38,732,554
Emp.: 2,297
Fiscal Year-end: 12/31/12
Business Description:
Holding Company; Ceramic Products Mfr
S.I.C.: 6719
N.A.I.C.S.: 551112
Personnel:
Jia Dong Huang *(Chm)*
Edmund Man Hen *(CFO)*
Wei Feng Su *(Sec)*
Board of Directors:
Jia Dong Huang
Davis Yan Cheng
Shen Cheng Liang
Jianwei Liu
William L. Stulginsky
Pei Zhi Su
Wei Feng Su

CHINA CGAME, INC.

Research Building No 801 Wuzhong Road
Science & Education Indus Park
Wujin District, Changzhou, Jiangsu, 213164, China
Tel.: (86) 756 853 8908
Fax: (86) 756 853 8919
E-Mail: zh@kge-group.com
Web Site: www.caebuilding.com
Year Founded: 2004
CCGM—(OTC)
Sales Range: $25-49.9 Million
Emp.: 416
Business Description:
Designs, Engineers & Installs Curtain Wall Systems Including Wooden & Metal Curtain Walls
S.I.C.: 8711
N.A.I.C.S.: 541330
Personnel:
Jun Tang *(Chm)*
Luo Ken Yi *(Pres)*
Zhixin Xing *(CEO)*
Qin Lu *(Acting CFO & Sec)*
Board of Directors:
Jun Tang
Chen Huang
Shibin Jo
Kelly Wang
Chia Yong Whatt
Zhixin Xing
Ping Xu
Luo Ken Yi

Non-U.S. Subsidiary:

Techwell Engineering Ltd. **(1)**
Room 403 Lu Plaza 2 Wing Yip Street
Kwun Tong, Kowloon, China (Hong Kong) (100%)
Tel.: (852) 2793 1083
Manufactures & Constructs External Building Facades Including Roofing Systems for Buildings & Curtain Walls
S.I.C.: 8711
N.A.I.C.S.: 541330

CHINA CHANGJIANG MINING & NEW ENERGY CO., LTD.

Seventeenth Floor Xinhui Mansion
Gaoxin Road
Hi-Tech Zone, Xi'an, China 710075
Tel.: (86) 29 88331685
Fax: (86) 29 88332335
Web Site: www.sxcjny.cn
Year Founded: 1969
Rev.: $1,188,119
Assets: $23,333,023
Liabilities: $10,604,487
Net Worth: $12,728,536
Earnings: $615,507
Emp.: 16
Fiscal Year-end: 12/31/12
Business Description:
Gold & Other Metal Mining Services
Import Export
S.I.C.: 1041
N.A.I.C.S.: 212221
Personnel:
Wei Dong Chen *(Chm, Pres & CEO)*
Ping Li *(CFO)*

CHINA CHEMICAL & PHARMACEUTICAL CO., LTD.

No 23 Xiangyang Rd Zhongzheng District
100 Taipei, Taiwan
Tel.: (886) 223124239
Fax: (886) 223615143
E-Mail: info@ccpc.com.tw
Web Site: www.ccpc.com.tw
1701—(TAI)
Sales Range: $75-99.9 Million
Business Description:
Pharmaceutical Products Mfr & Distr
S.I.C.: 2834
N.A.I.C.S.: 325412
Personnel:
Shiun Sheng Wang *(Chm & Gen Mgr)*

Subsidiaries:

Chunghwa Yuming Healthcare Co., Ltd. **(1)**
No 23 Xiangyang Road
Zhongzheng Dist, 100 Taipei, Taiwan
Tel.: (886) 223124712
Fax: (886) 223753811
Web Site: www.cyh365.com.tw
Emp.: 1,200
Pharmaceutical Products Mfr & Distr
S.I.C.: 5122
N.A.I.C.S.: 424210

Tai Rung Development Co., Ltd. **(1)**
No 28 Dongsing St
Shulin District, Taipei, 238, Taiwan
Tel.: (886) 286863079
Fax: (886) 226810917
Web Site: www.ccpg.com.tw
Ampoules & Plastic Containers Mfr
S.I.C.: 3085
N.A.I.C.S.: 326160

Plants:

China Chemical & Pharmaceutical Co., Ltd. - Hsinfong Plant **(1)**
No 182-1 Kengzikou
Xinfeng Township, Hsin-chu, 304, Taiwan
Tel.: (886) 3 559 9866
Fax: (886) 3 559 9094
Web Site: www.ccpc.com.tw/english/05_about/01_detail.aspx?AID=6
Pharmaceutical Products Mfr
S.I.C.: 2834
N.A.I.C.S.: 325412

China Chemical & Pharmaceutical Co., Ltd. - Taichung Plant **(1)**
No 10 Gongyequ 15th Road
Xitun District, Taichung, 407, Taiwan
Tel.: (886) 423596818
Fax: (886) 423596823
Pharmaceutical Products Mfr
S.I.C.: 2834
N.A.I.C.S.: 325412

CHINA CHEMICAL CORP.

1 Electric Power Plant Road
Zhou Cun District, Zibo, China
Tel.: (86) 533 6166 8699
Web Site: www.chinachemicalcorp.com
Year Founded: 2008
CHCC—(OTC)
Sales Range: $75-99.9 Million
Emp.: 176
Business Description:
Chemical Producer
S.I.C.: 2899
N.A.I.C.S.: 325998
Personnel:
Feng Lu *(Chm, Pres & CEO)*
Lingliang Lu *(Vice Chm)*
Bin Li *(CFO & Chief Acctg Officer)*
Kai Yan *(COO & Chief Admin Officer)*
Lianjun Zhang *(CMO)*
Board of Directors:
Feng Lu
Hui Chen
Lingliang Lu
Fengzhen Zhou

CHINA CINDA ASSET MANAGEMENT CO., LTD.

1 Building 9 Yard Naoshikou Avenue
Xicheng District, Beijing, 100031, China
Tel.: (86) 10 63080000
Fax: (86) 10 63080266
Web Site: www.cinda.com.cn
1359—(HKG)
Business Description:
Asset Management & Consulting Services
S.I.C.: 6211
N.A.I.C.S.: 523999
Personnel:
Jianhang Hou *(Chm)*
Jingfan Zang *(Pres)*
Zhenhong Luo *(Chief Risk Officer)*
Xiaozhou Chen *(Member-Mgmt Bd)*
Junhua Yang *(Member-Mgmt Bd)*
Weidong Zhang *(Sec)*
Board of Directors:
Jianhang Hou
Stephen Tso Tung Chang
Xikui Li
Shengliang Lu
Dong Qiu
Shurong Wang
Yuping Xiao
Dingbo Xu
Zhichao Xu
Boqin Yin
Hong Yuan
Jingfan Zang

CHINA CITY RAILWAY TRANSPORTATION TECHNOLOGY HOLDINGS COMPANY LIMITED

Unit 4407 44/F Cosco Tower 183 Queen's Road
Central, China (Hong Kong)
Tel.: (852) 2545 1555
E-Mail: enquiry@ccrtt.com.hk
Web Site: www.ccrtt.com.hk
Year Founded: 2011
CN6—(DEU HKG)
Rev.: $32,770,708
Assets: $89,307,933
Liabilities: $26,205,993
Net Worth: $63,101,940
Earnings: $7,613,466
Emp.: 190
Fiscal Year-end: 06/30/13
Business Description:
Railway Application Software Development Services
S.I.C.: 7371
N.A.I.C.S.: 541511
Personnel:
Wei Cao *(CEO & Compliance Officer)*
Patrick Kwok Fai Lau *(Sec)*
Board of Directors:
Zhenqing Tian
Jinrong Bai
Wei Cao
Rui Chen
Steven Bruce Gallagher
Weiya Hao
Zhaoguang Hu
Zhenbang Luo

Royal Bank of Canada Trust Company (Cayman) Limited
4th Floor Royal Bank House 24 Shedden Road
Georgetown, Cayman Islands

Transfer Agents:
Tricor Investor Services Limited
26th Floor Tesbury Centre 28 Queens Road East
Wanchai, China (Hong Kong)

Royal Bank of Canada Trust Company (Cayman) Limited
4th Floor Royal Bank House 24 Shedden Road
Georgetown, Cayman Islands

CHINA CLEAN ENERGY INC.

Jiangyin Industrial Zone
Jiangyin Town, Fuqing, Fujian, 350309, China
Tel.: (86) 59185773387
E-Mail: william.chen@chinacleanenergyinc.com
Web Site: www.chinacleanenergyinc.com
Year Founded: 2006
CCGY—(OTC)
Sales Range: $50-74.9 Million
Emp.: 120
Business Description:
Biodiesel Fuel & Chemicals Mfr
S.I.C.: 2999
N.A.I.C.S.: 324199
Personnel:
Tai-ming Ou *(CEO)*
Hua Shan Wang *(CFO & Chief Acctg Officer)*
Ri-wen Xue *(COO)*
Yun He *(Sr VP-Sls & Distr)*
Board of Directors:
Yu Lin
Tai-ming Ou
Qin Yang

Subsidiary:

Fujian Zhongde Technology Co., Ltd. **(1)**
Fulu Industry District
Longtian Town, Fuqing, 350315, China
Tel.: (86) 59185773387
Fax: (86) 591 28397168

CHINA CLEAN ENERGY INC.—(Continued)

E-Mail: sales@fj-zd.com
Web Site: www.fj-zd.com
Emp.: 200
Industrial Chemicals Mfr
S.I.C.: 2819
N.A.I.C.S.: 325180
Kiaming Ou *(Gen Mgr)*

CHINA CNR CORPORATION LIMITED

CNR Mansion 15 Area One
Fangchengyuan
Fengtai District, Beijing, 100078, China
Tel.: (86) 1051897277
Fax: (86) 1052608280
Web Site: www.chinacnr.com
Year Founded: 1880
601299—(SHG)
Sales Range: $1-4.9 Billion

Business Description:
Holding Company; Diesel & Electric Locomotive Engine, Rolling Stock & Other Locomotive Parts & Equipment Designer, Mfr, Refurbisher & Maintenance Services
S.I.C.: 6719
N.A.I.C.S.: 551112

Personnel:
Dianguo Cui *(Chm)*

Subsidiaries:

Beijing February 7th Railway Transportation Equipment Co., Ltd. **(1)**
No 1 Yanggongzhuang
Fengtai District, Beijing, 100072, China
Tel.: (86) 10 8330 6001
Fax: (86) 10 8330 3736
Web Site: www.27rail.chinacnr.com
Railway Locomotive Mfr
S.I.C.: 4789
N.A.I.C.S.: 488210

Beijing Nankou Railway Transportation Machinery Co., Ltd. **(1)**
Nankou
Changping District, Beijing, 102202, China
Tel.: (86) 1051013361
Fax: (86) 10 6977 1809
E-Mail: info@nkgc.com.cn
Web Site: www.njgs.chinacnr.com
Locomotives Mfr
S.I.C.: 3743
N.A.I.C.S.: 336510

Changchun Railway Vehicle Co., Ltd. **(1)**
435 Qingyin Road
Changchun, Jilin, 130062, China
Tel.: (86) 431 87831651
Fax: (86) 4312930792
Web Site: www.cccar.com.cn
Emp.: 10,000
Railway Vehicles Mfr
S.I.C.: 3743
N.A.I.C.S.: 336510
Lucy Ray *(Gen Mgr)*

CNR Dalian Locomotive Research Institute Co., Ltd. **(1)**
No 49 Zhongchang Street
Shahekou District, Dalian, Liaoning, 116021, China
Tel.: (86) 411 84601010
Fax: (86) 411 84601617
E-Mail: dlri@dlri.chinacnr.com
Emp.: 800
Railway Transportation Equipment Mfr
S.I.C.: 3799
N.A.I.C.S.: 336999

LORIC Import & Export Corp., Ltd. **(1)**
No 11 Yangtangdian Road
Haidian District, Beijing, 100038, China CN
Tel.: (86) 1051862369
Fax: (86) 1051862374
Locomotive & Rolling Stock Distr
Import Export
S.I.C.: 7389
N.A.I.C.S.: 425120
Guobing Cao *(Chm)*
Dayong Cheng *(Pres)*

Qiqihar Railway Rolling Stock Co., Ltd. **(1)**
36 ChangQian 1 Lu
Qiqihar, Heilongjiang, 161002, China
Tel.: (86) 4522938472
Fax: (86) 452 2516723
E-Mail: zxb@qrrsintl.com
Web Site: www.qrrs.com.cn
Railway Wagons & Cranes Mfr
S.I.C.: 3536
N.A.I.C.S.: 333923
Wei Yan *(Chm)*

Taiyuan Railway Rolling Stock Co., Ltd. **(1)**
No 10 Jiefang North Road
Taiyuan, Shanxi, 030001, China
Tel.: (86) 3514063799
Fax: (86) 351 4063773
E-Mail: sales@railway-vehicle.com
Web Site: www.railway-vehicle.com
Emp.: 700
Railroad Rolling Stock Mfr
S.I.C.: 3743
N.A.I.C.S.: 336510
Xiaojian Wang *(Mng Dir)*

Tangshan Railway Vehicle Co., Ltd **(1)**
No 3 Changqian Road
Fengrun District, Tangshan, Hebei, 63035, China
Tel.: (86) 315 3089103
Fax: (86) 315 3089838
E-Mail: export@tangche.com
Web Site: www.tangche.com
Emp.: 13,000
Railway Transportation Equipment Mfr
S.I.C.: 3743
N.A.I.C.S.: 336510

Tianjin JL Railway Transport Equipment Ltd. **(1)**
No 22 Nankou Road
Hebei District, Tianjin, 300232, China
Tel.: (86) 22 26243376
Fax: (86) 22 26271234
E-Mail: int.trade@tlr.cn
Web Site: www.tlr.cn
Emp.: 3,000
Locomotives & Freight Cars Mfr
S.I.C.: 3999
N.A.I.C.S.: 339999
Siu Ling Cheng *(Gen Mgr)*

CHINA COAL CORPORATION

Suite 675 340 12th Avenue
Southwest
Calgary, AB, T2R 1L5, Canada
Tel.: (403) 452-8806
Fax: (403) 452-8892
E-Mail: info@chinacoalcorporation.com
Web Site: chinacoalcorporation.com
Year Founded: 2006
CKO—(TSXV)
Sales Range: Less than $1 Million

Business Description:
Coal Mining Services
S.I.C.: 1241
N.A.I.C.S.: 213113

Personnel:
Xinlang Feng *(Chm)*
Lishe Feng *(Pres)*
Raymond Fong *(CEO)*
Mark J. Roth *(CFO)*

Board of Directors:
Xinlang Feng
Lishe Feng
Raymond Fong
Stephen Hume
Alvin Jackson
Mark J. Roth

Legal Counsel:
McLeod & Company LLP
Calgary, AB, Canada

Transfer Agent:
Computershare Investor Services Inc.
3rd Floor 510 Burrard St
V6C 3B9 Vancouver, BC, Canada

CHINA COAL ENERGY COMPANY LIMITED

1 Huangsi Street Chaoyang
Beijing, 100011, China
Tel.: (86) 1082256688
Fax: (86) 1082236008
E-Mail: bgs@chinacoal.com
Web Site: www.chinacoalenergy.com
1898—(HKG)
Rev.: $13,866,281,780
Assets: $29,496,491,304
Liabilities: $13,385,857,905
Net Worth: $16,110,633,399
Earnings: $1,520,944,907
Emp.: 54,964
Fiscal Year-end: 12/31/12

Business Description:
Coal Mining & Processing Operations
S.I.C.: 2999
N.A.I.C.S.: 324199

Personnel:
An Wang *(Chm)*
Xi Wang *(Chm-Supervisory Bd)*
Yanjiang Li *(Vice Chm)*
Lieke Yang *(Pres)*
Qing'an Weng *(CFO)*
Dongzhou Zhou *(Sec)*

Board of Directors:
An Wang
Yanjiang Li
Yanmeng Li
Wai Fung Ngai
Yi Peng
Lieke Yang
Jiaren Zhang
Pei Zhao
Qinye Zhou

Supervisory Board of Directors:
Xi Wang
Shaoping Zhang
Litao Zhou

PricewaterhouseCoopers
22nd Floor Prince's Building
Central, China (Hong Kong)
Tel.: (852) 2 826 2111

Legal Counsel:
DLA Piper Hong Kong
17th Fl Edinburgh Tower The Landmark No 15 Queens Rd
Central, China (Hong Kong)

Beijing Jiayuan Law Firm
R407 Ocean Plaza 158 Fuxingmennei Avenue
Xicheng, Beijing, China

China Securities Depository & Clearing Corporation Limited
36/F China Insurance Bldg
166 Lu Jia Zui Rd E, Shanghai, PRC, China 20012

Transfer Agent:
Computershare Hong Kong Investor Services Limited
Rooms 1806-1807 18/F Hopewell Centre
183 Queen's Road East, Wanchai, China (Hong Kong)
Tel.: (852) 2862 8555

Subsidiaries:

China Coal Energy Shandong Co., Ltd. **(1)**
No 135 Tianjin Road
Rizhao, Shandong, 276826, China
Tel.: (86) 633 8333626
Fax: (86) 633 8332371
Web Site: www.chinacoalenergy.com
Coal Mining & Distr
S.I.C.: 1241
N.A.I.C.S.: 213113

China Coal Handan Design Engineering Co.,Ltd. **(1)**
No 114 Fu He Bei Dajie
Handan, Hebei, 56031, China
Tel.: (86) 310 7106407
Fax: (86) 310 3014959
Web Site: www.chinacoalenergy.com
Coal Mining & Distr
S.I.C.: 1241
N.A.I.C.S.: 213113

China National Coal Industry Qinhuangdao Imp. & Exp. Co., Ltd. **(1)**
No 252 Minzu Road
Qinhuangdao, Hebei, 0660011, China
Tel.: (86) 3353878888
Fax: (86) 335 3877877
Web Site: www.chinacoalenergy.com
Coal Mining Services
S.I.C.: 1241
N.A.I.C.S.: 213113

China National Coal Mining Equipment Co., Ltd. **(1)**
No 192 Anwai Dajie
Beijing, 100011, China
Tel.: (86) 10 64268372
Fax: (86) 10 64249352
E-Mail: cmeoffice@263.net
Web Site: www.chinacoal-cme.com
Coal Mining Machinery Mfr & Leasing Services
S.I.C.: 3532
N.A.I.C.S.: 333131

Shanghai ChinaCoal East China Co., Ltd. **(1)**
6th Floor No 899 Orient Road
Pudong New District, Shanghai, 200122, China
Tel.: (86) 21 68764227
Fax: (86) 21 58305093
Web Site: www.chinacoalenergy.com
Coal Mining & Whslr
S.I.C.: 1241
N.A.I.C.S.: 213113

Shanghai Datun Energy Resources Technology Development Company Limited **(1)**
Pei Xian
Xuzhou, Jiangsu, 211611, China
Tel.: (86) 51689025204
Fax: (86) 51689025878
Energy Saving Equipments Mfr
S.I.C.: 3433
N.A.I.C.S.: 333414

Xi an Engineering Design Co., Ltd. **(1)**
No 64 Yanta Beiduan Heping Men Wai
Xi'an, Shaanxi, 710054, China
Tel.: (86) 29 87857449
Fax: (86) 29 87855534
Web Site: www.chinacoalenergy.com
Coal Mining & Distr
S.I.C.: 1241
N.A.I.C.S.: 213113

Non-U.S. Subsidiary:

Sunfield Resources Pty. Limited **(1)**
Unit 2802 Level 28 31 Market St
Sydney, NSW, 2000, Australia
Tel.: (61) 292837611
Fax: (61) 292838885
Web Site: www.chinacoal.com.au
Emp.: 6
Coal Trading
S.I.C.: 2999
N.A.I.C.S.: 324199

CHINA COMMERCIAL CREDIT, INC.

No 1688 Yunli Road
Tongli, Wujiang, Jiangsu, China
Tel.: (86) 512 6396 0022
Fax: (86) 512 6396 0011
Web Site: www.chinacommercialcredit.com
CCCR—(NASDAQ)
Int. Income: $12,289,059
Assets: $100,004,819
Liabilities: $32,755,740
Net Worth: $67,249,079
Earnings: $8,312,469
Emp.: 22
Fiscal Year-end: 12/31/12

Business Description:
Commercial Banking
S.I.C.: 6029

N.A.I.C.S.: 522110
Personnel:
Huichun Qin *(Chm & CEO)*
Long Yi *(CFO)*
Board of Directors:
Huichun Qin
John F. Levy
Jingeng Ling
Arnold Staloff
Xiangdong Xiao
Jianmin Yin

CHINA COMMUNICATIONS CONSTRUCTION COMPANY LTD.

No 85 Deshengmenwai Street
Xicheng District, Beijing, 100088, China
Tel.: (86) 10 82016655
Fax: (86) 10 82016500
E-Mail: ir@ccccltd.cn
Web Site: www.ccccltd.cn
Year Founded: 2006
01800—(HKG OTC)
Rev.: $46,911,740,850
Assets: $68,911,512,750
Liabilities: $53,629,666,200
Net Worth: $15,281,846,550
Earnings: $1,863,628,200
Emp.: 94,629
Fiscal Year-end: 12/31/12
Business Description:
Transport Infrastructure, Dredging & Port Machinery Mfr; Port, Highway, Road & Bridge Construction
S.I.C.: 1629
N.A.I.C.S.: 237990
Personnel:
Qitao Liu *(Chm & Pres)*
Xiangdong Liu *(Chm-Supervisory Bd)*
Junyuan Fu *(CFO)*
Wensheng Liu *(Sec)*
Board of Directors:
Qitao Liu
Junyuan Fu
Chuangshun Liang
Zhangmin Liu
Hongjun Lu
Yaohui Yuan
Changfu Zhang
Qiao Zou
Supervisory Board of Directors:
Xiangdong Liu
Yongbin Wang
Sanhao Xu

PricewaterhouseCoopers
22nd Floor Prince's Building
Central, China (Hong Kong)
Tel.: (852) 2 826 2111
Legal Counsel:
Jia Yuan Law Firm
F407 Ocean Plaza 158 Fuxing Men Nei Avenue
Beijing, China
Freshfields Bruckhaus Deringer
11th Floor Two Exchange Square
Hong Kong, China (Hong Kong)
Transfer Agent:
Computershare Hong Kong Investor Services Limited
Shops 1712-1716 17th Floor Hopewell Centre
183 Queens Road East
Wanchai, China (Hong Kong)
Subsidiaries:

CCCC First Harbour Consultants Co., Ltd. **(1)**
1472 Dagunan Road
Hexi District, Tianjin, 300222, China
Tel.: (86) 2228160808
Fax: (86) 22 28341925
E-Mail: fdine@fdine.com.cn
Web Site: www.fdine.com.cn
Construction Engineering Services
S.I.C.: 8711
N.A.I.C.S.: 541330
Feng Zhongwu *(CEO)*
Zhu Jiquan *(Sec-Party Committee & VP)*

CCCC Guangzhou Dredging Co., Ltd. **(1)**
362 Binjiang Road Binjiangzhong Road
Guangzhou, Guangdong, 510221, China
Tel.: (86) 2089004418
Fax: (86) 20 8900 4453
Web Site: www.ccgdc.com
Dredging Contractors
S.I.C.: 1629
N.A.I.C.S.: 237990

CCCC Investment Co., Ltd. **(1)**
Deshengmenwai Street No 85
Xicheng District, Beijing, 100088, China
Tel.: (86) 1082017966
Fax: (86) 10 82017967
Web Site: www.ccccic.com.cn
Investment Management Services
S.I.C.: 6211
N.A.I.C.S.: 523999

CCCC Shanghai Equipment Engineering Co., Ltd. **(1)**
12F 3456 Pu Dong Nan Road
Shanghai, 200125, China
Tel.: (86) 2150390000
Fax: (86) 2150890068
E-Mail: jblv@ccccsh.com
Web Site: www.ccccsh.com
Emp.: 30
Port Machinery Installation & Mfr
S.I.C.: 3531
N.A.I.C.S.: 333120
Yang Tian *(Gen Mgr)*

CCCC Xi'an Road Construction Machinery Co., Ltd. **(1)**
No 8 West Section Jinggao South Road
Jingwei Industrial Park
Xi'an, Shaanxi, 710200, China
Tel.: (86) 29 86966698
Fax: (86) 29 86966699
Web Site: www.rm.com.cn
Road Construction Machinery Mfr & Sales
S.I.C.: 3531
N.A.I.C.S.: 333120
Zhou Chunping *(Mgr-Africa)*

China Harbour Engineering Company Ltd. **(1)**
9 Chun Xiu Rd
Dong Zhi Men Wai, Beijing, 100027, China
Tel.: (86) 1064175744
Fax: (86) 1064154455
E-Mail: marketing@chec.bj.cn
Web Site: www.chec.bj.cn/
Emp.: 6,000
Marine Engineering, Dredging, Reclamation & Road & Bridge Design Services
S.I.C.: 8711
N.A.I.C.S.: 541330
Ziyu Sun *(Chm & CEO)*
Yuqi Zhao *(Chief Engr)*

Shanghai Zhenhua Heavy Industry Co., Ltd **(1)**
3470 Pudong Nan-Lu
200125 Shanghai, China CN
Tel.: (86) 2158396666
Fax: (86) 2158399555
E-Mail: mail@zpmc.com
Web Site: www.zpmc.com
600320—(SHG)
Sales Range: $1-4.9 Billion
Large Port Loading Equipment & Steel Bridge Mfr
S.I.C.: 3559
N.A.I.C.S.: 333249
Jichang Zhou *(Chm)*
Xuezeng Kang *(Pres)*
Jue Wang *(CFO)*

Zhenhua Logistics Group Co., Ltd. **(1)**
No 158 Jingmen Avenue
Xingang, Tianjin, 300461, China
Tel.: (86) 2225762168
Fax: (86) 2225762268
E-Mail: zhh@zh-logistics.com
Web Site: www.eng.zh-logistics.com.cn
Logistics Consulting Services
S.I.C.: 4731
N.A.I.C.S.: 541614

Non-U.S. Subsidiary:

Chuwa Bussan Co., Ltd. **(1)**
Chuwa Bussan Honsha Building 2-8-14 Higashikanda
Chiyoda-Ku, Tokyo, 101-0031, Japan
Tel.: (81) 3 5821 6011
Fax: (81) 3 5821 1392
Web Site: chuwa.com
Industrial Machinery Distr
S.I.C.: 5082
N.A.I.C.S.: 423810
Shi Su Sheng *(Gen Mgr)*

CHINA CONCH VENTURE HOLDINGS LIMITED

1011 Jiuhua South Road
Wuhu, 241070, China
Tel.: (86) 553 8399135
Fax: (86) 553 8399065
E-Mail: hlcy@conch.cn
Web Site: www.conchventure.com
586—(HKG)
Business Description:
Holding Company; Energy Preservation, Environmental Protection Solutions & Building Materials
S.I.C.: 6719
N.A.I.C.S.: 551112
Personnel:
Jingbin Guo *(Chm)*
Zhongping Zhu *(CFO)*
Mao Shu *(Sec)*
Board of Directors:
Jingbin Guo
Chi On Chan
Kai Wing Chan
Chi Wah Lau
Daming Li
Jian Li
Qinying Li

CHINA CONSTRUCTION BANK CORPORATION

25 Finance Street
Beijing, 100032, China
Tel.: (86) 10 6759 8628
Fax: (86) 10 6360 3194
E-Mail: ccb@bj.china.com
Web Site: www.ccb.com
Year Founded: 1954
601939—(HKG OTC SHG)
Sales Range: $50-74.9 Billion
Emp.: 313,867
Business Description:
State-Owned Commercial Bank
S.I.C.: 6029
N.A.I.C.S.: 522110
Personnel:
Shuqing Guo *(Chm)*
Furong Zhang *(Chm-Supervisory Bd)*
Jianguo Zhang *(Vice Chm & Pres)*
Xiusheng Pang *(CFO & Exec VP)*
Jianhua Zeng *(CFO)*
Zhiling Huang *(Chief Risk Officer)*
Jingbo Yu *(Chief Audit Officer)*
Yongshun Yu *(Chief Audit Officer)*
Mei Sheung Chan *(Sec)*
Zuofu Chen *(Exec VP)*
Zheyi Hu *(Exec VP)*
Huan Zhao *(Exec VP)*
Board of Directors:
Shuqing Guo
Yuanling Chen
Zuofu Chen
Joseph Yam Chi Kwong
Peter Keith Levene
Xiaoling Li
Xiaoma Lu
Jenny Shipley
Yang Sue
Shumin Wang
Yong Wang
Kai-Man Wong
Jianguo Zhang
Xijun Zhao
Zhenmin Zhu
Supervisory Board of Directors:
Furong Zhang
Deming Dai
Feng Guo
Shuping Huang
Panshi Jin
Weiping Li
Jin Liu
Fengming Song
Legal Counsel:
Freshfields Bruckhaus Deringer
11F Two Exchange Square
Central, China (Hong Kong)
Beijing Commerce & Finance Law Offices
6/F NCI Tower A12 Jianuomenwal Avenue
Beijing, China
China Securities Depository & Cleaning Corporation Limited
36/F China Insurance Building 166 East Lujiazui Road
Shanghai, China
Non-U.S. Subsidiaries:

CCB International (Holdings) Limited **(1)**
12/F CCB Tower 3 Connaught Road Central
Central, China (Hong Kong)
Tel.: (852) 2532 6100
Fax: (852) 2530 1496
Web Site: www.ccbintl.com.hk
Investment Services
S.I.C.: 6211
N.A.I.C.S.: 523999
Zhanghong Hu *(CEO)*

China Construction Bank (Asia) Corporation Limited **(1)**
16F York House The Landmark 15 Queens Road
Central, China (Hong Kong)
Tel.: (852) 27795533
Telex: 75679 BAAL
Fax: (852) 37183273
Web Site: www.asia.ccb.com
Sales Range: $200-249.9 Million
Personal & Commercial Banking Services
S.I.C.: 6029
N.A.I.C.S.: 522110

CHINA CORD BLOOD CORPORATION

48th Floor Bank of China Tower 1 Garden Road
Central, China (Hong Kong)
Tel.: (852) 36058180
Fax: (852) 36058181
Web Site: www.chinacordbloodcorp.com
CO—(NYSE)
Rev.: $83,574,639
Assets: $474,369,943
Liabilities: $277,163,545
Net Worth: $197,206,398
Earnings: $19,005,132
Emp.: 890
Fiscal Year-end: 03/31/13
Business Description:
Cord Blood Storage Services
S.I.C.: 8071
N.A.I.C.S.: 621511
Personnel:
Yuen Kam *(Chm)*
Tina Ting Zheng *(CEO)*
Albert Bing Cheun Chen *(CFO)*
Xin Xu *(CTO)*
Rui Arashiyama *(CEO-Guangdong & Zhejiang)*
Yue Deng *(CEO-Beijing)*
Board of Directors:
Yuen Kam
Albert Bing Cheun Chen
Mark D. Chen
Yungang Lu
Jennifer J. Weng
Tina Ting Zheng

CHINA CULTURE INDUSTRIAL INVESTMENT FUND MANAGEMENT CO., LTD.

12/F No 28 Fengsheng Hutong
Xicheng District, Beijing, China

China Culture Industrial Investment Fund Management Co., Ltd.—(Continued)

Tel.: (86) 10 57503518
E-Mail: info@chinacf.com
Web Site: www.chinacf.com
Business Description:
Private Equity Firm
S.I.C.: 6211
N.A.I.C.S.: 523999
Personnel:
Hang Chen *(Mng Dir)*

CHINA DAIRY GROUP LIMITED

8 Wilkie Road 03 01 Wilkie Edge
Singapore, 228095, Singapore
Tel.: (65) 65337600
Fax: (65) 65947855
Web Site: www.chinadairygroup.cn
Year Founded: 1979
T16—(SES)
Rev.: $293,415,330
Assets: $151,621,848
Liabilities: $101,632,865
Net Worth: $49,988,983
Earnings: $1,704,143
Emp.: 1,510
Fiscal Year-end: 12/31/12
Business Description:
Holding Company; Dairy Products Mfr
S.I.C.: 0241
N.A.I.C.S.: 112120
Personnel:
Huaguo Liu *(Chm)*
Kim Swee Seah *(Sec)*
Board of Directors:
Huaguo Liu
Sik Ting Chau
Jing Kong
Kain Sze Kwok
Huafeng Lei
Jingji Wang
Puhui Zhang

Non-U.S. Subsidiary:

Xian Yinqiao Biological Science and Technology Co., Ltd. (1)
No 01 9/f Building A Gaoke Plaza Hi-Tech Zone
Xi'an, Shaanxi, 710075, China
Tel.: (86) 2983886888
Fax: (86) 2988361209
Dairy Products Mfr & Distr
S.I.C.: 0241
N.A.I.C.S.: 112120

CHINA DAQING M&H PETROLEUM, INC.

Jiangiao Road 3rd Floor Song Yuan City
Economic & Tech Devel District
Jilin, 138000, China
Year Founded: 2005
CHDP—(OTC)
Sales Range: $10-24.9 Million
Emp.: 105
Business Description:
Development of Oil Wells & Oil Extraction & Sales; Steel & Steel Related Products Sales
S.I.C.: 1381
N.A.I.C.S.: 213111
Personnel:
Yongjun Wang *(Chm & Pres)*
Linan Gong *(CEO & Sec)*
Dehai Yin *(CFO & Chief Acctg Officer)*
Board of Directors:
Yongjun Wang
Haimiao Sun
Changming Zhang

CHINA DATA BROADCASTING HOLDINGS LIMITED

(Acquired by Sichuan Changhong Electric Co., Ltd. & Name Changed to Changhong Jiahua Holdings Limited)

CHINA DATANG CORPORATION

(d/b/a Datang Group)
No 1 Guangningbo Str
Xicheng District, 10032 Beijing, China
Tel.: (86) 1066586666
Fax: (86) 10 66586677
E-Mail: webmaster@china-cdt.com
Web Site: www.china-cdt.com
Year Founded: 2002
Sales Range: $25-49.9 Billion
Emp.: 99,132
Business Description:
Extra Large Scaled Power Generation Services
S.I.C.: 4939
N.A.I.C.S.: 221122
Personnel:
Shunda Liu *(Chm)*
Jinhang Chen *(Pres)*

Subsidiaries:

China Datang Corporation Renewable Power Co., Limited (1)
8/F Building 1 No 1 Caishikou Street
Xicheng District, Beijing, 100053, China
Tel.: (86) 10 83956262
Fax: (86) 10 83956555
Web Site: www.dtxny.com.cn
1798—(HKG)
Rev.: $693,859,183
Assets: $8,956,386,653
Liabilities: $7,130,144,436
Net Worth: $1,826,242,217
Earnings: $29,634,103
Emp.: 3,448
Fiscal Year-end: 12/31/12
Wind Power Generation
S.I.C.: 4911
N.A.I.C.S.: 221118
Yongsheng Hu *(Pres)*
Xuefeng Zhang *(CFO)*
Wenpeng Wang *(Co-Sec & VP)*
Gloria Sau-kuen Ma *(Co-Sec)*

Datang International Power Generation Co., Ltd. (1)
9 Guangningbo Street Xicheng District
Beijing, 100140, China (35.43%)
Tel.: (86) 10 83581901
Fax: (86) 10 83581907
E-Mail: zhangshaopeng@dtpower.com
Web Site: www.dtpower.com
0991—(HKG LSE)
Rev.: $12,326,465,016
Assets: $43,727,860,898
Liabilities: $34,727,478,513
Net Worth: $9,000,382,384
Earnings: $988,880,963
Emp.: 22,012
Fiscal Year-end: 12/31/12
Power Distr
S.I.C.: 3612
N.A.I.C.S.: 335311
Jingshan Cao *(Vice Chm)*
Xianzhou Wang *(CFO)*

Subsidiary:

Shanxi Datang International Shentou Power Generation Company Limited (2)
Zhenhua St Shentou Town
Shuocheng District, Shentou, Shanxi, 036011, China
Tel.: (86) 3492045495
Power Generation Services
S.I.C.: 4931
N.A.I.C.S.: 221111

CHINA DAYE NON-FERROUS METALS MINING LIMITED

Unit 2001 20/F Worldwide House 19 Des Voeux Road
Central, China (Hong Kong)
Tel.: (852) 28682101
Fax: (852) 28682302
E-Mail: info@hk661.com
Web Site: www.hk661.com
0661—(HKG)
Rev.: $4,587,289,839
Assets: $2,756,959,776
Liabilities: $1,815,696,007
Net Worth: $941,263,769
Earnings: $25,996,120
Emp.: 10,608
Fiscal Year-end: 12/31/12
Business Description:
Investment Services
S.I.C.: 6282
N.A.I.C.S.: 523920
Personnel:
Lin Zhang *(Chm)*
Zhong Sheng Long *(CEO)*
Wing Kwan Yeung *(Sec)*
Board of Directors:
Lin Zhang
Zhong Sheng Long
Quan Zhou Qiu
Yaoyu Tan
Guoqi Wang
Qihong Wang
Baojin Zhai

Butterfield Fund Services (Bermuda) Limited
Rosebank Centre 11 Bermudiana Rd
Pembroke, Bermuda

CHINA DEVELOPMENT BANK CORPORATION

No 18 Fuxingmennei Street Xicheng District
Beijing, China 100031
Tel.: (86) 10 6830 6789
Fax: (86) 10 6830 6699
E-Mail: webmaster@cdb.com.cn
Web Site: www.cdb.com.cn
Year Founded: 1994
Int. Income: $61,459,859,250
Net Worth: $79,083,631,350
Earnings: $10,018,987,200
Emp.: 592
Fiscal Year-end: 12/31/12
Business Description:
Bank Holding Company; Commercial & Investment Banking
S.I.C.: 6712
N.A.I.C.S.: 551111
Personnel:
Yuan Chen *(Chm)*
Zhongmin Yao *(Chm-Supervisory Bd)*
Zhijie Zheng *(Vice Chm & Pres)*
Jiawei Shu *(CFO)*
Qingyu Zhou *(Chief Compliance Officer)*
Qiying Xu *(Chief Risk Officer)*
Jizhong Chen *(Chief Audit Officer)*
Jiping Li *(Exec VP)*
Yongsheng Wang *(Exec VP)*
Li Yuan *(Exec VP)*
Board of Directors:
Yuan Chen
Xiaoyun Chen
Jian Du
Hao Huang
Weijia Huang
Weiwen Lai
Mi Luo
Jiying Pang
Aiwu Song
Gongxia Yue
Shude Zhang
Xinli Zheng
Zhijie Zheng
Supervisory Board of Directors:
Zhongmin Yao
Jianyun Geng
Hongzhuan Hu
Xiangyang Leng
Wenqi Yang

Non-U.S. Subsidiary:

China Development Bank International Investment Limited (1)
(Formerly New Capital International Investment Limited)
Suites 4506-4509 Two International Finance Centre
No 8 Finance Street, Central, China (Hong Kong) Ky
Tel.: (852) 29736883
Fax: (852) 29736889
Web Site: www.cdb-intl.com
1062—(HKG)
Rev.: $196,345
Assets: $136,965,010
Liabilities: $1,637,439
Net Worth: $135,327,571
Earnings: ($1,117,873)
Emp.: 9
Fiscal Year-end: 12/31/12
Investment Services
S.I.C.: 6211
N.A.I.C.S.: 523999
Rongsong Teng *(CEO)*
Yong Mao *(Chief Investment Officer)*
Kwok Ho Wong *(Sec)*

Non-U.S. Joint Venture:

Taurus Mineral Limited (1)
Room 1901 CC Wu Bldg 302 Hennessy Road
Wanchai, China (Hong Kong) HK
Investment Holding Company
S.I.C.: 6719
N.A.I.C.S.: 551112

Non-U.S. Subsidiary:

Kalahari Minerals Plc (2)
1B 38 Jermyn Street
London, SW1Y 6DN, United Kingdom UK
Tel.: (44) 20 7292 9110
Fax: (44) 20 3214 0079
E-Mail: reception@kalahari-minerals.com
Web Site: www.kalahari-minerals.com
Sales Range: $1-9.9 Million
Emp.: 7
Holding Company; Metal Ore Exploration & Mining Services
S.I.C.: 6719
N.A.I.C.S.: 551112
Zhiping Yu *(Chm)*
Duncan Craib *(CFO & Co-Sec)*
Janis Sawyer *(Co-Sec)*

CHINA DEVELOPMENT FINANCIAL HOLDING CORP.

125 Nanjing East Road
Section 5, Taipei, 10504, Taiwan
Tel.: (886) 2 2753 2201
Fax: (886) 2 2753 2203
E-Mail: cdibhuser@cdibh.com
Web Site: www.cdibh.com
Year Founded: 2001
2883—(TAI)
Emp.: 2,126
Business Description:
Financial Holding Company
S.I.C.: 6712
N.A.I.C.S.: 551111
Personnel:
Mu-Tsai Chen *(Chm)*
Paul Yang *(Pres & CEO)*
Long-I Liao *(Mng Dir)*
Sherie Chiu *(CFO & Sr Exec VP)*
Melanie Y.C. Nan *(Gen Counsel & Exec VP)*
Jane Lai *(Exec VP & Head-Risk Mgmt)*
Kenneth Huang *(Exec VP & Gen Auditor)*
Beatrice Chou *(Exec VP-Ops & Tech)*
David D. Chow *(Exec VP)*
Daw-Yi Hsu *(Exec VP)*
Yuling Lee *(Exec VP)*
Bing-Huang Shih *(Exec VP)*
Eddie Yu-Chang Wang *(Exec VP)*
Reddy Hoe-Choon Wong *(Exec VP-Global Equities & Global Fixed Income)*

Board of Directors:
Mu-Tsai Chen
Gilbert T.C. Bao
Eddy Chang
David Chen
Daw-Yi Hsu
Howe-Yong Lee
Long-I Liao
Melanie Y.C. Nan
Jen-Chieh Pan
Hue-Sun Teng
Ching-Yen Tsay
Mark Wei
Paul Yang
Supervisory Board of Directors:
Chia-Juch Chang
Cheng-Ming Chou
Howard N.H. Wang

Subsidiaries:

China Development Industrial Bank, Inc. **(1)**
10/F No 125 Nanking E Rd
Section 5, Taipei, Taiwan (100%)
Tel.: (886) 227638800
Fax: (886) 227562144
E-Mail: ir@cdibh.com
Web Site: www.cdibank.com
Investment Banking
S.I.C.: 6211
N.A.I.C.S.: 523110
Chao Chin Tung *(Chm)*
Simon Dzeng *(Pres)*
Meng-Horng Peng *(Sec & Sr VP)*
David S. Chen *(Sr Exec VP-Direct Investments)*
Arthur Chiang *(Exec VP-HR)*
Beatrice Chou *(Exec VP-Ops & Tech Center)*
Eddie Yu-Chang Wang *(Exec VP-Corp & Investment Banking)*
Jamie Huang *(Sr VP-Treasury Dept)*
Kenneth Huang *(Sr VP)*
David Kuo *(Sr VP-Equity Derivative & Principal Trading)*
Jane Lai *(Sr VP & Acting Head-Risk Mgmt)*

Subsidiaries:

CDC Finance & Leasing Corp. **(2)**
3F 125 Nanking E Road Section 5
Taipei, 105, Taiwan
Tel.: (886) 227611758
Fax: (886) 227606031
Emp.: 50
Financial Investment Services
S.I.C.: 6211
N.A.I.C.S.: 523999
Chao Ming Meng *(Pres)*

CDIB Asset Management Co., Ltd. **(2)**
125 Nanking East Road Section 5
Taipei, Taiwan
Tel.: (886) 227568968
Financial Management Services
S.I.C.: 6211
N.A.I.C.S.: 523999

CDIB Capital International Corporation **(2)**
125 Nanking East Road
Section 5, Taipei, 105, Taiwan
Tel.: (886) 2 2763 8800
Fax: (886) 2 2756 2144
Web Site: www.cdibcapital.com
Equity Investment Firm
S.I.C.: 6211
N.A.I.C.S.: 523999
Paul Yang *(Co-Founder & Chm)*
Steven Wu *(Sr VP)*

Co-Headquarters:

CDIB Capital International (Hong Kong) Corporation Limited **(3)**
Suites 701-4 ICBC Tower Citibank Plaza 3
Garden Road
Central, China (Hong Kong) HK
Tel.: (852) 2231 8600
Fax: (852) 2231 8601
Web Site: www.cdibcapital.com
Equity Investment Firm
S.I.C.: 6211
N.A.I.C.S.: 523999
Paul Yang *(Co-Founder & Chm)*
Lionel de Saint-Exupery *(Co-Founder & CEO)*
Justin Busarakamwong *(Sr VP)*
Neville Chan *(Sr VP-Fin, Compliance, Ops & Admin)*
Stephen Choi *(Sr VP)*

Non-U.S. Subsidiary:

CDIB Capital International (Korea) Corporation Ltd. **(4)**
City Air Tower 17/F 159-9 Samsung-Dong
Gangnam-gu, Seoul, 135-973, Korea (South)
Tel.: (82) 2 551 8700
Fax: (82) 2 551 8711
Web Site: www.cdibcapital.com
Emp.: 6
Equity Investment Firm
S.I.C.: 6211
N.A.I.C.S.: 523999
H.Y. Kim *(Mng Dir & Head-Korea)*

China Development Asset Management Corp. **(2)**
7F 125 Section 5 Nanjing East Road
Taipei, 10504, Taiwan
Tel.: (886) 2 2756 8968
Fax: (886) 2 2756 8977
Asset Management Services
S.I.C.: 8748
N.A.I.C.S.: 541618

China Venture Management Inc. **(2)**
12F 125 Nanking E Rd Section 5
Taipei, 10504, Taiwan
Tel.: (886) 227673668
Fax: (886) 227677008
Emp.: 10
Fund Management Services
S.I.C.: 6371
N.A.I.C.S.: 524292
Wen Chun Yang *(Pres)*

KGI Securities Co., Ltd. **(1)**
700 Mingshui Road
Zhongshan District, Taipei, 104, Taiwan (81.7%)
Tel.: (886) 2 2181 8888
Fax: (886) 2 85011856
Web Site: www.kgi.com
Rev.: $434,607,613
Assets: $4,330,562,179
Liabilities: $2,700,111,387
Net Worth: $1,630,450,792
Earnings: $56,709,049
Emp.: 4,805
Fiscal Year-end: 12/31/12
Securities Brokerage Services
S.I.C.: 6211
N.A.I.C.S.: 523120
Mark P. Wei *(Chm)*

Subsidiaries:

Grand Cathay Securities Corporation **(2)**
14F No 2 Chongqing South Road
Section 1, Taipei, ROC, 100, Taiwan
Tel.: (886) 223148800
Fax: (886) 223142206
E-Mail: ir@cdibh.com
Web Site: www.gcsc.com.tw
Securities Trading & Brokerage Services
S.I.C.: 6211
N.A.I.C.S.: 523120
Daw-Yi Hsu *(Chm & Acting Pres)*
Shuzhen Chiu *(CFO)*

Non-U.S. Subsidiary:

Grand Cathay Securities (Hong Kong) Limited **(3)**
17th Fl LHT Tower No 31 Queens Rd
Central, China (Hong Kong)
Tel.: (852) 25212982
Fax: (852) 25210085
E-Mail: cs@grandcathay.com.hk
Web Site: www.grandcathay.com.hk
Emp.: 30
Securities Brokerage Services
S.I.C.: 6211
N.A.I.C.S.: 523120

KGI Futures Co. Ltd. **(2)**
8F No 35 Bo-ai Road
Zhongzheng District, Taipei, 100, Taiwan
Tel.: (886) 2 2361 9889
Fax: (886) 2 2371 2867
Web Site: www.KGIfutures.com.tw
Financial Future Brokerages Services
S.I.C.: 6221
N.A.I.C.S.: 523140

KGI Securities Investment Trust Co., Ltd. **(2)**
No 698 Mingshui Road
Zhongshan District, Taipei, 104, Taiwan
Tel.: (886) 2 2181 5678
Fax: (886) 2 8501 2388
E-Mail: service@kgifund.com.tw
Web Site: www.kgifund.com.tw
Managed Assets: $397,243,000
Emp.: 70
Investment Funds
S.I.C.: 6722
N.A.I.C.S.: 525910

KGI Securities (Taiwan) Co., Ltd. **(2)**
No 700 Mingshui Road
Zhongshan District, Taipei, 104, Taiwan
Tel.: (886) 2 2181 8888
Fax: (886) 2 8501 2944
Web Site: www.kgi.com
Securities Brokerages Services
S.I.C.: 6211
N.A.I.C.S.: 523120

Non-U.S. Subsidiaries:

KGI Hong Kong Limited **(2)**
41/F Central Plaza 18 Harbour Road
Wanchai, China (Hong Kong)
Tel.: (852) 2878 6888
Fax: (852) 2878 6800
E-Mail: info@kgi.com
Web Site: www.kgieworld.com
Emp.: 700
Securities Brokerage Services
S.I.C.: 6211
N.A.I.C.S.: 523120

KGI Securities (Singapore) Pte Ltd **(2)**
65 Chulia Street 37-06 OCBC Centre
Singapore, 049513, Singapore
Tel.: (65) 62362643
Fax: (65) 62362648
Emp.: 5
Securities Brokerage Services
S.I.C.: 6211
N.A.I.C.S.: 523120
Rebecca Lo *(Mgr)*

One Asset Management Limited **(2)**
24th Floor Siam Tower Discovery Center
989 Rama I Road
Pathumwan, Bangkok, 10330, Thailand
Tel.: (66) 2 659 8888
Fax: (66) 2 659 8860
Web Site: www.one-asset.com
Emp.: 200
Fund Management Services
S.I.C.: 6211
N.A.I.C.S.: 523120
Monrat Phadungsit *(Mng Dir)*

CHINA DIGITAL ANIMATION DEVELOPMENT, INC.

30 Ganshui Road diwang Dasha
Room 605
Xiangfang District, Harbin, 150090, China
Tel.: (86) 3982 966108
Web Site:
CHDA—(OTC OTCB)
Sales Range: $1-9.9 Million
Emp.: 27
Business Description:
Animation Services
S.I.C.: 7819
N.A.I.C.S.: 512199
Personnel:
Qiang Fu *(Chm & CEO)*
Yumei Hu *(CFO)*
Hong Huo *(COO)*
Board of Directors:
Qiang Fu
Shaoqiu Xia
Transfer Agent:
American Registrar & Transfer Co.
342 E 900 S
Salt Lake City, UT 84111

CHINA DIGITAL MEDIA CORPORATION

2505-06 25th Floor Stelux House
698 Prince Edward Road East,
Kowloon, China (Hong Kong)
Tel.: (852) 23908600
Fax: (852) 21277515
E-Mail: ir@chinadigimedia.com
Web Site: www.chinadigimedia.com
Year Founded: 1987
Sales Range: $1-9.9 Million
Emp.: 200
Fiscal Year-end: 12/31/12
Business Description:
Cable Television Operations
S.I.C.: 4841
N.A.I.C.S.: 515210
Personnel:
Daniel Chi Shing Ng *(Chm & CEO)*
Chung Lai Lok *(CFO)*

CHINA DIGITAL TV HOLDING CO., LTD.

Jingmeng High-Tech Building B 4th
Floor No 5 Shangdi East Road
Haidian District, Beijing, 100085, China
Tel.: (86) 10 62971199
Web Site: ir.chinadtv.cn
Year Founded: 2004
STV—(NYSE)
Rev.: $90,244,000
Assets: $193,565,000
Liabilities: $110,402,000
Net Worth: $83,163,000
Earnings: $5,538,000
Emp.: 778
Fiscal Year-end: 12/31/12
Business Description:
Conditional Access Systems to Digital Television Market
S.I.C.: 3663
N.A.I.C.S.: 334220
Personnel:
Jianhua Zhu *(Chm & CEO)*
Zhenwen Liang *(CFO)*
Dong Li *(CMO)*
Huiqing Chen *(Chief Admin Officer)*
Zengxiang Lu *(Chief Strategy Officer)*
Tianxing Wang *(CTO)*
Jian Han *(CEO-Cyber Cloud)*
Board of Directors:
Jianhua Zhu
Michael Elyakim
Zengxiang Lu
Gongquan Wang
Songzuo Xiang
Eric Xu
Andrew Y. Yan

CHINA DISPLAY TECHNOLOGIES, INC.

12A Block Xinhe Road Xinqiao 3
Industrial District
Baoan Town, Shenzhen, 150090, China
Tel.: (86) 755 29758811
Year Founded: 2004
Sales Range: $25-49.9 Million
Emp.: 597
Business Description:
LEDs & Cold Cathode Fluorescent Lamps For Displays Developer, Mfr & Marketer
S.I.C.: 3841
N.A.I.C.S.: 339112
Personnel:
Lawrence Kwok-Yan Chan *(CEO)*
Jason Ye *(CFO & Sec)*
Jason Wong *(Exec VP)*
Board of Directors:
Lawrence Kwok-Yan Chan
Liang Hong
Sen Li

CHINA DISTANCE EDUCATION HOLDINGS LIMITED
18th Floor Xueyuan International Tower 1 Zhichun Road
Haidian District, Beijing, 100083, China
Tel.: (86) 10 82319999
Fax: (86) 10 82337887
Web Site: www.cdeledu.com
Year Founded: 2000
DL—(NYSE)
Rev.: $71,360,000
Assets: $105,994,000
Liabilities: $41,474,000
Net Worth: $64,520,000
Earnings: $13,564,000
Emp.: 1,118
Fiscal Year-end: 09/30/13
Business Description:
Online Education & Test Preparation Courses & Other Related Services & Products
S.I.C.: 9411
N.A.I.C.S.: 923110
Personnel:
Zhengdong Zhu *(Co-Founder, Chm & CEO)*
Baohong Yin *(Co-Founder & Deputy Chm)*
Hongfeng Sun *(Co-Founder & VP)*
Ping Wei *(CFO)*
Guojie Hu *(Sr VP)*
Feijia Ji *(Sr VP)*
Zheng Liang *(Sr VP)*
Songjiang Qin *(Sr VP)*
Board of Directors:
Zhengdong Zhu
Xiaoshu Chen
Liankui Hu
Annabelle Yu Long
Hongfeng Sun
Baohong Yin
Carol Yu
Yu Gao
Dazhong Qin
Bing Xiang
Yudi Xu
Computershare Hong Kong Investor Services Limited
Shops 1712-1716 17th Floor Hopewell Centre
183 Queens Road East
Wanchai, China (Hong Kong)
Transfer Agents:
Royal Bank of Canada Trust Company (Cayman) Limited
4th Floor Royal Bank House 24 Shedden Road
Georgetown, Cayman Islands
Computershare Hong Kong Investor Services Limited
Shops 1712-1716 17th Floor Hopewell Centre
183 Queens Road East
Wanchai, China (Hong Kong)

Subsidiary:

China Distance Education Limited **(1)**
18th Floor Xue Yuan International Towers
No 1 Zhichun Road
Hai Dian District, Beijing, 100083, China
Tel.: (86) 10 8231 9999
Fax: (86) 10 8233 7887
Online Education Support Services
S.I.C.: 8299
N.A.I.C.S.: 611710

CHINA DONGXIANG (GROUP) COMPANY LIMITED
Building 21 No 2 Jingyuanbei Street
Beijing Economic & Technology Development Zone, Beijing, 100176, China
Tel.: (86) 10 6783 6666
Fax: (86) 10 6785 6626
Web Site: www.dxsport.com
4C1—(DEU HKG)
Rev.: $281,453,130
Assets: $1,164,224,199
Liabilities: $61,098,952
Net Worth: $1,103,125,247
Earnings: $30,785,765
Emp.: 507
Fiscal Year-end: 12/31/12
Business Description:
Sportswear Products Mfr
S.I.C.: 2299
N.A.I.C.S.: 314999
Personnel:
Yihong Chen *(Founder, Chm & CEO)*
Dazhong Qin *(COO)*
Jianjun Sun *(CEO-Japan Phenix Corporation)*
Pui Man Wai *(Sec)*
Board of Directors:
Yihong Chen

CHINA DREDGING GROUP CO., LTD.
(Acquired by China Growth Equity Investment Ltd. to form Pingtan Marine Enterprise Ltd.)

CHINA DU KANG CO., LTD.
Town of Dukang Baishui County A 28
Van Metropolis 35 Tangyan Road
Xi'an, Shaanxi, 710065, China
Tel.: (86) 29 88830106
CDKG—(OTC)
Rev.: $5,076,665
Assets: $17,608,341
Liabilities: $7,240,447
Net Worth: $10,367,894
Earnings: $924,661
Emp.: 192
Fiscal Year-end: 12/31/12
Business Description:
White Wines Mfr, Licensor, Distr & Sales
S.I.C.: 2084
N.A.I.C.S.: 312130
Personnel:
Yongsheng Wang *(CEO)*
Su Ying Liu *(CFO)*
Board of Directors:
Su Ying Liu
Fen Ying Nie
Yongsheng Wang
Transfer Agent:
Island Stock Transfer Inc
100 Second Avenue South Suite 705S
Saint Petersburg, FL 33701

CHINA EASTERN AIRLINES CORPORATION LTD.
Kong Gang San Lu Number 92
Shanghai, 200335, China
Tel.: (86) 21 6268 6268
Fax: (86) 21 6268 6116
E-Mail: ir@ce-air.com
Web Site: www.ce-air.com
CEA—(HKG LSE NYSE SHG)
Rev.: $13,542,489,405
Assets: $19,668,578,733
Liabilities: $15,768,271,619
Net Worth: $3,900,307,113
Earnings: $445,987,737
Emp.: 66,207
Fiscal Year-end: 12/31/12
Business Description:
Domestic, Regional & International Passenger & Cargo Airline Services
S.I.C.: 4512
N.A.I.C.S.: 481111
Personnel:
Shaoyong Liu *(Chm)*
Faming Yu *(Chm-Supervisory Bd)*
Xulun Ma *(Vice Chm & Pres)*
Yongliang Wu *(CFO & VP)*
Zhuping Luo *(Sec)*
Board of Directors:
Shaoyong Liu
Jiadan Gu
Weidong Ji
Yangmin Li
Sandy Ke-Yaw Liu
Zhuping Luo
Xulun Ma
Ruiqing Shao
Bing Tang
Xiaogen Wu
Zhao Xu
Supervisory Board of Directors:
Faming Yu
Jinxiong Feng
Jiashun Lu
Shang Xi
Taisheng Yan
China Securities Depository & Clearing Corporation Limited
36/F China Insurance Building No 166 Lujiazui Dong Road
Pudong New Area, Shanghai, China
The Bank of New York
22F 101 Barclay Street
New York, NY 10286

CHINA EDUCATION ALLIANCE, INC.
58 Heng Shan Road Kun Lun Shopping Mall
Harbin, China 150090
Tel.: (86) 45182335794
Web Site: www.chinaeducationalliance.com
Year Founded: 1996
CEAI—(OTC)
Rev.: $11,725,109
Assets: $94,171,636
Liabilities: $1,932,598
Net Worth: $92,239,038
Earnings: ($14,447,027)
Emp.: 615
Fiscal Year-end: 12/31/12
Business Description:
Educational Services Including On-Line Portal, Training Centers, Software & Media
S.I.C.: 8299
N.A.I.C.S.: 611519
Personnel:
Xiqun Yu *(Chm, Pres & CEO)*
Cloris Li *(CFO)*
Board of Directors:
Xiqun Yu
Xiaohua Gu
Liansheng Zhang
Transfer Agent:
Vstock Transfer LLC
77 Spruce St Ste 20
Cedarhurst, NY 11598

CHINA EDUCATION, INC.
Suite 2504 China World Tower 1
China World Trade Center
1 Jian Guo Men Wai Avenue, Beijing, China
Tel.: (86) 1065059478
Sales Range: $10-24.9 Million
Emp.: 1,170
Business Description:
Elementary & High Schools Owner & Operator
S.I.C.: 8211
N.A.I.C.S.: 611110
Personnel:
Lawrence Lee *(Co-Chm)*
Yaoliang Ge *(CEO)*
Helen Yang *(CFO)*
Board of Directors:
Lawrence Lee
Avi Suriel

CHINA EDUCATION RESOURCES INC.
Suite 300 515 West Pender Street
Vancouver, BC, V6B 6H5, Canada
Tel.: (604) 331-2388
Fax: (604) 682-8131
E-Mail: admin@chinaeducationresources.com
Web Site: www.chinaeducationresources.com
Year Founded: 2000
CHN—(TSXV)
Rev.: $7,391,934
Assets: $7,259,378
Liabilities: $7,896,685
Net Worth: ($637,307)
Earnings: ($1,503,652)
Fiscal Year-end: 12/31/12
Business Description:
Educational Products Including Textbooks & Software
S.I.C.: 9411
N.A.I.C.S.: 923110
Personnel:
Chengfeng Zhou *(Chm & CEO)*
Danny Hon *(CFO)*
Board of Directors:
Chengfeng Zhou
Danny Hon
Wang Li
Mark Scott
Legal Counsel:
Borden Ladner Gervais LLP
Vancouver, BC, Canada

Subsidiary:

CEN China Education Network Ltd. **(1)**
Suite 1818 Cathedral Place
925 West Georgia Street, Vancouver, BC, V6C 3L2, Canada
Tel.: (604) 683-6865
Fax: (604) 681-5636
E-Mail: Admin@chinaeducationresources.com
Emp.: 2
Educational Products & Services
S.I.C.: 8299
N.A.I.C.S.: 611710
C. F. Zhou *(CEO & Dir)*

CHINA ELECTRIC MFG. CORPORATION
No 9 Sec 2 Chung Shiao E Rd
100 Taipei, Taiwan
Tel.: (886) 223914311
Fax: (886) 223962720
E-Mail: info@toa.com.tw
Web Site: www.chinaelectric.com.tw
1611—(TAI)
Sales Range: $75-99.9 Million
Business Description:
Lighting Products Mfr
S.I.C.: 3645
N.A.I.C.S.: 335121
Personnel:
Julie Chou *(Chm & Gen Mgr)*

CHINA ELECTRIC MOTOR, INC.
Sunna Motor Industry Park
Jianan Fuyong Hi-Tech Park
Baoan District, Shenzhen, Guangdong, China
Tel.: (86) 7558149969
CELM—(OTC)
Sales Range: $75-99.9 Million
Emp.: 920
Business Description:
Micro-Motor Products Designer, Mfr, Marketer & Sales
S.I.C.: 3621
N.A.I.C.S.: 335312
Personnel:
Xiaohui Li *(Chm, Pres & CEO)*
Xinming Xiao *(COO)*
Xiaobo Zhang *(Chief Admin Officer)*
Dehe Wang *(CTO)*
Hongyang Chen *(Exec VP)*
Board of Directors:

Xiaohui Li
Liang Tang
Xiaoying Zhou

CHINA ELECTRONICS CORPORATION

No 27 Wanshou Road
Haidian District, Beijing, 100846, China
Tel.: (86) 1068218529
Fax: (86) 1068213745
E-Mail: webmaster@cec.com.cn
Web Site: www.cec.com.cn
Year Founded: 1989
Sales Range: $5-14.9 Billion
Business Description:
Holding Company; Information Technology Products Mfr & Services
S.I.C.: 6719
N.A.I.C.S.: 551112
Personnel:
Qunli Xiong *(Chm)*
Liehong Liu *(Pres)*
Jia Lang *(Head-Discipline Inspection Team & Chief Legal Officer)*
Board of Directors:
Qunli Xiong
Yunting Dong
Hongfu Hu
Jia Lang
Kecheng Li
Liehong Liu
Xiaowu Rui
Duan Su
Songlin Xie
Xiaotie Zhang
Subsidiaries:

China National Software & Service Co., Ltd **(1)**
No 18 Changsheng Road Changping District
Beijing, 102200, China
Tel.: (86) 10 51508665
Fax: (86) 10 51508661
Web Site: www.css.com.cn
600536—(SHG)
Emp.: 10,554
Software Development, Distribution & Services
S.I.C.: 7372
N.A.I.C.S.: 511210
Chunping Cheng *(Chm)*
Jun Fang *(CFO)*

Subsidiary:

Great Wall Computer Software & Systems Co., Ltd **(2)**
5/F Gaode Building 10 Huayuan Dong Road
Haidian District, Beijing, 100083, China CN
Tel.: (86) 1082038899
Fax: (86) 1082038812
E-Mail: huangig@gwssi.com.cn
Web Site: www.gwssi.com.cn
Software Equipment Services
S.I.C.: 7376
N.A.I.C.S.: 541513
Keqin Gao *(Mgr)*

Great Wall Technology Co., Ltd. **(1)**
No 2 Keyuan Road Technology & Industry Park
Nanshan District, Shenzhen, 518057, China
Tel.: (86) 755 2672 8686
Fax: (86) 755 2650 4493
E-Mail: webmaster@greatwalltech.com
Web Site: www.greatwalltech.com
0074—(HKG)
Sls.: $15,231,221,849
Assets: $8,367,921,268
Liabilities: $5,925,228,744
Net Worth: $2,442,692,524
Earnings: $20,214,139
Emp.: 60,000
Fiscal Year-end: 12/31/12
Computer Mfr & Computer Services
S.I.C.: 3571
N.A.I.C.S.: 334111
Liehong Liu *(Chm)*
Jia Lang *(Chm-Supervisory Bd)*
Heping Du *(CEO)*
Yan Zhong *(Sec)*

Subsidiaries:

China Great Wall Computer Shenzhen Co., Ltd. **(2)**
Kefa Road
Science & Industry Park
Nanshan District, Shenzhen, 518057, China CN
Tel.: (86) 75526639997
Fax: (86) 75526631695
E-Mail: mobingyu@greatwall.com.cn
Web Site: www.gwoversea.com
000066—(SSE)
Emp.: 1,000
Computer Parts & Products Mfr
S.I.C.: 3571
N.A.I.C.S.: 334111
Mo Bing Yu *(Mgr-Intl Bus)*

Shenzhen ExcelStor Technology, Ltd. **(2)**
5F #8 Bldg Kaifa Industrial Complex
7006 Caitian Rd
Futian District, Shenzhen, China CN
Tel.: (86) 75583346668
Fax: (86) 755 8327 5922
E-Mail: sales@excelstor.com
Web Site: www.excelstor.com
Mfr of Computer Hard Drive Disks & Equipment
S.I.C.: 3571
N.A.I.C.S.: 334111

Shenzhen Kaifa Technology Co., Ltd. **(2)**
Caitan Rd
7006
Futian District, Shenzhen, China
Tel.: (86) 75583275000
Fax: (86) 75583275054
E-Mail: webmaster@kaifa.cn
Web Site: www.kaifa.com.cn
000021—(HKG)
Sales Range: $800-899.9 Million
Computer & Video Equipment Mfr
S.I.C.: 3571
N.A.I.C.S.: 334111
Tam Man Chi *(Chm & Pres)*
Cheng Kwok Wing *(Sr VP)*

Subsidiary:

Shenzhen Kafia Magnetic Recording Co., Ltd **(3)**
Caitian Rd 7006
Futian Distric, Shenzhen, 518035, China
Tel.: (86) 75583275000
Fax: (86) 755 83275376
Web Site: www.kaifa.cn/eng/about/contactus.asp
Disk Mfr
S.I.C.: 3577
N.A.I.C.S.: 334118

GreatWall Information Industry Co., Ltd. **(1)**
161 Yuhua Road
Changsha, Hunan, 410007, China CN
Tel.: (86) 731 5554610
Fax: (86) 731 5553061
E-Mail: gwizqb@gwi.com.cn
Web Site: www.gwi.com.cn
000748—(SSE)
Sales Range: $50-74.9 Million
Emp.: 1,450
Computer Devices & Application Software Mfr
S.I.C.: 3571
N.A.I.C.S.: 334111
Yuchun Nie *(Chm)*
Yuejin Yi *(Vice Chm)*
Zhigang Li *(Pres)*
Kui Zhang *(CFO)*
Wan Zhu *(CTO & VP)*

Non-U.S. Subsidiary:

China Electronics Corporation Holdings Company Limited **(1)**
Room 3403 34th Floor China Resources Building 26 Harbour Road
Wanchai, China (Hong Kong) (74.98%)
Tel.: (852) 25989088
Fax: (852) 25989018
E-Mail: investor@cecholdings.com.hk
Web Site: www.cecholding.com
0085—(HKG)
Rev.: $149,018,746
Assets: $173,915,639
Liabilities: $70,007,471
Net Worth: $103,908,168
Earnings: $25,478,457
Emp.: 330
Fiscal Year-end: 12/31/12
Electronics Products Mfr
S.I.C.: 3999
N.A.I.C.S.: 327110
Qinghua Xie *(Mng Dir)*
Kui Kwan Ng *(Sec)*

CHINA ELECTRONICS HOLDINGS, INC.

Building 3 Longhe East Road Binhe District
Lu'an, Anhui, 237000, China
Tel.: (86) 564 3224888
Web Site: www.chinaelectronicsholdings.com
CEHD—(OTC)
Rev.: $58,082,897
Assets: $59,940,697
Liabilities: $5,772,865
Net Worth: $54,167,832
Earnings: ($1,101,341)
Emp.: 66
Fiscal Year-end: 12/31/12
Business Description:
Consumer Electronics & Appliances Retailer
S.I.C.: 5722
N.A.I.C.S.: 443141
Personnel:
Hailong Liu *(Chm, Pres, CEO & CFO)*
Board of Directors:
Hailong Liu
Haibo Liu

CHINA EMEDIA HOLDINGS CORPORATION

Suite 2302 Seaview Commercial Building
21 Connaught Road West, Sheung Wan, China (Hong Kong)
Tel.: (852) 90099119
Fax: (852) 28558158
Web Site: www.smartcntv.com
Year Founded: 2009
Business Description:
Internet Marketing Solutions
S.I.C.: 8742
N.A.I.C.S.: 541613
Personnel:
Kai Lun Ng *(Chm)*
Chang Zhong Ge *(Vice Chm)*
Kenneth Kwan *(CEO)*
Fred Cheng *(CFO)*
Board of Directors:
Kai Lun Ng
Fred Cheng
Chang Zhong Ge
Kenneth Kwan

CHINA ENERGINE INTERNATIONAL (HOLDINGS) LIMITED

Suite 4701 47/F Central Plaza 18 Harbour Road
Beijing, China
Tel.: (86) 85225861185
Fax: (86) 85225310088
E-Mail: energine@energine.hk
Web Site: www.energine.hk
Year Founded: 1997
CT1—(DEU)
Sls.: $127,645,671
Assets: $588,218,449
Liabilities: $332,743,612
Net Worth: $255,474,837
Earnings: $699,038
Emp.: 707
Fiscal Year-end: 12/31/12
Business Description:
Wind Energy Related Products Mfr
S.I.C.: 3534
N.A.I.C.S.: 333921
Personnel:
Shuwang Han *(Chm)*
Xiaodong Wang *(Vice Chm)*
Guang Li *(CEO)*
Steve Au-Yeung Keung *(Sec)*
You Li *(Exec VP)*
Board of Directors:
Shuwang Han
Shili Fang
Alice Lai Kuen Kan
Guang Li
Gordon Ng
Dechen Wang
Lijun Wang
Xiaodong Wang
Jianhua Zhang

Royal Bank of Canada Trust Company (Cayman) Limited
4th Floor Royal Bank House 24 Shedden Road
Georgetown, Cayman Islands

Subsidiary:

Beijing Wanyuan-Henniges Sealing Systems Co., Ltd **(1)**
No 1 Nan Da Hong Men Road
Beijing, Fengtai District, 100076, China
Tel.: (86) 68374743
Web Site: www.hennigesautomotive.com
Vehicle Sealing Systems & Anti-Vibration Products Mfr
S.I.C.: 3714
N.A.I.C.S.: 336390

CHINA ENERGY CORPORATION

No 57 Xinhua East Street
Hohhot, Inner Mongolia, 010010, China
Tel.: (86) 4714668870
Web Site: www.ceccec.com
Rev.: $246,062,847
Assets: $231,437,511
Liabilities: $132,890,622
Net Worth: $98,546,889
Earnings: $12,303,316
Emp.: 304
Fiscal Year-end: 11/30/12
Business Description:
Coal Mining & Production Services
S.I.C.: 1221
N.A.I.C.S.: 212111
Personnel:
Wenxiang Ding *(Pres, CEO, Treas & Sec)*
Fu Xu *(Acting CFO)*
Transfer Agent:
QuickSilver Stock Transfer LLC
6623 Las Vegas Blvd South
Las Vegas, NV 89119

CHINA ENERGY DEVELOPMENT HOLDINGS LIMITED

Units 5611-12 56th Floor The Center
99 Queen's Road Central
Central, China (Hong Kong)
Tel.: (852) 2169 3382
Fax: (852) 2169 3002
Web Site: www.cnenergy.com.hk
Year Founded: 2001
HPG1—(DEU HKG)
Sls.: $7,988,581
Assets: $517,768,809
Liabilities: $74,600,283
Net Worth: $443,168,526
Earnings: ($4,428,788)
Emp.: 46
Fiscal Year-end: 12/31/12

China Energy Development Holdings Limited—(Continued)

Business Description:
Oil & Gas Exploration Services
S.I.C.: 1389
N.A.I.C.S.: 213112
Personnel:
Guoqiang Zhao *(CEO)*
Board of Directors:
Kwong Kau Chui
Ewing Wing Kwok Fu
Changbi Huang
Baohe Liu
Xiaoli Sun
Yongguang Wang
Zhenming Zhang
Guoqiang Zhao

Royal Bank of Canada Trust Company (Cayman) Limited
4th Floor Royal Bank House 24 Shedden Road
Georgetown, Cayman Islands
Transfer Agents:
Tricor Tengis Limited
26th Floor Tesbury Centre 28 Queen's Road East
Wanchai, China (Hong Kong)
Tel.: (852) 29801333
Fax: (852) 28108185

Royal Bank of Canada Trust Company (Cayman) Limited
4th Floor Royal Bank House 24 Shedden Road
Georgetown, Cayman Islands

CHINA ENERGY LIMITED
6 Battery Road 10-01
Singapore, 049909, Singapore
Tel.: (65) 38169666
Fax: (65) 3816967
Web Site: www.chinaenergy.com.sg
A0G—(SES)
Rev.: $1,734,789,600
Assets: $2,266,366,382
Liabilities: $1,848,525,350
Net Worth: $417,841,032
Earnings: ($231,471,318)
Fiscal Year-end: 12/31/12
Business Description:
Dimethyl Ether Mfr
S.I.C.: 2899
N.A.I.C.S.: 325199
Personnel:
Lianguo Cui *(Chm & CEO)*
Qiang Li *(Deputy CEO)*
Leslie Wei Hsein Ying *(CFO)*
Lawrence Chee Meng Wong *(Sec)*
Board of Directors:
Lianguo Cui
Hock Meng Lai
Horn Kee Leong
Qiang Li
Kian Min Ong
William Wong

Moore Stephens LLP
10 Anson Road 29 15 International Plaza
Singapore, Singapore
Transfer Agent:
Boardroom Corporate & Advisory Services Pte. Ltd.
50 Raffles Place 32-01 Singapore Land Tower
Singapore, Singapore

CHINA ENERGY RECOVERY INC.
Building 26 No 1388 Zhangdong Road Zhangjiang Hi-Tech Park
Shanghai, 201203, China
Tel.: (86) 21 20281866
Fax: (86) 21 20282378
E-Mail: hudie@cerenergy.com
Web Site: www.chinaenergyrecovery.com
CGYV—(OTC)
Rev.: $92,461,713
Assets: $84,098,535
Liabilities: $76,175,706
Net Worth: $7,922,829
Earnings: $97,293
Emp.: 420
Fiscal Year-end: 12/31/12
Business Description:
Waste Energy Management Services
S.I.C.: 4959
N.A.I.C.S.: 562998
Personnel:
Qinghuan Wu *(Chm & CEO)*
Simon Dong *(Acting CFO & Controller)*
Qi Chen *(COO)*
Board of Directors:
Qinghuan Wu
Qi Chen
Yan Sum Kung
Estelle Lau
Jules Silbert

CHINA ENGINE GROUP LIMITED
27/F Hopewell Centre 183 Queens Road East
Hong Kong, China (Hong Kong)
Tel.: (852) 59585739836
Fax: (852) 59585739797
Web Site: www.chinaengine.co.kr
Year Founded: 1987
900080—(KRS)
Business Description:
Automobile Parts Mfr
S.I.C.: 3711
N.A.I.C.S.: 336111
Personnel:
Geng Sheng Wang *(Pres & CEO)*

CHINA ENTERPRISES LIMITED
25th Floor Paul Y Centre 51 Hung To Road
Kwun Tong, Kowloon, China (Hong Kong)
Tel.: (852) 31510300
Fax: (852) 23720620
Web Site: www.chinaenterpriseslimited.com
Year Founded: 1993
CSHEF—(OTC)
Sales Range: Less than $1 Million
Business Description:
Holding Company; Tire Mfr
S.I.C.: 3011
N.A.I.C.S.: 326211
Personnel:
Allan Yap *(Chm & CEO)*
Eva Chan Ling *(Deputy Chm)*
Jimmy Chun Man Chow *(CFO)*
Board of Directors:
Allan Yap
Eva Chan Ling
Sin Chi Fai
Dorothy Kam T. Law
Lien Kait Long
Richard Whittall

CHINA ENVIRONMENT LTD.
133 Cecil Street 18-03 Keck Seng Tower
Singapore, 069535, Singapore
Tel.: (65) 62259921
Fax: (65) 62259908
E-Mail: ir@ce-dy.com
Web Site: www.chinaenv.net
5OU—(SES)
Rev.: $64,993,160
Assets: $128,011,496
Liabilities: $38,820,081
Net Worth: $89,191,416
Earnings: $6,464,242
Fiscal Year-end: 12/31/12
Business Description:
Waste Gas Treatment Services
S.I.C.: 4959
N.A.I.C.S.: 562998
Personnel:
Min Huang *(Chm & CEO)*
Choon Teck Chiar *(CFO)*
Liangfang Li *(Pres-Technical & R&D Centre)*
Guoxin Wu *(Pres-Sls & Mktg)*
Yoen Har Wong *(Sec)*
Board of Directors:
Min Huang
Andrew Bek
Song Lin
Wei Ping Loh
Jida Wu
Yu Liang Wu

CHINA ENVIRONMENTAL ENERGY INVESTMENT LIMITED
Room 2211 22/F Lippo Centre Tower Two 89 Queensway
Hong Kong, China (Hong Kong)
Tel.: (852) 24759105
Fax: (852) 24822692
Web Site: www.986.com.hk
Year Founded: 1965
986—(HKG)
Sls.: $12,850,512
Assets: $71,627,599
Liabilities: $50,740,536
Net Worth: $20,887,063
Earnings: ($50,449,237)
Emp.: 230
Fiscal Year-end: 03/31/13
Business Description:
Holding Company; Electro-Deposited Copper Foil, Copper Clad Laminates & Printed Circuit Boards Mfr
S.I.C.: 6719
N.A.I.C.S.: 551112
Personnel:
Tong Chen *(Chm & CEO)*
Hang Yin Tam *(Sec)*
Board of Directors:
Tong Chen
Kitty Ching Ho Chan
Wing Kiu Kwok
Jian Hua Liang
Lin Lin
King Keung Ong
Kwong Chan Tse
Zhenghua Wang
Liang Xiang
Zhengwei Yao
Jue Zhou

Butterfield Fulcrum Group (Bermuda) Limited
26 Burnaby Street
Hamilton, HM 11, Bermuda
Transfer Agents:
Tricor Tengis Limited
26th Floor Tesbury Centre 28 Queen's Road East
Wanchai, China (Hong Kong)
Tel.: (852) 29801333
Fax: (852) 28108185

Butterfield Fulcrum Group (Bermuda) Limited
26 Burnaby Street
Hamilton, HM 11, Bermuda
Subsidiaries:

Nam Hing Circuit Board Company Limited **(1)**
27 F Yuen Long Trade Ctr 99-109 Castle Peak Rd
PO Box 267
Yuen Long, New Territories, China (Hong Kong)
Tel.: (852) 24716438
Fax: (852) 24822692
E-Mail: namhing1@nh-circuitboard.com.hk
Web Site: www.namhing-pcb.com.hk
Emp.: 300
Printed Circuit Boards Mfr
S.I.C.: 3672
N.A.I.C.S.: 334412
Michael Lo *(Gen Mgr)*

Nam Hing Industrial Laminate Limited **(1)**
Unit 4 7/F Yuen Long Trading Ctr 33 Wang Yip St W Yuen Long
PO Box 267
Yuen Long, New Territories, China (Hong Kong)
Tel.: (852) 24759105
Fax: (852) 24822692
E-Mail: nhillhkg@nh-laminate.com.hk
Web Site: www.nh-laminate.com.hk
Emp.: 100
Copper Clad Laminates Mfr
S.I.C.: 3083
N.A.I.C.S.: 326130
Lau Pherick *(Mng Dir)*

Non-U.S. Subsidiary:

Zhongshan Nam Hing Insulating Material Limited **(1)**
Dongsheng Indus Dev Estate
Lan Wang, Zhongshan, Guangdong, China
Tel.: (86) 76085601415
Fax: (86) 76085600945
E-Mail: nhillhkg@nh-laminate.com.hk
Industrial Laminates Mfr
S.I.C.: 3083
N.A.I.C.S.: 326130

CHINA ENVIRONMENTAL RESOURCES GROUP LIMITED
2F Shui On Centre 6-8 Harbour Road
Wanchai, China (Hong Kong)
Tel.: (852) 39043300
Fax: (852) 39043303
E-Mail: info@cergreen.com
Web Site: www.cergreen.com
1130—(HKG SES)
Sls.: $3,999,255
Assets: $119,708,025
Liabilities: $28,062,228
Net Worth: $91,645,797
Earnings: ($5,432,921)
Emp.: 56
Fiscal Year-end: 06/30/13
Business Description:
Fertilizers Mfr
S.I.C.: 2875
N.A.I.C.S.: 325314
Personnel:
Hongbo Zhou *(Chm & CEO)*
Tai On Lo *(Sec)*
Board of Directors:
Hongbo Zhou
Ka Yin Chan
Wilfred Wai Kwok
James Kwong Choi Leung
Christopher David Thomas
Kays Kwai Sang Wong

Computershare Hong Kong Investor Services Limited
17M Floor Hopewell Centre 183 Queen's Road East
Wanchai, China (Hong Kong)
Transfer Agents:
Maples Fund Services (Cayman) Limited
Boundary Hall Cricket Square
PO Box 1093
Georgetown, Cayman Islands

Computershare Hong Kong Investor Services Limited
17M Floor Hopewell Centre 183 Queen's Road East
Wanchai, China (Hong Kong)

CHINA ENVIRONMENTAL TECHNOLOGY HOLDINGS LIMITED
Unit 1003-5 10/F Shui On Centre 6-8 Harbour Road
Wanchai, China (Hong Kong)
Tel.: (852) 2511 1870
Fax: (852) 2511 1878
E-Mail: ceth_po@cethl.com
Web Site: www.cethl.com
Year Founded: 2001
646—(HKG)

Sales Range: $10-24.9 Million
Emp.: 158
Business Description:
Sewage Treatment Services
S.I.C.: 4952
N.A.I.C.S.: 221320
Personnel:
Zhong Ping Xu *(Chm)*
Fang Hong Zhang *(CEO)*
Nelson Wang Hing Li *(Sec)*
Board of Directors:
Zhong Ping Xu
Ze Min Ge
Tianfu Ma
Yutang Pan
Kam Wah Wong
Luo Lin Xin
Xiao Yang Xu
Fang Hong Zhang
Nan Wen Zhu
Jiane Zuo

CHINA ERZHONG GROUP DEYANG HEAVY INDUSTRIES CO., LTD.

(d/b/a China National Erzhong Group)
460 West Zhujiang Road
Deyang, Sichuan, 618013, China
Tel.: (86) 8382343088
Fax: (86) 838 2343066
E-Mail: jinck@china-erzhong.com
Web Site: www.china-erzhong.com
601268—(SHG)
Emp.: 12,650
Business Description:
Heavy Technical Equipment Mfr; Steel Products Casting & Forging
S.I.C.: 3559
N.A.I.C.S.: 333249
Personnel:
Ke Shi *(Chm)*
Derun Sun *(Vice Chm & Gen Mgr)*
Board of Directors:
Ke Shi
Derun Sun

CHINA ESSENCE GROUP LTD.

Unit 2607 26/F Inspring Space 25 Ganluyuan Nanli
Qingnian Road Chaoyang Area, Beijing, China
Tel.: (86) 1085590127
Fax: (86) 1085591026
Web Site: www.chinaessence.com
G54—(SES)
Rev.: $63,151,771
Assets: $220,697,930
Liabilities: $134,813,295
Net Worth: $85,884,635
Earnings: ($88,270,721)
Fiscal Year-end: 03/31/13
Business Description:
Potato Starch Mfr
S.I.C.: 2046
N.A.I.C.S.: 311221
Personnel:
Libin Zhao *(Founder & Chm)*
Changling Liu *(CEO)*
Guolin Wu *(Chief R&D Officer)*
Meng Keong Teo *(Co-Sec)*
Board of Directors:
Libin Zhao
Kwong Wah Er
Peter Hock Meng Lai
Jiquan Li
Changling Liu
Jianwei Shen
BDO Limited
25th Floor Wing On Centre 111 Connaught Road
Central, China (Hong Kong)
Legal Counsel:
Wong Partnership
1 George St 20 01
Singapore, 049145, Singapore
Jingtian & Gongcheng
34th Floor Tower 3 China Central Place 77 Jianguo Road
Beijing, China
Conyers Dill & Pearman
2901 One Exchange Square 8 Connaught Place
Central, China (Hong Kong)
Codan Trust Company (Cayman) Limited
Cricket Square Hutchins Drive
PO Box 2681
Georgetown, Grand Cayman, Cayman Islands

CHINA EVERBRIGHT BANK CO., LTD.

No 25 Taipingqiao Ave Everbright Center
Xicheng District, Beijing, 100033, China
Tel.: (86) 10 6363 6363
Fax: (86) 10 6363 9066
Web Site: www.cebbank.com
Year Founded: 1992
601818—(HKG SHG)
Sales Range: $5-14.9 Billion
Emp.: 22,267
Business Description:
Banking Services
S.I.C.: 6029
N.A.I.C.S.: 522110
Personnel:
Shuangning Tang *(Chm)*
Haoyi Cai *(Chm-Supervisory Bd)*
Zhefu Luo *(Vice Chm)*
Huijun Mu *(Vice Chm-Supervisory Bd)*
You Guo *(Pres)*
Hong Lu *(Sec & Exec VP)*
Qing Wu *(Exec Dir)*
Jie Li *(Exec VP)*
Jun Liu *(Exec VP)*
Teng Ma *(Exec VP)*
Huofa Qiu *(Exec VP)*
Jianbao Shan *(Exec VP)*
Huayu Zhang *(Exec VP)*
Board of Directors:
Shuangning Tang
Catherine Oi Ling Fok
You Guo
Zhefu Luo
Zhimin Qiao
Shumin Wang
Zhongxin Wang
Gang Wu
Gaolian Wu
Jian Wu
Qing Wu
Rong Xie
Xinze Zhang
Daojiong Zhou
Supervisory Board of Directors:
Haoyi Cai
Shuang Chen
Yu Chen
Ning Ma
Huijun Mu
James Parks Stent
Pingsheng Wang
Junhao Wu
Donghai Ye
Erniu Yu
Chuanju Zhang
Subsidiary:
Shanghai Everbright Convention and Exhibition Centre Limited **(1)**
5F B Block 66 Caobao Road
Xuhui District, Shanghai, China 200235
Tel.: (86) 21 64753288
Fax: (86) 21 64820944
E-Mail: ebhotel@secec.com
Web Site: www.secec.com
Exhibition & Convention Center Operating Services
S.I.C.: 7389
N.A.I.C.S.: 561591

CHINA EVERBRIGHT INTERNATIONAL LIMITED

Rm 2703 27/F Far East Finance Centre 16 Harcourt Road
Hong Kong, China (Hong Kong)
Tel.: (852) 28041886
Fax: (852) 25284228
E-Mail: info1@ebchinaintl.com
Web Site: www.ebchinaintl.com
0257—(HKG OTC)
Sls.: $439,711,505
Assets: $2,138,392,550
Liabilities: $1,020,343,310
Net Worth: $1,118,049,241
Earnings: $148,821,711
Emp.: 1,650
Fiscal Year-end: 12/31/12
Business Description:
Construction Company
S.I.C.: 1442
N.A.I.C.S.: 212321
Personnel:
Shuangning Tang *(Chm)*
Qiutao Zang *(Vice Chm)*
Xiaoping Chen *(CEO)*
Raymond Kam Chung Wong *(CFO)*
Zhiqiang Yang *(Chief Legal Officer)*
Yuen Ling Poon *(Sec)*
Board of Directors:
Shuangning Tang
Shuguang Cai
Xiaoping Chen
Philip Yan Hok Fan
Aubery Kwok Sing Li
Selwyn Mar
Tianyi Wang
Raymond Kam Chung Wong
Qiutao Zang
Haitao Zhai

CHINA EVERBRIGHT LIMITED

46th Floor Far East Finance Center
16 Harcourt Road
Central, China (Hong Kong)
Tel.: (852) 25289882
Fax: (852) 25290177
E-Mail: investorrelations@everbright165.com
Web Site: www.everbright165.com
0165—(HKG)
Sls.: $522,332,220
Assets: $4,159,679,287
Liabilities: $296,817,110
Net Worth: $3,862,862,177
Earnings: $176,367,752
Emp.: 218
Fiscal Year-end: 12/31/12
Business Description:
Investment Holding
S.I.C.: 6799
N.A.I.C.S.: 523920
Personnel:
Shuangning Tang *(Chm)*
Qiutao Zang *(Deputy Chm)*
Shuang Chen *(CEO)*
Richard Chi Chun Tang *(CFO)*
Ling He *(Co-Chief Investment Officer)*
Yuanzhi Jiang *(Co-Chief Investment Officer)*
John Shen *(Co-Chief Investment Officer)*
Tung Hung Wong *(Chief Admin Officer)*
Ping Yang *(Co-Chief Investment Officer)*
Lian Chen Yin *(Co-Chief Investment Officer)*
Frederick Sui Cheong Tsang *(Chief Risk Officer)*
Desmond Ming Kin Chan *(Sec)*
Board of Directors:
Shuangning Tang
Shuang Chen
Yuanzhi Jiang
Zhijun Lin
John Gin Chung Seto
Richard Chi Chun Tang
Weimin Wang
Qiutao Zang

CHINA EVERGREEN ACQUISITION CORPORATION

B-2102 CaiZhi Tower Zhongguancun Rd E
Haidian, Beijing, 100083, China
Tel.: (86) 13901174642
Fax: (86) 1082600567
Year Founded: 2007
Emp.: 10
Business Description:
Investment Services
S.I.C.: 6211
N.A.I.C.S.: 523999
Personnel:
Gui Fa Cao *(Chm)*
Quan Sheng Li *(Co-CEO)*
Yi Shen *(Co-CEO)*

CHINA EXECUTIVE EDUCATION CORP.

c/o Hangzhou MYL Business Administration Consulting Co. Ltd.
Room 307 Hualong Business Bldg
110 Moganshan Road, Hangzhou, 310005, China
Tel.: (86) 57188808109
Web Site: www.myl101.com
Year Founded: 2008
Sales Range: $10-24.9 Million
Emp.: 294
Business Description:
Executive Management Training Services
S.I.C.: 8299
N.A.I.C.S.: 611430
Personnel:
Kaien Liang *(Chm & CEO)*
Zhiwei Huang *(CFO)*
Pokai Hsu *(COO)*
Tingyuan Chen *(Chief Strategy Officer)*
Board of Directors:
Kaien Liang
Hongmiao Chen
Pokai Hsu
Hongbo Shen

CHINA FARM EQUIPMENT LTD.

10 Anson Rd 30 07 International Plaza
Singapore, 079903, Singapore
Tel.: (65) 63234598
Fax: (65) 63234558
E-Mail: info@chinafarmequipment.com
Web Site: www.chinafarmequipment.com
A8J—(SES)
Sales Range: $50-74.9 Million
Business Description:
Farm Equipment & Diesel Engine Mfr
S.I.C.: 3523
N.A.I.C.S.: 333111
Personnel:
Shuping Wang *(Chm & CEO)*
Kian Hin Sho *(CFO)*
Busarakham Kohsikaporn *(Co-Sec)*
Lei Mui Toh *(Co-Sec)*
Board of Directors:
Shuping Wang
See Juan Kuik
Joo Khin Ng

China Farm Equipment Ltd.—(Continued)

Kian Hin Sho
Weiping Wang
Transfer Agent:
BACS Private Limited
63 Cantonment Rd
Singapore, 089758, Singapore
Tel.: (65) 323 6200

CHINA FAW GROUP CORPORATION

2259 Dongfeng Street
Changchun, Jilin, 130011, China
Tel.: (86) 431 85900715
Fax: (86) 431 85730707
Web Site: www.faw.com
Year Founded: 1953
Sales Range: $25-49.9 Billion
Emp.: 118,000
Business Description:
Automobile & Commercial Truck Mfr
S.I.C.: 3711
N.A.I.C.S.: 336111
Personnel:
Jianyi Xu *(Chm)*
Xianping Xu *(Pres)*

Subsidiary:

Faw Car Co., Ltd. **(1)**
No 4888 Weishan Road
High-Tech Industrial Dev Zone
Changchun, Jilin, 130012, China
Tel.: (86) 431 8578 1108
Fax: (86) 431 8578 1100
Web Site: www.fawcar.com.cn
000800—(SSE)
Sales Range: $5-14.9 Billion
Emp.: 7,836
Automobile Mfr & Sales
S.I.C.: 3711
N.A.I.C.S.: 336211
Jianyi Xu *(Chm)*
Shaoming Wu *(Vice Chm)*
Wenquan Wang *(Sec)*

Joint Ventures:

FAW-Volkswagen Automotive Co., Ltd. **(1)**
Dongfeng Street
Changchun, Jilin, 130011, China CN
Tel.: (86) 431 85990151
E-Mail: pengcheng.li@fw-vw.com
Web Site: www.faw-volkswagen.com
Emp.: 9,800
Motor Vehicle Mfr & Distr
S.I.C.: 3711
N.A.I.C.S.: 336111
Li Pengcheng *(Gen Mgr)*

Tianjin FAW Toyota Motor Co., Ltd. **(1)**
No 2 Liuli Road
Yangliuqing Village, Tianjin, Xiqing, 300380, China
Tel.: (86) 22 2794 4050
Fax: (86) 2227944060
E-Mail: info@tjfaw.com
Web Site: en.tjfaw.com
Motor Vehicle Mfr; Owned by China First Automotive Works & Toyota Motor Corporation
S.I.C.: 3714
N.A.I.C.S.: 336390

CHINA FIBER OPTIC NETWORK SYSTEM GROUP LTD.

Suite 2001 20th Floor Shui On Centre 6-8 Harbour Road
Wanchai, China (Hong Kong)
Tel.: (852) 28778033
Fax: (852) 28778083
E-Mail: randyhung@chinafiberoptic.com
Web Site: www.chinafiberoptic.com
3777—(HKG)
Rev.: $237,357,324
Assets: $407,432,777
Liabilities: $170,245,422
Net Worth: $237,187,354
Earnings: $43,234,522
Emp.: 405
Fiscal Year-end: 12/31/12
Business Description:
Fiber Optic Cords
S.I.C.: 3357
N.A.I.C.S.: 335921
Personnel:
Bing Zhao *(Chm)*
Randy King Kuen Hung *(CFO & Sec)*
Board of Directors:
Bing Zhao
Xuejun Deng
Randy King Kuen Hung
Pan Lui
Kwai Yuen Ma
Yuxiao Meng
Cuiming Shi
Ni Xia

Computershare Hong Kong Investor Services Limited
46th Floor Hopewell Centre 183 Queen's Road East
Wanchai, China (Hong Kong)

CHINA FIBRETECH LTD.

Wubao Industrial Zone
Shishi, Fujian, 362700, China
Tel.: (86) 595 88904838
Fax: (86) 595 88980858
E-Mail: chinafibretech@chinafibretech.com
Web Site: www.china-fibretech.com
Year Founded: 1995
F6D—(SES)
Rev.: $7,714,074
Assets: $86,385,013
Liabilities: $9,511,779
Net Worth: $76,873,234
Earnings: ($1,844,407)
Emp.: 510
Fiscal Year-end: 12/31/12
Business Description:
Fabric Processing Services
S.I.C.: 2269
N.A.I.C.S.: 313310
Personnel:
Xinhua Wu *(Chm & CEO)*
Yan Gao *(COO)*
Chris Chee Keong Chong *(Co-Sec)*
Benny Heng Chong Lim *(Co-Sec)*
Board of Directors:
Xinhua Wu
Yan Gao
Yoke Hean Lim
Qingguo Lin
Wai Cheong Low
Dezhi Wu

Boardroom Corporate & Advisory Services Pte. Ltd.
50 Raffles Place 32-01 Singapore Land Tower
Singapore, Singapore
Transfer Agent:
Boardroom Corporate & Advisory Services Pte. Ltd.
50 Raffles Place 32-01 Singapore Land Tower
Singapore, Singapore

CHINA FILMS TECHNOLOGY INC.

Yunmeng Economic and Technological Development Zone
Firsta Road, Yunmeng, Hubei, 432500, China
Tel.: (86) 7124326146
Fax: (86) 7124338866
Web Site: www.debangtech.com
Sales Range: $25-49.9 Million
Emp.: 145
Business Description:
Flexible Film Mfr
S.I.C.: 2672
N.A.I.C.S.: 322220
Personnel:
Zhian Zhang *(Chm)*
Yongsheng Yang *(CEO)*
Keng Swee Goh *(CFO)*
Board of Directors:
Zhian Zhang
Keng Swee Goh
Yongsheng Yang

CHINA FINANCE ONLINE CO. LIMITED

9th Floor of Tower C Corporate Square 35 Financial Street
Xicheng District, Beijing, 100033, China
Tel.: (86) 10 58325288
Fax: (86) 10 58325200
E-Mail: ir@jrj.com
Web Site: www.jrj.com.cn
JRJC—(NASDAQ)
Rev.: $29,599,486
Assets: $121,370,995
Liabilities: $40,654,444
Net Worth: $80,716,551
Earnings: ($11,960,147)
Emp.: 590
Fiscal Year-end: 12/31/12
Business Description:
Chinese Financial & Market Information Services
S.I.C.: 6211
N.A.I.C.S.: 523999
Personnel:
Zhiwei Zhao *(CEO)*
Jeff Jun Wang *(CFO)*
Board of Directors:
Kheng Nam Lee
Chee Beng Neo
Zhiwei Zhao
Legal Counsel:
O'Melveny & Myers LLP
400 S. Hope St.
Los Angeles, CA 90071-2899
Tel.: (323) 669-6000

Subsidiaries:

China Finance Online (Beijing) Co., Ltd. **(1)**
Corporate Square 35 Financial St
Xicheng District, Beijing, 100032, China
Tel.: (86) 1086325288
Chinese Financial & Market Information Services
S.I.C.: 6211
N.A.I.C.S.: 523999

China Finance Online **(1)**
No 690 Pibo Rd
Shanghai, 201203, China
Tel.: (86) 2150819999
Fax: (86) 2150819798
Web Site: www.stockstar.com
Emp.: 1,000
Online Comprehensive, Timely & Professional Financial Information & Data Services
S.I.C.: 4899
N.A.I.C.S.: 517919

Fortune Software (Beijing) Co., Ltd **(1)**
Corporate Square
35 Financial Street
Xicheng District, Beijing, 100032, China
Tel.: (86) 10 8632 5288
Online Information Storage & Retieval Services
S.I.C.: 7389
N.A.I.C.S.: 561499

Shenzhen Genius Information Technology Co., Ltd. **(1)**
11/F Aolin Pike Building Shangbao Lu Futian Qu
Shenzhen, 518034, China
Tel.: (86) 21 5081 9999
Software Development Services
S.I.C.: 7371
N.A.I.C.S.: 541511

Non-U.S. Subsidiaries:

Daily Growth Futures Limited **(1)**
Room 3705-07 The Center 99 Queen's Road
Central, China (Hong Kong)
Tel.: (852) 3900 1701
Fax: (852) 3900 1705
Emp.: 3
Commodity Futures Brokerage Services
S.I.C.: 6221
N.A.I.C.S.: 523140

Daily Growth Securities Limited **(1)**
Room 3705 The Center 99 Queen's Road
Central, China (Hong Kong)
Tel.: (852) 3900 1701
Fax: (852) 3900 1705
Securities Brokerage Services
S.I.C.: 6211
N.A.I.C.S.: 523120

CHINA FINANCIAL LEASING GROUP LIMITED

Room A-C 3/F Golden Sun Centre 59 Bonham Strand West
Sheung Wan, China (Hong Kong)
Tel.: (852) 37582328
Fax: (852) 31042882
E-Mail: info@CFLG.com.hk
Web Site: www.CFLG.com.hk
2312—(HKG)
Rev.: $28,756
Assets: $6,879,740
Liabilities: $56,222
Net Worth: $6,823,518
Earnings: ($2,948,055)
Emp.: 17
Fiscal Year-end: 12/31/12
Business Description:
Financial Leasing Services
S.I.C.: 6719
N.A.I.C.S.: 551112
Personnel:
Patrick Kwok Hung Choy *(Chm)*
Anthony Chi Hung Chan *(Mng Dir)*
Hing Bun Tsang *(Sec)*
Board of Directors:
Patrick Kwok Hung Choy
Anthony Chi Hung Chan
Man Yi Chan
Wai King Choi
William Keith Jacobsen
Ka Ki Kwong
Jackie Man Yi Mak
Yiu Wing Tang
Nai Jiang Yang
John Jong Ling Yen
Transfer Agent:
Tricor Tengis Limited
26/F Tesbury Centre, 28 Queens Road East
Hong Kong, China (Hong Kong)

CHINA FINANCIAL SERVICES HOLDINGS LIMITED

Suite 5606 56/F Central Plaza 18 Harbour Road
Wanchai, China (Hong Kong)
Tel.: (852) 25986183
Fax: (852) 25988305
Web Site: www.cfsh.com.hk
605—(HKG)
Sls.: $38,762,499
Assets: $308,005,328
Liabilities: $74,619,883
Net Worth: $233,385,444
Earnings: $32,965,939
Emp.: 110
Fiscal Year-end: 12/31/12
Business Description:
Holding Company; Supermarket Chain Operations; Financial Services
S.I.C.: 6719
N.A.I.C.S.: 551112
Personnel:
Siu Lam Cheung *(Founder & Chm)*
Yuk Ming Chan *(Vice Chm)*
Chin Keung Chung *(Sec)*

Board of Directors:
Siu Lam Cheung
Chun Keung Chan
Yuk Ming Chan
Hui Liu
Wan Lo
Ye Tao
Kwok Wai Tsang
Jian Sheng Wang

Subsidiary:

K.P.A. Company Limited (1)
Rm 5606 56 F Cent Plz 18 Harbour Rd
Wanchai, China (Hong Kong)
Tel.: (852) 25986183
Fax: (852) 25988305
E-Mail: info@kpi.com.hk
Emp.: 20
Property Investment Services
S.I.C.: 6513
N.A.I.C.S.: 531110
Siu Lam Cheung *(Mgr)*

CHINA FIRE SAFETY ENTERPRISE GROUP LIMITED

Units A-B 16/F China Overseas
Building No 139 Hennessy Road
Wanchai, China (Hong Kong)
Tel.: (852) 2960 1688
Fax: (852) 2960 1166
Web Site: www.chinafire.com.cn
0445—(HKG)
Sls.: $159,409,629
Assets: $288,306,396
Liabilities: $90,265,242
Net Worth: $198,041,154
Earnings: ($3,516,304)
Emp.: 1,021
Fiscal Year-end: 12/31/12
Business Description:
Fire Engines, Fire & Safety Equipment Mfr & Sales
S.I.C.: 9224
N.A.I.C.S.: 922160
Personnel:
Xiong Jiang *(Chm)*
Qing Jiang *(CEO & Compliance Officer)*
Ching Wah Li *(Sec)*
Board of Directors:
Xiong Jiang
Ja Wei Heng
Yong Hu
Qing Jiang
Yu Loke
Guo Li Sun
De Feng Wang
Xiu Xia Weng
Hai Yan Zhang

Butterfield Fulcrum Group (Cayman) Limited
Butterfield House 68 Fort Street
609
Georgetown, Grand Cayman, KY1 1107, Cayman Islands
Transfer Agents:
Computershare Hong Kong Investor Services Limited
17M Floor Hopewell Centre 183 Queens Road East
Hong Kong, China (Hong Kong)

Butterfield Fulcrum Group (Cayman) Limited
Butterfield House 68 Fort Street
609
Georgetown, Grand Cayman, KY1 1107, Cayman Islands

Non-U.S. Subsidiaries:

Beijing City Chongzheng Huasheng Emergency Appliances System Co., Ltd. (1)
Beiqijia Hongxiang Hung Industrial Incubator Base 3
Changping District, Beijing, 102209, China
Tel.: (86) 10 81784092
Fax: (86) 10 81784093
E-Mail: sales@czhs.com.cn
Web Site: www.czhs.com.cn
Fire Fighting Equipments Mfr
S.I.C.: 9224
N.A.I.C.S.: 922160

Wanyou Fire Engineering Group Company Limited (1)
51 N Rd Fuzhou City No 158 Eight-story High-King Trade Ctr
Fuzhou, China
Tel.: (86) 59187562228
Fax: (86) 59187670532
E-Mail: wygc@wanyoufire.com
Web Site: www.wanyoufire.com
Fire Fighting Equipments Mfr
S.I.C.: 9224
N.A.I.C.S.: 922160

CHINA FIRST HEAVY INDUSTRIES CO., LTD.

Changqian Road 9
Fularji, Qiqihar, Heilongjiang, 161042, China
Tel.: (86) 452 6810123
Fax: (86) 452 6810111
E-Mail: zjlb@cfhi.com
Web Site: www.cfhi.com
Year Founded: 1954
601106—(SHG)
Business Description:
Heavy Steel Machinery Mfr
S.I.C.: 3559
N.A.I.C.S.: 333249
Personnel:
Shengfu Wu *(Chm)*

CHINA FLAVORS AND FRAGRANCES COMPANY LIMITED

Room 2101-02 21st Floor Wing On House 71 Des Voeux Road
Central, China (Hong Kong)
Tel.: (852) 28380095
Fax: (852) 31040438
E-Mail: cf@chinaffl.com
Web Site: www.chinaffl.com
3318—(HKG)
Rev.: $120,845,455
Assets: $199,263,187
Liabilities: $27,522,986
Net Worth: $171,740,201
Earnings: $9,547,997
Emp.: 977
Fiscal Year-end: 12/31/12
Business Description:
Flavors & Fragrance Sales & Mfr
S.I.C.: 5122
N.A.I.C.S.: 446120
Personnel:
Ming Fan Wang *(Chm & CEO)*
Man Wai Ma *(Sec)*
Board of Directors:
Ming Fan Wang
Roger Wai Man Leung
Qing Long Li
Kwun Wan Ng
Wu Qian
Xiao Xiong Zhou

Bank of Bermuda (Cayman) Limited
PO Boy 513 68 West Bay Road
Georgetown, Grand Cayman, KY-1106, Cayman Islands
Transfer Agents:
Tricor Investor Services Limited
26/F Tesbury Centre 28 Queen's Road East
Hong Kong, China (Hong Kong)

Bank of Bermuda (Cayman) Limited
PO Boy 513 68 West Bay Road
Georgetown, Grand Cayman, KY-1106, Cayman Islands

CHINA FLEXIBLE PACKAGING HOLDINGS LIMITED

No 689 Xiguan Road
Rongcheng District, Jieyang, Guangdong, 522000, China
Tel.: (86) 6638811898
Fax: (86) 663 8821336
E-Mail: info@cnflexpack.com
Web Site: www.cnflexpack.com
C59—(SES)
Sales Range: $125-149.9 Million
Emp.: 350
Business Description:
Flexible Packaging Material Mfr
S.I.C.: 2671
N.A.I.C.S.: 326112
Personnel:
Hanming Zeng *(Chm & CEO)*
Zeyu Li *(Chief R&D Officer)*
Foon Kuen Lai *(Sec)*
Board of Directors:
Hanming Zeng
Jinmin Du
Tiew Siam Ong
Tung Leung Wong
Koon Sang Yeung

Foo Kon Tan Grant Thornton LLP
47 Hill Street 05 01 Singapore Chinese Chamber Of Commerce
Industry Building, 179365 Singapore, Singapore
Transfer Agent:
Boardroom Corporate & Advisory Services Pte. Ltd.
50 Raffles Place 32-01 Singapore Land Tower
Singapore, Singapore

CHINA FLOORING HOLDING COMPANY LIMITED

Unit 3401 34/F West Tower Shun Tak Centre
168-200 Connaught Road, Central, China (Hong Kong)
Tel.: (852) 28586665
Fax: (852) 28589700
E-Mail: info@nature-hk.hk
Web Site: www.china-flooring.com.hk
2083—(HKG)
Sls.: $177,579,050
Assets: $490,067,658
Liabilities: $83,068,542
Net Worth: $406,999,116
Earnings: $18,899,179
Emp.: 2,389
Fiscal Year-end: 12/31/12
Business Description:
Wood Flooring
S.I.C.: 2421
N.A.I.C.S.: 321918
Personnel:
Hok Pan Se *(Chm & Pres)*
Chun Yiu Tsang *(CFO & Sec)*
Board of Directors:
Hok Pan Se
Raymond Siu Wing Chan
Savio Chi Keung Chow
Eric King Fung Ho
Arthur Kwok Cheung Li
Jian Bin She
Homer Sun
Chun Ming Teoh
Son I Un
Sen Lin Zhang

Computershare Hong Kong Investor Services Limited
Shops 1712-1716 17th Floor Hopewell Centre
183 Queens Road East
Wanchai, China (Hong Kong)
Transfer Agents:
Royal Bank of Canada Trust Company (Cayman) Limited
4th Floor Royal Bank House 24 Shedden Road
Georgetown, Cayman Islands

Computershare Hong Kong Investor Services Limited
Shops 1712-1716 17th Floor Hopewell Centre
183 Queens Road East
Wanchai, China (Hong Kong)

CHINA FOOD COMPANY PLC

49 51 Whitehall
London, SW1A 2BX, United Kingdom
Tel.: (44) 20 7930 8888
Web Site: www.chinafoodcompany.com
CFC—(AIM)
Rev.: $31,745,308
Assets: $109,579,037
Liabilities: $59,561,343
Net Worth: $50,017,694
Earnings: ($8,564,490)
Emp.: 1,082
Fiscal Year-end: 12/31/12
Business Description:
Cooking Sauces & Animal Feed Mfr
S.I.C.: 2047
N.A.I.C.S.: 311111
Personnel:
John McLean *(Chm)*
Feng Bo *(CEO)*
Ricky Mak King Pui *(CFO)*
Fu Guoping *(CEO-China)*
Nigel Cartwright *(Sec)*
Board of Directors:
John McLean
Feng Bo
Clifford Halvorsen
Daniel Saw
Raphael Wai Mun Tham
Legal Counsel:
Stephenson Harwood
1 Finsbury Circus
London, United Kingdom

Stephenson Harwood
1 Raffles Place #12-00 OUB Centre
Singapore, Singapore

Non-U.S. Holding:

Full Fortune Holdings Pte Ltd (1)
36 Robinson Road
Singapore, Singapore
Tel.: (65) 65360880
Investment Management Services
S.I.C.: 6282
N.A.I.C.S.: 523920

CHINA FOOD PACKING INC., LTD.

Flat RM 1407 City Landmark 1 69 Chung On Street
Tsuen Wan, Hong Kong, China (Hong Kong)
Tel.: (852) 29407730
Fax: (852) 29407718
Web Site: www.chinafoodpack.com
Year Founded: 2007
Business Description:
Metal Can Mfr
S.I.C.: 3411
N.A.I.C.S.: 332431
Personnel:
Man Chan *(CEO)*

CHINA FOREST INDUSTRY HOLDINGS LIMITED

Room 2206 22nd Fl Office Tower,Convention Plaza 1
Harbour Road, Wanchai, China (Hong Kong)
Tel.: (852) 35718680
Fax: (852) 35719990
E-Mail: lionaxmarc@163.com
Web Site: www.chinaforestindustry.com
MLCFI—(EUR)
Sales Range: $1-9.9 Million
Business Description:
Forest Plantation, Logging, Standing Wood Transfer, Timber Production & Forestry Management Services
S.I.C.: 0831
N.A.I.C.S.: 113210
Personnel:
Daofang Zhou *(Chm & CEO)*
Tong Jiang *(Vice Chm)*
Luler Tang *(CFO)*
Sizu Lin *(CTO)*
Gaoping Zhou *(Vice Gen Dir)*
Chen Jiang *(Sec)*

China Forest Industry Holdings Limited—(Continued)

Board of Directors:
Daofang Zhou
Lui Cheung
Tong Jiang
Sebastien Tran
Gaoping Zhou

CHINA FORESTRY HOLDINGS CO., LTD.

Room 2507 Floor 25 America Bank Center Harcourt Road 12
Central Ring, Hong Kong, China (Hong Kong)
Tel.: (852) 2519 7288
Fax: (852) 2519 6629
Web Site: www.chinaforestryholding.com
930—(HKG)
Sls.: $22,866,775
Assets: $515,619,952
Liabilities: $296,890,809
Net Worth: $218,729,143
Earnings: ($188,514,126)
Emp.: 715
Fiscal Year-end: 12/31/12

Business Description:
Forest Management Services
S.I.C.: 0851
N.A.I.C.S.: 115310

Personnel:
Kwok Cheong Li *(Chm)*
Raymond Wai Kit Tong *(CFO & Sec)*
Ning Jiang *(Chief Sls Officer)*
Ying Meng Xiang *(Chief Resource Officer)*

Board of Directors:
Kwok Cheong Li
Helen Wai Man Hsu
Zhi Tong Li
Pu Lin
Can Liu
Yong Ping Liu
Fan Zhi Meng
Feng Xiao

Legal Counsel:
Orrick, Herrington & Sutcliffe
43rd Floor Gloucester Tower The Landmark 15 Queens Road Central
Hong Kong, China (Hong Kong)

Computershare Hong Kong Investor Services Limited
Shops 1712-1716 17th Floor Hopewell Centre 183 Queens Road East
Wanchai, China (Hong Kong)

Transfer Agent:
Royal Bank of Canada Trust Company (Cayman) Limited
4th Floor Royal Bank House 24 Shedden Road
Georgetown, Cayman Islands

CHINA FORESTRY INC.

Economic Development Zone
Hanzhong, Shaan'xi, China
Tel.: (86) 2985257870
Web Site: www.chinaforestryinc.com
CHFYD—(OTC OTCB)
Rev.: $1,546,063
Assets: $2,657,649
Liabilities: $3,296,364
Net Worth: ($638,715)
Earnings: $123,169
Emp.: 29
Fiscal Year-end: 12/31/12

Business Description:
Commercial Forest Management Services
S.I.C.: 0851
N.A.I.C.S.: 115310

Personnel:
Yuan Tian *(CEO)*
Man Ha *(CFO & Treas)*

Board of Directors:
Man Ha
Yuan Tian

Transfer Agent:
Interwest Transfer Co., Inc.
1981 E 4800 S Ste 100
Salt Lake City, UT 84117
Tel.: (801) 272-9294
Fax: (801) 277-3147

CHINA FORTUNE FINANCIAL GROUP LIMITED

35th Floor Office Tower Convention Plaza
1 Harbour Road, Wanchai, China (Hong Kong)
Tel.: (852) 31051863
Fax: (852) 31051862
E-Mail: info@290.com.hk
Web Site: www.290.com.hk
0290—(HKG)
Sls.: $6,036,150
Assets: $63,769,772
Liabilities: $25,215,012
Net Worth: $38,554,761
Earnings: ($8,944,746)
Emp.: 128
Fiscal Year-end: 03/31/13

Business Description:
Security Management Services
S.I.C.: 6211
N.A.I.C.S.: 523999

Personnel:
Min Zhang *(Chm)*
Keith Cheuk Fan Ng *(Mng Dir)*
Chun Fai Cai *(Sec)*

Board of Directors:
Min Zhang
Chun Yu Hon
Graham Ka Wai Lam
Kay Kwok Ng
Keith Cheuk Fan Ng
B. Ray Billy Tam
Tony Kam Fat Wong
Ling Wu
Yingyan Xia

Royal Bank of Canada Trust Company (Cayman) Limited
4th Floor Royal Bank House 24 Shedden Road
Georgetown, Cayman Islands

Transfer Agents:
Union Registrars Limited
18/F Fook Lee Commercial Centre Town Place
33 Lockhart Road
Wanchai, China (Hong Kong)

Royal Bank of Canada Trust Company (Cayman) Limited
4th Floor Royal Bank House 24 Shedden Road
Georgetown, Cayman Islands

Subsidiaries:

Excalibur Futures Limited **(1)**
Rm 2512 Cosco Tower 83 Queens Rd
Central, China (Hong Kong)
Tel.: (852) 28449862
Fax: (852) 25260618
E-Mail: info@excalibur.com.hk
Web Site: www.excalibur.com.hk
Emp.: 30
Securities Trading Services
S.I.C.: 6211
N.A.I.C.S.: 523110
Allan Poon *(Mng Dir)*

Excalibur Securities Limited **(1)**
2512 Cosco Tower 183 Queen's Road
Central, China (Hong Kong)
Tel.: (852) 25260388
Fax: (852) 25260618
E-Mail: cs@excalibur.com.hk
Web Site: www.excalibur.com.hk
Emp.: 20
Securities Trading Services
S.I.C.: 6211
N.A.I.C.S.: 523110
Allan Poon *(Pres)*

Fortune (HK) Securities Limited **(1)**
35th Fl Office Tower Convention Plaza 1 Harbour Road
Wanchai, China (Hong Kong)
Tel.: (852) 31051029
Fax: (852) 3105 1892
Web Site: www.hths.com.hk
Emp.: 35
Securities Trading Services
S.I.C.: 6211
N.A.I.C.S.: 523110

Fortune Wealth Management Limited **(1)**
Unit 1609 16 F 113 Argyle St
Mongkok, Kowloon, China (Hong Kong)
Tel.: (852) 2541 6608
Fax: (852) 2541 3355
E-Mail: admin@fortunewealth.com.hk
Web Site: www.fortune-wealth.com.hk
Portfolio Management & General Insurance Services
S.I.C.: 6799
N.A.I.C.S.: 523920

Non-U.S. Subsidiary:

China Fortune Group Strategic Investment Company Limited **(1)**
Fl 32 Fortune Plz Jintian Rd
Futian Dist, Shenzhen, China
Tel.: (86) 75533335566
Fax: (86) 75533335575
E-Mail: ir@cfortgroup.com
Web Site: www.cfortgroup.com
Investment Management Services
S.I.C.: 6211
N.A.I.C.S.: 523999
Zhou Wentao *(Chm)*
Huang Yue *(Pres & Mng Dir)*

CHINA FORTUNE GROUP LIMITED

(See Under China Fortune Financial Group Limited)

CHINA FORTUNE HOLDINGS LIMITED

Room 1505-7 15/F Tower A Regent Centre 63 Wo Yi Hop Road
Kwai Chung, New Territories, China (Hong Kong)
Tel.: (852) 24220811
Fax: (852) 24280988
E-Mail: info@chinafortune.com
Web Site: www.fortunetele.com
0110—(HKG)
Sls.: $80,342,169
Assets: $75,470,695
Liabilities: $22,140,973
Net Worth: $53,329,723
Earnings: ($9,018,634)
Emp.: 159
Fiscal Year-end: 12/31/12

Business Description:
Telecommunication & Investment Services
S.I.C.: 8748
N.A.I.C.S.: 541618

Personnel:
Kin Kiu Fong *(CTO)*
Jason Man Kit Lam *(Sec)*

Board of Directors:
Victor Wing Seng Chang
Chun Kwan Law
Peter Xi Zhi Luo
Carl Yu Wang
Alexis Lit Chor Wong

The Bank of Bermuda Limited
Bank of Bermuda Building 6 Front Street
Hamilton, Bermuda

Transfer Agents:
Tricor Abacus Limited
26/F Tesbury Centre 28 Queen's Road East
Hong Kong, China (Hong Kong)

The Bank of Bermuda Limited
Bank of Bermuda Building 6 Front Street
Hamilton, Bermuda

CHINA FORTUNE LAND DEVELOPMENT CO., LTD.

No 18 Xia Guang Li Gateway Plaza 9th Floor Block A
East Third Ring Road Chaoyang, Beijing, China 100027
Tel.: (86) 10 59115000
Fax: (86) 10 59115088
Web Site: www.cfldcn.com
Year Founded: 1998
600340—(SHG)

Business Description:
Real Estate Development Services
S.I.C.: 6531
N.A.I.C.S.: 531390

Personnel:
Wenxue Wang *(Chm & Pres)*

CHINA FRUITS CORP.

Fu Xi Technology & Industry Park
Nan Feng County, Jiangxiang, Jiang Xi, China
Tel.: (86) 7943266199
CHFR—(OTC)
Sls.: $3,709,101
Assets: $6,246,186
Liabilities: $3,754,781
Net Worth: $2,491,405
Earnings: $128,421
Emp.: 60
Fiscal Year-end: 12/31/12

Business Description:
Tangerine Non-Alcoholic & Alcoholic Beverages
S.I.C.: 2037
N.A.I.C.S.: 311411

Personnel:
Quan Long Chen *(Chm, Pres & CEO)*
Ze Li *(CFO)*

Board of Directors:
Quan Long Chen

Transfer Agent:
Guardian Registrar & Transfer, Inc.
7951 SW 6th St Ste 216
Plantation, FL 33324-3276

CHINA GALAXY SECURITIES COMPANY LIMITED

Tower C Corporate Square 35 Finance Street
Xicheng District, Beijing, 100033, China
Tel.: (86) 4008888888
Fax: (86) 1066568532
E-Mail: webmaster@chinastock.com.cn
Web Site: www.chinastock.com.cn
Year Founded: 2007
6881—(HKG)
Sales Range: $900-999.9 Million
Emp.: 8,600

Business Description:
Securities brokerage, Investment Consulting & Financial Advisory Services
S.I.C.: 6211
N.A.I.C.S.: 523110

Personnel:
Youan Chen *(Chm)*
Weiguo Gu *(Pres)*
Chengming Wu *(Sec)*

Board of Directors:
Youan Chen
Weiguo Gu
Chenghui Li
Feng Liu
Xiaoli Qi
Xun Shi
Shiding Wang
Chengming Wu
Yuwu Wu
Guoping Xu

CHINA GAOXIAN FIBRE FABRIC HOLDINGS LTD.

Industrial Area of Balidian Town
Wuxing District, Huzhou, 313002, China
Tel.: (86) 5722561700
Fax: (86) 5722560131
Web Site: www.chinagaoxian.com

I4U—(SES)
Sales Range: $250-299.9 Million
Emp.: 736
Business Description:
Polyester Yarn & Knit Fabric Mfr
S.I.C.: 2299
N.A.I.C.S.: 313110
Personnel:
Xiangbin Cao *(Chm & CEO)*
Raymond Wai Kan Wong *(CFO)*
Board of Directors:
Xiangbin Cao
Wai Meng Chan
Fen Chen
Chung Kong Lau
Yijie Liu
Wan Loong Tham

CHINA GAS HOLDINGS LIMITED
Room 1601 16th Floor AXA Centre
151 Gloucester Road
Wanchai, China (Hong Kong)
Tel.: (852) 28770800
Fax: (852) 28770633
E-Mail: 384hk@chinagasholdings.com.hk
Web Site: www.chinagasholdings.com.hk
384—(HKG OTC)
Rev.: $2,740,221,801
Assets: $4,560,646,862
Liabilities: $2,905,350,529
Net Worth: $1,655,296,334
Earnings: $263,227,956
Emp.: 28,000
Fiscal Year-end: 03/31/13
Business Description:
Natural Gas Production
S.I.C.: 1311
N.A.I.C.S.: 211111
Personnel:
Ming Hui Liu *(Pres & Mng Dir)*
Yingxue Pang *(Deputy Pres & CEO-Shanghai Zhongyou Energy Holdings Limited)*
Eric Wing Cheong Leung *(CFO & Deputy Mng Dir)*
Feona Yuk Yee Ng *(Sec)*
Board of Directors:
Cynthia Sin Yue Wong
Xinguo Chen
Zhuozhi Feng
P. K. Jain
Eric Wing Cheong Leung
Ming Hui Liu
Jinlong Ma
Erwan Mao
Yingxue Pang
Jeong Joon Yu
Yuhua Zhao
Weiwei Zhu

Butterfield Fulcrum Group (Bermuda) Limited
Rosebank Centre 11 Bermudiana Road
Pembroke, Bermuda
Transfer Agents:
Computershare Hong Kong Investor Services Limited
17M Floor Hopewell Centre 183 Queen's Road East
Wanchai, China (Hong Kong)

Butterfield Fulcrum Group (Bermuda) Limited
Rosebank Centre 11 Bermudiana Road
Pembroke, Bermuda

CHINA GENERAL PLASTICS CORPORATION
7F No 37 Ji-Hu Rd Nei Hu District
114 Taipei, Taiwan
Tel.: (886) 287516888
Fax: (886) 226599553
E-Mail: cgpcstkqa@cgpc.com.tw
Web Site: www.cgpc.com.tw
1305—(TAI)
Sales Range: $250-299.9 Million
Business Description:
Polyvinyl Chloride Resin Mfr
S.I.C.: 2821
N.A.I.C.S.: 325211
Personnel:
Quintin Wu *(Chm)*

CHINA GENGSHENG MINERALS, INC.
No 88 Gengsheng Road
Dayugou Town, Gongyi, Henan, 451271, China
Tel.: (86) 371 6405 9863
Fax: (86) 371 6405 9846
E-Mail: ir@gengsheng.com
Web Site: www.gengsheng.com
Year Founded: 1986
CHGS—(NYSEMKT)
Rev.: $73,534,827
Assets: $162,405,310
Liabilities: $121,923,395
Net Worth: $40,481,915
Earnings: ($13,539,454)
Emp.: 1,200
Fiscal Year-end: 12/31/12
Business Description:
Mineral Products Mfr
S.I.C.: 3299
N.A.I.C.S.: 327999
Personnel:
Shunqing Zhang *(Chm, Pres & CEO)*
Weina Zhang *(Interim CFO)*
Xiangyang Zhang *(Sec)*
Board of Directors:
Shunqing Zhang
Jeffrey Friedland
Hsin-I Lin
Jingzhong Yu
Ningsheng Zhou

CHINA GERUI ADVANCED MATERIALS GROUP LIMITED
1 Shuanghu Development Zone
Xinzheng City, Zhengzhou, Henan, 451191, China
Tel.: (86) 37162568634
Fax: (86) 371 6771 8787
Web Site: www.geruigroup.com
CHOP—(NASDAQ)
Rev.: $265,486,082
Assets: $673,369,602
Liabilities: $343,302,282
Net Worth: $330,067,320
Earnings: $26,133,088
Emp.: 1,070
Fiscal Year-end: 12/31/12
Business Description:
Cold-Rolled Specialty Steel Products Mfr
S.I.C.: 3399
N.A.I.C.S.: 331221
Personnel:
Mingwang Lu *(Chm & CEO)*
Edward Meng *(CFO)*
Board of Directors:
Mingwang Lu
Harry Edelson
J. P. Huang
Yi Lu
Yunlong Wang
Kwok Keung Wong
Maotong Xu

CHINA GEZHOUBA GROUP CORPORATION
21F Tower A Gemdale Plaza No 91 Jianguo Road
Chaoyang District, Beijing, 100022, China
Tel.: (86) 10 59525952
Fax: (86) 10 59525951
E-Mail: cggc@cggcintl.com
Web Site: www.gzbgj.com
Year Founded: 1970
600068—(SHG)
Sales Range: $5-14.9 Billion
Emp.: 40,000
Business Description:
Construction Engineering Services
S.I.C.: 8711
N.A.I.C.S.: 541330
Personnel:
Chen Xiaohua *(Gen Mgr)*

CHINA GINSENG HOLDINGS, INC.
64 Jie Fang Da Road Ji Yu Building A Suite 1208
Changchun, China 130022
Tel.: (86) 43185790039
Web Site: www.chinaginsengs.com
Year Founded: 2004
CSNG—(OTC)
Rev.: $3,563,165
Assets: $5,367,231
Liabilities: $6,528,120
Net Worth: ($1,160,889)
Earnings: ($3,646,004)
Emp.: 122
Fiscal Year-end: 06/30/13
Business Description:
Ginseng Mfr, Distr & Marketer
S.I.C.: 2833
N.A.I.C.S.: 325411
Personnel:
Changzhen Liu *(Chm & CEO)*
Ying Ren *(CFO)*
Xiaohua Cai *(CMO)*
Board of Directors:
Changzhen Liu
Qing Ouyang
Jiankun Song
Hui Sun
Yuxiang Zhang

CHINA GLASS HOLDINGS LIMITED
Room 2608 26/F West Tower Shun Tak Centre 168-200 Connaught Road
Central, China (Hong Kong)
Tel.: (852) 25592996
Fax: (852) 25597669
Web Site: www.chinaglassholdings.com
3300—(HKG)
Sls.: $405,095,299
Assets: $908,323,839
Liabilities: $539,674,131
Net Worth: $368,649,708
Earnings: ($29,440,941)
Emp.: 5,963
Fiscal Year-end: 12/31/12
Business Description:
Glass Products Mfr & Sales
S.I.C.: 3231
N.A.I.C.S.: 327215
Personnel:
Cheng Zhou *(Chm)*
Zhaoheng Zhang *(CEO)*
Jianxun Wang *(CTO)*
Hiu Ling Li *(Sec)*
Xiangdong Cui *(Sr VP)*
Ping Li *(Sr VP)*
Board of Directors:
Cheng Zhou
Huachen Chen
Shuai Chen
Xiangdong Cui
Ping Li
Wei Ni
Min Ning
Baiheng Zhang
Zhaoheng Zhang
John Ling Huan Zhao
Lihua Zhao

Appleby Management (Bermuda) Ltd.
Canon's Court 22 Victoria Street
HM 12 Hamilton, Bermuda
Transfer Agents:
Computershare Hong Kong Investor Services Limited
46th Floor Hopewell Centre 183 Queen's Road East
Wanchai, China (Hong Kong)

Appleby Management (Bermuda) Ltd.
Canon's Court 22 Victoria Street
HM 12 Hamilton, Bermuda

CHINA GLAZE CO., LTD.
No 136 Sector 4 Chung Hsing Road
Chutung, Hsin-chu, Taiwan
Tel.: (886) 35824128
Fax: (886) 35820543
E-Mail: info@mail.china-glaze.com.tw
Web Site: www.china-glaze.com.tw
1809—(TAI)
Sales Range: $125-149.9 Million
Business Description:
Glaze & Ceramic Products Mfr & Distr
S.I.C.: 3229
N.A.I.C.S.: 327212
Personnel:
Xianchang Tsai *(Pres)*

Non-U.S. Subsidiaries:

Guangdong Sanshui T&H glaze Co., Ltd. **(1)**
Da-Busha Industry Zone Datang Town
Sanshui District, Foshan, Guangdong, 528143, China
Tel.: (86) 75787293010
Fax: (86) 75783386998
E-Mail: service@china-glaze.com.cn
Web Site: www.china-glaze.com.tw/eng/about/liaison.htm
Emp.: 300
Ceramic Glazing Services
S.I.C.: 1793
N.A.I.C.S.: 238150

PT. China Glaze Indonesia **(1)**
Kawasan Industri Suryacipta Jl Surya Lestari Kav 1-17C Kutamekar
Ciampel, Karawang, West Java, 41361, Indonesia
Tel.: (62) 267440938
Fax: (62) 267440 889
Web Site: www.china-glaze.com.tw/eng/about/liaison.htm
Ceramic Mfr
S.I.C.: 3255
N.A.I.C.S.: 327120

Shandong T&H glaze Co., Ltd. **(1)**
Bai-E Road North Side Economic Development Zone
Gaoqing, Zibo, Shandong, 256300, China
Tel.: (86) 533 6258888
Fax: (86) 533 6256666
Web Site: www.china-glaze.com.tw/EN/AboutUs.aspx?pkid=125
Ceramic Glazing Services
S.I.C.: 1793
N.A.I.C.S.: 238150

Shanghai Che-hung system glaze Ltd. **(1)**
Jindu Road 618
Meilong Town Minhang District, Shanghai, China
Tel.: (86) 2164975566
Fax: (86) 2164973535
Ceramic Glazes Mfr
S.I.C.: 3999
N.A.I.C.S.: 327110

Shanghai T&H glaze Co., Ltd. **(1)**
No 538 Side Jindu Road Meilong Town
Minhang District, Shanghai, 200237, China
Tel.: (86) 2164975566
Fax: (86) 2164973538
Web Site: www.china-glaze.com.tw/eng/about/liaison.htm
Ceramic Glazing Services
S.I.C.: 1793
N.A.I.C.S.: 238150

CHINA GLOBAL MEDIA, INC.

25-26F Wanxiang Enterprise Building
No 70 Station North Road
Changsha, Hunan, 410001, China
Tel.: (86) 73189970899
Year Founded: 1980
CGLO—(OTC)
Sls.: $59,725,182
Assets: $48,138,842
Liabilities: $23,869,508
Net Worth: $24,269,334
Earnings: $6,763,817
Emp.: 125
Fiscal Year-end: 12/31/12

Business Description:
Advertisement & Brand Name Development
S.I.C.: 7319
N.A.I.C.S.: 541890

Personnel:
Guolin Yang *(Chm, Pres, CEO, Treas & Sec)*
Jun Liang *(CFO & Chief Scientific Officer)*
Hongdong Xu *(COO)*

Board of Directors:
Guolin Yang
Jun Liang
Bingchuan Xiao
Hongdong Xu

Transfer Agent:
Action Stock Transfer Corp.
2469 E Fort Union Blvd Ste 214
Salt Lake City, UT 84121

CHINA GOGREEN ASSETS INVESTMENT LIMITED

(Name Changed to Jun Yang Solar Power Investments Limited)

CHINA GOLD INTERNATIONAL RESOURCES CORP. LTD.

Suite 1030 One Bentall Centre 505 Burrard Street
PO Box 31
Vancouver, BC, V7X 1M5, Canada
Tel.: (604) 609-0598
Fax: (604) 688-0598
E-Mail: info@chinagoldintl.com
Web Site: www.chinagoldintl.com
2099—(HKG TSX)
Rev.: $332,387,000
Assets: $1,806,264,000
Liabilities: $438,470,000
Net Worth: $1,367,794,000
Earnings: $73,514,000
Emp.: 1,276
Fiscal Year-end: 12/31/12

Business Description:
Gold & Nonferrous Metal Mining & Production Services
S.I.C.: 1041
N.A.I.C.S.: 212221

Personnel:
Xin Song *(Chm)*
Bing Liu *(CEO)*
Derrick Zhang *(CFO)*
Jerry Xie *(Sec & Exec VP)*
Zhanming Wu *(Sr Exec VP)*

Board of Directors:
Xin Song
John King Burns
Yunfei Chen
Greg Hall
Y. B. Ian He
Xiangdong Jiang
Bing Liu
Lianzhong Sun
Zhanming Wu

Legal Counsel:
Kirkland & Ellis
26/F Gloucester Tower The Landmark 15 Queen's Road
Central, China (Hong Kong)

Fraser Milner Casgrain LLP
20th Floor 250 Howe Street
Vancouver, BC, V6C 3R8, Canada

CIBC Mellon Trust Company
1066 West Hastings Street Suite 1600
Vancouver, BC, V6E 3X1, Canada

Transfer Agents:
Computershare Hong Kong Investor Services Limited
Shops 1712-1716 17th Floor Hopewell Centre
183 Queens Road East
Wanchai, China (Hong Kong)

CIBC Mellon Trust Company
1066 West Hastings Street Suite 1600
Vancouver, BC, V6E 3X1, Canada

CHINA GRAND FORESTRY GREEN RESOURCES GROUP LIMITED

(Name Changed to China Sandi Holdings Limited)

CHINA GRAND RESORTS, INC.

RM 1901 Reignwood Center No 8
Yong'an Dongli Jianguomen Outer Street
Chaoyang District, Beijing, 100022, China
Tel.: (86) 10 6482 7785
Year Founded: 1989
CGND—(OTC OTCB)
Int. Income: $30
Assets: $25,535
Liabilities: $1,313,674
Net Worth: ($1,288,139)
Earnings: ($210,830)
Emp.: 4
Fiscal Year-end: 09/30/13

Business Description:
Advertising, Media & Marketing Solutions
S.I.C.: 7319
N.A.I.C.S.: 541890

Personnel:
Menghua Liu *(Chm, CEO & Acting CFO)*

Board of Directors:
Menghua Liu
Yanhong Deng
Xiangyang Liu

CHINA GREAT WALL ASSET MANAGEMENT CORPORATION

Floors 9-12 Yuetan DaSha Office Bldg A
No 2 YueTan Beijie Xichengqu,
Beijing, 100 045, China
Tel.: (86) 1068054068
Fax: (86) 1068082784
E-Mail: jiangyh@gwamcc.com
Web Site: www.gwamcc.com
Emp.: 4,000

Business Description:
Financial Asset Management Services
S.I.C.: 6282
N.A.I.C.S.: 523920

Personnel:
Dongping Zhao *(CEO)*

Joint Venture:

Nissay-Greatwall Life Insurance Co., Ltd. **(1)**
37th Floor United Plaza 1468
Nanjing Road West, Shanghai, 200 040, China CN
Tel.: (86) 38999888
Fax: (86) 2162470739
Web Site: www.nissay.co.jp/english/network/
Life Insurance Products & Services; Owned 50% by Nippon Life Insurance Co. & 50% by China Great Wall Asset Management Corporation
S.I.C.: 6311
N.A.I.C.S.: 524113
Yasushi Ozaki *(Pres)*

CHINA GREEN AGRICULTURE, INC.

3rd Floor Borough A Block A 181
South Taibai Road
Xi'an, Shaanxi, China 710065
Tel.: (86) 29 88266368
Fax: (86) 29 88231590
E-Mail: info@cgagri.com
Web Site: www.cgagri.com
CGA—(NYSE)
Sls.: $216,897,956
Assets: $348,728,342
Liabilities: $51,875,050
Net Worth: $296,853,292
Earnings: $44,774,048
Emp.: 501
Fiscal Year-end: 06/30/13

Business Description:
Humic Acid Organic Liquid Compound Fertilizer Researcher, Developer, Mfr & Distr
S.I.C.: 2875
N.A.I.C.S.: 325314

Personnel:
Tao Li *(Chm, Pres & CEO)*
Ken Ren *(CFO)*

Board of Directors:
Tao Li
Yu Hao
Lianfu Liu
Yiru Shi
Philip Yizhao Zhang

CHINA GREEN CREATIVE, INC.

18/F Development Centre Building
South of Renmin Rd
LuoHu District, Shenzhen, Guangdong, China
Tel.: (86) 75523998799
CNGVD—(OTC)
Rev.: $6,870,194
Assets: $6,356,193
Liabilities: $8,064,589
Net Worth: ($1,708,396)
Earnings: $635,873
Emp.: 42
Fiscal Year-end: 12/31/12

Business Description:
Electronic Products & Consumer Goods Distr
S.I.C.: 5065
N.A.I.C.S.: 423690

Personnel:
Xing Hua Chen *(Pres)*
Xin Zhang Ye *(CEO)*
Deng Lin *(CFO)*

Board of Directors:
Feng Chen
Xing Hua Chen
Xin Zhang Ye

CHINA GREEN ENERGY INDUSTRIES, INC.

Jingsu Wujin Lijia Industrial Park
Lijia Town
Wujin District, Changzhou, Jiangsu, 213176, China
Tel.: (86) 519 86230102
CGRE—(OTCB)
Sales Range: $10-24.9 Million
Emp.: 575

Business Description:
Holding Company; Clean Technology-Based Consumer Products Mfr & Distr
S.I.C.: 6719
N.A.I.C.S.: 551112

Personnel:
Jianliang Shi *(Chm & CEO)*
Jianfeng Xu *(CFO)*
Zhengxing Shangguan *(Exec VP)*

Board of Directors:
Jianliang Shi
Zhengxing Shangguan
Jinrong Shen
Ying Wang

CHINA GREEN, INC.

Room 3601 The Centre Queen's Road 99
Central, China (Hong Kong)
Tel.: (852) 36918831
Fax: (852) 36918821
Web Site: www.chinagreeninc.com
Sales Range: $10-24.9 Million
Emp.: 8

Business Description:
Landscaping & Environmental Consulting Services
S.I.C.: 0783
N.A.I.C.S.: 561730

Personnel:
Wei Guo Wang *(CEO)*

Board of Directors:
Wei Guo Wang

CHINA GREEN MATERIAL TECHNOLOGIES, INC.

1 Yantai Third Road Centralism Area
Haping Road
Harbin Economic and Technological Development Zone
Harbin, Heilongjiang, 150060, China
Tel.: (86) 451 5175 0888
Fax: (86) 451 8281 2677
Web Site: www.sinogreenmaterial.com
Sales Range: $10-24.9 Million
Emp.: 245

Business Description:
Starch-Based Biodegradable & Disposable Food Trays, Containers, Tableware & Packaging Materials
S.I.C.: 2899
N.A.I.C.S.: 325998

Personnel:
Zhonghao Su *(Pres & CEO)*
Yang Li *(Sec)*

Board of Directors:
Zhonghao Su
Guiguo Wu
Youwei Xing

Subsidiary:

Harbin ChangFangYuan Hi-Tech Environment-Friendly Industrial Co., Ltd **(1)**
No 172 Zhongshan Road
Harbin, Heilongjiang, 150040, China
Tel.: (86) 45182811855
Fax: (86) 45182812677
Disposable Tableware Distr
S.I.C.: 5199
N.A.I.C.S.: 424990

CHINA GREEN STAR AGRICULTURAL CORPORATION

100 King Street West Suite 5700
Toronto, ON, M5X 1C7, Canada
Tel.: (416) 849-3858
Fax: (416) 849-3859
Web Site: www.greenstaragricultural.com
Year Founded: 2007
GRE—(TSXV)
Rev.: $38,767,953
Assets: $46,335,585
Liabilities: $6,268,902
Net Worth: $40,066,683

Earnings: $10,259,546
Fiscal Year-end: 12/31/12
Business Description:
Investment Services
S.I.C.: 6211
N.A.I.C.S.: 523999
Personnel:
Lianyun Guan *(Founder, Chm, Pres & CEO)*
Michael Lam *(CFO)*
Judith Hong Wilkin *(Sec)*
Board of Directors:
Lianyun Guan
Frank Galati
Bob Jian Gou
Bryan Knebel
Huirong Luo
G. Michael Newman
Huoyun Ye
Legal Counsel:
Fogler, Rubinoff LLP
Toronto Dominion Centre Suite 3300
Toronto, ON, M5K 1G8, Canada
Tel.: (416) 864-9700
Fax: (416) 941-8852
Transfer Agent:
Olympia Transfer Services Inc.
Suite 920 120 Adelaide Street West
Toronto, ON, Canada

CHINA GRENTECH CORPORATION LIMITED

15th Floor Block A Guoren Building
Keji Central 3rd Road
Hi-Tech Park Nanshan District,
Shenzhen, 518057, China
Tel.: (86) 755 8350 1796
E-Mail: investor@powercn.com.cn
Web Site: www.grentech.com.cn
Year Founded: 1999
Sales Range: $250-299.9 Million
Emp.: 4,443
Business Description:
Designer & Mfr of Wireless Telecommunications Equipment
S.I.C.: 4812
N.A.I.C.S.: 517210
Personnel:
Huang Yin *(Founder)*
Yingjie Gao *(Chm, Pres & CEO)*
Rong Yu *(CFO)*
Board of Directors:
Yingjie Gao
Jing Fang
Cuiming Shi
Gordon Hing Lun Tsang
Qi Wang
Xiaohu You
Rong Yu
Subsidiaries:

Quanzhou Lake Communication Co., Ltd. **(1)**
1306 Tower A Tiancheng Square 324
Longkou East Tianhe North, Guangzhou, 518040, China
Tel.: (86) 20 85266957
Fax: (86) 20 85266957
Designer & Mfr of Wireless Telecommunications Equipment
S.I.C.: 4812
N.A.I.C.S.: 517210

Shenzhen GrenTech Co., Ltd. **(1)**
Tower B Zhongyin Building
Caitian Road North, Futian District
Shenzhen, China
Tel.: (86) 75526503007
Web Site: www.grentech.com
Designer & Mfr of Wireless Telecommunications Equipment
S.I.C.: 4812
N.A.I.C.S.: 517210

CHINA GROWTH EQUITY INVESTMENT LTD.

(Name Changed to Pingtan Marine Enterprise Ltd.)

CHINA GROWTH OPPORTUNITIES LIMITED

1st Floor Royal Chambers St Julian's Avenue
PO Box 650
Saint Peter Port, Guernsey GY1 3JX
Tel.: (44) 1481 810 100
Web Site: www.chinagrowthopportunities.com
Year Founded: 2006
CGOP—(LSE)
Rev.: $1,579
Assets: $439,043
Liabilities: $123,185
Net Worth: $315,858
Earnings: ($476,946)
Fiscal Year-end: 03/31/13
Business Description:
Real Estate Investment Services
S.I.C.: 6519
N.A.I.C.S.: 531190
Personnel:
Rhys Davies *(Chm)*
Board of Directors:
Rhys Davies
Kevin McCabe
Legal Counsel:
Stephenson Harwood
1 Finsbury Circus
London, United Kingdom
Mourant Ozannes
1 Le Marchant Street
186
Saint Peter Port, Guernsey

CHINA GUANGDONG NUCLEAR POWER HOLDING CO., LTD.

(d/b/a China Guangdong Nuclear Power Group)
Keji Building No 1001 ShangbuZhong Road
Futian District, Shenzhen, Guangdong, 518028, China
Tel.: (86) 55 8367 1581
Year Founded: 1994
Sales Range: $1-4.9 Billion
Business Description:
Holding Company; Nuclear Power Plant Developer & Operator
S.I.C.: 6719
N.A.I.C.S.: 551112
Personnel:
Zhimin Qian *(Chm)*
Yu He *(Pres)*
Subsidiary:

CGNPC Uranium Resources Co., Ltd. **(1)**
30/F Bldg A The International Center of Times
No 101 Shaoyaoju Beili
Chaoyang District, Beijing, 100031, China CN
Tel.: (86) 10 6811 8820 (100%)
Fax: (86) 10 5732 1800
Web Site: www.cgnpc.com.cn
Holding Company; Uranium Exploration, Development, Mining, Trading & Power Plant Supplier
S.I.C.: 6719
N.A.I.C.S.: 551112
Zhenxing Zhou *(Chm)*

Non-U.S. Joint Venture:

Taurus Mineral Limited **(2)**
Room 1901 CC Wu Bldg 302 Hennessy Road
Wanchai, China (Hong Kong) HK
Investment Holding Company
S.I.C.: 6719
N.A.I.C.S.: 551112

Non-U.S. Subsidiaries:

Kalahari Minerals Plc **(3)**
1B 38 Jermyn Street
London, SW1Y 6DN, United Kingdom UK
Tel.: (44) 20 7292 9110
Fax: (44) 20 3214 0079
E-Mail: reception@kalahari-minerals.com
Web Site: www.kalahari-minerals.com
Sales Range: $1-9.9 Million
Emp.: 7
Holding Company; Metal Ore Exploration & Mining Services
S.I.C.: 6719
N.A.I.C.S.: 551112
Zhiping Yu *(Chm)*
Duncan Craib *(CFO & Co-Sec)*
Janis Sawyer *(Co-Sec)*

CHINA GUANGFA BANK CO., LTD.

Room 3008 Guangfa Building No 713
Dongfengdong Road Xuexiu
Guangzhou, Guangdong, 510080, China
Tel.: (86) 20 3832 2888
Fax: (86) 20 8731 1722
E-Mail: webmaster@gdb.com.cn
Web Site: www.cgbchina.com.cn
Int. Income: $8,277,708,924
Assets: $185,560,605,738
Liabilities: $175,469,169,118
Net Worth: $10,091,436,620
Earnings: $1,782,274,602
Emp.: 15,939
Fiscal Year-end: 12/31/12
Business Description:
Commercial Banking Services
S.I.C.: 6029
N.A.I.C.S.: 522110
Personnel:
Jinsheng Li *(Chm-Supervisory Bd)*
Morris Li *(Pres)*
James Morrow *(Chief Risk Officer & Deputy Pres)*
Edward Chou *(Deputy Pres)*
Guizhi Wang *(Deputy Pres)*
Fengming Zhang *(Deputy Pres)*
Lianming Zheng *(Deputy Pres)*
Larry Zong *(Deputy Pres)*
Xiaolong Zheng *(Sec)*
Board of Directors:
Tai Lo Chan
Yongguang Gai
Frederick Shing Ip Kwun
Dianjun Li
Morris Li
Zimin Li
Jiade Liu
James Morrow
Jian Pu
Feng Wan
Fenghua Wang
Lo Weber
Fengming Zhang
Shengman Zhang
Xifang Zhang
Larry Zong
Supervisory Board of Directors:
Jinsheng Li
Jianhua Deng
Junxiong Fan
Xuejin Gu
Jinsong Tan
Feng Zhai
Meiqing Zhai
Lanping Zheng
Yingyu Zhu

CHINA GUODIAN CORPORATION

6-8 Fuchengmeng Bei Street
Xicheng District, Beijing, 100034, China
Tel.: (86) 1058682001
Fax: (86) 1058683900
E-Mail: cgdc@cgdc.com.cn
Web Site: www.cgdc.com.cn
Business Description:
Holding Company; Power Generation & Distribution
S.I.C.: 6719
N.A.I.C.S.: 551112
Personnel:
Song Gao *(Exec VP)*
Shuhua Mi *(Exec VP)*
Haibin Yang *(Exec VP)*
Chongde Yu *(Exec VP)*
Chengjie Zhang *(Exec VP)*
Subsidiary:

GD Power Development Co., Ltd. **(1)**
No 19 Anyuan Anhui Bei Li
Chaoyang District, Beijing, 100101, China CN
Tel.: (86) 10 5868 2200 (53.42%)
Fax: (86) 10 5855 3800
E-Mail: gddl@600795.com.cn
Web Site: www.600795.com.cn —(SHG)
Holding Company; Power Generation & Distribution
S.I.C.: 6719
N.A.I.C.S.: 551112
Yongpeng Zhu *(Chm)*
Baoping Qiao *(Vice Chm)*
Shuchen Feng *(Gen Mgr)*
Hongyuan Jiang *(Chief Acctg Officer & Sec)*

CHINA HAIDA LTD.

420 North Bridge Road 04-06 North Bridge Centre
Singapore, 188727, Singapore
Tel.: (65) 65336360
Fax: (65) 6565336020
Web Site: www.haida.com.sg
C92—(SES)
Rev.: $61,697,975
Assets: $54,361,488
Liabilities: $10,674,402
Net Worth: $43,687,086
Earnings: $874,469
Emp.: 231
Fiscal Year-end: 12/31/12
Business Description:
Aluminum Products Mfr
S.I.C.: 3354
N.A.I.C.S.: 331318
Personnel:
Youcai Xu *(CEO)*
Lai Yoke Chan *(CFO)*
Zaiquan Wang *(CMO)*
Guohong Gong *(Chief Production Officer)*
Gang Xu *(Chief Engrg Officer)*
Yunlong Zhang *(Vice Mktg Officer)*
Stella Ah Chit Chan *(Sec)*
Board of Directors:
Guiying Zhao
Yun Guo
Joshua Kian Guan Ong
Beng Keng Soh
Liangfa Wang
Youcai Xu
Non-U.S. Subsidiary:

Jiangyin Litai Decorative Materials Co., Ltd. **(1)**
Huashi Town
214421 Wuxi, Jiangsu, China
Tel.: (86) 51086213931
E-Mail: info@jshdia.com
Laminated Plastics & Sheets Mfr
S.I.C.: 3083
N.A.I.C.S.: 326130
Youcai Xu *(Pres)*

CHINA HAIDIAN HOLDINGS LIMITED

Units 1902 04 Level 19 International Commerce Center
1 Austin Road West, Kowloon, China (Hong Kong)
Tel.: (852) 28050607
Fax: (852) 28652583
E-Mail: info@chinahaidian.com
Web Site: www.chinahaidian.com
0256—(HKG)

China Haidian Holdings Limited—(Continued)

Rev.: $288,887,201
Assets: $678,423,616
Liabilities: $168,282,071
Net Worth: $510,141,545
Earnings: $40,011,509
Emp.: 4,000
Fiscal Year-end: 12/31/12

Business Description:
Watches & Timepieces Mfr
S.I.C.: 3829
N.A.I.C.S.: 334519

Personnel:
Kwok Lung Hon *(Chm)*
Jianguang Shang *(CEO)*
Chi Wah Fong *(CFO & Sec)*
Antonio Calce *(CEO-Eterna)*

Board of Directors:
Kwok Lung Hon
Bo Bi
Tze Wa Fung
Michael Chun Wai Kwong
Toi Man Lam
Qiang Li
Jianguang Shang
Tao Shi
Lai Hei Sit

Non-U.S. Subsidiaries:

EBOHR Luxuries International Co., Limited **(1)**
7 Fl Ste B Xinnengyuan Mansion Nanhai Rd
Nanshan Dist, Shenzhen, Guangdong, 518054, China
Tel.: (86) 75526645021
Fax: (86) 75526649255
Emp.: 300
Watches Mfr
S.I.C.: 3829
N.A.I.C.S.: 334519
Li Tao *(Mgr)*

Ocean Montres SA **(1)**
Rte Du Platy 7A
1752 Villars-sur-Glane, Fribourg, Switzerland
Tel.: (41) 264010233
Fax: (41) 264010083
E-Mail: ocean-sa@bluewin.ch
Watches Mfr & Distr
S.I.C.: 3829
N.A.I.C.S.: 334519
Yongning Wang *(Chm)*

Zhuhai Rossini Glasses Industry Limited **(1)**
No 12 Jingle Rd Jida
Xiangzhou Dist, Zhuhai, Guangdong, China
Tel.: (86) 7563956303
Fax: (86) 7563332799
E-Mail: glasses@rossini.com.cn
Web Site: www.rossini.com.cn
Emp.: 100
Eyeglasses Distr
S.I.C.: 5048
N.A.I.C.S.: 423460
Chen Si Chu *(Mgr)*

Zhuhai Rossini Watch Industry Limited **(1)**
No 12 Jingle Rd Jida
Xiangzhou Dist, Zhuhai, Guangdong, 519015, China
Tel.: (86) 7563333805
Fax: (86) 7563332799
E-Mail: info@rossini.com.cn
Web Site: www.rossini.com.cn
Emp.: 400
Watches Mfr & Distr
S.I.C.: 3829
N.A.I.C.S.: 334519

CHINA HANKING HOLDINGS LIMITED

227 Youth Avenue Shenhe District
Shenyang, Liaoning, 110016, China
Tel.: (86) 2431298820
Fax: (86) 2431298860
E-Mail: ir@hanking.com
Web Site: www.hanking.com
3788—(HKG)
Rev.: $216,216,771
Assets: $424,397,957
Liabilities: $214,486,418
Net Worth: $209,911,538
Earnings: $57,210,781
Emp.: 2,095
Fiscal Year-end: 12/31/12

Business Description:
Iron Ore Mining
S.I.C.: 1011
N.A.I.C.S.: 212210

Personnel:
Guocheng Pan *(Pres & CEO)*
Xuezhi Zheng *(CFO)*
Ming Wai Mok *(Co-Sec)*
Zhuo Xia *(Co-Sec)*

Board of Directors:
Min Yang
Yuchuan Chen
Johnson Chi-King Fu
Fusheng Lan
Kenneth Jue Lee
Guocheng Pan
Yumin Qiu
Anjian Wang
Ping Wang
Zhuo Xia
Jiye Yang
Xuezhi Zheng

Legal Counsel:
Clifford Chance
28th Floor Jardine House One Connaught Place
Central, China (Hong Kong)

Codan Trust Company (Cayman) Limited
Cricket Square Hutchins Drive
PO Box 2681
Georgetown, Grand Cayman, Cayman Islands

CHINA HEALTH INDUSTRIES HOLDINGS, INC.

168 Binbei Street Songbei District
Harbin, Heilongjiang, China 150028
Tel.: (86) 451 88100688
Web Site:
CHHE—(OTCB)
Rev.: $7,727,040
Assets: $54,438,375
Liabilities: $992,469
Net Worth: $53,445,906
Earnings: ($552,923)
Emp.: 95
Fiscal Year-end: 06/30/13

Business Description:
Medical Drug Mfr & Sales
S.I.C.: 2834
N.A.I.C.S.: 325412

Personnel:
Sun Xin *(Chm, CEO, CFO & Treas)*

Board of Directors:
Sun Xin

Transfer Agent:
Interwest Transfer Co. Inc.
1981 E Murray Holladay Rd Ste 100
Salt Lake City, UT 84101

CHINA HEALTH LABS & DIAGNOSTICS LTD.

(d/b/a Biochem Group)
Room 2111 No 1 Kun Tai International Plaza
Chaoyang, Beijing, China
Tel.: (86) 10 5879 0928
E-Mail: info@chinahealthlabs.com
Web Site: www.chinahealthlabs.com
Year Founded: 2009
Rev.: $45,507,230
Assets: $57,605,447
Liabilities: $23,178,558
Net Worth: $34,426,889
Earnings: $6,788,163
Emp.: 173
Fiscal Year-end: 12/31/12

Business Description:
Holding Company; Medical Diagnostic Equipment, Medical Reagents & Supplies Developer, Mfr & Distr
S.I.C.: 6719
N.A.I.C.S.: 551112

Personnel:
Shiping Yao *(Founder, Chm, Pres & CEO)*
Chao Zhang *(CFO)*
Yuqiang Tang *(COO)*
Stephen D. Wortley *(Sec)*

Board of Directors:
Shiping Yao
Hong Chang
Paul Haber
Kim David Morris Oishi
Yuqiang Tang
Bill Tunbrant
Yumin Zhuang

CHINA HEALTH RESOURCE, INC.

343 Sui Zhou Zhong Road
Suining, Sichuan, China 629000
Tel.: (86) 8252391788
E-Mail: info@chinahealthresource.com
Web Site: www.chinahealthresource.com
Year Founded: 2002
CHRI—(OTC)
Rev.: $22,927,862
Assets: $25,831,204
Liabilities: $12,449,666
Net Worth: $13,381,538
Earnings: $1,684,568
Emp.: 230
Fiscal Year-end: 12/31/12

Business Description:
Pharmaceutical Mfr
S.I.C.: 2834
N.A.I.C.S.: 325412

Personnel:
Jiayin Wang *(Pres & CEO)*
Weihai Liu *(CFO)*

Board of Directors:
Ping Gao
Bing Wang
Jiayin Wang

CHINA HEALTHCARE HOLDINGS LIMITED

Unit 801 8/F China Insurance Group Building 141 Des Voeux Road
Central, China (Hong Kong)
Tel.: (852) 8226 1583
Fax: (852) 3585 1822
E-Mail: info@chinahealthcareholdings.com
Web Site: www.chinahealthcareltd.com
0673—(HKG)
Sales Range: $1-9.9 Million
Emp.: 48

Business Description:
Holding Company; Medical Products & Health Related Communication Services
S.I.C.: 5047
N.A.I.C.S.: 423450

Personnel:
Hong Sheng Jia *(Chm)*
Amy Yu *(COO & VP)*
Raymond Siu Hung Tsui *(Sec)*

Board of Directors:
Hong Sheng Jia
Ho Chung
Bo Jiang
Zhong Yuan Li
Xiang Ming Mu
Shi Yun Yan
Hua Zhao
Bao Yi Zhou

Legal Counsel:
King & Wood Mallesons
13th Floor Gloucester Tower The Landmark 15 Queens Road Central
Central, China (Hong Kong)

Butterfield Fund Services (Bermuda) Limited
Rosebank Centre 11 Bermudiana Rd
Pembroke, Bermuda

Transfer Agents:
Tricor Tengis Limited
26th Floor Tesbury Centre 28 Queen's Road East
Wanchai, China (Hong Kong)
Tel.: (852) 29801333
Fax: (852) 28108185

Butterfield Fund Services (Bermuda) Limited
Rosebank Centre 11 Bermudiana Rd
Pembroke, Bermuda

CHINA HEALTHCARE LIMITED

20 Jalan Afifi CISCO Centre II #06-02/03/04
409179 Singapore, Singapore
Tel.: (65) 64478788
Fax: (65) 64497707
E-Mail: econ@econhealthcare.com
Web Site: www.econhealthcare.com
Year Founded: 1987
592—(SES)
Sales Range: $10-24.9 Million
Net Worth: $28,294,985

Business Description:
Nursing Home Services
S.I.C.: 8361
N.A.I.C.S.: 623312

Personnel:
Chu Poh Ong *(Chm)*
Song Khim Chua *(CEO)*
Yong Soon Soh *(CFO & Controller-Fin)*
Cheng Liew *(Sr Resident Medical Officer)*
Chan Meng Lim *(Resident Medical Officer)*

Board of Directors:
Chu Poh Ong
Hin Ling Koh

Transfer Agent:
M & C Services Private Limited
138 Robinson Road 17-00 The Corporate Office
Singapore, 068906, Singapore
Tel.: (65) 6227 6660

Subsidiaries:

Econ Ambulance Services Pte Ltd **(1)**
10 Buangkok View
Singapore, 539747, Singapore
Tel.: (65) 63828888
Fax: (65) 64685708
E-Mail: ambulance@econhealthcare.com
Web Site: www.econhealthcare.com
Emp.: 10
Ambulance services
S.I.C.: 8099
N.A.I.C.S.: 621910
Henry Lim *(Gen Mgr)*

Econ Careskill Training Centre Pte Ltd **(1)**
260 Sims Ave No 04-01
Singapore, 387604, Singapore
Tel.: (65) 67418640
Fax: (65) 67480564
E-Mail: enquiry@econcareskill.com
Web Site: www.econcareskill.com
Emp.: 4
Health Care Training Services
S.I.C.: 8099
N.A.I.C.S.: 621999

Econ Healthcare (S) Pte Ltd **(1)**
20 Jalan Afifi Cisco Ctr No 06-02
Singapore, 409179, Singapore
Tel.: (65) 64478788
Fax: (65) 64961339
E-Mail: econ@econhealthcare.com
Web Site: www.econhealthcare.com
Emp.: 500

Nursing Homes
S.I.C.: 8051
N.A.I.C.S.: 623110

Econ Medicare Centre Pte Ltd (1)
58 Braddell Rd
Singapore, 359905, Singapore
Tel.: (65) 64931336
Fax: (65) 64873033
Nursing Homes
S.I.C.: 8051
N.A.I.C.S.: 623110

Econ Nursing Home Services (1987) Pte Ltd (1)
452 Upper E Coast Rd
Singapore, 466500, Singapore
Tel.: (65) 64961338
Fax: (65) 64961339
E-Mail: lizapoh@econhealthcare.com
Web Site: www.econhealthcare.com
Nursing Homes
S.I.C.: 8051
N.A.I.C.S.: 623110

Sunnyville Nursing Home (1996) Pte Ltd (1)
10 Ama Keng Rd
Singapore, 709828, Singapore
Tel.: (65) 67937009
Fax: (65) 67937000
Web Site: www.econhealthcare.com
Emp.: 20
Nursing Homes
S.I.C.: 8051
N.A.I.C.S.: 623110

West Point Hospital Pte Ltd (1)
235 Corporation Dr
Singapore, 619771, Singapore
Tel.: (65) 62625858
Fax: (65) 62625859
E-Mail: enquiry@westpointhospital.com
Web Site: www.westpointhospital.com
Emp.: 50
Hospital
S.I.C.: 8062
N.A.I.C.S.: 622110

Non-U.S. Subsidiaries:

Econ Healthcare (M) Sdn Bhd (1)
6th & 7th Fl Chinese Maternity Hospital
106 Jln Pudu, 55100 Kuala Lumpur, Malaysia
Tel.: (60) 320267118
Fax: (60) 320263118
E-Mail: k.l@econhealthcare.com
Web Site: www.econhealthcare.com
Emp.: 40
Nursing Homes
S.I.C.: 8051
N.A.I.C.S.: 623110
Yong Lailatun *(Gen Mgr)*

Econ Medicare Centre Sdn Bhd (1)
6th & 7th Fl Chinese Maternity Hospital
106 Jalan Pudu, 55100 Kuala Lumpur, Malaysia
Tel.: (60) 320267118
Fax: (60) 320263118
Web Site: www.econhelpcare.com
Emp.: 50
Nursing Homes
S.I.C.: 8051
N.A.I.C.S.: 623110
Lai Yong Lian *(Mng Dir)*

CHINA HEFENG RESCUE EQUIPMENT, INC.

88 Taishan Street Beijing Industrial Zone
Longgang District, Huludao, Liaoning, 125000, China
Tel.: (86) 429 3181998
Web Site: www.hefengrescue.com
Year Founded: 2010
CHRE—(OTC OTCB)
Rev.: $3,657,524
Assets: $8,582,668
Liabilities: $1,899,126
Net Worth: $6,683,542
Earnings: $4,411,577
Emp.: 90
Fiscal Year-end: 12/31/12

Business Description:
Mining Equipment Distr
S.I.C.: 5082
N.A.I.C.S.: 423810

Personnel:
Baoyuan Zhu *(Chm)*
Zhengyuan Yan *(CEO)*
Wenqi Yao *(CFO)*

Board of Directors:
Baoyuan Zhu
Jianjun Gao
Zhengyuan Yan

CHINA HERB GROUP HOLDINGS CORPORATION

(Formerly Island Radio, Inc.)
4th Fl Airport Industrial Park Business Ctr No 35 Changjiang South Rd
New District, Wuxi, Jiangsu, China
Tel.: (86) 13909 840703
Web Site:
Year Founded: 2010
ISLD—(OTC OTCB)
Earnings: ($34,170)
Fiscal Year-end: 12/31/12

Business Description:
Holding Company
S.I.C.: 6719
N.A.I.C.S.: 551112

Personnel:
Qiuping Lu *(Pres, CEO, CFO & Treas)*
Yubo Zheng *(Sec)*

Board of Directors:
Fumin Feng
Chin Yung Kong
Qiuping Lu
Yubo Zheng

Transfer Agent:
Island Stock Transfer Inc
100 Second Avenue South Suite 705S
Saint Petersburg, FL 33701

CHINA HGS REAL ESTATE INC.

6 Xinghan Road 19th Floor
Hanzhong, Shaanxi, 723000, China
Tel.: (86) 9162622612
Web Site: www.chinahgs.com
HGSH—(NASDAQ)
Sls.: $67,809,073
Assets: $177,827,914
Liabilities: $78,678,750
Net Worth: $99,149,164
Earnings: $20,791,565
Emp.: 116
Fiscal Year-end: 09/30/13

Business Description:
Real Estate Development Including Residential Apartments & Commercial Properties
S.I.C.: 1531
N.A.I.C.S.: 236117

Personnel:
Xiaojun Zhu *(Chm, Pres & CEO)*
Samuel Wei Shen *(CFO)*

Board of Directors:
Xiaojun Zhu
John Chen
Shenghui Luo
Luo Shenghui
Christy Young Shue
Yuankai Wen

CHINA HIGH PRECISION AUTOMATION GROUP LIMITED

Rm 2805 China Resources Building
26 Harbour Road
Wanchai, China (Hong Kong)
Tel.: (852) 28771809
Fax: (852) 28771807
E-Mail: info@chpag.com
Web Site: www.chpag.net
0591—(HKG)
Sls.: $82,053,809
Assets: $376,409,213
Liabilities: $17,405,353
Net Worth: $359,003,859
Earnings: $5,762,601
Emp.: 1,067
Fiscal Year-end: 06/30/13

Business Description:
High Precision Industrial Automation Instrument Mfr
S.I.C.: 3823
N.A.I.C.S.: 334513

Personnel:
Fun Chung Wong *(Founder, Chm & CEO)*
Chuen Cheung *(Sec)*

Board of Directors:
Fun Chung Wong
Taylor Yuk Hiu Chan
Chuen Cheung
Guo Qing Hu
Qin Zhi Ji
Fang Zhong Su
Chong Zou

Royal Bank of Canada Trust Company (Cayman) Limited
4th Floor Royal Bank House 24 Shedden Road
Georgetown, Cayman Islands

Transfer Agents:
Tricor Investor Services Limited
26th Floor Tesbury Centre 28 Queens Road East
Wanchai, China (Hong Kong)

Royal Bank of Canada Trust Company (Cayman) Limited
4th Floor Royal Bank House 24 Shedden Road
Georgetown, Cayman Islands

Non-U.S. Subsidiary:

Fujian Wide Plus Precision Instruments Co., Ltd. (1)
No 1 Chashan Rd Mawei Hi-tech Dev Zone
Fuzhou, Fujian, 350015, China
Tel.: (86) 59183969908
Fax: (86) 59183969600
E-Mail: info@wideplus.com
Web Site: www.wideplus.com
Emp.: 1,500
Precision Tools Mfr & System Integration Services
S.I.C.: 3425
N.A.I.C.S.: 332216
Allan Wu *(Mgr)*

CHINA HIGH SPEED TRANSMISSION EQUIPMENT GROUP CO., LTD.

Room 1302 13th Floor Top Glory Tower 262 Gloucester Road
Causeway Bay, China (Hong Kong)
Tel.: (852) 25376689
Web Site: www.chste.com
0658—(HKG OTC)
Rev.: $1,011,686,580
Assets: $3,158,292,871
Liabilities: $1,928,069,038
Net Worth: $1,230,223,833
Earnings: $20,407,777
Emp.: 9,267
Fiscal Year-end: 12/31/12

Business Description:
Transmission Devices Provider
S.I.C.: 5063
N.A.I.C.S.: 423610

Personnel:
Yueming Hu *(Chm & CEO)*
Edward Wing Hong Lui *(CFO, Sec & Controller-Fin)*

Board of Directors:
Yueming Hu
Shimin Chen
Yongdao Chen
Jianhua Jiang
Xihe Jiang
Maoji Jin
Shengqiang Li
Enrong Liao
Jianguo Liu
Xun Lu
Junsheng Zhu

Computershare Hong Kong Investor Services Limited
17M Floor Hopewell Centre 183 Queen's Road East
Wanchai, China (Hong Kong)

Transfer Agents:
Royal Bank of Canada Trust Company (Cayman) Limited
4th Floor Royal Bank House 24 Shedden Road
Georgetown, Cayman Islands

Computershare Hong Kong Investor Services Limited
17M Floor Hopewell Centre 183 Queen's Road East
Wanchai, China (Hong Kong)

Non-U.S. Subsidiary:

Zhenjiang Tongzhou Propeller Co., Ltd. (1)
Dingmao Economic Dev Zone
Zhenjiang, Jiangsu, China
Tel.: (86) 51185370789
Fax: (86) 51185370787
E-Mail: Tongzhou@zjtpp.com
Web Site: www.zjtpp.com
Marine Propellers Mfr
S.I.C.: 3369
N.A.I.C.S.: 331529
Joui Goo *(Mgr)*

CHINA-HONG KONG PHOTO PRODUCTS HOLDINGS LIMITED

8th Floor Tsuen Wan Industrial Centre 220-248 Texaco Road
Tsuen Wan, China (Hong Kong)
Tel.: (852) 24088663
Fax: (852) 24090294
E-Mail: enquiry@chinahkphoto.com.hk
Web Site: www.chinahkphoto.com.hk
Year Founded: 1968
1123—(HKG)
Rev.: $61,332,360
Assets: $123,195,348
Liabilities: $14,261,999
Net Worth: $108,933,349
Earnings: $4,199,257
Emp.: 386
Fiscal Year-end: 03/31/13

Business Description:
Holding Company; Photographic Equipment & Supplies Distr
S.I.C.: 6719
N.A.I.C.S.: 551112

Personnel:
Dennis Tai Lun Sun *(Chm)*
Stanley Tao Hung Sun *(Deputy Chm)*
Rita Wai Kwan Chan *(Sec)*

Board of Directors:
Dennis Tai Lun Sun
Malcolm Man Chung Au
David Ka Fai Li
Allan Hui Liu
Eileen Yuk Wah Ng
Stanley Tao Hung Sun
Simon Kwok Tong Tang
Allan Chi Yun Wong

Legal Counsel:
Gallant Y.T. Ho & Co.
5th Floor Jardine House 1 Connaught Place
Central, China (Hong Kong)
Tel.: (852) 2526 3336
Fax: (852) 2845 9294

Butterfield Fulcrum Group (Bermuda) Limited
26 Burnaby Street
Hamilton, HM 11, Bermuda

Transfer Agents:
Tricor Tengis Limited
26th Floor Tesbury Centre 28 Queen's Road East
Wanchai, China (Hong Kong)

China-Hong Kong Photo Products Holdings Limited—(Continued)

Tel.: (852) 29801333
Fax: (852) 28108185

Butterfield Fulcrum Group (Bermuda) Limited
26 Burnaby Street
Hamilton, HM 11, Bermuda

Subsidiaries:

Fotomax (F.E.) Ltd. **(1)**
Unit 02-04 West Wing 8/F Tsuen Wan Ind Centre
220 Texaco Road, Tsuen Wan, China (Hong Kong) HK
Tel.: (852) 31891648 (100%)
Fax: (852) 31891608
Web Site: www.fotomaxonline.com
Retail Photographic Developing & Processing Services & Supplies Stores Operator
S.I.C.: 5734
N.A.I.C.S.: 443142
Dennis Tai-Lun Sun *(Chm)*

Fuji Photo Products Company, Limited **(1)**
8th Floor Tsuen Wan Industrial Centre
220-248 Texaco Road, Tsuen Wan, China (Hong Kong) HK
Tel.: (852) 24088663 (100%)
Fax: (852) 24089443
E-Mail: enquiry@chinahkphoto.com.hk
Web Site: www.fujifilm.com.hk
Emp.: 60
Photographic Developing & Processing Supplies Marketer & Distr
S.I.C.: 5043
N.A.I.C.S.: 423410
Dennis Tai-Lun Sun *(Chm)*

CHINA HONGQIAO GROUP LIMITED

Huixian One Road Zouping Economic Development District
Zouping County, Binzhou, Shandong, 256200, China
Tel.: (86) 543 4166008
Fax: (86) 543 4166001
Web Site: www.hongqiaochina.com
1378—(HKG)
Rev.: $3,940,233,267
Assets: $7,049,241,495
Liabilities: $3,500,866,557
Net Worth: $3,548,374,938
Earnings: $866,144,239
Emp.: 29,296
Fiscal Year-end: 12/31/12
Business Description:
Aluminum Products Mfr
S.I.C.: 3354
N.A.I.C.S.: 331318
Personnel:
Shiping Zhang *(Founder & Chm)*
Shuliang Zheng *(Vice Chm)*
Bo Zhang *(CEO)*
Xingli Qi *(CFO)*
Wing Yan Ho *(Co-Sec)*
Yuexia Zhang *(Co-Sec)*
Board of Directors:
Shiping Zhang
Yinghai Chen
Benwen Han
Xingli Qi
Jian Xing
Congsen Yang
Bo Zhang
Jinglei Zhang
Shuliang Zheng
Legal Counsel:
Orrick, Herrington & Sutcliffe
43rd Floor Gloucester Tower The Landmark 15 Queens Road Central
Hong Kong, China (Hong Kong)
Computershare Hong Kong Investor Services Limited
Shops 1712-1716 17th Floor Hopewell Centre
183 Queens Road East
Wanchai, China (Hong Kong)
Transfer Agents:
Royal Bank of Canada Trust Company (Cayman) Limited
4th Floor Royal Bank House 24 Shedden Road
PO Box 1586
Georgetown, Cayman Islands
Computershare Hong Kong Investor Services Limited
Shops 1712-1716 17th Floor Hopewell Centre
183 Queens Road East
Wanchai, China (Hong Kong)

CHINA HONGXING SPORTS LIMITED

Jiangnan Torch Development Area
Licheng District
362000 Quanzhou, Fujian, China
Tel.: (86) 59522462620
Fax: (86) 59522485777
Web Site: www.chinahongxing.org
BR9—(SES)
Sales Range: $250-299.9 Million
Business Description:
Footwear Mfr
S.I.C.: 2389
N.A.I.C.S.: 316210
Personnel:
Zhongming Lan *(CEO)*
Kelvin Yeung *(CFO & Co-Sec)*
Kok Liang Chew *(Co-Sec)*
Board of Directors:
Wai Meng Chan
Alfred Keng Chuan Cheong
Zhongming Lan
Bernard Ah Kong Tay
Rongguang Wu

Subsidiaries:

Hongrong Light Industry Co., Ltd. **(1)**
Jiangnan Hi Tec Area
Licheng, Quanzhou, 362000, China
Tel.: (86) 15960221545
Sports Apparels Mfr
S.I.C.: 2389
N.A.I.C.S.: 316210

Hongxing Erke Sports Goods Co., Ltd **(1)**
Jiangnan Torch Development Area
Licheng District, Quanzhou, Fujian, 362000, China
Tel.: (86) 5922951388
Fax: (86) 5922951399
Sport Goods Mfr
S.I.C.: 2389
N.A.I.C.S.: 316210
Kenny Lin *(Mgr-Sls)*

CHINA HOUSEHOLD HOLDINGS LIMITED

(Formerly Bao Yuan Holdings Ltd.)
Suite no 1001B 10/F Tower 1
33 Canton Road, Kowloon, Tsim Sha Tsui, China (Hong Kong)
Tel.: (852) 2377 9262
Fax: (852) 2377 9611
E-Mail: nfo@chh.hk
Web Site: www.chh.hk/html/about_company.php
0692—(HKG)
Rev.: $2,230,835
Assets: $257,925,790
Liabilities: $42,991,930
Net Worth: $214,933,860
Earnings: ($2,114,780)
Emp.: 86
Fiscal Year-end: 12/31/12
Business Description:
Investment Holding Company; Titanium Exploration; Textile Mfr & Sales
S.I.C.: 6719
N.A.I.C.S.: 551112
Personnel:
Man Pan Wong *(Chm)*
Board of Directors:
Kaneko Hiroshi
Xie Jianming
Edmond To Yan Ming
Tommy Yiu Kwok Ming
Zhu Qi
Tsang King Sun
Kuang Yuanwei
Fu Zhenjin
Transfer Agent:
Computershare Hong Kong Investor Services Limited
17th Floor, Hopewell Centre 183 Queens Road East
Hong Kong, China (Hong Kong)

Subsidiaries:

Ching Hing Weaving Dyeing & Printing Factory Limited **(1)**
10 F Intl Indus Bldg 501-503 Castle Peak Rd
Kowloon, China (Hong Kong)
Tel.: (852) 22669107
Fax: (852) 27860993
E-Mail: info@ching-hing.com.hk
Web Site: www.ching-hing.com.hk
Fabrics Processing Services
S.I.C.: 2299
N.A.I.C.S.: 313210

CHINA HOUSING & LAND DEVELOPMENT, INC.

1008 Liuxue Road
Baqiao District, Xi'an, Shaanxi, China 710038
Tel.: (86) 29 82582632
Fax: (86) 29 8258 2640
E-Mail: chld@chldinc.com
Web Site: www.chldinc.com
Year Founded: 1999
CHLN—(NASDAQ)
Rev.: $148,979,260
Assets: $524,585,930
Liabilities: $375,499,535
Net Worth: $149,086,395
Earnings: $16,547,718
Emp.: 611
Fiscal Year-end: 12/31/12
Business Description:
Real Estate Development
S.I.C.: 6726
N.A.I.C.S.: 525990
Personnel:
Pingji Lu *(Chm)*
Xiaohong Feng *(CEO & Co-Mng Dir)*
Cangsang Huang *(CFO & Co-Mng Dir)*
Jing Lu *(COO & Sec)*
Board of Directors:
Pingji Lu
Xiaohong Feng
Heung Sang Fong
Suiyin Gao
Cangsang Huang
Yusheng Lin
Albert S. McLelland

Non-U.S. Subsidiary:

Aura Gold Mineracao Ltda-Brasilia **(1)**
SRTVS Q 701 bl O Ed Multiempresarial sala 528 a
Brasilia, Brazil
Tel.: (55) 6130350300
Fax: (55) 6130350310
E-Mail: icampos@auraminerals.com
Web Site: www.auraminerals.com
Emp.: 20
Gol Mining & Exploration
S.I.C.: 1041
N.A.I.C.S.: 212221
Carlos Bertoni *(Gen Mgr)*

CHINA HUANCHI BEARING GROUP CO., LTD.

(d/b/a HCH Bearing Group)
Henghe Industry Zone
Cixi City, Ningbo, 315318, China
Tel.: (86) 574 63198088
Fax: (86) 574 63197548
Web Site: www.hchbearing.com
Year Founded: 1973
Emp.: 2,500
Business Description:
Ball & Roller Bearing Mfr
S.I.C.: 3562
N.A.I.C.S.: 332991
Personnel:
Chengjiang Hu *(Pres)*

U.S. Subsidiary:

HCH Bearing Americas **(1)**
14476-406 Duval Pl W
Jacksonville, FL 32218
Tel.: (904) 374-7471
Fax: (904) 379-2328
E-Mail: sales@hchbearingamericas.com
Web Site: www.hchbearingamericas.com
Ball & Roller Bearing Mfr
S.I.C.: 3562
N.A.I.C.S.: 332991
Douglas Robbie, *(Gen Mgr)*

CHINA HUANENG GROUP CO., LTD.

4 Fu Xing Men Nei Street
Xicheng District, Beijing, 100031, China
Tel.: (86) 1063228800
Fax: (86) 1063226888
Web Site: www.chng.com.cn
Business Description:
Holding Company; Power Generation
S.I.C.: 6719
N.A.I.C.S.: 551112
Personnel:
Peixi Cao *(Pres)*

CHINA HUARONG ASSET MANAGEMENT CORP.

10 Baiyun Road
Xicheng District, Beijing, 100045, China
Tel.: (86) 1063409999
Fax: (86) 1063477644
Web Site: www.chamc.com.cn
Year Founded: 1999
Emp.: 3,000
Business Description:
Non-Performing Loan Acquirer, Manager & Retailer for Chinese Government-Owned Banks; Asset Resolution, Debt Restructuring & Investment Banking Services
S.I.C.: 6163
N.A.I.C.S.: 522310
Personnel:
Ding Zhongchi *(Pres & CEO)*
Dong Dongqing *(Exec VP)*
Yunsheng Sui *(Exec VP)*
Zheng Wanchun *(Exec VP)*
Xu Zhaohong *(Exec VP)*

Holding:

D'Long International Strategic Investment Co., Ltd. **(1)**
1155 Yuanshen Road
Pudong New Area, Shanghai, 200135, China
Tel.: (86) 2168624600
Fax: (86) 2158545400
Web Site: www.d-long.com
Holding Company
S.I.C.: 6719
N.A.I.C.S.: 551112

Subsidiary:

Shenyang Hejin Holding Investment Co., Ltd. **(2)**
No 55 New Century Road Hunnan
Shenyang, Liaoning, China
Tel.: (86) 24 62336790
Fax: (86) 24 62336799
E-Mail: hjtz@hjinv.com
Web Site: www.hjinv.com

Holding Company: Non-Ferrous Metal Alloy Material Smelting, Processing, Manufacture & Marketing
S.I.C.: 6719
N.A.I.C.S.: 551112
Yan Wu *(Chm)*
Wei Yu *(CEO)*
Dongwen Zhang *(VP & CFO)*
Yingjie Li *(Exec VP)*

CHINA HUISHAN DAIRY HOLDINGS COMPANY LIMITED

101 Huishan Broad Road
Shenyang, 110163, China
Tel.: (86) 24 23964378
Fax: (86) 24 88081665
E-Mail: ir@huishangroup.com
Web Site: www.huishandairy.com
6863—(HKG)
Rev.: $405,454,776
Earnings: $150,172,025
Emp.: 2,154
Fiscal Year-end: 03/31/13
Business Description:
Dairy Products
S.I.C.: 0241
N.A.I.C.S.: 112120
Personnel:
Kai Yang *(Chm & CEO)*
Wing Hoi So *(CFO)*
Michael Chou *(Sec)*
Board of Directors:
Kai Yang
Chi Heng Cheng
Kun Ge
Ruixia Gu
Hok Yin Kwok
Kar Cheung Li
Francis Wai Keung Siu
Wing Hoi So
Kungang Song
Kei Pang Tsui
Guangyi Xu

CHINA HUIYUAN JUICE GROUP LTD

Edinburgh Tower 33/F The Landmark
15 Queen's Road
Central, China (Hong Kong)
Tel.: (852) 21368072
Fax: (852) 31706606
Web Site: www.huiyuan.com.cn
1886—(HKG)
Rev.: $632,344,679
Assets: $1,253,877,710
Liabilities: $371,835,604
Net Worth: $882,042,106
Earnings: $2,566,857
Emp.: 9,048
Fiscal Year-end: 12/31/12
Business Description:
Beverages Mfr
S.I.C.: 2086
N.A.I.C.S.: 312111
Personnel:
Xinli Zhu *(Founder & Chm)*
Daniel Saw *(CEO)*
Gloria Sau Kuen Ma *(Sec)*
Board of Directors:
Xinli Zhu
Xu Jiang
Wen-chieh Lee
Man Kit Leung
Quanhou Song
Andrew Y. Yan
Chen Zhao
Yali Zhao

Computershare Hong Kong Investor Services Limited
Shops 1712-1716 17th Floor Hopewell Centre
183 Queens Road East
Wanchai, China (Hong Kong)

Transfer Agents:
Royal Bank of Canada Trust Company (Cayman) Limited
4th Floor Royal Bank House 24 Shedden Road
Georgetown, Cayman Islands

Computershare Hong Kong Investor Services Limited
Shops 1712-1716 17th Floor Hopewell Centre
183 Queens Road East
Wanchai, China (Hong Kong)

Non-U.S. Subsidiaries:

Jilin Huiyuan Food & Beverage Co., Ltd. **(1)**
No 12 Xinghua Rd Jishu Econ Dev Zone
Jilin, 132000, China
Tel.: (86) 4328866608
Fax: (86) 4328866608
Canned Fruit & Vegetable Juices Mfr
S.I.C.: 2033
N.A.I.C.S.: 311421

Jiujiang Huiyuan Food & Beverage Co., Ltd. **(1)**
No 1 Huiyuan Rd State Export Processing Zone
Jiujiang, Jiangxi, 332000, China
Tel.: (86) 7928431202
Fax: (86) 7928431216
Soft Drinks Mfr
S.I.C.: 2086
N.A.I.C.S.: 312111

Luzhong Huiyuan Food & Beverage Co., Ltd. **(1)**
Huiyuan Ave N Side Hi-New Dev Zone
Laiwu, Shandong, 271100, China
Tel.: (86) 6346251688
Fax: (86) 6346251112
Fruit & Vegetable Juices Mfr
S.I.C.: 2033
N.A.I.C.S.: 311421

CHINA HYDROELECTRIC CORPORATION

2105A Ping'an International Financial Center No 3 South Xinyuan Str
Chaoyang District, Beijing, 100027, China
Tel.: (86) 10 6408 2341
Fax: (86) 10 64941540
E-Mail: info@chinahydroelectric.com
Web Site: www.chinahydroelectric.com
CHC—(NYSE)
Rev.: $85,388,000
Assets: $754,316,000
Liabilities: $361,801,000
Net Worth: $392,515,000
Earnings: ($1,149,000)
Emp.: 609
Fiscal Year-end: 12/31/12
Business Description:
Hydroelectric Power Generation & Distribution Services
S.I.C.: 4911
N.A.I.C.S.: 221111
Personnel:
Amit Gupta *(Chm)*
You-Su Lin *(Interim CEO)*
Daniel Chan *(COO)*
Board of Directors:
Amit Gupta
Yong Cao
Daniel Chan
Anthony H. Dixon
Richard H. Hochman
Min Lin
You-Su Lin
Allard M. Nooy
Stephen Outerbridge

CHINA INDUSTRIAL WASTE MANAGEMENT, INC.

1 Huaihe West Road
Dalian, 116600, China
Tel.: (86) 41182595129
Fax: (86) 41182595169
E-Mail: darcy.zhang@chinaciwt.com
Web Site: www.chinaciwt.com
Year Founded: 1987
CIWT—(OTC)
Sales Range: $25-49.9 Million
Emp.: 570
Business Description:
Industrial Waste Collection, Treatment, Disposal & Recycling Services
S.I.C.: 4953
N.A.I.C.S.: 562211
Personnel:
Jinqing Dong *(Chm & CEO)*
Xin Guo *(CFO)*
Jun Li *(COO)*
Dazhi Zhang *(Sec)*
Board of Directors:
Jinqing Dong
Jun Li
Yangzu Wang
Chunyou Wu

Subsidiary:

Dalian Lipp Environmental Energy Engineering & Technology Co., Ltd **(1)**
Rm 1510 Rainbow Bldg
No 23 Renmin Rd Zhongshan Dist, Dalian, Liaoning, China
Tel.: (86) 41182595129
Fax: (86) 41182565119
E-Mail: info@lipp-system.cn
Web Site: www.lipp-system.cn
Waste Disposals & Sewage Treatment Services
S.I.C.: 4952
N.A.I.C.S.: 221320
Dong Jinqing *(CEO)*

CHINA INFORMATION TECHNOLOGY, INC.

21st Floor Everbright Bank Building
Zhuzilin
Futian District, Shenzhen, Guangdong, 518040, China
Tel.: (86) 755 83708333
Web Site: www.chinacnit.com
CNIT—(NASDAQ)
Rev.: $86,377,455
Assets: $287,421,889
Liabilities: $123,407,956
Net Worth: $164,013,933
Earnings: ($90,622,558)
Emp.: 1,438
Fiscal Year-end: 12/31/12
Business Description:
Information Technology Software & Equipment Mfr
S.I.C.: 7372
N.A.I.C.S.: 511210
Personnel:
Jiang Huai Lin *(Chm & CEO)*
Daniel K. Lee *(CFO)*
Zhi Qiang Zhao *(COO)*
Yi Fu Liu *(CMO)*
Board of Directors:
Jiang Huai Lin
Remington Chia-Hung Hu
Yun Sen Huang
Qiang Lin
Zhi Qiang Zhao

Subsidiary:

Wuda Geoinformatics Co., Ltd. **(1)**
Whu S&T Park East Lake Development Zone
430223 Wuhan, China
Tel.: (86) 2787196368
Fax: (86) 2787196133
Emp.: 515
Prepackaged Software Services
S.I.C.: 7372
N.A.I.C.S.: 511210
Liu Yi Fu *(Gen Mgr)*

CHINA INFRASTRUCTURE CONSTRUCTION CORPORATION

Shidai Caifu Tiandi Building Suite 1906-09
1 Hangfeng Road
Fengtai District, Beijing, 100070, China
Tel.: (86) 10 51709287
E-Mail: chncir@hotmail.com
Web Site:
Year Founded: 2003
CHNC—(OTCB)
Sales Range: $75-99.9 Million
Emp.: 389
Business Description:
Ready-Mix Concrete & Cement Mfr
S.I.C.: 3273
N.A.I.C.S.: 327320
Personnel:
Rong Yang *(Chm, Pres & CEO)*
John Bai *(Acting CFO)*

CHINA INFRASTRUCTURE INVESTMENT LIMITED

16/F Agricultural Bank China Tower
50 Connaught Road
Central, China (Hong Kong)
Tel.: (852) 2383 6868
Fax: (852) 2698 8188
E-Mail: hkoffice@china-infrastructure.com
Web Site: www.china-infrastructure.com
Year Founded: 1992
600—(HKG)
Sls.: $1,755,912
Assets: $147,097,907
Liabilities: $20,642,574
Net Worth: $126,455,333
Earnings: ($2,166,231)
Emp.: 31
Fiscal Year-end: 12/31/12
Business Description:
Investment Management Services
S.I.C.: 6282
N.A.I.C.S.: 523920
Personnel:
De Chao Ye *(Chm & CEO)*
Hai Hua Zhu *(Vice Chm)*
Markson Kim Sun Chan *(Sec)*
Board of Directors:
De Chao Ye
Jin Geng He
Xu Dong Ji
Eliza Siu Yuk Lee
Xiao Jun Xu
Hong Gao Yu
Edwin Hon Ming Yuen
Guo Chang Zhou
Hai Hua Zhu

The R&H Trust Co. Ltd
Windward 1 Regatta Office Park
897
Georgetown, Cayman Islands

Transfer Agents:
Tricor Standard Limited
26/F Tesbury Centre 28 Queen's Road East
Wanchai, China (Hong Kong)
Tel.: (852) 2980 1333
Fax: (852) 2810 8185

The R&H Trust Co. Ltd
Windward 1 Regatta Office Park
897
Georgetown, Cayman Islands

CHINA INNOVATION INVESTMENT LIMITED

26/F No 9 Des Voeux Road West
Sheung Wan, China (Hong Kong)
Tel.: (852) 2111 9988
Fax: (852) 2111 9989
E-Mail: info@1217.com.hk
Web Site: www.1217.com.hk
Year Founded: 2002

China Innovation Investment Limited—(Continued)

1217—(HKG)
Rev.: $85,365
Assets: $42,336,606
Liabilities: $2,787,641
Net Worth: $39,548,965
Earnings: ($11,014,522)
Emp.: 11
Fiscal Year-end: 12/31/12
Business Description:
Investment Management Services
S.I.C.: 6282
N.A.I.C.S.: 523920
Personnel:
Xin Xiang *(CEO)*
Chi Wing Fok *(Sec)*
Board of Directors:
Yaomin Wang
Cheong Yee Chan
Raymond Chun Kui Jook
Wing Hang Lee
Zhou Li
David Xin Wang
Xin Xiang
Hong Liang Zang

Royal Bank of Canada Trust Company (Cayman) Limited
4th Floor Royal Bank House 24 Shedden Road
Georgetown, Cayman Islands
Transfer Agents:
Union Registrars Limited
18/F Fook Lee Commercial Centre Town Place
33 Lockhart Road
Wanchai, China (Hong Kong)

Royal Bank of Canada Trust Company (Cayman) Limited
4th Floor Royal Bank House 24 Shedden Road
Georgetown, Cayman Islands

CHINA INTEGRATED ENERGY, INC.

10F Western International Square
2 Gaoxin Road, Xi'an, Shaanxi, 710043, China
Tel.: (86) 29 8268 3920
Web Site: www.cbeh.net.cn
Year Founded: 1998
CBEH—(OTC)
Sales Range: $400-449.9 Million
Emp.: 373
Business Description:
Oil & Gasoline Exploration, Production & Distribution Services
S.I.C.: 1311
N.A.I.C.S.: 211111
Personnel:
Xincheng Gao *(Chm, Pres & CEO)*
Gaihong Li *(CFO & Exec VP)*
Board of Directors:
Xincheng Gao
Gaihong Li
Stephen Markscheid
Liren Wei

CHINA INTEGRATED MEDIA CORPORATION LIMITED

Suite 5 Level 2 Malcolm Reid Building 187 Rundle Street
Adelaide, SA, 5000, Australia
Tel.: (61) 8 8232 0180
Fax: (61) 8 8312 0248
E-Mail: info@chinamedia.com.au
Web Site: www.chinamedia.com.au
Year Founded: 2008
CIK—(ASX)
Business Description:
Digital Advertising, Gaming & Entertainment
S.I.C.: 7319
N.A.I.C.S.: 541890
Personnel:
Con Unerkov *(Chm & Sec)*
Board of Directors:
Con Unerkov
Bing He
Loui Kotsopoulous
Herbert Ying Chiu Lee

CHINA INTELLIGENCE INFORMATION SYSTEMS, INC.

11th Floor Tower B1 Yike Industrial Base
Shinhua Road
High-tech Industrial Dev Zone, Jinan, 250101, China
Tel.: (86) 531 55585742
Web Site: www.chinavoip-telecom.com
IICN—(OTC)
Sales Range: $1-9.9 Million
Emp.: 90
Business Description:
VoIP Software Products & Services
S.I.C.: 7372
N.A.I.C.S.: 511210
Personnel:
Kunwu Li *(Chm, Pres, CEO & Interim CFO)*
Dawei Qi *(CTO)*
Board of Directors:
Kunwu Li
Xiaodong Ding
Shile Dong
Yanli Jiang
Kaili Kan
Dawei Qi
Ruzhi Xu
Yinyi Xu

CHINA INTELLIGENT LIGHTING AND ELECTRONICS, INC.

29 & 31 Huanzhen Road
Shuikou Town, Huizhou, Guangdong, 516005, China
Tel.: (86) 752 3138511
Year Founded: 2007
CILE—(OTC)
Sales Range: $25-49.9 Million
Emp.: 645
Business Description:
LED & Other Lighting Products Designer, Mfr & Sales
S.I.C.: 3648
N.A.I.C.S.: 335129
Personnel:
Xuemei Li *(Chm, Pres & CEO)*
Bin Dong *(COO)*
Shiliang Wu *(Exec VP-Sls & Mktg)*
Board of Directors:
Xuemei Li
Zhang Hongfeng
Ruxiang Niu
Shiliang Wu

CHINA INTERACTIVE EDUCATION, INC.

Block C Zhennan Road
South District, Zhongshan, Guangdong, China
Tel.: (86) 760 2819888
Web Site: www.menq.com.cn
Year Founded: 2000
CIVN—(OTC)
Sales Range: $25-49.9 Million
Emp.: 420
Business Description:
Development of Information Technology for Education; E-Classroom & E-Library Solutions
S.I.C.: 9411
N.A.I.C.S.: 923110
Personnel:
Tiannan Chen *(Chm)*
Ruofei Chen *(Pres & CEO)*
Hon Wan Chan *(CFO)*
Wei Dong He *(COO)*
Yi Zhou *(CTO)*
Board of Directors:
Tiannan Chen
Ruofei Chen
Wei Dong He
Zijian Wu
Yi Zhou

CHINA INTERNATIONAL MARINE CONTAINERS (GROUP) CO., LTD.

CIMC R&D Center No 2 Gangwan Avenue Shekou Industrial Zone
Shenzhen, Guangdong, 518067, China
Tel.: (86) 75526691130
Fax: (86) 75526692707
E-Mail: email@cimc.com
Web Site: www.cimc.com
Year Founded: 1980
000039—(HKG SSE)
Rev.: $8,630,964,954
Assets: $10,006,339,563
Liabilities: $6,493,029,174
Net Worth: $3,513,310,389
Earnings: $306,648,806
Emp.: 58,535
Fiscal Year-end: 12/31/12
Business Description:
Tank Container, Trailer & Road Transport Equipment Mfr
S.I.C.: 3412
N.A.I.C.S.: 332439
Personnel:
Jianhong Li *(Chm)*
Xingru Wang *(Vice Chm & Mng Dir)*
Minjie Xu *(Vice Chm)*
Boliang Mai *(Pres)*
Yuqun Yu *(Sec)*
Board of Directors:
Jianhong Li
Huiping Ding
Qingjun Jin
Boliang Mai
Jiakang Sun
Hong Wang
Xingru Wang
Jing'an Xu
Minjie Xu
Supervisory Board of Directors:
Wanguang Feng
Qianru Huang
Shijie Lv
Legal Counsel:
Paul Hastings
21-22/F Bank of China Tower 1 Garden Road
Hong Kong, China (Hong Kong)
Subsidiaries:

CIMC Jidong (Qinhuangdao) Vehicles Manufacture Co., Ltd. **(1)**
No 9 Weihai Ave East Side Of Zhejiang North Road East Area
Qinhuangdao, Hebei, 066004, China
Tel.: (86) 3355181939
Fax: (86) 3355181918
Automobile Mfr
S.I.C.: 3711
N.A.I.C.S.: 336111

CIMC Vehicle (Group) Co., Ltd. **(1)**
CIMC R & D Centre No 2 Gangwan Avenue Shekou
Nanshan District, Shenzhen, Guangdong, 518067, China
Tel.: (86) 755 26691130
Fax: (86) 755 2682 6579
Truck Trailer Mfr & Distr
S.I.C.: 3715
N.A.I.C.S.: 336212

Subsidiaries:

Liaoning CIMC Vehicle Logistics Equipments Co., Ltd. **(2)**
No 254 Northeast Road
Dadong, Shenyang, 110044, China
Tel.: (86) 24 88902000
Fax: (86) 24 88099322
Logistics Container Equipment Mfr
S.I.C.: 3412
N.A.I.C.S.: 332439

Shenzhen CIMC Vehicle Sales Co., Ltd. **(2)**
5th Floor CIMC R&D Center No 2 GangWan Avenue
Nanshan, Shenzhen, 518067, China
Tel.: (86) 13823579670
Automobile Parts Distr
S.I.C.: 3291
N.A.I.C.S.: 327910

Yangzhou CIMC Tonghua Tank Equipment Co., Ltd. **(2)**
No 139 Yangzijiang M Rd
Yangzhou, China
Tel.: (86) 51487872332
Motor Truck Trailer Mfr
S.I.C.: 3715
N.A.I.C.S.: 336212

CIMC Vehicle (Guangxi) Co., Ltd. **(1)**
3 Xiuxiang Ave Xixiangtang
Nanning, Guangxi, 530003, China
Tel.: (86) 771 3213559
Heavy Trailer & Truck Mfr
S.I.C.: 3711
N.A.I.C.S.: 336120

CIMC Vehicle (Liaoning) Co., Ltd. **(1)**
No 88 Binhai South Road
Yingkou, Liaoning, China
Tel.: (86) 417 3286900
Fax: (86) 417 3286666
Auto Parts & Accessories Mfr
S.I.C.: 3714
N.A.I.C.S.: 336390

CIMC Vehicle (Shandong) Co., Ltd. **(1)**
No 8001 E Jingshi Rd
250200 Jinan, Shandong, China (87.01%)
Tel.: (86) 53185833023
Fax: (86) 53185833027
E-Mail: cimcgm@yahoo.com
Web Site: www.cimc-shandong.com
Emp.: 10
Nonmetallic Mineral Product Mfr
S.I.C.: 3299
N.A.I.C.S.: 327999
Happle Hoo *(Mgr-Sls)*

Dalian CIMC Container Co., Ltd **(1)**
IIIB-2 Dalian Free Trade Zone
116-600 Dalian, China (100%)
Tel.: (86) 41139968185
Fax: (86) 41139968317
E-Mail: qingyu.meng@cimc.com
Web Site: www.palletcenter.com
Emp.: 1,000
Power Boiler & Heat Exchanger Mfr
S.I.C.: 3443
N.A.I.C.S.: 332410
Qing Yu Meng *(Mgr-Pur)*

Dalian CIMC Logistics Equipment Co., Ltd. **(1)**
No 2 Gangwan Avenue
Shekou Industrial Zone, Shenzhen, Guangdong, China (100%)
Tel.: (86) 75526802601
Fax: (86) 75526688171
E-Mail: le@cimc.com
Web Site: www.cimc.com
Emp.: 50,000
Metal Container Mfr
S.I.C.: 3412
N.A.I.C.S.: 332439

Dalian CIMC Railway Equipment Co., Ltd. **(1)**
Free Trade Zone IIIB-2
Dalian, Liaoning, China 116600
Tel.: (86) 411 3921 6026
Fax: (86) 411 3921 6066
Railroad Rolling Stock Mfr
S.I.C.: 3743
N.A.I.C.S.: 336510

Donghwa Container Transportation Service Co., Ltd. **(1)**
5th Floor No 500 Changjiang Road
Shanghai, China 200431
Tel.: (86) 21 66151717
Fax: (86) 21 66155700
E-Mail: info@donghwa.com.cn

Web Site: www.donghwa.com.cn
Emp.: 500
Container Transportation Services
S.I.C.: 4789
N.A.I.C.S.: 488999
Wu Yimin *(Gen Mgr)*

Enric (Bengbu) Compressor Co., Ltd. (1)
187 Yanshan Road
Bengbu, Anhui, 233052, China
Tel.: (86) 552 3139287
Fax: (86) 552 3139193
Emp.: 640
Compressor Machinery Mfr
S.I.C.: 3563
N.A.I.C.S.: 333912

Enric Energy Equipment Holdings Limited (1)
Cimc R D Center Number 2 Gangwan Avenue Shekou Industrial Zone
Shenzhen, Guangdong, 518067, China
Tel.: (86) 755 26802050
Fax: (86) 755 26693117
Investment Management Services
S.I.C.: 6211
N.A.I.C.S.: 523999

Enric (Lang fang) Energy Equipment integration Co., Ltd. (1)
No 106 Huaxiang Road Economic And Technique Development Zone
Langfang, Hebei, China 065001
Tel.: (86) 316 6079954
Fax: (86) 316 6079321
Web Site: www.cimc.com
Industrial Equipment Mfr
S.I.C.: 3559
N.A.I.C.S.: 333249

Gansu CIMC Huajun Vehicle Co., Ltd. (1)
No 26 Changan Road
Baiyin, Gansu, China 730900
Tel.: (86) 943 8250666
Fax: (86) 943 8233286
E-Mail: gszjhj@gszjhj.com
Web Site: www.gszjhj.com
Motor Vehicle Mfr
S.I.C.: 3711
N.A.I.C.S.: 336111

Jingmen Hongtu Special Aircraft manufacturing Co., Ltd (1)
1 Hongtu Road
Dongbao District, Jingmen, 448134, China
Tel.: (86) 72 4888 9000
Fax: (86) 72 4888 9379
E-Mail: hongtu@enricgroup.com
Seaplanes Supplies Pressure Vessel Mfr
S.I.C.: 3499
N.A.I.C.S.: 332439

Luoyang CIMC Lingyu Automobile CO., LTD. (1)
West Section of Guanlin Road
Luolong District, 471004 Luoyang, Henan, China
Tel.: (86) 379 65937665
Fax: (86) 379 65937693
Emp.: 1,000
Trailer & Container Mfr
S.I.C.: 3715
N.A.I.C.S.: 336212
Guo Fang *(Gen Mgr)*

Luoyang Linyu Automobile Co., Ltd (1)
West Section of Guanlin Road
Luolong District, 471023 Luoyang, Henan, China
Tel.: (86) 379 65937678
Fax: (86) 379 65937693
E-Mail: overseasales@lingyu.com
Emp.: 100
Automobile Mfr
S.I.C.: 3711
N.A.I.C.S.: 336111
Yonghua Guo *(Gen Mgr)*

Nantong CIMC Special Transportation Equipment Manufacture Co., Ltd. (1)
No 159 Chenggang Road
Gangzha District, Nantong, Jiangsu, 226003, China
Tel.: (86) 51385066888
Fax: (86) 51385565155
Transportation Equipment Mfr
S.I.C.: 3799
N.A.I.C.S.: 336999

Nantong CIMC Tank Equipment Co., Ltd. (1)
No159 ChengGang Road
Nantong, Jiangsu, China (100%)
Tel.: (86) 51385066888
Fax: (86) 51385564961
Emp.: 5,000
Nonmetallic Mineral Product Mfr
S.I.C.: 3299
N.A.I.C.S.: 327999
Guocai Tang *(Gen Mgr)*

Ningbo CIMC Container Service Co., Ltd. (1)
No 255 Zhujiang Road Beilun Zone
Ningbo, China
Tel.: (86) 574 26883553
Fax: (86) 574 26883536
E-Mail: info@cimc-services.com
Container Trucking Services
S.I.C.: 4214
N.A.I.C.S.: 484110
Huang Lupeng *(Gen Mgr)*

Ningbo CIMC Logistics Equipment Co., Ltd. (1)
Ningbo Export-Processing Zone
Ningbo, Zhejiang, China
Tel.: (86) 574 8682 5122
Fax: (86) 574 8682 5120
Logistic Metal Container Mfr
S.I.C.: 3412
N.A.I.C.S.: 332439

Qingdao CIMC Container Manufacture Co., Ltd (1)
No 1 East Kaifa Road E&T Development Zone
Qingdao, 266500, China
Tel.: (86) 532 86935706
Fax: (86) 532 86859288
Metal Container Mfr
S.I.C.: 3499
N.A.I.C.S.: 332439

Qingdao CIMC Eco - Equipment Co., Ltd. (1)
No 1 Huanghedong Road Economic Technological Development Zone
Qingdao, China
Tel.: (86) 532 86935712
Fax: (86) 532 86935720
Web Site: www.cimc.com
Automobile Spare Parts Mfr
S.I.C.: 3714
N.A.I.C.S.: 336390

Qingdao CIMC Reefer Container Manufacture Co., Ltd. (1)
No 586 East Lanzhou Road Jiaozhou
Qingdao, Shandong, China
Tel.: (86) 532 81121097
Fax: (86) 532 81121111
Reefer Container Mfr
S.I.C.: 3412
N.A.I.C.S.: 332439

Qingdao CIMC Special Reefer Co., Ltd. (1)
12 Dongwaihuan Road
266300 Jinan, Shandong, China (100%)
Tel.: (86) 53282279978
Fax: (86) 53282279978
Nonmetallic Mineral Product Mfr
S.I.C.: 3299
N.A.I.C.S.: 327999
Tianhua Huang *(Gen Mgr)*

Qingdao Kooll Logistics Co., Ltd. (1)
No 6 Qianwangang Road Economy Technology Development Zone
Qingdao, Shandong, 266510, China
Tel.: (86) 532 86828666
Fax: (86) 532 86828080
E-Mail: info@kooll.cn
Web Site: www.kooll.cn
Logistics Consulting Services
S.I.C.: 4731
N.A.I.C.S.: 541614

Shanghai CIMC Baowell Industries Co. Ltd (1)
No 1881 Yueluo Road
Baoshan District, Shanghai, 201908, China
Tel.: (86) 2156860000
Fax: (86) 2156863985
Wood Container & Pallet Mfr
S.I.C.: 2448
N.A.I.C.S.: 321920

Shanghai CIMC Reefer Containers Co., Ltd. (1)
No 6888 Hutai Rd
Baoshan Dist, Shanghai, China (100%)
Tel.: (86) 2156010088
Fabricated Structural Metal Mfr
S.I.C.: 3441
N.A.I.C.S.: 332312
Jianhong Li *(Chm)*

Shanghai CIMC Special Vehicle Co., Ltd. (1)
No 1771 Fuyuan Road
Baoshan District, Shanghai, China
Tel.: (86) 21 56861100
Fax: (86) 21 56863985
Automobile Mfr
S.I.C.: 3711
N.A.I.C.S.: 336111

Shanghai CIMC Yangshan Container Service Co., Ltd. (1)
5th Floor No 500 Changjiang Road
Shanghai, 200431, China
Tel.: (86) 21 66151717
Fax: (86) 21 66155700
E-Mail: dw@donghwa.com.cn
Warehousing & Logistics Services
S.I.C.: 4225
N.A.I.C.S.: 493110

Shenzhen CIMC Tianda Airport Equipment Co., Ltd. (1)
Shekou Industrial Zone Gulf Road On The 19
Nanshan District, Shenzhen, Guangdong, 518067, China
Tel.: (86) 755 26688488
Trailer & Container Mfr
S.I.C.: 3715
N.A.I.C.S.: 336212

Shenzhen CIMC Wood Co., Ltd. (1)
5/F No 2 Gangwan Avenue Shekou Industrial Zone
Nanshan District, Shenzhen, 518067, China
Tel.: (86) 755 26691129
Transportation Equipment Mfr & Distr
S.I.C.: 3799
N.A.I.C.S.: 336999

Shenzhen CIMC Yantian Port Container Service Co., Ltd (1)
Mingzhu 3rd Street
Yantian Road, Shenzhen, China (55%)
Tel.: (86) 75525283836
Fax: (86) 75525283336
E-Mail: depotservice1.sscm@cimc.com
Web Site: www.cimc-services.com
Emp.: 200
Nonmetallic Mineral Product Mfr
S.I.C.: 3299
N.A.I.C.S.: 327999

Shenzhen Southern CIMC Containers Service Co., Ltd. (1)
Qianhaiwan Logistics Zone Yue Liang Wan Avenue
Shenzhen, China 518067
Tel.: (86) 755 26691131
Fax: (86) 755 26453616
E-Mail: skdepot@cimc.com
Web Site: www.cimc.com
Metal Container Mfr
S.I.C.: 3499
N.A.I.C.S.: 332439

Shenzhen Southern CIMC Eastern Logistics Equipment Manufacturing Co., Ltd. (1)
3th Jinglong Avenue Pingshan Town
Longgang District, Shenzhen, 518118, China
Tel.: (86) 755 89663666, ext. 3020
Fax: (86) 755 89663517
Web Site: www.cimcsouth.com
Logistic Conatiner Equipment Mfr
S.I.C.: 3499
N.A.I.C.S.: 332439
Wendy Cheng *(Mgr-Overseas Sls)*

Taicang CIMC Containers Co., Ltd. (1)
No 96 Binjiang Avenue Gangkou Development Zone
Taicang, Jiangsu, China
Tel.: (86) 512 53782629
Emp.: 200
Freight Forwarding Services
S.I.C.: 4731
N.A.I.C.S.: 488510
Hu Jianming *(Gen Mgr)*

Tianjin CIMC Logistics Equipments Co., Ltd. (1)
No 21 No 5 Street Economic And Technological Development Zone
Tianjin, 300457, China
Tel.: (86) 2259887105
Fax: (86) 2259887106
Logistics Equipment & Container Mfr
S.I.C.: 3499
N.A.I.C.S.: 332439

Wuhu CIMC RuiJiang Automobile CO LTD (1)
205 High-tech Industries In Wuhu City of The Road
Wuhu, China
Tel.: (86) 553 3025150
Fax: (86) 553 3023120
E-Mail: cimc.rj@gmail.com
Web Site: www.cimc-whrj.com
Heavy Vehicle & Automobile Mfr
S.I.C.: 3711
N.A.I.C.S.: 336111
Wang Zhu Jiang *(Mgr-Sls)*

Xinhui CIMC Container Co., Ltd. (1)
Xinhui Zhongji Industrial Park Da Ao Town
Xinhui District, Jiangmen, Guangdong, 529144, China
Tel.: (86) 7506248888
Fax: (86) 7506248555
Fabricated Metal Container Mfr
S.I.C.: 3412
N.A.I.C.S.: 332439

Xinhui CIMC Special Transportation Equipment Co., Ltd. (1)
Da Ao Town
Xinhui Dist, Jiangmen, Guangdong, 529144, China
Tel.: (86) 7506248888
Fax: (86) 7506248555
Transportation Equipment Mfr
S.I.C.: 3799
N.A.I.C.S.: 336999

Xinhui CIMC Wood Co., Ltd. (1)
Xinhui Cimc Industrial Park Da Ao Town
Xinhui District, Jiangmen, Guangdong, 529144, China
Tel.: (86) 7506248906
Fax: (86) 7506248555
Industrial Timber Products Distr
S.I.C.: 5099
N.A.I.C.S.: 423990

Yangzhou CIMC Tong Hua Special Vehicles Co., Ltd. (1)
No 139 Middle Yangzijiang Road
Yangzhou, Jiangsu, 225009, China
Tel.: (86) 51487867220
Fax: (86) 51487873290
Heavy Trailer Mfr
S.I.C.: 3715
N.A.I.C.S.: 336212

Yangzhou Runyang Logistics Equipments Co., Ltd. (1)
99 Yangwei Road Dev Zone
Yangzhou, Jiangsu, China 225102
Tel.: (86) 514 87576699
Fax: (86) 514 87573880
E-Mail: sales@yzryc.com
Web Site: www.yzryc.com
Logistics Metal Container Mfr
S.I.C.: 3499
N.A.I.C.S.: 332439

Yangzhou Tonglee Reefer Container Co., Ltd. (1)
Liuwei
Yangzhou, Jiangsu, China (51%)
Tel.: (86) 51487585823
Fax: (86) 51487582196
E-Mail: sales@tonglee-reefer.com
Web Site: www.tlc-yz.com
Emp.: 1,800
Nonmetallic Mineral Product Mfr
S.I.C.: 3299
N.A.I.C.S.: 327999
Hongzhou Zhao *(Gen Mgr)*

China International Marine Containers (Group) Co., Ltd.—(Continued)

Yangzhou Tonglee Reefer Equipment Co.,Ltd (1)
Dev Zone
225102 Yangzhou, Jiangsu, China (100%)
Tel.: (86) 51487585823
Fax: (86) 51487582196
Web Site: www.tlc-yz.com
Nonmetallic Mineral Product Mfr
S.I.C.: 3299
N.A.I.C.S.: 327999
Hongzhou Zhao *(Gen Mgr)*

Yantai CIMC Raffles Ship Co., Ltd. (1)
No 70 Zhifu E Rd Zhijiedao
Zhifu Dist, Yantai, 264000, China
Tel.: (86) 5356801451
Fax: (86) 5356828419
Ship Building Services
S.I.C.: 3731
N.A.I.C.S.: 336611
George Lee *(Gen Mgr)*

Zhangjiagang CIMC Sanctum Cryogenic Equipment Machinery Co., Ltd. (1)
GangxiRd M Economic
Jinggang Town, Zhangjiagang, 215632, China
Tel.: (86) 512 58391235
Fax: (86) 12 5837 0701
E-Mail: sdy@sdy-cn.com
Web Site: www.sdy-cn.com
Cryogenic Tank Mfr
S.I.C.: 3443
N.A.I.C.S.: 332420
Shi Cai-xing *(Gen Mgr)*

Zhangzhou CIMC Container Co., Ltd. (1)
China Merchants Zhangzhou Development Zone
Zhangzhou, China
Tel.: (86) 596 685 6179
Fax: (86) 596 685 9862
Fabricated Metal Container Mfr
S.I.C.: 3499
N.A.I.C.S.: 332439
Tony Chang *(Gen Mgr)*

Zhumadian CIMC Huajun Vehicle Co.,Ltd (1)
Zhumadian yicheng area Middle section of Xuesong Rd
463000 Zhengzhou, Henan, China (75%)
Tel.: (86) 3963810953
Fax: (86) 3963810953
Web Site: www.hjcl.com
Emp.: 3,500
Nonmetallic Mineral Product Mfr
S.I.C.: 3299
N.A.I.C.S.: 327999
Fapei Wu *(VP)*

Zhumadian CIMC Huajun Vehicle Trading Co., Ltd (1)
Middle Section of Xuesong Road
Zhumadian, 463500, China
Tel.: (86) 39 6381 0953
Truck & Trailer Distr
S.I.C.: 5013
N.A.I.C.S.: 423120
Guo Yonghua *(Gen Mgr)*

U.S. Subsidiaries:

CIMC USA Inc. (1)
289 E Water Tower Dr
Monon, IN 47959
Tel.: (219) 253-2054
Fax: (219) 253-8033
Web Site: www.cimc.com
Emp.: 500
Industrial Equipment Mfr
S.I.C.: 3559
N.A.I.C.S.: 333249
Densil William *(Gen Mgr)*

Direct Chassis LLC (1)
700 Rockmead Dr Ste 250
Kingwood, TX 77339-2106
Tel.: (281) 812-3462
Fax: (281) 540-3411
E-Mail: info@directchassis.com
Web Site: www.directchassis.com
Chassis Distr
S.I.C.: 5012
N.A.I.C.S.: 423110

Vanguard National Trailer Corporation (1)
289 E Water Tower Dr
Monon, IN 47959 (100%)
Tel.: (219) 253-2008
Fax: (219) 253-7386
Toll Free: (888) 253-3008
Web Site: www.vanguardtrailer.com
Emp.: 100
Trailer Mfr
S.I.C.: 3715
N.A.I.C.S.: 336212
Charlie Mudd *(Pres)*

Non-U.S. Subsidiaries:

Beheermaatschappij Burg B.V (1)
Katwijkerlaan 75
Pijnacker, Zuid-Holland, 2641 PD, Netherlands
Tel.: (31) 153694340
Fax: (31) 153615400
Management Consulting Services
S.I.C.: 8748
N.A.I.C.S.: 541618

Burg Carrosserie B.V. (1)
Lakenblekerstraat 26
1431 GG Aalsmeer, North Holland, Netherlands
Tel.: (31) 297 324 553
Fax: (31) 297 321 440
E-Mail: info@burgers-carrosserie.nl
Web Site: www.burgers-carrosserie.nl
Emp.: 5
Automotive Body Mfr
S.I.C.: 3711
N.A.I.C.S.: 336211
A. G. H. Burgess *(Gen Mgr)*

Burg Service B.V. (1)
Middenweg 6
PO Box 299
4760 AG Moerdijk, Netherlands
Tel.: (31) 88 00 30 800
Fax: (31) 88 00 30 882
E-Mail: info@burgservice.nl
Web Site: www.burgservice.nl
Emp.: 65
Stainless Steel Storage Tank Mfr
S.I.C.: 3317
N.A.I.C.S.: 331210
Cor den Ridder *(Sr Mgr-Ops & Plant Mgr)*

Caspian Driller Pte. Ltd. (1)
08-04 Orchard Towers
Singapore, 229594, Singapore
Tel.: (65) 6735 8690
Fax: (65) 6734 5449
Metal Container Mfr
S.I.C.: 3499
N.A.I.C.S.: 332439

China International Marine Containers (Hong Kong) Limited (1)
Rm 3101-2 31th Fl Vicwood Plz
Central District, Central, China (Hong Kong) (100%)
Tel.: (852) 28051268
Fax: (852) 28051835
Web Site: www.cinc.com
Emp.: 200
Industrial Supplies Whslr
S.I.C.: 5085
N.A.I.C.S.: 423840
Jianhong Li *(Mng Dir)*

CIMC Australia Pty Ltd. (1)
U 2 14 Monterey Road
Dandenong, 3175, Australia (100%)
Tel.: (61) 397972100
Fax: (61) 397972199
Web Site: www.cimc.com.au
Emp.: 150
Metal Container Mfr
S.I.C.: 3412
N.A.I.C.S.: 332439
Hector Ojea *(Gen Mgr)*

CIMC Burg B.V. (1)
Katwijkerlaan 75
Pijnacker, Zuid-Holland, 2641 PD, Netherlands
Tel.: (31) 153694340
Fax: (31) 153615400
Emp.: 25
Transportation Services
S.I.C.: 4789
N.A.I.C.S.: 488999
Jan Bunk *(Plant Mgr)*

CIMC Holdings Australia Pty Ltd (1)
U 2 14 Monterey Rd
Dandenong, VIC, 3175, Australia
Tel.: (61) 3 9797 2100
Fax: (61) 3 9797 2199
Investment Management Services
S.I.C.: 6211
N.A.I.C.S.: 523999

CIMC Raffles Offshore (Singapore) Limited (1)
No 1 Claymore Drive 08-04 Orchard Towers
Singapore, 229594, Singapore
Tel.: (65) 6735 8690
Fax: (65) 6734 5449
Web Site: www.yantai-raffles.com
Oil & Gas Offshore Services
S.I.C.: 1389
N.A.I.C.S.: 213112
Malcolm Chang *(Mng Dir)*

CIMC Rolling Stock Australia Pty Ltd. (1)
Unit 1 138 Ashley Street
Underdale, Adelaide, SA, 5032, Australia
Tel.: (61) 8 8351 8111
Fax: (61) 8 8351 8822
Web Site: www.cimc.com.au/ContactUs
Rail Road Rolling Stock Mfr
S.I.C.: 3743
N.A.I.C.S.: 336510
Brad Usher *(Gen Mgr)*

CIMC Vehicle Australia Pty Ltd (1)
Unit 2 14 Monterey Road
Dandenong, VIC, 3175, Australia
Tel.: (61) 3 9797 2100
Fax: (61) 3 9797 2199
E-Mail: reception@cimc.com.au
Transportation Equipment Mfr
S.I.C.: 3799
N.A.I.C.S.: 336999
Hector Ojea *(Mng Dir)*

Exploitatiemaatschappij Intraprogres B.V (1)
Katwijkerlaan 75
2641 PD Pijnacker, Netherlands
Tel.: (31) 15 3694340
Fax: (31) 15 3693385
Freight Trucking Services
S.I.C.: 4213
N.A.I.C.S.: 484121

Hobur Twente B.V. (1)
Bedrijvenpark Twente 115
7602 KE Almelo, Netherlands
Tel.: (31) 546 573 665
Fax: (31) 546 573 695
E-Mail: info@hobur.nl
Web Site: www.hobur.nl
Road Tanker Mfr
S.I.C.: 3795
N.A.I.C.S.: 336992

Holvrieka Danmark A/S (1)
Kulholmsvej 24
DK-8930 Randers, Denmark
Tel.: (45) 86 428400
Fax: (45) 86 403335
E-Mail: holvrieka@holvrieka.dk
Emp.: 65
Metal Container Mfr
S.I.C.: 3412
N.A.I.C.S.: 332439
Bo Mortensen *(Mng Dir)*

Holvrieka Holding B.V. (1)
Kapitein Grantstraat 8
Postbus 2044
Emmen, 7801 CA, Netherlands
Tel.: (31) 591 61 48 88
Fax: (31) 591 61 72 34
E-Mail: info@holvrieka-ido.nl
Web Site: www.holvrieka.com
Emp.: 65
Financial Management Services
S.I.C.: 6211
N.A.I.C.S.: 523999
Ko Brink *(Gen Mgr)*

Holvrieka Ido B.V. (1)
Kapitein Grantstraat 8
7821 AR Emmen, Netherlands
Tel.: (31) 591 614888
Fax: (31) 591 617234
E-Mail: info@holvrieka-ido.nl
Emp.: 60
Stainless Steel Tanks Mfr
S.I.C.: 3317
N.A.I.C.S.: 331210
Ko Brink *(Gen Mgr)*

Holvrieka Nirota B.V. (1)
Lorentzstraat 7
8606 JP Sneek, Netherlands
Tel.: (31) 515 43 53 73
Fax: (31) 515 41 80 65
E-Mail: info@holvrieka-nirota.nl
Emp.: 100
Stainless Steel Tank Mfr
S.I.C.: 3317
N.A.I.C.S.: 331210
Ko Brink *(Mng Dir)*

Holvrieka N.V. (1)
Wervikstraat 350
PO Box 19
8930 Menen, Belgium
Tel.: (32) 56 514251
Fax: (32) 56 510728
E-Mail: info@holvrieka.be
Web Site: www.holvrieka.net
Emp.: 50
Stainless & Fabrication Steel Container Mfr
S.I.C.: 3412
N.A.I.C.S.: 332439
Anton Dirven *(Gen Mgr)*

Immoburg N.V. (1)
Kanaallaan 54
Bree, Limburg, 3960, Belgium
Tel.: (32) 89 46 91 11
Fax: (32) 89 46 91 10
Real Estate Development Services
S.I.C.: 6531
N.A.I.C.S.: 531390

LAG Trailers N.V. (1)
IT Kanaal Zuid 3613 - Kanaallaan 54
3960 Bree, Belgium
Tel.: (32) 89 46 91 11
Fax: (32) 89 46 91 10
E-Mail: info@lag.be
Web Site: www.lag.be
Emp.: 450
Truck Tankers Mfr
S.I.C.: 3711
N.A.I.C.S.: 336120

Marshall Lethlean Industries Pty Ltd (1)
291 - 293 Hammond Road
Dandenong, VIC, 3164, Australia
Tel.: (61) 3 8788 5400
Fax: (61) 3 9794 7624
E-Mail: info@mli.com.au
Web Site: www.mli.com.au
Emp.: 10
Transporting Equipment Mfr
S.I.C.: 3799
N.A.I.C.S.: 336999
Geoff Purcell *(Gen Mgr)*

Noordkoel B.V. (1)
Kapitein Grantstraat 8
Emmen, Drenthe, 7821 AR, Netherlands
Tel.: (31) 591614888
Business Support Services
S.I.C.: 7389
N.A.I.C.S.: 561499

Tacoba Consultant Forestry N.V (1)
Mataal Straal 16
Paramaribo, Suriname
Tel.: (597) 401485
Fax: (597) 404290
E-Mail: tacoba@cimc.com
Forestry Consulting Services
S.I.C.: 0851
N.A.I.C.S.: 115310

TGE Gas Engineering GmbH (1)
Mildred-Scheel-Strasse 1
53175 Bonn, Germany De
Tel.: (49) 228 60448 0
Fax: (49) 228 60448 888
E-Mail: info@tge-gas.com
Web Site: www.tge-gas.com
Engineering Services
S.I.C.: 8711
N.A.I.C.S.: 541330
Vladimir Puklavec *(Chm-Supervisory Bd)*
Werner Schlott *(CEO & Chm-Exec Bd)*
Klaus Nussbaum *(Dir-Fin & Member-Exec Bd)*

Vela Holding B.V. (1)
Katwijkerlaan 75
Pijnacker, Zuid-Holland, 2641 PD, Netherlands
Tel.: (31) 153694340
Investment Management Services
S.I.C.: 6211
N.A.I.C.S.: 523999

CHINA INTERNET CAFE HOLDINGS GROUP, INC.

1707 Block A Genzon Times Square
Longcheng Blvd Centre City
Longgang District, Shenzhen, Guangdong, 518172, China
Tel.: (86) 755 8989 6008
Fax: (86) 755 89899013
E-Mail: kerban@sina.com
Web Site: www.chinainternetcafe.com
Year Founded: 2006
CICC—(OTC)
Rev.: $29,575,042
Assets: $39,257,358
Liabilities: $10,590,364
Net Worth: $28,666,994
Earnings: $4,776,485
Emp.: 656
Fiscal Year-end: 12/31/12
Business Description:
Internet Cafe Owner & Operator
S.I.C.: 5812
N.A.I.C.S.: 722514
Personnel:
Dishan Guo *(Chm, CEO & CFO)*
Board of Directors:
Dishan Guo
Wenbin An
Lei Li
Luke Liu
Lizong Wang
Transfer Agent:
VStock Transfer LLC
77 Spruce St Ste 201
Cedarhurst, NY 11516

CHINA INVESTMENT AND FINANCE GROUP LIMITED

Unit 5801-03 The Center 99 Queen's Road
Central, China (Hong Kong)
Tel.: (852) 2180 7788
Fax: (852) 2180 7798
Web Site: www.chnif.com
1226—(HKG)
Rev.: $981,310
Assets: $70,549,190
Liabilities: $129,853
Net Worth: $70,419,337
Earnings: ($1,903,818)
Emp.: 7
Fiscal Year-end: 03/31/13
Business Description:
Investment Holding Services
S.I.C.: 6282
N.A.I.C.S.: 523920
Personnel:
Chi Fai Li *(Sec)*
Board of Directors:
Jintian Liao
Cheong Yee Chan
Kaizhi Chen
Tak-kong Ha
Kwong Kin Leung
Chi Ming Lo
Weiquan Zhou
Transfer Agent:
Tricor Standard Limited
26/F Tesbury Centre 28 Queen's Road East
Wanchai, China (Hong Kong)
Tel.: (852) 2980 1333
Fax: (852) 2810 8185

CHINA INVESTMENT CORPORATION

New Poly Plaza No 1 Chaoyangmen Beidajie
Dongcheng District, Beijing, 100010, China
Tel.: (86) 10 8409 6277
Fax: (86) 10 6408 6908
E-Mail: pr@china-inv.cn
Web Site: www.china-inv.cn
Year Founded: 2007
Business Description:
Investment Management Services
S.I.C.: 6799
N.A.I.C.S.: 523920
Personnel:
Xuedong Ding *(Chm)*
Liqun Jin *(Chm-Supervisory Bd)*
Keping Li *(Vice Chm & Pres)*
Xiang Liang *(Exec VP & Sec-Discipline Inspecting Commission)*
Yifei Fan *(Exec VP)*
Chun Peng *(Exec VP)*
Jianxi Wang *(Exec VP)*
Ping Xie *(Exec VP)*
Board of Directors:
Xuedong Ding
Jian Chen
Shangpu Fang
Xiaolian Hu
Keping Li
Xin Li
Yong Li
Zhongli Liu
Chunzheng Wang
Xiaoqiang Zhang
Supervisory Board of Directors:
Liqun Jin
Guangqing Cui
Dasheng Dong
Mubing Zhou
Xinyi Zhuang

Subsidiary:

Central Huijin Investment Ltd. (1)
New Poly Plaza 1 Chaoyangmen Beidajie
Dongcheng District, Beijing, 100010, China
Tel.: (86) 10 6408 6638
Fax: (86) 10 6408 6605
E-Mail: huijinpr@huijin-inv.cn
Web Site: www.huijin-inv.cn
Investment Management Services
S.I.C.: 6211
N.A.I.C.S.: 523999
Jiange Li *(Vice Chm)*
Chun Peng *(Pres)*
You'an Chen *(Exec VP)*
Hong'an Zhang *(Exec VP)*
Haiying Zhao *(Exec VP)*

CHINA INVESTMENT DEVELOPMENT LIMITED

Units 7809-13 78/F Center 99 Queen's Road
Central, China (Hong Kong)
Tel.: (852) 3102 1690
Fax: (852) 3102 1695
E-Mail: info@cidl.com.hk
Web Site: www.cidl.com.hk
Year Founded: 1998
204—(HKG)
Rev.: $98,518
Assets: $4,978,760
Liabilities: $582,726
Net Worth: $4,396,034
Earnings: ($1,156,939)
Fiscal Year-end: 03/31/13
Business Description:
Investment Management Services
S.I.C.: 6799
N.A.I.C.S.: 523920
Personnel:
Xuming Zhang *(CEO)*
Chak Keung Wong *(Sec)*
Board of Directors:
Cheong Yee Chan
Felix Wo Fong
Wing Kin Leung
Ping Sum Tang
Chak Keung Wong

Butterfield Fulcrum Group (Bermuda) Limited
26 Burnaby Street
Hamilton, HM 11, Bermuda

CHINA ITS (HOLDINGS) CO., LTD.

10-12/F Nexus Center 19A East 3rd Ring Road North
Chaoyang District, Beijing, 100020, China
Tel.: (86) 1059330088
Fax: (86) 1059330999
Web Site: www.its.cn
1900—(HKG)
Sales Range: $200-249.9 Million
Emp.: 562
Business Description:
Transportation Infrastructure Technology Services
S.I.C.: 7373
N.A.I.C.S.: 541512
Personnel:
Hailin Jiang *(Chm)*
Board of Directors:
Hailin Jiang
Onward Choi
Xiao Lu
Jianguo Pan
Lu Sun
Jing Wang
Chunsheng Zhou

CHINA IVY SCHOOL, INC.

1 Suhua Road Shiji Jinrong Building Suite 801
Suzhou Industrial Park, Suzhou, Jiangsu, 215020, China
Tel.: (86) 51267625632
E-Mail: cnivy@126.com
Web Site: www.chinaivyschool.com
CIVS—(OTC)
Sales Range: $1-9.9 Million
Business Description:
Schools
S.I.C.: 8211
N.A.I.C.S.: 611110
Personnel:
Yongqi Zhu *(CEO)*
Jian Xue *(CFO)*
Qian Gao *(Sec)*
Board of Directors:
Qian Gao
Yipeng Lu
Fugeng Xia
Haiming Zhang
Yongqi Zhu

CHINA JISHAN HOLDINGS LIMITED

1 Sophia Road 05-03 Peace Centre
Singapore, 228149, Singapore
Tel.: (65) 63371295
Fax: (65) 63374225
Web Site: www.jishantextile.com
J18—(SES)
Rev.: $78,096,379
Assets: $161,711,683
Liabilities: $135,529,232
Net Worth: $26,182,451
Earnings: $773,917
Fiscal Year-end: 12/31/12
Business Description:
Textile Svcs
S.I.C.: 2299
N.A.I.C.S.: 313310
Personnel:
Guan Liang Jin *(Chm)*
Rong Hai Jin *(CEO)*
Michael Jong Yeat Chin *(CFO)*
Priscilla Wai Teng Chan *(Sec)*
Board of Directors:
Guan Liang Jin
Rong Hai Jin
Kait Long Lien
Ping Wen Xu
Wei Jen Yip
Ming Hai Yu
Transfer Agent:
Intertrust Singapore Corporate Services Pte. Ltd
3 Anson Road #27-01 Springleaf Tower
Singapore, Singapore

CHINA JIUHAO HEALTH INDUSTRY CORPORATION LIMITED

(Formerly Media China Corporation Limited)
No 9 Anwai Beihu Chaoyang District
Beijing, China
Tel.: (86) 10 6491 8888
Fax: (86) 10 6419 8017
Web Site: www.juhaohealth.com
0419—(HKG)
Sls.: $26,221,052
Assets: $480,641,341
Liabilities: $226,974,252
Net Worth: $253,667,088
Earnings: ($6,924,113)
Emp.: 485
Fiscal Year-end: 12/31/12
Business Description:
Health Industry, Media & Real Estate Investment Services
S.I.C.: 6211
N.A.I.C.S.: 523999
Personnel:
Hoi Po Yuen *(Chm & CEO)*
Changsheng Zhang *(Vice Chm)*
Raymond Wai Man Hau *(CFO & Sec)*
Board of Directors:
Hoi Po Yuen
Hugo Shong
Edward Suning Tian
Xin Wei
David Yau Kar Wong
Kin Yuen
Changsheng Zhang
Legal Counsel:
Fred Kan & Co
Suite 3104-7 31st Floor Central Plaza 18 Harbour Road
Hong Kong, China (Hong Kong)
D.S. Cheung & Co.
29 F Bank of East Asia Harbour View Centre 56 Gloucester Road
Wanchai, China (Hong Kong)
Transfer Agent:
Tricor Tengis Limited
26th Floor Tesbury Centre 28 Queen's Road East
Wanchai, China (Hong Kong)
Tel.: (852) 29801333
Fax: (852) 28108185

CHINA JO-JO DRUGSTORES, INC.

Room 507-513 5th Floor A Building Meidu Plaza
Gongshu District, Hangzhou, Zhejiang, China
Tel.: (86) 57188077078
Web Site: www.chinajojodrugstores.com
Year Founded: 2006
CJJD—(NASDAQ)
Rev.: $89,495,546
Assets: $67,838,021
Liabilities: $29,690,412
Net Worth: $38,147,609
Earnings: ($14,334,525)
Emp.: 690
Fiscal Year-end: 03/31/13
Business Description:
Drug Store & Pharmacy Owner & Operator

CHINA JO-JO DRUGSTORES, INC.—(Continued)

S.I.C.: 5912
N.A.I.C.S.: 446110
Personnel:
Lei Liu *(Chm & CEO)*
Frank Ming Zhao *(CFO)*
Li Qi *(Sec & Gen Mgr)*
Board of Directors:
Lei Liu
Genghua Gu
Taihong Guo
Li Qi
Zhimin Su
Transfer Agent:
American Stock Transfer & Trust Co.
6201 15th Ave
Brooklyn, NY 11219
Tel.: (718) 921-8124

CHINA KANGDA FOOD COMPANY LIMITED
1 Hai Nan Road Economic & Technology Development Zone
Jiaonan City, Qingdao, Shandong, China
Tel.: (86) 532 86171115
Fax: (86) 532 86161323
Web Site: www.kangdafood.com
0834—(HKG SES)
Rev.: $236,660,766
Assets: $255,683,372
Liabilities: $143,622,321
Net Worth: $112,061,050
Earnings: $95,945
Emp.: 5,529
Fiscal Year-end: 12/31/12
Business Description:
Food Mfr & Distr
S.I.C.: 2099
N.A.I.C.S.: 311999
Personnel:
Fengjun An *(CEO)*
William Fong *(CFO & Co-Sec)*
Josephine Lei Mui Toh *(Co-Sec)*
Board of Directors:
Sishi Gao
Fengjun An
Yanxu Gao
DingDing He
Choon Hoong Lau
Yamada Naoki
Chung Leung Yu
Qi Zhang
BDO Limited
25th Floor Wing On Centre 111 Connaught Road
Central, China (Hong Kong)
Legal Counsel:
WongPartnership LLP
One George Street #20-01
Singapore, Singapore
P. C. Woo & Co
12th Floor Princes Building 10 Chater Road
Central, China (Hong Kong)
Hitrust & Co
2401 02 Gang Ao Bldg No2, Shandong Rd
Qingdao, China
B.A.C.S. Private Limited
63 Cantonment Road
Singapore, 089758, Singapore
Tel.: (65) 3236 2000

CHINA KANGTAI CACTUS BIO-TECH INC.
99 Taibei Road Limin Economic and Technological Development Zone
Harbin, Heilongjiang, 150025, China
Tel.: (86) 451 57351189
Fax: (86) 451 57351551
E-Mail: biocactus@gmail.com
Web Site: www.biocactus.com
Year Founded: 2000
CKGT—(OTC)
Sales Range: $25-49.9 Million
Emp.: 132
Business Description:
Cactus-Based Products Including Nutraceuticals, Beverages (Juices, Wine & Beer), Packaged Foods & Other Products Containing Cactus, Cactus Fruit & Cactus Derivatives
S.I.C.: 2836
N.A.I.C.S.: 325414
Personnel:
Jinjiang Wang *(Chm, Pres & CEO)*
Hong Bu *(CFO)*
Board of Directors:
Jinjiang Wang
Hong Bu
Chengzhi Wang
Jiping Wang
Song Yang
John Zhang
Subsidiary:

Harbin Hainan Kangda Cacti Hygienical Foods Co., Ltd **(1)**
No 99 Taibei Road
Harbin, 150001, China
Tel.: (86) 451 5735 1189
Fax: (86) 451 5735 1551
Web Site: www.xrz.cn
Cactus & Cut Products Mfr
S.I.C.: 0179
N.A.I.C.S.: 111339

CHINA KELI ELECTRIC COMPANY LTD.
Two Bentall Center Suite 900 555 Burrard Street
Vancouver, BC, V7X 1M8, Canada
Tel.: (604) 893-7007
Web Site: www.zkl.cc
ZKL—(TSXV)
Rev.: $17,184,634
Assets: $34,431,640
Liabilities: $18,887,987
Net Worth: $15,543,653
Earnings: $437,853
Fiscal Year-end: 04/30/13
Business Description:
Electronic Component Mfr
S.I.C.: 3679
N.A.I.C.S.: 334419
Personnel:
Sou Wa Wong *(Chm)*
Lou Meng Cheong *(CEO)*
Kelvin Zhang *(CFO)*
Board of Directors:
Sou Wa Wong
Lou Meng Cheong
George Graham Dorin
Michael Raymont
Jian Wen Wu
Yan Zhang
Non-U.S. Subsidiary:

Zhuhai Keli Electronic Co., Ltd. **(1)**
No 32 Jinfeng West Road Jinding Technology Industrial Park Xi
Zhuhai, 519085, China
Tel.: (86) 75 6338 2666
Electrical Equipment & Component Mfr
S.I.C.: 3699
N.A.I.C.S.: 335999

CHINA KINGHO ENERGY GROUP CO., LTD.
Floor 36 Middle Tower China Overseas Plaza No 8 Yard Guanghua Dongli
Jianguomenwai Chaoyang Dist,
Beijing, 100020, China
Tel.: (86) 10 5630 7890
Fax: (86) 10 5630 7822
Web Site: www.chinakingho.com
Year Founded: 2011
Sales Range: $1-4.9 Billion
Emp.: 20,000
Business Description:
Holding Company; Coal Mining, Processing & Wholesale Distribution
S.I.C.: 6719
N.A.I.C.S.: 551112
Personnel:
Qinghua Huo *(Chm)*
Non-U.S. Subsidiary:

Carabella Resources Limited **(1)**
Level 1 1 Breakfast Creek Road
Newstead, QLD, 4006, Australia
Tel.: (61) 7 3135 9900
Fax: (61) 7 3216 1138
E-Mail: info@carabellaresources.com.au
Web Site: www.carabellaresources.com
Rev.: $709,670
Assets: $55,483,488
Liabilities: $1,267,194
Net Worth: $54,216,295
Earnings: ($8,441,010)
Emp.: 11
Fiscal Year-end: 06/30/13
Coal Mining Services
S.I.C.: 1222
N.A.I.C.S.: 212112
Anthony Quin *(CEO)*
G. J. Taggart *(CFO)*
Kylie Anderson *(Sec)*

CHINA KINGSTONE MINING HOLDINGS LIMITED
Units 6812-13 The Center 99 Queens Road
Central, China (Hong Kong)
Tel.: (852) 2527 4999
Fax: (852) 2527 5666
E-Mail: ir@kingstonemining.com
Web Site: www.kingstonemining.com
1380—(HKG)
Rev.: $2,551,449
Assets: $88,623,527
Liabilities: $5,224,418
Net Worth: $83,399,109
Earnings: ($91,556,216)
Emp.: 59
Fiscal Year-end: 12/31/12
Business Description:
Marble Mining Services
S.I.C.: 1499
N.A.I.C.S.: 212399
Personnel:
Hongyu Liu *(Chm)*
Jianhong Chen *(CEO)*
Wai Fai Law *(Sec)*
Board of Directors:
Hongyu Liu
Raymond Wai Man Chung
Tin Faat Lam
Patrick Ka Wing Mak
Cuiwei Zhang
Hongjun Zhu
Legal Counsel:
Orrick, Herrington & Sutcliffe
43rd Floor Gloucester Tower The Landmark 15 Queens Road Central
Hong Kong, China (Hong Kong)
Computershare Hong Kong Investor Services Limited
Shops 1712-1716 17th Floor Hopewell Centre
183 Queens Road East
Wanchai, China (Hong Kong)
Transfer Agents:
Royal Bank of Canada Trust Company (Cayman) Limited
4th Floor Royal Bank House 24 Shedden Road
PO Box 1586
Georgetown, Cayman Islands
Computershare Hong Kong Investor Services Limited
Shops 1712-1716 17th Floor Hopewell Centre
183 Queens Road East
Wanchai, China (Hong Kong)

CHINA KUNDA TECHNOLOGY HOLDINGS LIMITED
24 Raffles Place 25-03 Clifford Centre
Singapore, 048621, Singapore
Tel.: (65) 65343567
Fax: (65) 65343566
E-Mail: ir@chinakunda.com
Web Site: www.chinakunda.com
GU5—(SES)
Rev.: $41,139,563
Assets: $46,083,248
Liabilities: $26,477,690
Net Worth: $19,605,558
Earnings: ($6,460,395)
Emp.: 40
Fiscal Year-end: 03/31/13
Business Description:
Precision Molds & Plastic Injection Parts Mfr
S.I.C.: 3544
N.A.I.C.S.: 333511
Personnel:
Kaoqun Cai *(Chm & CEO)*
Khee Wee Hau *(CFO)*
Jinbiao Yang *(COO)*
Wei Lin Goh *(Co-Sec)*
Wei Jin Ong *(Co-Sec)*
Board of Directors:
Kaoqun Cai
Kaobing Cai
Khee Wee Hau
Chew Thim Ho
Koon Weng Leong
Yit Keong Lim
Jinbiao Yang
Transfer Agent:
Boardroom Corporate & Advisory Services Pte. Ltd.
50 Raffles Place 32-01 Singapore Land Tower
Singapore, Singapore
Non-U.S. Subsidiary:

Yick Kwan Tat Enterprise Company Limited **(1)**
Osaka Tamura Sakata Ave S 6 South Bantian Rd
Buji Town, Shenzhen, China
Tel.: (86) 755 28778999
Fax: (86) 755 84165762
E-Mail: imd16@kunda.com
Web Site: www.kundamould.com
Emp.: 900
Plastic Injection & IMD Products Mfr
S.I.C.: 3089
N.A.I.C.S.: 326199

CHINA LIANSU GROUP HOLDINGS LIMITED
Liansu Industrial Estate Longjiang Town
Shunde Zone, Foshan, Guangdong, 528318, China
Tel.: (86) 75723888333
Fax: (86) 75723888555
E-Mail: northeramerica@liansu.com
Web Site: www.liansu.com
Year Founded: 1996
2128—(HKG)
Rev.: $1,730,093,013
Assets: $1,553,995,556
Liabilities: $596,460,782
Net Worth: $957,534,774
Earnings: $195,587,398
Emp.: 7,100
Fiscal Year-end: 12/31/12
Business Description:
Plastic Pipes & Pipe Fittings Mfr
S.I.C.: 3089
N.A.I.C.S.: 326122
Personnel:
Luen Hei Wong *(Founder & Chm)*
Manlun Zuo *(CEO)*
Guanggen Liu *(CFO)*
Samuel Chi Wai Kwan *(Co-Sec)*
Shuixian Yuan *(Co-Sec)*
Board of Directors:
Luen Hei Wong
Chongen Bai
Guonan Chen
Man Yu Cheung
Pui Cheung Fung
Lixin Gao

Guirong Huang
Zhaocong Kong
Zhiqiang Lai
Dewei Lin
Shaoquan Lin
Jianfeng Luo
Jonathan Kwok Ho Wong
Manlun Zuo
Xiaoping Zuo

Computershare Hong Kong Investor Services Limited
Shops 1712-1716 17th Floor Hopewell Centre
183 Queens Road East
Wanchai, China (Hong Kong)

Transfer Agents:
Maples Finance Limited
Queengate House
P.O.Box 1093
Georgetown, Cayman Islands

Computershare Hong Kong Investor Services Limited
Shops 1712-1716 17th Floor Hopewell Centre
183 Queens Road East
Wanchai, China (Hong Kong)

CHINA LIAONING DINGXU ECOLOGICAL AGRICULTURE DEVELOPMENT, INC.

Room 2119 Mingyong Building No 60 Xian Road
Shahekou District, Dalian, 116021, China
Tel.: (86) 13909 840703
Year Founded: 2010
CLAD—(OTC OTCB)
Rev.: $8,617,176
Assets: $19,226,696
Liabilities: $9,751,731
Net Worth: $9,474,965
Earnings: $1,409,556
Emp.: 36
Fiscal Year-end: 12/31/12

Business Description:
Mushrooms & Related Products
S.I.C.: 0182
N.A.I.C.S.: 111411

Personnel:
Yung Kong Chin *(Pres, CEO, CFO, Treas & Sec)*

Board of Directors:
Yung Kong Chin

Transfer Agent:
Island Stock Transfer
15500 Roosevelt Blvd Ste 301
Clearwater, FL 33760

CHINA LIFE INSURANCE COMPANY LIMITED

16 Financial Street Xicheng District
Beijing, 100033, China
Tel.: (86) 10 6363 1191
Fax: (86) 10 6657 5112
E-Mail: serve@e-chinalife.com
Web Site: www.chinalife.com.cn
LFC—(HKG NYSE SHG)
Rev.: $59,010,392,250
Assets: $301,642,806,600
Liabilities: $266,203,212,750
Net Worth: $35,439,593,850
Earnings: $1,790,557,200
Emp.: 99,271
Fiscal Year-end: 12/31/12

Business Description:
Insurance Services
S.I.C.: 6311
N.A.I.C.S.: 524113

Personnel:
Yang Mingsheng *(Chm)*
Feng Wan *(Pres)*
Zheng Yang *(CFO)*
Yingqi Liu *(Sec & VP)*

Board of Directors:
Yang Mingsheng
Dairen Lin
Yingqi Liu
Jianmin Miao
Bruce Douglas Moore
Changji Sun
Feng Wan

Legal Counsel:
King & Wood
40th Floor Office Tower A Beijing Fortune Plaza 7
Beijing, China

Subsidiary:

China Life Insurance Asset Management Company Limited **(1)**
9/F Suite A Tongtai Mansion No 33 Jinrong Street
Xicheng District, Beijing, 100032, China CN
Tel.: (86) 1088088866 (60%)
Fax: (86) 1088087798
Web Site: www.clamc.com
Asset Management Services
S.I.C.: 6411
N.A.I.C.S.: 524298
Jianmin Miao *(Chm)*

CHINA LIFESTYLE FOOD AND BEVERAGES GROUP LIMITED

(Name Changed to Labixiaoxin Snacks Group Limited)

CHINA LILANG LIMITED

200 Chang xing Road
Jinjiang, Fujian, China 362200
Tel.: (86) 4008879888
Fax: (86) 59585622555
E-Mail: lilanz@lilanz.com
Web Site: www.lilanz.com
Year Founded: 1987
1234—(HKG)
Sls.: $443,726,825
Assets: $522,499,745
Liabilities: $144,118,092
Net Worth: $378,381,653
Earnings: $99,566,703
Emp.: 2,900
Fiscal Year-end: 12/31/12

Business Description:
Apparel Mfr
S.I.C.: 2389
N.A.I.C.S.: 315990

Personnel:
Dong Xing Wang *(Chm)*
Liang Xing Wang *(Vice Chm & CEO)*
Cong Xing Wang *(Vice Chm)*
Brenda Yuk Lan Ko *(CFO & Sec)*

Board of Directors:
Dong Xing Wang
Rong Hua Cai
Tien Tui Chen
Cheng Chu Hu
Shixian Lai
Hong Te Lu
Xing Nie
Rong Bin Pan
Cong Xing Wang
Liang Xing Wang
Ru Ping Wang

Computershare Hong Kong Investor Services Limited
Shops 1712-1716 17th Floor Hopewell Centre
183 Queens Road East
Wanchai, China (Hong Kong)

Transfer Agent:
Royal Bank of Canada Trust Company (Cayman) Limited
4th Floor Royal Bank House 24 Shedden Road
Georgetown, Cayman Islands

CHINA LINEN TEXTILE INDUSTRY, LTD.

Chengdong Street
Lanxi, Heilongjiang, China
Tel.: (86) 4555635885
Fax: (86) 45182309971
E-Mail: xiaoweixing@chinalinen.cc
Web Site: www.chinalinen.cc
Year Founded: 2000
CTXIF—(OTCB)
Sales Range: $50-74.9 Million
Emp.: 1,408

Business Description:
Linen Textile Products Mfr & Sales
S.I.C.: 2299
N.A.I.C.S.: 314999

Personnel:
Ren Gao *(Chm & CEO)*
Jodie Zheng Wehner *(CFO)*
Songyun Li *(CMO)*
Chunfu Zhao *(Sec & Vice Gen Mgr)*

Board of Directors:
Ren Gao
Xu Jianzhong
Xu Jixiang
Stephen Paul Monticelli
Chunfu Zhao

Transfer Agent:
Island Stock Transfer
15500 Roosevelt Blvd Ste 301
Clearwater, FL 33760

CHINA LODGING GROUP, LIMITED

No 2266 Hongqiao Road
Changning District, Shanghai, 200336, China
Tel.: (86) 21 6195 2011
Fax: (86) 21 6195 9597
E-Mail: ir@htinns.com
Web Site: www.htinns.com
HTHT—(NASDAQ)
Rev.: $543,152,310
Assets: $687,850,205
Liabilities: $292,223,955
Net Worth: $395,626,250
Earnings: $28,514,210
Emp.: 12,833
Fiscal Year-end: 12/31/12

Business Description:
Economy Hotels Owner & Operator
S.I.C.: 7011
N.A.I.C.S.: 721110

Personnel:
Qi Ji *(Founder, Chm & CEO)*
Min Zhang *(CFO)*
Yunhang Xie *(COO)*

Board of Directors:
Qi Ji
Joseph Chow
Alfred Min Fan
Yan Huang
Yongjian Sun
John Jiong Wu
Tongtong Zhao

CHINA LOGISTICS GROUP, INC.

23F Gutai Beach Building No 969 Zhongshan Road South
Shanghai, 200011, China
Tel.: (86) 21 63355100
E-Mail: info@chinalogisticsinc.com
Web Site: www.chinalogisticsinc.com
CHLO—(OTC OTCB)
Sls.: $23,133,394
Assets: $4,172,007
Liabilities: $4,413,244
Net Worth: ($241,237)
Earnings: ($836,660)
Emp.: 126
Fiscal Year-end: 12/31/12

Business Description:
International Freight Forwarding & Logistics Services
S.I.C.: 4731
N.A.I.C.S.: 488510

Personnel:
Wei Chen *(Chm, Pres, CEO, Treas & Sec)*
Yuan Huang *(CFO)*

Board of Directors:
Wei Chen
Hui Liu

Transfer Agent:
Interwest Transfer Co. Inc.
1981 E Murray Holladay Rd Ste 100
Salt Lake City, UT 84101

CHINA LONGYI GROUP INTERNATIONAL HOLDINGS LIMITED

8/F East Area Century Golden Resources Business Center 69 Banjing Road
Haidian District, Beijing, China 100089
Tel.: (86) 1088452568
CGYG—(OTCB)
Sls.: $256,304
Assets: $1,153,995
Liabilities: $1,072,478
Net Worth: $81,517
Earnings: ($421,506)
Emp.: 69
Fiscal Year-end: 12/31/12

Business Description:
Holding Company
S.I.C.: 6719
N.A.I.C.S.: 551112

Personnel:
Changde Li *(Chm)*
Jie Chen *(CEO)*
Xinmin Pan *(CFO)*

Board of Directors:
Changde Li
Hui Chen
Jie Chen
Hongliang Li
Wei Wang

Transfer Agent:
Securities Transfer Corporation
2591 Dallas Pkwy Ste 102
Frisco, TX 75034
Tel.: (469) 633-0101
Fax: (469) 633-0088

CHINA LONGYUAN POWER GROUP CORP LTD.

(d/b/a Longyuan Group)
Room 1206 12th Floor 7 Baishiqiao Street
Haidian District, Beijing, China
Tel.: (86) 10 66579822
Fax: (86) 10 66579899
Web Site: www.clypg.com.cn
0916—(HKG OTC)
Rev.: $2,746,228,187
Assets: $17,130,361,602
Liabilities: $11,344,738,657
Net Worth: $5,785,622,945
Earnings: $528,222,952
Emp.: 6,269
Fiscal Year-end: 12/31/12

Business Description:
Wind Energy Producer & Distr
S.I.C.: 4911
N.A.I.C.S.: 221118

Personnel:
Baoping Qiao *(Chm-Supervisory Bd)*
Enyi Li *(Pres)*
Nansong Jia *(Co-Sec)*
Yuk Tai Soon *(Co-Sec)*

Board of Directors:
Yongpeng Zhu
Bin Chen
Qun Huang
Baoxing Luan
Congmin Lv
Yan Meng
Baole Wang
Changjun Xie
Songyi Zhang

Supervisory Board of Directors:
Baoping Qiao

China Longyuan Power Group Corp Ltd.—(Continued)

Shen He
Yongping Yu
KPMG
8th Floor Princes Building 10 Chater Road
Central, China (Hong Kong)
Legal Counsel:
Clifford Chance
28th Floor Jardine House One Connaught Place
Central, China (Hong Kong)
Beijing Tianchi Law Firm
14th Floor Tower A Huixin Plaza Asian Games Village No 8 Beishihuan
Beijing, China
Beijing Jiayuan Law Firm
F407-F408 Ocean Plaza 158 Fuxingmennei Avenue
Beijing, China

CHINA LOTSYNERGY HOLDINGS LTD

Unit 3308 33/F Office Tower
Convention Plaza 1 Harbour Road
Wanchai, China (Hong Kong)
Tel.: (852) 2136 6618
Fax: (852) 2136 6608
Web Site: www.chinalotsynergy.com
1371—(DEU HKG)
Sls.: $78,305,532
Assets: $257,681,817
Liabilities: $95,908,239
Net Worth: $161,773,578
Earnings: $26,090,840
Emp.: 480
Fiscal Year-end: 12/31/12
Business Description:
Lottery Products Distr
S.I.C.: 7389
N.A.I.C.S.: 561499
Personnel:
Ivy Ting Lau *(Chm & Co-CEO)*
Jingwei Wu *(Co-CEO)*
Donna Tan Na Chan *(CFO & Compliance Officer)*
Hengben Chen *(Chm-CTG Bus-Guangdong & VP)*
Hiu Wong Wong *(Sec)*
Board of Directors:
Ivy Ting Lau
Donna Tan Na Chan
Ming Fai Chan
Shuming Cui
Chris Cheong Thard Hoong
Shenglan Huang
Zi Kui Li
Jingwei Wu
Butterfield Fulcrum Group (Bermuda) Limited
26 Burnaby Street
Hamilton, HM 11, Bermuda
Transfer Agent:
Butterfield Fulcrum Group (Bermuda) Limited
26 Burnaby Street
Hamilton, HM 11, Bermuda

CHINA LUDAO TECHNOLOGY COMPANY LIMITED

Flat B 17th Floor Harvest Building
29-35 Wing Kut Street
Central, China (Hong Kong)
Tel.: (852) 3184 7410
Web Site: www.ludaocn.com
2023—(HKG)
Business Description:
Cleaning & Personal Care Products Mfr
S.I.C.: 2841
N.A.I.C.S.: 325611
Personnel:
Yuerong Yu *(Chm & CEO)*

CHINA LUMENA NEW MATERIALS CORP.

Suites 7503-05 International Commerce Centre 1 Austin Road West
Kowloon, China (Hong Kong)
Tel.: (852) 31022031
Fax: (852) 31020109
E-Mail: lumena_ir@lumena.hk
Web Site: www.lumena.hk
0067—(HKG OTC)
Rev.: $716,012,404
Assets: $3,313,365,100
Liabilities: $989,111,772
Net Worth: $2,324,253,329
Earnings: $213,705,829
Emp.: 2,512
Fiscal Year-end: 12/31/12
Business Description:
Thenardite Exploration & Mining Services
S.I.C.: 1499
N.A.I.C.S.: 212399
Personnel:
Zhigang Zhang *(Chm)*
Daming Zhang *(CEO)*
Hua Luo *(CFO)*
Kui Tong Wong *(Sec & Mgr-Fin)*
Board of Directors:
Zhigang Zhang
Xingwu Gou
John Tiong Lu Koh
Jianyong Tan
Chun Keung Wong
Lichuan Xia
Rudolf Man Chiu Yu
Daming Zhang
Appleby Trust (Cayman) Ltd.
Clifton House 75 Fort Street
PO Box 1350
Grand Cayman, Cayman Islands
Transfer Agent:
Appleby Trust (Cayman) Ltd.
Clifton House 75 Fort Street
PO Box 1350
Grand Cayman, Cayman Islands

CHINA MACHINERY ENGINEERING CORPORATION

CMEC Mansion No 178
Guanganmenwai Street
Xicheng District, Beijing, China 100055
Tel.: (86) 10 63451188
Fax: (86) 10 63261865
E-Mail: cmec@mail.cmec.com
Web Site: www.cmec.com
Year Founded: 1978
1829—(HKG)
Rev.: $3,382,879,608
Assets: $5,523,187,337
Liabilities: $3,947,804,693
Net Worth: $1,575,382,644
Earnings: $306,288,534
Emp.: 2,384
Fiscal Year-end: 12/31/12
Business Description:
Construction Engineering Services
S.I.C.: 1629
N.A.I.C.S.: 237990
Personnel:
Bai Sun *(Chm)*
Taifang Li *(Vice Chm)*
Chun Zhang *(Pres)*
Yamin Zhou *(CFO)*
Minjian Chen *(Co-Sec)*
Fung Chu Tsang *(Co-Sec)*
Board of Directors:
Bai Sun
Philip Kin Ho Chan
Yongzhong Fang
Taifang Li
Hongyu Liu
Li Liu
Chongyi Pan
Zhian Wang
Chun Zhang
Legal Counsel:
Shearman & Sterling
12th Floor Gloucester Tower The Landmark 15 Queen's Road
Central, China (Hong Kong)

CHINA MAGNESIUM CORPORATION LIMITED

Seabank Building Level 10 12-14 Marine Parade
PO Box 3767
Southport, QLD, 4215, Australia
Tel.: (61) 7 55311808
Fax: (61) 7 55911059
E-Mail: info@chinamagnesiumcorporation.com
Web Site: www.chinamagnesiumcorporation.com
CMC—(ASX)
Rev.: $850,688
Assets: $17,535,979
Liabilities: $3,310,160
Net Worth: $14,225,820
Earnings: ($2,029,995)
Emp.: 20
Fiscal Year-end: 06/30/13
Business Description:
Magnesium MIning Services
S.I.C.: 1099
N.A.I.C.S.: 212299
Personnel:
Tom Blackhurst *(Co-Founder, CEO & Mng Dir)*
Xinping Liang *(Co-Founder & COO)*
Damien Kelly *(Sec)*
Board of Directors:
William Bass
Tom Blackhurst
Xinping Liang
Peter Robertson
Legal Counsel:
Thomsons Lawyers
Level 16 Waterfront Place 1 Eagle Street
Brisbane, Australia

CHINA MAN-MADE FIBER CORPORATION

10-11 F No 50 Sec 1 Xinsheng S Rd
100 Taipei, Taiwan
Tel.: (886) 223937111
Fax: (886) 223910462
E-Mail: stock@cmfc.com.tw
Web Site: www.cmfc.com.tw
1718—(TAI)
Sales Range: $450-499.9 Million
Business Description:
Fiber Products Mfr
S.I.C.: 2299
N.A.I.C.S.: 313110
Personnel:
Kuei-Tseng Wang *(Chm)*

CHINA MARINE FOOD GROUP, LTD.

Da Bao Industrial Zone
Shishi, Fujian, 362700, China
Tel.: (86) 59588987588
Web Site: www.china-marine.cn/eng/p5.asp
Year Founded: 1999
CMFO—(OTC)
Rev.: $157,317,347
Assets: $146,220,850
Liabilities: $19,526,118
Net Worth: $126,694,732
Earnings: ($4,485,052)
Emp.: 517
Fiscal Year-end: 12/31/12
Business Description:
Seafood Products Processor, Distr & Sales
S.I.C.: 2092
N.A.I.C.S.: 311710
Personnel:
Pengfei Liu *(Chm, CEO & Sec)*
Board of Directors:
Pengfei Liu
Xiaochuan Li
Weipeng Liu
Honkau Wan
Changhu Xue

CHINA MARKETING MEDIA HOLDINGS, INC.

RMA 901 KunTai International Mansion
12 Chaowai Street, Beijing, 100020, China
Tel.: (86) 1059251090
CMKM—(OTCB)
Sales Range: $10-24.9 Million
Emp.: 364
Business Description:
Holding Company; Magazine Publisher & Sales; Electronic & Computer Products Sales
S.I.C.: 6719
N.A.I.C.S.: 551112
Personnel:
Yingsheng Li *(Pres & CEO)*
Zhen Zhen Peri *(CFO)*
Wengao Luo *(COO)*
Board of Directors:
Li Shuang Cai
Xiaofeng Ding
Wengao Luo
Dongsheng Ren

CHINA MASS MEDIA CORP.

6/F Tower B Corporate Square 35 Finance Street
Xicheng District, Beijing, 100033, China
Tel.: (86) 1088091099
Fax: (86) 1088091088
Web Site: www.chinammia.com
Year Founded: 2003
Sales Range: $25-49.9 Million
Emp.: 151
Business Description:
Television Advertising Services
S.I.C.: 7319
N.A.I.C.S.: 541890
Personnel:
Shengcheng Wang *(Chm & CEO)*
Haiyan Xing *(Chief Admin Officer)*
Board of Directors:
Shengcheng Wang
Haiyan Xing

CHINA MEDIA GROUP CORPORATION

No 55 Salan Snuker 13/28
Tadisma Business Park Section 13, 40100 Shah Alam, Selangor, Malaysia
Tel.: (60) 3 5519 7079
Fax: (60) 3 5519 0839
E-Mail: info@chinamediagroup.net
Web Site: www.chinamediagroup.net
Year Founded: 2002
CHMD—(OTCB)
Sales Range: Less than $1 Million
Emp.: 5
Business Description:
Advertising & Telecommunications Services
S.I.C.: 7319
N.A.I.C.S.: 541890
Personnel:
Mohd Mahyudin Zainal *(Pres & CEO)*
Mohd Suhaimi Rozali *(CFO, Sec & Treas)*
Norlizah Zainal *(CTO)*
Board of Directors:
Mohd Khairudin Ramli

Mohd Mahyudin Zainal
Norlizah Zainal

CHINA MEDIA INC.

Room 10128 No 269-5-1 Taibai South Road
Yanta District, Xi'an, ShaanXi, China 710068
Tel.: (86) 2987651114
Web Site: www.xatvm.com
CHND—(OTCB)
Rev.: $1,672,656
Assets: $7,629,216
Liabilities: $577,000
Net Worth: $7,052,216
Earnings: $52,927
Emp.: 11
Fiscal Year-end: 06/30/13
Business Description:
Holding Company; Television Broadcasting
S.I.C.: 6719
N.A.I.C.S.: 551112
Personnel:
Dean Li *(Pres, CEO & Sec)*
Shuncheng Ma *(CFO & Treas)*
Board of Directors:
Bin Li
Dean Li
Shengli Liu

CHINA MEDIAEXPRESS HOLDINGS, INC.

Room 2805 Central Plaza
Wanchai, China (Hong Kong)
Tel.: (852) 2827 6100
Web Site: www.ccme.tv
Year Founded: 2007
CCME—(OTC)
Sales Range: $75-99.9 Million
Emp.: 161
Business Description:
Entertainment & Media Investment Services
S.I.C.: 6211
N.A.I.C.S.: 523999
Personnel:
Zheng Cheng *(Chm, Pres & CEO)*
Board of Directors:
Zheng Cheng
Yingshou Huang
George Zhou

CHINA MEDICAL SYSTEM HOLDINGS LTD.

6F/8F Building A Tongfang Information Harbour 11 Langshan Road
Shenzhen Hi-tech Industry Park, Shenzhen, Nanshan, 518057, China
Tel.: (86) 75582416868
Fax: (86) 75582416622
E-Mail: info@cms.net.cn
Web Site: www.cms.net.cn
867—(HKG)
Sls.: $281,866,000
Assets: $552,767,000
Liabilities: $101,793,000
Net Worth: $450,974,000
Earnings: $85,128,000
Emp.: 2,091
Fiscal Year-end: 12/31/12
Business Description:
Pharmaceutical Mfr
S.I.C.: 2834
N.A.I.C.S.: 325412
Personnel:
Kong Lam *(Chm & CEO)*
Yanling Chen *(CFO)*
Hongbing Chen *(COO)*
Wai Ming Wong *(CTO)*
Jonathan Zheng *(Chief Intl Ops Officer)*
Vincent Wing Sin Hui *(Sec)*
Board of Directors:
Kong Lam
Hongbing Chen
Yanling Chen
Terry Kam Shing Cheung
Ki Fat Hui
Huaizheng Peng
Manlin Sa
Chi Keung Wu

Computershare Hong Kong Investor Services Limited
Shops 1712-1716 17th Floor Hopewell Centre
183 Queens Road East
Wanchai, China (Hong Kong)

Non-U.S. Subsidiary:

Sky United Trading Limited **(1)**
Rm 2106 21F Island Pl Tower 510 Kings Rd
North Point, China (Hong Kong)
Tel.: (852) 23693889
Fax: (852) 23891320
Emp.: 5
Pharmaceuticals Mfr
S.I.C.: 2834
N.A.I.C.S.: 325412

CHINA MEDICAL TECHNOLOGIES, INC.

24 Yong Chang North Road
Beijing Economic-Technological Development Area, Beijing, 100176, China
Tel.: (86) 10 67871166
Fax: (86) 10 67889588
Web Site: www.chinameditech.com
Year Founded: 1999
CMEDY—(OTC)
Sales Range: $125-149.9 Million
Emp.: 897
Business Description:
Medical Device Developer, Mfr & Distr
S.I.C.: 3841
N.A.I.C.S.: 339112
Personnel:
Xioadong Wu *(Chm & CEO)*
Takyung Tsang *(CFO)*
Minshi Shen *(COO)*
Zhong Chen *(CTO)*
Board of Directors:
Xioadong Wu
Iain Ferguson Bruce
Lawrence A. Crum
Ruyu Du
Yuedong Li
Guoming Qi
Takyung Tsang

Subsidiary:

Beijing Yuande Bio-Medical Engineering Co., Ltd. **(1)**
No 24 North Yongchang Road
Economic Tech Development Zone, Beijing, 100176, China CN
Tel.: (86) 1067871166 (100%)
Fax: (86) 1067889588
Web Site: www.chinameditech.com
Emp.: 1,000
Electromedical Equipment Mfr
S.I.C.: 3845
N.A.I.C.S.: 334510
Xiaodong Wu *(CEO)*

CHINA MEDICINE CORPORATION

Guangri Tower 2/F 9 Siyounan Rd 1st St
Yuexiu District, Guangzhou, 510600, China
Tel.: (86) 2087391718
Fax: (86) 2087373030
E-Mail: ir@cmc621.com
Web Site: www.cmc621.com
Year Founded: 2005
CHME—(OTC)
Sales Range: $50-74.9 Million
Emp.: 281
Business Description:
Pharmaceutical & Medical Products Developer & Distr
S.I.C.: 2834
N.A.I.C.S.: 325412
Personnel:
Senshan Yang *(Chm & CEO)*
Henry Chi Fung Ho *(CFO)*
Minhua Liu *(Exec VP)*
Board of Directors:
Senshan Yang
Rachel Gong
Ryan JH. Shih
Transfer Agent:
Continental Stock Transfer & Trust Co.
17 Battery Pl
New York, NY 10004
Tel.: (212) 509-4000
Fax: (212) 509-5150

Subsidiary:

Konzern US Holding Corporation **(1)**
Rm 702 Guangri Mansion No 9 Siyou Nan Rd
Wuyang Xincheng, Guangzhou, Guangdong, 510600, China
Tel.: (86) 2087391718
Fax: (86) 2087379184
E-Mail: konzern09@uskonzern.com
Web Site: www.chinamedicinecorp.com
Emp.: 100
Pharmaceutical Services
S.I.C.: 5122
N.A.I.C.S.: 424210

CHINA MENGNIU DAIRY COMPANY LIMITED

Suite 1602 16th Floor Top Glory Tower 262 Gloucester Road
Causeway Bay, China (Hong Kong)
Tel.: (852) 2180 9050
Fax: (852) 2180 9039
E-Mail: info@mengniuir.com
Web Site: www.mengniuir.com
2319—(HKG OTC)
Rev.: $5,731,364,074
Assets: $3,334,378,096
Liabilities: $1,257,914,882
Net Worth: $2,076,463,214
Earnings: $228,673,788
Emp.: 28,000
Fiscal Year-end: 12/31/12
Business Description:
Dairy Products Mfr & Distr
S.I.C.: 5143
N.A.I.C.S.: 424430
Personnel:
Xubo Yu *(Vice Chm)*
Yiping Sun *(CEO)*
Wennan Wu *(CFO)*
Jianjun Lu *(Chief Admin Officer)*
Chris Wai Cheong Kwok *(Sec & Controller-Fin)*
Board of Directors:
Gaoning Ning
Ying Bai
Finn S. Hansen
Shuge Jiao
Ding Liu
Fuchun Liu
Jianping Ma
Christian Nèu
Gensheng Niu
Yiping Sun
Julian Juul Wolhardt
Andrew Kwok Keung Wu
Jingshui Wu
Andrew Y. Yan
Xubo Yu
Xiaoya Zhang

Computershare Hong Kong Investor Services Limited
46th Floor Hopewell Centre 183 Queen's Road East
Wanchai, China (Hong Kong)

Non-U.S. Subsidiaries:

Mengniu Dairy (Dengkou Bayan Gaole) Co., Ltd. **(1)**
Inside Mengniu Indus Park Zone
Hohhot, Inner Mongolia, China
Tel.: (86) 4782207888
Fax: (86) 3913963505
Dairy Products Mfr & Sales
S.I.C.: 0241
N.A.I.C.S.: 112120

Mengniu Dairy (Tangshan) Co., Ltd. **(1)**
Waihuan Rd S
Fengrun Dist, Tangshan, Hebei, 064000, China
Tel.: (86) 3155167666
Fax: (86) 3155159378
Dairy Products Mfr & Sales
S.I.C.: 0241
N.A.I.C.S.: 112120

Yashili International Holdings Ltd. **(1)**
Yashili Industrial City Chaoan Ave
Chaozhou, Guangdong, China Ky
Tel.: (86) 7685819077 (89.82%)
Fax: (86) 7685820311
Web Site: www.yashili.hk
1230—(HKG)
Sls.: $580,619,466
Assets: $884,773,691
Liabilities: $236,293,029
Net Worth: $648,480,662
Earnings: $74,733,842
Emp.: 5,929
Fiscal Year-end: 12/31/12
Holding Company; Food Products Mfr
S.I.C.: 6719
N.A.I.C.S.: 551112
Lidian Zhang *(Co-Founder)*
Jieping Wen *(CFO)*
Xiaonan Wu *(Co-Sec, Gen Mgr-Investment Center & Dir-Legal)*
Siu Pik Ho *(Co-Sec)*

CHINA MERCHANTS GROUP LIMITED

40/F China Merchants Tower Shun Tak Centre 168-200 Connaught Rd
Central, China (Hong Kong)
Tel.: (852) 25428288
Fax: (852) 25448851
E-Mail: cmhk@cmhk.com
Web Site: www.cmhk.com
Year Founded: 1872
Sales Range: $100-124.9 Million
Emp.: 1,000
Business Description:
Holding Company; Transportation, Financial Investment, Property Development & Management Services
S.I.C.: 6719
N.A.I.C.S.: 551112
Personnel:
Yuning Fu *(Chm)*
Jianhong Li *(Pres)*
Gangfeng Fu *(CFO)*
Weihua Ma *(Pres/CEO-China Merchants Bank)*

Subsidiaries:

China Merchants Holdings (International) Company Limited **(1)**
38/F East China Merchants Tower Shun Tak Centre
168-200 Connaught Road, Central, China (Hong Kong) HK
Tel.: (852) 21028888 (55.82%)
Fax: (852) 28512173
E-Mail: relation@cmhi.com.hk
Web Site: www.cmhi.com.hk
0144—(HKG)
Rev.: $1,421,286,900
Assets: $9,989,240,700
Liabilities: $3,066,946,800
Net Worth: $6,922,293,900
Earnings: $736,046,600
Emp.: 6,226
Fiscal Year-end: 12/31/12

China Merchants Group Limited—(Continued)

Industrial & Commercial Conglomerate; Shipping Services; Public Port Operator
S.I.C.: 4491
N.A.I.C.S.: 488320
Yuning Fu *(Chm)*
Jianhong Li *(Vice Chm)*
Jianhua Hu *(Mng Dir)*
Yunshu Liu *(Overseas Ops Officer)*
Chong Shun Leung *(Sec)*

Non-U.S. Subsidiaries:

China Merchants Holdings (Pacific) Limited **(2)**
8 Temasek Boulevard
38-01 Suntec Tower 3, 038988 Singapore, Singapore
Tel.: (65) 68360200
Fax: (65) 68364776
E-Mail: relation@cmhp.com.sg
Web Site: www.cmhp.com.sg
Emp.: 10
Activities Related to Real Estate
S.I.C.: 6531
N.A.I.C.S.: 531390
Wu Xinhua *(COO)*

Hempel-Hai Hong Coatings (Kunshan) Co., Ltd **(2)**
No 1 Haihong Rd
Zhangpu Town, Kunshan, China
Tel.: (86) 51257440388
Fax: (86) 51257440389
Web Site: www.hempel.com
Emp.: 200
Chemical & Allied Products Whslr
S.I.C.: 5169
N.A.I.C.S.: 424690
Shan Gang Zhang *(Mgr)*

Shekou Container Terminals (Phase III) Co., Ltd **(2)**
Jetty Three Harbour Road
Shekou, 518069 Shenzhen, China
Tel.: (86) 75526822199
Fax: (86) 75526677755
E-Mail: marketing@sctcn.com
Web Site: www.sctcn.com
Security Systems Services
S.I.C.: 7382
N.A.I.C.S.: 561621

Shenzhen Cyber-Harbour Network Co. Limited **(2)**
7th Floor Finance Centre No 22
Taizi Road, Shenzhen, China
Tel.: (86) 75526856200
Fax: (86) 75526852033
E-Mail: contact@chnetcn.com
Web Site: www.chnetcn.com
Emp.: 100
Security Systems Services
S.I.C.: 7382
N.A.I.C.S.: 561621

Hong Kong Ming Wah Shipping Co., Ltd. **(1)**
Room 3701 37/F China Merchants Tower
Shun Tak Centre
Connaught Road, Central, China (Hong Kong) HK
Tel.: (852) 25172128
Fax: (852) 25473482
E-Mail: mwex@hkmw.com.hk
Web Site: www.hkmw.com.hk
Emp.: 100
Deep Sea Freight Transportation Services
S.I.C.: 4412
N.A.I.C.S.: 483111
Xingang Su *(Chm)*

Affiliate:

China Merchants China Direct Investments Limited **(1)**
1803 China Merchants Tower Shun Tak Centre 168 200 Connaught Road
Central, China (Hong Kong) HK
Tel.: (852) 28589089 (24.65%)
Fax: (852) 28588455
E-Mail: info@cmcdi.com.hk
Web Site: www.cmcdi.com.hk
0133—(HKG)
Rev.: $13,679,480
Assets: $568,776,594
Liabilities: $90,374,232
Net Worth: $478,402,362
Earnings: $9,883,248
Fiscal Year-end: 12/31/12
Security Management Services
S.I.C.: 6726
N.A.I.C.S.: 525990
Yinquan Li *(Chm)*
Chong Shun Leung *(Sec)*

Non-U.S. Subsidiaries:

China Merchants Shekou Industrial Zone Co., Ltd. **(1)**
1 New Times Plaza Room 2901
Prince Edward Road
Shekou Industrial Zone, Shenzhen, Guangdong, 518080, China CN
Tel.: (86) 755 2681 8928
Fax: (86) 755 2669 1325
Web Site: skiz.shekou.com
Real Estate Investment Trust
S.I.C.: 6726
N.A.I.C.S.: 525990
Sunchent Chemming *(Chm)*

Subsidiary:

China Merchants Property Development Co., Ltd. **(2)**
9/F New Times Plaza
Shekou Industrial Zone
Nanshan District, Shenzhen, Guangdong, 518067, China CN
Tel.: (86) 75526818600 (50.86%)
Fax: (86) 75526691037
E-Mail: investor@cmpd.cn
Web Site: www.cmpd.cn
200024—(SSE)
Sales Range: $1-4.9 Billion
Emp.: 9,236
Real Estate Management & Development Services
S.I.C.: 6531
N.A.I.C.S.: 531390
Shaobin Lin *(Chm)*
Gangfeng Fu *(Chm-Supervisory Bd)*
Peikun Huang *(CFO)*

Non-U.S. Subsidiary:

China Merchants Land Limited **(3)**
(Formerly Tonic Industries Holdings Limited)
Room 3111 31/F China Merchants Tower
Shun Tak Centre
168-200 Connaught Road, Central, China (Hong Kong) Ky
Tel.: (852) 3976 5300 (70.18%)
Fax: (852) 2116 0057
E-Mail: ir@cmland.hk
Web Site: ir.cmland.hk
978—(HKG)
Sales Range: $10-24.9 Million
Emp.: 310
Investment Holding Company
S.I.C.: 6211
N.A.I.C.S.: 523999
Wing Yan Chan *(Deputy CFO, Sec & Gen Mgr-Fin)*

China Merchants Technology Holdings Co., Ltd. **(1)**
5/F Innovation Centre Nanhai Road North Branch No 1077
Shekou Industrial Zone, Shenzhen, Guangdong, China CN
Tel.: (86) 75526888600
Fax: (86) 75526888628
E-Mail: cmtech@cmtech.net
Web Site: www.cmtech.net
Emp.: 20
Holding Company
S.I.C.: 6719
N.A.I.C.S.: 551112
Liji Gu *(Chm)*

Non-U.S. Affiliates:

China Merchants Bank Co., Ltd. **(1)**
49/F China Merchants Bank Tower
No 7088 Shennan Boulevard, Shenzhen, 518040, China (18.03%)
Tel.: (86) 755 8319 8888
Fax: (86) 755 8319 5109
Web Site: www.cmbchina.com
600036—(HKG OTC SHG)
Int. Income: $23,843,543,850
Assets: $541,395,588,150
Liabilities: $509,545,051,200
Net Worth: $31,850,536,950
Earnings: $7,192,251,450
Emp.: 1,725
Fiscal Year-end: 12/31/12
Banking Services
S.I.C.: 6029
N.A.I.C.S.: 522110
Mingzhi Han *(Chm-Supervisory Bd)*
Weihua Ma *(Pres & CEO)*
Hao Li *(CFO & Exec VP)*
Lianfeng Xu *(CTO)*
Qi Lan *(Co-Sec)*
Natalia Sze Ka Mee Seng *(Co-Sec)*
Wei Ding *(Exec VP)*
Xiaoqing Tang *(Exec VP)*
Zhihong Tang *(Exec VP)*
Qingbin Wang *(Exec VP)*
Fenglan Yin *(Exec VP)*
Guanghua Zhang *(Exec VP)*
Qi Zhu *(Exec VP)*

Subsidiary:

China Merchants Fund Management Co., Ltd. **(2)**
28th Floor China Merchants Bank Tower
7088 Shennan Blvd
Shenzhen, 518040, China (55%)
Tel.: (86) 755 8319 6666
Web Site: www.cmfchina.com
Managed Assets: $9,503,400,000
Emp.: 179
Asset Management Services
S.I.C.: 6282
N.A.I.C.S.: 523920
Yuhui Chen *(Dir-Equity Res)*

Non-U.S. Subsidiaries:

CMB International Capital Corporation Limited **(2)**
Unit 1803 18 F Bank of America Tower 12 Harcourt Road
Central, China (Hong Kong)
Tel.: (852) 37618888
Fax: (852) 37618788
E-Mail: info@cmbi.com.hk
Web Site: www.cmbi.com.hk
Securities Brokerage Services
S.I.C.: 6211
N.A.I.C.S.: 523120

Wing Lung Bank Limited **(2)**
45 Des Voeux Road
Central, China (Hong Kong)
Tel.: (852) 23095555
Fax: (852) 28100592
E-Mail: wlb@winglungbank.com
Web Site: www.winglungbank.com
Int. Income: $655,768,391
Assets: $23,074,470,577
Liabilities: $20,854,780,210
Net Worth: $2,219,690,367
Earnings: $275,113,149
Emp.: 1,725
Fiscal Year-end: 12/31/12
Commercial Banking Services
S.I.C.: 6029
N.A.I.C.S.: 522110
Weihua Ma *(Chm)*
Guanghua Zhang *(Vice Chm)*
Qi Zhu *(CEO)*
Chung Keung Cheung *(CFO)*
Yiu Lung Cheng *(COO)*
Zhiqiang Wang *(CIO)*
Jun Liu *(Chief Risk Officer & Gen Mgr)*
Hon Yee Iva Chu *(Sec)*

Subsidiaries:

Wing Lung Bank (Trustee) Ltd. **(3)**
45 Des Voeux Road
Central, China (Hong Kong)
Tel.: (852) 28268404
Fax: (852) 25372301
Web Site: www.winglungbank.com
Rental Agency & Financial Property Management Services
S.I.C.: 6726
N.A.I.C.S.: 525990

Wing Lung Finance Ltd. **(3)**
45 Des Voeux Road 4th Floor
Central, China (Hong Kong)
Tel.: (852) 28268333
Fax: (852) 28100592
Web Site: www.winglungbank.com
Hire Purchase, Stocking Loan & Leasing Financial Services
S.I.C.: 6726
N.A.I.C.S.: 525990

Wing Lung Futures Limited **(3)**
45 Des Voeux Road
Central, China (Hong Kong)
Tel.: (852) 28268333
Fax: (852) 28100592
E-Mail: wlb@winglungbank.com
Web Site: www.winglungbank.com
Emp.: 50
Futures & Options Trading Services
S.I.C.: 6221
N.A.I.C.S.: 523140

Wing Lung Insurance Co. Ltd. **(3)**
10th Floor Wing Lung Bank Building
45 Des Voeux Road, Central, China (Hong Kong)
Tel.: (852) 28268229
Fax: (852) 25267045
E-Mail: enquiry@wlins.com
Web Site: www.winglungbank.com
Emp.: 100
Insurance Services
S.I.C.: 6311
N.A.I.C.S.: 524113
James Cy Chan *(CEO)*

Wing Lung Property Management Limited **(3)**
45 Des Voeux Road
Central, China (Hong Kong)
Tel.: (852) 28268333
Fax: (852) 25372301
E-Mail: trust01@winglungbank.com
Web Site: www.winglungbank.com
Property Management & Rental Agency Services
S.I.C.: 6531
N.A.I.C.S.: 531390

Wing Lung Securities Ltd. **(3)**
BFF Bank Center 636 Nathan Rd
Mongkok, Kowloon, China (Hong Kong)
Tel.: (852) 21714987
Fax: (852) 21714995
E-Mail: securities@winglungbank.com
Web Site: www.winglungsec.com
Securities Brokerage
S.I.C.: 6211
N.A.I.C.S.: 523120
Mukyiu Wong *(CEO)*

China Merchants Securities Co., Ltd. **(1)**
45F Block A Jiangsu Bldg Yitian Road
Futian District, Shenzhen, Guandong, 518026, China
Tel.: (86) 755 2695 1111
E-Mail: sbox@cmschina.com.cn
Web Site: www.cmschina.com.cn
600999—(SHG)
Sales Range: $800-899.9 Million
Securities Dealing & Brokerage Services
S.I.C.: 6211
N.A.I.C.S.: 523110
Shaolin Gong *(Chm)*
Yan Wang *(Pres & CEO)*
Jian Guo *(Sec & VP)*

CHINA METAL RECYCLING (HOLDINGS) LIMITED

Rm 3003A-5 30/F The Centrium 60 Wyndham Street 1 Harbour Road
Central, China (Hong Kong)
Tel.: (852) 25474725
Fax: (852) 25403693
E-Mail: admin@cmr773.com
Web Site: www.chinametalrecycle.com
Sales Range: $1-4.9 Billion
Emp.: 600

Business Description:
Scrap Metal Recycling Services
S.I.C.: 5051
N.A.I.C.S.: 423510

Personnel:
Chi Wai Chun *(Chm & CEO)*
Yan Zhang Jiang *(COO)*
Po Kei Lam *(Sec)*

Board of Directors:
Chi Wai Chun
Kam Hung Chan
Ka Lun Fung
Yan Zhang Jiang
Wun Yin Lai

Chuang Shun Leung
Qi Ping Yan
Butterfield Fulcrum Group (Cayman) Limited
Butterfield House 68 Fort Street
609
Georgetown, Grand Cayman, KY1 1107, Cayman Islands
Transfer Agents:
Tricor Investor Services Limited
26th Floor Tesbury Centre 28 Queens Road East
Wanchai, China (Hong Kong)
Butterfield Fulcrum Group (Cayman) Limited
Butterfield House 68 Fort Street
609
Georgetown, Grand Cayman, KY1 1107, Cayman Islands
Non-U.S. Subsidiary:
Guangzhou Asia Steel Co., Ltd. **(1)**
15 F Yagang Mansion No 3401
Huangpu Dist, Guangzhou, Guangdong, 510735, China
Tel.: (86) 2082221668
Fax: (86) 82087187
Web Site: www.cmr773.com
Scrap Metals Recycling Services
S.I.C.: 5093
N.A.I.C.S.: 423930

CHINA METRO-RURAL HOLDINGS LIMITED

Suite 2204 22/F Sun Life Tower The Gateway 15 Canton Road
Tsimshatsui, Kowloon, China (Hong Kong)
Tel.: (852) 2317 9888
Fax: (852) 2317 5243
Web Site: www.chinametrorural.com
Year Founded: 1980
CNR—(NYSEMKT)
Rev.: $36,719,673
Assets: $413,011,118
Liabilities: $259,636,054
Net Worth: $153,375,064
Earnings: ($12,311,114)
Emp.: 461
Fiscal Year-end: 03/31/13
Business Description:
Holding Company; Agricultural Logistics Services; Jewelry Mfr
S.I.C.: 6719
N.A.I.C.S.: 551112
Personnel:
Kam Seng Sio *(Acting CFO)*
Phyllis Lai Ping Chan *(Sec)*
Board of Directors:
Min Sang Ho
Wan Fai Hui
Matthew Chau Ming Lai
Wai Yan Leung
Shaobin Su
Francis King Chung Tsui
Henry Gee Hang Wong
Ernest Ka Lok Yuen
Legal Counsel:
Paul, Hastings, Janofsky & Walker
Nine W. 57th St., 47th Fl.
New York, NY 10019
Tel.: (212) 832-6100
Kaye, Scholer, Fierman, Hays & Handler
425 Park Ave.
New York, NY 10022
Tel.: (217) 836-8000
Transfer Agent:
American Stock Transfer & Trust Company
6201 15th Ave 3rd Fl
Brooklyn, NY 11219
Tel.: (718) 921-8206
Fax: (718) 236-2641
Toll Free: (800) 937-5449
Holding:
Man Sang International Limited **(1)**
Suites 2208-14 22/F Sun Life Tower The Gateway 15 Canton Road
Tsimshatsui, Kowloon, China (Hong Kong) BM
Tel.: (852) 23175300
Fax: (852) 23175243
E-Mail: pearl@man-sang.com
Web Site: www.man-sang.com
0938—(HKG)
Rev.: $59,469,806
Assets: $258,117,797
Liabilities: $128,801,321
Net Worth: $129,316,476
Earnings: $8,287,230
Emp.: 914
Fiscal Year-end: 03/31/13
Pearl Processor & Distr
S.I.C.: 3914
N.A.I.C.S.: 339910
Chung Hing Cheng *(Chm)*
Tai Po Cheng *(Deputy Chm)*
Alex Leung *(CFO & Sec)*
Subsidiary:
Man Sang Jewellery Company Limited **(2)**
220 A 14 22nd Fl Sun Life Canton Road
Kowloon, China (Hong Kong) HK
Tel.: (852) 23175300 (100%)
Fax: (852) 23175243
Web Site: www.man-sang.com
Emp.: 55
Pearl Products Trader & Distr
S.I.C.: 7389
N.A.I.C.S.: 425120
Ricky Chung Hing Cheng *(Chm)*
Subsidiary:
Arcadia Jewellery Limited **(3)**
220 A 22nd Fl Sunlife Tower The Gateway 1515 Carton Rd
Kowloon, China (Hong Kong) HK
Tel.: (852) 23179138 (100%)
Fax: (852) 23179139
Web Site: www.arcadia-jewellery.com
Emp.: 50
Pearl Jewelry Products Exporter, Whlsr & Mfr
S.I.C.: 5094
N.A.I.C.S.: 423940
Ricky Chung Hing Cheng *(Chm)*

CHINA MILK PRODUCTS GROUP LIMITED

North Band 104 Farm Daqing High-Tech Development Zone
163316 Daqing, Heilongjiang, China
Tel.: (86) 4596280860
Fax: (86) 4596280865
E-Mail: chinamilkgroup@listedcompany.com
Web Site: www.chinamilkgroup.com
G86—(SES)
Sales Range: $75-99.9 Million
Business Description:
Milk Products Mfr
S.I.C.: 0241
N.A.I.C.S.: 112120
Personnel:
Shuqing Liu *(Chm)*
Hailong Liu *(CEO)*
Yuxia Li *(Deputy CEO-Admin)*
Ho Yan Choi *(CFO & Co-Sec)*
Joo Khin Ng *(Co-Sec)*
Board of Directors:
Shuqing Liu
Hailong Liu
Litao Liu
Choon Chiaw Loo
Yee Loong Sum
Xiaolai Xie

CHINA MINERALS MINING CORPORATION

Suite 717 1030 West Georgia Street
Vancouver, BC, Canada V6E 2Y3
Tel.: (604) 629-1505
Fax: (604) 629-0923
Toll Free: (888) 629-1505
Web Site: www.chinamineralsmining.com
Year Founded: 2006
CMV—(TSXV)
Rev.: $319,345
Assets: $22,503,377
Liabilities: $1,057,239
Net Worth: $21,446,139
Earnings: ($1,868,467)
Fiscal Year-end: 11/30/12
Business Description:
Mineral Exploration Services
S.I.C.: 1081
N.A.I.C.S.: 213114
Personnel:
Ling Zhu *(Chm)*
Patricia Fong *(CFO)*
Board of Directors:
Ling Zhu
Harvey Brooks
Bernard Kahlert
Zheng Zhou
Legal Counsel:
McMillan LLP
1500 1055 West Georgia Street
V6E4N7 Vancouver, BC, Canada
Transfer Agent:
Computershare Trust Company of Canada
510 Burrard St 2nd Fl
Vancouver, BC, Canada

CHINA MING YANG WIND POWER GROUP LIMITED

(d/b/a Guangdong Mingyang Wind Power)
Jianye Road Mingyang Industry Park National Hi-Tech Industrial Development Zone,
Zhongshan, Guangdong, 528437, China
Tel.: (86) 76028138888
Fax: (86) 76028138511
Web Site: www.mywind.com.cn
MY—(NYSE)
Rev.: $459,568,935
Assets: $1,896,877,729
Liabilities: $1,319,052,911
Net Worth: $577,824,818
Earnings: $47,788,434
Emp.: 2,107
Fiscal Year-end: 12/31/12
Business Description:
Wind Turbine Mfr
S.I.C.: 3511
N.A.I.C.S.: 333611
Personnel:
Chuanwei Zhang *(Chm & CEO)*
Calvin Lau *(CFO)*
Jiawan Cheng *(COO)*
Renjing Cao *(CTO)*
Song Wang *(Sr VP-Tech Dev, Mktg & Sls Svcs)*
Board of Directors:
Chuanwei Zhang
Leo Austin
Cole R. Capener
Stephen Markscheid
Song Wang
Dabing Zhou

CHINA MINING INTERNATIONAL LIMITED

6 Battery Road Level 31 Raffles Place
Singapore, 049909, Singapore
Tel.: (65) 6320 8485
Fax: (65) 6320 8484
E-Mail: hq@sunshine-holdings.com
Web Site: www.chinamining-international.com
Y34—(SES)
Rev.: $14,311,273
Assets: $119,729,693
Liabilities: $39,185,912
Net Worth: $80,543,781
Earnings: ($31,637,837)
Fiscal Year-end: 12/31/12
Business Description:
Holding Company; Iron Ore Mining; Property Development Services
S.I.C.: 6719
N.A.I.C.S.: 551112
Personnel:
Yinghui Guo *(Chm)*
Bin Li *(CEO)*
Tze Khern Yeo *(CFO & Co-Sec)*
Soon Soo Foo *(Co-Sec)*
Board of Directors:
Yinghui Guo
Siew Wei Chan
Lingling Dong
Bin Li
Han Boon Lim
Jincheng Ning
Xiaoying Zhang
Transfer Agent:
KCK CorpServe Pte. Ltd.
333 North Bridge Road 08-00 KH KEA Building
Singapore, Singapore

CHINA MINING RESOURCES GROUP LIMITED

Room 1306, 13-F Bank of America Tower 12 Harcourt Road
Admiralty, Hong Kong, China (Hong Kong)
Tel.: (852) 2295 0822
Fax: (852) 2295 0990
E-Mail: enquiry@chinaminingresources.com
Web Site: www.chinaminingresources.com
INU—(DEU)
Business Description:
Molybdenum Mining Services
S.I.C.: 1099
N.A.I.C.S.: 212299
Personnel:
Xian Sheng You *(Chm & Exec Dir)*
Shou Wu Chen *(Deputy Chm, CEO & Exec Dir)*
Kwok Kuen Yeung *(CFO & Exec Dir)*
Lai Ming Leung *(Sec & Mgr-Acctg)*
Board of Directors:
Shou Wu Chen
Xian Sheng You
Cha Hwa Chong
Kang Nam Chu
Yi Quan Fang
Ming Yung Lam
Xiang Min Lin
Hui Wang
Kwok Kuen Yeung
Subsidiary:
Wuyi Star Tea Industrial Co., Ltd. **(1)**
Room 701 7/F Fortune Centre 44-48 Yun Ping Road
Causeway Bay, China (Hong Kong)
Tel.: (852) 3153 4430
Fax: (852) 3153 4425
E-Mail: info@brightease.com.hk
Web Site: www.wuyistar.com.hk
Emp.: 10
Tea Mfr
S.I.C.: 2099
N.A.I.C.S.: 311920

CHINA MINING UNITED FUND

22/F IFC Building No 8 Jianguomenwai Avenue
Chao Yang District, Beijing, 100020, China
Tel.: (86) 10 85660017
Fax: (86) 10 85660589
Web Site: www.cmufund.com
Business Description:
Mining & Related Assets Closed-End Investment Fund
S.I.C.: 6726
N.A.I.C.S.: 525990
Personnel:
Zhi Zheng *(Chm)*

CHINA MINMETALS CORPORATION
(d/b/a Minmetals Group)
5 Sanlihe Road
Haidian District, Beijing, 100044, China
Tel.: (86) 1068495888
Fax: (86) 1068335570
E-Mail: zc@minmetals.com.cn
Web Site: www.minmetals.com
Year Founded: 1950
Sales Range: $15-24.9 Billion
Emp.: 2,000

Business Description:
Holding Company; Minerals & Metals Production & Trading Services
S.I.C.: 6719
N.A.I.C.S.: 551112
Personnel:
Zhongshu Zhou *(Pres)*

Subsidiaries:

China International Engineering & Materials Corp. **(1)**
Minmetals Plaza 5 Sanlihe Road
Haidian District, Beijing, 100044, China
Tel.: (86) 10 68495194
Fax: (86) 10 68495073
Web Site: www.minmetals.com
Metal Distr
S.I.C.: 5051
N.A.I.C.S.: 423510

China Minmetals Hainan Trading Development Corp. **(1)**
16th Floor Shenfa Building 22 Jinlong Road
Finance and Trade District, 570125 Haikou, China
Tel.: (86) 89868520885
Fax: (86) 89868523079
E-Mail: minmetals@hk.hi.cn
Web Site: www.minmetals.com
Trading in Metals, Minerals & Electrical Products
Export
S.I.C.: 1081
N.A.I.C.S.: 213114

China Minmetals Ningbo Trading Corp. **(1)**
4/F 88 Zhongshan Road West
Ningbo, 315010, China (100%)
Tel.: (86) 57487349848
Fax: (86) 57487349848
E-Mail: mntc@mail.nbptt.zj.cn
Metal Distr
Export
S.I.C.: 5051
N.A.I.C.S.: 423510
Sun Tingshe *(Gen Mgr)*

China Minmetals Non-Ferrous Metals Co. Ltd. **(1)**
Block A Minmetals Building 6 Sanlihe Road
Haidian District, Beijing, 100044, China (82.23%)
Tel.: (86) 1068495202
Fax: (86) 1068495215
E-Mail: info@cmnltd.com
Web Site: www.cmnltd.com
Rev.: $3,205,488,128
Copper, Aluminum, Tungsten, Tin, Antimony, Lead, Zinc, Precious Metals & Rare Earth Metals Distr
S.I.C.: 5051
N.A.I.C.S.: 423510
Zhou Zhongshu *(Chm)*
Lixin Wang *(Pres)*
Jiqing Xu *(CFO & VP)*

Non-U.S. Subsidiary:

MMG Limited **(2)**
(Formerly Minmetals Resources Limited)
Units 8501 8503 Level 85 International Commerce Centre
1 Austin Road, Kowloon, China (Hong Kong) (72%)
Tel.: (852) 2216 9688
Fax: (852) 2840 0580
Web Site: www.mmg.com
1208—(HKG)
Rev.: $2,499,400,000
Assets: $4,659,200,000
Liabilities: $2,973,400,000
Net Worth: $1,685,800,000
Earnings: $217,500,000
Emp.: 8,500
Fiscal Year-end: 12/31/12
Holding Company; Zinc, Copper & Other Metals Exploration, Development & Mining
S.I.C.: 6719
N.A.I.C.S.: 551112
Andrew Gordon Michelmore *(CEO)*
David Mark Lamont *(CFO)*
Marcelo Bastos *(COO)*
Nick Myers *(Gen Counsel)*
Lucia Suet Kam Leung *(Sec)*

Corporate Headquarters:

MMG Limited - Corporate Office **(3)**
Level 23 28 Freshwater Place
Southbank, VIC, 3006, Australia
Tel.: (61) 392880888
Fax: (61) 392880800
Web Site: www.mmg.com
Emp.: 400
Corporate Office; Zinc, Copper & Other Metals Exploration, Development & Mining
S.I.C.: 8741
N.A.I.C.S.: 551114
Andrew Gordon Michelmore *(CEO)*
David Mark Lamont *(CFO)*
Marcelo Bastos *(COO)*

Subsidiaries:

MMG Australia Limited **(4)**
Level 23 28 Freshwater Place
Southbank, VIC, 3006, Australia AU
Tel.: (61) 3 9288 0888 (100%)
Fax: (61) 3 9288 0800
E-Mail:
Web Site: www.mmg.com
Emp.: 200
Metallic Mineral & Metal Ore Exploration, Development & Mining
S.I.C.: 1031
N.A.I.C.S.: 212231
Andrew Gordon Michelmore *(CEO)*
David Mark Lamont *(Grp CFO)*
Brett Fletcher *(COO)*

Non-U.S. Subsidiary:

MMG Canada **(4)**
2600-1177 West Hastings Street
Vancouver, BC, V6E 2K3, Canada
Tel.: (778) 373-5600
Web Site: www.mmg.com
Metallic Mineral Exploration & Development Services
S.I.C.: 1081
N.A.I.C.S.: 213114

Non-U.S. Joint Venture:

Changzhou Jinyuan Copper Co., Ltd. **(4)**
776 Zhongwu Road
Changzhou, Jiangsu, China JP
Tel.: (86) 51988830226
Fax: (86) 51988829456
E-Mail: cjcco@jsmail.com.cn
Web Site: www.jinyuan-copper.com
Copper Wire & Rod Mfr
S.I.C.: 3351
N.A.I.C.S.: 331420

China Minmetals Zhuhai Import and Export Trading Co., Ltd. **(1)**
Room 2703 Bright Intl Trade Center
47 Haibin Rd S Jida, Zhuhai, 519015, China CN
Tel.: (86) 7563222358 (100%)
Fax: (86) 7563222351
E-Mail: zhcnmnmt@pub.zhuhai.gd.cn
Web Site: www.minmetals.com
Metal Distr
Export
S.I.C.: 5051
N.A.I.C.S.: 423510
Liu Minxin *(Gen Mgr)*

China National Metal Products Imp/Exp Company **(1)**
Minmetals Plz 5 Sanlihe Rd
Beijing, 100044, China
Tel.: (86) 1068494508
Fax: (86) 1068495409
E-Mail: zp@minmetals.com.cn
Web Site: www.minmetals.com
Emp.: 15
Metal & Electrical Products Importer & Exporter
S.I.C.: 5051
N.A.I.C.S.: 423510
Fang Gang *(Gen Mgr)*

China National Metals & Minerals Imp. & Exp. Shanghai Pudong Corp. **(1)**
16A Bao Ding Building 550 Xujiahui Road
Shanghai, 200025, China
Tel.: (86) 2164739872
Fax: (86) 2164735525
E-Mail: mmpd@sh163a.sta.net.cn
Metal & Mineral Importer & Exporter
S.I.C.: 5051
N.A.I.C.S.: 423510

China National Metals & Minerals Imp/Exp Shenzhen Corp. **(1)**
15 Fl Times Financial Ctr 4001 Shen Nan Rd
Shenzhen, 518034, China
Tel.: (86) 75582389287
Fax: (86) 75583025341
E-Mail: mmsz@163.net
Emp.: 20
Metal & Mineral Importer & Exporter
S.I.C.: 5051
N.A.I.C.S.: 423510

China National Minerals Co., Ltd. **(1)**
5 Sanlihe Road Haidian District
Beijing, 100044, China
Tel.: (86) 1068494481
Fax: (86) 1068494450
E-Mail: yclbk@minmetals.com
Web Site: www.minerals.minmetals.com.cn
Sales Range: $1-4.9 Billion
Emp.: 250
Iron Ore, Billets, Pig Iron, Steel Scraps, Demo-Vessel, Coke, Coal, Ferroalloys, Refractory Raw Materials, Barite, Fluorspars & Talc Importer & Exporter
S.I.C.: 5051
N.A.I.C.S.: 423510
Jinzeng He *(Mng Dir)*

China Palace International Travel Service **(1)**
15 Garden Road
Haidian District, Beijing, 100088, China
Tel.: (86) 1062052214
Fax: (86) 1062054357
Travel Services
S.I.C.: 4729
N.A.I.C.S.: 561599

Hanxing Metallurgical Mine Administration **(1)**
No 54 Northern Zhainghua Road
Handan, Hebei, China
Tel.: (86) 31030233951
Fax: (86) 3103023392
E-Mail: hxks@hxks.com
Web Site: www.hxks.com
Metals, Minerals & Electrical Products Import Export
S.I.C.: 1081
N.A.I.C.S.: 213114

Minmetals Development Co., Ltd. **(1)**
5 Sanlihe Road Building B
Haidian District, Beijing, 100044, China
Tel.: (86) 10 68494206
Fax: (86) 10 68494207
Web Site: www.minlist.com.cn
600058—(SHG)
Sales Range: $5-14.9 Billion
Emp.: 4,100
Freight Transportation, Logistics, Storage & Mineral Trading Services; Hotel Management & Technology Services
S.I.C.: 4731
N.A.I.C.S.: 488510
Zhou Zhongshu *(Chm)*
Guiquan Feng *(Vice Chm)*

Minmetals Finance Company **(1)**
Minmetals Plaza 5 Sanlihe Road
Haidian District, Beijing, China
Tel.: (86) 1068495359
Fax: (86) 1068495353
E-Mail: cw@minmetals.com.cn
Financial Services
S.I.C.: 6211
N.A.I.C.S.: 523999

Minmetals International Tendering Co., Ltd. **(1)**
5 Sanlihe Road
Haidian District, Beijing, 100044, China
Tel.: (86) 1068495888
Fax: (86) 1068494524
E-Mail: zb@minmetals.com.cn
Web Site: mitc.minmetals.com
Emp.: 10,000
Mechanical & Electrical Product Importer
S.I.C.: 5051
N.A.I.C.S.: 423510
Jzhou Zhong Shu *(Pres)*

Minmetals Nanjing International Trading Co., Ltd. **(1)**
Room 1509 Longsheng Building
23 Hongwu Road, Nanjing, 210005, China
Tel.: (86) 2586899367
Fax: (86) 2586899366
E-Mail: jind@minmetals.com
Web Site: www.minmetals.com.cn
Emp.: 24
International Metal Wholesale Trading Services
S.I.C.: 5051
N.A.I.C.S.: 423510
Liu Weidong *(Gen Mgr)*

Minmetals Real Estate Company **(1)**
Minmetals Plz 5 Sanlihe Rd
Haidian District, Beijing, 100044, China
Tel.: (86) 1068495117
Fax: (86) 1068495086
E-Mail: fd@minmetals.com.cn
Web Site: www.minmetals.com
Real Estate Services
S.I.C.: 6531
N.A.I.C.S.: 531390

Minmetals Tongling Gem Stone Co., Ltd. **(1)**
Minmetals Plaza 5 Sanlihe Road
Haidian District, Beijing, 100044, China
Tel.: (86) 1068495057
Fax: (86) 1068495157
Gem Stone Distr
S.I.C.: 5094
N.A.I.C.S.: 423940

Minmetals Xiamen Enterprises Co., Ltd. **(1)**
11/F Huicheng Commercial Centre
Xiamen, China
Tel.: (86) 898 58566930
Fax: (86) 898 5851568
Metal Distr
S.I.C.: 5051
N.A.I.C.S.: 423510

Minmetals Xinjiang Ala-Shankou Trading Co., Ltd. **(1)**
Zhungeer Road
Ala-Shankou, Xinjiang, 833418, China
Tel.: (86) 9096993966
Fax: (86) 9096993965
Metals Distr
S.I.C.: 5051
N.A.I.C.S.: 423510

Minmetals Yantai Co., Ltd. **(1)**
Room 1005 1010 Qili Mansion
Yantai, 264001, China
Tel.: (86) 5356627672
Fax: (86) 5356627671
E-Mail: minmetals@public.ytptt.sd.cn
Web Site: www.minmetal-yantai.com
Emp.: 19
Metal Distr
S.I.C.: 5051
N.A.I.C.S.: 423510
Ciang Huagun *(CFO)*

Minmetals Zhejiang International Trading Co., Ltd. **(1)**
3 Jiefang Road
Hangzhou, 315009, China
Tel.: (86) 57185802578
Fax: (86) 57185802448
E-Mail: mntc@mail.nbptt.zj.cn
International Metal Wholesale Trading Services
S.I.C.: 5051
N.A.I.C.S.: 423510

Affiliate:

Shangri-La International Hotel Marketing Ltd. **(1)**
The Kerry Centre Hotel No 1 Guang Hua Road
Chao Yang District, Beijing, 100020, China

Tel.: (86) 1065618833
Fax: (86) 1065612626
E-Mail: info@shangri-la.com
Web Site: www.shangri-la.com
Emp.: 700
Hotel Operations
S.I.C.: 7011
N.A.I.C.S.: 721110
Jeremy Aniere *(Gen Mgr)*

Joint Ventures:

ICBC-AXA-Minmetals Assurance Co., Ltd. **(1)**
12/F China Merchants Tower 161 Lu Jai Zui Road
Pudong New District, Shanghai, 200120, China
Tel.: (86) 2158792288
Fax: (86) 21 5879 2299
E-Mail:
Web Site: www.icbc-axa.com
Sales Range: $10-24.9 Million
Insurance Services in Life, Education, Retirement, Health & Wealth Management
S.I.C.: 6311
N.A.I.C.S.: 524113

Shanghai Oriental Futures Co., Ltd. **(1)**
Room 704 22 417 Street Lancun Road
Shanghai, 200122, China
Tel.: (86) 2168401560
Fax: (86) 21 68401559
Futures Trading Services; Owned by China Minmetals Corporation & by Huadong Supply Company of China Non-Ferrous Metals Industrial Corporation
S.I.C.: 6231
N.A.I.C.S.: 523210

U.S. Subsidiary:

Minmetals, Inc. **(1)**
1200 Harbor Blvd
Weehawken, NJ 07086 NJ
Tel.: (201) 809-1898 (100%)
Fax: (201) 809-1899
E-Mail: mininc@minmetalsusa.com
Web Site: www.minmetalsusa.com
Sales Range: $50-74.9 Million
Emp.: 20
Metal Products Mfr
Export
S.I.C.: 5052
N.A.I.C.S.: 423520
Caojing Liu *(Pres)*

Subsidiaries:

Minmetals, Inc. (L.A.) **(2)**
1037 Walnut Ave
Pomona, CA 91766 CA
Tel.: (909) 627-8258
Fax: (909) 627-8830
E-Mail: info@minmetals.com
Web Site: www.minmetalsusa.com
Metal Distr
S.I.C.: 5051
N.A.I.C.S.: 423510
Bai Li *(Gen Mgr)*

Non-U.S. Subsidiaries:

Cheeminmet Finance Limited **(1)**
16/F China Minmetals Tower 79 Chatham Road
Tsimshatsui, Kowloon, China (Hong Kong)
Tel.: (852) 26136000
Fax: (852) 23695501
E-Mail: public@cheerglory.com
Emp.: 20
Financial Services
S.I.C.: 6726
N.A.I.C.S.: 525990

Cheerglory Traders Limited **(1)**
11 F China Minmetals Tower 79 Chatham Road S
Tsimshatsui, Kowloon, China (Hong Kong)
Tel.: (852) 26136000
Fax: (852) 28106187
E-Mail: public@cheerglory.com
Web Site: www.cheerglory.com
Emp.: 200
Metal Distr
S.I.C.: 5051
N.A.I.C.S.: 423510
Liu Qingchun *(Mng Dir)*

China Expand Development Ltd. **(1)**
79 Chathan Rd S Tsimshatsui
Kowloon, China (Hong Kong)
Tel.: (852) 26136000
Fax: (852) 27212079
E-Mail: minmet04@netvigator.com
Web Site: www.minmetals.com
Emp.: 40
Real Estate Services
S.I.C.: 6531
N.A.I.C.S.: 531390
Qian Zigang *(Gen Mgr)*

China Metals E Minerals (Brazil) Ltd. **(1)**
Rua da Assembleia 10 Sala 3420
20119-900 Rio de Janeiro, Brazil
Tel.: (55) 2125312321
Fax: (55) 25312383
E-Mail: zhidl@minmetal.com
Web Site: www.Minmetal.com
Emp.: 100
Metal Distr
S.I.C.: 5051
N.A.I.C.S.: 423510
Lefsheng Guo *(Mng Dir)*

China Minmet Investment Limited **(1)**
79 Chatham Road South Tsimshatsui
Kowloon, China (Hong Kong)
Tel.: (852) 26136000
Fax: (852) 23695501
Web Site: www.chinaminmetals.com
Emp.: 150
Investment Services
S.I.C.: 6211
N.A.I.C.S.: 523999
Liang Qing *(Gen Mgr)*

China Minmetals H.K. (Holding) Limited **(1)**
19/F China Minmetals Tower 79 Chatham Road South
Tsimshatsui, Kowloon, China (Hong Kong)
Tel.: (852) 26136000
Fax: (852) 26136333
E-Mail: public@cheerglory.com
Web Site: www.minmetals.com.cn/detail_news.jsp?article_millseconds=1207039175547
Emp.: 20
Metal Distr
S.I.C.: 5051
N.A.I.C.S.: 423510
Qingchun Liu *(Gen Mgr)*

China Minmetals South America (Holding) Ltd. **(1)**
Rua Assembleia 10-S 3420
CEP 20011-901 Rio de Janeiro, RJ, Brazil
Tel.: (55) 2125312321
Fax: (55) 2125311577
E-Mail: minmetalsbr@minmetalsbr.com.br
Web Site: www.minmetalsbr.com
Emp.: 2
Metal Distr
S.I.C.: 5051
N.A.I.C.S.: 423510
Dai Baolong *(Mng Dir)*

Minmetals Australia Pty. Ltd. **(1)**
Level 8 564 Saint Kilda Road
Melbourne, VIC, 3004, Australia AU
Tel.: (61) 395206800 (100%)
Fax: (61) 395211815
E-Mail: enquires@minmetals.com.au
Web Site: www.australia.minmetals.com.cn
Emp.: 25
Metal Distr
S.I.C.: 5051
N.A.I.C.S.: 423510
Zhilong Liu *(Mng Dir)*

Minmetals Capitals & Securities, Inc. **(1)**
16 F China Minmetals Tower 79 Chatham Rd S
Kowloon, China (Hong Kong)
Tel.: (852) 26136000
Fax: (852) 23695501
Web Site: www.chinaminmetals.com
Emp.: 50
Metal Investments
S.I.C.: 3324
N.A.I.C.S.: 331512

Minmetals Germany GmbH **(1)**
Kaiserswerther Strasse 22
Dusseldorf, Germany (100%)
Tel.: (49) 21149680
Fax: (49) 211496875
E-Mail: info@minmetals.de
Web Site: www.minmetals.de
Sales Range: $150-199.9 Million
Emp.: 20
Metal Distr
Import Export
S.I.C.: 5051
N.A.I.C.S.: 423510
Jianxun Yan *(Gen Mgr)*

Minmetals Japan Corporation **(1)**
2-7-15 Fukagawa Koto-Ku
Tokyo, 135-0033, Japan
Tel.: (81) 356399555
Fax: (81) 356399557
E-Mail: chenshr@minmetals.com
Emp.: 10
Metal Distr
S.I.C.: 5051
N.A.I.C.S.: 423510
Pugang Pon *(Gen Mgr)*

Minmetals Korea Co., Ltd. **(1)**
Room 1103 Hyoryung Building 1 Mugyo-Dong Jung-Gu
Seoul, 100170, Korea (South)
Tel.: (82) 27794741
Fax: (82) 27794745
E-Mail: yangh@minmetals.com
Web Site: www.minmetals.com
Emp.: 6
Metal Distr
S.I.C.: 5051
N.A.I.C.S.: 423510

Minmetals Land Limited **(1)**
18th Floor China Minmetals Tower 79 Chatham Road South
Tsimshatsui, Kowloon, China (Hong Kong)
Tel.: (852) 26136363
Fax: (852) 25819823
E-Mail: info@minmetalsland.com
Web Site: www.minmetalsland.com
0230—(HKG OTC)
Rev.: $555,317,243
Assets: $2,258,664,215
Liabilities: $1,239,797,512
Net Worth: $1,018,866,703
Earnings: $55,385,057
Emp.: 1,090
Fiscal Year-end: 12/31/12
Real Estate Services
S.I.C.: 6531
N.A.I.C.S.: 531390
Jianbo He *(Deputy Chm & Mng Dir)*
Patrick Yiu Wing Law *(COO)*
Xiaoli He *(Deputy Mng Dir & Gen Mgr-Fin Dept)*
Liang Yin *(Sr Deputy Mng Dir)*
Zoe Wing Yee Chung *(Sec)*

Minmetals North Europe AB **(1)**
Arenavagen 41
PO Box 10114
121 28 Stockholm, Sweden
Tel.: (46) 86699001
Fax: (46) 86699012
E-Mail: info@minmetals.se
Web Site: www.minmetals.se
Emp.: 5
Metal Distr
S.I.C.: 5051
N.A.I.C.S.: 423510

Minmetals R.S.A. (PTY) Ltd. **(1)**
Gillooly's View Office Park Bldd A 1st Fl
Osborne Lane Bedfordview, 2007
Johannesburg, South Africa
Mailing Address:
PO Box 1192
Bedfordview, 2008, South Africa
Tel.: (27) 116150029
Fax: (27) 116150051
E-Mail: info@minmetals.co.za
Web Site: www.minmetals.co.za
Emp.: 5
Metal Distr
S.I.C.: 5051
N.A.I.C.S.: 423510
Jingbo Li *(Gen Mgr)*

Minmetals South-East Asia Corporation Pte. Ltd. **(1)**
19-04 Clifford Ctr 24 Raffles Pl
Singapore, 048621, Singapore
Tel.: (65) 356566
Fax: (65) 320508
E-Mail: sales@minmetals.com.sg
Web Site: www.minmetals.com.sg
Emp.: 10
Metal Distr
S.I.C.: 5051
N.A.I.C.S.: 423510

Minmetals Spain S.A. **(1)**
1 Piso 4 128-130 Plaza
P Taulat, 08005 Barcelona, Spain
Tel.: (34) 933072007
Web Site: www.minmetals.com
Metal Distr
S.I.C.: 5051
N.A.I.C.S.: 423510

Minmetals (UK) Ltd. **(1)**
Mimet House 5A Praed Street
London, W2 1NJ, United Kingdom
Tel.: (44) 2074114012
Fax: (44) 2074114016
E-Mail: info@minmetals.co.uk
Web Site: www.minmetals.co.uk
Emp.: 8
Metal Distr
S.I.C.: 5051
N.A.I.C.S.: 423510

Minnat Resources Pte. Ltd. **(1)**
24 Raffles Place
#19-03 Clifford Centre
048621 Singapore, Singapore SG
Tel.: (65) 65357406
Fax: (65) 65325825
Web Site: www.minmetals.com.sg
Administration & Metal Mining Services
Export
S.I.C.: 1081
N.A.I.C.S.: 213114

Non-U.S. Affiliates:

China Stone Corporation **(1)**
Daini-Nakamura Building 9-5 Shinkawa 2-chome Chuo-ku
Tokyo, 104-0033, Japan
Tel.: (81) 335519881
Fax: (81) 335519885
E-Mail: csc@chinastone.co.jp
Web Site: www.chinastone.co.jp
Sales Range: $10-24.9 Million
Emp.: 15
Stone & Brick Distr
S.I.C.: 5032
N.A.I.C.S.: 423320
Han Yaguang *(VP-Sls)*

Janfair Pty. Ltd. **(1)**
Level 15 215 Adelaide Street
Brisbane, QLD, 4000, Australia
Tel.: (61) 738326755
Fax: (61) 738326672
E-Mail: janfairqld@hotmail.com
Web Site: www.janfair.com
Emp.: 5
Real Estate Services
S.I.C.: 6531
N.A.I.C.S.: 531390

CHINA MINSHENG BANKING CORPORATION LTD.

7th Floor Jiabin Building of Freindship Hotel 1
Zhongguancun South Street
Haidian District, Beijing, 100873, China
Tel.: (86) 10 68946790
Fax: (86) 10 68466796
E-Mail: cmbc@cmbc.com.cn
Web Site: www.cmbc.com.cn
Year Founded: 1996
600016—(HKG OTC SHG)
Sales Range: $15-24.9 Billion
Emp.: 40,820

Business Description:
Commercial Banking Services
S.I.C.: 6029
N.A.I.C.S.: 522110

Personnel:
Wenbiao Dong *(Chm)*
Qi Hong *(Vice Chm & Pres)*
Yutang Liang *(Vice Chm)*
Yonghao Liu *(Vice Chm)*
Zhiqiang Lu *(Vice Chm)*
Hongwei Zhang *(Vice Chm)*

China Minsheng Banking Corporation Ltd.—(Continued)

Jie Shi *(Asst Pres & Gen Mgr-Credit Assessment & Risk Mgmt Dept)*
Dan Bai *(CFO)*
Bin Li *(Asst Pres)*
Qingyuan Wan *(Sec)*
Xiaofeng Mao *(Exec VP)*
Benxiu Xing *(Exec VP)*
Pinzhang Zhao *(Exec VP)*
Board of Directors:
Wenbiao Dong
Qi Hong
Yutang Liang
Yonghao Liu
Zhiqiang Lu
Qingyuan Wan
Di Wu
Hongwei Zhang
Supervisory Board of Directors:
Ying Hu
Yuan Li
Zhongnan Lu
Liang Wang
Disheng Zhang
Ke Zhang

KPMG
8th Floor Prince's Building 10 Chater Road
Central, China (Hong Kong)

China Securities Depository & Clearing Corporation Limited
36th Floor China Insurance Building 166 Luijiazui Road East Pudong New
Shanghai, China

CHINA MINZHONG FOOD CORPORATION LIMITED
(Acquired by First Pacific Company Limited)

CHINA MOBILE COMMUNICATIONS CORPORATION
60F The Center
99 Queen's Road, Central, China (Hong Kong)
Tel.: (852) 31218888
Fax: (852) 25119092
E-Mail: ir@chinamobilehk.com
Web Site: www.chinamobileltd.com
Sales Range: $25-49.9 Billion
Emp.: 127,959
Business Description:
Holding Company; Mobile Telecommunications
S.I.C.: 6719
N.A.I.C.S.: 551112
Personnel:
Guohua Xi *(Chm)*
Yue Li *(Pres)*
Board of Directors:
Guohua Xi
Wenlin Huang
Yue Li
Yuejia Sha
Taohai Xue
Non-U.S. Subsidiary:

China Mobile Limited (1)
60th Floor The Center 99 Queen's Road
Central, China (Hong Kong) (74.08%)
Tel.: (852) 3121 8888
Fax: (852) 2511 9092
E-Mail: ca@chinamobilehk.com
Web Site: www.chinamobileltd.com
CHL—(HKG NYSE SHG)
Rev.: $89,021,605,050
Assets: $167,127,514,650
Liabilities: $51,912,180,000
Net Worth: $115,215,334,650
Earnings: $20,552,171,850
Fiscal Year-end: 12/31/12
Cellular Telecommunication Services
S.I.C.: 4812
N.A.I.C.S.: 517210
Yue Li *(CEO)*
Taohai Xue *(CFO & VP)*
Wai Lan Wong *(Sec)*

CHINA MODERN AGRICULTURAL INFORMATION, INC.
No A09 Wuzhou Sun Town Limin Avenue
Limin Development District, Harbin, Heilongjiang, China 150000
Tel.: (86) 451 8480 0733
Year Founded: 2008
CMCI—(OTC)
Rev.: $46,766,281
Assets: $90,415,393
Liabilities: $21,822,149
Net Worth: $68,593,244
Earnings: $21,853,516
Emp.: 137
Fiscal Year-end: 06/30/13
Business Description:
Agricultural Services
S.I.C.: 0241
N.A.I.C.S.: 112120
Personnel:
Enjia Liu *(Chm)*
Youliang Wang *(CEO)*
Yanyan Liu *(CFO)*
Qin Libei *(COO)*
Liu Zhengxin *(Chief HR Officer)*
Board of Directors:
Enjia Liu
Yanqin Shan
Youliang Wang

CHINA MODERN DAIRY HOLDINGS LTD.
Economic Technological Development Zone
Ma'anshan, Anhui, 243121, China
Tel.: (86) 555 7167700
Fax: (86) 555 7167770
E-Mail: info@moderndairyir.com
Web Site: www.moderndairyir.com
1117—(HKG)
Sls.: $394,037,115
Assets: $1,773,347,868
Liabilities: $898,287,060
Net Worth: $875,060,807
Earnings: $54,326,065
Emp.: 4,955
Fiscal Year-end: 06/30/13
Business Description:
Raw Milk Production & Dairy Farming
S.I.C.: 0241
N.A.I.C.S.: 112120
Personnel:
Lina Gao *(Deputy Chm & CEO)*
Yugang Sun *(CFO)*
Chunlin Han *(COO)*
Kai Hing Wong *(Sec)*
Board of Directors:
Xubo Yu
Sheng Ding
Lina Gao
Chunlin Han
Max Chi Kin Hui
Yan Kang
Conway Kong Wai Lee
Yongsheng Lei
Shengli Li
Fuchun Liu
Yugang Sun
Julian Juul Wolhardt

Computershare Hong Kong Investor Services Limited
Shops 1712-1716 17th Floor Hopewell Centre
183 Queens Road East
Wanchai, China (Hong Kong)

Transfer Agents:
Maples Finance Ltd
Queensgate House
Grand Cayman, Cayman Islands

Computershare Hong Kong Investor Services Limited
Shops 1712-1716 17th Floor Hopewell Centre
183 Queens Road East
Wanchai, China (Hong Kong)

CHINA MOLYBDENUM CO., LTD.
North of Yihe Huamei Shan Road
Chengdong New District
Luanchuan, Luoyang, Henan, China 471500
Tel.: (86) 379 6865 8031
Fax: (86) 379 6865 8030
Web Site: www.chinamoly.com
3993—(HKG)
Rev.: $907,175,497
Assets: $2,501,778,718
Liabilities: $536,582,758
Net Worth: $1,965,195,961
Earnings: $161,451,276
Emp.: 8,139
Fiscal Year-end: 12/31/12
Business Description:
Molybdenum Mining & Processing Services
S.I.C.: 1099
N.A.I.C.S.: 212299
Personnel:
Wenjun Wu *(Chm)*
Zhenhao Zhang *(Chm-Supervisory Bd)*
Chaochun Li *(Vice Chm)*
Meifeng Gu *(CFO)*
Siu Pik Ho *(Co-Sec)*
Xinhui Zhang *(Co-Sec)*
Board of Directors:
Wenjun Wu
Yanchun Bai
Gordon Cheng
Chaochun Li
Faben Li
Hedong Shu
Qinxi Wang
Shan Xu
Xu Xu
Yufeng Zhang
Supervisory Board of Directors:
Zhenhao Zhang
Jiaoyun Deng
Dongfang Yin
Legal Counsel:
Morrison & Foerster
33/F Edinburgh Tower The Landmark 15 Queen's Road
Central, China (Hong Kong)

Llinks Law Offices
19 F One Lujiazui 68 Yin Cheng Road Middle
Shanghai, China

China Securities Depository & Clearing Corporation Limited
36/F China Insurance Building 166 Lujiazui East Road Pudong New Area
Shanghai, China

Non-U.S. Subsidiary:

Northparkes Mines (1)
Bogan Rd
Goonumbla, Parkes, New South Wales, 2870, Australia (100%)
Mailing Address:
PO Box 995
Parkes, NSW, 2870, Australia
Tel.: (61) 268613000
Fax: (61) 268613102
E-Mail: northparkes@riotinto.com
Web Site: www.northparkes.com
Emp.: 300
S.I.C.: 1479
N.A.I.C.S.: 212393

CHINA MOTION TELECOM INTERNATIONAL LIMITED
Rooms 3505-3506 35th Floor
Edinburgh Tower The Landmark
15 Queen's Road Central, Central, China (Hong Kong)
Tel.: (852) 22092888
Fax: (852) 22091888
Web Site: www.chinamotion.com
Year Founded: 1990
0989—(HKG)
Sales Range: $1-9.9 Million
Emp.: 304
Business Description:
Telecommunications Management & Services
S.I.C.: 4899
N.A.I.C.S.: 517919
Personnel:
Raymond Pang Wan Ting *(Chm)*
Zuguang Ji *(Deputy CEO)*
Yuet Kwan Lung *(Sec)*
Board of Directors:
Raymond Pang Wan Ting
An Guo Huang
Zuguang Ji
Ka Man Sin
Fei Tat Wong

MUFG Fund Services (Bermuda) Limited
26 Burnaby Street
Hamilton, Bermuda

Subsidiary:

China Motion Holdings Limited (1)
Unit 3101 Level 31 Tower 1 Enterprise Square Five 38 Wang Chiu Road
Kowloon Bay, Hong Kong, China (Hong Kong) VG
Tel.: (852) 22092888 (100%)
Fax: (852) 22091888
E-Mail:
Emp.: 200
Holding Company
S.I.C.: 6719
N.A.I.C.S.: 551112
Ting Reymond *(Chm)*

Subsidiaries:

China Motion United Telecom Limited (2)
Unit 3101 Level 31 Tower 1 Enterprise Square Five 38 Wang Chiu Road
Kowloon Bay, Hong Kong, China (Hong Kong) HK
Tel.: (852) 22092888 (70%)
Fax: (852) 22091888
Investment Holding Company
S.I.C.: 6719
N.A.I.C.S.: 551112

CHINA MOWIN HOLDING LTD
12th Floor Grand Building 15-18 Connaught Road
Central, China (Hong Kong)
Tel.: (852) 25216838
Fax: (852) 28106317
E-Mail: tcwsn@hk.tcw.com
Web Site: www.chinamowin.com
MLWIN—(EUR)
Emp.: 1,300
Business Description:
Holding Company; Mobile Communications Services
S.I.C.: 6719
N.A.I.C.S.: 551112
Personnel:
Bill Yang *(Chm & Pres)*
Feilight Chen *(COO)*
Randy Zhang *(CTO)*
Board of Directors:
Bill Yang
George Yi

CHINA NATIONAL AVIATION FUEL GROUP CORPORATION
China National Aviation Fuel Plaza
No 2 Madian Road
Haidian District, Beijing, 100088, China
Tel.: (86) 10 5989 0754
Fax: (86) 10 5989 0766
Web Site: www.cnaf.com
Sales Range: $25-49.9 Billion
Emp.: 9,300
Business Description:
Air Transportation Logistics Services
S.I.C.: 4581
N.A.I.C.S.: 488190

Personnel:
Sun Li *(Pres)*

Non-U.S. Subsidiary:

China Aviation Oil (Singapore) Corporation Ltd. (1)
8 Temasek Boulevard 31-02 Suntec Tower Three
Singapore, 038988, Singapore (51%)
Tel.: (65) 63348979
Fax: (65) 63335283
E-Mail: admin@caosco.com
Web Site: www.caosco.com
G92—(SES)
Rev.: $14,807,984,000
Assets: $1,650,340,000
Liabilities: $1,190,407,000
Net Worth: $459,933,000
Earnings: $66,189,000
Fiscal Year-end: 12/31/12
Jet Fuel Distribution
S.I.C.: 5989
N.A.I.C.S.: 454310
Kai Yuen Wang *(Deputy Chm)*
Fanqiu Meng *(CEO)*
Chunyan Wang *(CFO)*
Jean Teo *(COO)*
Doreen Nah *(Sec & Head-Legal)*

CHINA NATIONAL AVIATION HOLDING COMPANY

Guohang Bldg 36 Xiaoyun Rd
Beijing, 100027, China
Tel.: (86) 1084488888
Fax: (86) 1084475400
Web Site: www.airchinagroup.com
Sales Range: $5-14.9 Billion
Emp.: 100
Business Description:
Holding Company; Passenger Transportation
S.I.C.: 6719
N.A.I.C.S.: 551112
Personnel:
Jianjiang Cai *(Gen Mgr)*

Non-U.S. Subsidiary:

Air China Ltd. (1)
Blue Sky Mansion 28 Tianzhu Road Airport Economic Development Zone
Beijing, Shunyi, China
Tel.: (86) 10 6146 2799
Fax: (86) 10 6146 2805
E-Mail: ir@airchina.com
Web Site: www.airchina.com.cn
601111—(HKG OTC SHG)
Rev.: $16,018,065,786
Assets: $29,798,783,330
Liabilities: $21,494,482,440
Net Worth: $8,304,300,890
Earnings: $782,813,594
Emp.: 25,269
Fiscal Year-end: 12/31/12
Provider of Commercial Airline Services
S.I.C.: 4512
N.A.I.C.S.: 481111
Jianjiang Cai *(Chm)*
Song Zhiyong *(Pres)*
Qiang Long *(Chief Svc Officer)*
Chuanyu Xu *(Chief Safety Officer)*
Rune Feng *(Pres-Labour Union)*
Xinyu Rao *(Co-Sec)*
Shuit Mui Tam *(Co-Sec)*

Joint Venture:

Aircraft Maintenance & Engineering Corp. (2)
Beijing Capital International Airport
Beijing, 100621, China
Tel.: (86) 10645611224
Fax: (86) 1064561517
Web Site: www.ameco.com.cn
Emp.: 3,600
Aircraft Maintenance, Repair & Overhaul Services; Owned 60% by China National Aviation Holding Company & 40% by Deutsche Lufthansa AG
S.I.C.: 4581
N.A.I.C.S.: 488190
Chai Weixi *(CEO)*

Subsidiary:

Air Macau Co., Ltd. (1)
398 Alameda Drive Carlos D'Assumpcao 12-18 andar, Macau, China (Macau) (51%)
Tel.: (853) 3966888
Fax: (853) 3966866
Web Site: www.airmacau.com.mo
Sales Range: $5-14.9 Billion
Regional Airline Services
Import Export
S.I.C.: 4512
N.A.I.C.S.: 481111
Gu Tiefei *(Chm)*
Zheng Yan *(Pres)*

CHINA NATIONAL BUILDING MATERIALS GROUP CORPORATION

No 2 South Zi Zhu Yuan Road
Haidian District, Beijing, 100048, China
Tel.: (86) 1088416688
Fax: (86) 1068422743
E-Mail: cnbmadmin@cnbm.com.cn
Web Site: www.cnbm.com.cn
Year Founded: 1984
Emp.: 100,000
Business Description:
Holding Company; Building Materials Mfr & Distr
S.I.C.: 6719
N.A.I.C.S.: 551112
Personnel:
Zhiping Song *(Chm)*
Yan Yao *(Pres)*
Jinhua Xu *(Gen Counsel & VP)*
Board of Directors:
Zhiping Song
Desheng Cao
Jianglin Cao
Jiantang Guo
Zhenhua Hao
Junlu Jiang
Xizhong Lin
Zhenhou Wang
Jiwen Xiong
Yan Yao
Jian Zhang

Holding:

China National Building Material Company Limited (1)
17th Floor Zhong Guo Jian Cai Da Sha San Lihe Road No 11
Haidian District, Beijing, China 100037 CN
Tel.: (86) 10 88082366 (48.82%)
Fax: (86) 10 88082383
E-Mail: cnbmltd@cnbm.com.cn
Web Site: www.cnbmltd.com
3323—(HKG OTC)
Rev.: $13,854,520,367
Assets: $39,145,968,941
Liabilities: $32,146,267,995
Net Worth: $6,999,700,946
Earnings: $1,229,020,226
Emp.: 121,657
Fiscal Year-end: 12/31/12
Building Products Mfr
S.I.C.: 3241
N.A.I.C.S.: 327310
Zhiping Song *(Chm)*
Jiwei Wu *(Chm-Supervisory Bd)*
Jianglin Cao *(Pres)*
Xuean Chen *(CFO & VP)*
Zhangli Chang *(Co-Sec & VP)*
Susan Yee Har Lo *(Co-Sec)*

Subsidiary:

China Triumph International Engineering Co., Ltd. (2)
2000 Zhongshanbei Road
Shanghai, China
Tel.: (86) 21 62030071
Fax: (86) 21 62033390
E-Mail: shanghai@ctiec.net
Web Site: www.ctiec.net
Engineering Services
S.I.C.: 8711
N.A.I.C.S.: 541330

Non-U.S. Subsidiary:

CTF Solar GmbH (3)
Manfred-von-Ardenne-Ring 20 Haus F
01099 Dresden, Germany
Tel.: (49) 6195 6796 0
Fax: (49) 6195 6763 19
E-Mail: info@ctf-solar.com
Web Site: www.ctf-solar.com
Emp.: 18
Solar Modules Mfr
S.I.C.: 3674
N.A.I.C.S.: 334413
Sven Frauenstein *(CTO)*

CHINA NATIONAL CHEMICAL CORPORATION

(d/b/a ChemChina)
No 62 Beisihuan Xilu
Haidian District, Beijing, PRC, 100080, China
Tel.: (86) 10 8267 7234
Fax: (86) 10 8267 7088
E-Mail: zghg@chemchina.com
Web Site: www.chemchina.com.cn
Year Founded: 2004
Emp.: 100,000
Business Description:
Holding Company; Chemicals
S.I.C.: 6719
N.A.I.C.S.: 551112
Personnel:
Ren Jianxin *(Chm & Gen Mgr)*

Subsidiary:

China National Bluestar (Group) Co., Ltd. (1)
No 19 East Road North No 3 Ring Road
ChaoYang District, Beijing, 100029, China CN
Tel.: (86) 1064429448
Fax: (86) 1064429446
E-Mail: cbsc@china-bluestar.com
Web Site: www.china-bluestar.com
Sales Range: $1-4.9 Billion
Emp.: 37,000
Petroleum Products, Organic & Inorganic Chemicals Developer & Mfr
S.I.C.: 2899
N.A.I.C.S.: 325998

Non-U.S. Subsidiaries:

Adisseo France S.A.S. (2)
10 Place De General Gaulle
F-92160 Antony, France FR
Tel.: (33) 146747000
Telex: 610500 F
Fax: (33) 140969696
E-Mail: info@adisseo.com
Web Site: www.adisseo.com
Sales Range: $750-799.9 Million
Emp.: 1,200
Animal Vitamins & Nutritional Food Additives Developer & Mfr
S.I.C.: 2048
N.A.I.C.S.: 311119
Gerard Deman *(CEO)*

Elkem ASA (2)
Hoffsveien 65B
N 0303 Oslo, Norway
Mailing Address:
PO Box 5211
Majorstuen, 0303 Oslo, Norway
Tel.: (47) 22450100
Fax: (47) 22450155
E-Mail: info@elkem.com
Web Site: www.elkem.com
Sales Range: $1-4.9 Billion
Emp.: 150
Development & Production of Advanced Ceramics & Environmental Technology
Export
S.I.C.: 3365
N.A.I.C.S.: 331524
Morten Viga *(CFO & Sr VP)*
Karin Aslaksen *(Sr VP-HR)*
Inge Grubben-Stromnes *(Sr VP-Strategy, Bus Dev & R&D)*

Divisions:

Deepsea Elkem Chartering AS (3)
Lilleakeerveien 4
PO Box 53
N 0216 Oslo, Norway
Tel.: (47) 22527800
Telex: 71247 elkch n
Fax: (47) 23501460
E-Mail: chartering@elkem-chartering.no
Web Site: www.elkem.com
Emp.: 100
Deep Sea Logistics Services
S.I.C.: 4731
N.A.I.C.S.: 541614
Joel Baardson *(Mng Dir)*

Elkem ASA - Materials Division (3)
PO Box 8126
Vaagsbygd, N 4675 Kristiansand, Norway
Tel.: (47) 38017500
Fax: (47) 38014970
E-Mail: elkem.materials@elkem.no
Web Site: www.materials.elkem.com
Sales Range: $25-49.9 Million
Emp.: 80
Microsilica Products, Cement Building Products, Silicon Metal Powders & Silicon Nitride Mfr
S.I.C.: 3241
N.A.I.C.S.: 327310

Non-U.S. Division:

Elkem Japan K.K. (4)
Nikko Sanno Bldg
401 5 3 Akasaka 2 Chome, Tokyo, 107-0052, Japan
Tel.: (81) 335847711
Fax: (81) 335840437
E-Mail: chikashi.aso@elkem.no
Web Site: www.elkem.co.jp
Sales Range: $25-49.9 Million
Emp.: 12
Construction Materials Mfr
S.I.C.: 5039
N.A.I.C.S.: 423390
Aso Chikashi *(Mgr-Fin)*

Elkem ASA - Silicon Division (3)
PO Box 5211
NO 0303 Oslo, Norway
Tel.: (47) 22450100
Fax: (47) 4722450495
E-Mail: info@elkem.no
Web Site: www.elkem.com
Emp.: 120
Silicon Products
S.I.C.: 3365
N.A.I.C.S.: 331524
Halge Aasin *(Pres)*

Divisions:

Elkem Marnes Kvartsittbrudd (4)
Elkem Marnes
N 8130 Sandhorney, Norway
Tel.: (47) 75758502
Fax: (47) 75758695
Web Site: www.elkem.no
Silicon Products Mfr
S.I.C.: 3365
N.A.I.C.S.: 331524
Kjell Sture Hugaas *(Mgr)*

Elkem Solar Research (4)
Vaagsbygd
PO Box 8040
NO-4675 Kristiansand, Norway
Tel.: (47) 38017000
Fax: (47) 38017040
Web Site: www.elkem.com
Research Services
S.I.C.: 8731
N.A.I.C.S.: 541712
Ragnar Tronstad *(Dir-R&D)*

Elkem Tana (4)
Austertana
NO-9845 Tana, Norway
Tel.: (47) 78926140
Fax: (47) 78926150
Web Site: www.elkem.no
Sls.: $2,145,000
Emp.: 18
Quartzite Quarrying
S.I.C.: 1429
N.A.I.C.S.: 212319

Elkem Thamshavn (4)
PO Box 10
NO-7301 Orkanger, Norway
Tel.: (47) 72488200
Telex: 55628 thavn n
Fax: (47) 72488300
Web Site: www.elkem.no

China National Chemical Corporation—(Continued)

Emp.: 130
Ferrosilicon Mfr
S.I.C.: 3312
N.A.I.C.S.: 331110
Alf Tore Haug *(Plant Mgr)*

U.S. Division:

Elkem Silicon Materials-Pittsburgh (4)
Airport Office Park Bldg 2 400 Rouser Rd
Moon Township, PA 15108-2749
Mailing Address:
PO Box 266
Pittsburgh, PA 15230-0266
Tel.: (412) 299-7200
Fax: (412) 299-7238
Web Site: www.elkem.com
Emp.: 16
Silicon Metal & Calcium Carbide Mfr
S.I.C.: 3365
N.A.I.C.S.: 331524
Mark Nilsen *(Pres)*

Non-U.S. Subsidiary:

Elkem Iceland (4)
Grundartangi
Skilmannahreppur, IS-301 Akranes, Iceland
Tel.: (354) 04320200
Telex: 2131 alloys is
Fax: (354) 04320101
Emp.: 120
Ferrosilicon Mfr
S.I.C.: 3312
N.A.I.C.S.: 331110
Einar Thorsteinsson *(Mng Dir)*

Elkem ASA-Carbon Division (3)
PO Box 8040
Kristiansand, 4675, Norway
Tel.: (47) 38017500
Fax: (47) 38017641
E-Mail: info@elkem.com
Web Site: www.elkem.nl
Emp.: 400
Carbon Products Mfr
S.I.C.: 3624
N.A.I.C.S.: 335991
Johannes Toste *(Gen Mgr)*

Non-U.S. Subsidiary:

Carboderivados S.A. (4)
Rua Atalydes
Moreira De Souza
n245 CIVIT I, CEP 29168 060 Serra, Espirito Santo, Brazil
Tel.: (55) 27 2123 200
Telex: 272657 crbd br
Fax: (55) 2733410077
Emp.: 34
Carbon Products Mfr
S.I.C.: 2819
N.A.I.C.S.: 325180

Elkem Bjolvefossen (3)
Hoffsveien 65B
Majorstua, N 5614 Alvik, Norway
Tel.: (47) 56550800
Telex: 42146 ferro n
Fax: (47) 56550951
E-Mail: bjolvefossen@elkem.com
Web Site: www.elkem.com
Emp.: 110
Foundry Products
S.I.C.: 3365
N.A.I.C.S.: 331524
Sroda Nummetal *(Mng Dir)*

Non-U.S. Subsidiaries:

Elkem Ltd. (3)
305 Glossop Rd
Sheffield, South Yorkshire, S10 2HL, United Kingdom
Tel.: (44) 42700334
Telex: 83733 elchem g
Fax: (44) 4442753103
Web Site: www.elkem.com
Emp.: 10
Foundry Products
S.I.C.: 3364
N.A.I.C.S.: 331523

Elkem Metal Canada Inc. (3)
2020 Chemin De La Reserve
Chicoutimi, QC, G7J0E1, Canada
Tel.: (418) 549-4171
Fax: (418) 549-4352
E-Mail: chris.lisso@elkem.com
Web Site: www.elkem.com
Emp.: 80
Ferrosilicon Mfr
S.I.C.: 3399
N.A.I.C.S.: 331110
Leo Bertrand *(Gen Mgr)*

Division:

Elkem Metals Canada Inc.-Hamilton (4)
1685 Main St W Ste 303
Hamilton, ON, L8S 1G5, Canada
Tel.: (905) 572-6722
Fax: (905) 572-6741
E-Mail: ham.sales@elkem.com
Web Site: www.elkem.com
Emp.: 4
Metals Sales & Distr
S.I.C.: 6029
N.A.I.C.S.: 522110
Chris Lisso *(Dir-Sls & Mktg)*

Euro Nordic Logistics B.V. (3)
Klompenmakerstraat 3
2984 BB Ridderkerk, Netherlands
Mailing Address:
PO Box 9234
3007AE Rotterdam, Netherlands
Tel.: (31) 180441144
Fax: (31) 180441100
E-Mail: logistics@euronordic.nl
Web Site: www.euronordic.nl
Emp.: 55
Logistics Services
S.I.C.: 4731
N.A.I.C.S.: 541614

Makhteshim-Agan Industries Ltd. (2)
Golan Street Airport City
Tel Aviv, 70151, Israel IL
Tel.: (972) 73 232 1000 (60%)
Fax: (972) 73 232 1074
E-Mail: ir@ma-industries.com
Web Site: www.ma-industries.com
MAIN—(TAE)
Rev.: $2,834,503,000
Assets: $3,975,023,000
Liabilities: $2,646,247,000
Net Worth: $1,328,776,000
Earnings: $122,573,000
Emp.: 4,508
Fiscal Year-end: 12/31/12
Crop Protection Products Mfr
Import Export
S.I.C.: 2879
N.A.I.C.S.: 325320
Xingqiang Yang *(Chm)*
Ami Erel *(Vice Chm)*
Chen Lichtenstein *(Deputy CEO)*
Aviram Lahav *(CFO & Sr VP)*
Ignacio Dominguez *(Chief Comml Officer, Sr VP & Head-Global Products & Mktg Div)*
Michal Arlosoroff *(CSR Officer, Gen Counsel, Sec & Sr VP)*
Shaul Friedland *(CEO-Americas)*
Anders Harfstrand *(CEO-Europe)*
Ran Maidan *(CEO-Asia Pacific, Africa & Middle East)*
Eli Abramov *(Sr VP-Global Resources)*
Rony Patishi-Chillim *(Sr VP-Global Corp Comm)*
Amos Rabin *(Sr VP-Global HR)*

Subsidiary:

Makhteshim Chemical Works Ltd. (3)
Derech Hebron Industrial Zone
PO Box 60
Industrial Zone, Beersheba, 84100, Israel IL
Tel.: (972) 86296611
Fax: (972) 86296846
E-Mail: rachell@mcw.co.il
Web Site: www.mcw.co.il
Emp.: 200
Agricultural Chemicals Mfr
S.I.C.: 2879
N.A.I.C.S.: 325320
Robert Schachter *(Mgr)*

Non-U.S. Subsidiaries:

Aragonesas Agro S.A. (3)
Paseo de Recoletos 16 3rd Floor
28001 Madrid, Spain ES
Tel.: (34) 91 585 2380
Fax: (34) 915852310
E-Mail: aragro@aragro.es
Web Site: www.aragro.es
Emp.: 100
Agricultural Chemicals Mfr
S.I.C.: 2879
N.A.I.C.S.: 325320

Farmoz Pty Ltd. (3)
Suite 1 Level 4 Building B
207 Pacific Highway, Saint Leonards, NSW, 2065, Australia
Tel.: (61) 294317800
Fax: (61) 294317700
E-Mail: farmoz@farmoz.com.au
Web Site: www.farmoz.com.au
Sales Range: $50-74.9 Million
Emp.: 30
Agricultural Product Mfr & Distr
S.I.C.: 2879
N.A.I.C.S.: 325320
David Peters *(Mng Dir)*
Stuart Deer *(CFO)*

Magan Argentina S.A. (3)
Cerrito 1186 8th Floor
Buenos Aires, C1010AAX, Argentina
Tel.: (54) 1148136040
Fax: (54) 1148136082
E-Mail: info@magan.com.ar
Web Site: www.magan.com.ar
Emp.: 30
Agricultural Chemicals Mfr
S.I.C.: 2879
N.A.I.C.S.: 325320

MAGAN Korea Co. Ltd. (3)
Ste 201 Hosan Bldg 61-4 Nonhyun-Dong
Kangnam-Gu, Seoul, 135 010, Korea (South)
Tel.: (82) 234446883
Fax: (82) 234446880
Emp.: 3
Agricultural Chemicals Mfr
S.I.C.: 2879
N.A.I.C.S.: 325320
Is Yoon *(CEO)*

Makhteshim-Agan Espana SA (3)
C/San Vicente N 16
Entresuelo Puertas 3-5, 46002 Valencia, Spain ES
Tel.: (34) 963519534
Fax: (34) 963519846
E-Mail: mcwagan@mcwagan.com
Web Site: www.ma-industries.com
Emp.: 10
Agricultural Chemicals Mfr
S.I.C.: 2879
N.A.I.C.S.: 325320

Makhteshim-Agan France Sarl (3)
2 Rue Troyon
92316 Sevres, Cedex, France FR
Tel.: (33) 141901696
Fax: (33) 146626497
E-Mail: accueil@ma-france.com
Web Site: www.ma-france.com
Emp.: 64
Agricultural Chemicals Mfr
S.I.C.: 2879
N.A.I.C.S.: 325320
Eve Leconte *(Mgr-HR)*

Makhteshim-Agan Italia S.r.l. (3)
Zenita 19 Grassobbio
24126 Bergamo, Italy IT
Tel.: (39) 035 328 811
Fax: (39) 035 328 888
E-Mail: mait@ma-italia.it
Web Site: www.ma-italia.it
Emp.: 40
Agricultural Chemicals Mfr
S.I.C.: 2879
N.A.I.C.S.: 325320

Makhteshim-Agan MAROM S.R.L. (3)
Sos Bucuresti-Nord nr 10 Global City
Business Park Cladirea O21 Et 6
Voluntari Jud Ilfov, 77190 Bucharest, Romania RO
Tel.: (40) 213077612
Fax: (40) 212720015
E-Mail: marom@makhte.ro
Web Site: www.makhteshim-agan.ro
Emp.: 25
Agricultural Chemicals Mfr
S.I.C.: 2879
N.A.I.C.S.: 325320
Elizer Frumerman *(Mgr)*

Makhteshim-Agan (U.K.) Ltd. (3)
Unit 16 Thatcham Business Village
Colthrop Way, Thatcham, Berks, RG19 4LW, United Kingdom UK
Tel.: (44) 635860555
Fax: (44) 1635 861555
E-Mail: admin@mauk.co.uk
Web Site: www.mauk.co.uk
Emp.: 12
Agricultural Chemicals Mfr
S.I.C.: 2879
N.A.I.C.S.: 325320
Mike Barrett *(Mng Dir)*

Milenia Agrociencias S.A. (3)
Av Pedro Antonio de Souza 400
Jardim Eucaliptos, Londrina, PR, 86031 610, Brazil
Tel.: (55) 4333719000
Fax: (55) 4333719299
E-Mail: milenia@milenia.com.br
Web Site: www.milenia.com.br
Emp.: 500
Agricultural Chemicals Mfr
S.I.C.: 2879
N.A.I.C.S.: 325320
Rodrigo Guiterrez *(Pres)*

Proficol Andina B.V. - Colombia (3)
Carrera 11 No 87-51 Piso 4
Bogota, 29611, Colombia Co
Tel.: (57) 1 6446730
Fax: (57) 1 6401201
E-Mail: contact.us@proficol.com
Web Site: www.proficol.com
Sales Range: Less than $1 Million
Emp.: 112
Agricultural Chemicals Mfr
S.I.C.: 2879
N.A.I.C.S.: 325320
Steiner Jorge *(Mng Dir)*

Non-U.S. Affiliate:

Alfa Agricultural Supplies S.A. (3)
73 Ethnikis Antistasseos St
Chalandri, 152 31 Athens, Greece GR
Tel.: (30) 2111205555
Fax: (30) 2111205559
E-Mail: alfa@alfagro.gr
Web Site: www.alfagro.gr
Emp.: 85
Mfr of Agricultural Chemicals
S.I.C.: 2879
N.A.I.C.S.: 325320
Vasilis Paissios *(Mgr-Sls)*

CHINA NATIONAL COMPLETE PLANT IMPORT & EXPORT CORPORATION

(d/b/a China Complant Group)
Mansion 9 Xi Bin He Lu An Ding Men
Beijing, 100011, China
Tel.: (86) 1064253388
Fax: (86) 1064211382
E-Mail: info@complant.com
Web Site: www.complant.com
Year Founded: 1959

Business Description:
Construction & Engineering Services
S.I.C.: 1629
N.A.I.C.S.: 237990
Personnel:
Zhimin Li *(Chm)*

CHINA NATIONAL MACHINERY INDUSTRY CORPORATION

No 3 Danling Street
Haidian District, Beijing, 100080, China
Tel.: (86) 10 82688888
Fax: (86) 10 82688811
E-Mail: office@sinomach.com.cn
Web Site: www.sinomach.com.cn
Year Founded: 1997
Sales Range: $25-49.9 Billion
Emp.: 100,000

Business Description:
Investment Management Services
S.I.C.: 6799

N.A.I.C.S.: 523920
Personnel:
Ren Hongbin *(Chm)*
Chen Zhi *(Vice Chm)*
Xu Jian *(Pres)*
Luo Jiamang *(CFO)*
Board of Directors:
Ren Hongbin
An Dewu
Wei Feng
Liu Gaozhuo
Xu Jian
Zhang Lailiang
Lian Weizeng
Wu Xiaogen
Han Xizheng
Chen Zhi

CHINA NATIONAL MATERIALS COMPANY LIMITED

(d/b/a SINOMA)
11 Beishuncheng Street Xizhimennei
Xicheng District, Beijing, 100035, China
Tel.: (86) 10 82229925
Fax: (86) 10 82228800
E-Mail: sinomaltd@sinoma-ltd.cn
Web Site: en.sinoma-ltd.cn
1893—(HKG OTC)
Sls.: $7,350,396,791
Assets: $13,954,085,640
Liabilities: $9,653,220,937
Net Worth: $4,300,864,703
Earnings: $248,810,091
Emp.: 56,325
Fiscal Year-end: 12/31/12
Business Description:
Cement & Engineering Equipment & Materials
S.I.C.: 3531
N.A.I.C.S.: 333120
Personnel:
Zhijiang Liu *(Chm)*
Weibing Xu *(Chm-Supervisory Bd)*
Xinhua Li *(Vice Chm & Pres)*
Kaijun Yu *(CFO)*
Chao Gu *(Co-Sec & VP)*
Leung Fai Yu *(Co-Sec)*
Board of Directors:
Zhijiang Liu
Chong Shun Leung
Xinhua Li
Zhengfei Lu
Baoqi Tang
Shimin Wang
Shiliang Yu
Hai Zhang
Zude Zhou
Supervisory Board of Directors:
Weibing Xu
Xiaoli Qu
Jianguo Wang
Xingmin Yu
Renjie Zhang
Transfer Agent:
Computershare Hong Kong Investor Services Limited
17M Floor Hopewell Centre 183 Queen's Road East
Wanchai, China (Hong Kong)
Subsidiaries:

Beijing Composite Material Co., Ltd. **(1)**
261 Kangxi Rd Badaling Industry Development Zone
Yanqing, 102101 Beijing, China
Tel.: (86) 10 61161236
Fax: (86) 10 61162500
E-Mail: composite@sinoma.cn
Web Site: www.sinoma-composite.cn
Water Tanks & Pipes Mfr
S.I.C.: 3443
N.A.I.C.S.: 332420

Jiangxi Sinoma New Solar Materials Co., Ltd. **(1)**
No 1859 Economic Development Zone
Xinyu, Jiangxi, China
Tel.: (86) 7906863333
Fax: (86) 790 6863666
E-Mail: jxzc@sinomasolar.com
Web Site: www.sinomasolar.com
Silica Crucibles Mfr & Distr
S.I.C.: 3255
N.A.I.C.S.: 327120
Tan Zhongming *(Gen Mgr)*

Sinoma Advanced Materials Co. Ltd. **(1)**
16 Wangjing North Road
Chaoyang District, Beijing, 100102, China
Tel.: (86) 10 64390145
Fax: (86) 10 64399496
E-Mail: zoomber@sinoma.cn
Web Site: www.sinoma-zoomber.cn
Quartz Crystals Mfr & Engineering Services
S.I.C.: 3679
N.A.I.C.S.: 334419

Sinoma Jinjing Fiber Glass Co., Ltd. **(1)**
No 122 Yumin Road Zibo National New Hi-Tech Industrial Park
Zibo, Shandong, 255086, China
Tel.: (86) 5333919112
Fax: (86) 5333919156
E-Mail: fiberjj@sinoma.cn
Web Site: www.sinoma-fiberjj.cn
Fiberglass Products Mfr
S.I.C.: 3088
N.A.I.C.S.: 326191
Wang Baoguo *(Chm)*

Sinoma Yanzhou Mining Engineering Co., Ltd. **(1)**
No 136 Zhongqiao North Street
Yanzhou, Shandong, 272100, China
Tel.: (86) 5373413645
Fax: (86) 537 3413645
E-Mail: yzhgs@sinoma.cn
Web Site: old.sinoma.cn/connect_us.asp
Engineering Services
S.I.C.: 8711
N.A.I.C.S.: 541330

Suzhou Tianshan Cement Co.,Ltd. **(1)**
North End of Gaodian Bridge
Chefang Town, Suzhou, Jiangsu, 215125, China
Tel.: (86) 51265922579
Portland Cement Mfr
S.I.C.: 3241
N.A.I.C.S.: 327310

Taishan Fiberglass Inc. **(1)**
Economic Development Zone
Tai'an, Shandong, 271000, China
Tel.: (86) 5386627910
Fax: (86) 5386627917
E-Mail: ctgf@ctgf.com
Web Site: www.ctgf.com
Fiberglass Products Mfr & Distr
S.I.C.: 2299
N.A.I.C.S.: 313210
Zhiyao Tang *(Chm & Pres)*

Taishan Fiberglass Zoucheng Co., Ltd. **(1)**
Liyan Industrial Park
Taiping Town, Zoucheng, Shandong, 273517, China
Tel.: (86) 5375463988
Fiber Glass Mfr
S.I.C.: 3229
N.A.I.C.S.: 327212

Xiamen ISO Standard Sand Co., Ltd. **(1)**
No 45 Yanghe Road Xinyang Industrial Zone
Haicang Investment Zone, 361022 Xiamen, Fujian, China
Tel.: (86) 592 6516879
Fax: (86) 592 6516860
E-Mail: salesmanager@isosand.com
Web Site: www.isosand.com
Sands Distr
S.I.C.: 5032
N.A.I.C.S.: 423320

U.S. Subsidiary:

CTG International Inc. **(1)**
1268 E Edna Pl
Covina, CA 91724-2509
Tel.: (626) 332-0800
Fax: (626) 332-2226
Web Site: www.ctgf.com
Emp.: 5
Glass Fiber Distr
S.I.C.: 3229
N.A.I.C.S.: 327212
Calvin Lee *(Pres)*

CHINA NATIONAL NUCLEAR CORPORATION

No 1 Nanasanxiang
Sanlihe, Beijing, 100822, China
Tel.: (86) 10 6851 2211
Fax: (86) 10 6853 3989
Web Site: www.cnnc.com.cn
Emp.: 100,000
Business Description:
Nuclear Technology Industries Holding Company
S.I.C.: 6719
N.A.I.C.S.: 551112
Personnel:
Qin Sun *(Pres)*
Non-U.S. Holding:

CNNC International Limited **(1)**
Unit 2809 28th Floor China Resources Building 26 Harbour Road
Wanchai, China (Hong Kong) Ky
Tel.: (852) 2598 1010
Fax: (852) 2598 6262
E-Mail: info@cnncintl.com
Web Site: www.cnncintl.com
2302—(HKG)
Rev.: $53,829,146
Assets: $179,962,491
Liabilities: $55,558,365
Net Worth: $124,404,126
Earnings: ($3,370,495)
Emp.: 16
Fiscal Year-end: 12/31/12
Holding Company
S.I.C.: 6719
N.A.I.C.S.: 551112
Hongqing Zhang *(CEO)*
Philip Sau Yan Li *(Sec & Controller-Fin)*
Ying Wang *(Exec VP)*

CHINA NATIONAL OFFSHORE OIL CORP.

No 25 Chaoyangmenbei Dajie
Box 4705
Beijing, Dongcheng, 100010, China
Tel.: (86) 1084521010
Fax: (86) 1064602600
E-Mail: cnooc@cnooc.com.cn
Web Site: www.cnooc.com.cn
Rev.: $83,645,009,100
Assets: $129,954,708,450
Liabilities: $47,282,179,050
Net Worth: $82,672,529,400
Earnings: $11,879,914,950
Emp.: 102,562
Fiscal Year-end: 12/31/12
Business Description:
Oil Production Services
S.I.C.: 1311
N.A.I.C.S.: 211111
Personnel:
Yilin Wang *(Chm)*
Hua Yang *(Pres)*
Guangyu Yuan *(Asst Pres)*
Changbo Zheng *(Asst Pres)*
Mengfei Wu *(CFO)*
Jianwei Zhang *(Chief Compliance Officer)*
Liguo Zhao *(Chief Legal Officer)*
Yongzhi Jiang *(Co-Sec)*
Weilin Zhu *(Exec VP & Gen Mgr-Exploration Dept)*
Bi Chen *(Exec VP)*
Guohua Zhang *(Sr VP)*
Board of Directors:
Yilin Wang
Swan Foo Boon
Wei Chen
Gong He
Kaiyuan Wang
Dawei Xia
Zhongyu Xie
Hua Yang
Jianwei Zhang
Subsidiary:

China Oilfield Services Limited **(1)**
Room 610 B CNOOC Plaza 25
Chaoyangmen North Avenue
Dongcheng District, Beijing, 100010, China CN
Tel.: (86) 10 84522840 (54.74%)
Fax: (86) 10 84522131
E-Mail: cosl@cnoocs.com
Web Site: www.cosl.com.cn
2883—(HKG OTC SHG)
Rev.: $3,538,978,167
Assets: $11,857,918,673
Liabilities: $6,742,168,084
Net Worth: $5,115,750,589
Earnings: $725,907,965
Emp.: 12,991
Fiscal Year-end: 12/31/12
Holding Company; Offshore Oil & Gas Drilling, Well & Marine Support Services
S.I.C.: 6719
N.A.I.C.S.: 551112
Xuefen An *(Chm-Supervisory Bd)*
Yong Li *(Pres & CEO)*
Feilong Li *(CFO & Exec VP)*
Haijiang Yang *(Sec)*
Weiliang Dong *(Exec VP)*

Joint Venture:

Eastern Marine Services Limited **(2)**
Room 1008-1010 10F Building B
No 317 Xianxia Road
Shanghai, 200051, China
Tel.: (86) 62706737
Fax: (86) 6270673789
Web Site: www.emsl.com.cn/contact.htm
Sales Range: $250-299.9 Million
Offshore Oil & Gas Exploration, Production Support & Pipeline Construction Services; Owned 51% by China Oilfield Services Limited & 49% by Trico Marine Services, Inc.
S.I.C.: 1389
N.A.I.C.S.: 213112

Non-U.S. Subsidiary:

CNOOC Limited **(1)**
65th Floor Bank of China Tower One Garden Road
Central, China (Hong Kong) HK
Tel.: (852) 2213 2500 (66%)
Fax: (852) 2525 9322
E-Mail: contact@cnooc.com.cn
Web Site: www.cnoocltd.com
CEO—(HKG NYSE TSX)
Rev.: $39,335,548,950
Assets: $72,446,719,500
Liabilities: $23,238,166,500
Net Worth: $49,208,553,000
Earnings: $10,117,315,350
Emp.: 10,063
Fiscal Year-end: 12/31/12
Offshore Oil & Gas Exploration & Production Services
Import Export
S.I.C.: 1311
N.A.I.C.S.: 211111
Fanrong Li *(Chm, Pres & CEO)*
Hua Yang *(Vice Chm)*
Hua Zhong *(CFO, Sec & Gen Mgr-IR Dept)*

Non-U.S. Subsidiaries:

China Offshore Oil (Singapore) International Pte. Ltd. **(2)**
20 Cecil St
27-01/08 Equity Plz, Singapore, 049705, Singapore SG
Tel.: (65) 65356995 (100%)
Fax: (65) 65352976
Oil Exploration & Drilling Services
S.I.C.: 1381
N.A.I.C.S.: 213111

CNOOC Canada Inc. **(2)**
Suite 1600 555 4th Avenue South West
Calgary, AB, T2P 3E7, Canada Ca
Tel.: (403) 249-9425
Fax: (403) 225-2606

China National Offshore Oil Corp.—(Continued)

Sales Range: $250-299.9 Million
Emp.: 20
Holding Company; Oil Exploration & Extraction Services
S.I.C.: 6719
N.A.I.C.S.: 551112
David Bowes *(Treas)*

Subsidiary:

Nexen Energy ULC (3)
(Formerly Nexen Inc.)
801 7th Avenue SW
Calgary, AB, T2P 3P7, Canada Ca
Tel.: (403) 699-4000 (100%)
Fax: (403) 699-5800
E-Mail: info@nexeninc.com
Web Site: www.nexeninc.com
Rev.: $6,670,868,220
Assets: $20,414,188,740
Liabilities: $11,661,842,640
Net Worth: $8,752,346,100
Earnings: $331,008,660
Emp.: 3,228
Fiscal Year-end: 12/31/12
Holding Company; Diversified Energy Resource Exploration, Extraction & Specialty Chemical Distribution Services
S.I.C.: 6719
N.A.I.C.S.: 551112
Fanrong Li *(Chm)*
Zhi Fang *(Vice Chm)*
Kevin J. Reinhart *(CEO)*
Una M. Power *(CFO & Sr VP-Corp Plng, Bus Dev, Mktg & IT)*
Alan O'Brien *(Gen Counsel, Sec & Sr VP)*
Jim Arnold *(Sr VP-Oil Sands)*
Ron Bailey *(Sr VP-Operational Svcs, Tech & Canadian Natural Gas)*

Subsidiaries:

Nexen Marketing Inc. (4)
801 7th Avenue SW
Calgary, AB, T2P 3P7, Canada AB
Tel.: (403) 699-4400
Fax: (403) 699-5707
Web Site: www.nexeninc.com
Crude Oil, Natural Gas & Natural Gas Liquids Wholesale Trade Agency
S.I.C.: 7389
N.A.I.C.S.: 425120

U.S. Subsidiary:

Nexen Energy Marketing U.S.A. Inc. (5)
Murphy Bldg 5th Fl 9805 Katy Fwy
Houston, TX 77024
Tel.: (281) 295-5500
Fax: (281) 295-5599
Web Site: www.nexeninc.com
Crude Oil, Natural Gas & Natural Gas Liquids Wholesale Trade Agency
S.I.C.: 7389
N.A.I.C.S.: 425120

Non-U.S. Subsidiary:

Nexen Energy Marketing Europe Limited (5)
Charter Place Vine Street
Uxbridge, Mddx, UB8 1JG, United Kingdom UK
Tel.: (44) 1895 275 900
Fax: (44) 1895 275 901
Web Site: www.nexeninc.com
Emp.: 20
Crude Oil, Natural Gas & Natural Gas Liquids Wholesale Trade Agency
S.I.C.: 7389
N.A.I.C.S.: 425120

Nexen Oil Sands Partnership (4)
801 7 Ave Sw 34 Fl
Calgary, AB, T2P 3P7, Canada
Tel.: (780) 334-3400
Fax: (403) 699-5800
Web Site: www.nexeninc.com
Oil Sands Exploration & Petroleum Extraction Services
S.I.C.: 1311
N.A.I.C.S.: 211111
Jim Arnold *(Sr VP)*

Unit:

Nexen Shale Gas (Canada) (4)
Fort Nelson
PO Box 3202
Fort Nelson, BC, V0C 1R0, Canada
Tel.: (250) 774-5150
Web Site: www.nexeninc.com
Shale Gas Extraction Services
S.I.C.: 1311
N.A.I.C.S.: 211111

U.S. Subsidiary:

Nexen Petroleum U.S.A. Inc. (4)
945 Bunker Hill Rd Ste 1400
Houston, TX 77024 DE
Tel.: (832) 714-5000
E-Mail: info@nexeninc.com
Web Site: www.nexeninc.com
Emp.: 168
Petroleum & Natural Gas Extraction Services
S.I.C.: 1311
N.A.I.C.S.: 211111
Peter D. Addy *(VP & Gen Mgr)*

Subsidiaries:

Nexen Petroleum Offshore U.S.A. Inc. (5)
945 Bunker Hill Rd Ste 1400
Houston, TX 77024 DE
Tel.: (832) 714-5000
Offshore Petroleum & Natural Gas Extraction Services
S.I.C.: 1311
N.A.I.C.S.: 211111
Peter D. Addy *(VP & Gen Mgr)*

Non-U.S. Subsidiaries:

Nexen Petroleum Colombia Limited (4)
Carrera #9 76-49 Piso 6
Nogal Centre, Bogota, Colombia Co
Tel.: (57) 1 319 1330
Web Site: www.nexeninc.com
Petroleum & Natural Gas Extraction Services
S.I.C.: 1311
N.A.I.C.S.: 211111
Alistair Mooney *(VP & Gen Mgr)*

Nexen Petroleum Nigeria Ltd. (4)
The Octagon 7th Fl 13A AJ Marinho Dr
Victoria Island
Lagos, Nigeria NG
Tel.: (234) 1 774 1267 (100%)
Web Site: www.nexeninc.com
Petroleum & Natural Gas Extraction Services
S.I.C.: 1311
N.A.I.C.S.: 211111
Alistair Mooney *(VP & Gen Mgr)*

Nexen Petroleum UK Limited (4)
Upper Ground Floor Charter Place Vine Street
Uxbridge, Mddx, UB8 1JG, United Kingdom UK
Tel.: (44) 1895 237 700 (100%)
Fax: (44) 1895 237 232
Web Site: www.nexeninc.com
Emp.: 200
Petroleum & Natural Gas Extraction Services
S.I.C.: 1311
N.A.I.C.S.: 211111
Archie Kennedy *(Mng Dir)*

CHINA NATIONAL PETROLEUM CORPORATION

(d/b/a CNPC)
9 Dongzhimen North Street
Dongcheng District
Beijing, 100007, China
Tel.: (86) 10 6209 4114
Fax: (86) 10 6209 4205
E-Mail: admin_eng@cnpc.com.cn
Web Site: www.cnpc.com.cn
Year Founded: 1988
Rev.: $426,270,845,655
Assets: $541,586,425,775
Liabilities: $245,472,452,199
Net Worth: $296,113,973,576
Earnings: $22,107,883,622
Fiscal Year-end: 12/31/12

Business Description:
Holding Company; Oil & Gas Products & Services
Import Export
S.I.C.: 6719
N.A.I.C.S.: 551112

Personnel:
Jiping Zhou *(Chm)*
Yongyuan Liao *(Pres)*
Guoliang Wang *(CFO)*

Subsidiary:

PetroChina Company Limited (1)
9 Dongzhimen North Street
Dongcheng District, Beijing, 100007, China CN
Tel.: (86) 10 5998 6223 (86.42%)
Fax: (86) 10 6209 9557
E-Mail: suxinliang@petrochina.com.cn
Web Site: www.petrochina.com.cn
PTR—(HKG NYSE SHG)
Sls.: $348,722,769,600
Assets: $344,529,129,600
Liabilities: $156,967,309,800
Net Worth: $187,561,819,800
Earnings: $20,748,987,000
Emp.: 548,355
Fiscal Year-end: 12/31/12
Oil & Natural Gas Producer
S.I.C.: 1311
N.A.I.C.S.: 211111
Jiping Zhou *(Chm)*
Dongjin Wang *(Pres)*
Yibo Yu *(CFO & Gen Mgr-M&A Dept)*
Hualin Li *(Sec & VP)*

Subsidiaries:

PetroChina International Co. Ltd. (2)
Building A Fl 22 23 Vantone New World Plaza
2 Fuwai Street, Beijing, 100037, China
Tel.: (86) 1068041188
Fax: (86) 1068587901
Web Site: www.petrochinaintl.com.cn
Emp.: 300
Petroleum Producer
S.I.C.: 1311
N.A.I.C.S.: 211111

Non-U.S. Subsidiaries:

PetroChina International (Indonesia) (3)
Gedung Menara Kuningan 17th-27th Floors
Jl Hr Rasuna Said Blok X/7
Kav 5, Jakarta, 12940, Indonesia
Tel.: (62) 21 579 45300
Fax: (62) 21 579 45301
Web Site: www.petrochina.co.id/address.html
Petroleum Producer
S.I.C.: 1311
N.A.I.C.S.: 211111

PetroChina International (London) Co., Limited (3)
8th Floor Marble Arch Tower
55 Bryanston Street, London, W1H 7AA, United Kingdom
Tel.: (44) 2078680856
Fax: (44) 2078680855
Web Site: www.petrochina.com.cn/Ptr/About_PetroChina/Contact_Us/picl.htm
Emp.: 7
Petroleum & Natural Gas
S.I.C.: 4924
N.A.I.C.S.: 221210
Si Bingjun *(Gen Mgr)*

U.S. Subsidiary:

PetroChina International (America) Inc. (2)
Plaza Ten Ste 302 #3 2nd St
Jersey City, NJ 07311
Tel.: (201) 716-1818
Fax: (201) 716-1819
Oil & Natural Gas Producer
S.I.C.: 1311
N.A.I.C.S.: 211111

Non-U.S. Subsidiaries:

PetroChina International (Japan) Co., Ltd. (2)
14F Shiodome Sumitomo Bldg.9-2
Higashi-Shimbashi 1-Chome, Tokyo, Minato-ku, 105-0021, Japan
Tel.: (81) 3 3575 8881
Fax: (81) 3 3575 8882
Oil & Natural Gas Producer
S.I.C.: 1311
N.A.I.C.S.: 211111

PetroChina International (Kazakhstan) Co., Ltd (2)
110 Str Furmanov
Almaty, Kazakhstan
Tel.: (7) 3272 596315
Fax: (7) 3272 596318
Oil & Natural Gas Producer
S.I.C.: 3291
N.A.I.C.S.: 327910

PetroChina International (Middle East) Company Limited (2)
102-104 The Gate Village 04 Dubai International Finance Centre
Dubai International Financial, Dubai, United Arab Emirates
Tel.: (971) 44407800
Fax: (971) 44407801
E-Mail: wang-nazd@petrochina.com.cn
Web Site: www.petrochina.com
Emp.: 8
Oil & Natural Gas Producer
S.I.C.: 1311
N.A.I.C.S.: 211111

PetroChina International (Rus) Co., Ltd (2)
117198 E303-305
Leninsky Prospekt 113/1, Moscow, Russia
Tel.: (7) 95 9565771
Fax: (7) 95 9565770
Oil & Natural Gas Producer
S.I.C.: 1311
N.A.I.C.S.: 211111

PetroChina International (Turkmenistan) Ltd. (2)
48 Garashizlik Street
Turmenistan, Ashkhabad, Turkmenistan TM
Tel.: (993) 9312 48176
Fax: (993) 9312 48176
Oil & Natural Gas Producer
S.I.C.: 3291
N.A.I.C.S.: 327910

Singapore Petroleum Company Limited (2)
One Temasek Avenue 27-00 Millenia Twr
Singapore, 039192, Singapore (96.2%)
Tel.: (65) 62766006
Telex: SPC RS 21430
Fax: (65) 62756006
E-Mail: spccc@spc.com.sg
Web Site: www.spc.com.sg
Emp.: 180
Oil & Gas Field Development & Production Services; Petroleum Refining; Petroleum Production & Distr
Import Export
S.I.C.: 1311
N.A.I.C.S.: 211111
Helen Chong *(Mgr-HR)*

Joint Venture:

Singapore Refining Co. Pte. Ltd. (3)
1 Merlimau Rd
Singapore, 628260, Singapore SG
Tel.: (65) 63570100
Fax: (65) 68677182
Web Site: www.src.com.sg
Sales Range: $1-4.9 Billion
Emp.: 500
Petroleum Refinery
S.I.C.: 2911
N.A.I.C.S.: 324110
Chiau Beng Choo *(Chm)*

Non-U.S. Subsidiary:

Singapore Petroleum Co. (HK) Ltd. (3)
908 China Resources Bldg 26 Harbour Rd
Hong Kong, China (Hong Kong) (100%)
Tel.: (852) 25110693
Fax: (852) 25110867
E-Mail: hkspc@netvigator.com
Web Site: www.spc.com.sg/aboutspc/regional_operations.asp
Petroleum Products Distr
S.I.C.: 5172
N.A.I.C.S.: 424720

Sinooil Mongolia LLC (2)
Central Tower 508-509 Sukhbaatar Square
Sukhbaatar District-8, Ulaanbaatar, 210620, Mongolia

Tel.: (976) 7737 7777
Oil & Natural Gas Producer
S.I.C.: 3291
N.A.I.C.S.: 327910

Non-U.S. Joint Venture:

Arrow Energy Pty. Ltd. (2)
Level 39 111 Eagle Street
Brisbane, QLD, 4000, Australia
Mailing Address:
GPO Box 5262
Brisbane, QLD, 4001, Australia
Tel.: (61) 730124000
Fax: (61) 7 3012 4001
E-Mail: info@arrowenergy.com.au
Web Site: www.arrowenergy.com.au
Sales Range: $50-74.9 Million
Coal Seam Gas Extraction Services
S.I.C.: 1311
N.A.I.C.S.: 211111
Andrew Faulkner *(CEO)*
Minjie Li *(CFO)*
Jianhua Feng *(COO)*

Subsidiaries:

CH4 Operations Pty Ltd (3)
Level 19 42-60 Albert St
Brisbane, Queensland, 4000, Australia
Tel.: (61) 7 32282300
Fax: (61) 7 30124001
E-Mail: info@arrowenergy.com.au
Emp.: 200
Oil & Gas Supplier
S.I.C.: 1389
N.A.I.C.S.: 213112
Shawn Scott *(Gen Mgr)*

Non-U.S. Subsidiary:

Kunlun Energy Co. Ltd. (1)
39/F 118 Connaught Road West
Hong Kong, China (Hong Kong)
Tel.: (852) 25222282
Fax: (852) 28681741
E-Mail: info@kunlun.com.hk
Web Site: www.kunlun.com.hk
0135—(HKG OTC)
Rev.: $4,249,289,350
Assets: $13,996,490,900
Liabilities: $5,978,637,800
Net Worth: $8,017,853,100
Earnings: $1,278,410,300
Emp.: 17,475
Fiscal Year-end: 12/31/12
Crude Oil & Natural Gas Exploration, Development & Production
S.I.C.: 1321
N.A.I.C.S.: 211112
Hualin Li *(Chm)*
Bowen Zhang *(Pres)*
Hak Woon Lau *(Sec)*
Cheng Cheng *(Sr VP)*

Non-U.S. Joint Venture:

PetroKazakhstan Inc. (1)
Sun Life Plz N Tower
Calgary, AB, T2P 3N3, Canada
Tel.: (403) 221-8435
Fax: (403) 221-8425
Web Site: www.petrokazakhstan.com
Sales Range: $1-4.9 Billion
Oil & Gas Exploration, Acquisition & Refinement: Owned 67% by China National Petroleum Corporation & 33% by JSC KazMunayGas Exploration
S.I.C.: 1311
N.A.I.C.S.: 211111
Zhongcai Wang *(Pres)*

CHINA NATIONAL PHARMACEUTICAL GROUP CORPORATION

(d/b/a SINOPHARM Group)
20 Zhichun Road
Haidian District, Beijing, 100088, China
Tel.: (86) 10 6201 9988
Fax: (86) 10 6203 3332
Web Site: www.sinopharm.com
Year Founded: 1998

Business Description:
Pharmaceuticals Mfr
S.I.C.: 2834
N.A.I.C.S.: 325412

Personnel:
Cuzhou Liu *(Chm)*
Lulin She *(Vice Chm & Pres)*

Subsidiaries:

China National Group Corporation of Traditional & Herbal Medicine (1)
Floor 12 Machinery Building No 248
Guang'an Men Wai Street, Beijing, 100055, China
Tel.: (86) 10 633 172 20
Fax: (86) 10 633 172 21
Web Site: www.sino-tcm.com
Sales Range: $100-124.9 Million
Medicinal Products Developer, Mfr & Distr
S.I.C.: 2833
N.A.I.C.S.: 325411

China National Medical Equipment Industry Corporation (1)
20 Zhichun Road
Haidian District, Beijing, 100088, China
Tel.: (86) 1082029999
Fax: (86) 10 820 222 33
Web Site: www.cmic.com.cn
Medical Equipment Mfr & Distr
S.I.C.: 3841
N.A.I.C.S.: 339112

Subsidiary:

CMICS Medical Electronic Instrument Co., Ltd. (2)
45, Huifeng 4 Road, Zhongkai Hi-tech Development Zone
Guangdong, Huizhou, 516006, China
Tel.: (86) 7522775520
Fax: (86) 7522775501
E-Mail: info@cmics.com.cn
Web Site: www.cmics.com.cn
Emp.: 120
Medical Electronic Instruments
S.I.C.: 3841
N.A.I.C.S.: 339112
Zhu Ai Cheng *(Gen Mgr)*

China National Medicines Corporation Ltd. (1)
12A Sanyuan Xi Xiang Yongwai
Chongwen District, Beijing, 10007, China
Tel.: (86) 10 672 544 49
Fax: (86) 10 672 629 19
Web Site: www.cncm.com.cn
Pharmaceutical Distribution
S.I.C.: 5122
N.A.I.C.S.: 424210

China National Pharmaceutical Foreign Trade Corporation (1)
20 Zhichun Road
Haidian District, Beijing, 100088, China
Tel.: (86) 1062026699
Fax: (86) 1068354539
Web Site: www.sino-pharm.com
Sales Range: $100-124.9 Million
Pharmaceutical Wholesale Trade Agency
S.I.C.: 7389
N.A.I.C.S.: 425120

China National Pharmaceutical Industry Corporation Ltd. (1)
F/3-4 Sinopharm Building 20 Zhichun Road
Haidian District, Beijing, 100088, China CN
Tel.: (86) 1062026699
Fax: (86) 1062032345
Web Site: www.sino-pharm.com
Sales Range: $100-124.9 Million
Pharmaceutical Research & Development, Production, Trade & Investment Services
S.I.C.: 2834
N.A.I.C.S.: 325412
Yan Bing *(Pres)*

China Pharmaceutical Advertising Limited Company (1)
7th Floor 20 Zhichun Rd
Haidian District, Beijing, 100088, China
Tel.: (86) 1082074512
Fax: (86) 1082074536
E-Mail: admin@spadv.com
Web Site: www.spadv.com
Advertising Agency
S.I.C.: 7311
N.A.I.C.S.: 541810

Sichuan Industrial Institute of Antibiotics (1)
18 Shanbanqiao Road
Chengdu, Sichuan, 610051, China
Tel.: (86) 28 438 46 63
Fax: (86) 10 433 32 18
Web Site: www.siia.ac.cn
Medicinal Research & Development
S.I.C.: 8731
N.A.I.C.S.: 541711

SINOPHARM United Engineering Company Ltd. (1)
8 Daping Zheng Street
Yuzhong District, Chongqing, 400042, China
Tel.: (86) 23 688 108 52
Fax: (86) 23 688 108 52
E-Mail: market@cpidi.com
Web Site: www.cpidi.com
Emp.: 50
Engineering & Project Design Services
S.I.C.: 8711
N.A.I.C.S.: 541330
Xie You Qiang *(Pres)*

Joint Ventures:

HM Science Inc. (1)
Room 719/706 20 Zhichun Road
Haidian District, Beijing, 100088, China CN
Tel.: (86) 1062362317
Fax: (86) 1062352617
E-Mail: sales@hm-science.com
Web Site: www.hm-science.com
Emp.: 8
Medicinal Wholesale Trade Agency; Owned by Kracie Holdings, Ltd. & by China National Pharmaceutical Group Corporation (SINOPHARM)
S.I.C.: 7389
N.A.I.C.S.: 425120

Qingdao Huazhong Pharmaceuticals Co., Ltd. (1)
202 Chong Qing Nan Road
Qingdao, Shangdong, 266100, China CN
Tel.: (86) 53284961075
Fax: (86) 53284961078
Web Site: www.phm-huazhong.com
Traditional Chinese Medicinal Mfr; Owned by Kracie Holdings, Ltd. & by China National Pharmaceutical Group Corporation (SINOPHARM)
S.I.C.: 2833
N.A.I.C.S.: 325411

Reed Sinopharm Exhibitions Co., Ltd. (1)
15th Floor Tower B Ping An International Finance Center
No 1-3 Xinyuan South Rd, Beijing, 100027, China
Tel.: (86) 1084556677
Fax: (86) 1062033210
E-Mail: pharmexpo@cpec.com.cn
Web Site: www.reed-sinopharm.com
Emp.: 100
Pharmaceutical, Medical & Health Care Exhibition & Trade Show Organizer
S.I.C.: 7389
N.A.I.C.S.: 561920
KunPing Hu *(Mng Dir)*
Joe Zhou *(CFO)*

Sino-Swed Pharmaceutical Corp., Ltd. (1)
Unit 1801-1805 China Resources Building
No 8 Jianguomenbei Avenue, Beijing, 100005, China
Tel.: (86) 1065189090
Fax: (86) 1085192301
E-Mail: webmaster@sspc.com.cn
Web Site: www.sspc.com.cn
Emp.: 1,000
Parenteral Nutrition, Enteral Nutrition & Application Device Mfr; Owned 51% by Fresenius SE & 49% by China National Pharmaceutical Group Corporation (SINOPHARM)
S.I.C.: 2833
N.A.I.C.S.: 325411

Non-U.S. Holding:

Winteam Pharmaceutical Group Limited (1)
Rooms 2801-5 China Insurance Group Building 141 Des Voeux Road
Central, China (Hong Kong) HK
Tel.: (852) 28543393 (56.97%)
Fax: (852) 25441269
E-Mail: publicrelation@winteamgroup.com.hk
Web Site: www.winteamgroup.com
0570—(HKG)
Sls.: $163,527,040
Assets: $247,173,939
Liabilities: $112,667,355
Net Worth: $134,506,584
Earnings: $27,421,733
Emp.: 3,167
Fiscal Year-end: 12/31/12
Pharmaceutical Mfr
S.I.C.: 2834
N.A.I.C.S.: 325412
Xian Wu *(Chm)*
Bin Yang *(Mng Dir)*
Po Wah Huen *(Sec)*

Non-U.S. Subsidiary:

Foshan Dezhong Pharmaceutical Co., Ltd. (2)
No 89 Foping Rd
Foshan, Guangdong, 528000, China
Tel.: (86) 757 82286 327
Web Site: www.dezhong.com
Pharmaceuticals Mfr
S.I.C.: 2834
N.A.I.C.S.: 325412

CHINA NATIONAL RAILWAY SIGNAL & COMMUNICATION CORP.

B 49 Xisihuan Nanlu
Beijing, Fengtai, 100071, China
Tel.: (86) 10 51846108
Fax: (86) 01051846610
E-Mail: wd@crsc.com.cn
Web Site: www.crsc.com.cn
Year Founded: 1953
Emp.: 30,000

Business Description:
Train Control Systems
S.I.C.: 4789
N.A.I.C.S.: 488210

Personnel:
Zhou Zhiliang *(Pres & Vice Sec)*

Joint Venture:

CASCO Signal Ltd. (1)
27 Floor Room C D Triumphal Arch Building
No 428 Tian Mu Zhong Road, Shanghai, 200070, China CN
Tel.: (86) 163543654
Fax: (86) 163542837
E-Mail: mkting@casco.com.cn
Web Site: www.casco.com.cn
Emp.: 100
Supplies Complete Signaling Systems, Communications Equipment, Project Design, Engineering & Consulting Services for Railroad & Transit Authorities: Joint Venture of Casco Signal Ltd (50%) & Alstom Signalling Inc (50%)
S.I.C.: 8711
N.A.I.C.S.: 541330

CHINA NATURAL GAS, INC.

(Filed Ch 11 Bankruptcy #13-10419 on 7/1/13 in U.S. Bankruptcy Ct, Southern Dist of NY)
19th Floor Building B Van Metropolis
Tang Yan Road
High-Tech Zone, Xi'an, Shaanxi, 710065, China
Tel.: (86) 2988323325
Fax: (86) 2988319221
E-Mail: ir.chng@naturalgaschina.com
Web Site: www.naturalgaschina.com
Year Founded: 1999
CHNG—(OTC)
Rev.: $145,281,288
Assets: $288,500,809
Liabilities: $84,259,850
Net Worth: $204,240,959
Earnings: $11,037,269
Emp.: 1,056
Fiscal Year-end: 12/31/12

CHINA NATURAL GAS, INC.—(Continued)

Business Description:
Natural Gas Exploration, Construction & Distribution Services
S.I.C.: 1311
N.A.I.C.S.: 211111
Personnel:
Qinan Ji *(Chm)*
Zhiqiang Wang *(Vice Chm)*
Shuwen Kang *(CEO)*
Zhaoyang Qiao *(CFO)*
Wilson Qu *(Chief Acctg Officer)*
Board of Directors:
Qinan Ji
Lawrence W. Leighton
Zhiqiang Wang
Frank Waung

Subsidiary:

Xi' An Xilan Natural Gas Co., Ltd. **(1)**
19th Floor Building B Van Metropolis Tang Yan Road Hi-Tech Zone
Xi'an, Shaanxi, 710065, China
Tel.: (86) 29 8832 3325
Fax: (86) 29 8831 9221
Web Site: www.naturalgaschina.com
Natural Gas Distribution Services
S.I.C.: 4924
N.A.I.C.S.: 221210

CHINA NATURAL RESOURCES, INC.

Room 2205 22/F West Tower Shun Tak Centre 168-200 Connaught Road Central, Sheung Wan, China (Hong Kong)
Tel.: (852) 2810 7205
Fax: (852) 2810 6963
E-Mail: info@chnr.net
Web Site: www.chnr.netcontact.asp
Year Founded: 1986
CHNR—(HKG NASDAQ)
Rev.: $24,886,553
Assets: $453,399,201
Liabilities: $366,528,107
Net Worth: $86,871,094
Earnings: ($12,937,856)
Emp.: 2,009
Fiscal Year-end: 12/31/12
Business Description:
Holding Company
S.I.C.: 6719
N.A.I.C.S.: 551112
Personnel:
Feilie Li *(Chm, Pres & CEO)*
Wah On Edward Wong *(CFO & Sec)*
Cheuk Ho Tam *(Exec VP)*
Board of Directors:
Feilie Li
Kwan Sing Lam
Kin Sing Ng
Cheuk Ho Tam
Wah On Edward Wong
Wing Hang Yip

Subsidiary:

Feishang Mining Holding Limited **(1)**
Room 2105 West Tower Shun Tak Centre
200 Connaught Road C, Sheung Wan, China (Hong Kong) VG
Tel.: (852) 2810 7205
Fax: (852) 2810 6963
Holding Company
S.I.C.: 6719
N.A.I.C.S.: 551112
Feilie Li *(CEO)*
Alfred Him Chan *(CFO)*

Non-U.S. Subsidiary:

Wuhu Feishang Mining Development Co., Ltd. **(2)**
Fanxin Road
Fanchang, Wuhu, 243601, China CN
Tel.: (86) 5537337566 (100%)
Zinc, Iron & Other Minerals Mining
S.I.C.: 1031
N.A.I.C.S.: 212231
Mian Tang *(CEO)*

CHINA NEPSTAR CHAIN DRUGSTORE LTD.

6th Floor Tower B Xinnengyuan Building Nanhai Road
Nanshan District, Shenzhen, Guangdong, 518054, China
Tel.: (86) 755 26433366
Fax: (86) 755 26401549
Web Site: www.nepstar.cn
NPD—(NYSE)
Rev.: $405,044,626
Assets: $261,151,147
Liabilities: $98,154,686
Net Worth: $162,996,462
Earnings: $14,311,114
Emp.: 14,500
Fiscal Year-end: 12/31/12
Business Description:
Drug Store Owner & Operator
S.I.C.: 5912
N.A.I.C.S.: 446110
Personnel:
Simin Zhang *(Chm)*
Fuxiang Zhang *(CEO)*
Zixin Shao *(CFO)*
Board of Directors:
Simin Zhang
Alan Au
Barry John Buttifant
Stephanie Hui
Alistair Eric MacCallum Laband
Zixin Shao

Subsidiaries:

Guangzhou Nepstar Chain Co., Ltd. **(1)**
No 281 Chigang E Rd
Haizhu Dist, Guangzhou, Guangdong, 510310, China
Tel.: (86) 2034029301
Fax: (86) 2034029309
Pharmaceutical Products Retailer
S.I.C.: 5912
N.A.I.C.S.: 446110

Shenzhen Nepstar Chain Co., Ltd. **(1)**
Haiwang Xingchen 7 F Fumin Plaza Qifeng Road
Guancheng District, Dongguan, Guangdong, 523000, China
Tel.: (86) 76922366079
Fax: (86) 76922363959
Retail Drug Store Operation Services
S.I.C.: 5912
N.A.I.C.S.: 446110

CHINA NETWORKS INTERNATIONAL HOLDING LTD.

801 Block C Central International Trade Center 6A Jianguomenwai Avenue
Chaoyang District, Beijing, 100022, China
Tel.: (86) 1085911829
Year Founded: 2008
CNWHF—(OTC OTCB)
Int. Income: $113,165
Assets: $2,632,224
Liabilities: $2,488,546
Net Worth: $143,678
Earnings: ($4,141,618)
Emp.: 4
Fiscal Year-end: 12/31/12
Business Description:
Television Broadcasting Services
S.I.C.: 4833
N.A.I.C.S.: 515120
Personnel:
Shuangqing Li *(Chm & CEO)*
Xin Yan Li *(Interim CFO)*
Board of Directors:
Shuangqing Li
Michael E. Weksel

CHINA NEW BORUN CORPORATION

Bohai Industrial Park
Yangkou Town, Shouguang, Shandong, 262715, China
Tel.: (86) 536 5451199
Web Site: ir.chinanewborun.com
BORN—(NYSE)
Rev.: $411,015,122
Assets: $388,069,385
Liabilities: $147,001,321
Net Worth: $241,068,064
Earnings: $29,887,858
Emp.: 1,113
Fiscal Year-end: 12/31/12
Business Description:
Corn-Based Edible Alcohol Mfr & Distr
S.I.C.: 2899
N.A.I.C.S.: 325998
Personnel:
Jinmiao Wang *(Chm, Pres & CEO)*
Yuanqin Chen *(CFO)*
Hengxiu Song *(COO)*
Wei Qi *(CTO)*
Bing Yu *(Chief Strategy Officer)*
Rongjian Wang *(Controller-Fin & Treas)*
Board of Directors:
Jinmiao Wang
Rong Chen
Hengxiu Song
Ruiping Wang
Yibin Wei

CHINA NEW ECONOMY FUND LIMITED

17/F Chuangs Tower 30-32 Connaught Road Central
Central, China (Hong Kong)
Tel.: (852) 2826 2900
Fax: (852) 2530 0727
Web Site: www.chinaneweconomyfund.com
Year Founded: 2010
80—(HKG)
Sales Range: Less than $1 Million
Business Description:
Closed-End Investment Fund
S.I.C.: 6726
N.A.I.C.S.: 525990
Personnel:
Craig Blaser Lindsey *(Chm)*
Junyan Wang *(CEO)*
Winston Sze Wai Wong *(Sec)*
Board of Directors:
Craig Blaser Lindsey
Doyle Ainsworth Dally
Xu Gu
Kam Chau Siu
Junyan Wang
Yangsheng Xu
Legal Counsel:
Maples & Calder
Ugland House South Church St
Georgetown, Cayman Islands

Clifford Chance
28th Floor Jardine House One Connaught Place
Central, China (Hong Kong)
Transfer Agent:
Computershare Hong Kong Investor Services Limited
Shops 1712-16 17th Floor Hopewell Centre 183 Queen's Road East
Hong Kong, China (Hong Kong)

CHINA NEW ENERGY GROUP COMPANY

1703-1704 A Building No 1 Hongji Apartment
Jin Wei Road
He Bei District, Tianjin, China
Tel.: (86) 22 5829 9778
Web Site: www.cnegc.com
CNER—(OTC)
Sales Range: $10-24.9 Million
Emp.: 130
Business Description:
Energy Utitlity Holding Company; Natural Gas Distribution, Network Development, Pipeline Construction, Operation & Maintenance Services
S.I.C.: 6719
N.A.I.C.S.: 551112
Personnel:
Jiaji Shang *(Chm)*
Yangkan Chong *(CEO)*
Eric Yu Tak Shing *(CFO)*
Changli Li *(CTO)*
Board of Directors:
Jiaji Shang
Yangkan Chong
Chunming Guo
John Douglas Kuhns
James Tie Li
Transfer Agent:
Corporate Stock Transfer, Inc.
3200 Cherry Creek Dr S Ste 430
Denver, CO 80209
Tel.: (303) 282-4800
Fax: (303) 282-5800

Subsidiary:

Willsky Development Ltd. **(1)**
1703-1704 A Building No 1 Hongji Apartment
Jin Wei Road
He Bei District, Tianjin, China VG
Tel.: (86) 22 5829 9778 (100%)
Energy Utitlity Holding Company
S.I.C.: 6719
N.A.I.C.S.: 551112
Jiaji Shang *(Chm, Pres & CEO)*

CHINA NEW ENERGY LIMITED

8/F Technology Integration Building 4 Nengyuan Road
Tianhe District, Guangzhou, Guangdong, 510640, China
Tel.: (86) 20 8705 7185
Fax: (86) 20 8705 7162
E-Mail: secretary@zkty.com.cn
Web Site: www.chinanewenergy.co.uk
Year Founded: 2006
CNEL—(AIM)
Rev.: $23,216,563
Assets: $34,777,825
Liabilities: $23,317,592
Net Worth: $11,460,233
Earnings: $3,455,305
Fiscal Year-end: 12/31/12
Business Description:
Bioethanol, Biobutanol & Biogas Plant & Equipment Mfr & Engineering
S.I.C.: 1629
N.A.I.C.S.: 237990
Personnel:
Weijun Yu *(Chm)*
Zhaoxing Tang *(CEO)*
Xiaoyi Wen *(CFO)*
Liren Ding *(Chief Admin Officer)*
Board of Directors:
Weijun Yu
Richard Bennett
Yong Chen
Zhaoxing Tang

Legal Counsel:
Stephenson Harwood LLP
One Raffles Place 12 00
Singapore, 048616, Singapore
Jingtian & Gongcheng
Room 2401 2402 New World Center 6009
Yitian Road Futian District
Shenzhen, 518026, China
Bird & Bird LLP
15 Fetter Lane
London, EC4A 1JP, United Kingdom
Appleby LLP
PO Box 207 13 14 Esplanade
Saint Helier, JE1 1BD, Jersey
Subsidiary:
Guangdong Zhongke Tianyuan New Energy Technology Co., Ltd. **(1)**
8/F Technology Integration Building of GIEC No 4 Nengyuan Road
Wushan Tianhe District, Guangzhou, 510640, China CN
Tel.: (86) 20 8705 7185
Fax: (86) 20 8705 7162
E-Mail: zkty@zkty.com.cn
Web Site: www.zkty.com.cn
Emp.: 80
Bio-Energy Technologies Developer, Mfr & Installation Services
S.I.C.: 3559
N.A.I.C.S.: 333249
Zhaoxing Tang *(Pres)*
Subsidiary:
Guangdong Boluo Jiuneng High-New Technology Engineering Co., Ltd. **(2)**
Zhouji High & New Technology Industrial Zone
Boluo County, Huizhou, Guangdong, 516100, China
Tel.: (86) 7526221499
Fax: (86) 7526221165
Web Site: www.zkty.com.cn/en/about.asp?n_id=226&cur=Subsidiary
Emp.: 20
Environmental Engineering Services
S.I.C.: 8711
N.A.I.C.S.: 541330

CHINA NEW TOWN DEVELOPMENT COMPANY LIMITED

2/F Palm Grove House
PO Box 3340
Road Town, Tortola, Virgin Islands (British)
Tel.: (284) 4946004
Fax: (284) 4946404
E-Mail: info@china-newtown.com
Web Site: www.china-newtown.com
D4N—(SES)
Rev.: $148,517,443
Assets: $1,868,248,670
Liabilities: $1,353,487,779
Net Worth: $514,760,891
Earnings: $7,264,687
Emp.: 1,175
Fiscal Year-end: 12/31/12
Business Description:
Holding Company; Commercial Real Estate Developer & Property Manager
S.I.C.: 6719
N.A.I.C.S.: 551112
Personnel:
Jian Shi *(Founder & Co-Chm)*
Yao Min Li *(Co-Chm & Co-CEO)*
Stan Wai Leung Yue *(Vice Chm)*
Janson Bing Shi *(Co-CEO)*
Songmin Yu *(Asst Pres)*
Xin Zuo *(Asst Pres)*
Lijun Cai *(CFO)*
Biya Gu *(COO)*
Sau Ling Chan *(Co-Sec)*
Siew Tian Low *(Co-Sec)*
Board of Directors:
Yao Min Li
Jian Shi
Biya Gu
Siu Chee Kong
Philip Bing Lun Lam
Yiping Mao
Yifeng Qian
Janson Bing Shi
Yiqing Song
Henry Song Kok Tan
Yonggang Yang
E Hock Yap
Stan Wai Leung Yue
Hao Zhang
Tricor Investor Services Limited
26th Floor Tesbury Centre 28 Queens Road East
Wanchai, China (Hong Kong)
Transfer Agent:
Tricor Barbinder Share Registration Services
80 Robinson Road 02-00
Singapore, Singapore
Corporate Headquarters:
China New Town Development Company Limited - Corporate Office **(1)**
2503 Convention Plaza Office Tower No 1 Harbour Road
Wanchai, China (Hong Kong)
Tel.: (852) 3965 9000
Fax: (852) 3965 9111
E-Mail: Contact2012@china-newtown.com
Web Site: www.china-newtown.com
Corporate Office; Commercial Real Estate Developer & Property Manager
S.I.C.: 8741
N.A.I.C.S.: 551114
Jian Shi *(Founder & Co-Chm)*
Yao Min Li *(Co-Chm & Co-CEO)*
Janson Bing Shi *(Vice Chm, Co-CEO & Exec Dir)*
Stan Wai Leung Yue *(Vice Chm)*
Songmin Yu *(Asst Pres)*
Xin Zuo *(Asst Pres)*
Lijun Cai *(CFO)*
Biya Gu *(COO)*
Sau Ling Chan *(Co-Sec)*
Siew Tian Low *(Co-Sec)*

CHINA NICKEL RESOURCES HOLDINGS CO. LTD.

Room 3501 China Merchants Tower
Shun Tak Centre 168-200 Connaught Road
Sheung Wan, Central, China (Hong Kong)
Tel.: (852) 2110 0836
Fax: (852) 2110 0826
Web Site: www.cnrholdings.com
2889—(HKG)
Rev.: $233,124,606
Assets: $1,007,964,566
Liabilities: $491,915,402
Net Worth: $516,049,164
Earnings: ($36,026,227)
Emp.: 3,000
Fiscal Year-end: 12/31/12
Business Description:
Steel Mfr & Sales
S.I.C.: 3312
N.A.I.C.S.: 331110
Personnel:
Shutong Dong *(Chm & CEO)*
Shyh-yi Chiang *(Deputy CEO)*
Rowena See Wai Ng *(Deputy CEO)*
Yee Lok Chan *(Sec & Controller-Fin)*
Board of Directors:
Shutong Dong
Baohua Bai
Shyh-yi Chiang
Chengzhe Dong
Changhuai Huang
Fahmi Idris
Rowena See Wai Ng
Wenzhou Song
Chi Keung Wong
Fei Yang
Tianjun Yang
Computershare Hong Kong Investor Services Limited
17M Floor Hopewell Centre 183 Queen's Road East
Wanchai, China (Hong Kong)
Transfer Agents:
Royal Bank of Canada Trust Company (Cayman) Limited
4th Floor Royal Bank House 24 Shedden Road
Georgetown, Cayman Islands
Computershare Hong Kong Investor Services Limited
17M Floor Hopewell Centre 183 Queen's Road East
Wanchai, China (Hong Kong)

CHINA NONFERROUS METAL MINING (GROUP) CO., LTD.

CNMC Building No 10 Anding Road
Chaoyang District, Beijing, 100029, China
Tel.: (86) 10 84426666
Fax: (86) 10 84426699
E-Mail: cnmc@cnmc.com.cn
Web Site: www.cnmc.com.cn
Year Founded: 1983
Sales Range: $15-24.9 Billion
Emp.: 27,798
Business Description:
Mineral Exploration Services
S.I.C.: 1099
N.A.I.C.S.: 212299
Personnel:
Yan Diyong *(Vice Gen Mgr)*

CHINA NONFERROUS MINING CORPORATION LIMITED

CNMC Building 10 Anding Road
Chaoyang District, Beijing, China
Tel.: (86) 10 8442 6666
Web Site: www.cnmcl.net
1258—(HKG)
Business Description:
Copper Mining
S.I.C.: 1021
N.A.I.C.S.: 212234
Personnel:
Tao Luo *(Chm)*
Xinghu Tao *(Vice Chm & Pres)*
Hong Han *(CFO)*
Board of Directors:
Tao Luo
Shuang Chen
Jingwei Liu
Xingeng Luo
Chuanyao Sun
Xinghu Tao
Chunlai Wang
Kaishou Xie
Xinguo Yang

CHINA NORTH INDUSTRIES GROUP CORPORATION

(d/b/a NORINCO Group)
No 46 Sanlihe Road
Xicheng District, Beijing, 100821, China
Tel.: (86) 1063529988
E-Mail: webmaster@norincogroup.com.cn
Web Site: www.norincogroup.com.cn
Sales Range: $200-249.9 Billion
Emp.: 280,000
Business Description:
Holding Company; Military, Industrial, Chemical & Opto-Electronic Information Technology Products Mfr
S.I.C.: 6719
N.A.I.C.S.: 551112
Personnel:
Guoqing Zhang *(Pres)*
Qianyi Luo *(CFO)*
Subsidiary:
North Lingyun Industrial Group Co., Ltd. **(1)**
Songlindian
Zhuozhou, Hebei, 072761, China CN
Tel.: (86) 31 2367 6616
Fax: (86) 31 2395 2235
Web Site: www.lyig.com.cn
Plastic Automotive Components Mfr
S.I.C.: 3714
N.A.I.C.S.: 336390
Xizeng Li *(Pres)*
Non-U.S. Subsidiary:
Kiekert AG **(2)**
Hoeseler Platz 2
42579 Heiligenhaus, Germany De
Tel.: (49) 2056150
Fax: (49) 205612569
Web Site: www.kiekert.de
Sales Range: $650-699.9 Million
Emp.: 3,380
Automotive Latching Systems Mfr
S.I.C.: 3714
N.A.I.C.S.: 336390
Karl Krause *(CEO & Chm-Exec Bd)*
Stephan Espelage *(CFO & Member-Exec Bd)*
Ulrich-Nicholas Kranz *(Corp Counsel & Member-Exec Bd-Legal, Mergers & Acq)*
Jurgen Wenzel *(Member-Exec Bd-Sls & Pur)*
Michael M. Merget *(Exec VP-Product Dev)*
Jurgen Peulen *(Exec VP-Production)*
U.S. Subsidiary:
Keykert USA, Inc. **(3)**
46941 Liberty Dr
Wixom, MI 48393 DE
Tel.: (248) 960-4100
Fax: (248) 960-5391
E-Mail: tech_support@keykertusa.com
Web Site: www.kiekert.com
Emp.: 100
Automotive Latching Systems Mfr
S.I.C.: 3714
N.A.I.C.S.: 336390
Jurgen Peulen *(Exec VP-Production)*
Non-U.S. Subsidiary:
Kiekert CS s.r.o. **(3)**
Jaselska 593
CZ-535 01 Prelouc, Czech Republic CZ
Tel.: (420) 468 88 1111
Fax: (420) 468 88 2111
Web Site: www.kiekert.cz
Automotive Latching Systems Mfr
S.I.C.: 3714
N.A.I.C.S.: 336390
Georg Stappan *(Gen Mgr)*

CHINA NORTHERN MEDICAL DEVICE, INC.

70 Daxin Jie
Daowai District, Harbin, Heilongjiang, 150020, China
Tel.: (86) 45182280845
Year Founded: 2007
CNMV—(OTC OTCB)
Assets: $913
Liabilities: $6,604
Net Worth: ($5,691)
Earnings: ($13,627)
Fiscal Year-end: 12/31/12
Business Description:
Medical Device Mfr
S.I.C.: 3841
N.A.I.C.S.: 339112
Personnel:
Sotirios Leontaritis *(Pres & Treas)*
Grigorios Tsourtos *(CFO)*
Nicolaos Kardaras *(Sec)*
Board of Directors:
Christos Kapatos
Nicolaos Kardaras
Sotirios Leontaritis

CHINA NT PHARMA GROUP COMPANY LIMITED

(d/b/a NT Pharma Group)

China NT Pharma Group Company Limited—(Continued)

Unit 1505 15/F Bank of East Asia
Harbour View Centre
56 Gloucester Road, Wanchai, China (Hong Kong)
Tel.: (852) 28081606
Fax: (852) 25089459
Web Site: www.ntpharma.com
1011—(HKG)
Sls.: $117,411,118
Assets: $353,439,979
Liabilities: $212,858,682
Net Worth: $140,581,297
Earnings: ($176,214,847)
Emp.: 927
Fiscal Year-end: 12/31/12
Business Description:
Pharmaceutical Mfr
S.I.C.: 2834
N.A.I.C.S.: 325412
Personnel:
Tit Ng *(Co-Founder, Chm & CEO)*
Yu Chin *(Co-Founder)*
Charles Chong Guang Wang *(CFO)*
Ming Wai Mok *(Sec)*
Board of Directors:
Tit Ng
Yu Chin
Leung Hung
Wei Qian
Patrick Sun
Martin Yue Nien Tang
Lap-Chee Tsui
Fan Wang
Codan Trust Company (Cayman) Limited
Cricket Square Hutchins Drive
PO Box 2681
Georgetown, Grand Cayman, Cayman Islands
Transfer Agents:
Tricor Investor Services Limited
26th Floor Tesbury Centre 28 Queens Road East
Wanchai, China (Hong Kong)
Codan Trust Company (Cayman) Limited
Cricket Square Hutchins Drive
PO Box 2681
Georgetown, Grand Cayman, Cayman Islands

CHINA NUCLEAR INDUSTRY 23 INTERNATIONAL CORPORATION LIMITED

Room 2801 28/F China Resources Building 26 Harbour Road
Wanchai, China (Hong Kong)
Tel.: (852) 3983 0923
Fax: (852) 3983 0999
E-Mail: info@cni23intl.com
Web Site: www.cni23intl.com
Year Founded: 1983
611—(HKG)
Rev.: $30,125,557
Assets: $79,631,525
Liabilities: $23,380,827
Net Worth: $56,250,698
Earnings: $4,735,173
Emp.: 496
Fiscal Year-end: 12/31/12
Business Description:
Hotel Management Services
S.I.C.: 7011
N.A.I.C.S.: 721110
Personnel:
Shu Kit Chan *(Vice Chm)*
Limin Song *(CEO)*
Siu Cheung Ng *(Sec)*
Board of Directors:
Yuchuan Dong
Edmond Ka Ling Chan
Shu Kit Chan
Nan Chang
Chi Shing Chung
Jinping Dai
Shuwei Guo
Naishan Han
Qing Jian
Jian Lei
Limin Song
Lei Yu
Legal Counsel:
Conyers Dill & Pearman
2901 One Exchange Square 8 Connaught Place
Central, China (Hong Kong)

CHINA NUOKANG BIO-PHARMACEUTICAL INC.

18-1 East Nanping Road Hunnan National New High-tech Development Zone
Shenyang, Liaoning, 110171, China
Tel.: (86) 24 24696033
Fax: (86) 24 24696133
E-Mail: info@lnnk.net
Web Site: www.lnnk.com
Sales Range: $25-49.9 Million
Emp.: 449
Business Description:
Pharmaceutical Mfr
S.I.C.: 2834
N.A.I.C.S.: 325412
Personnel:
Baizhong Xue *(Chm & CEO)*
Felix Chungfai Wong *(CFO)*
Steven Shizheng Duan *(Sec & VP-IR)*
Hongying Wang *(Exec VP)*
Board of Directors:
Baizhong Xue
Huining Cao
David Xiaoying Gao
Qiang Liu
Sean S. Shao
Neil Nanpeng Shen
Mingde Yu

CHINA NUTRIFRUIT GROUP LIMITED

5th Floor Chuangye Building
Chuangye Plaza Industrial Zone 3
Daqing Hi-Tech Indus Dev Zone,
Daqing, Heilongjiang, 163316, China
Tel.: (86) 4598972870
Web Site: www.chinanutrifruit.com
Sales Range: $75-99.9 Million
Emp.: 516
Business Description:
Fruit Products Developer, Processor, Marketer & Distr
S.I.C.: 2037
N.A.I.C.S.: 311411
Personnel:
Changjun Yu *(Chm, Pres & CEO)*
Board of Directors:
Changjun Yu
Jingfu Li
Jizeng Zhang

CHINA OCEAN SHIPPING (GROUP) COMPANY

(d/b/a COSCO)
Ocean Plz 158 Fuxingmennei St
Beijing, 100031, China
Tel.: (86) 1066493388
Fax: (86) 1066492288
Web Site: www.cosco.com.cn
Year Founded: 1961
Sales Range: $15-24.9 Billion
Emp.: 80,000
Business Description:
International Shipping; Forwarding, Air Freight, Terminals, Warehousing, Inland Haulage, Trade, Financial Affairs, Insurance, Ship Building, Ship Repairing & Real Estate Development
S.I.C.: 4731
N.A.I.C.S.: 488510
Personnel:
Yun Peng Li *(Chm)*
Yueying Sun *(CFO)*
Xu Minjie *(Exec VP)*
Lirong Xu *(Exec VP)*
Fusheng Zhang *(Exec VP)*
Liang Zhang *(Exec VP)*

Subsidiaries:

China COSCO Holdings Company Limited **(1)**
3rd Floor No 1 Tongda Square
Tianjin Port Free Trade Zone, Tianjin, 300461, China
Tel.: (86) 10 6641 8665
Fax: (86) 10 6649 2211
E-Mail: investor@chinacosco.com
Web Site: www.chinacosco.com
601919—(HKG OTC SHG)
Rev.: $14,031,083,571
Assets: $26,243,276,345
Liabilities: $19,619,625,134
Net Worth: $6,623,651,211
Earnings: ($1,292,632,503)
Emp.: 46,221
Fiscal Year-end: 12/31/12
Holding Company; Container Shipping Services
S.I.C.: 6719
N.A.I.C.S.: 551112
Jaifu Wei *(Chm & CEO)*
Dawei Song *(Chm-Supervisory Bd)*
Ze Hua Ma *(Vice Chm)*
Lijun Jiang *(Pres)*
Runjiang Tang *(CFO)*
Huawei Guo *(Co-Sec)*
Michelle Man Hung *(Co-Sec)*

Affiliate:

COSCO Pacific Ltd. **(2)**
49/F COSCO Tower 183 Queen's Road
Central, China (Hong Kong) (43.21%)
Tel.: (852) 28098188
Fax: (852) 29076088
E-Mail: info@coscopac.com.hk
Web Site: www.coscopac.com.hk
1199—(HKG)
Rev.: $735,500,000
Assets: $3,743,881,000
Liabilities: $1,333,498,000
Net Worth: $2,410,383,000
Earnings: $354,469,000
Emp.: 3,142
Fiscal Year-end: 12/31/12
Holding Company; Marine Terminal Operation, Logistics & Cargo Handling Services
S.I.C.: 6719
N.A.I.C.S.: 551112
Xingru Wang *(Vice Chm & Mng Dir)*
Jinguang Qiu *(Deputy Mng Dir & Gen Mgr-Strategy & Dev Dept)*
Ken Hang Chan *(Deputy Mng Dir)*
Haimin Wang *(Deputy Mng Dir)*
Kelvin Tin Yau Wong *(Deputy Mng Dir)*
Michelle Man Hung *(Sec & Gen Counsel)*

Subsidiary:

COSCO Container Industries Limited **(3)**
49/F COSCO Tower 183 Queen's Road
Central, China (Hong Kong) VG
Tel.: (852) 2809 8188
Fax: (852) 2907 6088
Holding Company
S.I.C.: 6719
N.A.I.C.S.: 551112

COSCO Container Lines Co., Ltd. **(1)**
No 378 Dong Da Ming Road
Shanghai, 200080, China CN
Tel.: (86) 21 3512 4888
Fax: (86) 21 6545 8984
Web Site: www.coscon.com
Rev.: $7,695,647,100
Fiscal Year-end: 12/31/12
Deep Sea Freight Container Transportation Services
S.I.C.: 4412
N.A.I.C.S.: 483111
Chao Han *(Chm-Supervisory Bd)*
Min Wan *(Mng Dir)*
Huang-jun Deng *(CFO)*
Xiang Chen *(Deputy Mng Dir)*
Liping Hou *(Deputy Mng Dir)*
Hu Zhou *(Deputy Mng Dir)*
De-zhang Zhu *(Deputy Mng Dir)*

U.S. Subsidiary:

COSCO Container Lines Americas, Inc. **(2)**
100 Lighting Way
Secaucus, NJ 07094 DE
Tel.: (201) 422-0500
Fax: (201) 422-8928
Toll Free: (800) 242-7354
E-Mail: webcontact@cosco-usa.com
Web Site: www.cosco-usa.com
Sales Range: $50-74.9 Million
Emp.: 591
Deep Sea Freight Container Transportation Services
S.I.C.: 4412
N.A.I.C.S.: 483111
Howard Finkel *(Exec VP)*
Frank Grossi *(Exec VP)*
Timothy E. Marsh *(Exec VP-Trade)*

COSCO Shipping Co., Ltd. **(1)**
20 Guangzhou Ocean Plaza Zhujiang New Town
Guangzhou, China CN
Tel.: (86) 2038161888 (50.52%)
Fax: (86) 2038162888
E-Mail: info@coscol.com.cn
Web Site: www.coscol.com.cn
600428—(SHG)
Rev.: $1,001,513,806
Assets: $2,304,307,176
Liabilities: $1,248,630,549
Net Worth: $1,055,676,627
Earnings: $6,121,663
Fiscal Year-end: 12/31/12
Ocean Shipping Services
S.I.C.: 4412
N.A.I.C.S.: 483111
Weilong Ye *(Chm)*
Zhenyu Li *(Vice Chm & Deputy Gen Mgr)*
Guomin Han *(CEO)*
Xueliang Liu *(CFO)*
Jundong Xue *(Sec)*

Subsidiary:

Guangzhou Ocean Shipping Co., Ltd. **(2)**
412 Huanshi Road East
Guangzhou, 510061, China CN
Tel.: (86) 20 8776 5567 (100%)
Fax: (86) 20 8776 5636
Web Site: www.coscogz.com.cn
Marine Freight Transportation Services
S.I.C.: 4412
N.A.I.C.S.: 483111

U.S. Subsidiary:

China Ocean Shipping Company Americas, Inc. **(1)**
100 Lighting Way
Secaucus, NJ 07094-3681 (100%)
Tel.: (201) 422-0500
Fax: (201) 422-8956
Toll Free: (800) 242-7354
E-Mail:
Web Site: www.coscoamericas.com
Emp.: 600
Freight Transportation Arrangement Import Export
S.I.C.: 4731
N.A.I.C.S.: 488510
Howard Finkel *(Exec VP-Trade Div)*
Frank Grossi *(Exec VP-OMD Div)*

Subsidiary:

COSCO North America, Inc. **(2)**
100 Lighting Way
Secaucus, NJ 07094-3681 DE
Tel.: (201) 422-0500
Fax: (201) 422-8928
Holding Company; Regional Managing Office
S.I.C.: 6719
N.A.I.C.S.: 551112

Subsidiaries:

CCLA Secaucus **(3)**
100 Lighting Way
Secaucus, NJ 07094-3681
Tel.: (201) 422-8888
Fax: (201) 422-8955

Web Site: www.cosco.com
Sales Range: $50-74.9 Million
Emp.: 200
Freight Transportation Arrangement
Import Export
S.I.C.: 4731
N.A.I.C.S.: 488510
Mary DiCarlo *(Mgr-Northeast)*

COSCO Agencies (Los Angeles) Inc. **(3)**
588 Harbor Scenic Way 3rd Fl
Long Beach, CA 90802 (100%)
Tel.: (213) 689-6700
Fax: (213) 689-6777
Web Site: www.cosco-usa.com
Sls.: $6,500,000
Emp.: 75
Marine Cargo Handling
Import Export
S.I.C.: 4731
N.A.I.C.S.: 488510
Jin Guoqiang *(Pres)*
Thomas C. Somma *(Exec VP)*

Sea Trade International **(3)**
100 Lighting Way
Secaucus, NJ 07094-3681
Tel.: (201) 422-8688
Fax: (201) 422-8687
Web Site: www.seatrade-usa.com
Sls.: $1,800,000
Emp.: 20
Deep Sea Foreign Transportation of Freight
Import Export
S.I.C.: 4412
N.A.I.C.S.: 483111
Yachun Wu *(Pres)*

World Ocean America Inc. **(3)**
100 Lighting Way
Secaucus, NJ 07094-3681
Tel.: (201) 422-0500
Fax: (201) 422-8931
Web Site: www.cosco-usa.com
Sls.: $1,800,000
Emp.: 6
Deep Sea Foreign Transportation of Freight
Import Export
S.I.C.: 4412
N.A.I.C.S.: 483111
Liu Hanbo *(Pres)*

Yuan Hua Technical & Supply Corporation **(3)**
100 Lighting Way
Secaucus, NJ 07094-3681 (100%)
Tel.: (201) 422-8810
Fax: (201) 422-8989
E-Mail: yuanhua@cosco-usa.com
Web Site: www.coscoamericas.com
Emp.: 5
Management Services
Import Export
S.I.C.: 8742
N.A.I.C.S.: 541611

Non-U.S. Subsidiaries:

COSCO Holdings (Singapore) Pte. Ltd. **(1)**
9 Temasek Boulevard
07-00 Suntec City Tower Two, Singapore, 038989, Singapore
Tel.: (65) 68850888
Fax: (65) 63361217
E-Mail: enquiry@cosco.com.sg
Web Site: www.cosco.com.sg
Emp.: 23
Holding Company
S.I.C.: 6719
N.A.I.C.S.: 551112
Wu Ziheng *(Pres)*

Subsidiary:

COSCO Corporation (Singapore) Ltd. **(2)**
9 Temasek Boulevard 07-00 Suntec Tower 2
Singapore, 038989, Singapore (53.35%)
Tel.: (65) 68850888
Fax: (65) 63369006
E-Mail: enquiry@cosco.com.sg
Web Site: www.cosco.com.sg
F83—(OTC SES)
Sls.: $3,023,556,446
Assets: $5,986,415,232
Liabilities: $4,327,214,927
Net Worth: $1,659,200,304
Earnings: $137,466,661
Emp.: 90
Fiscal Year-end: 12/31/12
Shipping, Ship Repair & Other Shipping Related Services
S.I.C.: 4412
N.A.I.C.S.: 483111
Zi Heng Wu *(Vice Chm & Pres)*
Hong Han Ma *(CFO)*
Siew Tian Low *(Co-Sec)*
Meng Keong Teo *(Co-Sec)*

COSCO (Hong Kong) Group Ltd. **(1)**
52nd Floor COSCO Tower
183 Queens Road, Central, China (Hong Kong)
Tel.: (852) 28098888
Fax: (852) 28098826
Web Site: www.cosco.com.hk
Holding Company
S.I.C.: 6719
N.A.I.C.S.: 551112
Futian Wang *(Vice Chm & Pres)*
Guoyuan Liu *(Vice Chm)*

Subsidiary:

COSCO International Holdings Limited **(2)**
47/F COSCO Tower 183 Queen's Road
Central, China (Hong Kong) (60%)
Tel.: (852) 28097888
Fax: (852) 81690678
E-Mail: info@coscointl.com
Web Site: www.coscointl.com
00517—(HKG OTC)
Rev.: $1,290,235,660
Assets: $1,240,162,183
Liabilities: $262,702,614
Net Worth: $977,459,569
Earnings: $51,954,858
Emp.: 782
Fiscal Year-end: 12/31/12
Diversified Investment & Holding Company; Ship Trading; Supplying Services; Property Investment & Development; Infrastructure Investment; Building Construction
S.I.C.: 6211
N.A.I.C.S.: 523999
Sun Jiakang *(Chm)*
Liang Zhang *(Vice Chm)*
Zhengjun Xu *(Mng Dir)*
Shui Suet Chiu *(Sec)*

Non-U.S. Joint Venture:

Tianjin Cosco Kansai Paint & Chemicals Co., Ltd. **(3)**
42 5th Avenue
TEDA, Tianjin, 300457, China CN
Tel.: (86) 22 2529 2004
Fax: (86) 22 2532 1821
Web Site: www.kansai.com.cn
Paint & Chemical Mfr; Owned by Kansai Paint Co., Ltd & by COSCO International Holdings Limited
S.I.C.: 2851
N.A.I.C.S.: 325510

CHINA OIL & GAS GROUP LIMITED

Suite 2805 28th Floor Sino Plaza
255-257 Gloucester Road
Causeway Bay, China (Hong Kong)
Tel.: (852) 22002222
Fax: (852) 28272808
E-Mail: info@hk603.com
Web Site: www.hk603.com
0603—(HKG)
Rev.: $630,491,741
Assets: $1,184,856,301
Liabilities: $536,646,573
Net Worth: $648,209,729
Earnings: $94,673,285
Emp.: 3,435
Fiscal Year-end: 12/31/12
Business Description:
Oil & Gas Exploration
S.I.C.: 1389
N.A.I.C.S.: 213112
Personnel:
Tieliang Xu *(Chm & CEO)*
Jenny Yin Shan Law *(CFO)*
Stella Yuen Ying Chan *(Sec)*
Board of Directors:
Tieliang Xu
Shing Cheung
Yijun Guan
Yunlong Li
Xunzhi Shi
Guangtian Wang
Yuan Zhu

Butterfield Fulcrum Group (Bermuda) Limited
Rosebank Centre 11 Bermudiana Road
Pembroke, Bermuda

Transfer Agent:
Computershare Hong Kong Investor Services Limited
Shops 1712-1716 17th Floor Hopewell Centre
183 Queens Road East
Wanchai, China (Hong Kong)

Non-U.S. Subsidiary:

Accelstar Pacific Limited **(1)**
C/o Overseas Mgmt Company Trust BVI Ltd
2nd Fl RG Hodge Plz
Road Town, Tortola, Virgin Islands (British) VG1110
Tel.: (284) 494 4693
Fax: (284) 494 4627
Investment Holding Services
S.I.C.: 6211
N.A.I.C.S.: 523999
Sandra Zasquez *(Mgr)*

CHINA OIL HBP SCIENCE & TECHNOLOGY CO., LTD.

(d/b/a China Oil HBP Group/Beijing Oil HBP Group)
7 Floor 1 De Sheng Zhi Ye Building 26
Huang Si Avenue
Xicheng District, Beijing, 100120, China
Tel.: (86) 10 82809807
E-Mail: hbp@china-hbp.com
Web Site: www.china-hbp.com
Year Founded: 1998
002554—(SSE)
Emp.: 380
Business Description:
Oil & Gas Field Equipment Mfr
S.I.C.: 3533
N.A.I.C.S.: 333132
Personnel:
Song Huang *(Chm)*

CHINA OILFIELD TECHNOLOGY SERVICES GROUP LIMITED

28 Xin Fa Street Hi-Tech Development Zone
Daqing, Heilongjiang, China 163316
Tel.: (86) 4596030223
Fax: (86) 4596293888
Web Site: www.chinaoilfieldtech.com
DT2—(SES)
Rev.: $521,346
Assets: $21,793,743
Liabilities: $38,344,643
Net Worth: ($16,550,899)
Earnings: ($76,661,169)
Fiscal Year-end: 12/31/12
Business Description:
Crude Oil Mfr
S.I.C.: 2046
N.A.I.C.S.: 311221
Personnel:
Yanming Gao *(Chm)*
Zhehui Xu *(CFO)*
Vincent Bock Hui Lim *(Sec)*
Board of Directors:
Yanming Gao
Wah Kwong
Hock Meng Lai
Yansong Liang
Fengwu Wu

BDO Limited
25th Floor Wing On Centre 111 Connaught Road
Hong Kong, China (Hong Kong)

Legal Counsel:
Vincent Lim & Associates LLC
18 Cross Street No 07-11 China Square Central
Singapore, 048423, Singapore

Transfer Agent:
Boardroom Corporate & Advisory Services Pte. Ltd.
50 Raffles Place 32-01 Singapore Land Tower
Singapore, Singapore

CHINA ORIENTAL GROUP CO., LTD.

Suites 901 2 & 10 Great Engle Centre 23 Harbour Road
Wanchai, China (Hong Kong)
Tel.: (852) 25111369
Fax: (852) 25111301
E-Mail: info@chinaorientalgroup.com
Web Site: www.chinaorientalgroup.com
0581—(HKG)
Rev.: $5,738,036,568
Assets: $3,931,852,500
Liabilities: $2,414,038,208
Net Worth: $1,517,814,292
Earnings: $23,267,871
Emp.: 14,000
Fiscal Year-end: 12/31/12
Business Description:
Iron & Steel Mfr
S.I.C.: 3312
N.A.I.C.S.: 331110
Personnel:
Jingyuan Han *(Chm & CEO)*
Xiaoling Shen *(CFO & Deputy Gen Mgr)*
Jun Zhu *(COO & Exec Deputy Gen Mgr)*
Siu Kei Au Yeung *(Sec & Controller-Fin)*
Board of Directors:
Jingyuan Han
Vijay Kumar Bhatnagar
Li Han
Lei Lui
Ondra Otradovec
Xiaoling Shen
Tianyi Wang
Francis Man Chung Wong
Tung Ho Yu
Guoping Zhou
Hao Zhu
Jun Zhu

Butterfield Fulcrum Group (Bermuda) Limited
Rosebank Centre 11 Bermudiana Rd
Pembroke, Bermuda

Transfer Agents:
Tricor Investor Services Limited
26th Floor Tesbury Centre 28 Queens Road East
Wanchai, China (Hong Kong)

Butterfield Fulcrum Group (Bermuda) Limited
Rosebank Centre 11 Bermudiana Rd
Pembroke, Bermuda

CHINA OUHUA WINERY HOLDINGS LIMITED

3 Wolong North Road Wolong Foreign Trade Invest Dev Centre
Yantai, China
Tel.: (86) 5356019888
Fax: (86) 5356012999
Web Site: www.ohuawine.com
CNOUHUA—(KLS)
Sales Range: $50-74.9 Million
Emp.: 110
Business Description:
Wine Producer & Distr
S.I.C.: 2084
N.A.I.C.S.: 312130
Personnel:
Chao Wang *(Chm & CEO)*

CHINA OUMEI REAL ESTATE INC.

Floor 28 Block C Longhai Mingzhu Building
182 Haier Road, Qingdao, 266000, China
Tel.: (86) 532 8099 7969
Web Site: www.chinaoumeirealestate.com
OMEI—(NASDAQ)
Sales Range: $100-124.9 Million
Emp.: 203
Business Description:
Real Estate Development Services
S.I.C.: 1542
N.A.I.C.S.: 236220
Personnel:
Antoine Cheng *(Chm)*
Yang Chen *(Pres)*
Weiqing Zhang *(CEO)*
Zhaohui John Liang *(CFO)*
Board of Directors:
Antoine Cheng
Lawrence Lee
Peter D. Linneman
Ruiping Tao
Weiqing Zhang

CHINA OUTDOOR MEDIA GROUP LIMITED

Unit 1803 18th Floor Sun Hung Kai Centre 30 Harbour Road
Wanchai, China (Hong Kong)
Tel.: (852) 25223080
Fax: (852) 25220709
E-Mail: admin@comg.com.hk
Web Site: www.comg.com.hk
0254—(HKG)
Rev.: $5,066,059
Assets: $8,487,876
Liabilities: $4,356,963
Net Worth: $4,130,913
Earnings: ($54,106,904)
Emp.: 27
Fiscal Year-end: 06/30/13
Business Description:
Real Estate Investment Trust
S.I.C.: 6514
N.A.I.C.S.: 531110
Personnel:
Joseph Chi Yuen Lau *(CEO)*
Richard Lap Chin Tang *(COO)*
Pik Kwan Wong *(Sec)*
Board of Directors:
Alexander Kwong Choi Cheng
Sheung Hing Cheng
Hong Xing Gao
Wei Hu
Joseph Chi Yuen Lau
Ning Qiao Li
Liang Lu
Richard Lap Chin Tang
Sheve Li Tay
Qun Wang
Fan Yang
Transfer Agent:
Tricor Abacus Limited
26/F Tesbury Centre 28 Queen's Road East
Hong Kong, China (Hong Kong)
Subsidiary:

iKanTV Limited (1)
17 F Bangkok Bank Bldg 18 Bonham Strand W
Sheung Wan, China (Hong Kong)
Tel.: (852) 34237100
Fax: (852) 34237199
E-Mail: info@chinapost-te.com
Web Site: www.ikantv.com
Emp.: 25
Outdoor Advertising & Television Broadcasting Services
S.I.C.: 4833
N.A.I.C.S.: 515120

CHINA PACIFIC INSURANCE (GROUP) CO., LTD.

South Tower Bank of Communications Financial Building
190 Central Yincheng Road Pudong
New District, Shanghai, China
Tel.: (86) 2158767282
Fax: (86) 2168870791
E-Mail: ir@cpic.com.cn
Web Site: www.cpic.com.cn
601601—(HKG OTC SHG)
Premiums: $25,928,767,800
Assets: $108,256,592,700
Liabilities: $92,757,757,050
Net Worth: $15,498,835,650
Earnings: $814,900,500
Emp.: 85,137
Fiscal Year-end: 12/31/12
Business Description:
Life & Property Insurance Services
S.I.C.: 6311
N.A.I.C.S.: 524113
Personnel:
Guofu Gao *(Chm)*
Zhuping Zhou *(Chm-Supervisory Bd)*
Lianhong Huo *(Pres)*
Yue Gu *(Fin Officer & Exec VP)*
Xueying Huang *(Chief IT Officer)*
Lin Fang *(Co-Sec)*
Gloria Sau Kuen Ma *(Co-Sec)*
Jinghui Xu *(Exec VP)*
Board of Directors:
Guofu Gao
Stephen Tso Tung Chang
Janine Junyuan Feng
Lianhong Huo
Ruoshan Li
Chengran Wang
Jumin Wu
Junhao Wu
Wei Xiao
Fei Xu
Shanda Xu
Xiangdong Yang
Xianghai Yang
Tin Fan Yuen
Anguo Zheng
Supervisory Board of Directors:
Zhuping Zhou
Jihai He
Lichun Lin
Junxiang Song
Jianwei Zhang
Ernst & Young
22/ F CITIC Tower 1 Tim Mei Ave
Central, China (Hong Kong)
Subsidiary:

China Pacific Property Insurance Co., Ltd. (1)
190 Cent Yincheng Rd
Shanghai, 200120, China
Tel.: (86) 21 5877 6688
Fax: (86) 21 6887 1218
Web Site: www.cpic.com.cn/cpic/en/about/view_info.jsp?idinfo=news991id
Property Insurance Services
S.I.C.: 6331
N.A.I.C.S.: 524126
Zongmin Wu *(Pres)*
Kaixu Huang *(Chief Compliance Officer)*

CHINA PACKAGING GROUP COMPANY LIMITED

Room 912 9/F New East Ocean Centre 9 Science Museum Road
TST East, Kowloon, China (Hong Kong)
Tel.: (852) 2311 7728
Fax: (852) 2311 7738
Web Site: www.cpackaging.com.hk
Year Founded: 1997
572—(HKG)
Rev.: $11,768,402
Assets: $10,007,868
Liabilities: $2,514,437
Net Worth: $7,493,431
Earnings: ($13,611,856)
Emp.: 85
Fiscal Year-end: 12/31/12
Business Description:
Tinplate Can Mfr
S.I.C.: 3411
N.A.I.C.S.: 332431
Personnel:
Jianhong He *(Chm)*
Cheuk Pun Lau *(Sec)*
Board of Directors:
Jianhong He
Robert Siu Ling Siu
Tak Wah Tam
Zhantao Zhang

CHINA PACKAGING HOLDINGS DEVELOPMENT LIMITED

Hong Sheng Industrial Park Fengxin Industrial Zone
Yichun, Jiangxi, China
Tel.: (86) 795 4588155
Fax: (86) 795 4604258
E-Mail: pack@hs-pack.com
Web Site: www.hs-pack.com
1439—(HKG)
Sales Range: $25-49.9 Million
Business Description:
Packaging Products Mfr
S.I.C.: 2657
N.A.I.C.S.: 322212
Personnel:
Weiwei Chen *(Chm)*
Chung Ming Hu *(CFO & Sec)*
Board of Directors:
Weiwei Chen
Li Yu Hu
Da Jin Liu
Peter Yiu Ho Ma
Shao Hua Sun
Ping Wu

CHINA PAPER HOLDINGS LIMITED

South Part Jianshe Road
Linyi, Shandong, China
Tel.: (86) 5398500106
Fax: (86) 5398501066
Web Site: www.chinapaper-holdings.com
C71—(SES)
Rev.: $148,281,551
Assets: $288,223,794
Liabilities: $18,996,077
Net Worth: $269,227,717
Earnings: $8,710,381
Fiscal Year-end: 12/31/12
Business Description:
Paper Mfr
S.I.C.: 2299
N.A.I.C.S.: 313110
Personnel:
Yong Chen *(Co-Founder & Chm)*
Hanpu Li *(Co-Founder & Mng Dir)*
Board of Directors:
Yong Chen
Hanpu Li
Jun Li
Pengju Li
Song Kwang Tan
Transfer Agents:
Tricor Barbinder Share Registration Services
80 Robinson Road 02-00
Singapore, Singapore
HSBC Securities Services (Bermuda) Limited
Bank of Bermuda Building 6 Front Street
Hamilton, Bermuda

CHINA PEDIATRIC PHARMACEUTICALS, INC.

Room 403 Block H NO1 Bldg Qujiang Conference Exhibition International
Yanta District, Xi'an, China 710061
Tel.: (86) 2989120908
Web Site: www.chinapediatricpharma.com
Year Founded: 2005
CPDU—(OTC)
Sls.: $16,391,702
Assets: $12,119,512
Liabilities: $500,048
Net Worth: $11,619,464
Earnings: ($9,152,318)
Emp.: 135
Fiscal Year-end: 12/31/12
Business Description:
Pharmaceutical Mfr
S.I.C.: 2834
N.A.I.C.S.: 325412
Personnel:
Jun Xia *(Chm, Pres & CEO)*
Minggang Xiao *(CFO)*
Jing Fu *(Sr VP)*
Board of Directors:
Jun Xia
Wanxiang Li
Nanjing Lin
Minggang Xiao
Xiaoying Zhang
Transfer Agent:
Transhare
Greenwood Village, CO 80110

CHINA PETROCHEMICAL CORPORATION

(d/b/a Sinopec Group)
22 Chaoyangmen North Street
Chaoyang District, Beijing, 100728, China
Tel.: (86) 1059960114
Fax: (86) 1059760111
Web Site: www.sinopecgroup.com
Year Founded: 1983
Business Description:
Holding Company; Petrochemical Mfr
S.I.C.: 6719
N.A.I.C.S.: 551112
Personnel:
Fu Chengyu *(Chm)*
Tianpu Wang *(Pres)*
Subsidiary:

Sinopec International Petroleum Exploration & Production Corporation (1)
No 263 North Fourth Ring Road
Haidian District, Beijing, 100083, China CN
Tel.: (86) 1082310862
Fax: (86) 1082310841
Holding Company; Petroleum Upstream & Downstream Properties Investment & Management
S.I.C.: 6719
N.A.I.C.S.: 551112
Jifeng Liu *(CFO)*

Non-U.S. Subsidiaries:

Sinopec Daylight Energy Ltd. (2)
Sun Life Plaza East Tower Suite 2700
112 4th Avenue SW, Calgary, AB, T2P 0H3, Canada
Tel.: (403) 266-6900
Fax: (403) 266-6988
Toll Free: (866) 616-6300
E-Mail: ir@daylightenergy.com
Web Site: www.sinopec.com
Sales Range: $650-699.9 Million
Emp.: 252
Oil & Natural Gas Exploration & Production Services
S.I.C.: 1311
N.A.I.C.S.: 211111
Feng Zhiqiang *(Chm & CEO)*
Steve Nielsen *(CFO & VP)*

Stacy Knull *(COO & VP)*
Cam Proctor *(Chief Legal Officer)*
Ted Hanbury *(Exec VP)*

Non-U.S. Joint Venture:

Mansarovar Energy Colombia Ltd. (2)
13-76 Calle 100
Bogota, Colombia
Tel.: (57) 14858762
Fax: (57) 16011972
Web Site: www.mansarovar.com.co
Crude Petroleum Production & Transportation; Owned by Oil & Natural Gas Corporation & by China Petrochemical Corporation
S.I.C.: 1311
N.A.I.C.S.: 211111
Sidhartha Sur *(CEO)*

Holding:

China Petroleum & Chemical Corporation (1)
22 Chaoyangmen North Street
Chaoyang District, Beijing, 100728, China CN
Tel.: (86) 1059960028
Fax: (86) 1059960386
E-Mail: ir@sinopec.com.cn
Web Site: english.sinopec.com
SNP—(HKG NYSE SHG)
Rev.: $442,563,248,250
Assets: $201,214,183,050
Liabilities: $114,158,664,450
Net Worth: $87,055,518,600
Earnings: $10,610,544,600
Emp.: 376,201
Fiscal Year-end: 12/31/12
Holding Company; Petroleum Production & Refining Services & Petrochemical Mfr
S.I.C.: 6719
N.A.I.C.S.: 551112
Fu Chengyu *(Chm)*
Zuoran Wang *(Chm-Supervisory Bd)*
Tianpu Wang *(Vice Chm)*
Yaocang Zhang *(Vice Chm)*
Youcai Zhang *(Vice Chm-Supervisory Bd)*
Chunguang Li *(Pres)*
Xinhua Wang *(CFO)*
Ge Chen *(Sec)*
Xiyou Cai *(Sr VP)*
Houliang Dai *(Sr VP)*
Zhigang Wang *(Sr VP)*
Jianhua Zhang *(Sr VP)*

Subsidiaries:

Sinopec Beijing Yanhua Petrochemical Company Limited (2)
No 1 Gangnan
Yanshan Fangshan District, Beijing, 102500, China
Tel.: (86) 1069342295
Fax: (86) 1069342736
E-Mail: office@bypc.com.cn
Web Site: www.bypc.com.cn
00325—(HKG)
Emp.: 16,000
Provider of Petrochemical Products
S.I.C.: 2869
N.A.I.C.S.: 325110
Wang Yong Jian *(Chm & Gen Mgr)*

Sinopec Chemical Sales Company (2)
A6 Huixin East Street
Chaoyang District
100029 Beijing, China
Tel.: (86) 10 8464 5788
Fax: (86) 10 8464 1775
Chemical Product Sales
S.I.C.: 5169
N.A.I.C.S.: 424690

Sinopec Guangzhou Company (2)
No 239 Shihua Road
Huangpu District, Guangzhou, 510726, China
Tel.: (86) 2082123888
Fax: (86) 2082396591
Web Site: english.sinopec.com
Petrochemical Mfr
S.I.C.: 2869
N.A.I.C.S.: 325110

Sinopec Qilu Petrochemical Co., Ltd. (2)
15 Huangong Road Linzi
Zibo, Shandong, 255408, China
Tel.: (86) 5337180777
Fax: (86) 5337180406
E-Mail: bgs.qlsh@sinopec.com
Web Site: english.sinopec.com
Petrochemical Processing Services
S.I.C.: 2869
N.A.I.C.S.: 325110

Sinopec Sales Company, Ltd. (2)
No A6 Huisingong Street
Chaoyan District, Beijing, China CN
Tel.: (86) 1064998828
Fax: (86) 10 8464 1014
Petrochemical Sales Services
S.I.C.: 5169
N.A.I.C.S.: 424690

Sinopec Shanghai Petrochemical Company Limited (2)
No 48 Jinyi Road
Jinshan District, Shanghai, PRC, 200540, China CN
Tel.: (86) 21 5794 1941 (55.56%)
Fax: (86) 21 5794 0050
E-Mail: spc@spc.com.cn
Web Site: www.spc.com.cn
SHI—(HKG NYSE SHG)
Sls.: $14,774,374,491
Assets: $5,792,075,432
Liabilities: $3,202,193,133
Net Worth: $2,589,882,299
Earnings: ($239,091,807)
Emp.: 15,007
Fiscal Year-end: 12/31/12
Mfr. of Ethylene, Deisel Fuel, Gasoline, Synthetic Fibers & Petrochemicals
S.I.C.: 2821
N.A.I.C.S.: 325211
Guangdao Rong *(Chm & Sec)*
Zhiqing Wang *(Vice Chm, Pres & Deputy Sec)*
Haijun Wu *(Vice Chm)*
Ye Guohua *(CFO)*
Jingming Zhang *(Gen Legal Counsel & Sec)*

Subsidiary:

China Jinshan Associated Trading Corp. (3)
4 F Information Ctr Bldg Weier Rd
Shanghai, 200540, China CN
Tel.: (86) 2157940433 (67.33%)
Telex: 33100 CJATC CN
Fax: (86) 2157942248
E-Mail: cjatc@cjatc.com
Web Site: www.cjatc.com
Emp.: 60
Import & Export Technology, Equipment & Spare Parts of Petrochemical, Synthetic Fiber & Plastic
S.I.C.: 2869
N.A.I.C.S.: 325110
Wu Huili *(Mgr-Trading Mgmt)*

Non-U.S. Subsidiary:

Amodaimi Oil Company, Ltd. (3)
Av 12 de Octubre N24 593 & Francisco Salazar 1 - 3 Edificio Plaza
2000 Ofic 3 A, Quito, Ecuador EC
Tel.: (593) 2 2976600 (100%)
Emp.: 400
Oil & Gas Exploration Services
S.I.C.: 1389
N.A.I.C.S.: 213112
Luis Garcia *(Gen Mgr)*

Sinopec Shengli Oilfield Co., Ltd. (2)
258 Jinan Road
Dongying District, Dongying, Shandong, 257001, China
Tel.: (86) 5468552074
Fax: (86) 5468221719
E-Mail: ljz22@slof.com
Petrochemical Products Mfr
S.I.C.: 2869
N.A.I.C.S.: 325110

Sinopec Taishan Oil Products Co., Ltd. (2)
No 104 Dongyue Street
Tai'an, Shandong, 27100, China
Tel.: (86) 3588265105
Fax: (86) 5388265450
Petrochemical Products Mfr
S.I.C.: 2869
N.A.I.C.S.: 325110

Sinopec Wuhan Oil Products Co., Ltd. (2)
No 18 Wangsong District
Wuhan, Hubei, China
Tel.: (86) 2785797018
Fax: (86) 2785778551
E-Mail: whoil@whoil.com
Web Site: www.whoil.com
Petrochemical Products Mfr
S.I.C.: 2869
N.A.I.C.S.: 325110

Sinopec Wuhan Phoenix Co., Ltd. (2)
Changqing Road
Qingshan District, Wuhan, Hubei, 430082, China
Tel.: (86) 2786515662
Fax: (86) 27 86515 043
E-Mail: snpcwhpw@public.wh.hb.cn
Web Site: english.sinopec.com
Petrochemical Products Mfr
S.I.C.: 2869
N.A.I.C.S.: 325110

Sinopec Yangzi Petrochemical Co., Ltd. (2)
777 Xinhua Road Yanjlan Development Zone
Luhe District, Nanjing, Jiangsu, 210048, China CN
Tel.: (86) 2557782114
Fax: (86) 2557784389
E-Mail: yzshgs@ypc.com.cn
Web Site: www.ypc.com.cn
Sales Range: $1-4.9 Billion
Ethylene, Butadiene, Polyethylene & Other Chemicals Mfr
S.I.C.: 2869
N.A.I.C.S.: 325110
Jiaren Zhang *(CFO & Sr VP)*

Sinopec Zhenhai Refining & Chemical Co., Ltd. (2)
Ahenhai District
Ningbo, Zhejiang, 315207, China
Tel.: (86) 444238
Fax: (86) 57486270077
Web Site: www.zrcc.com.cn
Emp.: 6
Petrochemical Products Mfr
S.I.C.: 2869
N.A.I.C.S.: 325110

Affiliates:

Petro-Cyberworks Information Technology Co., Ltd. (2)
1208 Nanxincang Tower A A22 Dongsishitiao
Dongcheng District, Beijing, 100007, China
Tel.: (86) 1084191188
Fax: (86) 1064096213
E-Mail: pcitcbdd@pcitc.com
Web Site: www.pcitc.com
Emp.: 700
Information Technology Services
S.I.C.: 7373
N.A.I.C.S.: 541512

Sinopec Fujian Refining & Chemical Co., Ltd. (2)
Quangang District
Quanzhou, China
Tel.: (86) 59587789188
Fax: (86) 59587789130
E-Mail: gsb@mail.fipcl.com
Chemical Processing Services
S.I.C.: 2869
N.A.I.C.S.: 325110

Weihai Weiyang Petroleum Co. Ltd. (2)
East Haibucun Economy & Tech Development Area
Weihai, 264205, China
Tel.: (86) 6315901550
Fax: (86) 631 5901551
Emp.: 100
Oil & Liquefied Chemicals Storage & Sales
S.I.C.: 5989
N.A.I.C.S.: 454310

Joint Ventures:

BASF-YPC Company Limited (2)
Luhe District
Nanjing, Jiangsu, 210048, China
Tel.: (86) 2558569999
Fax: (86) 2558569966
E-Mail: wanh@basf-ypc.com.cn
Web Site: www.basf-ypc.com.cn
Emp.: 2,000
Petrochemical Products Mfr
S.I.C.: 2869
N.A.I.C.S.: 325110
Houliang Dai *(Chm)*
Bernd Blumenberg *(Pres)*

Shanghai Gaoqiao BASF Dispersions Co., Ltd. (2)
No 99 Ln 1929 Pudong Bei Road
Pudong New Area, Shanghai, 200137, China CN
Tel.: (86) 2158670303
Fax: (86) 21558675050
E-Mail: sgbd@sgbd.com.cn
Web Site: www.sgbd.com.cn
Emp.: 200
Adhesive Raw Material Mfr; Owned 50% by BASF SE & 50% by China Petrochemical Corporation
S.I.C.: 2891
N.A.I.C.S.: 325520

Shanghai SECCO Petrochemical Co., Ltd. (2)
29/30F A Building Far East International Plaza
No 299 Xian Xia Road, Shanghai, 200051, China CN
Tel.: (86) 2152574688
Fax: (86) 2162097070
E-Mail: contacts@secco.com.cn
Web Site: www.secco.com.cn
Emp.: 500
Petrochemical Products Mfr; Owned 50% by BP plc & 50% by China Petrochemical Corporation
S.I.C.: 2869
N.A.I.C.S.: 325110
Xin Hua *(Dir-Fin)*

Non-U.S. Subsidiaries:

UNIPEC Asia Co. Ltd. (2)
Room 1202 12th Floor Convention Plaza Office Tower 1
Harbour Road, Wanchai, China (Hong Kong)
Tel.: (852) 28796688
Fax: (852) 25272868
E-Mail: info@unipec.net
Emp.: 40
Petrochemical Trading Services
S.I.C.: 1389
N.A.I.C.S.: 213112

UNIPEC UK Co. Ltd. (2)
20th Floor Marble Arch Tower
55 Bryanston Street
London, W1H 7AA, United Kingdom
Tel.: (44) 2076169888
Fax: (44) 2076169889
Web Site: www.sinopec.com
Petrochemical Trading Services
S.I.C.: 1389
N.A.I.C.S.: 213112

CHINA PETROCHEMICAL DEVELOPMENT CORP.

10-11F No 12 Tunghsing Rd
Taipei, Taiwan
Tel.: (886) 287878187
Fax: (886) 287878400
E-Mail: list1314@ms.tse.com.tw
Web Site: www.cpdc.com.tw
1314—(TAI)
Sales Range: $1-4.9 Billion
Emp.: 982

Business Description:
Resins & Plastics Products Distr
S.I.C.: 2821
N.A.I.C.S.: 325211

Personnel:
Henry Heng Feng *(Chm)*

Subsidiaries:

Chemax International Corporation (1)
8F No 12 Tunghsing Road
Songshan District, Taipei, 105, Taiwan
Tel.: (886) 287878577
Fax: (886) 287872487

China Petrochemical Development Corp.—(Continued)

Web Site: www.chemax.com.tw
Emp.: 10
Petrochemicals Import & Distr
S.I.C.: 5169
N.A.I.C.S.: 424690
Shun Wang Ko *(Gen Mgr)*

Tsou Seen Chemical Industries Corporation (1)
8F 12 Tunghsing Rd
Taipei, 105, Taiwan
Tel.: (886) 287878459, ext. 73302299
Fax: (886) 287878453
E-Mail: tsci@tsou-seen.com.tw
Web Site: www.tsou-seen.com.tw
Dicalcium Phosphate & Liquid Fertilizers Mfr
S.I.C.: 2874
N.A.I.C.S.: 325312

Joint Venture:

Taiwan Chlorine Industries Ltd. (1)
25 Chungchih Street Hsiaokang District
Kaohsiung, 812, Taiwan TW
Tel.: (886) 7 8715 171
Fax: (886) 7 8717 289
E-Mail: tcics@ppg.com
Web Site: www.tci-ppg.com
Chlorine Mfr
S.I.C.: 2819
N.A.I.C.S.: 325180

Plants:

China Petrochemical Development Corp. - Da-Sheh Plant (1)
No 1 Chinchian Road
Da-Sheh Hsiang, Kaohsiung, 815, Taiwan
Tel.: (886) 7 351 3521
Web Site: www.cpdc.com.tw/english/01_about/01about_01company.php?ID=6
Petrochemicals Mfr
S.I.C.: 2911
N.A.I.C.S.: 324110

China Petrochemical Development Corp. - Hsiaokang Plant (1)
No 34 Chunglin Road
Hsiaokang District, Kaohsiung, 81208, Taiwan
Tel.: (886) 78711160
Fax: (886) 78715487
Emp.: 350
Petrochemicals Mfr
S.I.C.: 2911
N.A.I.C.S.: 324110

China Petrochemical Development Corp. - Tou-Fen Plant (1)
No 217 Section 2 Tzyh-Chyang Road
Tou-Fen, Miao-li, Taiwan
Tel.: (886) 37623381
Fax: (886) 37637040
Web Site: www.cpdc.com.tw
Petrochemicals Mfr
S.I.C.: 2911
N.A.I.C.S.: 324110

Eternal Chemical Co., Ltd. - Lu-Chu Plant (1)
22 Changhsing Road
Luchu District, Kaohsiung, 821, Taiwan
Tel.: (886) 76963331
Fax: (886) 7 696 8705
Web Site: www.eternal-group.com
Emp.: 3,000
Unsaturated Polyester Resins Mfr
S.I.C.: 2821
N.A.I.C.S.: 325211
Shihfeng Huang *(Mgr)*

CHINA PHARMA HOLDINGS, INC.

Second Floor 17 Jinpan Road
Haikou, Hainan, 570216, China
Tel.: (86) 898 66811730
Fax: (86) 89866819024
CPHI—(NYSEMKT)
Rev.: $32,806,678
Assets: $157,610,954
Liabilities: $24,666,513
Net Worth: $132,944,441
Earnings: ($20,008,049)
Emp.: 400
Fiscal Year-end: 12/31/13
Business Description:
Pharmaceutical Mfr
S.I.C.: 2834
N.A.I.C.S.: 325412
Personnel:
Zhilin Li *(Chm, Pres & CEO)*
Board of Directors:
Zhilin Li
Gene Michael Bennett
Baowen Dong
Heung Mei Tsui
Yingwen Zhang
Transfer Agent:
Securities Transfer Corporation
2591 Dallas Pkwy Ste 102
Frisco, TX 75034
Tel.: (469) 633-0101
Fax: (469) 633-0088

CHINA PHARMACEUTICAL GROUP LIMITED

(Name Changed to CSPC Pharmaceutical Group Limited)

CHINA PHARMACEUTICALS, INC.

24th Floor Building A Zhengxin Mansion 1st Gaoxin Road No 5
Hi-Tech Development Zone, 710075
Xi'an, China
Tel.: (86) 2984067215
E-Mail: admin@chinapharmaceuticalsinc.com
Web Site: www.chinapharmaceuticalsinc.com
Year Founded: 2004
CFMI—(OTC)
Sales Range: $10-24.9 Million
Emp.: 344
Business Description:
Pharmaceutical Products Mfr
S.I.C.: 2834
N.A.I.C.S.: 325412
Personnel:
Guozhu Wang *(Chm & CEO)*

CHINA PIONEER PHARMA HOLDINGS LIMITED

No 1000 Wangqiao Road
Pudong New District, Shanghai, 201201, China
Tel.: (86) 21 50498987
Fax: (86) 21 50498986
Web Site: www.pioneer-pharma.com
Year Founded: 1996
1345—(HKG)
Rev.: $152,293,149
Assets: $137,718,820
Liabilities: $103,911,569
Net Worth: $33,807,251
Earnings: $29,501,145
Fiscal Year-end: 12/31/12
Business Description:
Pharmaceuticals & Medical Products Distr
S.I.C.: 5122
N.A.I.C.S.: 424210
Personnel:
Paul Xinzhou Li *(Chm & CEO)*
Mengjun Zhu *(CFO & Deputy Gen Mgr)*
Board of Directors:
Paul Xinzhou Li
Chanshu Lai
Chi Hung Wong
Zhonghai Xu
Mengjun Zhu

CHINA PIPE GROUP LTD

12/F Phase 1 Austin Tower 22-26A Austin Avenue
Tsim Sha Tsui, Kowloon, China (Hong Kong)
Tel.: (852) 27287237
Fax: (852) 23872999
E-Mail: info@chinapipegroup.com
Web Site: www.bunkeeintl.com.hk
0380—(HKG)
Rev.: $58,688,627
Assets: $56,181,065
Liabilities: $15,867,942
Net Worth: $40,313,123
Earnings: $1,766,615
Emp.: 187
Fiscal Year-end: 12/31/12
Business Description:
Pipes & Fittings Mfr & Sales
S.I.C.: 3931
N.A.I.C.S.: 339992
Personnel:
Guanglin Lai *(Chm)*
Ben Ansheng Yu *(CEO)*
Siu Kwan Cheng *(Sec)*
Board of Directors:
Guanglin Lai
Wei Wen Chen
Fulin Lai
Patrick Wai Yip Tsang
Kean Seng U
Wilson Yee Shuen Wong
Li Yang
Ben Ansheng Yu

Appleby Management (Bermuda) Ltd.
Canon's Court 22 Victoria Street
HM 12 Hamilton, Bermuda
Transfer Agent:
Appleby Management (Bermuda) Ltd.
Canon's Court 22 Victoria Street
HM 12 Hamilton, Bermuda

CHINA POLY GROUP CORPORATION

1 North Street Chaoyangmen
Beijing, Dongcheng, 100010, China
Tel.: (86) 10 64082288
Fax: (86) 10 64082008
Web Site: www.poly.com.cn
Year Founded: 1993
Sales Range: $700-749.9 Million
Business Description:
Real Estate Developments, International Trade of Military & Civil Products, Culture & Arts & Mineral Resources Investments
S.I.C.: 6531
N.A.I.C.S.: 531390
Personnel:
Chen Hongshen *(Chm)*
Zhengao Zhang *(Pres & Chief Acct)*
Board of Directors:
Chen Hongshen
Lingjian Kong
Xiaochao Wang
Jiajin Xie
Donggen Xu
Bo Yu
Liansheng Zhang
Zhengao Zhang
Zhong Zhang

Subsidiary:

Poly Southern Group Co., Ltd. (1)
1801 Office Building CITIC Plaza
233 Tianhe Rd (N)
Guangzhou, P.C., 1801, China CN
Tel.: (86) 20 38911822
Fax: (86) 20 38911813
Web Site: www.poly.com.cn
Real Estate Development
S.I.C.: 6519
N.A.I.C.S.: 531190

Subsidiary:

Poly Real Estate (Group) Co., Ltd. (2)
Floor 29-33 Poly International Plaza
Yuejiang Road
510308 Guangzhou, Haizhu, China CN
Tel.: (86) 20 89898000 (100%)
Fax: (86) 20 89898666
E-Mail: stock@polycn.com
Web Site: www.polycn.com
600048—(SHG)
Emp.: 8,482
Real Estate Developments
S.I.C.: 6519
N.A.I.C.S.: 531190
Song Guangiu *(Chm)*
Peng Bihong *(CFO)*
Hu Zaixin *(CMO)*
Wu Zhangyan *(CTO)*
Yue Yongiian *(Sec)*

CHINA POLYMETALLIC MINING LIMITED

22/F South Tower 145 Tiantai Road
High-Tech District, Chengdu, China
Tel.: (86) 28 6555 7858
Fax: (86) 28 6555 7861
E-Mail: cpm@chinapolymetallic.com
Web Site: www.chinapolymetallic.com
Year Founded: 2009
2133—(HKG)
Rev.: $75,788,288
Assets: $299,396,668
Liabilities: $50,890,934
Net Worth: $248,505,734
Earnings: $28,412,229
Emp.: 396
Fiscal Year-end: 12/31/12
Business Description:
Non Ferrous Metal Mining Services
S.I.C.: 3369
N.A.I.C.S.: 331529
Personnel:
Xiaochuan Ran *(Chm)*
Ji He *(CEO)*
Tao Li *(CFO)*
Dejun Lei *(COO)*
Zhonglin Guo *(CTO)*
Yang Shen *(Chief Admin Officer)*
Siu Pik Ho *(Sec)*
Board of Directors:
Xiaochuan Ran
Christopher Michael Casey
Andrew Joseph Dawber
William Beckwith Hayden
Ji He
Kenneth Jue Lee
Edward Kwok Chi Miu
Xiangdong Shi

Codan Trust Company (Cayman) Limited
Cricket Square Hutchins Drive
PO Box 2681
Georgetown, Grand Cayman, Cayman Islands
Transfer Agent:
Codan Trust Company (Cayman) Limited
Cricket Square Hutchins Drive
PO Box 2681
Georgetown, Grand Cayman, Cayman Islands

CHINA POLYPEPTIDE GROUP, INC.

No 11 Jianda Road
Jinghan Economic Devel Zone
Wuhan, 430023, China
Tel.: (86) 27 8351 8396
Year Founded: 2007
CHPN—(OTC)
Sales Range: $25-49.9 Million
Business Description:
Polypeptide-Based Nutritional Supplements & Health Food Research, Development & Sales
S.I.C.: 0182
N.A.I.C.S.: 111419
Personnel:
Yihua Zhan *(Chm & CEO)*
Shengfan Yan *(Pres)*
Lirong Hu *(Interim CFO)*
Board of Directors:
Yihua Zhan
Kaichao Peng
Shengfan Yan

CHINA POST E-COMMERCE (HOLDINGS) LIMITED
Room 702 7/F Goodluck Industrial Centre 808 Lai Chi Kok Road
Lai Chi Kok, Kowloon, China (Hong Kong)
Tel.: (852) 2520 6020
Fax: (852) 2520 6086
E-Mail: admin@cpech.com
Web Site: www.cpech.com
IH1A—(DEU)
Business Description:
Shopping & Direct Mailing Services
S.I.C.: 7331
N.A.I.C.S.: 541860
Personnel:
Joseph Chi Yuen Lau *(Chm & Exec Dir)*
Board of Directors:
Man Wai Chung
Chan Man Fung
Chung Mong Lee
Wing Kin Tam

CHINA POST GROUP
No 3 Financial Street
Beijing, Xicheng District, 100808, China
Tel.: (86) 10 6885 9944
E-Mail: feedback@chinapost.com.cn
Web Site: www.chinapost.com.cn/
Sales Range: $25-49.9 Million
Emp.: 927,800
Business Description:
Newspaper Distribution, Postal Remittances, Stamp Distribution, Logistics & Postal Services
S.I.C.: 4311
N.A.I.C.S.: 491110
Personnel:
Li Guohua *(Pres & CEO)*

CHINA POWER EQUIPMENT, INC.
Yongle Industry Zone Jingyang Industry Concentration Area
Xi'an, Shaanxi, China 713702
Tel.: (86) 29 6261 9758
Fax: (86) 2988312081
E-Mail: saj@xa-fj.com
Web Site: www.chinapower-equipment.com
Year Founded: 2006
CPQQ.OB—(OTCB)
Rev.: $36,768,911
Assets: $45,312,764
Liabilities: $3,725,129
Net Worth: $41,587,635
Earnings: $6,407,072
Emp.: 75
Fiscal Year-end: 12/31/12
Business Description:
Electrical Power Transformer Products Mfr
S.I.C.: 3675
N.A.I.C.S.: 334416
Personnel:
Yongxing Song *(Chm, Pres & CEO)*
Elaine Lanfeng Zhao *(CFO)*
Board of Directors:
Yongxing Song
Dangsheng Chen
Yarong Feng
Sue Kuen Leung
Michael Segal
Transfer Agent:
Worldwide Stock Transfer, LLC
433 Hackensack Ave Level L
Hackensack, NJ 07601

CHINA POWER INTERNATIONAL DEVELOPMENT LIMITED
Suite 6301 63/F Central Plaza 18 Harbour Road
Wanchai, China (Hong Kong)
Tel.: (852) 28023861
Fax: (852) 28023922
Web Site: www.chinapower.hk
2380—(HKG)
Rev.: $2,807,927,116
Assets: $11,105,107,872
Liabilities: $8,098,169,188
Net Worth: $3,006,938,685
Earnings: $267,070,693
Emp.: 7,669
Fiscal Year-end: 12/31/12
Business Description:
Hydroelectric Power Generation
S.I.C.: 4911
N.A.I.C.S.: 221111
Personnel:
Xiaolin Li *(Chm & CEO)*
Dake Gu *(Pres)*
Shengrong Wang *(Chief Admin Officer)*
Bin Li *(Chief Corp Culture Officer)*
Siu Lan Cheung *(Sec)*
Board of Directors:
Xiaolin Li
Dake Gu
Qihong Guan
Gordon Che Keung Kwong
Fang Li
Alec Yiu Wa Tsui
Zichao Wang
Transfer Agent:
Computershare Hong Kong Investor Services Limited
Shops 1712-1716 17th Floor Hopewell Centre
183 Queens Road East
Wanchai, China (Hong Kong)

CHINA POWER INVESTMENT CORPORATION
Building 3 No 28 Financial Street
PO Box 2201
Xicheng District, Beijing, 100033, China
Tel.: (86) 10 66298000
Fax: (86) 10 66298095
Web Site: www.cpicorp.com.cn
Sales Range: $25-49.9 Billion
Business Description:
Electric Power Generation Services
S.I.C.: 4911
N.A.I.C.S.: 221118
Personnel:
Qizhou Lu *(Pres)*
Zhenping Meng *(CFO & VP)*

CHINA POWER NEW ENERGY DEVELOPMENT COMPANY LIMITED
Rooms 3801-05 38th Floor China Resources Building 26 Harbour Road
Wanchai, China (Hong Kong)
Tel.: (852) 36078888
Fax: (852) 36078899
Web Site: www.cpne.com.hk
0735—(HKG)
Rev.: $249,345,733
Assets: $2,554,683,204
Liabilities: $1,407,801,771
Net Worth: $1,146,881,433
Earnings: $33,640,776
Emp.: 1,013
Fiscal Year-end: 12/31/12
Business Description:
Construction & Power Generation Services
S.I.C.: 1541
N.A.I.C.S.: 236210
Personnel:
Xiaolin Li *(Chm)*
Yaxiong Bi *(Vice Chm)*
Lian Yin *(Vice Chm)*
Xuezhi Chen *(CFO)*
Chun Nam Fung *(Sec)*
Board of Directors:
Xiaolin Li
Yaxiong Bi
Chi Cheng
Kar Wing Chu
Hongxin He
Fang Li
Hao Wang
Kwok Tai Wong
Lian Yin
Xinyan Zhao
HSBC Securities Services (Bermuda) Limited
6 Front Street
Hamilton, Bermuda
Transfer Agent:
Tricor Tengis Limited
26/F Tesbury Centre, 28 Queens Road East
Hong Kong, China (Hong Kong)

CHINA POWER TECHNOLOGY, INC.
12 Gongyuan Road
Kaifeng, Henan, 475002, China
Tel.: (86) 378 299 6222
Fax: (86) 378 299 6111
E-Mail: info@kfboler.com
Web Site: www.chinapowerti.com
Year Founded: 2007
CNPI—(OTC)
Sales Range: $100-124.9 Million
Emp.: 1,470
Business Description:
Boiler Mfr
S.I.C.: 3443
N.A.I.C.S.: 332410
Personnel:
Honghai Zhang *(Chm & CEO)*
Shiyong Fan *(COO)*
Wuling Fu *(CTO)*
Board of Directors:
Honghai Zhang
Shiyong Fan
Remington Chia-Hung Hu
Zhenduo Liu

CHINA POWERPLUS LIMITED
39 Fishery Port Road
Singapore, 619745, Singapore
Tel.: (65) 62663502
Fax: (65) 62682447
Web Site: www.chinapowerplus.com
Z02—(SES)
Rev.: $271,270,329
Assets: $238,817,545
Liabilities: $40,809,491
Net Worth: $198,008,054
Earnings: ($40,722,046)
Fiscal Year-end: 12/31/12
Business Description:
Portable Power Tools Mfr
S.I.C.: 3499
N.A.I.C.S.: 332999
Personnel:
Yongwen Xue *(Chm & Mng Dir)*
Desmond Tai Tiong Ong *(Deputy Chm)*
Dianyan Guo *(Deputy Mng Dir)*
Min-Li Tan *(Sec)*
Board of Directors:
Yongwen Xue
Dianyan Guo
Yanping Hao
Danny Beng Teck Oh
Desmond Tai Tiong Ong
Damien Yang Hwee Seah
Legal Counsel:
Colin Ng & Partners LLP
36 Carpenter Street
Singapore, Singapore

CHINA PRECISION STEEL, INC.
18th Floor Teda Building 87 Wing Lok Street
Sheungwan, Hong Kong, China (Hong Kong)
Tel.: (852) 2543 2290
Web Site: www.chinaprecisionsteelinc.com
CPSL—(NASDAQ)
Rev.: $36,527,550
Assets: $119,927,678
Liabilities: $67,017,943
Net Worth: $52,909,735
Earnings: ($68,939,386)
Emp.: 231
Fiscal Year-end: 06/30/13
Business Description:
Cold-Rolled Steel Products Mfr
S.I.C.: 3312
N.A.I.C.S.: 331221
Personnel:
Leada Tak Tai Li *(Chm & CFO)*
Hai Sheng Chen *(CEO)*
Zu De Jiang *(COO)*
Board of Directors:
Leada Tak Tai Li
Hai Sheng Chen
Jian Lin Li
Tung Kuen Tsui
Wei Hong Xiao
U.S. Subsidiary:

OraLabs, Inc. **(1)**
18685 E Plz Dr
Parker, CO 80134
Tel.: (303) 783-9499
Fax: (303) 783-5759
Web Site: www.oralabs.com
Emp.: 150
Oral Care Products Retailer
S.I.C.: 5047
N.A.I.C.S.: 423450
Mark Hayes *(Dir-Mfg)*

CHINA PREMIUM LIFESTYLE ENTERPRISE, INC.
28/F King Palace Plaza 52A Sha Tsui Road
Tsuen Wan, China (Hong Kong)
Tel.: (852) 2954 2469
E-Mail: ir@chinapremiumlifestyle.com
Web Site: www.chinapremiumlifestyle.com
CPLY—(OTC)
Sales Range: $150-199.9 Million
Emp.: 222
Business Description:
Luxury Sports Car Dealer
S.I.C.: 5511
N.A.I.C.S.: 441110
Subsidiary:

Auto Italia Limited **(1)**
3S Center Unit C Ground Floor 2 Yuen Shun Circuit
Sha Tin, China (Hong Kong)
Tel.: (852) 2365 0269
New Car Dealer
S.I.C.: 5511
N.A.I.C.S.: 441110

Non-U.S. Subsidiaries:

Dalian Auto Italia Car Trading Co., Ltd **(1)**
No 2-7 Yi Pin Xing Hai B3 Area Xing Hai Square
Dalian, Liaoning, 116023, China
Tel.: (86) 411 84804789
Fax: (86) 411 84805867
E-Mail: ferrari-maserati@163.com
Emp.: 21
New Car Dealer
S.I.C.: 5511
N.A.I.C.S.: 441110

Nanjing Auto Italia Car Trading Co., Ltd **(1)**
No 48 Ningnan Avenue
Yuhua District, Nanjing, Jiangsu, 210012, China

CHINA PREMIUM LIFESTYLE ENTERPRISE, INC.—(Continued)

Tel.: (86) 25 58077888
Fax: (86) 25 52323350
New Car Dealer
S.I.C.: 5511
N.A.I.C.S.: 441110

CHINA PRINT POWER GROUP LIMITED

Unit 2 13/F Kodak House II 39
Healthy Street East
North Point, China (Hong Kong)
Tel.: (852) 31241243
Fax: (852) 31241242
E-Mail: sales@powerprinting.com.hk
Web Site: www.powerprinting.com.hk
6828—(HKG SES)
Rev.: $24,742,152
Assets: $36,025,664
Liabilities: $7,998,253
Net Worth: $28,027,411
Earnings: ($1,899,949)
Emp.: 157
Fiscal Year-end: 12/31/12

Business Description:
Printing Services
S.I.C.: 2759
N.A.I.C.S.: 323111

Personnel:
Chun Lee Sze *(CEO)*
Wai Ming Chan *(COO)*
Gwendolyn Jong Yuh Gn *(Co-Sec)*
Kan Chun Tsui *(Co-Sec)*

Board of Directors:
Siang Kai Lim
Wai Ming Chan
Stella Oi Ling Chung
Wing Hang Kwan
Shek Kin Lam
Nelson Kwong Chi Liu
Chun Lee Sze
Piew Wee
Fei Tat Wong

BDO Limited
25th Floor Wing On Centre 111 Connaught Road
Central, China (Hong Kong)

Codan Services Limited
Clarendon House 2 Church Street
Hamilton, Bermuda

Transfer Agent:
Boardroom Corporate & Advisory Services Pte. Ltd.
50 Raffles Place 32-01 Singapore Land Tower
Singapore, Singapore

CHINA PRINTING & PACKAGING, INC.

Xiandong Road Shangsong Villing
Fufeng County, Baoji, Shaanxi, 722205, China
Tel.: (86) 907 547 1054
Year Founded: 2007
CHPI—(OTC)
Sales Range: $10-24.9 Million
Emp.: 150

Business Description:
Paper Packaging & Paperboard Products Mfr
S.I.C.: 2679
N.A.I.C.S.: 322299

Personnel:
Yongming Feng *(Chm & CEO)*
Jinrong Shi *(CFO)*

Board of Directors:
Yongming Feng
Michael Segal

Transfer Agent:
Pacific Stock Transfer Company
4045 S Spencer St Ste 403
Las Vegas, NV 89119
Tel.: (702) 361-3033

CHINA PRIVATE EQUITY INVESTMENT HOLDINGS LIMITED

(Name Changed to Adamas Finance Asia Limited)

CHINA PROPERTIES GROUP LTD

14th Fl Wheelock House 20 Pedder St
Central, China (Hong Kong)
Tel.: (852) 23116788
Fax: (852) 23111818
E-Mail: cpg@cpg-group.com
Web Site: www.cpg-group.com
1838—(HKG)
Sales Range: $125-149.9 Million
Emp.: 374

Business Description:
Property Development in Residential & Commercial Sectors
S.I.C.: 6531
N.A.I.C.S.: 531210

Personnel:
George Shih Chang Wang *(Chm)*
Sai Chung Wong *(Mng Dir)*
Ling Ling Yu *(Sec)*

Board of Directors:
George Shih Chang Wang
Warren Talbot Beckwith
Michael Chaun Kwan Cheng
Kai Cheong Kwan
Koon Hoo Luk
Garry Alides Willinge
Sai Chung Wong
Zhi Gao Wu
Li Chang Xu

HSBC Trustee (Cayman) Limited
HSBC House 68 West Bay Road
PO Box 484
Georgetown, Cayman Islands

Transfer Agents:
Tricor Investor Services Limited
26th Floor Tesbury Centre 28 Queens Road East
Wanchai, China (Hong Kong)

HSBC Trustee (Cayman) Limited
HSBC House 68 West Bay Road
PO Box 484
Georgetown, Cayman Islands

CHINA PROPERTIES INVESTMENT HOLDINGS LIMITED

Room 2001 20/F Lippo Centre Tower Two 89 Queensway Road
Hong Kong, China (Hong Kong)
Tel.: (852) 25360991
Fax: (852) 25360990
Web Site: www.736.com.hk
0736—(HKG)
Rev.: $1,495,732
Assets: $83,598,148
Liabilities: $11,660,543
Net Worth: $71,937,605
Earnings: ($20,338,836)
Emp.: 41
Fiscal Year-end: 03/31/13

Business Description:
Investment Holding Company
S.I.C.: 6799
N.A.I.C.S.: 523920

Personnel:
Dong Xu *(Chm)*
Yuk Sing Yip *(Sec)*

Board of Directors:
Dong Xu
Tat On Au
Jie Min Cao
Wilson Wai Yin Lai
Kwong Wah Tse
Wai Fong Yu

HSBC Securities Services (Bermuda) Limited
6 Front Street
Hamilton, Bermuda

Transfer Agent:
HSBC Securities Services (Bermuda) Limited
6 Front Street
Hamilton, Bermuda

Subsidiary:

Lok Wing group Limited (1)
1B Kai Yee Ct 58 Battery St
Yau Ma Tei, Kowloon, China (Hong Kong)
Tel.: (852) 81022703
Fax: (852) 25525848
Real Estate Property Management Services
S.I.C.: 6531
N.A.I.C.S.: 531311

CHINA PROSPEROUS CLEAN ENERGY CORPORATION

West Side Public Transportation Gas Filling Center
Angang Avenue-Middle Part
Yindu Dsitrict, Anyang, Henan, 455000, China
Tel.: (86) 3723166864
Fax: (86) 3723166864
Web Site: www.otcpb.com
Year Founded: 2006
CHPC—(OTC)
Sales Range: $25-49.9 Million
Emp.: 260

Business Description:
Natural & Liquefied Petroleum Gas Distr & Retailer; Gas Filling Stations Construction Services
S.I.C.: 4924
N.A.I.C.S.: 221210

Personnel:
Wei Wang *(Chm, CEO, Treas & Sec)*
Hongjie Zhou *(Acting CFO)*

CHINA PUBLIC PROCUREMENT LIMITED

Suites 2805-2810 Dah Sing Financial Centre 108 Gloucester Road
Wanchai, China (Hong Kong)
Tel.: (852) 2114 0101
Fax: (852) 2114 0309
E-Mail: enquiry@cpphk.com
Web Site: www.cpphk.com
1094—(HKG)
Rev.: $35,735,011
Assets: $241,754,944
Liabilities: $21,202,604
Net Worth: $220,552,340
Earnings: ($2,175,386)
Emp.: 116
Fiscal Year-end: 12/31/12

Business Description:
Information Technology Services
S.I.C.: 7373
N.A.I.C.S.: 541512

Personnel:
Shulin Chen *(Co-Chm)*
Yuanzhong Cheng *(Co-Chm)*
Dingbo Wang *(CEO)*
Kening Li *(CFO)*
Charles Kin Shing Lau *(Chief Investment Officer & Sec)*

Board of Directors:
Shulin Chen
Yuanzhong Cheng
Kevin Tze See Chan
Bojie Chen
Wai Kong Ho
Charles Kin Shing Lau
Kening Li
Jie Liu
Ru Chuan Peng
Zhiyong Peng
Shaoji Shen
Dingbo Wang
Ning Wang
Fred Fong Wu
Haigen Xu
Wei Ying

Butterfield Fulcrum Group (Bermuda) Limited
26 Burnaby Street
Hamilton, HM 11, Bermuda

CHINA PUTIAN FOOD HOLDING LIMITED

Room 3312 33/F West Tower Shun Tak Centre
200 Connaught Road, Central, China (Hong Kong)
Tel.: (852) 35824666
Fax: (852) 35824567
Web Site: www.putian.com.hk
1699—(HKG)
Sales Range: $75-99.9 Million
Emp.: 550

Business Description:
Hog Farming, Slaughtering & Sales
S.I.C.: 0213
N.A.I.C.S.: 112210

Personnel:
Chenyang Cai *(Chm & CEO)*
Haifang Cai *(Deputy CEO-Admin)*
Shengyin Cai *(CFO)*
Kin Shing Ku *(Sec & Controller)*

Board of Directors:
Chenyang Cai
Haifang Cai
Shengyin Cai
Zirong Cai
Shiming Wu
Wenquan Yu

CHINA QINBA PHAMACEUTICALS, INC.

24th Floor Building A Zhengxin Mansion Hi-Tech Development Zone
5 of 1st Gaoxin Road, Xi'an, China
Tel.: (86) 2982098912
Web Site: www.chinapharmaceuticalsinc.com
Sales Range: $10-24.9 Million
Emp.: 486

Business Description:
Pharmaceuticals Mfr
S.I.C.: 2834
N.A.I.C.S.: 325412

Personnel:
Wang Guozhu *(Chm & CEO)*
Gao Lei *(CFO)*
Qiao Yufei *(Sec)*

Board of Directors:
Wang Guozhu
Zhang Guiping
Chen Xi Huang Wong

CHINA QINFA GROUP LIMITED

(d/b/a Qinfa Group)
22nd Floor South Tower Poly International Plaza 1 Pazhou East Road
Haizhu, Guangzhou, Guangdong, China 510308
Tel.: (86) 2089898239
Web Site: www.qinfagroup.com
Year Founded: 1996
866—(HKG)
Sls.: $1,760,897,522
Assets: $2,888,955,230
Liabilities: $2,271,240,636
Net Worth: $617,714,594
Earnings: $52,920,878
Emp.: 1,745
Fiscal Year-end: 12/31/12

Business Description:
Coal Operations
S.I.C.: 1241
N.A.I.C.S.: 213113

Personnel:
Jihua Xu *(Chm)*
Jianfei Wang *(CEO)*
Chi Kin Wong *(CFO & Sec)*

Board of Directors:
Jihua Xu
Guosheng Huang
Sik Yuen Lau
Xiaomei Liu
Jianfei Wang
Li Weng
Zhiying Xing
Legal Counsel:
Zhong Lun Law Firm
36-37/F SK Tower 6A Jianguomenwai Avenue
Beijing, China
Squire Sanders
24th Floor, Central Tower 28 Queen's Road
Central, China (Hong Kong)
Hasting & Co
5th Floor Gloucester Tower The Landmark 11
Pedder Street
Central, China (Hong Kong)
Royal Bank of Canada Trust
Company (Cayman) Limited
4th Floor Royal Bank House 24 Shedden Road
Georgetown, Cayman Islands
Transfer Agents:
Union Registrars Limited
18/F Fook Lee Commercial Centre Town Place
33 Lockhart Road
Wanchai, China (Hong Kong)
Royal Bank of Canada Trust
Company (Cayman) Limited
4th Floor Royal Bank House 24 Shedden Road
Georgetown, Cayman Islands

CHINA RAILWAY CONSTRUCTION CORPORATION LIMITED

40 Fuxing Road Haidian District
Beijing, 100855, China
Tel.: (86) 1051888114
Fax: (86) 1068217382
E-Mail: ir@crcc.cn
Web Site: www.crcc.cn
Year Founded: 2007
601186—(HKG SHG)
Rev.: $76,933,108,613
Assets: $76,353,047,982
Liabilities: $64,704,687,565
Net Worth: $11,648,360,417
Earnings: $1,353,500,487
Emp.: 244,523
Fiscal Year-end: 12/31/12
Business Description:
Railroad Construction Services
S.I.C.: 1629
N.A.I.C.S.: 237990
Personnel:
Fengchao Meng *(Chm)*
Shugui Peng *(Chm-Supervisory Bd)*
Guangfa Zhao *(Pres)*
Chun Biu Law *(Co-Sec)*
Xingxi Yu *(Co-Sec)*
Board of Directors:
Fengchao Meng
Kecheng Li
Weifeng Wei
Taishi Wu
Guangfa Zhao
Guangjie Zhao
Mingxian Zhu
Supervisory Board of Directors:
Shugui Peng
Shaojun Huang
Liangcai Zhang
Legal Counsel:
Beijing Deheng Law Office
12/F Tower B Focus Place 19 Finance Street
Beijing, China
Baker & Mckenzie
23rd Floor Pacific Place 88 Queensway
Hong Kong, China (Hong Kong)
Subsidiaries:

China Civil Engineering Construction Corporation **(1)**
4 Beifengwo
Haidian District, Beijing, China
Tel.: (86) 1063263392
Fax: (86) 1063263864
E-Mail: zongban@ccecc.com.cn
Web Site: www.ccecc.com.cn
Engineering & Construction Services
S.I.C.: 8711
N.A.I.C.S.: 541330
Rongxin Lin *(Chm)*
Zhiming Liu *(Vice Chm)*
Li Yuan *(Pres)*

Subsidiaries:

CCECC International Trading Co. Ltd. **(2)**
11/f Dacheng Plaza No 28 Xuanwumen
West Avenue Xuanwu District
Beijing, 100053, China
Tel.: (86) 1063600935
Fax: (86) 1063600940
Civil Engineering Services
S.I.C.: 8711
N.A.I.C.S.: 541330
Fong Ta Wei *(Mgr)*

Shanghai CCECC Enterprises Company Ltd. **(2)**
27/F Shanghai CCECC Mansion No 666
Gonghexin Road
Shanghai, 200070, China
Tel.: (86) 2166531726
Fax: (86) 2156637234
E-Mail: shanghai@ccecc.com.cn
Civil Engineering Services
S.I.C.: 8711
N.A.I.C.S.: 541330

Non-U.S. Subsidiaries:

CCECC (Botswana) (Pty) Ltd. **(2)**
Plot 153 Commerce Park
Private Bag T08
Tlokweng, Gaborone, Botswana
Tel.: (267) 3925332
Fax: (267) 392 5586
E-Mail: ccecc-botswana@ccecc.com.cn
Civil Engineering Services
S.I.C.: 8711
N.A.I.C.S.: 541330

CCECC Nigeria Ltd. **(2)**
46 Nnamdi Azikiwe Drive Ebute Metta
Lagos Minland
Lagos, Nigeria
Tel.: (234) 8033154680
E-Mail: ccecc-nigeria@ccecc.com.cn
Civil Engineering Services
S.I.C.: 8711
N.A.I.C.S.: 541330

China Civil Engineering Construction Company(Macau) Ltd.. **(2)**
Assumpcao No 263 22 Andar C H Edif
China Civil Plaza
Macau, China (Macau)
Tel.: (853) 28781160
Fax: (853) 2878 1242
E-Mail: ccecc-macao@ccecc.com.cn
Emp.: 30
Civil Engineering Services
S.I.C.: 8711
N.A.I.C.S.: 541330
Fasheng Li *(Mgr)*

China Railway 13th Bureau Group Co., Ltd. **(1)**
No 2138 Lingdong Road
Erdao District, Changchun, Jilin, 130033, China
Tel.: (86) 43186161114
Fax: (86) 43184647191
Construction Engineering Services
S.I.C.: 1629
N.A.I.C.S.: 237990

China Railway 19th Bureau Group Co., Ltd. **(1)**
No 137 Nanjiao Street
Liaoyang, Liaoning, 111000, China
Tel.: (86) 4192326114
Fax: (86) 4192326200
Construction Engineering Services
S.I.C.: 1629
N.A.I.C.S.: 237990

China Railway Electrification Bureau (Group) Co., Ltd. **(1)**
Baoman Road Mancheng County
Baoding, Hebei, 072150, China
Tel.: (86) 3127065872
Web Site: www.eeb.cn
Railway Road Construction Services
S.I.C.: 1542
N.A.I.C.S.: 236220
Gao Shutang *(Chm)*
Wang Qizeng *(Sec-Party Committee)*

China Railway Fourth Survey and Design Institute Group Co., Ltd **(1)**
Room B 5 F Building B Huifangyuan
Nanshan District, Shenzhen, 518052, China
Tel.: (86) 75526530649
Fax: (86) 75526530649
Engineering Consulting Services
S.I.C.: 8711
N.A.I.C.S.: 541330

Non-U.S. Subsidiary:

China Railway Construction (HK) Limited **(1)**
Room 207 MTR Hung Hom Building
MTR Hung Hom Station, Hung Hom,
Kowloon, China (Hong Kong)
Tel.: (852) 27749886
Fax: (852) 27740197
Emp.: 10
Railway Construction Services
S.I.C.: 1629
N.A.I.C.S.: 237990
Zheng Zheong *(Mgr)*

Non-U.S. Joint Venture:

Corriente Resources, Inc. **(1)**
5811 Cooney Road Suite S209
Richmond, BC, V6X 3M1, Canada BC
Tel.: (604) 282-7212
Fax: (604) 282-7568
E-Mail: copper@corriente.com
Web Site: www.corriente.com
Emp.: 252
Copper & Gold Mining Services
S.I.C.: 1021
N.A.I.C.S.: 212234
Shouhua Jin *(Chm & Mng VP)*
Dongqing Li *(Pres)*
Zhaoqi Wang *(CFO)*
Guobin Hu *(Sec & VP)*

CHINA RAILWAY GROUP LIMITED

No 1 Xinghuo Road Fengtai District
Beijing, 100070, China
Tel.: (86) 1051845717
Fax: (86) 1051842057
E-Mail: ir@crecg.com
Web Site: www.crecg.com
601390—(SHG)
Rev.: $73,964,531,250
Assets: $87,455,820,600
Liabilities: $73,414,592,550
Net Worth: $14,041,228,050
Earnings: $1,276,042,050
Emp.: 289,343
Fiscal Year-end: 12/31/12
Business Description:
Holding Company; Railway & Other Infrastructure Engineering & Construction Services
S.I.C.: 6719
N.A.I.C.S.: 551112
Personnel:
Changjin Li *(Chm)*
Qiuming Wang *(Chm-Supervisory Bd)*
Guiqing Yao *(Vice Chm)*
Jiansheng Li *(CFO & VP)*
Chun Chung Tam *(Co-Sec)*
Tengqun Yu *(Co-Sec)*
Board of Directors:
Changjin Li
Zhongren Bai
Huazhang Gong
Xiuguo Han
Gong He
Patrick Sun
Taiwen Wang
Guiqing Yao
Supervisory Board of Directors:
Qiuming Wang
Wenxin Chen
Longbiao Lin
Jianyuan Liu
Xixue Zhang
Deloitte Touche Tohmastu CPA LLP
8/F Deloitte Tower The Towers Oriental Plaza 1
East Chang An Avenue
Beijing, China
Legal Counsel:
Linklaters
10th Floor, Alexandra House, 18 Chater Road
Hong Kong, China (Hong Kong)
Jia Yuan Law Firm
F407 Ocean Plaza 158 Fuxing Men Nei Avenue
Beijing, China
China Securities Depository & Clearing Corporation Limited
36/F China Insurance Bldg
166 Lu Jia Zui Rd E, Shanghai, PRC, China
20012
Subsidiaries:

China Railway Major Bridge Engineering Group Co., Ltd. **(1)**
38 Hanyang Avenue
Wuhan, Hubei, 430050, China
Tel.: (86) 2784596949
E-Mail: mbecjb@ztmbec.com
Web Site: www.ztmbec.com
Construction Engineering Services
S.I.C.: 6552
N.A.I.C.S.: 237210
Mei Quan *(Chm)*
Liu Ziming *(Sec-Communist Party)*

China Railway Real Estate Group Co Ltd **(1)**
9 F No 15 Guangan Road
Fengtai District, Beijing, 100055, China
Tel.: (86) 1058095852
Fax: (86) 1058095852
Real Estate Development Services
S.I.C.: 1522
N.A.I.C.S.: 236116

China Railway Shanhaiguan Bridge Group Co., Ltd. **(1)**
35 Nanhaixi Road
Shanhaiguan District, Qinhuangdao, Hebei, 066205, China
Tel.: (86) 335 7940128
Fax: (86) 335 5152849
E-Mail: impexp@crsbg.com
Web Site: www.crsbg.com
Emp.: 1,300
Railway Steel Structure Mfr
S.I.C.: 3441
N.A.I.C.S.: 332312
Wu Zhao an *(Chm)*
Guo Changjiang *(Sec-Party & Vice Chm)*
Liu Enguo *(CEO)*
Liao Ke *(CFO)*
Zhao Yingjie *(Chm-Labor Party)*

China Railway Southwest Research Institute Co., Ltd. **(1)**
No 118 Xiyuecheng Street
Chengdu, Sichuan, 610031, China
Tel.: (86) 2886643703
Fax: (86) 2886643703
Web Site: www.swi.com.cn
Emp.: 1,000
Engineering Consulting Services
S.I.C.: 8711
N.A.I.C.S.: 541330
Huang Xiaomei *(Mgr)*

Non-U.S. Subsidiaries:

China Railway Engineering (HK) Limited **(1)**
5 Cambridge Rd
Kowloon, China (Hong Kong)
Tel.: (852) 28318341
Fax: (852) 28335604
Heavy & Civil Engineering Construction
S.I.C.: 1629
N.A.I.C.S.: 237990
Qin Jiaming *(Pres)*

Sino Railway Engineering Corporation Sdn. Bhd. **(1)**
Lot 1903 1904 Menara 1 Faber Twr
Jalan Desa Bahagia Taman Desa, 58100
Kuala Lumpur, Malaysia
Tel.: (60) 379811616
Fax: (60) 379818194

China Railway Group Limited—(Continued)

Heavy & Civil Engineering Construction
S.I.C.: 1629
N.A.I.C.S.: 237990

CHINA RAILWAY MATERIALS CO., LTD.

No 11 Huayuan Street
Xicheng District, Beijing, 100032, China
Tel.: (86) 10 51895188
Fax: (86) 10 51895028
E-Mail: crm@crmsc.com.cn
Web Site: www.crmsc.com.cn
Year Founded: 1979
Sales Range: $25-49.9 Billion
Emp.: 1,000
Business Description:
Railway Material Whslr
S.I.C.: 5039
N.A.I.C.S.: 423390
Personnel:
Li Wenke *(Pres)*

CHINA RARE EARTH HOLDINGS LIMITED

15/F Club Lusitano 16 Ice House Street
Central, China (Hong Kong)
Tel.: (852) 28696283
Fax: (852) 21360030
E-Mail: info@creh.com.hk
Web Site: www.creh.com.hk
0769—(HKG)
Sls.: $271,042,326
Assets: $469,528,356
Liabilities: $26,467,632
Net Worth: $443,060,723
Earnings: ($90,202,975)
Emp.: 1,100
Fiscal Year-end: 12/31/12
Business Description:
Holding Company; Rare Earth Materials Processor & Distr
S.I.C.: 6719
N.A.I.C.S.: 551112
Personnel:
Quanlong Jiang *(Co-Founder & Chm)*
Yuanying Qian *(Co-Founder, Deputy Chm & CEO)*
Desmond Lap Tak Law *(Sec & Controller-Fin)*
Board of Directors:
Quanlong Jiang
Charles Chunhua Huang
Cainan Jiang
Zhong Jin
Yuanying Qian
Guozhen Wang
Computershare Hong Kong Investor Services Limited
17th Floor, Hopewell Centre 183 Queens Road East
Hong Kong, China (Hong Kong)
Transfer Agents:
Royal Bank of Canada Trust Company (Cayman) Limited
4th Floor Royal Bank House 24 Shedden Road
Georgetown, Cayman Islands
Computershare Hong Kong Investor Services Limited
17th Floor, Hopewell Centre 183 Queens Road East
Hong Kong, China (Hong Kong)
Non-U.S. Subsidiary:

Yixing Xinwei Leeshing Rare Earth Company Limited **(1)**
Yangan Vlg
Dingshu Town, Yixing, Jiangsu, China
Tel.: (86) 51087457060
Fax: (86) 51087451186
Web Site: www.creh.com.hk/eng/index_com2.htm
Emp.: 500
Rare Earth Materials Processor & Distr
S.I.C.: 3259
N.A.I.C.S.: 327120
Jianwen Zhao *(Head-Tech Dept)*

CHINA RECYCLING ENERGY CORPORATION

12/F Tower A Chang An International Building
88 Nan Guan Zheng Jie, Xi'an, Shanxi, 710068, China
Tel.: (86) 2987691097
Fax: (86) 2987651099
E-Mail: tch@creg-cn.com
Web Site: www.creg-cn.com
CREG—(NASDAQ)
Rev.: $1,245,805
Assets: $202,296,601
Liabilities: $82,940,964
Net Worth: $119,355,637
Earnings: $3,222,504
Emp.: 166
Fiscal Year-end: 12/31/12
Business Description:
Recovered Energy Power Plants Development, Construction & Operation
S.I.C.: 4911
N.A.I.C.S.: 221118
Personnel:
Guohua Ku *(Chm & CEO)*
David Chong *(CFO & Sec)*
Lanwei Li *(COO & VP-Bus Dev)*
Board of Directors:
Guohua Ku
Timothy F. Driscoll
Lanwei Li
Albert S. McLelland
Chungui Shi

CHINA REDSTONE GROUP, INC.

239 Jianxin Road
Jiangbei District, Chongqing, 400000, China
Tel.: (86) 23 4025 1111
Fax: (86) 23 4025 6358
Web Site: www.chinaredstone.com
CGPI—(OTC)
Sales Range: $25-49.9 Million
Emp.: 43
Business Description:
Funeral Services & Cemeteries; Hospitality Services
S.I.C.: 7261
N.A.I.C.S.: 812220
Personnel:
Yiyou Ran *(Chm, Pres & CEO)*
Michael Wang *(CFO)*
Board of Directors:
Yiyou Ran
Jianquan Chen
Ray Hsu
Tim Hudson
S. Michael Rudolph
Michael Wang
Lihua Zhang

CHINA RENJI MEDICAL GROUP LTD

Unit 3001 30th Floor Hopewell Centre
183 Queen's Road East
Wanchai, China (Hong Kong)
Tel.: (852) 21552688
Fax: (852) 21559898
E-Mail: contact@renjimedical.com
Web Site: www.renjimedical.com
0648—(HKG)
Sls.: $17,335,780
Assets: $86,153,558
Liabilities: $18,222,698
Net Worth: $67,930,860
Earnings: $7,899,606
Emp.: 141
Fiscal Year-end: 12/31/12
Business Description:
Consultancy Services For Medical Equipment
S.I.C.: 3845
N.A.I.C.S.: 334510
Personnel:
Chi Chiu Tang *(Chm & CEO)*
Gatson Sung Him Lam *(Sec)*
Board of Directors:
Chi Chiu Tang
Chung On Kwok
Jianguo Wang
Chi Keung Wu
Yan Wu

CHINA RERUN CHEMICAL GROUP LIMITED

Room 407 Block B-11 Service Outsourcing Industrial Park
Hi-tech Industrial Development Zone, Daqing, Heilongjiang, 163316, China
Tel.: (86) 459 6669777
E-Mail: 777@chinarerun.com
Web Site: www.chinarerun.com
CHRR—(AIM)
Business Description:
Lubricants Mfr
S.I.C.: 2992
N.A.I.C.S.: 324191
Personnel:
Xinghe Wu *(Chm)*
Board of Directors:
Xinghe Wu
Nicholas Lyth
Zhongzhi Zhao
Jane Zhu

CHINA RESOURCES AND TRANSPORTATION GROUP LIMITED

Room 1801-07 18/F China Resources Building 26 Harbour Road
Wanchai, China (Hong Kong)
Tel.: (852) 31767100
Fax: (852) 31767122
E-Mail: info@crtg.com.hk
Web Site: www.crtg.com.hk
0269—(HKG)
Sls.: $589,245,794
Assets: $2,278,176,542
Liabilities: $1,618,675,049
Net Worth: $659,501,493
Earnings: ($33,596,504)
Emp.: 267
Fiscal Year-end: 03/31/13
Business Description:
Expressway & Toll Road Construction Services
S.I.C.: 1611
N.A.I.C.S.: 237310
Personnel:
Zhong Cao *(Chm)*
Tsun Pong Fung *(Vice Chm)*
Jingquan Duan *(CEO)*
Sharon Wai Kam Ngan *(Sec)*
Board of Directors:
Zhong Cao
Liang Ming Bao
Jingquan Duan
Tsun Pong Fung
Zhiping Gao
Baoli Jing
David Kam Ching Tsang
Tak On Yip
Transfer Agent:
Tricor Progressive Limited
26/F Tesbury Centre 28 Queen's Road
Wanchai, China (Hong Kong)
Subsidiary:

Glory Success Trading Limited **(1)**
Ste 1606 16 F Ofc Tower Convention Plz 1 Harbour Rd
Wanchai, China (Hong Kong)
Tel.: (852) 31767100
Fax: (852) 3176 7122
Timber Logs Trading & Furniture Mfr
S.I.C.: 2512
N.A.I.C.S.: 337121

CHINA RESOURCES CEMENT HOLDINGS LIMITED

Room 4606-08 China Resources Building 26 Harbour Road
Wanchai, China (Hong Kong)
Tel.: (852) 3118 6800
Fax: (852) 3118 6830
E-Mail: crcement@crc.com.hk
Web Site: www.crcement.com.hk
Year Founded: 2003
1313—(HKG OTC)
Sls.: $3,268,280,046
Assets: $6,725,919,942
Liabilities: $3,894,410,052
Net Worth: $2,831,509,890
Earnings: $302,410,574
Emp.: 23,296
Fiscal Year-end: 12/31/12
Business Description:
Cement Mfr
S.I.C.: 3241
N.A.I.C.S.: 327310
Personnel:
Longshan Zhou *(Chm)*
Zhongliang Yu *(Vice Chm)*
Yonghong Pan *(CEO)*
Robert Chung Kwok Lau *(CFO)*
Peter Chi Lik Lo *(Sec)*
Board of Directors:
Longshan Zhou
Ying Chen
Wenmin Du
Daoguo Huang
Stephen Shu Kwan Ip
Nelson Chi Yuen Lam
Robert Chung Kwok Lau
Yonghong Pan
Abraham Lai Him Shek
Bin Wei
Yongmo Xu
Zhongliang Yu
Xuemin Zeng
Transfer Agent:
Tricor Investor Services Limited
26th Floor Tesbury Centre 28 Queens Road East
Wanchai, China (Hong Kong)

CHINA RESOURCES DEVELOPMENT INC.

1402 China Resources Bldg
Wanchai, China (Hong Kong)
Tel.: (852) 25042333
Fax: (852) 250423232
E-Mail: info@sscmandarin.com
Web Site: www.sscmandarin.com
Year Founded: 2010
Emp.: 4
Business Description:
Investment Services
S.I.C.: 6211
N.A.I.C.S.: 523999
Personnel:
Seng Leong Lee *(Chm & CEO)*
Wing Kai Ho *(CFO, Sr VP-Fin, Treas & Sec)*
Board of Directors:
Seng Leong Lee
John Ambruz
Paul Bernards
Wing Kai Ho
Pieter van Aswegen
Qiaolian Wang
Shaonan Xing

CHINA RESOURCES (HOLDINGS) CO., LTD.

49th Floor China Resources Building
26 Harbour Road, Wanchai, China (Hong Kong)

Tel.: (852) 28797888
Fax: (852) 28275774
E-Mail: crc@crc.com.hk
Web Site: www.crc.com.hk
Year Founded: 1938
Sales Range: $15-24.9 Billion
Emp.: 80,000
Business Description:
Holding Company
S.I.C.: 6719
N.A.I.C.S.: 551112
Personnel:
Lin Song *(Chm)*
Yin Wang *(Vice Chm)*
Shibo Qiao *(Mng Dir)*
Bin Wei *(CFO)*
Wenmin Du *(Chief HR Officer)*
Lang Chen *(Deputy Mng Dir)*
Wei Jiang *(Deputy Mng Dir)*
Biao Yan *(Gen Counsel)*
Board of Directors:
Lin Song
Lang Chen
Wei Jiang
Guoan Ma
Chuandong Wang
Yin Wang
Biao Yan

Subsidiaries:

China Resources Chemicals Holdings Ltd. **(1)**
49/F China Resources Building
26 Harbour Road, Wanchai, China (Hong Kong) HK
Tel.: (852) 28797888 (100%)
Telex: 65053 CIREO HX
Fax: (852) 28275774
Web Site: www.crc.com.hk
Emp.: 20
Chemical Products Distr
S.I.C.: 5169
N.A.I.C.S.: 424690
Chu Tan *(Gen Mgr)*

China Resources Enterprise, Limited **(1)**
39/F China Resources Building 26 Harbour Road
Wanchai, China (Hong Kong) HK
Tel.: (852) 28271028 (51.69%)
Fax: (852) 25988453
E-Mail: info@cre.com.hk
Web Site: www.cre.com.hk
0291—(HKG)
Sls.: $16,278,132,200
Assets: $16,439,577,600
Liabilities: $9,504,130,800
Net Worth: $6,935,446,800
Earnings: $647,586,900
Emp.: 211,000
Fiscal Year-end: 12/31/12
Holding Company
S.I.C.: 6719
N.A.I.C.S.: 551112
Lang Chen *(Chm)*
Hongji Liu *(Vice Chm)*
Hong Jie *(CEO)*
Frank Ni Hium Lai *(CFO & Sec)*

Subsidiaries:

China Resources Logistics (Holdings) Co., Ltd. **(2)**
Yuen Fat Administration Building 89 Yen Chow St W
West Kowloon Reclamation, Kowloon, China (Hong Kong) HK
Tel.: (852) 23746688 (100%)
Fax: (852) 28271670
E-Mail: contact@crclogistics.com
Web Site: www.crclogistics.com
Holding Company; Warehousing, Supply Chain Management, Freight Forwarding & Other Logistics Services
S.I.C.: 6719
N.A.I.C.S.: 551112
PakShing Lau *(Chm & Gen Mgr)*

China Resources Retail (Group) Co., Ltd. **(2)**
4/F Yuen Fat Bldg 89 Yen Chow Street West
West Kowloon Reclamation, Kowloon, China (Hong Kong) HK
Tel.: (852) 28391888 (100%)
Fax: (852) 25775063
E-Mail: retail@crcretail.com
Web Site: www.crcretail.com
Holding Company; Arts & Crafts Retail & Pharmacy Stores Operator
S.I.C.: 6719
N.A.I.C.S.: 551112

China Resources Textiles (Holdings) Co., Ltd. **(2)**
11/F China Resources Building
26 Harbour Road, Wanchai, China (Hong Kong) HK
Tel.: (852) 25938111 (100%)
Fax: (852) 28274211
E-Mail: info@crlintex.com
Web Site: www.crlintex.com
Sales Range: $600-649.9 Million
Emp.: 1,000
Holding Company; Textiles Processing & Garments Mfr & Distr
S.I.C.: 6719
N.A.I.C.S.: 551112

Division:

China Resources Textiles Co., Ltd. **(3)**
China Resources Building 10th FL 5001 Shennan Road East
Luohu District, Shenzhen, China HK
Tel.: (86) 755 8269 1888 (100%)
Fax: (86) 755 8269 1898
E-Mail: info@crlintex.com
Web Site: www.crlintex.com
Emp.: 40
Textiles Processing & Garments Mfr & Distr
S.I.C.: 2299
N.A.I.C.S.: 313110
Ming Xiang *(Gen Mgr)*

CRE Properties (Hong Kong) Ltd. **(2)**
Yuen Fat Administration Building 89 Yen Chow Street West
West Kowloon Reclamation, Kowloon, China (Hong Kong) HK
Tel.: (852) 28277333 (100%)
Fax: (852) 27283322
E-Mail: cppgw@crc.com.hk
Emp.: 50
Commercial Property Investment, Development & Management Services
S.I.C.: 6531
N.A.I.C.S.: 531390
PakShing Lau *(Chm & Gen Mgr)*

Ng Fung Hong Limited **(2)**
8/F China Resources Building
26 Harbour Road, Wanchai, China (Hong Kong) HK
Tel.: (852) 25938777 (100%)
Fax: (852) 28275985
E-Mail: nfh@nfh.com.hk
Web Site: www.nfh.com.hk
Fresh, Live & Frozen Seafood, Meat, Poultry & Other Foodstuffs Distr
S.I.C.: 5142
N.A.I.C.S.: 424420
Mark Shulin Chen *(Chm & Mng Dir)*
Jinqing Guo *(Mng Dir)*

Non-U.S. Subsidiaries:

China Resources Vanguard Co., Ltd. **(2)**
No 27 Water Bay Road
Luohu District, Shenzhen, Guangdong, 518020, China CN
Tel.: (86) 75525685001 (100%)
Fax: (86) 75525614744
Web Site: www.crvanguard.com.cn
Supermarkets Owner & Operator
S.I.C.: 5411
N.A.I.C.S.: 445110
Shuo Chen *(COO)*
Lan Yi *(Sr VP)*

Non-U.S. Subsidiary:

China Resources Vanguard (Hong Kong) Co., Ltd. **(3)**
B 84 Paksik Godown No 2
15 29 Wo Shui St, Hong Kong, China (Hong Kong) HK
Tel.: (852) 28278333 (100%)
Fax: (852) 28279975
Web Site: www.crvanguard.com.hk
Emp.: 1,000
Supermarkets Owner & Operator
S.I.C.: 5411
N.A.I.C.S.: 445110

Non-U.S. Joint Venture:

China Resources Snow Breweries Ltd. **(2)**
Room 306 China Resources Bldg 8 Jianguomen N Ave
Dongcheng District, Beijing, 100005, China VG
Tel.: (86) 1065179898
Fax: (86) 1085191900
E-Mail: crboffice@crp.cn
Web Site: www.snowbeer.com.cn
Emp.: 2,000
Holding Company; Beer Breweries & Whslr
S.I.C.: 6719
N.A.I.C.S.: 551112
Ari Mervis *(Chm)*
Ghang Shuzhong *(CFO)*

China Resources Gas Group Limited **(1)**
Room 1901-05 China Resources Building
26 Harbour Road
Wanchai, China (Hong Kong) BM
Tel.: (852) 25937388 (74.94%)
Fax: (852) 25988228
E-Mail: investor-relations@crgas.com.hk
Web Site: www.crgas.com.hk
1193—(HKG OTC)
Sls.: $2,526,209,546
Assets: $5,467,333,384
Liabilities: $3,558,354,231
Net Worth: $1,908,979,153
Earnings: $262,375,210
Emp.: 30,000
Fiscal Year-end: 12/31/12
Investment Holding Company
S.I.C.: 6719
N.A.I.C.S.: 551112
Chuandong Wang *(Chm)*
Thiam Kin Ong *(CFO & Sec)*
Bin Ge *(Sr VP-Customer Rels-China Resources Gas Holdings Ltd)*

Subsidiary:

China Resources Gas (Holdings) Ltd. **(2)**
19/F China Resources Building
26 Harbour Road, Wanchai, China (Hong Kong) HK
Tel.: (852) 25937375 (100%)
Fax: (852) 28022154
Web Site: www.crcgas.com
Liquefied Petroleum Gas Distr
S.I.C.: 5989
N.A.I.C.S.: 454310
Guoan Ma *(Chm)*

Non-U.S. Holding:

Zhengzhou China Resources Gas Co., Ltd. **(2)**
352 Longhai Road West
Zhengzhou, Henan, 450006, China CN
Tel.: (86) 371 6885 5777 (56.87%)
Fax: (86) 371 6888 1042
Web Site: www.hnzzgas.com
Sales Range: $200-249.9 Million
Emp.: 1,656
Holding Company; Natural Gas Distr, Pressure Control Equipment Mfr & Gas Pipeline Construction Services
S.I.C.: 6719
N.A.I.C.S.: 551112
Guoqi Yan *(Chm & Compliance Officer)*
Cheuk Lam Wong *(Sec)*

China Resources Land Limited **(1)**
46th Floor China Resources Building 26 Harbour Road
Wanchai, China (Hong Kong) Ky
Tel.: (852) 2877 2330 (67.3%)
Fax: (852) 2877 9068
Web Site: www.crland.com.hk
1109—(HKG)
Rev.: $5,720,689,960
Assets: $29,433,547,112
Liabilities: $19,568,899,965
Net Worth: $9,864,647,147
Earnings: $1,443,851,861
Emp.: 17,301
Fiscal Year-end: 12/31/12
Commercial & Residential Property Investment, Development & Management
S.I.C.: 6726
N.A.I.C.S.: 525990
Xiangdong Wu *(Chm)*
Zhuoying Zhao *(Co-CFO & VP)*
Guohua Wang *(Co-CFO)*
Peter Chi Lik Lo *(Sec)*
Yong Tang *(Sr VP & Gen Mgr-Chengdu Reg)*
Hong Kun Wang *(Sr VP & Gen Mgr-Hainan Province)*

China Resources Microelectronics Ltd. **(1)**
4609-10 China Resources Building
26 Harbour Road, Wanchai, China (Hong Kong) Ky
Tel.: (852) 22999188 (60.11%)
Fax: (852) 22999300
E-Mail: ir.crmicro@crc.com.hk
Web Site: www.crmicro.com
Sales Range: $450-499.9 Million
Emp.: 7,751
Holding Company; Semiconductors Developer & Mfr
S.I.C.: 6719
N.A.I.C.S.: 551112
Elvis Mao-song Deng *(CEO)*

Co-Headquarters:

China Resources Microelectronics Ltd. **(2)**
No 14 Liangxi Road
Wuxi, Jiangsu, 214061, China
Tel.: (86) 51085807123
Fax: (86) 51085804647
Web Site: www.crmicro.com
Holding Company
S.I.C.: 6719
N.A.I.C.S.: 551112
Guoping Wang *(CEO)*
Frank Ni Hium Lai *(CFO)*
Qing Peng *(Deputy CFO)*

Division:

CSMC Technologies **(3)**
No 14 Liangxi Road
Wuxi, Jiangsu, 214061, China (100%)
Tel.: (86) 51088118888
Fax: (86) 51085877352
Web Site: www.crmicro.com.cn
Semiconductor Mfr
S.I.C.: 3674
N.A.I.C.S.: 334413
Elvis Mao-Song Deng *(Pres)*

Subsidiaries:

ANST, China Resources Micro-Assembly Technology Co., Ltd. **(3)**
B-27 Ximei Road Wuxi New-High Technology
Industrial Development Zone, Wuxi, Jiangsu, 214028, China CN
Tel.: (86) 51082990111 (100%)
Fax: (86) 51082990288
E-Mail: anst@anst.com.cn
Web Site: www.anst.com.cn
Integrated Circuit Testing & Packaging Services
S.I.C.: 8734
N.A.I.C.S.: 541380
Xiaojian Zhang *(Gen Mgr)*

Wuxi China Resources Huajing Microelectronics Co., Ltd. **(3)**
No 14 Liangxi Road
Wuxi, Jiangsu, 214061, China CN
Tel.: (86) 510 8580 7228 (100%)
Fax: (86) 510 8580 0864
E-Mail: sales@hj.crmicro.com
Web Site: www.crhj.com.cn
Power Transistor Chips Mfr
S.I.C.: 3674
N.A.I.C.S.: 334413

Wuxi China Resources Semico Co., Ltd. **(3)**
No 14 Liangxi Road
Wuxi, Jiangsu, 214061, China CN
Tel.: (86) 510 8581 0118 (100%)
Fax: (86) 510 8581 0407
E-Mail: info@semico.com.cn
Web Site: www.semico.com.cn
Integrated Circuit Design Services

China Resources (Holdings) Co., Ltd.—(Continued)

S.I.C.: 7389
N.A.I.C.S.: 541490

China Resources Power Holdings Co., Ltd. (1)
Rooms 2001 2005 20th Floor China Resources Building 26 Harbour Road
Wanchai, China (Hong Kong) HK
Tel.: (852) 25937530 (65.3%)
Fax: (852) 25937531
E-Mail: crp-ir@crc.com.hk
Web Site: www.cr-power.com
0836—(HKG OTC)
Sls.: $8,051,060,304
Assets: $22,925,984,136
Liabilities: $14,041,844,807
Net Worth: $8,884,139,329
Earnings: $1,125,030,336
Emp.: 38,118
Fiscal Year-end: 12/31/12
Holding Company; Electric Power Plant Investment, Development, Operation & Management Services
S.I.C.: 6719
N.A.I.C.S.: 551112
Junqing Zhou *(Chm)*
Shen Wen Zhang *(Vice Chm)*
Yu Jun Wang *(Pres)*
Xing An *(Asst Pres & Dir-Info Mgmt)*
Yi Jian *(Asst Pres & Dir-Strategic Dev)*
Xiao Bin Wang *(Co-CFO & Sec)*
Guo Lin Zhu *(Co-CFO & VP)*
Ya Ping Wang *(COO & Exec VP)*
Fan Sen Bu *(Chief Dev Officer & Exec VP)*
Hou Chang Zhao *(CTO & Exec VP)*
Chun Gui Liu *(CTO/Deputy Gen Mgr-CR Coal)*
Yuan Kui Ding *(Chief HR Officer & VP)*
Li Hui Jiang *(Sr VP)*
Ping Liu *(Sr VP)*

CHINA RITAR POWER CORP.

Room 405 Tower C Huahan Building
16 Langshan Road
North High-Tech Indus Park
Nanshan District, Shenzhen, 518057, China
Tel.: (86) 75583475380
Web Site: www.ritarpower.com
Sales Range: $75-99.9 Million
Emp.: 1,700

Business Description:
Lead-Acid Battery Mfr
S.I.C.: 3692
N.A.I.C.S.: 335912

Personnel:
Jiada Hu *(Pres, CEO, Treas & Sec)*
Aijun Liu *(CFO)*
Jianjun Zeng *(COO)*
Degang He *(CTO)*

Board of Directors:
Paul Kam Shing Chiu
Jiada Hu
Yaofu Tang
Xiongjie Wang
Jianjun Zeng

CHINA RONGSHENG HEAVY INDUSTRIES CO., LTD.

No 31 Lane 168 Daduhe Road
Putuo District, Shanghai, China
Tel.: (86) 21 51198888
Fax: (86) 21 31357788
E-Mail: sales@rshi.cn
Web Site: www.rshi.cn
1101—(HKG OTC)
Rev.: $1,263,865,721
Assets: $7,969,319,757
Liabilities: $5,572,558,393
Net Worth: $2,396,761,364
Earnings: ($89,279,260)
Emp.: 6,594
Fiscal Year-end: 12/31/12

Business Description:
Construction, Engineering & Ship Building Services
S.I.C.: 1629
N.A.I.C.S.: 237990

Personnel:
Qiang Chen *(Chm & CEO)*
Zhen Guo Wu *(Vice Chm)*
Sean S. J. Wang *(CFO)*
Xiao Ming Luan *(COO)*
Zheng Yu *(Chm-Rongsheng Machinery)*
Guo Rong Chen *(Pres-Rongsheng Heavy Industries & Gen Dir-Plant Construction)*
Urs Karl Huwiler *(Pres-Rong An Power Machinery)*
Guang Shan Yao *(Pres-Rongsheng Machinery)*
Don Fook Kang Lee *(CEO-Rongsheng Offshore & Marine)*
Man Yee Lee *(Sec)*
Kai Guo Chen *(Exec VP-Ship Building)*

Board of Directors:
Qiang Chen
Liang Hong
Wei Ping Hu
Xiao Ming Luan
Hing Lun Tsang
Jin Lian Wang
Sean S. J. Wang
Tao Wang
A. Ning Wei
Zhen Guo Wu
Da Wei Xia

Codan Trust Company (Cayman) Limited
Cricket Square Hutchins Drive
PO Box 2681
Georgetown, Grand Cayman, Cayman Islands

Transfer Agent:
Codan Trust Company (Cayman) Limited
Cricket Square Hutchins Drive
PO Box 2681
Georgetown, Grand Cayman, Cayman Islands

CHINA RUIFENG GALAXY RENEWABLE ENERGY HOLDINGS LIMITED

(Name Changed to Galaxy Semiconductor Co., Ltd.)

CHINA RUITAI INTERNATIONAL HOLDINGS CO., LTD.

Wenyang Town
Feicheng, Shandong, 271603, China
Tel.: (86) 538 3850 703
Fax: (86) 538 3850 247
E-Mail: info@ruitai.com
Web Site: www.rutocel.com
Sales Range: $25-49.9 Million
Emp.: 530

Business Description:
Chemical Products Mfr
S.I.C.: 2899
N.A.I.C.S.: 325998

Personnel:
Xing Fu Lu *(Pres)*
Dian Min Ma *(CEO & Sec)*
Gang Ma *(CFO)*

Board of Directors:
Xing Fu Lu
Dian Min Ma
Jin Tian

CHINA SAITE GROUP COMPANY LIMITED

Unit 6105 61/F The Center 99 Queen's Road
Central, China (Hong Kong)
Tel.: (852) 2126 7434
Fax: (852) 3691 8124
Web Site: www.chinasaite.com.cn
Year Founded: 1998
153—(HKG)

Business Description:
Steel Structure Construction
S.I.C.: 1791
N.A.I.C.S.: 238120

Personnel:
Jianqiang Jiang *(Chm)*
Xiaoqiang Shao *(CEO)*
Kwok Kuen Wong *(CFO & Sec)*

Board of Directors:
Jianqiang Jiang
Tiegang Chen
Horace Chun Fung Ma
Xiaoqiang Shao
Yimin Wu
Jiaming Xu

CHINA SANDI HOLDINGS LIMITED

(Formerly China Grand Forestry Green Resources Group Limited)
Units 3309 33/F West Tower
Shun Tak Centre 168 200 Connaught Road, Central, China (Hong Kong)
Tel.: (852) 2587 7786
Fax: (852) 2587 7763
E-Mail: info@chinasandi.com.hk
Web Site: www.chinasandi.com.hk
0910—(HKG)
Rev.: $36,733,987
Assets: $821,105,631
Liabilities: $296,395,057
Net Worth: $524,710,574
Earnings: $20,066,425
Emp.: 154
Fiscal Year-end: 03/31/13

Business Description:
Forestry Business Services
S.I.C.: 0851
N.A.I.C.S.: 115310

Personnel:
Kenneth Chi Hung Chi *(CEO & Sec)*
Man Tak Lau *(CFO)*

Board of Directors:
Chi Yuen Chan
Kenneth Chi Hung Chi
Man Tak Lau
Yun Kuen Wong
Peter Pak Yan Yu
Jianchan Zhang
Jinyun Zheng
Yurui Zheng

HSBC Securities Services (Bermuda) Limited
6 Front Street
Hamilton, Bermuda

Transfer Agents:
Tricor Tengis Limited
26th Floor Tesbury Centre 28 Queen's Road East
Wanchai, China (Hong Kong)
Tel.: (852) 29801333
Fax: (852) 28108185

HSBC Securities Services (Bermuda) Limited
6 Front Street
Hamilton, Bermuda

Non-U.S. Subsidiary:

Yunnan ShenYu New Energy Company Limited (1)
Building No 8 Floor 9 Hongxing International Plaza Guangfu Rd
Kunming, Yunnan, China 650051
Tel.: (86) 871 63131938
Fax: (86) 871 63131786
E-Mail: ynshenyu@yahoo.com.cn
Web Site: www.syxny.cn
Biodiesel Fuel Research
S.I.C.: 4911
N.A.I.C.S.: 221112

CHINA SANJIANG FINE CHEMICALS COMPANY LIMITED

Pinghai Road
Jiaxing, Zhejiang, China
Tel.: (86) 57385286861
Fax: (86) 573 8528 6856
Web Site: www.chinasanjiang.com
2198—(HKG)
Rev.: $400,532,015
Assets: $724,646,537
Liabilities: $414,767,199
Net Worth: $309,879,338
Earnings: $74,184,539
Emp.: 518
Fiscal Year-end: 12/31/12

Business Description:
Chemical Mfr
S.I.C.: 2899
N.A.I.C.S.: 325998

Personnel:
Jianzhong Guan *(Chm)*
Lixin Cha *(Asst Pres)*
Ngai Hang Yip *(Sec & Controller-Fin)*

Board of Directors:
Jianzhong Guan
Jianhong Han
Jianping Han
Gary Ho Cheung Mui
Yingshan Niu
Kaijun Shen
Wanxu Wang

Legal Counsel:
Chiu & Partners
40th Fl Jardine House 1 Connaught Place
Central, China (Hong Kong)

Butterfield Fulcrum Group (Cayman) Limited
Butterfield House 68 Fort Street
PO Box 609
Georgetown, Cayman Islands

Transfer Agents:
Tricor Investor Services Limited
26th Floor Tesbury Centre 28 Queens Road East
Wanchai, China (Hong Kong)

Butterfield Fulcrum Group (Cayman) Limited
Butterfield House 68 Fort Street
PO Box 609
Georgetown, Cayman Islands

CHINA SCE PROPERTY HOLDINGS LIMITED

SCE Building 208 Gaoqi Nanwu Road
Xiamen, Fujian, China 361006
Tel.: (86) 592 6676666
Fax: (86) 592 6676688
E-Mail: ir@sce-re.com
Web Site: www.sce-re.com
Year Founded: 1987
1966—(HKG)
Rev.: $577,683,123
Assets: $3,181,563,761
Liabilities: $2,082,181,337
Net Worth: $1,099,382,423
Earnings: $143,127,662
Emp.: 1,600
Fiscal Year-end: 12/31/12

Business Description:
Holding Company; Residential Property Developer; Construction Machinery & Electric Power Equipment Mfr & Sales
S.I.C.: 6719
N.A.I.C.S.: 551112

Personnel:
Chiu Yeung Wong *(Founder & Chm)*
Yuanlai Chen *(Founder & Vice Chm)*
Hui Lok Cheng *(Founder & Vice Chm)*
Yinghua Bian *(Asst Pres)*
Sui Po Li *(Sec & Controller-Fin)*
Wei Li *(Exec VP)*

Board of Directors:
Chiu Yeung Wong
Yuanlai Chen
Hui Lok Cheng
Yiyi Dai
Youquan Huang
Wei Li
Hong Te Lu

Stephen Leung Huel Ting
Codan Trust Company (Cayman) Limited
Hutchins Drive
PO Box 2681
Georgetown, Cayman Islands
Transfer Agent:
Codan Trust Company (Cayman) Limited
Hutchins Drive
PO Box 2681
Georgetown, Cayman Islands

CHINA SECURITY & SURVEILLANCE TECHNOLOGY, INC.

13/F Shenzhen Special Zone Press Tower
Shennan Road
Shenzhen, Futian, 518034, China
Tel.: (86) 755 8351 0888
Fax: (86) 755 8351 0815
E-Mail: csst@csst.com
Web Site: www.csst.com
Sales Range: $650-699.9 Million
Emp.: 3,500
Business Description:
Security & Surveillance Solutions
S.I.C.: 7382
N.A.I.C.S.: 561621
Personnel:
Guoshen Tu *(Chm & CEO)*
Terence Wing Khai Yap *(Vice Chm & CFO)*
Lizhong Wang *(COO)*
Daiyou Qian *(Chief Strategy Officer)*
Zhongxin Xie *(Chief Audit Officer)*
Board of Directors:
Guoshen Tu
Runsen Li
Peter Mak
Peter Kin Kwong Mak
Terence Wing Khai Yap
Subsidiaries:

Changzhou Minking Electronics Co., Ltd. (1)
No 65-12 Xinggang Road Zhonglou Economic Development Zone
Changzhou, Jiangsu, 213000, China
Tel.: (86) 519 86666112
Fax: (86) 519 86699917
E-Mail: sales@minking.cc
Web Site: www.minking.cc
Emp.: 300
Surveillance Equipment Mfr
S.I.C.: 3679
N.A.I.C.S.: 334419
Annie King *(Gen Mgr)*

China Security & Surveillance Distribution (PRC), Inc (1)
Building 6th Tong Fuyu
Gongming Town, 518107 Shenzhen, China
Tel.: (86) 755 33265722
Fax: (86) 755 33265700
Security & Surveillance Equipment Distr
S.I.C.: 5065
N.A.I.C.S.: 423690

China Security & Surveillance Manufacturing (PRC), Inc. (1)
Floor 1 Sector 6 Tong Fu Yu CSST Science & Tech Park
Guang Ming New District, Shenzhen, China
Tel.: (86) 75533265694
Fax: (86) 755 33265699
Web Site: www.hts.cn
Surveillance Equipment Mfr
S.I.C.: 3679
N.A.I.C.S.: 334419
Ivan Vhao *(Gen Mgr)*

Guangdong Stonesonic Digital Technique Co., Ltd. (1)
Stonesonic Digital Zone North Chaozhou Avenue
Chaozhou, China
Tel.: (86) 7682802892
Fax: (86) 768 2801617
Web Site: www.stonesonic.com
Emp.: 300
Surveillance Systems Mfr
S.I.C.: 3679
N.A.I.C.S.: 334419
Zoe Zhao *(Mgr-Intl Dept)*

Shenzhen Coson Electronic Co. Ltd. (1)
01 17th Floor Yinglong Building 6025 Shennan Mid Road
Shenzhen, 518040, China
Tel.: (86) 755 33358689
Fax: (86) 755 33358689
E-Mail: asia@coson.com
Web Site: www.coson.com
Emp.: 250
Security Equipment Mfr
S.I.C.: 3679
N.A.I.C.S.: 334419

Shenzhen Longhorn Security Technology Co., Ltd. (1)
The 4th Building New High Technology Industrial Park
Guangming Wandaiheng, Shenzhen, China
Tel.: (86) 75533265555
Fax: (86) 755 33265577
Web Site: www.csst-longhorn.com
Emp.: 600
Security Devices Mfr
S.I.C.: 3679
N.A.I.C.S.: 334419

CHINA SEVEN STAR SHOPPING LIMITED

Unit A02 11/F Bank of East Asia Harbour View Centre 56 Gloucester Road
Wanchai, China (Hong Kong)
Tel.: (852) 28028188
Fax: (852) 25960223
E-Mail: ir@sevenstar.hk
Web Site: www.sevenstar.hk
0245—(HKG)
Sls.: $79,546,289
Assets: $20,830,841
Liabilities: $16,208,370
Net Worth: $4,622,471
Earnings: $2,226,322
Emp.: 71
Fiscal Year-end: 12/31/12
Business Description:
Real Estate Management Services
S.I.C.: 6552
N.A.I.C.S.: 237210
Personnel:
Xinguang Ni *(Chm)*
Zhiming Wang *(Mng Dir)*
Gerald Edwin Law *(Sec)*
Board of Directors:
Xinguang Ni
Yu Zhang Ling
Wei Lu
Zhiming Wang
Chak Keung Wong
Transfer Agent:
Tricor Tengis Limited
26/F Tesbury Centre, 28 Queens Road East
Hong Kong, China (Hong Kong)

CHINA SHANSHUI CEMENT GROUP LTD.

Sunnsy Industrial Park Gushan Town
Changqing District, Jinan, Shandong, China 250307
Tel.: (86) 53188360218
Fax: (86) 53188360218
E-Mail: ir@shanshuigroup.com
Web Site: www.shanshuigroup.com
0691—(HKG OTC)
Rev.: $2,567,171,832
Assets: $4,453,101,936
Liabilities: $2,960,467,594
Net Worth: $1,492,634,343
Earnings: $254,757,753
Emp.: 21,576
Fiscal Year-end: 12/31/12
Business Description:
Cement Mfr
S.I.C.: 3241
N.A.I.C.S.: 327310
Personnel:
Bin Zhang *(Chm, Co-Sec & Gen Mgr)*
Yongkui Zhao *(CFO & Deputy Gen Mgr)*
Cheung Hung Li *(Co-Sec)*
Board of Directors:
Bin Zhang
Shuge Jiao
Homer Sun
Jianguo Sun
Jian Wang
Yanmou Wang
Xiao Yu
Yuchuan Yu
Caikui Zhang
Transfer Agent:
Computershare Hong Kong Investor Services Limited
Shops 1712-1716 17th Floor Hopewell Centre
183 Queens Road East
Wanchai, China (Hong Kong)
Subsidiaries:

Pingyin Shanshui Cement Co.,Ltd (1)
Dongmaopu Vlg Ancheng Town
Pingyin County, 250409 Jinan, Shandong, China
Tel.: (86) 531 87659296
Fax: (86) 531 87659202
E-Mail: pingyinshuini@shanshuigroup.com
Cement Products Whslr
S.I.C.: 5032
N.A.I.C.S.: 423320

Shandong Shanshui Cement Group Ltd. Qingdao Branch (1)
1701 6 Zhongshan Rd
Qingdao, Shandong, China 266071
Tel.: (86) 532 82877597
Fax: (86) 532 85830651
Web Site: www.shanshui.com
Emp.: 30
Cement Mfr
S.I.C.: 3241
N.A.I.C.S.: 327310
Steven Zhan *(Sls Mgr)*

Yantai Shanshui Cement Co.,Ltd (1)
Qixia Economic Dev Zone
Yantai, Shandong, 264000, China
Tel.: (86) 5355571036
Cement Mfr
S.I.C.: 3241
N.A.I.C.S.: 327310

Zibo Shuangfeng Shanshui Cement Co., Ltd. (1)
Shuanggou Town Zichuan District
Zibo, China
Tel.: (86) 53382070036
Cement Plant Construction Services
S.I.C.: 1541
N.A.I.C.S.: 236210

CHINA SHENGDA PACKAGING GROUP INC.

No 2 Beitang Road Xiaoshan Economic & Technological Development Zone
Hangzhou, Zhejiang, 311215, China
Tel.: (86) 571 82838805
E-Mail: office@cnpti.com
Web Site: www.cnpti.com
Year Founded: 2007
CPGI—(NASDAQ)
Rev.: $125,308,951
Assets: $167,148,591
Liabilities: $61,705,467
Net Worth: $105,443,124
Earnings: $5,570,003
Emp.: 1,412
Fiscal Year-end: 12/31/12
Business Description:
Corrugated Paperboards, Flexo-Printed & Color-Printed Paper Cartons Mfr
S.I.C.: 2653
N.A.I.C.S.: 322211
Personnel:
Nengbin Fang *(Chm)*
Daliang Teng *(CEO)*
Ken He *(CFO)*
Board of Directors:
Nengbin Fang
Congyi Fang
Zhihai Mao
Zhang Yaoquan
Michael Yadong Zhang

Bernstein & Carter
Subsidiary:

Zhejiang Great Shengda Packaging Co., Ltd. (1)
No 2 Beitang Road Xiaoshan Economic and Technological Development Zone
Hangzhou, 311215, China
Tel.: (86) 57182838411
Corrugated & Solid Fiber Box Mfr
S.I.C.: 2653
N.A.I.C.S.: 322211

CHINA SHENGHUO PHARMACEUTICAL HOLDINGS, INC.

Kunming National Economy & Technology Dev District
No 2 Jing You Road
Kunming, 650217, China
Tel.: (86) 871 728 2628
Fax: (86) 871 727 4648
E-Mail: qionghua_kmsh@163.com
Web Site: www.shenghuo.com.cn/en/
Sales Range: $25-49.9 Million
Emp.: 416
Business Description:
Phamaceutical Mfr
S.I.C.: 2834
N.A.I.C.S.: 325412
Personnel:
Gui Hua Lan *(Chm & CEO)*
Feng Lan *(Pres)*
Song Fang *(CTO-Kunming Shenghuo Pharmaceutical (group) Co Ltd)*
Zheng Yi Wang *(Sec & Exec Dir-Exports)*
Board of Directors:
Gui Hua Lan
Yunhong Guan
Feng Lan
Zheng Yi Wang
Subsidiary:

Kunming Shenghuo Pharmaceutical (Group) Co., Ltd., (1)
No 2 Jing You Road Kunming National Economy & Technology Developing
Kunming, China
Tel.: (86) 8717282628
Fax: (86) 8717282620
Web Site: www.shenghuo.com.cn
Emp.: 350
Pharmaceutical Mfr
S.I.C.: 2834
N.A.I.C.S.: 325412
Lan Guihaualen *(Mng Dir)*

CHINA SHENZHOU MINING & RESOURCES, INC.

Suite 305 Zeyang Tower No 166 Fushi Road
Shijingshan District, Beijing, China 100043
Tel.: (86) 1088906927
E-Mail: investors@chinaszky.com
Web Site: www.chinaszmg.com
SHZ—(NYSEMKT)
Sales Range: $25-49.9 Million
Emp.: 317
Business Description:
Nonferrous Metals Mining & Exploration Services
S.I.C.: 1499
N.A.I.C.S.: 212399

China Shenzhou Mining & Resources, Inc.—(Continued)

Personnel:
Xiaojing Yu *(Chm & CEO)*
Helin Cui *(Pres & COO)*
Jiayin Zhu *(CFO)*
Board of Directors:
Xiaojing Yu
Helin Cui
Liancheng Li
Shing Mun Wong
Xueming Xu
Jian Zhang
Transfer Agent:
Standard Registrar & Transfer, Inc.
12528 S 1840
Draper, UT 84020

CHINA SHESAYS MEDICAL COSMETOLOGY INC.

New No 83 Xinnan Road
Wuhou District, Chengdu, Sichuan, 610041, China
Tel.: (86) 2885482277
Year Founded: 2005
CSAY—(OTC)
Sales Range: $10-24.9 Million
Emp.: 313
Business Description:
Professional Medical Beauty, Cosmetic Surgery & Cosmetic Dentistry Services
S.I.C.: 8062
N.A.I.C.S.: 622110
Personnel:
Yixiang Zhang *(Chm & CEO)*
Wenhui Shao *(Pres)*
Wenbin Zhu *(CFO)*
Wei Chen *(CMO)*
Xingwang Pu *(CTO)*
Board of Directors:
Yixiang Zhang
Xingwang Pu
Wenhui Shao
Transfer Agent:
Island Stock Transfer
100 2nd Ave S Suite 705S
Saint Petersburg, FL 33701
Tel.: (727) 289-0010

CHINA SHINEWAY PHARMACEUTICAL GROUP LTD.

Suite 5201 52/F Central Plaza 18 Harbour Road
Wanchai, China (Hong Kong)
Tel.: (852) 3521 0816
Fax: (852) 3521 0821
Web Site: www.shineway.com.hk
2877—(HKG OTC)
Sls.: $338,707,754
Assets: $753,431,110
Liabilities: $118,568,341
Net Worth: $634,862,769
Earnings: $102,879,997
Emp.: 3,758
Fiscal Year-end: 12/31/12
Business Description:
Manufacturing & Trading Of Chinese Medicines
S.I.C.: 6321
N.A.I.C.S.: 524114
Personnel:
Zhenjiang Li *(Co-Founder, Chm, Pres & CEO)*
Yunxia Xin *(Co-Founder)*
Zheng Pin Wang *(Chief Scientific Officer)*
Mei Shan Wong *(Sec)*
Board of Directors:
Zhenjiang Li
Li Cheng
Randy King Kuen Hung
Brandelyn Ching Ton Lee
Huimin Li
Dequan Ren
Liutai Sun
Zheng Pin Wang
Yunxia Xin
Computershare Hong Kong Investor Services Limited
Shops 1712-1716 17th Floor Hopewell Centre
183 Queens Road East
Wanchai, China (Hong Kong)
Transfer Agents:
Royal Bank of Canada Trust Company (Cayman) Limited
4th Floor Royal Bank House 24 Shedden Road
Georgetown, Cayman Islands
Computershare Hong Kong Investor Services Limited
Shops 1712-1716 17th Floor Hopewell Centre
183 Queens Road East
Wanchai, China (Hong Kong)

CHINA SHIPBUILDING INDUSTRY COMPANY LIMITED

No 72 Kunminghu Nan Lu
Haidian District, Beijing, 100097, China
Tel.: (86) 10 8859 8000
Fax: (86) 10 8859 9000
E-Mail: csic@csic.com.cn
Web Site: www.csic.com.cn
Year Founded: 1999
601989—(SHG)
Sales Range: $25-49.9 Billion
Emp.: 140,000
Business Description:
Ship Repairer, Refitter & Mfr; Ship Equipment & Engineering Services
S.I.C.: 3731
N.A.I.C.S.: 336611
Personnel:
Changyin Li *(Chm & Pres)*
Biyi Zhang *(CFO & VP)*
Zhensheng Zhu *(Chief Legal Officer & VP)*

CHINA SHIPPING (GROUP) COMPANY

450 Fu Shan Lu Oudong New District
Shanghai, China
Tel.: (86) 2165967456
Fax: (86) 2165966068
Web Site: www.cnshipping.com
Year Founded: 1997
Sales Range: $1-4.9 Billion
Business Description:
Freight Shipping Services
S.I.C.: 4731
N.A.I.C.S.: 488510
Personnel:
Shaode Li *(Pres)*

Subsidiary:

China Shipping Container Lines Co., Ltd. **(1)**
450 Fu Shan Road Pudong New Area
Shanghai, 200122, China
Tel.: (86) 2165966105
Fax: (86) 2165966813
E-Mail: gyuzhou@cnsipping.com
Web Site: www.cscl.com.cn
2866—(HKG OTC)
Rev.: $5,170,737,470
Assets: $8,133,956,028
Liabilities: $3,769,764,978
Net Worth: $4,364,191,050
Earnings: $91,117,949
Emp.: 4,806
Fiscal Year-end: 12/31/12
Container Shipping Services
S.I.C.: 4731
N.A.I.C.S.: 488510
Shaode Li *(Chm)*
De Cheng Chen *(Chm-Supervisory Bd)*
Xiaowen Huang *(Vice Chm)*
Lirong Xu *(Vice Chm)*
Yu Mang Ye *(Sec)*

Non-U.S. Holding:

China Shipping Development Co., Ltd. **(1)**
700 East Daming Road China Marine Tower 16
Shanghai, 200080, China
Tel.: (86) 21 65967160
Fax: (86) 21 65966160
E-Mail: csd@cnshipping.com
Web Site: www.cnshippingdev.com
600026—(HKG SHG)
Oil, Coal & Dry Bulk Cargo Shipping
S.I.C.: 4731
N.A.I.C.S.: 488510
Shaode Li *(Chm)*

CHINA SHIPPING NETWORK TECHNOLOGY CO., LTD.

600 Minsheng Road
Pudong New District, Shanghai, 200135, China
Tel.: (86) 21 58856638
Fax: (86) 21 58520383
E-Mail: dsh@sctd.com.cn
Web Site: www.sctd.com.cn
002401—(SSE)
Business Description:
Intelligent Transportation Systems & Industrial Automation Products Mfr
S.I.C.: 3823
N.A.I.C.S.: 334513
Personnel:
Yihua Shen *(Chm)*

CHINA SHOUGUAN MINING CORPORATION

6009 Yitian Road New World Center Rm 3207
Futian District, Shenzhen, China
Tel.: (86) 75582520008
Fax: (86) 75582520156
Web Site:
CHSO—(OTC)
Sls.: $5,039,321
Assets: $14,718,496
Liabilities: $9,256,589
Net Worth: $5,461,907
Earnings: ($1,697,023)
Emp.: 1
Fiscal Year-end: 12/31/12
Business Description:
Gold Mining Services
S.I.C.: 1041
N.A.I.C.S.: 212221
Personnel:
Feize Zhang *(Chm & CEO)*
Hoi Ho Tsao *(CFO)*
Jingfeng Lv *(CTO)*
Board of Directors:
Feize Zhang

CHINA SILVER GROUP LIMITED

21/F The Center 99 Queen's Road Central
Central, China (Hong Kong)
Tel.: (852) 3478 3704
Fax: (852) 3478 3880
E-Mail: mmoy@chinasilver.hk
Web Site: www.chinasilver.hk
Year Founded: 2002
815—(HKG)
Emp.: 680
Business Description:
Silver Ingot & Other Non-Ferrous Metal Products Mfr
S.I.C.: 3499
N.A.I.C.S.: 332999
Personnel:
Wantian Chen *(Chm & CEO)*
Matthew Moy *(CFO & Sec)*
Board of Directors:
Wantian Chen
Guoyu Chen
Tao Jiang
Haitao Li
Guosheng Song
Yilong Zeng

CHINA SINGYES SOLAR TECHNOLOGIES HOLDINGS LIMITED

8 Hongda Road Nanping Technology Industry Park
Zhuhai, Guangdong, China
Tel.: (86) 7568682222
Fax: (86) 8930865
E-Mail: business@zhsye.com
Web Site: www.zhsye.com
0750—(HKG)
Rev.: $492,039,622
Assets: $645,515,886
Liabilities: $351,339,665
Net Worth: $294,176,221
Earnings: $51,932,989
Emp.: 2,100
Fiscal Year-end: 12/31/12
Business Description:
Holding Company; Curtain Walls Designer, Mfr, Supplier & Installer
S.I.C.: 8711
N.A.I.C.S.: 541330
Personnel:
Hongwei Liu *(Founder, Chm & CEO)*
Wen Xie *(Founder & Pres)*
Jinli Sun *(Founder & Deputy Pres)*
Shi Xiong *(Founder & Chief Engr)*
Zhijun Wang *(CFO)*
Chon Man Yu *(Sec & Controller-Fin)*
Board of Directors:
Hongwei Liu
Zhirong Cao
Jinshu Cheng
Huizhong Li
Jinli Sun
Ching Wang
Wen Xie
Simon Wing Fat Yick
Legal Counsel:
DLA Piper
17 F Edinburgh Tower The Landmark 15 Queen's Road
Central, China (Hong Kong)
Butterfield Fulcrum Group (Bermuda) Limited
Rosebank Centre 11 Bermudiana Rd
Pembroke, Bermuda

Subsidiaries:

Zhuhai Singyes Curtain Wall Engineering Co., Ltd **(1)**
Zhuhai Singyes Curtain Wall Engineering Co., Ltd
Nanping Technology Park, Zhuhai, Guangdong, 519060, China
Tel.: (86) 7568682222
Fax: (86) 7568689121
E-Mail: business@zhsye.com
Curtain Walls Design & Mfr
S.I.C.: 2672
N.A.I.C.S.: 322220
Chao Zhang *(Deputy Gen Mgr)*

Zhuhai Singyes Renewable Energy Technology Co., Ltd. **(1)**
No 8 Hongda Rd
Nanping Technology Park, Zhuhai, Guangdong, China
Tel.: (86) 7568911890
Fax: (86) 7568689121
Curtain Walls Design & Mfr
S.I.C.: 2671
N.A.I.C.S.: 322220

CHINA SKY CHEMICAL FIBRE CO., LTD.

Jiangnan Industrial Garden Licheng
362000 Quanzhou, Fujian, China
Tel.: (86) 59522463111
Fax: (86) 59522480333
Web Site: www.chsky.hk
E90—(SES)
Sales Range: $350-399.9 Million

Business Description:
Textile & Garment Mfr
S.I.C.: 3199
N.A.I.C.S.: 316998
Personnel:
Zhong Xuan Huang *(CEO)*
San Wing Hui *(Co-Sec)*
Li Tao *(Co-Sec)*
Board of Directors:
Wing Lin Cheung
Kwong Wah Er
Zhong Xuan Huang
Seng Kwoon Lai
Jian Sheng Song
Zhi Wei Wang

CHINA SKY ONE MEDICAL, INC.

No 2158 North Xiang An Road
Song Bei District, Harbin, 150001, China
Tel.: (86) 451 87032617
Fax: (86) 451 82541840
Web Site: www.cski.com.cn
Year Founded: 1986
CSKI—(OTC)
Sales Range: $125-149.9 Million
Emp.: 2,279
Business Description:
Pharmaceutical Mfr
S.I.C.: 2834
N.A.I.C.S.: 325412
Personnel:
Yan-Qing Liu *(Chm, Pres & CEO)*
Bing Liu *(Sec)*
Board of Directors:
Yan-Qing Liu
Zhao Jie
Jian-ping Li
Xu-feng Qian
Chun-fang Song
Wen-chao Zhang

Subsidiary:

Harbin Tian Di Ren Medical Science and Technology Company (1)
Rm 1706 Diwang Bldg 30 Ganshui Rd
Nangang Heilongjiang, 150090 Harbin, China
Tel.: (86) 45153994064
Fax: (86) 45187000451
Emp.: 1,515
Chinese Herbal Medicines Research & Development Services
S.I.C.: 8731
N.A.I.C.S.: 541712
Liu Yan Quing *(Mgr)*

CHINA SKYRISE DIGITAL SERVICE INC.

4/F M-3rd Building
Hi-tech Industrial Park
Nanshan District, Shenzhen, 518070, China
Tel.: (86) 755 26012511
Fax: (86) 755 26012468
E-Mail: skyrise@chinaskyrise.com
Web Site: www.chinaskyrise.com
Year Founded: 2006
CSKD—(OTC)
Sales Range: $10-24.9 Million
Emp.: 145
Business Description:
Digital Residential Safety & Video Surveillance Products
S.I.C.: 3651
N.A.I.C.S.: 334310
Personnel:
Mingchun Zhou *(Chm, Pres & CEO)*
Jiabo Fan *(CFO)*
Board of Directors:
Mingchun Zhou
Shengrong Dong
Weibing Wang

CHINA SLP FILTRATION TECHNOLOGY, INC.

Shishan Industrial Park
Nanhai District, Foshan, Guangdong, China
Tel.: (86) 75786683197
Web Site: www.silepu.com
Sales Range: $10-24.9 Million
Emp.: 176
Business Description:
Nonwoven Fabrics Mfr
S.I.C.: 2297
N.A.I.C.S.: 313230
Personnel:
Jie Li *(CEO)*
Eric Gan *(CFO)*
Shijun Zeng *(CTO)*
Wawai Law *(Pres-Sls)*
Board of Directors:
Chris Bickel
Richard M. Cohen
Wawai Law
Su Lei
Jie Li
Jun Li

CHINA SOLAR & CLEAN ENERGY SOLUTIONS, INC.

3rd Floor West Wing Dingheng Plaza
45A North Fengtai Road
Beijing, 100071, China
Tel.: (86) 1063860500
Web Site: www.delisolar.com
CSOL—(OTC)
Sales Range: $25-49.9 Million
Emp.: 700
Business Description:
Renewable Energy Services
S.I.C.: 4911
N.A.I.C.S.: 221118
Personnel:
Deli Du *(Pres & CEO)*
Board of Directors:
Zhaolin Ding
Deli Du
Zhenhang Jia

Subsidiaries:

Beijing Ailiyang Solar Energy Technology Co. Ltd. (1)
No 45 North Road
Fengtai, Beijing, China
Tel.: (86) 13311318578
Fax: (86) 139 021 06418
Web Site: www.ailiyang.cn
Solar Heating Products Mfr
S.I.C.: 3433
N.A.I.C.S.: 333414
Du Mobile *(Gen Mgr)*

Beijing Deli Solar Technology Development Co., Ltd. (1)
28 Fengtai N Rd Fengtai
Beijing, China
Tel.: (86) 1063869399
Fax: (86) 10 63866173
Solar Energy Heating Products Mfr
S.I.C.: 3433
N.A.I.C.S.: 333414

CHINA SOLAR ENERGY HOLDINGS LIMITED

Room 4003-05 40/F China Resources Building 26 Harbour Road
Wanchai, China (Hong Kong)
Tel.: (852) 31042820
Fax: (852) 31065294
E-Mail: info@chinasolar-energy.com
Web Site: www.chinasolar-energy.com
0155—(HKG OTC)
Rev.: $23,275,346
Assets: $129,957,357
Liabilities: $28,420,709
Net Worth: $101,536,648
Earnings: ($18,531,018)
Emp.: 114
Fiscal Year-end: 03/31/13
Business Description:
Solar Cells Mfr
S.I.C.: 3674
N.A.I.C.S.: 334413
Personnel:
Ngo Yeung *(Chm)*
Kin Wai Ting *(CFO & Sec)*
Board of Directors:
Ngo Yeung
Aiguo Ding
Chuan Fan
Yi Zhong Gu
Lijie Guo
Guojun Hao
Yan Jin
Xiaofeng Kong
Jian Li
Junhai Liu
Yanfeng Sun
Yuchun Yang
Tat Man Yin
Jing Zhang

Computershare Hong Kong Investor Services Limited
Shops 1712-1716 Hopewell Centre 183 Queens Road East
Hong Kong, China (Hong Kong)

Transfer Agents:
HSBC Securities Services (Bermuda) Limited
6 Front Street
Hamilton, Bermuda

Computershare Hong Kong Investor Services Limited
Shops 1712-1716 Hopewell Centre 183 Queens Road East
Hong Kong, China (Hong Kong)

U.S. Subsidiary:

Terra Solar North America, Inc. (1)
522 SW 5th Ave Ste 915
Portland, OR 97204 OR
Tel.: (503) 227-2023
Fax: (503) 227-2925
E-Mail: solarinfo@terrasolar.com
Photovoltaic Modules Mfr
S.I.C.: 3674
N.A.I.C.S.: 334413
Jack Chik Ming Chu *(Pres & CEO)*
Sandor Caplan *(CTO)*

CHINA SOUTH CITY HOLDINGS LIMITED

Suite 2205-07 Sun Life Tower The Gateway 15 Canton Road Tsim Sha Tsui
Kowloon, China (Hong Kong)
Tel.: (852) 31883118
Fax: (852) 31881323
E-Mail: inquiry@chinasouthcity.com
Web Site: www.chinasouthcity.com
Year Founded: 2002
1668—(HKG)
Rev.: $965,585,466
Assets: $5,460,390,974
Liabilities: $3,391,676,943
Net Worth: $2,068,714,031
Earnings: $369,656,839
Emp.: 3,730
Fiscal Year-end: 03/31/13
Business Description:
Large Scale Integrated Logistics & Trade Centers Developer & Operator
S.I.C.: 1542
N.A.I.C.S.: 236220
Personnel:
Chung Hing Cheng *(Chm)*
Moon Lam Leung *(CEO)*
Stephen Sing Hong Fung *(CFO)*
Michelle Man Yu Tse *(Deputy CFO, Sec & Head-IR)*
Board of Directors:
Chung Hing Cheng
Kai Cheung Ma
Tai Po Cheng
Stephen Chiu Chung Hui
Andrew Kwan Yuen Leung
Moon Lam Leung
Wai Keung Li
Wai Mo Ma
Cliff Kai Lit Sun
Yang Xu
Samuel Wing Ki Yung

CHINA SOUTH INDUSTRIES GROUP CORPORATION

69 Zizhuyuan Road
Haidian District, Beijing, China
Tel.: (86) 1068963980
Fax: (86) 1068963688
Web Site: www.csgc.com.cn
Sales Range: $25-49.9 Billion
Business Description:
Automobile Mfr
S.I.C.: 3711
N.A.I.C.S.: 336111
Personnel:
Bin Xu *(Pres)*

CHINA SOUTH LOCOMOTIVE & ROLLING STOCK CORPORATION LIMITED

(Name Changed to CSR Corporation Limited)

CHINA SOUTHERN AIRLINES CO., LTD.

278 Ji Chang Road
Guangzhou, 510405, China
Tel.: (86) 20 8612 4462
Fax: (86) 20 8665 9040
E-Mail: csn@cs-air.com
Web Site: www.csair.com
ZNH—(HKG NYSE SHG)
Rev.: $15,807,798,900
Assets: $22,628,817,900
Liabilities: $16,317,072,000
Net Worth: $6,311,745,900
Earnings: $601,088,400
Emp.: 44,935
Fiscal Year-end: 12/31/12
Business Description:
Domestic, Regional & International Passenger & Cargo Airline Services
S.I.C.: 4512
N.A.I.C.S.: 481111
Personnel:
Wan Geng Tan *(Vice Chm, Pres & CEO)*
Jie Bo Xu *(CFO & Sr Exec VP)*
Chen Jie Hu *(CIO)*
Guo Zhi Qiang *(CMO)*
Bing Xie *(Sec)*
Gang Chen *(Exec VP)*
Ren Ji Dong *(Exec VP)*
Chen Gang *(Exec VP)*
Zhou Yue Hai *(Exec VP)*
Ren Jidong *(Exec VP)*
Dong Suguang *(Exec VP)*
Wang Zhi Xue *(Exec VP)*
Board of Directors:
Xian Min Si
Zhen You Chen
Hua Zhang Gong
Wang Quan Hua
Kwong Yu Lam
Wen Xin Li
Xiang Dong Ning
Wan Geng Tan
Jin Cai Wei
Jie Bo Xu

China Southern Airlines Co., Ltd.—(Continued)

Legal Counsel:
O'Melveny & Myers LLP
Citicorp Center 153 E. 53rd St.
New York, NY 10022-4611

China Securities Depository & Clearing Corporation Limited
36/F China Insurance Building No 166 Lujiazui Dong Road
Pudong New Area, Shanghai, China

BNY Mellon Shareowner Services
PO Box 358516
Pittsburgh, PA 15252-8516

Subsidiary:

Xiamen Airlines Co., Ltd. (1)
Xiamen Gaoqi International Airport
Xiamen, Fujian, China (60%)
Tel.: (86) 5925739888
Web Site: www.xiamenair.com.cn
Commercial Aviation Services
S.I.C.: 4512
N.A.I.C.S.: 481111
Guanghua Yang *(Pres)*

CHINA SOUTHERN POWER GRID CO., LTD.

(d/b/a CSG)
6 Huasui Road Zhujiang Xingcheng
Tianhe District, Guangzhou, Guangdong, 510623, China
Tel.: (86) 2038121080
Fax: (86) 20 3812 1080
E-Mail: international@csg.net.cn
Web Site: eng.csg.cn
Year Founded: 2002
Emp.: 130,000
Business Description:
Investments, Construction & Power Networks Operations
S.I.C.: 4939
N.A.I.C.S.: 221121
Personnel:
Jinguo Zhao *(Chm)*
Jun Zhong *(Pres)*
Wenzhong Li *(CFO)*
Xiao Peng *(VP & CIO)*
Board of Directors:
Jinguo Zhao
Xiao Peng
Dacai Qi
Jiuling Wang
Jun Zhong

Subsidiary:

Hainan Power Grid Company (1)
No 34 Haifu Road
Haikou, 570203, China
Tel.: (86) 89865343312
Fax: (86) 89865366066
Electric Power Generation
S.I.C.: 4939
N.A.I.C.S.: 221122
Qiang Li *(Gen Mgr)*

CHINA SPECIALTY GLASS AG

Maximiliansplatz 15
80333 Grunwald, Germany
Tel.: (49) 40609186
Fax: (49) 40609186
E-Mail: ir@csg-ag.com
Web Site: www.csg-ag.com
8GS—(DEU)
Rev.: $153,068,952
Assets: $226,086,559
Liabilities: $71,485,666
Net Worth: $154,600,894
Earnings: $21,962,764
Emp.: 588
Fiscal Year-end: 12/31/12
Business Description:
Glass Mfr
S.I.C.: 3211
N.A.I.C.S.: 327211
Personnel:
Chun Chang Hao *(Chm-Supervisory Bd)*
Yong Shi Xin *(Deputy Chm-Supervisory Bd)*
Li Shi Chun *(Co-CEO)*
Heung Sze Nang *(Co-CEO)*
Jing He *(CFO)*
Zhou Chao *(COO)*
Supervisory Board of Directors:
Chun Chang Hao
Andreas Grosjean
Yong Shi Xin

CHINA SPORTS INTERNATIONAL LIMITED

Dingxing Industrial Zone Yangdai
Jinjiang, Fujian, China
Tel.: (86) 59585095555
Fax: (86) 59585080789
E-Mail: ir@chinasportsintl.com
Web Site: www.chinasportsintl.com
FQ8—(SES)
Rev.: $120,767,301
Assets: $230,633,044
Liabilities: $43,383,682
Net Worth: $187,249,362
Earnings: $2,574,800
Fiscal Year-end: 12/31/12
Business Description:
Sports Shoes Mfr
S.I.C.: 2389
N.A.I.C.S.: 316210
Personnel:
Shaoxiong Lin *(Chm & CEO)*
Alex Chiu Hung Chan *(CFO)*
Nicole Siew Ping Tan *(Sec)*
Board of Directors:
Shaoxiong Lin
Chin Yee Lai
Shaoqin Lin
Hong Boon Sim
Hock Chee Tham
Transfer Agent:
B.A.C.S. Private Limited
63 Cantonment Road
Singapore, 089758, Singapore
Tel.: (65) 3236 2000

CHINA STAR ENTERTAINMENT LIMITED

Unit 3409 Shun Tak Centre West Tower 168 200 Connaught Road
Central, China (Hong Kong)
Tel.: (852) 23131888
Fax: (852) 21919888
E-Mail: mail@chinastar.com.hk
Web Site: www.chinastar.com.hk
0326—(HKG)
Sls.: $188,909,042
Assets: $358,559,144
Liabilities: $153,888,414
Net Worth: $204,670,730
Earnings: $12,189,128
Emp.: 744
Fiscal Year-end: 12/31/12
Business Description:
Motion Picture Producer & Distr
S.I.C.: 7812
N.A.I.C.S.: 512110
Personnel:
Wah Keung Heung *(Chm)*
Tiffany Ming Yin Chen *(Vice Chm)*
Dorothy Shuk Han Wong *(Sec & Controller-Fin)*
Board of Directors:
Wah Keung Heung
Tiffany Ming Yin Chen
Paul Wai Chi Ho
Cho Sing Hung
Yuk Sheung Li
Gilbert Chak Lam Tang

Butterfield Fulcrum Group (Bermuda) Limited
Rosebank Centre 11 Bermudiana Road
Pembroke, Bermuda

Transfer Agents:
Computershare Hong Kong Investor Services Limited
Shops 1712-1716 17th Floor Hopewell Centre
183 Queens Road East
Wanchai, China (Hong Kong)

Butterfield Fulcrum Group (Bermuda) Limited
Rosebank Centre 11 Bermudiana Road
Pembroke, Bermuda

Subsidiaries:

China Star Entertainment Holding Company (1)
Unit 3409 Shun Tak Centre West Tower
1682-200 Connaught Road
Central, China (Hong Kong)
Tel.: (852) 23131888
Fax: (852) 23779400
E-Mail: mail@chinastar.com.hk
Emp.: 30
Television Show Production Services
S.I.C.: 7812
N.A.I.C.S.: 512110
Charles Heung *(Mgr)*

China Star HK Distribution Limited (1)
Rm 3409 Shun Tak Ctr W Tower
168 Connaught Rd C, Hong Kong, China (Hong Kong)
Tel.: (852) 23131888
Fax: (852) 21919888
E-Mail: mail@chinastar.com.hk
Emp.: 50
Motion Picture Distr
S.I.C.: 7812
N.A.I.C.S.: 512110
Anna Tsang *(Mgr)*

China Star International Distribution Limited (1)
Ste 503 C Miramar Tower
132 Nathan Rd TST, Kowloon, China (Hong Kong)
Tel.: (852) 23131888
Fax: (852) 21919888
E-Mail: mail@chinastar.com.hk
Emp.: 30
Television Show Production Services
S.I.C.: 7812
N.A.I.C.S.: 512110
Charles Heung *(Mgr)*

CHINA STATE CONSTRUCTION ENGINEERING CORPORATION

CSCEC Mansion 15 Sanlihe Road
Haidian Districr, Beijing, 100037, China
Tel.: (86) 1088082888
Web Site: www.app.cscec.com.cn
Sales Range: $1-4.9 Billion
Business Description:
Construction & Engineering Services
S.I.C.: 1541
N.A.I.C.S.: 236210
Personnel:
Jinzhang Liu *(Deputy Pres)*
Zhaohe Zeng *(Deputy Pres)*
Wenjie Sun *(Pres)*

Subsidiaries:

China Construction Decoration Engineering Co. (1)
6th Floor B Building CSCEC Mansion 15 Sanlihe Rd
Haidian District, Beijing, 100037, China
Tel.: (86) 1088082736
Fax: (86) 1088082752
E-Mail: zsgcb@cscec.com.cn
Web Site: www.cscec-zs.com
Emp.: 200
Engineering Services
S.I.C.: 8711
N.A.I.C.S.: 541330
Wang Wensheng *(Gen Mgr)*

China Construction Development Co. Ltd. (1)
11th Floor CSCEC Mansion
15 Sanlihe Road
Haidian District, Beijing, 100037, China
Tel.: (86) 1088082888
E-Mail: zhaopin@cscec.com
Web Site: www.cscec.com
Heavy Construction Services
S.I.C.: 1541
N.A.I.C.S.: 236210

China Construction First Building (Group) Corporation Ltd. (1)
52 Xisihuan Road
Beijing, 1000073, China
Tel.: (86) 10 8398 2062
Fax: (86) 10 8398 2068
E-Mail: bgs@cscec1b.net
Web Site: www.cscec1b.net
Heavy Construction Services
S.I.C.: 1629
N.A.I.C.S.: 236210

China Construction Import & Export Co. (1)
14 Fuwai Avenue
Xincheng District, Beijing, 100037, China
Tel.: (86) 10 8603 6253
Fax: (86) 10 6803 3559
Web Site: www.cscec.com.cn/english/co_ji goushezhi.htm
Import & Export Services
S.I.C.: 7389
N.A.I.C.S.: 561499

China Overseas Holding Ltd. (1)
10/F Three Pacific Place
1 Queen's Road East
Central, China (Hong Kong)
Tel.: (852) 282378888
Fax: (852) 28655939
E-Mail: cohl@cohl.com
Web Site: www.cohl.com
Construction Services
S.I.C.: 1541
N.A.I.C.S.: 236210

Non-U.S. Branch:

China Overseas Holding Ltd. (2)
27th Floor China Overseas Mansion
139 Hennessy Road, Wanchai, China (Hong Kong)
Tel.: (852) 2823 7888
Fax: (852) 2865 5828
Web Site: www.cscec.com.cn
Construction Services
S.I.C.: 1541
N.A.I.C.S.: 236210

Non-U.S. Subsidiaries:

China Overseas Grand Oceans Group Ltd. (2)
Unit 6703 Level 67 International Commerce Centre 1 Austin Road
Kowloon, China (Hong Kong)
Tel.: (852) 2988 0600
Fax: (852) 2988 0606
E-Mail:
Web Site: www.cogogl.com.hk
0081—(HKG OTC)
Rev.: $1,252,994,513
Assets: $3,990,298,820
Liabilities: $2,880,155,633
Net Worth: $1,110,143,187
Earnings: $320,523,149
Emp.: 677
Fiscal Year-end: 12/31/12
Electric Fans & Electrical Household Appliances Mfr; Real Estate Development Services
S.I.C.: 3564
N.A.I.C.S.: 333413
Bin Chen *(CEO)*
Yi Ting Fan *(Asst Pres)*
Wendong Liu *(Asst Pres)*
Ai Guo Xu *(Asst Pres)*
Paul Man Kwan Wang *(CFO)*
Edmond Wai Sang Chong *(Sec)*

China Overseas Land & Investment Limited (2)
10/F Three Pacific Place 1 Queen's Road East
Hong Kong, China (Hong Kong)
Tel.: (852) 28237888
Fax: (852) 28655939
E-Mail: cohl@cohl.com
Web Site: www.cohl.com.hk
0688—(HKG OTC)
Sls.: $8,327,680,491
Assets: $29,635,893,518
Liabilities: $18,345,424,041

Net Worth: $11,290,469,476
Earnings: $2,428,447,135
Emp.: 18,849
Fiscal Year-end: 12/31/12
Property Development & Investment Services
S.I.C.: 6531
N.A.I.C.S.: 531390
Qingping Kong *(Chm)*
Jian Min Hao *(Vice Chm & CEO)*
Xiao Xiao *(Vice Chm & Sr VP)*
Hongbo Kan *(Asst Pres & Gen Mgr-Dev Mgmt Dept)*
Guoxin Ouyang *(Asst Pres & Gen Mgr-China Overseas Property Co Ltd-Beijing)*
Min Bai *(Asst Pres)*
Yong Guo *(Asst Pres & Gen Mgr-China Overseas Property Grp Co Ltd)*
Yun Wing Nip *(CFO)*
Qi Wang *(Pres-China Overseas Property Svcs Ltd & Asst Pres)*
Keith Cheung *(Sec)*

China State Construction International Co. **(1)**
12th Floor Beijing Sunflower Tower 37 Maizzidian St
Chaoyang District, Beijing, 100026, China
Tel.: (86) 1085276299
Fax: (86) 1085275660
Web Site: www.cscec.com
Heavy Construction Services
S.I.C.: 1629
N.A.I.C.S.: 236210

CSCEC Property Management Co. **(1)**
8th Floor B Building CSEC Mansion 15 Sanlihe Road
Haidian District, Beijing, 100037, China
Tel.: (86) 10 8808 2702
Fax: (86) 10 8808 2677
Web Site: www.cscec.com.cn
Property Management Services
S.I.C.: 6531
N.A.I.C.S.: 531312

U.S. Subsidiary:

China Construction American Co. **(1)**
525 Washington Blvd Ste 1668
Jersey City, NJ 07310
Tel.: (201) 876-2788
Fax: (201) 876-6737
E-Mail: us@chinaconstruction.com
Web Site: www.cscec.com.cn
Construction Services
S.I.C.: 1541
N.A.I.C.S.: 236210
Ning Yuan *(Pres)*

Non-U.S. Subsidiaries:

China Construction (South Pacific) Development Co. Pte. Ltd. **(1)**
10 Hoe Chiang Rd No 27-02
Keppel Towers, Singapore, 089315, Singapore
Tel.: (65) 62274537
Fax: (65) 62275073
E-Mail: sg@chinaconstruction.com
Web Site: www.chinaconstruction.com.sg
Emp.: 100
Construction Services
S.I.C.: 1541
N.A.I.C.S.: 236210
Chen Guo Cai *(CEO)*

CSC & EC (Pty) Ltd. **(1)**
PO Box 00335
Gaborone, Botswana
Tel.: (267) 301 427
Fax: (267) 357 826
E-Mail: bw@chinaconstruction.com
Web Site: www.cscec.com.cn/english/co_jigoushezhi.htm
Construction Services
S.I.C.: 1541
N.A.I.C.S.: 236210

CHINA STATE CONSTRUCTION INTERNATIONAL HOLDINGS LIMITED

29/F China Overseas Building 139 Hennessy Road
Wanchai, China (Hong Kong)
Tel.: (852) 28237888
Fax: (852) 25276782
Web Site: www.csci.com.hk
3311—(HKG OTC)
Rev.: $2,548,697,782
Assets: $4,798,589,915
Liabilities: $3,012,249,692
Net Worth: $1,786,340,224
Earnings: $275,501,804
Emp.: 8,266
Fiscal Year-end: 12/31/12

Business Description:
Professional & Management Services
S.I.C.: 8711
N.A.I.C.S.: 541330

Personnel:
Yong Zhou *(Vice Chm & CEO)*
Sui Ha Tse *(Sec)*

Board of Directors:
Qingping Kong
Raymond Chung Tai Ho
Cheung Shew Hung
Shing See Lee
Raymond Hai Ming Leung
Adrian David Man Kiu Li
Jian Li
Shujie Pan
Shuchen Tian
Hancheng Zhou
Yong Zhou

Royal Bank of Canada Trust Company (Cayman) Limited
4th Floor Royal Bank House 24 Shedden Road
Georgetown, Cayman Islands

Transfer Agents:
Tricor Standard Limited
26/F Tesbury Centre 28 Queens Road East
Hong Kong, China (Hong Kong)

Royal Bank of Canada Trust Company (Cayman) Limited
4th Floor Royal Bank House 24 Shedden Road
Georgetown, Cayman Islands

Holding:

Far East Global Group Ltd. **(1)**
16/F Eight Commercial Tower 8 Sun Yip Street
Chai Wan, China (Hong Kong) (74.2%)
Tel.: (852) 2557 3121
Fax: (852) 2595 8811
E-Mail: info@fareastglobal.com
Web Site: www.fareastglobal.com
830—(HKG)
Rev.: $167,099,471
Assets: $211,065,231
Liabilities: $65,463,144
Net Worth: $145,602,087
Earnings: ($19,978,223)
Emp.: 1,429
Fiscal Year-end: 12/31/12
Construction & Engineering Services
S.I.C.: 1629
N.A.I.C.S.: 237990
Chit Sun Cheong *(Vice Chm & CEO)*
Sim Wang Chan *(CFO)*
Hai Wang *(COO)*
Ronald G. Kloepper *(CTO)*
Raymond Wai Man Ho *(Pres-Asia Pacific & VP-Overseas Bus Dev)*
Elliot Kracko *(Pres-North America & VP)*
Connie Shuk Yin Lau *(Sec)*

Subsidiary:

Far East Aluminium Works Company Limited **(2)**
16 F Eight Com Tower 8 Sun Yip St
Chai Wan, China (Hong Kong)
Tel.: (852) 25573121
Fax: (852) 25958811
E-Mail: info@fareastglobal.com
Web Site: www.fareastglobal.com
Emp.: 100
Aluminum Window & Curtain Walls Installation Services
S.I.C.: 1793
N.A.I.C.S.: 238150
Jacob James Chen *(Mng Dir)*

U.S. Subsidiaries:

Far East Aluminum Works (U.S.) Corporation **(2)**
353 Pilot Rd Ste B
Las Vegas, NV 89119
Tel.: (702) 796-8818
Fax: (702) 227-9757
Emp.: 4
Aluminium Forgings Mfr
S.I.C.: 3463
N.A.I.C.S.: 332112

Far East Facade, Inc. **(2)**
353 Pilot Rd Ste B
Las Vegas, NV 89119
Tel.: (702) 796-8818
Fax: (702) 656-0454
Emp.: 6
Aluminum Window & Curtain Walls Installation Services
S.I.C.: 1793
N.A.I.C.S.: 238150
Ronnie Wong *(VP)*

Non-U.S. Subsidiaries:

Far East Aluminium Works Canada Corporation **(2)**
Unit 2001 1700 Langstaff Road
Concord, ON, L4K 3S3, Canada
Tel.: (905) 695-6996
Fax: (905) 695-3469
Aluminum Windows & Claddings Installation Services
S.I.C.: 1751
N.A.I.C.S.: 238350
Rebecca Tock *(Mgr-Admin)*

Far East Aluminium Works (Singapore) Pte. Ltd. **(2)**
No 10 Jalan Besar 12-01 Sim Lim Tower
Singapore, Singapore
Tel.: (65) 62971638
Fax: (65) 62962638
E-Mail: lim.fuiling@fareastglobal.com
Aluminum Window & Cladding Installation Services
S.I.C.: 1751
N.A.I.C.S.: 238350

Netfortune (Shanghai) Aluminium Works Co. Ltd. **(2)**
Rm 606 Golden Magnolia Plz No 1 Dapu Rd
Luwan Dist, Shanghai, 200023, China
Tel.: (86) 2153960151
Fax: (86) 2153960462
Web Site: www.fareastglobal.com
Emp.: 100
Aluminum Window & Claddings Installation Services
S.I.C.: 1751
N.A.I.C.S.: 238350
Sunny Lee *(Gen Mgr)*

CHINA STATE SHIPBUILDING CORPORATION

5 Yuetan
Beijing, 100861, China
Tel.: (86) 10 6803 8833
Fax: (86) 10 6803 4592
E-Mail: cssc@cssc.net.cn
Web Site: www.cssc.net.cn
Year Founded: 1999

Business Description:
Shipbuilding, Ship Repair, Shipboard Equipment Mfg, Marine Design & Research Services
S.I.C.: 3731
N.A.I.C.S.: 336611

Personnel:
Wenming Hu *(Chm)*

Subsidiary:

China CSSC Holdings Limited **(1)**
Room 12803 No 1 Pudong Avenue
Pudong New District, Shanghai, 200129, China
Tel.: (86) 21 6886 1666
Fax: (86) 21 6886 0568
Web Site: www.cssholdings.com
600150—(SHG)
Sales Range: $1-4.9 Billion
Ship Building & Maintenance Services
S.I.C.: 3731
N.A.I.C.S.: 336611
Xiaojin Chen *(Chm)*

Subsidiary:

CSSC Jiangnan Heavy Industry Co., Ltd. **(2)**
Floor 11-13 No 600 Luban Road
Shanghai, China 200023
Tel.: (86) 2153023456
Fax: (86) 2163141103
E-Mail: mail@jnhi.com
Web Site: www.jnhi.com
600072—(SHG)
Sales Range: $200-249.9 Million
Emp.: 876
Steel Structures Mfr & Sales
S.I.C.: 3441
N.A.I.C.S.: 332312
Zuojun Tan *(Chm)*
Dade Ren *(Vice Chm)*

Joint Venture:

TTS Hua Hai Ships Equipment Co., Ltd. **(1)**
18th Fl 3255 Zhou Jia Zui Road
CN-200093 Shanghai, China
Tel.: (86) 2165398257
Fax: (86) 2165397400
E-Mail: info@tts-huahai.com
Web Site: www.tts-se.com
Emp.: 80
Marine Cargo Vessel Equipment Mfr
S.I.C.: 3799
N.A.I.C.S.: 336999

CHINA STATIONERY LIMITED

Donglou Village Wuli Ting
Jiangkou Town
Hangjiang District, Putian, China
Tel.: (86) 594 369 7883
Web Site: www.sakura-china.com
Year Founded: 2007
CSL—(KLS)

Business Description:
Stationery Products
S.I.C.: 2678
N.A.I.C.S.: 322230

Personnel:
Fung Chan *(Chm)*
Danping Jiang *(CEO)*
Poay Lin Tan *(CFO)*

Board of Directors:
Fung Chan
Danping Jiang
Angus Chun Jut Kwan
Nik Hashim Nik Ab Rahman
Richard Izaac Risambessy
Choon Hwa Tan

CHINA STEEL AUSTRALIA LIMITED

Level 28 Waterfront Place 1 Eagle Street
GPO Box 1142
Brisbane, QLD, 4001, Australia
Tel.: (61) 7 3123 4472
E-Mail: info@cnsteel.com.au
Web Site: www.cnsteel.com.au
Sales Range: $10-24.9 Million

Business Description:
Nickel Pig Iron Producer
S.I.C.: 3321
N.A.I.C.S.: 331511

Personnel:
Li Dong Chen *(CEO & Mng Dir)*
Leanne Ralph *(Sec)*

Board of Directors:
Yongwen Xue
Brian Fai Ho Chee
Li Dong Chen
Chung Leung Cheung

Legal Counsel:
Thomsons Lawyers
Level 16 Waterfront Place 1 Eagle Street
Brisbane, Australia

China Steel Australia Limited—(Continued)

Non-U.S. Subsidiaries:

China Steel Pte Ltd **(1)**
7500a Beach Road 11-310 The Plaza
Singapore, 199591, Singapore
Tel.: (65) 62665967
Fax: (65) 62682447
Stainless Steel Mfr
S.I.C.: 3312
N.A.I.C.S.: 331221

Linyi Yilida Steel Co., Ltd. **(1)**
Yi Meng Experimental Development Zone
Zhudi Da Zhuang Town, Linyi, Shandong, 276000, China
Tel.: (86) 5398065509
Fax: (86) 5398065509
Web Site: www.cnsteel.com.au/contact.php
Stainless Steel Products Mfr
S.I.C.: 3312
N.A.I.C.S.: 331221

CHINA STEEL CORPORATION

1 Chung Kang Road
Siaogang District, Kaohsiung, 81233, Taiwan
Tel.: (886) 78021111
Telex: 71108 STLMILL
Fax: (886) 78022511
E-Mail: y81@mail.csc.com.tw
Web Site: www.csc.com.tw
Year Founded: 1971
2002—(TAI)
Rev.: $12,143,638,097
Assets: $20,928,001,634
Liabilities: $10,580,738,378
Net Worth: $10,347,263,255
Earnings: $216,412,602
Emp.: 23,000
Fiscal Year-end: 12/31/12

Business Description:
Steel Mfr
Import Export
S.I.C.: 3325
N.A.I.C.S.: 331513

Personnel:
Jo-Chi Tsou *(Chm)*
Jyh-Yuh Sung *(Pres)*
Kin-Tsau Lee *(Exec VP)*

Board of Directors:
Jo-Chi Tsou
Juu-En Chang
Kin-Tsau Lee
Shen-Yi Lee
Ting-Peng Liang
Ming-Jong Liou
Jih-Gang Liu
Jerry J. R. Ou
Jyh-Yuh Sung
Chao-Chin Wei
Cheng-I Weng

Supervisory Board of Directors:
I-lin Cheng
Andrew Deng
Feng-Ming Hao

Legal Counsel:
Lee & Li
7th Floor 201, Tun Hua North Road
Taipei, Taiwan
Tel.: (886) 2 2715 3300
Fax: (886) 2 2713 3966

Subsidiaries:

China Prosperity Development Corporation **(1)**
Rm 2406 24th Fl 31 Hai Bien Rd
Kaohsiung, 802, Taiwan TW
Tel.: (886) 75362500 (100%)
Fax: (886) 75362413
E-Mail: cpdc7@mail.csc.com.tw
Web Site: www.cpdc-csc.com.tw
Emp.: 9
Real Estate Development
S.I.C.: 6531
N.A.I.C.S.: 531390

China Steel Express Corporation **(1)**
32F No 8 Ming Chuan 2nd Rd
Kaohsiung, 806, Taiwan (100%)
Tel.: (886) 73378888
Telex: 73336 CSETWN
Fax: (886) 73381310
E-Mail: atm@mail.csebulk.com
Web Site: www.csebulk.com.tw
Emp.: 55
Bulk & General Cargo, Shipping & Chartering Service
S.I.C.: 4522
N.A.I.C.S.: 481212
Donald K.L. Chao *(Pres)*
H. C. Ko *(CFO)*

China Steel Global Trading Corporation **(1)**
31st Fl Bao Chen Enterprise Bldg No 8
Ming Chuan 2nd Rd
Kaohsiung, 806, Taiwan TW
Tel.: (886) 73322168 (100%)
Fax: (886) 3356411
E-Mail: csgt@mail.csc.com.tw
Web Site: www.csgt.com.tw
Sales Range: $125-149.9 Million
Emp.: 70
Steel Product Trading Business, Industrial Materials Trading Business & Sales Agent for Steel and Aluminium Products
S.I.C.: 7389
N.A.I.C.S.: 425120
Lai Nee *(Pres)*

China Steel Machinery Corporation **(1)**
3 Tai-Chi Road
Hsiao Kang, Kaohsiung, Taiwan
Tel.: (886) 78020111
Fax: (886) 78022177
E-Mail: c21@csmc.com.tw
Web Site: www.csmc.com.tw
Industrial Steel Machinery Mfr
S.I.C.: 3559
N.A.I.C.S.: 333249
Kao Tong-Seng *(Chm)*
Hsu Wen-Du *(Pres)*

China Steel Management consulting Corporation **(1)**
Chung Kang Road
Hsiao Kang District, Kaohsiung, Taiwan
Tel.: (886) 7 8010723
Fax: (886) 7 8033568
Web Site: www.csc.com.tw/csc_e/ss/a n_9224e.htm
Management Consulting Services
S.I.C.: 8748
N.A.I.C.S.: 541618
C. T. Wong *(Chm)*
Y. C. Guu *(Pres)*

China Steel Security Corporation **(1)**
17th Fl No 247 Ming Sheng 1st Rd Shin Shing District
Kaohsiung, 800, Taiwan TW
Tel.: (886) 72299678 (100%)
Fax: (886) 72264078
Web Site: www.csccss.com.tw
Sls.: $178,740
Emp.: 1,147
Security Services & Systems
S.I.C.: 7382
N.A.I.C.S.: 561621
M. L. Chou *(Chm)*

Chung Hung Steel Corporation **(1)**
317 Yu Liao Road
Chiao Tou, Kaohsiung, 82544, Taiwan
Tel.: (886) 76117171
Fax: (886) 76110594
E-Mail: ch21@chsteel.com.tw
Web Site: www.chsteel.com.tw
2014—(TAI)
Sls.: $1,488,010,778
Assets: $1,146,901,029
Liabilities: $845,363,294
Net Worth: $301,537,734
Earnings: ($117,637,657)
Emp.: 931
Fiscal Year-end: 12/31/12
Rolled Steel Pipes Mfr
S.I.C.: 3399
N.A.I.C.S.: 331110
Yu-Soong Chen *(Chm)*
Joun-Chen King *(Pres)*

C.S. Aluminium Corporation **(1)**
No 17 Tung Lin Rd
Hsiao Kang, Kaohsiung, 812, Taiwan TW
Tel.: (886) 78718666 (98%)
Fax: (886) 78721852
E-Mail: csacm2@mail.csc.com.tw
Web Site: www.csalu.com.tw
Emp.: 500
Mfr of Aluminum Alloy Ingot, Aluminum Plate, Aluminum Sheet/Coil & Aluminum Foil
S.I.C.: 3365
N.A.I.C.S.: 331524

Gains Investment Corporation **(1)**
30F No 6 Ming Chuan 2nd Rd
Kaohsiung, 806, Taiwan (100%)
Tel.: (886) 73382288
Fax: (886) 73387110
E-Mail:
Web Site: www.gains.com.tw
Sales Range: $1-9.9 Million
Emp.: 20
Direct Investments Focusing on Industrial Materials, Electronic Related Industries, Telecommunication Industries & Other High-Tech Industries
S.I.C.: 6282
N.A.I.C.S.: 523930
L.R. Hu *(Pres)*

HIMAG Magnetic Corporation **(1)**
24 1 Chien Kuo Rd
Nei Pu Industrial District, Ping-tung, Taiwan TW
Tel.: (886) 87780222 (50%)
Fax: (886) 87780226
E-Mail: kiki@himag.com.tw
Web Site: www.himag.com.tw
Sales Range: $1-9.9 Million
Emp.: 30
Mfr. of Ferrite Materials Such As Iron Oxide, Ferrite Powder & Ferrite Core
S.I.C.: 3269
N.A.I.C.S.: 327110
Kiki Kuo *(Mgr-Sls)*

InfoChamp Systems Corporation **(1)**
11th Fl 6 Ming Chuan 2nd Rd
Kaohsiung, Chien Chen, 806, Taiwan TW
Tel.: (886) 75350101 (100%)
Fax: (886) 75350110
E-Mail: icsc@mail.cse.com.tw
Web Site: www.icsc.com.tw
Emp.: 300
Enterprise Resource Planning; Supply Chain Management; Information System Design,
S.I.C.: 7373
N.A.I.C.S.: 541512
Chung Chih Wu *(Pres)*

United Steel Engineering & Constrution Corp. **(1)**
No 1 Jhonggang Rd
Siaogang District, Kaohsiung, Taiwan
Tel.: (886) 7 806 2555, ext. 721
Fax: (886) 7 801 9150
E-Mail: usyc7@ms45.hinet.net
Web Site: www.usec.com.tw
Construction Engineering Services
S.I.C.: 1629
N.A.I.C.S.: 237990

Affiliates:

China Ecotek Corporation **(1)**
8F No 8 Ming Chuan 2nd Rd
Kaohsiung, 806, Taiwan TW
Tel.: (886) 73306138 (50%)
Fax: (886) 73394016
E-Mail: ecotek@ecotek.com.tw
Web Site: www.ecotek.com.tw
Rev.: $951,141
Emp.: 250
Environment Protection Industries, Steel & Related Industries, Waste Treatment & Facility Maintenance, Co-Generation Plant Planning, Design, Construction & Feasibility Study
S.I.C.: 4953
N.A.I.C.S.: 562219
My Tsuei *(Gen Mgr)*

China Hi-Ment Corp. **(1)**
10F 243 I Hsin 1st Rd Chien Chen
Kaohsiung, 806, Taiwan TW
Tel.: (886) 73368377 (35%)
Fax: (886) 73368433
Web Site: www.chc.com.tw
Emp.: 200
Mfr. & Sales of Cement & Slag Powder, Waste Treatment & International Trade
S.I.C.: 3241
N.A.I.C.S.: 327310
S. W. Kuan Donny *(Pres)*

China Steel Chemical Corp. **(1)**
5th Floor 47 Chung Hua 4th Road
Ling Ya District, Kaohsiung, Taiwan TW
Tel.: (886) 73383515 (31%)
Fax: (886) 73383516
E-Mail: jenny@e-cscc.com.tw
Web Site: www.cscc.com.tw
Sales Range: $1-4.9 Billion
Emp.: 140
Mfr. of Coal Tar, Coke, Coke Breeze, Coal Chemical, Anti-Corrosion & Water Proof Coating Material for Construction
S.I.C.: 2999
N.A.I.C.S.: 324199
James Wang *(Mgr-Comml)*

China Steel Structure Co., Ltd. **(1)**
1 Chung Kang Road
Kaohsiung, Taiwan TW
Tel.: (886) 78023433 (19%)
Telex: 72234 cssc
Fax: (886) 78063243
E-Mail: 232@cssc.com.tw
Web Site: www.cssc.com.tw
Emp.: 400
Build-Up Steel Sections & Other Steel Structures
S.I.C.: 3441
N.A.I.C.S.: 332312
Wentuan Chen *(Pres)*
H.W. Shen *(CFO)*

Dragon Steel Corporation **(1)**
No 100 Lung Chang Rd
Lishui Vlg Lung Ching Hsia, Taichung, Hsien, 434, Taiwan TW
Tel.: (886) 426306088 (30%)
Fax: (886) 426306066
Web Site: www.dragonsteel.com.tw
Emp.: 441
H-Sections & Hot Rolled Steel Coils
S.I.C.: 3312
N.A.I.C.S.: 331110

OIDC **(1)**
Rm 2406 24 Fl
333 Keelung Rd Section 1, Taipei, 110, Taiwan TW
Tel.: (886) 227576965 (20%)
Fax: (886) 227576932
E-Mail: oidc@ms5.hinet.net
Web Site: www.oidc.com.tw
Sales Range: $1-9.9 Million
Emp.: 15
Oversea Investments
S.I.C.: 6211
N.A.I.C.S.: 523110

Tang Eng Iron Works Co., Ltd. **(1)**
458 Hsin Hsing Road Feng-Shan Village
Hu Kou Hsiang, Hsin-chu, 300, Taiwan (8%)
Tel.: (886) 35981721
Fax: (886) 3 598 1646
E-Mail: sb@mail.tessco.com.tw
Emp.: 1,848
Stainless Steel & Construction
S.I.C.: 3325
N.A.I.C.S.: 331513

Non-U.S. Subsidiaries:

Group Steel Corporation (M) Sdn. Bhd. **(1)**
180 Kawasan Industri Ayer Keroh
Melaka, 75450, Malaysia (90%)
Tel.: (60) 62319990
Fax: (60) 62310167
E-Mail: info@cscmalaysia.com.my
Web Site: www.cscmalaysia.com
Sls.: $117,624,024
Emp.: 600
Mfr. of Hot-Dip Galvanized Steel Coils & Color Steel Sheets
S.I.C.: 3399
N.A.I.C.S.: 331110
Su Weikin *(Pres)*

CSC Steel Sdn. Bhd. **(1)**
(Formerly Ornasteel Enterprise Corp. (M) Sdn. Bhd.)
180 Kawasan Industri Ayer Keroh
75450 Melaka, Malaysia (70%)
Tel.: (60) 6 231 0169
Fax: (60) 6 231 0167
E-Mail: info@cscmalaysia.com
Web Site: www.cscmalaysia.com

Emp.: 700
Mfr of Cold Rolled Steel Products
S.I.C.: 3399
N.A.I.C.S.: 331221
Soon Hockchiew *(Mgr-Fin)*

CHINA SUCCESS FINANCE GROUP HOLDINGS LIMITED

West Wing 21st Floor Guangfa B #29
Jihua 5th Road
Foshan, China
Tel.: (86) 757 83994802
Web Site: www.gdjcrzdb.cn
3623—(HKG)
Sales Range: $1-9.9 Million
Emp.: 50
Business Description:
Financial Loans
S.I.C.: 6163
N.A.I.C.S.: 522310
Personnel:
Tiewei Zhang *(Chm)*
Bin Li *(Pres)*

CHINA SUN GROUP HIGH-TECH CO.

1 Hutan Street Zhongshan District
Dalian, PRC, 116015, China
Tel.: (86) 411 8288 9800
E-Mail: ir@china-sun.cn
Web Site:
CSGH—(OTC OTCB)
Sales Range: $25-49.9 Million
Emp.: 264
Business Description:
Cobaltosic Oxide & Lithium Iron Phosphate Mfr
S.I.C.: 2899
N.A.I.C.S.: 325998
Personnel:
Bin Wang *(Chm)*
Guosheng Fu *(CEO)*
Board of Directors:
Bin Wang
Ren Fuqiu
Zhi Li
Fudong Sui
Jiao Wang
Karlton S. M. Wong

CHINA SUNERGY CO., LTD.

123 Focheng West Road Jiangning Economic & Technical Development Zone
Nanjing, Jiangsu, 211100, China
Tel.: (86) 2552766666
Fax: (86) 2552766882
Web Site: www.n-pv.com
CSUN—(NASDAQ)
Rev.: $292,721,361
Assets: $923,085,343
Liabilities: $916,765,366
Net Worth: $6,319,977
Earnings: ($133,593,621)
Emp.: 2,867
Fiscal Year-end: 12/31/12
Business Description:
Solar Cell Products Mfr
S.I.C.: 3699
N.A.I.C.S.: 335999
Personnel:
Tingxiu Lu *(Chm)*
Jianhua Zhao *(Vice Chm & CTO)*
Stephen Cai *(CEO)*
Yongfei Chen *(CFO)*
Board of Directors:
Tingxiu Lu
Shiliang Guo
Jian Li
Steve Morgan
Ruennsheng Allen Wang
Wang Wenze
Jianhua Zhao
Xiaoqian Zhou

CHINA SUNSHINE PAPER HOLDINGS COMPANY LIMITED

Changle Economic Developed Zone
Weifang, 262400, China
Tel.: (86) 5362181001
Fax: (86) 5362186006
Web Site: www.sunshinepaper.co m.cn
Year Founded: 2000
2002—(HKG)
Rev.: $588,408,993
Assets: $1,187,808,500
Liabilities: $938,441,799
Net Worth: $249,366,701
Earnings: $8,667,809
Emp.: 3,000
Fiscal Year-end: 12/31/12
Business Description:
Paper Products Mfr
S.I.C.: 2679
N.A.I.C.S.: 322299
Personnel:
Dongxing Wang *(Chm & Gen Mgr)*
Weixin Shi *(Vice Chm)*
Cheuk Him Ng *(CFO, Sec & Controller-Fin)*
Board of Directors:
Dongxing Wang
Xiaolei Ci
Ping Shing Leung
Weixin Shi
Junfeng Wang
Zefeng Wang
Fang Xu
Ye Xu
Zengguo Zhang
Legal Counsel:
Orrick, Herrington & Sutcliffe
43rd Floor Gloucester Tower The Landmark 15 Queens Road
Central, China (Hong Kong)

Computershare Hong Kong Investor Services Limited
Shops 1712-1716 17th Floor Hopewell Centre
183 Queens Road East
Wanchai, China (Hong Kong)
Transfer Agents:
Royal Bank of Canada Trust Company (Cayman) Limited
4th Floor Royal Bank House 24 Shedden Road
Georgetown, Cayman Islands

Computershare Hong Kong Investor Services Limited
Shops 1712-1716 17th Floor Hopewell Centre
183 Queens Road East
Wanchai, China (Hong Kong)

Subsidiary:

Shandong Century Sunshine Paper Group Co., Ltd. (1)
Changle Ecnomic Development Zone
Weifang, Shandong, 262400, China
Tel.: (86) 536 218 1001
Fax: (86) 536 218 6006
E-Mail: sgygbcs@126.com
Emp.: 150
Paper Product Mfr
S.I.C.: 2679
N.A.I.C.S.: 322299

U.S. Subsidiary:

Century Sunshine Paper (USA) Inc. (1)
1000 Lakes Dr Ste 430
West Covina, CA 91790-2928
Tel.: (626) 502-1360
Paper Product Distr
S.I.C.: 5113
N.A.I.C.S.: 424130

CHINA SUNSINE CHEMICAL HOLDINGS LTD

112 Robinson Rd 12-04
Singapore, 068902, Singapore
Tel.: (65) 62209070
Fax: (65) 62239177
E-Mail: info@chinasunsine.com
Web Site: www.chinasunsine.com
CH8—(SES)
Rev.: $1,147,544,890
Assets: $911,739,354
Liabilities: $295,541,297
Net Worth: $616,198,058
Earnings: $25,915,428
Fiscal Year-end: 12/31/12
Business Description:
Rubber Chemical Products Mfr
S.I.C.: 3011
N.A.I.C.S.: 326211
Personnel:
Cheng Qiu Xu *(Chm & Gen Mgr)*
Dave Thian Huat Yak *(CFO & Co-Sec)*
Chee Tong Ho *(Co-Sec)*
Board of Directors:
Cheng Qiu Xu
Choon Kong Koh
Benny Heng Chong Lim
Yong Wah Ling
Jing Fu Liu
Ying Qun Ma
Paul Lye Heng Tan
Chun Hua Xu
Jun Xu

CHINA SUPER POWER SAVING HOLDINGS CO., LTD.

17/F Eastern Comm Centre
393-399 Hennessy Road, Hong Kong, China (Hong Kong)
Tel.: (852) 23828488
Fax: (852) 23828456
Web Site: www.csps.hk
Year Founded: 1999
MLCSP—(EUR)
Sales Range: $50-74.9 Million
Emp.: 240
Business Description:
Energy Saving Solutions
S.I.C.: 4931
N.A.I.C.S.: 221118
Personnel:
Cho Man Wong *(Chm)*
Ian Chang *(CEO)*

CHINA SYNTHETIC RUBBER CORPORATION

(d/b/a CSRC)
7th Floor Taiwan Cement Building
113 Zhongshan North Road
Section 2, Taipei, 104, Taiwan
Tel.: (886) 225316556
Fax: (886) 225316558
E-Mail: csyc@tpe.csrc.com.tw
Web Site: www.csrc.com.tw
Year Founded: 1973
Sales Range: $350-399.9 Million
Business Description:
Mfr. of Carbon Black & Gelatine
S.I.C.: 2819
N.A.I.C.S.: 325180
Legal Counsel:
Lee & Li
7th Floor 201, Tun Hua North Road
Taipei, Taiwan
Tel.: (886) 2 2715 3300
Fax: (886) 2 2713 3966

Subsidiary:

Synpac-Kingdom Pharmaceutical Co., Ltd. (1)
7th Fl 113 Zhong Shan N Rd Section 2
Taipei, 104, Taiwan TW
Tel.: (886) 225818887 (60%)
Fax: (886) 225816608
E-Mail: lynn.lin@sking.com.tw
Web Site: www.sking.com.tw
Emp.: 146
Generic Pharmaceutical Mfr & Marketer
S.I.C.: 2834
N.A.I.C.S.: 325412

U.S. Subsidiary:

Continental Carbon Company (1)
16850 Park Row
Houston, TX 77084-5023 TX
Tel.: (281) 647-3700 (66.67%)
E-Mail: info@continentalcarbon.com
Web Site: www.continentalcarbon.com
Emp.: 259
Carbon Black Developer & Mfr
S.I.C.: 2819
N.A.I.C.S.: 325180

Non-U.S. Subsidiary:

Continental Carbon India Ltd. (1)
A-14 Industrial Area 1 South Side of GT Rd
Ghaziabad, 201 001, India (66.7%)
Tel.: (91) 1202840505
Fax: (91) 1202840504
Web Site: www.continentalcarbon.com
Emp.: 156
Mfr & Marketer of Carbon Black
S.I.C.: 2819
N.A.I.C.S.: 325180

CHINA TAIFENG BEDDINGS HOLDINGS LIMITED

(Formerly International Taifeng Holdings Limited)
Room 911 9/F Block A Hunghom Commercial 39 Ma Tau West
Hung Hom, China (Hong Kong)
Tel.: (852) 2230 8913
E-Mail: ir@taifeng.cc
Web Site: www.taifeng.cc
Year Founded: 2009
873—(HKG)
Sales Range: $300-349.9 Million
Emp.: 5,384
Business Description:
Cotton Yarns & Bedding Products Mfr & Distr
S.I.C.: 2823
N.A.I.C.S.: 325220
Personnel:
Qingping Liu *(Chm)*
Dengxiang Li *(Vice Chm)*
Chunwei Liu *(CEO)*
Wai Hong Pang *(Sec & Controller-Fin)*
Board of Directors:
Qingping Liu
Kin Sang Chan
Shunlin Dai
Dengxiang Li
Yuchun Li
Chunwei Liu
Tongli Qi
Shengzhong Zou
Transfer Agent:
Computershare Hong Kong Investor Services Limited
Shops 1712-1716 17th Floor Hopewell Centre
183 Queens Road East
Wanchai, China (Hong Kong)

CHINA TAIPING INSURANCE HOLDINGS COMPANY LIMITED

12/F China Taiping Tower Phase II 8 Sunning Road
Causeway Bay, China (Hong Kong)
Tel.: (852) 36029800
Fax: (852) 28662262
E-Mail: mail@ctih.cntaiping.com
Web Site: www.ctih.cntaiping.com
0966—(HKG)
Rev.: $8,128,044,744
Assets: $31,326,920,993
Liabilities: $28,619,948,821
Net Worth: $2,706,972,172
Earnings: $190,039,418
Emp.: 37,187
Fiscal Year-end: 12/31/12
Business Description:
Capital Management Services
S.I.C.: 6282

China Taiping Insurance Holdings Company Limited—(Continued)

N.A.I.C.S.: 523920
Personnel:
Bin Wang *(Chm)*
Shuguang Song *(Vice Chm & CEO)*
Man Ko Chan *(CFO & Sec)*
Board of Directors:
Bin Wang
Shujian Che
Conway Kong Wai Lee
Tao Li
Wei Peng
Shuguang Song
Jiesi Wu
Yiqun Xie
Transfer Agent:
Hong Kong Registrars Limited
46th Floor Hopewell Centre 183 Queen's Road East
Wanchai, China (Hong Kong)

CHINA TAISAN TECHNOLOGY GROUP HOLDINGS LIMITED

Zhengdong Development Area
362271 Dongcheng
Dongshi Town, Jingjiang, Fujian, China
Tel.: (86) 59585507565
Fax: (86) 595 85587422
E-Mail: lianjie@china-taisan.com
Web Site: www.china-taisan.com
F2X—(SES)
Rev.: $94,099,563
Assets: $227,790,582
Liabilities: $38,665,679
Net Worth: $189,124,904
Earnings: ($14,453,603)
Fiscal Year-end: 12/31/12
Business Description:
Sports & Leisure Apparel Mfr
S.I.C.: 2389
N.A.I.C.S.: 315280
Personnel:
Wen Chang Lin *(CEO)*
Swee Gek Tan *(Sec)*
Board of Directors:
Cheung Kong Choi
Jiaji Chen
Xiao Bin Fu
Wen Chang Lin
John See Juan Ngan
Thomas Siu For Tsang
Transfer Agent:
M & C Services Private Limited
112 Robinson Road 05-01
Singapore, 068902, Singapore

CHINA TECHFAITH WIRELESS COMMUNICATION TECHNOLOGY LIMITED

Building C No 5A Rong Chang East Street
Economic Tech Area Yi Zhuang, Beijing, 100176, China
Tel.: (86) 10 5822 8390
E-Mail: jj@techfaith.cn
Web Site: www.techfaithwireless.com
Year Founded: 2002
CNTF—(NASDAQ)
Rev.: $137,663,000
Assets: $386,346,000
Liabilities: $54,657,000
Net Worth: $331,689,000
Earnings: ($1,845,000)
Emp.: 358
Fiscal Year-end: 12/31/12
Business Description:
Mobile Handset Software & Design Solutions
S.I.C.: 7389
N.A.I.C.S.: 541990
Personnel:
Defu Dong *(Chm & CEO)*
Shugang Li *(Pres)*
Yuping Ouyang *(CFO)*
Changke He *(CTO)*
Xiaonong Cai *(Sr VP)*
Yibo Fang *(Sr VP)*
Board of Directors:
Defu Dong
Xiaonong Cai
Jy-Ber Gilbert Lee
Yungang Lu
Ling Sui
Hui Zhang
Subsidiaries:

TechFaith Intelligent Handset Technology Limited **(1)**
No 10A Tower D2 IT Park Electronoic Town
Jiun Xian Qiao North Road
Chao Yang District, Beijing, 0100015, China
Tel.: (86) 1058229999
Fax: (86) 1058227200
E-Mail: zhenqingwei@techfaith.cn
Emp.: 100
Mobile Phones & Related Products Development
S.I.C.: 4812
N.A.I.C.S.: 517210
Daood Zhen *(Mgr-Sls)*

TechFaith (Shanghai) **(1)**
6F No 8 Building 3000 LongDong Avenue
RiverFront Harbor, Shanghai, 201203, China
Tel.: (86) 2161005656
Fax: (86) 2161005849
Mobile Handset Software & Design Solutions
S.I.C.: 4812
N.A.I.C.S.: 517210

TechFaith (Shenzhen) **(1)**
A Block 6 Floor Building B1 Cyber Tech Zone Gaoxin Ave 7 s
Hi-tech Industrial District, Shenzhen, 518057, China
Tel.: (86) 755 3330 0202
Fax: (86) 755 3330 0206
Mobile Handset Software & Design Solutions
S.I.C.: 4812
N.A.I.C.S.: 517210

CHINA TECHNOLOGY DEVELOPMENT GROUP CORPORATION

(Name Changed to Renewable Energy Trade Board Corporation)

CHINA TELECOMMUNICATIONS CORPORATION

31 Jinrong Street
Xicheng, Beijing, 100032, China
Tel.: (86) 1058501800
Fax: (86) 1058501060
E-Mail: info@chinatelecom.com.cn
Web Site: www.chinatelecom.com.cn
Year Founded: 1991
Business Description:
Holding Company;
Telecommunications Services
S.I.C.: 4812
N.A.I.C.S.: 517210
Personnel:
Xiaochu Wang *(Chm & CEO)*
Wei Leping *(CTO)*
Andi Wu *(Chief Acctg Officer, Member & Grp VP-Party Leadership)*
Shang Bing *(Sec & VP-Party Leadership Grp)*
Board of Directors:
Xiaochu Wang
Xiaowei Yang
Subsidiaries:

China Communications Services Corporation Limited **(1)**
Level 5 No 2 & B Fuxingmen South Avenue
Xicheng District
Beijing, China 100032
Tel.: (86) 10 5850 2290
E-Mail: service@chinaccs.com.hk
Web Site: www.chinaccs.com.hk
0552—(HKG OTC)
Rev.: $9,772,035,019
Assets: $7,141,996,711
Liabilities: $3,805,803,754
Net Worth: $3,336,192,957
Earnings: $388,525,496
Emp.: 130,000
Fiscal Year-end: 12/31/12
Infrastructure, Business Process Outsourcing, Applications & Content Services
S.I.C.: 4812
N.A.I.C.S.: 517210
Ping Li *(Chm)*
Jianghua Xia *(Chm-Supervisory Bd)*
Qibao Zheng *(Pres)*
Rui Hou *(CFO & Exec VP)*
Terence Wai Cheung Chung *(Asst CFO & Sec)*
Shiping Liang *(Exec VP)*
Qi Wang *(Exec VP)*
Jianxing Yuan *(Exec VP)*

China Telecom Corporation Limited **(1)**
31 Jinrong Street
Xicheng District, Beijing, 100033, China (70.89%)
Tel.: (86) 10 6642 8166
Fax: (86) 10 5850 1504
E-Mail: information@chinatelecom-h.com
Web Site: www.chinatelecom-h.com
CHA—(HKG NYSE)
Rev.: $44,966,146,050
Assets: $86,584,687,200
Liabilities: $44,325,821,700
Net Worth: $42,258,865,500
Earnings: $2,389,104,000
Emp.: 305,676
Fiscal Year-end: 12/31/12
Wire-Line Telecommunications Services
S.I.C.: 4812
N.A.I.C.S.: 517210
Xiaochu Wang *(Chm & CEO)*
Jie Yang *(Pres & COO)*
Andi Wu *(CFO & Exec VP)*
Jacky Shun Loy Yung *(Asst CFO & Sec)*
Kangmin Sun *(Exec VP)*
Gao Tongqing *(Exec VP)*
Xiaowei Yang *(Exec VP)*
Jiping Zhang *(Exec VP)*

Subsidiary:

Jiangsu Telecom Company Limited **(2)**
268 Hanzhong Road
Nanjing, 210029, China (100%)
Tel.: (86) 256588577
Fax: (86) 256588888
Web Site: www.telecomjs.com
Telecommunications Services
S.I.C.: 4813
N.A.I.C.S.: 517110

U.S. Subsidiary:

China Telecom Americas **(2)**
607 Herndon Pkwy Ste 201
Herndon, VA 20170
Tel.: (703) 787-0088
Fax: (703) 787-0086
E-Mail: sales@ctamericas.com
Web Site: www.ctamericas.com
Emp.: 20
Telecommunication Services
S.I.C.: 4813
N.A.I.C.S.: 517110
YiJun Tan *(Pres)*
LingPing Kong *(Exec VP)*

Joint Venture:

Yangtze Optical Fibre & Cable Co. Ltd. **(1)**
4 Guanshan Er Road
Wuhan, 430073, China
Tel.: (86) 2787802541
Fax: (86) 277802536
E-Mail: marketing@yofc.com
Web Site: www.yofc.com
Emp.: 1,500
Fiber Optic Cable Mfr
S.I.C.: 3357
N.A.I.C.S.: 335921

Dan Zhuang *(Gen Mgr)*

CHINA TIAN LUN GAS HOLDINGS LIMITED

(d/b/a Tian Lun Gas)
4th FloorTianlun Group Building No 6
Huanghe Dong Rd
Zhengzhou, Henan, China 450003
Tel.: (86) 371 68081771
Fax: (86) 371 63979930
E-Mail: Tianlunranqi@tianlungas.com
Web Site: www.tianlungas.com
1600—(HKG)
Rev.: $113,794,104
Assets: $321,189,458
Liabilities: $178,817,604
Net Worth: $142,371,854
Earnings: $23,705,662
Emp.: 1,420
Fiscal Year-end: 12/31/12
Business Description:
Gas Pipeline Transportation
S.I.C.: 4923
N.A.I.C.S.: 486210
Personnel:
Yingcen Zhang *(Founder & Chm)*
Xiaoming Hu *(CEO)*
Xinjian Li *(CFO)*
Dicson Man Yuk Hung *(Sec)*
Board of Directors:
Yingcen Zhang
Yi Feng
Xiaoming Hu
Liuqing Li
Tao Li
Heng Sun
Zhenyuan Xian
Jiaming Zhang
Jun Zhao
Legal Counsel:
Loong & Yeung
Suites 2001 2005 20/F Jardine House
1 Connaught Place, Central, China (Hong Kong)

Appleby Trust (Cayman) Ltd.
Clifton House 75 Fort Street
PO Box 1350
Grand Cayman, Cayman Islands
Transfer Agents:
Computershare Hong Kong Investor Services Limited
Rooms 1712-1716 17/F Hopewell Centre 183 Queen's Road East
Wanchai, China (Hong Kong)
Tel.: (852) 2862 8628
Fax: (852) 2865 0990

Appleby Trust (Cayman) Ltd.
Clifton House 75 Fort Street
PO Box 1350
Grand Cayman, Cayman Islands

CHINA TIANRUI GROUP CEMENT COMPANY LIMITED

63 Guangcheng Road East
Ruzhou, Henan, 467500, China
Tel.: (86) 375 6030133
Fax: (86) 375 6056211
E-Mail: yucl@tianruigroup.cn
Web Site: www.trcement.com
1252—(HKG)
Rev.: $1,205,813,988
Assets: $2,992,781,020
Liabilities: $1,985,122,399
Net Worth: $1,007,658,621
Earnings: $121,169,033
Emp.: 6,996
Fiscal Year-end: 12/31/12
Business Description:
Cement Mfr
S.I.C.: 3241
N.A.I.C.S.: 327310
Personnel:
Liufa Li *(Chm)*
DeLong Wang *(Deputy CEO & Exec Dir)*
Wuxue Xu *(CFO & Exec Dir)*

Board of Directors:
Liufa Li
Horace Chun Fung Ma
Ming Chien Tang
DeLong Wang
Wuxue Xu

Non-U.S. Division:

China Tianrui Group Cement Company Limited (1)
Hong Kong Universal Building 22
Hong Kong, China (Hong Kong)
Tel.: (852) 2501 0088
Fax: (852) 2501 0028
E-Mail: ycl6906@sina.com
Cement Mfr
S.I.C.: 3241
N.A.I.C.S.: 327310

CHINA TIANYI HOLDINGS LIMITED

Suite 2311 Tower One Times Square
1 Matheson Street
Causeway Bay, China (Hong Kong)
Tel.: (852) 3163 1000
Fax: (852) 3163 1122
E-Mail: adminhk@hksummi.com
Web Site: www.tianyi.com.hk
Year Founded: 1993
756—(HKG)
Rev.: $83,519,200
Assets: $296,990,726
Liabilities: $77,755,804
Net Worth: $219,234,921
Earnings: $10,654,705
Emp.: 850
Fiscal Year-end: 06/30/13

Business Description:
Juice Mfr & Whslr
S.I.C.: 2037
N.A.I.C.S.: 311411

Personnel:
Ke Sin *(Chm)*
Yuang-whang Liao *(CEO)*
Pui Shan Leung *(Sec)*

Board of Directors:
Ke Sin
Kwan San
Jianchong Zeng
Weidong Zhuang
Xueyuan Zhuang

Appleby Trust (Cayman) Ltd.
Clifton House 75 Fort Street
PO Box 1350
Grand Cayman, Cayman Islands

Transfer Agent:
Appleby Trust (Cayman) Ltd.
Clifton House 75 Fort Street
PO Box 1350
Grand Cayman, Cayman Islands

CHINA TIME SHARE MEDIA CO. LTD.

Chuanban Dayu Building 312 Long Zhua Shu Xiao Hong M
Chaoyang District, Beijing, 100078, China
Tel.: (86) 1087695559
Web Site: www.dytsm.com
Sales Range: $25-49.9 Million
Emp.: 586

Business Description:
Advertising Services
S.I.C.: 7319
N.A.I.C.S.: 541890

Personnel:
Jilun He *(Chm & CEO)*
Yifan Li *(CFO)*

Board of Directors:
Jilun He
Wayne W. Tsou
Yafei Wang
Feng Xiao
Jiaju Zeng
Changwen Zhou

CHINA TING GROUP HOLDINGS LIMITED

27/F King Palace Plaza 55 King Yip Street
Kwun Tong, Kowloon, China (Hong Kong)
Tel.: (852) 2950 9788
Fax: (852) 2790 6802
E-Mail: info@chinatingholdings.com
Web Site: www.chinatingholdings.com
Year Founded: 1992
3398—(HKG)
Rev.: $332,954,058
Assets: $463,671,189
Liabilities: $96,350,924
Net Worth: $367,320,265
Earnings: $19,827,868
Emp.: 10,000
Fiscal Year-end: 12/31/12

Business Description:
Holding Company; Apparel Mfr & Retailer
Import Export
S.I.C.: 6719
N.A.I.C.S.: 551112

Personnel:
Man Yi Ting *(Chm)*
Hung Yi Ting *(CEO)*
Tony Ren Shen *(Pres-China Ting Fashion Group (USA) LLC)*
Raymond Ho Lung Cheng *(Sec & Mgr-Fin & Acctg)*

Board of Directors:
Man Yi Ting
Chi Pang Cheng
Peter Ting Yin Cheung
Jianer Ding
Man Kit Leung
Hung Yi Ting
Chi Keung Wong

Legal Counsel:
Squire Sanders
24th Floor, Central Tower 28 Queen's Road
Central, China (Hong Kong)

Computershare Hong Kong Investor Services Limited
Shops 1712-16 17th Floor Hopewell Centre 183 Queen's Road East
Hong Kong, China (Hong Kong)

Subsidiary:

China Ting Garment Mfg (Group) Limited (1)
27/F King Palace Plaza 55 King Yip Street
Kwun Tong, China (Hong Kong) HK
Tel.: (852) 29509788 (100%)
Fax: (852) 27906802
E-Mail: info@chinatingholdings.com
Web Site: www.chinating.com.hk
Emp.: 70
Finished Garment International Trade Whslr
S.I.C.: 7389
N.A.I.C.S.: 425120
Man Yi Ting *(Chm)*

CHINA TITANS ENERGY TECHNOLOGY GROUP CO., LTD.

Titans Industrial Park Shihuaxilu
Zhuhai, China 519015
Tel.: (86) 756 3325412
E-Mail: titans@titans.com.cn
Web Site: www.titans.com.cn
Year Founded: 1992
2188—(HKG)
Sls.: $37,912,730
Assets: $127,519,856
Liabilities: $47,864,682
Net Worth: $79,655,174
Earnings: $1,866,805
Emp.: 460
Fiscal Year-end: 12/31/12

Business Description:
Power Electronics & Automation Control Mfr
S.I.C.: 3676
N.A.I.C.S.: 334416

Personnel:
Xin Qing Li *(Chm)*
Wei An *(CEO)*
Yiu Hung Wong *(Sec)*

Board of Directors:
Xin Qing Li
Wei An
Wan Jun Li
Xiao Hui Li
Zhuo Ping Yu

Legal Counsel:
P. C. Woo & Co
12th Floor Princes Building 10 Chater Road
Central, China (Hong Kong)

Computershare Hong Kong Investor Services Limited
Shops 1712-1716 17th Floor Hopewell Centre
183 Queens Road East
Wanchai, China (Hong Kong)

Transfer Agent:
Royal Bank of Canada Trust Company (Cayman) Limited
4th Floor Royal Bank House 24 Shedden Road
Georgetown, Cayman Islands

CHINA TMK BATTERY SYSTEMS INC.

Sanjun Industrial Park No 2
Huawang Road Dalang Street
Bao'an District, Shenzhen, 518109, China
Tel.: (86) 755 2810 9908
Web Site:
Year Founded: 2006
Sales Range: $50-74.9 Million
Emp.: 671

Business Description:
Nickel Metal Hydride Cell (Ni-MH) Rechargeable Batteries Mfr & Sales
S.I.C.: 3691
N.A.I.C.S.: 335911

Personnel:
Henian Wu *(Chm)*

Transfer Agent:
Island Stock Transfer
100 2nd Ave S Suite 705S
Saint Petersburg, FL 33701
Tel.: (727) 289-0010

CHINA TONTINE WINES GROUP LIMITED

Unit No 3612 36th Floor West Tower
Shun Tak Centre
Nos 168-200 Connaught Road,
Central, China (Hong Kong)
Tel.: (852) 25211628
Fax: (852) 25211323
E-Mail: chinatontine@sprg.com.hk
Web Site: www.tontine-wines.com.hk
0389—(HKG)
Rev.: $104,540,932
Assets: $307,261,490
Liabilities: $13,141,502
Net Worth: $294,119,988
Earnings: $14,116,682
Emp.: 425
Fiscal Year-end: 12/31/12

Business Description:
Wine Producer & Distr
S.I.C.: 2084
N.A.I.C.S.: 312130

Personnel:
Guangyuan Wang *(Chm & CEO)*
Chi Kan Sum *(Sec)*

Board of Directors:
Guangyuan Wang
Albert Chi Keung Lai
Changgao Li
Daniel Wai Kin Sih
Lijuan Wang
Hebin Zhang

Legal Counsel:
Jingtian & Gongcheng
34/F Tower 3 China Central Place 77 Jianguo Rd Chaoyang District
Beijing, China

Conyers Dill & Pearman
Clarendon House, 2 Church Street
Hamilton, Bermuda

Chiu & Partners
40 Floor Jardine House 1 Connaught Place
Hong Kong, China (Hong Kong)

Butterfield Fulcrum Group (Bermuda) Limited
Burnaby Street
Hamilton, HM 11, Bermuda

Transfer Agents:
Tricor Investor Services Limited
26th Floor Tesbury Centre 28 Queens Road East
Wanchai, China (Hong Kong)

Butterfield Fulcrum Group (Bermuda) Limited
Burnaby Street
Hamilton, HM 11, Bermuda

CHINA TOPREACH INC.

6th Floor San Shan Tower 59 Dongjie Street
Fuzhou, China 350001
Tel.: (86) 591 88310920
Fax: (86) 591 83302585
Web Site: www.chinatopreach.com
CGSXF—(OTC)
Sales Range: $75-99.9 Million
Emp.: 1,070

Business Description:
Newpaper & Online Publisher
S.I.C.: 2711
N.A.I.C.S.: 511110

Personnel:
Zhi Chen *(CEO)*
Tiezhu Zhang *(CFO)*

Board of Directors:
Min Chen
Zhi Chen
Peifeng Hong
Toshihiro Nakamura
Jingfeng Wang
Michael Weichun Zhang
Tiezhu Zhang

CHINA TRANSINFO TECHNOLOGY CORP.

Vision Bldg 39 Xueyuan Rd 9th Floor
Haidian District, Beijing, 100191, China
Tel.: (86) 1051691999
E-Mail: contact@ctfo.com
Web Site: www.chinatransinfo.com
Sales Range: $150-199.9 Million
Emp.: 946

Business Description:
Traffic Information Systems Mfr
S.I.C.: 3714
N.A.I.C.S.: 336320

Personnel:
Shudong Xia *(Chm, Pres, CEO & Sec)*
Rong Zhang *(CFO)*
Danxia Huang *(Treas & VP-Ops)*

Board of Directors:
Shudong Xia
Zhongsu Chen
Danxia Huang
Walter Teh Ming Kwauk
Brandon Ho-Ping Lin
Dan Liu
Xingming Zhang

CHINA TRAVEL INTERNATIONAL INVESTMENT HONG KONG LTD

12th Floor CTS House 78-83
Connaught Road
Central, China (Hong Kong)

China Travel International Investment Hong Kong Ltd—(Continued)

Tel.: (852) 2853 3888
Fax: (852) 28517538
E-Mail: ctiiadm@hkcts.com
Web Site: www.hkcts.com
308—(HKG)
Rev.: $601,994,177
Assets: $2,245,061,538
Liabilities: $403,857,731
Net Worth: $1,841,203,806
Earnings: $116,287,755
Emp.: 11,879
Fiscal Year-end: 12/31/12

Business Description:
Tour Operations, Hotels, Theme Parks, Passenger & Freight Transportation, Golf Club & Infrastructure Investment Services
S.I.C.: 4725
N.A.I.C.S.: 561520

Personnel:
Shuai Ting Wang *(Chm)*
Sui On Lo *(Vice Chm)*
Siu Chung Lai *(Sec)*

Board of Directors:
Shuai Ting Wang
Wing Kee Chan
Yun Wah Fong
Zhuoyang Fu
Yan Jiang
Sui On Lo
Robert Tsai To Sze
Peter Man Kong Wong
Muhan Xu
Fengchun Zhang

CHINA TREASURE MINE TECHNOLOGY HOLDINGS CO., LTD.

(d/b/a Treasure Mine)
Oxford Commercial Building 18F 494-496 Nathan Road
Kowloon, China (Hong Kong)
Tel.: (852) 277 18608
E-Mail: bomkon@126.com
Web Site: www.bomkon.com
MLTMT—(EUR)
Sales Range: $1-9.9 Million

Business Description:
Internet & Mobile Application Software
S.I.C.: 7372
N.A.I.C.S.: 511210

Personnel:
Jingshan Yu *(Chm)*

CHINA TYCOON BEVERAGE HOLDINGS LIMITED

18th Fl Wing Wong Commercial Bldg
557 & 559 Nathan Rd, Kowloon, China (Hong Kong)
Tel.: (852) 3919 9933
Fax: (852) 3919 9922
E-Mail: info@chinatycoon.com.hk
Web Site: www.chinatycoon.com.hk
0209—(HKG)
Sales Range: $25-49.9 Million
Emp.: 4,300

Business Description:
Beverage Products Mfr; Toy Mfr
S.I.C.: 2037
N.A.I.C.S.: 311411

Personnel:
Ka Lok Sue *(Chm)*
Charles Ming Chi Lo *(Deputy Chm & CEO)*
Danita On *(COO)*
Yuk Yee Chan *(Sec)*

Board of Directors:
Ka Lok Sue
Yuk Yee Chan
Ming Fai Kwok
Christine Pik Har Leung
Charles Ming Chi Lo
Danita On
Zhiqiang Shi
Jingyu Wang
Kwok Tai Wong

CHINA UNITED INSURANCE SERVICE, INC.

7F No 311 Section 3 Nan-King East Road
Taipei, Taiwan
Tel.: (886) 2 871 26958
CUII—(OTC OTCB)
Rev.: $37,842,246
Assets: $23,212,445
Liabilities: $7,723,835
Net Worth: $15,488,610
Earnings: $8,604,024
Emp.: 218
Fiscal Year-end: 06/30/13

Business Description:
Life Insurance Services
S.I.C.: 6311
N.A.I.C.S.: 524113

Personnel:
Chung Mei Lo *(CEO)*
Yung Chi Chuang *(CFO)*
Tung Chi Hsieh *(COO)*
Wen Yuan Hsu *(CMO)*
Te Yun Chiang *(CTO)*
Shu-Fen Lee *(Sec)*

Board of Directors:
Chen Kuei Chiao
Shu-Fen Lee
Chwan Hau Li
Fu Chang Li
Yi Hsiao Mao

Transfer Agent:
Glendale Securities Inc
15233 Ventura Blvd Ste 712
Sherman Oaks, CA 91403

CHINA UNITED NETWORK COMMUNICATIONS GROUP COMPANY LIMITED

No 21 Financial Street
Xicheng District, Beijing, P.R., 100140, China
Tel.: (86) 10 10010
Fax: (86) 10 661 10009
Web Site: eng.chinaunicom.com
600050—(SHG)

Business Description:
Holding Company
S.I.C.: 6719
N.A.I.C.S.: 551112

Personnel:
Xiaobing Chang *(Chm & Sec)*
Yimin Lu *(Vice Chm, Pres & Co-Deputy Sec)*
Xunsheng Zuo *(Vice Chm, VP & Co-Deputy Sec)*

Board of Directors:
Xiaobing Chang
Yimin Lu
Jilu Tong
Xunsheng Zuo

Subsidiary:

China United Network Communications Limited **(1)**
29th Floor No 1033 Changning Road
Changning District, Shanghai, 200050, China
Tel.: (86) 21 527 322 28
Fax: (86) 21 527 322 20
Web Site: eng.chinaunicom.com
Telecommunications
S.I.C.: 4899
N.A.I.C.S.: 517919

Non-U.S. Subsidiary:

China Unicom (Hong Kong) Limited **(1)**
75th Floor The Center 99 Queens Road Central
Hong Kong, China (Hong Kong) HK
Tel.: (852) 2126 2018
Fax: (852) 2121 3232
E-Mail: info@chinaunicom.com.hk
Web Site: www.chinaunicom.com.hk
CHU—(HKG NYSE)
Rev.: $39,541,895,100
Assets: $81,986,297,400
Liabilities: $48,706,428,150
Net Worth: $33,279,869,250
Earnings: $1,127,199,600
Emp.: 289,015
Fiscal Year-end: 12/31/12
Telecommunications & Internet Services
S.I.C.: 4813
N.A.I.C.S.: 517110
Xiaobing Chang *(Chm & CEO)*
Yimin Lu *(Pres)*
Fushen Li *(CFO)*
Ka Yee Chu *(Sec)*
Zhengxin Jiang *(Sr VP)*
Jianguo Li *(Sr VP)*
Jilu Tong *(Sr VP)*
Junan Zhang *(Sr VP)*

U.S. Subsidiaries:

China Netcom (USA) Operations Limited **(2)**
707 Wilshire Blvd Ste 3088
Los Angeles, CA 90017
Tel.: (213) 489-5636
Fax: (213) 489-5480
Web Site: www.chinaunicomamericas.com
Emp.: 30
Telecommunications
S.I.C.: 4899
N.A.I.C.S.: 517919

China Unicom USA Corporation **(2)**
624 S Grant Ave Ste 900
Los Angeles, CA 90017
Tel.: (213) 624-1038
Fax: (213) 683-9903
Web Site: www.unicomus.com
Telecommunications
S.I.C.: 4899
N.A.I.C.S.: 517919

Non-U.S. Subsidiaries:

China Unicom (Europe) Operations Limited **(2)**
Level 32 25 Canada Square
London, Canary Wharf, E14 5LQ, United Kingdom
Tel.: (44) 2077151999
Fax: (44) 2077151994
Telecommunications Services
S.I.C.: 4813
N.A.I.C.S.: 517110

China Unicom (Japan) Operations Corporation **(2)**
2403-B Mita Kokusai Building
1-4-28 Mita Minato-ku, Tokyo, 108-0073, Japan
Tel.: (81) 354396698
Fax: (81) 354393666
Telecommunications Services
S.I.C.: 4813
N.A.I.C.S.: 517110

Unicom New Century Telecommunications Corporation Limited **(2)**
No 133A Xidan North St
Xicheng District, Beijing, 100032, China
Tel.: (86) 1066505588
Fax: (86) 1066114366
Emp.: 400
Telecommunications Services
S.I.C.: 4813
N.A.I.C.S.: 517110

Subsidiary:

China Netcom Group Corporation (Hong Kong) Limited **(2)**
46 Floor Cheung Kong Centre
2 Queens Road, Central, China (Hong Kong) HK
Tel.: (852) 2626 8888
Fax: (852) 2626 8862
E-Mail: info@china-netcom.com
Web Site: www.china-netcom.com
Sales Range: $5-14.9 Billion
Emp.: 142,110
Broadband Internet Access & Telecom Services
S.I.C.: 4813
N.A.I.C.S.: 517110
Zuo Xunsheng *(CEO)*
Teng Yong *(Chief Tech Officer)*
Pei Aihua *(Sr VP)*
Zhao Jidong *(Sr VP)*

CHINA UPTOWN GROUP COMPANY LIMITED

Suite 1501 15/F Tower 1 Silvercord
30 Canton Road
Tsimshatsui, Kowloon, China (Hong Kong)
Tel.: (852) 35824878
Fax: (852) 38834898
E-Mail: info@chinauptown.com.hk
Web Site: www.chinauptown.com.hk
2330—(HKG)
Sls.: $155,581,502
Assets: $239,094,031
Liabilities: $170,939,915
Net Worth: $68,154,116
Earnings: $22,381,330
Emp.: 56
Fiscal Year-end: 12/31/12

Business Description:
Investment Holding Services
S.I.C.: 6719
N.A.I.C.S.: 551112

Personnel:
Feng Liu *(Chm)*
Xian Chen *(Vice Chm)*
Anthony Sai Chung Lau *(CEO)*
Lui Fu *(Sec)*

Board of Directors:
Feng Liu
Chun Fai Chan
Xian Chen
Anthony Sai Chung Lau
Winfield Kwok Chu Ng
Michael Lai Yin Poon
Dan Xia

Royal Bank of Canada Trust Company (Cayman) Limited
4th Floor Royal Bank House 24 Shedden Road
Georgetown, Cayman Islands

Transfer Agents:
Union Registrars Limited
18/F Fook Lee Commercial Centre Town Place
33 Lockhart Road
Wanchai, China (Hong Kong)

Royal Bank of Canada Trust Company (Cayman) Limited
4th Floor Royal Bank House 24 Shedden Road
Georgetown, Cayman Islands

CHINA VALVES TECHNOLOGY, INC.

93 West Xinsong Road
Kaifeng, Henan, China 475002
Tel.: (86) 371 8601877
Fax: (86) 378 2913714
E-Mail: ir@cvalve.com
Web Site: www.cvvt.cc
Year Founded: 1997
Sales Range: $150-199.9 Million
Emp.: 1,900

Business Description:
Metal Valves Mfr
S.I.C.: 3494
N.A.I.C.S.: 332919

Personnel:
Siping Fang *(Chm, Pres & Sec)*
Kaixiang Du *(CEO)*
Renrui Tang *(CFO)*
Binjie Fang *(COO)*
Qizhong Xiang *(CTO)*
Crocker Coulson *(Pres-CCG IR)*

Board of Directors:
Siping Fang
Zhaonian Du
Binjie Fang
Yinli Song
Zengbiao Yu

Legal Counsel:
Pillsbury Winthrop Shaw Pittman LLP
Washington, DC 20001

Transfer Agent:
PacWest Tansfer LLC
500 East Warm Springs Rd Ste 240
Las Vegas, NV 89119

CHINA VANADIUM TITANO-MAGNETITE MINING COMPANY LIMITED

7th Floor Longwei Mansion 198
Longdu South Road
Longquanyi District, Chengdu, 610100, China
Tel.: (86) 2888433449
Fax: (86) 2888433449
E-Mail: ir@chinavtmmining.com
Web Site: www.chinavtmmining.com
0893—(HKG)
Rev.: $243,633,328
Assets: $860,326,358
Liabilities: $296,969,122
Net Worth: $563,357,236
Earnings: $65,224,128
Emp.: 2,051
Fiscal Year-end: 12/31/12

Business Description:
Iron Ore Mining Services
S.I.C.: 1011
N.A.I.C.S.: 212210

Personnel:
Zhongping Jiang *(Chm)*
Wei Tang *(CEO)*
Roy Chi Mo Kong *(CFO & Sec)*

Board of Directors:
Zhongping Jiang
Peidong Gu
Roy Chi Mo Kong
Yi Liu
Wei Tang
Cheng Kwee Teo
Jin Wang
Haizong Yu
Xing Yuan Yu

Legal Counsel:
Minter Ellison
15F Hutchison House 10 Harcourt Road
Central, China (Hong Kong)

Conyers Dill & Pearman
Cricket Square Hutchins Drive
PO Box 2681
Georgetown, Grand Cayman, Cayman Islands

Computershare Hong Kong Investor Services Limited
Shops 1712-1716 17th Floor Hopewell Centre
183 Queens Road East
Wanchai, China (Hong Kong)

Transfer Agent:
Royal Bank of Canada Trust Company (Cayman) Limited
4th Floor Royal Bank House 24 Shedden Road
Georgetown, Cayman Islands

CHINA VANKE CO., LTD.

Vanke Center No 33 Huanmei Road
Dameisha
Yantian District, Shenzhen, 518083, China
Tel.: (86) 755 256 06666
Fax: (86) 755 255 31696
E-Mail: ir@vanke.com
Web Site: www.vanke.com
000002—(SSE)
Rev.: $15,386,197,339
Assets: $60,219,217,876
Liabilities: $47,171,565,600
Net Worth: $13,047,652,276
Earnings: $2,488,002,104
Emp.: 31,019
Fiscal Year-end: 12/31/12

Business Description:
Property Development
S.I.C.: 6531
N.A.I.C.S.: 531390

Personnel:
Shi Wang *(Chm)*
Fuyuan Ding *(Chm-Supervisory Bd)*
Shibo Qiao *(Deputy Chm)*
Liang Yu *(Pres)*
Changfeng Ding *(Exec VP)*
Daqing Mao *(Exec VP)*
Jun Mo *(Exec VP)*
Wenjin Wang *(Exec VP)*
Li Xiao *(Exec VP)*
Dong Xie *(Exec VP)*
Jiwen Zhang *(Exec VP)*
Weijun Zhou *(Exec VP)*

Board of Directors:
Shi Wang
Sheng Hua
Wei Jiang
Elizabeth Law
Daqing Qi
Shibo Qiao
Jianyi Sun
Yin Wang
Li Xiao
Liang Yu
Liping Zhang

Supervisory Board of Directors:
Fuyuan Ding
Ding Wu
Qingping Zhou

Subsidiaries:

Chengdu Vanke Real Estate Company Limited **(1)**
4/f Building 98 Wanke City Garden No 1 Jingan Road
Jinjian, Chengdu, Sichuan, 610066, China
Tel.: (86) 2884096445
Fax: (86) 2884781888
Real Estate Management Services
S.I.C.: 6531
N.A.I.C.S.: 531390

Dongguan Vanke Real Estate Company Limited **(1)**
11/f Dongshen Mansion Dongcheng South Road
Dongcheng District, Dongguan, Guangdong, 523000, China
Tel.: (86) 76922306868
Fax: (86) 76922303989
Real Estate Management Services
S.I.C.: 6531
N.A.I.C.S.: 531390

Guangzhou Vanke Real Estate Company Limited **(1)**
No 42 Yanyu Road Ershadao
Yuexiu District, Guangzhou, Guangdong, 510105, China
Tel.: (86) 2087351866
Fax: (86) 2087351822
Property Management Services
S.I.C.: 6531
N.A.I.C.S.: 531390

Non-U.S. Holding:

Vanke Property (Overseas) Limited **(1)**
55/F Bank of China Tower 1 Garden Road
Central, China (Hong Kong) Ky
Tel.: (852) 2309 8888 (73.9%)
Fax: (852) 2328 8097
E-Mail: vkoverseas.ir@vanke.com
Web Site: www.vankeoverseas.com
1036—(HKG)
Sales Range: $300-349.9 Million
Emp.: 273
Holding Company; Commercial Property Investment, Development & Management
S.I.C.: 6719
N.A.I.C.S.: 551112
Peter Chi Chung Luk *(CFO)*

Subsidiary:

Winsor Properties (Hong Kong) Ltd. **(2)**
55/F Bank of China Tower No 1 Garden Road
Central, China (Hong Kong) HK
Tel.: (852) 2810 8008 (100%)
Fax: (852) 2810 0664
Property Investment & Development
S.I.C.: 6531
N.A.I.C.S.: 531312

CHINA VEHICLE COMPONENTS TECHNOLOGY HOLDINGS LIMITED

76 Lao Street
Xichuan Town, Nanyang, China
Tel.: (86) 377 6921 9800
Fax: (86) 377 6921 3107
E-Mail: ir@china-cvct.com
Web Site: www.china-cvct.com
1269—(HKG)
Rev.: $81,429,662
Assets: $154,325,627
Liabilities: $108,367,200
Net Worth: $45,958,426
Earnings: $1,211,567
Emp.: 1,400
Fiscal Year-end: 12/31/12

Business Description:
Shock Absorber Mfr
S.I.C.: 3714
N.A.I.C.S.: 336330

Personnel:
Chunylng Xi *(Chm)*
Zhijun Zhao *(CEO)*
Ping Wang *(CFO)*
Man Yuk Hung *(Sec)*

Board of Directors:
Chunying Xi
Peleus Kin Wang Chu
Pengxu Fu
Zhiqiang Li
Wenbo Wang
Qingxi Xie
Weixia Yang
Jinhua Zhang
Zhijun Zhao

Transfer Agent:
Royal Bank of Canada Trust Company (Cayman) Limited
4th Floor Royal Bank House 24 Shedden Road
Georgetown, Cayman Islands

Subsidiary:

Nanyang Cijan Auto Shock Absorber Co., Ltd. **(1)**
No 76 Laojie Rd
Xichuan County, Nanyang, Henan, 474450, China
Tel.: (86) 37769219933
Fax: (86) 37769219937
Web Site: www.china-shock-absorber.com
Emp.: 150
Automotive Parts Mfr
S.I.C.: 3714
N.A.I.C.S.: 336390
Chun Zhi Zhao *(Gen Mgr)*

CHINA VITUP HEALTH CARE HOLDINGS, INC.

108-1 Nashan Road
Zhongshan District, Dalian, China
Tel.: (86) 41182653668
Web Site: www.vitup.cn
Year Founded: 2003
CVPH—(OTC)
Sales Range: $1-9.9 Million
Emp.: 107

Business Description:
Holding Company; Medical Clinics Owner & Operator
S.I.C.: 6719
N.A.I.C.S.: 551112

Personnel:
ShuBin Wang *(Chm)*
Feng Gu *(CEO)*
Chunxiang Li *(CFO)*
Charles Guo *(COO)*

Board of Directors:
ShuBin Wang
Liming Gong
Feng Gu
Xun Yuan
Laifu Zhong

CHINA WATER AFFAIRS GROUP LTD

Suite 6408 64/F Central Plaza 18 Harbour Road
Wanchai, China (Hong Kong)
Tel.: (852) 39686666
Fax: (852) 29509642
E-Mail: info@chinawatergroup.com
Web Site: www.chinawatergroup.com
0855—(HKG OTC)
Rev.: $290,224,541
Assets: $1,502,257,571
Liabilities: $832,499,911
Net Worth: $669,757,660
Earnings: $67,768,254
Emp.: 5,500
Fiscal Year-end: 03/31/13

Business Description:
Utilities Supplying Services
S.I.C.: 4941
N.A.I.C.S.: 221310

Personnel:
Chuan Liang Duan *(Chm)*
Aston Chi Wing Lie *(Scc)*

Board of Directors:
Chuan Liang Duan
Kam Wing Chau
Guo Ru Chen
Shao Yun Huang
Makoto Inoue
Ji Sheng Li
Dong Liu
King Keung Ong
Jiesi Wu
Hai Hu Zhao
Wen Zhi Zhou

Subsidiary:

Ming Hing Waterworks Engineering (PRC) Limited **(1)**
Rm 1809 18 F Telford House 16 Wang Hoi Rd
Kowloon Bay, Kowloon, China (Hong Kong)
Tel.: (852) 23808265
Fax: (852) 23975975
E-Mail: mail@minghing.com.hk
Web Site: www.minghing.com.hk
Emp.: 200
Water & Sewer System Construction Services
S.I.C.: 1629
N.A.I.C.S.: 237110

CHINA WATER GROUP, INC.

Suite 7A01 Baicheng Building 584 Yingbin Road Dashi
Panyu District, Guangzhou, Guangdong, China
Tel.: (86) 20 3479 9768
CHWG—(OTC)
Sales Range: Less than $1 Million
Emp.: 72

Business Description:
Bottled Water Mfr & Distr
S.I.C.: 2086
N.A.I.C.S.: 312112

Personnel:
Chong Liang Pu *(Chm)*
Wenge Fang *(Pres & CEO)*
Rencai Ding *(CFO)*

Board of Directors:
Chong Liang Pu
Rencai Ding
Wenge Fang

CHINA WATER INDUSTRY GROUP LIMITED

Room 1207 12/ F West Tower Shun Tak Centre 168-200 Connaught Road
Central, Sheung Wan, China (Hong Kong)
Tel.: (852) 25476382
Fax: (852) 25476629
E-Mail: info@chinawaterind.com
Web Site: www.chinawaterind.com
1129—(HKG)

China Water Industry Group Limited—(Continued)

Rev.: $42,280,771
Assets: $159,824,499
Liabilities: $68,972,518
Net Worth: $90,851,980
Earnings: ($5,921,642)
Emp.: 1,008
Fiscal Year-end: 12/31/12

Business Description:
Water Supply & Sewage Treatment Services
S.I.C.: 4952
N.A.I.C.S.: 221320

Personnel:
De Yin Wang *(Chm & CEO)*
Georgiana Yin Yin Chu *(Sec)*

Board of Directors:
De Yin Wang
Georgiana Yin Yin Chu
Xiao Ting Deng
Chao Tian Guo
Jian Jun Li
Yue Hui Lin
Feng Liu
Joe Siu Keung Wong

Royal Bank of Canada Trust Company (Cayman) Limited
4th Floor Royal Bank House 24 Shedden Road
Georgetown, Cayman Islands

Transfer Agents:
Union Registrars Limited
18/F Fook Lee Commercial Centre Town Place 33 Lockhart Road
Wanchai, China (Hong Kong)

Royal Bank of Canada Trust Company (Cayman) Limited
4th Floor Royal Bank House 24 Shedden Road
Georgetown, Cayman Islands

CHINA WATER PROPERTY GROUP LIMITED

Suite 6208 62/F Central Plaza 18 Harbour Road
Wanchai, China (Hong Kong)
Tel.: (852) 2827 0088
Fax: (852) 2827 0303
E-Mail: info@waterpropertygroup.com
Web Site: www.waterpropertygroup.com
2349—(HKG)
Sls.: $34,993,677
Assets: $532,479,683
Liabilities: $304,451,595
Net Worth: $228,028,088
Earnings: $8,595,807
Emp.: 412
Fiscal Year-end: 12/31/12

Business Description:
Investment Holding Company
S.I.C.: 6719
N.A.I.C.S.: 551112

Personnel:
Wenxia Wang *(Vice Chm & CEO)*
Tak Yip Yeung *(Sec)*

Board of Directors:
Chuan Liang Duan
Pok Hiu Chan
Qian Ren
Jian Wang
Wenxia Wang
Chi Ming Wong
Kun Zhou

HSBC Trustee (Cayman) Limited
HSBC House 68 West Bay Road
PO Box 484
Georgetown, Grand Cayman, Cayman Islands

Transfer Agents:
Tricor Tengis Limited
26th Floor Tesbury Centre 28 Queen's Road East
Wanchai, China (Hong Kong)
Tel.: (852) 29801333
Fax: (852) 28108185

HSBC Trustee (Cayman) Limited
HSBC House 68 West Bay Road
PO Box 484
Georgetown, Grand Cayman, Cayman Islands

CHINA WEAVING MATERIALS HOLDINGS LIMITED

Fengtian Development Zone
Fengxin, Yichun, Jiangxi, 330700, China
Tel.: (86) 795 4509998
Fax: (86) 795 4509999
E-Mail: ir@chinaweavingmaterials.com
Web Site: www.chinaweavingmaterials.com
3778—(HKG)
Emp.: 1,850

Business Description:
Yarn & Cotton Mfr
S.I.C.: 2299
N.A.I.C.S.: 313110

Personnel:
Hong Zheng *(Chm)*

Board of Directors:
Hong Zheng
Mabel Mei Bo Chan
Wing Ka Ng
Jianxin Nie
Irons J.P. Sze
Yongxiang Zheng

CHINA WESTERN POWER INDUSTRIAL CO., LTD.

5/F Maike Building 5 Jiuxing Avenue
Chengdu, 610041, China
Tel.: (86) 28 8558 6440
Fax: (86) 28 8558 6400
E-Mail: cwpc@westernpower.cn
Web Site: www.westernpower.cn
002630—(SSE)
Sales Range: $200-249.9 Million

Business Description:
Boiler Mfr
S.I.C.: 3443
N.A.I.C.S.: 332410

Personnel:
Renchao Li *(Chm)*

CHINA WIND POWER INTERNATIONAL CORP.

150 York Street Ste 818
Toronto, ON, M5H 3S5, Canada
Tel.: (416) 916-4205
Fax: (416) 916-5463
E-Mail: wzhang@chinawindpowerinternational.com
Web Site: www.chinawindpowerinternational.com
Year Founded: 1987
Sales Range: $1-9.9 Million
Emp.: 35

Business Description:
Wind Power Generation & Development Services
S.I.C.: 4931
N.A.I.C.S.: 221118

Personnel:
Jun Liu *(Chm & CEO)*
Wendell Zhang *(CFO)*
Walter Huang *(Sr VP-Strategic Dev, Corp Fin, IR & Clean Dev Mechanism)*

Board of Directors:
Jun Liu
Linda Dundas
Joshua J. Gerstein
Walter Huang
Hongliang Xu

CHINA WINDPOWER GROUP LIMITED

Suite 3901 Far East Finance Centre
16 Harcourt Road
Admiralty, Hong Kong, China (Hong Kong)
Tel.: (852) 37661066
Fax: (852) 28660281
E-Mail: agitacheung@uhr.com.hk
Web Site: www.cwpgroup.com.hk
0182—(HKG)
Rev.: $141,821,660
Assets: $968,159,953
Liabilities: $393,687,961
Net Worth: $574,471,992
Earnings: $5,275,602
Emp.: 1,586
Fiscal Year-end: 12/31/12

Business Description:
Investment Holding Company
S.I.C.: 6282
N.A.I.C.S.: 523920

Personnel:
Shunxing Liu *(Chm & CEO)*
Johnson Chun Shun Ko *(Vice Chm)*
Mingyang Hu *(CFO)*
Jason Kam Kwan Chan *(Sec)*
Xun Wang *(Exec VP)*

Board of Directors:
Shunxing Liu
Jason Kam Kwan Chan
Huang Jian
Johnson Chun Shun Ko
Samantha Wing Yan Ko
Shang Li
Jianhong Liu
Tony Tong Hoo Tsoi
Xun Wang
David Yau Kar Wong
Zhifeng Yang
Fat Suan Yap
Weizhou Yu
Dadi Zhou
Zhizhong Zhou

Transfer Agent:
Tricor Tengis Limited
26th Floor Tesbury Centre 28 Queen's Road East
Wanchai, China (Hong Kong)
Tel.: (852) 29801333
Fax: (852) 28108185

CHINA WIRELESS TECHNOLOGIES LIMITED

No 2 Flat Coolpad Cyber Park
Mengxi Boulevard
Northern Part of Science & Technology Park Nanshan
District518057, Shenzhen, 518057, China
Tel.: (86) 75533023607
Web Site: www.chinawireless.cn
2369—(HKG)
Rev.: $1,851,571,129
Assets: $1,044,933,559
Liabilities: $733,778,885
Net Worth: $311,154,674
Earnings: $41,818,872
Emp.: 3,900
Fiscal Year-end: 12/31/12

Business Description:
Holding Company; Wireless Telecommunications Solutions & Equipment Whslr
S.I.C.: 4812
N.A.I.C.S.: 517210

Personnel:
Deying Guo *(Chm & CEO)*
Chao Jiang *(CFO, Sec & VP)*

Board of Directors:
Deying Guo
King Chung Chan
Dazhan Huang
Chao Jiang
Bin Li
Wang Li
Weixin Xie
Xianzu Yang

Legal Counsel:
DLA Piper Hong Kong
17th Fl Edinburgh Tower The Landmark No 15 Queens Rd
Central, China (Hong Kong)

Conyers Dill & Pearman
2901 One Exchange Square 8 Connaught Place
Central, China (Hong Kong)

Computershare Hong Kong Investor Services Limited
Shops 1712-16 17th Floor Hopewell Centre 183 Queen's Road East
Hong Kong, China (Hong Kong)

Transfer Agents:
Royal Bank of Canada Trust Company (Cayman) Limited
4th Floor Royal Bank House 24 Shedden Road
Georgetown, Cayman Islands

Computershare Hong Kong Investor Services Limited
Shops 1712-16 17th Floor Hopewell Centre 183 Queen's Road East
Hong Kong, China (Hong Kong)

CHINA WOOD, INC.

Daizhuang Industry Zone
Yitang Town
Lanshan District, Linyi, Shandong, 276000, China
Tel.: (86) 5398566168
Fax: (86) 75786259293
CNWD—(OTC)
Sales Range: $25-49.9 Million
Emp.: 430

Business Description:
Plywood Mfr
S.I.C.: 2435
N.A.I.C.S.: 321211

Personnel:
Xiaoling Ye *(Chm)*
Zhikang Li *(CEO)*
Hang Sang Lau *(CFO)*

Board of Directors:
Xiaoling Ye
Zhikang Li

CHINA WOOD OPTIMIZATION (HOLDINGS) LIMITED

Room 09-10 41/F China Resources Building
26 Harbour Road, Wanchai, China (Hong Kong)
Tel.: (852) 2527 1196
Web Site: www.chinawood.com.hk
8099—(HKG)

Business Description:
Processed Wood Products Mfr & Distr
S.I.C.: 2499
N.A.I.C.S.: 321999

Personnel:
Tsun Yim *(Chm)*
Li Li *(CEO)*
Ngai Chor *(CFO)*

Board of Directors:
Tsun Yim
Ying Kit Lau
Li Li
Junwen Pu
Dali Zhang

CHINA WORLD TRADE CENTER CO., LTD.

1 Jian Guo Men Wai Avenue
Beijing, 100004, China
Tel.: (86) 10 65052288
Fax: (86) 10 65053862
E-Mail: cwtc@cwtc.com
Web Site: www.cwtc.com
600007—(SHG)
Sales Range: $150-199.9 Million

Business Description:
Commercial & Residential Buildings & Facilities Operation & Management
S.I.C.: 6531
N.A.I.C.S.: 531312
Personnel:
Jingnan Hong *(Chm)*

CHINA XD ELECTRICITY CO., LTD.

7 Tangxing Road
Xi'an, 710075, China
Tel.: (86) 29 88832222
Fax: (86) 29 84242679
Web Site: www.xdect.com.cn
601179—(SHG)
Emp.: 15,800
Business Description:
Power Transmission, Distribution & Control Equipment Mfr & Sales
S.I.C.: 3612
N.A.I.C.S.: 335311
Personnel:
Yalin Zhang *(Chm)*

CHINA XD PLASTICS COMPANY LTD.

No 9 Dalian North Road Haping Road Centralized Industrial Park
Harbin Development Zone, Harbin, Heilongjiang, China 150060
Tel.: (86) 451 8434 6600
E-Mail: cxdc@chinaxd.net
Web Site: www.chinaxd.net
CXDC—(NASDAQ)
Rev.: $599,818,968
Assets: $611,584,309
Liabilities: $347,221,485
Net Worth: $264,362,824
Earnings: $85,867,747
Emp.: 606
Fiscal Year-end: 12/31/12
Business Description:
Modified Plastic Products Mfr & Distr
S.I.C.: 3089
N.A.I.C.S.: 326199
Personnel:
Jie Han *(Chm, Pres & CEO)*
Taylor Dahe Zhang *(CFO)*
Qingwei Ma *(COO)*
Junjie Ma *(CTO)*
Board of Directors:
Jie Han
Lawrence W. Leighton
Feng Li
Qingwei Ma
Homer Sun
Jun Xu
Linyuan Zhai
Taylor Dahe Zhang
Transfer Agent:
Interwest Transfer Company, Inc.
1981 Murray Holladay Road Suite 100
Salt Lake City, UT 84117

CHINA XIBOLUN TECHNOLOGY HOLDINGS CORPORATION

No 587 15th Road 3rd Avenue
Binhai Industrial Park Eco & Tech Development Zone, Wenzhou, 325088, China
Tel.: (86) 1309 9840703
Web Site:
Year Founded: 2008
CXBL—(OTC OTCB)
Liabilities: $20,983
Net Worth: ($20,983)
Earnings: ($35,425)
Fiscal Year-end: 04/30/13
Business Description:
Strategic, Financial & Operational Consulting Services
S.I.C.: 8742
N.A.I.C.S.: 541611
Personnel:
Chin Yung Kong *(Pres, CEO, CFO, Treas & Sec)*
Board of Directors:
Chin Yung Kong
Anyuan Sun

CHINA XINGBANG INDUSTRY GROUP INC.

7/F West Tower Star International Mansion 6-20 Jinsui Rd
Tianhe District, Guangzhou, Guangdong, China
Tel.: (86) 20 38296988
Fax: (86) 20 38296977
Web Site: www.ju51.com
CXGP—(OTC OTCB)
Rev.: $625,323
Assets: $1,857,174
Liabilities: $2,514,903
Net Worth: ($657,729)
Earnings: ($1,828,546)
Emp.: 30
Fiscal Year-end: 12/31/12
Business Description:
E-Commerce Related & Marketing Consulting Services
S.I.C.: 8742
N.A.I.C.S.: 541613
Personnel:
Xiaohong Yao *(Chm, Pres & CEO)*
Haigang Song *(Interim CFO, Treas & Sec)*
Board of Directors:
Xiaohong Yao
Joseph Levinson
Haigang Song
Gangxian Su
Xingzheng Tan
Fei Wu
Xiaole Zhan
Transfer Agent:
Island Stock Transfer
15500 Roosevelt Blvd Ste 301
Clearwater, FL 33760

CHINA XINIYA FASHION LIMITED

4th Floor 33 Wang Hai Road Xiamen Software Park Phase II
Xiamen, Fujian, 361000, China
Tel.: (86) 592 331 5667
Fax: (86) 592 331 5677
Web Site: www.xiniya.com
XNY—(NYSE)
Rev.: $219,798,680
Assets: $261,839,603
Liabilities: $38,971,941
Net Worth: $222,867,662
Earnings: $27,870,391
Emp.: 276
Fiscal Year-end: 12/31/12
Business Description:
Men's Business Casual Apparel Mfr
S.I.C.: 2329
N.A.I.C.S.: 315220
Personnel:
Qiming Xu *(Chm & CEO)*
Chee Jiong Ng *(CFO)*
Kangkai Zeng *(COO)*
Board of Directors:
Qiming Xu
Alvin Ang
Peter M. McGrath
Bin Yang
Kangkai Zeng

CHINA XLX FERTILISER LTD

Xinxiang High Technology Development Zone
Henan, 453731, China
Tel.: (86) 3735592888
Fax: (86) 3735592527
E-Mail: ir@chinaxlx.com.hk
Web Site: www.chinaxlx.com.hk
1866—(HKG)
Rev.: $626,756,018
Assets: $812,869,920
Liabilities: $442,998,497
Net Worth: $369,871,423
Earnings: $49,402,509
Emp.: 3,834
Fiscal Year-end: 12/31/12
Business Description:
Fertilzer Mfr
S.I.C.: 2875
N.A.I.C.S.: 325314
Personnel:
Xingxu Liu *(Chm & CEO)*
Yunhua Yan *(CFO)*
Yuk Tai Soon *(Co-Sec)*
Meng Keong Teo *(Co-Sec)*
Board of Directors:
Xingxu Liu
Buwen Li
Shengxiao Li
Jie Lian
Kian Guan Ong
Wei Jin Ong
Yunhua Yan
Tricor Barbinder Share Registration Services
80 Robinson Road 02-00
Singapore, Singapore

CHINA XUEFENG ENVIRONMENTAL ENGINEERING INC.

(Formerly NYC Moda Inc.)
C214 Fitting Integration Building
Fazhan Road to Sugian Gate Section, Nanjing, Jiangsu, 223800, China
Tel.: (86) 527 8437 0508
Web Site: www.cxfee.com
Year Founded: 2011
CXEE—(OTC OTCB)
Rev.: $5,426,435
Assets: $17,602,633
Liabilities: $2,155,320
Net Worth: $15,447,313
Earnings: $3,372,718
Emp.: 32
Fiscal Year-end: 04/30/13
Business Description:
Environmental Engineering Services
S.I.C.: 8711
N.A.I.C.S.: 541330
Personnel:
Li Yuan *(Chm & CEO)*
Kuanfu Fan *(CFO, Treas & Sec)*
Board of Directors:
Li Yuan
Yi Yuan
Xiaojun Zhuang

CHINA YANGTZE POWER CO., LTD.

Block B Focus Place 19 Financial Street
Xicheng District, Beijing, 100032, China
Tel.: (86) 10 5868 8999
Fax: (86) 10 5868 8888
E-Mail: cypc@cypc.com.cn
Web Site: www.cypc.com.cn
Year Founded: 2002
600900—(SHG)
Sales Range: $1-4.9 Billion
Emp.: 2,570
Business Description:
Hydroelectric Power Generation
S.I.C.: 4939
N.A.I.C.S.: 221111
Personnel:
Yong'an Li *(Chm)*
Ya Yang *(Chm-Supervisory Bd)*
Zhenbang Fu *(Sec)*
Board of Directors:
Yong'an Li
Yaxiong Bi
Guangjing Cao
Jianmin Cui
Qixiang Fan
Huazhang Gong
Chuxue Lin
Yougi Sun
Xiaosong Wang
Guangqi Wu
Jingru Wu
Qing Yang
Supervisory Board of Directors:
Ya Yang
Guoqing Chen
Xiaohong Chen
Zhengang Wang
Chongqiu Zhang

CHINA YIDA HOLDING, CO.

28/F Yifa Building 111 Wusi Road
Fuzhou, Fujian, China 350003
Tel.: (86) 591 28308388
E-Mail: jocelynchen@yidacn.net
Web Site: www.yidacn.net
CNYD—(NASDAQ)
Rev.: $27,605,889
Assets: $218,779,737
Liabilities: $60,046,687
Net Worth: $158,733,050
Earnings: ($607,187)
Emp.: 523
Fiscal Year-end: 12/31/12
Business Description:
Holding Company; Advertising Services; Tourism
S.I.C.: 6719
N.A.I.C.S.: 551112
Personnel:
Minhua Chen *(Chm & CEO)*
Yongxi Lin *(CFO & Controller-Fin)*
Yanling Fan *(COO)*
Board of Directors:
Minhua Chen
Yanling Fan
Fucai Huang
Renjiu Pei
Chunyu Yin

CHINA YILI PETROLEUM COMPANY

Tongliao Economic Development District
Tongliao, Inner Mongolia, 638229, China
Tel.: (86) 9735069295
Year Founded: 2004
CYIP—(OTC)
Emp.: 10
Business Description:
Oil Refining Services
S.I.C.: 2911
N.A.I.C.S.: 324110
Personnel:
Chunshi Li *(Chm, CEO & CFO)*
Board of Directors:
Chunshi Li

CHINA YONGDA AUTOMOBILES SERVICES HOLDINGS LIMITED

299 Ruijin Road S
Shanghai, 200023, China
Tel.: (86) 21 63026789
Fax: (86) 21 53522427
E-Mail: yongdaauto@ydauto.com.cn
Web Site: www.ydauto.com.cn
3669—(HKG)
Sales Range: $1-4.9 Billion
Emp.: 6,400
Business Description:
Car Retail, Rental, Insurance & Inspection Services

China Yongda Automobiles Services Holdings Limited—(Continued)

S.I.C.: 5511
N.A.I.C.S.: 441110
Personnel:
Tak On Cheung *(Chm & CEO)*
Yingjie Cai *(Vice Chm & Gen Mgr)*
Zhigao Wang *(Vice Chm)*
Board of Directors:
Tak On Cheung
Yingjie Cai
Xianglin Chen
Wei Lu
Liqun Wang
Zhigao Wang
Zhiqiang Wang

CHINA YOUNGMAN AUTOMOBILE GROUP CO., LTD.

No 501 BaDa Street
Jinhua, Zhejiang, 321016, China
Tel.: (86) 57989186133
Fax: (86) 57989186790
E-Mail: overseas@young-man.cn
Web Site: www.young-man.cn
Business Description:
Holding Company; Motor Vehicle & Motor Vehicle Components Mfr & Distr
S.I.C.: 6719
N.A.I.C.S.: 551112
Personnel:
Qingnian Pang *(Chm)*
Subsidiaries:

Jinhua Youngman Automobile Co., Ltd **(1)**
No 501 BaDa Street
Jinhua, Zhejiang, 321016, China CN
Tel.: (86) 57989186133
Fax: (86) 57989186790
E-Mail: overseas@yo-man.cn
Web Site: www.yo-man.cn
Heavy Duty Truck Mfr
S.I.C.: 3711
N.A.I.C.S.: 336120

Zhejiang Youngman Lotus Automobile Co., Ltd. **(1)**
No 501 BaDa Street
Jinhua, Zhejiang, 321016, China CN
Tel.: (86) 57989186388
Web Site: www.youngmanlotus.com
Car & Sport Utility Vehicle Mfr & Distr
S.I.C.: 3711
N.A.I.C.S.: 336111

CHINA YUAN HONG FIRE CONTROL GROUP HOLDINGS LTD

(d/b/a Yuanhong)
Baisha Meilin Industrial Area
Nan'an, Fujian, 362300, China
Tel.: (86) 595 86278200
Fax: (86) 595 86288675
E-Mail: willinzhu@gmail.com
Web Site: www.en.baishafire.com
Sales Range: $50-74.9 Million
Emp.: 350
Business Description:
Fire Safety Products Mfr
S.I.C.: 9224
N.A.I.C.S.: 922160
Personnel:
Zhuge Zhuang *(Chm, Founder & CEO)*
Pengyun Zhao *(CFO)*
Zhuangzhi Li *(Sec)*

CHINA YUANBANG PROPERTY HOLDINGS LIMITED

9th Floor Yuanbang Building No 599 Huangshi West Road
Baiyun District, Guangzhou, Guangdong, China 510430
Tel.: (86) 2026272116
Fax: (86) 2026272202
Web Site: www.yuanbang.com
B2X—(SES)
Rev.: $137,806,187
Assets: $719,337,293
Liabilities: $577,904,878
Net Worth: $141,432,415
Earnings: $17,226,329
Fiscal Year-end: 06/30/13
Business Description:
Property Development Services
S.I.C.: 6531
N.A.I.C.S.: 531312
Personnel:
Jianfeng Chen *(Founder & Chm)*
Xiaoxiong Zhou *(CEO)*
Ching Hoi Chong *(CFO & Sec)*
Board of Directors:
Jianfeng Chen
Zhangxin Huang
See Juan Kuik
Sheng Ouyang
Yi-Dar Teo
Shaorong Zheng

BDO Limited
25th Floor Wing On Centre 111 Connaught Road
Central, China (Hong Kong)

Transfer Agent:
B.A.C.S. Private Limited
63 Cantonment Road
Singapore, 089758, Singapore
Tel.: (65) 3236 2000

CHINA YUNNAN TIN MINERALS GROUP COMPANY LIMITED

Units 2502 5 25th Floor Harbour Centre 25 Harbour Road
Wanchai, China (Hong Kong)
Tel.: (852) 39261888
Fax: (852) 39261999
E-Mail: info@cytmg.com
Web Site: www.cytmg.com
0263—(HKG)
Sls.: $1,740,825
Assets: $174,564,257
Liabilities: $17,294,000
Net Worth: $157,270,257
Earnings: ($31,967,479)
Emp.: 68
Fiscal Year-end: 12/31/12
Business Description:
Minerals Exploration & Sales
S.I.C.: 1481
N.A.I.C.S.: 213115
Personnel:
Guoqing Zhang *(Chm)*
Ka Wai Leung *(Sec & Mgr-Fin)*
Board of Directors:
Guoqing Zhang
Ah Fei Chan
Shuda Chen
Chao Hu
Jalen Lee
Yuk Fat Lee
Christine Shin Kwan Ng
Shun Loy Wong
Yun Kuen Wong
Transfer Agent:
Tricor Secretaries Limited
26th Floor Tesbury Centre 28 Queen's Road East
Wanchai, China (Hong Kong)

Subsidiaries:

GT Capital Limited **(1)**
Ste 1502-1503 15 F Great Eagle Ctr 23 Harbour Rd
Wanchai, China (Hong Kong)
Tel.: (852) 31626688
Fax: (852) 31626668
E-Mail: cs@gtcapital.com.hk
Web Site: www.gtcapital.com.hk
Emp.: 10
Securities Brokerage Services
S.I.C.: 6211
N.A.I.C.S.: 523120
Freddie Leung *(Mgr)*

Poly Metal and Minerals Limited **(1)**
Rm 1502-3 15 F Great Eagle Ctr 23 Harbour Rd
Wanchai, China (Hong Kong)
Tel.: (852) 31626666
Fax: (852) 31626669
E-Mail: info@bejingyst.com
Web Site: www.bejingyst.com
Emp.: 10
Iron Ore Processing Services
S.I.C.: 1011
N.A.I.C.S.: 212210
Paul Cho Hung Suen *(Mng Dir)*

CHINA YURUN FOOD GROUP LIMITED

10 Yurun Road
Jianye District, Nanjing, China 210041
Tel.: (86) 25 6663 8888
E-Mail: ir@yurun.com.hk
Web Site: www.yurun.com.hk
C7Y—(DEU)
Sls.: $3,453,491,446
Assets: $3,307,286,002
Liabilities: $1,302,571,662
Net Worth: $2,004,714,341
Earnings: ($78,802,248)
Emp.: 26,000
Fiscal Year-end: 12/31/12
Business Description:
Processed Meat Mfr
S.I.C.: 5147
N.A.I.C.S.: 311612
Personnel:
Zhangli Yu *(Chm)*
Shibao Li *(CEO)*
Rosa Wing Sze Lee *(Sec)*
Board of Directors:
Zhangli Yu
Jianguo Chen
Kuande Feng
Hui Gao
Yuqi Ge
Chenghua Li
Shibao Li
Jun Qiao
Kaitian Wang

Butterfield Fulcrum Group (Bermuda) Limited
26 Burnaby Street
Hamilton, HM 11, Bermuda

Transfer Agents:
Tricor Investor Services Limited
26th Floor Tesbury Centre 28 Queens Road East
Wanchai, China (Hong Kong)

Butterfield Fulcrum Group (Bermuda) Limited
26 Burnaby Street
Hamilton, HM 11, Bermuda

CHINA ZENITH CHEMICAL GROUP LIMITED

Unit 1101-12 Sun Hung Kai Centre 30 Harbour Road
Wanchai, China (Hong Kong)
Tel.: (852) 28453131
Fax: (852) 28453535
E-Mail: info@chinazenith.com.hk
Web Site: www.chinazenith.com.hk
0362—(HKG)
Sls.: $38,355,662
Assets: $525,708,905
Liabilities: $124,369,309
Net Worth: $401,339,596
Earnings: ($41,895,468)
Emp.: 866
Fiscal Year-end: 06/30/13
Business Description:
Chemical Mfr & Sales
S.I.C.: 2869
N.A.I.C.S.: 325199
Personnel:
Yuk Foebe Chan *(Chm & CEO)*
Chiu Hung Tsang *(CFO & Sec)*
Jianwei Wu *(COO)*
Board of Directors:
Yuk Foebe Chan
Che Kong Chiau
Bryan Wing Yun Ma
Zhanrong Peng
Ching Ho Tam
Sin Just Wong
Jianwei Wu
Legal Counsel:
Jones Day
29th Floor Edinburgh Tower The Landmark 15 Queen's Road
Central, China (Hong Kong)

HSBC Trustee (Cayman) Limited
HSBC House 68 West Bay Road
PO Box 484
Georgetown, Cayman Islands

Transfer Agents:
Tricor Tengis Limited
22/F Hopewell Centre 183 Queens Road East
Wanchai, China (Hong Kong)

HSBC Trustee (Cayman) Limited
HSBC House 68 West Bay Road
PO Box 484
Georgetown, Cayman Islands

CHINA ZENIX AUTO INTERNATIONAL LIMITED

No 1608 North Circle Road State Highway
Zhangzhou, Fujian, 363000, China
Tel.: (86) 5962600308
Fax: (86) 5962600558
E-Mail: joinsun@zxwheel.com
Web Site: www.zenixauto.com
ZX—(NYSE)
Rev.: $593,775,740
Assets: $657,940,180
Liabilities: $295,809,993
Net Worth: $362,130,186
Earnings: $57,445,243
Emp.: 5,070
Fiscal Year-end: 12/31/12
Business Description:
Steel Wheel Mfr
S.I.C.: 3714
N.A.I.C.S.: 336390
Personnel:
Jianhui Lai *(Chm & CEO)*
Junqiu Gao *(Deputy CEO)*
Martin Cheung *(CFO)*
Guohe Zhang *(CTO)*
Jiangjun Yang *(Chief Production Officer)*
Board of Directors:
Jianhui Lai
Junqiu Gao
William John Sharp
Ian Frances Wade
Yichun Zhang

CHINA ZHENGTONG AUTO SERVICES HOLDINGS LIMITED

(d/b/a ZhengTong Auto)
59 West Third Ring South Road
FengTai District, Beijing, China
Tel.: (86) 10 63829393
Fax: (86) 10 63855726
Web Site: www.zhengtongauto.com
Year Founded: 1999
1728—(HKG)
Sls.: $4,392,113,544
Assets: $2,691,273,553
Liabilities: $1,611,000,308
Net Worth: $1,080,273,245
Earnings: $100,645,930
Emp.: 7,258
Fiscal Year-end: 12/31/12
Business Description:
Car Dealership Owner & Operator
S.I.C.: 5511

N.A.I.C.S.: 441110
Personnel:
Muqing Wang *(Founder)*
Kunpeng Wang *(CEO)*
Zhubo Li *(CFO)*
Wei Li *(COO)*
Guoqing Wang *(Chief HR Officer)*
Xiao Jing Luo *(Sec)*
Board of Directors:
Tao Chen
Zhubo Li
Yongjun Yong Jun Shao
Xiangyong Tan
Kunpeng Wang
Muqing Wang
Kelvin Tin Yau Wong
Yansheng Zhang

Codan Trust Company (Cayman) Limited
Cricket Square Hutchins Drive
PO Box 2681
Georgetown, Grand Cayman, Cayman Islands

Transfer Agent:
Computershare Hong Kong Investor Services Limited
Shops 1712-1716 17th Floor Hopewell Centre
183 Queens Road East
Wanchai, China (Hong Kong)

CHINA ZHONGHUA GEOTECHNICAL ENGINEERING CO., LTD.

(d/b/a CGE)
Aoyu Mansion 2 Jinyuan Road
Daxing Industrial Devel Zone, Beijing, 102600, China
Tel.: (86) 10 61271720
Fax: (86) 10 61271705
E-Mail: cge@cge.com.cn
Web Site: www.cge.com.cn
002542—(SSE)
Emp.: 210
Business Description:
Dynamic Consolidation Foundation Treatment Services
S.I.C.: 1541
N.A.I.C.S.: 236210
Personnel:
Yanwei Wu *(Chm)*

CHINA ZHONGWANG HOLDINGS LIMITED

299 Wensheng Road
Liaoyang, 111003, China
Tel.: (86) 4193688888
Fax: (86) 4194152332
E-Mail: admin@zhongwang.com
Web Site: www.zhongwang.com
1333—(HKG)
Rev.: $2,144,025,455
Assets: $5,345,254,527
Liabilities: $2,564,111,428
Net Worth: $2,781,143,100
Earnings: $287,007,480
Emp.: 5,349
Fiscal Year-end: 12/31/12
Business Description:
Aluminum Products Mfr
S.I.C.: 3355
N.A.I.C.S.: 331318
Personnel:
Zhongtian Liu *(Founder, Chm & Pres)*
Vincent Lap Kei Cheung *(CFO & Co-Sec)*
Changqing Lu *(Co-Sec & VP-Strategic Plng, Capital Ops & Mgmt)*
Board of Directors:
Zhongtian Liu
Yan Chen
Xihui Gou
Roy Wa Kei Lo
Changqing Lu
Ketong Shi
Xianjun Wen
Chun Wa Wong
Hong Zhong
Legal Counsel:
Morrison & Foerster
33/F Edinburgh Tower The Landmark 15 Queen's Road
Central, China (Hong Kong)

Commerce & Finance Law Offices
6F NCI Tower A12 Jianguomenwai Avenue
Beijing, China

Computershare Hong Kong Investor Services Limited
Shops 1712-1716 17th Floor Hopewell Centre
183 Queens Road East
Wanchai, China (Hong Kong)

CHINACACHE INTERNATIONAL HOLDINGS LTD.

Section A Building 3 Dian Tong Creative Square No 7 Jiuxianqiao North
Chaoyang District, Beijing, 100015, China
Tel.: (86) 10 6408 4466
Fax: (86) 10 6437 4251
E-Mail: info@chinacache.com
Web Site: www.chinacache.com
CCIH—(NASDAQ)
Rev.: $129,261,328
Assets: $143,106,377
Liabilities: $37,965,309
Net Worth: $105,141,068
Earnings: ($2,699,020)
Emp.: 900
Fiscal Year-end: 12/31/12
Business Description:
Internet Content & Application Delivery Services
S.I.C.: 7372
N.A.I.C.S.: 511210
Personnel:
Song Wang *(Founder, Chm & CEO)*
Jean Xiaohong Kou *(Co-Founder & Sr VP)*
Ken Zhang *(Pres)*
Jing An *(Acting CFO)*
Board of Directors:
Song Wang
Jean Xiaohong Kou
Duane Ziping Kuang
Bin Laurence
Yunjie Liu
Michael David Ricks

CHINACAST EDUCATION CORPORATION

Suite 08 20th Floor 1 International Financial Centre
1 Harbour View Street
Central, China (Hong Kong)
Tel.: (852) 3960 6506
E-Mail: mjsantos@chinacasteducation.com
Web Site: www.chinacast.com.cn
CAST—(OTC)
Sales Range: $75-99.9 Million
Emp.: 1,600
Business Description:
E-Learning, Post Secondary Education Long Distance, K-12 Education, Vocational Training, Career Training, Enterprise Training & Government Training Services
S.I.C.: 2741
N.A.I.C.S.: 611710
Personnel:
Derek Feng *(Chm & Interim CEO)*
Douglas N. Woodrum *(Interim CFO & Interim Sec)*
Wei Li *(COO)*
Michael J. Santos *(Pres-Intl)*
Board of Directors:
Derek Feng
Stephen Markscheid
Ned L. Sherwood
Daniel Kar Keung Tseung
Douglas N. Woodrum
Subsidiary:

ChinaCast Technology (HK) Limited (1)
Rm C 16/F Hamilton Coml Bldg 558 560 Nathan Rd
Mongkok, Kowloon, China (Hong Kong)
Tel.: (852) 28112389
Fax: (852) 28112973
Telecommunication Network Services
S.I.C.: 4813
N.A.I.C.S.: 517110

CHINA.COM INC.

11/F ING Tower 308 Des Voeux Road Central, China (Hong Kong)
Tel.: (852) 2371 6603
E-Mail: mail@hongkong.com
Web Site: www.inc.china.com
HKM1—(DEU)
Rev.: $18,341,332
Assets: $50,850,788
Liabilities: $6,743,956
Net Worth: $44,106,832
Earnings: $2,677,389
Emp.: 258
Fiscal Year-end: 12/31/12
Business Description:
Directory Publishing Services
S.I.C.: 2741
N.A.I.C.S.: 511140
Personnel:
Simon Kwong Chi Wong *(CEO)*
Partick Yuk Hay Ho *(CFO)*
Chi Wa Chow *(Compliance Officer)*
Chung Yung Cheng *(Gen Counsel & Sec)*
Board of Directors:
Chi Wa Chow
Yun Xu
Honghua Huang
Hongcheng Mao
Jiang Peng
Guilong Wu
Hua Xiao
Xiangrong Zhu

Computershare Hong Kong Investor Services Limited
Shops 1712-1716 17th Floor Hopewell Centre
183 Queens Road East
Wanchai, China (Hong Kong)

Transfer Agents:
HSBC Trustee (Cayman) Limited
HSBC House 68 West Bay Road
PO Box 484
Georgetown, Cayman Islands

Computershare Hong Kong Investor Services Limited
Shops 1712-1716 17th Floor Hopewell Centre
183 Queens Road East
Wanchai, China (Hong Kong)

CHINAEDU CORPORATION

4th Floor-A GeHua Building No 1 Qinglong Hutong
Dongcheng District, Beijing, 100007, China
Tel.: (86) 10 84186655
Fax: (86) 10 83913165
Web Site: www.chinaedu.com
Year Founded: 1999
CEDU—(NASDAQ)
Rev.: $80,068,660
Assets: $197,331,889
Liabilities: $62,769,736
Net Worth: $134,562,153
Earnings: $13,233,635
Emp.: 2,137
Fiscal Year-end: 12/31/12
Business Description:
Online Educational Services
S.I.C.: 9411
N.A.I.C.S.: 923110
Personnel:
Julia Huang *(Chm)*
Shawn Ding *(CEO)*
Simon Mei *(CFO)*
Board of Directors:
Julia Huang
Benjamin Cheng
Shawn Ding
Alfred Min Fan
Zonglian Gu
Tianwen W. Liu
Samuel Yen

CHINALCO YUNNAN COPPER RESOURCES LIMITED

Level 8 320 Adelaide Street
Brisbane, QLD, 4000, Australia
Mailing Address:
GPO Box 216
Brisbane, QLD, 4001, Australia
Tel.: (61) 7 3211 9013
Fax: (61) 7 3010 9001
E-Mail: admin@cycal.com.au
Web Site: www.cycal.com.au
CYU—(ASX)
Rev.: $108,319
Assets: $21,126,218
Liabilities: $1,040,934
Net Worth: $20,085,284
Earnings: ($8,136,975)
Fiscal Year-end: 06/30/13
Business Description:
Mineral Exploration Services
S.I.C.: 1021
N.A.I.C.S.: 212234
Personnel:
Paul Williams *(Mng Dir)*
Paul K. Marshall *(CFO & Sec)*
Board of Directors:
Zhihua Yao
Paul Williams
Robert Zewen Yang
Legal Counsel:
Hopgood Ganim Lawyers
Level 8 Waterfront Place 1 Eagle Street
Brisbane, QLD, 4000, Australia

CHINANET ONLINE HOLDINGS, INC.

No 3 Min Zhuang Road Building 6 Yu Quan Hui Gu Tuspark
Haidian District, Beijing, China
Tel.: (86) 1051600828
E-Mail: zhanglifeng1@gmail.com
Web Site: www.chinanet-online.com
Year Founded: 2003
CNET—(NASDAQ)
Sls.: $46,600,000
Assets: $56,918,000
Liabilities: $12,073,000
Net Worth: $44,845,000
Earnings: $3,408,000
Emp.: 462
Fiscal Year-end: 12/31/12
Business Description:
Holding Company; Full-Service Media Development & Advertising Services
S.I.C.: 6719
N.A.I.C.S.: 551112
Personnel:
Handong Cheng *(Chm, Pres & CEO)*
Zhige Zhang *(CFO & Treas)*
George Kai Chu *(COO)*
Zhenghong Yang *(CTO)*
Board of Directors:
Handong Cheng
Zhiqing Chen
Douglas C. MacLellan
Mototake Watanabe
Zhige Zhang

CHINANETCENTER CO., LTD.

Rm 5M Tower A Guomen Bldg
Sanyuan Bridge East 3rd Ring Rd
Chaoyang Dist, Beijing, 100028, China

ChinaNetCenter Co., Ltd.—(Continued)

Tel.: (86) 1084519900
Fax: (86) 1084515152
E-Mail: ibs@chinanetcenter.com
Web Site: www.chinanetcenter.com
Year Founded: 2000
300017—(CHIN)
Sales Range: $50-74.9 Million
Emp.: 582
Business Description:
Online Business Solutions
S.I.C.: 7379
N.A.I.C.S.: 518210
Personnel:
Cheng Yan Liu *(CEO)*

CHINASOFT INTERNATIONAL LTD.

Room 4607-8 46/F Cosco Tower 183 Queens Road
Central, China (Hong Kong)
Tel.: (852) 2915 2830
Fax: (852) 2915 2285
E-Mail: carol@chinasofti.com
Web Site: www.chinasofti.com
0354—(HKG)
Sls.: $439,723,963
Assets: $546,817,298
Liabilities: $219,223,643
Net Worth: $327,593,655
Earnings: $23,850,057
Emp.: 18,946
Fiscal Year-end: 12/31/12
Business Description:
Information Technology Outsourcing Services & Software
S.I.C.: 7379
N.A.I.C.S.: 541519
Personnel:
Yuhong Chen *(Chm, CEO & Compliance Officer)*
Frank Waung *(CFO)*
Simon Chung *(COO)*
Hui Wang *(Chief Strategic Officer & Sr VP)*
Simon Zhang *(Chief HR Officer & Sr VP)*
Shenyao Han *(CEO-Pro Svcs & Sr VP)*
William Ming Fuk Fok *(Sec)*
Zhenming Tang *(Sr VP)*
Board of Directors:
Yuhong Chen
Sam Goodner
Xiaohai Jiang
Patrick Wing Yin Leung
Sheng Lin
Lipu Shen
Jun Song
Zhenming Tang
Hui Wang
Zeshan Xu
Zhijie Zeng
Yaqin Zhang
John Ling Huan Zhao

Computershare Hong Kong Investor Services Limited
46th Floor Hopewell Centre 183 Queen's Road East
Wanchai, China (Hong Kong)
Transfer Agents:
Royal Bank of Canada Trust Company (Cayman) Limited
4th Floor Royal Bank House 24 Shedden Road
Georgetown, Cayman Islands

Computershare Hong Kong Investor Services Limited
46th Floor Hopewell Centre 183 Queen's Road East
Wanchai, China (Hong Kong)

Subsidiaries:

Chinasoft Resource (International) Limited (1)
Unit 333 1st FL Core Bldg 2
Central, China (Hong Kong)
Tel.: (852) 24432790
Fax: (852) 29446870
E-Mail: wingtam@chinasoftinc.com
Web Site: www.chinasoft-resource.com
Emp.: 10
IT Outsourcing Services
S.I.C.: 8742
N.A.I.C.S.: 541613

U.S. Subsidiary:

Chinasoft International Inc. (1)
2535 152nd Ave NE Ste B2
Redmond, WA 98052
Tel.: (425) 296-6253
Fax: (425) 883-0246
E-Mail: hr@chinasoftus.com
Web Site: www.chinasoftus.com
Emp.: 35
IT Outsourcing Services
S.I.C.: 8742
N.A.I.C.S.: 541613
Al Buckingham *(VP)*

Non-U.S. Subsidiaries:

Beijing Chinasoft International Education Technology Co., Ltd. (1)
N Wing 15 F Raycom Infotech Park Tower C No 2 Kexueyuan Nanlu
Haidian District, Beijing, 100190, China
Tel.: (86) 10 82862006
Fax: (86) 10 82862809
Web Site: www.chinasofti.com
Training & Outsourcing Services
S.I.C.: 8299
N.A.I.C.S.: 611710

Chinasoft International (Guang Zhou) Information Technology Limited (1)
Unit B F 16 Gaosheng Bldg No 109 Tiyu W Rd
Guangzhou, 510620, China
Tel.: (86) 2038792990
Fax: (86) 2038785271
E-Mail: liyp@chinasofti.com
Emp.: 50
IT Consulting & Training Services
S.I.C.: 8742
N.A.I.C.S.: 541613

CS&S Cyber Resources Software Technology (Tianjin) Co., Ltd. (1)
4 F Xinzheng Bldg 1 Changwa Zhonglu
Haidian, Beijing, 100089, China
Tel.: (86) 1059715666
Fax: (86) 1062186582
Web Site: www.chinasoftinc.com
IT Outsourcing Services
S.I.C.: 8742
N.A.I.C.S.: 541613
Flora Wang *(Mgr-Bus Dev)*

Dalian Xinhua Infotech Co., Ltd (1)
601 No.5 Software Park E Rd
Dalian, 116023, China
Tel.: (86) 41184760101
Fax: (86) 411 84760108
E-Mail: info@digittime.com
Web Site: www.digittime.com
Emp.: 600
Business & Engineering Process Outsourcing Services
S.I.C.: 7389
N.A.I.C.S.: 561499
Fan Yang *(Gen Mgr)*

Shanghai Chinasoft Resources Information Technology Services Limited (1)
Ln 879 Zhongjiang Rd 4th Fl Bldg 15
Shanghai, 200333, China
Tel.: (86) 2152829078
Fax: (86) 2152807506
E-Mail: jack_huang@chinasoftinc.com
Web Site: www.chinasoft-resource.com
Emp.: 1,300
IT Training & Outsourcing Services
S.I.C.: 8299
N.A.I.C.S.: 611710
Celina Shen *(Mgr)*

Shanghai Huateng Software Systems Co., Ltd. (1)
11 F No 481 Hongcao Rd
Shanghai, 200233, China (91.22%)
Tel.: (86) 2151751660
Fax: (86) 2151751661
Web Site: www.huateng.com
Application Software Development Services
S.I.C.: 7371
N.A.I.C.S.: 541511
Shenyao Han *(Pres & CEO)*

CHINATRUST FINANCIAL HOLDING CO., LTD.

(Name Changed to CTBC Financial Holding Co., Ltd.)

CHINAVISION MEDIA GROUP LIMITED

33/F Far East Finance Centre No 16 Harcourt Road
Admiralty, Hong Kong, China (Hong Kong)
Tel.: (852) 39718888
Fax: (852) 39718800
Web Site: www.chinavision.hk
1060—(HKG)
Rev.: $131,075,870
Assets: $271,522,020
Liabilities: $97,240,034
Net Worth: $174,281,986
Earnings: $23,221,316
Emp.: 1,700
Fiscal Year-end: 12/31/12
Business Description:
Holding Company
S.I.C.: 6719
N.A.I.C.S.: 551112
Personnel:
Ping Dong *(Chm & Acting CEO)*
Qing Hai Ng *(Pres)*
Fuk Tak Lam *(CFO)*
Ada Ching Man Fung *(Sec)*
Board of Directors:
Ping Dong
Ching Chen
Hui Zhi Jin
Muk Yin Kong
Chak Hung Li
Qing Hai Ng
Chao Zhao

Butterfield Fulcrum Group (Bermuda) Limited
26 Burnaby Street
Hamilton, HM 11, Bermuda
Transfer Agents:
Tricor Secretaries Limited
26th Floor Tesbury Centre 28 Queen's Road East
Wanchai, China (Hong Kong)

Butterfield Fulcrum Group (Bermuda) Limited
26 Burnaby Street
Hamilton, HM 11, Bermuda

Boardroom Corporate & Advisory Services Pte. Ltd.
50 Raffles Place 32-01 Singapore Land Tower
Singapore, Singapore

CHINESE ESTATES HOLDINGS LIMITED

26/F MassMutual Tower 38 Gloucester Rd
Wanchai, China (Hong Kong)
Tel.: (852) 28666999
Fax: (852) 28662822
E-Mail: contactus@chineseestates.com
Web Site: www.chineseestates.com
0127—(HKG OTC)
Sales Range: $300-349.9 Million
Emp.: 331
Business Description:
Real Estate Investment, Brokerage & Development Services
S.I.C.: 6726
N.A.I.C.S.: 525990
Personnel:
Ming-Wai Lau *(Chm & Acting CEO)*
Kwong-wai Lam *(Sec & Controller-Fin)*
Board of Directors:
Ming-Wai Lau
Kwok-wai Chan
Amy Yuk-Wai Lau
Phillis Lai-ping Loh
Tsz-chun Ma
Transfer Agent:
Butterfield Fulcrum Group (Bermuda) Limited
Rosebank Centre 11 Bermudiana Rd
Pembroke, Bermuda
Subsidiaries:

Chinese Estates (Harcourt House) Limited (1)
26th Fl Mass Mutual Tower
38 Gloucester Rd, Wanchai, China (Hong Kong)
Tel.: (852) 28655266
Fax: (852) 28662822
Real Estate Property Leasing Services
S.I.C.: 6513
N.A.I.C.S.: 531110
Matthew Cheong *(Gen Mgr)*

Chinese Estates Limited (1)
26 F Massmutual Tower 38 Gloucester Rd
Hong Kong, China (Hong Kong)
Tel.: (852) 28666999
Fax: (852) 28662833
Web Site: www.chineseestates.com
Emp.: 250
Property Investment Managing Services
S.I.C.: 6726
N.A.I.C.S.: 525990
Matthew Cheong *(Mng Dir)*

Dollar Union Limited (1)
26 F MassMutual Tower 38 Gloucester Rd
Wanchai, China (Hong Kong)
Tel.: (852) 28666999
Fax: (852) 28615881
Web Site: www.chineseestate.com
Real Estate Agency & Brokerage Services
S.I.C.: 6531
N.A.I.C.S.: 531210

The House of Kwong Sang Hong Limited (1)
G F MassMutual Tower 38 Gloucester Rd
Wanchai, China (Hong Kong)
Tel.: (852) 28615808
Fax: (852) 28451102
E-Mail: twogirlsclub@ksh.com.hk
Web Site: www.twogirls.hk
Cosmetics Distr
S.I.C.: 5122
N.A.I.C.S.: 446120
Sue Chan *(Mgr)*

Speed Win Limited (1)
26 F MassMutual Tower 38 Gloucester Rd
Wanchai, China (Hong Kong)
Tel.: (852) 28666999
Fax: (852) 28615818
Emp.: 300
Property Development Services
S.I.C.: 6531
N.A.I.C.S.: 531311

CHINESE GLOBAL INVESTORS GROUP LTD.

(d/b/a CGI Group)
3 Shenton Way 11-10 Shenton House
Singapore, 068805, Singapore
Tel.: (65) 6438 2286
Fax: (65) 6438 9789
Web Site: www.chineseglobalinvestors.com
5CJ—(CAT)
Rev.: $9,545,477
Assets: $13,093,738
Liabilities: $6,203,231
Net Worth: $6,890,507
Earnings: ($890,025)
Emp.: 149
Fiscal Year-end: 06/30/13
Business Description:
Building Protection, Restoration & Waterproofing Systems Mfr
S.I.C.: 7349
N.A.I.C.S.: 561790
Personnel:
Kemmy Koh *(CFO)*
Benny Heng Chong Lim *(Co-Sec)*
Wai Cheong Low *(Co-Sec)*

Board of Directors:
Henry Poy-Wu Chin
Yong Cao
Tian Huat Ng
Yuen Chun So
Tua Ba Tee
Keng Tin U

CHINESE MARITIME TRANSPORT LTD.

Chinese Maritime Building 15 JiNan Road Sect 1
Taipei, 10051, Taiwan
Tel.: (886) 223963282
Fax: (886) 223916165
E-Mail: cmt@agcmt.com.tw
Web Site: www.cmt.tw
2612—(TAI)
Rev.: $124,028,011
Assets: $762,044,551
Liabilities: $431,492,115
Net Worth: $330,552,436
Earnings: $19,401,007
Emp.: 427
Fiscal Year-end: 12/31/12
Business Description:
Inland Container Transportation Services
S.I.C.: 3621
N.A.I.C.S.: 335312
Personnel:
John Y. K. Peng *(Chm)*
Muh-Haur Jou *(Vice Chm)*

Subsidiary:

CMT Logistics Co., Ltd. **(1)**
No 27 Tsao Nan Pohsia
Puhsin, Yang-mei, Taoyuan, 326, Taiwan
Tel.: (886) 223936242
Fax: (886) 223413539
E-Mail: loiaowh@cntl.com.tw
Web Site: www.agcnt.com.tw
Emp.: 100
Warehousing & Logistics Services
S.I.C.: 4225
N.A.I.C.S.: 493110
Y. M. Wang *(VP)*

Non-U.S. Subsidiaries:

Chinese Maritime Transport (Hong Kong), Limited **(1)**
Rm 2202C 22th Fl Fairmont House 8 Cotton Tree Dr
Central, China (Hong Kong)
Tel.: (852) 28277928
Fax: (852) 28277818
Web Site: www.agcmt.com.tw
Emp.: 10
Management Services
S.I.C.: 8741
N.A.I.C.S.: 551114
Emily Tam *(Office Mgr)*

Chinese Maritime Transport (S) Pte. Ltd. **(1)**
111 North Bridge Road 20-05 Peninsula Plaza
Singapore, Singapore 179098
Tel.: (65) 6 337 6556
Fax: (65) 6 337 4266
Marine Shipping Services
S.I.C.: 4499
N.A.I.C.S.: 488330

CHINESE PEOPLE HOLDINGS COMPANY LIMITED

Unit 1101 11th Floor Tung Ning Building 2 Hillier Street
Central, China (Hong Kong)
Tel.: (852) 29022008
Fax: (852) 28030108
E-Mail: info@681hk.com
Web Site: www.681hk.com
0681—(HKG)
Sls.: $195,860,737
Assets: $292,548,994
Liabilities: $108,212,132
Net Worth: $184,336,862
Earnings: ($51,782,580)
Emp.: 3,400
Fiscal Year-end: 03/31/13
Business Description:
Natural Gas Sales
S.I.C.: 1311
N.A.I.C.S.: 211111
Personnel:
Shikang Mo *(Chm)*
Hesheng Zhang *(Deputy Chm)*
Song Jin *(Mng Dir)*
Fun Replen Li *(Sec)*
Board of Directors:
Shikang Mo
Peleus Kin Wang Chu
Song Jin
Jialin Li
Junmin Liu
Ka Man Sin
Qinglian Tan
Ruixin Xu
Hesheng Zhang
Yanyun Zhao

The Bank of Bermuda Limited
6 Front Street
Hamilton, HM 11, Bermuda

Transfer Agents:
Tricor Tengis Limited
26/F Tesbury Centre, 28 Queens Road East
Hong Kong, China (Hong Kong)

The Bank of Bermuda Limited
6 Front Street
Hamilton, HM 11, Bermuda

CHINESEWORLDNET.COM INC.

Suite 368 1199 West Pender Street
Vancouver, BC, V6E 2R1, Canada
Tel.: (604) 488-8878
Fax: (604) 488-0868
Web Site: www.chineseworldnet.com
Year Founded: 2000
CWNOF—(OTC)
Rev.: $1,243,638
Assets: $2,571,264
Liabilities: $546,060
Net Worth: $2,025,204
Earnings: ($128,931)
Emp.: 23
Fiscal Year-end: 12/31/12
Business Description:
Online Translation Services
S.I.C.: 2741
N.A.I.C.S.: 519130
Personnel:
Joe Kin Foon Tai *(Pres & CEO)*
Kelvin Fu Szeto *(CFO & COO)*
Chi Cheong Liu *(Treas)*
Gilbert Chan *(Sr VP-Mktg & IR)*
Board of Directors:
Andy Siu Wing Lam
Chi Cheong Liu
Chi Kong Liu
Joe Kin Foon Tai

CHINHUNG INTERNATIONAL (INC.)

807 69 Convensia-daero
Yeongsu-gu, Incheon, Korea (South)
Tel.: (82) 32 432 0658
Fax: (82) 32 432 0659
Web Site: www.chinhung.co.kr
Year Founded: 1959
002780—(KRS)
Business Description:
Construction Engineering Services
S.I.C.: 8711
N.A.I.C.S.: 541330
Personnel:
Cheon Su Cha *(CEO)*

CHINLINK INTERNATIONAL HOLDINGS LIMITED

7 F Two Exchange Square 8 Connaught Place
Central, China (Hong Kong)
Tel.: (852) 21680777
Fax: (852) 21680780
E-Mail: decca@decca.com.hk
Web Site: www.decca.com.hk
0997—(HKG)
Rev.: $20,808,017
Assets: $23,888,374
Liabilities: $18,747,654
Net Worth: $5,140,721
Earnings: ($2,894,412)
Emp.: 45
Fiscal Year-end: 03/31/13
Business Description:
Conglomerates & Holding Companies
S.I.C.: 6719
N.A.I.C.S.: 551112
Personnel:
Weibin Li *(Chm & Mng Dir)*
Shirley Suk Ling Lam *(CFO & Sec)*
Board of Directors:
Weibin Li
Irene Sim Ling Chan
Sau Mui Fung
May Ka Fung Lai
Shirley Suk Ling Lam
Chi Kit Lau
Wai Yip Siu
Legal Counsel:
DLP Piper
Hong Kong, China (Hong Kong)

HSBC Securities Services (Bermuda) Limited
6 Front Street
Hamilton, Bermuda

Transfer Agents:
Tricor Standard Limited
26/F Tesbury Centre 28 Queen's Road East
Wanchai, China (Hong Kong)
Tel.: (852) 2980 1333
Fax: (852) 2810 8185

HSBC Securities Services (Bermuda) Limited
6 Front Street
Hamilton, Bermuda

CHINO CORPORATION

32-8 Kumano-Cho
Itabashi-Ku, Tokyo, 173-8632, Japan
Tel.: (81) 3 3956 2171
Fax: (81) 3 3956 0915
E-Mail: inter@chino.co.jp
Web Site: www.chino.co.jp
Year Founded: 1913
6850—(TKS)
Emp.: 505
Business Description:
Controlling Equipment Mfr & Whslr
S.I.C.: 3823
N.A.I.C.S.: 334513
Personnel:
Takao Kariya *(Pres)*

CHINOOK ENERGY INC.

Suite 700 700 - 2nd Street SW
Calgary, AB, T2P 2W1, Canada
Tel.: (403) 261-6883
Fax: (403) 266-1814
E-Mail: info@chinookenergyinc.com
Web Site: www.chinookenergyinc.com
CKE—(TSX)
Rev.: $192,636,106
Assets: $618,753,594
Liabilities: $277,206,334
Net Worth: $341,547,260
Earnings: ($90,483,653)
Emp.: 119
Fiscal Year-end: 12/31/12
Business Description:
Oil & Gas Exploration Services
S.I.C.: 1311
N.A.I.C.S.: 211111
Personnel:
Matthew Joseph Brister *(Chm & CEO)*
Walter J. Vrataric *(Pres)*
L. Geoffrey Barlow *(CFO & VP-Fin)*
Fred Davidson *(Sec)*
Board of Directors:
Matthew Joseph Brister
Donald Archibald
John A. Brussa
Stuart G. Clark
Robert C. Cook
Robert J. Herdman
Townes Pressler, Jr.
P. Grant Wierzba
Legal Counsel:
Burnet, Duckworth & Palmer LLP
Calgary, AB, Canada
Transfer Agent:
Alliance Trust Company
Calgary, AB, Canada

CHINOOK INDUSTRIAL LTD.

516 60 Avenue SE
Calgary, AB, T2H 0P9, Canada
Tel.: (403) 253-8291
Fax: (403) 255-5565
Web Site: www.chinook.ca
Rev.: $16,954,265
Emp.: 65
Business Description:
Industrial Products Mfr
S.I.C.: 3563
N.A.I.C.S.: 333912
Personnel:
Bill Bracko *(Pres)*

CHINT GROUP CORP.

CHINT High-Tech Industrial Zone
North Baixiang, Wenzhou, Zhejiang, 325603, China
Tel.: (86) 57762777777
Fax: (86) 577 62775769
E-Mail: global-sales@chint.com
Web Site: www.chint.com
Sales Range: $1-4.9 Billion
Emp.: 18,000
Business Description:
Holding Company; Power & Transmission Products Mfr
S.I.C.: 6719
N.A.I.C.S.: 551112
Personnel:
Cunhui Nan *(Chm & CEO)*

Subsidiary:

Zhejiang CHINT Electrics Co., Ltd. **(1)**
1255 Wenhe Road
Songjiang District, Shanghai, 201614, China
Tel.: (86) 2167777777
Fax: (86) 21 6777 7999
E-Mail: zyin@chint.com
Web Site: www.chintelectric.com
601877—(SHG)
Sales Range: $500-549.9 Million
Emp.: 4,300
Power Transmission & Distribution Products Mfr
S.I.C.: 3612
N.A.I.C.S.: 335311
Cunhui Nan *(Chm)*

CHINTZ & COMPANY

1720 Store St
Victoria, BC, V8W 1V5, Canada
Tel.: (250) 388-0996
E-Mail: info@chintz.com
Web Site: www.chintz.com
Rev.: $14,615,598
Emp.: 200
Business Description:
Home Furnishing Stores
S.I.C.: 5719
N.A.I.C.S.: 442299
Personnel:
Nicole Degoutiere *(Owner)*

CHINVEST SAS
(d/b/a Chazelles)
Route de Marthon
16380 Chazelles-sur-Lyon, France
Tel.: (33) 545235050
Fax: (33) 545235309
E-Mail: anso@chazelles.com
Web Site: www.chazelles.com
Year Founded: 1979
Sales Range: $10-24.9 Million
Emp.: 130
Business Description:
Fireplaces, Inserts, Stoves & Barbecues Mfr & Distr
S.I.C.: 3433
N.A.I.C.S.: 333414
Personnel:
Dominique Combeau *(Chm & Pres)*

CHINYANG CHEMICAL CORPORATION
300-1 Yeocheondong
Namgu, Ulsan, Korea (South)
Tel.: (82) 52 278 0701
Fax: (82) 52 278 0848
E-Mail: export@cycc.co.kr
Web Site: www.chinyang.co.kr
Year Founded: 1963
051630—(KRS)
Emp.: 185
Business Description:
Polyvinyl Chloride Product Mfr
S.I.C.: 2821
N.A.I.C.S.: 325211
Personnel:
Jin-Ug Jeung *(Co-CEO)*
Gyu-Ho Lim *(Co-CEO)*

CHIOME BIOSCIENCE INC.
Sumitomo Fudosan Nishi-shinjuku Bldg No 6 3-12-1 Honmachi
Shibuya-ku, Tokyo, 151-0071, Japan
Tel.: (81) 3 63833561
Web Site: www.chiome.co.jp
Year Founded: 2005
4583—(TKS)
Sls.: $3,565,397
Assets: $14,264,074
Liabilities: $2,847,240
Net Worth: $11,416,834
Earnings: ($4,695,790)
Emp.: 32
Fiscal Year-end: 03/31/13
Business Description:
Pharmaceutical Mfr
S.I.C.: 2834
N.A.I.C.S.: 325412
Personnel:
Masa Fujiwara *(CEO)*
Board of Directors:
Masa Fujiwara
Tsutomu Kawaguchi
Keiichi Kiyota
Shigeru Kobayashi
Kunihiro Ohta

CHIP ENG SENG CORPORATION LTD.
69 Ubi Crescent 06-01
Singapore, 408561, Singapore
Tel.: (65) 68480848
Fax: (65) 68480838
E-Mail: enquiry@chipengseng.com.sg
Web Site: www.chipengseng.com.sg
Year Founded: 1998
C29—(SES)
Rev.: $499,679,438
Assets: $935,646,776
Liabilities: $562,801,281
Net Worth: $372,845,495
Earnings: $65,804,313
Emp.: 700
Fiscal Year-end: 12/31/12
Business Description:
Building Construction & Real Estate Management
S.I.C.: 1542
N.A.I.C.S.: 236220
Personnel:
Tiam Seng Lim *(Chm)*
Raymond Lee Meng Chia *(Deputy Chm & CEO)*
Tiang Chuan Lim *(Deputy Chm)*
Siang Thong Yeo *(Mng Dir)*
Beng Chuan Lim *(CFO)*
Abdul Jabbar Karam Din *(Co-Sec)*
Lee Eng Loh *(Co-Sec)*
Board of Directors:
Tiam Seng Lim
Mong Seng Ang
Heng Tan Cheng
Raymond Lee Meng Chia
Chee Wee Goh
Tai Meng Hoon
Dawn Sock Kiang Lim
Tiang Chuan Lim

Subsidiaries:

ACP Metal Finishing Pte Ltd **(1)**
No 6 Joo Koon Circle
629037 Singapore, Singapore
Tel.: (65) 68638318
Fax: (65) 68622989
Web Site: www.acpanode.com.sg
Emp.: 150
Metal Service Centers
S.I.C.: 5051
N.A.I.C.S.: 423510
Chan Seng Koh *(Mgr-Mktg)*

CEL Development Pte. Ltd. **(1)**
69 Ubi Crescent 01-01
Singapore, 408561, Singapore
Tel.: (65) 65000065
Fax: (65) 65000064
E-Mail: cel.marketing@chipengseng.com.sg
Web Site: www.celdevelopment.com.sg
Residential Property Development Services
S.I.C.: 1522
N.A.I.C.S.: 236116
Raymond Lee Meng Chia *(CEO)*

CES Engineering & Construction Pte. Ltd **(1)**
69 Ubi Crescent 06-01 Ces Bldg
Singapore, 408561, Singapore
Tel.: (65) 68480848
Fax: (65) 68480838
Property Development Services
S.I.C.: 1522
N.A.I.C.S.: 236116
Siang Thong Yeo *(Mng Dir)*

CES Land Pte. Ltd. **(1)**
69 Ubi Crescent 06-01 Ces Building
Singapore, 408561, Singapore
Tel.: (65) 65000065
Fax: (65) 65000066
E-Mail: enquiries@chipengseng.com.sg
Web Site: www.chipengseng.com.sg
Property Development Services
S.I.C.: 1542
N.A.I.C.S.: 236220

CES-Precast Pte. Ltd. **(1)**
3 Tampines Industrial Street 61
Singapore, 528816, Singapore
Tel.: (65) 65828488
Fax: (65) 65831028
Emp.: 25
Precast Products Mfr & Distr
S.I.C.: 3272
N.A.I.C.S.: 327390
Chin Hah Koh *(Gen Mgr)*

Chip Eng Seng Contractors (1988) Pte Ltd. **(1)**
69 Ubi Cres No 06-01 CES Bldg
408561 Singapore, Singapore
Tel.: (65) 68480848
Fax: (65) 68480838
E-Mail: enquiry@chipengseng.com.sg
Web Site: www.chipengseng.com.sg/contact.aspx
Building Construction
S.I.C.: 1542
N.A.I.C.S.: 236220
Siang Thong Yeo *(Mng Dir)*

Subsidiary:

CES Building and Construction Pte Ltd **(2)**
69 Ubi Crescent 06-01 Ces Bldg
Singapore, 408561, Singapore
Tel.: (65) 68480848
Fax: (65) 68480838
E-Mail: enquiry@chipengseng.com.sg
Commercial Property Development Services
S.I.C.: 1542
N.A.I.C.S.: 236220

CHIPITA S.A.
12th km National Road
Metamorphosis, 144 52 Athens, Attica, Greece
Tel.: (30) 210 288 5000
Fax: (30) 2885032
Web Site: www.chipita.com
Business Description:
Cakes, Pastries, Cookies & Bread Chips Mfr & Marketer
S.I.C.: 2099
N.A.I.C.S.: 311999
Personnel:
Spyros Theodoropoulos *(CEO)*

U.S. Subsidiary:

Chipita America, Inc. **(1)**
1 Westbrook Corporate Ctr Ste 640
Westchester, IL 60154-5701 FL
Tel.: (708) 731-2430
Web Site: www.chipita.us.com
Emp.: 60
Soft Croissant Mfr
S.I.C.: 2051
N.A.I.C.S.: 311812
George Chalkias *(Pres & CEO)*
Antonios Pouftis *(CFO)*

Unit:

Chipita America, Inc. - Tulsa **(2)**
601 S Boulder Ave Ste 900
Tulsa, OK 74119
Tel.: (918) 560-4100
Fax: (918) 560-4108
Web Site: www.chipita.us.com
Soft Croissant Mfr
S.I.C.: 2051
N.A.I.C.S.: 311812
Chris Gunsch *(Dir-Mktg)*

CHIPMOS TECHNOLOGIES (BERMUDA) LTD.
No 1 R&D Road 1 Hsinchu Science Park
Hsin-chu, Taiwan
Tel.: (886) 35633988
Fax: (886) 35668981
E-Mail: chipmos_bermuda@chipmos.com.tw
Web Site: www.chipmos.com.tw
Year Founded: 2000
IMOS—(NASDAQ)
Rev.: $651,000,367
Assets: $973,741,941
Liabilities: $432,869,269
Net Worth: $540,872,672
Earnings: $24,448,653
Emp.: 5,629
Fiscal Year-end: 12/31/12
Business Description:
Computer Chip Testing Services
S.I.C.: 3674
N.A.I.C.S.: 334413
Personnel:
Shih Jye Cheng *(Chm & CEO)*
Chin-Shyh Ou *(Deputy Chm)*
Lafair Cho *(Pres)*
Shou-Kang Chen *(CFO)*
Board of Directors:
Shih Jye Cheng
Chin-Shyh Ou
Antonio R. Alvarez
Shou-Kang Chen
Rong Hsu
Cao Rong Tsai
Chao-Jung Tsai
Hsing-Ti Tuan
Yeong-Her Wang
John Woon Seto Yee

Non-U.S. Subsidiary:

ChipMOS Japan Inc. **(1)**
Robot FA Bldg 1-9-1 Nakasa
Mihama-Ku, Chiba, 261-0023, Japan
Tel.: (81) 43 299 6914
Fax: (81) 43 299 6924
E-Mail: ray_lin@cmosj.co.jp
Web Site: www.chipmos.com.tw
Semiconductor & Related Device Mfr
S.I.C.: 3674
N.A.I.C.S.: 334413
Ray Lin *(Gen Mgr)*

U.S. Subsidiary:

ChipMOS U.S.A., Inc. **(1)**
2890 N 1st St
San Jose, CA 95134 (100%)
Tel.: (408) 922-2777
Fax: (408) 922-7275
Web Site: www.chipmos.com.tw
Emp.: 4
Semiconductor & Related Device Mfr
S.I.C.: 3674
N.A.I.C.S.: 334413
Steve Cheng *(Pres)*

Divisions:

ChipMOS Assembly Fab **(1)**
No 5 Nan-Ko Rd 7
Southern Taiwan Science Pk, Taipei, ROC, Taiwan
Tel.: (886) 65052388
Fax: (886) 065052388
Emp.: 3,000
Semiconductor & Related Device Mfr
S.I.C.: 3674
N.A.I.C.S.: 334413

ChipMOS Gold Bumping Fab **(1)**
No 37 Hsin Tai Road
Jhubei, Hsin-chu, 302, Taiwan
Tel.: (886) 36562078
Fax: (886) 55532715
E-Mail: s7898@chipmos.com
Web Site: www.chipmos.com
Emp.: 600
Semiconductor & Related Device Mfr
S.I.C.: 3674
N.A.I.C.S.: 334413

ChipMOS Testing Fab **(1)**
No 1 R and D Road 1
Hsinchu Science Park, Hsin-chu, Taiwan
Tel.: (886) 35770055
Fax: (886) 35668995
E-Mail: Fiyontaih@Choipmos.com
Semiconductor & Related Device Mfr
S.I.C.: 3674
N.A.I.C.S.: 334413

Subsidiary:

ChipMOS Taiwan **(1)**
1 R&D Road 1 Hsinchu Science Park
Hsin-chu, Taiwan
Tel.: (886) 035770055
Fax: (886) 6 505 2336
Web Site: www.chipmos.com
Semiconductor & Related Device Mfr
S.I.C.: 3674
N.A.I.C.S.: 334413
Jeff Chang *(Mng Dir)*

CHIPS&MEDIA, INC.
11/12/13F V&S Building 891-46 55 Daechi-dong
Gangnam-gu, Seoul, 135-502, Korea (South)
Tel.: (82) 2 568 3767
Fax: (82) 2 568 3768
Web Site: www.chipsnmedia.com
Year Founded: 2003
094360—(KRS)
Sales Range: $1-9.9 Million
Emp.: 60
Business Description:
Semiconductor Device Mfr
S.I.C.: 3674
N.A.I.C.S.: 334413

Personnel:
Steve Sang-Hyun Kim *(CEO)*
Gus Ho Lee *(CFO)*
Mickey Min-Yong Jeon *(CTO)*

CHIRANA T. INJECTA, A.S.

Nam Dr A Schweitzera 194
916 01 Stara Tura, Slovakia
Tel.: (421) 327752801
Fax: (421) 327753854
E-Mail: sales@t-injecta.sk
Web Site: www.t-injecta.sk
Year Founded: 1947
Sales Range: $10-24.9 Million
Emp.: 470
Business Description:
Medical Instruments Mfr
S.I.C.: 3841
N.A.I.C.S.: 339112
Personnel:
Gabriela Vdoviakova *(Asst Gen Dir)*

CHIRIPAL INDUSTRIES LTD.

(d/b/a Chiripal Group)
Chiripal House Shivranjani Cross Roads
Satellite, Ahmedabad, Gujarat, 380 015, India
Tel.: (91) 7926734660
Fax: (91) 7926768656
E-Mail: info@chiripalgroup.com
Web Site: www.chiripalgroup.com
Year Founded: 1972
Sales Range: $200-249.9 Million
Emp.: 1,470
Business Description:
Fabric & Textile Mfr & Exporter
S.I.C.: 2299
N.A.I.C.S.: 313310
Personnel:
Vedprakash Chiripal *(Chm & Mng Dir)*
Brijmohan D. Chiripal *(Mng Dir)*
Board of Directors:
Vedprakash Chiripal
Rajesh Bindal
Jaiprakash Chiripal
Jyotiprasad Chiripal

Subsidiary:

Nandan Denim Limited (1)
(Formerly Nandan Exim Limited)
Chirpal House Shivranjani Cross Road Satellite
Ahmedabad, 380015, India
Tel.: (91) 9879 201438
E-Mail: nishant.giri@live.com
Web Site: nandandenim.com
NANDAN—(BOM)
Sales Range: $100-124.9 Million
Emp.: 950
Denim Fabrics Mfr
S.I.C.: 2299
N.A.I.C.S.: 314999
Vedprakash D. Chiripal *(Chm)*
Deepak J. Chiripal *(CEO)*
Brijmohan D. Chiripal *(Mng Dir)*
Purvee D. Roy *(Sec)*

Subsidiary:

CIL Nova Petrochemicals Limited (2)
Survey No 396 P 395/4 P Moraiya Village
Sarkhej - Bavla Highway
Tal Sanad, Ahmedabad, Gujarat, 382 210, India
Tel.: (91) 2717250556
Fax: (91) 2717251612
E-Mail: cs.cilnova@chiripalgroup.com
Web Site: www.chiripalgroup.com
533407—(BOM)
Rev.: $54,943,216
Assets: $32,419,915
Liabilities: $22,949,869
Net Worth: $9,470,047
Earnings: $512,668
Fiscal Year-end: 03/31/13
Petrochemical Products Mfr
S.I.C.: 2869
N.A.I.C.S.: 325110
Vedprakash D. Chiripal *(Compliance Officer)*
Payal Agarwal *(Sec)*

CHITRCHATR COMMUNICATIONS INC.

76 Marlyn Court Northeast
Calgary, AB, T2A 7H5, Canada
Tel.: (702) 475-5636
E-Mail: info@chitrchatr.com
Web Site: www.chitrchatr.com
Year Founded: 2013
CHA—(CNSX)
Business Description:
Software Publisher
S.I.C.: 7372
N.A.I.C.S.: 511210
Personnel:
Rahim Mohamed *(CEO)*

CHITTAGONG STOCK EXCHANGE LTD.

CSE Bldg 1080 Sk Mujib Rd
4100 Chittagong, Agrabad, Bangladesh
Tel.: (880) 31714632
Fax: (880) 88031714101
E-Mail: abs@csebd.com
Web Site: www.cse.com.bd
Emp.: 80
Business Description:
Stock Exchange Services
S.I.C.: 6211
N.A.I.C.S.: 523120
Personnel:
Nasiruddin Ahmed Chowdhury *(Pres)*
Al Maruf Khan *(Pres)*
Syed Sajid Husain *(CEO)*
Board of Directors:
Abu Ahmed
Ali Ahmed
Waliur Rahman Bhuiyan
Bijan Chakroborty
A. Q.I. Chowdhury
Amir Humayun Mahmud Chowdhury
Syed Mahmudul Huq
Rabiul Husain
Morshed Murad Ibrahim
Mirza Salman Ispahani
Tareq Kamal
A. Majeed Khan
Al Maruf Khan
Anis A. Khan
Yasmeen Murshed
A. S. M. Nayeem
Mamun Rashid
Abdul Rauf
Farooq Sobhan

CHIU TING MACHINERY CO., LTD.

80 Yuang Cheng Rad Taiping
41161 Taichung, Taiwan
Tel.: (886) 422792345
Fax: (886) 422737298
E-Mail: mc@geetech.com.tw
Web Site: www.geetech.com.tw
1539—(TAI)
Sales Range: $10-24.9 Million
Business Description:
Machinery & Hardware Components Mfr
S.I.C.: 1796
N.A.I.C.S.: 238290
Personnel:
Po Yen Chuang *(Chm & Gen Mgr)*

U.S. Subsidiary:

Oliver Machinery Co. (1)
6902 S 194th St
Kent, WA 98032
Tel.: (253) 867-0334
Fax: (253) 867-0387
E-Mail: info@olivermachinery.net
Web Site: www.olivermachinery.net
Woodworking Machinery Mfr
S.I.C.: 3554
N.A.I.C.S.: 333243

Non-U.S. Subsidiary:

Chiu Ting Industrial (Huizhou) Co., Ltd. (1)
Yu Fang Industrial Park
Chenjian, Huizhou, Guangdong, 516000, China
Tel.: (86) 7523089556
Fax: (86) 752 308 9558
E-Mail: hzcnc@geetech.com.tw
Web Site: www.cnc-geetech.com
Industrial Machinery Mfr
S.I.C.: 3541
N.A.I.C.S.: 333517

CHIYODA CORPORATION

Minatomirai Grand Central Tower 4-6-2 Minatomirai Nishi-ku
Yokohama, 220-8765, Japan
Tel.: (81) 452257777
Fax: (81) 45 503 0200
E-Mail: chyod@ykh.chiyoda.co.jp
Web Site: www.chiyoda-corp.com
Year Founded: 1948
6366—(OTC TKS)
Sls.: $4,388,098,000
Assets: $4,789,169,000
Liabilities: $2,706,253,000
Net Worth: $2,082,916,000
Earnings: $176,847,000
Emp.: 4,915
Fiscal Year-end: 03/31/13
Business Description:
Construction & Engineering Services
S.I.C.: 1629
N.A.I.C.S.: 236210
Personnel:
Takashi Kubota *(Chm)*
Shogo Shibuya *(Pres & CEO)*
Masahito Kawashima *(CFO & Exec VP)*
Keiichi Nakagaki *(Sr Exec VP & Dir-Corp Plng, Mgmt & Fin Ops-Offshore & Upstream Pr)*
Hiroshi Ogawa *(Sr Exec VP & Dir-Global Project Mgmt Div)*
Katsuo Nagasaka *(Exec VP & Dir-Bus Dev Div)*
Satoru Yokoi *(Exec VP & Dir-Downstream & Non Hydrocarbon Project Ops)*
Mamoru Nakano *(Sr VP, Gen Mgr-Intl Gas & LNG Project Unit & Dir-Gas & LNG Projec)*
Takao Kamiji *(Sr VP & Dir-Infrastructure Project Ops)*
Katsutoshi Kimura *(Sr VP & Dir-Risk Mgmt & CSR Div)*
Masahiko Kojima *(Sr VP & Dir-Corp Plng, Mgmt & Fin Div)*
Hiromi Koshizuka *(Sr VP & Dir-ChAS Project Ops)*
Kenjiro Miura *(Sr VP & Dir-Project Logistics & Construction Div)*
Ryosuke Shimizu *(Sr VP & Dir-Tech & Engrg Div)*
Koichi Shirakawa *(Sr VP & Deputy Dir-Gas & LNG Project Ops)*
Tadashi Izawa *(Sr VP-Bus Dev Div)*
Sumio Nakashima *(Sr VP-Gas & LNG Project Ops)*
Board of Directors:
Takashi Kubota
Masahito Kawashima
Masahiko Kojima
Katsuo Nagasaka
Keiichi Nakagaki
Hiroshi Ogawa
Masaji Santo
Shogo Shibuya
Ryosuke Shimizu

Transfer Agent:
Mitsubishi UFJ Trust & Banking Corporation
1 4 5 Marunouchi Chiyoda ku
Tokyo, 1008212, Japan

Subsidiaries:

Arrow Business Consulting Corporation (1)
432-1 Tsurumichuo 4-Chome
Tsurumi-Ku, Yokohama, Kanagawa, 230-0051, Japan
Tel.: (81) 455025774
Fax: (81) 455025753
Financial & Accounting Consulting Services
S.I.C.: 8721
N.A.I.C.S.: 541219

Arrowhead International Corporation (1)
1-7-8 Shibakoen
Minato-Ku, Tokyo, 105-0011, Japan
Tel.: (81) 354700880
Fax: (81) 0354700890
E-Mail: infomed@arrowhead.co.jp
Web Site: www.arrowhead.co.jp
Emp.: 54
Air Cargo Services
S.I.C.: 4522
N.A.I.C.S.: 481212
Naomitsu Wakame *(Pres)*

Chiyoda Advanced Solutions Corporation (1)
Technowave 100 Building 1-25 Shin-Urashima-Cho 1-chome
Kanagawa-Ku, Yokohama, Kanagawa, 221-0031, Japan
Tel.: (81) 454411260
Fax: (81) 454411264
Web Site: www.chiyoda-as.co.jp
Engineering Consulting Services
S.I.C.: 8711
N.A.I.C.S.: 541330
Masahiro Watanabe *(Pres & CEO)*

Chiyoda Keiso Co., Ltd. (1)
3-13 Moriya-Cho Kanagawa-Ku Yokohama-Shi
Yokohama, Kanagawa, 221-0022, Japan
Tel.: (81) 45 441 9600
Fax: (81) 45 441 1434
Web Site: www.cst.chiyoda.co.jp
Oil & Gas Field Construction Services
S.I.C.: 1389
N.A.I.C.S.: 213112

Chiyoda Kosho Co., Ltd. (1)
34-26 Tsurumichuo 4-Chome
Tsurumi-Ku Yokohama, Yokohama, Kanagawa, 230 0051, Japan
Tel.: (81) 455067662
Fax: (81) 455067667
Construction Engineering Services
S.I.C.: 8711
N.A.I.C.S.: 541330

Chiyoda TechnoAce Co., Ltd. (1)
3-13 Moriya-cho Kanagawa-Ku Yokohama-shi
Yokohama, 221-0022, Japan
Tel.: (81) 4 54419600
Fax: (81) 4 54505236
Web Site: www.cta.chiyoda.co.jp
Emp.: 100
Construction Engineering Services
S.I.C.: 8711
N.A.I.C.S.: 541330
Ishiwatari Takao *(Pres)*

Chiyoda U-Tech Co., Ltd. (1)
4-32-1 Tsurumichuo
Tsurumi-Ku, Yokohama, 230-0051, Japan
Tel.: (81) 455027618
Fax: (81) 455035399
E-Mail: utc@utc-yokohama.com
Web Site: www.utc-yokohama.com
Emp.: 200
Software Consulting Services
S.I.C.: 7373
N.A.I.C.S.: 541512
Ishyama Tatsuo *(Mgr)*

IT Engineering Limited (1)
1 25 Shinurashima-cho 1-Chome
Kanagawa-Ku, Yokohama, 221-0031, Japan
Tel.: (81) 454419123
Fax: (81) 454411466

Chiyoda Corporation—(Continued)

Web Site: www.ite.co.jp
Information Technology Consulting Services
S.I.C.: 7373
N.A.I.C.S.: 541512

U.S. Subsidiary:

Chiyoda International Corporation **(1)**
1177 W Loop S Ste 680
Houston, TX 77027
Tel.: (713) 965-9005
Fax: (713) 965-0075
E-Mail: sstrobel@chiyoda-us.com
Web Site: www.chiyoda-us.com
Emp.: 2
Construction & Engineering Services
S.I.C.: 1629
N.A.I.C.S.: 236210
Koji Okamoto *(Dir-Sls & Mktg)*

Non-U.S. Subsidiaries:

Chiyoda Almana Engineering LLC **(1)**
12th Floor Al-Qassar Tower Taawon Street
West Bay
PO Box 22961
Doha, Qatar
Tel.: (974) 44074666
Fax: (974) 44074650
E-Mail:
Web Site: www.chiyoda-almana.com
Emp.: 300
Construction Engineering Services
S.I.C.: 8711
N.A.I.C.S.: 541330
Kazumi Ikeda *(Mng Dir)*

Chiyoda & Public Works Co., Ltd. **(1)**
Room 308-309 Sedona Hotel No 1 Kaba Aye Pagoda Road
Yankin Township, Yangon, Myanmar
Tel.: (95) 1 545605
Fax: (95) 1 545227
E-Mail: yanmon-cpw@wimaxmail.net.mm
Web Site: www.chiyoda-corp.com
Emp.: 13
Industrial Facilities Design & Construction Services
S.I.C.: 1629
N.A.I.C.S.: 236210
Daniel Tin *(Gen Mgr)*

Chiyoda Corporation (Shanghai) **(1)**
Room 606 UC Tower No 500 Fushan Road
Pu Dong New Area
Shanghai, 200122, China
Tel.: (86) 2168761500
Fax: (86) 2168761300
Industrial Facilities Design & Construction Services
S.I.C.: 1623
N.A.I.C.S.: 237130

Chiyoda do Brasil Representacoes Ltda. **(1)**
Praia de Botafogo 228 Sala 501
22250-040 Botafogo, Rio de Janeiro, Brazil
Tel.: (55) 2137388280
Fax: (55) 2137386835
E-Mail: tomoyuki.tsukamoto@chiyoda-corp.com
Web Site: www.chiyoda-corp.com
Emp.: 2
Oil & Gas Field Engineering Services
S.I.C.: 1389
N.A.I.C.S.: 213112
Tomoyuki Tsukamoto *(Mgr)*

Chiyoda Malaysia Sdn. Bhd. **(1)**
15th Floor Menara Maxisegar Jalan Pandan Indah 4/2
Pandan Indah, 55100 Kuala Lumpur, Malaysia
Tel.: (60) 3 4297 0988
Fax: (60) 3 4297 0800
E-Mail: chiyoda@chiyoda.com.my
Web Site: www.chiyoda.com.my
Construction Engineering Services
S.I.C.: 8711
N.A.I.C.S.: 541330

Chiyoda Oceania Pty Limited **(1)**
Level 28 AMP Tower 140 St Georges Terrace
Perth, WA, 6000, Australia
Tel.: (61) 892782599
Fax: (61) 892782727
Web Site: www.chiyoda-corp.com
Emp.: 1
Industrial Facilities Design & Construction Services
S.I.C.: 1629
N.A.I.C.S.: 236210
Yasuji Ichinose *(Mgr-Bus Dev)*

Chiyoda Philippines Corporation. **(1)**
15 22F Sun Plz Bldg 1507 Shaw Blvd Cor Princeton St
Barangay Wack-Wack, 1555 Mandaluyong, Philippines
Tel.: (63) 25717596
Fax: (63) 25717599
Web Site: www.chiyodaphil.com.ph
Emp.: 625
Civil Engineering Services
S.I.C.: 8711
N.A.I.C.S.: 541330
Haruki Yoshiike *(Mgr-HR)*

Chiyoda Singapore (Pte) Limited **(1)**
14 International Business Park
Jurong East, Singapore, Singapore
Tel.: (65) 65633488
Fax: (65) 65675231
Web Site: www.chiyoda.com.sg
Emp.: 180
Construction & Engineering Services
S.I.C.: 1541
N.A.I.C.S.: 236210

Chiyoda (Thailand) Limited **(1)**
140/42 ITF Tower II 20th Floor Silom Road
Kwaeng Suriyawong
Khet Bangrak, Bangkok, 10500, Thailand
Tel.: (66) 22316441
Fax: (66) 22316443
Web Site: www.chiyoda-corp.com
Emp.: 10
Industrial Facilities Design & Construction Services
S.I.C.: 1623
N.A.I.C.S.: 237130
Tatsuo Iwaizumi *(Deputy Mng Dir)*

PT. Chiyoda International Indonesia **(1)**
9th Floor Mid-Plaza Building Jalan Jenderal Sudirman Kav 10-11
10220 Jakarta, Indonesia
Tel.: (62) 215704693
Fax: (62) 215735723
Web Site: www.chiyoda-corp.com
Emp.: 9
Construction Engineering Services
S.I.C.: 8711
N.A.I.C.S.: 541330
Kimiho Sakurai *(Mgr)*

Non-U.S. Joint Venture:

L&T-Chiyoda Limited **(1)**
BP Estate NH-8 Chhani
Vadodara, 391 740, India
Tel.: (91) 2652771003
Fax: (91) 2652774985
E-Mail: info@lntchiyoda.com
Web Site: www.lntchiyoda.com
Emp.: 600
Engineering Consulting Services; Owned 50% by Larsen & Toubro Limited & 50% by Chiyoda Corporation
S.I.C.: 8999
N.A.I.C.S.: 541690
M. Habibulla *(CEO)*
Kiyomi Inoue *(COO)*

CHIYODA INTEGRE CO., LTD.

4-5 Akashi-cho
Chuo-ku, Tokyo, 104-0044, Japan
Tel.: (81) 3 3542 3410
Fax: (81) 3 3541 3554
Web Site: www.chiyoda-i.co.jp
Year Founded: 1955
6915—(TKS)
Emp.: 4,634

Business Description:
Office Automation Equipment Mfr & Whslr
S.I.C.: 3589
N.A.I.C.S.: 333318

Personnel:
Kaname Maruyama *(Chm)*
Mitsuaki Koike *(Pres)*
Takumi Murasawa *(Co-Mng Dir)*
Akira Sato *(Co-Mng Dir)*

Board of Directors:
Kaname Maruyama
Hiroyasu Kanabe
Mitsuaki Koike
Takumi Murasawa
Akira Oikawa
Akira Sato

CHL LIMITED

Hotel The Suryaa New Delhi New Friends Colony
New Delhi, 110 025, India
Tel.: (91) 11 2683 5070
Fax: (91) 11 2683 7758
E-Mail: chl@chl.co.in
Web Site: www.chl.co.in
Year Founded: 1979
532992—(BOM)
Rev.: $11,237,761
Assets: $46,999,475
Liabilities: $27,098,806
Net Worth: $19,900,669
Earnings: $1,088,409
Fiscal Year-end: 03/31/13

Business Description:
Hotel Management Services
S.I.C.: 7011
N.A.I.C.S.: 721110

Personnel:
Lalit Kumar Malhotra *(Chm & Co-Mng Dir)*
Luv Malhotra *(Co-Mng Dir)*
N. K. Goel *(CFO & VP-Fin)*
G. J. Varadarajan *(Compliance Officer & Sec)*

Board of Directors:
Lalit Kumar Malhotra
O. P. Bajaj
Lalit Bhasin
Subhash Ghai
A. K. Malhotra
D. V. Malhotra
Gagan Malhotra
Luv Malhotra
Yash Kumar Sehgal
R. C. Sharma

Transfer Agent:
Beetal Financial & Computer Services Pvt. Ltd
Beetal House 3rd Floor 99 Madangir Behind Local Shopping Centre
New Delhi, India

CHL S.P.A.

Via G Marconi 128
50131 Florence, Italy
Tel.: (39) 05550517211
Fax: (39) 05550517235
E-Mail: customersupport@chl.it
Web Site: www.chl.it
Year Founded: 1993
CHL—(ITA)
Sales Range: $25-49.9 Million
Emp.: 45

Business Description:
Products & Services for Information Technology, Multi-Media & Telecommunications
S.I.C.: 5734
N.A.I.C.S.: 443142

Personnel:
Federigo Franchi *(Chm)*
Fernando Franchi *(Mng Dir)*

Board of Directors:
Federigo Franchi
Massimo Dal Piaz
Enrico Fini
Fernando Franchi
Francesco Guzzinati
Andrea Tognetti

CHLITINA HOLDING LIMITED

10F No 107 Songren Road
Xinyi District, Taipei, 110, Taiwan
Tel.: (886) 87580364
Fax: (886) 87580369
Web Site: www.chlitina.com
4137—(TAI)
Sls.: $79,391,280
Fiscal Year-end: 12/31/12

Business Description:
Beauty & Skin Care Products
S.I.C.: 2844
N.A.I.C.S.: 325620

Personnel:
Pi Hua Chen *(Chm)*
Ching Lun Yu *(Pres)*

CHO THAVEE DOLLASIEN PUBLIC COMPANY LIMITED

265 Moo 4 Muangkhao
Muang, Khon Kaen, 4000, Thailand
Tel.: (66) 43 341412
Fax: (66) 43 341410
E-Mail: info@ctvdoll.co.th
Web Site: www.ctvdoll.co.th
CHO—(THA)
Rev.: $22,898,131
Fiscal Year-end: 12/31/12

Business Description:
Truck Bodies & Trailers Mfr
S.I.C.: 3711
N.A.I.C.S.: 336120

Personnel:
Suradech Thaveesaengsakulthai *(Pres & CEO)*

CHOCOLATS CAMILLE BLOCH S.A.

Grand Rue 21
CH 2608 Courtelary, Switzerland
Tel.: (41) 329451200
Telex: 952403 cbsa ch
Fax: (41) 329451201
E-Mail: info@camillebloch.ch
Web Site: www.camillebloch.ch
Year Founded: 1929
Sales Range: $25-49.9 Million
Emp.: 180

Business Description:
Chocolate Products Mfr
Export
S.I.C.: 2064
N.A.I.C.S.: 311352

Personnel:
Daniel Bloch *(CEO)*

CHOFU SEISAKUSHO CO., LTD.

2-1 Chofuohgimachi Shimonoseki-City
Yamaguchi, 881, Japan
Tel.: (81) 832483980
Fax: (81) 832481906
Web Site: www.chofu.co.jp
Year Founded: 1954
5946—(TKS)
Rev.: $525,998,000
Assets: $1,314,478,000
Liabilities: $117,986,000
Net Worth: $1,196,492,000
Earnings: $38,830,000
Emp.: 1,136
Fiscal Year-end: 12/30/12

Business Description:
Air Conditioners, Boilers, Water Heaters & Other Related Appliances Mfr & Distr
S.I.C.: 5075
N.A.I.C.S.: 423730

Personnel:
Kazuhiro Hashimoto *(Pres)*

CHOICE GOLD CORP.

1110 - 925 West Georgia St
Vancouver, BC, V6C 3L2, Canada

Fax: (604) 408-9301
Toll Free: (800) 975-7152
E-Mail: info@choicegoldcorp.com
Web Site: www.choicegoldcorp.com
Year Founded: 2009
CHF—(CNSX)
Rev.: $41,985
Assets: $118,203
Liabilities: $33,942
Net Worth: $84,261
Earnings: ($202,185)
Fiscal Year-end: 06/30/13
Business Description:
Metal Mining Services
S.I.C.: 1099
N.A.I.C.S.: 212299
Personnel:
Gianni Kovacevic *(Chm, Pres & CEO)*
Jamie Lewin *(CFO)*
Loraine Pike *(Sec)*
Board of Directors:
Gianni Kovacevic
Jamie Lewin
Terence S. Ortslan
Legal Counsel:
Miller Thompson
Robson Court 1000 840 Howe St
Vancouver, BC, Canada
Transfer Agent:
Computershare Trust Company of Canada
510 Burrard St 2nd Fl
Vancouver, BC, Canada

CHOICE INFRA VENTURES LIMITED

Shree Shakambhari Corporate Park
156-158 Chakravorty Ashok Society
Near Bombay Cambridge School J B Nagar Andheri E, Mumbai, 400099, India
Tel.: (91) 22 6707 9999
Fax: (91) 22 6707 9959
E-Mail: info@choiceinfraventures.com
Web Site: www.choiceindiagroup.com
Year Founded: 1992
531364—(BOM)
Rev.: $5,813,614
Assets: $6,981,926
Liabilities: $199,362
Net Worth: $6,782,564
Earnings: $155,659
Fiscal Year-end: 03/31/13
Business Description:
Highway & Bridge Construction Services
S.I.C.: 1611
N.A.I.C.S.: 237310
Personnel:
Kamal Poddar *(Chm, CEO & Mng Dir)*
Sandeep Likhamania *(Compliance Officer & Sec)*
Board of Directors:
Kamal Poddar
Sanwarmal Ramgopal Jangid
Hashmukh Mehta
Lalit Menghnani
Govind Patodia
Arun Poddar
Rameshchandra Purohit
Transfer Agent:
Link Intime India Pvt. Ltd
C-13 Pannalal Silk Mills Compound LBS Marg
Bhandup (West)
Mumbai, India

CHOICE INTERNATIONAL LIMITED

Shree Shakambhari Corporate Plt No 156-158 Chakravarti Ashok Complex Near Cambridge School Andheri, Mumbai, 400 099, India
Tel.: (91) 22 6707 9999
Fax: (91) 22 6707 9959
E-Mail: info@choiceindia.com
Web Site: www.choiceindia.com
531358—(BOM)
Rev.: $7,700,792
Assets: $21,121,335
Liabilities: $11,201,669
Net Worth: $9,919,666
Earnings: $677,941
Fiscal Year-end: 03/31/13
Business Description:
Investment Banking Services
S.I.C.: 6211
N.A.I.C.S.: 523110
Personnel:
Kamal Poddar *(Mng Dir)*
Mahavir Toshniwal *(Compliance Officer & Sec)*
Board of Directors:
Brijmohan Agarwal
Pankaj Bhansali
Kali Mohan Bhattacharya
Debkumar Goswami
Ajay Kejriwal
Satish Chandra Kulhari
Hemlata Poddar
Kamal Poddar
Bhagyam Ramani
Alexander Koshy Prince Vaidyan
Transfer Agent:
Sharex Dynamic (India) Pvt Limited
Unit-1 Luthra Ind Premises 1st Fl 44-E M
Vasanti Marg Andheri-Kurla Rd
Safed Pool Andheri E, Mumbai, India
Subsidiaries:

Choice Capital Advisors Private Limited **(1)**
Shree Shakambhari Corporate Park Plot No 156-158 Chakravarti Ashok Society JB Nagar Andheri East, Mumbai, 400 099, India
Tel.: (91) 22 6707 9999
Fax: (91) 22 6707 9959
Emp.: 500
Financial Management Services
S.I.C.: 6282
N.A.I.C.S.: 523930
Shilpa Khetan *(Mgr)*

Choice Equity Broking Private Limited **(1)**
Shree Shakambhari Corporate Park 156-158 Chakravarti Ashok Society
JB Nagar Off Sahar Road, Mumbai, 400 099, India
Tel.: (91) 22 67079999
Fax: (91) 22 67079898
Security Brokerage Services
S.I.C.: 6211
N.A.I.C.S.: 523120
Sandeep B. Jhunjhunwala *(VP)*

CHOICE PROPERTIES REAL ESTATE INVESTMENT TRUST

22 Saint Clair Avenue East Suite 800
Toronto, ON, M4T 2S5, Canada
Tel.: (905) 459-2500
Fax: (905) 861-2326
E-Mail: investor@choicereit.ca
Web Site: www.choicereit.ca
Year Founded: 2013
CHP.UN—(TSX)
Business Description:
Real Estate Investment Trust
S.I.C.: 6726
N.A.I.C.S.: 525990
Personnel:
Galen G. Weston *(Chm)*
John Morrison *(Pres & CEO)*
Bart Munn *(CFO)*
S. Jane Marshall *(COO)*
Transfer Agent:
CIBC Mellon Trust Company
PO Box 7010
Adelaide Street Postal Station, Toronto, ON, M5C 2W9, Canada
Tel.: (416) 643-5500
Fax: (416) 643-5501
Toll Free: (800) 387-0825

CHOICES MARKETS LTD.

8188 River Way
Delta, BC, V4G 1K5, Canada
Tel.: (604) 952-2266
Fax: (604) 940-8845
E-Mail: comments@choicesmarket.com
Web Site: www.choicesmarket.com
Rev.: $28,032,560
Emp.: 200
Business Description:
Grocery Stores
S.I.C.: 5411
N.A.I.C.S.: 445110
Personnel:
Wayne Lockhart *(Owner)*

CHOIL ALUMINUM CO., LTD.

1207-10 Sinsang-ri Jinryang-eup
Gyeongsan, Gyeongsan-do, Korea (South)
Tel.: (82) 538565252
Fax: (82) 538565257
E-Mail: choilal@choilal.co.kr
Web Site: www.choilal.co.kr
Year Founded: 1975
018470—(KRS)
Business Description:
Aluminum Products Mfr & Sales
S.I.C.: 3353
N.A.I.C.S.: 331315
Personnel:
Youngho Lee *(Pres)*

CHOKHANI SECURITIES LTD

5A Maker Bhavan II 5th Floor New Marine Lines
Mumbai, 400020, India
Tel.: (91) 2222007772
Fax: (91) 2222007722
E-Mail: contact@rrcfinancials.com
Web Site: www.rrcfinancials.com
CHOKSEC—(BOM)
Rev.: $776,283
Assets: $4,413,369
Liabilities: $5,770
Net Worth: $4,407,599
Earnings: $310,605
Emp.: 25
Fiscal Year-end: 03/31/13
Business Description:
Merchant Banking, Mutual Fund, Debt Market Operations, Insurance & Depository Services
S.I.C.: 6411
N.A.I.C.S.: 524210
Personnel:
Manish Parikh *(Compliance Officer)*
Upendera C. Shukla *(Sec)*
Board of Directors:
Ramakant R. Chokhani
Rajesh Chokhani
Pravin Gupta
Yogesh Raja
Transfer Agent:
Universal Capital Securities Pvt. Ltd
21 Shakil Niwas Mahakali Caves Road Andheri East
Mumbai, India

CHOKSI IMAGING LTD.

4th Floor C Wing Classique Centre
Plot No 26 Mahal Industrial Premises
Off Mahakali Caves Road Near Paper Box Andheri East, Mumbai, 400093, India
Tel.: (91) 22 42287555
Fax: (91) 22 42287588
E-Mail: imaging@choksiworld.com
Web Site: www.choksiworld.com
530427—(BOM)
Rev.: $42,624,888
Assets: $19,087,857
Liabilities: $15,537,855
Net Worth: $3,550,002
Earnings: $42,308
Emp.: 208
Fiscal Year-end: 03/31/13
Business Description:
Photographic Product Mfr & Distr
S.I.C.: 3081
N.A.I.C.S.: 326113
Personnel:
Anil V. Choksi *(Mng Dir)*
Gaurav S. Choksi *(Pres-Fin)*
Sunil A. Choksi *(Pres-Mktg)*
Tushar K. Choksi *(Pres-Admin)*
Board of Directors:
Sharadchandra Pendse
Anil V. Choksi
Gaurav S. Choksi
Naimish N. Choksi
Samir K. Choksi
Himanshu Kishnadwala
Vikram V. Maniar
Tushar M. Parikh
Transfer Agent:
Adroit Corporate Services Pvt. Ltd.
19 20 Jaferbhoy Industrial Estate Makwana Road Marol Naka Andheri E
Mumbai, India

CHOKSI LABORATORIES LIMITED

6/3 Manoramaganj
Indore, MP, 452001, India
Tel.: (91) 731 4243888
Fax: (91) 731 2490593
E-Mail: info@choksilab.com
Web Site: www.choksilab.com
Year Founded: 1982
526546—(BOM)
Sales Range: $1-9.9 Million
Business Description:
Pharmaceutical Products Mfr
S.I.C.: 2834
N.A.I.C.S.: 325412
Personnel:
Sunil Choksi *(Mng Dir)*
Himika Choksi Varma *(Mng Dir)*
Board of Directors:
Stela Choksi
Sunil Choksi
Vyangesh Choksi
Satish Joshi
Pradip Karmakar
N. K. Mani
Sudarshan Shastri
Himika Choksi Varma
Transfer Agent:
Link Intime India Pvt. Ltd
C-13 Pannalal Silk Mills Compound LBS Marg
Bhandup (West)
Mumbai, India

CHOLNIZ

Lieu Dit Pont De 1 Tigny Route De Roanne
42190 Lyon, France
Tel.: (33) 477602733
Fax: (33) 477602602
E-Mail: pgvdc10656@mousquetaeres.com
Sales Range: $10-24.9 Million
Emp.: 55
Business Description:
Grocery Stores
S.I.C.: 5411
N.A.I.C.S.: 445110
Personnel:
Jean-Paul Champailler *(Pres)*
Board of Directors:
Marc Montagnon

CHONBANG CO., LTD.

13th Fl Chungjung Tower Building
464 Chungjeongno 3 ga
Seodaemun Gu, Seoul, 120013, Korea (South)
Tel.: (82) 221226000
Fax: (82) 223923923
Web Site: www.chonbang.co.kr
000950—(KRS)
Sls.: $249,798,000
Assets: $490,575,000
Liabilities: $311,457,000
Net Worth: $179,118,000
Earnings: $33,108,000
Emp.: 1,200
Fiscal Year-end: 12/31/12

Business Description:
Yarns & Fabrics Mfr
S.I.C.: 2299
N.A.I.C.S.: 313110

Personnel:
Kyoo-Ok Cho *(Chm & CEO)*

Subsidiary:

Cheonbang Auto Co., Ltd. **(1)**
No 100 Im-dong Buk-gu
Gwangju, Gyeonggi, Korea (South)
Tel.: (82) 62 529 2002
Fax: (82) 62 514 5956
Web Site: www.chonbangauto.co.kr
Automobile Sales & Services
S.I.C.: 5012
N.A.I.C.S.: 423110

Plants:

Chonbang Co., Ltd. - Gwangju Factory **(1)**
No 100 Im-dong
Buk-gu, Gwangju, Korea (South)
Tel.: (82) 62 520 3300
Fax: (82) 62 520 3330
Cotton Yarn Mfr
S.I.C.: 0724
N.A.I.C.S.: 115111
Yeong Su Kim *(Mgr)*

Chonbang Co., Ltd. - Youngam Factory **(1)**
Shinbuk Nonggong K-1 Complex Galgok-ri
Shinbuk-myeon, Yeongam, Jeollanam-do, Korea (South)
Tel.: (82) 614729191
Fax: (82) 614729126
Fabric Mfr
S.I.C.: 2299
N.A.I.C.S.: 313210
Yong Seo Kim *(Gen Mgr)*

Non-U.S. Subsidiary:

Qingdao Tracon Electronic Co., Ltd. **(1)**
266-100 He-Ma-Shi Vlg Subdistrict office of Fu-Shan-Hou
Shi-Bei Dist, Qingdao, Shandong, China
Tel.: (86) 53285692388
Fax: (86) 53285692200
Film Condenser Mfr
S.I.C.: 3081
N.A.I.C.S.: 326113

CHONBURI CONCRETE PRODUCT PUBLIC COMPANY LIMITED

39/1 Moo1 Sukhumvit Road Huaykapi Muang
Chon Buri, 20000, Thailand
Tel.: (66) 3826 5400
Fax: (66) 3827 2443
E-Mail: ir@ccp.co.th
Web Site: www.ccp.co.th
Year Founded: 1983
CCP—(THA)
Rev.: $86,226,093
Assets: $80,895,608
Liabilities: $62,495,471
Net Worth: $18,400,137
Earnings: $7,245,034
Fiscal Year-end: 12/31/12

Business Description:
Concrete Product Mfr & Distr
S.I.C.: 3272
N.A.I.C.S.: 327390

Personnel:
Pratheep Theepakornsukkasem *(Chm)*
Artit Theepakornsukkasame *(Mng Dir)*
Sittichai Vinichsorn *(Sr VP-Production & Concrete Quality)*

Board of Directors:
Pratheep Theepakornsukkasem
Narong Banyen
Anupong Natpisarnwanit
Preecha Ratthayanon
Surapon Sukamongkol
Cholticha Teepakornsookkasem
Artit Theepakornsukkasame
Yuan Wang Tzu

Subsidiary:

Chonburi Kanyong Co., Ltd. **(1)**
39/1-4 Moo 1 Sukhumvit Road Huaykapi
Muang, Chon Buri, Thailand
Tel.: (66) 3826 5400 99
Fax: (66) 3827 2400 1
Construction Material Retailer
S.I.C.: 5211
N.A.I.C.S.: 444190

CHONG HING BANK LTD.

(Acquired by Yue Xiu Enterprises (Holdings) Limited)

CHONG KUN DANG PHARMACEUTICAL CORP.

368 3-ga Chungjeong-ro
Seodaemun-gu, Seoul, 120-756, Korea (South)
Tel.: (82) 2 2194 0300
Fax: (82) 2 2194 0369
Web Site: www.ckdpharm.com
Year Founded: 1941
001630—(KRS)

Business Description:
Pharmaceutical Product Mfr
S.I.C.: 2834
N.A.I.C.S.: 325412

Personnel:
Jang Han Lee *(Chm)*

CHONGHERR INVESTMENTS LTD.

Level 34 Central Plaza One 345 Queen Street
Brisbane, QLD, 4000, Australia

Mailing Address:
PO Box 2917
Brisbane, QLD, 4001, Australia
Tel.: (61) 732211166
Fax: (61) 732212188
E-Mail: info@chongherr.com.au
Web Site: www.chongherr.com.au
CDH—(ASX)
Sls.: $2,626,364
Assets: $6,019,395
Liabilities: $1,158,554
Net Worth: $4,860,841
Earnings: ($427,126)
Emp.: 15
Fiscal Year-end: 12/31/12

Business Description:
Sandstone Mining, Mfr & Exporter Export
S.I.C.: 1429
N.A.I.C.S.: 212319

Personnel:
Densen De-Hui Liu *(Chm, CEO & Mng Dir)*
Sophia Xiaoqing Kong *(Sec)*

Board of Directors:
Densen De-Hui Liu
Sophia Xiaoqing Kong
Zhen Lu
Peijuan Zhuang

Legal Counsel:
Hemming+Hart Lawyers
Level 2 307 Queen Street
Brisbane, 4000, Australia

Transfer Agent:
Link Market Services Ltd
Level 12 300 Queen Street
Brisbane, QLD, 4000, Australia

Subsidiary:

Australian Sandstone Industries Pty. Ltd. **(1)**
Level 34 Central Plz One 345 Queen St
Brisbane, QLD, 4000, Australia AU
Tel.: (61) 732218999
Fax: (61) 732212188
E-Mail: info@asisandstone.com.au
Web Site: www.asisandstone.com.au
Emp.: 10
Sandstone Quarrying & Processing Services
S.I.C.: 1411
N.A.I.C.S.: 212311

CHONGQING CHANGAN AUTOMOBILE COMPANY LTD

260 Jianxin East Road
Jianxin Donglu
Jiangbei District, Chongqing, 400023, China
Tel.: (86) 2367591888
Fax: (86) 2367852882
E-Mail: export@changan.com.cn
Web Site: www.globalchana.com
200625—(SSE)
Sales Range: $1-4.9 Billion
Emp.: 9,000

Business Description:
Automobile Mfr & Sls
S.I.C.: 3711
N.A.I.C.S.: 336111

Personnel:
Liuping Xu *(Chm)*

CHONGQING FUAN PHARMACEUTICAL (GROUP) CO., LTD.

Changshou Chemical Park Zone
Chongqing, Fuan, 401254, China
Tel.: (86) 23 61028798
Fax: (86) 23 61028787
E-Mail: sales@fapharm.com
Web Site: www.fapharm.com
Year Founded: 2004
300194—(CHIN)
Sales Range: $50-74.9 Million
Emp.: 640

Business Description:
Pharmaceutical Mfr
S.I.C.: 2834
N.A.I.C.S.: 325412

Personnel:
Xudong Zhou *(Vice Gen Mgr)*

CHONGQING FULING ZHACAI GROUP CO., LTD.

(d/b/a Fuling Zhacai)
29 Sports South Road
Fuling District, Chongqing, 408000, China
Tel.: (86) 237 2231475
E-Mail: chenli198212@sina.com
Web Site: www.flzc.com
002507—(SSE)
Emp.: 900

Business Description:
Mustards & Sauces Mfr
S.I.C.: 2035
N.A.I.C.S.: 311941

Personnel:
Bin Zhou *(Chm)*

CHONGQING HELICOPTER INVESTMENT CO. LTD.

6th Floor Building C1 No 68 Uranus Building
Avenue of the Stars, 401121
Chongqing, China
Tel.: (86) 23 67886800
Web Site: www.cqhic.cn
Sales Range: $500-549.9 Million

Business Description:
Holding Company
S.I.C.: 6719
N.A.I.C.S.: 551112

Personnel:
Huang Yong *(Chm)*

Board of Directors:
Huang Yong

U.S. Subsidiary:

The Enstrom Helicopter Corp. **(1)**
2209 22nd St
Menominee, MI 49858 DE
Tel.: (906) 863-1200
Fax: (906) 863-6244
Web Site: www.enstromhelicopter.com
Sales Range: $10-24.9 Million
Emp.: 100
Helicopter Mfr
S.I.C.: 3721
N.A.I.C.S.: 336411
Jerry Mullins *(Pres & CEO)*
Charles Chumacher *(CFO)*

CHONGQING IRON & STEEL CO LTD

30 Gangtie Rd
Dadukou District
400084 Chongqing, Sichuan, China
Tel.: (86) 2368845030
Fax: (86) 2368849520
Web Site: www.cqgt.cn
601005—(SHG)
Sales Range: $1-4.9 Billion

Business Description:
Iron & Steel Mfr
S.I.C.: 3315
N.A.I.C.S.: 331222

Personnel:
Jian Pai Zhu *(Chm-Supervisory Bd)*
Xiao An You *(Sec)*

Board of Directors:
Hong Chen
Shan Chen
Ren Sheng Li
Tian Ni Liu
Xing Liu
Deng Qiang
Yi Jie Sun
Jin Fu Yuan
Guo Lin Zhang

Supervisory Board of Directors:
Jian Pai Zhu
Shou Lun Gao
Jun Gong
You He Huang

KPMG
8th Floor Princes Building 10 Chater Road
Central, China (Hong Kong)

CHONGQING LIFAN INDUSTRY (GROUP) IMP. & EXP. CO., LTD.

(d/b/a Lifan Group)
60 Zhangjiawan Shangqiao
Shapingba, Chongqing, China
Tel.: (86) 2361663388
Fax: (86) 2361663299
E-Mail: iec031@lifan.com
Web Site: www.lifan.com
Year Founded: 1992
Sales Range: $1-4.9 Billion
Emp.: 13,200

Business Description:
Engine, Motorcycle & Automobile Mfr, Marketer, Exporter & Importer

S.I.C.: 3711
N.A.I.C.S.: 336310
Personnel:
Minshan Yin *(Chm)*

CHONGQING MACHINERY & ELECTRIC CO LTD
Ste 2208 22nd Fl Jardine House
1 Connaught Place
Central, China (Hong Kong)
Tel.: (852) 21670000
Fax: (852) 21670050
2722—(HKG)
Sales Range: $800-899.9 Million
Business Description:
Motor Vehicle Parts Mfr
S.I.C.: 3714
N.A.I.C.S.: 336310
Personnel:
Hua Jun Xie *(Chm)*
Xiaojun Wang *(Sec)*
Board of Directors:
Hua Jun Xie
Xianzheng Chen
Yong He
Yong Huang
Shaohua Liao
Jian Wu
Jingpu Yang
Gang Yu

CHONGQING MAS SCI. & TECH. CO., LTD.
Erlang Technology Park Chongqing
Hi-Tech Venture Park 6F C2
Chongqing, 400039, China
Tel.: (86) 23 68460850
Fax: (86) 23 68465683
E-Mail: mas@cqmas.com
Web Site: www.cqmas.com
300275—(CHIN)
Emp.: 380
Business Description:
Coal Mine Safety & Security Monitoring Systems
S.I.C.: 1241
N.A.I.C.S.: 213113
Personnel:
Yan Ma *(Chm)*

CHONGQING NEW CENTURY CRUISE CO., LTD.
(d/b/a Century Cruises)
7/8 Floors Nanping Mansion Building B
6 East Nanping Street
Southern District, Chongqing, 400060, China
Tel.: (86) 23 62948994
Fax: (86) 23 62949900
E-Mail: usadept@centuryrivercruises.com
Web Site: www.centuryrivercruises.com
002558—(SSE)
Emp.: 790
Business Description:
Cruise & Tour Operator
S.I.C.: 4489
N.A.I.C.S.: 487210
Personnel:
Jianhu Peng *(Chm)*

CHONGQING RURAL COMMERCIAL BANK CO., LTD.
10 Yanghe East Road
Jiangbei District, Chongqing, China 400020
Tel.: (86) 236 7637508
Fax: (86) 236 7740888
E-Mail: cqrcb@cqrcb.com
Web Site: www.cqrcb.com
3618—(HKG OTC)
Int. Income: $3,547,376,090
Assets: $68,912,698,883
Liabilities: $63,793,040,902
Net Worth: $5,119,657,981
Earnings: $854,248,122
Emp.: 14,800
Fiscal Year-end: 12/31/12
Business Description:
Banking Services
S.I.C.: 6029
N.A.I.C.S.: 522110
Personnel:
Jianzhong Liu *(Chm)*
Mingping Yang *(Chm-Supervisory Bd)*
Yuansheng Tan *(Pres)*
Jun Sui *(Co-Sec & VP)*
Patsy Pik Yuk Cheng *(Co-Sec)*
Board of Directors:
Jianzhong Liu
Zhengsheng Chen
Xiaodong Gao
Yusheng Hua
Weili Liu
Jun Sui
Leland Li Hsun Sun
Yuansheng Tan
Jun Tao
Yongshu Wang
Honghai Wen
Qing Wu
Xiufeng Wu
Mengbo Yin
Supervisory Board of Directors:
Mingping Yang
Huiming Chen
Yunling Dong
Bentong Shi
Jianwu Zeng
Xinyu Zhang
Yi Zheng
Yuzhou Zhu
Ruilan Zuo
Legal Counsel:
Paul Hastings
21-22/F Bank of China Tower 1 Garden Road
Hong Kong, China (Hong Kong)
Chongqing Jingsheng Law Firm
Level 18 Business Tower InterContinental Hotel
101 Minzu Road
Yuzhong District, Chongqing, China
China Securities Depository & Clearing Co Ltd
No 17 Taipingqiao Avenue
Xicheng District, Beijing, China

CHONGQING THREE GORGES WATER CONSERVANCY AND ELECTRIC POWER CO., LTD.
12/F Yide Building 183 Bayi Road
Yuzhong District, Chongqing, 400010, China
Tel.: (86) 23 63801161
Fax: (86) 23 63801165
Web Site: www.cqsxsl.com
600116—(SHG)
Sales Range: $75-99.9 Million
Emp.: 2,100
Business Description:
Hydraulic Power Generation & Distribution Services
S.I.C.: 4939
N.A.I.C.S.: 221111
Personnel:
Jianquiao Ye *(Chm)*

CHONGQING ZHIFEI BIOLOGICAL PRODUCTS CO.,LTD
Chongqing Golden Resources Road
25th Floor No 7
Jiangbei District, Chongqing, 400020, China
Tel.: (86) 2386358226
Fax: (86) 2386358685
E-Mail: zhifeishengwu@sina.com
Web Site: www.zhifeishengwu.com
Year Founded: 1995
300122—(CHIN)
Sales Range: $100-124.9 Million
Emp.: 647
Business Description:
Pharmaceutical Products Mfr
S.I.C.: 2834
N.A.I.C.S.: 325412
Personnel:
Rensheng Jiang *(Chm & Gen Mgr)*
Guanjiang Wu *(Vice Chm & Deputy Gen Mgr)*
Xu Chang *(CFO & Deputy Gen Mgr)*
Board of Directors:
Rensheng Jiang
Yufeng Chen
Lingfeng Jiang
Guanjiang Wu
Nong Yu

CHONGYI ZHANGYUAN TUNGSTEN CO., LTD.
Xiancheng Chongyi
Ganzhou, Jiangxi, 341300, China
Tel.: (86) 797 3812666
Fax: (86) 797 3816889
E-Mail: bgs@zy-tungsten.com
Web Site: www.zy-tungsten.com
002378—(SSE)
Business Description:
Tungsten Mining & Production Services
S.I.C.: 1099
N.A.I.C.S.: 212299
Personnel:
Huang Zelan *(Chm)*

CHOO BEE METAL INDUSTRIES BERHAD
Wisma Soon Teik Aun Jalan Bendahara
31650 Ipoh, Perak, Malaysia
Tel.: (60) 52558111
Fax: (60) 52550573
E-Mail: enquiries@choobee.com.my
Web Site: www.choobee.com.my
CHOOBEE—(KLS)
Rev.: $147,451,196
Assets: $142,875,400
Liabilities: $9,028,621
Net Worth: $133,846,778
Earnings: $3,161,149
Fiscal Year-end: 12/31/12
Business Description:
Steel Pipe Mfr
S.I.C.: 3312
N.A.I.C.S.: 331110
Personnel:
Ah Khun Soon *(Chm)*
Cheng Hai Soon *(Mng Dir)*
Yoke Yin Chan *(Co-Sec)*
Cindy Chiew *(Co-Sec)*
Board of Directors:
Ah Khun Soon
Shahrizan Abdullah
Choon Yam Khoo
Sieng Tzi Lee
Chee Hoong Lim
Poh Tat Ng
Cheng Boon Soon
Cheng Hai Soon
Hean Hooi Soon

CHOONGANG VACCINE LABORATORY CO., LTD.
59-3 Hwaamdong Daedeok Valley
Yuseonggu, Daejeon, Korea (South) 305-348
Tel.: (82) 42 863 9322
Fax: (82) 42 863 8454
Web Site: www.cavac.co.kr
Year Founded: 1968
072020—(KRS)
Business Description:
Biological Product Mfr
S.I.C.: 2834
N.A.I.C.S.: 325412
Personnel:
In-Joong Yoon *(CEO)*

CHOONGANGOCEAN CO., LTD.
8th Fl Green Building 28-1 Jamwon-dong
Seoul, Seocho, Korea (South)
Tel.: (82) 232189500
Fax: (82) 232189595
Web Site: www.c-ocean.co.kr
Year Founded: 1999
054180—(KRS)
Business Description:
LCE Display Panel Mfr
S.I.C.: 3999
N.A.I.C.S.: 339999
Personnel:
Jun Byungchul *(Pres & CEO)*

CHOONGWAE PHARMA CORPORATION
698 Sindehbahng Dong
Dongjahk Gu
156010 Seoul, Korea (South)
Tel.: (82) 28406777
Fax: (82) 28437696
E-Mail: info@cwholdings.co.kr
Web Site: www.cwp.co.kr
Year Founded: 1945
001060—(KRS)
Sales Range: $350-399.9 Million
Emp.: 1,300
Business Description:
Pharmaceutical Products Mfr
S.I.C.: 2834
N.A.I.C.S.: 325412
Personnel:
Chong-Ho Lee *(Chm)*
Gyeong Ha Lee *(Pres & CEO)*

CHOPARD & CIE S.A.
Ruee De Veyrot 8
CH 1217 Meyrin, Geneva, Switzerland
Tel.: (41) 227193131
Fax: (41) 227193135
E-Mail: info@chopard.ch
Web Site: www.chopard.com
Sales Range: $450-499.9 Million
Emp.: 800
Business Description:
Watches, Jewelry & Accessories Mfr & Sales
S.I.C.: 5944
N.A.I.C.S.: 448310
Personnel:
Karl Friedrich Scheufele *(Pres)*

U.S. Subsidiary:

Chopard USA Ltd. **(1)**
21 E 63rd St
New York, NY 10065
Tel.: (212) 821-0300
Fax: (212) 821-0325
E-Mail: reception@chopard.com
Web Site: www.chopard.com
Emp.: 55
Watches, Jewelry & Accessories Sales
S.I.C.: 5094
N.A.I.C.S.: 423940
Marc Hruschka *(Pres & CEO)*

CHORDIA FOOD PRODUCTS LTD.
48/A Parvati Industrial Estate Pune-Satara Road
Pune, Maharashtra, 411009, India
Tel.: (91) 20 24220022
Fax: (91) 20 24215190
E-Mail: admin@chordia.com

Chordia Food Products Ltd.—(Continued)

Web Site: www.chordia.com
Year Founded: 1960
519475—(BOM)
Sales Range: $1-9.9 Million
Business Description:
Processed Foods Mfr
S.I.C.: 2037
N.A.I.C.S.: 311411
Personnel:
Hukmichand Sukhlal Chordia *(Chm)*
Pradeep Hukmichand Chordia *(Mng Dir)*
B. R. Gavhane *(Sec)*
Board of Directors:
Hukmichand Sukhlal Chordia
Pradeep Hukmichand Chordia
Pravin H. Chordia
Hiralal N. Lunkad
Mahendra S. Mehta

CHORI CO., LTD.

1-7-3 Awajimachi
Chuo-ku, Osaka, 541-8603, Japan
Tel.: (81) 662285000
Telex: 63322
Fax: (81) 662285546
Web Site: www.chori.co.jp
Year Founded: 1948
8014—(TKS)
Sls.: $2,440,317,000
Assets: $790,361,000
Liabilities: $445,126,000
Net Worth: $345,235,000
Earnings: $32,384,000
Emp.: 1,286
Fiscal Year-end: 03/31/13
Business Description:
Trading House; Import; Export & Brokerage of Textile Materials & Products; Metal Products, Plastic Resins, Chemicals, Fertilizers
S.I.C.: 2389
N.A.I.C.S.: 314999
Personnel:
Shuji Yamazaki *(Pres & CEO)*
Masayuki Hatsuya *(Co-Mng Dir)*
Nagao Iseda *(Co-Mng Dir)*
Jun Kobayashi *(Co-Mng Dir)*
Noburo Kojima *(Co-Mng Dir)*
Jun Furuya *(Exec Officer)*
Jun Hayami *(Exec Officer)*
Kunihisa Inoue *(Exec Officer)*
Akira Marui *(Exec Officer)*
Hideki Masahiro *(Exec Officer)*
Makoto Miura *(Exec officer)*
Funki Ou *(Exec Officer)*
Kazuo Sakihama *(Exec Officer)*
Shigemasa Yabu *(Exec Officer)*
Tetsuji Yamaguchi *(Exec Officer)*
Hiroshi Yoshida *(Exec Officer)*
Board of Directors:
Masayuki Hatsuya
Kunihisa Inoue
Nagao Iseda
Jun Kobayashi
Noburo Kojima
Makoto Miura
Kazuo Sakihama
Shuji Yamazaki

Subsidiaries:

Business Anchor Corporation (1)
1-7-3 Awajimachi
Chuo-ku, Osaka, Japan
Tel.: (81) 6 6228 5528
Web Site: www.chori.co.jp/bac/
Business Support Services
S.I.C.: 7389
N.A.I.C.S.: 561499

Chori Imaging Corporation (1)
3-13-6 Shinyokohama
Kouhoku-ku, Yokohama, Japan
Tel.: (81) 45 476 2260
Web Site: www.chori-imaging.com
Image Processing Apparatus Distr
S.I.C.: 5063
N.A.I.C.S.: 423610

Chori MODA Co., Ltd. (1)
4-20-9 Sendagaya
Shibuya-ku, Tokyo, Japan
Tel.: (81) 3 5414 8261
Web Site: www.chori-moda.com
Apparel Retailer
S.I.C.: 5699
N.A.I.C.S.: 448150

Chori Urban Development Co., Ltd. (1)
2-4-3 Horidomecho Nihonbashi
Chuo-ku, Tokyo, Japan
Tel.: (81) 3 3665 2527
Web Site: www.cud.co.jp
Real Estate Management Services
S.I.C.: 6531
N.A.I.C.S.: 531390

Dijion Co., Ltd (1)
23-3 Sakuragaoka
Shibuya-ku, Tokyo, Japan
Tel.: (81) 3 3780 0891
Web Site: www.dijon.co.jp
Ladies Apparel Whslr
S.I.C.: 5137
N.A.I.C.S.: 424330

Tohcho Co., Limited (1)
2-4-3 Horidome cho Nihonbashi
Chuo-ku, Tokyo, 103-8652, Japan
Tel.: (81) 3 3665 2472
Fax: (81) 3 3665 2751
Chemical Products Whslr
S.I.C.: 5169
N.A.I.C.S.: 424690

Tokyo Kutsushita Co., Ltd. (1)
1-1-6 Saga
Koto-ku, Tokyo, Japan
Tel.: (81) 3 5639 9570
Fax: (81) 3 5639 9575
Web Site: www.k-tk.com
Inner Socks Mfr & Distr
S.I.C.: 2252
N.A.I.C.S.: 315110

U.S. Subsidiary:

Chori America, Inc. (1)
30 Montgomery St Ste 1230
Jersey City, NJ 07302-3834 (100%)
Tel.: (212) 642-0400
Telex: ITT 420235
Fax: (212) 642-0480
Web Site: www.chori.com
Emp.: 30
Trading House
S.I.C.: 5199
N.A.I.C.S.: 424310
Yoshi Suzuki *(Mgr-Sls)*

Non-U.S. Subsidiaries:

Chori Australia Pty Ltd. (1)
Ste 642 Level 6 149 Castlereaugh St
Sydney, 2000, Australia
Tel.: (61) 292672622
Fax: (61) 292675353
Web Site: www.chori.com.au
Emp.: 3
Financial Services
S.I.C.: 6282
N.A.I.C.S.: 523930

Chori Co. (Hong Kong) Ltd. (1)
Unit 1308, Telecom Tower Wharf Ent Square
123 Harpen rd
Kowloon, China (Hong Kong)
Tel.: (852) 27242333
Fax: (852) 23117198
Web Site: www.chori.co.jp/english/network/kaigai.html
S.I.C.: 6221
N.A.I.C.S.: 523130

Chori (Dalian) Trading Co., Ltd. (1)
5F MORI Bldg No 147 Zhongshan Road
Xigang District, Dalian, China
Tel.: (86) 411 8369 1785
Fax: (86) 411 8369 1792
Web Site: www.chori.co.jp/english/network/kaigai.html
Emp.: 20
Textile Products Distr
S.I.C.: 5137
N.A.I.C.S.: 424330

Chori Europe GmbH (1)
Zeil 81
60313 Frankfurt, Germany (100%)
Tel.: (49) 696698510
Fax: (49) 66162880
Emp.: 3
Trading House; Import; Export & Brokerage of Textile Materials & Products; Metal Products, Plastic Resins, Chemicals, Fertilizers
S.I.C.: 2299
N.A.I.C.S.: 314999

Chori Fashion Network Co., Ltd. (1)
Rm 606 6/F Mirror Tower 61 Mody Rd
Hong Kong, China (Hong Kong)
Fax: (852) 27394775
S.I.C.: 6221
N.A.I.C.S.: 523130

Chori Middle East FZE (1)
PO BOX 17334
Jebel Ali, Dubai, United Arab Emirates
Tel.: (971) 4 8814742
Fax: (971) 4 8814745
Web Site: www.chori.co.jp/english/network/kaigai.html
Chemical & Textile Products Mfr
S.I.C.: 2899
N.A.I.C.S.: 325998
Takayuki Kunugihara *(Gen Mgr)*

Chori Shanghai Ltd. (1)
Rm 1201 International Trade Ctr No 2201 Yan An Rd
Shanghai, 200336, China (100%)
Tel.: (86) 2162780886
Fax: (86) 2162780616
Web Site: www.chori.com.cn
Emp.: 90
Financial Services
S.I.C.: 6282
N.A.I.C.S.: 523930
Mao Inoue *(Gen Mgr)*

Chori Singapore Pte. Ltd. (1)
10 Hoe Chiang Rd Unit 20-06
Keppel Towers, Singapore, 089315, Singapore (100%)
Tel.: (65) 62501177
Fax: (65) 62502265
Web Site: www.chori.co.jp/english/network/kaigai.html
Emp.: 9
Trading House; Import; Export & Brokerage of Textile Materials & Products; Metal Products, Plastic Resins, Chemicals, Fertilizers
S.I.C.: 2299
N.A.I.C.S.: 314999

Chori (Tianjin) Co., Ltd. (1)
Room No 2105 Exchange North Tower 189 Nanjing Road
Heping District, Tianjin, 300051, China
Tel.: (86) 22 8319 1606
Fax: (86) 22 8319 1605
Web Site: www.chori.co.jp
Emp.: 7
Textile Products Mfr
S.I.C.: 2389
N.A.I.C.S.: 314999

Chori Trading Malaysia Sdn Bhd (1)
Suite 13A 04-13A Floor Wisma MCA 163 Jalan Ampang
50450 Kuala Lumpur, Malaysia
Tel.: (60) 3 2162 2773
Fax: (60) 3 2162 9773
Web Site: www.chori.co.jp
Emp.: 5
Trading House; Import; Export & Brokerage of Textile Materials & Products; Metal Products, Plastic Resins, Chemicals & Fertilizers
S.I.C.: 2299
N.A.I.C.S.: 314999

Dalian Anchor Business Service Co., Ltd. (1)
Central Plaza Hotel Dalian Rm No 904 No 145 Zhongshan Road
Xigang District, Dalian, China
Tel.: (86) 411 83700273
Office Outsourcing Services
S.I.C.: 7389
N.A.I.C.S.: 561499

P.T. Chori Indonesia (1)
World Trade Centre I Lt 12
Jl Jend Sudirman Kav 29 31, Jakarta, 12920, Indonesia
Tel.: (62) 215211288
Fax: (62) 215211184
E-Mail: sebrig@chori.co.jp
Web Site: www.chori.co.jp/english/network/kaigai.html
Emp.: 14
Provider of Trading & Import & Export Services
S.I.C.: 7389
N.A.I.C.S.: 561990
Ank Sakamoto *(Pres)*

Red Butterfly Strontium Industry Co., Ltd. (1)
29 Xia he road
Longshui Town, Chongqing, Dazu, China
Tel.: (86) 23 67961322
Fax: (86) 23 67961321
Carbonic Strontium Mfr & Distr
S.I.C.: 3299
N.A.I.C.S.: 327999

Thai Chori Co., Ltd. (1)
Thaniya Plz Building 25 Fl 52 Silom Rd
Bangrak, Bangkok, 10500, Thailand
Tel.: (66) 22670230
Fax: (66) 22676533
Web Site: www.chori.co.th
Emp.: 20
Trading House; Import; Export & Brokerage of Textile Materials & Products; Metal Products, Plastic Resins, Chemicals, Fertilizers
S.I.C.: 2389
N.A.I.C.S.: 314999
Kotalo Moai *(Pres)*

Non-U.S. Joint Ventures:

Hangzhou Itokin Fashion Co., Ltd. (1)
98 Beside Jianshe Er Rd
Hangzhou, 311215, China
Tel.: (86) 5712635600
Mfr. of Women's Clothing; Joint Venture
S.I.C.: 5699
N.A.I.C.S.: 315240

Shanghai Beidie Adornment Co., Ltd. (1)
No. 81, Anjian Rd., Beicai Town
Pudongxinqu, 201204 Shanghai, China
Mfr. of Women's Clothing; Joint Venture
S.I.C.: 5699
N.A.I.C.S.: 315240

Shanghai Xindie Tanaka Garments Co., Ltd. (1)
No.1678, Liyue Lu, Pujiang Zhen
Minhang, 201114 Shanghai, China
Mfr. of Knitted Garments
S.I.C.: 2259
N.A.I.C.S.: 315190

CHORUS AVIATION INC.

310 Goudey Drive Halifax Stanfield International Airport
Enfield, NS, B2T 1E4, Canada
Tel.: (902) 873-5000
Fax: (902) 873-2098
E-Mail: investorsinfo@chorusaviation.ca
Web Site: www.chorusaviation.ca
Year Founded: 2005
CHR.A—(TSX)
Rev.: $1,700,456,098
Assets: $807,449,404
Liabilities: $676,124,452
Net Worth: $131,324,952
Earnings: $100,502,380
Emp.: 4,558
Fiscal Year-end: 12/31/12
Business Description:
Holding Company
S.I.C.: 6719
N.A.I.C.S.: 551112
Personnel:
Richard H. McCoy *(Chm)*
Joseph D. Randell *(Pres & CEO)*
Richard Flynn *(CFO)*

Jolene Mahody *(COO)*
Colin Copp *(Chief Admin Officer)*
Barbara Snowdon *(Gen Counsel & Sec)*
Board of Directors:
Richard H. McCoy
Gary M. Collins
Karen Cramm
Benjamin C. Duster IV
Richard Douglas Falconer
Sydney John Isaacs
G. Ross MacCormack
John Thomas McLennan
Joseph D. Randell
Transfer Agent:
CIBC Mellon Trust Company
Montreal, QC, Canada
Holdings:

Jazz Aviation LP (1)
310 Goudey Drive Halifax International Airport
Enfield, NS, B2T 1E4, Canada (100%)
Tel.: (902) 873-5000
Fax: (902) 873-2098
Web Site: www.flyjazz.ca
Sales Range: $1-4.9 Billion
Emp.: 4,144
Air Transportation Services
S.I.C.: 4512
N.A.I.C.S.: 481111
Joseph D. Randell *(Pres & CEO)*
Richard Flynn *(CFO)*
Jolene Mahody *(COO)*
Colin Copp *(Chief Admin Officer)*
Barbara Snowdon *(Gen Counsel & Sec)*

Divisions:

Air Canada Express (2)
1000 Air Ontario Dr
London, ON, N5V 3S4, Canada
Tel.: (519) 457-8071
Fax: (519) 452-9425
Web Site: www.flyjazz.ca
Airline Services
S.I.C.: 4512
N.A.I.C.S.: 481111
Debra Williams *(Mgr-Corp Comm)*

Air Canada Express (2)
5520 Miller Road
Richmond, BC, V7B 1L9, Canada
Tel.: (604) 244-2600
Fax: (604) 244-2676
Web Site: www.flyjazz.ca
Emp.: 1,200
Airline Services
Import Export
S.I.C.: 4512
N.A.I.C.S.: 481111
Colin Copp *(Sr VP-Employee Rels)*

CHORUS LIMITED

Level 9 North Tower Datacom House
68-86 Jervois Quay
Wellington, 6011, New Zealand
Mailing Address:
PO Box 632
Wellington, 6140, New Zealand
Tel.: (64) 4 471 0220
E-Mail: info@chorus.co.nz
Web Site: www.chorus.co.nz
CNU—(ASX NZE OTC)
Sales Range: $500-549.9 Million
Emp.: 532
Business Description:
Telecommunications Services
S.I.C.: 4813
N.A.I.C.S.: 517110
Personnel:
Susan Jane Sheldon *(Chm)*
Mark Ratcliffe *(CEO)*
Andrew Carroll *(CFO)*
Ewen Powell *(CIO)*
Vanessa Oakley *(Gen Counsel & Sec)*
Board of Directors:
Susan Jane Sheldon
Prudence Mary Flacks
Jonathan Peter Hartley
Mark Ratcliffe
Keith S. Turner
Anne Urlwin
Clayton Gordon Wakefield

CHOSEIDO PHARMACEUTICAL CO., LTD.

(Acquired by Nihon Chouzai Co., Ltd.)

CHOSEN HOLDINGS LIMITED

No 17 Woodlands Terrace Woodlands East Industrial Estate
Singapore, 738442, Singapore
Tel.: (65) 67530800
Fax: (65) 67537988
E-Mail: enquiries@chosen.com.sg
Web Site: www.chosen.com.sg
Year Founded: 1986
C10—(SES)
Rev.: $81,376,181
Assets: $78,616,454
Liabilities: $25,121,961
Net Worth: $53,494,493
Earnings: $951,290
Emp.: 1,075
Fiscal Year-end: 06/30/13
Business Description:
Ceramic Products Mfr
S.I.C.: 3259
N.A.I.C.S.: 327120
Personnel:
Aloysius Cher Kia Lim *(Chm & Mng Dir)*
Kok Hwee Chow *(CEO)*
Wee Choo Soong *(CFO & Co-Sec)*
Meng Ling Liew *(Co-Sec)*
Board of Directors:
Aloysius Cher Kia Lim
Heng Ching Chew
Kok Hwee Chow
Kok Kee Chow
Wee Choo Soong
Henry Song Kok Tan
Subsidiaries:

Chosen Investment Pte Ltd (1)
17 Woodlands Terrace Woodlands East Industrial Estate
Singapore, 738442, Singapore
Tel.: (65) 67530800
Fax: (65) 67537988
Plastics Product Mfr
S.I.C.: 3089
N.A.I.C.S.: 326199

Chosen Plastic Pte Ltd. (1)
17 Woodlands Terrace Woodlands East Indstrial Estate
Singapore, Singapore
Tel.: (65) 67530800
E-Mail: enquiries@chosen.com.sg
Plastic Injection Molding
S.I.C.: 3089
N.A.I.C.S.: 326199
Aloysius Cher Kia Lim *(Chm)*

Subsidiaries:

Chosen Dzios Pte Ltd (2)
2 Woodlands Sector 1 03-22 Woodlands Spectrum
Singapore, 738068, Singapore
Tel.: (65) 67536911
Fax: (65) 67533261
Web Site: www.chosen.com.sg/files/ct.htm
Emp.: 130
Plastics Product Mfr
S.I.C.: 3089
N.A.I.C.S.: 326199
Mike Lim *(Gen Mgr)*

Chosen Plastic Pte Ltd. (2)
Woodlands East Industrial Estate
17 Woodlands Terrace, Singapore, 738442, Singapore
Tel.: (65) 67530800
Fax: (65) 67537988
E-Mail: chosen@singnet.com.sg
Web Site: www.chosenplastic.com
Emp.: 50
Molded Plastic Mfr
S.I.C.: 3089
N.A.I.C.S.: 326199

Chosen Technologies Pte Ltd. (2)
2 Woodlands Sector 1 #03-22
Woodlands Spectrum, Singapore, 738068, Singapore
Tel.: (65) 67536911
Fax: (65) 67533261
Web Site: www.chosen.com.sg/files/ct.htm
Emp.: 25
Molded Plastic Parts Mfr
S.I.C.: 3089
N.A.I.C.S.: 326199
Mike Lim *(Gen Mgr)*

Unit:

Chosen Toolroom - Singapore (2)
01-55 Woodlands Spectrum II
207 Woodlands Avenue 9, Singapore, 738958, Singapore
Tel.: (65) 67541663
Fax: (65) 67541698
E-Mail: design@chosen.com.sg
Web Site: www.chosen.com.sg/files/cppltr.htm
Sls.: $7,000,000
Emp.: 60
Molded Plastics Mfr
S.I.C.: 3089
N.A.I.C.S.: 326199
Mike Lim *(Gen Mgr)*

Non-U.S. Subsidiaries:

Chosen Electronics Assembly (Shanghai) Co., Ltd. (2)
Wai Gao Qiao Free Trade Zone
238 Ri Ying Road S Pudong, Shanghai, 200131, China
Tel.: (86) 2150481138
Fax: (86) 2150481003
Emp.: 3,000
Contract Electronic Mfg Services
S.I.C.: 3089
N.A.I.C.S.: 326199
Jeffrey Hoo *(Gen Mgr)*

Chosen Enterprise (Dongguan) Co., Ltd. (2)
18 Xihu Hi-Tech Information Industrial Park
Shilong, Dongguan, Guangdong, 523325, China
Tel.: (86) 76988493338
Fax: (86) 76988493238
E-Mail: enquiries@chosen.com.sg
Web Site: www.chosen.com.sg/files/cedg.htm
Molded Plastic Mfr
S.I.C.: 3089
N.A.I.C.S.: 326199

Chosen Enterprise (Shanghai) Co., Ltd. (2)
Wai Gao Qiao Free Trade Zone 238 Ri Ying Road South
Pudong, Shanghai, 200131, China
Tel.: (86) 2150480118
Fax: (86) 21050481119
E-Mail: hoo_jeffrey@chosen.com.sg
Web Site: www.chosen.com.sg
Emp.: 300
Molded Plastic Mfr
S.I.C.: 3089
N.A.I.C.S.: 326199
Hoo Jeffrey *(Gen Mgr)*

Chosen Manufacturing Sdn. Bhd. (2)
Kawasan Perindustrian Tebrau IV PLO 268
Jalan Firma 3
Johor Bahru, 81100 Johor, Malaysia
Tel.: (60) 73577861
Fax: (60) 73579961
E-Mail: admin_cm@chosen.com.sg
Web Site: www.chosen.com.sg/files/cmsb.htm
Emp.: 100
Molded Plastic Products Mfr
S.I.C.: 3089
N.A.I.C.S.: 326199
Tay Say Kiat *(Sr Mgr)*

Chosen Plastic Sdn. Bhd. (2)
Taman Perindustrian Cemerlang
No 21 Jalan Gemilang 1
Ulu Tiram Johor Bahru, 81800 Johor, Malaysia
Tel.: (60) 78677867
Fax: (60) 8677767
Web Site: www.chosen.com.sg/files/cpsb.htm
Emp.: 300
Molded Plastic Mfr
S.I.C.: 3089
N.A.I.C.S.: 326199
Lye Kong Sang *(Gen Mgr-Ops)*

Chosen (Thailand) Company Limited (2)
107 Moo 1 Hi-Tech Industrial Estate Asia-Nakornsawan Road
Tambol Banlane Amphur Bangpa-i, Ayutthaya, 13160, Thailand
Tel.: (66) 35351571
Fax: (66) 35351576
Web Site: www.chosen.com.sg/files/cth.htm
Emp.: 200
Molded Plastics Mfr
S.I.C.: 3089
N.A.I.C.S.: 326199

Non-U.S. Unit:

Chosen Toolroom - Shanghai (2)
Wai Gao Qiao Free Trade Zone
238 Ri Ying Road S Pudong, Shanghai, 200131, China
Tel.: (86) 2150480118
Fax: (86) 2150481119
E-Mail: ces_admin@chosen.com.sg
Web Site: www.chosen.com.sg/files/cestr.htm
Molded Plastics Mfr
S.I.C.: 3089
N.A.I.C.S.: 326199

CHOSUN REFRACTORIES CO., LTD.

Taeindong 1657-9
Kwangyang, Jeonlanam-do, Korea (South)
Tel.: (82) 61 798 8114
Fax: (82) 61 792 2139
Web Site: www.chosunref.co.kr
Year Founded: 1947
000480—(KRS)
Business Description:
Refractory Mfr
S.I.C.: 3259
N.A.I.C.S.: 327120
Personnel:
Sam Ryul Yang *(Pres)*

CHOSUN WELDING CO., LTD.

865 Jangheung-Dong
Nam-Gu, Pohang, 790-240, Korea (South)
Tel.: (82) 54 2898200
Fax: (82) 2 5536117
Web Site: www.chosunwelding.com
Year Founded: 1949
120030—(KRS)
Business Description:
Welding Material Mfr & Distr
S.I.C.: 3548
N.A.I.C.S.: 333992
Personnel:
Won Yeong Jang *(CEO)*

CHOW SANG SANG HOLDINGS INTERNATIONAL LIMITED

4/F Chow Sang Sang Building 229 Nathan Road
Kowloon, China (Hong Kong)
Tel.: (852) 2192 3123
Fax: (852) 2730 9683
E-Mail: cs@chowsangsang.com
Web Site: www.chowsangsang.com
Year Founded: 1934
116—(HKG)
Sls.: $2,354,656,916
Assets: $1,344,375,317
Liabilities: $431,013,054
Net Worth: $913,362,263
Earnings: $127,507,565

Chow Sang Sang Holdings International Limited—(Continued)

Emp.: 7,013
Fiscal Year-end: 12/31/12
Business Description:
Jewelry Mfr & Whslr
S.I.C.: 3911
N.A.I.C.S.: 339910
Personnel:
Kwen Lim Chow *(Chm)*
Theodore Shing Chi Tam *(Sec)*
Board of Directors:
Kwen Lim Chow
Bing Fun Chan
Gerald King Sing Chow
Kwen Ling Chow
Vincent Wing Shing Chow
Winston Wun Sing Chow
Pui Lam Chung
Stephen Man Lung Lau
Ka Lun Lee
King Man Lo
Stephen Leung Huel Ting

Butterfield Fulcrum Group (Bermuda) Limited
26 Burnaby Street
Hamilton, HM 11, Bermuda

CHOW STEEL INDUSTRIES PUBLIC COMPANY LIMITED

209/1 K Tower 18th Floor Unit 3
Sukhumvit 21 (Asoke)
Klongtoey Nua
Wattana, Bangkok, 10110, Thailand
Tel.: (66) 22603101
Fax: (66) 22603100
E-Mail: info@chowsteel.com
Web Site: www.chowsteel.com
Year Founded: 2000
CHOW—(THA)
Emp.: 250
Business Description:
Steel Billets Mfr
S.I.C.: 3399
N.A.I.C.S.: 331110
Personnel:
Pruchya Piumsomboon *(Chm)*
Narong Yoothanom *(Vice Chm)*
Anavin Jiratomsiri *(CEO)*
Koo Man Wai *(Deputy Mng Dir & VP-Procurement)*
Board of Directors:
Pruchya Piumsomboon
Kanawath Aran
Noppadon Chirasanti
Anavin Jiratomsiri
Sharhuta Jiratomsiri
Sanguankiat Lewmanomont
Kalyaporn Pan-ma-rerng
Mark D. Remijan
Koo Man Wai
Narong Yoothanom

CHOW TAI FOOK ENTERPRISES LTD.

38/F, New World Tower
16-18 Queen's Road, Central, China (Hong Kong)
Tel.: (852) 25268649
Fax: (852) 28104297
E-Mail: enquiry@chowtaifook.com
Web Site: www.chowtaifook.com
Business Description:
Investment Holding Company
S.I.C.: 6719
N.A.I.C.S.: 551112
Personnel:
Henry Kar-Shun Cheng *(Chm)*
Kent Siu-Kee Wong *(Mng Dir)*
Board of Directors:
Henry Kar-Shun Cheng
Sai-Cheong Chan
Adrian Chi-Kong Cheng
Conroy Chi-Heng Cheng
Hamilton Pin-Hei Cheng
Peter Kar-Shing Cheng
Wilson Kam-Biu Cheng
Tong-Fat Koo
Kent Siu-Kee Wong

Holdings:

Chow Tai Fook Jewellery Group Limited **(1)**
38/F New World Tower
16-18 Queen's Road, Central, China (Hong Kong) Ky
Tel.: (852) 2526 8649
E-Mail: enquiry@chowtaifook.com
Web Site: www.chowtaifook.com
1929—(HKG OTC)
Emp.: 6,000
Holding Company; Jewelry & Watch Retailer
S.I.C.: 6719
N.A.I.C.S.: 551112
Henry Kar-Shun Cheng *(Chm)*
Kent Siu-Kee Wong *(Mng Dir)*
Hamilton Ping-Hei Cheng *(Fin Dir & Sec)*

Subsidiaries:

Chow Tai Fook Jewellery Co., Ltd. **(2)**
38/F New World Tower
Central, China (Hong Kong) HK
Tel.: (852) 2526 8649
E-Mail: enquiry@chowtaifook.com
Web Site: www.chowtaifook.com
Jewelry Mfr & Retail Stores Operator
S.I.C.: 5944
N.A.I.C.S.: 448310
Henry Kar-Shun Cheng *(Chm)*
Kent Siu-Kee Wong *(Mng Dir)*

CTF Watch Limited **(2)**
38/F New World Tower 16-18 Queen's Road
Central, China (Hong Kong) VG
Tel.: (852) 2526 8649
Web Site: watch.chowtaifook.com
Watch Retailer
S.I.C.: 5944
N.A.I.C.S.: 448310
Kent Siu-Kee Wong *(Mng Dir)*

New World Development Company Limited **(1)**
30/F New World Tower 18 Queen's Road
Central, China (Hong Kong) HK
Tel.: (852) 25231056
Fax: (852) 28104673
E-Mail: newworld@nwd.com.hk
Web Site: www.nwd.com.hk
0017—(HKG)
Rev.: $6,032,268,105
Assets: $42,835,784,445
Liabilities: $19,915,566,695
Net Worth: $22,920,217,750
Earnings: $2,387,689,780
Emp.: 47,000
Fiscal Year-end: 06/30/13
Properties, Infrastructure, Service & Telecommunications Businesses & Strategic Investments
S.I.C.: 6552
N.A.I.C.S.: 237210
Henry Kar-Shun Cheng *(Chm)*
Man-Hoi Wong *(Sec)*

Subsidiaries:

New World China Land Limited **(2)**
9/F New World Tower 1 18 Queen's Road
Central, China (Hong Kong) Ky
Tel.: (852) 21310201 (70%)
Fax: (852) 21310216
E-Mail: enquiry@nwcl.com.hk
Web Site: www.nwcl.com.hk
0917—(HKG)
Rev.: $2,083,041,794
Assets: $15,196,279,998
Liabilities: $7,755,397,039
Net Worth: $7,440,882,960
Earnings: $626,098,156
Emp.: 9,172
Fiscal Year-end: 06/30/13
Investment Property for Lease, Develop & Manage Resort & Hotel Projects
S.I.C.: 6211
N.A.I.C.S.: 523999
Henry Kar-Shun Cheng *(Chm & Mng Dir)*
Benny Yiu-ho Chan *(Deputy CEO-Shenyang & Anshan)*
Steward Lee *(Deputy CEO-Beijing, Tianjin, Jinan, Tangshan & Langfang)*
Ronald Kwok-Siu Yau *(Deputy CEO-Tangshan & Beijing)*
Wingo Chi-wing Chan *(CEO-Beijing, Tianjin, Tangshan, Langfang & Jinan)*
Desmond Chung-chun Lau *(CEO-Shenyang & Anshan)*
Sau-lung Li *(CEO-Wuhan)*
Guo-qiang Liang *(CEO-Guiyang)*
Li-qun Liu *(CEO-Changsha & Yiyang)*
See-yuen Wong *(CEO-Chengdu)*
Simon Siu-man Wong *(CEO-Wuhan)*
Titus Zhi-hai Yuan *(CEO-Ningbo)*
Lynda Man-ying Ngan *(Sec)*

Subsidiaries:

Dalian New World Hotel Co., Ltd. **(3)**
Hong Kong Corporate Office 36/F New World Tower 1
18 Queen's Road, Central, China (Hong Kong) (100%)
Tel.: (852) 21382222
Fax: (852) 21382233
E-Mail: office@rosewoodhotelgroup.com
Web Site: www.rosewoodhotelgroup.com
Emp.: 60
Hotels & Motels
S.I.C.: 7011
N.A.I.C.S.: 721110
Symon Britle *(Mng Dir)*

New World China Land Investments Company Limited **(3)**
9th Floor New World Twr I
18 Queens Rd, Central, China (Hong Kong) (100%)
Tel.: (852) 21382222
Fax: (852) 21382233
E-Mail: office@newworldhospitality.com
Web Site: www.newworldhospitality.com
Emp.: 30
Real Estate Property Lessors
S.I.C.: 6519
N.A.I.C.S.: 531190

Non-U.S. Subsidiary:

Shenyang New World Hotel Co Ltd **(3)**
No 2 Nanjing S St
Heping District, Shenyang, China (100%)
Tel.: (86) 2423869888
Fax: (86) 2423860018
E-Mail: fo@nwhsy.china.com
Web Site: www.newworldhotels.com
Hotels & Motels
S.I.C.: 7011
N.A.I.C.S.: 721110
Michael Fu *(Pres)*

New World Department Store China Limited **(2)**
7th Floor 88 Hing Fat Street Causeway Bay
Hong Kong, China (Hong Kong) Ky
Tel.: (852) 27533988 (72%)
Fax: (852) 23180884
E-Mail: nwdscad@nwds.com.hk
Web Site: www.nwds.com.hk
0825—(HKG OTC)
Rev.: $517,288,728
Assets: $1,654,978,472
Liabilities: $854,378,341
Net Worth: $800,600,131
Earnings: $82,721,812
Emp.: 6,616
Fiscal Year-end: 06/30/13
Departmental Store
S.I.C.: 5311
N.A.I.C.S.: 452111
Philip Fai-yet Cheung *(Mng Dir)*
Kenneth Kwok-kan Wong *(CFO)*
Catherine Yuk-Kwai Wu *(Sec)*

New World Hotels (Holdings) Limited **(2)**
36/F New World Tower 1
18 Queen's Road, Central, China (Hong Kong) HK
Tel.: (852) 2138 2222 (64%)
Fax: (852) 2138 2233
Web Site: www.newworldhotels.com
Emp.: 50
Holding Company; Hotel Owner & Operator
S.I.C.: 6719
N.A.I.C.S.: 551112
Yu-Tung Cheng *(Chm)*
Henry Kar-Shun Cheng *(Mng Dir)*

Subsidiary:

New World Hotel Management Limited **(3)**
36/F New World Tower 1
18 Queen's Road, Central, China (Hong Kong) HK
Tel.: (852) 2138 2222 (70%)
Fax: (852) 2138 2233
E-Mail: office@newworldhospitality.com
Web Site: www.newworldhospitality.com
Emp.: 9,000
Hotel Developer & Operator
S.I.C.: 7011
N.A.I.C.S.: 721110
Sonia Chi-man Cheng *(Vice Chm)*
Symon Bridle *(COO)*
John Shamon *(Sr VP-Technical Svcs)*

U.S. Subsidiary:

Rosewood Hotels & Resorts LLC **(3)**
500 Crescent Ct Ste 300
Dallas, TX 75201
Tel.: (214) 880-4200
Fax: (214) 880-4201
Web Site: www.rosewoodhotels.com
Emp.: 55
Hotel Owner & Operator
S.I.C.: 7011
N.A.I.C.S.: 721110
Radha Arora *(Pres)*
Robert Boulogne *(COO)*
Susan Aldridge *(Gen Counsel & Sr VP-Legal)*
George Fong *(Sr VP-Architecture & Design)*

Subsidiaries:

Caneel Bay **(4)**
Route 20 N Shore Rd PO Box 720
Saint John, VI 00830
Tel.: (340) 776-6111
Fax: (340) 693-8280
E-Mail: caneelres@rosewoodhotels.com
Web Site: www.caneelbay.com
Emp.: 500
Hotel
S.I.C.: 7011
N.A.I.C.S.: 721110
Nikoley Hotze *(Mng Dir)*

The Carlyle, A Rosewood Hotel **(4)**
35 E 76th St
New York, NY 10021
Tel.: (212) 744-1600
Fax: (212) 717-4682
E-Mail: thecarlyle@rosewoodhotels.com
Web Site: www.thecarlyle.com
Emp.: 500
Hotel
S.I.C.: 7521
N.A.I.C.S.: 812930
John Scott *(CEO)*
Giovanni Beretta *(Mng Dir)*

Hotel Crescent Court **(4)**
400 Crescent Ct
Dallas, TX 75201
Tel.: (214) 871-3200
Fax: (214) 871-3272
E-Mail: crescentcourt@rosewoodhotels.com
Web Site: www.rosewoodhotels.com
Emp.: 100
Hotel
S.I.C.: 7011
N.A.I.C.S.: 721110
Adrian Norbury *(Dir-Mktg)*

Little Dix Bay **(4)**
Cruz Bay
Saint John, VI 00831-0720
Tel.: (284) 495-5555
Fax: (284) 495-5661
E-Mail: littledixbay@rosewoodhotels.com
Web Site: www.littledixbay.com
Emp.: 350
Hotel
S.I.C.: 7011
N.A.I.C.S.: 721110
Lily Carr *(Mgr-Sls)*

The Mansion on Turtle Creek **(4)**
2821 Turtle Creek Blvd
Dallas, TX 75219

Tel.: (214) 559-2100
Fax: (214) 528-4187
E-Mail: themansion@rosewoodhotels.com
Web Site: www.themansiononturtlecreek.com
Hotel
S.I.C.: 5812
N.A.I.C.S.: 722511
John Scott *(CEO)*
Duncan Grham *(Mng Dir)*

Non-U.S. Subsidiaries:

Al Faisaliah Hotel **(4)**
King Fahad Rd
PO Box 4148
Olaya, Riyadh, 11491, Saudi Arabia
Tel.: (966) 12732000
Fax: (966) 12732001
E-Mail: alfaisaliah@rosewoodhotels.com
Web Site: www.alfaisaliahhotel.com
Emp.: 950
Hotel
S.I.C.: 7011
N.A.I.C.S.: 721110
Alex Pichel *(Mng Dir)*

The Dharmawangsa **(4)**
Jalan Brawijawa Raya No 26
Jakarta, 12160, Indonesia
Tel.: (62) 217258181
Fax: (62) 217258383
E-Mail: hotel@the-dharmawangsa.com
Web Site: www.the-dharmawangsa.com
Emp.: 500
Hotel
S.I.C.: 7011
N.A.I.C.S.: 721110

Hotel Al Khozama **(4)**
Olaya Rd
PO Box 4148
Riyadh, 11491, Saudi Arabia
Tel.: (966) 1462732000
Fax: (966) 14648576
E-Mail: alkhozama@rosewoodhotels.com
Web Site: www.al-khozama.com
Emp.: 400
Hotel
S.I.C.: 7011
N.A.I.C.S.: 721110
Alex Pichel *(Mng Dir)*

Jumba Bay **(4)**
PO Box 243
Saint John's, Antigua & Barbuda
Tel.: (268) 4626000
Fax: (268) 4626020
E-Mail: jumbabay@rosewoodhotels.com
Web Site: www.jumbybayresort.com
Emp.: 230
Hotel
S.I.C.: 7011
N.A.I.C.S.: 721110
Andrew Hedley *(Gen Mgr)*

King Pacific Lodge **(4)**
255 W 1st St Ste 214
North Vancouver, BC, V7M 3G8, Canada
Tel.: (604) 987-5452
Fax: (604) 987-5472
E-Mail: info@kingpacificlodge.com
Web Site: www.kingpacificlodge.com
Emp.: 40
Hotel
S.I.C.: 7011
N.A.I.C.S.: 721110

NWS Holdings Limited **(2)**
28F New World Tower 18 Queen's Road
Central, China (Hong Kong) BM
Tel.: (852) 21310600 (60%)
Fax: (852) 21316250
E-Mail: news@nws.com.hk
Web Site: www.nws.com.hk
0659—(HKG OTC)
Rev.: $2,095,166,705
Assets: $8,642,590,060
Liabilities: $3,352,932,110
Net Worth: $5,289,657,950
Earnings: $526,412,585
Emp.: 26,000
Fiscal Year-end: 06/30/13
Holding Company; Infrastructure & Facilities Support Services
S.I.C.: 6719
N.A.I.C.S.: 551112
Henry Kar Shun Cheng *(Chm)*
Tak Wing Chow *(Sec & Controller-Fin)*

CHOWGULE & COMPANY PVT. LTD.

Chowgule House Mormugao Harbour
Goa, 403 803, India
Tel.: (91) 832-2525000
Fax: (91) 8322521011
E-Mail: ccl@chowgule.co.in
Web Site: www.chowgule.co.in
Year Founded: 1941
Sales Range: $400-449.9 Million
Business Description:
Holding Company; Activities in Mining, Transportation, Export of Iron Ore, Shipbuilding & Material Handling & Construction Equipment
S.I.C.: 6719
N.A.I.C.S.: 551112
Personnel:
Vijay Vishwasrao Chowgule *(Chm & CEO)*

Subsidiaries:

Chowgule & Company (Salt) Private Limited **(1)**
Chowgule House Mormugao Harbour
Goa, 403 803, India In
Tel.: (91) 832 252 5047
Fax: (91) 832 252 1011
E-Mail: mahadevan.ccl@chowgule.co.in
Web Site: www.chowgule.co.in/salt/index.html
Industrial Salt Production & Export
S.I.C.: 3299
N.A.I.C.S.: 327999
Nathan Ramesh Chowgule *(Exec Dir)*

Chowgule Brothers Pvt. Ltd **(1)**
Chowgule House Mormugao Harbour
Goa, 403 803, India
Tel.: (91) 8322525107
Web Site: www.chowgulebros.com
Sales Range: $1-9.9 Million
Emp.: 98
Shipping, Insurance, Freight Forwarding, Warehousing & Custom Broking
S.I.C.: 4731
N.A.I.C.S.: 488510
Jaywant Yeshwantrao Chowgule *(Exec Dir)*

Chowgule Industries Pvt. Ltd. **(1)**
Chowgule House
Mormugao Harbour, Goa, 403 803, India
Tel.: (91) 832 2525000
Fax: (91) 832 2521011
Web Site: www.chowguleindustries.com
Trading Services; Motor Vehicle Sales, Marketing of Pipes, Chemicals & Waste Water Systems
S.I.C.: 5012
N.A.I.C.S.: 423110

Chowgule Steamships Limited **(1)**
Chowgule House Mormugao Harbour
Goa, 403 803, India
Tel.: (91) 832 2525000
Fax: (91) 832 2521011
E-Mail: csl@chowgule.co.in
Web Site: www.chowgulesteamships.co.in
501833—(BOM)
Rev.: $17,441,227
Assets: $152,522,666
Liabilities: $73,975,768
Net Worth: $78,546,898
Earnings: ($25,669,779)
Fiscal Year-end: 03/31/13
Bulk Cargo Shipping Services
S.I.C.: 4412
N.A.I.C.S.: 483111
Mangesh Sawant *(CFO)*
Suhas Joshi *(Compliance Officer & Sec)*

Deccan Alloy Metal Industries Pvt. Ltd. **(1)**
2095 E Ward Vikram Nagar near Tembalai Hill
Kolhapur, 416 005, India
Tel.: (91) 2312655115
Fax: (91) 2312668515
Web Site: www.chowgule.co.in/koapl/kolhapur_oxygen.asp
Industrial & Medical Oxygen Mgr
S.I.C.: 2813
N.A.I.C.S.: 325120
Satish Chowgule *(Chm)*
Umaji Chowgule *(Mng Dir)*

Keltech Energies Ltd. **(1)**
32/1-2 6th Floor Crescent Towers
Crescent Road, Bengaluru, 560 001, India
Tel.: (91) 8022257900
Fax: (91) 80 22253857
E-Mail: info@keltechenergies.com
Web Site: www.keltechenergies.com
Explosives Mfr
S.I.C.: 2892
N.A.I.C.S.: 325920

Kolhapur Gases (Carbon Dioxide) Pvt. Ltd. **(1)**
295 E Ward Vikram Nagar near Tembalai Hill
Kolhapur, 416 005, India
Tel.: (91) 2312655115
Fax: (91) 231 266 8515
Web Site: www.chowgule.co.in/koapl/kolhapur_oxygen.asp
Industrial & Medical Gases Mfr
S.I.C.: 2813
N.A.I.C.S.: 325120
Umaji Chowgule *(Mng Dir)*

Kolhapur Oxygen and Acetylene Private Limited **(1)**
2095 E Ward Vikram Nagar near Tembalai Hill
Kolhapur, 416 005, India
Tel.: (91) 2312655115
Fax: (91) 231 266 8515
E-Mail: koapl@chowgule.co.in
Web Site: www.chowgule.co.in/koapl/kolhapur_oxygen.asp
Industrial & Medical Oxygen & Nitrogen Mfr
S.I.C.: 2813
N.A.I.C.S.: 325120
Vijay Chowgule *(Chm)*
Umaji Chowgule *(Mng Dir)*

Joint Venture:

Chowgule Koster (India) Construction Chemicals Pvt. Ltd. **(1)**
Bakhtawar 4th Floor Namiman Point
Mumbai, Maharashtra, 400021, India
Tel.: (91) 22 66202500
Fax: (91) 22 66202570
E-Mail: contactus@chowgulekoster.com
Web Site: www.chowgulekoster.com
Waterproofing Products Mfr & Distr
S.I.C.: 2899
N.A.I.C.S.: 325998

CHP CONSULTING LIMITED

20 Gresham Street
London, EC2V 7JE, United Kingdom
Tel.: (44) 2075881800
Fax: (44) 2075881802
E-Mail: sales@chp.co.uk
Web Site: www.chpconsulting.com
Rev.: $35,270,901
Emp.: 100
Business Description:
Software Services
S.I.C.: 7371
N.A.I.C.S.: 541511
Personnel:
Andrew Page *(CEO)*
Ian Hargrave *(CFO)*
Andrew Denton *(COO)*

CHRIS JOANNOU PUBLIC LTD

51 Stigos Street
3117 Limassol, Cyprus
Tel.: (357) 25 333779
Fax: (357) 25 332605
E-Mail: cjoannou@cjoannou.com
Web Site: www.chrisjoannouplc.com
Year Founded: 1957
CJ—(CYP)
Business Description:
Food Products Machinery & Equipment Supplier
S.I.C.: 5087
N.A.I.C.S.: 423850
Personnel:
Chris Joannou *(Founder & Chm)*

CHRISLIS

Route Nationale 151
Jardres, 86800 Poitiers, France
Tel.: (33) 549463858
Sales Range: $10-24.9 Million
Emp.: 64
Business Description:
Grocery Stores
S.I.C.: 5411
N.A.I.C.S.: 445110
Personnel:
Lisiane Plaisant *(HR Dir)*

CHRISTENSEN MOTORS LTD.

2525 Bowen Road
Nanaimo, BC, V9T 3L2, Canada
Tel.: (250) 758-9125
Fax: (250) 758-6322
E-Mail: christensenmazda@shaw.ca
Year Founded: 1970
Rev.: $18,107,735
Emp.: 40
Business Description:
New & Used Car Dealers
S.I.C.: 5511
N.A.I.C.S.: 441110
Personnel:
Dan Jones *(Mgr-Sls)*

CHRISTIAN DIOR S.A.

30 Ave Montaigne
75008 Paris, France
Tel.: (33) 144132232
Fax: (33) 147200060
E-Mail: info@christiandior.com
Web Site: www.dior.com
Year Founded: 1946
CDI—(EUR OMX OTC)
Sales Range: $25-49.9 Million
Emp.: 84,497
Business Description:
Mfr & Distr of Apparel, Luggage & Fine Leather Goods, Perfumes & Beauty Products, Champagne, Brandy, Wines, Watches & Jewelry
S.I.C.: 3171
N.A.I.C.S.: 316992
Personnel:
Bernard Arnault *(Chm)*
Eric Guerlain *(Vice Chm)*
Sidney Toledano *(CEO)*
Pierre Gode *(Mng Dir)*
Patricia Malone *(Pres/COO-Americas)*
Board of Directors:
Bernard Arnault
Delphine Arnault
Denis Dalibot
Christian de Labriffe
Jaime de Marichalar y Saenz de Tejada
Renaud Donnedieu de Vabres
Helene Desmarais
Segolene Gallienne
Pierre Gode
Eric Guerlain
Sidney Toledano

Ernst & Young et Autres
1 2 Place des Saisons
Courbevoie, France

Subsidiaries:

CD INVESTISSEMENTS SARL **(1)**
Espace de Comboire
38130 Echirolles, France
Tel.: (33) 4 76 09 72 12
Fax: (33) 4 76 33 13 46
Investment Management Services
S.I.C.: 6211
N.A.I.C.S.: 523999

Christian Dior Couture S.A. **(1)**
11 Bis Rue Francios 1er
75008 Paris, France (100%)
Tel.: (33) 140735444
Fax: (33) 147200060
Web Site: www.christiandior.com
Sales Range: $1-4.9 Billion
Emp.: 200
Fashion Designer & Mfr

Christian Dior S.A.—(Continued)

Export
S.I.C.: 2389
N.A.I.C.S.: 315280
Sidney Toledano *(Chm & CEO)*

CHRISTIAN LOUBOUTIN SARL

19 Rue Jean-Jacques Rousseau
75001 Paris, France
Tel.: (33) 142360531
Fax: (33) 0142369973
E-Mail: standard@christianlouboutin.fr
Web Site: www.christianlouboutin.fr
Year Founded: 1992
Sales Range: $10-24.9 Million
Emp.: 15

Business Description:
Shoe Mfr & Retailer
S.I.C.: 2389
N.A.I.C.S.: 316210

Personnel:
Bruno Chambelland *(Pres)*
Alexis Mourot *(Mng Dir)*

CHRISTIAN MAYR GMBH & CO. KG

Eichenstrasse 1
D-87665 Mauerstetten, Germany
Tel.: (49) 8341 804 0
Fax: (49) 8341 804 421
E-Mail: info@mayr.com
Web Site: www.mayr.com
Emp.: 800

Business Description:
Industrial Equipment Mfr
S.I.C.: 3559
N.A.I.C.S.: 333249

Personnel:
Gunther Klingler *(CEO)*

U.S. Subsidiary:

Mayr Corp. (1)
4 North St Ste 300
Waldwick, NJ 07463 NJ
Tel.: (201) 445-7210
Web Site: www.mayr.com
Industrial Machinery Mfr
S.I.C.: 3559
N.A.I.C.S.: 333249
Hans Eberle *(Pres)*

Non-U.S. Subsidiary:

Mayr Transmissions Ltd. (1)
Units 10-11 Valley Road Business Park
Keighley, West Yorkshire, BD21 4L, United Kingdom
Tel.: (44) 1535 663900
Fax: (44) 1535 663261
E-Mail: sales@mayr.co.uk
Web Site: www.mayr.co.uk
Industrial Machinery Mfr
S.I.C.: 3559
N.A.I.C.S.: 333249

CHRISTIAN POTIER S.A.

1819 chemin de Beauchamp
CS2008 Monteux, 84207 Carpentras, Cedex, France
Tel.: (33) 4 90 60 67 00
Fax: (33) 4 90 60 77 13
E-Mail: commercial@christian-potier.fr
Web Site: www.christian-potier.fr
Year Founded: 1985
MLCHP—(EUR)
Sales Range: $10-24.9 Million

Business Description:
Sauce Mfr
S.I.C.: 2099
N.A.I.C.S.: 311942

Personnel:
Olivier Potier *(CEO)*

CHRISTIANI & NIELSEN (THAI) PUBLIC COMPANY LIMITED

451 La Salle Road Sukhumvit 105
Bangna
Bangkok, 10260, Thailand
Tel.: (66) 2398 0158
Fax: (66) 2398 9860
E-Mail: cnt@cn-thai.co.th
Web Site: www.cn-thai.co.th
Year Founded: 1930
CNT—(THA)
Rev.: $242,542,160
Assets: $150,772,033
Liabilities: $90,236,753
Net Worth: $60,535,280
Earnings: $15,434,434
Fiscal Year-end: 12/31/12

Business Description:
Construction Services
S.I.C.: 1541
N.A.I.C.S.: 236210

Personnel:
Santi Grachangnetara *(Chm)*
Kirit Shah *(Vice Chm)*
Somchai Jongsililerd *(Mng Dir & Sec)*
Surasak Osathanugraha *(Asst Mng Dir)*

Board of Directors:
Santi Grachangnetara
John Scott Heinecke
Somchai Jongsililerd
Paniti Junhasavasdikul
Surasak Osathanugraha
Kasemsit Pathomsak
Anumolu Ramakrishna
Ishaan Shah
Kirit Shah
Kris Thirakaosal
Khushroo Kali Wadia

CHRISTIE & SON SALES LTD

24 Forest Hills Parkway
Dartmouth, NS, B2W 6E4, Canada
Tel.: (902) 462-6107
Year Founded: 1976
Rev.: $11,998,403
Emp.: 100

Business Description:
Automotive Parts & Accessories Stores
S.I.C.: 5531
N.A.I.C.S.: 441310

Personnel:
Archie Christie *(Pres)*

CHRISTIE GROUP PLC

Whitefriars House 6 Carmelite Street
London, EC4Y 0BS, United Kingdom
Tel.: (44) 2072270707
Fax: (44) 2072270708
E-Mail: executive@christiegroup.com
Web Site: www.christiegroup.com
CTG—(LSE)
Rev.: $88,667,658
Assets: $28,262,974
Liabilities: $25,230,737
Net Worth: $3,032,237
Earnings: $110,550
Emp.: 1,350
Fiscal Year-end: 12/31/12

Business Description:
Software Sector
S.I.C.: 3652
N.A.I.C.S.: 334614

Personnel:
Philip Gwyn *(Chm)*
David Rugg *(CEO)*
Dan Prickett *(CFO & Sec)*

Board of Directors:
Philip Gwyn
Tony Chambers
Chris Day
Paul Ian Harding
Dan Prickett
David Rugg
Pommy Sarwal

Subsidiaries:

Christie, Owen & Davies Ltd. (1)
Whitefriars House
6 Carmelite Street, London, EC4Y 0BS, United Kingdom
Tel.: (44) 2072270700
Fax: (44) 2072270701
E-Mail: enquiries@christie.com
Web Site: www.christie.com
Emp.: 50
Professional Brokerage & Advisory Services
S.I.C.: 6411
N.A.I.C.S.: 524210
Simon Chaplin *(Dir-Corp Pubs)*

Orridge & Co Ltd. (1)
Unit 4 Essex House Astra Ctr Edinburgh Way
Harlow, Essex, CM20 2BN, United Kingdom
Tel.: (44) 1279775600
Fax: (44) 1279451660
E-Mail: contact@orridge.co.uk
Web Site: www.orridge.co.uk
Emp.: 12
Stocktaking Solutions
S.I.C.: 7389
N.A.I.C.S.: 561990
Paul Harding *(Mng Dir)*

Pinders Professional & Consultancy Services Ltd. (1)
Pinder House 249 Upper Third St
Cent Milton Keynes, Milton Keynes, Buckinghamshire, MK9 1DS, United Kingdom
Tel.: (44) 1908350500
Fax: (44) 1908350501
E-Mail: info@pinders.co.uk
Web Site: www.pinders.co.uk
Business Appraising & Surveying Services
S.I.C.: 6531
N.A.I.C.S.: 531320
Justin Cain *(Mng Dir)*

RCC Business Mortgage Brokers Ltd. (1)
39 Victoria St
London, SW1H 0EU, United Kingdom
Tel.: (44) 207 227 0774
Fax: (44) 844 4124925
E-Mail: london@christiefinance.com
Web Site: www.christiefinance.com
Emp.: 5
Business Mortgage Broker Services
S.I.C.: 6163
N.A.I.C.S.: 522310
Philip Roberts *(Head-Compliance)*

RCC Insurance Brokers Ltd. (1)
10 Finsbury Sq
London, EC2A 1AD, United Kingdom
Tel.: (44) 844 4124924
Fax: (44) 207 4488830
E-Mail: enquiries@christieinsurance.com
Web Site: www.christieinsurance.com
Emp.: 20
Commercial Insurance Brokerage Services
S.I.C.: 6411
N.A.I.C.S.: 524210
Walter Murray *(Mng Dir)*

Venners Systems & Services Ltd. (1)
249 Upper Third St Witan Gate W
Milton Keynes, Buckinghamshire, MK9 1DS, United Kingdom
Tel.: (44) 1908350650
Fax: (44) 1908350551
E-Mail: contact@vennersys.com
Web Site: www.vennersys.co.uk
Emp.: 10
Leisure & Hospitality Solutions
S.I.C.: 8742
N.A.I.C.S.: 541611
Paul Harding *(Mng Dir)*

Venners Ltd. (1)
Essex House Astra Ctr Edinburgh Way
Harlow, Essex, CM20 2BN, United Kingdom
Tel.: (44) 1279620820
Fax: (44) 1279620821
E-Mail: enquiries@venners.co.uk
Web Site: www.venners.com
Emp.: 20
Stocktake & Auditing Services
S.I.C.: 7389
N.A.I.C.S.: 561990
Trevor Heyburn *(Mng Dir)*

Non-U.S. Subsidiaries:

Christie + Co GmbH (1)
Bockenheimer Landstrasse 93
Frankfurt, Hesse, 60325, Germany
Tel.: (49) 699074570
Fax: (49) 6990745710
E-Mail: frankfurt@christie.com
Web Site: www.christie.com
Emp.: 20
Business Valuing & Surveying Services
S.I.C.: 7389
N.A.I.C.S.: 561499
Markus Beike *(Mng Dir)*

Christie + Co OY (1)
Tammasaarenlaituri 3
00180 Helsinki, Finland
Tel.: (358) 941378500
Fax: (358) 941378510
E-Mail: kimmo.virtanen@christie.com
Web Site: www.christiecorporate.com
Emp.: 3
Business Valuers & Surveying Services
S.I.C.: 8741
N.A.I.C.S.: 561110

Christie + Co SARL (1)
5 Rue Meyerbeer
75008 Paris, France
Tel.: (33) 153967272
Fax: (33) 153967282
E-Mail: paris@christie.com
Web Site: www.christie.com
Emp.: 10
Business Valuing & Surveying Services
S.I.C.: 8741
N.A.I.C.S.: 561110
Philippe Souterbicq *(Mng Dir)*

Christie, Owen & Davies SL (1)
Paseo de Gracia 11 Esc B 4 3
08007 Barcelona, Spain
Tel.: (34) 933436161
Fax: (34) 933436160
E-Mail: barcelona@christie.com
Web Site: www.christie.com
Emp.: 3
Business Valuers & Surveying Services
S.I.C.: 7389
N.A.I.C.S.: 561499
Inmaculada Ranera *(Mng Dir)*

Orridge SA (1)
Renbaanlaan 60
Brussels, 1050, Belgium
Tel.: (32) 2 646 25 4747
Fax: (32) 2 646 78 37
E-Mail: contact@orridge.eu
Emp.: 3
Stocktake & Inventory Management Services
S.I.C.: 8748
N.A.I.C.S.: 541618
Pearl Hardeng *(Mgr)*

Venners Systems & Services Corporation (1)
200-1920 Yonge St
Toronto, ON, M4S 3E2, Canada
Tel.: (416) 572-7784
Fax: (416) 572-7772
E-Mail: alan.magrowski@vennersys.com
Web Site: www.vennersys.com
Emp.: 4
Software Development & Consulting Services
S.I.C.: 7371
N.A.I.C.S.: 541511
Alan Magrowski *(Gen Mgr)*

CHRISTIE LITES INC.

100 Carson St Unit A
Toronto, ON, M8W 3R9, Canada
Tel.: (416) 644-1010
Fax: (416) 644-0404
Web Site: www.christielites.com
Year Founded: 1985
Sales Range: $10-24.9 Million
Emp.: 65

Business Description:
Stage Lighting Services
S.I.C.: 5049
N.A.I.C.S.: 423490

Personnel:
Huntly Christie *(CEO)*
Michael Rawson *(Treas)*

CHRISTINE INTERNATIONAL HOLDINGS LIMITED

No 33 Jinshajiang Road
Putuo District, Shanghai, China
Tel.: (86) 21 6286 6666
Fax: (86) 21 6286 3333
E-Mail: info@christine.com.cn
Web Site: www.christine.com.cn
Year Founded: 2008
1210—(HKG)
Rev.: $220,488,883
Assets: $325,375,632
Liabilities: $143,611,519
Net Worth: $181,764,113
Earnings: $3,190,502
Emp.: 8,776
Fiscal Year-end: 12/31/12

Business Description:
Bakery Product Mfr & Whslr
S.I.C.: 2053
N.A.I.C.S.: 311813

Personnel:
Tien-An Lo *(Chm & CEO)*
Eddie Kun Chiu Liou *(Sec)*

Board of Directors:
Tien-An Lo
Chi-Ming Chou
Toshihito Hirasawa
Dun-Ching Hung
Weide Luo
Wanwen Su
Nianlin Zhu

Legal Counsel:
O' Melveny & Myers
31/F AIA Central 1 Connaught Road
Central, China (Hong Kong)

Boardroom Share Registrars (HK) Limited
12th Floor The Lee Gardens 33 Hysan Avenue
Causeway Bay, China (Hong Kong)

Transfer Agents:
Royal Bank of Canada Trust Company (Cayman) Limited
4th Floor Royal Bank House 24 Shedden Road
Georgetown, Cayman Islands

Boardroom Share Registrars (HK) Limited
12th Floor The Lee Gardens 33 Hysan Avenue
Causeway Bay, China (Hong Kong)

CHRISTOF HOLDING AG

Plabutscherstrasse 115
8051 Graz, Austria
Tel.: (43) 316 685500 0
Fax: (43) 316 685500 3800
E-Mail: contact@christof-group.com
Web Site: www.christof-group.com
Year Founded: 1966
Sales Range: $400-449.9 Million
Emp.: 2,700

Business Description:
Holding Company
S.I.C.: 6719
N.A.I.C.S.: 551112

Personnel:
Johann Christof, Sr. *(Chm-Supervisory Bd)*
Johann Christof *(Chm-Mgmt Bd & CEO)*
Gunter Dorflinger *(Member-Mgmt Bd)*
Gernot Schieszler *(Member-Mgmt Bd)*

Supervisory Board of Directors:
Johann Christof, Sr.
Stefan Christof
Peter Hadl
Peter Kollegger
Wolfgang Nossing

Subsidiaries:

ace Apparatebau construction & engineering GmbH **(1)**
Hans Thalhammer Strasse 18
8501 Lieboch, Austria
Tel.: (43) 3136 63600 0
Fax: (43) 3136 63600 4600
E-Mail: ace.office@christof-group.com
Industrial Equipment Mfr
S.I.C.: 3559
N.A.I.C.S.: 333249
Markus Fuchsbichler, *(Mng Dir)*

apb Apparatebau Schweisstechnik GmbH **(1)**
Gustav-Kramer-Strasse 5b
8605 Kapfenberg, Austria
Tel.: (43) 3862 25025
Fax: (43) 3862 25050
E-Mail: apb.office@christof-group.com
Industrial Equipment Mfr
S.I.C.: 3559
N.A.I.C.S.: 333249
Josef Habe, *(Mng Dir)*

Christof Electrics GmbH & Co KG **(1)**
Lastenstrasse 19
1230 Vienna, Austria
Tel.: (43) 1 86386-0
Fax: (43) 1 86386 5002
E-Mail: info@christof-electrics.at
Electrical Engineering Services
S.I.C.: 8711
N.A.I.C.S.: 541330
Hans Joachim Rinner, *(Gen Mgr)*

Greentech Energiesysteme GmbH **(1)**
Plabutscherstrasse 115
8051 Graz, Austria
Tel.: (43) 316 685500 3730
Fax: (43) 316 685500 3800
E-Mail: greentech@christof-group.com
Web Site: www.greentech.co.at
Biomass Heating System Mfr
S.I.C.: 3433
N.A.I.C.S.: 333414
Heinz Kaller, *(Mng Dir)*

J. Christof Gesellschaft m.b.H. **(1)**
Plabutscherstrasse 115
8051 Graz, Austria
Tel.: (43) 316 685500 0
Fax: (43) 316 685500 3800
E-Mail: jch@christof-group.com
Plant Design & Construction Services
S.I.C.: 7389
N.A.I.C.S.: 541420

PMS Elektro- und Automationstechnik GmbH **(1)**
Wolkersdorf 46
9431 Sankt Stefan im Lavanttal, Austria
Tel.: (43) 4352 36688 0
Fax: (43) 4352 366 88 510
Web Site: www.pms-elektrotechnik.at
Engineering Services
S.I.C.: 8711
N.A.I.C.S.: 541330

Quality-Safety-Engineering GmbH **(1)**
Plabutscherstrasse 115
8051 Graz, Austria
Tel.: (43) 316 686300 0
Fax: (43) 316 686300 3888
E-Mail: qse@qse.co.at
Web Site: www.qse.co.at
Quality, Safety & Environmental Consulting Services
S.I.C.: 8999
N.A.I.C.S.: 541690
Manfred Strecker, *(Mng Dir)*

Renewable Energy Products GmbH **(1)**
Concept Strasse 1
8101 Gratkorn, Austria
Tel.: (43) 316 685500 3471
Fax: (43) 316 685500 63471
Wood Gas Power Station Engineering Services
S.I.C.: 7389
N.A.I.C.S.: 541420
Franz Krammer *(Mng Dir)*

RIA Rohr- und Industrieanlagenbau GmbH **(1)**
Glacisstrasse 37
8010 Graz, Austria
Tel.: (43) 316 327643
Fax: (43) 316 327903
E-Mail: ria@christof-group.com
Technical Staffing Services
S.I.C.: 7361
N.A.I.C.S.: 561311
Felix Jud *(Mng Dir)*

Schoeller-Bleckmann Nitec GmbH **(1)**
Hauptstrasse 2
A 2630 Ternitz, Austria AT
Tel.: (43) 26303190 (100%)
Fax: (43) 263034119
E-Mail: sbn@christof-group.com
Web Site: www.sbn.at
Emp.: 100
High-Pressure Equipment Mfr
S.I.C.: 3443
N.A.I.C.S.: 332420
Othmar Posch *(CEO)*

Tank Farm Revamp GmbH **(1)**
Plabutscherstrasse 115
8051 Graz, Austria
Tel.: (43) 316 685500 3721
Fax: (43) 316 685500 63721
E-Mail: tfr@christof-group.com
Petrochemical Tank Mfr
S.I.C.: 3443
N.A.I.C.S.: 332420

Non-U.S. Subsidiaries:

J. Christof E & P Services S.R.L. **(1)**
Strada Trandafirilor 49 A
107084 Brazii, Romania
Tel.: (40) 344 401027
Fax: (40) 344 401026
Oil & Gas Equipment Maintenance & Support Services
S.I.C.: 7699
N.A.I.C.S.: 811310

J. Christof Romania S.R.L. **(1)**
Strada Trandafirilor 49 A
107084 Brazii, Romania
Tel.: (40) 344 401027
Fax: (40) 344 401026
Management Services
S.I.C.: 8748
N.A.I.C.S.: 541618
Markus Gran, *(Mng Dir)*

JCR-Christof Consulting S.R.L. **(1)**
Strada Trandafirilor 49 A
107084 Brazii, Romania
Tel.: (40) 344 401027
Fax: (40) 344 401027
E-Mail: jcr@christof-group.com
Plant Design & Construction Services
S.I.C.: 7389
N.A.I.C.S.: 541420
Franz Kitting-Muhr, *(Mng Dir)*

PMSR Electro si Automatizare S.R.L. **(1)**
Strada Trandafirilor 49 A/1
107084 Brazii, Romania
Tel.: (40) 344 802048 0
Fax: (40) 344 802049
E-Mail: pmsr@christof-group.com
Electrical Instrumentation & Control Mfr
S.I.C.: 3625
N.A.I.C.S.: 335314
Edgar Beer *(Mng Dir)*

SC Dinafit SRL **(1)**
Strada Trandafirilor 49 A
107084 Brazii, Romania
Tel.: (40) 344 401027
Fax: (40) 344 401026
E-Mail: office.dinafit@christof-group.com
Rotating Equipment Repair & Maintenance Services
S.I.C.: 7699
N.A.I.C.S.: 811310
Wolfgang Koch, *(Mng Dir)*

Non-U.S. Joint Venture:

Ferrostaal Christof Romania SRL **(1)**
Strada Trandafirilor 49 A
107084 Brazii, Romania
Tel.: (40) 344 401027
Fax: (40) 344 401026
E-Mail: fcr@christof-group.com
Plant Design & Construction Services
S.I.C.: 7389
N.A.I.C.S.: 541420
Markus Gran *(Mng Dir)*

CHROMA ATE INC.

66 Hwaya 1st Rd Kueishan Hwaya Technology Park
Taoyuan, 33383, Taiwan
Tel.: (886) 33279999
Fax: (886) 33278898
E-Mail: info@chromaate.com
Web Site: www.chromaate.com
2360—(TAI)
Rev.: $398,730,883
Assets: $382,456,213
Liabilities: $114,834,338
Net Worth: $267,621,874
Earnings: $31,872,449
Emp.: 2,247
Fiscal Year-end: 12/31/12

Business Description:
Test & Measurement Instruments Mfr
S.I.C.: 3825
N.A.I.C.S.: 334515

Personnel:
Leo Huang *(Chm & CEO)*
Paul Ying *(CFO)*

Subsidiaries:

Chroma New Material Corporation **(1)**
4F 68 Hua Ya 1st Road
Kueishan Hsiang, Taoyuan, 33383, Taiwan
Tel.: (886) 33279998
Fax: (886) 33273500
Web Site: www.Chroma.ate.com.tw
Emp.: 2,000
Wiring Supplies Distr
S.I.C.: 5063
N.A.I.C.S.: 423610
Leo Huang *(Gen Mgr)*

Testar Electronic Corporation **(1)**
4F No 68 Huaya 1st Road
Gueishan Township, Taoyuan, 333, Taiwan
Tel.: (886) 33279600
Fax: (886) 33185442
E-Mail: testarservice@testar.com.tw
Web Site: www.testar.com.tw
Rev.: $2,200,000
Emp.: 127
Electronic Testing Equipments Mfr
S.I.C.: 3825
N.A.I.C.S.: 334515
Leo Huang *(Chm)*
C. C. Ho *(Pres)*

Plant:

Chroma ATE Inc. - Lin-Kou Factory **(1)**
No 66 & 68 Hwa Ya 1st Road Hwa Ya-Technical Park
Kuei-ShanHsiang, Taoyuan, 33350, Taiwan
Tel.: (886) 33279999
Fax: (886) 33278898
E-Mail: chroma@chroma.com.tw
Emp.: 2,000
Measuring & Testing Equipments Mfr
S.I.C.: 3823
N.A.I.C.S.: 334513
Leo Huang *(Gen Mgr)*

U.S. Subsidiary:

Chroma ATE Inc. **(1)**
7 Chrysler
Irvine, CA 92618 CA
Tel.: (949) 421-0355
Fax: (949) 421-0353
Toll Free: (800) 478-2026
E-Mail: info@chromaus.com
Web Site: www.chromaus.com
Emp.: 15
Automatic Testing Equipments Distr
S.I.C.: 5084
N.A.I.C.S.: 423830
Scott Wang *(VP)*

Subsidiary:

Chroma Systems Solutions, Inc. **(2)**
25612 Commercentre Dr
Lake Forest, CA 92630-8813 CA
Tel.: (949) 600-6400
Fax: (949) 600-6401
E-Mail: sales@chromausa.com
Web Site: www.chromausa.com
Emp.: 70
Power Supplies Distr
S.I.C.: 5063
N.A.I.C.S.: 423610
Fred Sabatine *(Pres)*

Chroma ATE Inc.—(Continued)

Non-U.S. Subsidiaries:

Chroma ATE Europe B.V. (1)
Morsestraat 32
6716 AH Ede, Gelderland, Netherlands
Tel.: (31) 318648282
Fax: (31) 318648288
E-Mail: sales@chromaeu.com
Web Site: www.chromaeu.com
Emp.: 11
Measuring & Testing Equipments Distr
S.I.C.: 5084
N.A.I.C.S.: 423830
Rob Overdijkink *(Mgr)*

Chroma Electronics (Shanghai) Co., Ltd. (1)
3F Building 40 No 333 Qin Jiang Road
Shanghai, Guangdong, China
Tel.: (86) 2164959900
Fax: (86) 2164953964
E-Mail: chroma@chroma.com.cn
Web Site: www.chromaate.com
Emp.: 50
Measuring & Testing Equipments Distr
S.I.C.: 5084
N.A.I.C.S.: 423830
Emma Chan *(Mng Dir)*

Chroma Electronics (Shenzhen) Co., Ltd. (1)
8F No 4 Nanyou Tian An Industrial Estate
Shenzhen, Guangdong, China
Tel.: (86) 75526644598
Fax: (86) 75526419620
E-Mail: michael.tien@chroma.cn
Web Site: www.chromaate.com
Emp.: 100
Measuring & Testing Equipments Distr
S.I.C.: 5084
N.A.I.C.S.: 423830
Michael Tien *(Mgr-Sls)*

Chroma Japan Corp. (1)
472 Nippa-cho
Kouhoku-ku, Yokohama, Kanagawa, 223-0057, Japan
Tel.: (81) 45 470 2285
Fax: (81) 45 470 2287
E-Mail: chroma@chroma.com.tw
Web Site: www.chromaate.com
Measuring & Testing Equipments Distr
S.I.C.: 5084
N.A.I.C.S.: 423830

Chroma Systems Solutions, Inc. (1)
2757 Galleon Crescent
Mississauga, ON, L5M5T9, Canada
Tel.: (905) 821-1094
Fax: (905) 821-1094
Web Site: www.chromaate.com
Measuring & Testing Equipments Distr
S.I.C.: 5084
N.A.I.C.S.: 423830

Neworld Electronics Ltd. (1)
Unit 6 6th Floor Shui Hing Centre No 13
Sheung Yuet Road
Kowloon Bay, Kowloon, China (Hong Kong)
Tel.: (852) 23319350
Fax: (852) 23319406
E-Mail: neworld_nwd94@neworld.com.hk
Web Site: www.chromaate.com
Emp.: 6
Measuring & Testing Equipments Distr
S.I.C.: 5084
N.A.I.C.S.: 423830
Randy Chau *(Mgr)*

Weikuang Mech. Eng. (NANJING) Co., Ltd. (1)
811 Hushan Raod Jiangning District
Nanjing, Jiangsu, 211100, China
Tel.: (86) 25 5217 8501
Fax: (86) 25 5217 8502
Web Site: www.chromaate.com
Measuring & Testing Equipments Distr
S.I.C.: 5084
N.A.I.C.S.: 423830

CHROMATIC INDIA LIMITED

207 Vardhaman Complex Premises
co-op Soc Ltd L B S Marg
Vikhroli W, Mumbai, 400083, India
Tel.: (91) 22 61369800
Fax: (91) 22 25793973
E-Mail: dyestuff@bom3.vsnl.net.in
Web Site: www.chromatic.in
530191—(BOM)
Rev.: $17,296,108
Assets: $73,613,409
Liabilities: $15,510,257
Net Worth: $58,103,152
Earnings: $33,780
Fiscal Year-end: 03/31/13

Business Description:
Specialty Chemicals Mfr
S.I.C.: 2899
N.A.I.C.S.: 325998

Personnel:
Harmeet Singh *(Sec)*

Board of Directors:
Vinod Kumar Kaushik
Ajay Singh Sethi
Chirag Shah

Transfer Agent:
Bigshare Services Private Limited
E-2 Ansa Industrial Estate Sakivihar Road Saki Naka Andheri (E)
Mumbai, India

CHROMETCO LIMITED

Building 2 Country Club Estate
Woodlands Drive
Woodmead, South Africa

Mailing Address:
PO Box 3787
Johannesburg, 2055, South Africa
Tel.: (27) 11 258 8660
Fax: (27) 86 679 3589
E-Mail: info@chrometco.co.za
Web Site: www.chrometco.co.za
Year Founded: 2003
CMO—(JSE)
Rev.: $173,490
Assets: $25,866,886
Liabilities: $5,844,021
Net Worth: $20,022,865
Earnings: ($1,401,766)
Fiscal Year-end: 02/28/13

Business Description:
Mineral Exploration Services
S.I.C.: 1099
N.A.I.C.S.: 212299

Personnel:
Petrus Cilliers *(Mng Dir)*

Board of Directors:
Jonathan Scott
Edward Bramley
Petrus Cilliers
Ivan Collair
Trevor Scott

Legal Counsel:
Pietersens Incorporated
28 Fricker Road
Illovo, 2196, South Africa

DLA Cliffe Dekker Hofmeyer Incorporated
1 Protea Place Sandown
Sandton, 2196, South Africa

Transfer Agent:
Computershare Investor Services (Pty) Ltd
70 Marshall Street
Johannesburg, South Africa

CHROMOGENEX TECHNOLOGIES LTD.

Unit 1-2 Heol Rhosyn Dafen Ind Est
Llanelli, Carmarthenshire, SA14 8QG, United Kingdom
Tel.: (44) 1554 755444
Fax: (44) 1554 755333
E-Mail: sales@chromogenex.com
Web Site: www.chromogenex.com
Year Founded: 1985
Sales Range: $10-24.9 Million
Emp.: 36

Business Description:
Medical Equipment Mfr
S.I.C.: 3841
N.A.I.C.S.: 339112

Personnel:
Roland Denning *(Chm)*
Peter McGuinness *(CEO)*

CHRYSALIS CAPITAL VII CORPORATION

(Name Changed to Spectra7 Microsystems Inc.)

CHRYSALIS RESOURCES LIMITED

Unit 2 Level 1 331-335 Hay Street
Subiaco, WA, 6008, Australia

Mailing Address:
PO Box 226
Wembley, WA, 6913, Australia
Tel.: (61) 8 9380 4430
Fax: (61) 8 9481 5044
E-Mail: info@chrysalisresources.com.au
Web Site: www.chrysalisresources.com.au
Year Founded: 2007
C56—(ASX DEU)
Rev.: $34,280
Assets: $6,650,027
Liabilities: $424,068
Net Worth: $6,225,959
Earnings: ($4,069,407)
Emp.: 13
Fiscal Year-end: 06/30/13

Business Description:
Mineral Exploration Services
S.I.C.: 1481
N.A.I.C.S.: 213115

Personnel:
Leigh Ryan *(CEO)*
Kevin Hart *(Sec)*

Board of Directors:
Neale Fong
Trevor Benson
Michael Griffiths
Grant Kidner
Adrian Paul
Jing Wang

Legal Counsel:
Steinepreis Paganin Lawyers & Consultants
Level 4 Next Bldg 16 Milligan Street
6000 Perth, WA, Australia

CHRYSCAPITAL

Suite 101 The Oberoi Dr Zakir Hussain Marg
New Delhi, 110003, India
Tel.: (91) 1141291000
Fax: (91) 1142191010
E-Mail: info@chryscapital.com
Web Site: www.chryscapital.com
Managed Assets: $2,000,000,000
Emp.: 20

Business Description:
Private Equity Firm
S.I.C.: 6211
N.A.I.C.S.: 523999

Personnel:
Ashish Dhawan *(Founder)*

CHS CONTAINER HANDEL GMBH

Tillmannstrasse 19
D-28239 Bremen, Germany
Tel.: (49) 421643960
Fax: (49) 4216439699
E-Mail: info@chs-container.de
Web Site: www.chs-container.de
Year Founded: 1986
Sales Range: $10-24.9 Million
Emp.: 58

Business Description:
Containers Rental & Leasing Services
S.I.C.: 7359
N.A.I.C.S.: 532490

Personnel:
Ayca Turkantos *(Mng Dir-Istanbul)*

CHU KAI PUBLIC COMPANY LIMITED

42/62 Moo 14 Bangna-Trad Km 7
Road Bangkaew
Bangplee, Samut Prakan, 10540, Thailand
Tel.: (66) 2715 0000
Fax: (66) 2715 0055
Web Site: www.chukai.co.th
Year Founded: 1990
CRANE—(THA)
Rev.: $42,289,973
Assets: $92,747,077
Liabilities: $55,157,845
Net Worth: $37,589,232
Earnings: $6,351,574
Fiscal Year-end: 12/31/12

Business Description:
Repair & Maintenance Services
S.I.C.: 7549
N.A.I.C.S.: 811198

Personnel:
Piboon Limprapat *(Chm)*
Thongchai Prarangsi *(Deputy Chm & Acting CEO)*
Chamnan Ngampojanavong *(CFO & Acting Exec VP/Mgr-Acctg & Fin)*
Lert Nitheranont *(COO & Acting Exec VP-Bus Mgmt)*
Wanida Darachai *(Sec & Exec VP-Org Support)*
Nateeporn Doungsawasdi *(Exec VP-Mktg & Engrg)*

Board of Directors:
Piboon Limprapat
Werawan Boonkwan
Wanida Darachai
Vacharin Duangdara
Nateeporn Duangsawasdi
Chamnan Ngampojanavong
Jiraporn Praerangsri
Thongchai Prarangsi
Surin Premamornkit
Jessada Promjart
Somsak Sivapaiboon

Subsidiaries:

The Crane Laem Chabang Co., Ltd. (1)
195/95 Moo 5 Nhongkham
Si Racha, Chonburi, 20230, Thailand
Tel.: (66) 38 481 888
Fax: (66) 38 481 777
E-Mail: junjira@thecrane-lcb.com
Crane Rental Services
S.I.C.: 7359
N.A.I.C.S.: 532490

The Crane Rayong Co., Ltd. (1)
4/2 Moo 4
21180 Nikom Pattana, Rayong, Thailand
Tel.: (66) 38 897 041
Fax: (66) 38 897 045
E-Mail: allan@thecranerayong.com
Crane Rental Services
S.I.C.: 7359
N.A.I.C.S.: 532490

The Crane Service Co., Ltd. (1)
42/51 Moo 14 Bangna-Trad Rd Km 7
Bangkaew, Bang Phli, Samutprakarn, 10540, Thailand
Tel.: (66) 2 720 9933
Fax: (66) 2 720 9915
E-Mail: nonthaporn@thecraneservice.com
Crane Rental Services
S.I.C.: 7359
N.A.I.C.S.: 532490

CHU KONG PETROLEUM AND NATURAL GAS STEEL PIPE HOLDINGS LIMITED

Qinghe Road Shiji Town
Panyu District, 511450 Guangzhou, Guangdong, China

Tel.: (86) 2084558888
Fax: (86) 2084850688
E-Mail: pipe@pck.com.cn
Web Site: www.pck.todayir.com
1938—(HKG)
Rev.: $623,644,306
Assets: $1,077,129,127
Liabilities: $686,312,060
Net Worth: $390,817,067
Earnings: $49,255,890
Emp.: 3,964
Fiscal Year-end: 12/31/12
Business Description:
Steel Pipe Mfr
S.I.C.: 3317
N.A.I.C.S.: 331210
Personnel:
Chang Chen *(Chm & CEO)*
Cammy Pui Shan Wong *(CFO & Sec)*
Board of Directors:
Chang Chen
Ping Chen
Zhao Hua Chen
Zhao Nian Chen
Guo Yao Liang
Tak Wah See

Royal Bank of Canada Trust Company (Cayman) Limited
4th Floor Royal Bank House 24 Shedden Road Georgetown, Cayman Islands

Transfer Agents:
Tricor Investor Services Limited
26/F Tesbury Centre 28 Queen's Road East Hong Kong, China (Hong Kong)

Royal Bank of Canada Trust Company (Cayman) Limited
4th Floor Royal Bank House 24 Shedden Road Georgetown, Cayman Islands

CHU KONG SHIPPING ENTERPRISES (HOLDING) CO. LTD.

Chu Kong Shipping Tower
143 Connaught Road Central, Hong Kong, China (Hong Kong)
Tel.: (852) 25471528
Fax: (852) 25599622
Web Site: www.cks.com.hk
Business Description:
Holding Company
S.I.C.: 6719
N.A.I.C.S.: 551112
Personnel:
Weiqing Liu *(Chm)*
Bangming Yang *(Vice Gen Mgr & CFO)*
Board of Directors:
Weiqing Liu
Honglin Hua
Liezhang Huang
Yuanrong Huang
Bangming Yang

Subsidiary:

Chu Kong Shipping Enterprises (Group) Company Limited (1)
(Formerly Chu Kong Shipping Development Co. Limited)
24th Floor Chu Kong Shipping Tower 143 Connaught Road
Central, China (Hong Kong) (71%)
Tel.: (852) 2581 3799
Fax: (852) 2851 0389
E-Mail: info@cksd.com
Web Site: www.cksd.com
560—(HKG)
Rev.: $195,313,731
Assets: $412,951,930
Liabilities: $143,386,468
Net Worth: $269,565,462
Earnings: $18,730,116
Emp.: 462
Fiscal Year-end: 12/31/12
Cargo Shipping & Port Operation Services
S.I.C.: 4491
N.A.I.C.S.: 488320
Weiqing Liu *(Chm)*
Gebing Xiong *(Mng Dir)*
Maggie Mei Ki Cheung *(Sec & Gen Mgr-Assurance)*

CHUAN HUAT RESOURCES BERHAD

Wisma Lim Kim Chuan Lot 50A Jalan 1/89B Off Jalan Sungai Besi
57100 Kuala Lumpur, Malaysia
Tel.: (60) 379833333
Fax: (60) 379803333
E-Mail: enquiries@chuanhuat.com.my
Web Site: www.chuanhuat.com.my
CHUAN—(KLS)
Rev.: $232,271,204
Assets: $134,557,669
Liabilities: $77,752,152
Net Worth: $56,805,517
Earnings: $4,359,656
Fiscal Year-end: 12/31/12
Business Description:
Computer Diskettes Mfr
S.I.C.: 3695
N.A.I.C.S.: 334613
Personnel:
Patrick Khoon Heng Lim *(CEO & Mng Dir)*
Mark Loong Heng Lim *(Deputy Mng Dir)*
Siew Loon Foo *(Sec)*
Board of Directors:
Zaki Muda
Dali Kumar
Bock Lim Leow
Mark Loong Heng Lim
Nicholas Kean Hoong Lim
Patrick Khoon Heng Lim
Keat Chai Tai

CHUAN HUP HOLDINGS LIMITED

390 Jalan Ahmad Ibrahim
Singapore, 629155, Singapore
Tel.: (65) 65599700
Fax: (65) 62681937
Web Site: www.chuanhup.com.sg
C33—(SES)
Rev.: $246,477,000
Assets: $455,158,000
Liabilities: $142,289,000
Net Worth: $312,869,000
Earnings: $19,172,000
Fiscal Year-end: 06/30/13
Business Description:
Marine Transportation Services
S.I.C.: 4412
N.A.I.C.S.: 483111
Personnel:
Terence Siong Woon Peh *(CEO)*
Valerie May Wei Tan *(Sec & Head-Legal & Secretarial)*
Board of Directors:
Cheng Han Tan
Kwee Siah Lim
Kwee Chim Peh
Terence Siong Woon Peh
Joanna Sau Kwan Young

Subsidiaries:

Beauford Marine Pte Ltd (1)
390 Jalan Ahmad Ibrahim
Singapore, 629155, Singapore
Tel.: (65) 6559 9700
Fax: (65) 6268 1937
Web Site: www.Chuanhup.com.sg
Emp.: 20
Cruise Line Services
S.I.C.: 4482
N.A.I.C.S.: 483114
William Chan *(Mgr-Ops)*

Cresta Investment Pte Ltd (1)
390 Jalan Ahmad Ibrahim
Jurong, Singapore
Tel.: (65) 68611711
Fax: (65) 6862 2336
Investment Management Services
S.I.C.: 6282
N.A.I.C.S.: 523920

PCI Limited (1)
386 Jalan Ahmad Ibrahim
Singapore, 629156, Singapore (76.16%)
Tel.: (65) 62658181
Fax: (65) 62653333
E-Mail: info@pciltd.com.sg
Web Site: www.pciltd.com.sg
P19—(SES)
Rev.: $183,659,000
Assets: $122,983,000
Liabilities: $39,529,000
Net Worth: $83,454,000
Earnings: $3,505,000
Fiscal Year-end: 06/30/13
Electronic Products & Components Designer & Mfr
S.I.C.: 3679
N.A.I.C.S.: 334419
Kwee Chim Peh *(Chm)*
Terence Siong Woon Peh *(Vice Chm)*
Eng Lin Teo *(CEO)*
Keng Poh Lee *(CFO)*
Valerie May Wei Tan *(Sec)*

Subsidiary:

Quijul Pte. Ltd. (2)
322 Jalan Ahmad Ibrahim
Jurong Indus Estate, Singapore, Singapore
Tel.: (65) 66638244
Fax: (65) 62626456
Emp.: 10
Property Rental Services
S.I.C.: 6519
N.A.I.C.S.: 531190
Teo Teck Chuan *(Mng Dir)*

U.S. Subsidiaries:

PCI Limited (2)
2276 Hartfield Cir
Winston Salem, NC 27103
Tel.: (804) 737-7979
E-Mail: nasales@pciltd.com
Web Site: www.pciltd.com
Emp.: 4,000
Electronic Components Whslr
S.I.C.: 3676
N.A.I.C.S.: 334416
Steve Conner *(Dir-Sls)*

Printed Circuits International Incorporated (2)
407 Lee Ave
Highland Springs, VA 23075-1514
Tel.: (804) 737-7979
Electronic Components Whslr
S.I.C.: 3677
N.A.I.C.S.: 334416

Non-U.S. Subsidiary:

PCI-Shanghai Electronic Company Ltd. (2)
No 1199 Blk 87 Shanghai Caohejing Hi-tech Park
Qin Zhou Bei Lu, Shanghai, 200233, China
Tel.: (86) 2164852487
Fax: (86) 2164850942
E-Mail: sales@pciltd.com.sg
Web Site: www.pciltd.com.sg
Emp.: 700
Electronic Components Mfr
S.I.C.: 3679
N.A.I.C.S.: 334419
Victor Liu *(Mgr-Fin)*

CHUAN SENG LEONG PTE. LTD.

No 521 Bukit Batok Street 23
Singapore, 659544, Singapore
Tel.: (65) 6366 5733
Fax: (65) 6366 3528
E-Mail: admin@csl.com.sg
Web Site: www.csl.com.sg
Year Founded: 1976
Sales Range: $10-24.9 Million
Emp.: 45
Business Description:
Household & Personal Care Products Distr
S.I.C.: 5149
N.A.I.C.S.: 424490
Personnel:
Amos Chong How Lee *(Gen Mgr)*

CHUANG'S CHINA INVESTMENTS LIMITED

25th Floor Alexandra House 18 Chater Road
Central, China (Hong Kong)
Tel.: (852) 2522 2013
Fax: (852) 2810 6213
E-Mail: chuangs@chuangs.com.hk
Web Site: www.chuangs-china.com
CUG—(DEU HKG)
Rev.: $65,700,283
Assets: $484,231,879
Liabilities: $157,283,152
Net Worth: $326,948,728
Earnings: $4,663,090
Emp.: 516
Fiscal Year-end: 03/31/13
Business Description:
Real Estate Development Services
S.I.C.: 6531
N.A.I.C.S.: 531390
Personnel:
Albert Ka Pun Chuang *(Deputy Chm)*
Sai Wai Lee *(Deputy Chm)*
Ann Mee Sum Li *(Mng Dir)*
Wai Ching Lee *(Sec)*
Board of Directors:
Abraham Lai Him Shek
Ka Fung Chong
David Yu Lin Chu
Albert Ka Pun Chuang
Andrew Chun Wah Fan
Sai Wai Lee
Ann Mee Sum Li
Sunny Chun Kit Pang
Chung Wai Wong

Butterfield Fulcrum Group (Bermuda) Limited
26 Burnaby Street
Hamilton, HM 11, Bermuda

CHUANG'S CONSORTIUM INTERNATIONAL LIMITED

25/F Alexandra House 18 Chater Road
Central, China (Hong Kong)
Tel.: (852) 2522 2013
Fax: (852) 2810 6213
E-Mail: chuangs@chuangs.com.hk
Web Site: www.chuangs-consortium.com
367—(HKG)
Rev.: $150,352,476
Assets: $1,658,057,411
Liabilities: $517,705,881
Net Worth: $1,140,351,530
Earnings: $146,877,403
Emp.: 2,510
Fiscal Year-end: 03/31/13
Business Description:
Investment Management Services
S.I.C.: 6799
N.A.I.C.S.: 523920
Personnel:
Alan Shaw Swee Chuang *(Chm)*
Alice Siu Suen Siu Chuang *(Vice Chm)*
Sheung Chi Ko *(Mng Dir)*
Tee Way Teo *(CEO-Malaysia Div)*
Wai Ching Lee *(Sec)*
Board of Directors:
Alan Shaw Swee Chuang
Ka Fung Chong
David Yu Lin Chu
Albert Ka Pun Chuang
Candy Ka Wai Chuang
Shing Kwong Fong
Sheung Chi Ko
Lop Kay Lui
Abraham Lai Him Shek
Alice Siu Suen Siu Chuang

Chuang's Consortium International Limited—(Continued)

Chung Wai Wong
Chi Ming Yau

Butterfield Fulcrum Group (Bermuda) Limited
26 Burnaby Street
Hamilton, HM 11, Bermuda

CHUBU ELECTRIC POWER CO., INC.

1 Higashi-shincho
Higashi-ku, Nagoya, Aichi, 461-8680, Japan
Tel.: (81) 52 951 8211
Fax: (81) 52 962 4624
Web Site: www.chuden.co.jp
Year Founded: 1951
9502—(TKS)
Rev.: $29,138,934,000
Assets: $64,710,525,000
Liabilities: $48,308,370,000
Net Worth: $16,402,155,000
Earnings: ($353,771,000)
Emp.: 17,345
Fiscal Year-end: 03/31/13

Business Description:
Electric Utility Services
S.I.C.: 4931
N.A.I.C.S.: 221122

Personnel:
Toshio Mita *(Chm)*
Akihisa Mizuno *(Pres)*
Kazuhiro Matsubara *(Exec VP & Gen Mgr-Legal Affairs, Fin, Acctg, Pur & Contracting)*
Tomohiko Ohno *(Exec VP & Gen Mgr-Secretarial Svcs, Corp Comm & Personnel Dept)*
Masatoshi Sakaguchi *(Exec VP & Gen Mgr-Nuclear Power Div)*

Board of Directors:
Toshio Mita
Yoshifumi Iwata
Hideko Katsumata
Satoru Katsuno
Kazuhiro Matsubara
Masanori Matsuura
Akihisa Mizuno
Ryousuke Mizutani
Tomohiko Ohno
Satoshi Onoda
Masatoshi Sakaguchi
Yutaka Watanabe

Transfer Agent:
Mitsubishi UFJ Trust & Banking Corporation
21-24 Nishiki 3-chome Naka-ku Nagoya
Aichi, Japan

U.S. Subsidiary:

Chubu Electric Power Company U.S.A. Inc. **(1)**
900 17th St NW Ste 1220
Washington, DC 20006-2514 DE
Tel.: (202) 775-1960
Fax: (202) 331-9256
E-Mail: info@chuden.co.jp
Web Site: www.chuden.co.jp/english
Emp.: 6
Electric Utility Services
S.I.C.: 4931
N.A.I.C.S.: 221118
Masahiro Takizawa *(Gen Mgr)*

Non-U.S. Branch:

Chubu Electric Power Co., Inc. - UK Office **(1)**
Nightingale House 65 Curzon St
London, W1J 8PE, United Kingdom
Tel.: (44) 2074090142
Fax: (44) 2074080801
Web Site: www.chuden.co.jp/english
Emp.: 4
Electric Utility Services
S.I.C.: 4911
N.A.I.C.S.: 221122

Munekazu Uchikawa *(Gen Mgr)*

CHUGAI MINING CO. LTD.

Marunouchi Bldg 12F 2-4-1
Marunouchi
Chiyoda-ku, Tokyo, 100-6312, Japan
Tel.: (81) 332011541
Fax: (81) 332015019
Web Site: www.chugaikogyo.co.jp
1491—(TKS)
Rev.: $215,116,000
Assets: $100,584,000
Liabilities: $14,575,000
Net Worth: $86,009,000
Earnings: $2,651,000
Emp.: 90
Fiscal Year-end: 03/31/13

Business Description:
Precious Metals
S.I.C.: 3339
N.A.I.C.S.: 331410

Personnel:
Katsuyama Minoru *(CEO)*
Manami Mikami *(Gen Dir)*
Atsushi Ohara *(Gen Dir)*
Yoshiaki Tanaka *(Gen Dir)*

Board of Directors:
Mamoru Abe
Manami Mikami
Katsuyama Minoru
Atsushi Ohara
Yoshiaki Tanaka

Plants:

Chugai Mining Co. Ltd. - Mochikoshi Plant **(1)**
892 41 Yugashima Izu
Shizuoka, Japan
Tel.: (81) 558850762
Fax: (81) 558851547
Web Site: www.chugaikogyo.co.jp/eng/list.html
Gold & Silver Products Mfr
S.I.C.: 3471
N.A.I.C.S.: 332813

Chugai Mining Co. Ltd. - Tokyo Plant **(1)**
2-12-16 Keihinjima
Ota-ku, Tokyo, 143-0003, Japan
Tel.: (81) 337907130
Fax: (81) 337994091
Web Site: www.chugaikogyo.co.jp
Gold Mining Services
S.I.C.: 1041
N.A.I.C.S.: 212221

CHUGAI RO CO., LTD.

3-6-1 Hiranomachi
Chuo-ku, Osaka, 541-0046, Japan
Tel.: (81) 662211251
Fax: (81) 662211411
Web Site: www.chugai.co.jp
Year Founded: 1945
1964—(TKS)
Sls.: $366,278,000
Assets: $424,468,000
Liabilities: $201,058,000
Net Worth: $223,410,000
Earnings: ($5,885,000)
Emp.: 479
Fiscal Year-end: 03/31/13

Business Description:
Industrial Furnaces, Incinerators & Ovens Mfr
S.I.C.: 3567
N.A.I.C.S.: 333994

Personnel:
Tadashi Tanigawa *(Chm)*
Yuji Nishimoto *(Pres)*
Tsunehiko Magara *(Exec Officer-Overseas Sls)*
Kiyoshi Tsujino *(Sr Exec Officer-Production Engrg Dept)*
Tetsuo Akiyama *(CEO-Thailand & Indonesia)*

Board of Directors:
Tadashi Tanigawa
Kengo Ichizen
Kinya Kisoda
Kenichiro Nanba
Yuji Nishimoto

Subsidiaries:

Chugai Air System Co., Ltd. **(1)**
94-7 Ishizunishimachi Nichi-ku Sakai-city
Osaka, 592-8332, Japan
Tel.: (81) 722801661
Fax: (81) 722801662
E-Mail: jun.kusunoki@casco-jp.com
Web Site: www.casco-jp.com
Emp.: 12
Wet & Dry Type Dehumidifiers, Clean Dryers, Environmental Testing Systems, Aging Systems & Air Conditioners
S.I.C.: 3585
N.A.I.C.S.: 333415

Chugai Engineering Co.,Ltd. **(1)**
94-7 Ishizunisimachi
Nishi-ku, Sakai, Osaka, 592-8332, Japan
Tel.: (81) 722800791
Fax: (81) 722800792
Web Site: www.chugai.co.jp/crp_e/05_4.html
Emp.: 64
Industrial Furnace Mfr
S.I.C.: 3567
N.A.I.C.S.: 333994
Kazutoshi Mimura *(Pres)*

Chugai Environmental Engineering Co., Ltd. **(1)**
2-12-7 Higashisinbashi Minato-ku
Tokyo, 105-0021, Japan
Tel.: (81) 335784753
Fax: (81) 335784755
Web Site: www.chugai.com
Emp.: 62
Environmental-Related Systems Operator, Maintenance, Repair & Modification Services
S.I.C.: 3822
N.A.I.C.S.: 334512

Chugai Plant Co., Ltd. **(1)**
2-4 Chikko-Shinmachi Sakai
Osaka, 592-8331, Japan
Tel.: (81) 722471360
Fax: (81) 722470178
Web Site: www.chugai-pharm.co.jp
Emp.: 200
Industrial Furnace Designer, Mfr, Operator, Maintenance & Sales
S.I.C.: 3567
N.A.I.C.S.: 333994

CR Co., Ltd. **(1)**
2-4-7 Kyomachibori Nishi-ku
Osaka, 550-0003, Japan
Tel.: (81) 664477253
Fax: (81) 664457845
Life & Non-Life Insurance Agent; Parking Lot Operator; Temporary Employment Services
S.I.C.: 6411
N.A.I.C.S.: 524298

Harmotec Co., Ltd. **(1)**
525-20 Hirakata Ageo
Saitama, 362-0059, Japan
Tel.: (81) 487817741
Fax: (81) 48 781 7710
Web Site: www.chugai.co.jp/crp_e/05_7.html
Metal Heat Treating Services
S.I.C.: 3398
N.A.I.C.S.: 332811

Kyoshin Co., Ltd. **(1)**
2-4 Chikko-Shinmachi Sakai
Osaka, 592-8331, Japan
Tel.: (81) 722456154
Fax: (81) 722456429
Web Site: www.chugai.co.jp/crp_e/05_6.html
Industrial Machinery, Heat Furnaces, Environmental Equipment, Combustion Equipment & FPD Manufacturing Systems Designer & Mfr
S.I.C.: 3559
N.A.I.C.S.: 333249

Unit:

Chugai Ro Co., Ltd. - Sakai Works **(1)**
2-4 Chikko-Shinmachi
Nishi-ku, Sakai, 592-8331, Japan
Tel.: (81) 722472501
Fax: (81) 722472508
Web Site: www.chugai.co.jp/crp_e/04shokai.html
Emp.: 469
Industrial Furnace Mfr
S.I.C.: 3567
N.A.I.C.S.: 333994

Plant:

Chugai Ro Co., Ltd. - Kokura Factory **(1)**
2-2-1 Higashiminato
Kokura-Kita-ku, Kitakyushu, 803-0802, Japan
Tel.: (81) 935715788
Fax: (81) 935716268
Industrial Furnace Mfr
S.I.C.: 3567
N.A.I.C.S.: 333994

Non-U.S. Subsidiaries:

Chugai Ro Aluminum (Shandong) Co., Ltd. **(1)**
South of Road 10 High-New Technology Industrial Development Zone, Tai'an, Shandong, China
Tel.: (86) 5386928799
Fax: (86) 5386928766
Web Site: www.chugai.co.jp
Emp.: 50
Industrial Furnaces & Ovens
S.I.C.: 3567
N.A.I.C.S.: 333994
Suiguo Zong *(Pres)*

Chugai Ro Shanghai Co., Ltd. **(1)**
26F Shanghai International Trade Center
2200 Yan-An Road West, Shanghai, China
Tel.: (86) 2162950081
Fax: (86) 2162350301
E-Mail: coo@Chugai.com
Web Site: www.Chugai.com
Emp.: 60
Industrial Furnaces & Ovens
S.I.C.: 3567
N.A.I.C.S.: 333994

Taiwan Chugai Ro Co., Ltd. **(1)**
A1C21F 6 Swei 3rd Rd
Lingya Chiu, Kaohsiung, 802, Taiwan
Tel.: (886) 75357898
Fax: (886) 75357897
E-Mail: chugairo@ms17.hinet.net
Emp.: 7
Industrial Furnaces & Ovens
S.I.C.: 3567
N.A.I.C.S.: 333994
M Michicu *(Pres)*

THE CHUGOKU BANK, LIMITED

1-15-20 Marunouchi Kita-ku
Okayama, Japan
Tel.: (81) 862233111
Web Site: www.chugin.co.jp
Year Founded: 1930
8382—(TKS)
Rev.: $1,289,266,000
Assets: $74,574,445,000
Liabilities: $69,656,444,000
Net Worth: $4,918,001,000
Earnings: $202,686,000
Emp.: 3,101
Fiscal Year-end: 03/31/13

Business Description:
Banking Services
S.I.C.: 6029
N.A.I.C.S.: 522110

Personnel:
Fumihiro Izumi *(Chm)*
Masato Miyanaga *(Pres)*
Hiromichi Tsuboi *(Sr Mng Dir)*
Hajime Aoyama *(Mng Dir)*
Yoshimasa Asama *(Mng Dir)*

Masahiko Fukuda *(Mng Dir)*
Hiroyuki Hanazawa *(Mng Dir)*
Yoshinori Yamamoto *(Mng Dir)*
Board of Directors:
Fumihiro Izumi
Hiromichi Ando
Hajime Aoyama
Yoshimasa Asama
Masahiko Fukuda
Hiroyuki Hanazawa
Hitoshi Ikeda
Sadanori Kato
Masato Miyanaga
Kazushi Shiwaku
Koji Terasaka
Hiromichi Tsuboi
Tokikazu Tsurui
Shunji Watanabe
Yoshinori Yamamoto

Subsidiaries:

Chugin Asset Management Company, Limited (1)
2-10-17 Marunouchi
Kita-ku, Okayama, 700-0823, Japan
Tel.: (81) 862241512
Fax: (81) 862246131
Web Site: www.chugin-am.jp
Asset Management Services
S.I.C.: 8741
N.A.I.C.S.: 561110

The Chugin Credit Guarantee Co., Limited (1)
2-10-17 Marunouchi
Kita-ku, Okayama, 700-0823, Japan
Tel.: (81) 862311266
Fax: (81) 862258355
Credit Guarantee Services
S.I.C.: 7323
N.A.I.C.S.: 561450

The Chugin Lease Company, Limited (1)
Chugoku Ginko Honten Bekkan Nai
Okayama, Japan
Tel.: (81) 862327060
Fax: (81) 862328731
E-Mail: coc7060@to9.ominet.jp
Emp.: 50
Equipment Rental & Leasing
S.I.C.: 7377
N.A.I.C.S.: 532420
Makoto Shimitz *(Pres)*

The Chugin Operation Center, Co., Limited (1)
1-15-20 Marunouchi
Kita-ku, Okayama, 700-0823, Japan
Tel.: (81) 862764144
Deposit & Bank Remittance Services
S.I.C.: 6099
N.A.I.C.S.: 522320

Chugin Securities Co., Ltd. (1)
6-8 Ote-machi
Tsuyama, Okayama, 708-0023, Japan
Tel.: (81) 868224111
Fax: (81) 862120262
Web Site: www.chugin-sec.jp
Securities Brokerage Services
S.I.C.: 6211
N.A.I.C.S.: 523120

THE CHUGOKU ELECTRIC POWER CO., INC.

4-33 Komachi Naka-ku
Hiroshima-shi, Hiroshima, 730-8701, Japan
Tel.: (81) 822410211
Fax: (81) 825442792
Web Site: www.energia.co.jp
Year Founded: 1951
9504—(OTC TKS)
Rev.: $13,197,008,000
Assets: $31,892,674,000
Liabilities: $25,121,613,000
Net Worth: $6,771,061,000
Earnings: ($241,461,000)
Emp.: 9,814
Fiscal Year-end: 03/31/13

Business Description:
Electric Services
S.I.C.: 4911
N.A.I.C.S.: 221122
Personnel:
Takashi Yamashita *(Chm)*
Tomohide Karita *(Pres)*
Yukio Furubayashi *(Mng Dir)*
Masaki Hirano *(Mng Dir)*
Hideo Matsumura *(Mng Dir)*
Shigehiko Morimae *(Mng Dir)*
Kazuyuki Nobusue *(Mng Dir)*
Moriyoshi Ogawa *(Mng Dir)*
Akira Sakotani *(Mng Dir)*
Nobuo Watanabe *(Mng Dir)*
Satoshi Kumagai *(Exec VP)*
Hirofumi Obata *(Exec VP)*
Mareshige Shimizu *(Exec VP)*
Board of Directors:
Takashi Yamashita
Yukio Furubayashi
Masaki Hirano
Tomohide Karita
Satoshi Kumagai
Hideo Matsumura
Shigehiko Morimae
Kazuyuki Nobusue
Hirofumi Obata
Moriyoshi Ogawa
Masaki Ono
Akira Sakotani
Mareshige Shimizu
Hiroaki Tamura
Nobuo Watanabe
Transfer Agent:
Sumitomo Trust and Banking Co Limited
5-33 Kitahama 4 Cho-me
Chuo-ku, Osaka, Japan

Subsidiaries:

Chuden Kogyo Co Ltd (1)
2-2-5 House fl electrical 13
Sakae-ku, Nagoya, Aichi, 460 0008, Japan
Tel.: (81) 522230810
Electrical Equipment Mfr
S.I.C.: 3825
N.A.I.C.S.: 334515

Chuden Plant Co Ltd (1)
Deshio 2 3 18 Minami Ward
Hiroshima, Hiroshima, 734 0001, Japan
Tel.: (81) 822524311
Fax: (81) 822524392
E-Mail: eigyo@chuden-plant.co.jp
Web Site: www.chuden-plant.co.jp
Emp.: 2,000
Construction Repair of Equipment
S.I.C.: 1629
N.A.I.C.S.: 237990
Kozo Kaneda *(Pres)*
Koike Takao *(Mng Dir)*

The Chugoku Electric Manufacturing Co., Inc (1)
4 chome Minami ku Hiroshima Oozu 32
Issue No. 4, 732 8564 Hiroshima, Hiroshima, Japan
Tel.: (81) 822863411
Fax: (81) 822863458
Emp.: 431
Electric Power Meter Repair Services
S.I.C.: 7539
N.A.I.C.S.: 811118
Hiraoka Kazushi *(Pres)*

Energia Communications Inc (1)
HK Hiroshima Broadcasting Ctr Bldg 2 11 10
Otemachi, Naka, Hiroshima, 730 0051, Japan
Tel.: (81) 825233300
Fax: (81) 825233301
E-Mail: info@enecom.co.jp
Web Site: www.enecom.co.jp
Emp.: 778
Information Processing
S.I.C.: 4899
N.A.I.C.S.: 517919
Minoru Sato *(Pres)*

International Standard Management Center Inc. (ISM) (1)
No 9-5 chome Naka-ku
Toukaichimachi, Hiroshima, 730 0805, Japan
Tel.: (81) 829420001
Fax: (81) 82 942 0011
Web Site: www.ismc.co.jp/
Environmental Consulting Services
S.I.C.: 8999
N.A.I.C.S.: 541690
Ramesh Chandak *(Pres)*

Ozuki Steel Industries Co Ltd (1)
2316-1 Yoshida
Shimonoseki, 750 1101, Japan
Tel.: (81) 832821111
Fax: (81) 832820970
E-Mail: d-ozuki@pnet.gr.energia.co.jp
Steel Castings
S.I.C.: 1791
N.A.I.C.S.: 238120

Tempearl Industrial Co Ltd (1)
3-1-42 Ohzu Minami-ku
Hiroshima, 732-0802, Japan
Tel.: (81) 822821341
Fax: (81) 822828680
E-Mail: sakai@tempearl.co.jp
Web Site: www.tempearl.co.jp
Emp.: 370
Circuit Breaker Mfr
S.I.C.: 3674
N.A.I.C.S.: 334413
Cheng Umeji *(Pres)*

CHUGOKU MARINE PAINTS, LTD.

Tokyo Club Building 2-6
Kasumigaseki 3-chome Chiyoda-ku
Tokyo, 100-0013, Japan
Tel.: (81) 3 35063951
Fax: (81) 355118541
Web Site: www.cmp.co.jp
Year Founded: 1917
4617—(TKS)
Sls.: $920,216,000
Assets: $1,168,640,000
Liabilities: $544,951,000
Net Worth: $623,689,000
Earnings: $32,758,000
Emp.: 2,386
Fiscal Year-end: 03/31/13
Business Description:
Marine Paints & Adhesives Mfr & Sales
S.I.C.: 2851
N.A.I.C.S.: 325510
Personnel:
Masataka Uetake *(Pres & CEO)*
Masashi Ono *(Mng Dir & Chief-Technical)*
Toshiaki Kondo *(Pres-Chugoku Samhwa Paints Ltd)*
Board of Directors:
Tsuneo Doi
Hidenori Miyoshi
Masashi Ono
Junji Tomochika
Masataka Uetake

Divisions:

Chugoku Marine Paints, Ltd. - Domestic Sales & Marketing Division (1)
Tokyo Club Building 2-6 Kasumigaseki 3-chome
Chiyoda-ku, Tokyo, 100-0013, Japan
Tel.: (81) 3 3506 5844
Fax: (81) 3 5511 8542
Paint & Coating Distr
S.I.C.: 5198
N.A.I.C.S.: 424950

Chugoku Marine Paints, Ltd. - Overseas Sales & Marketing Division (1)
Tokyo Club Building 2-6 Kasumigaseki 3-chome
Chiyoda-ku, Tokyo, 100-0013, Japan
Tel.: (81) 3 3506 3971
Fax: (81) 3 5511 8542
Paint & Coating Mfr
S.I.C.: 2851
N.A.I.C.S.: 325510

Subsidiaries:

Bunsei Trading Co. Ltd. (1)
1-6-18 Hikoshimaenoura-Cho
Shimonoseki-Shi, 750-0075 Yamaguchi, Japan
Tel.: (81) 832665271
Fax: (81) 832679828
Web Site: www.cmp.co.jp/en/network/inetwork.php?kind=sub
Adhesive Mfr
S.I.C.: 2891
N.A.I.C.S.: 325520

Chugoku Marine Paints (Nagasaki), Ltd. (1)
1-16 Saiwaimachi
Nagasaki, 850-0046, Japan
Tel.: (81) 95 826 0256
Fax: (81) 95 821 8871
Marine Coating Mfr
S.I.C.: 2851
N.A.I.C.S.: 325510

Chugoku Soft Development Co. Ltd. (1)
1-7 Meijishinkai Otake-Shi
Hiroshima, 739-0652, Japan
Tel.: (81) 827578569
Fax: (81) 827578522
Paint & Coating Mfr
S.I.C.: 2851
N.A.I.C.S.: 325510
T. Yamazumi *(Mng Dir)*

Chugoku Technical Support Co. Ltd. (1)
1-7 Meijishinkai Otake-Shi
739-0652 Hiroshima, Japan
Tel.: (81) 827578569
Fax: (81) 827578522
Web Site: www.cmp.co.jp/en/network/inetwork.php?kind=sub
Emp.: 100
Other Scientific & Technical Consulting Services
S.I.C.: 8999
N.A.I.C.S.: 541690
Tetsuo Yamazumi *(Chm)*

CMP Planning Ltd. (1)
1-15-2 Yoshijimahigashi
Naka-Ku, Hiroshima, 730-0822, Japan
Tel.: (81) 822419188
Fax: (81) 822419938
Web Site: www.cmp.co.jp
Urban Planning & Community & Rural Development Administration
S.I.C.: 9532
N.A.I.C.S.: 925120

Global Engineering Service Co., Ltd. (1)
1-7 Meijishinkai Otake-Shi
Hiroshima, 739-0652, Japan
Tel.: (81) 827578535
Fax: (81) 827 578 571
Web Site: www.gmp.company.jp
Emp.: 20
Engineering Services
S.I.C.: 8711
N.A.I.C.S.: 541330
Koji Mikamy *(Pres)*

Kobe Paints, Ltd. (1)
1321-1 Rokubuichi Aza Hyakuchobu
Inami-Cho Kako-Gun, 675-1112 Hyogo, Japan
Tel.: (81) 794950301
Fax: (81) 794952386
E-Mail: info@cmp.co.jp
Web Site: www.cmp.co.jp/en/network/inetwork.php?kind=sub
Emp.: 70
Paint & Coating Mfr
S.I.C.: 2851
N.A.I.C.S.: 325510
Hisaya Shigemoatsu *(Gen Mgr)*

Ohtake-Meishin Chemical Co., Ltd. (1)
1-7 Meijishinkai
Otake, Hiroshima, 739-0652, Japan JP
Tel.: (81) 827577955
Fax: (81) 827577572

Chugoku Marine Paints, Ltd.—(Continued)

E-Mail:
Web Site: www.cmp.co.jp/en/network/inetwork.php?kind=sub
Emp.: 25
Other Chemical & Allied Products Merchant Whslr
S.I.C.: 5169
N.A.I.C.S.: 424690
T. Yamazumi *(Mng Dir)*

Sanyo Kosan Co., Ltd. (1)
352-2 Noji
788-0036 Sukumo, Kouchi, Japan
Tel.: (81) 880 63 0892
Fax: (81) 880 63 0896
Web Site: www.cmp.co.jp/en/network/_1061/group.html
Fabricated Textile Products Mfr
S.I.C.: 2389
N.A.I.C.S.: 314999

Plants:

Chugoku Marine Paints, Ltd. - Kyushu Factory (1)
2783 Tade Yoshinogari -Cho
Kanzaki-Gun, 842-0035 Saga, Japan
Tel.: (81) 952 52 1313
Fax: (81) 952 52 1317
Web Site: www.cmp.co.jp/en/company/establishment/kyusyu.html
Industrial Equipment Mfr
S.I.C.: 3559
N.A.I.C.S.: 333249

Chugoku Marine Paints, Ltd. - Shiga Factory (1)
2306-7 Mikami
520-2323 Yasu, Shiga, Japan
Tel.: (81) 77 587 0488
Fax: (81) 77 588 0521
Web Site: www.cmp.co.jp/en/company/establishment/shiga-en.html
Industrial Machinery Mfr
S.I.C.: 3559
N.A.I.C.S.: 333249

U.S. Subsidiary:

CMP Coatings Inc (1)
1610 Engineers Rd
Belle Chasse, LA 70037
Tel.: (504) 392-4817
Fax: (504) 392-2979
Toll Free: (800) 747-7241
E-Mail: cmpcoatings@worldnet.att.net
Web Site: www.cmp.co.jp/en/network/onetwork.php?kind=factory
Emp.: 24
Paint Varnish & Supplies Whslr
S.I.C.: 5198
N.A.I.C.S.: 424950
Kevin Casey *(Pres)*

Non-U.S. Subsidiaries:

Camrex Chugoku Ltd (1)
Godliman House 21 Godliman Street
EC4V5BD London, United Kingdom
Tel.: (44) 2077780021
Fax: (44) 2074897302
E-Mail: mailbox-uk@cmpeurope.eu
Web Site: www.cmp.co.gp
Emp.: 8
Paint Varnish & Supplies Whslr
S.I.C.: 5198
N.A.I.C.S.: 424950
Bob Cain *(Mng Dir)*

Charter Chemical & Coating Corporation (1)
1 Mercedes Ave
San Miguel, 1600 Pasig, Philippines
Tel.: (63) 26417101
Fax: (63) 26412724
Web Site: www.bh.com
Emp.: 200
Paint & Coating Mfr
S.I.C.: 2851
N.A.I.C.S.: 325510
Albert Taenlee *(Mng Dir)*

Chugoku Marine Paints (Guangdong) Ltd (1)
Industrial Development Area
Lunjiao Shunde, 528308 Foshan, Guangdong, China
Tel.: (86) 75727736170
Fax: (86) 75727736171
E-Mail: cmpgds@cmpgd.com.cn
Other Chemical & Allied Products Merchant Whslr
S.I.C.: 5169
N.A.I.C.S.: 424690

Chugoku Marine Paints (Hellas) S.A. (1)
8 Kanari St
18538 Piraeus, Greece
Tel.: (30) 2104522489
Fax: (30) 2104180868
E-Mail: cmp-hellas@cmpeurope.eu
Web Site: www.cmp.co.jp/en/network/onetwork.php?kind=europe
Emp.: 14
Paint Varnish & Supplies Whslr
S.I.C.: 5198
N.A.I.C.S.: 424950
Makis Kalomamas *(Gen Mgr)*

Chugoku Marine Paints (Hongkong) Ltd (1)
Unit 5-6 P 23rd Floor Island Place Tower 510 Kings Road
North Point, China (Hong Kong)
Tel.: (852) 25766376
Fax: (852) 25763607
E-Mail: marine@cmp-hk.com.hk
Web Site: www.cmp.com
Emp.: 15
Paint Varnish & Supplies Whslr
S.I.C.: 5198
N.A.I.C.S.: 424950

Chugoku Marine Paints (Shanghai), Ltd. (1)
Room 2001 20th Floor Ludi Hechuang Bldg No 450 Caoyang Road
Putuo District, Shanghai, China CN
Tel.: (86) 21 5235 7799
Fax: (86) 21 5236 0952
E-Mail: cmpshanghai@cmp.com.cn
Paint Mfr & Distr
S.I.C.: 2851
N.A.I.C.S.: 325510

Plant:

Chugoku Marine Paints (Shanghai), Ltd. - Factory & Technical Center (2)
4677 Jiasong Road North
Jiading, 201814 Shanghai, China
Tel.: (86) 21 59501000
Fax: (86) 21 59501300
Web Site: www.csp.co.kr/vol2/company4.asp
Emp.: 600
Paint Mfr
S.I.C.: 2851
N.A.I.C.S.: 325510
Hiroshi Hasegawa *(Gen Mgr)*

Chugoku Marine Paints (Singapore) Pte. Ltd. (1)
22 Tuas Street
Singapore, 638459, Singapore SG
Tel.: (65) 6861 6500
Fax: (65) 6861 3002
E-Mail: salesmarine@cmpsin.com.sg
Emp.: 10
Paint & Adhesive Mfr & Distr
S.I.C.: 2851
N.A.I.C.S.: 325510
Junji Tomochika *(Mng Dir)*

Chugoku Marine Paints (Taiwan) Ltd (1)
5th Floor -2 No 146 Sung Chiang Road
10458 Taipei, Taiwan
Tel.: (886) 225110106
Fax: (886) 225710618
E-Mail: cmptpe@ms19.hinet.net
Web Site: www.cmp.co.jp/en/network/onetwork.php?kind=asia
Emp.: 10
Other Chemical & Allied Products Merchant Whslr
S.I.C.: 5169
N.A.I.C.S.: 424690

Chugoku Paints BV (1)
Sluisweg 12
Heijningen, 4794 SW Moerdijk, Netherlands
Tel.: (31) 167526100
Fax: (31) 167522059
E-Mail: sales@cmp.europe.eu
Web Site: www.chugoku.com
Emp.: 50
Paint Varnish & Supplies Whslr
S.I.C.: 5198
N.A.I.C.S.: 424950
Kenichi Date *(Mng Dir)*

Chugoku Paints (Germany) GmbH (1)
Johannisbollwerk 19
20459 Hamburg, Germany
Tel.: (49) 4031796480
Fax: (49) 4031796476
E-Mail: mailbox-de@cmpeurope.eu
Web Site: www.germany.chugoku.nl
Emp.: 6
Other Chemical & Allied Products Merchant Whslr
S.I.C.: 3291
N.A.I.C.S.: 327910
Wols Ruedigern *(Mng Dir)*

Chugoku Paints (India) Private Limited (1)
405 Raheja Chambers Free Press Journal Marg Nariman Point
400021 Mumbai, Maharashtra, India In
Tel.: (91) 22 43550600
Fax: (91) 22 43550625
E-Mail: sales@cmpindia.net
Web Site: www.cmp.co.jp
Emp.: 18
Paint & Coating Mfr
S.I.C.: 2851
N.A.I.C.S.: 325510
K. L. Batra *(Mng Dir)*

Chugoku Paints (Malaysia) Sdn. Bhd. (1)
9 02 9th floor Menara PJ AMCORP Trade Center No 18
No 18 Persiaran Barat, 46050 Petaling Jaya, Selangor, Malaysia MY
Tel.: (60) 379564373
Fax: (60) 379560219
E-Mail: sally@cmp.com.my
Emp.: 20
Painting & Wall Covering Contractors
S.I.C.: 1721
N.A.I.C.S.: 238320

Plant:

Chugoku Paints (Malaysia) Sdn. Bhd. - Johor Factory (2)
Plo 430 Jalan Emas Dua Pasir Gudang Industrial Estate
Johor, 81700 Pasir Gudang, Malaysia
Tel.: (60) 7 2511502
Fax: (60) 7 2511871
Paint Mfr
S.I.C.: 2851
N.A.I.C.S.: 325510
Toru Tanaka *(Asst Gen Mgr)*

Chugoku-Samhwa Paints Ltd. (1)
Toerae-ri Hallim-myeon Ste 972
Gimhae-si, 621-873 Changwon, Korea (South) Ks
Tel.: (82) 553400777
Fax: (82) 553400739
E-Mail: cspaint@csp.co.kr
Web Site: www.csp.Chugoku.com
Emp.: 50
Paint & Coating Mfr
S.I.C.: 2851
N.A.I.C.S.: 325510
M. C. Mckim *(Mng Dir)*

Plant:

Chugoku-Samhwa Paints Ltd. - Gyeongnam Factory (2)
972 Toerae-ri Hallim-myeon
621-873 Kimhae, Gyeongnam, Korea (South)
Tel.: (82) 55 340 0777
Fax: (82) 55 340 0719
E-Mail: cspaint@csp.co.kr
Web Site: www.csp.co.kr/vol2/company4.asp
Paint & Coating Mfr
S.I.C.: 2851
N.A.I.C.S.: 325510

P.T. Chugoku Paints Indonesia (1)
8th Floor Midplaza 1 Bldg
Jalan Jendral Sudirman Kav 10, Jakarta, Indonesia
Tel.: (62) 215700515
Fax: (62) 215733787
E-Mail: cpi_of2@biz.net.id
Paint & Coating Mfr
S.I.C.: 2851
N.A.I.C.S.: 325510
Kamine Ainaho *(Mng Dir)*

Shipping, Trading & Lighterage Co. LLC (1)
6th Floor Shipping Tower Al Mina Road Al Rifa'a
PO Box 464
Dubai, United Arab Emirates
Tel.: (971) 43934666
Fax: (971) 43934888
E-Mail: comm@stalco.ae
Web Site: www.stalcouae.com
Emp.: 75
Navigational Services to Shipping
S.I.C.: 4499
N.A.I.C.S.: 488330

THE CHUKYO BANK, LTD.

3-33-13 Sakae
Naka-ku, Nagoya, Aichi, 460-8681, Japan
Tel.: (81) 522626111
Fax: (81) 522522602
E-Mail: koks_gyo@chukyo-bank.co.jp
Web Site: www.chukyo-bank.co.jp
Year Founded: 1943
8530—(NGO TKS)
Sales Range: $400-449.9 Million
Emp.: 1,364

Business Description:
Banking Services
S.I.C.: 6029
N.A.I.C.S.: 522110

Personnel:
Masakazu Fukamachi *(Pres)*
Shunji Banno *(Sr Mng Dir)*
Hiromasa Ueyama *(Mng Dir)*
Yukio Yoshida *(Mng Dir)*

Board of Directors:
Shunji Banno
Masakazu Fukamachi
Hiroshi Ishikawa
Shigeo Muro
Fukuo Sugai
Hiromasa Ueyama
Yukio Yoshida

CHULARAT HOSPITAL PUBLIC COMPANY LIMITED

88/8-9 Thepharak Road KM 14.5
Bangpla
Bangphli, Samut Prakan, 10540, Thailand
Tel.: (66) 27692900
Fax: (66) 27692967
Web Site: www.chularat.com
Year Founded: 1986
CHG—(THA)
Rev.: $62,098,872
Fiscal Year-end: 12/31/12

Business Description:
Hospital Owner & Operator
S.I.C.: 8062
N.A.I.C.S.: 622110

Personnel:
Kriangsak Phlatsin *(Chm)*

CHUM MINING GROUP INC.

14727 129th Street
Edmonton, AB, T6V 1C4, Canada
Tel.: (780) 887-4998
Year Founded: 2012

Business Description:
Uranium & Other Metal Mining
S.I.C.: 1094
N.A.I.C.S.: 212291

Personnel:
Wayne Cadence *(Pres, CEO, CFO, Treas & Sec)*

Board of Directors:
Wayne Cadence

CHUMPORN PALM OIL INDUSTRY PUBLIC COMPANY LIMITED
1168/91 30th Floor Lumpini Tower
Rama IV Rd
Sathorn, Bangkok, 10120, Thailand
Tel.: (66) 2 679 9166
Fax: (66) 2 285 6369
E-Mail: info@cpi-th.com
Web Site: www.cpi-th.com
Year Founded: 1979
CPI—(THA)
Rev.: $133,574,660
Assets: $95,569,735
Liabilities: $43,767,256
Net Worth: $51,802,480
Earnings: $1,048,526
Fiscal Year-end: 12/31/12
Business Description:
Palm Oil Mfr
S.I.C.: 2075
N.A.I.C.S.: 311224
Personnel:
Somchai Sakulsurarat *(Chm)*
Karoon Nuntileepong *(Mng Dir)*
Takon Tawintermsup *(Deputy Mng Dir)*
Board of Directors:
Somchai Sakulsurarat
Kitti Chatlekhavanich
Pichet Nithivasin
Songridth Niwattisaiwong
Karoon Nuntileepong
Ninnat Olanvoravuth
Chusak Prachayangprecha
Voravit Rojrapitada
Takon Tawintermsup
Pornchai Techawatanasuk
Santi Vilassakdanont
Suthep Wongvorazathe
Suntaree Yingjajaval

Subsidiary:

CPI Agrotech Co., Ltd. **(1)**
16 Moo 16
Thasae District, 86140 Chumphon, Thailand
Tel.: (66) 77 599 680
Fax: (66) 77 599 943
E-Mail: admin@cpiagrotech.com
Web Site: www.cpiagrotech.com
Soybean Oil Mfr
S.I.C.: 2075
N.A.I.C.S.: 311224

CHUN WO DEVELOPMENT HOLDINGS LIMITED
5C Hong Kong Spinners Industrial Building 601-603 Tai Nan West Street
Cheung Sha Wan, Kowloon, China (Hong Kong)
Tel.: (852) 37588711
Fax: (852) 27446937
E-Mail: info@chunwo.com
Web Site: www.chunwo.com
0711—(HKG)
Rev.: $490,697,432
Assets: $586,441,389
Liabilities: $389,023,452
Net Worth: $197,417,937
Earnings: $10,029,086
Emp.: 3,640
Fiscal Year-end: 03/31/13
Business Description:
Construction Industry
S.I.C.: 1522
N.A.I.C.S.: 236116
Personnel:
Dominic Yat Ting Pang *(Chm)*
Derrick Yat Bond Pang *(Deputy Chm)*
Clement Yuk Chiu Kwok *(Mng Dir)*
Robin Chun Ming Liu *(CFO)*
Andy Chi Sang Yiu *(Deputy Mng Dir-Construction)*
Juanna Sau Mui Chan *(Sec)*
Board of Directors:
Dominic Yat Ting Pang
Son Yiu Au
Alec Chiu Ying Chan
Stephen Chiu Chung Hui
Clement Yuk Chiu Kwok
Shing See Lee
Christina Wai Hang Li
Derrick Yat Bond Pang

Butterfield Fulcrum Group (Bermuda) Limited
26 Burnaby Street
Hamilton, HM 11, Bermuda

Subsidiaries:

Chun Wo Building Construction Limited **(1)**
Rm C2 5 Fl Hong Kong Spinners Indus Bldg Block 1 & 2
601-603 Tai Nan W St, Cheung Sha Wan, Kowloon, China (Hong Kong)
Tel.: (852) 27458389
Fax: (852) 27446937
E-Mail: info@chunwo.com
Emp.: 1,700
Building Construction & Design Services
S.I.C.: 1542
N.A.I.C.S.: 236220
Derrick Pang *(Exec Dir)*

Chun Wo (China) Limited **(1)**
Rm C2 5 F Hong Kong Spinners Indus Bldg
601-603 Tai Nan W St, Cheung Sha Wan, Kowloon, China (Hong Kong)
Tel.: (852) 27458389
Fax: (852) 27446937
E-Mail: info@chunwo.com
Emp.: 2,000
Building Construction Services
S.I.C.: 1542
N.A.I.C.S.: 236220
Dominic Pang Yat Ting *(Chm)*

Chun Wo Civil Engineering Limited **(1)**
Rm C2 5 F Hong Kong Spinners Indus Bldg
Cheung Sha Wan, Kowloon, China (Hong Kong)
Tel.: (852) 27458389
Fax: (852) 23701791
E-Mail: info@chunwo.com
Web Site: www.chunwo.com
Emp.: 300
Civil Engineering Services
S.I.C.: 8711
N.A.I.C.S.: 541330
Clement Kwok *(Mng Dir)*

Chun Wo Construction and Engineering Company Limited **(1)**
Rm C2 5 F Hong Kong Spinners Indus Bldg Block 1 & 2
Cheung Sha Wan, Kowloon, China (Hong Kong)
Tel.: (852) 27458389
Fax: (852) 27446937
E-Mail: info@Chunwo.com
Web Site: www.chun.wo.com
Emp.: 2,000
Commercial Building Construction Services
S.I.C.: 1542
N.A.I.C.S.: 236220
Clement Kwok *(Mng Dir)*

Chun Wo Contractors Limited **(1)**
Rm C2 5 F Hong Kong Spinners Indus Bldg Block 1 & 2
Cheung Sha Wan, Kowloon, China (Hong Kong)
Tel.: (852) 27458389
Fax: (852) 27446937
E-Mail: info@chunwo.com
Web Site: www.chunwo.com
Emp.: 2,000
Commercial Building Construction Services
S.I.C.: 1542
N.A.I.C.S.: 236220
Clement Kwok *(Mng Dir)*

Chun Wo E & M Engineering Limited **(1)**
Rm C2 5 F Hong Kong Spinners Indus Bldg Block 1 & 2
Cheung Sha Wan, Kowloon, China (Hong Kong)
Tel.: (852) 27457292
Fax: (852) 27446937
Electrical & Mechanical Engineering Services
S.I.C.: 8711
N.A.I.C.S.: 541330

Chun Wo Elegant Decoration Engineering Company Limited **(1)**
Rm C2 5 F Hong Kong Spinners Indus Bldg Block 1 & 2
Cheung Sha Wan, Kowloon, China (Hong Kong)
Tel.: (852) 27458389
Fax: (852) 27446937
E-Mail: info@Chunwo.com
Emp.: 420
Interior Design & Decorating Services
S.I.C.: 7389
N.A.I.C.S.: 541410
Clement Kwok *(Mng Dir)*

Chun Wo Foundations Limited **(1)**
Rm C2 5 F Hong Kong Spinners Indus Bldg Block 1 & 2
601-603 Tai Nan W St, Cheung Sha Wan, Kowloon, China (Hong Kong)
Tel.: (852) 27458389
Fax: (852) 27446937
E-Mail: info@chunwo.com
Web Site: www.chunwo.com
Emp.: 3,000
Foundation & Underground Construction Services
S.I.C.: 1629
N.A.I.C.S.: 237990
Clement Kwok *(Mng Dir)*

City Professional Management Limited **(1)**
Unit 5C Hong Kong Spinners Indus Bldg Phase 1-2 No 760-762
Cheung Sha Wan Rd, Kowloon, China (Hong Kong)
Tel.: (852) 37588988
Fax: (852) 29590761
E-Mail: info@citysecurity.com
Web Site: www.citysecurity.com
Emp.: 2,000
Property & Facility Management Services
S.I.C.: 6531
N.A.I.C.S.: 531312
Michael Wong *(Mng Dir)*

City Security Company Limited **(1)**
5C Hong Kong Spinners Indus Bldg Phase 5 760-762 Cheung Sha Wan Rd
Kowloon, China (Hong Kong)
Tel.: (852) 37588988
Fax: (852) 29590761
E-Mail: info.security@chunwo.com
Web Site: www.citysecurity.com.hk
Security System Installation & Guarding Services
S.I.C.: 1731
N.A.I.C.S.: 238210
Michael W. T. Wong *(Mng Dir)*

CHUN YU WORKS & CO., LTD.
No 100 Tapao St
82063 Kangshan, Kaohsiung, Taiwan
Tel.: (886) 76224111
Fax: (886) 76216697
E-Mail: lion.service@chunyu.com.tw
Web Site: www.chunyu.com.tw
2012—(TAI)
Sales Range: $100-124.9 Million
Emp.: 450
Business Description:
Aerospace Fasteners & Medical Equipment Mfr
S.I.C.: 3812
N.A.I.C.S.: 334511
Personnel:
Chin-Fu Kan *(Chm)*
Simon Lee *(Pres)*

Subsidiaries:

Chun Yu Bio-Tech Co., Ltd. **(1)**
No 269 Jiahua Road
Gangshan District, Kaohsiung, 82056, Taiwan
Tel.: (886) 7 621 8318
Fax: (886) 7 621 0665
E-Mail: sales@chunyubio.com
Web Site: www.chunyubio.com
Emp.: 25
Industrial Fasteners Mfr
S.I.C.: 3452
N.A.I.C.S.: 332722
Christina Cheng *(Mgr)*

Chun Zu Machinery Ind. Co., Ltd. **(1)**
No 50 Tapao Street
Gangshan, Kaohsiung, 82063, Taiwan
Tel.: (886) 7 6212196
Fax: (886) 7 6221718
E-Mail: chunzu@ms9.hinet.net
Web Site: www.chunzu.com.tw
Sls.: $67,000,000
Emp.: 170
Metal Parts Forming Machinery Mfr
S.I.C.: 3541
N.A.I.C.S.: 333517
H. C. Lee *(Asst Mgr)*

Hi-Ace Trading Co., Ltd. **(1)**
3F No 132 Section 3 Chengde Road
Datong District, Taipei, 10363, Taiwan
Tel.: (886) 225925167
Fax: (886) 2 25940724
Web Site: www.chunyu.com.tw/EN/about_01.html
Industrial Fasteners Distr
S.I.C.: 5072
N.A.I.C.S.: 423710

Plants:

Chun Yu Works & Co., Ltd. - Chiashing Plant **(1)**
No 1 Chiashing Road
Kangshan, Kaohsiung, 82057, Taiwan
Tel.: (886) 76214121
Fax: (886) 7 622 3256
Fasteners Mfr
S.I.C.: 3452
N.A.I.C.S.: 332722

Chun Yu Works & Co., Ltd. - Kangshan Plant **(1)**
No 100 Tapao Street
Kangshan Town, Kaohsiung, 82063, Taiwan
Tel.: (886) 7 622 4111
Fax: (886) 7 621 6697
Web Site: www.chunyu.com.tw/EN/about_05.html
Industrial Fasteners Mfr
S.I.C.: 3399
N.A.I.C.S.: 331110

USI Corporation - Kaohsiung Plant **(1)**
330 Feng Jen Road Jen Wu Hsiang
Kaohsiung, 814, Taiwan
Tel.: (886) 73711721
Fax: (886) 7 371 4268
Polyethylene Resins Mfr
S.I.C.: 2821
N.A.I.C.S.: 325211
Martin Yo *(Gen Mgr-Engrg)*

Non-U.S. Subsidiaries:

Chun Yu (DongGuan) Metal Products Co., Ltd. **(1)**
Song Mu Shan Administration Zone
Dalang, Dongguan, Guangdong, 523795, China
Tel.: (86) 769 83310921
Fax: (86) 769 83181001
Web Site: www.chunyu.com.cn
Structured Steel Products Mfr
S.I.C.: 3312
N.A.I.C.S.: 331221

PT. Moonlion Industries Indonesia **(1)**
Jl Rawa Bali No 8 Industrial Estate
Pulogadung, Jakarta, 13920, Indonesia
Tel.: (62) 21 4602888
Fax: (62) 21 4602887
Web Site: www.chunyu.com.tw/EN/about_05.html
Hardware Mfr
S.I.C.: 3452
N.A.I.C.S.: 332722

Shanghai Chun Zu Machinery Industry Co., Ltd. **(1)**
6639 Jihe Road Baihe Town
Qingpu District, Shanghai, 201709, China
Tel.: (86) 2159742888
Fax: (86) 2159742882
E-Mail: service@chunzu.com.cn

Chun Yu Works & Co., Ltd.—(Continued)

Emp.: 220
Hardware Mfr
S.I.C.: 3452
N.A.I.C.S.: 332722
Bruce T. Sun *(Chm)*

Shanghai Tongsheng Trading Co., Ltd. **(1)**
No 9088 Hutai Road Luojing Town
Baoshan District, Shanghai, 200949, China
Tel.: (86) 21 66877015
Fax: (86) 21 66877012
Web Site: www.chunyu.com.tw/EN/about_05.html
Fastener Distr
S.I.C.: 5072
N.A.I.C.S.: 423710

Shanghai Uchee Hardware Products CO., LTD **(1)**
No 5 Minying Road Luojing Town
Baoshan District, Shanghai, 200949, China
Tel.: (86) 21 66877022
Fax: (86) 21 66877011
Web Site: www.chunyu.com.tw/EN/about_05.html
Fastener Distr
S.I.C.: 5072
N.A.I.C.S.: 423710

CHUN YUAN STEEL INDUSTRY CO., LTD.

6th-7th Fl No 502 Fu-Hsing N Rd
Taipei, Taiwan
Tel.: (886) 225018111
Fax: (886) 225055390
E-Mail: ak500@cysco.com.tw
Web Site: www.cysco.com.tw
2010—(TAI)
Sales Range: $350-399.9 Million

Business Description:
Steel Coil Mfr
S.I.C.: 3444
N.A.I.C.S.: 332322
Personnel:
Wen Lung Lee *(Chm)*

Divisions:

Chun Yuan Steel Industry Co., Ltd. - Automated Storage System Division **(1)**
No 236 Bate Section Shangting Road
Longtan Hsiang, Taoyuan, 32571, Taiwan
Tel.: (886) 33 489 2131
Fax: (886) 33 489 5294
E-Mail: 720558@cysco.com.tw
Web Site: www.cysco.com.tw/eng/contact/main_total.htm
Global Logistics Engineering & Steel Material Processing, Stamping Technology & Steel Racks Mfr
S.I.C.: 4731
N.A.I.C.S.: 541614
Jen-Chuan Weng *(Gen Mgr)*

Chun Yuan Steel Industry Co., Ltd. - Special Steel Strip Division **(1)**
No 236 Bate Section Shang Ting Road
Longtan Hsiang, Taoyuan, 32571, Taiwan
Tel.: (886) 34892131
Fax: (886) 34798544
Stainless Steel Products Mfr
S.I.C.: 3312
N.A.I.C.S.: 331110

Subsidiary:

Chun Yuan Construction Co., Ltd. **(1)**
3F 1 No 502 Fusing N Road Jhongshan District
Taipei, 10364, Taiwan
Tel.: (886) 225018111
Fax: (886) 2 2501 5481
E-Mail: admin@chunyuan.com.tw
Web Site: www.chunyuan.com.tw
Commercial Building Construction & Architectural Services
S.I.C.: 1542
N.A.I.C.S.: 236220

Plants:

Chun Yuan Steel Industry Co., Ltd. - Kaohsiung plant **(1)**
No 5 Shihchuan Road
Hsiao-Kang District, Kaohsiung, 81245, Taiwan
Tel.: (886) 2 2268 5209
Fax: (886) 2 2268 4585
Web Site: www.cysco.com.tw/eng/contact/main_total.htm
Fabricated Steel Products Mfr
S.I.C.: 3443
N.A.I.C.S.: 332313

Chun Yuan Steel Industry Co., Ltd. - Shi Tsu Plant **(1)**
6th F No 502 Fu-Hsing N Road
Taipei, 10476, Taiwan
Tel.: (886) 2 2501 8111
Fax: (886) 2 2505 0690
Web Site: www.cysco.com.tw/eng/l/contact.htm
Metal Stampings Mfr
S.I.C.: 3466
N.A.I.C.S.: 332119

Chun Yuan Steel Industry Co., Ltd. - Special Steel Kao Hsiung Plant **(1)**
No 10 Yenhai 2nd Road
Hsiao Kang District, Kaohsiung, 81249, Taiwan
Tel.: (886) 78060888
Fax: (886) 78070777
Metal Stampings Mfr
S.I.C.: 3469
N.A.I.C.S.: 332119
Chen Ruey-Jye *(Mgr)*

Chun Yuan Steel Industry Co., Ltd. - Special Steel Tai Chung Plant **(1)**
No 501-1 Wuguang Road
Wu Jih Hsiang, Taichung, 414, Taiwan
Tel.: (886) 4 2338 4688
Fax: (886) 4 2338 4663
Steel Strips Mfr
S.I.C.: 3312
N.A.I.C.S.: 331110

Chun Yuan Steel Industry Co., Ltd. - Taichung plant **(1)**
13 25th Road Taichung Industrial Zone
Taichung, 40850, Taiwan
Tel.: (886) 423592111
Fax: (886) 423590911
Motor & Ceiling Fan Blades Mfr
S.I.C.: 3423
N.A.I.C.S.: 332216

Non-U.S. Subsidiary:

Shanghai Chun Yuan Steel Industry Co., LTD **(1)**
No 3030 Tanglu Road Tangzhen Town
Pudong New Territory, Shanghai, 201203, China
Tel.: (86) 21 5896 1652
Fax: (86) 21 5896 5187
Web Site: www.cysco.com.tw/eng/shcy/contact.htm
Container Angles Mfr
S.I.C.: 3999
N.A.I.C.S.: 339999

CHUNG-HSIN ELECTRIC & MACHINERY MANUFACTURING CORP.

25 Wen-Te Rd Lo Shan Tsun Kwei Shan Hsiang
Taoyuan, Hsien, 33383, Taiwan
Tel.: (886) 33284170
Fax: (886) 33274155
E-Mail: services@chem.com.tw
Web Site: www.chem.com.tw
Year Founded: 1956
1513—(TAI)
Rev.: $329,220,126
Assets: $465,382,166
Liabilities: $205,081,292
Net Worth: $260,300,874
Earnings: $18,489,057
Emp.: 2,289
Fiscal Year-end: 12/31/12

Business Description:
Electric Equipment Mfr
S.I.C.: 3699
N.A.I.C.S.: 335999
Personnel:
Yi Fu Chiang *(Pres)*

U.S. Subsidiary:

CHEM USA Corp. **(1)**
38507A Cherry St
Newark, CA 94560-4743
Tel.: (510) 608-8818
Fax: (510) 608-8828
E-Mail: sales@chemusa.com
Web Site: www.chemusa.com
Sales Range: $10-24.9 Million
Emp.: 30
Notebook Computers Sales
S.I.C.: 5045
N.A.I.C.S.: 423430
Richard Liu *(VP-Sls & Mktg)*

Subsidiaries:

Etrovision Technology Co., Ltd. **(1)**
2nd Floor Blk C Nan Kang Software Park
19-5 San Chung Rd Nan Kang Dis, Taipei, 115, Taiwan
Tel.: (886) 226551518
Fax: (886) 226551540
E-Mail: etrosales@etrovision.com
Web Site: www.etrovision.com
Emp.: 50
Semiconductor & Device Mfr
S.I.C.: 3674
N.A.I.C.S.: 334413
Ming Jang Lee *(Mng Dir)*

Global-Entech Co., Ltd **(1)**
8th Floor No 766 Chung Cheng Rd
Taipei County Chung Ho, Taipei, Taiwan
Tel.: (886) 232345700
Web Site: www.geinc.com.tw
Professional Scientific & Technical Services
S.I.C.: 7389
N.A.I.C.S.: 541990

Parktron Technology Co., Ltd **(1)**
8th Fl No 801 Chung Cheng Rd
Taipei County Chung-Ho, Taipei, Taiwan
Tel.: (886) 282276186
Fax: (886) 282276185
E-Mail: info@parktron.com
Web Site: www.parktron.com
Emp.: 25
Automatic Vending Machine Mfr
S.I.C.: 3589
N.A.I.C.S.: 333318
Richard Hsieh *(Mgr-Mktg)*

CHUNGDAHM LEARNING, INC.

14 15F Shinyoung Bldg 68-5 Chungdahm-dong
Gangnam-gu, Seoul, 135-953, Korea (South)
Tel.: (82) 2 3429 9407
Web Site: www.cdiholdings.co.kr
Year Founded: 1998
096240—(KRS)
Sales Range: $75-99.9 Million
Emp.: 348

Business Description:
Online Educational Services
S.I.C.: 8299
N.A.I.C.S.: 611710
Personnel:
Young-Hwa Kim *(CEO)*

CHUNGHO COMNET CO., LTD.

15th Floor SB-TOWER 318 Dosan Daero
Gangnam Gu, Seoul, Korea (South)
Tel.: (82) 2 3670 7788
Fax: (82) 2 3670 7636
E-Mail: Global@chunghocomnet.com
Web Site: www.chunghocomnet.com
Year Founded: 1977
012600—(KRS)
Emp.: 618

Business Description:
Automatic Teller Machine & Office Automation Equipment Mfr
S.I.C.: 3575
N.A.I.C.S.: 334118
Personnel:
Jung Woo Lee *(CEO)*

CHUNGHWA CHEMICAL SYNTHESIS & BIOTECH CO., LTD.

1 Tung-Hsing Street
Shu-Lin City, Taipei, Hsien, Taiwan
Tel.: (886) 2 86843318
Fax: (886) 2 86843202
Web Site: www.ccsb.com.tw
Year Founded: 1964
1762—(TAI)
Sales Range: $25-49.9 Million
Emp.: 200

Business Description:
Chemical, Pharmaceutical & Biotechnology Mfr
S.I.C.: 2899
N.A.I.C.S.: 325998
Personnel:
Shiun-Sheng Wang *(Chm)*

Subsidiary:

Chunghwa Biomedical Technology Co Ltd **(1)**
8F No 73 Zhouzi Street
Neihu District, Taipei, 114, Taiwan
Tel.: (886) 226599070
Fax: (886) 2 2659 9076
Web Site: www.cbt365.com.tw
Emp.: 40
Health Care Products Mfr
S.I.C.: 2841
N.A.I.C.S.: 325611
Mango Hoo *(Mgr)*

U.S. Subsidiary:

Pharmaports LLC **(1)**
1 E Uwchlan Ave Ste 116
Exton, PA 19341
Tel.: (610) 524-7888
Fax: (610) 524-7288
E-Mail: info@pharmaports.com
Pharmaceutical Products Distr
S.I.C.: 5122
N.A.I.C.S.: 424210
Amy Liang *(Asst Mgr)*

CHUNGHWA TELECOM CO., LTD.

No 21-3 Hsinyi Road Section 1
Taipei, Taiwan
Tel.: (886) 2 2344 5488
Fax: (886) 2 2356 8306
E-Mail: chtir@cht.com.tw
Web Site: www.cht.com.tw
Year Founded: 1996
2412—(NYSE TAI)
Rev.: $7,455,836,970
Assets: $14,884,069,890
Liabilities: $2,355,218,190
Net Worth: $12,528,851,700
Earnings: $1,389,957,060
Emp.: 30,432
Fiscal Year-end: 12/31/12

Business Description:
Telecommunications Services
S.I.C.: 4812
N.A.I.C.S.: 517210
Personnel:
Rick L. Tsai *(Chm & CEO)*
Mu-Piao Shih *(Interim CFO)*
Board of Directors:
Rick L. Tsai
Gordon Shu Chen
Guo Shin Lee
Mu Shun Lin
Yi Bing Lin
Shih Wei Pan
Mu-Piao Shih
Shih Peng Tsai
Zse Hong Tsai
Jennifer Yuh Jen Wu
Transfer Agent:
Taiwan Securities Co., Ltd.
B1 No 96 Sector 1
Chien-Kuo North Road, Taipei, Taiwan

Tel.: (886) 2 2504 8125
Fax: (886) 2 2515 4900

Subsidiaries:

Chief Telecom Inc. **(1)**
No 250 Yangguang Street
11491 Taipei, Taiwan (69%)
Tel.: (886) 226576688
Fax: (886) 226576728
Web Site: www.chief.com.tw
International Telecommunications Services
S.I.C.: 4813
N.A.I.C.S.: 517110

Subsidiary:

Unigate Telecom Inc. **(2)**
No 250 Yuang Guang St Neihu Chiu
Taipei, Taiwan 11483
Tel.: (886) 2 2657 6688
Fax: (886) 2 2657 6728
E-Mail: UniGate@UniGate.net.tw
Web Site: www.unigate.net.tw
Emp.: 160
Telecommunication Services
S.I.C.: 4899
N.A.I.C.S.: 517919
Johnny Liu *(Gen Mgr)*

Chunghwa Precision Test Tech. Co., Ltd **(1)**
2F No 15 Gongye 3rd Rd
Pingjhen, Taoyuan, 324, Taiwan
Tel.: (886) 3 469 1234
Fax: (886) 3 469 1511
Web Site: www.cht-pt.com.tw
Emp.: 250
Test Board Mfr
S.I.C.: 3699
N.A.I.C.S.: 335999
Hank Wang *(Pres)*

Chunghwa System Integration Co., Ltd. **(1)**
24F 458 Xinyi Rd Sec 4
Xinyi District, Taipei, 11012, Taiwan
Tel.: (886) 2 2345 4666
Fax: (886) 2 2345 7749
Information Technology Consulting Services
S.I.C.: 7373
N.A.I.C.S.: 541512

Light Era Development Co., Ltd. **(1)**
2F No 102 Hengyang Road
Zhongzheng District, Taipei, 100, Taiwan
Tel.: (886) 2 27039789
Fax: (886) 2 27008998
Web Site: www.light-era.com.tw
Real Estate Development Services
S.I.C.: 6531
N.A.I.C.S.: 531390

Spring House Entertainment Tech. Inc. **(1)**
10F No 480 Rueiguang Rd
Neihu Taipei, Taiwan
Tel.: (886) 2 8751 8399
Fax: (886) 2 8751 9689
E-Mail: service@kland.com.tw
Web Site: www.springhouse.com.tw
Mobile Application Software Development Services
S.I.C.: 7371
N.A.I.C.S.: 541511

Affiliates:

ELTA Technology Co., Ltd **(1)**
4th Fl 41 Jhong Hua Rd
Taipei, Taiwan (32%)
Tel.: (886) 223411100
Fax: (886) 233933095
E-Mail: kjen@elta.com.tw
Web Site: www.elta.com.tw
Emp.: 120
Computer Related Services
S.I.C.: 7379
N.A.I.C.S.: 541519
Sally Chan *(Gen Mgr)*

Senao International Co., Ltd. **(1)**
2nd Floor 531 Chung Cheng Rd
Hsin-Tie, Taipei, Taiwan (31%)
Tel.: (886) 033289289
Fax: (886) 222183608
Computer Communication Based Consumer Electronics
S.I.C.: 5045
N.A.I.C.S.: 423430

Subsidiary:

Senao Networks, Inc. **(2)**
No 500 Fusing 3rd Road
Hwa Technology Park, Taoyuan, Kuei-shan Hsiang, Taiwan
Tel.: (886) 33289289
Fax: (886) 33961112
Web Site: www.senao.com
Data Networking & Wireless Voice Communication Products
S.I.C.: 7374
N.A.I.C.S.: 518210

U.S. Subsidiaries:

Chunghwa Precision Test Tech. USA Corporation **(1)**
3120 De La Cruz Blvd Ste 110
Santa Clara, CA 95054
Tel.: (408) 380-0008
Fax: (408) 380-0019
Semiconductors & Equipment Mfr
S.I.C.: 3674
N.A.I.C.S.: 334413

Chunghwa Telecom Global, Inc. **(1)**
2107 N 1st St Ste 580
San Jose, CA 95131 CA
Tel.: (408) 988-1898 (100%)
Fax: (408) 573-7168
Toll Free: (877) 998-1898
E-Mail: info@chtglobal.com
Web Site: www.chtglobal.com
Emp.: 20
International Telecommunications Services
S.I.C.: 4812
N.A.I.C.S.: 517210

Non-U.S. Subsidiaries:

Chunghwa Telecom Japan Co., Ltd **(1)**
Level 5 Asagawa Building 2-1-17 Shiba Daimon
Minato-Ku, Tokyo, 105 0012, Japan (100%)
Tel.: (81) 3 4590 2288
Fax: (81) 3 3436 7599
Telecommunications Services
S.I.C.: 4812
N.A.I.C.S.: 517210
Michael Chow *(Pres)*

Chunghwa Telecom Singapore Pte Ltd **(1)**
20 Kallang Avenue Level 1 Lobby A Pico Creative Centre
Singapore, 339411, Singapore (100%)
Tel.: (65) 6392 2164
Fax: (65) 6392 3962
E-Mail: bencht@cht.sg
Telecommunications Services
S.I.C.: 4812
N.A.I.C.S.: 517210
Benjamin Liu *(Pres)*

Donghwa Telecom Co. Ltd **(1)**
Unit A 7/F Tower A Billion Centre 1 Wang Kwong Road
Kowloon Bay, Kowloon, China (Hong Kong) (100%)
Tel.: (852) 3586 2600
Fax: (852) 3586 3936
E-Mail: sconnie@Donghwatele.com
Emp.: 13
International Telecommunications Services
S.I.C.: 4812
N.A.I.C.S.: 517210
Edwin Yu *(Pres)*

CHUNGKWANG CONSTRUCTION CO., LTD.

550 Eonju-ro Gangnam-gu
Seoul, Korea (South)
Tel.: (82) 2 34616393
Fax: (82) 2 34616396
140290—(KRS)
Business Description:
Highway & Street Construction
S.I.C.: 1622
N.A.I.C.S.: 237310
Personnel:
Sung Heo *(CEO)*

CHUNICHI SHIMBUN CO., LTD.

1-6-1 Sannomaru
Naka-Ku, Nagoya, Aichi, 460-0001, Japan
Tel.: (81) 522018811
Fax: (81) 522014331
E-Mail: shakai@chunichi.co.jp
Web Site: www.chunichi.co.jp
Year Founded: 1886
Sales Range: $1-4.9 Billion
Emp.: 3,500
Business Description:
Newpaper Publishing & News Distribution
S.I.C.: 2711
N.A.I.C.S.: 511110
Personnel:
Bungo Shirai *(Chm)*
Nobuake Koide *(Pres)*

Subsidiary:

Chunichi Dragons Co., Inc. **(1)**
Chunichi Bldg 6th FL 4-1-1 Sakae
Naka-ku, Nagoya, Aichi, 460-0008, Japan
Tel.: (81) 522618811
Fax: (81) 522518649
E-Mail: office@dragons.com.jp
Web Site: www.dragons.co.jp
Emp.: 250
Professional Baseball Team
S.I.C.: 7941
N.A.I.C.S.: 711211
Katstsuhiko Sakai *(Pres)*

CHUNTEX ELECTRONIC CO., LTD.

1st Floor No 136 Alley 6 Lane 235
Pao Chiao Road, Hsin Tien, Taiwan
Tel.: (886) 289121889
Fax: (886) 289121660
E-Mail: marketing@ctx.com.tw
Web Site: www.ctx.com.tw
Year Founded: 1981
Sales Range: $150-199.9 Million
Emp.: 230
Business Description:
Computer Terminal Mfr
S.I.C.: 3575
N.A.I.C.S.: 334118
Personnel:
Million Lin *(Gen Mgr)*

CHUO DENKI KOGYO CO., LTD.

Chiyoda First Bldg 3-2-1 Nishikanda
Chiyoda-ku, Tokyo, 101-0065, Japan
Tel.: (81) 3 3514 0511
Fax: (81) 3 3514 0560
Web Site: www.chu-den.co.jp
Year Founded: 1934
5566—(TKS)
Emp.: 758
Business Description:
Alloy Iron Mfr & Whslr
S.I.C.: 3312
N.A.I.C.S.: 331110
Personnel:
Takao Nishino *(Pres)*

CHUO ELECTRONICS CO., LTD.

Hachioji Sq Bldg 7 Fl 3-20-6 Myojin Cho
Tokyo, 192-0046, Japan
Tel.: (81) 426565811
Fax: (81) 426565808
E-Mail: sakurada@cec.co.jp
Web Site: www.cec.co.jp
Year Founded: 1960
Sales Range: $50-74.9 Million
Emp.: 70
Business Description:
Electronics Components Mfr
S.I.C.: 5065
N.A.I.C.S.: 423690
Personnel:
Hitoshi Miyata *(Gen Mgr)*

CHUO MITSUI TRUST & BANKING COMPANY, LIMITED

33-1 Shiba 3-chome Minato-ku
Tokyo, 105-8574, Japan
Tel.: (81) 352328111
Fax: (81) 352328506
Web Site: www.chuomitsui.co.jp
Year Founded: 1924
Emp.: 5,197
Business Description:
Asset Management & Other Financial Services
S.I.C.: 6211
N.A.I.C.S.: 523999

CHUO SENKO ADVERTISING CO., LTD.

6-1 Ginza 2-Chome
Chuo-ku, Tokyo, 104-8211, Japan
Tel.: (81) 335620151
Telex: J 28210
Fax: (81) 335643822
E-Mail: sfukui@chusen.co.jp
Web Site: www.chusen.co.jp
Year Founded: 1954
Billings: $197,022,376
Emp.: 630
Business Description:
Advertising Agency
S.I.C.: 7311
N.A.I.C.S.: 541810
Personnel:
Shigeru Ohsawa *(Chm & Pres)*

CHUO SPRING CO., LTD.

68 Aza Kamishiota Narumi-cho
Midori-ku, Nagoya, Aichi, 458-8505, Japan
Tel.: (81) 52 623 1111
Fax: (81) 52 624 5717
Web Site: www.chkk.co.jp
Year Founded: 1925
5992—(TKS)
Emp.: 4,346
Business Description:
Spring Product Mfr & Distr
S.I.C.: 3493
N.A.I.C.S.: 332613
Personnel:
Tokuyuki Takahashi *(Pres)*
Akio Makino *(Sr Mng Officer)*
Takefumi Habu *(Officer)*
Hiroyuki Hamaguchi *(Sr Mng Officer)*
Keiji Hasegawa *(Officer)*
Yuichi Hirata *(Officer)*
Yusuke Kajiwara *(Mng Officer)*
Kiyoaki Kuwayama *(Mng Officer)*
Takeshi Matsumoto *(Officer)*
Norifumi Miura *(Officer)*
Satoshi Suzuki *(Officer)*
Manabu Tsuboi *(Mng Officer)*
Board of Directors:
Hiroyuki Hamaguchi
Yusuke Kajiwara
Kiyoaki Kuwayama
Akio Makino
Tokuyuki Takahashi
Manabu Tsuboi

CHURCH INTERNATIONAL LTD

Kestrel House Knightrider Court
Maidstone, Kent, ME15 6LU, United Kingdom
Tel.: (44) 1622675126
Fax: (44) 1622764660
E-Mail: info@church-int.com
Web Site: www.church-int.com
Year Founded: 1984
Emp.: 25
Business Description:
Management Consultant Services
S.I.C.: 8742
N.A.I.C.S.: 541611

Church International Ltd—(Continued)

Personnel:
Brian Fitzgerald *(Mng Dir)*
Board of Directors:
Brian Fitzgerald

CHURCHILL CHINA PLC

Marborough Works High Street
Tunstall
Stoke-on-Trent, ST6 5NZ, United Kingdom
Tel.: (44) 1782577566
Fax: (44) 1782 524355
E-Mail: churchill@churchillchina.plc.uk
Web Site: www.churchillchina.com
Year Founded: 1795
CHH—(AIM)
Rev.: $65,437,881
Assets: $64,104,960
Liabilities: $22,315,368
Net Worth: $41,789,593
Earnings: $3,832,937
Emp.: 520
Fiscal Year-end: 12/31/12
Business Description:
China Dishes & Tableware Mfr
S.I.C.: 3999
N.A.I.C.S.: 327110
Personnel:
Andrew D. Roper *(CEO)*
David J. S. Taylor *(Fin Dir & Sec)*
David M. O'Connor *(COO)*
Board of Directors:
Alan McWalter
Jonathan W. Morgan
David M. O'Connor
Andrew D. Roper
David J. S. Taylor
Legal Counsel:
Addleshaw Goddard
100 Barbirolli Square
Manchester, United Kingdom

THE CHURCHILL CORPORATION

400 4954 Richard Road SW
Calgary, AB, T3E 6L1, Canada
Tel.: (403) 685-7777
Fax: (403) 685-7770
E-Mail: inquiries@churchill-cuq.com
Web Site: www.churchillcorporation.com
Year Founded: 1981
CUQ—(TSX)
Rev.: $1,214,748,105
Assets: $738,001,203
Liabilities: $504,257,400
Net Worth: $233,743,803
Earnings: ($61,492,065)
Emp.: 3,239
Fiscal Year-end: 12/31/12
Business Description:
Commercial & Industrial Construction Services
S.I.C.: 1542
N.A.I.C.S.: 236220
Personnel:
Albrecht W. A. Bellstedt *(Chm)*
Ian M. Reid *(Vice Chm)*
David J. LeMay *(Pres & CEO)*
Daryl E. Sands *(CFO & Exec VP)*
Gord Broda *(Pres/COO-Broda Construction)*
Al Miller *(Pres-Canem Sys)*
Allan Tarasuk *(Pres-Churchill Svcs Grp)*
Evan T. Johnston *(Gen Counsel, Sec & VP)*
Board of Directors:
Albrecht W. A. Bellstedt
Wendy L. Hanrahan
Harry A. King
Carmen R. Loberg
Allister J. McPherson
Henry R. Reid
Ian M. Reid
George M. Schneider
Brian W. L. Tod
Legal Counsel:
Miller Thomson LLP
840 Howe Street, Suite 8000
Vancouver, BC, V6Z 2M1, Canada
Tel.: (604) 687-2422
Fax: (604) 643-1200

Borden Ladner Gervais LLP
1000 Canterra Tower 400 3rd Ave SW
Calgary, AB, T2P 4H2, Canada

CIBC Mellon Trust Company
600 The Dome Tower 333 7th Avenue S.W.
Calgary, AB, T2P 2Z1, Canada
Tel.: (800) 387-0825
Fax: (416) 643-5501
Transfer Agents:
Valiant Trust Company
Suite 310 606 4th Street S.W.
Calgary, AB, Canada

CIBC Mellon Trust Company
600 The Dome Tower 333 7th Avenue S.W.
Calgary, AB, T2P 2Z1, Canada
Tel.: (800) 387-0825
Fax: (416) 643-5501
Subsidiaries:

Broda Construction Inc. (1)
4271 5th Ave E
Prince Albert, SK, S6V 7V6, Canada
Tel.: (306) 764-5337
Fax: (306) 763-5788
Web Site: www.brodaconstruction.com
Emp.: 150
Construction Engineering Services
S.I.C.: 1629
N.A.I.C.S.: 237990
Gord Broda *(Pres & COO)*

Canem Holdings Ltd. (1)
Business Bldg
Richmond, BC, V6V 2X7, Canada
Tel.: (604) 214-8650
Fax: (604) 214-8651
Investment Management Services
S.I.C.: 6211
N.A.I.C.S.: 523999
Al Miller *(Pres)*

Fuller Austin Insulation, Inc. (1)
11540 184th St
Edmonton, AB, T5S 2W7, Canada (100%)
Tel.: (780) 452-1701
Fax: (780) 452-4129
E-Mail: info@fulleraustininsulation.ca
Web Site: www.fulleraustininsulation.ca
Emp.: 30
Provider of Commercial & Industrial Construction Services
S.I.C.: 1542
N.A.I.C.S.: 236220
Ronald L. Martineau *(Pres)*

Insulation Holdings Inc. (1)
11825-149 St
Edmonton, AB, T5L 2J1, Canada
Tel.: (780) 481-9600
Fax: (780) 468-3136
Web Site: www.churchillcorporation.com
Construction Engineering Services
S.I.C.: 1629
N.A.I.C.S.: 236210
Ronald L. Martineau *(Pres & COO)*

Kam-Crete Ltd. (1)
529 Pk St W
Kamsack, SK, S0A 1S0, Canada
Tel.: (306) 542-2060
Fax: (306) 542-2110
E-Mail: kamcrete@sasktel.net
Web Site: www.brodaconstruction.com
Emp.: 15
Precast Concrete Products Mfr
S.I.C.: 3272
N.A.I.C.S.: 327390
Bob Hellegards *(Gen Mgr)*

Laird Electric Inc. (1)
6707-59 St NW
Edmonton, AB, T6B 3P8, Canada
Tel.: (780) 450-9636
Fax: (780) 469-6924
Toll Free: (888) 450-9636
E-Mail: info@lairdelectric.com
Web Site: www.lairdelectric.com
Electrical Contractors
S.I.C.: 1731
N.A.I.C.S.: 238210
David LeMay *(Pres & COO)*

North American Rock & Dirt Inc. (1)
4271 5th Ave E
Prince Albert, SK, S6V 7V6, Canada
Tel.: (306) 764-5337
Fax: (306) 763-5788
Web Site: www.brodaconstructons.com
Emp.: 150
Construction Engineering Services
S.I.C.: 1622
N.A.I.C.S.: 237310
Gordie Broda *(Gen Mgr)*

Northern Industrial Insulation Contractors, Inc. (1)
18910 111 Ave
Edmonton, AB, T5S 1E6, Canada (100%)
Tel.: (780) 483-1850
Fax: (780) 484-0004
E-Mail: info@northern-insulation.ca
Web Site: www.churchillcorporation.com
Emp.: 150
Provider of Commercial & Industrial Construction Services
S.I.C.: 1542
N.A.I.C.S.: 236220
Shelborn Dolbish *(VP)*

Stuart Olson Dominion Construction Ltd. (1)
Ste 400 4954 Richard Rd SW
Calgary, AB, T3E 6L1, Canada (100%)
Tel.: (403) 520-2767
Fax: (403) 520-1250
Web Site: www.sodcl.com
Emp.: 60
Commercial & Industrial Construction Services
S.I.C.: 1542
N.A.I.C.S.: 236220
Mick Howven *(VP-Fin)*

CHURCHILL MINING PLC

41 York Street
Subiaco, WA, 6008, Australia
Mailing Address:
PO Box 8050
Subiaco, WA, 6008, Australia
Tel.: (61) 8 6382 3737
Fax: (61) 8 6382 3777
Web Site: www.churchillmining.com
R9W—(AIM DEU)
Rev.: $4,000
Assets: $8,370,000
Liabilities: $4,011,000
Net Worth: $4,359,000
Earnings: ($11,601,000)
Fiscal Year-end: 06/30/13
Business Description:
Thermal Coal Mining Services
S.I.C.: 1221
N.A.I.C.S.: 212111
Personnel:
Nicholas Smith *(Mng Dir)*
Russell P. Hardwick *(Co-Sec)*
Stephen R. Ronaldson *(Co-Sec)*
Board of Directors:
David F. Quinlivan
Rachmat Gobel
Fara Luwia
Jon Nagulendran
Gregory Radke
Nicholas Smith
Legal Counsel:
Ronaldsons LLP
55 Gower Street
London, EC1E 6HQ, United Kingdom
Non-U.S. Subsidiary:

PT Indonesia Coal Development (1)
Wisma Kosgoro Buiding 18th Floor
Jl MH Thamrin 53, Jakarta, Pusat, 10350, Indonesia
Tel.: (62) 21398 2398
Fax: (62) 21319 22877
E-Mail: admin@icd.co.id
Coal Mining Services
S.I.C.: 1222
N.A.I.C.S.: 212112

C.I. BANACOL S.A.

Calle 26 Sur 48 12
Envigado, Atioquia, Colombia
Tel.: (57) 43396262
Fax: (57) 43396207
E-Mail: info@banacol.com
Web Site: www.banacol.com
Sales Range: $100-124.9 Million
Emp.: 5,000
Business Description:
Wholesaler of Fresh Fruits & Vegetables
S.I.C.: 5431
N.A.I.C.S.: 445230
Personnel:
Victor Henriquez *(Gen Mgr)*
U.S. Subsidiary:

Banacol Marketing Corp. (1)
355 Alhambra Cir Ste 1510
Coral Gables, FL 33134 FL
Tel.: (305) 441-9036
Fax: (305) 446-4291
E-Mail: info@banacol.com
Web Site: www.banacol.com
Emp.: 120
Importer & Distributor of Bananas & Fruits
S.I.C.: 5148
N.A.I.C.S.: 424480
Mario Tello *(Controller)*

CI FINANCIAL CORPORATION

2 Queen Street East 20th Floor
Toronto, ON, M5C 3G7, Canada
Tel.: (416) 364-1145
Fax: (416) 364-6299
Toll Free: (800) 268-9374
Web Site: www.cifinancial.com
Year Founded: 1965
CIX—(TSX)
Rev.: $1,449,024,703
Assets: $2,953,844,742
Liabilities: $1,287,879,151
Net Worth: $1,665,965,592
Earnings: $350,057,065
Emp.: 1,287
Fiscal Year-end: 12/31/12
Business Description:
Holding Company; Investment & Wealth Management Services
S.I.C.: 6719
N.A.I.C.S.: 551112
Personnel:
William T. Holland *(Chm)*
Stephen A. MacPhail *(Pres & CEO)*
Douglas J. Jamieson *(CFO & Exec VP)*
David C. Pauli *(COO & Exec VP)*
Sheila A. Murray *(Gen Counsel, Sec & Exec VP)*
Board of Directors:
William T. Holland
Sonia Baxendale
Ronald Duncan Besse
G. Raymond Chang
Paul W. Derksen
Clay Horner
Stephen A. MacPhail
David Miller
Stephen T. Moore
Tom P. Muir
A. Winn Oughtred
David J. Riddle
Transfer Agent:
Computershare Investor Services Inc.
100 University Avenue 9th Floor
Toronto, ON, Canada
Subsidiaries:

Assante Wealth Management (Canada) Ltd. (1)
2 Queen Street East 19th Floor
Toronto, ON, M5C 3G7, Canada
Tel.: (416) 348-9994

Fax: (866) 645-4447
E-Mail: service@assante.com
Web Site: www.assante.com
Investment Advisory & Wealth Management Services
S.I.C.: 6799
N.A.I.C.S.: 523930
Steven J. Donald, *(Pres)*
Robert J. Dorrell *(Sr VP-Distr Svcs)*
James E. Ross *(Sr VP-Wealth & Estate Plng)*

CI Investments Inc. (1)
2 Queen Street East 20th Floor
Toronto, ON, M5C 3G7, Canada
Tel.: (416) 364-1145
Fax: (416) 364-6299
Toll Free: (800) 268-9374
E-Mail: service@ci.com
Web Site: www.ci.com
Investment Fund Management Services
S.I.C.: 6799
N.A.I.C.S.: 523920
Derek J. Green *(Pres & CEO)*
Douglas J. Jamieson *(CFO & Exec VP)*
David C. Pauli *(COO & Exec VP)*
Tony Issa *(CTO & Exec VP)*
Chris von Boetticher *(Gen Counsel, Sec & VP)*
Lorraine P. Blair *(Sr VP-HR)*
K. Michael Kelly *(Sr VP-Sls-Ontario)*
Neal A. Kerr *(Sr VP-Ontario)*
Roy Ratnavel *(Sr VP)*
Alain Ruel *(Sr VP-Sls-Quebec & Eastern Provinces)*

Affiliates:

CI Master Limited Partnership (2)
2 Queen Street East Twentieth Floor
Toronto, ON, M5C 3G7, Canada
Tel.: (416) 364-1145
Fax: (416) 364-4990
CIP.UN—(TSX)
Rev.: $575,111
Assets: $299,299
Liabilities: $288,479
Net Worth: $10,820
Earnings: $181,255
Fiscal Year-end: 12/31/12
Closed-End Investment Fund
S.I.C.: 6726
N.A.I.C.S.: 525990
Stephen A. MacPhail *(Pres)*

High Yield & Mortgage Plus Trust (2)
2 Queen Street East 20th Floor
Toronto, ON, M5C 3G7, Canada
Tel.: (416) 364-1145
Fax: (416) 364-6299
Web Site: www.skyloncapital.com
HYM.UN—(TSX)
Assets: $39,851,256
Liabilities: $541,741
Net Worth: $39,309,515
Earnings: ($419,476)
Fiscal Year-end: 12/31/12
Closed-End Investment Fund
S.I.C.: 6726
N.A.I.C.S.: 525990
Derek J. Green *(CEO)*

Skylon All Asset Trust (2)
c/o CI Investments Inc 2 Queen Street East Twentieth Floor
Toronto, ON, M5C 3G7, Canada
Tel.: (416) 364-1145
Fax: (416) 365-0501
Web Site: www.skyloncapital.com
SKA.UN—(TSX)
Rev.: $32,803
Assets: $12,640,952
Liabilities: $3,744,473
Net Worth: $8,896,479
Earnings: ($134,193)
Fiscal Year-end: 12/31/12
Closed-End Investment Fund
S.I.C.: 6726
N.A.I.C.S.: 525990
Derek J. Green *(CEO)*

Skylon Growth & Income Trust (2)
2 Queen Street East 20th Floor
Toronto, ON, M5C 3G7, Canada
Tel.: (416) 364-1145
Fax: (416) 364-6299
Web Site: www.skyloncapital.com
SKG.UN—(TSX)
Rev.: $2,554,631
Assets: $60,907,581
Liabilities: $5,998,910
Net Worth: $54,908,671
Earnings: $1,408,526
Fiscal Year-end: 12/31/12
Closed-End Investment Fund
S.I.C.: 6726
N.A.I.C.S.: 525990
Derek J. Green *(CEO)*

Skylon International Advantage Yield Trust (2)
2 Queen Street East 20th Floor
Toronto, ON, M5C 3G7, Canada
Tel.: (416) 364-1145
Fax: (416) 364-6299
Web Site: www.skyloncapital.com
Rev.: $1,988
Assets: $8,437,242
Liabilities: $666,988
Net Worth: $7,770,254
Earnings: ($62,623)
Fiscal Year-end: 12/31/12
Closed-End Investment Fund
S.I.C.: 6726
N.A.I.C.S.: 525990
Derek J. Green *(CEO)*

Trident Performance Corp. (2)
2 Queen Street E 20th Floor
Toronto, ON, M5C 3G7, Canada ON
Tel.: (416) 364-1145
Fax: (416) 364-6299
Toll Free: (800) 268-9374
TCP—(TSX)
Rev.: $5,964
Assets: $11,261,253
Liabilities: $3,232,553
Net Worth: $8,028,700
Earnings: ($224,649)
Fiscal Year-end: 12/31/12
Closed-End Investment Fund
S.I.C.: 6726
N.A.I.C.S.: 525990
David C. Pauli *(CEO)*
Douglas J. Jamieson *(CFO)*
Chris von Boetticher *(Sec)*

Yield Advantage Income Trust (2)
2 Queen Street East 20th Floor
Toronto, ON, M5C 3G7, Canada
Tel.: (416) 364-1145
Fax: (416) 364-6299
Web Site: www.skyloncapital.com
YOU.UN—(TSX)
Assets: $12,547,514
Liabilities: $1,037,756
Net Worth: $11,509,758
Earnings: ($116,300)
Fiscal Year-end: 12/31/12
Closed-End Investment Fund
S.I.C.: 6726
N.A.I.C.S.: 525990
Derek J. Green *(CEO)*

C.I. GROUP PUBLIC COMPANY LIMITED

1/1 Moo 7 Bangkoowad Road
Bangkoowad
Amphoe Muang, Pathumthani, 12000, Thailand
Tel.: (66) 2976 5290
Fax: (66) 2976 5023
E-Mail: cigroup@coilinter.com
Web Site: www.coilinter.com
Year Founded: 1983
CIG—(THA)
Rev.: $34,186,723
Assets: $41,008,916
Liabilities: $27,270,170
Net Worth: $13,738,746
Earnings: ($2,806,930)
Emp.: 1,000
Fiscal Year-end: 12/31/12

Business Description:
Air Conditioning Product Mfr & Distr
S.I.C.: 3585
N.A.I.C.S.: 333415

Personnel:
Prung Boonpadung *(Chm)*
Aree Poomsanoh *(Vice Chm)*
Theera Poomsanoh *(Mng Dir)*
Sawai Chatchairungruang *(Pres-Corp Fin & Bus Dev)*
Phrom Jitravitavaj *(Deputy Mng Dir)*
Chankapaw Dissakul *(Sec)*

Board of Directors:
Prung Boonpadung
Songphol Annanon
Chankapaw Dissakul
Aree Poomsanoh
Theera Poomsanoh
Nadith Rodpet
Taweesak Wangkorkiat
Wongsawat Wongsawang

Plants:

C.I. Group Public Company Limited - Factory 2 (1)
789/75 Moo 1 Pinthong Industrial Park
Nongkham, Si Racha, Chonburi, 20230, Thailand
Tel.: (66) 3829 6920
Fax: (66) 3829 6919
Heat Exchanger Mfr
S.I.C.: 3443
N.A.I.C.S.: 332410

C.I. Group Public Company Limited - Factory 3 (1)
526/1-3 Moo3 Teparak Road
Amphoe Muang, Samut Prakan, 10270, Thailand
Tel.: (66) 2758 3034
Fax: (66) 2758 3085
Heat Exchanger Mfr
S.I.C.: 3559
N.A.I.C.S.: 332410

C.I. HOLDINGS BERHAD

Suite A-11-1 Level 11 Hampshire Office Place 157 Hampshire
No 1 Jalan Mayang Sari, 50450
Kuala Lumpur, Malaysia
Tel.: (60) 3 2182 7333
Fax: (60) 3 2166 7208
E-Mail: info@cih.com.my
Web Site: www.cih.com.my
CIHLDG—(KLS)
Rev.: $12,911,194
Assets: $41,000,821
Liabilities: $2,769,612
Net Worth: $38,231,209
Earnings: ($174,781)
Fiscal Year-end: 06/30/13

Business Description:
Plumbing Products Mfr
S.I.C.: 3432
N.A.I.C.S.: 332913

Personnel:
Johari Abdul Ghani *(Mng Dir)*
Loke Yean Foo *(CEO-Doe Grp)*
Azlan Ahmad *(Co-Sec)*
Ngeok Mui Chin *(Co-Sec)*

Board of Directors:
Abdul Ghani Abdul Aziz
Johari Abdul Ghani
Joha Abdul Rahman
Nor Hishammuddin Mohd Nordin
Bee Tein Teh
Kasinathan Tulasi
Mariam Prudence Yusof

CI RESOURCES LIMITED

12 Lyall Street
South Perth, WA, 6151, Australia
Tel.: (61) 8 9489 4444
Fax: (61) 8 9381 4963
E-Mail: info@ciresources.com.au
Web Site: www.ciresources.com.au
CII—(ASX)
Rev.: $161,130,544
Assets: $176,443,162
Liabilities: $59,935,339
Net Worth: $116,507,822
Earnings: $25,387,640
Fiscal Year-end: 06/30/13

Business Description:
Phosphate & Chalk Mining, Processing & Sales
S.I.C.: 1475
N.A.I.C.S.: 212392

Personnel:
Elizabeth Lee *(Sec)*

Board of Directors:
David Somerville
Adrian Gurgone
Kamaruddin Mohammed
Kelvin Keh Feng Tan
Lip Jen Tee
Lip Sin Tee

Legal Counsel:
Steinepreis Paganin Lawyers
Level 4 Next Building 16 Milligan Street
Perth, WA, Australia

CIA. HERING

Street Hermann Hering 1790 - Bom Retiro
89010-900 Blumenau, SC, Brazil
Tel.: (55) 47 3321 3544
E-Mail: assessoria@hering.com.br
Web Site: www.ciahering.com.br
Year Founded: 1880
HGTX3—(BRAZ)
Rev.: $733,563,427
Assets: $581,578,271
Liabilities: $195,936,511
Net Worth: $385,641,760
Earnings: $152,984,676
Emp.: 8,858
Fiscal Year-end: 12/31/12

Business Description:
Apparel Mfr & Whslr
S.I.C.: 2399
N.A.I.C.S.: 315990

Personnel:
Ivo Hering *(Chm)*
Fabio Hering *(CEO)*
Frederico de Aguiar Oldani *(CFO & IR Officer)*
Marcos Ribeiro Gomes *(CMO)*
Carlos Tavares D'Amaral *(Chief Admin Officer)*
Ronaldo Loos *(Chief Comml Officer)*
Edgar de Oliveira *(Chief Production Officer)*
Moacyr Jose Matheussi *(Chief Supply Chain Officer)*

Board of Directors:
Ivo Hering
Fabio Hering
Patrick Charles Morin, Jr
Arthur Eduardo Negri
Marcio Guedes Pereira, Jr
Nei Schilling Zelmanovits

CIA IGUACU DE CAFE SOLUVEL

BR 369 - Rodovia Mello Peixoto Km 88
86300-000 Cornelio Procopio, Parana, Brazil
Tel.: (55) 43 3401 1211
Fax: (55) 43 3401 2542
E-Mail: iguacu@iguacu.com.br
Web Site: www.iguacu.com.br
Year Founded: 1967
IGUA3—(BRAZ)

Business Description:
Coffee Mfr & Whslr
S.I.C.: 2095
N.A.I.C.S.: 311920

Personnel:
Edivaldo Barrancos *(Dir-IR)*

CIAM GROUP LIMITED

23/F Bank of America Tower 12 Harcourt Road
Central, China (Hong Kong)
Tel.: (852) 28430290
Fax: (852) 25253688
E-Mail: ciam.info@ciamgroup.com
Web Site: www.ciamgroup.com
0378—(HKG)

CIAM Group Limited—(Continued)

Rev.: $2,845,540
Assets: $74,040,898
Liabilities: $3,063,723
Net Worth: $70,977,175
Earnings: ($1,894,404)
Emp.: 12
Fiscal Year-end: 12/31/12

Business Description:
Investment Management Services
S.I.C.: 6282
N.A.I.C.S.: 523920

Personnel:
Jianzhong Dou *(Chm)*
Kelvin Wing Yat Lo *(Vice Chm & CEO)*
William Chein Kwong Chan *(COO)*
Kyna Yuen Ching Wong *(Sec)*
Fung Philip Lam *(Sr VP)*

Board of Directors:
Jianzhong Dou
Peng Kuan Chan
Andrew Chi Yuen Hung
Kelvin Wing Yat Lo
Zhicheng Lu
Victor Fung Shuen Sit
Hock Ghim Toh
David Yau Kar Wong

Butterfield Fulcrum Group (Bermuda) Limited
26 Burnaby Street
Hamilton, HM 11, Bermuda

Transfer Agent:
Computershare Hong Kong Investor Services Limited
17M Floor Hopewell Centre 183 Queens Road East
Hong Kong, China (Hong Kong)

CIBT EDUCATION GROUP INC.

Suite 1200 777 West Broadway
Vancouver, BC, V5Z 4J7, Canada
Tel.: (604) 871-9909
Fax: (604) 871-9919
Toll Free: (888) 865-0901
E-Mail: info@cibt.net
Web Site: www.cibt.net
Year Founded: 1986
MBA—(OTC TSX)
Rev.: $30,969,308
Assets: $40,200,170
Liabilities: $24,601,377
Net Worth: $15,598,793
Earnings: ($912,178)
Emp.: 547
Fiscal Year-end: 08/31/13

Business Description:
Education, Training, Graphic Design & Advertising Services
S.I.C.: 9411
N.A.I.C.S.: 923110

Personnel:
David Hsu *(Chm)*
Toby Chu *(Vice Chm, Pres & CEO)*
Dennis Huang *(CFO, Sec & Exec VP)*
Patrick Dang *(Pres-Sprott-Shaw Community College)*
David An *(Exec VP-Bus Dev-China)*
Maggie Harvie *(Exec VP-Sprott-Shaw Community College)*
Jane Li *(Exec VP-China)*

Board of Directors:
David Hsu
Toby Chu
Tony Haskell David
Derek Feng
Troy Rice
Shane Frederick Weir

Transfer Agent:
Computershare Investor Services Inc.
510 Burrard Street 2nd Floor
Vancouver, BC, V6C 3B9, Canada

CIC HOLDINGS LIMITED

Tuscany Office Park
PO Box 3581
2128 Rivonia, South Africa
Tel.: (27) 118070109
Fax: (27) 118071316
E-Mail: sarah.loots@cicholdings.com
Web Site: www.cicholdings.com
CCI—(JSE)
Sales Range: $300-349.9 Million

Business Description:
Holding Company; Business Support Services
S.I.C.: 6719
N.A.I.C.S.: 551112

Personnel:
Bryan H. Kent *(Chm)*
Trevor P. Rogers *(CEO)*
Frans W. Britz *(CFO)*
J. F. B. Smit *(Sec)*

Board of Directors:
Bryan H. Kent
Hosea Angula
Cornelius J. Bezuidenhout
Frans W. Britz
Hans-Bruno Gerdes
Johan A. Holtzhausen
Martina Kohler
Marcel Lamprecht
Pierre Malan
Piet Pieterse
Trevor P. Rogers
Milton Vellios

Subsidiaries:

CIC Marketing (Pty) Limited **(1)**
Tuscany Block 5 Coonbe Pl
Johannesburg, Gauteng, 2128, South Africa
Tel.: (27) 118070109
Fax: (27) 118071316
E-Mail: sarah.loots@cicholdings.com
Consumer Goods Distr
S.I.C.: 5064
N.A.I.C.S.: 423620

Non-U.S. Subsidiaries:

Commercial Investment Corporation (Pty) Limited **(1)**
Corner Iscor & Solingen St Northern Indus Area
Windhoek, Namibia
Tel.: (264) 612855800
Fax: (264) 612855879
Emp.: 250
Insurance Underwriting Services
S.I.C.: 6321
N.A.I.C.S.: 524114
Marcel Lamprecht *(Mng Dir)*

Global Holdings (Botswana) (Pty) Limited **(1)**
Plot 20774 Old Hyundai Plant Broadhurst Industrial
Gaborone, Botswana
Tel.: (267) 3904941
Fax: (267) 3904965
Emp.: 600
General Warehousing & Distribution Services
S.I.C.: 4225
N.A.I.C.S.: 493110
Piet Pieterse *(Mng Dir)*

CIC MINING RESOURCES LIMITED

802 Office Tower The St Regis Beijing
No 21 Jianguomenwai Dajie, Beijing, 100020, China
Tel.: (86) 10 8532 2861
Fax: (86) 10 8532 2681
E-Mail: bromley@cicresources.com
Web Site: www.cicresources.com
Year Founded: 2003
Sales Range: Less than $1 Million

Business Description:
Mining Investment & Royalty Services
S.I.C.: 1081
N.A.I.C.S.: 213114

Personnel:
Stuart J. Bromley *(Chm & CEO)*
Hu Ye *(CFO)*
YuQin Song *(COO)*

Board of Directors:
Stuart J. Bromley
Hongguang Li
Robert Rhodes

CICADA VENTURES LTD.

401 - 850 West Hastings Street
Vancouver, BC, V6C 1E1, Canada
Tel.: (604) 662-8130
Fax: (604) 662-8090
Year Founded: 1980
CID—(TSXV)
Int. Income: $2,312
Assets: $314,905
Liabilities: $498,873
Net Worth: ($183,968)
Earnings: ($347,247)
Fiscal Year-end: 01/31/13

Business Description:
Mineral Exploration Services
S.I.C.: 1499
N.A.I.C.S.: 212399

Personnel:
Sammy Cheng *(Pres & CEO)*
Danielle Alleyn *(CFO)*

Board of Directors:
Sammy Cheng
Elvis Glazier
Hayden Ross

CICCOLELLA SPA

Parasacco Indl Zone San Nicola
Melfi, 85025, Italy
Tel.: (39) 0972255200
Fax: (39) 0972255650
E-Mail: ciccolella@ciccolella.eu
Web Site: www.ciccolella.eu
CC—(ITA)
Sales Range: $450-499.9 Million
Emp.: 1,225

Business Description:
Production and marketing of cut flowers and potted plants.
S.I.C.: 5193
N.A.I.C.S.: 424930

Personnel:
Corrado Ciccolella *(Chm & CEO)*
Francesco Ciccolella *(Vice Chm)*

Board of Directors:
Paolo Giorgi Bassi
Carlo Andrea Bollino
Alberto Bombassei
Antonio Ciccolella
Corrado Ciccolella
Francesco Ciccolella
Giantivo Giannelli

CICLAD SA

22 Ave Franklin Roosevelt
75008 Paris, France
Tel.: (33) 156597733
Fax: (33) 153762210
E-Mail: info@ciclad.com
Web Site: www.ciclad.com
Emp.: 10

Business Description:
Private Equity Firm
S.I.C.: 6211
N.A.I.C.S.: 523999

Personnel:
Thierry Thomann *(Founder)*
Jean-Francois Vaury *(Founder)*

CICOR TECHNOLOGIES LTD.

Route de l'Europe 8
2017 Boudry, Switzerland
Tel.: (41) 438114405
Fax: (41) 438114409
E-Mail: info@cicor.ch
Web Site: www.cicor.ch
CICN—(SWX)
Sls.: $189,977,589
Assets: $228,391,667
Liabilities: $99,266,140
Net Worth: $129,125,528
Earnings: $6,760,860
Emp.: 1,512
Fiscal Year-end: 12/31/12

Business Description:
Printed Circuit Boards Mfr
S.I.C.: 3672
N.A.I.C.S.: 334412

Personnel:
Antoine Kohler *(Chm)*
Patric Schoch *(CEO & Interim CFO)*
Urs Wehinger *(Sec)*
Heinz Gloor *(Exec VP-ME Div)*
Pascal Keller *(Exec VP-PCB Div)*
Gim Hong Sng *(Exec VP-Asia Div)*
Erich Trinkler *(Exec VP-ES Div)*

Board of Directors:
Antoine Kohler
Robert Demuth
Andreas Dill
Heinrich J. Essing
Hans Knopfel

Subsidiaries:

Cicor Management AG **(1)**
World Trade Ctr Leutschenbachstrasse 95
8050 Zurich, Switzerland
Tel.: (41) 438114405
Fax: (41) 438114409
E-Mail: info@cicor.com
Web Site: www.cicor.com
Emp.: 1,700
Business Management Services
S.I.C.: 8741
N.A.I.C.S.: 561110
Antoine Kohler *(Pres)*

Cicorel SA **(1)**
Route de l Europe 8
2017 Boudry, Neuchatel, Switzerland
Tel.: (41) 328430500
Fax: (41) 328430599
E-Mail: sales@cicorel.ch
Web Site: www.cicorel.ch
Emp.: 100
Flexible Printed Circuit Boards Mfr
S.I.C.: 3672
N.A.I.C.S.: 334412
Pascal Keller *(Gen Mgr)*

Electronicparc Holding AG **(1)**
C/o Swisstronics Contract Manufacturing Ag
Industriestrasse 8
Bronschhofen, Saint Gallen, 9552, Switzerland
Tel.: (41) 719137373
Fax: (41) 719137374
E-Mail: info@cicor.ch
Web Site: www.cicor.ch
Emp.: 200
Investment Holding Services
S.I.C.: 6719
N.A.I.C.S.: 551112

Photochemie AG **(1)**
Gewerbestrasse 1
6314 Unterageri, Zug, Switzerland
Tel.: (41) 417544545
Fax: (41) 417544555
E-Mail: sales@photochemie.ch
Web Site: www.photochemie.ch
Emp.: 80
Circuit Boards Mfr
S.I.C.: 3672
N.A.I.C.S.: 334412
Pascal Keller *(Gen Mgr)*

Reinhardt Microtech AG **(1)**
Aeulistrasse 10
Wangs, 7323 Saint Gallen, Switzerland
Tel.: (41) 817200456
Fax: (41) 817200450
E-Mail: info@reinhardt-microtech.ch
Web Site: www.reinhardt-microtech.ch
Emp.: 48
Thin Film Circuits Mfr
S.I.C.: 3674
N.A.I.C.S.: 334413
Andrew Steward Barnett *(Mng Dir)*
Hans Tratschin *(Mng Dir)*

Swisstronics Contract Manufacturing AG (1)
Industriestrasse 8
9552 Bronschhofen, Switzerland
Tel.: (41) 719137373
Fax: (41) 719137374
E-Mail: info@swisstronics.ch
Web Site: www.swisstronics.ch
Emp.: 180
Circuit Boards Mfr
S.I.C.: 3672
N.A.I.C.S.: 334412
Erich Kuenzle *(COO)*

Systel SA (1)
Via Luserte Sud 7
6572 Quartino, Ticino, Switzerland
Tel.: (41) 918503811
Fax: (41) 91 850 39 88
E-Mail: info@systel.ch
Web Site: www.systel.ch
Emp.: 50
Circuit Boards Mfr
S.I.C.: 3672
N.A.I.C.S.: 334412
Urs Schlosser *(Head-Fin & Admin)*

Non-U.S. Subsidiaries:

Cicor Anam Ltd. (1)
15 VSIP St 4
Thuan An, Binh Duong, Vietnam
Tel.: (84) 650 75 6623
Fax: (84) 650 75 6624
E-Mail: info-asia@cicor.com
Web Site: www.cicor.com
Electronic Products Assembling Services
S.I.C.: 3679
N.A.I.C.S.: 334418
Gim Hong Sng *(Exec VP-Asia)*

Cicor Ecotool Pte Ltd. (1)
45 Changi South Ave 2# 04-00
Singapore, 486133, Singapore
Tel.: (65) 65 455 030
Fax: (65) 65 450 032
E-Mail: info-asia@cicor.com
Web Site: www.cicor.com
Emp.: 50
Electronic Components & Systems Mfr
S.I.C.: 3679
N.A.I.C.S.: 334419
Emil Strickler *(CEO)*
Chye Hock Yap *(Mng Dir)*

PT ESG Panatec (1)
Batamindo Indus Park Lot 338 Jalan Beringin Muka Kuning
Batam, Riau Islands, 29433, Indonesia
Tel.: (62) 770612233
Fax: (62) 770612266
Emp.: 300
Electronic Products Assembling Services
S.I.C.: 3679
N.A.I.C.S.: 334419

Reinhardt Microtech GmbH (1)
Seebahnstrasse 14
89077 Ulm, Germany
Tel.: (49) 731 392 56 46
Fax: (49) 731 98588 411
E-Mail: info@reinhardt-microtech.de
Web Site: www.cicor.com
Emp.: 30
Thin Film Circuits Mfr
S.I.C.: 3674
N.A.I.C.S.: 334413

RHe Microsystems GmbH (1)
Heidestrasse 70
01454 Radeburg, Saxony, Germany
Tel.: (49) 352841990
Fax: (49) 3528419999
E-Mail: info@rhe.de
Web Site: www.rhe.de
Emp.: 80
Semiconductor Integrated Circuits Mfr
S.I.C.: 3674
N.A.I.C.S.: 334413
Udo Dehne *(Mng Dir)*
Dietrich Zahn *(Mng Dir)*

Systronics S.R.L. (1)
Zona Parc Indus FN CP Nr 117 Of P Nr 8
2900 Arad, Romania
Tel.: (40) 257216684
Fax: (40) 257216733
E-Mail: info@systronics.ro
Web Site: www.systronics.ro
Emp.: 300
Printed Circuit Boards Mfr
S.I.C.: 3672
N.A.I.C.S.: 334412
Cosmin Popa *(Mng Dir)*

CID GROUP

19F Tower B CCIG International
Plaza 333 Cao Xi North Road
Shanghai, China
Tel.: (86) 21 3397 3678
Fax: (86) 21 3397 3599
Web Site: www.cidgroup.com
Year Founded: 1998

Business Description:
Private Equity Firm
S.I.C.: 6211
N.A.I.C.S.: 523999

Personnel:
Steven Chang *(Mng Partner)*
Charles Chang *(Sr Partner)*
Vincent Hou *(Partner)*
Jason Hsieh *(Partner)*
Tony Huang *(Partner)*
Howard S. Lee *(Partner)*
James Liang *(Partner)*
Hanfei Lin *(Partner)*
Lisa Lo *(Partner)*
Po Yen Lu *(Partner)*
Jack Tsai *(Partner)*
David K. Yang *(Partner)*

CIE AMENAGEMENT COTEAUX DE GASCOGNE

Chemin De Lalette
65000 Tarbes, Hautes Pyrenees, France
Tel.: (33) 562517149
Rev.: $23,500,000
Emp.: 209

Business Description:
Engineering Services
S.I.C.: 8711
N.A.I.C.S.: 541330

Personnel:
Francis Daguzan *(Pres)*

Board of Directors:
Francis Daguzan
Henri Tardieu

CIE IMPORT PRODUITS ALIMENTAIRES

Les Neufs Arpents 394 Rue De Flins
Bouafle, 78410 Paris, France
Tel.: (33) 130904600
Fax: (33) 130904601
E-Mail: qualite@delicemer.fr
Web Site: www.delicemer.fr
Sales Range: $10-24.9 Million
Emp.: 21

Business Description:
Fish & Seafoods
S.I.C.: 5146
N.A.I.C.S.: 424460

Personnel:
Jean-Luc Paviot *(Gen-Mgr)*

CIE INTL ANDRE TRIGANO

Num 111-113 111 Reuilly
75012 Paris, France
Tel.: (33) 144681747
E-Mail: djimili.boudis@atciat.com
Sls.: $21,500,000
Emp.: 429

Business Description:
Fabricated Textile Products
S.I.C.: 2399
N.A.I.C.S.: 314999

Personnel:
Andre Trigano *(Pres)*

CIECH S.A.

182 Pulawska Street
02 670 Warsaw, Poland
Tel.: (48) 226391000
Fax: (48) 226391451
E-Mail: ciech@ciech.com
Web Site: www.ciech.com
CIE—(WAR)
Sls.: $1,388,379,918
Assets: $1,182,271,740
Liabilities: $903,137,719
Net Worth: $279,134,020
Earnings: ($137,966,772)
Emp.: 5,682
Fiscal Year-end: 12/31/12

Business Description:
Chemical Mfr
S.I.C.: 2899
N.A.I.C.S.: 325199

Personnel:
Ewa Sibrecht-Oska *(Chm-Supervisory Bd)*
Dariusz Krawczyk *(Chm-Mgmt Bd)*
Przemyslaw Cieszynski *(Deputy Chm-Supervisory Bd)*
Andrzej Kopec *(Member-Mgmt Bd)*
Artur Osuchowski *(Member-Mgmt Bd)*

Supervisory Board of Directors:
Ewa Sibrecht-Oska
Przemyslaw Cieszynski
Arkadiusz Grabalski
Zygmunt Kwiatkowski
Maciej Lipiec
Waldemar Maj
Mariusz Obszynski
Slawomir Stelmasiak

Subsidiaries:

Agrochem Czluchow Sp. z.o.o. (1)
Mickiewicza 5
77 300 Czluchow, Poland
Tel.: (48) 598345670
Fax: (48) 598345670
E-Mail: czluchow@agrochem.com.pl
Web Site: www.agrochem.com.pl
Emp.: 80
Agro Chemicals Mfr & Distr
S.I.C.: 2879
N.A.I.C.S.: 325320

Agrochem Dobre Miasto Sp. z.o.o. (1)
Ul Spichrzowa 13
Dobre Miasto, 11 040, Poland
Tel.: (48) 896151861
E-Mail: dobremiasto@agrochem.com.pl
Web Site: www.agrochem.com.pl
Agro Chemicals Mfr & Distr
S.I.C.: 2879
N.A.I.C.S.: 325320

Alwernia Fosforany Sp. z.o.o. (1)
Olszewskiego 25
Alwernia, Poland
Tel.: (48) 122589100
Fax: (48) 122832199
E-Mail: alwernia@alwernia.pl
Web Site: www.alwernia.com
Emp.: 300
Chemicals Producer & Distr
S.I.C.: 2899
N.A.I.C.S.: 325998
Agnieszka Lisowska *(Mgr-Sls)*

Cheman S.A. (1)
Ul Polczynska 10
01 378 Warsaw, Poland
Tel.: (48) 222105800
Fax: (48) 223803685
E-Mail: ekorzeniewicz@cheman.pl
Web Site: www.cheman.pl
Emp.: 100
Chemicals Mfr & Distr
S.I.C.: 2899
N.A.I.C.S.: 325998
Ludwik Majewski *(Pres)*

Chemia.Com S.A. (1)
182 Pulwaska St
02 670 Warsaw, Poland
Tel.: (48) 22 639 11 96
Fax: (48) 22 639 11 97
E-Mail: biuro@chemia.com
Web Site: www.chemia.com
Application Software Development Services
S.I.C.: 7371
N.A.I.C.S.: 541511

Ciech Service Sp. z.o.o. (1)
ul. Rakowiecka 41 Lok 15
02 521 Warsaw, Poland
Tel.: (48) 22 409 3617
Fax: (48) 22 409 3489
E-Mail: sekretariat@ciechservice.com.pl
Web Site: www.ciech-service.home.pl
Personal & Property Protection Services
S.I.C.: 7381
N.A.I.C.S.: 561612
Matthew Heron *(Chm)*
Marian Zurek *(Chm)*
Zbigniew Jerzy Kucinski *(Vice Chm)*
Paul Matusik Wojciech *(Sec)*

Gdanskie Zaklady Nawozow Fosforowych Fosfory Sp. z o.o. (1)
2 Kujawska St
Gdansk, 80550, Poland
Tel.: (48) 58 343 82 71
Fax: (48) 58 303 85 55
E-Mail: sekretariat@fosfory.pl
Web Site: www.fosfory.com.pl
Fertilizers Mfr
S.I.C.: 2873
N.A.I.C.S.: 325311

GZNF Fosfory Sp z.o.o. (1)
2 Kujawska St
80 550 Gdansk, Poland
Tel.: (48) 583438235
Fax: (48) 58 763 43 03
E-Mail: fosfory@fosfory.pl
Web Site: fosfory.pl/main.php?strona=aktualnosci&podstrona=przetargi
Agricultural Chemical Products Mfr
S.I.C.: 2879
N.A.I.C.S.: 325320

Huta Szkla Wymiarki S.A. (1)
ul. Ksiecia Witolda 11
68 131 Wymiarki, Poland
Tel.: (48) 683604450
Fax: (48) 683604460
E-Mail: marketing.hs@hs-wymiarki.com.pl
Web Site: www.hs-wymiarki.com.pl
Emp.: 1,500
Glass Products Mfr
S.I.C.: 3229
N.A.I.C.S.: 327212
Przemyslaw Rzezniczak *(Gen Mgr)*

Polfa Sp. z o.o. (1)
69 Prosta St
00 838 Warsaw, Poland PL
Tel.: (48) 224441166
Fax: (48) 224441188
E-Mail: polfa@polfa.eu
Web Site: www.polfa.eu
Emp.: 40
Chemicals Distr
S.I.C.: 5169
N.A.I.C.S.: 424690
Grzegorz Dworak *(Mng Dir)*

Soda Polska Ciech Sp. z.o.o. (1)
4 Fabryczna St
88 101 Inowroclaw, Poland
Tel.: (48) 523541500
Fax: (48) 523537043
E-Mail: izch@izch.com.pl
Web Site: www.sodapolska.pl
Emp.: 700
Chemicals Mfr
S.I.C.: 2899
N.A.I.C.S.: 325998
Jan Szczepanski *(Pres)*

Transoda Sp. z.o.o. (1)
Ul Fabryczna 4
88 101 Inowroclaw, Poland
Tel.: (48) 523541474
Fax: (48) 523537104
E-Mail: transoda@transoda.com.pl
Web Site: www.transoda.com.pl
Railway Transportation Services
S.I.C.: 4789
N.A.I.C.S.: 488210

Vitrosilicon S.A. (1)
27 Zaganska St
68 120 Ilowa, Poland
Tel.: (48) 683600747
Fax: (48) 683600700
E-Mail: vitro@vitrosilicon.com.pl
Web Site: www.vitrosilicon.com.pl
Smelted Glass & Chemical Products Mfr
S.I.C.: 2899
N.A.I.C.S.: 325998

Ciech S.A.—(Continued)

Zachem UCR Sp. z.o.o. (1)
Ul Wojska Polskiego 65
85 825 Bydgoszcz, Poland
Tel.: (48) 523747676
Fax: (48) 523747744
E-Mail: ucr@zachem.com.pl
Web Site: www.zachemucr.com.pl
Emp.: 300
Organization Development Consulting Services
S.I.C.: 8999
N.A.I.C.S.: 541612
Wlodzimierz Wozniak *(Acct Mgr)*

Zaklady Chemiczne Zachem S.A. (1)
65 Wojska Polskiego St
85 825 Bydgoszcz, Poland
Tel.: (48) 52 374 71 00
Fax: (48) 52 361 02 82
E-Mail: zachem@zachem.com.pl
Web Site: www.zachem.com.pl
Chemicals Mfr
S.I.C.: 2899
N.A.I.C.S.: 325998

ZCh Alwernia S.A. (1)
25 K Olszewskiego St
32 566 Alwernia, Poland
Tel.: (48) 122589100
Fax: (48) 122832188
E-Mail: alwernia@alwernia.com.pl
Web Site: www.alwernia.com.pl
Emp.: 300
Chemicals Producer & Distr
S.I.C.: 2899
N.A.I.C.S.: 325998
Wieslaw Halucha *(Pres & CEO)*

ZCh Organika Sarzyna S.A. (1)
1 Chemikow st
37 310 Nowa Sarzyna, Poland
Tel.: (48) 172407100
Fax: (48) 172407102
E-Mail: zch@zch.sarzyna.pl
Web Site: www.zch.sarzyna.pl
Emp.: 700
Chemicals Producer & Distr
S.I.C.: 2899
N.A.I.C.S.: 325998
Andrzej Miazga *(Pres)*

Non-U.S. Subsidiaries:

Daltrade Ltd (1)
94 Haligate Howden
Goole, East Yorkshire, DN147SZ, United Kingdom
Tel.: (44) 1430 430 041
Fax: (44) 1430 430 477
E-Mail: info@daltrade.co.uk
Web Site: www.daltrade.co.uk
Emp.: 15
Chemical Distr
S.I.C.: 5169
N.A.I.C.S.: 424690
Andrew Aleksanrowicz *(Mng Dir)*

Nordiska Unipol AB (1)
Arstaangsvagen 1C
PO Box 47040
S 10074 Stockholm, Sweden
Tel.: (46) 87445575
Fax: (46) 8182219
E-Mail: nordiska@unipol.se
Web Site: www.nordiskaunipol.se
Emp.: 3
Polish Chemicals Distr
S.I.C.: 5169
N.A.I.C.S.: 424690
Dariusz Januszewski *(Mng Dir)*

Polcommerce GmbH (1)
Billroth St 2 4 44
A 1190 Vienna, Austria
Tel.: (43) 14081511
Fax: (43) 14084561
E-Mail: office@polcommerce.at
Web Site: www.ciech.com
Emp.: 35
Chemicals Mfr & Distr
S.I.C.: 2899
N.A.I.C.S.: 325998
Wojciech Swider *(Mng Dir)*

Polsin Private Ltd (1)
20 Bendemeer Rd No 02-01
Cyberhub, Singapore, 339914, Singapore
Tel.: (65) 62238182
Fax: (65) 62989585
E-Mail: polsin.spore@polsin.com.sg
Web Site: www.polsin.com.sg
Emp.: 11
Chemicals Producer & Distr
S.I.C.: 2899
N.A.I.C.S.: 325998
Wlodzimierz Paczesny *(Mng Dir)*

Non-U.S. Subsidiary:

Polisin Overseas Shipping Ltd (2)
Ul Armii Krajowej 116 16
81 824 Sopot, Poland
Tel.: (48) 585552791
Fax: (48) 585552780
E-Mail: spedycja@polsin.com.pl
Web Site: www.polsin.com.pl
Emp.: 17
Sea Freight Forwarding Services
S.I.C.: 4412
N.A.I.C.S.: 483111
Andrzej Smejlis *(Gen Mgr)*

S.C. Uzinele Sodice Govora Ciech Chemical Group S.A. (1)
St Uzinei N 2 Judetul Valcea
240007 Ramnicu Valcea, Valcea County, Romania (92.91%)
Tel.: (40) 250731852
Fax: (40) 250733382
E-Mail: secretariat@usg.ro
Web Site: www.usg.ro
UZIM—(BUC)
Emp.: 700
Chemicals Producer & Distr
S.I.C.: 5169
N.A.I.C.S.: 424690
Jan Szczepanski *(Chm-Supervisory Bd)*
Witold Urbanowski *(Chm-Mgmt Bd, CEO & Gen Dir)*
Robert Pietrowski *(Member-Mgmt Bd, CFO & Dir-Fin)*

Sodawerk Stassfurt GmbH & Co. KG (1)
An der Loderburger Bahn 4a
39418 Stassfurt, Germany
Tel.: (49) 39252630
Fax: (49) 00493925263
E-Mail: info@sodawerk.de
Web Site: www.sodawerk.de
Emp.: 420
Chemicals Producer & Distr
S.I.C.: 2899
N.A.I.C.S.: 325998

CIELO GOLD CORP.

1250 West Hastings Street
Vancouver, BC, V6E 2M4, Canada
Tel.: (604) 685-2542
Fax: (604) 408-9301
Web Site: www.cielows.com
Year Founded: 2011
CMC—(CNSX)
Business Description:
Gold Mining
S.I.C.: 1041
N.A.I.C.S.: 212221
Personnel:
Lucky Janda *(Pres & CEO)*
Board of Directors:
Lucky Janda
Rana Vig

CIELO S.A.

(d/b/a VisaNet Brasil)
Alameda Grajau 219 Alphaville
Barueri
Sao Paulo, 06454050, Brazil
Tel.: (55) 1121847600
Fax: (55) 1121847850
Web Site: www.cielo.com.br
CIEL3—(BRAZ OTC)
Rev.: $2,669,686,737
Assets: $4,937,192,897
Liabilities: $3,812,679,725
Net Worth: $1,124,513,172
Earnings: $1,141,488,788
Emp.: 55,680
Fiscal Year-end: 12/31/12
Business Description:
Electronic Payment Solutions
S.I.C.: 7389
N.A.I.C.S.: 425110
Personnel:
Romulo de Mello Dias *(CEO)*
Clovis Poggetti, Jr. *(CFO & IR Officer)*
Dilson Tadeu da Costa Ribeiro *(Exec Officer-Products & Bus Dev Area)*
Claudio Eduardo Vianna de Oliveira *(Exec Officer-Corp Comml Area)*
Eduardo Chedid Simoes *(Exec Officer-Retail Bus Area)*
Pilnio Cardoso da Costa Patrao *(Member-Exec Bd)*
Roberto Menezes Dumani *(Exec VP-Org Dev Dept)*
Board of Directors:
Alexandre Correa Abreu
Jose Mauricio Pereira Coelho
Francisco Augusto da Costa e Silva
Domingos Figueiredo de Abreu
Maria Izabel Gribel de Castro
Gilberto Mifano
Raul Francisco Moreira
Marcelo Araujo Noronha
Alexandre Rapapport
Milton Almicar Silva Vargas

U.S. Subsidiary:

Merchant e-Solutions, Inc. (1)
3400 Bridge Pkwy Ste 100
Redwood City, CA 94065 DE
Tel.: (650) 628-6850
Toll Free: (888) 288-2692
E-Mail: sales@merchante-solutions.com
Web Site: www.merchante-solutions.com
Sales Range: $100-124.9 Million
Electronic Payment Software Developer
S.I.C.: 7372
N.A.I.C.S.: 511210
Paulo Guzzo *(Pres & CEO)*
Marcelo F. Perez *(CFO & Exec VP-Corp Dev)*
James M. Aviles *(COO & Mgr-Products & Tech)*
Sharif M. Bayyari *(Pres-US)*
Charles Jadallah *(Exec VP-Sls & Bus Dev)*

CIENTIFICA PLC

(Formerly Avia Health Informatics Plc)
3 Noble Street
London, EC2V 7EE, United Kingdom
Tel.: (44) 203 126 4933
E-Mail: info@cientifica.com
Web Site: www.cientifica.com
CTFA.L—(AIM)
Emp.: 45
Business Description:
Technology Investment Services
S.I.C.: 6211
N.A.I.C.S.: 523999
Personnel:
Tim Harper *(CEO)*
Legal Counsel:
EMW Picton Howell LLP
Procter House 1 Procter Street
London, United Kingdom

DLA Piper LLP
3 Noble Street
EC2V 7EE London, United Kingdom

CIFI HOLDINGS (GROUP) CO. LTD.

5th Floor Block 3 Lane 288 Tongxie Road
Changning District, Shanghai, 200335, China
Tel.: (86) 21 60701010
Fax: (86) 21 60701999
E-Mail: office@cifi.com.cn
Web Site: www.cifi.com.cn
Year Founded: 2000
884—(HKG)
Sales Range: $650-699.9 Million
Emp.: 2,700
Business Description:
Real Estate Developer
S.I.C.: 6552
N.A.I.C.S.: 237210
Personnel:
Zhong Lin *(Chm)*
Wei Lin *(Vice Chm)*
Feng Lin *(CEO)*
Tai On Lo *(Sec)*
Board of Directors:
Zhong Lin
Yunchang Gu
Feng Lin
Wei Lin
Wee Seng Tan
Yongyue Zhang

CIG PANNONIA ELETBIZTOSITO NYRT

(d/b/a CIG Pannonia Life Insurance)
Florian ter 1
Pf 516
1033 Budapest, Hungary
Tel.: (36) 4153730444
Fax: (36) 1 2472021
E-Mail: info@cig.eu
Web Site: www.cigpannonia.hu
CIGPANNONIA—(BUD)
Premiums: $181,636,385
Assets: $223,322,714
Liabilities: $29,488,711
Net Worth: $193,834,003
Earnings: ($9,642,927)
Emp.: 95
Fiscal Year-end: 12/31/12
Business Description:
Life Insurance Services
S.I.C.: 6311
N.A.I.C.S.: 524113
Personnel:
Bela Horvath *(Chm)*
Zsigmond Jarai *(Chm-Supervisory Bd)*
Jozsef Bayer *(Deputy Chm-Supervisory Bd)*
Otto Csurgo *(CEO)*
Balazs Birkas *(Deputy CEO-Customer Svc)*
Zoltan Busa *(Deputy CEO-Product Dev & Risk Mgmt-CIG Pannonia EMABIT Zrt)*
Gabriella Kadar *(Deputy CEO-Sls)*
Andras Kovacs *(Deputy CEO-Sls Dev)*
Linda Sallai *(Deputy CEO-Product Dev & Risk Manipulation)*
Sandor Vigh *(Deputy CEO-IT)*
Tibor Zarnoczi *(Deputy CEO-Alternative Sls Dev)*
Miklos Barta *(CFO)*
Balazs Hamori *(Chief Actuary)*
Antal Csevar *(Consumer Protection Officer)*
Katalin Halasz *(Sr Medical Officer)*
Balazs Pap *(CEO-Sls Grp)*
Board of Directors:
Bela Horvath
Miklos Barta
Balazs Birkas
Otto Csurgo
Gabriella Kadar
Supervisory Board of Directors:
Zsigmond Jarai
Laszlo Gyorgy Asztalos
Jozsef Bayer
Imre Fekete
Peter Kostevc
Sandor Ormandi
Bela Erno Preisinger
Attila Tamas Solymar

CIGMA METALS CORPORATION

Calle Zurbano 46 2C
Madrid, Spain 28010

Tel.: (34) 91 4516157
Year Founded: 1989
C9K.FSE—(DEU)
Sales Range: Less than $1 Million
Business Description:
Gold & Silver Mining Services
S.I.C.: 1041
N.A.I.C.S.: 212221
Personnel:
Antonio Jaramillo *(Pres, CEO & CFO)*
Board of Directors:
Antonio Jaramillo
Michelle Robinson
Transfer Agent:
Interwest Transfer Co. Inc.
1981 E Murray Holladay Rd Ste 100
Salt Lake City, UT 84101

CIGNITI TECHNOLOGIES LTD.

6th Floor ORION Block The V (Ascendas) Plot No 17
Software Units Layout
Madhapur, Hyderabad, 500081, India
Tel.: (91) 40 30702250
Fax: (91) 40 30702255
E-Mail: info.hyd@cigniti.com
Web Site: www.cigniti.com
590089—(BOM)
Business Description:
Software Testing Services
S.I.C.: 7373
N.A.I.C.S.: 541512
Personnel:
C. V. Subramanyam *(Chm-Supervisory Bd & Mng Dir)*
Sudhakar Pennam *(Pres & CEO)*
Raj Neravati *(COO)*
Mahendra Alladi *(CTO)*
Sanjay Jupudi *(Pres-Americas)*
Sriram Rajaram *(Pres-Strategy & Corp Dev)*
Gary L. Smith *(Exec VP-Sls)*
Sai Chintala *(Sr VP-Pre-Sls-Global)*
Kalyana Rao Konda *(Sr VP-Delivery-Global)*

Corporate Headquarters:

Cigniti, Inc. (1)
433 E Las Colinas Blvd #1240
Irving, TX 75039 IA
Tel.: (972) 756-0622
Fax: (972) 767-0948
E-Mail: info@cigniti.com
Web Site: www.cigniti.com
Sales Range: $10-24.9 Million
Emp.: 155
Computer Systems Design Services
S.I.C.: 7373
N.A.I.C.S.: 541512
Sanjay Jupudi *(Pres-Americas)*
Gary L. Smith *(Exec VP-Sls)*

CIMA CO., LTD.

5F Hulic Ginza Building 1-7-10 Ginza
Chuo-ku, Tokyo, 104 0061, Japan
Tel.: (81) 3 3567 8091
Fax: (81) 3 3567 8092
E-Mail: soumu@bridaldiamond.co.jp
Web Site: www.cima-ir.jp
Year Founded: 1994
7638—(JAS)
Sls.: $94,116,000
Assets: $81,785,000
Liabilities: $37,642,000
Net Worth: $44,143,000
Earnings: ($13,376,000)
Emp.: 460
Fiscal Year-end: 03/31/13
Business Description:
Bridal Jewelry Designer & Mfr
S.I.C.: 3911
N.A.I.C.S.: 339910
Personnel:
Katsuyo Shiraishi *(Pres)*
Takuma Izumi *(Exec Officer-Sls Div-Japan)*
Keita Seo *(Exec Officer-Sls Div-West)*
Board of Directors:
Lior Kunstler
Tomoyuki Marunaka
Eiichi Matsuhashi
Katsuyo Shiraishi
Yutaro Tamaki
Jean-Paul Tolkowsky

CIMATRON LTD.

11 Gush Etzion St
Giv'at Shemu'el, 54030, Israel
Tel.: (972) 732370237
Fax: (972) 3 531 2097
E-Mail: info@cimatron.com
Web Site: www.cimatron.com
Year Founded: 1982
CIMT—(NASDAQ)
Rev.: $42,314,000
Assets: $34,410,000
Liabilities: $15,945,000
Net Worth: $18,465,000
Earnings: $3,709,000
Emp.: 281
Fiscal Year-end: 12/31/12
Business Description:
Computer Software Developer & Mfr
S.I.C.: 7373
N.A.I.C.S.: 541512
Personnel:
Yossi Ben-Shalom *(Chm)*
Danny Haran *(Pres & CEO)*
Ilan Erez *(CFO & VP-Ops)*
William F. Gibbs *(Pres-North America)*
Board of Directors:
Yossi Ben-Shalom
Barak Dotan
Rami Entin
William F. Gibbs
David Golan

U.S. Subsidiaries:

Cimatron Technologies Inc. (1)
41700 Gardenbrook Rd Ste 100
Novi, MI 48375-1320
Tel.: (248) 596-9700
Fax: (248) 596-9741
Toll Free: (877) 596-9700
E-Mail: info@cimatrontech.com
Web Site: www.cimatrontech.com
Emp.: 21
Provider of Computer Software
S.I.C.: 7699
N.A.I.C.S.: 811212
Sam Golan *(Pres & CEO)*

Non-U.S. Subsidiaries:

Cimatron (Beijing) Technology Co. Ltd. (1)
Huibin Office B0415 No 8 Beichendon St
Chaoyang District, Beijing, 100101, China
Tel.: (86) 1084978229
E-Mail: langyan@cimatron.com.cn
Web Site: www.cimatron.com.cn
Emp.: 41
Computer Software
S.I.C.: 7373
N.A.I.C.S.: 541512

Cimatron France Sarl (1)
Cei 66 Blvd Niels Bohr
BP 2132, 69603 Villeurbanne, Cedex, France
Tel.: (33) 474129056
Fax: (33) 478892703
E-Mail: foinso@cimatron.fr
Web Site: www.cimatron.fr
Emp.: 5
Provider of Computer Software
S.I.C.: 7373
N.A.I.C.S.: 541512
Danny Haran *(Pres & CEO)*
Ilan Erez *(CFO & VP-Ops)*

Cimatron GmbH (1)
Ottostrasse 2
76275 Ettlingen, Germany (100%)
Tel.: (49) 724353880
Fax: (49) 7243538855
E-Mail: webinfo@cimatron.de
Web Site: www.cimatron.de
Emp.: 40
Provider of Computer Software
S.I.C.: 7373
N.A.I.C.S.: 541512
Dirk Doberg *(Mng Dir)*

Cimatron Japan KK (1)
Nihonbashi Honcho Bldg 10th Fl 1-3-5
Nihonbashi Honcho Chuo-ku, Tokyo, 103-0023, Japan
Tel.: (81) 335481147
E-Mail: marketing@cimatron.co.jp
Web Site: www.metalcam.com
Emp.: 10
Provider of Computer Software
S.I.C.: 7373
N.A.I.C.S.: 541512

Cimatron UK Limited (1)
The Media Centre
Huddersfield, W Yorkshire, HD1 1RL, United Kingdom
Tel.: (44) 8709905216
Fax: (44) 8709905217
Emp.: 2
Provider of Computer Software
S.I.C.: 7373
N.A.I.C.S.: 541512

CIMB GROUP HOLDINGS BERHAD

5th Floor Bangunan CIMB Jalan
Semantan Damansara Heights
50490 Kuala Lumpur, Malaysia
Tel.: (60) 3 2093 0379
Fax: (60) 3 2093 9688
E-Mail: ir@cimb.com
Web Site: www.cimb.com
CIMB—(KLS OTC)
Int. Income: $4,440,235,192
Assets: $110,527,693,401
Liabilities: $100,902,767,229
Net Worth: $9,624,926,172
Earnings: $1,441,800,951
Emp.: 41,993
Fiscal Year-end: 12/31/12
Business Description:
Bank Holding Company
S.I.C.: 6712
N.A.I.C.S.: 551111
Personnel:
Nazir Razak *(CEO & Mng Dir)*
Charon Wardini Mokhzani *(CEO-CIMB Investment Bank & Deputy CEO-Investment Banking)*
Sooi Lin Kong *(Deputy CEO-CIMB Investment Bank & Head-Corp Client Solutions)*
Renzo Christopher Viegas *(Deputy CEO & Head-Consumer Banking)*
Kok Kwan Lee *(Deputy CEO-Corp Banking, Treasury & Markets)*
Kenny Kim *(CFO & Head-Grp Strategy & Strategic Investment Div)*
David Richard Thomas *(Chief Risk Officer)*
Arwin Rasyid *(Pres/CEO-CIMB Niaga & Head-Indonesia)*
Subhak Siwaraksa *(Pres/CEO-CIMB Thai Bank & Head-Thailand)*
Badlisyah Abdul Ghani *(CEO-CIMB Islamic Bank & Head-Islamic Banking Div & Middle East)*
Lye Mun Mak *(CEO-CIMB Bank & Head-Singapore)*
Rossaya Mohd Nashir *(Sec)*
Board of Directors:
Mohammed Nor Yusof
Muhamad Abdul Kadir
Zainal Abidin Putih
Hamzah Bakar
Robert Dau Meng Cheim
Katsumi Hatao
Watanan Petersik
Nazir Razak
Glenn Muhammad Surya Yusuf

Subsidiaries:

CIMB Group Sdn. Bhd. (1)
10th Floor Bangunan CIMB Jalan Semantan
50490 Kuala Lumpur, Malaysia MY
Tel.: (60) 320848888
Fax: (60) 320849888
Web Site: www.cimb.com.my
Sales Range: $50-74.9 Million
Emp.: 3,000
Investment Holding
S.I.C.: 6712
N.A.I.C.S.: 551111
Mohammed Nor Yusof *(Chm)*
Nazir Razak *(CEO & Grp Mng Dir)*

Subsidiaries:

CIMB Private Equity Sdn Bhd (2)
Level 33 Menara Bumiputra Commerce 11
Jalan Raja Laut, 50350 Kuala Lumpur, Malaysia
Tel.: (60) 326192827
Fax: (60) 26923650
Emp.: 25
Commercial Banking Services
S.I.C.: 6029
N.A.I.C.S.: 522110

Commerce Asset Ventures SDN BHD (2)
6 Commerce House 22-24 Jalan Sri
Semantan Satu
50490 Kuala Lumpur, Malaysia
Tel.: (60) 0327325577
Fax: (60) 0327321343
Web Site: www.cinb.com
Emp.: 30
Investment Management Services
S.I.C.: 8742
N.A.I.C.S.: 541611
Lee Yu Lian *(COO)*

Goodmaid Chemical Corporation Sdn Bhd (2)
Suite C-12-12 Plaza Mont Kiara No 2 Jalan Kiara
Mont Kiara, 70450 Kuala Lumpur, Malaysia
Tel.: (60) 362039558
Fax: (60) 3 6203 9557
E-Mail: enquiries@goodmaid.net
Web Site: www.goodmaid.net
Household Cleaning Products Mfr
S.I.C.: 2842
N.A.I.C.S.: 325612

Goodmaid Marketing Sdn Bhd (2)
Ste C 12 12 Plz Mont Kiara No 2
Jalan Kiara Mont Kiara, 50480 Kuala Lumpur, Malaysia
Tel.: (60) 362039558
Fax: (60) 362039557
E-Mail: enquiries@goodmaid.net
Household Cleaning Products Mf
S.I.C.: 2842
N.A.I.C.S.: 325612
Lim Dik *(Gen Mgr)*

Kibaru Manufacturing Sdn Bhd (2)
A83 Jalan 1 B 3 Kawasan MIEL Sungai Petani Phase I
08000 Sungai Petani, Kedah Darul Aman, Malaysia
Tel.: (60) 44421222
Fax: (60) 44421223
E-Mail: sales4@kibaru.com.my
Web Site: www.kibaru.com.my
Emp.: 175
Rubber Component Mfr
S.I.C.: 3069
N.A.I.C.S.: 326299

Joint Ventures:

CIMB-Principal Asset Management Berhad (2)
Level 5 Menara Milenium 8 Jalan Damanlela
Bukit Damansara, Kuala Lumpur, 50490, Malaysia
Tel.: (60) 3 2084 2000
Fax: (60) 20842004
Web Site: www.cimb-principal.com.my
Emp.: 185
Asset Management
S.I.C.: 6282
N.A.I.C.S.: 523920
Ken Goh *(CEO)*
Munirah Khairuddin *(CEO)*
Pedro Esteban Borda *(CEO-ASEAN Reg)*

CIMB Group Holdings Berhad—(Continued)

Subsidiary:

CIMB Wealth Advisors Berhad (3)
50 52 54 Jalan ss 21/39 Damansara Utama
47400 Petaling Jaya, Selangor, Malaysia
Tel.: (60) 3 7718 3000
Fax: (60) 3 7718 3003
E-Mail: cwa.custsupport@cwealthadvisors.com.my
Web Site: www.cwealthadvisors.com.my
Financial Advisory Services
S.I.C.: 6211
N.A.I.C.S.: 523999

Non-U.S. Subsidiaries:

CIMB-Principal Asset Management Company Limited (3)
44 CIMB THAI Bank Building 16th Floor Langsuan Road
Lumpini Pathumwan, Bangkok, 10330, Thailand
Tel.: (66) 26869595
Web Site: www.cimb-principal.co.th
Financial Management Services
S.I.C.: 6211
N.A.I.C.S.: 523999

CIMB-Principal Asset Management (Singapore) Pte Ltd (3)
50 Raffles Place 22-03A Singapore Land Tower
Singapore, 48623, Singapore
Tel.: (65) 6210 8488
Fax: (65) 6562108489
Web Site: www.cimb-principal.com.my
Emp.: 1
Asset Management Services
S.I.C.: 6799
N.A.I.C.S.: 523920
Bent Hov *(CEO)*

PT CIMB-Principal Asset Management (3)
The Jakarta Stock Exchange Building II 20th Floor Jl Jend
Sudirman Kav 52-53, Jakarta, 12190, Indonesia Id
Tel.: (62) 21 515 1180
Fax: (62) 21 515 1178
Web Site: www.cimb-principal.co.id
Emp.: 55
Commercial Banking Services
S.I.C.: 6029
N.A.I.C.S.: 522110
Fadlul Imansyah *(VP-Equity)*

CIMB Principal Islamic Asset Management Sdn. Bhd. (2)
Menara Bumiputra-Commerce
Kuala Lumpur, Malaysia
Tel.: (60) 3 2084 2288
E-Mail: noripah.kamso@cimb.com
Web Site: www.cimb-principalislamic.com
Asset Management Services
S.I.C.: 6282
N.A.I.C.S.: 523920
Noripah Kamso *(CEO)*
Zeid Ayer *(Chief Investment Officer)*

Non-U.S. Subsidiaries:

Armada Investment Holding Ltd (2)
30 Shotover Street Queenstown Town Centre
Queenstown-Lakes, Queenstown, Otago, New Zealand
Tel.: (64) 34412100
Fax: (64) 3 441 3900
Investment Management Services
S.I.C.: 6211
N.A.I.C.S.: 523999

CIMB Research Pte Ltd (2)
50 Raffles Place 19-00
Singapore, 048623, Singapore
Tel.: (65) 62251228
Fax: (65) 65389889
Web Site: www.cimbsecurities.com
Commercial Banking Services
S.I.C.: 6029
N.A.I.C.S.: 522110

CIMB Securities International Pte Ltd (2)
50 Raffles Place 19-00 Singapore Land Tower
Singapore, 48623, Singapore
Tel.: (65) 62251228
Fax: (65) 62251522
Commercial Banking Services
S.I.C.: 6029
N.A.I.C.S.: 522110

Subsidiary:

CIMB Securities (Singapore) Pte Ltd (3)
50 Raffles Pl 01-01 Singapore Land Tower
Singapore, 048623, Singapore
Tel.: (65) 65389889
Fax: (65) 63231176
E-Mail: clientsservices.sg@cimb.com
Web Site: www.cimbsecurities.COM
Security Brokerage Services
S.I.C.: 6211
N.A.I.C.S.: 523120
Carol Fong *(CEO)*

Non-U.S. Subsidiaries:

CIMB Securities (HK) Ltd (3)
Units 7706-08 Level 77 International Commerce Centre 1
Austin Road West, Kowloon, China (Hong Kong)
Tel.: (852) 28680380
Fax: (852) 2537 1928
Commercial Banking Services
S.I.C.: 6029
N.A.I.C.S.: 522110
Soolik Keoy *(Gen Mgr)*

Subsidiary:

CIMB Securities (HK) Nominees Ltd (4)
Units 7706-08 Level 77 International Commerce Centre 1
Austin Road West, Kowloon, China (Hong Kong)
Tel.: (852) 2868 0380
Fax: (852) 2537 1928
Emp.: 200
Commercial Banking Services
S.I.C.: 6029
N.A.I.C.S.: 522110

CIMB Securities (UK) Ltd (3)
27 Knightbridge
London, SW1X 7YB, United Kingdom
Tel.: (44) 2072012199
Fax: (44) 20 7201 2191
Web Site: www.cimb.com
Emp.: 15
Financial Security Services
S.I.C.: 6211
N.A.I.C.S.: 523999

PT CIMB Securities Indonesia (3)
The Jakarta Stock Exchange Building II 20th Floor Jl Jend, Jakarta, Indonesia
Tel.: (62) 215151330
Fax: (62) 215151335
Commercial Banking Services
S.I.C.: 6029
N.A.I.C.S.: 522110

CIMB Thai Bank Public Company Limited (2)
44 North Sathon
Silom Bangrak, Bangkok, 10500, Thailand (93.15%)
Tel.: (66) 2633 9000
Fax: (66) 2633 9026
Web Site: www.bankthai.co.th
CIMBT—(THA)
Sales Range: $200-249.9 Million
Emp.: 2,783
Banking & Financial Services
S.I.C.: 6029
N.A.I.C.S.: 522110
Chakramon Phasukavanich *(Chm)*
Robert Cheim Dau Meng *(Vice Chm)*
Subhak Siwaraksa *(Pres, CEO & Head-Investment Banking Grp)*
Thaphop Kleesuwan *(Sec)*

Subsidiary:

BT Asset Management Company Limited (3)
44 Bank Thai Tower 24-26 th Floor
Soi Langsuan Ploenchit Rd Lump, 10330
Bangkok, Thailand
Tel.: (66) 26869500
Fax: (66) 26571307
Web Site: www.cimbprinciple.co.th
Emp.: 70
Real Estate Services
S.I.C.: 6531
N.A.I.C.S.: 531390
Anusorn Buranakanonda *(Mng Dir)*

PT Bank Niaga TBK (2)
Graha Niaga
Jl Jend Sudirman Kav 58
Jakarta, 12190, Indonesia
Tel.: (62) 212505151
Fax: (62) 21 250 5205
Web Site: www.cimbniaga.com
Banking Services
S.I.C.: 6029
N.A.I.C.S.: 522110
Yosef Antonius Boliona Badilangoe *(Exec VP & Head-Retail Sls & Svcs)*
Agos Cholan *(Exec VP & Head-Mortgage Banking)*
Paul S. Hasjim *(Exec VP & Head-Ops & IT)*
Lynna A. Muliawan *(Exec VP & Head-Preferred Banking)*

iCIMB (MSC) Sdn Bhd (1)
19th Floor Menara Atlas 5 Jalan 4/83a
Kuala Lumpur, 59200, Malaysia
Tel.: (60) 322960000
Fax: (60) 322836982
Financial Management Services
S.I.C.: 6211
N.A.I.C.S.: 523999

Non-U.S. Subsidiary:

PT Kencana Internusa Artha Finance (1)
Gedung Kita Finance Jl R S Fatmawati No 16
Jakarta, 12420, Indonesia
Tel.: (62) 21 7590 8899
Fax: (62) 21 7590 6875
E-Mail: sales@kitafinance.com
Web Site: www.kitafinance.com
Automobile Financing Services
S.I.C.: 6726
N.A.I.C.S.: 525990
Daniel Hutapea *(Corp Sec)*

CIMCORP OY

Satakunnantie 5
28400 Ulvila, Finland
Tel.: (358) 26775111
Fax: (358) 26775200
E-Mail: info@cimcorp.com
Web Site: www.cimcorp.com
Sales Range: $25-49.9 Million
Emp.: 200
Fiscal Year-end: 12/31/12

Business Description:
Developer of Robotic Distribution Systems
S.I.C.: 8711
N.A.I.C.S.: 541330
Personnel:
Marrkku Vesa *(Pres)*

Non-U.S. Subsidiary:

RMT Robotics Ltd. (1)
635 South Service Road
Grimsby, ON, L3M 4E8, Canada
Tel.: (905) 643-9700
Fax: (905) 643-9666
Web Site: www.rmtrobotics.com
Emp.: 75
Automated Material Handling System Mfr & Whslr
S.I.C.: 3569
N.A.I.C.S.: 333999
Don Heelis *(Mgr-Global Sls-Tire Sys)*

CIMENTAS IZMIR CIMENTO FABRIKASI TURK A.S.

Kemalpasa Caddesi No 4 Isikkent
35070 Izmir, Turkey
Tel.: (90) 2324721050
Web Site: www.cimentas.com
CMENT—(IST)
Rev.: $3,374,391,230
Assets: $7,187,888,470
Liabilities: $1,962,131,360
Net Worth: $5,225,757,110
Earnings: $55,382,740
Fiscal Year-end: 12/31/12

Business Description:
Cement Mfr
S.I.C.: 3241
N.A.I.C.S.: 327310
Personnel:
Walter Montevecchi *(Chm & CEO)*
Francesco Gaetano Caltagirone *(Vice Chm)*
Board of Directors:
Walter Montevecchi
Mehmet Nazmi Akduman
Marco Maria Bianconi
Alessandro Caltagirone
Francesco Gaetano Caltagirone
Mario Ciliberto
Massimiliano Capece Minutolo
Riccardo Nicolini

CIMINO & ASSOCIATI PRIVATE EQUITY S.P.A.

(d/b/a Cape)
Via Monte Rosa 88
The Private Equity House
20149 Milan, Italy
Tel.: (39) 027636131
Fax: (39) 02 773 31617
E-Mail: info@cape.it
Web Site: www.cape.it
Year Founded: 1999
Managed Assets: $730,056,000
Emp.: 7,000

Business Description:
Private Equity Firm
S.I.C.: 6211
N.A.I.C.S.: 523999
Personnel:
Simone Cimino *(Founder, Chm & Mng Partner)*
Marco Visarma *(CEO & Mng Partner)*
Guido De Vecchi *(Mng Partner)*
Annamaria Petrillo *(Partner)*
Francesco Sala *(Partner)*
Emanuela Trezzi *(Partner)*
Maddalena De Liso *(CFO)*

Joint Venture:

Cape-Natixis S.G.R. S.p.A. (1)
Monte Rosa No 88
I-20149 Milan, Italy
Tel.: (39) 027636131
Fax: (39) 0277331617
E-Mail: info@cape.it
Web Site: www.cape.it
Emp.: 25
Private Equity Funds Management Services
S.I.C.: 6211
N.A.I.C.S.: 523999
Simone Cimino *(Founder, Chm & Mng Partner)*
Marco Visarma *(CEO & Mng Partner)*
Guido De Vecchi *(Mng Partner)*
Annamaria Petrillo *(Partner)*
Emanuela Trezzi *(Partner)*
Maddalena De Liso *(CFO)*

CIMMCO BIRLA LIMITED

Indra Palace 3rd Floor H Block
Connaught Circle
New Delhi, 110001, India
Tel.: (91) 11 23356463
Fax: (91) 11 41516793
E-Mail: info@cimmco.in
Web Site: www.cimmco.in
505230—(BOM NSE)
Emp.: 1,000

Business Description:
Heavy Engineering Services
S.I.C.: 1629
N.A.I.C.S.: 237990
Personnel:
Jagdish Prasad Chowdhary *(Chm & Mng Dir)*
Umesh Chowdhary *(Vice Chm, CEO & Mng Dir)*
Vinay Mohan *(CFO)*
Dipankar Ganguly *(Sec)*

Board of Directors:
Jagdish Prasad Chowdhary
Anil Kumar Agarwal
Rakesh Mohan Agarwal
Umesh Chowdhary
D.N. Davar
Ravi Kumar
Vinay Mohan
G.B. Rao
Jagdish Kumar Shukla

CIMOS D.D.

C Marezganskega upora 2
6000 Koper, Slovenia
Tel.: (386) 56658100
Fax: (386) 56658299
E-Mail: info@cimos.eu
Web Site: www.cimos.eu
Sales Range: $300-349.9 Million
Emp.: 3,480
Business Description:
Automotive Components Mfr
S.I.C.: 3795
N.A.I.C.S.: 336111
Personnel:
Vojko Anton Antoncic *(Chm-Supervisory Bd)*
Jerko Bartolic *(Chm-Mgmt Bd)*
Zvonimir Grgurovic *(Deputy Chm-Supervisory Bd)*
Janez Gradisek *(Member-Mgmt Bd-Production)*
Supervisory Board of Directors:
Vojko Anton Antoncic
Zvonimir Grgurovic
Stojan Nikolic
Andro Ocvirk
Marjan Podgorsek
Meta Berk Skok
Subsidiaries:

Cimos Titan d.o.o. **(1)**
28 Kovinarska Cesta
Kamnik, 1241, Slovenia (100%)
Tel.: (386) 018309144
Fax: (386) 18309179
E-Mail: titan.livarna@cimos.eu
Web Site: www.cimos.com
Emp.: 300
Steel Foundry
S.I.C.: 3325
N.A.I.C.S.: 331513
Ivan Batagelj *(Mng Dir)*

Livarna Vuzenica d.o.o. **(1)**
21 A Livarska Cesta
Vuzenica, 2367, Slovenia (62.4%)
Tel.: (386) 28764200
Fax: (386) 28764075
Emp.: 345
Steel Foundry
S.I.C.: 3325
N.A.I.C.S.: 331513
Vojko Jeznik *(Gen Mgr)*

PS Cimos Tan Avtomobilska Industrija, d.o.o. **(1)**
21 Perhavceva ulica
Maribor, 2000, Slovenia (100%)
Tel.: (386) 24501111
Fax: (386) 24614299
Web Site: www.cimos.eu/index.php?item=145&page=search&query=perhav%C4%8Deva&search=1
Emp.: 712
Motor Vehicle Component Mfr
S.I.C.: 3714
N.A.I.C.S.: 336390
Miroslav Skapin *(Mng Dir)*

CINAPORT ACQUISITION CORP.

Suite 2706 40 King Street West
Toronto, ON, M5H 3Y2, Canada
Tel.: (416) 213-8118
Fax: (416) 213-8668
E-Mail: schari@cinaport.com
Year Founded: 2011
CPQ.P—(TSXV)
Business Description:
Investment Services
S.I.C.: 6211
N.A.I.C.S.: 523999
Personnel:
Donald Wright *(Chm)*
Avininder Grewal *(CEO)*
Board of Directors:
Donald Wright
Seshadri Chari
Avininder Grewal
John O'Sullivan
Transfer Agent:
Equity Financial Trust Company
Toronto, ON, Canada

CINCO INVESTMENTS PLC

3rd Floor 14 Hanover Street Hanover Square
London, W1S1 YH, United Kingdom
Tel.: (44) 2075145872
Fax: (44) 2075149911
E-Mail: info@cincoinvestments.eu
Web Site: www.cincoinvestments.eu
1CC—(DEU)
Business Description:
Oil Refineries
S.I.C.: 2911
N.A.I.C.S.: 324110
Personnel:
Wassim Ashi *(Chm)*
Board of Directors:
Wassim Ashi
Javad Ashi

CINDA INTERNATIONAL HOLDINGS LIMITED

45th Floor COSCO Tower 183 Queen's Road
Central, China (Hong Kong)
Tel.: (852) 22357888
Fax: (852) 22357878
E-Mail: cs@cinda.com.hk
Web Site: www.cinda.com.hk
0111—(HKG)
Rev.: $14,806,684
Assets: $100,901,957
Liabilities: $29,113,042
Net Worth: $71,788,915
Earnings: $1,354,233
Emp.: 110
Fiscal Year-end: 12/31/12
Business Description:
Securities & Commodities Brokerage Services; Investment Advisory Services
S.I.C.: 6211
N.A.I.C.S.: 523120
Personnel:
Xiaozhou Chen *(Chm)*
Guanjiang Gao *(Deputy Chm)*
Hongwei Zhao *(Mng Dir)*
Mun Chung Lau *(Sec & Deputy Gen Mgr)*
Board of Directors:
Xiaozhou Chen
Gongmeng Chen
Kwok Wai Chow
Guanjiang Gao
Zhijian Gong
Muk Ming Hung
Mun Chung Lau
Tongsan Wang
Hongwei Zhao
Legal Counsel:
Tung & Co.
19th Floor 8 Wyndham Street
Central, China (Hong Kong)

Conyers Dill & Pearman
2901 One Exchange Square 8 Connaught Place
Central, China (Hong Kong)

Butterfield Fulcrum Group (Bermuda) Limited
26 Burnaby Street
Hamilton, HM 11, Bermuda
Transfer Agents:
Tricor Secretaries Limited
26th Floor Tesbury Centre 28 Queens Rd E
Hong Kong, China (Hong Kong)

Butterfield Fulcrum Group (Bermuda) Limited
26 Burnaby Street
Hamilton, HM 11, Bermuda

CINDERELLA MEDIA GROUP LIMITED

26/F 625 King's Road
North Point, Hong Kong, China (Hong Kong)
Tel.: (852) 2976 2000
Fax: (852) 2595 9118
E-Mail: info@cinderellagroup.com.hk
Web Site: www.cinderellagroup.com.hk
550—(HKG)
Sls.: $196,782,987
Assets: $172,455,280
Liabilities: $67,515,125
Net Worth: $104,940,155
Earnings: $24,360,976
Emp.: 1,136
Fiscal Year-end: 12/31/12
Business Description:
Media Advertising Services
S.I.C.: 7319
N.A.I.C.S.: 541890
Personnel:
Chuk Kin Lau *(Compliance Officer)*
Mei Lan Lam *(Sec)*
Board of Directors:
Siu Kau Wan
Franco Ping Kuen Cheng
Peter Stavros Patapios Christofis
David Ho
Mei Lan Lam
Chuk Kin Lau
Adrian Ching Ming Lee
Eleanor Lee Ching Man Ling
Legal Counsel:
Cheung, Tong & Rosa
Rooms 501, 5/F, Sun Hung Kai Cenre, 30 Harbour Road
Hong Kong, China (Hong Kong)

Butterfield Fulcrum Group (Bermuda) Limited
26 Burnaby Street
Hamilton, HM 11, Bermuda

CINDRELLA HOTELS LTD.

3rd Mile Sevoke Road
Kolkata, 734401, India
Tel.: (91) 353 2544130
Fax: (91) 353 2531173
E-Mail: cindrela@bsnl.in
Web Site: www.cindrellahotels.com
526373—(BOM)
Sales Range: $25-49.9 Million
Business Description:
Hotel Service
S.I.C.: 7011
N.A.I.C.S.: 721120
Personnel:
Rajendra Kumar Baid *(Chm)*
Board of Directors:
Rajendra Kumar Baid
Sangita Devi Baid
Surajmal Kundalia
Kumaresh Lahiri
Rajendra Lakhotia
Transfer Agent:
Niche Technologies Private Limited
D-511 Bagree Market 71 B. R. B. Basu Road
Kolkata, India

CINEPLEX INC.

1303 Yonge St
Toronto, ON, M4T 2Y9, Canada
Tel.: (416) 323-6600
Fax: (416) 323-6683
E-Mail: guestservices@cineplex.com
Web Site: www.cineplex.com
CGXL—(TSX)
Rev.: $1,085,336,641
Assets: $1,319,517,813
Liabilities: $576,672,751
Net Worth: $742,845,062
Earnings: $119,763,506
Emp.: 10,000
Fiscal Year-end: 12/31/12
Business Description:
Holding Company
S.I.C.: 6719
N.A.I.C.S.: 551112
Personnel:
Phyllis N. Yaffe *(Chm)*
Ellis Jacob *(Pres & CEO)*
Gord Nelson *(CFO)*
Dan McGrath *(COO)*
Anne Fitzgerald *(Chief Legal Officer & Sec)*
Jeffrey Kent *(CTO)*
Michael Kennedy *(Exec VP-Filmed Entertainment)*
Heather Briant *(Sr VP-HR)*
Board of Directors:
Phyllis N. Yaffe
Rob Bruce
Joan T. Dea
Ian Greenberg
Ellis Jacob
Sarabjit Marwah
Anthony Munk
Edward Sonshine
Robert J. Steacy
Legal Counsel:
Goodmans LLP
333 Bay Street Suite 3400
Toronto, ON, Canada
Transfer Agent:
CIBC Mellon Trust Company
Toronto, ON, Canada
Tel.: (416) 643-5500
Subsidiary:

Cineplex Entertainment LP **(1)**
1303 Yonge St
Toronto, ON, M4T 2Y9, Canada (76%)
Tel.: (416) 323-6600
Web Site: www.cineplex.com
Sales Range: $500-549.9 Million
Emp.: 130
Movie Theater Operator
S.I.C.: 7832
N.A.I.C.S.: 512131
Ellis Jacob *(Pres & CEO)*
Gordon Nelson *(CFO)*
Dan McGrath *(COO)*
Anne Fitzgerald *(Chief Legal Officer)*
Jeffrey Kent *(CTO)*
Salah Bachir *(Pres-Cineplex Media)*
Michael Kennedy *(Exec VP-Filmed Entertainment)*
Michael McCartney *(Exec VP-Film Programming)*
Heather Briant *(Sr VP-HR)*
Susan Mandryk *(Sr VP-Customer Strategies)*
Paul Nonis *(Sr VP-Ops)*
Fab Stanghieri *(Sr VP-Real Estate & Construction)*

CINERAD COMMUNICATIONS LIMITED

Subol Dutt Building 13 Brabourne Road Mezzanine Floor
Kolkata, West Bengal, 700 001, India
Tel.: (91) 33 2231 5686
Fax: (91) 33 2231 5683
E-Mail: info@cineradcommunications.com
Web Site: www.cineradcommunications.com
Year Founded: 1986
530457—(BOM)
Rev.: $19,080
Assets: $439,585
Liabilities: $36,235
Net Worth: $403,350

Cinerad Communications Limited—(Continued)

Earnings: ($71,384)
Fiscal Year-end: 03/31/13

Business Description:
Advertising & Promotional Film Production Services
S.I.C.: 7812
N.A.I.C.S.: 512110

Personnel:
Pradeep Kumar Daga *(Mng Dir)*
Sweta Sethia *(Compliance Officer & Sec)*

Board of Directors:
Pradeep Kumar Daga
Vinita Daga
Dilip Kumar Hela
Bishambar Pachisia
Manmohan R. Prahladka

Transfer Agent:
System Support Services
209 Shivai Industrial Estate 89 Andheri Kurla Road Sakinaka
Near L.I.C, Mumbai, 400 072, India

CINEVISTAAS LTD

Plot No 1 L.B.S. Marg
Gandhi Nagar Kanjurmarg W
400078 Mumbai, Maharashtra, India
Tel.: (91) 2225787622
Fax: (91) 2225770446
E-Mail: helpdesk@cinevistaas.com
Web Site: www.cinevistaas.com
532324—(BOM)
Sales Range: $10-24.9 Million
Emp.: 16

Business Description:
Media & Entertainment Services
S.I.C.: 7832
N.A.I.C.S.: 512131

Personnel:
Prem Krishen Malhotra *(Chm)*
Sunil Mehta *(Vice Chm & Mng Dir)*
K. B. Nair *(CFO)*
Abraham Mathew *(Chief Accounts Officer)*

Board of Directors:
Prem Krishen Malhotra
Renu Anand
Talat Aziz
Sunil Mehta
Bharti Sareen
Sulochana Talreja

CINEWORLD GROUP PLC

Power Road Studios 114 Power Road Chiswick
London, W4 5PY, United Kingdom
Tel.: (44) 2089875000
Fax: (44) 2087422998
E-Mail: corporate@cineworld.co.uk
Web Site: www.cineworldplc.com
CINE—(LSE)
Rev.: $566,491,323
Assets: $754,584,762
Liabilities: $456,730,668
Net Worth: $297,854,094
Earnings: $43,746,333
Emp.: 5,441
Fiscal Year-end: 12/27/12

Business Description:
Cinema Operator
S.I.C.: 7832
N.A.I.C.S.: 512131

Personnel:
Anthony Herbert Bloom *(Chm)*
Stephen Mark Wiener *(CEO)*
Philip Bowcock *(CFO)*

Board of Directors:
Anthony Herbert Bloom
Philip Bowcock
Martina Ann King
David Ossian Maloney
Eric Hartley Senat
Stephen Mark Wiener
Peter Wodehouse Williams

Legal Counsel:
Olswang LLP
90 High Holborn
London, United Kingdom

Non-U.S. Subsidiary:

Adelphi-Carlton Limited (1)
Parnell Ctr Parnell St
Co Dublin, Dublin, 1, Ireland
Tel.: (353) 18728895
Fax: (353) 18728575
E-Mail: dublin@cineworld.ie
Movie Theaters
S.I.C.: 7832
N.A.I.C.S.: 512131
Lorraine Pierce *(Gen Mgr)*

Subsidiary:

Cineworld Cinema Properties Limited (1)
Power Rd Studios
London, W4 5PY, United Kingdom
Tel.: (44) 2089875000
Fax: (44) 2087422998
E-Mail: customer.services@cineworld.co.uk
Web Site: www.cineworld.co.uk
Emp.: 150
Film Production Services
S.I.C.: 7929
N.A.I.C.S.: 711510
Katy Thomas *(Office Mgr)*

CINKARNA CELJE D.D.

Kidriceva 26
3001 Celje, Slovenia
Tel.: (386) 34276000
Fax: (386) 34276106
E-Mail: info@cinkarna.si
Web Site: www.cinkarna.si
CICG—(LJU)
Rev.: $233,180,222
Assets: $263,851,030
Liabilities: $84,341,472
Net Worth: $179,509,558
Earnings: $24,626,571
Emp.: 1,005
Fiscal Year-end: 12/31/12

Business Description:
Titanium Dioxide Pigment Mfr
S.I.C.: 2899
N.A.I.C.S.: 325998

Personnel:
Milan Medved *(Chm-Supervisory Bd)*
Tomaz Bencina *(Chm-Mgmt Bd & Gen Mgr)*
Barbara Gorjup *(Vice Chm-Supervisory Bd)*
Nikolaja Podgorsek Selic *(Member-Mgmt Bd & Mgr-Technical)*
Marko Cvetko *(Member-Mgmt Bd)*
Jurij Vengust *(Member-Mgmt Bd-Fin, Acctg & IT)*

Supervisory Board of Directors:
Milan Medved
Barbara Gorjup
Matjaz Jansa
Dusan Mestinsek
Jozica Tominc
Marin Zagar

CINS HOLDING CORP.

5148 Williams Road
Richmond, BC, V7E 1K1, Canada
Tel.: (604) 773-1339
Fax: (604) 909-4701
E-Mail: samwang@crif.ca
Web Site: www.cins.cn
Year Founded: 2007
CHD—(CNSX)
Int. Income: $81
Assets: $55,421
Liabilities: $572,621
Net Worth: ($517,201)
Earnings: ($1,555,037)
Fiscal Year-end: 12/31/12

Business Description:
Holding Company; Online Gaming Software
S.I.C.: 6719
N.A.I.C.S.: 551112

Personnel:
Chung Yan Lee *(CEO)*
Sam Sheng Wang *(CFO)*

Board of Directors:
Shu Wai Chan
George Graham Dorin
Chung Yan Lee
Stephen Hon Cheung So
Sam Sheng Wang

CINVEN LIMITED

(d/b/a Cinven Group of Companies)
Warwick Court Paternoster Square
London, EC4M 7AG, United Kingdom
Tel.: (44) 20 7661 3333
Fax: (44) 20 7661 3888
E-Mail: info@cinven.com
Web Site: www.cinven.com
Year Founded: 1987

Business Description:
Private Equity Firm
S.I.C.: 6211
N.A.I.C.S.: 523999

Personnel:
Hugh Langmuir *(Mng Partner)*
David R. Barker *(Partner-Indus & TMT)*
Caspar Berendsen *(Partner-Fin Svcs)*
Peter Catterall *(Partner-Consumer & Fin Svcs)*
Soren Christensen *(Partner-Financing)*
Guy Davison *(Partner-Consumer)*
Xavier Geismar *(Partner-Consumer)*
Rebecca Gibson *(Partner-Consumer)*
Alexandra Hess *(Partner-IR)*
Roberto Italia *(Partner-Indus)*
Stuart McAlpine *(Partner-Bus Svcs & Healthcare)*
Nicolas Paulmier *(Partner-Bus Svcs & TMT)*
Jorge Quemada *(Partner-Bus Svcs)*
Supraj Rajagopalan *(Partner-Healthcare)*
Matthew Sabben-Clare *(Partner-Financing)*
Thilo Sautter *(Partner-Bus Svcs)*
Bruno Schick *(Partner-Indus)*
Benoit Valentin *(Partner-Indus)*
Christoph Hobo *(Principal-Bus Svcs)*
Yalin Karadogan *(Principal-Bus Svcs)*
Charles Miller-Jones *(Principal-Consumer)*

Holdings:

EnServe Group Limited (1)
Freedom House 111 Bradford Rd Tingley
Wakefield, Leeds, WF3 1SD, United Kingdom
Tel.: (44) 1132012120
Fax: (44) 8451642021
E-Mail: info@enservegroup.com
Web Site: www.enservegroup.com
Sales Range: $400-449.9 Million
Emp.: 120
Commercial, Public & Utilities Support Services
S.I.C.: 7389
N.A.I.C.S.: 561499
Roy A. Gardner *(Chm)*
David Owens *(CEO)*
David Cruddance *(CFO)*

Subsidiaries:

The Freedom Group of Companies Limited (2)
Freedom House Bradford Rd
Tingley, Wakefield, WF3 1SD, United Kingdom
Tel.: (44) 1924887766
Fax: (44) 1924887788
E-Mail: info@freedom-group.co.uk
Web Site: www.freedom-group.co.uk
Emp.: 200
Electrical Engineering Services
S.I.C.: 8711
N.A.I.C.S.: 541330
David Owens *(Mng Dir)*

H2O Water Services Limited (2)
Freedom House 111 Bradford Road
cingley, Wakefield, WS31SD, United Kingdom
Tel.: (44) 1132820820
Fax: (44) 08451643004
E-Mail: info@h2owater.co.uk
Web Site: www.h2owater.co.uk
Emp.: 100
Water Meter Services, New Mains Installation & Services, Leakage Detection & Repair Services
S.I.C.: 1711
N.A.I.C.S.: 238220

The IT&T Department Limited (2)
Freedom House Bradford Rd
Tingley, Wakefield, West Yorkshire, WF3 1SD, United Kingdom
Tel.: (44) 1924885777
Fax: (44) 1924887788
E-Mail: enquiries@itandt.it
Web Site: www.itandt.it
Software Services
S.I.C.: 7371
N.A.I.C.S.: 541511
Ken Pugh *(Mng Dir)*

Mechanical and Electrical Training Limited (2)
Unit 1 Eden Close
Hellaby Lane Industrial Estate, Rotherham, South Yorkshire, S66 8RW, United Kingdom
Tel.: (44) 1709709525
Fax: (44) 1709704415
E-Mail: info@met-uk.com
Web Site: www.met-uk.com
Training & Consulting Services
S.I.C.: 8742
N.A.I.C.S.: 541611
Andy Macdonald *(Mng Dir)*

Meter U Limited (2)
PO Box 9725
Hucknall, Nottingham, Nottinghamshire, NG15 5DF, United Kingdom
Tel.: (44) 8450505102
Fax: (44) 1159630816
E-Mail: enquiries@meter-u.com
Web Site: www.meter-u.co.uk
Emp.: 6
Meter Reading Services
S.I.C.: 7389
N.A.I.C.S.: 561499

Metro Rod plc (2)
Metro House Churchill Way
Macclesfield, Cheshire, SK11 6AY, United Kingdom
Tel.: (44) 1625888100
Fax: (44) 1625 616687
E-Mail: enquiries@metrorod.co.uk
Web Site: www.metrorod.co.uk
Waste Water Network Maintenance Services
S.I.C.: 7349
N.A.I.C.S.: 561790
Leanne Ronan *(Team Leader-Further Recommendations)*

National Industrial Fuel Efficiency Limited (2)
NIFES House Sinderland Rd Broadheath
Altrincham, Cheshire, WA14 5HQ, United Kingdom
Tel.: (44) 1619285791
Fax: (44) 1619268718
E-Mail: hoffice@nifes.co.uk
Web Site: www.nifes.co.uk
Emp.: 45
Energy Management Services
S.I.C.: 8999
N.A.I.C.S.: 541690
Anthony Mayall *(Mng Dir)*

Revenue Assurance Consulting Limited (2)
Hertsmere House
Shenley Road, Borehamwood, Herts, WD6 1TE, United Kingdom
Tel.: (44) 8451303593
Fax: (44) 2082073499
E-Mail: enquiry@rasplc.co.uk

Web Site: www.rasplc.com
Emp.: 50
Imbalance Analysis & Recovery Services for Utility Industry
S.I.C.: 8748
N.A.I.C.S.: 541618
David Owens *(Acting Mng Dir)*

Gondola Group Ltd. **(1)**
5th Floor 2 Balcombe Street
London, NW1 6NW, United Kingdom
Tel.: (44) 8453899489
Fax: (44) 8453899488
Web Site: www.gondolaholdings.co.uk
Sls.: $954,364,947
Assets: $1,485,480,174
Liabilities: $2,075,029,131
Net Worth: ($589,548,957)
Earnings: ($121,289,472)
Emp.: 15,124
Fiscal Year-end: 06/30/13
Holding Company; Casual Dining Restaurants
S.I.C.: 6719
N.A.I.C.S.: 551112
Harvey Smyth *(CEO)*
Nick Carter *(Sec & Dir-Fin)*

Subsidiary:

PizzaExpress Ltd. **(2)**
Hunton House Highbridge Estate
Uxbridge, Mddx, UB8 1HU, United Kingdom UK
Tel.: (44) 8453899489 (100%)
Fax: (44) 8453899488
E-Mail: feedback@pizzaexpress.com
Web Site: www.pizzaexpress.com
Emp.: 60
Pizza Restaurants Operator
S.I.C.: 5812
N.A.I.C.S.: 722511
Richard Hodgson *(CEO)*

Guardian Financial Services Ltd. **(1)**
1 North Wall Quay
Lytham Saint Anne's, FY8 4JZ, United Kingdom
Tel.: (44) 845 7010210
Fax: (44) 1253663232
E-Mail: uks.life.servicing@aegon.co.uk
Web Site: www.guardianfs.co.uk
Life Insurance & Pension Services
S.I.C.: 6311
N.A.I.C.S.: 524113

Helix Industries Ltd. **(1)**
2B Sidings Court
Doncaster, South Yorkshire, DN4 5NU, United Kingdom
Tel.: (44) 1302762700
Holding Company
S.I.C.: 6719
N.A.I.C.S.: 551112

Subsidiaries:

Bypy Hydraulics & Transmissions Ltd. **(2)**
8 Lingen Road Industrial Estate
Ludlow, SY8 1XD, United Kingdom (40%)
Tel.: (44) 584873012
Telex: 35472
Fax: (44) 1584876647
E-Mail: sales@bypy.co.uk
Web Site: www.bypy.co.uk
Emp.: 16
Hydraulic & Transmission Component Mfr
S.I.C.: 3593
N.A.I.C.S.: 333995
Ian Beece *(Mng Dir)*

K.J.P. Ltd. **(2)**
93-103 Drummond Street
London, NW1 2HJ, United Kingdom
Agricultural, Photographic & Technical Services
S.I.C.: 7389
N.A.I.C.S.: 541990

Host Europe Group Limited **(1)**
c/o Webfusion Ltd.
5 Roundwood Avenue
Stockley Park, Uxbridge, UB11 1FF, United Kingdom UK
Tel.: (44) 808 252 3452 (Sls)
Web Site: www.hosteurope.com
Emp.: 600
Domain Registrar Services
S.I.C.: 4899
N.A.I.C.S.: 517919
Thomas Vollrath *(CEO)*

Subsidiary:

Webfusion Ltd. **(2)**
5 Roundwood Ave
Stockley Park, Uxbridge, UB11 1FF, United Kingdom UK
Tel.: (44) 8453660845
Fax: (44) 8450791030
E-Mail: contact@gxn.net
Web Site: www.corporate.webfusion.co.uk
Sales Range: $200-249.9 Million
Emp.: 170
Custom Web Hosting Services
S.I.C.: 4899
N.A.I.C.S.: 517919
Michael Read *(CEO)*

Non-U.S. Subsidiary:

Host Europe GmbH **(2)**
Welserstrasse 14
Cologne, 51149, Germany (100%)
Tel.: (49) 2203 1045 1040
Fax: (49) 2203 1045 1042
E-Mail: info@hosteurope.de
Web Site: www.hosteurope.de
Internet & Web Hosting Services
S.I.C.: 4899
N.A.I.C.S.: 517919
Patrick Pulvermuller *(Mng Dir & COO)*

Non-U.S. Holdings:

Avio S.p.A. **(1)**
Via Ariana km 5 2
00034 Colleferro, RO, Italy IT
Tel.: (39) 06 9728 5111 (81%)
Web Site: www.avio.com
Rev.: $383,705,566
Assets: $6,305,125,646
Liabilities: $5,252,079,572
Net Worth: $1,053,046,074
Earnings: $43,989,384
Emp.: 4,800
Fiscal Year-end: 12/31/12
Missile & Space Vehicle Propulsion Systems & Components Designer & Mfr
S.I.C.: 3764
N.A.I.C.S.: 336415
Alan J. Bowkett *(Chm)*
Sandro Maria Ferracuti *(Vice Chm)*
Pier Giuliano Lasagni *(Sr VP-Space Sys)*

CeramTec GmbH **(1)**
CeramTec-Platz 1-9
D-73207 Plochingen, Germany De
Tel.: (49) 71536110
Telex: 726 6930
Fax: (49) 715325421
E-Mail: info@ceramtec.de
Web Site: www.ceramtec.de
Sales Range: $550-599.9 Million
Emp.: 3,000
Production of Innovative Ceramics for High-Duty Applications.
S.I.C.: 3291
N.A.I.C.S.: 327910
Ulf D. Zimmermann *(CEO)*

Subsidiaries:

CeramTec-ETEC GmbH **(2)**
An der Burg Sulz 17
53797 Lohmar, Germany
Tel.: (49) 2205 9200 0
Fax: (49) 2205 9200 144
E-Mail: info@etec-ceram.de
Web Site: www.etec-ceram.de
Emp.: 14
Cermaics Mfr
S.I.C.: 1459
N.A.I.C.S.: 212325

Emil Muller GmbH **(2)**
Durrnbucher Strasse 10
91452 Wilhermsdorf, Germany
Tel.: (49) 9102 9935 35
Fax: (49) 9102993560
Web Site: www.ceramtec.com
Ceramics Mfr
S.I.C.: 1459
N.A.I.C.S.: 212325
Gudrun Schiller *(Gen Mgr)*

U.S. Subsidiaries:

CeramTec North America Electronic Applications, Inc. **(2)**
1 Technology Pl
Laurens, SC 29360 DE
Tel.: (864) 682-3215
Fax: (864) 682-1140
E-Mail: sales@ceramtec.com
Web Site: www2.ceramtec.com
Sales Range: $350-399.9 Million
Emp.: 1,900
Advanced Technical Ceramics, Including Substrates, Packages & Seals Laser Facility
S.I.C.: 3299
N.A.I.C.S.: 327999
Roberto Vigo *(Mgr-Mktg)*

CeramTec North America Inc **(2)**
1 Technology Pl
Laurens, SC 29360-1669
Tel.: (864) 682-3215
Fax: (864) 682-1140
Toll Free: (800) 845-9761
E-Mail: sales@ceramtec.com
Web Site: www.ceramtec.com
Sales Range: $100-124.9 Million
Emp.: 200
Ceramic Engineering
S.I.C.: 3299
N.A.I.C.S.: 327999
Brent Pahach *(Pres)*
Patrick Mcpoland *(CFO, VP-Fin & Admin)*

Durawear Corporation **(2)**
2598 Alton Rd
Birmingham, AL 35210
Tel.: (205) 833-1210
Fax: (205) 836-8182
E-Mail: sales@durawear.net
Web Site: www.durawear.net
Ceramics Mfr
S.I.C.: 1459
N.A.I.C.S.: 212325
Paul Yandora *(Gen Mgr)*

Non-U.S. Subsidiaries:

CeramTec Commerciale Italiana **(2)**
40 Via Campagnola
24126 Bergamo, Italy
Tel.: (39) 35 32 23 82
Fax: (39) 35 42 43 200
Ceramics Mfr
S.I.C.: 1459
N.A.I.C.S.: 212325

CeramTec Czech Republic s.r.o. **(2)**
Zerotinova 62
78701 Sumperk, Czech Republic
Tel.: (420) 583 369 111
Fax: (420) 583 369 190
Ceramics Mfr
S.I.C.: 1459
N.A.I.C.S.: 212325

CeramTec GmbH **(2)**
Carre 92 Immeuble G2
8 avenue des Louvresses, 92622 Gennevilliers, France
Tel.: (33) 1 30 90 00 80
Fax: (33) 1 30 90 00 23
Ceramics Mfr
S.I.C.: 1459
N.A.I.C.S.: 212325

CeramTec Iberica, Innovative Ceramic Engineering, S.L. **(2)**
Santa Marta 23-25
Barcelona, Spain
Tel.: (34) 93 7 50 65 60
Fax: (34) 93 7 50 18 12
Ceramics Mfr
S.I.C.: 1459
N.A.I.C.S.: 212325

CeramTec Innovative Ceramic Engineering, (M) Sdn. Bhd. **(2)**
Lot 17 & 18 Lorong Bunga Tanjung 3/1
Senawang Industrial Park, 70400
Seremban, Malaysia
Tel.: (60) 6 6 77 93 00
Fax: (60) 6 6 77 93 88
Ceramics Mfr
S.I.C.: 1459
N.A.I.C.S.: 212325

CeramTec Korea Ltd. **(2)**
398-17 Shin-Dong, Yeong tong-ku
Suwon, 442-390, Korea (South)
Tel.: (82) 31 2 04 06 63
Fax: (82) 31 2 04 06 65
Ceramics Mfr
S.I.C.: 1459
N.A.I.C.S.: 212325

CeramTec Medical Products China **(2)**
Room 2101 Building 2
Fuxing Road 11, Beijing, 100038, China
Tel.: (86) 10 68570805
Fax: (86) 10 68532808
Ceramics Mfr
S.I.C.: 1459
N.A.I.C.S.: 212325

CeramTec Press and Sinter Technics de Mexico, S.A. de C.V. **(2)**
Resurreccion Oriente 10
Parque Industrial Resurreccion, 72228
Puebla, Mexico
Tel.: (52) 9102 9935 35
Ceramics Mfr
S.I.C.: 1459
N.A.I.C.S.: 212325

CeramTec Suzhou Ltd. **(2)**
728 Fengting Rd
Weiting Sub-district, 215122 Suzhou, China
Tel.: (86) 512 62 74 07 88 507
Fax: (86) 512 62 74 59 28
Ceramics Mfr
S.I.C.: 1459
N.A.I.C.S.: 212325

CeramTec UK Ltd. **(2)**
Sidmouth Road Colyton
Devon, EX24 6JP, United Kingdom
Tel.: (44) 1297 55 27 07
Ceramics Mfr
S.I.C.: 1459
N.A.I.C.S.: 212325

PST Press + Sintertechnik Sp.z.o.o. **(2)**
Ul Odlewnikow 52
39-432 Gorzyce, Poland
Tel.: (48) 9102 9935 35
Ceramics Mfr
S.I.C.: 1459
N.A.I.C.S.: 212325

PST Press Sintertecnica Brasil Ltda **(2)**
Rodovia Arnaldo Julio Mauerberg 3960
Distrito Industrial 1 Predio, 13460000 Sao Paulo, Brazil
Tel.: (55) 91029935 35
E-Mail: g.schiller@emil-mueller-gmbh.de
Web Site: www.ceramtec.com
Ceramics Mfr
S.I.C.: 1459
N.A.I.C.S.: 212325
Gudrun Schiller *(Mng Dir)*

Coor Service Management Group AB **(1)**
Knarrarnasgatan 7
173 11 Kista, Sweden
Tel.: (46) 855395000
Fax: (46) 8279335
E-Mail: info@coor.com
Web Site: www.coor.com
Sls.: $1,090,544,018
Assets: $1,142,724,312
Liabilities: $1,063,281,726
Net Worth: $79,442,586
Earnings: $10,057,356
Emp.: 7,100
Fiscal Year-end: 12/31/12
Integrated Facilities Management Services
S.I.C.: 8744
N.A.I.C.S.: 561210
Anders Narvinger *(Chm)*
Mikael Stohr *(Pres & CEO)*
Olof Stalnacke *(CFO)*
AnnaCarin Grandin *(Pres-Norway)*
Johan Mild *(Pres-Finland)*
Jorgen Utzon *(Pres-Denmark)*
Ulf Wretskog *(Pres-Sweden)*
Anders Asplund *(Sr VP-HR)*
Jens Ebbe Rasmussen *(Sr VP-Bus Dev)*
Rikard Wannerholt *(Sr VP-Ops Dev)*

Non-U.S. Subsidiaries:

Coor Service Management A/S **(2)**
Bregnerodvej 133
3460 Birkerod, Denmark
Tel.: (45) 44 77 88 88
Fax: (45) 44 77 88 99
E-Mail: info.dk@coor.com
Web Site: www.coor.dk
Facilities Support Services
S.I.C.: 8744

Cinven Limited—(Continued)

N.A.I.C.S.: 561210
Jorgen Utzon *(Pres)*
Jacob T. Dohn *(Sr VP-Bus & Ops Dev)*

Coor Service Management AS (2)
Veritasveien 3
1363 Hovik, Norway
Mailing Address:
Postboks 101
1322 Hovik, Norway
Tel.: (47) 6757 9200
Fax: (47) 6757 9945
E-Mail: firmapost@coor.com
Web Site: www.coor.no
Facilities Support Services
S.I.C.: 8744
N.A.I.C.S.: 561210
AnnaCarin Grandin *(Pres)*
Nikolai Utheim *(CFO)*

Coor Service Management NV (2)
Pantserschipstraat 181/5
9000 Gent, Belgium
Tel.: (32) 9 223 19 99
Fax: (32) 9 223 86 20
Facilities Support Services
S.I.C.: 8744
N.A.I.C.S.: 561210

Coor Service Management Oy (2)
Mannerheimintie 117
00280 Helsinki, Finland
Mailing Address:
PL 108
00101 Helsinki, Finland
Tel.: (358) 10 234 3400
Fax: (358) 10 234 3470
Facilities Support Services
S.I.C.: 8744
N.A.I.C.S.: 561210
Johan Mild *(Pres)*
Henri Turunen *(CFO)*
Jukka Tuominen *(Bus Unit Pres & Exec VP)*
Jari Mansikkaoja *(Bus Unit Pres)*
Jaska Mertaharju *(Bus Unit Pres)*
Tarja Vasara *(Bus Unit Pres)*

JOST-Werke GmbH (1)
Siemensstrasse 2
63263 Neu-Isenburg, Germany
Tel.: (49) 61022950
Fax: (49) 6102295298
E-Mail: jost-info@jost-werke.de
Web Site: www.jost-werke.com
Sales Range: $450-499.9 Million
Emp.: 500
Commercial Vehicle Component Mfr
S.I.C.: 3714
N.A.I.C.S.: 336390
Lars Brorsen *(Chm-Mgmt Bd)*
Alexander Kleinke *(Member-Mgmt Bd)*
Dirk Schmidt *(Member-Mgmt Bd)*

Sebia SA (1)
Parc Technologique Leonard de Vinci
Lisses, 91008, France
Tel.: (33) 69 89 80 80
E-Mail: sebia@sebia.com
Web Site: www.sebia.com
Sales Range: $125-149.9 Million
Emp.: 400
Medical Diagnostic Equipment Mfr
S.I.C.: 3841
N.A.I.C.S.: 339112
Benoit Adelus *(Chm & CEO)*

U.S. Subsidiary:

Sebia, Inc. (2)
1705 Corporate Dr
Norcross, GA 30093
Tel.: (770) 446-3707
Toll Free: (800) 835-6497
Web Site: www.sebia-usa.com
Rev.: $3,300,000
Emp.: 22
Medical Diagnostic Equipment Mfr
S.I.C.: 3841
N.A.I.C.S.: 339112
Theresa Heslin *(CEO)*

Non-U.S. Joint Venture:

Truvo NV/SA (1)
Uitbreidingstraat 80 bus 3
2600 Berchem, Belgium BE
Tel.: (32) 32856411
Fax: (32) 32856400
E-Mail: info@truvo.com
Web Site: www.truvo.com
Sales Range: $500-549.9 Million
Emp.: 2,200
Online & Print Directory Publisher
S.I.C.: 2741
N.A.I.C.S.: 511140
Andrew Day *(Chm)*
Donat Retif *(CEO & Mng Dir)*
Pierre Gatz *(CTO)*
Wim van Neutegem *(Treasury & VP-Tax)*

U.S. Subsidiary:

Axesa Servicios de Informacion, S. en C. (2)
1001 San Roerto St Ste 500
San Juan, PR 00926
Tel.: (787) 758-2828
Fax: (787) 771-6451
E-Mail: newmedia@axesa.com
Web Site: www.axesa.com
Sales Range: $25-49.9 Million
Emp.: 250
Directory Publisher; Owned 39.6% by Truvo & 59.4% by Local Insight Media
S.I.C.: 2741
N.A.I.C.S.: 511140
Linda Martin *(Mng Dir)*

Non-U.S. Subsidiaries:

Gouden Gids B.V. (2)
Harkerbergweg 88
1101 CM Amsterdam, Zuidoost, Netherlands NL
Tel.: (31) 205676767
Fax: (31) 205676950
Web Site: www.truvo.nl
Emp.: 400
Business & Services Contact Information Directory
S.I.C.: 2741
N.A.I.C.S.: 511140
Ian Harrison *(Mng Dir)*

Paginas Amarelas S.A. (2)
Ave D Joao II No 1 17 01 74 Piso
1990 083 Lisbon, Portugal PT
Tel.: (351) 218989500
Fax: (351) 218989510
E-Mail: pa@paginasamarelas.pt
Web Site: www.paginasamarelas.pt
Emp.: 200
Yellow Pages for Telephone Directories Export
S.I.C.: 4899
N.A.I.C.S.: 517919
Marco Goncalvaf *(Dir-Mktg)*

Publitec B.V. (2)
Herikerberweg 88
1101 CM Amsterdam, Netherlands NL
Tel.: (31) 205676869
Fax: (31) 206910374
E-Mail: info@publitec.nl
Web Site: www.publitec.nl
Emp.: 100
Marketing, Media Measurement, Business & Directory Information
S.I.C.: 2741
N.A.I.C.S.: 511140
Peter Gatz *(Gen Mgr)*

CIPHER PHARMACEUTICALS INC.

5650 Tompken Road Unit 16
Mississauga, ON, L4W 4P1, Canada
Tel.: (905) 602-5840
Fax: (905) 602-0628
E-Mail: info@cipherpharma.com
Web Site: www.cipherpharma.com
DND—(TSX)
Rev.: $8,407,421
Assets: $21,823,709
Liabilities: $9,491,897
Net Worth: $12,331,812
Earnings: $2,528,787
Emp.: 12
Fiscal Year-end: 12/31/12
Business Description:
Drug Developer
S.I.C.: 2834
N.A.I.C.S.: 325412
Personnel:
Gerald McDole *(Chm)*
Larry Andrews *(Pres & CEO)*
Norman C. Evans *(CFO)*
Board of Directors:
Gerald McDole
Stefan Aigner
Larry Andrews
William D. Claypool
John D. Mull
Stephen R. Wiseman
Transfer Agent:
Computershare Investor Services Inc.
Montreal, QC, Canada

CIPI SPA

(Acquired by Emmegi S.p.a.)

CIPLA LTD.

Mumbai Central
Mumbai, 400 008, India
Tel.: (91) 22 2308 2891
Fax: (91) 22 2307 0013
Web Site: www.cipla.com
500087—(BOM)
Rev.: $1,576,172,538
Assets: $2,161,350,558
Liabilities: $489,287,286
Net Worth: $1,672,063,272
Earnings: $286,415,190
Fiscal Year-end: 03/31/13
Business Description:
Pharmaceutical Mfr
S.I.C.: 2834
N.A.I.C.S.: 325412
Personnel:
M. K. Hamied *(Vice Chm)*
Subhanu Saxena *(Global CEO & Mng Dir)*
V. S. Mani *(CFO)*
Mital Sanghvi *(Sec)*
Board of Directors:
Yusuf K. Hamied
M. K. Hamied
V. C. Kotwal
H. R. Manchanda
Peter Mugyenyi
Pankaj Patel
S. Radhakrishnan
M. R. Raghavan
Subhanu Saxena
Ashok Sinha
R.G.N. Price & Co.
Mumbai, India
Transfer Agent:
Karvy Computershare Private Limited
Plot No 17-24 Vittal Rao Nagar Madhapur
Hyderabad, 500 081, India
Tel.: (91) 40 2342 0818

Non-U.S. Subsidiary:

Cipla Medpro South Africa Limited (1)
Unit 9 10 Rosen Heights Rosen Park Pasita Street
Bellville, South Africa ZA
Tel.: (27) 219140520
Fax: (27) 219174688
E-Mail: admin@ciplamedpro.co.za
Web Site: www.cipla.co.za
Rev.: $256,599,921
Assets: $336,543,834
Liabilities: $116,923,986
Net Worth: $219,619,849
Earnings: $18,806,259
Emp.: 696
Fiscal Year-end: 12/31/12
Pharmaceuticals Mfr
S.I.C.: 2834
N.A.I.C.S.: 325412
Johan du Preez *(Acting CEO)*
Skhumbuzo Ngozwana *(Deputy CEO)*
Mark Sardi *(Deputy CEO)*
Mark W. Daly *(CFO)*

Subsidiaries:

Cipla Medpro Distribution Centre (Pty) Limited (2)
Unit 2A & B and Ubit 4 Lillie St
Cape Town, Western Cape, 7550, South Africa
Tel.: (27) 219751901
Fax: (27) 219751909
E-Mail: Joseph@ciplamedpro.co.za
Emp.: 60
Pharmaceutical Products Distr
S.I.C.: 5122
N.A.I.C.S.: 424210
Joseph Ludorf *(Mng Dir)*

Cipla Medpro Manufacturing (Pty) Limited (2)
Belvedere Ofc Park Block F Bella Rosa St
Bellville, Cape Town, Western Cape, 7530, South Africa
Tel.: (27) 219140520
Fax: (27) 314627774
Emp.: 460
Pharmaceutical Products Mfr
S.I.C.: 2834
N.A.I.C.S.: 325412
Imtiaz Hoosen *(Gen Mgr)*

Cipla-Medpro (Pty) Limited (2)
Rosen Heights Rosen Park
Bellville, Cape Town, Western Cape, 7530, South Africa
Tel.: (27) 219140520
Fax: (27) 219140123
E-Mail: medical@ciplamedpro.co.za
Web Site: www.ciplamedpro.co.za
Emp.: 400
Pharmaceutical Products Mfr
S.I.C.: 2834
N.A.I.C.S.: 325412
Jerome Smith *(CEO)*
Skhumbuzo Ngozwana *(Deputy CEO)*

Cipla Vet (Pty) Limited (2)
Rosen Heights Rosen Park
Bellville, Cape Town, Western Cape, 7530, South Africa
Tel.: (27) 219434220
Fax: (27) 219143986
E-Mail: info@ciplavet.co.za
Web Site: www.ciplavet.co.za
Emp.: 9
Veterinary Medicines Mfr
S.I.C.: 2834
N.A.I.C.S.: 325412
Craig Mincher *(Mng Dir)*

Medpro Gen (Pty) Limited (2)
Rosen Heights Pasita St Rosen Park
Bellville, Cape Town, Western Cape, 7530, South Africa
Tel.: (27) 219140520
Fax: (27) 219140247
E-Mail: admin@ciplamedpro.co,za
Web Site: www.cipla.co.za
Emp.: 450
Pharmaceutical Products Mfr
S.I.C.: 2834
N.A.I.C.S.: 325412
Skhumbuzo Ngozwana *(Deputy CEO)*
Mark Sadi *(Deputy CEO)*

Medpro Pharmaceutica (Pty) Limited (2)
Unit 9 and 10 Rosen Heights Pasita St
Cape Town, Western Cape, 7530, South Africa
Tel.: (27) 219140520
Fax: (27) 219100096
Emp.: 340
Pharmaceutical Products Mfr
S.I.C.: 2834
N.A.I.C.S.: 325412

CIPLA MEDPRO SOUTH AFRICA LTD.

(Acquired by Cipla Ltd.)

CIRCA ENTERPRISES INC.

206 5 Richard Way SW
Calgary, AB, T2G 4M6, Canada
Tel.: (403) 258-2011
Fax: (403) 255-2595
Toll Free: (877) 257-4588
E-Mail: investor@circaent.com

Web Site: www.circaent.com
CTO—(TSXV)
Rev.: $22,500,637
Assets: $9,844,774
Liabilities: $2,212,689
Net Worth: $7,632,086
Earnings: $549,693
Emp.: 132
Fiscal Year-end: 12/31/12
Business Description:
Voice & Data Telecommunications Services
S.I.C.: 4812
N.A.I.C.S.: 517210
Personnel:
Peter C. Bourgeois *(Chm)*
Grant Reeves *(Interim CEO)*
Cory Tamagi *(CFO & VP-Fin)*
Board of Directors:
Peter C. Bourgeois
Robert B. Johnston
Grant Reeves
Ivan W. Smith
Brice Sweatt
Warren White
Legal Counsel:
Bennett Jones L.L.P.
855 2nd St SW Ste 4500
Calgary, AB, T2P 4K7, Canada
Tel.: (403) 298-3100
Fax: (403) 233-0353
Transfer Agent:
Computershare Trust Corporation of Canada
600 530 8 th Avenue SW
T2P 3S8 Calgary, AB, Canada
Subsidiary:

Circa Metals Inc. (1)
206 Great Gulf Dr
Vaughan, ON, L4K 5W1, Canada
Tel.: (905) 669-5511
Fax: (905) 669-4518
Toll Free: (800) 263-4579
E-Mail: info@circahydel.com
Web Site: www.circametals.com
Fabricated Metal Products Mfr
S.I.C.: 3441
N.A.I.C.S.: 332312
Tom Maxwell *(Gen Mgr)*

U.S. Subsidiary:

Circa Telecom USA Inc (1)
6293 W Linebaugh Ave
Tampa, FL 33625
Tel.: (813) 676-2050
Fax: (813) 676-2060
E-Mail: info@circatelecom.com
Web Site: www.circatelecom.com
Sales Range: $10-24.9 Million
Emp.: 16
Provider of Voice & Data Telecommunications Services
S.I.C.: 5065
N.A.I.C.S.: 423690
Ivan Smith *(Pres & CEO)*

CIRCADIAN TECHNOLOGIES LIMITED

Suite 0403 Level 4 650 Chapel Street
South Yarra, VIC, 3141, Australia
Tel.: (61) 3 9826 0399
Fax: (61) 3 9824 0083
E-Mail: info@circadian.com.au
Web Site: www.circadian.com.au
CIR—(ASX OTC)
Rev.: $1,202,257
Assets: $17,102,902
Liabilities: $2,139,445
Net Worth: $14,963,458
Earnings: ($5,215,196)
Emp.: 25
Fiscal Year-end: 06/30/13
Business Description:
Biomedical Research
S.I.C.: 8732
N.A.I.C.S.: 541720
Personnel:
Robert Klupacs *(CEO & Mng Dir)*
Megan Baldwin *(CEO)*
Mark Pryn *(Sec & Head-Fin)*
Board of Directors:
Dominique Fisher
Robert Klupacs
Tina McMeckan
Legal Counsel:
Minter Ellison
Level 23 Rialto Towers 525 Collins Street
Melbourne, VIC, 3000, Australia
Subsidiaries:

CancerProbe Pty Ltd (1)
10 Wallace Ave
Toorak, Victoria, 3142, Australia
Tel.: (61) 398260399
Fax: (61) 398240083
Health Care Services
S.I.C.: 8099
N.A.I.C.S.: 621999
Robert Klupacs *(Mng Dir)*

Neuro Therapeutics Limited (1)
10 Wallace Ave
Toorak, Victoria, 3142, Australia
Tel.: (61) 398260399
Fax: (61) 398240083
Health Care Services
S.I.C.: 8099
N.A.I.C.S.: 621999
Robert Klupacs *(Mng Dir)*

CIRCLE HOLDINGS PLC

32 Welbeck Street
London, W1G 8EU, United Kingdom
Tel.: (44) 207 034 5250
Fax: (44) 207 034 5251
Web Site: www.circleholdingsplc.com
CIRC—(AIM)
Rev.: $115,676,675
Assets: $202,641,858
Liabilities: $135,163,535
Net Worth: $67,478,324
Earnings: ($48,048,319)
Emp.: 583
Fiscal Year-end: 12/31/12
Business Description:
Holding Company; Healthcare Services
S.I.C.: 6719
N.A.I.C.S.: 551112
Personnel:
Steve Andrew Melton *(CEO)*
Paolo Pieri *(CFO)*
Massoud Keyvan-Fouladi *(Chief Medical Officer)*
Board of Directors:
Michael James Kirkwood
Lorraine Baldry
Anthony Bromovsky
Timothy Bunting
Massoud Keyvan-Fouladi
Paolo Pieri
Andrew B. Shilston
Legal Counsel:
Ogier
Ogier House The Esplanade
Saint Helier, Jersey

Lawrence Graham
4 More London Riverside
London, United Kingdom

CIRCLE OIL PLC

2 New Wellington Terrace O'Connell Avenue
Limerick, Ireland
Tel.: (353) 61319366
Fax: (353) 61310210
E-Mail: info@circleoil.net
Web Site: www.circleoil.net
COP—(LSE)
Rev.: $73,270,000
Assets: $260,913,000
Liabilities: $44,938,000
Net Worth: $215,975,000
Earnings: $25,243,000
Emp.: 21
Fiscal Year-end: 12/31/12
Business Description:
Oil & Gas Exploration Services
S.I.C.: 1389
N.A.I.C.S.: 213112
Personnel:
Stephen Ian Jenkins *(Chm)*
Christopher Green *(CEO)*
Brendan McMorrow *(CFO & Sec)*
Board of Directors:
Thomas Anderson
Stephen Ian Jenkins
Nicholas Clayton
Christopher Green
Keith Adams Morris
Mohammad Sultan
Legal Counsel:
O'Flynn Exhams & Partner
58 South Mall
Cork, Ireland
Non-U.S. Subsidiaries:

Circle Oil Maroc Limited (1)
2 Rue Ghzaoua Souissi La Pineped
10000 Rabat, Morocco
Tel.: (212) 537635656
Fax: (212) 537656314
E-Mail: morocco@circleoil.net
Emp.: 1
Oil & Gas Exploration Services
S.I.C.: 1389
N.A.I.C.S.: 213112
Anal Lenrahi *(Office Mgr)*

Circle Oil Oman Limited (1)
Al Khuwair 25 College Street Way No 4927
Villa No 2084
PO Box No 270
134 Muscat, Oman
Mailing Address:
PO Box 270
Muscat, 134, Oman
Tel.: (968) 24483006
Fax: (968) 24487114
E-Mail: oman@circleoil.net
Emp.: 3
Oil & Gas Exploration Services
S.I.C.: 1389
N.A.I.C.S.: 213112
Hassan Husain Al Lawati *(Gen Mgr)*

CIRCUIT ELECTRONIC INDUSTRIES PUBLIC COMPANY LIMITED

45 Moo 12 Rojana Industrial Park
Tambol Thanu
Amphur Uthai, Ayutthaya, 13210, Thailand
Tel.: (66) 35 226280
Fax: (66) 35 226714
E-Mail: marketing@cei.co.th
Web Site: www.cei.co.th
Year Founded: 1984
CIRKIT—(THA)
Rev.: $6,430,202
Assets: $9,411,239
Liabilities: $127,843,369
Net Worth: ($118,432,130)
Earnings: $1,298,365
Fiscal Year-end: 12/31/12
Business Description:
Communication Device Mfr
S.I.C.: 3674
N.A.I.C.S.: 334413
Personnel:
Akamin Nganthavee *(Pres)*

CIRCUIT SYSTEMS (INDIA) LIMITED

B-24 GIDC Electronics Estate
Sector-25, Gandhinagar, Gujarat, 382044, India
Tel.: (91) 79 2328 7086
Fax: (91) 79 2328 7089
E-Mail: info@mycsil.com
Web Site: www.mycsil.com
532913—(BOM)
Sales Range: $1-9.9 Million
Emp.: 120
Business Description:
Printed Circuit Boards Mfr
S.I.C.: 3672
N.A.I.C.S.: 334412
Personnel:
Magan H. Patel *(Chm)*
Paresh N. Vasani *(Mng Dir)*
Board of Directors:
Magan H. Patel
Ambalal C. Patel
Anand A. Patel
Ishwar H. Patel
Paresh N. Vasani
Transfer Agent:
Cameo Corporate Services Limited
Subramanian Building No 1 Club House Road
5th Floor
Chennai, India

CIRKEL GMBH & CO.KG

Flaesheimer Strasse 605
45721 Recklinghausen, Germany
Tel.: (49) 236493810
Fax: (49) 2364938199
E-Mail: info@cirkel.de
Web Site: www.cirkel.de
Year Founded: 1898
Rev.: $70,349,400
Emp.: 120
Business Description:
Construction Products Mfr
S.I.C.: 5032
N.A.I.C.S.: 423320
Personnel:
Jan-Friedrich Cirkel *(Co-Mng Dir)*
Attila Dal *(Co-Mng Dir)*

CIRQUE DU SOLEIL INC.

8400 2nd Ave
Montreal, QC, H1Z 4M6, Canada
Tel.: (514) 722-2324
Fax: (514) 722-3692
Toll Free: (800) 678-2119
E-Mail: mediainfo@cirquedusoleil.com
Web Site: www.cirquedusoleil.com
Year Founded: 1984
Emp.: 4,000
Business Description:
Theatrical & Music Producer
S.I.C.: 5812
N.A.I.C.S.: 711110
Personnel:
Guy Laliberte *(Founder)*
Daniel Lamarre *(Pres & CEO)*
Jacques Methe *(Pres-Cirque du Soleil Media)*
Gilles Ste-Croix *(Sr VP-Creation Content)*
Subsidiary:

Cirque du Soleil Musique Inc. (1)
8400 2nd Avenue
Montreal, QC, H1Z 4M6, Canada
Tel.: (514) 722-2324
Fax: (514) 722-3692
E-Mail: contact@cirquedusoleil.com
Web Site: www.cirquedusoleil.com
Emp.: 2,000
Music Producer
S.I.C.: 2741
N.A.I.C.S.: 512230
Guy Laliberte *(Founder)*

U.S. Subsidiary:

Cirque du Soleil Orlando Inc. (1)
1478 E Buena Vista Dr
Lake Buena Vista, FL 32830
Tel.: (407) 934-9200
Fax: (407) 934-9148
Web Site: www.cirquedusoleil.com
Emp.: 200
Theatrical Services
S.I.C.: 5812
N.A.I.C.S.: 711110
Neil Boyd *(Gen Mgr)*

CIRTEK HOLDINGS PHILIPPINES CORPORATION

116 East Main Avenue Phase V SEZ
Laguna Technopark
Binan, Laguna, 4024, Philippines
Tel.: (63) 49 5412310
Fax: (63) 49 5412317
E-Mail: jorge.aguilar@cirtek.com.ph
Web Site: www.cirtekholdings.com
Business Description:
Holding Company; Electronics
S.I.C.: 6719
N.A.I.C.S.: 551112
Personnel:
Jerry Liu *(Chm)*
Anthony S. Buyawe *(CFO, Compliance Officer & Treas)*
Board of Directors:
Jerry Liu
Jorge Aguilar
Anthony S. Buyawe
Justin T. Liu
Michael Stephen Liu
Nelia T. Liu
Nicanor P. Lizares
Martin Lorenzo
Ernest Fritz Server

CIS ACQUISITION LTD.

89 Udaltsova Street Suite 84
Moscow, 119607, Russia
Tel.: (7) 917 514 1310
CISAU—(NASDAQ)
Int. Income: $14,621
Assets: $41,819,280
Liabilities: $39,689,440
Net Worth: $2,129,840
Earnings: ($3,429,198)
Emp.: 4
Fiscal Year-end: 10/31/13
Business Description:
Investment Services
S.I.C.: 6211
N.A.I.C.S.: 523999
Personnel:
Anatoly Danilitskiy *(Chm & CEO)*
Kyle Shostak *(CFO & Sec)*
Board of Directors:
Anatoly Danilitskiy
David R. Ansell
Kyle Shostak
Levan Vasadze
Taras Vazhnov

CIS PROMOTION

116 Quai Charles Roissard
73025 Chambery, Savoie, France
Tel.: (33) 479691645
Fax: (33) 479969985
E-Mail: info@cis-promotion.com
Web Site: www.cis-promotion.com
Sls.: $20,500,000
Emp.: 20
Business Description:
Real Estate Agents & Managers
S.I.C.: 6531
N.A.I.C.S.: 531210
Personnel:
Bernard Sevez *(Chm)*

CISCAR

104 Rue Michel Ange
75016 Paris, France
Tel.: (33) 153842323
Fax: (33) 153842324
Web Site: www.ciscar.fr
Sls.: $23,900,000
Emp.: 21
Business Description:
Industrial Machinery & Equipment
S.I.C.: 5084
N.A.I.C.S.: 423830
Personnel:
Jean-Claude Noyer *(Chm)*
Board of Directors:
Jean-Claude Noyer
Cyril Florent

CISION AB

(d/b/a Cision Group)
Linnegatan 87A
PO Box 24194
SE-104 51 Stockholm, Sweden
Tel.: (46) 850741000
Fax: (46) 850741025
E-Mail: info.corporate@cision.com
Web Site: corporate.cision.com
CSN—(OMX)
Rev.: $151,075,667
Assets: $277,226,521
Liabilities: $121,248,338
Net Worth: $155,978,183
Earnings: $9,729,490
Emp.: 1,049
Fiscal Year-end: 12/31/12
Business Description:
Holding Company; Business Communication Media Planning, Connection, Monitoring & Analysis Products & Services
S.I.C.: 6719
N.A.I.C.S.: 551112
Personnel:
Hans-Erik Andersson *(Chm)*
Peter Granat *(Pres & CEO)*
Charlotte Hansson *(CFO)*
Anna-Karin Samuelson *(Sr VP-HR)*
Board of Directors:
Hans-Erik Andersson
Alf Blomqvist
Peter Granat
Scott Raskin
Catharina Stackelberg-Hammaren
Rikard Steiber
Thomas Tarnowski

Subsidiaries:

Atodia AB (1)
Linnegatan 87A
Stockholm, 115 23, Sweden
Tel.: (46) 850741400
Fax: (46) 850743309
Computer Software Development Services
S.I.C.: 7371
N.A.I.C.S.: 541511

Cision Global Solutions AB (1)
Linnegatan 87
Stockholm, 115 23, Sweden
Tel.: (46) 850741000
Computer Software Development Services
S.I.C.: 7371
N.A.I.C.S.: 541511

Cision Sverige AB (1)
Linnegatan 87 A
Box 24194
104 51 Stockholm, Sweden
Tel.: (46) 8 507 410 00
E-Mail: info.se@cision.com
Web Site: www.se.cision.com
Public Relations & Communication Services
S.I.C.: 8743
N.A.I.C.S.: 541820
Magnus Thell *(CEO)*
Anders Kall *(CFO)*

Public and Investor Relations PIR Sverige AB (1)
Saltmatargatan 9
Stockholm, 113 59, Sweden
Tel.: (46) 8 20 17 00
E-Mail: info@pirab.se
Web Site: www.pirab.se
Public Relations & Communication Consulting Services
S.I.C.: 8743
N.A.I.C.S.: 541820

Unit:

Cision Scandinavia (1)
Linnegatan 87A
SE-114 88 Stockholm, Sweden
Tel.: (46) 850741000
Fax: (46) 850743309
E-Mail: support.se@cision.com
Web Site: se.cision.com
Sales Range: $10-24.9 Million
Emp.: 225
Business Communication Media Planning & Connection Products & Services
S.I.C.: 7389
N.A.I.C.S.: 561499
Yann Blandy *(Mng Dir)*

U.S. Subsidiaries:

Cision US Inc. (1)
332 S Michigan Ave Ste 900
Chicago, IL 60604-4393 DE
Tel.: (312) 922-2400 (100%)
Fax: (312) 922-3126
Toll Free: (866) 639-5087
E-Mail: info.us@cision.com
Web Site: www.us.cision.com
Emp.: 346
Business Communication Media Planning, Connection, Monitoring & Analysis Products & Services
S.I.C.: 7389
N.A.I.C.S.: 561499
Peter Granat *(Pres & CEO)*
Mike Czlonka *(CFO & Sr VP)*
Dawn Conway *(COO)*
K. C. Brown *(Sr VP & Head-Cision's Analysis Svcs)*
Steven Brown *(Sr VP-Sls-North America)*
Vanessa Bugasch *(Sr VP-Global Mktg & Product Mktg)*
Wayne Bullock *(Sr VP-Analysis Ops)*
Scott Thompson *(Sr VP-IT)*
Randy Zierfuss *(Sr VP-HR)*

Non-U.S. Subsidiaries:

Cision Canada Inc. (1)
150 Ferrand Dr Ste 1100
Toronto, ON, M3E 3E5, Canada Ca
Tel.: (416) 750-2220 (100%)
Fax: (416) 750-2233
Toll Free: (877) 269-3367
E-Mail: info.ca@cision.com
Web Site: www.ca.cision.com
Emp.: 310
Business Communication, Media Planning, Connection, Monitoring & Analysis Products & Services
S.I.C.: 7389
N.A.I.C.S.: 561499
Terry Foster *(Pres)*
Phil Crompton *(Sr VP-Brdcst Monitoring-North America & Gen Mgr)*

Subsidiary:

Cision Quebec Inc. (2)
1001 Sherbrooke Street East Suite 410
Montreal, QC, H2L 1L3, Canada QC
Tel.: (514) 878-9979 (100%)
Fax: (514) 878-9118
Web Site: qc.ca.cision.com
Emp.: 35
Business Communication Media Planning, Connection, Monitoring & Analysis Products & Services
S.I.C.: 7389
N.A.I.C.S.: 561499
Caroline Gregoire *(VP-Ops)*

Cision Germany GmbH (1)
Hanauer Landstr 291 b
60314 Frankfurt am Main, Germany
Tel.: (49) 69 710475 180
Fax: (49) 69 710475 220
E-Mail: info@de.cision.com
Web Site: www.de.cision.com
Telecommunications Services
S.I.C.: 4899
N.A.I.C.S.: 517919
Yann Blandy *(Mng Dir)*

Cision Norge AS (1)
Akersgata 16
0158 Oslo, Norway
Tel.: (47) 46 8 507 410 00
E-Mail: info.no@cision.com
Web Site: www.no.cision.com
Public Relations Consulting Services
S.I.C.: 8743
N.A.I.C.S.: 541820

Cision Portugal S.A. (1)
Avenida Fontes Pereira de Melo No 21 5o
1050-116 Lisbon, Portugal (100%)
Tel.: (351) 213190570
Fax: (351) 213190578
E-Mail: info.pt@cision.com
Web Site: www.pt2.cision.com
Business Communication Media Planning, Connection, Monitoring & Analysis Products & Services
S.I.C.: 7389
N.A.I.C.S.: 561499
Jose Santos *(Mng Dir)*

Cision UK Ltd. (1)
16-22 Baltic Street West
London, EC1Y 0UL, United Kingdom (100%)
Tel.: (44) 2072517220
Fax: (44) 2076891117
E-Mail: info.uk@cision.com
Web Site: www.cision.com
Emp.: 100
Business Communication Media Planning, Connection, Monitoring & Analysis Products & Services
S.I.C.: 7389
N.A.I.C.S.: 561499
Tom Ritchi *(Mng Dir)*

Cision Finland Oy (1)
Salmisaarenkatu 1 B
00180 Helsinki, Finland FI
Tel.: (358) 20 786 2590 (100%)
E-Mail: info@cision.com
Web Site: fi.cision.com
Emp.: 120
Business Communication Media Planning, Connection, Monitoring & Analysis Products & Services
S.I.C.: 7389
N.A.I.C.S.: 561499
Tapio Ignatius *(Mng Dir)*

Romeike Monitoring Ltd (1)
16-22 Baltic Street
London, EC1Y 0UL, United Kingdom
Tel.: (44) 2072517220
Fax: (44) 2076891117
Emp.: 100
Computer Software Development Services
S.I.C.: 7371
N.A.I.C.S.: 541511
Torsten Bruce-Morgan *(Gen Mgr)*

THE CISNEROS GROUP OF COMPANIES

Edificio Venevision Quinto Piso Final
Avenida La Salle
Caracas, 1050, Venezuela
Tel.: (58) 2127815066
Fax: (58) 2127818286
E-Mail: info@cisneros.com
Web Site: www.cisneros.com
Year Founded: 1929
Emp.: 10,000
Business Description:
Holding Company; Broadcast & Pay Television, Radio & the Internet
S.I.C.: 6719
N.A.I.C.S.: 551112
Personnel:
Gustavo A. Cisneros *(Co-Chm & CEO)*
Steven I. Bandel *(Co-Chm)*
Ricardo J. Cisneros *(Vice Chm)*
Miguel Dvorak *(Pres & COO)*
Yolanda Talamo *(Chief HR Officer)*

Subsidiaries:

Americatel Sistemas de Comunicacion C.A. (1)
C C Pza Aeropuerto 2 2-10 Zona Industrial Unare I
Puerto Ordaz, Bolivar, Venezuela
Tel.: (58) 212 700 47 00
E-Mail: info@americatel.com.ve
Web Site: www.americatel.com.ve
Telecommunication Management Services
S.I.C.: 8748
N.A.I.C.S.: 541618

Cuponidad Venezuela CA (1)
Av Tamanaco Edif La Union Piso 6 Ofic 6-A
El Rosal, Caracas, 1060, Venezuela
Tel.: (58) 212 953 6562
E-Mail: soporte.ve@cuponidad.com
Web Site: www.cuponidad.com.ve

Telecommunication Services
S.I.C.: 8748
N.A.I.C.S.: 541618

U.S. Subsidiaries:

RedMas (1)
121 Alhambra Plz Ste 1400
Coral Gables, FL 33134
Tel.: (305) 442-3411
Fax: (305) 446-4772
E-Mail: operations@redmas.com
Web Site: www.redmas.com
Advertising Services
S.I.C.: 7311
N.A.I.C.S.: 541810
Alejandro Leon Navas *(Reg Dir-Ventas Pan)*

Non-U.S. Subsidiary:

Cuponidad Peru (1)
Miguel Dasso 117 Piso 9
San Isidro, Lima, Peru
Tel.: (51) 1 422 4649
Telecommunication Services
S.I.C.: 8748
N.A.I.C.S.: 541618

CISTRO TELELINK LIMITED

206 Airen Heights AB Road
Indore, Madhya Pradesh, 452010, India
Tel.: (91) 731 2555022
Fax: (91) 731 2555722
E-Mail: cistrotelelink@gmail.com
Web Site: www.cistrotelelink.net
Year Founded: 1992
531775—(BOM)
Rev.: $4,504
Assets: $973,251
Liabilities: $57,573
Net Worth: $915,678
Earnings: ($4,893)
Fiscal Year-end: 03/31/13

Business Description:
Telecom Services
S.I.C.: 4899
N.A.I.C.S.: 517919

Personnel:
Satyendersingh Gupta *(CEO)*
Arunkumar Sharma *(CFO & Compliance Officer)*

Board of Directors:
Sanjay Agrawal
Jatin Chawla
Satyendersingh Gupta
Arunkumar Sharma
Prahalad Singh Tomar
Pyarelal Varma

Transfer Agent:
Ankit Consultancy Pvt Ltd
60 Electronics Complex Pardehsipura
Indore, India

CITADEL CAPITAL CO.

1089 Corniche El Nile Four Seasons Nile Plaza Office Building 3rd fl
Garden City, Cairo, 11519, Egypt
Tel.: (20) 227914440
Fax: (20) 227914448
E-Mail: ykhattab@citadelcapital.com
Web Site:
Year Founded: 2004

Business Description:
Private Equity Firm
S.I.C.: 6211
N.A.I.C.S.: 523999

Personnel:
Ahmed Hassanein Heikal *(Co-Founder & Chm)*
Hisham El-Khazindar *(Co-Founder & Mng Partner)*
Ahmed El Shamy *(Mng Partner)*
Amr El-Garhy *(Mng Dir & Head-Corp Fin & Investment Review Function)*
Ahmed El-Houssieny *(Mng Dir)*
Marwan El Araby *(Mng Dir)*
Karim Sadek *(Mng Dir)*
Amr Seif *(CEO-Fin Unlimited)*

Non-U.S. Subsidiary:

Rally Energy Limited (1)
444 5th Ave SW Ste 1120
Calgary, AB, T2P 2T8, Canada ON
Tel.: (403) 538-0000
Fax: (403) 538-3705
E-Mail: info@rallyenergy.com
Web Site: www.rallyenergy.com
Sales Range: $50-74.9 Million
Emp.: 65
Oil & Gas Exploration Services
S.I.C.: 1311
N.A.I.C.S.: 211111
Gawdat Tadros *(Mgr-Fin)*

Holding:

ASEC Cement Co. (1)
Kafr El Elw-Helwan z
P O Box 11421
Cairo, Egypt
Tel.: (20) 250107719
Fax: (20) 25010428
Web Site: www.asec-egypt.com
Cement Manufacturing
S.I.C.: 3241
N.A.I.C.S.: 327310

CITAIR INC.

(d/b/a General Coach Canada)
73 Mill Street
Hensall, ON, N0M 1X0, Canada
Tel.: (519) 262-2600
Fax: (519) 262-2340
E-Mail: info@generalcoachcanada.com
Web Site: www.generalcoach.on.ca
Emp.: 120

Business Description:
Mobile Home Mfr
S.I.C.: 2452
N.A.I.C.S.: 321992

Personnel:
Roger W. Faulkner *(Pres)*

CITATION RESOURCES LTD.

Level 7 1008 Hay Street
Perth, WA, 6000, Australia

Mailing Address:
PO Box 7209
Cloisters Square, Perth, WA, 6850, Australia
Tel.: (61) 8 9389 2000
Fax: (61) 8 9389 2099
E-Mail: info@citation.net.au
Web Site: www.cleanglobalenergy.net.au
CTR—(ASX)
Rev.: $749,817
Assets: $12,040,675
Liabilities: $4,600,844
Net Worth: $7,439,830
Earnings: ($538,769)
Fiscal Year-end: 06/30/13

Business Description:
Coal Mining & Processing Services
S.I.C.: 1241
N.A.I.C.S.: 213113

Personnel:
Sara Kelly *(Sec)*

Board of Directors:
Michael Curnow
Peter Neil Landau
Brett Mitchell

CITIBASE HOLDINGS PLC

1 Warwick Row
London, SW1E 5ER, United Kingdom
Tel.: (44) 2078087444
Fax: (44) 2078087028
E-Mail: citibaseplc@citibase.co.uk
Web Site: www.citibase.co.uk
Emp.: 75

Business Description:
Holding Company; Office Leasing Services
S.I.C.: 6519
N.A.I.C.S.: 531190

Personnel:
Ian Read *(Co-Founder, Chm & Co-Mng Dir)*
David Joseph *(Co-Founder & Co-Mng Dir)*

Board of Directors:
Ian Read
David Joseph

CITIC DAMENG HOLDINGS LIMITED

Suites 3501-02 35/F Bank of America Tower No 12 Harcourt Road
Central, China (Hong Kong)
Tel.: (852) 2179 1310
Fax: (852) 2537 0168
E-Mail: ir@citicdameng.com.hk
Web Site: www.dameng.citic.com
Year Founded: 2005
00D—(DEU)
Rev.: $385,101,954
Assets: $1,200,951,196
Liabilities: $696,437,931
Net Worth: $504,513,264
Earnings: ($64,324,129)
Emp.: 9,032
Fiscal Year-end: 12/31/12

Business Description:
Manganese Mining Services
S.I.C.: 1099
N.A.I.C.S.: 212299

Personnel:
Yiyong Qiu *(Chm)*
Weijian Li *(Vice Chm)*
Yuchuan Tian *(CEO)*
Wai Yip Lau *(CFO & Sec)*

Board of Directors:
Yiyong Qiu
Jiqiu Chen
Weijian Li
Zengxin Mi
Shijian Mo
Zhuzhong Tan
Yuchuan Tian
Zhi Jie Yang
Chen Zeng

Codan Services Limited
Clarendon House 2 Church Street
Hamilton, Bermuda

Transfer Agents:
Computershare Hong Kong Investor Services Limited
Shops 1712-1716 17th Floor Hopewell Centre
183 Queens Road East
Wanchai, China (Hong Kong)

Codan Services Limited
Clarendon House 2 Church Street
Hamilton, Bermuda

CITIC GROUP CORPORATION

Capital Mansion 6 Xinyuan Nanlu
Chaoyang District, Beijing, 100004, China
Tel.: (86) 3596792457
Fax: (86) 3596563425
Web Site: www.citicgroup.com.cn
Year Founded: 1979
Sales Range: $50-74.9 Billion
Emp.: 125,215

Business Description:
Holding Company
S.I.C.: 6719
N.A.I.C.S.: 551112

Personnel:
Zhenming Chang *(Chm)*
Meifang Lin *(Interim Chm-Supervisory Bd)*

Board of Directors:
Zhenming Chang
Pu Cao
Jianzhong Dou
Zhiqiang Liu
Yonglan Qu
Jiong Wang
Jinming Yang
Zhensheng Yu

Supervisory Board of Directors:
Meifang Lin
Hongquan Dou
Zengyuan Li
Xiaoping Zhang
Yongqin Zheng

Subsidiaries:

Bohai Aluminium Industries Ltd. (1)
95 Beihuan Rd
Halgang District, Qinhuangdao, Hebei, China
Tel.: (86) 335302000000
Fax: (86) 3353016007
Web Site: www.bail.com.cn
Emp.: 1,400
Aluminum Whslr
S.I.C.: 3334
N.A.I.C.S.: 331313
Wang Jun *(Legal Rep)*

China International Economic Consultants Co., Ltd. (1)
13th Fl Capital Mansion 6 Xinyuan Nanlu
Chaoyang District, Beijing, 100004, China (100%)
Tel.: (86) 1084861313
Fax: (86) 10 84865509
E-Mail: ciec-info@citic.com.con
Web Site: www.ciec.cc
Consulting Services
S.I.C.: 8748
N.A.I.C.S.: 541618

CITIC Automobile Co., Ltd. (1)
8 Fangyuan Nanjie St
Chaoyang District, Lanzhou, 471039, China (100%)
Tel.: (86) 64359780
Fax: (86) 1064350678, ext. 6492880
E-Mail: auto.citic@263.net
Web Site: www.citic.com
Emp.: 50
S.I.C.: 3714
N.A.I.C.S.: 336340
Mi Zengxin *(Chm)*

CITIC Development Co., Ltd. (1)
Capital Mansion 6 Xinyuan Nanlu
Beijing, 100004, China
Tel.: (86) 10 646 62243
Fax: (86) 10 646 62250
E-Mail: dev@citic.com.cn
Financial Services
S.I.C.: 6211
N.A.I.C.S.: 523999

CITIC East China Group (1)
1085 Pudong Avenue
Shanghai, 200135, China (100%)
Tel.: (86) 21 6105 1166
Fax: (86) 21 6105 1111
E-Mail: citicsh@citic.com
Web Site: futures.ecitic.com
Emp.: 40
Industrial Investment, Domestic Trade & Real Estate Services
S.I.C.: 6211
N.A.I.C.S.: 523999
Wang Jiong *(Chm)*

CITIC Guoan Co., Ltd. (1)
Guoan Mansion 7th Floor One Guoan Dong Dian Street
Dong Da Qiao
Chao Yang District, Beijing, 100020, China CN
Tel.: (86) 10 695 3760 (50%)
Fax: (86) 10 650 61482
Emp.: 11,059
Industrial Development Services
S.I.C.: 9532
N.A.I.C.S.: 925120

Subsidiary:

CITIC Guoan Information Industry Co., Ltd. (2)
Guoan Mansion 1 Guoan Dong Beije
Chaoyang District, Beijing, 100020, China (100%)
Tel.: (86) 10 6501 0855
Fax: (86) 10 6501 0854
E-Mail: giuo@citicguoaninfo.com
Web Site: www.guoan.citic.com
Emp.: 60

CITIC Group Corporation—(Continued)

Investment Holdings; Industrial Development Services
S.I.C.: 6211
N.A.I.C.S.: 523999
Li Shilin *(Pres)*

CITIC Institute of Architecture & Design Research (1)
Capital Mansion 6 Xinyuannanlu
100004 Beijing, China (100%)
Tel.: (86) 10 6466 0088
Fax: (86) 27 827 26178
Web Site: www.whadi.com.cn
Emp.: 200
Contract Engineering Services
S.I.C.: 8711
N.A.I.C.S.: 541330

CITIC Limited (1)
Capital Mansion 6 Xinyuan Nanlu
Chaoyang District, Beijing, 100004, China
Tel.: (86) 3596792457
Web Site: www.citic.com
Bank Holding Company
S.I.C.: 6712
N.A.I.C.S.: 551111
Xiaoxian Chen *(VP)*

Subsidiary:

China CITIC Bank Corporation Limited (2)
Block C Fuhua Mansion No 8
Chaoyangmen Beidajie
Dongcheng District, Beijing, 100027, China (66.95%)
Tel.: (86) 10 6555 8000
Fax: (86) 10 6555 0809
E-Mail: ir_cncb@citicbank.com
Web Site: www.ecitic.com
601998—(HKG OTC SHG)
Int. Income: $22,049,968,500
Assets: $470,186,310,150
Liabilities: $437,926,099,050
Net Worth: $32,260,211,100
Earnings: $4,985,507,250
Emp.: 41,365
Fiscal Year-end: 12/31/12
Banking Services
S.I.C.: 6029
N.A.I.C.S.: 522110
Xiaohuang Zhu *(Pres)*
Lianfu Wang *(Chief Compliance Officer)*
Wendy Mei Ha Kam *(Co-Sec)*
Zhengyue Lin *(Co-Sec)*

Non-U.S. Subsidiary:

CITIC International Financial Holdings Limited (3)
Ste 2701 2709 CITIC Tower
1 Tim Mei Avenue, Central, China (Hong Kong) (70%)
Tel.: (852) 36073000
Fax: (852) 25253303
E-Mail: info@citicifh.com
Web Site: www.citicifh.com
Emp.: 1,500
Financial Services; Holding Company
S.I.C.: 6712
N.A.I.C.S.: 551111
Dan Kong *(Chm)*
Zhenming Chang *(Vice Chm)*
Kelvin Wing Yat Lo *(Mng Dir)*
Kyna Y.C. Wong *(Sec)*

U.S. Subsidiary:

Citic Bank International Ltd. (4)
323 W Valley Blvd
Alhambra, CA 91803
Tel.: (626) 282-9820
Fax: (626) 282-9399
E-Mail: labranch@cncbinternational.com
Emp.: 12
Banking Services
S.I.C.: 6029
N.A.I.C.S.: 522110
Ben Cheng *(Branch Mgr)*

CITIC Machinery Manufacturing Co., Ltd. (1)
Jianxi District
Luoyang, Henan, 471039, China (100%)
Tel.: (86) 357 391 3008
Fax: (86) 357 391 3007
E-Mail: citicmmi@public.yc.sx.cn
Web Site: www.machine.citic.com
Emp.: 20
Heavy Machinery Mfr
S.I.C.: 3559
N.A.I.C.S.: 333249

CITIC Networks Management Co., Ltd. (1)
Capital Mansion 6 Xinyuannanlu
Chaoyang District, Beijing, 100004, China (100%)
Tel.: (86) 10 8486 8800
Fax: (86) 10 8486 8080
Web Site: www.netmgt.citic.com
Emp.: 50
Digital Network Development & Marketing Services
S.I.C.: 7379
N.A.I.C.S.: 541519
Luo Ning *(Gen Mgr)*

Joint Venture:

Great Wall Broadband Network Service Co., Ltd. (2)
68 ZijinBuilding Floor 17th Wanquan Road
Haidian District, Beijing, 100086, China CN
Tel.: (86) 1082659931
Fax: (86) 1082659790
Sales Range: $1-4.9 Billion
Computer Storage Technology Mfr
S.I.C.: 3572
N.A.I.C.S.: 334112

CITIC Ningbo Group (1)
29 Jiangdong Road N Citic Mansion
Ningbo, Zhejiang, 315040, China
Tel.: (86) 574 8657 3176
Fax: (86) 574 733 2566
Real Estate Services
Import Export
S.I.C.: 6531
N.A.I.C.S.: 531390

CITIC Ocean Helecopter Co., Ltd. (1)
19th Fl Agricultural Bank Tower
188 Jiefang Rd W Shinzhen, Guangzhou, Guangjong, China (100%)
Tel.: (86) 7555590796
Fax: (86) 7555590757
Web Site: www.china-cohc.com
Harbor Pilot Delivery Services
S.I.C.: 7359
N.A.I.C.S.: 532411

CITIC Private Equity Funds Management Co., Ltd. (1)
11/F Jinbao Tower No 89 Jinbao Street
Dongcheng District
Beijing, 100005, China
Tel.: (86) 10 8507 9000
Fax: (86) 10 8522 1872
E-Mail: BusinessContact@citicpe.com
Web Site: www.citicpe.com
Private Equity Firm
S.I.C.: 6211
N.A.I.C.S.: 523999
Lefei Liu *(Chm & CEO)*

CITIC Publishing House (1)
Ta Yuan Diplomatic Office Bldg 14
Liangmahe St
Chaoyang District, Beijing, 100600, China
Tel.: (86) 1085323366
Fax: (86) 1085322505
Web Site: www.publish.citic.com
Publishing Services
S.I.C.: 2741
N.A.I.C.S.: 511199

CITIC Qinhuangdao Co., Ltd. (1)
Don Wang Ling Haigang District
Qinhuangdao, Hebei, 66003, China
Tel.: (86) 353100888
Fax: (86) 3353010518
Aluminum Curtain Wall, Doors & Windows Mfr
S.I.C.: 3442
N.A.I.C.S.: 332321
Chen Xiaoping *(Gen Mgr)*

CITIC Real Estate Co., Ltd. (1)
Capital Mansion 6 Xinyuan Nanlu
Chaoyang District, Beijing, 100004, China
Tel.: (86) 1064666052
Fax: (86) 10 646 66090
E-Mail: bangong-crec@citic.com.cn
Provider of Real Estate Investing Services
S.I.C.: 6726
N.A.I.C.S.: 525990

CITIC South China Group (1)
75th Fl CITIC Plz 233 Tianhe Beilu
Guangzhou, 510613, China (100%)
Tel.: (86) 2038770068
Fax: (86) 2038770668
Web Site: www.citicsouth.com.cn
Emp.: 50
Property Investment & Real Estate Services
S.I.C.: 6531
N.A.I.C.S.: 531390

CITIC Travel Co., Ltd. (1)
7th Fl Ste 2 Bld CITIC Bldg
19 Jianguomenwai Dajie, Beijing, 100004, China (100%)
Tel.: (86) 85263636
Fax: (86) 85263737
E-Mail: citicttvl@public3.bta.net.cn
Web Site: www.citictravel.com
Emp.: 120
Provider of Travel & Tourism Services
S.I.C.: 4724
N.A.I.C.S.: 561510

Jiangyin Xingcheng Special Steel Works Co., Ltd. (1)
No 297 Binjiang East Road
214400 Jiangyin, Jiangsu, China
Tel.: (86) 51086271692
Fax: (86) 51086271729
E-Mail: jyxczjb@public1.wx.js.cn
Web Site: www.jyxc.com
Special Steel Manufacturing
S.I.C.: 3312
N.A.I.C.S.: 331110
Peter Lee Chung Hing *(Chm)*

Ningbo Daxie Development Zone (1)
Daxie Island, Beilun District
Ningbo Development Zone, Ningbo, Zhejiang, 315812, China
Tel.: (86) 574 7332022
Fax: (86) 574 7331006
E-Mail: citicdx@mail.nbptt.zj.cn
Web Site: www.citic-daxie.com
Emp.: 150
Land Development Services
S.I.C.: 6531
N.A.I.C.S.: 531390

Joint Venture:

Citic GSI Tomida Group Co., Ltd. (1)
The Business Building Second Happiness Village
Chayang District, Beijing, China
Tel.: (86) 1064673002
Fax: (86) 10 6467 3013
Textiles
S.I.C.: 2299
N.A.I.C.S.: 313310

Non-U.S. Subsidiaries:

CITIC Pacific Ltd. (1)
32nd Floor CITIC Tower 1 Tim Mai Avenue
Central, China (Hong Kong) (100%)
Tel.: (852) 28202111
Fax: (852) 28772771
E-Mail: contact@citicpacific.com
Web Site: www.citicpacific.com
CTPCY—(HKG OTCB)
Rev.: $12,027,424,400
Assets: $31,900,424,700
Liabilities: $20,054,304,000
Net Worth: $11,846,120,700
Earnings: $1,063,579,600
Emp.: 34,781
Fiscal Year-end: 12/31/12
Holding Company; Telecommunications, Power Generation, Property Investment & Industrial Manufacturing
S.I.C.: 6719
N.A.I.C.S.: 551112
Zhenming Chang *(Chm)*
Jijing Zhang *(Pres)*
Shuchun Liu *(Mng Dir & COO-CITIC Pacific Mining Management Pty Ltd)*
Vernon Francis Moore *(CFO)*
Yue Jiang Xin *(Chm-CITIC Telecom)*
Wei Xie *(Pres-CITIC Pacific Special Steel Co Ltd)*
Moon Tong Yip *(CEO-DCH Holdings)*
Norman Kee Tong Yuen *(CEO-CITIC Telecom)*
Ricky Wing Kay Choy *(Gen Counsel, Sec & VP)*
Zhenjun Luan *(Treas & VP)*

Subsidiaries:

CITIC Hong Kong (Holdings) Ltd. (2)
32nd Fl Citic Tower 1 Tim Mei Ave
NIL Central, China (Hong Kong) (100%)
Tel.: (852) 28202111
Fax: (852) 28772771
E-Mail: contact@citicpacific.com
Web Site: www.citicpacific.com
Emp.: 200
Investment & Holding Services
S.I.C.: 6211
N.A.I.C.S.: 523999
Chang Ming *(Chm)*

CITIC Resources Holdings Limited (2)
Suites 3001-3006 30/F One Pacific Place
88 Queensway
Hong Kong, China (Hong Kong) (54%)
Tel.: (852) 2899 8200
Fax: (852) 2815 9723
E-Mail: ir@citicresources.com
Web Site: www.citicresources.com
1205—(HKG OTC)
Rev.: $6,245,559,658
Assets: $3,890,406,284
Liabilities: $2,118,553,335
Net Worth: $1,771,852,949
Earnings: ($162,728,066)
Emp.: 4,700
Fiscal Year-end: 12/31/12
Forest Products
S.I.C.: 2411
N.A.I.C.S.: 113310
Yiyong Qiu *(CEO)*
Johnathan Jen Wah Cha *(Gen Counsel)*
So Mui Li *(Sec)*

CITIC Telecom International Holdings Limited (2)
25/F CITIC Telecom Tower 93 Kwai Fuk Road
Kwai Chung, China (Hong Kong)
Tel.: (852) 23778888
Fax: (852) 23762063
E-Mail: contact@citictel.com
Web Site: www.citictel.com
1883—(HKG)
Sls.: $465,485,000
Assets: $603,532,164
Liabilities: $162,391,119
Net Worth: $441,141,045
Earnings: $59,960,332
Emp.: 900
Fiscal Year-end: 12/31/12
Telecommunication Services
S.I.C.: 4899
N.A.I.C.S.: 517919
Yue Jiang Xin *(Chm)*
Brook Ching Wa Wong *(Pres & Head-Bus-China)*
Kee Tong Yuen *(CEO)*
David Tin Wai Chan *(CFO)*
Sutton Yuet Pun Cheung *(CTO)*

CPCNet Hong Kong Limited (2)
20th Fl Lincoln House Taikoo Pl
979 King's Road, Quarry Bay, China (Hong Kong)
Tel.: (852) 21707101
Fax: (852) 27951262
E-Mail: info@cpcnet.com
Web Site: www.cpcnet.com
Network Communications & Security Solutions
S.I.C.: 7389
N.A.I.C.S.: 561499
Stephen Ho *(CEO)*
Esmond Li *(CFO)*
Joel Ma *(Exec VP-Intl Bus & Partnership)*
Ivan Tang *(Sr VP-Sls)*

New Hong Kong Tunnel Company Limited (2)
The Administration Building NKIL 6047
Cha Kwo Ling East Kwun Tong, Kowloon, China (Hong Kong)
Tel.: (852) 23480011
Fax: (852) 23475037
E-Mail: eht@nhkt.com
Web Site: www.easternharbourtunnel.com.hk
Emp.: 200
Eastern Harbour Tunnel Construction & Maintenance
S.I.C.: 4789
N.A.I.C.S.: 488490

Sims Trading Company Ltd. (2)
7th Floor DCH Building
20 Kai Cheung Road, Kowloon, China (Hong Kong)
Tel.: (852) 22621798
Fax: (852) 27570208
Web Site: www.simshk.com
Emp.: 100
Consumer & Healthcare Products Importer, Distributor & Wholesaler
S.I.C.: 5149
N.A.I.C.S.: 424490
Glenn Robert Sturrock Smith *(CEO)*

Non-U.S. Subsidiaries:

CITIC Australia Pty. Ltd. (2)
CITIC House Level 7 99 King St
Melbourne, VIC, 3000, Australia (100%)
Tel.: (61) 396148000
Fax: (61) 396148800
E-Mail: info@citic.com.au
Emp.: 45
Investment & Trading Services
S.I.C.: 6211
N.A.I.C.S.: 523999
Chen Zeng *(Pres & CEO)*
Irwan Kam *(CFO)*

Subsidiary:

CITIC Australia Trading Limited (3)
Level 7 CITIC House 99 King St
3000 Melbourne, VIC, Australia AU
Tel.: (61) 396148000
Fax: (61) 396148800
Aluminium & Alumina Mfg
Export
S.I.C.: 3334
N.A.I.C.S.: 331313
Tinghu Guo *(Exec Dir)*

CITIC New Zealand Ltd. (2)
Level 24 ASB Bank Ct 135 Albert St
PO Box 7348
Auckland, 1015, New Zealand (100%)
Tel.: (64) 93091528
Fax: (64) 93091525
E-Mail: cui@citic.co.nz
Lumber Production Services
S.I.C.: 0811
N.A.I.C.S.: 113110

Dah Chong Hong Holdings Ltd. (2)
8th Floor DCH Building
20 Kai Cheung Road, Kowloon, Japan
Tel.: (81) 27683388
Fax: (81) 27968838
E-Mail: dch@dch.com.hk
Web Site: www.dch.com.hk
1828—(HKG OTC)
Holding Company
S.I.C.: 6719
N.A.I.C.S.: 551112
Hui Ying Bun *(Chm)*
Chu Hon Fai *(Deputy Chm)*

Macao Cement Manufacturing Co., Ltd. (1)
Estrada De Nossa Senhora De Ka Ho
PO Box 1106
Coloane, Macau, China (Macau) (100%)
Tel.: (853) 28870511
Fax: (853) 28870273
E-Mail: mocement@macau.ctm.net
Web Site: www.mocement.com.mo/intro/eng.html
Cement Mfr
S.I.C.: 3241
N.A.I.C.S.: 327310

Non-U.S. Affiliate:

CITIC Capital Holdings Limited (1)
28/F CITIC Tower 1 Tim Mei Avenue
1 Tim Mei Avenue, Central, China (Hong Kong)
Tel.: (852) 37106888
Fax: (852) 25238312
E-Mail: info@citiccapital.com
Web Site: www.citiccapital.com
Emp.: 150
Private Equity Firm
S.I.C.: 6211
N.A.I.C.S.: 523999
Miu Cheung *(Mng Dir & Head-Structured Fin Grp)*
Annie Fung *(Mng Dir & Head-Bus Dev)*

U.S. Subsidiary:

CITIC Capital Partners (2)
1120 Avenue Of The Americas Ste 1501
New York, NY 10036
Tel.: (212) 395-9767
Fax: (212) 395-9787
E-Mail: mmiller@citiccapital.com
Web Site: www.citiccapital.com
Emp.: 10
Private Equity Firm
S.I.C.: 6211
N.A.I.C.S.: 523999
Brian J. Doyle *(Exec VP)*

Holding:

The Colibri Group, Inc. (3)
25 Fairmount Ave
East Providence, RI 02914
Tel.: (401) 943-2100
Fax: (401) 943-1027
Web Site: www.colibri.com
Sales Range: $100-124.9 Million
Emp.: 500
Mfr & Distr of Jewelry, Lighters, Accessories & Clocks; Owned by Founders Equity Inc., Main Street Resources & CITIC Group
Import Export
S.I.C.: 5094
N.A.I.C.S.: 423940

Non-U.S. Holdings:

AsiaInfo-Linkage, Inc. (2)
4th Floor Zhongdian Information Tower 6
Zhongguancun South Street
Haidian District, Beijing, 100086, China DE
Tel.: (86) 10 82166688
Fax: (86) 10 82166699
E-Mail: info@asiainfo.com
Web Site: www.asiainfo.com
Rev.: $547,872,000
Assets: $1,282,323,000
Liabilities: $263,983,000
Net Worth: $1,018,340,000
Earnings: $29,953,000
Emp.: 11,246
Fiscal Year-end: 12/31/12
Holding Company; Telecom Network Integration & Software Solution Services
S.I.C.: 6719
N.A.I.C.S.: 551112
Jian Ding *(Chm)*
Steve Zhang *(Pres & CEO)*
Jun Wu *(CFO & Exec VP)*
Yadong Jin *(CTO & Exec VP)*
Guoxiang Liu *(Exec VP)*

Subsidiaries:

AsiaInfo Technologies (Chengdu), Inc (3)
6th Floor Wukuang Mansion No 310
Zhongshan North Road
Xiacheng District, Hangzhou, China
Tel.: (86) 57185789290
Custom Computer Programming Services
S.I.C.: 7371
N.A.I.C.S.: 541511
Qindai Wang *(Pres)*

AsiaInfo Technologies (China), Ltd. (3)
4F Zhongdian Info Tower 6 Zhongguancun S St
Haidian District, Beijing, 100086, China CN
Tel.: (86) 1062501658 (100%)
Fax: (86) 1062501893
E-Mail: info@asiainfo.com
Web Site: www.asiainfo.com
Emp.: 500
Telecom Network Integration & Software Solutions
S.I.C.: 7373
N.A.I.C.S.: 541512

U.S. Subsidiary:

Lenovo-AsiaInfo Technologies, Inc (3)
2137 Hwy Rt 35
Holmdel, NJ 07733
Tel.: (732) 383-9066
Web Site: www.lenovoai.com
Computer Equipment & Software Whslr
S.I.C.: 5045
N.A.I.C.S.: 423430
Jian Qi *(Chm)*

Non-U.S. Subsidiary:

AsiaInfo International Pte. Ltd. (3)
391B Orchard Road Ngee Ann City 23-01
Singapore, 238874, Singapore
Tel.: (65) 6832 5918
Fax: (65) 6491 1284
Information Technology Consulting Services
S.I.C.: 7373
N.A.I.C.S.: 541512

Narumi China Corporation (2)
3 Denjiyama Narumi-cho
Midori-ku, Nagoya, 458 8530, Japan JP
Tel.: (81) 528962205
Telex: 447-3562 NARUTO J
Fax: (81) 528962293
E-Mail: export@narumi.co.jp
Web Site: www.narumi.co.jp
Sales Range: $75-99.9 Million
Emp.: 343
Designer, Mfr & Marketer of Bone China Dinnerware
Import Export
S.I.C.: 3269
N.A.I.C.S.: 327110
Rikizo Matsukawa *(Pres)*

Non-U.S. Joint Venture:

Asia Satellite Telecommunications Holdings Limited (1)
19F Sunning Plaza 10 Hysan Avenue
Causeway Bay, China (Hong Kong)
Tel.: (852) 2500 0880
Fax: (852) 2500 0895
E-Mail: wpang@asiasat.com
Web Site: www.asiasat.com
1135—(HKG)
Sls.: $229,472,328
Assets: $1,117,069,607
Liabilities: $144,869,264
Net Worth: $972,200,343
Earnings: $117,908,269
Emp.: 124
Fiscal Year-end: 12/31/12
Satellite Telecommunication Services
S.I.C.: 4899
N.A.I.C.S.: 517410
William Wade *(Pres & CEO)*
Sue Ching Yeung *(CFO, Sec & VP-Fin)*
Catherine Chang *(Gen Counsel)*

Non-U.S. Representative Offices:

CITIC Europe Representative Office (1)
Saalburgstrasse 155
61350 Bad Homburg, Germany (100%)
Tel.: (49) 617293060
Fax: (49) 172930621
E-Mail: info@normag.de
Web Site: www.normag.de
Business Consulting Services
S.I.C.: 7389
N.A.I.C.S.: 561499

CITIC Japan Representative Office (1)
3rd Fl The Landic Third Akadaka Bldg
2 3 2 Akasaka Minato Ku, Tokyo, 1070052, Japan (100%)
Tel.: (81) 335842635
Fax: (81) 335056235
E-Mail: citic.tyo@nifpy.com
Web Site: www.citic.com.cn
Emp.: 2
Provider of Financial Services
S.I.C.: 6282
N.A.I.C.S.: 523930

CITIC SECURITIES CO., LTD.

Citic Securities Tower No 48
Liangmaqiao Road Chaoyang District
Beijing, 100125, China
Tel.: (86) 10 6083 6888
Fax: (86) 10 6083 6031
Web Site: www.cs.ecitic.com
Year Founded: 1995
600030—(HKG SHG)
Rev.: $2,076,366,633
Assets: $26,767,425,112
Liabilities: $12,997,624,533
Net Worth: $13,769,800,578
Earnings: $684,135,657
Emp.: 10,452
Fiscal Year-end: 12/31/12

Business Description:
Holding Company; Securities & Commodities Futures Brokerage, Dealing & Investing Services
S.I.C.: 6719
N.A.I.C.S.: 551112

Personnel:
Dongming Wang *(Chm)*
Ke Yin *(Vice Chm)*
Boming Cheng *(Pres)*
Xiaobo Ge *(Mng Dir & Head-Fin, Capital Ops, Alternative Investments & Risk)*
Weidong Huang *(Mng Dir & Head-Asset Mgmt Bus)*
Tatsuhito Tokuchi *(Mng Dir & Head-Investment Banking & Fixed Income Bus)*
Gang Xu *(Mng Dir & Head-Res Dept)*
Jianwei Wu *(Chief Compliance Officer)*
Jing Zheng *(Sec)*

Board of Directors:
Dongming Wang
Boming Cheng
Jun Fang
Weimin Ju
Conway Kong Wai Lee
Geping Rao
Benhua Wei
Xiaoqiu Wu
Ke Yin

Ernst & Young
22/ F CITIC Tower 1 Tim Mei Ave
Central, China (Hong Kong)

China Securities Depository & Clearing Corporation Limited
36/F China Insurance Building 166 Lujiazui East Road Pudong New Area
Shanghai, China

Subsidiaries:

CITIC Securities (Zhejiang) Co., Ltd. (1)
20/F Hengxin Tower 588 Jiangnan Avenue
Binjiang District, Hangzhou, 310052, China CN
Tel.: (86) 571 8578 3737 (100%)
Fax: (86) 571 8578 3721
E-Mail: 96598@bigsun.com.cn
Web Site: www.bigsun.com.cn
Securities Brokerage, Investment Advisory & Dealing Services
S.I.C.: 6211
N.A.I.C.S.: 523120
Qiang Shen *(CEO)*

CITIC Wantong Securities Co., Ltd. (1)
21/F Tower 1 Qingdao International Finance Center 222 Shenzhen Road
Laoshan District, Qingdao, 266061, China CN
Tel.: (86) 532 8502 2313 (96%)
Fax: (86) 532 8502 2301
E-Mail: 95548@zxwt.com.cn
Web Site: www.zxwt.com.cn
Securities Brokerage, Investment Advisory & Dealing Services
S.I.C.: 6211
N.A.I.C.S.: 523120
Baolin Yang *(CEO)*

CITICS Futures Co., Ltd. (1)
14/F Excellence Times Plaza Phase II 3rd Zhongxin Road No 8
Futian District, Shenzhen, 518048, China CN
Tel.: (86) 755 8322 2970 (100%)
Fax: (86) 755 8321 7421
E-Mail: csf@citicsf.com
Web Site: www.citicsf.com
Commodities Futures Broker & Dealer
S.I.C.: 6221
N.A.I.C.S.: 523140
Lei Zhang *(CEO)*

Goldstone Investment Co., Ltd. (1)
17/F CITIC Securities Tower No 48
Liangmaqiao Road

CITIC Securities Co., Ltd.—(Continued)

Chaoyang District, Beijing, 100026, China CN
Tel.: (86) 10 6083 7800 (100%)
Fax: (86) 10 6083 7899
Web Site: www.goldstone-investment.com
Private Equity Firm
S.I.C.: 6211
N.A.I.C.S.: 523999
Shuguang Qi *(CEO)*

Non-U.S. Subsidiaries:

CITIC Securities International Co., Ltd. (1)
26/F CITIC Tower 1 Tim Mei Avenue
Central, China (Hong Kong) HK
Tel.: (852) 2237 6899 (100%)
Fax: (852) 2104 6862
E-Mail: info@citics.com.hk
Web Site: www.citics.com.hk
Emp.: 200
Investment Banking, Securities Brokerage & Asset Management Services
S.I.C.: 6211
N.A.I.C.S.: 523110
Ke Yin *(CEO)*

CLSA Limited (1)
18/F One Pacific Place 88
Queensway, Hong Kong, China (Hong Kong)
Tel.: (852) 2600 8888
Fax: (852) 2868 0189
Web Site: www.clsa.com
Emp.: 1,500
Securities Brokerage Services
S.I.C.: 6211
N.A.I.C.S.: 523120
Jonathan Slone *(Mng Dir)*

Subsidiary:

CLSA Capital Partners (HK) Limited (2)
Room 1906-9 19th Floor Tower II Lippo Centre
89 Queensway, Hong Kong, China (Hong Kong)
Tel.: (852) 2600 8888
Fax: (852) 2868 0189
Web Site: www.clsacapital.com
Private Equity Firm
S.I.C.: 6211
N.A.I.C.S.: 523999
Richard Pyvis *(Chm)*
Michael McCoy *(Vice Chm)*
Randy Wilbert *(COO)*

CITIGOLD CORPORATION LIMITED

Level 13 500 Queen St
Brisbane, QLD, 4000, Australia
Tel.: (61) 7 3834 0000
Fax: (61) 7 3834 0011
E-Mail: info@citigold.com
Web Site: www.citigold.com
CTO—(ASX)
Rev.: $3,607,215
Assets: $216,587,423
Liabilities: $10,150,708
Net Worth: $206,436,715
Earnings: ($7,068,270)
Emp.: 70
Fiscal Year-end: 06/30/13

Business Description:
Gold Mining
Export
S.I.C.: 1041
N.A.I.C.S.: 212221

Personnel:
Mark J. Lynch *(Chm)*
Matthew B. Martin *(CEO)*
Dave Ang *(CFO)*
Brent Van Staden *(Sec)*

Board of Directors:
Mark J. Lynch
John J. Foley
Nicholas Ng
Arun Panchariya
Raymond Tan
Christopher Towsey

Subsidiary:

Charters Towers Gold Pty Ltd (1)
Clermont Hwy
Charters Towers, Queensland, 4820, Australia
Tel.: (61) 747877550
Fax: (61) 747878600
E-Mail: mine@citigold.com
Emp.: 90
Mining & Agriculture
S.I.C.: 1041
N.A.I.C.S.: 212221
Danny Stanford *(Gen Mgr)*

CITIPOST GROUP

51 Hailey Road
Erith, DA18 4AA Kent, SE18 6SW, United Kingdom
Tel.: (44) 2032600100
Fax: (44) 2032600150
E-Mail: sales@citipost.co.uk
Web Site: www.citipost.co.uk
Sales Range: $50-74.9 Million
Emp.: 400

Business Description:
Business-to-Business Mail Services
S.I.C.: 4311
N.A.I.C.S.: 491110

Personnel:
Kim Michael *(Mng Dir)*

Board of Directors:
Rob Bradford
Kim Michael
John Payne

Divisions:

Citipost AMP Ltd. (1)
51 Hailey Rd
Erith, DA184AA, United Kingdom
Tel.: (44) 02032600100
Fax: (44) 2032600150
E-Mail: admin@citipost.com
Web Site: www.citipost.com
Emp.: 50
Catalogue & Directory Delivery Services
S.I.C.: 4311
N.A.I.C.S.: 491110
Kim Michael *(Mng Dir)*

Citipost Direct Distribution Ltd. (1)
51 Hailey Rd
Erith, Kent, DA18 4AA, United Kingdom
Tel.: (44) 2032600100
Fax: (44) 2032600150
Web Site: www.citipost.com
Emp.: 30
Magazine, Newspaper & Journal Fulfillment & Distribution Services
S.I.C.: 4311
N.A.I.C.S.: 491110
John Payne *(Mng Dir)*

Citipost DSA Ltd. (1)
51 Hailey Rd
Erith, Kent, DA18 4AA, United Kingdom
Tel.: (44) 2032600100
Fax: (44) 2032600150
E-Mail: administrator@citipost.co.uk
Web Site: www.citipost.com
Emp.: 50
Postal Delivery Services
S.I.C.: 4311
N.A.I.C.S.: 491110
Rob Bradford *(Mng Dir)*

Non-U.S. Subsidiaries:

Citipost UK Ltd (1)
Russelsheimer Strasse 22
60326 Frankfurt, Germany
Tel.: (49) 69 97390252
Fax: (49) 69 73900697
Business-to-Business Mail Services
S.I.C.: 4311
N.A.I.C.S.: 491110

CITITEC ASSOCIATES LIMITED

50 Featherstone Street
London, EC1Y 8RT, United Kingdom
Tel.: (44) 207 608 5858
Fax: (44) 207 608 5888
E-Mail: info@cititec.com
Web Site: www.cititec.com
Year Founded: 1998
Sales Range: $75-99.9 Million
Emp.: 83

Business Description:
Employee Recruitment Services
S.I.C.: 7361
N.A.I.C.S.: 561311

Personnel:
Stephen Grant *(Mng Dir)*

CITIZEN HOLDINGS CO., LTD.

6-1-12 Tanashi-cho Nishi-Tokyo-shi
Tokyo, 188-8511, Japan
Tel.: (81) 424661280
Fax: (81) 424661280
Web Site: www.citizen.co.jp
Year Founded: 1930
7762—(OTC TKS)
Sls.: $2,992,550,000
Assets: $3,901,370,000
Liabilities: $1,784,871,000
Net Worth: $2,116,499,000
Earnings: $97,405,000
Emp.: 18,459
Fiscal Year-end: 03/31/13

Business Description:
Holding Company; Watch & Timepiece Component Mfr
S.I.C.: 6719
N.A.I.C.S.: 551112

Personnel:
Toshio Tokura *(Pres & CEO)*

Board of Directors:
Teruaki Aoki
Ryota Aoyagi
Kenji Ito
Shigeru Kabata
Keiichi Nakajima
Takao Nakajima
Toshio Tokura

Subsidiaries:

Citizen Business Expert Co., Ltd. (1)
6-1-12 Tanashi-Cho
Nishi-Tokyo, Tokyo, 188-8511, Japan JP
Tel.: (81) 42 461 1211
Watch & Parts Mfr
S.I.C.: 3829
N.A.I.C.S.: 334519

Citizen Financial Service Co., Ltd. (1)
6-1-12 Tanashi-Cho
Nishi-Tokyo, Tokyo, 188-8511, Japan JP
Tel.: (81) 424 68 4934
Financial Management Services
S.I.C.: 6211
N.A.I.C.S.: 523999
Toshio Tokura *(Gen Mgr)*

Citizen Finetech Miyota Co., Ltd. (1)
4107-5 Miyota Miyota-Machi
Kitasaku-Gun, Nagano, 389-0295, Japan JP
Tel.: (81) 267 32 3232
Fax: (81) 267 32 3930
Web Site: cfm.citizen.co.jp
Emp.: 539
Electronic Component Mfr
S.I.C.: 3679
N.A.I.C.S.: 334419
Toshihiko Sato *(Pres)*

Plant:

Citizen Finetech Miyota Co., Ltd. - Kitamimaki Works (2)
353 Yaehara
Tomi, Nagano-ken, 389-0406, Japan
Tel.: (81) 268 67 1800
Fax: (81) 268 67 1819
Web Site: cfm.citizen.co.jp/english/company/group.html
Electronic Component Mfr
S.I.C.: 3679
N.A.I.C.S.: 334419

U.S. Subsidiary:

Miyota Development Center of America, Inc. (2)
2602 Clover Basin Dr
Longmont, CO 80503
Tel.: (303) 772-2191
Fax: (303) 772-2193
Toll Free: (800) 397-8124
E-Mail: info@displaytech.com
Web Site: www.displaytech.com
Sales Range: $25-49.9 Million
Emp.: 20
Microdisplays Mfr
S.I.C.: 3674
N.A.I.C.S.: 334413
Takahiro Fujisawa *(Pres)*

Citizen Jewelry Co., Ltd. (1)
3F Homat Horizon Bldg 6-2 Gobancho
Chiyoda-Ku, Tokyo, 102-0076, Japan JP
Tel.: (81) 3 5215 2136
Jewelry & Precious Metal Mfr
S.I.C.: 3911
N.A.I.C.S.: 339910

Citizen Machinery Miyano Co., Ltd. (1)
4107-6 Miyota Miyota-machi
Kitasaku-gun, Karuizawa, Nagano, 389-0206, Japan JP
Tel.: (81) 267 32 5900
Fax: (81) 267 32 5928
Web Site: cmj.citizen.co.jp
Emp.: 1,500
Machine Tool Mfr & Distr
S.I.C.: 3542
N.A.I.C.S.: 333517
Keiichi Nakajima *(Pres & CEO)*
Atsuya Abe *(Operating Officer)*
Kenji Aoki *(Operating Officer)*
Hiromitsu Kamata *(Operating Officer)*
Akihide Kanaya *(Operating Officer)*
Norimitsu Katoh *(Operating Officer)*
Mamoru Kubota *(Operating Officer)*
Hiroyoshi Miyajima *(Operating Officer)*
Takayuki Satoh *(Operating Officer)*
Hiroshi Shinohara *(Operating Officer)*
Hidenori Yamazaki *(Operating Officer)*
Masayuki Yoshimuta *(Operating Officer)*

Affiliates:

Alps Tool Co., Ltd. (2)
10070 Oaza Sakaki
Nagano, Japan
Tel.: (81) 268822511
Fax: (81) 268827368
E-Mail: arai-y@markalpstool.co.jp
Web Site: www.alpstool.co.jp
Sales Range: $1-9.9 Million
Emp.: 300
Tools & Accessories; Bar Feeders
S.I.C.: 3425
N.A.I.C.S.: 332216

Mectron Japan, Inc. (2)
11240 Oaza Shomotakeshi
Nagano, 3852507, Japan
Tel.: (81) 268852345
Fax: (81) 268852347
Emp.: 80
Drilling & Tapping Machines & Equipment
S.I.C.: 3425
N.A.I.C.S.: 332216

Ocean Machinery (2)
1263 Oaza-Shomotakeshi
Takeshi-mura
Chiisagata-gun, Nagano, Japan
Tel.: (81) 268853431
Fax: (81) 268 85 343
Lathes Mfr
S.I.C.: 3542
N.A.I.C.S.: 333517

Non-U.S. Branch:

Citizen (China) Precision Machinery Co., Ltd. - Shanghai Branch (2)
Room 101 Bldg B The Rainbow Centre No 3051 Hechuan Road
Shanghai, 201103, China
Tel.: (86) 21 5868 1740
Fax: (86) 21 5868 1264
E-Mail:
Emp.: 24
Precision Instruments Distr
S.I.C.: 5099

N.A.I.C.S.: 423990
Yoshiharu Saito *(Pres & CEO)*

Non-U.S. Subsidiaries:

Citizen Machinery Europe GmbH (2)
Mettinger Strasse 11
73728 Esslingen, Germany De
Tel.: (49) 711 3906 100
Fax: (49) 711 3906 106
E-Mail:
Web Site: www.citizen.de
Emp.: 15
Industrial Machinery
S.I.C.: 5084
N.A.I.C.S.: 423830

Citizen Machinery Philippines Inc. (2)
First Philippine Industrial Park FPIP Lot No 29 Barangay Ulango
Tanauan, Batangas, 4232, Philippines PH
Tel.: (63) 43 405 6241
Fax: (63) 43 405 6145
Emp.: 30
Casting & Machine Tool Mfr
S.I.C.: 3541
N.A.I.C.S.: 333517
Yasuji Takahashi *(Pres)*

Citizen Machinery United Kingdom, Ltd. (2)
1 Park Avenue
Bushey, WD23 2DA, United Kingdom UK
Tel.: (44) 1923 691500
Fax: (44) 1923 691599
E-Mail: sales@citizenmachinery.co.uk
Web Site: www.citizenmachinery.co.uk
Emp.: 4
Automatic Lathe Machinery Distr
S.I.C.: 5085
N.A.I.C.S.: 423840
Daniel Marcoux *(Gen Mgr)*

Citizen Micro Co., Ltd. (1)
15-1 2 Chome Fujimi
Sayama, Saitama, 350-1393, Japan JP
Tel.: (81) 42 959 7220
Fax: (81) 42 959 7220
E-Mail: motor@micro.citizen.co.jp
Web Site: www.citizen-micro.com
Emp.: 422
Precision Electronic Equipment Mfr
S.I.C.: 3679
N.A.I.C.S.: 334419
Mamoru Ogura *(Pres)*

Subsidiary:

Citizen Yubaril Co., Ltd. (2)
4-107-6 Chome Minami Shimizusawa
Yubari, Hokkaido, 068-0536, Japan JP
Tel.: (81) 1235 9 6221
Fax: (81) 1235 9 6223
Web Site: www.citizen-yubari.jp
Wrist Watch Parts Mfr
S.I.C.: 3829
N.A.I.C.S.: 334519

Non-U.S. Subsidiary:

Citizen Micro Devices (Suzhou) Co., Ltd. (2)
No 388 South-Jinfeng Road Mudu Town
Wuzhong District, 215101 Suzhou, Jiangsu, China CN
Tel.: (86) 512 6655 3232
Fax: (86) 512 6651 3930
Web Site: www.citizen.co.jp/english/corporate/group/group02.html
Emp.: 600
Electronic Component Mfr
S.I.C.: 3679
N.A.I.C.S.: 334419

Citizen Plaza Co., Ltd. (1)
4-29-27 Takadanobaba
Shinjuku-Ku, Tokyo, 169-0075, Japan JP
Tel.: (81) 3 3363 2211
Fax: (81) 3 33632858
E-Mail: culture@citizen-plaza.co.jp
Emp.: 6
Shopping Mall Management Services
S.I.C.: 6512
N.A.I.C.S.: 531120
Diana Duran *(Pres)*

Citizen Sakae Trading Co., Ltd. (1)
7F Yushima Sakae Bldg 3-39-3 Yushima
Bunkyo-Ku, Tokyo, 113-0034, Japan JP
Tel.: (81) 3 3833 3811
Electronic Component Distr
S.I.C.: 5065
N.A.I.C.S.: 423690

Citizen Systems Japan Co., Ltd. (1)
6-1-12 Tanashi-cho
Nishi-Tokyo, Tokyo, 188-8511, Japan JP
Tel.: (81) 42 468 4771
Fax: (81) 24 468 4740
E-Mail: sales-op@systems.citizen.co.jp
Web Site: www.citizen-systems.co.jp
Emp.: 20
Electronic Component Mfr & Distr
S.I.C.: 3679
N.A.I.C.S.: 334419

Non-U.S. Subsidiaries:

Citizen Systems Europe Corporation (2)
Mettingerstrasse 11
73728 Esslingen, Germany
Tel.: (49) 711 3906 400
Fax: (49) 711 3906 405
E-Mail: sales@citizen-europe.com
Web Site: www.citizen-europe.com
Emp.: 12
Printer & Electronic Component Mfr
S.I.C.: 3575
N.A.I.C.S.: 334118
Takeshi Kakishima *(Pres & CEO)*

Citizen Systems (Jiangmen) Co., Ltd. (2)
Block C N0 399 Jinxing Road Jianghai Area
Jiangmen, Guangdong, China 529040 CN
Tel.: (86) 750 3870833
Fax: (86) 750 3870127
Electrical Equipment Mfr
S.I.C.: 3699
N.A.I.C.S.: 335999

Citizen T.I.C. Co., Ltd. (1)
5-16-12 Maehara-Cho
Koganei, Tokyo, 184-0013, Japan JP
Tel.: (81) 42 386 2261
Fax: (81) 42 386 2222
E-Mail: info@tic-citizen.co.jp
Timing Device Mfr
S.I.C.: 3824
N.A.I.C.S.: 334514

Citizen Watch Co., Ltd. (1)
6-1-12 Tanashi-Cho
Nishi-Tokyo-Shi, Tokyo, 188 8511, Japan JP
Tel.: (81) 424661231
Fax: (81) 424661280
E-Mail: support@cb.citizen.co.jp
Web Site: www.citizen.co.jp
Emp.: 1,500
Mfr & Sales of Watches & Parts, Information Equipment & Parts, Electronic Equipment & Parts & Industrial Machinery & Parts
S.I.C.: 3829
N.A.I.C.S.: 334519
Mikio Unno *(Pres & CEO)*
Mitsuyuki Kanamori *(Pres/CEO-Citizen Holdings)*

Subsidiaries:

Citizen Electronics Co., Ltd. (2)
1-23-1Kamikurechi
Fujiyoshida, Yamanashi, 403-0001, Japan JP
Tel.: (81) 555234121
Fax: (81) 555242426
Web Site: ce.citizen.co.jp/e/
Sales Range: $900-999.9 Million
Emp.: 1,351
Watch Parts, Buzzers, LEDs, Sensors, Electronic Thermometers & Electronic Blood Pressure Monitors Mfr
S.I.C.: 3829
N.A.I.C.S.: 334519
Yoshihiro Gohta *(Pres)*
Hirohiko ishii *(Operating Officer)*
Seigo Togashi *(Operating Officer)*
Yasunori Toyama *(Operating Officer)*

Subsidiaries:

Citizen Electronics Funehiki Co., Ltd. (3)
6-2 Kouyoudai
Funehiki, Tamura, Fukushima, 963-4300, Japan JP
Tel.: (81) 247 61 1160
Fax: (81) 247 82 1711
Electronic Component Mfr
S.I.C.: 3679
N.A.I.C.S.: 334419

Citizen Electronics Timel Co., Ltd. (3)
539-21 Koasumi
Fujiyoshida, Yamanashi-ken, 403-0002, Japan JP
Tel.: (81) 555 23 4351
Fax: (81) 555234741
Light Emitting Diode Mfr
S.I.C.: 3679
N.A.I.C.S.: 334419

U.S. Subsidiary:

CECOL, Inc. (3)
Ste C 951 N Plum Grove Rd
Schaumburg, IL 60173
Tel.: (847) 619-6700
Fax: (847) 619-6708
E-Mail: info@cecol.com
Web Site: www.cecol.com
Electronic Products Distr
S.I.C.: 5065
N.A.I.C.S.: 423690
Osamu Yamada *(Pres)*

Non-U.S. Subsidiaries:

C-E (Deutschland) GmbH (3)
Schafergasse 33
60313 Frankfurt am Main, Germany De
Tel.: (49) 69 299248 0
Fax: (49) 69 299248 50
E-Mail: inquiry@ce.citizen.co.jp
Web Site: ce.citizen.co.jp
Emp.: 1
Electronic Component Distr
S.I.C.: 5065
N.A.I.C.S.: 423690
Atsuro Ijichi *(Mng Dir)*

Citizen Electronics (China) Co., Ltd. (3)
D505 Orient International Plaza 85 Loushanguan Road
Changning District, Shanghai, 200336, China CN
Tel.: (86) 21 6295 5510
Fax: (86) 21 6295 5570
Emp.: 8
Electronic Component Mfr
S.I.C.: 3679
N.A.I.C.S.: 334419
Kiyoshi Naka *(Mng Dir)*

Citizen Heiwa Watch Co., Ltd. (2)
435 Shimotonooka
Iida, Nagano-Ken, 395-0195, Japan JP
Tel.: (81) 265 28 1500
Fax: (81) 265 28 1502
Web Site: www.citizen.co.jp/english/corporate/group/group01.html
Watch Mfr
S.I.C.: 3829
N.A.I.C.S.: 334519

Citizen Iwate Co. Ltd. (2)
2-15-5 Chome Mitake
Morioka, Iwate, 020 0122, Japan JP
Tel.: (81) 196410130
Fax: (81) 196417820
Web Site: www.citizen-iwate.com
Emp.: 150
Mfr. of Watch Parts, Coils, Printer Heads & FDD Carriages
S.I.C.: 3829
N.A.I.C.S.: 334519

Citizen Kohatsu Co., Ltd. (2)
29-27-4 Chome Takadanobaba
Shinjuku Ku, Tokyo, 169 0075, Japan
Tel.: (81) 333632211
Fax: (81) 333632663
Web Site: www.citizen-plaza.co.jp
Sales Range: $1-9.9 Million
Emp.: 55
Leisure Business Facilities for Bowling, Skating, Tennis, Etc.
S.I.C.: 7999
N.A.I.C.S.: 713940

Citizen Precision Machine Co., Ltd. (2)
41067 Oaza Miyota Miyotamachi
Kitasaku Gun, Nagano, 389 0206, Japan
Tel.: (81) 267325900
Fax: (81) 267325903
E-Mail: info@citizen.com
Web Site: www.citizen.com
Emp.: 400
Mfr. of Industrial Machinery & Equipment
S.I.C.: 3829
N.A.I.C.S.: 334519
Kenji Sugimoto *(CEO)*

Citizen Seimitsu Co., Ltd. (2)
6663-2 Funatsu Fujikawaguchiko
Yamanashi, 401 0395, Japan JP
Tel.: (81) 555231231
Fax: (81) 555246500
Web Site: www.seimitsu.citizen.co.jp
Emp.: 700
Mfr of Watch Parts, Cases, Dials, Watch Glass, Liquid Crystal Cells, Gauges, Videocassettes & Plastic Parts Molds
S.I.C.: 3829
N.A.I.C.S.: 334519
Shuichi Ishiwata *(Pres)*

Subsidiaries:

Citizen Chiba Precision Co., Ltd. (3)
1811-3 Yoshihashi
Yachiyo, Chiba, 276-0047, Japan JP
Tel.: (81) 47 458 7935
Fax: (81) 47 458 7962
E-Mail: info@ccj.citizen.co.jp
Web Site: ccj.citizen.co.jp
Emp.: 10
Electric Motor Mfr
S.I.C.: 3621
N.A.I.C.S.: 335312
Nobuyuki Tanaka *(Pres)*

Citizen Precision Hachinohe Co., Ltd. (3)
1-1-39 Kita-inter-kogyodanchi
Hachinohe, Aomori, 039-2245, Japan JP
Tel.: (81) 178 28 1211
Fax: (81) 178 28 1215
Electronic Component Mfr
S.I.C.: 3679
N.A.I.C.S.: 334419

Non-U.S. Subsidiary:

Citizen Precision Guangzhou Ltd. (3)
Wang-ting Road Xinhua Street Huadu Region
Guangzhou, Guang Dong, China 510812 CN
Tel.: (86) 20 8687 6014
Fax: (86) 20 8687 3087
Electronic Component Mfr
S.I.C.: 3679
N.A.I.C.S.: 334419

Citizen Techno Co., Ltd. (2)
3 Floor Homat Horizon Bldg 6-2
Tokyo, Iwate, 024 0051, Japan
Tel.: (81) 352152136
Fax: (81) 352152138
Mfr. of IC Packaging
S.I.C.: 3829
N.A.I.C.S.: 334519

Citizen Tokorozawa Works (2)
840 Shimotomi
Tokorozawa, Saitama, 359 8511, Japan JP
Tel.: (81) 4 2942 6271
Fax: (81) 4 2942 6241
Web Site: www.citizen.co.jp
Emp.: 200
Mfr. of Precision Industrial Machinery
S.I.C.: 3829
N.A.I.C.S.: 334519

Citizen Yoshimi Co., Ltd. (2)
1006 Oaza Shimohosoya
Yoshimimachi, Hiki, Saitama, 355 0118, Japan
Tel.: (81) 493542211
Fax: (81) 493542219
Web Site: www.citizenyoshimi.co.jp
Emp.: 169
Assembler of Information Equipment & Manufacturer of Watch Parts
S.I.C.: 3829
N.A.I.C.S.: 334519

Funehiki Seimitsu Co., Ltd. (2)
6-2 Koyodai Funehiki Cho
Tamura Gun, Fukushima, 963 4000, Japan JP

Citizen Holdings Co., Ltd.—(Continued)

Tel.: (81) 247611160
Fax: (81) 247611711
Web Site: www.funehikiseimitu.co.jp
Mfr. of Parts for Watches & Electronic Equipment
S.I.C.: 3829
N.A.I.C.S.: 334519

The Grace Limited (2)
3 4 33 Kokubun Cho
Sendai, Miyagi Aoba Ku, 980 0803, Japan
Tel.: (81) 222636801
Fax: (81) 22 262 6348
Wholesalers of Jewelry, Etc.
S.I.C.: 5944
N.A.I.C.S.: 448310

Heiwa Tokei Manufacturing Co., Ltd. (2)
435 Shimotonooka
Iida, Nagano, 395 0195, Japan
Tel.: (81) 265281500
Fax: (81) 265281502
E-Mail: tanakah@heiwa.citizen.co.jp
Web Site: www.heiwatokei.co.jp
Emp.: 500
Assembler of Watches & Manufacturer of Automation, Information & Electronic Equipment
S.I.C.: 3829
N.A.I.C.S.: 334519
Atsuo Kawaguchi *(Mng Dir)*

Hi-Mecha Co., Ltd. (2)
2534-6 Kubota Kubota-machi Yonezawa-shi
Yamagata-ken, Yamagata, 992 0003, Japan JP
Tel.: (81) 238372905
Fax: (81) 238372904
E-Mail: info@hi-mecha.co.jp
Web Site: www.hi-mecha.co.jp
Emp.: 25
Mfr of Watch Parts
S.I.C.: 3829
N.A.I.C.S.: 334519
Toshihiro Kamemori *(Pres)*

Miyota Co., Ltd. (2)
4107 5 Oaza Miyota Miyotamachi
Kitasaku Gun, Nagano, 389 0294, Japan
Tel.: (81) 267323331
Fax: (81) 267326327
Web Site: www.miyota.com
Emp.: 100
Assembler of Watches & Manufacturer of Quartz Oscillators, Electronic Viewfinders, LC Backlight & CCD Camera Modules
S.I.C.: 3829
N.A.I.C.S.: 334519

Sakae Shokai Co., Ltd. (2)
18 9 1 Chome Ueno
Tokyo, Taito Ku, 110 0005, Japan JP
Tel.: (81) 338333811
Fax: (81) 338370614
Real Estate Leasing
S.I.C.: 6519
N.A.I.C.S.: 531190

Sayama Precision Industries Co., Ltd. (2)
15 1 2 Chome Fujimi
Sayama, Saitama, 350 1393, Japan
Tel.: (81) 429597221
Fax: (81) 429585749
E-Mail: motor@micro.citizen.co.jp
Web Site: www.micro.citizen.co.jp
Emp.: 180
Mfr. of Watch Parts, Decelerators & Game Machines
S.I.C.: 3829
N.A.I.C.S.: 334519
Mamoru Ogura *(Pres)*

Silver Denken Co., Ltd. (2)
1-14-11 Shimoigusa
Suginami-Ku, Tokyo, 167 0022, Japan JP
Tel.: (81) 333102700
Fax: (81) 333102730
Web Site: www.silver-denken.co.jp
Emp.: 20
Retailer of Game Machines
S.I.C.: 5941
N.A.I.C.S.: 451110

T.I.C.-Citizen Co., Ltd. (2)
5 6 12 Maehara cho Koganei shi
Tokyo, 184 0013, Japan JP
Tel.: (81) 423862261
Fax: (81) 0423862222
Mfr. of Institutional & Outdoor Clocks & Indicators
S.I.C.: 3829
N.A.I.C.S.: 334519

Tohoku Citizen Corporation (2)
4 F Sendai Juzenji Bldg 4 33 3 Chome Kokubucho
Aoba Ku, Sendai, Miyagi, 980 0803, Japan
Tel.: (81) 222631881
Fax: (81) 222131031
Emp.: 50
Retailer of Watches, Clocks & Jewelry
S.I.C.: 5944
N.A.I.C.S.: 448310

Tokyo Bijutsu Co., Ltd. (2)
31 15 3 Chome Ikebukuro Honcho
Tokyo, 170 0011, Japan JP
Tel.: (81) 339823111
Fax: (81) 339823295
Web Site: www.tokyo-bijutsu.co.jp
Emp.: 130
Printing & Publishing; Manufacture & Sale of Pictures
S.I.C.: 7812
N.A.I.C.S.: 512110
Yasuo Kato *(Pres)*

Tokyo Citizen Corporation (2)
Citizen Ueno Bldg 2 18 5 Higashi Ueno
Taito Ku, Tokyo, 110 0015, Japan
Tel.: (81) 338334915
Fax: (81) 338334920
Emp.: 25
Sales of Watches, Clocks & Jewelry
S.I.C.: 5944
N.A.I.C.S.: 448310

Affiliate:

Star Micronics Co., Ltd. (2)
20 10 Nakayoshida
Shizuoka, 422 8654, Japan
Tel.: (81) 542631111
Fax: (81) 0542661057
Web Site: www.star-micronics.co.jp
Emp.: 909
Mfr. of Information & Electronic Equipment, Precision Industrial Machinery & Watch Parts
S.I.C.: 3699
N.A.I.C.S.: 335999
Yamanachi Masato *(Gen Mgr)*

U.S. Subsidiaries:

Bulova Corporation (2)
One Bulova Ave
Woodside, NY 11377-7826 NY
Tel.: (718) 204-3300
Fax: (718) 204-3546
Toll Free: (800) 228-5682
E-Mail: info@bulova.com
Web Site: www.bulova.com
Sales Range: $150-199.9 Million
Emp.: 210
Mfr. & Retailer of Watches & Clocks
Import Export
S.I.C.: 3829
N.A.I.C.S.: 334519
Gregory Thumm *(Pres)*
Ron Spencer *(COO)*
Charles Kriete *(Exec VP-Sls)*
James Chan *(Sr VP)*

Non-U.S. Subsidiaries:

Bulova de Mexico, SRL (3)
Magdalena 211 Piso 2
Col de Valle, 03100 Mexico, Mexico
Tel.: (52) 5555435800
Fax: (52) 5555433581
E-Mail: ventas@bulovawatch.com.mx
Web Site: www.bulova.ch
Emp.: 30
Watch & Clock Mfr & Distr
S.I.C.: 3829
N.A.I.C.S.: 334519
Carolina Sepulveda *(Gen Mgr)*

Bulova Swiss, SA (3)
Rte des Arsenaux 41
1705 Fribourg, Switzerland
Tel.: (41) 264255700
Fax: (41) 264255701
E-Mail: bulovaswiss@bulova.ch
Web Site: www.bulova.ch
Emp.: 15
Watch Mfr & Distr
S.I.C.: 3829
N.A.I.C.S.: 334519
Gaelle Ranchon *(Mng Dir)*

Bulova Watch Company Limited (3)
39 Casebridge Ct
Toronto, ON, M1B 5N4, Canada
Tel.: (416) 751-7151
Fax: (416) 751-4763
Toll Free: (800) 268-6562
E-Mail: jcameron@wittnaur.ca
Web Site: www.Bulova.com
Emp.: 70
Watch & Clocks Distr
S.I.C.: 5094
N.A.I.C.S.: 423940
William C. Stoner *(Pres)*

Citizen America Corp. (2)
Ste 404 363 Van Ness Way
Torrance, CA 90501-6282
Tel.: (949) 428-3700
Fax: (949) 428-3719
Toll Free: (800) 421-6516
Web Site: www.citizen-america.com
Emp.: 25
Sale of Information Equipment
S.I.C.: 5045
N.A.I.C.S.: 423430

Citizen Systems America Corporation (2)
363 Van Ness Way Ste 404
Torrance, CA 90501-6282 CA
Tel.: (310) 781-1460
Fax: (310) 781-9152
Toll Free: (800) 421-6516
Web Site: www.citizen-systems.com
Emp.: 15
Business Machines, Citizen Dot Matrix Printers, Thermal Printers, Calculators, Audio Products LCD Products & Portable Hand-Held Televisions Distr & Mfr
Import Export
S.I.C.: 5044
N.A.I.C.S.: 423420
Max Yamazaki *(Pres & CEO)*

Citizen Watch Co. of America, Inc. (2)
1200 Wall St W
Lyndhurst, NJ 07071-3680 NJ
Tel.: (201) 438-8150
Fax: (201) 438-4161
Web Site: www.citizenwatch.com
Watch Retailer
S.I.C.: 5094
N.A.I.C.S.: 423940
Jeffrey Cohen *(Pres)*
James Shada *(Sr VP-Natl Accts)*
Michael Springer *(Sr VP)*

U.S. Joint Venture:

Marubeni Citizen-Cincom Inc. (2)
40 Boroline Rd
Allendale, NJ 07401-1613 NJ
Tel.: (201) 818-0100
Fax: (201) 818-1877
Web Site: www.marucit.com
Emp.: 25
Mfr. of Precision Industrial Machinery
S.I.C.: 5084
N.A.I.C.S.: 423830
Shigeyuki Baba *(Pres)*
John Antignani *(Exec VP-Sls & Mktg)*

Non-U.S. Subsidiaries:

C-E (Hong Kong) Ltd. (2)
Rm 1204 12th Fl Telford House
16 Wang Hoi Rd, Kowloon, China (Hong Kong) HK
Tel.: (852) 27930613
Fax: (852) 23444916
E-Mail: enquiry@c-e.co.jp
Web Site: www.c-e.co.jp
Emp.: 10
Electronic Components Mfr
S.I.C.: 3679
N.A.I.C.S.: 334419
Yasuhiro Kapsunata *(Mng Dir)*

C-E (Singapore) Pte. Ltd. (2)
96 Somerset Rd
9 7 8 UOL Bldg
Singapore, 238163, Singapore SG
Tel.: (65) 67341398
Fax: (65) 67340218
Web Site: www.c-e.co.jp
Sales Range: $10-24.9 Million
Emp.: 8
Provider of Electronic Equipment
S.I.C.: 5731
N.A.I.C.S.: 443142

Citizen de Mexico, S.A. de C.V. (2)
Periferico Sur No 4690 local 417-M Col
Ampl Pedregal de San Angel
CP 04500 Mexico, DF, Mexico MX
Tel.: (52) 55 5606 2552
Fax: (52) 5555230713
Web Site: www.citizen.com.mx
Emp.: 130
Mfr of Watches & Cases
S.I.C.: 3911
N.A.I.C.S.: 339910

Citizen Latinamerica Corp. (2)
Balboa Ave Plz Balboa Commercial Ctr
PO Box 873479
Fl 4 Offices 401 402, Panama, 7, Panama
Tel.: (507) 2238943
Fax: (507) 5072654919
E-Mail: edith@citizenlatic.com.pa
Web Site: www.citizenlatic.com.pa
Emp.: 20
Retailer of Watches & Clocks
S.I.C.: 5944
N.A.I.C.S.: 448310
Katsuhiro Shoji *(Gen Mgr)*

Citizen Machinery Asia Co., Ltd. (2)
69 Moo 1 Phaholyothin Road Sanubtube
Wang Noi, Ayutthaya, 13170, Thailand TH
Tel.: (66) 35721833
Fax: (66) 35721835
E-Mail: aokik@cmj.citizen.co.jp
Emp.: 160
Watches & Clocks
S.I.C.: 3829
N.A.I.C.S.: 334519
Kenji Aoki *(Mng Dir)*

Citizen Machinery Europe GmbH (2)
Mettinger Strasse 11
D-73728 Esslingen, Germany De
Tel.: (49) 7113906100
Fax: (49) 7113906106
E-Mail: cme@citizen.de
Web Site: www.citizen.de
Emp.: 100
Holding Company; Commercial Printing Equipment Mfr & Distr
S.I.C.: 6719
N.A.I.C.S.: 551112
Kenichiro Hanyu *(Member-Mgmt Bd)*
Hiromitsu Kamata *(Member-Mgmt Bd)*
Jurgen Lindenberg *(Member-Mgmt Bd)*

Subsidiary:

Citizen Systems Europe GmbH (3)
Mettinger Strasse 11
D-73728 Esslingen, Germany De
Tel.: (49) 7113906400
Fax: (49) 7113906405
Web Site: www.citizen-europe.com
Emp.: 50
Printers & Calculators Mfr & Whslr
S.I.C.: 3555
N.A.I.C.S.: 333244
Morihito Suzuki *(Mng Dir)*

Citizen Systems Europe GmbH (2)
Mettinger Strasse 11
Esslingen, Taden Wuerttempeg, 73728, Germany
Tel.: (49) 7113906400
Fax: (49) 7113906405
E-Mail: info@citizen-europe.com
Web Site: www.citizen-europe.com
Emp.: 5
Mfr. of Precision Industrial Machinery
S.I.C.: 5084
N.A.I.C.S.: 423830
Morihito Suzuki *(Mng Dir-Europe, Middle East & South Africa)*

Citizen Watch (China) Co., Ltd. (2)
Tian Zhu Lu 7 Hao Tian Wai 2 Jie Kong Gang Gong Ye Qu
Shun Yi Xian, Beijing, China CN
Tel.: (86) 80486655
Fax: (86) 10 8048 6655
E-Mail: zhangjy@citizen.com.cn
Web Site: www.citizen.com.cn
Mfr. of Watches

S.I.C.: 3829
N.A.I.C.S.: 334519
Mikio Unno *(Pres & CEO)*

Citizen Watch Co. of Canada, Ltd. **(2)**
380 Bentley St Unit 2
Markham, ON, L3R3L2, Canada
Tel.: (905) 415-1100
Fax: (905) 415-1122
Toll Free: (800) 263-7799
E-Mail: info@citizenwatch.com
Web Site: www.citizenwatch.com
Emp.: 25
Mfr. of Watches
S.I.C.: 3829
N.A.I.C.S.: 334519
Kevin Kaye *(VP-Ops)*

Citizen Watch do Brasil S.A. **(2)**
Av Marques De Sao Vicente 121-Bloco B
CJ 1 702 17 Andar-Barra Funda
01139-001 Sao Paulo, Brazil BR
Tel.: (55) 11 3392 2820
Fax: (55) 11 3825 7968
Watch Mfr
S.I.C.: 3829
N.A.I.C.S.: 334519

Citizen Watch Espana S.A. **(2)**
Cityparc Ronda de Dalt-Edificio Londres
Crtra de L'Hospitalet
No 147-149, 8940 Cornella, Barcelona, Spain
Tel.: (34) 934753131
Fax: (34) 933778582
E-Mail: info@citizen.es
Web Site: www.citizen.es
Emp.: 12
Retailer of Watches & Clocks
S.I.C.: 3829
N.A.I.C.S.: 334519
Aoige Riota *(Pres & CEO)*

Citizen Watch Europe GmbH **(2)**
Hans Dunker Strasse 8
D 21035 Hamburg, Germany
Tel.: (49) 40734620
Fax: (49) 4073462201
E-Mail: info@citizenwatch.de
Web Site: www.citizenwatch.de
Emp.: 100
Retailer of Watches, Clocks & Jewelry
S.I.C.: 5944
N.A.I.C.S.: 448310
Dante Grossi *(Mng Dir)*

Citizen Watch Goodrington (Hong Kong) Ltd. **(2)**
64 Hung To Road
Kwun Tong, Kowloon, China (Hong Kong) HK
Tel.: (852) 2790 3188
Watch Mfr
S.I.C.: 3829
N.A.I.C.S.: 334519

Citizen Watch Italy S.p.A. **(2)**
Via G Di Vittorio N 9 11
Inzago, I 20065 Milan, Italy
Tel.: (39) 295311100
Fax: (39) 0295311111
Web Site: www.citizen.it
Emp.: 27
Retailer of Watches & Clocks
S.I.C.: 5944
N.A.I.C.S.: 448310

Citizen Watch (Switzerland) AG **(2)**
Zurich Strasse 17
CH-2504 Biel/Bienne, Switzerland
Tel.: (41) 323424931
Fax: (41) 323425781
E-Mail: citizen@bluewin.ch
Web Site: www.citizenwatch.ch
Emp.: 4
Mfr of Watches & Clocks
S.I.C.: 3829
N.A.I.C.S.: 334519

Citizen Watch (U.K.) Ltd. **(2)**
19 Busines Center Molly Millars Lane
Wokingham, Berks, RG41 2QY, United Kingdom
Tel.: (44) 01189890333
Fax: (44) 1189890536
E-Mail: info@citizenwatch.co.uk
Web Site: www.citizenwatch.co.uk
Emp.: 35
Retailer of Watches & Clocks
S.I.C.: 5944
N.A.I.C.S.: 448310
Alan Nice *(Gen Mgr)*

Citizen Watches Australia Pty. Ltd. **(2)**
122 Old Pittwater Rd
PO Box 218
Brookvale, NSW, 2100, Australia
Tel.: (61) 299397077
Fax: (61) 299050149
Web Site: www.citizenwatches.com.au
Emp.: 100
Mfr. of Watches & Clocks
S.I.C.: 5944
N.A.I.C.S.: 448310

Citizen Watches Gulf Co. **(2)**
Jebel Alifz Factory Units FC 2 3 4 5 6
Rd No 628, 16772 Dubai, United Arab Emirates
Mailing Address:
PO Box 6772
Jabelali Free Zone, Dubai, United Arab Emirates
Tel.: (971) 48815171
Fax: (971) 48815164
E-Mail: citizen@citizengulf.ae
Web Site: www.citizen-ne.com
Sls.: $810,000
Emp.: 25
Mfr. of Watches & Clocks
S.I.C.: 3829
N.A.I.C.S.: 334519
Faisal Mohamed *(Mgr-Sls)*

Citizen Watches (H.K.) Ltd. **(2)**
4 Fl 64 Hung Tong Rd Kwuntong
Kowloon, Hong Kong, China (Hong Kong)
Tel.: (852) 23640251
Fax: (852) 27640574
E-Mail: petty@citizen.com.hk
Web Site: www.citizen.com.hk
Emp.: 100
Retailer of Watches & Clocks
S.I.C.: 5944
N.A.I.C.S.: 448310
Francis Yu *(Mgr-Sls)*

Non-U.S. Subsidiary:

Citizen Watches (Malaysia) Sdn. Bhd. **(3)**
Suite A605 West Wing 6th Floor Wisma
Consplant 2 No 7 Jalan SS 16/1
47500 Subang Jaya, Selangor Darul Ehsan, Malaysia MY
Tel.: (60) 3 5637 9811
Fax: (60) 3 5637 9812
E-Mail: ctzmy@citizen.com.my
Web Site: www.citizen.com.my
Emp.: 7
Watch Mfr
S.I.C.: 3829
N.A.I.C.S.: 334519

Citizen Watches (India) Pvt. Ltd. **(2)**
299 6th Main HAL 2nd Stage
Indiranagar, Bengaluru, 560 038, India IN
Tel.: (91) 8043473777
Fax: (91) 8043479788
E-Mail: bangalore@citizenwatches.co.in
Web Site: www.citizenwatches.co.in
Emp.: 55
Watches Assembler & Retailer
S.I.C.: 3829
N.A.I.C.S.: 334519
Satish Halageri *(Mgr-Mktg)*

Citizen Watches (N.Z.) Ltd. **(2)**
10 Eden St
Private Bag 99902
Newmarket, Auckland, 1149, New Zealand
Tel.: (64) 95233393
Fax: (64) 95244177
E-Mail: info@citizen.co.nz
Web Site: www.citizenwatches.co.nz
Emp.: 8
Watches & Clocks Mfr
S.I.C.: 3829
N.A.I.C.S.: 334519

Farbest Industries Ltd. **(2)**
64 Hung To Rd
Kwun Tong, Kowloon, Hong Kong, China (Hong Kong)
Tel.: (852) 23442618
Fax: (852) 27905353
Web Site: www.citizen.co.jp/english/corporate/group/group02.html
Emp.: 14
Mfr of Watches & Watch Accessories
S.I.C.: 5094
N.A.I.C.S.: 423940
Lau Peng Leung *(Mng Dir)*

Firstcome Electronics Ltd. **(2)**
Block E G H 6th Fl Phase II Yip Fat Factory Bldg 73
75 Hoi Yuen Rd, Kwun Tong, China (Hong Kong) HK
Tel.: (852) 22652175
Fax: (852) 23414649
E-Mail: takao.watanabe@ce.citizen.co.jp
Web Site: www.citizen.co.jp/english/corporate/group/group02.html
Emp.: 10
Electronic Equipment Mfr
S.I.C.: 3679
N.A.I.C.S.: 334419
Takao Watanabe *(Gen Mgr)*

Goodrington Co., Ltd. **(2)**
64 Hung To Road
Kwun Tong, Kowloon, China (Hong Kong) HK
Tel.: (852) 23640251
Web Site: www.citizen.co.jp/company/group/group02.html
Assembler of Watches & Manufacturer of Watch Cases
S.I.C.: 3829
N.A.I.C.S.: 334519

Most Crown Industries Ltd. **(2)**
1701 17th Floor Fotan Ind Centre 26-28 Au Pui Wan Street
Sha Tin, China (Hong Kong)
Tel.: (852) 26996000
Fax: (852) 26015141
Web Site: cfm.citizen.co.jp/english/company/group.html
Emp.: 20
Assembler of Watches & Manufacturer of Quartz Oscillators
S.I.C.: 3829
N.A.I.C.S.: 334519
Miura Shoichioo *(Gen Mgr)*

Shiang Pao Precision Co., Ltd. **(2)**
No 5 Lane 108 An Her Road
Tantzu, Taichung, Taiwan TW
Tel.: (886) 425339674
Fax: (886) 425333740
Web Site: www.sip.com.cn
Mfr. of Molds, Watch Parts & Plastic Mold Parts
S.I.C.: 3829
N.A.I.C.S.: 334519

Sunciti Manufacturers Ltd. **(2)**
64 Hung To Rd
Kwun Tong, Kowloon, China (Hong Kong) HK
Tel.: (852) 27903188
Fax: (852) 27634452
Web Site: www.citizen.co.jp/english/corporate/group/group02.html
Emp.: 90
Assembler of Watches & Manufacturer of Watch Cases
S.I.C.: 3829
N.A.I.C.S.: 334519

Walop Ltd. **(2)**
1st Fl 64 Hung PO Rd Kwun Tong
Kowloon, China (Hong Kong) HK
Tel.: (852) 26932056
Fax: (852) 26932065
Sales Range: $25-49.9 Million
Emp.: 12
Mfr. of Watch Parts, Cases, Watch Glass, Dials & Liquid Crystal Panels
S.I.C.: 3829
N.A.I.C.S.: 334519
Charles Auo *(Mng Dir)*
Shigeyuki Gomi *(Mng Dir)*

Non-U.S. Affiliates:

Brasciti Industria e Comercio de Relogios da Amazonia, S.A. **(2)**
Av Abiurana No 1799
Distrio Industrial, Manaus, AM, Brazil BR
Tel.: (55) 926152169
Fax: (55) 92 615 2117
Assembler of Watches
S.I.C.: 3829
N.A.I.C.S.: 334519

CITIZENS BANK INTERNATIONAL LIMITED

Sharda Sadan
PO Box 19681
Kamaladi, Kathmandu, Nepal
Tel.: (977) 1 4169067
Fax: (977) 1 4169077
E-Mail: info@ctznbank.com
Web Site: www.ctznbank.com
CZBIL—(NEP)

Business Description:
Financial Services
S.I.C.: 6211
N.A.I.C.S.: 523999

Personnel:
Pradeep Jung Pandey *(Chm)*
Rajan Singh Bhandari *(CEO)*
Samir Prasad Dahal *(COO)*
Bodh Raj Devkota *(Chief Credit Officer)*
Shrijana Nepal *(HR Officer)*
Ganesh Raj Pokharel *(Sec & Asst Gen Mgr-Ops & IT)*

Board of Directors:
Pradeep Jung Pandey
Bijaya Dhoj Karki
Pavitra Kumar Karki
Prakash Chandra Mainali
Manohar Das Mool
Abinash Pant
Bal Krishna Prasai
Arjun Lal Rajbanshi

CITROEN UK LIMITED

221 Bath Rd
Slough, Berks, SL1 4BA, United Kingdom
Tel.: (44) 8444630010
Telex: 847053
Fax: (44) 1753748100
Web Site: www.citroen.co.uk
Year Founded: 1919
Emp.: 500

Business Description:
Automobiles Mfr & Distr
Import
S.I.C.: 5599
N.A.I.C.S.: 441228

Personnel:
Scott Michael *(Head-Comml Vehicles & Bus Centre Programme)*

CITRUS LEISURE PLC

02 Police Park Avenue
Colombo, 5, Sri Lanka
Tel.: (94) 115755055
Fax: (94) 112593455
E-Mail: info@citrusleisure.com
Web Site: www.citrusleisure.com
REEF—(COL)
Rev.: $1,862,020
Assets: $41,099,924
Liabilities: $8,963,785
Net Worth: $32,136,139
Earnings: ($805,223)
Emp.: 13
Fiscal Year-end: 03/31/13

Business Description:
Hotel Owner & Operator
S.I.C.: 7011
N.A.I.C.S.: 721110

Personnel:
Priya Chandana Bandara Talwatte *(CEO)*

Board of Directors:
Emilianus Prema Alphonse Cooray
Suresh Dayanath De Mel
Varuni Sonali Amunugama Fernando
Dilith Susantha Jayaweera
Janesh Manoj Bandara Pilimatalawwe
Pathiranage Vasula Sanjeewa Premawardhana
Rajinda Seneviratne
Priya Chandana Bandara Talwatte

THE CITY BANK LIMITED
City Bank Center 136 Gulshan Avenue
Gulshan-2, Dhaka, 1212, Bangladesh
Tel.: (880) 2 881 3483
Fax: (880) 2 988 4446
Web Site: www.thecitybank.com
Year Founded: 1983
CITYBA—(DHA)
Rev.: $153,857,374
Assets: $1,613,285,757
Liabilities: $1,389,801,808
Net Worth: $223,483,949
Earnings: $9,835,338
Emp.: 2,765
Fiscal Year-end: 12/31/12
Business Description:
Banking Services
S.I.C.: 6029
N.A.I.C.S.: 522110
Personnel:
Rubel Aziz *(Chm)*
Meherun Haque *(Vice Chm)*
Kazi Mahmood Sattar *(CEO & Mng Dir)*
Sohail Reza Khaled Hussain *(Mng Dir & Chief Bus Officer)*
Faruq Moinuddin *(Mng Dir & Chief Risk Officer)*
Md. Mahbubur Rahman *(CFO)*
Mashrur Arefin *(COO, Chief Comm Officer & Deputy Mng Dir)*
Kazi Azizur Rahman *(CIO)*
Badrudduza Choudhury *(Deputy Mng Dir & Head-Branch Banking)*
Mohammad Maroof *(Deputy Mng Dir & Head-Wholesale Banking)*
Md. Kafi Khan *(Sec)*
Board of Directors:
Rubel Aziz
Aziz Al Kaiser
Aziz Al Mahmood
Syeda Shaireen Aziz
Rajibul Huq Chowdhury
Meherun Haque
Tabassum Kaiser
Hossain Khaled
Rafiqul Islam Khan
Hossain Mehmood
Deen Mohammad
Evana Fahmida Mohammad
Kazi Mahmood Sattar
Mohammad Shoeb

CITY BUICK CHEVROLET CADILLAC GMC
1900 Victoria Park Ave
Toronto, ON, M1R 1T6, Canada
Tel.: (416) 288-5492
Fax: (416) 751-0568
Toll Free: (877) 794-7650
Web Site: www.citybuick.com
Rev.: $74,685,712
Emp.: 147
Business Description:
New & Used Car Dealers
S.I.C.: 5511
N.A.I.C.S.: 441110
Personnel:
Dean Fera *(Gen Mgr-Sls)*

CITY CEMENT COMPANY
Office 102 & 106 1st Floor Home Center Building Tahliya Street
PO Box 859
Sulemaniya, 11421 Riyadh, Saudi Arabia
Tel.: (966) 1 4620011
Fax: (966) 1 4624111
E-Mail: info@citycement.com
Web Site: www.citycement.com
3003—(SAU)
Business Description:
Cement Mfr
S.I.C.: 3241
N.A.I.C.S.: 327310
Personnel:
Mishaal bin Abdul-Aziz Al-Saud *(Chm)*
Omar Sulaiman Al-Abdullatif *(Vice Chm)*
Ahmed Omar Al-Abdullatif *(CEO)*
Board of Directors:
Mishaal bin Abdul-Aziz Al-Saud
Ahmed Omar Al-Abdullatif
Badr Omar Al-Abdullatif
Omar Sulaiman Al-Abdullatif
Sulaiman Omar Al-Abdullatif
Saleh Abdulrahman Al-Qifary

CITY DEVELOPMENT BANK LIMITED
Chippledhunga
PO Box 372
Pokhara, Nepal
Tel.: (977) 61 521505
Fax: (977) 61 533038
E-Mail: mail@citybanknepal.com
Web Site: www.citybanknepal.com
CDBL—(NEP)
Business Description:
Banking Services
S.I.C.: 6029
N.A.I.C.S.: 522110
Personnel:
Rajendra Kumar Batajoo *(Chm)*
Bishwo Mohan Adhikari *(CEO)*
Board of Directors:
Rajendra Kumar Batajoo
Bishwo Mohan Adhikari
Rabindra Nath Banstola
Pritam Man Buddhacharya
Jyendra Gauchan
Karma Kumari Gurung
ShreeKrishna Regmi
Nagendra Lal ShreeBastav

CITY E-SOLUTIONS LIMITED
390 Havelock Road 02-05 King's Centre
Singapore, 169662, Singapore
Tel.: (65) 6839 2888
Fax: (65) 6735 8924
E-Mail: enquires@ceslimited.com
Web Site: www.ceslimited.com
HO5—(DEU HKG)
Sls.: $17,419,211
Assets: $86,821,648
Liabilities: $9,619,154
Net Worth: $77,202,494
Earnings: $356,418
Emp.: 68
Fiscal Year-end: 12/31/12
Business Description:
Business Consulting Services
S.I.C.: 8742
N.A.I.C.S.: 541611
Personnel:
Leng Beng Kwek *(Chm & Mng Dir)*
Greg Mount *(Pres)*
Sherman Kwek *(CEO)*
Derek Mang Wo Man *(CFO)*
Bill Linehan *(CMO-Richfield Hospitality & Mng Dir-Sceptre Hospitality Resources)*
Rodrigo Jimenez *(CTO-Sceptre Hospitality Resources)*
Ho Yan Wan *(Sec)*
Johnathan Sze *(Sr VP-Investments)*
Board of Directors:
Leng Beng Kwek
Bernard Charnwut Chan
Khai Choon Gan
Lee Jackson
Leng Joo Kwek
Ka Shui Lo
Teik Kee Teoh
Lawrence Wai Lam Yip

CITY FORD SALES LTD.
14750 Mark Messier Trail
Edmonton, AB, T6V 1H5, Canada
Tel.: (780) 454-2000
Fax: (780) 447-2912
Toll Free: (800) 454-8675
E-Mail: sales@cityfordsales.com
Web Site: www.cityfordsales.com
Year Founded: 1985
Rev.: $51,341,268
Emp.: 100
Business Description:
New & Used Car Dealers
S.I.C.: 5511
N.A.I.C.S.: 441110
Personnel:
Mike Vida *(Gen Mgr)*

CITY GENERAL INSURANCE COMPANY LIMITED
Baitul Hossain Building 3rd Floor 27 Dilkusha Commercial Area
Dhaka, 1000, Bangladesh
Tel.: (880) 29557735
Fax: (880) 27169498
E-Mail: info@cityinsurance.com.bd
Web Site: www.cityinsurance.com.bd
25734—(CHT DHA)
Business Description:
Insurance Services
S.I.C.: 6411
N.A.I.C.S.: 524298
Personnel:
Hossain Ahktar *(Chm)*

CITY GROUP COMPANY KSC
Sulaibia Industrial Area Block No 2 Building No 800100
PO Box 24611
Safat, Kuwait, 13107, Kuwait
Tel.: (965) 188 2211
Fax: (965) 24677945
E-Mail: info@citygroupco.com
Web Site: www.citygroupco.com
CITYGROUP—(KUW)
Rev.: $55,633,300
Assets: $116,769,965
Liabilities: $29,098,806
Net Worth: $87,671,159
Earnings: $12,684,188
Emp.: 1,719
Fiscal Year-end: 12/31/12
Business Description:
Passenger & Cargo Transportation Services; Warehousing Services
S.I.C.: 4789
N.A.I.C.S.: 488999
Personnel:
Yacoub Saleh Al Sharhan *(Chm)*
Nabil Abdullah Al Jeraisy *(Vice Chm)*
Richard Paul Woods *(CEO)*
Deepak Narayan Juvekar *(CFO)*
Board of Directors:
Yacoub Saleh Al Sharhan
Nabil Abdullah Al Jeraisy
Suhail Kamel Homsi
Mukund G. Korde
Hany Shawky

Boubyan Auditing Office
PO Box 17445 Khalidiya
Kuwait, Kuwait

Subsidiaries:

Boubai Aviation Agencies Co WLL **(1)**
P O Box 5798
Kuwait, 13058, Kuwait
Tel.: (965) 22413716
Fax: (965) 22419025
Web Site: www.boodaiaviation.com
Emp.: 146
Travel Agency Services
S.I.C.: 4724
N.A.I.C.S.: 561510
Monzer Najia *(CEO)*

Boodai Aviation Co. WLL **(1)**
P O Box 5698
Safat, Kuwait, 13058, Kuwait
Tel.: (965) 2413713
Fax: (965) 2419025
E-Mail: ba@boodai.com
Web Site: www.boodai.com
Travel Agency Services
S.I.C.: 4724
N.A.I.C.S.: 561510

Non-U.S. Subsidiary:

Comprehensive Multiple Transportations Company **(1)**
Ain El Basha Street
PO Box 739
Amman, 11118, Jordan
Tel.: (962) 6 4022141
Fax: (962) 6 4022147
ABUS—(AMM)
Rev.: $12,730,242
Assets: $45,992,395
Liabilities: $43,265,499
Net Worth: $2,726,896
Earnings: ($9,989,955)
Emp.: 628
Fiscal Year-end: 12/31/12
Public Transportation Services
S.I.C.: 4789
N.A.I.C.S.: 488999
Nabil Abdullah Ali Al Jarici, *(Chm)*

CITY LODGE HOTELS LIMITED
Corner Homestead Ave Main Road
Bryanston, South Africa
Mailing Address:
PO Box 97
Cramerview, 2060, South Africa
Tel.: (27) 115572600
Fax: (27) 11 557 2601
E-Mail: info@citylodge.co.za
Web Site: www.citylodge.co.za
CLH—(JSE)
Rev.: $109,007,248
Assets: $153,464,965
Liabilities: $105,886,015
Net Worth: $47,578,950
Earnings: $24,398,296
Emp.: 1,530
Fiscal Year-end: 06/30/13
Business Description:
Hotel Owner & Operator
S.I.C.: 7011
N.A.I.C.S.: 721110
Personnel:
Bulelani Ngcuka *(Chm)*
Clifford Ross *(CEO)*
Melanie C. van Heerden *(Sec)*
Board of Directors:
Bulelani Ngcuka
Frank Kilbourn
Nigel I. Matthews
Ndumi Medupe
Stuart Morris
Clifford Ross
Keith Shongwe
Wendy Tlou
Andrew Widegger
Transfer Agent:
Computershare Investor Services (Pty) Ltd
70 Marshall Street
Johannesburg, South Africa
Subsidiaries:

City Lodge Holdings (Share Block) (Pty) Ltd **(1)**
R2 305 Herman St
Germiston, Gauteng, 1429, South Africa
Tel.: (27) 114445300
Fax: (27) 114445315
Hotel Management Services
S.I.C.: 8741
N.A.I.C.S.: 561110
James Van Rooyen *(Gen Mgr)*

City Lodge Bryanston (Pty) Limited **(1)**
Corner Main Road & Peter Place
Bryanston West, Sandton, Gauteng, South Africa

Mailing Address:
PO Box X10039
Randburg, 2125, South Africa
Tel.: (27) 11 706 7800
Fax: (27) 11 706 7819
E-Mail: clbryan.resv@citylodge.co.za
Web Site: www.citylodge.co.za
Emp.: 30
Hotel Management Services
S.I.C.: 8741
N.A.I.C.S.: 561110
Jason Viljoen *(Gen Mgr)*

CITY OF LONDON GROUP PLC

30 Cannon Street
London, EC4M 6XH, United Kingdom
Tel.: (44) 2076285518
Fax: (44) 2076288555
E-Mail: office@cityoflondongroup.com
Web Site: www.cityoflondongroup.com
Year Founded: 1985
CIN—(LSE)
Rev.: $51,058,446
Assets: $58,575,866
Liabilities: $43,913,738
Net Worth: $14,662,128
Earnings: ($2,809,557)
Emp.: 38
Fiscal Year-end: 03/31/13

Business Description:
Equity Investment Firm
S.I.C.: 6211
N.A.I.C.S.: 523999

Personnel:
Eric Anstee *(CEO)*
John Kent *(Deputy CEO)*
Lorraine Young *(Sec)*

Board of Directors:
Eric Anstee
Tony Brierley
Howard C. Goodbourn
John Greenhalgh
John Kent

Legal Counsel:
Fox Williams LLP
10 Dominion St
London, United Kingdom

Transfer Agent:
Capita Registrars Limited
The Registry 34 Beckenham Road
Beckenham, BR3 4TU, United Kingdom

Subsidiaries:

City of London Financial Services Limited (1)
30 Cannon St
London, EC4M 6XH, United Kingdom
Tel.: (44) 2076285518
Fax: (44) 2076288555
E-Mail: office@cityoflondongroup.com
Web Site: www.cityoflondongroup.com
Emp.: 3
Investment Management Services
S.I.C.: 6211
N.A.I.C.S.: 523999
Eric Anstee *(CEO)*

Tavernier Limited (1)
17 Albemarle St
London, W1S 4HP, United Kingdom
Tel.: (44) 2074933322
Web Site: www.tavernier.co.uk/
Investment Holding Services
S.I.C.: 6211
N.A.I.C.S.: 523999

CITY OF LONDON INVESTMENT GROUP PLC

77 Gracechurch Street
London, EC3V 0AS, United Kingdom
Tel.: (44) 2077110771
Fax: (44) 2077110772
E-Mail: info@citlon.co.uk
Web Site: www.citlon.com
CLIG—(LSE)
Rev.: $46,373,851
Assets: $29,252,920
Liabilities: $6,147,851
Net Worth: $23,105,070
Earnings: $9,896,529
Emp.: 77
Fiscal Year-end: 05/31/13

Business Description:
Asset Management & Investment Services
S.I.C.: 6211
N.A.I.C.S.: 523999

Personnel:
Barry M. Olliff *(Interim CEO & Chief Investment Officer)*
Thomas W. Griffith *(COO)*
Philippa A. Keith *(Sec)*

Board of Directors:
David M. Cardale
Barry A. Aling
Allan S. Bufferd
Rian A. Dartnell
Thomas W. Griffith
Barry M. Olliff
Carlos M. Yuste

Subsidiaries:

City of London Investment Management Company Limited (1)
77 Grace Church St
London, EC3V 0AS, United Kingdom
Tel.: (44) 2077110771
Fax: (44) 2077110772
E-Mail: info@citlon.co.uk
Web Site: www.citlon.co.uk
Emp.: 30
Investment Management Services
S.I.C.: 6799
N.A.I.C.S.: 523920
Barry Olliss *(Gen Mgr)*

City of London US Investments Limited (1)
77 Grace Church St
London, EC3V 0AS, United Kingdom
Tel.: (44) 2077110771
Fax: (44) 2077110774
E-Mail: info@citlon.co.uk
Web Site: www.citlon.co.uk
Emp.: 25
Unit Trust Brokerage & Managing Services
S.I.C.: 6211
N.A.I.C.S.: 523120

CITY OFFICE REIT, INC.

1075 West Georgia Street Suite 2600
Vancouver, BC, V6E 3C9, Canada
Tel.: (604) 806-3366
Sales Range: $10-24.9 Million

Business Description:
Real Estate Investment Trust
S.I.C.: 6726
N.A.I.C.S.: 525990

Personnel:
Gregory Tylee *(Pres & COO)*
James Farrar *(CEO)*
Anthony Maretic *(CFO, Treas & Sec)*

Board of Directors:
James Farrar

CITY PHARMACY LTD

Lot 01 Section 38 Waigani Dr
PO Box 1663
Port Moresby, Papua New Guinea
Tel.: (675) 325 9044
Fax: (675) 325 0942
E-Mail: sales@citypharmacy.com.pg
Web Site: www.cpl.com.pg
Year Founded: 1986
Sales Range: $10-24.9 Million
Emp.: 240

Business Description:
Pharmaceutical Retailer
S.I.C.: 5912
N.A.I.C.S.: 446110

Personnel:
Alan John Jarvis *(Chm)*
Mahesh Patel *(Mng Dir)*

Board of Directors:
Alan John Jarvis
Peter John Aitsi

CITY REFRIGERATION HOLDINGS (UK) LIMITED

Caledonia House Lawmoor Street
Glasgow, G5 0US, United Kingdom
Tel.: (44) 141 418 9000
Web Site: www.city-holdings.co.uk
Year Founded: 1985
Sales Range: $550-599.9 Million
Emp.: 10,707

Business Description:
Investment Management Services
S.I.C.: 6799
N.A.I.C.S.: 523920

Personnel:
William Haughey *(Founder & Chm)*

CITY SITE ESTATES PLC

145 St Vincent Street
Glasgow, G2 5JF, United Kingdom
Tel.: (44) 1412482534
Fax: (44) 1412263321
E-Mail: info@cseplc.co.uk
Web Site: www.cseplc.co.uk
BB38—(LSE)

Business Description:
Residential Property Management Services
S.I.C.: 6531
N.A.I.C.S.: 531311

Personnel:
Louis M. Goodman *(Mng Dir)*

Board of Directors:
Richard Gilliland
Louis M. Goodman

CITY SPORTS AND RECREATION PUBLIC COMPANY LIMITED

22 Navatanee Rd Kwaeng Ramintra
Khet Kannayao, Bangkok, 10230, Thailand
Tel.: (66) 2 376 1034
Fax: (66) 2 376 1685
E-Mail: info@navatanee.com
Web Site: ww.navatanee.com
CSR—(THA)
Rev.: $5,038,954
Assets: $57,851,507
Liabilities: $684,917
Net Worth: $57,166,590
Earnings: $2,125,477
Emp.: 107
Fiscal Year-end: 12/31/12

Business Description:
Golf Course & Clubs
S.I.C.: 7999
N.A.I.C.S.: 713910

Personnel:
Sukum Navapan *(Chm & CEO)*
Sukuma Jayananda *(Mng Dir)*
Patcharaporn Jultothai *(Sec & Mgr-Admin)*

Board of Directors:
Sukum Navapan
Nibhond Charanvas
Kittidej Charusathiara
Sukuma Jayananda
Paiboon Kanchanapiboon
Maevadi Navapan
Chackchai Panichapat
A. C. M. Kamthon Sindhvananda

CITY STEEL PUBLIC COMPANY LIMITED

88 3 Moo 4 Bypass Road
Nongmaidaeng Muang
Chon Buri, 20000, Thailand
Tel.: (66) 38 782 064
Fax: (66) 38 782 069
E-Mail: city@wkpgroup.com
Web Site: www.citysteelpcl.com
Year Founded: 1995
CITY—(THA)

Business Description:
Metal Product Mfr
S.I.C.: 3499
N.A.I.C.S.: 332999

Personnel:
Wibool Phongratanadechachai *(Chm)*
Komgrich Phongratanadechachai *(CEO)*
Satit Phongratanadechachai *(Mng Dir)*
Suputtra Phongratanadechachai *(CFO & Deputy Mng Dir)*
Charoenpong Ongwongsakul *(Deputy Mng Dir)*
Parichard Phongratanadechachai *(Sec)*

Board of Directors:
Wibool Phongratanadechachai
Manop Chivatanasoontorn
Charoenpong Ongwongsakul
Komgrich Phongratanadechachai
Satit Phongratanadechachai
Suputtra Phongratanadechachai
Anutara Tantraporn
Pattarathon Thatsanasuwan

CITY TELECOM (H.K.) LIMITED

(Name Changed to Hong Kong Television Network Limited)

CITY UNION BANK LTD

No 149 TSR Big Street
Kumbakonam, 612001, India
Tel.: (91) 4352432322
Fax: (91) 4352431746
E-Mail: co@cityunionbank.com
Web Site: www.cityunionbank.com
532210—(BOM)
Rev.: $456,526,513
Assets: $4,259,951,040
Liabilities: $3,955,771,100
Net Worth: $304,179,940
Earnings: $59,701,970
Emp.: 3,785
Fiscal Year-end: 03/31/13

Business Description:
Banking Services
S.I.C.: 6029
N.A.I.C.S.: 522110

Personnel:
N. Kamakodi *(CEO & Mng Dir)*
S. Sundar *(CFO & Sr Gen Mgr)*
V. Ramesh *(Compliance Officer, Sec & Deputy Gen Mgr)*

Board of Directors:
S. Balasubramanian
S. Bernard
N. Kamakodi
V. Kamakodi
N. Kantha Kumar
S. Mahalingam
R. G. Chandra Mogan
C. R. Muralidharan
T. K. Ramkumar
S. R. Singharavelu

Transfer Agent:
Karvy Computershare Private Limited
Plot No 17 to 24 Vittalrao Nagar Madhapur
Hyderabad, India

Division:

City Union Bank Ltd - International Banking Division (1)
No 706 Mount Rd Thousand Lights
Chennai, Tamil Nadu, 600006, India
Tel.: (91) 4428297202
Fax: (91) 4428297359
E-Mail: treasury@cityunionbank.com
Web Site: www.cityunionbank.com
Emp.: 35
Banking Services

City Union Bank Ltd—(Continued)

S.I.C.: 6029
N.A.I.C.S.: 522110
N. Kamakodi *(Mng Dir & CEO)*
S Balasubramanian *(Mng Dir)*

CITY WINDMILLS LTD.

Suite 72 Carioca Business Park
2 Sawley Road, Manchester, Lancs, M40 8BB, United Kingdom
Tel.: (44) 22 310 8603
Fax: (44) 22 310 8605
E-Mail: contact@citywindmills.com
Web Site: www.citywindmills.com
Year Founded: 2010
CYW—(DEU)

Business Description:
Windmill Mfr
S.I.C.: 3612
N.A.I.C.S.: 335311

Personnel:
Sean Kelly *(Founder & CFO)*
Peter Kazimirski *(CEO)*
Marc Alexandre Erbeia *(CTO)*

CITYCHAMP DARTONG CO., LTD.

26 Yuanhong Building 32 Wuyi Middle Road
Gulou District, Fuzhou, 350005, China
Tel.: (86) 591 83353338
Fax: (86) 591 83350013
E-Mail: gcdt@gcdt.net
Web Site: www.gcdt.net
600067—(SHG)
Sales Range: $1-4.9 Billion
Emp.: 1,100

Business Description:
Real Estate Developer; Enameled Wire Mfr
S.I.C.: 6552
N.A.I.C.S.: 237210

Personnel:
Guolong Han *(Chm)*
Xiaojie Han *(Pres)*

CITYCON OYJ

Korkeavuorenkatu 35
00130 Helsinki, Finland
Tel.: (358) 207664400
Fax: (358) 207664499
E-Mail: info@citycon.fi
Web Site: www.citycon.fi
Year Founded: 1988
CTY1S—(HEL)
Rev.: $322,003,864
Assets: $3,794,180,145
Liabilities: $2,367,374,562
Net Worth: $1,426,805,583
Earnings: $118,059,109
Emp.: 129
Fiscal Year-end: 12/31/12

Business Description:
Real Estate Sector
S.I.C.: 6531
N.A.I.C.S.: 531390

Personnel:
Chaim Katzman *(Chm)*
Ronen Ashkenazi *(Deputy Chm)*
Bernd Knobloch *(Deputy Chm)*
Marcel Kokkeel *(CEO)*
Eero Sihvonen *(CFO & Exec VP)*
Harri Holmstrom *(COO)*
Nils Styf *(Chief Investment Officer)*
Anu Tuomola *(Gen Counsel)*

Board of Directors:
Chaim Katzman
Ronen Ashkenazi
Bernd Knobloch
Kirsi Komi
Karine Ohana
Claes Ottosson
Per-Anders Ovin
Jorma Sonninen
Yuval Yanai
Ariella Zochovitzky

Subsidiaries:

Forssan Hameentie 3 Koy (1)
Haemeentie 3
31100 Forssa, Finland
Tel.: (358) 207 664 510
Shopping Mall Operator
S.I.C.: 6512
N.A.I.C.S.: 531120

Heikintori Oy (1)
Kauppamiehentie 1
Tapiola, Espoo, 2130, Finland
Tel.: (358) 2076 64641
Web Site: www.heikonteri.fi
Emp.: 5
Shopping Mall Leasing Services
S.I.C.: 6512
N.A.I.C.S.: 531120
Jakob Thoisen *(Gen Mgr)*

Jyvaskylan Kauppakatu 31 Koy (1)
Kauppakatu 31 3 krs
40100 Jyvaskyla, Finland
Tel.: (358) 400 783 811
Shopping Mall Operator
S.I.C.: 6512
N.A.I.C.S.: 531120

Karjaan Ratakatu 59 Koy (1)
Ratakatu 59
10300 Karjaa, Finland
Tel.: (358) 10 2287047
Shopping Mall Operator
S.I.C.: 6512
N.A.I.C.S.: 531120
Timo Mandila *(Mng Dir)*

Kauppakeskus Isokarhu Oy (1)
Saaristenkatu 3
13100 Hameenlinna, Finland
Tel.: (358) 10 228 70 47
Fax: (358) 10 228 7041
Shopping Mall Operator
S.I.C.: 6512
N.A.I.C.S.: 531120

Koskikeskuksen Huolto Oy (1)
Koskikeskus Lok 7
33100 Tampere, Finland
Tel.: (358) 3 274 0470
Fax: (358) 3 212 1879
Web Site: www.koskikeskus.fi
Real Estate Management Services
S.I.C.: 6531
N.A.I.C.S.: 531390
Kai Niinimaeki *(Gen Mgr)*

Kuusankosken Kauppakatu 7 Koy (1)
Kauppakatu 7
45700 Kuusankoski, Finland
Tel.: (358) 10 228 7047
Real Estate Management Services
S.I.C.: 6531
N.A.I.C.S.: 531390

Laajasalon Liikekeskus Oy (1)
Kauppakaarre 1
00700 Helsinki, Finland
Tel.: (358) 20 743 8340
Fax: (358) 20 743 8349
Residential Property Management Services
S.I.C.: 6531
N.A.I.C.S.: 531311
Juha Herno *(Mng Dir)*

Lahden Trio Koy (1)
Aleksanterinkatu 18
15140 Lahti, Finland
Tel.: (358) 3 878 5710
Fax: (358) 3 878 5770
Real Estate Management Services
S.I.C.: 6531
N.A.I.C.S.: 531390
Ulla-Maija Kemppi *(Gen Mgr)*

Lappeenrannan Brahenkatu 7 Koy (1)
Laserkatu 6
53850 Lappeenranta, Finland
Tel.: (358) 207 438 405
Shopping Mall Operator
S.I.C.: 6512
N.A.I.C.S.: 531120

Lappeenrannan Villimiehen Vitonen Oy (1)
Saaristenkatu 3
13100 Hameenlinna, Finland
Tel.: (358) 10 228 7047
Fax: (358) 10 228 7041
Real Estate Management Services
S.I.C.: 6531
N.A.I.C.S.: 531390

Lentolan Perusyhtio Oy (1)
Saaristenkatu 3
33100 Tampere, Finland
Tel.: (358) 10 228 7047
Fax: (358) 10 228 7041
Shopping Mall Operator
S.I.C.: 6513
N.A.I.C.S.: 531110

Myyrmanni Koy (1)
Elisa Komi Patotie 2
PO Box 33
01601 Vantaa, Finland
Tel.: (358) 9 70084141
Fax: (358) 9 53061460
Web Site: www.myyrmanni.fi
Real Estate Management Services
S.I.C.: 6531
N.A.I.C.S.: 531390
Elena Stenholm *(Gen Mgr)*

Oulun Galleria Koy (1)
Isokatu 23
Oulu, 90100, Finland
Tel.: (358) 20 766 4474
Web Site: www.citycon.com
Emp.: 10
Shopping Mall Operator
S.I.C.: 6512
N.A.I.C.S.: 531120
Brad Paul *(Gen Mgr)*

Porin Asema-Aukio Koy (1)
Satakunnankatu 23 B
28130 Pori, Finland
Tel.: (358) 2 633 7046
Real Estate Management Services
S.I.C.: 6531
N.A.I.C.S.: 531390

Porin Isolinnankatu 18 Koy (1)
Isolinnankatu 18
28100 Pori, Finland
Tel.: (358) 10 228 7047
Shopping Mall Operator
S.I.C.: 6512
N.A.I.C.S.: 531120

Sakylan Liiketalo Koy (1)
Saaristenkatu 3
13100 Hameenlinna, Finland
Tel.: (358) 10 228 7047
Shopping Mall Operator
S.I.C.: 6512
N.A.I.C.S.: 531120

Tampereen Hatanpaa Koy (1)
Saaristenkatu 3
13100 Hameenlinna, Finland
Tel.: (358) 10 2287047
Fax: (358) 10 2287041
Real Estate Property Development Services
S.I.C.: 6531
N.A.I.C.S.: 531390

Tampereen Suvantokatu Koy (1)
Pohjoisesplanadi 35 A b
00100 Helsinki, Finland
Tel.: (358) 102287047
Real Estate Manangement Services
S.I.C.: 6531
N.A.I.C.S.: 531390

Valkeakosken Torikatu 2 Koy (1)
Saaristenkatu 3
13100 Hameenlinna, Finland
Tel.: (358) 10 228 7047
Fax: (358) 10 228 7041
Real Estate Management Services
S.I.C.: 6531
N.A.I.C.S.: 531390

Non-U.S. Subsidiaries:

Citycon AB (1)
Box 47 203
100 74 Stockholm, Sweden
Tel.: (46) 8 522 80 317
Fax: (46) 8 645 41 65
Real Estate Leasing Services
S.I.C.: 6519
N.A.I.C.S.: 531190
Jonas Tapio *(Dir-Leasing)*

Citycon Development AB (1)
Liljeholmstorget 7
PO Box 47203
Stockholm, 117 63, Sweden
Tel.: (46) 8 522 803 10
Commercial Building Construction Services
S.I.C.: 1542
N.A.I.C.S.: 236220

Citycon Estonia Ou (1)
Paldiski mnt 102
13522 Tallinn, Estonia
Tel.: (372) 6659100
Fax: (372) 6659101
Emp.: 10
Hotel Management Services
S.I.C.: 7011
N.A.I.C.S.: 721110

Citycon Jakobsbergs Centrum AB (1)
PO Box 47203
100 74 Stockholm, Sweden
Tel.: (46) 8 58430470
Shopping Mall Operator
S.I.C.: 6512
N.A.I.C.S.: 531120

Citycon Liljeholmstorget Galleria AB (1)
Nybohovsbacken 38
117 63 Stockholm, Sweden
Tel.: (46) 8 522 80 310
Shopping Mall Operator
S.I.C.: 6512
N.A.I.C.S.: 531120

Kristiine Keskus Ou (1)
Endla 45
Tallinn, 10615, Estonia
Tel.: (372) 665 9100
Fax: (372) 665 9101
E-Mail: info@kristiine.com
Web Site: www.kristiine.com
Emp.: 10
Shopping Mall Operator
S.I.C.: 6512
N.A.I.C.S.: 531120
Mati Pops *(Gen Mgr)*

Magistral Kaubanduskeskuse Ou (1)
Sopruse pst 201/203
Tallinn, Estonia
Tel.: (372) 665 9100
Fax: (372) 665 9101
E-Mail: info@magistral.ee
Web Site: www.magistral.ee
Emp.: 1
Shopping Mall Operator
S.I.C.: 6512
N.A.I.C.S.: 531120

Rocca al Mare Kaubanduskeskuse AS (1)
Paldiski mnt 102
13522 Tallinn, Estonia
Tel.: (372) 665 9100
Fax: (372) 665 9101
E-Mail: info@roccaalmare.ee
Web Site: www.roccaalmare.ee
Emp.: 1
Shopping Mall Operator
S.I.C.: 6512
N.A.I.C.S.: 531120
Muammer Abali *(Mgr)*

Stenungs Torg Fastighets AB (1)
Strandvagen 15
Stenungsund, 444 30, Sweden
Tel.: (46) 30 36 91 05
Fax: (46) 30 36 91 05
Shopping Mall Operator
S.I.C.: 6512
N.A.I.C.S.: 531120

Strompilen AB (1)
Stroempilsplatsen 10
907 43 Umea, Sweden
Tel.: (46) 90 71 96 10
Shopping Mall Operator
S.I.C.: 6512
N.A.I.C.S.: 531120

UAB Prekybos Centras Mandarinas (1)
Ateities g 91
06324 Vilnius, Lithuania

Tel.: (370) 52794177
Fax: (370) 52794248
E-Mail: info@mandarinas.lt
Web Site: www.mandarinas.lt
Emp.: 1
Shopping Mall Operator
S.I.C.: 6512
N.A.I.C.S.: 531120

CITYFIBRE INFRASTRUCTURE HOLDINGS PLC
53 Chandos Place
London, WC2N 4HS, United Kingdom
Tel.: (44) 845 293 0774
E-Mail: info@cityfibre.com
Web Site: www.cityfibre.com
CFHL—(AIM)
Business Description:
Transformational Fibre Optic Infrastructure Builder
S.I.C.: 3357
N.A.I.C.S.: 335921
Personnel:
Greg Mesch *(CEO)*
Terry Hart *(CFO)*
Board of Directors:
Sally Davis
Greg Mesch

CITYLAND DEVELOPMENT CORPORATION
2 Fl Cityland 10 Tower I 156 HV Dela Costa Street
Salcedo Village, Makati, 1226, Philippines
Tel.: (63) 28936060
Fax: (63) 28928656
Web Site: www.citylandcondo.com
CDC—(PHI)
Rev.: $46,849,581
Assets: $207,393,561
Liabilities: $66,645,807
Net Worth: $140,747,754
Earnings: $12,974,487
Emp.: 216
Fiscal Year-end: 12/31/12
Business Description:
Real Estate Services
S.I.C.: 6531
N.A.I.C.S.: 531210
Personnel:
Washington Z. SyCip *(Chm)*
Andrew I. Liuson *(Vice Chm)*
Grace C. Liuson *(Deputy Vice Chm)*
Josef C. Gohoc *(Pres)*
Emma A. Choa *(Treas & Sr VP)*
Emma G. Jularbal *(Sec & VP-Legal Affairs)*
Rufina C. Buensuceso *(Exec VP)*
Board of Directors:
Washington Z. SyCip
Peter S. Dee
Alice C. Gohoc
Josef C. Gohoc
Andrew I. Liuson
Grace C. Liuson
Sabino R. Padilla Jr.
Helen C. Roxas
Stephen C. Roxas

CITYMAN LIMITED
153 Old No 43/35 2nd Floor
Promenade Road 2nd Cross
Frazer Town, Bengaluru, 560 005, India
Tel.: (91) 80 25540183
Fax: (91) 80 25540193
E-Mail: info@cityman.co.in
Web Site: www.cityman.co.in
Year Founded: 1992
521210—(BOM)
Sales Range: Less than $1 Million
Business Description:
Readymade Garments Mfr & Distr
S.I.C.: 2329
N.A.I.C.S.: 315220
Personnel:
Santhosh J. Karimattom *(Chm & Mng Dir)*
T. N. Sajeevan *(CFO)*
D. E. Chandrasekaran *(Compliance Officer & Sec)*
Board of Directors:
Santhosh J. Karimattom
Anup Kumar
Rajendra Patil
Kandumpully Rajesh

CITYNEON HOLDINGS LIMITED
Cityneon Design Centre 84 Genting Lane 06-01
Singapore, 349584, Singapore
Tel.: (65) 65716338
Fax: (65) 67493633
E-Mail: info@cityneon.com.sg
Web Site: www.cityneon.net
5HJ—(SES)
Rev.: $67,192,245
Assets: $40,429,745
Liabilities: $23,195,652
Net Worth: $17,234,093
Earnings: $3,844,554
Fiscal Year-end: 12/31/12
Business Description:
Event & Exhibition Services
S.I.C.: 7999
N.A.I.C.S.: 711310
Personnel:
Chee Wah Ko *(Mng Dir)*
Lee Ing Ng *(Sec)*
Board of Directors:
Weng Ho Lew
Soo Chiew Chua
Chee Wah Ko
Vincent Lee
Poh Hock Lim
Seng Kok Loh
Yuen Yow Loke
Hup Foi Tan
Chun Wai Wong

CITYSPRINT (UK) LIMITED
58-62 Scrutton Street
London, EC2A 4PH, United Kingdom
Tel.: (44) 2078801111
Fax: (44) 2078804901
E-Mail: info@citysprint.co.uk
Web Site: www.citysprint.co.uk
Sales Range: $50-74.9 Million
Emp.: 268
Business Description:
Courier Services
S.I.C.: 4215
N.A.I.C.S.: 492110
Personnel:
Andrew R. Bernard *(CEO)*
Ben Haynes *(Mng Dir)*

CITYSTATE SAVINGS BANK, INC.
Citystate Centre Building 709 Shaw Boulevard
Pasig, 1600, Philippines
Tel.: (63) 4701497
Fax: (63) 7065848
Web Site: www.citystatesavings.com
Year Founded: 1997
CSB—(PHI)
Int. Income: $5,785,748
Assets: $70,950,176
Liabilities: $51,602,676
Net Worth: $19,347,500
Earnings: $41,209
Emp.: 266
Fiscal Year-end: 12/31/12
Business Description:
Banking Services
S.I.C.: 6029
N.A.I.C.S.: 522110
Personnel:
Antonio L. Cabangon Chua *(Founder & Chm)*
Alfonso G. Sy *(Vice Chm)*
Rey D. Delfin *(Pres)*
J. Antonio A. Cabangon, Jr. *(Mng Dir & Sec)*
Meliton A. Narciso *(Chief Risk Officer & Asst VP-Risk Mgmt Dept)*
Ruel L. Angga *(Compliance Officer & VP-Compliance)*
D. Arnold A. Cabangon *(Treas)*
Board of Directors:
Antonio L. Cabangon Chua
Feorelio M. Bote
D. Alfred A. Cabangon
D. Arnold A. Cabangon
J. Antonio A. Cabangon, Jr.
J. Wilfredo A. Cabangon
Rey D. Delfin
Jose Armando R. Melo
Andres Y. Narvasa, Jr.
Pedro E. Paraiso
Benjamin V. Ramos
Ramon L. Sin
Lucito L. Sioson
Emmanuel R. Sison
Alfonso G. Sy

CITYWIDE SERVICE SOLUTIONS PTY LTD
Level 1 150 Jolimont Road
Melbourne, VIC, 3002, Australia
Tel.: (61) 392615000
Fax: (61) 392615005
E-Mail: citywide@citywide.com.au
Web Site: www.citywide.com.au
Emp.: 1,049
Business Description:
Environmental, Civil Infrastructure, Engineering & Maintenance Services
S.I.C.: 8711
N.A.I.C.S.: 541330
Personnel:
John Lyn Davies *(Chm)*
Kerry F. Osborne *(Mng Dir)*
John Collins *(CFO & Sec)*
Board of Directors:
John Lyn Davies
Alan H. Evans
Peter S. Lowe
Kerry F. Osborne
Janice B. C. van Reyke

CITYWIRE HOLDINGS LTD.
87 Vauxhall Walk
London, SE11 5HJ, United Kingdom
Tel.: (44) 2078402250
Fax: (44) 2078402279
E-Mail: info@citywire.co.uk
Web Site: www.citywire.co.uk
Emp.: 140
Business Description:
Holding Company; Internet & Magazine Publisher
S.I.C.: 2741
N.A.I.C.S.: 519130
Personnel:
Lawrence Lever *(Chm)*

Subsidiary:

Citywire Financial Publishers Ltd. **(1)**
87 Vauxhall Walk
London, SE11 5HJ, United Kingdom
Tel.: (44) 2078402250
Fax: (44) 2078402279
E-Mail: editors@citywire.co.uk
Web Site: www.citywire.co.uk
Emp.: 150
Financial Information Publisher
S.I.C.: 2741
N.A.I.C.S.: 519130
Lawrence Lever *(Founder & Chm)*
David Turner *(CEO)*

CITYXPRESS CORPORATION
200-1727 West Broadway
Vancouver, BC, V6J 4W6, Canada
Tel.: (604) 638-3820
Web Site: www.cityxpress.com
Year Founded: 1997
Sales Range: $1-9.9 Million
Emp.: 50
Business Description:
Software Developer for Online Auctions, Marketplaces & E-Commerce Classifieds for Newspapers
S.I.C.: 7372
N.A.I.C.S.: 511210
Personnel:
Phil Dubois *(Pres & CEO)*
Ken Bradley *(CFO & COO)*
Board of Directors:
Phil Dubois
Chris Hendricks
Jeff Herr
Derek Mather
Greg Schermer
Pascal Spothelfer
Pat Talamantes

CIVIC MOTORS LTD
1171 St Laurent Blvd
Ottawa, ON, K1K 3B7, Canada
Tel.: (613) 741-6676
Fax: (613) 728-2045
Toll Free: (866) 979-3384
Web Site: www.civicmotors.com
Year Founded: 1975
Rev.: $31,600,800
Emp.: 65
Business Description:
New & Used Car Dealers
S.I.C.: 5511
N.A.I.C.S.: 441110
Personnel:
Arnis Mierins *(Owner)*

CIVIL MERCHANT BITTIYA SANSTHA LIMITED
Kuleshwor MM Complex
Kathmandu, Nepal
Tel.: (977) 1 4289524
Fax: (977) 1 4289596
E-Mail: civilmbsl@hotmail.com
Web Site: www.civilmbsl.com.np
Year Founded: 2005
CMBSL—(NEP)
Business Description:
Financial Services
S.I.C.: 6211
N.A.I.C.S.: 523999
Personnel:
Jayandra Lal Shrestha *(CEO)*
Ram Kumar Thapa *(Sec & Asst Mgr)*
Board of Directors:
Debendra Babu Adhikari
Sanju Bhattarai
Bhaskar Raj Panta
Arun Raj Shrestha
Binod Lal Shrestha
Indira Shrestha
Narayan Lal Shrestha
Prithu Raj Shrestha
Sarad Prakash Shrestha

CIVITAS INTERNATIONAL MANAGEMENT CONSULTANTS GMBH
Possartstrasse 12
D-81679 Munich, Germany
Tel.: (49) 893838590
Fax: (49) 8938385930
E-Mail: office-muenchen@civitas.com
Web Site: www.civitas.com
Year Founded: 1971
Rev.: $19,311,600
Emp.: 35

CIVITAS INTERNATIONAL Management Consultants GmbH—(Continued)

Business Description:
Business Consulting Services
S.I.C.: 8748
N.A.I.C.S.: 541618
Personnel:
Christian G. Hirsch *(Partner)*
Reiner Hoock *(Partner)*
Roman A. Sauermann *(Partner)*
Ulrich Thess *(Partner)*
Klaus Ewerth *(Mng Dir)*
Rupert Nesselhauf *(Mng Dir)*
Bernd-M. Schroter *(Mng Dir)*
Gabriele Werner *(Mng Dir)*

CIVRAY DISTRIBUTION SOCIDIS

Route De Limoges
86400 Niort, France
Tel.: (33) 549870589
Sales Range: $10-24.9 Million
Emp.: 47
Business Description:
Grocery Stores
S.I.C.: 5411
N.A.I.C.S.: 445110
Personnel:
Yves Gaudineau *(Pres)*

C.J. COLEMAN & COMPANY LIMITED

Port Soken House 155 Minories
London, EC3 N1BT, United Kingdom
Tel.: (44) 2074882211
Fax: (44) 2074884436
E-Mail: inbox@cjcoleman.com
Web Site: www.cjcoleman.com
Year Founded: 1973
Sales Range: $10-24.9 Million
Emp.: 40
Fiscal Year-end: 12/31/12
Business Description:
Liability Insurance
S.I.C.: 6399
N.A.I.C.S.: 524128
Personnel:
Ben Coleman *(Chm)*
Board of Directors:
Mark Aspinall
Jim Foster
Nancy Layton-Cook
Graham Nash
Subsidiary:

Coleman & Large Ltd. (1)
4th Floor Europa House 49 Sandgate Road
Folkestone, Kent, CT20 1RQ, United Kingdom
Tel.: (44) 1303223883
Fax: (44) 1303223881
Web Site: www.cjcoleman.com
Emp.: 3
Liability Insurance
S.I.C.: 6399
N.A.I.C.S.: 524128
David Merry *(Chm)*

CJ CORPORATION

500 Narndaemunno 5-ga
Jung-Gu, Seoul, 100-095, Korea (South)
Tel.: (82) 27268114
Fax: (82) 27268112
E-Mail: webmaster@cj.net
Web Site: english.cj.net
Year Founded: 1953
001040—(KRS)
Sls.: $16,394,400,873
Assets: $19,888,088,005
Liabilities: $12,090,913,890
Net Worth: $7,797,174,116
Earnings: $530,338,647
Emp.: 3,669
Fiscal Year-end: 12/31/12
Business Description:
Holding Company; Food, Animal Feed, Home Shopping, Entertainment, Infrastructure, Pharmaceuticals & Biotechnologies
S.I.C.: 6719
N.A.I.C.S.: 551112
Personnel:
Jayhyun Lee *(Co-Chm & Co-CEO)*
KyungShik Sohn *(Co-Chm & Co-CEO)*
Gwan Hoon Lee *(Co-CEO)*
Board of Directors:
Jayhyun Lee
KyungShik Sohn
Gwan Hoon Lee
Sang Don Lee
Dae Sik Oh
Je Chan Park
Sang Goo Shin
Affiliates:

CJ Cheiljedang Corp. (1)
500 Namdaemoon-ro 5-Ga Jung-Gu
Seoul, 100-802, Korea (South)
Tel.: (82) 2 7268114
Fax: (82) 2 7268112
Web Site: www.cj.co.kr
097950—(KRS)
Sls.: $9,186,104,930
Assets: $10,545,752,949
Liabilities: $5,690,190,451
Net Worth: $4,855,562,498
Earnings: $288,965,573
Emp.: 4,500
Fiscal Year-end: 12/31/12
Food Products, Animal Feed & Life Science Products Mfr & Retailer
S.I.C.: 2099
N.A.I.C.S.: 311999
Kyung Shik Sohn *(Chm & Co-CEO)*
Chul Ha Kim *(Co-CEO)*
Jay Hyun Lee *(Co-CEO)*

CJ Korea Express Corporation (1)
58 12 Seosomun Dong Chung Ku
Seoul, 100814, Korea (South) Ks
Tel.: (82) 237820114
Fax: (82) 237820098
Web Site: www.korex.co.kr
000120—(KRS)
Sales Range: $1-4.9 Billion
Emp.: 5,700
Logistics Services
S.I.C.: 4731
N.A.I.C.S.: 541614
Won-Tae Lee *(CEO)*

Subsidiary:

CJ GLS Corporation (2)
2-5F CJ Korea Express Bldg 58-12
Seosomun-dong
Jung-gu, Seoul, Korea (South) Ks
Tel.: (82) 2 870 6185
Fax: (82) 2 870 6114
Web Site: www.cjgls.com
Third Party Logistics Services
S.I.C.: 4731
N.A.I.C.S.: 488510
Kwan Soo Shon *(CEO)*

U.S. Subsidiary:

CJ GLS America, Inc. (3)
5801 S Malt Ave
Commerce, CA 90040 AL
Tel.: (323) 278-5280
Web Site: www.cjgls.com
Third Party Logistics Services
S.I.C.: 4731
N.A.I.C.S.: 488510
Henry Tan *(Chm)*
Hyeong Kim *(CEO)*

Non-U.S. Subsidiaries:

CJ GLS Asia Pte Ltd (3)
20 Toh Guan Road
#08-00 CJ GLS Building, 608839
Singapore, Singapore
Tel.: (65) 64102800
Fax: (65) 64102801
Web Site: www.cjgls.com
Emp.: 100
Logistics Consulting Services
S.I.C.: 4731
N.A.I.C.S.: 541614
Cheong Kwok Weng *(Mng Dir)*

Subsidiaries:

CJ GLS (S) Airfreight Pte Ltd (4)
119 Airport Cargo Road
02-07/08 Changi Cargo Agents, 819454
Singapore, Singapore
Tel.: (65) 65430338
Fax: (65) 65468436
E-Mail: gsa-enquiry@cj.net
Web Site: www.cjgls.com
Emp.: 25
Scheduled Freight Air Transportation
S.I.C.: 4512
N.A.I.C.S.: 481112
Tommy Lin *(Mgr-Ops)*

CJ GLS (S) Infotech Pte Ltd (4)
20 Toh Guan Road
#08-00 CJ GLS Building, 608839
Singapore, Singapore
Tel.: (65) 64102800
Fax: (65) 64102801
Web Site: www.cjgls.com
Logistics Consulting Services
S.I.C.: 4731
N.A.I.C.S.: 541614

CJ GLS (S) Shipping Pte Ltd (4)
20 Toh Guan Road
#08-00 CJ GLS Building, 608839
Singapore, Singapore
Tel.: (65) 64102800
Fax: (65) 64102801
Web Site: www.cjgls.com
Emp.: 300
Navigational Services to Shipping
S.I.C.: 4499
N.A.I.C.S.: 488330
Cheong Kwok Weng *(Mng Dir)*

Qingdao CJ GLS Inc (3)
Qingdao Guangdong Development bank
B/D 1803 No 40
Shangdong Road, Qingdao, Shangdong, China
Tel.: (86) 53285015660
Fax: (86) 53285015565
Logistics Consulting Services
S.I.C.: 4731
N.A.I.C.S.: 541614

U.S. Subsidiary:

Korea Express U.S.A. Inc. (2)
11 Commerce Ct W S
New Brunswick, NJ 08810 NY
Tel.: (609) 860-3070
Fax: (609) 395-9772
E-Mail: keusa@keusa.com
Web Site: www.korex.co.kr/kxusa/
Logistics & Parcel Delivery Services
S.I.C.: 4215
N.A.I.C.S.: 492110
Sang-gil Lee *(Pres)*

Non-U.S. Subsidiaries:

Korea Express Europe GmbH (2)
Cargo City Sued Geb 558E
60549 Frankfurt am Main, Germany De
Tel.: (49) 69 6860 3991, ext. 3
Fax: (49) 69 6860 3999
E-Mail: info@koreaexpress.de
Web Site: www.koreaexpress.de
Freight Forwarding Services
S.I.C.: 4731
N.A.I.C.S.: 488510
Young-Jo Kim *(Mgr)*

Korea Express Hong Kong Co., Ltd. (2)
Unit A 9/F Dynamic Cargo Centre 188
Yeung UK Road
Tsuen Wan, New Territories, China (Hong Kong) HK
Tel.: (852) 3126 9640
Fax: (852) 3126 9613
E-Mail: hkg@korex.com.hk
Freight Forwarding Services
S.I.C.: 4731
N.A.I.C.S.: 488510
Young-Ho Jang *(Mgr)*

Korea Express Japan Co., Ltd. (2)
3F Toranomon 1 Chome MG B/D 1-16-16
Toranomon
Minato-Ku, 105-0001 Tokyo, Japan JP
Tel.: (81) 3 3500 5841
Fax: (81) 3 3500 5170
E-Mail: korexjp@korex.co.jp
Web Site: www.korex.co.jp
Emp.: 27
Freight Forwarding Services
S.I.C.: 4731
N.A.I.C.S.: 488510
Han-Bok Woo *(Pres & CEO)*

Korea Express Tianjin Co., Ltd. (2)
Room No 806 8/F Tower C City Center Bldg
Xigang Street
Heping District, Tianjin, China CN
Tel.: (86) 22 2351 1009
Fax: (86) 22 2351 1129
E-Mail: tsn@korexchina.com
Freight Forwarding Services
S.I.C.: 4731
N.A.I.C.S.: 488510
Kwan-Sik Yun *(Mgr)*

U.S. Subsidiary:

CJ America, Inc. (1)
3530 Wilshire Blvd Ste 1220
Los Angeles, CA 90010
Tel.: (213) 427-5566
Fax: (213) 380-5433
E-Mail: info@cjamerica.net
Web Site: www.cjamerica.net
Emp.: 50
Public Relations Services
S.I.C.: 8743
N.A.I.C.S.: 541820
Jin-Soo Kim *(Pres)*

Subsidiaries:

CJ Bakery, Inc. (2)
3530 Wilshire Blvd Ste 1220
Los Angeles, CA 90010-2341
Tel.: (213) 427-5566
Fax: (213) 380-5433
Web Site: www.cjamerica.net
Emp.: 50
Commercial Bakeries
S.I.C.: 2051
N.A.I.C.S.: 311812
Jin-Soo Kim *(Pres)*

CJ Entertainment America Corp. (2)
5670 Wilshire Blvd Ste 2450
Los Angeles, CA 90036
Tel.: (310) 557-3050
Fax: (323) 930-1015
Web Site: www.us.cjcgv.com
Emp.: 20
Entertainers & Entertainment Groups
S.I.C.: 7389
N.A.I.C.S.: 711410
Ted Kim *(Exec VP)*

CJ Internet Inc. (2)
1298 Kifer Rd Ste 507
Sunnyvale, CA 94086-5321
Tel.: (408) 232-5487
Fax: (408) 232-5488
Internet Publishing & Broadcasting
S.I.C.: 2741
N.A.I.C.S.: 519130
Young-jong Jung *(CEO)*

CJ Pacific Corporation (2)
141 W Jackson Blvd Ste 2194
Chicago, IL 60604
Tel.: (503) 223-6555
Fax: (503) 223-1461
Web Site: www.cjpis.co.kr/eng/03/09.html
Food Mfr
S.I.C.: 2099
N.A.I.C.S.: 311999
Jae Hyun Chun *(Gen Mgr)*

Non-U.S. Subsidiaries:

CJ Beijing Bakery Co.,Ltd (1)
Songlanpu Shahe Town
Changping District, 102206 Beijing, China
Tel.: (86) 1051087711
Fax: (86) 1051087765
E-Mail: thyoun@cj.net
Web Site: www.english.cj.net
Emp.: 3,000
Cookie & Cracker Mfr
S.I.C.: 2052
N.A.I.C.S.: 311821
Kim Taek *(Mng Dir)*

CJ Beijing Foods Co.,Ltd (1)
Songlanpu Shahe Town
Changping District, 102206 Beijing, China

Tel.: (86) 1080723171
Fax: (86) 1080722994
Web Site: english.cj.net
Food Mfr
S.I.C.: 2099
N.A.I.C.S.: 311999
Soo-Hyun Tark *(Mng Dir)*

CJ Cambodia Co., Ltd (1)
No 279 Norodom Boulevards
Sangkat Tonle Bassac, Phnom Penh, Cambodia
Tel.: (855) 23218729
Fax: (855) 23218730
Web Site: www.cj.net
Food Mfr
S.I.C.: 2099
N.A.I.C.S.: 311999

CJ China Ltd (1)
Suite 3003 30th Floor Central plaza
18 Harbour Road, Wanchai, China (Hong Kong)
Tel.: (852) 28029909
Fax: (852) 28661351
E-Mail: info@cj.net
Web Site: www.cj.net
Emp.: 50
Chemical & Allied Products Merchant Whslr
S.I.C.: 5169
N.A.I.C.S.: 424690

CJ Europe GmbH (1)
Ober Der Roeth 4
65824 Schwalbach, Germany
Tel.: (49) 6196590126
Fax: (49) 619645418
E-Mail: shawnkim@cj-europe.com
Web Site: www.cjpis.co.kr
Emp.: 21
Farm Supplies Whslr
S.I.C.: 5191
N.A.I.C.S.: 424910
Seong-Jin Bae *(Mng Dir)*

CJ Japan Corp. (1)
2-7-4 Nishishinbashi
Minato-Ku, 105-0003 Tokyo, Japan
Tel.: (81) 335801050
Fax: (81) 335801055
E-Mail: isobe@cj.net
Web Site: www.cjjapan.net
Emp.: 25
Durable Goods Whslr
S.I.C.: 5099
N.A.I.C.S.: 423990
Kil-Whan Chun *(Pres)*

CJ Media Japan Corp. (1)
2-7-4 Nishishinbashi
Minato-Ku, 105-0003 Tokyo, Japan
Tel.: (81) 335194551
Fax: (81) 335801051
E-Mail: masaru911@cj.net
Web Site: www.mnetjapan.com
Emp.: 100
Radio Broadcasting Stations
S.I.C.: 3663
N.A.I.C.S.: 334220

CJ Philippines Inc. (1)
Barangay Sampaioc
San Rafael, Makati, Bulacan, Philippines
Tel.: (63) 447666235
Fax: (63) 447666231
Web Site: english.cj.net
Animal Food Mfr
S.I.C.: 2048
N.A.I.C.S.: 311119

CJ Vina Agri Co., Ltd (1)
National Highway No 1 My Yen Village
Ben Luc District, Ho Chi Minh City, LongAn, Vietnam
Tel.: (84) 723641114
Fax: (84) 723870366
Web Site: english.cj.net
Emp.: 270
Animal Feed Mfr
S.I.C.: 2048
N.A.I.C.S.: 311119
Jay-hyun Lee *(CEO)*

PT. CJ Feed Jombang (1)
Jl Raya Mojoagung-Jombang Km 2
Desa Gambiran-Mojoagung Jomban, Bali, Jawa Timur, Indonesia
Tel.: (62) 321497200
Fax: (62) 321497555
E-Mail: vibrie_seni@cj.co.id
Emp.: 130
Animal Food Mfr
S.I.C.: 2048
N.A.I.C.S.: 311119
Haris Muhcadi *(Mgr-Mktg)*

CJ E&M CORPORATION

CJ E&M Center 66 Sangamsan-ro
Mapo-gu, Seoul, Korea (South)
Tel.: (82) 2 371 5501
Web Site: www.cjenm.com
Year Founded: 1993
130960—(KRS)
Rev.: $1,296,963,952
Assets: $1,944,609,041
Liabilities: $757,421,656
Net Worth: $1,187,187,385
Earnings: ($11,332,162)
Fiscal Year-end: 12/31/12

Business Description:
Television Broadcasting Services
S.I.C.: 4833
N.A.I.C.S.: 515120

Personnel:
Seok Hee Kang *(CEO)*

Board of Directors:
Seok Hee Kang
Jay Hyun Lee

CJ HELLOVISION CO., LTD.

10F Nurikkumsquare 1606 Sangam-dong
Mapo-gu, Seoul, 158070, Korea (South)
Tel.: (82) 15441002
Fax: (82) 23766191
Web Site: www.cjhellovision.com
037560—(KRS)
Sales Range: $350-399.9 Million
Emp.: 1,000

Business Description:
Cable TV Operator
S.I.C.: 4841
N.A.I.C.S.: 515210

Personnel:
Dong-Sik Byon *(CEO)*

CJ O SHOPPING CO., LTD.

2724 Bangbae Dong Seocho Gu
137060 Seoul, Korea (South)
Tel.: (82) 221070114
Fax: (82) 221070560
Web Site: company.cjmall.com
Year Founded: 1995
035760—(KRS)
Sales Range: $750-799.9 Million
Emp.: 700

Business Description:
Television Home Shopping Services
S.I.C.: 5961
N.A.I.C.S.: 454113

Personnel:
Hae-Sun Lee *(Pres)*

U.S. Subsidiary:

CJ America, Inc. (1)
3530 Wilshire Blvd Ste 1220
Los Angeles, CA 90010
Tel.: (213) 427-5566
Fax: (213) 427-7878
E-Mail:
Web Site: www.cjamerica.com
Emp.: 25
Food Products Mfr
S.I.C.: 2679
N.A.I.C.S.: 322299
Joon Thoi *(CEO)*

Non-U.S. Subsidiaries:

CJ Corp. (Moscow) (1)
Ul Ordjonikidz 11 Block 1 2
Moscow, 115419, Russia
Tel.: (7) 4959373457
Fax: (7) 4959373458
Emp.: 1
Chemicals Mfr
S.I.C.: 2833
N.A.I.C.S.: 325411
Kim Seong Min *(Mng Dir)*

CJ Corp.(Beijing) (1)
32 Fl Eagle Run Plz No 26 Xiaoyun Rd
Chaoyang Dist, Beijing, China
Tel.: (86) 1051087711
Fax: (86) 10 5108 8236
Convenience Foods Mfr
S.I.C.: 2099
N.A.I.C.S.: 311999

CJ do Brasil Ltda (1)
Alameda Vicente Pinzon 173 8th Fl
Sao Paulo, 04547-130, Brazil
Tel.: (55) 11 3717 8700
Fax: (55) 11 3717 8800
E-Mail: lliggiaevaki@cj.net
Web Site: www.cjbio.net
Emp.: 30
Lysine Mfr
S.I.C.: 3826
N.A.I.C.S.: 334516
Bruno Lee *(Mgr)*

CJ Harbin Feed Co., Ltd. (1)
Bohaidong Rd Haping Rd Haerbin City Dev Zone
Jizhong Dist, Harbin, Heilongjiang, 150060, China
Tel.: (86) 45186786068
Fax: (86) 45186786009
E-Mail: mchang@cj.net
Web Site: www.cj.net
Emp.: 90
Animal Feed Mfr
S.I.C.: 2048
N.A.I.C.S.: 311119
Kangsewon Kang *(Mgr)*

CJ Tur Yem Sanayi ve Ticaret Anonim Sirketi (1)
Organize Sanayi Bolgesi 1 Cad No 9 Inegol
Bursa, Turkey
Tel.: (90) 2247148731
Fax: (90) 2247148722
Emp.: 30
Food Processing Services
S.I.C.: 2034
N.A.I.C.S.: 311423
Byungki Roh *(Mgr)*

PT.Cheil Jedang Indonesia(Pasuruan) (1)
DS Arjosari Kec Rejoso
67 181 Pasuruan, East Java, Indonesia
Tel.: (62) 343401349
Fax: (62) 343482788
Food Additives Mfr
S.I.C.: 2869
N.A.I.C.S.: 325199

PT.Cheil Jedang Superfeed (1)
Jl Lanud Gorda Desa Julang Kec Cikande Kab
Serang, Banten, Indonesia 42101
Tel.: (62) 254400660
Fax: (62) 254400442
Animal Feeds Mfr
S.I.C.: 2048
N.A.I.C.S.: 311119

C.J.GELATINE PRODUCTS LIMITED

Acharya Donde Marg Tokersi Jivraj Wadi
Sewree, Mumbai, Maharashtra, 400 015, India
Tel.: (91) 22 4131790
Fax: (91) 22 4133193
E-Mail: cjgelatine@airtelmail.in
Web Site: www.cjgelatineproducts.com
Year Founded: 1980
507515—(BOM)
Sls.: $2,943,188
Assets: $4,264,086
Liabilities: $1,689,526
Net Worth: $2,574,560
Earnings: $3,041
Fiscal Year-end: 03/31/13

Business Description:
Gelatin Mfr
S.I.C.: 2899
N.A.I.C.S.: 325998

Personnel:
Sachiv Sahni *(Chm & Co-Mng Dir)*
Jaspal Singh *(Co-Mng Dir)*
Harman Singh *(Sec)*

Board of Directors:
Sachiv Sahni
Vikas Gupta
Sandeep S. Sahni
Jaspal Singh

Transfer Agent:
Adroit Corporate Services Pvt. Ltd
19/20 Jaferbhoy Industrial Estate 1st Floor
Makwana Road Marol Naka
Andheri East, Mumbai, 400 059, India

CJL CAPITAL INC.

116 rue Saint-Pierre
bureau 100
Quebec, QC, G1K 4A7, Canada
Tel.: (418) 653-9339
Fax: (418) 692-3969
E-Mail: mjacob@maximuscap.ca
Year Founded: 2007
CJL.P—(TSXV)

Business Description:
Investment Services
S.I.C.: 6211
N.A.I.C.S.: 523999

Personnel:
Mario Jacob *(Pres, CEO, CFO & Sec)*

Board of Directors:
Michel Berger
Mario Jacob
Denis M. Sirois

Transfer Agent:
CIBC Mellon Trust Company
2001 University St 16th Fl
Montreal, QC, H3A 2A6, Canada
Tel.: (514) 285-3649
Fax: (514) 285-3640
Toll Free: (800) 387-0825

CJSC GLOBEXBANK

(d/b/a GLOBEX Bank)
Zemlyanoy Val Street 59 Building 2
109004 Moscow, Russia
Tel.: (7) 4957852222
Fax: (7) 4955140903
E-Mail: post@globexbank.ru
Web Site: www.globexbank.ru
Year Founded: 1992
Rev.: $580,965,393
Assets: $7,542,856,800
Liabilities: $6,668,249,450
Net Worth: $874,607,350
Earnings: $14,183,954
Fiscal Year-end: 12/31/12

Business Description:
Retail, Commercial & Investment Banking
S.I.C.: 6029
N.A.I.C.S.: 522110

Personnel:
Dmitriev Vladimir Alexandrovich *(Chm)*
Kosov Nikolay Nikolayevich *(Deputy Chm)*
Vavilin Vitaly Vladimirovich *(Pres)*
Ivanov Alexey Nikolaevich *(Sr VP)*
Yatsenko Vladimir Petrovich *(Sr VP)*
Lebedeva Svetlana Sergeyevna *(Sr VP)*
Aldyuhov Sergey Viktorovich *(Sr VP)*
Filippov Sergey Vladimirovich *(Sr VP)*

Board of Directors:
Dmitriev Vladimir Alexandrovich
Ballo Anatoly Borisovich
Kosov Nikolay Nikolayevich
Nikanov Oleg Olegovich
Gruzinov Alexander Sergeyevich
Karpova Yulia Stanislavovna
Zelenov Alexander Viktorovich
Minin Vladimir Vladimirovich
Vavilin Vitaly Vladimirovich

CJSC GLOBEXBANK—(Continued)

Non-U.S. Holding:

RGI International Ltd. (1)
Frances House Sir William Place St Peter Port
PO Box 175
Saint Peter Port, GY1 4HQ, Guernsey GY
Tel.: (44) 1481723573 (51.4%)
Fax: (44) 1481732131
E-Mail: info@rgi-international.com
Web Site: www.rgi-international.com
RGI—(AIM)
Rev.: $19,809,000
Assets: $838,244,000
Liabilities: $415,725,000
Net Worth: $422,519,000
Earnings: ($58,832,000)
Fiscal Year-end: 12/31/12
Real Estate Development & Management Services
S.I.C.: 6531
N.A.I.C.S.: 531390
Andrey Nesterenko *(CEO)*
Petr Isaev *(Deputy CEO & Head-Comml Property)*
Leonid Jeliazko *(Deputy CEO & Head-Construction & Design)*
Artem Azizbaev *(Deputy CEO & Chief Legal Advisor)*
David Wood *(CFO)*

CJSC GLORIA JEANS CORPORATION

184 Stachki Str
344090 Rostov-na-Donu, Russia
Tel.: (7) 8632618901
Fax: (7) 8632618902
E-Mail: info@gloria-jeans.ru
Web Site: www.gloria-jeans.ru
Year Founded: 1988
Emp.: 200

Business Description:
Denim Garments Mfr & Distr
S.I.C.: 2399
N.A.I.C.S.: 315210

Personnel:
Brian Egan *(Pres & COO)*
Vladimir Melnikov *(Gen Dir)*

CJSC INVESTLESPROM

4 Brodnikov Per
119180 Moscow, Russia
Tel.: (7) 495 500 30 51

Business Description:
Holding Company
S.I.C.: 6719
N.A.I.C.S.: 551112

Personnel:
Anton Zavalkovsky *(Dir Gen)*

Subsidiary:

Segezha Pulp & Paper Mill (1)
Zavodskaya Street 1
Segezha, 186420 Karelia, Russia
Tel.: (7) 81431 34 000
Fax: (7) 81431 43253
E-Mail: office@scbk.ru
Web Site: www.scbk.ru
Sales Range: $125-149.9 Million
Emp.: 5,300
Paper Products & Paper Bags Mfr; Wood Processing Services
S.I.C.: 2611
N.A.I.C.S.: 322110
Alexander Uvarov *(Head-Mktg Res)*

Non-U.S. Subsidiary:

Segezha Packaging Limited (1)
Unit 1 Block 4 Ashbourne Business Park
Ashbourne, Ireland
Tel.: (353) 1 835 8866
Fax: (353) 1 835 2068
Web Site: www.segezha-packaging.com
Sales Range: $350-399.9 Million
Emp.: 1,300
Packaging Paper Mfr
S.I.C.: 2679
N.A.I.C.S.: 322299
Andrey Prokopov *(CEO)*

Non-U.S. Subsidiaries:

Sacchificio Tordera S.p.A. (2)
Via S Michele Del Carso 163
IT 21100 Varese, Italy
Tel.: (39) 0332261549
Fax: (39) 0332265807
E-Mail: mail@tordera.it
Web Site: www.tordera.it
Emp.: 80
Packaging Paper Mfr
S.I.C.: 2671
N.A.I.C.S.: 322220
Mike Graglia *(Gen Mgr)*

Segezha Packaging A/S (2)
Stigsborgvej 36
DK 9400 Norresundby, Denmark
Tel.: (45) 96323232
Fax: (45) 98170274
Web Site: www.segezha-packaging.com
Sls.: $59,297,000
Emp.: 200
Paper Sack Mfr
S.I.C.: 2679
N.A.I.C.S.: 322299

Segezha Packaging GmbH (2)
Fautenbacher Str 24
Postfach 1560
DE 77855 Achern, Germany
Tel.: (49) 78416460
Telex: 752221
Fax: (49) 7841646105
E-Mail: germany@segezha.com
Web Site: www.laundrysystems.electrolux.com
Emp.: 16
Paper Sack Mfr
S.I.C.: 2679
N.A.I.C.S.: 322299
Jim Krawczyk *(Gen Mgr)*

Segezha Packaging S.A.S. (2)
Immeuble Atria
21 avenue Edouard Belin, 92500 Paris, France
Tel.: (33) 155 479 560
Fax: (33) 1 55 47 95 75
Web Site: www.korsnas.se
Paper Mfr
S.I.C.: 2679
N.A.I.C.S.: 322299

Segezha Packaging S.A.U. (2)
Cruce Ctra Pulpi S N
E 04600 Huercal-Overa, Spain
Tel.: (34) 950470725
E-Mail: spain@korsnas-packaging.com
Emp.: 70
Paper Sack Mfr
S.I.C.: 2671
N.A.I.C.S.: 322220

Segezha Packaging Spain S.A. (2)
Urb. Industrial El Goro C/ Josefina Mayor, s/n
E-35219 Telde, Gran Canaria, Spain
Tel.: (34) 928683054
Fax: (34) 928 692 077
Mfr. of Paper Sacks
S.I.C.: 2672
N.A.I.C.S.: 322220

Segezha Packaging Spain S.A. (2)
PO Box 106
Casetas, ES 50620 Zaragoza, Spain
Tel.: (34) 976462020
Fax: (34) 976774160
Emp.: 50
Paper Product Mfr
S.I.C.: 2671
N.A.I.C.S.: 322220

Segezha Packaging, s.r.o. (2)
Uvalno 343
CZ 79391 Uvalno, Czech Republic (100%)
Tel.: (420) 554699111
Fax: (420) 652699699
E-Mail:
Web Site: www.segezha-packaging.com
Sales Range: $10-24.9 Million
Emp.: 80
Paper Sack Mfr
S.I.C.: 2671
N.A.I.C.S.: 322220
Ales Fischer *(Product Dir)*

CJSC RUSSIAN STANDARD CORPORATION

(d/b/a Russian Standard Corporation)
World Trade Center Office 1507
Krasnopresnenskaya Nab 12
1233610 Moscow, Russia
Tel.: (7) 495 967 0990
Fax: (7) 495 967 0991
Web Site: www.russianstandard.com
Year Founded: 1992
Sales Range: $5-14.9 Billion
Emp.: 20,000

Business Description:
Holding Company; Banking, Insurance & Distilled Beverages
S.I.C.: 6719
N.A.I.C.S.: 551112

Personnel:
Roustam V. Tariko *(Founder, Chm & CEO)*

Division:

Russian Standard Vodka (1)
World Trade Center Office 1507 Entrance 3
12 Krasnopresenskaya NAB
123610 Moscow, Russia
Tel.: (7) 495 967 0990
Fax: (7) 495 967 0991
Web Site: www.russianstandardvodka.com
Distillery
S.I.C.: 2085
N.A.I.C.S.: 312140
Roustam V. Tariko *(Chm & CEO)*

Subsidiaries:

JSC Russian Standard Bank (1)
36 Tkatskaya Street
105187 Moscow, Russia
Tel.: (7) 495 797 8402
Fax: (7) 495 797 8440
E-Mail: bank@rsb.ru
Web Site: www.russianstandardbank.com
Int. Income: $1,670,507,107
Assets: $9,539,803,433
Liabilities: $8,565,520,028
Net Worth: $974,283,405
Earnings: $196,374,852
Fiscal Year-end: 12/31/12
Commercial & Investment Banking
S.I.C.: 6029
N.A.I.C.S.: 522110
Roustam V. Tariko *(Chm)*
Dmitry Olegovich Levin *(CEO & Chm-Mgmt Bd)*
Vladimir N. Pyshnyi *(First Deputy CEO)*
Nikolai A. Itskov *(CFO)*

JSC Russian Standard Insurance (1)
2nd Floor Bldg 1 Entrance 1
Semeyonovskaya Street 9
107023 Moscow, Russia RU
Tel.: (7) 495 980 7760
Fax: (7) 495 926 8927
E-Mail: info@rslife.ru
Web Site: www.rsins.ru
Life & Other Insurance Products & Services
S.I.C.: 6311
N.A.I.C.S.: 524113

Roust Inc. (1)
World Trade Center Office 1507
Krasnopresnenskaya Nab 12
123610 Moscow, Russia
Tel.: (7) 495 727 1075
E-Mail: roust@roust.com
Distilled Spirits Distr
Import Export
S.I.C.: 5182
N.A.I.C.S.: 424820
Roustam V. Tariko *(Founder, Chm & CEO)*

U.S. Subsidiary:

Central European Distribution Corporation (1)
3000 Atrium Way Ste 265
Mount Laurel, NJ 08054 DE
Tel.: (856) 273-6980
E-Mail: info@cedc.com.pl
Web Site: www.cedc.com
Sls.: $1,745,315,000
Assets: $1,767,552,000
Liabilities: $1,964,461,000
Net Worth: ($196,909,000)
Earnings: ($363,238,000)
Emp.: 4,067
Fiscal Year-end: 12/31/12
Holding Company; Distilled Beverages Mfr & Distr
S.I.C.: 6719
N.A.I.C.S.: 551112
Roustam V. Tariko *(Interim Pres)*
Grant Winterton *(CEO)*
Ryan Lee *(CFO & VP)*
Bartosz Kolacinski *(Deputy CFO)*
Vladimir Filiptsev *(CEO-Russian Alcohol Grp)*

Non-U.S. Subsidiaries:

Agis SA (2)
Szosa Chelminska 26
Torun, 87 100, Poland
Tel.: (48) 566225658
Fax: (48) 566221852
Web Site: www.agis.com.pl
Sales Range: $150-199.9 Million
Distributes Wines, Beers & other Beverages
S.I.C.: 5921
N.A.I.C.S.: 445310

Bols Hungary, Kft (2)
Alkotas Point Irodahaz Alkotas u 50
1123 Budapest, Hungary
Tel.: (36) 13252500
Fax: (36) 13252501
E-Mail: info@bols.hu
Web Site: www.bols.hu
Emp.: 5
Alcoholic Beverages Mfr
S.I.C.: 2085
N.A.I.C.S.: 312140
Mariusz Chrobot *(Gen Mgr)*

CEDC International sp. z o.o. (2)
Kowanowska 48
64-600 Oborniki, Poland
Tel.: (48) 612974300
Fax: (48) 612974301
Alcoholic Beverages Mfr
S.I.C.: 2085
N.A.I.C.S.: 312140

CK POWER PUBLIC COMPANY LIMITED

587 Viriyathavorn Building Sutthisarn Road
Dindaeng Subdistrict
Dindaeng District, Bangkok, 10400, Thailand
Tel.: (66) 2691 9720
Fax: (66) 2691 9723
Web Site: www.ckpower.co.th
CKP—(THA)

Business Description:
Electric Power
S.I.C.: 4931
N.A.I.C.S.: 221122

Personnel:
Thanong Bidaya *(Chm)*
Plew Trivisvavet *(Chm-Exec Bd)*
Supamas Trivisvavet *(Mng Dir)*

Board of Directors:
Thanong Bidaya
Vicharn Aramvareekul
Supong Chayutsahakij
Alvin Gee
Prawet Ingadapa
Prasert Marittanaporn
Techapit Sangsingkeo
Narong Sangsuriya
Sompodh Sripoom
Plew Trivisvavet
Supamas Trivisvavet
Thanawat Trivisvavet

Joint Venture:

Bangpa-in Cogeneration Limited (1)
No 587 Sutthisarnvinijchai Road
Dindaeng District, Bangkok, Thailand TH
Tel.: (66) 2 275 0026
Fax: (66) 2 275 7029
Electric Power & Steam Generation & Distribution Services
S.I.C.: 4939
N.A.I.C.S.: 221118

C.K. TANG LIMITED

310 & 320 Orchard Rd
Singapore, 238864, Singapore

Tel.: (65) 67375500
Fax: (65) 67351130
E-Mail: corporate@tangs.com.sg
Web Site: www.tangs.com
Year Founded: 1932
Sales Range: $150-199.9 Million
Emp.: 686
Business Description:
Department Stores Owner & Operator
S.I.C.: 5311
N.A.I.C.S.: 452111
Personnel:
Ernest Teng Peng Seow *(Chm)*
Tiang Sooi Foo *(CEO)*
Siang Yarng Foo *(Sec & Legal Counsel)*
Juliet Ting Willcox *(Sr VP-Tangs Stores Singapore)*
Board of Directors:
Ernest Teng Peng Seow
Tiang Sooi Foo
Michael Grunberg
Cecil Vivian Richard Wong

CKD CORPORATION
250 Ouji 2-chome Komaki
Nagoya, Aichi, 485-8551, Japan
Tel.: (81) 568771111
Fax: (81) 568773412
E-Mail: pd@ckd.co.jp
Web Site: www.ckd.co.jp
Year Founded: 1943
6407—(NGO TKS)
Sls.: $715,341,000
Assets: $789,162,000
Liabilities: $229,790,000
Net Worth: $559,372,000
Earnings: $26,972,000
Emp.: 3,273
Fiscal Year-end: 03/31/13
Business Description:
Automatic Machinery, Labor-Saving Components, Pneumatic Valves & Cylinders & Auxiliary Components, Fluid Control Components Mfr & Sales
S.I.C.: 3593
N.A.I.C.S.: 333995
Personnel:
Kazunori Kajimoto *(Pres)*
Noriaki Ichimura *(Exec Officer)*
Tsuyoshi Kanada *(Mng Exec Officer)*
Akihiro Kojima *(Exec Officer)*
Masahiro Nagamatsu *(Exec Officer)*
Tatsuya Nishio *(Exec Officer)*
Yoshinori Nozawa *(Mng Exec Officer)*
Takuya Takahashi *(Exec Officer)*
Masahisa Tanase *(Exec Officer)*
Shigetomo Tokuda *(Exec Officer)*
Masahiko Tsukahara *(Mng Exec Officer)*
Kyoichi Uchinaga *(Exec Officer)*
Yoshikazu Yamauchi *(Exec Officer)*
Shinji Yuhara *(Exec Officer)*
Board of Directors:
Jyunichi Kagawa
Kazunori Kajimoto
Yoshinori Nozawa
Chiaki Takahata
Shigetomo Tokuda
Masahiko Tsukahara
Kyoichi Uchinaga

Plants:

CKD Corporation - Kasugai Plant **(1)**
1-850 Horinouchi-cho-kita
Kasugai, Aichi, 486-8530, Japan
Tel.: (81) 568816221
Web Site: www.ckd.co.jp/english/company/introduction/plant/index.htm
Emp.: 900
Semiconductor Equipment Mfr
S.I.C.: 3674
N.A.I.C.S.: 334413
Akihiro Kojima *(Plant Mgr)*

CKD Corporation - Yokkaichi Plant **(1)**
2800 Takayama Komaki-cho
Yokkaichi, Mie, 512-1303, Japan
Tel.: (81) 593392140
Fax: (81) 593992144
Web Site: www.ckd.co.jp/english/company/introduction/plant/index.htm#top
Automated Industrial Machinery Mfr
S.I.C.: 3559
N.A.I.C.S.: 333249

U.S. Subsidiaries:

CKD Corporation **(1)**
2700 Augustine Dr Ste 135
Santa Clara, CA 95054
Tel.: (408) 327-9000
Fax: (408) 327-9004
Web Site: www.ckdusa.com
Emp.: 3
Develops, Manufactures & Sells Fluid Power Cylinders
S.I.C.: 5099
N.A.I.C.S.: 423990

CKD Corporation **(1)**
3940 Olympic Blvd Ste 380
Erlanger, KY 41018-3973
Tel.: (859) 283-2776
Fax: (859) 283-2785
Web Site: www.ckdusa.com
Emp.: 3
Pneumatic Cylinder Developer, Mfr & Whslr
S.I.C.: 5251
N.A.I.C.S.: 444130

CKD Corporation **(1)**
595 Round Rock W Dr
Round Rock, TX 78681
Tel.: (512) 339-3035
Fax: (512) 339-3161
Web Site: www.ckd.com
Emp.: 2
Develops, Manufactures & Sells Fluid Power Cylinders
S.I.C.: 5065
N.A.I.C.S.: 423690

CKD USA Corporation **(1)**
4080 Winnetka Ave
Rolling Meadows, IL 60008 (100%)
Tel.: (847) 368-0539
Fax: (847) 788-0575
E-Mail: ckdusa@ckdusa.com
Web Site: www.ckdusa.com
Sales Range: $500-549.9 Million
Emp.: 18
Develops, Manufactures & Sells Fluid Power Cylinders
S.I.C.: 3491
N.A.I.C.S.: 332911
Tim Cochrane *(Treas & Sec)*

Non-U.S. Subsidiaries:

CDK Korea Corporation **(1)**
3rd Floor Sam Young B D 371-20 Sinsu-dong
Mapo-gu, Seoul, 121-110, Korea (South)
Tel.: (82) 27835201
Fax: (82) 27835204
E-Mail: ckdkorea@ckd-k.co.kr
Web Site: www.ckdkorea.co.kr
Pharmaceutical Preparation Products Mfr
S.I.C.: 2834
N.A.I.C.S.: 325412

CKD (China) Corporation **(1)**
No 101-C Wuxi High-New Tech Industrial Development Zone
Wuxi, Jiangsu, 214023, China
Tel.: (86) 510 5345300
Fax: (86) 510 5345320
Web Site: www.ckd.co.jp
Develops, Manufactures & Sells Fluid Power Cylinders
S.I.C.: 3593
N.A.I.C.S.: 333995

CKD (SHANGHAI) CORPORATION **(1)**
Room 601 Yuan Zhong Scientific Reseach Building 1905 Hongmei Road
Shanghai, 200233, China
Tel.: (86) 2161911888
Fax: (86) 2160905356
Web Site: www.ckd.co.jp/english/glblinfo/global/index.htm
Electrical Components Mfr
S.I.C.: 3679
N.A.I.C.S.: 334419

CKD Singapore Pte Ltd **(1)**
33 Tannery Lane
04-01 Hoesteel Indus Bldg, Singapore, 347789, Singapore (100%)
Tel.: (65) 67442623
Fax: (65) 67442486
E-Mail: ckdsin@ckdsin.com.sg
Web Site: www.ckdsin.com.sg
Emp.: 22
Develops, Manufactures & Sells Fluid Power Cylinders
S.I.C.: 3593
N.A.I.C.S.: 333995

CKD Thai Corporation Ltd. **(1)**
Amata Nakorn Industrial Estate 700/58 Moo 1
Tambol Bankao Amphur Panthong, Chon Buri, 20160, Thailand (100%)
Tel.: (66) 38214646
Fax: (66) 38459037
E-Mail: cst@ckdthai.com
Web Site: www.ckdthai.com
Emp.: 291
Develops, Manufactures & Sells Fluid Power Cylinders
S.I.C.: 3593
N.A.I.C.S.: 333995

M-CKD Precision Sdn. Bhd. **(1)**
Lot 6 Jalan Modal 23 2
Seksyen 23 Kaw Miel Fasa 8, 40300 Shah Alam, Selangor Darul Ehsan, Malaysia (100%)
Tel.: (60) 355411468
Fax: (60) 355411533
E-Mail: mckd@mckd.com.my
Web Site: www.mckd.com.my
Sales Range: $1-9.9 Million
Emp.: 56
Develops, Manufacures & Sells Fluid Power Cylinders
S.I.C.: 3593
N.A.I.C.S.: 333995
K. C. Wong *(Gen Mgr)*

Taiwan CKD Corporation **(1)**
16F-3 No 109 Sec 1 Jhongshan Road
Shinjhuang City, Taipei, 242, Taiwan (100%)
Tel.: (886) 285228198
Fax: (886) 285228128
E-Mail: info@ckdtaiwan.com.tw
Web Site: www.ckd.co.jp/english/glblinfo/global/index.htm
Emp.: 19
Develops, Manufactures & Sells Fluid Power Cylinders
S.I.C.: 3593
N.A.I.C.S.: 333995
Shigeru Takano *(Mgr-Admin)*

CKF, INC.
48 Prince St
Hantsport, NS, B0P 1P0, Canada
Tel.: (902) 684-3231
Fax: (902) 684-9703
Toll Free: (877) 425-3462
Web Site: www.ckfinc.com
Sales Range: $75-99.9 Million
Emp.: 500
Fiscal Year-end: 12/31/12
Business Description:
Pulp Fibre Tableware Products Mfr
S.I.C.: 2519
N.A.I.C.S.: 337125
Personnel:
Ian Anderson *(CEO)*

CL ASSET HOLDINGS, LIMITED
Level 2 28 34 Clarke Street
Crows Nest, NSW, 2065, Australia
Tel.: (61) 294323999
Fax: (61) 294609888
E-Mail: info@cl.com.au
Web Site: www.cl.com.au
Emp.: 3
Business Description:
Property Investor, Developer, Operator & Manager
S.I.C.: 6531
N.A.I.C.S.: 531390
Personnel:
Theodore Baker *(Chm, CEO & Mng Dir)*
Henry Kam *(Sec & Controller-Fin)*
Board of Directors:
Theodore Baker
Gary Dainton
Peter Mitropoulos
Legal Counsel:
HWL Ebsworth Lawyers
Level 14 Australia Sq 264 278 George St
Sydney, Australia

CL FINANCIAL LIMITED
1 Herbert St
Saint Claire, Port of Spain, Trinidad & Tobago
Tel.: (868) 6287589
Fax: (868) 6283766
Web Site:
Sales Range: Less than $1 Million
Emp.: 5
Fiscal Year-end: 12/31/12
Business Description:
Holding Company
S.I.C.: 6719
N.A.I.C.S.: 551112
Personnel:
Marlon Holder *(CEO)*

CLAAS KGAA MBH
(d/b/a Claas Gruppe)
Munsterstrasse 33
33428 Harsewinkel, Germany
Tel.: (49) 52 4712 0
Fax: (49) 52 4712 1926
E-Mail: investorrelations@claas.com
Web Site: www.claas-group.com
Year Founded: 1913
Sls.: $5,252,960,049
Assets: $3,988,816,067
Liabilities: $2,270,516,121
Net Worth: $1,718,299,946
Earnings: $291,641,120
Emp.: 9,697
Fiscal Year-end: 09/30/13
Business Description:
Holding Company; Agricultural Machinery Mfr & Distr
S.I.C.: 6719
N.A.I.C.S.: 551112
Personnel:
Cathrina Claas-Muhlhauser *(Chm-Supervisory Bd)*
Jurgen Schmidt *(Deputy Chm-Supervisory Bd)*
Theo Freye *(Member-Exec Bd)*
Hermann Garbers *(Member-Exec Bd-Tech & Quality)*
Lothar Kriszun *(Member-Exec Bd-Tractors)*
Hans Lampert *(Member-Exec Bd-Fin & Controlling)*
Jan-Hendrik Mohr *(Member-Exec Bd-Sls)*
Henry Puhl *(Member-Exec Bd-Grain Harvest)*
Supervisory Board of Directors:
Cathrina Claas-Muhlhauser
Christian Ernst Boehringer
Helmut Claas
Patrick Claas
Reinhold Claas
Michael Kohler
Gunter Linke
Ulrich Nickol
Gerd Peskes
Jurgen Schmidt
Heinrich Strotjohann
Carmelo Zanghi

Claas KGaA mbH—(Continued)

Subsidiaries:

Brotje Automation GmbH (1)
Stahlstrasse 1 5
Wiefelstede, 26215 Oldenburg, Germany (100%)
Tel.: (49) 4402966162
Fax: (49) 4402966290
E-Mail: info@broetjeautomation.de
Web Site: www.broetjeautomation.de
Emp.: 250
S.I.C.: 1731
N.A.I.C.S.: 238210
Bernd Schroeder *(Mng Dir)*

Claas Bordesholm GmbH (1)
Dieselstrasse 3
Wattenbek, 24582 Bordesholm, Germany (74.4%)
Tel.: (49) 4322754961
Fax: (49) 4322754969
Web Site: www.claas-bordesholm.de/de/
Farm & Garden Machinery & Equipment Whslr
S.I.C.: 3523
N.A.I.C.S.: 333111

Claas Industrietechnik GmbH (1)
Halberstadter Str 15-19
33106 Paderborn, Germany (100%)
Tel.: (49) 52517050
Fax: (49) 52517055030
E-Mail: bolweg@class.com
Web Site: www.claas-cit.com
Emp.: 500
Industrial Machinery & Equipment Whslr
S.I.C.: 5084
N.A.I.C.S.: 423830
Uwe Bolweg *(Mng Dir)*
Henry Puho *(Mng Dir)*

Claas Saulgau GmbH (1)
Zeppelinstr 2
88348 Saulgau, Germany (100%)
Tel.: (49) 75812030
Fax: (49) 75812036225
E-Mail: info@class.com
Web Site: www.claas.com
Emp.: 50
Farm Machinery & Equipment Mfr
S.I.C.: 3523
N.A.I.C.S.: 333111
Rolf Meuther *(Exec Dir & Head-Mgmt-Forage Harvest Machinery)*

Claas Selbstfahrende Erntemaschinen GmbH (1)
Munsterstr 33
Harsewinkel, 33428 Gutersloh, Germany (100%)
Tel.: (49) 5247120
Fax: (49) 5247122225
E-Mail: info@claas.de
Web Site: www.claas.de
Emp.: 2,000
Farm Machinery & Equipment Mfr
S.I.C.: 3523
N.A.I.C.S.: 333111
Hans-Peter Grothaus *(Mgr)*

Claas Vertriebsgesellschaft mbH (1)
Munsterstr 33
Harsewinkel, 33428 Gutersloh, Germany (100%)
Tel.: (49) 5247120
Fax: (49) 122721
E-Mail: infoclasse@claas.com
Web Site: www.claas.de
Emp.: 1,500
Farm Machinery & Equipment Mfr
S.I.C.: 3523
N.A.I.C.S.: 333111
Henning Rabe *(Dir-Mktg)*

U.S. Subsidiary:

Claas Omaha Inc. (1)
8401 S 132nd St
Omaha, NE 68138-5600 (100%)
Tel.: (402) 861-1000
Fax: (402) 861-1003
Web Site: www.claas.com
Farm Machinery & Equipment Mfr
S.I.C.: 3523
N.A.I.C.S.: 333111

Non-U.S. Subsidiaries:

Claas Argentina S.A. (1)
Lainez 58
Sunchalez, Santa Fe, 2322, Argentina (100%)
Tel.: (54) 3493423433
Fax: (54) 3493423259
Web Site: www.claas.com.ar
Harvesting Machinery & Equipment Mfr
S.I.C.: 3523
N.A.I.C.S.: 333111

Claas France Holding S.A.S. (1)
Avenue Du Parc Medicis
94260 Fresnes, France (100%)
Tel.: (33) 146748181
Fax: (33) 146747482
Web Site: www.claas.fr
Emp.: 80
Holding Company
S.I.C.: 6719
N.A.I.C.S.: 551112
Thierry Lemaire *(Mng Dir)*

Subsidiary:

Claas France S.A.S. (2)
Ave du Parc Medicis
Fresnes, France (100%)
Tel.: (33) 146748181
Fax: (33) 146748182
E-Mail: maariawlle.chevassu@claas.com
Web Site: www.claas.fr
Emp.: 180
Lawn & Garden Tractor & Home Lawn & Garden Equipment Mfr
S.I.C.: 3524
N.A.I.C.S.: 333112
Thierry Lemaire *(Mng Dir)*

Subsidiary:

Claas Reseau Agricole S.A.S. (3)
Route De Joinville Zone Artisanale
Rupt-sur-Moselle, France (100%)
Tel.: (33) 325949500
Fax: (33) 325949505
Web Site: www.claas.fr
Emp.: 69
Industrial Machinery & Equipment Whslr
S.I.C.: 5084
N.A.I.C.S.: 423830
Patrick Lombard *(Mng Dir)*

Claas Hungaria Kft. (1)
Dozsa Gyorgy Ut 17
Torokszentmiklos, Kecskemet, Hungary (100%)
Tel.: (36) 56597600
Web Site: www.claas.com
Farm Machinery & Equipment Mfr
S.I.C.: 3523
N.A.I.C.S.: 333111

Claas Iberica S.A. (1)
Apartado 19
Avenida de la Constitucion N 2, 28850 Madrid, Spain (100%)
Tel.: (34) 916559152
Web Site: www.claas.com
Farm & Garden Machinery & Equipment Whslr
S.I.C.: 3523
N.A.I.C.S.: 333111

Claas India Ltd. (1)
15/3 Mathura Rd
121003 Faridabad, Haryana, India (100%)
Tel.: (91) 1294297000
Fax: (91) 1295042764
Web Site: www.claas.com
Emp.: 50
Farm Machinery & Equipment Mfr
S.I.C.: 3523
N.A.I.C.S.: 333111
P. K. Malik *(Mng Dir)*

Claas U.K. Ltd. (1)
Saxham Business Park Saxham
Bury Saint Edmunds, IP286QZ, United Kingdom (100%)
Tel.: (44) 1284763100
Fax: (44) 1284769839
Web Site: www.claas.com
Emp.: 100
Farm & Garden Machinery & Equipment Whslr
S.I.C.: 3523
N.A.I.C.S.: 333111

Clive Last *(Chm)*

CLAIM POST RESOURCES INC.

Suite 903 141 Adelaide Street West
Toronto, ON, M5H 3L5, Canada
Tel.: (416) 203-5248
Fax: (416) 203-1254
Web Site: www.claimpostresources.com
Year Founded: 2005
CPS—(TSXV)
Int. Income: $213
Assets: $1,325,539
Liabilities: $744,052
Net Worth: $581,487
Earnings: ($532,350)
Fiscal Year-end: 09/30/12

Business Description:
Gold Mining Services
S.I.C.: 1041
N.A.I.C.S.: 212221

Personnel:
Charles M. Gryba *(Pres & CEO)*
Rebecca Hudson *(CFO)*
Richard D. Williams *(Sec)*

Board of Directors:
Charles M. Gryba
Julian B. Kemp
Joel D. Schneyer
Phillip Walford
Richard D. Williams

CLAIMPICKER AG

1st Floor 9 Building Shilong Road
Shanghai, China
Tel.: (86) 21 51699668
Fax: (86) 21 54085665
Web Site: www.claimpicker.de
OOV—(DEU)

Business Description:
Photo & Video Filing Sharing Services
S.I.C.: 2741
N.A.I.C.S.: 519130

Personnel:
Andre Muller *(Chm)*

CLAIMSECURE INC.

City Centre Plaza 1 City Centre Drive Suite 620
Mississauga, ON, L5B 1M2, Canada
Tel.: (905) 949-2322
Fax: (905) 949-3029
Toll Free: (888) 479-7587
Web Site: www.claimsecure.com
Year Founded: 1982
Rev.: $218,753,494
Emp.: 300

Business Description:
Healthcare Management Services
S.I.C.: 8082
N.A.I.C.S.: 621610

Personnel:
Peter Craig *(Chm & CEO)*
Paul Hardwick *(Pres)*
Greg Sawyer *(CFO & Controller)*
Danica Riengeutte *(COO)*

CLAIRGUIL

RN 165 Zac Kervidanou 3
Mellac, 29300 Quimper, France
Tel.: (33) 298719191
Sls.: $20,300,000
Emp.: 61

Business Description:
Grocery Stores
S.I.C.: 5411
N.A.I.C.S.: 445110

Personnel:
Xavier Le Jouan *(Mng Dir)*

Board of Directors:
Xavier Le Jouan

CLAIRVEST GROUP INC.

22 St Clair Avenue East Suite 1700
Toronto, ON, M4T 2S3, Canada
Tel.: (416) 925-9270
Fax: (416) 925-5753
Web Site: www.clairvest.com
CVG—(TSX)
Rev.: $46,745,779
Assets: $376,669,963
Liabilities: $29,073,097
Net Worth: $347,596,866
Earnings: $35,549,137
Emp.: 25
Fiscal Year-end: 03/31/13

Business Description:
Merchant Banking Services
S.I.C.: 6211
N.A.I.C.S.: 523110

Personnel:
Joseph L. Rotman *(Founder)*
Joseph J. Heffernan *(Chm)*
B. Jeffrey Parr *(Co-CEO & Mng Dir)*
Kenneth B. Rotman *(Co-CEO & Mng Dir)*
Michael Castellarin *(Mng Dir)*
Mitchell S. Green *(Mng Dir)*
Michael A. Wagman *(Mng Dir)*
Daniel Cheng *(CFO)*
Aly Champsi *(Principal)*
Sebastien Dhonte *(Principal)*
Steve Frenkiel *(Principal)*
Robbie Isenberg *(Principal)*
Adrian Pasricha *(Principal)*
Heather G. Crawford *(Gen Counsel & Sec)*

Board of Directors:
Joseph J. Heffernan
John Barnett
Michael Bregman
Sydney C. Cooper
Gerald R. Heffernan
G. John Krediet
B. Jeffrey Parr
Joseph L. Rotman
Kenneth B. Rotman
Lionel H. Schipper
Isadore Sharp

Transfer Agent:
CIBC Mellon Trust Company
PO Box 700 Station B
Montreal, QC, Canada

CLAMART AUTOMOBILES

185 Avenue Victor Hugo
92140 Clamart, France
Tel.: (33) 141331919
Web Site: www.clamartautomobiles.fr
Sls.: $20,700,000
Emp.: 33

Business Description:
New & Used Car Dealers
S.I.C.: 5511
N.A.I.C.S.: 441110

Board of Directors:
Jean-Claude Jacquetin

CLANCY CONSULTING LTD

2 Dunham Court
Altrincham, Cheshire, WA14 4NX, United Kingdom
Tel.: (44) 1616136000
Fax: (44) 1616136099
E-Mail: enquries@clancy.co.uk
Web Site: www.clancy.co.uk
Year Founded: 1972
Rev.: $11,525,866
Emp.: 110

Business Description:
Building Consulting Services
S.I.C.: 8748
N.A.I.C.S.: 541618

Personnel:
Alan Bramwell *(CEO)*

CLANCY EXPLORATION LIMITED

3 Corporation Place
PO Box 7040
Orange, NSW, 2800, Australia
Tel.: (61) 2 6361 1285
Fax: (61) 2 6361 1202
E-Mail: info@clancyexploration.com
Web Site: www.clancyexploration.com
Year Founded: 2003
CLY—(ASX DEU)
Rev.: $1,018,204
Assets: $3,884,492
Liabilities: $1,454,701
Net Worth: $2,429,791
Earnings: ($2,012,682)
Fiscal Year-end: 12/31/12

Business Description:
Copper & Gold Exploration Services
S.I.C.: 1021
N.A.I.C.S.: 212234

Personnel:
Gordon Barnes *(Mng Dir)*
Natalie Forsyth-Stock *(CFO)*
Rowan Caren *(Sec)*

Board of Directors:
Michael Etheridge
Gordon Barnes
Natalie Forsyth-Stock
James Macdonald

Legal Counsel:
Watson Mangioni
Level 13 50 Carrington Street
Sydney, NSW, 2000, Australia

Holborn Lenhoff Massey
3rd Floor Irwin Chambers 16 Irwin Street
Perth, WA, 6000, Australia

Hilary Macdonald
Suite 29 18 Stirling Highway
Nedlands, WA, 6009, Australia

CLARANET LIMITED

21 Southampton Row
London, WC1B 5HA, United Kingdom
Tel.: (44) 2076858310
Fax: (44) 2076858001
E-Mail: info@uk.claranet.net
Web Site: www.uk.claranet.net
Emp.: 250

Business Description:
Internet Access Services
S.I.C.: 7373
N.A.I.C.S.: 541512

Personnel:
Charles Costandi Nasser *(CEO)*
Olivier Beaudet *(CEO-France)*

Subsidiary:

Netscalibur Ltd. (1)
21 Southampton Row
London, WC1B 5HA, United Kingdom
Tel.: (44) 8708878800
Fax: (44) 8708878855
E-Mail: provisioning@netscalibur.co.uk
Web Site: www.netscalibur.co.uk
Emp.: 600
Online Business Services
S.I.C.: 7389
N.A.I.C.S.: 561499

CLARIANT AG

Rothausstrasse 61
4132 Muttenz, Switzerland
Tel.: (41) 61 469 5111
Fax: (41) 61 469 6512
E-Mail: info@clariant.com
Web Site: www.clariant.com
Year Founded: 1995
CLN—(SWX)
Sls.: $6,516,934,160
Assets: $10,280,523,000
Liabilities: $6,999,390,200
Net Worth: $3,281,132,800
Earnings: $256,878,160
Emp.: 21,202
Fiscal Year-end: 12/31/12

Business Description:
Dyes, Colorants, Additives, Master Batches & Specialty Chemicals for Dyeing, Finishing Textiles, Paper, Leather, Plastics & Aluminum Mfr
S.I.C.: 2899
N.A.I.C.S.: 325199

Personnel:
Rudolf Wehrli *(Chm)*
Gunter von Au *(Vice Chm)*
Hariolf Kottmann *(CEO)*
Patrick Jany *(CFO)*
Martin Vollmer *(CTO)*

Board of Directors:
Rudolf Wehrli
Peter Chen
Peter R. Isler
Dominik S. Koechlin
Hariolf Kottmann
Carlo G. Soave
Dolf Stockhausen
Gunter von Au
Konstantin Winterstein

Subsidiaries:

Clariant Beteiligungen AG (1)
Rothausstrasse 61
4132 Muttenz, Switzerland
Tel.: (41) 61 469 51 11
Chemical Product Mfr & Distr
S.I.C.: 2899
N.A.I.C.S.: 325998

Clariant Chemiebeteiligungen AG (1)
Rothausstrasse 61
4132 Muttenz, Switzerland
Tel.: (41) 61 4695111
Chemical Product Mfr & Distr
S.I.C.: 2899
N.A.I.C.S.: 325998

Clariant Products (Schweiz) AG (1)
Rothaus strasse 61
4132 Muttenz, Switzerland (100%)
Tel.: (41) 614695111
Fax: (41) 614695901
E-Mail: info@clariant.com
Web Site: www.clariant.com
Sales Range: $125-149.9 Million
Emp.: 1,000
Specialty Chemicals
S.I.C.: 2869
N.A.I.C.S.: 325998
Hariolf Kottmann *(CEO)*

EBITO Chemiebeteiligungen AG (1)
Rothausstrasse 61
4132 Muttenz, Switzerland
Tel.: (41) 61 469 51 11
Chemical Product Mfr
S.I.C.: 2899
N.A.I.C.S.: 325998

swissnovaChem Ltd. (1)
c/o Novac AG Uferstrasse 90
CH 4051 Basel, Switzerland
Tel.: (41) 23417730305
Fax: (41) 23415875440
Web Site: www.clariant.com
Mfr. of Dyes & Paints
S.I.C.: 2816
N.A.I.C.S.: 325130

U.S. Subsidiary:

Clariant Corporation (1)
4000 Monroe Rd
Charlotte, NC 28205
Tel.: (704) 331-7000
Fax: (704) 377-1063
E-Mail: info@clariant-northamerica.com
Web Site: www.clariant-northamerica.com
Emp.: 3,700
Specialty Chemicals Mfr
Import Export
S.I.C.: 2869
N.A.I.C.S.: 325199
Kenneth Golder *(CEO)*

Divisions:

Clariant Corporation (2)
(Formerly Sud-Chemie Inc.)
1600 W Hill St
Louisville, KY 40210-1750
Mailing Address:
PO Box 32370
Louisville, KY 40232-2370
Tel.: (502) 634-7200
Telex: 204190; 204239
Fax: (502) 637-3732
E-Mail:
Emp.: 750
Catalyst & Specialty Chemical Mfr
Import Export
S.I.C.: 2819
N.A.I.C.S.: 325180
John A. Ray *(CEO)*

Division:

Sud-Chemie Inc.-Air Purification (3)
32 Fremont St
Needham, MA 02494-2933 (100%)
Tel.: (781) 444-5188
Fax: (781) 444-0130
E-Mail: scpsales@sud-chemieinc.com
Web Site: www.sud-chemieinc.com
Emp.: 35
Precious Metal Based Catalyst Mfr
S.I.C.: 2819
N.A.I.C.S.: 325180
Martin Morrow *(Gen Mgr)*

Joint Venture:

Scientific Design Company, Inc. (3)
49 Industrial Ave
Little Ferry, NJ 07643-1901 DE
Tel.: (201) 641-0500
Fax: (201) 641-6986
E-Mail: sdci@scidesign.com
Web Site: www.scidesign.com
Emp.: 70
Process Technology Licensor
S.I.C.: 2819
N.A.I.C.S.: 325180
Darren S. Adams *(Pres & CEO)*

Clariant-Masterbatches Division (2)
85 Industrial Dr
Holden, MA 01520
Tel.: (508) 829-6321
Fax: (508) 829-6230
Web Site: www.clariant.masterbatches.com
Emp.: 3,500
Color & Additive Masterbatches & Specialty Compounding
Export
S.I.C.: 3087
N.A.I.C.S.: 325991

Units:

Clariant Corporation (3)
3023 Mayo St
Dalton, GA 30720
Tel.: (706) 275-8567
Fax: (706) 275-8570
Web Site: www.clariant.com
S.I.C.: 2821
N.A.I.C.S.: 325211

Clariant Corporation (3)
926 Elliot Rd Albion Industrial Park
Albion, MI 49224
Tel.: (517) 629-9101
Fax: (517) 629-5877
Toll Free: (877) 546-2885
Web Site: www.clariant.com
Emp.: 90
S.I.C.: 2821
N.A.I.C.S.: 325211

Subsidiaries:

Archroma Global Services (2)
4331 Chesapeake Dr
Charlotte, NC 28216
Tel.: (704) 395-6569
E-Mail: archroma.services@clariant.com
Web Site: www.archroma.com
Printing Services
S.I.C.: 2299
N.A.I.C.S.: 313110
Brad McClanahan *(Head-Global Bus)*

Katapullt LLC (2)
30 Ramland Rd Ste 103
Orangeburg, NY 10962
Tel.: (800) 424-9300
Chemical Product Distr
S.I.C.: 5169
N.A.I.C.S.: 424690

Kion Corp. (2)
1957 Pioneer Road Bldg A
Huntingdon Valley, PA 19006
Tel.: (215) 957-6100
Web Site: www.kioncorp.com
Emp.: 15
Plastics Material & Resin Mfr
S.I.C.: 2821
N.A.I.C.S.: 325211

Octagon Process, L.L.C. (2)
625 E Catawba Ave
Mount Holly, NC 28012
Tel.: (704) 822-2677
Fax: (704) 822-2193
E-Mail: deicers.us@clariant.com
Web Site: www.octagonprocess.com
Aircraft Runway De-icing & Anti-icing Product Mfr
S.I.C.: 2899
N.A.I.C.S.: 325998

Sud-Chemie North America Inc. (2)
1600 W Hill St
Louisville, KY 40210-1750
Tel.: (502) 634-7200
Industrial Chemical Product Mfr
S.I.C.: 2899
N.A.I.C.S.: 325998

Non-U.S. Subsidiaries:

Clariant (Argentina) S.A. (1)
Av Jose Garibaldi 2401
Lomas De Zamora, 1836 Buenos Aires, 1836, Argentina (100%)
Tel.: (54) 1142390600
Fax: (54) 1142390630
Web Site: www.clariant.com.ar
Emp.: 120
Mfr. of Dyes & Paints
S.I.C.: 2819
N.A.I.C.S.: 325130

Clariant (Australia) Pty. Ltd. (1)
100 Heales
Lara, VIC, 3212, Australia (100%)
Tel.: (61) 352759400
Fax: (61) 352759440
E-Mail: ainn.taooidie@clariant.com
Web Site: www.clariant.com
Sales Range: $100-124.9 Million
Emp.: 65
Mfr. of Dyes & Paints
S.I.C.: 2819
N.A.I.C.S.: 325130
Lynn Lirkin *(Mng Dir)*

Clariant Benelux SA/NV (1)
Parc Scientifique Fleming Fond Jean Paques 1
Louvain-la-Neuve, 1348, Belgium (100%)
Tel.: (32) 0010480511
Fax: (32) 10480666
Rev.: $114,000,000
Emp.: 200
Mfr. of Dyes & Paints
S.I.C.: 2819
N.A.I.C.S.: 325130
Marcel Dechear *(Mgr-Fin)*

Subsidiary:

Clariant Masterbatches Benelux SA (2)
Parc Scientifique Fleming Fond Jean Paques 1
1348 Louvain-la-Neuve, Belgium
Tel.: (32) 10 48 06 77
Fax: (32) 10 48 05 00
Chemical Product Mfr & Distr
S.I.C.: 2899
N.A.I.C.S.: 325998

Clariant (Canada), Inc. (1)
4600 Rue Cousens
Saint Laurent, QC, H41X3, Canada (100%)
Tel.: (514) 334-1117
Fax: (514) 334-6746
E-Mail: infocan@clariant.com
Web Site: www.clariant.com.ca
Emp.: 52
Mfr. of Dyes & Paints
S.I.C.: 2816
N.A.I.C.S.: 325130

Subsidiaries:

Phostech Lithium Inc. (2)
280 Avenue Liberte
Candiac, QC, J5R 6X1, Canada

Clariant AG—(Continued)

Tel.: (514) 906-1359
Fax: (450) 638-5995
E-Mail: info@phostechlithium.com
Web Site: www.phostechlithium.com
Lithium Product Mfr
S.I.C.: 2869
N.A.I.C.S.: 325199

Prairie Petro-Chem Ltd. (2)
738-6th St
Estevan, SK, S4A 1A4, Canada
Tel.: (306) 634-5808
Fax: (306) 634-6694
Chemical Product Mfr & Distr
S.I.C.: 2899
N.A.I.C.S.: 325998
Clinton Lund *(Mgr-Laboratory)*

Clariant Chemicals (Taiwan) Co., Ltd (1)
5/F No 96 Chien Kuo N Road Sec 1
Taipei, 10489, Taiwan
Tel.: (886) 2 25166886
Fax: (886) 2 25055588
Chemical Product Mfr & Distr
S.I.C.: 2899
N.A.I.C.S.: 325998

Clariant (China) Ltd. (1)
5/F Sandoz Center 178-182 Texaco Road
Tsuen Wan, NT, China (Hong Kong) (100%)
Tel.: (852) 24064189
Fax: (852) 24076046
Web Site: www.clariant.com
Emp.: 150
Mfr. of Dyes & Paints
S.I.C.: 2819
N.A.I.C.S.: 325130

Non-U.S. Subsidiaries:

Clariant Chemicals (China) Ltd. (2)
No 2 Lane 168 Linhong Rd
200335 Shanghai, China (100%)
Tel.: (86) 2122483000
Fax: (86) 2164952628
Web Site: www.clariant.com
Sales Range: $25-49.9 Million
Emp.: 300
Mfr. of Dyes & Paints
S.I.C.: 2816
N.A.I.C.S.: 325130

Clariant Chemicals (Guangzhou) Ltd. (2)
No 2 Nan Yun San Road Science City
Guangzhou Hi-Tech Indus Dev Zone
510665 Guangzhou, China (100%)
Tel.: (86) 20 2820 2222
Fax: (86) 20 2820 2111
Web Site: www.clariant.masterbatches.com
Mfr of Dyes & Paints
S.I.C.: 2816
N.A.I.C.S.: 325130

Clariant Masterbatches (Beijing) Ltd (2)
2 Yan Qi North No 2 Street Yan Qi
Industrial Development Zone
Huai Rou, Beijing, 101407, China
Tel.: (86) 10 6166 5500
Fax: (86) 10 6166 5050
Web Site: www.clariant.in
Plastic Colorant Mfr & Distr
S.I.C.: 2899
N.A.I.C.S.: 325998

Clariant Masterbatches (Shanghai) Ltd (2)
No 88 Lane 4377 Jin Du Road
Ming Hang District, Shanghai, 201108, China
Tel.: (86) 21 5442 6515
Fax: (86) 21 5442 7962
Web Site: www.clariant.in
Chemical Product Mfr & Distr
S.I.C.: 5169
N.A.I.C.S.: 424690

Clariant (Tianjin) Ltd. (2)
7 Sanwei Rd Dong Li Economic
Development Zone
Dongli District, Tianjin, 300300, China (100%)
Tel.: (86) 2224994288
Fax: (86) 2224990146
Web Site: www.clariant.com
Emp.: 300
Mfr. of Dyes & Paints
S.I.C.: 2819
N.A.I.C.S.: 325130
Yangy Gun *(Gen Mgr)*

Subsidiaries:

Clariant Pigments (Tianjin) Ltd (3)
Guihua No 2 Rd Bohai Fine Chemical
Industrial Park Dagang
Petrochemical Industrial Park, Tianjin, 300270, China
Tel.: (86) 22 6323 3737
Fax: (86) 22 6323 3738
Chemical Product Mfr
S.I.C.: 2899
N.A.I.C.S.: 325998

Clariant (Tianjin) Pigments Co. Ltd. (3)
Ji An St Zhanggui Zhuang Rd
Dongli District, 300163 Tianjin, China (100%)
Tel.: (86) 2224722778
Fax: (86) 22 247 298 34
Web Site: www.clariant.in
Mfr. of Dyes & Paints
S.I.C.: 2816
N.A.I.C.S.: 325130

Clariant (Colombia) S.A. (1)
Calle 18 Nr 43 A 72
Bogota, Colombia (100%)
Tel.: (57) 15781200
Fax: (57) 15781290
Web Site: www.clariant.com.co
Emp.: 140
Mfr. of Dyes & Paints
S.I.C.: 2819
N.A.I.C.S.: 325130

Clariant Colorquimica (Chile) Ltda. (1)
Camino A Melipilla 15 170
Santiago, 9260075, Chile (100%)
Tel.: (56) 23734100
Fax: (56) 23734190
E-Mail: andreaerrazuriz@clariant.com
Web Site: www.clariant.com.cl
Emp.: 120
Mfr. of Dyes & Paints
S.I.C.: 2816
N.A.I.C.S.: 325130
Orlando Gachter *(Mgr)*

Clariant Consulting AG (1)
Novocheryomushkinskaya street 61
117418 Moscow, Russia
Tel.: (7) 495 787 50 50
Fax: (7) 495 787 50 43
Chemical Product Distr
S.I.C.: 5169
N.A.I.C.S.: 424690

Clariant (Denmark) A/S (1)
Naverland 8
DK 2600 Glostrup, Denmark (100%)
Tel.: (45) 43241700
Fax: (45) 43241727
Mfr. of Dyes & Paints
S.I.C.: 2816
N.A.I.C.S.: 325130

Clariant (Egypt) S.A.E. (1)
19 Khalil El Aroussi St
Heliopolis, 11757 Cairo, Egypt
Tel.: (20) 26350709
Fax: (20) 26350580
Web Site: www.clariant.com
Emp.: 50
Mfr. of Dyes & Paints
S.I.C.: 2819
N.A.I.C.S.: 325130

Unit:

Clariant (Egypt) S.A.E.-EGCODAR (2)
23 Alexandria Cairo Desert Rd
21311 Alexandria, 21311, Egypt (100%)
Tel.: (20) 34701149
Fax: (20) 34701104
E-Mail: gaber.abdelhameed@clariant.com
Web Site: www.clariant.com
Emp.: 80
Dyes & Paints Mfr
S.I.C.: 2819
N.A.I.C.S.: 325130
Gaber Abdel Hameed *(Mgr-Site)*

Clariant Finance (Luxembourg) S.A. (1)
12 Rue Guillaume Kroll
Luxembourg, 1882, Luxembourg
Tel.: (352) 261 890 20
Financial Management Services
S.I.C.: 6211
N.A.I.C.S.: 523999

Clariant (Finland) Oy (1)
Robert Huberin Tie 3 B
1510 Vantaa, Finland (100%)
Tel.: (358) 984554200
Fax: (358) 984554250
Web Site: www.clariant.com
Emp.: 20
Mfr. of Dyes & Paints
S.I.C.: 2816
N.A.I.C.S.: 325130
Ter Sjoberg *(Gen Mgr)*

Subsidiary:

Clariant Masterbatches (Finland) Oy (2)
Ayritie 8 D
01510 Vantaa, Finland
Tel.: (358) 10 680 8500
Fax: (358) 10 680 8550
Chemical Product Mfr & Distr
S.I.C.: 2899
N.A.I.C.S.: 325998

Clariant (France) (1)
52 Ave Deschamps Pierreuh
92000 Puteaux, France (100%)
Tel.: (33) 146969600
Fax: (33) 146969601
Web Site: www.clariant.fr
Emp.: 100
Mfr. of Dyes & Paints
S.I.C.: 2819
N.A.I.C.S.: 325130
Arnaud Frete *(Mgr)*

Subsidiaries:

Airsec S.A.S. (2)
6 Rue Louise Michel
94603 Choisy-le-Roi, France
Tel.: (33) 1 41 76 20 00
Fax: (33) 1 41 76 20 57
Chemical Product Mfr & Distr
S.I.C.: 2899
N.A.I.C.S.: 325998

Bentofrance S.A.S. (2)
ZI et Portuaire Rue Louis Saillant
Portes-les-Valence, 26800, France
Tel.: (33) 4 75 57 30 22
Fax: (33) 4 75 57 44 89
E-Mail: btfrsales@clariant.com
Emp.: 10
Chemical Product Mfr
S.I.C.: 2899
N.A.I.C.S.: 325998
Laurent Nicolas *(Gen Mgr)*

Clariant Huningue (2)
Ave De Bale
68331 Huningue, France (100%)
Tel.: (33) 389896000
Fax: (33) 389896195
E-Mail: felix.grimm@clariant.com
Web Site: www.clariant.fr
Emp.: 350
Mfr. of Dyes & Paints
S.I.C.: 2816
N.A.I.C.S.: 325130
Felix Grimm *(Mng Dir)*

Clariant Production (France) S.A.S. (2)
52 Ave des Champs-Pierreux
Nanterre, 389896000, France
Tel.: (33) 389896000
Chemical Product Mfr
S.I.C.: 2899
N.A.I.C.S.: 325998

K.J. Quinn S.A.S. (2)
14/16 Boulevard du Docteur Pontier Zone
Ind De Rieutord
81304 Graulhet, France
Tel.: (33) 5 63428374
Fax: (33) 5 63428384
Leather Product Mfr
S.I.C.: 3199
N.A.I.C.S.: 316998

Clariant GmbH (1)
Am Unisyspark 1
65843 Sulzbach, Hellen, Germany (100%)
Tel.: (49) 619675760
Fax: (49) 61967578856
E-Mail: kontakt@clariant.com
Web Site: www.clariant.de
Emp.: 600
Mfr of Printing Inks & Pigments for Paints, Lacquers, Plastics & Specialty Applications
S.I.C.: 2819
N.A.I.C.S.: 325130

Subsidiaries:

Clariant Beteiligungs GmbH (2)
Am Unisys Park 1
65843 Sulzbach, Germany
Tel.: (49) 6196 757 60
Chemical Product Mfr & Distr
S.I.C.: 2899
N.A.I.C.S.: 325998

Clariant (Deutschland) GmbH (2)
Benzstrasse 11
70771 Leinfelden, Germany (100%)
Tel.: (49) 71190320
Fax: (49) 7119032335
E-Mail: Info@clariant.com
Web Site: www.clariant.com
Sls.: $226,456,736
Emp.: 120
Mfr. of Dyes & Paints
S.I.C.: 2816
N.A.I.C.S.: 325130
Martin Wissner *(Mgr-Site)*

Subsidiaries:

Clariant Advanced Materials GmbH (3)
Am Unisys Park 1
65843 Sulzbach, Germany
Tel.: (49) 6196 757 7893
Fax: (49) 6196 757 8906
E-Mail: contact@clariant.com
Web Site: www.advancedmaterials.clariant.com
Emp.: 600
Plastic Material Mfr & Distr
S.I.C.: 2821
N.A.I.C.S.: 325211

Clariant Masterbatch GmbH & Co. OHG (3)
Hohenrhein 1
56112 Lahnstein, Rheinland Tfalz, Germany (100%)
Tel.: (49) 2621140
Fax: (49) 262114245
E-Mail: uwe.chrecusch@clariant.com
Web Site: www.clariant.masterbaches.com
Emp.: 350
Mfr. of Dyes & Paints
S.I.C.: 2819
N.A.I.C.S.: 325130
Wolsgamg Shadt *(Mng Dir)*

Subsidiary:

Clariant Masterbatches (Deutschland) GmbH (4)
Andrea Heser Hohenrhein 1
56112 Lahnstein, Germany
Tel.: (49) 2621 14 213
Fax: (49) 2621 14 261
Web Site: www.clariant.de
Chemical Product Distr
S.I.C.: 5169
N.A.I.C.S.: 424690

Clariant Vertrieb (Deutshland) GmbH und Co. KG (3)
Am Unisyspark 1
65843 Sulzbach, Germany
Tel.: (49) 6196 757 60
Fax: (49) 6196 757 8856
E-Mail: contact@clariant.com
Emp.: 600
Specialty Chemical Mfr
S.I.C.: 2899
N.A.I.C.S.: 325998

Clariant Verwaltungsgesellschaft mbH (3)
Am Unisys Park 1
65843 Sulzbach, Hellen, Germany (100%)
Tel.: (49) 619675760
Fax: (49) 61967578856

E-Mail: kontact@clariant.com
Web Site: www.clariant.com
Emp.: 350
Mfr. of Dyes & Paints
S.I.C.: 2819
N.A.I.C.S.: 325130
Ulrich Ott *(Mng Dir)*

Sud-Chemie AG (2)
Lenbachplatz 6
80333 Munich, Germany De
Tel.: (49) 89 51100 (100%)
Telex: 523872 scmu d
Fax: (49) 89 5110 375
E-Mail: info@sud-chemie.com
Web Site: www.sud-chemie.com
Sales Range: $1-4.9 Billion
Emp.: 6,500
Mfr of Waste Water Chemical Treatments, Bleaching Earths, Sulfuric Acid, Dessicants & Phosphorus Fertilizers
S.I.C.: 2899
N.A.I.C.S.: 325199
Hariolf Kottmann *(Chm-Supervisory Bd)*
Gunter von Au *(Chm-Mgmt Bd)*
Ralf-Henri Schlomer *(Deputy Chm-Supervisory Bd)*
Udo de Wall *(Member-Mgmt Bd-Fin, Acctg, Tax & Legal Affairs)*
Hans-Joachim Muller *(Member-Mgmt Bd-Catalysts Div & Info Mgmt)*

Subsidiaries:

SC Beteiligungsgesellschaft mbH (3)
Robert-Bosch-Str 32b
Bensheim, Hessen, 64625, Germany
Tel.: (49) 6950607470
Financial Management Services
S.I.C.: 6211
N.A.I.C.S.: 523999

Sud-Chemie Zeolites GmbH (3)
Tricat-Strasse OT Greppin Chemie Park
Bitterfeld-Wolfen Areal B
Wolfen, Bitterfeld, 06803, Germany
Tel.: (49) 3493 7 5810
Fax: (49) 3493 7 6442
Zeolite Mfr
S.I.C.: 2899
N.A.I.C.S.: 325998
Franz Boehm *(Mgr-Site)*

Joint Venture:

ASK Chemicals GmbH (3)
Reisholzstrasse 16-18
PO Box 440
40721 Hilden, Germany De
Tel.: (49) 211711030
Fax: (49) 2117110335
E-Mail: info@ask-chemicals.de
Web Site: www.ask-chemicals.de
Sales Range: $300-349.9 Million
Emp.: 1,300
Foundry Supply Chemicals Mfr
S.I.C.: 2899
N.A.I.C.S.: 325998
Thomas Oehmichen *(CEO)*

Plant:

ASK Chemicals GmbH - Werk Wulfrath (4)
Dieselstrasse 35-41
D-42489 Wulfrath, Germany
Tel.: (49) 20587850
Fax: (49) 20582523
E-Mail: info@ask-chemicals.com
Web Site: www.ask-chemicals.com
Sales Range: $75-99.9 Million
Emp.: 220
Phenolic Resins Mfr
S.I.C.: 2821
N.A.I.C.S.: 325211
Stefan Sommer *(Gen Mgr)*

Non-U.S. Subsidiaries:

ASK Chemicals Benelux B.V. (4)
Industrieweg 73c
NL 5145 PD Waalwijk, Netherlands
Tel.: (31) 416674590
Fax: (31) 416674599
E-Mail: info.benelux@ask-chemicals.com
Web Site: www.ask-chemicals.com
Sales Range: $50-74.9 Million
Emp.: 9
Oil Based Chemical Intermediates Marketer
S.I.C.: 5169
N.A.I.C.S.: 424690
G. VanDyk *(Gen Mgr)*

Non-U.S. Subsidiaries:

Panjin Sud-Chemie Liaohe Catalyst Co., Ltd (3)
Hongqi Street
Shuangtaizi, Panjin, Liaoning, 124021, China
Tel.: (86) 427 5855154
Fax: (86) 427 5855947
Chemical Product Mfr
S.I.C.: 2899
N.A.I.C.S.: 325998

P.T. Sud-Chemie Indonesia (3)
Jl Raya Narogong KM 14 Pangkalan 10
Desa Limusnunggal Cileungsi
Bogor, 16820, Indonesia
Tel.: (62) 21 82497445
Fax: (62) 2182496060
Chemical Product Mfr
S.I.C.: 2899
N.A.I.C.S.: 325998

Shanghai Sud-Chemie Catalysts Co., Ltd (3)
No 18 HaiJin Road Second Industrial
Jin Shan District, Shanghai, 201512, China
Tel.: (86) 21 57266660
Web Site: www.clariant.cn
Chemical Product Mfr
S.I.C.: 2899
N.A.I.C.S.: 325998

Societa Sarda di Bentonite S.r.l. (3)
Strada St 293 Km 063
09010 Piscinas, Italy
Tel.: (39) 0781964095
Fax: (39) 0781964516
E-Mail: info@clariant.com
Emp.: 30
Chemical Product Mfr
S.I.C.: 2899
N.A.I.C.S.: 325998
Massimo Zedda *(Gen Mgr)*

Sud-Chemie Adsorbents Pvt. Ltd (3)
DBS House Prescott Road
Mumbai, 400 001, India
Tel.: (91) 2240779100
Fax: (91) 9870067779
Chemical Product Mfr
S.I.C.: 2899
N.A.I.C.S.: 325998
Ketan Premani *(Head-Chemical Mfg)*

Sud-Chemie Australia Pty Ltd (3)
12 Peachtree Rd
Penrith, NSW, 2750, Australia
Tel.: (61) 2 47321 421
Fax: (61) 2 47321 678
E-Mail: info.australia@sud-chemie.com.au
Web Site: www.sud-chemie.com.au
Chemical Product Mfr & Distr
S.I.C.: 2899
N.A.I.C.S.: 325998
Harry Brooks *(Grp Mgr-Civil Engrg)*

Sud Chemie Catalysts Italia S.r.l. (3)
Via G Fauser 36/B
28100 Novara, Italy
Tel.: (39) 0321 676430
Fax: (39) 0321 676491
Web Site: www.sued-chemie-mt.it
Emp.: 65
Chemical Product Mfr
S.I.C.: 2899
N.A.I.C.S.: 325998
Uwe Duerr *(Gen Mgr)*

Sud-Chemie Catalysts (Nanjing) Co., Ltd (3)
299 Zhanshui Road
Luhe District, 210048 Nanjing, China
Tel.: (86) 25 57060606
Fax: (86) 25 57025689
Web Site: www.clariant.cn
Chemical Product Mfr
S.I.C.: 2899
N.A.I.C.S.: 325998

Sud-Chemie CIS LLC (3)
Mosenka Park Towers Taganskaya Street 17-23
109147 Moscow, Russia
Tel.: (7) 4952585912
Fax: (7) 4952585911
Emp.: 8
Plastic Colorant Mfr
S.I.C.: 2899
N.A.I.C.S.: 325998
Pahritdin Yusupov *(Gen Mgr)*

Sud-Chemie do Brasil Ltda (3)
Rua Industrial 802 Bairro do Rio Abaixo
Jacarei, Sao Paulo, 12321-500, Brazil
Tel.: (55) 1221282288
Fax: (55) 1221282287
Specialty Chemical Mfr
S.I.C.: 2899
N.A.I.C.S.: 325998

Sud-Chemie Espana, S.L. (3)
Camino de la Magdalena s/n
Yuncos, 45210 Toledo, Spain ES
Tel.: (34) 925 53 70 83 (100%)
Telex: 41204
Fax: (34) 925 53 75 75
E-Mail: spain@sud-chemie.com
Web Site: www.sud-chemie.com
Mfr of Chemical Absorbents, Additives & Catalysts
S.I.C.: 2899
N.A.I.C.S.: 325998

Sud-Chemie France S.A.S. (3)
6 Rue Louise Michel
94600 Choisy-le-Roi, France
Tel.: (33) 1 41 76 20 00
Fax: (33) 1 41 76 20 20
Chemical Product Distr
S.I.C.: 5169
N.A.I.C.S.: 424690

Sud-Chemie Korea Co., Ltd (3)
527 Okmyung-Ri Daesong-Myun
Nam-Gu, Pohang, Gyungbuk, Korea (South)
Tel.: (82) 54 278 2141
Fax: (82) 54 278 2147
Chemical Product Distr
S.I.C.: 5169
N.A.I.C.S.: 424690
Sang-Hyun Lee, *(Pres & CEO)*

Sud-Chemie Redhill Bentonite (Liaoning) Co., Ltd (3)
Lucky Tower A 1306 3 Dong San Huan Bei Lu
Chaoyang, Beijing, 100027, China
Tel.: (86) 10 84487021
Fax: (86) 10 84487014
Chemical Product Mfr
S.I.C.: 2899
N.A.I.C.S.: 325998

Sud-Chemie South East Asia Pte. Ltd (3)
11A Chin Bee Ave
Singapore, 619936, Singapore
Tel.: (65) 6897 7231
Fax: (65) 6897 8393
E-Mail: info.scsea@clariant.com
Emp.: 26
Chemical Product Mfr
S.I.C.: 2899
N.A.I.C.S.: 325998
Meng Hwee Toh *(Gen Mgr)*

Sud-Chemie (TR) Madencilik Sanayi ve Ticaret A.S. (3)
Izmir Yolu 14 Km Kesirven Koyu Mevkii P K 195
Balikesir, 10034, Turkey
Tel.: (90) 266 264 87 57
Fax: (90) 266 264 87 52
Chemical Product Mfr
S.I.C.: 2899
N.A.I.C.S.: 325998

Sud-Chemie (UK) Limited (3)
3 Drake Mews Gadbrook Park
Northwich, Cheshire, United Kingdom
Tel.: (44) 1606 813060
Chemical Product Distr
S.I.C.: 5169
N.A.I.C.S.: 424690

Clariant (Gulf) FZE (1)
Jafzaview 19 15th Fl Jebel Ali Free Zone South
PO Box 2326
Dubai, United Arab Emirates
Tel.: (971) 4 88 65 588
Fax: (971) 4 88 65 585
Emp.: 20
Chemical Product Mfr & Distr
S.I.C.: 2899
N.A.I.C.S.: 325998
Robert Elisha *(Area Mgr-Mktg)*

Clariant (Hellas) S.A. (1)
Lelas Karadianne 67
Lykovrisi, 14123 Athens, Greece (100%)
Tel.: (30) 2102896100
Fax: (30) 2102851330
E-Mail: vaios.barlas@clariant.com
Web Site: www.clariant.com
Sales Range: $10-24.9 Million
Emp.: 53
Mfr. of Dyes & Paints
S.I.C.: 2816
N.A.I.C.S.: 325130
Vaios Barlas *(Mng Dir)*

Clariant Iberica S.A. (1)
Via Augusta 252 260
8017 Barcelona, Spain (100%)
Tel.: (34) 933068121
Fax: (34) 933768482
Web Site: www.clariant.es
Emp.: 100
Mfr. of Dyes & Paints
S.I.C.: 2816
N.A.I.C.S.: 325130

Subsidiaries:

Clariant Iberica Servicios S.L. (2)
Recursos Humanos Zal - Prat C/ Cal Coracero 46-56
El Prat del Llobregat, 08820 Barcelona, Spain
Tel.: (34) 93 479 82 00
Chemical Product Mfr & Distr
S.I.C.: 2899
N.A.I.C.S.: 325998

Clariant Masterbatch Iberica (2)
Carretera N II Km 592 4
08740 Barcelona, Spain (100%)
Tel.: (34) 936356100
Fax: (34) 936533861
E-Mail: infocmbi@clariant.com
Web Site: www.clariant.masterbatches.com
Emp.: 75
S.I.C.: 2899
N.A.I.C.S.: 325998

Non-U.S. Subsidiary:

Clariant Quimicos (Portugal) Ltd. (2)
Estrada Nacional 249 Km 15
2725 397 Mem Martins, Portugal (100%)
Tel.: (351) 219269762
Fax: (351) 219219767
Web Site: www.clariant.com
Emp.: 50
Mfr. of Dyes & Paints
S.I.C.: 2816
N.A.I.C.S.: 325130

Clariant (India) Ltd. (1)
Paville House 3rd Fl Of Veer Savarkar Marg
Opposite Siddhivinayak Temp
Mumbai, Maharashtra, 400025, India (51%)
Tel.: (91) 2224323434
Fax: (91) 2224229020
Web Site: www.clariantindia.com
Sales Range: $75-99.9 Million
Emp.: 400
Mfr. of Dyes & Paints
S.I.C.: 2819
N.A.I.C.S.: 325130

Subsidiaries:

BTP India Private Limited (2)
2nd Fl Kences Towers No 1 Ramakrishna St
T Nagar, Chennai, 600 017, India (100%)
Tel.: (91) 4428144136
Fax: (91) 4428144151
E-Mail: btpho@clariant.com
Web Site: www.btpindia.com
Sls.: $11,628,200
Emp.: 83
Mfr. of Dyes & Paints
S.I.C.: 2819
N.A.I.C.S.: 325130
G. Ramachandran *(Mgr)*

Clariant Chemicals (India) Limited (2)
Kolshet Road
PO Sandoz Baug
Thane, 400 607, India

Clariant AG—(Continued)

Tel.: (91) 22 2531 5330
Fax: (91) 22 2531 5666
E-Mail: clariant@clariant.com
Web Site: www.clariant.in
506390—(BOM NSE)
Rev.: $206,799,628
Assets: $152,288,265
Liabilities: $59,307,272
Net Worth: $92,980,992
Earnings: $18,781,094
Fiscal Year-end: 12/31/12
Paint & Coatings Mfr
S.I.C.: 2851
N.A.I.C.S.: 325510
R. A. Shah *(Chm)*
Deepak Parikh *(Vice Chm & Mng Dir)*
B. L. Gaggar *(Sec & Exec Dir-Fin)*

Colour-Chem Ltd. **(2)**
Ravindra Anx 194 Churchgate Reclamation
Mumbai, Maharashtra, 400020,
India (70%)
Tel.: (91) 2222022161
Fax: (91) 2222029781
Web Site: www.colour-chem.com
Sls.: $103,600,176
Emp.: 800
Mfr. of Dyes & Paints
S.I.C.: 2816
N.A.I.C.S.: 325130

Clariant Industries (Korea) Ltd. **(1)**
84-7 Chungdam-dong
Kangnam-ku, Seoul, Korea (South) (100%)
Tel.: (82) 2 510 8000
Fax: (82) 2 514 4147
Web Site: www.clariant.com
Emp.: 75
Mfr. of Dyes & Paints
S.I.C.: 2816
N.A.I.C.S.: 325130

Clariant Insurance AG **(1)**
Erlenweg 3
9495 Triesen, Liechtenstein
Tel.: (423) 231 20 00
Insurance Management Services
S.I.C.: 6411
N.A.I.C.S.: 524298

Clariant (Italia) S.p.A. **(1)**
Via A Manzoni
20030 Milan, Italy
Tel.: (39) 299181
Fax: (39) 0299188789
Web Site: www.clariant.com
Emp.: 300
Mfr. of Dyes & Paints
S.I.C.: 2816
N.A.I.C.S.: 325130

Subsidiary:

Clariant Masterbatches (Italia) S.p.A. **(2)**
Via Bergamo 77
23807 Merate, Lecco, Italy
Tel.: (39) 02 9918 4326
Fax: (39) 02 9918 9598
E-Mail: colorworksmerate@clariant.com
Web Site: www.colorworks.clariant.com
Chemical Product Mfr & Distr
S.I.C.: 2899
N.A.I.C.S.: 325998

Clariant (Japan) K.K. **(1)**
9/F Bunkyo Green Court Center Office
2-28-8 Honkomagome
Bunkyo-ku, Tokyo, 113 8662, Japan (100%)
Tel.: (81) 359777880
Fax: (81) 359777886
E-Mail: info-jp@clariant.com
Web Site: www.clariant.co.jp
Emp.: 450
Mfr. of Dyes & Paints
S.I.C.: 2816
N.A.I.C.S.: 325130
Yukako Nishiyama *(Mgr-Comm)*

Clariant (Korea) Ltd **(1)**
Yundang Bdg 11th floor 144-23 Samsung
2-dong Kangnam-ku
Seoul, Korea (South)
Tel.: (82) 2 510 8300
Fax: (82) 2 514 5747
Chemical Product Mfr & Distr
S.I.C.: 2899
N.A.I.C.S.: 325998

Clariant (Malaysia) Sdn. Bhd. **(1)**
No 79 And 80 Hicom Sector B Jalan Teluk
Gadung 27-93 A
40000 Shah Alam, Selangor,
Malaysia (100%)
Tel.: (60) 351012888
Fax: (60) 351012881
Web Site: www.clariant.com
Emp.: 40
Mfr. of Dyes & Paints
S.I.C.: 2819
N.A.I.C.S.: 325130
Walter Mohr *(Mng Dir)*

Subsidiary:

Clariant Masterbatches (Malaysia) Sdn Bhd **(2)**
No 79 & 80 Hicom Sector B Jalan Teluk
Gadung 27/93A
40000 Shah Alam, Selangor Darul Ehsan,
Malaysia
Tel.: (60) 3 5101 2888
Fax: (60) 3 5101 2881
Web Site: www.seap.clariant.com
Emp.: 100
Chemical Product Distr
S.I.C.: 5169
N.A.I.C.S.: 424690
Alex Lin *(Mgr-Mktg)*

Clariant (Maroc) S.A. **(1)**
13 Rue Zoubeir Bnou El Aouam
Roches Noires, Casablanca, 20303,
Morocco
Tel.: (212) 22401333
Fax: (212) 22249772
Emp.: 40
Mfr. of Dyes & Paints
S.I.C.: 2819
N.A.I.C.S.: 325130

Clariant Masterbatches Ireland Limited **(1)**
Monread Industrial Estate Monread Road
Naas, Co Kildare, Ireland IE
Tel.: (353) 45866565 (100%)
Fax: (353) 45875765
E-Mail: masterplast@clariant.com
Emp.: 40
Chemical Preparation
S.I.C.: 2899
N.A.I.C.S.: 325998
Peter Joyce *(Gen Mgr)*

Clariant Masterbatches (Saudi Arabia) Ltd **(1)**
Al Kharj Road 201
PO Box 5882
Riyadh, 11432, Saudi Arabia
Tel.: (966) 1 265 2828
Fax: (966) 1 265 1413
E-Mail: info.saudiarbia@clariant.com
Emp.: 125
Chemical Product Mfr & Distr
S.I.C.: 2899
N.A.I.C.S.: 325998
Nabil Abi Nadher *(Gen Mgr)*

Clariant (Mexico) S.A. de C.V. **(1)**
Plasticos No 28
55540 Santa Clara, Edo De Mexico, 55540,
Mexico (100%)
Tel.: (52) 5553291800
Fax: (52) 5555763259
E-Mail: information@clariant.com
Web Site: www.clariant.com
Sales Range: $150-199.9 Million
Emp.: 750
Mfr. of Dyes & Paints
S.I.C.: 2816
N.A.I.C.S.: 325130

Subsidiary:

Clariant Productos Quimicos S.A. de C. V. **(2)**
Plasticos 28
Morelos, Naucalpan, 54540, Mexico (100%)
Tel.: (52) 5552295500
Fax: (52) 5555697518
E-Mail: gabraelcurbo@clariant.com
Web Site: www.clariant.com.mx
Emp.: 345
Mfr. of Dyes & Paints
S.I.C.: 2819
N.A.I.C.S.: 325130
Gabrael Curbo *(CEO)*

Clariant (New Zealand) Ltd. **(1)**
4 Rothwell Ave Albany Industrial Ests
PO Box 300009
Auckland, 1310, New Zealand (100%)
Tel.: (64) 99145566
Fax: (64) 99145565
E-Mail: roy.grave@clariant.com
Web Site: www.clariant.com
Sls.: $31,663,696
Emp.: 60
Mfr. of Dyes & Paints
S.I.C.: 2816
N.A.I.C.S.: 325130
Roy Grave *(Mng Dir)*

Clariant (Norge) AS **(1)**
Solheimsviken
PO Box 2313
Bergen, 5008, Norway (100%)
Tel.: (47) 55363450
Fax: (47) 55363498
Web Site: www.clariant.com
Emp.: 25
Mfr. of Dyes & Paints
S.I.C.: 2819
N.A.I.C.S.: 325130
Srode Bekkeseat *(Mng Dir)*

Subsidiary:

Clariant Oil Services Scandinavia AS **(2)**
Thormolensgate 53 D
5892 Bergen, Norway
Tel.: (47) 55 36 34 50
Fax: (47) 55 36 34 98
Web Site: www.clariant.com
Chemical Product Distr
S.I.C.: 5169
N.A.I.C.S.: 424690

Clariant (Osterreich) GmbH **(1)**
Lnisinger Flur 8 23rd St
Vienna, 1230, Austria (100%)
Tel.: (43) 1801220
Fax: (43) 3180122925
Web Site: www.clariant.at
Sales Range: $1-9.9 Million
Emp.: 70
Mfr. of Dyes & Paints
S.I.C.: 2819
N.A.I.C.S.: 325130

Clariant (Pakistan) Ltd. **(1)**
1-A/1 Sector 20 Korangi Industrial Area
74900 Karachi, Pakistan
Tel.: (92) 111275000
Fax: (92) 5032337
Web Site: www.clariant.com.pk/
Dye & Paint Mfr
S.I.C.: 2819
N.A.I.C.S.: 325130

Clariant (Peru) S.A. **(1)**
Carretera Central Km 3 7 Casilla 460 Ate
Vitarte
Lima, 3, Peru (100%)
Tel.: (51) 013171500
Fax: (51) 014372444
Web Site: www.clariant.com.pe
Emp.: 71
Mfr. of Dyes & Paints
S.I.C.: 2816
N.A.I.C.S.: 325130

Clariant Polska Sp. z.o.o. **(1)**
Ul Pulawska 303
02785 Warsaw, Poland (100%)
Tel.: (48) 225494200
Fax: (48) 225494201
Web Site: www.clariant.pl
Emp.: 23
Mfr. of Dyes & Paints
S.I.C.: 2816
N.A.I.C.S.: 325130

Subsidiary:

COLEX Spolka z o.o. **(2)**
Ul Kolorowa 14
Zgierz, 95-100, Poland
Tel.: (48) 42 714 0200
Fax: (48) 42 716 13 25
E-Mail: office@colex.com.pl
Web Site: www.colex.com.pl
Chemical Product Mfr
S.I.C.: 2899
N.A.I.C.S.: 325998
Katarzyna Krajewska *(Sr Officer-Bus Support)*
Ewa Olczak *(Officer-Bus Support)*

Clariant S.A. **(1)**
Avenida de Nacoes Unidas 18001
CEP-04795 900 Sao Paulo, SP, Brazil BR
Tel.: (55) 11 568 372 33 (100%)
Fax: (55) 11 564 216 54
Web Site: www.clariant.com.br
Emp.: 1,900
Mfr. of Dyes & Paints
S.I.C.: 2819
N.A.I.C.S.: 325130

Clariant Sangho Ltd. **(1)**
84 7 Chungdam Dong
Kangnam Ku, Seoul, 135 100, Korea
(South) (80%)
Tel.: (82) 2510800
Fax: (82) 25404807
Web Site: www.clariantsangho.co.kr
Emp.: 120
S.I.C.: 2899
N.A.I.C.S.: 325998

Clariant (Singapore) Pte. Ltd. **(1)**
1 International Business Park
#08-01/02/02/04 The Synergy, Singapore,
609917, Singapore SG
Tel.: (65) 6563 0288 (100%)
Fax: (65) 6563 0200
Web Site: www.seap.clariant.com
Emp.: 112
Mfr. of Dyes & Paints
S.I.C.: 2819
N.A.I.C.S.: 325130
Mohr Walter *(Mng Dir)*

Clariant (Sverige) AB **(1)**
Goteborgsvagen 91 B
PO Box 5415
Molndal, 40229, Sweden (100%)
Tel.: (46) 31678500
Fax: (46) 31678585
E-Mail: info@clariant.com
Web Site: www.clariant.com
Sales Range: $25-49.9 Million
Emp.: 20
Mfr. of Dyes & Paints
S.I.C.: 2819
N.A.I.C.S.: 325130
Mark Mario Weilert *(Mgr)*

Subsidiary:

Clariant Masterbatches Norden AB **(2)**
Jarnyxegatan 7
PO Box 905
200 39 Malmo, Sweden
Tel.: (46) 40 671 72 00
Fax: (46) 40 671 72 48
Chemical Product Mfr & Distr
S.I.C.: 2899
N.A.I.C.S.: 325998

Clariant (Taiwan) Co. Ltd. **(1)**
5th Fl No 96 Chien Kuo N Rd Sec 1
Taipei, 00104, Taiwan (100%)
Tel.: (886) 225166886
Fax: (886) 225055588
E-Mail: jennifer.yu@clariant.com
Web Site: www.clariant.com
Emp.: 100
Mfr. of Dyes & Paints
S.I.C.: 2816
N.A.I.C.S.: 325130
Jennifer Yu *(Mng Dir)*

Clariant (Thailand) Ltd. **(1)**
3195/11 6th Fl Vibulthani Tower 1 Rama 4
Road
Klongton Klongtoey, 10110 Bangkok,
Thailand
Tel.: (66) 2 661 5360
Fax: (66) 2 661 4060
E-Mail: info.TH@clariant.com
Web Site: www.seap.clariant.com
Chemical Product Mfr & Distr
S.I.C.: 2899
N.A.I.C.S.: 325998

Subsidiaries:

Clariant Chemicals (Thailand) Ltd. **(2)**
No 3195 Flat 11 6th Fl Vibulthani Tower 1
Klongtoey
Rama 4 Rd Klongton, Bangkok, 10110,
Thailand (100%)
Tel.: (66) 26615360
Fax: (66) 26614060
E-Mail: clariant@clariant.com

Web Site: www.clariant.co.th
Sls.: $48,615,300
Emp.: 300
Mfr. of Dyes & Paints
S.I.C.: 2816
N.A.I.C.S.: 325130
Danial Hug *(Pres)*

Clariant Masterbatches Thailand Ltd **(2)**
700/848 Amata Nakorn Industrial Estate Phase 8 Moo 1
Tambol Phan Thong Chonburi, Bangkok, Amphur Phan Thong, 20160, Thailand (100%)
Tel.: (66) 38 939 599
Fax: (66) 38 939 500
Web Site: www.seap.clariant.com
Emp.: 215
Mfr of Dyes & Paints. Testing Laboratories & Warehousing
S.I.C.: 2819
N.A.I.C.S.: 325130

Clariant Tunisie S.A. **(1)**
19 rue de l'Artisanat
BP 2
TN-1080 Tunis, Cedex, Tunisia (100%)
Tel.: (216) 70 837 667
Fax: (216) 70 836 539
Mfr. of Dyes & Paints
S.I.C.: 2819
N.A.I.C.S.: 325130

Clariant (Turkiye) A.S. **(1)**
Tahsin Tekoglu Caddesi No 1 3
Sefakoy, TR 34620 Istanbul, Turkey (100%)
Tel.: (90) 2124134100
Fax: (90) 2125409554
Web Site: www.clariant.com
Sales Range: $125-149.9 Million
Emp.: 200
Mfr. of Dyes & Paints
S.I.C.: 2819
N.A.I.C.S.: 325130

Clariant UK Ltd. **(1)**
Clariant House Unit 2 Rawdon Park
Yeadon, Leeds, Hartford, LS19 7BA, United Kingdom (100%)
Tel.: (44) 113 239 7936
Fax: (44) 1132398473
E-Mail: clariant.uk@clariant.com
Web Site: www.clariant.co.uk
Sales Range: $400-449.9 Million
Emp.: 250
Dyes & Paints Mfr
S.I.C.: 2816
N.A.I.C.S.: 325130

Subsidiaries:

Clariant Distribution UK Limited **(2)**
Unit 2 Rawdon Park Yeadon
Leeds, LS19 7BA, United Kingdom
Tel.: (44) 1454 411 789
Chemical Product Distr
S.I.C.: 5169
N.A.I.C.S.: 424690

Clariant Holdings UK Ltd. **(2)**
Clariant House Unit 2 Rawdon Park
Yeadon Leeds, Leeds, LS19 7BA, United Kingdom UK (100%)
Tel.: (44) 1132397936
Fax: (44) 1132397974
E-Mail: clariant.uk@clariant.com
Web Site: www.clariant.com
Emp.: 80
Holding Company
S.I.C.: 6719
N.A.I.C.S.: 551112

Clariant Oil Services UK Ltd. **(2)**
Howe Moss Pl Dyce
Aberdeen, Scotland, AB21 0GS, United Kingdom UK (100%)
Tel.: (44) 224797400
Fax: (44) 1224770118
E-Mail: oilservices@clariant.com
Web Site: www.clariant.co.uk
Sales Range: $50-74.9 Million
Emp.: 80
S.I.C.: 2851
N.A.I.C.S.: 325998

Clariant Services UK Ltd **(2)**
Unit 2 Rawdon Park Green Lawe
Leeds, West Yorkshire, United Kingdom
Tel.: (44) 113 239 7936
Chemical Product Distr
S.I.C.: 5169
N.A.I.C.S.: 424690

Clariant (Uruguay) SA **(1)**
Zonamerica Of 704 A Ruta 8 - Km 17
500 San Isidro, Montevideo, 91600, Uruguay
Tel.: (598) 2 518 2261
Fax: (598) 2 518 2264
Chemical Product Mfr & Distr
S.I.C.: 2899
N.A.I.C.S.: 325998

Clariant (Venezuela) S.A. **(1)**
Zn Indus San Vicente Av Anton Philips
Maracay, Edo Aragua, 2104, Venezuela (100%)
Tel.: (58) 2435503111
Fax: (58) 2435503127
E-Mail: info@clariant.com
Web Site: www.clariant.com
Emp.: 249
Mfr. of Dyes & Paints
S.I.C.: 2816
N.A.I.C.S.: 325130

Clearwater Technologies Ltd **(1)**
Welsh Road East
Road Town, Virgin Islands (British)
Tel.: (284) 4944742
Financial Management Services
S.I.C.: 6211
N.A.I.C.S.: 523999

Italtinto S.r.l. **(1)**
Via Piani 82
16042 Carasco, Genova, Italy
Tel.: (39) 0185 350151
Fax: (39) 0185 350153
E-Mail: italtinto@italtinto.com
Web Site: www.italtinto.com
Color Pigment Mfr
S.I.C.: 2816
N.A.I.C.S.: 325130

Non-U.S. Subsidiary:

Italtinto India Private Limited **(2)**
EL 33 MIDC - Mahape
Navi Mumbai, 400 705, India
Tel.: (91) 2227613907
Fax: (91) 2227613908
E-Mail: italtintoindia@italtinto.com
Web Site: www.italtinto.com
Automatic Colorant Machinery & Gyro Mixer Mfr
S.I.C.: 3569
N.A.I.C.S.: 333999

P.T. Clariant Indonesia **(1)**
Gatot Subroto KM 4 Jl Kalisabi No 1 Kec
15138 Tangerang, Indonesia (100%)
Tel.: (62) 215538589
Fax: (62) 215520390
Web Site: www.clairant.com
Emp.: 500
Mfr. of Dyes & Paints
S.I.C.: 2819
N.A.I.C.S.: 325130
Hans Gert Herrel *(Pres)*

CLARIDGE HOMES INC.

2001 210 Gladstone Avenue
Ottawa, ON, K2P 0Y6, Canada
Tel.: (613) 233-6030
Fax: (613) 233-8290
E-Mail: sales@claridgehomes.com
Web Site: www.claridgehomes.com
Rev.: $25,669,350
Emp.: 90
Business Description:
Home Builders
S.I.C.: 1522
N.A.I.C.S.: 236116
Personnel:
Bill Malhotra *(Founder)*
Subhash Malhotra *(Pres)*

CLARINS S.A.

(d/b/a Groupe Clarins)
4 Rue Berteaux Dumas
PO Box 174
92203 Neuilly-sur-Seine, Cedex, France
Tel.: (33) 147381212
Fax: (33) 147383588
Web Site: www.clarins.com
Year Founded: 1954
Sales Range: $1-4.9 Billion
Emp.: 6,200
Business Description:
Perfume, Cosmetic & Skin Care Products Mfr, Distr & Marketer
Export
S.I.C.: 2844
N.A.I.C.S.: 325620
Personnel:
Christian Courtin-Clarins *(Pres)*
Pankaj Chandarana *(CFO)*
Gerard Delcour *(Chm-Azzaro Brand)*
Philip Shearer *(Exec VP)*

Subsidiaries:

Azzaro SAS **(1)**
16 Rue Montrosier
92201 Neuilly-sur-Seine, France FR (100%)
Tel.: (33) 55622500
Fax: (33) 55622525
Web Site: www.azzaroparis.com
Emp.: 50
Mfr. of Perfumes
S.I.C.: 2844
N.A.I.C.S.: 325620
Mathilde Castello Branco *(Dir-Creative)*

Cosmeurop S.A. **(1)**
43 Rue Des Comtes
PO Box 44
67034 Strasbourg, France FR (100%)
Tel.: (33) 388308686
Fax: (33) 388308696
Emp.: 200
Mfr. of Perfume
S.I.C.: 2844
N.A.I.C.S.: 325620
Jean Paul Foery *(Mng Dir)*

Laboratoires Clarins **(1)**
31 Chaussee Jules Cesar
95300 Pontoise, France (100%)
Tel.: (33) 134351515
Fax: (33) 130384148
Web Site: www.claris.net
Emp.: 500
Mfr. of Perfumes & Cosmetics
S.I.C.: 2844
N.A.I.C.S.: 325620

Thierry Mugler Parfums **(1)**
16 Rue Montrosier
92200 Neuilly-sur-Seine, France (100%)
Tel.: (33) 1 55 62 25 38
Fax: (33) 146745982
E-Mail: relations.clientele@mugler.net
Web Site: www.thierrymugler.com
Emp.: 100
Mfr of Perfumes
S.I.C.: 2844
N.A.I.C.S.: 325620

U.S. Subsidiary:

Clarins USA Inc. **(1)**
1 Park Ave 19th Fl
New York, NY 10016 (100%)
Tel.: (212) 980-1800
Fax: (212) 752-5910
Web Site: www.clarinsusa.com
Emp.: 150
Skin Care, Make-up Products & Perfume Distribution
Import
S.I.C.: 5122
N.A.I.C.S.: 424210
Erick Horowitz *(Pres-Clarins Brand Div)*
Marc Rosenblum *(Pres-Ops Svcs)*

Non-U.S. Subsidiaries:

Clarins BV **(1)**
Laan Van Westenenk 64
7336 AZ Apeldoorn, Netherlands NL (100%)
Tel.: (31) 555428842
Fax: (31) 555429010
E-Mail: clarins@clarins.com
Emp.: 55
Perfumes & Toiletries Distr
S.I.C.: 5122
N.A.I.C.S.: 424210
Jan Talboom *(Gen Mgr)*

Clarins Canada Inc. **(1)**
815 desserte St
Laval, QC, H7W 5N4, Canada (100%)
Tel.: (450) 688-0144
Fax: (450) 688-0087
Emp.: 100
Cosmetics & Perfumes Distr
S.I.C.: 5122
N.A.I.C.S.: 446120
Patricia Abergel *(VP)*

Clarins GmbH **(1)**
Petersbrunner Strasse 13
D 82319 Starnberg, Germany De (100%)
Tel.: (49) 815126030
Fax: (49) 81512603252
E-Mail: petera.lienen@clarins.de
Web Site: www.clarins.de
Emp.: 70
Cosmetics Distr
Import
S.I.C.: 5122
N.A.I.C.S.: 446120
Stephan Seidel-Jarleton *(Mng Dir)*

Clarins K.K. **(1)**
6-8-10 Roppongi
Tokyo, 106 0032, Japan (100%)
Tel.: (81) 334708554
Fax: (81) 334705813
Web Site: www.jp.clarins.com
Emp.: 40
Cosmetic Product Distribution
Import
S.I.C.: 5122
N.A.I.C.S.: 446120
Sumiko Kobayashi *(Pres)*

Clarins Korea Ltd. **(1)**
A Fl Daedong Bldg 823 -21
Kangnam Ku Yeoksam-Dong, Seoul, 135 933, Korea (South) (100%)
Tel.: (82) 25429045
Fax: (82) 8225425827
E-Mail: reception@kr.clarins.com
Web Site: kr.clarins.com
Perfumes & Cosmetics Distr
S.I.C.: 5122
N.A.I.C.S.: 446120

Clarins Ltd. **(1)**
Unit 12 K World Tech Ctr 95 How Ming St
Kwun Tong, Kowloon, China (Hong Kong) (100%)
Tel.: (852) 27901883
Fax: (852) 27902192
E-Mail: cherry.psahe@clarins.com.hk
Sls.: $6,814,493
Emp.: 170
Skin Care, Makeup Product & Perfume Distribution
S.I.C.: 5122
N.A.I.C.S.: 446120

Clarins Paris SA **(1)**
Edificio Bruselas Avenida De Europa 4 3rd Fl
28108 Alcobendas, Moraleja, Spain ES (100%)
Tel.: (34) 916572159
Fax: (34) 916572160
E-Mail: atencionalcliente@clarins.es
Web Site: www.clarins.es
Emp.: 60
Distributor of Perfumes & Cosmetics
S.I.C.: 5122
N.A.I.C.S.: 446120
Juan Migul Ualiente *(Mng Dir)*

Clarins Pte. Ltd. **(1)**
302 Orchard Rd 05 01 Tong Bldg
Singapore, 238 862, Singapore (100%)
Tel.: (65) 68386334
Fax: (65) 67320038
Web Site: www.clarins.com.sg
Emp.: 200
Skin Care, Makeup Products & Perfumes Distribution
S.I.C.: 5122
N.A.I.C.S.: 446120
Larry Soo *(Gen Mgr)*

Clarins SA **(1)**
2 Rte De La Galaise
Plan-les-Ouates, 1228, Switzerland CH (100%)
Tel.: (41) 228841212
Fax: (41) 228841201
E-Mail: direction@clarins.com
Web Site: www.clarins.com
Emp.: 180

Clarins S.A.—(Continued)

Distributor of Skin Care, Make-up & Perfume
Import Export
S.I.C.: 5122
N.A.I.C.S.: 446120
Elisabeth Metzger *(Mng Dir)*

Clarins Sdn Bhd (1)
Unit 6 05 6 07 Level 6 Amoda
22 Jalan Imbi, 55100 Kuala Lumpur, Malaysia (100%)
Tel.: (60) 321414076
Fax: (60) 321447847
E-Mail: info@clarins.com
Web Site: www.clarins.com
Rev.: $2,847,328
Emp.: 20
Skin Care & Makeup Products & Perfume Distribution
S.I.C.: 5122
N.A.I.C.S.: 446120
Tan Seong Teck *(COO)*

Clarins (U.K.) Ltd. (1)
10 Cavendish Place
London, W1G 9DN, United Kingdom UK (100%)
Tel.: (44) 2073076700
Fax: (44) 2073076701
Web Site: www.clarins.com.uk
Emp.: 100
Distribution & Sales of Cosmetics Import
S.I.C.: 5122
N.A.I.C.S.: 446120
Debbie Lewis *(Mng Dir)*

Monarimport S.p.A. (1)
Via Di Vittorio 13
40050 Castenaso, BO, Italy IT (100%)
Tel.: (39) 0516055111
Fax: (39) 0516055274
Emp.: 119
Cosmetics Distr
Import
S.I.C.: 5122
N.A.I.C.S.: 446120
Valentino Biffoni *(Dir-Comml)*

Non-U.S. Affiliates:

Bubbe S.A. (1)
11 Ave De l Artisanat
1420 Braine-l'Alleud, Belgium BE
Tel.: (32) 23850280
Fax: (32) 23843780
E-Mail: info@bubbe.be
Web Site: www.clarins.com
Emp.: 25
Distributor of Cosmetics
S.I.C.: 5122
N.A.I.C.S.: 424210
Charles Van Der Meulen *(Gen Mgr)*

Nevinar Cosmetics Ltd. (1)
92 Upper Georges St
Dun Laoghaire, S Dublin, Ireland IE (100%)
Tel.: (353) 12846477
Fax: (353) 12846488
E-Mail: clarins@nevinar.com
Web Site: www.clarins.com
Emp.: 15
Cosmetics Distr
S.I.C.: 5122
N.A.I.C.S.: 424210
Jerry Hickey *(Mng Dir)*

Talboom B.V. (1)
Laan Van Westenenk 64
7336 AZ Apeldoorn, Netherlands NL (100%)
Tel.: (31) 555428842
Fax: (31) 555429010
E-Mail: clarins@clarins.com
Emp.: 40
Distributor of Cosmetics
S.I.C.: 5122
N.A.I.C.S.: 424210
Jan Talboom *(Gen Mgr)*

CLARION S.A. AGROINDUSTRIAL

Rua Frei Egidio Laurent 308
06298-020 Osasco, SP, Brazil
Tel.: (55) 11 3604 8111
E-Mail: contato@clarionsa.com.br
Web Site: www.clarionsa.com.br
CLAN3—(BRAZ)

Business Description:
Edible Oil Whslr
S.I.C.: 5149
N.A.I.C.S.: 424490
Personnel:
Alexandre Bride *(Dir-IR)*

CLARIS LIFESCIENCES LTD.

Nr Parimal Crossing Ellisbridge
Ahmedabad, 380 006, India
Tel.: (91) 79 26563331
Fax: (91) 79 26565879
E-Mail: media.corp@clarislifesciences.com
Web Site: www.clarislifesciences.com
CLARIS—(BOM)
Rev.: $144,178,516
Assets: $371,224,047
Liabilities: $158,224,105
Net Worth: $212,999,942
Earnings: $19,265,136
Emp.: 1,558
Fiscal Year-end: 12/31/12
Business Description:
Pharmaceutical Mfr
S.I.C.: 2834
N.A.I.C.S.: 325412
Personnel:
Surrinder Lal Kapur *(Chm)*
Arjun S. Handa *(CEO & Mng Dir)*
Rajesh Kumar Modi *(Compliance Officer, Sec & Gen Mgr-Compliance)*
Chetan S. Majmudar *(Pres-Tech & CQA)*
Chandrasingh Purohit *(Pres-Fin)*
Bharat Shah *(Pres-Bus-India)*
Shyam Sharma *(Pres-HR Mgmt & Corp Comm)*
Board of Directors:
Surrinder Lal Kapur
T. V. Ananthanarayanan
Aditya S. Handa
Arjun S. Handa
Chetan S. Majmudar
Chandrasingh Purohit
Anup P. Shah
Transfer Agent:
Link Intime India Private Limited
C-13 Pannalal Silk Mills Compound LBS Rd
Bhandup W
Mumbai, India

CLARITY OSS LIMITED

Level 3 15 Blue Street
North Sydney, NSW, 2060, Australia
Tel.: (61) 2 9925 5000
Fax: (61) 299559999
E-Mail: info@clarity.com
Web Site: www.powerlan.com
CYO—(ASX)
Rev.: $41,009,761
Assets: $37,837,609
Liabilities: $51,161,900
Net Worth: ($13,324,291)
Earnings: ($3,956,854)
Emp.: 213
Fiscal Year-end: 06/30/13
Business Description:
Technology Products & Services
S.I.C.: 7379
N.A.I.C.S.: 541519
Personnel:
Jon Newbery *(CEO)*
Andrew Wrigglesworth *(CFO & Sec)*
S. Allaway *(Pres-CT)*
W. Tickner *(CEO-IMX)*
Board of Directors:
Ian Campbell
Ian M. Lancaster
Fiona McLeod
Jon Newbery
Legal Counsel:
Henry Davis York
44 Martin Place
Sydney, NSW, 2000, Australia

Subsidiaries:

Clarity International (1)
Level 3 15 Bule Street
North Sydney, NSW, 2060, Australia
Tel.: (61) 299255000
Fax: (61) 299559999
E-Mail: marketing@clarity.com
Web Site: www.clarity.com
Emp.: 60
Operational Support & Network Management Systems
S.I.C.: 7373
N.A.I.C.S.: 541512
Jon Newbery *(CEO)*

Non-U.S. Subsidiaries:

CG Philippines Inc (1)
37th Floor LKG Tower 6801 Ayala Avenue
Makati, 1226, Philippines
Tel.: (63) 2 859 2802
Fax: (63) 2 859 2970
Emp.: 15
Software Consulting Services
S.I.C.: 7371
N.A.I.C.S.: 541511
Catherine de Vera *(Mgr-HR & Admin)*

Clarity OSS Limited (1)
The Quorum Bond Street South
Bristol, BS1 3AE, United Kingdom
Tel.: (44) 117 906 0300
Fax: (44) 117 925 5801
Web Site: www.clarity.com
Emp.: 22
Software Development Services
S.I.C.: 7371
N.A.I.C.S.: 541511
Susan Frost *(Office Mgr)*

Clarity OSS (Malaysia) Sdn Bhd (1)
Level 28 The Gardens South Tower Mid Valley City Lingkaran Syed Putra
Kuala Lumpur, 59200, Malaysia
Tel.: (60) 3 2298 7294
Fax: (60) 3 2298 7333
Software Development Services
S.I.C.: 7371
N.A.I.C.S.: 541511

Omnix Holdings Limited (1)
174 Whiteladies Road
Bristol, BS8 2XU, United Kingdom
Tel.: (44) 117 906 0300
Fax: (44) 117 925 5801
Web Site: www.omnixholdings.com
Management Services
S.I.C.: 8741
N.A.I.C.S.: 551114

Subsidiary:

Omnix Software Limited (2)
The Quorum Bond Street South
Bristol, BS1 3AE, United Kingdom
Tel.: (44) 117 906 0300
Fax: (44) 117 925 5801
E-Mail: info@omnixsoftware.com
Web Site: www.omnixsoftware.com
Software Consulting Services
S.I.C.: 7373
N.A.I.C.S.: 541512
Jill Fitzgerald *(Controller-Fin-Global Projects)*

PT Clarity Systems Indonesia (1)
Wisma Nusantara 7th Floor Jl MH Thamrin No 59
Jakarta, 10350, Indonesia
Tel.: (62) 21 3983 5884
Fax: (62) 21 3983 5882
Software Consulting Services
S.I.C.: 7371
N.A.I.C.S.: 541511

CLARIUS GROUP LTD.

Level 9 1 York Street
Sydney, NSW, 2000, Australia
Tel.: (61) 292508100
Fax: (61) 292477930
E-Mail: feedback@clarius.com.au
Web Site: www.clarius.com.au
CND—(ASX)
Rev.: $234,762,204
Assets: $60,483,484
Liabilities: $21,946,626
Net Worth: $38,536,858
Earnings: ($43,991,209)
Emp.: 290
Fiscal Year-end: 06/30/13
Business Description:
Employment Services
S.I.C.: 7361
N.A.I.C.S.: 561311
Personnel:
Geoffrey J. Moles *(Founder)*
Kym L. Quick *(CEO & Mng Dir)*
Anne L. Bastock *(CFO)*
Nicholas J. V. Geddes *(Sec)*
Board of Directors:
Garry Sladden
Penelope Morris
Kym L. Quick
Legal Counsel:
Lander & Rogers Lawyers
Level 5 123 Pitt Street
Sydney, NSW, 2000, Australia

Subsidiaries:

Alliance Recruitment Pty Limited (1)
Level 5 1 York St
Sydney, NSW, 2000, Australia
Tel.: (61) 292508100
Fax: (61) 292477930
E-Mail: sydney@alliancerecruitment.com.au
Web Site: www.alliancerecruitment.com.au
Emp.: 50
Recruitment Services
S.I.C.: 7361
N.A.I.C.S.: 561311
Geoffrey Moles *(Gen Mgr)*

Candle IT & T Recruitment Limited (1)
L14 333 Colin St
Melbourne, Victoria, 3000, Australia
Tel.: (61) 398328000
Fax: (61) 298328008
Web Site: www.candlerecruit.com
Emp.: 50
Recruitment Services
S.I.C.: 7361
N.A.I.C.S.: 561311
Rob Fortescue *(Gen Mgr)*

Candle IT & T Recruitment Pty Limited (1)
Level 9 1 York St
Sydney, NSW, 2000, Australia
Tel.: (61) 292508100
Fax: (61) 292477930
E-Mail: inquiry@clarius.com.au
Emp.: 500
IT Recruitment Services
S.I.C.: 7361
N.A.I.C.S.: 561311

JAV IT Group Pty Limited (1)
Level 14 333 Collins St
Melbourne, Victoria, 3000, Australia
Tel.: (61) 396213344
Fax: (61) 396211388
E-Mail: south-oz@jav.com.au
Web Site: www.jav.com.au
Emp.: 100
Outsourcing Solutions & Services
S.I.C.: 7389
N.A.I.C.S.: 561499
Joseph Vella *(CEO)*

Lloyd Morgan International Pty Limited (1)
Level 14 333 Collins St
Melbourne, Victoria, 3000, Australia
Tel.: (61) 396835200
E-Mail: melbourne@lloydmorgan.com.au
Web Site: www.lloydmorgan.com
Emp.: 60
Employment Services
S.I.C.: 7361
N.A.I.C.S.: 561311
Goeff Moles *(Gen Mgr)*

Lloyd Morgan Sydney Pty Limited (1)
Level 5 1 York St
Sydney, NSW, 2000, Australia
Tel.: (61) 292253700
Fax: (61) 292253766
E-Mail: sydney@lloydmorgan.com.au
Web Site: www.lloydmorgan.com
Emp.: 8

Employment Services
S.I.C.: 7361
N.A.I.C.S.: 561311
Adam Kolokotsas *(Gen Mgr)*

The One Umbrella Pty Limited (1)
Level 9 1 York St
Sydney, New South Wales, 2000, Australia
Tel.: (61) 292630000
Fax: (61) 292253744
E-Mail: nsw@oneumbrella.com.au
Web Site: www.oneumbrella.com.au
Emp.: 8
Employment Services
S.I.C.: 7361
N.A.I.C.S.: 561311
Catherine Hill *(Gen Mgr)*

Non-U.S. Subsidiaries:

Lloyd Morgan China Limited (1)
2W Guomen Bldg No 1 Zuojiazhuang
Beijing, 10002, China
Tel.: (86) 10 6461 4931
Fax: (86) 10 6461 4942
E-Mail: beijing@lloydmorgan.com.cn
Web Site: www.lloydmorgan.com
Emp.: 30
Employment Services
S.I.C.: 7361
N.A.I.C.S.: 561311
Christian Buttrose *(Mng Dir)*

Lloyd Morgan Hong Kong Limited (1)
2403 A World Trade Ctr 24th Fl 280 Gloucester Rd
Causeway Bay, China (Hong Kong)
Tel.: (852) 28955282
Fax: (852) 25775902
E-Mail: hongkong@lloydmorgan.com.hk
Web Site: www.lloydmorgan.com
Emp.: 30
Employment Services
S.I.C.: 7361
N.A.I.C.S.: 561311
Alfred Chown *(Mng Dir)*

Lloyd Morgan Singapore Pte Limited (1)
10 Hoe Chiang Rd 14-02 Keppel Towers
Singapore, 089315, Singapore
Tel.: (65) 6323 1108
Fax: (65) 6323 1208
E-Mail: singapore@lloydmorgan.com.sg
Web Site: www.lloydmorgan.com
Employment Services
S.I.C.: 7361
N.A.I.C.S.: 561311

CLARK CONTRACTS LTD

23 McFarlane Street
Paisley, PA3 1RY, United Kingdom
Tel.: (44) 1418478787
Fax: (44) 1418478700
E-Mail: info@clarkcontracts.com
Web Site: www.clarkcontracts.com
Year Founded: 1978
Rev.: $46,973,614
Emp.: 186

Business Description:
Construction Services
S.I.C.: 1542
N.A.I.C.S.: 236220

Personnel:
Steve Clark *(Chm)*
Gordon Cunningham *(Mng Dir)*

THE CLARKE GROUP

33610 E Broadway Ave
Mission, BC, V2V 4M4, Canada
Tel.: (604) 826-9531
Fax: (604) 820-3872
Web Site: www.clarkegroup.com
Sales Range: $10-24.9 Million
Emp.: 100

Business Description:
Mfr. of Cedar Shingle Siding Panels, Cedar Shingle Roofing Panels & Fancy Cut Shingles
S.I.C.: 3089
N.A.I.C.S.: 326199

Personnel:
Louis Clarke *(Pres & COO)*

U.S. Subsidiary:

Shakertown 1992, Inc. (1)
1200 Kerron St
Winlock, WA 98596
Mailing Address:
PO Box 400
Winlock, WA 98596-0400
Tel.: (360) 785-3501
Fax: (360) 785-3076
Toll Free: (800) 426-8970
Web Site: www.shakertown.com
Emp.: 65
Cedar Shingles Mfr
S.I.C.: 2499
N.A.I.C.S.: 321999

CLARKE INC.

6009 Quinpool Road 9th Floor
Halifax, NS, B3K 5J7, Canada
Tel.: (902) 442-3000
Fax: (902) 442-0187
Web Site: www.clarkeinc.com
Year Founded: 1921
CKI—(TSX)
Rev.: $232,122,556
Assets: $231,346,227
Liabilities: $138,003,773
Net Worth: $93,342,454
Earnings: $2,876,694
Emp.: 777
Fiscal Year-end: 12/31/12

Business Description:
Investment Holding Company
S.I.C.: 6719
N.A.I.C.S.: 551112

Personnel:
George S. Armoyan *(Pres & CEO)*
Andrew Snelgrove *(CFO)*
Tim Rorabeck *(Gen Counsel & VP-Corp)*

Board of Directors:
Rex C. Anthony
Blair Cook
Charles Pellerin
Pat Powell
Michael Rapps

Legal Counsel:
Stewart McKelvey
Purdy's Wharf Tower I Suite 900 1959 Upper Water Street
PO Box 997
Halifax, NS, Canada

Transfer Agent:
Computershare Trust Company of Canada
1969 Upper Water Street Suite 2008 Purdy's Wharf Tower II
Halifax, NS, Canada

CLARKE REAL ESTATE LTD.

117 Columbus Drive
Carbonear, NL, A1Y 1A6, Canada
Tel.: (709) 596-4444
Fax: (709) 596-4408
Toll Free: (800) 982-5224
Web Site: www.barryclarke.ca
Rev.: $11,427,000
Emp.: 10

Business Description:
Real Estate Services
S.I.C.: 6531
N.A.I.C.S.: 531390

Personnel:
Barry Clarke *(Founder)*

CLARKSON PLC

St Magnus House 3 Lower Thames Street
London, EC3R 6HE, United Kingdom
Tel.: (44) 2073340000
Fax: (44) 2076264189
E-Mail: clarksons@clarksons.com
Web Site: www.clarksons.com
Year Founded: 1852
CKN—(LSE)
Rev.: $278,270,898
Assets: $336,862,557
Liabilities: $137,872,017
Net Worth: $198,990,540
Earnings: $25,584,498
Emp.: 939
Fiscal Year-end: 12/31/12

Business Description:
Integrated Shipping Services
S.I.C.: 4731
N.A.I.C.S.: 488510

Personnel:
Andi Case *(CEO)*
Nicholas Bucksey *(Sec)*

Board of Directors:
Robert Benton
Peter Backhouse
Andi Case
Philip Green
James Morley
Edmond Warner
Jeff Woyda

Subsidiaries:

Clarkson Overseas Shipbroking Limited (1)
St Magnus House 3 Lower Thames Street
London, EC3R 6HE, United Kingdom
Tel.: (44) 2073343440
Fax: (44) 2076262967
Ship Brokerage Services
S.I.C.: 4499
N.A.I.C.S.: 488390

Non-U.S. Subsidiaries:

Clarkson (Hellas) Limited (2)
95 Akti Miaouli
Piraeus, Greece 185 38
Tel.: (30) 210 458 6700
Fax: (30) 210 458 6799
Cargo Handling Services
S.I.C.: 4491
N.A.I.C.S.: 488320

Clarkson Shipping Services India Private Limited (2)
Flat number 124-125 Rectangle 1 Plot D-4
Saket District Centre, New Delhi, 110017, India
Tel.: (91) 11477 74444
Fax: (91) 11477 74400
E-Mail: tankers.india@clarksons.com
Emp.: 1
Marine Shipping Transportation Services
S.I.C.: 4412
N.A.I.C.S.: 483111
Amit Mehta *(Mng Dir)*

Clarkson Research Holdings Limited (1)
Homend Ho 15 Homend
Ledbury, HR8 1BN, United Kingdom
Tel.: (44) 1531634561
Fax: (44) 1531634239
E-Mail: sales@clarksons.com
Emp.: 16
Shipping Agency Services
S.I.C.: 4731
N.A.I.C.S.: 488510
Shaun Sturge *(Gen Mgr)*

Subsidiary:

Clarkson Research Services Limited (2)
St Magnus House 3 Lower Thames Street
London, EC3R 6HE, United Kingdom
Tel.: (44) 20 7334 3134
Fax: (44) 20 7522 0330
E-Mail: sales@crsl.com
Web Site: www.crsl.com
Emp.: 300
Shipping Related Services
S.I.C.: 4499
N.A.I.C.S.: 488390
Andi Case *(Mng Dir)*

Clarkson Securities Limited (1)
St Magnus House 3 Lower Thames Street
London, EC3R 6HE, United Kingdom
Tel.: (44) 207 334 3151
Fax: (44) 207 283 9412
Web Site: www.clarksonsecurities.com
Financial & Brokerage Services
S.I.C.: 6211
N.A.I.C.S.: 523120
Alex Gray *(CEO)*

Clarkson Valuations Limited (1)
St Magnus House 3 Lower Thames Street
London, EC3R 6HE, United Kingdom
Tel.: (44) 20 7334 3489
Fax: (44) 20 7623 0539
E-Mail: shipvalue@clarksons.co.uk
Web Site: www.shipvalue.net
Emp.: 350
Offshore Unit Valuation Services
S.I.C.: 7389
N.A.I.C.S.: 541990

Genchem Holdings Limited (1)
Maritime House 19A St Helens St
Ipswich, IP4 1HE, United Kingdom
Tel.: (44) 1473231121
Fax: (44) 1473297310
E-Mail: adminipswich@clarksons.com
Web Site: www.clarkson.com
Emp.: 16
Integrated Shipping Services
S.I.C.: 4499
N.A.I.C.S.: 488330
David Ramsey *(Gen Mgr)*

H Clarkson & Company Limited (1)
St Magnus House 3 Lower Thames St
London, EC3R 6HE, United Kingdom
Tel.: (44) 2073340000
Web Site: www.clarksons.com
Emp.: 350
Integrated Shipping Services
S.I.C.: 4499
N.A.I.C.S.: 488330

Subsidiary:

Clarkson Port Services Limited (2)
Grain Terminal Tilbury Docks
Tilbury, Essex, RM18 7LS, United Kingdom
Tel.: (44) 1375 859711
Fax: (44) 1375 842902
E-Mail: tilbury@clarksons.com
Web Site: www.clarksons.com
Emp.: 2
Integrated Shipping Services
S.I.C.: 4499
N.A.I.C.S.: 488330
Andy Rham *(Mng Dir)*

HC Shipping and Chartering Ltd (1)
6 Prince Street Dagger Lane
Hull, HU1 2LJ, United Kingdom
Tel.: (44) 1482586760
Fax: (44) 1482 590759
E-Mail: chartering@hcshipping.com
Web Site: www.hcshipping.com
Emp.: 7
Ship Chartering Services
S.I.C.: 4412
N.A.I.C.S.: 483111
Kristian Barford *(Dir-Chartering)*

U.S. Subsidiary:

Clarkson Shipping Services USA Inc. (1)
1333 W Loop S Ste 1525
Houston, TX 77027
Tel.: (713) 235-7400
Fax: (713) 235-7449
E-Mail: tankers@clarksons-houston.com
Web Site: www.clarksons-houston.com
Emp.: 100
Freight Transportation Arrangement
S.I.C.: 4731
N.A.I.C.S.: 488510
Roger Horten *(Mng Dir)*

U.S. Affiliate:

Overseas Wiborg Chartering Co. (1)
7 Mount Lassen Dr Ste A-121
San Rafael, CA 94903 (50%)
Tel.: (415) 479-2706
Fax: (415) 479-2841
E-Mail: all@overseaswiborg.com
Freight Transportation Arrangement
S.I.C.: 4731
N.A.I.C.S.: 488510

Non-U.S. Subsidiaries:

Clarkson Asia Ltd. (1)
1706-1713 Sun Hung Kai Centre
30 Harbour Road, Wanchai, China (Hong Kong)

Clarkson PLC—(Continued)

Tel.: (852) 28663111
Fax: (852) 28663068
E-Mail: clarksons@clarksons.com.hk
Web Site: www.clarksons.com.hk
Emp.: 20
Freight Transportation Arrangement
S.I.C.: 4731
N.A.I.C.S.: 488510
Martin Rowe *(Mng Dir)*

Clarkson Asia Pte Ltd. **(1)**
8 Shenton Way #23-01 Temasek Tower
Singapore, 068811, Singapore
Tel.: (65) 63390036
Fax: (65) 63340012
E-Mail: tankerops.spore@clarksons.com
Web Site: www.clarkson.co.uk
Emp.: 100
Freight Transportation Arrangement
S.I.C.: 4731
N.A.I.C.S.: 488510
Giles Rickwood Lane *(Mng Dir)*

Clarkson Australia Holdings Pty Ltd **(1)**
L 12 157 Walker St
North Sydney, Sydney, NSW, 2060, Australia
Tel.: (61) 2 9954 0200
E-Mail: sydney@clarksons.com
Emp.: 15
Ship Broking Services
S.I.C.: 6799
N.A.I.C.S.: 523910

Clarkson Australia (Pty) Limited **(1)**
11th Floor 157 Walker Street North
Sydney, NSW, 2000, Australia
Tel.: (61) 299540200
Fax: (61) 299540202
E-Mail: brokers@clarksonaustralia.com.au
Web Site: www.clarksonaustralia.com
Emp.: 11
Freight Transportation Arrangement
S.I.C.: 4731
N.A.I.C.S.: 488510
Peter Quirk *(Mng Dir)*

Subsidiary:

Clarkson Melbourne Pty Limited **(2)**
Level 12 636 St Kilda Road
Melbourne, VIC, 3004, Australia
Tel.: (61) 398676800
Fax: (61) 3 9867 6622
E-Mail: australia@clarksons.com
Emp.: 12
Marine Shipping Services
S.I.C.: 4412
N.A.I.C.S.: 483111
David Mullin *(Mng Dir)*

Clarkson (Deutschland) GmbH **(1)**
Johannisbollwerk 20 5 Fl
Hamburg, Germany
Tel.: (49) 40319766110
Fax: (49) 40 3197 66116
E-Mail: hamburg@clarksons.com
Emp.: 8
Chemical Product Distr
S.I.C.: 5169
N.A.I.C.S.: 424690

Clarkson Investment Services (DIFC) Limited **(1)**
Liberty House C/o Dubai International Financial Center
PO Box 506827
Office No 615 616 & 617, Dubai, United Arab Emirates
Tel.: (971) 4 4037000
Fax: (971) 4 4037900
E-Mail: info@clarksons.com
Web Site: www.clarksons.com
Emp.: 15
Cargo Handling Services
S.I.C.: 4491
N.A.I.C.S.: 488320

Clarkson Italia Srl **(1)**
Piazza Rossetti 3A 13
16129 Genoa, Italy
Tel.: (39) 01055401
Fax: (39) 010591695
E-Mail: fix@clarksons.it
Web Site: www.clarksons.com
Emp.: 20
Freight Transportation Arrangement
S.I.C.: 4731
N.A.I.C.S.: 488510
Massimo Dentici *(Pres)*

Clarkson Norway AS **(1)**
Godt Haab Strandveien 50
Lysaker, 1366, Norway
Tel.: (47) 67 10 23 00
Fax: (47) 67 10 23 23
Petrochemical Gas Broking Services
S.I.C.: 1389
N.A.I.C.S.: 213112
Karl Ekerholt *(Mng Dir)*

Clarkson Paris SAS **(1)**
90 Avenue Des Champs Elysees
75008 Paris, France
Tel.: (33) 1 74 31 11 16
Fax: (33) 1 74 31 10 00
Marine Shipping Services
S.I.C.: 4499
N.A.I.C.S.: 488390

Clarkson South Africa (Pty) Limited **(1)**
Heron House 33 Wessel Road
Rivonia, Johannesburg, 2128, South Africa
Tel.: (27) 11 803 0008
E-Mail: drycargo.za@clarksons.com
Emp.: 2
Shipping Services
S.I.C.: 4499
N.A.I.C.S.: 488330
Michael Rimm *(Gen Mgr)*

CLAS OHLSON AB

793 85 Insjon, Sweden
Tel.: (46) 247 44400
Fax: (46) 247 44425
E-Mail: kundtjanft@clasohlson.se
Web Site: www.clasohlson.se
CLAS—(OMX)
Sls.: $1,009,125,720
Assets: $481,149,360
Liabilities: $196,859,160
Net Worth: $284,290,200
Earnings: $51,316,200
Emp.: 2,524
Fiscal Year-end: 04/30/13

Business Description:
Retail Trading Company
S.I.C.: 5719
N.A.I.C.S.: 442299

Personnel:
Anders Moberg *(Chm)*
Klas Balkow *(Pres & CEO)*
Goran Melin *(CFO)*
Anders Lundsten *(CIO & Mgr-IT)*
Rosie Lewis *(Comm Officer-UK)*
Tina Englyst *(Gen Counsel)*
Peter Jelkeby *(Exec VP & Acting Dir-Sls & Comm)*

Board of Directors:
Anders Moberg
Johan Ahlberg
Henrik Andersson
Klas Balkow
Kenneth Bengtsson
Bjorn Haid
Urban Jansson
Cecilia Marlow
Katarina Sjogren Petrini
Edgar Rosenberger
Josefin Salminen
Sanna Suvanto-Harsaae
Lasse Zwetsloot

Non-U.S. Subsidiaries:

Clas Ohlson AS **(1)**
Stromgaten 8
5015 Bergen, Norway
Tel.: (47) 55308660
Fax: (47) 55308661
Web Site: www.clasohlson.no
Emp.: 25
Department Stores
S.I.C.: 5311
N.A.I.C.S.: 452111

Clas Ohlson Ltd. **(1)**
1013 Market Pl
Kingston upon Thames, KT1 1JZ, United Kingdom
Tel.: (44) 8456718215
Fax: (44) 8456718215
E-Mail: customerservices@clasohlson.co.uk
Web Site: www.clasohlson.co.uk
Electrical & Hardware Online Retailer
S.I.C.: 5961
N.A.I.C.S.: 454111
Isabel Abrahall *(Mgr-Store)*

Clas Ohlson OY **(1)**
Yrjonkatu 23 A
00101 Helsinki, Finland (100%)
Tel.: (358) 201112230
Fax: (358) 201112234
Web Site: www.clasohlson.com
Emp.: 500
Department Stores
S.I.C.: 5311
N.A.I.C.S.: 452111
Tapio Kuittene *(CEO)*

CLASQUIN S.A.

235 cours Lafayette
69451 Lyon, Cedex 06, France
Tel.: (33) 472831700
Fax: (33) 472831717
E-Mail: info@clasquin.com
Web Site: www.clasquin.com
ALCLA—(EUR)
Sls.: $248,502,982
Earnings: $3,096,191
Emp.: 562
Fiscal Year-end: 12/31/12

Business Description:
Logistic Services
S.I.C.: 4731
N.A.I.C.S.: 488510

Personnel:
Yves Revol *(Chm & CEO)*
Philippe Lons *(CFO & Deputy Gen Mgr)*
Alain Dumoulin *(COO)*
David Canard-Volland *(CIO)*
Emmanuel Thual *(Deputy Mng Dir & Dir-Sls-France)*
Yves Barnoud *(Gen Sec)*

Board of Directors:
Yves Revol
Ham San Chap
Philippe Le Bihan
Philippe Lons
Hugues Morin

Mazars
Lyon, France

U.S. Subsidiary:

Clasquin USA Inc. **(1)**
10 5th St
Valley Stream, NY 11581
Tel.: (516) 823-0000
Fax: (516) 823-9091
E-Mail: jfk@clasquin.com
Emp.: 20
Freight Transportation Services
S.I.C.: 4731
N.A.I.C.S.: 488510
Didier Vanderperre *(Pres)*

Non-U.S. Subsidiaries:

Clasquin Australia Pty Ltd. **(1)**
Unit 25 Noble St Allawah
2218 Sydney, NSW, Australia
Tel.: (61) 289866600
Fax: (61) 289866699
E-Mail: syd@clasquin.com
Web Site: www.clasquin.com
Freight Transportation Arrangement
S.I.C.: 4731
N.A.I.C.S.: 488510
David Finnie *(Mng Dir)*

Clasquin Espana S.L. **(1)**
Centro de Carga Aerea Oficina 208
Madrid-Barajas, 28042 Madrid, Spain
Tel.: (34) 917478586
Fax: (34) 917471838
E-Mail: everyone.mad@clasquin.com
Emp.: 2
Freight Transportation Arrangement
S.I.C.: 4731
N.A.I.C.S.: 488510
Jean Christophe *(Dir-Ops)*

Clasquin Far East Ltd. **(1)**
Rm E 11th Floor Apartment D Oriental Kenzo Plaza
48 Dongzhimen Wai Street, Dongcheng Dist Beijing, 100027, China
Tel.: (86) 1084549490
Fax: (86) 1084549498
E-Mail: bjs@clasquin.com
Web Site: www.clasquin.com
Emp.: 6
Freight Transportation Arrangement
S.I.C.: 4731
N.A.I.C.S.: 488510
Fabian Giordano *(Gen Mgr)*

Clasquin Germany GmbH **(1)**
Langenstrasse 52- 54
28195 Bremen, Germany
Tel.: (49) 421 517 001 20
Fax: (49) 421 517 001 25
E-Mail: bre@clasquin.com
Emp.: 3
Freight Forwarding Transportation Services
S.I.C.: 4731
N.A.I.C.S.: 488510
Dirk Bukowski *(Mng Dir)*

Clasquin International Taiwan Ltd. **(1)**
4th Floor No 16 Lane 345 Yangkuang St
Neihu District, 11491 Taipei, Taiwan
Tel.: (886) 226595840
Fax: (886) 226594922
Web Site: www.clasquin.com
Freight Transportation Arrangement
S.I.C.: 4731
N.A.I.C.S.: 488510

Clasquin Italia S.R.L. **(1)**
Via Dante 144
20 090 Limito de Pioltello
Milan, Italy
Tel.: (39) 0292169218
Fax: (39) 0292160164
E-Mail: mil@clasquin.com
Freight Transportation Arrangement
S.I.C.: 4731
N.A.I.C.S.: 488510

Clasquin Japan Co. Ltd. **(1)**
Gotanda Koyo Building 4F
1-9-4 Higashi Gotanda
Shinagawa-ku, Tokyo, 141-0022, Japan
Tel.: (81) 332807951
Fax: (81) 3 3280 7978
E-Mail: tyo@clasquin.com
Freight Transportation Arrangement
S.I.C.: 4731
N.A.I.C.S.: 488510

Clasquin Korea Co. Ltd. **(1)**
5th Fl Teopless Bldg 630-9 Hamnan Tong-Yong Sangu
Seoul, 140-210, Korea (South)
Tel.: (82) 23223500
Fax: (82) 23227793
E-Mail: sel@clasquin.com
Web Site: www.clasquin.com
Emp.: 50
Freight Transportation Arrangement
S.I.C.: 4731
N.A.I.C.S.: 488510

Clasquin Malaysia Sdn Bhd **(1)**
1-3 Jalan USJ1/B
47620 Subang Jaya, Malaysia
Tel.: (60) 380242886
Fax: (60) 380243301
E-Mail: kul@clasquin.com
Web Site: www.clasquin.com
Emp.: 10
Freight Transportation Arrangement
S.I.C.: 4731
N.A.I.C.S.: 488510

Clasquin Shanghai Ltd. **(1)**
Room 203 Qingke Mansion No 138 Fen Yang Road
Shanghai, 200031, China
Tel.: (86) 2164451452
Fax: (86) 2164457483
E-Mail: sha@clasquin.com
Logistics Consulting Management Services
S.I.C.: 4731
N.A.I.C.S.: 541614

Clasquin Singapore Pte. Ltd. **(1)**
19 Tai Seng Avenue 05-6 Home-Fix Building
PO Box 625
Changi Airfreight Centre, Singapore, 918105, Singapore

Tel.: (65) 426490
Fax: (65) 426487
E-Mail: sin@clasquin.com
Web Site: www.clasquin.com
Emp.: 20
Freight Transportation Arrangement
S.I.C.: 4731
N.A.I.C.S.: 488510
John Teo *(CFO)*

Clasquin Thailand (Co.) Ltd. **(1)**
12th Floor Unit 12D 163 Ocean Insurance Bldg
Surawongse Road, Bangkok, 10500, Thailand
Tel.: (66) 26342360
Fax: (66) 26342370
E-Mail: bkk@clasquin.com
Web Site: www.clasquin.com
Emp.: 20
Freight Transportation Arrangement
S.I.C.: 4731
N.A.I.C.S.: 488510
Claùde Goalec *(Gen Mgr)*

CLASS EDITORI S.P.A.

5 Via Marco Burigozzo
20122 Milan, Italy
Tel.: (39) 02582191
Fax: (39) 0258317376
E-Mail: ir@class.it
Web Site: www.e-class.it
Year Founded: 1986
CLE—(ITA)
Sales Range: $150-199.9 Million
Emp.: 299
Business Description:
Newspaper, Magazine & Electronic Publisher; Radio, TV & Satellite Broadcasting Services
S.I.C.: 2711
N.A.I.C.S.: 511110
Personnel:
Viktor Ukmar *(Chm)*
Paulo Panerai *(Vice Chm & Mng Dir)*
Pierluigi Magnaschi *(Vice Chm)*
Vittorio Terrenghi *(Vice Chm)*
Board of Directors:
Viktor Ukmar
William L. Bolster
Gabriele Capolino
Maurizio Carfagna
Paolo del Bue
Peter R. Kann
Samanta Librio
Pierluigi Magnaschi
Maria Martellini
Luca Nicolo Panerai
Paulo Panerai
Angelo Eugenio Riccardi
Vittorio Terrenghi

Subsidiaries:

MF Dow Jones News S.r.l. **(1)**
Via Marco Burigozzo 5
20122 Milan, 20122, Italy (50%)
Tel.: (39) 258219715
Fax: (39) 258219752
Web Site: www.dowjones.com
Newspaper Publishers
S.I.C.: 2711
N.A.I.C.S.: 511110
Stefano Nardelli *(Gen Mgr)*

CLASSIC DIAMONDS (INDIA) LIMITED

1002 Prasad Chambers
Opera House
Mumbai, Maharashtra, 400 004, India
Tel.: (91) 2240361000
Fax: (91) 2240361002
E-Mail: compsec@classicdiamondsindia.com
Web Site: www.classicdiamondsindia.com
523200—(BOM NSE)
Sales Range: $100-124.9 Million
Business Description:
Diamond & Gold Jewelry Exporter
S.I.C.: 5094
N.A.I.C.S.: 423940
Personnel:
Kumar C. Bhansali *(Chm & Mng Dir)*
Board of Directors:
Kumar C. Bhansali
Nirav K. Bhansali
Nishikant S. Jha
Madhukar Patankar
Transfer Agent:
Link Intime India Private Limited
C-13 Pannalal Silk Mills Compound L.B.S. Marg Bhandup
Mumbai, India

CLASSIC DREAM PROPERTIES LTD.

c/o Shuion Garden Office 2/F
Guangfo Road Huangqi Dali Town
Nanhai, Foshan, Guangdong, China 528248
Fax: (86) 75785999391
Web Site: www.classicdream.com.hk
5CD—(DEU)
Rev.: $31,579,081
Assets: $78,762,015
Liabilities: $37,831,609
Net Worth: $40,930,406
Earnings: $9,987,178
Fiscal Year-end: 06/30/13
Business Description:
Real Estate Development
S.I.C.: 6531
N.A.I.C.S.: 531210
Personnel:
Zhu Bang Shen *(Chm-Supervisory Bd)*
Xi Hua Deng *(Vice Chm-Supervisory Bd & COO)*
Ming Liang Guang *(CFO & Member-Mgmt Bd)*
Alan Yi Lun Cen *(Member-Mgmt Bd & Head-After Sls & Market Res Dept)*
Pin Xuan Cen *(Member-Mgmt Bd & Head-Project Mgmt Dept)*
Sha Hong She *(Member-Mgmt Bd & Head-Sls & Mktg Dept)*
Cheng Jian Li *(Member-Mgmt Bd & Exec Dir-Ops)*
Hong Wa Shum *(Member-Mgmt Bd & Exec Dir-Market Res)*
Supervisory Board of Directors:
Zhu Bang Shen
Xi Hua Deng
Ming Liang Guang
Cheng Jian Li
Hong Wa Shum

CLASSIC HONDA

30 Van Kirk Drive
Brampton, ON, L7A 2Y4, Canada
Tel.: (905) 454-1434
Fax: (905) 454-5013
Toll Free: (866) 671-2681
E-Mail: Info@Classichonda.ca
Web Site: www.classichonda.ca
Sales Range: $50-74.9 Million
Emp.: 103
Business Description:
Car Dealership
S.I.C.: 5511
N.A.I.C.S.: 441110
Personnel:
Glen Alizadeh *(Owner)*

CLASSIC MINERALS LIMITED

Unit 7 30 Hasler Road
Osborne Park, WA, 6017, Australia
Mailing Address:
PO Box 487
Osborne Park, WA, 6917, Australia
Tel.: (61) 8 9445 3008
Fax: (61) 8 9445 3008
E-Mail: admin@classicminerals.com.au
Web Site: www.classicminerals.com.au
CLZ—(ASX)
Rev.: $47,581
Assets: $3,068,062
Liabilities: $801,665
Net Worth: $2,266,398
Earnings: ($3,341,927)
Fiscal Year-end: 06/30/13
Business Description:
Metal Mining
S.I.C.: 1099
N.A.I.C.S.: 212299
Personnel:
Justin Doutch *(Chm & Mng Dir)*
Kent Hunter *(Sec)*
Board of Directors:
Justin Doutch
Kent Hunter
Stanislaw Procak
Legal Counsel:
Lawton Gillon
Level 11 16 St Georges Terrace
Perth, Australia

CLASSIC SCENIC BERHAD

Lot 12 Jalan RP3 Taman Rawang Perdana
48000 Rawang, Selangor Darul Ehsan, Malaysia
Tel.: (60) 360917477
Fax: (60) 360916766
E-Mail: marketing@classicscenic.com
Web Site: www.classicscenic.com
CSCENIC—(KLS)
Rev.: $20,438,988
Assets: $34,860,047
Liabilities: $2,746,181
Net Worth: $32,113,866
Earnings: $4,352,217
Emp.: 350
Fiscal Year-end: 12/31/12
Business Description:
Wooden Picture Frame Mfr
S.I.C.: 2499
N.A.I.C.S.: 321999
Personnel:
Richard Chee Keong Lim *(Chm)*
Samuel Chee Beng Lim *(Mng Dir)*
Chooi Yoong Chow *(Sec)*
Board of Directors:
Richard Chee Keong Lim
Thin An Au
Kong Weng Lee
Jeffery Chee Khoon Lim
Samuel Chee Beng Lim
Simon Chee Hwa Lim
Sau Tou Yeh

CLAUDE RESOURCES INC.

224 4th Ave S Ste 200
Saskatoon, SK, S7K 5M5, Canada
Tel.: (306) 668-7505
Fax: (306) 668-7500
E-Mail: clauderesources@clauderesources.com
Web Site: www.clauderesources.com
CGR—(OTC TSX)
Rev.: $80,324,768
Assets: $233,114,588
Liabilities: $41,900,925
Net Worth: $191,213,663
Earnings: $5,535,697
Emp.: 330
Fiscal Year-end: 12/31/12
Business Description:
Gold Mining & Exploration Services; Oil & Natural Gas Production
S.I.C.: 1041
N.A.I.C.S.: 212221
Personnel:
Ted J. Nieman *(Chm)*
Rick G. Johnson *(CFO)*
Brian Skanderbeg *(COO & Sr VP)*
Board of Directors:
Ted J. Nieman
Brian R. Booth
Ronald J. Hicks
J. Robert Kowalishin
Raymond A. McKay
Rita M. Mirwald
Michel Sylvestre
Legal Counsel:
MacPherson Leslie & Tyerman LLP
Suite 1500 410 22nd Street East
Saskatoon, SK, Canada
Transfer Agent:
Valiant Trust Company
606 4th Street SW Suite 310
Calgary, AB, T2P 1T1, Canada
Tel.: (403) 233-2801
Fax: (403) 233-2857

CLAUSAL COMPUTING OY

Kutojantie 3
02630 Espoo, Finland
Tel.: (358) 9 278 2200
E-Mail: info@clausal.com
Web Site: www.clausal.com
Business Description:
Computer Software Developer
S.I.C.: 7372
N.A.I.C.S.: 511210
Personnel:
Tatu Ylonen *(Owner)*

CLAVIS PHARMA ASA

(Name Changed to Aqualis ASA)

CLAVIS TECHNOLOGIES INTERNATIONAL CO., LTD.

1564-1 Seojin Bldg 3rd Floor
Seocho3-Dong
Seocho-Gu, Seoul, 137-874, Korea (South)
Tel.: (82) 234719340
Fax: (82) 234719337
E-Mail: sales@clavistech.com
Web Site: www.clavistech.com
Year Founded: 2003
CTLH—(OTC)
Sales Range: Less than $1 Million
Emp.: 7
Business Description:
Radio Frequency Identification (RFID Products & Solutions
S.I.C.: 3663
N.A.I.C.S.: 334220
Personnel:
Hwan Sup Lee *(Chm & Pres)*
So Lim Lee *(CFO)*
Kiyoung You *(CMO & Sec)*
Board of Directors:
Hwan Sup Lee
So Lim Lee
Kiyoung You
Transfer Agent:
Olde Monmouth Stock Transfer Company
200 Memorial Parkway
Atlantic Highlands, NJ 07716

CLAYMORE GOLD BULLION ETF

200 University Avenue 13th Floor
Toronto, ON, M5H 3C6, Canada
Tel.: (416) 813-2006
Fax: (416) 813-2020
E-Mail: info@claymoreinvestments.ca
Web Site: www.claymoreinvestments.ca
Year Founded: 2009
CGL—(TSX)
Business Description:
Investment Services
S.I.C.: 6211
N.A.I.C.S.: 523999

Claymore Gold Bullion ETF—(Continued)

Personnel:
David C. Hooten *(Chm)*
Som Seif *(Pres & CEO)*
Bruce Albelda *(CFO)*
Kevin M. Robinson *(Sec)*
Board of Directors:
David C. Hooten
Bruce Albelda
J. Thomas Futrell
Som Seif

CLAYMORE SILVER BULLION TRUST

200 University Avenue 13th Floor
Toronto, ON, M5H 3C6, Canada
Tel.: (416) 813-2006
Fax: (416) 813-2020
E-Mail: info@claymoreinvestments.ca
Web Site: www.claymoreinvestments.ca
Year Founded: 2009
SVR.UN—(TSX)
Business Description:
Financial Services
S.I.C.: 6091
N.A.I.C.S.: 523991
Personnel:
Som Seif *(Pres & CEO)*
Bruce Albelda *(CFO)*

CLAYTON CONSTRUCTION CO. LTD.

PO Box 11577
Lloydminster, AB, T9V 38B, Canada
Tel.: (306) 344-4649
Fax: (306) 344-2373
Web Site: www.claytonconstruction.ca
Rev.: $11,919,728
Emp.: 25
Business Description:
Oilfield Services
S.I.C.: 1389
N.A.I.C.S.: 213112
Personnel:
Glenn Clayton *(Pres)*

CLC GROUP LIMITED

Vincent Avenue
Shirley, Southampton, Hants, SO16 6PQ, United Kingdom
Tel.: (44) 2380 701 111
Fax: (44) 2380 701 171
E-Mail: mail@clcgroup.com
Web Site: www.clcgroup.com
Year Founded: 1969
Business Description:
Holding Company; Property & Building Maintenance & Refurbishment Services
S.I.C.: 6719
N.A.I.C.S.: 551112
Personnel:
Peter B. Armitage *(Mng Dir)*
Nick Hilton *(Deputy Mng Dir)*

Subsidiary:

CLC Contractors Ltd. **(1)**
Vincent Avenue
Shirley, Southampton, Hants, SO16 6PQ, United Kingdom UK
Tel.: (44) 2380 701 111
Fax: (44) 2380 701 171
Web Site: www.clcgroup.com
Property & Building Maintenance & Refurbishment Services
S.I.C.: 7349
N.A.I.C.S.: 561790
Peter B. Armitage *(Mng Dir)*
Nick Hilton *(Deputy Mng Dir)*

CLEAN AIR POWER LTD

Aston Way
Leyland, Lancashire, PR26 7UX, United Kingdom
Tel.: (44) 1772624499
Fax: (44) 1772436495
E-Mail: cleanairleyland@cleanairpower.com
Web Site: www.cleanairpower.com
Year Founded: 1991
CAP—(AIM)
Rev.: $12,542,721
Assets: $14,856,381
Liabilities: $3,594,464
Net Worth: $11,261,917
Earnings: ($3,506,024)
Emp.: 60
Fiscal Year-end: 12/31/12
Business Description:
Hydraulic Valves & Natural Gas Injector Components For Natural Gas Engines
S.I.C.: 3714
N.A.I.C.S.: 336310
Personnel:
John Pettitt *(Pres & CEO)*
Neill Skinner *(CFO)*
Board of Directors:
Rodney Westhead
Bernard Lord
John Pettitt
Karl-Viktor Schaller
Ulrich Wohr
Legal Counsel:
Pillsbury Winthrop Shaw Pittman LLP
Tower 42 Level 23 25 Old Broad St
London, United Kingdom
Transfer Agent:
Capita IRG (Offshore) Limited
Victoria Chambers Liberation Square 1/3 The Esplanade
Saint Helier, Jersey

CLEAN & SCIENCE CO., LTD.

903-1 Trade Centre 159-1
Samseong-Dong
Gangnam-Ku, Seoul, Korea (South)
Tel.: (82) 2 550 0800
Fax: (82) 2 551 0394
Web Site: www.cands.co.kr
Year Founded: 1973
045520—(KRS)
Business Description:
Filter Paper Mfr
S.I.C.: 2679
N.A.I.C.S.: 322299
Personnel:
Gyu-beom Gwak *(CEO)*

CLEAN BIOENERGY INC.

3352 11215 Jasper Ave
Edmonton, AB, T5K 0L5, Canada
Tel.: (780) 669-6604
E-Mail: ceo@cleanbioenergyinc.com
Web Site: www.cleanbioenergyinc.com
Year Founded: 2010
CJ7—(DEU)
Business Description:
Zero Emissions Sanitary Combustion & Incinerator Mfr
S.I.C.: 4953
N.A.I.C.S.: 562213
Personnel:
Bruce Youb *(CEO)*
John Comeau *(CFO)*
Board of Directors:
Gordie Mah
Gary Repchuk
James Timothy White
Bruce Youb

CLEAN COAL POWER R&D CO., LTD.

102-3 Iwamamachi-Kawada
Iwaki-City, Fukushima, 974-8222, Japan
Tel.: (81) 246773111
Fax: (81) 246773199
Web Site: www.ccpower.co.jp
Year Founded: 2001
Emp.: 63
Business Description:
Energy Research & Development
S.I.C.: 8731
N.A.I.C.S.: 541712
Personnel:
Tsutomu Watamabe *(Pres & CEO)*

CLEAN ENERGY BRAZIL PLC

IOMA House Hope Street
Douglas, Isle of Man IM1 1AP
Tel.: (44) 2078394321
Fax: (44) 2072424202
E-Mail: info@cleanenergybrazil.com
Web Site: www.cleanenergybrazil.com
CEB—(AIM)
Rev.: $1,024,000
Assets: $10,528,000
Liabilities: $333,000
Net Worth: $10,195,000
Earnings: ($85,000)
Fiscal Year-end: 04/30/13
Business Description:
Sugar & Ethanol Investment Services
S.I.C.: 6211
N.A.I.C.S.: 523999
Personnel:
Josef Raucher *(Chm)*
Philip Peter Scales *(Sec)*
Board of Directors:
Josef Raucher
Eitan Milgram
Timothy Walker

CLEAN ENERGY DEVELOPMENT BANK LIMITED

Suryodaya Bhawan Sitapaila Chowk Ring Road
PO Box 24773
Kathmandu, Nepal
Tel.: (977) 1 4671444
Fax: (977) 1 4277013
E-Mail: info@cedbl.com
Web Site: www.cedbl.com
Year Founded: 2006
CEDBL—(NEP)
Sales Range: $1-9.9 Million
Emp.: 131
Business Description:
Banking Services
S.I.C.: 6029
N.A.I.C.S.: 522110
Personnel:
Dhananjay Prasad Acharya *(Chm)*
Kapil Sharma *(Acting CEO)*
Barsha Shrestha *(Deputy CEO)*
Harihar Nidhi Tiwari *(Sec)*
Board of Directors:
Dhananjay Prasad Acharya
Anup Acharya
Manish Kumar Agrawal
Alwin B. Kool
Rajendra Raut
Laxmi Prasad Shrestha

J. Santhosh & Co.
Kamalpokhari
Kathmandu, Nepal
Legal Counsel:
Pioneer Law Associates Pvt. Ltd.
Pioneer House-246 Sahayog Marg Anamnagar
Kathmandu, Nepal

CLEAN LINEN SERVICES LIMITED

54 Furze Platt Road
Maidenhead, Berkshire, SL6 7NL, United Kingdom
Tel.: (44) 1628645900
Fax: (44) 1628674099
E-Mail: info@cleanservices.co.uk
Web Site: www.cleanservices.co.uk
Rev.: $33,736,753
Emp.: 530
Business Description:
Laundry Services
S.I.C.: 7219
N.A.I.C.S.: 812320
Personnel:
Jason Miller *(Mng Dir)*

CLEAN POWER CONCEPTS INC.

1620 McAra Street
Regina, SK, S4N 6H6, Canada
Tel.: (306) 546-8327
Fax: (306) 543-6580
E-Mail: corporate@cleanpowerconcepts.com
Web Site: cpowoil.com
Year Founded: 2005
CPOW—(OTC)
Sales Range: Less than $1 Million
Emp.: 5
Business Description:
Fuel Grade Oilseed Product Mfr
S.I.C.: 2075
N.A.I.C.S.: 311224
Personnel:
Michael Shenher *(Chm, Pres, CEO, CFO & Chief Acctg Officer)*

CLEAN POWER TECHNOLOGIES INC.

Unit 7 W E-Plan Industrial Estate
New Road, Newhaven, E Sussex, BN9 OEX, United Kingdom
Tel.: (44) 1273516013
Fax: (44) 1273612309
E-Mail: mail@cleanpowertechnologies.com
Web Site: www.cleanpowertechnologies.com
Year Founded: 2003
CPWE—(DEU OTC)
Sales Range: $1-9.9 Million
Emp.: 11
Business Description:
Hybrid Fuel Engine Power Trains Developer
S.I.C.: 3714
N.A.I.C.S.: 336350
Personnel:
David Anthony *(CFO)*
Board of Directors:
David Anthony
Abdul A. Mitha

Subsidiary:

Clean Power Technologies Ltd. **(1)**
Unit 7 W E Plan Industrial Estate New Road
Newhaven, E Sussex, BN9 OEX, United Kingdom UK
Tel.: (44) 1273516013
Fax: (44) 1273612309
E-Mail: mail@cleanpowertechnologies.com
Web Site: www.cleanpowertech.co.uk
Steam Hybrid Engine Mfr
S.I.C.: 3519
N.A.I.C.S.: 333618
David Anthony *(CFO)*
Michael Burns *(CTO)*

CLEAN SEAS TUNA LTD

7 North Quay Boulevard
PO Box 159
Port Lincoln, SA, 5606, Australia
Tel.: (61) 886212910
Fax: (61) 886212990
E-Mail: reception@cleanseas.com.au
Web Site: www.cleanseastuna.com.au
CSS—(ASX)
Rev.: $16,179,645
Assets: $30,433,488
Liabilities: $6,176,527

Net Worth: $24,256,962
Earnings: ($35,907,640)
Fiscal Year-end: 06/30/13
Business Description:
Seafood Producer
S.I.C.: 5142
N.A.I.C.S.: 424420
Personnel:
Hagen H. Stehr *(Founder)*
Craig Foster *(CEO)*
Frank Knight *(CFO & Sec)*
Board of Directors:
Paul Steere
Nick Burrows
Hagen H. Stehr
Marcus A. Stehr

CLEAN SEED CAPITAL GROUP LTD.

#14 7541 Conway Avenue
Burnaby, BC, V5E 2P7, Canada
Tel.: (604) 566-9895
Fax: (604) 566-9896
E-Mail: info@cleanseedcapital.com
Web Site: www.cleanseedcapital.com
Year Founded: 2010
CSX—(TSXV)
Business Description:
Investment Services; Agriculture
S.I.C.: 6211
N.A.I.C.S.: 523999
Personnel:
Graeme Lempriere *(Pres & CEO)*
Murray Swales *(CFO)*
Gord Wilson *(CTO & Mgr-Mfg)*
Lehla Moran *(Sec & Controller)*
Board of Directors:
Jason Birmingham
Neil Carnell
Ward Jensen
Graeme Lempriere
Murray Swales
Mark Tommasi
Transfer Agent:
Computershare Investor Services Inc.
3rd Floor 510 Burrard St
V6C 3B9 Vancouver, BC, Canada

CLEAN TEQ HOLDINGS LIMITED

270-280 Hammond Road
Dandenong, VIC, 3175, Australia
Tel.: (61) 3 9797 6700
Fax: (61) 3 9706 8344
E-Mail: info@cleanteq.com
Web Site: www.cleanteq.com
CLQ—(ASX)
Rev.: $10,862,850
Assets: $20,550,212
Liabilities: $8,883,903
Net Worth: $11,666,310
Earnings: ($4,825,965)
Emp.: 23
Fiscal Year-end: 06/30/13
Business Description:
Industrial Water Producer
S.I.C.: 1623
N.A.I.C.S.: 237110
Personnel:
Peter Voigt *(Founder)*
Cory Williams *(CEO)*
Tony Panther *(CFO)*
Melanie Leydin *(Sec)*
Board of Directors:
Sam Riggall
Roger Harley
Ian Knight
Greg Toll
Peter Voigt
Legal Counsel:
Minter Ellison
Level 23 S Rialto Tower 525 Collins St
Melbourne, Australia
Subsidiary:

Clean TeQ Limited **(1)**
270 280 Hammond Rd
Dandenong S, Melbourne, Victoria, 3175, Australia
Tel.: (61) 397068244
Fax: (61) 397068344
E-Mail: info@cleanteq.com
Web Site: www.cleanteq.com
Emp.: 30
Air & Water Purification Equipment Mfr
S.I.C.: 3564
N.A.I.C.S.: 333413
Melanie Leydin *(CFO)*

CLEAN TRANSPORTATION GROUP, INC.

7810 Marchwood Place
Vancouver, BC, V5S 4A6, Canada
Tel.: (604) 202-3212
Web Site: www.ctgiinc.com
Year Founded: 1978
CLNZ—(OTC)
Sales Range: Less than $1 Million
Business Description:
Automotive Engine Maintenance Service Products Mfr
S.I.C.: 3714
N.A.I.C.S.: 336310
Personnel:
Harold Schneider *(Treas)*
Delbert G. Blewett *(Sec)*
Board of Directors:
Delbert G. Blewett
Vernon L. Lewis
Harold Schneider

CLEANAWAY COMPANY LIMITED

1F 15 Min-Tsu Road
Kangshan District, Kaohsiung, 820, Taiwan
Tel.: (886) 76264853
Fax: (886) 76260286
E-Mail: 8422@cleanaway.tw
Web Site: www.cleanaway.tw
Year Founded: 1999
8422—(TAI)
Sales Range: $75-99.9 Million
Emp.: 140
Business Description:
Hazardous & Non-Hazardous Industrial Waste Treatment & Disposal
S.I.C.: 4953
N.A.I.C.S.: 562211
Personnel:
Ching-Hsiang Yang *(Chm)*
Cheng-Lun Tao *(Pres & Gen Mgr)*
Tsung-Tien Chen *(CFO)*
Board of Directors:
Ching-Hsiang Yang
Kun Yu Chang
Ta-Tai Chen
Chong Meng Lai
Cheng-Lun Tao
Chien-Hsun Wu
Wen-Tsai Yang

CLEANFIELD ALTERNATIVE ENERGY INC.

774 Gordon Baker Road
North York, ON, M2H 3B4, Canada
Tel.: (416) 756-4890
Fax: (416) 756-4837
E-Mail: info@cleanfieldenergy.com
Web Site: www.cleanfieldenergy.com
AIR—(TSXV)
Business Description:
Electric Power Generation Services
S.I.C.: 4931
N.A.I.C.S.: 221118
Personnel:
Tony Verrelli *(Pres & CEO)*
Henry Kroeze *(CFO)*
Mihail Stern *(CTO & VP)*
Board of Directors:
Khris Kline
Brian Miloski
Sureshlal Kamalalal Shrivastav
Mihail Stern
Tony Verrelli
Transfer Agent:
Olympia Transfer Service Inc
Suite 920 120 Adelaide Street West
Toronto, ON, Canada

CLEANTECH CAPITAL INC.

25 Adelaide Street East Suite 1900
Toronto, ON, M5C 3A1, Canada
Tel.: (416) 828-2077
Year Founded: 2013
YES.P—(TSXV)
Business Description:
Investment Services
S.I.C.: 6211
N.A.I.C.S.: 523999
Personnel:
James Srbolla *(Pres, CEO & Sec)*
James P. Boyle *(CFO)*
Board of Directors:
Ian Anderson
James P. Boyle
Lyle Clarke
Andrew Horsman
Gord Miller
James Srbolla
William White
Transfer Agent:
Equity Financial Trust Company
200 University Avenue Suite 400
Toronto, ON, M5H 4H1, Canada
Tel.: (416) 361-0152
Fax: (416) 361-0470
Toll Free: (866) 393-4891

CLEANTECH INNOVATIONS, INC.

C District Maoshan Industry Park
Tieling Economic Devel Zone
Tieling, Liaoning, 112616, China
Tel.: (86) 410 6129922
E-Mail: investors@ctiproduct.com
Web Site: www.ctiproduct.com
CTEK—(OTC)
Sales Range: $1-9.9 Million
Emp.: 240
Business Description:
Turbine Engines & Specialty Metal Products Mfr
S.I.C.: 3511
N.A.I.C.S.: 333611
Personnel:
Bei Lv *(Chm & CEO)*
Fegjun Sun *(CFO)*
Limin Han *(COO & Gen Mgr)*
Board of Directors:
Bei Lv
Shuyuan Liu
Dianfu Lv
Terry K. McEwen
Zili Zhao

CLEANTECH SOLUTIONS INTERNATIONAL, INC.

No 9 Yanyu Middle Road
Qianzhou Village Huishan Distr,
Wuxi, Jiangsu, China 214181
Tel.: (86) 510 8339 7559
Fax: (86) 510 8338 0099
E-Mail: Info@cleantechsolutionsinternational.com
Web Site: www.cleantechsolutionsinternational.com
Year Founded: 1995
CLNT—(NASDAQ)
Rev.: $57,199,221
Assets: $89,936,284
Liabilities: $11,942,626
Net Worth: $77,993,658
Earnings: $4,198,580
Emp.: 205
Fiscal Year-end: 12/31/12
Business Description:
High Precision Forged Rolled Rings, Yaw Bearings & Shafts Mfr
S.I.C.: 3499
N.A.I.C.S.: 332999
Personnel:
Jianhua Wu *(Chm & CEO)*
Adam C. Wasserman *(CFO)*
Board of Directors:
Jianhua Wu
Fu Ren Chen
Xi Liu
Bao Wen Wang
Tianxiang Zhou
Legal Counsel:
Asher S. Levitsky P.C
61 Broadway
New York, NY 10086
Transfer Agent:
Empire Stock Transfer, Inc.
1859 Whitney Mesa Dr
Henderson, NV 89009
Subsidiary:

Wuxi Huayang Electrical Power Equipment Co., Ltd **(1)**
No 9 Yanyu Middle Rd
Qianzhou Huishan, Wuxi, Jiangsu, China
Tel.: (86) 51083381199
Fax: (86) 51083380099
Electric Power Equipments Mfr
S.I.C.: 3511
N.A.I.C.S.: 333611

CLEANUP CORPORATION

6-22-22 Nishi-nippori
Arakawa-ku, Tokyo, 116-8587, Japan
Tel.: (81) 3 3894 4771
E-Mail: cl-customercenter@cleanup.co.jp
Web Site: www.cleanup.co.jp
Year Founded: 1949
7955—(TKS)
Sales Range: $1-4.9 Billion
Emp.: 2,674
Business Description:
Household Equipment Mfr & Whslr
S.I.C.: 2514
N.A.I.C.S.: 337124
Personnel:
Kyoichi Inoue *(Pres & CEO)*

CLEAR LEISURE PLC

1 Grosvenor Crescent
London, SW1X 7EF, United Kingdom
Tel.: (44) 20 3 021 0000
E-Mail: info@clearleisure.com
Web Site: www.clearleisure.com
Year Founded: 1999
CLP—(LSE)
Rev.: $11,660,525
Assets: $109,018,231
Liabilities: $55,755,669
Net Worth: $53,262,562
Earnings: ($3,211,962)
Emp.: 13
Fiscal Year-end: 12/31/12
Business Description:
Investment Management Services
S.I.C.: 6282
N.A.I.C.S.: 523920
Personnel:
Alfredo Villa *(CEO)*
Nilesh Jagatia *(CFO & Sec)*
Cesare Suglia *(COO)*
Board of Directors:
Luke Johnson
Francesco Emilani
Nilesh Jagatia
Cesare Suglia
Alfredo Villa
Legal Counsel:
CFMP
Studio Legale Associato Via Fatebenefratelli 22
20121 Milan, Italy

CLEAR LIGHT DIGITAL PTY. LTD.

Level 3 47 Wellington Street
Saint Kilda, VIC, 3182, Australia
Tel.: (61) 3 8530 1000
Fax: (61) 3 8530 1010
E-Mail: seethelight@clearlightdigital.com
Web Site: www.clearlightdigital.com
Year Founded: 2005
Sales Range: $1-9.9 Million
Emp.: 20

Business Description:
Internet Marketing Services
S.I.C.: 7319
N.A.I.C.S.: 541890

Personnel:
Jamie Silver *(Mng Dir)*

CLEAR MEDIA LIMITED

16/F Sunning Plaza 10 Hysan Avenue
Causeway Bay, China (Hong Kong)
Tel.: (852) 29601229
Fax: (852) 22353911
E-Mail: info@c1energy.ca
Web Site: www.clear-media.net
0100—(HKG)
Rev.: $196,266,542
Assets: $517,995,503
Liabilities: $82,476,162
Net Worth: $435,519,341
Earnings: $31,435,431
Emp.: 537
Fiscal Year-end: 12/31/12

Business Description:
Outdoor Media Company
S.I.C.: 7319
N.A.I.C.S.: 541890

Personnel:
Mark Thewlis *(Chm)*
Zi Jing Han *(CEO)*
Hong Kiong Teo *(CFO)*
Huai Jun Zhang *(COO)*
Jeffrey Yip *(Sec)*

Board of Directors:
Mark Thewlis
Jonathan David Bevan
Peter Maxwell Cosgrove
William Eccleshare
Zi Jing Han
Leonie Man Fung Ki
Thomas Manning
Desmond Murray
Hong Kiong Teo
Shou Zhi Wang
Huai Jun Zhang
Jia Zhu

Butterfield Fulcrum Group (Bermuda) Limited
26 Burnaby Street
Hamilton, HM 11, Bermuda

CLEAR MOUNTAIN RESOURCES CORP.

Suite 1220-1111 Melville Street
Vancouver, BC, V6E 3V6, Canada
Tel.: (604) 761-8597
Fax: (604) 608-4936
Web Site: www.clearmountainresources.com
Year Founded: 2010
CY—(TSXV)
Int. Income: $66
Assets: $533,321
Liabilities: $60,336
Net Worth: $472,985
Earnings: ($411,843)
Fiscal Year-end: 05/31/13

Business Description:
Metal Mining
S.I.C.: 1099
N.A.I.C.S.: 212299

Personnel:
Richard Barth *(Pres & CEO)*
Michael N. Waldkirch *(CFO)*

Board of Directors:
Richard Barth
Thomas Clarke
Craig Taylor
Michael N. Waldkirch

Legal Counsel:
Gregory T. Chu
Ste 650 1188 W Georgia St
Vancouver, BC, Canada

Transfer Agent:
Equity Transfer & Trust Company
1185 West Georgia Street Suite 1620
Vancouver, BC, V6E 4E6, Canada

CLEAR SYSTEM RECYCLING, INC.

73 Raymar Place
Oakville, ON, L6J 6M1, Canada
Tel.: (905) 302-3843
Web Site:
Year Founded: 2011
CLSR—(OTC OTCB)
Liabilities: $50,420
Net Worth: ($50,420)
Earnings: ($71,362)
Fiscal Year-end: 12/31/12

Business Description:
Hospital Recycling Services
S.I.C.: 4953
N.A.I.C.S.: 562211

Personnel:
Arthur John Carter *(Pres)*
Roy Rose *(Interim CEO)*
Kenneth R. Kepp *(CFO & COO)*

Board of Directors:
Gary Arford
Michael Balter
Arthur John Carter
Thomas Keith
Michael D. Noonan
Roy Rose

CLEAR2PAY NV/SA

De Kleetlaan 6a Mechelen Campus
Diegem, 1831, Belgium
Tel.: (32) 24025200
Fax: (32) 24025201
E-Mail: info@clear2pay.com
Web Site: www.clear2pay.com
Emp.: 1,000

Business Description:
Automated Payment Solutions
S.I.C.: 8721
N.A.I.C.S.: 541214

Personnel:
Michel Akkermans *(Co-Founder, Chm & CEO)*
Jurgen Ingels *(Co-Founder & CFO)*

Board of Directors:
Michel Akkermans
Dominique Illien

U.S. Subsidiary:

ISTS Worldwide, Inc. (1)
39300 Civic Center Dr Ste 390
Fremont, CA 94538
Tel.: (510) 794-1400
Fax: (510) 742-9269
E-Mail: sales@istsinc.com
Web Site: www.istsinc.com
Sales Range: $10-24.9 Million
Emp.: 65
Credit, Debit & Gift-Card Processing Services
S.I.C.: 7379
N.A.I.C.S.: 541519
Virendar Rana *(CEO)*

Non-U.S. Subsidiary:

ISTS Infotech Solutions Pvt Ltd. (2)
C 111 Sector 63
Noida, NP, 201301, India
Tel.: (91) 1204021400
Fax: (91) 1204021445
E-Mail: info@istsinc.com
Web Site: www.istsinc.com
Emp.: 137
Electronic Payment Processing Services
S.I.C.: 7379
N.A.I.C.S.: 541519
Viren Rana *(Pres)*

CLEARDEBT GROUP PLC

Nelson House Park Road
Timperley, Manchester, Cheshire, WA14 5BZ, United Kingdom
Tel.: (44) 1619692030
Fax: (44) 1619692207
Web Site: www.cleardebtgroup.co.uk
Sales Range: $10-24.9 Million
Emp.: 135

Business Description:
Holding Company; Financial Services
S.I.C.: 6719
N.A.I.C.S.: 551112

Personnel:
Gerald Carey *(Chm)*
David Emanuel Merton Mond *(CEO & Sec)*
Simon Lee *(COO)*

Board of Directors:
Gerald Carey
Simon Lee
Anthony J. Leon
David Emanuel Merton Mond
David M. Shalom

Legal Counsel:
DWF LLP
1 Scott Place 2 Hardman Street
Manchester, United Kingdom

DAC Beachcroft
100 Fetter Lane
London, United Kingdom

Subsidiaries:

Abacus (Financial Consultants) Limited (1)
Nelson House Park Rd
Timperley, Altrincham, Cheshire, WA14 5BZ, United Kingdom
Tel.: (44) 1619058810
Fax: (44) 161 972 0700
E-Mail: enquiries@abacusfinance.co.uk
Web Site: www.abacusfinance.co.uk
Emp.: 40
Debt Management Services
S.I.C.: 7322
N.A.I.C.S.: 561440
David E. Mond *(CEO)*

ClearCash Limited (1)
Nelson House Pk Rd
Timperley, Altrincham, Cheshire, WA14 5BZ, United Kingdom
Tel.: (44) 1619686823
Fax: (44) 1619692207
E-Mail: info@clearcash.co.uk
Web Site: www.clearcash.co.uk
Emp.: 120
Prepaid Cash Cards & Online Bill Payment Services
S.I.C.: 6099
N.A.I.C.S.: 522320
Samuel Mond *(Mng Dir)*

ClearDebt Limited (1)
Nelson House Park Rd
Timperley, Altrincham, Cheshire, WA14 5BZ, United Kingdom
Tel.: (44) 1619692030
Fax: (44) 1619692207
E-Mail: enquiries@cleardebt.co.uk
Web Site: www.cleardebt.co.uk
Emp.: 100
Debt Management Services
S.I.C.: 6211
N.A.I.C.S.: 523999
Andrew Smith *(Dir-Mktg)*

The Debt Advice Portal Limited (1)
Nelson House Park Road
Timperley, Altrincham, Cheshire, WA14 5BZ, United Kingdom
Tel.: (44) 20 7193 4143
E-Mail: b2b@debtadviceportal.com
Web Site: www.thedebtadviceportal.com
Debt Management Services
S.I.C.: 7322
N.A.I.C.S.: 561440

CLEARFORD INDUSTRIES INC.

515 Legget Drive Suite 100
Ottawa, ON, K2K 3G4, Canada
Tel.: (613) 599-6474
Fax: (613) 599-7478
E-Mail: info@clearford.com
Web Site: www.clearford.com
CLI—(TSXV)
Rev.: $881,740
Assets: $3,831,541
Liabilities: $6,160,216
Net Worth: ($2,328,676)
Earnings: ($3,537,392)
Fiscal Year-end: 12/31/12

Business Description:
Waste Water Management Services
S.I.C.: 4953
N.A.I.C.S.: 562219

Personnel:
Roderick M. Bryden *(Chm)*
Kevin Loiselle *(Pres & CEO)*
Mark McGuire *(CFO & VP-Fin)*
Wilf Stefan *(CTO & VP-Engrg)*
Mark Goudie *(Exec VP)*

Board of Directors:
Roderick M. Bryden
Glenn Gold
John B. Kelly
Daniel Kenney
Bruce Linton
C. Ian Ross
Andrew Szonyi

Transfer Agent:
Olympia Trust Company
Suite 920, 120 Adelaide Street West
M5H 1T1 Toronto, ON, Canada

CLEARSPEED TECHNOLOGY PLC

130 Aztec West
Park Avenue, Bristol, BS32 4UB, United Kingdom
Tel.: (44) 1454629623
Fax: (44) 1454629624
E-Mail: info@clearspeed.com
Web Site: www.clearspeed.com
Year Founded: 2001
Sales Range: $1-9.9 Million
Emp.: 6

Business Description:
Semiconductor Products Developer & Mfr
S.I.C.: 3674
N.A.I.C.S.: 334413

Personnel:
Russell David *(COO)*
Kenneth Innocent *(Sec)*

Board of Directors:
Russell David
Richard Bruce Farleigh

CLEARVIEW WEALTH LIMITED

Level 12 20 Bond Street
Sydney, NSW, 2000, Australia
Mailing Address:
GPO Box 4232
Sydney, NSW, 2001, Australia
Tel.: (61) 2 8095 1300
Fax: (61) 2 9233 1960
E-Mail: ir@clearview.com.au
Web Site: www.clearview.com.au
CVW—(ASX)
Rev.: $179,530,904
Assets: $1,636,851,480
Liabilities: $1,375,581,379
Net Worth: $261,270,102
Earnings: $1,954,980
Fiscal Year-end: 06/30/13

Business Description:
Financial Investment & Life Insurance Services

S.I.C.: 6211
N.A.I.C.S.: 523999
Personnel:
Simon Swanson *(Mng Dir)*
Athol Chiert *(CFO & Co-Sec)*
Justin McLaughlin *(Chief Investment Officer)*
Greg Martin *(Chief Actuary Officer & Chief Risk Officer)*
Chris Robson *(Gen Counsel & Co-Sec)*
Board of Directors:
Gary Weiss
Michael Alscher
David Brown
Gary Burg
Bruce Edwards
Les Fallick
Simon Swanson
Nathanial Thomas
Jenny Weinstock

CLEARWATER SEAFOODS INCORPORATED
757 Bedford Highway
Bedford, NS, B4A 3Z7, Canada
Tel.: (902) 443-0550
Fax: (902) 443-8365
Toll Free: (888) 722-5567
E-Mail: investorinquiries@clearwater.ca
Web Site: www.clearwater.ca
Year Founded: 1976
CLR—(TSX)
Sls.: $348,351,327
Assets: $409,685,343
Liabilities: $303,801,339
Net Worth: $105,884,004
Earnings: $22,568,230
Emp.: 1,400
Fiscal Year-end: 12/31/12
Business Description:
Wholesale Seafood
S.I.C.: 5421
N.A.I.C.S.: 445220
Personnel:
Ian D. Smith *(CEO)*
Robert D. Wight *(CFO & VP-Fin)*
Eric R. Roe *(COO & VP)*
John Burwash *(CIO)*
Greg Morency *(Chief Comml Officer & Exec VP)*
David Rathbun *(Chief Talent Officer & VP)*
David Kavanagh *(Gen Counsel & VP)*
Tyrone D. Cotie *(Treas)*
Board of Directors:
Harold Giles
Larry Hood
Mickey MacDonald
Brendan Paddick
John C. Risley
Stan Spavold
Thomas D. Traves
Transfer Agent:
Computershare Investor Services Inc.
Montreal, QC, Canada
Subsidiary:

Clearwater Seafoods Limited Partnership **(1)**
757 Bedford Highway
Bedford, NS, B4A 3Z7, Canada
Tel.: (902) 443-0550
Fax: (902) 443-8365
E-Mail: service@clearwater.ca
Web Site: www.clearwater.ca
Emp.: 150
Fresh & Frozen Seafood Processing
S.I.C.: 2092
N.A.I.C.S.: 311710
Colin MacDonald *(CEO)*
Robert Wight *(CFO & VP-Fin)*
Eric Roe *(COO)*

Non-U.S. Subsidiary:

Glaciar Pesquera S.A. **(2)**
Santiago Del Estero 1718 Piso 1 Oficina 7
Mar del Plata, Buenos Aires, 7600, Argentina
Tel.: (54) 2234922215
Fax: (54) 2234922216
Emp.: 150
Seafood Whslr
S.I.C.: 5146
N.A.I.C.S.: 424460
Eduardo Lemmi *(Pres)*

CLEEVE TECHNOLOGY INCORPORATED
716 Colonel Sam Drive
Oshawa, ON, L1H 7Y2, Canada
Tel.: (905) 579-9502
Fax: (905) 579-9991
E-Mail: solutions@cleevetech.com
Web Site: www.cleevetech.com
Year Founded: 1998
Rev.: $41,759,619
Emp.: 25
Business Description:
Electrical Products Supplier
S.I.C.: 5063
N.A.I.C.S.: 423610
Personnel:
Paul Church *(Pres)*

CLEGHORN MINERALS LTD.
152 Chemin de la Mine Ecole
Val d'Or, QC, J9P 7B6, Canada
Tel.: (819) 824-2808
Fax: (819) 824-3379
E-Mail: glenn.mullan@goldenvalleymines.com
Year Founded: 2010
JZZ.P—(TSXV)
Business Description:
Investment Services
S.I.C.: 6211
N.A.I.C.S.: 523999
Personnel:
Glenn J. Mullan *(Pres, CEO & Sec)*
Jens Zinke *(CFO)*
Board of Directors:
Joseph Groia
Glenn J. Mullan
Jens Zinke

CLEMEX TECHNOLOGIES INC
800 Guimond
Longueuil, QC, J4G 1T5, Canada
Tel.: (450) 651-6573
Fax: (450) 651-9304
Toll Free: (888) 651-6573
E-Mail: info@clemex.com
Web Site: www.clemex.com
CXG.A—(TSXV)
Sls.: $5,849,441
Assets: $4,774,633
Liabilities: $1,582,126
Net Worth: $3,192,507
Earnings: $100,696
Emp.: 29
Fiscal Year-end: 04/30/13
Business Description:
Image Analysis Solutions
S.I.C.: 3823
N.A.I.C.S.: 334513
Personnel:
Me Lisane Dostie *(Chm & Sec)*
Clement Forget *(Pres & CEO)*
Monique Dallaire *(COO)*
Caroline Trudel *(Treas & VP-Fin & Admin)*
Board of Directors:
Me Lisane Dostie
Yves Bassat
Normand Beauregard
Clement Forget
Jan Stephan Roell

Legal Counsel:
Miller, Thompson, Pouliot
Montreal, QC, Canada
Transfer Agent:
Computershare
Montreal, QC, Canada

CLEOPATRA INTERNATIONAL GROUP, INC.
12 Ying Chun Road 9th Floor
Hai Wai Lian Yi Building
Luo Hu District, Shenzhen, Guangdong, China
Tel.: (86) 755 8230 9541
Fax: (86) 755 8261 1003
CLIN—(OTC)
Sales Range: $1-9.9 Million
Emp.: 225
Business Description:
Beauty, Hair & Spa Services
S.I.C.: 7231
N.A.I.C.S.: 812112
Personnel:
Haiying Guan *(Chm & Pres)*
Yongping Xu *(CEO)*
Lixin Zhang *(CFO)*
Board of Directors:
Haiying Guan
Deng Hua
Yongping Xu
Howard Li Guo Zhao

CLERMONT CAPITAL INC.
Suite 100 736 Granville Street
Vancouver, BC, V6Z 1G3, Canada
Tel.: (604) 561-8196
Fax: (604) 684-6740
E-Mail: neil@stockpools.com
Year Founded: 2011
XYZ.P—(TSXV)
Business Description:
Investment Services
S.I.C.: 6211
N.A.I.C.S.: 523999
Personnel:
James Currie *(Chm & CFO)*
John Arlen Hansen *(Pres & CEO)*
Neil Currie *(Sec)*
Board of Directors:
James Currie
John Arlen Hansen
Marc Prefontaine
Sophia Shane
Transfer Agent:
Computershare Investor Services Inc.
3rd Floor 510 Burrard Street
Vancouver, BC, Canada

CLESSIDRA SGR S.P.A.
(d/b/a Clessidra Capital Partners)
Via del Lauro 7
20121 Milan, Italy
Tel.: (39) 28695221
Fax: (39) 02869522522
E-Mail: info@clessidrasgr.it
Web Site: www.clessidrasgr.it
Year Founded: 2003
Emp.: 30
Business Description:
Private Equity Firm
S.I.C.: 6211
N.A.I.C.S.: 523999
Personnel:
Claudio Sposito *(Chm & CEO)*
Joint Venture:

Prime European Therapeuticals S.p.A. **(1)**
Viale Milano 86/88
26900 Lodi, LO, Italy IT
Tel.: (39) 0371 49 021
Fax: (39) 0371 61 0019
Web Site: www.euticals.com
Sales Range: $250-299.9 Million
Emp.: 900
Pharmaceutical Ingredient & Fine Chemical Products Mfr
S.I.C.: 2869
N.A.I.C.S.: 325199
Maurizio Silvestri *(Pres & CEO)*

Plant:

Prime European Therapeuticals S.p.A. - Origgio Plant **(2)**
Viale Europa 5
21040 Origgio, VA, Italy
Tel.: (39) 02969531
Fax: (39) 0296730456
Web Site: www.euticals.com
Fine Chemical Mfr
S.I.C.: 2899
N.A.I.C.S.: 325998

U.S. Subsidiary:

Euticals Inc. **(2)**
2460 W Bennett St
Springfield, MO 65807-1229 DE
Tel.: (302) 994-3043
Fax: (302) 994-3475
Web Site: www.euticals.com
Pharmaceutical Ingredient Mfr
S.I.C.: 2869
N.A.I.C.S.: 325199
Steve Hancock *(Dir-Ops-US)*

Non-U.S. Subsidiaries:

Euticals GmbH **(2)**
Industriepark Hochst
65926 Frankfurt am Main, Germany De
Tel.: (49) 69 305 22055
Fax: (49) 69 305 17562
Web Site: www.euticals.com
Emp.: 60
Pharmaceutical Ingredient Mfr
S.I.C.: 2869
N.A.I.C.S.: 325199
Jurgen Brockmann *(Sls Dir & Mktg Dir)*

Euticals Limited **(2)**
Prince William Avenue
Sandycroft, Deeside, Flintshire, CH5 2PX, United Kingdom UK
Tel.: (44) 1244 520 777
Fax: (44) 1244 537 216
E-Mail:
Web Site: www.euticals.com
Pharmaceutical Ingredient Mfr
S.I.C.: 2869
N.A.I.C.S.: 325199
Tim Reeve *(Sr Mgr-Sls & Mktg)*

Euticals SAS **(2)**
Zone Industrielle de Laville
F-47240 Bon Encontre, France FR
Tel.: (33) 5 5369 1300
Fax: (33) 5 5369 1310
E-Mail:
Web Site: www.euticals.com
Fine Chemical Mfr
S.I.C.: 2899
N.A.I.C.S.: 325998

CLESTRA HAUSERMAN S.A.
56 Rue Jean Giraudoux
PO Box 46
67200 Strasbourg, Cedex, France
Tel.: (33) 388276800
Telex: 870.820
Fax: (33) 388276801
E-Mail: grh@clestra.com
Web Site: www.clestra.com
Emp.: 1,000
Business Description:
Furniture Systems Mfr
S.I.C.: 2599
N.A.I.C.S.: 337215
Personnel:
Xavier P. Negiar *(Chm, Pres & CEO)*
U.S. Subsidiary:

Clestra Hauserman, Inc. **(1)**
259 Veterans Ln Ste 201
Doylestown, PA 18901 DE
Tel.: (267) 880-3700
Fax: (267) 880-3705
E-Mail: clestra.usa@clestra.com
Web Site: www.clestra.com

Clestra Hauserman S.A.—(Continued)

Sales Range: $25-49.9 Million
Emp.: 14
Movable Walls & Partitions Mfr, Designer & Installer
Import
S.I.C.: 1799
N.A.I.C.S.: 238990
David R. Harkins, Jr. *(COO)*

Non-U.S. Affiliates:

Clestra Hauserman **(1)**
Via Legnano 21
20015 Milan, Parabiago, Italy (100%)
Tel.: (39) 331499701
Fax: (39) 0331499720
Web Site: www.clestra.it
Sales & Distribution of Office Furniture
S.I.C.: 5712
N.A.I.C.S.: 442110

Clestra Hauserman Korea **(1)**
9th Fl Kotef Bldg 35 3 Yeido Dong
Yongdungpo Po Gu, 150 704 Seoul, Korea (South) (50%)
Tel.: (82) 27846274
Fax: (82) 27846270
Web Site: www.clestra.co.kr
Emp.: 30
Provider of Furniture; Joint Venture of Posco, Korea & Clestra Hauserman S.A.
S.I.C.: 2521
N.A.I.C.S.: 337211
Taeyong Lee *(Chm)*

Clestra Hauserman Switzerland **(1)**
Ctr De Construction Crissier Chemin Du Closalet 4
1023 Cressier, Switzerland (100%)
Tel.: (41) 216376622
Fax: (41) 21637662
E-Mail: sav.crissier@clestra.com
Emp.: 30
Furniture Systems Mfr.
S.I.C.: 2599
N.A.I.C.S.: 337215
Niteo Migile *(Mng Dir)*

THE CLEVELAND GROUP OF COMPANIES LIMITED

Yarm Rd
PO Box 27
Darlington, Durham, DL1 4DE, United Kingdom
Tel.: (44) 325381188
Telex: 58313 CLEDLN G
Fax: (44) 325382320
E-Mail: info@clevelandbridge.com
Web Site: www.clevelandbridge.com
Year Founded: 1877
Sales Range: $75-99.9 Million
Emp.: 400
Business Description:
Designer, Supplier, Fabrication & Erection of Bridges, Power Stations & Commercial & Industrial Structures
S.I.C.: 8711
N.A.I.C.S.: 541330
Personnel:
Emad Kamil *(CEO)*

Subsidiaries:

Cleveland Bridge International Ltd **(1)**
19D Yu Jia Building 1336 Huashan Rd
Shanghai, Changning District, China HK
Tel.: (86) 2162110500 (100%)
Fax: (86) 2162110523
E-Mail: andy.wong@clevelandbridge.com
Web Site: www.clevelandbridge.com
Engineering & Construction Services
S.I.C.: 8711
N.A.I.C.S.: 541330

Cleveland Bridge UK Ltd. **(1)**
Cleveland House Yarm Rd
PO Box 27
Darlington, Durham, DL1 4DE, United Kingdom UK
Tel.: (44) 1325381188 (100%)
Fax: (44) 1325382320
E-Mail: info@clevelandbridge.com
Web Site: www.clevelandbridge.com
Emp.: 200
Holding Company; Bridge & Civil Engineering Construction Services
S.I.C.: 6719
N.A.I.C.S.: 551112
Brian Rogan *(Mng Dir)*

Subsidiary:

Cleveland Bridge & Engineering Co. Ltd. **(2)**
Yarm Rd
PO Box 27
Darlington, DL1 4DE, United Kingdom UK
Tel.: (44) 1325381188 (100%)
Fax: (44) 1325382320
E-Mail: info@clevelandbridge.com
Web Site: www.clevelandbridge.com
Emp.: 200
Bridge & Civil Engineering Construction Services
S.I.C.: 1622
N.A.I.C.S.: 237310
Andy Hall *(Mng Dir)*
Brian Rogan *(Mng Dir)*

Subsidiary:

Cleveland Bridge & Engineering Middle East (Pvt) Ltd **(3)**
9 Fl 7 8 Elleble Alli
PO Box 16765
Dubai, United Arab Emirates AE
Tel.: (971) 48835551 (100%)
Fax: (971) 48835416
E-Mail: contact@clevelandbridge.co.ae
Web Site: www.clevelandbridge.co.ae
Emp.: 100
Engineering Services
S.I.C.: 8711
N.A.I.C.S.: 541330
Michael Mack *(Mng Dir)*

Dorman Long UK Ltd **(1)**
Yarm Rd
PO Box 27
Darlington, DL1 4DE, United Kingdom UK
Tel.: (44) 1325390000 (100%)
E-Mail: chris.wilkinson@dormanlongtechnology.com
Web Site: www.dormanlongtechnology.com
Emp.: 50
Engineering Services
S.I.C.: 8711
N.A.I.C.S.: 541330

Subsidiaries:

Dorman Long Technology Ltd **(2)**
Yarm Rd
PO Box 27
Darlington, DL1 4DE, United Kingdom UK
Tel.: (44) 1325390000 (100%)
Fax: (44) 1325382320
Web Site: www.dormanlongtechnology.com
Emp.: 60
Engineering Services
S.I.C.: 8711
N.A.I.C.S.: 541330
David Dyer *(Mng Dir)*

Dorman Long Zalcon Ltd **(2)**
19D Yu Jia Building 1336 Huashan Rd
Shanghai, Changning District, China HK
Tel.: (86) 21 6211 0500 (100%)
Fax: (86) 21 6211 0523
E-Mail: andy.wong@clevelandbridge.com
Web Site: www.dormanlongtechnology.com
Engineering Services
S.I.C.: 8711
N.A.I.C.S.: 541330

CLEVELAND MINING COMPANY LIMITED

1/387 Hay Street
Subiaco, WA, 6008, Australia
Tel.: (61) 893813391
Fax: (61) 893821186
E-Mail: info@clevelandmining.com.au
Web Site: www.clevelandmining.com.au
CDG—(ASX)
Business Description:
Gold Mining & Exploration Services
S.I.C.: 1041
N.A.I.C.S.: 212221
Personnel:
Peter Fisher *(CEO)*
David Mendelawitz *(Mng Dir)*
Board of Directors:
Russell Scrimshaw
Rod Campbell
David Mendelawitz
Rick Stroud
Legal Counsel:
Mendelawitz morton Corporate Lawyers
Gryphon House 39 Richardson Street
West Perth, Australia

CLEVERBRIDGE AG

Brabanter Str 2-4
50764 Cologne, Germany
Tel.: (49) 221 222 45 0
Fax: (49) 221 222 45 19
E-Mail: cs@cleverbridge.com
Web Site: www.cleverbridge.com
Sales Range: $125-149.9 Million
Emp.: 100
Business Description:
E-Commerce Software & Services
S.I.C.: 7372
N.A.I.C.S.: 511210
Personnel:
Christian Blume *(CEO)*
Oliver Breme *(CFO & Gen Counsel)*
Martin Trzaskalik *(CTO)*

U.S. Subsidiary:

Cleverbridge, Inc. **(1)**
360 N Michigan Ave Ste 1900
Chicago, IL 60601-3805
Tel.: (312) 922-8693
Fax: (312) 376-1854
Web Site: www.cleverbridge.com
Emp.: 70
E-Commerce Software & Services
S.I.C.: 7372
N.A.I.C.S.: 511210
Christian Blume *(Pres)*

CLEVO COMPANY

No 129 Hsing Te Rd
241 San Chung, Taipei, Taiwan
Tel.: (886) 222789696
Fax: (886) 222789696
E-Mail: marketing@clevo.com.tw
Web Site: www.clevo.com.tw
2362—(TAI)
Sales Range: $150-199.9 Million
Business Description:
Laptop Computers Mfr
S.I.C.: 3571
N.A.I.C.S.: 334111
Personnel:
Kun-Tai Hsu *(Chm)*

CLICK&PHONE SECURITIES JOINT STOCK COMPANY

4 Lieu Giai Street
Ba Dinh District, Hanoi, Vietnam
Tel.: (84) 437621717
Fax: (84) 437930588
E-Mail: csc@clifone.com.vn
Web Site: www.clifone.com.vn
GBS—(HNX)
Emp.: 60
Business Description:
Investment Banking & Securities Dealing
S.I.C.: 6211
N.A.I.C.S.: 523110
Personnel:
Goo Sang Moon *(Chm)*

CLICK TRAVEL LTD.

Alpha Tower Suffolk Street
Queensway
Birmingham, B1 1TT, United Kingdom
Tel.: (44) 844 745 2121
E-Mail: support@clicktravel.com
Web Site: www.clicktravel.com
Year Founded: 1999
Sales Range: $75-99.9 Million
Emp.: 76
Business Description:
Travel Management Services
S.I.C.: 4725
N.A.I.C.S.: 561520
Personnel:
Simon McLean *(Mng Dir)*

CLICKS GROUP LIMITED

Cnr Searle & Pontac Streets
PO Box 5142
Cape Town, 8000, South Africa
Tel.: (27) 21 460 1911
Fax: (27) 21 460 8221
Web Site: www.clicksgroup.co.za
Year Founded: 1968
CLS—(JSE OTC)
Rev.: $1,686,264,149
Assets: $497,694,433
Liabilities: $371,947,818
Net Worth: $125,746,615
Earnings: $68,640,705
Emp.: 8,385
Fiscal Year-end: 08/31/13
Business Description:
Health & Beauty Products Retailer; DVDs, CDs & Gaming Software Retailer
S.I.C.: 5122
N.A.I.C.S.: 446120
Personnel:
David Kneale *(CEO)*
Michael Fleming *(CFO)*
Keith Warburton *(COO)*
David W. Janks *(Sec)*
Board of Directors:
David Nurek
Fatima Abrahams
John Bester
Bertina Engelbrecht
Michael Fleming
Fatima Jakoet
David Kneale
Nkaki Matlala
Martin Rosen
Transfer Agent:
Computershare Investor Services Limited
70 Marshall Street
Johannesburg, South Africa

Subsidiaries:

Clicks Direct Medicines (Proprietary) Limited **(1)**
36 Ayrshire Rd Longmeadow Business Park Ext 1
Modderfontein, 1645, South Africa
Tel.: (27) 119973000
Fax: (27) 861444413
E-Mail: clicksdirectmedicines@dirmed.co.za
Web Site: www.clicksdirectmedicines.co.za
Pharmaceutical Products Whslr
S.I.C.: 5122
N.A.I.C.S.: 424210

New Clicks South Africa (Proprietary) Limited **(1)**
14 Tamar Avenue
Florida, Western Cape, 1709, South Africa
Tel.: (27) 114701000
Fax: (27) 866819713
Pharmaceutical Products Mfr
S.I.C.: 2834
N.A.I.C.S.: 325412

United Pharmaceutical Distributors (Proprietary) Limited **(1)**
14 Tamar Ave
Randburg, 1709, South Africa
Tel.: (27) 11 470 1000
Fax: (27) 11 470 1083
Web Site: www.upd.co.za
Emp.: 125
Pharmaceutical Products Whslr
S.I.C.: 5122
N.A.I.C.S.: 424210

Vikesh Ramsunder *(Mng Dir)*

Non-U.S. Subsidiary:

Kalahari Medical Distributors (Proprietary) Limited **(1)**
Plot 20668/20669 Block 3
Broadhurst Industrial, Gaborone, Botswana
Tel.: (267) 393 4750
Fax: (267) 393 4748
Emp.: 25
Pharmaceutical Products Distr
S.I.C.: 5122
N.A.I.C.S.: 424210
Vishwas Divekar *(Gen Mgr)*

CLICKSOFTWARE TECHNOLOGIES LTD.

Azorim Park Oren Building 94 Em Hamoshavot Road
Petah Tiqwa, 49527, Israel
Tel.: (972) 3 7659 400
Fax: (972) 3 7659 401
Web Site: www.clicksoftware.com
CKSW—(NASDAQ)
Rev.: $100,046,000
Assets: $94,469,000
Liabilities: $31,551,000
Net Worth: $62,918,000
Earnings: $7,488,000
Emp.: 509
Fiscal Year-end: 12/31/12

Business Description:
Workforce & Service Management Software Products & Services
S.I.C.: 7372
N.A.I.C.S.: 511210

Personnel:
Moshe BenBassat *(Founder & CEO)*
Shmuel Arvatz *(CFO)*
Zvi Piritz *(Exec VP-Sls & Mktg-Worldwide)*
Israel Beniaminy *(Sr VP-Product Strategy)*
Nigel Clark *(Sr VP-Bus Dev)*

Board of Directors:
Israel Borovich
Shai Beilis
Nira Dror
Shlomo Nass
Menahem Shalgi
Gil Weiser

U.S. Subsidiaries:

ClickSoftware, Inc. **(1)**
35 Corporate Dr Ste 400
Burlington, MA 01803
Tel.: (781) 272-5903
Fax: (972) 272-6409
Toll Free: (888) 438-3308
E-Mail: sales@ClickSoftware.com
Web Site: www.clicksoftware.com
Emp.: 45
Workforce & Service Management Software Products & Services
S.I.C.: 7372
N.A.I.C.S.: 511210
Steve Lawrence *(VP-Sls-North America)*

Xora, Inc. **(1)**
1890 N Shoreline Blvd
Mountain View, CA 94043
Tel.: (650) 314-6470
Fax: (650) 938-8401
Toll Free: (877) 477-9672
E-Mail: sales@xora.com
Web Site: www.xora.com
Mobile Resource Management Software & Services
S.I.C.: 7372
N.A.I.C.S.: 511210
Anne Bonaparte *(Pres & CEO)*
Rodney Dabagian *(CFO)*
Oswald D'sa *(CIO)*
Tom Miltonberger *(CTO & VP-Products)*
Ananth Rani *(Sr VP-Products & Svcs)*

Subsidiary:

Gearworks, Inc. **(2)**
2770 Blue Water Rd Ste 400
Eagan, MN 55121-1500 NJ
Tel.: (651) 209-0350
Fax: (651) 209-0351
Toll Free: (800) 735-3457
E-Mail: info@gearworks.com
Web Site: www.gearworks.com
Emp.: 40
Mobile Telecommunications & Wireless Software Application Development
S.I.C.: 3625
N.A.I.C.S.: 335314
Howard Latham *(VP-Customers)*

Non-U.S. Subsidiaries:

ClickSoftware Australia Pty Limited **(1)**
Level 1 256 Queen Street
Melbourne, Victoria, 3000, Australia AU
Tel.: (61) 399466400
Fax: (61) 399466401
E-Mail: info@clicksoftware.com
Web Site: www.clicksoftware.com
Emp.: 20
Developer of Service Chain Optimization Software
S.I.C.: 7372
N.A.I.C.S.: 511210
Ofra Mosesson *(Mgr-Ops)*

ClickSoftware Central Europe GmbH **(1)**
Hanauer Landstr 293 P
60314 Frankfurt, Germany De
Tel.: (49) 694898130
Fax: (49) 6948981399
E-Mail: info@clicksoftware.com
Emp.: 10
Developer of Service Chain Optimization Software
S.I.C.: 7372
N.A.I.C.S.: 511210
Moshe Penpassat *(Mng Dir)*

ClickSoftware Europe, Limited **(1)**
270 Bath Road
Slough, Berks, SL1 4DX, United Kingdom UK
Tel.: (44) 01753511166
Fax: (44) 1753553127
Developer of Service Chain Optimization Software
S.I.C.: 7372
N.A.I.C.S.: 511210

CLICKTALE LTD.

2 Shoham Street
52521 Ramat Gan, Israel
Tel.: (972) 36138152
E-Mail: info@clicktale.com
Web Site: www.clicktale.com
Year Founded: 2006
Sales Range: $10-24.9 Million

Business Description:
Computer Related Customer Experience Analytics
S.I.C.: 7372
N.A.I.C.S.: 511210

Personnel:
Tal Schwartz *(Co-Founder, Chm & CEO)*
Arik Yavilevich *(Co-Founder & CTO)*
Yoav Persky *(CFO)*
David Dror Davidoff *(Chief Revenue Officer)*

Board of Directors:
Tal Schwartz
Richard Anton
David Ram

CLIENTELE LIMITED

Clientele Office Park Corner Rivonia & Alon Road
Morningside, Sandton, Gauteng, 2196, South Africa
Tel.: (27) 11 320 3000
Fax: (27) 11 320 3133
E-Mail: services@clientele.co.za
Web Site: www.clientele.co.za
CLI—(JSE)
Rev.: $136,772,070
Assets: $330,309,522
Liabilities: $271,173,308
Net Worth: $59,136,214
Earnings: $32,773,450
Fiscal Year-end: 06/30/13

Business Description:
Holding Company; Insurance & Investment Products & Services
S.I.C.: 6719
N.A.I.C.S.: 551112

Personnel:
Gavin John Soll *(Vice Chm)*
Basil William Reekie *(Mng Dir)*
Gary Owen Simpson *(Compliance Officer)*
Wilna van Zyl *(Sec)*

Board of Directors:
Gavin Quentin Routledge
Adrian Domoniq T'hooft Enthoven
Brenda-Lee Frodsham
Pheladi Raesebi Gwangwa
Iain Bruce Hume
Basil William Reekie
Gavin John Soll
Barry Anthony Stott
Robert Donald Williams

Transfer Agent:
Computershare Investor Services (Pty) Ltd.
70 Marshall Street
Johannesburg, 2001, South Africa
Tel.: (27) 11 370 5000
Fax: (27) 11 370 5487

Subsidiary:

Clientele Life Assurance Company Limited **(1)**
Clientele Office Park Corner Rivonia & Alon Road
Morningside, Sandton, Gauterng, 2196, South Africa
Tel.: (27) 113203333
Fax: (27) 11 320 3133
E-Mail: services@clientel.co.za
Web Site: www.clientele.co.za/life
Life Insurance Products & Services
S.I.C.: 6311
N.A.I.C.S.: 524113
Basil William Reekie *(Mng Dir)*

CLIFFMONT RESOURCES LTD.

1305 - 1090 West Georgia Street
Vancouver, BC, V6E 3V7, Canada
Tel.: (604) 568-6894
Fax: (604) 558-0506
E-Mail: info@cliffmontresources.com
Web Site: www.cliffmontresources.com
Year Founded: 2006
CVE1—(DEU TSXV)
Rev.: $6,060
Assets: $12,426,013
Liabilities: $1,123,562
Net Worth: $11,302,451
Earnings: ($2,489,098)
Emp.: 25
Fiscal Year-end: 09/30/13

Business Description:
Mineral Exploration Services
S.I.C.: 1481
N.A.I.C.S.: 213115

Personnel:
Jeff Tindale *(Pres & CEO)*
Darren Urquhart *(CFO)*

Board of Directors:
Nick Demare
Bruce Fair
Jeff Tindale
Antonio Uribe

Legal Counsel:
Axium Law Corporation
Suite 3350 Four Bentall Centre 1055 Dunsmuir Street
PO Box 49222
Vancouver, BC, Canada

Transfer Agent:
Computershare Investor Services Inc
Vancouver, BC, Canada

CLIFTON ASSET MANAGEMENT PLC

The Pavilions Eden Park
Ham Green, Bristol, BS20 0DD, United Kingdom
Tel.: (44) 1275 813 700
Fax: (44) 1275 813 701
E-Mail: webenquiries@cliftonasset.co.uk
Web Site: www.cliftonasset.co.uk
Year Founded: 1986
Sales Range: $1-9.9 Million
Emp.: 90

Business Description:
Financial & Consulting Services
S.I.C.: 6726
N.A.I.C.S.: 525990

Personnel:
Neil Greenaway *(Mng Dir)*

Subsidiaries:

Clifton Consulting Ltd **(1)**
The Pavilions Ham Green
Bristol, BS20 0DD, United Kingdom
Tel.: (44) 1275 813700
Fax: (44) 1275 813701
E-Mail: enquiries@clifton-asset.co.uk
Web Site: www.cliftonasset.co.uk
Emp.: 10
Business & Exit Strategy Planning
S.I.C.: 8742
N.A.I.C.S.: 541611
Neil Greenaway *(Mng Dir)*

Clifton Wealth Ltd **(1)**
The Pavilions Ham Green
Bristol, BS20 0DD, United Kingdom
Tel.: (44) 1275 813700
Fax: (44) 1275 813701
E-Mail: enquiries@clifton-asset.co.uk
Web Site: www.clifton-wealth.com
Emp.: 20
Wealth Management, Employee Benefits & Protection
S.I.C.: 6799
N.A.I.C.S.: 523920
Jo Purcell *(Gen Mgr)*

CLIFTON STAR RESOURCES INC.

1040 Avenue Belvedere Suite 217
Quebec, QC, G1S 3G3, Canada
Tel.: (418) 914-9922
Fax: (418) 914-9687
Web Site: www.cfo-star.com
CFO—(OTC TSXV)
Int. Income: $102,997
Assets: $49,775,250
Liabilities: $4,899,687
Net Worth: $44,875,564
Earnings: ($3,846,314)
Emp.: 10
Fiscal Year-end: 06/30/13

Business Description:
Mining Exploration Services
S.I.C.: 1081
N.A.I.C.S.: 213114

Personnel:
Ross Glanville *(Chm)*
Michel F. Bouchard *(Pres & CEO)*
Louis Dufour *(CFO)*
Harry Miller *(Sec)*

Board of Directors:
Ross Glanville
Michel F. Bouchard
Peter V. Gundy
Yves Harvey
Philip Nolan

Transfer Agent:
Computershare Trust Company
510 Burrard Street
Vancouver, BC, Canada

CLIMATE HUMAN CAPITAL PLC

104A Park Street
Mayfair, London, W1K 6NG, United Kingdom

Climate Human Capital plc—(Continued)

Tel.: (44) 20 7318 1244
E-Mail: info@climatehumancapital.com
Web Site: www.climatehumancapital.com
CLIP—(ISDX)
Business Description:
Recruitment Services
S.I.C.: 8999
N.A.I.C.S.: 541612
Personnel:
Michael Brennan *(CEO)*
Paul Turner *(CFO)*
Board of Directors:
Peter Evans
Michael Brennan
Wayne Holtshausen
Eduard Sparkes
Paul Turner
Legal Counsel:
Halliwells LLP
3 Hardman Square
Spinningfields, Manchester, M3 3EB, United Kingdom
Tel.: (44) 844 875 8000
Fax: (44) 844 875 8001

CLIMATE TECHNOLOGIES PTY LTD

26 Nylex Ave
Salisbury, SA, 5108, Australia
Tel.: (61) 883075100
Fax: (61) 882830401
Web Site: www.climatetechnologies.com.au
Sales Range: $50-74.9 Million
Emp.: 400
Business Description:
Refrigeration & Heating Equipment Mfr
S.I.C.: 3585
N.A.I.C.S.: 333415
Personnel:
Ted Celi *(Mng Dir)*

CLIMAX INTERNATIONAL COMPANY LIMITED

Clarendon House 2 Church Street
Hamilton, HM11, Bermuda
E-Mail: info@climax-intl.com
Web Site: www.climaxintl-co.com
0439—(HKG)
Sls.: $10,467,903
Assets: $34,606,440
Liabilities: $11,237,864
Net Worth: $23,368,577
Earnings: $287,816
Emp.: 550
Fiscal Year-end: 03/31/13
Business Description:
Paper Product Services
S.I.C.: 2671
N.A.I.C.S.: 322220
Personnel:
Hin Shek Wong *(CEO)*
Ming Kei Chan *(Sec)*
Board of Directors:
Man Tak Lau
Kwok Leung Man
Man Chan Ng
Hin Shek Wong
Hung Ki Wong
Yun Kuen Wong
Codan Services Limited
2 Church Street
Hamilton, Bermuda

CLIME CAPITAL LIMITED

Level 5 352 Kent Street
Sydney, NSW, 2000, Australia
Tel.: (61) 292528522
Fax: (61) 289172155
E-Mail: info@climecapital.com.au
Web Site: www.clime.com.au
CAM—(ASX)
Rev.: $9,492,683
Assets: $89,353,864
Liabilities: $4,902,150
Net Worth: $84,451,714
Earnings: $6,464,419
Fiscal Year-end: 06/30/13
Business Description:
Investment Management Services
S.I.C.: 6211
N.A.I.C.S.: 523999
Personnel:
Richard Proctor *(Sec)*
Board of Directors:
John Abernethy
Julian Gosse
Brett Spork
Geoffrey Wilson

CLIME INVESTMENT MANAGEMENT LIMITED

Level 5 352 Kent Street
Sydney, NSW, 2000, Australia
Tel.: (61) 292528522
Fax: (61) 289172155
E-Mail: info@clime.com.au
Web Site: www.clime.com.au
CIW—(ASX)
Rev.: $7,982,242
Assets: $31,744,220
Liabilities: $4,167,068
Net Worth: $27,577,152
Earnings: $1,481,856
Emp.: 7
Fiscal Year-end: 06/30/13
Business Description:
Investment Fund Management Services
S.I.C.: 6722
N.A.I.C.S.: 525910
Personnel:
Richard Proctor *(COO & Co-Sec)*
John B. Abernethy *(Chief Investment Officer)*
Biju Vikraman *(Co-Sec)*
Board of Directors:
Mark Osborn
John B. Abernethy
Neil Schafer
David J. Schwartz

Subsidiary:

Clime Asset Management Pty. Ltd. (1)
352 Kent Street
PO Box Q 1286
Queen Victoria Building, Sydney, New South Wales, 1230, Australia
Tel.: (61) 292528522
Fax: (61) 292528422
E-Mail: info@clime.com.au
Emp.: 16
Financial Management Services
S.I.C.: 8742
N.A.I.C.S.: 541611
Paul Jensen *(Mng Dir)*

CLINE MINING CORPORATION

181 Bay Street Brookfield Place
Heritage Building 3rd Floor
Toronto, ON, M5J 2T3, Canada
Tel.: (416) 504-7600
Fax: (416) 981-7316
E-Mail: info@clinemining.com
Web Site: www.clinemining.com
Int. Income: $128,852
Assets: $288,237,788
Liabilities: $52,004,819
Net Worth: $236,232,969
Earnings: ($4,929,078)
Emp.: 29
Fiscal Year-end: 11/30/12
Business Description:
Mineral Resource Development & Exploration Services
S.I.C.: 3299
N.A.I.C.S.: 327999
Personnel:
Matthew Goldfarb *(Acting CEO & Chief Restructuring Officer)*
Paul Haber *(CFO & Sec)*
Board of Directors:
Matthew Goldfarb
Dale M. Hendrick
Vincent James Sardo
Transfer Agent:
Canadian Stock Transfer Company Inc
1066 West Hastings Street
Vancouver, BC, Canada

U.S. Subsidiary:

New Elk Coal Company LLC (1)
122 W 1st St
Trinidad, CO 81082-2957
Tel.: (719) 845-0090
Fax: (719) 845-0077
Emp.: 350
Coal Mining Services
S.I.C.: 1222
N.A.I.C.S.: 212112
Darren Nicholls *(Deputy COO)*
David Stone *(COO)*

CLINICAL COMPUTING PLC

IP City Centre 1 Bath Street
Ipswich, IP2 8SD, United Kingdom
Tel.: (44) 1473 694770
Fax: (44) 1473 694761
E-Mail: support@ccl.com
Web Site: www.ccl.com
Year Founded: 1979
Sales Range: $1-9.9 Million
Emp.: 40
Business Description:
Clinical Information Management Software Developer
S.I.C.: 7372
N.A.I.C.S.: 511210
Personnel:
Gerry Musgrave *(Chm)*
Joseph G. Marlovits *(CEO, Sec & Dir-Fin)*
Board of Directors:
Gerry Musgrave
Howard E. Kitchner
Joseph G. Marlovits

Subsidiary:

Hydra Management Limited (1)
Riverview Ct Castlegate
Wetherby, Leeds, West Yorkshire, LS22 6LE, United Kingdom
Tel.: (44) 1937589560
Fax: (44) 1937584087
E-Mail: info@hydra-management.com
Web Site: www.hydra-management.com
Emp.: 9
Software Sales & Support Services
S.I.C.: 7371
N.A.I.C.S.: 541511
Juan Manrique *(CEO)*

U.S. Subsidiary:

Clinical Computing, Inc. (1)
205 W 4th St Ste 810
Cincinnati, OH 45202
Tel.: (513) 651-3803
Fax: (513) 651-5813
Toll Free: (800) 888-1140
E-Mail: barbrobinette@us.ccl.com
Web Site: www.ccl.com
Emp.: 7
Software Development & Support Services
S.I.C.: 7371
N.A.I.C.S.: 541511
Barb Robinette *(Office Mgr)*

CLINICAL GENOMICS PTY. LTD.

11 Julius Ave
North Ryde, NSW, 2113, Australia
Tel.: (61) 2 9888 9065
Fax: (61) 2 9475 4678
E-Mail: info@clinicalgenomics.com
Web Site: www.clinicalgenomics.com
Business Description:
Molecular Diagnostics Products Mfr
S.I.C.: 8071
N.A.I.C.S.: 621512
Personnel:
Robert Max Mawhinney *(Chm)*
Lawrence LaPointe *(CEO)*
Richard Sands *(CFO)*
Susanne Pedersen *(Chief Scientific Officer)*
Board of Directors:
Robert Max Mawhinney
Nicholas Cont
Peter Jollie

U.S. Subsidiary:

Enterix Inc. (1)
236 Fernwood Ave
Edison, NJ 08837
Tel.: (732) 346-1111
BiotechnologyProducts Mfr
S.I.C.: 8731
N.A.I.C.S.: 541711

CLINIGEN GROUP PLC

Pitcairn House Crown Square
Centrum 100
Burton-on-Trent, Staffs, DE14 2WW, United Kingdom
Tel.: (44) 1283 495 010
Web Site: www.clinigengroup.com
CLIN—(AIM)
Sales Range: $50-74.9 Million
Business Description:
Pharmaceutical Mfr & Distr
S.I.C.: 2834
N.A.I.C.S.: 325412
Personnel:
Andrew Leaver *(Chm)*
Peter George *(CEO)*
Shaun Chilton *(COO)*
Lorann Morse *(Sr VP-Clinical Trial Supply)*
Board of Directors:
Andrew Leaver
Shaun Chilton
John Hartup

CLINUVEL PHARMACEUTICALS LIMITED

Level 14 190 Queen Street
Melbourne, VIC, 3000, Australia
Tel.: (61) 396604900
Fax: (61) 396604999
E-Mail: investorrelations@clinuvel.com
Web Site: www.clinuvel.com
CUV—(ASX)
Rev.: $3,022,599
Assets: $16,480,594
Liabilities: $2,058,670
Net Worth: $14,421,924
Earnings: ($7,089,222)
Emp.: 40
Fiscal Year-end: 06/30/13
Business Description:
Pharmaceuticals Mfr
S.I.C.: 2834
N.A.I.C.S.: 325412
Personnel:
Philippe Wolgen *(CEO & Mng Dir)*
Darren M. Keamy *(CFO & Sec)*
Dennis Wright *(Acting Chief Scientific Officer)*
Board of Directors:
Stanley McLiesh
Elie Ishag
Brenda Shanahan
Philippe Wolgen
L. Jack Wood

Legal Counsel:
FAL Lawyers
Level 16 356 Collins Street
Melbourne, VIC, 3000, Australia
Bristows
100 Victoria Embankment
London, EC4Y 0DH, United Kingdom
Arnold Bloch Leibler
Level 21 333 Collins Street
Melbourne, VIC, 3000, Australia

Non-U.S. Subsidiary:

Clinuvel AG (1)
Neuhosstrasse 3D
6340 Baar, Switzerland
Tel.: (41) 442537500
Fax: (41) 417674546
Emp.: 15
Pharmaceutical Preparations Mfr
S.I.C.: 2834
N.A.I.C.S.: 325412
Isabelle Srancois *(Office Mgr)*

CLIO
27 Rue Du Hameau
75015 Paris, France
Tel.: (33) 826101082
Fax: (33) 153688260
Web Site: www.clio.fr
Sales Range: $25-49.9 Million
Emp.: 51
Business Description:
Travel Agency
S.I.C.: 4724
N.A.I.C.S.: 561510
Personnel:
Remy Boucharlat *(Dir-CNRS Research)*

CLIPPER LOGISTICS GROUP LTD.
Gelderd Road
Leeds, LS12 6LT, United Kingdom
Tel.: (44) 113 204 2050
E-Mail: info@clippergroup.co.uk
Web Site: www.clippergroup.co.uk
Year Founded: 1992
Sales Range: $250-299.9 Million
Emp.: 1,957
Business Description:
Logistics Services
S.I.C.: 4731
N.A.I.C.S.: 541614
Personnel:
Steve Parkin *(Chm)*
Tony Mannix *(Mng Dir)*
Paul White *(Sec)*
Board of Directors:
Steve Parkin
Sean Fahey
Sean Hallows
Nigel Hinds
David Hodkin
Derek Hunt
Ted Johnson
Tony Mannix
Carl Moore
Gary Walker
Paul White

CLIPPER VENTURES LTD.
Unit 1 A Granary & Bakery Royal Clarence Marina
Weevil Lane, Gosport, PO12 1FX, United Kingdom
Tel.: (44) 2392526000
Fax: (44) 2392526252
E-Mail: info@clipper-ventures.com
Web Site: www.clipper-ventures.com
Emp.: 62
Business Description:
Boat & Yacht Race Organizer
S.I.C.: 7999
N.A.I.C.S.: 711320
Personnel:
Robin Knox-Johnston *(Chm)*
William Ward *(CEO)*
Jeremy Knight *(COO)*
Board of Directors:
Robin Knox-Johnston
Bob Dench
Jeremy Knight
David Stubley
William Ward

CLIQ DIGITAL AG
Immermanstrasse 13
40210 Dusseldorf, Germany
Tel.: (49) 211380570
Fax: (49) 2113805720
Web Site: www.cliqdigital.com
B4B—(DEU)
Emp.: 135
Business Description:
Mobile Entertainment & Game Development Services
S.I.C.: 7372
N.A.I.C.S.: 511210
Personnel:
Andreas Hoyingg *(Chm-Supervisory Bd)*
Luc Voncken *(Chm-Mgmt Bd & CEO)*
Darren Ian Trussell *(Vice Chm-Supervisory Bd)*
Thomas Kothuis *(Member-Mgmt Bd & COO)*
Alexander Reitsma *(Member-Mgmt Bd)*
George Ursateanu *(Member-Mgmt Bd)*
Supervisory Board of Directors:
Andreas Hoyingg
Rudolf Christian de Back
Karel Gustaaf Tempelaar
Darren Ian Trussell
Cornelis H. van der Steenstraten
Rene van Dijk

CLIQ ENERGY BERHAD
Suite 0202 Level 2 Block B Peremba Square
Saujana Resort Section U2, Shah Alam, Selangor, 40150, Malaysia
Tel.: (60) 3 77342727
Fax: (60) 3 77342580
E-Mail: info@cliqenergy.com
Web Site: www.cliqenergy.com
5234—(KLS)
Business Description:
Oil & Gas Exploration & Production
S.I.C.: 1311
N.A.I.C.S.: 211111
Personnel:
Azmi Mohd Ali *(Chm)*
Ahmad Ziyad Elias *(CEO & Mng Dir)*
Kamarul Baharin Albakri *(CFO)*
Board of Directors:
Azmi Mohd Ali
Rosman Abdullah
Kamarul Baharin Albakri
Ahmad Ziyad Elias
Abd Hamid Ibrahim
Andrew Alexander Young

CLIVE CHRISTIAN PLC
56 Haymarket
London, SW1 Y4RN, United Kingdom
Tel.: (44) 2078395345
Web Site: www.clive.com
Year Founded: 1978
Emp.: 100
Business Description:
Holding Company; Perfume & Luxury Wood Home Interior Products Designer, Mfr & Distr
S.I.C.: 6719
N.A.I.C.S.: 551112
Personnel:
Clive Christian *(Founder & Chm)*
Subsidiaries:

Clive Christian Furniture Limited (1)
St Germaine St
Farnworth, Bolton, BL4 7 BG, United Kingdom UK
Tel.: (44) 1204702200
Fax: (44) 1204702217
E-Mail: reception@clivechristianfurniture.co.uk
Web Site: clivechristianinteriors.clive.com
Sls.: $16,266,971
Emp.: 150
Luxury Wood Home Interior Products Designer, Mfr & Distr
S.I.C.: 2511
N.A.I.C.S.: 337122
Clive Christian *(Founder & Chm)*

Clive Christian Perfume Limited (1)
56 Haymarket
London, SW1Y 4RN, United Kingdom UK
Tel.: (44) 2078393434
Fax: (44) 2078390799
E-Mail: londonoffice@clive.com
Web Site: perfume.clive.com
Emp.: 7
Perfume Developer & Distr
S.I.C.: 5122
N.A.I.C.S.: 424210
Clive Christian *(Chm)*

CLOETTA AB
Kista Science Tower
SE-164 51 Kista, Sweden
Tel.: (46) 852728800
Fax: (46) 13 655 60
Web Site: www.cloetta.se
CLA B—(OMX)
Sls.: $752,173,200
Assets: $1,445,832,000
Liabilities: $930,967,200
Net Worth: $514,864,800
Earnings: ($11,300,400)
Emp.: 2,579
Fiscal Year-end: 12/31/12
Business Description:
Chocolate Mfr
S.I.C.: 2066
N.A.I.C.S.: 311351
Personnel:
Lennart Bylock *(Chm)*
Bengt Baron *(Pres & CEO)*
Danko Maras *(CFO)*
Erwin Segers *(CMO)*
Giorgio Boggero *(Pres-Italy)*
Ewald Frenay *(Pres-Middle)*
Jacqueline Hoogerbrugge *(Pres-Ops)*
David Nuutinen *(Pres-Finland)*
Lars Pahlson *(Pres-Scandinavia)*
Jacob Broberg *(Sr VP-Corp Comm & IR)*
Johnny Engman *(Sr VP-Corp Dev & M&A)*
Edwin Kist *(Sr VP-HR)*
Board of Directors:
Lennart Bylock
Shahram Nikpour Badr
Lilian Fossum Biner
Hans Eckerstrom
Lena Gronedal
Hakan Kirstein
Adriaan Nuhn
Mikael Svenfelt
Olof Svenfelt
Meg Tiveus
Peter Tornquist
Robert-Jan van Ogtrop
Subsidiaries:

Cloetta Sverige AB (1)
Hjalmar Svenfelts vaeg
590 69 Ljungsbro, Ostergotland, Sweden
Tel.: (46) 13285000
Fax: (46) 13285403
Emp.: 200
Chocolate Mfr
S.I.C.: 2066
N.A.I.C.S.: 311351
Kent Sandin *(Mgr-Fin)*

CLONTARF ENERGY PLC
162 Clontarf Road
Dublin, 3, Ireland
Tel.: (353) 1 8332833
Fax: (353) 1 8333505
E-Mail: info@clontarfenergy.com
Web Site: www.clontarfenergy.com
CLON—(AIM)
Business Description:
Oil & Gas Exploration & Production Services
S.I.C.: 1311
N.A.I.C.S.: 211111
Personnel:
John J. Teeling *(Chm)*
David Horgan *(Mng Dir)*
Board of Directors:
John J. Teeling
Jim Finn
David Horgan
Manouchehr Takin
Legal Counsel:
McEvoy & Partners
Connaught House Burlington Road
Dublin, 4, Ireland

CLOSE BROTHERS GROUP PLC
10 Crown Place
London, EC2A 4FT, United Kingdom
Tel.: (44) 2076553100
Fax: (44) 2076558967
E-Mail: enquiries@closebrothers.com
Web Site: www.closebrothers.com
CBG—(LSE)
Int. Income: $710,996,358
Assets: $10,794,447,150
Liabilities: $9,467,053,905
Net Worth: $1,327,393,245
Earnings: $190,304,445
Emp.: 2,601
Fiscal Year-end: 07/31/13
Business Description:
Bank Holding Company; Merchant Banking, Securities Brokerage & Portfolio Management Services
S.I.C.: 6719
N.A.I.C.S.: 551112
Personnel:
Preben Prebensen *(CEO)*
Stephen R. Hodges *(Mng Dir & CEO-Banking)*
Martin Andrew *(CEO-Asset Mgmt)*
Julian Palfreyman *(CEO-Winterflood)*
Board of Directors:
P. Strone S. Macpherson
Bruce Carnegie-Brown
Raymond Greenshields
Stephen R. Hodges
Geoffrey Howe
Jonathan A. G. Howell
Shonaid C. R. Jemmett-Page
Lesley Jones
Elizabeth Lee
Bridget Macaskill
Preben Prebensen
Legal Counsel:
Slaughter & May
One Bunhill Row
London, EC1Y 8YY, United Kingdom
Tel.: (44) 20 7600 1200
Fax: (44) 20 7600 0289
Subsidiaries:

Close Asset Finance Limited (1)
11th Floor Tolworth Tower Ewell Rd
Tolworth, Surbiton, Surrey, KT6 7EL, United Kingdom
Tel.: (44) 2083394949
Fax: (44) 2083906168
Web Site: www.closeassetfinance.co.uk
Equipment Leasing Services

Close Brothers Group plc—(Continued)

S.I.C.: 7353
N.A.I.C.S.: 532412

Close Asset Management Holdings Limited (1)
10 Exchange Square Primrose Street
London, EC2A 2BY, United Kingdom
Tel.: (44) 20 7426 4000
Property Management Services
S.I.C.: 6531
N.A.I.C.S.: 531311

Subsidiaries:

Cavanagh Wealth Management (2)
The Courtyard Staplefield Road
Cuckfield, W Sussex, RH17 5JT, United Kingdom
Tel.: (44) 1444475400
E-Mail: financialadvice@closebrothersam.com
Web Site: www.closebrothersam.com
Sales Range: $10-24.9 Million
Emp.: 179
Investment Management Services
S.I.C.: 6211
N.A.I.C.S.: 523999
Andrew Fay *(CEO)*
Simon Redgrove *(Mng Dir)*
Ian Henson *(Sec & Grp Dir-Fin)*

Chartwell Group Limited (2)
Kings Orchid 1 Queen Street
Bristol, BS2 0HQ, United Kingdom UK
Tel.: (44) 1179170700
Fax: (44) 1179170701
E-Mail: advice@chartwell.co.uk
Web Site: www.chartwell.co.uk
Sales Range: $10-24.9 Million
Emp.: 80
Corporate & Private Investment & Fund Management Services
S.I.C.: 6282
N.A.I.C.S.: 523930
Mark Nish *(CEO)*

Close Brothers Private Equity LLP (1)
2 George Yard
London, EC3V 9DH, United Kingdom
Tel.: (44) 2070651100
Fax: (44) 2075886815
E-Mail: enquiries@cbpel.com
Web Site: www.cbpel.com
Emp.: 25
Private Equity Firm
S.I.C.: 6211
N.A.I.C.S.: 523999
Sean Dinnen *(Partner)*
Matthew Hutchinson *(Partner)*
Nick MacNay *(Partner)*
Iain Slater *(Partner)*
Simon Wildig *(Partner)*

Subsidiary:

Aqualisa Products Limited (2)
The Flyers Way
Westerham, Kent, TN16 1DE, United Kingdom (100%)
Tel.: (44) 1959560000
Fax: (44) 1959560045
E-Mail: marketing@aqualisa.co.uk
Web Site: www.aqualisa.co.uk
Rev.: $72,696,000
Emp.: 340
Shower Mfr & Distr
S.I.C.: 3088
N.A.I.C.S.: 326191
Harry Rawlinson *(Mng Dir)*

Holding:

Warwick International Group Limited (2)
Mostyn
Holywell, Flintshire, CH8 9HE, United Kingdom UK
Tel.: (44) 1745560651
Fax: (44) 1745561190
E-Mail: info@warwickchen.com
Web Site: www.warwicktchen.com
Sales Range: $150-199.9 Billion
Emp.: 180
Specialty Chemicals Mfr
S.I.C.: 2899
N.A.I.C.S.: 325998
Peter Bradley *(CEO)*

Close Premium Finance (1)
21st Floor Tolworth Tower Ewell Road
Toworth, Surbiton, Surrey, KT6 7EL, United Kingdom
Tel.: (44) 8702430026
Fax: (44) 8702430029
E-Mail: info@closepf.com
Web Site: www.closepf.com
Emp.: 300
Premium Finance Products & Services
S.I.C.: 6726
N.A.I.C.S.: 525990
Bob Golden *(CEO)*
Nigel Mottershead *(Mng Dir)*

Non-U.S. Subsidiary:

Close Premium Finance Ireland (2)
Alexandra House The Sweepstakes
Ballsbridge, Dublin, 4, Ireland
Tel.: (353) 1890 928 281
Fax: (353) 1890 886 190
E-Mail: cpfi@closepf.com
Web Site: www.closepf.com
Premium Finance Products & Services
S.I.C.: 6726
N.A.I.C.S.: 525990
Stuart Reid *(Gen Mgr)*

Close Wealth Management (1)
Nelson House Datbrook Business Ctr
CW9 7TN Northwich, United Kingdom UK
Tel.: (44) 606810100
Fax: (44) 606810181
Web Site: www.closewealth.co.uk
Emp.: 180
Provider of Investment Advise & Investment Management Services to Retired Individuals
S.I.C.: 6282
N.A.I.C.S.: 523930

Winterflood Securities Limited (1)
The Atrium Building Cannon Bridge House
25 Dowgate Hill
London, EC4R 2GA, United Kingdom
Tel.: (44) 20 3100 0000
Fax: (44) 20 7623 9482
E-Mail: enquiries@wins.co.uk
Web Site: www.wins.co.uk
Securities Brokerage Services
S.I.C.: 6211
N.A.I.C.S.: 523120

CLOUDTAG INC.

Kitwell House The Warren
Radlett, Herts, WD7 7DU, United Kingdom
Tel.: (44) 207 747 5100
E-Mail: contact@cloudtag.com
Web Site: www.cloudtag.com
CTAG—(AIM)
Business Description:
Physiological Monitoring Technology
S.I.C.: 3841
N.A.I.C.S.: 339112
Personnel:
Anthony Henry Reeves *(Chm)*
Board of Directors:
Anthony Henry Reeves
Alexander Mark Butcher
Michael Brian Victor Cudworth Hirschfield

CLOUDYN LTD.

10 HaYetzira St
43663 Ra'anana, Israel
Tel.: (972) 73 706 6967
Web Site: www.cloudyn.com
Year Founded: 2011
Business Description:
Optimization Engine Software Publisher
S.I.C.: 7372
N.A.I.C.S.: 511210
Personnel:
Sharon Wagner *(Co-Founder & CEO)*
Boris Goldberg *(Co-Founder & CTO)*
Vittaly Tavor *(Co-Founder & VP-Products)*

CLOVER CORPORATION LIMITED

Level 2 160 Pitt Street
Sydney, New South Wales, 2000, Australia
Tel.: (61) 292107000
Fax: (61) 292107099
E-Mail: info@clovercorp.com.au
Web Site: www.clovercorp.com.au
CLV—(ASX)
Rev.: $45,954,526
Assets: $43,230,476
Liabilities: $9,457,058
Net Worth: $33,773,419
Earnings: $6,488,115
Emp.: 37
Fiscal Year-end: 07/31/13
Business Description:
Natural Oils Sales
S.I.C.: 1321
N.A.I.C.S.: 211112
Personnel:
Ian L. Brown *(CEO & Mng Dir)*
Darren Callahan *(CFO)*
Jaime Pinto *(Sec)*
Board of Directors:
Peter R. Robinson
Graeme A. Billings
Ian L. Brown
Cheryl L. Hayman
Merilyn J. Sleigh
Subsidiary:

Nu-Mega Ingredients Pty. Ltd. (1)
31 Pinnacle Rd
Altona N, Melbourne, Victoria, 3025, Australia
Tel.: (61) 383692100
Fax: (61) 393698900
E-Mail: sales@nu-mega.com
Web Site: www.nu-mega.com
Emp.: 30
Fatty Acids Mfr
S.I.C.: 2869
N.A.I.C.S.: 325199
Peter Lancaster *(CEO)*

CLOVER INDUSTRIES LIMITED

Clover Park 200 Constantia Drive
Constantia Kloof, Roodepoort, South Africa 1709
Mailing Address:
PO Box 6161
Weltevreden Park, Roodepoort, South Africa 1715
Tel.: (27) 114711400
Fax: (27) 866836599
E-Mail: sales@clover.co.za
Web Site: www.clover.co.za
CLR—(JSE)
Rev.: $893,204,694
Assets: $495,307,624
Liabilities: $259,014,651
Net Worth: $236,292,973
Earnings: $26,792,250
Emp.: 6,533
Fiscal Year-end: 06/30/13
Business Description:
Dairy Products Mfr
S.I.C.: 2023
N.A.I.C.S.: 311514
Personnel:
Johann Hendrik Vorster *(CEO)*
Louis Jacques Botha *(CFO)*
Elton Ronald Bosch *(Exec-Bus Dev, Risk & Afrika)*
James Henry Ferreira Botes *(Exec-Comml)*
Hendrikus Lubbe *(Exec-Supply Chain & CIS)*
Marcelo Marques Palmeiro *(Exec-Corp & Brands Dev)*
Board of Directors:
Werner Ignatius Buchner
Stefanes Francois Booysen
Louis Jacques Botha
Johannes Nicolaas Stephanus Du Plessis
Martin Geoff Elliott
Jacobus Christoffel Hendriks
Christiaan Philippus Lerm
Nkateko Peter Mageza
Nigel Athol Smith
Johann Hendrik Vorster
Thomas Alexander Wixley
Transfer Agent:
Computershare Investor Services (Pty) Ltd
70 Marshall Street
Johannesburg, South Africa

CLOVER PAKISTAN LTD.

Lakson Square Building No 2
Sarwar Shaheed Road, Karachi, 74200, Pakistan
Tel.: (92) 215698000
Fax: (92) 215685489
E-Mail: clover@clover.com.pk
Web Site: www.clover.com.pk
Year Founded: 1986
CLOV—(KAR)
Sales Range: $10-24.9 Million
Business Description:
Food Products Mfr & Sales
S.I.C.: 2099
N.A.I.C.S.: 311999
Personnel:
Iqbal Ali Lakhani *(Chm)*
Zulfiqar Ali Lakhani *(CEO)*
Mansoor Ahmed *(Sec)*
Board of Directors:
Iqbal Ali Lakhani
Tasleemuddin Ahmed Batlay
A. Aziz H. Ebrahim
Shahid Ahmed Khan
Amin Mohammed Lakhani
Zulfiqar Ali Lakhani
M. A. Qadir

CLOVERDALE PAINT INC.

6950 King George Boulevard
Surrey, BC, V3W 4Z1, Canada
Tel.: (604) 596-6261
Fax: (604) 597-2677
Toll Free: (800) 279-7780
E-Mail: helpdesk@cloverdalepaint.com
Web Site: www.cloverdalepaint.com
Year Founded: 1933
Rev.: $111,000,000
Emp.: 100
Business Description:
Paints Mfr & Distr
S.I.C.: 2851
N.A.I.C.S.: 325510
Personnel:
C. A. Mordy *(Pres & CEO)*

CLP HOLDINGS LIMITED

8 Laguna Verde Avenue Hung Hom
Kowloon, China (Hong Kong)
Tel.: (852) 26788111
Fax: (852) 27604448
E-Mail: clp_info@clp.com.hk
Web Site: www.clpgroup.com
Year Founded: 1998
0002—(HKG OTC)
Rev.: $13,521,825,950
Assets: $29,498,086,200
Liabilities: $17,737,717,250
Net Worth: $11,760,368,950
Earnings: $1,069,253,400
Emp.: 6,518
Fiscal Year-end: 12/31/12
Business Description:
Holding Company; Electricity Investor-Operator
S.I.C.: 4939
N.A.I.C.S.: 221111

Personnel:
Andrew Clifford Winawer Brandler *(CEO)*
Mark Takahashi *(CFO)*
Quince Wai Yan Chong *(Chief Corp Dev Officer-CLP Power Hong Kong)*
Albert Sui Cheong Poon *(Deputy Mng Dir-CLP Power Hong Kong)*
April Yiu Wai Yee Chan *(Sec)*
Board of Directors:
Michael David Kadoorie
Nicholas Charles Allen
Ian Duncan Boyce
Andrew Clifford Winawer Brandler
Vincent Hoi Cheun Cheng
Roderick Ian Eddington
Peter William Greenwood
Richard Kendall Lancaster
Fanny Fan Chiu Fun Law
Irene Yun Lien Lee
Yui Bor Lee
John Andrew Harry Leigh
Ronald James McAulay
William Elkin Mocatta
Vernon Francis Moore
Paul Arthur Theys
Peter Pak Wing Tse
Judy Lam Sin Lai Tsui

Subsidiaries:

CLP Engineering Limited (1)
36F Asia Trade Centre 79 Lei Muk Road
Kwai Chung, New Territories, China (Hong Kong)
Tel.: (852) 26787900
Fax: (852) 2424 1155
E-Mail: clp_info@clp.com.hk
Web Site: www.clpgroup.com
Emp.: 200
Electrical Engineering Services
S.I.C.: 8711
N.A.I.C.S.: 541330
K. B. Lam *(Gen Mgr)*

CLP Power Hong Kong Limited (1)
8 Laguna Verde Avenue Hung Hom
Kowloon, China (Hong Kong) HK
Tel.: (852) 26788111 (100%)
Fax: (852) 27604448
E-Mail: clp_info@clp.com.hk
Web Site: www.clpgroup.com
Emp.: 6,000
Electric Power Distr
S.I.C.: 4931
N.A.I.C.S.: 221122
Betty So Siu Mai Yuen *(Vice Chm)*
Siu Hung Chan *(Mng Dir)*
Paul Wai Yin Poon *(COO)*

Hong Kong Nuclear Investment Company Limited (1)
147 Argyle Street
Kowloon, China (Hong Kong)
Tel.: (852) 26788111
Fax: (852) 26788491
E-Mail: clp_info@clp.com.hk
Web Site: www.clp.com.hk
Nuclear Power Generation Services
S.I.C.: 4939
N.A.I.C.S.: 221113
Siu Hung Chan *(Mng Dir)*

Non-U.S. Subsidiaries:

CLP Huanyu (Shandong) Biomass Heat and Power Company Limited (1)
Zhaihao Village Hubin Town
Boxing County, Binzhou, Shandong, China
Tel.: (86) 5432169299
Fax: (86) 5432169277
Biomass Mfr
S.I.C.: 2834
N.A.I.C.S.: 325412
Yingwei Lin *(Chm)*

CLP Power India Pvt. Ltd. (1)
15th Floor Oberoi Commerz International Business Park
Goregaon East, Mumbai, Maharashtra, 400 063, India
Tel.: (91) 2267588800
Fax: (91) 2267588811
E-Mail: indiapa@clpindia.in
Web Site: www.clpindia.in
Emp.: 55
Power Generation Services
S.I.C.: 4939
N.A.I.C.S.: 221112
Rajiv Ranjan Mishra *(Mng Dir)*
Samir Ashta *(CFO)*
Nabeel Saleem *(Gen Counsel)*

Gujarat Paguthan Energy Corporation Private Limited (1)
Plant Bharuch Palej Rd Village Paguthan
Bharuch, Gujarat, 392 015, India In
Tel.: (91) 2642671501 (100%)
Fax: (91) 2642671521/3
Web Site: www.clpgroup.com
Emp.: 35
Combined Cycle Power Plant
S.I.C.: 4931
N.A.I.C.S.: 221113
Rajiv Ranjan Mishra *(Mng Dir)*

TRUenergy Holdings Pty. Ltd. (1)
Level 33 385 Bourke St
Melbourne, VIC, 3000, Australia
Tel.: (61) 386281000
Fax: (61) 386281050
Web Site: www.energyaustralia.com.au
Solar Power Generation Services
S.I.C.: 4939
N.A.I.C.S.: 221118
Richard McIndoe *(Mng Dir)*

Subsidiary:

TRUenergy Pty Ltd (2)
Level 33 385 Bourke St
Melbourne, VIC, 3000, Australia AU
Tel.: (61) 386281000 (100%)
Fax: (61) 386281050
E-Mail: customerservice@truenergy.com.au
Web Site: www.truenergy.com.au
Emp.: 1,000
Gas & Electricity Distr
S.I.C.: 4924
N.A.I.C.S.: 221210
Richard Iain James McIndoe *(Mng Dir)*

CLPG PACKAGING INDUSTRIES SDN. BHD.

Plot 181 Jalan Perindustrian Bukit Minyak 7
Kawasan Perindustrian
Bukit Minyak, 14100 Bukit Mertajam, Penang, Malaysia
Tel.: (60) 604 501 0202
Fax: (60) 604 508 0202
E-Mail: sales@clpg.com.my
Web Site: www.clpg.com.my
Year Founded: 2002
Business Description:
Plastic Corrugated Sheet, Box & Partition Mfr
S.I.C.: 3083
N.A.I.C.S.: 326130

Subsidiary:

Corplast Packaging Industries Sdn. Bhd. (1)
No 10 Jalan Sungai Chadong 8 Casin Industrial Park
Batu 5 Off Jalan Kapar, 42100 Kelang, Selangor Darul Ehsan, Malaysia MY
Tel.: (60) 332918898
Fax: (60) 332919198
E-Mail: sales@corplast.com
Web Site: www.corplast.com
Emp.: 36
Profile Plastic Sheets Mfr
S.I.C.: 3081
N.A.I.C.S.: 326113
Tanchoon Hock *(Mgr-Production)*

CLS HOLDINGS PLC

86 Bondway
London, SW8 1SF, United Kingdom
Tel.: (44) 2075827766
Fax: (44) 2078207728
E-Mail: enquiries@clsholdings.com
Web Site: www.clsholdings.com
CLI—(LSE)
Rev.: $126,659,058
Assets: $1,935,735,753
Liabilities: $1,277,013,894
Net Worth: $658,721,859
Earnings: $73,752,843
Emp.: 65
Fiscal Year-end: 12/31/12
Business Description:
Holding Company; Commercial Property Investment, Development & Management Services
S.I.C.: 6719
N.A.I.C.S.: 551112
Personnel:
Sten A. Mortstedt *(Chm)*
Henry Klotz *(Vice Chm)*
Richard Tice *(CEO)*
John Whiteley *(CFO)*
Alain Millet *(Treas)*
David Fuller *(Sec)*
Board of Directors:
Sten A. Mortstedt
Malcolm C. Cooper
Joseph A. Crawley
Christopher P. Jarvis
Henry Klotz
Thomas Lundqvist
Jennica Mortstedt
Brigith Terry
Thomas J. Thomson
Richard Tice
John Whiteley
Transfer Agent:
Computershare Investor Services PLC
The Pavilions Bridgewater Road
PO Box 82
Bristol, BS13 8AE, United Kingdom
Tel.: (44) 870 702 0000
Fax: (44) 870 703 6119

Subsidiaries:

Apex Tower Limited (1)
86 Bondway
London, SW8 1SF, United Kingdom
Tel.: (44) 207582 7766
Fax: (44) 2078280218
Real Estate Development Services
S.I.C.: 6531
N.A.I.C.S.: 531390

Brent House Limited (1)
86 Bond Way
London, SW8 1SF, United Kingdom (100%)
Tel.: (44) 2075827766
E-Mail: enquiries@clsholdings.com
Emp.: 38
Other Real Estate Property Lessors
S.I.C.: 6519
N.A.I.C.S.: 531190
Sten Mortstedt *(Mng Dir)*

CI Tower Investments Limited (1)
86 Bondway
SW658J London, United Kingdom (100%)
Tel.: (44) 2075827766
Fax: (44) 2079620005
E-Mail: enquires@clsholdings.com
Emp.: 50
Real Estate Investment Trusts
S.I.C.: 6726
N.A.I.C.S.: 525990
Sten Mortstedt *(Mng Dir)*

CLSH Management Limited (1)
86 Bond Way
SW8 1SS London, United Kingdom (100%)
Tel.: (44) 2075827766
Fax: (44) 2075822363
E-Mail: enquiries@clsholdings.com
Web Site: www.clsholdings.com
Emp.: 50
Nonresidential Buildings Lessors
S.I.C.: 6512
N.A.I.C.S.: 531120
Sten Mortstedt *(Mng Dir)*

Great West House Limited (1)
86 Bondway
London, SW6 5HG, United Kingdom(100%)
Tel.: (44) 2075827766
Emp.: 40
Real Estate Agents & Brokers Offices
S.I.C.: 6531
N.A.I.C.S.: 531210
Sten Mortstedt *(Chm)*

Spring Gardens Limited (1)
1 Spring Gdns
SW8 1SF London, United Kingdom (100%)
Tel.: (44) 2075827766
Fax: (44) 2075870110
E-Mail: enquiries@clsholdings.com
Emp.: 38
Real Estate Investment Trusts
S.I.C.: 6726
N.A.I.C.S.: 525990
Sten Mortstedt *(Mng Dir)*

Three Albert Embankment Limited (1)
86 Bondway
Tinworth Street, London, SW8 1SF, United Kingdom (100%)
Tel.: (44) 2075827766
Fax: (44) 2078207728
E-Mail: enquiries@clsholdings.com
Web Site: www.clsholdings.com
Emp.: 50
Other Real Estate Property Lessors
S.I.C.: 6519
N.A.I.C.S.: 531190
Sten Mortstedt *(Mng Dir)*

Vauxhall Cross Limited (1)
1 Citadel Place
London, SE11 5EF, United Kingdom (100%)
Tel.: (44) 2075827766
Fax: (44) 2075870110
E-Mail: enquiries@clsholdings.com
Emp.: 55
Nonresidential Buildings Lessors
S.I.C.: 6512
N.A.I.C.S.: 531120
Sten Mortstedt *(Mng Dir)*

Non-U.S. Subsidiaries:

Adlershofer Sarl (1)
Avenue de la Gare 65
1611 Luxembourg, Luxembourg
Tel.: (352) 26684881
Fax: (352) 26687910
Property Management Services
S.I.C.: 6531
N.A.I.C.S.: 531311

Grossglockner Sarl (1)
Ave De La Gare 65
1611 Luxembourg, Luxembourg
Tel.: (352) 24527534
Property Management Services
S.I.C.: 6531
N.A.I.C.S.: 531311

Hamersley International BV (1)
Meridiaan 51
2801 DA Gouda, Netherlands (100%)
Tel.: (31) 182507775
Real Estate Investment Trusts
S.I.C.: 6726
N.A.I.C.S.: 525990
Per Sjoberg *(Mng Dir)*

Hermalux SARL (1)
55th Ave De La Gare
1611 Luxembourg, Luxembourg
Tel.: (352) 26684020
Fax: (352) 24527584
E-Mail: scaazaruso@clsholdings.com
Other Holding Companies Offices
S.I.C.: 6719
N.A.I.C.S.: 551112

Kapellen Sarl (1)
Rue Leon Thyes 12
2636 Luxembourg, Luxembourg
Tel.: (352) 26684756
Property Management Services
S.I.C.: 6531
N.A.I.C.S.: 531311

Vanerparken Property Investment KB (1)
Vanerparken 1
46235 Vanersborg, Sweden
Tel.: (46) 52167555
Fax: (46) 52165618
Web Site: www.vanerparken.com
Other Real Estate Property Lessors
S.I.C.: 6519
N.A.I.C.S.: 531190

CLS Holdings plc—(Continued)

Non-U.S. Joint Venture:

Bulgarian Land Development EAD (1)
47A Tsarigradsko Shose Blvd
1124 Sofia, Bulgaria BG
Tel.: (359) 2 805 1910
Fax: (359) 2 805 1914
E-Mail: office@bld.bg
Web Site: www.bld.bg
Emp.: 15
Commercial & Residential Real Estate Development & Construction Management Services
S.I.C.: 6552
N.A.I.C.S.: 237210
Dimitar Safov *(Gen Mgr)*

CLUB DE HOCKEY CANADIEN, INC.

(d/b/a Montreal Canadiens)
Bell Centre 1260 De la Gauchetiere Street West
Montreal, QC, H3B 5E8, Canada
Tel.: (514) 932-2582
Fax: (514) 932-8736
Toll Free: (855) 310-2525
E-Mail: cec@centrebell.ca
Web Site: canadiens.nhl.com
Year Founded: 1909
Sales Range: $75-99.9 Million
Emp.: 150

Business Description:
Professional Hockey Franchise & Sports Arena Operator
S.I.C.: 7941
N.A.I.C.S.: 711211

Personnel:
Geoffrey E. Molson *(Owner, Pres & CEO)*
Andrew Molson *(Gen Partner)*
Justin Molson *(Gen Partner)*
Michael Andlauer *(Partner)*
Luc Bertrand *(Partner)*
Fred Steer *(CFO & Exec VP)*
Kevin Gilmore *(COO & Exec VP)*
France Margaret Belanger *(Chief Legal Officer & Sr VP)*
Rejean Houle *(Pres-Canadiens Alumni Association)*
Francois-Xavier Seigneur *(Pres-Effix)*
Marc Bergevin *(Exec VP & Gen Mgr-Hockey Ops)*
Alain Gauthier *(Exec VP & Gen Mgr-Facilities Ops-Bell Centre)*
Donald Beauchamp *(Sr VP-Comm & Community Rels)*

Subsidiary:

L'Arena des Canadiens, Inc. (1)
1909 avenue des Canadiens-de-Montreal
Montreal, QC, H4B 5G0, Canada QC
Tel.: (514) 932-2582
Toll Free: (800) 663-6786
Web Site: www.centrebell.ca
Sports Arena & Entertainment Complex Operator
S.I.C.: 7999
N.A.I.C.S.: 711310
Alain Gauthier *(Exec VP & Gen Mgr)*

Unit:

evenko (2)
1275 Saint-Antoine Ouest
Montreal, QC, H3C 5L2, Canada
Tel.: (514) 790-2525
Toll Free: (877) 668-8269 (Tickets)
Web Site: www.evenko.ca
Music, Sports & Entertainment Promotion Services
S.I.C.: 7999
N.A.I.C.S.: 711310
Jacques Aube *(VP & Gen Mgr)*

CLUB MEDITERRANEE S.A.

11 Rue de Cambrai
75957 Paris, Cedex 19, France
Tel.: (33) 153353553
Fax: (33) 153353616
E-Mail: scottsdale.internet@clubmed.com
Web Site: www.clubmed.com
Year Founded: 1950
CU—(EUR)
Rev.: $1,964,062,030
Assets: $1,708,289,730
Liabilities: $1,005,588,990
Net Worth: $702,700,740
Earnings: $2,692,340
Emp.: 12,827
Fiscal Year-end: 10/31/12

Business Description:
Vacation Villages, Holiday Residences & Tourist Hotels Owner & Operator
S.I.C.: 7011
N.A.I.C.S.: 721199

Personnel:
Henri Giscard d'Estaing *(Chm & CEO)*
Michel Wolfovski *(CFO & Exec VP)*
Sophie Reinach *(Press Officer)*
Laure Baume *(CEO-New Markets-Europe & Africa & VP-Worldwide Strategic Mktg)*
Heidi Kunkel *(CEO-East & South Asia & Pacific)*
Edouard Silvercio *(Gen Counsel & VP)*

Board of Directors:
Henri Giscard d'Estaing
Lama Al Sulaiman
Anass Houir Alami
Amine Benhalima
Thierry Delaunoy de La Tour d'Artaise
Alain Dinin
Guangchang Guo
Christina Jeanbart
Pascal Lebard
Georges Pauget
Gerard Pluvinet
Jiannong Quian
Isabelle Seillier
Anne-Claire Taittinger

Deloitte & Associes
185 avenue Charles-de-Gaulle
Neuilly-sur-Seine, France

Subsidiaries:

Club Med Amerique du Sud (1)
11 Rue De Cambrai
Paris, 75019, France
Tel.: (33) 810810810
Tour Operators
S.I.C.: 4725
N.A.I.C.S.: 561520

Club Med Ferias (1)
11 Rue De Cambrai
75019 Paris, France
Tel.: (33) 810810810
Travel & Tourism Operation Services
S.I.C.: 4729
N.A.I.C.S.: 561599

Club Med Villas et Chalets Holding (1)
11 Rue De Cambrai
Paris, 75019, France
Tel.: (33) 153353553
Fax: (33) 153353616
Web Site: www.clubmed.fr
Travel & Tourism Operation Services
S.I.C.: 4729
N.A.I.C.S.: 561599
Henri Giscard *(Mng Dir)*

Subsidiary:

Club Med Villas et Chalets (2)
11 Rue De Cambrai
Paris, 75019, France
Tel.: (33) 130830335
Web Site: www.villas-chalets.clubmed.fr
Travel & Tourism Operation Services
S.I.C.: 4729
N.A.I.C.S.: 561599

Club Med World Holding (1)
11 Rue De Cambrai
Paris, 75019, France
Tel.: (33) 153353553
Fax: (33) 153353616
Web Site: www.cubmed.fr
Emp.: 700
Travel & Tourism Operation Services
S.I.C.: 4729
N.A.I.C.S.: 561599
Henri Giscard D'estaing *(Pres)*

U.S. Subsidiaries:

Club Med Management Services Inc (1)
6505 Blue Lagoon Dr 225
Miami, FL 33126-6009
Tel.: (305) 925-9000
Fax: (305) 925-9045
E-Mail: reception.desk@clubmed.com
Web Site: www.clubmed.us
Emp.: 80
Travel & Tourism Operation Services
S.I.C.: 4729
N.A.I.C.S.: 561599
Xavier Mufraggi *(Pres & CEO)*

Club Med Sales, Inc. (1)
65005 Blue Lagoon Dr Ste 225
Miami, FL 33126 (100%)
Tel.: (305) 925-9000
Fax: (305) 925-9052
Toll Free: (800) CLUB-MED
E-Mail: reception.desk@clubmed.com
Web Site: www.clubmed.com
Emp.: 100
Tour Operator Services
S.I.C.: 4724
N.A.I.C.S.: 561510

Division:

Club Med (2)
7001 N Scottsdale Rd Ste 1010
Scottsdale, AZ 85253
Mailing Address:
PO Box 347258
Coral Gables, FL 33234-7258
Tel.: (480) 948-9190
Telex: 669496
Fax: (480) 443-2085
Toll Free: (800) CLUBMED
Web Site: www.clubmed.us.com
Emp.: 75
Reservation Center
S.I.C.: 7011
N.A.I.C.S.: 721110
Henri D'Estaing *(Pres)*

Holiday Village of Sandpiper Inc (1)
3500 Se Morningside Blvd
Port Saint Lucie, FL 34952-6116
Tel.: (772) 398-5100
Fax: (772) 398-5103
Travel & Tourism Operation Services
S.I.C.: 4729
N.A.I.C.S.: 561599
Henri Giscard D'estaing *(Pres)*

Non-U.S. Subsidiaries:

Club Med Australia Pty Ltd (1)
L 6 227 Elizabeth Street
Sydney, NSW, 2000, Australia
Tel.: (61) 292650500
Fax: (61) 292650599
Web Site: www.clubmed.com.au
Emp.: 89
Holiday Resorts Management Services
S.I.C.: 7011
N.A.I.C.S.: 721110
Quentin Briard *(Gen Mgr)*

Club Med Brasil SA (1)
Lauro Muller 116
Rio de Janeiro, 22290-160, Brazil
Tel.: (55) 2121234500
Fax: (55) 21234501
Web Site: www.Clubmed.com
Travel & Tourism Operating Services
S.I.C.: 4729
N.A.I.C.S.: 561599

Club Med Sales Canada Inc (1)
1 Pl Alexis Nihon 15th Floor
Westmount, QC, H3Z 3C1, Canada
Tel.: (514) 937-7707
Fax: (514) 937-9661
Web Site: www.clubmed.ca
Travel & Tourism Operation Services
S.I.C.: 4729
N.A.I.C.S.: 561599

Club Med Vacances (Korea) Ltd (1)
5 F Doshim Gonghang Tower 159-9 Samsong-dong
Kangnam-gu, Seoul, Korea (South)
Tel.: (82) 52583726
Travel & Tourism Operation Services
S.I.C.: 4729
N.A.I.C.S.: 561599

Club Med Vacances (Taiwan) Ltd (1)
6F-1 No 358 Section 2 Pa Teh Road
Taipei, 10556, Taiwan
Tel.: (886) 227515511
Fax: (886) 287730800
E-Mail: contactus.tw@clubmed.com
Web Site: www.clubmed.com.tw
Travel & Tourism Operation Services
S.I.C.: 4729
N.A.I.C.S.: 561599

Club Med Viagens lda (1)
R Andrade Corvo 33 B
Lisbon, 1050-008, Portugal
Tel.: (351) 213309696
Fax: (351) 213537847
Web Site: www.clubmed.pt
Emp.: 10
Tours Operating Services
S.I.C.: 4729
N.A.I.C.S.: 561599
Jean Francois *(Gen Mgr)*

Club Mediterranee Australia Pty. Ltd. (1)
Level 9 55 Market St
Sydney, NSW, 2000, Australia (100%)
Tel.: (61) 292650500
Telex: 120-425
Fax: (61) 292650599
E-Mail: sales@clubmed.com.au
Web Site: www.clubmed.com.au
Emp.: 42
Travel Operator
S.I.C.: 4724
N.A.I.C.S.: 561510

Club Mediterranee Hellas (1)
161 Vouliagmenis Avenue Palama 2
Athens, 17237, Greece
Tel.: (30) 2109948600
Fax: (30) 2109948609
Emp.: 500
Tour Operators
S.I.C.: 4725
N.A.I.C.S.: 561520
Abate Alexander *(Gen Mgr)*

Club Mediterranee Holland BV (1)
Stadhouderskade 13
Amsterdam, 1054 ES, Netherlands
Tel.: (31) 206070607
Fax: (31) 206070670
Travel & Tourism Operation Services
S.I.C.: 4729
N.A.I.C.S.: 561599
Linda Kromhout *(Gen Mgr)*

Club Mediterranee Hong Kong Ltd (1)
13th Floor Winway Building 50 Wellington Street
Central, China (Hong Kong)
Tel.: (852) 3111 9388
Web Site: www.clubmed.com.hk
Travel & Tourism Operation Services
S.I.C.: 4729
N.A.I.C.S.: 561599

Club Mediterranee Italia S.p.A. (1)
Via del Governo Vecchio 5/6
00186 Rome, Italy (100%)
Tel.: (39) 066875361
Telex: 613 095
S.I.C.: 7011
N.A.I.C.S.: 721199

Club Mediterranee K.K. (1)
Azabu Green Terrace 6F 3-20-1 Minami Azabu Minato-ku
Tokyo, 106 0047, Japan (100%)
Tel.: (81) 3 5792 7627
Fax: (81) 352106727
Web Site: www.clubmed.co.jp
Emp.: 100
Tour Operator
S.I.C.: 4724

N.A.I.C.S.: 561510
Seguchi Mori Tadashi *(Pres)*

Club Mediterranee S.A. Belge **(1)**
59 Ave Louise
1050 Brussels, Belgium (99.6%)
Tel.: (32) 70660660
Telex: 21024
Web Site: www.clubmed.be
Travel Agency
S.I.C.: 4724
N.A.I.C.S.: 561510

Club Mediterranee Services India Private Ltd **(1)**
Ram Krishna Chambers Unit Nos 505 5th Floor Linking Road
Khar West, Mumbai, 400 052, India
Tel.: (91) 22 300 54109
E-Mail: sales.india@clubmed.com
Web Site: www.clubmed.co.in
Travel & Tourism Operation Services
S.I.C.: 4729
N.A.I.C.S.: 561599

Club Mediterranee Suisse **(1)**
Avenue D Aire 40
1203 Geneva, Switzerland
Tel.: (41) 223390909
Fax: (41) 22 339 09 84
Emp.: 20
Travel & Tourism Operation Services
S.I.C.: 4729
N.A.I.C.S.: 561599
Laure Baume *(Mng Dir)*

Club Mediterranee U.K. Ltd. **(1)**
Gemini House 10 18 Putney Hill
London, SW15 6AA, United Kingdom (100%)
Tel.: (44) 8453676767
Telex: 299.23.21
Fax: (44) 2087808602
Web Site: www.clubmed.co.uk
Emp.: 30
S.I.C.: 7011
N.A.I.C.S.: 721199
Laurent de Chorivit *(Mng Dir)*

CM World Montreal Inc **(1)**
540 Montee De Liesse
Saint Laurent, QC, H4T 1N8, Canada
Tel.: (514) 829-9505
Truck Repair Services
S.I.C.: 7538
N.A.I.C.S.: 811111

Vacances (Pty) Ltd **(1)**
212-214 2nd Floor Design Quarter Corner William Nicol and Leslie Road
Fourways, Johannesburg, Gauteng, 2021, South Africa
Tel.: (27) 118402600
Fax: (27) 118402616
Web Site: www.clubmed.co.za
Travel & Tourism Operation Services
S.I.C.: 4729
N.A.I.C.S.: 561599
David Randall *(Gen Mgr)*

CLUBLINK ENTERPRISES LIMITED

15675 Dufferin Street
King City, ON, L7B 1K5, Canada
Tel.: (905) 841-3730
Fax: (905) 841-1134
E-Mail: rsahi@morguard.com
Web Site: clublinkenterprises.ca
CLK—(TSX)
Rev.: $213,873,343
Assets: $648,686,518
Liabilities: $467,504,504
Net Worth: $181,182,013
Earnings: $14,463,985
Emp.: 550
Fiscal Year-end: 12/31/12

Business Description:
Holding Company; Golf Club Owner; Railway Operator
S.I.C.: 6719
N.A.I.C.S.: 551112

Personnel:
K. Rai Sahi *(Chm & CEO)*
Robert Visentin *(CFO)*
Eugene N. Hretzay *(Pres-White Pass & Yukon Route, Gen Counsel, Sec & VP)*

Board of Directors:
K. Rai Sahi
Patrick S. Brigham
Paul Campbell
David A. King
John Lokker
Samuel J.B. Pollock
Donald W. Turple
Jack D. Winberg

Transfer Agent:
Canada Stock Transfer Company Inc.
320 Bay Street
Toronto, ON, Canada

Subsidiary:

ClubLink Corporation **(1)**
15675 Dufferin St
King City, ON, L7B 1K5, Canada ON (100%)
Tel.: (905) 841-3730
Fax: (905) 841-1134
Toll Free: (800) 661-1818
Web Site: www.clublink.ca
Sales Range: $125-149.9 Million
Emp.: 3,500
Golf Clubs & Resorts
S.I.C.: 7999
N.A.I.C.S.: 713910
K. Rai Sahi *(Pres & CEO)*

CLUFF GOLD PLC

(Name Changed to Amara Mining plc)

CLUFF NATURAL RESOURCES PLC

Third Floor 5-8 The Sanctuary
London, SW1P 3JS, United Kingdom
Tel.: (44) 20 7887 2630
Fax: (44) 20 7887 2639
Web Site: www.cluffnaturalresources.com
Year Founded: 2012
CLNR—(LSE)
Rev.: $1,339
Assets: $4,700,602
Liabilities: $272,920
Net Worth: $4,427,682
Earnings: ($1,297,750)
Emp.: 9
Fiscal Year-end: 12/31/12

Business Description:
Coal Gasification Services
S.I.C.: 1311
N.A.I.C.S.: 211111

Personnel:
Algy Cluff *(Founder, Chm & CEO)*
Nicholas William Berry *(Deputy Chm)*

Board of Directors:
Algy Cluff
Nicholas William Berry
Peter Nigel Cowley
Robert Victor Danchin
Brian Anthony FitzGerald
William Herbrand
Christopher Matchette-Downes
Graham Swindells

Legal Counsel:
K&L Gates LLP
One New Change
London, United Kingdom

CLUJANA S.A.

Piata 1 Mai Square No 4-5
Cluj-Napoca, Romania
Tel.: (40) 264 437 157
Fax: (40) 264 437 044
E-Mail: office@clujana.com
Web Site: www.clujana.com
Year Founded: 1911
CLUJ—(BUC)

Business Description:
Footwear Mfr
S.I.C.: 2389
N.A.I.C.S.: 316210

Personnel:
Gliga Florin Valentin *(Pres)*

Board of Directors:
Adrian Radu Tarmure
Gliga Florin Valentin

CLUSTER TECHNOLOGY CO., LTD.

5-28 4-chome Shibukawa-cho Higashi
Osaka, 577-0836, Japan
Tel.: (81) 6 6726 2711
Fax: (81) 6 6726 2715
Web Site: www.cluster-tech.co.jp
Year Founded: 1996
4240—(JAS)
Emp.: 68

Business Description:
Metal Mold Mfr
S.I.C.: 3544
N.A.I.C.S.: 333511

Personnel:
Minoru Adachi *(Pres, CEO & Head-Sls & Mktg Div)*
Yoshinori Adachi *(Exec Officer & Dir-Dev Div)*
Seiichi Inada *(Exec Officer & Dir-Mfg Div I)*
Toshihiko Naruse *(Exec Officer & Dir-Control Div)*

CLUTCH AUTO LIMITED

2E/14 1st Fl
Jhandewalan Extn
110055 New Delhi, Delhi, India
Tel.: (91) 1123683548
Fax: (91) 11 2368 3548
E-Mail: cal@nda.vsnl.net.in
Web Site: www.clutchauto.com
Year Founded: 1971
CLUTCH—(BOM)

Business Description:
Clutch Mfr & Exporter
S.I.C.: 3714
N.A.I.C.S.: 336390

Personnel:
Vijay Krishan Metha *(Chm & Mng Dir)*

Board of Directors:
Vijay Krishan Metha
Chandra Shekar Agarwal
Avinish P. Gandhi
Pooja Kapur
Anuj Metha
Satish Sekhri
K. K. Taneja

CLYDE BLOWERS LTD.

(d/b/a Clyde Blowers Capital)
One Redwood Crescent
Peel Park, East Kilbride, G74 5PA, United Kingdom
Tel.: (44) 1355575000
Fax: (44) 1355579600
E-Mail: info@clydeblowers.co.uk
Web Site: www.clydeblowers.co.uk
Year Founded: 1934

Business Description:
Investment Holding Company
S.I.C.: 6719
N.A.I.C.S.: 551112

Personnel:
James Allan McColl *(Chm & CEO)*
Keith Gibson *(Mng Partner)*
Graham Lees *(CFO)*

Subsidiary:

David Brown Gear Systems Limited **(1)**
Park Road
Lockwood, Huddersfield, HD4 5DD, United Kingdom UK
Tel.: (44) 1484465500
Fax: (44) 1484465586
E-Mail: sales@davidbrown.textron.com
Web Site: www.davidbrown.com
Emp.: 400
Industrial & Marine Gears, Machinery Drives Systems & Pumps Mfr
S.I.C.: 3561
N.A.I.C.S.: 333911
Geoss Charlson *(CEO)*

Non-U.S. Subsidiaries:

David Brown Gear Industries Australia Pty. Ltd. **(2)**
13 to 19 Franklin Avenue Bulli
2516 Sydney, NSW, Australia AU
Tel.: (61) 242830300
Fax: (61) 242830333
E-Mail: productsales@davisbrown.com
Web Site: www.davidbrown.com
Emp.: 100
Speed Changers, Drivers & Gears Mfr
S.I.C.: 3566
N.A.I.C.S.: 333612
Ian Chew *(Gen Mgr)*

David Brown Guinard Pumps S.A.S. **(2)**
39 avenue Du Pont de Tasset
Meythet, 74960, France FR
Tel.: (33) 450055600
Fax: (33) 450055880
Web Site: www.clydeunion.com
Emp.: 320
Pumps & Pumping Equipments
S.I.C.: 3561
N.A.I.C.S.: 333911
Fouche Michel *(Plant Mgr)*

David Brown Radicon Inc. **(2)**
975 Dillingham Road
Pickering, ON, L1W 1Z7, Canada ON
Tel.: (905) 420-4141
Fax: (905) 420-9513
Web Site: www.textronpt.com
Emp.: 8
Power Transmission Products
S.I.C.: 3589
N.A.I.C.S.: 333318

Non-U.S. Group:

Clyde Bergemann Power Group **(1)**
Schillwiese 20
46485 Wesel, Germany
Tel.: (49) 281815101
Fax: (49) 281 815 184
E-Mail: info@clydebergemannpowergroup.com
Web Site: www.clydebergemannpowergroup.com
Emp.: 160
Holding Company; Power & Environmental Industry Cleaning, Air-Control & Ash Handling Equipment Developer & Mfr
S.I.C.: 6719
N.A.I.C.S.: 551112
Franz Bartels *(Pres & CEO)*

Subsidiary:

Clyde Bergemann GmbH **(2)**
Schillwiese 20
D-46485 Wesel, Germany (100%)
Tel.: (49) 281815100
Fax: (49) 281815185
E-Mail: info@clydebergemann.de
Web Site: www.clydebergemann.de
Emp.: 150
Industrial Boiler Cleaning Equipment Mfr & Distr
S.I.C.: 3823
N.A.I.C.S.: 334513
Bernard Rogalla *(Gen Mgr)*

Subsidiary:

Clyde Bergemann DRYCON GmbH **(3)**
Schillwiese 20
46485 Wesel, Germany De
Tel.: (49) 2818150
Fax: (49) 28153768
E-Mail: sales@cbw.de
Web Site: www.clydebergemann.de
Sls.: $8,177,605
Emp.: 40
Power & Industrial Boilers, Biomass Boilers & Waste Incinerators Manufacturing Services
S.I.C.: 3443
N.A.I.C.S.: 332410
Franz Bertels *(Pres & CEO)*

Clyde Blowers Ltd.—(Continued)

U.S. Subsidiary:

Clyde Bergemann Inc. (2)
4015 Presidential Pkwy
Atlanta, GA 30340-3707 (100%)
Tel.: (770) 557-3600
Fax: (770) 557-3651
E-Mail: info@clydebergermann.com
Web Site: www.boilercleaning.org
Emp.: 200
Industrial Boiler Cleaning Equipment Mfr & Distr
S.I.C.: 3569
N.A.I.C.S.: 333999

Subsidiary:

Anthony-Ross Company (3)
5600 SW Arctic Dr Ste 100
Beaverton, OR 97005-4101
Tel.: (503) 641-0545
Fax: (503) 643-1303
E-Mail: inforequest@anthonyross.com
Web Site: www.clydebergemann.com
Emp.: 100
Air System Solutions Mfr for Recovery Boilers
S.I.C.: 3554
N.A.I.C.S.: 333243
Gene Sullivan *(VP-Sls)*

Non-U.S. Subsidiaries:

Clyde Bergemann Canada (2)
19 Thorne St Ste 205
Cambridge, ON, N1R 1S3, Canada
Tel.: (866) 267-3068
Fax: (866) 599-3765
Industrial Boiler Cleaning Equipment Mfr & Distr
S.I.C.: 3823
N.A.I.C.S.: 334513

Clyde Bergemann Eesti AS (2)
Mustamae Tee 5A
10616 Tallinn, Estonia (100%)
Tel.: (372) 6259565
Fax: (372) 6541359
E-Mail: tlaaseq@cbw.de
Web Site: www.cdw.de
Emp.: 100
Industrial Boiler Cleaning Equipment Mfr & Distr
S.I.C.: 3823
N.A.I.C.S.: 334513
Tomas Laseq *(Mng Dir)*
Tina Taevere *(Sec)*

Clyde Bergemann Forest S.A. (2)
Avenue Jean Mermoz 29
6041 Gosselies, Belgium (100%)
Tel.: (32) 71919410
Fax: (32) 71919412
E-Mail: cbfsales@cbw.be
Web Site: www.clydebergemannforest.be
Emp.: 15
Mfr of Power Equipment
S.I.C.: 3612
N.A.I.C.S.: 335311
Jean-Michel Frech *(Mng Dir)*

Clyde Bergemann Limited (2)
47 Broad St Bridgeton
Glasgow, Scotland, G40 2QR, United Kingdom (100%)
Tel.: (44) 1415505400
Fax: (44) 1415505401
E-Mail: info@clydebergemann.co.uk
Web Site: www.clydebergemann.co.uk
Emp.: 60
Industrial Boiler Cleaning Equipment Mfr & Distr
S.I.C.: 3589
N.A.I.C.S.: 333318
Jeff Hudson *(Mng Dir)*

Clyde Bergemann Polska Sp. z o.o. (2)
Ul Murarska 27
43-100 Tychy, Poland (100%)
Tel.: (48) 322168412
Fax: (48) 322168818
E-Mail: biuro@clydebergemann.com.pl
Web Site: www.clydebergemann.com.pl
Industrial Boiler Cleaning Equipment Mfr & Distr
S.I.C.: 3823
N.A.I.C.S.: 334513

Shanghai Clyde Bergemann Machinery Company Ltd. (2)
No 2200 Yangshupu Road
Shanghai, 200090, China (100%)
Tel.: (86) 2165396385
Fax: (86) 2165661886
Web Site: www.clydebergemann.com.cn
Emp.: 100
Industrial Boiler Cleaning Equipment Mfr & Distr
S.I.C.: 3559
N.A.I.C.S.: 333249
Franz Bartels *(Chm)*

Non-U.S. Joint Venture:

Forest Espanola S.A. (1)
Menendez Pelayo 2
E 28009 Madrid, Spain (50%)
Tel.: (34) 915776277
Fax: (34) 915757495
E-Mail: forest@gosad.com
Web Site: www.gosad.com
Emp.: 25
Industrial Boiler Cleaning Equipment Mfr & Distr
S.I.C.: 3823
N.A.I.C.S.: 334513
Blas Moreno *(Gen Mgr)*

CLYDESTONE (GHANA) LIMITED

Ridge Tower Building 6th Avenue
PO Box 1003
Cantonments, Accra, Ghana
Tel.: (233) 21 660755
Fax: (233) 21 668232
Web Site: www.clydestone.com
Year Founded: 1989
CLYD—(GHA)
Emp.: 420

Business Description:
Information, Communication & Technology Solutions
S.I.C.: 7373
N.A.I.C.S.: 541512

Personnel:
George Prah *(Chm)*
Paul Tse Jacquaye *(Grp CEO & Mng Dir)*

Board of Directors:
George Prah
Ellis Badu
Nana Benyin Hutchful
Paul Tse Jacquaye

CMA CGM S.A.

4 quai d'Arenc
13235 Marseilles, Cedex 02, France
Tel.: (33) 488919000
Telex: 630 387 F GEMA
Fax: (33) 488919095
E-Mail: info@cma-cgm.com
Web Site: www.cma-cgm.com
Year Founded: 1977
Sales Range: $1-4.9 Billion
Emp.: 16,000

Business Description:
Holding Company for Shipping Activities
Import Export
S.I.C.: 4412
N.A.I.C.S.: 483111

Personnel:
Jacques R. Saade *(Chm & CEO)*
Michel Sirat *(CFO)*
Farid T. Salem *(Pres-Terminal Link)*

Board of Directors:
Jacques R. Saade
Jihad Azour
Dominique Bussereau
Ercument Erdem
Pierre Mongin
Evren Ozturk
Rodolphe Saade
Farid T. Salem
Robert Yuksel Yildirim
Tanya Saade Zeenny

Subsidiaries:

Compagnie Generale Maritime (1)
22 Quai De Galliene
92158 Suresnes, France (99%)
Tel.: (33) 146257000
Telex: 630 387 GEMAR
Fax: (33) 003488919095
Sls.: $1,033,000,000
Emp.: 290
Shipping
S.I.C.: 4412
N.A.I.C.S.: 483111
Jacques R. Saade *(Chm)*

Delmas (1)
1 Quai Colbert
BP 7007X
76080 Le Havre, France
Tel.: (33) 232741000
Fax: (33) 232741010
E-Mail: accueil@delmas.net
Web Site: www.delmas.com
Emp.: 600
Deep Sea Cargo Shipping
S.I.C.: 4412
N.A.I.C.S.: 483111
Mathieu Friedberg *(Gen Mgr)*

Non-U.S. Subsidiary:

Delmas (UK) Limited (2)
52 Charlotte Street
Birmingham, B3 1AR, United Kingdom UK
Tel.: (44) 1212365046
Fax: (44) 1212001196
E-Mail: bmm.sstocker@delmas.com
Web Site: www.delmas.com
Maritime Shipping Services
S.I.C.: 4412
N.A.I.C.S.: 483111

Progeco (1)
4 Qusuai Garenc
13002 Marseille, France
Tel.: (33) 495093760
Fax: (33) 495093546
E-Mail: ho-contact@progeco.fr
Web Site: www.progeco.fr
Emp.: 30
Purchasing, Renting & Repairing of Maritime Shipping Containers
S.I.C.: 4499
N.A.I.C.S.: 488390
Gallo Alexander *(Gen Mgr)*

River Shuttle Containers (1)
29 Boulevard Gay Lussac
Le Grand Bleu Entree B, 13014 Marseille, France
Tel.: (33) 488917500
Fax: (33) 491040316
E-Mail: ho.felamrani@rsc.fr
Web Site: www.rsc.fr
Sales Range: $10-24.9 Million
Emp.: 23
River Shipping Services in France
S.I.C.: 4449
N.A.I.C.S.: 483211
Fatiha El Amrani *(Mgr-Trade)*

Non-U.S. Subsidiaries:

ANL Container Line Pty Limited (1)
Level 7 ANL House
432 St Kilda Road, Melbourne, VIC, 3004, Australia (100%)
Tel.: (61) 3 9257 0555
Fax: (61) 3 9257 0619
Web Site: www.anl.com.au
Cargo Shipping
S.I.C.: 4412
N.A.I.C.S.: 483111

U.S. Subsidiary:

US Lines (2)
3601 S Harbor Blvd Ste 200
Santa Ana, CA 92704
Tel.: (714) 751-3333
Fax: (714) 751-3339
Toll Free: (866) 328-2308
Web Site: www.uslines.com
Emp.: 100
Deep Sea Shipping Services
S.I.C.: 4412
N.A.I.C.S.: 483111
Edward Aldridge *(CEO)*
Nick Hay *(Sr VP-Trades)*

Cheng Lie Navigation Co., Ltd. (1)
15F No 10 Sec 3 Minsheng East Road
Zhongshan District, Taipei, 10480, Taiwan
Tel.: (886) 221832888
Fax: (886) 225007588
E-Mail: general@cnc-line.com
Web Site: www.cncline.com.tw
Emp.: 107
Intra-Asia Shipping Services
S.I.C.: 4412
N.A.I.C.S.: 483111
Robert Sallons *(Mng Dir)*

Comanav (1)
7 bd de la Resistance
20300 Casablanca, Morocco
Tel.: (212) 22 30 30 12
Fax: (212) 22 30 20 06
E-Mail: comanav@comanav.com
Emp.: 2,740
Cargo & Passengers Sea Transport Services; Port Operations
S.I.C.: 4412
N.A.I.C.S.: 483111

MacAndrews & Company Limited (1)
6th Floor 75 King William Street
London, EC4N 7BE, United Kingdom
Tel.: (44) 2072206100
Fax: (44) 2072206101
E-Mail: marketing@macandrews.com
Web Site: www.macandrews.com
Emp.: 500
Ocean, Air & Land Transportation Services
S.I.C.: 4412
N.A.I.C.S.: 483111
Geoffrey Smith *(Mng Dir)*

CMA CORPORATION LIMITED

Level 5 160 Sussex Street
Sydney, NSW, 2000, Australia
Tel.: (61) 292003500
Fax: (61) 292003501
E-Mail: sydrection@cmacorp.net
Web Site: www.cmacorp.net
CMV—(ASX)

Business Description:
Metal Recycling
S.I.C.: 1081
N.A.I.C.S.: 213114

Personnel:
Parag-Johannes Bhatt *(Chm)*
John Pedersen *(CEO & Mng Dir)*
Trevor Schmitt *(CFO & Sec)*

Board of Directors:
Parag-Johannes Bhatt
Mike Greulich
Peter Lancken
John Pedersen
Trevor Schmitt
Oliver Scholz
Paul Whitehead

Subsidiaries:

CMA Recycling Australia Pty Limited (1)
Level 5 160 Sussex St
Sydney, NSW, 2000, Australia
Tel.: (61) 292003500
Fax: (61) 292003501
E-Mail: sydreception@cmacorp.net
Web Site: www.cmacorp.net
Emp.: 15
Integrated Metal Recycling Services
S.I.C.: 5051
N.A.I.C.S.: 423510
John Pedersen *(CEO)*

CMA Recycling Pty Limited (1)
Unit 1 160 Fison Ave W
Eagle Farm, Queensland, 4009, Australia
Tel.: (61) 738908443
Fax: (61) 1032601296
Web Site: www.cmacorp.net
Emp.: 2
Integrated Metal Recycling Services
S.I.C.: 5051
N.A.I.C.S.: 423510

CMA Recycling Victoria Pty Limited (1)
93 Heatherdale Rd
Ringwood, Victoria, 3134, Australia

Tel.: (61) 398732066
Fax: (61) 398732527
Web Site: www.cmacorp.net
Integrated Metal Recycling Services
S.I.C.: 5051
N.A.I.C.S.: 423510

T & T Metal & Asbestos Services Pty Limited (1)
52 Savage St
Eagle Farm, QLD, 4009, Australia
Tel.: (61) 732682699, ext. 38684392
Fax: (61) 7 32601620
Web Site: www.cmacorp.net
Emp.: 10
Scrap Metal Processing & Contracting Services
S.I.C.: 5051
N.A.I.C.S.: 423510

U.S. Subsidiary:

CMA Recycling Corporation, Ltd. (1)
415 E 151 St
East Chicago, IN 46312
Tel.: (219) 391-7075
Fax: (219) 391-7085
Web Site: www.cmacorp.net
Emp.: 50
Metal Recycling Services
S.I.C.: 5051
N.A.I.C.S.: 423510
Andrew Barker *(Gen Mgr)*

Non-U.S. Subsidiaries:

CMA Metals Limited (1)
273A Church St
Onehunga, Auckland, 1061, New Zealand
Tel.: (64) 96222226
Fax: (64) 96222223
E-Mail: cmaadminnz@cmacorp.net
Emp.: 70
Metal Recycling Services
S.I.C.: 5051
N.A.I.C.S.: 423510
Brett Howlitt *(Gen Mgr)*

CMA Peakmore Pte Limited (1)
25 Pioneer Sector 1
Singapore, Singapore
Tel.: (65) 62686436
Fax: (65) 62686694
Web Site: www.cmacorp.net
Emp.: 20
Metal Recycling Services
S.I.C.: 5051
N.A.I.C.S.: 423510

Scrap Metal Recyclers Limited (1)
273A Church St
Onehunga, Auckland, 1061, New Zealand
Tel.: (64) 96222226
Fax: (64) 96222223
Web Site: www.cmacorp.net
Emp.: 60
Scrap Metal Recycling Services
S.I.C.: 5051
N.A.I.C.S.: 423510
Bratt Howward *(Gen Mgr)*

Scrap Metal Recyclers (Waikato) Limited (1)
203 Ellis St
Frankton, Hamilton, New Zealand
Tel.: (64) 78479637
Fax: (64) 78479638
E-Mail: cmaadmin@cmacorp.net
Emp.: 30
Scrap Metal Recycling Services
S.I.C.: 5051
N.A.I.C.S.: 423510

CMB FINANCE LIMITED

MI Building Jamal Kamalakshi
PO Box 21507
Kathmandu, Nepal
Tel.: (977) 1 4223154
Fax: (977) 1 4232678
E-Mail: cmbfl@wlink.com.np
Web Site: www.cmbfinanceltd.com
Year Founded: 2008
CMBF—(NEP)
Business Description:
Financial Services
S.I.C.: 6211
N.A.I.C.S.: 523999
Personnel:
Mangal M. Bajracharya *(Chm)*
Rajendra Man Shakya *(CEO & Sec)*
Rajesh P. Manandhar *(COO)*
Hebendra Shakya *(Sr Officer-Admin)*
Rabindra Shrestha *(Sr Officer-Acct & Treasury Dept)*
Board of Directors:
Mangal M. Bajracharya
Prajwol R. Bajracharya
Prashant Manandhar
Gautam K. Shrestha
Mukunda K. Shrestha
Anil Ratna Tuladhar

CMC CORPORATION

1-1-19 Heiwa
Naka-ku, Nagoya, Aichi, 460-0021, Japan
Tel.: (81) 523223351
Web Site: www.cmc.co.jp
Year Founded: 1962
2185—(JAS)
Sales Range: $125-149.9 Million
Emp.: 555
Business Description:
Printing Services
S.I.C.: 2759
N.A.I.C.S.: 323111
Personnel:
Masumi Tatsuyama *(Pres)*

CMC-KAMAL TEXTILE MILLS LIMITED

Lotus Kamal Tower ONE 57
Zoarshahara C/A Nikunja-2 North Airport Road
Dhaka, 1229, Bangladesh
Tel.: (880) 2 8951989
Fax: (880) 2 8921587
E-Mail: lkc@bangla.net
Web Site: www.cmckamal.com
Year Founded: 1995
CMCKAMAL—(DHA)
Emp.: 900
Business Description:
Cotton Yarn Mfr
S.I.C.: 2299
N.A.I.C.S.: 313110
Personnel:
A. H. M. Mustafa Kamal *(Chm)*

CMC LIMITED

CMC Centre Old Mumbai Highway
Gachibowli
Hyderabad, 500 032, India
Tel.: (91) 4066578000
Fax: (91) 4023000509
Web Site: www.cmcltd.com
Year Founded: 1975
CMC—(NSE)
Rev.: $357,426,060
Assets: $267,467,755
Liabilities: $92,031,170
Net Worth: $175,436,585
Earnings: $42,684,661
Emp.: 10,663
Fiscal Year-end: 03/31/13
Business Description:
Software Development Services
S.I.C.: 7371
N.A.I.C.S.: 541511
Personnel:
Ramanathan Ramanan *(CEO & Mng Dir)*
J. K. Gupta *(CFO)*
Vivek Agarwal *(Compliance Officer & Sec)*
Board of Directors:
S. Ramadorai
M. S. Ananth
S. Mahalingam
Kalpana Morparia
Ramanathan Ramanan
Sudhakar Rao
Ashok Sinha
Transfer Agent:
Karvy Computershare Private Limited
Plot No 17 to 24 Vittalrao Nagar Madhapur
Hyderabad, India

CMC MAGNETICS CORPORATION

15th Floor 53 Ming Chuan West Road
Taipei, Taiwan
Tel.: (886) 2 2598 9890
Fax: (886) 225973008
E-Mail: ir@cmcnet.com.tw
Web Site: www.cmcnet.com.tw
2323—(TAI)
Sales Range: $800-899.9 Million
Business Description:
Optical Storage Media Developer
S.I.C.: 3559
N.A.I.C.S.: 333249
Personnel:
Ming-Sen Wong *(Chm & Gen Mgr)*
U.S. Subsidiary:

Hotan Corp. (1)
751 N Canyons Pkwy
Livermore, CA 94551
Tel.: (925) 290-1000
Fax: (925) 290-1002
E-Mail: info@hotan.com
Web Site: www.hotan.com
Optical Disk Distr
S.I.C.: 5065
N.A.I.C.S.: 423690
Tom Hsieh *(Gen Mgr)*

CMC METALS LTD.

Suite 605 - 369 Terminal Avenue
Vancouver, BC, V6A 4C4, Canada
Tel.: (604) 605-0166
Fax: (604) 692-0117
E-Mail: cmcmetals@shaw.ca
Web Site: www.cmcmetals.ca
CMB—(TSXV)
Rev.: $7,629
Assets: $6,827,003
Liabilities: $2,104,812
Net Worth: $4,722,190
Earnings: ($3,361,743)
Fiscal Year-end: 09/30/13
Business Description:
Mineral Exploration Services
S.I.C.: 1081
N.A.I.C.S.: 213114
Personnel:
Donald Wedman *(Pres & CEO)*
Michael Scholz *(CFO)*
Board of Directors:
Jatinder Bal
John Bossio
Mark Gunderson
Michael Scholz
Donald Wedman
Transfer Agent:
Computershare
3rd Floor 510 Burrard Street
V6C 3B9 Vancouver, BC, Canada

CMC TECHNOLOGIES ISRAEL LTD.

Harava 76
Ganot, Israel
Tel.: (972) 36316919
E-Mail: hotline@cmcltd.co.il
Web Site: www.cmcltd.co.il
Year Founded: 1999
Business Description:
Automation & Control Equipment Mfr
S.I.C.: 3559
N.A.I.C.S.: 333249
Personnel:
Niv Bass *(Engr)*
Subsidiary:

CMC Hi Tec Controlling Solutions Ltd. (1)
33 Alexandroni St
5225 Ramat Gan, Israel
Tel.: (972) 36316919
Fax: (972) 36316919
E-Mail: cmc-rafi@013.net.il
Web Site: www.cmcltd.co.il
Emp.: 4
Automated Electric Controls Mfr
S.I.C.: 3823
N.A.I.C.S.: 334513
Rafi Bass *(Chief Mgr)*

CMD, LTD.

Sycamore Rd Eastwood Trading Estate
Rotherham, S Yorkshire, S65 1EN, United Kingdom
Tel.: (44) 1709829511
Fax: (44) 1709378380
E-Mail: sales@cmd-ltd.com
Web Site: www.cmd-ltd.com
Sales Range: $1-9.9 Million
Emp.: 150
Business Description:
Commercial Lighting & Office Furniture Systems Developer & Mfr
S.I.C.: 2522
N.A.I.C.S.: 337214
Personnel:
Steve Cole *(Mng Dir)*

CME GORUP BERHAD

Lot 19 Jalan Delima 1/1 Subang Hi-Tech Indus Pk Batu Tiga
40000 Shah Alam, Selangor Darul Ehsan, Malaysia
Tel.: (60) 3 56331188
Fax: (60) 3 56343838
Web Site: www.cme.com.my
CME—(KLS)
Rev.: $7,499,858
Assets: $17,745,391
Liabilities: $4,331,495
Net Worth: $13,413,896
Earnings: $25,578
Fiscal Year-end: 12/31/12
Business Description:
Fire Fighting Vehicles Mfr
S.I.C.: 3711
N.A.I.C.S.: 336211
Personnel:
Nizamuddin Shahabuddin *(CEO)*
Ruey Shyan Tan *(Sec)*
Board of Directors:
Putra Azman Shah
Bee Hong Lim
Khairi Mohamad
Azlan Omry Omar
Suan Pin Ong
Nizamuddin Shahabuddin

CME HOLDCO L.P.

Walker House
PO Box 265 GT
Mary Street, Georgetown, Grand Cayman, E9 00000, Cayman Islands
Business Description:
Holding Company
S.I.C.: 6719
N.A.I.C.S.: 551112
Personnel:
Ronald S. Lauder *(Owner)*
Non-U.S. Subsidiary:

CENTRAL EUROPEAN MEDIA ENTERPRISES LTD. (1)
O'Hara House 3 Bermudiana Road
Hamilton, HM 08, Bermuda BM
Tel.: (441) 296 1431 (63.7%)
E-Mail: romana.tomasova@cme-net.com
Web Site: www.cme.net
CETV—(NASDAQ)

CME Holdco L.P.—(Continued)

Rev.: $691,034,000
Assets: $1,961,873,000
Liabilities: $1,520,872,000
Net Worth: $441,001,000
Earnings: ($281,533,000)
Emp.: 3,900
Fiscal Year-end: 12/31/13
TV Stations & Networks Operator
S.I.C.: 4833
N.A.I.C.S.: 515120
Christoph Mainusch *(Chm-BTV Media Grp EAD & Co-CEO)*
Michael Del Nin *(Co-CEO)*
David Sturgeon *(CFO)*
Pavel Stanchev *(CEO-Ops-Bulgaria)*
Daniel Penn *(Gen Counsel & Exec VP)*
Anthony Chhoy *(Exec VP & Head-Strategic Plng & Ops)*

CMG PTY. LTD.

19 Corporate Ave
Melbourne, 3178, Australia
Tel.: (61) 392374000
Fax: (61) 392374010
E-Mail: info@cmggroup.com.au
Web Site: www.cmggroup.com.au
Sales Range: $50-74.9 Million
Emp.: 300

Business Description:
Electric Motor Mfr & Distr
S.I.C.: 3621
N.A.I.C.S.: 335312

Personnel:
Jack Gringlas *(Mng Dir)*
Allan Sarjeand *(Mng Dir)*

Board of Directors:
Andrew Mitchell
Rohan Pollard
Dorian Turner

Subsidiary:

Sankey Australia (1)
15 Gaine Rd
Dandenong, VIC, 3175, Australia (100%)
Tel.: (61) 387875290
Fax: (61) 87875295
E-Mail: sankey@sankey.com.au
Web Site: www.sankey.com.au
Emp.: 45
Metal Products for Industry Designer & Mfr
S.I.C.: 3499
N.A.I.C.S.: 332999

Non-U.S. Subsidiaries:

CMG Electric Motors (Asia Pacific) Pte Ltd. (1)
12 Tuas loop
637346 Singapore, Singapore (100%)
Tel.: (65) 68633473
Fax: (65) 68633476
E-Mail: info@cmmggroup.com.sg
Web Site: www.cmggroup.com.sg
Emp.: 20
Motor & Generator Mfr
S.I.C.: 3621
N.A.I.C.S.: 335312
William Chua *(Mng Dir)*

CMG Electric Motors (Israel) Ltd. (1)
9 Bareket Street Zone 23
North Industrial Park, 38900 Caesarea, Israel
Tel.: (972) 46270777
Fax: (972) 46270779
E-Mail: info@cmmggroup.co.il
Web Site: www.cmmggroup.co.il
Emp.: 10
Motor & Generator Mfr
S.I.C.: 3621
N.A.I.C.S.: 335312
Amit Luski *(Mng Dir)*

CMG Electric Motors South Africa (Pty) Ltd. (1)
268 B Fleming Road Meadowdale
1610 Johannesburg, South Africa
Tel.: (27) 114531930
Fax: (27) 114539560
E-Mail: brian.campbell@cmggroup.co.za
Web Site: www.cmggroup.co.za
Emp.: 50
Motor & Generator Mfr
S.I.C.: 3621
N.A.I.C.S.: 335312
Brian Campbell *(CEO)*

CMG Electric Motors (UK) Ltd. (1)
Unit A Stafford Park 2
Telford, Shropshire, TF3 3AR, United Kingdom
Tel.: (44) 1952299606
Fax: (44) 1952299667
Web Site: www.cmggroup.co.uk
Emp.: 8
Electrical Apparatus & Equipment Wiring Supplies & Construction Material Whslr
S.I.C.: 5063
N.A.I.C.S.: 423610
Mark Williams *(Mng Dir)*

CMIC HOLDINGS CO., LTD.

7-10-4 Nishi-Gotanda
Shinagawa-ku, Tokyo, 141-0031, Japan
Tel.: (81) 357457070
Fax: (81) 357457077
E-Mail: information@cmic.co.jp
Web Site: www.cmic-holdings.co.jp
Year Founded: 1985
2309—(TKS)
Sls.: $553,333,000
Assets: $464,915,000
Liabilities: $259,182,000
Net Worth: $205,733,000
Earnings: $24,651,000
Emp.: 4,847
Fiscal Year-end: 09/30/12

Business Description:
Holding Company; Support Services for Pharmaceutical Development, Manufacturing & Sales
S.I.C.: 6719
N.A.I.C.S.: 551112

Personnel:
Kazuo Nakamura *(Chm & CEO)*
Kunihide Ichikawa *(Mng Dir)*
Keiko Nakamura *(Mng Dir)*
Nobuo Nakamura *(Mng Dir)*

Board of Directors:
Kazuo Nakamura
Kunihide Ichikawa
Keiko Nakamura
Nobuo Nakamura

Subsidiaries:

CMIC-BS Co.Ltd. (1)
Kongo Bldg 7-10-4 Nishi-Gotanda
Shinagawa-ku, 141-0031 Tokyo, Japan
Tel.: (81) 357457080
Fax: (81) 357457088
E-Mail: bs-haken@cmic.co.jp
Web Site: www.cmic-hordings.co.jp
Emp.: 700
All Other Business Support Services
S.I.C.: 7389
N.A.I.C.S.: 561499
Kazuo Nakanura *(Pres)*

CMIC CMO Co., Ltd. (1)
588 1-chome Kanaya-azuma
Shimada, Shizuoka, 428-0013, Japan
Tel.: (81) 547453191
Fax: (81) 547462801
E-Mail: cmic-cmo@cmic.co.jp
Web Site: www.cmic-cmo.com
Emp.: 370
Pharmaceutical Product Mfr & Distr
S.I.C.: 2834
N.A.I.C.S.: 325412
Kunihide Ichikawa *(Co-Chm)*
Tatsuro Miyagawa *(Co-Chm)*

CMIC CMO TOYAMA Co., Ltd. (1)
2-37 Ariso
Imizu, Toyama, 933-0251, Japan
Tel.: (81) 766863501
Fax: (81) 766863508
Web Site: www.cmiccmo-toyama.com
Pharmaceutical Product Mfr
S.I.C.: 2834
N.A.I.C.S.: 325412

CMIC-CP Co. Ltd. (1)
Kongo Bldg 7-10-4 Nishi-Gotanda
141-0031 Tokyo, Shinagawa-ku, Japan
Tel.: (81) 357457085
Fax: (81) 34932106
E-Mail: information@cmic.co.jp
Web Site: www.cmic.co.jp
Temporary Help Services
S.I.C.: 7363
N.A.I.C.S.: 561320
Fujio Nakamura *(Pres)*

CMIC-CRC Co. Ltd. (1)
2nd Floor Kongo Bldg 7-10-4 Nishi-Gotanda
Shinagawa-ku, 141-0031 Tokyo, Japan
Tel.: (81) 357456611
Fax: (81) 357456620
All Other Business Support Services
S.I.C.: 7389
N.A.I.C.S.: 561499
Akihiko Kobari *(Pres)*

CMIC MPSS Co. Ltd. (1)
Kongo Bldg 7-10-4 Nishi-Gotanda
Shinagawa-ku, 141-0031 Tokyo, Japan
Tel.: (81) 357456622
Fax: (81) 357456625
E-Mail: information@cmic.co.jp
Web Site: www.cmic-mpss.com
Emp.: 60,000
Pharmaceutical Preparation Mfr
S.I.C.: 2834
N.A.I.C.S.: 325412

CMIC SS CMO Co. Ltd. (1)
2-37 Ariso Izumi-shi
Toyama, 933-0251, Japan
Tel.: (81) 766863501
Fax: (81) 766863508
Web Site: www.cmic.co.jp/
Emp.: 50
Pharmaceutical Preparation Mfr
S.I.C.: 2834
N.A.I.C.S.: 325412
Shinya Yamaguchi *(Pres)*

Healthclick Co., Ltd. (1)
7-10-4 Nishigotanda Kongo Building 1 2f
Shinagawa-ku, Tokyo, 141-0031, Japan
Tel.: (81) 357456505
Fax: (81) 357456526
E-Mail: pcn@cmic.co.jp
Web Site: www.healthclick.co.jp
Health Care Services
S.I.C.: 8099
N.A.I.C.S.: 621999

Institute of Applied Medicine Inc. (1)
Sapporo Izumi 3rd Building 7 floor 2-32 North 2 West
Chuo-ku, 060-0002 Sapporo, Japan
Tel.: (81) 112077001
Fax: (81) 112077177
Web Site: www.oiken.co.jp
Medicinal & Botanical Mfr
S.I.C.: 2833
N.A.I.C.S.: 325411
Hiroshi Nakamura *(Pres)*

MDS Co. Ltd. (1)
1/7 ShimCMIC utomo Udosa Shumito
3-9-10 Shibuya Shibuya-ku, Tokyo, 150-0002, Japan
Tel.: (81) 357667161
Fax: (81) 357667162
Web Site: www.m-ds.co.jp
Emp.: 50
Power Distribution & Specialty Transformer Mfr
S.I.C.: 3612
N.A.I.C.S.: 335311
Kauko Oheda *(Pres)*

Site Support Institute Co., Ltd. (1)
Osaki Center Building 1-5-1 Osaki
Shinagawa-ku, Tokyo, 141-0032, Japan
Tel.: (81) 3 5436 2820
Fax: (81) 3 5436 2822
Web Site: www.j-smo.com
Emp.: 931
Pharmaceutical Products Mfr
S.I.C.: 2834
N.A.I.C.S.: 325412
Takayuki Nakano *(CEO)*

U.S. Subsidiary:

CMIC CMO USA Corporation (1)
3 Cedar Brook Dr N Ste 3
Cranbury, NJ 08512
Tel.: (609) 395-9700
Fax: (609) 395-8824
E-Mail: info@cmicvps.com
Web Site: www.cmiccmousa.com
Pharmaceutical Research & Development Services
S.I.C.: 8731
N.A.I.C.S.: 541711
Kunihide Ichikawa *(Pres)*
Masao Wakai *(Sec)*
Gary Wada *(Exec VP & Gen Mgr)*

Non-U.S. Subsidiaries:

CMIC Asia-Pacific, Pte. Ltd. (1)
6 Shenton Way #24-08A Tower Two
Singapore, 068809, Singapore
Tel.: (65) 6222 2655
Support Services for Pharmaceutical Development
S.I.C.: 2834
N.A.I.C.S.: 325412

CMIC (Beijing) Co.Ltd. (1)
A515 COFCO Plaza No 8
Jianguomennei Avenue, 100005 Beijing, China
Tel.: (86) 1065139211
Fax: (86) 1065139213
Web Site: www.cmic.co.jp/
Emp.: 20
Pharmaceutical Preparation Mfr
S.I.C.: 2834
N.A.I.C.S.: 325412
Wen He *(Pres)*

CMIC CMO Korea Co., Ltd (1)
157-3 Dodang-dong
Wonmi-gu, Bucheon, Gyeonggi-do, Korea (South)
Tel.: (82) 32 678 5771
Fax: (82) 32 675 3385
Web Site: www.cmic-cmo.co.kr
Pharmaceutical Products Mfr
S.I.C.: 2834
N.A.I.C.S.: 325412

CMIC Korea Co.Ltd. (1)
#702 Hanseong Bldg 47-2
Seosomun-dong Jung-gu, 100-110 Seoul, Korea (South)
Tel.: (82) 237083600
Fax: (82) 237896900
Web Site: www.cmic.co.kr
Pharmaceutical Preparation Mfr
S.I.C.: 2834
N.A.I.C.S.: 325412

Haedong SS Pharmaceutical Co. Ltd (1)
157-3 Dodang-dong Wonmi-gu Puchon-city
Seoul, Korea (South)
Tel.: (82) 326785771
Fax: (82) 326753385
Pharmaceutical Preparation Mfr
S.I.C.: 2834
N.A.I.C.S.: 325412
Jong Chul Kim *(CEO)*

CMK CORPORATION

43/F Shinjuku I-LAND TOWER Bldg
6-5-1 Nishi-Shinjuku
Shinjuku-ku, Tokyo, 163-1388, Japan
Tel.: (81) 3 5323 0231
Fax: (81) 3 5323 0071
E-Mail: customer-eng@cmk.co.jp
Web Site: www.cmk-corp.com
6958—(TKS)
Sls.: $799,447,000
Assets: $1,049,774,000
Liabilities: $414,271,000
Net Worth: $635,503,000
Earnings: $7,832,000
Emp.: 5,127
Fiscal Year-end: 03/31/13

Business Description:
Circuit Boards Mfr
S.I.C.: 3672
N.A.I.C.S.: 334412

Personnel:
Noboru Nakayama *(Chm)*
Kuniaki Kanemoto *(Pres & CEO)*
Sadanobu Kondo *(Mng Dir)*
Hiroshi Hanaoka *(Exec Officer)*
Kazuhiro Ito *(Exec Officer)*
Akiharu Nakayama *(Exec Officer)*
Takashi Ogasawara *(Exec Officer)*
Takaya Oguchi *(Exec Officer)*
Eizo Shibata *(Exec Officer)*

Board of Directors:
Noboru Nakayama
Kuniaki Kanemoto
Sadanobu Kondo
Akiharu Nakayama
Takaya Oguchi
Takeo Takai

Transfer Agent:
Japan Securities Agents, Ltd.
2-4, Nihonbashi Kayabacho 1-chome
Chuo-ku, Tokyo, 103-8202, Japan
Tel.: (81) 3 3668 9211

Subsidiaries:

CMK Finance Corporation **(1)**
Shinjuku I-Land Tower 43/F 6-5-1 Nishi-Shinjuku
Shinjuku-Ku, Tokyo, 163-1388, Japan
Tel.: (81) 353230237
Fax: (81) 353230072
Financial Support Services
S.I.C.: 6211
N.A.I.C.S.: 523999

CMK Kanbara Electronic Corporation **(1)**
1-2-5 Muramatsu-Kougyoudanchi
Gosen, Niigata, 959-1739, Japan
Tel.: (81) 250588737
Fax: (81) 250588759
E-Mail: shoji_komatsudara@cmk.co.jp
Emp.: 297
Printed Circuit Boards Mfr
S.I.C.: 3672
N.A.I.C.S.: 334412
Toshiaki Liyama *(Pres)*

CMK Mechanics Corporation **(1)**
560 Shimoyoshida Yoshida-machi
Chichibu, Saitama, 369-1503, Japan
Tel.: (81) 494771331
Fax: (81) 494771689
E-Mail: info@cmk-mechanics.co.jp
Web Site: www.cmk-mechanics.co.jp
Maintenance Machinery Equipment Mfr & Sales
S.I.C.: 3559
N.A.I.C.S.: 333249
Sumio Tashiro *(Pres)*

CMK Multi Corporation **(1)**
3-75-6 Higashi-ko Seirou-machi
Kitakanbara-gun, Niigata, 957-0101, Japan
Tel.: (81) 252561391
Fax: (81) 252561321
E-Mail: kazuo_inoue@cmk.co.jp
Web Site: www.cmk-corp.com
Sls.: $132,184,000
Emp.: 700
Printed Circuit Boards Mfr
S.I.C.: 3559
N.A.I.C.S.: 333249
Kazuo Inoue *(Mgr-General Affairs Dept)*

CMK Niigata Corporation **(1)**
3-75-6 Higashi-ko Seirou-machi
Kitakanbara-gun, Niigata, 957-0101, Japan
Tel.: (81) 252561311
Fax: (81) 252561321
E-Mail:
Web Site: www.cmk-corp.com
Printed Circuit Boards Mfr
S.I.C.: 3672
N.A.I.C.S.: 334412
Katuo Inone *(Mng Dir)*

CMK Products Corporation **(1)**
1-1-11 Shioda Tana
Sagamihara, Kanagawa, 229-1125, Japan
Tel.: (81) 427633188
Fax: (81) 42 763 5015
Web Site: www.cmkp.co.jp
Emp.: 350
Printed Circuit Boards Mfr
S.I.C.: 3672
N.A.I.C.S.: 334412

Yamanashi Sanko Co., Ltd. **(1)**
674 Shimojouminamiware Tatsuoka-cho
Nirasaki, Yamanashi, 407-0033, Japan
Tel.: (81) 551228065
Fax: (81) 551228069
E-Mail: customer-eng@cmk.co.jp
Web Site: www.cmk-corp.com
Emp.: 120
Electronic Printed Circuit Boards Mfr
S.I.C.: 3672
N.A.I.C.S.: 334412
Shigeru Oikawa *(Pres)*

Plants:

CMK Corporation - G Station Plant **(1)**
236 Imai Shiba-machi
Isesaki, Gunma, 372-0824, Japan
Tel.: (81) 270322063
Fax: (81) 270323655
E-Mail: customer-eng@cmk.co.jp
Web Site: www.cmk-corp.com
Circuit Boards Mfr
S.I.C.: 3672
N.A.I.C.S.: 334412
Takahiro Nakayama *(Pres)*

CMK Corporation - KIBAN Center Plant **(1)**
48-1 Toyatsuka-cho
Isesaki, Gunma, 372-0825, Japan
Tel.: (81) 270328585
Fax: (81) 270328595
Emp.: 2,000
Flat Screen Televisions Mfr
S.I.C.: 3663
N.A.I.C.S.: 334220
Masaaki Kanemoto *(Pres)*

CMK Corporation - Niigata Satellite Plant **(1)**
3-75-6 Higashi-ko Seiro-machi
Kitakanbara, Niigata, 957-0101, Japan
Tel.: (81) 252561311
Fax: (81) 252561321
E-Mail: pwb-inquiry@cmk.co.jp
Web Site: www.cmk-corp.com
Printed Circuit Boards Mfr
S.I.C.: 3672
N.A.I.C.S.: 334412

CMK Corporation - Technical Center Plant **(1)**
1744-1 Naganuma-cho
Isesaki, Gunma, 372-0855, Japan
Tel.: (81) 270324567
Fax: (81) 270329393
E-Mail: pwb-inquiry@cmk.co.jp
Web Site: www.cmk-corp.com
Industrial Technology Development Services
S.I.C.: 8731
N.A.I.C.S.: 541712

Non-U.S. Subsidiaries:

CMK Corporation (Thailand) Co., Ltd. **(1)**
334 Moo 7 Tambol Thatoom Amphur Srimahaphote
Prachin Buri, 25140, Thailand
Tel.: (66) 37207500
Fax: (66) 37207599
Web Site: www.cmk.co.th
Emp.: 1,000
Circuit Boards Mfr
S.I.C.: 3672
N.A.I.C.S.: 334412
Savanori Ogane *(Pres)*

CMK EUROPE N.V. **(1)**
Lammerdries 18 A
2440 Geel, Belgium
Tel.: (32) 14259400
Fax: (32) 14259435
Web Site: www.cmk-corp.com
Emp.: 10
Printed Circuit Boards Mfr
S.I.C.: 3672
N.A.I.C.S.: 334412
Danny Mattheus *(Mgr-Admin)*

CMKC (Hong Kong) Ltd. **(1)**
1215 12 F Exchange Tower 33 Wang Chiu Rd
Kowloon Bay, Kowloon, China (Hong Kong)
Tel.: (852) 27212252
Fax: (852) 27246622
Emp.: 120
Printed Circuit Boards Mfr
S.I.C.: 3672
N.A.I.C.S.: 334412

U.S. Subsidiary:

CMK America Corporation **(1)**
175 Handley Rd Ste 300
Tyrone, GA 30290
Tel.: (770) 632-7173
Fax: (770) 632-7175
Web Site: www.cmk-corp.com
Emp.: 5
Circuit Boards Distr
S.I.C.: 5065
N.A.I.C.S.: 423690
Kazahiro Ouchi *(Pres)*

CML GLOBAL CAPITAL LTD.

Suite 1200 833 4th Avenue Southwest
Calgary, AB, T2P 3T5, Canada
Tel.: (403) 216-3850
Fax: (403) 216-2661
Year Founded: 1992
Sales Range: $10-24.9 Million
Emp.: 150

Business Description:
Investment Services
S.I.C.: 6211
N.A.I.C.S.: 523999

Personnel:
Joy McDonald *(Office Mgr)*

Legal Counsel:
Lang Michener Lawrence & Shaw
595 Burrard Street
Vancouver, BC, Canada V7X 1L1

Subsidiary:

Aspen Property Management Ltd. **(1)**
444 5th Ave SW Ste 2100
Calgary, AB, T2P 2T8, Canada Ca
Tel.: (403) 216-2660
Fax: (403) 216-2661
E-Mail: apl@aspenpropertiesltd.com
Web Site: www.aspenpropertiesltd.com
Sales Range: $25-49.9 Million
Emp.: 162
Industrial & Warehouse Properties Acquirer & Developer
S.I.C.: 6726
N.A.I.C.S.: 525990
R. Scott Hutcheson *(Chm & CEO)*
Greg A. Guatto *(Pres & COO)*
Veronica D. Bouvier *(CFO & Exec VP)*

CML MICROSYSTEMS PLC

Oval Park
Langford, Maldon, Essex, CM9 6WG, United Kingdom
Tel.: (44) 1621875500
Fax: (44) 1621875606
E-Mail: group@cmlmicroplc.com
Web Site: www.cmlmicroplc.com
CML—(LSE)
Rev.: $39,858,025
Assets: $52,518,643
Liabilities: $18,775,703
Net Worth: $33,742,940
Earnings: $6,402,728
Emp.: 179
Fiscal Year-end: 03/31/13

Business Description:
Holding Company; Integrated Circuits Mfr
S.I.C.: 6719
N.A.I.C.S.: 551112

Personnel:
Chris A. Gurry *(Interim Chm & Mng Dir)*
Nigel G. Clark *(Fin Dir & Sec)*

Board of Directors:
Chris A. Gurry
Nigel G. Clark
James Lindop
Ronald J. Shashoua

Transfer Agent:
Neville Registrars Limited
Neville House 18 Laurel Lane
Halesowen, West Midlands, B63 3DA, United Kingdom

Subsidiaries:

Applied Technology (UK) Ltd. **(1)**
Chelynch Rd Doulting
Shepton Mallet, Somerset, BA4 4RQ, United Kingdom
Tel.: (44) 1749881130
Fax: (44) 1749881133
E-Mail: enquiries@app-tech.co.uk
Web Site: www.app-tech.co.uk
Emp.: 11
Application Software Development Services
S.I.C.: 7371
N.A.I.C.S.: 541511
Nigel Wilson *(Dir-Ops)*

CML Microcircuits (UK) Ltd. **(1)**
Oval Pk
Langford, Maldon, Essex, CM9 6WG, United Kingdom
Tel.: (44) 1621875500
Fax: (44) 1621875600
E-Mail: sales@cmlmicro.com
Web Site: www.cmlmicro.com
Emp.: 100
Communication Integrated Circuits Mfr & Distr
S.I.C.: 3674
N.A.I.C.S.: 334413
Neil Ball *(Dir-Sls)*

U.S. Subsidiary:

CML Microcircuits (USA) Inc. **(2)**
465 Corporate Sq Dr
Winston Salem, NC 27105
Tel.: (336) 744-5050
Fax: (336) 744-5054
E-Mail: us.sales@cmlmicro.com
Web Site: www.cmlmicro.com
Emp.: 20
Communication Integrated Circuits Mfr & Supplier
S.I.C.: 3674
N.A.I.C.S.: 334413
Jim Phillips *(VP-Sls)*

Non-U.S. Subsidiary:

CML Microcircuits (Singapore) Pte. Ltd. **(2)**
150 Kampong Ampat #05-03A KA Centre
368324 Singapore, Singapore
Tel.: (65) 62888 129
Fax: (65) 62888 230
E-Mail: sg.sales@cmlmicro.com
Web Site: www.cmlmicro.com
Emp.: 5
Communication Integrated Circuits Mfr & Supplier
S.I.C.: 3674
N.A.I.C.S.: 334413
Dennis Ng Wee Han *(Mng Dir-Sls)*

Radio Data Technology Ltd. **(1)**
Unit Bay 1 vitton Rd Industrial Estate E
Witham, Essex, CM8 3UJ, United Kingdom
Tel.: (44) 1376501255
Fax: (44) 1376501312
E-Mail: sales@radiodata.co.uk
Web Site: www.radiodata.co.uk
Emp.: 15
Wireless Data Video & Telemetry Products Mfr
S.I.C.: 3661
N.A.I.C.S.: 334210
Alan Hall *(Mng Dir)*

Non-U.S. Subsidiary:

Hyperstone GmbH **(1)**
Line-Eid-Strasse 3
78467 Konstanz, Baden-Wurttemberg, Germany
Tel.: (49) 753198030
Fax: (49) 753151725
E-Mail: info@hyperstone.de
Web Site: www.hyperstone.com
Emp.: 30
Semiconductor & Microprocessor Design Services
S.I.C.: 3674
N.A.I.C.S.: 334413
Steffen Allert *(VP-Sls & Field Application Support)*

U.S. Subsidiary:

Hyperstone Inc. **(2)**
465 Corporate Sq Dr
Winston Salem, NC 27105
Tel.: (336) 744-0724
Fax: (336) 744-5054
E-Mail: us.sales@hyperstone.com
Emp.: 20
Electronic Design Services
S.I.C.: 3674

CML Microsystems Plc—(Continued)

N.A.I.C.S.: 334413
Jim Phillips *(VP-Sls)*

Non-U.S. Subsidiary:

Hyperstone Asia Pacific Ltd. **(2)**
3F No 501 Sec 2 Tiding Blvd
Neihu Dist, Taipei, 114, Taiwan
Tel.: (886) 287510203
Fax: (886) 287972321
E-Mail: taiwan@hyperstone.com
Web Site: www.hyperstone.com
Emp.: 14
Semiconductor & Microprocessor Design & Mfr
S.I.C.: 3674
N.A.I.C.S.: 334413
Matthias Steck *(Deputy Gen Mgr)*

CMO PUBLIC COMPANY LIMITED

1471 Town in Town Soi 3/2 Ladphrao 94 Rd Phlabphla Wangthonglang
Bangkok, 10310, Thailand
Tel.: (66) 2 559 0505
Fax: (66) 2 559 3640
E-Mail: cmo@cmo-group.com
Web Site: www.cmo-group.com
Year Founded: 1991
CMO—(THA)
Rev.: $40,991,082
Assets: $24,332,510
Liabilities: $11,799,289
Net Worth: $12,533,221
Earnings: $3,061,968
Fiscal Year-end: 12/31/12

Business Description:
Marketing Communication Services
S.I.C.: 7389
N.A.I.C.S.: 561499

Personnel:
Ratanavudh Vajarodaya *(Chm)*
Sermkhun Kunawong *(CEO)*
Panitda Klaimanee *(Mng Dir)*
Jutiporn Mingkwanrungrueng *(Mng Dir)*
Rungarunothai Sraikit *(Mng Dir)*
Woraporn Teesirikaserm *(Mng Dir)*
Nongrat Thanjitt *(Mng Dir)*
Krongthong Tonarree *(Mng Dir)*

Board of Directors:
Ratanavudh Vajarodaya
Anant Gatepitthaya
Ausanee Kerdpheungboonpracha
Sermkhun Kunawong
Jumphol Rodcumdee
Suree Sirikorn

ANS Audit Company Limited
100/72 22nd Floor 100/2 Vongvanij Building B
Rama 9 Road Huaykwang
Bangkok, 10320, Thailand

Subsidiaries:

The Eyes Co., Ltd **(1)**
1603 Town-In-Town soi 5 Ladprao 94 Rd Phlabphla
Wang Thonglang, Bangkok, Thailand 10310
Tel.: (66) 2559 3437 8
Fax: (66) 2559 2629
E-Mail: theeyes@theeyes.co.th
Web Site: www.theeyes.co.th
Multimedia & Video Presentation Services
S.I.C.: 7832
N.A.I.C.S.: 512131
Nardnapin Sirihanyagorn *(Gen Mgr)*

PM Center Co., Ltd. **(1)**
PM Center Building 4/18-19 Moo 11
Nuanchan Road
Klongkum Bueng Kum, Bangkok, Thailand 10240
Tel.: (66) 2791 9400
Fax: (66) 2791 9401 2
E-Mail: info@pmcenter.co.th
Web Site: www.pmcenter.co.th
Light & Sound System Rental Services
S.I.C.: 7359
N.A.I.C.S.: 532490

CMP ADVANCED MECHANICAL SOLUTIONS LTD.

1241 Cascades St
Chateauguay, QC, J6J 4Z2, Canada
Tel.: (450) 691-5510
Fax: (450) 691-6467
Toll Free: (800) 363-9120
Web Site: www.cmpdifference.com
Year Founded: 1969
Rev.: $46,403,534
Emp.: 400

Business Description:
Metal Mfr
S.I.C.: 3411
N.A.I.C.S.: 332431

Personnel:
Steve Zimmermann *(Pres & CEO)*

CMP CAPITAL MANAGEMENT-PARTNERS GMBH

Mosse Palais
Leipziger Platz 15, 10117 Berlin, Germany
Tel.: (49) 30 39 40 69 0
Fax: (49) 30 39 40 69 25
E-Mail: kontakt@cm-p.de
Web Site: www.cm-p.de
Year Founded: 2000

Business Description:
Private Equity Firm
S.I.C.: 6211
N.A.I.C.S.: 523999

Personnel:
Kai Brandes *(Mng Partner)*
Ludger Vonnahme *(Mng Partner)*
Eric Sommer *(CFO & Dir-Investments)*

Holdings:

D+S communication center management GmbH **(1)**
Mexikoring 33
22297 Hamburg, Germany
Tel.: (49) 40 4114 0
Fax: (49) 40 4114 0099
E-Mail: info@ds-cc.de
Web Site: www.ds360grad.com
Sales Range: $100-124.9 Million
Call Center Services
S.I.C.: 7389
N.A.I.C.S.: 561422
Ludger Sieverding *(Chm-Mgmt Bd)*
Mario Bethune-Steck *(Member-Mgmt Bd)*
Bernhard Magin *(Member-Mgmt Bd)*
Bernd Rehder *(Member-Mgmt Bd)*

DRONCO GmbH **(1)**
Wiesenmuhle 1
95632 Wunsiedel, Germany
Tel.: (49) 92326090
Fax: (49) 9232609159
E-Mail: info@dronco.com
Web Site: www.dronco.com
Sales Range: $75-99.9 Million
Emp.: 300
Industrial Machines & Abrasive Products Mfr
S.I.C.: 3291
N.A.I.C.S.: 327910
Hermann Broker *(CEO)*
Jakob Jurgens *(Mng Dir)*

Pressmetall Gunzenhausen GmbH & Co. KG **(1)**
Alemannenstrasse 20
91710 Gunzenhausen, Germany De
Tel.: (49) 983150070
Fax: (49) 98315007177
E-Mail: info@pressmetall.de
Web Site: www.pressmetall.de
Sales Range: $125-149.9 Million
Emp.: 800
Precision Product Mfr
S.I.C.: 3451
N.A.I.C.S.: 332721
Peter Bohnlein *(CEO)*

UKM Fahrzeugteile GmbH **(1)**
Salzstrasse 3
D 09629 Reinsberg, Germany
Tel.: (49) 35 242 65 61 115
Fax: (49) 35 242 65 61 660
Web Site: www.ukm-gruppe.com
Emp.: 300
Automotive Component Mfr
S.I.C.: 3714
N.A.I.C.S.: 336390
Dieter Maier, *(Mng Dir)*

CMP - CLASSIC AUTOMOTIVE LTD

1313 36 St NE
Calgary, AB, T2A 6P9, Canada
Tel.: (403) 207-1000
Fax: (403) 207-1018
Toll Free: (888) 399-9199
E-Mail: info@cmpauto.com
Web Site: www.cmpauto.com
Sales Range: $150-199.9 Million
Emp.: 200

Business Description:
Automobile Sales & Servicing
S.I.C.: 5511
N.A.I.C.S.: 441110

Personnel:
Cathy Manten *(Controller)*

CMP GOLD TRUST

(Name Changed to Goodman Gold Trust)

CMQ RESOURCES INC.

400 407 8th Avenue SW
Calgary, AB, T2P 1E5, Canada
Tel.: (403) 261-4653
Fax: (403) 294-0105
E-Mail: info@cmqresources.com
Web Site: www.cmqresources.com
NV—(TSXV)
Rev.: $25,509
Assets: $8,047,055
Liabilities: $5,565,934
Net Worth: $2,481,121
Earnings: ($689,643)
Emp.: 2
Fiscal Year-end: 12/31/12

Business Description:
Gold Exploration Services
S.I.C.: 1041
N.A.I.C.S.: 212221

Personnel:
John Hogg *(CEO)*
David McGoey *(CFO)*

Board of Directors:
Odin Christensen
Ronald P. Mathison
Robert McKenzie

Legal Counsel:
Erwin & Thompson LLP
Reno, NV 89501

Bennett Jones LLP
Calgary, AB, Canada

Computershare Trust Company of Canada
Calgary, AB, Canada

Transfer Agents:
Computershare Trust Company of Canada
Toronto, ON, Canada

Computershare Trust Company of Canada
Calgary, AB, Canada

U.S. Subsidiary:

Montezuma Mines Inc. **(1)**
559 W Silver St Ste 301
Elko, NV 89801-3696
Tel.: (775) 778-3693
Fax: (775) 778-9137
Mineral Mining Services
S.I.C.: 1499
N.A.I.C.S.: 212399
John Hogg *(Gen Mgr)*

CMS COMPUTERS LTD.

CMS Lake Road Center 70 Lake Road
Kaycee Industries Compound,
Mumbai, 400 078, India
Tel.: (91) 2267489000
E-Mail: info@cms.co.in
Web Site: www.cms.com
Sales Range: $100-124.9 Million
Emp.: 6,000

Business Description:
IT Consulting & Product Design Services & Solutions
S.I.C.: 7379
N.A.I.C.S.: 541519

Personnel:
Rajiv Kaul *(Exec Vice Chm & CEO)*
Sudev Muthya *(Pres)*
Pankaj Khandelwal *(CFO)*

Subsidiaries:

CMS Computers Limited **(1)**
CMS Lake Rd Ctr 70 Lake Road Kaycee Industries Compound Bhandup, Mumbai, 400 078, India (100%)
Tel.: (91) 2267489000
Fax: (91) 2267489001
Web Site: www.cms.co.in
Emp.: 200
Computer Systems Services
S.I.C.: 7373
N.A.I.C.S.: 541512

CMS Traffic Systems Limited **(1)**
70 lake Road
Bhandup West, 400078 Mumbai, India
Tel.: (91) 2230780222
Fax: (91) 2225950169
Web Site: www.cmstraffic.in
ll Other Support Activities for Transportation
S.I.C.: 4789
N.A.I.C.S.: 488999
R. D. Grower *(Mng Dir)*

Kaycee Ind. Ltd. **(1)**
32 Ramjibhai Kamani Rd
Ballard Estate, 400001 Mumbai, India (100%)
Tel.: (91) 2222613521
Fax: (91) 2222616106
E-Mail: kayceeindltd@bsnl.com
Web Site: www.kayceeindustries.com
Emp.: 300
Switchgear & Switchboard Apparatus Mfr
S.I.C.: 3613
N.A.I.C.S.: 335313

SYSTIME Computer Systems (I) Ltd. **(1)**
SEEPZ Customs Wing
Andheri E, 400096 Mumbai, India (100%)
Tel.: (91) 2228290051
Fax: (91) 2228290126
Web Site: www.systime.net
Emp.: 80
Computer Systems Design Services
S.I.C.: 7373
N.A.I.C.S.: 541512
Vishal Grover *(Pres & CEO)*

SYSTIME **(1)**
155 Millennium Business Park Mahape
Navi, 400710 Mumbai, India (100%)
Tel.: (91) 2227783100
Fax: (91) 2227782291
Web Site: www.systime.net
Emp.: 40
Business Solutions & Computer Related Services
S.I.C.: 7379
N.A.I.C.S.: 541519
Vishal Grover *(Pres & CEO)*

CMST DEVELOPMENT CO., LTD.

18th Building of 6th section No 188 Western Road
South 4th Ring Road Fengtai District,
Beijing, China 100070
Tel.: (86) 10 83673331
Fax: (86) 10 83673332
Web Site: www.cmstd.com.cn
600787—(SHG)

Business Description:
Logistics Services
S.I.C.: 4731

N.A.I.C.S.: 541614
Personnel:
Tielin Han *(Chm & Pres)*

CMZ HOLDINGS LTD.

112 Robinson Road 12-04
Singapore, Singapore 068902
Tel.: (65) 62209070
Fax: (65) 62239177
E-Mail: ir@cmz-zipper.com
Web Site: www.cmzholdings.com
Business Description:
Garment Zipper Mfr
S.I.C.: 2389
N.A.I.C.S.: 315990
Personnel:
Kesheng Shao *(Chm)*
Dajun Shao *(CEO)*
Yoon Thim Wong *(CFO)*
Board of Directors:
Kesheng Shao
Kait Long Lien
Dajun Shao
Bin Shen
Chee Keong Siow

CN ASIA CORPORATION BHD.

Lot 7907 Batu 11 Jalan Balakong
43300 Seri Kembangan, Selangor
Darul Ehsan, Malaysia
Tel.: (60) 389426888
Fax: (60) 389423365
E-Mail: corporate@cnasia.com
Web Site: www.cnasia.com
CNASIA—(KLS)
Rev.: $6,687,202
Assets: $12,705,815
Liabilities: $3,414,230
Net Worth: $9,291,585
Earnings: ($510,085)
Emp.: 61
Fiscal Year-end: 12/31/12
Business Description:
Industrial Equipment Mfr
S.I.C.: 7699
N.A.I.C.S.: 811310
Personnel:
Cheng San Ho *(Mng Dir)*
Mui Tee Koh *(Co-Sec)*
Paik Goot Lim *(Co-Sec)*
Board of Directors:
Hilmi Mohd Noor
Ying Choy Chong
Cheng San Ho
Ab. Razak Idris
Lam Lee

CN DRAGON CORPORATION

16/F Paul Y Centre 51 Hung To Rd
Kwun Tong
Kowloon, China (Hong Kong)
Tel.: (852) 2772 9900
Web Site: www.wavelit.com
Year Founded: 2001
DRGN—(OTCB)
Rev.: $128,503
Assets: $130,489
Liabilities: $803,265
Net Worth: ($672,776)
Earnings: ($206,697)
Fiscal Year-end: 03/31/13
Business Description:
Internet Broadcasting Services
S.I.C.: 2741
N.A.I.C.S.: 519130
Personnel:
Teck Fong Kong *(Pres & CEO)*
Chong Him Lau *(CFO, Treas & Sec)*
Board of Directors:
Teck Fong Kong
Chong Him Lau
Shing Hing Li
Transfer Agent:
Action Stock Transfer Corporation
S Highland Drive Suite 300
Salt Lake City, UT 84124

CN NEGOCIOS, S.A.

Colima de Tibas de la Metalco 200 mts
Sur y 300 mts Este, San Jose, Costa Rica
Tel.: (506) 2240 0960
Fax: (506) 2240 0960, ext. 1002
E-Mail: info@cnnegocios.com
Web Site: www.cnnegocios.com
Year Founded: 1998
Sales Range: $1-9.9 Million
Business Description:
Computers, Software & Telecommunications Products Distr
S.I.C.: 5045
N.A.I.C.S.: 423430

CN RESOURCES INC.

255 Duncan Mill Road Suite 203
Toronto, ON, M3B 3H9, Canada
Tel.: (416) 510-2991
Web Site: www.cnmines.com
Year Founded: 2010
CNRR—(OTC)
Int. Income: $18,051
Assets: $445,271
Liabilities: $203,898
Net Worth: $241,373
Earnings: ($92,510)
Fiscal Year-end: 05/31/13
Business Description:
Mineral Exploration Services
S.I.C.: 1499
N.A.I.C.S.: 212399
Personnel:
Oliver Xing *(Pres, CEO, Treas & Sec)*
Board of Directors:
Oliver Xing

CNA GROUP LTD.

28 Kaki Bukit Crescent Kaki Bukit Techpark 1
Singapore, 416259, Singapore
Tel.: (65) 65110082
Fax: (65) 68429606
E-Mail: sales@cna.com.sg
Web Site: www.cna.com.sg
Year Founded: 1990
5GC—(SES)
Rev.: $63,625,464
Assets: $147,484,831
Liabilities: $100,235,955
Net Worth: $47,248,876
Earnings: ($2,675,992)
Fiscal Year-end: 12/31/12
Business Description:
Integrated System Solutions Services
S.I.C.: 7629
N.A.I.C.S.: 811211
Personnel:
Michael Liang Huat Ong *(Pres & Co-CEO)*
Sea Yeat Kua *(Co-CEO)*
Michael Thiam Chye Lee *(CFO & Co-Sec)*
Fook Chee Chue *(CEO-ASEAN)*
David Liang Eng Ong *(CEO-Greater China)*
Gumpalli Venkata Subarao *(CEO-CNA Integrated Tech)*
Chee Leong Lun *(Co-Sec)*
Amanda Meei Jiuan Shen *(Sr VP-Strategy Plng & Bus Dev)*
Board of Directors:
Bernard Tien Lap Chen
Shuaib Ahmed
Michael Liang Huat Ong
Toh Kang Pang
Chak Hung Siew
Choon Hock Tan
David Koon Sang Yeung

Subsidiary:

GETC Asia Private Limited (1)
25 Woodlands Industrial Park E1
5-5 Admiralty Industrial Park, Singapore, 757743, Singapore
Tel.: (65) 63647577
Fax: (65) 63647757
E-Mail: getc@getcasia.com
Web Site: www.getcasia.com
Emp.: 40
Environmental Engineering Services
S.I.C.: 8711
N.A.I.C.S.: 541330
Wing Sin Lui *(Gen Mgr)*

Non-U.S. Subsidiaries:

CNA Engineering PVT Ltd (1)
M12 Sector X 6th Main HAL III Stage
Jeevan Bheemanagar, Bengaluru, Karnataka, 560 075, India
Tel.: (91) 8025214096
Fax: (91) 8025214096
E-Mail: salesenquiry@cna.com.sg
Web Site: www.cna.com.sg
Emp.: 20
Automation Services
S.I.C.: 8711
N.A.I.C.S.: 541330
Ramesh V. Murthy *(Gen Mgr)*

CNA Integrated Technologies (LLC) (1)
Al Owais Bldg 2nd Fl No 206
PO Box 124276
BAI Karama, Dubai, United Arab Emirates
Tel.: (971) 43343642
Fax: (971) 43343641
E-Mail: cnaig@eim.ae
Web Site: www.cna.com.sg/contact.html
Emp.: 25
Plumbing Services
S.I.C.: 1711
N.A.I.C.S.: 238220
Gumpalli Subba Rao *(CEO)*

CNA Technology Inc (1)
Rm 501 Don Pablo Bldg
114 Amorsolo St, Makati, 1204, Philippines
Tel.: (63) 28940850
Fax: (63) 28933809
Emp.: 30
Communication Management Services
S.I.C.: 8748
N.A.I.C.S.: 541618
Ramon Tolentino *(Mgr)*

HTE Vietnam Co., Ltd. (1)
42 VSIP St 4 Vietnam Singapore Industrial Park
Thuan An, Binh Duong, Vietnam
Tel.: (84) 6503743045
Fax: (84) 6503743046
E-Mail: leepohkim@htevn.com
Web Site: www.htevn.com
Emp.: 150
Building Automation System Installation & Services
S.I.C.: 7349
N.A.I.C.S.: 561790

CNC HOLDINGS LIMITED

Rooms 2601-2605 26/F China Resources Building 26 Harbour Road
Wanchai, China (Hong Kong)
Tel.: (852) 31042962
Fax: (852) 26334691
E-Mail: cnc@cnctv.hk
Web Site: www.cnctv.hk
Year Founded: 1989
8356—(HKG)
Rev.: $37,630,447
Assets: $99,927,224
Liabilities: $104,582,705
Net Worth: ($4,655,482)
Earnings: ($14,982,572)
Emp.: 242
Fiscal Year-end: 03/31/13
Business Description:
Investment Holding Company
S.I.C.: 6211
N.A.I.C.S.: 523999
Personnel:
Jin Cai Wu *(Chm)*
Yuk Lun Lee *(Vice Chm)*
Chen Dong Zou *(CEO)*
Eric John Thien Loong Chia *(Compliance Officer)*
Mabel May Bo Kan *(Admin Officer)*
Yuet Tai Li *(Sec)*
Board of Directors:
Jin Cai Wu
Hon Yuen Chan
Eric John Thien Loong Chia
Ivan Siu Lun Chu
Chi Kit Hau
Hai Tao Jin
Kwok Cheung Kan
Yuk Lun Lee
Yong Sheng Li
Hui Liang
Chen Dong Zou
Codan Trust Company (Cayman) Limited
Cricket Square Hutchins Drive
PO Box 2681
Georgetown, Grand Cayman, Cayman Islands
Transfer Agents:
Tricor Investor Services Limited
26th Floor Tesbury Centre 28 Queens Road East
Wanchai, China (Hong Kong)
Codan Trust Company (Cayman) Limited
Cricket Square Hutchins Drive
PO Box 2681
Georgetown, Grand Cayman, Cayman Islands

CNC OFFICE SYSTEMS LTD.

241 Applewood Crescent
Vaughan, ON, L4K 4E6, Canada
Tel.: (416) 969-8288
Fax: (416) 969-8299
Toll Free: (800) 463-3271
E-Mail: sales@cncofficesystems.com
Web Site: www.cncofficesystems.com
Year Founded: 1979
Rev.: $10,433,394
Emp.: 60
Business Description:
Printing Services
S.I.C.: 2759
N.A.I.C.S.: 323111
Personnel:
J. Ross McKinney *(Pres)*

CNG TRAVEL GROUP PLC

Kilmurry
Kenmare, Co Kerry, Ireland
Tel.: (353) 64 40300
Fax: (353) 64 40155
E-Mail: info@cngplc.com
Web Site: www.cngtravel.com
Year Founded: 1999
Sales Range: $25-49.9 Million
Emp.: 65
Business Description:
Corporate Travel Management Services
S.I.C.: 4729
N.A.I.C.S.: 561599
Personnel:
Luke Mooney *(Chm)*
P. J. King *(CEO)*
William Lynch *(CFO)*
Board of Directors:
Luke Mooney
Ralph Manaker
Seamus Ross
Michael W. Smurfit Jr.

CNG VIETNAM JOINT STOCK COMPANY

No 35I Road 30 April Ward 9
Vung Tau, Vietnam
Tel.: (84) 64 3574618
Fax: (84) 64 3574619
E-Mail: info@cng-vietnam.com

CNG Vietnam Joint Stock Company—(Continued)

Web Site: www.cng-vietnam.com
Year Founded: 2007
CNG—(HOSE)
Rev.: $40,059,420
Assets: $31,186,623
Liabilities: $12,158,273
Net Worth: $19,028,350
Earnings: $5,896,312
Emp.: 169
Fiscal Year-end: 12/31/12

Business Description:
Gas Distribution Services
S.I.C.: 4924
N.A.I.C.S.: 221210

Personnel:
Tuan Ngoc Vu *(Chm)*
An Hoa Ngo *(Chm-Supervisory Bd)*
Van Vinh Dang *(CEO, Gen Dir & Member-Mgmt Bd)*
Van Dan Bui *(Member-Mgmt Bd & Deputy Gen Dir-Engrg)*
Thi Hong Hai Nguyen *(Member-Mgmt Bd & Deputy Gen Dir-Fin)*
Quang Dan Tran *(Member-Mgmt Bd & Deputy Gen Dir-Investment Plng)*

Board of Directors:
Tuan Ngoc Vu
Van Vinh Dang
Thi Thu Giang Le
Christopher Do Nghia
Quy Hieu Vu

Supervisory Board of Directors:
An Hoa Ngo
Quoc Vuong Dang
Van Hung Nguyen

CNH INDUSTRIAL N.V.

(Formerly FI CBM Holdings N.V.)
Cranes Farm Road
Basildon, Essex, SS14 3AD, United Kingdom
Tel.: (44) 1268 533 000
Web Site: www.cnhindustrial.com
Year Founded: 2013
CNHI—(ITA NYSE)
Sales Range: $25-49.9 Billion

Business Description:
Holding Company; Agricultural, Construction & Commercial Freight Vehicles & Power Train Parts Designer, Mfr & Distr
S.I.C.: 6719
N.A.I.C.S.: 551112

Personnel:
Sergio Marchionne *(Chm)*
Richard J. Tobin *(CEO & COO-NAFTA)*
Massimiliano Chiara *(CFO)*
Dario Ivaldi *(CTO & Sr VP-Agricultural Product Dev)*
Linda I. Knoll *(Chief HR Officer)*
Brad Crews *(Chief Quality Officer & Sr VP-Product Quality & Technical Support)*
Derek Neilson *(Chief Mfg Officer)*
Annalisa Stupenengo *(Chief Pur Officer)*
Andreas Klauser *(Pres-Case IH Agricultural Equipment & COO-EMEA)*
Dino Maggioni *(Pres-Parts & Svc & Head-Precision Solutions & Telematics)*
Alessandro Nasi *(Pres-Specialty Bus Unit & Exec Coord-GEC)*
Mario Gasparri *(Pres-Case Construction Equipment & New Holland Construction)*
Oddone Incisa *(Pres-Fin Svcs)*
Carlo Lambro *(Pres-New Holland Agricultural Equipment)*
Lorenzo Sistino *(Pres-Iveco)*

Board of Directors:
Sergio Marchionne
John Philip Elkann
Mina Gerowin
Maria Patrizia Grieco
Leo W. Houle
Peter P. Kalantzis
John B. Lanaway
Guido Tabellini
Jacqueline A. Tammenoms Bakker
Jacques Theurillat
Richard J. Tobin

Subsidiary:

CNH U.K. Limited **(1)**
Cranes Farm Road
Basildon, SS14 3AD, United Kingdom
Tel.: (44) 12 6853 3000
Fax: (44) 12 6829 2158
Emp.: 100
Farm Tractor & Engine Mfr
S.I.C.: 3523
N.A.I.C.S.: 333111

U.S. Subsidiary:

CNH America LLC **(1)**
6900 Veterans Blvd
Burr Ridge, IL 60527 NL
Tel.: (630) 887-2233 (83%)
E-Mail: investorrelations@cnh.com
Web Site: www.cnh.com
Agricultural, Construction & Mechanical Equipment Mfr
Import Export
S.I.C.: 3531
N.A.I.C.S.: 333120
Steven Bierman *(Pres-CNH Capital)*
Pierre Fleck *(Pres-CNH Parts & Svcs)*
Andreas Klauser *(Pres-Case IH Agricultural Equipment)*
Mark L. Mitchell *(Principal)*
Michael Going *(Gen Counsel, Sr VP & Sec)*
Giovanni Ravina *(Sr VP-HR)*

Units:

CNH America - New Holland **(2)**
500 Diller Ave
New Holland, PA 17557
Tel.: (717) 355-1121
Fax: (717) 355-1507
Web Site: www.cnh.com
Automotive Component Mfr
S.I.C.: 3711
N.A.I.C.S.: 336111

CNH America - Benson **(2)**
260 Hwy 12
Benson, MN 56215
Tel.: (320) 843-3333
Fax: (320) 843-2467
Web Site: www.caseih.com
Emp.: 300
Dry & Liquid Fertilizer Application Mfr
Import Export
S.I.C.: 3523
N.A.I.C.S.: 333111
Kim Heiden *(Plant Mgr & Chief Production Officer)*

CNH America - Fargo **(2)**
3401 7th Ave N
Fargo, ND 58102
Mailing Address:
PO Box 6006
Fargo, ND 58108-6006
Tel.: (701) 293-4400
Fax: (701) 293-4550
E-Mail: tmc.ash@tencarva.com
Web Site: www.cnh.com
Sls.: $80,000,000
Emp.: 500
Tractor Mfr
S.I.C.: 3523
N.A.I.C.S.: 333111

CNH America - Goodfield **(2)**
600 E Peoria St
Goodfield, IL 61742
Mailing Address:
PO Box 65
Goodfield, IL 61742-0065
Tel.: (309) 965-2233
Fax: (309) 965-2173
Web Site: www.cnh.com
Emp.: 350
Agricultural Soil Management Implements
S.I.C.: 0711
N.A.I.C.S.: 115112

CNH America - Racine **(2)**
700 State St
Racine, WI 53404
Tel.: (262) 636-6011
Web Site: www.cnh.com
Emp.: 150
Construction Machinery & Equipment Mfr
S.I.C.: 3531
N.A.I.C.S.: 333120
Rich Nelson *(Sr Dir-External Commun)*

CNH America - Wichita **(2)**
3301 South Hoover Rd
Wichita, KS 67215
Tel.: (316) 945-0111
Emp.: 600
Construction Equipment Mfr
S.I.C.: 3531
N.A.I.C.S.: 333120

New Holland Construction **(2)**
245 E N Ave
Carol Stream, IL 60188
Tel.: (262) 636-6011
Fax: (630) 462-1747
Web Site: www.newhollandconstruction.com
Emp.: 40
Construction & Earth Moving Equipment Sales & Distr
S.I.C.: 5082
N.A.I.C.S.: 423810
Mario Gasparri *(Pres-Brand)*

Non-U.S. Subsidiaries:

Afin Broker de Asigurare - Reasigurare S.r.l. **(1)**
11-15 Tipografilor
Bucharest, 13714, Romania
Tel.: (40) 213182862
Fax: (40) 213182824
Emp.: 5
Insurance Brokerage Services
S.I.C.: 6411
N.A.I.C.S.: 524210
Andreea Ceausescu *(Exec Dir)*

Afin Slovakia S.R.O. **(1)**
D Bravsk Cesta 2
841 04 Bratislava, Slovakia
Tel.: (421) 2 5941 8443
Fax: (421) 2 5941 8451
E-Mail: afin@afin.sk
Automobile Distr
S.I.C.: 5012
N.A.I.C.S.: 423110

Banco CNH Capital S.A. **(1)**
Av Juscelino Kubitscheck de Oliveira 11 825 CIC
Curitiba, 81450-903, Brazil
Tel.: (55) 41 2107 7035
Fax: (55) 4121077540
Web Site: www.bancocnh.com.br
Emp.: 20
Investment Management Services
S.I.C.: 6211
N.A.I.C.S.: 523999
Eric Hagen *(Pres)*

Case Construction Machinery (Shanghai) Co., Ltd **(1)**
No 29 Workshop No 376 Debao Rd
Waigaoqiao Free Trade Zone
Shanghai, 200131, China
Tel.: (86) 2150481306
Fax: (86) 2150481822
Construction Machinery Mfr
S.I.C.: 3531
N.A.I.C.S.: 333120
Howard Dale *(Mng Dir)*
Mario Gasparri *(Pres-Brand)*

CNH Belgium N.V. **(1)**
Leon Claeysstraat 3A
Zedelgem, 8210, Belgium
Tel.: (32) 5 025 31 26
Fax: (32) 5 025 36 40
Agricultural Farm Machinery Mfr
S.I.C.: 3523
N.A.I.C.S.: 333111

CNH Canada, Ltd. **(1)**
1000 71 St E
Saskatoon, SK, S7K 3S5, Canada
Tel.: (306) 934-3500
Fax: (306) 664-7672
Farm Equipment Mfr
S.I.C.: 3523
N.A.I.C.S.: 333111

CNH Deutschland GmbH **(1)**
Heinrich Fuchs Strasse 124
Heidelberg, 69126, Germany
Tel.: (49) 6221318500
Telex: 4191167
Fax: (49) 6221318798
Web Site: www.casece.com
Emp.: 12
Construction & Farm Equipment Mfr
S.I.C.: 3523
N.A.I.C.S.: 333111
Volker Hauf *(Gen Mgr)*

Subsidiaries:

CNH Baumaschinen GmbH **(2)**
Staakener Str 53-63
Berlin, 13581, Germany
Tel.: (49) 3033990
Fax: (49) 303399200
Web Site: www.newholland.de
Construction Equipment Mfr
S.I.C.: 3531
N.A.I.C.S.: 333120

Subsidiary:

O & K - Hilfe GmbH **(3)**
Staakener Str 53-63
13581 Berlin, Germany
Tel.: (49) 30 3 39 90
Fax: (49) 30 3399220
Construction Machinery Mfr
S.I.C.: 3531
N.A.I.C.S.: 333120

CNH Financial Services GmbH **(2)**
Salzstrasse 140
74076 Heilbronn, Germany
Tel.: (49) 7131 6440 0
Fax: (49) 7131 6440 255
Web Site: www.cnhcapital.com
Emp.: 25
Financial Management Services
S.I.C.: 6211
N.A.I.C.S.: 523999
Rolf Guenther *(Mgr)*

CNH France S.A. **(1)**
Rue Des Meuniers
Le Plessis-Belleville, 60330 Tracy-Le-Mont, France FR
Tel.: (33) 344742100
Web Site: www.cnh.com
Sales Range: $1-4.9 Billion
Emp.: 1,475
Construction & Farm Equipment Mfr
S.I.C.: 3523
N.A.I.C.S.: 333111
Sergio Marchionne *(Chm)*

CNH International S.A. **(1)**
Riva Paradiso 14
6902 Paradiso, Switzerland
Tel.: (41) 919 85 37 11
Fax: (41) 919 85 36 51
E-Mail: international@cnh.com
Web Site: www.cnh.com
Emp.: 10
Agricultural Machinery Distr
S.I.C.: 5083
N.A.I.C.S.: 423820
Sean Tay *(Gen Mgr)*

Subsidiaries:

MBA AG **(2)**
Zurichstrasse 50
8303 Bassersdorf, Switzerland
Tel.: (41) 44 838 61 11
Fax: (41) 44 838 62 22
E-Mail: info@mba-baumaschinen.ch
Construction Machinery Distr
S.I.C.: 5082
N.A.I.C.S.: 423810

CNH Italia S.p.A **(1)**
Viale Delle Nazioni 55
41100 Modena, Italy
Tel.: (39) 059591111
Telex: 510266 FIATMO I
Fax: (39) 059591996
Web Site: www.newholland.com
Tractors & Construction Machinery Mfr
S.I.C.: 3531
N.A.I.C.S.: 333120

Subsidiary:

CNH Services S.r.l. (2)
Viale Delle Nazioni 55
41122 Modena, Italy
Tel.: (39) 059 591 111
Fax: (39) 059 591 811
E-Mail: international@cnh.com
Agricultural & Construction Equipment Mfr
S.I.C.: 3523
N.A.I.C.S.: 333111

CNH Latin America Ltda. (1)
Avenida David Sarnoff 2 237 Cidade Industrial - Inconfidentes
32210-900 Contagem, Minas Gerais, Brazil
Tel.: (55) 3121043225
Fax: (55) 3121043400
Web Site: www.cnh.com
Construction Machinery Mfr
S.I.C.: 3531
N.A.I.C.S.: 333120
Paolo Bianco *(Mng Dir)*

CNH Portugal-Comercio de Tractores e Maquinas Agricolas Ltda (1)
Rua Quinta Do Paizinho Nr 2 1
Alfragide, 2794-083 Amadora, Portugal
Tel.: (351) 214 24 59 40
Fax: (351) 214 24 59 43
Emp.: 17
Farm Machinery & Equipment Distr
S.I.C.: 5083
N.A.I.C.S.: 423820
Fernando Garcia *(Mng Dir)*

CNH Trade N.V. (1)
Schiphol Boulevard 217
Schiphol, 1118 BH, Netherlands
Tel.: (31) 2 0446 0429
Agricultural Machinery Distr
S.I.C.: 5083
N.A.I.C.S.: 423820

Fiat Industrial Finance S.p.A. (1)
Via Nizza 250
10126 Turin, Italy IT
Tel.: (39) 011 0061111
Financial Management Services
S.I.C.: 6211
N.A.I.C.S.: 523999

U.S. Subsidiary:

Fiat Industrial Finance North America, Inc. (2)
7 Times Sq Tower Ste 4306
New York, NY 10036 DE
Tel.: (212) 207-0910
Fax: (212) 755-6152
Emp.: 6
Financial Management Services
S.I.C.: 6211
N.A.I.C.S.: 523999

FPT Industrial S.p.A. (1)
Via Puglia 35
10156 Turin, Italy
Tel.: (39) 011 0072111
Fax: (39) 011 0074555
E-Mail: sales1@fptindustrial.com
Web Site: www.fptindustrial.com
Automobile Mfr & Distr
S.I.C.: 3711
N.A.I.C.S.: 336111
Giovanni Bartoli *(CEO)*

Non-U.S. Subsidiary:

FPT Industrial Argentina S.A. (2)
Carlos Maria Della Paolera 299 Piso 27
Buenos Aires, 1001, Argentina
Tel.: (54) 1157765100
Fax: (54) 1157765123
Automotive Distr
S.I.C.: 5012
N.A.I.C.S.: 423110

Irisbus Deutschland GmbH (1)
Hauptstr 18
Mombach, 55120 Mainz, Germany
Tel.: (49) 6131962520
Fax: (49) 61319625210
E-Mail: info@irisbus.de
Web Site: www.irisbus.com
Bus & Coach Operating Services
S.I.C.: 4131
N.A.I.C.S.: 485210

Irisbus Iveco (1)
Parc Technologique de Lyon Bat B9 9 Allee Irene Joliot Curie
Saint Priest, 69800 Lyon, France
Tel.: (33) 472 796500
Fax: (33) 472 796559
E-Mail:
Web Site: www.irisbus.com
Emp.: 4,755
Bus & Coach Operating Services
S.I.C.: 4131
N.A.I.C.S.: 485210
Nicolas Tellier *(Office Mgr-Pres)*

Plant:

Irisbus Iveco - ANNONAY PLANT (2)
Rue Ferdinand Janvier
BP 138
7100 Annonay, France
Tel.: (33) 475326000
Fax: (33) 475326713
Automobile Mfr
S.I.C.: 3711
N.A.I.C.S.: 336111

Non-U.S. Plant:

Irisbus Iveco - VALLE UFITA PLANT (2)
Via Fondo Valle
83040 Flumeri, Avellino, Italy
Tel.: (39) 0825 4301
Fax: (39) 0825430407
Web Site: www.irisbus.com
Bus & Coach Mfr
S.I.C.: 3711
N.A.I.C.S.: 336111

Iveco S.p.A. (1)
Via Puglia 35
10156 Turin, Italy IT
Tel.: (39) 0110072111 (100%)
Telex: 221660 FIATVI I
Fax: (39) 0110074555
E-Mail: PressOffice@iveco.com
Web Site: www.iveco.com
Sales Range: $10-24.9 Million
Emp.: 31,000
Light, Medium & Heavy Commercial Vehicle Mfr
S.I.C.: 3711
N.A.I.C.S.: 336120
Alfredo Altavilla *(CEO)*

Subsidiary:

ASTRA Veicoli Industriali S.p.A. (2)
Via Caorsana 79
29122 Piacenza, PC, Italy
Tel.: (39) 0523543111
Telex: 530 148
Fax: (39) 0523591773
E-Mail: info@astraspa.com
Web Site: www.astraspa.com
Emp.: 450
Industrial Vehicles & Dumpers Mfr & Sales Import Export
S.I.C.: 5571
N.A.I.C.S.: 441228

Non-U.S. Subsidiaries:

Iveco Belgium NV SA (2)
Alfons Gossetlaan 28
1702 Groot-Bijgaarden, Belgium
Tel.: (32) 24671211
Fax: (32) 24671330
E-Mail: reception.grootbijgaarden@iveco.com
Web Site: www.ivecobenelux.com
Emp.: 50
Commercial Vehicles Marketer & Sales
S.I.C.: 5571
N.A.I.C.S.: 441228
Lorenzo Sistino *(Pres)*
Franco Fusignani *(COO)*

Iveco Capital SA (2)
Riva Paradiso 14
Lugano, 6900, Switzerland
Tel.: (41) 919853901
Fax: (41) 919853909
Emp.: 7
Financial Management Services
S.I.C.: 6211
N.A.I.C.S.: 523999
Valeria Roasio *(Gen Mgr)*

Iveco France S.A. (2)
6 Rue Nicolas Copernic
78083 Trappes, CEDEX, France
Tel.: (33) 130668394
Telex: UNIC 695-200 F
Fax: (33) 130668193
Web Site: www.iveco.com
Emp.: 3,000
Commercial Vehicle Sales
S.I.C.: 5012
N.A.I.C.S.: 423110
Alain Soudan *(Mgr)*

Subsidiaries:

FPT - Powertrain Technologies France S.A. (3)
5 Rue Pierre Timbaud
58600 Garchizy, France
Tel.: (33) 386907100
Fax: (33) 386388218
Truck Mfr
S.I.C.: 3715
N.A.I.C.S.: 336212

Iveco Est Sas (3)
10 rue des Tuileries Souffelweyesheim
57283 Mundolsheim, France
Tel.: (33) 3 87 80 24 22
Fax: (33) 3 87 51 62 07
Web Site: www.iveco-used.com
Automotive Dealer
S.I.C.: 5571
N.A.I.C.S.: 441228
Francis Di Nallo *(Gen Mgr)*

Iveco Participations S.A.S. (3)
6 Rue Nicolas Copernic
78190 Trappes, France FR
Tel.: (33) 1 30 66 80 00
Fax: (33) 1 30 66 82 10
Motor Vehicle Truck Rental Services
S.I.C.: 7519
N.A.I.C.S.: 532120

Subsidiary:

Provence Distribution Services S.a.r.l. (4)
135 R Mayor de Montricher
13854 Aix-en-Provence, France
Tel.: (33) 442549390
Fax: (33) 442549391
Motor Vehicle Truck Distr
S.I.C.: 5012
N.A.I.C.S.: 423110

Non-U.S. Subsidiary:

Iveco Czech Republic A.S. (3)
Dobrovskeho 74/II
Vysoke Myto, 566 03, Czech Republic
Tel.: (420) 4 6545 1111
Fax: (420) 4 6542 0386
E-Mail: info.cz@irisbus.iveco.com
Web Site: www.iveco.com
Emp.: 5
Buses & Coaches Mfr
S.I.C.: 3711
N.A.I.C.S.: 336111
Miroslav Nadvornik *(Mgr-Sls)*

Iveco International Trade Finance S.A. (2)
Via Balestra 3
6900 Lugano, Switzerland
Tel.: (41) 91985 37 11
Fax: (41) 91985 36 51
Financial Management Services
S.I.C.: 6211
N.A.I.C.S.: 523999

Iveco Ltd. (2)
Iveco House Station Rd
Watford, Herts, WD17 1SR, United Kingdom UK
Tel.: (44) 1923246400
Fax: (44) 1923240574
E-Mail: info@iveco.com
Web Site: www.iveco.com
Emp.: 150
Commercial Vehicles & Diesel Engines Mfr Import Export
S.I.C.: 3519
N.A.I.C.S.: 333618
Luca Sra *(Mng Dir-UK & Ireland)*

Iveco Magirus Brandschutztechnik GmbH (2)
Graf-Arco-Strasse 30
89079 Ulm, Germany
Tel.: (49) 7314080
Telex: 71255598 IM D
Fax: (49) 7314082410
E-Mail: magirus@iveco.com
Web Site: www.iveco.com
Emp.: 6,600
Commercial Vehicles & Trucks Mfr
S.I.C.: 3537
N.A.I.C.S.: 333924
Peter Barschkis *(CEO)*
Roel Nizet *(Mng Dir)*

Iveco Magirus Firefighting CAMIVA S.A.S. (2)
689 Avenue de Chambery
73231 Saint-Alban-Leysse, France FR
Tel.: (33) 4 79 75 66 66
Fax: (33) 4 79 70 54 40
E-Mail: contact@camiva.iveco.com
Web Site: www.camiva.com
Emp.: 220
Fire Fighting Vehicle Mfr
S.I.C.: 3711
N.A.I.C.S.: 336120

Iveco Motorenforschung AG (2)
Schlossgasse 2
9320 Arbon, Switzerland
Tel.: (41) 71 447 74 77
Fax: (41) 71 4463165
E-Mail: Info@Iveco-motorenforschung.ch
Web Site: www.iveco-arbon.ch
Emp.: 20
Automobile Engine Mfr
S.I.C.: 3714
N.A.I.C.S.: 336390
Meinrad Signer *(Gen Mgr)*

Iveco (Schweiz) AG (2)
Oberfeldstrasse 16
Kloten, 8302, Switzerland
Tel.: (41) 44 804 73 73
Fax: (41) 44 804 73 79
E-Mail: klotoen@iveco.com
Emp.: 10
Automobile Mfr
S.I.C.: 3711
N.A.I.C.S.: 336111
Franz Hafliger *(Gen Mgr)*

Iveco Slovakia, s.r.o. (2)
Dubravska Cesta 2
PO Box 138
Bratislava, 841 04, Slovakia
Tel.: (421) 2 5941 8440
Fax: (421) 2 5941 8451
E-Mail: iveco.slovakia@iveco.com
Automobile Mfr & Distr
S.I.C.: 3711
N.A.I.C.S.: 336111
Sergio Biancheri *(Gen Mgr)*

New Holland Fiat (India) Private Limited (1)
Plot No 09 Suite No - 301 Copia Corporate Suite
Jasola District Centre, New Delhi, 110 044, India
Tel.: (91) 11 49024000
Fax: (91) 11 49024015
E-Mail: nhidealerdevelopment@cnh.com
Web Site: www.newhollandindia.co.in
Agricultural Machinery Mfr
S.I.C.: 3523
N.A.I.C.S.: 333111
Rakesh Malhotra *(Mng Dir)*

Divisions:

New Holland Fiat (India) Pvt. Ltd. - Parts Division (2)
Plot No 03 Udyog Kendra
Dist Gautam Budh Nagar, 201 306 Noida, Uttar Pradesh, India
Tel.: (91) 120 3056000
Fax: (91) 120 3056929
Emp.: 150
Agricultural & Construction Equipment Mfr
S.I.C.: 3531
N.A.I.C.S.: 333120
Rakesh Malhotra *(Mng Dir)*

New Holland Fiat (India) Pvt. Ltd. - Tractor Division (2)
Plot No 03 Udyog Kendra
Distt Gautam Budh Nagar, 201 306 Noida, Uttar Pradesh, India
Tel.: (91) 120 3056000
Fax: (91) 120 3056929
Emp.: 150
Agricultural & Construction Equipment Mfr
S.I.C.: 3531

CNH Industrial N.V.—(Continued)

N.A.I.C.S.: 333120
Tsuyoshi Muramatsu *(Mng Dir)*

OOO Afin Leasing Vostok LLC (1)
Kosmonavta Volkova Str 10 Build 1
Moscow, Russia
Tel.: (7) 495 504 04 45
Fax: (7) 495 504 04 46
E-Mail: info@ivecofinance.com
Financial Leasing Services
S.I.C.: 6153
N.A.I.C.S.: 522220

Steyr Center Nord GmbH (1)
Kirchsee 1
Ruckersdorf, 2111 Harmannsdorf, Austria
Tel.: (43) 2264 6518
Fax: (43) 2264 6518 12
E-Mail: office@steyrcenternord.at
Agricultural Machinery Mfr
S.I.C.: 3523
N.A.I.C.S.: 333111

Non-U.S. Joint Venture:

TurkTraktor ve Ziraat Makineleri AS (1)
Guvercin Yolu No 111-112
Gazi, Ankara, 06560, Turkey TR
Tel.: (90) 312 233 33 33
Fax: (90) 312 233 33 73
E-Mail: turktraktor@turktraktor.com.tr
Web Site: www.turktraktor.com.tr
Emp.: 2,000
Agricultural Tractor Mfr & Distr
S.I.C.: 3523
N.A.I.C.S.: 333111
Marco Votta *(Gen Mgr)*

CNI HOLDINGS BERHAD

Wisma CNI No 2 Jalan U1/17
Seksyen U1 Hicom Glenmarie
Industrial Park
40000 Shah Alam, Selangor,
Malaysia
Tel.: (60) 3 5569 4000
Fax: (60) 3 5569 1078
E-Mail: info@cniholdings.com.my
Web Site: www.cniholdings.com.my
CNI—(KLS)
Rev.: $37,979,278
Assets: $43,272,618
Liabilities: $9,099,966
Net Worth: $34,172,652
Earnings: $434,874
Fiscal Year-end: 12/31/12

Business Description:
Management Services
S.I.C.: 8741
N.A.I.C.S.: 561110

Personnel:
Yoke Kwai Chin *(Sec)*

Board of Directors:
Peng Chor Koh
Huck Khoon Ch'ng
Chin Tai Cheong
Boon Swee Chew
How Loon Koh
Yang Ket Law
Lean Eng Lim
Zulkifli Mohamad Razali
Sia Swee Tan

CNI RESEARCH LTD

A/120 Gokul Arcade Opp Garware
House Sahar Road
Vile Parle E, Mumbai, 400 057, India
Tel.: (91) 22 28383889
E-Mail: support@cniglobalbiz.com
Web Site: www.cniglobalbiz.com
512018—(BOM)
Rev.: $2,803,480
Assets: $2,320,778
Liabilities: $110,980
Net Worth: $2,209,798
Earnings: $7,955
Fiscal Year-end: 03/31/13

Business Description:
Online Marketing Services
S.I.C.: 8742
N.A.I.C.S.: 541613

Personnel:
Kishor P. Ostwal *(Mng Dir)*

Board of Directors:
Mayur S. Doshi
Arun S, Jain
Kishor P. Ostwal
Sangita Ostwal

Transfer Agent:
Universal Capital Securities Private Limited
21 Shakil Niwas Mahakali Caves Road
Andheri-East, Mumbai, 400 093, India

CNIM CONSTRUCTIONS INDUSTRIELLES DE LA MEDITERRANEE SA

(d/b/a CNIM Group)
35 rue de Bassano
75008 Paris, France
Tel.: (33) 144311100
Fax: (33) 144311130
E-Mail: communication@cnim.com
Web Site: www.cnim.com
COM—(EUR)
Sls.: $972,004,741
Earnings: $26,779,360
Emp.: 2,660
Fiscal Year-end: 12/31/12

Business Description:
Industrial Construction Services
S.I.C.: 1629
N.A.I.C.S.: 237990

Personnel:
Vsevolod Dmitrieff *(Chm-Supervisory Bd)*
Nicolas Dmitrieff *(Chm-Mgmt Bd)*
Francois Canellas *(Vice Chm-Supervisory Bd)*
Catherine Delcroix *(Member-Mgmt Bd & Sec Gen)*
Stefano Costa *(Member-Mgmt Bd & Dir-Environment)*
Philippe Demigne *(Member-Mgmt Bd & Dir-Indus Sys)*

Supervisory Board of Directors:
Vsevolod Dmitrieff
Richard Armand
Francois Canellas
Christiane Dmitrieff
Lucile Dmitrieff
Agnes Herlicq
Andre Herlicq
Stephane Herlicq
Jean-Pierre Lefoulon
Johannes Martin
Jean-Francois Vaury
Ludwig von Mutius

Deloitte & Associes
Neuilly-sur-Seine, France

Subsidiaries:

Babcock Wanson Holding SA (1)
80 Rue Emile Zola
BP 95
93126 La Courneuve, France (100%)
Tel.: (33) 149373131
Fax: (33) 143520403
E-Mail: cnin@babcock.com
Web Site: www.cnin.com
Emp.: 3,500
Holding Company
S.I.C.: 6719
N.A.I.C.S.: 551112
Gumaa Hublot *(Mng Dir)*

Non-U.S. Subsidiaries:

Babcock Wanson Caldeiras Lda (2)
Rua Dos Transitarios 182 Salas Bs E Bt
4455-565 Perafita, Portugal
Tel.: (351) 229 999 490
Fax: (351) 229 999 659
E-Mail: info@babcock-wanson.pt
Web Site: www.babcock-wanson.pt
Motor & Generator Mfr
S.I.C.: 3621
N.A.I.C.S.: 335312

Babcock Wanson Espana SA (2)
Carretera Bilbao-Plencia 31 - Ed Inbisa Plt 1
Erandio, Spain
Tel.: (34) 94 452 30 36
Fax: (34) 94 452 30 54
E-Mail: comercial@babcock-wanson.es
Web Site: www.babcock-wanson.es
Steam Boiler & Air Generator Mfr
S.I.C.: 3585
N.A.I.C.S.: 333415

Babcock Wanson Italiana (2)
Via Roma 147
Cavenago Brianza, Milan, Italy
Tel.: (39) 02 95 91 21
Fax: (39) 02 95 01 92 52
E-Mail: bwi@babcock-wanson.com
Web Site: www.babcock-wanson.it
Steam Boiler Mfr
S.I.C.: 3433
N.A.I.C.S.: 333414

Babcock Wanson SA (1)
106-110 rue du Lt Petit-Le-Roy
Chevilly-Larue, 94 669 Paris, Cedex, France (100%)
Tel.: (33) 149784400
Fax: (33) 146861416
E-Mail: commercial@babcock-wanson.fr
Emp.: 40
Industrial Machinery Mfr
S.I.C.: 3559
N.A.I.C.S.: 333249

Plant:

Babcock Wanson SA - Manufacturing Facility (2)
7 boulevard Alfred Parent
BP 52
Nerac, France
Tel.: (33) 5 53 65 19 00
Fax: (33) 5 53 65 17 33
E-Mail: commercial@babcock-wanson.fr
Web Site: www.babcock-wanson.com
Steam Boiler & Generator Mfr
S.I.C.: 3443
N.A.I.C.S.: 332410

BERTIN PHARMA (1)
Parc d'activites du Pas du Lac 10 Bis Avenue Ampere
78180 Montigny-le-Bretonneux, France
Tel.: (33) 1 39 306 220
Fax: (33) 1 39 306 299
E-Mail: info@bertinpharma.com
Web Site: www.bertinpharma.com
Emp.: 10
Pharmaceutical Research & Development Services
S.I.C.: 8731
N.A.I.C.S.: 541711
Philippe Demigne *(Pres)*
Xavier Morge *(Mng Dir)*

Subsidiary:

VERBALYS (2)
Courtaboeuf 3 Rue De La Terre De Feu
Les Ulis, Essonne, 91940, France
Tel.: (33) 169298788
Business Management Consulting Services
S.I.C.: 8748
N.A.I.C.S.: 541618

Subsidiaries:

Vecsys Dataprod (3)
1 Rue De La Terre De Feu
Les Ulis, Essonne, 91940, France
Tel.: (33) 169298787
Fax: (33) 169075858
Construction Engineering Services
S.I.C.: 8711
N.A.I.C.S.: 541330

Vecsys SA (3)
3 Rue de la terre de Feu ZA
De Coutaboeuf, 91952 Les Ulis, France
Tel.: (33) 1 69 29 87 87
Fax: (33) 1 69 07 58 58
E-Mail: contact@vecsys.fr
Web Site: www.vecsys.fr
Automatic Speech Processing Services
S.I.C.: 8049
N.A.I.C.S.: 621340

BERTIN TECHNOLOGIES SAS (1)
10 B Avenue Ampere
78180 Montigny-le-Bretonneux, France
Tel.: (33) 139 306 110
Fax: (33) 1 39 30 09 50
E-Mail: communication@bertin.fr
Web Site: www.bertin.fr
Healthcare & Electronic Software Development Services
S.I.C.: 7371
N.A.I.C.S.: 541511
Philippe Demigne *(Chm & Mgr-Publ)*

CNIM Environnement SA (1)
35 Rue De Bassano
75008 Paris, France (100%)
Tel.: (33) 144311100
Fax: (33) 144311130
E-Mail: communication@cnim.com
Web Site: www.cnim.fr
Emp.: 40
Engineering Services
S.I.C.: 8711
N.A.I.C.S.: 541330
Nicolos Dimitriess *(Chm)*
Philippe Soulie *(Chm)*

CNIM Insertion (1)
Route des Nourrices
78850 Thiverval-Grignon, Yvelines, France
Tel.: (33) 1 30 79 03 68
Fax: (33) 1 30 54 00 17
Emp.: 5
Waste Treatment & Disposal Services
S.I.C.: 4953
N.A.I.C.S.: 562219
Marc-Henri Thimonier *(Gen Mgr)*

CNIM OUEST ARMOR (1)
Ld La Fontaine De Tremargat
Lantic, 22410, France
Tel.: (33) 296742527
Fax: (33) 296795913
Emp.: 5
Waste Treatment & Disposal Services
S.I.C.: 4953
N.A.I.C.S.: 562219

CNIM Transport Holding Srl (1)
35 Rue De Bassano
75008 Paris, France (100%)
Tel.: (33) 144311100
Fax: (33) 144311130
E-Mail: awcueilbsn@cnim.com
Web Site: www.cnim.com
Emp.: 60
Engineering Services
S.I.C.: 8711
N.A.I.C.S.: 541330
Philippe Soulie *(Chm)*

Non-U.S. Subsidiary:

CNIM Transport Equipment Co., Ltd (2)
Sanhe Road Cangjiang Industrial Park
Gaoming District, Foshan, Guangdong, 528500, China
Tel.: (86) 757 886 200 88
Fax: (86) 757 886 203 03
Web Site: www.cnim.com
Emp.: 200
Transportation Equipment Distr
S.I.C.: 5088
N.A.I.C.S.: 423860

Non-U.S. Subsidiaries:

Accord Lift Services Ltd. (1)
West Yoke Michaels Lane
Sevenoaks, TN15 7EP, United Kingdom (100%)
Tel.: (44) 1474879858
Fax: (44) 1474874143
E-Mail: info@accordlifts.co.uk
Web Site: www.accordlifts.co.uk
Emp.: 90
Engineering Services
S.I.C.: 8711
N.A.I.C.S.: 541330
Lian Ristery *(Mng Dir)*

Babcock Wanson AG (1)
Oberebene Strasse - 63
5620 Bremgarten, Switzerland (99.8%)
Tel.: (41) 566319580
Fax: (41) 566319588
E-Mail: bwag@babcock-wanson.com
Web Site: www.babcock-wanson.ch
Emp.: 680
Heavy & Civil Engineering Construction
S.I.C.: 1629
N.A.I.C.S.: 237990

Babcock Wanson Maroc (1)
Bd Ali Yaata
Ain Sebaa
20250 Casablanca, Morocco (100%)
Tel.: (212) 522355618
Fax: (212) 522352309
Web Site: www.babcock-wanson.ma/hi/index.htm
Engineering Services
S.I.C.: 8711
N.A.I.C.S.: 541330

Babcock Wanson UK Ltd. (1)
7 Elstree Way
Borehamwood, Hertfordshire, WD6 1SA, United Kingdom UK
Tel.: (44) 89537111 (25%)
Telex: 261169 Wanson G
Fax: (44) 2082075177
E-Mail: sales@babcock-wanson.co.uk
Web Site: www.babcockwanson.co.uk
Emp.: 50
Mfr. of Industrial Space & Process Heating Equipment
S.I.C.: 3433
N.A.I.C.S.: 333414

CNIM Babcock Central Europe S.r.o. (1)
Grafick A 848-18
15000 Prague, Czech Republic (100%)
Tel.: (420) 257286880
Fax: (420) 257310848
E-Mail: info@cnim.cz
Emp.: 10
Engineering Services
S.I.C.: 8711
N.A.I.C.S.: 541330
Gerard Hue *(Gen Mgr)*

CNIM Babcock Polska Sp. Z.o.o (1)
Kosciuszki 1C
44-100 Gliwice, Poland (100%)
Tel.: (48) 322306894
Fax: (48) 322327160
E-Mail: info@cnim.pl
Web Site: www.babcock-wanson.pl
Emp.: 10
Communication & Energy Wire Mfr
S.I.C.: 3357
N.A.I.C.S.: 335929

CNIM ECS LTD (1)
116-118 Chancery Lane
London, WC2A 1PP, United Kingdom
Tel.: (44) 20 7430 9362
Construction Engineering Services
S.I.C.: 8711
N.A.I.C.S.: 541330

CNIM Hong Kong Limited (1)
B 120324 O Estate
Weaston Rd, Sha Tin, China (Hong Kong) (99.99%)
Tel.: (852) 25703135
Fax: (852) 28071059
E-Mail: cnimhk@cnim.hk
Emp.: 120
Plumbing Heating & Air-Conditioning Contractors
S.I.C.: 1711
N.A.I.C.S.: 238220

CNIM Singapore Pte Ltd (1)
116 Lavender Street 03-08 Pek Chuan Building
Singapore, 338730, Singapore
Tel.: (65) 62990212
Fax: (65) 62993890
Escalator Installation Services
S.I.C.: 1799
N.A.I.C.S.: 238290

CNIM UK LTD (1)
116-118 Chancery Lane
London, WC2A 1PP, United Kingdom
Tel.: (44) 207 430 93 62
Fax: (44) 207 831 07 17
Waste Treatment & Disposal Services
S.I.C.: 4953
N.A.I.C.S.: 562219

Curtis Canada Inc. (1)
1225 Rue Industrielle
J5R2E4 La Prairie, QC, Canada (100%)
Tel.: (450) 619-2228
Fax: (450) 619-9496
Web Site: www.curtisdoorsystems.com
Emp.: 100
Engineering Services
S.I.C.: 8711
N.A.I.C.S.: 541330
Jean-Francois Vaury *(Mng Dir)*

LAB GmbH (1)
Bludenzer Str 6
70469 Stuttgart, Germany
Tel.: (49) 711 222 4935 0
Fax: (49) 711 222 493599
E-Mail: labgmbh@labgmbh.com
Web Site: www.lab-stuttgart.de
Emp.: 15
Waste Treatment Plant Operating Services
S.I.C.: 4953
N.A.I.C.S.: 562219
Stefano Costa *(Co-CEO)*
Thomas Feilenreiter *(Co-CEO)*

MES Environmental ltd. (1)
Crown Street
Wolverhampton, WV11QB, United Kingdom (100%)
Tel.: (44) 1902352864
Fax: (44) 1902352864
E-Mail:
Web Site: www.mes-e.co.uk/
Emp.: 30
Engineering Services
S.I.C.: 8711
N.A.I.C.S.: 541330

CNINSURE INC.

22/F Yinhai Building No 299 Yanjiang Zhong Road
Guangzhou, Guangdong, 510110, China
Tel.: (86) 20 61222777
Fax: (86) 20 61222329
Web Site: www.cninsure.net
Year Founded: 1999
CISG—(NASDAQ)
Rev.: $251,954,685
Assets: $540,215,333
Liabilities: $62,409,306
Net Worth: $477,806,027
Earnings: $19,814,472
Emp.: 4,108
Fiscal Year-end: 12/31/12

Business Description:
Insurance Brokerage Services
S.I.C.: 6411
N.A.I.C.S.: 524210

Personnel:
Yinan Hu *(Chm)*
Qiuping Lai *(Pres)*
Chunlin Wang *(CEO)*
Peng Ge *(CFO)*

Board of Directors:
Yinan Hu
Qiuping Lai
Allen Warren Lueth
Stephen Markscheid
Yunxiang Tang
Shangzhi Wu

Legal Counsel:
Commerce & Finance Law Offices
6F NCI Tower A12 Jianguomenwai Avenue
Beijing, China

CNMC GOLDMINE HOLDING LIMITED

745 Toa Payoh Lorong 5
#04-01 The Actuary, Singapore, 319455, Singapore
Tel.: (65) 62204621
Fax: (65) 62201270
Web Site: www.cnmc.com.sg
RTP—(CAT)

Business Description:
Gold Mining & Processing
S.I.C.: 1041
N.A.I.C.S.: 212221

Personnel:
Xiang Xiong Lin *(Chm)*
Vincent Bock Hui Lim *(Sec)*

CNP ASSURANCES SA

4 place Raoul Dautry
75716 Paris, Cedex 15, France
Tel.: (33) 142188888
Fax: (33) 142188655
E-Mail: infofi@cnp.fr
Web Site: www.cnp.fr
CNP—(EUR OTC)
Premiums: $35,591,388,630
Assets: $475,488,513,486
Liabilities: $454,504,415,526
Net Worth: $20,984,097,960
Earnings: $1,694,020,328
Emp.: 4,842
Fiscal Year-end: 12/31/12

Business Description:
Personal Life & Investment Products & Services
S.I.C.: 6411
N.A.I.C.S.: 524298

Personnel:
Jean-Paul Faugere *(Chm)*
Frederic Lavenir *(CEO)*
Xavier Larnaudie-Eiffel *(Deputy CEO-Intl Ops)*
Antoine Lissowski *(Deputy CEO-Fin)*
Thomas Behar *(Chief Actuary Officer)*
Thierry Marc Claude Claudon *(Member-Exec Bd)*

Board of Directors:
Jean-Paul Faugere
Jean-Paul Bailly
Valerie Baron-Loison
Patrick Berthelot
Michel Bouvard
Marcia Campbell
Virginie Chapron du Jeu
Marc-Andre Feffer
Ramon Fernandez
Jean-Yves Forel
Pierre Garcin
Anne-Sophie Grave
Jacques Hornez
Frederic Lavenir
Olivier Mareuse
Andre-Laurent Michelson
Pascal Oliveau
Stephane Pallez
Francois Perol
Henri Proglio
Alain Quinet
Nadia Remadna
Franck Silvent
Philippe Wahl

Mazars
61 rue Henri Regnault
Courbevoie, France

Subsidiaries:

Carres Blues (1)
Tour Maine Montparnasse 33 Ave Du Maine
4 place haoul dautri, 75015 Paris, cedex 15, France
Tel.: (33) 142188888
Fax: (33) 142188600
E-Mail: g.benoist@cnp.fr
Web Site: www.carresbleus.fr
Emp.: 100
Health Insurance Services
S.I.C.: 6311
N.A.I.C.S.: 524113
Benoist Gilles *(Pres)*
Marie Noelle *(Sec)*

CNP IAM (1)
4 Pl Raoul Dautry
Paris, 75716, France
Tel.: (33) 142189237
General Insurance Services
S.I.C.: 6411
N.A.I.C.S.: 524210

Fongepar (1)
10 Place de Catalogne
75680 Paris, Cedex 14, France
Tel.: (33) 144104900
Web Site: www.fongepar.fr
Insurance Services
S.I.C.: 6411
N.A.I.C.S.: 524298

Non-U.S. Subsidiaries:

Caixa Seguros (1)
Sector Comercial Norte 1 Padre 1
Edificio 1, 70711 900 Brasilia, DF, Brazil (51.75%)
Tel.: (55) 6121922995
Fax: (55) 614292407
E-Mail: inmperessa@caixaseguros.com.br
Web Site: www.caixaseguros.com.br
Emp.: 740
Insurance Services
S.I.C.: 6411
N.A.I.C.S.: 524298

CNP Assurances Compania de Seguros de Vida S.A (1)
M T De Alvear 1541
1001 Buenos Aires, Argentina
Tel.: (54) 1158117900
Fax: (54) 1158117962
E-Mail: cnp@cnpargentina.com.ar
Web Site: www.cnp.com.ar
Emp.: 70
Personal Insurance Services
S.I.C.: 6411
N.A.I.C.S.: 524298

CNP China (1)
2103 Full Link Plaza
18 Chaoyangmenwai Avenue, Beijing, 100020, China
Tel.: (86) 105882150
Fax: (86) 1065882152
E-Mail: info@cnp.com.cn
Web Site: www.cnp.fr
Insurance Services
S.I.C.: 6411
N.A.I.C.S.: 524298

CNP EUROPE LIFE LTD (1)
Embassy House Herbert Park Lane
Ballsbridge, Dublin, Ireland
Tel.: (353) 1 231 5080
Fax: (353) 1 231 5086
E-Mail: info@cnplife.ie
Web Site: www.cnplife.ie
General Insurance Services
S.I.C.: 6411
N.A.I.C.S.: 524210
Yann Illouz *(Gen Mgr)*

CNP Italia SpA (1)
Via Dante 14
20121 Milan, Italy
Tel.: (39) 0272601121
Fax: (39) 0272601150
Web Site: www.cnp.it
Emp.: 15
Loan Insurance Services
S.I.C.: 6411
N.A.I.C.S.: 524298
Marcello Mazzotte *(Mng Dir)*

CNP VIDA (1)
Chandiano 10-2 Planta
Madrid, 28023, Spain
Tel.: (34) 915243435
E-Mail: atencion@cnpvida.es
Web Site: www.cnpvida.es
General Insurance Services
S.I.C.: 6411
N.A.I.C.S.: 524210

CNPLUS CO., LTD.

Apartment Factory 222 722 Gojan-dong Namdong-gu
Incheon, 405821, Korea (South)
Tel.: (82) 32 8130970
Fax: (82) 32 8130977
Web Site: www.conn-net.co.kr
Year Founded: 2003
115530—(KRS)

Business Description:
High Precision Connector Mfr
S.I.C.: 3678
N.A.I.C.S.: 334417

Personnel:
Mu-Kun Han *(CEO)*

CNPV SOLAR POWER S.A.

Shengli Economic Development Zone
Dongying, Shangdong, 257000, China
Tel.: (86) 546 7795555

CNPV Solar Power S.A.—(Continued)

Fax: (86) 546 7795777
E-Mail: marketing@cnpv-power.com
Web Site: www.cnpv-power.com
Year Founded: 2006
ALCNP—(EUR)
Sales Range: $250-299.9 Million
Emp.: 573

Business Description:
Ingots, Wafers, Cells & Solar Modules Mfr
S.I.C.: 3612
N.A.I.C.S.: 335311

Personnel:
Anquan Wang *(Chm)*
Shunfu Zhang *(CEO)*
Shofeng Qi *(CFO)*
Bypina Veerraju Chaudary *(COO & CTO)*

Board of Directors:
Anquan Wang
Christophe Blondeau
Bypina Veerraju Chaudary
Shunfu Zhang
Chungfeng Zhao

Subsidiary:

CNPV Dongying Solar Power Company Limited, **(1)**
West No 19 Road South No 8 Road Victory Industrial Park
Dongying, Shandong, 257000, China
Tel.: (86) 5467795555
Fax: (86) 5467795777
Solar Power Equipment Mfr & Whslr
S.I.C.: 3699
N.A.I.C.S.: 335999

CNRP MINING INC.

208 Queens Way West #2506
Toronto, ON, M5J 2Y5, Canada
Tel.: (416) 628-9879
E-Mail: dw@CNRPMining.com
Web Site: www.cnrpmining.com
Year Founded: 2011
CND—(CNSX)

Business Description:
Gold Mining
S.I.C.: 1041
N.A.I.C.S.: 212221

Personnel:
Daniel Wettreich *(Chm & CEO)*
Mark Wettreich *(Sec & VP-Admin)*

Board of Directors:
Daniel Wettreich
Peter D. Wanner
Mark Wettreich
Scott F. White

CNSX MARKETS INC.

(d/b/a Canadian National Stock Exchange)
220 Bay St 9th Fl
Toronto, ON, M5J 2W4, Canada
Tel.: (416) 572-2000
Fax: (416) 572-4160
Web Site: www.cnsx.ca
Emp.: 20

Business Description:
Stock Exchange Services
S.I.C.: 6231
N.A.I.C.S.: 523210

Personnel:
Daniel T. Goodman *(Deputy Chm)*
Robert Cook *(Pres)*
Richard Carleton *(CEO)*
Robert Medland *(CFO)*

Board of Directors:
Bill Braithwaite
Gordon F. Cheesbrough
Adam Conyers
Daniel T. Goodman
Roy Hill
Thomas Lunan
Jeffrey MacIntosh
Steven Small
Joel Strickland

CNT GROUP LIMITED

31st Floor CNT Tower 338 Hennessy Road
Wanchai, China (Hong Kong)
Tel.: (852) 25733288
Fax: (852) 27927341
Web Site: www.cntgroup.com.hk
0701—(HKG)
Rev.: $169,646,233
Assets: $193,745,183
Liabilities: $72,755,137
Net Worth: $120,990,045
Earnings: $7,653,183
Emp.: 1,097
Fiscal Year-end: 12/31/12

Business Description:
Transportation
S.I.C.: 4111
N.A.I.C.S.: 485112

Personnel:
Paul Ting Ball Lam *(Chm)*
Philip Ho Chuen Tsui *(Deputy Chm & Mng Dir)*
Lai King Ma *(Sec)*

Board of Directors:
Paul Ting Ball Lam
David Akers-Jones
Wa Shek Chan
Chi Kwan Chong
Steven Chow
Sheung Chi Ko
Philip Ho Chuen Tsui
Danny T. Wong
Xiaojing Zhang
Yulin Zhang

HSBC Securities Services (Bermuda) Limited
6 Front Street
Hamilton, Bermuda

Subsidiary:

The China Paint Manufacturing Company (1932) Limited **(1)**
31 F CNT Tower 338 Hennessy Rd
Wanchai, China (Hong Kong)
Tel.: (852) 27920663
Fax: (852) 27927341
E-Mail: info@chinapaint.com
Web Site: www.chinapaint.com
Emp.: 80
Paint Mfr
S.I.C.: 2851
N.A.I.C.S.: 325510
Ricky Chuck *(CEO)*

Non-U.S. Subsidiary:

The China Paint Mfg. Co., (Xinfeng) Ltd. **(1)**
101 Fourth Ave S No 803 Block D Pioneer Home
Heping Dist, Shenyang, Liaoning, 110005, China
Tel.: (86) 2423502426
Fax: (86) 2423505406
Industrial Paints Mfr
S.I.C.: 2851
N.A.I.C.S.: 325510

CNTEE TRANSELECTRICA SA

str Olteni nr 2-4 sector 3
030786 Bucharest, Romania
Tel.: (40) 21 303 5822
Fax: (40) 21 303 5880
E-Mail: office@transelectrica.ro
Web Site: www.transelectrica.ro
TEL—(BUC)
Rev.: $861,819,680
Assets: $1,543,971,469
Liabilities: $784,961,831
Net Worth: $759,009,638
Earnings: $14,730,488
Emp.: 2,200
Fiscal Year-end: 12/31/12

Business Description:
Electricity Transmission, System & Market Operation
S.I.C.: 1629
N.A.I.C.S.: 237130

Personnel:
Marius Ion Mateescu *(Dir Gen)*
Ciprian Diaconu *(Deputy Dir Gen-Technical Mgmt)*
Corneliu Ene *(Deputy Dir Gen-Economic & Comml Mgmt)*

Board of Directors:
Stefan Doru Bucataru
Ioan Diaconu
Adrian Constantin Rusu
Constantin Vaduva

Subsidiaries:

Icemenerg SA **(1)**
Bd Energeticienilor 8
Sector 3, 032092 Bucharest, Romania
Tel.: (40) 213465241
Fax: (40) 213465310
E-Mail: icemenerg@icemenerg.ro
Web Site: www.icemenerg.ro
Emp.: 4
Electric Power Generation Services
S.I.C.: 4911
N.A.I.C.S.: 221111
Gheorghe Olteanu *(Pres & CEO)*

Icemenerg Service SA **(1)**
B-dul Energeticienilor 8
Sector 3, 032092 Bucharest, Romania
Tel.: (40) 213464786
Fax: (40) 21 3464365
Web Site: www.icemenerg-service.ro
Electricity Distribution Equipments & Control Devices Mfr
S.I.C.: 3822
N.A.I.C.S.: 334512

Smart SA **(1)**
Bucuresti B-dul Gen Gh Magheru nr 33
Sector 1, 010325 Bucharest, Romania
Tel.: (40) 213054402
Fax: (40) 213054470
Web Site: www.smart-sa.ro
Electrical Engineering Services
S.I.C.: 8711
N.A.I.C.S.: 541330

Teletrans SA **(1)**
16-18 Hristo Botev Boulevard
District 3, 030236 Bucharest, Romania
Tel.: (40) 213016014
Fax: (40) 21 301 60 14
E-Mail: office@teletrans.ro
Web Site: www.teletrans.ro
Emp.: 245
Telecommunication Services
S.I.C.: 4899
N.A.I.C.S.: 517919
Horia Hahaianu *(Gen Mgr)*

CO-OP ATLANTIC

123 Halifax St
PO Box 750
Moncton, NB, E1C 9R6, Canada
Tel.: (506) 858-6000
Fax: (506) 858-6637
Web Site: www.coopatlantic.ca
Year Founded: 1927
Emp.: 700

Business Description:
Groceries, Produce, General Merchandise, Petroleum, Feed & Farm Supplies Whslr
S.I.C.: 5191
N.A.I.C.S.: 424910

Personnel:
Bertha Campbell *(Chm)*
Adelard Cormier *(First Vice Chm)*
Wayne Lee *(Second Vice Chm)*
Paul-Emile Legere *(CEO)*
Leo LeBlanc *(Sec & VP-HR & Corp Affairs)*

Board of Directors:
Bertha Campbell
Adelard Cormier
Maggie Herbert
Reginald Larocque
Wayne Lee
Mary MacDonald
Robert Michael Oulton
George Trueman

Subsidiaries:

Avide Developments Inc. **(1)**
123 Halifax St
Moncton, NB, E1C 8N5, Canada
Tel.: (506) 858-6000
Fax: (506) 858-6283
Web Site: www.avide.com
Emp.: 20
Residential Development Services
S.I.C.: 1531
N.A.I.C.S.: 236117

Maximum Alarm & Security Inc. **(1)**
33 Henri Dunant Street
Moncton, NB, E1E 1E4, Canada
Tel.: (506) 858-6637
Fax: (506) 858-6639
E-Mail: info@maximumsecurity.ca
Web Site: www.maximumsecurity.ca
Business & Residential Security Systems
S.I.C.: 7382
N.A.I.C.S.: 561621
Mike Boudreau *(Mgr)*

THE CO-OPERATIVE BANK OF KENYA LIMITED

Co-operative House Haile Selassie Avenue
PO Box 48231
00100 Nairobi, Kenya
Tel.: (254) 203276000
Fax: (254) 20219831
E-Mail: customerservice@co-opbank.co.ke
Web Site: www.co-opbank.co.ke
COOP—(NAI)
Int. Income: $249,992,007
Assets: $2,255,956,316
Liabilities: $1,926,161,133
Net Worth: $329,795,183
Earnings: $86,738,925
Emp.: 3,367
Fiscal Year-end: 12/31/12

Business Description:
Investment Banking Services
S.I.C.: 6211
N.A.I.C.S.: 523110

Personnel:
Stanley Charles Muchiri *(Chm)*
Julius Riungu *(Vice Chm)*
Gideon Muriuki *(Mng Dir, CEO & Member-Mgmt Bd)*
Rosemary M. Githaiga *(Member-Mgmt Bd & Sec)*
Willis Osir *(Mng Dir-Co-Op Bank-South Sudan & Member-Mgmt Bd)*
Samuel Birech *(Member-Mgmt Bd & Dir-Retail Banking Div)*
Zachariah K. Chianda *(Member-Mgmt Bd & Dir-Ops Div)*
Titus Karanja *(Member-Mgmt Bd & Dir-Co-Op Banking Div)*
Anthony Mburu *(Member-Mgmt Bd & Dir-Credit Mgmt Div)*
Catherine Munyiri *(Member-Mgmt Bd & Dir-Corp & Institutional Banking Div)*
Patrick Nyaga *(Member-Mgmt Bd & Dir-Fin & Admin)*
Weda Welton *(Member-Mgmt Bd & Dir-HR Div)*

Board of Directors:
Stanley Charles Muchiri
Patrick Githendu
Cyrus Njine Kabira
James M. Kahunyo
Donald K. Kibera
Richard M. Kimanthi
Macloud Malonza
Elijah Kathuri Mbogo
Godfrey Mburia
Gideon Muriuki

John Murugu
Fredrick F. Odhiambo
Scholastica Odhiambo
Wilfred Ongoro
Julius Riungu
Rose Simani
Julius Sitienei
Gabriel J. S. Wakasyaka

CO-OPERATIVE GROUP LIMITED

1 Angel Square
Manchester, M60 0AG, United Kingdom
Tel.: (44) 1618341212
Fax: (44) 1618344507
E-Mail: customer.relations@co-op.co.uk
Web Site: www.co-operative.coop
Year Founded: 1844
Rev.: $19,659,001,920
Assets: $129,500,200,710
Liabilities: $122,353,913,460
Net Worth: $7,146,287,250
Earnings: ($819,651,510)
Emp.: 37,620
Fiscal Year-end: 01/05/13

Business Description:
Co-operative Business, Food Retailing, Funerals & Travel Agencies
S.I.C.: 7261
N.A.I.C.S.: 812210

Personnel:
Ursula Lidbetter *(Chm)*
Richard Pennycook *(CEO)*
Niall Booker *(Deputy CEO)*
Stephen Humes *(CFO)*
Andy Haywood *(CIO)*
Rebecca Skitt *(Chief HR Officer)*
Craig Brownsell *(Sr PR Officer)*
Andrew Torr *(Sr PR Officer)*
Steve Murrells *(CEO-Food)*
Alistar Asher *(Gen Counsel)*
Claire Davies *(Sec)*

Board of Directors:
Ursula Lidbetter
Jenny Barnes
Steven Bayes
Duncan Bowdler
John Brodie
Eric Calderwood
Martyn Cheatle
Herbert Daybell
Jenny de Villiers
Patrick Grange
Michael Harriot
Ray Henderson
Munir Malik
Liz Moyle
Paul Myners
David Pownall
Stuart Ramsay
Ben Reid
Mark Smith

Subsidiaries:

Aegis Security Services Limited (1)
5 Staithgate Lane
Bradford, BD6 1YA, United Kingdom
Tel.: (44) 12 7468 7288
Fax: (44) 12 7437 7347
E-Mail: enquiries@sunwin.co.uk
Web Site: www.sunwinservicesgroup.co.uk
Sales Range: $75-99.9 Million
Business Support Services
S.I.C.: 7389
N.A.I.C.S.: 561499

Co-op e-Store (1)
Sunwin House Chestergate
Merseyway, Stockport, Cheshire, SK1 1NT, United Kingdom
Tel.: (44) 8457000100
Web Site: www.coopelectricalshop.co.uk
Electronic Goods
S.I.C.: 5731
N.A.I.C.S.: 443142

Co-op Farmcare (1)
One Angel Square Hanover St
Manchester, M60 0AG, United Kingdom
Tel.: (44) 1618276117
Web Site: www.co-opfarmcare.com
Emp.: 8
Commercial Farming
S.I.C.: 0191
N.A.I.C.S.: 111998
Richard Quinn *(Mng Dir)*

Co-op Food (1)
Freepost MR9473
Manchester, M4 8BA, United Kingdom
Tel.: (44) 8000686727
E-Mail: customer.relations@co-operative.coop
Web Site: www.co-operative.coop/food
Emp.: 3,000
Community Food Retailer
S.I.C.: 5499
N.A.I.C.S.: 445299
Peter Mark *(CEO)*

Co-op Home Stores (1)
New Century House
Manchester, M60 4ES, United Kingdom
Tel.: (44) 1618341212
Web Site: www.co-operative.coop/legalservices/probate/
Home Decorating Stores
S.I.C.: 5719
N.A.I.C.S.: 442299

Co-operative Banking Group Limited (1)
New Century House
Manchester, M60 4ES, United Kingdom UK
Tel.: (44) 8457212212 (100%)
Web Site: www.co-operativebankinggroup.co.uk
Holding Company; Financial & Banking Services
S.I.C.: 6719
N.A.I.C.S.: 551112
Richard Pym *(Chm)*
Rod Bulmer *(Acting CEO)*
Bruce Hope-MacLellan *(COO)*
Grahame McGirr *(Interim Chief Risk Officer)*

Subsidiaries:

The Co-operative Bank p.l.c. (2)
1 Balloon St
PO Box 101
Manchester, M60 4EP, United Kingdom UK
Tel.: (44) 1618323456 (100%)
Fax: (44) 1618294475
Web Site: www.co-operativebank.co.uk
Commercial Banking Services
S.I.C.: 6029
N.A.I.C.S.: 522110
Graham R. Bennett *(Chm)*
William P. Morrissey *(Pres)*
Niall Booker *(CEO)*
Brona McKeown *(Gen Counsel & Sec)*

Subsidiaries:

Platform Funding Limited (3)
PO Box 237
Plymouth, PL1 1WG, United Kingdom
Tel.: (44) 1752236550
Fax: (44) 1752236557
E-Mail: info@platform.co.uk
Web Site: www.platform.co.uk
Emp.: 200
Mortgage & Nonmortgage Loan Brokers
S.I.C.: 6163
N.A.I.C.S.: 522310

Platform Home Loans Limited (3)
2 Harbour Exchange Square
London, E14 9FR, United Kingdom UK
Tel.: (44) 2075124006 (100%)
Fax: (44) 2075124071
E-Mail: igraham@platformhomeloans.com
Web Site: www.platform.co.uk/
Emp.: 200
Mortgage & Nonmortgage Loan Brokers
S.I.C.: 6163
N.A.I.C.S.: 522310

smile (3)
Delf House
PO Box 600
Skelmersdale, WN8 6GF, United Kingdom
Tel.: (44) 1614756108
Web Site: www.smile.co.uk
Internet Bank
S.I.C.: 6211
N.A.I.C.S.: 523110

Western Mortgage Services Limited (2)
The Moneycentre Precinct
Devon, PL1 1QH, United Kingdom
Tel.: (44) 1752236500
Fax: (44) 1752220016
E-Mail: greenaway@wmsl.co.uk
Web Site: www.wmsl.co.uk
Mortgage & Nonmortgage Loan Brokers
S.I.C.: 6163
N.A.I.C.S.: 522310
Mike Lewis *(Mng Dir)*

Co-operative Funeralcare (1)
2nd Floor Hanover Building
Hanover Street, Manchester, M60 08D, United Kingdom
Tel.: (44) 800289120
Fax: (44) 01618340768
Web Site: www.co-operativefuneralcare.co.uk
Emp.: 50
Funeral Services
S.I.C.: 7261
N.A.I.C.S.: 812210

Co-operative Group Pharmacy (1)
Brook House
Oldham Rd, Manchester, M24 1HF, United Kingdom
Tel.: (44) 1616544488
Fax: (44) 1706659644
Web Site: www.co-oppharmacy.co.uk
Emp.: 500
Pharmacy
S.I.C.: 5912
N.A.I.C.S.: 446110
John Nutttall *(Mng Dir)*

Co-operative Travel Limited (1)
New Century House
Corporation Street, Manchester, Lancanshire, M60 4ES, United Kingdom UK
Tel.: (44) 1782309100
Web Site: www.co-operativetm.co.uk/
Travel Arrangement Services
S.I.C.: 4724
N.A.I.C.S.: 561510
Jo Strange *(Head-Bus Dev)*

Branch:

Travelcare (2)
Trafford Plaza
PO Box 746
Seymour Grove, Manchester, Old Trafford, M16 0ZA, United Kingdom
Tel.: (44) 870 112 0101
Web Site: www.travelcare.co.uk
Travel Service
S.I.C.: 4729
N.A.I.C.S.: 561599

Shoefayre Limited (1)
Wigstone House
Kirkdale Road, Leicester, S Wigston, LE18 4SU, United Kingdom UK
Tel.: (44) 01162785264
Web Site: www.shoefayre.co.uk
Fashion Footwear & Accessories
S.I.C.: 5139
N.A.I.C.S.: 424340

CO-OPERATIVE INSURANCE SOCIETY LIMITED

Miller St
Manchester, M60 0AL, United Kingdom
Tel.: (44) 618328686
Fax: (44) 619034048
E-Mail: cfs@cfs.co.uk
Web Site: www.cfs.co.uk
Sales Range: $750-799.9 Million

Business Description:
Insurance & Other Financial Services
S.I.C.: 6399
N.A.I.C.S.: 524128

Personnel:
Neville Richardson *(CEO)*
Moira Lees *(Sec)*

Board of Directors:
Rodney Baker-Bates
Duncan Bowdler
Rod Bulmer
Peter Harvey
Paul Hewitt
Chris Jones
Stephen Kingsley
Phil Lee
Peter Marks
Bob Newton
Ben Reid
Neville Richardson
Len Wardle
Stephen Watts
Piers Williamson

CO-OPERATIVE PURCHASING SERVICES LTD.

2nd Level Suite 2
PO Box 812
420 Burwood Highway, Wantirna, VIC, 3152, Australia
Tel.: (61) 0398012811
Fax: (61) 0398016722
E-Mail: cps@cps.asn.au
Web Site: www.cps.asn.au
Emp.: 3

Business Description:
Co-operative Business Support Services
S.I.C.: 8742
N.A.I.C.S.: 541611

Personnel:
Max Fonovic *(Mktg Mgr)*

THE CO-OPERATORS GROUP LIMITED

130 Macdonell Street
Guelph, ON, N1H 6P8, Canada
Tel.: (519) 824-4400
Fax: (519) 823-9944
Toll Free: (800) 265-2662
E-Mail: service@cooperators.ca
Web Site: www.cooperators.ca
Year Founded: 1945
Rev.: $3,250,648,180
Assets: $11,345,395,379
Liabilities: $8,572,828,076
Net Worth: $2,772,567,303
Earnings: $234,273,616
Emp.: 5,017
Fiscal Year-end: 12/31/12

Business Description:
General Insurer
S.I.C.: 6411
N.A.I.C.S.: 524298

Personnel:
Richard Lemoing *(Chm)*
John Lamb *(First Vice Chm)*
Alexandra Wilson *(Second Vice Chm)*
Kathy Bardswick *(Pres & CEO)*
P. Bruce West *(CFO & Exec VP)*
Kevin Daniel *(COO/Exec VP-Co-operators Life Insurance Company)*
Carol Poulsen *(CIO & Exec VP)*
Michael White *(Pres/CEO-Addenda Capital Inc)*
Bob Hague *(Pres-Credit Union Distr)*
Robert Wesseling *(COO/Exec VP-The Sovereign General Insurance Co)*
Carol Hunter *(Exec VP-Member Rels & Corp Svcs)*
Rick McCombie *(Exec VP-Distr & Insurance Ops)*

Board of Directors:
Richard Lemoing
Denis Bourdeau
Daniel Burns
Albert De Boer
Connie Doucette
Paul Godin
Janet Grantham

The Co-operators Group Limited—(Continued)

Roger Harrop
John Harvie
Rowland Kelly
Rejean Laflamme
John Lamb
Denis Laverdiere
Jim Laverick
Sheena Lucas
Wayne McLeod
Terry Otto
Andre Perras
Dave Sitaram
Jack Wilkinson
Alexandra Wilson
Gordon Young

Subsidiaries:

Addenda Capital Inc. (1)
800 Blvd Rene-Levesque Ouest Ste 2750
Montreal, QC, H3B 1X9, Canada (71.4%)
Tel.: (514) 287-7373
Fax: (514) 287-7200
E-Mail: info@addenda-capital.com
Web Site: www.addenda-capital.com
Sales Range: $25-49.9 Million
Emp.: 130
Bond Portfolio Management
S.I.C.: 6211
N.A.I.C.S.: 523999
Carmand Normand *(Chm)*
Michael White *(Pres & CEO)*
Jim MacDonald *(Sr VP & Co-Chief Investment Officer)*
Benoit Durocher *(Exec VP & Chief Economic Strategist)*
Joe DiMassimo *(Sr VP-Client Servicing & Sls)*

Co-operators Financial Services Limited (1)
130 Macdonell Street
Guelph, ON, N1H 6P8, Canada
Tel.: (519) 824-4400
Fax: (519) 824-0599
Web Site: www.cooperators.ca
Insurance Holding Company
S.I.C.: 6411
N.A.I.C.S.: 524298
Kathy Bardswick *(Pres & CEO)*

Subsidiaries:

Co-operators General Insurance Company (2)
130 Macdonell Street
Guelph, ON, N1H 6P8, Canada Ca
Tel.: (519) 824-4400 (100%)
Fax: (519) 823-9944
E-Mail: service@cooperators.ca
Web Site: www.cooperators.ca
CCS.PR.C—(TSX)
Rev.: $2,208,871,483
Assets: $4,873,346,069
Liabilities: $3,441,845,939
Net Worth: $1,431,500,130
Earnings: $256,184,799
Emp.: 2,580
Fiscal Year-end: 12/31/12
General Insurance Services
S.I.C.: 6411
N.A.I.C.S.: 524298
Richard Lemoing *(Chm)*
John Lamb *(First Vice Chm)*
Alexandra Wilson *(Second Vice Chm)*
Kathy Bardswick *(Pres & CEO)*
P. Bruce West *(CFO & Exec VP-Fin)*
Carol Poulsen *(CIO & Exec VP)*
Michael White *(Pres/CEO-Addenda Capital Inc)*
Bob Hague *(Pres-Credit Union Distr-CUMIS Grp Limited)*
Kevin Daniel *(COO-Co-Operators Life Insurance Company & Exec VP)*
Rob Wesseling *(COO-Sovereign General Insurance Co & Exec VP-Natl P&C Product)*
Carol Hunter *(Exec VP-Member Rels & Corp Svcs)*
Rick McCombie *(Exec VP-Distr & Insurance Ops)*

Co-operators Life Insurance Company (2)
1920 College Ave
Regina, SK, S4P 1C4, Canada
Tel.: (306) 347-6200
Web Site: www.cooperators.ca/en/group/benefits/4_1_11.html
Managed Assets: $3,271,800,000
Emp.: 900
Direct Life Insurance Carriers
S.I.C.: 6311
N.A.I.C.S.: 524113
Kathy Bardswick *(Pres)*
Kevin Daniel *(COO)*
Frank Lowery *(Gen Counsel, Sec & VP)*

The CUMIS Group Limited (1)
151 N Service Rd
PO Box 5065
Burlington, ON, L7R 4C2, Canada ON
Tel.: (905) 632-1221
Fax: (905) 632-9412
Toll Free: (800) 263-9120
E-Mail: collin.hyslop@cumis.com
Web Site: www.cumis.com
Emp.: 400
Fire, Marine & Casualty Insurance Services
S.I.C.: 6351
N.A.I.C.S.: 524126
Russ Fast *(Chm)*
Craig Marshall *(Gen Counsel, Sec & VP)*

Subsidiary:

CUMIS Life Insurance Company (2)
151 North Service Rd
Burlington, ON, L7R 4C2, Canada
Tel.: (905) 632-1221
Fax: (905) 632-9412
Toll Free: (800) 263-9120
E-Mail: colleen.hyslop@cumis.com
Web Site: www.cumis.com
Life Insurance Carrier
S.I.C.: 6311
N.A.I.C.S.: 524113
Kathy Bardswick *(Pres & CEO)*

Federated Agencies Limited (1)
5600 Cancross Ct
Mississauga, ON, L5R 3E9, Canada
Tel.: (905) 507-9823
Fax: (905) 507-6223
E-Mail: special_lines@hbgrpins.com
Web Site: www.cooperators.ca/en/aboutus/companies/2_11_6.html
Emp.: 30
Personal, Commercial & Wealth Management Products
S.I.C.: 6282
N.A.I.C.S.: 523930
Rick McCombie *(Sr VP)*

HB Group Insurance Management Ltd. (1)
5600 Cancross Ct
Mississauga, ON, L5R 3E9, Canada
Tel.: (905) 507-6156
Fax: (905) 507-8661
E-Mail: facilitiesadministration@hpgrpins.com
Web Site: www.hbgroup.com
Emp.: 500
Automobile & Property Insurance
S.I.C.: 6331
N.A.I.C.S.: 524126
Geoffrey Beechey *(VP-Insurance Ops HB Grp-COSECO)*

The Sovereign General Insurance Company (1)
140-6700 MacLeod Trail Southeast
Sovereign Centre, Calgary, AB, T2H 0L3, Canada
Tel.: (403) 298-4200
Fax: (403) 298-4217
E-Mail: info@sovereigngeneral.com
Web Site: www.sovereigngeneral.com
Sales Range: $200-249.9 Million
Emp.: 80
General Insurance Carrier
S.I.C.: 6331
N.A.I.C.S.: 524126
Rob Wesseling *(COO)*

CO-PROSPERITY HOLDINGS LIMITED

Wu Bao Industry Area
Shishi, Fujian, China 362700
Tel.: (86) 595 88922222
Fax: (86) 595 88985888
Web Site: www.co-prosperity.com
707—(HKG)
Sls.: $81,932,606
Assets: $160,248,039
Liabilities: $116,410,522
Net Worth: $43,837,517
Earnings: ($11,016,883)
Emp.: 1,500
Fiscal Year-end: 12/31/12
Business Description:
Textile Product Mfr & Whslr
S.I.C.: 2269
N.A.I.C.S.: 313310
Personnel:
Siu Hung Sze *(Chm)*
Fengshou Qiu *(Vice Chm)*
Siu Bun Sze *(CEO)*
Hon Hung Chan *(Sec & Controller-Fin)*
Board of Directors:
Siu Hung Sze
Peilei Cai
Siu Keung Lui
Fengshou Qiu
Chin Pang Sze
Qingfu Zeng
Bei Zhao
HSBC Trustee (Cayman) Limited
HSBC House 68 West Bay Road
PO Box 484
Georgetown, Cayman Islands
Transfer Agents:
Tricor Investor Services Limited
26th Floor Tesbury Centre 28 Queens Road East
Wanchai, China (Hong Kong)
HSBC Trustee (Cayman) Limited
HSBC House 68 West Bay Road
PO Box 484
Georgetown, Cayman Islands

CO2 GROUP LIMITED

Level 11 225 St Georges Terrace
Perth, WA, 6000, Australia
Mailing Address:
Cloisters Square
PO Box 7312
Perth, WA, 6850, Australia
Tel.: (61) 8 9321 4111
Fax: (61) 8 9321 4411
E-Mail: info@co2australia.com.au
Web Site: www.co2australia.com.au
Year Founded: 1990
COZ—(ASX)
Rev.: $48,120,507
Assets: $43,212,077
Liabilities: $5,438,022
Net Worth: $37,774,055
Earnings: ($7,064,941)
Fiscal Year-end: 09/30/13
Business Description:
Environmental Engineering Services
S.I.C.: 8711
N.A.I.C.S.: 541330
Personnel:
Ian Norman Trahar *(Chm)*
Harley Ronald Whitcombe *(CFO & Sec)*
Board of Directors:
Ian Norman Trahar
Paul John Favretto
Malcolm Brian Hemmerling
Christopher David Mitchell
Harley Ronald Whitcombe
Legal Counsel:
Corrs Chambers Westgarth
Level 15 Woodside Building 240 St Georges Terrace
Perth, WA, 6000, Australia
Baker & McKenzie
Level 26 AMP Centre 50 Bridge Street
Sydney, NSW, 1223, Australia

CO2 SOLUTION, INC.

2300 Jean-Perrin Street
Quebec, QC, G2C 1T9, Canada
Tel.: (418) 842-3456
Fax: (418) 842-1732
Toll Free: (877) 884-3456
E-Mail: info@co2solution.com
Web Site: www.co2solution.com
CST—(TSXV)
Rev.: $750,024
Assets: $2,671,056
Liabilities: $717,804
Net Worth: $1,953,252
Earnings: ($2,528,124)
Fiscal Year-end: 06/30/13
Business Description:
Carbon Dioxide Recycling Services
S.I.C.: 1389
N.A.I.C.S.: 213112
Personnel:
Glenn R. Kelly *(Chm)*
Evan Price *(Pres & CEO)*
Thom Skinner *(CFO & Sr VP-Fin)*
Louis Fradette *(CTO & Sr VP-Process Engrg)*
Board of Directors:
Glenn R. Kelly
Robert Manherz
Kimberley Okell
Martin P. Pelletier
Evan Price
Jocelyn Proteau
Legal Counsel:
McCarthy Tetrault LLP / S.E.N.C.R.L s.r.l
Le Complexe St-Amable 1150 Claire-Fontaine Street 7th Floor
Quebec, QC, Canada
Leger Robic Richard S.E.N.C.R.L.
CDP Capital Center 1001 Square Victoria Bloc E 8th Floor
Montreal, QC, Canada
Transfer Agent:
Computershare Investor Services Inc
1500 University Street, Suite 700
Montreal, QC, Canada

COADNA HOLDINGS, INC.

87 Mary Street
Georgetown, Grand Kayman, KY1-9005, Cayman Islands
Tel.: (345) 945 1726
E-Mail: investor@coadna.com
Web Site: www.coadna.com
Year Founded: 2008
4984—(TAI)
Sales Range: $25-49.9 Million
Emp.: 260
Business Description:
Photonic Solutions
S.I.C.: 3674
N.A.I.C.S.: 334413
Personnel:
Jim Yuan *(Chm, Pres & CEO)*
Philip Lau *(CFO & Sec)*
Jack Kelly *(CTO & VP)*
Fang Wang *(Chief Comml Officer)*
Board of Directors:
Jim Yuan
David Y. Chang
Ronald Jen-Chuan Chwang
Ho-Ming Huang
Donny Kao
James Lung
Albert Wang

U.S. Subsidiary:

CoAdna Photonics, Inc. (1)
733 Palomar Ave
Sunnyvale, CA 94085
Tel.: (408) 736-1100
Fax: (408) 736-1106
E-Mail: sales@coadna.com
Photonic Component Mfr & Distr
S.I.C.: 3679
N.A.I.C.S.: 334419
Steven Liu *(VP-Ops)*

Non-U.S. Subsidiary:

CoAdna (HK) Limited (1)
Room 801-2 8/F Easey Commercial Building 253-261 Hennessy Road
Wanchai, China (Hong Kong)
Tel.: (852) 28249890
Fiber Optic Cable Mfr
S.I.C.: 3357
N.A.I.C.S.: 335921

COAL ASIA HOLDINGS INC.
3/F JTKC Centre 2155 Don Chino Roces Ave
Makati, 1231, Philippines
Tel.: (63) 2 8138892
Fax: (63) 2 8103536
Web Site: www.coalasiaholdings.com
COAL—(PHI)
Emp.: 60
Business Description:
Coal Mining
S.I.C.: 1222
N.A.I.C.S.: 212112
Personnel:
Harald R. Tomintz *(Chm)*
Jaime T. Ang *(Pres)*

COAL ENERGY S.A.
46A Avenue JF Kennedy
L-1855 Luxembourg, Luxembourg
Tel.: (352) 42 71 711
E-Mail: ir@coalenergy.com.ua
Web Site: www.coalenergy.com.ua
CLE—(WAR)
Business Description:
Coal Mining & Production Services
S.I.C.: 1222
N.A.I.C.S.: 212112
Personnel:
Viktor Vyshnevetskyy *(Chm-Mgmt Bd)*

COAL FE RESOURCES LIMITED
7 11 Exchange Road
Malaga, WA, 6090, Australia
Tel.: (61) 8 9209 2466
Fax: (61) 8 9248 9033
E-Mail: jatin@nexiacorp.com.au
Web Site: www.coalferesources.com
CES—(ASX)
Rev.: $257,224
Assets: $2,367,322
Liabilities: $2,039,868
Net Worth: $327,454
Earnings: ($2,658,034)
Fiscal Year-end: 06/30/13
Business Description:
Coal Exploration & Mining Services
S.I.C.: 1222
N.A.I.C.S.: 212112
Personnel:
Foo Khee Chan *(Chm)*
Kok Beng Ooi *(Pres-PT Techventure Indocoal)*
Jatin Cholera *(Sec)*
Board of Directors:
Foo Khee Chan
Julian Jew Keng Cheng
Hean Chong Moo
Faris Azmi Abdul Rahman
Wee Thow Yeo

COAL INDIA LIMITED
10 Netaji Subhas Road
Kolkata, West Bengal, 700001, India
Tel.: (91) 3322488099
Fax: (91) 3322435316
E-Mail: telecil@cal2.vsnl.net.in
Web Site: www.coalindia.in
Year Founded: 1975
COALINDIA—(BOM NSE)
Sls.: $16,367,356,728
Assets: $22,538,106,504
Liabilities: $13,539,608,118
Net Worth: $8,998,498,386
Earnings: $3,217,869,144
Emp.: 357,926
Fiscal Year-end: 03/31/13
Business Description:
Coal Production
S.I.C.: 2999
N.A.I.C.S.: 324199
Personnel:
S. Narsing Rao *(Chm & Mng Dir)*
M. Viswanathan *(Compliance Officer, Sec & Mgr-Fin)*
Manoj Kumar *(Chief Vigilance Officer)*
K. V. R. Murty *(Sr Officer-Secretarial)*
Board of Directors:
S. Narsing Rao
Abhijit Chatterjee
R. Mohan Das
A. K. Dubey
N. Kumar
Sujata Prasad
B. K. Saxena
Transfer Agent:
Karvy Computershare Pvt Ltd
Plot No 17 to 24 Vithal Rao Nagar Madhapur
Hyderabad, 500081, India
Subsidiaries:

Bharat Coking Coal Limited (1)
Koyla Bhawan
Koyla Nagar, Dhanbad, Jharkhand, 826005, India (100%)
Tel.: (91) 326 2330203
Fax: (91) 3262262227
E-Mail: bcclcmd@cmpdi.co.in
Web Site: www.bccl.gov.in
Emp.: 100,000
Coal Mining Services
S.I.C.: 1241
N.A.I.C.S.: 213113

Eastern Coalfields Limited (1)
10 Netaji Subhas Rd
Kolkata, 700001, India (100%)
Tel.: (91) 3322488099
Fax: (91) 3412520459
E-Mail: telecil@cal2.vsnl.net.in
Web Site: www.mahanadicoal.nic.in
Emp.: 200
Coal Mining Services
S.I.C.: 1241
N.A.I.C.S.: 213113
U. S. Upadhyay *(Dir-Technical Opers)*

Mahanadi Coalfields Limited (1)
Jagriti Vihar
PO Box UCE
Burla, Sambalpur, Orissa, 768020, India
Tel.: (91) 6632542461
Fax: (91) 6632542482
E-Mail: mcl@wb.nic.in
Web Site: www.mahanadicoal.nic.in
Coal Mining Services
S.I.C.: 1241
N.A.I.C.S.: 213113
G.D. Gulab *(Dir-HR)*

Northern Coalfields Limited (1)
Singrauli District
Sidhi, Singrauli, 486889, India (100%)
Tel.: (91) 7805266670
Fax: (91) 7805266640
E-Mail: cmdncl@nclhq.nic.in
Web Site: www.ncl.nic.in
Emp.: 1,100
Coal Mining Services
S.I.C.: 1241
N.A.I.C.S.: 213113
D. Kumar Singh *(Chm & Mng Dir)*

South Eastern Coalfields Limited (1)
SECL Bhawan
Seepat Rd, Bilaspur, 495006, India (100%)
Tel.: (91) 7752240582
Fax: (91) 7752240306
E-Mail: epsecl@bol6.vsln.net.in
Web Site: www.secl.nic.in
Sales Range: $1-4.9 Billion
Emp.: 86,000
Coal Mining Services
S.I.C.: 1241
N.A.I.C.S.: 213113

Western Coalfields Limited (1)
Coal Est
Nagpur, 440001, India (100%)
Tel.: (91) 7122511381
E-Mail: cmd.wcl@coalindia.in
Web Site: www.coalindia.in
Emp.: 2,000
Coal Mining Services
S.I.C.: 1241
N.A.I.C.S.: 213113
D. C. Garg *(Mng Dir)*

COAL OF AFRICA LIMITED
Suite 8 7 The Esplanade
Mount Pleasant, WA, 6153, Australia
Tel.: (61) 8 9316 9100
Fax: (61) 8 9315 5475
E-Mail: perth@coalofafrica.com
Web Site: www.coalofafrica.com
CZA—(AIM ASX JSE)
Rev.: $1,054,605
Assets: $445,392,498
Liabilities: $88,506,595
Net Worth: $356,885,903
Earnings: ($154,373,568)
Emp.: 440
Fiscal Year-end: 06/30/13
Business Description:
Coal Exploration Services
S.I.C.: 1222
N.A.I.C.S.: 212112
Personnel:
Bernard Robert Pryor *(Interim Chm)*
David Hugh Brown *(CEO)*
Michael Meeser *(CFO)*
C. Bronn *(COO)*
Tony Bevan *(Sec)*
Board of Directors:
Bernard Robert Pryor
David Hugh Brown
Peter Cordin
Michael Meeser
Brian Kgomotso Mosehla
David John Keir Murray
Rudolph Torlage
Legal Counsel:
Webber Wentzel
10 Fricker Road Illovo Boulevard
Johannesburg, South Africa

Hogan Lovells
Atlantic House Holborn Viaduct
London, EC1A 2FG, United Kingdom

Blakiston & Crabb
1202 Hay Street
West Perth, Australia

Computershare Investor Services
Ground Floor 70 Marshall Stree t
Johannesburg, South Africa

Computershare Investor Services
The Pavilions Bridgewater Road
Bristol, United Kingdom

Non-U.S. Subsidiaries:

Coal of Africa (SA) Ltd. (1)
2nd Floor Gabba Building The Campus 57 Sloane Street
Bryanston, South Africa ZA
Tel.: (27) 11 575 4363
Fax: (27) 11 576 4363
E-Mail: adminza@coalofafrica.co.za
Web Site: www.coalofafrica.com
Emp.: 35
Coal Mining Services
S.I.C.: 1241
N.A.I.C.S.: 213113
Simon J. Farrell *(Deputy Chm)*
Riaan van der Merwe *(COO)*

Magberg Manufacturing (Pty) Ltd (1)
Pinewood Ofc Park 33 Riley Rd
PO Box 1401
Woodmead, Sandton, Gauteng, 2199, South Africa
Tel.: (27) 118038247
Fax: (27) 118038323
E-Mail: info@nimagrout.com
Web Site: www.nimagrout.com
Emp.: 6
Magnesium Refining Services
S.I.C.: 3339
N.A.I.C.S.: 331410
Paul Holm *(Mng Dir)*

Metalloy Fibres (Pty) Ltd (1)
37 Lincoln St
Woodmead E, Sandton, Gauteng, South Africa
Tel.: (27) 11 803 8247
Fax: (27) 11 803 8323
E-Mail: info@nimaggroup.com
Emp.: 10
Stainless Steel Mfr
S.I.C.: 3399
N.A.I.C.S.: 331110
Godson Jaarth *(Mng Dir)*

COALBANK LIMITED
Level 6 344 Queen Street
Brisbane, QLD, 4000, Australia
Tel.: (61) 732296606
Fax: (61) 732216625
Web Site: www.coalbank.com
CBQ—(ASX)
Rev.: $24,856
Assets: $22,547,955
Liabilities: $5,040,791
Net Worth: $17,507,164
Earnings: ($24,741,723)
Fiscal Year-end: 06/30/13
Business Description:
Low Carbon Emission Coal Exploration & Production Services
S.I.C.: 1222
N.A.I.C.S.: 212112
Personnel:
Bruce Patrick *(CEO)*
Leni Stanley *(Sec)*
Board of Directors:
Anthony Wai-Lun Chan
Nick Bolkus
Daniel Kin-Wah Chan
George Lam
Ron Marks
Legal Counsel:
McCullough Robertson
Level 12 Central Plaza Two 66 Eagle Street
4000 Brisbane, QLD, Australia

COALFIELD RESOURCES PLC
(Formerly UK Coal plc)
Harworth Park Blyth Road
Harworth, Doncaster, S Yorkshire, DN11 8DB, United Kingdom
Tel.: (44) 1302755100
Web Site: www.coalfieldresources.com
CRES—(LSE)
Rev.: $12,634
Assets: $119,307,463
Liabilities: $43,613,673
Net Worth: $75,693,790
Earnings: $9,989,009
Emp.: 2,467
Fiscal Year-end: 12/29/12
Business Description:
Holding Company; Coal Mine Owner & Operator
S.I.C.: 6719
N.A.I.C.S.: 551112
Personnel:
Jonson Cox *(Chm)*
Geoff Mason *(Sec)*
Board of Directors:
Jonson Cox
Lisa Clement
Jeremy Hague
Peter Hickson
Steven Underwood
Legal Counsel:
Freshfields Bruckhaus Deringer LLP
65 Fleet Street
London, United Kingdom
Subsidiaries:

Harworth Insurance Company Limited (1)
Harworth Park Blyth Road
Harworth, Doncaster, S Yorkshire, DN11 8DB, United Kingdom
Tel.: (44) 1302751751

Coalfield Resources plc—(Continued)

Fax: (44) 1302752420
Emp.: 150
Insurance Services
S.I.C.: 6399
N.A.I.C.S.: 524128
David Carr *(Mgr-Admin)*

Harworth Power Limited (1)
Harworth Parkk Blyth Rd
Doncaster, DN11 8DB, United Kingdom (100%)
Tel.: (44) 1302751751
Fax: (44) 1302752420
E-Mail: enquire@ukcoal.com
Web Site: www.harworthpower.com
Emp.: 150
Holding Company
S.I.C.: 6719
N.A.I.C.S.: 551112
Jon Lloyd *(CEO)*

Mining Services Limited (1)
Harworth Pk Blyth Rd
Doncaster, TN11 8DB, United Kingdom (100%)
Tel.: (44) 1302751751
Fax: (44) 1302752420
E-Mail: enquire@ukcoal.com
Web Site: www.ukcoal.co.uk
Emp.: 150
Commercial & Industrial Machinery & Equipment Rental & Leasing
S.I.C.: 7359
N.A.I.C.S.: 532490

UK Coal Mining Limited (1)
Thoresby Colliery
NG219PS Nottingham, United Kingdom (100%)
Tel.: (44) 1623822238
Fax: (44) 1623822140
Emp.: 500
Bituminous Coal Underground Mining
S.I.C.: 1222
N.A.I.C.S.: 212112
Stewart Hoult *(Mng Dir)*
Derick Main *(Mng Dir)*

COALSPUR MINES LIMITED

Level 1 28 Ord Street
West Perth, WA, 6005, Australia
Tel.: (61) 8 6555 2945
Fax: (61) 8 8 6210 1153
E-Mail: info@coalspur.com
Web Site: www.coalspur.com
CPL—(ASX TSX)
Sales Range: Less than $1 Million
Emp.: 12

Business Description:
Coal Mining
S.I.C.: 1221
N.A.I.C.S.: 212111

Personnel:
Gill Winckler *(Pres & CEO)*
Robert Gough *(CFO)*
Colin Gilligan *(COO)*
Xenia Kritsos *(Gen Counsel, Co-Sec & VP)*
Simon Robertson *(Co-Sec)*

Board of Directors:
Colin Henri Steyn
Peter Binsteed Breese
Ted Mayers
David Murray
Mark Rodda
Denis Andre Turcotte
Gill Winckler

Legal Counsel:
Hardy Bowen Lawyers
PO Box 1364
West Perth, Australia
Tel.: (61) 8 9211 3600
Fax: (61) 8 6211 3690

Computershare Investor Services Inc
100 University Avenue
Toronto, ON, M5 J2Y1, Canada

Non-U.S. Subsidiary:

Coalspur Mines (Operations) Ltd. (1)
Ste 880 550 11th Ave SW
Calgary, AB, T2R 1M7, Canada
Tel.: (403) 261-9997
Fax: (403) 767-6378
Emp.: 13
Coal Mining Services
S.I.C.: 1222
N.A.I.C.S.: 212112

COAST & COUNTRY HOUSING LTD.

14 Ennis Sq
Dormanstown, Redcar, Cleveland, TS10 5JR, United Kingdom
Tel.: (44) 1642771300
Fax: (44) 1642771305
E-Mail: enquiries@cchousing.org.uk
Web Site: www.cchousing-online.org.uk
Sales Range: $50-74.9 Million
Emp.: 600

Business Description:
Housing Services
S.I.C.: 8322
N.A.I.C.S.: 624229

Personnel:
Paula Breen *(Chm)*
Vacant Position *(Vice Chm)*
Iain Sim *(CEO)*

Board of Directors:
Paula Breen
Timothy John Blackman
Amanda Coles
Frank Connorton
Nigel Johnston
Vacant Position

COAST INVESTMENT & DEVELOPMENT COMPANY K.S.C.C.

Coast Building Shuhada Street Al Sharq Area Near Sawaber Complex
Kuwait, Kuwait
Tel.: (965) 22230510
Fax: (965) 22415364
E-Mail: cidco@coast.com.kw
Web Site: www.coast.com.kw
COAST—(KUW)
Sls.: $399,178,326
Assets: $850,408,446
Liabilities: $450,379,658
Net Worth: $400,028,788
Earnings: ($40,616,629)
Fiscal Year-end: 12/31/12

Business Description:
Investment Services
S.I.C.: 6211
N.A.I.C.S.: 523999

Personnel:
Sulaiman Khaled Al Sahli *(Chm)*
Khaled Abdulaziz Al-Usaimi *(Vice Chm & CEO)*
Mohammad Rashed Al-Qaoud *(Sr VP-Support Grp)*
Muneer Abdulmuhsen Al-Sharhan *(Sr VP-Investment Grp)*

Board of Directors:
Sulaiman Khaled Al Sahli
Anwar Jassim Al Kharafi
Hamad Ahmad Al-Amiri
Abdulhadi Ahmed Al-Dosiri
Bader Yousef Al-Ghanim
Bader Mohammad Al-Qattan
Khaled Abdulaziz Al-Usaimi

Baker Tilly Kuwait
Sharq Area Omar Bin Khattab Street Shawafat Bldg Block No 5 1st Floor
PO Box 1486
Safat, Kuwait, 13015, Kuwait
Tel.: (965) 1828283
Fax: (965) 22461225

Albazie & Co.
Kuwait Airways Building 7th Floor Shuhada Street
PO Box 2115
Kuwait, Kuwait

Legal Counsel:
Al-Khebrah Legal Consultant & Lawyers
Al-Dawliya Building Fahd Al Salem Street
Kuwait, Kuwait

U.S. Subsidiary:

Coast Holding Corporation (1)
41 John St No 6
Babylon, NY 11702
Tel.: (631) 539-7441
Investment Management Services
S.I.C.: 8742
N.A.I.C.S.: 541611

COAST SPAS MANUFACTURING INC

6135 202 St
Langley, BC, V2Y 1N7, Canada
Tel.: (604) 514-8111
Fax: (604) 514-8165
Web Site: www.coastspas.com
Year Founded: 1997
Rev.: $19,000,000
Emp.: 200

Business Description:
Hot Tubs & Spas Mfr
S.I.C.: 3999
N.A.I.C.S.: 339999

Personnel:
Donald Elkington *(Pres & CEO)*

COAST TIRE & AUTO SERVICE, INC.

130 Somerset St Suite 150
Saint John, NB, E2K 2X4, Canada
Tel.: (506) 674-9620
Fax: (506) 674-9666
Web Site: www.coasttire.ca
Year Founded: 1984
Rev.: $44,519,850
Emp.: 300

Business Description:
Tire Supplier
S.I.C.: 5014
N.A.I.C.S.: 441320

Personnel:
Ron Outerbridge *(Pres & CEO)*

COAST WHOLESALE APPLIANCES INC.

8488 Main Street
Vancouver, BC, V5X 4W8, Canada
Tel.: (604) 301-3400
Fax: (604) 322-4911
E-Mail: invest@coastappliances.com
Web Site: www.coastwholesaleappliancesinc.com
Year Founded: 2010
CWA—(TSX)
Sls.: $144,327,498
Assets: $97,842,122
Liabilities: $40,529,342
Net Worth: $57,312,780
Earnings: $4,169,698
Fiscal Year-end: 12/31/12

Business Description:
Household Appliance Whslr
S.I.C.: 5064
N.A.I.C.S.: 423620

Personnel:
Stephen T. Bellringer *(Chm)*
Maurice E. Paquette *(Pres & CEO)*
Gordon Howie *(CFO)*
Stephen J. Raben *(Sr VP-Sls & Mktg-Single Family)*

Board of Directors:
Stephen T. Bellringer
Maurice E. Paquette
Jack G. Peck
Donald J. A. Smith
Anthony L. Soda

Transfer Agent:
Computershare Investor Services Inc.
3rd Floor 510 Burrard Street
Vancouver, BC, Canada

COASTAL CARIBBEAN OILS & MINERALS, LTD.

Clarendon House Church Street
Hamilton, HM 11, Bermuda
Tel.: (441) 2951422
Web Site: www.coastalcarib.com
COCBF—(OTC)
Sales Range: Less than $1 Million
Emp.: 1

Business Description:
Oil & Gas Exploration
S.I.C.: 1311
N.A.I.C.S.: 211111

Personnel:
Robert J. Angerer, Sr. *(Chm)*
Phillip W. Ware *(Pres, CEO & Chief Acctg Officer)*

Board of Directors:
Robert J. Angerer, Sr.
Herbert D. Haughton
Phillip W. Ware

COASTAL CONTACTS INC.

Suite 320 2985 Virtual Way
Vancouver, BC, V5M 4X7, Canada
Tel.: (604) 669-1555
Fax: (604) 669-6855
E-Mail: info@coastalcontacts.com
Web Site: www.coastalcontacts.com
COA—(NASDAQ TSX)
Sls.: $216,249,051
Assets: $92,702,305
Liabilities: $57,080,604
Net Worth: $35,621,701
Earnings: ($15,848,655)
Emp.: 626
Fiscal Year-end: 10/31/13

Business Description:
Optical Lenses Distr
S.I.C.: 5995
N.A.I.C.S.: 446130

Personnel:
Roger V. Hardy *(Founder, Chm & CEO)*
Nicholas Bozikis *(CFO)*
Steve Bochen *(COO)*

Board of Directors:
Roger V. Hardy
Jeffrey Robert Mason
Murray McBride
Michaela Tokarski

Legal Counsel:
Sangra Moller LLP
Vancouver, BC, Canada

Computershare Investor Services Inc.
510 Burrard St 2nd Floor
Vancouver, BC, V6C 3B9, Canada
Tel.: (604) 661-9400

Transfer Agents:
Computershare Trust Company, N.A
350 Indiana Street Suite 750
Golden, CO 80401

Computershare Investor Services Inc.
510 Burrard St 2nd Floor
Vancouver, BC, V6C 3B9, Canada
Tel.: (604) 661-9400

COASTAL CONTRACTS BHD.

Block G Lot 3B Bandar Leila WDT 259
90009 Sandakan, Sabah, Malaysia
Tel.: (60) 89616263
Fax: (60) 89616654
E-Mail: mail@coastalcontracts.com
Web Site: www.coastalcontracts.com
COASTAL—(KLS)
Rev.: $250,651,885
Assets: $380,632,221
Liabilities: $106,671,437
Net Worth: $273,960,784
Earnings: $38,975,969
Emp.: 253
Fiscal Year-end: 12/31/12

Business Description:
Marine Services
S.I.C.: 8711

N.A.I.C.S.: 541330
Personnel:
Chin Heng Ng *(Chm)*
Wei Ket Kong *(CFO)*
Dorothy Wei Kam Luk *(Sec)*
Board of Directors:
Chin Heng Ng
Thian Sang Loh
Chin Keuan Ng
Chin Shin Ng
Zainal Rajan

COASTAL ENERGY COMPANY

(Acquired & Absorbed by International Petroleum Investment Company PJSC)

COASTAL FORD SALES LTD

5750 Lougheed Highway
Burnaby, BC, V5B 2Z9, Canada
Tel.: (604) 294-6525
Fax: (604) 294-5068
E-Mail: info@coastalford.com
Web Site: www.coastalford.com
Year Founded: 1988
Rev.: $32,998,285
Emp.: 125
Business Description:
New & Used Car Dealers
S.I.C.: 5511
N.A.I.C.S.: 441110
Personnel:
Donald Carson *(Pres)*

COASTAL GOLD CORP.

(Formerly Castillian Resources Corp.)
65 Queen St W Suite 815
PO Box 75
Toronto, ON, M5H 2M5, Canada
Tel.: (416) 861-5899
Fax: (416) 861-8165
E-Mail: info@castillian.ca
Web Site: www.castillian.ca
Year Founded: 1987
COD—(OTC TSXV)
Assets: $14,310,461
Liabilities: $1,694,150
Net Worth: $12,616,311
Earnings: ($4,332,687)
Fiscal Year-end: 12/31/12
Business Description:
Gold Mining Services
S.I.C.: 1041
N.A.I.C.S.: 212221
Personnel:
Justin Reid *(Chm)*
William N. Pearson *(Pres & CEO)*
Gregory Duras *(CFO)*
Josh Van Deurzen *(Sec)*
Board of Directors:
Justin Reid
Bray P. Geo
David Patrick Gower
Michael L. Hoffman
William N. Pearson
Brian K. Penney
David S. Warner

Non-U.S. Subsidiary:

Castillian Metais Ltda **(1)**
Av Afonso Pena 2770 Sala 200
Belo Horizonte, 30130-007, Brazil
Tel.: (55) 31 3505 5200
Fax: (55) 31 3505 5200
E-Mail: info@castillian.ca
Emp.: 100
Gold Mining Services
S.I.C.: 1041
N.A.I.C.S.: 212221
Helio Diniz *(Mgr-South America)*

COASTAL GREENLAND LIMITED

Suite 1708 17th Fl One Exchange Square 8 Connaught Place
Central, China (Hong Kong)
Tel.: (852) 28779772
Fax: (852) 25240931
Web Site: www.coastal.com.cn
1124—(HKG)
Sales Range: $900-999.9 Million
Emp.: 2,500
Business Description:
Real Estate Investment & Property Management
S.I.C.: 6552
N.A.I.C.S.: 237210
Personnel:
Boon Teong Chan *(Chm)*
Ming Jiang *(Vice Chm & Mng Dir)*
Wing Bor Cheng *(Sec)*
Board of Directors:
Boon Teong Chan
Shaobin Cai
Wing Bor Cheng
Limin Guo
Ming Jiang
Kin Ho Law
Chen Hsin Lin
Lap Yan Tang
Lin Tao
Kai Cheong Wong
Ruxin Xu
Hong Qing Zheng

Butterfield Corporate Services Limited
Rosebank Centre, 11 Bermudiana Road
Pembroke, Bermuda

Subsidiary:

Coastal Realty Development Co. Limited **(1)**
Rm 1708 17 Fl One Exchange Sq 8
Connaught Pl
Central, China (Hong Kong)
Tel.: (852) 28779772
Fax: (852) 25240931
Real Estate Property Development Services
S.I.C.: 6531
N.A.I.C.S.: 531210

COASTAL PACIFIC MINING CORP.

927 Drury Avenue Northeast
Calgary, AB, T2E 0M3, Canada
Tel.: (403) 612-3001
Fax: (403) 313-5449
E-Mail: info@coastalpacificminingcorp.com
Web Site: www.coastalpacificminingcorp.com
Year Founded: 2007
CPMCF—(OTC)
Business Description:
Gold Mining Services
S.I.C.: 1041
N.A.I.C.S.: 212221
Personnel:
Joseph Bucci *(Pres, CEO, Interim CFO, Treas & Sec)*
Board of Directors:
Joseph Bucci
Dave L. Gibson
Richard Thomas Walker

COASTAL PACIFIC XPRESS INC.

Unit 105 5355 152 Street
Surrey, BC, V3S 5A5, Canada
Tel.: (604) 575-4200
Fax: (604) 575-0973
Toll Free: (888) 995-6995
E-Mail: info@cpx.ca
Web Site: www.cpx.ca
Year Founded: 1986
Rev.: $55,000,000
Emp.: 80
Business Description:
Trucking Services
S.I.C.: 4214
N.A.I.C.S.: 484110
Personnel:
Scott McIntosh *(Co-Owner & Pres-Ops)*
Jim Mickey *(Co-Owner & Pres-Admin)*

COBALT COAL LTD.

Suite 2000 840 7th Avenue Southwest
Calgary, AB, T2P 3G2, Canada
Tel.: (403) 538-8455
Fax: (403) 444-5042
E-Mail: info@cobaltcoalcorp.com
Web Site: cobaltcoalcorp.com
Year Founded: 2007
CCF—(TSXV)
Rev.: $3,885,847
Assets: $19,684,148
Liabilities: $20,819,839
Net Worth: ($1,135,691)
Earnings: ($6,949,728)
Fiscal Year-end: 12/31/12
Business Description:
Coal Mining Services
S.I.C.: 1222
N.A.I.C.S.: 212112
Personnel:
Al J. Kroontje *(Chm)*
Mike Crowder *(CEO)*
Robert L. Gilles *(CFO)*
Board of Directors:
Al J. Kroontje
Mike Crowder
Michael O. Kehler
Bill Lannaci

COBAR CONSOLIDATED RESOURCES LIMITED

Level 10 420 St Kilda Road
PO Box 33312
Melbourne, VIC, 3004, Australia
Tel.: (61) 3 9869 8200
Fax: (61) 3 9869 8299
E-Mail: admin@ccrlimited.com.au
Web Site: www.ccrlimited.com.au
R4R—(ASX DEU)
Rev.: $198,084
Assets: $89,235,138
Liabilities: $25,649,008
Net Worth: $63,586,129
Earnings: ($31,766,254)
Fiscal Year-end: 06/30/13
Business Description:
Silver Mining Services
S.I.C.: 1044
N.A.I.C.S.: 212222
Personnel:
Paul Bibby *(CEO)*
Alan Knights *(CFO)*
Claire Miller *(Sec)*
Board of Directors:
George A. Lefroy
Daniel Laurente
Kevin Tuckwell
Legal Counsel:
Lewis Holdway Commercial Lawyers
20 Queen Street
Melbourne, VIC, Australia

COBEPA S.A.

Rue de la Chancellerie 2 Box 1
1000 Brussels, Belgium
Tel.: (32) 2 213 32 10
Telex: 62574 COBEPA B
Fax: (32) 2 513 17 02
E-Mail: info@cobepa.be
Web Site: www.cobepa.be
Year Founded: 1957
Managed Assets: $1,750,021,000
Emp.: 15
Business Description:
Financial Investment Services
S.I.C.: 6211
N.A.I.C.S.: 523999
Personnel:
Jean-Marie Laurent Josi *(Mng Dir)*
Xavier de Walque *(CFO & Member-Exec Bd)*
Jean-Marc Crepin *(Member-Exec Bd & CEO-BeCapital)*
Dirk Broekhuyse *(Member-Exec Bd)*
Alfonso Pallavicini *(Member-Exec Bd)*
Board of Directors:
Francois Henrot
Philippe Bodson
Christophe d'Ansembourg
Charles de Liedekerke
Gregoire de Spoelberch
Olivier de Spoelberch
Philippe de Spoelberch
Hugo Ferreira
Jean-Marie Laurent Josi
Francois Pauly
Bart Van Malderen
William Wyatt

Non-U.S. Holdings:

Services Generaux de Gestion S.A. **(1)**
412F route d'Esch
L 2086 Luxembourg, Luxembourg (68%)
Tel.: (352) 46 6111 1
Fax: (352) 47 11 01
E-Mail: contact@sgg.lu
Web Site: www.sgg.lu
Rev.: $107,693,600
Emp.: 500
Accounting, Tax & Financial Services to Private Equity Industry
S.I.C.: 8721
N.A.I.C.S.: 541219
Carlo Schlesser *(Mng Dir)*

Non-U.S. Subsidiaries:

SGG Belgium S.A. **(2)**
147 avenue Brugmann
1190 Brussels, Belgium
Tel.: (32) 23468022
Fax: (32) 23467022
E-Mail: contact@sggbelgium.be
Emp.: 8
Corporate Administration Services
S.I.C.: 7389
N.A.I.C.S.: 561499
Hernans Thierry *(Gen Mgr)*

SGG (Nederland) B.V. **(2)**
Amsteldijk 166 Riverstaete Building
NL1079 LH Amsterdam, Netherlands
Tel.: (31) 20 644 4558
Fax: (31) 20 644 2735
E-Mail: info@sgg.nl
Web Site: www.sgg.nl
Emp.: 50
Corporate Administration Services
S.I.C.: 7389
N.A.I.C.S.: 561499
Sara Douwes *(Mgr-Comml)*

SGG Suisse S.A. **(2)**
Place Isaac-Mercier 3
1201 Geneva, Switzerland
Tel.: (41) 228070380
Fax: (41) 228070381
E-Mail: sgg@sggsa.ch
Web Site: www.sggsa.lu
Emp.: 5
Commercial Banking Services
S.I.C.: 6029
N.A.I.C.S.: 522110
Gregory Guissard *(Mng Dir)*

Socotec SA **(1)**
3 avenue du Centre
78280 Guyancourt, France (63%)
Tel.: (33) 1 30 12 80 00
Fax: (33) 1 30 12 82 61
Sales Range: $600-649.9 Million
Emp.: 5,000
Building Inspection Services
S.I.C.: 7389
N.A.I.C.S.: 541350
Vincent Oudin *(CEO)*
Thierry Schindele *(CFO)*

Cobepa S.A.—(Continued)

Subsidiary:

Societe Internationale de Controle et Approvisionnement SASU (2)
143 Avenue Charles de Gaulle
92200 Neuilly, France
Tel.: (33) 1 49 03 73 80
Fax: (33) 1 49 03 02 83
Web Site: www.sica.fr
Third Party Inspection Services to Oil & Gas Industry
S.I.C.: 7389
N.A.I.C.S.: 541350

Non-U.S. Subsidiaries:

Certification International (UK) Limited (2)
Delta 200 Delta Business Park
Great Western Way, Swindon, Wiltshire, SN5 7XP, United Kingdom
Tel.: (44) 1793 492892
Fax: (44) 1793 492692
E-Mail: emma@cert-int.com
Web Site: www.cert-int.com
Assessment, Analysis & Certification of Management Systems
S.I.C.: 7389
N.A.I.C.S.: 561499
John Pymer, *(Mng Dir)*

KHI Management International Ltd. (2)
Suite 308 3rd Floor 22 Park House
Park Street, Croydon, Surrey, CR0 1YE, United Kingdom
Tel.: (44) 208 688 2217
Fax: (44) 208 688 4336
E-Mail: contact@kmil.co.uk
Web Site: www.kmil.co.uk
Consulting Services to Oil & Gas & Energy Sectors
S.I.C.: 8999
N.A.I.C.S.: 541690

COBHAM PLC

Brook Road
Wimborne, Dorset, BH21 2BJ, United Kingdom
Tel.: (44) 1202882020
Telex: 41247
Fax: (44) 1202840523
E-Mail: info@cobham.com
Web Site: www.cobham.com
Year Founded: 1955
COB—(LSE)
Rev.: $2,762,809,926
Assets: $3,745,444,164
Liabilities: $2,080,240,788
Net Worth: $1,665,203,376
Earnings: $273,848,886
Emp.: 9,992
Fiscal Year-end: 12/31/12

Business Description:
Holding Company; Aerospace & Defense Systems Designer & Mfr
Import Export
S.I.C.: 6719
N.A.I.C.S.: 551112

Personnel:
Robert Murphy *(CEO)*
Simon Nicholls *(CFO)*
Richard Tyson *(Pres-Aerospace & Security)*
Robert E. Mullins *(Exec VP-Corp Strategy, Mergers & Acq-Arlington)*

Board of Directors:
John F. Devaney
D. Jonathan Flint
Michael W. Hagee
Robert Murphy
Simon Nicholls
John S. Patterson
Mark H. Ronald
Michael Wareing
Alison Wood

Divisions:

Cobham Mission Systems (1)
Brook Road
Wimborne Minster, Dorset, BH21 2BJ, United Kingdom
Tel.: (44) 1202882121
Fax: (44) 1202880096
E-Mail: communication@cobham.com
Emp.: 500
Military Aircraft Refueling, Life Support & Weapons Carriage Systems Developer & Mfr
S.I.C.: 3728
N.A.I.C.S.: 336413
David Squires *(Pres)*

U.S. Subsidiaries:

Carleton Life Support Systems Inc. (2)
2734 Hickory Grove Rd
Davenport, IA 52804-1203
Mailing Address:
2734 Hickory Grove Rd
Davenport, IA 52804-1203
Tel.: (563) 383-6000
Fax: (563) 383-6430
Web Site: www.cobham.com
Emp.: 375
Oxygen Systems for Aviation Applications
S.I.C.: 3559
N.A.I.C.S.: 333249
Dean Cantrill *(Pres & VP-Ops-Mission Sys Div)*

Carleton Technologies Inc. (2)
10 Cobham Dr
Orchard Park, NY 14127-4121 (100%)
Tel.: (716) 662-0006
Fax: (716) 662-0747
Web Site: www.carltech.com
Emp.: 300
Aerospace Systems Design & Mfr
S.I.C.: 3728
N.A.I.C.S.: 336413
K. N. Kota *(Gen Mgr)*

Subsidiaries:

Cobham Advanced Composites Ltd. (1)
Gelders Hall Rd
Shepshed, Loughborough, Leics, LE12 9NH, United Kingdom UK
Tel.: (44) 1509504541 (100%)
Fax: (44) 1509507563
Web Site: www.cobhamcomposites.co.uk
Emp.: 170
Aerospace, Defense & Industrial Composite Components Designer & Mfr
S.I.C.: 3479
N.A.I.C.S.: 332812
Gerry Masterson *(Deputy Mng Dir & Dir-Fin)*

Cobham Defence Communications Ltd. (1)
Haslingden Road
Blackburn, Lancs, BB1 2EE, United Kingdom UK
Tel.: (44) 1254292010 (100%)
Fax: (44) 1254292035
E-Mail: info@cobham.com
Web Site: www.cobham.com
Military Command, Control & Tactical Communication Systems Designer & Mfr
S.I.C.: 3669
N.A.I.C.S.: 334290
Steve Collier *(Mng Dir)*

Cobham Flight Inspection Limited (1)
Building 360 Durham Tees Valley Airport
Darlington, Co Durham, DL2 1NJ, United Kingdom
Tel.: (44) 1325 331360
Fax: (44) 1325 333591
Emp.: 40
Flight Inspection Services
S.I.C.: 9651
N.A.I.C.S.: 926150

Cobham MAL Limited (1)
Featherstone Road Wolverton Mill
Milton Keynes, Buckinghamshire, MK12 5EW, United Kingdom
Tel.: (44) 1908 574200
Fax: (44) 1908 574300
E-Mail: cobham.mal@cobham.com
Emp.: 6
Microwave Semiconductor Mfr
S.I.C.: 3674
N.A.I.C.S.: 334413
Karen Oddey *(CEO)*

Credowan Limited (1)
Stocks Lane Bracklesham Bay
Chichester, West Sussex, PO20 8NT, United Kingdom
Tel.: (44) 1243 670711
Fax: (44) 1243 672907
E-Mail: sales@credowan.co.uk
Web Site: www.credowan.com
Emp.: 70
Microwave Equipment Mfr & Distr
S.I.C.: 3679
N.A.I.C.S.: 334419

Domo Limited (1)
The Cobham Centre Solent Fusion 2 1100 Parkway
Whiteley, Fareham, Hampshire, PO15 7AB, United Kingdom
Tel.: (44) 1489 566750
Fax: (44) 1489 880538
Communication Equipment Mfr
S.I.C.: 3669
N.A.I.C.S.: 334290

Flight Refuelling Limited (1)
Brook Road
Wimborne, Dorset, BH21 2BJ, United Kingdom
Tel.: (44) 1202 882121
Fax: (44) 1202 880096
Aircraft Machinery Mfr
S.I.C.: 3728
N.A.I.C.S.: 336413

FR Aviation Limited (1)
Bournemouth International Airport
Christchurch, Dorsetshire, BH23 6NE, United Kingdom
Tel.: (44) 1202 409 000
Emp.: 400
Aircraft Surveillance Maintenance Services
S.I.C.: 7629
N.A.I.C.S.: 811219
Peter Nottage *(Mng Dir)*

Subsidiary:

FR Aviation Services Limited (2)
Bournemouth International Airport
Christchurch, Dorset, BH23 6NE, United Kingdom
Tel.: (44) 1202 409100
Fax: (44) 1202 478333
Emp.: 400
Aircraft Repair & Maintenance Services
S.I.C.: 7539
N.A.I.C.S.: 811198
Peter Nottage *(Gen Mgr)*

Lockman Electronic Holdings Limited (1)
4th Ave Globe Park
Marlow, Buckinghamshire, SL7 1YD, United Kingdom
Tel.: (44) 1628472072
Fax: (44) 1628890179
Investment Management Services
S.I.C.: 6211
N.A.I.C.S.: 523999

Micromill Electronics Limited (1)
Leydene House Waterberry Drive
Waterlooville, Hampshire, PO7 7XX, United Kingdom
Tel.: (44) 2392 366600
Fax: (44) 2392 366673
E-Mail: micromill.sales@cobham.com
Electronic Equipment Research & Development Services
S.I.C.: 8731
N.A.I.C.S.: 541712

U.S. Subsidiaries:

Chelton Avionics, Inc (1)
6400 Wilkinson Dr
Prescott, AZ 86301-6164
Tel.: (928) 708-1550
Fax: (928) 708-1532
Aircraft Communication System Mfr
S.I.C.: 3663
N.A.I.C.S.: 334220
John Payne *(Gen Mgr)*

Chelton Inc. (1)
Ste 200 1955 Lakeway Dr
Lewisville, TX 75057-6448
Tel.: (972) 221-1783
Fax: (972) 436-2716
E-Mail: info@cheltoninc.com
Web Site: www.chelton.com
Emp.: 50
Holding Company
S.I.C.: 6719
N.A.I.C.S.: 551112
Michael Wilkerson *(Pres)*

Non-U.S. Subsidiaries:

Chelton Antennas SA (2)
7 Chemin de Vaubesnard
91410 Dourdan, France
Tel.: (33) 1 60 81 5555
Fax: (33) 1 60 81 5556
E-Mail: cobham-antennas@cobham.com
Web Site: www.chelton-antennas.com
Emp.: 80
Aerospace Communication Equipment Mfr
S.I.C.: 3728
N.A.I.C.S.: 336413
Jean-Marc Billaud *(Gen Mgr)*

Chelton Limited (2)
The Chelton Centre 4th Ave
Marlow, Buckinghamshire, SL7 1TF, United Kingdom UK
Tel.: (44) 1628472072 (100%)
Fax: (44) 1628482255
E-Mail: info@chelton.co.uk
Web Site: www.chelton.co.uk
Emp.: 450
Aerospace Systems Design & Mfr
S.I.C.: 3812
N.A.I.C.S.: 334511
Chris Shaw *(Dir-Ops)*

Cobham Electronic Systems Inc. (1)
1011 Pawtucket Blvd
Lowell, MA 01853 DE
Tel.: (978) 442-4000
Fax: (978) 442-4001
Web Site: www.cobham.com
Sales Range: $200-249.9 Million
Emp.: 600
Microwave & Radio Communications Systems Developer & Mfr
S.I.C.: 3669
N.A.I.C.S.: 334290
Joe Thomas *(Pres & CEO)*

Unit:

Cobham Electronic Systems, Inc. - San Jose (2)
5300 Hellyer Ave
San Jose, CA 95138-1003
Tel.: (408) 624-3000
Fax: (408) 624-3905
Web Site: www.cobhamdes.com
Emp.: 345
Microwave & Radio Communications Systems Developer & Mfr
S.I.C.: 5065
N.A.I.C.S.: 423690
Kevin Carlson *(Mgr-IT)*

Comant Industries, Inc (1)
577 Burning Tree Rd
Fullerton, CA 92833
Tel.: (714) 870-2420
Fax: (714) 870-5133
E-Mail: ComantCustomerService@Cobham.com
Web Site: www.comant.com
Aircraft Communication Equipment Mfr
S.I.C.: 3663
N.A.I.C.S.: 334220
Walt Stierhoff *(Gen Mgr)*

Conax Florida Corporation (1)
2801 75th St N
Saint Petersburg, FL 33710
Tel.: (727) 345-8000
Fax: (727) 345-4217
E-Mail: sales@conaxfl.com
Web Site: www.conaxfl.com
Aircraft Parts Mfr
S.I.C.: 3728
N.A.I.C.S.: 336413
David Sapio *(Gen Mgr)*

Continental Microwave & Tool Co, Inc (1)
11 Continental Dr
Exeter, NH 03833
Tel.: (603) 775-5200
Fax: (603) 775-5201
Web Site: www.cobham.com
Electronic Component Mfr
S.I.C.: 3679

N.A.I.C.S.: 334419

DTC Communications, Inc. (1)
486 Amherst St
Nashua, NH 03063-1224 NH
Tel.: (603) 880-4411 (100%)
Fax: (603) 880-6965
Toll Free: (800) 233-8639
E-Mail: info@cobham.com
Web Site: www.dtccom.com
Sales Range: $10-24.9 Million
Emp.: 110
Miniature Wireless Audio & Video Communication Products Designer & Mfr Import Export
S.I.C.: 3663
N.A.I.C.S.: 334220
Henry W. Pomije *(Pres & CEO)*

Global Microwave Systems, Inc (1)
1916 Palomar Oaks Way Ste 100
Carlsbad, CA 92008-5523
Tel.: (760) 496-0055
Fax: (760) 496-0057
Toll Free: (888) 880-9339
E-Mail: sales@gmsinc.com
Web Site: www.gmsinc.com
Emp.: 48
Microwave Communication Equipment Mfr
S.I.C.: 3669
N.A.I.C.S.: 334290
Craig Herriott *(Mgr-Site)*

Kevlin Corporation (1)
596 Lowell St
Methuen, MA 01844 MA
Tel.: (978) 557-2400 (100%)
Fax: (978) 557-2800
Web Site: www.kevlin.com
Emp.: 75
Microwave Devices for Uses in Military Commercial Radar Systems Design & Mfr Export
S.I.C.: 3679
N.A.I.C.S.: 334419

Unit:

MAST Microwave (2)
5 Cornell Pl
Wilmington, MA 01887-2129 (100%)
Tel.: (978) 694-9595
Emp.: 10
Mfr. of Low Cost Rotary Couplers & Special Connectors
S.I.C.: 3679
N.A.I.C.S.: 334419

Nurad Technologies, Inc (1)
3310 Carlins Park Dr
Baltimore, MD 21215
Tel.: (410) 542-1700
Fax: (410) 542-9184
Web Site: www.nurad.com
Radar Communication Equipment Mfr
S.I.C.: 3669
N.A.I.C.S.: 334290
Larry Bielak *(Mgr-CADD)*

REMEC Defense & Space, Inc (1)
9404 Chesapeake Dr
San Diego, CA 92123
Tel.: (858) 560-1301
Fax: (858) 560-0291
Web Site: www.cobham.com
Aircraft Parts Mfr
S.I.C.: 3728
N.A.I.C.S.: 336413

RVision Inc. (1)
2365 Paragon Dr Ste A
San Jose, CA 95131 CA
Tel.: (408) 437-5777
Fax: (408) 437-9923
Web Site: www.rvisionusa.com
Emp.: 40
Photographic Equipment Mfr
S.I.C.: 3579
N.A.I.C.S.: 333316
Dermitt McCarthy *(VP-Sls)*

S-TEC Corporation (1)
1 S-Tec Way Municipal Airport
Mineral Wells, TX 76067
Tel.: (817) 215-7600
Fax: (940) 325-3904
E-Mail: info@s-tec.com
Web Site: www.s-tec.com
Aircraft Parts Mfr
S.I.C.: 3728
N.A.I.C.S.: 336413

SeaTel, Inc. (1)
4030 Nelson Ave
Concord, CA 94520 CA
Tel.: (925) 798-7979 (100%)
Fax: (925) 798-7986
Toll Free: (888) 798-7979
E-Mail: satcom.concordsales@cobham.com
Web Site: www.cobham.com
Sales Range: $25-49.9 Million
Emp.: 240
Marine Satellite Communication Antenna Systems Mfr
S.I.C.: 3663
N.A.I.C.S.: 334220
Paul H. Jona *(Sr VP)*

Sensor & Antenna Systems, Lansdale, Inc (1)
305 Richardson Rd
Lansdale, PA 19446
Tel.: (215) 996-2000
Fax: (215) 996-2088
Web Site: www.cobham.com
Aircraft Parts Mfr
S.I.C.: 3728
N.A.I.C.S.: 336413

TracStar Systems, Inc (1)
1551 College Park Business Ctr Rd
Orlando, FL 32804
Tel.: (407) 650-9054
Fax: (407) 650-9086
Toll Free: (888) 650-9054
E-Mail: sales@tracstar.net
Web Site: www.tracstar.net
Satellite Tracking System Mfr
S.I.C.: 3669
N.A.I.C.S.: 334290

Trivec-Avant Corporation (1)
17831 Jamestown Ln
Huntington Beach, CA 92647 CA
Tel.: (714) 841-4976
E-Mail: info@trivec.com
Web Site: www.trivec.com
Sales Range: $50-74.9 Million
Emp.: 75
Antenna Systems Mfr
S.I.C.: 3663
N.A.I.C.S.: 334220
Allen Muesse *(Pres)*

Non-U.S. Subsidiaries:

AFI Flight Inspection GmbH (1)
Hermann Blenk Strasse 34
Braunschweig, 38108, Germany
Tel.: (49) 531 235 27 0
Fax: (49) 531 235 27 99
Web Site: www.cobham.com
Emp.: 20
Flight Inspection Services
S.I.C.: 9651
N.A.I.C.S.: 926150
Wolfgang Joeres *(Gen Mgr)*

Air Precision SAS (1)
5 Avenue Denis Papin
BP 35
92393 Le Plessis-Robinson, France
Tel.: (33) 1 46 01 2124
Fax: (33) 1 46 61 8525
E-Mail: aerosales@airprecision.com
Web Site: www.airprecision.com
Aircraft Equipment Mfr
S.I.C.: 3728
N.A.I.C.S.: 336413

Cobham Antenna Systems (1)
Box 1134
16422 Kista, Sweden
Tel.: (46) 8 477 68 00
Fax: (46) 8 751 00 19
Microwave Component Mfr
S.I.C.: 3679
N.A.I.C.S.: 334419
Hans Wallgren *(Gen Mgr)*

Cobham Aviation Services Pty Limited (1)
National Drive Adelaide Airport
Adelaide, SA, 5950, Australia
Tel.: (61) 8 8154 7000
Fax: (61) 8 8154 7019
Contract Aviation Services
S.I.C.: 4581
N.A.I.C.S.: 488119
Peter Nottage *(CEO)*

Cobham (India) Pvt Limited (1)
Cobham India Liaison Office 4th Floor Birla Tower 25 Barakhamba Road
New Delhi, 110001, India
Tel.: (91) 11 451 72300
Fax: (91) 11 451 72310
E-Mail: cobhamindia@cobham.com
Web Site: www.cobham.com
Aircraft Parts Mfr
S.I.C.: 3728
N.A.I.C.S.: 336413
Lee Griffith *(Mng Dir)*

Cobham Tracking and Locating Limited (1)
120 Eileen Stubbs Ave Ste 200
Dartmouth, NS, B3B 1Y1, Canada
Tel.: (902) 468-3007
Fax: (902) 468-3009
E-Mail: sales1@cobhamtl.com
Web Site: www.cobhamtl.com
Emp.: 10
Electronic Tracking Machinery Mfr
S.I.C.: 3679
N.A.I.C.S.: 334419

Hyper-Technologies SAS (1)
28 Rue des Dames
78340 Les Clayes-sous-Bois, France
Tel.: (33) 1 305 507 05
Fax: (33) 1 305 419 40
Emp.: 115
Aircraft Equipment Mfr
S.I.C.: 3728
N.A.I.C.S.: 336413
Jean-luc Rodet *(CEO)*

Label SAS (1)
18 Rue de Montreal
BP 439
Ville la Grand, Annemasse, 74108, France
Tel.: (33) 450 87 7250
Fax: (33) 450 37 6751
E-Mail: label.sales@cobham.com
Web Site: www.label.fr
Emp.: 80
Aircraft Equipment Mfr
S.I.C.: 3728
N.A.I.C.S.: 336413
Bernard Meynet *(Mng Dir)*

Mastsystem International Oy (1)
Muovilaaksontie 8
Heinavaara, Finland
Tel.: (358) 13 737 7111
Fax: (358) 13 737 7113
E-Mail: mastsystems@cobham.com
Automotive Parts Mfr
S.I.C.: 3714
N.A.I.C.S.: 336390
Heikki Miettinen *(Mng Dir)*

National Air Support Pty Limited (1)
National Drive Adelaide Airport
Adelaide, SA, 5950, Australia
Tel.: (61) 8 8154 5600
Fax: (61) 8 8154 5624
Web Site: www.cobham.com
Aviation Support Services
S.I.C.: 4581
N.A.I.C.S.: 488190

NEC Aero SAS (1)
174 Quai De Jemmapes
75010 Paris, France
Tel.: (33) 153389898
Fax: (33) 142006783
E-Mail: avionics.necsales@cobham.com
Web Site: www.nec-aero.com
Emp.: 100
Aircraft Component Mfr
S.I.C.: 3728
N.A.I.C.S.: 336413
Eiji Kawaishi *(Chm)*

Omnipless Manufacturing (Proprietary) Limited (1)
PO Box 31093
Tokai, Cape Town, South Africa
Mailing Address:
PO Box 31093
Cape Town, 7966, South Africa
Tel.: (27) 21 700 7000
Fax: (27) 21 700 7199
E-Mail: omnipless@cobham.com
Web Site: www.omnipless.com
Emp.: 20
Electronic Equipment Mfr & Distr
S.I.C.: 3679

N.A.I.C.S.: 334419
Erwin Schumann *(Gen Mgr)*

Spectronic Denmark A/S (1)
Skindbjergvej 44
8500 Grena, Denmark
Tel.: (45) 8791 8100
Fax: (45) 8791 8181
E-Mail: tcs.grenaa.sales@cobham.com
Web Site: www.spectronic.com
Emp.: 70
Surveillance Equipment Mfr
S.I.C.: 3812
N.A.I.C.S.: 334511
Henrik Mortensen *(Gen Mgr)*

Surveillance Australia Pty Limited (1)
National Drive Adelaide Airport
Adelaide, SA, 5950, Australia
Tel.: (61) 8 81545670
Fax: (61) 8 8154 5674
Aircraft Surveillance System Mfr
S.I.C.: 3812
N.A.I.C.S.: 334511

TEAM SA (1)
35 Rue de Montlhery
Silic, 94563, France
Tel.: (33) 1 49 78 66 00
Fax: (33) 1 49 78 66 99
Web Site: www.team-avionics.com
Emp.: 70
Aircraft Machinery Mfr
S.I.C.: 3728
N.A.I.C.S.: 336413
Eiji Kawaishi *(Mng Dir)*

Thrane & Thrane A/S (1)
Lundtoftegaardsvej 93 D
DK-2800 Lyngby, Denmark DK
Tel.: (45) 39558800 (50.1%)
Fax: (45) 039558888
E-Mail: info@tt.dk
Web Site: www.thrane.com
THRAN—(CSE)
Emp.: 602
Terminals & Land Earth Stations for Global Mobile Satellite & Radio Communication Mfr
S.I.C.: 4899
N.A.I.C.S.: 517410
Niels Heering *(Chm)*
Svend Age Lundgaard Jensen *(CFO)*
Kim Gammelholm *(Sr VP-Sys)*

Subsidiary:

Thrane & Thrane Aalborg A/S (2)
Porsvej 93B
2800 Aalborg, Denmark
Tel.: (45) 39558800
Fax: (45) 39558888
E-Mail: info@thrane.com
Web Site: www.thranne.com
Emp.: 700
Measuring & Controlling Device Mfr
S.I.C.: 3829
N.A.I.C.S.: 334519
Walter Thygesen *(Mgr)*

U.S. Subsidiary:

Thrane & Thrane Inc. (2)
509 Viking Dr Ste KLM
Virginia Beach, VA 23452 (100%)
Tel.: (757) 463-9557
Fax: (757) 463-9581
E-Mail: writeus@thrane.com
Web Site: www.us.thrane.com
Emp.: 20
Distr of Satellite Communications Equipment
S.I.C.: 4899
N.A.I.C.S.: 517410
Christian Cock *(VP-Landmobile Bus Dev)*

Non-U.S. Subsidiaries:

European Satellite Link GmbH (2)
Muhlenstieg 5
D 22041 Hamburg, Germany
Tel.: (49) 40682770
Fax: (49) 4068277135
E-Mail: esl@thrane.com
Web Site: www.eslworld.eu
Emp.: 35
Supplier of Satellite Communications Equipment
S.I.C.: 4899
N.A.I.C.S.: 517410

Cobham plc—(Continued)

Henrick Christensen *(Mng Dir)*
Nekolai Hvegholm *(Mng Dir)*

Naval Electronics AB (2)
Hojdrodergatan 18
212 39 Malmo, Scania, Sweden
Tel.: (46) 40292045
Fax: (46) 40 18 74 13
E-Mail: sales@naval.se
Web Site: www.naval.se
Emp.: 15
Marine Communication Equipments Mfr
S.I.C.: 3663
N.A.I.C.S.: 334220

Thrane & Thrane Norge AS (2)
Bergerveien 12
PO Box 91
1375 Billingstad, Norway NO
Tel.: (47) 67244700
Fax: (47) 67244310
E-Mail: marketing_nera@thrane.com
Web Site: www.thrane.com
Emp.: 10
Supplier of Satellite Communications Equipment
S.I.C.: 4899
N.A.I.C.S.: 517410

Subsidiaries:

Thrane & Thrane Airtime A/S (3)
Bergerveien 12
PO Box 91
1375 Billingstad, Norway
Tel.: (47) 67244700
Fax: (47) 67 24 47 01
Mobile Communications Equipment Mfr
S.I.C.: 3663
N.A.I.C.S.: 334220

COBRA AUTOMOTIVE TECHNOLOGIES S.P.A.

Via Astico 41
21100 Varese, Italy
Tel.: (39) 0332825111
Fax: (39) 0332222005
E-Mail: info@cobra-at.com
Web Site: www.cobra-at.com
COB—(ITA)
Rev.: $210,862,723
Assets: $260,473,126
Liabilities: $207,987,304
Net Worth: $52,485,822
Earnings: ($20,060,625)
Emp.: 881
Fiscal Year-end: 12/31/12

Business Description:
Security Solutions for Automotive Market
S.I.C.: 7382
N.A.I.C.S.: 561621

Personnel:
Serafino Memmola *(Chm)*
Mario Rossetti *(CEO)*

Board of Directors:
Serafino Memmola
Paolo Alessandro Bonazzi
Angela Gamba
Diva Moriani
Giorgio Palli
Mario Rossetti

Subsidiary:

Cobra Italia S.p.A. (1)
SS Km 35 del Sempione 212
21052 Busto Arsizio, Varese, Italy
Tel.: (39) 0331 072200
Fax: (39) 0331 381212
Web Site: www.cobra-at.com
Automotive Security Device Mfr
S.I.C.: 3714
N.A.I.C.S.: 336320

Non-U.S. Subsidiaries:

Cobra Automotive Technologies UK Ltd. (1)
Cobra House Brooklands Close
Sunbury-on-Thames, Middlesex, TW16 7DX, United Kingdom
Tel.: (44) 1932772400
Fax: (44) 1932732338
E-Mail: info-uk@cobra-at.com
Web Site: www.cobrasecurity.couk
Emp.: 26
Automotive Security Systems Mfr
S.I.C.: 3714
N.A.I.C.S.: 336320

Cobra Beijing Automotive Technologies Co., Ltd. (1)
Building No 21 KangDing Rd 11
Beijing, 100176, China
Tel.: (86) 1067803288
Fax: (86) 1067803298
Emp.: 100
Design, Manufacture & Marketing of Electronic Automotive Security Systems
S.I.C.: 7382
N.A.I.C.S.: 561621
Fabrizio Finocchiaro *(Mng Dir)*

Cobra Deutschland GmbH (1)
Buschurweg 4
76870 Kandel, Rhineland-Palatinate, Germany
Tel.: (49) 7275 913260
Fax: (49) 7275 913274
E-Mail: info.de@cobra-at.com
Web Site: www.cobra-alarm.de
Emp.: 6
Automotive Security Systems Distr
S.I.C.: 5063
N.A.I.C.S.: 423610
Carmine Carella *(Mng Dir)*
Patrick de Bazin *(Mng Dir)*

Cobra do Brasil Servicos de Telematica Ltda. (1)
Ave Jose Rocha Bomfim 214 SL 228-229 Bloco H
Praca Santa Genebra, 13080-900
Campinas, Sao Paulo, Brazil
Tel.: (55) 19 3709 1670
Fax: (55) 19 3709 1673
Web Site: www.cobra-at.com
Emp.: 3
Vehicle Telemetry & Tracking Services
S.I.C.: 7389
N.A.I.C.S.: 561990

Cobra Japan K.K. (1)
Kakiya Building 2-7-17 Shin-Yokohama
Kohoku-ku, Yokohama, Kanagawa, 222-0033, Japan
Tel.: (81) 45 474 3610
Fax: (81) 45 474 3630
Security Systems Mfr
S.I.C.: 3679
N.A.I.C.S.: 334419

Cobra Telematics Development SA (1)
WTC 1 Bldg 1 1300 Route Des Cretes
06560 Sophia-Antipolis, France
Tel.: (33) 492383800
Fax: (33) 492383801
E-Mail: j.godare@cobratelematics.com
Web Site: www.cobratelematics.com
Emp.: 22
Software Development
S.I.C.: 7372
N.A.I.C.S.: 511210
Paolo De Giusti *(Gen Mgr)*

Cobra UK Ltd. (1)
Crossgate House Cross Street
Sale, Cheshire, M33 7FT, United Kingdom
Tel.: (44) 8700110050
Fax: (44) 8702390039
E-Mail: info-uk@cobra-at.com
Web Site: www.cobravehiclesecurity.co.uk
Emp.: 40
Vehicle Telemetry & Tracking Services
S.I.C.: 7389
N.A.I.C.S.: 561990
Andrew Smith *(Mng Dir)*

COBRA HOLDINGS PLC

110 Fenchurch Street
London, EC3M 5JT, United Kingdom
Tel.: (44) 2072040014
Fax: (44) 2072040019
Web Site: www.cobraholdings.co.uk
Year Founded: 2006
CBRA—(LSE)
Sales Range: $25-49.9 Million
Emp.: 272

Business Description:
Insurance Brokerage Services
S.I.C.: 6411
N.A.I.C.S.: 524298

Personnel:
Stephen Mark Burrows *(CEO)*
David Stanley *(COO)*

Board of Directors:
Peter James Robinson
Stephen Mark Burrows
David Harris
John Lincoln
David Stanley
Dominic Wainford

Legal Counsel:
ASB Law
Innovis House 108 High Street
Crawley, United Kingdom

ASB Law
Horizon House 1 Eclipse Park Sittingbourne Road
Maidstone, United Kingdom

Subsidiaries:

COBRA Financial Services Limited (1)
Canterbury House 2-6 Sydenham Road
Croydon, Surrey, CR0 9XE, United Kingdom
Tel.: (44) 20 8256 1910
Fax: (44) 20 8681 2174
E-Mail: enquiries@cobrafs.co.uk
Web Site: www.cobrafs.co.uk
Financial Advisory Services
S.I.C.: 6282
N.A.I.C.S.: 523930
Lee Wallis *(Mng Dir)*

COBRA Network Limited (1)
110 Fenchurch Street
London, EC3M 5JT, United Kingdom
Tel.: (44) 20 7204 0014
Fax: (44) 20 7204 0019
E-Mail: info@cobranetwork.co.uk
Web Site: www.cobranetwork.co.uk
Emp.: 10
Insurance Brokerage Services
S.I.C.: 6411
N.A.I.C.S.: 524210
Steve Burrows *(CEO)*
John Lincoln *(Mng Dir)*

COBRA Underwriting Agencies Limited (1)
1st Floor Canterbury House 2-6 Sydenham Road
Croydon, Surrey, CR0 9XE, United Kingdom
Tel.: (44) 20 8256 1910
Fax: (44) 20 8256 1975
E-Mail: enquiries@cobraunderwriting.co.uk
Web Site: www.cobraunderwriting.co.uk
Insurance Underwriting Services
S.I.C.: 6361
N.A.I.C.S.: 524127
Steve Burrows *(CEO)*
Michael Bowler *(Mng Dir)*

COBRA UK & Ireland Limited (1)
Old Lloyd's Chambers 139 Manchester Road
Broadheath, Altrincham, Cheshire, WA14 5HY, United Kingdom
Tel.: (44) 161 928 4444
Fax: (44) 161 928 4555
E-Mail: sales@uk-ireland-insurance.com
Web Site: www.cobrauki.co.uk
Emp.: 21
Insurance Brokerage Services
S.I.C.: 6411
N.A.I.C.S.: 524210
Martin Hoult *(Acct Dir)*

COBRA VENTURE CORPORATION

2489 Bellevue Avenue
West Vancouver, BC, V7V 1E1, Canada
Tel.: (604) 922-2030
Fax: (604) 922-2037
Toll Free: (888) 888-9122
E-Mail: cbv@telus.net
Web Site: www.cobraventure.com
Year Founded: 1999
CBV—(TSXV)
Rev.: $207,724
Assets: $7,239,672
Liabilities: $1,256,489
Net Worth: $5,983,183
Earnings: ($611,242)
Fiscal Year-end: 11/30/12

Business Description:
Oil & Gas Exploration Services
S.I.C.: 1389
N.A.I.C.S.: 213112

Personnel:
Daniel B. Evans *(Pres & CEO)*
Cyrus H. Driver *(CFO)*
Mike Perkins *(Sec)*

Board of Directors:
Cyrus H. Driver
Daniel B. Evans
David H. Evans
William Murray Rodgers

Legal Counsel:
Borden Ladner Gervais LLP
1000 Canterra Tower 400 3rd Ave SW
Calgary, AB, T2P 4H2, Canada

Transfer Agent:
Computershare Trust Company of Canada
9th Floor 100 University Avenue
Toronto, ON, Canada

COBRE MONTANA NL

(Formerly Midwinter Resources NL)
Suite 3 23 Belgravia Street
Belmont, WA, 6104, Australia 6005
Mailing Address:
PO Box 588
Belmont, WA, 6984, Australia
Tel.: (61) 8 6145 0288
Fax: (61) 8 9475 0847
E-Mail: info@cobremontana.com.au
Web Site: www.cobremontana.com.au
CXB—(ASX)
Sales Range: Less than $1 Million

Business Description:
Gold & Copper Exploration Services
S.I.C.: 1041
N.A.I.C.S.: 212221

Personnel:
Eduardo Javier Valenzuela *(Chm)*
Adrian Griffin *(Mng Dir)*
Belinda Ting *(CFO)*
Amanda Wilton-Heald *(Sec)*

Board of Directors:
Eduardo Javier Valenzuela
Bryan Dixon
Adrian Griffin

COBRIZA METALS CORP.

(Acquired & Absorbed by Candente Copper Corp.)

COBURG GROUP PLC

Unit 3 Harrington Way Warspite Road
Woolwich, London, SE18 5NU, United Kingdom
Tel.: (44) 2083170103
Fax: (44) 2088555664
E-Mail: info@coburg-group.com
Web Site: www.coburg-group.com
Sales Range: $1-9.9 Million
Emp.: 33

Business Description:
Investment Holding Company
S.I.C.: 6719
N.A.I.C.S.: 551112

Personnel:
Chris W. Birkle *(Chm)*
Bryan A. Stockley *(Mng Dir)*
Louisa E. Pino *(Sec)*

Board of Directors:
Chris W. Birkle
Christopher John Ells

Konrad P. Legg
Jeremy S.P. Maynard
Mark Edwin Parker
Bryan A. Stockley

COBURN JAPAN CORPORATION

1-6-11 Minato
Chuo-ku, Tokyo, 104-0043, Japan
Tel.: (81) 335535721
Fax: (81) 335535771
E-Mail: info@coburn.jp
Web Site: www.coburn.co.jp
Year Founded: 1978
Emp.: 29
Business Description:
Holographic Films Mfr
S.I.C.: 3081
N.A.I.C.S.: 326113
Personnel:
Toru Kojima *(Mng Dir)*

COCA-COLA AMATIL LIMITED

40 Mount Street
North Sydney, NSW, 2060, Australia
Tel.: (61) 2 9259 6159 (Investor Relations)
Fax: (61) 292596623
E-Mail: aus_investor_relations@anz.ccamatil.com
Web Site: www.ccamatil.com
Year Founded: 1904
CCL—(ASX)
Rev.: $5,355,560,320
Assets: $7,004,996,200
Liabilities: $4,838,887,140
Net Worth: $2,166,109,060
Earnings: $479,470,210
Emp.: 15,000
Fiscal Year-end: 12/31/12
Business Description:
Holding Company; Carbonated & Non-Carbonated Beverages Mfr & Distr
S.I.C.: 6719
N.A.I.C.S.: 551112
Personnel:
Alison Watkins *(Grp Mng Dir)*
Nessa O'Sullivan *(CFO)*
Barry Simpson *(CIO)*
Erich Rey *(Pres-Indonesia)*
George Forster *(Gen Counsel & Sec)*
Board of Directors:
David Michael Gonski
Ilana Rachel Atlas
Catherine Michelle Brenner
Anthony Froggatt
Martin Jansen
Geoffrey J. Kelly
Wal M. King
David E. Meiklejohn
Subsidiaries:

CCA Bayswater Pty Ltd (1)
41 Jersey Rd
Bayswater, VIC, 3153, Australia
Tel.: (61) 397296788
Fax: (61) 397204896
Canned Fruits Jam & Vegetables Mfr
S.I.C.: 2037
N.A.I.C.S.: 311411

Coca-Cola Amatil Pty Ltd (1)
40 Mount St
North Sydney, NSW, 2059, Australia AU
Tel.: (61) 292596800
Fax: (61) 292596681
E-Mail: consumer_information@ccamatil.com
Web Site: www.cocacola.com.au
Sales Range: $1-4.9 Billion
Emp.: 2,000
Carbonated & Non-Carbonated Beverages Mfr & Distr
S.I.C.: 2086
N.A.I.C.S.: 312111
Warrick White *(Mng Dir)*

Subsidiaries:

Can Recycling (S.A.) Pty Ltd (2)
16a Duncan Ct
Ottoway, Adelaide, SA, 5013, Australia
Tel.: (61) 883412511
Fax: (61) 83412494
Emp.: 12
Plastic Can Recycling Services
S.I.C.: 4953
N.A.I.C.S.: 562920
Tony Skidizecchia *(Mgr)*

Crusta Fruit Juices Proprietary Limited (2)
Virgo Rd
Ramco, SA, 5322, Australia
Tel.: (61) 885410100
Fax: (61) 883590022
Emp.: 40
Fresh Juice Mfr
S.I.C.: 2037
N.A.I.C.S.: 311411
Ashley Brown *(Mgr-Ops Excellence)*

Quenchy Crusta Sales Pty Ltd (2)
17 Duncan Rd
Dry Creek, Adelaide, SA, 5094, Australia
Tel.: (61) 883590011
Fax: (61) 883590022
Soft Drinks Distr
S.I.C.: 5149
N.A.I.C.S.: 424490

Quirks Australia Pty Ltd (2)
198 Power St
Glendenning, NSW, 2761, Australia
Tel.: (61) 288052500
E-Mail: sales@quirksaustralia.com.au
Web Site: www.quirksaustralia.com.au
Commercial Refrigeration Rental & Installation Services
S.I.C.: 1711
N.A.I.C.S.: 238220

Matila Nominees Pty Limited (1)
L 15 71 Macquarie St
Sydney, NSW, 2000, Australia
Tel.: (61) 292596130
Fax: (61) 292596233
Soft Drinks Mfr
S.I.C.: 2086
N.A.I.C.S.: 312111

Neverfail Bottled Water Co Pty Limited (1)
L7 Building 2 423 Pennant Hills Road
Pennant Hills, NSW, 2120, Australia
Tel.: (61) 294367000
Fax: (61) 0294367001
E-Mail: info@neverfail.com.au
Web Site: www.neverfail.com.au
Emp.: 200
Bottled Water Mfr & Distr
S.I.C.: 2086
N.A.I.C.S.: 312112

Subsidiary:

Piccadilly Natural Springs Pty Ltd (2)
70 Hardys Rd
Torrensville, SA, 5031, Australia
Tel.: (61) 294367000
Fax: (61) 130085803
Spring & Bottled Water Distr
S.I.C.: 5149
N.A.I.C.S.: 424490

Neverfail Springwater Co (Qld) Pty Limited (1)
1 Tolmer Pl
Chatswood, QLD, 4127, Australia
Tel.: (61) 1300 300204
Fax: (61) 1300 85803
Spring Water Distr
S.I.C.: 5149
N.A.I.C.S.: 424490

Neverfail Springwater Limited (1)
L 2 29-57 Christie St
Saint Leonards, NSW, 2065, Australia
Tel.: (61) 294367000
Fax: (61) 294367001
E-Mail: mhsoffer@neverfail.com.au
Web Site: www.neverfail.com.au
Emp.: 100
Spring & Bottled Water Distr
S.I.C.: 5149
N.A.I.C.S.: 424490
Glenn Gunston *(Gen Mgr)*

SPC Ardmona Limited (1)
50 Camberwell Rd
Hawthorn, VIC, 3123, Australia
Tel.: (61) 398618900
Fax: (61) 398618911
E-Mail: info@spcardmona.com.au
Web Site: www.spcardmona.com.au
Emp.: 100
Packaged Fruit Producer
S.I.C.: 2037
N.A.I.C.S.: 311411
John Deppe *(Gen Mgr-Intl Bus)*

Subsidiaries:

Ardmona Foods Limited (2)
Andrew Failey Ave
Shepparton, VIC, 3630, Australia
Tel.: (61) 358333777
Fax: (61) 358222131
Web Site: www.spcardmona.com.au
Emp.: 600
Canned Fruit Jam & Vegetable Mfr
S.I.C.: 2037
N.A.I.C.S.: 311411
Dince Pinneri *(CEO)*

Henry Jones Foods Pty Ltd (2)
PO Box 207
Shepparton, VIC, 3632, Australia
Tel.: (61) 358521111
Fax: (61) 358521178
Specialty Food Mfr & Distr
S.I.C.: 2038
N.A.I.C.S.: 311412

SPC Ardmona Operations Limited (2)
50 Camberwell Road
Hawthorn East, VIC, 3123, Australia
Tel.: (61) 398618900
Fax: (61) 398618911
E-Mail: webmail@spcardmona.com.au
Processed Fruit & Vegetable Mfr
S.I.C.: 2037
N.A.I.C.S.: 311411

Subsidiary:

Austral International Trading Company Pty Ltd (3)
50 Camberwell Rd
Hawthorn East, VIC, Australia
Tel.: (61) 398618900
Fax: (61) 398618911
Food Products Distr
S.I.C.: 5142
N.A.I.C.S.: 424420
Nigel Garrard *(DIR)*

Non-U.S. Subsidiaries:

SPC Ardmona (Germany) GmbH (2)
Agnesstrasse 30
22301 Hamburg, Germany
Tel.: (49) 4023841120
Fax: (49) 4023841118
E-Mail: info@spcardmona.de
Web Site: www.spcardmona.de
Emp.: 1
Packaged Fruits & Vegetables Distr
S.I.C.: 5148
N.A.I.C.S.: 424480
Jerold Obrien *(Gen Mgr)*

SPC Ardmona (Netherlands) BV (2)
Prins Bernhardplein 200
Amsterdam, Noord-Holland, 1097 JB, Netherlands
Tel.: (31) 205214777
Fruit Jam & Vegetable Mfr
S.I.C.: 2037
N.A.I.C.S.: 311411

SPC Ardmona (Spain), S.L.U. (2)
Carretera De Caravaca Moratalla km 1
Moratalla, Murcia, 30440, Spain
Tel.: (34) 968607500
Fax: (34) 968607917
Convenience Food Retailer
S.I.C.: 5411
N.A.I.C.S.: 445120

Non-U.S. Subsidiaries:

CCKBC Holdings Ltd (1)
Era House Floors 7-12 2 Diagorou Street
Nicosia, 1097, Cyprus
Tel.: (357) 22022999
Fax: (357) 22022900
Investment Management Services
S.I.C.: 6211
N.A.I.C.S.: 523999

Coca-Cola Amatil (Fiji) Ltd (1)
Laucala Beach Estate Ratu Dovi Rd
Nasinu, Fiji
Tel.: (679) 3394 333
Fax: (679) 39 44 06
Emp.: 10
Soft Drinks Mfr & Distr
S.I.C.: 2086
N.A.I.C.S.: 312111
Andrew Preece *(Gen Mgr)*

Coca-Cola Amatil (PNG) Ltd (1)
Erica St Lae
Lae, Morobe, Papua New Guinea
Tel.: (675) 4721033
Fax: (675) 4720443
Web Site: www.ccamatilpng.com
Soft Drink Mfr & Distr
S.I.C.: 5149
N.A.I.C.S.: 424490

Paradise Beverages (Fiji) Limited (1)
(Formerly Fosters Group Pacific Ltd.)
122-164 Foster Rd Walu Bay
PO Box 696
Suva, Fiji FJ
Tel.: (679) 3315811 (89.6%)
Telex: 2204 FJ
Fax: (679) 3300408
FGP—(SPSE)
Emp.: 300
Beer, Ready-to-Drink Alcoholic Beverages & Soft Drinks Mfr & Distr
S.I.C.: 2082
N.A.I.C.S.: 312120
Vinish Singh *(Sec)*

PT Coca-Cola Distribution Indonesia (1)
Jl Rawa Bulak I Kawasan Industri
Pulogadung Bl 3-T/11 Jatinegara
Cakung, Jakarta, Indonesia
Tel.: (62) 21 4603124
Fax: (62) 21 4602659
Soft Drink Distr
S.I.C.: 5149
N.A.I.C.S.: 424490

Vending Management Services Ltd (1)
67a Norfolk Road
Masterton, New Zealand
Tel.: (64) 6 377 0002
Fax: (64) 6 378 2468
E-Mail: info@vmsl.co.nz
Web Site: www.vmsl.co.nz
Emp.: 25
Soft Drink Vending Machine Software Development Services
S.I.C.: 7371
N.A.I.C.S.: 541511
Andy Kerr *(Gen Mgr)*

COCA-COLA CENTRAL JAPAN CO., LTD.

(Name Changed to Coca-Cola East Japan Co., Ltd.)

COCA-COLA EAST JAPAN CO., LTD.

(Formerly Coca-Cola Central Japan Co., Ltd.)
Kokusai Shin-Akasaka West Building
6-1-20 Akasaka
Minato-ku, Tokyo, 107-0052, Japan
Tel.: (81) 3 5575 3797 (IR)
E-Mail: ir@ccej.co.jp
Web Site: www.ccej.co.jp
Year Founded: 2001
2580—(NGO TKS)
Sales Range: $1-4.9 Billion
Emp.: 8,039
Business Description:
Holding Company; Soft Drink Mfr, Bottler & Distr
S.I.C.: 6719
N.A.I.C.S.: 551112
Personnel:
Calin Dragan *(Pres & CEO)*

Coca-Cola East Japan Co., Ltd.—(Continued)

Michael Coombs *(CFO)*
Yohei Yasumi *(Chief Pub Affairs & Comm Officer)*
Dan Nistor *(Chief Comml Officer)*
Takuya Arai *(Chief Procurement Officer)*
Koji Numahata *(Chief IT Officer)*
Pat Paya *(Chief Supply Chain Officer)*
Kannan Sethuraman *(Chief Bus Integration Officer)*

Board of Directors:
Fumio Akachi
Michael Coombs
Calin Dragan
Irial Finan
Haruhiko Inagaki
Masaki Ito
Shigehiko Kawamoto
Dan Nistor
Daniel Sayre
Keiji Takanashi
Hiroshi Yoshioka

Subsidiaries:

Coca-Cola Central Japan Co., Ltd. (1)
2-2-1 Minatomirai
Nishi-ku, Yokohama, Kanagawa, 220-8141, Japan JP
Tel.: (81) 4 5222 5850
Fax: (81) 4 5222 5857
Web Site: www.cccj.co.jp
Sales Range: $1-4.9 Billion
Soft Drink Bottler & Distr
S.I.C.: 2086
N.A.I.C.S.: 312111
Akimune Ozaki *(Pres)*

Mikuni Coca-Cola Bottling Co., Ltd. (1)
180 Kano
Okegawa, Saitama, 363-8601, Japan JP
Tel.: (81) 48 774 1103
Sales Range: $1-4.9 Billion
Emp.: 687
Soft Drink Mfr
S.I.C.: 2086
N.A.I.C.S.: 312111
Calin Dragan *(Pres & CEO)*

Tokyo Coca-Cola Bottling Co., Ltd. (1)
Seavans S Building 1-2-3 Shibaura
Minato-ku, Tokyo, 105-0023, Japan JP
Tel.: (81) 334537311
Fax: (81) 337982461
Emp.: 912
Soft Drink Mfr & Distr
S.I.C.: 2086
N.A.I.C.S.: 312111
Keiji Takanashi *(Pres)*

TONE Coca-Cola Bottling Co., Ltd. (1)
310 Nakane
Noda, 278-8686, Japan JP
Tel.: (81) 471231114
Fax: (81) 47125 1471
Sales Range: $25-49.9 Million
Soft Drink Mfr
S.I.C.: 2086
N.A.I.C.S.: 312111
Dan Nistor *(Pres)*

COCA-COLA EMBONOR S.A.

Av El Golf 40 piso 4
Las Condes, Santiago, Chile
Tel.: (56) 2 299 1400
Fax: (56) 2 206 7722
Web Site: www.embonor.cl
EMBONOR—(SGO)
Rev.: $806,551,880
Earnings: $80,152,960
Fiscal Year-end: 12/31/12

Business Description:
Beverage Bottling Services
S.I.C.: 2086
N.A.I.C.S.: 312111

Personnel:
Andres Vicuna Garcia-Huidobo *(Chm & Pres)*
Cristian Hohlberg Recabarren *(CEO)*
Jose Domingo Jaramillo Jimenez *(CEO-Chile)*
Orlando Piro Borquez *(CEO-Bolivia)*

Board of Directors:
Andres Vicuna Garcia-Huidobo
Jose Tomas Errazuriz Grez
Bernardo Fontaine Talavera
Jorge Lesser Garcia-Huidobo
Manuel Antonio Tocornal Astorega
Leonidas Vial Echeverria
Diego Hernan Vicuna Garcia-Huidobro

COCA-COLA HBC AG

Baarerstrasse 14
CH-6300 Zug, Switzerland
Tel.: (41) 41 561 3243
Web Site: www.coca-colahellenic.com
CCH—(ATH LSE NYSE)
Sales Range: $5-14.9 Billion
Emp.: 39,736

Business Description:
Holding Company; Soft Drink Bottler & Distr
S.I.C.: 6719
N.A.I.C.S.: 551112

Personnel:
Dimitris P. Lois *(CEO)*
Michalis Imellos *(CFO)*
Jan S. Gustavsson *(Gen Counsel, Sec & Dir-Strategic Dev)*

Non-U.S. Subsidiary:

Coca-Cola Hellenic Bottling Company S.A. (1)
9 Fragoklissias Street
15125 Maroussi, Athens, Greece GR
Tel.: (30) 210 618 3100
Fax: (30) 210 618 3274
E-Mail: investor.relations@cchbc.com
Web Site: www.coca-colahellenic.com
Rev.: $9,483,363,799
Assets: $9,759,867,117
Liabilities: $5,712,607,012
Net Worth: $4,047,260,105
Earnings: $260,349,278
Fiscal Year-end: 12/31/12
Beverage Bottling Services
S.I.C.: 2086
N.A.I.C.S.: 312111
George A. David *(Chm)*
Michalis Imellos *(CFO)*
Jan S. Gustavsson *(Gen Counsel & Dir-Strategic Dev)*

Subsidiary:

Tsakiris S.A. (2)
PO Box 8485
35200 Atalanti, Phthiotis, Greece
Tel.: (30) 22330 32510
Fax: (30) 22330 32471
E-Mail: tsakiris2@otenet.gr
Web Site: www.tsakiris.gr
Emp.: 65
Potato Chips Mfr & Distr
S.I.C.: 2096
N.A.I.C.S.: 311919
Aggelos Rorris *(Gen Mgr)*

Non-U.S. Subsidiaries:

3E (Cyprus) Limited (2)
66 Kyriakos Matsis Avenue
Engomi, Nicosia, CY-2409, Cyprus
Tel.: (357) 22885000
Fax: (357) 22358000
Investment Management Services
S.I.C.: 6719
N.A.I.C.S.: 551112

AS Coca-Cola HBC Eesti (2)
Mustamae Tee 16
10617 Tallinn, Estonia
Tel.: (372) 6 503 100
Fax: (372) 6 503 101
Emp.: 110
Beverage Products Mfr
S.I.C.: 2082
N.A.I.C.S.: 312120
Piret Jaaks *(Mgr-Pub Affairs)*

CCB Management Services GmbH (2)
Am Euro Platz 2
1120 Vienna, Austria
Tel.: (43) 1 81413 0
Fax: (43) 1 814132000
Business Management Consulting Services
S.I.C.: 8748
N.A.I.C.S.: 541618

CCB Services Limited (2)
29 Tanton Crescent
Clayton, BD14 6HD, United Kingdom
Tel.: (44) 1274 817686
Beverage Mfr
S.I.C.: 2082
N.A.I.C.S.: 312120

Coca-Cola Bevera Ceska republika, s.r.o.ges (2)
Eeskobrodska 1329
Kyje, Prague, 198 21, Czech Republic
Tel.: (420) 28 3015111
Fax: (420) 23 0230400
Emp.: 30
Beverage Products Mfr
S.I.C.: 2082
N.A.I.C.S.: 312120
Martina Stinglova *(Office Mgr)*

Coca-Cola Beverages Austria GmbH (2)
Triesterstrasse 91
Vienna, 1100, Austria
Tel.: (43) 1 61060 230
Fax: (43) 1 61060329
E-Mail: info@coke.at
Emp.: 500
Soft Drink Mfr
S.I.C.: 2086
N.A.I.C.S.: 312111
Felix Hug *(Project Mgr-Supply Chain Plng)*

Coca-Cola Beverages Slovenija d.o.o. (2)
9 Motnica Str
Trzin, 1236, Slovenia
Tel.: (386) 1 589 04 00
Fax: (386) 1 589 04 74
E-Mail: info@cchellenic.com
Web Site: www.coca-cola.si
Beverage Products Mfr
S.I.C.: 2082
N.A.I.C.S.: 312120

Coca-Cola Beverages Ukraine Ltd (2)
Sankt-Peterburzke Shose Km 51 Velyka Dymerka
Brovary District, Kiev, 07400, Ukraine
Tel.: (380) 44 490 0707
Fax: (380) 44 490 0701
E-Mail: ccbu@cchellenic.com
Web Site: www.en.coca-colahellenic.com.ua
Emp.: 2,300
Beverage Products Mfr
S.I.C.: 2082
N.A.I.C.S.: 312120
Andriy Bublyk *(Mgr-Govt Rels & Comm)*

Coca-Cola Bottlers Chisinau S.R.L. (2)
Chisinau Str Industriala 42
Chisinau, Moldova
Tel.: (373) 22 470 777
Fax: (373) 22 472 489
Beverage Mfr & Distr
S.I.C.: 2082
N.A.I.C.S.: 312120

Coca-Cola HBC B-H d.o.o. (2)
Mostarsko raskrsce bb
Hadzici, Sarajevo, 71240, Bosnia & Herzegovina
Tel.: (387) 33 284 100
Fax: (387) 33 284 111
Emp.: 300
Beverage Products Mfr
S.I.C.: 2082
N.A.I.C.S.: 312120

Coca-Cola HBC Finance B.V. (2)
Herengracht 556
Amsterdam, 1017 CG, Netherlands
Tel.: (31) 20 521 4777
Beverage Mfr
S.I.C.: 2082
N.A.I.C.S.: 312120

Coca-Cola HBC Hungary Ltd. (2)
Nemedi ut 104
2330 Dunaharaszti, Hungary
Tel.: (36) 2 450 01 00
Fax: (36) 2 420 11 01
Beverage Mfr
S.I.C.: 2082
N.A.I.C.S.: 312120

Coca-Cola HBC Ireland Limited (2)
Unit C1/C2 Huntstown Business Park
Cappagh Road
Ballycoolin, Dublin, Ireland
Tel.: (353) 1 880 7100
Fax: (353) 1 880 7101
E-Mail: info@coca-colabottlers.com
Web Site: www.coca-colahellenicireland.com
Beverages Bottler & Supplier
S.I.C.: 2082
N.A.I.C.S.: 312120

Coca-Cola HBC Italia S.r.l. (2)
Viale Monza 338
20128 Milan, Italy
Tel.: (39) 02 2707 71
Fax: (39) 02 2700 5761
Web Site: www.coca-colahellenic.it
Emp.: 3,000
Beverage Mfr & Distr
S.I.C.: 2086
N.A.I.C.S.: 312111
Giangiacomo Pierini *(Mgr-Pub Affairs & Comm)*

Coca-Cola HBC Northern Ireland Limited (2)
Knockmore Hill 12 Lissue Road
Lisburn, Antrim, BT28 2SZ, United Kingdom
Tel.: (44) 2892 642000
Fax: (44) 2892 642001
E-Mail: info@coca-colabottlers.com
Web Site: www.coca-colahellenicireland.com
Emp.: 800
Beverage Products Mfr
S.I.C.: 2082
N.A.I.C.S.: 312120
Jonathan Scott *(Mgr-Ireland Shopper & Category Insights)*

Coca-Cola HBC Polska sp. z o.o. (2)
Ul Annopol 20
03-236 Warsaw, Poland
Tel.: (48) 22 519 51 00
Fax: (48) 22 519 55 55
E-Mail: cocacola@cocacola.pl
Web Site: www.cocacola.com.pl/kontakt/dane-kontaktowe.html
Soft Drink Mfr
S.I.C.: 2086
N.A.I.C.S.: 312111

Coca-Cola HBC Serbia L.L.C. (2)
Magjistralja Prishtine-Shkup Kryqi i Lipjanit
14000 Lipljan, Kosovo, Serbia
Tel.: (381) 38 540 690
Fax: (381) 38 540 689
E-Mail: rs@cchellenic.com
Web Site: en.coca-colahellenic.rs
Emp.: 1,500
Soft Drink Mfr
S.I.C.: 2086
N.A.I.C.S.: 312111
Kreshnik Sinani *(Gen Mgr)*

Coca-Cola HBC-Srbija d.o.o. (2)
Batajnicki drum 14-16
Zemun, 11080 Belgrade, Serbia
Tel.: (381) 11 3073 100
Fax: (381) 11 3073 215
Web Site: en.coca-colahellenic.rs
Beverage Products Mfr
S.I.C.: 2082
N.A.I.C.S.: 312120

Coca-Cola HBC Switzerland Ltd (2)
Stationsstrasse 33
8306 Bruttisellen, Switzerland
Tel.: (41) 31 925 71 11
E-Mail: coca.cola@cchellenic.com
Web Site: en.coca-colahellenic.ch
Emp.: 1,300
Beverages Mfr & Distr
S.I.C.: 2086
N.A.I.C.S.: 312111

Coca-Cola Hellenic Bottling Company-Crna Gora d.o.o. (2)
Kuce Rakica bb
81000 Podgorica, Montenegro
Tel.: (382) 11 3020 030
Beverage Mfr
S.I.C.: 2082
N.A.I.C.S.: 312120

Coca-Cola Hellenic Procurement GmbH (2)
Am Euro Platz 2
Vienna, 1120, Austria
Tel.: (43) 1661710
Beverage Mfr & Whslr
S.I.C.: 2082
N.A.I.C.S.: 312120

Dunlogan Limited (2)
12 Lissue Road
Lisburn, Antrim, BT28 2SZ, United Kingdom
Tel.: (44) 121 415 7047
Beverage Mfr
S.I.C.: 2082
N.A.I.C.S.: 312120

Lanitis Bros Public Ltd. (2)
Kyriakou Matsi 66
PO Box 22000
2409 Nicosia, Cyprus (95.43%)
Tel.: (357) 22885000
Fax: (357) 22885000
E-Mail: info@lanitis-bros.com
Web Site: www.lanitis-bros.com
Emp.: 560
Soft Drink Mfr
S.I.C.: 2086
N.A.I.C.S.: 312111
Minas Angelides *(Mng Dir)*

LLC Coca-Cola HBC Eurasia (2)
6 Italyanskaya
Orel, 302024, Russia
Tel.: (7) 4862 42 12 34
Fax: (7) 4862 44 07 10
Beverage Products Mfr
S.I.C.: 2082
N.A.I.C.S.: 312120
Grigoriy Savin *(Mgr-Quality Control)*

The Nigerian Bottling Company Plc (2)
Iddo House
Iddo, Lagos, Nigeria
Tel.: (234) 12693030
Fax: (234) 12691521
Web Site: www.nbcplccareers.com
Soft Drink Mfr
S.I.C.: 2086
N.A.I.C.S.: 312111

SIA Coca-Cola HBC Latvia (2)
Ulbrokas 40
1021 Riga, Latvia
Tel.: (371) 67109900
Fax: (371) 67109911
Web Site: www.coca-cola.lv/contact.html
Emp.: 120
Beverage Products Mfr
S.I.C.: 2082
N.A.I.C.S.: 312120
Maris Berzins *(Mgr-Sls)*

UAB Coca-Cola HBC Lietuva (2)
Kirtim U G 47 B
Vilnius, Lithuania 02244
Tel.: (370) 5 2602222
Fax: (370) 5 2602020
Web Site: www.coca-cola.lt
Beverage Mfr & Distr
S.I.C.: 2082
N.A.I.C.S.: 312120

Valser Services AG (2)
Rothusstrasse 88
Bolligen, 3065 Bern, Switzerland
Tel.: (41) 31 925 73 11
E-Mail: info@valserservice.ch
Web Site: www.valserservice.ch
Beverage Products Retailer
S.I.C.: 5812
N.A.I.C.S.: 722515
Lorenz Erismann *(Mng Dir)*
Oliver Fritz *(CFO)*

COCA-COLA HELLENIC BOTTLING CO. S.A.

(Acquired by Coca-Cola HBC AG)

COCA-COLA ICECEK A.S.

Esenkent Mah Deniz Feneri Sk 4
Umraniye
34776 Istanbul, Turkey
Tel.: (90) 216 528 40 00
Fax: (90) 216 365 8457
Web Site: www.cci.com.tr
CCOLA—(IST OTC)
Emp.: 10,000

Business Description:
Soft Drink Bottler, Producer & Distr
S.I.C.: 2086
N.A.I.C.S.: 312111

Personnel:
Tuncay Ozilhan *(Chm)*
Kevin Andrew Warren *(Vice Chm)*
Michael A. O'Neill *(Mng Dir)*
Nusret Orhun Kostem *(CFO)*
Huseyin Murat Akin *(Pres-Intl Ops)*
Burak Basarir *(Pres-Turkey Reg)*

Board of Directors:
Tuncay Ozilhan
R. Yilmaz Arguden
Mehmet Mete Basol
Ahmet Cemal Dorduncu
Salih Metin Ecevit
Hamit Sedat Eratalar
Damian Paul Gammell
Michael A. O'Neill
Armagan Ozgorkey
Michael Spanos
Kevin Andrew Warren
Mehmet Hursit Zorlu

COCA-COLA WEST CO., LTD.

7-9-66 Hakozaki Higashi-ku
Fukuoka, 812-8650, Japan
Tel.: (81) 926418774
E-Mail: masahiro-takase@ccwh.co.jp
Web Site: www.ccwest.co.jp
Year Founded: 1960
2579—(OTC TKS)
Rev.: $4,253,007,000
Assets: $3,710,828,000
Liabilities: $1,169,212,000
Net Worth: $2,541,616,000
Earnings: $66,341,000
Emp.: 7,877
Fiscal Year-end: 12/31/12

Business Description:
Beverages Mfr & Sales
S.I.C.: 2086
N.A.I.C.S.: 312111

Personnel:
Norio Sueyoshi *(Chm)*
Tamio Yoshimatsu *(Pres)*
Nobuo Shibata *(Exec VP-Admin & SCM)*

Board of Directors:
Norio Sueyoshi
Yoshiki Fujiwara
Toshio Fukami
Shiro Kondo
Yoshinori Nakamura
Shigeki Okamoto
Nobuo Shibata
Hideharu Takemori
Vikas Tiku
Jiro Wakasa
Tamio Yoshimatsu

Subsidiaries:

Akiyoshi Systems Co Ltd (1)
2-14-14 Sonezaki
Kita-Ku, Osaka, Japan
Tel.: (81) 663656090
Web Site: www.ccwest.co.jp/english/corporate/group.php
Drinking Places
S.I.C.: 5813
N.A.I.C.S.: 722410

Coca-Cola West Daisen Products Co., Ltd. (1)
306-1 Kanayadani Hoki-cho
Saihaku-gun, Tottori, 689-4213, Japan
Tel.: (81) 859399881
Fax: (81) 859399885
Soft Drink Mfr
S.I.C.: 2086
N.A.I.C.S.: 312111

Coca-Cola West Japan Customer Service Co Ltd (1)
871 Taniyama
Koga, Fukuoka, Japan
Tel.: (81) 929446813
Web Site: www.ccwest.co.jp
Automatic Vending Machine Mfr
S.I.C.: 3589
N.A.I.C.S.: 333318
Mitsuo Isobe *(Pres)*

Coca-Cola West Logistics Co., Ltd. (1)
7-9-66 Hakozaki
Higashi-ku, Fukuoka, 812-8650, Japan JP
Tel.: (81) 926418816
Fax: (81) 926418818
Freight Truck Transportation Services
S.I.C.: 4212
N.A.I.C.S.: 484110

Coca-Cola West Products Co Ltd (1)
1670-2 Nihommatsu
Todorokimachi, Saga, Japan
Tel.: (81) 942836311
Web Site: www.ccwest.co.jp/english/corporate/group.php
Specialty Canning
S.I.C.: 2032
N.A.I.C.S.: 311422
Takuo Shibata *(VP)*

Coca-Cola West Retail Service Co., Ltd. (1)
7-9-66 Hakozaki
Higashi-Ku, Fukuoka, 812-0053, Japan
Tel.: (81) 926418867
Fax: (81) 0926418869
Web Site: www.ccwestccwst.co.jp
Emp.: 200
Soft Drink Retailer
S.I.C.: 5149
N.A.I.C.S.: 424490
Shigenori Urakawa *(Mng Dir)*

Coca-Cola West Service Co., Ltd. (1)
7-9-66 Hakozaki
Higashi-Ku, Fukuoka, 812-0053, Japan
Tel.: (81) 926510843
Fax: (81) 926510892
Real Estate Management Services
S.I.C.: 6531
N.A.I.C.S.: 531390

Coca-Cola West Vending Co., Ltd. (1)
7-9-66 Hakozaki
Higashi-Ku, Fukuoka, 812-0053, Japan
Tel.: (81) 926418554
Fax: (81) 926418568
Vending Machine Operators
S.I.C.: 5962
N.A.I.C.S.: 454210

Kadiac Co., Ltd (1)
1 Senshukukominami
Sennan, Osaka, Japan
Tel.: (81) 724566248
Fax: (81) 0724566345
Emp.: 25
Vending Machine Operations
S.I.C.: 3589
N.A.I.C.S.: 333318

Kansai Beverage Service Company Limited (1)
C-o Kinki Coca-Cola Bottling Co Ltd
Settsu, Osaka, Japan
Tel.: (81) 663302250
Web Site: www.ccwest.co.jp
Emp.: 700
Business Service Centers
S.I.C.: 7389
N.A.I.C.S.: 561439
Shingo Sakurai *(Pres)*

Nippon Supplement Inc. (1)
Applause Tower 19-19 Chayamachi
Kita-ku, Osaka, 530-0013, Japan
Tel.: (81) 663762220
Fax: (81) 663762234
E-Mail: global@nippon-sapuri.co.jp
Web Site: www.nippon-sapuri.com
Dietary Supplement Mfr
S.I.C.: 2099
N.A.I.C.S.: 311999
Tomohide Yamagami *(Pres)*

Nishinihon Beverage Co Ltd (1)
5-1-6 Hakozakifuto
Higashi-Ku, Fukuoka, 751, Japan
Tel.: (81) 926413220
Emp.: 500
Food Stores
S.I.C.: 5499
N.A.I.C.S.: 445299

Q SAI Co., Ltd. (1)
1-7-16 Kusagae
Chuo-ku, Fukuoka, 810-8606, Japan
Tel.: (81) 927240853
Fax: (81) 927243316
E-Mail: saiyou@kyusai.co.jp
Web Site: www.kyusai.co.jp
Emp.: 200
Health Food Products Mfr & Distr
S.I.C.: 2099
N.A.I.C.S.: 311999
Takashi Fujino *(Pres)*

Takamasamune Co Ltd (1)
297 Kuroda
Daizenjimachi Kurume, Fukuoka, Japan
Tel.: (81) 942268181
Web Site: www.takamasamune.com
Wine & Distilled Alcoholic Beverage Merchant Whlslr
S.I.C.: 5182
N.A.I.C.S.: 424820
Tsukasa Satou *(Pres)*

West Japan Service Company Limited (1)
7-9-66 Hakozaki
Higashi-Ku, Fukuoka, Japan
Tel.: (81) 926510843
Fax: (81) 0926510892
Insurance Agencies & Brokerages
S.I.C.: 6411
N.A.I.C.S.: 524210

Wex Co., Ltd. (1)
1806-74 Miyanogi-cho
Inage-ku, Chiba, 263-0054, Japan
Tel.: (81) 432570857
Vending Machine Operators
S.I.C.: 5962
N.A.I.C.S.: 454210

COCHIN MINERALS AND RUTILE LIMITED

VIII/224 Market Road
PB No 73
Aluva, Kerala, 683101, India
Tel.: (91) 484 2626789
Fax: (91) 484 2625674
E-Mail: investors@cmrlindia.com
Web Site: www.cmrlindia.com
Year Founded: 1989
513353—(BOM)
Rev.: $37,151,119
Assets: $26,016,403
Liabilities: $4,788,456
Net Worth: $21,227,948
Earnings: $8,035,829
Fiscal Year-end: 03/31/13

Business Description:
Synthetic Rutile Mfr & Whslr
S.I.C.: 5169
N.A.I.C.S.: 424690

Personnel:
R. K. Garg *(Chm)*
Mathew M. Cherian *(Vice Chm)*
S. N. Sasidharan Kartha *(Co-Mng Dir)*
Saran S. Kartha *(Co-Mng Dir)*
Suresh Kumar P. *(Compliance Officer & Sec)*

Board of Directors:
R. K. Garg
Mathew M. Cherian
Nabiel Mathew Cherian
Jaya S. Kartha
S. N. Sasidharan Kartha
Saran S. Kartha

Cochin Minerals and Rutile Limited—(Continued)

A. J. Pai
T. P. Thomaskutty
G. R. Warrier

Transfer Agent:
SKDC Consultants Ltd
Kanapathy Towers 3rd Floor 1391 A-1 Sathy Road Ganapathy Post
614008 Coimbatore, India

COCHIN SHIPYARD LIMITED

Perumanoor
Kochi, 682015, India
Tel.: (91) 4842380181
Fax: (91) 4842370897
E-Mail: info@cochinshipyard.com
Web Site: www.cochinshipyard.com
Year Founded: 1972
Sales Range: $300-349.9 Million
Emp.: 2,500

Business Description:
Ship Building & Repairing
S.I.C.: 3731
N.A.I.C.S.: 336611

Personnel:
Commodore K. Subramaniam *(Chm & Mng Dir)*
V. Kala *(Sec)*

Board of Directors:
Commodore K. Subramaniam
Rajeev Gupta
N. Kumar
P. Paleri
N.M. Paramesh
M.A. Pathan
S. Narasimha Rao
B. Sridhar
K. Subramaniam

COCHLEAR LIMITED

1 University Avenue Macquarie University
Sydney, NSW, 2109, Australia
Tel.: (61) 294286555
Fax: (61) 294286353
Web Site: www.cochlear.com
COH—(ASX)
Rev.: $783,941,609
Assets: $796,686,492
Liabilities: $424,747,455
Net Worth: $371,939,037
Earnings: $138,143,902
Emp.: 2,531
Fiscal Year-end: 06/30/13

Business Description:
Hearing Aid Mfr
S.I.C.: 3841
N.A.I.C.S.: 339112

Personnel:
Christopher Graham Roberts *(Pres & CEO)*
Neville Mitchell *(CFO & Sec)*
David Morris *(Chief Strategy Officer)*
Richard Brook *(Pres-European)*
Mark Salmon *(Pres-Asia Pacific)*
Christopher M. Smith *(Pres-Americas)*
Dig Howitt *(Sr VP-Mfg & Logistics)*
Jan Janssen *(Sr VP-Design & Dev)*
Michael Kavanagh *(Sr VP-Global Mktg)*
Anne-Marie Leslie *(Sr VP-HR)*
Jim Patrick *(Sr VP)*

Board of Directors:
Rick Holliday-Smith
Yasmin Allen
Paul Ronald Bell
Edward Byrne
Andrew Leslie Denver
Donal P. O'Dwyer
Christopher Graham Roberts

Subsidiary:

Cochlear Technologies Pty Limited (1)
14 Mars Road
Lane Cove, NSW, 2066, Australia
Tel.: (61) 294286555
Hearing Devices Mfr
S.I.C.: 3845
N.A.I.C.S.: 334510

U.S. Subsidiary:

Cochlear Americas Inc (1)
13059 E Peakview Ave
Centennial, CO 80111
Tel.: (303) 790-9010
Fax: (303) 792-9025
Toll Free: (800) 523-5798
E-Mail: info@cochlearamericas.com
Web Site: www.cochlearamericas.com
Emp.: 300
Hearing Device Mfr
S.I.C.: 3845
N.A.I.C.S.: 334510
Christopher M. Smith *(Pres)*

Non-U.S. Subsidiaries:

Cochlear AG (1)
Peter Merian-Weg 4
4052 Basel, Switzerland
Tel.: (41) 61 205 04 04
Fax: (41) 61 205 04 05
E-Mail: cagreception@cochlear.com
Web Site: www.cochlear-europe.com
Emp.: 70
Hearing Aids Mfr
S.I.C.: 3845
N.A.I.C.S.: 334510
Richard Brook *(Gen Mgr)*

Cochlear Benelux NV (1)
Schalienhoevedreef 20 Building I
2800 Mechelen, Belgium
Tel.: (32) 15 79 55 77
Fax: (32) 15 79 55 70
E-Mail: customerservice@cochlear.be
Web Site: www.cochlear.be
Hearing Aids Mfr
S.I.C.: 3845
N.A.I.C.S.: 334510

Cochlear Bone Anchored Solutions AB (1)
Konstruktionsvagen 14
435 33 Molnlycke, Sweden
Tel.: (46) 317924400
Fax: (46) 41 792 46 95
Web Site: www.cochlear.com
Emp.: 220
Hearing Aids Mfr
S.I.C.: 3845
N.A.I.C.S.: 334510
David Morris *(Pres)*

Cochlear Canada Inc (1)
120 Adelaide St W Ste 2500
Toronto, ON, M5H ITI, Canada
Tel.: (416) 972-5082
Toll Free: (800) 523-5798
Web Site: products.cochlearamericas.com
Hearing Device Mfr
S.I.C.: 3845
N.A.I.C.S.: 334510

Cochlear Deutschland GmbH & Co. KG (1)
Karl-Wiechert-Allee 76 A
30625 Hannover, Germany
Tel.: (49) 51 1 542 77 0
Fax: (49) 51 1 542 77 70
E-Mail: info@cochlear.de
Web Site: www.cochlear.de
Hearing Aids Mfr
S.I.C.: 3845
N.A.I.C.S.: 334510

Cochlear Europe Finance GmbH (1)
Karl-Wiechert-Allee 76a
30625 Hannover, Germany
Tel.: (49) 511542770
Fax: (49) 5115427770
Emp.: 80
Financial Support Services
S.I.C.: 6141
N.A.I.C.S.: 522291

Cochlear Europe Limited (1)
6 Dashwood Lang Road Bourne Business Park
Addlestone, Surrey, KT15 2HJ, United Kingdom
Tel.: (44) 1932871500
Fax: (44) 1932 871 526
Web Site: www.cochlear.co.uk
Hearing Aids Mfr
S.I.C.: 3845
N.A.I.C.S.: 334510
Darren Ransley *(Gen Mgr)*

Cochlear France SAS (1)
Route de l'Orme aux Merisiers Z I Les Algorithmes - Bat Homere
91190 Saint Aubin, France
Tel.: (33) 811111993
Fax: (33) 160196499
E-Mail: info-fr@cochlear.fr
Web Site: www.cochlear.fr
Emp.: 20
Hearing Aids Mfr
S.I.C.: 3845
N.A.I.C.S.: 334510

Cochlear GmbH (1)
Karl-Wiechert-Allee 76A
30625 Hannover, Germany
Tel.: (49) 511542770
Fax: (49) 51 1 542 7770
E-Mail: info@cochlear.de
Web Site: www.cochlear.de
Hearing Devices Mfr
S.I.C.: 3845
N.A.I.C.S.: 334510
Steffen Berenbold *(Bus Mgr & Coord-Clinic-Sudwestdeutschland Reg)*

Cochlear (HK) Limited (1)
Room 1810 18/F Hopewell Centre 183 Queen's Road East
Wanchai, China (Hong Kong)
Tel.: (852) 25305773
Fax: (852) 2530 5183
Web Site: www.cochlear.com
Hearing Aids Mfr
S.I.C.: 3845
N.A.I.C.S.: 334510

Cochlear Korea Limited (1)
Sungsan B/D 5/F 1689-5 Seocho-Dong
Seocho-Ku, Seoul, Korea (South)
Tel.: (82) 2 533 0114
Fax: (82) 2 533 6166
Web Site: www.cochlear.com
Hearing Devices Mfr
S.I.C.: 3845
N.A.I.C.S.: 334510

Cochlear Medical Device Company India Private Limited (1)
Ground Floor Platina Building Plot No C 59 Bandra Kurla Complex
Bandra East, Mumbai, 400051, India
Tel.: (91) 2261121111
Fax: (91) 22 61121100
E-Mail: cindcustumerservice@cochlear.com
Emp.: 2
Hearing Devices Mfr
S.I.C.: 3845
N.A.I.C.S.: 334510
Pisharody Vandana *(Country Mgr)*

Cochlear Nordic AB (1)
Konstruktionsvagen 14
PO Box 82
43522 Molnlycke, Sweden
Tel.: (46) 313351461
Fax: (46) 31335146
Web Site: www.cochlear.se
Hearing Aids Mfr
S.I.C.: 3845
N.A.I.C.S.: 334510

Cochlear Sweden Holdings AB (1)
Konstruktionsvagen 14
435 33 Molnlycke, Sweden
Tel.: (46) 317924400
Fax: (46) 31 7924400
Hearing Aids Mfr
S.I.C.: 3845
N.A.I.C.S.: 334510
David Morris *(Pres)*

Cochlear Tibbi Cihazlar ve Saglik Hizmetleri Limited Sirketi (1)
Cubuklu Mah Bogazici Cad Bogazici Plaza No 6/1 Kavacik
Beykoz, Istanbul, 34805, Turkey
Tel.: (90) 216 538 59 00
Fax: (90) 216 538 59 19
Web Site: www.cochlear.com.tr
Emp.: 20
Hearing Aids Mfr
S.I.C.: 3845
N.A.I.C.S.: 334510
Frank Koall *(Gen Mgr)*

Cochlear Verwaltungs GmbH (1)
Karl-Wiechert-Allee 76A
30625 Hannover, Germany
Tel.: (49) 511542770
Fax: (49) 511 5427770
Web Site: www.cochlear.com
Emp.: 10
Hearing Devices Mfr
S.I.C.: 3845
N.A.I.C.S.: 334510
Thomas Topp *(Gen Mgr)*

Nihon Cochlear Co Limited (1)
Ochanomizu-Motomachi Bldg Hongo 2-3-7
Bunkyo-ku, Tokyo, 113-0033, Japan
Tel.: (81) 338170241
Fax: (81) 338170245
Web Site: www.cochlear.com
Hearing Aids Distr
S.I.C.: 5047
N.A.I.C.S.: 423450

COCKATOO COAL LIMITED

Level 2 66 Hunter Street
Sydney, NSW, 2000, Australia
Tel.: (61) 2 9300 3333
Fax: (61) 2 9221 6333
E-Mail: info@cockatoocoal.com.au
Web Site: www.cockatoocoal.com.au
COK—(ASX)
Rev.: $68,893,103
Assets: $429,799,750
Liabilities: $167,260,654
Net Worth: $262,539,097
Earnings: ($33,894,069)
Emp.: 89
Fiscal Year-end: 06/30/13

Business Description:
Coal Mining Exploration
S.I.C.: 1241
N.A.I.C.S.: 213113

Personnel:
Mark Hamish Lochtenberg *(Chm)*
Andrew Lawson *(Mng Dir)*
Peter James Nightingale *(CFO)*
Luca Rocchi *(COO)*
Lee J. O'Dwyer *(Sec)*

Board of Directors:
Mark Hamish Lochtenberg
John Gillis Broinowski
Paul Gregory Chappell
Lindsay Ross Flint
Hyunsoo Kim
Andrew Lawson
Peter James Nightingale
Kenneth Scott Andrew Thompson
Robert Ainslie Yeates

Legal Counsel:
Minter Ellison
88 Phillip Street
Sydney, Australia

Subsidiaries:

Baralaba Coal Pty. Ltd. (1)
Lot 1 Baralaba Woorabinda Rd
Baralaba, Queensland, 4702, Australia
Tel.: (61) 749981592
Fax: (61) 749981693
E-Mail: info@cockatoocoal.com.au
Web Site: www.cockatoocoal.com.au
Emp.: 130
Coal Mining & Exploration Services
S.I.C.: 1241
N.A.I.C.S.: 213113

Blackwood Corporation Limited (1)
Level 9 288 Edward Street
Brisbane, QLD, 4000, Australia AU
Tel.: (61) 730340800
Fax: (61) 730340899
E-Mail: info@bwdcorp.com.au
Web Site: www.bwdcorp.com.au
BWD—(ASX)
Sales Range: Less than $1 Million
Coal Exploration & Development Services
S.I.C.: 1241
N.A.I.C.S.: 213113

Todd Harrington *(CEO)*
David Smith *(CFO)*
Patrick McCole *(Sec)*

COCKRAM CORPORATION

(d/b/a Cockram Construction)
Ground Floor 675 Victoria Stret
Abbotsford, VIC, 3067, Australia
Tel.: (61) 388628888
Fax: (61) 388628900
Web Site: www.cockram.com
Year Founded: 1861
Sales Range: $50-74.9 Million
Emp.: 400
Business Description:
Industrial Building Construction Services
S.I.C.: 1541
N.A.I.C.S.: 236210
Personnel:
Robert Milne *(Chm)*
Malcolm Batten *(Mng Dir)*
Louis Sciuto *(Fin Dir & Sec)*
Board of Directors:
Robert Milne
Malcolm Batten
David Judd
Darren Milne
Louis Sciuto

COCO HOMES INC.

Bay 2 2807 107 Avenue SE
Calgary, AB, T2Z 4M2, Canada
Tel.: (403) 212-8105
Fax: (403) 212-4860
E-Mail: info@cocohomes.com
Web Site: www.cocohomes.com
Year Founded: 1981
Rev.: $11,983,500
Emp.: 15
Business Description:
Home Building Construction Services
S.I.C.: 5211
N.A.I.C.S.: 444110
Personnel:
Doug Bennett *(Owner & Partner)*

COCOA PROCESSING COMPANY LIMITED

Heavy Industrial Area
Private Mail Bag
Tema, Ghana
Tel.: (233) 22 212153
Fax: (233) 22 206657
E-Mail: info@goldentreeghana.com
Web Site: www.goldentreeghana.com
Year Founded: 1981
CPC—(GHA)
Sales Range: $25-49.9 Million
Emp.: 430
Business Description:
Cocoa Processor
S.I.C.: 2066
N.A.I.C.S.: 311351
Personnel:
Nana Obiri Boahen *(Chm)*
Richard Amarh Tetteh *(Mng Dir)*
Stephen Ofori-Adjei *(Sec)*
Board of Directors:
Nana Obiri Boahen
John Amo Bediako
David Coleman
Dramani Egala
Osei Kyei Mensah-Bonsu
Charles Nimako
Isaac Osei
Richard Amarh Tetteh

COCOALAND HOLDINGS BERHAD

Lot 100 Jalan Industri 3/4 Rawang
Integrated Industrial Park
48000 Rawang, Selangor Darul Ehsan, Malaysia
Tel.: (60) 360913131
Fax: (60) 360912132
E-Mail: info@cocoaland.com
Web Site: www.cocoaland.com
COCOLND—(KLS)
Rev.: $73,194,275
Assets: $77,822,215
Liabilities: $13,497,557
Net Worth: $64,324,658
Earnings: $6,957,852
Fiscal Year-end: 12/31/12
Business Description:
Chocolate Mfr
S.I.C.: 2064
N.A.I.C.S.: 311340
Personnel:
Heng Hooi Ng *(Co-Sec)*
Mee Kiat Wong *(Co-Sec)*
Foo Teng Yap *(Co-Sec)*
Board of Directors:
Azman Mahmood
Kee Kan Chow
Kin Lip Koh
Kee Von Lau
Pak Lam Lau
Fook Meng Liew
Yoon Kee Liew
Jui Sia Ng
Swee Hock Soh
Chun Wah Tai

COCOKARA FINE INC.

Innotech Bldg 3-17-6 Shin-Yokohama
Kohoku-ku, Yokohama, Kanagawa, 222-0033, Japan
Tel.: (81) 45 548 5929
Web Site: www.cocokarafine.co.jp
Year Founded: 2008
3098—(TKS)
Sls.: $3,278,247,360
Assets: $1,461,403,840
Liabilities: $743,331,360
Net Worth: $718,072,480
Earnings: $77,094,240
Fiscal Year-end: 03/30/13
Business Description:
Holding Company; Pharmacy & Drug Store Owner & Operator; Nursing & Home Health Care Services; Online Healthcare Products Retailer
S.I.C.: 6719
N.A.I.C.S.: 551112
Personnel:
Masashi Hisamatsu *(Chm)*
Atsushi Tsukamoto *(Pres)*
Ichiro Ishibashi *(VP & Gen Mgr-Corp Strategy)*
Kazuo Hamano *(Mng Officer-Overseas Bus Div)*
Kaoru Hashizume *(Mng Officer)*
Shunji Uehara *(Mng Officer-Grp Mgmt Strategy)*
Board of Directors:
Masashi Hisamatsu
Kazuo Hamano
Kaoru Hashizume
Ichiro Ishibashi
Makoto Kitayama
Atsushi Tsukamoto
Shunji Uehara

Subsidiaries:

cocokara Healthcare Inc. **(1)**
Innotech Bldg 3-17-6 Shin-Yokohama
Kohoku-ku, Yokohama, Kanagawa, 222-0033, Japan JP
Tel.: (81) 45 548 5996
Web Site: www.cocokarafine.co.jp/healthcare
Drugstore & Pharmacy Operator
S.I.C.: 5912
N.A.I.C.S.: 446110
Atsushi Tsukamoto, *(Pres)*

cocokarafine OEC Co., Ltd. **(1)**
Innotech Bldg 3-17-6 Shin-Yokohama
Kohoku-ku, Yokohama, Kanagawa, 222-0033, Japan JP
Tel.: (81) 45 548 5992
Web Site: shop.cocokarafine.co.jp
Online Healthcare Products Retailer
S.I.C.: 5961
N.A.I.C.S.: 454111
Atsushi Tsukamoto, *(Pres)*

FINECARE Inc. **(1)**
2F Daily Care Seijo Minami Urawa
Nishiguchi Store 2-2-1 Bunzo
Minami-ku, Saitama, 336-0025, Japan JP
Tel.: (81) 48 710 6750
Web Site: www.finecare.co.jp
Nursing & Home Health Care Services
S.I.C.: 8082
N.A.I.C.S.: 621610
Atsushi Tsukamoto, *(Pres)*

COCOLONET CO., LTD.

15-1 Kamata
Fukushima-shi, Fukushima, 960-0102, Japan
Tel.: (81) 24 573 6556
Fax: (81) 245736560
Web Site: www.coclonet.jp
Year Founded: 1966
6060—(JAS)
Sls.: $115,544,000
Assets: $178,299,000
Liabilities: $106,931,000
Net Worth: $71,368,000
Earnings: $5,797,000
Emp.: 35
Fiscal Year-end: 03/31/13
Business Description:
Funeral & Wedding Services
S.I.C.: 7261
N.A.I.C.S.: 812210
Personnel:
Shoichi Kanno *(Chm)*

CODAN LIMITED

81 Graves Street
Newton, SA, 5074, Australia
Tel.: (61) 883050311
Fax: (61) 883050411
E-Mail: info@codan.com.au
Web Site: www.codan.com.au
CDA—(ASX)
Rev.: $243,680,496
Assets: $220,443,750
Liabilities: $90,460,533
Net Worth: $129,983,217
Earnings: $47,329,056
Emp.: 450
Fiscal Year-end: 06/30/13
Business Description:
Communications Equipment Mfr
S.I.C.: 3669
N.A.I.C.S.: 334290
Personnel:
Donald Shields McGurk *(CEO & Mng Dir)*
Michael Barton *(CFO & Sec)*
Board of Directors:
G. David Klingner
Peter R. Griffiths
David J. Klingberg
Peter F. Leahy
Donald Shields McGurk
Corinne S. Namblard
David J. Simmons

Subsidiaries:

IMP Printed Circuits Pty Ltd. **(1)**
6 CB Fisher Drive
Cavan, SA, 5094, Australia
Tel.: (61) 8 8262 1444
Fax: (61) 8 8262 2044
E-Mail: imp@imppc.com.au
Web Site: www.imppc.com.au
Emp.: 2
Printed Circuits, Membranes, Decals, Stencils & LCD Screens Mfr
S.I.C.: 3672
N.A.I.C.S.: 334412
Elio Franco *(Gen Mgr)*

Minelab Electronics Pty Ltd **(1)**
118 Hayward Avenue
Torrensville, SA, 5031, Australia
Tel.: (61) 8 8238 0888
Fax: (61) 8 8238 0890
E-Mail: minelab@minelab.com.au
Web Site: www.minelab.com.au
Emp.: 10
Metal Detecting Technologies
S.I.C.: 3499
N.A.I.C.S.: 332999

U.S. Subsidiary:

Minelab Americas Inc. **(2)**
2777 Finley Rd Unit 4
Downers Grove, IL 60515
Tel.: (630) 401-8150
Fax: (630) 401-8180
E-Mail: info@minelabamericas.com
Web Site: www.minelab.com
Metal Detectors Sales, Service & Support
S.I.C.: 7629
N.A.I.C.S.: 811219
Gary Schafer *(VP)*

Non-U.S. Subsidiary:

Minelab International Ltd **(2)**
Unit 207 Harbour Point Business Park
Little Island, Co Cork, Ireland
Tel.: (353) 21 423 2352
Fax: (353) 21 423 2353
E-Mail: minelab@minelab.ie
Web Site: www.minelab.com
Emp.: 22
Metal Detectors Sales, Service & Support
S.I.C.: 7629
N.A.I.C.S.: 811219
Hans Schild *(Mng Dir)*

Minetec Pty Ltd. **(1)**
10 Kembla Way
Willetton, WA, 6155, Australia
Tel.: (61) 8 9259 4955
Fax: (61) 89259 4090
E-Mail: minetec@minetec.com.au
Web Site: www.minetec.com.au
Emp.: 65
Designs & Manufactures Electronic Products & Associated Software for Communications Solutions for Mining Industry
S.I.C.: 3669
N.A.I.C.S.: 334290
Cassi Bokenfohr *(Gen Mgr)*

CODE 3 INC.

(See Under Public Safety Equipment (Intl) Ltd.)

CODE AGRICULTURE (HOLDINGS) LIMITED

Rooms 1120-26 11th Floor Sun Hung Kai Centre 30 Harbour Road
Wanchai, China (Hong Kong)
Tel.: (852) 3583 8488
Fax: (852) 3426 9830
E-Mail: info@code-hk.com
Web Site: www.code-hk.com
YM2A—(DEU)
Sls.: $94,734,407
Assets: $162,202,337
Liabilities: $187,199,810
Net Worth: ($24,997,473)
Earnings: ($32,571,996)
Emp.: 372
Fiscal Year-end: 03/31/13
Business Description:
Tobacco Machinery Mfr
S.I.C.: 3559
N.A.I.C.S.: 333249
Personnel:
Yingzi Jingquan *(Chm)*
Patrick Man Hung Wong *(Compliance Officer)*
Kwok Fat Li *(Sec)*
Board of Directors:
Yingzi Jingquan
Stephen William Frostick
Joshua Chi Hwa Lee
Guoshun Liu

Code Agriculture (Holdings) Limited—(Continued)

Richard Alvaro Sousa
Patrick Man Hung Wong
Zhongxin Wu
Zhizheng Zhao

Butterfield Fulcrum Group (Bermuda) Limited
Rosebank Centre 11 Bermudiana Road
Pembroke, Bermuda

Transfer Agents:
Tricor Abacus Limited
26/F Tesbury Centre 28 Queen's Road East
Hong Kong, China (Hong Kong)

Butterfield Fulcrum Group (Bermuda) Limited
Rosebank Centre 11 Bermudiana Road
Pembroke, Bermuda

CODERE S.A.

Avenida de Bruselas 26
28108 Alcobendas, Madrid, Spain
Tel.: (34) 913542800
Fax: (34) 913542890
E-Mail: inversor@codere.com
Web Site: www.codere.com
CDR—(MAD)
Rev.: $2,233,361,992
Assets: $2,602,907,196
Liabilities: $2,470,240,796
Net Worth: $132,666,400
Earnings: ($163,499,077)
Emp.: 21,182
Fiscal Year-end: 12/31/12
Business Description:
Casinos, Bingo Halls & Horse Racetracks Operator
S.I.C.: 7999
N.A.I.C.S.: 713210
Personnel:
Jose Antonio Martinez Sampedro *(Chm, Pres & CEO)*
Fernando Lorente Hurtado *(Deputy Chm)*
Luis Arguello Alvarez *(Sec)*
Board of Directors:
Jose Antonio Martinez Sampedro
Jose Ignacio Cases Mendez
Juan Junquera Temprano
Fernando Lorente Hurtado
Encarnacion Martinez Sampedro
Javier Martinez Sampedro
Jose Ramon Romero Rodriguez
Eugenio Vela Sastre
Joseph Zappala
Juan Jose Zornoza Perez

CO.DON AG

Warthestrasse 21
Teltow, D-14513, Germany
Tel.: (49) 3328 43 46 0
Fax: (49) 3328 43 46 43
E-Mail: info@codon.de
Web Site: www.codon.de
CNWK—(DEU)
Business Description:
Therapeutics & Neurosurgical Market Products Mfr
S.I.C.: 3841
N.A.I.C.S.: 339112
Personnel:
Bernd Wegener *(Chm-Supervisory Bd)*
Thommy Stahlin *(Vice Chm-Supervisory Bd)*
Andreas Baltrusch *(Member-Mgmt Bd)*
Vilma Siodla *(Member-Mgmt Bd)*
Supervisory Board of Directors:
Bernd Wegener
Barbara Sickmuller
Thommy Stahlin

CODORNIU, S.A.

Avda Jaume Codorniu Sant Sadurni d'Anoia
08770 Barcelona, Spain
Tel.: (34) 938 183 232
Telex: 52759 codor
Fax: (34) 938 910 822
E-Mail: codinfo@codorniu.es
Web Site: www.codorniu.es
Year Founded: 1551
Emp.: 900
Business Description:
Wines & Champagne Producer
Import Export
S.I.C.: 2084
N.A.I.C.S.: 312130
Personnel:
Maria del Mar Raventos *(Pres)*
Xavier Pages *(CEO)*

COECLERICI S.P.A.

Piazza Armando Diaz 7
20123 Milan, Italy
Tel.: (39) 02624691
Fax: (39) 0262469703
E-Mail: info@coeclerici.com
Web Site: www.coeclerici.com
Year Founded: 1895
Rev.: $793,120,287
Assets: $521,202,024
Liabilities: $405,566,021
Net Worth: $115,636,003
Earnings: $20,145,434
Emp.: 972
Fiscal Year-end: 12/31/12
Business Description:
Raw Material Sourcing, Marketing & Transporting Services
S.I.C.: 1241
N.A.I.C.S.: 213113
Personnel:
Paolo Clerici *(Chm & CEO)*
Corrado Papone *(Deputy Chm)*
Giorgio Invernizzi *(Interim CFO & Gen Mgr)*
Andrea Clavarino *(Exec VP-Gen & Institutional Affairs)*
Board of Directors:
Paolo Clerici
Antonio Belloni
Giorgio Cefis
Andrea Clavarino
Giacomo Clerici
Urbano Clerici
Nicolo Dubini
Teresio Gigi Gaudio
Hugh Malim
Corrado Papone
Riccardo Perissich
Lupo Rattazzi
Annibale Brivio Sforza
Jody Vender

Subsidiaries:

A. Billitz S.r.l. (1)
New Free Port Office Warehouse 72
34132 Trieste, Porto Franco, Italy (100%)
Tel.: (39) 040313941
Fax: (39) 040310266
E-Mail: info@billitztrieste.com
Web Site: www.billitztrieste.com
Emp.: 10
S.I.C.: 7389
N.A.I.C.S.: 425120

Adriafruit Italia S.r.l. (1)
Piazza Rossetti 2-8
16129 Genoa, Italy (100%)
Tel.: (39) 01057672
Fax: (39) 0105767235
E-Mail: info@adriafruit.it
Web Site: www.adriafruit.it
Emp.: 20
S.I.C.: 7389
N.A.I.C.S.: 425120

Coeclerici Bulk Terminal Torres S.p.A. (1)
Via Martin Piaggio 17
16122 Genoa, Italy (100%)
Tel.: (39) 0877285
Fax: (39) 0889852
S.I.C.: 5051
N.A.I.C.S.: 425120

Coeclerici Coal & Fuels S.p.A (1)
Via Manin 13
20121 Milan, Italy IT
Tel.: (39) 02624691 (100%)
Telex: 315051; 323335 clemi i
Fax: (39) 0262469703
E-Mail: coaldiv@coeclerici.com
Emp.: 20
S.I.C.: 5051
N.A.I.C.S.: 425120

Coeclerici Logistics S.p.A. (1)
Via Di Francia 28
16149 Genoa, Italy (100%)
Tel.: (39) 01060531
Fax: (39) 0106053444
E-Mail: newprojects@coeclerici.com
Web Site: www.coeclerici.com
Emp.: 20
Provider of Logistic & Transport Services of Raw Materials
S.I.C.: 4731
N.A.I.C.S.: 541614

Coeclerici Shipping S.p.A. (1)
Via De Francia 28
16149 Genoa, Italy (100%)
Tel.: (39) 01060531
Fax: (39) 0106053333
E-Mail: service@coeclerici.com
Emp.: 15
S.I.C.: 5051
N.A.I.C.S.: 425120

Coeclerici Coal & Fuels SpA (1)
7 Piazza Armando Diaz
20123 Milan, Italy (100%)
Tel.: (39) 2 62469756
Fax: (39) 2 62469705
E-Mail: coaldiv@coeclerici.com
Web Site: www.coeclerici.com
Emp.: 300
Coal & Fuel Management Services
S.I.C.: 7389
N.A.I.C.S.: 425120

Ing Ruggero Vio (1)
Via Portenari 1 Marghera
16149 Venice, Italy (100%)
Tel.: (39) 041931833
Fax: (39) 0106053525
E-Mail: service@coeclerici.com
Web Site: www.vio.it
Emp.: 15
Handling Raw Materials & Transhipment, Owners of Ships, Tugs, Coastal Barges & Ocean Barges
S.I.C.: 4412
N.A.I.C.S.: 483111

Sidermar Di Navigazione S.p.A. (1)
Via XX Settembre 41
16121 Genoa, Italy
Tel.: (39) 01056341
Fax: (39) 010 5634 313
S.I.C.: 7389
N.A.I.C.S.: 425120

Affiliate:

Solas Shipping Agency S.r.l. (1)
Via Carlo Barabino no.16 S 5
16129 Genoa, Italy
Tel.: (39) 0108681207
Fax: (39) 010 8681220
E-Mail: solas@solas.it
Web Site: www.solas.it
Emp.: 10
Shipping Agency Services; Chartering & Brokerage; Transports & Logistics
S.I.C.: 4731
N.A.I.C.S.: 488510

Non-U.S. Subsidiaries:

Coeclerici Coal & Fuels S.p.A. - Russia Branch (1)
4 Dobryninskij Pereulok 6/9
119049 Moscow, Russia (100%)
Tel.: (7) 0952376892
Telex: 413281 cocle su
Fax: (7) 0952302683
E-Mail: ccmoscow@coeclerici.com
Web Site: www.coeclerici.com
Emp.: 16
Coal & Other Raw Materials Distr, Marketer & Transporter
S.I.C.: 7389
N.A.I.C.S.: 425120

Citco Curacao (1)
Schottegatweg Oost 44,
PO Box 812
Willemstad, Curacao (100%)
Tel.: (599) 97322555
Fax: (599) 97322500
E-Mail: curacao-trust@citco.com
Web Site: www.citco.com
Emp.: 250
Trust & Fiduciuary Services
S.I.C.: 7389
N.A.I.C.S.: 425120

Somocar Overseas N.V. (1)
De Ruyterkade 62
Willemstad, Curacao (100%)
Tel.: (599) 9613077
Fax: (599) 9614375
S.I.C.: 7389
N.A.I.C.S.: 425120

COELI AB

Sveavagen 24
111 57 Stockholm, Sweden
Tel.: (46) 854591640
Fax: (46) 854591641
E-Mail: info@coeli.se
Web Site: www.coeli.se
Emp.: 100
Business Description:
Investment Services
S.I.C.: 6211
N.A.I.C.S.: 523999
Personnel:
Mikael Smedeby *(Chm)*
Magnus Wretholm *(CEO)*
Jan Sundqvist *(CEO-Private Equity)*

Holding:

Hanza AB (1)
Brovagen 5
182 76 Stocksund, Sweden
Tel.: (46) 86246200
Fax: (46) 86243060
E-Mail: info@hanza.com
Web Site: www.hanza.com
Sales Range: $150-199.9 Million
Emp.: 1,015
Contract Manufacturing Services
S.I.C.: 3999
N.A.I.C.S.: 339999
Per Tjernberg *(Chm)*
Erik Stenfors *(CEO)*
Lars Akerblom *(VP & CFO)*

Subsidiary:

HANZA Precision AB (2)
Verkstadsgatan 2
Box 93
SE-545 22 Toreboda, Sweden (100%)
Tel.: (46) 50618400
Fax: (46) 50618429
Sales Range: $10-24.9 Million
Emp.: 85
Mechanical Component Mfr
S.I.C.: 3499
N.A.I.C.S.: 332999

Unit:

HANZA Precision AB - Arjang (3)
Industrigatan 8
Box 34
SE-672 21 Arjang, Sweden
Tel.: (46) 317062800
Fax: (46) 317062850
Emp.: 53
Mechanical Component Mfr
S.I.C.: 3499
N.A.I.C.S.: 332999

COESIA SPA

(d/b/a/ COESIA Group)
Via Battindarno 91
40133 Bologna, Italy
Tel.: (39) 0516474111
Fax: (39) 0516474333
E-Mail: contact@coesia.com
Web Site: www.gede.it
Sales Range: $1-4.9 Billion
Emp.: 3,840

Business Description:
General Purpose Machinery Mfr
S.I.C.: 3569
N.A.I.C.S.: 333999
Personnel:
Isabella Seragnoli *(Chm & Pres)*
Angelos Papadimitriou *(CEO)*
Board of Directors:
Isabella Seragnoli
Roger Abravanel
Emilio Fossati
Umberto Paolucci
Angelos Papadimitriou
Maurizio Petta
Roberto Poli
Angelo Tantazzi
Francesco Tato

Subsidiary:

G.D SpA (1)
Via Battindarno 921
40133 Bologna, Italy
Tel.: (39) 0516474111
Fax: (39) 0516474333
E-Mail: info@gidi.it
Web Site: www.gidi.it
Sales Range: $600-649.9 Million
Emp.: 2,250
Mfr. of Cigarette Making & Packaging Machinery
S.I.C.: 3565
N.A.I.C.S.: 333993
Isabella Seragnoli *(Chm & Pres)*
Angelos Papadimitriou *(CEO)*

U.S. Subsidiary:

GD USA, Inc. (2)
501 Southlake Blvd
Richmond, VA 23236-3042
Tel.: (804) 794-9777
Fax: (804) 794-6187
Web Site: www.gdpackagemachinery.com
Emp.: 190
Mfr. of Packaging Machinery
Import Export
S.I.C.: 7699
N.A.I.C.S.: 811219
Guiseppi Venturi *(Exec VP-US Opers)*

Divisions:

ACMA GD (3)
501 Southlake Blvd
Richmond, VA 23236
Tel.: (804) 794-6688
Fax: (804) 379-2199
E-Mail: AcmaGD_USA@gidi.it
Web Site: www.gdpackagemachinery.com
Emp.: 150
Production & Packaging Machinery Mfr
S.I.C.: 3565
N.A.I.C.S.: 333993
Paolo Stagni *(VP-Ops)*

Corniani ACMA GD (3)
501 Southlake Blvd
Richmond, VA 23236
Tel.: (804) 794-6688
Fax: (804) 794-6187
Liquid Packaging Machinery Mfr
S.I.C.: 3565
N.A.I.C.S.: 333993

Volpak Packaging Machines (3)
501 Southlake Blvd
Richmond, VA 23236
Tel.: (804) 794-6688
Fax: (804) 379-2199
Packaging Machinery Mfr
S.I.C.: 3565
N.A.I.C.S.: 333993

Non-U.S. Subsidiaries:

G.D China Limited (2)
Suite 2105-2107 21Fl Tower 2 Ever Gain Plaza
88 Container Port Rd, Kwai Chung, NT, China (Hong Kong)
Tel.: (852) 25110888
Fax: (852) 25111068
E-Mail: general@gidichina.hk
Web Site: www.gidi.it
Emp.: 20
Cigarette Making & Packing Machinery Mfr
S.I.C.: 3565
N.A.I.C.S.: 333993
Tom Chung *(Mng Dir)*

G.D Do Brasil (2)
Rua Dr Alfonso Vergueiro 1101
Sao Paulo, SP, 02116-001, Brazil
Tel.: (55) 1127952000
Fax: (55) 1129547833
Web Site: www.coesia.com
Emp.: 200
Packaging Machinery Mfr
S.I.C.: 3565
N.A.I.C.S.: 333993
Stefano Nanni *(Pres)*

G.D Germany (2)
Hans Bockler Strasse 6 8
D 40764 Lagenfeld, Germany
Tel.: (49) 21739760
Fax: (49) 2173976149
E-Mail: gdlang@gd.it
Web Site: www.gidi.it
Sls.: $25,161,860
Emp.: 70
S.I.C.: 3499
N.A.I.C.S.: 332999
Rainhold Taesar *(Mng Dir)*

GD Indonesia (2)
Jalan Kig Raya Barat G8 Kawasan Industri Gresik
61121 Surabaya, East Java, Indonesia
Tel.: (62) 313985295
Fax: (62) 313985296
Cigarette Making & Packing Machinery Mfr
S.I.C.: 3565
N.A.I.C.S.: 333993

G.D Japan (2)
3-18-9 Tatsumi
Koto-ku, Tokyo, 135 0053, Japan
Tel.: (81) 335225360
Fax: (81) 335225361
E-Mail: gdj.administration@gidi.it
Web Site: www.gidi.it/gd/english/company/gd_world_japan.jsp
Emp.: 40
Cigarette Making & Packing Machinery Mfr
S.I.C.: 3565
N.A.I.C.S.: 333993
Shiyeyuki Suzuki *(Pres)*

G.D Russian Federation (2)
Panfilova street 19-1
Khimki, Moscow, 141407, Russia
Tel.: (7) 4957881000
Fax: (7) 4957394880
E-Mail: info@coesia.com
Web Site: www.coesia.com
Cigarette Making & Packing Machinery Mfr
S.I.C.: 3565
N.A.I.C.S.: 333993

G.D South East Asia (2)
1 Kaki Bukit View unit 04-01 Techview
04 05 KA Center, Singapore, 415941, Singapore
Tel.: (65) 63831711
Fax: (65) 63831911
E-Mail: sales@gidisingapore.com.sg
Emp.: 9
Cigarette Making & Packing Machinery Mfr
S.I.C.: 3565
N.A.I.C.S.: 333993

U.S. Subsidiaries:

Packaging Technologies, Inc. (1)
807 W Kimberly Rd
Davenport, IA 52806-5706
Tel.: (563) 391-1100
Fax: (563) 391-0017
Toll Free: (800) 257-5622
E-Mail: sales@packt.com
Web Site: www.packt.com
Emp.: 250
Packaging Machinery Mfr
Import Export
S.I.C.: 3565
N.A.I.C.S.: 333993
Barry W. Shoulders *(Pres & CEO)*

R.A. Jones & Co. Inc. (1)
2701 Crescent Springs Rd
Covington, KY 41017-1504
Tel.: (859) 341-0400
Fax: (859) 341-0519
Web Site: www.rajones.com
Sales Range: $1-4.9 Billion
Emp.: 5,000
Packaging Machinery Mfr
Import Export
S.I.C.: 3565
N.A.I.C.S.: 333993
Susan Awadalla *(CFO)*

Non-U.S. Subsidiaries:

Laetus GmbH (1)
Sandwiesenstrasse 27
Alsbach-Hahnlein, 64665, Germany
Tel.: (49) 625750090
Fax: (49) 62573119
E-Mail: contact@laetus.com
Web Site: www.laetus.com
Emp.: 90
Process & Packaging Solutions
S.I.C.: 3565
N.A.I.C.S.: 333993
Hendrik Hendrik *(Mng Dir)*
Hendrik Kneusels *(Mng Dir)*

Hapa AG (1)
Chriesbaumstrasse 4
8604 Volketswil, Switzerland
Tel.: (41) 433993299
Fax: (41) 433993201
E-Mail: info@hapa.ch
Web Site: www.hapa.ch
Emp.: 140
Process & Packaging Solutions
S.I.C.: 3565
N.A.I.C.S.: 333993
Mac Kenzie *(Dir-Sls)*

Sirius Machinery AB (1)
c/o Kalix 4 avenue du Parana
ZA Courtaboeuf n4 Les Ulis, F-91978
Courtaboeuf, Cedex, France FR
Tel.: (33) 1 69 18 05 90 (100%)
Fax: (33) 1 69 18 05 05
E-Mail: info@siriusmachinery.com
Web Site: www.siriusmachinery.com
Industrial Tube Filling Machinery Mfr
S.I.C.: 3559
N.A.I.C.S.: 333249
Goran Axelsson *(CFO)*

Subsidiaries:

ADMV (2)
ZA Les Triboulieres
38 460 Cremieu, France FR
Tel.: (33) 474904366 (100%)
Fax: (33) 474904677
E-Mail: commercial@admv.sa.fr
Web Site: www.admv.fr/
Emp.: 20
Feeding & Automation Equipment Mfr
S.I.C.: 3559
N.A.I.C.S.: 333249
Eric Viton *(Mng Dir)*

Kalix (2)
4 Avenue du Parana
91978 Les Ulis, Cedex, France FR
Tel.: (33) 33169180500 (100%)
Fax: (33) 169180501
E-Mail: sales@kalix.fr
Web Site: www.kalix.fr
Emp.: 55
Packaging Machinery Mfr
S.I.C.: 3559
N.A.I.C.S.: 333249

Volpak S.A (1)
Poligono Industrial Can Vinyalets
Santa Perpetua de Mogoda, Barcelona, 08130, Spain
Tel.: (34) 935446700
Fax: (34) 935741136
E-Mail: main@volpak.com
Web Site: www.volpak.com
Packaging Machinery Mfr
S.I.C.: 3565
N.A.I.C.S.: 333993
Gert Brinkman *(Mgr)*

COFCO LIMITED

Tower A COFCO Fortune Plaza
No 8 Chao Yang Men, Beijing, 100020, China
Tel.: (86) 1085006688
Fax: (86) 10 6527 8612
E-Mail: contact@cofco.com.cn
Web Site: www.cofco.com
Year Founded: 1952
Sales Range: $800-899.9 Million
Emp.: 12,000

Business Description:
Livestock & Poultry, Fruits, Vegetables, Canned Goods, Beverages, Confectionery & Condiments Import & Export Services
S.I.C.: 5154
N.A.I.C.S.: 424520
Personnel:
Gaoning Ning *(Chm)*
Xubo Yu *(Pres)*
Xiaohui Wu *(Chief Accountant)*
Hongbo Zheng *(Chief Economist)*
Liedong Liu *(Gen Counsel)*
Board of Directors:
Gaoning Ning
Jingtao Chi
Hua Jiang
Yongfu Liu
Zhiying Wang
Xubo Yu

Subsidiaries:

China National Native Produce & Animal By-Products Import & Export Corporation (1)
208 An Ding Men Wai Street
Beijing, 100011, China
Tel.: (86) 10 5123 6997
Fax: (86) 10 6420 4099
E-Mail: info@tuhsu.com.cn
Web Site: www.tuhsu.com.cn
Diversified Trading Company
S.I.C.: 5399
N.A.I.C.S.: 452990
Yongfu Liu *(Pres)*

Subsidiaries:

China Tea Co., Ltd. (2)
9th Fl 208 Andingmen Wai Street
Beijing, 100011, China
Tel.: (86) 1064204127
Fax: (86) 1064204101
E-Mail: info@teachina.com
Web Site: www.chinatea.com.cn
Tea Cultivation, Production, Processing, Research & Sales
S.I.C.: 2095
N.A.I.C.S.: 311920
Futang Zhu *(Chm)*

Subsidiary:

Fujian Tea Import & Export Co., Ltd. (3)
11 12 F Fortune Bldg 168 Hudong Rd
Fuzhou, Fujian, 350003, China
Tel.: (86) 59187853457
Fax: (86) 59187853402
E-Mail: ft@fteast.com
Web Site: www.fteast.com
Emp.: 80
Import & Export of Tea, Coffee & Other Miscellaneous Products
Import Export
S.I.C.: 2095
N.A.I.C.S.: 311920

China Tuhsu Flavours & Fragrances Import & Export Corporation (2)
COFCO Fortune Plaza No.8
Chao Yang Men South St, Beijing, 100020, China
Tel.: (86) 85018315
Fax: (86) 85623733
E-Mail: ctff@cofco.com
Web Site: www.ctff.com.cn
Processing, Domestic Marketing & Export of Natural Flavors, Synthetic Fragrances & Rosin & Turpentine Products
S.I.C.: 2819
N.A.I.C.S.: 325180

Non-U.S. Subsidiary:

Lihai International Shipping Co., Ltd. (2)
17 F East Asia Bank Harbor Center Building
56 Gloucester Road
Wanchai, China (Hong Kong)
Tel.: (852) 25289123
Fax: (852) 25200057
E-Mail: shipping@lihai.com.hk
Web Site: www.lihai.com.hk
Emp.: 10

COFCO Limited—(Continued)

Maritime Cargo Shipping Services
S.I.C.: 4491
N.A.I.C.S.: 488320
Pan Zhong Shan *(Gen Mgr)*

COFCO Commercial Property Investment Co., Ltd. **(1)**
Tower A COFCO Plaza
8 Jianguomennei Street, Beijing, 100005, China
Tel.: (86) 1085006688
Fax: (86) 1085612800
Web Site: www.cofco.com
Commercial Real Estate Development & Management
S.I.C.: 6531
N.A.I.C.S.: 531390

COFCO Property (Group) Co., Ltd. **(1)**
5 Hubin Road
Bao'an District, Shenzhen, Guangdong, 518101, China
Tel.: (86) 75527754517
Fax: (86) 755 2778 9701
E-Mail: cofco-property@cofco-property.cn
Web Site: www.cofco-property.cn
000031—(SSE)
Emp.: 485
Residential Real Estate Development & Sales; Leasing & Management of Properties
S.I.C.: 6531
N.A.I.C.S.: 531390
Jie Cui *(CFO)*
Hui Li *(Sec & Deputy Gen Mgr)*

COFCO Shenzhen Co., Ltd. **(1)**
F2 & F3 Xinglong Complex 9 Qingshui River Third Road
Hongling North Road
Luohu District, Shenzhen, 518024, China
Tel.: (86) 755 2231 6706
E-Mail: cofcosz@cofcosz.com.cn
Web Site: www.cofcosz.com.cn
Food Logistics & Warehousing Services; Property Management
S.I.C.: 4226
N.A.I.C.S.: 493190

COFCO Tunhe Co., Ltd. **(1)**
20/F China Merchants Bank Building 2 Huanghe Road
Urumqi, Xinjiang, 830000, China
Tel.: (86) 991 5571888
Fax: (86) 991 5571600
E-Mail: info@cofcotunhe.com
Web Site: www.cofcotunhe.com
600737—(SHG)
Emp.: 6,545
Food Processing & Sales of Tomato Sauce, Sugar, Fruit Jams & Other Agricultural By-Products
S.I.C.: 2099
N.A.I.C.S.: 311999
Hongbo Zheng *(Chm)*
Wei Zhao *(Chief Acctg Officer)*
Xuegong Jiang *(Sec)*

Non-U.S. Subsidiaries:

China Agri-Industries Holdings Limited **(1)**
31st Floor Top Glory Tower 262 Gloucester Road
Causeway Bay, China (Hong Kong)
Tel.: (852) 2833 0606
Fax: (852) 2833 0319
E-Mail: ir@cofco.com
Web Site: www.chinaagri.com
606—(HKG OTC)
Rev.: $11,775,609,035
Assets: $9,620,241,764
Liabilities: $5,689,328,804
Net Worth: $3,930,912,961
Earnings: $182,038,070
Emp.: 27,829
Fiscal Year-end: 12/31/12
Holding Company; Agricultural Products Processing
S.I.C.: 6719
N.A.I.C.S.: 551112
Xubo Yu *(Chm)*
Guojun Yue *(Mng Dir)*
Pui Fan Look *(Sec)*

China Foods Limited **(1)**
33rd Floor Top Glory Tower 262 Gloucester Road
Causeway Bay, China (Hong Kong)
Tel.: (852) 28330388
Fax: (852) 28330380
Web Site: www.chinafoodsltd.com
0506—(HKG OTC)
Rev.: $3,981,768,391
Assets: $2,606,360,740
Liabilities: $1,484,755,445
Net Worth: $1,121,605,295
Earnings: $76,358,774
Emp.: 17,288
Fiscal Year-end: 12/31/12
Holding Company; Beverages, Wine, Confectionery & Consumer Edible Oil
S.I.C.: 6719
N.A.I.C.S.: 551112
Xiuju Luan *(Mng Dir)*
Wenting Wu *(CFO & Deputy Gen Mgr)*
Kit Yee Linda Liu *(Sec)*

Non-U.S. Subsidiaries:

COFCO Food Marketing Services, Co., Ltd. **(2)**
Room 1321 Tower B COFCO Fortune plaza No 8
Chao Yang Men South St
Chao Yang, Beijing, 100020, China
Tel.: (86) 1085120501
Fax: (86) 1085120269
Web Site: www.cofco.com
Kitchen Products & Brands Promotion
S.I.C.: 5199
N.A.I.C.S.: 424990

COFCO Le Conte Food (Shenzhen) Co., Ltd. **(2)**
No 1 Meixiu Road Meilin Industrial Zone
Beihuan Road, Shenzhen, China (86%)
Tel.: (86) 755 8331 1056
Fax: (86) 755 8331 0971
E-Mail: leconte@leconte.com.cn
Web Site: www.leconte.com.cn
Chocolate & Nonchocolate Confections Mfr
S.I.C.: 2066
N.A.I.C.S.: 311351

COFCO Wines & Spirits Co. Ltd. **(2)**
11th Fl Tower A COFCO Plaza 8 Jianguomennei St
Dongcheng District, Beijing, 100005, China (100%)
Tel.: (86) 01085006688
Fax: (86) 1065278639
Web Site: www.cofco.com
Wine & Liquor Production & Whslr
S.I.C.: 5182
N.A.I.C.S.: 424820

The Hong Kong Parkview Group Limited **(1)**
33/F Top Glory Tower 262 Gloucester Road
Causeway Bay
Hong Kong, China (Hong Kong) BM
Tel.: (852) 28330338 (73.5%)
Fax: (852) 28330330
E-Mail: parkview@hongkongparkview.com
Web Site: www.hkparkviewgroup.com
0207—(HKG)
Sales Range: $1-9.9 Million
Emp.: 4
Property Holding & Investment Services
S.I.C.: 6719
N.A.I.C.S.: 551112
Jianping Ma *(Chm)*
Kin Wai Tse *(Sec)*

COFFEE REPUBLIC TRADING LTD.

10 Rochester Row
Victoria, London, SW1P 1BS, United Kingdom
Tel.: (44) 2078285800
Fax: (44) 2076309847
E-Mail: reception@coffeerepublic.com
Web Site: www.coffeerepublic.com
Sales Range: $10-24.9 Million
Emp.: 132

Business Description:
Holding Company; Coffee Shop Owner & Operator
S.I.C.: 6719
N.A.I.C.S.: 551112

Personnel:
Teric Affara *(CEO)*

Board of Directors:
Nicholas Jeffrey

Subsidiary:

Coffee Republic (UK) Limited **(1)**
109-123 Clifton St
London, EC2A 4LD, United Kingdom
Tel.: (44) 2070330600
Fax: (44) 2070330464
E-Mail: reception@coffeerepublic.com
Emp.: 6
Espresso & Coffee Bars Operating Services
S.I.C.: 5812
N.A.I.C.S.: 722515
David Reynolds *(CEO)*

COFFEY INTERNATIONAL LIMITED

Level 10 BT Tower 1 Market Street
Sydney, NSW, 2000, Australia
Tel.: (61) 2 9287 2100
Fax: (61) 2 9287 2188
E-Mail: investor.relations@coffey.com
Web Site: www.coffey.com.au
COF—(ASX)
Rev.: $715,499,607
Assets: $338,944,067
Liabilities: $195,920,011
Net Worth: $143,024,057
Earnings: ($949,353)
Emp.: 2,250
Fiscal Year-end: 06/30/13

Business Description:
Holding Company; Infrastructure Consultancy Services
S.I.C.: 6719
N.A.I.C.S.: 551112

Personnel:
John Douglas *(CEO & Mng Dir)*
Richard Biesheuvel *(Grp Exec-Projects)*
Chantalle Meijer *(Grp Exec-Mktg & Comm)*
Rebelle Moriarty *(Grp Exec-HR)*
Rob Morris *(Grp Exec-Environments)*
Sukumar Pathmanandavel *(Grp Exec-Geotechnics & Mining)*
Michael Renehan *(Grp Exec-Testing)*
Glen H. Simpson *(Grp Exec-Intl Dev)*
Bob Simpson *(Pres-Geosciences-Canada)*
Jennifer Waldegrave *(Sec)*

Board of Directors:
John Mulcahy
Stuart A. Black
Leeanne Bond
Guy Cowan
John Douglas
Urs Meyerhans
Susan Oliver

Subsidiaries:

Coffey Corporate Pty Ltd. **(1)**
Level 3 Twr 1 495 Victoria Ave
Chatswood, New South Wales, 2067, Australia
Tel.: (61) 284044300
Fax: (61) 294195689
Web Site: www.coffey.com
Emp.: 4,000
Engineering Services
S.I.C.: 8711
N.A.I.C.S.: 541330
Roger Olds *(CEO & Mng Dir)*

Coffey Geotechnics Pty. Ltd. **(1)**
8-12 Mars Rd
Lane Cove W, Sydney, New South Wales, 2066, Australia
Tel.: (61) 299111000
Fax: (61) 299111001
E-Mail: receptionist@coffey.com
Web Site: www.coffey.com.au
Emp.: 100
Geotechnical Engineering Services
S.I.C.: 8711
N.A.I.C.S.: 541330

Coffey Information Pty. Ltd. **(1)**
Bugden Lane
Alstonville, NSW, 2477, Australia
Tel.: (61) 266283224
Fax: (61) 266281833
Web Site: www.coffey.com.au
Emp.: 5
Professional Consulting Services
S.I.C.: 8748
N.A.I.C.S.: 541618
Christopher McNeil *(Mgr-Lab)*

Coffey International Development Pty. Ltd. **(1)**
Level 2 70 Hindmarsh Sq
Adelaide, South Australia, 5000, Australia
Tel.: (61) 884181500
Fax: (61) 882240453
Web Site: www.coffey.com.au
Emp.: 60
Professional Consulting Services
S.I.C.: 8748
N.A.I.C.S.: 541618

Coffey Mining Pty. Ltd. **(1)**
Lev 3 15 Astor Terr
Springhill, QLD, 4000, Australia
Tel.: (61) 736082500
Fax: (61) 38322994
Web Site: www.coffey.com.au
Emp.: 9
Mining Consultancy Services
S.I.C.: 1081
N.A.I.C.S.: 213114
Roger Olds *(Mng Dir)*

Coffey Projects (Australia) Pty. Ltd. **(1)**
Level 5 12 Creek St
Brisbane, Queensland, 4000, Australia
Tel.: (61) 735036200
Fax: (61) 730020444
E-Mail: receptionist@coffey.com
Web Site: www.coffey.com
Emp.: 20
Business Management Consulting Services
S.I.C.: 8742
N.A.I.C.S.: 541611
John Douglas *(Mng Dir)*

U.S. Subsidiaries:

Coffey International Development Inc. **(1)**
165 Seaman Ave Apt 6e
New York, NY 10034-1987
Tel.: (908) 517-5590
Fax: (908) 517-5591
Web Site: www.coffey.com
Emp.: 2
Business Management Consulting Services
S.I.C.: 8742
N.A.I.C.S.: 541611
Tom Fitch *(COO)*

Management Systems International Inc. **(1)**
600 Water St SW
Washington, DC 20024
Tel.: (202) 484-7170
Fax: (202) 488-0754
E-Mail: info@msi-inc.com
Web Site: www.msiworldwide.com
Emp.: 700
Economic Consulting Services
S.I.C.: 8748
N.A.I.C.S.: 541618
Lawrence Cooley *(Pres)*
Paul Wise *(CFO)*
Stacy Stacks *(Chief Mgmt Officer)*
Marina Fanning *(Exec VP)*
Keith Brown *(Sr VP-Programs)*
Malcolm Butler *(Sr VP-Emerging Markets)*

Non-U.S. Subsidiaries:

Coffey Environments (NZ) Ltd. **(1)**
7 City Rd
Grafton, 1010 Auckland, New Zealand
Tel.: (64) 95235626
Fax: (64) 3072654
Web Site: www.coffey.com
Emp.: 5
Environmental Consulting Services
S.I.C.: 8999
N.A.I.C.S.: 541620

Coffey Geotechnics (NZ) Ltd. (1)
Level 11 7 City Road
Epsom, 1023 Auckland, New Zealand
Tel.: (64) 95235626
Fax: (64) 95235627
Web Site: www.coffey.com
Geotechnical Engineering Services
S.I.C.: 8711
N.A.I.C.S.: 541330

Coffey International Development Holdings Ltd. (1)
The Malthouse 1 Northfield Rd
Reading, Berkshire, RG1 8AH, United Kingdom
Tel.: (44) 1189566066
Fax: (44) 1189576066
Web Site: www.coffey.com
Emp.: 30
Holding Company; Consultancy Services
S.I.C.: 6719
N.A.I.C.S.: 551112
Rod Reeve *(Gen Mgr)*

Subsidiary:

Coffey International Development Ltd. (2)
The Malthouse 1 Northfield Rd
Reading, Berkshire, RG1 8AH, United Kingdom
Tel.: (44) 1189566066
Fax: (44) 1189576066
E-Mail: contact@coffey.com
Web Site: www.coffey.com
Emp.: 40
Business Management Consultancy Services
S.I.C.: 8742
N.A.I.C.S.: 541611
Roger Olds *(CEO)*

Coffey International Development Sp. z.o.o. (1)
ul Krucza 16 22
00 526 Warsaw, Poland
Tel.: (48) 225782280
Fax: (48) 225782281
Web Site: www.coffey.com
Emp.: 10
Business Consulting Services
S.I.C.: 8742
N.A.I.C.S.: 541611
Richard Moreton *(Office Mgr)*

Coffey Mining (South Africa) Pty. Ltd. (1)
Block D Somerset Ofc Estate 604 Kudu St
Allens Nek, 1737 Roodepoort, Gauteng, South Africa
Tel.: (27) 116793331
Fax: (27) 116793272
E-Mail: adminzi@coffey.com
Web Site: www.coffey.com
Emp.: 23
Mining Consultancy Services
S.I.C.: 1081
N.A.I.C.S.: 213114
Feroza Sader *(Office Mgr)*

Coffey Projects (Africa) Pty. Ltd. (1)
13 Saddle Dr Woodmead Ofc Park
2191 Woodmead, Gauteng, South Africa
Tel.: (27) 116560950
Fax: (27) 116569523
Web Site: www.coffey.com
Emp.: 27
Project Management Services
S.I.C.: 8748
N.A.I.C.S.: 541618
Richard Bovell *(Mng Dir)*

Coffey Projects (New Zealand) Ltd. (1)
Level 11 7 City Road Grafton
Newmarket, Auckland, 1010, New Zealand
Tel.: (64) 93799463
Fax: (64) 93012654
E-Mail: rebecca.juson@coffey.com
Web Site: www.coffey.com
Emp.: 600
Business Management Services
S.I.C.: 7389
N.A.I.C.S.: 561499

Coffey (UK) Ltd. (1)
The Malthouse 1 Northfield Rd
Reading, Berkshire, RG1 8AH, United Kingdom
Tel.: (44) 1189566066
Fax: (44) 1189576066
Web Site: www.coffey.com
Emp.: 50
Business Management Services
S.I.C.: 7389
N.A.I.C.S.: 561499
Roger Olds *(CEO & Mng Dir)*

The Evaluation Partnership Ltd. (1)
83 Baker St
London, W1U 6AG, United Kingdom
Tel.: (44) 2070347026
Fax: (44) 2070347100
E-Mail: info@evaluationpartnership.com
Web Site: www.evaluationpartnership.com
Emp.: 50
General Management Consulting Services
S.I.C.: 8742
N.A.I.C.S.: 541611
John P. Watson *(Mng Dir)*

COFIDUR SA

(d/b/a Groupe Cofidur)
14 rue du Viaduc
94310 Nogent-sur-Marne, France
Tel.: (33) 1 48722163
Fax: (33) 1 48720296
Web Site: www.groupe-cofidur.com
ALCOF—(EUR)
Sales Range: $125-149.9 Million
Business Description:
Printed Circuit Mfr
S.I.C.: 3672
N.A.I.C.S.: 334412
Personnel:
Henri Tranduc *(Chm & CEO)*

COFINA SGPS, S.A.

Rua General Norton de Matos 68 - R/C
4050-424 Porto, Portugal
Tel.: (351) 22 834 65 00
Fax: (351) 22 834 65 09
E-Mail: sede@cofina.pt
Web Site: www.cofina.pt
Year Founded: 1995
CFN—(EUR)
Sls.: $80,872,918
Assets: $191,717,450
Liabilities: $171,877,110
Net Worth: $19,840,339
Earnings: $5,717,123
Emp.: 849
Fiscal Year-end: 12/31/12
Business Description:
Newspaper Publishing Services
S.I.C.: 2711
N.A.I.C.S.: 511110
Personnel:
Paulo Jorge dos Santos Fernandes *(Chm)*
Joao Manuel Matos Borges de Oliveira *(CFO)*
Board of Directors:
Paulo Jorge dos Santos Fernandes
Ana Rebelo de Carvalho Meneres de Mendonca Mariz Fernandes
Domingos Jose Vieira de Matos
Pedro Macedo Pinto de Mendonca
Joao Manuel Matos Borges de Oliveira
Pedro Miguel Matos Borges de Oliveira

COFINIMMO S.A./N.V.

Boulevard De La Woluwe 58
Woluwedal
1200 Brussels, Belgium
Tel.: (32) 23730000
Fax: (32) 23730010
E-Mail: info@cofinimmo.be
Web Site: www.cofinimmo.be
COFB—(EUR)
Rev.: $303,360,756
Assets: $4,903,408,071
Liabilities: $2,827,220,849
Net Worth: $2,076,187,222
Earnings: $138,244,928
Emp.: 109
Fiscal Year-end: 12/31/12
Business Description:
Nonresidential Property Manager & Real Estate Investment Trust
S.I.C.: 6726
N.A.I.C.S.: 525990
Personnel:
Andre A.G. Bergen *(Chm)*
Jean-Edouard Carbonnelle *(CEO)*
Marc Hellemans *(CFO)*
Xavier Denis *(COO)*
Francoise Roels *(Gen Counsel & Sec)*
Board of Directors:
Andre A.G. Bergen
Jean-Edouard Carbonnelle
Xavier de Walque
Xavier Denis
Chevalier Vincent Doumier
Robert Franssen
Gaetan Hannecart
Francoise Roels
Alain Schockert
Gilbert van Marcke de Lummen
Baudouin Velge

COFINLUXE S.A.

(d/b/a COFCI)
6 Rue Anatole de la Forge
75017 Paris, France
Tel.: (33) 155377172
Fax: (33) 146229827
Web Site: www.cofinluxe.fr
Sls.: $20,200,000
Emp.: 44
Business Description:
Toilet Preparations
S.I.C.: 2844
N.A.I.C.S.: 325620
Personnel:
Jean-Pierre Grivory *(Chm)*

COFITEM-COFIMUR SA

41 43 rue Saint-Dominique
75007 Paris, France
Tel.: (33) 1 5370 7777
Fax: (33) 1 5370 7778
Web Site: www.cofitem-cofimur.fr
Year Founded: 1984
CFTM—(EUR)
Rev.: $76,162,260
Assets: $1,447,753,334
Liabilities: $1,011,250,981
Net Worth: $436,502,353
Earnings: $48,440,581
Emp.: 14
Fiscal Year-end: 12/31/12
Business Description:
Real Estate Leasing & Development & Rental of Real Estate Property
S.I.C.: 6531
N.A.I.C.S.: 531390
Personnel:
Sophie Beuvaden *(Chm)*
Olivier Riche *(Mng Dir)*
Guy de Soucy *(Deputy Mng Dir)*
Alain Le Veel *(Deputy Mng Dir)*
Arnaud Pomel *(Deputy Mng Dir)*
Board of Directors:
Sophie Beuvaden
Michel Dufief
Jean-Paul Dumont
Peter Etzenbach
Juergen Gerke
Luc Guinefort
Olivier Le Borgne
Eric Le Gentil
Cyril Le Touze
Philippe Lepargneur
Olivier Riche
Francois Thomazeau
Cornel Widmer

Mazars
61 rue Henri Regnault
Courbevoie, France

COFLUSA S.A.

(d/b/a Camper)
Poligoni Industrial Inca s n
07300 Inca, Spain
Tel.: (34) 971507000
Fax: (34) 971507116
E-Mail: info@camper.com
Web Site: www.camper.com
Emp.: 600
Business Description:
Shoe Mfr, Retailer & Distr
S.I.C.: 2389
N.A.I.C.S.: 316210

COFRA HOLDING AG

(d/b/a COFRA Group)
Grafenau 10
6301 Zug, Switzerland
Mailing Address:
PO Box 151
6301 Zug, Switzerland
Tel.: (41) 417280000
Fax: (41) 417280099
E-Mail: mail@cofraholding.com
Web Site: www.cofraholding.com
Year Founded: 2001
Business Description:
Investment Holding Company
S.I.C.: 6719
N.A.I.C.S.: 551112
Personnel:
Erik Brenninkmeijer *(Chm-Supervisory Bd)*
Stan Brenninkmeijer *(CEO)*
Supervisory Board of Directors:
Erik Brenninkmeijer
Stan Brenninkmeijer
Richard M. Hayden

Non-U.S. Holdings:

Bregal Investments LLP (1)
81 Fulham Road 3rd Floor
London, SW3 6RD, United Kingdom UK
Tel.: (44) 207 408 1663
Fax: (44) 207 491 9228
Web Site: www.bregal.com
Private Equity Firm
N.A.I.C.S.: 523999
Steven Black *(Co-CEO)*
Quentin Van Doosselaere *(Co-CEO)*
Edwin Niers *(CFO)*

Co-Headquarters:

Bregal Investments, Inc. (2)
277 Park Ave 29th Fl
New York, NY 10172 DE
Tel.: (212) 573-6235
Fax: (212) 573-6234
E-Mail: management@bregal.com
Web Site: www.bregal.com
Private Equity Firm
N.A.I.C.S.: 523999
Steven Black *(Co-CEO)*
Quentin Van Doosselaere *(Co-CEO)*

Subsidiary:

Bregal Partners, L.P. (3)
277 Park Ave 29th Fl
New York, NY 10172
Tel.: (212) 704-5350
Fax: (212) 704-5351
Web Site: www.bregalpartners.com
Private Equity Firm
N.A.I.C.S.: 523999
Robert Bergmann *(Mng Partner)*
Scott Perekslis *(Mng Partner)*
Matthew Ford *(Principal)*
Paul McGill *(Principal)*

Holding:

Shock Doctor, Inc. (4)
110 Cheshire Ln Ste 120
Minnetonka, MN 55305

COFRA Holding AG—(Continued)

Tel.: (800) 233-6956
E-Mail: cs@shockdoctor.com
Web Site: www.shockdoctor.com
Sales Range: $75-99.9 Million
Sports Protective Equipment Mfr
N.A.I.C.S.: 339920
Kenneth B. Woodrow *(Chm)*
Tony Armand *(CEO)*

Subsidiary:

Bregal Capital LLP (2)
Michelin House 81 Fulham Road
London, SW3 6RD, United Kingdom UK
Tel.: (44) 2075914200
Fax: (44) 2075914222
E-Mail: bregal@bregalcapital.com
Web Site: www.bregalcapital.com
Managed Assets: $3,540,726,000
Private Equity Firm
S.I.C.: 6211
N.A.I.C.S.: 523999
Adam Barron *(Co-Founder & Partner)*
Edmund Lazarus *(Co-Founder & Partner)*
Dominic Shorthouse *(Chm & Mng Partner)*
Dwight Cupit *(CFO & Partner)*

Holding:

QA Ltd. (3)
Rath House 55 65 Uxbridge Road
Slough, Berks, SL1 1SG, United Kingdom (65%)
Tel.: (44) 8450747839
Fax: (44) 8450747840
E-Mail: info@qa.com
Web Site: www.qa.com
Emp.: 200
Professional Training Programs & Services
S.I.C.: 8299
N.A.I.C.S.: 611430
Christian Martin *(Chm)*
William Macpherson *(CEO)*

Non-U.S. Holdings:

Canopius Group Limited (3)
Ogier House Saint Julian's Avenue
Saint Peter Port, GY1 1WA, Guernsey GY
Tel.: (44) 1481721672 (85%)
Fax: (44) 1481721575
Web Site: www.canopius.com
Rev.: $1,092,368,045
Assets: $3,595,896,456
Liabilities: $3,029,371,968
Net Worth: $566,524,488
Earnings: $73,624,921
Fiscal Year-end: 12/31/12
Holding Company; Insurance & Reinsurance Products & Services
S.I.C.: 6719
N.A.I.C.S.: 551112
Michael Watson *(Chm)*
Inga Beale *(CEO)*
Paul Cooper *(CFO)*
Robert Law *(CFO)*
Stephen Manning *(COO)*
Jim Giordano *(Chief Underwriting Officer)*
Mike Duffy *(CEO-Global Property & Joint Active Underwriter)*
Stephen Gargrave *(CEO-Global Specialty & Joint Active Underwriter)*
Tim Rolfe *(CEO-Retail-UK)*

proALPHA Software GmbH (3)
Auf dem Immel 8
67685 Weilerbach, Germany
Tel.: (49) 6374 800 0
Fax: (49) 6374 800 199
E-Mail: info@proalpha.de
Web Site: www.proalpha.com
Sales Range: $50-74.9 Million
Emp.: 500
IT Consulting Services
S.I.C.: 8999
N.A.I.C.S.: 541690
Friedrich Neumeyer *(CEO)*

U.S. Subsidiary:

proALPHA Software Corporation (4)
20 Trafalgar Sq Ste 403
Nashua, NH 03063
Tel.: (603) 881-3635
Software Publisher
N.A.I.C.S.: 511210

C&A Mode GmbH & Co. KG (1)
Bleichstrasse 20
40211 Dusseldorf, Germany De
Mailing Address:
PO Box 101111
40002 Dusseldorf, Germany
Tel.: (49) 2111662747
Fax: (49) 2111662748
E-Mail: Presse@CundA.de
Web Site: www.cunda.de
Operator of Family Clothing Stores
S.I.C.: 5651
N.A.I.C.S.: 448140

Non-U.S. Subsidiary:

C&A Mode AG (2)
Ohmstrasse 11
CP 5247, 8050 Zurich, Switzerland CH
Tel.: (41) 432883766
Fax: (41) 432883740
E-Mail: ch@c-and-a.com
Web Site: www.c-e-a.ch
Sales Range: $250-299.9 Million
Emp.: 1,300
Family Clothing Stores Owner & Operator
Import Export
S.I.C.: 5651
N.A.I.C.S.: 448140

Non-U.S. Unit:

C&A - Europe Head Office (2)
Senneberg
Jean Monnetlaan, 1804 Vilvoorde, Belgium
Tel.: (32) 22576333
Fax: (32) 22576959
E-Mail:
Web Site: www.c-and-a.com
Sls.: $6,250,000,000
Emp.: 30,000
Operator of Family Clothing Stores
S.I.C.: 5651
N.A.I.C.S.: 448140
Marc Esgeourgie *(CEO)*

COGECO INC.

5 Place Ville Marie Suite 1700
Montreal, QC, H3B 0B3, Canada
Tel.: (514) 764-4700
Fax: (514) 874-2625
Web Site: www.cogeco.ca
CGO—(TSX)
Rev.: $1,823,288,143
Assets: $5,419,906,972
Liabilities: $4,058,715,865
Net Worth: $1,361,191,108
Earnings: $188,642,134
Emp.: 4,555
Fiscal Year-end: 08/31/13
Business Description:
Holding Company; Telecommunications
S.I.C.: 6719
N.A.I.C.S.: 551112
Personnel:
Jan E. Peeters *(Chm)*
Pierre L. Comtois *(Vice Chm)*
Louis Audet *(Pres & CEO)*
Pierre Gagne *(CFO & Sr VP)*
Christian Jolivet *(Chief Legal Officer, Sec & VP-Corp Affairs)*
Richard Lachance *(Pres/CEO-Cogeco Diffusion Inc.)*
Andree Pinard *(Treas & VP)*
Board of Directors:
Jan E. Peeters
Louis Audet
Elisabetta Bigsby
Pierre L. Comtois
Paule Dore
Claude A. Garcia
Normand Legault
David McAusland
Legal Counsel:
Stikeman Elliott
1155 Rene-Levesque Blvd West 40th Floor
Montreal, QC, H3B 3V2, Canada
Transfer Agent:
Computershare Trust Corporation of Canada
100 University Avenue 9th Floor
Toronto, ON, Canada

Subsidiary:

Cogeco Cable, Inc. (1)
5 Place Ville-Marie Office 1700
Montreal, QC, H3B 0B3, Canada (100%)
Tel.: (514) 764-4700
Fax: (514) 874-2625
Web Site: www.cogeco.ca
CCA—(MON TSX)
Rev.: $1,682,345,053
Assets: $5,221,683,480
Liabilities: $3,885,629,150
Net Worth: $1,336,054,330
Earnings: $183,976,204
Emp.: 4,059
Fiscal Year-end: 08/31/13
Telecommunications Company
S.I.C.: 4841
N.A.I.C.S.: 515210
Jan E. Peeters *(Chm)*
Louis Audet *(Pres & CEO)*
Pierre Gagne *(CFO & Sr VP)*
Philippe Jette *(CTO, Chief Strategy Officer & Sr VP)*
Christian Jolivet *(Chief Legal Officer, Sec & VP-Corp Affairs)*
Antonio P. Ciciretto *(Pres/CEO-Cogeco Data Services)*
Edward T. Holleran *(Pres/CEO-Atlantic Broadband Inc)*
Gary Sherlock *(Pres/CEO-PEER1 Hosting)*
Louise St-Pierre *(Pres/CEO-Canada)*
Andree Pinard *(Treas & VP)*

Divisions:

Cogeco Cable Ontario (2)
950 Syscon Rd
PO Box 5076
Burlington, ON, L7R4S6, Canada (100%)
Tel.: (905) 333-5343
Fax: (905) 333-8136
Web Site: www.cogeco.ca
Emp.: 700
Cable Communication Services
S.I.C.: 4899
N.A.I.C.S.: 517919
Ron A. Perrotta *(VP-Mktg & Strategic Plng)*

Cogeco Cable Quebec (2)
1630 6th Street Office 200
Trois Rivieres, QC, G8Y 5B8, Canada
Tel.: (819) 372-9292
Fax: (819) 372-3318
Web Site: www.cogeco.ca
Emp.: 32
Provider of Cable Television Services
S.I.C.: 4841
N.A.I.C.S.: 515210

Subsidiaries:

Cogeco Data Services Inc. (2)
413 Horner Avenue
Toronto, ON, M8W 4W3, Canada QC
Tel.: (416) 599-3282
Web Site: www.cogecodata.com
Data & Internet Telecommunications Services
S.I.C.: 7374
N.A.I.C.S.: 518210
Tony P. Ciciretto *(Pres)*

Peer 1 Network Enterprises, Inc. (2)
Suite 1000 555 W Hastings Street
Vancouver, BC, V6B 4N5, Canada BC
Tel.: (604) 683-7747
Fax: (604) 683-4634
Toll Free: (866) 683-7747
E-Mail: info@peer1.com
Web Site: www.peer1.com
Sales Range: $125-149.9 Million
Emp.: 540
Internet Infrastruction Solutions
S.I.C.: 4899
N.A.I.C.S.: 517919
Gary N. Sherlock *(Pres & CEO)*
Sheila Bouman *(Chief People & Performance Officer)*
Benjamin Young *(Gen Counsel & Sec)*
Dominic Monkhouse *(Sr VP-Customer Experience & Mng Dir-UK)*
Robert Miggins *(Sr VP-Bus Dev)*
Ted Smith, Jr. *(Sr VP-Ops)*

Subsidiary:

Peer 1 Network (Toronto) Inc. (3)
1 Yonge St
Toronto, ON, M5E 1E5, Canada
Tel.: (416) 815-7027
Fax: (416) 815-7330
Toll Free: (866) 579-9690
Emp.: 5
Web Hosting Services
S.I.C.: 7374
N.A.I.C.S.: 518210

U.S. Subsidiary:

Peer 1 Network (USA), Inc. (3)
75 Broad St Rm 280
New York, NY 10004 WA
Tel.: (866) 579-9690
Fax: (212) 742-1295
Toll Free: (866) 683-7747
E-Mail: sales@peer1.com
Web Site: www.peer1.com
Telecommunications Services
S.I.C.: 4899
N.A.I.C.S.: 517919

Division:

ServerBeach (4)
8500 Vicar Ste 500
San Antonio, TX 78218-1532
Tel.: (210) 798-4400
Fax: (210) 798-0109
E-Mail: Sales@serverbeach.com
Web Site: www.serverbeach.com
Emp.: 50
Web Hosting Services
S.I.C.: 2741
N.A.I.C.S.: 519130
Dax Moreno *(Dir-Customer Experience)*

U.S. Subsidiary:

Atlantic Broadband Group LLC (2)
1 Batterymarch Park Ste 405
Quincy, MA 02169
Tel.: (617) 786-8800
Web Site: www.atlanticbb.com
Sales Range: $300-349.9 Million
High Speed Broadband Services
S.I.C.: 4899
N.A.I.C.S.: 517919
Joe Dijulio *(Pres & Gen Mgr)*
Leslie Brown *(Gen Counsel & Sr VP)*

COGENT B2B LTD.

44 Tanners Drive
Milton Keynes, HP5 2SL, United Kingdom
Tel.: (44) 800 6899175
Web Site: www.cogentb2b.com
Business Description:
Business Consulting Services
S.I.C.: 8742
N.A.I.C.S.: 541611
Personnel:
Kevin Dunstall *(Mng Dir)*

Holding:

St. Ives Direct Bradford Limited (1)
Battye Street
Laisterdyke, Bradford, BD4 8AG, United Kingdom UK
Tel.: (44) 1274269300 (100%)
Fax: (44) 1274269355
Web Site: www.stivesdirect.com
Sales Range: $50-74.9 Million
Emp.: 200
Commercial Printing
S.I.C.: 2759
N.A.I.C.S.: 323111
Richard Armour *(Mgr-Production)*

COGENT HEALTH SOLUTIONS INC.

321 Water St Ste 501
Vancouver, BC, V6B 1B8, Canada
Tel.: (604) 708-9075
Fax: (604) 687-6942
E-Mail: info@cogenths.com
Web Site: www.cogenths.com
Emp.: 20
Business Description:
Healthcare Web-Based Solutions
S.I.C.: 7372
N.A.I.C.S.: 511210

Personnel:
Len Grenier *(Pres & CEO)*
Mark Thomson *(COO)*
Board of Directors:
Len Grenier
Amos Michelson
Greg Peet
Ian Robertson

COGENT HOLDINGS LIMITED
7 Penjuru Close 05-00
Singapore, 608779, Singapore
Tel.: (65) 62666161
Fax: (65) 62615730
Web Site: www.cogentholdingsltd.com
KJ9—(SES)
Rev.: $77,871,784
Assets: $87,154,765
Liabilities: $35,522,281
Net Worth: $51,632,484
Earnings: $6,282,307
Fiscal Year-end: 12/31/12
Business Description:
Warehousing Services
S.I.C.: 1542
N.A.I.C.S.: 236220
Personnel:
Yeow Khoon Tan *(Chm & CEO)*
Benson Min Cheow Tan *(Deputy CEO)*
Edwin Yeow Lam Tan *(Mng Dir)*
Bee Ka Lim *(Sec)*
Board of Directors:
Yeow Khoon Tan
Soo Sen Chan
Michael Cheow Khoon Chua
Benson Min Cheow Tan
Edwin Yeow Lam Tan
Benedict Lip Hua Teo

COGITO MEDIA GROUP INC.
279 Sherbrooke West Suite 305
Montreal, QC, H2X 1Y2, Canada
Tel.: (858) 531-5723
Web Site: www.cogitomedias.com
Year Founded: 2007
KRMC—(OTCB)
Business Description:
Business Services
S.I.C.: 7389
N.A.I.C.S.: 561499
Personnel:
Pierre Turgeon *(Pres & CEO)*
Jacques Arsenault *(CFO & Treas)*
Transfer Agent:
Corporate Stock Transfer, Inc.
3200 Cherry Creek Dr S Ste 430
Denver, CO 80209
Tel.: (303) 282-4800
Fax: (303) 282-5800

COGITORE RESOURCES INC.
1 Adelaide Street East Suite 2800
Toronto, ON, M5C 2V9, Canada
Tel.: (416) 924-9893
Fax: (416) 924-7997
Web Site: www.cogitore.com
Year Founded: 2002
WOO—(TSXV)
Int. Income: $4,833
Assets: $1,458,211
Liabilities: $497,390
Net Worth: $960,822
Earnings: ($2,883,047)
Fiscal Year-end: 12/31/12
Business Description:
Metal Mining Exploration Service
S.I.C.: 1081
N.A.I.C.S.: 213114
Personnel:
Mark E. Goodman *(Chm)*
Gerald Riverin *(Pres & CEO)*
Carmello Marrelli *(CFO)*
Board of Directors:
Mark E. Goodman
David Comba
Jonathan C. Goodman
Alain Krushnisky
Stephen Lidsky
Gerald Riverin

COGNITA SCHOOLS LIMITED
5 & 7 Diamond Court Opal Drive
Eastlake Park Fox Milne
Milton Keynes, MK15 0DU, United Kingdom
Tel.: (44) 1908 396 250
Fax: (44) 1908 396 251
E-Mail: info@cognitaschools.co.uk
Web Site: www.cognitaschools.com
Year Founded: 2004
Sales Range: $250-299.9 Million
Emp.: 3,553
Business Description:
School Operator
S.I.C.: 8211
N.A.I.C.S.: 611110
Personnel:
Chris Woodhead *(Chm)*
Rees Withers *(CEO)*
Gary Narunsky *(CFO)*
Dean Villa *(COO & Dir-Property)*
Josep Caubet *(CEO-Latin America)*
Ed Hyslop *(CEO-Europe)*
Brian Rogove *(CEO-Asia Pacific)*

COGNITEC SYSTEMS GMBH
Grossenhainer Str 101 Tower B
D-01127 Dresden, Germany
Tel.: (49) 351862920
Fax: (49) 3518629210
E-Mail: info@cognitec-systems.de
Web Site: www.cognitec-systems.de/
Emp.: 25
Business Description:
Developer of Facial Recognition Software
S.I.C.: 7372
N.A.I.C.S.: 511210
Personnel:
Alfredo Herrera Hernandez *(CEO)*
U.S. Subsidiary:

Cognitec Systems Corporation **(1)**
5201 Blue Lagoon Dr Ste 800
Miami, FL 33126
Tel.: (305) 629-3113
Fax: (305) 629-3112
E-Mail: info@cognitec.com
Web Site: www.cognitec.com
Emp.: 1
Distr of Facial Recognition Software
S.I.C.: 8741
N.A.I.C.S.: 551114
Alfredo Herrera *(CEO)*
Roger Kelesoglu *(Exec VP-Bus Dev)*

COGO GROUP, INC.
Room 1001 Tower C Skyworth
Building High-tech Industrial Park
Nanshan
Shenzhen, 518057, China
Tel.: (86) 75526743210
Fax: (86) 75526743508
E-Mail: communications@comtech.com.cn
Web Site: www.comtech.com.cn
Year Founded: 1995
COGO—(NASDAQ)
Rev.: $776,879,594
Assets: $376,753,758
Liabilities: $124,072,334
Net Worth: $252,681,424
Earnings: $7,737,107
Emp.: 540
Fiscal Year-end: 12/31/12
Business Description:
Mobile Handset & Telecom Equipment, Including LCD Modules, Camera Modules, Persistent Storage Modules, Input/Output Modules, Sound System & Power Supply Modules
S.I.C.: 1799
N.A.I.C.S.: 238990
Personnel:
Yi Yuan *(Pres)*
Andy Liu *(CFO, Treas & Sec)*
Board of Directors:
Andy Liu
Q. Y. Ma
George Mao
Subsidiary:

Comtech Communication Technology (Shenzhen) Co., Ltd. **(1)**
9th Fl Tower C Skyworth Bldg High-tech Industrial Park Nanshan
Nanshan Dist, Shenzhen, China
Tel.: (86) 75526743210
Fax: (86) 75526743006
E-Mail: scarlettwu@comtech.com.cn
Web Site: www.comtech.com.cn/
Emp.: 300
Electronics Components Mfr
S.I.C.: 3675
N.A.I.C.S.: 334416
Jeffrey Kang *(Gen Mgr)*

COGRA S.A.
Zone de Gardes
48000 Mende, France
Tel.: (33) 4 66 65 34 63
Fax: (33) 4 66 65 22 24
Web Site: www.cogra.fr
Year Founded: 1982
ALCOG—(EUR)
Sales Range: $10-24.9 Million
Emp.: 40
Business Description:
Wood Pellet Mfr
S.I.C.: 2499
N.A.I.C.S.: 321999
Personnel:
Bernard C. Chapon *(Chm & Mng Dir)*

COGSTATE LIMITED
Level 2 255 Bourke Street
Melbourne, VIC, 3000, Australia
Tel.: (61) 61396641300
Fax: (61) 61396641301
E-Mail: info@cogstate.com
Web Site: www.cogstate.com
Year Founded: 1999
CGS—(ASX)
Rev.: $13,131,012
Assets: $11,519,610
Liabilities: $2,339,421
Net Worth: $9,180,189
Earnings: ($2,039,633)
Fiscal Year-end: 06/30/13
Business Description:
Cognitive Testing Products Sales
S.I.C.: 5122
N.A.I.C.S.: 424210
Personnel:
Brad O'Connor *(CEO & Mng Dir)*
Paul Maruff *(Chief Scientific Officer)*
Sophie Egholm *(Pres-Clinical Trials)*
Jason Sada *(Pres-Axon Sports)*
Roger O'Sullivan *(Gen Counsel)*
Mark Edwards *(Co-Sec)*
Claire Newstead-Sinclair *(Co-Sec)*
Board of Directors:
Martyn Myer
Rodolfo Chapa
Brad O'Connor
David Simpson
Richard A. van den Broek
Legal Counsel:
Clayton Utz
333 Collins St
Melbourne, Vic, Australia

COHEN'S HOME FURNISHINGS LTD.
81 Kenmount Road
Saint John's, NL, A1B 4B7, Canada
Tel.: (709) 739-6631
Fax: (709) 739-4153
Web Site: www.cohens.ca
Year Founded: 1984
Rev.: $28,564,314
Emp.: 200
Business Description:
Furniture Stores
S.I.C.: 5712
N.A.I.C.S.: 442110
Personnel:
Randolph Bell *(Pres)*

COHERIS SA
22 quai Gallieni
F-92150 Suresnes, France
Tel.: (33) 1 57 32 60 60
Fax: (33) 1 57 32 62 00
E-Mail: contact@coheris.com
Web Site: www.coheris.com
COH—(EUR)
Sls.: $23,006,045
Earnings: ($1,911,561)
Emp.: 28
Fiscal Year-end: 12/31/12
Business Description:
Customer Relationship Management & Business Intelligence Software Publisher
S.I.C.: 7372
N.A.I.C.S.: 511210
Personnel:
Fabrice Roux *(Chm & CEO)*
Eric d'Andigne de Beauregard *(Mng Dir)*
Barbara Mus *(Sec)*
Board of Directors:
Fabrice Roux
Arnaud Creput
Eric d'Andigne de Beauregard
Claude Leclercq
Herve Marchyllie
Philippe Strosser
Non-U.S. Subsidiaries:

Coheris Benelux SA **(1)**
Rue De La Presse 4
1000 Brussels, Belgium
Tel.: (32) 22271143
Fax: (32) 22183141
E-Mail: gfmenager@coheris.com
Software Publisher
S.I.C.: 7372
N.A.I.C.S.: 511210

Coheris InfoCat Ltd. **(1)**
Riverside House
27-29 Vauxhall Grove, London, SW8 1SY, United Kingdom
Tel.: (44) 2077357711
Fax: (44) 2077358811
E-Mail: ukinfo@infocat.co.uk
Web Site: www.infocat.co.uk
Business Intelligence Consultancy
S.I.C.: 7389
N.A.I.C.S.: 561499

COHIBA MINERALS LIMITED
Suite 9 1200 Hay Street
West Perth, WA, 6005, Australia
Mailing Address:
PO Box 281
West Perth, WA, 6872, Australia
Tel.: (61) 8 6460 4960
Fax: (61) 8 9324 3045
E-Mail: admin@cohibaminerals.com.au
Web Site: www.cohibaminerals.com.au
CHK—(ASX)
Business Description:
Gold & Other Metal Mining
S.I.C.: 1041

Cohiba Minerals Limited—(Continued)

N.A.I.C.S.: 212221
Personnel:
Matthew Sheldrick *(Chm)*
James Robinson *(Mng Dir & Sec)*
Board of Directors:
Matthew Sheldrick
Simon Coxhell
David Herszberg
James Robinson
Legal Counsel:
Steinepreis Paganin
Level 4 Next Building 16 Milligan St
Perth, Australia

COHORT PLC

Arlington House 1025 Arlington Business Park
Theale, Reading, RG7 4SA, United Kingdom
Tel.: (44) 1189090390
Fax: (44) 1189090391
E-Mail: info@cohortplc.com
Web Site: www.cohortplc.com
CHRT—(LSE)
Rev.: $111,917,965
Assets: $118,239,863
Liabilities: $24,987,526
Net Worth: $93,252,337
Earnings: $13,176,016
Emp.: 513
Fiscal Year-end: 04/30/13
Business Description:
Information Management
S.I.C.: 7373
N.A.I.C.S.: 541512
Personnel:
Andrew Thomis *(CEO)*
Simon Walther *(Fin Dir & Sec)*
Board of Directors:
Stanley Carter
Nick Prest
Andrew Thomis
Robert Walmsley
Simon Walther
Legal Counsel:
Pitmans
The Anchorage 34 Bridge Street
Reading, United Kingdom
Subsidiaries:

MASS Consultants Limited **(1)**
Enterprise House Great N Rd
Little Paxton, Saint Neots, Cambridgeshire, PE19 6BN, United Kingdom
Tel.: (44) 1480222600
Fax: (44) 1480407366
E-Mail: systems@mass.co.uk
Web Site: www.mass.co.uk
Emp.: 90
Defence Security Consulting Services
S.I.C.: 9711
N.A.I.C.S.: 928110
Ashley Lane *(Mng Dir)*

Systems Consultants Services Limited **(1)**
Arlington House 1025 Arlington Bus Park
Theale, Reading, West Berkshire, RG7 4SA, United Kingdom
Tel.: (44) 1189090200
Fax: (44) 1189090202
E-Mail: info@scs-ltd.co.uk
Web Site: www.scs-ltd.co.uk
Emp.: 130
Defence & Security Consulting Services
S.I.C.: 8999
N.A.I.C.S.: 541690

Systems Engineering & Assessment Ltd. **(1)**
Beckington Castle 17 Castle Corner
Beckington, Frome, Somerset, BA11 6TA, United Kingdom
Tel.: (44) 1373852000
Fax: (44) 1373831133
E-Mail: info@sea.co.uk
Web Site: www.sea.co.uk
Emp.: 260
Defence & Aerospace Engineering Solutions
S.I.C.: 8711
N.A.I.C.S.: 541330
Steven Hill *(Mng Dir)*

COILLTE LTD.

The Irish Forestry Board
Dublin Rd Newtownmountkennedy, Wicklow, County Wicklow, Ireland
Tel.: (353) 12011111
Fax: (353) 12011119
E-Mail: pr@coillte.ie
Web Site: www.coillte.ie
Sls.: $226,191,943
Emp.: 900
Business Description:
Forestry, Engineered Wood Products & Land Development Services
S.I.C.: 0851
N.A.I.C.S.: 115310
Personnel:
Brendan McKenna *(Chm)*
Board of Directors:
Brendan McKenna
Breffni Byrne
Eugene Griffin
Grainne Hannon
Richard Howlin
Sinead Leech
Philip Lynch
Frank Toal
Subsidiaries:

Coillte Consult Limited **(1)**
Dublin Rd New Town Mount Kennedy County
Wicklow, Ireland (100%)
Tel.: (353) 12011111
Fax: (353) 12011199
Emp.: 110
Other Management Consulting Services
S.I.C.: 8748
N.A.I.C.S.: 541618
David Gunning *(Mng Dir)*

Medite Europe Ltd. **(1)**
Redmondstown
Clonmel, Co Tipperary, Ireland IE (100%)
Tel.: (353) 526182300
Fax: (353) 526121815
E-Mail: info@medite-europe.com
Web Site: www.medite-europe.com
Emp.: 160
Holding Company
S.I.C.: 6719
N.A.I.C.S.: 551112
Neill Foot *(Mng Dir)*

SmartPly Europe Limited **(1)**
Belview Slieverue
Waterford, Ireland (100%)
Tel.: (353) 51851233
Fax: (353) 51851130
E-Mail: reception@smartply.com
Web Site: www.smartply.com
Emp.: 250
Lumber Plywood Millwork & Wood Panel Whslr
S.I.C.: 5031
N.A.I.C.S.: 423310
Neil Foot *(Mng Dir)*

COKAL LIMITED

Level 34 Riverside Centre 123 Eagle Street
Brisbane, QLD, 4000, Australia
Mailing Address:
PO Box 7122
Brisbane, QLD, 4001, Australia
Tel.: (61) 7 3001 4100
Fax: (61) 7 3001 4195
E-Mail: info@cokal.com.au
Web Site: www.cokal.com.au
CKA—(ASX)
Rev.: $2,267,373
Assets: $62,510,362
Liabilities: $2,482,484
Net Worth: $60,027,878
Earnings: ($7,004,724)
Fiscal Year-end: 06/30/13
Business Description:
Coal Exploration Services
S.I.C.: 1222
N.A.I.C.S.: 212112
Personnel:
Peter Lynch *(Chm & CEO)*
Victor Kuss *(CFO & Co-Sec)*
Duncan Cornish *(Co-Sec)*
Board of Directors:
Peter Lynch
Patrick Hanna
Domenic Martino
Agus Widjojo
Legal Counsel:
Thomsons Lawyers
Level 16 Waterfront Place 1 Eagle Street
Brisbane, Australia

COKE RESOURCES LIMITED

36 Outram Street
West Perth, WA, 6005, Australia
Tel.: (61) 8 6336 6400
Fax: (61) 8 6336 6420
E-Mail: admin@cokeresources.com.au
Web Site: www.cokeresources.com
Year Founded: 2011
CKE—(ASX)
Business Description:
Mineral Exploration Services
S.I.C.: 1099
N.A.I.C.S.: 212299
Personnel:
Simon Penney *(Sec)*
Board of Directors:
James Carter
Rafael Nitiyudo
Simon Penney
Les Pereira
Claude Strnadica

COKO-WERK GMBH & CO. KG

Porschestrasse 3-11
32107 Bad Salzuflen, Germany
Tel.: (49) 522228990
Fax: (49) 5222289955
E-Mail: kontakt@coko-werk.de
Web Site: www.coko-werk.de
Year Founded: 1926
Rev.: $91,231,800
Emp.: 480
Business Description:
Vacuum Cleaner Mfr
S.I.C.: 3639
N.A.I.C.S.: 335210
Personnel:
Klaus Wilhelm Dreskruger *(Gen Mgr & Mng Dir)*
Heino Sander *(Gen Mgr & Mng Dir)*
Reinhard Spieker *(Gen Mgr & Mng Dir)*

COKYVINA JOINT STOCK COMPANY

178 Trieu Viet Vuong Street
Hai Ba Trung District, Hanoi, Vietnam
Tel.: (84) 4 39781323
Fax: (84) 4 39782368
E-Mail: info@cokyvina.com.vn
Web Site: www.cokyvina.com.vn
CKV—(HNX)
Sales Range: $1-9.9 Million
Business Description:
Electronic & Broadcasting Equipment Mfr
S.I.C.: 3679
N.A.I.C.S.: 334419
Personnel:
Thi Phuong Le *(Chm-Supervisory Bd)*
Ngoc Ninh Pham *(Chm-Mgmt Bd & Gen Dir)*
Dang Chieu Nguyen *(Member-Mgmt Bd)*
Minh Chau Nguyen *(Member-Mgmt Bd)*
Thi Tuyet Mai Tran *(Member-Mgmt Bd)*
Supervisory Board of Directors:
Thi Phuong Le
Xuan Hoang Le
Thi Anh Tuyet Pham

COL CAPITAL LIMITED

47 F China Online Centre 333 Lockhart Road
Wanchai, China (Hong Kong)
Tel.: (852) 31028500
Fax: (852) 29613500
E-Mail: general@colcapital.com.hk
Web Site: www.colcapital.com.hk
383—(HKG)
Rev.: $167,419,782
Assets: $681,541,627
Liabilities: $489,285,301
Net Worth: $192,256,326
Earnings: ($104,293,213)
Emp.: 2,113
Fiscal Year-end: 06/30/13
Business Description:
Financial Services
S.I.C.: 6211
N.A.I.C.S.: 523999
Personnel:
Sok Un Chong *(Chm)*
Ada Ching Man Fung *(Sec)*
Board of Directors:
Sok Un Chong
Muk Yin Kong
Siu Ki Lau
Wah Yan Ma
Peng Chong Wong
Jian Zhang
MUFG Fund Services (Bermuda) Limited
26 Burnaby Street
Hamilton, Bermuda
Transfer Agents:
Tricor Tengis Limited
26th Floor Tesbury Centre 28 Queen's Road East
Wanchai, China (Hong Kong)
Tel.: (852) 29801333
Fax: (852) 28108185
MUFG Fund Services (Bermuda) Limited
26 Burnaby Street
Hamilton, Bermuda

COL FINANCIAL GROUP, INC.

2401-B East Tower Philippine Stock Exchange Centre
Exchange Road Ortigas Center, Pasig, 1605, Philippines
Tel.: (63) 26333777
Fax: (63) 26346958
E-Mail: helpdesk@citiseconline.com
Web Site: www.citiseconline.com
COL—(PHI)
Rev.: $15,940,368
Assets: $103,568,629
Liabilities: $72,173,445
Net Worth: $31,395,184
Earnings: $7,490,808
Emp.: 91
Fiscal Year-end: 12/31/12
Business Description:
Online Securities Brokerage Services
S.I.C.: 6211
N.A.I.C.S.: 523120
Personnel:
Edward K. Lee *(Chm)*
Alexander C. Yu *(Vice Chm)*
Conrado F. Bate *(Pres & CEO)*
Edwin A. Mendiola *(CFO, Treas & Exec VP)*
Caesar A. Guerzon *(Sec, Sr VP & Head-Legal, HR & Admin)*
Catherine L. Ong *(Sr VP & Head-Ops)*

Board of Directors:
Edward K. Lee
Conrado F. Bate
Kho Boo Boon
Manuel S. Estacion
Paulwell Hann
Hernan G. Lim
Joel Litman
Edwin A. Mendiola
Catherine L. Ong
Alexander C. Yu
Raymond C. Yu
Wellington C. Yu

COLABOR GROUP INC.
1620 Montarville Blvd
Boucherville, QC, J4B 8P4, Canada
Tel.: (450) 449-4911
Fax: (450) 449-6180
E-Mail: info@colabor.com
Web Site: www.colabor.com
Year Founded: 1962
GCL—(OTC TSX)
Sls.: $1,458,076,249
Assets: $484,972,418
Liabilities: $324,935,198
Net Worth: $160,037,220
Earnings: $3,189,810
Emp.: 1,650
Fiscal Year-end: 12/31/12
Business Description:
Food & Non-Food Products Distr
S.I.C.: 5149
N.A.I.C.S.: 424490
Personnel:
Jacques Landreville *(Chm)*
Claude Gariepy *(Pres & CEO)*
Jean-Franois Neault *(CFO & VP)*
Jack Battersby *(Pres-Summit Food Svc-Ontario Div)*
Board of Directors:
Jacques Landreville
Donald Dube
Gilles C. Lachance
Richard Lord
Robert Panet-Raymond
Transfer Agent:
Computershare Investor Services Inc.
Montreal, QC, Canada
Subsidiaries:

Colabor LP (1)
1620 boulevard de Montarville
Boucherville, QC, J4B 8P4, Canada
Tel.: (450) 449-4911
Fax: (450) 449-2098
E-Mail: ltouchette@colabor.com
Web Site: www.colabor.com
Emp.: 100
Food Marketing & Distribution
S.I.C.: 5149
N.A.I.C.S.: 424490
Claude Gariepy *(Pres)*

Division:

Summit Food Service Distributors, Inc. (2)
580 Industrial Road
London, ON, N5V 1V1, Canada
Tel.: (519) 453-3410
Fax: (519) 453-5148
Toll Free: (800) 265-9267
Web Site: www.summitfoods.com
Emp.: 150
Wholesale Food Distr
S.I.C.: 5149
N.A.I.C.S.: 424490
Jack J. Battersby *(Pres)*

Colabor SKOR Distribution (1)
10 Ronrose Drive
Vaughan, ON, L4K 4R3, Canada
Tel.: (905) 660-1212
Fax: (905) 660-4848
E-Mail: sales@skor.colabor.com
Web Site: skor.colabor.com
Sales Range: $125-149.9 Million
Emp.: 350
Food Service & Retail Products Marketer & Distr
S.I.C.: 5812
N.A.I.C.S.: 722310
Bart Trentadue *(Pres)*

Subsidiaries:

SKOR Culinary Concepts Inc. (2)
1330 Crestlawn Dr
Mississauga, ON, L4W 1P8, Canada
Tel.: (905) 625-4447
Fax: (905) 625-3279
Web Site: skor.colabor.com
Food Production for Caterers
S.I.C.: 5812
N.A.I.C.S.: 722310
Sam Ruso *(Dir-Ops)*

Les Pecheries Norref Quebec Inc. (1)
4900 Rue Molson Rd
H1Y 3J8 Montreal, QC, Canada
Tel.: (514) 593-9999
Fax: (514) 593-8406
E-Mail: info@norref.com
Web Site: www.norref.com
Sea Food Distr
S.I.C.: 5146
N.A.I.C.S.: 424460

COLAND HOLDINGS LIMITED
1F 866 Halei Road Zhangjiang High Tech Park
Pudong District, Shanghai, China
Tel.: (86) 2151371880
Fax: (86) 2151371882
E-Mail: colandpharma@colandpharma.com
Web Site: www.colandpharma.com
4144—(TAI)
Sales Range: $50-74.9 Million
Business Description:
Pharmaceutical Mfr
S.I.C.: 2834
N.A.I.C.S.: 325412
Personnel:
William Keller *(Chm)*
Leo Lee *(CEO)*
Board of Directors:
William Keller
Leo Lee
Li-Da Tang
Xiaoping Ye
Subsidiary:

Coland Pharmaceutical Co., Ltd. (1)
No 866 Halei Road Room 103 Zhang Jiang Hi-Tech Park
Shanghai, 201203, China CN
Tel.: (86) 86 21 5137 1880
Fax: (86) 86 21 5137 1882
Web Site: www.colandpharma.com
Pharmaceutical Products Mfr & Distr
S.I.C.: 2834
N.A.I.C.S.: 325412
William Keller *(Chm)*
Leo Lee *(CEO)*

COLANDIS
Saint Elivet Route De Guingamp
22300 Lannion, Cotes D Armor, France
Tel.: (33) 296467666
Sales Range: $10-24.9 Million
Emp.: 64
Business Description:
Grocery Stores
S.I.C.: 5411
N.A.I.C.S.: 445110
Personnel:
Christian Coden *(Mgr-Mktg)*

COLBA.NET TELECOM INC.
6465 Trans-Canada Highway
Montreal, QC, H4T 1S3, Canada
Tel.: (514) 856-3500
Fax: (514) 856-9506
Toll Free: (888) 477-7189
E-Mail: joseph.bassili@colba.net
Web Site: www.colba.net
CB—(CNSX)
Rev.: $3,511,738
Assets: $840,371
Liabilities: $2,151,644
Net Worth: ($1,311,272)
Earnings: ($17,716)
Fiscal Year-end: 12/31/12
Business Description:
Telecommunications Services
S.I.C.: 4812
N.A.I.C.S.: 517210
Personnel:
Joseph Basili *(Pres & CEO)*
Michel Poissant *(CFO & VP)*
Jean-Paul Basili *(Treas & Sec)*
Board of Directors:
Jean-Paul Basili
Joseph Basili
Michael Karras
Guy Laflamme
Transfer Agent:
Computershare
100 University Avenue 9 Floor
Toronto, ON, Canada

COLDMATIC PRODUCTS INTERNATIONAL LLC
8500 Keele Street
Concord, ON, LAK 2A6, Canada
Tel.: (905) 326-7600
Fax: (905) 326-7601
E-Mail: sales@coldmatic.com
Web Site: www.coldmatic.com
Sales Range: $50-74.9 Million
Emp.: 1,000
Business Description:
Refrigeration Products Mfr
S.I.C.: 3585
N.A.I.C.S.: 333415
Personnel:
Mark Galea *(Pres)*
U.S. Subsidiary:

Clark Door Co., Inc. (1)
2564 Metro Blvd
Maryland Heights, MO 63043-2417 MO
Tel.: (314) 432-3112
Fax: (314) 432-2296
Toll Free: (800) 278-0090
Web Site: www.coldmatic.com
Emp.: 125
Automatic Doors; Shock Absorber; Fire Doors; Door Covering; Cold Storage & Fire Door Combination Mfr
S.I.C.: 5031
N.A.I.C.S.: 423310

COLEFAX GROUP PLC
19/23 Grosvenor Hill
London, W1K 3QD, United Kingdom
Tel.: (44) 2074932231
Fax: (44) 2074953123
E-Mail: reception@colefax.com
Web Site: www.colefaxgroupplc.com
Year Founded: 1957
CFX—(LSE)
Rev.: $111,527,881
Assets: $61,590,731
Liabilities: $23,240,832
Net Worth: $38,349,899
Earnings: $3,686,063
Emp.: 340
Fiscal Year-end: 04/30/13
Business Description:
Holding Company; Furnishing Fabrics & Wallpapers Designer & Distr
S.I.C.: 6719
N.A.I.C.S.: 551112
Personnel:
David B. Green *(Chm & CEO)*
Robert M. Barker *(Fin Dir & Sec)*
Key Hall *(CEO-Cowtan & Tout)*
Board of Directors:
David B. Green
Robert M. Barker
Key Hall
Wendy Nicholls
Alan K. P. Smith
Legal Counsel:
SJ Berwin
10 Queen Street Place
London, EC4R 1BE, United Kingdom
Transfer Agent:
Computershare Investor Services PLC
The Pavilions Bridgewater Road
PO Box 82
Bristol, BS13 8AE, United Kingdom
Tel.: (44) 870 702 0000
Fax: (44) 870 703 6119
Subsidiaries:

Jane Churchill Limited (1)
Garratt Lane Wandsworth
London, SW18 4DJ, United Kingdom (100%)
Tel.: (44) 2088746484
Fax: (44) 2088775413
E-Mail: info@colefax.co.uk
Web Site: www.colefax.co.uk
Emp.: 40
Home Furnishings Stores
S.I.C.: 5719
N.A.I.C.S.: 442299
David B. Green *(Chm & CEO)*

Kingcome Sofas Limited (1)
24 Old Newton Road Heathfield Newton Abbot
Devon, TQ12 6RA, United Kingdom (100%)
Tel.: (44) 1626834800
Fax: (44) 1626835866
E-Mail: frank.phipps@kingcomesofas.co.uk
Web Site: www.kingcomesofas.co.uk
Emp.: 50
Home Furnishings Stores
S.I.C.: 5719
N.A.I.C.S.: 442299
F. Phipps *(Mng Dir)*

Sibyl Colefax & John Fowler Limited (1)
39 Brook Street Mayfair
London, W1K 4JE, United Kingdom UK (100%)
Tel.: (44) 2074932231
Fax: (44) 2074999721
E-Mail: info@colefax.com
Web Site: www.colefaxantiques.com
Emp.: 35
Home Furnishings Stores
S.I.C.: 5719
N.A.I.C.S.: 442299
Ed Foster *(Mgr-Antiques)*

Non-U.S. Subsidiary:

Colefax & Fowler GmbH (2)
Ottostr 13
80333 Munich, Germany De (100%)
Tel.: (49) 893399720
Fax: (49) 8933997225
E-Mail: munich.showroom@colefax.co.uk
Web Site: www.colefax.com
Emp.: 3
Piece Goods Notions & Dry Goods Whslr
S.I.C.: 5199
N.A.I.C.S.: 424310

U.S. Subsidiary:

Cowtan & Tout, Inc. (1)
111 Ste 930
New York, NY 10011-5201
Mailing Address:
111 8th Ave Ste 930
New York, NY 10011-5220
Tel.: (212) 647-6900
Fax: (212) 647-6997
Web Site: www.colefaxgroup.com
Emp.: 140
Fabrics & Wallpaper
S.I.C.: 5131
N.A.I.C.S.: 424310
David B. Green *(Chm)*
Key Hall *(CEO)*
Larry Stern *(CFO)*

COLETTE
213 rue Saint-Honore
75001 Paris, France
Tel.: (33) 155353390

Colette—(Continued)

Fax: (33) 155353399
E-Mail: contact@colette.fr
Web Site: www.colette.fr
Year Founded: 1997
Sales Range: $10-24.9 Million
Emp.: 70
Business Description:
Clothing Retailer
S.I.C.: 5699
N.A.I.C.S.: 448150
Personnel:
Colette Roussaux *(Chm & Mng Dir)*

COLEXON ENERGY AG

Grosse Elbstrasse 45
22767 Hamburg, Germany
Tel.: (49) 40 2800 310
Fax: (49) 40 2800 31102
E-Mail: info@colexon.com
Web Site: www.colexon.com
HRP—(DEU)
Sls.: $34,865,803
Assets: $161,001,932
Liabilities: $130,982,341
Net Worth: $30,019,591
Earnings: ($2,423,106)
Emp.: 44
Fiscal Year-end: 12/31/12
Business Description:
Large-Scale Photovoltaic System Developer
S.I.C.: 3679
N.A.I.C.S.: 334419
Personnel:
Peter Dill *(Chm-Supervisory Bd)*
Joris de Meester *(Deputy Chm-Supervisory Bd)*
Volker Hars *(CEO & Member-Mgmt Bd)*
Supervisory Board of Directors:
Peter Dill
Joris de Meester
Markus Neumann

Subsidiaries:

COLEXON 1. Solar Verwaltungs GmbH **(1)**
Grosse Elbstr 45
Hamburg, 22767, Germany
Tel.: (49) 402800310
Fax: (49) 40280031101
Solar Power Plants Mfr
S.I.C.: 3679
N.A.I.C.S.: 334419

COLEXON 3. Solarprojektgesellschaft mbH & Co. KG, **(1)**
Grosse Elbstr 45
Hamburg, 22767, Germany
Tel.: (49) 402800310
Fax: (49) 40280031102
E-Mail: info@colexon.de
Web Site: www.colexon.com.de
Emp.: 37
Solar Power Generation Services
S.I.C.: 4931
N.A.I.C.S.: 221118
Volker Hars *(Mng Dir)*

COLEXON 6. Solarprojektgesellschaft mbH & Co. KG, **(1)**
Grosse Elbstr 45
Hamburg, 22767, Germany
Tel.: (49) 408222550
Solar Power Generation Services
S.I.C.: 4911
N.A.I.C.S.: 221118

U.S. Subsidiary:

COLEXON Corp. **(1)**
60 E Rio Salado Pkwy Ste 900
Tempe, AZ 85281
Tel.: (480) 366-5925
Fax: (480) 366-5801
E-Mail: info@colexon.us
Web Site: www.colexon.de/content/us/011_colexon_corp/010_colexon_corp.php
Solar Power Structure Construction Services
S.I.C.: 1629
N.A.I.C.S.: 237130

Non-U.S. Subsidiaries:

COLEXON Australia Pty. Ltd. **(1)**
181 Bay Street
Brighton, VIC, 3186, Australia
Tel.: (61) 3 9595 3863
E-Mail: info@colexon.com.au
Solar Power Plants Mfr
S.I.C.: 1629
N.A.I.C.S.: 237130

COLEXON Iberia S.L **(1)**
Calle Juan Ramon Jimenez 8 Primera
Planta Centro de Negocios EB
28036 Madrid, Spain
Tel.: (34) 9 12 77 64 00
Fax: (34) 9 13 50 47 52
E-Mail: info@colexoniberia.es
Web Site: www.colexon.com
Solar Power Plants Mfr & Whslr
S.I.C.: 3999
N.A.I.C.S.: 339999

Renewagy A/S **(1)**
Kongevejen 2100
2100 Virum, Denmark
Tel.: (45) 43331343
E-Mail: mgh@beierholm.dk
Web Site: www.renewagy.com
Sales Range: $1-9.9 Million
Emp.: 4
Investment Services
S.I.C.: 6282
N.A.I.C.S.: 523930

COLGATE-PALMOLIVE (PAKISTAN) LTD

Lakson Square Building No 2 Sarwar Shaheed Road
Karachi, 74200, Pakistan
Tel.: (92) 2135698000
Fax: (92) 215685489
Web Site: www.colgate.com.pk
COLG—(KAR)
Sls.: $258,469,634
Assets: $93,228,831
Liabilities: $26,052,567
Net Worth: $67,176,264
Earnings: $16,098,090
Emp.: 728
Fiscal Year-end: 06/30/13
Business Description:
Healthcare & Personal Products Mfr
S.I.C.: 2841
N.A.I.C.S.: 325611
Personnel:
Zulfiqar Ali Lakhani *(CEO)*
Mansoor Ahmed *(Sec)*
Board of Directors:
Iqbal Ali Lakhani
Tasleemuddin Ahmed Batlay
Mukul Deoras
A. Aziz Ebrahim
Amin Mohammad Lakhani
Zulfiqar Ali Lakhani
Jerome Graham Webb

COLIBRI RESOURCE CORPORATION

51A Commercial Street
PO Box 714
Nanaimo, BC, V9R 5M2, Canada
Tel.: (250) 755-7871
Fax: (250) 755-7876
E-Mail: info@colibriresourcecorp.com
Web Site: www.colibriresource.com
Year Founded: 2004
CBI—(TSXV)
Int. Income: $21,173
Assets: $8,077,582
Liabilities: $69,927
Net Worth: $8,007,655
Earnings: ($660,155)
Fiscal Year-end: 11/30/12
Business Description:
Mineral Exploration Services
S.I.C.: 1081
N.A.I.C.S.: 213114
Personnel:
James J. Irwin *(Founder & Mgr-Exploration)*
Paul Bartos *(Co-Chm)*
Ronald Goguen, Sr. *(Co-Chm)*
Lance D. Geselbracht *(Pres & CEO)*
Brian Lewicki *(CFO)*
Board of Directors:
Paul Bartos
Ronald Goguen, Sr.
Roger Doucet
Lance D. Geselbracht
Jonathan A. Nourse
William R. Walker

COLIN MEAR ENGINEERING LTD

Combe St Nicholas Chard
Somerset, TA20 3NL, United Kingdom
Tel.: (44) 1460269500
Fax: (44) 1460269550
E-Mail: cme@cme-ltd.com
Web Site: www.cme-ltd.com
Rev.: $21,102,593
Emp.: 133
Business Description:
Machinery Equipment Mfr
S.I.C.: 3559
N.A.I.C.S.: 333249
Personnel:
Paul Simmons *(Dir-Technical)*

COLINA HOLDINGS BAHAMAS LIMITED

308 East Bay Street
PO Box N-4728
Nassau, Bahamas
Tel.: (242) 396-2100
Fax: (242) 393-1710
Web Site: www.colina.com
CHL—(BISX)
Rev.: $157,330,060
Assets: $578,802,043
Liabilities: $451,835,881
Net Worth: $126,966,162
Earnings: $12,180,161
Fiscal Year-end: 12/31/12
Business Description:
Holding Company; Insurance, Mortgage, Investment & Retirement Products & Services
S.I.C.: 6719
N.A.I.C.S.: 551112
Personnel:
Emanuel M. Alexiou *(Vice Chm & CEO)*
Board of Directors:
Terence Hilts
Emanuel M. Alexiou
Glenn Bannister
Earle Bethell
John Farmer
Ednol Farquharson
Anthony Ferguson
Sandra Knowles
Willie Moss
Macgregor Robertson

Subsidiary:

Colina Insurance Limited **(1)**
308 East Bay Street
PO Box N-4728
Nassau, Bahamas BS
Tel.: (242) 396-2100 (100%)
Fax: (242) 393-1710
Web Site: www.colina.com
Life & Health Insurance Products & Services
S.I.C.: 6411
N.A.I.C.S.: 524298
Emanuel M. Alexiou, *(Vice Chm & CEO)*
Emmanuel Komolafe *(Chief Risk Officer)*

COLINZ LABORATORIES LIMITED

A/101 Pratik Estate Mulund Link Road Near Wockhardt Hospital
Mumbai, 400 078, India
Tel.: (91) 22 2590 8002
Fax: (91) 22 2590 8004
E-Mail: colinz@hathway.com
Web Site: www.colinz.com
Year Founded: 1987
531210—(BOM)
Sls.: $1,424,206
Assets: $1,827,191
Liabilities: $666,902
Net Worth: $1,160,289
Earnings: $14,795
Emp.: 300
Fiscal Year-end: 03/31/13
Business Description:
Pharmaceutical Product Mfr & Whslr
S.I.C.: 2834
N.A.I.C.S.: 325412
Personnel:
L. S. Mani *(Chm & Mng Dir)*
Vasant K. Bhat *(Compliance Officer)*
Board of Directors:
L. S. Mani
Krishna Kumar Attrassary
Vasant K. Bhat
N. K. Menon
Transfer Agent:
Bigshare Services Private Limited
E 2/3 Ansa Industrial Estate Sakivihar Road
Sakinaka Andheri(E)
Mumbai, India

COLIPAYS

Zone Aeroportuaire de Gillot
97438 Sainte-Marie, Reunion
Tel.: (262) 2 62 28 99 99
Fax: (262) 2 62 28 43 70
Web Site: www.colipays.com
MLCLP—(EUR)
Sales Range: $1-9.9 Million
Business Description:
Flower Packaging & Delivery
S.I.C.: 5992
N.A.I.C.S.: 453110
Personnel:
Frederic Faby *(Chm & CEO)*

COLLABRIUM JAPAN ACQUISITION CORPORATION

16 Old Bond Street
London, W1S 4PS, United Kingdom
Tel.: (44) 20 7408 4710
Year Founded: 2012
JACQU—(NASDAQ)
Int. Income: $15,733
Assets: $43,513,269
Liabilities: $37,253,267
Net Worth: $6,260,002
Earnings: ($4,397,547)
Emp.: 2
Fiscal Year-end: 09/30/13
Business Description:
Investment Services
S.I.C.: 6211
N.A.I.C.S.: 523999
Personnel:
Andrew C. Williams *(Chm)*
Koji Fusa *(CEO)*
Board of Directors:
Andrew C. Williams
Koji Fusa
Hiroshi Tamada

COLLECTION CONRAD C

9320 boul St-Laurent Suite 200
Montreal, QC, H2N 1N7, Canada
Tel.: (514) 385-9599

Fax: (514) 385-9594
Toll Free: (888) 561-4416
E-Mail: info@conradc.com
Web Site: www.conradc.com
Rev.: $10,433,394
Emp.: 120
Business Description:
Family Clothing Stores
S.I.C.: 5651
N.A.I.C.S.: 448140
Personnel:
Conrad Cape *(Pres)*

COLLECTION HOUSE LIMITED
Level 7 515 St Paul's Terrace
PO Box 2247
Fortitude Valley, QLD, 4006, Australia
Tel.: (61) 7 3292 1000
Fax: (61) 7 3832 0222
E-Mail: investor@collectionhouse.com.au
Web Site: www.collectionhouse.com.au
Year Founded: 1992
CLH—(ASX)
Rev.: $41,032,688
Assets: $249,664,234
Liabilities: $121,207,693
Net Worth: $128,456,541
Earnings: $16,271,349
Emp.: 730
Fiscal Year-end: 06/30/13
Business Description:
Debt Collection Services
S.I.C.: 7322
N.A.I.C.S.: 561440
Personnel:
Matthew Thomas *(CEO & Mng Dir)*
Adrian Ralston *(CFO)*
Paul Freer *(COO)*
Marcus Barron *(CIO)*
Michael Watkins *(Gen Counsel & Co-Sec)*
Julie Tealby *(Co-Sec)*
Board of Directors:
David Liddy
Tony Coutts
Kerry Daly
David Gray
Philip Hennessy
Dennis Punches
Matthew Thomas
Subsidiaries:

Collective Learning and Development Pty Ltd (1)
Level 7 Green Square 515 St Paul's Terrace
Fortitude Valley, Brisbane, QLD, 4006, Australia
Tel.: (61) 300 367 370
E-Mail: info@clad.net.au
Web Site: www.clad.net.au
Training Services
S.I.C.: 8299
N.A.I.C.S.: 611430
Gary Lung *(Mgr-Learning & Dev)*

Jones King Lawyers Pty Ltd (1)
Level 7 515 St Paul's Terrace
PO Box 2087
Fortitude Valley, QLD, 4006, Australia
Tel.: (61) 7 3225 0000
Fax: (61) 7 3225 0099
Web Site: www.collectionhouse.com.au/jones-king-legal-division-of-chl
Legal Services
S.I.C.: 8111
N.A.I.C.S.: 541110
Nathan Shaw *(Dir-Solicitor)*

Lion Finance Pty Ltd (1)
L 3 484-488 Queen St
Brisbane, QLD, 4000, Australia
Tel.: (61) 1300 133 667
Fax: (61) 3832 3728
Financial Management Services
S.I.C.: 8742
N.A.I.C.S.: 541611

Midstate CreditCollect Pty Ltd (1)
31 Grey Street
PO Box 1655
3844 Traralgon, VIC, Australia
Tel.: (61) 1300 551 055
Fax: (61) 3 5174 7088
E-Mail: creditcollect@creditcollect.com.au
Web Site: www.creditcollect.com.au
Credit Management Service
S.I.C.: 7322
N.A.I.C.S.: 561440
Mark Answerth *(Mng Dir)*

COLLEGE FORD LINCOLN LTD.
3975 - 1st Avenue South
Lethbridge, AB, T1J 4P8, Canada
Tel.: (403) 329-0333
Fax: (403) 329-3158
Toll Free: (800) 461-5276
E-Mail: info@collegefordlincoln.dealeremail.com
Web Site: www.collegefordlincoln.com
Rev.: $23,293,518
Emp.: 50
Business Description:
New & Used Car Dealers
S.I.C.: 5511
N.A.I.C.S.: 441110
Personnel:
Sandy Sutherland *(Owner)*

COLLEGE GROUP LIMITED
The Registry Royal Mint Ct
London, EC3N 4QN, United Kingdom
Tel.: (44) 2074572020
Fax: (44) 2078667900
E-Mail: pr@collegehill.com
Web Site: www.collegehill.com
Emp.: 200
Business Description:
Advertising Agency
S.I.C.: 7311
N.A.I.C.S.: 541810
Personnel:
Jurgen Muller *(Chm & CEO)*
Alex Sandberg *(Chm)*
Richard Nichols *(CEO)*

COLLEGE PARK MOTOR PRODUCTS LTD
4512 Railway Avenue
Vermilion, AB, T9X 1E9, Canada
Tel.: (780) 853-4646
Fax: (780) 853-5225
Toll Free: (888) 857-0514
E-Mail: sales@collegeparkgm.com
Web Site: www.collegeparkgm.com
Year Founded: 1997
Rev.: $11,476,733
Emp.: 25
Business Description:
New & Used Car Dealers
S.I.C.: 5511
N.A.I.C.S.: 441110
Personnel:
Larry Alward *(Gen Mgr)*

COLLER CAPITAL LTD.
33 Cavendish Square
London, W1G 0TT, United Kingdom
Tel.: (44) 2076318500
Fax: (44) 2076318555
E-Mail: mail@collercapital.com
Web Site: www.collercapital.com
Year Founded: 1990
Emp.: 50
Business Description:
Private Equity Secondaries Investment Services
S.I.C.: 6211
N.A.I.C.S.: 523999
Personnel:
Jeremy Coller *(Founder & Chm)*
Timothy Jones *(CEO)*
Jonathon Freeman *(Partner)*
Jonathon Gutstein *(Partner)*
Axel K. A. Hansing *(Partner)*
Hiromichi Mizuno *(Partner)*
Frank Morgan *(Partner)*
Erwin Roex *(Partner)*
Holdings:

Accentus Medical Plc (1)
528 10 Unit 2 Rutherford Ave
Didcot, Harwell, Oxfordshire, OX11 0DF, United Kingdom
Tel.: (44) 1235434320
Fax: (44) 1235434329
E-Mail: enquiries@accentus-medical.com
Web Site: www.accentus-medical.com
Emp.: 25
Developer of Medical Devices New Technology & Intellectual Property
S.I.C.: 3845
N.A.I.C.S.: 334510
Andrew Paszkowski *(Chm)*
Phillip Agg *(Mng Dir)*
Ralph Forster *(Sec & Dir-Investment)*
Martin Pickford *(Sr VP-Bus Dev)*

Risksol Consulting Ltd. (1)
59-60 Russell Square
London, WC1B 4HP, United Kingdom
Tel.: (44) 870 850 4889
Fax: (44) 870 850 4895
E-Mail: enquiries@risksol.co.uk
Web Site: www.risksol.co.uk
Emp.: 22
Business & Management Consulting
S.I.C.: 8742
N.A.I.C.S.: 541611
Andrew Paszkowski *(Chm)*
Mike Robertson *(Mng Dir)*
Ralph Forster *(Sec)*

Non-U.S. Subsidiary:

Credit Agricole Private Equity S.A. (1)
37-4 rue du Rocher
75682 Paris, France
Tel.: (33) 143232121
Fax: (33) 43 23 64 54
E-Mail: cape.contact@ca-privateequity.fr
Web Site: www.ca-privateequity.com
Private Equity Firm
S.I.C.: 6211
N.A.I.C.S.: 523999
Fabien Prevost *(Chm-Mgmt Bd)*
Bertrand Tissot *(Partner)*
Phillippe Zurawski *(Partner)*
Francois Lecointe *(Sec)*

Subsidiaries:

Ludovic Le Gall S.A.S. (2)
Z I Des Chatelets 22 Avenue Des Chatelets
22440 Ploufragan, Cotes-d'Armor, France (60%)
Tel.: (33) 296765781
Fax: (33) 296766308
E-Mail: contact@ludovic-legall.com
Web Site: www.ludovic-legall.com
Sales Range: $25-49.9 Million
Emp.: 100
S.I.C.: 5093
N.A.I.C.S.: 423930
Jean-Philippe Sepchat *(Chm)*
Philippe Le Gall *(CEO)*

Sepchat Flaysakier (2)
30 Ave Charles Bedaux
ZI du Menneton, 37000 Tours, France
Tel.: (33) 247376363
Fax: (33) 247377760
Web Site: www.slgrecycling.fr
Sales Range: $50-74.9 Million
Emp.: 250
Recycling Services
S.I.C.: 4212
N.A.I.C.S.: 562119
Jean-Philippe Sepchat *(CEO)*

COLLETTE DINNIGAN PTY. LTD.
22-24 Hutchinson St Surry Hills
Sydney, NSW, 2010, Australia
Tel.: (61) 293610110
Fax: (61) 293610029
E-Mail: mail@collettedinnigan.com.au
Web Site: www.collettedinnigan.com.au
Sales Range: $10-24.9 Million
Emp.: 100
Business Description:
Women's Clothing Designer
S.I.C.: 2259
N.A.I.C.S.: 315190
Personnel:
Robyn Holt *(CEO)*

COLLIER MOTOR GROUP LIMITED
1-41 Sutton Road
Erdington, Birmingham, W Midlands, B23 6QH, United Kingdom
Tel.: (44) 1213825000
Fax: (44) 1213776907
E-Mail: mail@colliers.seat.co.uk
Web Site: www.colliers.co.uk
Year Founded: 1926
Sales Range: $125-149.9 Million
Emp.: 300
Business Description:
Holding Company; New & Used Car Dealerships Owner & Operator
S.I.C.: 6719
N.A.I.C.S.: 551112
Personnel:
David Charles Clark *(Mng Dir & Grp CEO)*
Niall James Thomas Power *(Sec)*
Board of Directors:
David Charles Clark
Niall James Thomas Power
Michael J. Smith
Anthony M. Webster
Subsidiary:

Colliers of Birmingham Limited (1)
1-41 Sutton Rd
Erdington, Birmingham, W Midlands, B23 6QH, United Kingdom UK
Tel.: (44) 1213825000
Fax: (44) 1213776907
Web Site: www.colliers.co.uk
New & Used Car Dealer
S.I.C.: 5511
N.A.I.C.S.: 441110
David Charles Clark *(Mng Dir)*

COLLINS CO., LTD.
6/F No 201 Tunghua North Road
10544 Taipei, Taiwan
Tel.: (886) 227125311
Fax: (886) 227175408
E-Mail: cust@email.collins.com.tw
Web Site: www.collins.com.tw
2906—(TAI)
Sales Range: $250-299.9 Million
Business Description:
Diversified Trading Services
S.I.C.: 7389
N.A.I.C.S.: 561499
Personnel:
Leslie Lee *(Chm & Gen Mgr)*
Subsidiary:

Colltex Garment Mfy Co. Ltd. (1)
6th Floor Tung Hwa North Road
Taipei, 10508, Taiwan
Tel.: (886) 225460266
Fax: (886) 225148755
E-Mail: lchiou@email.collins.com.tw
Emp.: 16
Knitwear & Sweaters Mfr
S.I.C.: 2259
N.A.I.C.S.: 315190
Larry Chiou *(Pres)*

U.S. Subsidiary:

Collins International Co., Ltd. (1)
2100 Route 208
Fair Lawn, NJ 07410
Tel.: (201) 794-9200
Fax: (201) 794-3511

Collins Co., Ltd.—(Continued)

E-Mail: info@collinsinternational.com
Web Site: www.collinsinternational.com
Emp.: 7
Furnitures Distr
S.I.C.: 5021
N.A.I.C.S.: 423210
Steve Lin *(Pres)*

Non-U.S. Subsidiaries:

Collins Fashion (Pvt) Ltd. **(1)**
63 A Ward Place
Colombo, 00700, Sri Lanka
Tel.: (94) 112686203
Fax: (94) 112678089
E-Mail: collinscolombo@collinsfashion.com
Emp.: 600
Garments Mfr
S.I.C.: 2259
N.A.I.C.S.: 315190
Wenders Shieh *(Mng Dir)*

Commend (H.K.) Ltd. **(1)**
24 Room No 200681 Cable TV Tower 9 Hoi Shing Road
Tsuen Wan, New Territories, China (Hong Kong)
Tel.: (852) 27459878
Fax: (852) 27869311
Casual Apparels Retailer
S.I.C.: 5651
N.A.I.C.S.: 448140

COLLINS INDUSTRIES, LTD.

3740-73 Avenue
Edmonton, AB, Canada T6B 2Z2
Tel.: (780) 440-1414
Fax: (780) 466-6583
E-Mail: info@collinssteel.com
Web Site: www.collins-industries-ltd.com
Year Founded: 1984
Rev.: $17,085,026
Emp.: 92
Business Description:
Steel Products Mfr
S.I.C.: 3399
N.A.I.C.S.: 331221
Personnel:
Jason Collins *(COO)*

THE COLLINSON GROUP LIMITED

5 & 17 Devonshire Square
London, EC2M 4SQ, United Kingdom
Tel.: (44) 20 7422 1864
Fax: (44) 20 7630 6161
Web Site: www.thecollinsongroup.com
Year Founded: 1991
Sales Range: $300-349.9 Million
Business Description:
Holding Company; Marketing, Insurance, Travel Enhancement & Technology Products & Services
S.I.C.: 6719
N.A.I.C.S.: 551112
Personnel:
David Evans *(Dir-Insurance Grp)*

Subsidiaries:

Collinson Insurance Group Ltd. **(1)**
17 Devonshire Square
London, EC2M 4SQ, United Kingdom UK
Tel.: (44) 20 7422 4490
Web Site: www.collinsoninsurancegroup.com
Holding Company; Travel Insurance Products & Services
S.I.C.: 6719
N.A.I.C.S.: 551112
David Evans *(Mng Dir)*

Subsidiary:

Columbus Direct Limited **(2)**
19 Bartlett Street
Croydon, CR2 6TB, United Kingdom UK
Tel.: (44) 845 888 8893
E-Mail: admin@columbusdirect.com
Web Site: www.columbusdirect.com
Travel Insurance Products & Services
S.I.C.: 6399
N.A.I.C.S.: 524128
Greg Lawson *(Head-Retail)*

Priority Travel Group (Holdings) Limited **(1)**
520 Fulham Road
London, SW6 5NJ, United Kingdom UK
Tel.: (44) 20 8256 9035
Web Site: www.prioritytravelgroup.com
Holding Company; Travel Clubs & Enhancement Services
S.I.C.: 6719
N.A.I.C.S.: 551112
Tim Gregory *(Mgr-Bus Dev)*

Subsidiary:

Priority Pass Limited **(2)**
19 Bartlett Street
Croydon, Surrey, CR2 6TB, United Kingdom UK
Mailing Address:
PO Box 120
Croydon, Surrey, CR9 4NU, United Kingdom
Tel.: (44) 20 8680 1338
Fax: (44) 20 8688 6191
E-Mail: info@prioritypass.co.uk
Web Site: www.prioritypass.com
Emp.: 100
Airport Lounge Membership Network Operator
S.I.C.: 5813
N.A.I.C.S.: 722410
Errol McGlothan *(Gen Mgr)*

Units:

Lounge Club **(2)**
19 Bartlett Street
Croydon, Surrey, CR2 6TB, United Kingdom
Mailing Address:
PO Box 3312
Croydon, Surrey, CR2 1DR, United Kingdom
Tel.: (44) 20 8827 0089
Fax: (44) 20 8688 6191
E-Mail: info.london@loungeclub.com
Web Site: www.loungeclub.com
Airport Lounge Membership Network Operator
S.I.C.: 5813
N.A.I.C.S.: 722410

Lounge Pass **(2)**
19 Bartlett Street
Croydon, Surrey, CR2 6TB, United Kingdom
Mailing Address:
PO Box 1441
Croydon, Surrey, CR9 3XZ, United Kingdom
Tel.: (44) 20 8865 3280
Fax: (44) 870 366 7976
E-Mail: info@loungepass.com
Web Site: www.loungepass.com
Airport Lounge Membership Network Operator
S.I.C.: 5813
N.A.I.C.S.: 722410
Jacqui Bates *(Gen Mgr)*

COLOMBIA CREST GOLD CORP.

1055 West Hastings Street Suite 300
Vancouver, BC, V6E 2E9, Canada
Tel.: (604) 684-7160
E-Mail: info@colombiacrestgold.com
Web Site: www.colombiacrestgold.com
Year Founded: 1981
CLB—(TSXV)
Int. Income: $34,652
Assets: $11,780,476
Liabilities: $415,281
Net Worth: $11,365,195
Earnings: ($7,001,829)
Fiscal Year-end: 09/30/12
Business Description:
Gold Exploration Services
S.I.C.: 1041
N.A.I.C.S.: 212221
Personnel:
Carl B. Hansen *(Chm)*
Bill Jung *(CFO & Sec)*
Board of Directors:
Carl B. Hansen
Chris McKellar
Jeff Palmer
Thomas Pladsen
Legal Counsel:
Holmes & King
1300 -1111 West Georgia Street
Vancouver, BC, Canada
Transfer Agent:
Pacific Corporate Trust Company
2nd Floor 510 Burrard Street
Vancouver, BC, V6V 3B9, Canada

COLOMBIAN MINES CORPORATION

580 Hornby St 510
Vancouver, BC, V6C 3B6, Canada
Tel.: (604) 669-0868
Fax: (604) 558-4200
Web Site: www.colombianmines.com
Year Founded: 2006
CMJ—(TSXV)
Int. Income: $17,296
Assets: $2,576,623
Liabilities: $372,322
Net Worth: $2,204,301
Earnings: ($2,648,398)
Fiscal Year-end: 04/30/13
Business Description:
Metal Exploration Services
S.I.C.: 1081
N.A.I.C.S.: 213114
Personnel:
Robert G. Carrington *(Pres & CEO)*
David Cross *(CFO & Sec)*
Gloria Carrington *(Pres-Corporacion Minera De Colombia & Country Mgr)*
Board of Directors:
Donn Burchill
Robert G. Carrington
Peter Crescenzo
David Salari
Paul Wang
Legal Counsel:
Bull, Housser & Tupper LLP
3000 - 1055 West Georgia Street
Vancouver, BC, Canada
Transfer Agent:
Computershare Trust Company of Canada
510 Burrard St
Vancouver, BC, Canada

COLOMBO DOCKYARD PLC

Graving Docks
PO Box 906
Port of Colombo, Colombo, 15, Sri Lanka
Tel.: (94) 112429000
Fax: (94) 112446441
E-Mail: coldock@cdl.lk
Web Site: www.cdl.lk
Year Founded: 1974
DOCKN—(COL)
Rev.: $128,648,995
Assets: $144,005,503
Liabilities: $61,937,104
Net Worth: $82,068,398
Earnings: $15,627,395
Emp.: 1,775
Fiscal Year-end: 12/31/12
Business Description:
Ship Building & Repairing Services
S.I.C.: 3731
N.A.I.C.S.: 336611
Personnel:
Akihiko Nakauchi *(Chm)*
Sarath De Costa *(Vice Chm)*
Mangala P. B. Yapa *(CEO & Mng Dir)*
Manori P. Mallikarachchi *(Legal Officer & Sec)*
Board of Directors:
Akihiko Nakauchi
Sarath De Costa
L. Ganlath
Y. Kijima
Piyadasa Kudabalage
Janaki Kuruppu
T. Nakabe
H. A. R. K. Wickramathilake
Mangala P. B. Yapa

Subsidiary:

Dockyard General Engineering Services (Pvt) Ltd. **(1)**
223 Jayantha Mallimarachchi Mawatha
Colombo, 01400, Sri Lanka
Tel.: (94) 112527980
Fax: (94) 112522846
E-Mail: tgweera@dges.lk
Web Site: www.dges.lk
Emp.: 54
Civil & Mechanical Engineering Services
S.I.C.: 1629
N.A.I.C.S.: 237990
T. G. Weersinghe *(Gen Mgr)*

Division:

Dockyard General Engineering Services (Pvt) Ltd. - Marine & Industrial Hardware Division **(2)**
2 Srimath Bandaranayaka Mawatha
Colombo, 12, Sri Lanka
Tel.: (94) 112424708
Fax: (94) 11 471415
Web Site: www.cdl.lk/as_comp1.php
Marine & Indilstrial Hardware Mfr
S.I.C.: 3429
N.A.I.C.S.: 332510
F. J. L. Felix *(Mgr-Sls)*

COLOMBO STOCK EXCHANGE

04-01 West Block World Trade Center
Echelon Sq, Colombo, 1, Sri Lanka
Tel.: (94) 0112446581
Fax: (94) 2445279
E-Mail: info@cse.lk
Web Site: www.cse.lk
Rev.: $2,403,015
Emp.: 100
Business Description:
Stock Exchange Services
S.I.C.: 6231
N.A.I.C.S.: 523210
Personnel:
A.N. Fonseka *(Chm)*
Surekha Sellahewa *(CEO)*
Board of Directors:
A.N. Fonseka
Gomin Dayasri
Ashroff Omar
Anthony A. Page
Malik Ranasinghe
Dhakshitha T. W. Thalgodapitiya
M. Eraj Wijesinghe
Rienzie T. Wijetilleke

COLONIAL COAL INTERNATIONAL CORPORATION

Suite 200 595 Howe Street
Vancouver, BC, V6C 2T5, Canada
Tel.: (604) 568-4962
Fax: (604) 681-4692
Web Site: ccoal.ca
Year Founded: 2007
CAD—(TSXV)
Rev.: $83,421
Assets: $17,822,478
Liabilities: $365,766
Net Worth: $17,456,713
Earnings: ($2,010,953)
Fiscal Year-end: 07/31/13
Business Description:
Investment Services
S.I.C.: 6211
N.A.I.C.S.: 523999

Personnel:
David Austin *(Chm, Pres & CEO)*
William Filtness *(CFO & Sec)*
John Perry *(COO)*
Board of Directors:
David Austin
Ian Downie
Anthony Hammond
John Perry
Wayne Waters
Transfer Agent:
Computershare Trust Company of Canada
510 Burrard St 2nd Fl
Vancouver, BC, Canada

COLONIAL GARAGE AND DISTRIBUTORS LIMITED

(d/b/a Colonial Auto Parts Ltd.)
59 Majors Path
Saint John's, NL, A1A 4Z9, Canada
Tel.: (709) 576-7278
Fax: (709) 576-3389
Web Site: www.colonialautoparts.ca
Year Founded: 1926
Rev.: $14,393,160
Emp.: 110
Business Description:
Automotive Parts Supplier
S.I.C.: 5531
N.A.I.C.S.: 441310
Personnel:
Douglas Squires *(VP)*

THE COLONIAL MOTOR COMPANY LIMITED

Level 1 CMC Building 89 Courtenay Place
PO Box 6159
Wellington, 6141, New Zealand
Tel.: (64) 43849734
Fax: (64) 48017279
E-Mail: cmc@colmotor.co.nz
Web Site: www.colmotor.co.nz
CMO—(NZE)
Rev.: $514,258,659
Assets: $186,306,156
Liabilities: $74,420,181
Net Worth: $111,885,975
Earnings: $12,387,600
Emp.: 93
Fiscal Year-end: 06/30/13
Business Description:
Holding Company; New & Used Car, Heavy Truck & Tractor Dealerships Owner & Operator
S.I.C.: 6719
N.A.I.C.S.: 551112
Personnel:
Jim P. Gibbons *(Chm)*
Graeme D. Gibbons *(CEO)*
Nicholas K. Bartle *(Sec)*
Board of Directors:
Jim P. Gibbons
Peter John Aitken
Falcon R. S. Clouston
Graeme D. Gibbons
Matthew J. Newman
Denis M. Wood
Subsidiaries:

Advance Agricentre Ltd (1)
243 Dee Street
Invercargill, 9810, New Zealand
Tel.: (64) 32111333
Fax: (64) 32144578
E-Mail: admin@advanceagricentre.co.nz
Web Site: www.advanceagricentre.co.nz
Emp.: 12
New & Used Tractor Dealers
S.I.C.: 5083
N.A.I.C.S.: 423820

Avon City Motorcycles Ltd. (1)
Epsom Road
Sockburn, Christchurch, Canterbury, 8042, New Zealand
Tel.: (64) 33413490
Fax: (64) 3 341 3496
Emp.: 11
Motorcycle Retailer
S.I.C.: 5571
N.A.I.C.S.: 441228
John Luxton *(Mng Dir)*

Avon City Motors Ltd (1)
165 Main South Road
Sockburn, Christchurch, 8004, New Zealand
Tel.: (64) 33484129
Fax: (64) 33484414
E-Mail: ravon@acford.co.nz
Web Site: www.avoncityford.co.nz
Emp.: 100
New & Used Car Dealers
S.I.C.: 5511
N.A.I.C.S.: 441110
John Luxton *(Gen Mgr)*

Capital City Motors Ltd (1)
97 Taranaki Street
Wellington, 6141, New Zealand
Tel.: (64) 48028750
Fax: (64) 48028751
Web Site: www.capitalcitymotors.co.nz
New & Used Car Dealers
S.I.C.: 5511
N.A.I.C.S.: 441110
Hamish Jacob *(CEO)*

Dunedin City Motors Ltd (1)
Cnr Andersons Bay & Macandrew Rd
Dunedin, New Zealand
Tel.: (64) 34664060
Fax: (64) 34664071
E-Mail: sales@dcford.co.nz
Web Site: www.dcford.co.nz
Emp.: 50
New & Used Car Dealers
S.I.C.: 5511
N.A.I.C.S.: 441110
Keith Kippenberger *(Mgr-Sls-Ford New Vehicle)*

Fagan Motors Ltd. (1)
75 Dixon Street
5840 Masterton, New Zealand
Tel.: (64) 63786159
Fax: (64) 63786156
E-Mail: sales@faganmotors.co.nz
Web Site: www.faganmotors.co.nz
Emp.: 35
New Car Dealers
S.I.C.: 5511
N.A.I.C.S.: 441110
Keith Allen *(Mgr-Sls)*

Hutchinson Motors Ltd (1)
186 Tuam St
Christchurch, 8011, New Zealand
Tel.: (64) 33793440
Fax: (64) 33656347
E-Mail: info@teamhutchinsonford.co.nz
Web Site: www.teamhutchinsonford.co.nz
Emp.: 70
New & Used Car Dealers
S.I.C.: 5511
N.A.I.C.S.: 441110
Deb Macdonald *(Bus Mgr)*

Macaulay Motors Ltd (1)
270 Dee Street
Invercargill, 9810, New Zealand
Tel.: (64) 32111222
Fax: (64) 3 214 4367
E-Mail: sales@macaulayford.co.nz
Web Site: www.macaulayford.co.nz
Emp.: 50
New & Used Car Dealers
S.I.C.: 5511
N.A.I.C.S.: 441110
Grant Price *(Bus Mgr)*

Metro Training Services Ltd. (1)
23 Parumoana Street
Porirua, Wellington, 5022, New Zealand
Tel.: (64) 6442372240
Fax: (64) 42372243
Web Site: www.automotivetraining.co.nz
Emp.: 3
Automotive Repair Training Services
S.I.C.: 7549
N.A.I.C.S.: 811198
Frank Whitworth *(Mgr-Trng)*

M.S. Motors (1998) Ltd. (1)
157 Haven Road
PO Box 106
Nelson, 7040, New Zealand
Tel.: (64) 35489189
Fax: (64) 35484407
E-Mail: admin@msford.co.nz
Web Site: www.nelsonford.co.nz
Emp.: 15
New Car Dealers
S.I.C.: 5511
N.A.I.C.S.: 441110
Alan Kirby *(Mng Dir)*

Pukekohe Motors Ltd (1)
231 Minukau Rd
Pukekohe, 2120, New Zealand
Tel.: (64) 92384060
Fax: (64) 92383663
E-Mail: info@pukekohemotors.co.nz
Web Site: www.pukekohemotors.co.nz
Emp.: 12
New & Used Car Dealers
S.I.C.: 5511
N.A.I.C.S.: 441110
Matthew Newman *(Gen Mgr)*

Ruahine Motors Ltd. (1)
Ruataniwha Street Hawkes Bay
Poverty Bay, Waipukurau, 4200, New Zealand
Tel.: (64) 68588086
Fax: (64) 68588345
E-Mail: sales@ruahinemotors.co.nz
Web Site: www.ruahinemotors.co.nz
Emp.: 16
New & Used Car Dealers
S.I.C.: 5511
N.A.I.C.S.: 441110
David Wills *(Mng Dir)*

South Auckland Ford Ltd (1)
Corner Great South Road and Gladding Place
Manukau, Auckland, 2241, New Zealand
Tel.: (64) 92622739
Fax: (64) 92622750
E-Mail: info@southaucklandmotors.co.nz
Web Site: www.southaucklandmotors.co.nz
Emp.: 130
New & Used Car Dealers
S.I.C.: 5511
N.A.I.C.S.: 441110
Matthew Newman *(Principal)*

South Auckland Motors Ltd. (1)
Corner Great South Road & Gladding Place
PO Box 76 250
Manukau, Auckland, 2241, New Zealand
Tel.: (64) 92622739
Fax: (64) 92622750
E-Mail: sales@southaucklandmotors.co.nz
Web Site: www.southaucklandmotors.co.nz
Emp.: 120
New & Used Car Dealers
S.I.C.: 5511
N.A.I.C.S.: 441110
Matthew Newman *(CEO)*

Southland Tractors Ltd (1)
853 North Road
Lorneville, Invercargill, 9876, New Zealand
Tel.: (64) 32358741
Fax: (64) 32358713
E-Mail: admin@eastlandtractors.co.nz
Web Site: www.southlandtractors.co.nz
Emp.: 10
New & Used Tractor Dealers
S.I.C.: 5083
N.A.I.C.S.: 423820
Grant Price *(Mgr)*

Southpac Trucks Ltd. (1)
96-98 Wiri Station Road
PO Box 76463
Manukau, 2241, New Zealand
Tel.: (64) 92623181
Fax: (64) 92623184
E-Mail: info@spt.co.nz
Web Site: www.southpactrucks.co.nz
Emp.: 150
General Freight Trucking Services
S.I.C.: 4213
N.A.I.C.S.: 484121
Maarten Durent *(CEO)*

Stevens Motors Ltd (1)
434 High Street
Lower Hutt, 5010, New Zealand
Tel.: (64) 45703480
Fax: (64) 45703481
E-Mail: sales@stevensmotors.co.nz
Web Site: www.stevensmotors.co.nz
Emp.: 35
New & Used Car Dealers
S.I.C.: 5511
N.A.I.C.S.: 441110
Paul Dikens *(Bus Mgr)*

Timaru Motors Ltd (1)
207 Hilton Highway
Washdyke, Timaru, 7910, New Zealand
Tel.: (64) 36874133
Fax: (64) 36874123
E-Mail: sales@timarumotors.co.nz
Web Site: www.timarumotors.co.nz
Emp.: 16
New & Used Car Dealers
S.I.C.: 5511
N.A.I.C.S.: 441110
Wayne Patman *(Principal)*

COLONY FORD LINCOLN SALES INC

300 Queen Street E
Brampton, ON, L6V 1C2, Canada
Tel.: (905) 451-4094
Fax: (905) 451-0004
Toll Free: (866) 980-4686
Web Site: www.colonyfordlincoln.com
Rev.: $33,492,390
Emp.: 70
Business Description:
New & Used Car Dealers
S.I.C.: 5511
N.A.I.C.S.: 441110
Personnel:
David Kerr *(Pres)*
Keith Coulter *(CEO)*
Darlene Tolmie *(Treas & Sec)*

COLOPL INC.

4-20-3 Ebisu Shibuya-ku
Tokyo, 150-6032, Japan
Tel.: (81) 3 67217770
Web Site: www.colopl.co.jp
Year Founded: 2008
3668—(TKS)
Rev.: $66,083,886
Fiscal Year-end: 09/30/12
Business Description:
Game Applications
S.I.C.: 7372
N.A.I.C.S.: 511210
Personnel:
Naruatsu Baba *(Pres)*

COLOPLAST A/S

Holtedam 1
3050 Humlebaek, Denmark
Tel.: (45) 49111111
Fax: (45) 49111555
E-Mail: coloplast@coloplast.com
Web Site: www.coloplast.com
COLOB—(CSE OTC)
Rev.: $1,957,684,800
Assets: $1,807,257,600
Liabilities: $734,198,400
Net Worth: $1,073,059,200
Earnings: $389,654,400
Emp.: 7,875
Fiscal Year-end: 09/30/12
Business Description:
Mfr & Developer of Healthcare Products & Services
S.I.C.: 8049
N.A.I.C.S.: 621399
Personnel:
Michael Pram Rasmussen *(Chm)*
Niels Peter Louis-Hansen *(Deputy Chm)*
Lars Rasmussen *(Pres & CEO)*
Lene Skole *(CFO & Exec VP)*
Nicolai Buhl Andersen *(Sr VP)*
Anders Monrad Rendtorff *(Sr VP-People & Comm)*
Board of Directors:
Michael Pram Rasmussen
Thomas Barfod
Hakan Bjorklund
Jane Lichtenberg

Coloplast A/S—(Continued)

Niels Peter Louis-Hansen
Per Magid
Brian Petersen
Torben Rasmussen
Jorgen Tang-Jensen

Subsidiary:

Coloplast (1)
Holtedan 1 & 3
Humlebaek, 3050, Denmark (100%)
Tel.: (45) 49111111
Fax: (45) 49111555
E-Mail: coloplast@coloplast.com
Web Site: www.coloplast.com
Emp.: 900
S.I.C.: 8732
N.A.I.C.S.: 541720
Lars Arsmussen *(Mng Dir)*

U.S. Subsidiaries:

Coloplast Corp. (1)
200 S 6th St Ste 900
Minneapolis, MN 55402
Tel.: (507) 345-6200
Fax: (507) 345-3291
Toll Free: (800) 788-0293
E-Mail: usmedweb@coloplast.com
Web Site: www.us.coloplast.com
Developer & Mfr of Healthcare Products & Services
S.I.C.: 3841
N.A.I.C.S.: 339112
Kimberly Herman *(Pres & Sr VP)*

Coloplast Distribution Center (1)
1840 W Oak Pkwy
Marietta, GA 30062-2275
Tel.: (770) 281-8400
Web Site: www.us.coloplast.com
Medical Instrument Distr
S.I.C.: 5047
N.A.I.C.S.: 423450

Non-U.S. Subsidiaries:

AMOENA GmbH & Co. KG (1)
Kapellenweg 36
83064 Raubling, Germany (85%)
Tel.: (49) 80358710
Fax: (49) 8035871559
E-Mail: amoena@amoena.com
Web Site: www.amoena.de
Emp.: 120
S.I.C.: 7335
N.A.I.C.S.: 621410

Coloplast AB (1)
Kungsbacvagan 2
Kungsbacka, 43422, Sweden (100%)
Tel.: (46) 30033250
Fax: (46) 30018866
E-Mail: info@coloplast.com
Web Site: www.coloplast.se
Emp.: 30
S.I.C.: 8099
N.A.I.C.S.: 621410
Brecc Enger *(Mng Dir)*

Coloplast AG (1)
Euro Business Ctr Euro 1 Blegistrasse 1
Rotkreuz, 6343, Switzerland (100%)
Tel.: (41) 7997979
Fax: (41) 7997940
E-Mail: ch@coloplast.com
Web Site: www.coloplast.com
Emp.: 12
S.I.C.: 8099
N.A.I.C.S.: 621410

Coloplast Beteiligungs GmbH (1)
Kuehnstrasse 75
22045 Hamburg, Germany (100%)
Tel.: (49) 406698070
Fax: (49) 4066980748
E-Mail: dere@coloplast.com
Web Site: www.coloplast.de
Emp.: 200
S.I.C.: 8099
N.A.I.C.S.: 621410
Chima Abuba *(Pres)*

Coloplast B.V. (1)
Softwareweg 1
PO Box 1111
3821 BN Amersfoort, Netherlands (100%)
Tel.: (31) 334544444
Fax: (31) 334544455
E-Mail: nlpost@coloplast.com
Web Site: www.coloplast.nl
Emp.: 70
Healthcare Products & Services
S.I.C.: 8099
N.A.I.C.S.: 621999
Rachel Klauber *(Mng Dir)*

Coloplast Canada Corporation (1)
3300 Ridgeway Dr Unit 12
Mississauga, ON, L5L 5Z9, Canada (100%)
Tel.: (905) 820-7588
Fax: (905) 820-8218
E-Mail: ca@coloplast.com
Web Site: www.coloplast.ca
Emp.: 50
S.I.C.: 8099
N.A.I.C.S.: 621410
Michael Alderman *(Gen Mgr)*

Coloplast (China) Co. Ltd. (1)
265 Bldg 1 Chang Ping Rd
Gongbei Zhuhai, Guangzhou, Guangdong, 519020, China (70%)
Tel.: (86) 568150886
Fax: (86) 7568870087
Web Site: www.coloplast.com.cn
Emp.: 100
S.I.C.: 8099
N.A.I.C.S.: 621410

Coloplast Croatia (1)
Nova Cesta 60
10000 Zagreb, Croatia
Tel.: (385) 1 4550 101
Fax: (385) 1 4550 501
E-Mail: coloplast@zg.htnet.hr
Emp.: 11
Surgical Instrument Mfr
S.I.C.: 3841
N.A.I.C.S.: 339112
Albert Karner *(Reg Mgr)*

Coloplast Czech Republic (1)
Radlicka 740/113d
158 00 Prague, Czech Republic
Tel.: (420) 244 470 202
Fax: (420) 244 472 106
E-Mail: czlel@coloplast.com
Web Site: www.coloplast.cz
Emp.: 14
Surgical Instrument Mfr
S.I.C.: 3841
N.A.I.C.S.: 339112
Radoslav Stilla *(Gen Mgr)*

Coloplast de Argentina S.A. (1)
Bouchard 574 Piso 13
Buenos Aires, CP 1106, Argentina (100%)
Tel.: (54) 1143112999
Fax: (54) 1143134747
E-Mail: arsr@coloplast.com
Web Site: www.coloplast.com.ar
Emp.: 40
S.I.C.: 8099
N.A.I.C.S.: 621410
Sandigo Caratini *(Pres)*

Coloplast de Costa Rica S.A. (1)
Zona Franca Metropolitana Barreakde Heredia
1023006 Heredia, Costa Rica (100%)
Tel.: (506) 2933034
Fax: (506) 2933036
Web Site: www.coloplast.co.kr/company/worldwidecontact.html
Sales Range: $1-9.9 Million
Emp.: 240
S.I.C.: 7335
N.A.I.C.S.: 621410

Coloplast do Brasil Ltda. (1)
Rua Mexico 3 4th Fl
Rio de Janeiro, 20031-144, Brazil (100%)
Tel.: (55) 2122155842
Fax: (55) 2122155834
Web Site: www.colopast.com
Emp.: 6
S.I.C.: 8099
N.A.I.C.S.: 621410
Vitor Muniz *(Gen Mgr)*

Coloplast GmbH (1)
Thomas-Klestil-Platz 10
Schwechat, 2320 Vienna, Austria (100%)
Tel.: (43) 170757510
Fax: (43) 17075730
E-Mail: at@coloplast.com
Web Site: www.coloplast.at
Emp.: 20
S.I.C.: 8099
N.A.I.C.S.: 621410

Coloplast GmbH (1)
Kuehnstrasse 75
22045 Hamburg, 22045, Germany (100%)
Tel.: (49) 406698070
Fax: (49) 4066980772
E-Mail: info@coloplast.de
Web Site: www.coloplast.de
Emp.: 200
S.I.C.: 8099
N.A.I.C.S.: 621410
Greger Karlsson *(Mng Dir)*

Coloplast Greece (1)
Gionas 1A Str
Kypriadou, 11141 Metamorfosis, Greece
Tel.: (30) 210 202 0232
Fax: (30) 2102020775
E-Mail: info@coloplast.gr
Web Site: www.coloplast.gr
Medical Instrument Mfr
S.I.C.: 3841
N.A.I.C.S.: 339112

Coloplast (Hong Kong) Ltd. (1)
Units 2606-07 26/F Laws Commerical Plaza
788 Cheung Sha Wan Road
Tsimshatsui, Kowloon, Lai Chi Kok, China (Hong Kong)
Tel.: (852) 3628 7488
Fax: (852) 2302 1884
E-Mail: cnchk@coloplast.com
Web Site: www.coloplast.com
Surgical Instrument Mfr
S.I.C.: 3841
N.A.I.C.S.: 339112

Coloplast Hungary Kft. (1)
Buzadirag 15
Tkomarom, 2800 Tatabanya, Hungary (100%)
Tel.: (36) 34520500
Fax: (36) 34520586
E-Mail: info@coloplast.com
Web Site: www.colorplast.com
Emp.: 900
S.I.C.: 8099
N.A.I.C.S.: 621410
Boris Kovac *(Gen Mgr)*

Coloplast (India) Private Limited (1)
Unit 108 Plot 4 Salcon Aurum District Centre Jasola
New Delhi, 110025, India
Tel.: (91) 11 40800400
Fax: (91) 11 41676531
E-Mail: cin@coloplast.com
Emp.: 45
Surgical Instrument Mfr
S.I.C.: 3841
N.A.I.C.S.: 339112

Coloplast Israel (1)
Hataash 20 Beit Hapaamon Office 321
Kfar Saba, 44425, Israel
Tel.: (972) 9 766 7030
Fax: (972) 97669118
Web Site: www.coloplast.so.il
Emp.: 15
Medical Equipment Distr
S.I.C.: 5047
N.A.I.C.S.: 423450
Alex Glazer *(Gen Mgr)*

Coloplast K.K. (1)
11 fl Italian Culture Bldg 2-1-30 Kudan Minami
Chiyoda Ku, Tokyo, 102 0074, Japan
Tel.: (81) 334596641
Fax: (81) 3435144187
E-Mail: jp@coloplast.com
Web Site: www.coloplast.co.jp
Emp.: 90
S.I.C.: 8099
N.A.I.C.S.: 621410
Vagn Heiberg *(Gen Mgr)*

Coloplast Korea Limited (1)
Gwanghwamum Officia 624 Shinmoonro-1Ga
Jongno-Gu, 110-099 Seoul, Korea (South)
Tel.: (82) 27228004
Fax: (82) 27226002
Medical Instrument Mfr
S.I.C.: 3841
N.A.I.C.S.: 339112

Coloplast Norge AS (1)
Ryenstubben 10
0661 Oslo, Norway (100%)
Mailing Address:
PO Box 6287
0603 Etterstad, Norway
Tel.: (47) 22575000
Fax: (47) 22687813
E-Mail: kundeservice@coloplast.com
Web Site: www.coloplast.no
Sales Range: $25-49.9 Million
Emp.: 30
S.I.C.: 8099
N.A.I.C.S.: 621410

Coloplast N.V. (1)
Guido Gezellestraat 121
1601 Huizingen, Belgium (100%)
Tel.: (32) 23343535
Fax: (32) 23343536
E-Mail: beeb@coloplast.com
Web Site: www.coloplast.be
Emp.: 35
S.I.C.: 8099
N.A.I.C.S.: 621410
Gitte Hesselholt *(Country Mgr)*

Coloplast OOO (1)
Leningradsku Ave 72 Bldg 2
Moscow, 125335, Russia
Tel.: (7) 495 937 53 90
Fax: (7) 495 937 53 91
E-Mail: info@coloplast.ru
Web Site: www.coloplast.ru
Emp.: 2
Surgical Appliances Mfr
S.I.C.: 3842
N.A.I.C.S.: 339113
Taku Cheuk *(Gen Mgr)*

Coloplast OY (1)
Rajatorpantie 41 C
1640 Vantaa, Finland
Tel.: (358) 9 8946750
Fax: (358) 9 890 022
E-Mail: coloplast.fi@coloplast.com
Web Site: www.coloplast.fi
Emp.: 16
Medical Device Mfr
S.I.C.: 3841
N.A.I.C.S.: 339112
Kristina Jensen *(Country Mgr)*

Coloplast Portugal Lda. (1)
Avenida Jose Gomes Ferreira 15
Miraflores-Alges
1495-131 Alges, Portugal
Tel.: (351) 214 985 400
Fax: (351) 214 985 409
E-Mail: pt@coloplast.com
Web Site: www.coloplastportugal.pai.pt
Emp.: 6
Medical Device Mfr
S.I.C.: 3841
N.A.I.C.S.: 339112
Angelo Maria *(Gen Mgr)*

Coloplast Productos Medicos S.A. (1)
Comdesa De Venavito No 5 4th Fl
Madrid, 28027, Spain (100%)
Tel.: (34) 913141802
Fax: (34) 913141465
E-Mail: es@coloplast.com
Web Site: www.coloplast.es
Emp.: 40
S.I.C.: 8099
N.A.I.C.S.: 621410

Coloplast Pty. Ltd. (1)
33 Gilby Rd
Mount Waverley, Melbourne, VIC, 3149, Australia (100%)
Tel.: (61) 395411111
Fax: (61) 395411155
E-Mail: au.care@coloplast.com
Web Site: www.coloplast.com.au
Emp.: 40
S.I.C.: 8099
N.A.I.C.S.: 621410
Greger Karlsson *(Gen Mgr)*

Laboratoires Coloplast (1)
6 Rue de Rome Les Jardins du Golf
93561 Rosny-sous-Bois, France
Tel.: (33) 1 56 63 1700
Fax: (33) 1 56 63 18 07
Web Site: www.coloplast.fr
Developer of Custom Medical Care Products & Services
S.I.C.: 8071
N.A.I.C.S.: 621511

Coloplast Shared Services Sp. z.o.o (1)
ul Malczewskiego 26
71-612 Szczecin, Poland
Tel.: (48) 91 881 75 00
Fax: (48) 91 881 75 80
Financial Investment Services
S.I.C.: 6211
N.A.I.C.S.: 523999

Coloplast Slovakia (1)
Obchodne Zastupitelstvo Dolna 62
974 01 Banska Bystrica, Slovakia
Tel.: (421) 48 41 53 761
Fax: (421) 48 41 53 762
E-Mail: skima@coloplast.com
Surgical Instrument Mfr
S.I.C.: 3841
N.A.I.C.S.: 339112

Coloplast Slovenia (1)
Zelezna Cesta 16
1000 Ljubljana, Slovenia
Tel.: (386) 1 280 75 30
Fax: (386) 12807532
E-Mail: si@coloplast.com
Medical Device Mfr
S.I.C.: 3841
N.A.I.C.S.: 339112
Albert Karner *(Gen Mgr)*

Coloplast S.p.A. (1)
Via Ronzanei 7-29
40033 Casalecchio di Reno, Italy (100%)
Tel.: (39) 0514138000
Fax: (39) 0514138289
E-Mail: info@coloplast.com
Web Site: www.coloplast.it
Emp.: 120
S.I.C.: 8099
N.A.I.C.S.: 621410
Ulrik Berthelsen *(Country Mgr)*

Coloplast Spain (1)
Condesa Venadito 5 - Planta 4
28027 Madrid, Spain
Tel.: (34) 91 314 18 02
Fax: (34) 91 314 14 65
E-Mail: es@coloplast.com
Emp.: 120
Medical Device Mfr
S.I.C.: 3841
N.A.I.C.S.: 339112

Coloplast Sp.z.o.o. (1)
Ul Leszno 12
01192 Warsaw, Poland (100%)
Tel.: (48) 225357373
Fax: (48) 225357374
E-Mail: plgk@coloplast.com
Web Site: www.coloplast.pl
Emp.: 34
S.I.C.: 8099
N.A.I.C.S.: 621410
Grzegorz Kado *(Gen Mgr)*

Coloplast Ukraine A/S (1)
Gertzena Str 17-25 Office 20
Kiev, 4050, Ukraine
Tel.: (380) 44 507 2512
Fax: (380) 50 507 2512
E-Mail: uaty@coloplast.com
Emp.: 1
Medical Equipment Mfr
S.I.C.: 3845
N.A.I.C.S.: 334510
Tetiana Shamenko *(Gen Mgr)*

Coloplast UK Ltd. (1)
Nene Hall Peterborough Business Park
Orton, Peterborough, Cambs, PE2 6FX,
United Kingdom (100%)
Tel.: (44) 1733 392 000
Fax: (44) 1733 233 348
E-Mail: gbccare@coloplast.com
Web Site: www.coloplast.co.uk
Emp.: 180
S.I.C.: 8099
N.A.I.C.S.: 621410

COLOR CHIPS (INDIA) LIMITED

Plot No 91 Rd No 7-B Women's Co-operative housing Society
Jubilee Hills, Hyderabad, Andhra Pradesh, 500 033, India
Tel.: (91) 40 23550268
Fax: (91) 40 23559333
E-Mail: info@colorchipsindia.com
Web Site: www.colorchipsindia.com
532172—(BOM)
Business Description:
Integrated Design Services
S.I.C.: 7371
N.A.I.C.S.: 541511
Personnel:
Penugonda T. V. M. Suresh *(Mng Dir)*
K. Gurava Raju *(CFO)*
D. S. Subrahmanyam *(Compliance Officer)*
Board of Directors:
G. Chandra Bhushan
Kotturi Ravi Kumar
K. Ch A. V. S. N. Murthy
M. Krishnam Raju
Jagannadha Sastry Rani
D. S. Subrahmanyam
Penugonda T. V. M. Suresh
Transfer Agent:
Venture Capital & Corporate Investments Private Limited
12-10-167 Bharat Nagar
500018 Hyderabad, India

COLORADO RESOURCES LTD.

262 2300 Carrington Road
Kelowna, BC, V4T 2N6, Canada
Tel.: (250) 768-1511
Fax: (250) 768-0020
Web Site: www.coloradoresources.com
Year Founded: 2009
CXO—(OTC TSXV)
Business Description:
Metal Mining & Exploration Services
S.I.C.: 1099
N.A.I.C.S.: 212299
Personnel:
Adam Travis *(Pres & CEO)*
Terese J. Gieselman *(CFO & Sec)*
Board of Directors:
Brian Flower
Terese J. Gieselman
Carl Hering
Lawrence Nagy
Adam Travis
Transfer Agent:
Computershare Investor Services Inc.
2nd Fl 510 Burrard St
Vancouver, BC, Canada

COLORLAND ANIMATION LTD.

1802 Shatin Galleria Shan Meid St
18224 Fotan Shat
Hong Kong, China (Hong Kong)
Tel.: (852) 23669013
Fax: (852) 23679087
E-Mail: col@colorland.com.hk
Web Site: www.colorland-animation.com
Year Founded: 1991
Emp.: 194
Business Description:
Motion Picture & Video Animation Services
S.I.C.: 7819
N.A.I.C.S.: 512199
Personnel:
Louis Sek *(CEO)*

COLORPAK LIMITED

63-73 Woodlands Drive
Braeside, VIC, 3195, Australia
Tel.: (61) 3 9586 4700
Fax: (61) 3 9587 8162
E-Mail: colorpak@colorpak.com.au
Web Site: www.colorpak.com.au
CKL—(ASX)
Rev.: $184,989,424
Assets: $146,918,384
Liabilities: $72,037,247
Net Worth: $74,881,138
Earnings: $7,809,497
Fiscal Year-end: 06/30/13
Business Description:
Carton Mfr
S.I.C.: 2631
N.A.I.C.S.: 322130
Personnel:
Alex Commins *(Mng Dir)*
Stephen Nicholls *(CFO & Sec)*
Paul Grobler *(CIO)*
Board of Directors:
Geoffrey Livingston Willis
Alex Commins
Bronwyn Constance
David Heaney
Ian Wightwick

COLORSTARS GROUP

10th Floor 566 Jung Jeng Road
Sindian District, New Taipei City, 231, Taiwan
Tel.: (886) 2 8667 6600
Fax: (886) 2 8667 1400
E-Mail: sales@colorstars.com
Web Site: www.colorstars.com
Year Founded: 2002
CSTU—(OTC)
Sls.: $2,736,466
Assets: $2,273,763
Liabilities: $763,390
Net Worth: $1,510,373
Earnings: ($1,230,964)
Emp.: 11
Fiscal Year-end: 12/31/12
Business Description:
LED Lighting Products Developer & Mfr
S.I.C.: 3648
N.A.I.C.S.: 335129
Personnel:
Wei-Rur Chen *(Chm, Pres, CEO & CFO)*
Mei-Ying Chiu *(Sec)*
Board of Directors:
Wei-Rur Chen
Mei-Ying Chiu
Hsiu-Fu Liu

COLOSSUS MINERALS INC.

1 University Avenue Suite 401
Toronto, ON, M5J 2P1, Canada
Tel.: (416) 643-7655
Fax: (416) 643-3890
E-Mail: info@colossusminerals.com
Web Site: www.colossusminerals.com
Year Founded: 2006
COLUF—(OTC)
Rev.: $8,839,000
Assets: $279,642,000
Liabilities: $161,287,000
Net Worth: $118,355,000
Earnings: ($30,063,000)
Emp.: 485
Fiscal Year-end: 12/31/12
Business Description:
Gold & Platinum Mining Services
S.I.C.: 1041
N.A.I.C.S.: 212221
Personnel:
John Frostiak *(Chm)*
David Anthony *(Pres & COO)*
David Massola *(Inteirm CEO)*
Gregory Yuen Ho *(Sec & VP-Legal)*
Board of Directors:
John Frostiak
Legal Counsel:
Silva Martins, Vilas Boas, Lopes e Frattari Advogados
Rua Paraiba 476 8o. andar
Belo Horizonte, Brazil
Cassels, Brock & Blackwell LLP
2100 Scotia Plaza 40 King St W
Toronto, ON, M5H 3C2, Canada
Tel.: (416) 869-5300
Telex: 6-23415
Fax: (416) 360-8877
Transfer Agent:
Equity Financial Trust Company
Toronto, ON, Canada
Non-U.S. Subsidiary:

Colossus Mineracao Ltda. (1)
Avenida Getulio Vargas 1420 Sala
1303 Savassi, Belo Horizonte, Brazil
Tel.: (55) 31 3223 8825
Gold & Platinum Mining Services
S.I.C.: 1041
N.A.I.C.S.: 212221

COLOWIDE CO., LTD.

2-2-1 Landmark Tower Minatomirai
Nishi-ku, Yokohama, Kanagawa, 221-0835, Japan
Tel.: (81) 452745970
Web Site: www.colowide.co.jp
Sales Range: $450-499.9 Million
Emp.: 1,800
Business Description:
Restaurants & Bars Owner & Operator
S.I.C.: 5812
N.A.I.C.S.: 722511

COLT GROUP S.A.

K2 Building Forte 1 2a rue Albert Borschette
L-1246 Luxembourg, Luxembourg
Mailing Address:
BP 2174
L-1021 Luxembourg, Luxembourg
Tel.: (352) 27992703
Web Site: www.colt.net
Year Founded: 1992
COLT—(LSE)
Rev.: $2,146,602,682
Assets: $2,759,917,734
Liabilities: $763,278,390
Net Worth: $1,996,639,344
Earnings: $35,135,037
Emp.: 4,957
Fiscal Year-end: 12/31/12
Business Description:
Telecommunication Services
S.I.C.: 4813
N.A.I.C.S.: 517110
Personnel:
Simon Haslam *(Chm)*
Rakesh Bhasin *(CEO)*
Richard Blaustein *(Mng Dir)*
Andy Kankan *(Mng Dir)*
Mark Ferrari *(CFO)*
Andrew Powell *(COO)*
Carl Robertson *(CMO)*
Caroline Griffin Pain *(Sec)*
Francois Eloy *(Exec VP-Colt Comm Svcs)*
Jurgen Hernichel *(Exec VP-Bus Svcs Unit)*
Mark Leonard *(Exec VP-Infrastructure Svcs Unit)*
Paul Musson *(Exec VP-HR)*
Richard Oosterom *(Exec VP-Strategy & Bus Dev)*
Adriaan Oosthoek *(Exec VP-Data Centre Svcs)*
Simon Walsh *(Exec VP-Colt Enterprise Svcs)*
Board of Directors:
Simon Haslam
Andreas Barth
Rakesh Bhasin
Vincenzo Damiani
Mark Ferrari
Gene Gabbard
Sergio Giacoletto-Roggio
Tim Hilton
Katherine Innes
Anthony Rabin
Michael Wilens

COLT Group S.A.—(Continued)

Legal Counsel:
Slaughter & May
One Bunhill Row
London, EC1Y 8YY, United Kingdom
Tel.: (44) 20 7600 1200
Fax: (44) 20 7600 0289

Non-U.S. Subsidiaries:

COLT Telecom A/S (1)
Borgmester Christiansens Gade 55
2450 Copenhagen, Denmark (100%)
Tel.: (45) 70212330
Fax: (45) 70212331
E-Mail: dk.info@colt.net
Web Site: www.colt.net
Emp.: 38
Telecommunications Services
S.I.C.: 4813
N.A.I.C.S.: 517110
John Jacobsen *(Mng Dir)*

COLT Telecom AB (1)
Luntmakargatan 18
PO Box 3458
103 69 Stockholm, Sweden (100%)
Tel.: (46) 87818000
Fax: (46) 87818100
E-Mail: se.info@colt.net
Emp.: 29
Telecommunications Services
S.I.C.: 4813
N.A.I.C.S.: 517110
Victoria Karlsson *(Mng Dir)*

COLT Telecom AG (1)
Murtschenstrasse 27
8048 Zurich, Switzerland (100%)
Tel.: (41) 585601600
Fax: (41) 585602610
E-Mail: ch.info@colt.net
Web Site: www.colt.ch
Emp.: 120
Telecommunications Services
S.I.C.: 4813
N.A.I.C.S.: 517110
Joerg Dannheim *(Mgr-Fin)*

COLT Telecom Austria GmbH (1)
Karntner Ring 10-12
1010 Vienna, Austria (100%)
Tel.: (43) 1205000
Fax: (43) 120500199
E-Mail: office@colt.net
Web Site: www.colt.net
Emp.: 55
Telecommunications Services
S.I.C.: 4813
N.A.I.C.S.: 517110
Semih Calaskan *(Mng Dir)*

COLT Telecom B.V. (1)
Van der Madeweg 12-14a
PO Box 94014
1090 GA Amsterdam, Netherlands (100%)
Tel.: (31) 208882020
Fax: (31) 2028882010
E-Mail: nl.info@colt.net
Web Site: www.colt.net
Emp.: 120
Telecommunications Services
S.I.C.: 4813
N.A.I.C.S.: 517110
M. van Meensel *(Mgr-Fin)*

COLT Telecom Espana SA (1)
Calle Telemaco 5
28027 Madrid, Spain (100%)
Tel.: (34) 917899000
Fax: (34) 917899098
E-Mail: info.es@colt.net
Web Site: www.colt.net
Emp.: 50
Telecommunications Services
S.I.C.: 4813
N.A.I.C.S.: 517110
Steve Cahall *(VP)*

COLT Telecom GmbH (1)
Herriotstrasse 4
60528 Frankfurt am Main, Germany (100%)
Tel.: (49) 69566060
Fax: (49) 69566061000
E-Mail: de.info@colt.net
Web Site: www.colt.net
Telecommunications Services
S.I.C.: 4813
N.A.I.C.S.: 517110
Jurgen Hernithel *(Mng Dir)*

COLT Telecom Ireland Limited (1)
1st Fl 1 Gate Way E Wall Rd
Dublin, 3, Ireland (100%)
Tel.: (353) 14365900
Fax: (353) 14365901
E-Mail: info@colt.net
Web Site: www.colt.net
Emp.: 25
Telecommunications Services
S.I.C.: 4813
N.A.I.C.S.: 517110
Gary Keogh *(Mng Dir)*

COLT Telecom NV/SA (1)
Culliganlaan 2H
Rue du Planeur, 1130 Brussels, Belgium (100%)
Tel.: (32) 27901616
Fax: (32) 27901600
E-Mail: be.Info@colt.net
Telecommunications Services
S.I.C.: 4813
N.A.I.C.S.: 517110

COLT Telecom Portugal (1)
Estrada da Outurela 118
Edificio B, 2790 114 Carnaxide, Portugal (100%)
Tel.: (351) 211200000
Fax: (351) 211200009
E-Mail: geral@colt.net
Web Site: www.colt.net
Emp.: 40
Telecommunications Services
S.I.C.: 4813
N.A.I.C.S.: 517110
Catarina Pessanha *(Dir-Fin)*

COLT Telecom S.p.A. (1)
Viale E Jenner 56
20159 Milan, Italy (100%)
Tel.: (39) 02303331
Fax: (39) 0230333700
E-Mail: it.info@colt.net
Web Site: www.colt.net
Emp.: 100
Telecommunications Services
S.I.C.: 4813
N.A.I.C.S.: 517110

COLT Telecommunications France (1)
23-27 rue Pierre Valette
92247 Malakoff, Cedex, France (100%)
Tel.: (33) 170995500
Fax: (33) 170995880
E-Mail: accueil@colt.net
Emp.: 500
Telecommunications Services
S.I.C.: 4813
N.A.I.C.S.: 517110

COLT RESOURCES INC.

2000 McGill College Avenue Suite 2010
Montreal, QC, H3A 3H3, Canada
Tel.: (514) 843-7178
Fax: (514) 843-7704
E-Mail: nperrault@coltresources.com
Web Site: www.coltresources.com
Year Founded: 2000
GTP—(DEU OTC TSXV)
Int. Income: $51,866
Assets: $40,277,803
Liabilities: $9,162,745
Net Worth: $31,115,058
Earnings: ($9,380,469)
Fiscal Year-end: 12/31/12

Business Description:
Gold, Uranium & Other Metal-Based Mineral Mining & Resources
S.I.C.: 1041
N.A.I.C.S.: 212221

Personnel:
Richard Quesnel *(Chm)*
Nikolas Perrault *(Pres & CEO)*
Shahab Jaffrey *(CFO)*
Declan Costelloe *(COO & Exec VP)*
David A. Johnson *(Chief Legal Officer & Sec)*

Board of Directors:
Richard Quesnel
Declan Costelloe
David A. Johnson
James Franz Ladner
James Wayne Murton
Nikolas Perrault
Paul Yeou

Transfer Agent:
Computershare Investor Services Inc
100 University Avenue 9th Floor North Tower
Toronto, ON, Canada

COLTENE HOLDING AG

Feldwiesenstrasse 20
CH-9450 Altstatten, Switzerland
Tel.: (41) 71 757 53 00
Fax: (41) 71 757 53 01
E-Mail: info.ch@coltene.com
Web Site: www.coltene.com
CLTN—(SWX)
Sls.: $170,613,509
Assets: $164,878,003
Liabilities: $60,335,067
Net Worth: $104,542,935
Earnings: $10,285,920
Emp.: 899
Fiscal Year-end: 12/31/12

Business Description:
Holding Company; Dental Products & Devices Mfr & Distr
S.I.C.: 6719
N.A.I.C.S.: 551112

Personnel:
Nick Huber *(Chm)*
Martin Schaufelberger *(CEO)*
Hans Gruter *(CFO)*

Board of Directors:
Nick Huber
Robert Heberlein
Erwin Locher
Matthew Robin
Roland Weiger

Subsidiary:

Coltene / Whaledent AG (1)
Feldwiesenstrasse 20
9450 Altstatten, Switzerland
Tel.: (41) 71 757 53 00
Fax: (41) 71 757 53 01
E-Mail: info@coltenewhaledent.ch
Emp.: 100
Dental Equipment Mfr
S.I.C.: 3843
N.A.I.C.S.: 339114
Nick Huber *(Chm)*
Martin Schaufelberger *(CEO)*
Hans Gruter *(CFO)*

Non-U.S. Subsidiary:

Coltene / Whaledent S.a.r.l. (2)
19 Bld Alexandre Oyon
72058 Le Mans, France
Tel.: (33) 243393030
Fax: (33) 243393040
E-Mail: info@coltenewhaledent.fr
Web Site: www.coltene.com
Emp.: 16
Dental Equipment Mfr
S.I.C.: 3843
N.A.I.C.S.: 339114
Cynthia Vedel *(Office Mgr)*

U.S. Subsidiaries:

Coltene/Whaledent Inc. (1)
235 Ascot Pkwy
Cuyahoga Falls, OH 44223-3701
Tel.: (330) 916-8800
Fax: (330) 916-7077
Toll Free: (800) 221-3046
E-Mail: info@coltenewhaledent.com
Web Site: www.coltene.com
Emp.: 300
Dental Product & Device Mfr
S.I.C.: 3843
N.A.I.C.S.: 339114
Michael Nordahl *(Gen Mgr-Bus Dev)*

Non-U.S. Subsidiaries:

B+P Beatmungsprodukte GmbH (1)
Talstrasse 16
Neunkirchen-Seelscheid, 53819 Wurzburg, Germany
Tel.: (49) 224792160
Fax: (49) 22476733
E-Mail: info@b-und-p.com
Web Site: www.b-und-p.com
Medical Dental & Hospital Equipment & Supplies Whslr
S.I.C.: 5047
N.A.I.C.S.: 423450

Coltene / Whaledent GmbH + Co. KG (1)
Raiffeisenstrasse 30
89129 Langenau, Baden-Wurttemberg, Germany
Tel.: (49) 7345 805 0
Fax: (49) 7345 805 201
E-Mail: info@coltenewhaledent.de
Web Site: www.coltene.com
Emp.: 100
Dental Equipment Mfr
S.I.C.: 3843
N.A.I.C.S.: 339114
Werner Mannsehedel *(Mng Dir)*

U.S. Subsidiary:

Endodent Inc (2)
851 Meridian St
Duarte, CA 91010-3588 CA
Tel.: (626) 359-5715
Fax: (626) 303-1844
Dental Equipment Distr
S.I.C.: 5047
N.A.I.C.S.: 423450

Coltene / Whaledent Ltd (1)
The President Ste A Kendal House
Burgess Hill, West Sussex, RH15 9NF, United Kingdom
Tel.: (44) 1444235486
Fax: (44) 1444870640
E-Mail: info@coltenewhaledent.co.uk
Web Site: www.coltene.com
Emp.: 11
Dental Equipment Mfr
S.I.C.: 3843
N.A.I.C.S.: 339114
Karen Sewell *(Gen Mgr)*

Coltene / Whaledent Private Limited (1)
106/107 Hallmark Vasant Oscar LBS Marg
Mulund West, Mumbai, Maharashtra, 400080, India
Tel.: (91) 2225923626
Fax: (91) 2225623165
E-Mail: infoindia@coltenewhaledent.com
Dental Supplies Distr
S.I.C.: 5047
N.A.I.C.S.: 423450

Dentalia Kft (1)
Akacfa Utca 86
2060 Bicske, Fejer, Hungary
Tel.: (36) 22261159
Fax: (36) 22350139
Dental Equipment Mfr
S.I.C.: 3843
N.A.I.C.S.: 339114

COLTERRA CAPITAL CORPORATION

5100 De Maisonneuve Boulevard West Suite RC-08
Montreal, QC, H4A 3T2, Canada
Tel.: (514) 487-1515
Fax: (514) 487-0185
Web Site: www.colterracapital.com

Business Description:
Real Estate Investment Services
S.I.C.: 6211
N.A.I.C.S.: 523999

Personnel:
Richard Glickman *(Chm & CEO)*
Robert Berger *(Pres)*

COLTSTAR VENTURES INC.

1680 200 Burrard Street
Vancouver, BC, Canada V6C 3L6
Tel.: (604) 683-8236
Fax: (604) 683-3685
E-Mail: info@ColtstarVentures.com
Web Site: www.coltstarventures.com
Year Founded: 2007
CTR—(TSXV)

Sales Range: Less than $1 Million
Business Description:
Mineral Exploration Services
S.I.C.: 1081
N.A.I.C.S.: 213114
Personnel:
Damien Reynolds *(Chm, Pres & CEO)*
Garry Stock *(CFO)*
Board of Directors:
Damien Reynolds
Adrian Rolke
Peter Russell-Jones
Garry Stock
Transfer Agent:
Computershare Investor Services Inc.
100 University Ave 9th Floor
Toronto, ON, Canada

COLUMBIA CHRYSLER DODGE JEEP LTD.
5840 Minoru Boulevard
Richmond, BC, V6X 2A9, Canada
Tel.: (604) 273-8018
Fax: (604) 273-4149
Toll Free: (888) 265-5829
Web Site: www.columbiachryslerdodge.com
Year Founded: 1967
Sales Range: $25-49.9 Million
Emp.: 78
Business Description:
New & Used Car Dealer
S.I.C.: 5511
N.A.I.C.S.: 441110
Personnel:
Bob Hewitt *(Gen Mgr)*

COLUMBIA DBL (PTY) LIMITED
Waggie Rd
PO Box 287
Blackheath, Cape Town, Western Cape, 7581, South Africa
Tel.: (27) 219051665
Fax: (27) 219054049
E-Mail: info@columbiadbl.com
Web Site: www.columbiadbl.com
Emp.: 190
Business Description:
Masonry Bricks & Blocks Mfr
S.I.C.: 3271
N.A.I.C.S.: 327331
Personnel:
Luke Wightman *(Mng Dir)*

COLUMBIA DODGE 1967 LTD.
(See Under Columbia Chrysler Dodge Jeep Ltd.)

COLUMBIA MANUFACTURING CO LTD.
4575 Tillicum St
Burnaby, BC, V5J 3J9, Canada
Tel.: (604) 437-3377
Fax: (604) 437-4443
Toll Free: (888) 437-5557
E-Mail: info@columbiaskylights.com
Web Site: www.columbiaskylights.com
Year Founded: 1955
Sales Range: $10-24.9 Million
Emp.: 100
Fiscal Year-end: 12/31/12
Business Description:
Flat Glasses Mfr
S.I.C.: 3211
N.A.I.C.S.: 327211
Personnel:
Mike Williams *(Pres)*

COLUMBIA YUKON EXPLORATIONS INC.
2489 Bellevue Avenue
Vancouver, BC, V7V 1E1, Canada
Tel.: (604) 922-2030
Fax: (604) 922-2037
E-Mail: info@waterfrontgroup.com
Web Site: www.columbiayukon.com
Year Founded: 1984
CYU—(TSXV)
Rev.: $31,504
Assets: $16,225,871
Liabilities: $109,853
Net Worth: $16,116,017
Earnings: ($1,141,835)
Fiscal Year-end: 04/30/13
Business Description:
Mineral Exploration Services
S.I.C.: 1081
N.A.I.C.S.: 213114
Personnel:
Douglas L. Mason *(Chm & CEO)*
Ronald A. Coombes *(Pres)*
Sead Hamzagic *(CFO)*
Board of Directors:
Douglas L. Mason
Benjamin Ainsworth
Ronald A. Coombes
Sead Hamzagic
Andrzej Kowalski
Bruce E. Morley
Edward Alfred Yurkowski
Legal Counsel:
McCullough O'Connor Irwin
Suite 2610 Ocean Plaza 1066 West Hastings St
Vancouver, BC, Canada
Transfer Agent:
Computershare Trust Company of Canada
510 Burrard St 3rd Fl
Vancouver, BC, V6C 3B9, Canada

COLUMBUS A/S
Lautrupvang 6
DK- 2750 Ballerup, Denmark
Tel.: (45) 70 20 50 00
Web Site: www.columbusglobal.com
COLUM—(OMX)
Rev.: $160,972,202
Assets: $90,190,461
Liabilities: $39,593,529
Net Worth: $50,596,932
Earnings: $26,152
Emp.: 879
Fiscal Year-end: 12/31/12
Business Description:
Software Development & Services
S.I.C.: 7372
N.A.I.C.S.: 511210
Personnel:
Ib Kunoe *(Chm)*
Jorgen Cadovius *(Deputy Chm)*
Thomas Honore *(CEO)*
Hans Henrik Thrane *(CFO)*
Board of Directors:
Ib Kunoe
Jorgen Cadovius
Peter Skov Hansen
Ulla Krossteig
Sven Madsen
U.S. Subsidiary:

First Tech Direct, LLC **(1)**
26622 Woodward Ave
Royal Oak, MI 48067
Tel.: (248) 291-0138
Web Site: www.firsttechdirect.com
Sales Range: $1-9.9 Million
Emp.: 30
Custom Computer Programming Services
S.I.C.: 7371
N.A.I.C.S.: 541511
Mark LaBelle *(Pres & Co-Founder)*

COLUMBUS COPPER CORPORATION
(Formerly Empire Mining Corporation)
1090 Hamilton Street
Vancouver, BC, V6B 2R9, Canada
Tel.: (604) 634-0970
Fax: (604) 634-0971
Toll Free: (888) 818-1364
E-Mail: info@columbusgroup.com
Web Site: www.columbuscopper.com
Year Founded: 2005
CCU—(TSXV)
Int. Income: $518
Assets: $11,232,160
Liabilities: $423,542
Net Worth: $10,808,618
Earnings: ($1,781,220)
Fiscal Year-end: 05/31/13
Business Description:
Mineral Exploration Services
S.I.C.: 1081
N.A.I.C.S.: 213114
Personnel:
Robert Giustra *(Chm)*
David Cliff *(Pres & CEO)*
Akbar Hassanally *(CFO)*
Damyan Hristov *(COO)*
James Isaac *(Sec & VP-Legal)*
Board of Directors:
Robert Giustra
Nicholas Clarke
David Cliff
Michael David Johnson
Legal Counsel:
McMillan LLP
Suite 1500 1055 W Georgia Street
Vancouver, BC, Canada
Transfer Agent:
Computershare Investor Services Inc.
3rd Floor 510 Burrard St
V6C 3B9 Vancouver, BC, Canada

COLUMBUS ENERGY LIMITED
808 Nelson Street Suite 2103
Vancouver, BC, V6Z 2H2, Canada
Tel.: (604) 684-7619
Fax: (604) 684-7346
E-Mail: info@columbusenergy.ca
Web Site: www.columbusenergy.ca
CEL—(TSXV)
Assets: $14,930
Liabilities: $304,370
Net Worth: ($289,440)
Earnings: ($513,770)
Emp.: 3
Fiscal Year-end: 12/31/12
Business Description:
Oil & Gas Exploration Services
S.I.C.: 1311
N.A.I.C.S.: 211111
Personnel:
Bob Laslett *(Chm)*
Paul A. Ray *(CEO)*
Douglas W. Scheving *(CFO & Sec)*
William M. Houston *(COO)*
Board of Directors:
Bob Laslett
Jack N. BesMargian
William M. Houston
Paul A. Ray
Douglas W. Scheving
Legal Counsel:
DuMoulin Black LLP
10th Floor 595 Howe St
Vancouver, BC, Canada
Transfer Agent:
Computershare Investor Services Inc.
3rd Floor 510 Burrard Street
Vancouver, BC, Canada

COLUMBUS GOLD CORPORATION
475 Howe Street Suite 910
Vancouver, BC, V6C 2B3, Canada
Tel.: (604) 689-2599
Fax: (604) 689-3609
Toll Free: (866) 869-2599
E-Mail: info@columbusgoldcorp.com
Web Site: www.columbusgoldcorp.com
Year Founded: 2003
CGT—(OTC TSXV)
Sales Range: Less than $1 Million
Emp.: 10
Business Description:
Gold Mining Services
S.I.C.: 1041
N.A.I.C.S.: 212221
Personnel:
Robert Giustra *(Chm & CEO)*
Andy B. Wallace *(Pres)*
Akbar Hassanally *(CFO)*
Rock Lefrancois *(COO)*
Joel Schuster *(Sec & VP-Legal)*
Board of Directors:
Robert Giustra
Gil Atzmon
Peter Gianulis
Donald Gustafson
Legal Counsel:
McMillan LLP
Suite 1500 1055 W Georgia Street
Vancouver, BC, Canada
Transfer Agent:
Computershare Trust Company of Canada
Suite 200 510 Burrard Street
Vancouver, BC, Canada
U.S. Subsidiary:

Columbus Gold (U.S.) Corporation **(1)**
573 E 2nd St
Reno, NV 89502
Tel.: (775) 324-1226
Fax: (775) 324-4811
Web Site: www.columbusgoldcorp.com
Emp.: 4
Gold Mining Services
S.I.C.: 1041
N.A.I.C.S.: 212221
Andy Wallace *(Gen Mgr)*

COLUMBUS SILVER CORPORATION
1090 Hamilton Street
Vancouver, BC, V6B 2R9, Canada
Tel.: (604) 634-0970
Fax: (604) 634-0971
Toll Free: (888) 818-1364
E-Mail: info@columbussilvercorp.com
Web Site: www.columbussilvercorp.com
Year Founded: 2007
CSC—(TSXV)
Assets: $2,993,075
Liabilities: $424,548
Net Worth: $2,568,527
Earnings: ($873,461)
Emp.: 15
Fiscal Year-end: 09/30/12
Business Description:
Silver Mining Services
S.I.C.: 1044
N.A.I.C.S.: 212222
Personnel:
Robert F. Giustra *(Pres & CEO)*
Akbar Hassanally *(CFO)*
Joel Schuster *(Sec & VP-Legal)*
Drew Clark *(Sr VP)*
Board of Directors:
Gil Atzmon
Robert F. Giustra
Jim Greig
Donald Gustafson
Legal Counsel:
McMillan LLP
1500 1055 West Georgia Street
V6E4N7 Vancouver, BC, Canada
Transfer Agent:
Computershare Trust Company of Canada
Suite 200 510 Burrard Street
Vancouver, BC, Canada

COM DEV INTERNATIONAL LTD.

155 Sheldon Drive
Cambridge, ON, N1R 7H6, Canada
Tel.: (519) 622-2300
Fax: (519) 622-1691
E-Mail: investor.relations@comdev.ca
Web Site: www.comdev.ca
CDV—(OTC TSX)
Rev.: $208,085,841
Assets: $260,429,329
Liabilities: $79,614,264
Net Worth: $180,815,065
Earnings: $13,944,694
Emp.: 1,282
Fiscal Year-end: 10/31/12

Business Description:
Space & Ground-Based Wireless Communications Products & Subsystems Mfr
S.I.C.: 4812
N.A.I.C.S.: 517210

Personnel:
Terry Reidel *(Chm)*
Peter Scovell *(Vice Chm)*
Michael Pley *(CEO)*
Gary Calhoun *(CFO)*
David Lizius *(Pres-Canada)*
Peter Mabson *(Pres-exactEarth Ltd)*
Rob Spurrett *(Pres-Europe)*
Dan White *(Pres-USA)*
Michael Williams *(Pres-Intl Products)*

Board of Directors:
Terry Reidel
James C. Adamson
Kym Anthony
Roberta Bondar
David F. Masotti
Christopher O'Donovan
Michael Pley
Peter Scovell

Legal Counsel:
Gardiner Roberts LLP
Toronto, ON, Canada

Transfer Agent:
Computershare Trust Company of Canada
9th Floor 100 University Avenue
Toronto, ON, Canada

Subsidiaries:

COM DEV Limited (1)
155 Sheldon Dr
Cambridge, ON, N1R 7H6, Canada
Tel.: (519) 622-2300
Fax: (519) 622-1691
Space Communications Products Mfr
S.I.C.: 3663
N.A.I.C.S.: 334220

COM DEV Space (1)
155 Sheldon Dr
Cambridge, ON, N1R 7H6, Canada (100%)
Tel.: (519) 622-2300
Fax: (519) 622-1691
Web Site: www.comdev.ca
Emp.: 800
Space-Qualified Microwave, Electronic & Battery Subsystems Mfr for Communications & Science Satellites
S.I.C.: 3669
N.A.I.C.S.: 334290
Michael Pley *(CEO)*

U.S. Subsidiary:

COM DEV USA LLC (1)
2333 Utah Ave
El Segundo, CA 90245
Tel.: (424) 456-8000
Fax: (424) 456-8001
Web Site: www.comdevusa.com
Microwave Equipment Mfr
S.I.C.: 3663
N.A.I.C.S.: 334220

Non-U.S. Subsidiary:

COM DEV Europe Limited (1)
Triangle Bus Pk
Stoke Mandeville, Aylesbury, Bucks, HP225SX, United Kingdom
Tel.: (44) 1296616400
Fax: (44) 1296616500
E-Mail: info@comdev.co.uk
Web Site: www.comdev.co.uk
Emp.: 80
Electronic Component Mfr
S.I.C.: 3679
N.A.I.C.S.: 334419
Rob Sturrett *(Pres)*

COMARCH S.A.

Al Jana Pawla II 39a
31-864 Krakow, Poland
Tel.: (48) 126461000
Fax: (48) 126461100
E-Mail: info@comarch.pl
Web Site: www.comarch.com
CMR—(WAR)
Rev.: $280,303,596
Assets: $363,666,608
Liabilities: $165,478,751
Net Worth: $198,187,856
Earnings: $11,813,727
Emp.: 3,759
Fiscal Year-end: 12/31/12

Business Description:
Information Technology Solutions & Services
S.I.C.: 7372
N.A.I.C.S.: 511210

Personnel:
Janusz Filipiak *(Founder, Pres, CEO & Member-Mgmt Bd)*
Elzbieta Filipiak *(Chm-Supervisory Bd)*
Maciej Brzezinski *(Deputy Chm-Supervisory Bd)*
Konrad Taranski *(CFO, Member-Mgmt Bd & VP)*
Zbigniew Rymarczyk *(Member-Mgmt Bd, VP & Dir-ERP Bus Unit)*
Marcin Warwas *(Member-Mgmt Bd, VP & Dir-Svcs Bus)*
Piotr Piatosa *(Member-Mgmt Bd & VP)*
Pawel Prokop *(Member-Mgmt Bd & VP)*
Piotr Reichert *(Member-Mgmt Bd & VP)*

Supervisory Board of Directors:
Elzbieta Filipiak
Maciej Brzezinski
Danuta Drobniak
Wojciech Kucharzyk
Anna Lawrynowicz
Anna Pruska

Subsidiaries:

CA Consulting SA (1)
Jerozolimskie 81
02-001 Warsaw, Masovian, Poland
Tel.: (48) 126461000
Fax: (48) 126461100
Computer Software Consulting Services
S.I.C.: 7371
N.A.I.C.S.: 541511

iComarch24 SA (1)
al Jana Pawla II 41e
31-864 Krakow, Lesser Poland, Poland
Tel.: (48) 12 684 88 80
Fax: (48) 12 684 81 00
E-Mail: help@ibard24.com
Web Site: www.ibard24.com
Data Protection & Security Services
S.I.C.: 7376
N.A.I.C.S.: 541513

iFIN24 SA (1)
al Jana Pawla II 39a
31-864 Krakow, Lesser Poland, Poland
Tel.: (48) 12 68488 51
Fax: (48) 12 64611 00
E-Mail: helpdesk@ifin24.pl
Web Site: www.ifin24.pl
Financial Management Services
S.I.C.: 6099
N.A.I.C.S.: 522320

iReward24 SA (1)
Aleja Jana Pawla II 39A
31-864 Krakow, Lesser Poland, Poland
Tel.: (48) 126877000
Fax: (48) 12 687 71 00
E-Mail: info@iReward24.pl
Web Site: www.ireward24.com
Software Development & Consulting Services
S.I.C.: 7373
N.A.I.C.S.: 541512

Non-U.S. Subsidiaries:

Comarch AG (1)
Chemnitzer Str 50
01187 Dresden, Hesse, Germany
Tel.: (49) 35132013200
Fax: (49) 3514389710
E-Mail: info@comarch.de
Web Site: www.comarch.de
Emp.: 100
Information Technology Consulting Services
S.I.C.: 8742
N.A.I.C.S.: 541611
Catherine Bania *(CEO)*

Comarch R&D S.A.R.L. (1)
100A Allee Saint-Exupery
38330 Montbonnot-Saint-Martin, Isere, France
Tel.: (33) 457582300
E-Mail: comarch_rd_grenoble@comarch.com
Web Site: www.comarch.com
Software Development & Consulting Services
S.I.C.: 7371
N.A.I.C.S.: 541511

Comarch Schilling GmbH (1)
Anne-Conway-Strasse 2
28359 Bremen, Germany
Tel.: (49) 421201400
Fax: (49) 42120140140
E-Mail: info@comarch.com
Emp.: 30
Software Development & Consulting Services
S.I.C.: 7371
N.A.I.C.S.: 541511
Jens Goedel *(Mgr)*

Comarch Software S.A.R.L. (1)
19 avenue Le Corbusier
59000 Lille, Nord, France
Tel.: (33) 362534900
Fax: (33) 365244694
E-Mail: contact@lille.fr
Web Site: www.comarch.com
Emp.: 31
Software Development & Consulting Services
S.I.C.: 7371
N.A.I.C.S.: 541511
Arkadiusz Ilgowski *(Mng Dir)*

Comarch Solutions GmbH (1)
Pfalzburger Strasse 43-44
10717 Berlin, Germany
Tel.: (49) 30 7679670
Fax: (49) 30 767967 1467
E-Mail: info@comarch.com
Web Site: www.comarch.com
Software Development & Consulting Services
S.I.C.: 7371
N.A.I.C.S.: 541511
Ludwig Ametsbichler *(Co-Mng Dir)*
Piotr Piatosa *(Co-Mng Dir)*

Comarch Solutions GmbH (1)
Messerschmitt Str 4
Munich, Bayern, 80992, Germany
Tel.: (49) 89143290
Fax: (49) 89143291114
E-Mail: info@comarch.com.ge
Web Site: www.comarch.com
Emp.: 50
Software Development & Consulting Services
S.I.C.: 7371
N.A.I.C.S.: 541511
Lukasz Wasek *(Mng Dir)*

Comarch Solutions GmbH (1)
Nussdorfer Laende 23
Vienna, 1190, Austria
Tel.: (43) 1910660
Fax: (43) 19106666
E-Mail: info@comarch.com
Web Site: www.comarch.com
Emp.: 20
Software Development & Consulting Services
S.I.C.: 7371
N.A.I.C.S.: 541511
Janusz Filipiak *(Gen Mgr)*

Comarch Swiss AG (1)
Bahnhofstr 21b
9471 Buchs, St. Gallen, Switzerland
Tel.: (41) 817555500
Fax: (41) 817555501
E-Mail: info@comarch-swiss.ch
Emp.: 25
Software Development & Consulting Services
S.I.C.: 7371
N.A.I.C.S.: 541511
Michael Eberle *(Co-Mng Dir)*

Comarch Vietnam Co. Ltd. (1)
No 128 Nguyen Phi Khanh Street Tan Dinh Ward District 1
Ho Chi Minh City, Vietnam
Tel.: (84) 838206218
E-Mail: Comarch_vn@comarch.com
Software Development & Consulting Services
S.I.C.: 7371
N.A.I.C.S.: 541511

OOO Comarch (1)
Bakhrushina Street 32 build 1
115054 Moscow, Russia
Tel.: (7) 4952218901
E-Mail: finance@comarch.ru
Web Site: www.comarch.com
Software Development & Consulting Services
S.I.C.: 7371
N.A.I.C.S.: 541511

COMARGROS SA

Str Depozitelor Nr 17
Pitesti, Romania
Tel.: (40) 248 217201
Fax: (40) 248 217702
CORE—(BUC)
Rev.: $1,514,883
Assets: $4,531,898
Liabilities: $88,577
Net Worth: $4,443,321
Earnings: $81,945
Emp.: 26
Fiscal Year-end: 12/31/12

Business Description:
Food, Beverages & Tobacco Distr
S.I.C.: 5149
N.A.I.C.S.: 424490

Personnel:
Stefan Osiac *(Pres)*

COMAT AUTO SA

90 Timisoara Blvd Sector 6
061334 Bucharest, Romania
Tel.: (40) 21 4440223
Fax: (40) 21 4440918
E-Mail: office@comat-auto.ro
Web Site: www.comat-auto.ro
COTA—(BUC)
Sales Range: $1-9.9 Million
Emp.: 68

Business Description:
Motor Vehicle Parts & Accessories Distr
S.I.C.: 5013
N.A.I.C.S.: 423120

Personnel:
Eugen Stanculescu *(Pres)*

COMAT SA

Str Vilior 15
Alexandria, Romania
Tel.: (40) 247 314190
Fax: (40) 247 315296
COAD—(BUC)

Business Description:
Wood, Construction Materials & Sanitary Equipment Distr
S.I.C.: 5031
N.A.I.C.S.: 423310

Personnel:
Georgeta Iordan *(Pres)*

COMAT TECHNOLOGIES (P) LTD.

No 333 Nova Miller Thimmaiah Road
Vasanth Nagar, Bengaluru, 560052, India
Tel.: (91) 8022343000
E-Mail: info@comat.com
Web Site: www.comat.com
Year Founded: 1995
Sales Range: $1-9.9 Million
Business Description:
Business Consulting, Technology Integration, Back Office & Field Services to the Government, Public & Private Sectors
S.I.C.: 8742
N.A.I.C.S.: 541611
Personnel:
Sriram Raghavan *(Co-Founder & CEO)*
Shashi K. Patil *(COO)*
Board of Directors:
Sriram Raghavan
Ravi Rangan

Non-U.S. Subsidiary:

Comat Europe (1)
Eerste Helmersstraat 267 H
1054 DZ Amsterdam, Netherlands
Tel.: (31) 20 4123881
Fax: (31) 20 4120034
E-Mail: info.europe@comat.com
Business Consultants
S.I.C.: 8742
N.A.I.C.S.: 541611

U.S. Subsidiary:

Comat Technologies, Inc. (1)
14716 Maine Cove Terr Ste B
North Potomac, MD 20878
Tel.: (240) 498-5453
Fax: (201) 762-0377
E-Mail: info.usa@comat.com
Business Consultants
S.I.C.: 8742
N.A.I.C.S.: 541611

COMBA TELECOM SYSTEMS HOLDINGS LIMITED

611 East Wing No.8 Science Park
West Avenue Hong Kong Science Park
Hong Kong, China (Hong Kong)
Tel.: (852) 26366861
Fax: (852) 26370966
E-Mail: comba@comba-telecom.com
Web Site: www.comba-telecom.com
2342—(HKG)
Rev.: $816,623,200
Assets: $1,301,326,133
Liabilities: $803,300,730
Net Worth: $498,025,403
Earnings: ($27,807,423)
Emp.: 9,900
Fiscal Year-end: 12/31/12
Business Description:
Holding Company; Wireless Telecommunications Infrastructure & Services
S.I.C.: 6719
N.A.I.C.S.: 551112
Personnel:
Tung Ling Fok *(Chm)*
Yue Jun Zhang *(Vice Chm & Pres)*
Jiang Cheng Wu *(Sr VP-Mktg & Sls-PRC)*
Ji Ci Yan *(Sr VP-Production Ops)*
Simon Pui Sang Yeung *(Sr VP-Strategy & Ops-Intl)*
Yuan Jian Zhang *(Sr VP)*
Board of Directors:
Tung Ling Fok
Kevin Siu Ki Lau
Jin Tong Lin
Cai Liu
Ting Shuo Qian
Wilson Chak Wai Tong
Jiang Cheng Wu
Ji Ci Yan
Simon Pui Sang Yeung
Yuan Jian Zhang
Yue Jun Zhang
Guo Bao Zheng

Computershare Hong Kong Investor Services Limited
Shops 1712-1716 17th Floor Hopewell Centre
183 Queens Road East
Wanchai, China (Hong Kong)

Transfer Agents:
Royal Bank of Canada Trust Company (Cayman) Limited
4th Floor Royal Bank House 24 Shedden Road
Georgetown, Cayman Islands

Computershare Hong Kong Investor Services Limited
Shops 1712-1716 17th Floor Hopewell Centre
183 Queens Road East
Wanchai, China (Hong Kong)

U.S. Subsidiaries:

Comba Telecom Inc. (1)
2390 Bering Dr
San Jose, CA 95131-1121
Tel.: (408) 526-0180
Web Site: www.comba-telecom.com
Wireless Systems Mfr
S.I.C.: 3825
N.A.I.C.S.: 334515

WaveLab Inc. (1)
12007 Sunrise Valley Dr Ste 350
Reston, VA 20191-3489 (100%)
Tel.: (703) 860-3522
Fax: (703) 860-3599
E-Mail: info@wavelab.com
Web Site: www.wavelab.com
Emp.: 100
Other Computer Peripheral Equipment Mfr
S.I.C.: 3575
N.A.I.C.S.: 334118

Non-U.S. Subsidiaries:

Comba Telecom Co. Ltd. (1)
3rd Floor T Shinawatra Building 94
Sukhumvit Road
Klongtoeynua Wattana, Bangkok, 10110, Thailand (100%)
Tel.: (66) 26643440
Fax: (66) 26643442
E-Mail: eric@comba-telecom.com.th
Web Site: www.comba-telecom.com.th
Emp.: 4
Cellular & Other Wireless Telecommunications
S.I.C.: 4812
N.A.I.C.S.: 517210
Eric Ng *(Gen Mgr)*

Comba Telecom India Private Limited (1)
E 172 Greater Kailash Part I
New Delhi, 110048, India
Tel.: (91) 11 4173 9997
Fax: (91) 11 4173 9996
Web Site: www.comba-telecom.com
Telecommunications Equipment Mfr
S.I.C.: 3663
N.A.I.C.S.: 334220
Rajiv Girotra *(Gen Mgr)*

Comba Telecom Ltda (1)
Avenida Engenheiro Luiz Carlos Berrini 1297 cj 122
Brooklin Novo, 04571-090 Sao Paulo, Brazil
Tel.: (55) 11 3509 3700
Fax: (55) 11 3509 3720
Web Site: www.comba-telecom.com
Emp.: 4
Telecommunications Equipment Mfr
S.I.C.: 3661
N.A.I.C.S.: 334210
Johnny Prito *(Mgr)*

Comba Telecom Systems Limited (1)
611 East Wing No 8 Science Park West Avenue
Hong Kong, China (Hong Kong)
Tel.: (852) 26366861
Fax: (852) 2637 0966
E-Mail: comba@comba-telecom.com
Web Site: www.comba-telecom.com
Emp.: 60
Wireless Telecommunication Services
S.I.C.: 4813
N.A.I.C.S.: 517911
Milenda Ip *(Mgr-HR)*

Comba Telecom Systems (Singapore) Pte. Ltd. (1)
No1 kaki Bukit Ziew Unit 3 02-10 Techview
415941 Singapore, 415941, Singapore (100%)
Tel.: (65) 63454908
Fax: (65) 63451186
E-Mail: serene.liow@comba-telecom.com
Web Site: www.comba-telecom.com
Emp.: 200
Other Electronic Parts & Equipment Whslr
S.I.C.: 5065
N.A.I.C.S.: 423690
Ongsing Gye *(Mng Dir)*

Comba Telecom Technology (Guangzhou) Limited (1)
10 Shenzhou Rd
Guangzhou, Guangdong, China (100%)
Tel.: (86) 2028390000
Fax: (86) 2028390136
Web Site: www.comba.com.cn/get_content.aspx?channelID=8&ClassID=74
Other Communications Equipment Mfr
S.I.C.: 3669
N.A.I.C.S.: 334290

Comban Telecom Systems AB (1)
Gustavslundsvagen 147 Bromma
16751 Stockholm, Sweden (100%)
Tel.: (46) 8253870
Fax: (46) 8253871
Web Site: www.comba-telecom.com
Other Electronic Parts & Equipment Whslr
S.I.C.: 5065
N.A.I.C.S.: 423690

COMBAT DRUGS LIMITED

203 Kabra Complex 61 M G Road
Secunderabad, Andhra Pradesh, 500003, India
Tel.: (91) 40 39818888
E-Mail: enquiry@combatdrugs.in
Web Site: www.combatdrugs.in
Year Founded: 1986
524752—(BOM)
Rev.: $102,886
Assets: $1,608,637
Liabilities: $150,632
Net Worth: $1,458,005
Earnings: ($26,089)
Fiscal Year-end: 03/31/13
Business Description:
Pharmaceutical Product Mfr
S.I.C.: 2834
N.A.I.C.S.: 325412
Personnel:
Suchit Mohan Lal *(Mng Dir)*
Board of Directors:
Anjani Kumar Agarwal
Sanjay Kumar Agarwal
Suchit Mohan Lal
Sushant Mohan Lal
S. S. Marthi
Battula Narasimha Gnana Prakash
Transfer Agent:
Venture Capital & Corporate Investments Private Limited
12-10-167 Bharat Nagar
500018 Hyderabad, India

COMBI CORPORATION

6-7 Motoasakusa 2-Chome
Tokyo, 111-0041, Japan
Tel.: (81) 358287666
Fax: (81) 358287665
E-Mail: info@combi.co.jp
Web Site: www.combi.co.jp
Year Founded: 1957
Sales Range: $250-299.9 Million
Emp.: 247
Business Description:
Children's Products, Toys, Games, Exercise Machines, Home Health Apparatus & Medical Devices Mfr, Developer, Seller & Licenser
Export
S.I.C.: 3944
N.A.I.C.S.: 339930
Personnel:
Yasuo Matsuura *(Chm)*
Hiromasa Matsuura *(Pres & CEO)*
Sei Kasai *(Sr Mng Exec Officer)*
Michita Kinoshita *(Sr Mng Exec Officer)*
Board of Directors:
Yasuo Matsuura
Yoshichika Horino
Sei Kasai
Michita Kinoshita
Noboru Kotani

Subsidiaries:

CombiNext Corporation (1)
2-6-7 Moto-Asakusa
Taito-ku, Tokyo, 111 0041, Japan JP
Tel.: (81) 487971000 (100%)
Fax: (81) 48 798 6109
Development, Production & Sales of Baby Wear & Baby Bedding
S.I.C.: 2389
N.A.I.C.S.: 315240
Hiromasa Matsuura *(Pres)*

CombiWith Corporation (1)
2-6-7 Motoasakusa
Taito-ku, Tokyo, 111-0041, Japan (100%)
Tel.: (81) 358287631
Fax: (81) 358287630
E-Mail: t.mori@combiwith.co.jp
Web Site: www.combiwith.co.jp/biz/english/company/index.html
Emp.: 332
Sporting & Recreational Goods & Supplies Whslr
S.I.C.: 5091
N.A.I.C.S.: 423910
Ichiro Suzuki *(Pres)*

U.S. Subsidiary:

Combi USA, Inc. (1)
1962 Hwy 160 W Ste 100
Fort Mill, SC 29708-8027 (100%)
Tel.: (803) 548-6633
Fax: (803) 548-3663
Toll Free: (800) 992-6624
Web Site: www.combi-intl.com
Mfr & Marketer of Baby Products
S.I.C.: 5099
N.A.I.C.S.: 423990
Sei Kasai *(Chm)*

Non-U.S. Subsidiaries:

Combi Asia Limited (1)
Room 1003 10th Floor HK Pacific Center
Kowloon, China (Hong Kong) (100%)
Tel.: (852) 23662899
Fax: (852) 27240074
E-Mail: marketing@gobal.combi.co.jp
Web Site: www.combi.com.hk
Emp.: 60
Baby Products Whslr
S.I.C.: 5099
N.A.I.C.S.: 423990
Season Ip *(Mgr-Mktg)*

Non-U.S. Subsidiaries:

Combi Korea Co., Ltd. (2)
1805 Tower 2 No 3
Seongsu-gu, Seoul, Korea (South)
Tel.: (82) 24990872
Fax: (82) 8224990875
E-Mail: combi@combikorea.co.kr
Web Site: www.combi.co.kr
Emp.: 20
Baby Products Retailer
S.I.C.: 5641
N.A.I.C.S.: 448130
Takayuki Fujieda *(Chm)*

Combi (Taiwan) Co., Ltd. (2)
6F 6 Lane 360 Nei Hu Road Sec 1
Taipei, 11493, Taiwan
Tel.: (886) 226578822

Combi Corporation—(Continued)

Fax: (886) 226578685
Web Site: www.combi.com.tw
Baby Products Sales & Marketing
S.I.C.: 5092
N.A.I.C.S.: 423920
Yasuo Matsuura *(Chm)*

Ningbo Combi Baby Goods Co., Ltd **(2)**
No Cs4-1 Yuandong Industrial City
Yuyao, Ningbo, China (100%)
Tel.: (86) 57462729051
Web Site: www.combi.co.jp/en/company/group_e.htm
Baby Products Mfr
S.I.C.: 3942
N.A.I.C.S.: 339930
Kuo Che Cheng *(Chm)*

Combi (Shanghai) Co., Ltd. **(1)**
Huaihai Financial Mansion 23F No 200
Huaihai Zhong Road
Shanghai, 200021, China
Tel.: (86) 2163852688
Fax: (86) 2163858885
E-Mail: service@combi.com.cn
Web Site: www.combi.com.cn
Emp.: 200
Baby Products Sales & Marketing
S.I.C.: 5092
N.A.I.C.S.: 423920

COMBINE WILL INTERNATIONAL HOLDINGS LIMITED

Room 901-3 Block 4 Tai Ping Industrial Centre
51A Ting Kok Road, Tai Po, NT, China (Hong Kong)
Tel.: (852) 2665 1678
Fax: (852) 2665 6304
E-Mail: ir@combinewill.com
Web Site: www.combinewill.com
N02—(SES)
Rev.: $196,849,267
Assets: $176,030,419
Liabilities: $92,207,116
Net Worth: $83,823,303
Earnings: $4,448,904
Emp.: 10,000
Fiscal Year-end: 12/31/12

Business Description:
Holding Company; Plastic & Die-Cast Products Mfr
S.I.C.: 6719
N.A.I.C.S.: 551112

Personnel:
Dominic Jo Tak Tam *(Chm & CEO)*
Alan Hung Leung Tsang *(CFO & Co-Sec)*
Kevin Ka Keung Miu *(Chief Supervisory Officer)*
Joo Khin Ng *(Co-Sec)*

Board of Directors:
Dominic Jo Tak Tam
Alexander Hok Fung Cheung
Jack Seng Hee Chia
Simon Hau Shun Chiu
Li Ning
John Hing Wah Yau
Koulman Naiqiao Zheng

Transfer Agent:
Boardroom Corporate & Advisory Services Pte. Ltd.
50 Raffles Place 32-01 Singapore Land Tower
Singapore, Singapore

COMBINED GROUP CONTRACTING COMPANY KSCC

Block No 2 Plot No 284 Al Ardiya Industrial Area
Kuwait, Kuwait
Tel.: (965) 22254545
Fax: (965) 24344610
E-Mail: info@cgc-kw.com
Web Site: www.cgc-kw.com
Year Founded: 1965
CGC—(KUW)
Rev.: $626,375,000
Assets: $613,598,356
Liabilities: $455,950,437
Net Worth: $157,647,919
Earnings: $37,906,555
Emp.: 6,582
Fiscal Year-end: 12/31/12

Business Description:
Mechanical, Sanitary & Building Construction Contractor
S.I.C.: 1799
N.A.I.C.S.: 238190

Personnel:
Abdul Rahman Mousa Al Ma'rouf *(Chm & Mng Dir)*
Raad Khalaf Al Abdullah *(Vice Chm)*

Board of Directors:
Abdul Rahman Mousa Al Ma'rouf
Raad Khalaf Al Abdullah
Ahmad Khalid Ahmad Al Homaizi
Emad Ahmad Al Houti
Ma'rouf Abdul Rahman Al Ma'rouf
Mousa Ahmad Al Ma'rouf
Sulaiman Abdul Rahman Al Ma'rouf

COMBINED MOTOR HOLDINGS LIMITED

1 Wilton Crescent Umhlanga Ridge
4319 Durban, South Africa

Mailing Address:
PO Box 1033
Umhlanga Rocks, 4320 Durban, South Africa
Tel.: (27) 315804200
Fax: (27) 315804280
E-Mail: cmhinfo@cmh.co.za
Web Site: www.cmh.co.za
CMH—(JSE)
Rev.: $1,002,151,289
Assets: $305,387,465
Liabilities: $217,050,860
Net Worth: $88,336,605
Earnings: $22,778,646
Emp.: 2,840
Fiscal Year-end: 02/28/13

Business Description:
Holding Company; New Car Dealerships
S.I.C.: 6719
N.A.I.C.S.: 551112

Personnel:
Jebb D. McIntosh *(CEO)*
K. Fonseca *(Sec)*

Board of Directors:
Maldwyn Zimmerman
L. C. Zee Cele
Mark P. D. Conway
James S. Dixon
John T. M. Edwards
Stuart K. Jackson
Vusi P. Khanyile
Jebb D. McIntosh
Dineo Molefe

Transfer Agent:
Computershare Investor Services (Pty) Ltd
PO Box 61051
Marshalltown, South Africa

Subsidiaries:

Bonerts (Pty) Ltd **(1)**
11 Corner Barney and Ruven Rd
Johannesburg, Gauteng, 2094, South Africa
Tel.: (27) 115384600
Fax: (27) 115384630
E-Mail: carshop@cmh.co.za
Web Site: www.cmhbonerts.co.za
Emp.: 65
Used Automotives & Parts Retailer
S.I.C.: 5012
N.A.I.C.S.: 423110
Allen Laing *(Mgr-Sls)*

Cmh Autogas Products (Pty) Ltd **(1)**
1 Wilton Crescent
Umhlanga Ridge, Durban, Kwazulu-Natal, 4319, South Africa
Tel.: (27) 315804200
Fax: (27) 315804280
E-Mail: ianidp@cmh.co.za
Web Site: www.cmh.co.za
Emp.: 6
Automotive Gas Conversion Services
S.I.C.: 7538
N.A.I.C.S.: 811111
Jebb Mcintosh *(CEO)*

Cmh Car Hire (Pty) Ltd **(1)**
1st Fl CMH Bldg 206 W St
Durban, Kwazulu-Natal, 4001, South Africa
Tel.: (27) 112309999
Fax: (27) 313358439
E-Mail: reservations@cmh.co.za
Web Site: www.firstcarrental.co.za
Emp.: 383
Car Rental Services
S.I.C.: 7514
N.A.I.C.S.: 532111
Bruce Barritt *(Mng Dir)*

CMH Luxury Motors (Pty) Ltd **(1)**
115 Flanders Dr Mount Edgecombe
Durban, 4300, South Africa
Tel.: (27) 315029800
Fax: (27) 315394705
Web Site: www.autoumhlanga.co.za
Emp.: 200
Automotive Parts Retailer
S.I.C.: 5013
N.A.I.C.S.: 423120
Brent Cole *(Mgr)*

CMH Luxury Motors (Umhlanga) Pty. Ltd **(1)**
115 Flanders Dr
Mount Edgecombe, Durban, Kwazulu-Natal, 4300, South Africa
Tel.: (27) 315029800
Fax: (27) 315394705
Emp.: 100
Car Dealers
S.I.C.: 5511
N.A.I.C.S.: 441110

CMH Marine and Leisure (Pty) Ltd **(1)**
234 Malibongwe Dr
Johannesburg, Gauteng, 2194, South Africa
Tel.: (27) 114624390
Fax: (27) 117041669
Web Site: www.cmhmarineandleisure.co.za
Emp.: 48
Used Boats & Jet Ski Sales
S.I.C.: 5551
N.A.I.C.S.: 441222
Craig Lanham-Love *(COO-MG & Maxus)*

COMCATER PTY. LTD.

156 Swann Dr Derrimut
Melbourne, VIC, 3030, Australia
Tel.: (61) 3 8369 4600
Fax: (61) 3 8369 4666
E-Mail: sales@comcater.com.au
Web Site: www.comcater.com.au
Year Founded: 1979
Sales Range: $25-49.9 Million
Emp.: 60

Business Description:
Food Service Equipment Supplier
S.I.C.: 5049
N.A.I.C.S.: 423490

Personnel:
Michael Wood *(CEO)*
Nancy Mary Wood *(Mng Dir)*

COMCEREAL SA

Str Isaacei nr 73 et 3
Tulcea, Romania
Tel.: (40) 240 534061
Fax: (40) 240 534069
Web Site: www.comcerealtulcea.ro
CTUL—(BUC)
Rev.: $5,227,741
Emp.: 63
Fiscal Year-end: 12/31/12

Business Description:
Storage & Warehousing
S.I.C.: 4225
N.A.I.C.S.: 493110

Personnel:
Emilian-Mihai Niculescu *(Gen Mgr)*

COMDAT DATASYSTEMS AG

Wagistrasse 23
8952 Schlieren, Switzerland
Tel.: (41) 447382424
Fax: (41) 447382434
E-Mail: info@comdat.ch
Web Site: www.comdat.ch
Year Founded: 1988
Sales Range: $10-24.9 Million
Emp.: 72
Fiscal Year-end: 12/31/12

Business Description:
Computer Service & Network Building
S.I.C.: 7379
N.A.I.C.S.: 541519

Subsidiary:

ServiceOne AG **(1)**
Hertistrasse 26
Wallisellen, 8304 Bulach, Switzerland
Tel.: (41) 44 877 73 73
Fax: (41) 44 877 73 70
Information Technology Solutions & Services Specializing in Imaging, Printing & Multimedia; Supplier of Photocopying Machines & Other Imaging Products
S.I.C.: 7373
N.A.I.C.S.: 541512
Andreas Spahni *(Gen mgr)*

COME AND STAY S.A.

22 bis rue des Volontaires
75015 Paris, France
Tel.: (33) 142849696
Fax: (33) 145490029
E-Mail: investisseur@comeandstay.com
Web Site: www.comeandstay.fr
Year Founded: 2000
ALCSY—(EUR)
Sales Range: $25-49.9 Million
Emp.: 144

Business Description:
Email & Mobile Advertising Services
S.I.C.: 7319
N.A.I.C.S.: 541890

Personnel:
Carole Walter *(Chm, CEO & Dir Gen)*

Non-U.S. Subsidiaries:

Come&Stay DKH A/S **(1)**
Lindedej
655220 Odense, Denmark
Tel.: (45) 70260006
Fax: (45) 87345687
E-Mail: info@comeandstay.com
Web Site: www.comeandstay.com
Emp.: 10
Mobile Phone Advertising Services
S.I.C.: 7311
N.A.I.C.S.: 541810
Carol Volta *(Mgr)*

Come&Stay Spain SL. **(1)**
Zurdano 45 1Fl
28010 Madrid, Spain
Tel.: (34) 915343972
Fax: (34) 911853111
E-Mail: ingridveaurin@comeandstay.com
Web Site: www.comeandstay.com
Emp.: 6
Mobile Phone Advertising Services
S.I.C.: 7311
N.A.I.C.S.: 541810

COME SURE GROUP (HOLDINGS) LIMITED

Units 8-10 8th Floor Cornell Centre
50 Wing Tai Road
Chai Wan, China (Hong Kong)
Tel.: (852) 28890310
Fax: (852) 25587474

Web Site: www.comesure.com
0794—(HKG)
Sls.: $98,867,383
Assets: $140,100,564
Liabilities: $64,853,210
Net Worth: $75,247,354
Earnings: $2,170,357
Emp.: 1,702
Fiscal Year-end: 03/31/13

Business Description:
Paper Packaging Industry
S.I.C.: 2631
N.A.I.C.S.: 322130

Personnel:
Kam Chau Chong *(Founder & Chm)*
Wa Pan Chong *(Pres & CEO)*
Dicson Man Yuk Hung *(Sec)*

Board of Directors:
Kam Chau Chong
On Ta Yuen Chau
Wa Ching Chong
Wa Lam Chong
Wa Pan Chong
Tze Lun Law
Pui Man Tsui

Legal Counsel:
Loong & Yeung
Suites 2001 2005 20/F Jardine House 1
Connaught Place
Central, China (Hong Kong)

Guangdong Rongan
Room 704, Block 1 Dongjiang Haoyuan 1
Longjing Road
Baoan District, Shenzhen, China

Appleby
2206-19 Jardine House 1 Connaught Place
Central, China (Hong Kong)

Appleby Trust (Cayman) Ltd.
Clifton House 75 Fort Street
PO Box 1350
Grand Cayman, Cayman Islands

Transfer Agents:
Tricor Investor Services Limited
26th Floor Tesbury Centre 28 Queens Road
East
Wanchai, China (Hong Kong)

Appleby Trust (Cayman) Ltd.
Clifton House 75 Fort Street
PO Box 1350
Grand Cayman, Cayman Islands

COMEAUS SEA FOODS LIMITED

60 Saulnierville Rd
PO Box 39
Saulnierville, NS, B0W 2Z0, Canada
Tel.: (902) 769-2101
Fax: (902) 769-3594
E-Mail: info@comeausea.com
Web Site: www.comeausea.com
Year Founded: 1946
Rev.: $52,000,000
Emp.: 278

Business Description:
Sea Food Products
S.I.C.: 2092
N.A.I.C.S.: 311710

Personnel:
Bernardin J. Comeau *(Co-Founder)*
Clarence Comeau *(Co-Founder)*

COMELF SA

No 4 Industry Street
420063 Bistrita, Romania
Tel.: (40) 263234462
Fax: (40) 263238092
E-Mail: comelf@comelf.ro
Web Site: www.comelf.ro
CMF—(BUC)
Sls.: $52,178,768
Assets: $41,686,972
Liabilities: $19,489,479
Net Worth: $22,197,493
Earnings: $1,188,425
Emp.: 1,064
Fiscal Year-end: 12/31/12

Business Description:
Mining Machinery & Equipment Mfr
S.I.C.: 3559
N.A.I.C.S.: 332410

Personnel:
Constantin Savu *(Chm)*

COMER INDUSTRIES S.P.A.

Via Magellano 27
42046 Reggiolo, Italy
Tel.: (39) 0522974111
Fax: (39) 0522974378
E-Mail: info@comerindustries.com
Web Site: www.comerindustries.com
Rev.: $131,415,604
Emp.: 1,200

Business Description:
Mfr., Designs & Markets Engineering Systems & Mechatronic Solutions for Power Transmission
S.I.C.: 8711
N.A.I.C.S.: 541330

Personnel:
Fabio Storchi *(Co-Founder, Chm, Pres & CEO)*
Fabrizio Storchi *(Co-Founder, VP & Mng Dir)*

Board of Directors:
Fabio Storchi
Marino Battini
Giuliano Spaggiari
Aimone Storchi
Fabrizio Storchi

U.S. Subsidiaries:

Comer Inc. (1)
12730 Virkler Dr
Charlotte, NC 28273-3885 NC
Mailing Address: (100%)
PO Box 410305
Charlotte, NC 28241-0305
Tel.: (704) 588-8400
Fax: (704) 588-2222
E-Mail: getinfo@comerinc.com
Web Site: www.comerinc.com
Sales Range: $75-99.9 Million
Emp.: 38
Mfr. & Designer of Farm & Garden Machinery
Import Export
S.I.C.: 5083
N.A.I.C.S.: 423820
Caroline Arlinterry *(Pres)*

Comer Industries Inc (1)
12730 Virkler Dr
Charlotte, NC 28273-3882
Tel.: (704) 588-8400
Fax: (704) 588-2222
Web Site: www.comerinc.com
Emp.: 42
Heavy & Civil Engineering Construction
S.I.C.: 1629
N.A.I.C.S.: 237990
Fabio Storchi *(Owner)*

Non-U.S. Subsidiaries:

Comer Industries GmbH (1)
Albert Einstein Strasse 1
70806 Kornwestheim, Germany (100%)
Tel.: (49) 7154801100
Fax: (49) 71548011022
Web Site: www.comerindustries.com
Emp.: 5
Engineering Services
S.I.C.: 8711
N.A.I.C.S.: 541330

Comer Industries Sarl (1)
Parc de l'Esplanade
28 Rue Paul Henri Spaak, 77462 Paris, Saint Thibault des V, France (100%)
Tel.: (33) 160310371
Web Site: www.comerindustries.com
Emp.: 10
Farm & Garden Machinery & Equipment Whslr
S.I.C.: 5083
N.A.I.C.S.: 423820

Comer Industries U.K. Ltd (1)
Units 2-3 Heath Road
Merry Lees Industrial Estate D, Leicester, LE9 9FE, United Kingdom
Tel.: (44) 1530231504
Fax: (44) 1530231503
E-Mail: sales@comeindustriesr.com
Web Site: www.comeindustriesr.com
Emp.: 9
Farm & Garden Machinery & Equipment Whslr
S.I.C.: 5083
N.A.I.C.S.: 423820
Wincenzo Vanni *(Gen Mgr)*

Comer (Shanghai) Trading Company Ltd (1)
Room 2001 No 398 Sun Young Center
Jiangsu Road Changhing Distric, 200050
Shanghai, China
Tel.: (86) 2162112718
Fax: (86) 2162119454
E-Mail: michael_lin@comerindustries.com
Web Site: www.comerindustries.com.cn
Engineering Services
S.I.C.: 8711
N.A.I.C.S.: 541330

COMERCIAL GASSO SA

Poligon Industrial Can Calderon C/ Murcia 35 Nave C
08030 Sant Boi de Llobregat, Barcelona, Spain
Tel.: (34) 936529800
Fax: (34) 936529804
E-Mail: gasso@gasso.com
Web Site: www.gasso.com
Sales Range: $25-49.9 Million
Emp.: 60

Business Description:
Mfr & Distr of Hose, Hose Fittings & Hose Assemblies
S.I.C.: 3052
N.A.I.C.S.: 326220

Personnel:
Jordi Gasso *(CEO)*

Non-U.S. Subsidiary:

GASSO PORTUGAL Lda (1)
Praceta Emidio Santana Zona Industrial
Casal Do Marco Lote 13 B
2840-588 Aldeia de Paio Pires, Portugal
Tel.: (351) 21 2267850
Fax: (351) 21 2267859
E-Mail: gassopt@gasso.com
Emp.: 5
Rubber Hose Distr
S.I.C.: 5085
N.A.I.C.S.: 423840
Paulo Santos *(Mgr)*

COMET FARM LTD.

PO Box 22072
Nicosia, Cyprus
Tel.: (357) 22359059
Fax: (357) 22359062
E-Mail: info@komitis.com.cy
Web Site: www.komitis.com.cy
Year Founded: 1963
Emp.: 200

Business Description:
Poultry Hatchery Services
S.I.C.: 0254
N.A.I.C.S.: 112340

Personnel:
Savvas Papaefstathiou *(Owner & Mng Dir)*

Subsidiary:

Comet Hatcheries Ltd. (1)
PO Box 22072
Nicosia, Cyprus
Tel.: (357) 22359059
Fax: (357) 22359062
E-Mail: info@komitis.com.cy
Web Site: www.komitis.com.cy/profile.htm
Emp.: 40
Egg Hatchery Services
S.I.C.: 0259
N.A.I.C.S.: 112390
Nasavva Taefthiou *(Mgr)*

COMET HOLDING AG

Herrengasse 10
CH-3175 Flamatt, Switzerland
Tel.: (41) 317449000
Fax: (41) 317449090
E-Mail: info@comet-group.com
Web Site: www.comet-group.com
COTN—(SWX)
• Sls.: $231,407,287
Assets: $219,114,912
Liabilities: $91,986,126
Net Worth: $127,128,786
Earnings: $6,393,892
Emp.: 770
Fiscal Year-end: 12/31/12

Business Description:
Holding Company; Non-Destructive Testing, Security & Semiconductor Industry Equipment Systems & Components Mfr
S.I.C.: 6712
N.A.I.C.S.: 551111

Personnel:
Ronald Fehlmann *(CEO)*
Markus Portmann *(CFO)*
Eric Dubuis *(CIO)*
Charles Flukiger *(Pres-Indus X-Ray)*
Michael Kammerer *(Pres-Vacuum Capacitors)*
Stefan Moll *(Pres-X-Ray Sys)*

Board of Directors:
Hans Hess
G. L. Bona
Lucas A. Grolimund
Rolf Huber
Hans Leonz Notter

Subsidiary:

COMET AG (1)
Herrengasse 10
Flamatt, 3175, Switzerland
Tel.: (41) 31 744 90 00
Fax: (41) 31 744 90 90
Solar Cells Mfr & Distr
S.I.C.: 3674
N.A.I.C.S.: 334413
Ronald Fehlmann *(Mgr)*

U.S. Subsidiaries:

COMET TECHNOLOGIES USA, INC. (INDUSTRIAL X-RAY) (1)
76 Progress Dr
Stamford, CT 06902
Tel.: (203) 969-2161
Fax: (203) 969-2162
E-Mail: xray@cometusa.com
Web Site: www.comet-group.com
X-Ray Component Distr
S.I.C.: 5065
N.A.I.C.S.: 423690
Jeremy Simon *(Gen Mgr)*

COMET TECHNOLOGIES USA, INC. (X-RAY SYSTEMS) (1)
3400 Gilchrist Rd
Akron, OH 44260-1221
Tel.: (330) 798-4800
Fax: (330) 784-9854
Toll Free: (800) 334-7809
E-Mail: yxlon@akr.yxlon.com
Web Site: www.comet-group.com
Emp.: 8
X-Ray Equipment Distr
S.I.C.: 5047
N.A.I.C.S.: 423450

COMET Technologies USA, Inc. (1)
2360 Bering Dr
San Jose, CA 95131
Tel.: (408) 325-8770
Fax: (408) 325-8773
Web Site: www.comet-pct.com
Emp.: 49
Vacuum Capacitor Mfr
S.I.C.: 3677
N.A.I.C.S.: 334416
Paul Smith *(Gen Mgr)*

Non-U.S. Subsidiaries:

COMET Electronics Co. Ltd. (1)
1201 Guiqiao Road Building 10 1st Floor
Jin Qiao
Export Processing Zone Pudong, Shanghai, 201206, China

Comet Holding AG—(Continued)

Tel.: (86) 21 6879 9000
Fax: (86) 21 6879 9009
E-Mail: xray@cometchina.com
Web Site: www.comet-group.com
X-Ray Equipment Mfr
S.I.C.: 3845
N.A.I.C.S.: 334510

COMET Mechanical Equipment (Shanghai) Co. Ltd (1)
1201 Guiqiao Road Building 10 1st Floor
Jin Qiao Export
Processing Zone Pudong, Shanghai, 201206, China
Tel.: (86) 21 6879 9000
Fax: (86) 21 6879 9009
Web Site: www.comet-group.com
Vacuum Capacitor Mfr
S.I.C.: 3675
N.A.I.C.S.: 334416

YXLON International GmbH (1)
Essener Bogen 15
22419 Hamburg, Germany
Tel.: (49) 40 52729 0
Fax: (49) 40 52729 170
E-Mail: yxlon@hbg.yxlon.com
Web Site: www.yxlon.com
X-Ray Inspection Equipment Mfr
S.I.C.: 3845
N.A.I.C.S.: 334517

YXLON International X-Ray GmbH (1)
Essener Bogen 15
22419 Hamburg, Germany
Tel.: (49) 40527290
Fax: (49) 4052729170
E-Mail: yxlon@hbg.yxlon.com
Web Site: www.yxlon.com
Rev.: $66,402,050
Emp.: 150
X-Ray Testing Systems & Services
S.I.C.: 8734
N.A.I.C.S.: 541380
Joseph M. Kosanetzky *(Pres & CEO)*

Subsidiaries:

YXLON International CT Development GmbH (2)
Am Walzwerk 41
D 45527 Hattingen, Germany
Tel.: (49) 2324 5629 0
Fax: (49) 2324 5629 29
E-Mail: yxlon@dus.yxlon.xom
Web Site: www.yxlon.com
X-Ray Inspection & Diagnostic Services
S.I.C.: 8734
N.A.I.C.S.: 541380
Martin Munker *(Mgr)*

YXLON International Feinfocus GmbH (2)
Im Bahlbrink 11-13
30827 Garbsen, Germany
Tel.: (49) 513170980
Fax: (49) 5131709880
E-Mail: yxlon@han.yxlon.com
Web Site: www.yxlon.com
Emp.: 50
X-Ray Inspection & Diagnostic Services
S.I.C.: 8734
N.A.I.C.S.: 541380
Andreas Hadrich *(COO)*

U.S. Subsidiary:

YXLON International Inc. (2)
3400 Gilchrist Rd
Akron, OH 44260-1221
Tel.: (330) 798-4800
Fax: (330) 784-9854
E-Mail: yxlon@akr.yxlon.com
Web Site: www.yxlon.com
Emp.: 25
X-Ray Testing Systems & Services
S.I.C.: 8734
N.A.I.C.S.: 541380
Jason Robbins *(Head-Aerospace Sls)*

Non-U.S. Subsidiaries:

YXLON International A/S (2)
Helgeshoj Alle 38
DK 2630 Tastrup, Denmark
Tel.: (45) 72407700
Fax: (45) 72407701
E-Mail: yxlon@cph.yxlon.com
Web Site: www.cph.yxlon.com
Emp.: 38
X-Ray Testing & Diagnostic Services
S.I.C.: 8734
N.A.I.C.S.: 541380
Hans Rysgaart *(Gen Mgr)*

YXLON International K.K. (2)
New Stage Yokohama Bldg 1st Floor 1-1-32
Shinurashima-cho
Kanagawa-ku, Tokyo, 140-0013, Japan
Tel.: (81) 454501730
Fax: (81) 454501740
E-Mail: yxlon@jpn.yxlon.com
Web Site: www.yxlon.co.jp
Emp.: 20
X-Ray Inspection & Diagnostic Services
S.I.C.: 8734
N.A.I.C.S.: 541380
Shinichi Kamihara *(Gen Mgr)*

COMET RESOURCES LIMITED

Unit 2 23 Belgravia St
Belmont, WA, 6104, Australia
Tel.: (61) 8 9475 7100
Fax: (61) 8 9277 4147
E-Mail: comet@cometres.com.au
Web Site: www.cometres.com.au
CRL—(ASX)
Rev.: $106,028
Assets: $2,059,110
Liabilities: $29,542
Net Worth: $2,029,568
Earnings: ($653,214)
Emp.: 3
Fiscal Year-end: 06/30/13

Business Description:
Zinc & Lead Exploration & Mining Services
S.I.C.: 1031
N.A.I.C.S.: 212231

Personnel:
Robert Oswald Jones *(Founder & Chm)*
Anthony Roy Cooper *(CEO)*
Edmumd Czechowski *(Sec)*

Board of Directors:
Robert Oswald Jones
Anthony Roy Cooper
Edmumd Czechowski
Nathan J. Featherby

COMET RIDGE LIMITED

Level 3 283 Elizabeth Street
Brisbane, QLD, 4000, Australia
Mailing Address:
GPO Box 798
Brisbane, QLD, 4001, Australia
Tel.: (61) 732213661
Fax: (61) 732213668
E-Mail: info@cometridge.com.au
Web Site: www.cometridge.com.au
COI—(ASX)
Rev.: $337,986
Assets: $55,766,374
Liabilities: $6,659,284
Net Worth: $49,107,090
Earnings: ($7,280,680)
Fiscal Year-end: 06/30/13

Business Description:
Oil, Gas & Coal Exploration & Mining Services
S.I.C.: 1311
N.A.I.C.S.: 211111

Personnel:
Tor McCaul *(Mng Dir)*
Don Langdon *(CFO)*
Dale Aaskow *(COO)*
Stephen Rodgers *(Sec)*

Board of Directors:
James A. V. McKay
Anthony Gilby
Tor McCaul
Christopher Pieters
Jeffrey Schneider
Gillian Swaby

Legal Counsel:
Porter Davies Lawyers
Level 5 46 Edward St
Brisbane, Australia

Subsidiary:

Chartwell Energy Limited (1)
Level 13 145 Eagle St
Brisbane, QLD, Australia
Tel.: (61) 732213661
Fax: (61) 732213668
E-Mail: info@chartwellenergy.com.au
Web Site: www.chartwellenergy.com.au
Emp.: 10
Coal Seam Gas Exploration Services
S.I.C.: 1389
N.A.I.C.S.: 213112
Tor McCaul *(Mng Dir)*

U.S. Subsidiary:

Comet Ridge USA, Inc. (1)
600 17th St Ste 800-S
Denver, CO 80202 (100%)
Tel.: (303) 226-1300
Fax: (303) 226-1301
Web Site: www.cometridgeresources.com
Emp.: 20
Oil & Gas Exploration
S.I.C.: 1381
N.A.I.C.S.: 213111
Andy Lydyard *(CEO)*

Joint Venture:

Comet Ridge Resources, LLC (2)
600 17th St Ste 800-S
Denver, CO 80202
Tel.: (303) 226-1300
Fax: (303) 226-1301
E-Mail: info@cometridgeresources.com
Web Site: www.cometridgeresources.com
Oil & Gas Exploration
S.I.C.: 1381
N.A.I.C.S.: 213111
Andy Lydyard *(Pres & CEO)*
Randy Spaur *(CFO)*

COMET UMETNI BRUSI IN NEKOVINE, D.D.

Tovarniska 5
3214 Zrece, Slovenia
Tel.: (386) 386375750
Fax: (386) 37575101
E-Mail: comet@comet.si
Web Site: www.comet.si
Year Founded: 1958
Sales Range: $50-74.9 Million
Emp.: 750

Business Description:
Grinding Tools Mfr
S.I.C.: 3291
N.A.I.C.S.: 327910

Personnel:
Metka Hren *(Chief Controller)*

Supervisory Board of Directors:
Ida Basic
Borut Jamnik
Bozislav Jancic
Marko Novak
Rajko Vrecer

Non-U.S. Subsidiaries:

Cobra GmbH (1)
St Michael ob Bleiburg 47
9143 Saint Michael, Austria
Tel.: (43) 423535500
Fax: (43) 4235355015
E-Mail: office@cobra-austria.at
Web Site: www.cobra-austria.at
Sls.: $13,222,000
Emp.: 9
Abrasive Products Mfr & Whslr
S.I.C.: 3291
N.A.I.C.S.: 327910

Toroflex GmbH (1)
Esbachgraben 17
DE 95463 Bindlach, Germany
Tel.: (49) 920865810
Fax: (49) 9208658140
E-Mail: info@toroflex.de
Web Site: www.toroflex.de
Emp.: 15
Abrasive Products Mfr & Whslr
S.I.C.: 3291
N.A.I.C.S.: 327910
Uwe Kierzkowski *(Mng Dir)*

Subsidiary:

Ecopack, d.o.o. (1)
Tovarniska 5
3214 Zrece, Slovenia
Tel.: (386) 37575491
Fax: (386) 37575101
E-Mail: benjamin.macuh@ecopack.si
Web Site: www.ecopack.si
Emp.: 10
Gaskets, Packing & Sealing Devices Mfr
S.I.C.: 3053
N.A.I.C.S.: 339991
Benjamin Macuh *(Mgr)*

COMFORT COMMOTRADE LIMITED

A-301 Hetal Opposite Natraj Market
Arch SV Road
Malad (West), Mumbai, 400064, India
Tel.: (91) 22 28449765
Fax: (91) 22 28892527
E-Mail: ipo-Commotrade@comfortsecurities.co.in
Web Site: www.comfortcommotrade.com
534691—(BOM)
Rev.: $174,489
Assets: $2,083,936
Liabilities: $125,771
Net Worth: $1,958,165
Earnings: $20,540
Fiscal Year-end: 03/31/13

Business Description:
Commodity Brokerage Services
S.I.C.: 6221
N.A.I.C.S.: 523140

Personnel:
Raghav Jadhav *(Compliance Officer)*

Board of Directors:
Anil Beniprasad Agrawal
Sushil K. Jain
Anilkumar Shivkaran Nevatia
Bharat Shiroya

Transfer Agent:
Sharepro Services (India) Private Limited
13 AB Samhita Warehousing Complex II Floor
Sakinaka Telephone Lane
Off Andheri Kurla Rd Sakinaka, Mumbai, India

COMFORT INTECH LIMITED

106 Avkar Algani Nagar Kalaria
Daman, 396 210, India
Tel.: (91) 260 2240803
Fax: (91) 260 2242936
E-Mail: info@comfortintech.com
Web Site: www.comfortintech.com
Year Founded: 1994
531216—(BOM)
Rev.: $2,851,900
Assets: $20,864,311
Liabilities: $3,901,698
Net Worth: $16,962,613
Earnings: $491,600
Fiscal Year-end: 03/31/13

Business Description:
Financial Services
S.I.C.: 6141
N.A.I.C.S.: 522291

Personnel:
Anil B. Agrawal *(Founder, Chm & Mng Dir)*
Ramadevi Gundeti *(Compliance Officer & Sec)*

Board of Directors:
Anil B. Agrawal
Annu A. Agrawal
Janak G. Mehta
Anil Nevatia
Bharat N. Shiroya
Jugal C. Thacker

Transfer Agent:
Bigshare Services Private Limited
E/2 Ansa Industrial Estate Sakivihar Road
Sakinaka Andheri - East
Mumbai, India

COMFORTDELGRO CORPORATION LIMITED

205 Braddell Road
Singapore, 579701, Singapore
Tel.: (65) 63838833
Fax: (65) 62870311
E-Mail: info@comfortdelgro.com
Web Site: www.comfortdelgro.com.sg
Year Founded: 1971
C52—(OTC SES)
Rev.: $2,870,558,504
Assets: $3,923,547,344
Liabilities: $1,788,421,184
Net Worth: $2,135,126,160
Earnings: $251,405,640
Emp.: 20,275
Fiscal Year-end: 12/31/12

Business Description:
Public Passenger Transport Services
S.I.C.: 4119
N.A.I.C.S.: 485999

Personnel:
Hong Pak Kua *(CEO & Mng Dir)*
Daisy Mui Wah Chan *(HR Officer)*
Chek Siew Choo *(Fin Officer)*
Peng Yen Choo *(IR & Special Projects Officer)*
Sok Yong Eng *(Bus Dev Officer)*
Thio Li-Ping Lynn *(Officer-Legal Grp)*
Tong Sing Ng *(Info Officer)*
May Poh Sim Ong *(Internal Audit Officer)*
Tammy I-Lin Tan *(Corp Comm Officer)*
Jimmy Teck Leong Chua *(CEO-ComfortDelGro Insurance Brokers Pte Ltd)*
Juay Kiat Gan *(CEO-SBS Transit Ltd)*
Jim Glasson *(CEO-ComfortDelGro Cabcharge Pty Ltd)*
Chak Khoon Huam *(CEO-ComfortDelGro Driving Centre Pte Ltd)*
Jayne Kwek *(CEO-Moove Media Pte Ltd)*
Kwok Sun Leong *(CEO-Bus Unit-China North)*
Wing Yew Sim *(CEO-VICOM Ltd)*
Jaspal Singh *(CEO-Bus Unit-United Kingdom & Ireland)*
Kim Huat Tan *(CEO-Swan Taxis Limited)*
Simon Seow Boon Tan *(CEO-Bus Unit-West China)*
Richard Yew Meng Tang *(CEO-Bus Unit-East China)*
Marc Chew Liang Tay *(CEO-Bus Unit-South China)*
Richard Boon Leng Teo *(CEO-ComfortDelGro Rent-A-Car Pte Ltd)*
Ban Seng Yang *(CEO-Taxi Bus-Singapore)*
Chuen Huei Chia *(Gen Dir-Vietnam Taxi Co Ltd)*
Alan Meng Hock Lim *(Gen Dir-ComfortDelGro Savico Taxi Company)*
Wendy Wan Tak Chan *(Sec & VP-Fin)*

Board of Directors:
Jit Poh Lim
Hong Pak Kua
Ah Heng Ong
Soon Hee Oo
Adeline Wai Fun Sum
Heng Tan Tow
Kai Yuen Wang
David Chin Huat Wong

Subsidiaries:

SBS Transit Ltd. **(1)**
205 Braddell Road
Singapore, 579701, Singapore
Tel.: (65) 62848866
Fax: (65) 62870311
E-Mail: info@comfortdelgro.com
Web Site: www.sbstransit.com.sg
Sls.: $336,726,496
Emp.: 7,136
Bus Transportation Services
S.I.C.: 4111
N.A.I.C.S.: 485113
Lim Jit Poh *(Chm)*
Kua Hong Tak *(Mng Dir)*

VICOM Ltd. **(1)**
385 Sin Ming Drive
Singapore, 575718, Singapore
Tel.: (65) 64584555
Fax: (65) 64581040
E-Mail: customerservice@vicom.com.sg
Web Site: www.vicom.com.sg
V01—(SES)
Rev.: $78,621,547
Assets: $117,385,787
Liabilities: $22,250,006
Net Worth: $95,135,781
Earnings: $21,681,611
Emp.: 881
Fiscal Year-end: 12/31/12
Technical Testing & Inspection Services
S.I.C.: 8734
N.A.I.C.S.: 541380
Wing Yew Sim *(CEO)*
Peng Yen Choo *(Grp IR & Special Projects Officer)*
Wendy Wan Tak Chan *(Sec)*
Thiam Siong Sze *(Sr VP-Setsco Services Pte Ltd)*

Non-U.S. Joint Ventures:

ComfortDelGro Cabcharge Pty. Ltd. **(1)**
29 Foundry Rd,
Seven Hills, NSW, 2147, Australia
Tel.: (61) 298900000
Fax: (61) 298915900
Web Site: www.cdcbus.com
Emp.: 120
Passenger Bus Service Operator; Joint Venture of ComfortDelGro Corporation Limited (51%) & Cabcharge Australia Limited (49%)
S.I.C.: 4111
N.A.I.C.S.: 485113

COMINAR REAL ESTATE INVESTMENT TRUST

455 Du Marais Street
Quebec, QC, G1M 3A2, Canada
Tel.: (418) 681-8151
Fax: (418) 681-2946
Toll Free: (866) 266-4627
E-Mail: info@cominar.com
Web Site: www.cominar.com
Year Founded: 1998
CUF.UN—(TSX)
Rev.: $561,161,069
Assets: $5,583,459,047
Liabilities: $2,902,691,479
Net Worth: $2,680,767,568
Earnings: $340,124,817
Emp.: 440
Fiscal Year-end: 12/31/12

Business Description:
Real Estate Investment Trust
S.I.C.: 6726
N.A.I.C.S.: 525990

Personnel:
Robert Despres *(Chm)*
Michel Dallaire *(Pres & CEO)*
Michel Berthelot *(CFO & Exec VP)*
Sylvain Cossette *(COO & Exec VP)*
Roger Turpin *(Treas & VP)*
Michel Paquet *(Sec & Sr Exec VP)*
Todd Bechard *(Exec VP-Atlantic Provinces)*
Guy Charron *(Exec VP-Ops-Retail Sector)*
Alain Dallaire *(Exec VP-Ops)*
Michel Ouellette *(Exec VP-Acq & Dev)*

Legal Counsel:
Davies, Ward, Phillips & Vineberg LLP
Toronto, ON, Canada

Transfer Agent:
Computershare Trust Company of Canada
1500 University Street Suite 700
Montreal, QC, Canada

COMINCO S.A.

B-dul Gh Magheru nr 31 Sector 1
010335 Bucharest, Romania
Tel.: (40) 213165530
Fax: (40) 213165527
E-Mail: office@cominco.ro
Web Site: www.cominco.ro
COBS—(BUC)
Sales Range: $25-49.9 Million
Emp.: 336

Business Description:
General Contracting Services
S.I.C.: 1522
N.A.I.C.S.: 236116

Personnel:
Gheorghe Gemanar *(Chm)*
Adrian Andrici *(Vice Chm)*

Board of Directors:
Gheorghe Gemanar
Adrian Andrici
Grigore Chis
Rusu Florin
Gemanar Catalin Traian

COMINTEL CORPORATION BERHAD

No 37 Jalan Pelukis U1/46 Section U1 Temasya Industrial Park
Glenmarie
40150 Shah Alam, Selangor Darul Ehsan, Malaysia
Tel.: (60) 350399898
Fax: (60) 350399833
Web Site: www.comcorp.com.my
COMCORP—(KLS)
Rev.: $136,480,737
Assets: $85,339,207
Liabilities: $51,764,685
Net Worth: $33,574,522
Earnings: $911,218
Fiscal Year-end: 01/31/13

Business Description:
Communication & System Integration Services
S.I.C.: 1731
N.A.I.C.S.: 238210

Personnel:
Keng Hok Leng *(Mng Dir)*
Shuh Shiang Eng *(Co-Sec)*
Hock Chiang Loh *(Co-Sec)*

Board of Directors:
Samshuri Arshad
Ramli Abd Rahman
Mohamadon Abdullah
Kek Hoe Koh
Chai Bee Lee
Choon Lee
Keng Hok Leng
Hock Chiang Loh
Loga Bala Mohan
Abdul Majid Omar
Mun Wai Wong

COMISION FEDERAL DE ELECTRICIDAD

(d/b/a CFE)
Reforma 164 Col Juarez
06598 Mexico, DF, Mexico
Tel.: (52) 1 800 800 8765
Fax: (52) 555310461
Web Site: www.cfe.gob.mx
Year Founded: 1937
Sales Range: $15-24.9 Billion
Emp.: 77,000

Business Description:
Electrical Power Distr
S.I.C.: 4911
N.A.I.C.S.: 221122

Personnel:
Oscar H. Lara Andrade *(Deputy Dir-Fin Control)*

COMITAL S.P.A.

Strada Brandizzo 130
10088 Volpiano, Turin, Italy
Tel.: (39) 011 982 2111
E-Mail: comitalalluminio@comital.com
Web Site: www.comital.com
Year Founded: 1935
Sales Range: $500-549.9 Million
Emp.: 1,750

Business Description:
Reclaimed Aluminum & Rubber Products
S.I.C.: 3069
N.A.I.C.S.: 326299

Personnel:
Corrado Ariaudo *(Chm & Mng Dir)*

Subsidiaries:

Comital Alluminio Volpiano **(1)**
Strada Brandizzo 130
10088 Volpiano, Turin, Italy
Tel.: (39) 011 982 2111
Web Site: www.comitalalluminio.it
Rolled Aluminum
S.I.C.: 2672
N.A.I.C.S.: 322220

Comital Cofresco S.p.A. **(1)**
Strada Brandizzo 130
10088 Volpiano, Turin, Italy
Tel.: (39) 0119822111
Fax: (39) 0119828400
Flexible Food Wrap
S.I.C.: 2671
N.A.I.C.S.: 322220

COMJOYFUL INTERNATIONAL COMPANY

(Formerly Camelot Corporation)
J4-2-12 Diplomatic Residence
Compound No 1 Xiushui Street
Jianguomen Wan Chaoyang District, Beijing, 10060, China
Tel.: (86) 10 8589 2903
Year Founded: 1988
KJFI—(OTC OTCB)
Liabilities: $47,000
Net Worth: ($47,000)
Earnings: ($72,153)
Fiscal Year-end: 04/30/13

Business Description:
Investment Services
S.I.C.: 6211
N.A.I.C.S.: 523999

Personnel:
Yazhong Liao *(Pres & CEO)*
Gene Michael Bennett *(CFO)*

Transfer Agent:
Empire Stock Transfer, Inc.
1859 Whitney Mesa Dr
Henderson, NV 89009

COMLAND COMMERCIAL LIMITED

Lunar House Mercury Park
High Wycombe, HP10 0HH, United Kingdom
Tel.: (44) 1628535777
Fax: (44) 1628535700
E-Mail: info@comland.co.uk
Web Site: www.comland.co.uk
Sales Range: $25-49.9 Million
Emp.: 14

Comland Commercial Limited—(Continued)

Business Description:
Commercial Property Development Services
S.I.C.: 6531
N.A.I.C.S.: 531390
Personnel:
Stuart Crossley *(Chm & CEO)*
Christopher G. Martin *(Fin Dir & Sec)*
Board of Directors:
Stuart Crossley
Christopher G. Martin

COMMANDER RESOURCES LTD.
11th Floor 1111 Melville Street
Vancouver, BC, V6E 3V6, Canada
Tel.: (604) 685-5254
Fax: (604) 685-2814
Toll Free: (800) 667-7866
E-Mail: info@commanderresources.com
Web Site: www.commanderresources.com
Year Founded: 1987
CMD—(TSXV)
Business Description:
Gold & Base Metal Mining Services
S.I.C.: 1041
N.A.I.C.S.: 212221
Personnel:
David Harold Watkins *(Chm)*
Eric W. Norton *(Pres & CEO)*
Alnesh Mohan *(CFO)*
Janice Davies *(Sec)*
Board of Directors:
David Harold Watkins
Brian Abraham
William J. Coulter
Bernard H. Kahlert
Mark Lotz
Eric W. Norton
Legal Counsel:
Tupper, Johnson & Yeadon
1177 W Hastings St Ste 1710
Vancouver, BC, V6E 2L3, Canada
Transfer Agent:
CIBC Mellon Trust Company
Suite 1600 The Oceanic Plaza 1066 West Hastings Street
Vancouver, BC, Canada

COMMCENTER S.A.
Avenida Joaquin Planells 106
15008 La Coruna, Spain
Tel.: (34) 902222255
Fax: (34) 981169100
E-Mail: info@commcenter.es
Web Site: www.commcenter.es
CMM—(MAD)
Sales Range: $10-24.9 Million
Emp.: 100
Business Description:
Telecommunications Services
S.I.C.: 4813
N.A.I.C.S.: 517110
Personnel:
Jose Luis Otero Barros *(CEO)*

COMMERCE RESOURCES CORP.
Suite 1450 789 West Pender Street
Vancouver, BC, V6C 1H2, Canada
Tel.: (604) 484-2700
Fax: (604) 681-8240
Toll Free: (866) 484-2700
E-Mail: info@commerceresources.com
Web Site: www.commerceresources.com
Year Founded: 1999
CCE—(TSXV)
Int. Income: $39,970
Assets: $51,573,443
Liabilities: $1,516,539
Net Worth: $50,056,904
Earnings: ($198,884)
Fiscal Year-end: 10/31/12
Business Description:
Mineral Exploration Services
S.I.C.: 1081
N.A.I.C.S.: 213114
Personnel:
Axel Hoppe *(Chm)*
David Hodge *(Pres)*
Alicia Milne *(Sec)*
Board of Directors:
Axel Hoppe
Jody Richard Dahrouge
Ian Graham
Christopher Grove
Jenna Hardy
David Hodge
Sven Olsson

COMMERCIAL BAKERIES CORP.
45 Torbarrie Rd
Toronto, ON, M3L 1G5, Canada
Tel.: (416) 247-5478
Fax: (416) 242-4129
E-Mail: info@commercialbakeries.com
Web Site: www.commercialbakeries.com
Year Founded: 1950
Rev.: $22,000,000
Emp.: 200
Business Description:
Cookies & Biscuits Mfr
S.I.C.: 2052
N.A.I.C.S.: 311821
Personnel:
Anthony Fusco, Jr. *(VP)*

COMMERCIAL BANK OF CEYLON LTD.
Commercial House No 21 Sir Razik Fareed Mawatha
PO Box 856
Colombo, 1, Sri Lanka
Tel.: (94) 112486000
Fax: (94) 112449889
E-Mail: info@combank.net
Web Site: www.combank.net
COMB—(COL ISE)
Rev.: $497,483,961
Assets: $4,020,932,024
Liabilities: $3,604,877,620
Net Worth: $416,054,404
Earnings: $79,137,161
Emp.: 4,400
Fiscal Year-end: 12/31/12
Business Description:
Banking Services
S.I.C.: 6029
N.A.I.C.S.: 522110
Personnel:
Dinesh Weerakkody *(Chm)*
K. G. D. D. Dheerasinghe *(Deputy Chm)*
W. M. Ravi S. Dias *(CEO & Mng Dir)*
Nandika Buddhipala *(CFO)*
Jegan Durairatnam *(COO)*
Rohan Muttiah *(CIO)*
Sanath Manatunga *(Chief Risk Officer)*
S. M. Richard Rodrigo *(Compliance Officer)*
R. R. Dunuwille *(Sec)*
Board of Directors:
Dinesh Weerakkody
K. G. D. D. Dheerasinghe
W. M. Ravi S. Dias
Jegan Durairatnam
Lakshman Hulugalle
M. P. Jayawardena
Uditha Liyanage
S. Swarnajothi
Legal Counsel:
Julius & Creasy
No 41 Janadhipathi Mawatha
Colombo, 1, Sri Lanka
Subsidiaries:

Commercial Bank Primary Dealer Ltd. **(1)**
Commercial House No 21 Bristol Street
PO Box 856
Colombo, 1, Sri Lanka (100%)
Tel.: (94) 112445010
Fax: (94) 112423527
E-Mail: treasury@combank.net
Web Site: www.combank.net
Emp.: 450
Government Securities Dealer
S.I.C.: 6211
N.A.I.C.S.: 523120
Isuru Thilakawardana *(Deputy Gen Mgr-HR)*

Commercial Development Company Ltd. **(1)**
Commercial House No 21 Bristol Street
PO Box 856
Colombo, 1, Sri Lanka (94.55%)
Tel.: (94) 112445010
Property Development Services
S.I.C.: 6531
N.A.I.C.S.: 531390

ONEzero Company Ltd. **(1)**
3rd Floor Commercial Bank Building
Backup Center 2085 Galle Road
Colombo, Sri Lanka (100%)
Tel.: (94) 112445010
Fax: (94) 112574410
IT Services
S.I.C.: 7379
N.A.I.C.S.: 541519

COMMERCIAL BANK OF DUBAI PSC
Ittihad Rd
PO Box 2668
Dubai, United Arab Emirates
Tel.: (971) 42121000
Fax: (971) 42121911
E-Mail: cbd-ho@cbd.ae
Web Site: www.cbd.ae
Year Founded: 1969
CBD—(DFM)
Rev.: $455,997,035
Assets: $10,742,735,566
Liabilities: $8,884,078,498
Net Worth: $1,858,657,068
Earnings: $232,125,447
Fiscal Year-end: 12/31/12
Business Description:
Banking Services
S.I.C.: 6029
N.A.I.C.S.: 522110
Personnel:
Saeed Ahmed Ghobash *(Chm)*
Khaled Abdul Wahed Al Rostamani *(Deputy Chm)*
Peter Baltussen *(CEO)*
Yaqoob Yousuf Hassan *(Deputy CEO)*
Thomas Pereira *(CFO)*
Mahmoud Hadi *(COO)*
Asem Fikree *(CIO)*
Ahmed Shaheen *(Chief Risk Officer & Gen Mgr)*
Board of Directors:
Saeed Ahmed Ghobash
Ali Fardan Al Fardan
Omar Abdullah Al Futtaim
Abdulla Saif Al Hathboor
Mohammed Abdul Rahman Al Jallaf
Mana Mohamed Saeed Al Mulla
Abdulla Saeed Al Naboodah
Khaled Abdul Wahed Al Rostamani
Abdul Wahid Al Ulama
Hamed Ahmed Kazim
Shihab Mohammed Shihab Gargash
Subsidiary:

CBD Financial Services LLC **(1)**
PO Box 2668
Dubai, United Arab Emirates
Tel.: (971) 43055889
Fax: (971) 42121111
Web Site: www.cbdfs.ae/contact.aspx
Financial Investment & Brokerage Services
S.I.C.: 6211
N.A.I.C.S.: 523999

COMMERCIAL BANK OF KUWAIT S.A.K.
Mubarak Al Kabir Street
PO Box 2861
Safat, Kuwait, 13029, Kuwait
Tel.: (965) 22990000
Fax: (965) 22450150
E-Mail: mail@cbk.com
Web Site: www.cbk.com
Year Founded: 1960
CBK—(KUW)
Int. Income: $403,685,773
Assets: $12,998,228,305
Liabilities: $11,038,545,076
Net Worth: $1,959,683,229
Earnings: $4,085,759
Emp.: 12,092
Fiscal Year-end: 12/31/12
Business Description:
Banking Services
S.I.C.: 6029
N.A.I.C.S.: 522110
Personnel:
Ali Mousa M. Al Mousa *(Chm & Mng Dir)*
Abdulrazzak A. Al Kandari *(Deputy Chm)*
Nuhad Kalim Saliba *(CEO)*
Elham Yousry Mahfouz *(Deputy CEO)*
Adli Abdalla Ghazal *(Treas & Gen Mgr)*
Board of Directors:
Ali Mousa M. Al Mousa
Abdulrahman Abdullah Al Ali
Salem Ali Hassan Al Ali
Abdulrazzak A. Al Kandari
Ahmed Duaij Al Sabah
Majed Ali Owaid Awad
Mahmoud A. A. Behbehani

Deloitte & Touche
Kuwait, Kuwait

COMMERCIAL BANK OF QATAR Q.S.C.
Commercial Bank Plaza
PO Box 3232
Doha, Qatar
Tel.: (974) 4490000
Fax: (974) 4490070
E-Mail: info@cbq.com.qa
Web Site: www.cbq.qa
Year Founded: 1975
CBQK—(QE)
Int. Income: $774,107,350
Assets: $21,378,083,559
Liabilities: $17,387,775,695
Net Worth: $3,990,307,864
Earnings: $537,483,727
Emp.: 1,114
Fiscal Year-end: 12/31/12
Business Description:
Banking Services
S.I.C.: 6029
N.A.I.C.S.: 522110
Personnel:
Abdullah Khalifa al Attiyah *(Chm)*
Abdullah Ali Jabor Al Thani *(Vice Chm)*
Abdullah Al Raisi *(CEO)*
Andrew Charles Stevens *(Grp CEO)*
Hussain Ebrahim Alfardan *(Mng Dir)*
Nicholas Coleman *(CFO & Exec Gen Mgr)*
Sandeep Chouhan *(COO & Exec Gen Mgr)*
Jeremy Davies *(CMO & Exec Gen Mgr)*
Khoda Fartash *(Chief Legal Officer & Exec Gen Mgr)*

Rafed Al-Ani *(CTO)*
Jerold Williamson *(Chief Risk Officer & Exec Gen Mgr)*
Rajbushan Buddhiraju *(Chief Retail Banking Officer)*
Board of Directors:
Abdullah Khalifa al Attiyah
Abdulla Mohd Ibrahim Al Mannai
Jassim Al Mosallam
Khalifa Abdullah Al Subaey
Hussain Ebrahim Alfardan
Omar Hussain Alfardan
Ahmed Nasser Faleh Al Thani
Abdullah Ali Jabor Al Thani
Jabor Ali Jabor Al Thani

Non-U.S. Subsidiary:

Alternatifbank A.S. **(1)**
Cumhuriyet Caddesi No 46
Elmadag, 34367 Istanbul, Turkey (74.24%)
Tel.: (90) 2123156500
Fax: (90) 2122257615
E-Mail: fi@abank.com.tr
Web Site: wwweng.abank.com.tr
ALNTF—(IST)
Int. Income: $486,307,363
Assets: $4,460,291,916
Liabilities: $4,120,708,690
Net Worth: $339,583,226
Earnings: $45,933,201
Emp.: 1,230
Fiscal Year-end: 12/31/12
Commercial Banking Services
S.I.C.: 6029
N.A.I.C.S.: 522110
Tuncay Ozilhan *(Chm)*
Andrew Charles Stevens *(Vice Chm)*
Hamit Aydogan *(CEO)*
Dilek Algan *(Exec VP-Credit Monitoring Resturcturing & Legal Follow-Up)*
Isil Funda Oney Babacan *(Exec VP-IT)*
Murad Buyukkurkcu *(Exec VP-Credit Admin)*
Mutlu Caliskan *(Exec VP-Inspections Bd)*
Suat Cetin *(Exec VP-Ops)*
Murat Ozer *(Exec VP-HR)*
Muzaffer Ozturk *(Exec VP-Corp & Comml Banking)*
Tolga Senefe *(Exec VP-Treasury)*
Cem Sipal *(Exec VP-Fin Control)*
Sakir Somek *(Exec VP-Intl Fin Institutions Grp)*

COMMERCIAL ENGINEERS & BODY BUILDERS COMPANY LTD

124 Napier Town
Jabalpur, Madhya Pradesh, 482001, India
Tel.: (91) 761 2451941
Fax: (91) 761 2407009
E-Mail: info@cebbco.com
Web Site: www.cebbco.com
CEBBCO—(BOM NSE)
Rev.: $109,463,479
Assets: $115,646,513
Liabilities: $64,840,999
Net Worth: $50,805,514
Earnings: $3,430,938
Emp.: 230
Fiscal Year-end: 03/31/13
Business Description:
Vehicle & Locomotive Bodies Mfr
S.I.C.: 3711
N.A.I.C.S.: 336211
Personnel:
Kailash Gupta *(Chm & Mng Dir)*
Deepak Tiwary *(CEO)*
Abhijit Kanvinde *(CFO)*
Anurag Misra *(Compliance Officer & Sec)*
Board of Directors:
Kailash Gupta
Ravi Gupta
Praveen Kumar
Sevantilal Popatlal Shah
Sudhir Kumar Vadehra

Transfer Agent:
Karvy Computershare Private Limited
Plot No 17 to 24 Vittalrao Nagar Madhapur
Hyderabad, India

COMMERCIAL FACILITIES COMPANY S.A.K.C.

Sharq Abdullah Al-Ahmed Street
PO Box 24284
Safat, Kuwait, 13103, Kuwait
Tel.: (965) 1833232
Fax: (965) 22455275
E-Mail: info@cfc-kw.com
Web Site: www.cfc-kw.com
Year Founded: 1977
FACIL—(KUW)
Rev.: $68,614,533
Assets: $1,033,842,383
Liabilities: $433,179,072
Net Worth: $600,663,310
Earnings: $56,243,860
Emp.: 190
Fiscal Year-end: 12/31/12
Business Description:
Installment Credit & Loan Services
S.I.C.: 6163
N.A.I.C.S.: 522310
Personnel:
Abdallah Saud Abdulaziz Al-Humaidhi *(Chm & Mng Dir)*
Ali Ibrahim Marafi *(Vice Chm)*
Khaled A. Al-Ali *(Asst Mng Dir-Fin & Admin)*
Naser A. Al-Mannai *(Asst Mng Dir-Mktg)*
Board of Directors:
Abdallah Saud Abdulaziz Al-Humaidhi
Alhareth Abdulrazak Al-Khaled
Khalid Mishary Al-Khalid
Musaed Bader Al-Sayer
Abdulla M. H. Al-Sumait
Mohammed Reda Y. Behbehani
Ali Ibrahim Marafi

Ali Al Hassawi & Partners
Sharq Dasman Complex Block 2 9 Floor
PO Box 22351
Kuwait, 13084, Kuwait

COMMERCIAL INTERNATIONAL BANK (EGYPT) S.A.E.

Nile Tower Building 21/23 Charles De Gaulle
Cairo, Egypt
Tel.: (20) 237472000
Fax: (20) 235703172
E-Mail: info@cibeg.com
Web Site: www.cibeg.com
Year Founded: 1975
COMI—(EGX OTC)
Int. Income: $1,167,422,181
Assets: $13,964,906,448
Liabilities: $12,350,283,410
Net Worth: $1,614,623,038
Earnings: $330,797,165
Emp.: 5,181
Fiscal Year-end: 12/31/12
Business Description:
Banking Services
S.I.C.: 6029
N.A.I.C.S.: 522110
Personnel:
Hisham Ezz Al-Arab *(Chm & Mng Dir)*
Jawaid Mirza *(Mng Dir)*
Omar Khan *(COO)*
Hussien Abaza *(CEO-Instutional Banking)*
Mohamed Abdel Aziz El Toukhy *(CEO-Consumer Banking)*
Board of Directors:
Hisham Ezz Al-Arab
Nadia Makram Ebeid
Essam El Wakil
Mahmoud M. Fahmy
Paul Fletcher
Medhat Hassanein
Sherif H. Kamel
William M. Mikhail
Jawaid Mirza

Ernst & Young
Cairo, Egypt

COMMERCIAL LIGHTING PRODUCTS LTD.

1535 Cliveden Avenue
Delta, BC, V3M 6P7, Canada
Tel.: (604) 540-4999
Fax: (604) 540-2402
Toll Free: (800) 665-1021
E-Mail: sales@comlight.com
Web Site: www.comlight.com
Rev.: $13,041,743
Emp.: 60
Business Description:
Electrical Products Distr
S.I.C.: 5063
N.A.I.C.S.: 423610
Personnel:
Gord Carson *(Mgr-Calgary)*

THE COMMERCIAL REAL ESTATE COMPANY K.S.C.C.

(d/b/a Al-Tijaria)
Al-Sharq Jaber Al Mubarak St CRC Building
Kuwait, 13042, Kuwait
Tel.: (965) 22902900
Fax: (965) 22426848
E-Mail: info@altijaria.com
Web Site: www.altijaria.com
ALTIJARIA—(KUW)
Rev.: $40,967,444
Assets: $1,324,466,373
Liabilities: $383,827,494
Net Worth: $940,638,878
Earnings: $38,749,157
Emp.: 176
Fiscal Year-end: 12/31/12
Business Description:
Commercial Property Investment Services
S.I.C.: 6531
N.A.I.C.S.: 531390
Personnel:
Abdul Fatah M. R. Marafie *(Chm & Mng Dir)*
Adwan Mohammad Abdulaziz Aladwani *(Vice Chm)*
Vadakkanchery Veera Raghavan *(CFO)*
Saleh Ahmad Al-Aryan *(CEO-Admin & Legal Affairs Grp)*
Ali Mohamad Al-Kulaib *(CEO-Properties Grp)*
Abdulaziz I. Al-Mousa *(CEO-Investments)*
Khalil S. Al-Onaizi *(CEO-Technical Affairs Grp)*
Board of Directors:
Abdul Fatah M. R. Marafie
Adwan Mohammad Abdulaziz Aladwani
Talal Jassim M. Albahar
Ebrahim Mohammad Ali Alghanim
Abdulaziz M. A. Alhasawi
Ali Mousa M. Almousa
Faisal Ibrahim Ibrahim Almusallam
Fahad Yousif S. Alsabah

COMMERCIAL SPRING AND TOOL COMPANY LIMITED

160 Watline Avenue
Mississauga, ON, L4Z 1R1, Canada
Tel.: (905) 568-3899
Fax: (905) 568-1929
Web Site: www.commercialspring.com
Rev.: $51,007,704
Emp.: 450
Business Description:
Spring & Wire Mfr
S.I.C.: 3495
N.A.I.C.S.: 332613
Personnel:
Frank Martinitz *(Pres)*

COMMERZBANK AG

Kaiserplatz St 16
D 60311 Frankfurt am Main, Germany
Tel.: (49) 6913620
Telex: 4152530 c b d
Fax: (49) 69285389
E-Mail: info@commerzbank.com
Web Site: www.commerzbank.com
Year Founded: 1870
CBK100—(DEU EUR LSE OTC SWX)
Int. Income: $19,598,889,030
Assets: $855,999,887,260
Liabilities: $819,607,527,480
Net Worth: $36,392,359,780
Earnings: $146,732,530
Emp.: 58,160
Fiscal Year-end: 12/31/12
Business Description:
Bank Holding Company; Corporate Banking Services
S.I.C.: 6712
N.A.I.C.S.: 551111
Personnel:
Klaus-Peter Muller *(Chm-Supervisory Bd)*
Martin Blessing *(Chm-Mgmt Bd)*
Uwe Tschage *(Deputy Chm-Supervisory Bd)*
Stephen Engels *(CFO & Member-Mgmt Bd)*
Frank Annuscheit *(COO & Member-Mgmt Bd)*
Stefan Schmittmann *(Chief Risk Officer)*
Markus Beumer *(Member-Mgmt Bd-Mittelstandsbank Bus Segment)*
Michael Reuther *(Member-Mgmt Bd-Corp & Markets Bus Segment)*
Martin Zielke *(Member-Mgmt Bd-Private Customers Bus Segment)*
Supervisory Board of Directors:
Klaus-Peter Muller
Hans-Hermann Altenschmidt
Stefan Burghardt
Gunnar de Buhr
Karl-Heinz Flother
Hans-Peter Keitel
Markus Kerber
Alexandra Krieger
Oliver Leiberich
Beate Mensch
Ulrich Middelmann
Helmut Perlet
Barbara Priester
Mark Roach
Petra Schadeberg-Hermann
Marcus Schenck
Margit Schoffer
Uwe Tschage
Gertrude Tumpel-Gugerell
Nikolaus von Bomhard

Subsidiaries:

1. CR Fonds-Verwaltungsgesellschaft mbH **(1)**
Mercedesstr 6
40470 Dusseldorf, Germany
Tel.: (49) 21177080
Pension Fund Management Services
S.I.C.: 6371
N.A.I.C.S.: 525110

10. CR Fonds-Verwaltungsgesellschaft mbH **(1)**
Mercedesstr 6
40470 Dusseldorf, Germany
Tel.: (49) 211 77080
Fax: (49) 211 77083156

Commerzbank AG—(Continued)

Financial Investment Services
S.I.C.: 6282
N.A.I.C.S.: 523930

11. CR Fonds-Verwaltungsgesellschaft mbH (1)
Mercedesstr 6
40470 Dusseldorf, Germany
Tel.: (49) 211 77080
Fax: (49) 211 77083156
Financial Investment Services
S.I.C.: 6282
N.A.I.C.S.: 523930

12. CR Fonds-Verwaltungsgesellschaft mbH (1)
Mercedesstr 6
40470 Dusseldorf, Germany
Tel.: (49) 211 77080
Fax: (49) 211 77083156
Financial Investment Services
S.I.C.: 6282
N.A.I.C.S.: 523930

13. CR Fonds-Verwaltungsgesellschaft mbH (1)
Mercedesstr 6
40470 Dusseldorf, Germany
Tel.: (49) 211 77080
Fax: (49) 211 77083156
Financial Investment Services
S.I.C.: 6282
N.A.I.C.S.: 523930

14. CR Fonds-Verwaltungsgesellschaft mbH (1)
Mercedesstr 6
40470 Dusseldorf, Germany
Tel.: (49) 211 77080
Fax: (49) 211 77083156
Financial Investment Services
S.I.C.: 6282
N.A.I.C.S.: 523930

2. CR Fonds-Verwaltungsgesellschaft mbH (1)
Mercedesstr 6
40470 Dusseldorf, Germany
Tel.: (49) 211 77080
Fax: (49) 211 77083156
Financial Investment Services
S.I.C.: 6282
N.A.I.C.S.: 523930

3. CR Fonds-Verwaltungsgesellschaft mbH (1)
Mercedesstr 6
40470 Dusseldorf, Germany
Tel.: (49) 211 77080
Fax: (49) 211 77083156
Financial Investment Services
S.I.C.: 6282
N.A.I.C.S.: 523930

4. CR Fonds-Verwaltungsgesellschaft mbH (1)
Mercedesstr 6
40470 Dusseldorf, Germany
Tel.: (49) 211 77080
Fax: (49) 211 77083156
Financial Investment Services
S.I.C.: 6282
N.A.I.C.S.: 523930

5. CR Fonds-Verwaltungsgesellschaft mbH (1)
Mercedesstr 6
40470 Dusseldorf, Germany
Tel.: (49) 211 77080
Fax: (49) 211 77083156
Financial Investment Services
S.I.C.: 6282
N.A.I.C.S.: 523930

6. CR Fonds-Verwaltungsgesellschaft mbH (1)
Mercedesstr 6
40470 Dusseldorf, Germany
Tel.: (49) 211 77080
Fax: (49) 211 77083156
Financial Investment Services
S.I.C.: 6282
N.A.I.C.S.: 523930

7. CR Fonds-Verwaltungsgesellschaft mbH (1)
Mercedesstr 6
40470 Dusseldorf, Germany
Tel.: (49) 211 77080
Fax: (49) 211 77083156
Financial Investment Services
S.I.C.: 6282
N.A.I.C.S.: 523930

8. CR Fonds-Verwaltungsgesellschaft mbH (1)
Mercedesstr 6
40470 Dusseldorf, Germany
Tel.: (49) 211 77080
Fax: (49) 211 77083156
Financial Investment Services
S.I.C.: 6282
N.A.I.C.S.: 523930

ABANTITIM Grundstucks-Vermietungsgesellschaft mbH (1)
Mercedesstr 6
40470 Dusseldorf, Germany
Tel.: (49) 211 77080
Fax: (49) 211 77083156
Real Estate Management Services
S.I.C.: 6531
N.A.I.C.S.: 531390

ABANTUM Beteiligungsgesellschaft mbH (1)
Mercedesstr 6
40470 Dusseldorf, Germany
Tel.: (49) 211 77080
Fax: (49) 211 77083156
Financial Management Services
S.I.C.: 6211
N.A.I.C.S.: 523999

ABELASSA Grundstucks-Vermietungsgesellschaft mbH (1)
Mercedesstr 6
40470 Dusseldorf, Germany
Tel.: (49) 211 77080
Fax: (49) 211 77083156
Real Estate Management Services
S.I.C.: 6531
N.A.I.C.S.: 531390

ABENITA Photovoltaik Beteiligungsgesellschaft mbH (1)
Mercedesstr 6
40470 Dusseldorf, Germany
Tel.: (49) 211 77080
Fax: (49) 211 77083156
Photovoltaic Cell Mfr
S.I.C.: 3674
N.A.I.C.S.: 334413

ABESTA Grundstucks-Vermietungsgesellschaft mbH (1)
Mercedesstr 6
40470 Dusseldorf, Germany
Tel.: (49) 211 77080
Fax: (49) 211 77083156
Real Estate Management Services
S.I.C.: 6531
N.A.I.C.S.: 531390

ABORONUM Grundstucks-Vermietungsgesellschaft mbH (1)
Mercedesstr 6
40470 Dusseldorf, Germany
Tel.: (49) 211 77080
Fax: (49) 211 77083156
Real Estate Management Services
S.I.C.: 6531
N.A.I.C.S.: 531390

ABOTORIUM Finanz- und Verwaltungsgesellschaft mbH i.L. (1)
Mercedes Strasse 6
40470 Dusseldorf, Germany
Tel.: (49) 211 77080
Financial Investment Services
S.I.C.: 6282
N.A.I.C.S.: 523930

ACARINA Beteiligungsgesellschaft mbH (1)
Mercedesstr 6
40470 Dusseldorf, Germany
Tel.: (49) 211 77080
Fax: (49) 211 77083156
Financial Investment Services
S.I.C.: 6282
N.A.I.C.S.: 523930

ACCESSA Grundstucks-Vermietungsgesellschaft mbH (1)
Mercedesstr 6
40470 Dusseldorf, Germany
Tel.: (49) 211 77080
Fax: (49) 211 77083156
Real Estate Management Services
S.I.C.: 6531
N.A.I.C.S.: 531390

ACINA Grundstucks-Vermietungsgesellschaft mbH (1)
Mercedesstr 6
40470 Dusseldorf, Germany
Tel.: (49) 211 77080
Fax: (49) 211 77083156
Real Estate Management Services
S.I.C.: 6531
N.A.I.C.S.: 531390

ACOLA Grundstucks-Vermietungsgesellschaft mbH (1)
Mercedesstr 6
40470 Dusseldorf, Germany
Tel.: (49) 211 77080
Fax: (49) 211 77083156
Real Estate Management Services
S.I.C.: 6531
N.A.I.C.S.: 531390

ACREDA Grundstucks-Vermietungsgesellschaft mbH (1)
Mercedesstr 6
40470 Dusseldorf, Germany
Tel.: (49) 211 77080
Fax: (49) 211 77083156
Real Estate Management Services
S.I.C.: 6531
N.A.I.C.S.: 531390

ACRONA Photovoltaik-Beteiligungsgesellschaft mbH (1)
Mercedesstr 6
40470 Dusseldorf, Germany
Tel.: (49) 211 77080
Fax: (49) 211 77083156
Photovoltaic Cell Mfr
S.I.C.: 3674
N.A.I.C.S.: 334413

ACTOSA Grundstucks-Vermietungsgesellschaft mbH (1)
Mercedesstr 6
40470 Dusseldorf, Germany
Tel.: (49) 211 77080
Fax: (49) 211 77083156
Real Estate Management Services
S.I.C.: 6531
N.A.I.C.S.: 531390

ADAMANTA Grundstucks-Vermietungsgesellschaft mbH (1)
Mercedesstr 6
40470 Dusseldorf, Germany
Tel.: (49) 211 77080
Fax: (49) 211 77083156
Real Estate Management Services
S.I.C.: 6531
N.A.I.C.S.: 531390

ADELIA Grundstucks-Vermietungsgesellschaft mbH & Co. Objekt Berlin Teltow KG (1)
Mercedesstr 6
40470 Dusseldorf, Germany
Tel.: (49) 211 77080
Fax: (49) 211 77083156
Real Estate Management Services
S.I.C.: 6531
N.A.I.C.S.: 531390

ADELIA Grundstucks-Vermietungsgesellschaft mbH (1)
Mercedesstr 6
40470 Dusseldorf, Germany
Tel.: (49) 211 77080
Real Estate Management Services
S.I.C.: 6531
N.A.I.C.S.: 531390

ADENARA Flugzeug-Leasinggesellschaft mbH (1)
Geigerbergstr 37
76227 Karlsruhe, Germany
Tel.: (49) 721 42625
Aircraft Leasing Services
S.I.C.: 7359
N.A.I.C.S.: 532411

ADURAMA Verwaltung und Treuhand GmbH (1)
Mercedesstr 6
40470 Dusseldorf, Germany
Tel.: (49) 211 77080
Fax: (49) 211 77083156
Financial Management Services
S.I.C.: 6211
N.A.I.C.S.: 523999

AGALINA Grundstucks-Vermietungsgesellschaft mbH (1)
Mercedesstr 6
40470 Dusseldorf, Germany
Tel.: (49) 211 77080
Fax: (49) 211 77083156
Real Estate Management Services
S.I.C.: 6531
N.A.I.C.S.: 531390

AGARBA Grundstucks-Vermietungsgesellschaft mbH (1)
Mercedesstr 6
40470 Dusseldorf, Germany
Tel.: (49) 211 77080
Fax: (49) 211 77083156
Real Estate Management Services
S.I.C.: 6531
N.A.I.C.S.: 531390

AGASILA Grundstucks-Vermietungsgesellschaft mbH (1)
Mercedesstr 6
40470 Dusseldorf, Nordrhein-Westfalen, Germany
Tel.: (49) 211 77080
Fax: (49) 211 77083156
E-Mail: info@commerzbank.com
Emp.: 300
Real Estate Development Services
S.I.C.: 6531
N.A.I.C.S.: 531390
Sabine Brunk *(Gen Mgr)*

AJOLA Grundstucks-Vermietungsgesellschaft mbH (1)
Mercedesstr 6
40470 Dusseldorf, Germany
Tel.: (49) 211 77080
Fax: (49) 211 77083156
Real Estate Management Services
S.I.C.: 6531
N.A.I.C.S.: 531390

AKERA Verwaltung und Treuhand GmbH (1)
Mercedesstr 6
40470 Dusseldorf, Germany
Tel.: (49) 211 77080
Fax: (49) 211 77083156
Financial Management Services
S.I.C.: 6211
N.A.I.C.S.: 523999

ALACRITAS Verwaltungs- und Treuhand GmbH (1)
Mercedesstr 6
40470 Dusseldorf, Germany
Tel.: (49) 211 77080
Fax: (49) 211 77083156
Financial Management Services
S.I.C.: 6211
N.A.I.C.S.: 523999

ALBELLA Verwaltung und Treuhand GmbH (1)
Mercedesstr 6
40470 Dusseldorf, Germany
Tel.: (49) 211 77080
Fax: (49) 211 77083156
Financial Management Services
S.I.C.: 6211
N.A.I.C.S.: 523999

ALBOLA Verwaltungund Treuhand GmbH (1)
Mercedesstr 6
40470 Dusseldorf, Germany
Tel.: (49) 211 77080
Fax: (49) 211 77083156
Financial Management Services
S.I.C.: 6211
N.A.I.C.S.: 523999

ALCARDA Grundstucks-Vermietungsgesellschaft mbH (1)
Mercedesstr 6
40470 Dusseldorf, Nordrhein-Westfalen, Germany
Tel.: (49) 211 77080
Fax: (49) 211 77083156
E-Mail: info@commerzbank.com
Commercial Banking Services
S.I.C.: 6029
N.A.I.C.S.: 522110

ALDINGA Verwaltung und Treuhand GmbH (1)
Mercedesstr 6
40470 Dusseldorf, Germany
Tel.: (49) 211 77080
Fax: (49) 211 77083156
Financial Management Services
S.I.C.: 6211
N.A.I.C.S.: 523999

ALDULA Verwaltung und Treuhand GmbH (1)
Mercedesstr 6
40470 Dusseldorf, Germany
Tel.: (49) 211 77080
Fax: (49) 211 77083156
Financial Management Services
S.I.C.: 6211
N.A.I.C.S.: 523999

ALEMONA Verwaltung und Treuhand GmbH (1)
Mercedesstr 6
40470 Dusseldorf, Germany
Tel.: (49) 211 77080
Fax: (49) 211 77083156
Financial Management Services
S.I.C.: 6211
N.A.I.C.S.: 523999

ALIVERA Grundstucks-Vermietungsgesellschaft mbH (1)
Mercedesstr 6
40470 Dusseldorf, Germany
Tel.: (49) 211 77080
Fax: (49) 211 77083156
Real Estate Management Services
S.I.C.: 6531
N.A.I.C.S.: 531390

ALMARENA Grundstucks-Vermietungsgesellschaft mbH (1)
Mercedesstr 6
40470 Dusseldorf, Germany
Tel.: (49) 211 77080
Fax: (49) 211 77083156
Real Estate Management Services
S.I.C.: 6531
N.A.I.C.S.: 531390

ALMONDA Grundstucks-Vermietungsgesellschaft mbH (1)
Mercedesstr 6
40470 Dusseldorf, Germany
Tel.: (49) 211 77080
Fax: (49) 211 77083156
Real Estate Management Services
S.I.C.: 6531
N.A.I.C.S.: 531390

ALMURUS Grundstucks-Vermietungsgesellschaft mbH (1)
Mercedesstr 6
40470 Dusseldorf, Germany
Tel.: (49) 211 77080
Fax: (49) 211 77083156
Real Estate Management Services
S.I.C.: 6531
N.A.I.C.S.: 531390

ALONGA Grundstucks-Vermietungsgesellschaft mbH (1)
Mercedesstr 6
40470 Dusseldorf, Germany
Tel.: (49) 211 77080
Fax: (49) 211 77083156
Real Estate Management Services
S.I.C.: 6531
N.A.I.C.S.: 531390

ALSANTA Grundstucks-Vermietungsgesellschaft mbH (1)
Mercedesstr 6
40470 Dusseldorf, Nordrhein-Westfalen, Germany
Tel.: (49) 211 77080
Fax: (49) 211 77083156
Real Estate Development Services
S.I.C.: 6531
N.A.I.C.S.: 531390

ALSENNA Grundstucks-Vermietungsgesellschaft mbH (1)
Mercedesstr 6
40470 Dusseldorf, Germany
Tel.: (49) 211 77080
Fax: (49) 211 77083156
Real Estate Management Services
S.I.C.: 6531
N.A.I.C.S.: 531390

ALSTRUCTA Grundstucks-Vermietungsgesellschaft mbH (1)
Mercedesstr 6
40470 Dusseldorf, Germany
Tel.: (49) 69 13622255
Real Estate Management Services
S.I.C.: 6531
N.A.I.C.S.: 531390

ALUBRA Verwaltung und Treuhand GmbH (1)
Mercedesstr 6
40470 Dusseldorf, Germany
Tel.: (49) 211 77080
Fax: (49) 211 77083156
Financial Management Services
S.I.C.: 6211
N.A.I.C.S.: 523999

ALUDANTA Grundstucks-Vermietungsgesellschaft mbH (1)
Mercedesstr 6
40470 Dusseldorf, Germany
Tel.: (49) 211 77080
Financial Investment Services
S.I.C.: 6282
N.A.I.C.S.: 523930

ALVENTA Grundstucks-Vermietungsgesellschaft mbH (1)
Mercedesstr 6
40470 Dusseldorf, Germany
Tel.: (49) 211 77080
Fax: (49) 211 77083156
Real Estate Management Services
S.I.C.: 6531
N.A.I.C.S.: 531390

ALVINA Grundstucks-Vermietungsgesellschaft mbH (1)
Mercedesstr 6
40470 Dusseldorf, Germany
Tel.: (49) 211 77080
Fax: (49) 211 77083156
Real Estate Management Services
S.I.C.: 6531
N.A.I.C.S.: 531390

AMALIA Verwaltung und Treuhand GmbH (1)
Mercedesstr 6
40470 Dusseldorf, Germany
Tel.: (49) 211 77080
Fax: (49) 211 77083156
Financial Management Services
S.I.C.: 6211
N.A.I.C.S.: 523999

AMERA Verwaltung und Treuhand GmbH (1)
Mercedesstr 6
40470 Dusseldorf, Germany
Tel.: (49) 211 77080
Fax: (49) 211 77083156
Financial Management Services
S.I.C.: 6211
N.A.I.C.S.: 523999

AMONEUS Grundstucks-Vermietungsgesellschaft mbH (1)
Mercedesstr 6
40470 Dusseldorf, Germany
Tel.: (49) 211 77080
Fax: (49) 211 77083156
Real Estate Management Services
S.I.C.: 6531
N.A.I.C.S.: 531390

AMTERA Grundstucks-Vermietungsgesellschaft mbH (1)
Mercedesstr 6
40470 Dusseldorf, Germany
Tel.: (49) 211 77080
Fax: (49) 211 77083156
Real Estate Management Services
S.I.C.: 6531
N.A.I.C.S.: 531390

ANBANA Grundstucks-Vermietungsgesellschaft mbH (1)
Mercedesstr 6
40470 Dusseldorf, Germany
Tel.: (49) 211 77080
Fax: (49) 211 77083156
Real Estate Management Services
S.I.C.: 6531
N.A.I.C.S.: 531390

ANCAVA Grundstucks-Vermietungsgesellschaft mbH (1)
Mercedesstr 6
40470 Dusseldorf, Germany
Tel.: (49) 211 77080
Fax: (49) 211 77083156
Real Estate Management Services
S.I.C.: 6531
N.A.I.C.S.: 531390

ANDROMEDA Verwaltungsgesellschaft mbH (1)
Mercedesstr 6
40470 Dusseldorf, Germany
Tel.: (49) 211 77080
Investment Management Services
S.I.C.: 6282
N.A.I.C.S.: 523920

ANEA Grundstucks-Vermietungsgesellschaft mbH (1)
Mercedesstr 6
40470 Dusseldorf, Germany
Tel.: (49) 211 77080
Fax: (49) 211 77083156
Real Estate Management Services
S.I.C.: 6531
N.A.I.C.S.: 531390

ARAFINA Grundstucks-Vermietungsgesellschaft mbH (1)
Mercedesstr 6
40470 Dusseldorf, Germany
Tel.: (49) 211 77080
Fax: (49) 211 77083156
Real Estate Management Services
S.I.C.: 6531
N.A.I.C.S.: 531390

AREBA Verwaltung und Treuhand GmbH (1)
Mercedesstr 6
40470 Dusseldorf, Germany
Tel.: (49) 211 77080
Fax: (49) 211 77083156
Real Estate Management Services
S.I.C.: 6531
N.A.I.C.S.: 531390

ARMANDA Flugzeug-Leasinggesellschaft mbH (1)
Mercedesstr 6
40470 Dusseldorf, Germany
Tel.: (49) 211 77080
Fax: (49) 211 77083156
Aircraft Leasing Services
S.I.C.: 7359
N.A.I.C.S.: 532411

ARQUATUS Grundstucks-Vermietungsgesellschaft mbH i.L. (1)
Mercedesstr 6
40470 Dusseldorf, Germany
Tel.: (49) 211 77080
Fax: (49) 211 77083156
Real Estate Management Services
S.I.C.: 6531
N.A.I.C.S.: 531390

ASCETO Grundstucks-Vermietungsgesellschaft mbH (1)
Mercedesstr 6
40470 Dusseldorf, Germany
Tel.: (49) 211 77080
Fax: (49) 211 77083156
Real Estate Management Services
S.I.C.: 6531
N.A.I.C.S.: 531390

ASERTUNA Grundstucks-Vermietungsgesellschaft mbH (1)
Mercedesstr 6
40470 Dusseldorf, Germany
Tel.: (49) 211 77080
Fax: (49) 211 77083156
Real Estate Management Services
S.I.C.: 6531
N.A.I.C.S.: 531390

ASKANZA Grundstucks-Vermietungsgesellschaft mbH & Co. Objekt Ludenscheid KG (1)
Mercedesstr 6
40470 Dusseldorf, Germany
Tel.: (49) 211 77080
Fax: (49) 211 77083156
Real Estate Management Services
S.I.C.: 6531
N.A.I.C.S.: 531390

ASKANZA Grundstucks-Vermietungsgesellschaft mbH (1)
Mercedesstr 6
40470 Dusseldorf, Germany
Tel.: (49) 211 77080
Fax: (49) 211 77083156
Real Estate Management Services
S.I.C.: 6531
N.A.I.C.S.: 531390

ASKIBA Grundstucks-Vermietungsgesellschaft mbH (1)
Mercedesstr 6
40470 Dusseldorf, Germany
Tel.: (49) 211 77080
Fax: (49) 211 77083156
Real Estate Management Services
S.I.C.: 6531
N.A.I.C.S.: 531390

ASSANDRA Grundstucks-Vermietungsgesellschaft mbH (1)
Mercedesstr 6
40470 Dusseldorf, Germany
Tel.: (49) 211 77080
Fax: (49) 211 77083156
Real Estate Management Services
S.I.C.: 6531
N.A.I.C.S.: 531390

ASSENTO Photovoltaik-Beteiligungsgesellschaft mbH (1)
Mercedesstr 6
40470 Dusseldorf, Germany
Tel.: (49) 211 77080
Fax: (49) 211 77083156
Photovoltaic Cell Mfr
S.I.C.: 3674
N.A.I.C.S.: 334413

ASSERTA Flugzeug-Leasinggesellschaft mbH (1)
Mercedesstr 6
40470 Dusseldorf, Germany
Tel.: (49) 211 77080
Fax: (49) 211 77083156
Aircraft Leasing Services
S.I.C.: 7359
N.A.I.C.S.: 532411

ATERNA Mobilien-Vermietungsgesellschaft mbH (1)
Friedrichstrasse 50
10117 Berlin, Germany
Tel.: (49) 30 20174910
Fax: (49) 30 20174930
Real Estate Management Services
S.I.C.: 6531
N.A.I.C.S.: 531390

Atlas Vermoegensverwaltungs GmbH (1)
Baurs Park 9
22587 Hamburg, Germany De
Tel.: (49) 215991550 (100%)
Banking Opers.
S.I.C.: 6159
N.A.I.C.S.: 522298

ATUNO Verwaltungund Treuhand GmbH (1)
Mercedesstr 6
40470 Dusseldorf, Germany
Tel.: (49) 211 77080
Fax: (49) 211 77083156
Financial Management Services
S.I.C.: 6211
N.A.I.C.S.: 523999

AURESTA Grundstucks-Vermietungsgesellschaft mbH (1)
Mercedesstr 6
40470 Dusseldorf, Nordrhein-Westfalen, Germany
Tel.: (49) 211 77080
Fax: (49) 211 77083156
Real Estate Development Services
S.I.C.: 6531
N.A.I.C.S.: 531390

Non-U.S. Subsidiary:

Banque Bauer (Suisse) SA (2)
Rue Jean Petitot 7
CH 1211 Geneva, Switzerland (100%)
Tel.: (41) 228191570

Commerzbank AG—(Continued)

Fax: (41) 228191599
E-Mail: info@banquebauer.ch
Web Site: www.banquebauer.ch
Sales Range: $1-9.9 Million
Emp.: 11
Commercial Banking
S.I.C.: 6029
N.A.I.C.S.: 522110
Dirk Hoffman *(Chm)*
Seuferle Johannes *(Mng Dir)*

AVANCIA Vermietungsgesellschaft mbH (1)
Mercedesstr 6
40470 Dusseldorf, Germany
Tel.: (49) 211 77080
Fax: (49) 211 77083156
Real Estate Management Services
S.I.C.: 6531
N.A.I.C.S.: 531390

AVARICA Grundstucks-Vermietungsgesellschaft mbH & Co. Objekt Munchberg KG (1)
Mercedesstr 6
40470 Dusseldorf, Germany
Tel.: (49) 211 77080
Fax: (49) 211 77083156
Real Estate Brokerage Services
S.I.C.: 6531
N.A.I.C.S.: 531210

AVARICA Grundstucks-Vermietungsgesellschaft mbH (1)
Mercedesstr 6
40470 Dusseldorf, Germany
Tel.: (49) 211 77080
Fax: (49) 211 77083156
Real Estate Management Services
S.I.C.: 6531
N.A.I.C.S.: 531390

AVERTUM Flugzeug-Leasinggesellschaft mbH & Co. Zweite Legacy 600 KG (1)
Mercedesstr 6
40470 Dusseldorf, Germany
Tel.: (49) 211 77080
Fax: (49) 211 77083156
Aircraft Rental & Leasing Services
S.I.C.: 7359
N.A.I.C.S.: 532411

AVERTUM Flugzeug-Leasinggesellschaft mbH (1)
Mercedesstr 6
40470 Dusseldorf, Germany
Tel.: (49) 211 77080
Fax: (49) 211 77083156
Aircraft Leasing Services
S.I.C.: 7359
N.A.I.C.S.: 532411

Beteiligungsgesellschaft fur Industrie und Handel mbH (1)
Kaiserstr 16
60311 Frankfurt am Main, Germany
Tel.: (49) 211 7 70 830
Financial Investment Services
S.I.C.: 6282
N.A.I.C.S.: 523930

BFC Berliner Film Companie Beteiligungsgesellschaft mbH (1)
Johannisstr 20
10117 Berlin, Germany
Tel.: (49) 30 726194621
Fax: (49) 30 726194609
Video Production Services
S.I.C.: 7812
N.A.I.C.S.: 512110

BONITAS Mobilien-Vermietungsgesellschaft mbH & Co. Objekt Neustadt-Schwaig KG (1)
Mercedesstr 6
40470 Dusseldorf, Germany
Tel.: (49) 211 77080
Fax: (49) 211 77083156
Automobile Leasing Services
S.I.C.: 7515
N.A.I.C.S.: 532112

CASIA Grundstuecks - Vermietungs- und Verwaltungsgesellschaft (1)
Dusseldorf, Germany (97.6%)
S.I.C.: 6159
N.A.I.C.S.: 522298

CB Euregio GmbH (1)
Kaiserstr 16
60311 Frankfurt am Main, Germany
Tel.: (49) 69 13620
Real Estate Management Services
S.I.C.: 6531
N.A.I.C.S.: 531390

CB Lux Kirchberg GmbH (1)
Kaiserstr 16
60311 Frankfurt am Main, Germany
Tel.: (49) 69 13620
Real Estate Management Services
S.I.C.: 6531
N.A.I.C.S.: 531390

CBG Commerz Beteiligungsgesellschaft Holding mbH (1)
Kaiserplatz
PO Box 2
60311 Frankfurt am Main, Germany (100%)
Tel.: (49) 6913643049
Fax: (49) 6913629336
E-Mail: cbg@commerzbank.com
Web Site: www.cbg.commerzbank.com
Emp.: 13
Private Equity & Venture Capital
S.I.C.: 6799
N.A.I.C.S.: 523910
Armin Schuler *(Chm)*

CBG Commerz (1)
Kaiserplatz
60261 Frankfurt am Main, Germany (100%)
Tel.: (49) 6913644494
Fax: (49) 6913629336
E-Mail: cbg@commerzbank.com
Web Site: www.cbg.commerzbank.de
Rev.: $5,159,550
Emp.: 20
Private Equity & Venture Capital Management
S.I.C.: 6799
N.A.I.C.S.: 523910
Klaus Sachse *(Mng Dir)*

CGG Canada Grundbesitz GmbH (1)
Klopstockstr 5
65187 Wiesbaden, Germany
Tel.: (49) 61171050
Financial Management Services
S.I.C.: 6211
N.A.I.C.S.: 523999

CGI mbH (1)
Kraussbarger Reng 56
65205 Wiesbaden, Germany (75%)
Tel.: (49) 6117105285
Fax: (49) 6117105189
E-Mail: info@commerz.com
Web Site: www.hausinvest.de
Emp.: 250
Corporate Banking Services
S.I.C.: 6159
N.A.I.C.S.: 522298
Heiko Beck *(Mng Dir)*

Collegium Glashutten Zentrum fur Kommunikation GmbH (1)
Wuestemser St 1
61479 Glashutten, Germany (100%)
Tel.: (49) 6082200
Fax: (49) 608220640
E-Mail: collres@commerzbank.com
Web Site: www.collegium-glashuetten.de
Emp.: 45
S.I.C.: 6159
N.A.I.C.S.: 522298
Anita Gunia *(Mng Dir)*

Comdirect Bank AG (1)
Pascalkehre 15
D 25451 Quickborn, Germany DE
Tel.: (49) 41067040 (100%)
Fax: (49) 41067083213
E-Mail: info@comdirect.de
Web Site: www.comdirect.de
Sales Range: $10-24.9 Million
Emp.: 1,000
Full Banking Services
S.I.C.: 6159
N.A.I.C.S.: 522298
Andre Carls *(CEO)*
Michael Mandel *(CEO)*

Commerz Building and Management GmbH (1)
Ruttenscheider Str 2
45128 Essen, Germany
Tel.: (49) 201 8219700
Fax: (49) 201 82197019
Residential Property Management Services
S.I.C.: 6531
N.A.I.C.S.: 531311

Commerz Business Consulting GmbH (1)
Mainzer Landstrasse 185 - 189
60327 Frankfurt am Main, Germany
Tel.: (49) 69 136 49971
Fax: (49) 69 136 49986
E-Mail: info@commerz-business-consulting.de
Web Site: www.commerz-business-consulting.de
Business Management Consulting Services
S.I.C.: 8748
N.A.I.C.S.: 541618

Commerz Finanz-Management GmbH (1)
KaiserStrasse 16
60261 Frankfurt am Main, Germany (100%)
Tel.: (49) 6913620
Fax: (49) 69285389
E-Mail: info@commerzbank.com
Web Site: www.commerzbank.de
Emp.: 1,000
Personal Asset Planning Services
S.I.C.: 6282
N.A.I.C.S.: 523930

Commerz Grundbesitz Investmentgesellschaft mbH (1)
Friedrich Str 25
D 65183 Wiesbaden, Germany (75%)
Tel.: (49) 611710501
Fax: (49) 61171055189
E-Mail: info@commerzreal.com
Web Site: www.hausinvest.com
Sales Range: $100-124.9 Million
Emp.: 200
Investment Services
S.I.C.: 6282
N.A.I.C.S.: 523930
Michael Bucker *(Mgr)*

Commerz Real AG (1)
Mercedesstrasse 6
D 40470 Dusseldorf, Germany (100%)
Tel.: (49) 21177080
Fax: (49) 21177083156
Web Site: www.commerzreal.com
Emp.: 300
Lessor in Real Estate Leasing Contracts
S.I.C.: 6513
N.A.I.C.S.: 531110
Michael Bucker *(Gen Mgr)*

Subsidiaries:

Commerz Real Asset Verwaltungs gesellschaft mbH (2)
Tolzer Strasse 2
82031 Grunwald, Germany
Tel.: (49) 89 15709 800
Fax: (49) 89 15709 816
Asset Management Services
S.I.C.: 6282
N.A.I.C.S.: 523920

Commerz Real Baucontract GmbH (2)
Mercedesstrasse 6
40470 Dusseldorf, Germany
Tel.: (49) 211 77080
Fax: (49) 211 77083156
Real Estate Management Services
S.I.C.: 6531
N.A.I.C.S.: 531390

Commerz Real Baumanagement GmbH (2)
Tolzer Str 2
82031 Grunwald, Germany
Tel.: (49) 89 15709800
Construction Management Services
S.I.C.: 1629
N.A.I.C.S.: 237990

Commerz Real Finanzierungsleasing GmbH (2)
Mercedesstr 6
40470 Dusseldorf, Germany
Tel.: (49) 211 77080
Real Estate Management Services
S.I.C.: 6531
N.A.I.C.S.: 531390

Commerz Real Fonds Beteiligungs-gesellschaft mbH (2)
Mercedesstrasse 6
40470 Dusseldorf, Germany
Tel.: (49) 211 77082200
Fax: (49) 211 77083281
E-Mail: cfb-fonds@commerzreal.com
Web Site: www.cfb-fonds.com
Sls.: $22,067,213
Emp.: 475
Fund Management Services
S.I.C.: 6726
N.A.I.C.S.: 525990
Michael Kohl *(Mng Dir)*

Commerz Real Immobilien GmbH (2)
Mercedesstr 6
40470 Dusseldorf, Germany
Tel.: (49) 211 77080
Fax: (49) 211 77083156
Real Estate Management Services
S.I.C.: 6531
N.A.I.C.S.: 531390

Commerz Real Investmentgesellschaft mbH (2)
Friedrichstrasse 25
65185 Wiesbaden, Germany
Tel.: (49) 611 71050
Fax: (49) 611 71055189
E-Mail: info@commerzreal.com
Web Site: berater.commerzreal.com
Emp.: 300
Real Estate Investment Services
S.I.C.: 6531
N.A.I.C.S.: 531390
Michael Becker *(CEO)*

Commerz Real Mobilienleasing GmbH (2)
Mercedesstrasse 6
40470 Dusseldorf, Germany
Tel.: (49) 211 7708 2332
Fax: (49) 211 7708 3330
E-Mail: crm.gf@commerzreal.com
Web Site: www.commerzreal.com
Industrial Machinery Leasing Services
S.I.C.: 7359
N.A.I.C.S.: 532490
Christian Bremser *(Gen Mgr)*

Subsidiaries:

Commerz Real Direkt GmbH i.L. (3)
Mercedesstr 6
40470 Dusseldorf, Germany
Tel.: (49) 69 239121
Real Estate Management Services
S.I.C.: 6531
N.A.I.C.S.: 531390

Commerz Real IT-Leasing GmbH (3)
Mercedesstrasse 6
40470 Dusseldorf, Germany
Tel.: (49) 211 77082389
Fax: (49) 211 77083330
E-Mail: it@commerzreal.com
Web Site: www.commerzreal.com
Emp.: 500
Financial Management Services
S.I.C.: 6211
N.A.I.C.S.: 523999
Michael Buecker *(Gen Mgr)*

Commerz Real Mietkauf GmbH (3)
Mercedesstrasse 6
40470 Dusseldorf, Germany
Tel.: (49) 211 77080
Fax: (49) 211 77083156
Real Estate Management Services
S.I.C.: 6531
N.A.I.C.S.: 531390

Commerz Real Partner Sud GmbH (2)
Mercedesstr 6
40470 Dusseldorf, Germany
Tel.: (49) 211 77080
Fax: (49) 211 77083156
Real Estate Management Services
S.I.C.: 6531
N.A.I.C.S.: 531390

Commerz Real Projektconsult GmbH (2)
Mercedesstr 6
40470 Dusseldorf, Nordrhein-Westfalen, Germany
Tel.: (49) 0211 77080
Fax: (49) 211 770831
E-Mail: info@commerzreal.com
Emp.: 300
Real Estate Management Services
S.I.C.: 6531
N.A.I.C.S.: 531390

Commerz Real Vertrieb GmbH (2)
Mercedesstr 6
40470 Dusseldorf, Nordrhein-Westfalen, Germany
Tel.: (49) 211 77082131
Real Estate Development Services
S.I.C.: 6531
N.A.I.C.S.: 531390

Commerz Real Verwaltung und Treuhand GmbH (2)
Mercedesstr 6
40470 Dusseldorf, Germany
Tel.: (49) 211 77080
Fax: (49) 211 77083156
Real Estate Management Services
S.I.C.: 6531
N.A.I.C.S.: 531390

Non-U.S. Subsidiary:

CeGeREAL SA (2)
21-25 rue Balzac
75008 Paris, France (60%)
Tel.: (33) 142257636
Fax: (33) 142257637
E-Mail: info@cegereal.com
Web Site: www.cegereal.com
CGR—(EUR)
Rev.: $52,006,586
Assets: $1,231,325,545
Liabilities: $567,129,305
Net Worth: $664,196,239
Earnings: $22,696,426
Emp.: 3
Fiscal Year-end: 12/31/12
Real Estate Investments
S.I.C.: 6531
N.A.I.C.S.: 531390
Richard Wrigley *(Chm)*
Raphael Treguier *(CEO)*
Carl-Christian Siegel *(Deputy CEO-Real Estate)*

Commerz Real Autoservice GmbH i.L. (1)
Ludwig-Erhard-Allee 9
40227 Dusseldorf, Germany
Tel.: (49) 211 77080
Automobile Leasing Services
S.I.C.: 7515
N.A.I.C.S.: 532112

Commerz Real Western Europe GmbH (1)
Friedrichstr 25
65185 Wiesbaden, Germany
Tel.: (49) 611 7105 0
Real Estate Management Services
S.I.C.: 6531
N.A.I.C.S.: 531390

Commerz Systems GmbH (1)
Theodor-Heuss-Allee 80
60486 Frankfurt am Main, Germany
Tel.: (49) 69136 43100
Fax: (49) 69136 40033
E-Mail: info@commerzsystems.de
Web Site: www.commerzsystems.de
Information Technology Consulting Services
S.I.C.: 7373
N.A.I.C.S.: 541512
Wolfgang Ganzke *(CEO)*

Commerz Transaction Services Mitte GmbH (1)
Juri-Gagarin-Ring 86
99084 Erfurt, Germany
Tel.: (49) 361 67870
Fax: (49) 361 6787600
Financial Transaction Processing Services
S.I.C.: 6099
N.A.I.C.S.: 522320

Commerz Transaction Services Nord GmbH (1)
Lorenzweg 42
39124 Magdeburg, Germany
Tel.: (49) 391 74488100
Fax: (49) 391 74488110
Emp.: 260
Financial Transaction Processing Services
S.I.C.: 6099
N.A.I.C.S.: 522320
Lars Najda *(Gen Mgr)*

Commerz Transaction Services West GmbH (1)
Unionstr 3
Hamm, 59067, Germany
Tel.: (49) 691 3620
Financial Transaction Processing Services
S.I.C.: 6099
N.A.I.C.S.: 522320

Commerzbank Auslandsbanken Holding AG (1)
Kaiserstrasse 16
60311 Frankfurt am Main, Germany
Tel.: (49) 69 13620
Fax: (49) 69 285389
Investment Management Services
S.I.C.: 6799
N.A.I.C.S.: 523920

Commerzbank Auslandsbanken Holding Nova GmbH (1)
Kaiserstr 16
60311 Frankfurt, Hessen, Germany
Tel.: (49) 6913620
Investment Management Services
S.I.C.: 6799
N.A.I.C.S.: 523920

Commerzbank Immobilien- und Vermogensverwaltungsgesellschaft mbH (1)
Kaiserstr 16
60311 Frankfurt, Germany
Tel.: (49) 6913620
Fax: (49) 69285389
Commerical Banking Services
S.I.C.: 6029
N.A.I.C.S.: 522110
Martin Blessing *(CEO)*

Commerzbank Inlandsbanken Holding GmbH (1)
Kaiserstrasse 16
Frankfurt am Main, 60311, Germany
Tel.: (49) 69 271 190
Fax: (49) 69 285 389
Investment Management Services
S.I.C.: 6282
N.A.I.C.S.: 523920

Commerzbank (1)
Kaiserstrasse 16
60311 Frankfurt, Germany (100%)
Tel.: (49) 6913643049
Fax: (49) 6913629336
E-Mail: cbg@commerzbank.com
Web Site: www.cbg.commerzbank.de
Emp.: 11
Private Equity & Venture Capital Management
S.I.C.: 6799
N.A.I.C.S.: 523910
Armin Schuler *(Mng Dir)*

CommerzFactoring GmbH (1)
Grosse Bleiche 15
55116 Mainz, Germany
Tel.: (49) 6131261460
Fax: (49) 6131261459
E-Mail: info@commerzfactoring.de
Web Site: www.commerzfactoring.de
Financial Management Services
S.I.C.: 6211
N.A.I.C.S.: 523999
Julian Kox *(Mng Dir)*

CommerzKommunalbau GmbH (1)
Ludwig-Erhard-Allee 9
40227 Dusseldorf, Germany
Tel.: (49) 211 77080
Fax: (49) 211 77083156
Financial Investment Services
S.I.C.: 6282
N.A.I.C.S.: 523930

CommerzLeasing und Immobilien GmbH (1)
Mercedesstrasse 6
D 40470 Dusseldorf, Germany (100%)
Tel.: (49) 21177080
Fax: (49) 2117708156
E-Mail: info@commerzreal.com
Web Site: www.commerzreal.com
Emp.: 1,500
Leasing & Real Estate Financing
S.I.C.: 6159
N.A.I.C.S.: 522294
Jurgen A. Gawron *(Mng Dir)*
Ebernard Graf *(Mng Dir)*

Subsidiaries:

ALTINUM GVG mbH & Co. Sonnenhof (2)
Sonninstrasse 24-28
20097 Hamburg, Germany (100%)
Corporate Banking Services
S.I.C.: 6159
N.A.I.C.S.: 522298

CFB Commerz Fonds Beteiligungs GmbH (2)
Mercedesstrasse 6
40470 Dusseldorf, Germany (100%)
Tel.: (49) 2117708200
Fax: (49) 2117708280
Web Site: www.commerzleasing.com
Emp.: 300
Closed-End Funds for German Equity Market; Leasing Fund Service
S.I.C.: 6726
N.A.I.C.S.: 525990

Commerz Immobilien GmbH (2)
Mercedes Strasse 6
40470 Dusseldorf, Germany (100%)
Tel.: (49) 21177080
Fax: (49) 21177083367
E-Mail: info@commerzraal.com
Web Site: www.commerzleasing.com
Int. Income: $63,576,072
Emp.: 500
Corporate Banking Services
S.I.C.: 6211
N.A.I.C.S.: 523110
Monika Wirghs *(Mgr)*

CommerzLeasing GmbH (2)
Ludwig-Landmann-Str 349
60487 Frankfurt am Main, Germany
Tel.: (49) 69 979929 01
Fax: (49) 69 97992930
Investment Management Services
S.I.C.: 6282
N.A.I.C.S.: 523920

FABA Vermietungsgesellschaft mbH (2)
Kaiserplatz
D 60311 Frankfurt am Main, Germany (95%)
Tel.: (49) 69 13620
Banking Services
S.I.C.: 6159
N.A.I.C.S.: 522298

Non-U.S. Subsidiary:

BRE Leasing Sp. z o.o. (2)
Ul Ks I Skorupki 5
00 963 Warsaw, Poland PL (51%)
Tel.: (48) 223201800
Fax: (48) 226257236
E-Mail: info@bre-leasing.com.pl
Web Site: www.bre-leasing.com.pl
Emp.: 160
S.I.C.: 6159
N.A.I.C.S.: 522298

Subsidiary:

BREL-COM Sp. z o. o. (3)
ul Ks I Skorupki 5
00-963 Warsaw, Poland
Tel.: (48) 22 320 1800
Fax: (48) 22 625 7236
Financial Investment Services
S.I.C.: 6211
N.A.I.C.S.: 523999

CommerzTrust GmbH (1)
Gallusanlage 2
60329 Frankfurt am Main, Germany
Tel.: (49) 69 13654233
Fax: (49) 69 13655141
E-Mail: info@commerztrust.com
Web Site: www.commerztrust.de
Emp.: 9
Pension Fund Management Services
S.I.C.: 6371
N.A.I.C.S.: 525110
Joerg Haarhus *(Mng Dir)*

CRI Zweite Beteiligungsgesellschaft mbH (1)
Friedrichstr 25
65185 Wiesbaden, Germany
Tel.: (49) 611 71050
Fax: (49) 611 7105209
Real Estate Management Services
S.I.C.: 6531
N.A.I.C.S.: 531390

Deutsche Schiffsbank AG (1)
Domshof 17
D 28195 Bremen, Germany De
Mailing Address: (100%)
PO Box 10 62 69
D-28062 Bremen, Germany
Tel.: (49) 42136090
Fax: (49) 4213609326
E-Mail: info@schiffsbank.com
Web Site: www.schiffsbank.com
Emp.: 168
Cargo Ship Financing & Mortgage Loan Services
S.I.C.: 6153
N.A.I.C.S.: 522220
Jochen Klosgoo *(Chm-Supervisory Bd)*
Stefan Otto *(Chm-Mgmt Bd)*
Klaus Muller-Gebel *(Deputy Chm-Supervisory Bd)*
Rainer Jakubowski *(Member-Mgmt Bd)*
Tobias Muller *(Member-Mgmt Bd)*

Direktservice Commerz GmbH (1)
Am Silberpalais 1
47057 Duisburg, Germany
Tel.: (49) 1802266906
Fax: (49) 1802266905
E-Mail: kontakt@commerzdirektservice.de
Web Site: www.commerzdirektservice.com
Financial & Insurance Products Advisory & Support Service; Technical Assistance; Direct Sales; Consulting Services
S.I.C.: 6726
N.A.I.C.S.: 525990
Stefan Homp *(Mng Dir)*

Dr. Gubelt Immobilien Vermietungs-Gesellschaft mbH & Co. Objekt Chemnitz KG (1)
Mercedesstr 6
40470 Dusseldorf, Germany
Tel.: (49) 21 17 70 80
Real Estate Management Services
S.I.C.: 6531
N.A.I.C.S.: 531390

Dresdner Bank AG (1)
Jurgen Ponto Platz 1
60301 Frankfurt am Main, Germany
Tel.: (49) 692630
Telex: 415-240
Fax: (49) 692634831
E-Mail: info@dresdner-bank.com
Web Site: www.dresdner-bank.com
Sales Range: $800-899.9 Million
Emp.: 21,341
Banking Services
S.I.C.: 6029
N.A.I.C.S.: 522110
Klaus-Peter Muller *(Chm-Supervisory Bd)*
Claudia Eggert-Lehmann *(Vice Chm-Supervisory Bd)*
Martin Blessing *(Chm-Mng Dir-Commerzbank)*
Andree Moschner *(Mng Dir-Private & Corp Clients)*
Markus Beumer *(Mng Dir)*
Wolfgang Hartmann *(Mng Dir)*
Achim Kassow *(Mng Dir)*
Michael Reuther *(Mng Dir)*
Eric Strutz *(CFO)*
Frank Annuscheit *(COO-Commerzbank AG)*
Wulf Meier *(Chief HR Officer)*
Stefan Schmittmann *(Chief Risk Officer)*

Subsidiaries:

KGAL GmbH & Co. KG (2)
Tolzer Strasse 15
82031 Grunwald, Germany
Tel.: (49) 89641430
Fax: (49) 8964143150
E-Mail: kgal@kgal.de
Web Site: www.kgal-gruppe.de
Emp.: 500
Debt Financing
S.I.C.: 6141

Commerzbank AG—(Continued)

N.A.I.C.S.: 522293
Georg Reul *(CEO)*

Subsidiary:

AL.systems GmbH (3)
Toelzer Strasse 15
82031 Grunwald, Germany
Tel.: (49) 896283410
Fax: (49) 8964143612
E-Mail: maria.meier@kgal.de
Web Site: www.kgal.de
Emp.: 350
IT Support & Services
S.I.C.: 8748
N.A.I.C.S.: 541618
Maria Meier *(Mgr-Svc)*

Joint Ventures:

AL Ships GmbH (3)
Toelzer Strasse 15
82031 Grunwald, Germany
Tel.: (49) 8964143424
Fax: (49) 8964143612
Web Site: www.kgal.de
Emp.: 10
Ship Management Services
S.I.C.: 4499
N.A.I.C.S.: 488390
Jochen Korber *(Mng Dir)*

GOAL German Operating Aircraft Leasing GmbH (3)
Tolzer Str 15
Grunwald, 82031 Munich, Germany De
Tel.: (49) 8964143152
Fax: (49) 8964143611
Web Site: www.goal-leasing.de
Aircraft Leasing Services; Owned 60% by Commerzbank AG & 40% by Deutsche Lufthansa AG
S.I.C.: 7359
N.A.I.C.S.: 532411
Michael Radunz *(Mng Dir)*
Christian Schloemann *(Mng Dir)*

Lufthansa Leasing GmbH (3)
Toelzer Strasse 15
82031 Grunwald, Germany De
Tel.: (49) 8964143203
Fax: (49) 8964143611
Emp.: 10
Aircraft Leasing Services; Owned 51% by Commerzbank AG & 49% by Deutsche Lufthansa AG
S.I.C.: 7359
N.A.I.C.S.: 532411
Jochen Hoerger *(Mng Dir)*
Markus Ott *(Mng Dir)*

Non-U.S. Subsidiaries:

AL.I.NA Fund Management Inc. (3)
70 University Avenue, Suite 1410
Toronto, ON, M5J 2M4, Canada
Tel.: (416) 595-5335
Fax: (416) 595-5678
Real Estate Investments
S.I.C.: 6531
N.A.I.C.S.: 531390

EUROASSET Italia S.r.l. (3)
Piazza Velasca 4
20122 Milan, Italy
Tel.: (39) 028696101
Fax: (39) 028696102
Web Site: www.kgal-gruppe.de/web/content.jsp?nodeId=3853&lang=de
Real Estate Investments
S.I.C.: 6531
N.A.I.C.S.: 531390

KGAL Asset Management Osterreich GmbH (3)
BC 20 Dresdner Strasse 45
1200 Vienna, Austria
Tel.: (43) 133448290
Fax: (43) 1334482920
Web Site: www.kgal.de/web/content.jsp?nodeId=3998&lang=en
Real Estate Investment Services
S.I.C.: 6531
N.A.I.C.S.: 531390
Thomas Krischke *(Mng Dir)*

Reuschel & Co. Kommanditgesellschaft (2)
Maximiliansplatz 13
80285 Munich, Germany
Tel.: (49) 8923950
Fax: (49) 89291180
E-Mail: info@reuschel.com
Web Site: www.donner-reuschel.de
Emp.: 500
Banking Services
S.I.C.: 6029
N.A.I.C.S.: 522110

Non-U.S. Subsidiaries:

Commerzbank Holdings (UK) Limited (2)
30 Gresham Street
London, EC2V 3PG, United Kingdom UK
Mailing Address:
PO Box 52715
London, EC2P 2XY, United Kingdom
Tel.: (44) 2076537000
Web Site: www2.commerzbank.com
Emp.: 6,000
International Banking, Securities Trading & Venture Capital Services
S.I.C.: 6726
N.A.I.C.S.: 525990
Herbert Walter *(Chm)*
Martin Blessing *(CEO)*

U.S. Subsidiaries:

Commerzbank (3)
2 World Financial Ctr
New York, NY 10281 DE
Tel.: (212) 969-2700
Emp.: 766
Investment Banking Services
S.I.C.: 6211
N.A.I.C.S.: 523110

Non-U.S. Subsidiaries:

Dresdner Kleinwort Deutschland GmbH (3)
Theodor Heuss Allee 44 46
60486 Frankfurt, Germany
Mailing Address:
Juergen-Ponto-Platz 1
60301 Frankfurt, Germany
Tel.: (49) 697130
Fax: (49) 004969713
Web Site: www.dresdnerkleinwort.de
Investment Banking
S.I.C.: 6211
N.A.I.C.S.: 523110
Manfred Fleckenstein *(Head-Global Cash Mgmt)*

Dresdner Kleinwort France SA (3)
5 Blvd De La Madeleine
75001 Paris, France
Tel.: (33) 170368500
Telex: 630591
Fax: (33) 170368560
Web Site: www.bkid.com
Emp.: 40
Investment Banking
S.I.C.: 6211
N.A.I.C.S.: 523110
Pavid Manson *(Mng Dir)*

Dresdner Kleinwort Limited (3)
21/F Cheung Kong Ctr
2 Queens Rd, Central, China (Hong Kong)
Tel.: (852) 4724888
Telex: 73953
Emp.: 20
Investment Banking
S.I.C.: 6211
N.A.I.C.S.: 523110

Dresdner Kleinwort Malaysia (3)
9th Floor Wisma Genting
28 Jalan Sultan Ismail, Kuala Lumpur, 50250, Malaysia
Tel.: (60) 3 2072 1988
Investment Banking Services
S.I.C.: 6211
N.A.I.C.S.: 523110

Dresdner Kleinwort Shanghai (3)
39th Floor Jin Mao Tower
88 Century Boulevard, Shanghai, 200120, China
Tel.: (86) 21 3866 5588
Investment Banking Services
S.I.C.: 6211
N.A.I.C.S.: 523110

Dresdner Kleinwort Singapore (3)
20 Collyer Quay 22-00 Tung Ctr
Singapore, 049319, Singapore
Tel.: (65) 6222 8080
Fax: (65) 6224 4008
Emp.: 100
Investment Banking Services
S.I.C.: 6211
N.A.I.C.S.: 523110
Herbert Walter *(Mng Dir)*

Dresdner Kleinwort (3)
Plac Trzech Krzyzy 18
00-499 Warsaw, Poland
Tel.: (48) 225253000
Fax: (48) 225253409
Web Site: www.Dresdner-bank.pl
Emp.: 35
Investment Bank
S.I.C.: 6211
N.A.I.C.S.: 523110
Witold Grzeskowiak *(Mgr)*

Dresdner Bank Mexico S.A. (2)
Bosque De Alisos No 47 A 4th Fl
Col Bosques De Las Lomas
05120 Mexico, DF, Mexico
Tel.: (52) 5552583000
Telex: 1772518
Fax: (52) 52583199
E-Mail: Mexico@dbla.com
Web Site: www.dbla.com
Emp.: 21
Investment Bank
S.I.C.: 6211
N.A.I.C.S.: 523110

Dresdner Bank ZAO (2)
23 Malaya Morskaya Ul
190000 Saint Petersburg, Russia
Tel.: (7) 8121185151
Telex: 12.1086NPDBRU
Fax: (7) 8121185411
E-Mail: info.russia@bkid.com
Web Site: www.dresdner-bank.ru
Sales Range: Less than $1 Million
Emp.: 150
Banking Services
S.I.C.: 6099
N.A.I.C.S.: 522320
Igor Repin *(Pres)*

Branch:

Dresdner Bank Zao (3)
30 Podsosensky Pereulok
Moscow, 103062, Russia
Tel.: (7) 495737-3450
Fax: (7) 4957373451
Web Site: www.dresdner.ru
Emp.: 100
Investment Bank
S.I.C.: 6211
N.A.I.C.S.: 523110
Victor Shevchenko *(Gen Dir)*

DSB Vermogensverwaltungs-gesellschaft mbH (1)
Am Lunedeich 136
27572 Bremerhaven, Germany
Tel.: (49) 17664114963
Investment Management Services
S.I.C.: 6282
N.A.I.C.S.: 523920

Einunddreissigste DRESIB Beteiligungs-Gesellschaft mbH (1)
Jurgen-Ponto-Platz 1
60329 Frankfurt am Main, Germany
Tel.: (49) 69 13654233
Financial Investment Services
S.I.C.: 6282
N.A.I.C.S.: 523930

EuREAM GmbH (1)
Friedrichstr 25
65183 Wiesbaden, Germany
Tel.: (49) 61171050
Fax: (49) 61171055189
Emp.: 300
Financial Management Services
S.I.C.: 6211
N.A.I.C.S.: 523999
Michael Bucker *(Gen Mgr)*

Non-U.S. Subsidiary:

Eurohypo Europaische Hypothekenbank S.A. (2)
Airport Ctr 5 Rue Heienhaff
L-1736 Senningerberg, Luxembourg
Tel.: (352) 26345511
Fax: (352) 263455222
E-Mail: info.lux@hypothekenbankfranfurt.com
Web Site: www.hypothekenbankfranfurt.lu
Emp.: 34
Mortgage Banking Services
S.I.C.: 6163
N.A.I.C.S.: 522310
Ralf Woitschig *(Chm)*

Eurohypo AG (1)
Helfmann-Park 5
65760 Eschborn, Germany (100%)
Tel.: (49) 6925480
Telex: 41 855 43
Fax: (49) 69254888888
Web Site: www.eurohypo.com
Emp.: 100
Mortgage Lending Services
S.I.C.: 6159
N.A.I.C.S.: 522292
Jochen Klosges *(Chm-Supervisory Bd)*
Thomas Bley *(Member-Mgmt Bd-Risk Mgmt & Fin & Restructuring)*
Ralf Woitschig *(Member-Mgmt Bd-Pub Fin, IT & Treasury)*

Subsidiaries:

Forum Immobiliengesellschaft mbH (2)
Rosental 102
53111 Bonn, Germany
Tel.: (49) 2284490133
Fax: (49) 2284490153
E-Mail: info@forum-immo.de
Web Site: www.forum-immo.de
Real Estate Development Services
S.I.C.: 6531
N.A.I.C.S.: 531390

Futura Hochhausprojektgesellschaft mbH (2)
Helfmann-Park 5
65760 Eschborn, Germany
Tel.: (49) 69 25480
Construction Management Services
S.I.C.: 1629
N.A.I.C.S.: 237990

G-G-B Gebaude- und Grundbesitz GmbH (2)
Helfmann-Park 5
65760 Eschborn, Germany
Tel.: (49) 6925480
Real Estate Development Services
S.I.C.: 6531
N.A.I.C.S.: 531390

gr Grundstucks GmbH Objekt Corvus & Co. (2)
Eschborner Landstr 42
60489 Frankfurt, Germany
Tel.: (49) 6974749690
Fax: (49) 69747496910
E-Mail: info@commerzbankfrankfurt.de
Real Estate Development Services
S.I.C.: 6531
N.A.I.C.S.: 531390

IVV Immobilien-Verwaltungs- und Verwertungsgesellschaft mbH (2)
Helfmann-Park 5
65760 Eschborn, Germany
Tel.: (49) 69 25 48 0
Fax: (49) 69 25 48 81935
Real Estate Agencies
S.I.C.: 6531
N.A.I.C.S.: 531390

Nordboden Immobilien- und Handelsgesellschaft mbH (2)
Helfmann-Park 5
65760 Eschborn, Germany
Tel.: (49) 69 254827265
Real Estate Management Services
S.I.C.: 6531
N.A.I.C.S.: 531390

Property Invest GmbH (2)
Helfmann-Park 5
Eschborn, 65760, Germany
Tel.: (49) 69 25480
Real Estate Development Services
S.I.C.: 6531
N.A.I.C.S.: 531390

TARA Immobiliengesellschaft mbH (2)
Helfmann-Park 5
65760 Eschborn, Germany

Tel.: (49) 69 25480
Real Estate Development Services
S.I.C.: 6531
N.A.I.C.S.: 531390

TARA Immobilienprojekte GmbH (2)
Helfmann-Park 5
65760 Eschborn, Hessen, Germany
Tel.: (49) 69 25480
Real Estate Development Services
S.I.C.: 6531
N.A.I.C.S.: 531390

TARA Property Management GmbH (2)
Helfmann-Park 5
65760 Eschborn, Germany
Tel.: (49) 6925480
Real Estate Development Services
S.I.C.: 6531
N.A.I.C.S.: 531390

Unica Immobiliengesellschaft mbH (2)
Helfmann-Park 5
65760 Eschborn, Germany
Tel.: (49) 69 254821935
Real Estate Management Services
S.I.C.: 6531
N.A.I.C.S.: 531390

WESTBODEN-Bau- und Verwaltungsgesellschaft mbH (2)
Helfmann-Park 5
65760 Eschborn, Germany
Tel.: (49) 69 23820
Fax: (49) 69 2382526
Real Estate Development Services
S.I.C.: 6531
N.A.I.C.S.: 531390

Westend Grundstucksgesellschaft mbH (2)
Helfmann-Park 5
65760 Eschborn, Germany
Tel.: (49) 6925480
Real Estate Management Services
S.I.C.: 6531
N.A.I.C.S.: 531390

European Bank for Fund Services Gesellschaft mit beschrankter Haftung (1)
Bahnhofstrasse 20
85609 Aschheim, Germany
Tel.: (49) 89 4 54 60890
Fax: (49) 894 54 60892
Financial Investment Services
S.I.C.: 6282
N.A.I.C.S.: 523930

FM LeasingPartner GmbH (1)
Gewerbepark 33 - 35
49143 Bissendorf, Germany
Tel.: (49) 5402 9202100
Fax: (49) 5402 920299
E-Mail: info@fm-leasingpartner.de
Web Site: www.fm-leasingpartner.de
Financial Management Services
S.I.C.: 6211
N.A.I.C.S.: 523999
Wolfgang Muller *(Mng Dir)*

Gesellschaft fur Kreditsicherung mbH (1)
Burgstr 28
10178 Berlin, Germany
Tel.: (49) 30 16632301
Fax: (49) 30 16632299
Credit Protection Services
S.I.C.: 7299
N.A.I.C.S.: 812990

GRANADA Investment GmbH i.L. (1)
Mercedesstr 6
40470 Dusseldorf, Germany
Tel.: (49) 21177080
Financial Management Services
S.I.C.: 6211
N.A.I.C.S.: 523999

Grundbesitzgesellschaft Berlin mbH (1)
Helfmann-Park 5
65760 Eschborn, Germany
Tel.: (49) 6925480
Real Estate Management Services
S.I.C.: 6531
N.A.I.C.S.: 531390

Grundstucks- und Vermogensverwaltungsgesellschaft Geretsried mbH (1)
Oderstrasse 59
40470 Dusseldorf, Germany
Tel.: (49) 21177080
Financial Investment Services
S.I.C.: 6282
N.A.I.C.S.: 523930

GVG Gesellschaft zur Verwertung von Grundbesitz mit beschrankter Haftung (1)
Helfmann-Park 5
65760 Eschborn, Germany
Tel.: (49) 6925480
Real Estate Development Services
S.I.C.: 6531
N.A.I.C.S.: 531390

Non-U.S. Branch:

Eurohypo Europaische Hypothekenbank S.A. Dublin Branch (2)
Commerzbank House
Guild St, Dublin, 1, Ireland
Tel.: (353) 16491618
Fax: (353) 16491622
E-Mail: eurohypo.dublin@eurohypo.com
Web Site: www.eurohypo.lu
Emp.: 14
S.I.C.: 6159
N.A.I.C.S.: 522298

H 47 GmbH & Co. KG (1)
Mercedesstr 6
40470 Dusseldorf, Germany
Tel.: (49) 2177080
Fax: (49) 21177083156
Real Estate Agency Services
S.I.C.: 6531
N.A.I.C.S.: 531210

H 47 Verwaltungsgesellschaft mbH (1)
Mercedesstr 6
40470 Dusseldorf, Germany
Tel.: (49) 211 77080
Fax: (49) 211 77083156
Financial Investment Services
S.I.C.: 6282
N.A.I.C.S.: 523930

Hibernia Beta Beteiligungsgesellschaft mit beschrankter Haftung (1)
Kaiserstr 16
60311 Frankfurt am Main, Germany
Tel.: (49) 6913620
Fax: (49) 69 285389
Financial Management Services
S.I.C.: 6211
N.A.I.C.S.: 523999

Hibernia Gamma Beteiligungsgesellschaft mit beschrankter Haftung (1)
Kaiserstr 16
60311 Frankfurt am Main, Germany
Tel.: (49) 69 13620
Real Estate Management Services
S.I.C.: 6531
N.A.I.C.S.: 531390

Hibernia Sigma Beteiligungsgesellschaft mit beschrankter Haftung (1)
Neue Mainzer str 32-36
60311 Frankfurt am Main, Germany
Tel.: (49) 6913620
Fax: (49) 69285389
Financial Investment Services
S.I.C.: 6282
N.A.I.C.S.: 523930

HVI Handels- und Verwertungsgesellschaft fur Immobilien mbH (1)
Mercedesstr 6
40470 Dusseldorf, Germany
Tel.: (49) 21177080
Fax: (49) 211 77083156
Real Estate Management Services
S.I.C.: 6531
N.A.I.C.S.: 531390

Immobilien-Vermietungsgesellschaft Reeder & Co. Objekt Airport Burocenter Dresden KG (1)
Mercedesstr 6
40470 Dusseldorf, Germany
Tel.: (49) 21177080
Real Estate Brokerage Services
S.I.C.: 6531
N.A.I.C.S.: 531210

Immobilienverwaltungs- und Vertriebsgesellschaft Villen am Glienicker Horn mbH (1)
Potsdamer Str 125
10783 Berlin, Germany
Tel.: (49) 3026532633
Real Estate Management Services
S.I.C.: 6531
N.A.I.C.S.: 531390

Immobilienverwaltungsgesellschaft Grammophon Buropark mbH (1)
Potsdamer Str 125
Berlin, 10783, Germany
Tel.: (49) 30 26532633
Real Estate Management Services
S.I.C.: 6531
N.A.I.C.S.: 531390

Immobilienverwaltungsgesellschaft Schlachthof Offenbach mbH (1)
Helfmann-Park 5
65760 Eschborn, Germany
Tel.: (49) 69 298980
Property Management Services
S.I.C.: 6282
N.A.I.C.S.: 523920

IWP International West Pictures GmbH & Co. Erste Produktions KG (1)
Stadtwaldgurtel 13
50935 Cologne, Germany
Tel.: (49) 22194997166
Business Management Consulting Services
S.I.C.: 8748
N.A.I.C.S.: 541618

KENSTONE GmbH (1)
Helfmann-Park 5
65760 Eschborn, Germany
Tel.: (49) 307001765165
Fax: (49) 307001765199
E-Mail: info@kenstone.de
Web Site: www.kenstone.de
Emp.: 40
Real Estate Management Services
S.I.C.: 6531
N.A.I.C.S.: 531390
Christoph Kettel *(Chm-Supervisory Bd)*
Martinus Kurth *(Co-Mng Dir)*
Guenter Wattig *(Co-Mng Dir)*

Kommanditgesellschaft MS "CPO ALICANTE" Offen Reederei GmbH & Co. (1)
Bleichenbruke 10
20354 Hamburg, Germany
Tel.: (49) 40 348430
Marine Transportation Services
S.I.C.: 4499
N.A.I.C.S.: 488390

Kommanditgesellschaft MS CPO ANCONA Offen Reederei GmbH & Co. (1)
Bleichenbruke 10
20354 Hamburg, Germany
Tel.: (49) 40 348430
Freight Shipping Services
S.I.C.: 4731
N.A.I.C.S.: 488510

Kommanditgesellschaft MS "CPO BILBAO" Offen Reederei GmbH & Co. (1)
Bleichenbruke 10
20354 Hamburg, Germany
Tel.: (49) 40 348430
Commercial Banking Services
S.I.C.: 6029
N.A.I.C.S.: 522110

Kommanditgesellschaft MS CPO MARSEILLE Offen Reederei GmbH & Co. (1)
Bleichenbruke 10
20354 Hamburg, Germany
Tel.: (49) 40 348430
Fax: (49) 40 34843170
Freight Shipping Services
S.I.C.: 4731
N.A.I.C.S.: 488510

Kommanditgesellschaft MS CPO PALERMO Offen Reederei GmbH & Co. (1)
Bleichenbruke 10
20354 Hamburg, Germany
Tel.: (49) 40 348430
Freight Shipping Services
S.I.C.: 4731
N.A.I.C.S.: 488510

Kommanditgesellschaft MS "CPO TOULON" Offen Reederei GmbH & Co. (1)
Bleichenbruke 10
20354 Hamburg, Germany
Tel.: (49) 40 348430
Marine Transportation Services
S.I.C.: 4499
N.A.I.C.S.: 488390

Kommanditgesellschaft MS CPO VALENCIA Offen Reederei GmbH & Co. (1)
Bleichenbruke 10
20354 Hamburg, Germany
Tel.: (49) 40 348430
Fax: (49) 40 34843170
Freight Shipping Services
S.I.C.: 4731
N.A.I.C.S.: 488510

KTC Kommunikations- und Trainings-Center Konigstein GmbH (1)
Olmuhlweg 65
61462 Konigstein, Germany
Tel.: (49) 6174 29 51 00
Fax: (49) 6174 29 51 60
E-Mail: info@ktc-koenigstein.com
Web Site: www.ktc-koenigstein.com
Emp.: 120
Hotel Management Services
S.I.C.: 7011
N.A.I.C.S.: 721110
Sandra Trost *(Mng Dir)*

LAUREA MOLARIS Grundstucks-Vermietungsgesellschaft mbH & Co. Objekt Berlin Anthropolis KG (1)
Mercedesstr 6
40470 Dusseldorf, Germany
Tel.: (49) 211 77080
Real Estate Management Services
S.I.C.: 6531
N.A.I.C.S.: 531390

LAUREA MOLARIS Grundstucks-Vermietungsgesellschaft mbH (1)
Mercedesstr 6
40470 Dusseldorf, Germany
Tel.: (49) 21177080
Fax: (49) 21177083156
Real Estate Management Services
S.I.C.: 6531
N.A.I.C.S.: 531390

LOFRA GmbH & Co.KG (1)
80 Frankfurt Department
60261 Frankfurt am Main, Germany
Tel.: (49) 69 13620
Real Estate Development Services
S.I.C.: 6531
N.A.I.C.S.: 531390

LOFRA Verwaltungs-Gesellschaft mbH (1)
Jurgen-Ponto-Platz
60329 Frankfurt am Main, Germany
Tel.: (49) 21177080
Financial Investment Services
S.I.C.: 6282
N.A.I.C.S.: 523930

LUGO Photovoltaik-Beteiligungsgesellschaft mbH & Co. Objekt El Baldio 1 KG (1)
Mercedesstr 6
40470 Dusseldorf, Germany
Tel.: (49) 21177080
Photovoltaic Cell Mfr
S.I.C.: 3674
N.A.I.C.S.: 334413

Commerzbank AG—(Continued)

LUGO Photovoltaik Beteiligungsgesellschaft mbH (1)
Mercedesstr 6
40470 Dusseldorf, Germany
Tel.: (49) 211 77080
Fax: (49) 211 77083156
Photovoltaic Cell Mfr
S.I.C.: 3674
N.A.I.C.S.: 334413

Messestadt Riem Office am See I GmbH (1)
Helfmann-Park 5
65760 Eschborn, Germany
Tel.: (49) 69 254829242
Real Estate Management Services
S.I.C.: 6531
N.A.I.C.S.: 531390

Messestadt Riem Office am See II GmbH (1)
Helfmann-Park 5
65760 Eschborn, Germany
Tel.: (49) 69 254821316
Real Estate Management Services
S.I.C.: 6531
N.A.I.C.S.: 531390

MOLBINA Vermietungsgesellschaft mbH & Co. Objekt Dusseldorf Ludwig-Erhard-Allee KG (1)
Mercedesstr 6
40470 Dusseldorf, Germany
Tel.: (49) 211 77080
Fax: (49) 211 77083156
Real Estate Management Services
S.I.C.: 6531
N.A.I.C.S.: 531390

MOLMELFI Vermietungsgesellschaft mbH & Co. Objekt Burghausen KG (1)
Mercedesstr 6
40470 Dusseldorf, Germany
Tel.: (49) 211 77080
Fax: (49) 211 77083156
Real Estate Management Services
S.I.C.: 6531
N.A.I.C.S.: 531390

MOLRATUS Vermietungsgesellschaft mbH & Co. Objekt Loxstedt KG (1)
Mercedesstr 6
40470 Dusseldorf, Germany
Tel.: (49) 211 77080
Fax: (49) 211 77083156
Real Estate Management Services
S.I.C.: 6531
N.A.I.C.S.: 531390

MOLRATUS Vermietungsgesellschaft mbH (1)
Mercedesstr 6
40470 Dusseldorf, Germany
Tel.: (49) 211 77080
Fax: (49) 211 77083156
Real Estate Management Services
S.I.C.: 6531
N.A.I.C.S.: 531390

MONEA Vermietungsgesellschaft mbH (1)
Mercedesstr 6
40470 Dusseldorf, Germany
Tel.: (49) 211 77080
Fax: (49) 211 77083156
Real Estate Management Services
S.I.C.: 6531
N.A.I.C.S.: 531390

NACONEO Schiffsbetriebsgesellschaft mbH i.L. (1)
Am Sandtorkai 62
20457 Hamburg, Germany
Tel.: (49) 4034809010
Freight Shipping Services
S.I.C.: 4731
N.A.I.C.S.: 488510

NACONGA Schiffsbetriebsgesellschaft mbH (1)
Am Sandtorkai 62
20457 Hamburg, Germany
Tel.: (49) 40 348430
Investment Management Services
S.I.C.: 6282
N.A.I.C.S.: 523920

NACORINO Schiffsbetriebsgesellschaft mbH i.L. (1)
Am Sandtorkai 62
20457 Hamburg, Germany
Tel.: (49) 211 77080
Freight Shipping Services
S.I.C.: 4731
N.A.I.C.S.: 488510

NACORONA Schiffsbetriebsgesellschaft mbH i.L. (1)
Am Sandtorkai 62
20457 Hamburg, Germany
Tel.: (49) 211 77080
Freight Shipping Services
S.I.C.: 4731
N.A.I.C.S.: 488510

NACOTA Schiffsbetriebsgesellschaft mbH i.L. (1)
Am Sandtorkai 62
20457 Hamburg, Germany
Tel.: (49) 211 77080
Freight Shipping Services
S.I.C.: 4731
N.A.I.C.S.: 488510

NAFIRINA Schiffsbetriebsgesellschaft mbH (1)
Am Sandtorkai 62
20457 Hamburg, Germany
Tel.: (49) 211 77080
Freight Shipping Services
S.I.C.: 4731
N.A.I.C.S.: 488510

NAMINO Schiffsbetriebsgesellschaft mbH i.L. (1)
Am Sandtorkai 62
20457 Hamburg, Germany
Tel.: (49) 211 77080
Freight Shipping Services
S.I.C.: 4731
N.A.I.C.S.: 488510

NAROLA Schiffsbetriebsgesellschaft mbH i.L. (1)
Am Sandtorkai 62
20457 Hamburg, Germany
Tel.: (49) 211 77080
Freight Shipping Services
S.I.C.: 4731
N.A.I.C.S.: 488510

NAUCULA Schiffsbetriebsgesellschaft mbH (1)
Am Sandtorkai 62 Dock 4
20457 Hamburg, Germany
Tel.: (49) 40 349090 10
Fax: (49) 40 34809040
Freight Shipping Services
S.I.C.: 4731
N.A.I.C.S.: 488510

NAULUMO Schiffsbetriebsgesellschaft mbH (1)
Am Sandtorkai 62
20457 Hamburg, Germany
Tel.: (49) 211 77082802
Freight Shipping Services
S.I.C.: 4731
N.A.I.C.S.: 488510

NAUMOSA Schiffsbetriebsgesellschaft mbH i.L. (1)
Am Sandtorkai 62
Hamburg Hamburg, Germany
Tel.: (49) 4034809010
Fax: (49) 4034809040
Freight Shipping Services
S.I.C.: 4731
N.A.I.C.S.: 488510

NAUPEUS Schiffsbetriebsgesellschaft mbH i.L. (1)
Am Sandtorkai 62
20457 Hamburg, Germany
Tel.: (49) 4034809010
Freight Shipping Services
S.I.C.: 4731
N.A.I.C.S.: 488510

NAURANTO Schiffsbetriebsgesellschaft mbH (1)
Am Sandtorkai 62
20457 Hamburg, Germany
Tel.: (49) 4034809010
Fax: (49) 4034809040
Freight Shipping Services
S.I.C.: 4731
N.A.I.C.S.: 488510

NAURATA Schiffsbetriebsgesellschaft mbH (1)
Am Sandtorkai 62 Dock 4
20457 Hamburg, Germany
Tel.: (49) 40 348090 10
Fax: (49) 40 34809040
Freight Shipping Services
S.I.C.: 4731
N.A.I.C.S.: 488510

NAUSOLA Schiffsbetriebsgesellschaft mbH (1)
Am Sandtorkai 62 Dock 4
20457 Hamburg, Germany
Tel.: (49) 4034809010
Fax: (49) 4034809040
Freight Shipping Services
S.I.C.: 4731
N.A.I.C.S.: 488510

NAUTARO Schiffsbetriebsgesellschaft mbH (1)
Am Sandtorkai 62dock 4
20457 Hamburg, Germany
Tel.: (49) 40 34 80 90 10
Freight Shipping Services
S.I.C.: 4731
N.A.I.C.S.: 488510

NAUTESSA Schiffsbetriebsgesellschaft mbH (1)
Am Sandtorkai 62
20457 Hamburg, Germany
Tel.: (49) 2117082802
Freight Shipping Services
S.I.C.: 4731
N.A.I.C.S.: 488510

NAUTIS Schiffsbetriebsgesellschaft mbH (1)
Am Sandtorkai 62 Dock 4
20457 Hamburg, Germany
Tel.: (49) 40 34809010
Freight Shipping Services
S.I.C.: 4731
N.A.I.C.S.: 488510

NAUTLUS Schiffsbetriebsgesellschaft mbH (1)
Am Sandtorkai 62
20457 Hamburg, Germany
Tel.: (49) 4034809010
Fax: (49) 4034809040
Freight Shipping Services
S.I.C.: 4731
N.A.I.C.S.: 488510

NAUTORIA Schiffsbetriebsgesellschaft mbH (1)
Am Sandtorkai 62
20457 Hamburg, Germany
Tel.: (49) 69 13622255
Investment Management Services
S.I.C.: 6282
N.A.I.C.S.: 523920

NAUTUGO Schiffsbetriebsgesellschaft mbH (1)
Am Sandtorkai 62 Dock 4
20457 Hamburg, Germany
Tel.: (49) 4034809010
Freight Shipping Services
S.I.C.: 4731
N.A.I.C.S.: 488510

NAVALIS Schiffsbetriebsgesellschaft mbH (1)
Am Sandtorkai 62 Dock 4
20457 Hamburg, Germany
Tel.: (49) 40 34809010
Investment Management Services
S.I.C.: 6799
N.A.I.C.S.: 523920

NAVIGA Schiffsbeteiligung GmbH (1)
Am Sandtorkai 62
20457 Hamburg, Germany
Tel.: (49) 40 23909640
Financial Investment Services
S.I.C.: 6282
N.A.I.C.S.: 523930

NAVIGOLO Schiffsbetriebsgesellschaft mbH (1)
Am Sandtorkai 62
20457 Hamburg, Germany
Tel.: (49) 4034809010
Freight Shipping Services
S.I.C.: 4731
N.A.I.C.S.: 488510

NAVILO Vermietungsgesellschaft mbH (1)
Am Sandtorkai 62
20457 Hamburg, Germany
Tel.: (49) 40 34809010
Real Estate Management Services
S.I.C.: 6531
N.A.I.C.S.: 531390

NAVIPOS Schiffsbeteiligungsgesellschaft mbH (1)
Am Sandtorkai 62
20457 Hamburg, Germany
Tel.: (49) 40 348090
Investment Management Services
S.I.C.: 6799
N.A.I.C.S.: 523920

NAVIRENA Schiffsbetriebsgesellschaft mbH (1)
Am Sandtorkai 62
20457 Hamburg, Germany
Tel.: (49) 40 348430
Freight Shipping Services
S.I.C.: 4731
N.A.I.C.S.: 488510

NAVITA Schiffsbetriebsgesellschaft mbH (1)
Am Sandtorkai 62
20457 Hamburg, Germany
Tel.: (49) 4034809010
Freight Shipping Services
S.I.C.: 4731
N.A.I.C.S.: 488510

NAVITONI Schiffsbetriebsgesellschaft mbH (1)
Am Sandtorkai 62 Dock 4
20457 Hamburg, Germany
Tel.: (49) 4034809010
Freight Shipping Services
S.I.C.: 4731
N.A.I.C.S.: 488510

NAVITOSA Schiffsbetriebsgesellschaft mbH (1)
Am Sandtorkai 62
20457 Hamburg, Germany
Tel.: (49) 211 77080
Freight Shipping Services
S.I.C.: 4731
N.A.I.C.S.: 488510

NEPTANA Schiffsbetriebsgesellschaft mbH (1)
Am Sandtorkai 62
20457 Hamburg, Germany
Tel.: (49) 4034809010
Fax: (49) 4034809040
Business Management Consulting Services
S.I.C.: 8748
N.A.I.C.S.: 541618

NEPTILA Schiffsbetriebsgesellschaft mbH (1)
Am Sandtorkai 62
20457 Hamburg, Germany
Tel.: (49) 40 34809010
Freight Shipping Services
S.I.C.: 4731
N.A.I.C.S.: 488510

NEPTORA Schiffsbetriebsgesellschaft mbH (1)
Am Sandtorkai 62
20457 Hamburg, Germany
Tel.: (49) 211 77080
Freight Shipping Services
S.I.C.: 4731
N.A.I.C.S.: 488510

NEPTUNO Schiffsbetriebsgesellschaft mbH (1)
Am Sandtorkai 62
20457 Hamburg, Germany
Tel.: (49) 21177082200
Fax: (49) 21177083281
Financial Management Services

S.I.C.: 6211
N.A.I.C.S.: 523999

NESTOR Grundstucks-Vermietungsgesellschaft mbH (1)
Mercedesstr 6
40470 Dusseldorf, Germany
Tel.: (49) 211 77080
Fax: (49) 211 77083156
Real Estate Management Services
S.I.C.: 6531
N.A.I.C.S.: 531390

NORA Grundstucks-Vermietungsgesellschaft mbH & Co. Objekt Lampertheim KG (1)
Mercedesstr 6
40470 Dusseldorf, Germany
Tel.: (49) 211 77080
Fax: (49) 211 77083156
Real Estate Management Services
S.I.C.: 6531
N.A.I.C.S.: 531390

NORA Grundstucks-Vermietungsgesellschaft mbH & Co. Objekte Plon und Preetz KG (1)
Mercedesstr 6
40470 Dusseldorf, Germany
Tel.: (49) 211 77 08 2371
Fax: (49) 211 77 08 3156
Real Estate Management Services
S.I.C.: 6531
N.A.I.C.S.: 531390

NORA Grundstucks-Vermietungsgesellschaft mbH (1)
Mercedesstr 6
40470 Dusseldorf, Germany
Tel.: (49) 211 77080
Fax: (49) 211 77083156
Real Estate Management Services
S.I.C.: 6531
N.A.I.C.S.: 531390

NOSCO Grundstucks-Vermietungsgesellschaft mbH (1)
Grosse Bleiche 35-37
55116 Mainz, Germany
Tel.: (49) 61312020
Real Estate Brokerage Services
S.I.C.: 6531
N.A.I.C.S.: 531210

NOTITIA Grundstucks-Vermietungsgesellschaft mbH (1)
Friedrichstr 50-55
10117 Berlin, Germany
Tel.: (49) 211 77082372
Fax: (49) 211 77089372
Real Estate Management Services
S.I.C.: 6531
N.A.I.C.S.: 531390

NOVELLA Grundstucks-Vermietungsgesellschaft mbH (1)
Mercedesstr 6
40470 Dusseldorf, Germany
Tel.: (49) 211 77080
Fax: (49) 211 77083156
Real Estate Management Services
S.I.C.: 6531
N.A.I.C.S.: 531390

NOVELLA GV GmbH (1)
Ludwig-Erhard-Allee 9
40227 Dusseldorf, Germany (100%)
Corporate Banking Services
S.I.C.: 6159
N.A.I.C.S.: 522298

Number X Real Estate GmbH (1)
Helfmann-Park 5
65760 Eschborn, Germany
Tel.: (49) 69254821935
Fax: (49) 69254888888
Real Estate Development Services
S.I.C.: 6531
N.A.I.C.S.: 531390

NUMERIA Grundstucks-Vermietungsgesellschaft mbH (1)
Mercedesstr 6
40470 Dusseldorf, Germany
Tel.: (49) 211 77080
Financial Investment Services
S.I.C.: 6282
N.A.I.C.S.: 523930

NURUS Beteiligungsgesellschaft mbH (1)
Mercedesstr 6
40470 Dusseldorf, Germany
Tel.: (49) 211 77080
Fax: (49) 211 77083156
Real Estate Management Services
S.I.C.: 6531
N.A.I.C.S.: 531390

OLEANDRA Grundstucks-Vermietungs- gesellschaft mbH & Co. Objekt Luna KG (1)
Mercedesstr 6
40470 Dusseldorf, Germany
Tel.: (49) 211 770 80
Real Estate Management Services
S.I.C.: 6531
N.A.I.C.S.: 531390

OLEANDRA Grundstucks-Vermietungs- gesellschaft mbH & Co. Objekt Pluto KG (1)
Tolzer Str 2
82031 Grunwald, Germany
Tel.: (49) 211 77080
Real Estate Management Services
S.I.C.: 6531
N.A.I.C.S.: 531390

OLEANDRA Grundstucks-Vermietungs- gesellschaft mbH & Co. Objekt Venus KG (1)
Tolzer Str 2
82031 Grunwald, Germany
Tel.: (49) 211 77080
Financial Investment Services
S.I.C.: 6282
N.A.I.C.S.: 523930

OLEANDRA GV GmbH & Co. Objekt Luna KG (1)
Dusseldorf, Germany (100%)
S.I.C.: 6159
N.A.I.C.S.: 522298

OSKAR Medienbeteiligungsgesellschaft mbH (1)
Mercedesstr 6
40470 Dusseldorf, Germany
Tel.: (49) 211 77080
Fax: (49) 211 77083156
Financial Management Services
S.I.C.: 6211
N.A.I.C.S.: 523999

RAMONIA Grundstucks-Vermietungsgesellschaft mbH (1)
Mercedesstr 6
40470 Dusseldorf, Germany
Tel.: (49) 211 77080
Fax: (49) 211 77083156
Real Estate Management Services
S.I.C.: 6531
N.A.I.C.S.: 531390

RAPIDA Grundstucks-Vermietungsgesellschaft mbH (1)
Mercedesstr 6
40470 Dusseldorf, Germany
Tel.: (49) 211 77080
Fax: (49) 211 77083156
Real Estate Management Services
S.I.C.: 6531
N.A.I.C.S.: 531390

Real Estate TOP TEGEL Drei GmbH (1)
Wittestrasse 30 House J Level 1
13509 Berlin, Germany
Tel.: (49) 3088092113
Fax: (49) 3088092201
E-Mail: info@toptegel.de
Real Estate Development Services
S.I.C.: 6531
N.A.I.C.S.: 531390

Real Estate TOP TEGEL Eins GmbH (1)
Helfmann Park 5
65760 Eschborn, Germany
Tel.: (49) 6925480
Fax: (49) 6925486113
Real Estate Development Services
S.I.C.: 6531
N.A.I.C.S.: 531390

Real Estate TOP TEGEL Sechs GmbH (1)
Wittestrasse 30 Haus J Ebene 1
13509 Berlin, Germany
Tel.: (49) 30 43091219
Fax: (49) 30 88722875
Emp.: 10
Real Estate Development Services
S.I.C.: 6531
N.A.I.C.S.: 531390
Stephen Petersen *(Gen Mgr)*

Real Estate TOP TEGEL Vier GmbH (1)
Helfmann-Park 5
65760 Eschborn, Germany
Tel.: (49) 69254821935
Real Estate Development Services
S.I.C.: 6531
N.A.I.C.S.: 531390

Real Estate TOP TEGEL Zwei GmbH (1)
Helfmann-Park
65760 Eschborn, Germany
Tel.: (49) 69254821935
Real Estate Development Services
S.I.C.: 6531
N.A.I.C.S.: 531390

RESIDO Flugzeug-Leasinggesellschaft mbH (1)
Mercedesstr 6
40470 Dusseldorf, Germany
Tel.: (49) 211 77080
Fax: (49) 211 77083156
Aircraft Leasing Services
S.I.C.: 7359
N.A.I.C.S.: 532411

RIMA Medien-Beteiligungsgesellschaft mbH i.L. (1)
Ludwig-Erhard-Allee 9
40227 Dusseldorf, Germany
Tel.: (49) 211 77080
Fax: (49) 211 77083156
Investment Management Services
S.I.C.: 6282
N.A.I.C.S.: 523920

RIPA Medien-Beteiligungsgesellschaft mbH (1)
Mercedesstr 6
40470 Dusseldorf, Germany
Tel.: (49) 21177080
Fax: (49) 21177083156
Investment Management Services
S.I.C.: 6282
N.A.I.C.S.: 523920

ROSARIA Grundstucks-Vermietungsgesellschaft mbH & Co. Objekt Baden-Airpark KG (1)
Ludwig-Erhard-Allee 9
40227 Dusseldorf, Germany
Tel.: (49) 211 77080
Fax: (49) 211 77083156
Aircraft Leasing Services
S.I.C.: 7359
N.A.I.C.S.: 532411

ROSARIA Grundstucks-Vermietungsgesellschaft mbH (1)
Mercedesstr 6
40470 Dusseldorf, Germany
Tel.: (49) 211 77080
Fax: (49) 211 77083156
Real Estate Management Services
S.I.C.: 6531
N.A.I.C.S.: 531390

ROSATA Grundstucks-Vermietungsgesellschaft mbH (1)
Mercedesstr 6
40470 Dusseldorf, Germany
Tel.: (49) 211 77082429
Real Estate Management Services
S.I.C.: 6531
N.A.I.C.S.: 531390

ROSINTA Grundstucks-Vermietungsgesellschaft mbH (1)
Mercedesstr 6
40470 Dusseldorf, Germany
Tel.: (49) 21177080
Fax: (49) 21177083156
Real Estate Management Services
S.I.C.: 6531
N.A.I.C.S.: 531390

ROSOLA Grundstucks-Vermietungsgesellschaft mbH (1)
Mercedesstr 6
40470 Dusseldorf, Germany
Tel.: (49) 211 77080
Fax: (49) 211 77083156
Real Estate Management Services
S.I.C.: 6531
N.A.I.C.S.: 531390

ROTUNDA Grundstucks-Vermietungsgesellschaft mbH (1)
Ludwig-Erhard-Allee 9
40227 Dusseldorf, Germany
Tel.: (49) 211 77080
Fax: (49) 211 77 08 31 56
Real Estate Management Services
S.I.C.: 6531
N.A.I.C.S.: 531390

SECUNDO Grundstucks-Vermietungsgesellschaft mbH (1)
Mercedesstr 6
40470 Dusseldorf, Germany
Tel.: (49) 211 77080
Fax: (49) 211 77083156
Financial Investment Services
S.I.C.: 6282
N.A.I.C.S.: 523930

Service-Center Inkasso GmbH (1)
Fritz-Vomfelde-Strasse 12
Dusseldorf, 40547, Germany
Tel.: (49) 1622 158 753
Financial Investment Services
S.I.C.: 6282
N.A.I.C.S.: 523930

SOLTRX Transaction Services GmbH (1)
Wiesenstrasse 70 b 5
40549 Dusseldorf, Germany
Tel.: (49) 211506550
Fax: (49) 211506554220
E-Mail: info@s-t-services.com
Web Site: www.s-t-services.com
Financial Transaction Processing Services
S.I.C.: 6099
N.A.I.C.S.: 522320

Suddeutsche Industrie-Beteiligungs-GmbH (1)
Gallusanlage 8
Frankfurt am Main, 60329, Germany
Tel.: (49) 69 2633406
Financial Investment Services
S.I.C.: 6282
N.A.I.C.S.: 523930

TARA Immobilien-Besitz GmbH (1)
Helfmann-Park 5
65760 Eschborn, Germany
Tel.: (49) 69254821935
Real Estate Development Services
S.I.C.: 6531
N.A.I.C.S.: 531390

TIGNARIS Beteiligungsgesellschaft mbH & Co. Objekt Ostfildern KG (1)
Mercedesstr 6
40470 Dusseldorf, Germany
Tel.: (49) 211 77080
Fax: (49) 211 77083156
Investment Management Services
S.I.C.: 6799
N.A.I.C.S.: 523920

TIGNARIS Beteiligungsgesellschaft mbH & Co. Streubesitz KG (1)
Mercedesstr 6
40470 Dusseldorf, Germany
Tel.: (49) 211 77080
Fax: (49) 211 77083156
Financial Management Services
S.I.C.: 6211
N.A.I.C.S.: 523999

TOMO Vermogensverwaltungsgesellschaft mbH (1)
Kaiserstr 16
60311 Frankfurt am Main, Germany
Tel.: (49) 69 13649971
Asset Management Services
S.I.C.: 6282
N.A.I.C.S.: 523920

U.S. Subsidiaries:

Commerz Markets LLC (1)
2 World Financial Ctr
New York, NY 10281-1050

Commerzbank AG—(Continued)

Tel.: (212) 266-7200
Fax: (212) 266-7235
Securities Brokerage Services
S.I.C.: 6211
N.A.I.C.S.: 523120
John Geremia *(Mgr)*

Commerzbank Capital Markets Corporation **(1)**
2 World Financial Ctr 31st Fl
New York, NY 10281-1050 (100%)
Tel.: (212) 703-4000
Telex: 672 1062
Fax: (212) 703-4001
Web Site: www.commerzbank.us/commerzbank_us/en/metanavigation/locations_ny_popup.htm
Emp.: 270
Financial Services
S.I.C.: 6159
N.A.I.C.S.: 522298

Commerzbank Futures LLC **(1)**
2 World Financial Ctr
New York, NY 10281-1008 (100%)
Tel.: (312) 360-1175
Fax: (312) 360-1176
Emp.: 22
Financial & Banking Services
S.I.C.: 6221
N.A.I.C.S.: 523130

Commerzbank U.S. Finance, Inc. **(1)**
55 Broad St
New York, NY 10004-2501
Tel.: (212) 244-1500
Financial Management Services
S.I.C.: 6211
N.A.I.C.S.: 523999

Dresdner Kleinwort Holdings II, Inc. **(1)**
2 World Financial Ctr
New York, NY 10281
Tel.: (212) 969-2700
Investment Management Services
S.I.C.: 6799
N.A.I.C.S.: 523920

Dresdner Kleinwort Holdings LLC **(1)**
2 World Financial Ctr
New York, NY 10281
Tel.: (212) 969-2700
Investment Management Services
S.I.C.: 6282
N.A.I.C.S.: 523920

Dresdner Kleinwort Pfandbriefe Investments II, Inc. **(1)**
103 Foulk Rd
Wilmington, DE 19803-3742
Tel.: (302) 691-6328
Financial Investment Services
S.I.C.: 6211
N.A.I.C.S.: 523999

Sterling Energy LLC **(1)**
1225 17th St Ste 2520
Denver, CO 80202
Tel.: (720) 881-7100
Electric Power Generation Services
S.I.C.: 4931
N.A.I.C.S.: 221118
John Brouillette *(Dir-Land & Legal)*

U.S. Representative Office:

Commerzbank AG - New York Branch **(1)**
2 World Financial Ctr
New York, NY 10281-1008 (100%)
Tel.: (212) 266-7200
Telex: 667488 cbk
Fax: (212) 266-7235
E-Mail: cbmailbox@cbkna.com
Web Site: www.cbkna.com
Emp.: 300
Banking
S.I.C.: 6211
N.A.I.C.S.: 523110
Martin Preissler *(Mng Dir-Client Relationship Mgmt)*

Non-U.S. Subsidiaries:

AMBRESA Sp. z.o.o. **(1)**
Senatorska 18
Warsaw, Poland
Tel.: (48) 228291597
Fax: (48) 228291598
Financial Management Services
S.I.C.: 6211
N.A.I.C.S.: 523999

Bankowy Dom Hipoteczny Sp. z. o.o. **(1)**
M st Warszawa Armii Ludowej 26
00-609 Warsaw, Poland
Tel.: (48) 22 579 75 12
Real Estate Management Services
S.I.C.: 6531
N.A.I.C.S.: 531390

BRE Bank **(1)**
Ul Senatorska 18
PO Box 728
00 950 Warsaw, Poland (75%)
Tel.: (48) 228290000
Fax: (48) 228290033
E-Mail: info@brebank.de
Web Site: www.brebank.de
Emp.: 400
Corporate Banking Services
S.I.C.: 6029
N.A.I.C.S.: 522110
Cezary Stypulkowski *(Pres)*

Subsidiaries:

BRE Corporate Finance S.A. **(2)**
ul Wspolna 47/49
00-684 Warsaw, Poland
Tel.: (48) 22 33 22 000
Fax: (48) 22 33 22 001
E-Mail: office@bcf.pl
Web Site: www.bcf.pl
Emp.: 30
Investment Banking Services
S.I.C.: 6211
N.A.I.C.S.: 523110
Piotr Galazka *(Chm)*
Leszek Filipowicz *(Vice Chm)*

BRE Faktoring S.A. **(2)**
Ul Krolewska 14
00-065 Warsaw, Poland
Tel.: (48) 22 829 14 60
Fax: (48) 22 829 14 99
E-Mail: kontakt@brefaktoring.pl
Web Site: www.brefaktoring.pl
Emp.: 55
Factoring Services
S.I.C.: 6159
N.A.I.C.S.: 522298
Miroslaw Jakowiecki *(Chm)*

BRE Holding Sp. z o.o. **(2)**
Senatorska 18/3
Warsaw, Poland
Tel.: (48) 228291206
Investment Management Services
S.I.C.: 6282
N.A.I.C.S.: 523920

BRE Property Partner Sp. z o.o. **(2)**
ul Krolewska 14
00-065 Warsaw, Poland
Tel.: (48) 22 526 74 02
Fax: (48) 22 526 74 03
Web Site: www.brepp.pl
Real Estate Development Services
S.I.C.: 6531
N.A.I.C.S.: 531390

BRE Ubezpieczenia TUiR SA **(2)**
Ul Ks I Skorupki 5
00-963 Warsaw, Poland
Tel.: (48) 22 444 70 01
Fax: (48) 22 444 70 02
E-Mail: biuro@breubezpieczenia.pl
Web Site: www.breubezpieczenia.pl
Insurance Management Services
S.I.C.: 6411
N.A.I.C.S.: 524298
Pawel Zylm *(CEO)*

BRE Wealth Management S.A. **(2)**
ul Krolewska 14
00-065 Warsaw, Poland
Tel.: (48) 22 526 78 78
Fax: (48) 22 829 11 11
Web Site: www.brebank.pl/uslugi_finansowe/oferta_Grupy_BRE_Banku/BRE_Wealth_Management/kontakt/
Asset Management Services
S.I.C.: 6799
N.A.I.C.S.: 523920
Malgorzata Janczewska *(Pres)*

BRE.locum S.A. **(2)**
ul Piotrkowska 173
90-447 Lodz, Poland
Tel.: (48) 42 230 10 57
Fax: (48) 42 230 10 58
E-Mail: bre.locum@brelocum.pl
Web Site: www.brelocum.pl
Real Estate Development Services
S.I.C.: 6531
N.A.I.C.S.: 531390

Dom Inwestycyjny BRE Banku SA **(2)**
ul Wspolna 47/49
00-684 Warsaw, Poland
Tel.: (48) 22 697 47 00
Fax: (48) 22 697 48 20
E-Mail: brebrokers@dibre.pl
Web Site: www.dibre.pl
Securities Brokerage Services
S.I.C.: 6231
N.A.I.C.S.: 523210
Hans Dieter Kemler *(Chm-Supervisory Bd)*
Jaroslaw Kowalczuk *(Pres)*

Garbary Sp. z o.o. **(2)**
Ul Garbary 101/111
61-757 Poznan, Poland
Tel.: (48) 61 8513750
Fax: (48) 61 8513876
E-Mail: biuro@garbary.pl
Web Site: www.garbary.pl
Real Estate Development Services
S.I.C.: 6531
N.A.I.C.S.: 531390

Non-U.S. Subsidiary:

Transfinance a.s. **(2)**
Corso Karlin Krizikova 237/36a
PO BOX 13
186 00 Prague, Czech Republic
Tel.: (420) 225 98 25 11
Fax: (420) 225 98 25 61
E-Mail: info@transfinance.cz
Web Site: www.transfinance.cz
Emp.: 26
Financial Support Services
S.I.C.: 6211
N.A.I.C.S.: 523999
Jana Nemeckova *(Chm)*
Henryk Okrzeja *(Chm-Supervisory Bd)*

CG Real Estate Luxemburg S.a.r.l. **(1)**
25 Rue Edward Steichen
2540 Luxembourg, Luxembourg
Tel.: (352) 47 79 11 25 02
Fax: (352) 47 79 11 25 99
Real Estate Development Services
S.I.C.: 6531
N.A.I.C.S.: 531390

Commerz (East Asia) Ltd. **(1)**
29/F Two International Finance Ctr 8
Finance St Ctr
Hong Kong, China (Hong Kong) (100%)
Mailing Address:
GPO Box 11378
Hong Kong, China (Hong Kong)
Tel.: (852) 28429609
Fax: (852) 39880900
E-Mail: info@commerzbank.com
Web Site: www.commerzbank.com
Emp.: 80
Banking Services
S.I.C.: 6159
N.A.I.C.S.: 522298
Eberhard Brodhage *(Gen Mgr)*

Commerz Funds Solutions S.A. **(1)**
Rue Edward Steichen
2540 Luxembourg, Luxembourg
Tel.: (352) 2708 2641
Fax: (352) 2708 2650
E-Mail: cfs-info@commerzbank.lu
Web Site: www.commerzfundssolutions.com
Financial Management Services
S.I.C.: 6211
N.A.I.C.S.: 523999

Commerz Grundbesitz Gestao de Centros Commerciais, Sociedade Unipessoal, Lda. **(1)**
R Carmo 2
Lisbon, 1200-094, Portugal
Tel.: (351) 213210600
Fax: (351) 213210601
Emp.: 4
Financial Management Services
S.I.C.: 6211
N.A.I.C.S.: 523999

Commerz (Nederland) N.V. **(1)**
Strawinskylaan 2501
1077 ZZ Amsterdam, Netherlands
Tel.: (31) 205574911
Fax: (31) 205574618
Web Site: www.commerzbank.nl
Investment Banking Services
S.I.C.: 6211
N.A.I.C.S.: 523110
Dirk Dreiskamper *(Country Mgr)*

Commerz Nominees Limited **(1)**
30 Gresham Street
London, EC2V 7PG, United Kingdom
Tel.: (44) 20 7623 8000
Security Brokerage Services
S.I.C.: 6211
N.A.I.C.S.: 523120

Commerz Securities Hong Kong Limited **(1)**
29/F Two International Finance Centre 8
Finance Street
Central, China (Hong Kong)
Tel.: (852) 39 88 09 88
Fax: (852) 39 88 09 00
Security Brokerage Services
S.I.C.: 6211
N.A.I.C.S.: 523120

Commerzbank AG (South East Asia) Ltd. **(1)**
8 Shenton Way Temasek Tower 42 01
Singapore, 68811, Singapore (100%)
Tel.: (65) 63110000
Telex: rs 27189 cbksin
Fax: (65) 62253943
E-Mail: info@commerzbank.com.sg
Web Site: www.commerbank.com
Emp.: 150
Bank Holding Company; Regional Managing Office
S.I.C.: 6712
N.A.I.C.S.: 551111

Branch:

Commerzbank AG - Singapore Branch **(2)**
71 Robinson Road 12-01
68811 Singapore, Singapore (100%)
Tel.: (65) 62234855
Fax: (65) 62253943
E-Mail: info@commerzbank.com.sg
Web Site: www.commerzbank.com
Emp.: 250
S.I.C.: 6159
N.A.I.C.S.: 522298
Dirk Verlage *(Gen Mgr)*

Commerzbank Belgium S.A.N.V. **(1)**
Blvd Louis Schmidt 29
1040 Brussels, Belgium (100%)
Tel.: (32) 27431811
Fax: (32) 27431837
Web Site: www.commerzbank.com
Emp.: 51
International Banking Services
S.I.C.: 6159
N.A.I.C.S.: 522298
Andrew Gerland *(Mgr)*

Commerzbank (Budapest) RT **(1)**
Szechenyi Rakpart 8
H 1054 Budapest, Hungary (100%)
Tel.: (36) 013748100
Telex: 202663 cbkbp h
Fax: (36) 62549347
E-Mail: info.budapest@commerzbank.com
Web Site: www.commerzbank.hu
Emp.: 160
Corporate Banking Services
S.I.C.: 6159
N.A.I.C.S.: 522298
Andres Kozma *(CEO)*

Commerzbank Capital Investment Company Limited **(1)**
30 Gresham Street
London, EC2V 7PG, United Kingdom
Tel.: (44) 20 7623 8000
Fax: (44) 20 7621 1481
Investment Management Services
S.I.C.: 6799
N.A.I.C.S.: 523920

Commerzbank (Eurasija) SAO (1)
14/2 Kadashevskaya Nab
119017 Moscow, Russia (100%)
Tel.: (7) 4957974800
Fax: (7) 4957974828
Web Site: www.commerzbank.com
Emp.: 100
Corporate Banking Services
S.I.C.: 6159
N.A.I.C.S.: 522298
Gernot Kleckner *(Gen Mgr)*

Commerzbank Finance BV (1)
Strawinskylaan 2501
1077 ZZ Amsterdam, Netherlands
Tel.: (31) 20 5574911
Fax: (31) 20 5574618
Financial Management Services
S.I.C.: 6211
N.A.I.C.S.: 523999

Commerzbank Holdings France SAS (1)
23 Rue de la Paix
Paris, 75002, France
Tel.: (33) 1 44941700
Fax: (33) 1 44941800
Investment Management Services
S.I.C.: 6211
N.A.I.C.S.: 523999

Commerzbank International (Jersey) Limited (1)
PO Box 1075
Saint Helier, JE4 2QP, Jersey
Tel.: (44) 15347 000 00
Fax: (44) 15347 000 07
Financial Investment Services
S.I.C.: 6282
N.A.I.C.S.: 523930

Commerzbank International SA (1)
25 Edward Station
2540 Luxembourg, Luxembourg (100%)
Mailing Address:
PO Box 303
2013 Luxembourg, Luxembourg
Tel.: (352) 4779111
Telex: 1292, 1293, 2195 cbklxlu
Fax: (352) 4779112270
E-Mail: privatebanking@commerzbank.com
Web Site: www.commerzbank.lu
Sales Range: $50-74.9 Million
Emp.: 150
International Banking Services
S.I.C.: 6159
N.A.I.C.S.: 522298
Falk Fischer *(Chm)*

Unit:

Commerzbank International (2)
25 Rue Edward Steichen
2540 Luxembourg, Luxembourg (100%)
Tel.: (352) 4779111
Fax: (352) 4779112270
E-Mail: cisal@commerzbank.com
Web Site: www.commerzbank.lu
Emp.: 420
Investment Trust
S.I.C.: 6099
N.A.I.C.S.: 523991
Falk Fischer *(CEO & Mng Dir)*

Non-U.S. Subsidiary:

Commerzbank Europe (Ireland) (2)
Commerzbank House Guild St IFSC
Dublin, 1, Ireland (40%)
Tel.: (353) 16491100
Fax: (353) 16491199
Web Site: www.commerzbank.com
Emp.: 26
Corporate Banking Services
S.I.C.: 6159
N.A.I.C.S.: 522298
John Bowden *(Mgr)*

Commerzbank Investments (UK) Limited (1)
30 Gresham Street
London, EC2V 7PG, United Kingdom
Tel.: (44) 20 7623 8000
Fax: (44) 20 7623 4069
Investment Management Services
S.I.C.: 6282
N.A.I.C.S.: 523920
Jochen Muller *(Mng Dir & Country Mgr-Corp Client Bus)*

Commerzbank Leasing December - 1 Limited (1)
30 Gresham Street
London, EC2V 7PG, United Kingdom
Tel.: (44) 2076238000
Financial Leasing Services
S.I.C.: 6141
N.A.I.C.S.: 522220

Commerzbank Leasing December - 10 Ltd (1)
30 Gresham Street
London, EC2V 7PG, United Kingdom
Tel.: (44) 20 7623 8000
Financial Leasing Services
S.I.C.: 6141
N.A.I.C.S.: 522220

Commerzbank Leasing December - 11 Ltd (1)
30 Gresham Street
London, EC2V 7PG, United Kingdom
Tel.: (44) 20 7623 8000
Financial Leasing Services
S.I.C.: 6153
N.A.I.C.S.: 522220

Commerzbank Leasing December - 12 Limited (1)
30 Gresham Street
London, EC2V 7PG, United Kingdom
Tel.: (44) 20 7623 8000
Financial Leasing Services
S.I.C.: 6141
N.A.I.C.S.: 522220

Commerzbank Leasing December - 13 Limited (1)
35 Basinghall St
London, EC2V 5DB, United Kingdom
Tel.: (44) 20 7612 3846
Financial Leasing Services
S.I.C.: 6159
N.A.I.C.S.: 522220

Commerzbank Leasing December - 20 Limited (1)
30 Gresham Street
London, EC2V 7PG, United Kingdom
Tel.: (44) 2076537000
Financial Leasing Services
S.I.C.: 6153
N.A.I.C.S.: 522220

Commerzbank Leasing December - 22 Limited (1)
30 Gresham Street
London, EC2V 7PG, United Kingdom
Tel.: (44) 2076537000
Financial Leasing Services
S.I.C.: 6141
N.A.I.C.S.: 522220

Commerzbank Leasing December - 23 Limited (1)
30 Gresham Street
London, EC2V 7PG, United Kingdom
Tel.: (44) 2076537000
Financial Leasing Services
S.I.C.: 6141
N.A.I.C.S.: 522220

Commerzbank Leasing December - 24 Limited (1)
30 Gresham Street
London, EC2V 7PG, United Kingdom
Tel.: (44) ()20765370
Financial Leasing Services
S.I.C.: 6159
N.A.I.C.S.: 522220

Commerzbank Leasing December - 25 Limited (1)
30 Gresham Street
London, EC2V 7PG, United Kingdom
Tel.: (44) 2076537000
Financial Leasing Services
S.I.C.: 6141
N.A.I.C.S.: 522220

Commerzbank Leasing December - 26 Limited (1)
30 Gresham Street
London, EC2V 7PG, United Kingdom
Tel.: (44) 2076537000
Financial Leasing Services
S.I.C.: 6153
N.A.I.C.S.: 522220

Commerzbank Leasing December - 3 Limited (1)
30 Gresham Street
London, EC2V 7PG, United Kingdom
Tel.: (44) 20 7623 8000
Financial Leasing Services
S.I.C.: 6141
N.A.I.C.S.: 522220

Commerzbank Leasing December - 4 Limited (1)
30 Gresham Street
London, EC2V 7PG, United Kingdom
Tel.: (44) 20 7623 8000
Financial Leasing Services
S.I.C.: 6153
N.A.I.C.S.: 522220

Commerzbank Leasing December - 6 Limited (1)
30 Gresham Street
London, EC2V 7PG, United Kingdom
Tel.: (44) 20 7623 8000
Financial Leasing Services
S.I.C.: 6141
N.A.I.C.S.: 522220

Commerzbank Leasing December - 8 Limited (1)
30 Gresham Street
London, EC2V 7PG, United Kingdom
Tel.: (44) 20 7623 8000
Financial Leasing Services
S.I.C.: 6153
N.A.I.C.S.: 522220

Commerzbank Leasing December - 9 Limited (1)
30 Gresham Street
London, EC2V 7PG, United Kingdom
Tel.: (44) 20 7623 8000
Financial Leasing Services
S.I.C.: 6153
N.A.I.C.S.: 522220

Commerzbank Leasing Holdings Limited (1)
30 Gresham Street
London, EC2V 7PG, United Kingdom
Tel.: (44) 20 7623 8000
Fax: (44) 20 7475 7250
Investment Management Services
S.I.C.: 6282
N.A.I.C.S.: 523920

Commerzbank Leasing Limited (1)
30 Gresham Street
London, EC2V 7PG, United Kingdom
Tel.: (44) 20 7623 8000
Financial Leasing Services
S.I.C.: 6141
N.A.I.C.S.: 522220

Commerzbank Leasing March - 3 Limited (1)
Townsend House 160-174 Northolt Road
Harrow, HA2 0EG, United Kingdom
Tel.: (44) 20 7623 8000
Financial Leasing Services
S.I.C.: 6159
N.A.I.C.S.: 522220

Commerzbank Leasing September - 5 Limited (1)
30 Gresham Street
London, EC2V 7PG, United Kingdom
Tel.: (44) 20 7623 8000
Financial Leasing Services
S.I.C.: 6141
N.A.I.C.S.: 522220

Commerzbank Leasing September - 6 Limited (1)
30 Gresham Street
London, EC2V 7PG, United Kingdom
Tel.: (44) 2076537000
Financial Leasing Services
S.I.C.: 6153
N.A.I.C.S.: 522220

Commerzbank (Nederland) N.V. (1)
Strawinskylaan 2501
PO Box 75444
NL 1077 ZZ Amsterdam, Netherlands (100%)
Tel.: (31) 205574911
Telex: 18076 cbam nl
Fax: (31) 206272446
E-Mail: cbnl@commerzbank.com
Web Site: www.commerzbank.com
Sales Range: $10-24.9 Million
Emp.: 40
Corporate Banking Services
S.I.C.: 6159
N.A.I.C.S.: 522298
Dirk Dreiskaemper *(Gen Mgr)*

Commerzbank Online Ventures Limited (1)
30 Gresham Street
London, EC2V 7PG, United Kingdom
Tel.: (44) 20 7623 7000
Venture Capital Management Services
S.I.C.: 6799
N.A.I.C.S.: 523910

Commerzbank Overseas Holdings Limited (1)
30 Gresham Street
London, EC2V 7PG, United Kingdom
Tel.: (44) 20 7623 8000
Investment Management Services
S.I.C.: 6282
N.A.I.C.S.: 523920

Commerzbank Property Management & Services Limited (1)
30 Gresham Street
London, EC2V 7PG, United Kingdom
Tel.: (44) 20 7623 8000
Real Estate Management Services
S.I.C.: 6531
N.A.I.C.S.: 531390

Commerzbank Representative Office Nigeria Limited (1)
The Adunola House 5th Floor Wing A
Banana Island Ikoyi
Lagos, Nigeria
Tel.: (234) 807 472 80 82
Fax: (234) 1 260 00 84
Financial Investment Services
S.I.C.: 6282
N.A.I.C.S.: 523930
Florian M. Witt *(Mgr)*

Commerzbank Representative Office Panama, S.A. (1)
Ph Torre de las Americas Torre C Piso 27
Oficina 2701 Punta Pacifica
Panama, Panama
Tel.: (507) 340 31 01
Fax: (507) 340 35 95
Financial Investment Services
S.I.C.: 6211
N.A.I.C.S.: 523999

Commerzbank Sao Paulo Servicos Ltda. (1)
R Pedroso Alvarenga 1208 an16
Sao Paulo, 04531-004, Brazil
Tel.: (55) 11 30799790
Financial Investment Services
S.I.C.: 6282
N.A.I.C.S.: 523930

Commerzbank Securities Ltd. (1)
30 Gresham Street
London, EC2V 7PG, United Kingdom
Tel.: (44) 20 7623 8000
Security Brokerage Services
S.I.C.: 6211
N.A.I.C.S.: 523120

Commerzbank Securities Nominees Limited (1)
30 Gresham Street
London, WC2H 7WG, United Kingdom
Tel.: (44) 20 7623 8000
Security Brokerage Services
S.I.C.: 6211
N.A.I.C.S.: 523120

CSA COMMERZ SOUTH AFRICA (PROPRIETARY) LIMITED (1)
Le Val-North Block Ground Floor 45 Jan Smuts Avenue
Johannesburg, 2193, South Africa
Tel.: (27) 11 486 0565
Fax: (27) 11 486 1642
E-Mail: fi.Johannesburg@commerzbank.com
Emp.: 4
Commercial Banking Services
S.I.C.: 6029
N.A.I.C.S.: 522110

CSK Sp. z.o.o. (1)
ul Piotrkowska 173
90-447 Lodz, Poland

Commerzbank AG—(Continued)

Tel.: (48) 22 768 79 01
Fax: (48) 22 768 79 10
E-Mail: recepcja@csk-jachranka.pl
Web Site: www.csk-jachranka.pl
Facilities Management Services
S.I.C.: 8744
N.A.I.C.S.: 561210

Dresdner Kleinwort do Brasil Limitada (1)
Condominio Edificio Plaza Iguatemi Avenida Faria Lima 2277 7th Floor
01452-000 Sao Paulo, Brazil
Tel.: (55) 11 2202 8100
Financial Investment Services
S.I.C.: 6282
N.A.I.C.S.: 523930

Elco Leasing Limited (1)
30 Gresham Street
London, EC2V 7PG, United Kingdom
Tel.: (44) 2076537000
Financial Leasing Services
S.I.C.: 6159
N.A.I.C.S.: 522220

Erste Europaische Pfandbrief- und Kommunalkreditbank Aktiengesellschaft (1)
Postfach 2133
1021 Luxembourg, Luxembourg
Tel.: (352) 26 3481
E-Mail: info@eepk.lu
Web Site: www.eepk.lu
Financial Investment Services
S.I.C.: 6282
N.A.I.C.S.: 523930
Ralf Woitschig *(Chm)*
Hermann Rave *(Deputy Chm)*
Gerard-Jan Bais *(Mng Dir)*

Espacio Leon Propco S.L.U. (1)
Calle Pinar 7 - Piso 5 IZ
Madrid, 28006, Spain
Tel.: (34) 987237929
Real Estate Development Services
S.I.C.: 6531
N.A.I.C.S.: 531390

Forum Algarve - Gestao de Centro comercial, Sociedade Unipessoal, Lda. (1)
Avenida da Liberdade 224
1250-148 Lisbon, Portugal
Tel.: (351) 289 889 300
Fax: (351) 289 889 301
E-Mail: forumalgarve@multi-development.com
Web Site: www.forumalgarve.net
Shopping Center Management Services
S.I.C.: 6512
N.A.I.C.S.: 531120

Forum Almada, Gestao de Centro Comercial, Sociedade Unipessoal Lda. II & Comandita (1)
Estrada do Caminho Municipal 1011 Vale de Mourelos
2810-354 Almada, Portugal
Tel.: (351) 21 250 99 00
Fax: (351) 21 250 99 11
Shopping Center Management Services
S.I.C.: 6512
N.A.I.C.S.: 531120

Forum Almada-Gestao de Centro Commercial, Sociedade Unipessoal, Lda. (1)
Estrada do Caminho Municipal 1011 Vale de Mourelos
2810-354 Almada, Portugal
Tel.: (351) 21 250 99 00
Fax: (351) 21 250 99 11
Shopping Mall Operator
S.I.C.: 6512
N.A.I.C.S.: 531120

Forum Montijo, Gestao de Centro Comercial Sociedade Unipessoal, Lda (1)
Zona Industrial do Pau Queimado Rua da Azinheira - Afonsoeiro
2870-100 Montijo, Portugal
Tel.: (351) 212 307 800
Fax: (351) 212 307 801
E-Mail: forumontijo@multi-mallmanagement.com
Web Site: www.forumontijo.com
Emp.: 800
Shopping Center Operator
S.I.C.: 5411
N.A.I.C.S.: 445110

Immobiliengesellschaft Ost Hagle, spol. s.r.o (1)
Jugoslavska 1
12000 Prague, Czech Republic
Tel.: (420) 233321472
Real Estate Management Services
S.I.C.: 6531
N.A.I.C.S.: 531390

Limited Liability Company ABRIO (1)
Ul Korchagintsev 7a
Kharkiv, 61171, Ukraine
Tel.: (380) 57 7102810
Fax: (380) 57 7117780
Real Estate Management Services
S.I.C.: 6531
N.A.I.C.S.: 531390

Morris (S.P.) Holdings Limited (1)
30 Gresham Street
London, EC2V 7PG, United Kingdom
Tel.: (44) 2076238000
Investment Management Services
S.I.C.: 6799
N.A.I.C.S.: 523920

Pisces Nominees Limited (1)
30 Gresham Street
London, EC2V 7PG, United Kingdom
Tel.: (44) 2076238000
Financial Management Services
S.I.C.: 6211
N.A.I.C.S.: 523999

Public Joint Stock Company "Bank Forum" (1)
17/52 Bohdana Khmelnytskoho St
Kiev, 01030, Ukraine
Tel.: (380) 44581 04 34
Fax: (380) 44 200 24 52
E-Mail: info@forum.ua
Web Site: www.forum.ua
Emp.: 700
Financial Management Services
S.I.C.: 6211
N.A.I.C.S.: 523999
Vadym Berezovyk *(Chm-Mgmt Bd)*
Karsten Sieber *(Deputy Chm-Mgmt Bd)*
Sybille Kroiss *(Member-Mgmt Bd-Risks)*
Harald Muecke *(Member-Mgmt Bd-Ops)*
Taras Prots *(Member-Mgmt Bd-Fin Mgmt)*
Radik Valiullin *(Member-Mgmt Bd-Gen Support)*
Victor Zinchenko *(Member-Mgmt Bd-Fin Markets)*

RAVENNA Krakow Sp. z.o.o. (1)
Ks Skorupki 5
Warsaw, Poland
Tel.: (48) 223201805
Fax: (48) 223203904
Financial Management Services
S.I.C.: 6211
N.A.I.C.S.: 523999

Rood Nominees Limited (1)
30 Gresham Street
London, EC2V 7PG, United Kingdom
Tel.: (44) 2076238000
Security Brokerage Services
S.I.C.: 6211
N.A.I.C.S.: 523120

South East Asia Properties Limited (1)
30 Gresham Street
London, EC2V 7PG, United Kingdom
Tel.: (44) 2076238000
Financial Leasing Services
S.I.C.: 6159
N.A.I.C.S.: 522220

Wijkertunnel Beheer III B.V. (1)
Strawinskylaan 2501
1077ZZ Amsterdam, Netherlands
Tel.: (31) 205574660
Financial Investment Services
S.I.C.: 6282
N.A.I.C.S.: 523930

Non-U.S. Representative Offices:

Commerzbank AG - Antwerp Branch (1)
Uitbreidingstraat 46
2600 Antwerp, Belgium (100%)
Tel.: (32) 32810440
Telex: 62790 cbkbr b
Fax: (32) 32810989
E-Mail: antwerp@commerzbank.com
Web Site: www.commerzbank.com
Corporate Banking Services
S.I.C.: 6159
N.A.I.C.S.: 522298

Commerzbank AG - South Africa (1)
Le Val North Block Ground Floor 45 Jan Smuts Avenue
Westcliff, 2193, South Africa
Mailing Address:
PO Box 860
Parklands, 2121, South Africa
Tel.: (27) 11 486 0565
Fax: (27) 11 486 1642
Web Site: www2.commerzbank.com
Sales Range: $1-9.9 Million
Emp.: 60
Corporate Banking Services
S.I.C.: 6029
N.A.I.C.S.: 522110
Clive Kellow *(Gen Mgr)*

COMMEX TECHNOLOGY LTD.

3A Udyog Nagar SV Road Goregaon W
Mumbai, 400 062, India
Tel.: (91) 22 2778 0045
Fax: (91) 22 2778 0046
E-Mail: investor@commextechnology.com
Web Site: www.commextechnology.com
532342—(BOM)
Rev.: $4,604,724
Assets: $25,078,502
Liabilities: $4,447,783
Net Worth: $20,630,719
Earnings: $1,882,922
Fiscal Year-end: 03/31/13

Business Description:
Software Products & Solutions
S.I.C.: 7371
N.A.I.C.S.: 541511

Personnel:
Ketan Sheth *(Chm & Mng Dir)*
Vivek Thakur *(Sec)*

Board of Directors:
Ketan Sheth
Sudip Bandyopadhyay
Madhukar Nath Chaturvedi
Jayant Mitra

Transfer Agent:
Universal Capital Securities Pvt. Ltd
21 Shakil Niwas Opp.Satya Saibaba Temple
Mahakali Caves Road Andheri
Mumbai, India

COMMISSION DE LA SANTE ET DE LA SECURITE DU TRAVAIL

524 rue Bourdages CP 1200
Succursale Terminus
Quebec, QC, G1K 7E2, Canada
Tel.: (418) 266-4850
Fax: (418) 266-4398
Toll Free: (866) 302-2778
Web Site: www.csst.qc.ca
Year Founded: 1885
Rev.: $37,200,000
Emp.: 3

Business Description:
Insurance Services
S.I.C.: 6331
N.A.I.C.S.: 524126

Personnel:
Jacques Lamonde *(Chm)*

COMMISSIONERS GOLD LIMITED

Suite 18 47 Neridah Street
Chatswood, NSW, 2067, Australia
Tel.: (61) 2 9410 3445
Fax: (61) 2 9410 0458
Web Site: www.commissionersgold.com.au
CGU—(ASX)

Business Description:
Gold & Other Metal Mining
S.I.C.: 1041
N.A.I.C.S.: 212221

Personnel:
Christopher Battye *(Chm)*
Robert J. McCauley *(Mng Dir)*
Keith Taylor *(Sec)*

Board of Directors:
Christopher Battye
Wesley Martin Harder
Robert J. McCauley
Robert John Waring

COMMONWEALTH BANK OF AUSTRALIA

(d/b/a Commonwealth Bank Group)
Ground Floor Tower 1 201 Sussex Street
Sydney, NSW, 2000, Australia
Tel.: (61) 2 9378 2000
Telex: AA 120345
Fax: (61) 2 9118 7192
E-Mail: media_inquiries@cba.com.au
Web Site: www.commbank.com.au
Year Founded: 1911
CBA—(ASX)
Int. Income: $36,201,511,900
Assets: $785,614,179,600
Liabilities: $738,206,966,400
Net Worth: $47,407,213,200
Earnings: $8,016,875,300
Emp.: 44,969
Fiscal Year-end: 06/30/13

Business Description:
Retail, Commercial, Investment & Private Banking
S.I.C.: 6029
N.A.I.C.S.: 522110

Personnel:
Ian M. Narev *(CEO & Mng Dir)*
David Craig *(CFO)*
Michael Harte *(CIO & Grp Exec-Enterprise Svcs)*
Alden L. Toevs *(Chief Risk Officer)*
David Cohen *(Grp Exec-Corp Affairs & Gen Counsel)*
Simon Blair *(Grp Exec-Intl Fin Svcs)*
Matt Comyn *(Grp Exec-Retail Banking Svcs)*
Rob Jesudason *(Grp Exec-Strategic Dev)*
Melanie Laing *(Grp Exec-HR)*
Grahame Petersen *(Grp Exec-Bus & Private Banking)*
Kelly Bayer Rosmarin *(Grp Exec-Institutional Banking & Markets)*
Annabel Spring *(Grp Exec-Wealth Mgmt)*
Barbara Chapman *(CEO/Mng Dir-ASB)*
Margaret Taylor *(Sec)*

Board of Directors:
David J. Turner
John A. Anderson
Jane Sharman Hemstritch
Launa Karen Inman
S. Carolyn H. Kay
Brian J. Long
Andrew M. Mohl
Ian M. Narev
Harrison H. Young

Subsidiaries:

Bank of Western Australia Ltd. (1)
108 St Georges Terrace
Level 20 BankW Tower, Perth, WA, 6000, Australia
Mailing Address:
PO Box E237
6001 Perth, Australia
Tel.: (61) 894492840
Fax: (61) 8 9449 2570

Web Site: www.bankwest.com.au
Banking Services
S.I.C.: 6029
N.A.I.C.S.: 522110
Paul Clark *(CEO-BankWest Bus)*
Ian Corfield *(CEO-Retail Div)*

CBFC Limited (1)
Level 7 48 Martin Place
Sydney, NSW, 2000, Australia
Tel.: (61) 293783876
Fax: (61) 293782400
Web Site: www.cba.com
Financial Services
S.I.C.: 6159
N.A.I.C.S.: 522293

Colonial Holding Company Limited (1)
Ground Floor Tower 1 201 Sussex Street
Sydney, NSW, 2000, Australia AU
Tel.: (61) 291187220
Fax: (61) 291187192
CNG—(ASX)
Rev.: $6,529,798,600
Assets: $24,137,120,200
Liabilities: $19,344,502,300
Net Worth: $4,792,617,900
Earnings: $860,774,600
Fiscal Year-end: 06/30/13
Investment Management Services
S.I.C.: 6211
N.A.I.C.S.: 523999
Michael Venter *(Chm)*
John Greenhalgh *(Co-Sec)*
Bernadette Anne Watts *(Co-Sec)*

Subsidiaries:

Avanteos Investments Limited (2)
L 1 105 Camberwell Rd
Hawthorn East, VIC, 3123, Australia
Tel.: (61) 398055111
Fax: (61) 398134182
Investment Management Services
S.I.C.: 6211
N.A.I.C.S.: 523999

Avanteos Pty Limited (2)
105 Camberwell Rd
Hawthorn East, VIC, 3123, Australia
Tel.: (61) 398055111
Fax: (61) 398040398
Portfolio Management Services
S.I.C.: 6799
N.A.I.C.S.: 523920

Colonial First State Group Limited (2)
Level 29 52 Martin Place
Sydney, NSW, 2000, Australia AU
Mailing Address: (100%)
PO Box 3956
Sydney, NSW, 2001, Australia
Tel.: (61) 292733000
Fax: (61) 293033200
E-Mail: contactus@colonialfirststate.com.au
Web Site: www.cfsgam.com.au
Emp.: 200
Holding Company; Financial & Real Estate Asset Management Services
S.I.C.: 6719
N.A.I.C.S.: 551112
Mark Lazberger *(CEO)*
David Dixon *(Chief Investment Officer)*

Subsidiaries:

Colonial First State Investments Limited (3)
11 Harbour Street
Sydney, NSW, 2000, Australia AU
Mailing Address: (100%)
PO Box 3956
Sydney, NSW, 2001, Australia
Tel.: (61) 293033000
Fax: (61) 293033200
E-Mail: contactus@colonialfirststate.com.au
Web Site: www.colonialfirststate.com.au
Emp.: 1,000
Investment Services
S.I.C.: 6211
N.A.I.C.S.: 523110
John Dempsey *(Gen Mgr-Fin & Compliance)*

Colonial First State Property Limited (3)
Level 7 52 Martin Place
Sydney, NSW, 2000, Australia AU
Mailing Address: (100%)
PO Box 3892
Sydney, NSW, 2001, Australia
Tel.: (61) 293033500
Fax: (61) 293033622
E-Mail: cfxfeedback@colonialfirststate.com.au
Web Site: www.colonialfirststate.com.au
Emp.: 850
Property Acquisition, Development & Management Services
S.I.C.: 6531
N.A.I.C.S.: 531390

Subsidiary:

Colonial First State Property Management Pty Ltd (4)
1341 Dandenong Road Chadstone Shopping Ctr
Melbourne, VIC, 3148, Australia AU
Tel.: (61) 399361222 (100%)
Fax: (61) 399361333
E-Mail: info@cfsgam.com.au
Web Site: www.cfspm.com.au
Emp.: 300
Retail Properties Management & Development
S.I.C.: 6519
N.A.I.C.S.: 531190
Tony Gilchrist *(Head-Dev)*

Commonwealth Managed Investments Limited (3)
Darling Park Tower 1 201 Sussex Street
Sydney, NSW, 2000, Australia AU
Tel.: (61) 2 9303 3500
Fax: (61) 2 9303 3622
Investment Funds Trustee
S.I.C.: 6091
N.A.I.C.S.: 523991

Affiliate:

CFS Retail Property Trust Group (4)
Ground Floor Tower 1 201 Sussex Street
Sydney, NSW, 2000, Australia
Tel.: (61) 2 9303 3186
Fax: (61) 2 9118 7192
Web Site: www.cfsgam.com.au/cfx
CFX—(ASX)
Rev.: $769,590,850
Assets: $8,992,385,110
Liabilities: $2,985,303,870
Net Worth: $6,007,081,240
Earnings: $307,419,500
Fiscal Year-end: 06/30/13
Shopping Center Real Estate Investment Trust
S.I.C.: 6726
N.A.I.C.S.: 525990
Michael Gorman *(CEO)*

Non-U.S. Subsidiary:

First State Investments (UK) Limited (3)
30 Cannon Street
London, EC4M 6YQ, United Kingdom UK
Tel.: (44) 20 7332 6500
Fax: (44) 20 7332 6501
Web Site: www.firststate.co.uk
Emp.: 80
Investment Management Services
S.I.C.: 6799
N.A.I.C.S.: 523920
Chris Turpin *(Mng Dir-EMEA & Head-Product-Global)*

Non-U.S. Subsidiaries:

First State Investments (Hong Kong) Limited (4)
Level 6 Three Exchange Square 8 Connaught Place
Central, China (Hong Kong) HK
Tel.: (852) 2846 7566
Fax: (852) 2868 4742
E-Mail: info@firststate.com.hk
Web Site: www.firststateinvestments.com
Financial Management Services
S.I.C.: 6211
N.A.I.C.S.: 523999

First State Investments (Singapore) (4)
1 Temasek Avenue 17-01 Millenia Tower
Singapore, 039192, Singapore SG
Tel.: (65) 6538 0008
Fax: (65) 6538 0800
E-Mail: info@firststate.com.sg
Web Site: www.firststateinvestments.com
Investment Management Services
S.I.C.: 6211
N.A.I.C.S.: 523999

Non-U.S. Joint Venture:

Suomi Power Networks Oy (4)
c/o TMF Finland Oy Erottajankatu 9 B 3
00130 Helsinki, Finland FI
Tel.: (358) 9 3158 9000
Fax: (358) 9 3158 9001
Holding Company; Electric Power Distr
S.I.C.: 6719
N.A.I.C.S.: 551112

Non-U.S. Joint Venture:

Anglian Water Group Limited (3)
Anglian House Ambury Road
Huntingdon, Cambs, PE29 3NZ, United Kingdom JE
Tel.: (44) 1480323000
Fax: (44) 1480323115
E-Mail: enquiries@awg.com
Web Site: www.awg.com
Sls.: $2,203,899,195
Assets: $13,509,404,589
Liabilities: $13,347,053,577
Net Worth: $162,351,012
Earnings: ($75,805,920)
Emp.: 5,967
Fiscal Year-end: 03/31/13
Holding Company; Water Supply, Sewerage & Property Development Services
S.I.C.: 6719
N.A.I.C.S.: 551112
Claire Russell *(Sec)*

Subsidiaries:

Anglian Water Services Limited (4)
Anglian House Ambury Road
Huntingdon, Cambs, PE29 3NZ, United Kingdom UK
Tel.: (44) 1480323000
Fax: (44) 1480323115
Web Site: www.anglianwater.co.uk
Sls.: $1,836,714,270
Assets: $13,001,189,067
Liabilities: $11,435,007,174
Net Worth: $1,566,181,893
Earnings: $467,153,982
Emp.: 250
Fiscal Year-end: 03/31/13
Water Supply Distribution & Sewerage Services
S.I.C.: 4971
N.A.I.C.S.: 221310
Adrian Montague *(Chm)*
Peter Simpson *(Mng Dir & Member-Mgmt Bd)*
Claire Russell *(Member-Mgmt Bd, Sec & Dir-Legal)*
Scott Longhurst *(Member-Mgmt Bd & Mng Dir-Fin & Non Regulated Bus)*
Chris Boucher *(Member-Mgmt Bd & Dir-Info Svcs)*
Richard Boucher *(Member-Mgmt Bd & Dir-Bus Change & Strategy)*
Paul Gibbs *(Member-Mgmt Bd & Dir-Wastewater Svcs)*
Kate Kelly *(Member-Mgmt Bd & Dir-HR)*
Chris Newsome *(Member-Mgmt Bd & Dir-Asset Mgmt)*
Martyn Oakley *(Member-Mgmt Bd & Dir-Customer Svcs)*
Mark Pendlington *(Member-Mgmt Bd & Dir-Corp Affairs)*
Jean Spencer *(Member-Mgmt Bd & Dir-Regulation)*
Paul Valleley *(Member-Mgmt Bd & Dir-Water Svcs)*

AWG Property Limited (4)
47 Melville Street
Edinburgh, EH4 7HL, United Kingdom UK
Tel.: (44) 01313431000
Fax: (44) 01312004480
Web Site: www.awgproperty.co.uk
Emp.: 30
Commercial & Residential Property Investment & Development
S.I.C.: 6531
N.A.I.C.S.: 531390
Tony Donnelly *(Mng Dir)*

Count Financial Limited (2)
Level 19 Gold Fields House 1 Alfred Street
Sydney, NSW, 2000, Australia AU
Tel.: (61) 282720292
Fax: (61) 292417342
E-Mail: info@count.com.au
Web Site: www.count.com.au
Sales Range: $125-149.9 Million
Emp.: 100
Insurance Services
S.I.C.: 6321
N.A.I.C.S.: 524114
Barry Martin Lambert *(Chm)*
David Lane *(CEO)*
Anna Smith *(Gen Counsel & Sec)*

Subsidiaries:

CountGPS Pty. Ltd. (3)
Level 4 293 Queen St
Brisbane, Queensland, 4000, Australia
Tel.: (61) 732211100
Fax: (61) 732214130
E-Mail: info@countgps.com.au
Web Site: www.countgps.com.au
Emp.: 25
Internet Accounting Services
S.I.C.: 7371
N.A.I.C.S.: 541511

Countplus Limited (3)
Level 19 1 Alfred Street
Sydney, NSW, 2000, Australia
Mailing Address:
GPO Box 1453
Sydney, NSW, 2001, Australia
Tel.: (61) 2 8272 0491
Fax: (61) 2 9241 7342
E-Mail: info@countplus.com.au
Web Site: www.countplus.com.au
CUP—(ASX)
Rev.: $119,203,735
Assets: $105,904,455
Liabilities: $51,730,886
Net Worth: $54,173,569
Earnings: $11,549,594
Emp.: 600
Fiscal Year-end: 06/30/13
Holding Company; Accounting & Financial Services
S.I.C.: 6719
N.A.I.C.S.: 551112
Barry Martin Lambert *(Chm)*
Michael James Spurr *(CEO, Mng Dir & CFO)*
Arlette Jubian *(Sec & Controller-Fin)*

Equity Loan Broking Pty Ltd. (3)
PO Box 3323
Sydney, NSW, 2001, Australia
Tel.: (61) 282720291
Fax: (61) 92417342
E-Mail: info@equityloanbroking.com.au
Web Site: www.equityloanbroking.com.au
Emp.: 1
Broking Services
S.I.C.: 6211
N.A.I.C.S.: 523120

finconnect (australia) pty. ltd. (3)
Gold Fields House Level 19 1 Alfred St
PO Box 3323
Sydney, New South Wales, 2000, Australia
Tel.: (61) 282720440
Fax: (61) 292417342
E-Mail: info@finconnect.com.au
Web Site: www.finconnect.com.au
Emp.: 80
Financial Planning Accountants & Advisory Services
S.I.C.: 6211
N.A.I.C.S.: 523999
Kristy Coates *(Mgr-Admin)*

Financial Wisdom Limited (2)
Ground L Tower 1 201 Sussex St
Sydney, NSW, 2000, Australia
Tel.: (61) 1800024864
Fax: (61) 29303140
E-Mail: info@financialwisdom.com.au
Web Site: www.financialwisdom.com.au
Financial Advisory Services
S.I.C.: 6282
N.A.I.C.S.: 523930
Mark Ballantyne *(Gen Mgr)*

Whittaker Macnaught Pty Limited (2)
10/40 Creek St
Brisbane, QLD, 4000, Australia

Commonwealth Bank of Australia—(Continued)

Tel.: (61) 732211022
Fax: (61) 732219682
E-Mail: info@whittakermacnaught.com.au
Web Site: www.whittakermacnaught.com.au
Financial Advisory Services
S.I.C.: 6282
N.A.I.C.S.: 523930
Cheryl Macnaught *(Co-Founder)*
Noel Whittaker *(Co-Founder)*

Non-U.S. Subsidiary:

ASB Group (Life) Limited **(2)**
Cnr Albert Wellesley Streets
Auckland, 1141, New Zealand
Tel.: (64) 93778930
Insurance Management Services
S.I.C.: 6411
N.A.I.C.S.: 524298

Commonwealth Securities Limited **(1)**
Locked Bag 22
Australia Square, Sydney, NSW, 1215, Australia
Tel.: (61) 291151417
Fax: (61) 282924777
E-Mail: shares@commsec.com.au
Web Site: www.comsec.com.au
Security Brokerage Services
S.I.C.: 6211
N.A.I.C.S.: 523120
Ralph Norris *(CEO)*

Homepath Pty Limited **(1)**
Level 7 48 Martin Place
Sydney, NSW, 2000, Australia
Tel.: (61) 1300130852
Financial Credit Management Services
S.I.C.: 6159
N.A.I.C.S.: 522298

JDV Limited **(1)**
L7 141 St Georges Tce
Perth, WA, Australia (100%)
Tel.: (61) 892660222
Web Site: www.jdv.com.au
Securities Brokerage
S.I.C.: 6211
N.A.I.C.S.: 523120

Securitisation Advisory Services Pty Limited **(1)**
201 Sussex St
Sydney, NSW, 2000, Australia
Tel.: (61) 299534834
Investment Advisory Services
S.I.C.: 6282
N.A.I.C.S.: 523930

U.S. Representative Office:

Commonwealth Bank of Australia - U.S.A. **(1)**
599 Lexington Ave 17th Fl
New York, NY 10022-7664
Tel.: (212) 848-9200
Telex: TRT 177666
Fax: (212) 336-7725
Web Site: www.commbank.com.au
Emp.: 48
International Banking
S.I.C.: 6029
N.A.I.C.S.: 522110
Ian Phillips *(CEO)*

Non-U.S. Subsidiaries:

ASB Bank Limited **(1)**
ABB Bank Ctr Corner Albert And Wellesley Sq 135 Albert St
PO Box 35
Shortland St, 1140 Auckland, New Zealand (100%)
Tel.: (64) 93778930
Telex: NZ60881
Fax: (64) 93583511
E-Mail: info@asbbank.co.nz
Web Site: www.asbbank.co.nz
Emp.: 500
International Banking
S.I.C.: 6159
N.A.I.C.S.: 522293
G. J. Judd *(Chm)*
Jonathan Peter Hartley *(Deputy Chm)*
J. M.R. Syme *(Deputy Chm)*
Ian Park *(Acting CEO)*
Russel Jones *(COO)*
J. S. Barclay *(Chief HR Officer)*
K. D. Francis *(CEO-Corp & Institutional Banking)*
S. B. McRobie *(CEO-Relationship Banking)*
G. T. Edwards *(Gen Counsel & Sec)*

Subsidiaries:

AEGIS Limited **(2)**
Sovereign House 33-45 Hurstmere Road
PO Box 33 1068
Takapuna, North Shore, 0740, New Zealand
Tel.: (64) 9 487 9006
Fax: (64) 9 487 9493
E-Mail: enquire@aegisnet.co.nz
Web Site: www.aegis.co.nz
Investment Management Services
S.I.C.: 6211
N.A.I.C.S.: 523999

ASB Group Investments Limited **(2)**
Level 28 ASB Bank Centre 153 ALbert Street Auckland Central
Auckland, 1010, New Zealand
Tel.: (64) 93778930
Web Site: www.asb.co.nz/kiwisaver/asbGroupInvestments.aspx#1
Investment Management Services
S.I.C.: 6211
N.A.I.C.S.: 523999

ASB Holdings Limited **(2)**
Level 28 135 Albert Street Auckland Central
Auckland, 1010, New Zealand
Tel.: (64) 93778930
Commercial Banking Services
S.I.C.: 6029
N.A.I.C.S.: 522110

ASB Securities Limited **(2)**
135 Albert Street
PO Box 35
Shortland Street, Auckland, 1140, New Zealand
Tel.: (64) 9 369 4602
Fax: (64) 9 337 2425
E-Mail: asbsecinfo@asb.co.nz
Web Site: www.asb.co.nz
Emp.: 50
Online Securities Trading Services
S.I.C.: 7379
N.A.I.C.S.: 518210
Andrew Kelleher *(Gen Mgr)*

CBA Asia Limited **(1)**
1 Temasek Ave 17-01 Millenia Tower
Singapore, 039192, Singapore
Tel.: (65) 63497000
Fax: (65) 62245812
Emp.: 50
Commercial Banking Services
S.I.C.: 6029
N.A.I.C.S.: 522110

CommBank Europe Limited **(1)**
Level 3 Strand Towers 36 The Strand
Sliema, SLM07, Malta
Tel.: (356) 6 21 320812
Fax: (356) 21320811
Web Site: www.commbank.com.au/about-us/our-company/international-branches/europe/
Commercial Banking Services
S.I.C.: 6029
N.A.I.C.S.: 522110

CommBank Management Consulting (Asia) Co Limited **(1)**
Rm 1501-1505 15/F Chater Hse 8 Connaught Rd C
Central District, Hong Kong, China (Hong Kong)
Tel.: (852) 36678900
Fax: (852) 36678939
Emp.: 100
Insurance Management Services
S.I.C.: 6411
N.A.I.C.S.: 524298

CTB Australia Limited **(1)**
Rm 01-05 15/F Chater Hse 8 Connaught Rd C
Central, China (Hong Kong)
Tel.: (852) 28447500
Fax: (852) 28459194
E-Mail: cbahk@cba.com.au
Financial Management Services
S.I.C.: 6211
N.A.I.C.S.: 523999

PT. Bank Commonwealth **(1)**
Wisma Metropolitan II 1st Floor Jl Jend Sudirman Kav 29-31
Jakarta, 12920, Indonesia
Tel.: (62) 21 5296 1222
Fax: (62) 21 5296 2293
E-Mail: customercare@commbank.co.id
Web Site: www.commbank.co.id
Commercial Banking Services
S.I.C.: 6029
N.A.I.C.S.: 522110
Antonia Da Silva Costa *(Chm)*
Andriaan Laoh *(Vice Chm)*

Sovereign Group Limited **(1)**
74 Taharoto Road
Takapuna, Auckland, 1142, New Zealand
Tel.: (64) 9 487 9000
Fax: (64) 9 487 8003
E-Mail: enquire@sovereign.co.nz
Web Site: www.sovereign.co.nz
Emp.: 800
Investment Management Services
S.I.C.: 6211
N.A.I.C.S.: 523999
Symon Brewis-Weston *(Mng Dir)*

Non-U.S. Holding:

PT Bank Arta Niaga Kencana Tbk **(1)**
Jalan Bubutan 127-135
Surabaya, 60174, Indonesia
Tel.: (62) 313534123
Fax: (62) 313532039
Web Site: www.ank.co.id
Emp.: 452
Commercial & Retail Banking
S.I.C.: 6029
N.A.I.C.S.: 522110
Oma Emen Admadi *(Pres)*
Andry Wijaya *(Treas & Dir-Bus Dev)*

Non-U.S. Representative Offices:

Commonwealth Bank of Australia - Beijing **(1)**
2909 China World Towers
Beijing China World Trade Ctr, Beijing, 100004, China
Tel.: (86) 1065055350
Fax: (86) 1065055354
Web Site: www.commbank.au
Emp.: 5
S.I.C.: 6159
N.A.I.C.S.: 522298

Commonwealth Bank of Australia - Grand Cayman **(1)**
PO Box 501
CBA Grand Cayman, Georgetown, Grand Cayman, Cayman Islands
S.I.C.: 6159
N.A.I.C.S.: 522298

Commonwealth Bank of Australia - Hong Kong **(1)**
Room 1501-1505 Chater House 8 Connaught Road
Central, China (Hong Kong)
Tel.: (852) 2844 7500
Telex: 852-60466 CTB HX
Fax: (852) 28459194
E-Mail:
Web Site: www.commbank.com.au/about-us/our-company/international-branches/asia.html#HongKong
Emp.: 45
International Bankers
S.I.C.: 6159
N.A.I.C.S.: 522293
Stephen Poon *(Gen Mgr)*

Commonwealth Bank of Australia - Japan **(1)**
8th Fl Toranomon Waiko Bldg 12 1 Toranomon 5 Chome Minato Ku
Tokyo, 105 0001, Japan
Tel.: (81) 354007850
Telex: J 28167
Fax: (81) 354007288
E-Mail: info@commbank.co.jp
Web Site: www.commbank.co.jp
Emp.: 18
International Bankers
S.I.C.: 6159
N.A.I.C.S.: 522293
Martin Spann *(Gen Mgr)*

Commonwealth Bank of Australia - Shanghai **(1)**
Level 11 Azia Centre 1233 Lujiazui Ring Road
Pudong, Shanghai, China
Tel.: (86) 21 6123 8900
Fax: (86) 21 6165 0285
Web Site: www.commbank.com.au/about-us/our-company/international-branches/asia.html#China
Emp.: 3
Commercial Banking
S.I.C.: 6159
N.A.I.C.S.: 522298
Stanley Lo *(Gen Mgr)*

Commonwealth Bank of Australia - UK **(1)**
Senator House 85 Queen Victoria St
EC4 V4HA London, United Kingdom
Tel.: (44) 2077103999
Telex: 883864
Fax: (44) 2077103939
E-Mail: info@combank.com.au
Web Site: www.combank.com.au
Emp.: 100
International Bankers
S.I.C.: 6159
N.A.I.C.S.: 522293
Paul Orchard *(Gen Mgr)*

COMMONWEALTH PLYWOOD CO. LTD.

15 Blvd Labelle
PO Box 90
Sainte-Therese, QC, J7E 4H9, Canada
Tel.: (450) 435-6541
Fax: (450) 435-3814
Web Site: www.commonwealthplywood.com
Year Founded: 1940
Emp.: 2,500
Business Description:
Wood Products Mfr & Distr; Logging & Forest Management Services
S.I.C.: 2435
N.A.I.C.S.: 321113
Personnel:
W. T. Caine *(Pres)*

COMMSTRAT LIMITED

Lvl 8 574 St Kilda Rd
Melbourne, VIC, 3004, Australia
Mailing Address:
PO Box 6137
St Kilda Road Central, Melbourne, VIC, 8008, Australia
Tel.: (61) 3 8534 5000
Fax: (61) 3 9530 8911
E-Mail: enquiries@commstrat.com.au
Web Site: www.commstrat.com.au
COJ—(ASX)
Rev.: $6,387,625
Assets: $7,984,965
Liabilities: $6,507,945
Net Worth: $1,477,020
Earnings: $338,899
Emp.: 30
Fiscal Year-end: 06/30/13
Business Description:
Journals & Magazines Publication
S.I.C.: 2759
N.A.I.C.S.: 323111
Personnel:
Alexander McNab *(Chm)*
Chris Atkin *(CEO)*
Kim Clark *(Sec)*
Board of Directors:
Alexander McNab
Nicholas Love
Mark Sowerby
Legal Counsel:
Kain Lawyer
315 Wakefield Street
Adelaide, Australia

Subsidiary:

Hallmark Editions Pty Limited (1)
PO Box 6137
Brighton, Victoria, 8008, Australia
Tel.: (61) 385345000
Fax: (61) 395308911
E-Mail: reception@commstrat.com.au
Web Site: www.halledit.com.au
Magazine & Journal Publishers
S.I.C.: 2721
N.A.I.C.S.: 511120
Brad Gurrie *(CEO)*

COMMTOUCH SOFTWARE LTD.

1 Sapir Road 5th Floor Beit Ampa
PO Box 4014
Herzliyya, 46140, Israel
Tel.: (972) 9 863 6888
Fax: (972) 9 863 6863
E-Mail: info@commtouch.com
Web Site: www.commtouch.com
CTCH—(NASDAQ)
Rev.: $23,910,000
Assets: $59,133,000
Liabilities: $24,411,000
Net Worth: $34,722,000
Earnings: $1,485,000
Emp.: 198
Fiscal Year-end: 12/31/12
Business Description:
E-Mail Filtering & Management Applications
S.I.C.: 7372
N.A.I.C.S.: 511210
Personnel:
Lior Samuelson *(Chm)*
Shlomi Yanai *(CEO)*
Brian D. Briggs *(CFO)*
Lior Kohavi *(CTO)*
Gary Davis *(Gen Counsel, Sec & VP)*
Pete Shah *(Sr VP-Worldwide Sls)*
Board of Directors:
Lior Samuelson
Yair Bar-Touv
David Earhart
James A. Hamilton
Hila Karah
Aviv Raiz
Todd S. Thomson
Shlomi Yanai
Transfer Agent:
Wells Fargo Bank, N.A.
PO Box 64856
Saint Paul, MN 55164-0856

U.S. Subsidiaries:

Commtouch Inc. (1)
292 Zeigbraltar Dr
Sunnyvale, CA 94089
Tel.: (650) 864-2000
Fax: (650) 864-2002
E-Mail: sales-us@commtouch.com
Web Site: www.commtouch.com
Emp.: 20
Computer Virus Protection
S.I.C.: 3575
N.A.I.C.S.: 334118
Joy A. Nemitz *(CMO)*
Sue Perng Lee *(Gen Counsel & Sec)*

COMMUNICATION AND SYSTEM SOLUTION PUBLIC COMPANY LIMITED

475 477 Moo 9 Bondstreet Road
Bangpood Parkred, Nonthaburi, Thailand
Tel.: (66) 29601001
Fax: (66) 2960 0260
Web Site: www.cssthai.com
CSS—(THA)
Rev.: $109,398,904
Assets: $65,842,893
Liabilities: $52,345,069
Net Worth: $13,497,825
Earnings: $5,243,485
Fiscal Year-end: 12/31/12
Business Description:
Electrical Cable, Wire & Engineering Products Distribution & Installation
S.I.C.: 5063
N.A.I.C.S.: 423610
Personnel:
Sompong Kangsawiwat *(Chm & CEO)*

COMMUNICATION DESIGN INTERNATIONAL LIMITED

10 Bukit Batok Crescent 04-08 The Spire
Singapore, 658079, Singapore
Tel.: (65) 6342 0090
Fax: (65) 6342 0089
E-Mail: cdigroup@pacific.net.sg
Web Site: www.cdi-world.com
Year Founded: 1995
5HT—(SES)
Rev.: $16,238,132
Assets: $7,723,538
Liabilities: $5,458,863
Net Worth: $2,264,675
Earnings: ($677,702)
Fiscal Year-end: 06/30/13
Business Description:
Design Structures for Trade Shows, Museums, Visitor Centers; Outsourced Marketing Services
S.I.C.: 7389
N.A.I.C.S.: 541410
Personnel:
Robert Walter Dell *(Chm)*
David Cheow Guan Bay *(Pres & CEO)*
Geok Chng *(CFO & Co-Sec)*
Foon Kuen Lai *(Co-Sec)*
Board of Directors:
Robert Walter Dell
David Cheow Guan Bay
Robin Sin Beng Chin
Kiew Tee Pao
Chin Tiong Tan

Non-U.S. Subsidiary:

Clements and Street Ltd (1)
12 Broad Ground Rd
Lakeside, Redditch, Worcestershire, B98 8YP, United Kingdom
Tel.: (44) 1527513890
Fax: (44) 1527513891
E-Mail: paul.simpson@clementsandstreet.co.uk
Web Site: www.clementsandstreet.com
Exhibition Contractors
S.I.C.: 1799
N.A.I.C.S.: 238390
Paul Simson *(Dir-Comml & Mktg)*

COMMUNICATION WEAVER CO., LTD.

Coweaver B/D 446-19 Seogyo-dong
Mapo-gu, Seoul, 121-841, Korea (South)
Tel.: (82) 2 3140 3348
Fax: (82) 2 3140 3318
Web Site: www.coweaver.co.kr
Year Founded: 2000
056360—(KRS)
Business Description:
Optical Transmission Equipment Mfr
S.I.C.: 3661
N.A.I.C.S.: 334210
Personnel:
Daeyoung Lee *(Pres & Co-CEO)*
Su-Ha Whang *(Co-CEO)*
Ki-Hyuk Sung *(Sr Mng Dir)*
Board of Directors:
Chang-Seok Hwang
In-Heon Hwang
Seong-Kyu Hyun
Darl-Sug Kim
Dae-Ho Ko
Daeyoung Lee
Kyoung-Ho Lee
Ki-Hyuk Sung
Su-Ha Whang

COMMUNICATIONS INVESTMENT PARTNERS LIMITED

Suite 600, 570 Queen Street
Fredericton, NB, E3B 6Z6, Canada
Mailing Address:
Harneys Corporate Services Limited
P.O. Box 71
Craigmuir Chambers, Tortola, Road Town, Virgin Islands (British)
Web Site: www.ciplimited.com
Business Description:
Investment Activities
S.I.C.: 6211
N.A.I.C.S.: 523999
Personnel:
Hans Lipman *(Pres)*

COMMUNICORP GROUP LTD.

6th Floor 1 Grand Canal Quay
Dublin, 2, Ireland
Tel.: (353) 14325911
Fax: (353) 14325901
E-Mail: info@communicorp.ie
Web Site: www.communicorp.ie
Year Founded: 1989
Sales Range: $50-74.9 Million
Emp.: 1,200
Fiscal Year-end: 12/31/12
Business Description:
Radio Stations Owner & Operator
S.I.C.: 4832
N.A.I.C.S.: 515112
Personnel:
Denis O'Brien *(Founder & Owner)*
Lucy Gaffney *(Chm)*
Gervaise Slowey *(CEO)*
Board of Directors:
Lucy Gaffney
Paul Connolly
Ronan Harris
Maria Mahon
Denis O'Brien
Gervaise Slowey

Non-U.S. Subsidiary:

Oy Metroradio Finland AB (1)
Pursimiehenkatu 29-31 C
00150 Helsinki, Finland FI
Tel.: (358) 207768360 (100%)
Web Site: www.metroradio.fi
Emp.: 30
Radio Stations Owner & Operator
S.I.C.: 4832
N.A.I.C.S.: 515112

COMMUNISIS PLC

Wakefield Road
Leeds, LS10 1DU, United Kingdom
Tel.: (44) 1132770202
Fax: (44) 1132713503
E-Mail: enquiries@communisis.com
Web Site: www.communisis.com
CMS—(LSE)
Rev.: $362,879,780
Assets: $409,795,748
Liabilities: $212,089,171
Net Worth: $197,706,577
Earnings: $8,180,722
Emp.: 1,525
Fiscal Year-end: 12/31/12
Business Description:
Printing Management Services; Specialist Printing & Direct Mail Services
S.I.C.: 2759
N.A.I.C.S.: 323111
Personnel:
Andy Blundell *(CEO)*
Dave Rushton *(Grp Mng Dir)*
Sarah Caddy *(Sec)*
Board of Directors:
Peter Hickson
Andy Blundell
Michael Firth
Jane Griffiths
Peter Harris
Nigel Howes
Dave Rushton
John Wells
Legal Counsel:
Eversheds LLP
Bridgewater Pl Water Ln
Leeds, United Kingdom

Subsidiaries:

Communisis Europe Limited (1)
Wakefield Road
Leeds, West Yorkshire, LS10 1DU, United Kingdom
Tel.: (44) 113 277 0202
Fax: (44) 113 2713503
E-Mail: enquiries@communisis.com
Web Site: www.communisis.com
Emp.: 30
Management Services
S.I.C.: 8741
N.A.I.C.S.: 551114
Andy Blundell *(CEO)*

Communisis UK Limited (1)
Wakefield Road
Leeds, West Yorkshire, LS10 1DU, United Kingdom (100%)
Tel.: (44) 1132770202
Fax: (44) 1132713503
E-Mail: enquiries@communisis.com
Web Site: www.Communisis.co.uk
Emp.: 25
Commercial Printing
S.I.C.: 2759
N.A.I.C.S.: 323111
Andy Blundell *(Exec Dir)*

Subsidiary:

Absolute Intuistic Limited (2)
Ai House Holbrooke Pl
Hill Rise, Richmond, Surrey, TW10 6UD, United Kingdom
Tel.: (44) 2086147333
Fax: (44) 2086147300
E-Mail: info@aidataintelligence.com
Web Site: www.aidataintelligence.com
Emp.: 40
Data Processing Services
S.I.C.: 7379
N.A.I.C.S.: 518210
John Regan *(CEO)*
Jon Cano-Lopez *(Mng Dir)*
Jason Batten *(COO)*

COMMVESCO LEVINSON VINER GROUP INC

485 Bank St
Ottawa, ON, K2P 1Z2, Canada
Tel.: (613) 728-2000
Fax: (613) 728-1107
Toll Free: (877) 728-3003
E-Mail: info@clvgroup.com
Web Site: www.clvgroup.com
Rev.: $18,107,735
Emp.: 200
Business Description:
Real Estate Agents & Brokers
S.I.C.: 6411
N.A.I.C.S.: 524210
Personnel:
Michael Darryl McGahan *(CEO)*

COMNORD S.A.

Calea Grivitei 136 Sector 1
010741 Bucharest, Romania
Tel.: (40) 212066800
Fax: (40) 212066802
E-Mail: contact@comnord.ro
Web Site: www.comnord.ro
COSC—(BUC)
Sales Range: $10-24.9 Million
Emp.: 37
Business Description:
Civil & Industrial Construction Services

COMNORD S.A.—(Continued)

S.I.C.: 1542
N.A.I.C.S.: 236220
Personnel:
Oleana Negoita *(Pres)*

COMO DIFFUSION INC.
255 Boul Decarie
Saint Laurent, QC, H4N 2L7, Canada
Tel.: (514) 286-2666
Fax: (514) 286-2822
Toll Free: (800) 465-9711
Web Site: www.freddavid.com
Rev.: $73,764,000
Emp.: 75
Business Description:
Apparel Mfr
S.I.C.: 2389
N.A.I.C.S.: 315990
Personnel:
Helaine Peters *(Pres)*

COMO ENGINEERS PTY. LTD.
27 McCabe St
Mosman Park, Perth, WA, 6012, Australia
Tel.: (61) 8 9432 0100
Fax: (61) 8 9336 4900
E-Mail: como@comoeng.com.au
Web Site: www.comoeng.com.au
Year Founded: 1986
Emp.: 30
Business Description:
Mining Engineering Services
S.I.C.: 8711
N.A.I.C.S.: 541330
Personnel:
Richard Ladyman *(Mng Dir)*
Kevin Chong *(Sec)*

COMOPS LIMITED
Level 6 77 Pacific Highway
North Sydney, NSW, 2060, Australia
Tel.: (61) 299238000
Fax: (61) 299238099
E-Mail: info@comops.com.au
Web Site: www.comops.com.au
COM—(ASX)
Rev.: $10,156,833
Assets: $21,347,447
Liabilities: $13,641,919
Net Worth: $7,705,528
Earnings: ($13,128,875)
Emp.: 100
Fiscal Year-end: 12/31/12
Business Description:
Software Development
S.I.C.: 7372
N.A.I.C.S.: 511210
Personnel:
Colin Henson *(CEO)*
Christopher Brooke *(CFO & Sec)*
Board of Directors:
Murray A. Creighton
Niall Cairns
Phillip Carter
Tony Karabatsas
Alex Ninis
Legal Counsel:
Price Waterhouse Coopers Australia
201 Sussex Street
Sydney, NSW, 2000, Australia

COMOX VALLEY DODGE CHRYSLER JEEP LTD.
4847 Island Hwy North
Courtenay, BC, V9N 5Y8, Canada
Tel.: (250) 338-5451
Fax: (250) 338-1442
Toll Free: (877) 850-2828
E-Mail: info@comoxvalleydodge.com
Web Site: www.comoxvalleydodge.com
Rev.: $14,418,889
Emp.: 33
Business Description:
New & Used Car Dealers
S.I.C.: 5511
N.A.I.C.S.: 441110
Personnel:
Bill Eddy *(Mgr-Body Shop)*

COMP-U-LEARN TECH INDIA LIMITED
(Name Changed to CTIL Limited)

COMPA S.A.
Henri Coanda Street 8
550234 Sibiu, Romania
Tel.: (40) 269239400
Fax: (40) 269 237 770
E-Mail: office@compa.ro
Web Site: www.compa.ro
CMP—(BUC)
Sales Range: $75-99.9 Million
Emp.: 1,543
Business Description:
Motor Vehicle Parts & Accessories Mfr
S.I.C.: 3714
N.A.I.C.S.: 336340
Personnel:
Ioan Deac *(Chm, Pres & CEO)*
Board of Directors:
Ioan Deac
Florin Acu
Dan Baiasu
Tiberiu Bucur
Ioan Firiza
Ioan Miclea
Bogdon Muntenas
Ilie Nistor
Octavian Suciu

COMPACT DISC INDIA LTD
SCO 856 Chandigarh Kalka Rd
NAC Manimajra
160101 Chandigarh, Chandigarh, India
Tel.: (91) 1722734331
Fax: (91) 1722733014
E-Mail: info@compactdisc.co.in
Web Site: www.compactdisc.co.in
526141—(BOM)
Sales Range: $25-49.9 Million
Business Description:
Produce, Distribute & Finance Films & Television Serials Including Animation
S.I.C.: 7819
N.A.I.C.S.: 512191
Personnel:
Suresh Kumar *(Chm)*
Board of Directors:
Suresh Kumar
Santosh Grover
Vinod Kumar
Rashmee Seengal
Subsidiary:

Laser Infomedia Ltd. **(1)**
SCO 856 NAC Manimajra Chandigarh - Kalka Rd
Chandigarh, 160101, India
Tel.: (91) 1722734331
Fax: (91) 1722733014
Multimedia Production Services
S.I.C.: 7812
N.A.I.C.S.: 512110

COMPACT METAL INDUSTRIES LTD.
120 Pioneer Road
Singapore, 639597, Singapore
Tel.: (65) 68633268
Fax: (65) 68633968
E-Mail: info@compact.com.sg
Web Site: www.compact.com.sg
Year Founded: 1973
C02—(SES)
Rev.: $27,723,443
Assets: $51,398,486
Liabilities: $16,930,409
Net Worth: $34,468,078
Earnings: ($638,838)
Emp.: 1,192
Fiscal Year-end: 12/31/12
Business Description:
Aluminum Windows & Doors & Extruded Aluminum Mfr
S.I.C.: 3442
N.A.I.C.S.: 332321
Personnel:
Gim Huat Chng *(Chm)*
Beng Hua Chng *(CEO)*
Fook Chang Heng *(CFO & Co-Sec)*
Choon Seng Por *(COO)*
Li Yang *(CTO)*
Siew Koon Ang *(Co-Sec)*
Board of Directors:
Gim Huat Chng
Alex Beng Hock Chng
Beng Hua Chng
Lisa Sam Min Hui
Ah Chye Kan
Subsidiaries:

Aluform Marketing Pte Ltd. **(1)**
120 Pioneer Road #01-02
Singapore, 639597, Singapore
Tel.: (65) 68979780
Fax: (65) 68633968
E-Mail: info@aluform.com.sg
Web Site: www.aluform.com.sg
Emp.: 35
Building Architectural Products Supply & Installation
S.I.C.: 1799
N.A.I.C.S.: 238390
Chng Gim Huag *(Pres)*

FacadeMaster Pte Ltd. **(1)**
20 Pioneer Road #04-01
639597 Singapore, Singapore
Tel.: (65) 68631836
Fax: (65) 68630836
E-Mail: info@facademaster.com.sg
Building Facade Contracting Services
S.I.C.: 3448
N.A.I.C.S.: 332311

Integrate Marketing Pte Ltd. **(1)**
120 Pioneer Rd #01-02
Singapore, 639597, Singapore
Tel.: (65) 68979780
Fax: (65) 68979738
E-Mail: info@integrate.com.sg
Web Site: www.integrate.com.sg
Emp.: 25
Building Components & Accessories Mfr & Distr
S.I.C.: 5211
N.A.I.C.S.: 444190
Gary Ang *(Gen Mgr)*

Non-U.S. Subsidiaries:

Compact Metal Industries Sdn Bhd **(1)**
77 Jalan Riang 21
Taman Gembira Johore Baru, Johor, 81200, Malaysia
Tel.: (60) 73348370
Fax: (60) 73314448
E-Mail: cmisb01@po.jaring.my
Aluminum Window & Door Mfr
S.I.C.: 3442
N.A.I.C.S.: 332321

Non-U.S. Subsidiary:

INTEGRATE PTE LTD **(2)**
120 Pioneer Road 01-02
Singapore, 639597, Singapore
Tel.: (65) 6897 9780
Fax: (65) 6897 9738
E-Mail: info@integrate.com.sg
Web Site: www.integrate.com.sg
Steel Mfr
S.I.C.: 3312
N.A.I.C.S.: 331110
Garry Ang *(Gen Mgr)*

PT Cakra Compact Aluminium Industries **(1)**
Jl Raya Medan Tg Morawa Km 11
PO Box 2345
North Sumatera Medan, Indonesia
Tel.: (62) 617940246
Fax: (62) 617940244
Web Site: www.cakracompact.com
Aluminum Window & Door Mfr
S.I.C.: 3442
N.A.I.C.S.: 332321
Albert Quek *(Gen Mgr)*

Selaco Aluminium Berhad **(1)**
Lot 280 Jalan Timah
Pasir Gudang Ind Estate
Gudang Johore, Johor, 81700, Malaysia
Tel.: (60) 72514062
Fax: (60) 72515287
E-Mail: kylim@selaco.com.my
Web Site: www.selaco.com.my
Emp.: 300
Aluminum Window & Door Mfr
S.I.C.: 3442
N.A.I.C.S.: 332321
Ky Lim *(Gen Mgr)*

COMPAGNIA DELLA RUOTA S.P.A.
Via Aldo Moro 3/A
13900 Biella, Italy
Tel.: (39) 015 405679
Fax: (39) 015 8407120
E-Mail: info@compagniadellaruota.com
Web Site: www.compagniadellaruota.com
CDR—(ITA)
Business Description:
Investment, Financial & Advisory Services
S.I.C.: 6211
N.A.I.C.S.: 523999
Personnel:
Mauro Girardi *(Chm)*
Board of Directors:
Mauro Girardi
Michele Calzolari
Vincenzo Polidoro
Gabriella Tua
Andrea Zanelli

COMPAGNIA FINANZIARIA DE BENEDETTI S.P.A.
(d/b/a COFIDE)
Via Ciovassina 1
20121 Milan, Italy
Tel.: (39) 02722701
Fax: (39) 0272270202
E-Mail: info@cofide.it
Web Site: www.cofide.it
COF—(ITA)
Rev.: $6,815,629,094
Assets: $10,923,676,852
Liabilities: $7,806,710,410
Net Worth: $3,116,966,442
Earnings: ($158,559,980)
Emp.: 13,944
Fiscal Year-end: 12/31/12
Business Description:
Holding Company; Publishing, Food Machinery Manufacturing, Automotive Components, Tobacco Machinery, Specialty Foods, Real Estate & Financial Services
S.I.C.: 6719
N.A.I.C.S.: 551112
Personnel:
Rodolfo De Benedetti *(CEO)*
Board of Directors:
Silvia Candiani
Laura Cioli
Francesca Cornelli
Massimo Cremona
Carlo De Benedetti
Edurado De Benedetti

Marco De Benedetti
Paola Dubini
Pierluigi Ferrero
Francesco Guasti
Joseph Oughourlian
Roberto Robotti

Subsidiaries:

CIR S.p.A. **(1)**
Via Ciovassino 1
20121 Milan, Italy
Tel.: (39) 0272270
Fax: (39) 0272270259
E-Mail: info@cirgroup.it
Web Site: www.cirgroup.it
CIR—(ITA)
Assets: $10,890,851,843
Liabilities: $7,751,538,979
Net Worth: $3,139,312,864
Earnings: ($100,806,594)
Emp.: 13,940
Fiscal Year-end: 12/31/12
Holding Company; Publishing, Media, Automotive Components, Specialty Food, Real Estate, Utilities & Food Machinery
S.I.C.: 6719
N.A.I.C.S.: 551112
Rodolfo De Benedetti *(Chm)*
Monica Mondardini *(CEO)*
Giuseppe Gianoglio *(Chief Admin Officer)*

Subsidiaries:

Gruppo Editoriale L'Espresso S.p.A. **(2)**
Via Cristoforo Colombo n 98
00147 Rome, Italy IT
Tel.: (39) 0684781 (55%)
Fax: (39) 0684787371
E-Mail: investorrelations@gruppoespresso.it
Web Site: www.gruppoespresso.it
ES—(ITA OTC)
Rev.: $1,094,009,474
Assets: $1,768,093,332
Liabilities: $1,017,365,285
Net Worth: $750,728,047
Earnings: $29,549,778
Emp.: 2,536
Fiscal Year-end: 12/31/12
Magazine & Newspaper Publisher; Radio, Television & Internet Broadcasting Services
S.I.C.: 2711
N.A.I.C.S.: 511110
Carlo De Benedetti *(Chm)*
Monica Mondarini *(CEO)*
Massimo Ghedini *(CEO/Gen Mgr-A Manzoni & C SpA)*

Subsidiaries:

A.Manzoni And C. Spa **(3)**
Via Nervesa 21
20139 Milan, Italy (100%)
Tel.: (39) 02574941
Fax: (39) 0257400444
E-Mail: info@manzoni.it
Web Site: www.manzoniadvertising.com
Emp.: 200
Advertising Material Distribution Services
S.I.C.: 7319
N.A.I.C.S.: 541870
Sabio Vaccarono *(Mng Dir)*

Editoriale FVG Spa **(3)**
Viale Palmanova 290
33100 Udine, Italy (92.21%)
Tel.: (39) 0432527217
Fax: (39) 0432527240
E-Mail: direzione@messaggeroveneto.it
Emp.: 200
Newspaper Publishers
S.I.C.: 2711
N.A.I.C.S.: 511110
Omar Monestier *(Mng Dir)*

Editoriale La Nuova Sardegna Spa **(3)**
Preba niepda 31
07100 Sassari, Italy (100%)
Tel.: (39) 079222400
Fax: (39) 0792674086
E-Mail: lanuovasardegna@lanuovasardegna.it
Web Site: www.lanuovasardegna.it
Emp.: 100
Newspaper Publishers
S.I.C.: 2711
N.A.I.C.S.: 511110
Antonello Esposito *(Mng Dir)*

Editoriale Metropoli Spa **(3)**
Via Tortona 33
20144 Milan, Italy (100%)
Tel.: (39) 02489691
Fax: (39) 02489696439
E-Mail: velvet@larepubblicavelvet.it
Periodical Publishers
S.I.C.: 2721
N.A.I.C.S.: 511120
Nichela Gattermaeer *(Mng Dir)*

Ksolutions Spa **(3)**
Via Lenin 132 A 26
San giuliano Terme, 56017 Florence, Italy (100%)
Tel.: (39) 050898111
Fax: (39) 050898412
E-Mail: info@ksolutions.it
Office Equipment Whslr
S.I.C.: 5044
N.A.I.C.S.: 423420

Selpi Spa **(3)**
Via Francesco Ferruccio 8
20145 Milan, Italy (70%)
Tel.: (39) 0234811
Fax: (39) 023451937
E-Mail: info@selpi.it
Emp.: 5
Newspaper Publishers
S.I.C.: 2711
N.A.I.C.S.: 511110

Sogefi S.p.A. **(2)**
Via Flavio Gioia 8
Milan, Italy (52.43%)
Tel.: (39) 02467501
Fax: (39) 0243511348
Web Site: www.sogefi.it
Emp.: 6,100
Automotive Filters Mfr
S.I.C.: 3714
N.A.I.C.S.: 336390
Rodolfo De Benedetti *(Chm)*

Non-U.S. Subsidiaries:

Filtrauto S.A. **(3)**
7 Ave Du 8 Mai 1945
78280 Guyancourt, France
Tel.: (33) 161374300
Telex: 697084 F
Fax: (33) 161374301
E-Mail: accuilg@filtrauto.com
Web Site: www.filtrauto.com
Emp.: 1,050
Mfr of Automotive Filters
S.I.C.: 3711
N.A.I.C.S.: 336111
Emanuele Bosio *(Chm & Dir Gen)*

Non-U.S. Divisions:

Filtrauto Do Brasil Ltda. **(4)**
Avenue Piraporanha No 251
Sao Bernardo do Campo, MG, 019891000, Brazil
Tel.: (55) 01143412400
Industrial Filters Mfr
S.I.C.: 3714
N.A.I.C.S.: 336390

Filtrauto Slovenija **(4)**
Obrat Jesenice
C Franceta Mesarna 15
4270 Jesenice, Slovenia
Web Site: www.filtrauto.com
Industrial Filters Mfr
S.I.C.: 3714
N.A.I.C.S.: 336390

Sogefi Filtration Argentina S.A. **(3)**
Aguilar 3003
Remedios de Escalada, Buenos Aires, Argentina
Tel.: (54) 1142204600
E-Mail: sogefi@sogefi.com.ar
Web Site: www.sogefi.com.ar
Industrial Filters Mfr
S.I.C.: 3714
N.A.I.C.S.: 336390

Sogefi Filtration D.O.O. **(3)**
Ladja 11
1215 Medvode, Slovenia
Tel.: (386) 013629011
Fax: (386) 13613315
Web Site: www.sogeci.com
Emp.: 159
Industrial Filters Mfr
S.I.C.: 3569
N.A.I.C.S.: 333999
Veida Hrabar *(Sec)*

Sogefi Industria de Autopecas Ltda. **(3)**
Av Piraporinha 251
San Bernardo do Campo, 09891-000 Sao Paulo, Brazil
Tel.: (55) 11 759 2400
Telex: 114253 TRAM BR
Fax: (55) 11 759 5959
Web Site: www.sogefi.com.br
Mfr & Sales of Filters
S.I.C.: 3589
N.A.I.C.S.: 333318

Sorgenia S.p.A **(2)**
Via V Viviani 12
Milan, 20124, Italy
Tel.: (39) 02671941
Fax: (39) 02 6719 4210
E-Mail: info@sorgenia.it
Web Site: www.sorgenia.it
Emp.: 200
Natural Gas Production Services
S.I.C.: 1389
N.A.I.C.S.: 213112
Riccardo Bani *(Gen Mgr)*

Saire S.R.L **(1)**
9 Via Giotto
39100 Bolzano, Italy
Tel.: (39) 0471250006
Fax: (39) 0471 251 894
Non Flammable Materials Mfr
S.I.C.: 9224
N.A.I.C.S.: 922160

COMPAGNIA IMMOBILIARE AZIONARIA S.P.A.

Via G Borgazzi 2
Milan, MI, 20122, Italy
Tel.: (39) 02 58219347
Fax: (39) 02 58317376
E-Mail: ir@c-i-a.it
Web Site: www.c-i-a.it
Year Founded: 2002
CIA—(ITA)
Sales Range: $10-24.9 Million
Emp.: 3

Business Description:
Real Estate Management Services
S.I.C.: 6531
N.A.I.C.S.: 531390

Personnel:
Angelo Riccardi *(Chm)*
Paolo Panerai *(Vice Chm)*
Marco Fanfani *(Co-Mng Dir)*
Luca Nicolo Panerai *(Co-Mng Dir)*

Board of Directors:
Angelo Riccardi
Maurizio Carfagna
Giovanni Battista Cattaneo della Volta
Marco Fanfani
Andrea Morante
Nicoletta Costa Novaro
Beatrice Panerai
Luca Nicolo Panerai
Paolo Panerai
Vincenzo Truppa
Diego Della Valle
Umberto Vitiello

COMPAGNIE AERIENNE INTER REGIONALE EXPRESS SA

(d/b/a CAIRE)
Aeroport de Rochambeau
97351 Matoury, French Guiana
Tel.: (594) 293630
Fax: (594) 305437
Web Site: www.airguyane.com
MLAAE—(EUR)
Sales Range: $25-49.9 Million

Business Description:
Airline Operator
S.I.C.: 4512
N.A.I.C.S.: 481111

Personnel:
Christian Marchand *(Chm)*

COMPAGNIE DAPPAREILS ELECTRIQUES PEERLESS LIMITEE

(d/b/a Peerless Electric Company LTD.)
9145 Rue Boivin
Montreal, QC, H8R 2E5, Canada
Tel.: (514) 595-1671
Fax: (514) 595-4411
E-Mail: info@peerless-electric.com
Web Site: www.peerless-electric.com
Rev.: $18,645,116
Emp.: 130

Business Description:
Commercial & Industry Light Mfr
S.I.C.: 3646
N.A.I.C.S.: 335122

Personnel:
Barry Fagen *(Pres)*

COMPAGNIE DE FIVES LILLE SA

(d/b/a Fives Group)
27-29 rue de Provence
75009 Paris, France
Tel.: (33) 145237575
Fax: (33) 145237571
E-Mail: contact@fivesgroup.com
Web Site: www.fivesgroup.com
Year Founded: 1812
Sls.: $2,029,860,127
Assets: $1,669,755,614
Liabilities: $1,337,038,929
Net Worth: $332,716,685
Earnings: $70,436,999
Emp.: 6,521
Fiscal Year-end: 12/31/12

Business Description:
Cement, Mineral, Food Processing, Sugar & Waste Disposal Industries Equipment Supplier
S.I.C.: 3241
N.A.I.C.S.: 327310

Personnel:
Dominique Gaillard *(Chm-Supervisory Bd)*
Frederic Sanchez *(Chm-Exec Bd)*
Lise Fauconnier *(Vice Chm-Supervisory Bd)*
Lucile Ribot *(CFO & Member-Mgmt Bd)*
Shang Blao *(CEO-Stein Shanghai)*
Ron McCullough *(CEO-North America)*
Frederic Thrum *(CEO-Cail)*
Martin Duverne *(Member-Exec Bd-Energy & Logistics Div)*
Jean-Camille Uring *(Member-Exec Bd)*

Supervisory Board of Directors:
Dominique Gaillard
Lise Fauconnier
Alexandra Goltsova
Laurent Roquette

Deloitte & Associes
185 avenue Charles-de-Gaulle
Neuilly-sur-Seine, France

Subsidiary:

Fives DMS **(1)**
1 rue du Mont-de-Templemars
BP 30219
Z.I Lille Seclin, 59472 Seclin, Cedex, France (100%)
Tel.: (33) 320493500
Fax: (33) 320493501
E-Mail: fivesdms@fivesgroup.com
Web Site: www.fivesgroup.com
Emp.: 150
Rolling Mills & Allied Equipment for Ferrous & Nonferrous Metals, Hot Strip Downcoilers, Computerized Hydraulic Mill Automatic Gauge Control Systems, Mill Modernization of Existing Facilities

Compagnie de Fives Lille SA—(Continued)

S.I.C.: 3549
N.A.I.C.S.: 333519
Benoeit Caracge *(Gen Mgr)*

U.S. Subsidiaries:

Cinetic Automation (1)
23400 Halsted Rd
Farmington, MI 48335-2840
Tel.: (248) 477-0800
Fax: (248) 615-2452
Web Site: www.cineticusa.com
Emp.: 220
Mfr. of Automated Assembly Machines
S.I.C.: 3547
N.A.I.C.S.: 333519
Michael Di Michele *(Pres)*

Subsidiaries:

Cinetic Landis Ltd. (2)
16778 Halfway Blvd
Hagerstown, MD 21740
Tel.: (301) 797-3400
Fax: (301) 797-2480
E-Mail: landis-us-info@fivesgroup.com
Web Site: www.fivesgroup.com
Emp.: 130
Precision Grinding Machines
Export
S.I.C.: 3569
N.A.I.C.S.: 333999

Gardner Abrasives (2)
481 Gardner St
South Beloit, IL 61080
Tel.: (815) 389-2251
Fax: (815) 389-5024
Web Site: www.gardnerabrasives.com
Emp.: 100
Abrasive Wheel Mfr
Export
S.I.C.: 6062
N.A.I.C.S.: 522130

Cinetic Sorting Corp. (1)
500 E Burnett Ave
Louisville, KY 40217-1120 KY
Tel.: (502) 636-1414 (100%)
Fax: (502) 636-1491
Web Site: www.sorting.com
Emp.: 70
Sorting & Material Handling System Mfr
S.I.C.: 3535
N.A.I.C.S.: 333922
Chris Gatz *(VP-Sls & Mktg)*

Fives Machining Systems, Inc. (1)
(Formerly MAG IAS, LLC)
3940 Olympic Blvd
Erlanger, KY 41018 DE
Tel.: (859) 534-4600
Fax: (859) 669-1897
Web Site: www.fivesmsi.com
Sales Range: $400-449.9 Million
Emp.: 1,000
Metal Cutting Machines & Automated Systems for Automotive/Commercial Vehicle Industry
S.I.C.: 3542
N.A.I.C.S.: 333517
Mark Logan *(VP-Bus Dev & Mktg)*

Unit:

Fives Machining Systems, Inc. - Global Services, Chatsworth (2)
20701 Plummer St
Chatsworth, CA 91311-5002
Mailing Address:
PO Box 2477
Chatsworth, CA 91313-2477
Tel.: (818) 407-1400
Fax: (818) 407-0020
E-Mail:
Web Site: www.fivesmsi.com
Emp.: 6
Machine Tool Rebuild, Retrofit & Maintenance Services
S.I.C.: 7389
N.A.I.C.S.: 541990
Bill Wier *(Mgr-HR)*

Plants:

Fives Machining Systems, Inc. - Fond du Lac (2)
142 Doty St
Fond Du Lac, WI 54935-3331
Mailing Address:
PO Box 590
Fond Du Lac, WI 54936-0590
Tel.: (920) 921-9400
Fax: (920) 906-2522
E-Mail:
Web Site: www.fivesmsi.com
Emp.: 2,700
Machine Tools & Factory Automation Equipment Mfr & Services
Import Export
S.I.C.: 3541
N.A.I.C.S.: 333517
Linda Kieckhafer *(Mgr-Mktg)*

Fives Machining Systems, Inc. - Hebron (2)
2200 Litton Ln
Hebron, KY 41048
Tel.: (859) 534-4600
Fax: (859) 534-4995
E-Mail:
Web Site: www.fivesmsi.com
Emp.: 750
Machine Tools Mfr
S.I.C.: 3542
N.A.I.C.S.: 333517
Chip Storie *(VP & Gen Mgr)*

Fives North American Combustion, Inc. (1)
4455 E 71st St
Cleveland, OH 44105-5601 OH
Tel.: (216) 271-6000
Fax: (216) 641-7852
E-Mail: fna.sales@fivesgroup.com
Web Site: www.namfg.com
Emp.: 325
Mfr. of Industrial Furnace Components & Edge Guide Materials; Electrical & General Engineering
S.I.C.: 3433
N.A.I.C.S.: 333414
Wes Paisley *(Pres)*
Kathy Ruekberg *(CFO)*

Non-U.S. Subsidiaries:

Cinetic Giustina s.r.l. (1)
Corso Lombardia 79 Z.I. Pescarito
10099 San Mauro Torinese, Torino, Italy
Tel.: (39) 0112228611
Fax: (39) 0112228632
E-Mail: cinetic-giustina@fivesgroup.com
Emp.: 60
Grinding Machinery Mfr
S.I.C.: 3541
N.A.I.C.S.: 333517
Paolo Poletti *(Pres)*

Fives Fletcher Limited (1)
33 Brunel Parkway
Pride Park, Derby, DE24 8HR, United Kingdom (100%)
Tel.: (44) 1332636000
Fax: (44) 1332636020
E-Mail: fivesfletcher@fivesgroup.com
Web Site: www.fivesgroup.com
Sales Range: $10-24.9 Million
Emp.: 33
Sugar Processing Machinery Mfr
S.I.C.: 2061
N.A.I.C.S.: 311314

COMPAGNIE DE L'OCCIDENT POUR LA FINANCE ET L'INDUSTRIE S.A.

(d/b/a COFI SA)
2 rue de l'Eau
1449 Luxembourg, Luxembourg
Tel.: (352) 299 230
Fax: (352) 299 231
E-Mail: info@cofi.lu
Web Site: www.cofi.lu
Rev.: $170,532,816
Assets: $3,754,707,748
Liabilities: $3,205,384,233
Net Worth: $549,323,515
Earnings: $26,759,167
Fiscal Year-end: 12/31/12

Business Description:
Bank Holding Company
S.I.C.: 6712
N.A.I.C.S.: 551111

Personnel:
Frederic Wagner *(Chm)*
Massimo Trabaldo Togna *(Vice Chm)*
Bruno Panigaldi *(Sec)*

Board of Directors:
Frederic Wagner
Jean Bodoni
Americo Bortuzzo
Robert Hoffmann
Jean Noel Lequeue
Bruno Panigaldi
Massimo Trabaldo Togna

Non-U.S. Subsidiary:

PKB Privatbank SA (1)
Via S Balestra 1
6901 Lugano, Switzerland CH
Tel.: (41) 91 913 3535
Fax: (41) 91 923 3522
Web Site: www.pkb.ch
Private Banking
S.I.C.: 6211
N.A.I.C.S.: 523110
Henry Peter *(Chm)*
Maurizio Jesi Ferrari *(Vice Chm)*
Fernando Zari Malacrida *(Vice Chm)*
Umberto Trabaldo Togna *(Pres)*
Elena Trabaldo Togna *(Sec)*
Lorenzo Tavola *(Exec VP)*
Enrico Tonella *(Exec VP)*

COMPAGNIE DE SAINT-GOBAIN SA

Les Miroirs 18 Ave d'Alsace
92400 Courbevoie, France
Tel.: (33) 147623000
Telex: 611570SGF
E-Mail: actionnaires@saint-gobain.com
Web Site: www.saint-gobain.com
Year Founded: 1665
SGO—(EUR LSE OTC)
Sls.: $58,151,851,660
Assets: $63,974,036,910
Liabilities: $39,943,556,240
Net Worth: $24,030,480,670
Earnings: $1,071,551,320
Emp.: 192,781
Fiscal Year-end: 12/31/12

Business Description:
Glass, Plastics, Ceramics & Other Construction Materials Mfr
Import Export
S.I.C.: 3999
N.A.I.C.S.: 339999

Personnel:
Pierre-Andre de Chalendar *(Chm & CEO)*
Laurent Guillot *(CFO)*
Jerome Fessard *(Pres-Pkg Sector & Sr VP)*
Benoit Bazin *(Pres-Building Distr Sector & Sr VP)*
Jean-Pierre Floris *(Pres-Innovative Matls Sector & Sr VP)*
Claude Imauven *(Pres-Construction Products Sector & Sr VP)*
Antoine Vignial *(Sec)*
Jean-Francois Phelizon *(Sr VP & Dir-Audit & Internal Control)*
Jean-Claude Breffort *(Sr VP-Intl Dev)*
Gilles Colas *(Sr VP-Strategic Dev)*
John T. Crowe *(Sr VP-Gen Delegate-North America)*
Claire Pedini *(Sr VP-HR)*

Board of Directors:
Pierre-Andre de Chalendar
Isabelle Bouillot
Gerhard Cromme
Jean-Martin Folz
Bernard Gautier
Anne-Marie Idrac
Sylvia Jay
Frederic Lemoine
Gerard Mestrallet
Michel Pebereau
Jacques Pestre
Olivia Qiu
Denis Ranque
Gilles Schnepp
Jean-Dominique Senard
Jean-Cyril Spinetta

KPMG Audit
Patrick-Hubert Petit 1 cours Valmy
F-92923 Paris, La Defense Cedex, France

Divisions:

Saint-Gobain Distribution Batiment (1)
Les Miroirs 18 Ave Dalsace
92400 Courbevoie, France FR
Tel.: (33) 147623000 (100%)
Telex: 213 855
Fax: (33) 0147624387
Web Site: www.saint-gobain.com
Emp.: 60
Construction Materials Distr
Import Export
S.I.C.: 1442
N.A.I.C.S.: 212321
Benoit Bazin *(Mng Dir)*

Subsidiaries:

Gibbs and Dandy PLC (3)
226 Dallow Road
Luton, LU 1JG, United Kingdom
Tel.: (44) 1582798798
Fax: (44) 1582798799
E-Mail: mail@gibbsanddandy.com
Web Site: www.gibbsanddandy.com
Rev.: $124,045,186
Emp.: 345
Building Supply Store Operator
S.I.C.: 5251
N.A.I.C.S.: 444110
Mike Warner *(Chm)*
Amitabh Sharma *(Sec & Dir-Fin)*

Jewson Ltd. (3)
Merchant House Binley Business Park Binley
Coventry, Westmidland, CV3 2TT, United Kingdom (100%)
Tel.: (44) 2476438400
Fax: (44) 2476438401
E-Mail: peter.hindle@jewson.co.uk
Web Site: www.jewson.co.uk
Rev.: $665,396,992
Emp.: 450
Timber & Building Material Merchants
S.I.C.: 5211
N.A.I.C.S.: 444190
Peter Hindle *(Mng Dir)*

U.S. Subsidiary:

Meyer Decorative Surfaces, Inc. (2)
340 Patton Dr
Atlanta, GA 30336
Tel.: (404) 507-1200
Fax: (404) 222-1980
E-Mail:
Web Site: www.meyerdeco.com
Laminates, Cabinets, Custom Doors, Counter Tops, Adhesives, Hardware, Tools & Wood Products Whslr & Distr
S.I.C.: 5031
N.A.I.C.S.: 423310
David Sullivan *(CEO)*
Philippe Guerreau *(Sec)*

Subsidiaries:

Meyer Laminate Flooring, Inc. (4)
1900 Australian Ave
Riviera Beach, FL 33404-5322
Tel.: (561) 844-3434
Fax: (561) 844-6118
Web Site: www.meyerflooring.com
Distributor of Laminates & Related Products
S.I.C.: 5031
N.A.I.C.S.: 423310

Meyer Laminates (MA), Inc. (4)
330 Patton Dr SW
Atlanta, GA 30336-1841 (100%)
Tel.: (404) 699-3900
Fax: (404) 699-3914
Web Site: www.meyerdeco.com
Emp.: 100
Distributor of Laminates & Related Products
S.I.C.: 5031
N.A.I.C.S.: 423310
David Sullivan *(CEO)*

Meyer Laminates (SE), Inc. (4)
330 Patton Dr SW
Atlanta, GA 30336-1841 (100%)
Tel.: (404) 699-3900
Fax: (404) 699-3914
Web Site: www.meyerdeco.com
Emp.: 100
Distributor of Laminates & Related Products
S.I.C.: 5031
N.A.I.C.S.: 423310
Terry Miller *(Reg Mgr)*

Non-U.S. Subsidiaries:

Dahl International AB (3)
Karlsbodavagen 2
PO Box 11076
16811 Bromma, Sweden (100%)
Tel.: (46) 87642200
Fax: (46) 8212815
E-Mail: eva.hemb@dahlinternational.com
Web Site: www.dahlinternational.com
Emp.: 10
Wholesale Suppliers of Tubes, Pipes, Fittings, Non-ferrous Metals, Heating, Sanitary & Hospital Equipment, Industrial Supplies & Contractor's Tools
S.I.C.: 5065
N.A.I.C.S.: 423690

Subsidiary:

Dahl Sverige (4)
Ulcsattragagen 1
17722 Jarfalla, Sweden
Tel.: (46) 858359500
Fax: (46) 858359599
E-Mail: info@dahl.com
Web Site: www.dahl.se
Sls.: $18,938,220
Emp.: 1,000
Wholesale Distr. of Food
S.I.C.: 5149
N.A.I.C.S.: 424490
Goran Dahlin *(Dir-Mktg)*

Non-U.S. Subsidiaries:

Brodrene Dahl A/S (4)
Grenseveien 5
Oslo, 6146, Norway (100%)
Tel.: (47) 22725500
Fax: (47) 22658765
E-Mail: toft@dahl.no
Web Site: www.dahl.no
Emp.: 700
S.I.C.: 7389
N.A.I.C.S.: 425120
Arne-Erik Olsen *(Pres)*

Brodrene Dahl A/S (4)
Park Alle 370
2605 Brondby, Denmark (100%)
Tel.: (45) 43200202
Telex: 33145
Fax: (45) 43200201
E-Mail: bd@bd.dk
Web Site: www.bd.dk
Emp.: 150
Wholesale of Metal Products
S.I.C.: 5051
N.A.I.C.S.: 423510
Lars Fournais *(Pres)*

PDM Ltd. (3)
Old Milltown Kill
Kildare, Ireland (100%)
Tel.: (353) 45877165
Fax: (353) 45877467
E-Mail: enquiries@pdm.ie
Web Site: www.pdm.ie
Emp.: 30
Mfr. of Fencing & Fabricator of Transmission Poles
S.I.C.: 2499
N.A.I.C.S.: 321999
Brendan Giddonn *(Mng Dir)*

Non-U.S. Subsidiaries:

Raab Karcher Baustoffe GmbH (2)
Hanauer Landstrasse 150
60314 Frankfurt am Main, Germany
Tel.: (49) 694050502
Fax: (49) 6940505100
E-Mail: info@raabkarcher.de
Web Site: www.raabkarcher.de
Emp.: 5,400
Building Materials, Tiles, Sanitary Fittings & Heating
S.I.C.: 5211
N.A.I.C.S.: 444110
Udo Brand *(CEO)*

Subsidiaries:

Raab Karcher Hamm (3)
Hafenstrasse 142
59067 Hamm, Germany
Tel.: (49) 2381940800
Fax: (49) 23819408080
E-Mail: hamm@saint-gobain.com
Web Site: www.raabkarcher.de
Emp.: 24
Tile Mfr
S.I.C.: 3259
N.A.I.C.S.: 327120
Christoph Hornung *(Gen Mgr)*

Raab Karcher Sanitar Heizung Fliesen GmbH (3)
Muenchener Str. 101
85737 Ismaning, Germany
Heating Systems Mfr
S.I.C.: 3433
N.A.I.C.S.: 333414

Non-U.S. Subsidiaries:

Raab Karcher Bouwstoffen B.V. (3)
Huifakkerstraat 20
4824 BA Breda, Netherlands
Tel.: (31) 765731400
Fax: (31) 765731419
E-Mail: info@raabkracher.nl
Web Site: www.raabkarcher.nl
Sales Range: $250-299.9 Million
Emp.: 15
Tile Mfr
S.I.C.: 3255
N.A.I.C.S.: 327120
Rom Danver Looeg *(Gen Mgr)*

Raab Karcher Bouwstoffen (3)
Kanaalstraat 295
7547 Enschede, Netherlands
Tel.: (31) 534800150
Fax: (31) 534304305
E-Mail: info@raabkracher.nl
Web Site: www.raabkarcher.nl
Emp.: 8
Distr of Construction Materials
S.I.C.: 5211
N.A.I.C.S.: 444190
Jan Nijhuis *(Sr Mgr-Bldg)*

Raab Karcher France S.A. (3)
10, Quai Paul Doumer
92411 Courbevoie, Cedex, France
Tel.: (33) 1 47 68 45 65
Coal Preparation & Distribution Services
S.I.C.: 2999
N.A.I.C.S.: 324199

Raab Karcher Nederland B.V. (3)
Kamerlingh Onnesweg 10 A
3316 GL Dordrecht, Netherlands
Tel.: (31) 786521600
Fax: (31) 786521619
E-Mail: info@raabkarcher.nl
Web Site: www.raabkarcher.nl
Emp.: 10
Adhesive Tapes
S.I.C.: 2891
N.A.I.C.S.: 325520
Neck Hareng *(Mng Dir)*

Raab Karcher (U.K.) PLC (3)
Karcher House Beaumont Rd
Banbury, OX16 1TB, United Kingdom
Tel.: (44) 1295 752000
Web Site: www.karcher.co.uk/uk/Home.htm
Heating Systems Mfr
S.I.C.: 3433
N.A.I.C.S.: 333414

Saint-Gobain Building Distribution Ltd. (2)
Aldwych House 81 Aldwych
London, WC2B 4HQ, United Kingdom UK
Tel.: (44) 2074008888
Telex: 27451
Fax: (44) 2074008710
Web Site: www.saint-gobain.co.uk
Emp.: 20
Importer & Distributor of Wood Products & Building Materials
Import
S.I.C.: 5031
N.A.I.C.S.: 423310
Leo Quinn *(CEO)*

Saint-Gobain Emballage (1)
Les Miroirs
18 avenue d'Alsace, 92096 Courbevoie, France FR
Tel.: (33) 147623800
Fax: (33) 147625081
E-Mail: commercial.france.sge@saint-gobain.com
Web Site: www.saint-gobain-emballage.fr
Emp.: 1,862
Mfr. of Glass Containers, Bottles & Industrial Jars
S.I.C.: 3229
N.A.I.C.S.: 327212
Jerome Fessard *(Pres)*

Subsidiaries:

Saint-Gobain Desjonqueres (2)
Les Miroirs 18 Ave Dalsace
92400 Courbevoie, France (99.99%)
Tel.: (33) 147623330
Telex: 611570GD1
Fax: (33) 147624358
E-Mail: sgd.pharmacie@saint-gobain.com
Web Site: www.saint-gobain-desjonqueres.fr
Emp.: 2,000
Mfr. of Small Glass Bottles for Perfume & Pharmaceutical Industry
S.I.C.: 3229
N.A.I.C.S.: 327212

VOA Verrerie d'Albi SA (2)
Rue Francois Arago
81011 Albi, France
Tel.: (33) 5 63 78 10 36
Fax: (33) 5 63 78 10 11
Web Site: www.voa.fr
Emp.: 300
Glass Container Mfr
S.I.C.: 3221
N.A.I.C.S.: 327213
Fabian Marion *(Mng Dir)*

Subsidiary:

Saga Decor S.A.S. (2)
328 Rue Pasteur
60700 Pont-Saint-Maxence, France
Tel.: (33) 3 44 317 777
Fax: (33) 3 44 317 778
E-Mail: contact@saga-decor.com
Web Site: www.saga-decor.com
Emp.: 130
Glass Container Mfr
S.I.C.: 3221
N.A.I.C.S.: 327213
Marine Lemahieu *(Mgr-Sls-Wine Champagne Beer & Soft Drinks)*

Subsidiaries:

Saint-Gobain VG Emballage SA (3)
6062 Rue Hauteville
PO Box 279
F 75525 Paris, France (99.98%)
Tel.: (33) 149291313
Fax: (33) 149291363
E-Mail: infovg@saint-gobain.com
Web Site: www.vg-emballage.com
Emp.: 95
Distribution of Glass & Plastic Containers & Fittings
S.I.C.: 5085
N.A.I.C.S.: 423840

Verreries de l'Orne SAS (3)
Route De Joue Du Plain
61150 Ecouche, France (99.98%)
Tel.: (33) 233122810
Fax: (33) 233122819
Emp.: 200
Decoration of Glass Containers
S.I.C.: 3231
N.A.I.C.S.: 327215

U.S. Subsidiary:

Saint-Gobain Desjonqueres, Inc (3)
750 Lexington Ave Fl 5
New York, NY 10022-1200 NY
Tel.: (212) 753-4200
Fax: (212) 355-6073
Web Site: www.sgdgroup.com
Rev.: $20,000,000
Emp.: 25
Mfr. of Glass Bottles
S.I.C.: 5085
N.A.I.C.S.: 423840
Marie-Christine Revereau *(Gen Mgr)*

Non-U.S. Subsidiary:

Saint-Gobain Kipfenberg GmbH (3)
Altmuehlstrasse 2
D 85 110 Kipfenberg, Germany De
Tel.: (49) 84651710 (99.73%)
Fax: (49) 8465171127
E-Mail: info.kipfenberg@saint-gobain.com
Web Site: www.saint-gobain-kipfenberg.de
Emp.: 230
Mfr. of Small Glass Bottles
S.I.C.: 3221
N.A.I.C.S.: 327213

Saint-Gobain Vitrage (1)
Les Miroirs 18 Ave D Alsace
F 92400 Courbevoie, France (100%)
Tel.: (33) 147623030
Telex: 611570F
Fax: (33) 147623495
Web Site: www.saint-gobain-vitrage.com
Emp.: 1,000
Mfr. & Fabrication of Flat Glass
S.I.C.: 3211
N.A.I.C.S.: 327211
Jean-Pierre Floris *(Pres)*

Subsidiaries:

Eurofloat SAS (2)
Zone Industrielle Et Portuaire
38150 Salaise-sur-Sanne, France FR
Tel.: (33) 474293075 (100%)
Fax: (33) 474293086
E-Mail: euroflat@saint-gobain-glass.com
Web Site: www.saint-gobain-glass.com
Emp.: 194
Glass Products Mfr
S.I.C.: 3211
N.A.I.C.S.: 327211
Emmanuel Abt *(Gen Mgr)*

Le Vitrage du Midi (2)
ZI Sud
BP 68
30301 Beaucaire, Cedex, France (99.98%)
Tel.: (33) 466598080
Fax: (33) 466586110
Web Site: www.saint-gobain-glass.com
Emp.: 90
Mfr. of Tempered, Laminated & Double Glazed Glass
S.I.C.: 3229
N.A.I.C.S.: 327212

Miroiteries de l'Ouest Armorique (2)
ZI Kerpont 570 Rue Daniel Trudaine
56850 Caudan, France (99.93%)
Tel.: (33) 297765233
Fax: (33) 297767844
Emp.: 80
Holding Company, Distribution of Glass
S.I.C.: 5039
N.A.I.C.S.: 423390

Saint-Gobain Sekurit France (2)
Rue Du Marechal Joffre
60150 Thourotte, Puteaux, France (100%)
Tel.: (33) 344923700
Fax: (33) 344923939
E-Mail: info@saint-gobain-sekurit.com
Web Site: www.saint-gobain-sekurit.com
Emp.: 2,000
Mfr. of Glass Products
S.I.C.: 3211
N.A.I.C.S.: 327211
Lecomte Annesothie *(Sec)*

Non-U.S. Subsidiaries:

Saint-Gobain Sekurit Benelux S.A. (3)
Rue Des Glaces Nationales 169
B 5060 Sambreville, Belgium (99.79%)
Tel.: (32) 712161586
Fax: (32) 71261598
Web Site: www.saint-gobain-sekurit.com
Emp.: 450
Mfr. & Sale of Glass Products
S.I.C.: 3211
N.A.I.C.S.: 327211
Patrick Smeets *(Admin Officer)*

Subsidiary:

Saint-Gobain Autover Distribution SA (4)
Chaussee Romaine 60
6600 Bastogne, Belgium

Compagnie de Saint-Gobain SA—(Continued)

Tel.: (32) 61 210 940
Fax: (32) 61 210 976
Web Site: www.saint-gobain.de/benelux/en/produkte/gesellschaft.html?ks_remote_id=2&kt_remote_id=286&pe_id=122
Automotive Glass Product Distr
S.I.C.: 5013
N.A.I.C.S.: 423120

Saint-Gobain Sekurit CR Spol S.R.O. (3)
Masarykova 1404
268 01 Horovice, Czech Republic
Tel.: (420) 311 541 111
Fax: (420) 311 541 105
E-Mail: central@saint-gobain.com
Web Site: www.saint-gobain-sekurit.cz
Emp.: 500
Automotive Glass Product Mfr
S.I.C.: 3714
N.A.I.C.S.: 336390
Martina Hasmanova *(Gen Dir & Chm-Mgmt Bd)*
Jan Cerveny *(Member-Mgmt Bd & Fin Dir)*
Petr Rolak *(Member-Mgmt Bd & Dir-Technical)*
Jane Andrt *(Member-Mgmt Bd & Dir-Quality & Dev)*
Jiri Kovanda *(Member-Mgmt Bd & Dir-HR)*
Petr Kupka *(Member-Mgmt Bd & Dir-Comml & Supply Chain)*

Saint-Gobain Sekurit de Colombia S.A. (3)
Carrera 7 N 26-20 Piso 20
Bogota, 76164, Colombia
Tel.: (57) 1 255 7756
Fax: (57) 1 310 2939
Glass Product Mfr
S.I.C.: 3231
N.A.I.C.S.: 327215

Saint-Gobain Sekurit Deutschland Beteiligungen GmbH (3)
Viktoriaallee 3-5
52066 Aachen, Germany
Tel.: (49) 2419470
Fax: (49) 2419472368
Flat Glass Mfr
S.I.C.: 3211
N.A.I.C.S.: 327211
Stephan Mast *(Mgr)*

Subsidiary:

Saint-Gobain Autover Deutschland GmbH (4)
Huttenstrasse 115-131
50170 Kerpen, Germany
Tel.: (49) 22735680
Fax: (49) 227354803
E-Mail: autover@saint-gobain.com
Web Site: www.autover.de
Emp.: 67
Automotive Glass Product Mfr
S.I.C.: 3714
N.A.I.C.S.: 336390
Bernd Kummerle *(Mng Dir)*

Subsidiary:

Freudenberger Autoglas GmbH (5)
Karl-Weinmair-Strasse 5
80807 Munich, Germany De
Tel.: (49) 893582740
Fax: (49) 893507575
E-Mail: info@Freudenberger-Autoglas.de
Web Site: www.freudenberger-autoglas.de
Automotive Glass Mfr
S.I.C.: 3231
N.A.I.C.S.: 327215

Saint-Gobain Sekurit India Limited (3)
T-94-95 Bhosari Industrial Area Bhosari
Pune, 411002, India
Tel.: (91) 20 663116000
Fax: (91) 20 66311666
Web Site: www.sekuritindia.com
515043—(BOM)
Rev.: $22,675,083
Assets: $20,081,606
Liabilities: $6,518,146
Net Worth: $13,563,459
Earnings: $119,999
Emp.: 185
Fiscal Year-end: 03/31/13
Automotive Glass Distr
S.I.C.: 5013
N.A.I.C.S.: 423120
A. Dinakar *(Mng Dir)*
Madhura Joshi *(Compliance Officer & Sec)*

Saint-Gobain Sekurit Maroc (3)
Zone Franche d'Exportation de Kenitra
Kenitra, Morocco
Tel.: (212) 522 665 731
Fax: (212) 522 661 052
Flat Glass Mfr
S.I.C.: 3211
N.A.I.C.S.: 327211

Saint-Gobain Sekurit Mexico, S.A. de C.V. (3)
Avenida Nicolas Bravo 8 Parque Industrial
Cuautla Municipio de Ayala
62715 Morelos, Mexico (59.83%)
Tel.: (52) 7353548000
Fax: (52) 7353548019
E-Mail: lidir.campos@saint-gobain.com
Web Site: www.saint-gobain-sekurit.com
Emp.: 800
Automotive Glazing Mfr.
S.I.C.: 3211
N.A.I.C.S.: 327211
Jose Picadus *(Mng Dir)*

Saint-Gobain Sekurit Portugal Vidro Automovel SA (3)
Estrada Nacional 10 Apartado 1731
2696-652 Santa Iria de Azoia, Portugal PT
Tel.: (351) 219 429 600
Fax: (351) 219429603
Emp.: 100
Automotive Glass Product Mfr
S.I.C.: 3231
N.A.I.C.S.: 327215
Antonio Martinez Menendez *(Mgr-Technical)*

Subsidiary:

Saint-Gobain Autover Portugal S.A. (4)
Rua 25 de Abril 460
4405-445 Serzedo, Portugal PT
Tel.: (351) 227536140
Fax: (351) 227536159
Web Site: www.autover.pt
Automotive Glass Product Distr
S.I.C.: 5013
N.A.I.C.S.: 423120

Saint-Gobain Sekurit (Shanghai) Co., Ltd. (3)
No 45 Wen Jing Road Minhang Development Zone
Shanghai, 200245, China
Tel.: (86) 21 64626550
Fax: (86) 2164638325
E-Mail: marketing@sgh-china.com
Automotive Glass Mfr
S.I.C.: 3231
N.A.I.C.S.: 327215

Saint-Gobain Sekurit Thailand Co., Ltd. (3)
64/8 Moo 4 Tumbol Pluakdeng Amphur Pluakdeng
Rayong, 21140, Thailand
Tel.: (66) 38954477
Fax: (66) 38954490
Web Site: www.saint-gobain.co.th/sekurit.php
Automotive Glass Product Mfr
S.I.C.: 3231
N.A.I.C.S.: 327215

Societe Industrielle des Vitrages d'Aquitaine (2)
Zone Industrielle
PO Box 50
33230 Coutras, France FR
Tel.: (33) 557498100 (100%)
Fax: (33) 557490170
E-Mail: sivaq@saint-gobain.com
Web Site: www.saint-gobain-glass.com
Emp.: 150
Mfr. of Tempered & Laminated Glass & Double Glazing Products
S.I.C.: 3231
N.A.I.C.S.: 327215
Geanluc Camus *(Mng Dir)*

S.G. Materiaux de Construction (1)
Les Miroirs 18 avenue d'Alsace
F-92400 Courbevoie, France
Tel.: (33) 147623000
Telex: 611570 F Miroi
Fax: (33) 147623777
E-Mail: claude.imauven@saint-gobain.com
Web Site: www.saint-gobain.com
Emp.: 1,000
Construction Products Mfr
S.I.C.: 3297
N.A.I.C.S.: 327120
Claude Imauven *(Dir-Construction Products Sector)*

Subsidiaries:

BPB Paperboard Ltd. (2)
East Leake
Loughborough, Leics, LE12 6JU, United Kingdom
Tel.: (44) 1159451000
Fax: (44) 1159451199
Web Site: www.british-gypsum.com
Flexible Plastic Packaging Materials, Multi-Wall Paper Sacks, Solid Fibreboard Containers, Packaging Board, Cartons & Packaging Systems
S.I.C.: 3089
N.A.I.C.S.: 326199

Subsidiaries:

British Gypsum Ltd. (4)
East Leake
Loughborough, Leicestershire, LE12 6HX, United Kingdom
Tel.: (44) 1159451000
Fax: (44) 1159451901
Web Site: www.british-gypsum.com
Emp.: 1,040
Building & Industrial Plasters, Plasterboard, Partitioning, Ceiling & Lining Systems, Thermal, Fire & Sound Insulation Products, Floor Screed, Tools & Accessories Mfr Import Export
S.I.C.: 3275
N.A.I.C.S.: 327420
Mike Chaldecott *(Mng Dir)*

Gypsum Industries (UK) Ltd. (3)
East Leake
Loughborough, Leicestershire, LE12 6HX, United Kingdom
Tel.: (44) 1159451000
Fax: (44) 1159451901
E-Mail: bgtechnical.enquiries@bpb.com
Web Site: www.british-gypsum.com
Emp.: 1,000
Gypsum Products Mfr
S.I.C.: 3275
N.A.I.C.S.: 327420
Mike Chaldecott *(Mng Dir)*

Joint Venture:

British Gypsum-Isover Ltd. (3)
Whitehouse Industrial Estate Norwich Rd
Runcorn, Cheshire, WA7 3DP, United Kingdom
Tel.: (44) 928719197
Telex: 627011
Fax: (44) 928717125
Web Site: www.isowool.com
Emp.: 150
Insulation Product Mfr; Joint Venture of British Gypsum Ltd. & Isover Saint Gobain
S.I.C.: 3296
N.A.I.C.S.: 327993
Gerry Mitchell *(Mgr-Innovations)*

Non-U.S. Subsidiaries:

BPB Belgium (3)
Merksemsebaan 270
2110 Wijnegem, Belgium
Tel.: (32) 33602211
Fax: (32) 33602380
E-Mail: info@isogips.be
Web Site: www.bpbbelgium.be
Plasterboard & Gypsum Plasters
S.I.C.: 5039
N.A.I.C.S.: 423390
Bert van Buggenhout *(Mng Dir)*

BPB Gyproc (3)
ul Elektrozavodskaya 27/8
Moscow, 107023, Russia
Tel.: (7) 495 775 1510
Fax: (7) 495 775 1511
E-Mail: sergey.mukhin@gyproc.com
Web Site: www.gyproc.ru
Gypsum Product Mfr & Training Center
S.I.C.: 3275
N.A.I.C.S.: 327420

BPB Gypsum (Pty) Ltd. (3)
PO Box 700
1400 Germiston, South Africa
Tel.: (27) 3455300
Fax: (27) 113455302
E-Mail: enquiries@za.bpb.com
Web Site: www.bpbsi.com
Emp.: 376
Gypsum Product Mfr
S.I.C.: 3275
N.A.I.C.S.: 327420
Steven Dutoit *(CEO)*

BPB Gypsum Uretim ve Ticaret Ltd. Sti (Trading) (3)
Koroglu Caddesi Ugur Mumcu Nun
Gaziosmanpasa Sokagi 1 4, Ankara, 06700, Turkey
Tel.: (90) 3124481617
Fax: (90) 3124481612
Web Site: www.rigips.com
Emp.: 100
Gypsum Product Mfr
S.I.C.: 3275
N.A.I.C.S.: 327420
Mehmed Tunaman *(Gen Mgr)*

BPB Iberplaco SA (3)
Montaner 267 Principal 2 A
08021 Barcelona, Spain
Tel.: (34) 934141987
Fax: (34) 932021928
Web Site: www.placosa.es
Gypsum Product Mfr
S.I.C.: 3275
N.A.I.C.S.: 327420

BPB Industries Ltd. (3)
77 Ostend Rd
PO Box 700
Germiston, 1400, South Africa
Tel.: (27) 113455300
Fax: (27) 113455301
E-Mail: enquiries@za.bpb.com
Web Site: www.bpbsa.com
Emp.: 200
Gypsum Product Mfr
S.I.C.: 3275
N.A.I.C.S.: 327420
Steven Dupoit *(CEO)*

BPB Italia SpA (3)
Via Matteotti 62
Cinisello, 20092 Milan, Balsamo, Italy
Tel.: (39) 2611151
Fax: (39) 2611192900
Web Site: www.bpbitalia.it
Gypsum Product Mfr
S.I.C.: 3275
N.A.I.C.S.: 327420

BPB Limitada (3)
Av Das FPLM No 1839
Maputo, Mozambique
Tel.: (258) 21461388
Fax: (258) 21461389
E-Mail: bbpenka.popova@saintgobain.co.mz
Web Site: www.saintgobain.com
Emp.: 30
Gypsum Products Mfr
S.I.C.: 3275
N.A.I.C.S.: 327420
Penka Popova *(Mng Dir)*

BPB Netherlands B.V. (3)
Stuartweg 1B
4131 MH Vianen, Netherlands
Tel.: (31) 347325100
Fax: (31) 347325125
E-Mail: info@gyproc.nl
Web Site: www.gyproc.nl
Emp.: 50
Plasterboard & Gypsum Products Whslr
S.I.C.: 5039
N.A.I.C.S.: 423390
Peter Anmaat *(Gen Mgr)*

BPB Placo S.A. (3)
34 Ave Franklin Roosevelt
92282 Suresnes, Cedex, France
Tel.: (33) 146254625
Telex: 688360
Fax: (33) 141380808
E-Mail: jstern@bpb.fr
Sales Range: $900-999.9 Million
Emp.: 1,887
Gypsum Products

S.I.C.: 3275
N.A.I.C.S.: 327420

Subsidiaries:

Societe Industrielle de Contrecollage SA (SIC) (4)
Zone Industrielle 2 Ave Etienne Audibert
BP34 60302 Senlis, France
Tel.: (33) 344531098
Fax: (33) 344537320
E-Mail: elogie.ouillon@saint-gobain.com
Web Site: www.coramine.com
Emp.: 60
Gypsum Product Mfr
S.I.C.: 3275
N.A.I.C.S.: 327420
Maxime Berrios *(Gen Mgr)*

CIA Industrial El Volcan SA (3)
Agustinas 1357 Piso 10
Santiago, Chile
Tel.: (56) 24830500
E-Mail: mbarros@volcan.cl
Web Site: www.volcan.cl
Emp.: 1,500
Gypsum Products Mfr
S.I.C.: 3275
N.A.I.C.S.: 327420
Herman Phillip *(Plant Mgr)*

Donn Products (Pty) Ltd. (3)
PO Box 700
1400 Germiston, South Africa
Tel.: (27) 113455300
Fax: (27) 113455302
E-Mail: enquires@saint-gobain.co.za
Web Site: www.saint-gobain.co.za
Emp.: 86
Gypsum Product Mfr
S.I.C.: 3275
N.A.I.C.S.: 327420
Coenraad Hicge *(Dir-Fin)*

Donn South Africa (Pty) Ltd. (3)
77 Ostend Rd
PO Box 700
1400 Gauteng, South Africa
Tel.: (27) 113455300
Fax: (27) 860272329
E-Mail: enquiries@zabpb.com
Web Site: www.bpbsa.com
Emp.: 150
Gypsum Product Mfr
S.I.C.: 3275
N.A.I.C.S.: 327420
Steven Dutoit *(CEO)*

Fulmar Insurance Company Ltd. (3)
La Mielle La Rte De La Margion
Richmond, Saint Peter Port, GY7 9XH, Guernsey
Tel.: (44) 1481267618
Fax: (44) 1481267617
E-Mail: gayna.babinski@bpb.com
Emp.: 1
Insurance Services
S.I.C.: 6411
N.A.I.C.S.: 524298

Gypco Shanghai (3)
968 Wang Qiao Road Wang Qiao Industrial Zone
Pudong, Shanghai, 201201, China
Tel.: (86) 5838 5838
Fax: (86) 5838 1409
E-Mail: paul.shen@bpb.com
Gypsum Product Mfr
S.I.C.: 3275
N.A.I.C.S.: 327420

Gyproc A/S (3)
Hareskovvej 12
4400 Kalundborg, Denmark
Tel.: (45) 59570330
Fax: (45) 59570331
E-Mail: info@gyproc.com
Web Site: www.gyproc.com
Emp.: 100
Plasterboard & Gypsum Plasters
S.I.C.: 5039
N.A.I.C.S.: 423390
Niels Galsgaard *(Mng Dir)*

Gyproc AB (3)
Karlmarlde Den
PO Box 153
S 74624 Balsta, Sweden
Tel.: (46) 171415400
Telex: GYPROC S
Fax: (46) 171415450
Web Site: www.gyproc.se
Emp.: 100
Plasterboard Mfr
S.I.C.: 3275
N.A.I.C.S.: 327420
Kim Soini *(CFO)*

Gyproc AS (3)
Habornveien 59
1630 Fredrikstad, Norway
Mailing Address:
PO Box 1154
1631 Fredrikstad, Norway
Tel.: (47) 69357500
Fax: (47) 69357501
E-Mail: gyprocno@gyproc.com
Web Site: www.gyproc.no
Emp.: 65
Plasterboard & Gypsum Plasters
S.I.C.: 5039
N.A.I.C.S.: 423390
Niels Galsgaard *(Mng Dir-Denmark)*

Gypsum Industries (Ireland) Limited (3)
Unit 14 Park West Industrial Park
Dublin, 12, Ireland
Tel.: (353) 1 6298400
Fax: (353) 16237055
E-Mail: enquiries@gyproc.ie
Web Site: www.gyproc.ie
Emp.: 40
Gypsum Product Mfr
S.I.C.: 3275
N.A.I.C.S.: 327420
Mark O'Reilly *(Reg Mgr-Sls)*

Gypsum Industries (Pvt) Ltd. (3)
PO Box AY70
Amby, Harare, Zimbabwe
Tel.: (263) 4496392
Fax: (263) 4486314
E-Mail: enquiries@za.bpb.com
Gypsum Product Mfr
S.I.C.: 3275
N.A.I.C.S.: 327420

LM Materiaux SA (3)
150 Chaussee De Namur
1300 Wavre, Belgium
Tel.: (32) 482911
Fax: (32) 10452775
E-Mail: info@lmmateriaux.be
Web Site: www.lmmateriaux.be
Sales Range: $10-24.9 Million
Emp.: 40
Gypsum Product Mfr
S.I.C.: 3275
N.A.I.C.S.: 327420

Moy-Isover Ltd. (3)
Ardfinnan Clonmel
Tipperary, 14, Ireland
Tel.: (353) 5266100
Fax: (353) 5266372
E-Mail: info@moyisover.ie
Web Site: www.moyisover.ie
Emp.: 80
Insulation Material Mrr & Distr; Joint Venture between Gypsum Industries Ltd (50% & Isover-Saint Gobain (50%)
S.I.C.: 3296
N.A.I.C.S.: 327993
Padraig Barry *(Mng Dir)*

Placo Argentina S.A. (3)
556 Lavalle Piso 3e
Buenos Aires, Argentina
Tel.: (54) 11 51 734100
Fax: (54) 11 51 734111
Web Site: www.saint-gobain.com
Gypsum Products Mfr
S.I.C.: 3275
N.A.I.C.S.: 327420

Placo do Brasil Ltda. (3)
Av Valentina Mello Freire Borenstein 333
Bairro Jardim Sao Francisco
Mogi Das Cruzes, CEP 08735 270 Sao Paulo, SP, Brazil
Tel.: (55) 11 3186 8900
Fax: (55) 11 3186 8956
E-Mail: sac.placo@saint-gobain.com
Web Site: www.placo.com.br/
Emp.: 60
Gypsum Product Mfr
S.I.C.: 3275
N.A.I.C.S.: 327420

Rigips AG (3)
Gewerbepark
Postfach 5506
5506 Magenwil, Switzerland
Tel.: (41) 628874444
Fax: (41) 628874445
E-Mail: info@rigips.ch
Web Site: www.rigips.ch
Emp.: 160
Plasterboard & Gypsum Plasters
S.I.C.: 5039
N.A.I.C.S.: 423390
Thomas Breu *(Mng Dir)*

Rigips Austria GmbH (3)
Unterkainisch 24
A 8990 Bad Aussee, Austria
Tel.: (43) 36225050
Fax: (43) 3622505430
E-Mail: petra.zaintberter@saint-gobain.com
Web Site: www.rigips.com
Emp.: 60
Gypsum Products Mfr
S.I.C.: 3275
N.A.I.C.S.: 327420
Peter Giffinger *(Mng Dir)*
Peter Wichert *(Mng Dir)*

Rigips Bosnia (3)
Kolodvorska 12
71 000 Sarajevo, Bosnia & Herzegovina
Tel.: (387) 33660380
Fax: (387) 33660380
Web Site: www.rigips.com
Plasterboard & Gypsum Plasters
S.I.C.: 5039
N.A.I.C.S.: 423390
Haris Custovic *(Country Mgr)*

Rigips Bulgaria E.O.O.D. (3)
Buiness Park Sofia
Building 12B Office 307, 1766 Sofia, Bulgaria
Tel.: (359) 29769500
Fax: (359) 29769507
Web Site: www.rigips.com
Plasterboard & Gypsum Plasters
S.I.C.: 5039
N.A.I.C.S.: 423390
Mirena Georgieva *(Head Accountant)*

Rigips Croatia (3)
Predstavnistvo u RH
Hondlova 2, 10000 Zagreb, Croatia
Tel.: (385) 12335570
Fax: (385) 00351244290
E-Mail: office.hr@rigips.com
Web Site: www.rigips.com
Emp.: 4
Plasterboard & Gypsum Plasters
S.I.C.: 5039
N.A.I.C.S.: 423390
Hrvoje Miocic *(Country Mgr)*

Rigips Hungaria Gipszkarton Kft (3)
Zador U 4
1181 Budapest, Hungary
Tel.: (36) 12960500
Fax: (36) 12950662
E-Mail: rigips.vevoszolgalat@saintgobain.com
Web Site: www.rigips.hu
Emp.: 51
Gypsum Products Mfr
S.I.C.: 3275
N.A.I.C.S.: 327420

Rigips Polska-Stawiany Sp. z o.o. (3)
Szarbkow 73
PL 02 677 Pinczow, Poland
Tel.: (48) 224571457
E-Mail: rigips.polska@saint-gobain.com
Web Site: www.rigips.com
Emp.: 200
Gypsum Products Mfr
S.I.C.: 3275
N.A.I.C.S.: 327420
Malgorzata Piatek *(Dir-Factory)*

Rigips Slovakia sro (3)
Wlaisk 44
91701 Trnava, Slovakia
Tel.: (421) 335514376
Fax: (421) 335552250
E-Mail: office@rigips.sk
Web Site: www.rigips.sk
Emp.: 80
Gypsum Products Mfr
S.I.C.: 3275
N.A.I.C.S.: 327420
Roman Regec *(Mng Dir)*

Rigips Slovenia (3)
Ulica Bratov Babnik 10 1 Fl
1000 Ljubljana, Slovenia
Tel.: (386) 15197112
Fax: (386) 15197816
Web Site: www.rigips.com
Emp.: 5
Gypsum Products Mfr
S.I.C.: 3275
N.A.I.C.S.: 327420

Rigips SRO (3)
Pocernicka 96 272
10800 Prague, 10, Czech Republic
Tel.: (420) 267021777
Fax: (420) 267021790
E-Mail: info@rigips.cz
Web Site: www.rigips.com
Emp.: 25
Gypsum Product Mfr
S.I.C.: 3275
N.A.I.C.S.: 327420
Pavel Satny *(Mgr-Sls)*

Rigips Verwaltungs GmbH (3)
PO Box 110948
40509 Dusseldorf, Germany
Tel.: (49) 21155030
Fax: (49) 2115503208
E-Mail: info@rigips.de
Web Site: www.rigips.de
Emp.: 18
Gypsum Products
S.I.C.: 3275
N.A.I.C.S.: 327420

Subsidiaries:

Saint-Gobain Rigips GmbH (4)
Schanzenstrasse 84
40549 Dusseldorf, Germany
Mailing Address:
PO Box 11 09 48
40509 Dusseldorf, Germany
Tel.: (49) 2 11 55 03 0
Telex: 17 2 114 308
Fax: (49) 2 11 55 03 208
E-Mail: info@rigips.de
Web Site: www.rigips.de
Emp.: 100
Gypsum Products Mfr
S.I.C.: 3275
N.A.I.C.S.: 327420
Rudiger Vogel *(Chm)*
Werner Hansmann *(Mng Dir-Sls & Mktg)*
Christian Grimm *(Mng Dir)*

Holding:

Perlit Thermoputz Ersen GmbH (5)
Grimelsheimer Strasse 43
D 34396 Liebenau, Germany
Tel.: (49) 5676237
Fax: (49) 56768436
E-Mail: perlit-ersen@t-online.de
Emp.: 5
Building Material Mfr
S.I.C.: 3089
N.A.I.C.S.: 326199
Martin Pilger *(Mng Dir)*

SOVAC Grosshandel und Vertretungen in Industrieprodukten GmbH (4)
Feldhauser Str 261
45896 Gelsenkirchen, Germany
Tel.: (49) 209 3603996
Fax: (49) 209 3603998
Packaging Material Distr
S.I.C.: 5085
N.A.I.C.S.: 423840

Saint-Gobain Construction Products (Malaysia) Sdn Bhd (3)
No 1 Jalan Sultan Mohamad 4 Kawasan
Perindustrian Bandar
Sultan Suleiman, 42000 Port Klang, Selangor, Malaysia
Tel.: (60) 331695588
Fax: (60) 3 3169 5500
E-Mail: solutions.malaysia@saint-gobain.com
Web Site: www.bpbmalaysia.com
Plasterboard & Gypsum Plasters
S.I.C.: 5039
N.A.I.C.S.: 423390

Compagnie de Saint-Gobain SA—(Continued)

Lee Eam Hooi *(Dir-Sls)*

Saint-Gobain Hellas ABEE (3)
5 Kleisouras
Metamorfosi, 14452 Athens, Greece
Tel.: (30) 2102831804
Fax: (30) 2102830043
Web Site: www.rigips.com
Emp.: 28
Gypsum Products Mfr
S.I.C.: 3275
N.A.I.C.S.: 327420
Tatas George *(Gen Mgr)*

SIA Gyproc (3)
Daugavgrivas 93
LV-1007 Riga, Latvia
Tel.: (371) 7472999
Fax: (371) 7473039
Gypsum Products Mfr
S.I.C.: 3275
N.A.I.C.S.: 327420

Thai Gypsum (3)
Gypsum Metropolitan Tower 539 2 Si Ayutthaya Rd
Ratchathewi, Bangkok, 10400, Thailand
Tel.: (66) 26408600
Fax: (66) 26408766
Web Site: www.thaigypsum.com
Emp.: 600
Gypsum Product Mfr
S.I.C.: 3275
N.A.I.C.S.: 327420
Lalit Naik *(CEO)*

Saint-Gobain Weber (2)
Rue de Brie
77170 Servon, France FR
Mailing Address:
BP 84
77253 Brie-Comte-Robert, Cedex, France
Tel.: (33) 1 6062 1300
Fax: (33) 1 6405 4750
E-Mail:
Web Site: www.e-weber.com
Emp.: 200
Holding Company; Construction Mortar, Insulation & Other Building Materials Mfr & Distr
S.I.C.: 6719
N.A.I.C.S.: 551112
Jean-Luc Jargez *(Mng Dir)*

Subsidiaries:

Saint-Gobain Weber France (3)
Rue de Brie
77170 Servon, France FR
Mailing Address:
BP 84
77253 Brie-Comte-Robert, Cedex, France
Tel.: (33) 1 6062 1300
Fax: (33) 1 6405 4750
Web Site: www.weber.fr
Emp.: 1,000
Construction Mortar, Insulation & Other Building Materials Mfr & Distr
S.I.C.: 3255
N.A.I.C.S.: 327120
Jean-Luc Jargez *(Mng Dir)*

Subsidiary:

Optiroc SA (4)
1431 Chemin du Mas de Sorbier
ZI de Grezan, 30034 Nimes, Cedex 1, France FR
Tel.: (33) 466280020
Fax: (33) 466271540
E-Mail: info@optiroc.fr
Web Site: www.optiroc.fr
Emp.: 25
Pre-mix Mortar & Clay Products Mfr
S.I.C.: 3272
N.A.I.C.S.: 327390

Saint-Gobain Weber Netservices (3)
Le Closeau Rue de Brie
77170 Servon, France FR
Mailing Address:
BP 84
77253 Brie-Comte-Robert, Cedex, France
Tel.: (33) 1 6062 1300
Fax: (33) 1 6405 4750
Information Technology Services
S.I.C.: 7376
N.A.I.C.S.: 541513

Non-U.S. Subsidiaries:

Saint-Gobain Byggevarer AS (3)
Brobekkveien 84
0582 Oslo, Norway NO
Mailing Address:
Postboks 216
Alnabru, 0614 Oslo, Norway
Tel.: (47) 2288 7700
Fax: (47) 2264 5454
E-Mail: info@weber-norge.no
Web Site: www.weber-norge.no
Emp.: 300
Pre-mixed Mortar & Clay Products Mfr & Distr
S.I.C.: 3259
N.A.I.C.S.: 327120
Kristin Roed Eriksen *(Mng Dir)*

Saint-Gobain Byggprodukter AB (3)
Gardsvagen 18
169 70 Solna, Sweden SE
Mailing Address:
PO Box 707
169 27 Solna, Sweden
Tel.: (46) 86256100
Fax: (46) 86256180
E-Mail:
Web Site: www.weber.se
Emp.: 70
Pre-mixed Mortar & Clay Products Mfr & Distr
S.I.C.: 3255
N.A.I.C.S.: 327120
Lars-Erik Edgarsson *(Mng Dir)*

Saint-Gobain statybos gaminiai UAB (3)
Menulio 7
04326 Vilnius, Lithuania LT
Tel.: (370) 52301618
Fax: (370) 52301119
E-Mail: info@weber.lt
Web Site: www.weber.lt
Emp.: 25
Pre-mixed Mortar & Clay Products Mfr & Distr
S.I.C.: 3259
N.A.I.C.S.: 327120
Mart Arro *(Reg Dir-Balkans)*

Saint-Gobain Weber A/S (3)
Randersvej 75
DK 8940 Randers, Denmark DK
Tel.: (45) 70101025
Fax: (45) 87427205
E-Mail: weber@weber.dk
Web Site: www.weber.dk
Emp.: 100
Pre-mixed Mortar & Clay Products Mfr & Distr
S.I.C.: 3255
N.A.I.C.S.: 327120
Torben Dyrberg *(Mng Dir)*

Saint-Gobain Weber AG (3)
Tafernstrasse 11b
Dattwil, 5405 Baden, Switzerland CH
Tel.: (41) 56 484 2424
Fax: (41) 56 484 2400
Web Site: www.weber-marmoran.ch
Emp.: 100
Pre-mixed Mortar & Clay Products Mfr & Distr
S.I.C.: 3297
N.A.I.C.S.: 327120

Saint-Gobain Weber Beamix B.V. (3)
Hastelweg 161
5652 CJ Eindhoven, Netherlands NL
Mailing Address:
Postbus 7932
5605 SH Eindhoven, Netherlands
Tel.: (31) 40 259 7911
Fax: (31) 40 259 6250
E-Mail: info@weberbeamix.nl
Web Site: www.weber-beamix.nl
Emp.: 200
Pre-mixed Mortar & Clay Products Mfr & Distr
S.I.C.: 3259
N.A.I.C.S.: 327120
Mark Kooij *(Gen Mgr)*

Saint-Gobain Weber Belgium NV/SA (3)
Oostvaarrtdijk 10
1850 Grimbergen, Belgium BE
Tel.: (32) 2254 7854
Fax: (32) 2254 7855
E-Mail: info@weber-belgium.be
Web Site: www.weber-belgium.be
Emp.: 55
Pre-mixed Mortar & Clay Products Mfr & Distr
S.I.C.: 3297
N.A.I.C.S.: 327120
Fredrick Baurain *(Gen Mgr)*

Saint-Gobain Weber Cemarksa SA (3)
Ctra C-17 Km 2
Montcada, 08110 Barcelona, Spain
Tel.: (34) 935 72 65 00
Fax: (34) 935 64 50 05
E-Mail: info@weber.es
Web Site: www.weber.es
Concrete Product Mfr
S.I.C.: 3272
N.A.I.C.S.: 327390

Saint-Gobain Weber Co., Ltd. (3)
14th Fl Gypsum Metropolitan Bldg 539/3 Sri-Ayutthaya Rd
Phayathai Ratchathewi, Bangkok, 10400, Thailand TH
Tel.: (66) 2 245 8777
Fax: (66) 2 245 7425
E-Mail: contact-th@e-weber.com
Web Site: www.weberthai.com
Concrete Product Mfr
S.I.C.: 3272
N.A.I.C.S.: 327390

Saint-Gobain Weber GmbH (3)
Schanzenstrasse 84
40549 Dusseldorf, Germany De
Tel.: (49) 2363399332
E-Mail: info@sg-weber.de
Web Site: www.sg-weber.de
Insulation, Flooring & Tiling Systems Mfr
S.I.C.: 3259
N.A.I.C.S.: 327120
Alfred Horner *(Chm-Mgmt Bd & CEO)*
Roman Lackner *(Member-Mgmt Bd)*

Saint-Gobain Weber Limited (3)
Enterprise Way Maulden Road
Flitwick, Beds, MK45 5BY, United Kingdom UK
Tel.: (44) 870 333 0070
Fax: (44) 1525 718 988
E-Mail: mail@netweber.co.uk
Web Site: www.netweber.co.uk
Emp.: 200
Industrial Mortar Mfr
S.I.C.: 3482
N.A.I.C.S.: 332992
Allan Hodge *(Dir-Comml)*

Saint-Gobain Weber Lujian Building Materials (Shanghai) Co., Ltd. (3)
Rm 1816-1818 Ocean Tower 550 Yan
200001 Shanghai, China
Tel.: (86) 21 63618869
Fax: (86) 21 63618200
Web Site: www.weber-china.cn/en/weber/distributor-corner.html
Emp.: 100
Industrial Mortar Mfr
S.I.C.: 3297
N.A.I.C.S.: 327120
Wu Weiqun *(Area Dir-Sls)*

Saint-Gobain Weber Oy Ab (3)
Stromberginkuja 2
PL 70
FIN 00381 Helsinki, Finland FI
Tel.: (358) 10442200
Fax: (358) 10442295
Web Site: www.e-weber.fi
Sales Range: $150-199.9 Million
Emp.: 100
Pre-mixed Mortar & Clay Products Mfr & Distr
S.I.C.: 3255
N.A.I.C.S.: 327120
Magnus Holm *(Mng Dir)*

Saint-Gobain Weber Portugal S.A. (3)
Zona Industrial de Taboeira Apartado 3016
Esgueira, 3801-101 Aveiro, Portugal PT
Tel.: (351) 234 30 11 30
Fax: (351) 234 30 11 44
E-Mail: info@weber.com.pt
Web Site: www.weber.com.pt
Concrete Product Mfr
S.I.C.: 3272
N.A.I.C.S.: 327390

Saint-Gobain Weber South Africa (Pty) Ltd. (3)
77 Ostend Road
Germiston, South Africa ZA
Tel.: (27) 11 345 5300
Fax: (27) 11 345 5301
E-Mail: info@weber-tylon.co.za
Web Site: www.weber-tylon.co.za
Industrial Mortar Mfr
S.I.C.: 3255
N.A.I.C.S.: 327120

Plants:

Saint-Gobain Weber South Africa (Pty) Ltd. - Alrode Factory (4)
Corner Potgieter & Bosworth St
Alberton, Gauteng, 1451, South Africa
Tel.: (27) 116178500
Tile Adhesives Mfr
S.I.C.: 2891
N.A.I.C.S.: 325520

Saint-Gobain Weber South Africa (Pty) Ltd. - Cape Town Factory (4)
10 Grenville Avenue Epping 1
Cape Town, South Africa
Tel.: (27) 21 530 3800
Fax: (27) 215323735
Web Site: www.weber-tylon.co.za/weber/contact-us/weber-factories.html
Emp.: 30
Clay Refractory Mortar Mfr
S.I.C.: 3297
N.A.I.C.S.: 327120
Gary Mathews *(Plant Mgr)*

Saint-Gobain Weber South Africa (Pty) Ltd. - Kwazulu Natal Factory (4)
107 Eskom Road New Germany
3600 Durban, South Africa
Tel.: (27) 31 705 4569
Fax: (27) 31 705 8041
Web Site: www.weber-tylon.co.za/weber/contact-us/weber-factories.html
Emp.: 26
Industrial Mortar Mfr
S.I.C.: 3259
N.A.I.C.S.: 327120
James Hoad *(Gen Mgr)*

Saint-Gobain Weber South Africa (Pty) Ltd. - Port Elizabeth Factory (4)
1 Buick Street Markman
6061 Port Elizabeth, South Africa
Tel.: (27) 41 461 1508
Web Site: www.weber-tylon.co.za/weber/contact-us/weber-factories.html
Industrial Mortar Mfr
S.I.C.: 3259
N.A.I.C.S.: 327120

Saint-Gobain Weber Stahel-Keller AG (3)
Technoramastrasse 9
CH-8404 Winterthur, Switzerland (79.09%)
E-Mail: info@weber-stahel-keller.ch
Web Site: www.weber-stahel-keller.ch
Flat Glass Mfr.
S.I.C.: 3211
N.A.I.C.S.: 327211

Saint Gobain Weber Terranova, spol. s.r.o. (3)
Stara Vajnorska 139
831 04 Bratislava, Slovakia (79%)
Tel.: (421) 244453022
Fax: (421) 244451109
E-Mail: contact@weber-terranova.sk
Web Site: www.weber-terranova.sk
Emp.: 100
Construction Materials Mfr.
S.I.C.: 5039
N.A.I.C.S.: 423390
Daniel Balush *(Gen Mgr)*

Saint-Gobain Weber Yapi Kimyasallari San. ve Tic. A.S (3)
Ansizca Koyu Ansizca Ic Kisim Sanayi Sokak No 284
Kemalpasa, 35171 Izmir, Turkey
Tel.: (90) 232 397 07 00
Fax: (90) 232 397 08 00
E-Mail: info@weber.com.tr

Web Site: www.weber.com.tr
Emp.: 150
Construction Mortar Mfr
S.I.C.: 3259
N.A.I.C.S.: 327120
Levent Gokce *(Gen Mgr)*

Non-U.S. Subsidiaries:

BPB Plc (2)
Aldwych House
81 Aldwych, London, WC2B 4HQ, United Kingdom
Tel.: (44) 147625200
Telex: 847694
Fax: (44) 1753668888
E-Mail: bpb@finsbury.com
Web Site: www.bpb.com
Emp.: 12,689
Holding Company
S.I.C.: 6719
N.A.I.C.S.: 551112

Subsidiary:

BPB United Kingdom Ltd. (3)
Sefton Park Stoke Poges
Slough, SL2 4JS, United Kingdom
Tel.: (44) 1753668800
Fax: (44) 1753898888
Web Site: www.bpb.com
Emp.: 2,200
Holding Company; Gypsum Products
S.I.C.: 6719
N.A.I.C.S.: 551112

Saint-Gobain Construction Product Russia Insulation (2)
Smychka street 60
140301 Moscow, Russia
Tel.: (7) 495 775 15 12
Fax: (7) 495 775 15 13
Construction Material Distr
S.I.C.: 5039
N.A.I.C.S.: 423390

Saint-Gobain Construction Products Belgium NV (2)
Sint Jansweg 9 Haven 1602
9130 Kallo, Belgium BE
Tel.: (32) 3 360 22 11
Fax: (32) 3 360 23 80
E-Mail: info@gyproc.be
Web Site: www.gyproc.be/nl
Construction Material Whslr
S.I.C.: 5039
N.A.I.C.S.: 423390

Subsidiary:

Saint-Gobain Gyproc Belgium NV (3)
Sint-Jansweg 9 Haven 1602
9130 Kallo, Belgium
Tel.: (32) 3 3602211
Fax: (32) 33602409
E-Mail: info@gyproc.be
Web Site: www.gyproc.be
Construction Material Distr
S.I.C.: 5039
N.A.I.C.S.: 423390
Ludo Sterckx *(Product Mgr)*

Saint-Gobain Construction Products CZ A.S. (2)
Radiova 3
102 00 Prague, Czech Republic
Tel.: (420) 272 701 137
Fax: (420) 272 701 138
E-Mail: info@weber-terranova.cz
Web Site: www.weber-terranova.cz
Construction Material Mfr & Distr
S.I.C.: 3297
N.A.I.C.S.: 327120
Martin Soucek *(Gen Mgr)*

Saint-Gobain Construction Products Finland (2)
Stromberginkuja 2
00381 Helsinki, Finland
Tel.: (358) 10 44 22 00
Fax: (358) 10 44 22 300
Emp.: 100
Construction Material Distr
S.I.C.: 5033
N.A.I.C.S.: 423330
Magnus Holm *(Mgr)*

Saint-Gobain Construction Products Hungary Kft. (2)
46 Becsi ut 07/5 hrsz
2085 Pilisvorosvar, Hungary HU
Tel.: (36) 26 36 77 00
Fax: (36) 26 36 77 06
E-Mail: info@weber-terranova.hu
Web Site: www.weber-terranova.hu
Construction Material Distr
S.I.C.: 5039
N.A.I.C.S.: 423390

Saint-Gobain Construction Products Nederland BV (2)
Parallelweg 20
Etten-Leur, 4878 AH, Netherlands
Tel.: (31) 76 508 0000
Fax: (31) 76 501 7020
Emp.: 350
Construction Material Distr
S.I.C.: 5039
N.A.I.C.S.: 423390
Frank Poel *(Gen Mgr)*

Saint-Gobain Construction Products Romania SRL (2)
Str 22 Decembrie 1989 Nr 23
Turda, 401113, Romania
Tel.: (40) 264312044
Fax: (40) 264433428
E-Mail: office@weber.ro
Web Site: www.weber.ro
Gypsum Based Building Product Mfr
S.I.C.: 3275
N.A.I.C.S.: 327420

Saint-Gobain Construction Products Slovakia s.r.o. (2)
Stara Vajnorska 139
831 04 Bratislava, Slovakia
Tel.: (421) 2 4445 3022
Fax: (421) 24445 3030
Adhesive & Paint Product Mfr
S.I.C.: 2891
N.A.I.C.S.: 325520

Saint-Gobain Construction Products South Africa Ltd. (2)
77 Ostend Road Delville East Rand
Germiston, Gauteng, 1401, South Africa
Tel.: (27) 11 345 5300
E-Mail: talk2us@saint-gobain.com
Web Site: www.saint-gobain.co.za
Construction Material Mfr & Distr
S.I.C.: 3275
N.A.I.C.S.: 327420

Saint-Gobain Construction Products Ukraine (2)
Vul Maryny Raskovoi 13
02660 Kiev, Ukraine
Tel.: (380) 44 498 70 55
Fax: (380) 44 498 70 58
E-Mail: weber.ua@saint-gobain.com
Web Site: www.weber.ua
Plaster Mfr & Distr
S.I.C.: 3275
N.A.I.C.S.: 327420
Andrey Gluschenko *(Head-Mktg Dept)*

Saint-Gobain Construction Products Vietnam Limited (2)
Lot C23B Hiep Phuoc IP
Nha Be Dist, Ho Chi Minh City, Vietnam
Tel.: (84) 8 3781 8461
Fax: (84) 8 3781 8460
Web Site: www.gyproc.vn
Gypsum Product Mfr
S.I.C.: 3275
N.A.I.C.S.: 327420

Saint-Gobain Isover G+H AG (2)
Burgermeister Grunzweig Strasse 1
D 67059 Ludwigshafen, Germany (99.87%)
Tel.: (49) 6215010
Telex: 464851 und 464689
Fax: (49) 621501704
E-Mail: dialog@isover.de
Web Site: www.isover.de
Emp.: 1,300
Mfr. & Distributor of Thermal, Acoustic, Refrigeration & Fire-Protection Insulating Materials
S.I.C.: 2499
N.A.I.C.S.: 321999

Subsidiary:

Superglass Dammstoffe GmbH (3)
Industriestrasse 12
64297 Darmstadt, Germany
Tel.: (49) 6151153680
Fax: (49) 61511536899
E-Mail: service@superglass.de
Web Site: www.superglass.de
Emp.: 20
Insulation Material Distr
S.I.C.: 5033
N.A.I.C.S.: 423330
Danijel Lucic *(Mng Dir)*

Non-U.S. Subsidiaries:

Saint-Gobain Isover A/S (3)
Ostermarksvej 4
6580 Vamdrup, Denmark (98.75%)
Tel.: (45) 72171717
Fax: (45) 72171919
E-Mail: isover@isover.dk
Web Site: www.isover.dk
Emp.: 220
Mfr. of Insulation Materials & Systems
S.I.C.: 3296
N.A.I.C.S.: 327993
Dirk De Meulder *(Mng Dir)*

Saint-Gobain Isover AB (3)
Storgatan 29
26782 Billesholm, Sweden (99.66%)
Tel.: (46) 4284000
Telex: 72287 Gullbil
Fax: (46) 4284590
E-Mail: isover@isover.se
Web Site: www.isover.se
Emp.: 380
Mfr. & Distributor of Insulating Materials; Held 90.1% by International Saint-Gobain & 9.9% by Isover S.A.
S.I.C.: 3296
N.A.I.C.S.: 327993
Dirk de Meulder *(Gen Mgr)*

Saint-Gobain Isover Argentina S.A. (3)
Calle Bouchard y Enz
Llavallol, B 1836 AWB Buenos Aires, Argentina (76.26%)
Tel.: (54) 1142395200
Fax: (54) 1142395284
E-Mail: saint-gobain@isover-argentina.com.ar
Web Site: www.isover-argentina.com.ar
Emp.: 130
Manufacturing & Marketing of Glass Wool Products
S.I.C.: 3211
N.A.I.C.S.: 327211
Yanina Balboa *(Head-HR)*

Saint-Gobain Isover Austria AG (3)
Prager Str 77
2000 Stockerau, Austria (98.43%)
Tel.: (43) 22666060
Fax: (43) 2266606444
E-Mail: marketing@isover.at
Web Site: www.isover.at
Emp.: 180
Mfr. of Fiber Glass Products
S.I.C.: 3296
N.A.I.C.S.: 327993
Daniel Dominei *(CEO)*

Saint-Gobain Isover Benelux B.V. (3)
Parallelweg 20
NL 4878 AH Etten-Leur, Netherlands (98.75%)
Tel.: (31) 765080000
Fax: (31) 765017020
E-Mail: info@isover.nl
Web Site: www.isover.nl
Emp.: 400
Insulation Products Mfr.
S.I.C.: 3296
N.A.I.C.S.: 327993
S. Te Poel *(Mng Dir)*

Saint Gobain Isover Benelux (3)
Pleinlaan 5
1050 Brussels, Belgium (99%)
Tel.: (32) 26458821
Fax: (32) 26458858
E-Mail: info@isover.com
Web Site: www.isover.be
Emp.: 20
Insulation Products Mfr.
S.I.C.: 3296
N.A.I.C.S.: 327993

Saint Gobain Isover Italia S.p.A. (3)
Via Ettore Romagnoli 6
20146 Milan, Italy (91.35%)
Tel.: (39) 0000242431
Fax: (39) 0248953780
Web Site: www.isover.it/It/Contatti/Contatti.aspx
Emp.: 200
Producer & Distributor of Building & Industrial Glass Wool & Mineral Fibre Insulation
S.I.C.: 3296
N.A.I.C.S.: 327993

Saint Gobain Isover SA (3)
18 Ave Dalsace
La Defense, 92096 Paris, Cedex, France (100%)
Tel.: (33) 142566070
Fax: (33) 142566049
Web Site: www.isover.fr
Emp.: 1,500
Mineral Wool Mfr
S.I.C.: 3296
N.A.I.C.S.: 327993
Claude Imauven *(Pres & Dir Gen)*

Subsidiary:

Plafometal SAS (4)
Route de Phades
08800 Montherme, France
Tel.: (33) 324595400
Fax: (33) 324595401
E-Mail: plafometal@saint-gobain.com
Web Site: www.plafometal.com
Emp.: 94
Metal Product Mfr
S.I.C.: 3499
N.A.I.C.S.: 332999
Didier Basset *(Dir-Sls & Mktg)*

Saint-Gobain Isover S.A. (3)
Route De Payerne
PO Box 145
1522 Lucens, Switzerland (96.53%)
Tel.: (41) 219060111
Telex: 24379 FIVER
Fax: (41) 219060205
E-Mail: isover@isover.ch
Web Site: www.isover.ch
Emp.: 230
Mfr. & Distributor of Insulating Materials; Distribution of Fiber-Reinforcements
S.I.C.: 2499
N.A.I.C.S.: 321999

Saint-Gobain Rakennustuotteet Oy (3)
Kerkkolankatu 37 39
05801 Hyvinkaa, Finland (100%)
Tel.: (358) 1400684898
Fax: (358) 194560343
Web Site: www.isover.fi
Emp.: 200
Mfr. of Glass Products
S.I.C.: 3211
N.A.I.C.S.: 327211

Subsidiaries:

Alp'Verre (1)
8 Rue Des Terrasses
BP 48 74962 Cran-Gevrier, Cedex, France (100%)
Tel.: (33) 450572200
Fax: (33) 450578567
E-Mail: dertrand.juillouet@saint-gobain.com
Emp.: 70
Glass Mfr.
S.I.C.: 3211
N.A.I.C.S.: 327211

Autover France Glacauto (1)
41 Rue Des Bruyeres
69330 Pusignan, France (100%)
Tel.: (33) 472051919
Fax: (33) 478044166
Web Site: www.autover.fr
Emp.: 80
Mfr. of Glass Products
S.I.C.: 3211
N.A.I.C.S.: 327211
Nicolas Schild *(Mgr-Fin)*

Auvergne Isolation (1)
Montmurat
15600 Maurs, France (100%)
Tel.: (33) 471491900
E-Mail: auvergneisol@saint-gobain-glass.com
Web Site: www.saint-gobain-glass.com
Mfr. of Industrial Glass Products
S.I.C.: 3211

Compagnie de Saint-Gobain SA—(Continued)

N.A.I.C.S.: 327211

Barbe (1)
Roch Glas
29200 Brest, France (79.17%)
Tel.: (33) 298032982
Fax: (33) 298471447
Web Site: www.pointp.fr
Emp.: 50
Hardware Retailer
S.I.C.: 5251
N.A.I.C.S.: 444130
Yves Harster *(Mgr)*

Bourgeois (1)
3 rue de Langeais ZIL
BP 146
49301 Cholet, Cedex, France (79%)
Tel.: (33) 241461877
Hardware Retailer
S.I.C.: 5251
N.A.I.C.S.: 444130

Cedeo (1)
3 Ave John F Kennedy
62000 Arras, France (61.64%)
Tel.: (33) 321505252
Fax: (33) 321713424
E-Mail: cedeo-arras@saint-gobain.com
Web Site: www.cedeo.fr/agences-region/Nord-Pas-de-Calais-15
Hardware Retailer
S.I.C.: 5251
N.A.I.C.S.: 444130

Centre Est Vitrage (1)
27 Rue Paul Sabatier Prolongee Industrial Zone Confreries
71530 Crissey, France (80%)
Tel.: (33) 385464612
Fax: (33) 385415615
E-Mail: sebastien.raynal@saint-gobain.com
Emp.: 110
Mfr. of Glass Products
S.I.C.: 3211
N.A.I.C.S.: 327211
Sebastien Raynal *(Gen Mgr)*

Ceramidi (1)
Le Bugarel-Bruniquel
82800 Negrepelisse, France (61.41%)
Flat Glass Mfr.
S.I.C.: 3211
N.A.I.C.S.: 327211

Comptoir General des Glaces et Produits Verriers (1)
8 Route Des Champs Fourgons
P O Box 65
92233 Gennevilliers, France (100%)
Tel.: (33) 146139400
Telex: 698774 Glacyver
Fax: (33) 146139427
Emp.: 70
Distributor of Glass Products
S.I.C.: 5039
N.A.I.C.S.: 423390

Courbu Vitrages (1)
ZI Du Phare
33700 Merignac, France (100%)
Tel.: (33) 557923131
Fax: (33) 556479756
E-Mail: courbu@saint-gobain-glass.com
Web Site: www.saint-gobain-glass.com
Emp.: 70
Mfr. of Glass Products
S.I.C.: 3211
N.A.I.C.S.: 327211

Decoupage et Mecanique de l'Ouest (1)
68 Rue Denis Papin
49500 Segre, Cedex, France (100%)
Tel.: (33) 241921203
Fax: (33) 241928254
E-Mail: dmo49@club.fr
Web Site: www.d-m-o.fr
Emp.: 6
Flat Glass
S.I.C.: 3211
N.A.I.C.S.: 327211

Dispano (1)
8 Blvd Ferdinand De Lesseps
76000 Rouen, France (79.21%)
Tel.: (33) 235983838
Fax: (33) 235703185
E-Mail: info@dispano.com
Web Site: www.dispano.com
Emp.: 30
S.I.C.: 3211
N.A.I.C.S.: 327211

Distribution Sanitaire Chauffage SAS (1)
2 Avenue des Charmes - ZAC du Parc Alata
60550 Verneuil en Halatte, France
Tel.: (33) 3 44 55 82 00
Fax: (33) 3 44 55 27 06
Web Site: www.cedeo.fr
Sanitaryware Mfr
S.I.C.: 3499
N.A.I.C.S.: 332999

Eurocoustic (1)
7 Pl De Saverne
92400 Courbevoie, France (98.31%)
Tel.: (33) 156370240
Fax: (33) 156370269
E-Mail: info@eurocoustic.com
Web Site: www.eurocoustic.com
Emp.: 160
Provider of Thermal & Acoustic Insulation Services
S.I.C.: 3296
N.A.I.C.S.: 327993
Guillaume Loizeaud *(Gen Mgr)*

Expobois (1)
Les Perrasses
74230 Thones, France (79.19%)
Flat Glass Mfr.
S.I.C.: 3211
N.A.I.C.S.: 327211

Fabresines (1)
11-17, rue Constantin-Pecqueur
95157 Taverny, Cedex, France (79.05%)
Tel.: (33) 1 34 18 08 78
Fax: (33) 1 34 18 03 92
Paint Mfr.
S.I.C.: 2851
N.A.I.C.S.: 325510

Giraud (1)
Route De Roanne
69240 Pont-Trambouze, France (59.18%)
Tel.: (33) 474645476
Fax: (33) 4 74 64 42 70
E-Mail: info@giraud-freres.fr
Frames Mfr.
S.I.C.: 3442
N.A.I.C.S.: 332321

Glassver (1)
ZI Le Vivier
79700 Saint Pierre-des-Echaubrognes, France (99.71%)
Tel.: (33) 549821515
Fax: (33) 549821520
E-Mail: glassver@saint-gobain-glass.com
Web Site: www.saint-gobain-glass.com
Emp.: 140
Glass Mfr.
S.I.C.: 3211
N.A.I.C.S.: 327211

Gobba Vitrage (1)
21 Ave Marcellin Berthelot
PO Box 7
38200 Vienne, France (100%)
Tel.: (33) 474537553
Fax: (33) 474537541
Web Site: www.saint-gobain-glass.com
Emp.: 90
Flat Glass Mfr.
S.I.C.: 3211
N.A.I.C.S.: 327211

K par K (1)
66 Blvd Felix Faure
93300 Aubervilliers, France (59.15%)
Tel.: (33) 148344022
Fax: (33) 148343596
Web Site: www.kpark.fr
Emp.: 48
Windows Retailer.
S.I.C.: 5023
N.A.I.C.S.: 423220
Sfancois Rollet *(Mng Dir)*

La Basquaise de CD (1)
Rue de l'Industrie
ZI des Pontois, 64600 Anglet, France (79.23%)
Flat Glass Mfr.
S.I.C.: 3211
N.A.I.C.S.: 327211

La Savoisienne de CD (1)
84 BP 732
74015 Annecy, Cedex, France (79.23%)
Flat Glass Mfr.
S.I.C.: 3211
N.A.I.C.S.: 327211

Lagrange Production (1)
Route de Montauban 2
31340 La Magdeleine-sur-Tarn, France (59.17%)
Tel.: (33) 561378880
Fax: (33) 561350972
E-Mail: thierry.asselin@lapeyre.fr
Web Site: www.lapeyre.fr
Emp.: 200
Flat Glass Mfr.
S.I.C.: 3211
N.A.I.C.S.: 327211
Thierry Asselin *(Gen Mgr)*

Lapeyre Services (LGS) (1)
2 Rue Andre Karman
PO Box 149
93304 Aubervilliers, France (59.04%)
Tel.: (33) 148117400
Fax: (33) 148117401
Web Site: www.lapeyre.com
Emp.: 400
Data Processing
S.I.C.: 7379
N.A.I.C.S.: 518210

Lapeyre (1)
2 Rue Andre Karman
PO Box 149
93300 Aubervilliers, France (59.18%)
Tel.: (33) 148117400
Fax: (33) 148117401
Web Site: www.groupe-lapeyre.com
Emp.: 400
Hardware Retailer
S.I.C.: 5251
N.A.I.C.S.: 444130
Xaveier Besgoeert *(Mng Dir)*

Les Zelles (1)
ZI Les Ecorces
BP 7
88250 La Bresse, France (59.18%)
Tel.: (33) 329255311
Fax: (33) 329 2559 57
E-Mail: ressources.humaines@leszelles.fr
Web Site: www.leszelles.fr
Window Frame Mfr.
S.I.C.: 3089
N.A.I.C.S.: 326199

Menuiserie du Centre (1)
Ave Martial Lapeyre
15210 Ydes, France (59.18%)
Tel.: (33) 471679000
Fax: (33) 471679048
E-Mail: mc@menuiserie.fr
Emp.: 300
Furniture Mfr
S.I.C.: 3429
N.A.I.C.S.: 332510

Metz Woippy Cedeo (1)
34 36 Route De Thionville
57062 Metz, Cedex, 2, France (61.64%)
Tel.: (33) 387310266
Fax: (33) 387313854
E-Mail: cedeo-metz@saint-gobain.com
Web Site: www.cedeo.fr
Plumbing Supplies Retailer
S.I.C.: 5211
N.A.I.C.S.: 444190

Miroiterie du Rhin (1)
Rue De Industrie
PO Box 24
68126 Bennwihr Gare, 68126, France (100%)
Tel.: (33) 389208888
Fax: (33) 389232109
Web Site: www.saint-gobain-glass.com
Emp.: 100
Mfr. of Glass Products
S.I.C.: 3211
N.A.I.C.S.: 327211

Miroiteries de L'Ouest Atlantique (1)
Zone Des Rochettes
BP 56
44550 Montoir-de-Bretagne, France
Tel.: (33) 240002323
Fax: (33) 240002300
E-Mail: miroiteriesouest@saint-gobain-glass.com
Web Site: www.saint-gobain-glass.com
Rev.: $3,000,000
Emp.: 50
Mfr. of Glass Products
S.I.C.: 3211
N.A.I.C.S.: 327211
Courvoisies Dear *(Gen Mgr)*

Miroiteries de l'Ouest Semiver Climaver (1)
Rue D'Alembert
BP 510
22005 Saint-Brieuc, France (99.97%)
Tel.: (33) 296682268
Fax: (33) 296 3359 41
E-Mail: miroiteriesouestbretagne@saint-gobain-glass.com
Web Site: www.saint-gobain-glass.com
Mfr. of Industrial Products
S.I.C.: 3823
N.A.I.C.S.: 334513

MS Brico (1)
44 Rue De Rohrwiller
67240 Bischwiller, France (78.95%)
Tel.: (33) 388062857
Fax: (33) 388539026
Hardware Retailer
S.I.C.: 5251
N.A.I.C.S.: 444130

Natec (1)
Le Closeau rue de Brie
BP 84 77170 Servon, France (79.98%)
Flat Glass Mfr
S.I.C.: 3211
N.A.I.C.S.: 327211

Participations des Ardennes (1)
21-23, rue des Ardennes
75019 Paris, France (79.23%)
Flat Glass Mfr.
S.I.C.: 3211
N.A.I.C.S.: 327211

Partidis S.A.S. (1)
Les Miroirs 18 avenue d'Alsace
92400 Courbevoie, France
Tel.: (33) 1 47 62 53 00
Fax: (33) 1 47 62 53 80
Web Site: www.saint-gobain.fr/en/directory/company/search/country?
Building Material Distr
S.I.C.: 5211
N.A.I.C.S.: 444190

Subsidiary:

La Plateforme du Batiment (2)
7 Rue Benjamin Constant
75927 Paris, France
Tel.: (33) 1 42 03 85 00
Fax: (33) 1 42 02 24 28
Web Site: www.laplateforme.com
Building Material Distr
S.I.C.: 5211
N.A.I.C.S.: 444190

Pastural (1)
Allee de Cumieres
51200 Epernay, France (59.17%)
Tel.: (33) 326511551
Fax: (33) 326511561
E-Mail:
Web Site: www.pastural.fr
Emp.: 300
Wood Products
S.I.C.: 2431
N.A.I.C.S.: 321911

POINT P DEVELOPPEMENT (1)
Le Mozart 13/15 rue Germaine Tailleferre
75019 Paris, France
Tel.: (33) 140033300
Fax: (33) 140033304
E-Mail: enseigne.pointp@saint-gobain.com
Web Site: www.saint-gobain.com
Building Material Distr
S.I.C.: 5033
N.A.I.C.S.: 423330

Point P Est-Cibomat (1)
99 Rte De Bitche
PO Box 175
67506 Haguenau, France (61.41%)
Tel.: (33) 383256291

Fax: (33) 3 83 25 95 15
Web Site: www.pointp.fr/fiche-agence/hague nau-point-p-3145-92S7R335c9018
Hardware Retailer
S.I.C.: 5251
N.A.I.C.S.: 444130

Point P SA (1)
13-15 rue Germaine Tailleferre
75019 Paris, France (79.23%)
Tel.: (33) 140033300
Fax: (33) 140033304
E-Mail: enseigne.pointp@saint-gobain.com
Web Site: www.groupe-pointp.fr
Emp.: 20
Construction Materials Distr
S.I.C.: 5211
N.A.I.C.S.: 444190

Subsidiaries:

Brossette SAS (2)
23 rue Crepet
69007 Lyon, France
Tel.: (33) 472720505
Fax: (33) 437288733
E-Mail: contact@brossette.fr
Web Site: www.brossette.fr
Sales Range: $900-999.9 Million
Emp.: 2,650
Plumbing & Heating Supplies Distr
S.I.C.: 5074
N.A.I.C.S.: 423720

Non-U.S. Subsidiary:

SG DISTRIBUZIONE SRL (2)
6 Via Ettore Romagnoli
20146 Corsico, Italy
Tel.: (39) 02 89 30 16 14
Fax: (39) 02 82 67 250
Web Site: www.saint-gobain.com
Emp.: 39
Construction Material Distr
S.I.C.: 5039
N.A.I.C.S.: 423390
Mauro de Feudis *(Mgr-Comml)*

Point P Trouillard (1)
Zone Ouest De Malleve 4 Blvd Jean Moulin
44006 Nantes, France (79.21%)
Tel.: (33) 240384242
Fax: (33) 240384200
Web Site: www.pointp.fr
Hardware Retailer
S.I.C.: 5251
N.A.I.C.S.: 444130
Juy Piltric *(Pres)*

Point P (1)
12 Rue Curie Nord
6800 Colmars, France (78.96%)
Tel.: (33) 389201605
Fax: (33) 389201600
Web Site: www.pointp.fr
Emp.: 30
Hardware Retailer
S.I.C.: 5251
N.A.I.C.S.: 444130

Point P (1)
17, route de Bellevue
16710 Saint Yrieix, France (79.21%)
Tel.: (33) 555621084
Fax: (33) 5 45 92 20 84
Web Site: www.pointp.fr/fiche-agence /st-yrieix-point-p-3707
Hardware Retailer
S.I.C.: 5251
N.A.I.C.S.: 444130

Point P (1)
3 Rue Christian De Wett
69628 Villeurbanne, Cedex, France
Tel.: (33) 472134499
Fax: (33) 4 78 53 43 85
Web Site: www.pointp.fr/fiche-agence/villeu rbanne-bois-point-p-3792
Tile, Wood, Panels, Flooring & Structural Woodwork Mfr
S.I.C.: 2519
N.A.I.C.S.: 337125

Quincaillerie Lorraine (1)
13 Rue Gabriel Faure
54140 Jarville, France (61.54%)
Tel.: (33) 383562600
Fax: (33) 383567773
S.I.C.: 3211
N.A.I.C.S.: 327211

SAE Asti (1)
13, avenue de la Republique
92400 Courbevoie, France (100%)
Flat Glass Mfr.
S.I.C.: 3211
N.A.I.C.S.: 327211

Saint-Gobain Abrasifs (1)
ZI 8 Rue De La Taye
BP 45
28110 Luce, Cedex, France (99.9%)
Tel.: (33) 237916400
Fax: (33) 237342855
Abrasive Products Mfr.
S.I.C.: 3291
N.A.I.C.S.: 327910

Subsidiary:

Saint Gobain Abrasives (2)
Zides Vegnes 43 Rue Saint Andre
93012 Bobigny, France (99.9%)
Tel.: (33) 148432728
Fax: (33) 148436132
Emp.: 45
Mfr. Abrasive Products
S.I.C.: 3291
N.A.I.C.S.: 327910
Pierre Barrovecchio *(Gen Mgr)*

SAINT-GOBAIN ACHATS (1)
Les Miroirs 18 avenue d'Alsace
92400 Courbevoie, France
Tel.: (33) 1 47 62 48 00
Fax: (33) 1 47 62 49 96
Emp.: 1,000
Glass Product Mfr
S.I.C.: 3231
N.A.I.C.S.: 327215
David Turra *(Mgr-Pur)*

Saint Gobain Autover France S.A. (1)
Zac De Mariage 41 Rue De Bruyeres
69330 Pusignan, France (99.69%)
Tel.: (33) 557195800
Fax: (33) 557195801
Web Site: www.autover.fr
Mfr. of Glass Products
S.I.C.: 6351
N.A.I.C.S.: 524126

Saint Gobain Autover France S.A.S. (1)
ZI De La Bihardais
PO Box 73
35175 Bruz, France (80%)
Tel.: (33) 299058545
Fax: (33) 299058540
Web Site: www.autover.fr
Emp.: 18
Mfr. of Glass Products
S.I.C.: 3211
N.A.I.C.S.: 327211
Patrick Berranger *(Gen Mgr)*

SAINT-GOBAIN CONCEPTIONS VERRIERES (1)
Les Miroirs 18 avenue d'Alsace
92400 Courbevoie, France
Tel.: (33) 1 47 62 48 00
Fax: (33) 1 47 62 48 93
Glass Product Mfr
S.I.C.: 3231
N.A.I.C.S.: 327215

SAINT-GOBAIN CONSULTING INFORMATION AND ORGANIZATION (1)
Les Miroirs 18 avenue d'Alsace
92400 Courbevoie, France
Tel.: (33) 1 47 62 37 00
Fax: (33) 1 47 62 50 50
Web Site: www.saint-gobain.com
Business Management Consulting Services
S.I.C.: 8742
N.A.I.C.S.: 541611

Saint-Gobain Glass France SA (1)
Les Miroirs 18 avenue d'Alsace
92400 Courbevoie, France
Tel.: (33) 1 47 62 34 00
Fax: (33) 1 47 62 50 46
Web Site: www.saint-gobain.fr/en/directo ry/company/search/country?
Glass Product Mfr
S.I.C.: 3231
N.A.I.C.S.: 327215

Subsidiaries:

Saint-Gobain Glass Logistics S.A.S (2)
1 bis rue de Pise
BP 20074
60777 Thourotte, France
Tel.: (33) 344 906 161
Fax: (33) 344 760 102
E-Mail: sggl.thourotte@saint-gobain.com
Web Site: www.sggl.eu
Emp.: 40
Glass Transportation Services
S.I.C.: 4731
N.A.I.C.S.: 541614
Mouhssine Azziz *(Mgr-IT)*

Saint-Gobain Sovis SAS (2)
BP 202
02407 Chateau-Thierry, France
Tel.: (33) 323838300
Fax: (33) 323836515
Web Site: www.sovis.com
Glass Product Mfr
S.I.C.: 3231
N.A.I.C.S.: 327215
Omar El Karzazi *(Mng Dir)*

Saint-Gobain Sully S.A.S. (2)
16 Route d'Isdes
45600 Sully-sur-Loire, France
Tel.: (33) 2 38 37 30 00
Fax: (33) 2 38 37 30 05
E-Mail: sully@saint-gobain.com
Web Site: www.saint-gobain-sully.com
Emp.: 500
Automotive Glass Product Mfr
S.I.C.: 3231
N.A.I.C.S.: 327215
Francoise Roux *(Project Mgr)*

Samin S.A. (2)
18 Avenue Malvesin
92403 Courbevoie, France
Tel.: (33) 146919846
Fax: (33) 1 43348187
Web Site: www.samin.fr
Mineral Mining Services
S.I.C.: 1499
N.A.I.C.S.: 212399

SAINT-GOBAIN GLASS SOLUTIONS MENUISIERS INDUSTRIEL (1)
Z I de St-Pierre des Echaubrognes
79700 Mauleon, France
Tel.: (33) 5 49 82 15 15
Fax: (33) 5 49 65 51 91
E-Mail: glassver@saint-gobain-glass.com
Web Site: www.saint-gobain.fr/en/directo ry/company/search/country?
Flat Glass Mfr
S.I.C.: 3211
N.A.I.C.S.: 327211

SAINT-GOBAIN GLASS SOLUTIONS PARIS - NORMANDIE (1)
Zi Caen Ouest
BP 21
14650 Carpiquet, France
Tel.: (33) 2 31 71 14 14
Fax: (33) 2 31 26 99 73
E-Mail: vsgnormandie@saint-gobain-glass. com
Flat Glass Mfr & Whslr
S.I.C.: 3211
N.A.I.C.S.: 327211
Michel Claudon *(Gen Mgr)*

SAINT-GOBAIN GLASS SOLUTIONS SUD-OUEST (1)
ZI Du Phare 3 Rue Gay Lussac
33700 Merignac, France
Tel.: (33) 5 57 92 31 31
Fax: (33) 5 56 47 97 56
E-Mail: courbu@saint-gobain-glass.com
Flat Glass Mfr
S.I.C.: 3211
N.A.I.C.S.: 327211

SAINT-GOBAIN INTERSERVICES S.A. (1)
Les Miroirs 18 avenue d'Alsace
92400 Courbevoie, France
Tel.: (33) 1 47 62 48 00
Fax: (33) 1 47 62 48 93
Glass Product Mfr
S.I.C.: 3231
N.A.I.C.S.: 327215

Saint-Gobain Pam S.A. (1)
91 Ave De La Liberation
54076 Nancy, France (100%)
Tel.: (33) 383952000
Fax: (33) 383952757
Web Site: www.pont-a-mousson.com
Emp.: 2,000
Mfr. of Ductile Iron Pipes & Hydraulic Parts for Water Supply Systems, Irrigation, Sewerage & Drainage; Ductile Iron for Building
S.I.C.: 3317
N.A.I.C.S.: 331210
Pascal Queru *(Pres)*

Subsidiary:

Saint-Gobain Seva (2)
43 Rue Du Pont De Fer
PO Box 176
71100 Chalon-sur-Saone, France (100%)
Tel.: (33) 385472500
Fax: (33) 385742599
E-Mail: chrestothe.heugnault@saint-gobain. com
Web Site: www.saint-gobain-seva.com
Emp.: 360
Mfr. of Equipment for all Industries, Injection Moulds, Fibre Plates, Glass Moulds
S.I.C.: 3589
N.A.I.C.S.: 333318
Chrestothe heugnault *(Gen Mgr)*

Saint-Gobain Performance Plastics Europe, S.A. (1)
La Mothe-Aux-Aulnaies
89120 Charny, France
Tel.: (33) 3 86 63 78 78
Fax: (33) 3 86 63 77 77
E-Mail: info@Saint-gobain.com
Emp.: 160
Plastic Product Mfr
S.I.C.: 3089
N.A.I.C.S.: 326199
Xavier Hubert *(Mgr)*

Subsidiaries:

Saint-Gobain Adfors France (2)
517 Avenue de la Boisse
73025 Chambery, France
Tel.: (33) 4 79 68 32 18
Fax: (33) 4 79 68 32 40
Textile Fabric Product Mfr
S.I.C.: 2269
N.A.I.C.S.: 313310

Saint-Gobain Materiaux Innovants (2)
Les Miroirs 18 avenue d'Alsace
92400 Courbevoie, France
Tel.: (33) 1 47 62 30 00
Web Site: www.saint-gobain-materiaux-inno vants.com
Architectural Component Mfr
S.I.C.: 3446
N.A.I.C.S.: 332323

Saint-Gobain Performance Plastics Verneret (1)
La Mothe Aux Aulnaies
89120 Charny, France (100%)
Tel.: (33) 386637878
Fax: (33) 386637777
Emp.: 160
Silicone & Polymer Extruded Products Mfr.
S.I.C.: 2821
N.A.I.C.S.: 325211
Hubert Xavier *(Mng Dir)*

SAINT-GOBAIN PLACO SAS (1)
34 Avenue Franklin-Roosevelt
92282 Suresnes, France
Tel.: (33) 1 46 25 46 25
Fax: (33) 1 41 38 08 08
E-Mail: placoinfo@saint-gobain.com
Web Site: www.placo.fr
Plaster Board Mfr
S.I.C.: 3275
N.A.I.C.S.: 327420

Saint-Gobain Produits Industriels (1)
Commune De Condren
2700 Tergnier, France (100%)
Tel.: (33) 323578181
Fax: (33) 323576443
E-Mail: sgpi@saint-gobain-glass.com
Web Site: www.saint-gobain-glass.com
Mfr. of Glass Products
S.I.C.: 3211
N.A.I.C.S.: 327211

SAINT-GOBAIN PRODUITS POUR LA CONSTRUCTION SAS (1)
Les Miroirs 18 avenue d'Alsace
92400 Courbevoie, France

Compagnie de Saint-Gobain SA—(Continued)

Tel.: (33) 1 47 62 34 00
Fax: (33) 1 47 62 36 65
Web Site: www.saint-gobain.fr/en/directory/company/search/country#
Construction Material Mfr & Distr
S.I.C.: 3255
N.A.I.C.S.: 327120

SAINT-GOBAIN QUARTZ S.A.S. **(1)**
BP 102
Nemours, 77793, France
Tel.: (33) 1 64 45 45 00
E-Mail: quartz.sales.fr@saint-gobain.com
Quartz Product Mfr
S.I.C.: 3679
N.A.I.C.S.: 334419

SAINT-GOBAIN SERVICES RH FRANCE **(1)**
Rue de l Ambassadeur
78700 Conflans-Sainte-Honorine, France
Tel.: (33) 1 34 90 40 00
Human Resource Consulting Services
S.I.C.: 8999
N.A.I.C.S.: 541612

SAINT-GOBAIN SOLAR SYSTEMS S.A. **(1)**
18 Avenue d'Alsace
Courbevoie, 92400, France
Tel.: (33) 147623400
Photovoltaic Product Mfr
S.I.C.: 3674
N.A.I.C.S.: 334413

Saint-Gobain Stradal **(1)**
47 Avenue des Genottes
95800 Cergy, Pontoise, France (60%)
Tel.: (33) 1 34 25 5555
Fax: (33) 1 34 25 5585
Web Site: www.stradal.fr
Emp.: 60
Mfr of Construction Materials
S.I.C.: 3531
N.A.I.C.S.: 333120

Sanitaire Comtois **(1)**
6, avenue Gaulard
75019 Paris, France (61.4%)
Flat Glass Mfr.
S.I.C.: 3211
N.A.I.C.S.: 327211

Servibat **(1)**
ZI Bordilla
56360 Le Palais, France (61.49%)
Tel.: (33) 297313132
Fax: (33) 297313104
Flat Glass Mfr.
S.I.C.: 3211
N.A.I.C.S.: 327211

SFIC **(1)**
2 Route Du Bassin 5
92230 Gennevilliers, France (100%)
Tel.: (33) 140033426
Fax: (33) 140857475
Web Site: www.sfic.com
Emp.: 500
Hardware Retailer
S.I.C.: 5251
N.A.I.C.S.: 444130
Claude Bonnin *(Gen Mgr)*

Societe Atlantique de Prefabrication **(1)**
Chemin des Anglais
BP 101 44470 Carquefou, France (79.21%)
S.I.C.: 3211
N.A.I.C.S.: 327211

Societe de Commercialisation de Fournitures pour l'Industrie et la Construction **(1)**
13-15 Rue Germaine Tailleferre
75019 Paris, Cedex 19, France (99.91%)
Tel.: (33) 00140033411
Fax: (33) 140033449
Emp.: 50
Mfr. of Fabric Products
S.I.C.: 3499
N.A.I.C.S.: 332999
Claude Bonnin *(Dir Gen)*

Societe Verriere de l'Atlantique **(1)**
Zn Indus
BP 48
49800 Trelaze, France (99.99%)
Tel.: (33) 241376520
Fax: (33) 241376544
E-Mail: stevatlantique@saint-gobain-glass.com
Web Site: www.saint-gobain-glass.com
Emp.: 90
Tempered Glass & Double Glazing
S.I.C.: 3229
N.A.I.C.S.: 327212
Yannick Andre *(Mng Dir)*

Societe Verriere d'Encapsulation **(1)**
Rue Del Europe
60400 Noyon, France (100%)
Tel.: (33) 344098800
Fax: (33) 344098819
Emp.: 200
Flat Glass Mfr.
S.I.C.: 3211
N.A.I.C.S.: 327211
Draunu Oliviye *(Gen Mgr)*

Societe Verriere Francaise **(1)**
Centre De Commerce De Gross
PO Box 424
59814 Lesquin, France (100%)
Tel.: (33) 320870340
Telex: 132884F SVFLESQ
Fax: (33) 320875662
E-Mail: stevfrancaise@saint-gobain-glass.com
Web Site: www.saint-gobain-glass.com
Rev.: $4,041,473
Emp.: 175
Distributor of Glass Products & Automatic Doors
S.I.C.: 5039
N.A.I.C.S.: 423390
Arniod Besnard *(Mng Dir)*

Soprover **(1)**
LID 1 Ere Ave
PO Box 64
5 Eme Rue, 6510 Carros, France (100%)
Tel.: (33) 493291132
Telex: 47673
Fax: (33) 0493082363
E-Mail: michel.scotinni@soprover.com
Web Site: www.soprover.com
Emp.: 35
Distributor of Glass Products
S.I.C.: 5039
N.A.I.C.S.: 423390
Michel Scottini *(Mng Dir)*

Sovedys **(1)**
523 Rue Emile Zola
BP 67
73491 La Ravoire, Cedex, France (100%)
Tel.: (33) 4 79 72 99 60
Telex: 320454 SOVEDYS
Fax: (33) 4 79 72 79 96
Web Site: www.saint-gobain.com
Emp.: 80
Flat Glass Products & Automatic Doors Distr
S.I.C.: 5039
N.A.I.C.S.: 423390

Spafi **(1)**
Les Miroirs 18 Ave d'Alsace
92400 Courbevoie, France (100%)
Tel.: (33) 147623000
Fax: (33) 147623710
Emp.: 1,000
Holding Company
S.I.C.: 6719
N.A.I.C.S.: 551112

Stradal Environnement **(1)**
47 Ave des Genottes
95800 Cergy, Pontoise, France (61.64%)
Tel.: (33) 1 34 255555
Fax: (33) 1 34 255585
Web Site: www.stradal.fr
Sales Range: $250-299.9 Million
Emp.: 1,200
Mfr of Industrial Materials
S.I.C.: 3544
N.A.I.C.S.: 333511

Thuon SA **(1)**
53 Ave Gaston Cabannes
33270 Floirac, France (79.21%)
Tel.: (33) 557809809
Fax: (33) 556326904
Web Site: www.thuon.fr
Emp.: 55
Hardware Retailer.
S.I.C.: 5251
N.A.I.C.S.: 444130
Arthur Jean Pierre *(Mng Dir)*

Unicorn Precidia SA **(1)**
rue de la Vallee
14100 Lisieux, France (99%)
Flat Glass Mfr.
S.I.C.: 3211
N.A.I.C.S.: 327211

Verallia S.A. **(1)**
18 Avenue d'Alsace
92400 Courbevoie, France
Tel.: (33) 1 47 62 38 00
Fax: (33) 1 47 62 50 80
E-Mail: marketing.france.sge@saint-gobain.com
Web Site: www.verallia.com
Glass Bottle Mfr & Distr
S.I.C.: 3221
N.A.I.C.S.: 327213

Non-U.S. Subsidiaries:

Verallia Argentina **(2)**
6070 National Rail Rodeo de la Cruz
Mendoza, Argentina
Tel.: (54) 261 4130200
E-Mail: informes@saint-gobain.com
Web Site: www.verallia.com.ar
Glass Container Mfr
S.I.C.: 3221
N.A.I.C.S.: 327213

Verallia Chile **(2)**
Camino Rosario a Quinta de Tilcoco 1650
Rengo, Chile
Tel.: (56) 72959 100
Fax: (56) 72959 101
E-Mail: sgeinformaciones@saint-gobain.com
Web Site: www.verallia.cl
Glass Container Mfr
S.I.C.: 3221
N.A.I.C.S.: 327213

Verrerie Aurys **(1)**
ZI Pommenauque Rue Gravier
PO Box 170
50500 Carentan, France (100%)
Tel.: (33) 233716500
Fax: (33) 233716519
E-Mail: aurys@saint-gobain-glass.com
Web Site: www.saint-gobain-glass.com
Emp.: 250
Flat Glass Mfr.
S.I.C.: 3211
N.A.I.C.S.: 327211
Stephane Reyniers *(Gen Mgr)*

Verrerie de Saint-Just **(1)**
ZI La Verreie
42176 Saint Just-Saint Rambert, Cedex, France (100%)
Tel.: (33) 477362121
Fax: (33) 477362105
E-Mail: verrerie.st.just@saintgobain.com
Web Site: www.saint-just.com
Emp.: 49
Mfr. of Glass Products
S.I.C.: 3211
N.A.I.C.S.: 327211

Vertec **(1)**
Les Miroirs
18, avenue d'Alsace
92400 Courbevoie, France (100%)
Holding Company
S.I.C.: 6719
N.A.I.C.S.: 551112

Vetrotech Saint-Gobain Atlantique SarL **(1)**
21 Sq Saint Charles
75012 Paris, France (100%)
Tel.: (33) 53466789
Telex: 3209H5F VERTEX
Fax: (33) 43438330
E-Mail: vetrotex@vetrotex.fr
Web Site: www.vetrotex.com
Emp.: 12
Mfr. of Fiber Glass Reinforcements
S.I.C.: 3211
N.A.I.C.S.: 327211

VETROTECH SAINT-GOBAIN FRANCE **(1)**
21 Square Saint-Charles
75012 Paris, France
Tel.: (33) 1 534 66 789
Fax: (33) 1 434 38 330
Emp.: 11
Fire Resistant Glass Product Mfr
S.I.C.: 3231
N.A.I.C.S.: 327215
Jerome Bastien *(Gen Dir)*

Vitrages Isolants d'Auvergne **(1)**
BP 171
63020 Clermont-Ferrand, France (100%)
Tel.: (33) 473234800
Fax: (33) 473248409
E-Mail: viauvergne@saint-gobain-glass.com
Web Site: www.saint-gobain-glass.com
Emp.: 38
Mfr. of Glass Products
S.I.C.: 3211
N.A.I.C.S.: 327211

Wehr Miroiterie S.A.S. **(1)**
10 Rue Thomas Edison
BP 71081
67452 Mundolsheim, France
Tel.: (33) 3 90 24 90 90
Fax: (33) 3 90 24 90 91
E-Mail: info@wehr.fr
Web Site: www.wehr.fr
Commercial Glass Installation Services
S.I.C.: 1793
N.A.I.C.S.: 238150

Affiliates:

Atlantique Menuiseries Fermetures (A.M.F.) **(1)**
Route Du Poire
85190 Aizenay, France (46.08%)
Tel.: (33) 251455145
Fax: (33) 251347064
Web Site: www.saint-gobain.com
Flat Glass Mfr
S.I.C.: 3211
N.A.I.C.S.: 327211

Beton Manufacture de Vitre **(1)**
Rte de Plague
35500 Vitre, France (30.81%)
Tel.: (33) 223551320
Fax: (33) 299744625
Concrete Mfr.
S.I.C.: 3273
N.A.I.C.S.: 327320

Mabetoc **(1)**
87, rue de Paris
76800 Saint Etienne-du-Rouvray, France (30.82%)
Flat Glass Mfr.
S.I.C.: 3211
N.A.I.C.S.: 327211

Point P **(1)**
41 Rue De Tourville
76600 Le Havre, France (36.9%)
Tel.: (33) 235193800
Fax: (33) 235427940
Web Site: www.pointp.fr
Emp.: 100
Hardware Retailer
S.I.C.: 5251
N.A.I.C.S.: 444130

Servilog **(1)**
Routede Cholet
BP 389
85304 Challans, France (46.02%)
Flat Glass Mfr.
S.I.C.: 3211
N.A.I.C.S.: 327211

Societe des Tuyaux Armes de la Charente **(1)**
Les Maisons Rouges
16460 Chenon, France (39.61%)
Tel.: (33) 545225584
Fax: (33) 545225565
Concrete Products Mfr.
S.I.C.: 3272
N.A.I.C.S.: 327332

Tuyaux et Agglomeres Vendeens **(1)**
ZI LA Folie 5 rue Bollee La Chaise Vicomte
85310 Saint Florent-des-Bois, France (38.82%)
Concrete Mfr.
S.I.C.: 3272
N.A.I.C.S.: 327332

Joint Venture:

Keraglass SNC **(1)**
Rue Saint Laurent
77167 Bagneaux-sur-Loing, France

Tel.: (33) 164784700
Fax: (33) 164784757
E-Mail: info@eurokera.com
Sales Range: $50-74.9 Million
Emp.: 135
Clear Fire-Resistant Glass Ceramics Mfr & Distr; Owned 50% by Compagnie de Saint-Gobain SA & 50% by Corning Incorporated
S.I.C.: 3259
N.A.I.C.S.: 327120
Albert Di Giovanni *(Gen Mgr)*

U.S. Subsidiary:

Saint-Gobain Corporation (1)
750 E Swedesford Rd PO Box 860
Valley Forge, PA 19482-0101
Tel.: (610) 341-7000
Fax: (610) 341-7777
E-Mail: sgnorthamericainfo@saint-gobain.com
Web Site: www.saint-gobain-corporation.com
Emp.: 600
Holding Company
S.I.C.: 6719
N.A.I.C.S.: 551112
John Crowe *(Pres & CEO)*
Susan Nutson *(Sr VP-HR)*
M. Shawn Puccio *(Sr VP-Fin)*

Subsidiaries:

Carborundum Ventures Inc. (2)
23 Acheson Dr
Niagara Falls, NY 14303-1555 (100%)
Tel.: (716) 278-6299
Flat Glass Mfr.
S.I.C.: 8631
N.A.I.C.S.: 813930

CertainTeed Corporation (2)
750 E Swedesford Rd
Valley Forge, PA 19482 MD
Mailing Address: (100%)
PO Box 860
Valley Forge, PA 19482-0860
Tel.: (610) 341-7000
Telex: 845263
Fax: (610) 341-7777
Toll Free: (800) 233-8990
E-Mail: corporate@certainteed.com
Web Site: www.certainteed.com
Sales Range: $1-4.9 Billion
Emp.: 7,000
Insulation Products; Solid Vinyl Siding & Windows; Asphalt Roofing Materials; Polymerization; PVC Pipe; Clay Roof Tiles; Ventilation Products; Fiber Glass Reinforcements; PVC Fencing, Deck & Railing, Retractable Awning & Canopy Systems, Siding Mfr
Import Export
S.I.C.: 3221
N.A.I.C.S.: 327213
John Crowe *(Pres & CEO)*
Robert Panaro *(CFO, VP-Fin & Controller-Auster)*
Shawn Puccio *(CIO)*
Mark Rayfield *(Pres-Siding Products Grp)*
Tom Smith *(Pres-Roofing)*
Tim Feagans *(Gen Counsel, Sec & VP)*

Subsidiaries:

CertainTeed Ceilings (3)
750 E Swedesford Rd
Valley Forge, PA 19482 DE
Mailing Address: (100%)
PO Box 860
Valley Forge, PA 19482
Tel.: (610) 341-7000
Fax: (610) 341-7777
E-Mail: info@certainteed.com
Web Site: www.certainteed.com
Sales Range: $1-9.9 Million
Emp.: 12
Acoustic Ceiling Products
S.I.C.: 1742
N.A.I.C.S.: 238310
Peter Dechowski *(CEO)*

CertainTeed Corporation Foundation (3)
750 E Swedesford Rd
Valley Forge, PA 19482 DE
Tel.: (610) 341-7000 (100%)
Fax: (610) 341-7777
Web Site: www.certainteed.com
Emp.: 500
Mfr. of Flat Glass Products
S.I.C.: 3221
N.A.I.C.S.: 327213
Shawn Puccio *(CFO)*
John Sweeney *(Treas)*

CertainTeed Corporation Technical Center (3)
1400 Union Meeting Rd
Blue Bell, PA 19422 PA
Mailing Address: (100%)
PO Box 1100
Blue Bell, PA 19422
Tel.: (610) 341-7000
Fax: (610) 341-7777
Toll Free: (800) 274-8530
E-Mail: corporate@certainteed.com
Web Site: www.certainteed.com
Emp.: 600
Flat Glass, Glass Containers, Insulation, Reinforcements, Building Materials, Abrasives, Industrial Ceramics & Pipes Mfr
S.I.C.: 3221
N.A.I.C.S.: 327213

CertainTeed Foreign Sales Corp. (3)
PO Box 860
Valley Forge, PA 19482-0860 (100%)
Tel.: (610) 341-7000
Fax: (610) 341-7777
E-Mail: corporate@certainteed.com
Web Site: www.certainteed.com
Emp.: 600
Sales Services
S.I.C.: 3221
N.A.I.C.S.: 327213
Shawn Puccio *(CFO)*

CERTAINTEED GYPSUM AND CEILING MANUFACTURING, INC. (3)
4300 W Cypress St Ste 500
Tampa, FL 33607
Tel.: (813) 286-3900
Fax: (813) 286-3992
Web Site: www.saint-gobain.fr/en/directory/company/search/country
Gypsum Product Mfr
S.I.C.: 3275
N.A.I.C.S.: 327420

CERTAINTEED GYPSUM, INC. (3)
4300 500 W Cypress St
Tampa, FL 33607
Tel.: (813) 286-3900
Fax: (813) 286-3931
Web Site: www.saint-gobain.fr/en/directory/company/search/country
Gypsum Product Mfr
S.I.C.: 3275
N.A.I.C.S.: 327420

CertainTeed GYPSUM MANUFACTURING, INC (3)
4300 500 W Cypress St
Tampa, FL 33607
Tel.: (813) 286-3900
Fax: (813) 286-3931
Gypsum Product Mfr
S.I.C.: 3275
N.A.I.C.S.: 327420

CertainTeed GYPSUM WEST VRGINIA, INC. (3)
4300 500 W Cypress St
Tampa, FL 33607
Tel.: (813) 286-3900
Fax: (813) 286-3931
Gypsum Product Mfr
S.I.C.: 3275
N.A.I.C.S.: 327420

CertainTeed Saint-Gobain (3)
5931 E Marginal Way S
Seattle, WA 98134-2414 WA
Tel.: (206) 763-1550
Toll Free: (800) 562-9955
E-Mail:
Web Site: www.certainteed.com
Emp.: 120
Gypsum Wallboard Mfr
S.I.C.: 3275
N.A.I.C.S.: 327420

CertainTeed (3)
1077 Pleasant St
Norwood, MA 02062-4609 (100%)
Tel.: (781) 551-0656
Fax: (781) 551-9507
E-Mail: enquiries@texon.com
Web Site: www.certainteed.com
Sales Range: $75-99.9 Million
Emp.: 160
Mfr. of Building Materials & Machinery
Export
S.I.C.: 2952
N.A.I.C.S.: 324122
Patrick Widman *(Dir-Ops)*

CTKC Corporation (3)
c/o Deleware Management Co. 750 E. Swedesford Rd.
Valley Forge, PA 19482 (100%)
Tel.: (302) 574-8914
Flat Glass
S.I.C.: 3211
N.A.I.C.S.: 327211

Corhart Refractories Corp. (2)
10300 Ormsby Park Pl Ste 450
Louisville, KY 40223-6185 KY
Tel.: (502) 423-6324
Fax: (502) 775-7300
Emp.: 450
Fire Brick Mfr.
S.I.C.: 3297
N.A.I.C.S.: 327120
Richard Delcourt *(Plant Mgr)*

HCS Corporation (2)
22626 85th Pl S
Kent, WA 98031-2469 WA
Mailing Address:
PO Box 5729
Kent, WA 98064-5729
Tel.: (253) 854-4945
Fax: (253) 854-4947
E-Mail: hotcell@hotcell.com
Web Site: www.hotcell.com
Sls.: $3,800,000
Emp.: 13
Radiation Shielding Windows Mfr
S.I.C.: 3231
N.A.I.C.S.: 327215
Jean Philippe Lacharmme *(Pres & CEO)*

Marion Glass Equipment and Technology Company (2)
123 E Mckinley St
Marion, IN 46952 (50%)
Mailing Address:
PO Box 406
Marion, IN 46952-2271
Tel.: (765) 662-1172
Fax: (765) 662-1417
Web Site: www.gps-america.biz
Emp.: 95
Flat Glass
S.I.C.: 3559
N.A.I.C.S.: 333249
Tammy Whike *(Controller)*

Meyer International Inc. (2)
1 Meyer Plz
Vallejo, CA 94590
Tel.: (707) 552-2489
Gypsum Product Mfr
S.I.C.: 3275
N.A.I.C.S.: 327420

Meyer Laminates, Inc. (2)
1264 La Quinta Dr 41
Orlando, FL 32809 FL
Tel.: (407) 857-6353
Fax: (407) 856-9452
Rev.: $55,000,000
Emp.: 64
Lumber Plywood & Millwork
S.I.C.: 5031
N.A.I.C.S.: 423310

Norandex Building Material Distribution, Inc. (2)
300 Executive Pkwy W Ste 100
Hudson, OH 44236
Tel.: (800) 528-0942
E-Mail: info@norandex.com
Web Site: www.norandexhome.com
Building Material Distr
S.I.C.: 5032
N.A.I.C.S.: 423320

Norandex/Reynolds Distribution, Inc. (2)
300 Executive Pwy W Ste 100
Hudson, OH 44236
Tel.: (330) 656-8800
Fax: (330) 656-8996
Toll Free: (800) 528-0942
E-Mail: info@norandex.com
Web Site: www.norandex.com
Sales Range: $800-899.9 Million
Emp.: 2,200
Building Materials Distr & Vinyl Siding Mfr
S.I.C.: 5033
N.A.I.C.S.: 423330
Van L. Garber *(VP-Mktg)*

SAGE Electrochromics, Inc. (2)
1 Sage Way
Faribault, MN 55021 MN
Tel.: (507) 331-4848 (100%)
Fax: (507) 333-0145
Toll Free: (877) 724-3321
E-Mail: info@sageglass.com
Web Site: www.sageglass.com
Sales Range: $10-24.9 Million
Electronically Tintable Window Glass Mfr
S.I.C.: 3211
N.A.I.C.S.: 327211
John Van Dine *(Founder)*
Alan McLenaghan *(CEO)*
Chip Loeb *(CFO & Sr VP)*
Hong Mo Yang *(Chief Comml Officer)*
Erik Bjornard *(Sr VP-Strategic Technologies)*

Saint-Gobain Abrasives, Inc (2)
1 New Bond St PO Box 15008
Worcester, MA 01615-0008 NC
Tel.: (508) 795-5000
Fax: (508) 795-2688
Web Site: www.sgabrasives.com
Sales Range: $800-899.9 Million
Emp.: 1,200
Abrasive Materials Mfr
S.I.C.: 3291
N.A.I.C.S.: 327910
John Crowe *(Pres)*

Subsidiaries:

ABC Superabrasives (3)
1401 E Lackawanna St
Olyphant, PA 18447 FL
Mailing Address:
PO Box 811598
Boca Raton, FL 33481-1598
Tel.: (570) 383-3261
Fax: (561) 995-7979
Toll Free: (800) 368-5155
Web Site: www.abcsuperabrasives.com
Emp.: 32
Diamond Powder
S.I.C.: 3291
N.A.I.C.S.: 327910
Brian Schaffer *(Mgr)*

Norton Company (3)
1 New Bond St PO Box 15008
Worcester, MA 01606 MA
Tel.: (508) 795-5000 (100%)
Telex: 920428
Fax: (508) 795-2599
Toll Free: (800) 446-1119
Web Site: www.nortonabrasives.com
Emp.: 1,000
Abrasives, Grinding Wheels, Pulpstones, Diamond & CBN Diamond Dressing Tools & Wheels, Coated Abrasives, Floor Maintenance Products, Sharpening Stones, Masonry & Concrete Saws & Blades, Tower Packings, Polyvinyl Tubing, Safety Products, Plastic Components, Diamond Drilling & Coring Bits for Gas & Oil Exploration, Sealants & Fluoropolymers, Industrial Ceramics, Refractories, Igniters & Kiln Furniture Mfr
Import Export
S.I.C.: 6719
N.A.I.C.S.: 551112
Dean Arvidson *(Dir-Technical Mktg)*

Subsidiaries:

Norton Abrasive Exports (4)
1 New Bond St
Worcester, MA 01606 (100%)
Tel.: (508) 795-5000
Fax: (508) 795-2599
Web Site: www.sgabrasives.com
Emp.: 1,600
Mfr. of Automotive & Industrial Welding Products
S.I.C.: 6719
N.A.I.C.S.: 551112
Mark Rayfield *(VP)*

Compagnie de Saint-Gobain SA—(Continued)

Saint-Gobain Industrial Ceramics Inc. (4)
1 New Bond St
Worcester, MA 01606 (100%)
Tel.: (508) 795-5000
Fax: (508) 795-2599
Toll Free: (877) 281-3693
Web Site: www.refractories.saint-gobain.com
Emp.: 1,700
Flat Glass Mfr.
S.I.C.: 3291
N.A.I.C.S.: 327910
Mark Rayfield *(VP & Gen Mgr)*

Saint-Gobain NorPro (4)
3840 Fishcreek Rd
Stow, OH 44224-4305 (100%)
Tel.: (330) 673-5860
Fax: (330) 677-7247
Web Site: www.norpro.saint-gobain.com
Emp.: 65
Mfr. & Designer of Packings & Trays
S.I.C.: 3533
N.A.I.C.S.: 333132
Antonio Vilela *(VP & Gen Mgr)*

Saint-Gobain Performance Plastics Corp. (4)
150 Dey Rd
Wayne, NJ 07470-4670 (100%)
Tel.: (973) 696-4700
Fax: (973) 696-4056
E-Mail: info@saint-gobain.com
Web Site: www.plastics.saint-gobain.com
Sales Range: $800-899.9 Million
Emp.: 150
Mfr. of Engineered Plastic Products & Materials; High Performance Polymer Products
Import Export
S.I.C.: 3089
N.A.I.C.S.: 326199
Raymond Pace *(Dir-Worldwide Mktg)*

Subsidiaries:

Saint-Gobain Performance Plastics Corporation (5)
701 Daniel Webster Hwy
Merrimack, NH 03054-2713 DE
Tel.: (603) 424-9000 (100%)
Telex: 6817377 CHEMFAB UW
Fax: (603) 424-9012
E-Mail: info@fff.saint-gobain.com
Web Site: www.fff.saint-gobain.com
Emp.: 200
Developer, Manufacturer & Marketer of High Performance Engineered Products & Materials Systems
Import Export
S.I.C.: 2295
N.A.I.C.S.: 313320
Christain Marrow *(Gen Mgr)*

Non-U.S. Holdings:

Chemfab Japan, Ltd. (6)
3-20-1 Miyoshi-cho,
Fuchu
Tokyo, 183-0045, Japan
Tel.: (81) 42 358 5530
Fax: (81) 42 358-2887
E-Mail: risa.morisaki@saint-gobain.com
Industrial Plastics Mfr.
S.I.C.: 3544
N.A.I.C.S.: 333511

Saint-Gobain Performance Plastics Brasil (6)
Rodovia Regis Bittencourt
PO Box 3
06850-970 Sao Paulo, Brazil (100%)
Tel.: (55) 1141471499
Fax: (55) 1141471317
Web Site: www.ceramicmaterials.saint-gobain.com
Emp.: 30
Plastics Mfr
S.I.C.: 3086
N.A.I.C.S.: 326140

Saint-Gobain Performance Plastics Cologne GmbH (6)
Am Nordkanal 37
47877 Willich, Germany (100%)
Tel.: (49) 2154 60190
Fax: (49) 2154 60194
E-Mail: aff.germany@saint-gobain.com
Web Site: www.fff.saint-gobain.com
Sales Range: $10-24.9 Million
Emp.: 30
Performance Plastics Mfr
S.I.C.: 2821
N.A.I.C.S.: 325211
Jean-Dominique Gregoire *(Gen Mgr)*

Saint-Gobain Performance Plastics Ireland Ltd (6)
Cooraclare Rd
Kilrush, County Clare, Ireland IE
Tel.: (353) 659080170 (100%)
Telex: 852-70232
Fax: (353) 659080177
E-Mail: aff.europe@saint-gobain.com
Web Site: www.chemfab.com
Emp.: 80
Mfr of Coated Fabrics
S.I.C.: 2295
N.A.I.C.S.: 313320
John Costelloe *(Dir-Ops)*

Tygaflor Ltd. (6)
Bay 3 Transpennine Estate
Rochdale, Lancs, OL11 2PX, United Kingdom (100%)
Tel.: (44) 1706746900
Fax: (44) 1706746991
Web Site: www.fffeurope.saint-gobain.com
Emp.: 30
PTFE Coated Fabrics, Conveyor Belts & Films Mfr
S.I.C.: 2241
N.A.I.C.S.: 313220
Peter Appleton *(Gen Mgr)*

Saint-Gobain Performance Plastics Corp. (5)
1 Sealants Pk
Granville, NY 12832-1652 PA
Tel.: (518) 642-2200 (100%)
Fax: (518) 642-2793
Toll Free: (800) 724-0883
Web Site: www.fff.saint-gobain.com
Emp.: 100
Mfr. of Industrial Tapes Foams Films and Laminates Health Care Products
S.I.C.: 3089
N.A.I.C.S.: 326199

Saint Gobain Performance Plastics Corporation (5)
1199 S Chillicothe Rd
Aurora, OH 44202
Tel.: (216) 245-0529
Fax: (330) 562-3933
E-Mail: hosesupport@saint-gobain.com
Web Site: www.plastics.saint-gobain.com
Emp.: 60
Aircraft Body & Wing Assemblies & Parts
S.I.C.: 3728
N.A.I.C.S.: 336413
Tom Kinisky *(Pres)*

Non-U.S. Subsidiaries:

Al Rushaid Eastman Arabia Limited (5)
Dhahran Airport
PO Box 539
Dhahran, 31932, Saudi Arabia (37.5%)
Tel.: (966) 38980028
Mfr. of Glass Products
S.I.C.: 3211
N.A.I.C.S.: 327211

Bicron Products PPL (5)
SB Billimoria Co 70/3 Miller Road
Bengaluru, 560 052, India (100%)
Web Site: www.bicron.com
Crystals & Detectors Mfr
S.I.C.: 3231
N.A.I.C.S.: 327215

EFESIS Schleiftechnik GmbH (5)
Dr Georg Schafer Strasse 1
D 97447 Gerolzhofen, Germany (100%)
Tel.: (49) 93826020
Fax: (49) 9382602186
E-Mail: yerkauf@saint-gobain.com
Web Site: www.efesis.de
Emp.: 200
Mfr. of Glass Products
S.I.C.: 3211
N.A.I.C.S.: 327211
Ripp Stein *(Mgr)*

Grindwell Norton Ltd. (5)
Leela Business Park 5th Level
Andheri Kurla Road Andheri E, Mumbai, 400059, India (51%)
Tel.: (91) 2240212121
Telex: 11-2840 GNO-IN
Fax: (91) 2240212102
Emp.: 75
Mfr & Sales of Abrasive Products
S.I.C.: 3291
N.A.I.C.S.: 327910
Deepak Chindarkar *(CFO)*

Grindwell Norton Ltd (5)
Leela Business Park 5th Level Andheri-Kurla Road
Marol Andheri, Mumbai, 400 059, India (20%)
Tel.: (91) 2240212121
Fax: (91) 2240212102
Web Site: www.grindwellnorton.co.in
Emp.: 2,300
Mfr. of Fluoropolymers
S.I.C.: 2821
N.A.I.C.S.: 325211
Anand Mahajan *(Mng Dir)*

Norton Insurance Limited (5)
30 Cedar Avenue
Hamilton, 5, Bermuda (100%)
Captive Insurance Company
S.I.C.: 6411
N.A.I.C.S.: 524298

Norton Pampus GmbH (5)
Am Nordkanal 37
D-47877 Willich, Germany (100%)
Tel.: (49) 215460310
Telex: 8531924 TFE D
Fluoropolymers
S.I.C.: 2821
N.A.I.C.S.: 325211

Saint-Gobain Abrasifs SA (5)
Rue De l Ambassadeur
PO Box 8
78702 Conflans-Sainte-Honorine, France (99.91%)
Tel.: (33) 134904000
Telex: NORTON A 696844 F
Fax: (33) 139198956
Web Site: www.norton-abrasifs.com
Emp.: 500
Mfr. & Retailer of Abrasive Products, Sealants, Construction Products, Industrial Ceramics
S.I.C.: 3291
N.A.I.C.S.: 327910
Thomas Petuaud-Letang *(Mng Dir)*

SAINT-GOBAIN ABRASIVES A/S (5)
Korskildeeng 5
2670 Greve, Denmark
Tel.: (45) 467 552 44
Fax: (45) 467 550 60
E-Mail: sga.dk@saint-gobain.com
Web Site: www.s-ga.dk
Abrasive Product Mfr
S.I.C.: 3291
N.A.I.C.S.: 327910

Saint-Gobain Abrasives AB (5)
PO Box 305
177 25 Jarfalla, Sweden (99%)
Tel.: (46) 858088100
Telex: 109 34 NORSCAN S
Fax: (46) 858088101
E-Mail: sga.se@saint-gobain.com
Web Site: www.saint-gobain.se
Sls.: $21,909,816
Emp.: 27
Mfr. of Abrasive Products, Industrial Ceramics & Construction Products
S.I.C.: 3291
N.A.I.C.S.: 327910
Joost Morsink *(Gen Mgr)*

Saint-Gobain Abrasives BV (5)
Groenloseweg 28
7151 HW Eibergen, Netherlands (99%)
Mailing Address:
PO Box 10
7150 AA Eibergen, Netherlands
Tel.: (31) 545471766
Fax: (31) 545478007
Web Site: www.saint-gobain.com
Emp.: 20
Mfr. of Abrasive Products
S.I.C.: 3291
N.A.I.C.S.: 327910
Gui Bast *(Mng Dir)*

Saint-Gobain Abrasives Canada Inc (5)
3 Beach Road
PO Box 3008
Hamilton, ON, L8L 7Y5, Canada (100%)
Tel.: (905) 547-2551
Telex: 618648 NORTON HAM
Fax: (905) 547-9194
Web Site: www.sga.com
Emp.: 50
Mfr. of Grinding Wheels
S.I.C.: 3291
N.A.I.C.S.: 327910

Saint-Gobain Abrasives Gmbh (5)
Birkenstrasse 45-49
50387 Wesseling, Germany
Tel.: (49) 22367 031
Fax: (49) 22367 03367
E-Mail: info@cora-schleiftechnik.de
Web Site: www.saint-gobain-abrasives.com
Abrasive Product Mfr
S.I.C.: 3291
N.A.I.C.S.: 327910
Raphael Delhaye *(Dir-Fin)*

Saint-Gobain Abrasives Ltd (5)
70 Wharf Rd Te Atatu Peninsula
PO Box 45005
Auckland, New Zealand (100%)
Tel.: (64) 98347119
Telex: NZ 60703
Fax: (64) 98346623
E-Mail: sales.nz@saint-gobain.com
Web Site: www.saintgobain.com
Emp.: 45
Mfr. & Retailer of Pressure Sensitive Tapes, Abrasive Products, Construction Products
S.I.C.: 3291
N.A.I.C.S.: 327910
Kavin Dennis *(Mgr-Warehouse)*

Saint-Gobain Abrasives Limited (5)
Doxey Rd
Stafford, Staffordshire, ST16 1EA, United Kingdom UK
Tel.: (44) 1785223281 (100%)
Fax: (44) 8456026210
E-Mail: enquiry.sauk@saint-gobain.com
Web Site: www.saint-gobain.co.uk
Sls.: $1,243,386,752
Emp.: 180
Abrasive Products Mfr.
S.I.C.: 3291
N.A.I.C.S.: 327910
Alan Holcombe *(Mng Dir)*

Saint-Gobain Abrasives Malaysia (5)
Ste 210 1st Fl Block A Kelana Ctr Point No 3
Jalan SS7/19 Kalana Jaya, 47301 Petaling Jaya, Malaysia (100%)
Tel.: (60) 356389550
Telex: MA 37024
Fax: (60) 60378054389
E-Mail: info@sgabrasives.com
Web Site: www.sg-abrasives.com
Emp.: 10
Mfr. of Abrasive Products
S.I.C.: 3291
N.A.I.C.S.: 327910
David Yan *(Mgr-Sls)*

Saint-Gobain Abrasives (Pty.) Ltd. (5)
Unit 2 Monteer Road
Isando, 1600, South Africa (99.91%)
Tel.: (27) 119612000
Fax: (27) 119612005
Web Site: www.saint-gobain.com
Abrasive Products Mfr.
S.I.C.: 3291
N.A.I.C.S.: 327910
Duncan Whitehead *(Gen Mgr)*

Saint Gobain Abrasives Pty. Ltd. (5)
4 Colbert Rd
Campbellfield, 3061, Australia (99.97%)
Tel.: (61) 393586100
Telex: AA-20235
Fax: (61) 93586180
Web Site: www.saintgobain.com.au
Emp.: 100
Mfr. of Abrasive Products, Industrial Ceramics, Chemical Process Products, Sealants, Safety Products, Construction Products, Pressure Sensitive Tapes

S.I.C.: 3291
N.A.I.C.S.: 327910
Roger Freeman *(Mng Dir)*

Saint-Gobain Abrasives SA/NV (5)
Heide 10
B 1780 Wemmel, Belgium (99.91%)
Tel.: (32) 22672100
Fax: (32) 22678424
E-Mail: saies.be@saint-gobain.com
Web Site: www.saint-gobain.com
Emp.: 20
Mfr. of Abrasive Materials
S.I.C.: 3291
N.A.I.C.S.: 327910

Saint-Gobain Abrasives S.A. (5)
Bd J F Kennedy 190
4930 Bascharage, Luxembourg (99.9%)
Mailing Address:
PO Box 19
4901 Bascharage, Luxembourg
Tel.: (352) 504011
Telex: 2382 NORTON LU
Fax: (352) 503504
E-Mail: direction.nlx@saint-gobain.com
Web Site: www.construction.norton.eu
Emp.: 114
Mfr. & Sale of Construction & Abrasive Products
S.I.C.: 3291
N.A.I.C.S.: 327910
Marie Claire *(Mgr-HR)*

Saint-Gobain Abrasives S.R.O. (5)
Vinohradska 184
130 52 Prague, Czech Republic
Tel.: (420) 267 132 029
Fax: (420) 267 132 021
E-Mail: info@sgabrasives.cz
Web Site: www.sgabrasives.cz
Emp.: 29
Abrasive Product Mfr
S.I.C.: 3291
N.A.I.C.S.: 327910

Saint-Gobain Abrasives (Suzhou) Co., Ltd. (5)
No 45 Ting Lan Road Suzhou Industrial Park
215123 Suzhou, Jiangsu, China
Tel.: (86) 51262898050
Fax: (86) 51262898008
Emp.: 150
Abrasive Product Mfr
S.I.C.: 3291
N.A.I.C.S.: 327910
Franck Guo *(Gen Mgr)*

Saint-Gobain Abrasives Thailand Ltd. (5)
539/2 Gypsum Metropolitan Tower 13th Floor Sri Ayudhya Road
Phayathai Ratchathewi, Bangkok, 10400, Thailand
Tel.: (66) 26405440
Fax: (66) 26405441
Web Site: www.abrasivesthailand.com
Emp.: 130
Abrasive Product Mfr
S.I.C.: 3291
N.A.I.C.S.: 327910
Sitthichai Manasom *(Mgr-Production)*

Saint-Gobain Abrasivi S.p.A (5)
Via Per Cesano Boscone 4
I-20094 Milan, Italy (99.91%)
Tel.: (39) 0244851
Telex: 320407 Norton I
Fax: (39) 024402922
Mfr. & Retailer of Abrasive Products, Industrial Ceramics, Construction Products
S.I.C.: 3291
N.A.I.C.S.: 327910

Saint-Gobain Abrasivi S.p.A. (5)
Via 4 Novembre 228
21042 Caronno Pertus, Italy (99%)
Tel.: (39) 296450505
Fax: (39) 0296350456
E-Mail: tierre.barrovetthio@saint-gobain.com
Web Site: www.grinding.it
Emp.: 32
Mfr. of Abrasive Textiles & Related Products
S.I.C.: 3291
N.A.I.C.S.: 327910

Saint-Gobain Abrasivos CA (5)
Av Alberto Ravell Galpon Saint Gobain Urbanizacion
Los Teques, Venezuela
Tel.: (58) 212 210 48 00
Fax: (58) 212 210 48 14
Web Site: www.saint-gobain.com.mx/view/apven/apabrasivos.html
Abrasive Product Mfr
S.I.C.: 3291
N.A.I.C.S.: 327910
Paul Botello *(Gen Mgr)*

SAINT-GOBAIN ABRASIVOS COLOMBIA LTDA (5)
Km 20 Carretera Occidente
Mosquera, Colombia
Tel.: (57) 1 8933993
Fax: (57) 1 8276340
Web Site: www.carborundum.com.co/saintgobain-abrasivos-colombia.aspx
Abrasive Product Mfr
S.I.C.: 3291
N.A.I.C.S.: 327910

Saint-Gobain Abrasivos Lda (5)
122 Zona Industrial De Maia I Sector VIII
Apartado 6550
Gemunde, Maia, Portugal
Tel.: (351) 229 437 940
Fax: (351) 229 437 949
E-Mail: comercial.sga@saint-gobain.com
Web Site: www.sgabrasivos.com.br
Abrasive Product Mfr
S.I.C.: 3291
N.A.I.C.S.: 327910

SAINT-GOBAIN ABRASIVOS LIMITADA (5)
Av Vitacura 9990 - of 302 - Vitacura
Santiago, Chile
Tel.: (56) 2 342 3851
Fax: (56) 2 211 1337
Web Site: www.saint-gobain.com.br/versao2006/ingles/empresasEnderecos_chile_abrasivos.aspx
Abrasive Product Mfr
S.I.C.: 3291
N.A.I.C.S.: 327910

SAINT-GOBAIN ABRASIVOS, S.A. DE C.V. (5)
Carretera Matamoros Brecha E-99 Parque Industrial Reynosa
Reynosa, Tamps, Mexico 88780
Tel.: (52) 899131 07 40
Fax: (52) 899131 07 65
Web Site: www.saint-gobain-northamerica.com
Abrasive Product Mfr
S.I.C.: 3291
N.A.I.C.S.: 327910

Saint-Gobain Abrasivos SA (5)
Carretera De Guipuzcoa Km 7 5
162 Berrioplano, E 31195 Correos, Pamplona, Spain (100%)
Tel.: (34) 948306000
Telex: 37729 NORTO E
Fax: (34) 948306042
Web Site: www.norton.co.es
Emp.: 130
Mfr. & Sale of Abrasive & Construction Products
S.I.C.: 3291
N.A.I.C.S.: 327910

Saint-Gobain Ceramic Materials AS (5)
Mordhaim
PO Box 113
N 4790 Lillesand, Norway (100%)
Tel.: (47) 37260000
Telex: 21042 NORT N
Fax: (47) 37260150
Web Site: www.sic.saint-gobain.com
Emp.: 270
Mfr. of Abrasive Grain
S.I.C.: 3291
N.A.I.C.S.: 327910
Lars Maltby *(Gen Mgr)*

Saint-Gobain Ceramic Materials Canada Inc. (5)
8001 Daly St
Niagara Falls, ON, L2G 6S2, Canada (100%)
Tel.: (905) 295-4311
Fax: (905) 295-6462
Web Site: www.saint-gobain-northamerica.com
Emp.: 40
Mfr. of Industrial Ceramics
S.I.C.: 1459
N.A.I.C.S.: 212325
Chris Ciccarelli *(Mgr-Ops)*

Saint-Gobain Ceramic Materials Weilerswist GmbH (5)
Metternicher Strasse 3
D 53919 Weilerswist, Germany (100%)
Tel.: (49) 225496070
Fax: (49) 2254960760
E-Mail: info@saintgobain.com
Web Site: www.saintgobain.com
Emp.: 10
Mfr. of Textiles & Related Products
S.I.C.: 2299
N.A.I.C.S.: 313210
Hesse VOLKER Volker *(Gen Dir)*

Saint-Gobain Ceramicas Industriales S.A. (5)
Poligono Industrial Aquiberia
Castellbisbal, 8755 Barcelona, Spain (100%)
Tel.: (34) 936828140
Fax: (34) 936828143
Web Site: www.saintgobain.com
Emp.: 75
Mfr. of Glass & Plastic Products
S.I.C.: 3211
N.A.I.C.S.: 327211

Saint-Gobain Industrial Ceramics Ltd. (5)
Mill Ln Rainford Merseyside
Saint Helens, WA11 8LP, United Kingdom (100%)
Tel.: (44) 01744882941
Telex: 267291
Fax: (44) 01744883514
Web Site: www.refractories.saint-gobain.com
Emp.: 50
Specialised Refractory Materials Mfr.
S.I.C.: 3255
N.A.I.C.S.: 327120

Saint-Gobain K.K. (5)
Saint Gobain bldg 7 Koji-machi 3-chome
Chiyoda-ku, Tokyo, 102 0083, Japan (100%)
Tel.: (81) 332630281
Fax: (81) 332634011
Web Site: www.saint-gobain.com.jp
Emp.: 50
Provider of Management & Marketing Services & Sale of Chemical Process Products
S.I.C.: 5169
N.A.I.C.S.: 424690

Saint-Gobain Performance Plastics Chaineux SA (5)
Ave Du Parc 18
B 4650 Chaineux, Belgium (100%)
Tel.: (32) 87322011
Fax: (32) 87322051
E-Mail: gppl.chaineux@saint-gobain.com
Web Site: www.saint-goabin.com
Emp.: 70
Ceramics & Plastics Mfr.
S.I.C.: 3089
N.A.I.C.S.: 326199
Provost Laurent *(Gen Mgr)*

Saint-Gobain Performance Plastics Pampus GmbH (5)
Am Nordkanal 37
D 47877 Willich, Germany (100%)
Tel.: (49) 2154600
Telex: 8886966 NWSD
Fax: (49) 215460310
Web Site: www.saint-gobain-bearing.com
Emp.: 340
Mfr. of Engineered Plastic Products & Materials, High Performance Polymer Products
S.I.C.: 3089
N.A.I.C.S.: 326199
Ernst Breinig *(Gen Mgr)*

Saint-Gobain Performance Plastics Shanghai (5)
1468 Kun Yang Road Minhong Developement Zone
Shanghai, 200245, China (100%)
Tel.: (86) 2154721568
Fax: (86) 2154722378
E-Mail: info@saintgobain.com
Web Site: www.saintgobain.com
Emp.: 100
Mfr. of Plastic Products
S.I.C.: 3089
N.A.I.C.S.: 326199

Societe Europeenne des Produits Refractaires (5)
Les Miroirs La Defense
92096 Paris, Cedex, France (100%)
Tel.: (33) 0147623700
Telex: 630805 SEPR
Fax: (33) 147624242
Emp.: 1,000
Mfr. of Electro-Fused Refractory Products
S.I.C.: 3297
N.A.I.C.S.: 327120
Pierre-Andre De Chalendar *(CEO)*

Subsidiaries:

Saint-Gobain Centre de Recherche et d'Etudes Europeennes (6)
550 Avenue Alphonse Jauffret
84306 Cavaillon, France
Tel.: (33) 4 32 50 09 00
Fax: (33) 4 32 50 09 01
Laboratory Testing Services
S.I.C.: 8734
N.A.I.C.S.: 541380
Catherine Grange *(Mgr-HR)*

Saint-Gobain Cristaux (6)
104 Rue De Larchant
PO Box 521
77140 Nemours, France (100%)
Tel.: (33) 164451010
Telex: 650926 SILIS
Fax: (33) 164451001
E-Mail: sylvie.sargood@saint-gobain.com
Web Site: www.test-cdph.saint-gobain.com
Emp.: 100
Mfr. of Pure Fused Silica Tubing for the Lamp Industry; Silica Wool, Felts & Yarns
S.I.C.: 3356
N.A.I.C.S.: 331491
Tam Tinsty *(Pres)*

Saint-Gobain Materiaux Ceramiques SA (6)
Les Miroirs 18 avenue d'Alsace
92400 Courbevoie, France
Tel.: (33) 147623700
Web Site: www.saint-gobain.fr/en/directory/company/search/country#
Ceramic Wall Mfr
S.I.C.: 3255
N.A.I.C.S.: 327120

Subsidiary:

Saint-Gobain Coating Solutions (7)
50 Rue du Mourelet
BP 966
84000 Avignon, France
Tel.: (33) 4 9085 8500
Fax: (33) 4 9082 9452
Web Site: www.coatingsolutions.saint-gobain.com
Emp.: 25
Abrasive Product Mfr
S.I.C.: 3291
N.A.I.C.S.: 327910
Patrice Fournier *(Product Mgr-Mktg-Export Sls)*

Savoie Refractaires (6)
10 Rue Del Industrie
Venissieux, France (99.99%)
Tel.: (33) 478781300
Fax: (33) 478781350
E-Mail: info@sepr.fr
Web Site: www.sepr.fr
Emp.: 33
Mfr. of Special Refractories
S.I.C.: 3255
N.A.I.C.S.: 327120

Valoref SA (6)
Cruise Zone Industrielle
84500 Bollene, France
Tel.: (33) 4 90 40 5000
Fax: (33) 4 90 40 5001
E-Mail: marketing@valoref.com
Web Site: www.valoref.eu
Emp.: 20
Waste Management Services
S.I.C.: 4959
N.A.I.C.S.: 562998

Compagnie de Saint-Gobain SA—(Continued)

Non-U.S. Subsidiary:

SEPR Italia S.p.A. (6)
Via del Teroldego 1
I-38016 Mezzocorona, Trento, Italy (100%)
Tel.: (39) 0461616666
Telex: 311029 REFRAD I
Fax: (39) 0461601859
Web Site: www.saint-gobain-glass.com
Emp.: 1,000
Mfr. of Electrofused Refractory Products
S.I.C.: 3255
N.A.I.C.S.: 327120
Sargeo Mazzolane *(Gen Mgr)*

Warren Diamond Powder Company, Inc. (4)
1401 E Lackawanna St Mid Valley Industrial Park
Olyphant, PA 18447-2152 NY
Tel.: (570) 383-3261
Fax: (570) 383-3218
Toll Free: (800) 368-5155
E-Mail: info@warrendiamond.com
Web Site: www.warrendiamond.com
Sales Range: $1-9.9 Million
Emp.: 50
Diamond Wheels & Diamond Electroplated Products Mfr
Import Export
S.I.C.: 3291
N.A.I.C.S.: 327910
Phillipe Cruzet *(Pres)*

Saint-Gobain Abrasives, Inc. - Chicago (3)
200 E Fullerton
Carol Stream, IL 60188 (100%)
Tel.: (630) 868-8060
Web Site: www.saint-gobain-northamerica.com
Emp.: 125
Diamond Cutting Tools For Turning Boring Burnishing
S.I.C.: 3423
N.A.I.C.S.: 332216

Saint-Gobain Abrasives, Inc. - Philadelphia (3)
200 Commerce Dr
Montgomeryville, PA 18936-9640
Tel.: (215) 855-4300
Fax: (215) 362-3809
Toll Free: (800) 331-8837
E-Mail: moyco@moycotech.com
Web Site: www.moycotech.com
Sales Range: $1-9.9 Million
Emp.: 55
Abrasive Materials Mfr
S.I.C.: 3291
N.A.I.C.S.: 327910
Alexander Pecora *(Mgr-Site & Product-US)*

Saint-Gobain ADFORS America, Inc. (2)
1795 Baseline Rd
Grand Island, NY 14072-2010
Tel.: (716) 775-3900
Fax: (716) 775-3901
Toll Free: (800) 762-6694
Web Site: www.sg-adfors.com
Reinforcement Fabrics Mfr
S.I.C.: 2297
N.A.I.C.S.: 313230
Rudi Coetzee *(Gen Mgr)*

Subsidiary:

New York Wire Company (3)
500 E Middle St
Hanover, PA 17331-2027 PA
Tel.: (717) 637-3795
Fax: (717) 637-4549
E-Mail: mzammetti@newyorkwire.com
Web Site: www.newyorkwireind.com
Emp.: 500
Screening, Industrial Mesh & Drawn Wire Products
Export
S.I.C.: 3496
N.A.I.C.S.: 332618
Guy E. Fritz, Jr. *(CEO)*
Robert Kervian *(CFO)*

Branches:

Braeburn Alloy Steel (4)
101 Braeburn Rd
Lower Burrell, PA 15068-2259 DE
Tel.: (724) 224-6900
Fax: (724) 224-1958
Web Site: www.braeburnsteel.com
Sales Range: $10-24.9 Million
Emp.: 70
Mfr of Alloy Tool Steel
S.I.C.: 3399
N.A.I.C.S.: 331110
Clem Templeton *(Mktg Mgr)*

New York Wire Company (4)
1497 Industrial Rd
Walterboro, SC 29488 DE
Tel.: (843) 538-8041
Fax: (843) 538-2028
Toll Free: (800) 828-5329
Web Site: www.newyorkwire.com
Emp.: 300
Fiberglass Products
S.I.C.: 3089
N.A.I.C.S.: 326199
Butch Diehl *(Plant Mgr)*

SAINT-GOBAIN ADVANCED CERAMICS CORPORATION (2)
168 Creekside Dr
Amherst, NY 14228
Tel.: (716) 691-2051
Fax: (716) 691-2090
E-Mail: bnsales@saint-gobain.com
Web Site: www.bn.saint-gobain.com
Emp.: 75
Chemical Product Mfr
S.I.C.: 2899
N.A.I.C.S.: 325998
Scott Kuppinger *(Bus Mgr)*

Saint-Gobain Autover Inc (2)
3351 SW Blvd
Grove City, OH 43123
Tel.: (614) 801-2290
Fax: (614) 801-0303
Web Site: www.autover.us
Automotive Glass Product Mfr
S.I.C.: 3231
N.A.I.C.S.: 327215
Jim Stanley *(Controller)*

Saint Gobain BTI (2)
43 Bibber Pkwy
Brunswick, ME 04011-7357 TX
Tel.: (207) 729-7792
Fax: (207) 729-7280
Web Site: www.sgtf.com
Sales Range: $10-24.9 Million
Emp.: 139
Mfr of Reinforcement Fabrics for Composite Materials Used in Boats, Skis, Automotive Parts, & Industrial Tanks & Pipes
S.I.C.: 2299
N.A.I.C.S.: 313210

Saint-Gobain Ceramics & Plastics (2)
10300 Ormsby Park Pl Ste 450
Louisville, KY 40223-6185 KY
Mailing Address:
PO Box 740009
Louisville, KY 40201-7409
Tel.: (502) 423-6324
Fax: (502) 775-7478
Web Site: www.refractories.saint-gobain.com
Emp.: 450
Industrial Inorganic Chemicals
S.I.C.: 2819
N.A.I.C.S.: 325180

Subsidiaries:

Saint-Gobain Ceramics (3)
23 Acheson Dr
Niagara Falls, NY 14303-1555 DE
Tel.: (716) 278-6233 (100%)
Fax: (716) 278-2373
E-Mail: scd.sales@saint-gobain.com
Web Site: www.carbo.com
Sales Range: $50-74.9 Million
Emp.: 200
High Temperature Ceramic Fiber Insulation & Refractory Products, Polyester Resins & Resin Components Producer
Export
S.I.C.: 3269
N.A.I.C.S.: 327110
Curt Schmidt *(Mgr-Mktg)*

Saint-Gobain Ceramics Structural Ceramics Inc (2)
23 Acheson Dr
Niagara Falls, NY 14303
Tel.: (716) 278-6233
Fax: (716) 278-2373
E-Mail: scd.sales@saint-gobain.com
Web Site: www.hexoloy.com
Ceramic Material Mfr
S.I.C.: 3297
N.A.I.C.S.: 327120

Non-U.S. Subsidiary:

Saint-Gobain Ceramics SC (3)
3-7 Kojimachi
Chiyoda-ku, Tokyo, 102-0083, Japan
Tel.: (81) 332630289
Fax: (81) 332646010
Web Site: www.hexoloy.com
Glass Ceramic Mfr
S.I.C.: 3229
N.A.I.C.S.: 327212

Saint-Gobain Containers, Inc. (2)
1509 S Macedonia Ave
Muncie, IN 47302-3664 DE
Mailing Address: (100%)
PO Box 4200
Muncie, IN 47307
Tel.: (765) 741-7000
Fax: (765) 741-7012
Web Site: www.us.verallia.com
Sales Range: $1-4.9 Billion
Emp.: 4,395
Glass Bottle & Jar Mfr
S.I.C.: 3221
N.A.I.C.S.: 327213
Joseph R. Grewe *(Pres & CEO)*
Steve Rhea *(Sr VP-Strategic Dev)*

Subsidiary:

Saint-Gobain Containers, Inc. - Madera (3)
2441 Ave 12
Madera, CA 93637-9384
Tel.: (559) 675-4700
Web Site: www.sgcontainers.com
Glass Container Mfr
S.I.C.: 3221
N.A.I.C.S.: 327213

Saint-Gobain Desjonqueres Manufacturing, Inc (2)
9141 Technology Dr
Covington, GA 30014 (99.99%)
Tel.: (770) 786-1952
Fax: (770) 786-2140
Flat Glass Mfr.
S.I.C.: 3221
N.A.I.C.S.: 327213

SAINT-GOBAIN GLASS EXPROVER NORTH AMERICA CORP. (2)
15825 N 71st St Ste 205
Scottsdale, AZ 85254
Tel.: (480) 607-9400
Fax: (800) 511-2023
Toll Free: (800) 511-1930
Web Site: usa.saint-gobain-glass.com
Flat Glass Mfr
S.I.C.: 3211
N.A.I.C.S.: 327211

Saint-Gobain Sekurit USA (2)
38600 Van Dyke Ave Ste 350
Sterling Heights, MI 48312-1134 MI
Tel.: (586) 532-9500
Fax: (586) 532-9501
E-Mail: info@saint-gobain-sekurit.com
Web Site: www.saint-gobain-sekurit.com
Emp.: 8
Windshield Mfr.
S.I.C.: 3211
N.A.I.C.S.: 327211

SAINT-GOBAIN SOLAR GARD, LLC (2)
4540 Viewridge Ave
San Diego, CA 92123
Tel.: (877) 273-4364
E-Mail: info@solargard.com
Web Site: www.solargard.com
Window Film Mfr & Distr
S.I.C.: 3081
N.A.I.C.S.: 326113

Saint-Gobain Winter Inc (2)
100 Wilhelm Winter St
Travelers Rest, SC 29690-2226 (100%)
Mailing Address:
PO Box 1006
Travelers Rest, SC 29690-1006
Tel.: (864) 834-4145
Fax: (864) 834-3730
E-Mail: info@saintgobain.com
Web Site: www.saintgobain.com
Emp.: 80
Abrasive Products Mfr.
S.I.C.: 3291
N.A.I.C.S.: 327910

Saint Gobain (2)
5300 Gerber Rd
Fort Smith, AR 72904 (100%)
Tel.: (479) 782-2001
Fax: (479) 782-9984
Toll Free: (800) 643-2149
E-Mail: service@nortonproppants.com
Web Site: www.nortonproppants.com
Emp.: 150
Mfr. of Industrial Ceramic Products
S.I.C.: 3291
N.A.I.C.S.: 327910
Jack Larry *(Gen Mgr)*

Saint-Gobain (2)
1 New Bond St
Worcester, MA 01606 MA
Mailing Address:
PO Box 15008
Worcester, MA 01615-0008
Tel.: (508) 795-5000
Fax: (508) 795-5741
Web Site: www.nortonabrasives.com
Emp.: 1,200
Mfr. of Abrasives Products
S.I.C.: 6719
N.A.I.C.S.: 551112
Jean-Louis Beffa *(Chm)*
Bernard Field *(Sec)*
Jean-Claude Breffort *(Sr VP-HR & Dev-Intl)*
Jean-Pierre Floris *(Sr VP-Innovative Matls Sector)*
Jean-Francois Phelizon *(Sr VP)*

Unisul (2)
101 Hatfield Rd
Winter Haven, FL 33880-1325 FL
Tel.: (863) 294-3206
Fax: (863) 294-6771
E-Mail: unisul@unisul.com
Web Site: www.unisul.com
Emp.: 16
Distributors of Blowing Fans Industrial or Commercial
S.I.C.: 3564
N.A.I.C.S.: 333413
Gary Holliday *(Controller)*

Vetrotech Saint-Gobain North America Inc. (2)
2108 B St NW Ste 110
Auburn, WA 98001-1624 WA
Tel.: (253) 333-0660 (100%)
Fax: (253) 333-5166
Toll Free: (888) 803-9533
E-Mail: infoVSGNA.vetrotech@saint-gobain.com
Web Site: www.vetrotechusa.com
Emp.: 5
Mfr of Fire Rated Glass Products
S.I.C.: 3211
N.A.I.C.S.: 327211

Joint Venture:

Eurokera North America, Inc. (2)
140 Southchase Blvd
Fountain Inn, SC 29644 DE
Tel.: (864) 963-8082
Fax: (864) 963-8183
E-Mail: info@eurokera.com
Web Site: www.eurokera.com
Sales Range: $25-49.9 Million
Emp.: 50
Flat Glass Mfr.
S.I.C.: 3229
N.A.I.C.S.: 327212

Non-U.S. Subsidiaries:

CertainTeed Gypsum Canada, Inc. (2)
3304 58th Avenue S E
Calgary, AB, T2C 0B3, Canada
Tel.: (403) 279-2112
Fax: (403) 236-4880
Web Site: www.saint-gobain-northamerica.com
Gypsum Product Mfr
S.I.C.: 3275

N.A.I.C.S.: 327420
Sidney Anderson *(Gen Mgr)*

CERTAINTEED GYPSUM NORTH AMERICAN SERVICES, INC. (2)
2424 Lakeshore Road West
Mississauga, ON, L5J 1K4, Canada
Tel.: (905) 823-9881
Fax: (905) 823-4860
Gypsum Product Mfr
S.I.C.: 3275
N.A.I.C.S.: 327420
John Crowe *(Pres)*

CertainTeed Insulation (2)
3985 Belgreen Drive
Ottawa, ON, Canada K1G 3N2
Tel.: (613) 736-1215
Fax: (613) 736-1150
Web Site: www.saint-gobain-northamerica.com
Glass Product Mfr
S.I.C.: 3231
N.A.I.C.S.: 327215

Pyramid Specialities Products Ltd. (2)
17 Chemin De l Aviation
Pointe-Claire, QC, H9R 4Z2, Canada QC
Tel.: (514) 694-6788 (100%)
Emp.: 30
Glass Mfr
S.I.C.: 3231
N.A.I.C.S.: 327215
David Smith *(Mgr-Sls & Mktg)*

Saint-Gobain Adfors Canada Ltd (2)
201 Hugel Ave
Midland, ON, L4R 4G1, Canada
Tel.: (705) 526-7867
Fax: (705) 526-2801
Web Site: www.saint-gobain-northamerica.com
Fiber Glass Product Mfr
S.I.C.: 3089
N.A.I.C.S.: 326199

SAINT-GOBAIN SOLAR GARD CANADA, INC (2)
760 Pacific Road Unit 1
Oakville, ON, L6L 6M5, Canada
Tel.: (800) 595-8468
Fax: (905) 847-3190
Emp.: 4
Window Film Distr
S.I.C.: 5033
N.A.I.C.S.: 423330
Frank Mackay *(Gen Mgr)*

SG Ceramics Materials Canada Inc. (2)
8001 Daly St
Niagara Falls, ON, L2G 6S2, Canada
Tel.: (905) 295-4311
Fax: (905) 295-3521
Emp.: 36
Abrasive Product Mfr
S.I.C.: 3291
N.A.I.C.S.: 327910
Chris Ciccarelli *(Gen Mgr)*

Non-U.S. Subsidiaries:

Ashworth (1)
Hither Airsworth Rd
Radcliffe, M26 4AF, United Kingdom (100%)
Tel.: (44) 1617233468
Fax: (44) 1617246800
Web Site: www.ashworth.eu.com
Emp.: 100
Pipe & Tube Systems
S.I.C.: 3084
N.A.I.C.S.: 326122
Bill Willocks *(Mng Dir)*

Beijing SEPR Refracories Co., Ltd. (1)
No 10 Nan Xin Road Nan Kou County
Changping District, Beijing, 102202, China
Tel.: (86) 10 89791418
Fax: (86) 10 89791401
Web Site: www.saint-gobain.com.cn/html/companypages/SEPR_BJ.htm
Electro Fuse Product Mfr
S.I.C.: 3643
N.A.I.C.S.: 335931
Yuan He *(Dir-Sls)*

BPB GYPSUM BV (1)
20 Parallelweg
4878AH Etten-Leur, Netherlands
Tel.: (31) 76 5080000
Web Site: www.saint-gobain.fr/en/directory/company/search/country
Gypsum Product Mfr
S.I.C.: 3275
N.A.I.C.S.: 327420

Brasilit SA (1)
Avenida Santa Marina 482 1 Andar
05036 903 Sao Paulo, Agua Branca, Brazil (92.5%)
Tel.: (55) 11 2246 7000
Telex: 1137760 BLIT
Fax: (55) 11 36111598
Web Site: www.brasilit.com.br
Emp.: 600
Mfr of Fibre-Cement Sheets & Mouldings
S.I.C.: 2952
N.A.I.C.S.: 324122

CENTRAL SAINT-GOBAIN INVESTMENT CO LTD (1)
Kowa-Hitotsubashi Building 2F 7-1 Kanda-Nishikicho 3-chome
Chiyoda-ku, Tokyo, 101-0054, Japan
Tel.: (81) 332597694
Fax: (81) 332597687
Financial Investment Services
S.I.C.: 6211
N.A.I.C.S.: 523999

Consumers Sklo Zorya (1)
1 Promyslova St
Zorya Village, Rivne, 35314, Ukraine
Tel.: (380) 362692104
Fax: (380) 362692347
E-Mail: zorya@saint-gobain.com
Web Site: www.ua.verallia.com
Sls.: $57,876,882
Emp.: 542
Glass Container Mfr
S.I.C.: 3221
N.A.I.C.S.: 327213
Jean-Andre Barbosa *(Gen Dir)*

Deutsche Terranova Industrie (1)
Metternicher Strasse 17
D-53919 Weilerswist, Germany (79.09%)
Tel.: (49) 22546050
Fax: (49) 225460599
Flat Glass Mfr.
S.I.C.: 3211
N.A.I.C.S.: 327211

Doganer Alci Madencilik Enerji Ithalat Ihracat Pazarlama Ticaret Ve Sanayi A.S. (1)
Cetin Emec Bulvari 1042 Cadde 1296 Sokak No 7
Ovecler, Ankara, Turkey
Tel.: (90) 312478 26 01
Fax: (90) 312478 10 54
E-Mail: doganer@doganeralci.com.tr
Web Site: www.doganeralci.com.tr
Plaster Board Mfr
S.I.C.: 3275
N.A.I.C.S.: 327420
Bahri Akdag *(Chm)*
Durak Dogan *(Vice Chm)*

Eckelt Glas GmbH (1)
Resthofstrasse 18
4400 Steyr, Austria
Tel.: (43) 72528940
Fax: (43) 725289424
E-Mail: glas@eckelt.at
Web Site: www.eckelt.at
Emp.: 285
Flat Glass Mfr
S.I.C.: 3211
N.A.I.C.S.: 327211
Winfried Semling *(Mng Dir)*

Faba Autoglas Technik GmbH (1)
Blomberger Weg 6
13437 Berlin, Germany (99.79%)
Tel.: (49) 304147390
Fax: (49) 304112959
Web Site: www.faba-autoglas.com
Emp.: 30
Flat Glass Mfr.
S.I.C.: 3211
N.A.I.C.S.: 327211
Stefan Kranz *(Gen Mgr)*

FiberGlass Colombia S.A. (1)
Calle 3ra No 3 - 49 Este
Mosquera, Colombia
Tel.: (57) 18933030
E-Mail: contacto@fiberglascolombia.com.co
Web Site: www.fiberglasscolombia.com
Glass Product Mfr
S.I.C.: 3231
N.A.I.C.S.: 327215

Fibras Fivenglass SA (1)
Soco Industrial Zone North Facing Street Polifilm
Altimira, Venezuela
Tel.: (58) 2443220409
Fax: (58) 2443223494
E-Mail: contacto.fivenglass@saint-gobain.com
Web Site: www.fivenglass.com.ve
Emp.: 11
Glass Product Distr
S.I.C.: 5033
N.A.I.C.S.: 423330

Flachglas Torgau GmbH (1)
Solar St 1
04860 Torgau, Germany (99.79%)
Tel.: (49) 34217510
Fax: (49) 3421751701
Web Site: www.saint-gobain-glass.com
Emp.: 300
Mfr. of Glass Products
S.I.C.: 3211
N.A.I.C.S.: 327211

Galvano Groothandel BV (1)
Dillenburgstraat 12
5652 AP Eindhoven, Netherlands
Tel.: (31) 40214 14 14
Fax: (31) 40211 57 14
E-Mail: info@galvano.nl
Web Site: www.galvano.nl
Emp.: 85
Sanitaryware Distr
S.I.C.: 5074
N.A.I.C.S.: 423720
Erik van Stiphout *(Sr Product Mgr)*

Glaceries de Saint-Roch Germania (1)
Viktoriaallee 3 5
52066 Aachen, Germany (99.49%)
Tel.: (49) 2415160
Fax: (49) 2415162511
E-Mail: paul.meettson@saint-gobain.com
Web Site: www.saint-gobain-glass.com
Emp.: 300
Mfr. of Glass Products
S.I.C.: 3211
N.A.I.C.S.: 327211
Paul Meettson *(Gen Mgr)*

Glaceries de Saint-Roch SA (1)
World Trade Center Tour 1Bld E Jacqmain 162
Bte 48, 1210 Brussels, Belgium (99.54%)
Telex: 21263 SINROC
Fax: (32) 2217 2957
Emp.: 750
Mfr. & Transformer of Flat Glass
S.I.C.: 3211
N.A.I.C.S.: 327211

Non-U.S. Subsidiary:

Glasfabriek Sas van Gent B.V. (2)
Westkade 20
PO Box 4
4550 AA Sas-van-Gent, Netherlands NL
Tel.: (31) 115458000 (100%)
Telex: 55148 Glas
Fax: (31) 115453754
E-Mail: sunglass@saintgobain.com
Web Site: www.saint-gobain-glass.com
Rev.: $25,497,000
Emp.: 120
Fabricator of Reflective Glass; Tempered Glass; Enameled Glass; Insulating Glass
S.I.C.: 3211
N.A.I.C.S.: 327211
Mark Visser *(Gen Mgr)*

Glas Ziegler GesmbH (1)
Liesinger Flurgasse 10
1230 Vienna, Austria
Tel.: (43) 1869 26 460
Fax: (43) 1869 26 4611
E-Mail: info@glasziegler.at
Web Site: www.austria.sggs.com
Flat Glass Mfr
S.I.C.: 3211
N.A.I.C.S.: 327211

Glashuset i Sverige AB (1)
Annkristin Backstrom
Glashuset Burs
Burs Anges 231, 623 49 Gotland, Sweden (99.5%)
Tel.: (46) 498483077
Fax: (46) 70 497 88 64
Web Site: www.glashuset.se
Emp.: 10
Mfr. of Glass Products
S.I.C.: 3211
N.A.I.C.S.: 327211

International Saint-Gobain (1)
10 rue Saint-Pierre
CH-1700 Fribourg, Switzerland (100%)
Tel.: (41) 19 61 37 22 15 22
Holding Company
S.I.C.: 6719
N.A.I.C.S.: 551112

Jiangsu Donghai Saint-Gobain Co. Ltd. (1)
105 West Heping Road
Donghai, Jiangsu, 222 300, China (69.44%)
Flat Glass
S.I.C.: 3211
N.A.I.C.S.: 327211

KBS AG (1)
Industriestrasse 16
5106 Veltheim, Switzerland
Tel.: (41) 56 463 68 68
Fax: (41) 56 463 68 69
E-Mail: info@kbs-ag.ch
Web Site: www.kbs-ag.ch
Construction Material Distr
S.I.C.: 5039
N.A.I.C.S.: 423390

Koninklijke Saint-Gobain Glass Nederland NV (1)
Wageningselaan 42
PO Box 5073900
3903 Veenendaal, Netherlands (99.91%)
Tel.: (31) 318531311
Fax: (31) 318531305
E-Mail: info@saint-gobain-glass.com
Web Site: www.sggs.nl
Emp.: 100
Mfr. of Glass Products
S.I.C.: 3211
N.A.I.C.S.: 327211
Goost Morsink *(Mng Dir)*

La Venecia Iberiaglass S.L. (1)
Cima Do Alle-Filueira
36500 Lalin, Spain
Tel.: (34) 986 78 72 51
Fax: (34) 989 78 72 81
Flat Glass Mfr
S.I.C.: 3211
N.A.I.C.S.: 327211

La Veneciana Centro S.A. (1)
Edificio Ederra Centro Azca
Paseo de la Castellana 77, 28046 Madrid, Spain (73.1%)
Tel.: (34) 913972000
Fax: (34) 913972199
Web Site: www.saint-gobain-glass.com
Sls.: $97,447,100
Emp.: 849
Distributor, Processor & Installer of Glass Products & Mirrors
S.I.C.: 3211
N.A.I.C.S.: 327211
Santigao Cardantes *(Mng Dir)*

LIN YI SAINT-GOBAIN REFRACTORY CO., LTD (1)
Fuzhuang
Luozhuang District, Linyi, China
Tel.: (86) 539 850 8889
Fax: (86) 539 850 8669
Gypsum Product Mfr
S.I.C.: 3275
N.A.I.C.S.: 327420

LVI-DAHL OY (1)
Robert Huberin tie 5
01510 Vantaa, Finland
Tel.: (358) 20 759 4200
Fax: (358) 20 759 4300
Web Site: www.lvi-dahl.fi
Industrial Steel Pipe Distr
S.I.C.: 5051
N.A.I.C.S.: 423510
Erkki Stenberg *(CEO)*
Timo Kahila *(CFO)*
Barbro Dilen *(Sec)*

MAG Isover K.K. (1)
3-7 Kojimachi
Chiyoda-ku, 102-0083 Tokyo, Japan

Compagnie de Saint-Gobain SA—(Continued)

Tel.: (81) 3 3288 6300
Fax: (81) 3 3288 7361
Web Site: www.mag.co.jp
Fiber Glass Insulation Product Mfr & Distr
S.I.C.: 3296
N.A.I.C.S.: 327993

Modenfix Italia SRL (1)
Via Fosse Ardeatine 2
I-41042 Fiorano-Modenese, Italy (73.34%)
Tel.: (39) 59556115
S.I.C.: 3211
N.A.I.C.S.: 327211

Optimera A/S (1)
Ostre Aker Vei 260
0976 Oslo, Norway
Tel.: (47) 22 16 88 00
Fax: (47) 22 16 89 00
E-Mail: olsmar@optimera.no
Web Site: www.optimera.no
Building Material Distr
S.I.C.: 5032
N.A.I.C.S.: 423320
Asbjorn Vennebo *(CEO)*

PAM Colombia SA (1)
KM 3 5 Autopista Medellin Costado Sur
Terminal Terrestre De Carga
Etapa 1 Modulo 3 Bodega 9, 140165 Cota, Colombia
Tel.: (57) 317 657 47 23
Fax: (57) 1 841 58 33
Web Site: www.pamcol.com
Iron Pipe Mfr
S.I.C.: 3317
N.A.I.C.S.: 331210

Productora de Abrasivos Ltda. (1)
Km 20 Carretera Occidente Via Madrid
Cundinamarca, Colombia
Tel.: (57) 1893 3993
Abrasive Product Mfr
S.I.C.: 3291
N.A.I.C.S.: 327910

Productora de Abrasivos Pabsa Ltda (1)
Carrera 18 No 86-A-14
Bogota, Colombia (99.9%)
Tel.: (57) 1 82 76 266
Fax: (57) 1 827 6615
Abrasive Products Mfr.
S.I.C.: 3291
N.A.I.C.S.: 327910

PT Prima Rezeki Pertiwi (1)
Jl Jend Sudirman Kav 60 Menara Sudirman Lt 11
Jakarta, 12190, Indonesia
Tel.: (62) 21 52921135
Fax: (62) 21 52921136
Gypsum Product Mfr
S.I.C.: 3275
N.A.I.C.S.: 327420

PT. Saint-Gobain Abrasives Indonesia (1)
Jl Rungkut Industri IV/17 A-B
Surabaya, 60292, Indonesia
Tel.: (62) 31 8474358
Fax: (62) 31 8474385
E-Mail: CS.SGAI@saint-gobain.com
Web Site: www.sgabrasives-indonesia.com
Abrasive Product Mfr
S.I.C.: 3291
N.A.I.C.S.: 327910

PT Saint-Gobain Winter Diamas (1)
Jl Raya Bekasi Km 27 Pondok Ungu
Bekasi, 17124, Indonesia
Tel.: (62) 21 88986262
Fax: (62) 21 88986565
E-Mail: CS.SGWD@saint-gobain.com
Web Site: www.sgabrasives-indonesia.com
Abrasive Product Mfr
S.I.C.: 3291
N.A.I.C.S.: 327910

Rayen Cura Saic (1)
Carril Nacional 6070 Rodao De La Cruz
Mendoza, Argentina
Tel.: (54) 261 4130200
Fax: (54) 261 4130212
Web Site: www.rayencura.com
Glass Bottle Mfr
S.I.C.: 3221
N.A.I.C.S.: 327213

Rencol Tolerance Rings Ltd. (1)
Unit 16 Concorde Rd Patchway
Bristol, BS34 5TB, United Kingdom
Tel.: (44) 1179381700
Fax: (44) 1179157986
Automotive Fastener Mfr
S.I.C.: 3714
N.A.I.C.S.: 336390
Alan Holcombe *(Dir-Sls & Mktg)*

S-G API BV (1)
Newtonweg 1
3846 BJ Harderwijk, Netherlands
Tel.: (31) 341 474 600
Fax: (31) 341 474 626
E-Mail: sales@api.nl
Web Site: www.api.nl
Ceiling Product Mfr
S.I.C.: 3646
N.A.I.C.S.: 335122

Saint-Gobain Abrasives Nederland B.V. (1)
Prins Bernhardplein 200
Amsterdam, Netherlands
Tel.: (31) 20 521 4777
Fax: (31) 20 521 4824
Abrasive Product Mfr
S.I.C.: 3291
N.A.I.C.S.: 327910

Saint-Gobain Abrasivos Argentina SA (1)
Calle Peru 590 - 8VO
Buenos Aires, Argentina
Tel.: (54) 11 5901 3622
Fax: (54) 11 5901 3618
Abrasive Product Mfr
S.I.C.: 3291
N.A.I.C.S.: 327910

Saint-Gobain Abrasivos Brasil Ltda (1)
Av Santa Marina 482 - 4 andar
Sao Paulo, Brazil
Tel.: (55) 11 64 645206
Fax: (55) 4 64401477
Web Site: www.sgabrasivos.com.br
Abrasive Product Mfr
S.I.C.: 3291
N.A.I.C.S.: 327910

Saint-Gobain Adfors Austria GmbH (1)
Industriestrasse 11
7053 Hornstein, Austria
Tel.: (43) 2689 2234 0
Fax: (43) 2689 2234 85
Web Site: www.saint-gobain.fr/en/directory/company/search/country?
Emp.: 74
Glass Product Mfr
S.I.C.: 3231
N.A.I.C.S.: 327215
Milos Pavlis *(Gen Mgr)*

SAINT-GOBAIN ADFORS CZ FABRICS S.R.O. (1)
Sokolovska 106
570 21 Litomysl, Czech Republic
Tel.: (420) 461 651 111
Fax: (420) 461 651 350
Textile Fabric Product Mfr
S.I.C.: 2389
N.A.I.C.S.: 314999

SAINT-GOBAIN ADFORS CZ GLASS MAT S.R.O. (1)
Sokolovska 106
570 21 Litomysl, Czech Republic
Tel.: (420) 461 651 111
Fax: (420) 461 612 769
E-Mail: adfors-cz@saint-gobain.com
Web Site: www.vertex.cz
Glass Product Mfr
S.I.C.: 3231
N.A.I.C.S.: 327215

Saint-Gobain Adfors CZ S.R.O. (1)
Sokolovska 106
570 21 Litomysl, Czech Republic
Tel.: (420) 461 651 111
Fax: (420) 461 651 350
E-Mail: adfors-cz@saint-gobain.com
Web Site: www.vertex.cz
Fiber Glass Product Mfr
S.I.C.: 3231
N.A.I.C.S.: 327215

Saint-Gobain Adfors Italia S.p.A. (1)
Via Piave 29
17047 Vado Ligure, Savona, Italy
Tel.: (39) 019 2160013
Fax: (39) 019 885120
Web Site: www.saint-gobain.it/materiali_eng.php?num=41
Glass Veil Mfr
S.I.C.: 3231
N.A.I.C.S.: 327215

Saint-Gobain Advanced Ceramics (Shanghai) Co. Ltd (1)
No 12 Lane 3679 Jin Du Road Xin Zhuang Industrial Zone
Shanghai, 201108, China
Tel.: (86) 21 64899993
Fax: (86) 21 64422667
E-Mail: refractories.shanghai@saint-gobain.com
Web Site: www.saint-gobain.com.cn/html/companypages/SGAC_SH.htm
Emp.: 150
Ceramic Filter & Refractory Material Mfr
S.I.C.: 3297
N.A.I.C.S.: 327120

SAINT GOBAIN AMERICA S.A. DE C.V. (1)
AV Horacio 1855-502 Los Morales
Tijuana, Mexico
Tel.: (52) 6646254168
Fax: (52) 6646275272
Emp.: 282
Abrasive Product Mfr
S.I.C.: 3291
N.A.I.C.S.: 327910
Julio Leon *(Gen Mgr)*

SAINT-GOBAIN ASSESSORIA e ADMINISTRACAO LTDA. (1)
Avenida Santa Marina 482
Agua Branca, Sao Paulo, 05036-903, Brazil
Tel.: (55) 11 2246 7600
Fax: (55) 11 3611 1598
Flat Glass Product Mfr
S.I.C.: 3211
N.A.I.C.S.: 327211

Saint-Gobain Autover Direktglas AB (1)
Ellipsvagen 15
141 75 Kungens Kurva, Sweden
Tel.: (46) 8449 57 00
Fax: (46) 8449 57 10
E-Mail: info@autover.se
Web Site: www.direktglas.se
Emp.: 35
Automotive Glass Product Mfr
S.I.C.: 3231
N.A.I.C.S.: 327215
Jan Zetterstrom *(CEO)*

Saint-Gobain Autover Hellas S.A. (1)
Pontou B KTEO Area
57009 Kalochori, Greece
Tel.: (30) 2310 798770
Fax: (30) 2310 796116
E-Mail: info@autover.gr
Web Site: www.autover.gr
Automotive Glass Product Mfr
S.I.C.: 3231
N.A.I.C.S.: 327215

SAINT-GOBAIN AUTOVER OSTERREICH GMBH (1)
Brown-Boveri-Strasse 8 B17 Bauteil 2
2351 Wiener Neudorf, Austria
Tel.: (43) 2236 90 320
Fax: (43) 2236 90 321
E-Mail: autover.wien@saint-gobain.com
Web Site: www.autover.at
Automotive Glass Product Distr
S.I.C.: 5013
N.A.I.C.S.: 423120

Saint-Gobain Autover (1)
Chaussee Romaine 60
6600 Bastogne, Belgium
Tel.: (32) 61 210 940
Fax: (32) 61 210 976
Emp.: 21
Automotive Glass Product Mfr
S.I.C.: 3231
N.A.I.C.S.: 327215
Thierry Amerlynck *(Mgr)*

Saint-Gobain Bockmann A/S (1)
Habornveien 50
1602 Fredrikstad, Norway
Tel.: (47) 48 11 88 00
Fax: (47) 69 32 20 75
E-Mail: info@bockmann.no
Web Site: www.bockmann.sggs.com
Glass Product Mfr
S.I.C.: 3231
N.A.I.C.S.: 327215
Benoit Chatillon *(Gen Mgr)*

Saint-Gobain Building Distribution Deutschland GmbH (1)
Hanauer Landstrasse 150
60314 Frankfurt am Main, Germany
Tel.: (49) 694 05 0502
Fax: (49) 694 05 05 100
E-Mail: info@sgbd-deutschland.com
Web Site: www.sgbd-deutschland.de
Building Material Distr
S.I.C.: 5211
N.A.I.C.S.: 444190
Kathrin Will *(Head-Comm)*

Saint-Gobain Building Distribution (Ireland) Ltd. (1)
648 Springfield Road
Belfast, BT12 7EH, United Kingdom IE
Tel.: (44) 28 9024 3661
Fax: (44) 28 9023 2123
Emp.: 250
Timber Product Distr
S.I.C.: 5099
N.A.I.C.S.: 423990
Gary Hunter *(Branch Mgr)*

Saint-Gobain Canalizacao S.A. (1)
Via Dr Sergio Braga 452
27330-050 Barra Mansa, Brazil (81%)
Tel.: (55) 2440091300
Fax: (55) 2433255266
E-Mail: pamsac@saint-gobain.com
Web Site: www.saint-gobain-canalizacao.com.br
Emp.: 800
Mfr of Ductile Iron Pipes & Fittings; Hydraulic Valves
S.I.C.: 3494
N.A.I.C.S.: 332919

SAINT-GOBAIN CANALIZACION CHILE SA (1)
Antillanca Norte 600 Parque Industrial
Vespucio - Lo Echevers
Pudahuel, Santiago, Chile
Tel.: (56) 2444 1300
Fax: (56) 2 443 4502
E-Mail: info@saint-gobain.cl
Web Site: www.saint-gobain.com.br/versao2006/espanhol/empresasEnderecos_chile_canalizacao.aspx
Abrasive Product Mfr
S.I.C.: 3291
N.A.I.C.S.: 327910

SAINT-GOBAIN CERAMIC MATERIALS (ZHENGZHOU) CO. LTD (1)
DengFeng YangCheng Industrial Zone
Zhengzhou, Henan, China 452477
Tel.: (86) 371 6295 7959
Fax: (86) 371 6295 2244
E-Mail: SGCM_ZZ@saint-gobain.com
Ceramic Product Mfr
S.I.C.: 3229
N.A.I.C.S.: 327212

Saint-Gobain Ceramics & Plastics Plc (1)
Mill Lane Rainford
Saint Helens, WA11 8LP, United Kingdom
Tel.: (44) 1744 882941
Fax: (44) 1744 884746
Ceramic & Plastic Product Mfr
S.I.C.: 3229
N.A.I.C.S.: 327212

Saint-Gobain Condotte S.p.A. (1)
Via Allegro 1
I 16016 Cogoleto, Italy (100%)
Tel.: (39) 1091711
Fax: (39) 10 9171365
Web Site: www.tubighisa.it
Mfr. of Glass Products
S.I.C.: 3211
N.A.I.C.S.: 327211

Saint-Gobain Crystals NV (1)
Nieuwe weg 109
3765 GC Soest, Netherlands
Tel.: (31) 35 602 97 00
Fax: (31) 35 602 92 14

Web Site: www.saint-gobain.de/deutschland/en/produkte/gesellschaft.html?ks_remote_id=2&kt_remote_id=436&pe_id=123
Crystal Product Mfr
S.I.C.: 3231
N.A.I.C.S.: 327215

SAINT-GOBAIN DE COLOMBIA SA (1)
Carrera 7 North 26-20 Piso 20
76164 Bogota, Colombia
Tel.: (57) 1 255 7756
Fax: (57) 1 310 2939
Flat Glass Mfr
S.I.C.: 3211
N.A.I.C.S.: 327211

Saint-Gobain Deutsche Glas GmbH (1)
Viktoria Allee 3 5
D 52066 Aachen, Germany (99.79%)
Tel.: (49) 2415160
Telex: 887 4647 VGG
Fax: (49) 2415162166
E-Mail: vera.rutte@saint-gobain.com
Web Site: www.saint-gobain-glass.de
Rev.: $385,112,992
Emp.: 200
Holding Company; Distributor of Flat Glass for the Building Industry
S.I.C.: 6719
N.A.I.C.S.: 551112
Guerjn Peitz *(Mng Dir)*

SAINT-GOBAIN DEVELOPPEMENT MAROC (1)
2 Allee Des Figuiers Ain Sebaa
20250 Casablanca, Morocco
Tel.: (212) 522 665 731
Fax: (212) 522 350 965
Flat Glass Mfr
S.I.C.: 3211
N.A.I.C.S.: 327211

SAINT-GOBAIN DEVISA S.A. (1)
Paseo Castellana 77
28046 Madrid, Spain
Tel.: (34) 913 97 20 71
Fax: (34) 913 97 21 84
Flat Glass Mfr
S.I.C.: 3211
N.A.I.C.S.: 327211

SAINT-GOBAIN DIAMANTWERKZEUGE GMBH & CO. KG (1)
Schutzenwall 13-17
Norderstedt, 22844, Germany
Tel.: (49) 40 5258 0
Fax: (49) 5258215
E-Mail: info.winter@saint-gobain.com
Web Site: www.winter-superabrasives.com
Abrasive Product Mfr
S.I.C.: 3291
N.A.I.C.S.: 327910

Saint-Gobain Distribucion Construccion, S.L (1)
C/ Verneda del Congost s/n-Pol Ind El Pedregar
08160 Montmelo, Spain
Tel.: (34) 935723600
Fax: (34) 935720051
Building Material Distr
S.I.C.: 5211
N.A.I.C.S.: 444190

Saint-Gobain Distribution Denmark A/S (1)
Park Alle 370
2605 Brondby, Denmark
Tel.: (45) 48784000
Fax: (45) 48784201
Web Site: www.saint-gobain.de/deutschland/de/produkte/gesellschaft.html?ks_remote_id=1&kt_remote_id=451&pe_id=123
Rev.: $792,834,000
Emp.: 1,500
Construction Material Distr
S.I.C.: 5033
N.A.I.C.S.: 423330
Sus Nielsen *(Mgr)*

Saint-Gobain Distribution Nordic AB (1)
Box 67
177 22 Jarfalla, Sweden
Tel.: (46) 8 764 22 00
Fax: (46) 8 583 595 99
Building Material Distr
S.I.C.: 5033
N.A.I.C.S.: 423330

Saint-Gobain Distribution The Netherlands BV (1)
Atlasstraat 1
5047 RG Tilburg, Netherlands
Tel.: (31) 134580000
Fax: (31) 134580199
E-Mail: info@raabkarcher.nl
Emp.: 60
Construction Material Distr
S.I.C.: 5039
N.A.I.C.S.: 423390
Rian Mourik *(Dir-HR)*

Saint-Gobain Ecophon A/S (1)
Hammerholmen 18E
2650 Hvidovre, Denmark
Tel.: (45) 36 77 09 09
Fax: (45) 36 77 09 05
E-Mail: info@ecophon.dk
Web Site: www.ecophon.com
Acoustic Product Mfr
S.I.C.: 3446
N.A.I.C.S.: 332323

Saint Gobain Ecophon AB (1)
Yttervagen
PO Box 500
S 260 61 Hyllinge, Sweden (99.66%)
Tel.: (46) 42179900
Fax: (46) 42225555
E-Mail: jerald.saset@ecophon.se
Web Site: www.ecophon.com
Emp.: 350
Mfr. of Acoustic Ceilings & Wall Absorber Systems .
S.I.C.: 1742
N.A.I.C.S.: 238310
Jerald Saset *(Pres)*

Non-U.S. Subsidiary:

Decoustics Limited (2)
61 Royal Group Crescent
Woodbridge, ON, L4H 1X9, Canada ON (100%)
Tel.: (416) 675-3983
Fax: (905) 652-2505
E-Mail: sales@decoustics.com
Web Site: www.decoustics.com
Emp.: 100
Acoustic Paneling
S.I.C.: 1742
N.A.I.C.S.: 238310

Saint-Gobain Ecophon BV (1)
Parallelweg 17
4878 AH Etten-Leur, Netherlands
Tel.: (31) 76 502 00 00
Fax: (31) 76501 74 00
E-Mail: plafonds@ecophon.nl
Web Site: www.ecophon.nl
Acoustic Product Mfr
S.I.C.: 3259
N.A.I.C.S.: 327120
Boudewijn van Grinsven *(Project Mgr-Technical)*

SAINT-GOBAIN ECOPHON CZ S.R.O. (1)
Pekarska 695/10a
155 00 Prague, Czech Republic
Tel.: (420) 233 343 415
Fax: (420) 233 343 416
E-Mail: info@ecophon.cz
Web Site: www.ecophon.cz
Emp.: 7
Acoustic Product Mfr
S.I.C.: 3255
N.A.I.C.S.: 327120
Petr Magda *(Dir-Sls)*

Saint-Gobain Ecophon Ltd (1)
Old Brick Kiln Monk Sherborne
Tadley, RG26 5PP, United Kingdom
Tel.: (44) 1256 850977
Fax: (44) 1256 851550
E-Mail: marketing@ecophon.co.uk
Web Site: www.ecophon.com
Emp.: 50
Acoustic Wall Panel Mfr
S.I.C.: 3449
N.A.I.C.S.: 332323
Paul Lake *(Mng Dir)*

Saint-Gobain Ecophon Production A/S (1)
Hammerholmen 18E
2650 Hvidovre, Denmark DK
Tel.: (45) 36 77 09 09
Fax: (45) 36 77 09 05
Emp.: 20
Acoustic Product Mfr
S.I.C.: 3449
N.A.I.C.S.: 332323
Soren Jensen *(Mgr-Technical)*

Saint-Gobain Envases SA (1)
Km 1 5 caminoRosario a Quinto de Telcoco
Rengo, Chile
Tel.: (56) 7 295 9100
Fax: (56) 7 295 9101
Wine Bottle Mfr
S.I.C.: 3221
N.A.I.C.S.: 327213

Saint-Gobain Euroveder Italia SpA (1)
Via Maestri del Lavoro 12/14
12020 Cervasca, Italy
Tel.: (39) 0171 6851
Fax: (39) 0171 685484
Glass Product Mfr
S.I.C.: 3231
N.A.I.C.S.: 327215

Saint-Gobain Euroveder Operadora S.A. de C.V. (1)
Nicolas Bravo No 5 Parque Industrial Cuautla
62715 Mexico, Mexico MX
Tel.: (52) 5552791600
Fax: (52) 5552791619
Emp.: 3,000
Construction Material Distr
S.I.C.: 5039
N.A.I.C.S.: 423390
Dominique Sam *(Gen Mgr)*

SAINT-GOBAIN FACILITAS PORTUGAL, SOCIEDADE UNIPESS (1)
Estrada Nacional 10 Lugar de Dom Pedro
2690-364 Santa Iria de Azoia, Portugal
Tel.: (351) 219534622
Fax: (351) 219534607
Glass Product Mfr
S.I.C.: 3231
N.A.I.C.S.: 327215

SAINT-GOBAIN FORMULA GMBH (1)
Kutzhutte
37445 Walkenried, Germany
Tel.: (49) 5525 203 0
Fax: (49) 5525 203 58
E-Mail: info@saintgobainformula.com
Web Site: www.saintgobainformula.com
Gypsum Product Mfr
S.I.C.: 3275
N.A.I.C.S.: 327420
Jurgen Knetemann *(Mgr-North & Central Europe Reg)*

Saint-Gobain Foundry Co. Ltd. (1)
No 1 Huagong Road Cihu Industrial Zone
Ma'anshan, Anhui, 243052, China
Tel.: (86) 5553507801
Iron Foundry Services
S.I.C.: 3322
N.A.I.C.S.: 331511

Saint-Gobain Foundry (Ma'anshan) Co., Ltd. (1)
Huangong Road Cihu
Ma'anshan, Anhui, China 243052
Tel.: (86) 5553507801
Fax: (86) 5553507803
Iron Pipe Mfr
S.I.C.: 3317
N.A.I.C.S.: 331210

Saint-Gobain Glass Benelux SA (1)
Rue des Glaces Nationales 169
5060 Sambreville, Belgium
Tel.: (32) 71261211
Fax: (32) 71261293
E-Mail: glassinfo.be@saint-gobain-glass.com
Web Site: www.befr.saint-gobain-glass.com
Flat Glass Mfr
S.I.C.: 3211
N.A.I.C.S.: 327211

Subsidiary:

Techniver SA (2)
Zoning Industriel de Mornimont rue Isidor Derese 4
5190 Jemeppe-sur-Sambre, Belgium
Tel.: (32) 71755711
Fax: (32) 71755750
Web Site: www.belgique.sggs.com
Flat Glass Mfr
S.I.C.: 3211
N.A.I.C.S.: 327211

SAINT-GOBAIN GLASS ESTONIA SE (1)
Kirde 2
61506 Elva, Estonia
Tel.: (372) 7 303 300
Fax: (372) 7 303 333
E-Mail: info@sekurit.ee
Web Site: www.sekurit.ee
Emp.: 230
Glass Product Mfr
S.I.C.: 3231
N.A.I.C.S.: 327215
Andi Kasak *(Gen Mgr)*

Saint-Gobain Glass Finland Oy (1)
Koskelontie 21
02920 Espoo, Finland
Tel.: (358) 9854 5030
Fax: (358) 9854 50 345
E-Mail: autover@autover.fi
Web Site: www.autover.fi
Automobile Glass Product Mfr
S.I.C.: 3231
N.A.I.C.S.: 327215

SAINT-GOBAIN GLASS HELLAS (1)
Av Kalamakiou 37
Alimos, 17455 Athens, Greece
Tel.: (30) 210 9854407
Fax: (30) 210 9854408
Glass Product Mfr
S.I.C.: 3231
N.A.I.C.S.: 327215
Zafiris Primikirios *(Project Mgr)*

Saint-Gobain Glass India Ltd. (1)
A-1 SIPCOT Industrial Park Sriperumbudur
602105 Kanchipuram, Tamil Nadu, India
Tel.: (91) 4427162832
Web Site: www.saint-gobain.co.in/_contactUs.html
Float Glass Mfr
S.I.C.: 3211
N.A.I.C.S.: 327211

Saint-Gobain Glass Italia Logistica Servizi S.r.l. (1)
Via Ponte A Piglieri 2
1 56121 Pisa, Italy (100%)
Tel.: (39) 050516446
Fax: (39) 050516111
E-Mail: info@saint-gobain-glass.com
Web Site: it.saint-gobain-glass.com
Emp.: 600
Mfr. of Fabricated Glass Products for the Automotive & Building Industry
S.I.C.: 3211
N.A.I.C.S.: 327211

Non-U.S. Subsidiaries:

Emmaboda Glas AB (2)
PO Box 153
36122 Emmaboda, Sweden (99.64%)
Tel.: (46) 47118800
Telex: 43076 Emglass
Fax: (46) 47113526
E-Mail: info@emmabodaglas.se
Web Site: www.emmabodaglas.se
Sales Range: $25-49.9 Million
Emp.: 200
Fabrication of Insulating & Tempered Glass for the Building Industry
S.I.C.: 3221
N.A.I.C.S.: 327213
Peter Moller *(Gen Mgr)*

Scanglas A/S (2)
Glasvej 2
4220 Korsor, Denmark (100%)
Tel.: (45) 70332700
Telex: 45502 Scangl
Fax: (45) 58373700
E-Mail: peter.moller@scanglas.dk
Web Site: www.scanglas.dk

Compagnie de Saint-Gobain SA—(Continued)

Emp.: 450
Mfr. of Insulation & Tempered Glass
S.I.C.: 3231
N.A.I.C.S.: 327215
Peter Moller *(Mng Dir)*

Saint-Gobain Glass Italia SpA (1)
Via Ponte a Piglieri 2
56121 Pisa, Italy
Tel.: (39) 050 516111
Fax: (39) 050 48266
E-Mail: distribution.italia@saint-gobain.com
Web Site: www.saint-gobain.it
Glass Product Mfr
S.I.C.: 3231
N.A.I.C.S.: 327215

Saint-Gobain Glass Mexico, S.A. de C.V (1)
Av Nicolas Bravo 58 Parque Industrial Cuautla
Municipio De Ayala, Morelos, 62741, Mexico
Tel.: (52) 7353548100
Fax: (52) 7353548199
Web Site: www.saint-gobain-glass.com.mx
Emp.: 350
Mfr. of Glass Products
S.I.C.: 3211
N.A.I.C.S.: 327211

Saint-Gobain Glass Nordic A/S (1)
Dampfrgevej 26
DK 2100 Copenhagen, Denmark (99.64%)
Tel.: (45) 35256400
Fax: (45) 35436301
Web Site: www.saint-gobain-glass.dk
Flat Glass Mfr.
S.I.C.: 3211
N.A.I.C.S.: 327211

SAINT GOBAIN GLASS OPERADORA S.A. DE C.V. (1)
Av Nicolas Bravo No 5 Parque Industrial Cuautla
Ayala, Morelos, Mexico
Tel.: (52) 735 35 4 81 00
Fax: (52) 735 35 4 81 23
Flat Glass Mfr
S.I.C.: 3211
N.A.I.C.S.: 327211

Saint-Gobain Glass Polska (1)
Ul Szklanych Domow 1
PL 425320 Dabrowa Gornicza, Poland (99.87%)
Tel.: (48) 322954000
Fax: (48) 322954108
Web Site: www.saint-gobain-glass.com
Emp.: 280
Mfr. of Glass Products
S.I.C.: 3211
N.A.I.C.S.: 327211
Hugues Demissel *(Gen Mgr)*

Subsidiary:

Saint-Gobain Euroveder Polska Sp. z o.o. (2)
ul Szklarska 27
68-205 Zary, Poland
Tel.: (48) 68363 38 10
Fax: (48) 68363 38 15
Emp.: 100
Gypsum Product Mfr
S.I.C.: 3275
N.A.I.C.S.: 327420

Saint-Gobain Glass Portugal Vidro Plano SA (1)
EN 10 - Apartado 1713
2691-652 Santa Iria de Azoia, Portugal
Tel.: (351) 21 953 4600
Fax: (351) 21 953 4642
Flat Glass Mfr
S.I.C.: 3211
N.A.I.C.S.: 327211

Subsidiary:

Covipor-CIA Vidreira do Norte Ltda. (2)
Apartado 59 Santa Christina do Couto
4784-909 Santo Tirso, Portugal
Tel.: (351) 252 80 82 00
Fax: (351) 252 80 82 09
E-Mail: covipor@saint-gobain.com
Web Site: www.saint-gobain.fr/en/directory/company/search/country?
Emp.: 50
Flat Glass Mfr
S.I.C.: 3211
N.A.I.C.S.: 327211
Manuel Fernandes *(Mng Dir)*

Saint-Gobain Glass Romania SRL (1)
Str Varianta Nord 61
Calarasi, 910053 Bucharest, Romania
Tel.: (40) 242 305 164
Fax: (40) 242 305 109
E-Mail: office.sggr@saint-gobain.com
Emp.: 250
Glass Product Mfr
S.I.C.: 3231
N.A.I.C.S.: 327215
Ramona Avram *(Coord-Acctg)*

Saint-Gobain Glass Solar GmbH (1)
Julicher Str 495
D 52070 Aachen, Germany (99.81%)
Tel.: (49) 24196670
Telex: 832532 VGPAC
Fax: (49) 2419667354
E-Mail: dl_sgdg_kinona_achen@saint-gobain.com
Web Site: www.deutsche-glas.de
Emp.: 200
Glass Mfr
S.I.C.: 3211
N.A.I.C.S.: 327211

Saint-Gobain Glass Solution BURNIAT (1)
Industrielaan 129
1070 Brussels, Belgium
Tel.: (32) 25211071
Fax: (32) 25214959
E-Mail: sales.burniat@saint-gobain.com
Flat Glass Mfr
S.I.C.: 3211
N.A.I.C.S.: 327211

Saint-Gobain Glass Solution FRANKENGLAS NV (1)
Middenweg 11
3930 Hamont, Belgium
Tel.: (32) 11810820
Fax: (32) 2621778
E-Mail: Sales.frankenglas@saint-gobain.com
Web Site: www.belgique.sggs.com
Emp.: 50
Flat Glass Mfr
S.I.C.: 3211
N.A.I.C.S.: 327211
Rony Gielen *(Mgr-Sls)*

Saint-Gobain Glass Solution Glorious NV (1)
Kortrijksestraat 174
8520 Kuurne, Belgium
Tel.: (32) 56 365 365
Fax: (32) 56365 400
E-Mail: info.glorieux@saint-gobain.com
Web Site: www.glorieux.be
Emp.: 100
Flat Glass Mfr
S.I.C.: 3211
N.A.I.C.S.: 327211
Luc Barbier *(Gen Mgr)*

Saint-Gobain Glass Solution MIROVER NV (1)
Wervikstraat 225
8930 Menen, Belgium
Tel.: (32) 56521080
Fax: (32) 56521082
E-Mail: info.mirover@saint-gobain.com
Flat Glass Mfr
S.I.C.: 3211
N.A.I.C.S.: 327211

Saint-Gobain Glass Solution Sas Glas (1)
Westkade 20
4551 BV Sas-van-Gent, Netherlands
Tel.: (31) 115 458000
Fax: (31) 115 453754
E-Mail: marketing.sasglas@saint-gobain.com
Web Site: www.sasglas.nl
Emp.: 99
Glass Product Mfr
S.I.C.: 3231
N.A.I.C.S.: 327215
Kees Douma *(Mgr-Ops)*

Saint-Gobain Glass Solution WAGENER-JOWACO EUPEN (1)
rue de Herbesthal 303
4700 Eupen, Belgium
Tel.: (32) 87321111
Fax: (32) 87881461
E-Mail: sales.wagener@saint-gobain.com
Emp.: 17
Flat Glass Mfr
S.I.C.: 3211
N.A.I.C.S.: 327211
Sven Bertels *(CEO)*

SAINT-GOBAIN GLASS SOLUTIONS CZ, s.r.o. (1)
Sklenarska 7
Horni Herspice, 619 00 Brno, Czech Republic
Tel.: (420) 543 426 111
Fax: (420) 543 426 110
E-Mail: obchod@sggscz.com
Web Site: www.sggscz.com
Insulating Glass Mfr
S.I.C.: 3231
N.A.I.C.S.: 327215

Saint-Gobain Glass UK Ltd (1)
Weeland Road Eggborough
Goole, East Yorkshire, DN14 0FD, United Kingdom
Tel.: (44) 1977 666100
Fax: (44) 1977 666200
E-Mail: glassinfo.uk@saint-gobain-glass.com
Web Site: uk.saint-gobain-glass.com
Emp.: 200
Glass Product Mfr
S.I.C.: 3231
N.A.I.C.S.: 327215
Steve Severs *(Mng Dir)*

SAINT-GOBAIN GLASSOLUTIONS NITRASKLO, s.r.o. (1)
Levicka 3
950 15 Nitra, Slovakia
Tel.: (421) 37655 66 21
Fax: (421) 37655 54 82
E-Mail: info@nitrasklo.sk
Web Site: www.nitrasklo.sk/index.php?page=kontakty_interier
Flat Glass Mfr
S.I.C.: 3211
N.A.I.C.S.: 327211

SAINT-GOBAIN GRADBENI IZDELKI d.o.o. (1)
Ljubljanska cesta 68
1290 Grosuplje, Slovenia
Tel.: (386) 17818010
Fax: (386) 17818012
Adhesive & Ceramic Product Mfr
S.I.C.: 2891
N.A.I.C.S.: 325520

SAINT-GOBAIN GRADEVINSKI PROIZVODI HRVATSKA D.O.O. (1)
Hondlova 2/9 1 kat
Zagreb, 10 000, Croatia
Tel.: (385) 1 3010 202
Fax: (385) 1 3096 725
E-Mail: isover@isover.hr
Web Site: www.isover.hr
Emp.: 527
Adhesive Product Distr
S.I.C.: 5169
N.A.I.C.S.: 424690
Mirsad Begovic *(Gen Mgr)*

Saint-Gobain Gussrohr GmbH & Co. KG (1)
Saarbrucker Strasse 51
66130 Saarbrucken, Germany (100%)
Tel.: (49) 68187011
Fax: (49) 6818701603
E-Mail: tamara.bikelmamm@saint-gobain.com
Web Site: www.saint-gobain-gussrohr.de
Emp.: 400
Mfr. of Cast Iron Pipe, Joints, Machine & Rough Castings for Transportation Vehicles
S.I.C.: 3322
N.A.I.C.S.: 331511
Laurent Huwdlonjeau *(Mng Dir)*
Cal Ceran *(Mng Dir)*

SAINT-GOBAIN GUSSROHRVERTIEB OSTERREICH GMBH (1)
Archenweg 52
6020 Innsbruck, Austria
Tel.: (43) 5123417170
Fax: (43) 51234171720
E-Mail: office@saint-gobain-gussrohrvertrieb.at
Web Site: www.saint-gobain.de/deutschland/en/produkte/gesellschaft.html?ks_remote_id=2&kt_remote_id=171&pe_id=123
Steel Pipe Mfr
S.I.C.: 3317
N.A.I.C.S.: 331210

Saint-Gobain Gyproc India Ltd (1)
5th Level Leela Business Park Andheri Kurla Road
Andheri East, Mumbai, 400 059, India
Tel.: (91) 22 40212121
Fax: (91) 22 40212392
E-Mail: gyprocindia@saint-gobain.com
Web Site: www.saint-gobaingyproc.in
Emp.: 90
Gypsum Product Mfr
S.I.C.: 3275
N.A.I.C.S.: 327420
Tushar Jambekar *(Mgr-Mktg Comm)*

Plant:

Saint-Gobain Gyproc India Ltd - Bengaluru Plant (2)
Plot No 10-17 KIADB Industrial area
Haraohalli V & P Kanakapura TQ
Ramanagaram, Bengaluru, Karnataka, 562 112, India
Tel.: (91) 8027563370
Gypsum Product Mfr
S.I.C.: 3275
N.A.I.C.S.: 327420

Saint-Gobain Gyproc Nederland BV (1)
Stuartweg 1B
4131 NH Vianen, Netherlands
Tel.: (31) 347325 100
Fax: (31) 347325 125
E-Mail: info@gyproc.nl
Web Site: www.gyproc.nl
Emp.: 80
Architectural Facade Mfr
S.I.C.: 3446
N.A.I.C.S.: 332323
Peter Janmaat *(Gen Dir)*

Saint-Gobain Gyproc South Africa (Pty) Ltd (1)
77 Ostend Road
Germiston, 1400, South Africa
Tel.: (27) 11 345 5300
Fax: (27) 86 027 2329
E-Mail: za-enquiries@saint-gobain.com
Web Site: www.gyproc.co.za
Building Material Mfr
S.I.C.: 3259
N.A.I.C.S.: 327120

Saint-Gobain Gypsum (Changzhou) Co., Ltd. (1)
No 25 Tongjiang North Road Chunjiang Town
Xinbei District, 213022 Changzhou, China
Tel.: (86) 51988020300
Fax: (86) 51988020405
Emp.: 100
Gypsum Product Mfr
S.I.C.: 3275
N.A.I.C.S.: 327420
Gavin Tian *(Plant Mgr)*

Saint-Gobain Gypsum China (Shanghai) (1)
No 968 Wangqiao Road
Pudong New Area, Shanghai, China
Tel.: (86) 2158385838
Gypsum Product Mfr
S.I.C.: 3275
N.A.I.C.S.: 327420

Saint-Gobain Gypsum Materials Shanghai (1)
Wang Kiu Rd 968 Jinqiao Development Zone
Pudong New Area, Shanghai, 201201, China
Tel.: (86) 21 58385838

Fax: (86) 21 58382601
Emp.: 200
Gypsum Product Mfr
S.I.C.: 3275
N.A.I.C.S.: 327420

SAINT GOBAIN GYPSUM OPERADORA SA DE CV (1)
Av Nicolas Bravo 5
62715 Cuautla, Morelos, Mexico
Tel.: (52) 444 824 08 88
Fax: (52) 444 824 06 88
Emp.: 100
Gypsum Product Mfr
S.I.C.: 3275
N.A.I.C.S.: 327420

Saint-Gobain Gypsum SA de CV (1)
Av Industria No 4950
San Luis Potosi, 78395, Mexico
Tel.: (52) 444824 0888
Fax: (52) 444824 0688
Gypsum Product Mfr
S.I.C.: 3275
N.A.I.C.S.: 327420

Saint-Gobain Hanglas Japan K.K. (1)
3-7 Kojimachi
Chiyoda-ku, Tokyo, 102-0083, Japan JP
Tel.: (81) 352750889
Fax: (81) 352750913
Web Site: www.saint-gobain.co.jp/html_en/company/sghj.html#1
Emp.: 12
Glass Product Mfr
S.I.C.: 3231
N.A.I.C.S.: 327215
Philippe Schwindenhammer *(Pres)*

Saint-Gobain Hornstein Glastextil GmbH (1)
Industriestr II/7
7053 Hornstein, Austria
Tel.: (43) 2689 2234
Fax: (43) 2689 2234 90
E-Mail: office@hgt.at
Web Site: www.saint-gobain.de/deutschland/en/produkte/suche-nach-gesellschaften.html?pe_id=123&firmaname=&firmaland_id=8
Emp.: 70
Fiber Glass Product Mfr
S.I.C.: 3231
N.A.I.C.S.: 327215
Milos Pavlis *(Mgr)*

Saint-Gobain HPM Polska sp zoo (1)
Ul Torunska 239/241
62-600 Kolo, Poland
Tel.: (48) 63 261 71 00
Fax: (48) 63 272 04 01
E-Mail: info.kolo@saint-gobain.com
Web Site: www.saint-gobain.abrasives.pl
Emp.: 2,000
Abrasive Product Mfr
S.I.C.: 3291
N.A.I.C.S.: 327910
Arkadiusz Sokulski *(Mgr-Logistics)*

SAINT-GOBAIN HPM RUS. OOO (1)
58 Friedrich Engels srt bulding 2
Moscow, 105082, Russia
Tel.: (7) 495 937 32 23
Fax: (7) 495937 32 24
E-Mail: sg@sgabrasives.ru
Web Site: www.sgabrasives.ru
Emp.: 30
Abrasive Product Mfr
S.I.C.: 3291
N.A.I.C.S.: 327910
German Kuznetsov *(Reg Mgr-Sls)*

SAINT-GOBAIN IDAPLAC, S.L. (1)
C/ Albert Einstein 25
08940 Cornella de Llobregat, Barcelona, Spain
Tel.: (34) 93 475 11 62
Fax: (34) 93 474 33 28
E-Mail: info@distriplacyanner.com
Web Site: www.distriplac.com
Emp.: 45
Insulation Roofing Material Distr
S.I.C.: 5033
N.A.I.C.S.: 423330
Isabell Pla Gonzalez *(Dir-HR)*

SAINT-GOBAIN INDUSTRIAL CERAMICS PTY LTD (1)
326 Settlement Road
Thomastown, Melbourne, VIC, 3074, Australia
Tel.: (61) 394630050
Fax: (61) 394656015
Web Site: www.hexoloy.com
Emp.: 10
Ceramic Product Mfr
S.I.C.: 3259
N.A.I.C.S.: 327120
Jordy Schellebeck *(Controller-Fin)*

Saint-Gobain Isover Cz S.R.O (1)
Pocernicka 272/96
108 03 Prague, Czech Republic
Tel.: (420) 296 411 735
Fax: (420) 296 411 736
E-Mail: info@saint-gobain.com
Web Site: www.isover.com
Emp.: 350
Insulating Glass Mfr
S.I.C.: 3211
N.A.I.C.S.: 327211
Roman Janata *(Gen Mgr)*

Saint-Gobain Isover Espana (1)
Edificio Ederra Centro Azca
PO Box 77
28046 Madrid, Spain (73.13%)
Tel.: (34) 913972000
Fax: (34) 913972626
Web Site: www.isover.net
Mfr. of Glass Products
S.I.C.: 3211
N.A.I.C.S.: 327211

Saint-Gobain Isover (Gu'an) Glass Wool Co., Ltd. (1)
NO 5 Yong Kang Road Guan Town
65500 Langfang, China
Tel.: (86) 316 616 3540
Fax: (86) 316 616 4935
Gypsum Product Mfr
S.I.C.: 3275
N.A.I.C.S.: 327420

SAINT-GOBAIN LIMITED (1)
Saint-Gobain House Binley Business Park
Coventry, CV3 2TT, United Kingdom
Tel.: (44) 2476 56 0700
Fax: (44) 2476 56 0705
E-Mail: info@saint-gobain.co.uk
Web Site: www.saint-gobain.co.uk
Construction Material Distr
S.I.C.: 5033
N.A.I.C.S.: 423330
Peter Hindle *(CEO)*

SAINT-GOBAIN MALAYSIA SDN BHD. (1)
No. 1 Jalan Sultan Mohamad 4 Kawasan
Perindustrian Bandar Suleiman
42000 Port Klang, Selangor, Malaysia
Tel.: (60) 33169 5588
Fax: (60) 33169 5688
E-Mail: solutions.malaysia@bpb.co
Web Site: www.bpbmalaysia.com
Gypsum Board Mfr
S.I.C.: 3275
N.A.I.C.S.: 327420
Edward Loy *(Mng Dir)*

Saint-Gobain Materiaux Ceramiques Benelux SA (1)
Route de Villers 19
Hody, 4162 Anthisnes, Belgium
Tel.: (32) 4 383 98 34
Fax: (32) 4 383 72 09
E-Mail: sabine.radoux@saint-gobain.com
Abrasive Product Mfr
S.I.C.: 3291
N.A.I.C.S.: 327910

Saint-Gobain Mexico S.A. de C.V. (1)
Nicolas Bravo No 5 Parque Industrial
Cuautla Villa de Ayala
Cuautla, Morelos, 62741, Mexico
Tel.: (52) 7353548100
Fax: (52) 7353548123
E-Mail: glassinfo.mx@saint-gobain-glass.com
Web Site: www.saint-gobain-glass.com.mx
Emp.: 400
Glass Product Mfr
S.I.C.: 3231
N.A.I.C.S.: 327215

Juan Jose Sevilla *(Gen Mgr)*

Saint-Gobain Mondego S.A. (1)
Apto 2030 Fontela
3081 901 Figueira da Foz, Portugal (75.76%)
Tel.: (351) 233403100
Fax: (351) 233403112
E-Mail: alvaro.ferreira@saint-gobain.com
Web Site: www.sgmondego.com
Emp.: 250
Mfr. of Glass Products
S.I.C.: 3211
N.A.I.C.S.: 327211
Paulo Pinto *(Gen Mgr)*

Saint-Gobain Nederland Beheer BV (1)
Huifakkerstraat 18
Breda, 4815 PN, Netherlands
Tel.: (31) 76 548 1500
Glass Product Mfr
S.I.C.: 3211
N.A.I.C.S.: 327211

Saint-Gobain NorPro GmbH (1)
Am Bahnhof
56414 Steinefrenz, Germany
Tel.: (49) 64359657 0
Fax: (49) 64359657 19
E-Mail: olaf.emmerich@saint-gobain.com
Web Site: www.norpro.saint-gobain.com
Plastic Product Mfr
S.I.C.: 3089
N.A.I.C.S.: 326199

Saint-Gobain Oberland AG (1)
Oberlandstrasse
PO Box 1160
88410 Bad Wurzach, Germany (96.67%)
Tel.: (49) 7564180
Fax: (49) 756418600
E-Mail: info.oberland@saint-gobain.com
Web Site: www.saint-gobain-oberland.de
Emp.: 500
Mfr. of Glass Products
S.I.C.: 3221
N.A.I.C.S.: 327213
S. Jaenecke *(CEO & Mng Dir)*

Subsidiary:

GPS Glas Produktions Service GmbH (2)
Ruhrglasstrasse 50
45329 Essen, Germany
Tel.: (49) 201 36 00 771
Fax: (49) 201 36 00 737
E-Mail: info@gps-essen.de
Web Site: www.gps-essen.de
Emp.: 80
Glass Making Machinery Mfr
S.I.C.: 3559
N.A.I.C.S.: 333249
Mirko Muller *(Mng Dir)*

Saint-Gobain Orsil s.r.o. (1)
Cermakova # 7 Block 2
CZ 120 00 Prague, Czech Republic (100%)
Tel.: (420) 221429600
Fax: (420) 221429663
E-Mail: info@isover.cz
Web Site: www.isover.cz
Emp.: 30
Insulation Products Mfr.
S.I.C.: 3296
N.A.I.C.S.: 327993

Saint-Gobain PAM Cz S.R.O (1)
Tovarni 388
267 01 Kraluv Dvur, Czech Republic
Tel.: (420) 311 712 611
Fax: (420) 311 712 622
E-Mail: trubni.systemy@saint-gobain.com
Web Site: www.saint-gobain-pam.cz
Cast Iron Product Mfr
S.I.C.: 3317
N.A.I.C.S.: 331210

Saint-Gobain PAM Deutschland GmbH (1)
Saarbrucker Strasse 51
66130 Saarbrucken, Germany
Tel.: (49) 68187010
Fax: (49) 681874302
E-Mail: info@pam-d.saint-gobain.com
Web Site: www.pamline.de
Iron Pipe Distr
S.I.C.: 5051
N.A.I.C.S.: 423510
Burkhard Schmolck *(Gen Mgr)*

Subsidiary:

Saint-Gobain HES Gmbh (2)
Saarbrucker Str 51
66130 Saarbrucken, Germany
Tel.: (49) 220397840
Fax: (49) 22039784200
E-Mail: info@hes.saint-gobain.com
Web Site: www.saint-gobain-hes.de
Iron Pipe Distr
S.I.C.: 5051
N.A.I.C.S.: 423510

Saint-Gobain PAM Italia SpA (1)
Via Romagnoli 6
20146 Milan, Italy
Tel.: (39) 02 42 43 281
E-Mail: advpamitalia@saint-gobain.com
Web Site: www.pamline.it
Iron Pipe Mfr
S.I.C.: 3317
N.A.I.C.S.: 331210

Saint-Gobain PAM Portugal SA (1)
Est Nac 10 - Lugar de D Pedro - Apartado 1708
2691-901 Santa Iria de Azoia, Portugal
Tel.: (351) 218 925 000
Fax: (351) 218 925 009
E-Mail: sgpamportugal@saint-gobain.com
Web Site: www.saint-gobain-pam.pt
Emp.: 15
Steel Pipe Mfr
S.I.C.: 3317
N.A.I.C.S.: 331210
Sandra Sa *(Dir-Fin)*

Saint-Gobain PAM UK (1)
Sinclair Works Station Rd Ketley
Telford, Shropshire, TF1 5AD, United Kingdom (99%)
Tel.: (44) 1952262500
Fax: (44) 1952262555
Web Site: www.saint-gobain-pam.co.uk
Sales Range: $150-199.9 Million
Emp.: 140
Pipe Mfr
S.I.C.: 3498
N.A.I.C.S.: 332996
Andy Burnhan *(Dir-Site)*

Saint-Gobain PAM UK (1)
Lows Lane
Stanton-by-Dale, Ilkeston, Derbyshire, DE7 4QU, United Kingdom (100%)
Tel.: (44) 1159305000
Telex: 37671
Fax: (44) 1159329513
Web Site: www.saint-gobain-pam.co.uk/
Emp.: 1,400
Mfr Ductile Iron Pipes for Water Supply Systems & Sewerage
S.I.C.: 3322
N.A.I.C.S.: 331511
Paul Minchin *(Mng Dir)*

Saint-Gobain PAM UK (1)
Holwell Works Asfordby Hill
Melton Mowbray, Leicestershire, LE14 3RE, United Kingdom (100%)
Tel.: (44) 1664812812
Fax: (44) 1664812060
Web Site: www.saint-gobain-pam.co.uk/
Sls.: $212,544,752
Emp.: 800
Flat Glass Mfr
S.I.C.: 3211
N.A.I.C.S.: 327211
Paul Minchin *(Mng Dir)*

SAINT-GOBAIN PARTICIPACOES LTDA (1)
Av Santa Marina 482 - 4 andar
Agua Branca, Sao Paulo, 05036-903, Brazil
Tel.: (55) 11 22467600
Fax: (55) 11 22461598
Glass Product Mfr
S.I.C.: 3231
N.A.I.C.S.: 327215

Saint-Gobain Performance Plastics Corby Ltd. (1)
13 Earlstrees Rod
Corby, NN17 4NP, United Kingdom
Tel.: (44) 15 3627 6000
Fax: (44) 15 3620 3427
Emp.: 18
Adhesive Mfr & Distr
S.I.C.: 2891

Compagnie de Saint-Gobain SA—(Continued)

N.A.I.C.S.: 325520
Ian Beresford *(Product Mgr)*

Saint-Gobain Performance Plastics Espana S.A. (1)
Poligono El Sequero 45-46
26509 Agoncillo, La Rioja, Spain
Tel.: (34) 94 14 86 035
Fax: (34) 94 14 37 095
Emp.: 41
Plastic Product Mfr
S.I.C.: 3089
N.A.I.C.S.: 326199
Ribera Aldama *(Controller)*

Saint-Gobain Performance Plastics Kontich NV (1)
Heiveldekens 22
2550 Kontich, Belgium
Tel.: (32) 34 58 28 28
Fax: (32) 34 58 26 69
E-Mail: infoproduct.kontich@saint-gobain.com
Polymer Component Mfr
S.I.C.: 2822
N.A.I.C.S.: 325212

Saint-Gobain Performance Plastics Rencol Limited (1)
Unit 16 Concorde Road Patchway
Bristol, BS34 5TB, United Kingdom
Tel.: (44) 117 9381 700
Fax: (44) 117 9157 982
E-Mail: enquiries@rencol.co.uk
Web Site: www.rencol.co.uk
Precision Spring Component Mfr & Distr
S.I.C.: 3495
N.A.I.C.S.: 332613

Saint-Gobain Performance Plastics Sipro GmbH (1)
Zabernerstrasse 25
65203 Wiesbaden, Germany
Tel.: (49) 611 928 130
Fax: (49) 611 928 13 33
E-Mail: info.sipro@saint-gobain.com
Web Site: www.sipro.de
Emp.: 15
Plastic Product Mfr
S.I.C.: 3089
N.A.I.C.S.: 326199

SAINT GOBAIN PERU SA (1)
Av los Faisanes Nro 157 La Campina
Chorrillos, Lima, Peru
Tel.: (51) 12524034
Fax: (51) 12524035
E-Mail: sgobain@saint-gobain.com.pe
Web Site: www.saint-gobain.com.pe
Flat Glass Mfr
S.I.C.: 3211
N.A.I.C.S.: 327211
Hugo Blanco Frias *(Gen Dir)*

Saint-Gobain Pipe Systems Belgium SA/NV (1)
Raatshovenstraat 2
3400 Landen, Belgium
Tel.: (32) 11 88 01 00
Fax: (32) 11 88 63 01
E-Mail: sgps-be@saint-gobain.com
Web Site: www.sgps.be
Emp.: 25
Iron Pipe Mfr
S.I.C.: 3317
N.A.I.C.S.: 331210
Jean-Pierre Robert *(Controller-Fin)*

SAINT-GOBAIN PIPE SYSTEMS BV (1)
Markerkant 10-17
1316 AB Almere, Netherlands
Tel.: (31) 365333344
Fax: (31) 365335096
E-Mail: sgps.nl@saint-gobain.com
Web Site: www.sgps.nl
Emp.: 20
Iron Pipe Mfr
S.I.C.: 3317
N.A.I.C.S.: 331210
Anne-Michaelle Leroy *(Mgr-Mktg)*

Saint-Gobain Pipe Systems Oy (1)
Merstolantie 16
29200 Harjavalta, Finland
Tel.: (358) 207 424600
Fax: (358) 207 424601
E-Mail: sgps.finland@saint-gobain.com
Web Site: www.sgps.fi
Steel Pipe Mfr
S.I.C.: 3317
N.A.I.C.S.: 331210

Saint-Gobain Pipeline Hong Kong Ltd. (1)
15/F Hermes Commercial Centre 4-4A
Hillwood Road
Kowloon, China (Hong Kong)
Tel.: (852) 2735 7825
Fax: (852) 2735 7881
E-Mail: pipelines-HK@saint-gobain.com
Web Site: www.saint-gobain.com.cn/html/companypages/Pipeline_HK.htm
Iron Pipe Mfr
S.I.C.: 3317
N.A.I.C.S.: 331210
Eddy Yeung *(Mgr-Tech)*

Saint-Gobain Pipelines Co. Ltd. (1)
Huangong Road Cihu
Ma'anshan, Anhui, China 243052
Tel.: (86) 5553508041
Fax: (86) 5553506702
Web Site: www.saint-gobain.com.cn/html/companypages/Pipeline_com.htm
Sls.: $199,529,890
Emp.: 954
Steel Pipe Mfr
S.I.C.: 3317
N.A.I.C.S.: 331210

Saint-Gobain Pipelines South Africa (Pty) Limited (1)
200 Watt Road Pretoria West
PO Box 631
Pretoria, 0001, South Africa
Tel.: (27) 12 380 4600
Fax: (27) 12 386 5489
E-Mail: industrial@saint-gobain-pipelines.co.za
Web Site: www.saint-gobain-pipelines.co.za
Emp.: 580
Iron Pipe Mfr
S.I.C.: 3317
N.A.I.C.S.: 331210
Paul Martin *(Mgr-Mktg)*

SAINT-GOBAIN POLSKA SP. Z O.O. (1)
Al Jerozolimskie 204
02-486 Warsaw, Poland
Tel.: (48) 22 578 85 40
Fax: (48) 22 578 85 42
Web Site: www.sgdb.pl
Emp.: 30
Glass Product Mfr
S.I.C.: 3231
N.A.I.C.S.: 327215
Marcin Nowara *(Dir-Fin & Admin)*

Saint-Gobain PPC Italia SpA (1)
Via E Romagnoli 6
20146 Milan, Italy
Tel.: (39) 02 611151
Fax: (39) 02 611192400
E-Mail: gyproc.italia@saint-gobain.com
Web Site: www.gyproc.it
Gypsum Product Mfr
S.I.C.: 3275
N.A.I.C.S.: 327420

Saint-Gobain PPL Korea Co Ltd. (1)
13f Dongsin Bldg 141-28 Samseung1-dong
Gangnam-gu, Seoul, 135-090, Korea (South)
Tel.: (82) 2 3706 9334
Fax: (82) 2 554 1550
Web Site: www.sgppl.co.kr
Emp.: 30
Chemical Product Mfr
S.I.C.: 2899
N.A.I.C.S.: 325998
K. S. Chang *(Gen Mgr)*

Saint-Gobain Proppants (Guanghan) Co., Ltd. (1)
Anle Village Nan Xing Town
Guanghan, 618305, China
Tel.: (86) 83 8550 3612
Fax: (86) 83 8550 3600
Glass Product Mfr
S.I.C.: 3211
N.A.I.C.S.: 327211

Saint-Gobain Quartz (Jinzhou) Company Ltd. (1)
N 94A Jiefang West Road
Jinzhou, Liaoning, 121003, China
Tel.: (86) 4165172901
E-Mail: quartz.sales.cn@saint-gobain.com
Web Site: www.quartz.saint-gobain.com
Construction Material Distr
S.I.C.: 5039
N.A.I.C.S.: 423390

Saint-Gobain Rigips Alci Sanayi ve Ticaret Anonim A.S (1)
Ilkbahar Mahallesi 606 Sokak No 8
Cankaya, 06550 Ankara, Turkey
Tel.: (90) 312 463 63 63
Fax: (90) 312 463 63 64
E-Mail: info@rigips.com.tr
Web Site: www.rigips.com.tr
Gypsum Product Mfr
S.I.C.: 3275
N.A.I.C.S.: 327420
Ediz Koklu *(Mgr-Ops)*

Saint Gobain SA (1)
Paseo de La Castellana N 77
Edificio Ederra Planta 10, 28046 Madrid, Spain (100%)
Tel.: (34) 913972669
Fax: (34) 913972679
E-Mail: teresa.cinea@saint-gobain.com
Web Site: www.saintgobainglass.com
Emp.: 30
Mfr. of Cast Iron Pipes & Fittings
S.I.C.: 3322
N.A.I.C.S.: 331511
Francisco Ramirez *(Mng Dir)*

Saint-Gobain Schleifmittel GmbH (1)
Birkenstrasse 45-49
50389 Wesseling, Germany
Tel.: (49) 2236 89960
Fax: (49) 2236 899610
Abrasive Product Mfr
S.I.C.: 3291
N.A.I.C.S.: 327910
Michael Meding *(Gen Mgr)*

SAINT-GOBAIN SERVICES AUSTRIA GMBH (1)
Unterkainisch 24
8990 Bad Aussee, Austria
Tel.: (43) 3622 505 0
Fax: (43) 3622 505 430
Flat Glass Mfr
S.I.C.: 3211
N.A.I.C.S.: 327211

SAINT-GOBAIN SOLAR GARD AUSTRALIA PTY LTD. (1)
1/6 Stanton Rd
Seven Hills, NSW, 2147, Australia
Tel.: (61) 2 9838 8888
Fax: (61) 2 9838 8088
E-Mail: info.aus@solargard.com
Web Site: www.solargard.com.au
Safety Window Film Mfr & Distr
S.I.C.: 3081
N.A.I.C.S.: 326113
Luc Goemaere *(Head-Strategic Acct)*

SAINT-GOBAIN SOLAR GARD NV (1)
Karreweg 18
9870 Zulte, Belgium
Tel.: (32) 9240 95 69
Fax: (32) 9240 95 90
E-Mail: benelux.info@solargard.com
Web Site: www.solargard.be
Emp.: 25
Safety Window Film Mfr & Distr
S.I.C.: 3081
N.A.I.C.S.: 326113
Peter Staelens *(Reg Mgr)*

SAINT-GOBAIN SOLAR GARD UK, LTD (1)
Unit 13 Ball Mill Top Business Park
Grimley, Worcester, Worcestershire, WR2 6LS, United Kingdom
Tel.: (44) 1905 640400
Fax: (44) 1905 640500
E-Mail: solargarduk@saint-gobain.com
Web Site: www.solargard.co.uk
Safety Window Film Mfr & Distr
S.I.C.: 3081
N.A.I.C.S.: 326113
Ian Penfold *(Mgr-Sls)*

Saint-Gobain Solar S.r.l. (1)
Via Ettore Romagnoli n 6
20146 Milan, Italy
Tel.: (39) 02 4243798
Fax: (39) 02 42 43 424
Web Site: www.saint-gobain-solar.com
Photovoltaic Product Mfr
S.I.C.: 3674
N.A.I.C.S.: 334413

Saint-Gobain Solar Systems SA (1)
Ecostart 2 rue du Commerce
3895 Foetz, Luxembourg
Tel.: (352) 80 70 96 20
Fax: (352) 26 80 32 34
Emp.: 40
Photovoltaic Product Mfr
S.I.C.: 3674
N.A.I.C.S.: 334413
Jean-Clement Nugue *(Gen Mgr)*

Saint-Gobain South Africa Pty. Ltd. (1)
PO Box 30
Springs, 1560, South Africa ZA
Tel.: (27) 113608200
Fax: (27) 00118134414
E-Mail: info@isoder.co.za
Web Site: www.isoder.co.za
Emp.: 300
Mfr., Sales & Marketing of Composites, Raw Materials, & Insulation Products for Industrial & Building Applications.
S.I.C.: 3296
N.A.I.C.S.: 327993
Johan G. Oosthuizen *(Gen Mgr-Building Insulation)*

Saint-Gobain TM K.K. (1)
3-7 Kojimachi
Chiyoda-ku, Tokyo, 102-0083, Japan
Tel.: (81) 332631430
Fax: (81) 332631285
E-Mail: SGTM.Info@saint-gobain.com
Web Site: www.saint-gobain-tm.com
Emp.: 12
Ceramic Material Mfr
S.I.C.: 3255
N.A.I.C.S.: 327120
Kozaki Chiba *(Plant Mgr)*

Saint-Gobain Transformados S.A. (1)
C/ Los Corrales Parcelas C5 y C6 Poligono Industrial La Ballestera
Alovera, Spain ES
Tel.: (34) 949 20 98 93
Fax: (34) 949 20 98 95
E-Mail: info@achpaneles.com
Web Site: www.sgtransformados.com
Steel Structure Installation Services
S.I.C.: 1629
N.A.I.C.S.: 237990

Saint-Gobain Vetrerie SPA (1)
Via Del Lavoro 1
Lonigo, SV, 36045, Italy (92.51%)
Tel.: (39) 0444725700
Fax: (39) 0444830736
Web Site: www.verallia.it
Emp.: 1,126
Mfr. of Jars & Water Bottles
S.I.C.: 3221
N.A.I.C.S.: 327213

Saint-Gobain Vetrotex Deutschland GmbH (1)
Viktoriaallee 3 - 5
D-52066 Aachen, Germany (100%)
Tel.: (49) 2415160
Fax: (49) 2415162913
Web Site: www.vetrotextextiles.com
Emp.: 250
Mfr. of Textiles & Yarns
S.I.C.: 2299
N.A.I.C.S.: 313210

Saint-Gobain Vetrotex (Thailand) Ltd. (1)
79 24 Moo 2 Srinakharin Rd
Nongbon, Bangkok, 10260, Thailand (100%)
Tel.: (66) 236602408
Fax: (66) 236604245
Web Site: www.saint-gobain-vetrotex.co.th/
Emp.: 100
Mfr. of Glass-Fiber-Reinforced Precast Concrete
S.I.C.: 3211
N.A.I.C.S.: 327211

Saint-Gobain Vicasa SA (1)
Paseo de la Castellana 77
28046 Madrid, Spain (73.06%)

Tel.: (34) 913972336
Fax: (34) 91 3972179
E-Mail: laura.roldan@saint-gobain.com
Web Site: www.vicasa.es
Emp.: 100
Mfr of Glass & Bottle Products
S.I.C.: 3211
N.A.I.C.S.: 327211
Laura Roldan Pinedo *(Mgr-Export Sls)*

Subsidiary:

Saint-Gobain Montblanc SA (2)
Nacional 240 Km 38 900
43400 Montblanc, Spain
Tel.: (34) 977 86 17 00
Fax: (34) 977 86 17 41
Glass Product Mfr
S.I.C.: 3231
N.A.I.C.S.: 327215

Saint-Gobain Vidros S.A. (1)
Avenida Santa Marina 482 2nd Fl
05036 903 Sao Paulo, SP, Brazil (100%)
Tel.: (55) 1138747988
Fax: (55) 1136111680
Web Site: www.saint-gobain-vidros.com.br
Emp.: 2,000
Mfr. of Baking & Glass Products
S.I.C.: 3211
N.A.I.C.S.: 327211

Saint-Gobain Wanner SA (1)
Resina 16
Villaverde, 28021 Madrid, Spain (73.13%)
Tel.: (34) 917233410
Fax: (34) 915453012
E-Mail: wanneryvinyas@saint-gobain.com
Emp.: 200
Mfr. of Industrial & Insulation Products
S.I.C.: 3296
N.A.I.C.S.: 327993

Sanitas Troesch AG (1)
Hardturmstrasse 101
8031 Zurich, Switzerland
Tel.: (41) 44 446 10 10
Fax: (41) 44 446 11 50
E-Mail: zuerich@sanitastroesch.ch
Web Site: www.sanitastroesch.ch
Emp.: 120
Sanitaryware Mfr
S.I.C.: 3499
N.A.I.C.S.: 332999
Michael Schumacher *(CEO)*

Scandi-Glass A/S (1)
Ashaugveien 62
N 3107 Sem, Norway (99.64%)
Tel.: (47) 33300400
Fax: (47) 33300420
Web Site: www.scandi-glass.no
Emp.: 32
Mfr. of Glass Products
S.I.C.: 3211
N.A.I.C.S.: 327211

Scanpac AB (1)
Kemivagen 7
Glanshammar, 705 97 Orebro, Sweden
Tel.: (46) 19463400
Fax: (46) 19465731
E-Mail: info@dalapro.se
Web Site: www.dalapro.se
Concrete Ready Mix Mfr
S.I.C.: 3273
N.A.I.C.S.: 327320

Schafer GmbH (1)
Alfred-Weckesser-Strasse 6
76669 Bad Schonborn, Germany
Tel.: (49) 7253 94210
Fax: (49) 7253 9421 94
Roofing Product Distr
S.I.C.: 5033
N.A.I.C.S.: 423330

Sekurit Saint-Gobain Deutschland GmbH & Co. KG (1)
Viktoria Allee 3-5
D 52066 Aachen, Germany (100%)
Tel.: (49) 02419470
Fax: (49) 0415462166
E-Mail: info@saint-gobain-glass.com
Web Site: www.saint-gobain-glass.com
Rev.: $239,403,120
Emp.: 250
Mfr. of Glass Products
S.I.C.: 3211
N.A.I.C.S.: 327211
Gertrude Goeggert *(Sec & Gen Mgr)*

Sekurit Saint-Gobain Italia S.R.L. (1)
Via Saluzzo 95
I 12038 Savigliano, Cuneo, Italy (99.15%)
Tel.: (39) 172727111
Fax: (39) 172727120
Web Site: www.saintgobain.com
Mfr. of Glass Products
S.I.C.: 3211
N.A.I.C.S.: 327211

Subsidiaries:

S.G. Autover Italia S.R.L. (2)
Via Ettore Romagnoli 6
20146 Milan, Italy
Tel.: (39) 02 900 788 1
Fax: (39) 02 900 788 30
Web Site: www.autover.it/it_IT/conte nt/206/0/226/Contatti.html
Flat Glass Mfr
S.I.C.: 3211
N.A.I.C.S.: 327211

Sicurglass Sud SRL (2)
Via Riosecco localita Canfora
Fisciano, Salerno, 84084, Italy
Tel.: (39) 0898 283411
Fax: (39) 089 825588
Glass Product Mfr
S.I.C.: 3231
N.A.I.C.S.: 327215

Sekurit Saint-Gobain Scandinavia AB (1)
Bruksgatan 18
PO Box 84
S 241 22 Eslov, Gusdh, Sweden (99%)
Tel.: (46) 41366800
Fax: (46) 41316415
E-Mail: maria.nordberg@saint-gobain.com
Web Site: www.saint-gobain-sekurit.com
Emp.: 45
Mfr. & Sale of Glass Products
S.I.C.: 3211
N.A.I.C.S.: 327211
Helena Eklov-Siggeoin *(Gen Mgr)*

Sekurit Saint-Gobain Torgau GmbH (1)
Solarstr 5
D 04860 Torgau, Torgua, Germany (99.77%)
Tel.: (49) 34217530
Fax: (49) 3421751827
Web Site: www.saint-gobain-saturet.com
Rev.: $175,424,700
Emp.: 100
Mfr. of Glass Products
S.I.C.: 3211
N.A.I.C.S.: 327211
Juergen Koeppe *(Plant Mgr)*

SEPR India Limited (1)
Kanjikode West
PB No 1
678 623 Palakkad, Kerala, India
Tel.: (91) 4913080333
Fax: (91) 4913080354
E-Mail: mktg.seprindia@saint-gobain.com
Web Site: www.saint-gobain.co.in/SEPR%20Refactories%20India.html
Emp.: 500
Refractory Material Mfr
S.I.C.: 3259
N.A.I.C.S.: 327120
V. Venkatesh *(Head-Mfg)*

SEPR Keramik GmbH & CO KG (1)
Concordiaplatz 3
51143 Cologne, Germany
Tel.: (49) 2203 956 479
Fax: (49) 2203 956 430
Web Site: www.saint-gobain.de/benelux/en/produkte/suche.html?p_action=h_show&h_pcon_s_pe_id=20&pe_id=123
Emp.: 4
Refractory Material Distr
S.I.C.: 5085
N.A.I.C.S.: 423840
Axel Hesse *(Mgr)*

Subsidiaries:

Saint-Gobain Ceramic Materials GmbH (2)
Concordiaplatz 3
51143 Cologne, Germany
Tel.: (49) 2203 956 401
Fax: (49) 2203 956 421
Web Site: www.sic.saint-gobain.com
Silicon Carbide Powder Mfr
S.I.C.: 2819
N.A.I.C.S.: 325180

Saint-Gobain IndustrieKeramik Roedental GmbH (2)
Postfach 1144
96466 Rodental, Germany
Tel.: (49) 9563 724 0
Fax: (49) 9563 724 206
E-Mail: info@sgik.saint-gobain.de
Web Site: www.saint-gobain.de/deutschland/en/produkte/gesellschaft.html?ks_remote_id=2&kt_remote_id=27&pe_id=123
Refractory Product Mfr & Distr
S.I.C.: 3255
N.A.I.C.S.: 327120

Saint-Gobain Performance Plastics Isofluor GmbH (2)
Borsigstrasse 13 - 15
41469 Neuss, Germany
Tel.: (49) 2137917 890
Fax: (49) 2137 12 667
E-Mail: Service@Isofluor.de
Web Site: www.isofluor.de
Plastic Tubing Mfr
S.I.C.: 3089
N.A.I.C.S.: 326199
Thomas Rong *(Mng Dir)*

Subsidiary:

Saint-Gobain Performance Plastics MG Silikon GmbH (3)
Robert-Bosch-Str 17
88131 Lindau, Germany
Tel.: (49) 8382 70560
Fax: (49) 8382 75123
E-Mail: info.mgsilikon@saint-gobain.com
Web Site: www.process.saint-gobain.eu
Plastic Product Mfr
S.I.C.: 3089
N.A.I.C.S.: 326199

SEPR Refractories India Ltd (1)
Kanjikode West
PB No 1
Palakkad, Kerala, 678623, India
Tel.: (91) 3080333
Fax: (91) 3080347
Web Site: www.saint-gobain.co.in
Glass Product Mfr
S.I.C.: 3231
N.A.I.C.S.: 327215

Division:

Saint-Gobain Weber (India) Ltd (2)
Level 5 Leela Business Park Andheri-Kurla Road
Andheri East, Mumbai, 400059, India
Tel.: (91) 2240212121
E-Mail: weber-india@saint-gobain.com
Web Site: www.weber.co.in
Adhesive Product Mfr
S.I.C.: 2891
N.A.I.C.S.: 325520

SGGS Belgium SA (1)
Boulevard Industriel 129
1070 Brussels, Belgium
Tel.: (32) 2 556 37 10
Fax: (32) 2 556 37 29
E-Mail: glassinfo@glassolutions.be
Web Site: www.glassolutions.be
Emp.: 53
Flat Glass Mfr
S.I.C.: 3211
N.A.I.C.S.: 327211
Annie Coppins *(Gen Mgr)*

SGGS GLASINDUSTRIE BOERMANS (1)
Schampbergstraat 34
3511 Hasselt, Belgium
Tel.: (32) 11858585
Fax: (32) 11858586
E-Mail: info.boermans@saint-gobain.com
Emp.: 100
Flat Glass Mfr
S.I.C.: 3211
N.A.I.C.S.: 327211
Luc Barbier *(Mng Dir)*

SHANGHAI SEPR ZIRCONIUM PRODUCTS CO., LTD (1)
1441 Beidi Road
Minghang, Shanghai, 201106, China
Tel.: (86) 21 5218 9065
Fax: (86) 21 5218 6391
E-Mail: SEPR_SH@saint-gobain.com
Zirconia Powder & Zirconium Chemical Mfr
S.I.C.: 2899
N.A.I.C.S.: 325998
JingMei Liao *(Mgr-Sls)*

Solaglas Ltd. (1)
Binley 1 Herald Way
Coventry, West Midland, CV3 2ZJ, United Kingdom (99.85%)
Tel.: (44) 2476547400
Fax: (44) 2476457799
E-Mail: enquiries@solaglas.co.uk
Web Site: www.saint-gobain-glass.com
Rev.: $119,792,000
Emp.: 200
Mfr. of Glass Products
S.I.C.: 3211
N.A.I.C.S.: 327211
Simon Carin *(Mng Dir)*

SOLAR GARD NORDIC AB (1)
Stockholmsvagen 21
Rimbo, 762 21 Norrtalje, Sweden
Tel.: (46) 175748 80
Fax: (46) 175748 89
E-Mail: nordicinfo@saint-gobain.com
Web Site: www.solargard.se
Safety Window Film Mfr & Distr
S.I.C.: 3081
N.A.I.C.S.: 326113
Niklas Falck *(Mgr-Market)*

Van Keulen BV (1)
TT Vasumweg 151
1033 SG Amsterdam, Netherlands
Tel.: (31) 20 4604300
Fax: (31) 20 6930718
E-Mail: info@van-keulen.nl
Web Site: www.van-keulen.nl
Emp.: 60
Building Material Distr
S.I.C.: 5033
N.A.I.C.S.: 423330
Jan Visser *(Mgr-Pur)*

Vemac S.R.L (1)
Via Prati 67
65124 Pescara, Italy
Tel.: (39) 08541691
Fax: (39) 0854169210
E-Mail: infovemac@saint-gobain.com
Web Site: www.vemac.it
Emp.: 107
Building Material Distr
S.I.C.: 5032
N.A.I.C.S.: 423320
Carlo Giansante *(Gen Mgr)*

VETROTECH SAINT-GOBAIN BENELUX NV (1)
Hulsenweg 21
6031 SP Nederweert, Netherlands
Tel.: (31) 495 57 44 35
Fax: (31) 49557 44 36
E-Mail: vetrotech.benelux@saintgobain.com
Web Site: www.vetrotech.com
Emp.: 20
Fire Resistant Glass Product Mfr
S.I.C.: 3231
N.A.I.C.S.: 327215
Arnold Sirag *(Gen Mgr)*

Vetrotech Saint-Gobain Central & Eastern Europe AG (1)
Siegfried-Marcus-Strasse 1
4400 Steyr, Austria
Tel.: (43) 7252 90 90 90
Fax: (43) 7252 90 90 99
Web Site: www.vetrotech.com
Fire Resistant Glass Product Mfr
S.I.C.: 3231
N.A.I.C.S.: 327215

Vetrotech Saint-Gobain International AG (1)
Bernstrasse 43
3175 Flamatt, Switzerland
Tel.: (41) 31 336 81 81
Fax: (41) 31 336 81 89
Web Site: www.vetrotech.com
Emp.: 80
Fire Resistant Glass Product Mfr
S.I.C.: 3231
N.A.I.C.S.: 327215

VETROTECH Saint-Gobain Poland Sp. z o.o. (1)
ul Pilsudskiego 18
46-100 Namyslow, Poland

Compagnie de Saint-Gobain SA—(Continued)

Tel.: (48) 77 410 5420
Fax: (48) 77 410 5321
Web Site: www.vetrotech.com
Emp.: 6
Fire Resistant Glass Distr
S.I.C.: 5039
N.A.I.C.S.: 423390
Grzegorz Soltys *(Gen Mgr)*

Vetrotech Saint-Gobain UK Ltd **(1)**
Glenewes House Gtwy Dr
Leeds, Westyorkshire, LS19 7XY, United Kingdom (100%)
Tel.: (44) 1132391500
Fax: (44) 1132391511
E-Mail: infovsguk.vetrotech@saint-gobain.com
Web Site: www.vetrotech.com
Emp.: 50
Mfr. of Glass Products
S.I.C.: 3211
N.A.I.C.S.: 327211

Vetrotex Italia S.p.A. **(1)**
Via E Romagnoli 6
I 20146 Milan, Italy (100%)
Tel.: (39) 0000242431
Telex: 43 324 408
Web Site: www.vetrotexeurope.com
Emp.: 600
Fiber Reinforcement Materials
S.I.C.: 3211
N.A.I.C.S.: 327211

W.A.W. Spol S.R.O. **(1)**
Mlynske luhy 17
821 05 Bratislava, Slovakia
Tel.: (421) 2 48 20 98 01
Fax: (421) 2 43 41 11 30
Sanitaryware Distr
S.I.C.: 5074
N.A.I.C.S.: 423720
Andreas Heitmann *(Gen Mgr)*

ZAO "Saint-Gobain Kavminsteklo" **(1)**
Zavodskaya Str 1
357217 Mineralnye Vody, Russia
Tel.: (7) 87922 7 75 25
Fax: (7) 87922 4 36 21
Web Site: www.sgpackaging.ru
Glass Bottles Mfr
S.I.C.: 3221
N.A.I.C.S.: 327213

Zao Zavod Minplita **(1)**
Sosnovskiy r-n d Talovka
456538 Chelyabinsk, Russia
Tel.: (7) 351 247 17 01
Fax: (7) 351 247 17 00
Glass Product Mfr
S.I.C.: 3231
N.A.I.C.S.: 327215

Non-U.S. Affiliates:

Companhia Brasileira de Cristal **(1)**
Rua Jose Mattar, 201 Jardim Sao Dimas
Sao Jose dos Campos, SP, 12245-450, Brazil (38.13%)
Flat Glass Mfr.
S.I.C.: 3211
N.A.I.C.S.: 327211

TBF Malaisie **(1)**
N-2 Jalan Teknologi 8 Plo 26
Mengkibol Industrial Area
PO Box 135, 86000 Keluang, Malaysia (44.07%)
Mfr. of Glass Products
S.I.C.: 3211
N.A.I.C.S.: 327211

COMPAGNIE DES ALPES S.A.

89 Rue Escudier
92772 Boulogne-Billancourt, Cedex, France
Tel.: (33) 146848800
Fax: (33) 146848919
E-Mail: communication@compagniedesalpes.fr
Web Site: www.compagniedesalpes.com
Year Founded: 1989
CDA—(EUR)
Sls.: $912,271,139
Assets: $1,943,248,896
Liabilities: $895,706,518
Net Worth: $1,047,542,378
Earnings: $44,404,764
Emp.: 5,415
Fiscal Year-end: 09/30/12

Business Description:
Tourist Destination Operator
S.I.C.: 7999
N.A.I.C.S.: 713990

Personnel:
Dominique Marcel *(Chm & CEO)*
Bernard Blas *(Vice Chm)*
Agnes Pannier-Runacher *(Deputy Mng Dir-Fin Strategy, Dev, Legal & Info Svcs)*

Board of Directors:
Dominique Marcel
Jean-Yves Barnavon
Bernard Blas
Gilles Chabert
Giorgio Frasca
Antoine Gosset-Grainville
Julien Goubault
Noelle Lenoir
Pascal Marchetti
Stephanie Paix
Rachel Picard
Francis Szpiner

Cabinet Mazars
61 rue Henri Regnault
92075 Paris, France

Subsidiaries:

Aquarium Geant De Saint Malo SAS **(1)**
La Ville Jouan Rue Du General Patton
35400 Saint-Malo, Ille-et-Vilaine, France
Tel.: (33) 29 921 1900
Fax: (33) 29 921 1901
E-Mail: contact@aquarium-st-malo.com
Web Site: www.aquarium-st-malo.com
Emp.: 20
Aquarium Management Services
S.I.C.: 8422
N.A.I.C.S.: 712130
Arnaud Cosce *(Pres)*

CDA-DS SAS **(1)**
89 Rue Escudier
92100 Boulogne-Billancourt, Hauts De Seine, France
Tel.: (33) 146848800
Fax: (33) 146848919
Web Site: www.compagniedesalpes.fr
Emp.: 200
Recreational Services
S.I.C.: 7996
N.A.I.C.S.: 713110

CDA Financement SNC **(1)**
89 Rue Escudier
92100 Boulogne-Billancourt, Hauts De Seine, France
Tel.: (33) 146848800
Fax: (33) 146944699
Financial Support Services
S.I.C.: 8742
N.A.I.C.S.: 541611

ECOBIOGESTION SAS **(1)**
Le Bioscope
68190 Ungersheim, Haut-Rhin, France
Tel.: (33) 3 89 62 43 00
Fax: (33) 3 89 62 43 01
E-Mail: bioscope@compagniedesalpes.fr
Web Site: www.lebioscope.com
Recreational Services
S.I.C.: 7996
N.A.I.C.S.: 713110

France Miniature SAS **(1)**
Boulevard Andre Malraux
78990 Elancourt, Yvelines, France
Tel.: (33) 130161630
Fax: (33) 1 3016 1631
E-Mail: contactgroupe@franceminiature.com
Web Site: www.franceminiature.com
Emp.: 11
Recreational Services
S.I.C.: 7996
N.A.I.C.S.: 713110
Beatrice de Reynies *(Mgr-Publ)*

Grevin & Cie Touraine SAS **(1)**
les Hauts Boeufs
37400 Lussault-sur-Loire, Indre-et-Loire, France
Tel.: (33) 2 47 23 44 44
Fax: (33) 2 47 23 44 45
Recreational Services
S.I.C.: 7996
N.A.I.C.S.: 713110

Grevin & Cie **(1)**
BP 8
60128 Plailly, France
Tel.: (33) 344628787
Fax: (33) 344623440
Amusement Park Operator
S.I.C.: 7999
N.A.I.C.S.: 713990
Jean-Pierre Sonois *(Chm)*

Non-U.S. Subsidiaries:

Grevin Deutschland GmbH **(2)**
Aurorastrsse 51
59909 Bestwig, Nordrhein-Westfalen, Germany
Tel.: (49) 2905810
Fax: (49) 29 0581 118
Web Site: www.fortsun.de
Emp.: 40
Recreational Services
S.I.C.: 7996
N.A.I.C.S.: 713110
Jan Reuvers *(Mng Dir)*

Hellendoorn Avonturen Park BV **(2)**
Avonturenpark Hellendoorn
Luttenbergerweg 22
7447 PB Hellendoorn, Overijssel, Netherlands
Tel.: (31) 548655555
Fax: (31) 548656365
E-Mail: info@avonturenpark.nl
Web Site: www.avonturenpark.nl
Emp.: 400
Recreational Services
S.I.C.: 7996
N.A.I.C.S.: 713110
Marloes San Rooyen *(Mgr-Mktg)*

Parc Asterix SAS **(1)**
Parc Asterix
BP 8
60128 Plailly, Oise, France
Tel.: (33) 344623131
Fax: (33) 344623294
E-Mail: contact@parcasterix.com
Web Site: www.parcasterix.fr
Recreational Services
S.I.C.: 7996
N.A.I.C.S.: 713110
Claire Bounioux *(Mgr-Mktg)*

Safari Africain de Port Saint Pere SA **(1)**
La Chevallerie
44710 Port-Saint-Pere, Loire-Atlantique, France
Tel.: (33) 240048282
Fax: (33) 240048743
Recreational Services
S.I.C.: 7996
N.A.I.C.S.: 713110
Nathalie Thomas *(Mgr-Fin)*

Non-U.S. Subsidiaries:

Belpark BV **(1)**
Meenseweg 497
8902 Ieper, West Flanders, Belgium
Tel.: (32) 57468686
Fax: (32) 57467595
E-Mail: info-blw@cda-parks.com
Web Site: www.bellewaerdepark.be
Emp.: 100
Recreational Services
S.I.C.: 7996
N.A.I.C.S.: 713110
Stefaan Lemey *(Gen Dir)*

Pleasurewood Hills Ltd **(1)**
Leisure Way Corton
Lowestoft, Suffolk, NR32 5DZ, United Kingdom
Tel.: (44) 1502586000
Fax: (44) 1502 567393
E-Mail: info@pleasurewoodhills.com
Web Site: www.pleasurewoodhills.com
Recreational Services
S.I.C.: 7996
N.A.I.C.S.: 713110
Denise Thompson *(Mgr-PR)*

SwissAlp SA **(1)**
Chemin Frank Thomas 36
1208 Geneva, Switzerland
Tel.: (41) 227040670
Fax: (41) 22 704 06 71
Investment & Real Estate Management Services
S.I.C.: 6211
N.A.I.C.S.: 523999
Patrick Ciocco *(Mng Dir)*

COMPAGNIE DES LEVURES LESAFFRE SA

137 rue Gabriel Peri
Marcq-en-Baroeul, 59 700, France
Tel.: (33) 320816100
Fax: (33) 320916098
Web Site: www.lesaffre.com
Year Founded: 1853
Sales Range: $1-4.9 Billion
Emp.: 7,200

Business Description:
Yeast Production
S.I.C.: 2083
N.A.I.C.S.: 311213

Personnel:
Lucien Lesaffre *(Chm & CEO)*

U.S. Subsidiary:

Lesaffre International Corp. **(1)**
7475 W Main St
Milwaukee, WI 53214
Tel.: (414) 615-4120
Fax: (414) 615-4012
Web Site: www.lesaffre.com
Sls.: $139,800,000
Emp.: 100
Holding Company; Yeast Production
S.I.C.: 6719
N.A.I.C.S.: 551112
John Riesch *(Pres)*

Subsidiary:

Lesaffre Yeast Corp. **(2)**
7475 W Main St
Milwaukee, WI 53214
Tel.: (414) 615-4120
Fax: (414) 615-4012
Toll Free: (877) 677-7000
Web Site: www.lesaffreyeastcorp.com
Sls.: $37,100,000
Emp.: 50
Groceries & Related Products, Nec
S.I.C.: 5149
N.A.I.C.S.: 424490
James Geiger *(Mgr-Inventory Plng & Control)*

Non-U.S. Subsidiaries:

BFP Wholesale Ltd. **(1)**
Unit 8 Connections Indus Ctr Vestry Rd
Sevenoaks, Kent, TN14 5DF, United Kingdom UK
Tel.: (44) 1732228400 (100%)
Fax: (44) 1732228329
E-Mail: enquiries.dbi-bfpw@dsm.com
Web Site: www.bfpwholesale.com
Emp.: 13
Bakery Ingredients Mfr
S.I.C.: 5149
N.A.I.C.S.: 424490

Lesaffre Chile S.A. **(1)**
Las Esteras Norte 2751
Quilicura, Chile CL
Tel.: (56) 26233595 (100%)
Fax: (56) 262333640
E-Mail: alexandro.funzaleda@lefersa.cl
Web Site: www.lefersa.cl
Emp.: 200
Yeast Mfr
S.I.C.: 2099
N.A.I.C.S.: 311999
Alexandro Funzaleda *(Gen Mgr)*

Safmex SA de CV **(1)**
Km 57 5 Carretera Mexico Toluca
Parque Industrial, 52000 Toluca, Mexico

Tel.: (52) 7224624200
Fax: (52) 7222165142
E-Mail: jhdc@safmex.com
Web Site: www.safmex.com.mx
Emp.: 300
Yeast Production
S.I.C.: 2083
N.A.I.C.S.: 311213

COMPAGNIE DU BOIS SAUVAGE SA

Rue du Bois Sauvage 17
B-1000 Brussels, Belgium
Tel.: (32) 22275450
Fax: (32) 22192520
E-Mail: info@bois-sauvage.be
Web Site: www.bois-sauvage.be
COMB—(EUR)
Rev.: $224,049,804
Assets: $667,338,200
Liabilities: $173,647,853
Net Worth: $493,690,347
Earnings: $27,161,672
Fiscal Year-end: 12/31/12

Business Description:
Financial Management Services
S.I.C.: 6211
N.A.I.C.S.: 523999

Personnel:
Frederic Van Gansberghe *(Chm)*
Vincent Doumier *(Mng Dir)*
Bruno Spilliaert *(Sec)*

Board of Directors:
Frederic Van Gansberghe
Francois Blondel
Pierre-Yves de Laminne de Bex
Vincent Doumier
Frederic Jourdain
Valerie Paquot
Patrick Van Craen

COMPAGNIE DU MONT BLANC - SA

35 place de la Mer de Glace
74400 Chamonix-Mont-Blanc, France
Tel.: (33) 4 50 53 22 75
E-Mail: sales@compagniedumontblanc.fr
Web Site: www.compagniedumontblanc.fr
Year Founded: 2000
MLCMB—(EUR)
Sales Range: $75-99.9 Million
Emp.: 455

Business Description:
Ski Lift & Tow Operator
S.I.C.: 7999
N.A.I.C.S.: 713920

Personnel:
Mathieu Dechavanne *(Pres & Mng Dir)*

COMPAGNIE FINANCIERE RICHEMONT S.A.

(d/b/a Richemont SA)
50 Chemin de la Chenaie Bellevue
1293 Geneva, Switzerland
Tel.: (41) 227213500
Fax: (41) 227213550
E-Mail: info@richemont.com
Web site: www.richemont.com
Year Founded: 1988
CFR—(JSE OTC)
Sls.: $13,663,625,500
Assets: $19,515,426,490
Liabilities: $5,764,299,940
Net Worth: $13,751,126,550
Earnings: $2,699,070,850
Emp.: 27,666
Fiscal Year-end: 03/31/13

Business Description:
Holding Company; Jewelry, Watches, Writing Instruments & Other Luxury Goods Whslr & Retailer
Import Export
S.I.C.: 6719
N.A.I.C.S.: 551112

Personnel:
Johann P. Rupert *(Chm)*
Bernard Fornas *(Co-CEO)*
Richard Lepeu *(Co-CEO)*
Gary Saage *(CFO)*
Stanislas de Quercize *(CEO-Cartier)*
Georges Kern *(CEO-IWC Schaffhausen)*
Jerome Lambert *(CEO-Jaeger-LeCoultre)*
Philippe Leopold-Metzger *(CEO-Piaget)*
Albert Kaufmann *(Gen Counsel)*
Frederick Mostert *(Legal Counsel)*
Matthew Kilgarriff *(Sec)*

Board of Directors:
Johann P. Rupert
Franco Cologni
Charles Douro
Bernard Fornas
Yves-Andre Istel
Richard Lepeu
Ruggero Magnoni
Josua Dillie Malherbe
Frederick Mostert
Simon Murray
Alain Dominique Perrin
Guillaume Pictet
Norbert Adolf Platt
Alan Grant Quasha
Maria Ramos
Robin W. Renwick
Dominique Rochat
Jan Rupert
Gary Saage
Jurgen Erich Schrempp
Martha Wikstrom

Legal Counsel:
Lenz & Staehelin
30 route de Chene
Geneva, Switzerland

Cliffe Dekker Hofmeyr
6 Sandown Valley Crescent
Sandton, South Africa

Subsidiaries:

Baume & Mercier S.A. (1)
50 Chemin de la Chenaie
Bellevue, Geneva, 1293, Switzerland
Tel.: (41) 229995151
Fax: (41) 229995050
E-Mail: info@baume-et-mercier.com
Web Site: www.baume-et-mercier.com
Watch & Clocks
S.I.C.: 3829
N.A.I.C.S.: 334519
Alain Zimmernann *(CEO)*

U.S. Subsidiary:

Baume & Mercier, Inc. (2)
645 5th Ave Fl 6
New York, NY 10022-5346 NY
Tel.: (212) 593-0444
Fax: (212) 755-3138
Web Site: www.baume-and-mercier.com
Sales Range: $50-74.9 Million
Emp.: 90
Watches Whslr
S.I.C.: 5094
N.A.I.C.S.: 423940
Alain Zimmerman *(CEO)*
Rodolfo Chavez *(Pres-North America)*

Cartier International SA Geneve (1)
8 Blvd James-Fazy
1201 Geneva, Switzerland
Tel.: (41) 227212400
Fax: (41) 227212485
E-Mail: wilsrid.roulet@cartier.com
Web Site: www.cartier.com
Emp.: 100
Luxury Watches Mfr
S.I.C.: 3829
N.A.I.C.S.: 334519
Bernard Fornas *(Pres)*

Cartier SA (1)
Blvd James Fazy 8
Geneva, 1201, Switzerland
Tel.: (41) 227212400
Fax: (41) 264011869
E-Mail: reception.fazy@cartier.com
Luxury Watches & Jewelry Mfr
S.I.C.: 3829
N.A.I.C.S.: 334519

International Watch Co. Ag (1)
Baumgartenstr 15
Schaffhausen, 8201, Switzerland
Tel.: (41) 526356565
Fax: (41) 526356501
E-Mail: info@iwc.com
Web Site: www.iwc.com
Emp.: 715
Watch & Clock Mfr
S.I.C.: 3829
N.A.I.C.S.: 334519
George Kern *(CEO)*

Manufacture Jaeger-LeCoultre SA (1)
Rue de la Golisse 8
Le Sentier, Vaud, 1347, Switzerland
Tel.: (41) 218450202
Fax: (41) 218450550
E-Mail: info@jaeger-lecoultre.com
Web Site: www.jaeger-lecoultre.com
Luxury Watches Mfr
S.I.C.: 3829
N.A.I.C.S.: 334519

Manufacture Roger Dubuis SA (1)
2 rue Andre De Garrini
1217 Meyrin, Switzerland
Tel.: (41) 227832828
Fax: (41) 227832828
E-Mail: info@rogerdubuis.com
Web Site: www.rogerdubuis.com
Emp.: 400
Luxury Watches Mfr
S.I.C.: 3829
N.A.I.C.S.: 334519
Jean-Marc Pontroue *(CEO)*

Montblanc Montre SA (1)
Chemin des Tourelles 10
2400 Le Locle, Neuchatel, Switzerland
Tel.: (41) 329338888
Fax: (41) 329338880
Emp.: 100
Luxury Watches Mfr
S.I.C.: 3829
N.A.I.C.S.: 334519

Piaget S.A. (1)
37 chemin du champ des filles
La Cote aux Fees, 1228 Plan-les-Ouates, Switzerland
Tel.: (41) 228844844
Fax: (41) 228844119
E-Mail: accueil.piaget@piaget.com
Web Site: www.piaget.com
Emp.: 400
Luxury Watches Mfr
S.I.C.: 3829
N.A.I.C.S.: 334519
Yves G. Piaget *(Pres)*
Philippe Leopold Metzger *(CEO)*

Richemont Suisse SA (1)
50 Chemin de la Chenaie
Bellevue, 1293 Geneva, Switzerland CH
Tel.: (41) 223675330
Fax: (41) 22 3675331
Luxury Watches Mfr
S.I.C.: 3829
N.A.I.C.S.: 334519

Vacheron And Constantin S.A. (1)
Chemin du Tourbillon 10
1228 Plan-les-Ouates, Switzerland
Tel.: (41) 229302005
Fax: (41) 229302006
Web Site: www.vacheron-constantin.com
Emp.: 20
Luxury Watches Mfr
S.I.C.: 3829
N.A.I.C.S.: 334519
Gulien Marchemoir *(Mng Dir)*

Van Cleef & Arpels SA (1)
Route des Biches 8
1752 Villars-sur-Glane, Fribourg, Switzerland
Tel.: (41) 264079511
Web Site: www.vancleef-arpels.com
Emp.: 60
Luxury Watches Mfr
S.I.C.: 3829
N.A.I.C.S.: 334519
Nicolas Bos *(Pres & CEO)*
Catherine Renier *(Pres-Asia Pacific)*

Non-U.S. Subsidiaries:

Alfred Dunhill Limited (1)
5-7 Mandeville Pl
London, W1U 3AY, United Kingdom
Tel.: (44) 2078388000
Fax: (44) 2078388301
E-Mail: customer.services@dunhill.com
Web Site: www.dunhill.com
Emp.: 150
Luxury Watches Mfr
S.I.C.: 3829
N.A.I.C.S.: 334519
Fabrizio Cardinali *(CEO)*

James Purdey & Sons Limited (1)
Audley House
57-58 S Audley St, London, W1K 2ED, United Kingdom
Tel.: (44) 2074991801
Fax: (44) 2073553297
E-Mail: enquiries@purdey.com
Web Site: www.purdey.com
Gun & Rifles Mfr
S.I.C.: 3489
N.A.I.C.S.: 332994
Paul Cartledge *(Dir-Ops)*

Montblanc International BV (1)
Herengracht 436
1017 BZ Amsterdam, North Holland, Netherlands
Tel.: (31) 203428677
Fax: (31) 206969839
Web Site: www.montblanc.com
Emp.: 20
High Quality Writing Instruments Mfr
S.I.C.: 3579
N.A.I.C.S.: 339940
Van Holestien *(Mng Dir)*
Jan Van Holten *(Mng Dir)*

Montblanc-Simplo GmbH (1)
Hellgrundweg 100
Hamburg, 22525, Germany
Tel.: (49) 40840010
Fax: (49) 4084001341
E-Mail: service@montblanc.com
Web Site: www.montblanc.com
Emp.: 1,100
Luxury Watches & Writing Instruments Mfr
S.I.C.: 3829
N.A.I.C.S.: 334519
Lutz Bethge *(Mng Dir)*

Net-a-Porter Group Ltd. (1)
1 The Village Offices Westfield London Shopping Centre
London, W12 7GF, United Kingdom
Tel.: (44) 2034714510
E-Mail: press@net-a-porter.com
Web Site: www.net-a-porter.com
Sales Range: $150-199.9 Million
Emp.: 800
Online & Mail Order Fashion Retailer
S.I.C.: 5961
N.A.I.C.S.: 454111
Natalie Massenet *(Chm)*
Alison Loehnis *(Mng Dir)*

Richemont Asia Pacific Limited (1)
6 F Jardine House
1 Connaught Pl, Central, China (Hong Kong)
Tel.: (852) 25327200
Fax: (852) 25377866
Web Site: www.richemont.com
Emp.: 500
Luxury Watches Mfr
S.I.C.: 3829
N.A.I.C.S.: 334519

Richemont Holdings (UK) Limited (1)
15 Hill St
London, W1J 5QT, United Kingdom
Tel.: (44) 2074992539
Fax: (44) 2074910524
Web Site: www.richemont.com
Emp.: 50
Luxury Watches Mfr
S.I.C.: 3829
N.A.I.C.S.: 334519

Richemont Iberia SL (1)
Paseo de la castellana 141
Madrid, 28046, Spain

Compagnie Financiere Richemont S.A.—(Continued)

Tel.: (34) 91 4548972
Fax: (34) 91 4460925
Web Site: www.richemont.com
Emp.: 180
Luxury Watches Mfr
S.I.C.: 3829
N.A.I.C.S.: 334519
Philippe Guillaumet *(CEO)*

Richemont Northern Europe GmbH (1)
Landsberger Str 302 306
80687 Munich, Germany
Tel.: (49) 89559840
Fax: (49) 8955984274
Web Site: www.richemont.com
Emp.: 120
Luxury Watches Mfr
S.I.C.: 3829
N.A.I.C.S.: 334519
Robert Hell *(Mng Dir)*

COMPAGNIE GENERAL BEARING SERVICE, INC.

490 Kent Street
Ottawa, ON, K2P 2B7, Canada
Tel.: (613) 238-8100
Fax: (613) 236-8207
Rev.: $30,434,597
Emp.: 100

Business Description:
Industrial Supplies Whslr
S.I.C.: 5085
N.A.I.C.S.: 423840

Personnel:
Pierre Bouchard *(Pres)*

COMPAGNIE GENERALE DE GEOPHYSIQUE-VERITAS

(Name Changed to CGG)

COMPAGNIE GENERALE DES ETABLISSEMENTS MICHELIN SCA

(d/b/a Michelin SCA)
23 Place des Carmes-Dechau
63040 Clermont-Ferrand, Cedex 9, France
Tel.: (33) 473322000
Telex: 990022 F
Fax: (33) 473985904
Web Site: www.michelin.com
Year Founded: 1863
ML—(EUR OTC)
Sls.: $28,907,654,580
Assets: $29,053,040,940
Liabilities: $17,609,249,770
Net Worth: $11,443,791,170
Earnings: $2,114,833,070
Emp.: 107,300
Fiscal Year-end: 12/31/12

Business Description:
Holding Company for the Mfr of Tires & Tubes, Steel Cables, Maps & Tourist Guides
Import Export
S.I.C.: 6719
N.A.I.C.S.: 551112

Personnel:
Eric Bourdais de Charbonniere *(Chm-Supervisory Bd)*
Jean-Dominique Senard *(CEO & Mng Partner)*
Marc Henry *(CFO)*

Supervisory Board of Directors:
Eric Bourdais de Charbonniere
Pat Cox
Barbara Dalibard
Louis Gallois
Francois Grappotte
Pierre Michelin
Laurence Parisot
Benoit Potier

Deloitte & Associes
185 avenue Charles-de-Gaulle
Neuilly-sur-Seine, France

Subsidiaries:

Euromaster France S.N.C (1)
Immeuble Sun 180 Avenue de l'Europe
38330 Montbonnot-Saint-Martin, France
Tel.: (33) 4 76 61 28 00
Fax: (33) 4 76 61 29 03
E-Mail:
Tire & Automotive Maintenance Services
S.I.C.: 7549
N.A.I.C.S.: 811198

Manufacture Francaise des Pneumatiques Michelin (1)
23 Pl Des Carmes Dechaux
F 63040 Clermont-Ferrand, Cedex 9, France (100%)
Tel.: (33) 473322000
Fax: (33) 473322002
Web Site: www.michelin.fr
Emp.: 33
Mfr. of Tires & Tubes
S.I.C.: 3011
N.A.I.C.S.: 326211
Michel Rollier *(Mng Dir)*

Subsidiary:

Kleber Pneumatiques SA (2)
Place des Carmes Dechaux
63040 Clermont, Ferrand, France FR
Tel.: (33) 4 73 32 2000 (98.3%)
Web Site: www.kleber.fr
Emp.: 1,000
Mfr of Tires & Rubber Products
S.I.C.: 3011
N.A.I.C.S.: 326211

Non-U.S. Subsidiary:

Kleber Reifen GmbH (3)
Michelinstrasse 4
76185 Karlsruhe, Germany De
Tel.: (49) 7215300 (100%)
Telex: 4429421 kcag d
Fax: (49) 7215301290
E-Mail: gerhard.janotta@de.michelin.com
Web Site: www.kleber-reifen.de
Emp.: 2,000
Mfr. of Tires & Tubes
S.I.C.: 3011
N.A.I.C.S.: 326211
Weisseick Oliver *(Mgr-Fin)*

Michelin Air Services (1)
23 Place Des Carmes Dechaux
63040 Clermont-Ferrand, France
Tel.: (33) 473322000
Fax: (33) 473322202
Tire Mfr & Distr
S.I.C.: 3011
N.A.I.C.S.: 326211

Pneu Laurent S.N.C (1)
Route de Sauvigny-le-bois
PO Box 127
89204 Avallon, France
Tel.: (33) 386314300
Fax: (33) 386314435
E-Mail:
Web Site: www.pneulaurent.fr
Tire Retreading Services
S.I.C.: 7534
N.A.I.C.S.: 326212

Pneumatiques Kleber S.A (1)
Zoning Industriel Croix de Metz
Toul, 54200, France
Tel.: (33) 3 83 63 30 00
Fax: (33) 3 83 63 33 63
Automotive Tire Mfr
S.I.C.: 3011
N.A.I.C.S.: 326211

Simorep et Cie - Societe du Caoutchouc Synthetique Michelin (1)
Av De La Parqueyre
33530 Bassens, France
Tel.: (33) 556772000
Fax: (33) 556208011
Automotive Tire Mfr
S.I.C.: 3011
N.A.I.C.S.: 326211

S.O.D.G. (1)
Blvd Louis Chartoire
63100 Clermont-Ferrand, France
Tel.: (33) 473235713
Fax: (33) 473235712
Automotive Tire Mfr
S.I.C.: 3011
N.A.I.C.S.: 326211

U.S. Subsidiaries:

Michelin Corporation (1)
One Pkwy S
Greenville, SC 29615-5022 SC
Mailing Address:
PO Box 19001
Greenville, SC 29602-9001
Tel.: (864) 458-5000
Fax: (864) 458-5430
Web Site: www.michelin-us.com
Rev.: $200,000,000
Emp.: 1,500
Sales of Automobile Tires Pneumatic
S.I.C.: 3011
N.A.I.C.S.: 326211

Subsidiaries:

American Synthetic Rubber Company (2)
4500 Camp Ground Rd
Louisville, KY 40216-4675 KY
Mailing Address:
PO Box 32960
Louisville, KY 40232-2960
Tel.: (502) 449-8300
Fax: (203) 348-6203
E-Mail:
Web Site: www.americansyntheticrubberco.com
Sales Range: $25-49.9 Million
Emp.: 360
Production of Synthetic Rubber & Liquid Polymers
S.I.C.: 2822
N.A.I.C.S.: 325212
Guillaume Coiraton *(Ops Mgr)*

Uniroyal Goodrich Intellectual (2)
1 Pkwy S
Greenville, SC 29615-5022 SC
Tel.: (864) 458-5000
Web Site: www.michelin-us.com
Mfr. & Sales of Auotmobile Tires
S.I.C.: 3011
N.A.I.C.S.: 326211
James M. Micali *(CEO)*

Michelin North America, Inc. (1)
1 Pkwy S
Greenville, SC 29615
Tel.: (864) 458-5000
Fax: (864) 458-6764
Toll Free: (800) 847-3435
Web Site: www.michelin-us.com
Emp.: 22,300
Designs, Manufactures & Sells Tires for Every Type of Vehicle, Including Airplanes, Automobiles, Bicycles, Earthmovers, Farm Equipment, Heavy-Duty Trucks, Motorcycles & the Space Shuttle; Publishes Travel Guides, Hotel & Restaurant Guides, Maps & Road Atlases
Import Export
S.I.C.: 3011
N.A.I.C.S.: 326211
Pete Selleck *(Chm & Pres)*

Subsidiaries:

Michelin Aircraft Tire Corporation (2)
1 Pkwy S
Greenville, SC 29615 (100%)
Tel.: (864) 458-5000
Fax: (864) 458-6764
E-Mail: info@airmichelin.com
Web Site: www.airmichelin.com
Emp.: 150
Mfr. of Aircraft Tires
S.I.C.: 3011
N.A.I.C.S.: 326211

Michelin Americas Research & Development (2)
515 Michelin Rd
Greenville, SC 29605-6131 SC
Mailing Address:
PO Box 1987
Greenville, SC 29602-1987
Tel.: (864) 422-4000
Fax: (864) 422-4099
E-Mail: info@michelin-us.com
Web Site: www.michelin-us.com
Emp.: 900
Commercial Physical Research
S.I.C.: 8731
N.A.I.C.S.: 541712

Michelin Americas Small Tires (MAST) (2)
1 Parkway S
Greenville, SC 29615-5022 NY
Mailing Address:
PO Box 19001
Greenville, SC 29602-9001
Tel.: (864) 458-5000
Toll Free: (800) 847-3435
Web Site: www.michelinman.com
Emp.: 13,000
Tires Mfr
Import Export
S.I.C.: 3011
N.A.I.C.S.: 326211
James M. Micali *(Chm & Pres)*
Scott Clark *(COO)*

Oliver Rubber Company (2)
408 Telephone Ave
Asheboro, NC 27205 DE
Tel.: (336) 629-1436
Fax: (336) 629-1430
E-Mail: service@oliverrubber.com
Web Site: www.oliverrubber.com
Emp.: 285
Retread Rubber, Bonding Gum & Equipment Mfr
Import Export
S.I.C.: 3061
N.A.I.C.S.: 326291

TCI Tire Centers, LLC (2)
310 Inglesby Pkwy
Duncan, SC 29334
Mailing Address:
PO Box 218
Duncan, SC 29334-0218
Tel.: (864) 329-2700
Fax: (864) 329-2929
Toll Free: (800) 603-2430
E-Mail: humanresources@tirecenters.com
Web Site: www.tirecenters.com
Sales Range: $600-649.9 Million
Emp.: 2,400
Automotive Tires Whslr
S.I.C.: 5014
N.A.I.C.S.: 423130
Cara Cornelius *(Sr Dir-Supply Chain & Logistics)*

Subsidiary:

TCI Tire Centers (3)
4771 Hollins Ferry Rd
Baltimore, MD 21227
Tel.: (410) 247-4464
Fax: (410) 536-0454
E-Mail: tci310mgr@tirecenters.com
Web Site: www.tirecenters.com
Emp.: 24
Automotive Tires Whslr
S.I.C.: 5014
N.A.I.C.S.: 423130

Non-U.S. Subsidiaries:

Michelin North America (Canada) Inc. (2)
3020 Jacques Bureau Ave
Laval, QC, H7P 6G2, Canada (100%)
Tel.: (450) 978-4700
Fax: (450) 978-7600
Web Site: www.michelin.ca
Emp.: 150
Commercial Tire Distr
Export
S.I.C.: 5014
N.A.I.C.S.: 441320
Jean Moreau *(VP-Personnel)*

Non-U.S. Subsidiaries:

Associated Tyre Specialists Limited (1)
Brixton Hill
London, United Kingdom
Tel.: (44) 2086716800
Automotive Tire Mfr & Distr
S.I.C.: 3011
N.A.I.C.S.: 326211

Compagnie Financiere Michelin (1)
Route Louis-Braille 10-12
Granges-Paccot, 1763, Switzerland
Tel.: (41) 264674444
Fax: (41) 264674150

E-Mail:
Financial Management Services
S.I.C.: 6211
N.A.I.C.S.: 523999

Euromaster AB (1)
Stormhallsv 6
PO Box 1134
432 15 Varberg, Sweden
Tel.: (46) 34082900
Fax: (46) 34083175
E-Mail: gen.se.info@euromaster.com
Automotive Tire Distr
S.I.C.: 5014
N.A.I.C.S.: 423130

Euromaster Automocion y Servicios, S.A. (1)
Calle Albarracin 34
28037 Madrid, Spain
Tel.: (34) 913791200
Fax: (34) 913791230
Tire Retreading Services
S.I.C.: 3011
N.A.I.C.S.: 326211

Euromaster Bandenservice B.V. (1)
Lubeckstraat 2
PO Box 169
7418 EC Deventer, Netherlands
Tel.: (31) 570679790
Fax: (31) 570679750
Web Site: www.euromaster.nl
Tire Mfr & Distr
S.I.C.: 3011
N.A.I.C.S.: 326211
Frank Bokkers *(Gen Mgr)*

Euromaster Danmark A/S (1)
Erik Glippings Vej 11- 13
8800 Viborg, Denmark
Tel.: (45) 87282828
E-Mail: info@dk.euromaster.com
Automotive Tire Distr
S.I.C.: 5014
N.A.I.C.S.: 423130

Euromaster GmbH (1)
Mainzer Strasse 81
67657 Kaiserslautern, Germany
Tel.: (49) 63134220
Fax: (49) 63148853
E-Mail: info@de.euromaster.com
Web Site: www.euromaster.de
Emp.: 140
Automotive Wheel Maintenance Services
S.I.C.: 7532
N.A.I.C.S.: 811121
Matthias Schubert *(Gen Mgr)*

Euromaster (Suisse) S.A. (1)
Industriestrasse 30
3186 Dudingen, Switzerland
Tel.: (41) 264932988
Fax: (41) 264932901
Automotive Tire Mfr
S.I.C.: 3011
N.A.I.C.S.: 326211

Laurent Reifen GmbH (1)
Sachsenhausener Str 29a
16515 Oranienburg, Germany
Tel.: (49) 330183450
Fax: (49) 3301834551
E-Mail: vertrieb@laurentreifen.de
Tire Retreading Services
S.I.C.: 3011
N.A.I.C.S.: 326211

Michelin Algerie SPA (1)
Route De Birkhadem Bachdjerrah
16040 Algiers, Algeria
Tel.: (213) 21268197
Fax: (213) 21268400
Tire Mfr
S.I.C.: 3011
N.A.I.C.S.: 326211

Michelin America do Sul (1)
Ave das Americas 700
Bloco 4, Barra da Tijuca Rio de Janeiro, RJ,
CEP 22640-100, Brazil BR
Tel.: (55) 2124294646 (100%)
Telex: 1130218 MCHL
Fax: (55) 21 2429 4902
Web Site: www.michelin.com.br
Emp.: 6,000
Marketing of Tires
S.I.C.: 5014
N.A.I.C.S.: 441320

Michelin Argentina Sociedad Anonima, Industrial, Comercial y Financiera (1)
Calle Lascano
5130 Buenos Aires, Argentina
Tel.: (54) 1146303030
Fax: (54) 1146303089
Automotive Tire Mfr
S.I.C.: 3011
N.A.I.C.S.: 326211

Michelin Asia (Hong Kong) Limited (1)
3406 34/F West Tower Shun Tak Centre
168-200 Connaught Road Central
Sheung Wan, Hong Kong, China (Hong Kong)
Tel.: (852) 28817287
Fax: (852) 25768518
E-Mail: marketing.hk@cn.michelin.com
Web Site: www.michelin.com.hk
Automotive Tire Distr
S.I.C.: 5014
N.A.I.C.S.: 423130

Michelin Asia-Pacific Pte Ltd (1)
77 Robinson Rd 34-01 & 35-01 Robinson 77
Singapore, 068896, Singapore
Tel.: (65) 64389400
Fax: (65) 64389361
E-Mail:
Automotive Tire Mfr & Distr
S.I.C.: 3011
N.A.I.C.S.: 326211

Michelin Asia (Singapore) Co. Pte. Ltd. (1)
78 Shenton Way 23-01 & 24-02
Singapore, 79120, Singapore
Tel.: (65) 64389500
Fax: (65) 64389511
E-Mail: website.sg@michelin.asia
Web Site: www.michelin.com.sg
Automotive Tire Distr
S.I.C.: 5014
N.A.I.C.S.: 423130

Michelin Belux S.A. (1)
Brusselsesteenweg 494
Asse, 1731, Belgium
Tel.: (32) 22744211
Fax: (32) 22744212
E-Mail: info@be.michelin.com
Emp.: 150
Automotive Tire Distr
S.I.C.: 5014
N.A.I.C.S.: 423130
Paul Perriniaux *(Gen Mgr)*

Michelin Chile Ltda. (1)
Calle Luis Carrera 1131
Vitacura, Santiago, Chile
Tel.: (56) 26405959
Fax: (56) 26405960
Web Site: www.michelin.cl
Emp.: 80
Automotive Tire Mfr
S.I.C.: 3011
N.A.I.C.S.: 326211
Errol Passo *(Gen Mgr)*

Michelin Chun Shin Ltd. (1)
5F-1 No 190 Sec 3 Datong Rd
Xizhi Dist, Taipei, 22103, Taiwan
Tel.: (886) 286471111
Fax: (886) 286473608
Web Site: www.michelin.com.tw
Automotive Tire Mfr
S.I.C.: 3011
N.A.I.C.S.: 326211

Michelin Espana Portugal, S.A. (1)
Avda de Los Encuartes 19
28760 Tres Cantos, Spain
Tel.: (34) 914105000
Fax: (34) 914105010
E-Mail: cfam@es.michelin.com
Automotive Tire Mfr & Distr
S.I.C.: 3011
N.A.I.C.S.: 326211

Michelin Finance (Pays-Bas) B.V. (1)
Huub van Doorneweg 2
5151 DT Drunen, Netherlands
Tel.: (31) 416384142
Fax: (31) 416384253
Financial Management Services
S.I.C.: 6211
N.A.I.C.S.: 523999
John Corsen *(Gen Mgr)*

Michelin Finanz Gesellschaft fur Beteiligungen AG & Co. OHG (1)
Michelinstrasse 4
76185 Karlsruhe, Germany
Tel.: (49) 7215300
Fax: (49) 7215301290
Automotive Tire Mfr
S.I.C.: 3011
N.A.I.C.S.: 326211

Michelin Hungaria Tyre Manufacture Ltd. (1)
Kerepesi Ut 17
1087 Budapest, Hungary
Tel.: (36) 42 502 600
Fax: (36) 42 502 603
Automotive Tire Mfr
S.I.C.: 3011
N.A.I.C.S.: 326211

Michelin India TamilNadu Tyres Private Limited (1)
9th Floor Shyamala Towers No 136 Arcot Road Saligramam
Saligramam, Chennai, 600 093, India
Tel.: (91) 44 3993 6000
Fax: (91) 4466216100
Emp.: 100
Automotive Tire Mfr
S.I.C.: 3011
N.A.I.C.S.: 326211
Nicolas Beaumont *(Mng Dir)*

Michelin India Tyres Private Limited (1)
7th Fl The Pinnacle Business Tower
Shooting Range Rd Surajkund
Faridabad, 121001, India
Tel.: (91) 1293097777
Fax: (91) 1293097888
Web Site: www.michelin.in
Emp.: 300
Automotive Tire Mfr & Distr
S.I.C.: 3011
N.A.I.C.S.: 326211
Thom Clark *(Dir-Comml)*

Michelin Korea Company Limited (1)
15th Fl 157-1 Samsung Dong Kangnam
Seoul, Korea (South) KS
Tel.: (82) 262405590 (100%)
Fax: (82) 262405581
Web Site: www.michelin.co.kr
Emp.: 45
Distr of Tires
S.I.C.: 5014
N.A.I.C.S.: 441320

Michelin Lastikleri Ticaret A.S. (1)
Buyukdere Cad Yapi Kredi Plaza B Blok
34330 Istanbul, Turkey
Tel.: (90) 2123175200
Fax: (90) 2123175200
Automotive Tire Mfr
S.I.C.: 3011
N.A.I.C.S.: 326211

Michelin Nordic AB (1)
PO Box 47175
100 74 Stockholm, Sweden
Tel.: (46) 87090700
E-Mail: backoffice@se.michelin.com
Automotive Tire Distr
S.I.C.: 5014
N.A.I.C.S.: 423130

Michelin Polska S.A. (1)
ul Leonharda 9
10-454 Olsztyn, Poland
Tel.: (48) 8953940000
Fax: (48) 895394090
Web Site: www.michelin.pl
Tire Mfr
S.I.C.: 3011
N.A.I.C.S.: 326211

Michelin Recherche et Technique S.A. (1)
Route Louis-Braille 10
Granges-Paccot, 1763, Switzerland
Tel.: (41) 264674444
Fax: (41) 264605700
Automotive Tire Mfr
S.I.C.: 3011
N.A.I.C.S.: 326211

Michelin Reifenwerke KGaA (1)
Michelinstrasse 4
76185 Karlsruhe, Germany De
Mailing Address: (100%)
PO Box 210951
76159 Karlsruhe, Germany
Tel.: (49) 7215300
Telex: 7825868
Fax: (49) 7215301290
E-Mail: webmaster@michelin-online.de
Web Site: www.michelin.de
Emp.: 1,400
Mfr. of Tires
S.I.C.: 3011
N.A.I.C.S.: 326211

Michelin Romania S.A. (1)
Bucharest North No 10 Global City
Business Park Building 01
011469 Bucharest, Romania
Tel.: (40) 212026500
Fax: (40) 212026600
E-Mail:
Web Site: www.michelin.ro
Emp.: 150
Automotive Tire Mfr & Distr
S.I.C.: 3011
N.A.I.C.S.: 326211
Eric Faidy *(Gen Mgr)*

Michelin Siam Group Co., Ltd. (1)
252 Phaholyothin Road Samsaen Nai
Payathai, Bangkok, 10400, Thailand TH
Tel.: (66) 2 619 3000 (88%)
Fax: (66) 2 619 3179
Web Site: www.michelin.co.th
Emp.: 6,300
Holding Company; Automotive Tires Mfr
S.I.C.: 6719
N.A.I.C.S.: 551112

Subsidiary:

Michelin Siam Co., Ltd. (2)
252 Phaholyothin Road Samsaen Nai
Payathai, Bangkok, 10400, Thailand TH
Tel.: (66) 26193000
Fax: (66) 26193179
Web Site: www.michelin.co.th
Emp.: 6,800
Automotive Tires Mfr
S.I.C.: 3011
N.A.I.C.S.: 326211
Suchala Thephabutra *(Mng Dir-HR)*

Plants:

Michelin Siam Co., Ltd. - Nongkhae Plant (3)
Siam Cement Industrial Estate 57 Moo
6 Nongplakradee Road, Nongkhae, Sarburi, 18140, Thailand
Tel.: (66) 36373276-89
Fax: (66) 36373296
Web Site: www.michelin.co.th
Emp.: 900
Heavy Truck Tires & Bus Tires Mfr
S.I.C.: 3011
N.A.I.C.S.: 326211

Michelin Siam Co., Ltd. - Si Racha Plant (3)
87/11 Moo 2 Sukhumvit Road
Laemchabang Industrial Estate
Tung Sukhla, Si Racha, Chon Buri, 20230, Thailand
Tel.: (66) 384905349
Fax: (66) 38490545
Web Site: www.michelin.co.th
Emp.: 1,200
Automotive Tires Mfr
S.I.C.: 3011
N.A.I.C.S.: 326211

Michelin Thai Holding Co., Ltd. (1)
252 Paholyothin Rd
Phaya Thai, Bangkok, 10400, Thailand
Tel.: (66) 26193000
Fax: (66) 26193179
Investment Management Services
S.I.C.: 6211
N.A.I.C.S.: 523999

Michelin Tyre Company South Africa (Proprietary) Limited (1)
11B Riley Road Eastwood Office Park
Bedfordview, 2007, South Africa
Tel.: (27) 115790300
Fax: (27) 115790513

Compagnie Generale des Etablissements Michelin SCA—(Continued)

E-Mail: reception@za.michelin.co.za
Web Site: www.michelin.co.za
Emp.: 100
Automotive Tire Mfr & Distr
S.I.C.: 3011
N.A.I.C.S.: 326211
Guillermo Antunez *(Gen Mgr)*

Michelin Tyre P.L.C. **(1)**
Campbell Rd
Stoke-on-Trent, ST4 4EY, United Kingdom UK
Tel.: (44) 1782402000 (100%)
Telex: 919071
Fax: (44) 1782402011
E-Mail: webinfo@uk.michelin.com
Web Site: www.michelin.co.uk
Emp.: 500
Mfr. of Tires
S.I.C.: 3011
N.A.I.C.S.: 326211

Michelin Ukraine LLC **(1)**
19 G Skovorody St Podil Plaza BC 8 Fl
Kiev, 4070, Ukraine
Tel.: (380) 444903462
Fax: (380) 444903463
Automotive Tire Mfr
S.I.C.: 3011
N.A.I.C.S.: 326211

Michelin Vietnam Company Limited **(1)**
8th Floor VFC Tower 29 Ton Duc Thang Street
District 1, Ho Chi Minh City, Vietnam
Tel.: (84) 8 3911 8115
Fax: (84) 8 3910 5417
Automotive Tire Mfr & Distr
S.I.C.: 3011
N.A.I.C.S.: 326211

Nihon Michelin Tire Co., Ltd. **(1)**
Fujimi Bldg 6-1 Fujimi 1-chome
Chiyoda-ku, Tokyo, 102-8176, Japan
Tel.: (81) 352102732
Fax: (81) 352102703
Automotive Tire Mfr & Distr
S.I.C.: 3011
N.A.I.C.S.: 326211

Shanghai Michelin Warrior Tire Co., Ltd. **(1)**
No 2915 Jianchuan Rd
Minhang Dist, Shanghai, 201111, China
Tel.: (86) 2134054888
Fax: (86) 2133727711
Automotive Tire Mfr & Distr
S.I.C.: 3011
N.A.I.C.S.: 326211

Societe des Matieres Premieres Tropicales Pte. Ltd. **(1)**
78 Shenton Way 23-02
Singapore, 079120, Singapore
Tel.: (65) 64389500
Fax: (65) 64389501
E-Mail:
Emp.: 50
Automotive Tire Mfr
S.I.C.: 3011
N.A.I.C.S.: 326211

Suomen Euromaster Oy **(1)**
Nuolihaukantie 5
28220 Pori, Finland
Tel.: (358) 26340600
Fax: (358) 26393605
Automotive Tire Distr
S.I.C.: 5014
N.A.I.C.S.: 423130

Tigar Tyres d.o.o. **(1)**
213 Nikole Pasica Str
18300 Pirot, Serbia
Tel.: (381) 10304000
Fax: (381) 10313141
Web Site: www.tigarmh.tigar.com
Tire Mfr & Distr
S.I.C.: 3011
N.A.I.C.S.: 326211

Uniroyal Goodrich Canada, Inc. **(1)**
131 Goodrich Dr
9000
Kitchener, ON, N2G 4S5, Canada (100%)
Tel.: (519) 894-7800
Fax: (519) 894-7874
Web Site: www.michelin.ca
Emp.: 15
Mfr. of Tires
S.I.C.: 3011
N.A.I.C.S.: 326211

COMPAGNIE MARITIME BELGE S.A.

De Gerlachekaai 20
BE 2000 Antwerp, Belgium
Tel.: (32) 32475911
Fax: (32) 32480906
E-Mail: info@cmb.be
Web Site: www.cmb.be
Year Founded: 1895
CMB—(EUR)
Sls.: $656,389,000
Assets: $2,283,716,000
Liabilities: $1,224,212,000
Net Worth: $1,059,504,000
Earnings: $130,874,000
Fiscal Year-end: 12/31/12

Business Description:
Cargo Transportation Services
S.I.C.: 4412
N.A.I.C.S.: 483111

Personnel:
Marc Saverys *(CEO)*
Francis Sarre *(Sec)*

Board of Directors:
Etienne F. Davignon
Jean-Pierre Blumberg
Ludwig Criel
Jean-Pierre Hansen
Fiona Morrison
Alexander Saverys
Marc Saverys
Virginie Saverys
Benoit Timmermans
Eric Verbeeck

Subsidiaries:

Bocimar Belgium NV **(1)**
De Gerlachekaai 20
Antwerp, 2000, Belgium
Tel.: (32) 32475111
Fax: (32) 32480906
E-Mail: ict@cmb.be
Emp.: 40
Container Shipping Services
S.I.C.: 4499
N.A.I.C.S.: 488390
Marc Saverys *(Gen Mgr)*

Bocimar International N.V. **(1)**
De Gerlachekaai 20
2000 Antwerp, Belgium (100%)
Tel.: (32) 32475111
Fax: (32) 32475195
E-Mail: bocimar.management@cmb.be
Sales Range: $350-399.9 Million
Emp.: 30
Deep Sea Freight Transportation Services
S.I.C.: 4412
N.A.I.C.S.: 483111
Benoit Timmermans *(Pres)*

Bocimar NV **(1)**
De Gerlachekaai 20
2000 Antwerp, Belgium
Tel.: (32) 32475111
Fax: (32) 32475195
E-Mail: bocimar.chartering@cmb.be
Emp.: 30
Marine Cargo Handling Services
S.I.C.: 4491
N.A.I.C.S.: 488320
Benoit Timmermans *(Gen Mgr)*

CMB NV **(1)**
De Gerlachekaai 20
Antwerp, 2000, Belgium
Tel.: (32) 32475911
Fax: (32) 32480906
E-Mail: info@cmb.be
Emp.: 200
Maine Cargo Handling Services
S.I.C.: 4491
N.A.I.C.S.: 488320
Marc Saverys *(Mng Dir)*

Hessenatie Logistics NV **(1)**
Schalienstraat 3
2000 Antwerp, Belgium (100%)
Tel.: (32) 32165900
Fax: (32) 32165992
E-Mail: info@heslog.be
Web Site: www.heslog.be
Emp.: 25
Logistics Services
S.I.C.: 4731
N.A.I.C.S.: 541614

Non-U.S. Subsidiaries:

Bocimar Hong Kong Limited **(1)**
Room 3206 32nd Floor Lippo Centre Tower Two 89 Queensway
Admiralty, Central, China (Hong Kong)
Tel.: (852) 2861 3880
Fax: (852) 2861 3881
Marine Transportation Services
S.I.C.: 4499
N.A.I.C.S.: 488390

CMB Japan Limited **(1)**
Room 401 Authentic Hanzomon 2 Kojimachi 2 Chome
Chiyoda-ku, Tokyo, 102-0083, Japan
Tel.: (81) 332649861
Fax: (81) 3 3264 9866
E-Mail: cmbjp@cmb.jp
Marine Cargo Handling Services
S.I.C.: 4491
N.A.I.C.S.: 488320

CMB Services SA **(1)**
20 Rue de Hollerich
1740 Luxembourg, Luxembourg
Tel.: (352) 4828501
Fax: (352) 48 28 71
E-Mail: admin@cmbserv.lu
Emp.: 1
Water Transportation Services
S.I.C.: 4499
N.A.I.C.S.: 488390
Beersmans Ludo *(Gen Mgr)*

Portline-Transportes Maritimos Internacionais SA **(1)**
Avenida Infante D Henrique N 332-3rd Floor
1849-025 Lisbon, Portugal
Tel.: (351) 218391800
Fax: (351) 218376680
E-Mail: mail@portline.pt
Web Site: www.portline.pt
Cargo Handling Services
S.I.C.: 4491
N.A.I.C.S.: 488320
Manuel Magalhaes *(Mng Dir)*

Sakura International KK **(1)**
7-26-3 Kameido
Koto-Ku, Tokyo, 136-0071, Japan
Tel.: (81) 356273308
Cargo Handling Services
S.I.C.: 4491
N.A.I.C.S.: 488320

Non-U.S. Joint Venture:

ASL Aviation Group Ltd. **(1)**
No 3 Malahide Road
Swords, Dublin, Ireland
Tel.: (353) 1 892 8100
Fax: (353) 1 892 8150
E-Mail: info@aslaviationgroup.com
Web Site: www.aslaviationgroup.com
Rev.: $511,594,408
Assets: $554,359,537
Liabilities: $356,807,743
Net Worth: $197,551,794
Earnings: $35,086,575
Emp.: 987
Fiscal Year-end: 12/31/12
Passenger & Freight Air Transportation Services
S.I.C.: 4512
N.A.I.C.S.: 481111
Ludwig Criel *(Chm)*
Hugh Flynn *(CEO)*
N. O'Connor *(Sec)*

Subsidiary:

Air Contractors (Ireland) Limited **(2)**
3 Malahide Rd
Swords, Dublin, Ireland IE
Tel.: (353) 18121900
Fax: (353) 18121919
E Mail: info@aircontractors.com
Web Site: www.aircontractors.com
Emp.: 60
Freight Air Transportation Services
S.I.C.: 4512
N.A.I.C.S.: 481112
Hugh Flynn *(CEO)*

COMPAGNIE MONEGASQUE DE BANQUE

23 Ave de la Costa
98000 Monaco, Monaco
Tel.: (377) 93157777
Fax: (377) 93250869
E-Mail: cmb@cmb.mc
Web Site: www.cmb.mc
Rev.: $89,412,611
Assets: $2,766,098,000
Liabilities: $2,042,271,815
Net Worth: $723,826,186
Earnings: $65,571,941
Emp.: 177
Fiscal Year-end: 12/31/12

Business Description:
Banking Services
S.I.C.: 6029
N.A.I.C.S.: 522110

Personnel:
Etienne Franzi *(Chm)*
Aldo Civaschi *(Vice Chm)*
Werner Peyer *(CEO)*

Board of Directors:
Etienne Franzi
Francesco Carloni
Aldo Civaschi
Evelyne Genta
Claude Giordan
Michel-Yves Mourou
Giampiero Pesenti
Werner Peyer
Alberto Rosati
Giuseppe Sabato
Sveva Severi
Francesco Saverio Vinci
Marco Vittorelli

COMPAL ELECTRONICS, INC.

581 Ruiguang Rd
Neihu, Taipei, 11492, Taiwan
Tel.: (886) 2 8797 8588
Fax: (886) 226585001
E-Mail: investor@compal.com
Web Site: www.compal.com
Year Founded: 1984
2324—(TAI)
Sls.: $23,129,530,329
Assets: $10,475,432,551
Liabilities: $6,567,899,865
Net Worth: $3,907,532,687
Earnings: $245,743,277
Emp.: 20,000
Fiscal Year-end: 12/31/12

Business Description:
Computer Monitors & Notebook Computers & LCD Mfr
S.I.C.: 3577
N.A.I.C.S.: 334118

Personnel:
Rock Sheng-Hsiun Hsu *(Chm)*
Ray Jui-Tsung Chen *(Pres & CEO)*
Gary Lu *(CFO & Sr VP)*

Transfer Agent:
Chinatrust
5F No 83 Sec 1 Chung Ching Nan Road
Taipei, Taiwan

Subsidiary:

Arcadyan Technology Corporation **(1)**
4th Floor 9 Park Avenue II
Science-Based Industrial Park, Hsin-chu, 300, Taiwan (50%)
Tel.: (886) 35787000
Fax: (886) 35637326
E-Mail: taiwan@arcadyan.com
Web Site: www.arcadyan.com.tw
3596—(TAI)
Sales Range: $250-299.9 Million
Emp.: 2,600
Wireless Networking Equipment Mfr

S.I.C.: 3663
N.A.I.C.S.: 334220
Ray Chen *(Chm)*
Hong-Yuh Lee *(Pres)*
Andrew Lu *(CFO)*
Mike Lu *(Exec VP)*

U.S. Subsidiaries:

Bizcom Electronics, Inc. **(1)**
1171 Montague Express Way
Milpitas, CA 95035
Tel.: (408) 262-7877
Fax: (408) 262-3907
Web Site: www.bizcom-us.com
Emp.: 155
Computer Peripherals Distr
S.I.C.: 5045
N.A.I.C.S.: 423430
Duan Wang *(CEO)*

Sceptre Industries, Inc. **(1)**
16800 E Gale Ave
City of Industry, CA 91745
Tel.: (626) 968-8668
Toll Free: (800) 788-2878
E-Mail: marketing@sceptre.com
Web Site: www.sceptre.com
Emp.: 70
Computer Equipment Mfr
S.I.C.: 3575
N.A.I.C.S.: 334118

Non-U.S. Subsidiaries:

Toshiba Electromex, S.A. de C.V. **(1)**
Avenida Rio Bravo 1230
Zaragoza, Chihuahua, 32700, Mexico
Tel.: (52) 6566820340
Fax: (52) 6566820201
Emp.: 1,959
LCD TV Mfr
S.I.C.: 3679
N.A.I.C.S.: 334419

U.S. Subsidiaries:

Amexcom Electronics, Inc. **(2)**
9555 Plaza Cir Ste B
El Paso, TX 79927-2005 (100%)
Tel.: (915) 858-7533
Fax: (915) 858-6650
Emp.: 5
TV Components Mfr
S.I.C.: 3651
N.A.I.C.S.: 334310
Robert Lail *(Dir-IT)*

COMPANHIA BRASILEIRA DE DISTRIBUICAO

(d/b/a Grupo Pao de Acucar)
Avenida Brigadeiro Luis Antonio No 3142
01402-901 Sao Paulo, SP, Brazil
Tel.: (55) 11 3886 0421
Fax: (55) 11 3884 2677
Web Site: www.gpari.com.br
Year Founded: 1981
CBD—(BRAZ NYSE)
Sls.: $25,049,233,121
Assets: $17,411,053,542
Liabilities: $11,966,839,125
Net Worth: $5,444,214,417
Earnings: $568,839,304
Emp.: 151,037
Fiscal Year-end: 12/31/12

Business Description:
Supermarket & Hypermarket Owner & Operator
S.I.C.: 5399
N.A.I.C.S.: 445110

Personnel:
Abilio dos Santos Diniz *(Chm)*
Arnaud Daniel Charles Walter Joachim Strasser *(Vice Chm)*
Eneas Cesar Pestana Neto *(CEO)*
Paulo Gualtieri *(Deputy CEO-Strategic Dev)*
Caio Racy Mattar *(VP-Specialized Bus & Member-Exec Bd)*
Christophe Hidalgo *(Exec VP-Fin)*
Hugo A. Jorda Bethlem *(Exec VP-Corp Rels & Sustainability)*

Board of Directors:
Abilio dos Santos Diniz
Candido Botelho Bracher
Jean Louis Bourgier
Pedro Henrique Chermont de Miranda
Ana Maria Falleiros dos Santos Diniz D'Avila
Pedro Paulo Falleiros dos Santos Diniz
Joao Paulo Felleiros dos Santos Diniz
Guilherme Affonso Ferreira
Ulisses Kameyama
Geyze Marchesi Diniz
Jean-Charles Henri Naouri
Antonie Marie Remi Lazars Giscard D'Estaing
Fabio Schvartsman
Arnaud Daniel Charles Walter Joachim Strasser

Subsidiaries:

Auto Posto Imperio Ltda. **(1)**
Rua Joaquim Carlos 1380
03019-000 Sao Paulo, Brazil
Tel.: (55) 11 22917166
Supermarket Operator
S.I.C.: 5411
N.A.I.C.S.: 445110

Casa Bahia Contact Center Ltda **(1)**
Rua da Graca 873
Sao Paulo, Brazil
Tel.: (55) 1142256000
Business Consulting Services
S.I.C.: 8742
N.A.I.C.S.: 541611

Via Varejo S.A. **(1)**
R Joao Pessoa 83
09520-010 Sao Caetano do Sul, SP, Brazil
Tel.: (55) 11 4225 6989
Fax: (55) 11 4225 9905
Web Site: www.viavarejo.com.br
VVAR3—(BRAZ)
Emp.: 70,000
Electronic Retail Store Operator
S.I.C.: 5734
N.A.I.C.S.: 443142
Michael Klein *(Chm)*
Arnaud Daniel Charles Walter Joachim Strasser *(Vice Chm)*
Francisco Tosta Valim Filho *(CEO)*
Marcelo Lopes *(Deputy CEO-Infrastructure)*
Vitor Faga de Almeida *(CFO & IR Officer)*

COMPANHIA CACIQUE DE CAFE SOLUVEL

R Horacio Sabino Coimbra 100
86072900 Londrina, PR, Brazil
Tel.: (55) 43 4009 6186
Fax: (55) 43 4009 6363
E-Mail: cafepele@cafepele.com.br
Web Site: www.cafepele.com.br
Year Founded: 1959
CIQU3—(BRAZ)
Sales Range: $300-349.9 Million
Emp.: 1,322

Business Description:
Coffee Mfr & Whslr
S.I.C.: 2099
N.A.I.C.S.: 311920

Personnel:
Paulo Roberto Ferro *(Dir-IR)*

COMPANHIA CELG DE PARTICIPACOES - CELGPAR

R 2 - Quadra A-37 505 - Edif Gileno Godoi
74805180 Goiania, GO, Brazil
Tel.: (55) 62 3243 1122
Fax: (55) 62 3243 1461
Web Site: celgpar.celg.com.br
Year Founded: 1956
GPAR3—(BRAZ)
Sales Range: $25-49.9 Million

Business Description:
Investment Management Services
S.I.C.: 6799
N.A.I.C.S.: 523920

Personnel:
Braulio Afonso Morais *(Dir-IR)*

COMPANHIA DE CONCESSOES RODOVIARIAS, S.A.

(See Under CCR S.A.)

COMPANHIA DE FERRO LIGAS DA BAHIA - FERBASA

Estrada de Santiago s/n
Ipojuca, Bahia, 48120-000, Brazil
Tel.: (55) 7136458700
Fax: (55) 7136451211
E-Mail: ferbasa@ferbasa.com.br
Web Site: www.ferbasa.com.br
FESA4—(BRAZ)
Sales Range: $400-449.9 Million
Emp.: 2,800

Business Description:
Ferrochrome Alloy Mfr
S.I.C.: 3399
N.A.I.C.S.: 331110

Personnel:
Pedro Barbosa de Deus *(Chm)*
Mario Ordoniz Nacif *(Vice Chm)*
Geraldo de Oliveira Lopes *(CEO & Chief IR Officer)*
Marta T. Barroso Fernandes *(Admin Officer)*
Giorgio Boscaini *(Engrg Officer)*
Sebastiao da Cruz Andrade *(Forestry Officer)*
Oseias da Rocha Fiau *(Indus Officer)*
Jose Ronaldo Sobrinho *(Mining Officer)*
Victor Vieira Rodrigues *(Fin Officer)*

Board of Directors:
Pedro Barbosa de Deus
Sergio Curvelo Doria
Barbara Klein de Araujo Carvalho
Geraldo de Oliveira Lopes
Paulo Roberto Magalhaes Bastos
Adelmo Jose Melgaco
Mario Ordoniz Nacif
Marcos Sampaio

Plant:

Companhia de Ferro Ligas da Bahia - Ferbasa - The Pojuca Factory **(1)**
Estrada de Santiago
Ipojuca, 48120-000, Brazil
Tel.: (55) 7136458700
Fax: (55) 7136451211
Web Site: www.ferbasa.com.br
Steel Products Mfr
S.I.C.: 3399
N.A.I.C.S.: 331110

COMPANHIA DE FIACAO E. TECIDOS CEDRO E CACHOEIRA

R Paraiba 337
30130-140 Belo Horizonte, Brazil MG
Tel.: (55) 31 3235 5223
Fax: (55) 31 3235 5033
E-Mail: sac@cedro.ind.br
Web Site: www.cedro.ind.br
Year Founded: 1872
CEDO3—(BRAZ)

Business Description:
Textile Product Mfr
S.I.C.: 2299
N.A.I.C.S.: 313210

Personnel:
Fabio Mascarenhas Alves *(Dir-IR)*

COMPANHIA DE LOCACAO DAS AMERICAS

Avenida Raja Gabaglia n 1 781 Belo Horizonte 12 andar
Luxemburgo, Belo Horizonte, Brazil 30350-540
Tel.: (55) 31 3316 1981
Fax: (55) 31 3319 1573
E-Mail: ri@locamerica.com.br
Web Site: www.locamerica.com.br
Year Founded: 1993
LCAM3—(BRAZ)
Rev.: $218,430
Assets: $583,098
Liabilities: $434,648
Net Worth: $148,450
Earnings: $1,831
Emp.: 665
Fiscal Year-end: 12/31/12

Business Description:
Vehicle Leasing Services
S.I.C.: 7519
N.A.I.C.S.: 532120

Personnel:
Luis Fernando Memoria Porto *(Chm & CEO)*
Sergio Augusto Guerra de Resende *(Vice Chm)*
Joel Kos *(CFO & IR Officer)*

Board of Directors:
Luis Fernando Memoria Porto
Bruno Jacques Carneiro
Sergio Augusto Guerra de Resende
Francisco Nuno Pontes Correia Neves
Valter Pasquini

COMPANHIA DE PARTICIPACOES ALIANCA DA BAHIA

Rua Pinto Martins n 11 - Comercio
Salvador, Bahia, 40015-020, Brazil
Tel.: (55) 71 3616 1013
Fax: (55) 71 3616 1016
Web Site: www.aliancaparticipacoes.com.br
Year Founded: 1997
PEAB3—(BRAZ)
Sales Range: $75-99.9 Million
Emp.: 35

Business Description:
Investment Management Services
S.I.C.: 6282
N.A.I.C.S.: 523920

Personnel:
Antonio Tavares Da Camara *(Dir-IR)*

COMPANHIA DE SANEAMENTO BASICO DO ESTADO DE SAO PAULO - SABESP

Rua Costa Carvalho 300
05429-900 Sao Paulo, Brazil
Tel.: (55) 11 3388 8000
Fax: (55) 11 3813 0254
Web Site: www.sabesp.com.br
SBSP3—(BRAZ)
Rev.: $5,289,999,032
Assets: $13,121,555,819
Liabilities: $7,358,780,648
Net Worth: $5,762,775,171
Earnings: $940,444,491
Emp.: 15,019
Fiscal Year-end: 12/31/12

Business Description:
Public Water & Sewage Systems Operator
S.I.C.: 4941
N.A.I.C.S.: 221310

Personnel:
Edson de Oliveira Giriboni *(Chm)*
Dilma Seli Pena *(CEO)*
Rui de Britto Alvares Affonso *(CFO & IR Officer)*
Luiz Paulo de Almeida Neto *(Reg Sys Officer)*
Marcelo Salles Holanda de Freitas *(Officer-Tech, Enterprises & Environment)*
Manuelito Pereira Magalhaes, Jr. *(Officer-Corp Mgmt)*
Paulo Massato Yoshimoto *(Officer-Metropolitan Reg)*

Companhia de Saneamento Basico do Estado de Sao Paulo - SABESP—(Continued)

Board of Directors:
Edson de Oliveira Giriboni
Jeronimo Antunes
Sidney Estanislau Beraldo
Alexander Bialer
Andrea Sandro Calabi
Heraldo Gilberto de Oliveira
Alberto Goldman
Reinaldo Guerreiro
Dilma Seli Pena
Walter Tesch

COMPANHIA DE SANEAMENTO DO PARANA SANEPAR
Rua Engenheiros Reboucas
Curitiba, Parana, Brazil
Tel.: (55) 4133303636
Fax: (55) 4133338834
Web Site: www.sanepar.com.br
SAPR4—(BRAZ)
Emp.: 4,005
Business Description:
Water Supply & Treatment Services
S.I.C.: 4971
N.A.I.C.S.: 221310
Personnel:
Ivan Lelis Bonilha *(Chm)*

COMPANHIA DE SEGUROS ALIANCA DA BAHIA
Rua Pinto Martins 11 Ed
Comendador Pedreira - Comercio
Salvador, BA, 40015-020, Brazil
Tel.: (55) 71 3616 1055
Fax: (55) 71 3616 1073
Web Site: www.alba.com.br
Year Founded: 1870
CSAB3—(BRAZ)
Sales Range: $25-49.9 Million
Emp.: 133
Business Description:
Insurance Management Services
S.I.C.: 6411
N.A.I.C.S.: 524298
Personnel:
Antonio Tavares Da Camara *(Dir-IR)*

COMPANHIA ENERGETICA DE BRASILIA - CEB
Sgcvs Lote 15 - Edificio Jade - Bloco C - 2
71215100 Brasilia, DF, Brazil
Tel.: (55) 61 3799 2350
Fax: (55) 61 3799 2351
Web Site: www.ceb.com.br
Year Founded: 1968
CEBR3—(BRAZ)
Sales Range: $650-699.9 Million
Emp.: 693
Business Description:
Investment Management Services
S.I.C.: 6799
N.A.I.C.S.: 523920
Personnel:
Marcelo Gomes de Alencar *(Dir-IR)*

COMPANHIA ENERGETICA DE MINAS GERAIS - CEMIG
Avenida Barbacena 1200
Belo Horizonte, MG, 30190-131, Brazil
Tel.: (55) 31 3506 3711
Web Site: www.cemig.com.br
Year Founded: 1952
CIG—(BRAZ MAD NYSE)
Rev.: $9,080,289,400
Assets: $20,055,830,970
Liabilities: $14,131,507,810
Net Worth: $5,924,323,160
Earnings: $2,101,354,080
Emp.: 8,368
Fiscal Year-end: 12/31/12
Business Description:
Electricity Generation, Transmission & Distribution Services
S.I.C.: 9631
N.A.I.C.S.: 926130
Personnel:
Djalma Bastos de Morais *(Pres & CEO)*
Subsidiaries:

Cemig Distribuicao S.A. **(1)**
Av Barbacena 1 200 - 5 Andar - Ala B1 Bairro Santo Agostinho, Belo Horizonte, Minas Gerais, 30190-131, Brazil
Tel.: (55) 31 3506 5028
Fax: (55) 31 3506 5026
Electric Power Distribution Services
S.I.C.: 4911
N.A.I.C.S.: 221122

Cemig Geracao e Transmissao S.A. **(1)**
Avenida Barbacena n 1 200 12 Andar Ala B1 Bairro Santo Agostinho
Belo Horizonte, Minas Gerais, 30190-131, Brazil
Tel.: (55) 31 3506 5024
Fax: (55) 31 3506 5026
Electric Power Generation & Distribution Services
S.I.C.: 4939
N.A.I.C.S.: 221118
Djalma Bastos de Morais *(Pres & CEO)*
Luiz Fernando Rolla *(CFO)*

Cemig Telecomunicacoes S.A. **(1)**
Rua dos Inconfidentes 1051 - Terreo e 1a sobreloja
Funcionarios, 30140-120 Belo Horizonte, Minas Gerais, Brazil
Tel.: (55) 31 3307 6300
Fax: (55) 31 3307 6380
E-Mail: comercial@cemigtelecom.com
Web Site: www.infovias.com.br
Telecommunication Services
S.I.C.: 4899
N.A.I.C.S.: 517919

Cemig Trading S.A. **(1)**
Av Barbacena 1200 Ala 5 A1 Parte 1 Sto Agostinho
Belo Horizonte, Minas Gerais, 30190-131, Brazil
Tel.: (55) 3132993711
Electric Power Distribution Services
S.I.C.: 4931
N.A.I.C.S.: 221122

Central Termeletrica de Cogeracao S.A. **(1)**
Av Barbacena 1 200
Belo Horizonte, Minas Gerais, 30123-970, Brazil
Tel.: (55) 3132502015
Electric Power Distribution Services
S.I.C.: 4939
N.A.I.C.S.: 221122

Efficientia S.A. **(1)**
Rua Aimores 3000 12 Andar - Barro Preto Ed Minerva, 30140-073 Belo Horizonte, Minas Gerais, Brazil
Tel.: (55) 31 3273 8133
Fax: (55) 31 3274 1763
Web Site: www.efficientia.com.br
Electric Power Mfr & Distr
S.I.C.: 4931
N.A.I.C.S.: 221111

Empresa de Servicos e Comercializacao de Energia Eletrica S.A. **(1)**
Rua dos Aimores 3000 - Barro Preto
Belo Horizonte, Minas Gerais, 30140-073, Brazil
Tel.: (55) 31 3506 3838
Electric Power Generation Services
S.I.C.: 4931
N.A.I.C.S.: 221118

Horizontes Energia S.A. **(1)**
Praia do Flamengo 66 1509B
Flamengo, Rio do Janeiro, Brazil
Tel.: (55) 21 2225 2209
Fax: (55) 21 2225 1528
E-Mail: horizonte@horizonteenergia.com.br
Web Site: www.horizonteenergia.com.br
Electric Power Generation Services
S.I.C.: 4939
N.A.I.C.S.: 221118

Rio Minas Energia Participacoes S.A. **(1)**
Av Rio Branco 123
Marechal Falorinno 168 20080-0, Rio de Janeiro, 20040-005, Brazil
Tel.: (55) 2122112980
E-Mail: cristina.guedes@light.com.br
Web Site: www.light.com.br
Emp.: 4,000
Holding Company
S.I.C.: 6719
N.A.I.C.S.: 551112
Jose Alqueres *(Chm)*

Subsidiary:

Light Servicos de Eletricidade S.A. **(2)**
Avenida Marechal Floriano 168
Rio de Janeiro, 20080 002, Brazil
Tel.: (55) 2122112794
Fax: (55) 2122112530
E-Mail: ricardo.levis@light.com.br
Web Site: www.light.com.br
Emp.: 6,000
Electric Power Generalization, Transmission & Distribution
S.I.C.: 3612
N.A.I.C.S.: 335311

COMPANHIA ENERGETICA DE SAO PAULO
(See Under CESP - Companhia Energetica de Sao Paulo)

COMPANHIA HABITASUL DE PARTICIPACOES
R Gal Joao Manoel 157 - 17 Floor
90010030 Porto Alegre, RS, Brazil
Tel.: (55) 51 3220 3516
Fax: (55) 51 3220 3751
E-Mail: contatos@habitasul.com.br
Web Site: www.habitasul.com.br
HBTS3—(BRAZ)
Sales Range: $25-49.9 Million
Business Description:
Real Estate Development Services
S.I.C.: 6531
N.A.I.C.S.: 531390
Personnel:
Eurito de Freitas Druck *(Dir-IR)*

COMPANHIA INDUSTRIAL CATAGUASES
Praca Jose Inacio Peixoto 28
36772-900 Brasilia, MG, Brazil
Tel.: (55) 32 3422 2211
Fax: (55) 32 3421 1382
E-Mail: cic@cataguases.com.br
Web Site: www.cataguases.com.br
Year Founded: 1936
CATA3—(BRAZ)
Business Description:
Textile Product Mfr & Whslr
S.I.C.: 2299
N.A.I.C.S.: 313210
Personnel:
Jose Inacio Peixoto Neto *(Pres)*

COMPANHIA INDUSTRIAL SCHLOSSER S/A.
Avenida Getulio Vargas 63/87
Caixa postal 17
Centro, 88353-000 Brusque, Santa Catarina, Brazil
Tel.: (55) 47 3251 8000
Fax: (55) 47 3251 8004
E-Mail: schlosser@schlosser.com.br
Web Site: www.schlosser.com.br
Year Founded: 1911
SCLO3—(BRAZ)
Emp.: 565
Business Description:
Textile Product Mfr & Whslr
S.I.C.: 2299
N.A.I.C.S.: 313110
Personnel:
Joao Beckhauser *(Dir-IR)*

COMPANHIA MELHORAMENTOS DE SAO PAULO
Rua Tito 479 - Vila Romana Lapa
05051-000 Sao Paulo, Brazil
Mailing Address:
Cx Postal 1729
01031-970 Sao Paulo, Brazil
Tel.: (55) 11 3874 0600
Fax: (55) 11 3675 2875
E-Mail: ri_melhoramentos@melhoramentos.com.br
Web Site: www.melhoramentos.com.br
Year Founded: 1890
MSPA3—(BRAZ)
Sales Range: $25-49.9 Million
Business Description:
Investment Management Services
S.I.C.: 6282
N.A.I.C.S.: 523920
Personnel:
Sergio Sesiki *(Dir-IR)*

COMPANHIA PARANAENSE DE ENERGIA
(d/b/a COPEL)
Rua Coronel Dulcidio 800
80420-170 Curitiba, Parana, Brazil
Tel.: (55) 41 3322 3535
Fax: (55) 41 3331 4145
E-Mail: copel@copel.com
Web Site: www.copel.com
Year Founded: 1954
ELP—(BRAZ NYSE)
Rev.: $4,196,912,220
Assets: $10,433,751,297
Liabilities: $4,286,357,006
Net Worth: $6,147,394,291
Earnings: $357,367,923
Emp.: 9,629
Fiscal Year-end: 12/31/12
Business Description:
Electric Power Generator, Transporter & Distr; Communications & Telecommunications Services
S.I.C.: 4939
N.A.I.C.S.: 221122
Personnel:
Mauricio Schulman *(Chm)*
Ricardo Portugal Alves *(CFO & Chief IR & External Stockholding Officer)*
Julio Jacob Junior *(Chief Legal Officer)*
Vlademir Santo Daleffe *(Chief Distr Officer)*
Jaime de Oliveira Kuhn *(Chief Power Generation & Transmission Officer)*
Pedro Augusto do Nascimento Neto *(Chief Distr Officer)*
Yara Christina Eisenbach *(Chief Corp Mgmt Officer)*
Gilberto Mendes Fernandes *(Chief Environment & Corp Citizenship Officer)*
Jonel Nazareno Iurk *(Chief Environment & Corp Citizenship Officer)*
Jorge Andriguetto Junior *(Chief Engrg Officer)*
Lindolfo Zimmer *(Sec)*
Board of Directors:
Mauricio Schulman
Pedro Luiz Cerize
Fabiano Braga Cortes
Nilton Camargo Costa
Paulo Procopiak de Aguiar

Jose Richa Filho
Carlos Homero Giacomini
Lindolfo Zimmer

Banco Itau S.A.
Rua Boa Vista, 185-7 Andar
01092-900 Sao Paulo, SP, Brazil
Tel.: (55) 11 237 5151
Fax: (55) 11 237 5756

Subsidiaries:

CEOLPAR - CENTRAIS EOLICAS DO PARANA LTDA. (1)
Br 280 Km 26 S/n
Palmas, Parana, Brazil
Tel.: (55) 46 32626452
Electric Power Distribution Services
S.I.C.: 4911
N.A.I.C.S.: 221122

COMPAGAS - CIA. PARANAENSE DE GAS (1)
Pasteur 463
Curitiba, Parana, 80250-080, Brazil
Tel.: (55) 4133121900
Fax: (55) 4133121922
E-Mail: compagas@compagas.com.br
Web Site: www.compagas.com.br
Emp.: 130
Natural Gas Distr
S.I.C.: 4924
N.A.I.C.S.: 221210
Luciano Pizzatto *(Gen Mgr)*

Copel Companhia Energia S/A (1)
Rua Coronel Dulcidio 800
Curitiba, 80420-170, Brazil
Tel.: (55) 4133223535
Fax: (55) 4133312849
E-Mail: ri@copel.com
Web Site: www.copel.com
Emp.: 100
Holding Company
S.I.C.: 6719
N.A.I.C.S.: 551112
Solange Gomide *(Mng Dir-Industrial Rels)*

Copel Distribuicao SA (1)
Rua Coronel Dulcidio 800
Curitiba, Parana, 80420-170, Brazil
Tel.: (55) 4133223535
Fax: (55) 4133312849
E-Mail: ri@copel.com
Web Site: www.copel.com
Electric Power Distribution
S.I.C.: 4911
N.A.I.C.S.: 221122
Rubens Ghilardi *(CEO)*
Rafael Iatauro *(CFO)*

Copel Telecomunicacoes S.A. (1)
Rua Jose Izidoro Biazetto 158 - Bloco A - Mossungue
Curitiba, Parana, Brazil 81200-240
Tel.: (55) 41 3310 5050
Fax: (55) 41 3331 4145
E-Mail: copel@copel.com
Web Site: www.copel.com
Emp.: 500
Telecommunication Services
S.I.C.: 4899
N.A.I.C.S.: 517919
Lindolfo Zimmer *(CEO)*

Copel Transmissao SA (1)
Jose Izidoro Biazetto 158
Curitiba, 81200 240, Brazil
Tel.: (55) 4133314704
Fax: (55) 4133314112
E-Mail: copel@copel.com.br
Web Site: www.copel.com.br
Emp.: 1,000
Electric Power Distribution
S.I.C.: 4931
N.A.I.C.S.: 221122
Lindolfo Zimmer *(Gen Mgr)*

ELEJOR - CENTRAIS ELETRICAS DO RIO JORDAO S.A. (1)
Rua Jose de Alencar n 2021
Juveve, 80040-070 Curitiba, Parana, Brazil
Tel.: (55) 4132620106
Fax: (55) 4133620115
E-Mail: elejor@elejor.com.br
Web Site: www.elejor.com.br
Emp.: 10
Electric Power Generation Services
S.I.C.: 4939
N.A.I.C.S.: 221118
Rafael Latauro *(Pres)*

UEGA - USINA ELETRICA A GAS DE ARAUCARIA LTDA. (1)
Rua Visconde do Rio Branco 1341 9 Andar
Curitiba, Parana, Brazil
Tel.: (55) 83708 795
Fax: (55) 41 3075 8699
E-Mail: uega@uega.com.br
Web Site: www.uega.com.br
Emp.: 13
Electric Power Generation Services
S.I.C.: 4931
N.A.I.C.S.: 221118
Flavio Chiesa *(Dir-Tech)*

COMPANHIA PROVIDENCIA INDUSTRIA E COMERCIO

Rodovia BR 376 km 16 5 Barro Preto
Sao Jose dos Pinhais, Parana, 83015-000, Brazil
Tel.: (55) 4133817600
Fax: (55) 4133817656
Web Site: www.providencia.com.br
PRVI3—(BRAZ)
Sales Range: $250-299.9 Million

Business Description:
Disposable & Durable Goods Mfr
S.I.C.: 2676
N.A.I.C.S.: 322291

Personnel:
Renan Bergmann *(Chm)*
Herminio de Freitas *(CEO)*
Eduardo Feldmann *(CFO & IR Officer)*

Board of Directors:
Renan Bergmann
Henrique Constantino
Marcelo de Araujo
Manuel de Sousa
Antonio Kandir
Guido Padovano
Elemer Andre Suranyi

U.S. Subsidiary:

Providencia USA, Inc. (1)
200 Deer Ridge Dr
Statesville, NC 28625-2526
Tel.: (704) 247-9853
Fax: (704) 768-2800
Emp.: 64
Nonwoven Fabrics Mfr
S.I.C.: 2297
N.A.I.C.S.: 313230
Herminio Freitas *(Pres)*

COMPANHIA SIDERURGICA NACIONAL

(d/b/a National Steel Company)
Av Brigadeiro Faria Lima 3400 20th Floor
04538 132 Sao Paulo, SP, Brazil
Tel.: (55) 11 3049 7100
Fax: (55) 11 3049 7150
E-Mail: invrel@csn.com.br
Web Site: www.csn.com.br
Year Founded: 1941
SID—(BRAZ NYSE)
Rev.: $8,311,103,299
Assets: $24,247,829,701
Liabilities: $19,817,124,131
Net Worth: $4,430,705,570
Earnings: ($236,389,545)
Emp.: 21,232
Fiscal Year-end: 12/31/12

Business Description:
Steel & Tin Mfr
S.I.C.: 3399
N.A.I.C.S.: 331110

Personnel:
Benjamin Steinbruch *(Chm & CEO)*
Jacks Rabinovich *(Vice Chm)*
Eneas Garcia Diniz *(Exec Officer)*

Board of Directors:
Benjamin Steinbruch
Antonio Francisco Dos Santos
Yoshiaki Nakano
Fernando Perrone
Jacks Rabinovich

Subsidiaries:

CSN Cimentos (1)
Ave Brigadeiro Faria Lima 3400
20 deg andar Itaim Bibi, Sao Paulo, Sao Paulo, 04538-132, Brazil
Tel.: (55) 1130497100
Fax: (55) 1130497150
Web Site: www.csn.com.br/portal/page?_pageid=456,172427&_dad=portal&_schema=PORTAL
Emp.: 7,000
Steel Products Mfr
S.I.C.: 3312
N.A.I.C.S.: 331221

CSN Parana (1)
Rodovia PR 423 5500
Estacao, Araucaria, Parana, 83705 000, Brazil
Tel.: (55) 4136418015
Fax: (55) 4136418106
Web Site: www.csn.com.br/portal/page?_pageid=456,170713&_dad=portal&_schema=PORTAL
Emp.: 26
Galvanized Steel Products Mfr
S.I.C.: 3462
N.A.I.C.S.: 332111
Carlos Frederico Xavier *(Gen Mgr)*

CSN Porto Real (1)
Ave Renato Monteiro 7777
Porto Real, RJ, 27570 000, Brazil
Tel.: (55) 2433582900
Fax: (55) 2433582901
Emp.: 400
Galvanized Automotive Products Mfr
S.I.C.: 5013
N.A.I.C.S.: 441310
Milton Picinini Filho *(Gen Mgr)*

Estanho de Rondonia S.A. (1)
Rua do Estanho 123
Setor Apoio Rodoviario, Ariquemes, Rondonia, 78930 000, Brazil
Tel.: (55) 6935352160
Fax: (55) 6935363328
Iron Ore Mfr
S.I.C.: 1011
N.A.I.C.S.: 212210

Inal Nordeste S.A. (1)
Rua do Aluminio s/n Lotes de 01 a 06 - Quadra II
Polo de Apoio, Camacari, Bahia, 42 800 970, Brazil
Tel.: (55) 7121042104
Fax: (55) 7121042100
Steel Products Service Centre
S.I.C.: 3312
N.A.I.C.S.: 331110

Industria Nacional de Acos Laminados SA (1)
Avenida Inal 190 Vila Industrial
Mogi das Cruzes, Sao Paulo, Sao Paulo, 08770 042, Brazil
Tel.: (55) 1147917800
Fax: (55) 1147907900
Web Site: www.brada.br
Emp.: 250
Steel Distr
S.I.C.: 5051
N.A.I.C.S.: 423510
Fulvio Tomaselli *(Mgr)*

Subsidiary:

Companhia Metalurgica Prada (2)
Rua Engenheiro Francisco Pita Britto 138
04753 900 Sao Paulo, Sao Paulo, Brazil
Tel.: (55) 1156821000
Fax: (55) 11 5522 8302
Web Site: www.prada.com.br
Steel Packaging Mfr
S.I.C.: 3324
N.A.I.C.S.: 331512

Sepetiba Tecon S.A. (1)
Estrada da Ilha da Madeira s/n deg, parte, Porto de Itaguai
Ilha da Madeira, Itaguai, Rio de Janeiro, 23826 600, Brazil
Tel.: (55) 2126889366
Fax: (55) 2126889346
E-Mail: comercial@sepetibatecon.com.br
Web Site: www.sepetibatecon.com.br
Emp.: 500
Logistics Services
S.I.C.: 4731
N.A.I.C.S.: 541614
Mauricio Lopes *(Mgr)*

Terminal de Carvao (1)
Estrada da Ilha da Madeira s/n deg, Parte, Porto de Itaguai
Ilha da Madeira
Itaguai, Rio de Janeiro, Brazil
Tel.: (55) 21 26871787
Fax: (55) 21 26871775
Logistics Services
S.I.C.: 4731
N.A.I.C.S.: 541614
Guilherme Moretzsohn Andrade *(Mgr)*

U.S. Subsidiary:

Companhia Siderurgica Nacional LLC (1)
455 W Industrial Dr
Terre Haute, IN 47802 DE
Tel.: (812) 299-4157 (100%)
Fax: (812) 299-3938
E-Mail: sales@csnllc.com
Web Site: www.csnllc.com
Emp.: 200
Steel Mfr
S.I.C.: 3312
N.A.I.C.S.: 331110
Chris Biddle *(Controller)*

Non-U.S. Subsidiaries:

Lusosider Projectos Siderurgicos S.A. (1)
Paio Pires
2840-075 Seixal, Setubal, Portugal
Tel.: (351) 212278300
Fax: (351) 212 27 83 90
E-Mail: paulo.goncalves@lusosider.pt
Web Site: www.lusosider.pt
Emp.: 300
Metallurgy Machines Mfr & Distr
S.I.C.: 3559
N.A.I.C.S.: 333249
Romalo Mansur *(Gen Mgr)*

Stahlwerk Thuringen GmbH (1)
Kronacher Strasse 6
D-07333 Unterwellenborn, Germany De
Mailing Address:
PO Box 1163
D-07331 Unterwellenborn, Germany
Tel.: (49) 36714450
Fax: (49) 3671445107
E-Mail: info@stahlwerk-thueringen.de
Web Site: www.stahlwerk-thueringen.de
Sales Range: $500-549.9 Million
Emp.: 700
Steel Products Mfr
S.I.C.: 3399
N.A.I.C.S.: 331221
Inaki Escos Oyarzabal *(Mng Dir)*

COMPANHIA TECIDOS SANTANENSE

Av Osmane Barbosa 1235
39404-006 Montes Claros, MG, Brazil
Tel.: (55) 31 3349 9820
Fax: (55) 31 3349 9810
E-Mail: export.cts@santanense.com.br
Web Site: www.santanense.com.br
Year Founded: 1891
CTSA3—(BRAZ)

Business Description:
Textile Product Mfr
S.I.C.: 5136
N.A.I.C.S.: 424320

Personnel:
Joao Batista Da Cunha Bomfim *(Dir-IR)*

COMPANIA ANONIMA NACIONAL TELEFONOS DE VENEZUELA

Avenida Libertador Centro Nacional De Telecom
Apartado Postal 1226
Edificio NEA Piso 1, Caracas, 1010, Venezuela

Compania Anonima Nacional Telefonos de Venezuela—(Continued)

Tel.: (58) 2125006800
Fax: (58) 2125003472
E-Mail: info@movilnet.com.ve
Web Site: www.cantv.com.ve
Year Founded: 1930
TDV.D—(CAR)
Sales Range: $1-9.9 Million
Emp.: 8,623

Business Description:
Provider of Telecommunication Services
S.I.C.: 4813
N.A.I.C.S.: 517110

Personnel:
Manuel Fernandez *(Pres)*
Vicente Llatas *(COO & Exec VP)*

Board of Directors:
Ricardo Armas
Edgar Hernandez Behrens
Christopher Bennett
Imanol Valdes Cantolla
Nicolas Vegas Chumaceiro
Ruth De Krivoy
Charles Fallini
Yelitza Garcia
Lorenzo Mendoza Gimenez
Ricardo Hausmann
John Lack
Vicente Llatas
Edward McQuaid
Luis Esteban Palacios
Julio Cesar Perez
Daniel Petri
German Garcia Velutini

Subsidiaries:

Cantv.net **(1)**
2da Av con 3era Transversal Los Cortijos de Lourdes
Edif Cantv Los Cortijos, Caracas, 1060, Venezuela
Tel.: (58) 2 9013850
Fax: (58) 2 9013763
Wireless Communication Services
S.I.C.: 4812
N.A.I.C.S.: 517210

Caveguias **(1)**
2da Av con 3era Transversal Los Cortijos de Lourdes
Caracas, Venezuela
Tel.: (58) 5960110
Fax: (58) 5620855
Telephone Directory Services
S.I.C.: 2741
N.A.I.C.S.: 511140

Movilnet **(1)**
Calle Londres con New York - Edif Movilnet - Las Mercedes
Caracas, Venezuela
Tel.: (58) 212 9092443
E-Mail: info@movilnet.com.ve
Web Site: www.movilnet.com.ve
Wireless Communication Services
S.I.C.: 4812
N.A.I.C.S.: 517210

COMPANIA DE MINAS BUENAVENTURA S.A.A.

Carlos Villaran 790 Santa Catalina
La Victoria, Lima, 13, Peru
Tel.: (51) 4192540
Fax: (51) 4717349
Web Site: www.buenaventura.com
Year Founded: 1953
BVN—(LIM NYSE)
Rev.: $1,563,527,000
Assets: $4,588,653,000
Liabilities: $624,267,000
Net Worth: $3,964,386,000
Earnings: $742,790,000
Emp.: 2,647
Fiscal Year-end: 12/31/12

Business Description:
Ore Mining & Exploration Services
S.I.C.: 1099
N.A.I.C.S.: 212299

Personnel:
Alberto Benavides de la Quintana *(Founder)*
Roque Eduardo Benavides Ganoza *(Chm, Pres & CEO)*
Carlos E. Galvez Pinillos *(CFO & VP)*
Gulnara La Rosa *(Gen Counsel)*

Board of Directors:
Roque Eduardo Benavides Ganoza
German Seraez Chavez
Jose Miguel Morales Dasso
Alberto Benavides de la Quintana
Carlos W. del Solar Simpson
Felipe Ortiz-de-Zevallos
Aubrey Laurence Paverd
Timothy R. Snider

Subsidiaries:

Compania Minera Condesa S.A. **(1)**
Carlos Villaran No 790 Urb Santa Catalina
La Victoria, Lima, Peru
Tel.: (51) 1 419 2500
Fax: (51) 1 471 6522
Mining & Exploration Services
S.I.C.: 1081
N.A.I.C.S.: 213114

Consorcio Energetico de Huancavelica S.A. **(1)**
Av Carlos Villaran 790 Santa Catalina - La Victoria
Lima, Peru
Tel.: (51) 14717278
Fax: (51) 14197349
E-Mail: raspilcueta@buenaventura.com.pe
Emp.: 200
Electric Power Distr
S.I.C.: 4911
N.A.I.C.S.: 221122
Carlos Galvez *(Mng Dir)*

Contacto Corredores de Seguros S.A. **(1)**
Av Republic of Panama 3545 Office 1202
Tower B San Isidro It files, Lima, Peru
Tel.: (51) 14412441
Fax: (51) 12215636
Web Site: www.contacto.com.pe/
Emp.: 16
All Other Nonmetallic Mineral Mining
S.I.C.: 1499
N.A.I.C.S.: 212399
Ricardo Cortez *(Mng Dir)*

Inversiones Colquijirca S.A. **(1)**
Av Javier Prado Oeste 2173
Lima, 27, Peru
Tel.: (51) 16113900
Investment Management Services
S.I.C.: 6211
N.A.I.C.S.: 523999

Minera La Zanja S.R.L. **(1)**
Av Carlos Villaran 790 Santa Catalina
La Victoria, Lima, Peru
Tel.: (51) 14192500
Fax: (51) 14716522
E-Mail: president@buenaventur.com.pe
Web Site: www.buenaventur.com.pe
Emp.: 600
Gold Ore Mining
S.I.C.: 1041
N.A.I.C.S.: 212221
Roque Cortez *(Mng Dir)*

Sociedad Minera El Brocal S.A.A. **(1)**
Avda Javier Prado Oeste 2173 San Isidro
Lima, Peru
Tel.: (51) 16113900
Fax: (51) 012645373
E-Mail: j_cruz@elbrocal.com.pe
Web Site: www.elbrocal.com.pe
Emp.: 50
Lead Ore & Zinc Ore Mining
S.I.C.: 1031
N.A.I.C.S.: 212231
Jsacruz Ramiret *(Gen Mgr)*

Non-U.S. Subsidiary:

Minera Julcani S.A.de C.V. **(1)**
Calle Alce Blanco 8 El Venado
Hidalgo, Mexico, Mexico
Tel.: (52) 771 138 6142
Emp.: 5
Mineral Mining Services
S.I.C.: 1499
N.A.I.C.S.: 212399
Mario Calderon *(Gen Mgr)*

COMPANIA DE NAVIGATIE FLUVIALA ROMANA NAVROM S.A. GALATI

Str Portului nr 34
800025 Galati, Romania
Tel.: (40) 236 461022
Fax: (40) 236 460190
E-Mail: navrom@navrom.ro
Web Site: www.navrom.ro
Year Founded: 1890
COVG—(BUC)

Business Description:
Inland Freight Water Transport Services
S.I.C.: 4449
N.A.I.C.S.: 483211

Personnel:
Mircea-Alexandru Mihailescu *(Pres)*

Board of Directors:
Constantin Hartan
Mircea-Alexandru Mihailescu

Subsidiaries:

Navrom Bac S.R.L. **(1)**
Punct de Trecere Bac - Faleza Dunarii, Galati, Romania
Tel.: (40) 236 496627
Fax: (40) 236 460848
E-Mail: navrombac@rdslink.ro
Marine Transportation Services
S.I.C.: 4449
N.A.I.C.S.: 483211

Navrom Centru de Afaceri S.R.L. **(1)**
Str Portului 23 Hotel Mercur et 2
Galati, Romania
Tel.: (40) 236 411048
Fax: (40) 236 411048
E-Mail: navrom_nca@yahoo.com
Marine Transportation Services
S.I.C.: 4449
N.A.I.C.S.: 483211

Navrom Delta S.A. **(1)**
Str Portului 26
Tulcea, Romania
Tel.: (40) 240 511553
Fax: (40) 240 511528
E-Mail: navdelta@x3m.ro
Web Site: www.navromdelta.ro
Marine Transportation Services
S.I.C.: 4449
N.A.I.C.S.: 483211

Navrom Shipyard S.R.L. **(1)**
Str Portului 54
Galati, Romania
Tel.: (40) 236 460990
Fax: (40) 236 414443
E-Mail: officeshipyard@navrom.ro
Marine Transportation Services
S.I.C.: 4449
N.A.I.C.S.: 483211

COMPANIA DE SEGUROS DE VIDA CRUZ DEL SUR S.A

El Golf 150
Las Condes, Santiago, Chile
Tel.: (56) 2 461 8000
Fax: (56) 4618334
Web Site: www.cruzdelsur.cl
Year Founded: 1992
Emp.: 1,000

Business Description:
Insurance & Financial Services
S.I.C.: 6411
N.A.I.C.S.: 524298

Personnel:
Jose Antonio Llaneza *(CEO)*

Subsidiary:

Principal Creditos Hipotecarios, S.A. **(1)**
Avenida Apoquindo 3600 Piso 10 Las Condes
Santiago, Chile CL
Tel.: (56) 2 2810 7000 (100%)
Fax: (56) 2 2810 7167
Web Site: www.principal.cl
Sales Range: $1-9.9 Million
Emp.: 38
Mortgage Loans & Investments Services
S.I.C.: 6163
N.A.I.C.S.: 522310
Rodrigo O. Gonzalez *(Gen Mgr)*

COMPANIA GENERAL DE ELECTRICIDAD S.A.

Teatinos 280
Santiago, Chile
Tel.: (56) 2 680 7000
Fax: (56) 2 680 7104
Web Site: www.cge.cl
CGE—(SGO)
Sales Range: $1-4.9 Billion

Business Description:
Electric Power Generation & Distribution
S.I.C.: 4911
N.A.I.C.S.: 221118

Personnel:
Jorge Eduardo Marin Correa *(Chm)*
Jose Luis Hornauer Herrmann *(Vice Chm)*
Pablo Guarda Barros *(CEO)*
Gonzalo Rodriguez Vives *(CFO)*

Board of Directors:
Jorge Eduardo Marin Correa
Juan Antonio Guzman Molinari
Jose Luis Hornauer Herrmann
Juan Hornauer Lopez
Francisco Javier Marin Estevez
Francisco Marin Jordan
Pablo Jose Perez Cruz

Subsidiaries:

Autogasco S.A. **(1)**
Santo Domingo 1061
Santiago, Chile
Tel.: (56) 2 694 45 01
Web Site: www.autogasco.cl
Emp.: 96
Natural Gas Distribution Services
S.I.C.: 4924
N.A.I.C.S.: 221210

Centrogas S.A. **(1)**
Avenida Vitacura 7646
Santiago, 760510, Chile
Tel.: (56) 2 7509600
Fax: (56) 2 750 9604
E-Mail: info@centrogas.cl
Web Site: www.centrogas.com
Emp.: 9
Heating System Maintenance & Installation Services
S.I.C.: 7699
N.A.I.C.S.: 811310
Renato Palomino *(Gen Mgr)*

CGE Magallanes S.A. **(1)**
Presidente Riesco No 5561 17th Fl
Santiago, Chile
Tel.: (56) 26807431
Fax: (56) 26807104
E-Mail: cge@cge.cl
Emp.: 18
Electric Power Generation Services
S.I.C.: 4911
N.A.I.C.S.: 221118

Empresa Electrica de Antofagasta S.A. **(1)**
Avenida Pedro Aguirre Cerda 5558
Antofagasta, Chile
Tel.: (56) 55 681401
Fax: (56) 55 681445
E-Mail: elecda@elecda.cl
Emp.: 178
Electric Power Distribution Services
S.I.C.: 4911
N.A.I.C.S.: 221122
Orlando Assad *(Gen Mgr)*

Enerplus S.A. **(1)**
Av Presidente Riesco 5561 Piso 15
Las Condes, Santiago, Chile
Tel.: (56) 2 680 75 56

Fax: (56) 2 680 75 55
E-Mail: contacto@enerplus.cl
Web Site: www.enerplus.cl
Emp.: 66
Electric Power Generation Services
S.I.C.: 4931
N.A.I.C.S.: 221118
Carlos Hornauer Herrmann *(Pres)*

Gasco GLP S.A. **(1)**
Santo Domingo 1061
Santiago, 8320315, Chile
Tel.: (56) 26944444
Fax: (56) 26944370
E-Mail: info@gasco.cl
Natural Gas Extraction Services
S.I.C.: 1311
N.A.I.C.S.: 211111

Gasmar S.A. **(1)**
Av Apoquindo 3200 Piso 8 Fl 11
7550183 Las Condes, Santiago, Chile
Tel.: (56) 2 3283200
Fax: (56) 2 3283249
E-Mail: principal@gasmar.cl
Web Site: www.gasmar.cl
Emp.: 39
Liquefied Gas Distr
S.I.C.: 4924
N.A.I.C.S.: 221210
Francisco Marin Estevez *(Chm)*
Jorge Montt Guzman *(CEO)*

Inmobiliaria Coronel S.A. **(1)**
Avenida Cordillera 3633 Of 3
Coronel, Chile
Tel.: (56) 41 2790400
Fax: (56) 41 2790401
Real Estate Management Services
S.I.C.: 6531
N.A.I.C.S.: 531390

Transformadores Tusan S.A. **(1)**
Av Gladys Marin 6030
Estacion Central, Santiago, Chile
Tel.: (56) 2 7797636
Fax: (56) 2 7413998
E-Mail: infotusan@tusan.cl
Emp.: 200
Electric Power Transmission Equipment Mfr
S.I.C.: 3568
N.A.I.C.S.: 333613
Augusto Wiegand Puyssegur *(Gen Mgr)*

Subsidiaries:

Energy Sur S.A. **(2)**
Parque Industrial Michaihue - Calle Local N 55
San Pedro de la Paz, Concepcion, Chile
Tel.: (56) 41 2798266
Fax: (56) 41 2798268
E-Mail: energy@energysur.cl
Electric Power Transformer Maintenance Services & Distr
S.I.C.: 7629
N.A.I.C.S.: 811219

Ingenieria y Desarrollo Tecnologico S.A. **(2)**
Avda Las Parcelas 5490
Estacion Central, Santiago, Chile
Tel.: (56) 2 719 2200
Fax: (56) 2 742 3934
E-Mail: info@idt.cl
Web Site: www.idt.cl
Power Electronic Equipment Mfr
S.I.C.: 3679
N.A.I.C.S.: 334419

Transnet S.A. **(1)**
Presidente Riesco 5561 Piso 12
Las Condes, Santiago, 8340434, Chile
Tel.: (56) 2 280 7000
Fax: (56) 2 280 7376
E-Mail: info@transnet.cl
Web Site: www.transnet.cl
Emp.: 100
Electric Power Transmission Services
S.I.C.: 4931
N.A.I.C.S.: 221121

Non-U.S. Subsidiary:

Gasco Argentina S.A. **(1)**
Avenida Leandro N Alem 1050 Piso 4
Buenos Aires, 1001, Argentina
Tel.: (54) 1143154000
Natural Gas Distribution Services
S.I.C.: 4924
N.A.I.C.S.: 221210

COMPANIA INDUSTRIAL DE TABACOS MONTE PAZ S.A.

San Ramon 716
CP 11800 Montevideo, Uruguay
Tel.: (598) 22008821
Fax: (598) 22037890
E-Mail: info@montepaz.com.uy
Web Site: www.montepaz.com.uy
Year Founded: 1881
Sales Range: $25-49.9 Million
Emp.: 450
Business Description:
Cigarettes & Tobacco Products Mfr Export
S.I.C.: 2131
N.A.I.C.S.: 312230
Personnel:
Jorge Luis Mailhos *(Chm & Pres)*

COMPANIA LEVANTINA DE EDIFICACION Y OBRAS PUBLICAS SA

(d/b/a CLEOP SA)
C/Santa Cruz de la Zarza 3
Valencia, VAL 46021, Spain
Tel.: (34) 963 393090
Fax: (34) 963 390923
Web Site: www.cleop.es
Year Founded: 1946
CLEO—(EUR)
Sales Range: $200-249.9 Million
Business Description:
Heavy Construction & Public Works Management
S.I.C.: 1542
N.A.I.C.S.: 236220
Personnel:
Carlos Turro Homedes *(Chm & Pres)*
Juan Miguel Gonzalez Jimenez *(CFO)*
Francisco Goberna Ortiz *(CTO)*
Francisco Perello Ferreres *(Sec)*
Board of Directors:
Carlos Turro Homedes
Carlos Castellanos Escrig
Jose Antonio Noguera Puchol
Agnes Noguera
Francisco Perello Ferreres
Antonio Noblejas Sanchez-Migallon
Marcos Turro Ribalta

COMPANIA LOGISTICA DE HIDROCARBUROS CLH, S.A.

(d/b/a CLH Group)
Titan 13
28045 Madrid, Spain
Tel.: (34) 91 7746000
Telex: 23387 CAMP E
Fax: (34) 91 7746001
E-Mail: infoclh@clh.es
Web Site: www.clh.es
CLH.T—(MAD)
Rev.: $722,712,903
Assets: $2,541,222,994
Liabilities: $2,295,637,163
Net Worth: $245,585,832
Earnings: $199,064,889
Emp.: 1,461
Fiscal Year-end: 12/31/12
Business Description:
Logistics Services; Hydrocarbons, Chemical Products, Derivatives & Residues Storage, Transport & Distribution
S.I.C.: 4731
N.A.I.C.S.: 541614
Personnel:
Jose Luis Lopez de Silanes Busto *(Chm & CEO)*
Jesus Alba Novillo *(CFO & Chief Economic Officer)*
Juan Rafael Bonilla Abascal *(Gen Dir-Ops)*
Rafael Garcia Serrano *(Gen Dir-Ops)*
Jorge Guillen Garcia *(Gen Dir-CLH Aviacion)*
Salvador Guillen Vazquez *(Gen Dir-Sls & Mktg)*
Basilio Navarro Sanchez *(Gen Dir-Resources)*
Luis Valero Quiros *(Gen Sec)*
Board of Directors:
Jose Luis Lopez de Silanes Busto
Daniel Micheal Agostino
Hamed Sloom Mubarak Al Athobi
Ahmed Hassan Al-Dheeb
Jose Eulogio Aranguren Escobar
Mario Armero Montes
Guillermo Briones Godino
Mathias Burghadt
Tanya Covassin
Rui Nuno Tavares de Almeida Moreira da Cruz
Pedro Fernandez Frial
Miguel Iraburu Elizondo
Nicolas Villen Jimenez
Stanislav Michael Kolenc
Jorge Lanza Perea
Andrew Liau
Pedro Miro Roig
Carlos Moran Moya
Carlos Maria Olazabal Estecha
Fernando Vazquez de Lapuerta
Robert Edward Verrion

Subsidiary:

CLH Aviacion, S.A **(1)**
Calle Titan 13
Madrid, 28045, Spain
Tel.: (34) 917746188
Fax: (34) 917746189
Warehousing & Freight Forwarding Services
S.I.C.: 4225
N.A.I.C.S.: 493110

COMPANIA MINERA ANTAMINA S.A.

Avenida El Derby 055 Twr A Office801
District of Santiago de Surco, Lima, 41, Peru
Tel.: (51) 12173000
Fax: (51) 13726317
Web Site: www.antamina.com
Emp.: 1,500
Business Description:
Copper Ore Mining Services
S.I.C.: 1021
N.A.I.C.S.: 212234
Personnel:
Enrique Alania Vera *(Mgr-Logistics)*

COMPANIA MINERA MILPO S.A.A.

Av San Borja Norte 523
San Borja, Lima, 41, Peru
Tel.: (51) 17105500
Fax: (51) 17105544
E-Mail: comunicaciones@milpo.com
Web Site: www.milpo.com
MILPOI1—(LIM)
Sales Range: $250-299.9 Million
Emp.: 806
Business Description:
Zinc, Copper, Lead, Silver & Gold Mining Services
S.I.C.: 1099
N.A.I.C.S.: 212299
Personnel:
Ivo Ucovich Dorsner *(Chm)*
Abraham Chahuan Abedrrabo *(CEO)*
Claudia Torres Beltran *(CFO)*
Adalberto Rivadeneira Gamez *(COO)*

COMPANIA NATIONALA POSTA ROMANA S.A.

(d/b/a Romanian Post)
Blvd Dacia 140 Sector 2
020065 Bucharest, Romania
Tel.: (40) 219393111
Fax: (40) 212007307
E-Mail: international@posta-romana.ro
Web Site: www.posta-romana.ro
Emp.: 33,762
Business Description:
Postal Services
S.I.C.: 4311
N.A.I.C.S.: 491110
Personnel:
Dan Mihai Toader *(Chm & CEO)*

COMPANIA SUDAMERICANA DE VAPORES, S.A.

(d/b/a CSAV)
Plaza Sotomayor 50
Valparaiso, Chile
Tel.: (56) 322203000
Fax: (56) 322203333
E-Mail: info@casv.com
Web Site: www.csav.cl
VAPORES—(SGO)
Rev.: $3,431,782,000
Assets: $2,482,650,000
Liabilities: $1,617,131,000
Net Worth: $865,519,000
Earnings: ($309,468,000)
Emp.: 4,211
Fiscal Year-end: 12/31/12
Business Description:
Freight Shipping Services
S.I.C.: 4731
N.A.I.C.S.: 488510
Personnel:
Francisco Perez Mackenna *(Chm)*
Andronico Luksic Craig *(Vice Chm)*
Claudio Barroilhet Acevedo *(Sec)*
Juan Carlos Valenzuela Aguirre *(Sr VP-HR)*
Guillermo Ginesta Bascunan *(Sr VP-Asia)*
Dheeraj Bhatia *(Sr VP-India)*
Juan Pablo Richards Bravo *(Sr VP-Europe)*
Vivien Swett Brown *(Sr VP-Performance Control)*
Jose Miguel Respaldiza Chicharro *(Sr VP-Cargo Svcs)*
Enrique Arteaga Correa *(Sr VP-South America East Coast)*
Nicolas Burr Garcia de la Huerta *(Sr VP-Admin & Fin)*
Fernando Valenzuela Diez *(Sr VP-Sys)*
Alvaro Infante Gonzalez *(Sr VP-North America, Central America & Caribbean)*
Andres Kulka Kuperman *(Sr VP-Mktg & Comml)*
Mauricio Carrasco Medina *(Sr VP-Dev)*
Arturo Castro Miranda *(Sr VP-Sls)*
Alejandro Pattillo Moreira *(Sr VP-Life Plng)*
Rafael Ferrada Moreira *(Sr VP-Strategic Dev & Plng)*
Christian Seydewitz Munizaga *(Sr VP-Ops & Dev)*
Eugenio Cruz Novoa *(Sr VP-Mediterranean)*
Hector Arancibia Sanchez *(Sr VP-Ship Mgmt)*
Gonzalo Baeza Solsona *(Sr VP-South America West Coast)*
Santiago Bielenberg Vasquez *(Sr VP-Special Svcs)*
Board of Directors:
Francisco Perez Mackenna
Juan Antonio Alvarez Avendano
Hernan Buchi Buc
Andronico Luksic Craig
Jose de Gregorio Rebeco

Compania Sudamericana de Vapores, S.A.—(Continued)

Gonzalo Menendez Duque
Arturo Claro Fernandez
Juan Francisco Gutierrez Irarrazaval
Canio Corbo Lioi
Victor Toledo Sandoval
Christoph Schiess Schmitz

Subsidiaries:

CSAV Inversiones Navieras S.A. **(1)**
Plaza Sotomayor 50 Valparaiso
Valparaiso, Chile
Tel.: (56) 32 2203000
Fax: (56) 32 2203333
E-Mail: customerservice@csav.com
Web Site: www.csav.cl
Emp.: 400
Navigational Shipping Services
S.I.C.: 4499
N.A.I.C.S.: 488330
Arturo Racke *(Reg Mgr)*

Sudamericana, Agencias Aereas y Maritimas S.A. **(1)**
Blanco 895 Valparaiso
Valparaiso, 2370554, Chile
Tel.: (56) 600 600 72 26
Fax: (56) 32 220 14 81
E-Mail: customerservice@saamsa.com
Web Site: www.saam.cl
Emp.: 200
Navigational Shipping & Transportation Services
S.I.C.: 4499
N.A.I.C.S.: 488330
O. Alejandro Garcia Huidobro *(Mng Dir)*

Non-U.S. Subsidiary:

Tollo Shipping Co. S.A. **(2)**
Roberto Motta Ave Capital Blaza Building
15th Fl Costa Valeste
Panama, Panama
Tel.: (507) 2636066
Fax: (507) 2635305
Deep Sea Transportation Services
S.I.C.: 4412
N.A.I.C.S.: 483111

COMPANIA VINICOLA DEL NORTE DE ESPANA, S.A.

Barrio de la Estacion S/N
26200 Haro, La Rioja, Spain
Tel.: (34) 941 304 800
Fax: (34) 941 304 815
E-Mail: marketing@cvne.com
Web Site: www.cvne.com
Year Founded: 1879
CUN—(MAD)
Sales Range: $10-24.9 Million
Business Description:
Wine Mfr & Whslr
S.I.C.: 2084
N.A.I.C.S.: 312130
Personnel:
L. I. Vallejo Chalbaud *(Chm)*

THE COMPANY FOR COOPERATIVE INSURANCE

(d/b/a Tawuniya)
700 King Fahad Road Att'awunya Towers
PO Box 86959
Riyadh, 11632, Saudi Arabia
Tel.: (966) 1 2188405
Fax: (966) 1 218 0102
E-Mail: invest@tawuniya.com.sa
Web Site: www.tawuniya.com.sa
Year Founded: 1986
8010—(SAU)
Sales Range: $750-799.9 Million
Emp.: 430
Business Description:
Insurance Services
S.I.C.: 6321
N.A.I.C.S.: 524114
Personnel:
Soliman Saad Al-Humayyad *(Chm)*
Ali A. Al-Subaihin *(CEO)*
Board of Directors:
Soliman Saad Al-Humayyad
Muhammad A. Al Agil
Waleed Abdull Rahman Al-eisa
Abdullah M. Al-Fayaz
Saad A. Al-Marzoqi
Abdulaziz A. Al-Modaimigh
Ali A. Al-Subaihin

COMPARTAMOS, S.A.B. DE C.V.

Av Insurgentes Sur 553 piso 1 de oficinas
Col Escandon, CP 11800 Mexico, DF, Mexico
Tel.: (52) 55 5276 7250
E-Mail: investor-relations@compartamos.com
Web Site: www.compartamos.com
COMPARC—(MEX)
Int. Income: $794,825,360
Assets: $1,796,500,440
Liabilities: $1,116,390,520
Net Worth: $680,109,920
Earnings: $159,012,280
Emp.: 16,601
Fiscal Year-end: 12/31/12
Business Description:
Bank Holding Company
S.I.C.: 6712
N.A.I.C.S.: 551111
Personnel:
Carlos Antonio Danel Cendoya *(Chm)*
Patricio Diez de Bonilla Garcia Vallejo *(CFO)*
Manuel de la Fuente Morales *(Sec)*
Board of Directors:
Carlos Antonio Danel Cendoya
Alvaro Rodriguez Arregui
Martha Elena Gonzalez Caballero
Juan Jose Gutierrez Chapa
Carlos Labarthe Costas
Guillermo Jose Siman Dada
Claudio Xavier Gonzalez Guajardo
Jose Ignacio Avalos Hernandez
Jose Manuel Canal Hernando
Luis Fernando Narchi Karam
John Anthony Santa Maria Otazua
Juan Ignacio Casanueva Perez
Rose Nicole Dominique Reich Sapire

Subsidiary:

Banco Compartamos, S.A., Institucion de Banca Multiple **(1)**
Av Insurgentes Sur 553 piso 1 de oficinas
Col Escandon, CP 11800 Mexico, DF, Mexico MX
Tel.: (52) 5552766398
E-Mail: banco@compartamos.com
Web Site: www.compartamos.com
COMPART—(MEX)
Sales Range: $500-549.9 Million
Emp.: 9,773
General Banking & Financial Services
S.I.C.: 6029
N.A.I.C.S.: 522110
Alvaro Rodriguez Arregui *(Chm)*
Fernando Alvarez Toca *(CEO)*
Carlos Labarthe Costas *(Dir Gen)*
Patricio Diez de Bonilla Garcia Vallejo *(CFO)*
Federico Hernandez Martinez *(COO)*
Enrique Majos Ramirez *(Chief Bus Officer & Chief Sls Officer)*
Hector Cervino Iglesias *(Personnel Officer)*
Oscar Ivan Mancillas Gabriele *(Chief Talent Officer)*
Rolando Javier Rocha Ochoa *(Mktg Officer)*
Manuel de la Fuente Morales *(Gen Counsel & Sec)*
Carlos Antonio Danel Cendoya *(Exec VP)*

COMPASS DIRECTIONAL SERVICES LTD

400 525 11th Ave SW
Calgary, AB, T2R 0C9, Canada
Tel.: (403) 237-8799
Fax: (403) 237-8882
E-Mail: infoopportunities@compassdirectional.com
Web Site: www.compassdirectional.com
Rev.: $22,271,797
Emp.: 35
Business Description:
Drilling Contractor
S.I.C.: 1381
N.A.I.C.S.: 213111
Personnel:
Rob Savoy *(Pres)*

COMPASS EAST INDUSTRY (THAILAND) PUBLIC COMPANY LIMITED

419/12-14 Srinakarin Road Tumbol Samrongnua
Amphur Muang, Samut Prakan, 10280, Thailand
Tel.: (66) 2 745 8244
Fax: (66) 2 361 1859
E-Mail: juanming@ceifan.com
Web Site: www.ceifan.com
Year Founded: 1987
CEI—(THA)
Sales Range: $1-9.9 Million
Business Description:
Ceiling Fan Mfr & Distr
S.I.C.: 3999
N.A.I.C.S.: 339999
Personnel:
Jen Chung Lou *(Chm & Pres)*

COMPASS GOLD CORPORATION

Suite 800 - 789 West Pender Street
Vancouver, BC, V6C 1H2, Canada
Tel.: (604) 638-8067
Fax: (604) 648-8105
E-Mail: info@compassgoldcorp.com
Web Site: www.compassgoldcorp.com
CVB—(TSXV)
Assets: $10,044,672
Liabilities: $976,372
Net Worth: $9,068,300
Earnings: ($1,798,930)
Fiscal Year-end: 12/31/12
Business Description:
Mineral Exploration Services
S.I.C.: 1081
N.A.I.C.S.: 213114
Personnel:
James Henderson *(Chm)*
Ian Spence *(Pres & CEO)*
Lara Iacusso *(CFO)*
Darren Devine *(Sec)*
Board of Directors:
James Henderson
Malcolm Carson
Madani Diallo
Lara Iacusso
Larry E. Phillips
Ian Spence
Legal Counsel:
DuMoulin Black LLP
10th Floor 595 Howe St
Vancouver, BC, Canada
Transfer Agent:
Computershare
3rd Floor 510 Burrard Street
Vancouver, BC, Canada

COMPASS GROUP PLC

Compass House Guildford Street
Chertsey, Surrey, KT16 9BQ, United Kingdom
Tel.: (44) 1932573000
Fax: (44) 1932569956
E-Mail: investor.relations@compass-group.co.uk
Web Site: www.compass-group.com
Year Founded: 1987
CPG—(LSE)
Rev.: $29,169,902,080
Assets: $15,165,624,320
Liabilities: $10,528,545,280
Net Worth: $4,637,079,040
Earnings: $726,049,280
Emp.: 506,699
Fiscal Year-end: 09/30/13
Business Description:
Holding Company; Catering, Hospitality & Other Business Support Services
S.I.C.: 6719
N.A.I.C.S.: 551112
Personnel:
Richard Cousins *(CEO)*
Mark White *(Gen Counsel & Sec)*
Board of Directors:
Paul Walsh
John George Bason
Dominic Blakemore
Richard Cousins
Gary Green
Andrew Martin
Susan Murray
Don Robert
Ian Robinson
Transfer Agent:
Capita Registrars
The Registry 34 Beckenham Road
Beckenham, United Kingdom

Subsidiaries:

Compass Group Holdings PLC **(1)**
Compass House Guildford Street
Chertsey, KT16 9BQ, United Kingdom
Tel.: (44) 1932573000
Fax: (44) 1932569956
Web Site: compassgroup.co.uk
Holding Company
S.I.C.: 6719
N.A.I.C.S.: 551112
Richard Cousins *(CEO)*

Compass Group Procurement Ltd **(1)**
Compass House Guildford Street
Chertsey, KT16 9BQ, United Kingdom
Tel.: (44) 1932 573000
Fax: (44) 1932 569956
Web Site: www.compass-group.com
Emp.: 150
Restaurant Operating Services
S.I.C.: 5812
N.A.I.C.S.: 722511

Compass Group, UK & Ireland Limited **(1)**
Parkview 82 Oxford Road
Uxbridge, UB8 1UX, United Kingdom UK
Tel.: (44) 1895554554 (100%)
Fax: (44) 1895554555
Web Site: www.compass-group.co.uk
Emp.: 200
Catering & Hospitality Services
S.I.C.: 5812
N.A.I.C.S.: 722320
Dennis Hogan *(Mng Dir)*

Letheby & Christopher Ltd **(1)**
Rowley Mile Racecourse
Newmarket, United Kingdom
Tel.: (44) 1638662750
Fax: (44) 1638 660 312
Emp.: 10
Catering Services
S.I.C.: 5812
N.A.I.C.S.: 722320
Sean Curtis *(Gen Mgr)*

VSG Group Ltd **(1)**
650 Pavilion Drive Northampton Business Park
Brackmills, Northampton, NN4 7SL, United Kingdom
Tel.: (44) 1604 744 000
Fax: (44) 1604 700050
E-Mail: sales@vsg.co.uk
Web Site: www.vsg.co.uk
Security System Services
S.I.C.: 7382
N.A.I.C.S.: 561621
Keith Francis *(Mng Dir)*

U.S. Group:

Compass Group North America **(1)**
2400 Yorkmont Rd
Charlotte, NC 28217-4511 (100%)
Tel.: (704) 329-4000
Web Site: www.cgnad.com
Sales Range: $5-14.9 Billion
Emp.: 1,200
Regional Managing Office; Vending & Food Service Contractors
S.I.C.: 8741
N.A.I.C.S.: 551114
Gary Green *(Pres & CEO)*
Tom Ondrof *(CFO)*
Vincent L. Berkeley, Jr. *(Chief Diversity Officer)*
Rick Postiglione *(CEO-Contract Foodservices)*
C. Phillip Wells *(Gen Counsel)*
Kurt Kimball *(Exec VP-Sls)*
Amy Knepp *(Sr VP-Strategic Alliance Grp)*
Lisa McEuen *(Sr VP-Bus Excellence)*

Subsidiary:

Compass Group USA, Inc. **(2)**
2400 Yorkmont Rd
Charlotte, NC 28217-4511 DE
Tel.: (704) 329-4000
Fax: (704) 329-6029
Web Site: www.compass-usa.com
Sales Range: $650-699.9 Million
Emp.: 1,000
Holding Company; Vending & Food Services
S.I.C.: 6719
N.A.I.C.S.: 551112
Gary Green *(Pres & CEO)*

Subsidiaries:

Bon Appetit Management Co **(3)**
100 Hamilton Ave Ste 400
Palo Alto, CA 94301
Tel.: (650) 798-8000
Fax: (650) 798-8090
E-Mail: info@bamco.com
Web Site: www.bamco.com
Emp.: 10,400
Restaurant Operating Services
S.I.C.: 5812
N.A.I.C.S.: 722511
Fedele Bauccio *(Co-Founder & CEO)*
Maisie Greenawalt *(Pres & VP-Strategy)*
Liz Baldwin *(CFO)*
Michael Bauccio *(COO)*

Compass Group USA Investments, Inc **(3)**
216 W Diversey Ave
Elmhurst, IL 60126-1104
Tel.: (630) 833-3666
Fax: (630) 832-3927
Investment Management Services
S.I.C.: 6211
N.A.I.C.S.: 523999
Dwayne Kriegel *(Branch Mgr)*

Crothall Services Group, Inc. **(3)**
955 Chesterbrook Blvd Ste 300
Wayne, PA 19087
Tel.: (610) 249-0420
Fax: (610) 249-0405
E-Mail: info@crothall.com
Web Site: www.crothall.com
Sales Range: $25-49.9 Million
Emp.: 60
Building Maintenance Contracting Service
S.I.C.: 7349
N.A.I.C.S.: 561720
Bobby Kutteh *(Pres & CEO)*
Daniel E. Gatti *(CFO & Sr VP)*

Subsidiaries:

Clinical Resources for Equipment Support Tech, Inc. **(4)**
735 Plz Blvd Ste 210
Coppell, TX 75019 TX
Tel.: (214) 488-9301
Fax: (214) 488-9299
Toll Free: (888) 467-1536
Web Site: www.crestservices.com
Sales Range: $1-9.9 Million
Emp.: 39
Medical Equipment Maintenance Services
S.I.C.: 7699
N.A.I.C.S.: 811219

Brian Montgomery *(Pres)*

SSC Service Solutions **(4)**
1845 Midpark Rd Ste 201
Knoxville, TN 37921-5951
Tel.: (865) 546-8880
Fax: (865) 523-5560
E-Mail: sales@sscserv.com
Web Site: www.sscserv.com
Sales Range: $150-199.9 Million
Emp.: 45
Janitorial Service, Contract Basis
S.I.C.: 7349
N.A.I.C.S.: 561720
Don Williams *(Pres & CEO)*
James Given *(CFO & Pres-Mall Div)*

Eurest Services, Inc. **(3)**
955 Chesterbrook Blvd
Wayne, PA 19087 DE
Tel.: (610) 240-8094
Fax: (610) 993-7801
Toll Free: (800) 447-4476
E-Mail: sales@eurestservices.us
Web Site: www.eurestservices.us
Janitorial & Facility Support Services
S.I.C.: 8744
N.A.I.C.S.: 561210
Bobby Kutteh *(CEO)*

Subsidiary:

Kimco Corporation **(4)**
4700 N Oketo Ave
Harwood Heights, IL 60706 IL
Tel.: (708) 583-9800
Fax: (708) 583-9888
E-Mail: sglowinski@usservices.com
Web Site: www.kimcocorp.com
Emp.: 2,300
Building Maintenance Services
Import Export
S.I.C.: 7349
N.A.I.C.S.: 561720
Nathaniel B. Shaw *(Exec VP)*
Richard Wender *(Exec VP)*
Sean Letwat *(Sr VP)*
Robert McGrath *(Sr VP-CBSE)*
Sandra Melton *(Sr VP)*

Non-U.S. Subsidiaries:

Eurest Colectividades SA **(4)**
Caminodelazarzuela 19 21
28023 Madrid, Aravaca, Spain (69.54%)
Tel.: (34) 915425339
Fax: (34) 917402557
E-Mail: dgeneral@euroest.colectividades.com
Web Site: www.eurest-colectividades.com
Catering & Hospitality Services
S.I.C.: 5812
N.A.I.C.S.: 722320
Alfredo Ruis Plaza *(Mng Dir)*

Eurest Deutschland GmbH **(4)**
Helfmann Pk 2
Eschborn, Hessen, 65760, Germany (69.52%)
Tel.: (49) 6196478500
Fax: (49) 6196478569
Web Site: www.eurest.de
Emp.: 1,500
Catering & Hospitality Services
S.I.C.: 5812
N.A.I.C.S.: 722320
Juergen Thamm *(Mng Dir)*

Eurest Nederland BV **(4)**
Paasheuvelweg 40
Postbus 22875
1100 DJ Amsterdam, Netherlands (64.32%)
Catering & Hospitality Services
S.I.C.: 5812
N.A.I.C.S.: 722320

Eurest Services GmbH **(4)**
Helfmann-Park 2
65760 Eschborn, Germany
Tel.: (49) 61 96 478 790
Fax: (49) 61 96 478 58 790
E-Mail: info@eurest-services.de
Web Site: www.eurest-services.de
Restaurant Operating Services
S.I.C.: 5812
N.A.I.C.S.: 722511
Gerhard Schmidt *(Gen Mgr)*

Subsidiary:

Eurest Sports & Food GmbH **(5)**
Helfmann-Park 2
65760 Eschborn, Germany
Tel.: (49) 61 96 478 500
Fax: (49) 61 96 478 569
E-Mail: info.compass@compass-group.de
Web Site: www.sports-and-food.de
Emp.: 200
Sports Club Catering Services
S.I.C.: 5812
N.A.I.C.S.: 722320
Juergen Thamm *(Gen Mgr)*

Foodbuy LLC **(3)**
50 Mansell Ct E
Alpharetta, GA 30022
Tel.: (678) 256-8000
Fax: (678) 256-8100
Food Catering Services
S.I.C.: 5812
N.A.I.C.S.: 722320
Tony Shearer *(Chm)*
Dan Barney *(Pres)*
Bill Hodges *(COO)*

Levy Restaurants, Inc. **(3)**
980 N Michigan Ave
Chicago, IL 60611-4518 IL
Tel.: (312) 664-8200
Fax: (312) 280-2739
Web Site: www.levyrestaurants.com
Emp.: 170
Restaurant & Sports Arena Dining Services
S.I.C.: 5812
N.A.I.C.S.: 722511
Lawrence F. Levy *(Chm)*
Andrew J. Lansing *(Pres & CEO)*
Robert Seiffert *(CFO & Exec VP)*
Allison Webber *(Chief Innovation Officer)*
Jeffery Wineman *(Exec VP-New Bus Dev)*

Branch:

Levy Restaurants **(4)**
401 E Jefferson St
Phoenix, AZ 85004-2438
Tel.: (602) 462-3000
Fax: (602) 462-3060
Web Site: www.levyjobs.com
Emp.: 250
Food Service Operations
S.I.C.: 5813
N.A.I.C.S.: 722410
Larry Levy *(Founder & Chm)*

Morrison Management Specialists, Inc. **(3)**
5801 Peachtree Dunwoody Rd
Atlanta, GA 30342-1503 GA
Tel.: (404) 845-3330
Fax: (404) 845-3333
Toll Free: (800) 2CLIENT
E-Mail: webmaster@iammorrison.com
Web Site: www.iammorrison.com
Emp.: 10,000
Food, Nutrition & Dining Services to the Health Care & Senior Living Industries
S.I.C.: 8099
N.A.I.C.S.: 621999
Gene Dolloff *(Pres-Morrison Sr Dining)*
Michael Svagdis *(Pres-Morrison Healthcare Food Svcs)*

Restaurant Associates Corporation **(3)**
330 Fifth Ave 5th Fl
New York, NY 10001 DE
Tel.: (212) 613-5500
E-Mail: info@restaurantassociates.com
Web Site: www.restaurantassociates.com
Sales Range: $450-499.9 Million
Emp.: 50
Restaurant Management Services
S.I.C.: 5812
N.A.I.C.S.: 722511
Edward J. Sirhal *(Pres)*
Dick Cattani *(CEO)*
Michael Gallagher *(Sr VP-Ops)*
Andrew Ziobro *(Sr VP-Ops-Cultural Centers & Catering Div)*

Units:

Bateman Senior Meals **(3)**
3110 W Pinhook Rd Ste 201
Lafayette, LA 70508
Tel.: (337) 593-0433
Fax: (337) 593-0434
E-Mail: info@batemanseniormeals.com
Web Site: www.batemanseniormeals.com
Emp.: 3
Food Service
S.I.C.: 8322
N.A.I.C.S.: 624120
Magi Brettler *(Reg VP)*

Canteen Vending Company **(3)**
2400 Yorkmont Rd
Charlotte, NC 28216
Tel.: (704) 329-4000
Fax: (704) 329-6029
Toll Free: (800) 357-0012
Web Site: www.canteen.com
Emp.: 1,000
Vending Machine Operator
S.I.C.: 5962
N.A.I.C.S.: 454210
Dennis Hogan *(CEO)*

Subsidiary:

Covenco Inc. **(4)**
3201 Fulling Mill Rd
Middletown, PA 17057-3174 PA
Tel.: (717) 939-1200
Fax: (717) 939-5226
Emp.: 300
Merchandising Machine Services
S.I.C.: 5962
N.A.I.C.S.: 454210
Curt Smith *(CEO)*

Chartwells USA **(3)**
2400 Yorkmont Rd
Charlotte, NC 28217-4511
Tel.: (704) 329-4000
Fax: (704) 328-6029
Web Site: www.eatlearnlive.com
Sales Range: $650-699.9 Million
Emp.: 1,000
Food Service Contractor
S.I.C.: 5812
N.A.I.C.S.: 722310
Steven Sweeney *(CEO)*
Keith Cullinan *(Pres-School Dining Svcs)*

FLIK International **(3)**
3 International Dr
Rye Brook, NY 10573-1058
Tel.: (914) 935-5300
Fax: (914) 935-5551
Web Site: www.flik-usa.com
Emp.: 125
Food Service Contractor
S.I.C.: 5812
N.A.I.C.S.: 722310
Scott Davis *(Pres)*

Non-U.S. Subsidiary:

Compass Group Canada (Beaver) Ltd. **(2)**
493 Dundas St
London, ON, N6B 1W4, Canada ON
Tel.: (519) 679-2661 (100%)
Fax: (519) 679-6946
Web Site: www.compass-canada.com
Emp.: 130
Business Institutional Contract Caterer
S.I.C.: 5812
N.A.I.C.S.: 722320

Non-U.S. Subsidiaries:

Compass Group (Australia) Pty Ltd **(1)**
35-51 Mitchell Street McMahons Point
Sydney, NSW, 2060, Australia
Tel.: (61) 2 9797 4900
Fax: (61) 2 9797 0415
E-Mail: communications@compass-group.com.au
Web Site: www.compass-group.com.au
Emp.: 10
Restaurant & Catering Services
S.I.C.: 5812
N.A.I.C.S.: 722320
Gerhard Poelzl *(Grp Mng Dir-Pacific)*
Lara Peake *(Gen Counsel & Grp Sec)*

Compass Group Deutschland GmbH **(1)**
Helfmann-Park 2
65760 Eschborn, Germany
Tel.: (49) 6196478500
Fax: (49) 6196478569
E-Mail: info.compass@compass-group.de
Web Site: www.compass-group.de
Emp.: 200
Restaurant & Catering Services
S.I.C.: 5812
N.A.I.C.S.: 722320

Compass Group PLC—(Continued)

Juergen Thamm *(Gen Mgr)*

Compass Group France Holdings SAS (1)
200 Ave de Paris
92320 Chatillon, France
Tel.: (33) 1 76 61 00 00
Investment Management Services
S.I.C.: 6211
N.A.I.C.S.: 523999

Compass Group International BV (1)
Laarderhoogtweg 11
Amsterdam, Zuidoost, 1101 DZ, Netherlands
Tel.: (31) 204307177
Fax: (31) 204307170
Emp.: 5
Financial Management Services
S.I.C.: 6211
N.A.I.C.S.: 523999
Peter Frans *(Gen Mgr)*

Compass Group International (1)
89 91 Rue Du Faubourg Saint Honore
F 75008 Paris, France (100%)
Tel.: (33) 155272300
Fax: (33) 155272399
Emp.: 40
Catering & Hospitality Services
S.I.C.: 5812
N.A.I.C.S.: 722320

Compass Group Italia S.p.A (1)
Via degli Olivetani 4
Milan, 20123, Italy IT
Tel.: (39) 02 480531
Fax: (39) 02 48194011
E-Mail: eurend@compass-group.it
Web Site: www.compass-group.it
Catering Services
S.I.C.: 5812
N.A.I.C.S.: 722320

Compass Group Nederland Holding BV (1)
Laarderhoogtweg 11
Postbus 22875
1100 DJ Amsterdam, Netherlands
Tel.: (31) 20 564 37 70
Fax: (31) 20 565 93 70
Web Site: www.compass-group.nl
Emp.: 150
Investment Management Services
S.I.C.: 6211
N.A.I.C.S.: 523999

Compass Group (Schweiz) AG (1)
Oberfeldstrasse 14
8302 Kloten, Switzerland
Tel.: (41) 43 557 11 11
Fax: (41) 43 557 11 10
E-Mail: info@compass-group.ch
Web Site: www.compass-group.ch
Restaurant Operating Services
S.I.C.: 5812
N.A.I.C.S.: 722511
Hans Boesch *(CEO)*

Compass Group Southern Africa (Pty) Ltd (1)
12 Stirrup Lane Woodmead Office Park Van Reenens Avenue
Woodmead, 2191, South Africa
Tel.: (27) 11 209 2400, ext. 14
Web Site: www.compass-group.co.za
Emp.: 620
Restaurant Operating Services
S.I.C.: 5812
N.A.I.C.S.: 722511
Terry Greenslade *(CFO)*

Medirest GmbH & Co OHG (1)
Helfmann-Park 2
65760 Eschborn, Germany
Tel.: (49) 61 96 478 701
Fax: (49) 61 96 478 972
E-Mail: info@compass-group.de
Web Site: www.medirest.de
Food Catering Services
S.I.C.: 5812
N.A.I.C.S.: 722320
Kay Pilz *(Gen Mgr)*

Restorama AG (1)
Oberfeldstrasse 14
Kloten, 8302, Switzerland
Tel.: (41) 43 557 11 11
Fax: (41) 43 557 11 10
E-Mail:
Professional Catering Services
S.I.C.: 5812
N.A.I.C.S.: 722320

Seiyo Food-Compass Group, Inc. (1)
Seiwa Ikebukuro Bldg 3-13-3 Higashi Ikebukuro
Toshima-ku, Tokyo, 170-0013, Japan
Tel.: (81) 3 3984 0281
Web Site: www.seiyofood.co.jp
Emp.: 2,380
Food Service, Catering & Hospitality Services
S.I.C.: 5812
N.A.I.C.S.: 722310
Takeshi Kohjima *(Pres & CEO)*
Toshihiro Kusunoki *(CFO & Sr VP)*
Mitsuaki Fujishima *(Sr Exec Officer)*
Yoshinori Miyahara *(Sr Exec Officer)*
Hideo Mori *(Sr Exec Officer)*

COMPASS RESOURCES LIMITED

Suite 2 Level 15 3 Spring Street
Sydney, NSW, 2000, Australia
Tel.: (61) 2 9247 5352
Fax: (61) 2 9247 5553
E-Mail: admin@compassresources.com.au
CMR—(ASX)
Rev.: $1,649,644
Assets: $83,289,843
Liabilities: $67,099,777
Net Worth: $16,190,066
Earnings: ($13,238,838)
Fiscal Year-end: 12/31/12

Business Description:
Mineral Exploration Services
S.I.C.: 1099
N.A.I.C.S.: 212299

Personnel:
Philip Wood *(CEO)*
James Carr *(Mng Dir)*
Thomas Bloomfield *(Sec)*

Board of Directors:
Mark Angelo
John Allen
James Carr
Gerald Eicke
David Gonzalez
Philip Wood

COMPEQ MANUFACTURING CO., LTD.

No 91 Ln Taoyuan 814 Ta-Hsin Hsin-Chuang Vlg
Lu-Chu Hsiang, Taoyuan, Taiwan
Tel.: (886) 33231111
Fax: (886) 33235577
E-Mail: inquiry@compeq.com.tw
Web Site: www.compeq.com.tw
2313—(TAI)
Sales Range: $300-349.9 Million
Emp.: 3,100

Business Description:
Printed Circuit Boards Mfr
S.I.C.: 3672
N.A.I.C.S.: 334412

Personnel:
Charles Wu *(Chm)*
T. L. Liu *(Pres)*

Plant:

Compeq Manufacturing Co., Ltd. - Luchu Plant (1)
No 91 Lane 814 Ta-Hsin Road Shin Chuang Village
Lu Chu Hsiang, Taoyuan, Taiwan
Tel.: (886) 33231111
Fax: (886) 3 323 5577
E-Mail: inquiry@compeq.com.tw
Emp.: 3,859
Printed Circuit Boards Mfr
S.I.C.: 3672
N.A.I.C.S.: 334412
Charles Wu *(Chm)*

Non-U.S. Subsidiaries:

Compeq Manufacturing(Huizhou) Co., Ltd. (1)
No 168 Huguang Road Huzhen Town
Boluo County, Huizhou, Guangdong, China
Tel.: (86) 752 6301111
Fax: (86) 752 6301701
E-Mail: inquiry@compeq.com.tw
Web Site: www.compeq.com.tw/english/location/branch-mainland.htm
Emp.: 4,500
Printed Circuit Boards Mfr
S.I.C.: 3672
N.A.I.C.S.: 334412
Steve Chen *(Pres)*

COMPEQ Manufacturing(Suzhou) Co., Ltd. (1)
Building 20 Suchun Industrial Lane No 428 Xinglong Street
Suzhou, Jiangsu, 215021, China
Tel.: (86) 51262836001
Fax: (86) 51262836002
E-Mail: inquiry@compeq.com.tw
Printed Circuit Boards Distr
S.I.C.: 3672
N.A.I.C.S.: 334412

COMPEQ Technology (Huizhou) Co., Ltd. (1)
No 168 Huguang Road Huzhen Town
Boluo, Huizhou, Guangdong, 516139, China
Tel.: (86) 7526301111
Fax: (86) 7526657789
Printed Circuit Boards Distr
S.I.C.: 5065
N.A.I.C.S.: 423690

Initial Technology Pte Ltd (1)
Block 750A Chai Chee Road 07-13 Technopark
Singapore, Chai Chee, 469001, Singapore
Tel.: (65) 63387933
Fax: (65) 63451623
Web Site: www.compeq.com.tw
Emp.: 3
Printed Circuit Boards Mfr & Distr
S.I.C.: 3672
N.A.I.C.S.: 334412
Poong Dickson *(Mng Dir)*

COMPETENT AUTOMOBILES CO. LTD.

Competent House F-14 Connaught Place
New Delhi, 110 001, India
Tel.: (91) 11 45700000
Fax: (91) 11 23327640
E-Mail: ho@competent-maruti.com
Web Site: www.competent-maruti.com
Year Founded: 1985
531041—(BOM)
Rev.: $149,640,962
Assets: $26,029,467
Liabilities: $12,635,985
Net Worth: $13,393,481
Earnings: $1,444,208
Emp.: 1,175
Fiscal Year-end: 03/31/13

Business Description:
Automobile Sales & Services
S.I.C.: 7549
N.A.I.C.S.: 811198

Personnel:
Raj Chopra *(Chm & Mng Dir)*
Kamal K. Kumar *(COO)*
Yadvinder Goyal *(Compliance Officer & Sec)*

Board of Directors:
Raj Chopra
Kavita Ahuja
Gopi Dargan
Rohit Gogia
K. K. Mehta
Ramesh Chander Murada
O. P. Tandon
S. L. Tandon

Transfer Agent:
Skyline Financial Services Pvt Ltd.
D 153A 1st Floor Okhla Industrial Area Phase 1
New Delhi, India

COMPETITION CHEVROLET LTD.

40 Boulder Blvd
Stony Plain, AB, T7Z 1V7, Canada
Tel.: (780) 963-6121
Fax: (780) 963-0369
Toll Free: (877) 963-6121
E-Mail: info@competitionchevrolet.com
Web Site: www.competitionchevrolet.com
Rev.: $55,000,000
Emp.: 60

Business Description:
New & Used Car Dealers
S.I.C.: 5511
N.A.I.C.S.: 441110

Personnel:
Blair Polack *(Pres)*

COMPETITION TOYOTA LTD.

1206 Oxford St E
London, ON, N5Y 3M3, Canada
Tel.: (519) 451-3880
Fax: (519) 451-6267
Toll Free: (855) 781-8660
Web Site: www.comptoyota.com
Year Founded: 1964
Rev.: $14,172,027
Emp.: 31

Business Description:
New & Used Car Dealers
S.I.C.: 5511
N.A.I.C.S.: 441110

Personnel:
Dianne Taylor *(Controller)*

COMPETITIVE FOODS AUSTRALIA PTY. LTD.

L1 355 Scarborough Beach Rd
6017 Osborne Park, Western Australia, Australia
Tel.: (61) 892429400
Fax: (61) 892429401
E-Mail: wareception@cfal.com.au
Sales Range: $450-499.9 Million
Emp.: 13,063

Business Description:
Franchise Restaurant Operator
S.I.C.: 5812
N.A.I.C.S.: 722513

Personnel:
John Cowin *(Owner)*

COMPLETE GENOMICS, INC.

(Acquired by BGI-Shenzhen)

COMPLETE LOGISTIC SERVICES BERHAD

25 Jalan Berangan
42000 Port Klang, Selangor Darul Ehsan, Malaysia
Tel.: (60) 331680757
Fax: (60) 331671145
E-Mail: info@complete-group.com
Web Site: www.complete-group.com
COMPLET —(KLS)
Rev.: $33,577,226
Assets: $41,250,156
Liabilities: $12,402,681
Net Worth: $28,847,475
Earnings: $3,961,809
Fiscal Year-end: 03/31/13

Business Description:
Logistics Services
S.I.C.: 4731
N.A.I.C.S.: 541614

Personnel:
Ibrahim Ahmad *(Chm)*
Hee Ling Law *(Mng Dir)*
Kia Hock Chia *(Co-Sec)*
Ong Leong Chia *(Co-Sec)*
Board of Directors:
Ibrahim Ahmad
Kah Ying Chia
G. K. Alfred Kumaraseri
Hee Ling Law
Hieng Ding Law
Kok Onn Lim
Yoon Kin Ng
Kiong Siang Yet

COMPLIANCE ENERGY CORPORATION

550-800 West Pender Street
Vancouver, BC, Canada
Tel.: (604) 689-0489
Fax: (604) 681-5910
Web Site: www.complianceenergy.com
Year Founded: 2000
CEC—(TSXV)
Sales Range: Less than $1 Million
Business Description:
Coal Exploration Services
S.I.C.: 1241
N.A.I.C.S.: 213113
Personnel:
James C. O'Rourke *(Chm)*
John A. Tapics *(CEO)*
Michael Varabioff *(Corp Sec)*
Board of Directors:
James C. O'Rourke
Paul Krivokuca
Jamieson Merritt
Rodney A. Shier
John A. Tapics
Paul Willis
Legal Counsel:
Axium Law
3350-1055 Dunsmuir Street
Vancouver, BC, Canada
Transfer Agent:
Computershare Transfer Services
4th Floor 510 Burrard Street
Vancouver, BC, Canada

COMPLUS TECHNOLOGIES SE

Unter den Platanen 24
14774 Brandenburg, Germany
Tel.: (49) 3381804360
Fax: (49) 33818043629
E-Mail: info@complus-technologies.com
Web Site: www.complus-technologies.de
PCA—(DEU)
Business Description:
Information Technology Services
S.I.C.: 7389
N.A.I.C.S.: 519190
Personnel:
Uwe Maiberg *(Chm & Mng Dir)*
Board of Directors:
Uwe Maiberg
Daniel Garthe
Edward H. Pfeiffenberger

COMPONENTA CORPORATION

Panuntie 4
FI-00610 Helsinki, Finland
Tel.: (358) 1040300
Fax: (358) 104032721
E-Mail: ir.componenta@componenta.com
Web Site: www.componenta.com
CTH1V—(HEL)
Sls.: $733,393,416
Assets: $619,776,668
Liabilities: $507,506,090
Net Worth: $112,270,578
Earnings: ($32,308,080)
Emp.: 4,104
Fiscal Year-end: 12/31/12
Business Description:
Industrial & Automotive Components Mfr & Distr
S.I.C.: 3714
N.A.I.C.S.: 336350
Personnel:
Harri Suutari *(Chm)*
Matti Ruotsala *(Vice Chm)*
Heikki Lehtonen *(Pres & CEO)*
Mika Hassinen *(CFO)*
Pauliina Rannikko *(Gen Counsel & Sr VP-Legal & Risk Mgmt)*
Juha Alhonoja *(Sr VP-Machine Shop Dev)*
Seppo Erkkila *(Sr VP-Ops Finland)*
Yaylaly Gunay *(Sr VP-Investments)*
Olli Karhunen *(Sr VP-Foundry Div)*
Antti Lehto *(Sr VP-Sls & Customer Svcs)*
Anu Mankki *(Sr VP-HR)*
Sabri Ozdogan *(Sr VP-Aluminium Div)*
Furio Scolaro *(Sr VP-Sls & Product Dev)*
Patrick Steensels *(Sr VP-Heerlen Foundry)*
Board of Directors:
Harri Suutari
Heikki Lehtonen
Marjo Miettinen
Riitta Palomaki
Matti Ruotsala
Tommi Salunen

Subsidiaries:

Componenta Finland Oy Pietarsaari **(1)**
Birgerintie 3
PO Box 37
68601 Pietarsaari, Finland
Tel.: (358) 1040300
Fax: (358) 104033199
Web Site: www.componenta.com
Emp.: 200
Iron Castings Mfr
S.I.C.: 3321
N.A.I.C.S.: 331511
Hannu Jylha *(Dir-Bus Unit)*

Componenta Finland Oy **(1)**
PO Box 40
03601 Karkkila, Finland
Tel.: (358) 1040300
Fax: (358) 104032614
Emp.: 265
Cast Iron Components Mfr
S.I.C.: 3312
N.A.I.C.S.: 331110
Juha Vatanen *(Dir-Bus Unit)*

Karkkilan Laakarikeskus Oy **(1)**
Valurinkatu 2 A 1
03600 Karkkila, Finland
Tel.: (358) 104032633
Fax: (358) 92258706
Web Site: www.karkkilanlaakarikeskus.fi
Emp.: 10
General Medical Services
S.I.C.: 8062
N.A.I.C.S.: 622110
Jussi Piironen *(Mgr)*

Vanhan Ruukin Kiinteistopalvelu Oy **(1)**
Valurinkatu 4 A 1
03600 Karkkila, Finland
Tel.: (358) 10 40300
Fax: (358) 92 259424
Emp.: 20
Real Estate Management Services
S.I.C.: 6531
N.A.I.C.S.: 531390
Kalervo Saarimaa *(Mgr-Bus Unit)*

U.S. Subsidiary:

Componenta USA, LLC **(1)**
407 Northpark Blvd
Huxley, IA 50124
Tel.: (515) 597-4201
Fax: (515) 597-4202
E-Mail: us.sales@componenta.com
Web Site: www.componenta.com
Printed Circuit Board Components Distr
S.I.C.: 3678
N.A.I.C.S.: 334417

Non-U.S. Subsidiaries:

Componenta Albin AB **(1)**
Hantverkargatan 3
PO Box 115
SE 681 23 Kristinehamn, Sweden
Tel.: (46) 550410500
Fax: (46) 550410545
E-Mail: se.sales@componenta.com
Web Site: www.componenta.com
Emp.: 110
Industrial Components Mfr
S.I.C.: 3589
N.A.I.C.S.: 333318
Andrias Falcini *(Pres)*

Componenta A.S. (Manisa) **(1)**
Cad no 14
45000 Manisa, Turkey
Tel.: (90) 2362338057
Fax: (90) 236 233 8061
E-Mail: tr.sales@componenta.com
Web Site: www.componenta.com
Lathes & Drilling Machines Mfr
S.I.C.: 3542
N.A.I.C.S.: 333517

Componenta B.V. **(1)**
Copernicusstraat 9
PO Box 10212
NL-6000 GE Weert, Netherlands
Tel.: (31) 495513800
Telex: 58055
Fax: (31) 495513195
E-Mail: nl.sales@componenta.com
Emp.: 700
Casting & Machining Services
S.I.C.: 3325
N.A.I.C.S.: 331513
P. Speensels *(Mgr)*

Componenta Dokumculuk Ticaret ve Sanayi AS **(1)**
Golyolu No 26 PK 18
Bursa, Orhangazi, 16801, Turkey TR
Tel.: (90) 2245734263 (93.6%)
Fax: (90) 224 573 4273
E-Mail: tr.sales@componenta.com
Web Site: www.componenta.com
COMDO—(IST)
Emp.: 4,155
Iron Castings, Aluminium Castings & Light Alloy Wheel Mfr
S.I.C.: 3364
N.A.I.C.S.: 331523
Heikki Bergholm *(Chm)*
Heikki Lehtonen *(Pres & CEO)*
Mika Hassinen *(CFO)*
Yrjo Julin *(COO)*
Pauliina Rannikko *(Gen Counsel & Sr VP-Legal & Risk Mgmt)*
Olli Karhunen *(Sr VP-Ops-Finland)*
Anu Mankki *(Sr VP-HR)*
Patrick Steensels *(Sr VP-Ops-Holland)*

Non-U.S. Subsidiary:

Componenta UK Ltd. **(2)**
Unit 3 Upper Keys Business Park
Keys Park Road
Hednesford, Cannock, Staffs, WS12 2GE, United Kingdom
Tel.: (44) 1543495555
Fax: (44) 8700512061
E-Mail: sales@componenta.co.uk
Web Site: www.componenta.co.uk
Emp.: 11
Trade & Marketing Activities of Cast Iron & Aluminium Castings for Automotive Industry
S.I.C.: 5013
N.A.I.C.S.: 423120
Allen Hooper *(Gen Mgr)*

Componenta Frammestad AB **(1)**
Frammestadvagen 29
465 97 Nossebro, Sweden
Tel.: (46) 10 450 7500
Fax: (46) 51253437
E-Mail: se.sales@componenta.com
Web Site: www.componenta.com
Emp.: 125
Cast Components Distr
S.I.C.: 5051
N.A.I.C.S.: 423510
Clas Tengstroem *(Mgr)*

Componenta France S.A.S. **(1)**
16 Rue Ampere
95300 Pontoise, Val-d'Oise, France
Tel.: (33) 134246750
Fax: (33) 134246750
E-Mail: fr.sales@componenta.com
Web Site: www.componenta.com
Emp.: 3
Iron Castings Mfr
S.I.C.: 3321
N.A.I.C.S.: 331511
Furio Scolaro *(Dir Gen)*

Componenta Italy S.r.l. **(1)**
Corso Unione Sovietica 612/21
10135 Turin, Italy
Tel.: (39) 0110864811
Fax: (39) 0110864911
E-Mail: it.sales@componenta.com
Web Site: www.componenta.com
Emp.: 5
Cast Components Distr
S.I.C.: 5051
N.A.I.C.S.: 423510
Luca Paolo Ferroni *(Mng Dir)*

Componenta Netherlands B.V. **(1)**
Copernicusstraat 9
6003 DE Weert, Limburg, Netherlands
Tel.: (31) 495513800
Fax: (31) 495513195
E-Mail: receptie.weert@componenta.com
Emp.: 250
Cast Components Distr
S.I.C.: 5051
N.A.I.C.S.: 423510
Theo Hendrikx *(Mgr-HR)*

Componenta Wirsbo AB **(1)**
PO Box 102
730 61 Virsbo, Sweden
Tel.: (46) 22339500
Fax: (46) 223 347 19
E-Mail: info.wirsbo@componenta.com
Web Site: www.componentawirsbo.se
Emp.: 210
Axles & Transmission Components Mfr
S.I.C.: 3714
N.A.I.C.S.: 336390
Goran Jansson *(Dir-Bus Unit)*

COMPOSITE LIMITED

Eastleigh House Upper Market Street
Eastleigh, Hampshire, SO50 9RD, United Kingdom
Tel.: (44) 2380645700
Fax: (44) 2380643665
E-Mail: info@compositeltd.co.uk
Web Site: www.compositeltd.co.uk
Year Founded: 1989
Rev.: $26,863,705
Emp.: 55
Business Description:
Construction Services
S.I.C.: 1542
N.A.I.C.S.: 236220
Personnel:
Roy Nield-Dumper *(Mng Dir)*
David Smith *(Sec & Dir-Fin)*

COMPREHENSIVE LAND DEVELOPMENT & INVESTMENT PLC

Mekka Street Al-Hussaini Centre number 6
PO Box 739
Amman, 11118, Jordan
Tel.: (962) 6 5540541
Fax: (962) 6 5540648
ATTA—(AMM)
Rev.: $2,510,055
Assets: $12,563,315
Liabilities: $1,505,547
Net Worth: $11,057,768
Earnings: ($813,263)
Emp.: 5
Fiscal Year-end: 12/31/12

Comprehensive Land Development & Investment Plc—(Continued)

Business Description:
Land Acquisition Services
S.I.C.: 6552
N.A.I.C.S.: 237210
Personnel:
Amjad Ghareeb Al-Bakri *(Gen Mgr)*

COMPREHENSIVE LEASING CO.

Abdullah Ghosheh Street Building No 66
Amman, 11118, Jordan
Tel.: (962) 65822110
Fax: (962) 65815271
E-Mail: info@c-leasing.com
Web Site: www.c-leasing.com
Year Founded: 2004
LEAS—(AMM)
Sales Range: $1-9.9 Million
Emp.: 17
Business Description:
Industrial Machinery & Equipment Leasing Services
S.I.C.: 7359
N.A.I.C.S.: 532490
Personnel:
Eliya Jad Wakileh *(Gen Mgr)*

COMPREHENSIVE MULTIPLE PROJECTS COMPANY PLC

King Abdullah Second industrial city
PO Box 141220
Amman, 11814, Jordan
Tel.: (962) 64023540
Fax: (962) 64022729
Year Founded: 1994
INOH—(AMM)
Rev.: $10,308,328
Assets: $20,571,182
Liabilities: $12,702,720
Net Worth: $7,868,462
Earnings: $63,230
Emp.: 100
Fiscal Year-end: 12/31/12
Business Description:
Storage Battery Mfr
S.I.C.: 3691
N.A.I.C.S.: 335911
Personnel:
Manule Azzam *(Gen Mgr)*

COMPRENDIUM STRUCTURED FINANCING GMBH

Feringastrasse 10B
Unterfohring, D-85774 Munich, Germany
Tel.: (49) 89960740
Fax: (49) 8996074295
E-Mail: info@comprendium.com
Web Site: www.comprendium.com
Emp.: 100
Business Description:
Office Equipment Sales Financing & Leasing Services
S.I.C.: 7359
N.A.I.C.S.: 532420
Personnel:
John W. Boo *(CEO & Member-Mgmt Bd)*
Bruno Berjal *(CFO & Member-Mgmt Bd)*
Peter Kohler *(Mng Dir-Sls & Mktg & Member-Mgmt Bd)*

Non-U.S. Subsidiary:

Comprendium Finance SA **(1)**
Zugerstrasse 50
CH-6341 Baar, Switzerland (100%)
Tel.: (41) 417682828
Telex: 458180. CDCO CH
Fax: (41) 417682800
E-Mail: info@comprendiumfinance.com
Web Site: www.comprendium.com
Emp.: 4
Office Equipment Sales Financing & Leasing Services
S.I.C.: 7359
N.A.I.C.S.: 532420
Guenter Karl *(CEO)*

COMPTA - EQUIPAMENTOS E SERVICOS DE INFORMATICA, S.A.

Edificio Atlas III Av Jose Gomes Ferreira n 13 Miraflores
Alges, 1495-139, Portugal
Tel.: (351) 214 134 200
Fax: (351) 214 131 220
E-Mail: international@compta.pt
Web Site: www.compta.pt
Year Founded: 1972
COMAE—(EUR)
Emp.: 240
Business Description:
Information Technology Services
S.I.C.: 7373
N.A.I.C.S.: 541512
Personnel:
Armindo Lourenco Monteiro *(Chm & CEO)*
Jose Manuel Barris Ferreira de Almeida *(Gen Sec)*

COMPTEL CORPORATION

Salmisaarenkaukio 1
PO Box 1000
FI-00181 Helsinki, Finland
Tel.: (358) 97001131
Fax: (358) 970011375
E-Mail: europe@comptel.com
Web Site: www.comptel.com
CTL1V—(HEL)
Sls.: $110,962,101
Assets: $92,146,683
Liabilities: $55,859,324
Net Worth: $36,287,359
Earnings: ($17,236,361)
Emp.: 700
Fiscal Year-end: 12/31/12
Business Description:
Convergent Mediation & Provisioning Software Solutions
S.I.C.: 7373
N.A.I.C.S.: 541512
Personnel:
Pertti Ervi *(Chm)*
Hannu Vaajoensuu *(Vice Chm)*
Juhani Hintikka *(Pres, CEO & Member-Exec Bd)*
Mikko Hytonen *(CFO & Member-Exec Bd)*
Antti Koskela *(CTO & Member-Exec Bd)*
Mauro Carobene *(Chief Market Ops Officer & Member-Exec Bd)*
Ulla Koivukoski *(Member-Exec Bd & Sr VP-Analytics Bus Unit)*
Kari Onniselk *(Member-Exec Bd & Sr VP-Global Svcs)*
Niina Pesonen *(Member-Exec Bd & Sr VP-HR)*
Diego Becker *(Sr VP-Latin America & Caribbean)*
Timo Koistinen *(Sr VP-Europe East)*
Mika Korpinen *(Sr VP-Asia-Pacific)*
Arnhild Schia *(Sr VP-Strategic Mktg)*
Board of Directors:
Pertti Ervi
Eriikka Soderstrom
Hannu Vaajoensuu
Antti Vasara
Petteri Wallden

Subsidiaries:

Comptel Communications Oy **(1)**
Lapinrinne 3
00100 Helsinki, Finland
Tel.: (358) 97001131
Telecommunications Software Development Service
S.I.C.: 7371
N.A.I.C.S.: 541511

Non-U.S. Subsidiaries:

Axiom Systems Ltd **(1)**
Suttons Business Park Sutton Park Avenue Earley
Reading, Bershire, RG6 1AZ, United Kingdom
Tel.: (44) 1189 294 000
Fax: (44) 1189 294 001
E-Mail: info@axiom.co.uk
Web Site: www.comptel.com
Emp.: 50
Telecommunication Software Development Services
S.I.C.: 7371
N.A.I.C.S.: 541511

Comptel Communications AS **(1)**
Arnnsgin Rd Veei 28
PO Box 183
NO-0483 Oslo, Norway (100%)
Mailing Address:
PO Box 4664
Nydalen, 0405 Oslo, Norway
Tel.: (47) 81555880
Fax: (47) 22020500
E-Mail: emea@comptel.com
Web Site: www.comptel.com
Sales Range: $25-49.9 Million
Emp.: 90
Telecommunications Services
S.I.C.: 4812
N.A.I.C.S.: 517911
Arnhild Schia *(Sr VP-Strategic Mktg)*

Comptel Communications EOOD **(1)**
9 Shipchenski Prohod Boulevard 3rd Floor
1111 Sofia, Bulgaria
Tel.: (359) 24891777
Fax: (359) 28706378
E-Mail: europe@comptel.com
Telecommunications Software Distr
S.I.C.: 5045
N.A.I.C.S.: 423430

Comptel Communications Sdn Bhd **(1)**
Lot L5 E 6 Enterprise 4 Technology Park Malaysia
Lebuhraya Puchong Sungai Besi, 57000 Kuala Lumpur, Malaysia
Tel.: (60) 389956222
Fax: (60) 389961888
E-Mail: asia@comptel.com
Web Site: www.comptel.com
Emp.: 160
Telecommunications Software Distr
S.I.C.: 5045
N.A.I.C.S.: 423430

Comptel Ltd **(1)**
69 Suttons Business Park Sutton Park Avenue
Reading, Berkshire, RG6 1AZ, United Kingdom
Tel.: (44) 1189294000
Fax: (44) 1189294001
Technical Management Consulting Services
S.I.C.: 8999
N.A.I.C.S.: 541690

COMPU-CLEARING OUTSOURCING LIMITED

7 Drome Road
Lyndhurst, Johannesburg, 2192, South Africa
Tel.: (27) 11 012 8700
Fax: (27) 118827009
E-Mail: info@compuclearing.za.com
Web Site: www.compu-clearing.com
CCL—(JSE)
Rev.: $7,454,076
Assets: $6,861,173
Liabilities: $911,807
Net Worth: $5,949,365
Earnings: $1,208,817
Emp.: 83
Fiscal Year-end: 06/30/13
Business Description:
Software Hardware Rental & Services
S.I.C.: 7371
N.A.I.C.S.: 541511
Personnel:
Arnold Garber *(Chm)*
Johan Du Preez *(CEO)*
Board of Directors:
Arnold Garber
Mario Acosta-Alarcon
David Edward Cleasby
Jonathan Davis
Johan Du Preez
Ari Katz
Milton Lutrin
Gillian McMahon
Thomas Mogale
Legal Counsel:
Fluxmans Attorneys
11 Biermann Avenue
Rosebank, South Africa
Transfer Agent:
Computershare Investor Services (Proprietary) Limited
70 Marshall Street
Johannesburg, South Africa

Subsidiary:

Compu-Clearing (Pty) Limited **(1)**
7 Drome Rd
Johannesburg, Gauteng, 2090, South Africa
Tel.: (27) 118827300
Fax: (27) 866738170
E-Mail: helpdesk@compu-clearing.com
Web Site: www.compu-clearing.za
Emp.: 90
Freight Forwarding Software Development Services
S.I.C.: 4731
N.A.I.C.S.: 488510
Johan du Preez *(CEO)*
Mario Acosta-Alarcon *(Mng Dir)*

COMPU-QUOTE INC.

3600 Rhodes Drive
Windsor, ON, N8W 5A4, Canada
Tel.: (519) 974-7283
Fax: (519) 974-7290
Toll Free: (800) 265-0808
Web Site: www.compu-quote.com
Year Founded: 1983
Rev.: $10,588,370
Emp.: 175
Business Description:
Computer Programming Services
S.I.C.: 7371
N.A.I.C.S.: 541511
Personnel:
James Nickelo *(Sr VP)*

COMPUAGE INFOCOM LTD.

601 D-Wing Lotus Corporate Park
Ram Mandir Lane
Near Jai Coach Junction Western Express Highway Goregaon E,
Mumbai, 400 063, India
Tel.: (91) 22 67114444
Fax: (91) 22 67114446
Web Site: www.compuageindia.com
Year Founded: 1987
532456—(BOM)
Rev.: $363,643,782
Assets: $91,292,610
Liabilities: $80,204,559
Net Worth: $11,088,051
Earnings: $1,518,352
Fiscal Year-end: 03/31/13
Business Description:
Computer Peripherals Distr
S.I.C.: 7379
N.A.I.C.S.: 541519
Personnel:
Atul H. Mehta *(Chm & Mng Dir)*
Bhavesh H. Mehta *(COO)*
Shilpa Singh *(Compliance Officer & Sec)*
Board of Directors:
Atul H. Mehta
Vijay Agarwal

G. S. Ganesh
Bhavesh H. Mehta
Preeti Trivedi

Transfer Agent:
Link Intime India Private Limited
C-13 Pannalal Silk Mills Compound LBS Road
Bhandup W
Mumbai, India

Subsidiaries:

ADIT E-commerce Pvt. Ltd. (1)
B42 Building No 1 Mittal Estate Marol
Andheri East, Mumbai, 400 059, India
Tel.: (91) 22 4068 6868
Web Site: www.anythinginit.com
Computer Peripheral Equipment Whslr
S.I.C.: 5045
N.A.I.C.S.: 423430

Lancor Projects Limited (1)
No 78 Vbc Jewellery Building 2nd Floor G
N Chetty Road
Theagaraya Nagar, Chennai, 600 017, India
Tel.: (91) 44 28344708
Property Development Services
S.I.C.: 6519
N.A.I.C.S.: 531190
Jayant Thivy *(Gen Mgr)*

Non-U.S. Subsidiary:

Compuage Infocom (S) Pte. Ltd. (1)
69 Ubi Crescent 03 - 04 CES Building
Singapore, 408561, Singapore
Tel.: (65) 68444 356
Fax: (65) 68444 547
E-Mail: sales@compuageinfo.com
Web Site: www.compuageindia.com
Computer Hardware Distr
S.I.C.: 5072
N.A.I.C.S.: 423710
Atul Mehta *(Chm, CEO & Mng Dir)*

COMPUCASE ENTERPRISE CO., LTD.

No 225 Ln 54 Sec 2 An Ho Rd Sec 2
T'ainan, Taiwan
Tel.: (886) 63560606
Fax: (886) 63560505
E-Mail: service@hec-group.com.tw
Web Site: www.hec-group.com.tw
3032—(TAI)
Sales Range: $25-49.9 Million

Business Description:
Computer Peripherals Mfr
S.I.C.: 3575
N.A.I.C.S.: 334118

Personnel:
Dong-Fu Hus *(Chm)*
Chun-Tung Wang *(CEO)*

Non-U.S. Subsidiaries:

Compucase Europe GmbH (1)
Im Huelsenfeld 9
40721 Hilden, Nordrhein-Westfalen, Germany
Tel.: (49) 210398810
Fax: (49) 2103 988118
E-Mail: info@compucase.de
Web Site: www.compucase.de
Computer Peripheral Equipment Mfr
S.I.C.: 3575
N.A.I.C.S.: 334118

Compucase Japan Co., Ltd. (1)
3-24-5-7F Shin-Yokohama
Kouhoku-Ku, Yokohama, Kanagawa, Japan
Tel.: (81) 454705948
Fax: (81) 454705958
E-Mail: support@hec-group.jp
Web Site: www.hec-group.jp
Computer Peripherals Mfr
S.I.C.: 3575
N.A.I.C.S.: 334118

Compucase UK. Ltd. (1)
15 Alston Drive Bradwell
Abbey, Milton Keynes, Buckinghamshire, MK13 9HA, United Kingdom
Tel.: (44) 1908 317 666
Fax: (44) 1908 317 607
E-Mail: info@compucase-hec.co.uk
Web Site: www.compucase-hec.co.uk
Emp.: 2
Computer Hardware Accessories Mfr
S.I.C.: 3575
N.A.I.C.S.: 334118
Jannie Wu *(Mgr)*

HEC Korea Co.,Ltd. (1)
506 Unitechvil Ilsan-ku
Koyang, Gyeonggi-do, 411-842, Korea (South)
Tel.: (82) 31 909 7080
Fax: (82) 31 909 7091
E-Mail: service@hec-group.co.kr
Web Site: www.heckorea.co.kr
Computer Peripherals Mfr
S.I.C.: 3577
N.A.I.C.S.: 334118

COMPUCOM SOFTWARE LTD

IT 14-15 EPIP Sitapura
Jaipur, Rajasthan, 302022, India
Tel.: (91) 1415115908
Fax: (91) 1412770335
E-Mail: contact@compucom.co.in
Web Site: www.compucomtech.co.in
532339—(BOM)
Rev.: $14,207,869
Assets: $33,729,000
Liabilities: $13,417,387
Net Worth: $20,311,614
Earnings: $1,476,287
Emp.: 560
Fiscal Year-end: 03/31/13

Business Description:
Software Development
S.I.C.: 7371
N.A.I.C.S.: 541511

Personnel:
Surendra Kumar Surana *(CEO & Mng Dir)*
Vishnu Bargoti *(CFO)*
Swati Jain *(Compliance Officer & Sec)*

Board of Directors:
G. L. Chaudhary
Ramesh Chand Jain
Ajay Kumar Surana
Shubh Karan Surana
Surendra Kumar Surana
Rajendra Prasad Udawat
Stephen Carl Viehman

Transfer Agent:
MCS Limited
F-65 1st Floor Okhla Industrial Area Phase-I
New Delhi, India

COMPUCON S.A.

9th km of Thessaloniki Thermi
PO Box 60445
57001 Thessaloniki, Greece
Tel.: (30) 2310 490300
Fax: (30) 2310 490399
E-Mail: info@compucon.gr
Web Site: www.compucon.gr
Year Founded: 1993
COMP—(ATH)
Emp.: 27

Business Description:
Embroidery Software Development Services
S.I.C.: 7371
N.A.I.C.S.: 541511

Personnel:
Vasilis Thomaidis *(Pres & CEO)*

Board of Directors:
Zahos Aggelou
Anastasios Alexandridis
Sotiris Dourdoumas
Charalambos Filadarlis
Vasilis Thomaidis
Anna Thomaidou

COMPUGATES HOLDINGS BERHAD

No 3 Jalan PJU 1/41 Dataran Prima
47301 Petaling Jaya, Selangor, Malaysia
Tel.: (60) 378808133
Fax: (60) 378806133
E-Mail: sales@compugates.com
Web Site: www.compugates.com
COMPUGT—(KLS)
Rev.: $171,899,271
Assets: $35,604,570
Liabilities: $16,750,154
Net Worth: $18,854,416
Earnings: ($3,054,575)
Fiscal Year-end: 12/31/12

Business Description:
Holding Company; Cellular Phones & Accessories Distr
S.I.C.: 6719
N.A.I.C.S.: 551112

Personnel:
Kheng Peow Goh *(Mng Dir)*
Mei Ling Chew *(Co-Sec)*
Cynthia Gloria Louis *(Co-Sec)*
Li Chen Mah *(Co-Sec)*

Board of Directors:
Asmat Kamaludin
Kheng Peow Goh
Tai Wai Goh
Mohamed Fauzi Omar
Thoo Chan See

COMPUGEN INC.

100 Via Renzo Dr
Richmond Hill, ON, L4S 0B8, Canada
Tel.: (905) 707-2000
Fax: (905) 707-2020
Toll Free: (800) 387-5045
Web Site: www.compugen.com
Year Founded: 1981
Emp.: 350

Business Description:
IT Solutions & Services
S.I.C.: 2741
N.A.I.C.S.: 519130

Personnel:
Harry Zarek *(Pres & CEO)*
David Austin *(CFO)*

Subsidiary:

Compugen Finance Inc. (1)
25 Leek Cres
Richmond Hill, ON, L4B 4B3, Canada
Tel.: (905) 695-8237
Computer Hardware & Software Leasing Services
S.I.C.: 7359
N.A.I.C.S.: 532420

COMPUGEN LTD.

72 Pinchas Rosen Street
Tel Aviv, 6951294, Israel
Tel.: (972) 3 765 8585
Fax: (972) 3 765 8555
E-Mail: info@cgen.com
Web Site: www.cgen.com
Year Founded: 1993
CGEN—(NASDAQ TAE)
Rev.: $3,549,000
Assets: $56,711,000
Liabilities: $24,823,000
Net Worth: $31,888,000
Earnings: ($14,083,000)
Emp.: 57
Fiscal Year-end: 12/31/13

Business Description:
Biotechnology Therapeutic & Diagnostic Products Discovery & Developer
S.I.C.: 2836
N.A.I.C.S.: 325414

Personnel:
Martin S. Gerstel *(Chm)*
Anat Cohen-Dayag *(Pres & CEO)*
Dikla Czaczkes Axselbrad *(CFO)*

Board of Directors:
Martin S. Gerstel
Yair Aharonowitz
Ruth Arnon
Dov Hershberg
Alex Kotzer
Arie Ovadia
Joshua Shemer

Subsidiary:

Keddem Bioscience Ltd. (1)
11 Ha'amal Street
Southern Industrial Zone, Ashkelon, 78785, Israel (100%)
Tel.: (972) 86711859
Fax: (972) 86714733
E-Mail: info@cgen.com
Small Molecule Drug Discovery
S.I.C.: 8731
N.A.I.C.S.: 541712
Dror Ofer *(Co-CEO)*

U.S. Branch:

Compugen USA, Inc. (1)
560 S Winchester Blvd Ste 500
San Jose, CA 95128 (100%)
Tel.: (408) 236-7336
Fax: (408) 236-7334
Web Site: www.cgen.com
Biotechnology Therapeutic & Diagnostic Products Discovery & Developer
S.I.C.: 2836
N.A.I.C.S.: 325414
Martin S. Gerstel *(Pres & Co-CEO)*

Affiliate:

Evogene Ltd. (1)
13 Gad Feinstein st Park Rehovot
PO Box 2100
Rehovot, 76121, Israel
Tel.: (972) 89311900
Fax: (972) 89466724
E-Mail: info@evogene.com
Web Site: www.evogene.com
EVGN—(NYSE TAE)
Rev.: $17,072,000
Assets: $64,855,000
Liabilities: $16,596,000
Net Worth: $48,259,000
Earnings: ($2,522,000)
Emp.: 60
Fiscal Year-end: 12/31/12
Crop Genetics
S.I.C.: 0721
N.A.I.C.S.: 115112
Martin Gerstel *(Chm)*
Ofer Haviv *(Pres & CEO)*
Sigal Fattal *(CFO)*
Hagai Karchi *(CTO & Exec VP-Dev)*
Assaf Kacen *(Exec VP-Tech Platform)*
Assaf Oron *(Exec VP-Strategy & Bus Dev)*

COMPUGROUP MEDICAL AG

Maria Trost 21
56070 Koblenz, Germany
Tel.: (49) 261 80000
Fax: (49) 26180001166
E-Mail: holding@cgm.com
Web Site: www.cgm.com
COP—(DEU)
Rev.: $606,559,971
Assets: $876,738,982
Liabilities: $635,226,661
Net Worth: $241,512,321
Earnings: $40,954,530
Emp.: 3,563
Fiscal Year-end: 12/31/12

Business Description:
Holding Company; Healthcare Industry Software Publisher
S.I.C.: 6719
N.A.I.C.S.: 551112

Personnel:
Klaus Steffens *(Chm-Supervisory Bd)*
Frank Gotthardt *(Chm-Mgmt Bd & CEO)*
Klaus Esser *(Deputy Chm-Supervisory Bd)*
Christian B. Teig *(CFO & Member-Mgmt Bd)*
Uwe Eibich *(Member-Mgmt Bd & Exec VP-Central Europe)*
Norbert Fischl *(Sr VP-US & Canada)*
Willibald Salomon *(Sr VP-Central Eastern Europe)*

CompuGroup Medical AG—(Continued)

Supervisory Board of Directors:
Klaus Steffens
Klaus Esser
Ralf Glass
Daniel Gotthardt
Rolf Hinz
Mathias Lange

Subsidiaries:

Aescudata GmbH (1)
Bahnhofstrabe 37
21423 Winsen, Germany
Tel.: (49) 4171696100
Fax: (49) 4171696120
E-Mail: vertrieb@aescudata.de
Web Site: www.aescudata.de
Emp.: 45
Software Development Services
S.I.C.: 7371
N.A.I.C.S.: 541511
Karl Pranzl *(Mng Dir)*

ALBIS Arzteservice Product GmbH & Co KG (1)
Maria Trost 23
56070 Koblenz, Germany
Tel.: (49) 26180001600
Fax: (49) 61 8000 1650
E-Mail: info@albis.de
Web Site: www.albis.de
Emp.: 40
Software Development Services
S.I.C.: 7371
N.A.I.C.S.: 541511
Volker Scheuble *(Mng Dir)*

All For One Enterprise Solutions GmbH (1)
Unixstrasse 1
88436 Eberhardzell, Germany
Tel.: (49) 73557990
Fax: (49) 7355799222
E-Mail: info@all-for-one.de
Web Site: www.all-for-one.de
Software & Consulting Services
S.I.C.: 7371
N.A.I.C.S.: 541511

ChreMaSoft Datensysteme Verwaltungs-GmbH (1)
Maria Trost 25
Rheinland-Pfalz, Koblenz, 56070, Germany
Tel.: (49) 26180001820
Fax: (49) 26180001809
E-Mail: info@chremasoft.com
Web Site: www.chremasoft.com
Emp.: 3,000
Medical Software Services
S.I.C.: 7371
N.A.I.C.S.: 541511
Dirk Rumenapp *(CEO)*

CompuDENT Praxiscomputer GmbH & Co. KG (1)
Maria Trost 25
56070 Koblenz, Germany
Tel.: (49) 26180001900
Fax: (49) 2618000196
E-Mail: info@compudent.de
Web Site: www.compudent.de
Emp.: 100
Online Dental Information Provider
S.I.C.: 8731
N.A.I.C.S.: 541712
Mario Luna Stollmeier *(Mng Dir)*

Subsidiary:

Intermedix Deutschland GmbH (2)
Maria Trost 21
56070 Koblenz, Germany
Tel.: (49) 26180001740
Fax: (49) 26180001745
E-Mail: maike.dieckmann@intermedix.de
Web Site: www.intermedix.de
Emp.: 27
Medical Information Services
S.I.C.: 8011
N.A.I.C.S.: 621491
Wolfgang Hofers *(Mng Dir)*

CompuGroup Medical Dentalsysteme GmbH (1)
Maria Trost 25
56070 Koblenz, Germany
Tel.: (49) 26180001500
Fax: (49) 26180001596
E-Mail: info@z1-software.de
Web Site: www.z1-software.de
Emp.: 2,000
Software Development Services
S.I.C.: 7371
N.A.I.C.S.: 541511

CompuGroup Medical Deutschland AG (1)
Maria Trost 25
56070 Koblenz, Germany
Tel.: (49) 261 8000 8000
Fax: (49) 261 8000 8100
E-Mail: info@cgm.com
Web Site: www.cgm.com
Medical Software Publisher
S.I.C.: 7372
N.A.I.C.S.: 511210

CompuGroup Medical Managementgesellschaft mbH (1)
Maria Trost 21
56070 Koblenz, Germany
Tel.: (49) 261 8000 1352
Fax: (49) 261 8000 3360
Business Support Services
S.I.C.: 7389
N.A.I.C.S.: 561499

CompuGroup Services GmbH (1)
Maria Trost 21
56070 Koblenz, Germany
Tel.: (49) 26180001150
Fax: (49) 261 80001155
E-Mail: info@gti-ag.de
Software Development Services
S.I.C.: 7371
N.A.I.C.S.: 541511
Andreas Koll *(Gen Mgr)*

CompuGroup Medical Software GmbH (1)
Maria Trost 21
56070 Koblenz, Germany De
Tel.: (49) 26180001960
Fax: (49) 26180001596
Web Site: www.cgm.com
Emp.: 70
Software Development Services
S.I.C.: 7371
N.A.I.C.S.: 541511
Jochen Bruggemann *(Mng Dir)*
Udo Mueller Oest *(CTO & VP)*

CompuMED Praxiscomputer GmbH & Co KG (1)
Maria Trost 25
56070 Koblenz, Germany
Tel.: (49) 26180001400
Fax: (49) 26180001441
E-Mail: info@compumed.de
Web Site: www.compumed.de
Practice Management Software Development Services
S.I.C.: 7371
N.A.I.C.S.: 541511
Peter Taulka *(Mgr-Customer Care)*

DATA VITAL GmbH & Co KG (1)
Maria Trost 25
56070 Koblenz, Germany
Tel.: (49) 26180001460
Fax: (49) 261 8000 1441
E-Mail: info@data-vital.de
Web Site: www.data-vital.de
Health Care Services
S.I.C.: 8082
N.A.I.C.S.: 621610
Stefan Hahne *(Mng Dir)*

GiV mbH (1)
Maria Trost 21
56070 Koblenz, Germany
Tel.: (49) 26180001824
Fax: (49) 26180001155
E-Mail: info@giv-igv.de
Web Site: www.giv-igv.de
Health Care Services
S.I.C.: 8011
N.A.I.C.S.: 621491

ifap Service-Institut fur Arzte und Apotheker GmbH (1)
Bunsenstrasse 7
82152 Martinsried, Germany
Tel.: (49) 89 89744 0
Fax: (49) 89 89744 300
E-Mail: info@ifap.de
Web Site: www.ifap.de
Medical Information Data Bank Operator
S.I.C.: 2741
N.A.I.C.S.: 511140

INMEDEA GmbH (1)
Gerhard Kindler St 6
72770 Reutlingen, Germany
Tel.: (49) 7121127060
Fax: (49) 71211270620
E-Mail: info@inmedea.com
Web Site: www.inmedea.com
Emp.: 6
Medical Software Development Services
S.I.C.: 7371
N.A.I.C.S.: 541511
Axel Greiner *(Acct Mgr)*

ISPRO GmbH (1)
Werksstr 15
45527 Hattingen, Germany
Tel.: (49) 2324 920 90
Fax: (49) 2324 920 970
E-Mail: info@ispro.de
Web Site: www.ispro.de
Emp.: 25
Health Care Services
S.I.C.: 8011
N.A.I.C.S.: 621491
Michael Franz *(Mng Dir)*

Lauer-Fischer GmbH (1)
Dr Mack Strasse 95
Furth, Germany
Tel.: (49) 911 74320
Fax: (49) 911 7432100
E-Mail: info@lauer-fischer.de
Web Site: www.lauer-fischer.de
Medical Software Developer
S.I.C.: 7372
N.A.I.C.S.: 511210
Volker Hesse *(Dir-Mktg)*

Medi-cine Medienproduktions GmbH (1)
Lise Meitner Strabe 9
55129 Mainz, Germany
Tel.: (49) 6131952960
Fax: (49) 61319529610
E-Mail: info@medi-cine.de
Web Site: www.medi-cine.de
Emp.: 20
Television Programs Producer
S.I.C.: 7929
N.A.I.C.S.: 711510
Frank Nadzeika *(Gen Mgr)*

MEDISTAR Praxiscomputer GmbH (1)
Karl Wiechert Allee 64
30625 Hannover, Germany
Tel.: (49) 511540500
Fax: (49) 511 5405 109
E-Mail: info@medistar.de
Web Site: www.medistar.de
Emp.: 104
Software Development Services
S.I.C.: 7371
N.A.I.C.S.: 541511

Systema Deutschland GmbH (1)
Maria Trost 21
56070 Koblenz, Germany
Tel.: (49) 261 8000 1780
Fax: (49) 261 8000 1789
E-Mail: info@systema.de
Web Site: www.systema.de
Health Care Services
S.I.C.: 8011
N.A.I.C.S.: 621491

Telemed Online Service fur Heilberufe GmbH (1)
Maria Trost 21
56070 Koblenz, Germany
Tel.: (49) 1805040008
Fax: (49) 1805040009
E-Mail: info@telemed.de
Web Site: www.telemed.de
Emp.: 18
Online Health Care Services
S.I.C.: 8011
N.A.I.C.S.: 621491
Arthur Steinel *(Gen Mgr)*

TurboMed EDV GmbH (1)
Osterberg 2
24113 Molfsee, Germany
Tel.: (49) 431 65920 50
Fax: (49) 431 65920 65
E-Mail: info@turbomed.de
Web Site: www.turbomed.de
Medical Data Services
S.I.C.: 2741
N.A.I.C.S.: 511140

Vita-X AG (1)
Maria Trost 21
56070 Koblenz, Germany
Tel.: (49) 26180001320
Fax: (49) 26180001351
E-Mail: info@vita-X.de
Web Site: www.vita-X.de
Health Care Services
S.I.C.: 8011
N.A.I.C.S.: 621491
Sabine Lippert *(Pres)*

U.S. Subsidiary:

CompuGroup Medical Inc. (1)
125 High St 14th Fl Oliver Street Tower
Boston, MA 02110
Tel.: (617) 443-4060
Fax: (617) 507-5886
E-Mail: info@cgmus.com
Web Site: www.cgmus.com
Medical Software Publisher
S.I.C.: 7372
N.A.I.C.S.: 511210
Mark Conner *(Pres-eMedix Reimbursement Svcs)*
Jim Kasoff *(Pres-Laboratory Solutions)*

Non-U.S. Subsidiaries:

ADVANCE AB (1)
Datavagen 29
PO Box 9249
400 95 Gothenburg, Sweden
Tel.: (46) 317601800
Fax: (46) 31287940
E-Mail: info@advance.se
Web Site: www.advance.se
Emp.: 50
Online Health Care Services
S.I.C.: 8011
N.A.I.C.S.: 621491

AESCU DATA Gesellschaft fur Datenverarbeitung mbH (1)
Pachergasse 17
4400 Steyr, Austria
Tel.: (43) 7252477220
Fax: (43) 7252477222000
E-Mail: info@aescudata.at
Web Site: www.aescudata.at
Emp.: 22
Software Development Sservices
S.I.C.: 7371
N.A.I.C.S.: 541511
Karl Pranzl *(Gen Mgr)*

Ascon Automatisering B.V. (1)
Nobelweg 22
6101 Echt, Netherlands
Tel.: (31) 900 3876333
Web Site: www.euroned.eu
Healthcare Industry Software Publisher
S.I.C.: 7372
N.A.I.C.S.: 511210

Ascon Hosting Facilities B.V. (1)
Nobelweg 32
6101 Echt, Netherlands
Tel.: (31) 900 3876633
Web Site: www.euroned.eu
Healthcare Industry Software Publisher
S.I.C.: 7372
N.A.I.C.S.: 511210

Ascon Software B.V. (1)
Nobelweg 32
6101 Echt, Netherlands
Tel.: (31) 900 3876633
Web Site: www.euroned.eu
Healthcare Industry Software Publisher
S.I.C.: 7372
N.A.I.C.S.: 511210

CGM Bilgi Sistemleri A.S. (1)
Sokak No 26-28 Mecidiyekoy
34394 Istanbul, Turkey
Tel.: (90) 212 3060000
Fax: (90) 212 355 8449
Web Site: www.cgmturkiye.com
Healthcare Software Publisher
S.I.C.: 7372
N.A.I.C.S.: 511210

CGM South Africa (Pty) Ltd. (1)
1 Proton Street Techno Park
PO Box 6089
7612 Stellenbosch, South Africa
Tel.: (27) 21 8866160
Fax: (27) 21 8866150
E-Mail: marie.hunneyball@cgmsa.com
Web Site: www.cgm.com
Emp.: 2
Healthcare Industry Software Publisher
S.I.C.: 7372
N.A.I.C.S.: 511210
Eddie Ong *(Gen Mgr)*

CompuGROUP CEE GmbH (1)
Neulinggasse 29
1030 Vienna, Austria
Tel.: (43) 17151623
Fax: (43) 17151631525
Web Site: www.report.compugroup.com
Emp.: 3
Software Development Services
S.I.C.: 7371
N.A.I.C.S.: 541511
Willibald Salomon *(Mng Dir)*

Subsidiaries:

Intermedix Osterreich GmbH (2)
Neulinggasse 29
A 1030 Vienna, Austria
Tel.: (43) 171516310
Fax: (43) 17151631525
E-Mail: info@intermedix.at
Web Site: www.intermedix.at
Emp.: 2
Health Care Software Services
S.I.C.: 7371
N.A.I.C.S.: 541511
Martin Schauperl *(Mng Dir)*

Systema HIS Human Information Systems Gesellschaft mbH (2)
Pachergasse 4
4400 Steyr, Austria
Tel.: (43) 72525870
Fax: (43) 72525879555
E-Mail: ssc@systema.info
Web Site: www.systema.info
Emp.: 250
Software Development Services
S.I.C.: 7371
N.A.I.C.S.: 541511
Hannes Reichl *(Gen Mgr)*

CompuGroup Medical Belgium bvba (1)
Borrestraat 11 a
9850 Nevele, Belgium
Tel.: (32) 9 3719384
Fax: (32) 9 3718963
E-Mail: info@cgmbelgium.be
Web Site: www.cgmbelgium.be
Medical Industry Software Publisher
S.I.C.: 7372
N.A.I.C.S.: 511210
Norbert Fishl *(Gen Mgr)*

CompuGroup Medical Ceska republika s.r.o. (1)
Jeremiasova 1422/7
155 00 Prague, Czech Republic
Tel.: (420) 246 007 9000
Fax: (420) 246 007 915
Web Site: www.compugroup.cz
Healthcare Industry Software Publisher
S.I.C.: 7372
N.A.I.C.S.: 511210

CompuGroup Medical Denmark A/S (1)
Lyngbyvej 20
2100 Copenhagen, Denmark
Tel.: (45) 7030 1340
Fax: (45) 7030 1341
E-Mail: kontakt@compugroupmedical.dk
Web Site: www.compugroupmedical.dk
Healthcare Industry Software Publisher
S.I.C.: 7372
N.A.I.C.S.: 511210
Anita B. Christensen *(Dir-Admin)*

CompuGroup Medical Hellas S.A. (1)
Soumela St 23 Kalamaria
55 132 Thessaloniki, Greece
Tel.: (30) 2310 432 885
Fax: (30) 2310 432 840
E-Mail: info@profdoc.gr
Web Site: www.compugroup.com
Emp.: 3
Medical Software Development Services
S.I.C.: 7371
N.A.I.C.S.: 541511
Stelios Louropoulos *(Mng Dir)*

CompuGroup Medical Italia S.p.A. (1)
Via A Olivetti 10
70056 Molfetta, BA, Italy
Tel.: (39) 080 3383 111
Fax: (39) 080 3383 880
Web Site: www.cgm.com
Healthcare Industry Software Publisher
S.I.C.: 7372
N.A.I.C.S.: 511210

CompuGroup Medical Lab AB (1)
Cirkelgatan 14
781 05 Borlange, Sweden
Tel.: (46) 24 32 17 600
Fax: (46) 24 32 17 601
E-Mail: labinfo@profdoc.com
Web Site: www.compugroupmedical.se
Emp.: 50
Analytical Laboratory Information Development Services
S.I.C.: 8071
N.A.I.C.S.: 621511
Jonas Westbom *(CEO)*

CompuGroup Medical Malaysia Sdn Bhd (1)
Unit L3-1-2 Level 3 Enterprise 4 Technology Park Malaysia
Lebuhraya Puchong-Sg
Bess Bukit Jalil, 57000 Kuala Lumpur, Malaysia
Tel.: (60) 899 66 700
Fax: (60) 899 66 707
Web Site: www.cgm.com
Healthcare Industry Software Publisher
S.I.C.: 7372
N.A.I.C.S.: 511210

CompuGroup Medical Polska sp. z o.o. (1)
Ul Do Dysa 9
20-149 Lublin, Poland
Tel.: (48) 81 444 2015
Fax: (48) 81 444 2018
Web Site: www.cgmpolska.pl
Healthcare Industry Software Publisher
S.I.C.: 7372
N.A.I.C.S.: 511210

CompuGroup Medical Schweitz AG (1)
Riedstrasse 1
6330 Cham, Switzerland
Tel.: (41) 41 785 2300
Fax: (41) 41 785 2309
Web Site: www.compugroup-medical.ch
Healthcare Industry Software Publisher
S.I.C.: 7372
N.A.I.C.S.: 511210
Peter Zberg *(Mng Dir)*

CompuGroup Medical Slovensko s.r.o. (1)
Galvaniho 7/D
82101 Bratislava, Slovakia
Tel.: (421) 253 418073
Fax: (421) 253 418074
E-Mail: info.adam@cgm.com
Web Site: www.cgm.sk
Emp.: 2
Healthcare Industry Software Publisher
S.I.C.: 7372
N.A.I.C.S.: 511210
Ryan Nock *(Gen Mgr)*

CompuGroup Medical Solutions SAS (1)
59 A avenue de Toulouse
34076 Montpellier, Cedex 3, France
Tel.: (33) 8 2036 3605
Web Site: www.cgm-solutions.fr
Healthcare Industry Software Publisher
S.I.C.: 7372
N.A.I.C.S.: 511210

CompuGroup Medical Sweden AB (1)
Lill Bommen 2 5 van hiss 7 & 8
411 04 Gothenburg, Sweden
Tel.: (46) 300 56 8000
Fax: (46) 3115 0505
Web Site: www.compugroupmedical.se
Healthcare Industry Software Publisher
S.I.C.: 7372
N.A.I.C.S.: 511210

Subsidiary:

Lorensbergs Communication AB (2)
Lilla Bommen 4A
41104 Gothenburg, Sweden
Tel.: (46) 31 720 6300
Fax: (46) 31 720 6301
Healthcare Industry Software Publisher
S.I.C.: 7372
N.A.I.C.S.: 511210

CompuGroup Osterreich GmbH (1)
Kristein 30
4470 Enns, Austria
Tel.: (43) 50 818100
Fax: (43) 50 818199
E-Mail: office@compugroup.at
Web Site: www.compugroup.at
Healthcare Industry Software Publisher
S.I.C.: 7372
N.A.I.C.S.: 511210

Effepieffe S.r.l. (1)
Via Mazzini 13
20812 Limbiate, MB, Italy
Tel.: (39) 02 0061 9826
Fax: (39) 02 9139 0110
Web Site: www.effepieffe.it
Healthcare Industry Software Publisher
S.I.C.: 7372
N.A.I.C.S.: 511210

HCS - Health Communication Service GmbH (1)
Maiss 48
3033 Altlengbach, Austria
Tel.: (43) 2774 6003
Fax: (43) 2774 6002
Web Site: www.hcs.at
Healthcare Industry Software Publisher
S.I.C.: 7372
N.A.I.C.S.: 511210
Eduard Schebesta *(Gen Mgr)*

INNOMED Gesellschaft fur medizinische Softwareanwendungen GmbH (1)
Ricoweg 22
Wiener Neudorf, Austria
Tel.: (43) 2236 8000
Fax: (43) 2236 8000888
Web Site: www.innomed.at
Healthcare Industry Software Publisher
S.I.C.: 7372
N.A.I.C.S.: 511210

Intermedix Ceska republika s.r.o. (1)
Jeremiasova 1422/7
155 00 Prague, Czech Republic
Tel.: (420) 246 007 900
Fax: (420) 246 007 915
E-Mail: info@intermedix.cz
Web Site: www.intermedix.cz
Emp.: 2
Healthcare Industry Software Publisher
S.I.C.: 7372
N.A.I.C.S.: 511210
Sviatoslav Molnar *(Mng Dir)*

Intermedix France S.a.r.l. (1)
212 Ave Paul Doumer
92500 Rueil-Malmaison, France
Tel.: (33) 147162702
Fax: (33) 147162703
E-Mail: contact@intermedix.fr
Web Site: www.intermedix.fr
Emp.: 7
Software Development & Communications Services
S.I.C.: 7371
N.A.I.C.S.: 541511
Samera Achemaoui *(Acct Mgr)*

Intermedix Italia S.r.l. (1)
Piazza Castello 19
20121 Milan, Italy
Tel.: (39) 080 3383309
Fax: (39) 02 335178522
Web Site: www.intermedixitalia.it
Healthcare Industry Software Publisher
S.I.C.: 7372
N.A.I.C.S.: 511210

Le Reseau Sante Sociale SAS (1)
212 Ave Paul Doumer
92508 Rueil-Malmaison, France
Tel.: (33) 147162700
Fax: (33) 147162701
E-Mail: redaction@lereseausantesocial.fr
Web Site: www.lereseausantesocial.fr
Emp.: 41
Online Medical Services
S.I.C.: 6324
N.A.I.C.S.: 524114
Franck Frayer *(Mng Dir)*

Medical Net SAS (1)
59A Avenue de Toulouse
34070 Montpellier, France
Tel.: (33) 467271402
Fax: (33) 499513302
E-Mail: support.medicalnet@cgm.com
Web Site: www.medicalnet.fr
Emp.: 50
Online Medical Services
S.I.C.: 2741
N.A.I.C.S.: 519130
Frank Frager *(Gen Mgr)*

Medigest Consultores S.L. (1)
C/ General Peron 26 esc 2 3o A
28020 Madrid, Spain
Tel.: (34) 91 5974562
Fax: (34) 91 5569716
Web Site: www.medigest.com
Healthcare Industry Software Publisher
S.I.C.: 7372
N.A.I.C.S.: 511210

MedXpert Healthcare Ssolutions GmbH (1)
Innsbrucker Strabe 83
A 6060 Hall in Tirol, Tyrol, Austria
Tel.: (43) 5223 20 45 90
Fax: (43) 5223 2045 90900
E-Mail: info@compugroup.at
Emp.: 12
Health Care Services
S.I.C.: 8011
N.A.I.C.S.: 621491
Helmut Stecher *(Gen Mgr)*

Microbais Werkmaatschappij B.V. (1)
Hettenheuvelweg
1101 BN Amsterdam, Netherlands
Tel.: (31) 20 430 7777
Fax: (31) 20 430 7770
Web Site: www.microbais.nl
Healthcare Industry Software Publisher
S.I.C.: 7372
N.A.I.C.S.: 511210

Profdoc ASA (1)
Torg 15 4 etasje
Lysaker, Norway
Tel.: (47) 21936370
Fax: (47) 21936371
Web Site: www.profdoc.no
Emp.: 5
Healthcare & Software Development Services
S.I.C.: 7371
N.A.I.C.S.: 541511
Christian B. Teig *(Pres)*
Bjorn Lindholt *(CFO)*

Subsidiary:

CompuGroup Medical Norway AS (2)
Torg 15 2nd Fl
Postboks 163
1325 Lysaker, Norway
Tel.: (47) 815 69 069
Fax: (47) 21 93 63 01
Emp.: 50
Health Care & Software Services
S.I.C.: 7371
N.A.I.C.S.: 541511
Kim Oyvind Engebretsen *(Head-Team Support)*

Non-U.S. Subsidiaries:

Profdoc LINK AB (2)
Baverns grand 17
PO Box 1740
75 148 Uppsala, Sweden
Tel.: (46) 184744400
Fax: (46) 18101220
Web Site: www.profdoc.se/kontakta/
Health Care Services
S.I.C.: 8011
N.A.I.C.S.: 621491

CompuGroup Medical AG—(Continued)

Profdoc (PTY) LTD (2)
37 Herte St
PO Box 6089
7600 Stellenbosch, South Africa
Tel.: (27) 218866160
Fax: (27) 218866150
E-Mail: info@cgm.com
Web Site: www.profdoc.co.za
Emp.: 11
Health Care Services
S.I.C.: 8011
N.A.I.C.S.: 621491
Ake Nylund *(CTO)*

Profdoc Sdn Bhd (2)
Unit L3-I-2 Level 3 Enterprise 4 Tech Park Malaysia
Lebuhraya Puchong-Sg Bes, 57000 Kuala Lumpur, Malaysia
Tel.: (60) 389966700
Fax: (60) 389966707
E-Mail: info@profdoc.com.my
Web Site: www.profdoc.com.my
Emp.: 50
Health Care & Information Technology Services
S.I.C.: 8011
N.A.I.C.S.: 621491
Rolf Henry Gronlund *(Mng Dir)*

Profdoc SIA (2)
Duntes 6-207
Riga, LV 1013, Latvia
Tel.: (371) 67798802
Fax: (371) 67798801
E-Mail: info@profdoc.lv
Web Site: www.profdoc.lv
Emp.: 5
Health Care Services
S.I.C.: 8011
N.A.I.C.S.: 621491
Iva Selecka *(Mgr-Sls)*

Profdoc Care AB (1)
Olof Palmes Gata 23 2 Fl
111 22 Stockholm, Sweden
Tel.: (46) 84115550
Fax: (46) 84409379
E-Mail: info@profdoc.se
Web Site: www.profdoccare.se
Emp.: 20
Health Care Services
S.I.C.: 8011
N.A.I.C.S.: 621491
Martin Williamson *(CEO)*

PROMED A.S. (1)
Profilo Plz B Blok Zemin Kat Cemal Sahir Sokak No 26-28, 34394 Istanbul, Turkey
Tel.: (90) 2123060000
Fax: (90) 212 355 84 49
E-Mail: info@cgmturkiye.com
Web Site: www.promedtibbi.com
Emp.: 200
Third Party Administration Services
S.I.C.: 6371
N.A.I.C.S.: 524292

Tepe International Health Information Systems A.S. (1)
Cyberpark Ankara Tech Dev Zone
Cyberplaza C Block Kat 3 No 1, 06800 Ankara, Turkey
Tel.: (90) 3122918000
Fax: (90) 3122918099
E-Mail: info@tepeinternational.com.tr
Web Site: www.tepeinternational.com.tr
Emp.: 52
Software Development Services
S.I.C.: 7371
N.A.I.C.S.: 541511
Mehmeat Mirhinsoy *(CEO)*

Tepe International Health Information Systems A.S. (1)
Office No 307 Al Khozama Ctr
PO Box 53215
11583 Riyadh, Saudi Arabia
Tel.: (966) 1 219 1160
Fax: (966) 1 219 1170
E-Mail: info@cgm.com
Emp.: 15
Medical Information Services
S.I.C.: 8011
N.A.I.C.S.: 621491
Mehmet Bilginsoy *(Mng Dir)*

Tipdata Medical Software (1)
Plz B Block No 26-28
Ground Fl Profilo, 34394 Istanbul, Turkey
Tel.: (90) 2123060080
Fax: (90) 2123557572
E-Mail: info@tipdata.com.tr
Web Site: www.tipdata.com.tr
Emp.: 10
Medical Sofware Development Services
S.I.C.: 7371
N.A.I.C.S.: 541511
Fatna Zakaryan *(Gen Mgr)*

COMPUMEDICS LIMITED

30-40 Flockhart Street
Abbotsford, VIC, 3067, Australia
Tel.: (61) 384207300
Fax: (61) 384207399
Web Site: www.compumedics.com
CMP—(ASX)
Sls.: $28,293,015
Assets: $19,890,563
Liabilities: $11,185,901
Net Worth: $8,704,661
Earnings: ($1,551,687)
Emp.: 162
Fiscal Year-end: 06/30/13

Business Description:
Medical Diagnostic Equipment Mfr
S.I.C.: 3845
N.A.I.C.S.: 334510

Personnel:
David Burton *(Founder, Chm & CEO)*
David Lawson *(CFO & Sec)*
Warwick Freeman *(CTO)*
Kerry Hubick *(Legal Counsel)*

Board of Directors:
David Burton
Alan Anderson
Graham F. Mitchell

U.S. Subsidiaries:

Compumedics USA, Inc. (1)
6605 W WT Harris Blvd Ste F
Charlotte, NC 28269-1582 DE
Tel.: (704) 749-3200
Fax: (704) 749-3298
Toll Free: (877) 717-3975
Web Site: www.compumedicsusa.com
Emp.: 30
Neurodiagnostic Laboratory Products Whslr
S.I.C.: 5122
N.A.I.C.S.: 424210

Divisions:

Compumedics Limited - Compumedics Sleep Division (2)
6605 W WT Harris Blvd Ste F
Charlotte, NC 28269-1582
Tel.: (704) 749-3200
Fax: (704) 749-3299
Toll Free: (800) 814-8890
E-Mail: sales@neuroscan.com
Web Site: www.compumedicsusa.com
Diagnostic Equipment Mfr
S.I.C.: 3845
N.A.I.C.S.: 334510
David Burton *(CEO)*

Compumedics Limited - Neuroscan Division (2)
6605 W WT Harris Blvd Ste F
Charlotte, NC 28269-1582
Tel.: (704) 749-3200
Fax: (704) 749-3299
Toll Free: (800) 814-8890
E-Mail: sales@neuroscan.com
Web Site: www.neuroscan.com
Emp.: 15
Diagnostic Equipment Mfr
S.I.C.: 3845
N.A.I.C.S.: 334510
Curtis W. Ponton *(VP)*

Non-U.S. Subsidiary:

Compumedics Germany GmbH (1)
Josef-Schuttler-Strasse 2
78224 Singen, Germany
Tel.: (49) 7731797690
Fax: (49) 7731 79 76 9 99
E-Mail: info@dwl.de
Web Site: www.dwl.de
Emp.: 25
Doppler Systems & Accessories Mfr
S.I.C.: 3845
N.A.I.C.S.: 334510
David Burton *(Mng Dir)*

COMPUTACENTER PLC

Hatfield Business Park Hatfield Avenue
Hatfield, AL10 9TW, United Kingdom
Tel.: (44) 1707631000
Fax: (44) 1707639966
E-Mail: personell@computacenter.com
Web Site: www.computacenter.com
CCC—(LSE)
Rev.: $4,602,389,028
Assets: $1,759,595,960
Liabilities: $1,092,593,884
Net Worth: $667,002,076
Earnings: $77,574,725
Emp.: 12,342
Fiscal Year-end: 12/31/12

Business Description:
Holding Company; Information Technology Management & Outsourcing Services
S.I.C.: 6719
N.A.I.C.S.: 551112

Personnel:
Mike Norris *(CEO)*
Mike Rodwell *(Chief Comml Officer)*
Oliver Tuszik *(CEO-Germany)*

Board of Directors:
Greg Lock
Tony Conophy
Philip Hulme
Ian Lewis
Brian James McBride
Mike Norris
Peter Ogden
John Ormerod

Legal Counsel:
Linklaters
1 Silk Street
London, EC2Y 8HQ, United Kingdom

Transfer Agent:
Equiniti
Aspect House Spencer Road
Lancing, United Kingdom

Subsidiaries:

Computacenter (UK) Ltd. (1)
Hatfield Avenue
Hatfield, Herts, AL10 9TW, United Kingdom UK
Tel.: (44) 1707631000 (100%)
Fax: (44) 1707639966
Web Site: www.computacenter.com
Information Technology Management & Outsourcing Services
S.I.C.: 7373
N.A.I.C.S.: 541512
Tony Conophy *(Grp Dir-Fin)*

RD Trading Limited (1)
Tekhnicon Springwood
Braintree, Essex, CM7 2YN, United Kingdom
Tel.: (44) 1376503600
Fax: (44) 1376503744
E-Mail: ghackett@rdc.co.uk
Web Site: www.rdc.co.uk
Emp.: 200
IT Asset Management Services
S.I.C.: 6799
N.A.I.C.S.: 523920
Gerry Hackett *(Mng Dir)*

Non-U.S. Subsidiaries:

Computacenter France S.A. (1)
150 Rue De La Belle Etoile
Zone Industrielle ParisNord 2, Roissy-en-France, Cedex, F 95943, France
Tel.: (33) 148174100
Fax: (33) 170734222
E-Mail: contacts@computacenter.fr
Web Site: www.computacenter.fr
Emp.: 600
IT Infrastructure Services
S.I.C.: 7373
N.A.I.C.S.: 541512
Henri Viard *(Mng Dir)*

Computacenter GmbH (1)
Stachegasse 13
1120 Vienna, Austria
Tel.: (43) 1801910
IT Infrastructure Services
S.I.C.: 7373
N.A.I.C.S.: 541512

Computacenter Holding GmbH (1)
Horselbergstr 7
81677 Munich, Germany
Tel.: (49) 89457120
Fax: (49) 8945712333
E-Mail: mailbox.demuc_front@computacenter.com
Web Site: www.computacenter.de
Emp.: 500
IT Infrastructure Services
S.I.C.: 7373
N.A.I.C.S.: 541512
Oliver Tuszik *(CEO)*
Angelica Benson *(Mng Dir)*

Computacenter NV/SA (1)
Karoslaan 31
1930 Zaventem, Belgium
Tel.: (32) 27049411
Fax: (32) 27049595
E-Mail: infobelgium@computacenter.com
Web Site: www.eshop.computacenter.com
Emp.: 60
IT Infrastructure Services
S.I.C.: 7373
N.A.I.C.S.: 541512
Tom Struye *(Mgr-Sls)*

Computacenter PSF SA (1)
45 rue des Scillas
L 2529 Howald, Luxembourg
Tel.: (352) 262911
Fax: (352) 26291815
E-Mail: infolux@computacenter.com
Web Site: www.computacenter.com
Emp.: 50
IT Infrastructure Services
S.I.C.: 7373
N.A.I.C.S.: 541512
Deboeck Olivier *(Mng Dir)*

Computacenter Services (Iberia) SLU (1)
C Balmes 236
08006 Barcelona, Spain
Tel.: (34) 936207000
Fax: (34) 936 207 040
Web Site: www.computacenter.com
International Call Centre Services
S.I.C.: 7389
N.A.I.C.S.: 561422

COMPUTECH HOLDINGS LIMITED

Unit 1604 16F West Tower Shun Tak Centre 168-200 Connaught Road Central, China (Hong Kong)
Tel.: (852) 2549 2038
Fax: (852) 2549 2789
E-Mail: info@clts.com
Web Site: www.computech.com.hk
8081—(HKG)
Rev.: $13,746,586
Assets: $20,641,800
Liabilities: $6,001,075
Net Worth: $14,640,725
Earnings: ($2,717,750)
Emp.: 18
Fiscal Year-end: 12/31/12

Business Description:
Investment Holding Company
S.I.C.: 6719
N.A.I.C.S.: 551112

Personnel:
Yue Zhou Yang *(Chm)*
Kwong Yiu Mak *(Compliance Officer)*
Wing Tai Lam *(Sec)*

Board of Directors:
Yue Zhou Yang
Tan Shan Jiang
Shun Tim Kwok
Chi Shing Luk
Kwong Yiu Mak
Ching Yip Wong

Joe Siu Keung Wong
Hong Kong Registrars Limited
Rooms 1712-1716 17th Floor Hopewell Centre
183 Queen's Road East
Wanchai, China (Hong Kong)
Transfer Agents:
Royal Bank of Canada Trust Company (Cayman) Limited
4th Floor Royal Bank House 24 Shedden Road
Georgetown, Cayman Islands
Hong Kong Registrars Limited
Rooms 1712-1716 17th Floor Hopewell Centre
183 Queen's Road East
Wanchai, China (Hong Kong)

COMPUTER & TECHNOLOGIES HOLDINGS LIMITED

29/F & 30/F Prosperity Millennia Plaza 663 King's Road
North Point, China (Hong Kong)
Tel.: (852) 25038000
Fax: (852) 25038100
E-Mail: info@ctil.com
Web Site: www.ctil.com
Year Founded: 1991
0046—(HKG)
Rev.: $26,654,997
Assets: $63,711,487
Liabilities: $12,099,894
Net Worth: $51,611,593
Earnings: $6,060,908
Emp.: 284
Fiscal Year-end: 12/31/12
Business Description:
Information Technology Services
S.I.C.: 7373
N.A.I.C.S.: 541512
Personnel:
Cheung Shing Ng *(Founder & Chm)*
Kwok Keung Ng *(Sec & Controller-Fin)*
Board of Directors:
Cheung Shing Ng
Albert Shu Tong Ha
Matthew K. O. Lee
Sunny King San Leung
Stephen Leung Huel Ting
HSBC Securities Services (Bermuda) Limited
6 Front Street
Hamilton, Bermuda
Transfer Agents:
Tricor Tengis Limited
26th Floor Tesbury Centre 28 Queen's Road East
Wanchai, China (Hong Kong)
Tel.: (852) 29801333
Fax: (852) 28108185
HSBC Securities Services (Bermuda) Limited
6 Front Street
Hamilton, Bermuda

Subsidiaries:

Computer And Technologies International Limited (1)
30/F Prosperity Millennia Plz 663 Kings Road
North Point, China (Hong Kong)
Tel.: (852) 25038000
Fax: (852) 25038100
Web Site: www.ctil.com
Computer System Network Integration Services
S.I.C.: 7373
N.A.I.C.S.: 541512
Peter Yan *(CEO & Exec Dir)*

Computer & Technologies Solutions Limited (1)
29/30 F MLC Millennia Plaza
663 King's Rd, North Point, China (Hong Kong)
Tel.: (852) 25038222
Fax: (852) 25038300
Web Site: www.ctil.com
Emp.: 180
Applicaton Software Development Services & Internet Solutions with Related Consulting, Implementation & Outsourcing Services
S.I.C.: 7371
N.A.I.C.S.: 541511
Peter Yan *(CEO)*

Global e-Business Services Limited (1)
30/F MLC Millennia Plaza
663 King s Road, North Point, China (Hong Kong)
Tel.: (852) 25038333
Fax: (852) 25038400
E-Mail: csvmail@ge-ts.com.hk
Web Site: vip.ge-ts.com.hk
Emp.: 100
Internet & Related Business Process Outsourcing Services
S.I.C.: 7371
N.A.I.C.S.: 541511
Stephen Lau *(Mgr)*

Global e-Trading Services Limited (1)
30 F Prosperity Millennia Plz 663 Kings Road
North Point, China (Hong Kong)
Tel.: (852) 25038333
Fax: (852) 25038400
Web Site: www.ge-ts.com.hk
Electronic Shopping Services
S.I.C.: 7299
N.A.I.C.S.: 812990

IPL Research Limited (1)
29 F MLC Millennia Plz
663 King's Rd, North Point, China (Hong Kong)
Tel.: (852) 28034026
Fax: (852) 28388707
E-Mail: raymond_wang@ipl.com.hk
Web Site: www.ipl.com
Emp.: 17
Human Resource Management & Related Application Software
S.I.C.: 8748
N.A.I.C.S.: 541618
Peter Yan *(Mgr-Sls)*

Maxfair Technologies Holdings Ltd. (1)
1F Efficiency House 35 Tai Yau Street
San Po Kong, Kowloon, China (Hong Kong)
Tel.: (852) 21041828
Fax: (852) 25649939
E-Mail: info@maxfair.com
Web Site: www.maxfair.com
Emp.: 10
Digital Audio/Video Related Systems & Software Distr
S.I.C.: 5734
N.A.I.C.S.: 443142
Tony Ma Mok Hoi *(Mng Dir)*

Y&A Professional Services Limited (1)
29 F Prosperity Millennia Plaza 663 Kings Road
North Point, China (Hong Kong)
Tel.: (852) 2139 2121
Fax: (852) 2519 0311
Web Site: www.ctil.com
Emp.: 50
Information Technology Consulting Services
S.I.C.: 8748
N.A.I.C.S.: 541618
Derek Cheung *(Gen Mgr)*

Non-U.S. Subsidiaries:

Computer & Technologies Integration Limited (1)
Room 2218 22/F Shartex Plaza
88 Zun Yi Road South, Shanghai, 200336, China
Tel.: (86) 2162197131
Fax: (86) 2162197133
Web Site: www.ctil.com
Information Technology & Networks with Related Design, Implementation & Support Services
S.I.C.: 7373
N.A.I.C.S.: 541512

Computer & Technologies (Shanghai) Co., Ltd (1)
Room 2218 22 F Shartex Plaza 88 Zun Yi Road South
Shanghai, 200336, China
Tel.: (86) 2162197131
Fax: (86) 2162197133
Computer System Network Integration Services
S.I.C.: 7373
N.A.I.C.S.: 541512

Shanghai Shangluo Software Co., Ltd. (1)
Flat E 12 F Jinming Building 8 Zun Yi Road South
200336 Shanghai, China
Tel.: (86) 21 6270 0658
Fax: (86) 21 6219 4988
Web Site: www.iplresearch.com.hk/eng/shanghai.htm
Human Resource Software Development Services
S.I.C.: 7371
N.A.I.C.S.: 541511

COMPUTER BOULEVARD INC.

Unit B 1250 St James Street
Winnipeg, MB, Canada R3H 0L1
Tel.: (204) 772-1088
Fax: (204) 775-3202
Toll Free: (866) 255-0099
Web Site: www.cbit.ca
Year Founded: 2001
Rev.: $12,814,223
Emp.: 50
Business Description:
Computers Parts Supplies
S.I.C.: 5731
N.A.I.C.S.: 443142
Personnel:
George Yung *(Owner)*

COMPUTER ENGINEERING & CONSULTING LTD

JR Ebisu Bldg 5-5 Ebisu Minami 1-chome
Shibuya-ku, Tokyo, 150-0022, Japan
Tel.: (81) 357892442
Fax: (81) 357892585
Web Site: www.cec-ltd.co.jp
9692—(TKS)
Sls.: $436,182,791
Assets: $373,766,195
Liabilities: $155,537,954
Net Worth: $218,228,241
Earnings: $13,941,422
Emp.: 2,520
Fiscal Year-end: 01/31/13
Business Description:
Software Development Services
S.I.C.: 7371
N.A.I.C.S.: 541511
Personnel:
Hirosato Iwasaki *(Chm)*
Shigeru Kashiwagi *(Pres)*
Kiyomi Hashimura *(Mng Dir)*
Kazuhiro Osada *(Mng Dir)*
Fujio Tahara *(Mng Dir)*
Nobukazu Chiba *(Exec Officer)*
Kouzou Hasegawa *(Exec Officer)*
Yutaka Hattori *(Exec Officer)*
Masahiro Hirota *(Exec Officer)*
Toshirou Kawano *(Exec Officer)*
Kazuaki Matsumoto *(Exec Officer)*
Hitoshi Ooishi *(Exec Officer)*
Hiroshi Tateishi *(Exec Officer)*
Board of Directors:
Hirosato Iwasaki
Nobukazu Chiba
Kouzou Hasegawa
Kiyomi Hashimura
Shigeru Kashiwagi
Hitoshi Ooishi
Kazuhiro Osada
Fujio Tahara

Subsidiaries:

Foresight System Co., Ltd. (1)
4-6 Nagahama 1
Chuo-ku, Fukuoka, 810-0072, Japan
Tel.: (81) 927523580
Fax: (81) 927145665
E-Mail: fs@foresight.co.jp
Web Site: www.foresight.co.jp
Sls.: $75,751,600
Emp.: 468
Software Development Services
S.I.C.: 7371
N.A.I.C.S.: 541511
Shirou Endo *(Pres)*

Kyushu Foresight Co., Ltd. (1)
Mitsuiwa Kyushu Sougo Bldg Nagahama 1-4-6
Chuo-ku, Fukuoka, 810-0072, Japan
Tel.: (81) 927243096
Fax: (81) 927243098
E-Mail: soumu@kyushufs.com
Web Site: www.kyushufs.com
Emp.: 40
Software Development Services
S.I.C.: 7371
N.A.I.C.S.: 541511
Shirou Endo *(Pres)*

Nishitele Information & Science Co., Ltd (1)
1-12-17 Hakataeki-higashi
Hakata-ku, Fukuoka, 812-0013, Japan
Tel.: (81) 92 482 7907
Fax: (81) 92 482 7910
Web Site: www.nishitele.co.jp
Software Development Services
S.I.C.: 7371
N.A.I.C.S.: 541511

Oita Computer Engineering & Consulting, Ltd. (1)
21-1 Ohira Aza Oaza
Kitsuki, Oita, Japan
Tel.: (81) 975320414
Fax: (81) 978621441
E-Mail: ocec-web@ml.cec-ltd.co.jp
Web Site: www.oita-cec.co.jp
Emp.: 98
Software Development & Consulting Services
S.I.C.: 7373
N.A.I.C.S.: 541512

Non-U.S. Subsidiary:

Computer Engineering & Consulting (Shanghai), Ltd. (1)
11th Fl Spring Song Bldg 3323 N Zhongshan Rd
Putuo Dist, Shanghai, 200062, China
Tel.: (86) 21 5162 1088
Fax: (86) 21 5162 1077
E-Mail: marketing@cec-ltd.cn
Web Site: www.cec-ltd.cn
Emp.: 15
Software Development Services
S.I.C.: 7371
N.A.I.C.S.: 541511

COMPUTER FORMS (MALAYSIA) BERHAD

Lot 2 Jalan Usahawan 5 PKNS
Setapak Indus Area
Off Jalan Genting Kelang
53300 Kuala Lumpur, Malaysia
Tel.: (60) 340233611
Fax: (60) 340213033
E-Mail: info@cfm.com.my
Web Site: www.cfm.com.my
Year Founded: 1972
CFM—(KLS)
Sales Range: $10-24.9 Million
Business Description:
Computer Forms Mfr
S.I.C.: 2759
N.A.I.C.S.: 323111
Personnel:
Ibrahim Mahaludin Puteh *(Chm)*
Poh Wah Loh *(Sec)*
Board of Directors:
Ibrahim Mahaludin Puteh
Muhayuddin Musa
Wee Sun Ou
Poh Seng Thor

Subsidiaries:

CFM Printing & Stationery Sdn. Bhd (1)
Lot 14 Jalan Perusahaan Tengah
Setapak, 53200 Kuala Lumpur, Malaysia

MY

Computer Forms (Malaysia) Berhad—(Continued)

Tel.: (60) 340210888
Fax: (60) 3 4021 0808
E-Mail: cpssales@cfm.com.my
Web Site: www.cfm.com.my
Emp.: 150
Commercial Offset Printing Services
S.I.C.: 2759
N.A.I.C.S.: 323111

Contipak Noron Sdn. Bhd. **(1)**
Lot 2 Block A Jalan Usahawan 5 PKNS
Setapak Industrial Area
Off Jalan Genting Kelang, 53300 Kuala
Lumpur, Malaysia MY
Tel.: (60) 340238218
Fax: (60) 3 4025 1219
Flexible Packaging Materials Mfr
S.I.C.: 2672
N.A.I.C.S.: 322220

Joint Venture:

CFM Toppan Forms (Malaysia) Sdn. Bhd. **(1)**
Lot 2 Block B Jalan Usahawan 5 PKNS
Setapak Industrial Area
Off Jalan Genting Kelang, 53300 Kuala
Lumpur, Malaysia MY
Tel.: (60) 340237628
Fax: (60) 340247628
E-Mail: info@cfmtf.com.my
Web Site: www.cfmtf.com.my
Outsource Data Printing & Direct Mailer Services; Owned by Computer Forms (Malaysia) Berhad, by Toppan Forms (Singapore) Pte. Ltd. & by Cardsys Sdn. Bhd.
S.I.C.: 2759
N.A.I.C.S.: 323111

COMPUTER GRAPHICS INTERNATIONAL INC.

Room 01B 02/F Podium Building
Guodu Golf Garden North of Xinsha Road
Futian District, Shenzhen, 518048, China
Tel.: (86) 755 2221 1114
Year Founded: 2003
CGII—(OTC)
Sls.: $3,701,783
Assets: $1,395,722
Liabilities: $1,943,882
Net Worth: ($548,160)
Earnings: ($1,636,692)
Emp.: 104
Fiscal Year-end: 09/30/13
Business Description:
3D Digital Video Services
S.I.C.: 7812
N.A.I.C.S.: 512110
Personnel:
Hua Zeng *(Chm)*
Jin Wang *(Pres & CEO)*
Board of Directors:
Hua Zeng
Xiaohong Peng
Jin Wang

COMPUTER INSTITUTE OF JAPAN LTD.

Yokohama NT Bldg 1-2-24 Hiranuma
Nishi-ku, Yokohama, 220-0023, Japan
Tel.: (81) 453240111
Fax: (81) 453149865
E-Mail: info@cij.co.jp
Web Site: www.cij.com
Year Founded: 1976
4826—(TKS)
Sls.: $181,632,000
Assets: $132,264,000
Liabilities: $33,000,000
Net Worth: $99,264,000
Earnings: $9,427,000
Emp.: 1,585
Fiscal Year-end: 06/30/13
Business Description:
Computer Software & Systems Developer & Mfr
S.I.C.: 7373
N.A.I.C.S.: 541512
Personnel:
Shozo Nakano *(Chm)*
Shinichi Hori *(Pres & CEO)*
Takayuki Ishida *(Exec Officer)*
Akihiko Sakamoto *(Exec Officer)*
Mitsuru Sawada *(Sr Exec Officer)*
Yukitoshi Someya *(Exec Officer)*
Jun Suda *(Mng Exec Officer)*
Masami Takamisawa *(Sr Exec Officer)*
Kiyoshi Yoshiyama *(Exec Officer)*
Shigeyuki Onishi *(Exec VP)*
Board of Directors:
Shozo Nakano
Shinichi Hori
Shigeyuki Onishi
Makoto Oya
Akihiko Sakamoto
Mitsuru Sawada
Jun Suda
Masami Takamisawa

Subsidiaries:

BSC Co., Ltd. **(1)**
Higashikanda Kaneko Building 3-1-2 Higashikanda
Chiyoda-Ku, Tokyo, 101-0031, Japan
Tel.: (81) 338338281
Fax: (81) 3 3833 7130
Web Site: www.bsc-web.co.jp
Business Management Software Development Services
S.I.C.: 7371
N.A.I.C.S.: 541511

Business Soft Service Co., Ltd. **(1)**
Fujimoto Dai-Ichi Life Bldg 3-3-1 Chuo
Chuo-ku, Chiba, 260-0013, Japan
Tel.: (81) 432217800
Fax: (81) 432217900
E-Mail: pos@we-bss.com
Web Site: www.we-bss.com
Software Development Services
S.I.C.: 7371
N.A.I.C.S.: 541511

CIJ Manage System, Inc. **(1)**
Yokohama NT Bldg
1 2 24 Hiranuma Nishi Ku, Yokohama, 220 0023, Japan (100%)
Tel.: (81) 453240111
Fax: (81) 453149865
E-Mail: info@cij.co.jp
Web Site: www.cij.com
Emp.: 10
Computer Research
S.I.C.: 7373
N.A.I.C.S.: 541512

CIJ NExt Co., Ltd. **(1)**
4-8 Kagurazaka Plaza Bldg
Shinjuku-ku, Tokyo, 162-0825, Japan (100%)
Tel.: (81) 352067131
Fax: (81) 352067282
E-Mail: john@cij-next.co.jp
Web Site: www.cij-next.co.jp
Sales Range: Less than $1 Million
Emp.: 524
Business Systems Development & Design of Semiconductors, Temporary Personnel Placements & Sales of Packaged Software Products
S.I.C.: 7389
N.A.I.C.S.: 561499
Shozo Nakano *(Pres)*

CIJ Solutions, Ltd. **(1)**
Bunshodo Building 5-1-1 Ueno
Taito-ku, Tokyo, 110-0005, Japan
Tel.: (81) 358163100
Fax: (81) 358163235
E-Mail: info@ml.csol.jp
Web Site: www.csol.jp
Emp.: 19
Enterprise Management Software Development Services
S.I.C.: 7371
N.A.I.C.S.: 541511
Masaharu Matsuoka *(Pres)*

Subsidiary:

CIJ Wave Ltd. **(2)**
3-8-10 Gudotaguro
Shimanto, Kochi, 787-0051, Japan
Tel.: (81) 880311008
Fax: (81) 880375211
E-Mail: info@cijwave.co.jp
Web Site: www.cijwave.co.jp
Senior Citizen Nursing Homes Operation Services
S.I.C.: 8361
N.A.I.C.S.: 623312

Custanet Co., Ltd. **(1)**
Hakata 1091 Building 1-2-2 Hakata-Eki Minami
Hakata-Ku, Fukuoka, 812-0016, Japan
Tel.: (81) 924819560
Fax: (81) 924819563
E-Mail: info@custa-net.co.jp
Web Site: www.custa-net.co.jp
Emp.: 50
Enterprise Management Software Development Services
S.I.C.: 7371
N.A.I.C.S.: 541511
Shinichi Hori *(Pres)*

Kanazawa Software Co., Ltd. **(1)**
36-1 Nakanosato-Machiri Shiroyama
Kanazawa, Ishikawa, 920 2147, Japan
Tel.: (81) 76 273 5011
Fax: (81) 76 273 5012
Business Management Software Development Services
S.I.C.: 7371
N.A.I.C.S.: 541511

Kochi Software Center Ltd. **(1)**
105-25 Hongu-Cho
Kochi, 780 0945, Japan
Tel.: (81) 888509222
Fax: (81) 888036444
E-Mail: ueta@k-sc.co.jp
Web Site: www.k-sc.co.jp
Emp.: 6
Information Technology Training & Education Services
S.I.C.: 8243
N.A.I.C.S.: 611420

U.S. Subsidiary:

CIJSJ America, Inc. **(1)**
1952 Camden Ave Ste 201
San Jose, CA 95124-2816 (100%)
Tel.: (408) 559-6166
Web Site: www.cij.com
Computer Consulting Services
S.I.C.: 7371
N.A.I.C.S.: 541511
Kikuo Yoshimura *(Chm)*

Non-U.S. Subsidiary:

Shanghai Technodia System Integration Co., Ltd. **(1)**
Shanghai Jinling Business Plaza
1st Tower 3rd Floor
Yi Shan Road, Shanghai, 200233, China (100%)
Tel.: (86) 2154260606
Fax: (86) 21 6485 5238
E-Mail: webmaster@technodia.com.cn
Web Site: www.cij.com
Computer Systems Design
S.I.C.: 7373
N.A.I.C.S.: 541512
Kikuo Yoshimura *(Chm)*
Mitsuru Mizunuma *(Pres)*

COMPUTER MODELLING GROUP LTD.

200 1824 Crowchild Trail NW
Calgary, AB, T2M 3Y7, Canada
Tel.: (403) 531-1300
Fax: (403) 289-8502
E-Mail: cmgl@cmgl.ca
Web Site: www.cmgl.ca
CMG—(TSX)
Rev.: $68,209,652
Assets: $82,922,142
Liabilities: $31,819,574
Net Worth: $51,102,568
Earnings: $24,673,564
Emp.: 173
Fiscal Year-end: 03/31/13
Business Description:
Oil & Gas Reservoir Modelling & Simulation Software; Oil Recovery Processes, Reservoir Engineering, Consulting, Training & Technical Support
S.I.C.: 1389
N.A.I.C.S.: 213112
Personnel:
Frank L. Meyer *(Chm)*
Kenneth M. Dedeluk *(Pres & CEO)*
John Kalman *(CFO & VP-Fin)*
Kathy L. Krug *(Sec)*
Board of Directors:
Frank L. Meyer
Kenneth M. Dedeluk
Christopher L. Fong
Patrick R. Jamieson
Robert F. M. Smith
John B. Zaozirny
Transfer Agent:
Valiant Trust Company
Suite 310 606 4th Street S.W.
Calgary, AB, Canada

COMPUTER SOFTWARE INNOVATIONS, INC.

(Acquired by Constellation Software Inc.)

COMPUTER STATIONERY INDUSTRY S.A.O.G.

Road No 7 Rusayl Industrial Estate
PO Box 13
Muscat, Oman
Tel.: (968) 24446160
Fax: (968) 24446277
E-Mail: csiops@omantel.net.om
Web Site: www.csiops.com
Year Founded: 1985
CSII—(MUS)
Sls.: $9,596,039
Assets: $12,258,164
Liabilities: $7,370,409
Net Worth: $4,887,755
Earnings: $200,491
Emp.: 8
Fiscal Year-end: 12/31/12
Business Description:
Computer Sales & Services
S.I.C.: 5045
N.A.I.C.S.: 423430
Personnel:
Mehdi Mohammed Jawad Al Abduwani *(Chm)*
Ali Mohammed Zabnoot *(Vice Chm)*
Board of Directors:
Mehdi Mohammed Jawad Al Abduwani
Said Hilal Yaqoob Al Kharusi
Zaki Hassan Naseeb Al Naseeb
Ammar Maqbool Al Saleh
Ranga Gorur
Himansu Mohapatra
Ali Mohammed Zabnoot

COMPUTERSHARE LIMITED

Yarra Falls 452 Johnston Street
Abbotsford, VIC, 3067, Australia
Tel.: (61) 394155000
Fax: (61) 394152500
E-Mail: webquery@computershare.com.au
Web Site: www.computershare.com
Year Founded: 1978
CPU—(ASX)
Rev.: $2,019,949,000
Assets: $3,618,877,000
Liabilities: $2,487,942,000
Net Worth: $1,130,935,000
Earnings: $160,577,000
Emp.: 14,270
Fiscal Year-end: 06/30/13

Business Description:
Securities Registration & Transfer Services
S.I.C.: 7389
N.A.I.C.S.: 561499
Personnel:
William Stuart Crosby *(Pres & CEO)*
Mark B. Davis *(CFO)*
Stuart Irving *(CIO)*
Paul A. Conn *(Pres-Global Capital Markets)*
Wayne Newling *(Pres-Canada)*
Bernie O'Connor *(Pres-Computershare Comm Svcs)*
Steven Rothbloom *(Pres-USA)*
Naz Sarkar *(CEO-United Kingdom, Channel Islands, Ireland & Africa)*
James Wong *(CEO-Asia)*
Dominic Matthew Horsley *(Sec)*
Board of Directors:
Christopher John Morris
William Stuart Crosby
Simon David Jones
Markus Kerber
Penelope Jane Maclagan
Arthur Leslie Owen
Nerolie Phyllis Withnall
Legal Counsel:
Minter Ellison
Level 23 Rialto Towers 525 Collins Street
Melbourne, VIC, 3000, Australia
U.S. Subsidiaries:

Computershare Investor Services LLC (1)
2 N Lasalle St
Chicago, IL 60602
Tel.: (312) 588-4700, ext. 3125884993
Fax: (312) 601-4334
Web Site: corporate.computershare.com
Sls.: $38,300,000
Emp.: 315
Security Transfer Agents
S.I.C.: 6282
N.A.I.C.S.: 523930

Kurtzman Carson Consultants LLC (1)
2335 Alaska Ave
El Segundo, CA 90245 CA
Tel.: (310) 823-9000
Fax: (310) 823-9133
Toll Free: (866) 381-9100
E-Mail: info@kccllc.com
Web Site: www.kccllc.com
Sales Range: $10-24.9 Million
Emp.: 130
Legal & Financial Software
S.I.C.: 7372
N.A.I.C.S.: 511210
Eric S. Kurtzman *(Co-Founder & CEO)*
Jonathan A. Carson *(Co-Founder & Mng Dir)*
Bryan Butvick *(Pres)*
Peter Huh *(CTO)*
Drake D. Foster *(Gen Counsel)*
James Le *(Exec VP-Class Action Svcs)*

Non-U.S. Subsidiaries:

Pepper GmbH (1)
Prannerstr 8
80333 Munich, Germany
Tel.: (49) 89 30 90 3 0
Fax: (49) 89 30 90 3 99
E-Mail: info@pepperglobal.com
Web Site: www.pepperglobal.com
Sales Range: $10-24.9 Million
Emp.: 150
Marketing & Communications
S.I.C.: 8742
N.A.I.C.S.: 541613
Markus Dunz *(Mng Dir)*
Steffen Herfurth *(Mng Dir)*

Servizio Titoli S.p.A. (1)
Via Lorenzo Mascheroni
20145 Milan, Italy
Tel.: (39) 0246776811
Fax: (39) 0246776850
E-Mail: ufficiomi@serviziotitoli.it
Web Site: www.serviziotitoli.it
Sales Range: $10-24.9 Million
Emp.: 50
Corporate Finance Advisory Services
S.I.C.: 8748
N.A.I.C.S.: 541618
Luca Matteo Lombardo *(Mng Dir)*

COMPUTIME GROUP LIMITED

9/F Tower One Lippo Centre 89 Queensway
Hong Kong, China (Hong Kong)
Tel.: (852) 22600300
Fax: (852) 27903996
E-Mail: hq@computime.com
Web Site: www.computime.com
0320—(HKG)
Rev.: $325,803,394
Assets: $249,132,174
Liabilities: $112,622,996
Net Worth: $136,509,178
Earnings: $4,010,216
Emp.: 3,800
Fiscal Year-end: 03/31/13
Business Description:
Tools & Instruments
S.I.C.: 3823
N.A.I.C.S.: 334513
Personnel:
Ho Auyang *(Chm)*
King Owyang *(CEO)*
B. Gene Patton *(CFO)*
Philip John Stevens Cox *(Chm-Salus Holdings Limited)*
Yuk Tai Soon *(Sec)*
Wai Leung Ha *(Exec VP-Tech)*
Board of Directors:
Ho Auyang
David Ching Leung Cheung
Anthony Chi Chiu Kam
Koon Hoo Luk
King Owyang
Arvind Amratlal Patel
Patrick Thomas Siewert
Chun Kong Wong

Computershare Hong Kong Investor Services Limited
Shops 1712-1716 17th Floor Hopewell Centre
183 Queens Road East
Wanchai, China (Hong Kong)
Transfer Agents:
Royal Bank of Canada Trust Company (Cayman) Limited
4th Floor Royal Bank House 24 Shedden Road
Georgetown, Cayman Islands

Computershare Hong Kong Investor Services Limited
Shops 1712-1716 17th Floor Hopewell Centre
183 Queens Road East
Wanchai, China (Hong Kong)
Subsidiaries:

Asia Electronics HK Technologies Limited (1)
9/F Tower One Lippo Centre 89 Queensway
Wanchai, China (Hong Kong)
Tel.: (852) 22600300
Fax: (852) 27398583
Web Site: www.asiaelectronics.com.hk
Electronic Control Products Distr
S.I.C.: 5063
N.A.I.C.S.: 423610

Computime Limited (1)
9th Floor Tower One Lippo Centre 89 Queensway
Hong Kong, China (Hong Kong)
Tel.: (852) 22600300
Fax: (852) 27903996
E-Mail: hq@computime.com
Web Site: www.computime.com
Electronic Control Products Mfr & Distr
S.I.C.: 3829
N.A.I.C.S.: 334514

Non-U.S. Subsidiaries:

Salus Controls GmbH (1)
Dieselstr 34
63165 Muhlheim, Hesse, Germany
Tel.: (49) 6108825850
Fax: (49) 61088258529
E-Mail: info@salus-controls.de
Web Site: www.salus-controls.de
Emp.: 10
Electronic Control Products Distr
S.I.C.: 5063
N.A.I.C.S.: 423610
Deam Jetson *(Mgr)*

Salus Controls Plc (1)
Salus House Unit 1 Dodworth Bus Park S Whinby Rd
Dodworth, Barnsley, South Yorkshire, S75 3SP, United Kingdom
Tel.: (44) 1226323961
Fax: (44) 1226240588
E-Mail: sales@salus-tech.com
Web Site: www.salus-tech.com
Emp.: 35
Electronic Control Products Distr
S.I.C.: 5063
N.A.I.C.S.: 423610
Dean Jepson *(Mng Dir-Sls)*

COMPUTRONICS HOLDINGS LIMITED

Unit 1 103 Lewis Road
Knoxfield, VIC, 3180, Australia
Tel.: (61) 398012566
Fax: (61) 398004339
E-Mail: murray@computronics.com
Web Site: www.computronics.com.au
Year Founded: 1976
Sales Range: $5-14.9 Billion
Emp.: 65
Business Description:
Microcomputer-Based Products Developer & Mfr
S.I.C.: 3575
N.A.I.C.S.: 334118
Personnel:
Murray Smith *(Sec)*
Board of Directors:
John Hansen
Murray Smith
David Wu

COMPUVISION SYSTEMS INC.

310 Circle Drive
Saint Albert, AB, T8N 7L5, Canada
Tel.: (780) 415-5093
Fax: (780) 415-5095
Toll Free: (888) 800-1986
E-Mail: info@compuvision.biz
Web Site: www.compuvision.biz
Year Founded: 1992
Rev.: $15,751,883
Emp.: 104
Business Description:
Computer Related Works & IT Services
S.I.C.: 7379
N.A.I.C.S.: 541519
Personnel:
Bernie Bourgeois *(Founder)*
Paul Thorsteinson *(Pres & COO)*
Ryan Vestby *(CEO)*

COMS PLC

46 Cannon Street
London, EC4N 6JJ, United Kingdom
Tel.: (44) 20 7148 3000
Fax: (44) 20 7148 3001
Web Site: www.coms.com
COMS—(LSE)
Rev.: $2,561,545
Assets: $4,298,407
Liabilities: $1,027,887
Net Worth: $3,270,520
Earnings: ($1,938,608)
Emp.: 21
Fiscal Year-end: 01/31/13
Business Description:
Internet Telephony Services
S.I.C.: 2741
N.A.I.C.S.: 519130
Personnel:
David Breith *(CEO)*
David Cargill *(CTO)*
Board of Directors:
Iain Ross
David Breith
Stephen Squire Foster
Legal Counsel:
Marriott Harrison
11 Staple Inn Buildings
London, WC1 7QH, United Kingdom

COMSA EMTE S.L.

Edificio Numancia 1
08014 Barcelona, Spain
Tel.: (34) 933662100
Fax: (34) 934051340
E-Mail: comunicacion@comsa.com
Web Site: www.comsaemte.com
Sales Range: $1-4.9 Billion
Emp.: 9,095
Business Description:
Engineering & Construction Services
S.I.C.: 1629
N.A.I.C.S.: 237990
Personnel:
Jorge Miarnau Montserrat *(Chm)*
Carles Sumarroca *(Vice Chm)*
Subsidiaries:

EMTE Cleanroom S.A. (1)
Gran Via de les Corts Catalanes 184 5 3
08038 Barcelona, Spain
Tel.: (34) 932988980
Fax: (34) 93 431 39 99
E-Mail: info@luwa.es
Web Site: www.luwa.es
Emp.: 49
Clean Room Engineering & Construction Services
S.I.C.: 8711
N.A.I.C.S.: 541330

EMTE INSTALACIONES (1)
Avda Baix Llobregat 10 08950 Esplugues de Llobregat
Barcelona, Spain
Tel.: (34) 934809292
Fax: (34) 934809299
Web Site: www.grupoemte.com
Emp.: 100
Engineering Services
S.I.C.: 8711
N.A.I.C.S.: 541330
Carles Sumarroca *(Vice Chm)*

COMSTAR AUTOMOTIVE TECHNOLOGIES PVT LTD

Keelakaranai Village
Malrosapuram Post
Maraimalai Nagar, Chengalpattu, 603 204, India
Tel.: (91) 44 37473700
Fax: (91) 44 37473737
E-Mail: marketing@comstarauto.com
Web Site: www.comstarauto.com
Year Founded: 1998
Sales Range: $300-349.9 Million
Business Description:
Alternators & Starter Motors Mfr
S.I.C.: 3714
N.A.I.C.S.: 336390
Personnel:
Sat Mohan Gupta *(CFO)*

COMSTOCK CANADA LTD.

3455 Landmark Road
Burlington, ON, L7M 1T4, Canada
Tel.: (905) 335-3333
Fax: (905) 335-0304
E-Mail: info@comstockcanada.com
Web Site: www.comstockcanada.com
Year Founded: 1904
Sales Range: $300-349.9 Million
Emp.: 1,000
Business Description:
Mechanical & Electrical Construction & Energy Infrastructure Services
S.I.C.: 1731
N.A.I.C.S.: 238210
Personnel:
Geoffrey W. Birkbeck *(CEO)*
Dennis Forlin *(CFO)*

COMSTOCK METALS LTD.
701 675 West Hastings Street
Vancouver, BC, V6B 1N2, Canada
Tel.: (604) 639-4533
Fax: (604) 685-3764
Web Site: www.comstock-metals.com
Year Founded: 2007
CSL—(OTC TSXV)
Int. Income: $25,703
Assets: $6,173,318
Liabilities: $910,793
Net Worth: $5,262,525
Earnings: ($1,201,590)
Fiscal Year-end: 09/30/12
Business Description:
Metal Mining
S.I.C.: 1099
N.A.I.C.S.: 212299
Personnel:
Rasool Mohammad *(Pres & CEO)*
Larry Johnson *(CFO & Sec)*
Board of Directors:
Gordon Davidson
Larry Johnson
Rasool Mohammad
Douglas Turnbull

COMSYS HOLDINGS CORPORATION
17-1 Higashigotanda 2-chome
Shinagawa-ku, Tokyo, 141-8647, Japan
Tel.: (81) 334487000
Fax: (81) 334487001
Web Site: www.comsys-hd.co.jp
1721—(TKS)
Sls.: $3,477,012,000
Assets: $2,646,622,000
Liabilities: $739,101,000
Net Worth: $1,907,521,000
Earnings: $146,124,000
Emp.: 9,798
Fiscal Year-end: 03/31/13
Business Description:
Holding Company; Telecommunications Networks Construction, Information Technology Support & Social Systems Management Services
S.I.C.: 6719
N.A.I.C.S.: 551112
Personnel:
Hajime Takashima *(Pres)*
Noriaki Itoh *(Pres-Nippon COMSYS)*
Masaru Kudo *(Pres-COMSYS JOHO Sys)*
Hidetoshi Miura *(Pres-Tsuken)*
Akio Ogawa *(Pres-TOSYS)*
Hirofumi Yamasaki *(Pres-Sanwa COMSYS Engrg)*
Board of Directors:
Takeshi Gotoh
Noriaki Itoh
Masaru Kudo
Hitoshi Kumagai
Masanobu Kurokawa
Yoshihiro Mimata
Hidetoshi Miura
Tsuyoshi Nishiyama
Akio Ogawa
Hajime Takashima
Tomoaki Yamamoto
Hirofumi Yamasaki
Transfer Agent:
Mitsubishi UFJ Trust & Banking Corporation
10-11 Higashisuna 7-Chome Koto-Ku
Tokyo, Japan
Subsidiaries:

COMSYS JOHO System Corporation **(1)**
3-23-14 Takanawa
Minato-ku, Tokyo, Japan
Tel.: (81) 334488100
Web Site: www.comjo.co.jp
Information Technology Services
S.I.C.: 7379
N.A.I.C.S.: 541519

Comsys Shared Services Corporation **(1)**
23-14 Comsys Shianagawa Bldg 2f Takanawa
Tokyo, Japan
Tel.: (81) 334487141
Fax: (81) 334414083
E-Mail: info@comsys-ss.co.jp
Web Site: www.comsys-ss.co.jp
Emp.: 150
Business Development & Shared Services
S.I.C.: 8732
N.A.I.C.S.: 541720
Yoshiaki Miyawaki *(Pres)*

Nippon COMSYS Corporation **(1)**
2-17-1 Higashi-gohanda Shinagawa-Ku
Tokyo, 141-8647, Japan
Tel.: (81) 334487030
Fax: (81) 334473993
Web Site: www.comsys.co.jp
Emp.: 1,138
Telecommunications & Electrical Engineering Services
S.I.C.: 4899
N.A.I.C.S.: 517919
Hajime Takashima *(Pres)*

Subsidiaries:

COMSYS Engineering Co., Ltd. **(2)**
5-13-1 Minamisenju
Tokyo, Japan
Tel.: (81) 338024001
Engineering Services
S.I.C.: 8711
N.A.I.C.S.: 541330

COMSYS Net Corporation **(2)**
Jinnoshoji Bldg 8f 1-25-13 Higashigotanda
Tokyo, Japan
Tel.: (81) 334480921
Web Site: www.comsysnet.co.jp
Communication Equipment Installation Services
S.I.C.: 3669
N.A.I.C.S.: 334290

COMSYS Tohoku Techno Co., Ltd. **(2)**
Comsis Sendai Bldg 5F 8-36 Shimizukoji
Wakabayashi-Ku, Sendai, Miyagi, Japan
Tel.: (81) 222142211
Fax: (81) 222141011
E-Mail: hatakeyama@comsys-tt.co.jp
Web Site: www.comsys-tt.co.jp
Emp.: 50
Software Development Services
S.I.C.: 7371
N.A.I.C.S.: 541511
Saori Hatakeyama *(Mng Dir)*

COMSYS Tsusan Co., Ltd. **(2)**
3-21-12 Shirokane
Minato-Ku, Tokyo, 108-0072, Japan
Tel.: (81) 334487278
Fax: (81) 334486145
E-Mail: somu@tusan.co.jp
Web Site: www.tusan.co.jp
Emp.: 70
Telecommunications Equipment Leasing Services
S.I.C.: 7359
N.A.I.C.S.: 532490

Tokushima Tsushinkensetsu Co., Ltd. **(2)**
3-2-33 Shinhamacho
Tokushima, 770-8006, Japan
Tel.: (81) 886621060
Construction Engineering Services
S.I.C.: 1629
N.A.I.C.S.: 237990

Tsushin Densetsu Co., Ltd. **(2)**
5-35-10 Shimbashi Minato-ku
Tokyo, 105-0004, Japan
Tel.: (81) 334345101
Fax: (81) 334365655
E-Mail: info@tsuden.co.jp
Web Site: www.tsuden.co.jp
Engineering Services
S.I.C.: 8711
N.A.I.C.S.: 541330

SANWA COMSYS Engineering Corporation **(1)**
2-12-3 Koenji-minami Suginami-Ku
Tokyo, 166-0003, Japan
Tel.: (81) 363653111
Fax: (81) 353062151
E-Mail: tochimoto-hitoshi@sancom-eng.co.jp
Web Site: www.sancom-eng.co.jp
Emp.: 800
Telecommunications Engineering Services
S.I.C.: 8711
N.A.I.C.S.: 541330
Yoji Oku *(Pres)*

Subsidiaries:

Sannect Co., Ltd. **(2)**
5th Fl Sakurai Bldg 15-15 Shiba 3-chome Minato-ku
Tokyo, 105 0014, Japan
Tel.: (81) 3 3769 2189
Fax: (81) 3 3769 5545
Web Site: www.sannect.jp
Emp.: 45
General Construction & Infrastructure Services
S.I.C.: 1542
N.A.I.C.S.: 236220

SANWA Denshi Inc. **(2)**
2-1-6 Sarugakucho Chiyoda-ku
Tokyo, 101-0064, Japan
Tel.: (81) 332913131
Fax: (81) 332913155
E-Mail: sanwa@sanwadenshi.com
Web Site: www.sanwadenshi.com
Emp.: 450
Telecommunications & Electrical Engineering Services
S.I.C.: 8711
N.A.I.C.S.: 541330
Toshiako Ota *(Gen Mgr)*

SUNCOM Technology Corporation **(2)**
Higasshi Nihombashi 3-12-6 chuo-ku
Tokyo, 103-0004, Japan
Tel.: (81) 356521041
Fax: (81) 336682570
Web Site: www.s-tcn.com
Emp.: 100
Engineering Services
S.I.C.: 8711
N.A.I.C.S.: 541330
Nakatani Seiithro *(Pres)*

TOSYS Niigata Co., Ltd. **(1)**
2-4-1 Matobaryutsu
Nishi-Ku, Niigata, 950-2032, Japan
Tel.: (81) 252111600
Fax: (81) 252111580
Telecommunication Services
S.I.C.: 4812
N.A.I.C.S.: 517210

COMTEC INC.
Seavans N building 10F 1-2-1
Shibaura Minato-ku
105-6791 Tokyo, Japan
Tel.: (81) 3 5419 5551
Web Site: comtec.web.transer.com
Year Founded: 1976
9657—(JAS)
Sls.: $140,877,000
Assets: $77,473,000
Liabilities: $42,581,000
Net Worth: $34,892,000
Earnings: $3,300,000
Emp.: 816
Fiscal Year-end: 03/31/13
Business Description:
Marketing Support Services
S.I.C.: 8742
N.A.I.C.S.: 541613
Personnel:
Yoshinori Ikura *(Chm)*
Hiroshi Kanke *(Pres)*
Setuo Kaino *(Co-Mng Dir & Operating Officer)*
Masayuki Yahara *(Co-Mng Dir & Operating Officer)*
Satoshi Hiki *(Operating Officer)*
Toshio Imai *(Operating Officer)*
Katsuhisa Toya *(Operating Officer)*
Board of Directors:
Yoshinori Ikura
Setuo Kaino
Hiroshi Kanke
Masayuki Yahara

COMTEC SOLAR SYSTEMS GROUP LIMITED
16 Yuan Di Road Nanhui Industrial Zone
Shanghai, 201314, China
Tel.: (86) 2168043010
Fax: (86) 2168043023
E-Mail: sales@comtecsolar.com
Web Site: www.comtecsolar.com
0712—(HKG)
Rev.: $162,918,943
Assets: $387,609,726
Liabilities: $154,944,355
Net Worth: $232,665,371
Earnings: ($26,218,034)
Emp.: 807
Fiscal Year-end: 12/31/12
Business Description:
Semiconductor Related Products Mfr
S.I.C.: 3674
N.A.I.C.S.: 334413
Personnel:
John Zhang *(Chm & CEO)*
Kwok Keung Chau *(CFO & Sec)*
Cheng Qi Shi *(CTO)*
Board of Directors:
John Zhang
Kwok Keung Chau
Donald Huang
Sun Kang
Ming Shu Leung
Daniel DeWitt Martin
Cheng Qi Shi

Computershare Hong Kong Investor Services Limited
Shops 1712-1716 17th Floor Hopewell Centre
183 Queens Road East
Wanchai, China (Hong Kong)
Transfer Agent:
Royal Bank of Canada Trust Company (Cayman) Limited
4th Floor Royal Bank House 24 Shedden Road
Georgetown, Cayman Islands
Subsidiary:

Shanghai Comtec Solar Technology Co., Ltd. **(1)**
No 16 Yuandi Rd Nanhu Industrial Zone
Shanghai, China
Tel.: (86) 21 68043010
Fax: (86) 21 68043332
E-Mail: sales@comtecsolar.com
Solar Ingot & Wafer Mfr
S.I.C.: 3674
N.A.I.C.S.: 334413

COMTRADE GROUP B.V.
Savski nasip 7
11070 Belgrade, Serbia
Tel.: (381) 11 2015 600
Fax: (381) 11 2015 626
E-Mail: info@comtrade.com
Web Site: www.comtrade.com
Emp.: 1,500
Business Description:
Holding Company; Information Technology Solutions & Software Engineering Services
S.I.C.: 6719
N.A.I.C.S.: 551112
Personnel:
Veselin Jevrosimovic *(Chm)*
Alexis Lope-Bello *(CEO & COO)*
Terry T. Curtis *(CFO)*
Ljubomir Ristic *(CMO)*
Gordana Simic *(Chief Legal Officer)*
U.S. Subsidiary:

ComTrade USA West, Inc. **(1)**
625 Ellis St Ste 201 B
Mountain View, CA 94043 CA

Tel.: (650) 968-2562
Fax: (650) 968-5136
E-Mail: info.us@comtrade.com
Web Site: www.comtrade.com
Software Engineering Services
S.I.C.: 3652
N.A.I.C.S.: 334614

Non-U.S. Subsidiaries:

ComTrade d.o.o. (1)
Litijska 51
1000 Ljubljana, Slovenia SI
Tel.: (386) 15865200
Fax: (386) 15865270
E-Mail: info@comtrade.com
Web Site: www.comtrade.com
Software Engineering & Consulting Services
S.I.C.: 7373
N.A.I.C.S.: 541512
Branka Jerse *(Dir-Fin)*

ComTrade GmbH (1)
Hirschstettner Strasse 19-21/Z/109
A-1220 Vienna, Austria AT
Tel.: (43) 19949650
Fax: (43) 1994965050
E-Mail: info-at@comtrade.com
Web Site: www.hermes-softlab.de
Software Engineering Services
S.I.C.: 3652
N.A.I.C.S.: 334614

ComTrade Software Solutions GmbH (1)
Stefan-George-Ring 29
81929 Munich, Germany
Tel.: (49) 89309040222
Fax: (49) 89309040400
E-Mail: info.de@comtrade.com
Web Site: www.hermes-softlab.de
Emp.: 3
Information Retrieval Services
S.I.C.: 7371
N.A.I.C.S.: 541511
Michael Zitmann *(Mng Dir)*

ComTrade Software Solutions Limited (1)
14 Merrion Square
Dublin, 2, Ireland
Tel.: (353) 16614030
Fax: (353) 16619557
E-Mail: info.ie@comtrade.com
Web Site: www.comtrade.com
Emp.: 20
Software Engineering Services
S.I.C.: 3652
N.A.I.C.S.: 334614
Brendan Garland *(Controller-Fin)*

COMTRONIC COMPUTER INC.

30 Kinnear Court Unit 1
Richmond Hill, ON, L4B 1K8, Canada
Tel.: (905) 881-3606
Fax: (905) 881-6893
E-Mail: sales@comtronic.ca
Web Site: www.comtronic.ca
Year Founded: 1987
Rev.: $29,499,380
Emp.: 30
Business Description:
Computer System Distr
S.I.C.: 5045
N.A.I.C.S.: 423430
Personnel:
John Tse *(Pres)*

COMTURE CORPORATION

8F Gate City Ohsaki East Tower 1-11-2 Osaki
Shinagawa-ku, Tokyo, 141-0032, Japan
Tel.: (81) 3 57459700
Fax: (81) 3 57459715
Web Site: www.comture.com
3844—(TKS)
Emp.: 680
Business Description:
Computer Systems Design Services
S.I.C.: 7373
N.A.I.C.S.: 541512
Personnel:
Koichi Mukai *(Chm)*

COMVEX S.A.

Str Incinta Port Dana 80-84
Constanta, Romania
Tel.: (40) 241639016
Fax: (40) 241639010
E-Mail: office@comvex.ro
Web Site: www.comvex.ro
Year Founded: 1991
CMVX—(BUC)
Sales Range: $25-49.9 Million
Emp.: 247
Business Description:
Bulk Raw Material Handling
S.I.C.: 4491
N.A.I.C.S.: 488320
Personnel:
Viorel Panait *(Pres)*

COMWAVE NETWORKS, INC.

61 Wildcat Road
Toronto, ON, M3J 2P5, Canada
Tel.: (66)) 28-8-5779
Web Site: www.comwave.net
Business Description:
Telecommunicatiosn Services
S.I.C.: 4812
N.A.I.C.S.: 517210
Subsidiary:

Radiant Communications Corp. (1)
1600 1050 W Pender St
Vancouver, BC, V6E 4T3, Canada
Tel.: (604) 257-0500
Fax: (604) 608-0999
Toll Free: (888) 219-2111
E-Mail: vancouver@radiant.net
Web Site: www.radiant.net
Rev.: $32,484,674
Assets: $15,423,870
Liabilities: $7,856,689
Net Worth: $7,567,181
Earnings: $407,180
Emp.: 83
Fiscal Year-end: 12/31/12
Internet & Other Communication Services
S.I.C.: 4899
N.A.I.C.S.: 517919
Paul Healy *(Pres & CEO)*
Chuck Leighton *(CFO & Exec VP)*
Jason Leeson *(CTO & Exec VP)*
Craig White *(Exec VP-Sls & Customer Svc)*

COMWEST ENTERPRISE CORP.

333 Seymour Street Suite 780
Vancouver, BC, V6B 5A6, Canada
Tel.: (778) 370-1725
Fax: (778) 370-1726
Web Site: www.comwestenterprise.ca
Year Founded: 1940
CWP—(TSXV)
Rev.: $28,895,644
Assets: $20,062,687
Liabilities: $8,899,894
Net Worth: $11,162,793
Earnings: $3,074,164
Fiscal Year-end: 11/30/12
Business Description:
Garment Leather Mfr & Sales
S.I.C.: 2389
N.A.I.C.S.: 315280
Personnel:
Douglas F. Good *(Pres & CEO)*
Bruce W. Aunger *(CFO)*
David J. Selley *(Sec)*
Board of Directors:
Bruce W. Aunger
Darryl R. Eddy
Douglas F. Good
Chandru Narwani
C. Michael O'Brian
Transfer Agent:
Computershare Investor Services Inc.
100 University Ave 9th Floor
Toronto, ON, Canada
Subsidiaries:

Peerless Garments Inc. (1)
515 Notre Dame Avenue
Winnipeg, MB, R3B 1R9, Canada
Tel.: (204) 774-5428
Fax: (204) 786-7976
Fur & Leather Apparel Mfr
S.I.C.: 2389
N.A.I.C.S.: 315280

Peerless Garments LP (1)
515 Notre Dame Avenue
Winnipeg, MB, R3B 1R9, Canada
Tel.: (204) 774-5428
Fax: (204) 786-7976
Web Site: www.peerless.mb.ca
Leather Garment Mfr & Distr
S.I.C.: 2389
N.A.I.C.S.: 315280
Marshall Mitton *(Mgr-Sls)*

CON-PRO INDUSTRIES CANADA LTD.

765 Marion Street
Winnipeg, MB, R2J 0K6, Canada
Tel.: (204) 233-3717
Fax: (204) 237-3534
Web Site: www.conpro.mb.ca
Year Founded: 1969
Rev.: $14,345,917
Emp.: 40
Business Description:
Building Contractors
S.I.C.: 1796
N.A.I.C.S.: 238290
Personnel:
Don Snodgrass *(Pres)*

CON-SPACE COMMUNICATIONS LTD.

5600 Parkwood Way Suite 505
Richmond, BC, V6V 2M2, Canada
Tel.: (604) 244-9323
Fax: (604) 270-2138
Toll Free: (800) 546-3405
E-Mail: info@con-space.com
Web Site: www.con-space.com
Year Founded: 1991
Sales Range: $1-9.9 Million
Business Description:
Communications Equipment Mfr
S.I.C.: 4813
N.A.I.C.S.: 517210
Personnel:
Andrew Ibbetson *(Pres)*
Non-U.S. Subsidiary:

CON-SPACE Communications (Europe) Limited (1)
Stephenson Court 2
Brunel Park, Newark, Notts, NG24 2EG, United Kingdom
Tel.: (44) 1636642484
Fax: (44) 1636642485
E-Mail: nwhite@con-space.com
Web Site: www.con-space.com
Emp.: 2
Communications Equipment Mfr
S.I.C.: 3663
N.A.I.C.S.: 334220
Nick White *(Mgr)*

CONAFI PRESTITO S.P.A.

Via Cordero di Pamparato 15
10143 Turin, Italy
Tel.: (39) 0117710320
Fax: (39) 0117710634
E-Mail: investor_relator@conafi.it
Web Site: www.conafi.it
CNP—(ITA)
Sales Range: $10-24.9 Million
Emp.: 146
Business Description:
Personal Financial Services
S.I.C.: 6726
N.A.I.C.S.: 525990
Personnel:
Nunzio Chiolo *(Chm)*
Claudio Forte *(CFO)*
Marco Gerardo *(COO)*
Board of Directors:
Nunzio Chiolo
Fabio Alfieri
Carlo Colombotti
Massimiliano Naef
Giuseppe Vimercati

CONAIR GROUP INC.

1510 Tower Street
Abbotsford, BC, Canada V2T 6H5
Tel.: (604) 855-1171
Fax: (604) 855-1017
E-Mail: info@conair.ca
Web Site: www.conair.ca
Rev.: $15,670,987
Emp.: 165
Business Description:
Aerial Fire Control Products & Services
S.I.C.: 0851
N.A.I.C.S.: 115310
Personnel:
Barry Marsden *(Chm)*
Tony Quo Vadis *(Pres)*
David Schellenberg *(CEO)*
Rick Pedersen *(Sr VP)*

CONALVIAS S.A.

Carrera 3 Norte 39n 23
Cali, Colombia
Tel.: (57) 2 4411700
E-Mail: contactenos@conalvias.com
Web Site: www.conalvias.com
Sales Range: $250-299.9 Million
Emp.: 500
Business Description:
Highway & Street Construction
S.I.C.: 1622
N.A.I.C.S.: 237310
Personnel:
Andres Jaramillo Lopez *(CEO)*

CONART ENGINEERS LIMITED

35 Manoj Udyog 40 A G D Ambekar Marg
Mumbai, 400 031, India
Tel.: (91) 2240270999
Fax: (91) 2240270975
E-Mail: mumbai@conartengineers.com
Web Site: www.conartengineers.com
Year Founded: 1973
522231—(BOM)
Sales Range: $1-9.9 Million
Business Description:
Residential Building Construction Service
S.I.C.: 1542
N.A.I.C.S.: 236220
Personnel:
Jitendra S. Sura *(Chm & Mng Dir)*
Tejas V. Sura *(Mng Dir)*
Board of Directors:
Jitendra S. Sura
Harshad B. Jhaveri
Chandrakant R. Patel
Haresh V. Patel
Sevantilal P. Shah
Jimeish J. Sura
Pradip R. Sura
Tejas V. Sura
Transfer Agent:
Sharex Dynamic (India) Pvt. Ltd.
Unit-1 Luthra Ind Premises Safed Pool Andheri Kurla Rd Andheri (E)
Mumbai, India

Conart Engineers Limited—(Continued)

CONBRACO INDUSTRIES INC.
(See Under Aalberts Industries N.V.)

CONCENTRA CONSULTING LIMITED
Thames House 18 Park Street
London, SE1 9EQ, United Kingdom
Tel.: (44) 20 7099 6910
Fax: (44) 20 7099 6920
E-Mail: info@concentra.co.uk
Web Site: www.concentra.co.uk
Year Founded: 2005
Sales Range: $10-24.9 Million
Emp.: 80
Business Description:
Technology Consulting Services
S.I.C.: 8999
N.A.I.C.S.: 541690
Personnel:
Rupert Morrison *(Mng Dir)*

CONCENTRIC AB
Ringvagen 3
280 40 SK Fagerhult, Sweden
Tel.: (46) 433 32400
Fax: (46) 433 30546
E-Mail: careers@concentricab.com
Web Site: www.concentricab.com
COIC—(OMX)
Sls.: $329,569,200
Assets: $263,160,000
Liabilities: $117,183,600
Net Worth: $145,976,400
Earnings: $23,994,000
Emp.: 1,016
Fiscal Year-end: 12/31/12
Business Description:
Hydraulics & Diesel Engine Pump Mfr
S.I.C.: 3594
N.A.I.C.S.: 333996
Personnel:
Stefan Charette *(Chm)*
David Woolley *(CEO)*
David Bessant *(CFO, VP-Fin & IT & Head-IR)*
Lena Olofsdotter *(Sr VP-Corp Comm)*
Andreas Wolf *(Sr VP-Europe)*
Board of Directors:
Stefan Charette
Marianne Brismar
Kenth Eriksson
Claes Magnus Kesson
Martin Lundstedt
Martin Skold
U.S. Subsidiaries:

Concentric Itasca Inc. (1)
800 Hollywood Ave
Itasca, IL 60143-1353
Tel.: (630) 773-3355
Fax: (630) 773-1119
E-Mail: info.usit@concentricAB.com
Emp.: 100
Hydraulics & Diesel Engine Pump Mfr
S.I.C.: 3594
N.A.I.C.S.: 333996

Concentric Rockford Inc. (1)
2222 15th St
Rockford, IL 61107-1166
Tel.: (815) 398-4400
Fax: (815) 398-5977
Toll Free: (800) 572-7867
E-Mail: info.usro@concentricAB.com
Emp.: 375
Hydraulics & Diesel Engine Pump Mfr
S.I.C.: 3594
N.A.I.C.S.: 333996
Joe Garlick *(VP-Sls)*

Non-U.S. Subsidiaries:

Concentric Birmingham Ltd. (1)
Gravelly Park Tyburn Road
Birmingham, B24 8HW, United Kingdom
Tel.: (44) 121 327 2081
Fax: (44) 121 327 6187
E-Mail: info.gbbi@concentricab.com
Hydraulics & Diesel Engine Pump Mfr
S.I.C.: 3594
N.A.I.C.S.: 333996

Concentric Hof GmbH (1)
Seligenweg 12
Postfach 15 07
DE-95014 Hof, Germany
Tel.: (49) 92818950
Fax: (49) 928187133
E-Mail: info.deho@concentricab.com
Emp.: 170
Hydraulics & Diesel Engine Pump Mfr
S.I.C.: 3594
N.A.I.C.S.: 333996
Bernd Thoss *(Pres)*

Concentric Pumps Pune Pvt. Ltd. (1)
Gat No 26 1 27 28
Haveli, Pune, 412216, India
Tel.: (91) 98 8107 1264
Fax: (91) 20 27069658
E-Mail: info.inpu@concentricab.com
Hydraulics & Diesel Engine Pump Mfr
S.I.C.: 3594
N.A.I.C.S.: 333996

Concentric Pumps (Suzhou) Co. Ltd. (1)
47 Dongjing Industrial Park 9 Dong Fu Lu SIP
Suzhou, Jiangsu, China
Tel.: (86) 512 8717 5100
Fax: (86) 512 8717 5101
E-Mail: info.chsh@concentricab.com
Hydraulics & Diesel Engine Pump Mfr
S.I.C.: 3594
N.A.I.C.S.: 333996

CONCEP GROUP LIMITED
The Plaza 535 King's Rd
London, SW10 0SZ, United Kingdom
Tel.: (44) 20 7952 5570
Fax: (44) 20 7952 5571
E-Mail: europe@concep.com
Web Site: www.concep.com
Business Description:
Email Marketing Software
S.I.C.: 7372
N.A.I.C.S.: 511210
Personnel:
Daniel Morgan *(CEO)*
U.S. Subsidiary:

Concep Inc. (1)
11 Harrison St
New York, NY 10013
Tel.: (212) 925-0380
Fax: (212) 925-2127
E-Mail: northamerica@concep.com
Web Site: www.concep.com
Email Software Publisher
S.I.C.: 7372
N.A.I.C.S.: 511210
Mark Power *(CEO)*

Non-U.S. Subsidiary:

Concep Pty Ltd (1)
Suite 6 02 37 Pitt St
Surry Hills, Sydney, NSW, 2000, Australia
Tel.: (61) 2 8030 8810
Fax: (61) 2 8003 9141
E-Mail: asiapacific@concep.com
Web Site: www.concep.com
Emp.: 7
Email Software Publisher
S.I.C.: 7372
N.A.I.C.S.: 511210
Ralph Koschek *(Mng Dir)*

CONCEPCION INDUSTRIAL CORPORATION
308 Sen Gil Puyat Avenue
Makati, Metro Manila, 1209, Philippines
Tel.: (63) 2 7721819
E-Mail: investorrelations@cic.ph
Web Site: www.cic.ph
Year Founded: 1962
Business Description:
Air-Conditioning Products Distr
S.I.C.: 5075
N.A.I.C.S.: 423730
Personnel:
Raul Joseph A. Concepcion *(Chm, Pres & CEO)*
Renna C. Hechanova-Angeles *(Vice Chm & Treas)*
Victoria A. Betita *(CFO & CIO)*
Board of Directors:
Raul Joseph A. Concepcion
Cesar A. Buenaventura
Jose A. Concepcion, III
Raul Anthony A. Concepcion
Renna C. Hechanova-Angeles
Raissa C. Hechanova-Posadas
Melito S. Salazar, Jr.
Victoria Herminia C. Young

CONCEPT ET TRADITION SA
48 route de Beauvais
60460 Precy-sur-Oise, France
Tel.: (33) 3 44 27 64 98
Fax: (33) 3 44 27 77 19
E-Mail: secretariat@concept-et-tradition.com
Web Site: www.concept-et-tradition.com
MLCET—(EUR)
Business Description:
Single Family Home Construction
S.I.C.: 1521
N.A.I.C.S.: 236115
Personnel:
Denis Lewandowski *(Chm)*
Gilles Planchon-Tourly *(CEO)*

CONCEPT GROUP LIMITED
1260 Highfield Crescent S E
Calgary, AB, Canada T2G 5M3
Tel.: (403) 287-8777
Fax: (403) 287-8781
Toll Free: (877) 387-8777
Web Site: www.conceptgroup.ca
Rev.: $16,412,337
Emp.: 200
Business Description:
Electrical & Controls Installation Contractor
S.I.C.: 1731
N.A.I.C.S.: 238210
Personnel:
Dave Kinley *(Pres & CEO)*
Shirley Schmold *(CFO)*

CONCEPTUS, INC.
(Acquired by Bayer Aktiengesellschaft)

CONCERN ACHEMA GROUP
(See Under Koncernas Achemos Grupe)

CONCERN BELNEFTEKHIM
(d/b/a The Belarusian State Concern for Oil and Chemistry)
73 Dzerzhinfkogo Ave
220116 Minsk, Belarus
Tel.: (375) 172717901
Fax: (375) 172719700
E-Mail: koncbnx@belneftekhim.by
Web Site: www.belneftekhim.by
Sales Range: $1-4.9 Billion
Emp.: 120,000
Business Description:
Petroleum Refining Services
S.I.C.: 2911
N.A.I.C.S.: 324110
Personnel:
Valery Kazakeeich *(Pres)*
Subsidiaries:

Belorusneft Republican Unitary Enterprise (1)
ul Rogachevskaya 9
246003 Gomel, Belarus
Tel.: (375) 232579263
Fax: (375) 232551274
E-Mail: contact@beloil.gomel.by
Web Site: www.beloil.by
Oil Exploration & Production
S.I.C.: 1311
N.A.I.C.S.: 211111

Borisov Plastic Products Plant Open Joint-Stock Company (1)
Ul Daumana 97
Borisov, 222120 Minsk, Belarus
Tel.: (375) 177734356
Fax: (375) 177743610
E-Mail: bzpi@bzpi.com
Web Site: www.bzpi.com
Plastic Products Mfr
S.I.C.: 3089
N.A.I.C.S.: 326199

Grodno Azot JSC (1)
Slavinskogo Street 4
230026 Grodno, Belarus
Tel.: (375) 1522741980
Fax: (375) 1522 63971
E-Mail: office@grodno-khim.by
Web Site: www.grodno-khim.by
Composites & Other Chemicals Mfr
S.I.C.: 2899
N.A.I.C.S.: 325998

CONCERN WORLDWIDE
52-55 Lower Camden Street
Dublin, Ireland
Tel.: (353) 14177700
Fax: (353) 14757362
E-Mail: info@concern.net
Web Site: www.concern.net
Sales Range: $125-149.9 Million
Emp.: 285
Business Description:
Emergency & Development Services in Developing Countries
S.I.C.: 7389
N.A.I.C.S.: 541990
Personnel:
Dominic MacSorley *(CEO)*

CONCHA PLC
80 83 Long Lane
London, EC1A 9ET, United Kingdom
Tel.: (44) 20 7692 0589
Web Site: www.hottunaplc.com
CHA—(AIM)
Rev.: $56,854
Assets: $333,230
Liabilities: $108,971
Net Worth: $224,259
Earnings: ($2,921,686)
Emp.: 3
Fiscal Year-end: 06/30/13
Business Description:
Apparel Mfr
S.I.C.: 2389
N.A.I.C.S.: 315990
Personnel:
Chris Akers *(Chm)*
Board of Directors:
Chris Akers
Russell Backhouse
Legal Counsel:
Brown Rudnick LLP
8 Clifford Street
London, W1K 3SQ, United Kingdom
Non-U.S. Subsidiary:

Hot Tuna Australia Pty Ltd. (1)
Level 7 28 Foveaux Street
Surry Hills, NSW, 2010, Australia
Tel.: (61) 292804411
Web Site: www.hot-tuna.com.au
Surf Apparel Mfr & Marketer
S.I.C.: 5136
N.A.I.C.S.: 424320

CONCORD BLUE ENGINEERING GMBH
Konigsallee 6-8
Dusseldorf, 40212, Germany
Tel.: (49) 211 320364
Fax: (49) 211 3230505
Web Site: www.concordblueenergy.com
Year Founded: 1998
Sales Range: $10-24.9 Million
Emp.: 100
Business Description:
Waste To Energy Services
S.I.C.: 4959
N.A.I.C.S.: 562998
Subsidiary:
Blue Tower GmbH (1)
Konrad Adenauer Strasse 9-13
45699 Herten, Germany
Tel.: (49) 2366305268
Fax: (49) 2366305299
Web Site: www.blue-tower.de
Electric Power Generation Services
S.I.C.: 4939
N.A.I.C.S.: 221112
Heinz-Juergen Muehlen *(Mng Dir)*

CONCORD CONCRETE PUMPS INC.
1608 Broadway Street
Port Coquitlam, BC, V3C 2M8, Canada
Tel.: (604) 468-7867
Fax: (604) 468-7885
Web Site: www.concordpumps.ca
Year Founded: 1998
Rev.: $14,085,082
Emp.: 85
Business Description:
Trucks & Parts Mfr
S.I.C.: 3537
N.A.I.C.S.: 333924
Personnel:
Izidro Flores *(Owner)*
Christopher Flores *(Pres-Sls & Mktg)*

CONCORD INVESTMENTBANK AG
Grosse Gallusstr 9
D 60311 Frankfurt, Germany
Tel.: (49) 6950951270
Fax: (49) 6950951350
E-Mail: info@concord-ag.de
Web Site: www.concord-ag.de
Year Founded: 1998
Sales Range: $25-49.9 Million
Emp.: 76
Business Description:
Investment Banking & Securities Brokerage Services
S.I.C.: 6211
N.A.I.C.S.: 523110
Personnel:
Dirk Schaper *(Chm-Mgmt Bd)*
Mathias Schmid *(Member-Mgmt Bd)*
Subsidiary:
Concord Financial Intermediary GmbH (1)
Grosse Gallusstrasse 1-7
60311 Frankfurt, Germany De
Tel.: (49) 6950951600
Fax: (49) 6950951650
E-Mail: info@concord-ag.de
Web Site: www.concord-ag.de/index.aspx?menu=8
Securities Brokerage Services
S.I.C.: 6211
N.A.I.C.S.: 523120
Dirk Schaper *(Chm-Mgmt Bd)*

CONCORD MEDICAL SERVICES HOLDINGS LIMITED
18/F Tower A Global Trade Center 36 North Third Ring Road East
Dongcheng District, Beijing, 100013, China
Tel.: (86) 10 59036688
Fax: (86) 10 59575252
E-Mail: ir@cmsholdings.com
Web Site: www.cmsholdings.com
CCM—(NYSE)
Rev.: $105,214,139
Assets: $582,220,197
Liabilities: $210,525,494
Net Worth: $371,694,704
Earnings: $21,362,148
Emp.: 616
Fiscal Year-end: 12/31/12
Business Description:
Radiotherapy & Diagnostic Imaging Centers
S.I.C.: 8071
N.A.I.C.S.: 621512
Personnel:
Steve Xiaodi Sun *(Founder)*
Jianyu Yang *(Chm & CEO)*
Zheng Cheng *(Pres & COO)*
Adam Jigang Sun *(CFO)*
Jing Zhang *(Chief Admin Officer)*
Yaw Kong Yap *(Sr VP)*
Board of Directors:
Jianyu Yang
Shirley Chen
Zheng Cheng
Tian Ji
Wai Hong Ku
Yongjun Li
Yaw Kong Yap
Zhe Yin
Jing Zhang

CONCORD PROJECTS LTD.
1277 Henderson Highway
Winnipeg, MB, R2G 1M3, Canada
Tel.: (204) 339-1651
Fax: (204) 339-0146
E-Mail: info@concordprojects.com
Web Site: www.concordprojects.com
Year Founded: 1978
Rev.: $20,742,677
Emp.: 15
Business Description:
General Contractor & Construction Management
S.I.C.: 8711
N.A.I.C.S.: 541330
Personnel:
Will Slota *(Pres & Gen Mgr)*
Ted Paetkau *(CEO)*
Daniel Gauthier *(Sr VP-Project Dev)*
Harald Schulz *(Sr VP-Project Dev)*

CONCORD SECURITY CORP.
925 4710 Kingsway Metrotower I
Burnaby, BC, V5H 4M2, Canada
Tel.: (604) 689-4005
Fax: (604) 689-3244
Toll Free: (888) 689-4005
E-Mail: info@concordsecurity.com
Web Site: www.concordsecurity.com
Year Founded: 1983
Rev.: $15,404,713
Emp.: 800
Business Description:
Security Services Provider
S.I.C.: 7381
N.A.I.C.S.: 561612
Personnel:
John Henry *(Pres & CEO)*
Rob Davis *(COO)*

CONCORDIA HEALTHCARE CORP.
(Formerly Mercari Acquisition Corp.)
27 Lakeshore Road East Suite 302
Oakville, ON, L6J 1H9, Canada
Tel.: (905) 842-5150
Fax: (905) 842-5154
Web Site: www.concordiapharma.ca
Year Founded: 2010
CXR—(OTC TSX)
Int. Income: $176
Assets: $524,238
Liabilities: $73,909
Net Worth: $450,329
Earnings: ($3,988)
Fiscal Year-end: 01/31/13
Business Description:
Holding Company; Biopharmaceutical Products Developer, Mfr & Distr
S.I.C.: 6719
N.A.I.C.S.: 551112
Personnel:
Mark L. Thompson *(Pres & CEO)*
Leith Tessy *(CFO & Sec)*
Transfer Agent:
Equity Financial Trust Company
200 University Avenue Suite 400
Toronto, ON, Canada
Subsidiary:
Concordia Healthcare Inc. (1)
277 Lakeshore Road East Suite 302
Oakville, ON, L6J 1H9, Canada
Tel.: (905) 842-5150
Fax: (905) 842-5154
Web Site: www.concordiapharma.ca
Biopharmaceutical Developer, Mfr & Distr
S.I.C.: 2834
N.A.I.C.S.: 325412
Mark L. Thompson *(Founder, Pres & CEO)*

CONCORDIA RESOURCE CORP.
654 999 Canada Place
Vancouver, BC, V6C 3E1, Canada
Tel.: (604) 669-6446
Fax: (604) 681-3091
E-Mail: info@concordiaresourcecorp.com
Web Site: www.concordiaresourcecorp.com
Year Founded: 2000
CCN—(TSXV)
Rev.: $336,973
Assets: $43,205,079
Liabilities: $908,534
Net Worth: $42,296,545
Earnings: ($14,934,156)
Fiscal Year-end: 09/30/12
Business Description:
Mineral Exploration Services
S.I.C.: 1081
N.A.I.C.S.: 213114
Personnel:
David Birkenshaw *(Chm)*
Toby Mayo *(Pres)*
Terry J. Krepiakevich *(Interim CEO)*
Eduard Epshtein *(CFO)*
Tracy Hansen *(Sec & VP)*
Board of Directors:
David Birkenshaw
Gerard de la Vallee Poussin
Edward Flood
John D. Fognani
Peter Clark Jones
Pamela J. Klessig
Terry J. Krepiakevich
Pierre B. Lebel
Borden Putnam
Legal Counsel:
McCullough O'Connor Irwin LLP
2610 Oceanic Plaza 1066 West Hastings Street
Vancouver, BC, Canada
Transfer Agent:
Computershare Trust Company of Canada
510 Burrard St 3rd Fl
Vancouver, BC, V6C 3B9, Canada

CONCRETE AGGREGATES CORPORATION
9th Floor Ortigas Building Ortigas Avenue
Pasig, Philippines
Tel.: (63) 26311231
Fax: (63) 26316517
E-Mail: concreteaggregatescorp@ca c.com.ph
Web Site: www.cac.com.ph
CA—(PHI)
Rev.: $483,787
Assets: $7,763,857
Liabilities: $748,713
Net Worth: $7,015,144
Earnings: $239,779
Emp.: 3
Fiscal Year-end: 12/31/12
Business Description:
Concrete Mfr
S.I.C.: 1771
N.A.I.C.S.: 238110
Personnel:
J. Rowell L. Recinto *(Chm)*
Emmanuel A. Rapadas *(Pres & Gen Mgr)*
Michael David I. Abundo, III *(Compliance Officer, Sec & VP)*
Brigido Theodore R. Sarmiento *(Corp Info Officer)*
Jose C. Rodriguez IV *(Treas)*
Board of Directors:
J. Rowell L. Recinto
Samson C. Lazo
Alberto M. Montilla
Jose Luis O. Montilla
Francisco M. Ortigas, III
Jaime M. Ortigas
Ma. Victoria B. Ortigas-Borromeo
Roberto M. Paterno
Emmanuel A. Rapadas
Jose C. Rodriguez IV

CONCRETE ENGINEERING PRODUCTS BERHAD
Tingkat 22 Menara KH Jalan Sultan Ismail
PO Box 11919
50762 Kuala Lumpur, Malaysia
Tel.: (60) 321441066
Fax: (60) 321444885
E-Mail: nahar@cepco.com.my
Web Site: www.cepco.com.my
CEPCO—(KLS)
Rev.: $68,598,332
Assets: $64,871,698
Liabilities: $29,127,058
Net Worth: $35,744,641
Earnings: $8,251,771
Fiscal Year-end: 08/31/13
Business Description:
Concrete Piles & Poles Mfr & Distr
S.I.C.: 1791
N.A.I.C.S.: 238120
Personnel:
Kway Wah Leong *(Mng Dir)*
Norakhmar Baharom *(Sec)*
Board of Directors:
Abdul Khudus Mohd Naaim
Kay Ong Khoo
Kway Wah Leong
Nur Rahmah Mohd Zain
Davinia Rajadurai
Dennis Xavier

CONDMAG S.A.
52 Avram Iancu St
500075 Brasov, Romania
Tel.: (40) 268414954
Fax: (40) 268471706
E-Mail: condmag@condmag.ro
Web Site: www.condmag.ro
COMI—(BUC)

CONDMAG S.A.—(Continued)

Sls.: $28,567,869
Assets: $57,118,743
Liabilities: $31,770,585
Net Worth: $25,348,158
Earnings: ($8,026,265)
Emp.: 870
Fiscal Year-end: 12/31/12

Business Description:
Pipeline Construction Services
S.I.C.: 1623
N.A.I.C.S.: 237120

Personnel:
Gheorghe Calburean *(Chm-Mgmt Bd)*
Alexandru Liviu Tatar *(Member-Mgmt Bd & Gen Mgr)*
Mariana Pruteanu *(Member-Mgmt Bd & Mgr-Economic)*
Cristian Robert Fader *(Member-Mgmt Bd)*
Dana Elisabeta Nanu *(Member-Mgmt Bd)*

CONDOR BLANCO MINES LIMITED

Suite 1901 Level 19 109 Pitt St
Sydney, NSW, 2000, Australia
Tel.: (61) 2 9225 4070
Fax: (61) 2 9235 3889
E-Mail: info@condormines.com
Web Site: www.condormines.com
Year Founded: 2010
CDB—(ASX)
Rev.: $292
Assets: $10,362,059
Liabilities: $794,206
Net Worth: $9,567,853
Earnings: ($2,422,541)
Fiscal Year-end: 06/30/13

Business Description:
Gold, Silver & Copper Mining Services
S.I.C.: 1041
N.A.I.C.S.: 212221

Personnel:
Glen Darby *(Mng Dir)*
Peter Dunoon *(Sec)*

Board of Directors:
Paul Crosio
Glen Darby
John Shanahan
Carl Swensson

Legal Counsel:
Eakin McCaffery Cox
Level 28 1 Market street
Sydney, NSW, 2000, Australia
Tel.: (61) 2 9265 3075
Fax: (61) 2 9261 5918

CONDOR GOLD PLC

(Formerly Condor Resources Plc)
7th Floor 39 St James's Street
London, SW1A 1JD, United Kingdom
Tel.: (44) 20 7493 2784
Fax: (44) 20 7493 8633
E-Mail: information@condorgold.com
Web Site: www.condorgold.com
CNR—(LSE)
Assets: $21,289,927
Liabilities: $1,104,379
Net Worth: $20,185,548
Earnings: $5,142,189
Emp.: 114

Business Description:
Gold & Silver Exploration Services
S.I.C.: 3339
N.A.I.C.S.: 331410

Personnel:
Mark Child *(Chm & CEO)*
Chris Putt *(Sec)*

Board of Directors:
Mark Child
Roger Owen Davey
James Mellon

Crowe Clark Whitehill LLP
St Bride's House 10 Salisbury Square
EC4Y 8EH London, United Kingdom

Legal Counsel:
Speechly Bircham LLP
6 New Street Square
London, EC4A 3LX, United Kingdom

Arias & Munoz
Km 4 1/2 Carretera a Masaya Centro BAC 5to Piso
Managua, Nicaragua

Arias & Munoz
Calle La Mascota N 533 San Benito
San Salvador, El Salvador

CONDOR PETROLEUM INC.

Suite 2400 144 4th Ave SW
Calgary, AB, T2P 3N4, Canada
Tel.: (403) 201-9694
Fax: (403) 201-9607
E-Mail: mbliesner@condorpetroleum.com
Web Site: www.condorpetroleum.com
CPI—(TSX)
Sls.: $3,787,216
Assets: $186,917,509
Liabilities: $12,769,181
Net Worth: $174,148,328
Earnings: ($14,008,724)
Emp.: 145
Fiscal Year-end: 12/31/12

Business Description:
Oil & Gas Exploration Services
S.I.C.: 1311
N.A.I.C.S.: 211111

Personnel:
Sean Roosen *(Chm)*
Don Streu *(Pres & CEO)*
Sandy Quilty *(CFO & VP)*
William Hatcher *(COO)*

Board of Directors:
Sean Roosen
Dennis Balderston
Edward W. Bogle
John Burzynski
Walter Dawson
Stefan Kaltenbach
Don Streu
Donald A. Wright
Werner Zoellner

Transfer Agent:
Olympia Transfer Services Inc
Toronto, ON, Canada

CONDOR RESOURCES INC.

Suite 1700 750 West Pender St
Vancouver, BC, V6C 2T8, Canada
Tel.: (604) 642-5707
Fax: (604) 688-9895
Toll Free: (866) 642-5707
E-Mail: info@condorresources.com
Web Site: www.condorresources.com
Year Founded: 2004
CN—(TSXV)
Int. Income: $17,636
Assets: $4,013,411
Liabilities: $66,357
Net Worth: $3,947,055
Earnings: ($3,495,279)
Fiscal Year-end: 02/28/13

Business Description:
Mineral Exploration Services
S.I.C.: 1081
N.A.I.C.S.: 213114

Personnel:
Lyle Davis *(Pres)*
John S. Watt *(CFO)*
Graham H. Scott *(Sec)*

Board of Directors:
Robert T. Boyd
Lyle Davis
Francisco F. de Undurraga
Paul Anthony Larkin
Graham H. Scott

Transfer Agent:
Computershare
3rd Floor 510 Burrard Street
Vancouver, BC, Canada

Non-U.S. Subsidiary:

Condor Exploration Peru S.A.C. **(1)**
Av Javier Prado Este No 1184 Int 302 Urb Corpac
San Isidro, Lima, Peru
Tel.: (51) 1 2266267
Mineral Mining Services
S.I.C.: 1499
N.A.I.C.S.: 212399

CONDOR RESOURCES PLC

(Name Changed to Condor Gold Plc)

CONDOTO PLATINUM NL

Level 4 66 Kings Park Road
West Perth, WA, 6005, Australia
Mailing Address:
PO Box 52
West Perth, WA, 6872, Australia
Tel.: (61) 8 6141 3500
Fax: (61) 8 6141 3599
E-Mail: info@condotoplatinum.com.au
Web Site: www.condotoplatinum.com.au
CPD—(ASX)
Rev.: $174,241
Assets: $13,538,294
Liabilities: $351,728
Net Worth: $13,186,567
Earnings: ($3,644,881)
Fiscal Year-end: 06/30/13

Business Description:
Platinum & Gold Exploration Services
S.I.C.: 1041
N.A.I.C.S.: 212221

Personnel:
Philip O'Neill *(Mng Dir)*
David Forest *(COO)*
Jay Stephenson *(Sec)*

Board of Directors:
William Hayden
Andrew Lorne Johnstone
Philip O'Neill

CONDUCTORES Y CABLES DEL PERU S.A.C.

(d/b/a CEPER S.A.)
334 Av Los Frutales
Ate-Vitarte, Lima, 03, Peru
Tel.: (51) 1713 6000
Telex: 20259 PE COPIR
Fax: (51) 1713 6001
E-Mail: comercial@ccp.com.pe
Web Site: www.ceper.com.pe
Sales Range: $25-49.9 Million
Emp.: 150

Business Description:
Cable Mfr
S.I.C.: 3357
N.A.I.C.S.: 335929

Personnel:
Karl Wilhelm Reusche Arambulo *(CEO)*

CONDUIT CAPITAL LIMITED

Tulbagh 360 Oak Avenue Randburg
2194 Johannesburg, South Africa
Mailing Address:
PO Box 97
Melrose Arch, 2076 Johannesburg, South Africa
Tel.: (27) 11 686 4200
Fax: (27) 11 789 3709
E-Mail: info@conduitcapital.co.za
Web Site: www.conduitcapital.co.za
CND—(JSE)
Rev.: $130,484,031
Assets: $114,812,074
Liabilities: $78,216,361
Net Worth: $36,595,713
Earnings: $6,560,476
Emp.: 10
Fiscal Year-end: 08/31/13

Business Description:
Investment Holding Company
S.I.C.: 6211
N.A.I.C.S.: 523120

Personnel:
Jason Dean Druian *(CEO)*

Board of Directors:
Reginald Selwyn Berkowitz
Richard Bruyns
Scott MacGibbon Campbell
Jason Dean Druian
Lourens Erasmus Louw
Robert Lindsey Shaw
Gunter Zeno Steffens
Gavin Toet

Transfer Agent:
Computershare Investor Services 2004 (Pty) Ltd
Ground Floor 70 Marshall Street
Johannesburg, South Africa

Subsidiaries:

Constantia Life Limited **(1)**
PO Box 2215
Cape Town, Western Cape, 8000, South Africa
Tel.: (27) 214248040
Fax: (27) 214237995
Web Site: www.conduitcapital.com
Emp.: 50
Life Insurance Services
S.I.C.: 6411
N.A.I.C.S.: 524210
Gavin Toet *(CEO)*

Goodall and Bourne Properties (Proprietary) Limited **(1)**
10 Dorp St
Cape Town, 8000, South Africa
Tel.: (27) 214248040
Fax: (27) 214237995
Property Management Services
S.I.C.: 6531
N.A.I.C.S.: 531312
Christoph Hermann Kuhn *(Chm)*

On Line Lottery Services (Proprietary) Limited **(1)**
PO Box 97
Melrose Arch, Johannesburg, Gauteng, 2076, South Africa
Tel.: (27) 116864200
Fax: (27) 117893709
E-Mail: admin@lottofun.co.za
Web Site: www.loottofun.co.za
Online Lottery Services
S.I.C.: 7999
N.A.I.C.S.: 713290

CONE AUTOMOBILES

8 Bd Du President Wilson
Dole, 39100 Dijon, France
Tel.: (33) 384826701
Sls.: $23,600,000
Emp.: 54

Business Description:
New & Used Car Dealers
S.I.C.: 5511
N.A.I.C.S.: 441110

Personnel:
Vincent Deffeuille *(Pres)*

CONERGY AG

(d/b/a Conergy Group)
Anckelmannsplatz 1
20537 Hamburg, Germany
Tel.: (49) 40271421000
Fax: (49) 402371021100
E-Mail: info@conergy.de
Web Site: www.conergy-group.com
CGY—(DEU)
Sls.: $637,411,495
Assets: $325,234,672
Liabilities: $428,351,294
Net Worth: ($103,116,622)

Earnings: ($133,270,830)
Emp.: 1,144
Fiscal Year-end: 12/31/12

Business Description:
Holding Company; Regenerative Energy Systems Mfr
S.I.C.: 6719
N.A.I.C.S.: 551112

Personnel:
Andreas Plesske *(Chm-Supervisory Bd)*
Philip Comberg *(Chm-Mgmt Bd & CEO)*
Werner Gunter Paul Paschke *(Deputy Chm-Supervisory Bd)*
Alexander Gorski *(COO & Member-Mgmt Bd)*
Marc Lohoff *(Chief Sls Officer-APAC, North America & ME & Member-Mgmt Bd)*
Jan Vannerum *(Member-Mgmt Bd-Fin, Tax, Treasury, Internal Audit, IT & IR)*

Supervisory Board of Directors:
Andreas Plesske
Pepyn Rene Dinandt
Werner Gunter Paul Paschke
Klaus-Dieter Rasch

Subsidiaries:

Conergy Deutschland GmbH **(1)**
Anckelmannsplatz 1
20537 Hamburg, Germany
Tel.: (49) 40271421000
Fax: (49) 40271421100
E-Mail: info@conergy.de
Web Site: www.conergy.de
Solar Panels Whslr
S.I.C.: 5046
N.A.I.C.S.: 423440

Subsidiaries:

Conergy SolarModule GmbH & Co. KG **(2)**
Conergy-Strasse 8
5236 Frankfurt, Hesse, Germany De
Tel.: (49) 335521130
Fax: (49) 33552113491
E-Mail: info@conergy.de
Solar Modules Mfr
S.I.C.: 3674
N.A.I.C.S.: 334413
Sven Starke *(Gen Mgr)*

Mounting Systems GmbH **(2)**
Mittenwalder Strasse 9A
15834 Rangsdorf, Brandenburg, Germany
Tel.: (49) 337085290
Fax: (49) 33 708 529 199
E-Mail: info@mounting-systems.de
Web Site: www.mounting-systems.de
Emp.: 200
Solar Mounting Systems Mfr
S.I.C.: 3646
N.A.I.C.S.: 335122
Stefan Spork *(Mng Dir)*

EPURON GmbH **(1)**
Anckelmannsplatz 1
20537 Hamburg, Germany
Tel.: (49) 40 2714 23000
Fax: (49) 40 2714 23300
E-Mail: info@epuron.de
Web Site: www.epuron.de
Energy Projects Development Services
S.I.C.: 1623
N.A.I.C.S.: 237130
Markus Lesser *(Co-Mng Dir)*
Joachim Mueller *(Co-Mng Dir)*
Michael Weibflog *(Mng Dir)*

Non-U.S. Subsidiaries:

EPURON EPE **(2)**
Vouliagmenis 4
Glyfada, 166 75 Athens, Greece
Tel.: (30) 2109604205
Fax: (30) 2109604516
E-Mail: info@epuron.gr
Web Site: www.epuron.de/en/desktopdefault.aspx/tabid-484/
Photovoltaic Devices Mfr
S.I.C.: 3674
N.A.I.C.S.: 334413
Dieter Scamitt *(Gen Mgr)*

EPURON Pty Ltd **(2)**
Level 11 75 Miller St
North Sydney, Sydney, NSW, 2060, Australia
Tel.: (61) 284567400
Fax: (61) 299226645
E-Mail: info@epuron.com.au
Web Site: www.epuron.com.au
Emp.: 15
Power Plant Management Services
S.I.C.: 8748
N.A.I.C.S.: 541618
Martin Poole *(Mng Dir)*

EPURON SARL **(2)**
9 Avenue de Paris
94300 Vincennes, Val-de-Marne, France
Tel.: (33) 1 4174 7040
Fax: (33) 1 4174 7041
E-Mail: info@epuron.fr
Web Site: www.epuron.fr
Emp.: 15
Electric Power Generation Services
S.I.C.: 4911
N.A.I.C.S.: 221118
Jean-Baptiste Godmet *(Mng Dir)*

EPURON Spain SLU **(2)**
C Jazminero 1 1-6
Aguadulce, 04720 Almeria, Spain
Tel.: (34) 950 55 1408
Fax: (34) 950 55 1024
E-Mail: info@epuron.es
Web Site: www.epuron.es
Power Plant Financing & Development Services
S.I.C.: 1623
N.A.I.C.S.: 237130

U.S. Subsidiary:

Conergy, Inc. **(1)**
1730 Camino Carlos Rey Ste 103
Santa Fe, NM 87507
Tel.: (505) 473-3800
Fax: (505) 473-3830
Toll Free: (888) 396-6611
Web Site: www.conergy.us
Sales Range: $10-24.9 Million
Emp.: 18
Mfr of Solar-Powered Water Pumps
S.I.C.: 3561
N.A.I.C.S.: 333911

Non-U.S. Subsidiaries:

Conergy E.P.E. **(1)**
Vouliagmenis 4
Glyfada, 166 75 Athens, Greece
Tel.: (30) 2109651800
Fax: (30) 2109630768
E-Mail: info@conergy.gr
Web Site: www.conergy.gr
Emp.: 30
Photovoltaic System Mfr
S.I.C.: 3674
N.A.I.C.S.: 334413
Stratos Theodorou *(Project Mgr)*

Conergy Espana S.L.U. **(1)**
C/Arturo Soria 336 8th Fl
28033 Madrid, Spain
Tel.: (34) 902555112
Fax: (34) 917276110
E-Mail: info@conergy.es
Web Site: www.conergy.es
Emp.: 100
Renewable Energy Systems Mfr
S.I.C.: 3433
N.A.I.C.S.: 333414

Conergy Italia SpA **(1)**
Via Zamenhof 200
36100 Vicenza, Italy
Tel.: (39) 0444380131
Fax: (39) 0444580122
E-Mail: info@conergy.it
Web Site: www.conergy.it
Photovoltaic Modules Whslr
S.I.C.: 5065
N.A.I.C.S.: 423690
Giuseppe Sofia *(Pres & Owner)*

Conergy Ltd. **(1)**
107B Nikou Pattichi str
3070 Limassol, Cyprus
Tel.: (357) 25822314
Fax: (357) 25822315
E-Mail: info@conergy.com
Web Site: www.conergy.com.cy
Photovoltaic Systems Installation Services
S.I.C.: 7389
N.A.I.C.S.: 561990
George Georgiou *(Mgr)*

Conergy Pte Ltd **(1)**
120 Robinson Road 12-01 Parakou Building
Singapore, 068913, Singapore
Tel.: (65) 6849 5540
Renewable Energy System Mfr
S.I.C.: 3674
N.A.I.C.S.: 334413

Subsidiary:

Conergy Renewable Energy Singapore Pte. Ltd. **(2)**
120 Robinson Road 12-01
Singapore, 068913, Singapore
Tel.: (65) 68495540
Fax: (65) 6849 5559
E-Mail: info-apac@conergy.com
Web Site: www.conergy.in
Emp.: 25
Renewable Energy System Distr
S.I.C.: 5074
N.A.I.C.S.: 423720
Alexander Lenz *(Co-Pres-South East Asia & Middle East)*
Marc Lohoff *(Co-Pres-Asia Pacific & Middle East)*

Conergy Pty Limited **(1)**
Unit 6 44-48 O'Dea Avenue
Waterloo, NSW, 2017, Australia
Tel.: (61) 285072222
Fax: (61) 2 8507 2220
E-Mail: info@conergy.com.au
Web Site: www.conergy.com.au
Photovoltaic Systems Distr
S.I.C.: 5049
N.A.I.C.S.: 423490

Conergy SAS **(1)**
ZAC Nicopolis - Route Nationale 7
83170 Brignoles, Var, France
Tel.: (33) 4 9477 5400
Fax: (33) 4 9477 5401
E-Mail: contact@conergy.fr
Web Site: www.conergy.fr
Emp.: 17
Solar Panels Distr
S.I.C.: 5065
N.A.I.C.S.: 423690

SunTechnics Energy Systems Private Limited **(1)**
660/1 100 Feet Road
Indiranagar, Bengaluru, Karnataka, 560 038, India
Tel.: (91) 8041880900
Fax: (91) 8041261932
E-Mail: SunTechnics.india@SunTechnics.com
Web Site: www.suntechnics.com
Emp.: 90
Solar Integrated Equipments Mfr
S.I.C.: 3433
N.A.I.C.S.: 333414
Atreya Nagaraja *(Dir-Natl Sls)*

Unit:

SunTechnics Energy Systems Private Limited - System Integration Unit **(2)**
60/1 White Field Rd Singayanapalya
Mahdevapura, Bengaluru, Karnataka, 560 048, India
Tel.: (91) 8040223206
Fax: (91) 41261932
E-Mail: ST-India@conergy.com
Web Site: www.conergy.com
Emp.: 150
Solar Panels Mfr
S.I.C.: 3999
N.A.I.C.S.: 339999
Nagaraj Atreya *(Mgr)*

Non-U.S. Subsidiary:

SunTechnics Fabrisolar AG **(2)**
Untere Heslibachstrasse 39
8700 Kusnacht, Zurich, Switzerland
Tel.: (41) 44 9142 88 0
Fax: (41) 44 9142 88 8
E-Mail: info@suntechnics.ch
Web Site: www.suntechnics.ch
Power Plant Management Services
S.I.C.: 4931
N.A.I.C.S.: 221118

CONESTOGA COLD STORAGE

299 Trillium Drive
Kitchener, ON, N2E 1W9, Canada
Tel.: (519) 748-5415
Fax: (519) 748-9852
Web Site: www.coldstorage.com
Year Founded: 1974
Rev.: $18,519,274
Emp.: 160

Business Description:
Cold Storage Warehouses
S.I.C.: 4222
N.A.I.C.S.: 493120

Personnel:
Larry Laurin *(Chm)*
Greg Laurin *(Pres)*
Ed Shantz *(Sr VP-Sls & Admin)*

CONESTOGA-ROVERS & ASSOCIATES, LTD.

(d/b/a CRA)
651 Colby Drive
Waterloo, ON, N2V 1C2, Canada
Tel.: (519) 884-0510
Fax: (519) 884-0525
Web Site: www.craworld.com
Year Founded: 1976
Emp.: 3,000

Business Description:
Engineering, Construction, IT & Environmental Consulting Services
S.I.C.: 8748
N.A.I.C.S.: 541618

Personnel:
Ed Roberts *(Pres)*
Steve Quigley *(Sec)*
Ian Richardson *(Exec VP)*
Glenn Turchan *(Exec VP)*

Division:

CRA Contractors Limited **(1)**
140 Bathurst Dr
Waterloo, ON, N2V 1V7, Canada
Tel.: (519) 884-3363
Fax: (519) 725-1370
Environmental & Municipal Infrastructure Construction
S.I.C.: 8999
N.A.I.C.S.: 541620
Bruce Monteith *(Mgr)*

Subsidiaries:

CRA (Quebec) Inc. **(1)**
4610 De la Cote-Vertu Blvd
Montreal, QC, Canada
Tel.: (514) 336-0510
Fax: (514) 336-9434
Engineering, Environmental Consulting, Construction & IT Services
S.I.C.: 8748
N.A.I.C.S.: 541618
Marie-France Gravelle *(Branch Mgr)*

Branch:

CRA (Quebec) Inc.-Brossard **(2)**
9955 de Catania Avenue Suite 220
Brossard, QC, J4Z3V6, Canada
Tel.: (450) 618-0510
Fax: (450) 678-6306
Web Site: www.craworld.com
Emp.: 20
Engineering, Environmental Consulting, Construction, & IT Services
S.I.C.: 8748
N.A.I.C.S.: 541618
Guy Chateaunef *(Dir-Environmental)*

eSolutions Group **(1)**
651 Colby Drive
Waterloo, ON, N2V1C6, Canada
Tel.: (519) 884-3352
Fax: (519) 725-1394
E-Mail: support@help.esolutionsgroup.ca
Web Site: www.esolutionsgroup.ca
Marketing, Communications and Creative Services

Conestoga-Rovers & Associates, Ltd.—(Continued)

S.I.C.: 8742
N.A.I.C.S.: 541613
Karen Mayfield *(Branch Mgr)*

SECRA Quebec, Inc. **(1)**
4600 De la Cote-Vertu Blvd
Montreal, QC, H4S 1C7, Canada
Tel.: (514) 934-1225
Fax: (514) 333-3024
Environmental Services
S.I.C.: 8999
N.A.I.C.S.: 541620
Nathalie Houle *(Mgr)*

Affiliate:

Inspec-Sol Inc. **(1)**
4600 De la Cote-Vertu Blvd
Montreal, QC, H4S 1C7, Canada
Tel.: (514) 333-5151
Fax: (514) 333-4674
Web Site: www.inspecsol.com
Engineering Services
S.I.C.: 8711
N.A.I.C.S.: 541330
Nat Agensky *(Founder)*
Salvatore Oppedisano *(Pres)*
Steve Lecuyer *(Sec & VP-Metallurgy)*

Subsidiary:

Geo-Logic Inc. **(2)**
347 Pido Road Unit 29
Peterborough, ON, K9J 6X7, Canada
Tel.: (705) 749-3317
Fax: (705) 749-9248
E-Mail: general@geo-logic.ca
Web Site: www.geo-logic.ca
Emp.: 45
Geotechnical Engineering, Hydrogeology, Environmental Engineering, Construction Materials Testing & Inspection Services
S.I.C.: 8711
N.A.I.C.S.: 541330
Garnet Brenchley *(Branch Mgr)*

U.S. Subsidiary:

Conestoga-Rovers & Associates Inc. **(1)**
2055 Niagara Falls Blvd Ste 3
Niagara Falls, NY 14304 DE
Tel.: (716) 297-6150
Fax: (716) 297-2265
Engineering, Environmental, Construction, & IT Services
S.I.C.: 8711
N.A.I.C.S.: 541330
Tony Ying *(Treas)*

Subsidiaries:

CRA Engineering Group Inc. **(2)**
5551 Corporate Blvd Ste 200
Baton Rouge, LA 70808
Tel.: (225) 971-4249
Fax: (225) 925-2897
Engineering & Design Services
S.I.C.: 8711
N.A.I.C.S.: 541330
Bill Fisher *(Branch Mgr)*

CRA Infrastructure & Engineering, Inc. **(2)**
285 Delaware Ave Ste 500
Buffalo, NY 14202 NY
Tel.: (716) 856-2142
Sales Range: $1-9.9 Million
Emp.: 45
Environmental & Municipal Engineering
S.I.C.: 8711
N.A.I.C.S.: 541330
Bryan Smith *(Branch Mgr)*

HSA Engineers & Scientists **(2)**
4019 E Fowler Ave
Tampa, FL 33617
Tel.: (813) 971-3882
Fax: (813) 971-1862
Toll Free: (800) 200-5550
E-Mail: claims@hsa-env.com
Web Site: www.hsa-env.com
Sales Range: $25-49.9 Million
Emp.: 290
Engineering Services
S.I.C.: 8711
N.A.I.C.S.: 541330
Nicholas Albergo *(Pres)*
Brian Moore *(CEO)*
Ronald Maggard *(COO)*
David Scott *(Treas)*
Richard Lewis *(Sec)*
Kevin Ormsby *(Exec VP)*

Non-U.S. Subsidiaries:

Conestoga-Rovers & Associados Engenharia SA. **(1)**
Avenida Torquato Tapajos 1292 Sala B
Bairro da Paz, 69048-660 Manaus, Brazil
Tel.: (55) 92 4009 0461
Fax: (55) 92 8122 1000
Enivronmental Services
S.I.C.: 8999
N.A.I.C.S.: 541620
Jeancarlo de Azevedo *(Branch Mgr)*

CRA (Europe) Ltd. **(1)**
Synergy House Unit 1 Calverton Business Park
Hoyle Road, Nottingham, Calverton, United Kingdom
Tel.: (44) 115 965 6700
Fax: (44) 115 965 5282
E-Mail: info@cra.co.uk
Web Site: www.cra.co.uk
Environmental, Health, Safety & Engineering Services
S.I.C.: 8999
N.A.I.C.S.: 541620
Nigel Leehane *(Mng Dir)*

CONEX MD, INC.

PO Box 929
Ra'anana, Israel 45108
Tel.: (972) 579461249
Web Site: www.conexmd.com
Year Founded: 2007
CXMD.OB—(OTC OTCB)
Assets: $575
Liabilities: $34,361
Net Worth: ($33,786)
Earnings: ($40,881)
Fiscal Year-end: 12/31/12
Business Description:
Healthcare Staffing Services
S.I.C.: 7361
N.A.I.C.S.: 561311
Personnel:
Patrick Bragoli *(CEO)*
Sebastian Cliche *(COO)*
Board of Directors:
Patrick Bragoli
Sebastian Cliche

CONEXION MEDIA GROUP PLC

10 Heathfield Terrace Chiswick
London, W4 4JE, United Kingdom
Tel.: (44) 2089874150
E-Mail: info@conexion-media.com
Web Site: www.conexion-media.com
CXM—(AIM)
Rev.: $4,130,396
Assets: $8,842,895
Liabilities: $11,027,656
Net Worth: ($2,184,761)
Earnings: ($1,041,782)
Emp.: 14
Fiscal Year-end: 12/31/12
Business Description:
Music Administration, Film & Television Production Services
S.I.C.: 2741
N.A.I.C.S.: 512230
Personnel:
Justin Sherry *(CEO)*
Frank McAweaney *(Sec)*
Board of Directors:
Guy Fletcher
Justin Sherry
Transfer Agent:
Capita Registrars
The Registry 34 Beckenham Road
Beckenham, United Kingdom

U.S. Subsidiary:

Diamond Time (US) Ltd.. **(1)**
630 9th Ave Ste 1012
New York, NY 10036-3744
Tel.: (212) 274-1006
Fax: (212) 274-1938
E-Mail: info@diamondtime.net
Web Site: www.diamondtime.net
Emp.: 5
Media Licensing & Copyright Services
S.I.C.: 9651
N.A.I.C.S.: 926150
Cathy Carapella *(Pres)*

CONFECCOES PORTO GRANDE, LDA

Cha de Cricket
CP 587
Mindelo, Sao Vicente, Cape Verde
Tel.: (238) 303020
Fax: (238) 321403
E-Mail: info@portogrande.net
Web Site: www.portogrande.net
Year Founded: 1994
Emp.: 140
Business Description:
Shirt Mfr
S.I.C.: 2329
N.A.I.C.S.: 315220

CONFECTIA S.A.

Str Tudor Vladimirescu Nr 129
Targu Jiu, Gorj, Romania
Tel.: (40) 253 213401
Fax: (40) 253 215648
E-Mail: confectia@intergorj.ro
Web Site: www.intergorj.ro/confectia
CNFG—(BUC)
Business Description:
Outerwear Mfr
S.I.C.: 2259
N.A.I.C.S.: 315190
Personnel:
Ana Carstoiu *(Gen Mgr)*

CONFECTII VASLUI S.A.

Strada Maresal Constantin Prezan Nr 11
730091 Vaslui, Romania
Tel.: (40) 235311840
Fax: (40) 235311953
Web Site: www.confectiivaslui.com
Year Founded: 1965
COVB—(BUC)
Business Description:
Outerwear Products Mfr
S.I.C.: 2259
N.A.I.C.S.: 315190
Personnel:
Ioan Ciprian Jude *(Pres)*
Board of Directors:
Gabriela Mariana Dascalu
Ioan Ciprian Jude

CONFEDERATION MINERALS LTD.

Suite 1980 - 1075 West Georgia St
Vancouver, BC, V6E 3C9, Canada
Tel.: (778) 331-2099
Fax: (778) 329-9361
E-Mail: info@confederationmineralsltd.com
Web Site: www.confederationmineralsltd.com
Year Founded: 2005
CFM—(OTC TSXV)
Rev.: $54,173
Assets: $15,014,381
Liabilities: $311,238
Net Worth: $14,703,143
Earnings: ($2,045,817)
Fiscal Year-end: 06/30/13
Business Description:
Mineral Exploration Services
S.I.C.: 1081
N.A.I.C.S.: 213114
Personnel:
Brian Bapty *(Pres)*
Lawrence Allan Dick *(CEO)*
Savio Chiu *(CFO)*
Board of Directors:
Kent E. Ausburn
Brian Bapty
Lawrence Allan Dick
Kenneth Richard Holmes
Scott Parsons
Legal Counsel:
Davis LLP
2800 Park Place 666 Burrard Street
Vancouver, BC, Canada
Transfer Agent:
Computershare
510 Burrard St 2nd Floor
Vancouver, BC, Canada

CONFIDENCE PETROLEUM INDIA LTD

404 Satyam Appts 8 Wardha Road
Dhantoli
Nagpur, Maharashtra, 440 012, India
Tel.: (91) 712 3250318
Fax: (91) 7123250319
E-Mail: info@confidencepetro.com
Web Site: www.confidencepetro.com
526829—(BOM)
Rev.: $59,064,243
Assets: $76,586,477
Liabilities: $29,331,568
Net Worth: $47,254,909
Earnings: $386,923
Fiscal Year-end: 03/31/13
Business Description:
Oil Marketing Service & Distr
S.I.C.: 2992
N.A.I.C.S.: 324191
Personnel:
Nitin Khara *(Chm, CEO & Mng Dir)*
Board of Directors:
Nitin Khara
Ashish Bilakhiya
Elesh Khara
Nalin Khara
Sumant Sutaria
Transfer Agent:
Ajel Limited
106 Link Plaza Commercial Complex Building
New Link Road
Oshiwara Jogeshwari West, Mumbai, India

CONFIDENCE TRADING COMPANY LIMITED

9 Botawala Building 3rd Floor 11/13
Horniman Circle
Fort, Mumbai, 400 001, India
Tel.: (91) 22 22662150
E-Mail: ctclbse@gmail.com
Web Site: www.ctcl.co.in
504340—(BOM)
Rev.: $360,529
Assets: $3,262,317
Liabilities: $271,555
Net Worth: $2,990,762
Earnings: $135,175
Fiscal Year-end: 03/31/13
Business Description:
Commodity Trading Services
S.I.C.: 6221
N.A.I.C.S.: 523130
Personnel:
Amruth R. Coutinho *(Mng Dir)*
Lalitkumar Roshanlal Maroo *(Compliance Officer)*
Board of Directors:
Amruth R. Coutinho
Manoj Naginlal Jain
Lalitkumar Roshanlal Maroo

Transfer Agent:
Purva Shareregistry (India) Pvt Ltd
9 Shiv Shakti Industrial Estate JR Boricha Marg
Lower Parel(E)
Mumbai, India

CONFLANDEY INDUSTRIES SAS
(See Under Saarstahl AG)

CONFLOW LIMITED
President Park
President Way, Sheffield, S47 UR, United Kingdom
Tel.: (44) 1142240000
Fax: (44) 1142784974
E-Mail: info@conflow.com
Web Site: www.conflow.com
Year Founded: 1975
Emp.: 80
Business Description:
Mining Industry Machinery Mfr
S.I.C.: 3532
N.A.I.C.S.: 333131
Personnel:
Roger Creasey *(Dir-Tech)*
U.S. Division:

Conflow Inc. (1)
270 Meadowlands Blvd
Washington, PA 15301-8903 DE
Tel.: (724) 746-0200 (100%)
Fax: (724) 746-0940
E-Mail: sales.usa@conflow.com
Web Site: www.conflow.com
Emp.: 10
Mining Industry Machinery Mfr & Distr
S.I.C.: 5082
N.A.I.C.S.: 423810
Mike Goddard *(VP-Sls)*

CONFORCE INTERNATIONAL, INC.
51A Caldari Road 2nd Floor
Concord, ON, L4K 4G3, Canada
Tel.: (416) 234-0266
Fax: (416) 234-0026
E-Mail: info@conforceintl.com
Web Site: conforceinternational.com
CFRI—(OTC)
Sales Range: Less than $1 Million
Emp.: 11
Business Description:
Flooring for Container Shipping & Highway Trailer Businesses
S.I.C.: 2431
N.A.I.C.S.: 321918
Personnel:
Marino Kulas *(Chm & CEO)*
Mario Verrilli *(Acting CFO & VP-Corp Dev)*
Board of Directors:
Marino Kulas
Pieter Jacob Eekel
Michel Fortier
Subsidiary:

Conforce 1 Container Terminals Inc. (1)
584 Hazelhurst Dr
Mississauga, ON, L5J 4T8, Canada
Tel.: (905) 855-2171
Fax: (416) 234-0026
E-Mail: info@conforce1.com
Web Site: www.conforce1.buildingmy.com
Emp.: 5
Containers Handling & Storage Services
S.I.C.: 4491
N.A.I.C.S.: 488320
Marino Kulas *(Pres)*

CONGATEC AG
Auwiesenstrasse 5
94469 Deggendorf, Germany
Tel.: (49) 991 2700 0
Fax: (49) 991 2700 111
E-Mail: info@congatec.com
Web Site: www.congatec.com
Year Founded: 2004
Sales Range: $75-99.9 Million
Emp.: 142
Business Description:
Computer Parts Distr
S.I.C.: 5045
N.A.I.C.S.: 423430
Personnel:
Bernd Hacker *(VP-Sls & Mktg)*

CONGEBEC CAPITAL LTEE.
810 avenue Godin
Quebec, QC, G1M 2X9, Canada
Tel.: (418) 683-3491
Fax: (418) 683-6387
Toll Free: (877) 683-3491
E-Mail: godin@congebec.com
Web Site: www.congebec.com
Year Founded: 1974
Sales Range: $100-124.9 Million
Emp.: 500
Business Description:
Cold Storage & Logistics Services
S.I.C.: 4222
N.A.I.C.S.: 493120
Personnel:
Laurier Pedneault *(Founder & Pres)*
Subsidiary:

Westco MultiTemp Distribution Centres Inc. (1)
1555 Chevrier Blvd
Winnipeg, MB, R3T 1Y7, Canada Ca
Tel.: (204) 475-5570
Fax: (204) 477-1217
E-Mail: info@westco.ca
Web Site: www.westco.ca
Rev.: $21,388,458
Emp.: 165
Multi-Temperature Warehousing & Logistics Services
S.I.C.: 4225
N.A.I.C.S.: 493110

CONICO LIMITED
(Formerly Fission Energy Limited)
Level 15 197 St George's Terrace
Perth, WA, 6000, Australia
Tel.: (61) 892825889
Fax: (61) 892825866
E-Mail: mailroom@conico.com.au
Web Site: www.conico.com.au
CNJ—(ASX)
Rev.: $9,099
Assets: $15,406,354
Liabilities: $654,999
Net Worth: $14,751,355
Earnings: ($717,448)
Emp.: 40
Fiscal Year-end: 06/30/13
Business Description:
Cobalt, Nickel & Manganese Oxide Exploration
S.I.C.: 1099
N.A.I.C.S.: 212299
Personnel:
Gregory Howard Solomon *(Chm)*
Aaron P. Gates *(CFO & Sec)*
Board of Directors:
Gregory Howard Solomon
Guy Touzeau Le Page
James B. Richardson
Douglas Howard Solomon
Legal Counsel:
Solomon Brothers
Level 15 197 St Georges Terrace
Perth, Australia

CONNACHER OIL & GAS LIMITED
332 6th Avenue SW Suite 900
Calgary, AB, T2P 0B2, Canada
Tel.: (403) 538-6201
Fax: (403) 538-6225
E-Mail: inquiries@connacheroil.com
Web Site: www.connacheroil.com
CLL—(TSX)
Rev.: $383,086,362
Assets: $1,327,216,498
Liabilities: $986,367,040
Net Worth: $340,849,458
Earnings: ($83,963,875)
Emp.: 153
Fiscal Year-end: 12/31/12
Business Description:
Oil & Gas Services
S.I.C.: 1311
N.A.I.C.S.: 211111
Personnel:
Colin M. Evans *(Chm)*
Christopher Bloomer *(CEO)*
Greg Pollard *(CFO)*
Merle D. Johnson *(COO)*
Suzanne Loov *(Gen Counsel & Sec)*
Board of Directors:
Colin M. Evans
D. Hugh Bessell
Christopher Bloomer
Gregory A. Boland
Jennifer K. Kennedy
Garry Mihaichuk
Kelly J. Ogle
Glen D. Roane
W. C. Seth
Legal Counsel:
Norton Rose Canada LLP
Calgary, AB, Canada
Valiant Trust Company
Toronto, ON, Canada
Transfer Agents:
Valiant Trust Company
Calgary, AB, Canada
Valiant Trust Company
Toronto, ON, Canada
Subsidiaries:

Great Divide Pipeline Limited (1)
900 332-6 Ave SW
Calgary, AB, T2P 0B2, Canada
Tel.: (403) 538-6201
Fax: (403) 538-6225
Oil & Gas Exploration Services
S.I.C.: 1311
N.A.I.C.S.: 211111

CONNECT COMMUNICATIONS GROUP LTD
Hertford House 1 Cranwood Street
London, EC1V 9QP, United Kingdom
Tel.: (44) 20 7950 3200
Fax: (44) 20 7950 3209
E-Mail: info@connectcs.com
Web Site: www.connectcs.com
Sales Range: $10-24.9 Million
Emp.: 50
Fiscal Year-end: 12/31/12
Business Description:
Communications Integration Services
S.I.C.: 4899
N.A.I.C.S.: 517919
Personnel:
Andrew Thomas *(Mng Dir)*

CONNECT GROUP N.V.
Industriestraat 4
1910 Kampenhout, Belgium
Tel.: (32) 16618920
Fax: (32) 16617882
E-Mail: info@connectgroup.com
Web Site: www.connectgroup.com
Year Founded: 1987
CONN—(EUR)
Sls.: $190,669,412
Assets: $95,889,101
Liabilities: $60,602,530
Net Worth: $35,286,571
Earnings: $4,084,892
Emp.: 1,650
Fiscal Year-end: 12/31/12
Business Description:
Electronics Manufacturing Services
S.I.C.: 3679
N.A.I.C.S.: 334419
Personnel:
Dominique Moorkens *(Chm)*
Luc Switten *(CEO)*
Hugo Ciroux *(CFO)*
Flor Peersman *(COO)*
Herman Struiwigh *(Chief Comml Officer)*
Board of Directors:
Dominique Moorkens
Willy Hendrickx
Piet Serrure
Luc Switten
Guy van Dievoet
Peter Watteeuw
Non-U.S. Subsidiaries:

Connect Systems B.V. (1)
Provincienbaan 6
5121 DL Rijen, Netherlands
Tel.: (31) 161 24 34 00
Fax: (31) 161 23 10 16
Electronics Manufacturing Services
S.I.C.: 3679
N.A.I.C.S.: 334419

Connectronics GmbH (1)
Siemensstrasse 11
72636 Frickenhausen, Germany
Tel.: (49) 7022 9446 0
Fax: (49) 7022 9446 99
Electronics Manufacturing Services
S.I.C.: 3679
N.A.I.C.S.: 334419
Irmin Mack *(Dir)*

Connectronics Romania S.R.L. (1)
Sos Borsului 40
410605 Oradea, Romania
Tel.: (40) 259 457 681
Fax: (40) 259 457 689
Electronics Manufacturing Services
S.I.C.: 3679
N.A.I.C.S.: 334419
Calin Vesa *(Plant Mgr)*

Connectronics s.r.o. (1)
Billundska 2756
272 01 Kladno, Czech Republic
Tel.: (420) 312 518 311
Fax: (420) 312 518 314
Electronics Manufacturing Services
S.I.C.: 3679
N.A.I.C.S.: 334419

Halin Group B.V. (1)
De Run 4281
5503 LM Veldhoven, Netherlands
Tel.: (31) 40 84 44 999
Fax: (31) 40 84 44 990
Electronics Manufacturing Services
S.I.C.: 3679
N.A.I.C.S.: 334419
Niels van Zon *(Mgr-Sls & Mktg)*

CONNECT HOLDINGS, INC.
7-7-29 Nishi-Shinjuku Shinjuku-ku
Nishi Shinjuku Building 4F, Tokyo, 160-0023, Japan
Tel.: (81) 3 53326110
Fax: (81) 3 53326111
Web Site: www.connect-hd.co.jp
Year Founded: 2010
3647—(TKS)
Business Description:
Holding Company; IT Solutions
S.I.C.: 6719
N.A.I.C.S.: 551112
Personnel:
Nobumi Nagakura *(Pres & CEO)*
Subsidiary:

Connect Technologies Corporation (1)
Davinci Shinjuku Building 6F 4-3-17 Shinjuku
Tokyo, Shinjuku, 160 0022, Japan
Tel.: (81) 353685520
Fax: (81) 353685521

Connect Holdings, Inc.—(Continued)

E-Mail: info@connect-tech.co.jp
Web Site: www.connect-tech.co.jp
Sales Range: $10-24.9 Million
Emp.: 130
Mobile Phone Systems Developer
S.I.C.: 4812
N.A.I.C.S.: 517210

Subsidiaries:

B.U.G., Inc (2)
1-14 Techno-park 1-chome
Shimonopporo Atsubetsu-ku, Sapporo, Sapporo, 004 0015, Japan
Tel.: (81) 118076667
Fax: (81) 118076645
E-Mail: sales@bug.co.jp
Web Site: www.bug.co.jp
Sls.: $55,324,088
Emp.: 125
Software & Hardware Mfr & Sales
S.I.C.: 5045
N.A.I.C.S.: 423430
Kawashima Akihiko *(Pres)*

Honda Electron Co., Ltd. (2)
3rd Fl Kanematsu Bldg
2-14-1 Kyobashi Chuo-ku, Tokyo, 104 0031, Japan
Tel.: (81) 3 5250 7321
Fax: (81) 3 5250 7330
Emp.: 80
Mobile Phones Design & Mfr
S.I.C.: 3663
N.A.I.C.S.: 334220
Yoshikuni Tanaka *(Pres)*

CONNECT LOGISTICS SERVICES INC
50 Corriveau Avenue
Saint Albert, AB, T8N 3T5, Canada
Tel.: (780) 458-4492
Fax: (780) 458-8588
Toll Free: (800) 265-6784
E-Mail: connectcs@exel.com
Web Site: www.connect-logistics.com
Rev.: $22,070,400
Emp.: 230
Business Description:
Liquor Whslr
S.I.C.: 5182
N.A.I.C.S.: 424820
Personnel:
Greg Foreman *(VP-Ops)*

CONNEMARA MINING COMPANY PLC
162 Clontarf Road
Dublin, 3, Ireland
Tel.: (353) 18332833
Fax: (353) 18333505
E-Mail: info@connemaramining.com
Web Site: www.connemaramc.com
Year Founded: 2006
CON—(LSE)
Business Description:
Zinc & Lead Mining Services
S.I.C.: 1031
N.A.I.C.S.: 212231
Personnel:
John Teeling *(Chm)*
James Finn *(Fin Dir & Sec)*
Board of Directors:
John Teeling
Edward Vivion Byrne
James Finn
Graham Reid
Legal Counsel:
McEvoy Partners
Connaught House Burlington Road
Dublin, Ireland

CONNEX SEESERVICE INC.
44 East Beaver Creek Suite 16
Richmond Hill, ON, L4B 1G8, Canada
Tel.: (905) 944-6500
Fax: (905) 944-6520
Toll Free: (800) 429-4625
E-Mail: support@connexservice.ca
Web Site: www.connexservice.ca
Sales Range: $100-124.9 Million
Emp.: 456
Business Description:
Wireless Communication Network System Services
Import
S.I.C.: 3663
N.A.I.C.S.: 334220
Personnel:
Chris Pay *(Pres & CEO)*
Board of Directors:
Colin de la Court Watson
Legal Counsel:
McCarthy Tetrault LLP
Ste 4700 Box 48 Toronto Dominion Bank Tower
Toronto, ON, M5K 1E6, Canada
Transfer Agent:
CIBC Mellon Trust Company
Adelaide Street Postal Station
PO Box 7010
Toronto, ON, M5C 2W9, Canada
Tel.: (416) 643-5500
Fax: (416) 643-5501
Toll Free: (800) 387-0825

CONPOREC INC.
3125 Joseph-Simard
Sorel-Tracy, QC, J3P 5N3, Canada
Tel.: (450) 746-9996
Fax: (450) 746-7587
E-Mail: info@conporec.com
Web Site: www.conporec.com
Year Founded: 1987
Sales Range: Less than $1 Million
Emp.: 5
Business Description:
Waste Treatment & Disposal Services
S.I.C.: 4953
N.A.I.C.S.: 562219
Personnel:
Jean Shoiry *(Pres)*

Non-U.S. Subsidiary:

Conporec S.A.S. (1)
52 Rue de Emerainville
77183 Croissy-Beaubourg, France
Tel.: (33) 164078614
E-Mail: gbeaulieu@conporec.europe.com
Web Site: www.conporec.com
Waste Management Services
S.I.C.: 4952
N.A.I.C.S.: 221320
Jean Beaudoin *(Pres & CEO)*

CONQUEST AGRI LIMITED
Level 18 50 Cavill Avenue
PO Box 40
Surfers Paradise, QLD, 4217, Australia
Tel.: (61) 7 5538 2558
Fax: (61) 7 5526 8922
E-Mail: info@fwaus.com
Web Site: www.fwaus.com
CQA—(ASX)
Sales Range: Less than $1 Million
Emp.: 60
Business Description:
Agricultural Support Services
S.I.C.: 7389
N.A.I.C.S.: 561990
Personnel:
Steve Cole *(Sec)*
Board of Directors:
Larry Shutes
Kevin Dart
Mathew Denton
Legal Counsel:
McCullough Robertson Lawyers
Level 11 Central Plaza Two 66 Eagle Street
Brisbane, Australia

Subsidiary:

Conquest Crop Protection Pty. Ltd. (1)
Suite 9 41 Walters Drive Herdsman Business Park
6017 Osborne Park, WA, Australia
Tel.: (61) 8 9347 0500
Fax: (61) 8 9347 0551
E-Mail: enquiry@conquestag.com.au
Web Site: www.conquestag.com.au
Crop Protection Product Distr
S.I.C.: 5191
N.A.I.C.S.: 424910

CONQUEST RESOURCES LIMITED
220 Bay Street Suite 700
Toronto, ON, M5J 2W4, Canada
Tel.: (647) 728-4134
Fax: (416) 368-5344
E-Mail: info@conquestresources.net
Web Site: www.conquestresources.net
Year Founded: 1945
CQR—(OTC TSXV)
Assets: $8,600,261
Liabilities: $954,259
Net Worth: $7,646,002
Earnings: ($274,350)
Fiscal Year-end: 12/31/12
Business Description:
Mineral Exploration Services
S.I.C.: 1081
N.A.I.C.S.: 213114
Personnel:
John F. Kearney *(Chm)*
Robert J. Kinloch *(Pres & CEO)*
Danesh K. Varma *(CFO)*
Neil J. F. Steenberg *(Sec)*
Board of Directors:
John F. Kearney
Gerald J. Gauthier
Robert J. Kinloch
Terence N. McKillen
Peter Palframan
Neil J. F. Steenberg
D. Brett Whitelaw
Legal Counsel:
Barrister & Solicitor
220 Bay Street Suite 700
Toronto, ON, Canada
Transfer Agent:
Equity Financial Trust Company
200 University Avenue Suite 400
Toronto, ON, M5H 4H1, Canada
Tel.: (416) 361-0152
Fax: (416) 361-0470
Toll Free: (866) 393-4891

Non-U.S. Subsidiary:

African Gold B.V. (1)
Prinsengracht 701
Amsterdam, 1017 JV, Netherlands
Tel.: (31) 206163141
Gold Mining Services
S.I.C.: 1041
N.A.I.C.S.: 212221
Terence McKillen *(Mgr)*

CONRAN HOLDINGS LIMITED
22 Shad Phames
London, SE1 2YU, United Kingdom
Tel.: (44) 2073781161
Fax: (44) 2074034309
E-Mail: cp@conran.com
Web Site: www.conran.com
Year Founded: 1993
Emp.: 100
Business Description:
Holding Company
S.I.C.: 6719
N.A.I.C.S.: 551112
Personnel:
Terence Conran *(Chm & Owner)*
Roger Mavity *(CEO)*

Subsidiaries:

Conran & Partners Ltd. (1)
22 Shad Thames
London, SE1 2YU, United Kingdom UK
Tel.: (44) 20 7403 8899
Fax: (44) 1273 716 060
E-Mail: cp@conran.com
Web Site: www.conranandpartners.com
Emp.: 18
Brand, Product, Interior & Architectural Design Services
S.I.C.: 7389
N.A.I.C.S.: 541490
Terence Conran *(Chm)*
Tim Bowder-Ridger, *(Mng Dir)*

Conran Contracts Limited (1)
22 Shad Thames
London, SE1 2YU, United Kingdom UK
Tel.: (44) 20 7403 8899
E-Mail: contracts@conran.com
Web Site: www.conranshopcontracts.co.uk
Furniture Distr
S.I.C.: 5021
N.A.I.C.S.: 423210
Terence Conran *(Chm)*
Nick Moore *(Mng Dir)*

The Conran Shop Ltd. (1)
3 Flatten Way High Street
Syston, LE7 1GU, United Kingdom
Tel.: (44) 844 848 4000
E-Mail: orders@conran.com
Web Site: www.conranshop.co.uk
Home Furnishing Retailer
S.I.C.: 5719
N.A.I.C.S.: 442299
Jessica Rembert *(Mgr-Mktg)*

CONROS CORPORATION
125 Bermondsey Rd
Toronto, ON, Canada
Tel.: (416) 757-6700
Fax: (416) 757-8087
E-Mail: comments@conros.com
Web Site: www.conros.com
Year Founded: 1970
Rev.: $20,900,000
Emp.: 475
Business Description:
Adhesive Mfr
S.I.C.: 2891
N.A.I.C.S.: 325520
Personnel:
Navin Chandaria *(Pres)*

CONROY GOLD & NATURAL RESOURCES PLC
10 Upper Pembroke Street
Dublin, 2, Ireland
Tel.: (353) 16618958
Fax: (353) 16621213
E-Mail: info@conroygold.com
Web Site: www.conroygoldandnaturalresources.com
CGNR—(AIM ISE)
Rev.: $16
Assets: $20,282,729
Liabilities: $2,682,998
Net Worth: $17,599,731
Earnings: ($570,748)
Emp.: 11
Fiscal Year-end: 05/31/13
Business Description:
Gold Mining & Exploration Services
S.I.C.: 1041
N.A.I.C.S.: 212221
Personnel:
Richard T. W. L. Conroy *(Chm)*
Maureen T. A. Jones *(Mng Dir)*
James P. Jones *(Fin Dir & Sec)*
Board of Directors:
Richard T. W. L. Conroy
Sorca C. Conroy
Seamus P. FitzPatrick
James P. Jones
Maureen T. A. Jones
Louis J. Maguire
Michael E. Power

Henry H. Rennison
C. David Wathen
Legal Counsel:
William Fry Solicitors
Fitzwilton House Wilton Place
Dublin, Ireland
Roschier
Keskuskatu 7A
00100 Helsinki, Finland

CONSEGNA GROUP LIMITED
(Name Changed to Rhinomed Limited)

CONSEILS ET SYSTEMES INFORMATIQUES
(d/b/a CetSI)
93/105 rue Veuve Lacroix
92000 Nanterre, France
Tel.: (33) 141194040
Fax: (33) 147602216
E-Mail: cial@cetsi.fr
Web Site: www.cetsi.fr
Rev.: $20,700,000
Emp.: 80
Business Description:
Management Consulting Services
S.I.C.: 8742
N.A.I.C.S.: 541611
Personnel:
Patricia Poelaert *(Mng Dir)*
Board of Directors:
Patricia Poelaert
Olivier Poelaert

CONSERV BUFTEA SA
1A Industriei Street
Buftea, Ilfov, 070000, Romania
Tel.: (40) 21 350 49 01
Fax: (40) 21 350 49 00
E-Mail: office@conservbuftea.ro
Web Site: www.conservbuftea.ro
Year Founded: 1870
CONS—(BUC)
Business Description:
Preserved Fruits & Vegetables Whslr
S.I.C.: 5148
N.A.I.C.S.: 424480
Personnel:
Ihab Laoun *(Pres)*
Board of Directors:
Ihab Laoun
Georges Wadih

CONSERVES ET SALAISONS VANELLI
131 Avenue Jalday
64500 Saint-Jean-de-Luz, France
Tel.: (33) 559511770
Fax: (33) 559262850
E-Mail: vanelli@vanelli.com
Web Site: www.vanelli.com
Sales Range: $10-24.9 Million
Emp.: 62
Business Description:
Fish & Seafoods
S.I.C.: 5146
N.A.I.C.S.: 424460
Personnel:
Jean-Marc Lecompte *(Mgr-Fin)*

CONSILIUM AB
Vastra Finnbodavagen 2-4
PO Box 5028
131 05 Nacka, Sweden
Tel.: (46) 856305300
Fax: (46) 856305399
E-Mail: info@consilium.se
Web Site: www.consilium.se
CONS B—(OMX)
Sales Range: $100-124.9 Million
Emp.: 390
Business Description:
Safety, Environment & Navigation Products & Systems Mfr
S.I.C.: 9224
N.A.I.C.S.: 922160
Personnel:
Carl Rosenblad *(Chm)*
Ove Hansson *(Pres & CEO)*
Anna Holmgren *(CFO)*
Board of Directors:
Carl Rosenblad
Anne-Marie Astrom
Peter Carlberg
Fredrik Nygren
Carl Adam Rosenblad
Subsidiaries:

Consilium Fire & Gas AB **(1)**
PO Box 8763
40276 Gothenburg, Sweden
Tel.: (46) 317107700
Fax: (46) 317107800
E-Mail: info@consilium.com
Web Site: www.consilium.com.se/contact.html
Emp.: 200
Fire Alarm Solutions Provider
S.I.C.: 9224
N.A.I.C.S.: 922160
Carl Adam Rofenblad *(Mng Dir)*

Consilium Marine AB **(1)**
Salsmastaregatan 21
PO Box 8763
40276 Gothenburg, Sweden
Tel.: (46) 317107700
Fax: (46) 317107800
E-Mail: info@consilium.se
Emp.: 200
Marine Equipments Supply Services
S.I.C.: 3799
N.A.I.C.S.: 336999
Carl-Adam Rosenblad *(Dir-Mktg)*

Consilium Navigation AB **(1)**
PO Box 5021
13105 Nacka, Sweden
Tel.: (46) 856305100
Fax: (46) 856305199
E-Mail: service-navigation@consilium.se
Web Site: www.consilium.se/contacts
Navigational Products Supplier
S.I.C.: 3812
N.A.I.C.S.: 334511
Carladam Rosenblad *(Mng Dir)*

Consilium Transport Safety AB **(1)**
Salsmastaregatan 21
PO Box 8763
40276 Gothenburg, Sweden
Tel.: (46) 317107700
Fax: (46) 317107800
E-Mail: sales.transport@consilium.se
Emp.: 150
Fire Detection System Suppliers
S.I.C.: 9224
N.A.I.C.S.: 922160
Carl Adam Rosenblad *(Gen Mgr)*

CONSOLIDATED BOTTLE CORPORATION
77 Union Street
Toronto, ON, M6N 3N2, Canada
Tel.: (416) 656-7777
Fax: (416) 656-6394
Toll Free: (800) 561-1354
E-Mail: Info@consbottle.com
Web Site: www.consbottle.com
Year Founded: 1910
Rev.: $15,387,324
Emp.: 60
Business Description:
Injection Molding & Decorating Services
S.I.C.: 3559
N.A.I.C.S.: 333249
Personnel:
Mark Korolnek *(Pres)*

CONSOLIDATED CONSTRUCTION CONSORTIUM LTD
5 2nd Link Street CIT Colony
Mylapore, Chennai, 600004, India
Tel.: (91) 4424661083
Fax: (91) 4424990225
E-Mail: cccl@vsnl.com
Web Site: www.ccclindia.com
CCCL—(NSE)
Rev.: $329,042,325
Assets: $408,023,898
Liabilities: $307,046,105
Net Worth: $100,977,794
Earnings: ($14,720,061)
Emp.: 3,245
Fiscal Year-end: 03/31/13
Business Description:
Construction Engineering Services
S.I.C.: 8711
N.A.I.C.S.: 541330
Personnel:
R. Sarabeswar *(Chm & CEO)*
S. Sivaramakrishnan *(Mng Dir)*
T. R. Seetharaman *(CFO)*
P. K. Jeyasree *(Compliance Officer & Sec)*
Board of Directors:
R. Sarabeswar
P. K. Aravindan
V. G. Janarthanam
K. E. C. Rajakumar
Jayaram Rangan
S. Sivaramakrishnan
P. K. Sridharan
P. Venkatesh
Transfer Agent:
Karvy Computershare Private Limited
17-24 Vittal Rao Nagar Madhapur
Hyderabad, India
Subsidiary:

CCCL Infrastructure Ltd. **(1)**
No 1 Third St Luz Ave Behind Nageswara Rao Pk Mylapore
Chennai, Tamil Nadu, 600004, India
Tel.: (91) 4423454800
Fax: (91) 4423454805
E-Mail: ccclinfra@ccclindia.com
Emp.: 20
Construction Management Services
S.I.C.: 1542
N.A.I.C.S.: 236220
S Sivaramakrishnan *(Mng Dir)*

CONSOLIDATED CONTRACTORS INTERNATIONAL COMPANY S.A.L.
62B Kifissias Ave Amaroussion
PO Box 61092
15125 Athens, Greece
Tel.: (30) 2106182000
Fax: (30) 2106199224
E-Mail: cccmoamail@ccc.gr
Web Site: www.ccc.gr
Year Founded: 1952
Sales Range: $1-4.9 Billion
Emp.: 600
Business Description:
Construction & Engineering Services
S.I.C.: 8711
N.A.I.C.S.: 541330
Personnel:
Said T. Khoury *(Chm)*
Tawfic S. Khoury *(Deputy Chm)*
Jamal Nakhleh *(CFO)*
Zuhair I. Haddad *(CIO & Head-Corp Assets & Risk Mgmt)*
Samer S. Khoury *(Pres-Engrg & Construction)*
Wael S. Khoury *(Pres-Petroleum & Minerals)*
Suheil H. Sabbagh *(Pres-HR)*
Edgard Marina *(Corp Counsel-Legal)*
Walid Noureddin *(Sec & Head-Grp Governance)*
Board of Directors:
Said T. Khoury
Ibrahim S. Dabdoub
Samer S. Khoury
Tawfic S. Khoury
Wael S. Khoury
Antoine Mattar
Jamal Nakhleh
Suheil H. Sabbagh
Mohamad Seoudi
Wahbe Tamari
Mahmoud Zeibak
Non-U.S. Subsidiaries:

Consolidated Contractors Company (Kuwait) W.L.L. **(1)**
E Ahmadi Block 33
PO Box 509
Kuwait, 13006, Kuwait
Tel.: (965) 3980390
Fax: (965) 3980560
Web Site: www.ccc.gr/GroupDirectory_Offices.htm
Contracting Services
S.I.C.: 1542
N.A.I.C.S.: 236220

Consolidated Contractors Company Ltd. **(1)**
Jabal Amman Sinan Bin Khafaji Street
Near Zahran Post Office
PO Box 830392, Amman, 11183, Jordan
Tel.: (962) 64568403
Fax: (962) 64643071
Web Site: www.ccc.gr/GroupDirectory_Offices.htm
Contracting Services
S.I.C.: 1542
N.A.I.C.S.: 236220

Consolidated Contractors International (UK) Ltd. **(1)**
11A West Halkin Str
Belgravia, London, SW1X 8JL, United Kingdom
Tel.: (44) 2072595900
Fax: (44) 2072595544
Emp.: 30
Contracting Services
S.I.C.: 1542
N.A.I.C.S.: 236220

CONSOLIDATED FASTFRATE INC.
9701 Hwy 50
Woodbridge, Vaughan, ON, L4H 2G4, Canada
Tel.: (905) 893-2600
Fax: (905) 893-1575
Toll Free: (800) 268-1564
Web Site: www.fastfrate.com
Sales Range: $125-149.9 Million
Emp.: 1,310
Business Description:
Freight Forwarding Services
S.I.C.: 4212
N.A.I.C.S.: 484110
Personnel:
Ronald Tepper *(Pres & CEO)*
Leonard Wyss *(CFO & VP)*

CONSOLIDATED FISHERIES LTD.
Waverley House
PO Box 383
Stanley, Falkland Islands
Tel.: (500) 22277
Fax: (500) 22211
E-Mail: cfo.gm@verizon.co.fk
Web Site: www.consolidatedfisheries.com
Year Founded: 1994
Emp.: 60
Business Description:
Fishing Services; Vessel Owner & Operator
S.I.C.: 0919
N.A.I.C.S.: 114119
Personnel:
George Betts *(VP)*
Board of Directors:
Colleen Alazia
Tony Blake

Consolidated Fisheries Ltd.—(Continued)

Jan Cheek
Peter Davy
Roger Edwards
John Pollard
Stuart Wallace
Hamish Wylie

CONSOLIDATED GEMS, INC.

Level 8 580 Saint Kilda Road
Melbourne, VIC, 3004, Australia
Tel.: (61) 3 8532 2800
Fax: (61) 3 8532 2805
Web Site: www.electrumint.com
CGEM—(OTC)
Assets: $9,549
Liabilities: $322,240
Net Worth: ($312,691)
Earnings: ($179,281)
Fiscal Year-end: 12/31/12
Business Description:
Alternative Energy
S.I.C.: 4911
N.A.I.C.S.: 221118
Personnel:
Joseph Isaac Gutnick *(Chm, Pres & CEO)*
Peter James Lee *(CFO & Sec)*
Board of Directors:
Joseph Isaac Gutnick

CONSOLIDATED GENERAL MINERALS PLC

2nd Floor Vintners Place 68 Upper Thames Street
London, EC4V 3BJ, United Kingdom
Tel.: (44) 2077887621
E-Mail: info@cgmplc.com
Web Site: www.cgmplc.com
Emp.: 1
Business Description:
Mineral Processing Services
S.I.C.: 1481
N.A.I.C.S.: 213115
Personnel:
Jean-Pierre Conrad *(Exec Dir)*
Board of Directors:
Robert F. M. Adair
Jean-Pierre Conrad
Nicolas Rouveyre
Legal Counsel:
Ward Hadaway
Sandgate House 102 Quayside
Newcastle upon Tyne, United Kingdom

CONSOLIDATED GLOBAL INVESTMENTS LIMITED

Level 1 284 Oxford Street
Leederville, WA, 6007, Australia
Tel.: (61) 8 9242 2621
Fax: (61) 8 9443 2859
E-Mail: info@cgi.net.au
Web Site: www.cgi.net.au
CGI—(ASX)
Rev.: $2,586
Assets: $638,368
Liabilities: $891,706
Net Worth: ($253,339)
Earnings: ($815,532)
Fiscal Year-end: 06/30/13
Business Description:
Mineral Exploration Services
S.I.C.: 1099
N.A.I.C.S.: 212299
Personnel:
John Palermo *(Chm & Sec)*
Board of Directors:
John Palermo
Leigh Anthony Coleman
Paul Anthony Ingram
Legal Counsel:
Allion Legal
50 Kings Park Road
West Perth, Australia

CONSOLIDATED HCI HOLDINGS CORP.

100 Strider Drive Unit 3
Woodbridge, ON, L4L 5V7, Canada
Tel.: (905) 851-7741
Fax: (416) 253-5074
E-Mail: ewdl@bellnet.ca
Year Founded: 1986
CXA.A—(TSX)
Rev.: $8,485,949
Assets: $51,000,184
Liabilities: $7,156,944
Net Worth: $43,843,240
Earnings: $7,945,202
Emp.: 4
Fiscal Year-end: 09/30/12
Business Description:
Real Estate Development Services
S.I.C.: 6531
N.A.I.C.S.: 531390
Personnel:
Stanley Goldfarb *(Pres, CEO & Treas)*
Arnold Joseph Resnick *(CFO & Controller)*
John Hunter Craig *(Sec)*
Board of Directors:
Rudolph Peter Bratty
John Hunter Craig
John Henry Daniels
Richard Michael Gambin
Stanley Goldfarb
Marc Muzzo
Transfer Agent:
Computershare Investor Services Inc.
9th Floor North Tower 100 University Avenue
Toronto, ON, Canada

CONSOLIDATED INFRASTRUCTURE GROUP LIMITED

Commerce Square Office 5 Building 2 39 Rivonia Road cnr Mellville Road
Sandhurst, Sandton, 2196, South Africa
Mailing Address:
PO Box 651455
Benmore, 2010, South Africa
Tel.: (27) 112804040
Fax: (27) 867489169
E-Mail: info@ciglimited.co.za
Web Site: www.ciglimited.co.za
CIL—(JSE)
Rev.: $186,075,925
Assets: $253,741,134
Liabilities: $109,440,556
Net Worth: $144,300,578
Earnings: $15,674,603
Emp.: 1,164
Fiscal Year-end: 08/31/13
Business Description:
Building Materials Whslr
S.I.C.: 5032
N.A.I.C.S.: 423320
Personnel:
David van Zyl *(CEO-CONCO)*
Raoul Gamsu *(CEO)*
Ivor Klitzner *(CFO & Dir-Fin & Strategy)*
D. C. Moore *(Chief Investment Officer)*
Jannie Hooman *(CEO-Building Matls)*
Board of Directors:
Frank Boner
Bernard Berelowitz
Kofi Bucknor
Alex Darko
Anthony Dixon
Raoul Gamsu
Robert Horton
Ivor Klitzner
Judi Nwokedi
Transfer Agent:
Computershare Investor Services Proprietary Limited
70 Marshall Street
Johannesburg, South Africa
Subsidiaries:

Consolidated Power Maintenance (Pty) Limited (1)
37 Richards Road
Midrand, Gauteng, 1685, South Africa ZA
Tel.: (27) 118054281
Fax: (27) 118051132
Electric Power Generation Services
S.I.C.: 4931
N.A.I.C.S.: 221118

Consolidated Power Projects (Pty) Limited (1)
37 Richards Drive Halfway House
Midrand, 1685, South Africa
Tel.: (27) 11 805 4281
Fax: (27) 11 805 4281
E-Mail: conco@conco.co.za
Web Site: www.conco.co.za
Electric Power Distr
S.I.C.: 4911
N.A.I.C.S.: 221122
Bernard Berelowitz *(CEO)*
Harry Browne *(COO)*

Drift Supersand (Proprietary) Limited (1)
Plot 121 Abraham Van Wyk Road
Roodepoort, Gauteng, 1724, South Africa
Tel.: (27) 116621207
Fax: (27) 866965440
Construction Materials Distr
S.I.C.: 5039
N.A.I.C.S.: 423390
Jannie Hooman *(Gen Mgr)*

West End Claybrick (Proprietary) Limited (1)
Plot 70 Zuurbekom On N12 Highway Between Westonaria & Lenasia
Westonaria, South Africa
Tel.: (27) 11 851 1100
Fax: (27) 11 851 1234
E-Mail: clay.sales@westend.co.za
Web Site: www.westendclaybrick.co.za
Clay Bricks Mfr & Distr
S.I.C.: 5032
N.A.I.C.S.: 423320
Hendrik Jacobus du Preez *(Chm)*
Philip Spies *(Mng Dir)*

CONSOLIDATED MINERALS LTD.

28 Ventnor Ave
West Perth, WA, 6005, Australia
Tel.: (61) 893213633
Fax: (61) 893213644
Web Site: www.consminerals.com.au
Sales Range: $250-299.9 Million
Emp.: 450
Business Description:
Metal Mining & Exploration Services; Owned by Palmary Enterprises Ltd.
S.I.C.: 1021
N.A.I.C.S.: 212234
Personnel:
Gennadiy Bogolyubov *(Owner)*
David Slater *(CFO)*
John Abbott *(Sec)*
Subsidiaries:

Australian Nickel Mines NL (1)
L 1 24 Outram St
West Perth, WA, Australia (81%)
Tel.: (61) 894816040
Uranium-Radium-Vanadium Ore Mining
S.I.C.: 1094
N.A.I.C.S.: 212291
Don Watt *(Chm)*

Pilbara Chromite Pty Ltd (1)
28-42 Ventnor Avenue
West Perth, WA, 6005, Australia
Tel.: (61) 893213633
Fax: (61) 893213644
E-Mail: cnl@consminerals.com.au
Web Site: www.consmineral.com.au
Emp.: 60
Uranium-Radium-Vanadium Ore Mining
S.I.C.: 1094
N.A.I.C.S.: 212291
Glenn Baldwin *(Mng Dir)*

Pilbara Contracting Pty Ltd (1)
28 Ventnor Ave
08 West Perth, WA, 60005, Australia
Tel.: (61) 893213633
Fax: (61) 893213644
Emp.: 65
Support Activities for Nonmetallic Minerals
S.I.C.: 1481
N.A.I.C.S.: 213115

CONSOLIDATED PRESS HOLDINGS LIMITED

Level 3 54 Park Street
Sydney, NSW, 2000, Australia
Tel.: (61) 292828000
Fax: (61) 292672150
Sales Range: $200-249.9 Million
Business Description:
Investment Holding Company
S.I.C.: 6719
N.A.I.C.S.: 551112
Personnel:
James Douglas Packer *(Chm & CEO)*

CONSOLIDATED TIN MINES LIMITED

395 Lake Street
Cairns, QLD, 4870, Australia
Tel.: (61) 740323319
Fax: (61) 740279429
E-Mail: admin@csdtin.com.au
Web Site: www.csdtin.com.au
Year Founded: 2007
CSD—(ASX)
Rev.: $211,805
Assets: $10,512,456
Liabilities: $1,266,065
Net Worth: $9,246,391
Earnings: ($1,103,216)
Emp.: 17
Fiscal Year-end: 06/30/13
Business Description:
Tin Mining Services
S.I.C.: 1099
N.A.I.C.S.: 212299
Personnel:
Ralph De Lacey *(Chm)*
John Banning *(Mng Dir)*
Kevin Hart *(Sec)*
Board of Directors:
Ralph De Lacey
Darryl Harris
Andrew Kerr
Si He Tong

CONSOLIDATED WATER CO. LTD.

Regatta Office Park Windward Three 4th Fl West Bay Road
PO Box 1114
Georgetown, Grand Cayman, KY1-1102, Cayman Islands
Tel.: (345) 945 4277
Fax: (345) 949 2957
E-Mail: info@cwco.com
Web Site: www.cwco.com
Year Founded: 1973
CWCO—(BISX NASDAQ)
Rev.: $63,822,131
Assets: $165,364,854
Liabilities: $23,866,481
Net Worth: $141,498,373
Earnings: $9,148,489
Emp.: 123
Fiscal Year-end: 12/31/13
Business Description:
Seawater Desalination Plants & Water Distribution Systems Developer & Operator
S.I.C.: 4971
N.A.I.C.S.: 221310

Personnel:
Wilmer F. Pergande *(Chm)*
Frederick W. McTaggart *(Pres & CEO)*
David W. Sasnett *(CFO & Exec VP)*
John Tonner *(COO & VP)*
Board of Directors:
Wilmer F. Pergande
Brian E. Butler
Carson K. Ebanks
Richard L. Finlay
Clarence B. Flowers, Jr.
Frederick W. McTaggart
David W. Sasnett
Leonard Jay Sokolow
Raymond Whittaker
Transfer Agent:
American Stock Transfer & Trust Company
59 Maiden Ln Plz Level
New York, NY 10038
Tel.: (212) 936-5100
Toll Free: (800) 937-5449
Subsidiaries:

Cayman Water Company Limited **(1)**
Regatta Office Park Windward Three 4th Floor
West Bay Road, Georgetown, Grand Cayman, Cayman Islands
Tel.: (345) 9454277
Fax: (345) 9492957
E-Mail: info@cwco.com
Web Site: ir.cwco.com
Emp.: 70
Water Supply Services
S.I.C.: 4941
N.A.I.C.S.: 221310
Frederick W. McTaggart *(Pres & CEO)*

DesalCo Limited **(1)**
Windward Three 4th Floor
West Bay Road, Georgetown, Grand Cayman, Cayman Islands
Tel.: (345) 9454277
Fax: (345) 9492957
E-Mail: ginjohn@cwco.com
Emp.: 30
Water Supply Services
S.I.C.: 4941
N.A.I.C.S.: 221310

Ocean Conversion (Cayman) Limited **(1)**
PO Box is 30614 SMB
Georgetown, Grand Cayman, Cayman Islands
Tel.: (345) 949 5105
Web Site: www.cwco.com
Water Supply Services
S.I.C.: 4941
N.A.I.C.S.: 221310

Non-U.S. Subsidiaries:

DesalCo (Barbados) Ltd **(1)**
Golf Club Road
Sandy Lane, Saint James, Barbados
Tel.: (246) 432 1153
Water Supply Services
S.I.C.: 4941
N.A.I.C.S.: 221310

Waterfield Company Limited **(1)**
Corner of Windsor Field Road & J F Kennedy Drive
Nassau, CR-54030, Bahamas
Tel.: (242) 3773451
Fax: (242) 2423773459
Water Supply Services
S.I.C.: 4971
N.A.I.C.S.: 221310

CONSOLIDATED WOODJAM COPPER CORP.

Suite 110 325 Howe Street
Vancouver, BC, V6C 1Z7, Canada
Tel.: (604) 681-7913
Fax: (604) 681-9855
E-Mail: office@woodjamcopper.com
Web Site: www.woodjamcopper.com
Year Founded: 2011
WCC—(TSXV)
Business Description:
Copper & Gold Mining
S.I.C.: 1021
N.A.I.C.S.: 212234
Personnel:
William Morton *(Pres & CEO)*
Don Sharp *(CFO)*
Glen Garratt *(VP & Sec)*
Board of Directors:
Glen Garratt
Peter Krag-Hansen
G. Ross McDonald
William Morton
Don Sharp
Legal Counsel:
Miller Thompson LLP
1000-840 Howe Street
Vancouver, BC, Canada V6Z 2M1
Transfer Agent:
Olympia Trust Company
1900 925 W Georgia Street
Vancouver, BC, V6C 3L2, Canada

CONSORCIO ALFA DE ADMINISTRACAO S.A.

Al Santos 466 - 2 Floor
1418000 Sao Paulo, Brazil
Tel.: (55) 11 3175 5493
Fax: (55) 11 3251 5499
Year Founded: 1952
BRGE11—(BRAZ)
Sales Range: $400-449.9 Million
Business Description:
Investment Management Services
S.I.C.: 6282
N.A.I.C.S.: 523920
Personnel:
Marco Aurelio Neto Arnes *(Dir-IR)*

CONSORCIO ARA, S.A.B. DE C.V.

Arcos bosques Marco II Paseo de tamarindos 90 Tower 1 Floor 24
Bosques de las Lomas, 05120
Mexico, Mexico
Tel.: (52) 5555968864
Fax: (52) 5555968648
E-Mail: atnclientes@ara.com.mx
Web Site: www.consorcioara.com.mx
ARA—(MEX)
Rev.: $512,572,898
Assets: $1,288,459,117
Liabilities: $525,921,432
Net Worth: $762,537,684
Earnings: $44,643,504
Fiscal Year-end: 12/31/12
Business Description:
Construction & Property Development Services
S.I.C.: 1531
N.A.I.C.S.: 236117
Personnel:
German Ahumada Russek *(Chm & Co-CEO-Housing Div)*
Luis Felipe Ahumada Russek *(Vice Chm & Co-CEO-Shopping Malls Div)*
German Ahumada Alduncin *(Vice Chm)*
Ricardo Maldonado Yanez *(Sec)*
Board of Directors:
German Ahumada Russek
German Ahumada Alduncin
Luis Felipe Ahumada Russek
Pedro Alonso Angulo
Luis Ramon Carazo Preciado
Roberto Danel Diaz
Felix Gavito Marco
Francisco Javier Lomelin Anaya
Andres Massieu Berlanga
Ricardo Paullada Nevarez
Marcos Ramirez Miguel

Subsidiary:

Promotora y Desarrolladora de Centros Comerciales, S. A. de C. V. **(1)**
Paseo De Los Tamarindos No 90 Torre I Piso 24
Mexico, 06700, Mexico
Tel.: (52) 5555968864
Residential Building Construction Services
S.I.C.: 1521
N.A.I.C.S.: 236115

CONSORT MEDICAL PLC

Ground Floor Suite D Breakspear Park Breakspear Way
Hemel Hempstead, HP2 4TZ, United Kingdom
Tel.: (44) 1442 867920
Fax: (44) 1442 245237
E-Mail: enquiries@consortmedical.com
Web Site: www.consortmedical.com
Year Founded: 1957
CSRT—(LSE)
Rev.: $160,079,993
Assets: $224,999,867
Liabilities: $61,140,633
Net Worth: $163,859,234
Earnings: $38,525,200
Emp.: 1,130
Fiscal Year-end: 04/30/13
Business Description:
Holding Company; Drug Delivery Devices Mfr
Export
S.I.C.: 6719
N.A.I.C.S.: 551112
Personnel:
Jonathan Glenn *(CEO)*
John Slater *(Gen Counsel & Sec)*
Board of Directors:
Peter J. Fellner
Richard Cotton
Steve Crummett
Lynn Drummond
Jonathan Glenn
William Jenkins
Ian Nicholson
Legal Counsel:
Eversheds
Norfolk, United Kingdom
Division:

Bespak Europe Ltd. **(1)**
Bergen Way
King's Lynn, Norfolk, PE30 2JJ, United Kingdom UK
Tel.: (44) 1553691000 (100%)
Fax: (44) 1553693728
E-Mail: bizdev@bespak.com
Web Site: www.bespak.com
Emp.: 450
Mfr & Distr of Drug Delivery Devices Including Inhalers & Metered Dose Valves
S.I.C.: 5122
N.A.I.C.S.: 424210
Joe Barry *(Mng Dir)*

Unit:

Bespak Europe Ltd. - Injectables **(2)**
199 Newhall Road
Sheffield, South Yorkshire, S9 2QJ, United Kingdom
Tel.: (44) 1142619011
Fax: (44) 1142431597
E-Mail: info@bespakinjectables.com
Web Site: www.bespakinjectables.com
Emp.: 20
Injectors Mfr & Distr
S.I.C.: 3841
N.A.I.C.S.: 339113

Subsidiary:

Integrated Aluminium Components Limited **(1)**
Edward Street
Nelson, Lancashire, BB9 8TJ, United Kingdom
Tel.: (44) 1282699921
Fax: (44) 1282696705
E-Mail: enquiry@iacltd.uk.com
Web Site: www.iacltd.uk.com
Emp.: 130
Aluminum Components Mfr
S.I.C.: 3355
N.A.I.C.S.: 331318
Danielle Oliver *(Acct Mgr)*

U.S. Subsidiaries:

Consort Medical Inc. **(1)**
2500 Regency Pkwy
Cary, NC 27511-8549 NC
Tel.: (919) 387-0112 (100%)
E-Mail: bizdev@bespakinc.com
Web Site: www.bespak.com
Mfr & Distr of Drug Delivery Devices Including Inhalers & Metered Dose Valves
S.I.C.: 3499
N.A.I.C.S.: 332999
Peter J. Fellner *(Chm)*
Jenny Owen *(Gen Counsel & Sec)*

H&M Rubber Inc **(1)**
4200 Mogadore Rd
Kent, OH 44240-7258
Tel.: (330) 678-3323
Fax: (330) 678-8460
Emp.: 103
Rubber Product Mfr
S.I.C.: 3069
N.A.I.C.S.: 326299
Gary Harvey *(Mng Dir)*

CONSORTEUM HOLDINGS INC.

6-14845 Yonge Street Suite #348
Aurora, ON, L4G 6H8, Canada
Tel.: (745) 298-7001
Toll Free: (888) 702-3410
Web Site: www.consorteum.com
Year Founded: 2005
CSRH—(OTC)
Assets: $7,026
Liabilities: $8,066,516
Net Worth: ($8,059,490)
Earnings: ($4,808,568)
Emp.: 2
Fiscal Year-end: 06/30/13
Business Description:
Investment Services
S.I.C.: 6211
N.A.I.C.S.: 523999
Personnel:
Craig A. Fielding *(Chm, Pres, CEO & CFO)*
Patrick Shuster *(COO & Sec)*
Board of Directors:
Craig A. Fielding
Patrick Shuster

CONSTANCE HOTELS SERVICES LIMITED

Poste de Flacq
Port Louis, Mauritius
Tel.: (230) 402 2999
Fax: (230) 413 2909
E-Mail: mkt@constancehotels.com
Web Site: www.constancehotels.com
CHSL—(MAU)
Rev.: $63,188,073
Assets: $228,041,781
Liabilities: $143,217,064
Net Worth: $84,824,717
Earnings: ($5,668,163)
Fiscal Year-end: 12/31/12
Business Description:
Hotel Management Services
S.I.C.: 7011
N.A.I.C.S.: 721110
Personnel:
George Dumbell *(Chm)*
Jean-Jacques Vallet *(CEO)*
Andrew Milton *(COO)*
Siegfried Espitalier Noel *(CMO)*

CONSTANTIA FLEXIBLES GROUP GMBH

Rivergate Handelskai 92
1200 Vienna, Austria
Tel.: (43) 1 888 56 40 1000
Fax: (43) 1 888 56 40 1900
E-Mail: office@cflex.com
Web Site: www.cflex.com
Sls.: $1,777,470,752
Assets: $1,818,352,589
Liabilities: $1,202,915,973
Net Worth: $615,436,616
Earnings: $76,685,920
Emp.: 5,452
Fiscal Year-end: 12/31/12

Business Description:
Flexible Packaging
S.I.C.: 2671
N.A.I.C.S.: 326112

Personnel:
Christopher von Hugo *(Chm-Supervisory Bd)*
Wolfgang Pfarl *(Vice Chm-Supervisory Bd)*
Thomas Unger *(CEO)*
Peter Frauenknecht *(CFO)*
Gerold Riegler *(COO)*
Franz Reiterer *(Chief Sls Officer & Exec VP-Food-Europe)*
Friedrich Humer *(Exec VP-Food-Emerging Markets)*
Walter Ometto *(Exec VP-Pharma)*
Alexander van 't Riet *(Exec VP-Labels)*

Supervisory Board of Directors:
Christopher von Hugo
Johann Helmut Burmester
Thomas Geitner
Thomas Goeke
Ulrich Kostlin
Wolfgang Pfarl
Heinrich Stahl
Gerardus van Kesteren
Johann-Melchior von Peter

CONSTANTIN MEDIEN AG

Munchener Strasse 101g
85737 Ismaning, Bavaria, Germany
Tel.: (49) 89995000
Fax: (49) 8999500111
E-Mail: info@emsportmedia.ag
Web Site: www.constantin-medien.de
EV4—(DEU)
Rev.: $766,855,164
Assets: $635,191,661
Liabilities: $522,483,577
Net Worth: $112,708,083
Earnings: $16,845,971
Emp.: 1,488
Fiscal Year-end: 12/31/12

Business Description:
Sports Segment Media Company
S.I.C.: 7313
N.A.I.C.S.: 541840

Personnel:
Fred Kogel *(Chm-Supervisory Board)*
Bernhard Burgener *(Chm-Exec Bd & CEO)*
Werner E. Klatten *(Deputy Chm-Supervisory Bd)*
Antonio Arrigoni *(CFO & Member-Mgmt Bd)*

Supervisory Board of Directors:
Fred Kogel
Erwin Conradi
Dieter Hahn
Werner E. Klatten
Bernd Kuhn
Jan P. Weidner

Subsidiaries:

Constantin Sport Marketing GmbH (1)
Munchener Strasse 101g
85737 Ismaning, Bavaria, Germany
Tel.: (49) 89 960 66 2554
Fax: (49) 89 960 66 2409
E-Mail: info@constantin-sport-marketing.de
Web Site: www.constantin-sport-marketing.de/
Emp.: 200
Sports & Film Media Services
S.I.C.: 7999
N.A.I.C.S.: 711310
Bernhard Burgener *(Mng Dir)*

Subsidiary:

PLAZAMEDIA GmbH TV- und Film-Produktion (2)
Munchener Strasse 101
85737 Ismaning, Bavaria, Germany
Tel.: (49) 89996330
Fax: (49) 89996336990
E-Mail: info@plazamedia.de
Web Site: www.plazamedia.de
Emp.: 200
Motion Picture & Video Production Services
S.I.C.: 7812
N.A.I.C.S.: 512110
Florian Nowosad *(CEO)*
Markus Maximilian Sturm *(CFO)*
Zeljko Karajica *(COO)*

Non-U.S. Subsidiary:

PLAZAMEDIA Swiss AG (3)
Etzelstrasse 11
8832 Wollerau, Schwyz, Switzerland
Tel.: (41) 446874010
Fax: (41) 446874011
Web Site: www.plazamedia-swiss.ch
Television Program Production Services
S.I.C.: 7812
N.A.I.C.S.: 512110
Christoph Roost *(Mng Dir)*

EM.TV Beteiligungs GmbH & Co. KG (1)
Munchener Str 101g
Ismaning, Bavaria, Germany
Tel.: (49) 89995000
Television Program Production Services
S.I.C.: 7812
N.A.I.C.S.: 512110

Non-U.S. Subsidiary:

TRIDEM SPORTS AG (1)
Etzelstrasse 11
8832 Wollerau, Schwyz, Switzerland
Tel.: (41) 442246900
Fax: (41) 442246909
Web Site: www.tridemsports.com
Emp.: 6
Sports Management Services
S.I.C.: 7941
N.A.I.C.S.: 711211
Christian Pirze *(Founder & CEO)*

CONSTANTINE METAL RESOURCES LTD.

Suite 320 800 West Pender St
Vancouver, BC, V6C 2V6, Canada
Tel.: (604) 629-2348
Fax: (604) 608-3878
E-Mail: info@constantinemetals.com
Web Site: www.constantinemetals.com
Year Founded: 2006
CEM—(TSXV)
Int. Income: $7,956
Assets: $17,029,140
Liabilities: $56,091
Net Worth: $16,973,050
Earnings: ($765,877)
Fiscal Year-end: 10/31/12

Business Description:
Mineral Exploration Services
S.I.C.: 1081
N.A.I.C.S.: 213114

Personnel:
K. Wayne Livingstone *(Chm)*
J. Garfield MacVeigh *(Pres & CEO)*
Aris Morfopoulos *(CFO)*

Board of Directors:
K. Wayne Livingstone
David W. Adamson
Brian C. Irwin
J. Garfield MacVeigh
Ross McDonald

Transfer Agent:
Computershare Trust Company of Canada
510 Burrard St
Vancouver, BC, Canada

CONSTANTINOU BROS HOTELS LTD

77 Poseidonos Avenue
PO Box 60182
Paphos, Cyprus
Tel.: (357) 26933979
Fax: (357) 26934875
E-Mail: sales@cbh-cyprus.com
Web Site: www.cbh-cyprus.com
Year Founded: 1979
CBH—(CYP)

Business Description:
Hotels Management Services
S.I.C.: 7011
N.A.I.C.S.: 721110

Personnel:
Andreas Constantinou *(Gen Dir)*

Board of Directors:
Andreas Anastasiou
Andreas Constantinou
Andreas Grigoriou
Marios Spyrou

CONSTELLATION SOFTWARE INC.

1200 - 20 Adelaide Street East
Toronto, ON, M5C 2T6, Canada
Tel.: (416) 861-2279
Fax: (416) 861-2287
E-Mail: info@csisoftware.com
Web Site: www.csisoftware.com
Year Founded: 1995
CSU—(OTC TSX)
Rev.: $891,226,000
Assets: $812,679,000
Liabilities: $553,875,000
Net Worth: $258,804,000
Earnings: $92,632,000
Emp.: 4,576
Fiscal Year-end: 12/31/12

Business Description:
Software Developer
S.I.C.: 7372
N.A.I.C.S.: 511210

Personnel:
Mark Leonard *(Chm & Pres)*
Jamal Nizam Baksh *(CFO)*
Mark Miller *(COO & CEO-Volaris Group & Trapeze Group)*
Jeff Bender *(CEO-Harris Operating Grp)*
John Billowits *(CEO-Vela Software Intl)*

Board of Directors:
Mark Leonard
J. Brian Aune
Jeff Bender
Meredith Hall Hayes
Robert Terrance Kittel
Ian McKinnon
Mark Miller
Stephen Scotchmer

Transfer Agent:
Computershare Trust Company of Canada
Toronto, ON, Canada

Subsidiaries:

Constellation Homebuilder Systems Inc. (1)
75 Frontenac Dr W Wing
Markham, ON, L3R 6H2, Canada (100%)
Tel.: (905) 943-6140
Fax: (905) 475-7204
Toll Free: (888) 723-2222
E-Mail: sales@constellationhb.com
Web Site: www.constellationhb.com
Emp.: 100
Software for Homebuilders
S.I.C.: 3652
N.A.I.C.S.: 334614
Dexter Salna *(Pres)*

U.S. Subsidiaries:

G1440 Inc. (2)
2031 Clipper Park Rd 105
Baltimore, MD 21211-1446
Tel.: (410) 843-3800
Fax: (410) 843-3853
E-Mail: support@g1440.com
Web Site: www.g1440.com
Emp.: 40
Information Technology Consulting & Staffing Services
S.I.C.: 7389
N.A.I.C.S.: 519190
Larry Fiorino *(Pres & CEO)*
Bonnie Wilhelm *(CFO & VP)*

Integrated Dealer Systems, Inc. (2)
12339 Wake Union Church Rd Ste 107
Wake Forest, NC 27587 (100%)
Tel.: (919) 790-5442
Fax: (919) 790-0682
Toll Free: (800) 769-7425
E-Mail: s.raynor@ids-astra.com
Web Site: www.ids-astra.com
Sales Range: $25-49.9 Million
Emp.: 7
Software Solutions for the RV, Marine & Automotive Industries
S.I.C.: 7371
N.A.I.C.S.: 541511
Sean Raynor *(Gen Mgr & Dir-Sls & Mktg)*

Majiq Inc. (2)
8520 154th Ave NE
Redmond, WA 98052
Tel.: (425) 881-7100
Fax: (425) 881-5084
E-Mail: sales@majiq.com
Web Site: www.majiq.com
Emp.: 70
Paper Industry Software Development Services
S.I.C.: 3291
N.A.I.C.S.: 327910
Stephen Latham *(Pres)*

Monolith Corporation (2)
12339 Wake Union Church Rd Ste 107
Wake Forest, NC 27587-4512
Tel.: (919) 878-1900
Fax: (919) 878-8844
Toll Free: (800) 949-7425
Web Site: www.monolith.com
Sales Range: $50-74.9 Million
Emp.: 6
Information Technology Solutions
S.I.C.: 7379
N.A.I.C.S.: 541519

POMS Corp. (2)
13655 Dulles Technology Dr
Herndon, VA 20171-4633 VA
Tel.: (703) 793-4400
Fax: (703) 793-4401
Web Site: www.poms.com
Rev.: $11,600,000
Emp.: 50
Computer Related Consulting Services
S.I.C.: 7371
N.A.I.C.S.: 541511
Greg Clark *(Mgr-Bus)*

Quantitative Medical Systems, Inc. (2)
6001 Shellmound St
Emeryville, CA 94608
Tel.: (510) 654-9200
Fax: (510) 654-1168
Toll Free: (800) 752-4600
E-Mail: qms@qms-us.com
Web Site: www.qms-us.com
Sales Range: $1-9.9 Million
Emp.: 30
Custom Computer Programming Services
S.I.C.: 7371
N.A.I.C.S.: 541511
John A. Sargent *(Pres & CEO)*
Michael Davis *(COO)*

Jonas Software Ltd. (1)
45 Vogell Road Suite 500
Richmond Hill, ON, L4B 3P6, Canada (100%)

Tel.: (905) 886-0544
Fax: (905) 886-8511
Toll Free: (888) 789-9073 (Sales)
E-Mail: support@jonassoftware.com
Web Site: www.jonassoftware.com
Emp.: 170
Software Reproducing Services
S.I.C.: 3652
N.A.I.C.S.: 334614
Barry Symons *(CEO)*
Tracey Keates *(CFO)*

U.S. Subsidiaries:

Computrition, Inc. **(2)**
8521 Fallbrook Ave Ste 100
West Hills, CA 91304
Tel.: (800) 222-4488
Fax: (818) 961-0430
E-Mail: info@computrition.com
Web Site: www.computrition.com
Healthcare Software Development Services
S.I.C.: 7371
N.A.I.C.S.: 541511
Matt Otchet *(Pres)*
Scott Saklad *(CEO)*
Kim Goldberg *(Exec VP-Ops)*

Efficient Workflow Solutions LLC **(2)**
454 Main St
Grand Junction, CO 81501
Tel.: (970) 256-1616
Fax: (970) 256-1650
Toll Free: (866) 750-7255
Web Site: www.moverssuite.com
Emp.: 17
Software Publisher
S.I.C.: 7372
N.A.I.C.S.: 511210
James Saad *(Pres)*

Shortcuts Software, Inc. **(2)**
7777 Center Ave Ste 100
Huntington Beach, CA 92647
Tel.: (562) 491-1600
Fax: (714) 622-6602
Toll Free: (866) 678-7324
E-Mail: info@shortcuts.net
Web Site: www.shortcuts.net
Emp.: 139
Software Solutions for Salon & Spa Markets
S.I.C.: 7372
N.A.I.C.S.: 511210
Rebecca Randall *(CEO)*
Paul Tate *(CEO-North America)*

Non-U.S. Subsidiary:

Jonas Computing (UK) Ltd. **(2)**
Avenue House 17 East End Road
Finchley, London, N3 3QE, United Kingdom
Tel.: (44) 208 343 1119
Software Developer
S.I.C.: 7372
N.A.I.C.S.: 511210

Subsidiary:

AMI Education Solutions Ltd **(3)**
Hithercroft Rd
Wallingford, Oxfordshire, OX10 9BT, United Kingdom
Tel.: (44) 8456 717 101
Fax: (44) 8456 717 102
E-Mail: info@amieducation.com
Web Site: www.amieducation.com
Emp.: 20
Educational Support Services
S.I.C.: 8299
N.A.I.C.S.: 611710
Scott Saklad *(Mgr)*

N. Harris Computer Corporation **(1)**
1 Antares Drive Suite 400
Ottawa, ON, K2E 8C4, Canada (100%)
Tel.: (613) 226-5511
Fax: (613) 226-3377
Toll Free: (888) 847-7747
E-Mail: info@harriscomputer.com
Web Site: www.harriscomputer.com
Emp.: 1,000
Computer Systems Mfr
S.I.C.: 7373
N.A.I.C.S.: 541512
Jeff Bender *(CEO)*
Melanie Judge *(CFO)*

Subsidiaries:

Advanced Utility Systems Corporation **(2)**
2235 Sheppard Avenue East Suite 1400
Toronto, ON, M2J 5B5, Canada (100%)
Tel.: (416) 496-0149
Fax: (416) 496-3910
Web Site: www.advancedutility.com
Customer Information & Billing Solutions Software
S.I.C.: 3652
N.A.I.C.S.: 334614
Peter Fanous *(Gen Mgr)*

Cogsdale Corporation **(2)**
14 MacAleer Dr Ste 5
Charlottetown, PE, C1E 2A1, Canada
Tel.: (902) 892-3101
Fax: (902) 368-5960
Toll Free: (800) 533-9690
E-Mail: info@cogsdale.com
Web Site: www.cogsdale.com
Sales Range: $10-24.9 Million
Emp.: 130
Service-Oriented Business Solutions for Local Governments & Utilities
S.I.C.: 7372
N.A.I.C.S.: 511210
David Perry *(Co-Pres)*
Kelly Dawson *(COO)*

Copernic Inc. **(2)**
400 Jean-Lesage Blvd
Quebec, QC, G1K 8W1, Canada ON
Tel.: (418) 527-0528
Fax: (418) 527-1751
Toll Free: (888) 725-2271
E-Mail: mferland@copernic.com
Web Site: www.copernic.com
Sales Range: $1-9.9 Million
Emp.: 25
Internet Marketing & Information Retrieval Services
S.I.C.: 2741
N.A.I.C.S.: 519130
Benoit Godbout *(CTO & VP)*

Subsidiary:

LTRIM Technologies **(3)**
140440 Armand Frappier Blvd
Laval, QC, H7V 4B4, Canada (100%)
Tel.: (450) 681-3171
Fax: (450) 681-0370
E-Mail: info@ltrim.com
Web Site: www.ltrim.com
Emp.: 27
Semiconductors Mfr
S.I.C.: 3674
N.A.I.C.S.: 334413
Sean Long *(VP-Mktg-Bus Dev)*

MS Govern **(2)**
1 Antares Drive Suite 400
Ottawa, ON, K2E 8C4, Canada (100%)
Tel.: (613) 226-5511
Fax: (613) 226-3377
E-Mail: finance@msgovern.com
Web Site: www.msgovern.com
Software Solutions for Government & Publlic Safety Organizations
S.I.C.: 3652
N.A.I.C.S.: 334614
Dennis Asbury *(VP-Sls, Mktg & Client Svcs)*

U.S. Subsidiary:

Innoprise Software, Inc. **(3)**
520 Zang St Ste 200
Broomfield, CO 80021
Tel.: (303) 226-0050
Toll Free: (888) 298-2133
E-Mail: sls@msgovern.com
Web Site: www.msgovern.com
Emp.: 25
Software Developer
S.I.C.: 7372
N.A.I.C.S.: 511210
Dennis Asbury *(Exec VP)*

U.S. Subsidiaries:

Capital Computer Associates, Inc. **(2)**
1 Cerone Commercial Dr
Albany, NY 12205 NY
Tel.: (518) 435-0500
Fax: (518) 435-9464
E-Mail: info@wincap.com
Web Site: www.cap-comp.com
Sales Range: $1-9.9 Million
Emp.: 10
Custom Computer Programming Services
S.I.C.: 7371
N.A.I.C.S.: 541511

Computer Software Innovations, Inc. **(2)**
900 E Main St Ste T
Easley, SC 29640 DE
Tel.: (864) 855-3900
Fax: (864) 855-6266
E-Mail: investorrelations@csioutfitters.com
Web Site: www.csioutfitters.com
Emp.: 249
Computer Software Solutions
S.I.C.: 7371
N.A.I.C.S.: 541511
Jeff Bender *(Pres & CEO)*
William J. Buchanan *(Sr VP-Technical Delivery & Support)*
Beverly N. Hawkins *(Sr VP-Product Dev)*

Volaris Group Inc. **(1)**
5800 Explorer Drive 5th Floor
Mississauga, ON, L4W 5K9, Canada ON
Tel.: (905) 267-5400
Fax: (905) 238-8408
E-Mail: info@volarisgroup.com
Web Site: www.volarisgroup.com
Holding Company; Specialized Business Software Publisher
S.I.C.: 6719
N.A.I.C.S.: 551112
Mark Miller *(CEO)*

Subsidiary:

Trapeze Software Inc. **(2)**
5800 Explorer Drive 5th Floor
Mississauga, ON, L4W 5K9, Canada
Tel.: (905) 629-8727
Fax: (905) 238-8408
E-Mail: info@trapezesoftware.com
Web Site: www.trapezesoftware.com
Emp.: 1,000
Software Development Services
S.I.C.: 7371
N.A.I.C.S.: 541511
Jeff Lougheed *(Regional Mgr)*

U.S. Subsidiaries:

Cultura Technologies Inc. **(3)**
3820 Mansell Rd Ste 375
Alpharetta, GA 30022
Tel.: (678) 249-3200
Toll Free: (800) 795-7995
Web Site: www.culturatech.com
Agricultural Software Development Services
S.I.C.: 7371
N.A.I.C.S.: 541511

Subsidiary:

E-Markets Inc. **(4)**
807 Mountain Ave Ste 200
Berthoud, CO 80513
Tel.: (515) 233-8720
E-Mail: sales@e-markets.com
Web Site: www.e-markets.com
Emp.: 12
E-Commerce Solutions & Services
S.I.C.: 7379
N.A.I.C.S.: 541519
Scott Cavey *(Pres & CEO)*

Trapeze Software Group, Inc. **(3)**
8360 E Via de Ventura Ste L-200
Scottsdale, AZ 85258
Tel.: (480) 627-8400
Fax: (480) 627-8411
Web Site: www.trapezegroup.com
Software Development Services
S.I.C.: 7371
N.A.I.C.S.: 541511
Mark Miller *(CEO)*

Non-U.S. Subsidiaries:

Trapeze Group Deutschland GmbH **(3)**
Kurze Muhren 1
20095 Hamburg, Germany
Tel.: (49) 40 5300 31 0
Fax: (49) 40 5300 31 19
Web Site: www.trapezegroup.com
Transportation Software Development Services
S.I.C.: 7371
N.A.I.C.S.: 541511

Trapeze Group Europe A/S **(3)**
Soren Frichs Vej 38 K 2
Abyhoj, 8230 Arhus, Denmark
Tel.: (45) 87 44 1600
Fax: (45) 87 44 1601
Web Site: www.trapezegroup.com
Software Development Services
S.I.C.: 7371
N.A.I.C.S.: 541511
Klavs Vejlang *(Gen Mgr)*

Trapeze Group (UK) Limited **(3)**
The Mill
Staverton, Wiltshire, BA14 6PH, United Kingdom
Tel.: (44) 844 561 6771
Fax: (44) 1225 784 222
E-Mail: info@trapezegroup.co.uk
Web Site: www.trapezegroup.com
Emp.: 7
Transportation Software Development Services
S.I.C.: 7371
N.A.I.C.S.: 541511
Peter Bell *(Mng Dir)*

Trapeze ITS Germany GmbH **(3)**
Nonnendammallee 101
13629 Berlin, Germany
Tel.: (49) 30 386 20772
Fax: (49) 30 386 20652
E-Mail: info@trapezeits.com
Web Site: www.trapezeits.de
Emp.: 6
Transportation Software Development Services
S.I.C.: 7371
N.A.I.C.S.: 541511
Hans-Peter Schaer *(Mgr)*

Trapeze ITS Switzerland GmbH **(3)**
Industrieplatz 3
Neuhausen, 8212, Switzerland
Tel.: (41) 589111111
Fax: (41) 589111112
E-Mail: info.ch@trapezegroup.com
Emp.: 23
Transportation Software Development Services
S.I.C.: 7371
N.A.I.C.S.: 541511
Hans-Peter Schaer *(CEO)*
Markus Lohrer *(CFO)*

Trapeze Poland sp. z o.o. **(3)**
ul Muchoborska 18
54-424 Wroclaw, Poland
Tel.: (48) 71 7985 820
Fax: (48) 71 7985 821
E-Mail: office@trapezegroup.pl
Emp.: 6
Software Development Services
S.I.C.: 7371
N.A.I.C.S.: 541511
Wojciech Palczynski *(Mng Dir)*

U.S. Subsidiaries:

AssetWorks, Inc. **(2)**
998 Old Eagle School Rd Ste 1215
Wayne, PA 19087
Tel.: (610) 687-9202
Fax: (610) 971-9447
Web Site: www.assetworks.com
Enterprise Asset Management Software & Solutions
S.I.C.: 7372
N.A.I.C.S.: 511210
Ken Slaughter *(Sr VP)*

Constellation Justice Systems Inc. **(2)**
141 Sullys Trl Ste 3
Pittsford, NY 14534
Tel.: (585) 218-0420
Fax: (585) 218-0444
E-Mail: askdamion@cjs-inc.com
Web Site: www.cjs-inc.com
Emp.: 4
Software Reproducing
S.I.C.: 3652
N.A.I.C.S.: 334614

Courtview Justice Solutions Inc. **(2)**
5399 Lauby Rd
North Canton, OH 44720
Tel.: (330) 470-4280
Fax: (330) 494-2483
Toll Free: (800) 406-4333
E-Mail: info@courtview.com
Web Site: www.courtview.com
Software Development Services
S.I.C.: 7371
N.A.I.C.S.: 541511

Constellation Software Inc.—(Continued)

Kevin Bade *(Gen Mgr)*

Wynne Systems, Inc. **(2)**
2603 Main St Ste 710
Irvine, CA 92614 CA
Tel.: (949) 224-6300
Toll Free: (866) 901-9284
Web Site: www.wynnesystems.com
Rental Management Software Publisher
S.I.C.: 7372
N.A.I.C.S.: 511210
John Bureau *(Pres & Gen Mgr)*

U.S. Subsidiaries:

Emphasys Computer Solutions, Inc. **(1)**
3890 Charlevoix Ave Ste 370
Petoskey, MI 49770
Tel.: (231) 347-8787
Fax: (231) 347-2639
E-Mail: info@emphasys-software.com
Web Site: www.emphasys-software.com
Business Management Software Development Services
S.I.C.: 7371
N.A.I.C.S.: 541511

Subsidiaries:

Emphasys Software Inc. **(2)**
333 N Canyons Pkwy Ste 211
Livermore, CA 94551 (100%)
Tel.: (925) 243-9393
Fax: (925) 243-9911
Web Site: www.emphasys-software.com
Emp.: 100
Software Reproducing
S.I.C.: 3652
N.A.I.C.S.: 334614
Michael Byrne *(CEO)*

SymPro, Inc. **(2)**
2200 Powell St Ste 1170
Emeryville, CA 94608 CA
Tel.: (510) 655-0900
Fax: (510) 655-4064
E-Mail: support@sympro.com
Web Site: www.sympro.com
Sales Range: $1-9.9 Million
Emp.: 15
Treasury Management Software Solutions
S.I.C.: 7372
N.A.I.C.S.: 511210
James Connor *(Pres)*

Friedman Corporation **(1)**
1 Pkwy N 400S
Deerfield, IL 60015
Tel.: (847) 948-7180
Fax: (847) 948-9425
E-Mail: sales@friedmancorp.com
Web Site: www.friedmancorp.com
Emp.: 25
Software Development Services
S.I.C.: 7371
N.A.I.C.S.: 541511
Mark Thompson *(Pres)*

Subsidiaries:

ASA Automotive Systems, LLC **(2)**
25 Manchester St Ste 100
Merrimack, NH 03054
Tel.: (603) 889-8700
Fax: (603) 880-3438
E-Mail: info@asatire.com
Web Site: www.asatire.com
Emp.: 30
Tire Mfr
S.I.C.: 3011
N.A.I.C.S.: 326211
Wayne Croswell *(Pres)*

CORESense Inc. **(2)**
125 High Rock Ave
Saratoga Springs, NY 12866
Tel.: (518) 306-3043
Fax: (518) 934-8807
Toll Free: (866) 229-2804
E-Mail: info@coresense.com
Web Site: www.coresense.com
Ecommerce & Retail Management Software Solutions
S.I.C.: 7372
N.A.I.C.S.: 511210
Chris Martin *(CEO)*

Varsity Logistics, Inc. **(2)**
1111 Bayhill Dr Ste 210
San Bruno, CA 94066
Tel.: (650) 392-7979
Fax: (650) 392-7988
Toll Free: (800) 438-7447
E-Mail: info@varsitynet.com
Web Site: www.varsitylogistics.com
Shipping Software Development Services
S.I.C.: 7371
N.A.I.C.S.: 541511
Chris Anderson *(Pres)*

Viewlocity Technologies U.S. LLC **(2)**
5339 Alpha Rd Ste 170
Dallas, TX 75240 GA
Tel.: (972) 715-0300
Fax: (972) 715-0302
E-Mail: info.usa@viewlocity.com
Web Site: www.viewlocity.com
Supply Chain Software Developer & Publisher
S.I.C.: 7372
N.A.I.C.S.: 511210
Teresa M. Finn *(VP-Ops)*

XDATA Solutions Inc. **(2)**
129 Dixie Way S Ste A
South Bend, IN 46637
Tel.: (574) 968-8115
E-Mail: sales@xdata.com
Web Site: www.xdata.com
Rev.: $5,181,000
Emp.: 33
Enterprise Resource Planning Software Developer
S.I.C.: 7372
N.A.I.C.S.: 511210

Non-U.S. Subsidiaries:

Albat+Wirsam Software GmbH **(2)**
Konrad-adenauer-strasse 15
35440 Linden, Germany De
Tel.: (49) 6403 9700
Fax: (49) 6403 64390
E-Mail: info@a-w.com
Web Site: www.a-w.com
Emp.: 190
Software Development Services
S.I.C.: 7371
N.A.I.C.S.: 541511
Uwe Schmit *(CEO)*
George Evers *(Mng Dir)*

QuadraMed Corporation **(1)**
12110 Sunset Hills Rd Ste 600
Reston, VA 20190 DE
Tel.: (703) 709-2300
Fax: (703) 709-2490
Toll Free: (800) 393-0278
E-Mail: investorrelations2@quadramed.com
Web Site: www.quadramed.com
Sales Range: $150-199.9 Million
Emp.: 650
Software, Web-Enabled Solutions & Professional Consulting Services to Hospitals & Healthcare Providers for Information Management
S.I.C.: 7371
N.A.I.C.S.: 541511
Daniel Desaulniers *(Pres)*
Jim Dowling *(Exec VP)*
David L. Puckett *(Exec VP)*
Vicki Wheatley *(Exec VP)*
Sandi Williams *(Exec VP)*

CONSTRUCCIONES Y AUXILIAR DE FERROCARRILES S.A.

Jose Miguel Iturrioz 26 Beasain
20200 Guipuzcoa, Spain
Tel.: (34) 943880100
Fax: (34) 943881420
E-Mail: caf@caf.net
Web Site: www.caf.net
CAF—(MAD)
Rev.: $2,317,008,958
Assets: $3,592,737,920
Liabilities: $2,640,188,028
Net Worth: $952,549,892
Earnings: $134,689,693
Emp.: 6,979
Fiscal Year-end: 12/31/12

Business Description:
Railway Equipment & Components Mfr & Distr
S.I.C.: 3743
N.A.I.C.S.: 336510

Personnel:
Jose Maria Baztarrica Garijo *(Chm & Co-CEO)*
Andres Arizcorreta Garcia *(Co-CEO)*
Alejandro Legarda Zaragueta *(Mng Dir)*

Board of Directors:
Jose Maria Baztarrica Garijo
Fermin Arrese Arratibel
Jose Miguel De La Rica Basagoiti
Luis Miguel Arconada Echarri
Jose Ignacio Berroeta Echevarria
Andres Arizcorreta Garcia
Jose Antonio Mutiloa Izagirre
Xabier Garaialde Maiztegui
Juan Jose Arrieta Sudupe
Alejandro Legarda Zaragueta

Subsidiaries:

Inversiones en Concesiones Ferroviarias, S.A. **(1)**
Jose Miguel Iturrioz
26 Beasain, Guipuzcoa, 20200, Spain
Tel.: (34) 914352500
Fax: (34) 915778129
E-Mail: cas@cas.net
Web Site: www.cas.com
Emp.: 200
Railway Investment Services
S.I.C.: 6211
N.A.I.C.S.: 523999
Alejandro Legarda *(Mng Dir)*

Predictove Ingenieros, S.L. **(1)**
Po Mikeletegi 55 Miramon-Zorroaga
Donostia-San Sebastian, 20009 Guipuzcoa, Spain
Tel.: (34) 943322396
Fax: (34) 943292357
E-Mail: geminis@geminis.com
Web Site: www.geminis.com
Emp.: 4
Engineering Services
S.I.C.: 8711
N.A.I.C.S.: 541330
Isabel Azanza *(Gen Mgr)*

Trainelec, S.L. **(1)**
Polygon Katategi
Plot 3a Pavilion no 1, 20271 Guipuzcoa, Spain
Tel.: (34) 943690870
Fax: (34) 943690912
E-Mail: info@trainelec.com
Web Site: www.trainelec.com
Railway Trains Equipment Mfr
S.I.C.: 4789
N.A.I.C.S.: 488210

U.S. Subsidiary:

CAF USA, Inc. **(1)**
1401 K St NW Ste 803
Washington, DC 20005
Tel.: (202) 898-4848
Fax: (202) 216-8929
E-Mail: mail@cafusa.com
Web Site: www.cafusa.com
Railway Industries
S.I.C.: 4789
N.A.I.C.S.: 488210
Virginaa Verdeja *(VP)*

Non-U.S. Subsidiaries:

CAF Chile, S.A. **(1)**
Avenida de los Conquistadores 1700 27th fl
Comuna de Providencia, 06252 Santiago, Chile
Tel.: (56) 24737200
Fax: (56) 2 473 7290
Web Site: www.caf.es/ingles/compania/oficinas.php
Railway Equipment Mfr
S.I.C.: 3714
N.A.I.C.S.: 336350

CAF Francia, S.A.S. **(1)**
9 to 11 Rue Benoit Malon
Suresnes, Cedex, France
Tel.: (33) 145064400
Fax: (33) 147284884
Web Site: www.caf.fr
Emp.: 10
Railway Equipments Mfr
S.I.C.: 4789
N.A.I.C.S.: 488210
Ontoen Gonzalez *(Mgr)*

CAF Mexico, S.A. de C.V. **(1)**
Oriente 1 piso Col Buenavista Delegacion Cuauhtemoc
Cruz Atoyac, Mexico, 6350, Mexico
Tel.: (52) 5556887543
Fax: (52) 55 5688 1156
E-Mail: cafmex93@prodigy.net.mx
Web Site: www.caf.es/caste/compania/oficinas.php
Emp.: 80
Railway Equipments Mfr
S.I.C.: 4789
N.A.I.C.S.: 488210
Maximiliano Zurita *(Gen Mgr)*

CONSTRUCTII FEROVIARE CRAIOVA SA

Aleea I Bariera Vilcii nr 28
CP 200100 Craiova, Dolj, Romania
Tel.: (40) 251414073
Fax: (40) 251419161
E-Mail: constructii_feroviare@yahoo.com
Web Site: constructii.feroviare.angelfire.com
CFED—(BUC)
Emp.: 90

Business Description:
Road Construction
S.I.C.: 1611
N.A.I.C.S.: 237310

Personnel:
Florian-Teodor Buzatu *(Pres)*

CONSTRUCTION ALBERT JEAN LTD.

4045 Parthenais Street
Montreal, QC, H2K 3T8, Canada
Tel.: (514) 522-2121
Fax: (514) 522-7024
E-Mail: construction@albertjean.com
Web Site: www.albertjean.com
Rev.: $21,736,238
Emp.: 75

Business Description:
Building Construction Company
S.I.C.: 1542
N.A.I.C.S.: 236220

Personnel:
Pierre Jean *(Chm & CEO)*
Pierre Albert *(Pres & COO)*

CONSTRUCTION DISTRIBUTION & SUPPLY COMPANY INC

4630 Dufferin Street Unit 8A
North York, ON, Canada M3H 5S4
Tel.: (416) 665-8006
Fax: (416) 665-7400
Toll Free: (800) 237-5565
E-Mail: sales@cdsco.net
Web Site: www.cdsco.net
Year Founded: 1968
Rev.: $21,736,238
Emp.: 100

Business Description:
Building Construction
S.I.C.: 5039
N.A.I.C.S.: 423390

Personnel:
Stan Lazar *(VP)*

CONSTRUCTION LONGER INC.

175 rue Leger
Sherbrooke, QC, J1L 1M2, Canada
Tel.: (819) 564-0115
Fax: (819) 564-3178

E-Mail: info@constructionlonger.com
Web Site: www.constructionlonger.com
Year Founded: 1979
Rev.: $45,468,219
Emp.: 60
Business Description:
Building Contractors
S.I.C.: 1799
N.A.I.C.S.: 238390
Personnel:
Luc Auclair *(Chm & Pres)*
Board of Directors:
Luc Auclair
Mario Foley
Dominic Gendron
Andre Lavallee
Roger Paradis

CONSTRUCTION SOCAM LTEE
3300 ave Francis Hughes
Laval, QC, H7L 5A7, Canada
Tel.: (450) 662-9000
Fax: (450) 662-9838
E-Mail: socam@socam.ca
Web Site: www.socam.ca
Year Founded: 1985
Rev.: $11,563,678
Emp.: 40
Business Description:
Construction Management
S.I.C.: 1542
N.A.I.C.S.: 236220
Personnel:
Francois Chevrier *(Pres)*

CONSTRUCTIONS DE LA COTE D'EMERAUDE
2 Zone Industrielle rue du Petit Pre
BP 26318
22106 Rennes, Cedex, France
Tel.: (33) 296395091
Fax: (33) 296854046
E-Mail: info@cce-contructions.fr
Web Site: www.cce-constructions.com
Rev.: $20,700,000
Emp.: 76
Business Description:
Nonresidential Construction
S.I.C.: 1542
N.A.I.C.S.: 236220
Personnel:
Jean-Francois Berre *(Gen Mgr)*

CONSTRUCTIONS METALLIQUES CHARLES AUER
Route Rivieres
Occey, 52190 Dijon, Haute Marne, France
Tel.: (33) 325883162
Fax: (33) 25883784
E-Mail: auer.sa@auer-cm.com
Web Site: www.auer-cm.com
Sales Range: $25-49.9 Million
Emp.: 103
Business Description:
Steel Construction
S.I.C.: 3325
N.A.I.C.S.: 331513

CONSTRUCTIONS METALLIQUES D'OBERNAI
(d/b/a CMO Obernai)
2 rue des Bonnes Gens
67210 Obernai, France
Mailing Address:
BP 29
67210 Obernai, France
Tel.: (33) 388494750
Fax: (33) 388950445
E-Mail: info@cmo-obernai.fr
Web Site: www.cmo-obernai.fr
Year Founded: 1992
Sales Range: $10-24.9 Million
Emp.: 100
Business Description:
Fabricated Structural Metal
S.I.C.: 3441
N.A.I.C.S.: 332312
Personnel:
Francois Jehle *(Dir Gen)*

CONSTRUTORA BETER S.A.
Av Heitor Antonio Eiras Garcia 3270
5564100 Sao Paulo, Brazil
Tel.: (55) 11 3301 4400
Fax: (55) 11 3301 4438
Web Site: www.beter.com.br
COBE3B—(BRAZ)
Business Description:
Civil Engineering Construction Services
S.I.C.: 1542
N.A.I.C.S.: 236220
Personnel:
Alberto Jose Aulicino Neto *(Dir-IR)*

CONSTRUTORA LIX DA CUNHA S.A.
Av Dr Jesuino Marcondes Machado 329
Nova Campinas, 13092108
Campinas, SP, Brazil
Tel.: (55) 19 2129 7766
Fax: (55) 19 2129 7756
E-Mail: investidor@lix.com.br
Web Site: www.lix.com.br
Year Founded: 1924
LIXC3—(BRAZ)
Sales Range: $1-9.9 Million
Business Description:
Civil Engineering Construction Services
S.I.C.: 1629
N.A.I.C.S.: 237990
Personnel:
Marisa Braga da Cunha Marri *(Chief Legal Officer)*

CONSTRUTORA SULTEPA S.A.
Travessa Francisco Leonardo Truda 40 - 11 andar
90010-050 Porto Alegre, RS, Brazil
Tel.: (55) 51 3214 1200
E-Mail: sultepa@sultepa.com.br
Web Site: www.sultepa.com.br
Year Founded: 1956
SULT3—(BRAZ)
Business Description:
Construction Engineering Services
S.I.C.: 1629
N.A.I.C.S.: 237990
Personnel:
George Washington Vital Da Silva *(Dir-IR)*

CONSULT VOYAGES SA
2 rue Lhomond
75005 Paris, France
Tel.: (33) 1 40 46 69 70
E-Mail: informations@capunivers.com
Web Site: www.capunivers.com
MLCSV—(EUR)
Business Description:
Tour & Travel Services
S.I.C.: 4729
N.A.I.C.S.: 561599
Personnel:
Alain Clavel *(Chm & CEO)*
Joseph Asfar *(CFO)*

THE CONSULTANT & INVESTMENT GROUP P.L.C.
Wadi Saqrah - King Abdullah Gardens Cross
PO Box 840431
Amman, 11184, Jordan
Tel.: (962) 65001000
Fax: (962) 65698833
E-Mail: CICG@istisharihospital.com
Year Founded: 1995
CICO—(AMM)
Rev.: $19,745,716
Assets: $29,769,862
Liabilities: $7,302,523
Net Worth: $22,467,339
Earnings: $1,449,133
Emp.: 493
Fiscal Year-end: 12/31/12
Business Description:
Investment Management Services
S.I.C.: 6211
N.A.I.C.S.: 523999
Personnel:
Mazen Al-Bashir *(Gen Mgr)*

CONSULTANTS F.DRAPEAU INC.
1915 de l'industrie boulevard
Saint-Mathieu-de-Beloeil, QC, J3G 4S5, Canada
Tel.: (450) 467-2642
Fax: (450) 467-5416
Toll Free: (800) 234-2334
E-Mail: info@fdrapeau.com
Web Site: www.fdrapeau.com
Rev.: $13,092,890
Emp.: 30
Business Description:
Commercial & Industrial Machines Repair Services
S.I.C.: 7699
N.A.I.C.S.: 811310
Personnel:
Francois M. Drapeau *(Founder)*

CONSULTATIO SA
Avenida Eduardo Madero 900 Piso 28
C1106 ACV Buenos Aires, Argentina
Tel.: (54) 1143188000
Fax: (54) 1143188001
Web Site: www.consultatio.com.ar
CTIO1—(BUE)
Sales Range: $25-49.9 Million
Emp.: 120
Business Description:
Real Estate Services
S.I.C.: 6531
N.A.I.C.S.: 531390
Personnel:
Eduardo F. Costantini *(Chm)*

CONSUMERS CHOICE HOME IMPROVEMENTS CORP
445 Finchdene Square
Scarborough, ON, M1X 1B7, Canada
Tel.: (416) 335-8353
Fax: (416) 335-8327
Toll Free: (800) 565-7366
E-Mail: sales@consumerschoice.ca
Web Site: www.consumerschoice.ca
Year Founded: 1990
Rev.: $16,300,000
Emp.: 125
Business Description:
Doors & Windows Installation Service
S.I.C.: 2431
N.A.I.C.S.: 321911
Personnel:
Stan Greenberg *(CEO)*

CONSUN PHARMACEUTICAL GROUP LIMITED
71 Dongpeng Avenue Eastern Section
Guangzhou, 510760, China
Tel.: (86) 20 82264529
Fax: (86) 20 82261886
E-Mail: gaohe@chinaconsun.com
Web Site: www.chinaconsun.com
1681—(HKG)
Emp.: 1,080
Business Description:
Pharmaceutical Mfr
S.I.C.: 2834
N.A.I.C.S.: 325412
Personnel:
Yubao An *(Chm)*
Board of Directors:
Yubao An
Xinxin Cheng
Zhongshi Feng
Qian Li
Yuanfu Su
Shunlong Wang
Zi Han Wang
Peter Wai Po Young
Quan Zhu

CONTACT ENERGY LIMITED
Level 1 Harbour City Tower 29 Brandon Street
Wellington, New Zealand
Mailing Address:
PO Box 10742
The Terrace, Wellington, 6143, New Zealand
Tel.: (64) 44994001
Fax: (64) 44994003
E-Mail: help@contactenergy.co.nz
Web Site: www.contactenergy.co.nz
Year Founded: 1996
CEN—(NZE)
Rev.: $2,095,848,000
Assets: $5,186,889,000
Liabilities: $2,226,420,000
Net Worth: $2,960,469,000
Earnings: $166,563,000
Emp.: 995
Fiscal Year-end: 06/30/13
Business Description:
Gas & Electricity Services
S.I.C.: 1389
N.A.I.C.S.: 213112
Personnel:
Dennis Barnes *(CEO)*
Graham Cockroft *(CFO)*
Paul Ridley-Smith *(Gen Counsel & Sec)*
Board of Directors:
Grant King
David Baldwin
Bruce Gerard Beeren
Whaimutu Dewes
Karen Anne Moses
Phillip Pryke
Susan Jane Sheldon

Subsidiaries:

Empower Limited **(1)**
Level 1 Harbour City Tower 29 Brandon St
Wellington, 6011, New Zealand NZ
Tel.: (64) 44994001 (100%)
Fax: (64) 44994003
E-Mail: support@empower.co.nz
Web Site: www.empower.co.nz
Emp.: 65
Electricity Retailer
S.I.C.: 4911
N.A.I.C.S.: 221122
Dennis Barnes *(CEO)*

CONTACT EXPLORATION INC.
Suite 1520 700 6th Ave SW
Calgary, AB, T2P 0T8, Canada
Tel.: (403) 234-8663
Fax: (403) 695-3915

Contact Exploration Inc.—(Continued)

E-Mail: information@contactexp.com
Web Site: www.contactexp.com
CEX—(TSXV)
Sls.: $4,112,359
Assets: $39,618,406
Liabilities: $11,037,581
Net Worth: $28,580,824
Earnings: $2,078,966
Emp.: 90
Fiscal Year-end: 03/31/13
Business Description:
Oil & Gas Exploration Services
S.I.C.: 1381
N.A.I.C.S.: 213111
Personnel:
Steve Harding *(Pres & CEO)*
Ian Thomson *(CFO)*
Raymond Sully *(COO)*
Bruce Allford *(Sec)*
Board of Directors:
Bruce Allford
Ken Bowie
Steve Harding
Robert Bruce Hodgins
Transfer Agent:
Computershare Trust Company of Canada
Calgary, AB, Canada

CONTAINER CORPORATION OF INDIA LTD.

CONCOR Bhawan C-3 Mathura Road Opposite Apollo Hospital
New Delhi, 110076, India
Tel.: (91) 11 41673093
Fax: (91) 11 41673112
E-Mail: co.pro@concorindia.com
Web Site: www.concorindia.com
Year Founded: 1988
531344—(BOM)
Rev.: $885,759,624
Assets: $1,341,042,696
Liabilities: $187,767,558
Net Worth: $1,153,275,138
Earnings: $172,535,094
Emp.: 1,198
Fiscal Year-end: 03/31/13
Business Description:
Logistics Support Services
S.I.C.: 4731
N.A.I.C.S.: 541614
Personnel:
Anil Kumar Gupta *(Chm & Mng Dir)*
Harish Chandra *(Compliance Officer, Sec & Gen Mgr-Fin & CS)*
A. K. Poddar *(Chief Vigilance Officer)*
Board of Directors:
Anil Kumar Gupta
M. K. Akhouri
A. K. Bandyopadhyay
Pradeep Bhatnagar
Deepak Gupta
Kausik Gupta
Arvind Mahajan
Sudhir Mathur
P. Alli Rani
M. P. Shorawala
Harpreet Singh
Kundan Sinha
Yash Vardhan
Transfer Agent:
Beetal Financial & Computer Services Pvt. Ltd
Beetal House 3rd Floor 99 Madangir Behind Local Shopping Centre
New Delhi, India

CONTANGO GROUP PTY. LTD.

Level 27 35 Collins Street
Melbourne, VIC, 3000, Australia
Tel.: (61) 3 9222 2333
Fax: (61) 3 9222 2345
E-Mail: contango@contango.com.au
Web Site: www.contango.com.au
Emp.: 15
Business Description:
Holding Company; Asset Management Services
S.I.C.: 6719
N.A.I.C.S.: 551112
Personnel:
David I. Stevens *(Mng Dir)*
Subsidiary:

Contango Asset Management Limited (1)
Level 27 35 Collins Street
Melbourne, VIC, 3000, Australia AU
Tel.: (61) 3 9222 2333
Fax: (61) 3 9222 2345
E-Mail: support@contango.com.au
Web Site: www.contango.com.au
Asset Management Services
S.I.C.: 6282
N.A.I.C.S.: 523920
David I. Stevens *(Co-Founder, Mng Dir & Chief Investment Officer)*
Glenn Fowles *(CFO)*

Affiliate:

Contango MicroCap Limited (2)
Level 27 35 Collins Street
Melbourne, VIC, 3000, Australia AU
Tel.: (61) 3 9222 2333 (7.2%)
Fax: (61) 3 9222 2345
E-Mail: contango@contango.com.au
Web Site: www.contango.com.au
CTN—(ASX)
Rev.: $5,014,585
Assets: $163,106,366
Liabilities: $3,232,594
Net Worth: $159,873,772
Earnings: ($13,110,660)
Fiscal Year-end: 06/30/13
Equity Investment Firm
S.I.C.: 6211
N.A.I.C.S.: 523999
David I. Stevens *(Mng Dir)*
Glenn Fowles *(CFO & Sec)*

Subsidiary:

Contango Capital Partners Limited (3)
Level 27 35 Collins Street
Melbourne, VIC, 3000, Australia AU
Tel.: (61) 3 9222 2333 (74.8%)
Fax: (61) 3 9222 2345
E-Mail: contango@contango.com.au
Web Site: www.contango.com.au
Equity Investment Firm
S.I.C.: 6211
N.A.I.C.S.: 523999
David I. Stevens *(Mng Dir)*
Glenn Fowles *(CFO & Sec)*

CONTEC CO., LTD.

3-9-31 Himesato Nishiyodogawa-ku
Osaka, 555-0025, Japan
Tel.: (81) 664727130
Fax: (81) 664751728
E-Mail: ad@contec.jp
Web Site: www.contec.co.jp
Year Founded: 1975
6639—(TKS)
Sales Range: $100-124.9 Million
Emp.: 250
Business Description:
Computer & Electronic Products Mfr & Distr
S.I.C.: 3575
N.A.I.C.S.: 334118
Personnel:
Eijiro Urushizaki *(Pres)*
Shiro Hayano *(Sr Mng Dir)*
Takao Kanemaru *(Mng Dir)*
Board of Directors:
Mitsugi Fujii
Shiro Hayano
Takao Kanemaru
Shukichi Muramatsu
Chikashi Nakai
Takashi Seki
Eijiro Urushizaki

Subsidiary:

Contec EMS Co., Ltd. (1)
3 9 31 Himesato
Nishiyodogawa-ku, Osaka, 555 0025, Japan
Tel.: (81) 664777241
Emp.: 110
Electronic Components Mfr
S.I.C.: 3678
N.A.I.C.S.: 334417

U.S. Subsidiary:

CONTEC Microelectronics U.S.A Inc. (1)
1294 Lawrence Station Rd
Sunnyvale, CA 94089
Tel.: (408) 400-8700
Fax: (408) 400-9115
Web Site: www.contecusa.com
Electronic Components Mfr
S.I.C.: 3678
N.A.I.C.S.: 334417

CONTEL CORPORATION LIMITED

13th Fl Dawning Bldg 12 Keji Nan Road
Nanshan District, Shenzhen, China
Tel.: (86) 75533300988
Fax: (86) 75533300809
E-Mail: sales@conteldigital.com
Web Site: www.conteldigital.com
OJ4—(SES)
Sales Range: $50-74.9 Million
Emp.: 4,500
Business Description:
Digital Electronic Products Mfr
S.I.C.: 3679
N.A.I.C.S.: 334419
Personnel:
Chengqun Wang *(Founder, Chm & CEO)*
Choi Fan Toon *(Sec)*
Board of Directors:
Chengqun Wang
Chee Seng Chong
Ser Ko Tan
Thomas Siu For Tsang
Wilson Yee Shuen Wong
Transfer Agent:
Tricor Barbinder Share Registration Services
8 Cross St 11-00 PWC Bldg
Singapore, 048424, Singapore

CONTEMPRO FOR HOUSING PROJECTS PLC

AL-Swaifia-AL-Amad Complex
PO Box 831223
Amman, 11183, Jordan
Tel.: (962) 65859510
Fax: (962) 65865029
E-Mail: allmo.company12345@gmail.com
Year Founded: 2002
COHO—(AMM)
Rev.: $8,019,115
Assets: $12,592,553
Liabilities: $648,077
Net Worth: $11,944,476
Earnings: $848,195
Emp.: 11
Fiscal Year-end: 12/31/12
Business Description:
Real Estate Investment Services
S.I.C.: 6531
N.A.I.C.S.: 531390
Personnel:
Iyad M. Adul Ghani Al-Amad *(Gen Mgr)*

CONTENT MEDIA CORPORATION LTD.

19 Heddon Street
London, W1B 4BG, United Kingdom
Tel.: (44) 2078516500
Fax: (44) 2078516506
E-Mail: london@contentmediacorp.com
Web Site: www.contentmediacorp.com
Rev.: $74,081,335
Assets: $75,957,532
Liabilities: $62,735,716
Net Worth: $13,221,816
Earnings: $13,844,056
Emp.: 63
Fiscal Year-end: 03/31/13
Business Description:
Holding Company; Motion Picture & Home Entertainment Distr
S.I.C.: 6719
N.A.I.C.S.: 551112
Personnel:
John Schmidt *(CEO)*
Geoffrey Webb *(CFO & Sec)*
Rick Kwak *(Exec VP & Head-Bus & Legal Affairs)*
Board of Directors:
Huw Davies
Dewitt Kerry McCluggage
Jeffrey Sagansky
John Schmidt
Franz von Auersperg
Geoffrey Webb
Legal Counsel:
Olswang
90 High Holborn
London, WC1V 6XX, United Kingdom

Division:

Fireworks International Division (1)
19 Heddon St
London, W1B 4BG, United Kingdom
Tel.: (44) 2078516500
Fax: (44) 2078516504
E-Mail: london@contentmediacorp.com
Web Site: www.contentfilm.com
Emp.: 30
Television Programming & Motion Picture Distr
S.I.C.: 4813
N.A.I.C.S.: 517110
Greg Phillips *(Pres)*
Jonathan Ford *(Exec VP-Digital Acq & Distr)*
Robert Kennedy *(Exec VP-Non-Fiction Programming)*
Kathryn Rice *(Sr VP-Sls & Acq-Europe)*

Subsidiary:

ContentFilm International Limited (1)
19-21 Heddon St
London, W1B 4BG, United Kingdom UK
Tel.: (44) 2078516500 (100%)
Fax: (44) 2078516506
E-Mail: london@contentmediacorp.com
Web Site: www.contentmediacorp.com
Emp.: 20
Motion Picture & Home Entertainment Distr
S.I.C.: 7829
N.A.I.C.S.: 512120
Jamie Carmichael *(Pres)*
John Schmidt *(CEO)*

U.S. Branch:

ContentFilm International - Los Angeles (2)
225 Arizona Ave Ste 250
Santa Monica, CA 90401
Tel.: (310) 576-1059
Fax: (310) 576-1859
E-Mail: info@contencorp.com
Web Site: www.contencorp.com
Emp.: 11
Motion Picture & Home Entertainment Distr
S.I.C.: 7829
N.A.I.C.S.: 512120
Jamie Carmichael *(Pres)*

U.S. Subsidiary:

Allumination FilmWorks LLC (2)
225 Arizona Ave Ste 250
Santa Monica, CA 90401-1234 DE
Tel.: (310) 576-1059

Fax: (310) 576-1859
E-Mail: info@alluminationfilmworks.com
Web Site: www.alluminationfilmworks.com
Emp.: 20
Motion Picture & Home Entertainment Distr
S.I.C.: 7822
N.A.I.C.S.: 512120
Cheryl Freeman *(CEO)*
Joseph Duey *(CFO)*

CONTENT VENTURES LIMITED

Sheperds Central Sheperd's Bush
Charecroft Way, London, W14 0EH, United Kingdom
Tel.: (44) 2074719393
Fax: (44) 2074719383
E-Mail: info@contentventures.co.uk
Web Site: www.apacemedia.co.uk
Sales Range: $10-24.9 Million
Emp.: 50

Business Description:
Media Holding Company; Television Broadcasting, Program Distribution & Music Publishing Services
S.I.C.: 6719
N.A.I.C.S.: 551112

Personnel:
Robert Burke *(Chm)*
Robert Carter *(Sec)*

Board of Directors:
Robert Burke
Olivier Dorier
Vassil Ivanov
Martin Johnston
Charles Thompson
William Vanderfelt

Subsidiaries:

Apace Music Limited **(1)**
Unit LG3 Shepherds Bldg
Charecroft Way, London, W14 0EH, United Kingdom
Tel.: (44) 207 4719270
Fax: (44) 207 4719383
E-Mail: sales@apacemusic.co.uk
Web Site: www.apacemusic.co.uk
Emp.: 20
Music Publishing Services
S.I.C.: 2741
N.A.I.C.S.: 512230

Pro-Active Projects Limited **(1)**
Unit 10 Warren Bus Park
Knockdown, Tetbury, Gloucestershire, GL8 8QY, United Kingdom
Tel.: (44) 1454232212
Fax: (44) 1454238727
E-Mail: info@proactivetv.co.uk
Web Site: www.proactivetv.com
Emp.: 20
Television Production Services
S.I.C.: 3663
N.A.I.C.S.: 334220
Alan Morton *(Gen Mgr)*

Steadfast International Limited **(1)**
Shepherds Central Sheperd's Bush
Charecroft Way, London, W14 0EH, United Kingdom
Tel.: (44) 20 7471 9393
Fax: (44) 20 7471 9383
E-Mail: info@steadfast.tv
Web Site: www.steadfastinternational.tv
Television Program Distr
S.I.C.: 4813
N.A.I.C.S.: 517110
Charles Thompson *(CEO)*

Steadfast Television Limited **(1)**
Shepherds Central
Charecroft Way, London, W14 0EH, United Kingdom
Tel.: (44) 2074719250
Fax: (44) 20 7471 9383
E-Mail: info@steadfast.tv
Web Site: www.steadfasttelevision.tv
Television Program Distr
S.I.C.: 4813
N.A.I.C.S.: 517110

CONTEXTA AG

Wasserwerkgasse 17/19
CH-3000 Bern, 13, Switzerland
Tel.: (41) 31 310 88 88
Fax: (41) 31 311 48 77
E-Mail: contexta@contexta.ch
Web Site: www.contexta.ch
Year Founded: 1968
Sales Range: $10-24.9 Million
Emp.: 58

Business Description:
Advertising Agency
S.I.C.: 7311
N.A.I.C.S.: 541810

Personnel:
Nadine Borter *(Owner & CEO)*

CONTIKI TOURS INTERNATIONAL LIMITED

c/o Consolidated Services Limited
PO Box 2257
Hamilton, Bermuda
Tel.: (441) 2958313

Business Description:
Holding Company; Tour Operators & Travel Agencies
S.I.C.: 6719
N.A.I.C.S.: 551112

Non-U.S. Subsidiary:

Contiki Holidays (Australia) Pty Ltd **(1)**
Travel House 35 Grafton Street
Bondi Junction, Sydney, NSW, 2022, Australia
Tel.: (61) 295112200
Fax: (61) 295112291
Web Site: www.contiki.com
Sales Range: $25-49.9 Million
Emp.: 100
Travel Agency
S.I.C.: 4724
N.A.I.C.S.: 561510
John A. Weeks *(Mng Dir)*

CONTINENTAL AKTIENGESELLSCHAFT

(d/b/a Continental Group)
Vahrenwalder Strasse 9
30165 Hannover, Germany

Mailing Address:
PO Box 169
D 30001 Hannover, Germany
Tel.: (49) 51193801
Telex: 92170
Fax: (49) 5119381770
E-Mail: mailservice@conti.de
Web Site: www.conti-online.com
Year Founded: 1871
CONG—(DEU)
Rev.: $44,068,490,354
Assets: $36,801,460,843
Liabilities: $24,491,005,427
Net Worth: $12,310,455,416
Earnings: $2,649,127,943
Emp.: 169,639
Fiscal Year-end: 12/31/12

Business Description:
Automotive Braking & Suspension Systems, Electronic Motors & Components, Passenger & Commercial Vehicle Tires, Belts & Hoses Mfr
Import Export
S.I.C.: 3052
N.A.I.C.S.: 336390

Personnel:
Wolfgang W. Reitzle *(Chm-Supervisory Bd)*
Elmar Degenhart *(Chm-Exec Bd)*
Werner Bischoff *(Deputy Chm-Supervisory Bd)*
Elke Strathmann *(Member-Exec Bd-HR & Dir-Labor Rels)*
Jose A. Avila *(Member-Exec Bd-Powertrain Div)*
Ralf Cramer *(Member-Exec Bd-Chassis & Safety Div)*
Helmut Matschi *(Member-Exec Bd-Interior Div)*
Wolfgang Schafer *(Member-Exec Bd-Fin, IT, Law, Controlling & Compliance)*
Nikolai Setzer *(Member-Exec Bd-Tire Div)*
Heinz-Gerhard Wente *(Member-Exec Bd-ContiTech Div-Corp Pur)*

Supervisory Board of Directors:
Wolfgang W. Reitzle
Werner Bischoff
Michael Deister
Gunter Dunkel
Hans Fischl
Jurgen M. Geissinger
Hans-Olaf Henkel
Michael Iglhaut
Jorg Kohlinger
Klaus J. Mangold
Hartmut Meine
Dirk Nordmann
Artur Otto
Klaus Rosenfeld
Georg F. W. Schaeffler
Maria-Elisabeth Schaeffler
Jorg Schonfelder
Bernd W. Voss
Siegfried Wolf
Erwin Worle

Divisions:

Continental Chassis & Safety Division **(1)**
Geurickstrasse 7
60488 Frankfurt am Main, Germany
Tel.: (49) 6976031
Fax: (49) 69761061
Sales Range: $5-14.9 Billion
Emp.: 27,809
Automotive Brake & Chassis Component Developer & Mfr
S.I.C.: 3714
N.A.I.C.S.: 336340
Ralf Cramer *(Mng Dir)*

Subsidiaries:

Conti Temic Microelectonics GmbH **(2)**
Sieboldstrasse 19
90411 Nuremberg, Germany (100%)
Tel.: (49) 91195260
Fax: (49) 9119526235
E-Mail: maria.schmuck@contenintal-corporation.com
Web Site: www.temic.com
Emp.: 1,100
Automotive Electronic Component Mfr
S.I.C.: 3714
N.A.I.C.S.: 336390
Anton Elsen *(Gen Mgr-Electonics)*

Continental Automotive GmbH **(2)**
Siemensstrasse 12
93026 Regensburg, Germany De
Tel.: (49) 94179002
E-Mail: info@continental.com
Web Site: www.continental.com
Emp.: 30,000
Automotive Safety, Powertrain & Interior Component Developer & Mfr
S.I.C.: 3714
N.A.I.C.S.: 336390

Continental Automotive GmbH **(2)**
Sodener Str 9
65824 Schwalbach, Germany De
Tel.: (49) 6196870
Fax: (49) 619686571
E-Mail: elke.trettin@continentalcorporation.com
Web Site: www.continental-corporation.com
Emp.: 1,300
Automotive Brake & Safety Component Mfr
S.I.C.: 3714
N.A.I.C.S.: 336390

Continental Safety Engineering International GmbH **(2)**
Carl Zeiss Strasse 9
63755 Alzenau, Germany
Tel.: (49) 60239420
Fax: (49) 6023942133
E-Mail: stafety-engineering@continental-corporation.com
Web Site: www.continental-corporation.com
Emp.: 125
Automotive Safety Component & Restraint System Mfr
S.I.C.: 3714
N.A.I.C.S.: 336390
Gunnar Juergens *(Mng Dir)*

Continental Commercial Vehicle Tires Division **(1)**
Vahrenwalder Strasse 9
30165 Hannover, Germany
Tel.: (49) 51193801
Fax: (49) 51193881770
E-Mail: mailservice@continental.de
Web Site: www.continental.de
Emp.: 8,000
Commercial Vehicle Tire Mfr
S.I.C.: 3011
N.A.I.C.S.: 326211
Hans-Joachim Nikolin *(Member-Exec Bd-Comml Vehicle Tires Div & Corp Pur)*

Non-U.S. Subsidiaries:

Barum Continental spol. s.r.o. **(2)**
Objizdna 1628
76531 Otrokovice, Czech Republic CZ
Tel.: (420) 577511111 (70%)
Fax: (420) 5779020201
E-Mail: tomas.venera@barum.cz
Web Site: www.contionline.cz
Emp.: 4,300
Mfr. of Tires
S.I.C.: 3011
N.A.I.C.S.: 326211
Libro Lah Lisky *(Gen Mgr)*

Continental Matador s.r.o. **(2)**
Terezie Vansovej 1054 45
020 01 Puchov, Slovakia
Tel.: (421) 424612854
Fax: (421) 424612854
Web Site: www.continental.sk
Emp.: 1,000
Commercial Vehicle Tire Mfr
S.I.C.: 3011
N.A.I.C.S.: 326211
Ladislav Rosina *(Mng Dir)*

Continental Interior Division **(1)**
Siemensstrasse 12
93055 Regensburg, Germany
Tel.: (49) 9417900
E-Mail: contact@continental.com
Web Site: www.continental.com
Emp.: 33,000
Automobile Gauge, Display & Interior Component Mfr
S.I.C.: 2396
N.A.I.C.S.: 336360
Helmut Matschi *(Mng Dir)*

Subsidiary:

Continental Trading GmbH **(2)**
Kruppstrasse 105
60388 Frankfurt am Main, Germany De
Tel.: (49) 69408050
Fax: (49) 6940805210
Emp.: 300
Commercial Vehicle Information System Developer & Mfr
S.I.C.: 3714
N.A.I.C.S.: 336390
Christoph Eisenhardt *(CEO)*

Plant:

Continental Automotive GmbH **(2)**
Heinrich Hertz Strasse 45
78052 Villingen-Schwenningen, Germany
Tel.: (49) 7721670
Fax: (49) 7721672080
E-Mail: christa.vergin@continental-cooperation.com
Web Site: www.continental-cooperation.com
Emp.: 1,300
Commercial Vehicle Information System Developer & Mfr
S.I.C.: 3714
N.A.I.C.S.: 336390
George Fichermann *(Mng Dir)*

Non-U.S. Subsidiaries:

Continental Automotive Components Malaysia Sdn. Bhd. **(2)**
2455 MK 1 Tingkat Perusahaan 2 A Prai Industrial Estate
13600 Penang, Malaysia MY

Continental Aktiengesellschaft—(Continued)

Tel.: (60) 43819100
Fax: (60) 43818194
E-Mail: siok.mei.koh@continental-corporation.com
Web Site: www.continental-corporation.com
Emp.: 1,000
Automotive Electronic Components Developer & Mfr
S.I.C.: 3714
N.A.I.C.S.: 336390
Yen Siew San *(CEO)*

Continental Automotive Pte. Ltd. **(2)**
Block 28 Ayer Rajah Crescent 08 05 08
Singapore, 139959, Singapore SG
Tel.: (65) 67799714
Fax: (65) 67796979
E-Mail: esther.neo@continental-corporation.com
Web Site: www.continental-corporation.com
Emp.: 400
Automotive Multimedia & Navagation System Developer & Mfr
S.I.C.: 3714
N.A.I.C.S.: 336390
Lilian Tan *(CFO)*

Continental Automotive Switzerland AG **(2)**
Industriestrasse 18
9464 Ruthi, Switzerland CH
Tel.: (41) 717679111
Fax: (41) 717661642
E-Mail: info@continental-coroporation.com
Web Site: www.continental-coroporation.com
Emp.: 200
Automotive Electronic Component Developer & Mfr
S.I.C.: 3714
N.A.I.C.S.: 336390
Hans Pauer *(CEO)*

Continental Automotive Trading Nederland B.V. **(2)**
Luchthavenweg 48
5657 EB Eindhoven, Netherlands NL
Tel.: (31) 40 844 4888
Fax: (31) 40 844 4777
E-Mail: commercial-nl@continental-corporation.com
Web Site: www.continental-corporation.com
Emp.: 20
Commercial Vehicle Information System Developer & Mfr
S.I.C.: 3714
N.A.I.C.S.: 336390

Continental Automotive Trading UK Ltd. **(2)**
36 Gravelly Industrial Park
Birmingham, B24 8TA, United Kingdom UK
Tel.: (44) 1213261234
Fax: (44) 1213261299
E-Mail: uk@vdo.com
Web Site: www.vdo.com.uk
Emp.: 190
Commercial Vehicle Information System Developer & Mfr
S.I.C.: 3714
N.A.I.C.S.: 336390
Paul Jennings *(Gen Mgr)*

Continental Pty Ltd **(2)**
2 Scholar Dr
Bundoora, Victoria, VIC, 3083, Australia
Tel.: (61) 394681000
Fax: (61) 394681500
E-Mail: enquiries.au@continental-corporation.com
Web Site: www.continental-corporation.com
Emp.: 300
Automobile Instrumentation Equipment Developer & Mfr
S.I.C.: 3714
N.A.I.C.S.: 336390
Angie Angelovaski *(CEO)*

Plant:

Continental Pty. Ltd. - Melbourne Plant **(3)**
67 93 National Boulevard
Melbourne, VIC, 3061, Australia
Tel.: (61) 383594300
Fax: (61) 383594360
E-Mail: enquiries.au@continental-corporation.com
Emp.: 300
Automotive Instrumentation Equipment Mfr
S.I.C.: 3714
N.A.I.C.S.: 336390
Frank Schilke *(Reg Mgr)*

Continental Trading GmbH **(2)**
Flachgasse 54 58
1150 Vienna, Austria AT
Tel.: (43) 1981270
Fax: (43) 19812739
Emp.: 30
Commercial Vehicle Information System Developer & Mfr
S.I.C.: 3714
N.A.I.C.S.: 336390
Karl Geist *(Mng Dir)*

Continental VDO Automotive, S.A. **(2)**
Carretera Ullastrell S H
8191 Barcelona, Spain ES
Tel.: (34) 935862880
Fax: (34) 936996407
E-Mail: dull.guntir@continental-corporation.com
Web Site: www.vdo.es
Emp.: 500
Automotive Electronic Component Mfr
S.I.C.: 3714
N.A.I.C.S.: 336390
Guntir Dull *(Mng Dir)*

Non-U.S. Plants:

Continental Automotive Czech Republic s.r.o. **(2)**
Prumyslova 1851
250 01 Brandys nad Labem, Czech Republic CZ
Tel.: (420) 326931500
Fax: (420) 326938510
Web Site: www.conti-online.com
Emp.: 1,700
Automotive Components Mfr
S.I.C.: 3714
N.A.I.C.S.: 336390
Klaus Evers *(Gen Mgr)*

Continental Brasil Industria Automotiva Ltda. **(2)**
Rua Marechal Rongon 1768
13323-900 Salto, SP, Brazil BR
Tel.: (55) 1140288150
Fax: (55) 1140281838
E-Mail: juline.ambiel@continental-corporation.com.br
Web Site: www.continental-corporation.com.br
Emp.: 500
Automotive Interior Component Developer & Mfr
S.I.C.: 3714
N.A.I.C.S.: 336390
Mercelo Torrea *(Gen Mgr)*

Continental Brasil Industria Automotiva Ltda. **(2)**
Av Senador Adolf Schindling 131 Vila das Bandeiras
07042 020 Guarulhos, SP, Brazil BR
Tel.: (55) 1164233400
Fax: (55) 1164233615
Web Site: www.vdo.com.br
Emp.: 1,100
Automotive Electronics Mfr
S.I.C.: 3714
N.A.I.C.S.: 336390
Kurt Upperich *(CFO)*

VDO Automotive, S.A. **(2)**
Calle Sepulveda 11
28108 Alcobendas, Madrid, Spain ES
Tel.: (34) 916572121
Fax: (34) 914909006
Web Site: www.vdo.com
Emp.: 79
Commercial Vehicle Information System Developer & Mfr
S.I.C.: 3714
N.A.I.C.S.: 336390

Continental Passenger & Light Truck Tires Division **(1)**
Vahrenwalder Strasse 9
30165 Hannover, Germany
Tel.: (49) 51193801
Fax: (49) 51193881770
E-Mail: mailservice@conti.de
Web Site: www.conti.de
Emp.: 25,000
Passenger Vehicle & Light Truck Tire Developer & Mfr
S.I.C.: 3011
N.A.I.C.S.: 326211

Plant:

Continental Passenger & Light Truck Tires - Aachen Plant **(2)**
Philipsstrasse 15
PO Box 500351
52068 Aachen, Germany
Tel.: (49) 2415193541
Fax: (49) 2415193541
E-Mail: info@continental-corporation.com
Web Site: www.continental-corporation.com
Emp.: 1,400
Mfr. of Tires
S.I.C.: 3011
N.A.I.C.S.: 326211
Dirk Weber *(Plant Mgr)*

Non-U.S. Subsidiaries:

Continental Tyre Group Ltd. **(2)**
Continental House 191 High St
West Drayton, Middlesex, UB7 7XW, United Kingdom (100%)
Tel.: (44) 1895425900
Fax: (44) 1895425982
Emp.: 150
Passenger Vehicle Tire Mfr
S.I.C.: 3011
N.A.I.C.S.: 326211
David Smith *(Mng Dir)*

Semperit Reifen GesmbH **(2)**
Wienersdorfer Str 20 24
A 2514 Traiskirchen, Austria AT (100%)
Tel.: (43) 22525012660
Telex: 114511 semp a
Fax: (43) 22525014001
E-Mail: tr_servicecenter@conti.de
Web Site: www.semperit.com
Emp.: 300
Mfr. of Tires
S.I.C.: 3011
N.A.I.C.S.: 326211
Martin Pert *(Mng Dir)*

Continental Powertrain Division **(1)**
Siemensstrasse 12
93055 Regensburg, Germany
Tel.: (49) 9417900
Web Site: www.continental.de
Emp.: 27,000
Automotive Engine System & Powertrain Component Developer & Mfr
S.I.C.: 3714
N.A.I.C.S.: 336310

Subsidiary:

Continental Mechatronic Germany GmbH & Co. KG **(2)**
Auer Strasse 19
09366 Stollberg, Germany
Tel.: (49) 372965490
Fax: (49) 37296549129
Emp.: 200
Automotive Actuator & Fuel Supply Component Mfr
S.I.C.: 3714
N.A.I.C.S.: 336390

Plant:

Continental Automotive GmbH **(2)**
Schorndorfer Strasse 91
93426 Roding, Germany
Tel.: (49) 9461914407
Fax: (49) 946191413407
Web Site: www.continental-corporation.com
Emp.: 600
Automotive Engine Pump Mfr
S.I.C.: 3519
N.A.I.C.S.: 333618
Juergen Haga *(CEO)*

ContiTech AG **(1)**
Vahrenwalder Strasse 9
30165 Hannover, Germany De
Tel.: (49) 511 938 02
Fax: (49) 511 938 81770
E-Mail: mailservice@contitech.de
Web Site: www.contitech.de
Emp.: 27,249
Rubber & Plastic Products Mfr
S.I.C.: 3052
N.A.I.C.S.: 326220
Heinz-Gerhard Wente *(CEO & Member-Exec Bd)*

Subsidiaries:

ContiTech Techno-Chemie GmbH **(2)**
Dieselstrasse 4
61184 Karben, Germany
Tel.: (49) 6039 990 0
Fax: (49) 6039 990 117
E-Mail: mailservice@contitech.de
Web Site: www.contitech.de
Rubber & Plastic Products Mfr
S.I.C.: 3069
N.A.I.C.S.: 326299

Subsidiaries:

ContiTech Fluid Automotive GmbH **(3)**
Gothaer Str 4-6
99880 Waltershausen, Germany
Tel.: (49) 3622 633 529
Fax: (49) 3622 633 564
Automotive Tire & Tube Mfr
S.I.C.: 3011
N.A.I.C.S.: 326211

ContiTech Kuhner GmbH & Cie. KG **(3)**
Talstrasse 1-6
71570 Oppenweiler, Germany
Tel.: (49) 7191 4810
Fax: (49) 7191 481397
E-Mail:
Emp.: 40
Rubber & Plastic Products Mfr
S.I.C.: 3069
N.A.I.C.S.: 326299
Christian Noell *(Gen Mgr)*

ContiTech MGW GmbH **(3)**
Seehafenstr 16
21079 Hamburg, Germany
Tel.: (49) 40 7667 01
Fax: (49) 40 7667 3105
Web Site: www.ac-hoses.de
Plastic & Rubber Hoses Mfr
S.I.C.: 3052
N.A.I.C.S.: 326220
Heinz-Gerhard Wente *(Deputy Chm-Supervisory Bd)*
Florian Fauth *(Mng Dir)*

ContiTech Schlauch GmbH **(3)**
Continentalstr 3-5
34497 Korbach, Germany
Tel.: (49) 5631580
Fax: (49) 5631581205
E-Mail: industrial.hoses@fluid.contitech.de
Rubber & Plastic Hoses Mfr
S.I.C.: 3052
N.A.I.C.S.: 326220
Ulrich Spitzer *(Gen Mgr)*

U.S. Subsidiary:

ContiTech Thermopol LLC **(3)**
9 Interstate Dr
Somersworth, NH 03878-1210
Tel.: (603) 692-6300
Fax: (603) 692-3118
Silicone Rubber Hose Mfr
S.I.C.: 3052
N.A.I.C.S.: 326220
John Stokes *(Mgr-Pur)*

Non-U.S. Subsidiaries:

Continental do Brasil Produtos Automotivos Ltda. **(3)**
Rodovia Dom Gabriel Paulino Bueno Couto s/n Km 66
13212-240 Jundiai, Sao Paulo, Brazil
Tel.: (55) 11 4583 6161
Fax: (55) 11 4583 6200
E-Mail: conti@conti.com.br
Web Site: www.conti.com.br
Automotive Tyre Mfr & Distr
S.I.C.: 3011
N.A.I.C.S.: 326211
Renato Sarzano *(Gen Mgr)*

ContiTech Anoflex S.A.S. **(3)**
2-12 Avenue Barthelemy Thimonnier
69300 Caluire-et-Cuire, France

Tel.: (33) 4 78 98 70 70
Fax: (33) 4 78 98 70 04
E-Mail:
Web Site: www.contitech.fr/pages/meet-team/meet-team_fr.html
Rubber & Plastic Hoses Mfr
S.I.C.: 3052
N.A.I.C.S.: 326220

ContiTech Fluid Automotive Hungaria Kft. (3)
Rakosi Ut 3
Mako, 6900, Hungary
Tel.: (36) 62511766
Fax: (36) 62212372
E-Mail: sales@fluid.contitech.hu
Web Site: www.contitech.hu
Rubber & Plastic Fluid Hoses Mfr
S.I.C.: 3052
N.A.I.C.S.: 326220
Claudia Holtkemper *(Co-Mng Dir)*
Mihaly Nagy *(Co-Mng Dir)*

ContiTech Fluid Automotive Romania SRL (3)
Str Mihai Viteazu Nr 125
Carei, 445100, Romania
Tel.: (40) 261806110
Fax: (40) 261806140
Emp.: 140
Fluid Hoses Mfr
S.I.C.: 3492
N.A.I.C.S.: 332912
Rafael Mansurov *(Gen Mgr-Fluid Tech)*

ContiTech Fluid Korea Ltd. (3)
Palbok-dong 1-333 Jeon Buk
560-841 Jeonju, Korea (South)
Tel.: (82) 63 21437 40
Fax: (82) 63 7103701
E-Mail:
Web Site: www.contitech-korea.com
Emp.: 25
Automobile Hose Mfr
S.I.C.: 3714
N.A.I.C.S.: 336330
Danny Lee *(Mng Dir-Fluid Tech)*

ContiTech Fluid Shanghai Co., Ltd. (3)
No 588 XinRun Road XinQiao Town
Songjiang, 201612 Shanghai, China
Tel.: (86) 2167629375
Fax: (86) 2167629379
Power Steering Hose Line Mfr
S.I.C.: 3714
N.A.I.C.S.: 336390

ContiTech Romania S.R.L. (3)
Str Otto Rudolf nr 4
300522 Timisoara, Romania
Tel.: (40) 256301527
Fax: (40) 256301501
Web Site: www.contitech.ro
Emp.: 1,700
Automotive Parts Mfr
S.I.C.: 3714
N.A.I.C.S.: 336390
Bernd Steinebronn *(CEO-Fluid Tech)*

ContiTech Rubber Industrial Kft. (3)
Budapesti Ut 10
Szeged, 6728, Hungary
Tel.: (36) 62 566 700
Fax: (36) 62 566 713
E-Mail: sales@fluid.contitech.hu
Web Site: www.contitech.hu/pages/meet-team/meet-team_en.html
Textile Conveyor Belt & Industrial Hoses Mfr
S.I.C.: 3559
N.A.I.C.S.: 333249
Regina Gensigora *(Mng Dir)*

Non-U.S. Subsidiary:

Kolubara Univerzal d.o.o. (4)
Kosmajska Ulica bb
Veliki Crljeni, Belgrade, 11563, Serbia
Tel.: (381) 11 8120 759
Fax: (381) 11 8120 759
E-Mail: office@kolubarauniverzal.com
Web Site: www.kolubarauniverzal.com
Emp.: 190
Rubber Products Mfr
S.I.C.: 3069
N.A.I.C.S.: 326299
Danilo Vujosevic *(Gen Mgr)*

ContiTech Transportbandsysteme GmbH (2)
Breslauer Strasse 14
37154 Northeim, Germany
Tel.: (49) 5551 702 207
Fax: (49) 5551 702 500
E-Mail: transportbandsysteme@tbs.contitech.de
Steel Cable & Conveyor Belt Installation Services & Mfr
S.I.C.: 3535
N.A.I.C.S.: 333922

Branch:

ContiTech Transportbandsysteme GmbH (3)
Clausthalstrasse 2
47441 Moers, Germany
Tel.: (49) 28411440
Fax: (49) 2841144126
E-Mail:
Web Site: www.contitech.de/index_en.html
Emp.: 65
Mfr of Components for Industrial Conveying Equipment & Engineered Products
S.I.C.: 3535
N.A.I.C.S.: 333922

Non-U.S. Subsidiary:

ContiTech Conveyor Belt Group (3)
No 1 No 1333 Xin Da Road Qingpu Town
Qingpu District, Shanghai, 201700, China
Tel.: (86) 21 6921 4910
Fax: (86) 21 6921 4899
E-Mail: cprice@contitech-natco.com
Conveyor Belt Mfr
S.I.C.: 3535
N.A.I.C.S.: 333922

Phoenix Compounding Technology GmbH (2)
Hannoversche Strasse 88
21079 Hamburg, Germany
Tel.: (49) 40 76 67 01
Fax: (49) 40 76 67 26 33
Web Site: www.phoenix-compounding.eu
Rubber Products Mfr
S.I.C.: 3069
N.A.I.C.S.: 326299
Heinz-Gerhard Wente *(Chm-Supervisory Bd)*
Peter Scholtissek *(Mng Dir)*

Affiliate:

Benecke-Kaliko AG (2)
Benecke-kaiko 40
30419 Hannover, Germany (100%)
Tel.: (49) 51163020
Fax: (49) 5116302206
E-Mail: kontakt@krispin.net
Web Site: www.benecke-kaliko.de
Emp.: 1,800
Producer of Tires & Rubber & Plastic Industrial Articles, Mechanical, Electronic Brake Systems
S.I.C.: 2296
N.A.I.C.S.: 314994
Manfred Winnimir *(Chm)*

Units:

ContiTech Antriebssysteme GmbH (2)
Phillipsborn strasse 1
30165 Hannover, Germany
Tel.: (49) 05119385306
Fax: (49) 05119385282
E-Mail: mailservice@contitech.de
Web Site: www.contitech.de
Sls.: $321,106,816
Emp.: 1,559
Mfr of Automotive Drive Belts
S.I.C.: 3052
N.A.I.C.S.: 326220
Heinz-Derhard Wente *(CEO)*
Konrad Muller *(Mng Dir)*

Non-U.S. Subsidiaries:

ContiTech Power Transmission System (Shanghai) Co., Ltd. (3)
22F Tian An Center 338 Nanjing Road West
Shanghai, 200003, China
Tel.: (86) 21 6141 8325
Fax: (86) 21 6141 8326
E-Mail: service.china@contitech.cn
Automotive Power Transmission Equipment Distr
S.I.C.: 5013
N.A.I.C.S.: 423120

ContiTech Roulunds Rubber A/S (3)
Orstedsgade 19 st
5000 C Odense, Denmark
Tel.: (45) 63133400
Fax: (45) 63133401
E-Mail: roulundsrubber@ptg.contitech.dk
Web Site: www.roulundsrubber.com
Sales Range: $75-99.9 Million
Emp.: 4
Mfr of Rubber Belts
S.I.C.: 3052
N.A.I.C.S.: 326220
Uffe Petersen *(CEO)*

ContiTech Vibration Control GmbH (2)
Jadekamp 30
D-30419 Hannover, Germany
Tel.: (49) 5119766138
Fax: (49) 51197686740
E-Mail: vibrationcontrol@vc.contitech.de
Web Site: www.contitech.de
Sls.: $254,104,192
Emp.: 1,599
Mfr of Engine & Chassis Mounts, Dampers & Sealing Systems
S.I.C.: 3714
N.A.I.C.S.: 336330

U.S. Subsidiaries:

ContiTech Beattie Corp. (2)
11535 Brittmoore Park Dr
Houston, TX 77041
Tel.: (832) 327-0141
Fax: (832) 327-0148
E-Mail: mail@contitechbeattie.com
Web Site: www.contitechbeattie.com
Rubber Hose Mfr
S.I.C.: 3052
N.A.I.C.S.: 326220
Michael Jackson *(Co-Chm)*
Tamas Katona *(Co-Chm)*

ContiTech North America, Inc. (2)
136 Summit Ave
Montvale, NJ 07645
Tel.: (201) 930-0600
Fax: (201) 930-0050
E-Mail: info.contitech@contitech-usa.com
Web Site: www.contitech-usa.com
Emp.: 35
Automotive Hose, Belt & Spring Mfr
S.I.C.: 3714
N.A.I.C.S.: 336390
Francisco Hidalgo *(CEO)*

Non-U.S. Subsidiaries:

Continental Industrias del Caucho S.A. (2)
Cityparc Ronda De Dalt Ctra de Hospitalet 147
E 08940 Barcelona, Cornella, Spain (100%)
Tel.: (34) 93 480 0400
Fax: (34) 934800401
E-Mail:
Web Site: www.contitech.de/locations/index.aspx?idBU=0
Emp.: 10
Producer of Tires, Rubber & Plastic Industrial Articles, Mechanical & Electronic Brake Systems
S.I.C.: 2296
N.A.I.C.S.: 314994

Continental Tyre and Rubber Singapore Pte. Ltd. (2)
80 Boon Keng Road Continental Building
Singapore, 339780, Singapore
Tel.: (65) 6580 0000
Fax: (65) 6634 1651
E-Mail: conti@conti-sg.com
Web Site: www.contitech.sg
Emp.: 7
Rubber Products Distr
S.I.C.: 5199
N.A.I.C.S.: 424990

ContiTech Belgium BVBA (2)
Uitbreidingstraat 42-46
2600 Berchem, Belgium
Tel.: (32) 3 20674 20
Fax: (32) 3 20674 30
E-Mail: info@contitech.be
Web Site: www.contitech-benelux.com
Rubber & Plastic Products Mfr
S.I.C.: 3069
N.A.I.C.S.: 326299
Tobias Mahrenholz *(Mng Dir)*

ContiTech Continental Suisse S.A. (2)
Lerzenstrasse 19
8953 Dietikon, Switzerland
Tel.: (41) 433432010
Fax: (41) 433432011
E-Mail: info.ch@contitech.de
Web Site: www.contitech.ch
Emp.: 2
Automotive Belt, Spring & Hose Mfr
S.I.C.: 3714
N.A.I.C.S.: 336390
Bernd Hauser *(Mng Dir)*

ContiTech Fluid Monterrey Servicios, S.A. de C.V. (2)
(Formerly Parker Sistemas de Automatization S de R.L.)
Carretera Nacional Monterrey
Cd Victoria Km 205 +850, Montemorelos, NL, 67500, Mexico MX
Tel.: (52) 8262630000 (100%)
Fax: (52) 8262637050
E-Mail:
Sales Range: $125-149.9 Million
Emp.: 250
Automotive Air Conditioning Components Mfr
S.I.C.: 3714
N.A.I.C.S.: 336390
Martin Dimas *(Gen Mgr)*

ContiTech France SNC (2)
3 Rue Fulgence Bienvenue
92631 Gennevilliers, France
Tel.: (33) 1 41 47 92 92
Fax: (33) 1 47 98 72 00
Rubber & Plastic Products Mfr
S.I.C.: 3069
N.A.I.C.S.: 326299

Contitech Hycop AB (2)
Finlandsgatan 14
Box 38
164 93 Kista, Sweden (100%)
Tel.: (46) 0141290200
Fax: (46) 8750
E-Mail: info@contitech.se
Web Site: www.contitech.se
Sls.: $399,209
Emp.: 89
Producer of Tires & Rubber & Plastic Industrial Articles, Mechanical, Electronic Brake Systems
S.I.C.: 2298
N.A.I.C.S.: 314994

ContiTech Japan Co. Ltd. (2)
Technowave 100 Bldg 15 F 1-25 Shin Urashima-cho 1-chome
Kanagawa-ku, 221-0031 Yokohama, Japan
Tel.: (81) 45444 3659
Fax: (81) 45444 3837
E-Mail: info.contitech@continentalcorporation.com
Web Site: www.contitech.jp
Emp.: 11
Rubber & Plastic Products Distr
S.I.C.: 5199
N.A.I.C.S.: 424990

ContiTech Kautschuk- und Kunststoff-Vertriebsgesellschaft (2)
Gewerbestr 14
Postfach 115
2351 Wiener Neudorf, Austria
Tel.: (43) 2236 49 101
Fax: (43) 2236 49 101 49
E-Mail: info@contitech.at
Emp.: 16
Offset Printing Blanket Distr
S.I.C.: 5085
N.A.I.C.S.: 423840
Herr Stefan Fuhrmann *(Mng Dir)*

ContiTech Print Service (S) Pte. Ltd. (2)
1 Ubi View 03-17 Focus One
Singapore, 408555, Singapore
Tel.: (65) 65097603
Fax: (65) 67420548
E-Mail: admin1@contitechprintservice.com.sg
Emp.: 10
Offset Printing Blanket Distr
S.I.C.: 5085
N.A.I.C.S.: 423840

Continental Aktiengesellschaft—(Continued)

Thomas Christensen *(Mng Dir)*

ContiTech Printing Blanket Shanghai Ltd. (2)
No 16 Factory Zone A No 6999 Chuansha Road Chuansha Economic Park
Pudong New District, 201202 Shanghai, China
Tel.: (86) 21 5868 1050
Fax: (86) 21 5868 1048
E-Mail: contiair@contitech.com.cn
Emp.: 5
Offset Printing Blanket Distr
S.I.C.: 5085
N.A.I.C.S.: 423840

ContiTech Scandinavia AB (2)
Finlandsgatan 14
Box 38
164 74 Kista, Sweden
Tel.: (46) 8 444 1330
Fax: (46) 8 750 5566
E-Mail: info@contitech.se
Web Site: www.contitech.se
Automotive Parts Mfr
S.I.C.: 3714
N.A.I.C.S.: 336390
John Myoehaenen *(Product Mgr-Automotive)*

ContiTech United Kingdom Ltd. (2)
Chestnut Field House
Rugby, Warwickshire, CV21 2PA, United Kingdom
Tel.: (44) 17 8857 1482
E-Mail: sales@fluid.contitech.co.uk
Web Site: www.contitech.co.uk
Emp.: 1
Rubber & Plastic Products Mfr
S.I.C.: 3069
N.A.I.C.S.: 326299

Dunlop Oil & Marine Ltd. (2)
Moody Lane Pyewipe
Grimsby, DN31 2SY, United Kingdom
Tel.: (44) 1472 359281
Fax: (44) 1472 362948
E-Mail: dunlop.sales@dunoil.com
Web Site: www.dunlop-oil-marine.co.uk
Emp.: 180
Oil & Gas Hoses Mfr & Distr
S.I.C.: 3052
N.A.I.C.S.: 326220
Mike Sloan *(Mng Dir)*
A. R. Kambiez Zandiyeh *(Mng Dir)*

Non-U.S. Affiliate:

IMAS A.E. (2)
Industrial Zone
PO Box 1050
GR 38110 Volos, Greece GR
Tel.: (30) 2421096500 (94%)
Fax: (30) 2421096590
E-Mail: info@imas.contitech.de
Web Site: www.contitech.de
Sls.: $74,477,200
Emp.: 250
Industrial Rubber Goods and Elastometer Technology
S.I.C.: 3061
N.A.I.C.S.: 326291
Andreas Bakenhus *(Mng Dir)*

Subsidiaries:

Continental Mechanical Components Germany GmbH (1)
Schorndorfer Strasse 91
93426 Roding, Germany
Tel.: (49) 9461 914 407
Fax: (49) 9461 91413 407
Web Site: www.continental.com
Automotive Electronic Parts Mfr
S.I.C.: 3714
N.A.I.C.S.: 336320

Continental Teves AG & Co. oHG (1)
Guerickestrasse 7
Frankfurt am Main, 60488, Germany
Tel.: (49) 69 76031
Fax: (49) 69 761061
Automotive Braking System & Component Distr
S.I.C.: 5013
N.A.I.C.S.: 423120

Joint Ventures:

Emitec Gesellschaft fur Emissionstechnologie mbH (1)
Haupstrasse 128
53797 Lohmar, Germany
Tel.: (49) 22461090
Fax: (49) 2246109109
E-Mail: info@emitec.com
Web Site: www.emitec.com
Emp.: 900
Automotive Catalytic Converter Developer & Mfr
S.I.C.: 3714
N.A.I.C.S.: 336390
Wolfgang Maus *(CEO)*

U.S. Subsidiary:

Emitec Inc. (2)
3943 W Hamlin
Rochester Hills, MI 48309
Tel.: (248) 276-6430
Fax: (248) 276-6431
E-Mail: info@emitec.de
Web Site: www.emitec.com
Emp.: 8
Automotive Catalytic Converter Developer & Mfr
S.I.C.: 3714
N.A.I.C.S.: 336390
Claus Brustle *(Pres)*

Non-U.S. Subsidiaries:

Emitec Japan K.K. (2)
Cedar Shibaura 4F
3 13 16 Shibaura Minato Ku, Tokyo, 108 0023, Japan
Tel.: (81) 354186066
Fax: (81) 354186080
Web Site: www.emitec.com
Automotive Catalytic Converter Component Developer & Mfr
S.I.C.: 5571
N.A.I.C.S.: 441228

Emitec Korea Inc. (2)
Room 901 Baek Young Building 630 19 Sinsa Dong
Gangnam gu, Seoul, 135 895, Korea (South)
Tel.: (82) 251794913
Fax: (82) 25179497
E-Mail: daesup.lim@emitec.com
Web Site: www.emitec.com
Emp.: 3
Automotive Catalytic Converter Component Developer & Mfr
S.I.C.: 3714
N.A.I.C.S.: 336390
Wonsik Kim *(Gen Mgr)*

SAS Autosystemtechnik Verwaltungs GmbH (1)
Siemensallee 84
76187 Karlsruhe, Germany De
Tel.: (49) 721350550
Fax: (49) 7213505580
E-Mail: info@karlsruhe.sas-automotive.com
Web Site: www.sas-automotive.com
Emp.: 80
Automotive Safety Component Mfr
S.I.C.: 3714
N.A.I.C.S.: 336390
Christophe Schmitt *(Pres & CEO)*
Ekkehard Klautke *(CFO & Exec VP)*
Wolfgang Braun *(COO & Exec VP)*

U.S. Subsidiaries:

Continental Automotive Systems US, Inc. (1)
1 Continental Dr
Auburn Hills, MI 48326
Tel.: (248) 393-5300
Fax: (248) 393-5301
Web Site: continental-corpaoration.com
Emp.: 6,000
Automotive Brake System & Chassis Component Developer & Mfr
S.I.C.: 3714
N.A.I.C.S.: 336390
Jeff Klei *(Pres)*
Samir Salman *(CEO)*

Plants:

Continental Automotive Systems US, Inc. (2)
100 Electronics Blvd SW
Huntsville, AL 35824
Tel.: (256) 464-2000
Fax: (256) 464-2279
Web Site: www.conti-online.com
Emp.: 2,300
Automotive Brake System & Chassis Component Mfr
S.I.C.: 3714
N.A.I.C.S.: 336390

Continental Automotive Systems US, Inc. (2)
15001 Commerce Dr N
Dearborn, MI 48120
Tel.: (313) 583-5980
Fax: (313) 583-5989
Web Site: www.continental-corporation.com
Emp.: 70
Automotive Brake System & Chassis Component Mfr
S.I.C.: 3714
N.A.I.C.S.: 336390

Continental Automotive Systems US, Inc. (2)
2400 Executive Hills Blvd
Auburn Hills, MI 48326 DE
Tel.: (248) 209-4000
Fax: (248) 209-4040
E-Mail: contact_us@usa.contiteves.com
Web Site: usa.vdo.com
Emp.: 1,500
Automotive Electronics & Safety Equipment Developer & Mfr
Import Export
S.I.C.: 3714
N.A.I.C.S.: 336390
Kathryn Blackwell *(VP-Mktg & Comm-NAFTA Reg)*

Continental Teves Inc. (1)
13456 Lovers Ln
Culpeper, VA 22701
Tel.: (540) 825-4100
Fax: (540) 825-2366
E-Mail: contact_us@usa.contiteves.com
Web Site: www.vdo.com
Automotive Braking Component Mfr
S.I.C.: 3714
N.A.I.C.S.: 336340
Sharon Fisher *(CMO)*

Continental Tire North America, Inc. (1)
1830 MacMillan Park Dr
Fort Mill, SC 29707 (100%)
Tel.: (704) 588-5895
Telex: 986426
Fax: (704) 583-8540
Toll Free: (800) 847-3349
E-Mail: kathryn.blackwell@continental-corporation.com
Web Site: www.continentaltire.com
Sales Range: $1-4.9 Billion
Emp.: 230
Passenger Vehicle Tire Mfr
Import Export
S.I.C.: 3011
N.A.I.C.S.: 326211
Matthias Schoenberg *(CEO)*
Paul Williams *(Exec VP-Commercial Vehicle Tires)*

Joint Venture:

GTY Tire Co. (2)
Po Box 1029
Mount Vernon, IL 62864 OH
Tel.: (618) 246-2263
Fax: (618) 246-2493
Emp.: 400
Tire Mfr
S.I.C.: 3011
N.A.I.C.S.: 326211
John Curry *(Mng Dir)*

Plant:

Continental Tire North America (2)
11525 N Hwy 42
Mount Vernon, IL 62864-0022 (100%)
Tel.: (618) 242-7100
Fax: (618) 246-2555
Web Site: continentaltire.com
Emp.: 2,500
Commercial Vehicle Tire Developer & Mfr
S.I.C.: 3011
N.A.I.C.S.: 326211
Hank Eisenga *(VP-Mfg)*

Non-U.S. Subsidiaries:

Continental Automotive Austria GmbH (1)
Dresdner Strasse 91
1200 Vienna, Austria
Tel.: (43) 1 33144 0
Fax: (43) 1 33144 900
Emp.: 20
Automotive Parts Mfr
S.I.C.: 3714
N.A.I.C.S.: 336390
Klaus Muller *(Gen Mgr)*

Continental Automotive Belgium N.V. (1)
Ikaroslaan 8
1930 Zaventem, Belgium
Tel.: (32) 2 716 0151
Fax: (32) 2 716 0199
Web Site: www.conti-online.com
Emp.: 10
Automotive Parts Distr
S.I.C.: 5013
N.A.I.C.S.: 423120

Continental Automotive Canada, Inc. (1)
700 Park Avenue East
Chatham, ON, N7M 5M7, Canada
Tel.: (519) 352-6700
Fax: (519) 436-3666
Automobile Parts Mfr
S.I.C.: 3714
N.A.I.C.S.: 336390

Continental Automotive Components (India) Private Ltd. (1)
53B Bommasandra Industrial Area Phase 1
Bengaluru, 560 099, India
Tel.: (91) 80 6611 5645
Fax: (91) 80 6611 5115
E-Mail: automotive.india@continental-corporation.com
Automotive Parts Mfr & Distr
S.I.C.: 3714
N.A.I.C.S.: 336390
Debjani Roy *(Gen Mgr)*

Continental Automotive Electronics LLC. (1)
249 Geumho-ri Buyong-myeon
Cheongwon, Chungcheongbuk-do, 363-942, Korea (South)
Tel.: (82) 432706114
Fax: (82) 432776012
Web Site: www.continental-corporation.co.kr
Automotive Electronic Component Mfr
S.I.C.: 3714
N.A.I.C.S.: 336320
Joerg Kretzschma *(Co-Pres)*
Chil Joon Kwon *(Co-Pres)*

Continental Automotive France SAS (1)
1 Avenue Paul Ourliac
31100 Toulouse, Haute Garonne, France
Tel.: (33) 561198888
Fax: (33) 561192525
Automotive Electronic Parts Mfr
S.I.C.: 3714
N.A.I.C.S.: 336320

Continental Automotive Japan KK (1)
Technowave 100 Bldg 15F
Kanagawa-ku, 221-0031 Yokohama, Japan
Tel.: (81) 454444131
Fax: (81) 45444397
Web Site: www.vdo.com
Automotive Parts Mfr
S.I.C.: 3714
N.A.I.C.S.: 336390
Masayuki Morimoto *(VP)*

Continental Automotive S.A. de C.V (1)
Poniente Km 4 2
66350 Santa Catarina, Nuevo Leon, Mexico
Tel.: (52) 818 124 4001
Fax: (52) 818 340 1371
Automotive Accessories Mfr
S.I.C.: 3714
N.A.I.C.S.: 336390

Continental Automotive Spain S.A. (1)
Carretera Ullastrell s/n
08191 Rubi, Barcelona, Spain

Tel.: (34) 93 586 2880
Fax: (34) 93 669 6407
E-Mail: info@vdo.es
Web Site: www.vdo.es
Automotive Parts Mfr
S.I.C.: 3714
N.A.I.C.S.: 336390

Continental Automotive Systems Czech Republic s.r.o. (1)
Kopanska u 1713
744 01 Frenstat pod Radhostem, Czech Republic
Tel.: (420) 556 88 1111
Fax: (420) 556 88 1390
Automotive Electronic Parts Mfr
S.I.C.: 3714
N.A.I.C.S.: 336320

Continental Automotive Systems, Inc (1)
16 Ring Road LISP2-SEZ
4027 Calamba, Laguna, Philippines
Tel.: (63) 49 545 1463
Fax: (63) 49 545 1337
Automotive Electronic Parts Mfr
S.I.C.: 3714
N.A.I.C.S.: 336320

Continental Automotive Systems Management Co., Ltd (1)
Nanjing West Road 338 Tian An Center Building 23F
200003 Shanghai, China
Tel.: (86) 21 6141 8282
Fax: (86) 21 6141 8299
Automotive Parts Mfr
S.I.C.: 3714
N.A.I.C.S.: 336390

Continental Automotive Systems (Shanghai) Co., Ltd (1)
Continental Automotive Tech Center Jiading
100 Huirong Road
Jiading Industrial Zone, 201807 Shanghai, China
Tel.: (86) 21 3916 5000
Fax: (86) 21 5954 2573
Automotive Electronic Parts Mfr
S.I.C.: 3714
N.A.I.C.S.: 336320

Continental Automotive (Thailand) Co. Ltd (1)
444 Olympia Thai Tower 4F Ratchadapisek Road Samsennok
Huay Kwang, Bangkok, 10310, Thailand
Tel.: (66) 2 512 5658
Fax: (66) 2 513 1803
E-Mail: automotive.th@continental-corporation.com
Emp.: 49
Automotive Parts Distr
S.I.C.: 5013
N.A.I.C.S.: 423120

Continental Automotive Trading S.r.l. (1)
Via Vialba 50
20026 Novate Milanese, Milan, Italy
Tel.: (39) 02 356 801
Fax: (39) 02 3820 4339
E-Mail: info.consumatori@continental-corporation.com
Emp.: 30
Automotive Parts Distr
S.I.C.: 5013
N.A.I.C.S.: 423120
Matteo Zucchi *(Gen Mgr)*

Continental Benelux S.A. (1)
Avenue du Parc Industriel 1E Av 36
4040 Herstal, Liege, Belgium BE
Tel.: (32) 42485700 (100%)
Fax: (32) 42485790
E-Mail: info@conteonline.com
Web Site: www.conteonline.com
Emp.: 20
Motor Vehicle Parts Mfr
S.I.C.: 3714
N.A.I.C.S.: 336390
Jean-Paul Cambier *(Mng Dir)*

Continental General Tire Inc. (1)
6110 Cantay Rd
Mississauga, ON, L5R 3W5, Canada (100%)
Tel.: (905) 856-4363
Fax: (905) 856-4363
E-Mail: info@continentaltire.com
Web Site: www.continentaltire.com
Sales Range: $200-249.9 Million
Emp.: 25
Mfr. & Distributor of Tires
S.I.C.: 3011
N.A.I.C.S.: 326211
Oliver Winschiers *(Gen Mgr)*

Continental Italia S.p.A. (1)
Via Pietro Rondoni 1
Milan, 20146, Italy (100%)
Tel.: (39) 02424101
Fax: (39) 02471744
Web Site: www.contionline.com
Emp.: 115
Producer of Tires & Rubber & Plastic Industrial Articles, Mechanical, Electronic Brake Systems
S.I.C.: 2298
N.A.I.C.S.: 314994

Continental Mabor (1)
Rua Adelino Leitao 330
Lousado, 4760-906 Vila Nova de Famalicao, Portugal PT
Tel.: (351) 252499200 (100%)
Fax: (351) 252417350
Web Site: www.conti.online.com
Emp.: 1,455
Mfr. of Tires
S.I.C.: 3011
N.A.I.C.S.: 326211

Continental Properties Mexico SA de CV (1)
Camino a la Tijera No 3
45640 Guadalajara, Mexico
Tel.: (52) 33 381 820 03
Fax: (52) 33 368 432 00
E-Mail: nolia.saucedomiddlescoretorref@continentalmiddlescorecorporation.com
Web Site: www.continental.com
Emp.: 450
Real Estate Development Services
S.I.C.: 6531
N.A.I.C.S.: 531390
Alejandro Sauter *(Gen Mgr)*

Continental Suisse S A (1)
Lerzenstrasse 19
PO Box 840
8953 Dietikon, Zurich, Switzerland (100%)
Tel.: (41) 17455600
Fax: (41) 17455630
Web Site: www.contionline.de
Emp.: 100
Producer of Tires & Rubber & Plastic Industrial Articles, Mechanical, Electronic Brake Systems
S.I.C.: 2296
N.A.I.C.S.: 314994

Continental Temic Electronics Philippines Inc. (1)
16 Ring Road LISP2-SEZ
4027 Calamba, Laguna, Philippines
Tel.: (63) 27867001
Fax: (63) 495451326
Web Site: www.continental-corporation.com
Emp.: 80
Automotive Electronic Brake System & Sensor Cluster Mfr
S.I.C.: 3714
N.A.I.C.S.: 336340

Continental Teves Hungary Kft. (1)
Hazgyari Ut 6-8
8200 Veszprem, Hungary
Tel.: (36) 88 540100
Fax: (36) 88 540109
Automotive Parts Distr
S.I.C.: 5013
N.A.I.C.S.: 423120

Continental Teves Portugal Sistemas de Travagem LDA (1)
Estrada National 252 KM 11
2950-402 Palmela, Portugal
Tel.: (351) 21 238 7500
Fax: (351) 21 238 3830
Automotive Braking System Mfr & Distr
S.I.C.: 3714
N.A.I.C.S.: 336340
Markus Klein *(Gen Mgr)*

Continental Teves UK Ltd. (1)
Waun-y-Pound
Ebbw Vale, NP3 6PL, United Kingdom
Tel.: (44) 1495 350350
Fax: (44) 1495 350351
Emp.: 140
Motor Vehicle Brake System Mfr
S.I.C.: 3714
N.A.I.C.S.: 336340
Mark Langshaw *(Gen Mgr)*

Continental Trading France SAS (1)
1 Rue de Clairefontaine
78512 Rambouillet, France
Tel.: (33) 1 34 57 40 36
Fax: (33) 1 34 57 40 54
E-Mail: 07rafmcontact.contitrading@continental-corporation.com
Motor Vehicle Electronic Parts Distr
S.I.C.: 5065
N.A.I.C.S.: 423690

Continental Trading UK Ltd. (1)
36 Gravelly Industrial Park
Birmingham, B24 8TA, United Kingdom
Tel.: (44) 800 215 315
Fax: (44) 1213261299
Emp.: 10
Automotive Parts Distr
S.I.C.: 5013
N.A.I.C.S.: 423120
Paul Jennings *(Reg Head-Sls)*

ContiTech AGES S.P.A. (1)
Via Trinita 80
10026 Santena, Italy (100%)
Tel.: (39) 01194201
Fax: (39) 0119492000
Web Site: www.contitech.de
Emp.: 1,063
Producer of Tires & Rubber & Plastic Industrial Articles, Mechanical, Electronic Brake Systems
S.I.C.: 2296
N.A.I.C.S.: 314994

General Tyre East Africa Ltd. (1)
Chemi Industrial Area
P O Box 554
NIL Arusha, Tanzania TZ
Tel.: (255) 272503341 (15%)
Fax: (255) 272508228
E-Mail: info@generaltyretz.com
Emp.: 400
Mfr. & Sales of Tires
S.I.C.: 3011
N.A.I.C.S.: 326211

OOO Continental Automotive RUS (1)
Zolotorozhsky Val 34 Build 6
111033 Moscow, Russia
Tel.: (7) 495 646 76 88
Fax: (7) 495 646 76 81
Automotive Parts Distr
S.I.C.: 5013
N.A.I.C.S.: 423120
Alexey Pokatilov *(Head-Sls)*

Otomotiv Lastikleri Tevzi AS (1)
Aydinevler Mahallesi Dumluppinar Cad No 24
Kucukyali, 34854 Istanbul, Turkey (89.66%)
Tel.: (90) 2165870000
Fax: (90) 2165182426
E-Mail: info@oltas.com.tr
Web Site: www.oltas.com.tr
Emp.: 150
Automotive Tires Distr
Import
S.I.C.: 5014
N.A.I.C.S.: 423130
Serkan Erat *(Mgr-Sls)*

SC Continental Automotive Romania S.R.L. (1)
Strada Siemens Nr 1
300704 Timisoara, Romania
Tel.: (40) 256 25 35 02
Fax: (40) 256 29 44 55
Automotive Software Development Services
S.I.C.: 7371
N.A.I.C.S.: 541511
Elena-Daria Tanasa *(Coord-PR)*

Non-U.S. Joint Venture:

Continental Sime Tyre Sdn Bhd (1)
4 Jalan Tandang
46050 Petaling Jaya, Selangor Darul Ehsan, Malaysia MY
Tel.: (60) 377878888
Telex: MA 37589
Fax: (60) 377825414
Web Site: www.conti-online.com
Emp.: 1,500
Tire Mfr; Joint Venture of Continental AG & Sime Darby Berhad
S.I.C.: 3011
N.A.I.C.S.: 326211
Benoit Henry *(CEO)*
Stefan Schwass *(CFO)*

Division:

Continental Sime Tyre Marketing Sdn. Bhd. (2)
4 Jalan Tandang
PO Box 66
46050 Petaling Jaya, Selangor, Malaysia MY
Tel.: (60) 377818833
Telex: MA 37589
Fax: (60) 377825414
Web Site: www.conti-sime.com
Sales Range: $75-99.9 Million
Emp.: 1,400
Mfr. & Marketing of Aircraft Tires
S.I.C.: 3011
N.A.I.C.S.: 326211
Henry Benoit *(CEO)*

CONTINENTAL CARBONIC PRODUCTS, INC.
(Acquired by Taiyo Nippon Sanso Corporation)

CONTINENTAL COAL LIMITED
Ground Floor 20 Kings Park Road
West Perth, WA, 6005, Australia
Tel.: (61) 8 9389 2111
Fax: (61) 8 9389 2199
E-Mail: admin@conticoal.com
Web Site: www.conticoal.com
CCC—(AIM ASX OTC)
Rev.: $64,849,883
Assets: $176,951,706
Liabilities: $149,098,458
Net Worth: $27,853,249
Earnings: ($51,571,445)
Emp.: 10
Fiscal Year-end: 06/30/13

Business Description:
Mining Exploration
S.I.C.: 1081
N.A.I.C.S.: 213114

Personnel:
Don Turvey *(CEO)*
Lou Van Vuuren *(CFO)*
Johan Heystek *(COO)*
John Ribbons *(Co-Sec)*
Dennis William Wilkins *(Co-Sec)*

Board of Directors:
Michael James Kilbride
Johan Bloemsma
Jason Paul Brewer
Ronald Chamberlain
Connie Molusi
Zacharias Bernard Swanepoel
Don Turvey

Legal Counsel:
Memery Crystal LLP
44 Southampton Buildings
London, United Kingdom

Non-U.S. Subsidiary:

Continental Coal Limited (South Africa) (1)
9th Fl Fredman Towers 13 Fredman Dr
Sandton, Gauteng, 2196, South Africa
Tel.: (27) 118811420
Fax: (27) 118811423
E-Mail: info@conticoal.com
Web Site: www.conticoal.com
Emp.: 20
Coal Mining Services
S.I.C.: 1241
N.A.I.C.S.: 213113
Bruce Buthelezi *(Mng Dir)*
Don Turvey *(CFO)*
Lou Van Vuuren *(CFO)*
Jason Brewer *(COO)*

CONTINENTAL FARMERS GROUP PLC
(Acquired by Almarai Company Ltd.)

CONTINENTAL FILM D.O.O.
Zavrtnica 17 Hrvatska
10000 Zagreb, Croatia
Tel.: (385) 16194660
Fax: (385) 16194663
E-Mail: cf-info@continental-film.hr
Web Site: www.continental-film.hr
Sales Range: $1-9.9 Million
Emp.: 40
Business Description:
Motion Picture Distr
S.I.C.: 7829
N.A.I.C.S.: 512120
Personnel:
Enver Hadziabdic *(Pres)*
Biba Hadziabdic *(Sr VP)*

CONTINENTAL GOLD LIMITED
155 Wellington Street West Suite 2920
Toronto, ON, M5V 3H1, Canada
Tel.: (416) 583-5610
Fax: (416) 595-9918
E-Mail: info@continentalgold.com
Web Site: www.continentalgold.com
Year Founded: 1986
CNL—(OTC TSX)
Rev.: $1,358,000
Assets: $310,596,000
Liabilities: $13,940,000
Net Worth: $296,656,000
Earnings: ($7,929,000)
Emp.: 330
Fiscal Year-end: 12/31/12
Business Description:
Gold Mining Services
S.I.C.: 1041
N.A.I.C.S.: 212221
Personnel:
Robert Allen *(Chm)*
Mark Moseley-Williams *(Pres & COO)*
Ari B. Sussman *(CEO)*
Paul Begin *(CFO)*
Cheree Scott *(Sec)*
Gustavo Koch *(Exec VP)*
Board of Directors:
Robert Allen
Patrick F. N. Anderson
Gary P. Barket
Jaime I. Gutierrez
Paul J. Murphy
Ari B. Sussman
Kenneth G. Thomas
Timothy Warman
Legal Counsel:
Cassels, Brock & Blackwell LLP
2100 Scotia Plaza 40 King St W
Toronto, ON, M5H 3C2, Canada
Tel.: (416) 869-5300
Telex: 6-23415
Fax: (416) 360-8877
Transfer Agent:
Computershare Investor Services Inc.
100 University Avenue 8th Floor
Toronto, ON, M5J 2Y1, Canada
Tel.: (514) 982-7555

CONTINENTAL HOLDINGS CORP.
23F 95 Dun Hua South Road Sec 2
Taipei, 10682, Taiwan
Tel.: (886) 2 3701 2000
Fax: (886) 2 3701 2999
E-Mail: patrick-chou@mail.cec.com.tw
Web Site: www.continental-holdings.com
3703—(TAI)
Sales Range: $800-899.9 Million
Emp.: 2,220
Business Description:
Holding Company; Construction & Engineering Services
S.I.C.: 6719
N.A.I.C.S.: 551112
Personnel:
Ken Y.C. Hung *(CEO)*
Rex Yang *(CFO)*
Board of Directors:
Nita Ing
Christopher Chang
Charles Y. Huang
Teh-Jung Kao
Helena Kuo
Hendrick Lam
Ming-Teh Wang
Supervisory Board of Directors:
Cheng-Hsiung Kang
Mei-Hsiang Tzeng Wang

Subsidiary:

Continental Engineering Corporation **(1)**
95 Dun Hua South Road Section 2
Taipei, 10682, Taiwan
Tel.: (886) 237011000
Fax: (886) 237012888
E-Mail: info@mail.cec.com.tw
Web Site: www.cec.com.tw
Emp.: 791
Heavy Engineering Construction Services
S.I.C.: 8711
N.A.I.C.S.: 541330
Nita Ing *(Chm)*
Ken Y.C. Hung *(Pres)*
Mossy Chen *(Pres-Taiwan Bus Div)*
Robert M. Park *(Pres-Intl Bus Div)*
Sunil Shinde *(CEO-India Project Offices)*

Subsidiaries:

CEC Commercial Development Corporation **(2)**
B1 52 Hanzhong Street
Wanhua District, Taipei, 108, Taiwan
Tel.: (886) 285020208
Fax: (886) 285020207
E-Mail: mac@mail.cec.com.tw
Web Site: www.continental-holdings.com
Emp.: 7
Commercial Complex Development & Management Services
S.I.C.: 6531
N.A.I.C.S.: 531311
Max wu *(Gen Mgr)*

Hsin Dar Environment Corporation **(2)**
19F 95 Tun Hua South Road Section 2
Taipei, 10682, Taiwan
Tel.: (886) 237016212
Fax: (886) 237012333
E-Mail: vicky@mail.cec.com
Emp.: 26
Commercial Building Construction Services
S.I.C.: 1542
N.A.I.C.S.: 236220
Jerry Chou *(Pres)*

North Shore Corp. **(2)**
19F No 95 Section 2 Dunhua South Road
Da-an District, Taipei, 106, Taiwan
Tel.: (886) 2 3701 1000
Fax: (886) 2 3701 2555
E-Mail: info@northshore.com.tw
Web Site: www.northshore.com.tw
Emp.: 14
Commercial Building Construction Services
S.I.C.: 1542
N.A.I.C.S.: 236220
Jerry Chou *(Pres)*

U.S. Subsidiary:

American Bridge Holding Company **(2)**
1000 American Bridge Way
Coraopolis, PA 15108-1266 DE
Tel.: (412) 631-1000
Fax: (412) 631-2000
Web Site: www.americanbridge.net
Emp.: 300
Holding Company
S.I.C.: 6719
N.A.I.C.S.: 551112
Nita Ing *(Chm)*

Subsidiary:

American Bridge Company **(3)**
1000 American Bridge Way
Coraopolis, PA 15108 DE
Tel.: (412) 631-1000
Fax: (412) 631-2000
E-Mail: info@americanbridge.net
Web Site: www.americanbridge.net
Sales Range: $400-449.9 Million
Emp.: 400
Engineering Services; Manufacture, Erection & Rehabilitation of Bridges & Other Structures; Underwater & Heavy Concrete Construction
S.I.C.: 1791
N.A.I.C.S.: 238120
Michael D. Flowers *(Pres & CEO)*
Terry Poole *(COO)*
Michael Cegelis *(Exec VP-Special & Intl Projects)*
Pamela Bena *(Sr VP-Fin)*
Jake Bidosky *(Sr VP-Mfg)*
Lanny Frisco *(Sr VP-Estimating)*
Richard C. Kermode *(Sr VP-Tampa District)*
David T. Simmons *(Sr VP-Richmond District)*

Subsidiary:

American Bridge Manufacturing Company **(4)**
2000 American Bridge Way
Coraopolis, PA 15108 DE
Tel.: (412) 631-3000
Fax: (412) 631-4000
E-Mail: info@americanbridge.net
Web Site: www.americanbridge.net
Bridge Manufacturing
S.I.C.: 1622
N.A.I.C.S.: 237310
Jake Bidosky *(Sr VP)*

Non-U.S. Subsidiary:

CEC International Corporation (India) Private Limited **(2)**
Tower 9A Floor 9 Cyber City
DLF Phase 3, Gurgaon, Haryan, 122002, India In
Tel.: (91) 1244588888
Fax: (91) 1244588897
E-Mail: info@cici.co.in
Web Site: www.cici.co.in
Emp.: 110
Commercial Building Construction Services
S.I.C.: 1542
N.A.I.C.S.: 236220
Sunil Shinde *(Mng Dir)*

CONTINENTAL HOLDINGS LIMITED
Unit M 1/F Kaiser Estate Phase 3 11 Hok Yuen Street
Hunghom, Kowloon, China (Hong Kong)
Tel.: (852) 2363 8882
Fax: (852) 2765 7516
E-Mail: sales@continental.com.hk
Web Site: www.continental.com.hk
513—(HKG)
Rev.: $122,401,274
Assets: $355,743,392
Liabilities: $125,515,030
Net Worth: $230,228,362
Earnings: $11,135,735
Emp.: 1,020
Fiscal Year-end: 06/30/13
Business Description:
Investment Management Services
S.I.C.: 6211
N.A.I.C.S.: 523999
Personnel:
Shirley Siu Yin Cheng *(Founder & Mng Dir)*
Charles Sing Chuk Chan *(Chm)*
Chun Lam Hui *(Sec)*
Board of Directors:
Charles Sing Chuk Chan
Derek Ping Kuen Chan
Vicki Wai Kei Chan
Victor Wai Lap Chan
Shirley Siu Yin Cheng
Frank Chi Fai Cheung
Gang Fang
Irons Sze
Paul Shiu Tin Yu

CONTINENTAL MUSHROOM CORP.
2545 9th Line Rd
Metcalfe, ON, K0A 2P0, Canada
Tel.: (613) 821-1411
Fax: (613) 821-1770
E-Mail: info@continentalmushroom.ca
Web Site: www.continentalmushroom.ca
Year Founded: 1972
Rev.: $13,008,323
Emp.: 260
Business Description:
Mushroom Producer & Supplier
S.I.C.: 0182
N.A.I.C.S.: 111411
Personnel:
Nicholas Pora *(Founder)*

CONTINENTAL PETROLEUMS LIMITED
A-2 Opp Udyog Bhawan Tilak Marg C-Scheme
Jaipur, 302 005, India
Tel.: (91) 141 2222232
Fax: (91) 141 2221961
E-Mail: conpetco@gmail.com
Web Site: www.conpetco.com
Year Founded: 1986
523232—(BOM)
Sales Range: $1-9.9 Million
Business Description:
Lubricating Oil & Grease Mfr
S.I.C.: 2992
N.A.I.C.S.: 324191
Personnel:
M. L. Khandelwal *(Chm & Mng Dir)*

CONTINENTAL PRECIOUS MINERALS INC.
36 Toronto Street Suite 1000
Toronto, ON, M5C 2C5, Canada
Tel.: (416) 805-3036
Fax: (905) 276-1508
E-Mail: godine@rogers.com
Web Site: www.czqminerals.com
Year Founded: 1987
CZQ—(TSX)
Rev.: $113,528
Assets: $10,632,905
Liabilities: $597,400
Net Worth: $10,035,505
Earnings: ($7,951,608)
Fiscal Year-end: 05/31/13
Business Description:
Uranium Exploration Services
S.I.C.: 1094
N.A.I.C.S.: 212291
Personnel:
Rana Vig *(Vice Chm)*
Larry Tsang Chun *(CFO)*
Board of Directors:
Laurence Curtis
Carmen Diges
Robert Perry
Rana Vig
Legal Counsel:
Fogler Rubinoff LLP
77 King St W Suite 3000
Toronto, ON, M5K 1G8, Canada
Transfer Agent:
CIBC Mellon Trust Company
PO Box 7010
Adelaide Street Postal Station, Toronto, ON, M5C 2W9, Canada
Tel.: (416) 643-5500
Fax: (416) 643-5501
Toll Free: (800) 387-0825

CONTINENTALE HOLDING AG
Ruhrallee 92
44139 Dortmund, Germany
Tel.: (49) 2319190
Fax: (49) 2319193255

E-Mail: info@continentale.de
Web Site: www.continentale.de
Year Founded: 1926
Emp.: 3,000
Business Description:
Holding Company; Insurance Services
S.I.C.: 6719
N.A.I.C.S.: 551112
Personnel:
Rolf Bauer *(CEO)*

Holding:

Mannheimer AG Holding **(1)**
Augustaanlage 66
D 68165 Mannheim, Germany (100%)
Tel.: (49) 18022024
Fax: (49) 1802999992
Web Site: www.mannheimer.de
Property, Casualty & Re-Insurance Carrier
S.I.C.: 6331
N.A.I.C.S.: 524126
Helmut Posch *(CEO)*

Subsidiaries:

Mannheimer Krankenversicherung AG **(2)**
Augustaanlage 66
68165 Mannheim, Germany
Tel.: (49) 18022024
Fax: (49) 1802999992
E-Mail: service@mannheimer.de
Web Site: www.mannheimer.de
Emp.: 25
Health Insurance Carrier
S.I.C.: 6324
N.A.I.C.S.: 524114
Helmut Posch *(CEO)*

Mannheimer Versicherung AG **(2)**
Augustaanlage 66
D 68165 Mannheim, Germany
Tel.: (49) 18022024
Fax: (49) 6214578008
Web Site: www.mannheimer.de
Emp.: 350
Property & Casualty Insurance Carrier
S.I.C.: 6351
N.A.I.C.S.: 524126
Marcus Kremer *(CEO)*

CONTINUATION INVESTMENTS LIMITED

945 Wellington Street
West Perth, WA, 6005, Australia
Tel.: (61) 8 9322 7600
Fax: (61) 8 9322 7602
COT—(ASX)
Sales Range: $10-24.9 Million
Business Description:
Financial Services
S.I.C.: 6211
N.A.I.C.S.: 523999
Personnel:
Jeremy Philip King *(Chm)*
Mark Thomas *(CEO)*
Sarah Jayne Smith *(Sec)*
Board of Directors:
Jeremy Philip King
Alan Dixon
Chris Duffield
Alex MacLachlan
Stuart Nisbett
Mark Thomas
John Vatovec

CONTO RESOURCES LTD.

Level 4 20 Loftus Street
Sydney, NSW, 2000, Australia
Mailing Address:
PO Box 1974
West Perth, WA, 6872, Australia
Tel.: (61) 8 9322 9295
Fax: (61) 8 6314 1587
E-Mail: info@contoresources.com
Web Site: www.contoresources.com
CNO—(ASX)
Rev.: $137,335
Assets: $3,472,794
Liabilities: $105,022
Net Worth: $3,367,772
Earnings: ($874,140)
Fiscal Year-end: 06/30/13
Business Description:
Gold Mining Services
S.I.C.: 1041
N.A.I.C.S.: 212221
Personnel:
Mark Johnson *(Chm)*
Simon Penney *(Co-Sec)*
John Smith *(Co-Sec)*
Board of Directors:
Mark Johnson
Steve Gemell
George Niumataiwalu
Legal Counsel:
Steinepreis Paganin
Level 4 The Read Building 16 Milligan Street
Perth, WA, 6000, Australia
Tel.: (61) 8 9321 4000
Fax: (61) 8 9321 4333

CONTOR GROUP S.A

Calea Bodrogului Nr 2-4
Arad, 310059, Romania
Tel.: (40) 257208501
Fax: (40) 257208555
E-Mail: commercial@contorgroup.com
Web Site: www.contorgroup.ro
CGC—(BUC)
Sls.: $5,645,174
Assets: $14,996,325
Liabilities: $14,169,983
Net Worth: $826,343
Earnings: $3,996,825
Emp.: 228
Fiscal Year-end: 12/31/12
Business Description:
Measuring Instruments Mfr
S.I.C.: 3825
N.A.I.C.S.: 334515
Personnel:
Alida-Valeria Toma *(Member-Mgmt Bd & Gen Mgr)*
Martha Sas *(Member-Mgmt Bd & Deputy Gen Mgr)*
Mihai Androne *(Member-Mgmt Bd & Dir-Fin & Acctg)*
Iacint Micoara *(Member-Mgmt Bd & Dir-Mfg)*
Alina Petrisor *(Member-Mgmt Bd & Dir-Pur)*
Gabriel Ujj *(Member-Mgmt Bd & Dir-Technical)*
Cristian Varsan *(Member-Mgmt Bd & Dir-Comml)*

CONTOUR SHOWERS LIMITED

Siddom Street
Winsford, Cheshire, CW7 2BA, United Kingdom
Tel.: (44) 1606592586
Fax: (44) 1606861260
E-Mail: sales@contour-showers.co.uk
Web Site: www.contour-showers.co.uk
Year Founded: 1959
Rev.: $16,934,636
Emp.: 66
Business Description:
Shower Mfr
S.I.C.: 3432
N.A.I.C.S.: 332913
Personnel:
William Hogg *(Mng Dir)*

CONTRAC GMBH

Max Planck Ring 43
65205 Wiesbaden, Germany
Tel.: (49) 612295530
Fax: (49) 612251461
E-Mail: info@contrac-cobus.de
Web Site: www.contrac-cobus.de
Year Founded: 1978
Rev.: $47,161,750
Emp.: 65
Business Description:
Transportation Service
S.I.C.: 4581
N.A.I.C.S.: 488190
Personnel:
Andreas Funk *(Co-Mng Dir)*

CONTRACT CHEMICALS LTD.

Penrhyn Rd Knowsley Business Park
Prescot, Merseyside, L34 9HY, United Kingdom
Tel.: (44) 1515488840
Fax: (44) 1515486548
E-Mail: info@contract-chemicals.com
Web Site: www.contract-chemicals.com
Year Founded: 1977
Emp.: 100
Business Description:
Fine & Specialty Chemicals Mfr
S.I.C.: 2899
N.A.I.C.S.: 325998
Personnel:
David Jones *(Chm)*
Mike Holding *(Mng Dir)*

CONTRACT PHARMACEUTICALS LIMITED

7600 Danbro Crescent
Mississauga, ON, L5N 6L6, Canada
Tel.: (905) 821-7600
Fax: (905) 821-7602
Web Site: www.cplltd.com
Year Founded: 1991
Business Description:
Pharmaceutical Product Mfr
S.I.C.: 2834
N.A.I.C.S.: 325412
Personnel:
Ken Paige *(CEO)*
John Ross *(COO)*

CONTRAF-NICOTEX-TOBACCO GMBH

Herbststrasse 8
D-74072 Heilbronn, Germany
Tel.: (49) 7131898550
Fax: (49) 71318985560
E-Mail: info@cntgroup.de
Web Site: www.cntleaf.com
Year Founded: 1982
Rev.: $21,155,200
Emp.: 17
Business Description:
Pharmaceutical Ingredients Mfr
S.I.C.: 2899
N.A.I.C.S.: 325998
Personnel:
Dirk H. Siemann *(Mng Dir)*
Sascha Siemann *(Mng Dir)*
Torsten Siemann *(Mng Dir)*

CONTRANS GROUP INC.

1179 Ridgeway Road
PO Box 1669
Woodstock, ON, N4S 0A9, Canada
Tel.: (519) 421-4600
Fax: (519) 539-9220
E-Mail: info@contrans.ca
Web Site: www.contrans.ca
CSS—(TSX)
Rev.: $519,097,124
Assets: $381,717,596
Liabilities: $198,412,356
Net Worth: $183,305,240
Earnings: $28,117,844
Emp.: 1,374
Fiscal Year-end: 12/31/12
Business Description:
Holding Company; Freight Transportation Services
S.I.C.: 6719
N.A.I.C.S.: 551112
Personnel:
Stan G. Dunford *(Chm & CEO)*
Gregory W. Rumble *(Pres & COO)*
James S. Clark *(CFO & VP-Fin)*
D. Jamieson Miller *(Treas & Sec)*
Board of Directors:
Stan G. Dunford
G. Ross Amos
Robert B. Burgess
Archie M. Leach
Gregory W. Rumble
Legal Counsel:
Cassels, Brock & Blackwell LLP
2100 Scotia Plaza 40 King St W
Toronto, ON, M5H 3C2, Canada
Tel.: (416) 869-5300
Telex: 6-23415
Fax: (416) 360-8877
Transfer Agent:
Computershare Trust Company of Canada
100 University Ave
Toronto, ON, Canada

Subsidiaries:

564661 ONTARIO INC. **(1)**
235 County Rd 40
Norwood, ON, K0L 2V0, Canada
Tel.: (705) 639-5211
Fax: (705) 639-1917
Web Site: www.wilburnarchertrucking.com
Emp.: 5
General Freight Trucking Services
S.I.C.: 4213
N.A.I.C.S.: 484122
Chris Hoet *(Office Mgr)*

Brookville Carriers Flatbed LP **(1)**
79 Parkway Drive
1896 Truro, Truro, NS, B2N 6C97, Canada
Tel.: (902) 893-8805
Fax: (902) 895-0722
E-Mail: rhamilton@brookville.com
Web Site: www.contransflatbedgroup.com
Emp.: 12
Freight Transportation Arrangement
S.I.C.: 4731
N.A.I.C.S.: 488510
Harm Singh *(Gen Mgr)*

Brookville Carriers Van LP **(1)**
65 Alloy Drive
Saint John, NB, E2M 7S9, Canada (100%)
Tel.: (506) 633-7555
Fax: (506) 634-5614
Web Site: www.brookvillecarriers.com
Emp.: 9
Freight Transportation Arrangement
S.I.C.: 4731
N.A.I.C.S.: 488510
Laban Herr *(Gen Mgr)*

Contrans Corp **(1)**
1179 Ridgeway Rd
Woodstock, ON, N4V 1E3, Canada
Tel.: (519) 421-4600
Fax: (519) 421-3399
Transportation Services
S.I.C.: 4499
N.A.I.C.S.: 488390

Contrans Flatbed Group LP **(1)**
80 Third Line
Hagersville, ON, N0A 1H0, Canada
Tel.: (877) 790-1226
Fax: (905) 768-0846
E-Mail: marketing@contrans.ca
Web Site: www.contransflatbedgroup.com
Emp.: 125
Transportation Services
S.I.C.: 4789
N.A.I.C.S.: 488999
Steven Brookshaw *(VP)*

Contrans Holding LP **(1)**
1179 Ridgeway Rd
Woodstock, ON, N4V 1E3, Canada
Tel.: (519) 421-4600
Fax: (519) 421-3399
Emp.: 30

Contrans Group Inc.—(Continued)

Investment Management Services
S.I.C.: 6211
N.A.I.C.S.: 523999
Greg Rumble *(Gen Mgr)*

Contrans Services LP (1)
1179 Ridgeway Rd
Woodstock, ON, N4V 1E3, Canada
Tel.: (519) 421-3300
Fax: (519) 421-3399
Emp.: 3
Trucking & Transportation Services
S.I.C.: 4213
N.A.I.C.S.: 484122
Johannes Neteland *(Gen Mgr)*

Cornerstone Logistics LP (1)
2180 Buckingham Rd Unit 204
Oakville, ON, L6H 6H1, Canada
Tel.: (905) 339-1456
Fax: (905) 339-3226
Toll Free: (877) 388-2888
Web Site: www.cornerstonelogistics.com
Emp.: 20
Freight Transportation Arrangement
S.I.C.: 4731
N.A.I.C.S.: 488510
Brian Kempisty *(VP-Sls & Mktg)*

ECL Carriers LP (1)
7236 Colonel Talbot Road
London, ON, N6L 1H8, Canada
Tel.: (519) 652-3900
Fax: (519) 652-9726
Toll Free: (800) 265-0934
Web Site: www.elgincartage.com
General Freight Trucking Long-Distance Truckload
S.I.C.: 4213
N.A.I.C.S.: 484121
Peter Vanderwyst *(Gen Mgr)*

General Freight Carriers LP (1)
65 Alloy Drive Spruce Lake Industrial Park
Saint John, NB, E2M 7S9, Canada
Tel.: (506) 648-0499
Fax: (506) 648-0518
Emp.: 10
General Freight Trucking Local
S.I.C.: 4214
N.A.I.C.S.: 484110
Harm Singh *(Gen Mgr)*

Glen Tay Transportation LP (1)
42 Lanark Road
Perth, ON, K7H 3K5, Canada (100%)
Tel.: (613) 267-2007
Fax: (613) 267-3612
Web Site: www.contrans.ca/glentay.html
Emp.: 100
All Other Support Activities for Transportation
S.I.C.: 4789
N.A.I.C.S.: 488999
Dan Robert *(Gen Mgr)*

Hopefield Trucking LP (1)
2278 Lakeshore Road West
Mississauga, ON, L5J 1K2, Canada
Tel.: (905) 855-3906
Fax: (905) 855-6946
E-Mail: dispatch@contrans.ca
Web Site: www.contransflatbedgroup.com
Emp.: 53
General Freight Trucking Local
S.I.C.: 4214
N.A.I.C.S.: 484110
Bryan Dunford *(Gen Mgr)*

L.A. Dalton Systems LP (1)
1435 Hwy #56 RR 1
Caledonia, ON, N3W 1T1, Canada
Tel.: (905) 772-1042
Fax: (905) 772-1044
Toll Free: (800) 363-5912
Web Site: www.ladalton.com
Emp.: 60
General Freight Trucking Long-Distance Truckload
S.I.C.: 4213
N.A.I.C.S.: 484121

Laidlaw Carriers Bulk LP (1)
240 Universal Rd
Woodstock, ON, N4S 0A9, Canada
Tel.: (519) 539-0471
Fax: (519) 537-5321
Web Site: www.contrans.com
Emp.: 40
General Freight Trucking Long-Distance Truckload
S.I.C.: 4213
N.A.I.C.S.: 484121
Scott Talbot *(VP)*

Laidlaw Carriers Flatbed LP (1)
Highway 6 North 11
PO Box 430
Hagersville, ON, N0A 1H0, Canada
Tel.: (905) 768-3375
Fax: (905) 768-2236
Web Site: www.laidlaw.ca
Emp.: 100
General Freight Trucking Long-Distance Truckload
S.I.C.: 4213
N.A.I.C.S.: 484121
Steve Brookshaw *(VP)*

Laidlaw Carriers Tank LP (1)
605 Athlone Avenue
PO Box 1571
Woodstock, ON, N4S 7V8, Canada
Tel.: (519) 539-6103
Fax: (519) 539-0177
General Freight Trucking Long-Distance Truckload
S.I.C.: 4213
N.A.I.C.S.: 484121
Dave Golton *(Gen Mgr & VP)*

Laidlaw Carriers Van LP (1)
21 Kerr Crescent
Puslinch, ON, N0B 2J0, Canada
Tel.: (519) 766-0660
Fax: (519) 766-9800
Toll Free: (800) 263-8267
Web Site: www.laidlaw.ca
Emp.: 35
General Freight Trucking Local
S.I.C.: 4214
N.A.I.C.S.: 484110
Laban Herr *(VP-Van Ops)*

Peter Hodge Transport Limited (1)
100 Market Drive
Milton, ON, L9T 3H6, Canada
Tel.: (905) 693-8088
Fax: (905) 693-8087
Toll Free: (800) 387-6933
E-Mail: info@peterhodgetransport.com
Web Site: www.peterhodgetransport.com
Emp.: 15
Trucking & Transportation Services
S.I.C.: 4789
N.A.I.C.S.: 488999
Peter Hodge *(Pres-Ops)*
Beverly Hodge *(Treas & Sec)*

Tri-Line Carriers LP (1)
235185 Ryan Road Rocky View
Calgary, AB, T1X 0K1, Canada (100%)
Tel.: (403) 279-7070
Fax: (403) 279-6616
Toll Free: (800) 661-9191
Web Site: www.triline.ca
Emp.: 25
General Freight Trucking Local
S.I.C.: 4214
N.A.I.C.S.: 484110
Brent Ryan *(Gen Mgr)*

Tri-Line Disposal Inc. (1)
11907 - 154 Street NW
Edmonton, AB, T5V 1N5, Canada
Tel.: (780) 444-8805
Fax: (780) 444-8851
E-Mail: AR@trilinedisposal.com
Web Site: www.trilinedisposal.com
Waste Disposal & Recycling Services
S.I.C.: 4953
N.A.I.C.S.: 562920
David M. Appleton *(VP-Western Canada)*

Tripar Transportation LP (1)
2180 Buckingham Rd
Oakville, Toronto, ON, L6H 6H1, Canada
Tel.: (905) 829-8500
Fax: (905) 829-8513
Web Site: www.contrans.ca/tripar.html
Emp.: 30
General Freight Trucking Long-Distance Truckload
S.I.C.: 4213
N.A.I.C.S.: 484121
Don Burditt *(Gen Mgr & Mgr-Sls)*

U.S. Subsidiary:

Cornerstone Logistics Inc. (1)
2813 Wehrle Dr Ste 8210
Williamsville, NY 14221 (100%)
Tel.: (716) 565-9900
Fax: (716) 565-9800
E-Mail: earbaram@cornerstonelogistics.com
Web Site: www.cornerstonelogistics.com
Emp.: 18
Freight Transportation Arrangement
S.I.C.: 4731
N.A.I.C.S.: 488510
Andy Leloenski *(Gen Mgr)*

CONTRAST LIGHTING M.L. INC.

1009 rue du Parc Industriel
Saint-Jean-Chrysostome-De-Levi, QC, Canada
Tel.: (418) 839-4624
Fax: (418) 839-7057
Toll Free: (888) 839-4624
E-Mail: info@contrastlighting.com
Web Site: www.contrastlighting.com
Year Founded: 1989
Rev.: $10,100,000
Emp.: 85

Business Description:
Lighting Products Mfr
S.I.C.: 3645
N.A.I.C.S.: 335121

CONTROL AND APPLICATIONS GROUP

15th Floor Al Masraf Building
Sheikh Hamdan St, Abu Dhabi, United Arab Emirates
Tel.: (971) 2 6767 965
Fax: (971) 2 6767 956
E-Mail: cag@cagroup.ae
Web Site: www.cagroup.ae

Business Description:
Engineering Solutions
S.I.C.: 8711
N.A.I.C.S.: 541330

Personnel:
Rashed Bin Jabr Al Suwaidi *(Chm)*
Carlos Marques *(Vice Chm)*
Hans Niederlander *(CFO)*
Mohamud Hassan Haji *(COO)*

U.S. Subsidiary:

vMonitor LLC (1)
4321 W Sam Houston Pkwy N Ste 100
Houston, TX 77043
Tel.: (713) 467-3900
Fax: (713) 467-3999
E-Mail: info@vmonitor.com
Web Site: www.vmonitor.com
Emp.: 150
Wireless Technology Services
S.I.C.: 3663
N.A.I.C.S.: 334220

CONTROL INSTRUMENTS GROUP LIMITED

59 Merino Avenue City Deep
2197 Johannesburg, South Africa

Mailing Address:
PO Box 86222
City Deep, 2049 Johannesburg, South Africa
Tel.: (27) 116272500
Fax: (27) 116272600
E-Mail: info@ci.co.za
Web Site: www.ci.co.za
Year Founded: 1948
CNL—(JSE)
Rev.: $63,263,194
Assets: $36,740,252
Liabilities: $21,623,891
Net Worth: $15,116,361
Earnings: ($3,732,120)
Emp.: 587
Fiscal Year-end: 12/31/12

Business Description:
Car Audio, Navigation & Instrumentation Systems
S.I.C.: 3651
N.A.I.C.S.: 334310

Personnel:
Sean Rogers *(CEO)*
Sean Graham *(Sec)*

Board of Directors:
Sam O'Leary
Stuart Bromfield
Harry Coetzee
Eckert Giliomee
Sean Rogers
Peter Surgey
Alex Watson

Transfer Agent:
Computershare Investor Services (Proprietary) Limited
Ground Floor 70 Marshall St
Johannesburg, South Africa

Subsidiaries:

Control Instruments Automotive (Pty) Limited (1)
76 White Road
7945 Cape Town, South Africa ZA
Tel.: (27) 217106800 (100%)
Fax: (27) 217106022
E-Mail: anca.priscu@ci-automotive.com
Web Site: www.ci-automotive.com
Emp.: 300
Design, Manufacture, Sale & Distribution of Aftermarket Components
S.I.C.: 3452
N.A.I.C.S.: 332722
Anca Priscu *(Gen Mgr)*

Control Instruments Dana (Pty) Limited (1)
59 Merino Roads City Deep
PO Box 86222
2049 Johannesburg, South Africa (100%)
Tel.: (27) 116272500
Fax: (27) 116131569
E-Mail: info@ci-automotive.com
Web Site: www.ci-automotive.com
Emp.: 150
Measuring & Dispensing Pump Mfr
S.I.C.: 3586
N.A.I.C.S.: 333913
Richard Friedman *(Mng Dir)*

Control Instruments Shurlok (Pty) Limited (1)
28 Wiganthorpe Road
3201 Pietermaritzburg, South Africa (100%)
Tel.: (27) 338454700
Fax: (27) 0315710825
Web Site: www.cishurlok.com
Emp.: 110
Electronic Component Mfr
S.I.C.: 3679
N.A.I.C.S.: 334419
Dion Hardy *(Gen Mgr)*

Pi Shurlok Engineering (Pty) Limited (1)
66 Ring Rd
Port Elizabeth, Eastern Cape, 6045, South Africa
Tel.: (27) 414511100
Fax: (27) 338454762
Automotive Spare Parts Mfr
S.I.C.: 3714
N.A.I.C.S.: 336390

Pi Shurlok (Pty) Limited (1)
28 Wiganthorpe Road
Pietermaritzburg, 3201, South Africa
Tel.: (27) 338454700
Fax: (27) 315710825
Web Site: www.pfk.co.za
Emp.: 30
Automotive Parts Mfr
S.I.C.: 3714
N.A.I.C.S.: 336390
Daniel Cloutier *(Gen Mgr)*

Transport Lighting and Fleet Products (Pty) Limited (1)
PO Box 2661
Paarl, 7620, South Africa (100%)
Tel.: (27) 218763738
Fax: (27) 21 876 3777

Electric Lamp Bulb & Part Mfr
S.I.C.: 3641
N.A.I.C.S.: 335110
Sam O'Leary *(Chm)*

U.S. Subsidiaries:

Pi Shurlok LLC (1)
47023 5 Mile Rd
Plymouth, MI 48170-3589 (100%)
Tel.: (734) 656-0140
Fax: (734) 656-0141
Web Site: www.pi-shurlok.com
Emp.: 100
Automotive Mechanical & Electrical Repair & Maintenance
S.I.C.: 7539
N.A.I.C.S.: 811118
Walter Lucking *(CEO)*

Non-U.S. Subsidiaries:

Pi Shurlok GmbH (1)
Hagenauer Str 59
Wiesbaden, Hessen, 65203, Germany
Tel.: (49) 611188900
Automotive Electronic Parts Mfr
S.I.C.: 3714
N.A.I.C.S.: 336320

Pi Shurlok Limited (1)
Milton Hall Ely Road Milton
Cambridge, CB24 6WZ, United Kingdom (100%)
Tel.: (44) 1223441434
Fax: (44) 1223203999
E-Mail: info@pi-innovo.com
Web Site: www.pi-innovo.com
Emp.: 75
Electronic Component Mfr
S.I.C.: 3679
N.A.I.C.S.: 334419

CONTROL PRINT LTD.

C-106 Hind Saurashtra Industrial Estate Andheri-Kurla Road Marol Naka
Andheri East, Mumbai, 400059, India
Tel.: (91) 22 28599065
Fax: (91) 22 28528272
Web Site: www.controlprint.com
522295—(BOM)
Rev.: $15,029,185
Assets: $17,847,716
Liabilities: $4,635,241
Net Worth: $13,212,476
Earnings: $2,253,085
Emp.: 409
Fiscal Year-end: 03/31/13

Business Description:
Automotive Mfr
S.I.C.: 3711
N.A.I.C.S.: 336111

Personnel:
Basant S. Kabra *(Chm & Mng Dir)*
Saroj Agarwal *(CFO, Compliance Officer & Sec)*

Board of Directors:
Basant S. Kabra
Gaurav Himatsinghka
S. S. Jangid
Shiva Kabra
Ashok Lohiya

Legal Counsel:
Parimal K. Shroff & Co
Mumbai, India

Transfer Agent:
Sharepro Services (India) Private Limited
13 AB Samhita Warehousing Complex II Floor
Sakinaka Telephone Lane
Off Andheri Kurla Rd Sakinaka, Mumbai, India

CONTROL RISKS GROUP HOLDINGS LTD.

Cottons Centre Cottons Lane
London, SE1 2QG, United Kingdom
Tel.: (44) 20 7970 2100
E-Mail: enquiries@controlrisks.com
Web Site: www.controlrisks.com
Year Founded: 1975
Sales Range: $300-349.9 Million
Emp.: 1,983

Business Description:
Management Consulting Services
S.I.C.: 8742
N.A.I.C.S.: 541611

Personnel:
Crawford Gillies *(Chm)*
Richard Fenning *(CEO)*
Gary Carpenter *(CFO)*
Jim Brooks *(Pres/CEO-Americas)*
John Conyngham *(Gen Counsel)*

Board of Directors:
Crawford Gillies
Nick Allan
Jim Brooks
Andreas Carleton-Smith
Gary Carpenter
John Conyngham
Richard Fenning
Anthony Fry
Tim Levett
Lady Louise Patten
Chris I. Roberts

CONTROLADORA COMERCIAL MEXICANA, S.A. DE C.V.

Avenida Revolucion 780 Modulo 2
Colonia San Juan, 03730 Mexico, Mexico
Tel.: (52) 55 5270 9312
Fax: (52) 55 5270 9302
Web Site: www.comerci.com.mx
Year Founded: 1944
COMERCI—(MEX)
Rev.: $3,516,822,196
Assets: $3,281,741,620
Liabilities: $1,243,218,825
Net Worth: $2,038,522,795
Earnings: $524,929,828
Emp.: 41,004
Fiscal Year-end: 12/31/12

Business Description:
Groceries Distr & Whslr; Restaurant Owner & Operator
S.I.C.: 5411
N.A.I.C.S.: 445110

Personnel:
Guillermo Gonzalez Nova *(Chm)*
Carlos Gonzalez Zabalegui *(Vice Chm & CEO)*
Luis Felipe Gonzalez Solana *(Vice Chm)*

Board of Directors:
Guillermo Gonzalez Nova
Santiago Garcia Garcia
Rodolfo Garcia Gomez de Parada
Pablo J. Gonzalez Guerra
Luis Felipe Gonzalez Solana
Miguel Angel Gonzalez Solana
Carlos Gonzalez Zabalegui
Luis Felipe Gonzalez Zabalegui
Luis Felipe Guichard Gonzalez
Jose Ignacio Llano Gutierrez
Alberto G. Saavedra Olavrrieta
Fermin Sobero San Martin
Joaquin Solis Rivera

CONTROLADORA VUELA COMPANIA DE AVIACION, S.A.B. DE C.V.

(d/b/a Volaris)
Av Antonio Dovali Jaime No 70 13th Floor Tower B
Colonia Zedec Santa Fe, Mexico, 01210, Mexico
Tel.: (52) 55 1105 2300
Web Site: www.volaris.mx
Year Founded: 2005
VLRS—(NYSE)
Rev.: $919,487,132
Assets: $448,598,583
Liabilities: $364,043,784
Net Worth: $84,554,800
Earnings: $15,996,982
Emp.: 2,569
Fiscal Year-end: 12/31/12

Business Description:
Air Transportation
S.I.C.: 4512
N.A.I.C.S.: 481111

Personnel:
Gilberto Perez Alonso Cifuentes *(Chm)*
Enrique Beltranena *(CEO)*
Fernando Suarez *(CFO)*
James Nides *(COO)*
Holger Blankenstein *(Chief Compliance Officer)*
Jaime Pous *(Gen Counsel)*

Board of Directors:
Gilberto Perez Alonso Cifuentes
Pedro Carlos Aspe Armella
Jose Luis Fernandez Fernandez
Brian Hanna Franke
William A. Franke
Harry F. Krensky
Roberto Jose Kriete Avila
Rodolfo Montemayor Garza
Joaquin Alberto Palomo Deneke
John A. Slowik
Jorge Antonio Vargas Diez Barroso

CONTROLCIRCLE LTD.

Hertsmere House 2 Hertsmere Road
London, E14 4AB, United Kingdom
Tel.: (44) 8454591111
Fax: (44) 2075176501
E-Mail: sales@controlcircle.com
Web Site: www.controlcircle.com
Year Founded: 2001
Sales Range: $10-24.9 Million
Emp.: 51

Business Description:
IT Services
S.I.C.: 7373
N.A.I.C.S.: 541512

Personnel:
Colin Tenwick *(Chm)*
Carmen Carey *(CEO)*
Simon Hancock *(CFO)*

CONVENIENCE RETAIL ASIA LIMITED

5th Floor LiFung Tower 888 Cheung Sha Wan Road
Kowloon, NT, China (Hong Kong)
Tel.: (852) 29916300
Fax: (852) 29916302
E-Mail: investor@cr-asia.com
Web Site: www.cr-asia.com
831—(HKG)
Rev.: $550,657,506
Assets: $248,176,783
Liabilities: $117,269,193
Net Worth: $130,907,590
Earnings: $25,783,681
Emp.: 6,515
Fiscal Year-end: 12/31/12

Business Description:
Convenience Store Operator
S.I.C.: 5411
N.A.I.C.S.: 445120

Personnel:
Richard Lap Bun Yeung *(CEO)*
Chi Kin Pak *(COO)*
Srinivasan Parthasarathy *(Chief Compliance Officer)*
Maria Sau Ping Li *(Sec)*

Board of Directors:
Victor Kwok King Fung
Malcolm Man Chung Au
Raymond Kuo Fung Ch'ien
Benedict Yew Teck Chang
William Kwok Lun Fung
Jeremy Paul Egerton Hobbins
Anthony Kai Yiu Lo
Chi Kin Pak
Godfrey Ernest Scotchbrook
Richard Lap Bun Yeung
Hongyi Zhang

Royal Bank of Canada Trust Company (Cayman) Limited
4th Floor Royal Bank House 24 Shedden Road
PO Box 1586
Georgetown, Cayman Islands

Transfer Agents:
Tricor Abacus Limited
26/F Tesbury Centre 28 Queen's Road East
Hong Kong, China (Hong Kong)

Royal Bank of Canada Trust Company (Cayman) Limited
4th Floor Royal Bank House 24 Shedden Road
PO Box 1586
Georgetown, Cayman Islands

Subsidiary:

Saint Honore Holdings Co. Ltd (1)
5F Express Industrial Building
43 Heung Yip Road, Hong Kong, China (Hong Kong)
Tel.: (852) 28730032
Fax: (852) 2873 4975
E-Mail: feedback@sthonore.com
Web Site: www.sthonore.com
Sales Range: $75-99.9 Million
Emp.: 1,950
Bakery
S.I.C.: 5461
N.A.I.C.S.: 311811
Glenn Chan Wai Cheung *(Chm)*
Shum Wing Hon *(Deputy Chm)*
Carrina Chan Wong Man Li *(Mng Dir)*

CONVERGENET HOLDINGS LIMITED

Arcay House 3 Anerley Road
Parktown, 2193, South Africa
Tel.: (27) 128093368
Fax: (27) 866348480
E-Mail: arlenet@convergenet.co.za
Web Site: www.convergenet.co.za
Year Founded: 2005
CVN—(JSE)
Emp.: 1,000

Business Description:
Holding Company; Information & Communications Technology Products & Services
S.I.C.: 6719
N.A.I.C.S.: 551112

Personnel:
Daniel Frederik Bisschoff *(Interim CEO)*
Sandile Swana *(CEO)*
Hanno van Dyk *(COO)*

Board of Directors:
Dumisani Dumekhaya Tabata
Lerato Mangope
Tim Molefe Modise
Nkosemntu Gladman Nika
Charles Edward Pettit
Sandile Swana
Hanno van Dyk

Transfer Agent:
Computershare Investor Services (Pty) Ltd.
70 Marshall Street
Johannesburg, 2001, South Africa
Tel.: (27) 11 370 5000
Fax: (27) 11 370 5487

Subsidiaries:

Andrews Kit (Pty) Ltd (1)
3 Monza Close Kyalami Bus Park
Johannesburg, Gauteng, 1685, South Africa
Tel.: (27) 114662744
Fax: (27) 114662739
E-Mail: contkit@contkit.co.za
Web Site: www.contkit.co.za
Emp.: 131
Telecommunication Installation Solutions
S.I.C.: 1731
N.A.I.C.S.: 238210
Noel Andrews *(Mng Dir)*

ConvergeNet Holdings Limited—(Continued)

Contract Kitting (Pty) Ltd (1)
7 Monza Close
Kyalami Business Park, Kyalami, 1685, South Africa
Mailing Address:
PO Box 6285
Halfway House, Johannesburg, 1685, South Africa
Tel.: (27) 11 466 2744
Fax: (27) 11 466 2739
Web Site: www.contkit.co.za
Information & Communication Technology Services
S.I.C.: 7336
N.A.I.C.S.: 541430
Etienne Visser *(Mng Dir)*

ConvergeNet SA (Pty) Ltd (1)
1 Fl Unit 5 Tiger Vly Ofc Park Silverlakes Dr Tiger Vly, Pretoria, Gauteng, 0054, South Africa
Tel.: (27) 214186702
Fax: (27) 866351393
E-Mail: arlenet@convergenet.co.za
Emp.: 5
Used Network Equipments Sales
S.I.C.: 5065
N.A.I.C.S.: 423690
Pieter Willem Johannes Bouwer *(CEO)*

Interface Network Technology (Pty) Ltd (1)
1016 Pretorius Ave
PO BOX 10524
Centurion, Pretoria, Gauteng, 0046, South Africa
Tel.: (27) 126442466
Fax: (27) 126442465
E-Mail: riza@intafrica.co.za
Web Site: www.intafrica.co.za
Emp.: 12
Data Communication Software Development Services
S.I.C.: 7371
N.A.I.C.S.: 541511
Christian de Waal *(Project Mgr-Sls)*

Navix Distribution (Pty) Ltd (1)
7 Monza Close
Kyalami Business Park, Kyalami, 1684, South Africa
Tel.: (27) 11 466 3936/7
Information & Communication Technology Services
S.I.C.: 7336
N.A.I.C.S.: 541430

netXcom (Pty) Ltd (1)
Prosperitas Building Unit 5 Tiger Valley Office Park
Silver Lakes Drive, Pretoria, 0081, South Africa
Tel.: (27) 128093368
Fax: (27) 866351393
E-Mail: nico@netxcom.co.za
Web Site: www.convergenet.com
Emp.: 2
Information & Communication Technology Services
S.I.C.: 7336
N.A.I.C.S.: 541430
Nico Wosthuizen *(Mgr)*

Sizwe Africa IT Group (Pty) Ltd (1)
Cnr's Landmark 35 Waterloo Ave
Kosmosdal
Samrand, Centurion, Gauteng, 0157, South Africa
Tel.: (27) 126575300
Fax: (27) 126570548
E-Mail: sales@sizwegroup.co.za
Web Site: www.sizwegroup.co.za
Emp.: 500
Information & Communication Technology Services
S.I.C.: 7336
N.A.I.C.S.: 541430
Kgaume Benjamin James Kekana *(Chm)*
Tim Molefe Modise *(CEO)*

Subsidiaries:

Sizwe Business Networking (Pty) Ltd (2)
Sizwe House Corner Landmarks and Waterloo Ave
Centurion, Kosmosdel, 0157, South Africa
Tel.: (27) 126575300
Fax: (27) 120570548
E-Mail: bongi.radvbe@sizwegroup.co.za
Web Site: www.sizwegroup.co.za
Emp.: 590
Information Communications Technology Support Services
S.I.C.: 4813
N.A.I.C.S.: 517110

Smart Box Support Services (Pty) Ltd (2)
35 Landmarks Rd Sizwe House
Samrand, Pretoria, Gauteng, 0002, South Africa
Tel.: (27) 126570619
Fax: (27) 865049505
Information Communications Technology Support Services
S.I.C.: 4813
N.A.I.C.S.: 517110

Subsidiaries:

Leboa IT Solutions (Pty) Ltd (3)
58B King Edward Dr Willows
Bloemfontein, Free State, 9300, South Africa
Tel.: (27) 514472206
Fax: (27) 514486215
E-Mail: support@leboa.co.za
Web Site: www.leboa.co.za
Emp.: 10
Information & Communication Technology Services
S.I.C.: 4899
N.A.I.C.S.: 517919
Faye Delport Cader *(Mng Dir)*

Setsibi IT Support Services (Pty) Ltd (3)
91 Retief St
Potchefstroom, 2520, South Africa
Tel.: (27) 182978518
Fax: (27) 182977060
Web Site: www.setsibi.co.za
Emp.: 11
Information Technology Support Services
S.I.C.: 7371
N.A.I.C.S.: 541511
Hosmeyer Devos *(Mgr)*

Tswelopele Technological Solutions (Pty) Ltd (2)
Sizwe House 35 Landmarks Waterloo Ave
Pretoria, Gauteng, South Africa
Tel.: (27) 126575300
Fax: (27) 865543650
Web Site: www.sizwegroup.co.za
Communication Software Development Services
S.I.C.: 7371
N.A.I.C.S.: 541511
Timothy Modise *(Mng Dir)*

Structured Connectivity Solutions (Pty) Ltd (1)
Unit 14 a Wild Fig Bus Park 1494
Cranberry St Honeydew Ext 1919
Johannesburg, Gauteng, 2170, South Africa
Tel.: (27) 117942240
Fax: (27) 117945162
Web Site: www.scs-za.com
Emp.: 15
Information Technology Solutions
S.I.C.: 7373
N.A.I.C.S.: 541512
Andrew Scheepers *(Exec Dir)*

Telesto Communications (Pty) Ltd (1)
The Greens Ofc Park Mount Edgecomb
Bldg 26 Charles De Gaulle Crescent
Centurion, Gauteng, 0169, South Africa
Tel.: (27) 126653010
Fax: (27) 866175106
E-Mail: kellyn@telesto.co.za
Emp.: 9
Call Center Operation Services
S.I.C.: 7389
N.A.I.C.S.: 561422

XDSL Networking Solutions (Pty) Ltd (1)
977 Schoeman Street
Arcadia, Pretoria, 0083, South Africa
Tel.: (27) 86 100 9375
Fax: (27) 86 673 8150
Information & Communication Technology Services
S.I.C.: 7336
N.A.I.C.S.: 541430

CONVERGENT MINERALS LTD.

Suite 702 Level 7 121 Walker Street
North Sydney, NSW, 2060, Australia
Tel.: (61) 2 9956 8750
Fax: (61) 2 9956 8751
E-Mail: info@convergentminerals.com
Web Site: www.convergentminerals.com
CVG—(ASX)
Rev.: $72,293
Assets: $10,945,453
Liabilities: $282,633
Net Worth: $10,662,820
Earnings: ($1,271,116)
Fiscal Year-end: 06/30/13
Business Description:
Mineral Exploration
S.I.C.: 1481
N.A.I.C.S.: 213115
Personnel:
David W. Price *(CEO)*
Hamlet Hacobian *(CFO & Sec)*
Board of Directors:
Robert Gordon Reynolds
Glenn E. Goodacre
John Haggman

Subsidiary:

Montague Resources Australia Pty Ltd. (1)
Level 2 45 Stirling Hwy
Inglewood, WA, 6052, Australia
Tel.: (61) 8 9423 3233
Fax: (61) 8 9271 2911
Nickel Ore Mining Services
S.I.C.: 1021
N.A.I.C.S.: 212234

CONVERSION CAPITAL PARTNERS LTD.

Craven House 16 Northumberland Avenue
London, WC2N 5AP, United Kingdom
Tel.: (44) 20 7808 4758
Year Founded: 2003
Business Description:
Private Investment Firm
S.I.C.: 6211
N.A.I.C.S.: 523999
Personnel:
William Ty Comfort, III *(Principal)*

U.S. Holding:

Vendome Group, LLC (1)
6 E 32nd St 8th Fl
New York, NY 10016-5422
Tel.: (212) 812-8420
Fax: (212) 228-1308
E-Mail: info@vendomegrp.com
Web Site: www.vendomegrp.com
Emp.: 33
Periodicals Publisher
S.I.C.: 2721
N.A.I.C.S.: 511120
Jane Butler *(Founder & CEO)*
Mark Fried *(Pres)*

CONVERSUS CAPITAL, L.P.

Trafalgar Court Les Banques
Saint Peter Port, Guernsey GY1 3QL
Tel.: (44) 1481745175
Fax: (44) 1481745176
E-Mail: ccap@conversus.com
Web Site: www.conversus.com
Year Founded: 2007
CCAP—(EUR)
Business Description:
Investment Mangement Services
S.I.C.: 6211
N.A.I.C.S.: 523999
Personnel:
Paul G. Guilbert *(Chm)*
Timothy A. Smith *(CFO)*
Board of Directors:
Paul G. Guilbert
Hoagland R. Hoagland, Jr.
Kathryn A. Matthews
Per Johan Stromberg

Subsidiary:

Conversus GP, Limited (1)
Trafalgar Court Les Banques
Saint Peter Port, Guernsey GY1 3QL
Tel.: (44) 1481 745 175
Fax: (44) 1481 745 176
Web Site: www.conversus.com
Emp.: 28
Investment Management Services
S.I.C.: 6799
N.A.I.C.S.: 523920
Tim Smith *(CFO)*

CONVERTO AS

Fjordalleen 16
0250 Oslo, Norway
Mailing Address:
Postboks 1423
0115 Oslo, Norway
Tel.: (47) 24 13 00 00
Fax: (47) 24 13 01 01
E-Mail: mail@converto.no
Web Site: www.converto.no
Year Founded: 2009
Business Description:
Investment Management & Advisory Services
S.I.C.: 6799
N.A.I.C.S.: 523920
Personnel:
Frank Reite *(CEO)*

Holding:

Norway Seafoods Group AS (1)
Inkognitogaten 8
0258 Oslo, Norway (73.63%)
Mailing Address:
PO Box 1301
Vika, NO 0112 Oslo, Norway
Tel.: (47) 70 11 86 00
Fax: (47) 70 11 86 92
E-Mail: norway@norwayseafoods.com
Web Site: www.norwayseafoods.com
NWSF—(OSL)
Seafood Producer & Distr
S.I.C.: 5146
N.A.I.C.S.: 424460
Bjarne Borgersen *(Chm)*
Niclas Ljungblom *(Vice Chm)*
Thomas H. Farstad *(CEO)*
Anna Nord Bjercke *(CFO)*

CONVEY-ALL INDUSTRIES INC.

130 Canada Street
PO Box 2008
Winkler, MB, R6W 4B7, Canada
Tel.: (204) 325-4195
Fax: (204) 325-8116
Toll Free: (800) 418-9461
E-Mail: info@convey-all.com
Web Site: www.convey-all.com
Year Founded: 1983
Rev.: $12,744,604
Emp.: 115
Business Description:
Conveyor Systems Mfr
S.I.C.: 3535
N.A.I.C.S.: 333922
Personnel:
Bob Toews *(Pres)*

CONVISUAL AG

Essener Strasse 99
46047 Oberhausen, Germany
Tel.: (49) 208 97 69 5 100
Fax: (49) 208 97 69 5 134
E-Mail: info@convisual.com

Web Site: www.convisual.com
C1V—(DEU)
Business Description:
Communication Software Publishing Services
S.I.C.: 7372
N.A.I.C.S.: 511210
Personnel:
Thomas Wolf *(CEO)*
Markus Hussmann *(CMO)*

CONVOY FINANCIAL SERVICES HOLDINGS LIMITED

39/F Convoy 169 Electric Road North Point
Hong Kong, China (Hong Kong)
Tel.: (852) 3601 3601
Fax: (852) 2311 1300
E-Mail: info@convoy.com.hk
Web Site: www.convoy.com.hk
1019—(HKG)
Rev.: $90,745,468
Assets: $50,972,001
Liabilities: $26,585,622
Net Worth: $24,386,379
Earnings: ($881,502)
Emp.: 325
Fiscal Year-end: 12/31/12
Business Description:
Insurance & Financial Services
S.I.C.: 6411
N.A.I.C.S.: 524298
Personnel:
Quincy Lee Man Wong *(Chm)*
Rosetta Sut Sam Fong *(CEO)*
Mark Kwong Yiu Mak *(CFO)*
Iris May Ling Law *(COO)*
Ernest Tsz Kin Chan *(Chief Comml Officer)*
Wan Chong Mok *(Compliance Officer)*
Henry Kin Man Shin *(Chief Distr Officer)*
Kim Hang Chow *(Sec)*
Board of Directors:
Quincy Lee Man Wong
Rosetta Sut Sam Fong
Francine Kwong Wing Ting Fu
Peter Yiu Ho Ma
Mark Kwong Yiu Mak
Davy Ka Chee Wu
Legal Counsel:
Tsun & Partners
Suites 1002-03 10th Floor Aon China Building
29 Queen's Road, Central, China (Hong Kong)

Conyers Dill & Pearman
Cricket Square Hutchins Drive
PO Box 2681
Georgetown, Grand Cayman, Cayman Islands

Butterfield Fulcrum Group (Cayman) Limited
Butterfield House 68 Fort Street
PO Box 609
Georgetown, Cayman Islands
Transfer Agents:
Tricor Investor Services Limited
26th Floor Tesbury Centre 28 Queens Road East
Wanchai, China (Hong Kong)

Butterfield Fulcrum Group (Cayman) Limited
Butterfield House 68 Fort Street
PO Box 609
Georgetown, Cayman Islands

CONWAY MARSH GARRETT TECHNOLOGIES LIMITED

(Formerly Egide UK Limited)
Egide House Thompson Drive
Bentwaters Parks
Rendlesham, Woodbridge, Suffolk, IP12 2TW, United Kingdom
Tel.: (44) 1394 445 100
Fax: (44) 1394 445 109
E-Mail: sales@egideuk.com
Web Site: www.egideuk.com
Business Description:
Metal, Ceramic & Plastic Injected Moulding Mfr
S.I.C.: 3364
N.A.I.C.S.: 331523
Personnel:
Christopher Conway *(Mng Dir)*

CONWAY RESOURCES INC.

2900 Chemin des Quatre Bourgeois
Suite 207
Quebec, QC, G1V 1Y4, Canada
Tel.: (418) 871-3334
Fax: (418) 871-8333
E-Mail: info@ressources-conway.com
Web Site: www.ressources-conway.com
Year Founded: 2005
CWY—(TSXV)
Rev.: $6,587
Assets: $7,732,852
Liabilities: $1,431,668
Net Worth: $6,301,184
Earnings: ($223,758)
Fiscal Year-end: 05/31/13
Business Description:
Mineral Exploration Services
S.I.C.: 1081
N.A.I.C.S.: 213114
Personnel:
Laurent Beaudoin *(Pres & CEO)*
Sylvie Mazuet *(CFO & Sec)*
Board of Directors:
Laurent Beaudoin
Sylvie Mazuet
David Quessy
Philippe Quessy
Transfer Agent:
Computershare Investor Services Inc
1100 University Street 12 Floor
Montreal, QC, Canada

CONWERT IMMOBILIEN INVEST SE

Alserbachstrasse 32
1090 Vienna, Austria
Tel.: (43) 1521450
Fax: (43) 152145 8111
E-Mail: cw@conwert.at
Web Site: www.conwert.at
CWI—(VIE)
Rev.: $841,490,867
Assets: $3,836,315,266
Liabilities: $2,456,491,016
Net Worth: $1,379,824,250
Earnings: ($231,675,857)
Emp.: 651
Fiscal Year-end: 12/31/12
Business Description:
Real Estate Investment Services
S.I.C.: 6211
N.A.I.C.S.: 523999
Personnel:
Johannes Meran *(Chm)*
Franz Pruckner *(Vice Chm)*
Board of Directors:
Johannes Meran
Kerstinn Gelbmann
Franz Pruckner
Eveline Steinberger-Kern
Alexander Tavakoli

Subsidiaries:

1010 Wien, Marc-Aurel-Strasse 7 Immobilientreuhand GmbH (1)
Albertgasse 35
1080 Vienna, Austria
Tel.: (43) 1 521 45 0
Fax: (43) 1 521 45 111
Residential Property Management Services
S.I.C.: 6531
N.A.I.C.S.: 531311

Centum Immobilien GmbH (1)
Albertg 35
1080 Vienna, Austria
Tel.: (43) 1521450
Fax: (43) 1 52145 111
Web Site: www.conwert.at
Emp.: 50
Real Estate Management Services
S.I.C.: 6531
N.A.I.C.S.: 531390
Thomas Doll *(Gen Mgr)*

Chorherr & Reiter okologische Bauprojekte GmbH (1)
Karte von Albertgasse 35
Vienna, 1080, Austria
Tel.: (43) 1 52145 0
Fax: (43) 1 52145111
Residential Property Development Services
S.I.C.: 1522
N.A.I.C.S.: 236116

Con Tessa Immobilienverwertung GmbH (1)
Albertgasse 35
1080 Vienna, Austria
Tel.: (43) 152145450
Fax: (43) 152145111
E-Mail: ofice@conwert.at
Residential Property Management Services
S.I.C.: 6531
N.A.I.C.S.: 531311

Con value one Immobilien GmbH (1)
Albertg 35
1080 Vienna, Austria
Tel.: (43) 1521450
Fax: (43) 152145111
E-Mail: valentino.donau@conwert.ag
Web Site: www.conwert.ag
Emp.: 60
Real Estate Management Services
S.I.C.: 6531
N.A.I.C.S.: 531390
Donau Valentino *(Gen Mgr)*

Con Wert Handelsges.m.b.H. (1)
Albertgasse 35
1080 Vienna, Austria
Tel.: (43) 1521450
Fax: (43) 152145111
Residential Property Management Services
S.I.C.: 6531
N.A.I.C.S.: 531311

conwert Baudevelopment GmbH (1)
Albertgasse 35
Vienna, 1080, Austria
Tel.: (43) 152145658
Fax: (43) 152145111
E-Mail: office@conwert.at
Web Site: www.conwert-bautraeger.at
Residential Property Development Services
S.I.C.: 1522
N.A.I.C.S.: 236116
Thomas Dooll *(Mng Dir)*

conwert Bautrager GmbH (1)
Albertgasse 35
1080 Vienna, Austria
Tel.: (43) 1 521 45 0
Fax: (43) 1 521 45 111
E-Mail: office@conwert-bautraeger.at
Web Site: www.conwert-bautraeger.at
Residential Property Development Services
S.I.C.: 1522
N.A.I.C.S.: 236116

conwert Invest GmbH (1)
Albertgasse 35
Vienna, Wien, 1080, Austria
Tel.: (43) 1521450
Fax: (43) 1 521 45 111
Real Estate Investment Services
S.I.C.: 6211
N.A.I.C.S.: 523999

conwert Management GmbH (1)
Albertgasse 35
Vienna, 1080, Austria
Tel.: (43) 1521450
Fax: (43) 1 521 45111
Web Site: www.conwert.at/web/en/view.php?MENUEID=25&USERNAME=&TEMPID=
Emp.: 100
Real Estate Management Services
S.I.C.: 6531
N.A.I.C.S.: 531390
Folker Reibel *(CEO)*

Conwert Securitisation Holding GmbH (1)
Albertgasse 35
Vienna, 1080, Austria
Tel.: (43) 1521450
Fax: (43) 1 521 45 111
Real Estate Investment Services
S.I.C.: 6211
N.A.I.C.S.: 523999

Cw Bautrager Projekt Eins GmbH (1)
Albertgasse 35
1080 Vienna, Austria
Tel.: (43) 1521450
Fax: (43) 1 521 45 111
Real Estate Management Services
S.I.C.: 6531
N.A.I.C.S.: 531390

G-Unternehmensbeteiligung GmbH (1)
Albertgasse 35
1080 Vienna, Austria
Tel.: (43) 1521450
Real Estate Management Services
S.I.C.: 6531
N.A.I.C.S.: 531390

G1 Immobilienverwertung GmbH (1)
Albertgasse 35
Vienna, 1080, Austria
Tel.: (43) 152145
Fax: (43) 152145111
Real Estate Management Services
S.I.C.: 6531
N.A.I.C.S.: 531390

GGJ Beteiligungs GmbH (1)
Albertgasse 35
Vienna, 1080, Austria
Tel.: (43) 1521450
Fax: (43) 152145111
Property Development Services
S.I.C.: 6531
N.A.I.C.S.: 531311

GJ-Beteiligungs GmbH (1)
alserpathstrasse 32
Vienna, 1090, Austria
Tel.: (43) 1521450
Fax: (43) 152145111
E-Mail: cw@conwert.at
Emp.: 100
Investment Management Services
S.I.C.: 6211
N.A.I.C.S.: 523999
Thomas Doll *(CFO)*

GK Immobilienverwertung GmbH (1)
Albertgasse 35
1080 Vienna, Austria
Tel.: (43) 1 52145 0
Fax: (43) 1 52145 111
Real Estate Management Services
S.I.C.: 6531
N.A.I.C.S.: 531390

GKB Beteiligungs GmbH (1)
Albertgasse 35
Vienna, 1080, Austria
Tel.: (43) 1521450
Fax: (43) 152145111
E-Mail: cw@conwert.at
Emp.: 50
Property Management Servcies
S.I.C.: 6531
N.A.I.C.S.: 531311
Volker Riebel *(Mng Dir)*

KALLCO PROJEKT Wienerberg City Entwicklungsgesellschaft m.b.H (1)
Albertgasse 35
1080 Vienna, Austria
Tel.: (43) 154625
Fax: (43) 1 546 25 33
Commercial Property Development Services
S.I.C.: 1542
N.A.I.C.S.: 236220

mog-Projektentwicklung GmbH (1)
Albertgasse 35
Vienna, 1080, Austria
Tel.: (43) 1521450
Fax: (43) 152145111
Commercial Property Development Services
S.I.C.: 1542
N.A.I.C.S.: 236220

RESAG Insurance Broker GmbH (1)
Albertgasse 35
1080 Vienna, Austria
Tel.: (43) 1 408 31 57
Fax: (43) 1 408 31 57 99

Conwert Immobilien Invest SE—(Continued)

E-Mail: resag@resag-insurance.com
Web Site: www.resag-insurance.com
Insurance Brokerage Services
S.I.C.: 6411
N.A.I.C.S.: 524210
K. R. Manfred Heiss *(Mgr)*

RESAG Properties Management GmbH (1)
Albertgasse 35
Vienna, 1080, Austria
Tel.: (43) 1262600
Fax: (43) 126260333
E-Mail: resag@resag-property.com
Web Site: www.resag-property.com
Real Estate Management Services
S.I.C.: 6531
N.A.I.C.S.: 531390

Rossauer Lande 47 - 49 Liegenschaftsverwaltungs GmbH (1)
Alserbachstrasse 32
Vienna, 1090, Austria
Tel.: (43) 1521450
Web Site: www.conwert.com
Real Estate Management Services
S.I.C.: 6531
N.A.I.C.S.: 531390

SHG 6 Immobilienentwicklungs GmbH (1)
Albertgasse 35
Vienna, Wien, 1080, Austria
Tel.: (43) 1 521 45 0
Fax: (43) 1 521 45 111
Residential Building Remodeling Services
S.I.C.: 1522
N.A.I.C.S.: 236118

Stadiongasse 4 Liegenschaftsverwertungs GmbH (1)
Albertgasse 35
1080 Vienna, Austria
Tel.: (43) 1521450
Fax: (43) 152145111
E-Mail: cw@conwert.at
Emp.: 100
Real Estate Management Services
S.I.C.: 6531
N.A.I.C.S.: 531390
Thomas Doll *(Mng Dir)*

Stubenbastei 10 und 12 Immobilien GmbH (1)
Albertgasse 35
1080 Vienna, Austria
Tel.: (43) 1521450
Property Management Services
S.I.C.: 6531
N.A.I.C.S.: 531312

TPI Immobilien Holding GmbH (1)
Albertgasse 35
Vienna, 1080, Austria
Tel.: (43) 1 5214 5
Real Estate Investment Services
S.I.C.: 6211
N.A.I.C.S.: 523999

WZH Projektentwicklung GmbH (1)
Albertgasse 35
1080 Vienna, Austria
Tel.: (43) 1521450
Fax: (43) 152145111
Residential Property Management Services
S.I.C.: 6531
N.A.I.C.S.: 531311

Non-U.S. Subsidiaries:

alt+kelber Eigenheim GmbH (1)
Bahnhofstreet 7
Heilbronn, Baden-Wurttemberg, 74072, Germany
Tel.: (49) 713160900
Fax: (49) 7131609019
Apartment Construction & Sales
S.I.C.: 1531
N.A.I.C.S.: 236117

alt+kelber Immobiliengruppe GmbH (1)
Bahnhofstrasse 7
74072 Heilbronn, Baden-Wurttemberg, Germany
Tel.: (49) 713160900
Fax: (49) 7131 6090 19
E-Mail: info@altundkelber.de
Web Site: www.altundkelber.de
Emp.: 300
Residential Real Estate Management Services
S.I.C.: 6531
N.A.I.C.S.: 531311

alt+kelber Immobilienkontor GmbH (1)
Strasse Des Friedens 104
Gera, Thuringen, 07548, Germany
Tel.: (49) 365 82180
Fax: (49) 365 82181
Apartment Construction & Sales
S.I.C.: 1522
N.A.I.C.S.: 236116

alt+kelber Immobilienmanagement GmbH (1)
Bahnhofstreet 7
74072 Heilbronn, Baden-Wurttemberg, Germany
Tel.: (49) 713160900
Fax: (49) 7131609019
Real Estate Management Servcies
S.I.C.: 6531
N.A.I.C.S.: 531390

alt+kelber Immobilienverwaltung GmbH (1)
Bahnhofstrasse 7
74072 Heilbronn, Baden-Wurttemberg, Germany
Tel.: (49) 713160900
Fax: (49) 7131 6090 19
Emp.: 25
Real Estate Management Services
S.I.C.: 6531
N.A.I.C.S.: 531390

alt+kelber Wohnungsprivatisierung GmbH (1)
Frau Obrikatis Charlottenstreet 18
Berlin, 10117, Germany
Tel.: (49) 30 897840 30
Fax: (49) 30 897840 11
E-Mail: cw@conwert.at
Real Estate Management Services
S.I.C.: 6531
N.A.I.C.S.: 531390
Worpi Berlin *(Gen Mgr)*

Bokreta Management Kft (1)
IX ker Viola u 13 15 Fsz 2
1094 Budapest, Hungary
Tel.: (36) 14570757
Fax: (36) 14570760
E-Mail: info@bokreta.hu
Web Site: www.bokreta.hu
Emp.: 2
Real Estate Management Services
S.I.C.: 6531
N.A.I.C.S.: 531390

conwert Alfhild Invest GmbH (1)
Auf der Eierwiese 10
82031 Grunwald, Bavaria, Germany
Tel.: (49) 896496000
Fax: (49) 8964960020
Real Estate Management Services
S.I.C.: 6531
N.A.I.C.S.: 531390

conwert & kelber Besitz 11/2007 GmbH (1)
Bahnhofstreet 7
74072 Heilbronn, Baden-Wurttemberg, Germany
Tel.: (49) 7131 60900
Real Estate Management Services
S.I.C.: 6531
N.A.I.C.S.: 531390

conwert & kelber Bestand 10/2007 GmbH (1)
Bahnhofstreet 7
Heilbronn, Baden-Wurttemberg, 74072, Germany
Tel.: (49) 7131609010
Fax: (49) 7131609019
Residential Property Development Services
S.I.C.: 1521
N.A.I.C.S.: 236115

Conwert Aries Invest GmbH (1)
Charlottenstreet 18
Berlin, 10117, Germany
Tel.: (49) 30240830000
Fax: (49) 30 240830240
Residential Property Development Services
S.I.C.: 1522
N.A.I.C.S.: 236116

conwert Berlin 2 Immobilien Invest GmbH (1)
Charlotten Street 18
Berlin, 10117, Germany
Tel.: (49) 30 240830000
Fax: (49) 30 240830240
Residential Property Development Services
S.I.C.: 6531
N.A.I.C.S.: 531311

conwert Capricornus Invest GmbH (1)
Charlottenstreet 18
Berlin, 10117, Germany
Tel.: (49) 30240830000
Investment Management Services
S.I.C.: 6211
N.A.I.C.S.: 523999

Conwert Carina Invest Gmbh (1)
Charlottenstreet 18
Berlin, 10117, Germany
Tel.: (49) 30 240830 000
Fax: (49) 30 240830 240
Residential Property Development Services
S.I.C.: 1522
N.A.I.C.S.: 236116

conwert Cassiopeia Invest GmbH (1)
Bahnhostreet 7
Heilbronn, Baden-Wurttemberg, 74072, Germany
Tel.: (49) 7131 60900
Fax: (49) 7131 609019
Residential Property Development Services
S.I.C.: 1521
N.A.I.C.S.: 236115

conwert Deutschland Beteiligungsholding GmbH (1)
Charlottenstreet 18
Berlin, 10117, Germany
Tel.: (49) 30240830000
Fax: (49) 30240830240
Investment Management Services
S.I.C.: 6211
N.A.I.C.S.: 523999

conwert Deutschland Holding GmbH & Co KG (1)
Bahnhofstreet 7
Heilbronn, Baden-Wurttemberg, 74072, Germany
Tel.: (49) 713160900
Fax: (49) 7131609019
Residential Property Development Services
S.I.C.: 1521
N.A.I.C.S.: 236115

conwert Deutschland Immobilien GmbH (1)
Charlottenstreet 18
Berlin, 10117, Germany
Tel.: (49) 3089784063
Real Estate Management Services
S.I.C.: 6531
N.A.I.C.S.: 531390

conwert Dresden Zwei Invest GmbH (1)
Charlottenstreet 18
Berlin, 10117, Germany
Tel.: (49) 30 240830000
Fax: (49) 30 240830240
Residential Property Development Services
S.I.C.: 6531
N.A.I.C.S.: 531311

conwert Eisa III Invest GmbH (1)
Auf Der Eierwiese 10a
Grunwald, Bavaria, 82031, Germany
Tel.: (49) 30240830000
Residential Property Development Services
S.I.C.: 6531
N.A.I.C.S.: 531311

conwert epsilon Invest GmbH (1)
Reinhardtstreet 58
Berlin, 10117, Germany
Tel.: (49) 30240830000
Fax: (49) 30240830240
Residential Property Development Services
S.I.C.: 1522
N.A.I.C.S.: 236116

conwert Grazer Damm Development GmbH (1)
Charlottenstreet 18
Berlin, 10117, Germany
Tel.: (49) 30240830000
Fax: (49) 30240830240
Residential Property Development Services
S.I.C.: 1522
N.A.I.C.S.: 236116

conwert Kirchsteigfeld 11 Invest GmbH (1)
Charlottenstreet 18
Berlin, 10117, Germany
Tel.: (49) 30240830000
Fax: (49) 30240830240
Residential Property Development Services
S.I.C.: 1522
N.A.I.C.S.: 236116

conwert Kirchsteigfeld 12 Invest GmbH (1)
Charlottenstreet 18
Berlin, 10117, Germany
Tel.: (49) 30240830000
Fax: (49) 30240830240
Residential Property Development Services
S.I.C.: 1522
N.A.I.C.S.: 236116

conwert Kirchsteigfeld 13 Invest GmbH (1)
Charlottenstreet 18
Berlin, 10117, Germany
Tel.: (49) 30240830000
Fax: (49) 30 240830240
Residential Property Development Services
S.I.C.: 1521
N.A.I.C.S.: 236115

conwert Kirchsteigfeld 15 Invest GmbH (1)
Charlottenstreet 18
Berlin, 10117, Germany
Tel.: (49) 30 240830000
Fax: (49) 30 240830240
Residential Property Development Services
S.I.C.: 1522
N.A.I.C.S.: 236116

conwert Kirchsteigfeld 16 Invest GmbH (1)
Charlottenstreet 18
Berlin, 10117, Germany
Tel.: (49) 30240830000
Residential Property Development Services
S.I.C.: 1522
N.A.I.C.S.: 236116

conwert Kirchsteigfeld 18 Invest GmbH (1)
Charlottenstreet 18
Berlin, 10117, Germany
Tel.: (49) 30240830000
Residential Property Development Services
S.I.C.: 1522
N.A.I.C.S.: 236116

conwert Kirchsteigfeld Beteiligungs GmbH (1)
Charlottenstreet 18
Berlin, 10117, Germany
Tel.: (49) 30240830000
Fax: (49) 30 240830240
Residential Property Development Services
S.I.C.: 6531
N.A.I.C.S.: 531311

conwert lambda Invest GmbH (1)
Charlottenstreet 27
4105 Leipzig, Saxony, Germany
Tel.: (49) 3419804669
Investment Management Services
S.I.C.: 6211
N.A.I.C.S.: 523999

conwert Leo Invest GmbH (1)
Bahnhofstr 7
74072 Heilbronn, Baden-Wurttemberg, Germany
Tel.: (49) 7131 60900
Fax: (49) 7131 609019
Real Estate Property Investment Services
S.I.C.: 6726
N.A.I.C.S.: 525990

conwert Libra Invest GmbH (1)
Charlottenstrasse 18
Berlin, 10117, Germany

Tel.: (49) 30 240830000
Fax: (49) 30 240830240
Residential Property Development Services
S.I.C.: 1522
N.A.I.C.S.: 236116

Conwert Omega Invest GmbH (1)
Charlotten Strasse 18
10117 Berlin, Germany (100%)
Tel.: (49) 30240830000
Fax: (49) 30240830240
Real Estate Agents & Brokers Offices
S.I.C.: 6531
N.A.I.C.S.: 531210

conwert Phoenix Invest GmbH (1)
Charlottenstrasse 18
Berlin, 10117, Germany
Tel.: (49) 30 240830000
Fax: (49) 30 240830240
Investment Management Services
S.I.C.: 6211
N.A.I.C.S.: 523999

conwert Taurus Invest GmbH (1)
Bahnhofstrasse 7
Heilbronn, Baden-Wurttemberg, 74072, Germany
Tel.: (49) 30 240830000
Investment Management Services
S.I.C.: 6211
N.A.I.C.S.: 523999

conwert Vela Invest GmbH (1)
Charlottenstrasse 18
Berlin, 10117, Germany
Tel.: (49) 30240830000
Fax: (49) 30 240830240
Investment Management Services
S.I.C.: 6211
N.A.I.C.S.: 523999

conwert Virgo Invest GmbH (1)
Charlottenstrasse 18
Berlin, 10117, Germany
Tel.: (49) 30240830000
Investment Management Services
S.I.C.: 6211
N.A.I.C.S.: 523999

conwert Wali III Invest GmbH (1)
Auf Der Eierwiese 10
Grunwald, Bavaria, 82031, Germany
Tel.: (49) 896496000
Investment Management Services
S.I.C.: 6211
N.A.I.C.S.: 523999

conwert Wali Invest GmbH (1)
Auf Der Eierwiese 10
Grunwald, Bavaria, 82031, Germany
Tel.: (49) 896496000
Investment Management Services
S.I.C.: 6211
N.A.I.C.S.: 523999

Deutsche Heimstatten Omega GmbH & Co KG (1)
Bahnhofstrasse 7
74072 Heilbronn, Baden-Wurttemberg, Germany
Tel.: (49) 30240830000
Real Estate Management Services
S.I.C.: 6531
N.A.I.C.S.: 531390

Hornby Deutschland GmbH (1)
Ostpreubenstrasse 13
Rodental, Bavaria, 96472, Germany
Tel.: (49) 9563 5036 0
Fax: (49) 9563 3071 24
E-Mail: office@hornby.de
Web Site: www.hornby.de
Model Railway Equipment Distr
S.I.C.: 5088
N.A.I.C.S.: 423860

Kiraly utca 77 Kft (1)
Kiraly St 77
James Dean Shop, 1077 Budapest, Hungary
Tel.: (36) 13528739
Residential Property Development Services
S.I.C.: 6531
N.A.I.C.S.: 531311

KKS Projektentwicklung GmbH (1)
Haferkornstrasse 22
Leipzig, Saxony, 04129, Germany
Tel.: (49) 3419085555
Fax: (49) 341 9085556
Real Estate Management Services
S.I.C.: 6531
N.A.I.C.S.: 531390

KWG Kommunale Wohnen AG (1)
Alstertor 9
20095 Hamburg, Germany
Tel.: (49) 402263088100
Fax: (49) 402263088200
E-Mail: info@kwg-ag.de
Web Site: www.kwg-ag.de
BIW—(DEU)
Rev.: $112,859,285
Assets: $636,698,197
Liabilities: $405,449,200
Net Worth: $231,248,997
Earnings: $62,592,858
Emp.: 60
Fiscal Year-end: 12/31/12
Real Estate Development Services
S.I.C.: 6531
N.A.I.C.S.: 531390
Peer Witten *(Chm-Supervisory Bd)*
Torsten P. Hoffmann *(Member-Mgmt Bd)*

Subsidiaries:

KWG Grundbesitz I Verwaltungs GmbH (2)
Alstertor 9
20095 Hamburg, Germany
Tel.: (49) 402263088100
Fax: (49) 402263088200
E-Mail: ir@kwg-ag.de
Emp.: 20
Residential Property Management Services
S.I.C.: 6531
N.A.I.C.S.: 531311
Stavros Efremidis *(Mng Dir)*

KWG Grundbesitz II GmbH & Co. KG (2)
Alstertor 9
20095 Hamburg, Germany
Tel.: (49) 402263088100
Fax: (49) 402263088200
Emp.: 20
Residential Property Management Services
S.I.C.: 6531
N.A.I.C.S.: 531311

KWG Grundbesitz III GmbH (2)
ABC-Strasse 19
20354 Hamburg, Germany
Tel.: (49) 40 34962830
Fax: (49) 4034962832
Web Site: www.kwg-ag.de
Residential Property Management Services
S.I.C.: 6531
N.A.I.C.S.: 531311

KWG Grundbesitz IV GmbH (2)
ABC-Strasse 19
20354 Hamburg, Germany
Tel.: (49) 40 263088100
Residential Property Management Services
S.I.C.: 6531
N.A.I.C.S.: 531311

KWG Grundbesitz IX GmbH (2)
Alstertor 9
20095 Hamburg, Germany
Tel.: (49) 40226308810
Fax: (49) 402226308200
Web Site: www.kwgag-online.de
Emp.: 20
Residential Property Management Services
S.I.C.: 6531
N.A.I.C.S.: 531311
Stavros Efremidis *(Mng Dir)*

KWG Grundbesitz V GmbH (2)
Alstertor 9
20095 Hamburg, Germany
Tel.: (49) 40226308810
Fax: (49) 40226308820
E-Mail: einhaus@kwg-ag.de
Web Site: www.kwgag-online.de
Emp.: 20
Residential Property Management Services
S.I.C.: 6531
N.A.I.C.S.: 531311

KWG Grundbesitz VIII GmbH (2)
Alstertor 9
20095 Hamburg, Germany
Tel.: (49) 40226308810
Fax: (49) 40226308800
Emp.: 20
Residential Property Management Services
S.I.C.: 6531
N.A.I.C.S.: 531311

Siedlungs- und Wohnhausgesellschaft Sachsen Gesellschaft mit beschrankter Haftung (2)
Leipzigerstrasse 30
08371 Glauchau, Saxony, Germany
Tel.: (49) 3763778132
Fax: (49) 3763488504
E-Mail: info@swg-sachsen.de
Web Site: www.swg-sachsen.de
Residential Property Management Services
S.I.C.: 6531
N.A.I.C.S.: 531311

Pd sk Bratislava s.r.o. (1)
Venturska 16
811 01 Bratislava, Slovakia
Tel.: (421) 254410248
Fax: (421) 254410255
E-Mail: pdsk@pdsk.sk
Web Site: www.pdsk.sk
Emp.: 1
Residential Property Development Services
S.I.C.: 1522
N.A.I.C.S.: 236116
Viktor Magic *(Project Mgr)*

Pdcz brno s.r.o (1)
Hybesova 42
602 00 Brno, Czech Republic
Tel.: (420) 736533003
E-Mail: pdcz@pdcz.cz
Web Site: www.pdcz.cz
Property Development Services
S.I.C.: 6531
N.A.I.C.S.: 531312
Pavlina Vrbova *(Mgr)*

XX. Fiume utca I Kft (1)
Munkacsy
Budapest, Hungary
Tel.: (36) 14570758
Real Estate Management Services
S.I.C.: 6531
N.A.I.C.S.: 531390

THE CONYGAR INVESTMENT COMPANY PLC

Fourth Floor 110 Wigmore Street
London, W1U 3RW, United Kingdom
Tel.: (44) 2072588670
Fax: (44) 2074874641
E-Mail: admin@conygar.com
Web Site: www.conygar.com
CIC—(AIM)
Rev.: $26,573,071
Assets: $387,220,191
Liabilities: $129,489,311
Net Worth: $257,730,880
Earnings: $10,319,204
Emp.: 9
Fiscal Year-end: 09/30/13

Business Description:
Property Investment Services
S.I.C.: 6211
N.A.I.C.S.: 523999

Personnel:
Robert Thomas Ernest Ware *(CEO)*
Freddie Jones *(Exec-Property)*
Peter A. Batchelor *(Sec & Dir-Fin)*

Board of Directors:
Nigel J. Hamway
Peter A. Batchelor
Preston M. C. Rabl
Steven M. Vaughan
Robert Thomas Ernest Ware
Michael D. Wigley

Legal Counsel:
Wragge & Co. LLP
55 Colmore Row
Birmingham, United Kingdom

CONZZETA HOLDING AG

Giesshuebelstr 45
8045 Zurich, Switzerland
Tel.: (41) 444682444
Fax: (41) 444682481
E-Mail: info@conzzeta.ch
Web Site: www.conzzeta.ch
CZH—(SWX)
Rev.: $1,253,639,894
Assets: $1,369,920,434
Liabilities: $336,549,245
Net Worth: $1,033,371,189
Earnings: $50,024,323
Emp.: 3,627
Fiscal Year-end: 12/31/12

Business Description:
Holding Company; Sheet Metal Processing Systems, Glass Processing Systems, Automation Systems, Foam Materials, Sporting Goods, Graphic Coatings & Real Estate
S.I.C.: 6719
N.A.I.C.S.: 551112

Personnel:
Jacob Schmidheiny *(Chm)*
Robert Suter *(CEO & Member-Exec Bd)*
Kaspar W. Kelterborn *(CFO & Member-Exec Bd)*
Andre Brutsch *(Member-Exec Bd & Head-Glass Processing Sys Bus)*
Jakob Rohner *(Member-Exec Bd & Head-Graphic Coatings Bus)*
Rolf G. Schmid *(Member-Exec Bd & Head-Sporting Goods Bus)*
Guy Sellier *(Member-Exec Bd & Head-Automation Sys Bus)*
Ralph Siegle *(Member-Exec Bd & Head-Real Estate Bus)*
Bart J. ten Brink *(Member-Exec Bd & Head-Foam Matls Bus)*
Alex Waser *(Member-Exec Bd & Head-Sheet Metal Processing Sys Bus)*
Barbara Senn *(Gen Counsel)*

Board of Directors:
Jacob Schmidheiny
Matthias Auer
Thomas W. Bechtler
Werner Dubach
Philip Mosimann
Robert F. Spoerry

Subsidiaries:

Buttikofer AG (1)
Zetzwilerstrasse 763
Gontenschwil Aargau, 5728 Aarau, Switzerland (100%)
Tel.: (41) 627670000
Fax: (41) 627670001
E-Mail: buettikofer@foampartner.com
Web Site: www.buettikofer.ch
Emp.: 20
All Other Plastics Product Mfr
S.I.C.: 3089
N.A.I.C.S.: 326199
Herbert Abele *(Mng Dir)*

Bystronic Laser AG (1)
Industriestr 21
3362 Niederlenz, Switzerland (100%)
Tel.: (41) 629563333
Fax: (41) 629563380
E-Mail: info.laser@bystronic.com
Web Site: www.bystronic.com
Sales Range: $400-449.9 Million
Emp.: 1,390
Machine Tool Metal Forming Types Mfr
S.I.C.: 3541
N.A.I.C.S.: 333517
Ferdi Tongi *(CEO)*

Subsidiaries:

Bystronic Maschinen AG (2)
Industriestrasse 5
4922 Butzberg, Switzerland (100%)
Tel.: (41) 629587777
Fax: (41) 629587676
E-Mail: bystronic@bystronic-glass.com
Web Site: www.bystronic-glass.com
Emp.: 220
Machine Tool Metal Cutting Types Mfr
S.I.C.: 3541
N.A.I.C.S.: 333517
Richard Jacob *(CEO)*

Conzzeta Holding AG—(Continued)

Bystronic Sales AG (2)
Industriestrasse 21
Niederoenz, 3362 Niederlenz, Switzerland (100%)
Tel.: (41) 629563783
Fax: (41) 629563381
E-Mail: info.sales@bystronic.com
Web Site: www.bystronic.ch
Emp.: 500
Industrial Machinery & Equipment Whslr
S.I.C.: 3541
N.A.I.C.S.: 333517
Hugo Allemann *(Mng Dir)*

U.S. Subsidiary:

Bystronic Inc. (2)
200 Airport Rd
Elgin, IL 60123 (100%)
Tel.: (847) 214-0300
Fax: (631) 231-1040
E-Mail: info@bystronic.com
Web Site: www.bystronic.com
Flat Glass Mfr
S.I.C.: 3211
N.A.I.C.S.: 327211
Gary Wisniewski *(Mgr-Sls Admin)*

Non-U.S. Subsidiaries:

Bystronic Asia Pte. Ltd. (2)
2 Leng Kee Road # 03-05
Thye Hong Centre, 159086 Singapore, Singapore (100%)
Tel.: (65) 64722478
Fax: (65) 64722418
E-Mail: enquiry@bystronic.com.sg
Web Site: www.bystronic.com
Emp.: 13
Industrial Machinery & Equipment Merchant Whslr
S.I.C.: 5084
N.A.I.C.S.: 423830
Kwan Hoong Mak *(Mng Dir)*

Bystronic Austria GmbH (2)
Viennese Road 131
4020 Linz, Austria (100%)
Tel.: (43) 732341155
Fax: (43) 732341153
E-Mail: office@bystronic.at
Web Site: www.bystronic.at
Machine Tool Metal Forming Types Mfr
S.I.C.: 3541
N.A.I.C.S.: 333517
Purtenes Philpp *(Mng Dir)*

Bystronic Benelux B.V. (2)
Stek 8 3371 KG
Postbus 153, 3371 Hardinxveld-Giessendam, Netherlands (100%)
Tel.: (31) 184611020
Fax: (31) 184617774
E-Mail: sales.nl@bystronic.com
Web Site: www.bystronic.nl/cutting_and_bending/nl/nl/contact/index.php?navid=86&nl=1
Emp.: 24
Construction & Mining except Oil Well Machinery & Equipment Whslr
S.I.C.: 5082
N.A.I.C.S.: 423810
Twes Wolters *(Office Mgr)*

Bystronic Deutschland GmbH (2)
Romerstrasse 14
71296 Heimsheim, Germany (100%)
Tel.: (49) 703346990
Fax: (49) 70334699222
E-Mail: info.de@bystronic.com
Web Site: www.bystronic.de/
Industrial Machinery & Equipment Whslr
S.I.C.: 5084
N.A.I.C.S.: 423830

Bystronic do Brasil Ltda (2)
Rua Arapongas 285
83040-200 Sao Jose dos Pinhais, Brazil (100%)
Tel.: (55) 4133982000
Fax: (55) 4133981789
E-Mail: bystronic.br@bystronic.com
Web Site: www.bystronic.com
Emp.: 15
All Other Automotive Repair & Maintenance
S.I.C.: 7539
N.A.I.C.S.: 811198
Leonardo Olsen *(Mng Dir)*

Bystronic France SAS (2)
Parc Technopolis 3rd Ave du Canada
91940 Les Ulis, France (35%)
Tel.: (33) 169419984
Fax: (33) 169419951
E-Mail: info.fr@bystronic.com
Web Site: www.bystronic.com
Emp.: 45
Machine Tool Metal Cutting Types Mfr
S.I.C.: 5084
N.A.I.C.S.: 423830
Franck Cavalin *(Mng Dir)*

Bystronic Glass UK Ltd. (2)
Lodge Park
Hortonwood 30, TF1 7ET Telford, Shropshire, United Kingdom (100%)
Tel.: (44) 1952677971
Fax: (44) 1952670637
Web Site: www.bystronic-glass.com
Emp.: 18
Glass Product Mfr Made by Purchased Glass
S.I.C.: 3231
N.A.I.C.S.: 327215
Steven Powell *(Mng Dir)*

Bystronic Iberica S.A. (2)
Av Tenerife N 2 Edificio 1 3a Planta
Oficina D San Sebastian de los, 28700 Madrid, Spain (100%)
Tel.: (34) 916544878
Fax: (34) 916524983
E-Mail: sales.es@bystronic.com
Web Site: www.bystronic.com
Farm & Garden Machinery & Equipment Whslr
S.I.C.: 5083
N.A.I.C.S.: 423820

Bystronic Polska Sp. z o.o. (2)
Al Krakowska 81 Sekocin Nowy
05090 Raszyn, Poland (100%)
Tel.: (48) 223313770
Fax: (48) 223313771
E-Mail: info.pl@bystronic.com
Web Site: www.bystronic.pl
Emp.: 17
Engineering Services
S.I.C.: 8711
N.A.I.C.S.: 541330
Hugo Allemann *(Mng Dir)*

Bystronic Scandinavia AB (2)
Ostra Bangatan 18
19560 Arlandastad, Sweden (100%)
Tel.: (46) 859441550
Fax: (46) 859441555
E-Mail: sales.se@bystronic.com
Web Site: www.bystronic.se
Industrial Machinery & Equipment Whslr
S.I.C.: 5084
N.A.I.C.S.: 423830
Michael Kron *(Mng Dir)*

Bystronic (Tianjin) Machinery Co. Ltd. (2)
Economic Development Zone
Ninghe County, 301500 Tianjin, China (100%)
Tel.: (86) 2269589988
Fax: (86) 2269588168
E-Mail: sales@afmtianjin.com
Web Site: www.afmtianjin.com
Emp.: 100
Machine Tool Metal Cutting Types Mfr
S.I.C.: 3542
N.A.I.C.S.: 333517
Adam Lee *(Mgr-Prochaic)*

Bystronic UK Ltd. (2)
Maple Park Lowfields Avenue
LS126HH Leeds, West Yorkshire, United Kingdom (100%)
Tel.: (44) 1132976666, ext. 8448485850
Fax: (44) 1132223198
E-Mail: sales@bystronic.co.uk
Web Site: www.bystronic.com
Emp.: 80
Machine Tool Metal Forming Types Mfr
S.I.C.: 3541
N.A.I.C.S.: 333517
David Larcombe *(Mgr)*

Bystronic UK Ltd. (2)
6 Wayside Business Park Wilsons Lane
Coventry, Warwickshire, CV6 6NY, United Kingdom (100%)
Tel.: (44) 844 848 5850
Fax: (44) 844 848 5851
E-Mail: sales.uk@bystronic.com
Web Site: www.bystronic.co.uk
Laser Cutting, Waterjet Cutting, Bending & Shearing Systems Mfr
S.I.C.: 3545
N.A.I.C.S.: 333515

Colorsud SA (1)
Via Industria
6814 Lamone, Switzerland
Tel.: (41) 919452461
Fax: (41) 919453303
Web Site: www.novacolor.it/public/sito/EN/partnership.asp
Paint Varnish & Supplies Whslr
S.I.C.: 5198
N.A.I.C.S.: 424950

Conzzeta Management AG (1)
Giesshubelstrasse 45
8045 Zurich, Switzerland (100%)
Tel.: (41) 444682466
Fax: (41) 444682480
E-Mail: info@conzzeta.ch
Web Site: www.conzzeta-versicherungen.ch
Emp.: 2
All Other Business Support Services
S.I.C.: 7389
N.A.I.C.S.: 561499
Rolf Meyer *(VP)*

Farben Isler AG (1)
Rufacherstrasse 78
4055 Basel, Switzerland
Tel.: (41) 613810072
Fax: (41) 613810002
Web Site: www.swisslack.ch
Paint Varnish & Supplies Merchant Whslr
S.I.C.: 5198
N.A.I.C.S.: 424950

Fritz Nauer AG (1)
Oberwolfhauserstrasse 9
Wolfhausen, 8633 Hinwil, Switzerland (100%)
Tel.: (41) 552536363
Fax: (41) 552536373
E-Mail: fritznauer@foampartner.com
Web Site: www.foampartner.com
Emp.: 200
Polystyrene Foam Product Mfr
S.I.C.: 3086
N.A.I.C.S.: 326140
Part Tenbrink *(Mng Dir)*

Jordan Peinture SA (1)
2 Chemin de la Colice
Crissier, 1023 Lausanne, Switzerland
Tel.: (41) 216376655
Fax: (41) 216376650
E-Mail: jordan-crissier@jordan-peinture.ch
Web Site: www.jordan-peinture.ch
Emp.: 40
Paint Varnish & Supplies Merchant Whslr
S.I.C.: 5198
N.A.I.C.S.: 424950

Mammut Sports Group AG (1)
Industriestr Birren 5
5703 Seon, Switzerland (100%)
Tel.: (41) 627698181
Fax: (41) 627698311
E-Mail: info@mammut.ch
Web Site: www.mammut.ch
Emp.: 200
Sporting and Athletic Goods Manufacturing
S.I.C.: 3949
N.A.I.C.S.: 339920
Rolf Schmid *(Mng Dir)*

Neutex AG (1)
Oberwolfhauserstrasse 9
8633 Zurich, Wolfhausen, Switzerland (100%)
Tel.: (41) 552536363
Web Site: www.foampartner.com
Emp.: 33
All Other Miscellaneous Textile Product Mills
S.I.C.: 2399
N.A.I.C.S.: 314999

Plazza Immobilien (1)
Im Tiergarten 22
Postfach 523, 8045 Zurich, Switzerland (100%)
Tel.: (41) 444686070
Fax: (41) 444513456
E-Mail: info@plazza.ch
Web Site: www.plazza.ch
Real Estate Agents & Brokers Offices
S.I.C.: 6531
N.A.I.C.S.: 531210
Ralph Siegle *(Mng Dir)*

Schmid Rhyner AG (1)
Soodring 29
8134 Adliswil, Switzerland (100%)
Tel.: (41) 447126400
Fax: (41) 447090804
E-Mail: infopf@schmid-rhyner.ch
Web Site: www.schmid-rhyner.ch
Emp.: 35
Printing Ink Mfr
S.I.C.: 2893
N.A.I.C.S.: 325910
Jakob Rohner *(Mng Dir)*

Seckler AG (1)
Moosstrasse 3
Pieterlen, 2542 Bern, Switzerland (100%)
Tel.: (41) 323760730
Fax: (41) 323760736
E-Mail: info@seckler.ch
Web Site: www.seckler.ch
Emp.: 30
Other Commercial & Service Industry Machinery Mfr
S.I.C.: 3589
N.A.I.C.S.: 333318
Jacques Hess *(CEO)*

Swiss Lack Theler Perren AG (1)
Nellenstadel 3
Glis, 3902 Wallis, Switzerland
Tel.: (41) 279233939
Fax: (41) 279239112
Web Site: www.thelerperren.ch/
Paint Varnish & Supplies Merchant Whslr
S.I.C.: 5198
N.A.I.C.S.: 424950

Theler Morand SA (1)
23 route de Riddes
Isvicre, 1950 Sion, Switzerland
Tel.: (41) 272035556
Fax: (41) 272035576
Paint & Coating Mfr
S.I.C.: 5198
N.A.I.C.S.: 424950

Transall AG (1)
Giesshubelstrasse 45
Zurich, Switzerland (100%)
Tel.: (41) 433994060
General Freight Trucking Local
S.I.C.: 4212
N.A.I.C.S.: 484110

U.S. Subsidiaries:

ixmation Inc. (1)
31 Presidential Dr
Roselle, IL 60172-3914 (100%)
Tel.: (630) 351-3000
Fax: (630) 671-2600
E-Mail: info@ixmation.us
Web Site: www.ixmation.com
Emp.: 150
Custom Tailored Automation Systems
S.I.C.: 3589
N.A.I.C.S.: 333318

Mammut Sports Group Inc. (1)
135 Northside Dr
Shelburne, VT 05482 (100%)
Tel.: (802) 985-5056
Fax: (802) 985-9141
E-Mail: info@mammutusa.com
Web Site: www.mammutusa.com
Emp.: 20
Sporting & Recreational Goods & Supplies Whslr
S.I.C.: 5091
N.A.I.C.S.: 423910
William Supple *(CEO)*

Swisstex Inc. (1)
325 Bessie Rd
Piedmont, SC 29673 (100%)
Mailing Address:
PO Box 9258
Greenville, SC 29604-9258
Tel.: (864) 845-7541
Fax: (864) 845-5699
E-Mail: swisstex@foampartner.com
Web Site: www.swisstex.com
Emp.: 15
Plastics Pipe & Pipe Fitting Mfr

S.I.C.: 3089
N.A.I.C.S.: 326122
Melissa Carver *(Mgr-HR)*

Non-U.S. Subsidiaries:

Ajungilak AS **(1)**
Professor Birkelandsvei 36
1008 Oslo, Norway (100%)
Tel.: (47) 23143700
Fax: (47) 23143701
E-Mail: mail@ajungilak.no
Web Site: www.ajungilak.no
Emp.: 10
Toy & Hobby Goods & Supplies Whslr
S.I.C.: 5092
N.A.I.C.S.: 423920
John Garrison *(CEO)*

Beyeler Maschinenbau GmbH **(1)**
Muhlhauser Str 3
Thuringen, 99867 Gotha, Germany (100%)
Tel.: (49) 36213830
Fax: (49) 3621383383
Web Site: www.bystronic.com
Sheet Metal Work Mfr
S.I.C.: 3444
N.A.I.C.S.: 332322

Frina Mousse France S.a.r.l. **(1)**
Boite Postale 55
1 Rue du Jasmin, 51381 Wittenheim, France (100%)
Tel.: (33) 389526652
Fax: (33) 389538252
E-Mail: patrick.stadelmann@foampartner.com
Web Site: www.foampartner.com
Emp.: 23
Polystyrene Foam Product Manufacturing
S.I.C.: 3086
N.A.I.C.S.: 326140
Patrick Stadelmann *(Mng Dir)*

Mammut Sports Group GmbH **(1)**
Anschutzstr 5
87700 Memmingen, Germany (100%)
Tel.: (49) 833183920
Fax: (49) 83318392229
E-Mail: info@mammut.ch
Web Site: www.mammut.ch
Emp.: 150
Sporting & Recreational Goods & Supplies Whslr
S.I.C.: 5091
N.A.I.C.S.: 423910
Frank Trommar *(Product Mgr)*

Reisgies Schaumstoff e GmbH **(1)**
Dieselstrasse 7
51381 Leverkusen, Germany (100%)
Tel.: (49) 21715080
Fax: (49) 2171569133
E-Mail: reisgies@foampartner.com
Web Site: www.foampartner.com
Emp.: 415
All Other Rubber Product Mfr
S.I.C.: 3069
N.A.I.C.S.: 326299
Micheal Krause *(Mgr)*

COOGEE CHEMICALS PTY LTD.

Corner Patterson & Kwinana Beach Roads
PO Box 5051
Rockinghim Beach, 6969 Kwinana, WA, 6969, Australia
Tel.: (61) 894398200
Fax: (61) 894398300
E-Mail: ccadmin@coogee.com.au
Web Site: www.coogee.com.au
Year Founded: 1971
Sales Range: $50-74.9 Million
Emp.: 350

Business Description:
Industrial, Agricultural & Mineral Processing Chemical Mfr
S.I.C.: 2899
N.A.I.C.S.: 325998

Personnel:
William Gordon Martin *(Chm)*
Phil Thick *(CEO)*

Board of Directors:
William Gordon Martin
Peter Knowles
Ms Lied-Cordruwisch
Tim Martin
Phil Thick

Non-U.S. Joint Venture:

Pride Chem Industries Sdn Bhd **(1)**
Plo 232 Jalan Keluli 1
Pasir Gudang Industrial Estate, 81700 Pasir Gudang, Johor Bahru, Malaysia (50%)
Tel.: (60) 72526755
Fax: (60) 72526741
E-Mail: pcjb01@streamyx.com
Web Site: www.coogee.com.au/op_jv.html
Emp.: 7
Chemical & Fertilizer Mineral Mining
S.I.C.: 1479
N.A.I.C.S.: 212393
Lim Kaming *(Gen Mgr)*

COOKE AQUACULTURE INC.

874 Main St
Blacks Harbour, NB, E5H 1E6, Canada
Tel.: (506) 456-6600
Fax: (506) 456-6652
E-Mail: info@cookeaqua.com
Web Site: www.cookeaqua.com
Year Founded: 1993
Sales Range: $25-49.9 Million
Emp.: 1,500

Business Description:
Salmon Farming, Processing & Sales
S.I.C.: 0921
N.A.I.C.S.: 112511

Personnel:
Glenn Cooke *(CEO)*
Michael Cooke *(COO)*
Nitin Soni *(CIO)*

Subsidiaries:

Kelly Cove Salmon Ltd. **(1)**
61 Wallace Cove Rd
Blacks Harbour, NB, E5H 1E6, Canada
Tel.: (506) 456-6600
Fax: (506) 456-6652
Web Site: www.cookeaqua.com
Sales Range: $1-9.9 Million
Emp.: 60
Salmon Farming
S.I.C.: 0921
N.A.I.C.S.: 112511
Michael Szemerda *(Gen Mgr)*

True North Salmon Co. Ltd. **(1)**
874 Main Street
Blacks Harbour, NB, E5H 1E6, Canada
Tel.: (506) 456-6600
Fax: (506) 456-6652
Web Site: www.truenorthsalmon.com
Emp.: 55
Salmon Harvesting, Processing & Marketing
S.I.C.: 5146
N.A.I.C.S.: 424460
Peter Groom *(Controller)*

COOKPAD INC.

5-12-7 Shiroganedai Minato-ku
Tokyo, 108-0071, Japan
Tel.: (81) 364086520
Fax: (81) 364086522
E-Mail: pr@cookpad.com
Web Site: www.cookpad.com
Year Founded: 1997
2193—(TKS)
Sales Range: $10-24.9 Million
Emp.: 50

Business Description:
Online Cooking Recipe Website Operator
S.I.C.: 2741
N.A.I.C.S.: 519130

Personnel:
Yoko Sano *(Pres)*

COOKSVILLE DODGE CHRYSLER INC.

290 Dundas Street East
Mississauga, ON, L5A 1W9, Canada
Tel.: (905) 279-3031
Fax: (905) 279-9686
Toll Free: (888) 329-6412
Web Site: www.cooksvilledodgechrysler.com
Rev.: $21,973,050
Emp.: 60

Business Description:
New & Used Car Dealers
S.I.C.: 5511
N.A.I.C.S.: 441110

Personnel:
Sean Kelly *(Owner)*

COOLGIANTS AG

Julius-Bamberger-Str 1
28279 Bremen, Germany
Tel.: (49) 4218392110
Fax: (49) 4218392280
E-Mail: info@coolgiants.de
Web Site: www.coolgiants.de

Business Description:
Household Appliances Distr
S.I.C.: 5074
N.A.I.C.S.: 423720

Personnel:
Kersten Hoppe *(Co-CEO)*
Jan Oetjen *(Co-CEO)*

COOP FORESTIERE BOURGOGNE LIMOUSIN

Zone Artisanale Du Theil
19200 Ussel, Correze, France
Tel.: (33) 555463500
Sales Range: $25-49.9 Million
Emp.: 66

Business Description:
Forestry Services
S.I.C.: 0851
N.A.I.C.S.: 115310

Personnel:
Elie De Cosnac *(Pres)*

COOP FRUIT CANTON ROUSSILLON

Rue D Alembert
38150 Salaise-sur-Sanne, Isere, France
Tel.: (33) 474864068
Sales Range: $10-24.9 Million
Emp.: 63

Business Description:
Fresh Fruits & Vegetables
S.I.C.: 5148
N.A.I.C.S.: 424480

Personnel:
Yves Pascal *(Pres)*

COOP NORGE SA

Kirkegata 4
0153 Oslo, Norway
Tel.: (47) 22 89 95 95
Fax: (47) 22 41 14 42
Web Site: www.coop.no
Emp.: 2,600

Business Description:
Grocery Store Operator
S.I.C.: 5411
N.A.I.C.S.: 445110

Personnel:
Ola H. Strand, *(CEO)*

Subsidiaries:

Coop Norge Grorud Eiendom AS **(1)**
Akeroveien 264
Oslo, Norway
Tel.: (47) 22899595
Fax: (47) 22899745
Web Site: www.coop.no
All Other General Merchandise Stores
S.I.C.: 5399
N.A.I.C.S.: 452990

Coop Norge Industri AS **(1)**
Ostre Aker Vei 264
0977 Oslo, Norway
Tel.: (47) 22899500
Fax: (47) 22411138
Web Site: www.coop.no
Emp.: 800
Dairy Product except Dried or Canned Whslr
S.I.C.: 5143
N.A.I.C.S.: 424430
Svein Fanebust *(Pres)*

Coop Norge Kaffe AS **(1)**
Filipstadveien 15
0250 Oslo, Norway (100%)
Tel.: (47) 22899999
Fax: (47) 22830905
E-Mail: torgeir.sveine@coopnorge.co.no
Web Site: www.coopnorge.co.no
Emp.: 100
Roasted Nuts & Peanut Butter Mfr
S.I.C.: 2068
N.A.I.C.S.: 311911
Torgeir Sveine *(Mng Dir)*

Coop Norge Stavanger Eiendom AS **(1)**
Akeroveien 264
Oslo, Norway
Tel.: (47) 73514222
All Other General Merchandise Stores
S.I.C.: 5399
N.A.I.C.S.: 452990

Goman Bakeriet AS **(1)**
Lorenveien 55
0580 Oslo, Norway (100%)
Tel.: (47) 22078650
Fax: (47) 22655264
E-Mail: svine.torgeer@coop.no
Web Site: www.coop.no
Commercial Bakeries
S.I.C.: 2052
N.A.I.C.S.: 311812
Torgeer Svine *(Gen Mgr)*

Non-U.S. Joint Venture:

Coop Trading A/S **(1)**
Helgeshoj Alle 57
DK-2620 Hoje Taastrup, Denmark
Tel.: (45) 8853 0000
E-Mail:
Web Site: www.cooptrading.com
Emp.: 114
Internordic Procurement of Branded Products
S.I.C.: 5399
N.A.I.C.S.: 452990
Per Bank *(Mng Dir)*

COOP SCHWEIZ

Thiersteinerallee 12
Postfach 2550
CH-4002 Basel, Switzerland
Tel.: (41) 613366666
Telex: 962133 csb ch
Fax: (41) 613366040
E-Mail: felix.wehrle@coop.ch
Web Site: www.coop.ch
Year Founded: 1890
Sls.: $28,851,302,920
Assets: $18,218,921,600
Liabilities: $10,380,899,760
Net Worth: $7,838,021,840
Earnings: $487,852,640
Emp.: 64,416
Fiscal Year-end: 12/31/12

Business Description:
Retail Store Operator
Import Export
S.I.C.: 5999
N.A.I.C.S.: 453998

Personnel:
Hansueli Loosli *(Chm)*
Irene Kaufmann-Brandli *(Vice Chm)*
Joos Sutter *(CEO & Head-Retail Bus Unit)*

Board of Directors:
Hansueli Loosli
Peter Eisenhut
Michela Ferrari-Testa
Hans-Jurg Kaser

Coop Schweiz—(Continued)

Irene Kaufmann-Brandli
Beth Krasna
Roman Kuhn
Lillia Rebsamen-Sala
Bernard Rueger
Giusep Valaulta

Subsidiaries:

Argo AG (1)
Baumlimattstrasse
CH 4313 Mohlin, Switzerland (100%)
Tel.: (41) 618559900
Fax: (41) 618514928
E-Mail: argoag@argo-ag.ch
Web Site: www.argo-ag.ch
Emp.: 50
Hosiery
S.I.C.: 2252
N.A.I.C.S.: 315110

Bank Coop AG (1)
Aechenplatz 3
CH 4002 Basel, Switzerland (100%)
Tel.: (41) 612862121
Fax: (41) 612714595
E-Mail: info@bankcoop.ch
Web Site: www.bankcoop.ch
Sales Range: $50-74.9 Million
Emp.: 650
Full-Service Banking
S.I.C.: 6712
N.A.I.C.S.: 551111
Andreas Waespi *(Gen Mgr)*

Bell AG (1)
Elsasserstrasse 174
4056 Basel, Switzerland (66.29%)
Tel.: (41) 613262626
Fax: (41) 613262170
E-Mail: info@bell.ch
Web Site: www.bell.ch
BELL—(SWX)
Sales Range: $1-4.9 Billion
Emp.: 6,500
Meat Sales & Production
S.I.C.: 5147
N.A.I.C.S.: 424470
Hansueli Loosli *(Chm)*
Leo Ebneter *(Vice Chm)*
Lorenz Wyss *(CEO)*
Martin Gysin *(Deputy CEO & CFO)*
Elisabeth Wegeleben *(Sec)*

Subsidiaries:

Bell Schweiz AG (2)
Elsasserstrasse 174
Basel, 4056, Switzerland (60%)
Tel.: (41) 613262626
Fax: (41) 613262170
E-Mail: info@bell.ch
Web Site: www.bell.ch
Sales Range: $800-899.9 Million
Emp.: 1,000
Meat Processing & Marketing
S.I.C.: 2011
N.A.I.C.S.: 311611
Loranz Wyss *(CEO)*

Frigo St. Johann AG (2)
Neudorfstrasse 90
4056 Basel, Switzerland
Tel.: (41) 61 327 1133
Fax: (41) 61 327 1233
E-Mail: info@frigo-ag.ch
Web Site: www.frigo-ag.ch
Meat Products Processing & Sales
S.I.C.: 5147
N.A.I.C.S.: 424470

SBA Schlachbetrieb Basel AG (2)
Schlachthofstrasse 55
4056 Basel, Switzerland
Tel.: (41) 61 385 3232
Fax: (41) 61 322 6663
Meat Products Processing & Sales
S.I.C.: 5147
N.A.I.C.S.: 424470

Non-U.S. Subsidiaries:

Abraham GmbH (2)
Brookdamm 21
21217 Seevetal, Germany
Tel.: (49) 40 7680050
Fax: (49) 40 768005 305
E-Mail: info@abraham.de
Web Site: www.abraham.de
Meat Products Processing & Sales
S.I.C.: 5147
N.A.I.C.S.: 424470
Christian Schroder *(CEO & Head-Distr & Mktg)*

Salaison Polette & Cie SAS (2)
Champ Saint-Pierre
63460 Teilhet, France
Tel.: (33) 473 64 3131
Fax: (33) 473 64 3140
E-Mail: salaison@polette.fr
Web Site: www.bell.ch
Meat Products Processing & Sales
S.I.C.: 5147
N.A.I.C.S.: 424470
Philippe Polette *(Pres & Dir Gen)*

ZIMBO Fleisch- und Wurstwaren GmbH & Co. KG (2)
Wasserstrasse 223
44799 Bochum, Germany
Tel.: (49) 234 9553 7000
Fax: (49) 234 9553 7208
E-Mail: info@zimbo.de
Web Site: www.zimbo.de
Meat Products Processing & Sales
S.I.C.: 5147
N.A.I.C.S.: 424470
Cristof Queisser *(CEO & Head-Mktg & Sls)*
Manfred Dahmen *(Deputy CEO & Head-Fin & Controlling)*

Chocolats Halba (1)
Alte Winterthurstrasse 1
PO Box
CH 8304 Wallisellen, Switzerland (100%)
Tel.: (41) 448771010
Fax: (41) 4487741999
E-Mail: info@halba.ch
Emp.: 250
Mfrs. of Chocolate Products
S.I.C.: 2064
N.A.I.C.S.: 311352

Coop Hostellerie AG (1)
Thiersteinerallee 12
Basel, 2550, Switzerland (100%)
Tel.: (41) 613366666
Fax: (41) 613366040
S.I.C.: 5311
N.A.I.C.S.: 452112
Hansueli Loosli *(CEO)*

Coop Mineraloel AG (1)
Hegenheimermattweg 65
CH 4123 Allschwil, Switzerland (51%)
Tel.: (41) 614854141
Fax: (41) 614820366
E-Mail: info@coop-mineraloel.ch
Web Site: www.coop-mineraloel.ch
Emp.: 17
Service Station Chain
S.I.C.: 4899
N.A.I.C.S.: 517919
Roger Oser *(Mng Dir)*

CWK AG (1)
St Galler Strasse 180
CH 8411 Winterthur, Switzerland CH
Tel.: (41) 522344444 (100%)
Fax: (41) 522344343
E-Mail: info@cwk-scs.ch
Web Site: www.cwk-scs.ch
Sales Range: $25-49.9 Million
Emp.: 100
Mfr. of Cosmetics & Chemcial Cleaning Products
S.I.C.: 2844
N.A.I.C.S.: 325620
Christain Koch *(Mng Dir)*

Dipl. Ing. Fust AG (1)
Buchental 4
9245 Oberburen-Uzwil, Switzerland
Tel.: (41) 719555050
Fax: (41) 719512934
E-Mail: info@fust.ch
Web Site: www.fust.ch
Emp.: 50
Domestic Appliance Retailer
S.I.C.: 3631
N.A.I.C.S.: 335221
Thomas Cecar *(Mng Dir)*

Subsidiaries:

Service 7000 AG (2)
Mollíserstrasse 41
Wiggis Park, CH 8754 Netstal, Glarus, Switzerland
Tel.: (41) 556453700
Fax: (41) 556453707
E-Mail: service7000@service7000.ch
Web Site: www.service7000.ch
Emp.: 100
Repair Services
S.I.C.: 7699
N.A.I.C.S.: 811412
Martin Reithebuch *(Mgr)*

Import Parfumerien AG (1)
Postfach 336
9004 Saint Gallen, Switzerland (100%)
Tel.: (41) 712254028
Fax: (41) 712254021
E-Mail: info@impo.ch
Web Site: www.impo.ch
Emp.: 40
S.I.C.: 5311
N.A.I.C.S.: 452112

Nutrex AG (1)
Juraweg 5
CH 3292 Busswil, Switzerland (100%)
Tel.: (41) 323842141
Fax: (41) 323867919
E-Mail: info@nutrex.ch
Web Site: www.nutrex.ch
Sls.: $20,026,100
Emp.: 15
Vinegar Production & Pickled Products
S.I.C.: 2034
N.A.I.C.S.: 311423
Mark Burkhalter *(Mgr)*

Panofina AG (1)
Alte Winterthurer strasse 1
CH 8304 Wallisellen, Switzerland (100%)
Tel.: (41) 18771111
Fax: (41) 8448771250
Web Site: www.halba.ch
Sales Range: $50-74.9 Million
Emp.: 290
Bakery & Confectionery Products
S.I.C.: 2052
N.A.I.C.S.: 311812

Pasta Gala SA (1)
Rue du Dr-Yersin 10
CH-1110 Morges, Switzerland (100%)
Tel.: (41) 218011332
Fax: (41) 21 802 20 49
Web Site: www.pastagala.com
Emp.: 51
Mfr. & Sales of Pasta
S.I.C.: 2045
N.A.I.C.S.: 311824

Steinfels Cleaning Systems (1)
St Galler Strasse 180
CH 8411 Winterthur, Switzerland (100%)
Tel.: (41) 522344400
Fax: (41) 522344401
E-Mail: scs@cwk-scs.ch
Web Site: www.scs-ag.ch
Rev.: $5,224,200
Emp.: 75
S.I.C.: 5311
N.A.I.C.S.: 452112
Christian Coch *(Mng Dir)*

TopTip (R. Muller AG) (1)
Kollikerstrasse 80
CH-5036 Oberentfelden, Switzerland (100%)
Tel.: (41) 627371111
Fax: (41) 627371112
Web Site: www.toptip.ch
Sls.: $100,130,500
Emp.: 241
S.I.C.: 5311
N.A.I.C.S.: 452112

COOPER ENERGY LIMITED

Level 10 60 Waymouth Street
Adelaide, SA, 5000, Australia
Tel.: (61) 881004900
Fax: (61) 881004997
E-Mail: customerservice@cooperenergy.com.au
Web Site: www.cooperenergy.com.au
COE—(ASX)
Rev.: $58,086,654
Assets: $168,877,516
Liabilities: $25,890,975
Net Worth: $142,986,541
Earnings: $1,373,488
Emp.: 58
Fiscal Year-end: 06/30/13

Business Description:
Oil & Gas Exploration & Well Drilling
S.I.C.: 1311
N.A.I.C.S.: 211111

Personnel:
David P. Maxwell *(Mng Dir)*
Jason de Ross *(CFO)*
Alison N. Evans *(Legal Counsel & Sec)*

Board of Directors:
John C. Conde
Hector M. Gordon
David P. Maxwell
Jeffrey W. Schneider
Alice J. M. Williams

Legal Counsel:
Squire Sanders
Level 21 300 Murray Street
Perth, WA, 6000, Australia

COOPER MINERALS INC.

(Name Changed to United Coal Holdings Ltd.)

COOPERATIEVE CENTRALE RAIFFEISEN-BOERENLEENBANK B.A.

(d/b/a Rabobank Nederland)
Croeselaan 18
3521 CB Utrecht, Netherlands

Mailing Address:
PO Box 17100
3500 HG Utrecht, Netherlands
Tel.: (31) 302160000
Fax: (31) 302162672
E-Mail: bestuurssecratarea@rn.rabobank.nl
Web Site: www.rabobank.com
Year Founded: 1898
Sales Range: $25-49.9 Billion
Emp.: 60,568

Business Description:
Bank Holding Company; Banking & Financial Management Services
S.I.C.: 6712
N.A.I.C.S.: 551111

Personnel:
Lense Koopmans *(Chm-Supervisory Bd)*
Antoon Vermeer *(Deputy Chm-Supervisory Bd)*
Bert Bruggink *(CFO & Member-Exec Bd)*
Rudi Kleijwegt *(Chief Compliance Officer)*
Rens Dinkhuijsen *(Sec-Exec Bd)*
Gerlinde Silvis *(Member-Exec Bd & Head-HR)*
Berry Marttin *(Member-Exec Bd)*
Sipko N. Schat *(Member-Exec Bd)*
Piet van Schijndel *(Member-Exec Bd)*
Sjoerd Eisma *(Sec-Supervisory Bd)*

Supervisory Board of Directors:
Lense Koopmans
Irene Petronella Asscher-Vonk
Bernard Bijvoet
Anthonie de Bruijn
Wout Dekker
Louise O. Fresco
Leo S. L.J. Graafsma
Rinus Minderhoud
Martin Tielen
Erik A. J. van de Merwe
Cees P. Veerman
Antoon Vermeer
Arnold Walravens

Subsidiaries:

De Lage Landen International BV (1)
Vestdijk 51
PO Box 652
5600 AR Eindhoven, Netherlands

Tel.: (31) 402339911
Fax: (31) 402338600
E-Mail: ra.m.slaats@delagelanden.com
Web Site: www.delagelanden.com
Int. Income: $2,262,057,216
Emp.: 5,000
Asset Based Financing Services
S.I.C.: 6726
N.A.I.C.S.: 525990
Ronald Slaats *(Chm & CEO)*
Steve Riggs *(Pres-Healthcare & Clean Tech)*

Subsidiary:

Athlon Holding N.V. (2)
Boeing Ave 280 119cz
Amersfoort, Netherlands
Tel.: (31) 235675700
Fax: (31) 207525715
E-Mail: info@athloncarlease.com
Web Site: www.athloncarlease.com
Sales Range: $900-999.9 Million
Emp.: 600
Car Leasing & Car Body Repair Services
S.I.C.: 7538
N.A.I.C.S.: 811111
Richard Sikkel *(Chm)*
Jan E. Demper *(Sec)*

Non-U.S. Subsidiaries:

De Lage Landen Leasing GmbH (2)
Hansaallee 249
40549 Dusseldorf, Germany (100%)
Tel.: (49) 21152680
Fax: (49) 2115268217
E-Mail: kundenbetreuung@delagelanden.com
Web Site: www.delagelanden.com
Emp.: 150
Leasing, Business & Consumer Finance Solutions
S.I.C.: 6726
N.A.I.C.S.: 525990
Thomas Stahl *(Mgr)*

De Lage Landen Leasing Ltd. (2)
1 George's Dock House IFSC
Dublin, 1, Ireland (100%)
Tel.: (353) 14814100
Fax: (353) 14814158
E-Mail: info@delagelanden.com
Web Site: www.delagelanden.com
Emp.: 45
Leasing, Business & Consumer Finance Solutions
S.I.C.: 6726
N.A.I.C.S.: 525990
Fergal O'Mongain *(Mng Dir)*
David Ritchie *(Mng Dir)*

De Lage Landen Leasing Ltd. (2)
Building 7 Croxley Green Business Park
PO Box 430
Hatters Lane, Watford, Hertfordshire, WD18 8EZ, United Kingdom (100%)
Tel.: (44) 1923810083
Fax: (44) 1923233500
Web Site: www.delagelanden.com
Emp.: 100
Leasing, Business & Consumer Finance Solutions
S.I.C.: 6726
N.A.I.C.S.: 525990
Robert Ceribelli *(Gen Mgr)*

De Lage Landen Leasing N.V. (2)
Lozenberg 5
1932 Zaventem, Belgium (100%)
Tel.: (32) 27180411
Fax: (32) 27180497
E-Mail: salesdesk.be@delagelanden.com
Web Site: www.delagelanden.com
Emp.: 40
Leasing, Business & Consumer Finance Solutions
S.I.C.: 6726
N.A.I.C.S.: 525990
Erwin Ollivier *(Mng Dir)*

De Lage Landen Leasing S.A.F (2)
Tour Manhattan 5-6 Place de l'Iris
92095 Paris, la Defense, France
Tel.: (33) 145192105
Fax: (33) 145192196
Web Site: www.delangelanden.com
Emp.: 100
Leasing, Business & Consumer Finance Solutions
S.I.C.: 6726
N.A.I.C.S.: 525990

De Lage Landen Leasing S.p.A. (2)
Viale Monte Grappa 4
20124 Milan, Italy
Tel.: (39) 02636941
Fax: (39) 0229062051
E-Mail: operations.italy@delagelanden.com
Web Site: www.delagelanden.com
Emp.: 80
Leasing, Business & Consumer Finance Solutions
S.I.C.: 6726
N.A.I.C.S.: 525990

Rabo Vastgoedgroep Holding N.V. (1)
Westerdorpsstraat 66
3871 AZ Hoevelaken, Netherlands NL
Mailing Address:
Postbus 15
NL-3870 DA Hoevelaken, Netherlands
Tel.: (31) 332539111
Fax: (31) 332539555
E-Mail: info@raborealestategroup.com
Web Site: www.raborealestategroup.com
Rev.: $2,054,543,500
Assets: $31,820,396,263
Liabilities: $29,657,288,191
Net Worth: $2,163,108,072
Earnings: ($146,140,215)
Emp.: 2,076
Fiscal Year-end: 12/31/12
Holding Company; Real Estate Development, Finance & Asset Management Services
S.I.C.: 6719
N.A.I.C.S.: 551112
L.C. Brinkman *(Chm-Supervisory Bd)*
Hans van der Linden *(Chm-Exec Bd)*
Sipko N. Schat *(Vice Chm-Supervisory Bd)*
Peter C. Keur *(Vice Chm-Exec Bd)*
Jos H. P. M. van Lange *(CFO, Chief Risk Officer & Member-Exec Bd)*
Walter P. de Boer *(Chm-Bouwfonds Property Dev & Member-Exec Bd)*
Isaac M. Kalisvaart *(CEO-MAB Dev & Member-Exec Bd)*
Jaap C. M. A. Gillis *(Member-Exec Bd)*

Subsidiaries:

Bouwfonds Property Development B.V. (2)
Westerdorpsstraat 66
NL-3871 AZ Hoevelaken, Netherlands NL
Mailing Address: (100%)
Postbus 15
NL-3870 DA Hoevelaken, Netherlands
Tel.: (31) 332539700
Fax: (31) 332539685
E-Mail: bpd@bouwfonds.nl
Web Site: www.bouwfonds.com
Sales Range: $1-4.9 Billion
Emp.: 1,100
Residential Real Estate Development
S.I.C.: 6552
N.A.I.C.S.: 237210
Walter P. de Boer *(CEO)*
J.C. Kreikamp *(Mng Dir-Fin)*
W.C.T.F. de Zeeuw *(Mng Dir-New Markets)*
H.W.J. Doornink *(Mng Dir-Ops)*
J.J.M. Franck *(Mng Dir-Intl)*

Bouwfonds Real Estate Investment Management B.V. (2)
De Beek 18
NL-3871 MS Hoevelaken, Netherlands NL
Mailing Address: (100%)
Postbus 15
NL-3870 DA Hoevelaken, Netherlands
Tel.: (31) 337504750
Fax: (31) 337504777
Web Site: www.bouwfonds.com
Emp.: 130
Real Estate Portfolio Development, Structuring & Management Services
S.I.C.: 6282
N.A.I.C.S.: 523920
Jean L.M.J. Klijnen *(Sr Mng Dir)*

FGH Bank N.V. (2)
Leidseveer 50
NL-3511 SB Utrecht, Netherlands NL
Mailing Address: (100%)
Postbus 2244
NL-3500 GE Utrecht, Netherlands
Tel.: (31) 302323911
Fax: (31) 302334572
E-Mail: info@fgh.nl
Web Site: www.fgh.nl
Emp.: 250
Real Estate Banking Services
S.I.C.: 6159
N.A.I.C.S.: 522292
Peter C. Keur *(Chm-Mgmt Bd & CEO)*
Frans B. Overdijk *(CFO)*

Fondsenbeheer Nederland B.V. (2)
Westerdorpsstrasse 68
NL-3871 AZ Hoevelaken, Netherlands NL
Mailing Address: (100%)
Postbus 15
NL-3870 DA Hoevelaken, Netherlands
Tel.: (31) 332539428
Fax: (31) 332531142
E-Mail: info@fondsenbeheer.nl
Web Site: www.fondsenbeheer.nl
Emp.: 90
Public Fund & Trust Management
S.I.C.: 6091
N.A.I.C.S.: 523991
Peter Bouwman *(Mng Dir)*

MAB Development Group B.V. (2)
Wijnhaven 60
NL-2511 GA Hague, Netherlands NL
Mailing Address: (100%)
Postbus 19412
NL-2500 CK Hague, Netherlands
Tel.: (31) 703068400
Fax: (31) 703543618
E-Mail: info@mab.com
Web Site: www.mab.com
Emp.: 80
Holding Company; Commercial Real Estate Development & Construction Services
S.I.C.: 6719
N.A.I.C.S.: 551112
Isaac M. Kalisvaart *(CEO)*
J.G.F. Eijkemans *(Mng Dir-Intl)*

Subsidiary:

MAB Development Nederland B.V. (3)
Wijnhaven 60
NL-2511 GA Hague, Netherlands NL
Tel.: (31) 703068400 (100%)
Fax: (31) 703543618
E-Mail: info@mab.com
Web Site: www.mab.com
Emp.: 100
Commercial Real Estate Development & Construction Services
S.I.C.: 6552
N.A.I.C.S.: 237210
Isaac Kalisvaart *(CEO)*
F.E.A. Dechesne *(Mng Dir)*
Cees B. van Boven *(Mng Dir)*

U.S. Subsidiaries:

Rabo Capital Services, Inc. (1)
245 Park Ave
New York, NY 10167 DE
Tel.: (212) 916-7800
Web Site: www.rabobankamerica.com
Emp.: 200
Corporate Banking, Financial Market & Merger Advisory Services
S.I.C.: 6211
N.A.I.C.S.: 523110
Christopher W. Nolan, Sr. *(Mng Dir-Merger & Acq Grp)*

Rabobank, N.A. (1)
1498 W Main St
El Centro, CA 92243-2819
Tel.: (760) 370-3600
Fax: (760) 353-7487
Web Site: www.rabobankamerica.com
Emp.: 1,700
Retail & Commercial Banking Services Import Export
S.I.C.: 6036
N.A.I.C.S.: 522120
Rick Arredondo *(Pres & COO)*
John J. Ryan *(CEO)*
Daniel C. Stevens *(CFO & Exec VP)*
Erwin Martinez *(CIO)*
Chris Nelson *(Exec VP & Dir-Mktg)*
Anker Fanoe *(Exec VP & Dir-Retail & Bus Banking)*
Jeff Paul *(Exec VP-Community Banking)*
Kim Hval *(Sr VP & Dir-Retail Sls)*
Bob Dingler *(Sr VP & Mgr-Agribusiness Div)*

Subsidiaries:

Rabo AgriFinance, Inc. (2)
1 CityPlace Dr Ste 200
Saint Louis, MO 63141 DE
Tel.: (314) 687-4000
Fax: (314) 687-4430
Web Site: www.raboag.com
Emp.: 100
Agricultural Real Estate Lending & Financing Services
S.I.C.: 6159
N.A.I.C.S.: 522291
Neil Dobbin *(CEO)*
John Johnson *(Mng Dir)*
Brian Newcomer *(Exec VP-Bus Dev)*

Subsidiaries:

Rabo AgriInsurance Services, Inc. (3)
6919 Chancellor Dr
Cedar Falls, IA 50613 DE
Tel.: (319) 277-4444
Fax: (319) 277-0144
Web Site: www.rabobankamerica.com
Emp.: 100
Agricultural Insurance & Lending Services
S.I.C.: 6411
N.A.I.C.S.: 524210
Kevin D. Schipper *(Pres)*

Unit:

Butte Community Payroll Systems (2)
2041 Forest Ave
Chico, CA 95928
Tel.: (530) 899-1636
Fax: (530) 899-4430
Web Site: www.buttecommunitypayroll.com
Sales Range: $75-99.9 Million
Emp.: 2
Payroll & Tax Services
S.I.C.: 8721
N.A.I.C.S.: 541214

Non-U.S. Group:

Rabobank Australia & New Zealand Group (1)
Level 16 Darling Park Tower 3
201 Sussex St, Sydney, NSW, 2000, Australia
Tel.: (61) 281154000
Fax: (61) 280834995
E-Mail: info@rabobank.com.au
Web Site: www.rabobank.com.au
Emp.: 700
Regional Managing Office
S.I.C.: 8741
N.A.I.C.S.: 551114
Thos Gieskes *(CEO)*

Subsidiaries:

Rabo Australia Limited (2)
Level 16 Darling Park Tower 3
201 Sussex Street, Sydney, NSW, 2000, Australia AU
Tel.: (61) 281154000
Fax: (61) 0280834995
E-Mail: sydney.webmaster@rabobank.com
Web Site: www.rabobank.com.au
Emp.: 700
Corporate Banking, Financial Market & Merger Advisory Services
S.I.C.: 6211
N.A.I.C.S.: 523110
William P. Gurry *(Chm)*

Rabobank Australia Limited (2)
Level 16 Darling Park Tower 3
201 Sussex Street, 2000 Sydney, NSW, Australia AU
Tel.: (61) 292344200
Fax: (61) 292337946
E-Mail: sydney.enquiry@rabobank.com
Web Site: www.rabobank.com.au
Emp.: 700
Commercial Banking
S.I.C.: 6029
N.A.I.C.S.: 522110
Thos Gieskes *(CEO & Reg Mgr)*
Ruurd Weulen Kranenberg *(Deputy CEO, CFO & Chief Risk Officer)*

Non-U.S. Subsidiary:

Rabobank New Zealand Limited (2)
Level 23 Vodafone Quay 157
PO Box 38396
6011 Wellington, New Zealand

Cooperatieve Centrale Raiffeisen-Boerenleenbank B.A.—(Continued)

Tel.: (64) 44625650
Fax: (64) 48192706
E-Mail: wellington@rabobank.com
Web Site: www.rabobank.co.nz
Emp.: 100
Commercial Banking
S.I.C.: 6029
N.A.I.C.S.: 522110
Ruurd Weulen Kranenberg *(Deputy CEO, CFO & Chief Risk Officer)*
Thos Gieskes *(CEO)*

Non-U.S. Subsidiaries:

Banco Rabobank International Brasil S.A. **(1)**
Av Nacoes Unidas 12995 6 andar 7th Floor
04578-000 Sao Paulo, SP, Brazil
Tel.: (55) 1155037000
Fax: (55) 1155037005
E-Mail: sandra.dantas@rabobank.com
Web Site: www.rabobank.com.br
Emp.: 250
Commercial Banking
S.I.C.: 6029
N.A.I.C.S.: 522110
Erik Peek Y. Van Eyken *(Pres)*

Banco Surinvest S.A. **(1)**
Rincon 530
11000 Montevideo, Uruguay
Tel.: (598) 29162300
Fax: (598) 9829160241
E-Mail: banque@heritage.com.uy
Web Site: www.heritage.com.uy
Emp.: 50
S.I.C.: 6153
N.A.I.C.S.: 522210
Graciela Reybaud *(Gen Mgr)*

Bank Gospodarki Zywnosciowej S.A. **(1)**
ul Kasprzaka 10/16
01-211 Warsaw, Poland (59%)
Tel.: (48) 22 8604400
Fax: (48) 22 8605000
E-Mail: relacje.inwestorskie@bgz.pl
Web Site: www.bgz.pl
BGZ—(WAR)
Int. Income: $683,883,868
Assets: $11,796,177,737
Liabilities: $10,694,906,708
Net Worth: $1,101,271,029
Earnings: $41,242,439
Emp.: 5,684
Fiscal Year-end: 12/31/12
Banking Services
S.I.C.: 6029
N.A.I.C.S.: 522110
Jan Alexander Pruijs *(Chm-Supervisory Bd)*
Dariusz Filar *(Vice Chm-Supervisory Bd)*
Jacek Bartkiewicz *(Pres & Member-Mgmt Bd)*
Gerardus Cornelis Embrechts *(Member-Mgmt Bd & First VP)*
Johannes Gerardus Beuming *(Member-Mgmt Bd & VP)*
Magdalena Legec *(Member-Mgmt Bd & VP)*
Dariusz Odzioba *(Member-Mgmt Bd & VP)*
Witold Okarma *(Member-Mgmt Bd & VP)*
Wojciech Sass *(Member-Mgmt Bd & VP)*
Andrzej Sieradz *(Member-Mgmt Bd & VP)*

PT. Bank Rabobank International Indonesia **(1)**
Plaza 89 Lantai 9 Jl HR Rasuna Said
Kav X-7 No 6, Jakarta, 12940, Indonesia Id
Tel.: (62) 21 252 0876
Fax: (62) 21 252 0875
E-Mail: indonesia@rabobank.com
Web Site: www.rabobank.co.id
Emp.: 50
Commercial Banking
S.I.C.: 6029
N.A.I.C.S.: 522110
Felix I. Hartadi *(Dir-Compliance)*

P.T. Rabo Finance Indonesia **(1)**
Plz 89 9th Fl Jl HR Rasuna Said
Kav X 7 6, Jakarta, 12940, Indonesia (100%)
Tel.: (62) 212520876
Fax: (62) 212520875
S.I.C.: 6153
N.A.I.C.S.: 522210

Rabo India Finance Pvt Ltd **(1)**
Forbes Building 2nd Floor
Mumbai, 400 001, India
Tel.: (91) 2222034567
Fax: (91) 2222035544
E-Mail: india@rabobank.com
Web Site: www.rabobank.com
Emp.: 70
Commercial Banking
S.I.C.: 6029
N.A.I.C.S.: 522110
Srijit Ramakrishnana *(Head-Facility)*

Rabobank Curacao NV **(1)**
Kayamensing Jombi 14
Zeelandia Office Park, Willemstad, 3876, Curacao
Tel.: (599) 94652011
Fax: (599) 5994652066
Web Site: www.rabobank.nl
Emp.: 15
S.I.C.: 6141
N.A.I.C.S.: 522210
Thomas Steven *(Gen Mgr)*

Rabobank France **(1)**
69 Blvd Haussmann
75008 Paris, France (100%)
Tel.: (33) 144718200
Fax: (33) 144710060
E-Mail: accueil.paris@rabobank.com
Web Site: www.rabobank.com
Emp.: 20
S.I.C.: 6141
N.A.I.C.S.: 522210
Laurem Gacom *(Mng Dir)*

Rabobank Ireland plc **(1)**
George's Dock House
tharlemont place, Dublin, 2, Ireland
Tel.: (353) 16076100
Fax: (353) 16701724
E-Mail: info@rabobank.ie
Web Site: www.rabobank.ie
Emp.: 80
Commercial Banking
S.I.C.: 6029
N.A.I.C.S.: 522110
Justin Sheridan *(Chief Admin Officer)*

Rabobank Polska S.A. **(1)**
Al Jana Pawla II 27
PO Box 75
00-958 Warsaw, 66, Poland
Tel.: (48) 226535000
Fax: (48) 22 653 5004
E-Mail: info-waw@rabobank.com
Web Site: www.rabobank.pl
Commercial Banking
S.I.C.: 6029
N.A.I.C.S.: 522110

Rabobank Singapore **(1)**
77 Robinson Rd 08-00
Singapore, 068896, Singapore (100%)
Tel.: (65) 65363363
Fax: (65) 65363236
E-Mail: connie.lee@rabobank.com
Web Site: www.rabobank.com.sg
Emp.: 180
S.I.C.: 6141
N.A.I.C.S.: 522210
Soh Hang Kwang *(CEO)*
Chong Goh *(Mng Dir)*

COOPERATIVE CENTRAL BANK LTD.

8 Gregorios Afxentiou Street
PO Box 24537
1096 Nicosia, Cyprus
Tel.: (357) 22743000
Fax: (357) 22670261
E-Mail: coopbank.gm@cytanet.com.cy
Web Site: www.coopbank.com.cy
Sales Range: $50-74.9 Million
Emp.: 220
Business Description:
Banking Services
S.I.C.: 6029
N.A.I.C.S.: 522110
Personnel:
Demetris Stavrou *(CEO & Bd Mem)*

COOPERS BREWERY LIMITED

461 South Rd
Regency Park
Adelaide, South Australia, 5010, Australia
Tel.: (61) 8440 1800
Fax: (61) 8440 1888
Web Site: www.coopers.com.au
Year Founded: 1862
Sales Range: $50-74.9 Million
Emp.: 125
Business Description:
Malt Beverage Brewery
S.I.C.: 2082
N.A.I.C.S.: 312120
Personnel:
Glenn Cooper *(Chm & Dir-Mktg)*
Timothy Cooper *(Mng Dir & Chief Brewer)*

U.S. Subsidiary:

Catalina Products, LLC **(1)**
5620 N Kolb Rd Ste 205
Tucson, AZ 85750 AZ
Tel.: (520) 529-0839
Fax: (800) 949-8542
Toll Free: (800) 852-4263
E-Mail: customerservices@mrbeer.com
Web Site: www.mrbeer.com
Emp.: 20
Home Brewery Systems & Supplies
S.I.C.: 2082
N.A.I.C.S.: 312120
Rick Zich *(CFO)*

COOPERS PARK CORPORATION

900-1095 West Pender St
Vancouver, BC, V6E 2M6, Canada
Tel.: (604) 662-8383
Fax: (604) 662-3878
E-Mail: info@cooperspark.com
Web Site: www.cooperspark.com
XCP—(TSXV)
Rev.: $1,961,235
Assets: $130,460,788
Liabilities: $412,570
Net Worth: $130,048,218
Earnings: $846,137
Fiscal Year-end: 12/31/12
Business Description:
Construction Services
S.I.C.: 1542
N.A.I.C.S.: 236220
Personnel:
Terence Hui *(Pres & CEO)*
Dennis Au-Yeung *(CFO, Sec & VP-Fin)*
Board of Directors:
Thomas S. Chambers
Terence Hui
Gerald Meerkatz
Transfer Agent:
Computershare Investor Services Inc.
3rd Floor 510 Burrard St
V6C 3B9 Vancouver, BC, Canada

Subsidiary:

Coopers Park Investment Holdings Limited **(1)**
1095 Pender St W Ste 900
Vancouver, BC, V6E 2M6, Canada
Tel.: (604) 662-8383
Fax: (604) 662-3878
Investment Management Services
S.I.C.: 6211
N.A.I.C.S.: 523999

COPA HOLDINGS, S.A.

(d/b/a Copa Airlines)
Avenida Principal y Avenida de la Rotonda Costa del Este
Complejo Business Park, Panama, Panama
Tel.: (507) 3042677
Fax: (507) 3042535
Web Site: www.copaair.com
CPA—(NYSE)
Rev.: $2,249,388,000
Assets: $3,479,500,000
Liabilities: $1,942,956,000
Net Worth: $1,536,544,000
Earnings: $326,476,000
Emp.: 8,277
Fiscal Year-end: 12/31/12
Business Description:
International Airline Passenger & Cargo Services
S.I.C.: 4512
N.A.I.C.S.: 481111
Personnel:
Stanley Motta *(Chm)*
Pedro Heilbron *(CEO)*
Jose Montero *(CFO)*
Daniel Gunn *(Sr VP-Ops)*
Board of Directors:
Stanley Motta
Jaime A. Arias C.
Alfredo Arias Loredo
Ricardo Alberto Arias
Roberto Artavia Loria
Jose Castaneda Velez
Joseph Fidanque, III
Osvaldo Heilbron
Pedro Heilbron
Douglas Leo
Alberto C. Motta, Jr.

Subsidiary:

Compania Panamena de Aviacion, S.A. **(1)**
Boulevard Costa del Este
Avenida Principal y Avenida de, Panama, Panama (99.8%)
Tel.: (507) 3033348
Web Site: www.copaair.com
Other Support Activities for Air Transportation
S.I.C.: 4581
N.A.I.C.S.: 488190
Alberto Motta *(Chm & Pres)*
Pedro Heilbron *(CEO)*
Victor Vial *(CFO)*

Non-U.S. Subsidiary:

AeroRepublica, S.A. **(1)**
Street 40A 13 13 1st Floor
Bogota, Colombia (99.8%)
Tel.: (57) 13209090
Fax: (57) 1 3209095
Web Site: www.aerorepublica.com
Other Support Activities for Air Transportation
S.I.C.: 4581
N.A.I.C.S.: 488190

COPAP INC.

755 boul St Jean Suite 305
Pointe-Claire, QC, H9R 5M9, Canada
Tel.: (514) 693-9150
Web Site: www.copap.com
Year Founded: 1990
Rev.: $104,300,000
Emp.: 14
Business Description:
Pulp & Paper Products Distr
S.I.C.: 2611
N.A.I.C.S.: 322110
Personnel:
David B. Sela *(Pres)*
Ronald Carriere *(CFO)*
Laurent J. Barbe *(COO & VP)*
Denys Lamarre *(Corp Sec & VP-Legal Affairs)*

COPARTNER TECHNOLOGY CORPORATION

4F No 16 Jian 8th Road
Zhonghe District, New Taipei City, Taiwan
Tel.: (886) 8226 5658
Fax: (886) 8226 5659
E-Mail: contact@copartner.com.tw
Web Site: www.copartner.com.tw

Year Founded: 1987
3550—(TAI)
Sales Range: $75-99.9 Million
Business Description:
Cable & Wire Mfr & Distr
S.I.C.: 3357
N.A.I.C.S.: 335921
Personnel:
Shin-Tsung Wang *(Pres)*

Non-U.S. Subsidiaries:

Copartner Wire & Cable (ShenZhen) Co Ltd **(1)**
No 68 Xintang Road XianTian Village
FuYong Town Baoan
Shenzhen, Guangdong, China
Tel.: (86) 75527312988
Fax: (86) 75527312165
Insulated Wire & Cable Mfr
S.I.C.: 3354
N.A.I.C.S.: 331318

Huisheng Plastics (Shen Zhen) Co Ltd **(1)**
No 2 Ninety Nine Industrial Area Minzhu Village Sha Jing Town
Baoan District, Shenzhen, Guangdong, China
Tel.: (86) 75533867988
Fax: (86) 755 33867990
Web Site: www.copartner.com.tw/english/01_about/05_copartner.php?pid=14
Cable & Wire Mfr
S.I.C.: 3355
N.A.I.C.S.: 331318

Shen Zhen Copartner Communication Co Ltd **(1)**
No 19 Dayangtian Industrial Area Wanfeng Village Shajing Town
Baoan District, Shenzhen, Guangdong, China
Tel.: (86) 75561573111
Fax: (86) 75561573166
Insulated Wire & Cable Mfr
S.I.C.: 3355
N.A.I.C.S.: 331318

Yanfu Copartner Technology (ShenZhen) Co Ltd **(1)**
No 68 Xintang Road XianTian Village
FuYong Town, Shenzhen, Guangdong, China
Tel.: (86) 75527312988
Fax: (86) 755 27312071
Cable & Wire Mfr
S.I.C.: 3354
N.A.I.C.S.: 331318
Michael Chen *(Gen Mgr)*

COPEINCA ASA
(Acquired by Pacific Andes International Holdings Limited)

COPENHAGEN MALMO PORT
Containervej 9
PO Box 900
DK 2100 Copenhagen, Denmark
Tel.: (45) 35461111
Fax: (45) 35461164
E-Mail: cmport@cmport.com
Web Site: www.cmport.com
Sales Range: $100-124.9 Million
Emp.: 450
Business Description:
Cargo Transportation Administration
S.I.C.: 9621
N.A.I.C.S.: 926120
Personnel:
Lennart Pettersson *(Mng Dir)*
Joham Roestin *(Mng Dir)*
Board of Directors:
Niels Bach
Kerry Forsberg
Rolf Hansson
Joen Magnusson
Peter Maskell
Soren A. Nyegaard
Anders Rubin
Kaj Schmidt
Mogens Worre Sorensen
Ake Svensson
Alfred Voldum

Non-U.S. Subsidiary:

Copenhagen Malmo Port **(1)**
Terminalgatan 18
PO Box 566
201 25 Malmo, Sweden (100%)
Tel.: (46) 406804100
Fax: (46) 40180501
E-Mail: cmport@cmport.com
Web Site: www.cmport.com
Rev.: $1,431,587
Emp.: 400
Shipping Terminal
S.I.C.: 4491
N.A.I.C.S.: 488320
Jopam Roestim *(Mng Dir)*
Lennart Pettersson *(Deputy Mng Dir)*

COPERSUCAR S.A.
Avenida Paulista 287
01311-000 Sao Paulo, SP, Brazil
Tel.: (55) 1126188166
Fax: (55) 1126188355
E-Mail: comercial@copersucar.com.br
Web Site: www.copersucar.com.br
Year Founded: 2008
Sales Range: $1-4.9 Billion
Emp.: 7,851
Business Description:
Sugar & Ethanol Production
Export
S.I.C.: 2061
N.A.I.C.S.: 311314
Personnel:
Luis Roberto Pogetti *(Chm)*
Paulo Roberto de Souza *(CEO)*
Board of Directors:
Luis Roberto Pogetti
Clesio Antonio Balbo
Norberto Bellodi
Carlos Dinucci
Leopold Titoto
Antonio Jose Zillo

COPITRAK INC.
8390 Mayrand Street
Montreal, QC, H4P 2C9, Canada
Tel.: (514) 737-7747
Fax: (514) 737-9155
Year Founded: 1976
Sales Range: $10-24.9 Million
Emp.: 25
Business Description:
Expense Management Hardware Developer & Software Designer
S.I.C.: 7372
N.A.I.C.S.: 511210
Personnel:
Mark Levine *(Pres & CEO)*
Legal Counsel:
Ravinsky Ryan
Montreal, QC, Canada

COPOL INTERNATIONAL LTD.
69 Hartigan Drive
PO Box 70
North Sydney, NS, B2A 3M4, Canada
Tel.: (902) 794-9685
Fax: (902) 794-7592
Toll Free: (800) 668-2700
Web Site: www.copolinternational.com
Year Founded: 1992
Rev.: $10,899,234
Emp.: 55
Business Description:
Film Products Mfr
S.I.C.: 3081
N.A.I.C.S.: 326113
Personnel:
Denis Lanoe *(VP-Ops)*

COPPEL S.A. DE C.V.
Republica 2859 Poniente
Col Recursos Hidraulicos, 80100
Culiacan, Sinaloa, Mexico
Tel.: (52) 6677594200
Fax: (52) 6677594223
E-Mail: informacion@int.coppel.com
Web Site: seguro.coppel.com
Year Founded: 1965
Sales Range: $1-4.9 Billion
Emp.: 30,910
Business Description:
Department Store Operator
Import
S.I.C.: 5311
N.A.I.C.S.: 452111
Personnel:
Enrique Coppel Luken *(Gen Dir)*
Agustin Coppel Luken *(Sec)*
Board of Directors:
Enrique Coppel Luken
Guillermo Alvarez Lopez
Agustin Coppel Luken
Enrique Coppel Tamayo
Jose Coppel
Ruben Coppel
Ricardo Martin Bringas

COPPER CORE LTD.
275 Carrier Dr
Toronto, ON, M9W 5Y8, Canada
Tel.: (416) 675-1177
Fax: (416) 675-0400
Toll Free: (800) 668-2588
E-Mail: sales@coppercore.com
Web Site: www.coppercore.com
Emp.: 80
Business Description:
Automotive Radiators, Oil Coolers & Air Coolers Mfr
S.I.C.: 3714
N.A.I.C.S.: 336390
Personnel:
Dan Pawlick *(Pres & CEO)*

COPPER COWBOY RESOURCES INC.
1220 Ottaburn Road
West Vancouver, BC, V7S 2J8, Canada
Tel.: (778) 227-6482
E-Mail: michael_mulberry@yahoo.ca
Year Founded: 2007
CCQ—(CNSX)
Assets: $30,855
Liabilities: $91,332
Net Worth: ($60,476)
Earnings: ($391,889)
Fiscal Year-end: 04/30/13
Business Description:
Metal Mining
S.I.C.: 1099
N.A.I.C.S.: 212299
Personnel:
Michael Mulberry *(Pres & CEO)*
James Henning *(CFO)*
Board of Directors:
Abby Farrage
Michael Mulberry
Leonard Vernon Senft

COPPER CREEK GOLD CORP.
700 West Pender Street Suite 615
Vancouver, BC, V6C 1G8, Canada
Tel.: (604) 662-3004
Fax: (604) 662-3063
Toll Free: (888) 957-0398
Web Site: www.coppercreekgold.com
CPV—(TSXV)
Int. Income: $96
Assets: $2,550,377
Liabilities: $468,702
Net Worth: $2,081,675
Earnings: ($73,718)
Fiscal Year-end: 12/31/12
Business Description:
Mineral Exploration Services
S.I.C.: 1081
N.A.I.C.S.: 213114
Personnel:
James E. Anderson *(Pres)*
Bing Jung *(CEO)*
Ken Leong *(Sec)*
Board of Directors:
James E. Anderson
Bob Culbert
Bing Jung
Gordon Jung
Gerry Olmstead
Transfer Agent:
Computershare Investor Services Inc.
100 University Ave 9th Floor
Toronto, ON, Canada

COPPER DEVELOPMENT CORPORATION
Viking House Nelson Street
Douglas, IM1 2AH, Isle of Man
Tel.: (44) 1624 639396
Fax: (44) 1624 661009
E-Mail: info@copperdevelopmentcorp.com
Web Site: www.copperdevelopmentcorp.com
Year Founded: 2009
CDC—(AIM OTC)
Rev.: $131,271
Assets: $35,717,346
Liabilities: $193,071
Net Worth: $35,524,275
Earnings: ($19,288,696)
Emp.: 61
Fiscal Year-end: 12/31/12
Business Description:
Copper Mining Services
S.I.C.: 1021
N.A.I.C.S.: 212234
Personnel:
Mitchell Alland *(Chm & CEO)*
Denham Eke *(CFO & Sec)*
Board of Directors:
Mitchell Alland
Denham Eke
Guy Elliott
Legal Counsel:
Kerman & Co. LLP
200 Strand
London, EC1V 9EE, United Kingdom

COPPER FOX METALS INC.
650 340 12th Avenue SW
Calgary, AB, T2R 1L5, Canada
Tel.: (403) 264-2820
Fax: (403) 264-2920
Toll Free: (866) 913-1910
E-Mail: info@copperfoxmetals.com
Web Site: www.copperfoxmetals.com
CUU—(OTC TSXV)
Assets: $89,728,118
Liabilities: $11,693,638
Net Worth: $78,034,479
Earnings: ($3,190,007)
Fiscal Year-end: 10/31/12
Business Description:
Copper Exploration & Development Services
S.I.C.: 1021
N.A.I.C.S.: 212234
Personnel:
Elmer B. Stewart *(Chm, Pres & CEO)*
Catherine Henderson *(CFO)*
Board of Directors:
Elmer B. Stewart
Ernesto Echavarria
Erik Koudstaal
David M. MacDonald
R. Hector Mackay-Dunn
J. Michael Smith

Copper Fox Metals Inc.—(Continued)

Legal Counsel:
Farris, Vaughan, Wills & Murphy LLP
25th Floor 700 W Georgia St
Vancouver, BC, Canada

Transfer Agent:
Canadian Stock Transfer Company Inc
600 The Dome Tower, 333 7th Ave SW
Calgary, AB, Canada

COPPER MOUNTAIN MINING CORPORATION

1700-700 West Pender Street
Vancouver, BC, V6C 1G8, Canada
Tel.: (604) 682-2992
Fax: (604) 682-2993
E-Mail: rod@cumtn.com
Web Site: www.cumtn.com
Year Founded: 2006
CUM—(OTC TSX)
Rev.: $228,101,358
Assets: $612,330,185
Liabilities: $369,784,308
Net Worth: $242,545,877
Earnings: $27,257,902
Fiscal Year-end: 12/31/12

Business Description:
Copper Mining Services
S.I.C.: 1021
N.A.I.C.S.: 212234

Personnel:
James C. O'Rourke *(CEO)*
Rodney A. Shier *(CFO)*

Board of Directors:
Bruce Aunger
Allan Cloke
Marin Katusa
James C. O'Rourke
Carl L. Renzoni
Rodney A. Shier
John Tapics

Legal Counsel:
Farris, Vaughan, Wills & Murphy
25th Floor 700 West Georgia Street
Vancouver, BC, Canada

Transfer Agents:
Computershare Trust Company of Canada
510 Burrard St
Vancouver, BC, Canada

Computershare Transfer Services
4th Floor 510 Burrard Street
Vancouver, BC, Canada

Subsidiary:

Similco Mines Ltd (1)
Ste 1700 700 W Pender St
Vancouver, BC, V6C 1G8, Canada
Tel.: (604) 682-2992
Fax: (604) 681-5910
E-Mail: info@cumtn.com
Web Site: www.cumtn.com
Emp.: 400
Mineral Mining Services
S.I.C.: 1499
N.A.I.C.S.: 212399
Rodney A. Shier *(CFO)*

COPPER NORTH MINING CORP.

2050 1111 W Georgia St
Vancouver, BC, V6E 4M3, Canada
Tel.: (604) 638-2505
Fax: (604) 669-2926
E-Mail: info@coppernorthmining.com
Web Site: www.coppernorthmining.com
Year Founded: 2011
COL—(TSXV)

Business Description:
Copper Mining
S.I.C.: 1021
N.A.I.C.S.: 212234

Personnel:
Dale Corman *(Chm)*
Harlan Meade *(Pres & CEO)*
Julien Francois *(CFO)*

Board of Directors:
Dale Corman
Bill Koutsouras
Bill LeClair
Harlan Meade

COPPER ONE INC.

2000 McGill College Suite 250
Montreal, QC, H3A 3H3, Canada
Tel.: (604) 688-9588
Fax: (778) 329-9361
E-Mail: info@continentresources.com
Web Site: www.continentresources.com
Year Founded: 2006
CUO—(TSXV)
Int. Income: $39,705
Assets: $10,708,271
Liabilities: $803,933
Net Worth: $9,904,339
Earnings: ($3,280,367)
Fiscal Year-end: 12/31/12

Business Description:
Copper Mining Services
S.I.C.: 1021
N.A.I.C.S.: 212234

Personnel:
G. Scott Moore *(Pres & CEO)*
Deborah Battiston *(CFO)*
Valery Zamuner *(Sec)*

Board of Directors:
Paul Cowley
Simon Marcotte
Justin Reid

Transfer Agent:
Equity Financial Trust Company
200 University Avenue Suite 400
Toronto, ON, M5H 4H1, Canada
Tel.: (416) 361-0152
Fax: (416) 361-0470
Toll Free: (866) 393-4891

COPPER RANGE LIMITED

(Name Changed to Caravel Energy Limited)

COPPER REEF MINING CORPORATION

12 Mitchell Rd
PO Box 306
Flin Flon, MB, R8A 1N1, Canada
Tel.: (204) 687-3500
Fax: (204) 687-4762
Web Site: www.copperreef.com
Year Founded: 1973
CZC—(CNSX)
Assets: $11,161,792
Liabilities: $1,464,483
Net Worth: $9,697,309
Earnings: ($599,683)
Emp.: 5
Fiscal Year-end: 11/30/12

Business Description:
Copper Mining Services
S.I.C.: 1021
N.A.I.C.S.: 212234

Personnel:
Robert N. Granger *(Chm)*
Stephen L. Masson *(Pres & CEO)*
David W. Kendall *(CFO & Treas)*
Laara Shaffer *(Sec)*

Board of Directors:
Robert N. Granger
Harry Barr
Gregory J. Campbell
David S. Kennedy
Stephen L. Masson
William J. Phillips
Edward G. Thompson

COPPER STRIKE LIMITED

Level 9 356 Collins Street
Melbourne, VIC, 3000, Australia
Tel.: (61) 396400955
Fax: (61) 396420698
E-Mail: info@copperstrike.com.au
Web Site: www.copperstrike.com.au
CSE—(ASX)
Rev.: $147,655
Assets: $27,604,135
Liabilities: $7,079,940
Net Worth: $20,524,195
Earnings: ($267,169)
Emp.: 2
Fiscal Year-end: 06/30/13

Business Description:
Mineral Exploration Services
S.I.C.: 1481
N.A.I.C.S.: 213115

Personnel:
Thomas Eadie *(Chm & Mng Dir)*
Melanie Leydin *(Sec)*

Board of Directors:
Thomas Eadie
John Stuart Ferguson Dunlop
Barrie Laws

Legal Counsel:
Baker & McKenzie
Level 19 181 William Street
Melbourne, Australia

COPPERMOLY LIMITED

Level 1 94 Bundall Road
Bundall, QLD, 4217, Australia
Tel.: (61) 755921001
Fax: (61) 755921011
E-Mail: info@coppermoly.com.au
Web Site: www.coppermoly.com.au
COY—(ASX)
Rev.: $21,635
Assets: $9,683,554
Liabilities: $524,349
Net Worth: $9,159,204
Earnings: ($1,042,523)
Fiscal Year-end: 06/30/13

Business Description:
Copper & Gold Mining & Exploration Services
S.I.C.: 1021
N.A.I.C.S.: 212234

Personnel:
Maurice J. Gannon *(Mng Dir)*
Paul Schultz *(Sec)*

Board of Directors:
Tom Revy
Ben Faulkner
Maurice J. Gannon
Michael Howard
Natalia Streltsova

Boardroom Pty Ltd
Level 7 207 Kent Street
Sydney, NSW, Australia

Subsidiary:

Copper Quest PNG Ltd (1)
Level 1
94 Bundall Rd, Bundall, Queensland, 4217, Australia
Tel.: (61) 755921001
Fax: (61) 755921011
Web Site: www.coppermoly.com.au/contact-us/index.htm
Emp.: 3
Copper Exploration Services
S.I.C.: 1021
N.A.I.C.S.: 212234
Peter Swiridiuk *(Mng Dir)*

COPYSOURCE INCORPORATED

(Acquired by Konica Minolta, Inc.)

COQUITLAM CHRYSLER DODGE JEEP LTD.

2960 Christmas Way
Coquitlam, BC, V3C4E6, Canada
Tel.: (604) 469-5600
Fax: (604) 464-0030
Toll Free: (800) 705-5338
E-Mail: cchry@telus.net
Web Site: www.coquitlamchryslerdodge.com
Year Founded: 1975
Rev.: $42,831,828
Emp.: 85

Business Description:
New & Used Car Dealers
S.I.C.: 5511
N.A.I.C.S.: 441110

Personnel:
Jeff Kornatowsky *(Gen Mgr)*

COR&FJA AG

Humboldtstrasse 35
70771 Leinfelden-Echterdingen, Germany
Tel.: (49) 711 94958 0
Fax: (49) 711 94958 49
E-Mail: investor.relations@cor.fja.com
Web Site: www.cor.fja.com
FJH—(DEU)
Sls.: $183,994,985
Assets: $142,629,195
Liabilities: $75,385,532
Net Worth: $67,243,663
Earnings: ($33,074,052)
Emp.: 1,178
Fiscal Year-end: 12/31/12

Business Description:
Software & Consulting Services
S.I.C.: 7372
N.A.I.C.S.: 511210

Personnel:
Elmar Helten *(Chm-Supervisory Bd)*
Christian Hofer *(Chm-Exec Bd)*
Klaus Kuhnle *(Deputy Chm-Supervisory Bd)*
Volker Weimer *(Member-Exec Bd-Banking, Non-Life & IT-Svcs)*
Rolf Zielke *(Member-Exec Bd-Life, P&C & Natl Market)*

Supervisory Board of Directors:
Elmar Helten
Klaus Kuhnle
Thomas Nievergelt
Jens Seehusen
Johann Zehetmaier

Subsidiaries:

COR&FJA Consulting GmbH (1)
Pascalstrasse 12
52076 Aachen, Germany
Tel.: (49) 2408 93801 0
Information Technology Consulting Services
S.I.C.: 7373
N.A.I.C.S.: 541512

COR&FJA Deutschland GmbH (1)
Prinzenallee 11
40549 Dusseldorf, Germany
Tel.: (49) 211 520659 00
Information Technology Consulting Services
S.I.C.: 7373
N.A.I.C.S.: 541512

U.S. Subsidiary:

FJA-US, Inc. (2)
1040 Avenue of the Americas 4th Fl
New York, NY 10018
Tel.: (212) 840-2618
E-Mail: support@fja-us.com
Web Site: www.fja-us.com
Information Technology Consulting Services
S.I.C.: 7373
N.A.I.C.S.: 541512
Marc Dutton, *(CEO)*
Carl-Arndt Krapp *(Mng Dir & CIO)*
Joe Wilds *(Sr VP)*

Non-U.S. Subsidiary:

COR&FJA Slovakia s.r.o. (2)
Hranicna 18
82105 Bratislava, Slovakia
Tel.: (421) 2 32221 270
Information Technology Consulting Services
S.I.C.: 7373
N.A.I.C.S.: 541512

COR&FJA Metris GmbH (1)
Leopoldstr 1
78112 Saint Georgen, Germany
Tel.: (49) 7724 88070 0
Fax: (49) 7724 8807 115
Information Technology Consulting Services
S.I.C.: 7373
N.A.I.C.S.: 541512

FJA bAV Service GmbH (1)
Elsenheimerstr 65
80687 Munich, Germany
Tel.: (49) 89 76901 0
Information Technology Consulting Services
S.I.C.: 7373
N.A.I.C.S.: 541512

PYLON GmbH (1)
Suderstrasse 77
20097 Hamburg, Germany
Tel.: (49) 40 99996 600
Information Technology Consulting Services
S.I.C.: 7373
N.A.I.C.S.: 541512

Non-U.S. Subsidiaries:

COR&FJA Austria Ges.m.b.H. (1)
Wiedner Hauptstr 76/1/4
1040 Vienna, Austria
Tel.: (43) 1 58070 0
Fax: (43) 1 51330 41
Information Technology Consulting Services
S.I.C.: 7373
N.A.I.C.S.: 541512

COR&FJA Benelux B.V (1)
De Witbogt 26
5652 AG Eindhoven, Netherlands
Tel.: (31) 40 2026337
Information Technology Consulting Services
S.I.C.: 7373
N.A.I.C.S.: 541512
Erwin van der Wal *(Mng Dir)*

COR&FJA Czech, spol. s r.o. (1)
Na Strzi 1702/65
140 00 Prague, Czech Republic
Tel.: (420) 222 191 507
Information Technology Consulting Services
S.I.C.: 7373
N.A.I.C.S.: 541512

COR&FJA OdaTeam d.o.o. (1)
Titova cesta 8
2000 Maribor, Slovenia
Tel.: (386) 22356200
Information Technology Consulting Services
S.I.C.: 7373
N.A.I.C.S.: 541512
Andrej Kline *(Mng Dir)*

COR&FJA Polska Sp. z o.o. (1)
Al Jerozolimskie 96
00-807 Warsaw, Poland
Tel.: (48) 22 275 56 71
Information Technology Consulting Services
S.I.C.: 7373
N.A.I.C.S.: 541512
Tomasz Dybowski *(Head-Insurance Market Dev)*

COR&FJA Schweiz AG (1)
Kaiserstrasse 8
4310 Rheinfelden, Switzerland
Tel.: (41) 61 90691 20
Information Technology Consulting Services
S.I.C.: 7373
N.A.I.C.S.: 541512

COR&FJA Systems Portugal, Unipessoal Lda (1)
Avenida dos Aliados n 54 5 Andar
4000-064 Porto, Portugal
Tel.: (351) 2 23203110
Information Technology Consulting Services
S.I.C.: 7373
N.A.I.C.S.: 541512

Wagner & Kunz Aktuare AG (1)
Henric Petri-Str 19
4051 Basel, Switzerland
Tel.: (41) 61 205 03 70
Fax: (41) 61 205 03 71
Web Site: www.aktuare.ch
Information Technology Consulting Services
S.I.C.: 7373
N.A.I.C.S.: 541512

CORAC GROUP PLC

Technology Centre 683-685 Stirling Road
Slough, Berkshire, SL1 4ST, United Kingdom
Tel.: (44) 1753 285800
Fax: (44) 1753 285801
E-Mail: info@corac.co.uk
Web Site: www.corac.co.uk
CRA—(LSE)
Rev.: $24,161,558
Assets: $46,029,986
Liabilities: $17,034,222
Net Worth: $28,995,764
Earnings: ($8,250,211)
Emp.: 131
Fiscal Year-end: 12/31/12

Business Description:
Air Compressor Technology Developer
S.I.C.: 3563
N.A.I.C.S.: 333912

Personnel:
Mark Crawford *(Mng Dir & CFO)*
Mike Webb *(Sec)*

Board of Directors:
Rohan Richard Courtney
Mark Crawford
Julia Henderson
Richard King

Legal Counsel:
Nabarro LLP
84 Theobalds Road
London, WC1X 8RW, United Kingdom

CORAL GOLD RESOURCES LTD.

570 Granville Street Suite 900
Vancouver, BC, V6C 3P1, Canada
Tel.: (604) 682-3701
Fax: (604) 682-3600
E-Mail: ir@coralgold.com
Web Site: www.coralgold.com
Year Founded: 1981
CLHRF—(OTCB)
Rev.: $4,228
Assets: $20,208,971
Liabilities: $3,414,461
Net Worth: $16,794,511
Earnings: ($1,533,339)
Emp.: 1
Fiscal Year-end: 01/31/13

Business Description:
Gold Mining Services
S.I.C.: 1041
N.A.I.C.S.: 212221

Personnel:
Gary R. Robertson *(Chm)*
David Wolfin *(Pres & CEO)*
Malcolm Davidson *(CFO)*
Pamela Saulnier *(Sec)*

Board of Directors:
Gary R. Robertson
Ronald Andrews
Andrew J. Kaplan
Chris Sampson
David Wolfin

Transfer Agent:
Computershare Investor Services Inc.
510 Burrard St 2nd Floor
Vancouver, BC, V6C 3B9, Canada
Tel.: (604) 661-9400

CORAL HUB LIMITED

Kingsley Chambers Block No 26
Ramasamy Street off Usmal Road
T Nagar Mambalam Guindy Taluk, Chennai, 600 017, India
Tel.: (91) 4424362751
Fax: (91) 4424362756
E-Mail: investors@coralhublimited.com
Web Site: www.coralhublimited.com
533011—(BOM NSE)
Sales Range: $10-24.9 Million
Emp.: 200

Business Description:
E-Publishing, E-Book, Print on Demand, Data & Document Management, Data Conversion, Digital Library Management Servcies
S.I.C.: 7374
N.A.I.C.S.: 518210

Personnel:
G. S. Chandrashekar *(Chm)*

Board of Directors:
G. S. Chandrashekar
Ghanshyam Joshi
Dilip Parekh
Harish Kumar Sahu
D. M. Shirodkar

Transfer Agent:
Link Intime India Pvt. Ltd.
C-13 Pannalal Silk Mills Compound
LBS Marg
Bhandup, Mumbai, 400 078, India
Tel.: (91) 22 2596 3838
Fax: (91) 22 2594 6969

Subsidiaries:

Basiz Fund Service Pvt Ltd. (1)
No 26 Ramasamy St Off Usman Rd
Tyagaraya Nagar, Chennai, India
Tel.: (91) 44 2436 2751
Fax: (91) 44 2436 2756
Accounting Services
S.I.C.: 8721
N.A.I.C.S.: 541219

Tutis Digital Publishing Pvt Ltd (1)
C-409 Solaris 1 Opp to L & T Gate No 6
Saki Vihar Rd Andheri E, Mumbai, 400 072, India
Tel.: (91) 2228578240
Fax: (91) 2226873413
Web Site: www.tutisdigitalpublishing.com
Emp.: 110
Electronic Publishing Services
S.I.C.: 7389
N.A.I.C.S.: 561410
G S Chandrasekar *(Mng Dir)*

Non-U.S. Subsidiary:

Digital Content Solutions Limited (1)
2nd Fl Titan Ct 3 Bishops Sq
Hatfield, Hertfordshire, AL10 9NA, United Kingdom
Tel.: (44) 1707 226045
Fax: (44) 1707 226244
E-Mail: info@digitalcontentsolutions.co.uk
Web Site: www.digitalcontentsolutions.co.uk
Database Management Services
S.I.C.: 7376
N.A.I.C.S.: 541513

CORAL LABORATORIES LTD.

503 Dalamal House J B Road
Nariman Point
Mumbai, 400021, India
Tel.: (91) 22 22873698
Fax: (91) 22 22873694
E-Mail: exports@corallab.com
Web Site: www.corallab.com
524506—(BOM)

Business Description:
Medical Laboratory Services
S.I.C.: 8071
N.A.I.C.S.: 621511

Personnel:
Daisy Thomas *(Compliance Officer)*

Board of Directors:
Kishor R. Mehta
S. Ramamurthy

CORAL PRODUCTS PLC

North Florida Road Haydock
Industrial Estate
Haydock, Merseyside, WA11 9TP, United Kingdom
Tel.: (44) 1942272882
Fax: (44) 1942726116
E-Mail: sales@coralproducts.com
Web Site: www.coralproducts.com
CRU—(AIM)
Rev.: $27,288,552
Assets: $24,725,364
Liabilities: $11,100,829
Net Worth: $13,624,535
Earnings: $674,357
Emp.: 110
Fiscal Year-end: 04/30/13

Business Description:
Video & DVD Packaging Mfr
S.I.C.: 2671
N.A.I.C.S.: 322220

Personnel:
Warren Ferster *(CEO & Mng Dir)*
Stephen D. Fletcher *(Sec & Dir-Fin)*

Board of Directors:
Joseph Grimmond
Stuart Ferster
Warren Ferster
Stephen D. Fletcher
Jonathan Lever

Legal Counsel:
Davies Arnold Cooper LLP
6-8 Bouverie Street
London, United Kingdom

CORAL SEA PETROLEUM LIMITED

Level 5 56 Pitt Street
Sydney, NSW, 2000, Australia
Tel.: (61) 2 8823 3177
Fax: (61) 2 8823 3188
E-Mail: info@coralseapetroleum.co.au
Web Site: www.coralseapetroleum.co.au
CSP—(ASX)
Rev.: $184,781
Assets: $3,018,180
Liabilities: $417,416
Net Worth: $2,600,764
Earnings: ($1,260,977)
Fiscal Year-end: 06/30/13

Business Description:
Investment Services
S.I.C.: 6211
N.A.I.C.S.: 523999

Personnel:
Domenic Martino *(Mng Dir)*
Louisa Martino *(Sec)*

Board of Directors:
Joseph Goldberg
Domenic Martino
Julian Lionel Sandt
Alvin Tan

CORAZON GOLD CORP.

1060-1055 West Hastings
Vancouver, BC, V6E 2E9, Canada
Tel.: (604) 629-9670
Fax: (604) 629-9671
E-Mail: info@corazongold.com
Web Site: www.corazongold.com
CGW—(TSXV)
Int. Income: $62,982
Assets: $6,803,058
Liabilities: $498,256
Net Worth: $6,304,802
Earnings: ($3,689,401)
Fiscal Year-end: 12/31/12

Business Description:
Gold Mining Services
S.I.C.: 1041
N.A.I.C.S.: 212221

Personnel:
Patrick Brauckmann *(Pres & CEO)*
Maricruz Alvarado *(CFO)*
Lynne Crouch *(Sec)*

Board of Directors:
Patrick Brauckmann
John King Burns
Carl Hering
Rosie Moore

Corazon Gold Corp.—(Continued)

Legal Counsel:
Fasken Martineau DuMoulin LLP
Suite 2900 550 Burrard Street
Vancouver, BC, Canada

CORAZON MINING LIMITED
Suite 5 Level 1 350 Hay St
PO Box 8187
Subiaco, WA, 6008, Australia
Tel.: (61) 8 6142 6366
Fax: (61) 8 6210 1872
E-Mail: info@corazon.com.au
Web Site: www.corazon.com.au
CZN—(ASX)
Rev.: $109,223
Assets: $2,159,277
Liabilities: $678,960
Net Worth: $1,480,317
Earnings: ($3,663,928)
Emp.: 2
Fiscal Year-end: 06/30/13
Business Description:
Exploration Services
S.I.C.: 1081
N.A.I.C.S.: 213114
Personnel:
Brett Smith *(Mng Dir)*
Robert Orr *(CFO & Sec)*
Board of Directors:
Clive Jones
Adrian Byass
Jonathan Downes
Brett Smith
Legal Counsel:
Steinepreis Paganin
Level 4 Next Building 16 Milligan St
Perth, Australia

CORDANT GROUP PLC.
Chevron House 346 Long Lane
Hillingdom, Middlesex, UB10 9PF, United Kingdom
Tel.: (44) 1895 201 800
Fax: (44) 1895 201 801
E-Mail: info@cordantgroup.com
Web Site: www.cordantgroup.com
Year Founded: 1957
Sales Range: $750-799.9 Million
Emp.: 30,000
Business Description:
Investment Management Services
S.I.C.: 6282
N.A.I.C.S.: 523920
Personnel:
Guy Pakenham *(Mng Dir)*

CORDLIFE GROUP LIMITED
61 Science Park Road No 05-16/18
Singapore, 117525, Singapore
Tel.: (65) 6238 0808
Fax: (65) 6238 1108
Web Site: www.cordlife.com
Year Founded: 2001
P8A—(OTC SES)
Business Description:
Stem Cell Banking Services
S.I.C.: 8071
N.A.I.C.S.: 621511
Personnel:
Jeremy Yee *(Exec Dir & CEO)*
Board of Directors:
Jeremy Yee

CORDOBA MINERALS CORP.
200 Burrard Street Suite 650
Vancouver, BC, V6C 3L6, Canada
Tel.: (604) 801-5432
Fax: (604) 662-8829
Toll Free: (888) 627-9378
E-Mail: info@cordobamineralscorp.com
Web Site: www.cordobamineralscorp.com
Year Founded: 2009
CDB—(TSXV)
Rev.: $11,176
Assets: $7,857,073
Liabilities: $65,733
Net Worth: $7,791,340
Earnings: ($2,167,076)
Fiscal Year-end: 04/30/13
Business Description:
Gold Mining Services
S.I.C.: 1041
N.A.I.C.S.: 212221
Personnel:
Simon T. P. Ridgway *(Chm & CEO)*
Peter Thiersch *(Pres)*
Kevin Bales *(CFO)*
Board of Directors:
Simon T. P. Ridgway
Harmen J. Keyser
G. Ross McDonald
Ralph Rushton
Peter Thiersch
Tod Turley
Transfer Agent:
Olympia Trust Company
Suite 1003 750 West Pender Street
Vancouver, BC, V6C 2T8, Canada

CORDS CABLE INDUSTRIES LTD.
B1/A26 Mohan Cooperative Industrial Estate
Mathura Road, New Delhi, 110044, India
Tel.: (91) 11 40551200
Fax: (91) 11 26951196
E-Mail: ccil@cordscable.com
Web Site: www.cordscable.com
532941—(BOM)
Rev.: $71,776,083
Assets: $53,489,591
Liabilities: $34,072,725
Net Worth: $19,416,867
Earnings: $1,127,385
Fiscal Year-end: 03/31/13
Business Description:
Cable Mfr
S.I.C.: 3357
N.A.I.C.S.: 335921
Personnel:
V. K. Beri *(CEO)*
D. K. Prashar *(Co-Mng Dir)*
Naveen Sawhney *(Co-Mng Dir)*
Dinesh Shukla *(Pres-Ops)*
Garima Pant *(Sec)*
Board of Directors:
N. K. Balasubramanian
Om Prakash Bhandari
D. K. Prashar
Ajit Kumar Sahay
Naveen Sawhney
Transfer Agent:
Link Intime India Private Limited
44 Community Centre 2nd Floor Naraina Industrial Area Phase-I
Near PVR Naraina, New Delhi, India

CORDSTRAP NETHERLANDS B.V.
Nobelstraat 1
5807 GA Oostrum, Netherlands
Mailing Address:
PO Box 5155
5800 GD Venray, Netherlands
Tel.: (31) 478 519 000
Fax: (31) 478 519 111
E-Mail: sales.nl@cordstrap.net
Web Site: www.cordstrap.net
Emp.: 400
Business Description:
Cargo Securing System Mfr
S.I.C.: 3089
N.A.I.C.S.: 326199
Personnel:
Sander Lossie *(Mgr-Export)*

U.S. Subsidiary:

Cordstrap USA, Inc. (1)
2000 S Sylvania Ave Ste 101
Sturtevant, WI 53177-2102
Tel.: (262) 898-6670
Fax: (262) 898-6677
E-Mail: sales.mw.usa@cordstrap.net
Web Site: www.cordstrap.net
Emp.: 49
Cargo Securing System Mfr
S.I.C.: 3089
N.A.I.C.S.: 326199
Tom Keefe *(VP-Sls)*

Non-U.S. Subsidiaries:

Cordstrap Deutschland GmbH (1)
Tackweg 41
47918 Tonisvorst, Germany
Tel.: (49) 2151 78880
E-Mail: sales.de@cordstrap.net
Web Site: www.cordstrap.net
Emp.: 2
Cargo Securing System Mfr
S.I.C.: 3089
N.A.I.C.S.: 326199
Frank Zielke *(Mgr-Comml)*

Cordstrap Espana s.l.u. (1)
Avenida Francesc Macia 60 13 fl Door 3
8207 Sabadell, Spain
Tel.: (34) 90 2565 071
Fax: (34) 93 7462 795
E-Mail: ventas@cordstrap.net
Web Site: www.cordstrap.net
Emp.: 12
Cargo Securing System Mfr
S.I.C.: 3089
N.A.I.C.S.: 326199
Jose Garcia *(Mgr-Comml)*

Cordstrap France Sarl (1)
5 7 Ave du General de Gaulle
60300 Senlis, France
Tel.: (33) 3 44258181
Fax: (33) 3 44258896
E-Mail: sales.fr@cordstrap.net
Cargo Securing System Mfr
S.I.C.: 3089
N.A.I.C.S.: 326199
Fabrice Lecat *(Mgr-Comml)*

Cordstrap India Private Limited (1)
Suite 47 Vatika Business Centre Level 5
Tech Park 1 Airport Road Y
Yerwada, Pune, 411006, India
Tel.: (91) 20 4011 1420
Fax: (91) 20 4011 1105
E-Mail: sales.in@cordstrap.net
Web Site: www.cordstrap.net
Emp.: 4
Cargo Securing System Mfr
S.I.C.: 3089
N.A.I.C.S.: 326199
Jon Blower *(Mng Dir)*

Cordstrap Ireland Limited (1)
41 Percy Place
Dublin, 4, Ireland
Tel.: (353) 1 4977660
Fax: (353) 1 7977455
E-Mail: sales.ie@cordstrap.net
Web Site: www.cordstrap.net
Emp.: 25
Cargo Securing System Mfr
S.I.C.: 3089
N.A.I.C.S.: 326199
Henk Van Zijl *(Country Mgr)*

Cordstrap Italia S.r.l. (1)
Via Papa Giovanni Paolo1 No 422
21040 Uboldo, Italy
Tel.: (39) 02 96783625
Fax: (39) 02 96782157
E-Mail: sales.it@cordstrap.net
Cargo Securing System Mfr
S.I.C.: 3089
N.A.I.C.S.: 326199
Dario Tofani *(Mng Dir)*

Cordstrap Load Securing Systems (Wuxi) Co., Ltd (1)
No 168 Yu an Road Shuofang Industrial Park
Wuxi, China 214142
Tel.: (86) 510 853 11 666
Fax: (86) 510 853 10 066
E-Mail: sales.cn@cordstrap.net
Cargo Securing System Mfr
S.I.C.: 3089
N.A.I.C.S.: 326199

Cordstrap Malaysia Sdn Bhd (1)
No 28 Jalan Kasuarina 12 Bandar Ambang Botanic
41200 Kelang, Malaysia
Tel.: (60) 3 3325 1616
Fax: (60) 3 3325 1661
E-Mail: sales.my@cordstrap.net
Web Site: www.cordstrap.net
Emp.: 9
Cargo Securing System Mfr
S.I.C.: 3089
N.A.I.C.S.: 326199
Stefan Becker *(Mgr-Comml)*

Cordstrap Mexico, S.A. de C.V. (1)
Av Manuel Gomez Morin No 3881 Oficina 2
Colonia Centro Sur
76090 Queretaro, Mexico
Tel.: (52) 442 229 1561
Fax: (52) 442 229 1562
E-Mail: sales.mx@cordstrap.net
Web Site: www.cordstrap.net
Emp.: 1
Cargo Securing System Mfr
S.I.C.: 3089
N.A.I.C.S.: 326199
Barry van Soest *(Mgr-Comml)*

Cordstrap Polska SP. Z O.O. (1)
Wysogotowo ul Kamienna 22
62 081 Przezmierowo, Poland
Tel.: (48) 61 652 51 52
Fax: (48) 61 652 51 57
E-Mail: sales.pl@cordstrap.net
Web Site: www.cordstrap.pl
Emp.: 17
Cargo Securing System Mfr
S.I.C.: 3089
N.A.I.C.S.: 326199
Okko Ten Hoff *(Gen Mgr)*

Cordstrap SA (Pty) Ltd (1)
Unit 3 Paddy Close Ottery
Cape Town, 7800, South Africa
Tel.: (27) 21 704 0090
Fax: (27) 21 704 2526
E-Mail: sales.za@cordstrap.net
Web Site: www.cordstrap.co.za
Emp.: 2
Cargo Securing System Mfr
S.I.C.: 3089
N.A.I.C.S.: 326199
Barry Hugo *(Mgr-Comml)*

Cordstrap, s.r.o. (1)
Jakubska 2
Prague, 11000, Czech Republic
Tel.: (420) 776 772 171
E-Mail: sales.cz@cordstrap.net
Cargo Securing System Mfr
S.I.C.: 3089
N.A.I.C.S.: 326199
David Marous *(Mgr-Comml)*

Cordstrap UK Ltd. (1)
Paddock Road West Pimbo
Skelmersdale, Lancashire, WN8 9PL, United Kingdom
Tel.: (44) 1695 554700
Fax: (44) 1695 556644
E-Mail: sales.uk@cordstrap.net
Web Site: www.cordstrap.net
Emp.: 2
Cargo Securing System Mfr
S.I.C.: 3089
N.A.I.C.S.: 326199
Alan Green *(Country Mgr)*

CORDY OILFIELD SERVICES INC.
1000 1520 4th Street SW
Calgary, AB, T2R 1H5, Canada
Tel.: (403) 266-2067
Fax: (403) 266-2087
E-Mail: info@cordy.ca
Web Site: www.cordy.ca
Year Founded: 1998
CKK—(TSXV)
Rev.: $111,681,129
Assets: $76,399,383
Liabilities: $34,535,237
Net Worth: $41,864,146
Earnings: ($3,212,673)
Emp.: 406

Fiscal Year-end: 12/31/12
Business Description:
Oilfield & Construction Services
S.I.C.: 1389
N.A.I.C.S.: 213112
Personnel:
David Mullen *(Chm & CEO)*
David J. Boomer *(CFO)*
Board of Directors:
David Mullen
David E. Olson
Melvin Ternan
Timothy H. Urquhart
Robert N. Waddell
Legal Counsel:
Davis LLP
Calgary, AB, Canada
Transfer Agent:
Computershare
Calgary, AB, Canada
Subsidiaries:

Battle River Oilfield Construction Ltd. (1)
1301 3rd St Ne
Manning, AB, T0H 2M0, Canada
Tel.: (780) 836-3498
Fax: (780) 836-3468
E-Mail: broffice@cordy.ca
Web Site: www.battleriveroilfield.com
Emp.: 15
Oil & Gas Pipeline Construction Services
S.I.C.: 1629
N.A.I.C.S.: 237120
Keith Hutchison *(Mgr-Ops & PR)*

Calgary Septic Ltd. (1)
5366 55 St SE
Calgary, AB, T2C 3G9, Canada
Tel.: (403) 262-7667
Fax: (403) 237-6278
E-Mail:
Web Site: www.cordy.ca
Emp.: 30
Septic Sludge Disposal Services
S.I.C.: 4953
N.A.I.C.S.: 562212
Franck Haettel *(Pres)*

Cordy Drilling Innovations Inc. (1)
3112 80th Ave SE
Calgary, AB, T2C1J3, Canada
Tel.: (403) 720-7600
Fax: (403) 236-2010
Toll Free: (855) 720-7600
E-Mail: info@cordy.com
Emp.: 1
Drilling Machinery Mfr
S.I.C.: 3532
N.A.I.C.S.: 333131
Luke Wilson *(Gen Mgr)*

Coverall Pipeline Construction Ltd. (1)
1101 Main Avenue East
Box 769
Sundre, AB, T0M 1X0, Canada
Tel.: (403) 638-2666
Fax: (403) 638-9131
E-Mail: info@coverallpipeline.com
Web Site: www.coverallpipeline.com
Oil & Gas Pipeline Construction Services
S.I.C.: 1623
N.A.I.C.S.: 237120

Hartwell Oilfield Ltd. (1)
4707 41st Street
PO Box 479
Stettler, AB, T0C 2L0, Canada
Tel.: (403) 358-4278
Fax: (403) 358-5219
Toll Free: (888) 742-6686
E-Mail: hartwell@telus.net
Web Site: www.hartwell.ca
Emp.: 25
Oil Drilling & Trucking Services
S.I.C.: 1381
N.A.I.C.S.: 213111
Amit Arora *(Office Mgr)*

Lamont Bit Services Ltd. (1)
6-1304 44 Avenue NE
Calgary, AB, T2E 6L6, Canada
Tel.: (403) 291-3711
Fax: (403) 250-8428
Web Site: www.lamontbits.com
Drill Bit & Down Hole Tool Mfr & Distr
S.I.C.: 3533
N.A.I.C.S.: 333132

New West Pipelines Ltd. (1)
14801-89 Street
Grande Prairie, AB, T8X 0J2, Canada
Tel.: (780) 513-2223
Fax: (780) 513-2677
E-Mail: newwest@cordy.ca
Web Site: www.newwestpipelines.com
Emp.: 200
Oil & Gas Pipeline Construction Services
S.I.C.: 1623
N.A.I.C.S.: 237120
Lorna Wold *(Controller)*

Nohels Group Inc. (1)
200 Industrial Road 1
PO Box 1227
Sparwood, BC, Canada V0B 2G0
Tel.: (250) 425-2519
Fax: (250) 425-0144
Web Site: www.nohels.com
Mining Equipment Distr
S.I.C.: 5082
N.A.I.C.S.: 423810
Michael Sharp *(Gen Mgr)*

Subsidiaries:

Elkford Industries Ltd. (2)
200 Industrial Rd Unit 1
Sparwood, BC, V0B 2G0, Canada
Tel.: (250) 425-2519
Oil & Gas Pipeline Construction Services
S.I.C.: 1623
N.A.I.C.S.: 237120

Fernie Contractors Ltd. (2)
200 Industrial Rd Unit 1
Sparwood, BC, V0B 2G0, Canada
Tel.: (250) 425-2519
Fax: (250) 425-0144
Oil & Gas Pipeline Construction Services
S.I.C.: 1623
N.A.I.C.S.: 237120

Hi-Hevi Rigging Ltd. (2)
200 Industrial Rd Unit 1
Sparwood, BC, V0B 2G0, Canada
Tel.: (250) 425-2519
Fax: (250) 425-0144
Heavy Machinery Transportation Services
S.I.C.: 4212
N.A.I.C.S.: 484220

Northern Glory Dredging Ltd. (2)
200 Industrial Rd 1 Rr 1 Unit 1
Sparwood, BC, V0B 2G1, Canada
Tel.: (250) 425-2519
Fax: (250) 425-0144
Heavy Machinery Transportation Servies
S.I.C.: 4212
N.A.I.C.S.: 484220
Mike Starr *(Gen Mgr)*

RB2 Energy Services Inc. (1)
5366 55 St SE
Calgary, AB, T2C 3G9, Canada
Tel.: (403) 203-2344
Fax: (403) 237-6278
Oil & Gas Pipeline Construction Services
S.I.C.: 1629
N.A.I.C.S.: 237120

Sphere Drilling Supplies Ltd. (1)
3112 - 80th Avenue S E
Calgary, AB, T2C 1J3, Canada
Tel.: (403) 720-9333
Fax: (403) 236-2010
Toll Free: (800) 230-8472
E-Mail: info.sphere@cordy.ca
Web Site: www.sphere-drilling.com
Emp.: 30
Drilling Machinery Mfr
S.I.C.: 3532
N.A.I.C.S.: 333131
Fred Lamont *(Gen Mgr)*

Tawow Resources Inc. (1)
9911 Chiila Blvd
Box 415
Tsuu T'ina, AB, T3W 6H6, Canada
Tel.: (403) 238-5190
Fax: (403) 238-5178
Toll Free: (877) 707-5190
E-Mail: admin@tawowresources.com
Web Site: www.tawowresources.com
Seismic Line Clearing Services
S.I.C.: 8713
N.A.I.C.S.: 541360
Darryl Bouvier *(Pres)*

CORDYS BV

(Acquired & Absorbed by Open Text Corporation)

CORE CANADIAN DIVIDEND TRUST

Standard Life Centre 121 King Street West Suite 2600
Toronto, ON, M5H 3T9, Canada
Tel.: (416) 681-3990
Fax: (416) 681-3901
Year Founded: 2006
CDD.UN—(TSX)
Rev.: $453,944
Assets: $10,994,706
Liabilities: $2,164,218
Net Worth: $8,830,488
Earnings: $92,438
Fiscal Year-end: 12/31/12
Business Description:
Financial Investment Services
S.I.C.: 6211
N.A.I.C.S.: 523999
Personnel:
John P. Mulvihill *(CEO)*
Transfer Agent:
Computershare Investor Services Inc
100 University Avenue 8th Floor
Toronto, ON, Canada

CORE COMMUNICATION SERVICES LTD.

6-7 Ludgate Square
London, EC4M7AS, United Kingdom
Tel.: (44) 8081300808
Fax: (44) 8081300809
E-Mail: enquiries@coretel.co.uk
Web Site: www.coretel.co.uk
Year Founded: 2005
Sales Range: $25-49.9 Million
Emp.: 15
Business Description:
International Mobile Telecommunications Services
S.I.C.: 4812
N.A.I.C.S.: 517210
Personnel:
Tony Greaves *(Founder)*

CORE CORPORATION

1-22-3 Sangenjaya Setagaya-ku
Tokyo, 154-8552, Japan
Tel.: (81) 3 3795 5111
Fax: (81) 3 3795 5110
E-Mail: public@core.co.jp
Web Site: www.core.co.jp
Year Founded: 1969
2359—(TKS)
Sales Range: $200-249.9 Million
Emp.: 1,279
Business Description:
IT Services
S.I.C.: 7379
N.A.I.C.S.: 541519
Personnel:
Ryohei Tanemura *(CEO)*
Minoru Yanada *(COO)*
Toshiyuki Kinoshita *(Mng Exec Officer)*
Morikazu Noaki *(Mng Exec Officer)*
Shigeru Ohira *(Mng Exec Officer)*
Kohji Ohuchi *(Mng Exec Officer)*
Board of Directors:
Toshiyuki Kinoshita
Morikazu Noaki
Shigeru Ohira
Kohji Ohuchi
Ryohei Tanemura
Minoru Yanada

Subsidiaries:

Accord System Co., Ltd. (1)
Second Core Bldg 2-11-26 Sangenjaya
Setagaya-ku, Tokyo, 154-0024, Japan
Tel.: (81) 3 5433 6640
Fax: (81) 3 3410 4661
Web Site: www.accordsystem.co.jp
Electronic Calculator Equipment Distr
S.I.C.: 5065
N.A.I.C.S.: 423690

Active Brains & Trust Co., Ltd. (1)
Sumitomo-Ohimachi Building
1-20-10 Ohi.Shinagawa-ku, 140-0014
Tokyo, Japan
Tel.: (81) 387183277
Fax: (81) 357183279
Web Site: www.core.co.jp/english/profile/prof_branch_list.html
Custom Computer Programming Services
S.I.C.: 7371
N.A.I.C.S.: 541511

Answer and Consulting Co., Ltd (1)
Suzawa Building 4-7-10 Honmachi Nihonbashi
Chuo-ku, Tokyo, 103-0023, Japan
Tel.: (81) 3 3242 2671
Fax: (81) 03 3242 2679
Web Site: www.core.co.jp/english/profile/prof_branch_list.html
Custom Computer Programming Services
S.I.C.: 7371
N.A.I.C.S.: 541511

CORE Industries Co., Ltd (1)
1-22-3 Sangenjaya
Setagaya-ku, 154-8552 Tokyo, Japan
Tel.: (81) 337955111
Fax: (81) 337955100
Web Site: www.core.co.jp
Computer & Computer Peripheral Equipment & Software Whslr
S.I.C.: 5045
N.A.I.C.S.: 423430
Ryohei Tanemura *(CEO)*

CORENet International Co., Ltd. (1)
11-1 Minami-Kurokawa
Asao-ku, Kawasaki, Kanagawa, 215-0034, Japan
Tel.: (81) 44 988 7711
Fax: (81) 44 988 7750
Information Technology Consulting Services
S.I.C.: 7373
N.A.I.C.S.: 541512

DISEC Co., Ltd (1)
Hiroshima Mixis Building
1-21-35 Kusatsu Shinmachi, Hiroshima, 7330834, Japan
Tel.: (81) 822788777
Fax: (81) 822788781
E-Mail: info@disec.co.jp
Web Site: www.disec.co.jp
Emp.: 50
Custom Computer Programming Services
S.I.C.: 7371
N.A.I.C.S.: 541511
Hiromitsu Yokota *(Pres)*

GIGA Co., Ltd (1)
Nikko Shibuya Nanpeidai Building
Nanpeidaichou 2-17 Shibuya-Ku, 150-0036
Tokyo, Japan
Tel.: (81) 357840022
Fax: (81) 334631488
Web Site: www.giga.com.hk
Custom Computer Programming Services
S.I.C.: 7371
N.A.I.C.S.: 541511
Alraki Ishii *(Pres)*

Institute of Bio-Medical and Welfare Engineering Co., Ltd (1)
Yamaguchi University Business Incubator Building
Tokiwadai 2-16-1 Ube-Shi, 755-0097
Yamaguchi, Japan
Tel.: (81) 836351354
Fax: (81) 836351354
Web Site: www.core.co.jp/english/profile/prof_branch_list.html
Surgical & Medical Instruments Mfr
S.I.C.: 3841
N.A.I.C.S.: 339112

K.N. Information System Co., Ltd (1)
Hikashiku Hikarimacuh
Rokuban 6 San Juyichu, Hiroshima, 732-0052, Japan

Core Corporation—(Continued)

Tel.: (81) 822611256
Fax: (81) 822618858
E-Mail: wangge@knc.co.jp
Web Site: www.knc.co.jp
Emp.: 26
All Other Information Services
S.I.C.: 7389
N.A.I.C.S.: 519190
Sakamoto Tatsuo *(Gen Mgr)*

Koga-city Information Center Co., Ltd. (1)
2-3-50 Chuo-cho
Koga, Ibaraki, 306-0033, Japan
Tel.: (81) 280 22 0701
Fax: (81) 280 22 0705
Information Technology Consulting Services
S.I.C.: 7373
N.A.I.C.S.: 541512

Lambda System Co., Ltd (1)
The Second CORE BLDG 2-11-26
Sangenjaya Setagaya-ku, 154-0024 Tokyo, Japan
Tel.: (81) 357873366
Fax: (81) 357873578
Web Site: www.core.co.jp/english/profile/pro f_branch_list.html
Emp.: 100
Wood Container & Pallet Mfr
S.I.C.: 2448
N.A.I.C.S.: 321920
Koyama Yuji *(Mng Dir)*

PRONET Co., Ltd (1)
11-1 Minami-kurokawa Asao-ku
Nishi-ku, Yokohama, Kanagawa, 215-0034, Japan
Tel.: (81) 0453283271
Fax: (81) 0453283270
Web Site: www.core.co.jp/english/profile/pro f_branch_list.html
Wood Container & Pallet Mfr
S.I.C.: 2448
N.A.I.C.S.: 321920

System Creative Co., Ltd (1)
8272-2 Minamiyokoichicho
Miyakonojo-shi, 885-0092 Miyazaki, Japan
Tel.: (81) 986222937
Fax: (81) 986222937
Web Site: www.core.co.jp/english/profile/pro f_branch_list.html
Custom Computer Programming Services
S.I.C.: 7371
N.A.I.C.S.: 541511

Tohoku Information Center Co., Ltd. (1)
6162-10 Tookamachi
Shinjo, Yamagata, 996-0091, Japan
Tel.: (81) 233 29 2411
Fax: (81) 233 29 2488
Information Technology Consulting Services
S.I.C.: 7373
N.A.I.C.S.: 541512

Non-U.S. Subsidiaries:

Beijing CORE Software Co., Ltd. (1)
Room 809 Run Yu Building 10 East Road
An Wai Xiao Guan
Chao Yang District, 100029 Beijing, China
Tel.: (86) 1084511277
Fax: (86) 1084511278
Web Site: www.coresoftware.com.in
Emp.: 50
Software Publishers
S.I.C.: 7372
N.A.I.C.S.: 511210
Cong Ma *(Pres)*

Shanghai CORE Co., Ltd (1)
Room 11501 SPSP Building 498 498
GuoShouJing Rd
Pudong New Area, 201203 Shanghai, China
Tel.: (86) 2150802815
Fax: (86) 2150802814
Custom Computer Programming Services
S.I.C.: 7371
N.A.I.C.S.: 541511

CORE EDUCATION AND TECHNOLOGIES LTD.

Block No 1-8 Building No 4 Sector 3
Millennium Business Park Mahape
Navi Mumbai, 400 710, India
Tel.: (91) 2239914800
Fax: (91) 2239914880
E-Mail: info@core-edutech.com
Web Site: www.core-edutech.com
Year Founded: 2003
COREEDUTEC—(NSE)
Rev.: $359,780,406
Assets: $793,751,783
Liabilities: $399,651,445
Net Worth: $394,100,337
Earnings: $50,224,435
Emp.: 2,000
Fiscal Year-end: 03/31/13

Business Description:
Educational Software Development Services
S.I.C.: 7371
N.A.I.C.S.: 541511

Personnel:
Sanjeev Mansotra *(Chm & CEO)*
Anshul Sonak *(Pres)*
Ganesh Umashankar *(Compliance Officer & Sec)*
Brian Keenan *(Pres-Consulting & Staffing-US)*
N. M. Kondap *(Pres-Higher Education)*
Nicole Neal *(Pres-Assessment & Solutions-US)*
Paul Sprayberry *(Pres-Advanced Tech-US)*
Anwar Ahmed Khan *(Exec VP-K-12 Education)*
Anandkumar Sanganeria *(Exec VP-Fin)*
Atul Jaiswal *(Sr VP-Sls-K-12 Bus)*
Yogesh Kamat *(Sr VP-Fin)*
Deepak Mehrotra *(Sr VP-Bus Dev-Vocational Education)*
Sucheta Phadke *(Sr VP-Content & New Initiatives)*
Rupamala Singh *(Sr VP-Mktg & Corp Comm)*

Board of Directors:
Sanjeev Mansotra
Sunder Shyam Dua
Harihar Iyer
Nikhil Champaklal Morsawala
Arun S. Nigavekar
Naresh Kumar Sharma

Asit Mehta & Associates
501 4 Midas Chambers Near Fun Republic
Multiplex Off Andheri Link Road
Andheri West, Mumbai, 400 053, India

Transfer Agent:
Adroit Corporate Services Pvt. Ltd.
19 20 Jaferbhoy Industrial Estate Makwana
Road Marol Naka Andheri E
Mumbai, India

Subsidiary:

CORE Projects and Technologies Ltd. (1)
10th Floor Plot No C-21 Lotus Business
Park Dalia Industrial Estate
Off Link Road Andheri, Mumbai, Maharashtra, 400 053, India
Tel.: (91) 2233066800
Fax: (91) 2233066880
E-Mail: info@core-edutech.com
Emp.: 70
Information Technology Consulting Services
S.I.C.: 7373
N.A.I.C.S.: 541512

U.S. Subsidiaries:

CORE Careers & Skill Developments Limited (1)
Harborside Financial Ctr Plz 10 Ste 208 3
2nd St
Jersey City, NJ 07311
Tel.: (888) 778-7737
Fax: (201) 743-7930
Emp.: 50
Educational Support Services
S.I.C.: 8299
N.A.I.C.S.: 611710
Irene Campbell *(Gen Mgr)*

CORE Education & Consulting Solutions, Inc. (1)
3 Ravinia Dr
Atlanta, GA 30346
Tel.: (678) 578-7711
Fax: (770) 234-5327
E-Mail: info@coreecs.com
Web Site: www.coreecs.com
Emp.: 60
Educational Consulting Services
S.I.C.: 8299
N.A.I.C.S.: 611710
Shekhar Iyer *(Pres)*

Non-U.S. Subsidiaries:

CORE Education & Consulting Solutions FZ-LLC (1)
Office No 207-10 Block No 17 2nd Floor
Knowledge Village
Dubai, United Arab Emirates
Tel.: (971) 4 4508801
Fax: (971) 4 4508802
Web Site: www.coreedutech.com
Educational Consulting Services
S.I.C.: 8299
N.A.I.C.S.: 611710

CORE Education & Consulting Solutions (UK) Ltd. (1)
Brough Business Centre Skillings Lane
Brough, HU15 1EN, United Kingdom
Tel.: (44) 1482 601100
Fax: (44) 1482 601101
E-Mail: info@coreecs.co.uk
Web Site: www.coreeducation.co.uk
Educational Software Publishing & Consulting Services
S.I.C.: 8299
N.A.I.C.S.: 611710

Subsidiary:

ITN Mark (UK) (2)
313 Boston Manor Road
London, TW8 9LX, United Kingdom
Tel.: (44) 20 8326 1100
Fax: (44) 20 8569 9532
E-Mail: west.london@itnmark.com
Web Site: www.itnmark.com
Teacher Recruitment Services
S.I.C.: 7361
N.A.I.C.S.: 561311
Sharon Bullock *(Dir-Comml)*

CORE Projects & Technologies FZC (1)
Dubai Knowledge Village
Dubai, United Arab Emirates
Tel.: (971) 44508801
Fax: (971) 44508802
E-Mail: info@core-edutech.com
Web Site: www.core-edutech.com
Emp.: 12
Software Development Services
S.I.C.: 7371
N.A.I.C.S.: 541511
Medeni Menekse *(Pres)*

CORE EXPLORATION LIMITED

Level 2 143 Hutt Street
PO Box 7298
Adelaide, SA, 5000, Australia
Tel.: (61) 7324 2987
Fax: (61) 8 8312 2002
E-Mail: info@coreexploration.com.au
Web Site: www.coreexploration.co m.au
Year Founded: 2010
CXO—(ASX)
Int. Income: $73,090
Assets: $4,725,808
Liabilities: $255,885
Net Worth: $4,469,923
Earnings: ($2,018,639)
Emp.: 6
Fiscal Year-end: 06/30/13

Business Description:
Copper & Uranium Exploration Services
S.I.C.: 1021
N.A.I.C.S.: 212234

Personnel:
Stephen Biggins *(Mng Dir)*
Jaroslaw Kopias *(CFO & Sec)*

Board of Directors:
Greg English
Stephen Biggins
Michael Schwarz

Legal Counsel:
Piper Alderman
Level 16 70 Franklin St
Adelaide, SA, 5000, Australia

CORE INVESTMENTS LTD.

Power House Whitehall Rd
Halesowen, West Midlands, B63 3JS, United Kingdom
Tel.: (44) 1215506313
Fax: (44) 1215855197
E-Mail: Halesowendepot@powerpla nthire.co.uk
Web Site: www.powerplanthire.co.uk
Sales Range: $50-74.9 Million
Emp.: 110

Business Description:
Holding Company
S.I.C.: 6719
N.A.I.C.S.: 551112

Personnel:
David Sairl *(Mng Dir)*

CORE LABORATORIES N.V.

Strawinskylaan 913 Tower A Level 9
1077 XX Amsterdam, Netherlands
Tel.: (31) 20 420 3191
Fax: (31) 20 627 9886
E-Mail: clb.webmaster@corelab.com
Web Site: www.corelab.com
Year Founded: 1936
CLB—(EUR NYSE)
Rev.: $1,073,508,000
Assets: $661,010,000
Liabilities: $491,621,000
Net Worth: $169,389,000
Earnings: $243,194,000
Emp.: 5,000
Fiscal Year-end: 12/31/13

Business Description:
Petroleum Reservoir Optimization & Management Services
S.I.C.: 1389
N.A.I.C.S.: 213112

Personnel:
David M. Demshur *(Chm-Supervisory Bd, Pres & CEO)*
Richard L. Bergmark *(CFO & Exec VP)*
M. L. Davis *(COO & Sr VP)*
C. Brig Miller *(Chief Acctg Officer, Treas & VP)*
Mark F. Elvig *(Gen Counsel, Sec & VP)*

Supervisory Board of Directors:
David M. Demshur
Richard L. Bergmark
Rene R. Joyce
Michael C. Kearney
D. John Ogren
Joseph R. Perna
Jan Willem Sodderland

Transfer Agent:
American Stock Transfer Co.
40 Wall St.
New York, NY 10005
Tel.: (212) 936-5100

Subsidiaries:

Core Laboratories International B.V. (1)
Stoomloggerweg 12
Vlaardingen, 3133 KT, Netherlands
Tel.: (31) 10 434 2503
Fax: (31) 10 434 2641
Reservoir Management Services
S.I.C.: 4971
N.A.I.C.S.: 221310

Saybolt Nederland B.V. (1)
Stoomloggerweg 12
3133 KT Vlaardingen, Netherlands
Tel.: (31) 10 4609 978

Fax: (31) 10 4353 600
E-Mail: saybolt.bunkerfueldesk@corelab.com
Web Site: www.corelab.com
Oil & Gas Exploration Services
S.I.C.: 1389
N.A.I.C.S.: 213112
Andre Hoogland *(Mgr-Laboratory)*

U.S. Subsidiaries:

Core Laboratories LP **(1)**
6316 Windfern Rd
Houston, TX 77040-4916 (100%)
Tel.: (713) 328-2673
Fax: (713) 328-2150
Web Site: www.corelab.com
Emp.: 400
Support Activities for Oil & Gas Operations
S.I.C.: 1389
N.A.I.C.S.: 213112
David M. Demshur *(Chm-Supervisory Bd, Pres & CEO)*

Owen Oil Tools LP **(1)**
12001 County Rd 1000
Godley, TX 76044
Tel.: (817) 551-0540
Fax: (817) 551-0795
Emp.: 400
Perforating Equipment Mfr
S.I.C.: 3533
N.A.I.C.S.: 333132
Jeffrey West *(Pres)*

Saybolt, LP **(1)**
3113 Red Bluff Rd
Pasadena, TX 77503
Tel.: (713) 477-8171
Fax: (713) 477-5380
E-Mail: saybolt.pasadena@corelab.com
Sales Range: $1-9.9 Million
Emp.: 10
Oil & Gas Exploration Services
S.I.C.: 1389
N.A.I.C.S.: 213112
Joseph Brown *(Gen Mgr)*

Stim-Lab, Inc. **(1)**
7406 N Hwy 81
Duncan, OK 73533
Tel.: (580) 252-4309
Fax: (580) 252-6979
Web Site: www.corelab.com
Oil & Gas Engineering Services
S.I.C.: 1389
N.A.I.C.S.: 213112
Michael F. Conway *(Pres)*

Non-U.S. Subsidiaries:

Core Lab de Mexico S.A. de C.V. **(1)**
Cda Universidad S/N
Villahermosa, 86020, Mexico
Tel.: (52) 9933580451
Oil & Gas Exploration Services
S.I.C.: 1389
N.A.I.C.S.: 213112

Core Laboratories Australia PTY LTD **(1)**
447 Belmont Ave
Kewdale, WA, 6105, Australia
Tel.: (61) 8 9353 3944
Fax: (61) 8 9353 1369
E-Mail: corelab.australia@corelab.com
Emp.: 35
Waste Management Services
S.I.C.: 9511
N.A.I.C.S.: 924110
Kevin Daken *(Mng Dir)*

Core Laboratories Canada Ltd. **(1)**
2810 12 Street NE
Calgary, AB, T2E 7P7, Canada
Tel.: (403) 250-4000
Fax: (403) 250-5120
Emp.: 200
Oil & Gas Drilling Services
S.I.C.: 1381
N.A.I.C.S.: 213111
Stephen J. Lee *(Pres)*

Core Laboratories Malaysia SDN BHD **(1)**
17 Jalan U1/23 Section U1 Hicom
Glenmarie Industrial Park
Shah Alam, Selangor, 40150, Malaysia
Tel.: (60) 3 5031 0088
Fax: (60) 3 5031 1122
Reservoir Management Services
S.I.C.: 4941
N.A.I.C.S.: 221310

Core Laboratories (U.K.) Limited **(1)**
Howe Moss Drive Kirkhill Industrial Estate Dyce
Aberdeen, United Kingdom AB21 0GL
Tel.: (44) 1224 421000
Fax: (44) 1224 421003
Emp.: 150
Reservoir Management Services
S.I.C.: 1389
N.A.I.C.S.: 213112
George Bruce *(Gen Mgr)*

PT Corelab Indonesia **(1)**
Cilandak Commercial Estate Building 303 Jl Cilandak KKO
Jakarta, 12560, Indonesia
Tel.: (62) 21 7801533
Fax: (62) 21 7802042
E-Mail: corelab.indonesia@corelab.com
Emp.: 150
Oil & Gas Exploration Services
S.I.C.: 1389
N.A.I.C.S.: 213112
Gunadie Tanuatmadja *(Mgr-Acctg)*

Saybolt Belgium N.V. **(1)**
Zwarte Weg 60 Kaai 371-373
2030 Antwerp, Belgium
Tel.: (32) 3 5400080
Fax: (32) 3 5448418
E-Mail: saybolt.belgium@corelab.com
Oil & Gas Exploration Services
S.I.C.: 1389
N.A.I.C.S.: 213112

Saybolt (Singapore) PTE LTD **(1)**
50 Science Park Road 04-06
Singapore, 117406, Singapore
Tel.: (65) 6775 2922
Fax: (65) 6779 1797
E-Mail: saybolt.singapore.ops@corelab.com
Emp.: 50
Bunker Surveying Services
S.I.C.: 4499
N.A.I.C.S.: 488390
Susan Jacob *(Mng Dir)*

CORE LOGIC, INC.

11th F 1-B U-Space 670 Sampyeong-Dong
Bundang-Gu, Seongnam, Gyeonggi-Do, Korea (South)
Tel.: (82) 2 2191 0716
Fax: (82) 2 2191 0878
Web Site: www.corelogic.co.kr
Year Founded: 1998
048870—(KRS)
Business Description:
Semiconductor Product Mfr
S.I.C.: 3674
N.A.I.C.S.: 334413
Personnel:
Han Ki Kim *(CEO)*

CORE SERVICES GROUP LIMITED

70B Kishorn Road
Mount Pleasant, WA, 6153, Australia
Tel.: (61) 8 9364 1129
Fax: (61) 8 9364 2954
E-Mail: info@coreservicesgroup.au
Web Site: www.coreservicesgroup.au
CRV—(ASX)
Int. Income: $45,007
Assets: $1,182,252
Liabilities: $227,539
Net Worth: $954,713
Earnings: ($1,190,826)
Fiscal Year-end: 06/30/13
Business Description:
Electronic Communication Services
S.I.C.: 7389
N.A.I.C.S.: 541990
Personnel:
Steve Dropulich *(Mng Dir)*
Ranko Matic *(Sec)*
Board of Directors:
Stephen Zurhaar
Steve Dropulich
Vincent Goss
Ranko Matic
Legal Counsel:
Steinepreis Paganin
Level 4 16 Milligan Street
Perth, WA, 6000, Australia

CORE SOFTWARE CORPORATION

555 Legget Drive Suite 301
Ottawa, ON, K2K 2X3, Canada
Tel.: (613) 727-5051
Fax: (613) 727-2603
Toll Free: (877) 768-2673
E-Mail: info@coremigration.com
Web Site: www.coremigration.com
Year Founded: 1997
Sales Range: $1-9.9 Million
Business Description:
Computer System Updating & Converting
S.I.C.: 7379
N.A.I.C.S.: 541519

CORECOMM SOLUTIONS INC.

(Formerly Venza Gold Corp.)
810 789 West Pender Street
Vancouver, BC, V6C 1H2, Canada
Tel.: (604) 424-4180
Year Founded: 2010
COCMF—(OTC OTCB)
Assets: $17,923
Liabilities: $73,453
Net Worth: ($55,530)
Earnings: ($153,164)
Fiscal Year-end: 10/31/13
Business Description:
Correlation Technology Developer
S.I.C.: 7379
N.A.I.C.S.: 541519
Personnel:
Patrick Fitzsimmons *(Pres & CEO)*
James Hyland *(CFO)*
Board of Directors:
Stephen Gerald Diakow
Patrick Fitzsimmons
Transfer Agent:
Empire Stock Transfer
1859 Whitney Mesa Dr
Henderson, NV 89014

CORECROSS, INC.

170-5 6F E-BIZ Center Gurodong
Guro-gu, Seoul, Korea (South)
Tel.: (82) 2 2029 0700
Fax: (82) 2 2029 0707
Web Site: www.corecross.com
038530—(KRS)
Business Description:
Semiconductor Product Mfr
S.I.C.: 3674
N.A.I.C.S.: 334413
Personnel:
Jong Ju Lee *(CEO)*

COREMAR S.A.

Constanta Port Berth 0
507051 Constanta, Romania
Tel.: (40) 241601104
Fax: (40) 241611450
E-Mail: office@coremar.ro
Web Site: www.coremar.ro
REMO—(BUC)
Sales Range: $1-9.9 Million
Emp.: 271
Business Description:
Marine Towage Services
S.I.C.: 4499
N.A.I.C.S.: 488390
Personnel:
Mihai Dede *(Gen Mgr)*

COREMEDIA AG

Ludwig-Erhard-Str 18
20459 Hamburg, Germany
Tel.: (49) 40 325587 0
Web Site: www.coremedia.com
Year Founded: 1996
Sales Range: $10-24.9 Million
Emp.: 150
Business Description:
Web Content Management Software Publisher
S.I.C.: 7372
N.A.I.C.S.: 511210
Personnel:
Florian Matthes *(Chm-Supervisory Bd)*
Gerrit Kolb *(CEO)*
Klemens Kleiminger *(CFO)*
Supervisory Board of Directors:
Florian Matthes
Jan Kuhne
Patrick Meisberger

U.S. Subsidiary:

CoreMedia Corporation **(1)**
118 2nd St 5th Fl
San Francisco, CA 94105
Tel.: (415) 371-0400
Web Content Management Software Publisher
S.I.C.: 7372
N.A.I.C.S.: 511210
Glenn Conradt *(VP-Global Mktg-North America)*

Non-U.S. Subsidiaries:

CoreMedia Asia Pacific Pte. Ltd. **(1)**
#03-106 25 International Business Park
Singapore, 609916, Singapore
Tel.: (65) 6562 8866
Web Content Management Software Publisher
S.I.C.: 7372
N.A.I.C.S.: 511210
Martin Pakendorf *(VP-Pro Svcs & Sls-Asia Pacific)*

CoreMedia UK Ltd. **(1)**
90 Long Acre Covent Garden
London, WC2E 9RZ, United Kingdom
Tel.: (44) 207 849 3317
Web Content Management Software Publisher
S.I.C.: 7372
N.A.I.C.S.: 511210
Florian Grebe *(VP-Sls-EMEA)*

CORENTEC CO., LTD.

11F Chungho Tower 748-1 Banpo 1-dong Seocho-gu
Seoul, 137-810, Korea (South)
Tel.: (82) 2 3445 5492
Fax: (82) 2 3445 5497
Web Site: www.corentec.com
Year Founded: 2000
104540—(KRS)
Sales Range: $10-24.9 Million
Emp.: 90
Business Description:
Medical Device Mfr
S.I.C.: 3841
N.A.I.C.S.: 339112
Personnel:
Sung Taek Hong *(CEO)*

COREP LIGHTING GROUP

ZAC Rives d'Arcins Rue Denis Papin
33130 Begles, France
Tel.: (33) 5 56 49 96 00
Fax: (33) 5 56 85 08 28
Web Site: www.coreplighting.com
Year Founded: 1970
MLCOR—(EUR)
Sales Range: $25-49.9 Million
Emp.: 256
Business Description:
Lampshade & Decorative Lamp Mfr
S.I.C.: 3641

Corep Lighting group—(Continued)

N.A.I.C.S.: 335110
Personnel:
Arnaud Champion *(Chm)*
Alain Petit *(CEO)*

CORERO NETWORK SECURITY PLC

169 High Street
Rickmansworth, Hertfordshire, WD3 1AY, United Kingdom
Tel.: (44) 1923897333
E-Mail: enquiries@corero.com
Web Site: www.coreroplc.com
CNS—(AIM)
Rev.: $20,565,000
Assets: $39,367,000
Liabilities: $20,072,000
Net Worth: $19,295,000
Earnings: ($5,889,000)
Emp.: 144
Fiscal Year-end: 12/31/12
Business Description:
Network Security Software Products Developer
S.I.C.: 7372
N.A.I.C.S.: 511210
Personnel:
Marty Meyer *(Pres)*
Ashley Stephenson *(CEO)*
Andrew Douglas Miller *(CFO & COO)*
Duncan Swallow *(Sec & Controller-Fin)*
David Ahee *(Sr VP-Worldwide Sls Div)*
Board of Directors:
Jens Peter Montanana
Richard Last
Andrew Trevor Lloyd
Ashley Stephenson
Legal Counsel:
Dorsey & Whitney (Europe) LLP
21 Wilson Street
London, EC2M 2TD, United Kingdom
Transfer Agent:
Capita Registrars Ltd
The Registry 34 Beckenham Road
Beckenham, United Kingdom
Subsidiary:

Corero Systems Limited (1)
3rd Fl 3 London Wall Bldg
London Wall, London, EC2M 5SY, United Kingdom
Tel.: (44) 1923897333
Software Design & Development Services
S.I.C.: 7371
N.A.I.C.S.: 541511

CORESA S.A.

San Nicolas 630
San Miguel, Santiago, 8930088, Chile
Tel.: (56) 25108800
Fax: (56) 25108888
E-Mail: coresa@coresa.cl
Web Site: www.coresa.cl
Year Founded: 1966
Sales Range: $25-49.9 Million
Emp.: 700
Business Description:
Containers, Meshes & Polyethylene Film Mfr
S.I.C.: 3053
N.A.I.C.S.: 339991
Personnel:
Francisco Javier Vial Herrera *(Chm & Pres)*
Eduardo Klinger *(CEO)*
Non-U.S. Subsidiary:

Coresa Argentina S.A. (1)
General Alvear 21
San Antonio de Areco, Buenos Aires, 2760, Argentina
Tel.: (54) 2326455400
Fax: (54) 2326455700
E-Mail: coresa@coresa.com.ar
Web Site: www.coresa.com.ar
Emp.: 73
Production & Commercialization of Sacks & Cloths
S.I.C.: 2671
N.A.I.C.S.: 322220

CORESLAB INTERNATIONAL, INC.

332 Jones Rd
Stoney Creek, ON, L8E 5N2, Canada
Tel.: (905) 643-0220
Fax: (905) 643-0233
Web Site: www.coreslab.com
Year Founded: 1975
Sales Range: $300-349.9 Million
Emp.: 2,700
Business Description:
Precast Concrete Products Mfr
S.I.C.: 1791
N.A.I.C.S.: 238120
Personnel:
Mark Simpson *(VP & Gen Mgr)*
U.S. Subsidiaries:

Coreslab Structures, Inc. (1)
802 Allied Rd
Bellevue, NE 68123
Tel.: (402) 291-0733
Fax: (402) 291-8834
E-Mail: jblahn@corelab.com
Web Site: www.coreslab.com
Emp.: 200
Precast & Prestressed Concrete Products Mfr & Sales
S.I.C.: 3272
N.A.I.C.S.: 327390
Todd Ceulp *(Gen Mgr)*

Coreslab Structures, Inc. (1)
1030 S Kitley Ave
Indianapolis, IN 46203-2623
Tel.: (317) 353-2118
Fax: (317) 357-6012
E-Mail: info@coreslab.com
Web Site: www.coreslab.com
Emp.: 80
Precast Concrete Mfr
S.I.C.: 3272
N.A.I.C.S.: 327390
Matt Ballain *(Gen Mgr)*

Coreslab Structures, Inc. (1)
7000 S Sunnyland Rd
Oklahoma City, OK 73135-1714
Tel.: (405) 672-2325
Fax: (405) 670-2651
E-Mail: info@coreslab.com
Web Site: www.coreslab.com
Emp.: 40
Precast & Prestressed Concrete Products Mfr
S.I.C.: 3272
N.A.I.C.S.: 327390
David Hellyer *(Gen Mgr)*

CORETRACK LIMITED

Suite 25 145 Stirling Highway
Nedlands, WA, 6009, Australia
Tel.: (61) 8 9389 3180
Fax: (61) 8 9389 3199
E-Mail: admin@coretrack.com.au
Web Site: www.coretrack.com.au
CKK—(ASX)
Sales Range: Less than $1 Million
Business Description:
Oil & Gas Industry
S.I.C.: 1311
N.A.I.C.S.: 211111
Personnel:
Winton Willesee *(Sec)*
Board of Directors:
Matthew Birney
Trevor Philip Beazley
Bernard Kelly
Winton Willesee
Legal Counsel:
Rockwell Olivier
Level 8 Wesfarmers House 40 The Esplanade
Perth, WA, 6000, Australia

CORETRONIC CORPORATION

No 2 Ke Bei 5th Road Science Park
Chunan, 35053, Taiwan
Tel.: (886) 37777000
Fax: (886) 37778358
Web Site: www.coretronic.com
5371—(TAI)
Sales Range: $1-4.9 Billion
Emp.: 2,878
Business Description:
Projection & Display Solutions
S.I.C.: 3575
N.A.I.C.S.: 334118
Personnel:
Weiyi Zhang *(Chm & CEO)*
Subsidiaries:

Coretronic System Engineering Corporation (1)
12F No 219 Sec 3 Beixin Road
Xindian District, New Taipei City, 23143, Taiwan (100%)
Tel.: (886) 2 2910 2955
Integrated Imaging Systems Developer
S.I.C.: 3575
N.A.I.C.S.: 334118

Liuli Optoma Technology Corp. (1)
12F No 215 Sec 3 Beixin Road
Xindian District, New Taipei City, 23143, Taiwan
Tel.: (886) 2 8219 1658
Projector Distr
S.I.C.: 5043
N.A.I.C.S.: 423410

Subsidiary:

Liuligongfang Corporation (2)
10F No 108 Minquan Road
Xindian District, New Taipei City, Taiwan
Tel.: (886) 2 8219 1658
Web Site: www.liuli.com
Projector Distr
S.I.C.: 5043
N.A.I.C.S.: 423410

Young Green Energy Co., Ltd. (1)
No 2 Ke Bei 5th Road Science Park
Chunan, Mial-Li, 35053, Taiwan (100%)
Tel.: (886) 37 777000
Energy Saving Technologies Research & Development Services
S.I.C.: 8731
N.A.I.C.S.: 541712

YOUNG Lighting Technology Inc. (1)
No 11 Li Hsing Road Science Park
Hsin-chu, Taiwan (100%)
Tel.: (886) 3 577 2000
Web Site: www.younglighting.com
Backlight Modules for TVs, Monitors, Tablet PCs & Mobile Phone Screens
S.I.C.: 3577
N.A.I.C.S.: 334118

Subsidiaries:

Coretronic Display Solution Corporation (2)
3F No 2 Ke Bei 5th Road Science Park
Chunan, Miao-Li, 350, Taiwan
Tel.: (886) 37 777 000
Medical Monitors & Clinical Ultrasonic Micro-Imaging Systems
S.I.C.: 3841
N.A.I.C.S.: 339112

Nano Precision Corporation (2)
No 5 Wen Hua Road Fengshan Vil
Hukou, Hsin-chu, Taiwan (100%)
Tel.: (886) 3 5986 200
Light Guide Plate Mfr
S.I.C.: 3577
N.A.I.C.S.: 334118

YoungOptics Inc. (1)
No 7 Xin'an Road Science Park
Hsin-chu, Taiwan
Tel.: (886) 3 620 6789
Web Site: www.youngoptics.com
Optical Lense Mfr & Distr
S.I.C.: 3827
N.A.I.C.S.: 333314

COREX GOLD CORPORATION

Suite 350 - 409 Granville Street
Vancouver, BC, V6C 1T2, Canada
Tel.: (604) 683-2505
Fax: (604) 683-2506
Toll Free: (866) 683-2505
E-Mail: info@corexgold.com
Web Site: www.corexgold.com
CGE—(TSXV)
Int. Income: $12,856
Assets: $10,376,004
Liabilities: $518,282
Net Worth: $9,857,722
Earnings: ($1,543,581)
Business Description:
Gold Exploration Services
S.I.C.: 1041
N.A.I.C.S.: 212221
Personnel:
Craig Schneider *(Pres & CEO)*
Terese J. Gieselman *(CFO & Sec)*
Board of Directors:
Bruno Barde
Patrick Downey
Hamish Greig
Craig Schneider
Mark Vanry
Legal Counsel:
DuMoulin Black LLP
10th Floor 595 Howe St
Vancouver, BC, Canada
Transfer Agent:
Computershare
510 Burrard St 2nd Floor
Vancouver, BC, Canada
Non-U.S. Subsidiary:

Corex Global S. de R.L. de C.V. (1)
Boulevard Juan Navarrete 84-1 Cole
Valle Escondido, Hermosillo, Sonora, Mexico 83207
Tel.: (52) 662 210 4080
Emp.: 1
Mineral Exploration Services
S.I.C.: 1481
N.A.I.C.S.: 213115
Craig Schneider *(Gen Mgr)*

CORIMON, C.A.

Calle Hans Neumann Edificio Corimon
Caracas, Venezuela
Tel.: (58) 2124005530
Fax: (58) 2124005507
E-Mail: info@corimon.com
Web Site: www.corimon.com
Year Founded: 1949
CRM.A—(CAR)
Emp.: 1,361
Business Description:
Paint, Coatings & Resins Mfr, Distr & Sales; Flexible Packaging Services
S.I.C.: 2851
N.A.I.C.S.: 325510
Personnel:
Amelia Ibafa *(Chm)*
Esteban Szekely *(Gen Dir)*
Board of Directors:
Alejandro Alfonzo-Larrain
Oswaldo Cisneros Fajardo
Celestino Diaz
Angel Eduardo Gomez Sigala
Omar Pernia
Alberto Sosa Schlageter
David Tomasello
Fernando Z. Volante
Subsidiaries:

Corimon Pinturas, C.A. (1)
Urbanizacion Industrial El Bosque
Av Hans Neumann, Valencia, Edo Carabobo, Venezuela
Tel.: (58) 2416131777
E-Mail: corimonpinturas@corimon.com
Web Site: www.corimonpinturas.com
Paint & Coatings Mfr
S.I.C.: 2851
N.A.I.C.S.: 325510
Bernardo Vera *(CEO)*

Resimon, C.A. (1)
Carretera Flor Amarillo Km 4
Zona Industrial 1, Valencia, Estado Carabobo, Venezuela
Tel.: (58) 2416131432
Fax: (58) 2416131416
E-Mail: info@resimon.com
Web Site: www.resimon.com
Synthetic Resin & Other Chemical Products Mfr
Export
S.I.C.: 2821
N.A.I.C.S.: 325211

Non-U.S. Subsidiary:

Sissons Paints Limited (1)
Uriah Butler Highway
Chaguanas, Trinidad & Tobago
Tel.: (868) 665-5721
Fax: (868) 665-1577
E-Mail: sissons@sissonspaints.com
Web Site: www.sissonspaints.com
Emp.: 100
Paint Products Mfr & Marketer
S.I.C.: 2851
N.A.I.C.S.: 325510
Umanath Maharagh *(Mgr-Comml)*

Non-U.S. Subsidiary:

Sissons Paints (Grenada) Limited (2)
Frequente Industrial Park
Grand Anse, 473 Saint George's, Grenada
Tel.: (473) 4441457
Fax: (473) 4441676
E-Mail: gsissons@spiceisle.com
Web Site: www.sissonspaints.com
Emp.: 30
Paint Products Mfr & Marketer
S.I.C.: 2851
N.A.I.C.S.: 325510
Christopher De Allie *(Mng Dir)*

CORIN GROUP PLC

The Corinium Centre
Cirencester, Gloucestershire, GL7 1YJ, United Kingdom
Tel.: (44) 1285659866
Fax: (44) 1285658960
E-Mail: info@coringroup.com
Web Site: www.corin.co.uk
Rev.: $45,076,145
Emp.: 249
Business Description:
Orthopedic Devices
S.I.C.: 3842
N.A.I.C.S.: 339113
Personnel:
Stefano Alfonsi *(Acting Chm & CEO)*
Russell Mably *(COO)*
Board of Directors:
Stefano Alfonsi
Enrico Amo
Pierluca Antolini
Marco Fumagalli
Russell Mably

CORINEX COMMUNICATIONS CORP.

12th Floor 570 Granville Street
Vancouver, BC, V6C 3P1, Canada
Tel.: (604) 692-0520
Fax: (604) 694-0061
Web Site: www.corinex.com
Sales Range: $25-49.9 Million
Business Description:
IP Communications System Mfr
S.I.C.: 3669
N.A.I.C.S.: 334290
Personnel:
Peter Sobotka *(Co-CEO)*
Sam Shi *(CTO)*
Norbert Benko *(Sr VP & Gen Mgr-Europe)*

CORINTHIA HOTELS INTERNATIONAL

22 Europa Centre
Floriana, SRN 1400, Malta
Tel.: (356) 21233141
Fax: (356) 21234219
E-Mail: chi@corinthia.com
Web Site: www.corinthia.com
Year Founded: 1960
Sales Range: $650-699.9 Million
Emp.: 5,000
Business Description:
Hotels
S.I.C.: 7011
N.A.I.C.S.: 721110
Personnel:
Alfred Pisani *(Founder & Chm)*
Simon Naudi *(CEO)*
Tony Potter *(Mng Dir)*
Liam Lambert *(COO)*

CORIO N.V.

Van Duvenborch Building
Stationsplein 97
3511 ED Utrecht, Netherlands
Mailing Address:
PO Box 8243
3503 RE Utrecht, Netherlands
Tel.: (31) 302346464
Fax: (31) 302333578
E-Mail: info@nl.corio-eu.com
Web Site: www.corio-eu.com
CORA—(EUR)
Rev.: $640,238,452
Assets: $10,272,623,270
Liabilities: $4,712,268,085
Net Worth: $5,560,355,185
Earnings: $21,134,869
Emp.: 549
Fiscal Year-end: 12/31/12
Business Description:
Real Estate Investment & Management Services
S.I.C.: 6519
N.A.I.C.S.: 531190
Personnel:
Derk C. Doijer *(Chm-Supervisory Bd)*
Robert A. H. van der Meer *(Vice Chm-Supervisory Bd)*
Gerard H. W. Groener *(CEO & Member-Mgmt Bd)*
Ben A. van der Klift *(CFO & Member-Mgmt Bd)*
Frederic Fontaine *(COO, Chief Dev Officer & Member-Mgmt Bd)*
Paul Tankink *(Chief Dev Officer-Nederland)*
Cem Alfar *(CEO-Turkiye)*
Jorg Banzhaf *(CEO-Deutschland)*
Eric Damiron *(CEO-France)*
Christophe Mouton *(CEO-Espana)*
Ermanno Niccoli *(CEO-Italia)*
Jan Willem H. Weissink *(CEO-Nederland)*
Maud de Vries *(Gen Counsel & Sec)*
Supervisory Board of Directors:
Derk C. Doijer
Gobert A. Beijer
John A. Carrafiell
Roel C. van den Berg
Robert A. H. van der Meer

Subsidiaries:

Corio Nederland B.V. (1)
Stationsplein 97
3511 ED Utrecht, Netherlands
Tel.: (31) 302346464
Fax: (31) 302333578
E-Mail: info@nl.corio-eu.com
Web Site: www.corio-eu.com
Emp.: 200
Propetry Investment Managing Services
S.I.C.: 6211
N.A.I.C.S.: 523999
Gerard Groener *(CEO)*

Corio Vastgoed Ontwikkeling (1)
St Jacobsstraat 200
3511 BT Utrecht, Netherlands
Tel.: (31) 302346123
Emp.: 200
Property Investment Managing Services
S.I.C.: 6211
N.A.I.C.S.: 523999
J. Haaren *(CEO)*

Non-U.S. Subsidiaries:

Corio Italia S.r.l. (1)
Via Fabio Filzi 25 A
20124 Milan, Italy
Tel.: (39) 026696349
Fax: (39) 026697711
E-Mail: info@it.corio-eu.com
Web Site: www.corio-eu.com
Emp.: 80
Real Estate Investment Services
S.I.C.: 6531
N.A.I.C.S.: 531390
Ermanno Niccoli *(Gen Mgr)*

Corio Real Estate Espana SL (1)
C Maria de Molina 40 8 Degree Planta
28006 Madrid, Spain
Tel.: (34) 914261777
Fax: (34) 914355644
E-Mail: info@es.corio-eu.com
Real Estate Investment Services
S.I.C.: 6531
N.A.I.C.S.: 531390

CORMER GROUP INDUSTRIES, INC.

1445 Church Avenue
Winnipeg, MB, R2X 2X9, Canada
Tel.: (204) 987-6400
Fax: (204) 988-3808
Web Site: www.cormeraerospace.com
Year Founded: 1988
Rev.: $12,600,000
Emp.: 125
Business Description:
Aircraft Parts Mfr
S.I.C.: 3728
N.A.I.C.S.: 336413
Personnel:
Andrew D. Corner *(CEO & Chm-Fin & Admin)*

CORNEC SAS

18 rue Jacquard
77400 Lagny, Seine Et Marne, France
Tel.: (33) 164022910
Fax: (33) 164304621
Web Site: www.cornec.fr
Sls.: $27,100,000
Emp.: 14
Business Description:
Recyclable Material Whslr
S.I.C.: 5093
N.A.I.C.S.: 423930
Personnel:
Patrick Cornec *(Pres)*

CORNERSTONE CAPITAL RESOURCES INC.

26 Kyle Avenue
Mount Pearl, NL, A1N 4R5, Canada
Tel.: (709) 745-8377
Fax: (709) 747-1183
Toll Free: (877) 277-8377
E-Mail: communications@crigold.com
Web Site: www.cornerstoneresources.com
CGP—(TSXV)
Rev.: $640,500
Assets: $4,263,977
Liabilities: $543,765
Net Worth: $3,720,212
Earnings: ($7,345,734)
Fiscal Year-end: 12/31/12
Business Description:
Mineral Exploration Services
S.I.C.: 1081
N.A.I.C.S.: 213114
Personnel:
W. John Clarke *(Co-Founder)*
John M. Fleming *(Chm)*
H. Brooke Macdonald *(Pres & CEO)*
David Loveys *(CFO & VP-Fin)*
Board of Directors:
John M. Fleming
W. John Clarke
Beverley A. Evans
David Loveys
H. Brooke Macdonald
Colin McKenzie
Donald J. Worth
Legal Counsel:
Ottenheimer & Baker
A1C 2B9 Saint John's, NL, Canada
Transfer Agent:
Computershare Trust Company
Halifax, NS, Canada

CORNERSTONE METALS INC.

(Formerly Appleton Exploration Inc.)
Suite 880 580 Hornby Street
Vancouver, BC, V6C 3B6, Canada
Tel.: (403) 804-8636
Fax: (604) 684-0642
E-Mail: info@cornerstonemetals.ca
Web Site: www.cornerstonemetals.ca
Year Founded: 2006
AEX—(TSXV)
Int. Income: $5,065
Assets: $1,054,331
Liabilities: $81,631
Net Worth: $972,700
Earnings: ($361,764)
Fiscal Year-end: 11/30/12
Business Description:
Mineral Exploration Services
S.I.C.: 1081
N.A.I.C.S.: 213114
Personnel:
Courtney Shearer *(Interim Pres & CEO)*
Robert G. McMorran *(CFO)*
Board of Directors:
Paul S. Cowley
Jason A. Nickel
Courtney Shearer
Fred Sveinson
Legal Counsel:
Thomas Rondeau LLP
300 576 Seymour Street
Vancouver, BC, V6B 3K1, Canada
Transfer Agent:
Computershare Ltd
510 Burrard Street 2nd Floor
Vancouver, BC, Canada

CORNERSTONE THERAPEUTICS INC.

(See Under Chiesi Farmaceutici SpA)

CORNEY & BARROW LIMITED

1 Thomas More Street
London, E1W 1YZ, United Kingdom
Tel.: (44) 20 7265 2400
Fax: (44) 20 7265 2444
E-Mail: wine@corneyandbarrow.com
Web Site: www.corneyandbarrow.com
Year Founded: 1780
Sales Range: $100-124.9 Million
Emp.: 406
Business Description:
Wine Whslr
S.I.C.: 5182
N.A.I.C.S.: 424820
Personnel:
Adam Brett-Smith *(Mng Dir)*
Board of Directors:
Simon Brown
Bryce Fraser
David McLaren

CORNU S.A.

Le Moulin 1424
Champagne, Switzerland

Cornu S.A.—(Continued)

Tel.: (41) 244361542
Fax: (41) 244361243
E-Mail: cornu@cornu.ch
Web Site: www.cornu.ch
Emp.: 150
Business Description:
Cookie & Cracker Mfr
S.I.C.: 2052
N.A.I.C.S.: 311821
Personnel:
Marc-Andre Cornu *(CEO)*

Non-U.S. Subsidiary:

Cornu Sas Fontain **(1)**
Route de Pugey
25660 Fontaine, Doubs, France
Tel.: (33) 381572983
Fax: (33) 381573096
E-Mail: cornu@cornu.ch
Web Site: www.cornu.ch/en/contacts/
Sls.: $20,100,000
Emp.: 29
Cookies & Crackers
S.I.C.: 2052
N.A.I.C.S.: 311821
Marc Cornu *(Dir-Pur)*

Subsidiary:

Roland Murten AG **(1)**
Freiburgstrasse 49
CH 3280 Murten, Switzerland
Tel.: (41) 266728222
Telex: 942030
Fax: (41) 266728230
E-Mail: info@roland.ch
Web Site: www.rolandch.ch
Emp.: 100
Mfr of Cookies, Crackers & Pretzels
S.I.C.: 2052
N.A.I.C.S.: 311821
Benno Piller *(Mgr-Production)*

CORNWALL GRAVEL CO. LTD.
390 11th St W
PO Box 67
Cornwall, ON, K6J 3B2, Canada
Tel.: (613) 932-6571
Fax: (613) 937-3634
Web Site: www.cornwallgravel.ca
Year Founded: 1949
Sales Range: $10-24.9 Million
Emp.: 90
Fiscal Year-end: 12/31/12
Business Description:
Construction Services
S.I.C.: 1542
N.A.I.C.S.: 236220
Personnel:
Fraser Ouderkirk *(Gen Mgr)*

CORNWALL MOTOR SALES (2002) LTD.
(See Under Seaway Chevrolet Cadillac Buick GMC Ltd)

CORO MINING CORP.
Suite 1280 625 Howe Street
Vancouver, BC, V6C 2T6, Canada
Tel.: (604) 682-5546
Fax: (604) 682-5542
E-Mail: investor.info@coromining.com
Web Site: www.coromining.com
Year Founded: 2004
COP—(TSX)
Rev.: $62,000
Assets: $32,598,000
Liabilities: $297,000
Net Worth: $32,301,000
Earnings: ($8,973,000)
Emp.: 14
Fiscal Year-end: 12/31/12
Business Description:
Copper Mining Services
S.I.C.: 1021
N.A.I.C.S.: 212234
Personnel:
Robert A. Watts *(Chm)*
Alan Stephens *(Pres & CEO)*
Damian Towns *(CFO)*
Marcelo Cortes *(Pres-Minera Cielo Azul & VP-Project Dev)*
Fabian Gregorio *(Pres-Minera San Jorge)*
Michael D. Philpot *(Sec & Exec VP)*
Board of Directors:
Robert A. Watts
Gordon J. Fretwell
Alvin Jackson
Michael D. Philpot
Alan Stephens
Rod Webster
Legal Counsel:
McCullough O'Connor Irwin, LLP
Ste 2610 Oceanic Plz 1066 W Hastings St
Vancouver, BC, V6E 3X1, Canada

Computershare Investor Services Inc.
510 Burrard St 2nd Floor
Vancouver, BC, V6C 3B9, Canada
Tel.: (604) 661-9400
Transfer Agents:
Computershare Investor Services Inc.
Toronto, ON, Canada

Computershare Investor Services Inc.
510 Burrard St 2nd Floor
Vancouver, BC, V6C 3B9, Canada
Tel.: (604) 661-9400

COROMANDEL ENGINEERING COMPANY LIMITED
Parry House 3rd Floor 43 Moore Street
Po Box 1698
Chennai, 600 001, India
Tel.: (91) 4425341513
Fax: (91) 4425342822
E-Mail: coromandelengg@cec.murugappa.com
Web Site: www.coromandelengg.com
COROENGG—(NSE)
Rev.: $40,286,530
Assets: $46,626,394
Liabilities: $43,426,631
Net Worth: $3,199,763
Earnings: ($1,008,669)
Fiscal Year-end: 03/31/13
Business Description:
Construction Engineering Services
S.I.C.: 8711
N.A.I.C.S.: 541330
Personnel:
M. M. Venkatachalam *(Chm & Mng Dir)*
R. Narayanan *(Compliance Officer, Sec & Head-Fin)*
G. Viswanath Kumar *(Sr VP)*
Board of Directors:
M. M. Venkatachalam
M. A. M. Arunachalam
Sridhar Ganesh
S. S. Rajsekar
N. V. Ravi
J. Srinivasan
V. Venkiteswaran
Transfer Agent:
Karvy Computershare Private Limited
Plot No 17 to 24 Vittalrao Nagar Madhapur
Hyderabad, India

CORONA CORPORATION
7-7 Higashi-shinbo
Sanjo, Niigata, 955-8510, Japan
Tel.: (81) 256 32 2111
Fax: (81) 256 35 6892
Web Site: www.corona.co.jp
Year Founded: 1937
5909—(TKS)
Sls.: $916,113,000
Assets: $1,044,142,000
Liabilities: $277,365,000
Net Worth: $766,777,000
Earnings: $33,011,000
Emp.: 2,237
Fiscal Year-end: 03/31/13
Business Description:
Heating Equipment Mfr & Whslr
S.I.C.: 3433
N.A.I.C.S.: 333414
Personnel:
Tsutomu Uchida *(Pres)*

CORONADO RESOURCES LTD.
507-595 Howe Street
Vancouver, BC, V6C 2T5, Canada
Tel.: (604) 683-6338
Fax: (604) 681-2161
Toll Free: (800) 811-2322
Web Site: www.coronadoresourcesltd.com
Year Founded: 1999
CRD—(OTC TSXV)
Int. Income: $38,073
Assets: $11,400,389
Liabilities: $77,363
Net Worth: $11,323,026
Earnings: ($322,950)
Fiscal Year-end: 02/28/13
Business Description:
Mining Exploration Services
S.I.C.: 1081
N.A.I.C.S.: 213114
Personnel:
Daniel Brown *(CEO)*
Barry MacNeil *(CFO)*
Giuseppe Perone *(Sec)*
Board of Directors:
Daniel Brown
Ashley Garnot
Douglas Lynes
John Vaccaro
Transfer Agent:
Computershare
510 Burrard St 2nd Floor
Vancouver, BC, Canada

CORONATION FUND MANAGERS LIMITED
7 Flr MontClare Place Cnr Camp Ground Rd
7700 Claremont, South Africa
Tel.: (27) 216802000
Fax: (27) 216802500
E-Mail: clientservice@coronation.co.za
Web Site: www.coronation.com
Rev.: $87,573,704
Emp.: 250
Business Description:
Asset Management Services
S.I.C.: 6211
N.A.I.C.S.: 523999
Personnel:
Shams Pather *(Chm)*
Hugo Nelson *(CEO)*
Anton Pillay *(COO)*
Board of Directors:
Shams Pather
Winston Floquet
Hugo Nelson
Anton Pillay

CORONET METALS INC.
1066 West Hastings Street Suite 2680
Vancouver, BC, Canada V6E 3X1
Tel.: (604) 648-3506
Fax: (604) 682-1288
Web Site: www.coronetmetals.com
CRF—(OTC TSXV)
Business Description:
Mineral Exploration Services
S.I.C.: 1081
N.A.I.C.S.: 213114
Personnel:
Stephen Stine *(Pres & COO)*
Joel Dumaresq *(CEO)*
Theo van der Linde *(CFO)*
June Hamilton *(Corp Sec)*
Board of Directors:
Miguel Aramburu
Joel Dumaresq
Len Harris
David Kaplan
Douglas Newby
Stephen Stine
Legal Counsel:
McCullough O'Connor Irwin, LLP
Ste 2610 Oceanic Plz 1066 W Hastings St
Vancouver, BC, V6E 3X1, Canada
Transfer Agent:
Computershare
3rd Floor 510 Burrard Street
Vancouver, BC, Canada

CORONUS SOLAR INC.
1100-1200 West 73rd Avenue
Vancouver, BC, V6P 6G5, Canada
Tel.: (604) 267-7078
Year Founded: 2001
CRNSF—(OTCB)
Int. Income: $90
Assets: $4,516,256
Liabilities: $3,785,923
Net Worth: $730,333
Earnings: ($1,390,123)
Fiscal Year-end: 03/31/13
Business Description:
Solar Electric Power Generation Services
S.I.C.: 4931
N.A.I.C.S.: 221114
Personnel:
Jefferson Thachuk *(Pres, CEO, CFO, Chief Acctg Officer, Treas & Sec)*
Board of Directors:
Kaitlyn Bogas
David Holmes
Jefferson Thachuk

COROPLAST FRITZ MULLER GMBH UND CO. KG
Wittener Strasse 271
42279 Wuppertal, Germany
Tel.: (49) 20226810
Fax: (49) 2022681375
E-Mail: coroplast@coroplast.de
Web Site: www.coroplast.de
Year Founded: 1928
Rev.: $195,576,089
Emp.: 554
Business Description:
Adhesive tapes Mfr
S.I.C.: 3999
N.A.I.C.S.: 339999
Personnel:
Natalie Mekelburger *(Chm-Mgmt Bd)*
Marcus Sohngen *(Deputy Chm-Mgmt Bd)*
Wolfram Berns *(Member-Mgmt Bd-Fin, Controlling & IT)*
Torben Kammerer *(Member-Mgmt Bd-Cable Assemblies)*

CORPBANCA SA
Avenida Rosario Norte 660 piso 7
Las Condes, Santiago, Chile
Tel.: (56) 2 2687 8000
Fax: (56) 2 2672 6729
E-Mail: corpbanca@corpbanca.cl
Web Site: www.corpbanca.cl
BCA—(NYSE)
Int. Income: $1,617,543,040
Assets: $28,676,230,880
Liabilities: $26,538,153,640
Net Worth: $2,138,077,240
Earnings: $252,604,360
Emp.: 5,163
Fiscal Year-end: 12/31/12

Business Description:
Banking, Wealth Management, Investment & Financial Advisory Services
S.I.C.: 6029
N.A.I.C.S.: 522110
Personnel:
Jorge Andres Saieh Guzman *(Chm)*
Fernando Aguad Dagach *(First Vice Chm)*
Jorge Selume Zaror *(Second Vice Chm)*
Fernando Massu Tare *(CEO)*
Eugenio Barriga Gigogne Miqueles *(CFO)*
Board of Directors:
Jorge Andres Saieh Guzman
Fernando Aguad Dagach
Gustavo Arriagada Morales
Francisco Leon Delano
Rafael Guilisasti Gana
Jose Luis Mardones Santander
Francisco Mobarec Asfura
Jorge Selume Zaror
Hugo P. Verdegaal

Subsidiary:

CorpBanca Asesorias Financieras S.A. **(1)**
Rosario Norte 660 15th Fl
Las Condes, Santiago, Chile CL
Tel.: (56) 2 660 2185
Fax: (56) 2 660 3731
Web Site: www.corpbanca.cl
Financial Advisory Services
S.I.C.: 6282
N.A.I.C.S.: 523930
Roberto Baraona Undurraga *(CEO & Gen Mgr)*

Non-U.S. Subsidiary:

Banco Santander Colombia, S.A. **(1)**
Carrera 7 No 99-53
Centro de Costos, Bogota, Colombia Co
Tel.: (57) 1 283 7313 (91.93%)
Fax: (57) 1 283 2930
Emp.: 200
Banking Services
S.I.C.: 6029
N.A.I.C.S.: 522110
Jaime Munita Valdivieso *(Pres)*

CORPORACION AMERICA S.A.
Honduras 5663 C1414BNE
Buenos Aires, Argentina
Tel.: (54) 114899 6600
Web Site: www.corporacionamerica.com
Sales Range: $900-999.9 Million
Emp.: 5,000
Business Description:
Investment Holding Company
S.I.C.: 6719
N.A.I.C.S.: 551112
Personnel:
Ernesto Gutierrez *(CEO)*

CORPORACION ANDINA DE FOMENTO
Ave Luis Roche Torre CAF Altamira
Caracas, Venezuela
Tel.: (58) 2122092111
Fax: (58) 2122092444
E-Mail: infocaf@caf.com
Web Site: www.caf.com
Sales Range: $400-449.9 Million
Emp.: 400
Business Description:
Banking Services
S.I.C.: 6029
N.A.I.C.S.: 522110
Personnel:
Juan Carlos Echeverry *(Chm)*
Luis Enrique Garcia Rodriguez *(Pres & CEO)*
Andres Rugeles *(Sec & Dir-Secretariat & External Rels)*
Luis Enrique Berrizbeitia *(Exec VP)*
Board of Directors:
Juan Carlos Echeverry
Luis Alberto Arce
Miriam Belchior
Amado Boudou
Edmee Betancourt de Garcia
Frank De Lima
Jorge Giordani
Carlos Gonzalez-Taboada
Elba Viviana Caro Hinojosa
Fernando Lorenzo
Alfonso Zarate Rivas
Patricio Rivera
Luis Miguel Castilla Rubio
Camilo Saman Salem
Elena Salgado
Jose Dario Uribe

CORPORACION DERMOESTETICA, S.A.
Calle Pizarro 11-13
46004 Valencia, Spain
Tel.: (34) 902252525
Fax: (34) 963178358
E-Mail: inversores@corpderm.com
Web Site: www.corporaciondermoestetica.com
Sales Range: $50-74.9 Million
Emp.: 777
Business Description:
Health Centers, Hospitals & Clinical Laboratories Owner & Operator
S.I.C.: 8069
N.A.I.C.S.: 622310
Personnel:
Jose Maria Suescun Verdugo *(Chm & CEO)*
Asuncion Vivancos Matellanos *(Vice Chm)*
Carlos Peiro Sendra *(Sec)*
Board of Directors:
Jose Maria Suescun Verdugo
Jacobo Llanza Figueroa
Fernando Garcia Llinares
Asuncion Vivancos Matellanos
Antonio Sanchez Rodado
Carlos Senent Sales

CORPORACION EG S.A.
Niquel # 9204
Monterrey, N.L., 64640, Mexico
Tel.: (52) 8181585500
Fax: (52) 8181585501
Web Site: www.corporacioneg.com
Business Description:
Mfr, Designer & Marketer of Centrifugal Pumps; Operator of Iron & Steel Foundry; Mfr of Machine Parts for Industrial & Consumer OEM's
S.I.C.: 3561
N.A.I.C.S.: 333911

Subsidiary:

Ruhrpumpen Inc. **(1)**
4501 S 86th E Ave
Tulsa, OK 74145
Tel.: (918) 627-8400
Fax: (918) 624-2461
Toll Free: (800) 334-2553
E-Mail: info@ruhrpumpen.com
Web Site: www.ruhrpumpen.com
Sales Range: $25-49.9 Million
Emp.: 100
Industrial Pumps & Parts
S.I.C.: 3561
N.A.I.C.S.: 333911
Sernando Elizondo *(Pres)*

Non-U.S. Subsidiary:

Ruhrpumpen GmbH **(2)**
Stockumer Strasse 28
D 58453 Witten, Germany De
Tel.: (49) 230266103
Fax: (49) 2032661303
E-Mail: info@ruhrpumpen.de
Web Site: www.ruhrpumpen.com
Emp.: 270
Mfr. of Pumps
S.I.C.: 3561
N.A.I.C.S.: 333911
Stephan Frieds *(Mng Dir)*

CORPORACION GESTAMP SL
Alfonso XII 16
28014 Madrid, Spain
Tel.: (34) 91 379 19 99
Fax: (34) 91 379 19 98
E-Mail: yentarnacion@gestamp.com
Web Site: www.gestamp.com
Sales Range: $1-4.9 Billion
Business Description:
Industrial Holding Company
S.I.C.: 6719
N.A.I.C.S.: 551112
Personnel:
Francisco Riberas Pampliega *(Pres)*

Divisions:

Gestamp Automacion S.A. **(1)**
Poligono Industrial Lebario S N
48220 Abadiano Celayeta, Spain
Tel.: (34) 944507010
Fax: (34) 946811858
E-Mail: gabadiano@gestamp.com
Web Site: www.gestamp.com
Sales Range: $1-4.9 Billion
Emp.: 8,000
Automotive Component & Structural System Mfr
S.I.C.: 3465
N.A.I.C.S.: 336370
Francisco Jose Riberas Mera *(CEO)*

U.S. Subsidiary:

Gestamp North America, Inc. **(2)**
2701 Troy Centre Dr Ste 150
Troy, MI 48084
Tel.: (248) 743-3400
Fax: (248) 743-3401
Automotive Component & Structural System Mfr
S.I.C.: 3465
N.A.I.C.S.: 336370
Jeff Wilson *(Pres)*

Subsidiary:

Gestamp Alabama, Inc. **(3)**
7000 Jefferson Metro Pkwy
Bessemer, AL 35111
Tel.: (205) 497-6400
Sls.: $27,100,000
Emp.: 250
Automotive Component & Structural System Mfr
S.I.C.: 3465
N.A.I.C.S.: 336370
Jeffrey Wilson *(Pres)*
Jim Barry *(CFO)*

Non-U.S. Subsidiary:

Edscha Holding GmbH **(2)**
Hohenhagener Strasse 26-28
42855 Remscheid, Germany De
Tel.: (49) 21913630
Fax: (49) 2191 363 549
E-Mail: info@edscha.com
Web Site: www.edscha.com
Emp.: 3,000
Holding Company; Motor Vehicle Hinge Systems & Driver Controls Developer & Mfr
S.I.C.: 6719
N.A.I.C.S.: 551112
Francisco Jose Riberas Mera *(Chm-Mgmt Bd)*
Mario Eikelmann *(Member-Mgmt Bd)*
Francisco Lopez Pena *(Member-Mgmt Bd)*
Juan Maria Riberas Mera *(Member-Mgmt Bd)*
Hans-Peter Schulz *(Member-Mgmt Bd)*
David Vazquez Pascual *(Member-Mgmt Bd)*
Volker Weiss *(Member-Mgmt Bd)*

Grupo Gonvarri **(1)**
Prolongacion de Embajadores S N
28053 Madrid, Spain
Tel.: (34) 913791900
Flat Steel Product Mfr
S.I.C.: 3399
N.A.I.C.S.: 331110

CORPORACION GRUPO QUIMICO, S.A.C.A.
Avenida Rio De Janeiro
Local Pinta Casa Entre Carohi, Las Mercedes, Caracas, 1060, Venezuela
Tel.: (58) 2129930557
Fax: (58) 2129915455
Year Founded: 1953
Emp.: 720
Business Description:
Paint, Resin, Pigment, Chemical Additive & Auxiliary Chemical Product Mfr
S.I.C.: 2899
N.A.I.C.S.: 325998
Personnel:
Lope Mendoza *(Chm)*

CORPORACION NACIONAL DEL COBRE DE CHILE
(d/b/a CODELCO)
Huerfanos 1270
PO Box 150 D
Santiago, Chile
Tel.: (56) 26903000
Telex: 240672 CUPRU CL
Fax: (56) 26903059
E-Mail: comunica@stgo.codelco.cl
Web Site: www.codelco.cl
Year Founded: 1976
Sales Range: $1-4.9 Billion
Emp.: 16,800
Business Description:
Copper & Molybdenum Mfr & Sales Export
S.I.C.: 1021
N.A.I.C.S.: 212234
Personnel:
Diego Hernandez Cabrera *(CEO)*
Juan Eduardo Herrera Correa *(CFO)*
Mario Espinoza Duran *(Sr VP-Bus Dev)*

Divisions:

Codelco Andina Division **(1)**
Ave Santa Teresa 513
Los Andes, Chile (100%)
Tel.: (56) 34 4980000
Fax: (56) 34495342
Web Site: www.codelco.com
Emp.: 1,126
Copper Mine
S.I.C.: 1021
N.A.I.C.S.: 212234
Armando Ola Vieira *(Gen Mgr)*

Codelco Chuquicamata Division **(1)**
Casilla 9 D
Chuquicamata, Chile (100%)
Tel.: (56) 55323100
Fax: (56) 322332
Web Site: www.codelco.cl
Emp.: 7,694
Copper Mine
S.I.C.: 1021
N.A.I.C.S.: 212234

Codelco El Teniente Division **(1)**
Millan 1020
Rancagua, Chile (100%)
Tel.: (56) 72292800
Fax: (56) 72292795
Web Site: www.teneiente.cl
Emp.: 300
S.I.C.: 1021
N.A.I.C.S.: 212234

Codelco Salvador Division **(1)**
Casilla 79
El Salvador, Chile (100%)
Tel.: (56) 52472103
Fax: (56) 52 47 2387
Web Site: www.codelco.com
Emp.: 2,247
Copper Mine
S.I.C.: 1021

Corporacion Nacional del Cobre de Chile—(Continued)

N.A.I.C.S.: 212234

Codelco Talleres Division (1)
Ave Estacion 01200
Rancagua, Chile (100%)
Tel.: (56) 26903000
Fax: (56) 26903151
Web Site: www.codelco.com
Emp.: 600
S.I.C.: 1021
N.A.I.C.S.: 212234
Alex A. Maluenda *(Gen Mgr)*

Subsidiaries:

Agua De La Falda S.A. (1)
Barrio Industrial Sitio 58 Alto Penuelas
Coquimbo, Chile
Tel.: (56) 23402000
Fax: (56) 23402069
Web Site: www.barricksudamerica.com
Metal & Gold Mining
S.I.C.: 1041
N.A.I.C.S.: 212221
Felipe Nunez Cordero *(Gen Mgr)*

Complejo Portuario Mejillones S.A. (1)
Coronel Tereira 72
Santiago, Chile
Tel.: (56) 26903850
Fax: (56) 26903851
E-Mail: cpnsa@codelco.cl
Web Site: www.mejillones.com
Emp.: 100
Real Estate
S.I.C.: 6531
N.A.I.C.S.: 531390
Rodrigo Toro *(VP)*

Fundicon Talleres S.A. (1)
Avenida Estacion
Rancagua, 01200, Chile
Tel.: (56) 72292083
Fax: (56) 72 292636
E-Mail: talleres@talleres.codelco.cl
Web Site: www.talleres.cl
Scrap Steel Castings Mfr
S.I.C.: 3324
N.A.I.C.S.: 331512
Mario Espinoza Duran *(Pres)*

Isapre San Lorenzo Ltda (1)
Pasaje Cuatro de Julio 694
El Salvador, Chile
Tel.: (56) 52475315
Web Site: www.isl.cl
Financing of Health Care Services & Benefits
S.I.C.: 6371
N.A.I.C.S.: 525120
Hernan Sandoval Orellana *(Pres)*

Sociedad Contractual Minera El Abra (1)
Kilometro 75 Camino Conchi Viejo
Antofagasta, Chile
Tel.: (56) 55818300
Fax: (56) 55818709
Web Site: www.codelco.com
Metal Ore Mining
S.I.C.: 1099
N.A.I.C.S.: 212299
Diego Hernandez Cabrera *(Pres & CEO)*

Sociedad Contractual Minera Puren (1)
Los Carrera N 6651
Copiapo, Chile
Tel.: (56) 52221043
Fax: (56) 52221159
Web Site: www.codelco.de
Support Activities for Metal Mining
S.I.C.: 1099
N.A.I.C.S.: 212299

Joint Venture:

BioSigma S.A. (1)
Carretera General San Martin #16 500 Lote #106 Colina Parque
Industrial Los Libertadores, Santiago, Chile CL
Mailing Address:
Casilla 100
Correo El Cortijo, Santiago, Chile
Tel.: (56) 24379030
Fax: (56) 24600416
E-Mail: informacion@biosigma.cl
Web Site: www.biosigma.cl
Emp.: 70
Mining Proteomics & Bioinformatics Research & Development; Owned by Corporacion Nacional del Cobre de Chile & by JX Holdings, Inc.
S.I.C.: 8731
N.A.I.C.S.: 541711
Ricardo Badilla Ohlbaum *(CEO & Gen Mgr)*

U.S. Subsidiary:

Corporacion del Cobre (U.S.A.), Inc. (1)
177 Broad St 11th Fl
Stamford, CT 06901-5003 DE
Tel.: (203) 425-4321
Fax: (203) 425-4322
Web Site: www.codelco.com
Emp.: 2
Sales of Copper & Molybdenum
S.I.C.: 5052
N.A.I.C.S.: 423520

Non-U.S. Subsidiaries:

CK Metall Agentur GmbH (1)
Louise Dumont Str 25
40211 Dusseldorf, Germany (100%)
Mailing Address:
Postfach 24 02 26
Dusseldorf, Germany
Tel.: (49) 211173690
Fax: (49) 2111736818
E-Mail: ck@codelco.de
Web Site: www.codelco.de
Emp.: 6
S.I.C.: 1021
N.A.I.C.S.: 212234
Heribert Heitling *(Gen Mgr)*

Codelco-Asia (1)
Unit E & F 26 Fl Mirae Asset No-166
Lujiazui Ring Rd
Shanghai, 200120, China
Tel.: (86) 2161090260
Telex: RS 26170
Fax: (86) 2161090277
E-Mail: codelco_sh@codelco.com.cn
Web Site: www.codelco.com
Sales of Copper
S.I.C.: 1021
N.A.I.C.S.: 212234
Carlos Alvarado *(Mng Dir)*

Codelco-Kupferhandel GmbH (1)
Louise Dumont Strasse 25
40211 Dusseldorf, Germany (100%)
Mailing Address:
Postfach 24 02 26
Dusseldorf, Germany
Tel.: (49) 211173680
Fax: (49) 2111736922
E-Mail: ck@codelco.de
Web Site: www.codelco.de
Emp.: 6
S.I.C.: 1021
N.A.I.C.S.: 212234
Heriberg Heidiling *(Gen Mgr)*

Coppermol S.A. (1)
Ricardo Rojas 401 Piso 4
C 1001 AEA Buenos Aires, Argentina
Tel.: (54) 11 4312 7086
Telex: 23644 COMOL AR
Fax: (54) 11 4311 4007
Web Site: www.codelco.com
Emp.: 8
Sales of Copper & Molybdenum Metals
S.I.C.: 1021
N.A.I.C.S.: 212234

CORPORACION PATRICIO ECHEVERRIA, S.A.

Urola 10
20230 Guipuzcoa, Legazpi, Spain
Tel.: (34) 943739000
Fax: (34) 943733363
E-Mail: comercial@bellota.com
Web Site: www.bellota.com
Year Founded: 1908
Sales Range: $250-299.9 Million
Emp.: 1,800

Business Description:
Holding Company
Import Export
S.I.C.: 6719
N.A.I.C.S.: 551112

Personnel:
Enrique Mir Sagardia *(Gen Mgr)*

Subsidiary:

Bellota Herramientas S.A. (1)
Urola 10 Apdo 1
Guipuzcoa, Barcelona, 20230, Spain (100%)
Tel.: (34) 943739000
Fax: (34) 943731501
E-Mail: comercial@bellota.com
Web Site: www.bellota.com
Emp.: 500
Mfr of Gardening & Agricultural Supplies
S.I.C.: 5083
N.A.I.C.S.: 423820
Edwardo Urrutia *(Mgr-Export)*

U.S. Subsidiary:

Corona Clipper (1)
22440 Temescal Canyon Rd
Corona, CA 92883 (100%)
Tel.: (951) 737-6515
Fax: (951) 737-8657
Toll Free: (800) 234-2547
E-Mail: info@coronaclipper.com
Web Site: www.coronaclipper.com
Emp.: 185
Gardening Tools Mfr
S.I.C.: 3423
N.A.I.C.S.: 332216
Al Schulten *(Controller)*

Non-U.S. Subsidiaries:

Bellota Brasil, Ltda. (1)
Rodovia BR470 Km 73 5 No 3500
PO Box 248
Indaial, SC, 89130004, Brazil (100%)
Tel.: (55) 473338011
Fax: (55) 473338512
E-Mail: mkt@bra.bellota.com
Web Site: www.bellota.com
Sales Range: $10-24.9 Million
Emp.: 300
Mfr. of Garden & Agricultural Machinery
S.I.C.: 5083
N.A.I.C.S.: 423820

Bellota Colombia, S.A. (1)
Parque Ind Juanchiquito Terraza 8
Manizales, Caladas, Colombia (100%)
Tel.: (57) 68748585
Fax: (57) 68748860
E-Mail: coprcion.exterior@bellota.com
Web Site: www.bellota.com
Emp.: 300
Mfr. of Garden & Agricultural Machinery
S.I.C.: 5083
N.A.I.C.S.: 423820
Carlos Polo *(Dir-Comml)*

Bellota Mexico, S.A. de C.V. (1)
Prolo Ave 16 Esq Number 400 Km 1
Fortin, Veracruz, 94470, Mexico (100%)
Tel.: (52) 2717170207
Fax: (52) 2717170212
E-Mail: mkt@mex.bellota.com
Web Site: www.bellota.com
Sales Range: $1-9.9 Million
Emp.: 300
Mfr. of Garden & Agricultural Machinery
S.I.C.: 5083
N.A.I.C.S.: 423820
Alvedo Salesus *(Gen Mgr)*

Bellota Venezuela C.A. (1)
Urbanizacion Ind Corinsa C/ Lazo 1
Cagua, Aragua, Venezuela
Tel.: (58) 44 395 3011
Fax: (58) 44 395 4277
E-Mail: mkt@ven.bellota.com
Web Site: www.bellota.com
Mfr. of Garden & Agricultural Machinery
S.I.C.: 5083
N.A.I.C.S.: 423820

Solbjerg Staalvarefabrik A/S (1)
Industriomradet 107
8732 Hovedgard, Denmark (100%)
Tel.: (45) 75662022
Fax: (45) 75662024
E-Mail: mkt@solbjerg.bellota.com
Web Site: www.bellota.com
Rev.: $6,613,840
Emp.: 5
Mfr. of Garden & Agricultural Machinery
S.I.C.: 5083
N.A.I.C.S.: 423820
Eric Madsen *(Mgr-Sls)*

CORPORACION VENEZOLANA DE GUAYANA

(d/b/a CVG)
Avenida Guayana con Carrera
Cuchivero Edificio Sede CVG
Altavista, Puerto Ordaz, Bolivar, Venezuela
Tel.: (58) 286 966 1930
Fax: (58) 286 966 1932
E-Mail: presidencia@cvg.com
Web Site: www.cvg.com
Year Founded: 1960
Emp.: 22,000

Business Description:
Business & Economic Development Services
S.I.C.: 8742
N.A.I.C.S.: 541611

Personnel:
Rafael Hill *(Pres)*
Carlos Osorio *(Pres)*

Holdings:

Complejo Siderurgico de Guayana, C.A. (1)
Parque Industrial CVG-Minorca Sector Punta Chichillo
8050 Puerto Ordaz, Bolivar, Venezuela VE
Tel.: (58) 2869520080
Fax: (58) 2869526440
E-Mail: agonzalez@comsigua.com.ve
Web Site: www.comsigua.net
Sales Range: $50-74.9 Million
Emp.: 245
Hot Briquette Iron Production & Sales
S.I.C.: 3462
N.A.I.C.S.: 332111
Ivan Hernandez *(Pres)*

Rialca (1)
Zona Industrial Sur II Avda Henry Ford
Apartado 1183
Valencia, 46023, Venezuela
Tel.: (58) 2418748411
Fax: (58) 2418322094
E-Mail: webmaster@rualca.com.ve
Web Site: www.rualca.com.ve
Emp.: 530
Aluminum Wheels & Other Aluminum Products Mfr & Sales
S.I.C.: 3353
N.A.I.C.S.: 331315
Leslie Turmero *(Pres)*

CORPORATE & RESOURCE CONSULTANTS PTY LTD

Level 1, Suite 5, The Business Centre, 55 Salvado Road
Subiaco, Western Australia, 6008, Australia
Tel.: (61) 8 9380 6789
Fax: (61) 8 9380 6761
E-Mail: reception@crcpl.com.au
Web Site: www.crcpl.com.au
Emp.: 15

Business Description:
Financial Management Consulting Services
S.I.C.: 8748
N.A.I.C.S.: 541618

Personnel:
Reg Gillard *(Mgr)*

CORPORATE COMMERCIAL BANK AD

10 Graf Ignatiev Street
Sofia, 1000, Bulgaria
Tel.: (359) 2 93 75 606
Fax: (359) 2 93 75 607
E-Mail: corpbank@corpbank.bg
Web Site: www.corpbank.bg
6C9—(BUL)

Int. Income: $221,584,549
Assets: $3,853,005,012
Liabilities: $3,545,248,884
Net Worth: $307,756,128
Earnings: $38,606,814
Emp.: 944
Fiscal Year-end: 12/31/12

Business Description:
Commercial Banking Services
S.I.C.: 6029
N.A.I.C.S.: 522110

Personnel:
Tzvetan Vassilev *(Chm-Supervisory Bd)*
Orlin Rusev *(Chm-Mgmt Bd)*

Supervisory Board of Directors:
Tzvetan Vassilev
Warith Mubarak Said Al Kharusi
Faisal Amur Mohamed Al Riyami
Lyubomir Denev
Zlatozar Surlekov

Joint Venture:

Bulgarian Telecommunications Company AD (1)
115I Tsarigradsko Shose Blvd
Hermes Park Building A, 1784 Sofia, Bulgaria BG
Tel.: (359) 2 949 43 31
Fax: (359) 2 951 50 60
E-Mail: ir@vivacom.bg
Web Site: www.vivacom.bg
5BT—(BUL)
Rev.: $586,249,570
Assets: $936,791,430
Liabilities: $729,820,112
Net Worth: $206,971,319
Earnings: ($24,826,770)
Fiscal Year-end: 12/31/12
Telecommunication Services
S.I.C.: 4899
N.A.I.C.S.: 517919
Vladimir Penkov Penkov *(Chm-Supervisory Bd)*
Bernard Jean Luc Moscheni *(CEO)*
Atanas Dobrev *(CFO)*
Alexander Dimitrov *(Chief Comml Officer)*
Mihaela Kalaydjieva *(Sec)*

CORPORATE DEVELOPMENT BANK LIMITED

Adarshnagar Main Road Parsa
Birgunj, 44313, Nepal
Tel.: (977) 51 531031
Fax: (977) 51 527843
E-Mail: info@corporatebank.com.np
Web Site: www.corporatebank.com.np
Year Founded: 2007
CORBL—(NEP)

Business Description:
Banking Services
S.I.C.: 6029
N.A.I.C.S.: 522110

Personnel:
Mohan Raj Regmi *(Chm)*
Binay Raj Pokhrel *(CEO)*

Board of Directors:
Mohan Raj Regmi
Binod Kumar Khandelwal
Ram Kumar Lamichhane
Binay Raj Pokhrel
Bissu Prasad Subedi

CORPORATE TRAVEL MANAGEMENT LIMITED

27A/52 Charlotte Street
Brisbane, QLD, 4000, Australia
Tel.: (61) 732112400
Fax: (61) 732297522
E-Mail: marketing@travelctm.com
Web Site: www.travelctm.com
Year Founded: 1994
CTD—(ASX)
Rev.: $82,288,384
Assets: $126,194,142
Liabilities: $50,136,473
Net Worth: $76,057,669
Earnings: $12,915,787
Emp.: 616
Fiscal Year-end: 06/30/13

Business Description:
Travel Services
S.I.C.: 4729
N.A.I.C.S.: 561599

Personnel:
Jamie Pherous *(Founder, CEO & Mng Dir)*
Steve Fleming *(CFO & Co-Sec)*
Robert A. Polk *(CEO-Polk Corporate Travel Management-USA)*
Laura Ruffles *(CEO-AU & NZ)*
Lyndall McCabe *(Co-Sec)*

Board of Directors:
Tony Bellas
Claire Gray
Stephen Lonie
Greg Moynihan
Jamie Pherous

Subsidiaries:

Corporate Travel Management Group Pty Ltd (1)
27A / 52 Charlotte Street
Brisbane, QLD, 4000, Australia
Tel.: (61) 7 3211 2400
Fax: (61) 7 3229 7522
E-Mail: reception@travelctm.com
Web Site: www.travelctm.com
Emp.: 14
Travel Management Services
S.I.C.: 4724
N.A.I.C.S.: 561510
Laura Ruffles *(CEO)*
Jamie Pherous *(Mng Dir)*
Steve Fleming *(CFO)*

Sainten Pty Ltd (1)
L 30 Margaret St
Sydney, NSW, 2000, Australia
Tel.: (61) 292301000
Fax: (61) 292301090
Travel Management Services
S.I.C.: 4724
N.A.I.C.S.: 561510
Claire Lesley Gray *(Mgr)*

U.S. Subsidiary:

R A Travel, Inc. (1)
39 W 14th St Ste 306
New York, NY 10011 NY
Tel.: (212) 633-8300
Fax: (212) 727-3768
Toll Free: (800) 788-0777
E-Mail: ratravel@mindspring.com
Web Site: www.ratravel.com
Sales Range: $10-24.9 Million
Emp.: 15
Travel Agencies
S.I.C.: 4724
N.A.I.C.S.: 561510
Rose Aiello *(Pres)*

CORPORATION BANK

Mangaladevi Temple Road
Pandeshwar, Mangalore, Karnataka, 575 001, India
Tel.: (91) 8242426416
Fax: (91) 8242440964
E-Mail: query@corpbank.co.in
Web Site: www.corpbank.com
532179—(BOM)
Rev.: $3,143,274,696
Assets: $35,869,523,474
Liabilities: $34,089,217,212
Net Worth: $1,780,306,262
Earnings: $267,577,104
Emp.: 15,908
Fiscal Year-end: 03/31/13

Business Description:
Banking Services
S.I.C.: 6029
N.A.I.C.S.: 522110

Personnel:
Sadhu Ram Bansal *(Chm & Mng Dir)*
C. G. Pinto *(CFO & Gen Mgr)*
K. S. Somayaji *(Chief Vigilance Officer & Gen Mgr)*
S. K. Dash *(Sec)*

Board of Directors:
Sadhu Ram Bansal
Ekanath Baliga
Bonam Venkata Bhaskar
Vincent D'Souza
Amar Lal Daultani
Kawaljit Singh Oberoi
Uma Shankar Paliwal
S. Shabbeer Pasha
Anna Roy
Sushobhan Sarker
Bibhas Kumar Srivastav

V. Narayanan & Co
Mumbai, India

Suresh Chandra & Associates
Mumbai, India

Rajendra K. Goel & Co
Mumbai, India

O.P. Totla & Co
Mumbai, India

K Varghese & Co
Mumbai, India

Transfer Agent:
Karvy Computershare Private Limited
Plot No 17-24 Vittal Rao Nagar Madhapur
Hyderabad, 500 081, India
Tel.: (91) 40 2342 0818

Subsidiary:

Corp Bank Securities Ltd (1)
21 Dalal st Fort
Veen Chambers, Mumbai, Maharashtra, 400001, India
Tel.: (91) 22 2670105
Fax: (91) 22 8663102
Web Site: www.corpbank.com
Securities Trading & Related Services
S.I.C.: 6211
N.A.I.C.S.: 523110

CORPORATION TSESNA JSC

43 Beibitshilik Street
010000 Astana, Kazakhstan
Tel.: (7) 7172 317399
Fax: (7) 7172 318290
E-Mail: info@tsesna.kz
Web Site: www.tsesna.kz
TSNA—(KAZ)

Business Description:
Investment Holding Company
S.I.C.: 6719
N.A.I.C.S.: 551112

Personnel:
Epkegali Edenbaev *(Chm-Mgmt Bd)*

Subsidiaries:

Concern Tsesna-Astyk LLP (1)
24 Akzhol Street
10000 Astana, Kazakhstan
Tel.: (7) 7172 700500
Fax: (7) 7172 546 092
E-Mail: pr@concern.kz
Web Site: www.tsesnaastyk.kz/
TSAS—(KAZ)
Sales Range: $100-124.9 Million
Flour, Cereals, Mixed Feeds, Flakes, Bread, Bakery Products, Confectionery & Pasta Mfr, Distr & Retailer
S.I.C.: 2041
N.A.I.C.S.: 311211
Nikolay Mescheryakov *(Chm-Mgmt Bd)*

Tsesnabank JSC (1)
29 Zhenis Ave
Astana, 010000, Kazakhstan
Tel.: (7) 7172 587711
Fax: (7) 7172 770195
E-Mail: info@tsb.kz
Web Site: www.tsb.kz
TSBN—(KAZ)
Int. Income: $368,291,022
Assets: $4,070,382,351
Liabilities: $3,753,130,881
Net Worth: $317,251,470
Earnings: $71,249,184
Emp.: 2,900
Fiscal Year-end: 12/31/12
Banking Services
S.I.C.: 6029
N.A.I.C.S.: 522110
Yerkegali Yedenbayev *(Chm)*
Dauren Zhaksybek *(Chm-Mgmt Bd & CEO)*
Rustam Yakupbayev *(First Deputy Chm-Mgmt Bd)*
Mars Aldashov *(Deputy Chm-Mgmt Bd)*
Samat Balkenov *(Deputy Chm-Mgmt Bd)*
Olga Boiko *(Deputy Chm-Mgmt Bd)*
Marat Mukhambetov *(Deputy Chm-Mgmt Bd)*
Murat Nurgazin *(Deputy Chm-Mgmt Bd)*
Galym Ordabayev *(Deputy Chm-Mgmt Bd)*
Serizhan Yegizbayev *(Deputy Chm-Mgmt Bd)*
Zhamila Batyrbekova *(Mng Dir & Member-Mgmt Bd)*
Saule Shaimerdenova *(Mng Dir & Member-Mgmt Bd)*

CORPORATIVO COPAMEX, S.A. DE C.V.

Montes Apalaches 101
Residencial San Agustin, 66260
Garza Garcia, Nuevo Leon, Mexico
Tel.: (52) 8181526000
Fax: (52) 8181526159
E-Mail: miguel.garcia@copamex.com
Web Site: www.copamex.com
Year Founded: 1987
Sales Range: $400-449.9 Million
Emp.: 6,800

Business Description:
Holding Company; Paper & Paper Products Mfr
S.I.C.: 6719
N.A.I.C.S.: 551112

Personnel:
Juan Bosco Maldonado Quiroga *(Chm)*

Board of Directors:
Juan Bosco Maldonado Quiroga

Subsidiaries:

Copamex Corrugados, S.A. De C.V. (1)
Poniente 134 No 649
Col Industrial Vallejo, 02300 Mexico, Mexico (100%)
Tel.: (52) 5550028200
Fax: (52) 5550028249
Web Site: www.copamex.com
Paperboard Mills
S.I.C.: 2631
N.A.I.C.S.: 322130

Copamex Empaque, S.A. De C.V. (1)
Montes Apalaches 101-28 Residencial San Agustin
San Pedro Garza Garcia, Nuevo Leon, Mexico (100%)
Tel.: (52) 8150006000
Fax: (52) 8150006209
E-Mail: contacto.mercadotecnia@copamex.com
Web Site: www.copamex.com
Emp.: 200
Paper Mills
S.I.C.: 2621
N.A.I.C.S.: 322121
Antonio Zarate *(Gen Mgr)*

Higiene Infantil de Mexico, S.A. De C.V. (1)
Valdepenas #2030
Anexo Lomas de Zapopan, 45130 Jalisco, Mexico (100%)
Tel.: (52) 3330033800
Fax: (52) 3330033900
Sanitary Paper Product Mfr
S.I.C.: 2676
N.A.I.C.S.: 322291

Papelera de Chihuahua, S.A. De C.V. (1)
Plz Ferrocarril Kansas No 1
Colonia Popular, Chihuahua, Mexico (100%)
Tel.: (52) 6144394200
Fax: (52) 6144159992
Web Site: www.copamex.com
Paper Mills

Corporativo Copamex, S.A. de C.V.—(Continued)

S.I.C.: 2621
N.A.I.C.S.: 322121

Papelera Mexicana SA de CV, Industrial (1)
Blvd Industrial 3201
Colonia La Cofradia, 60000 Uruapan, Michoacan, Mexico (100%)
Tel.: (52) 4525280173
Fax: (52) 4525280182
Web Site: www.copamex.mx
Emp.: 360
Mfr. of Paper & Paper Products
S.I.C.: 2621
N.A.I.C.S.: 322122

U.S. Subsidiary:

Copamex North America (1)
1201 N Watson Rd Ste 268
Arlington, TX 76006
Tel.: (817) 652-8932
Fax: (817) 652-8976
E-Mail: Radcliffe@Copamex.com
Emp.: 3
Paper Bag Distr
S.I.C.: 5113
N.A.I.C.S.: 424130
Raymond A. Radcliffe *(Reg Mgr-Sls)*

CORREA RIBEIRO S/A COMERCIO E INDUSTRIA

Av Centenario 2411 - Ed Emp
Centenario / Sa
40155151 Salvador, BA, Brazil
Tel.: (55) 71 2108 6200
Fax: (55) 71 2108 6202
Web Site: www.crci.com.br
CORR3—(BRAZ)
Sales Range: Less than $1 Million

Business Description:
Real Estate Management Services
S.I.C.: 6531
N.A.I.C.S.: 531390

Personnel:
Jose Carlos Da Costa Gomes *(Dir-IR)*

CORRIDOR RESOURCES INC.

301 5475 Spring Garden Road
Halifax, NS, B3J 3T2, Canada
Tel.: (902) 429-4511
Fax: (902) 429-0209
Toll Free: (888) 429-4511
E-Mail: info@corridor.ca
Web Site: www.corridor.ca
CDH—(TSX)
Sls.: $14,706,526
Assets: $157,033,292
Liabilities: $9,122,122
Net Worth: $147,911,170
Earnings: ($47,602,624)
Emp.: 17
Fiscal Year-end: 12/31/12

Business Description:
Pipeline Transporting Natural Gas Services
S.I.C.: 1311
N.A.I.C.S.: 211111

Personnel:
J. Douglas Foster *(Chm)*
Phillip R. Knoll *(Pres & CEO)*
Lisette F. Hachey *(CFO)*

Board of Directors:
J. Douglas Foster
Achille E. Desmarais
Martin Fraess-Ehrfeld
Phillip R. Knoll
Norman W. Miller
Robert David Penner
W. C. Seth

Legal Counsel:
Bennett Jones LLP
Calgary, AB, Canada

Transfer Agent:
Computershare Trust Company of Canada
600 530 8th Avenue SW
Calgary, AB, T2P 3S8, Canada
Tel.: (403) 267-6555
Toll Free: (800) 558-0046

CORROSION SERVICE COMPANY LIMITED

205 Riviera Drive
Markham, ON, L3R 5J8, Canada
Tel.: (416) 630-2600
Fax: (416) 630-2393
Web Site: www.corrosionservice.com
Year Founded: 1950
Rev.: $11,859,557
Emp.: 40

Business Description:
Engineering Services
S.I.C.: 8711
N.A.I.C.S.: 541330

Personnel:
Douglas Downing *(Pres)*

CORRUVEN, INC.

264 Notre Dame Street
Kedgwick, NB, E8B 1H9, Canada
Tel.: (506) 284-3100
Fax: (506) 284-3153
Toll Free: (877) 284-3101
E-Mail: info@corruven.com
Web Site: www.corruven.com
Year Founded: 2010
Emp.: 2

Business Description:
Composite Panel Mfr
S.I.C.: 2435
N.A.I.C.S.: 321211

Personnel:
Alain Belanger *(CEO)*
Denis Duguay *(CFO & Sec)*

Board of Directors:
Daniel Beauregard-Long
Alain Belanger
Denis Duguay
Patrick J. Durepos
Thomas Soucy

CORSA COAL CORP.

110 Yonge St Suite 601
Toronto, ON, M5C 1T4, Canada
Tel.: (416) 214-9800
Toll Free: (855) 214-9800
E-Mail: communication@corsacoal.com
Web Site: www.corsacoal.com
Year Founded: 2007
CSO—(TSXV)
Sls.: $53,568,000
Assets: $126,125,000
Liabilities: $52,114,000
Net Worth: $74,011,000
Earnings: ($27,792,000)
Fiscal Year-end: 11/30/12

Business Description:
Coal Mining Services
S.I.C.: 1499
N.A.I.C.S.: 212399

Personnel:
Michael Harrison *(Chm)*
Donald K. Charter *(Pres & CEO)*
Paul D. Caldwell *(CFO & Sec)*
Joseph Gallo *(Pres-Wilson Creek)*

Board of Directors:
Michael Harrison
Donald K. Charter
Patrick Connolly
John H. Craig
Timothy Phillips
Charles Pitcher
Robert Scott

U.S. Subsidiary:

Wilson Creek Energy, LLC (1)
140 W Union St
Somerset, PA 15501
Tel.: (814) 443-4600
Mineral Mining Services
S.I.C.: 1499
N.A.I.C.S.: 212399
Steve Meehan *(VP-Mktg)*

CORTEX BUSINESS SOLUTIONS INC.

3404 25th Street NE
Calgary, AB, T1Y 6C1, Canada
Tel.: (403) 219-2838
Fax: (403) 717-9692
Toll Free: (866) 716-6272
E-Mail: investor-relations@cortex.net
Web Site: www.cortex.net
Year Founded: 1999
CBX—(OTC TSXV)
Rev.: $6,127,276
Assets: $10,735,986
Liabilities: $1,937,414
Net Worth: $8,798,572
Earnings: ($7,103,954)
Fiscal Year-end: 07/31/13

Business Description:
Business Automation Solution Services
S.I.C.: 7389
N.A.I.C.S.: 561990

Personnel:
Art Smith *(Pres)*
Sandra Weiler *(CFO)*
Trudy Curry *(COO)*
Ryan D. Lailey *(Sr VP-US Ops & Bus Dev)*

Board of Directors:
Grant Billing
Randy Henderson
Keith Powell
Mark Ripplinger
Art Smith

Transfer Agent:
Computershare Trust Company of Canada
600 530 8th Avenue SW
Calgary, AB, T2P 3S8, Canada
Tel.: (403) 267-6555
Toll Free: (800) 558-0046

Subsidiary:

Cortex Business Solutions Ltd. (1)
3412 25 St NE
Calgary, AB, T1Y 6C1, Canada
Tel.: (866) 716-6272
Business Software Development Services
S.I.C.: 7371
N.A.I.C.S.: 541511

CORTEZ GOLD CORP.

Suite 750-580 Hornby Street
Vancouver, BC, V6C 3B6, Canada
Tel.: (604) 602-4935
Fax: (604) 602-4936
Toll Free: (866) -6024935
E-Mail: info@cortezgoldcorp.com
Web Site: www.cortezgoldcorp.com
Year Founded: 2007
CUT.P—(TSXV)
Rev.: $8,116
Assets: $1,117,349
Liabilities: $28,359
Net Worth: $1,088,990
Earnings: ($396,736)
Emp.: 120
Fiscal Year-end: 02/28/13

Business Description:
Investment Services
S.I.C.: 6211
N.A.I.C.S.: 523999

Personnel:
Robert Eadie *(Pres)*
Jose Antonio Berlanga Balderas *(CEO)*
Gary Arca *(CFO & Sec)*

Board of Directors:
Gary Arca
Jose Antonio Berlanga Balderas
Andrew de Verteuil
Robert Eadie

Legal Counsel:
Lang Michener
1500-1055 West Georgia Street
Vancouver, BC, Canada

Transfer Agent:
Computershare Investor Services
3rd Floor, 510 Burrard Street
Vancouver, BC, Canada

CORTICEIRA AMORIM, S.G.P.S., S.A.

Rua de Meladas 380
PO Box 20
4536-902 Lisbon, Portugal
Tel.: (351) 227475400
Fax: (351) 227475410
E-Mail: amorim@amorim.com
Web Site: www.amorim.pt
COR—(EUR)
Sls.: $719,177,861
Assets: $866,619,822
Liabilities: $469,168,515
Net Worth: $397,451,308
Earnings: $42,718,013
Emp.: 3,501
Fiscal Year-end: 12/31/12

Business Description:
Wine Cork Mfr
S.I.C.: 2499
N.A.I.C.S.: 321999

Personnel:
Antonio Rios de Amorim *(Chm)*
Durval Ferreira Marques *(Chm-Supervisory Bd)*
Nuno Filipe Vilela Barroca de Oliveira *(Vice Chm)*

Board of Directors:
Antonio Rios de Amorim
Luisa Alexandra Ramos Amorim
Cristina Rios de Amorim Baptista
Fernando Jose de Araujo dos Santos Almeida
Nuno Filipe Vilela Barroca de Oliveira
Juan Ginesta Vinas

Supervisory Board of Directors:
Durval Ferreira Marques
Gustavo Jose de Noronha da Costa Fernandes
Joaquim Alberto Hierro Lopes

CORTINA HOLDINGS LIMITED

391B Orchard Road 18-01 Ngee Ann City Tower B
Singapore, 238874, Singapore
Tel.: (65) 6339 9447
Fax: (65) 6336 7913
E-Mail: info@cortina.com.sg
Web Site: www.cortina.com.sg
Year Founded: 1972
C41—(SES)
Rev.: $297,515,297
Assets: $231,615,441
Liabilities: $122,707,814
Net Worth: $108,907,628
Earnings: $13,842,289
Emp.: 173
Fiscal Year-end: 03/31/13

Business Description:
Luxury Watches Distr
S.I.C.: 5094
N.A.I.C.S.: 423940

Personnel:
Anthony Keen Ban Lim *(Co-Founder, Chm & CEO)*
Michael See Jin Foo *(Co-Founder)*
Raymond Jit Ming Lim *(Deputy Chm & Deputy CEO)*
Soon Soo Foo *(Co-Sec)*
Prisca Low *(Co-Sec)*

Board of Directors:
Anthony Keen Ban Lim
Michael Sek Peng Chin
Michael See Jin Foo
Pearce Ping Sum Lau
James Ah Fong Lee

Jeremy Jit Yaw Lim
Raymond Jit Ming Lim
Benny Foo Pieng Long
Victor Chuen Tek Yu

Transfer Agent:
KCK CorpServe Pte. Ltd.
333 North Bridge Road 08-00 KH KEA Building
Singapore, Singapore

Subsidiaries:

Chronoswiss Asia Pte Ltd (1)
391 B Orchard Rd 18-06 Ngee Ann City Tower B
Singapore, 238874, Singapore
Tel.: (65) 62719600
Fax: (65) 62714711
E-Mail: enquiry@cortinawatch.com
Web Site: www.cortina.com.sg/2011/rn_cortina.htm
Emp.: 12
Chronoswiss Watches Whslr
S.I.C.: 5094
N.A.I.C.S.: 423940
Sharon Lim *(Exec Dir)*

Cortina Watch Pte Ltd. (1)
391B 15-01 LeeAnn Tower B
238874 Singapore, Singapore
Tel.: (65) 63399447
Fax: (65) 6563367913
E-Mail: enquiries@cortinawatch.com
Web Site: www.cortinawatch.com
Emp.: 30
Luxury Watch Distr
S.I.C.: 5094
N.A.I.C.S.: 423940
Anthony Keen Ban Lim *(CEO)*
Jit Yaw Lim *(COO)*

Pacific Time Pte Ltd. (1)
391B Orchard Rd No 18-06
Ngee Ann City Tower B, 238874 Singapore, Singapore
Tel.: (65) 62719600
Fax: (65) 62714711
E-Mail: enquiry@cortinawatch.com
Web Site: www.pacifictime.com.sg
Emp.: 100
Luxury Watch Distr
S.I.C.: 5094
N.A.I.C.S.: 423940
Sharon Yin Chian Lim *(Exec Dir)*

Non-U.S. Subsidiaries:

Cortina Watch Co., Ltd (1)
Room C 10F No 3 Section 1 Dunhua S Road
Songshan District, Taipei, Taiwan
Tel.: (886) 225796186
Fax: (886) 2 2579 6185
Emp.: 40
Watches & Clocks Whslr
S.I.C.: 5094
N.A.I.C.S.: 423940
Douglas Shih *(Mng Dir)*

Cortina Watch HK Limited (1)
53 Queen's Road
Central, China (Hong Kong)
Tel.: (852) 25220645
Fax: (852) 25228898
E-Mail: info@cortinawatch.com
Web Site: www.cortinawatch.com
Emp.: 8
Luxury Watch Distr
S.I.C.: 5094
N.A.I.C.S.: 423940
Lee Wai Chung *(Gen Mgr)*

Cortina Watch Sdn Bhd (1)
G32 KL Plaza
179 Jalan Bukit Bintang, 55100 Kuala Lumpur, Malaysia
Tel.: (60) 21455171
Web Site: www.blancpain.com
Luxury Watch Distr
S.I.C.: 5094
N.A.I.C.S.: 423940
Ivan Kin Chon Tshai *(Gen Mgr)*

Cortina Watch (Thailand) Co., Ltd. (1)
Room 110 112 116 1st Fl 494 Ploenchit Rd
Erawan, Bangkok, 10330, Thailand
Tel.: (66) 22507999
Fax: (66) 22507799
E-Mail: eiawan@cortina.com
Web Site: www.cortina.com
Emp.: 150
Luxury Watch Distr
S.I.C.: 5094
N.A.I.C.S.: 423940
Krist Chatikaratana *(Exec Dir)*

Pacific Time Co., Ltd (1)
7F1-2 No 21 Section 1 Tunhus South Road
Taipei, Taiwan
Tel.: (886) 2 25706789
Fax: (886) 2 25702341
Web Site: www.cortina.com.sg/2005/rn_cortina.htm
Watches & Parts Whslr
S.I.C.: 5094
N.A.I.C.S.: 423940
Douglas Shih *(Mng Dir)*

CORTUS ENERGY AB

Skalholtsgatan 2
Kista, 16440 Stockholm, Sweden
Tel.: (46) 8 588 866 30
Fax: (46) 8 752 8105
Web Site: www.cortus.se
CE—(OMX)

Business Description:
Gas Power
S.I.C.: 4924
N.A.I.C.S.: 221210

Personnel:
Rolf Ljunggren *(Mng Dir)*
Mats Thideman *(CFO)*

CORUM GROUP LIMITED

Level 17 24 Campbell Street
Sydney, NSW, 2000, Australia
Mailing Address:
PO Box K404
Sydney, NSW, 1240, Australia
Tel.: (61) 2 9289 4699
Fax: (61) 2 9212 5931
Web Site: www.corumgroup.com.au
COO—(ASX)
Rev.: $22,267,593
Assets: $26,381,804
Liabilities: $9,335,132
Net Worth: $17,046,672
Earnings: $6,622,546
Fiscal Year-end: 06/30/13

Business Description:
Software Development Services
S.I.C.: 7371
N.A.I.C.S.: 541511

Personnel:
Geoffrey John Broomhead *(Mng Dir)*
David Clarke *(CFO)*
George Nicolaou *(Sec)*

Board of Directors:
Michael John Shehadie
Geoffrey John Broomhead
Michael A. Cleary

CORUM WATCHES S.A.R.L.

1 Rue Du Petit Chateau
2301 La Chaux-de-Fonds, Switzerland
Tel.: (41) 329670670
Fax: (41) 329670600
E-Mail: info@corum.ch
Web Site: www.corum.ch
Emp.: 100

Business Description:
Mfr. & Seller of Watches
S.I.C.: 3829
N.A.I.C.S.: 334519

Personnel:
Serge Weinberg *(Chm)*
Antonio Calce *(CEO)*

Board of Directors:
Serge Weinberg
Richard Tomlin, Jr.

U.S. Subsidiary:

Corum USA LLC (1)
12 H Mauchly
Irvine, CA 92618 (100%)
Tel.: (949) 788-6200
Fax: (949) 453-9345
E-Mail: info@corum.ch
Web Site: www.corumtimepieces.com
Sales Range: $10-24.9 Million
Emp.: 15
Watches & Parts Distr
S.I.C.: 5094
N.A.I.C.S.: 423940

CORUS ENTERTAINMENT INC.

Corus Quay 25 Dockside Drive
Toronto, ON, M5A 0B5, Canada
Tel.: (416) 479-7000
Fax: (416) 479-7006
Web Site: www.corusent.com
Year Founded: 1999
CJR.B—(OTC TSX)
Rev.: $722,664,598
Assets: $1,971,896,823
Liabilities: $873,940,664
Net Worth: $1,097,956,159
Earnings: $149,066,363
Emp.: 1,523
Fiscal Year-end: 08/31/13

Business Description:
Media & Entertainment Services
S.I.C.: 4833
N.A.I.C.S.: 515120

Personnel:
Heather A. Shaw *(Chm)*
Julie M. Shaw *(Vice Chm)*
John M. Cassaday *(Pres & CEO)*
Thomas C. Peddie *(CFO & Exec VP)*
Doug Murphy *(COO & Exec VP)*
Scott Dyer *(CTO & Exec VP-Strategic Plng)*
Kathleen McNair *(Chief Integration Officer & Exec VP-HR & Corp Comm)*
Chris Pandoff *(Pres-Corus Radio)*
Gary A. Maavara *(Gen Counsel, Sec & Exec VP)*

Board of Directors:
Heather A. Shaw
Fernand Belisle
John M. Cassaday
Dennis M. Erker
Carolyn Hursh
Barry James
Wendy A. Leaney
Ronald D. Rogers
Catherine Roozen
Terrance E. Royer
Julie M. Shaw

Transfer Agent:
CST Trust Company
PO Box 700 Station B
Montreal, QC, Canada

Division:

Womens Network (1)
25 Dockside Dr
Toronto, ON, M5A 0, Canada (100%)
Tel.: (416) 479-7000
Fax: (416) 533-0346
E-Mail: comments@wnetwork.com
Web Site: www.wnetwork.com
Emp.: 400
Television Service Specialized for Women
S.I.C.: 4833
N.A.I.C.S.: 515120
Joanne Webb *(VP-Programming)*

Subsidiaries:

CFNY-FM Radio (1)
1 Dundas St W Ste 1600
Toronto, ON, M5G 1Z3, Canada
Tel.: (416) 408-3343
Fax: (416) 847-3300
E-Mail: info@edge.ca
Web Site: www.edge.ca
Sales Range: $10-24.9 Million
Emp.: 200
Radio Broadcasting
S.I.C.: 4832
N.A.I.C.S.: 515112
Kelly Beveridge *(Dir-Prog & Interactions)*

CHEX Television - Peterborough (1)
743 Monaghan Rd
Peterborough, ON, K9J 5K2, Canada
Tel.: (705) 742-0451
Fax: (705) 742-7274
E-Mail: michael.harris@corusent.com
Web Site: www.chextv.com
Emp.: 80
Television Broadcasting Network Services
S.I.C.: 4833
N.A.I.C.S.: 515120
Michael Harris *(Gen Mgr)*

CHEX TV - Durham (1)
10 Simcoe St N
Oshawa, ON, L1G 4R8, Canada
Tel.: (905) 434-5030
Fax: (905) 432-3315
Web Site: www.channel12.ca
Emp.: 15
Television Broadcasting Network Services
S.I.C.: 4833
N.A.I.C.S.: 515120
Elaine Garnett *(Gen Mgr-Sls)*

CKWS TV - Kingston (1)
170 Queen St Kingston
Kingston, ON, K7K 1B2, Canada
Tel.: (613) 544-2340
Fax: (613) 544-5508
Web Site: www.ckwstv.com
Emp.: 50
Television Broadcasting Network Services
S.I.C.: 4833
N.A.I.C.S.: 515120
Michael Harris *(Gen Mgr)*

Corus Premium Television Ltd. (1)
25 Dockside Dr
Toronto, ON, M5A 0B5, Canada (100%)
Tel.: (416) 479-6784
E-Mail: info@moviecentral.ca
Web Site: www.moviecentral.ca
Rev.: $23,628,393
Emp.: 85
Television Programming
S.I.C.: 4841
N.A.I.C.S.: 515210

Corus Radio Ltd. (1)
5204 84th St
Edmonton, AB, T6E 5N8, Canada (100%)
Tel.: (780) 440-6300
Fax: (780) 469-5937
E-Mail: info@corusent.com
Emp.: 110
Operate Twelve Radio Stations & Three Radio Networks
S.I.C.: 4833
N.A.I.C.S.: 515120
Chris Pandoff *(Pres)*
John M. Cassaday *(CEO)*

Nelvana Limited (1)
25 Dockside Dr
Toronto, ON, M5A 0B5, Canada
Tel.: (416) 479-7000
Fax: (416) 530-2832
Web Site: www.nelvana.com
Emp.: 1,200
Animation Programme Production Services
S.I.C.: 7819
N.A.I.C.S.: 512191
Colin Bohm *(Mng Dir)*

Telelatino Network Inc. (1)
5125 Steeles Ave W
North York, ON, M9L 1R5, Canada
Tel.: (416) 744-8200
Fax: (416) 744-0966
E-Mail: info@tlntv.com
Web Site: www.tlntv.com
Emp.: 50
Television Broadcasting Network Services
S.I.C.: 4833
N.A.I.C.S.: 515120
Aldo Di Felice *(Pres)*

Joint Venture:

Canadian Broadcast Sales (1)
45 St Clair Ave W 5th Fl
Toronto, ON, M4V 1K9, Canada
Tel.: (416) 961-4770
Fax: (416) 960-9067
E-Mail: info@radiocbs.com
Web Site: www.radiocbs.com
Emp.: 32
National Radio Advertising Sales Representation; Owned 50% by Corus Entertainment Inc. & 50% by Rogers Communications, Inc.

Corus Entertainment Inc.—(Continued)

S.I.C.: 7313
N.A.I.C.S.: 541840
Patrick Grierson *(Pres)*
Jerome Gignac *(Exec VP & Mgr-Vancouver)*
Leon Hildebrandt *(Exec VP)*

U.S. Subsidiary:

Country Music Television Limited **(1)**
330 Commerce St
Nashville, TN 37201-1805
Tel.: (615) 335-8400
Fax: (615) 335-8620
E-Mail: info@cmt.com
Web Site: www.cmt.com
Emp.: 30
Television Broadcasting Network Services
S.I.C.: 4833
N.A.I.C.S.: 515120

CORVUS CAPITAL LTD.

3rd Fl 13 charles 2nd St
London, SW1Y 4QU, United Kingdom
Mailing Address:
Palm Chambers
Po Box 119 Road Town
Tortola, Virgin Islands (British)
Tel.: (44) 2074519800
Fax: (44) 2077475101
E-Mail: ir@corvus.com
Web Site: www.corvuscapital.com
Sales Range: $25-49.9 Million
Emp.: 18
Business Description:
Investment Management Services
S.I.C.: 6211
N.A.I.C.S.: 523999
Personnel:
Andrew Regan *(CEO)*

CORVUS GOLD INC.

Suite 1920 1188 West Georgia St
Vancouver, BC, V6E 4A2, Canada
Tel.: (604) 683-3246
Fax: (604) 408-7499
E-Mail: info@corvusgold.com
Web Site: www.corvusgold.com
Year Founded: 2010
KOR—(OTC TSX)
Business Description:
Gold Mining Services
S.I.C.: 1041
N.A.I.C.S.: 212221
Personnel:
Jeffery A. Pontius *(Chm & CEO)*
Russell B. Myers *(Pres)*
Peggy Wu *(CFO)*
Carl Brechtel *(COO)*
Lawrence W. Talbot *(Gen Counsel & VP)*
Marla K. Ritchie *(Sec)*
Board of Directors:
Jeffery A. Pontius
Steve K. Aaker
Anton J. Drescher
Catherine A. Gignac
Rowland Perkins
Ed Yarrow
Legal Counsel:
Gowlings, Lafleur Henderson LLP
Four Bentall Centre Suite 2300
1055 Dunsmuir Street, Vancouver, BC, V7X 1J1, Canada
Tel.: (604) 683-6498
Fax: (604) 683-3558
Transfer Agent:
Computershare Trust Company of Canada
510 Burrard St 2nd Fl
Vancouver, BC, Canada

COSALT PLC

Origin 4 Genesis Park Origin Way
Grimsby, Lincs, DN31 3NW, United Kingdom
Tel.: (44) 1472 725560
Fax: (44) 1472 725569
E-Mail: enquiries@cosalt.com
Web Site: www.cosalt.plc.uk
Year Founded: 1873
Business Description:
Holding Company
S.I.C.: 6719
N.A.I.C.S.: 551112
Personnel:
David Ross *(Chm)*
Denise Robinson *(Sec)*
Legal Counsel:
Wilkin Chapman
New Oxford House Osborne Street
Grimsby, DN31 1HE, United Kingdom
Pinsent Masons
1 Park Row
Leeds, United Kingdom
Subsidiaries:

Cosalt Ballyclare Limited **(1)**
Banner House Greg Street
Reddish, Stockport, SK5 7BP, United Kingdom UK
Tel.: (44) 1614291100
Fax: (44) 8708502378
Web Site: www.cosalt.com
Emp.: 40
Personal Protective Equipment & Workwear Mfr & Distr
S.I.C.: 5084
N.A.I.C.S.: 423830
John Crossland *(Mng Dir)*

COSAN LIMITED

Av Juscelino Kubitschek 1327 4th Floor
Sao Paulo, SP 04543-000, Brazil
Tel.: (55) 11 3897 9797
Fax: (55) 11 3897 9799
E-Mail: ri@cosan.com.br
Web Site: www.cosan.com.br
CZZ—(NYSE)
Sls.: $14,764,810,282
Assets: $16,624,067,418
Liabilities: $10,083,910,275
Net Worth: $6,540,157,143
Earnings: $471,082,561
Emp.: 34,227
Fiscal Year-end: 03/31/13
Business Description:
Holding Company; Sugar & Ethanol Production, Marketing & Distribution
S.I.C.: 6719
N.A.I.C.S.: 551112
Personnel:
Rubens Ometto Silveira Mello *(Chm & CEO)*
Marcus Vinicius Pratini de Moraes *(Vice Chm)*
Marcelo Eduardo Martins *(CFO & Chief IR Officer)*
Pedro Isamu Mizutani *(COO)*
Marcos Marinho Lutz *(Chief Comml Officer)*
Marcelo de Souza Scarcela Portela *(Legal Officer)*
Board of Directors:
Rubens Ometto Silveira Mello
Burkhard Otto Cordes
Roberto de Rezende Barbosa
Mailson Ferreira da Nobrega
Helio Franca Filho
Pedro Isamu Mizutani
Marcos Marinho Lutz
Marcelo Eduardo Martins
George E. Pataki
Marcus Vinicius Pratini de Moraes
Marcelo de Souza Scarcela Portela
Jose Alexandre Scheinkman
Serge Varsano
Subsidiaries:

Agricola Ponte Alta S.A. **(1)**
Pte Alta s/n Predio I Barra Bonita
Barra Bonita, 17340-000, Brazil
Tel.: (55) 1436044400
Sugarcane Farming Services
S.I.C.: 0133
N.A.I.C.S.: 111930

Centro de Tecnologia Canavieira S.A. **(1)**
Fazenda Santo Antonio S/N
Caixa Postal 162
Piracicaba, 13400-970, Brazil
Tel.: (55) 19 3429 8199
Fax: (55) 19 3429 8105
E-Mail: comunicacao@ctc.com.br
Web Site: www.ctcanavieira.com.br
Emp.: 200
Sugarcane Research & Development Services
S.I.C.: 8731
N.A.I.C.S.: 541711
Luis Roberto Pogetti *(Pres)*

Companhia de Gas de Sao Paulo - Comgas **(1)**
Rua Olimpiadas 205 10 andar Vila Olimpia
04551 000 Sao Paulo, Brazil (60.1%)
Tel.: (55) 1145045000
Fax: (55) 45045257
Web Site: www.comgas.com.br
CGAS3—(BRAZ)
Rev.: $2,596,944,568
Assets: $2,935,652,152
Liabilities: $1,825,322,136
Net Worth: $1,110,330,016
Earnings: $180,353,928
Emp.: 1,041
Fiscal Year-end: 12/31/12
Natural Gas Distr
S.I.C.: 4924
N.A.I.C.S.: 221210
Rubens Ometto Silveira Mello *(Pres)*
Luiz Augusto Domenech *(CEO)*
Luis Henrique Cals de Beauclair Guimaraes *(Mng Dir)*
Roberto Collares Lage *(CFO)*
Leonardo Serra Netto Lerner *(Chief Legal Officer)*

Cosan S.A. Industria e Comercio **(1)**
Av Juscelino Kubitschek 1726 6th Floor
04530-000 Sao Paulo, Brazil
Tel.: (55) 1138979797
Fax: (55) 1138979799
E-Mail: rosm@cosan.com.br
Web Site: www.cosan.com.br/ —(BRAZ)
Sugar Cane & Ethanol Producer
S.I.C.: 2061
N.A.I.C.S.: 311314
Rubens Ometto Silveira Mello *(CEO)*

Subsidiary:

Handson Participacoes S.A. **(2)**
Fazenda Pau Dalho S/N Sala 20 B Predio Administrativo
Barra Bonita, Sao Paulo, Brazil 17340-000
Tel.: (55) 51 3204 5500
Agricultural Chemical Product Mfr
S.I.C.: 2879
N.A.I.C.S.: 325320

Non-U.S. Subsidiaries:

Comma Oil & Chemicals Limited **(2)**
Dering Way
Gravesend, Kent, United Kingdom DA12 2QX
Tel.: (44) 1474 564 311
Fax: (44) 1474 333 000
E-Mail: enquiries@commaoil.com
Web Site: www.commaoil.com
Emp.: 210
Automotive Lubricant Distr
S.I.C.: 5172
N.A.I.C.S.: 424720

Cosan Cayman Finance Limited **(2)**
494 Shedden Road Suite 2
PO Box 11048
Georgetown, KY1-1007, Cayman Islands
Tel.: (345) 623 6700
Fax: (345) 769 6700
E-Mail: info@caymanfinances.com
Web Site: www.caymanfinances.com
Financial Management Services
S.I.C.: 6211
N.A.I.C.S.: 523999
Richard Coles *(Chm)*
David Roberts *(Treas)*

Esso Brasileira de Petroleo Limitada **(1)**
Rua Victor Civita 77 Bldg 1
22775-905 Rio de Janeiro, Barra da Tijuca, Brazil BR
Tel.: (55) 2134332000
Telex: 2123380 ESSO
Fax: (55) 34332037
Web Site: www.esso.com
Emp.: 1,500
Gasoline Service Stations
S.I.C.: 5541
N.A.I.C.S.: 447110

COSBOARD INDUSTRIES LIMITED.

16-10 1/5/345 1&2 Sai Krupa Market
Malakpet, Hyderabad, Andhra Pradesh, 500036, India
Tel.: (91) 40 64515015
Fax: (91) 40 24555528
E-Mail: info@cosboard.com
Web Site: www.cosboard.com
530859—(BOM)
Rev.: $4,151,853
Assets: $4,483,334
Liabilities: $4,152,861
Net Worth: $330,472
Earnings: ($7,073)
Fiscal Year-end: 03/31/13
Business Description:
Paper Board Mfr
S.I.C.: 2631
N.A.I.C.S.: 322130
Personnel:
Ratan Kumar Gilra *(Mng Dir)*
Board of Directors:
Ratan Kumar Gilra
Anil Kumar Gilra
Vijay Kumar
Mahadev Rathi
Lalit Narayan Sarda
Shiv Shankar Taparia
Transfer Agent:
Bigshare Services (P) Ltd
E-2/3 Ansa Industrial Estate Saki Vihar Road Sakinaka
Andheri East, Mumbai, India

COSCO CAPITAL, INC.

(Formerly Alcorn Gold Resources Corporation)
2F Tabacalera Building No 2
900 D Romualdez Sr Street Paco, Manila, 1007, Philippines
Tel.: (63) 2524 9236
Fax: (63) 2524 7452
Web Site:
COSCO—(PHI)
Sales Range: Less than $1 Million
Emp.: 10
Business Description:
Oil & Gas Exploration Services
S.I.C.: 1311
N.A.I.C.S.: 211111
Personnel:
Eduardo F. Hernandez *(Chm, Pres & CEO)*

COSCO (INDIA) LIMITED

2/8 Roop Nagar
Delhi, 110 007, India
Tel.: (91) 11 23843000
Fax: (91) 11 23846000
E-Mail: mail@cosco.in
Web Site: www.coscoindia.com
Year Founded: 1980
530545—(BOM)
Sales Range: $700-749.9 Million
Business Description:
Health & Fitness Equipment Mfr
S.I.C.: 3949
N.A.I.C.S.: 339920
Personnel:
Pankaj Jain *(Compliance Officer)*

COSEL CO., LTD.
1-6-43 Kamiakae-machi
Toyama, 930-0816, Japan
Tel.: (81) 76 432 8152
Fax: (81) 76 442 9660
E-Mail: sales@cosel.co.jp
Web Site: www.cosel.co.jp
6905—(TKS)
Sls.: $193,314,000
Assets: $418,187,000
Liabilities: $29,832,000
Net Worth: $388,355,000
Earnings: $16,632,000
Emp.: 421
Fiscal Year-end: 05/31/13
Business Description:
Industrial Machinery Mfr
S.I.C.: 3613
N.A.I.C.S.: 335313
Personnel:
Toshimichi Machino *(Chm)*
Keiichi Fukumura *(Vice Chm)*
Masato Tanikawa *(CEO)*
Board of Directors:
Toshimichi Machino
Keiichi Fukumura
Satoshi Kiyosawa
Yukichi Konishi
Morio Saito
Yutaka Tamo
Masato Tanikawa
Takashi Yamakage
Isao Yasuda

Non-U.S. Subsidiaries:

Cosel Asia Ltd. **(1)**
Rm 601 9 Chong Yip St
Kwun Tong, Kowloon, China (Hong Kong)
Tel.: (852) 23052712
Fax: (852) 23053006
E-Mail: sales@coselasia.com
Web Site: www.coselasia.com
Emp.: 8
Power Supplies Mfr
S.I.C.: 3612
N.A.I.C.S.: 335311
Tatsuo Yamamoto *(Mng Dir)*

Cosel Europe GmbH **(1)**
Berner Str 51
60437 Frankfurt am Main, Hesse, Germany
Tel.: (49) 699500790
Fax: (49) 6950830200
E-Mail: sales@cosel.de
Web Site: www.coseleurope.eu
Emp.: 7
Power Supplies Mfr
S.I.C.: 3612
N.A.I.C.S.: 335311
Masahiro Miyamae *(Mng Dir)*

Cosel (Shanghai) Electronics Co., Ltd. **(1)**
Rm 3F2 Zhao Feng Universe Bldg
1800 Zhong Shan W Rd, Shanghai, 200235, China
Tel.: (86) 2164400381
Fax: (86) 2164400380
E-Mail: sales@coselasia.com
Web Site: www.coselasia.com
Emp.: 10
Power Supplies Mfr
S.I.C.: 3612
N.A.I.C.S.: 335311
Leo Au *(Mng Dir)*

COSET INC.
958-3 Daechon-dong Buk-gu
Technopark Venture Centre 2F
Gwangju, 500-706, Korea (South)
Tel.: (82) 62 6027765
Fax: (82) 62 6027770
E-Mail: info@coset.com
Web Site: www.coset.com
Year Founded: 1999
189350—(KRS)
Business Description:
Packaging Solutions & Services
S.I.C.: 2671
N.A.I.C.S.: 326112
Personnel:
Chi-Hyung Oh *(Chm)*
Jae-Hun Kim *(CEO)*

COSIGO RESOURCES LTD.
Suite 1500 885 West Georgia Street
Vancouver, BC, V6C 3E8, Canada
Tel.: (604) 515-5970
Toll Free: (877) 866-8688
E-Mail: info@cosigo.com
Web Site: www.cosigo.com
CSG—(TSXV)
Assets: $2,026,881
Liabilities: $148,044
Net Worth: $1,878,837
Earnings: ($3,301,337)
Fiscal Year-end: 12/31/12
Business Description:
Gold Exploration Services
S.I.C.: 1041
N.A.I.C.S.: 212221
Personnel:
Dennis W. Milburn *(Pres & CEO)*
Christine K. M. Aney *(CFO & Sec)*
Joseph Hilton Montgomery *(Exec VP)*
Board of Directors:
Magnus Haglund
Dennis W. Milburn
Joseph Hilton Montgomery
Patrick R. Mooney
Andres M. Rendle
Edward G. Robinson
Legal Counsel:
McCullough O'Connor Irwin, LLP
Ste 2610 Oceanic Plz 1066 W Hastings St
Vancouver, BC, V6E 3X1, Canada
Cardenas & Cardenas Abogados Ltda
Carrera 7a No 71-52 Torre B - PISO 9
Bogota, DC, Colombia
Transfer Agent:
Computershare Trust Company of Canada
600 538th Ave SW
Calgary, AB, Canada

COSLIGHT TECHNOLOGY INTERNATIONAL GROUP LIMITED
No 68 Dianlan Street Xuefu Road
Nangang District, Harbin, China 150086
Tel.: (86) 451 86677970
Fax: (86) 451 86678032
Web Site: www.cncoslight.com
Year Founded: 1994
1043—(HKG)
Rev.: $424,946,624
Assets: $906,279,598
Liabilities: $646,170,348
Net Worth: $260,109,250
Earnings: ($248,124)
Emp.: 9,452
Fiscal Year-end: 12/31/12
Business Description:
Battery Mfr
S.I.C.: 3691
N.A.I.C.S.: 335911
Personnel:
Dian Quan Song *(Co-Founder & Chm)*
Ke Xue Li *(Co-Founder & Deputy Gen Mgr)*
Ming Hua Luo *(Deputy Chairman & CEO)*
Kar Keung Ng *(Sec)*
Board of Directors:
Dian Quan Song
Ke Xue Li
Zeng Lin Li
Xing Quan Liu
Ming Hua Luo
Jian Min Xiao
Kai Xing
Ge Ping Yin
Li Ming Zhang
Legal Counsel:
DLA Piper Hong Kong
17/F Edinburgh Tower The Landmark 15 Queen's Road
Central, China (Hong Kong)
Butterfield Corporate Services Limited
Rosebank Centre, 11 Bermudiana Road
Pembroke, Bermuda
Transfer Agents:
Tricor Secretaries Limited
26th Floor Tesbury Centre 28 Queens Rd E
Hong Kong, China (Hong Kong)
Butterfield Corporate Services Limited
Rosebank Centre, 11 Bermudiana Road
Pembroke, Bermuda

COSMO BIO CO., LTD.
Toyo-Ekimae Bldg 2-20 Toyo 2-Chome Koto-ku
Tokyo, 135-0016, Japan
Tel.: (81) 3 5632 9617
Fax: (81) 3 5632 9618
E-Mail: export@cosmobio.co.jp
Web Site: www.cosmobio.co.jp
Year Founded: 1978
3386—(JAS)
Sales Range: $75-99.9 Million
Business Description:
Research Reagents Sales & Services
S.I.C.: 8731
N.A.I.C.S.: 541711
Personnel:
Toshiaki Kasamatsu *(Pres)*

U.S. Subsidiary:

Cosmo Bio USA, Inc. **(1)**
2792 Loker Ave W Ste 101
Carlsbad, CA 92010
Tel.: (760) 431-4600
Fax: (760) 431-4604
E-Mail: info@cosmobiousa.com
Web Site: www.cosmobiousa.com
Chemical Product Mfr
S.I.C.: 2899
N.A.I.C.S.: 325998
Haruhisa Sakurai, *(Pres & CEO)*
Yoshi Takehana *(CFO)*

COSMO COMMUNICATIONS CORPORATON
Unit 2 - 55 Travail Road
Markham, ON, L3S-3J1, Canada
Tel.: (905) 209-0488
Fax: (905) 209-0489
E-Mail: info@cosmocanada.ca
Web Site: www.cosmocanada.ca
Year Founded: 1983
CSMO—(OTC)
Sales Range: $10-24.9 Million
Emp.: 14
Business Description:
Consumer Electronic Equipment Mfr
S.I.C.: 3679
N.A.I.C.S.: 334419
Personnel:
Peter Horak *(CEO)*

COSMO COMMUNICATIONS INC.
Aoyama Tower Building 10th & 11th Floors 2-24-15 Minami-Aoyama
Minato-ku, Tokyo, 107-0062, Japan
Tel.: (81) 3 3405 8111
Fax: (81) 3 3405 8215
E-Mail: info@comnet.co.jp
Web Site: www.cosmo-com.jp
Year Founded: 1966
Sales Range: $50-74.9 Million
Emp.: 85
Business Description:
Advertising Agency
S.I.C.: 7311
N.A.I.C.S.: 541810
Personnel:
Iehito Edahiro *(Pres)*

COSMO ELECTRONICS CORPORATION
8F No 258 Lian Cheng Rd
Chang-Hua, Taipei, Taiwan
Tel.: (886) 282271877
Fax: (886) 282271855
Web Site: www.cosmo-ic.com
2466—(TAI)
Sales Range: $25-49.9 Million
Business Description:
Light Emitting Diode Mfr
S.I.C.: 3674
N.A.I.C.S.: 334413
Personnel:
Kenneth Tsai *(Chm)*
Morris Wang *(CFO)*

Plant:

Cosmo Electronics Corp. - Yilan Plant **(1)**
No 396 Lupu Road
Dongshan, Yilan, Taiwan
Tel.: (886) 39583455
Fax: (886) 39583521
E-Mail: peggy_kuo@cosmo-ic.com
Web Site: www.cosmo.com.tw
Circuit Relays Mfr
S.I.C.: 3625
N.A.I.C.S.: 335314

COSMO FILMS LTD.
1008 DLF Tower A Jasola District Centre
New Delhi, 110 025, India
Tel.: (91) 1149494949
Fax: (91) 1149494950
Web Site: www.cosmofilms.com
COSMOFILMS—(NSE)
Rev.: $244,459,170
Assets: $191,306,844
Liabilities: $127,058,328
Net Worth: $64,248,516
Earnings: $2,100,582
Emp.: 642
Fiscal Year-end: 03/31/13
Business Description:
Packaging Films Mfr
S.I.C.: 2672
N.A.I.C.S.: 322220
Personnel:
Ashok Jaipuria *(Chm & Mng Dir)*
Pankaj Poddar *(Pres & CEO)*
Neeraj Jain *(CFO)*
Jyoti Dixit *(Compliance Officer & Sec)*
Govi Reddy *(Pres-US)*
Tanuj Agarwal *(Sr VP-Subsidiary & Exports)*
Board of Directors:
Ashok Jaipuria
Badri Agarwal
H. K. Agrawal
Rajeev Gupta
Anil Kumar Jain
Surinder Kapur
Alpana Parida
Suresh Chandra Rajpal
Rangarajan Vasudevan
Transfer Agent:
Alankit Assignments Limited
Alankit House 2E/21Jhandewalan Extention
New Delhi, India

Subsidiary:

Cosmo Ferrites Ltd. **(1)**
Jabli
Solan, Himachal Pradesh, 173209, India
Tel.: (91) 1792 277231
Fax: (91) 1792277234
E-Mail: plant@cosmoferrites.com
Web Site: www.cosmoferrites.com
523100—(BOM)
Rev.: $9,160,002
Assets: $10,824,746
Liabilities: $6,743,480

Cosmo Films Ltd.—(Continued)

Net Worth: $4,081,266
Earnings: ($308,153)
Emp.: 300
Fiscal Year-end: 03/31/13
Soft Ferrites Mfr
S.I.C.: 3999
N.A.I.C.S.: 339999
Ambrish Jaipuria *(CEO & Dir-Bus Dev)*
Neha Pawar *(Sec)*

COSMO MOTORS LTD

3511 No 3 Road
Richmond, BC, V6X 2B8, Canada
Tel.: (604) 273-0333
Fax: (604) 273-0317
Toll Free: (877) 780-6994
Year Founded: 1993
Rev.: $35,212,705
Emp.: 70

Business Description:
New & Used Car Dealers
S.I.C.: 5511
N.A.I.C.S.: 441110

Personnel:
Thomas Glen *(Owner)*

COSMO OIL COMPANY, LIMITED

1-1-1 Shibaura
Minato-ku, Tokyo, 105-8528, Japan
Tel.: (81) 3 3798 3211
Fax: (81) 3 3798 3841
E-Mail: webmaster@cosmo-oil.co.jp
Web Site: www.cosmo-oil.co.jp
Year Founded: 1986
5007—(NGO OTC TKS)
Sls.: $34,833,579,000
Assets: $19,178,412,000
Liabilities: $16,352,160,000
Net Worth: $2,826,252,000
Earnings: ($944,702,000)
Emp.: 6,496
Fiscal Year-end: 03/31/13

Business Description:
Petroleum Trading, Refining & Marketing Services
Import Export
S.I.C.: 2911
N.A.I.C.S.: 324110

Personnel:
Yaichi Kimura *(Chm)*
Keizo Morikawa *(Pres & CEO)*
Hiroshi Kiriyama *(Sr Exec Officer-Corp Plng Unit)*
Hisashi Kobayashi *(Sr Exec Officer-Supply Bus Unit)*
Isao Kusakabe *(Sr Exec Officer-Resources E&P Bus Unit)*
Hideto Matsumura *(Sr Mng Exec Officer-Risk Mgmt, Tech & Res Unit)*
Hirohiko Ogiwara *(Sr Exec Officer-Sls Bus Unit)*
Yasushi Ohe *(Sr Exec Officer-Project Dev Bus Unit)*
Muneyuki Sano *(Sr Exec Officer)*
Atsuto Tamura *(Sr Mng Exec Officer-Corp Mgmt Unit)*

Board of Directors:
Yaichi Kimura
Mohamed Al Hamli
Mohamed Hamad Al Mehairi
Hiroshi Kiriyama
Hisashi Kobayashi
Isao Kusakabe
Hideto Matsumura
Keizo Morikawa
Hirohiko Ogiwara
Atsuto Tamura

Subsidiaries:

CM Aromatics Co Ltd (1)
1 1 1 Shibaura
Minato-ku, Tokyo, 105 8528, Japan
Tel.: (81) 337983262
Fax: (81) 337983157
Web Site: www.cosmo-oil.co.jp/eng/company/group.html
Emp.: 3
Oil Refining Services
S.I.C.: 1389
N.A.I.C.S.: 213112
Keizo Morikawa *(Pres)*

Cosmo Business Support Co., Ltd. (1)
2 2 2 Kaji cho
Tokyo, Chiyodaku, 101 0044, Japan
Tel.: (81) 332516714
Fax: (81) 332516724
Web Site: www.cosmo-business-support.co.jp
Emp.: 60
Brokerage & management of real estate
S.I.C.: 6531
N.A.I.C.S.: 531210
Hiroshi Matsushita *(Mgr)*

COSMO COMPUTER CENTER CO., LTD. (1)
2-35-4 Hama-cho Nihonbashi
Chuo-ku, Tokyo, Japan
Tel.: (81) 356421311
Web Site: www.cosmo-oil.co.jp/eng/company/group.html
Computer Software Development Services
S.I.C.: 7371
N.A.I.C.S.: 541511

Cosmo Delivery Service Co., Ltd. (1)
Chiba Makuhari Techno Garden D Ridge 6th Fl
1 3 Nakase Mihama-ku, Chiba, 261 8501, Japan
Tel.: (81) 433513351
Web Site: www.cosmo-oil.co.jp/eng/company/group.html
Delivery Service
S.I.C.: 4215
N.A.I.C.S.: 492210

Cosmo Energy Exploration and Development Ltd. (1)
2 2 24 Higashi Shinagawa
Tennouzu Central Tower, Tokyo, 140 0002, Japan
Tel.: (81) 367180950
Fax: (81) 367180951
E-Mail: osamu_idachita@cosmo-oil.co.jp
Crude Oil Development
S.I.C.: 2999
N.A.I.C.S.: 324199

Cosmo Engineering Co., Ltd. (1)
2 5 8 Higashi-Shinagawa, Shinagawa ku
Tokyo, 140 0002, Japan
Tel.: (81) 354620150
Fax: (81) 354620159
E-Mail: s_nakayama@cosmoeng.co.jp
Web Site: www.cosmoeng.co.jp
Emp.: 500
General plant and equipment engineering
S.I.C.: 2869
N.A.I.C.S.: 325110
Yasuo Sakata *(Chm)*
Hiroaki Sugioka *(Pres)*

Cosmo Kaiun Co., Ltd. (1)
Tokyo Sawanotsuru Ningyo-cho Bldg
1 3 8 Ningyo-cho Nihonbashi, Tokyo, 103 0013, Japan
Tel.: (81) 336620591
Fax: (81) 336620596
Web Site: www.cosmo-kaiun.co.jp
Emp.: 100
Marine transportation and shipping agency
S.I.C.: 4491
N.A.I.C.S.: 488320

Cosmo Matsuyama Oil Co., Ltd. (1)
3 580 Okaga
Matsuyama, Ehime, 791 8057, Japan
Tel.: (81) 899511111
Fax: (81) 899531535
Web Site: www.cosmo-oil.co.jp/eng/company/group.html
Emp.: 150
Oil Refining Services
S.I.C.: 1311
N.A.I.C.S.: 211111
Hiroyuki Tabuchi *(Gen Mgr)*

Cosmo Oil Ashmore, Ltd (1)
2-2-24 Higashi-Shinagawa Tennouzu Central Tower
Shinagawa-ku, Tokyo, Japan
Tel.: (81) 367180950
Fax: (81) 367180951
Web Site: www.cosmo-oil.co.jp/eng/company/group.html
Emp.: 10
Oil Exploration Services
S.I.C.: 1389
N.A.I.C.S.: 213112
Hideo Matsushita *(Pres)*

Cosmo Oil Lubricants Co., Ltd. (1)
5-33-7 Shiba
Minato-ku, Tokyo, 108-0014, Japan
Tel.: (81) 337983831
Fax: (81) 337983185
Web Site: www.cosmo-lube.co.jp
Emp.: 80
Lubricating Oil Mfr
S.I.C.: 2992
N.A.I.C.S.: 324191
Torigoe Shiyunsuke *(Pres)*

Cosmo Oil Sales Co., Ltd. (1)
Tokyo Tennouzu Yusen Bldg 20th Fl
2-2-20 Higashi Shinagawa, Tokyo, 140 8628, Japan
Tel.: (81) 367101616
Fax: (81) 367101617
E-Mail: info@cosmo-sales.com
Web Site: www.cosmo-sales.com
Emp.: 1,790
Oil Products Selling
S.I.C.: 1389
N.A.I.C.S.: 213112

COSMO PETRO SERVICE CO., LTD. (1)
2 Goikaigan
Ichihara, Chiba, Japan
Tel.: (81) 436210452
Web Site: www.cosmo-oil.co.jp/eng/company/group.html
Petroleum Refinery Services
S.I.C.: 2911
N.A.I.C.S.: 324110

Cosmo Petroleum Gas Co., Ltd . (1)
5-29-14 Shiba Minato-ku
Tokyo, Japan
Tel.: (81) 337983171
Fax: (81) 337982137
Emp.: 50
Import & Sales of LPG
S.I.C.: 1389
N.A.I.C.S.: 213112
Tamba Yoshini *(Gen Mgr)*

Cosmo Research Institute (1)
4-9-25 Shibaura Minato-ku
Tokyo, 108 8564, Japan
Tel.: (81) 337983552
Fax: (81) 337983288
E-Mail: mitsunori_tomida@cosmo-oil.co.jp
Web Site: www.cosmo-oil.co.jp/eng/company/group.html
Emp.: 50
Research And Technical Cooperation
S.I.C.: 8999
N.A.I.C.S.: 541690
Mitsunori Tomida *(Mgr-Gen Affairs)*

Cosmo Techno Yokkaichi Co., Ltd. (1)
1-1 Daikyo-cho
Yokkaichi, Mie, Japan
Tel.: (81) 593548773
Web Site: www.cosmo-oil.co.jp/eng/company/group.html
Petroleum Refinery Services
S.I.C.: 2911
N.A.I.C.S.: 324110

Cosmo Trade and Service Co., Ltd. (1)
2 5 8 Higashi Shinagawa 2-chome
Shinagawa, Tokyo, 140 8614, Japan
Tel.: (81) 354622800
Fax: (81) 354622809
E-Mail: info@cosmo-trade.com
Web Site: www.cosmo-trade.com
Emp.: 120
General trading
S.I.C.: 1799
N.A.I.C.S.: 238990
Yoshihisa Matsumiya *(Pres)*

Hokuto Kogyo Co.,Ltd. (1)
6 4 1 Nanaehama
Hokuto, Hokkaido, 049 0111, Japan
Tel.: (81) 138492021
Fax: (81) 138493348
E-Mail: info@hokuto-kougyo.co.jp
Web Site: www.hokuto-kougyo.co.jp
Construction, oil receiving & shipment works
S.I.C.: 4491
N.A.I.C.S.: 488320
Asai Tetsu *(Pres)*

KANSAI COSMO LOGISTICS CO., LTD. (1)
3-14, Chikkoshin-machi
Nishi-ku, Sakai, Osaka, Japan
Tel.: (81) 722470803
Petroleum Refinery Services
S.I.C.: 2911
N.A.I.C.S.: 324110

SAKAIDE COSMO KOSAN CO., LTD. (1)
1-1 Bannosu-Midori-cho
Sakaide, Kagawa, Japan
Tel.: (81) 877467119
Web Site: www.cosmo-oil.co.jp/eng/company/group.html
Marine Transportation Services
S.I.C.: 4412
N.A.I.C.S.: 483111

Joint Venture:

SBI ALApromo Co., Ltd. (1)
Izumi Garden Tower 1-6-1 Roppongi
Minato-ku, Tokyo, Japan
Tel.: (81) 362290095
Fax: (81) 335890761
Web Site: www.sbi-alapromo.co.jp
Emp.: 37
Development, Manufacturing & Distribution of Cosmetics, Health Foods, Dietary Supplements & Medicines Containing 5-Aminolevulinic Acid; Joint Venture of SBI Holdings, Inc. & COSMO OIL Co., Ltd.
S.I.C.: 2099
N.A.I.C.S.: 311999
Yoshitaka Kitao *(Pres & CEO)*
Satafumi Kawata *(COO)*
Tohru Tanaka *(CTO)*

U.S. Subsidiaries:

Cosmo Oil of U.S.A Inc (1)
21250 Hawthorne Blvd Ste 550
Torrance, CA 90503
Tel.: (310) 792-3863
Fax: (310) 792-3906
Crude Oil Merchants & Whslr
S.I.C.: 1389
N.A.I.C.S.: 213112

Non-U.S. Subsidiaries:

Cosmo Oil International Pte Ltd (1)
6 Battery Road Ste 26-06
049909 Singapore, Singapore
Tel.: (65) 63243722
Fax: (65) 63241022
Web Site: www.cosmo-oil.co.jp/eng/company/group.html
Emp.: 8
Crude Oil Merchants & Whslr
S.I.C.: 1389
N.A.I.C.S.: 213112
Kenichi Abe *(Mng Dir)*
T Abe *(Mng Dir)*

Cosmo Oil (Shanghai) Co., Ltd. (1)
Room 4105A Band Center
222 Yan An East Road, Shanghai, 200002, China
Tel.: (86) 21 6335 0206
Web Site: www.cosmo-oil.co.jp/eng/company/office.html
Oil Distr
S.I.C.: 4612
N.A.I.C.S.: 486110

Cosmo Oil U K PLC (1)
7 Old Park Ln
London, W1K 1QR, United Kingdom
Tel.: (44) 2076293031
Fax: (44) 2074913205
Web Site: www.cosmo-oil.co.jp
Emp.: 3
Crude Oil Merchants & Whslr
S.I.C.: 1389
N.A.I.C.S.: 213112
Hidefumi Takasu *(Mng Dir)*

COSMO PHARMACEUTICALS S.P.A.

Via C Colombo 1
I-20020 Lainate, Italy
Tel.: (39) 0293337614
Fax: (39) 0293337663
E-Mail: info@cosmopharmaceuticals.com
Web Site: www.cosmopharmaceuticals.com
COPN—(SWX)
Rev.: $80,146,923
Assets: $204,409,184
Liabilities: $36,675,055
Net Worth: $167,734,128
Earnings: $26,013,389
Emp.: 160
Fiscal Year-end: 12/31/12

Business Description:
Pharmaceuticals Mfr
S.I.C.: 5912
N.A.I.C.S.: 446110

Personnel:
Mauro Severino Ajani *(Chm & CEO)*
Hans Christoph Tanner *(CFO)*
Giuseppe Cipriano *(COO)*
Giuseppe Celasco *(Chief Medical Officer)*
Luigi Moro *(Chief Scientific Officer)*
Roberto Villa *(Chief Mfg Officer)*

Board of Directors:
Mauro Severino Ajani
Gianluigi Bertolli
Alessandro E. Della Cha
Dieter A. Enkelmann
Maria Grazia Roncarolo
Hans Christoph Tanner
Friedrich von Bohlen und Halbach

Subsidiaries:

Cosmo Research & Development S.R.L. **(1)**
Via Cristoforo Colombo 1
Lainate, 20020 Milan, Italy
Tel.: (39) 0293337276
Fax: (39) 02 9333 7663
Pharmaceutical Products Whslr
S.I.C.: 5122
N.A.I.C.S.: 424210

Cosmo S.p.A., **(1)**
Via Cristoforo Colombo 1
Lainate, 20020 Milan, Italy
Tel.: (39) 0293337614
Fax: (39) 0293337663
E-Mail: info@cosmopharmaceuticals.com
Emp.: 20
Parmaceutical Products Whslr
S.I.C.: 5122
N.A.I.C.S.: 424210
Gian Carlo Naccari *(Mgr-Mktg)*

COSMOS INITIA CO., LTD.

Shintamachi Bldg Shiba 5-34-6
Minato-ku
Tokyo, 108-8416, Japan
Tel.: (81) 3 3571 1111
Web Site: www.cigr.co.jp
Year Founded: 1969
8844—(JAS)
Sls.: $944,064,000
Assets: $529,870,000
Liabilities: $385,671,000
Net Worth: $144,199,000
Earnings: ($11,803,000)
Emp.: 239
Fiscal Year-end: 03/31/13

Business Description:
Real Estate Brokerage
S.I.C.: 6531
N.A.I.C.S.: 531210

Personnel:
Yoshiyuki Takagi *(Pres)*
Koji Kashiwagi *(Officer)*
Etsuko Souchi *(Officer)*
Hidenobu Tsuda *(Officer)*

Board of Directors:
Hisao Edahiro
Saburo Kobayashi
Shinichiro Kuwahara
Eiichi Shibata
Kei Sugitani
Yoshiyuki Takagi
Mototsugu Takai

COSMOS INSURANCE COMPANY PUBLIC LTD

46 Griva Digeni Avenue
1080 Nicosia, Cyprus
Tel.: (357) 22 796 000
Fax: (357) 22 022 000
E-Mail: info@cosmosinsurance.com.cy
Web Site: www.cosmosinsurance.com.cy
Year Founded: 1981
COS—(CYP)

Business Description:
Insurance Services
S.I.C.: 6411
N.A.I.C.S.: 524298

Personnel:
Andreas P. Erotokritou *(Chm)*
Andreas K. Tyllis *(Mng Dir)*
Elias Nissiotis *(CIO)*
Christiana A. Erotokritou *(Sec)*
Michael K. Tyllis *(Exec VP)*

Board of Directors:
Andreas P. Erotokritou
Costas Agathokleous
Andreas Efthimiou
Christiana A. Erotokritou
Frixos Kitromilides
Nikolaos Plakides
Michael Skoufarides
Andreas K. Tyllis
Michael K. Tyllis

COSMOS MACHINERY ENTERPRISES LIMITED

Units 1217 1223A 12th Floor Trade Square No 681 Cheung Sha Wan Road
Kowloon, China (Hong Kong)
Tel.: (852) 23766188
Fax: (852) 23759626
E-Mail: cmel@cosmel.com
Web Site: www.cosmel.com
0118—(HKG)
Sls.: $273,579,666
Assets: $364,430,503
Liabilities: $160,960,047
Net Worth: $203,470,456
Earnings: ($1,694,143)
Emp.: 6,000
Fiscal Year-end: 12/31/12

Business Description:
Industrial Machinery Mfr
S.I.C.: 5084
N.A.I.C.S.: 423830

Personnel:
To Tang *(Chm)*
Yiu Ming Wong *(CEO)*
Kar Shun Yip *(Mng Dir-Gainbase Industrial Limited)*
Ming Sang Wan *(Mng Dir)*
Kwong Sang Ho *(CFO & Co-Sec)*
Pui Ling Tam *(Co-Sec)*

Board of Directors:
To Tang
Tak Yin Cheng
Wei Sem Ho
Zhi Wei Huang
Wei Jiang
Wai Wah Kan
Jinping Qu
Freeman Yu Tang
Yiu Ming Wong
Ding Wu
Shuk Fan Yeung

Subsidiaries:

Cosmos i-Tech Solutions Ltd. **(1)**
8 Fl Tai Tung Indus Bldg 29-33 Tsing Yi Rd
Tsing Yi, New Territories, China (Hong Kong)
Tel.: (852) 23766160
Fax: (852) 23766161
E-Mail: sales.hk@cits.hk
Web Site: www.cits.hk
Information Technology Services
S.I.C.: 7371
N.A.I.C.S.: 541511
Anthony Chung *(CEO)*

Cosmos Machinery International Ltd. **(1)**
1 Fl Cheong Fat Factory Bldg 269-271 Un Chau St
Kowloon, China (Hong Kong)
Tel.: (852) 23608111
Fax: (852) 27854023
E-Mail: cmil@cmil.com.hk
Web Site: www.cmil.com.hk
Machinery Tools Distr
S.I.C.: 5084
N.A.I.C.S.: 423830

Cosmos Machinery Limited **(1)**
8 Fl Tai Tung Indus Bldg 29-33 Tsing Yi Rd
Tsing Yi, New Territories, China (Hong Kong)
Tel.: (852) 24312111
Fax: (852) 24361337
Industrial Machinery Mfr
S.I.C.: 3559
N.A.I.C.S.: 333249
Tang To *(Mng Dir)*

Gainbase Industrial Limited **(1)**
No 3-4 6 Fl World-Wide Indus Ctr 43-47 Shan Mei St
Shatin, Fotan, New Territories, China (Hong Kong)
Tel.: (852) 26011286
Fax: (852) 26012446
E-Mail: info@gainbase.com.cn
Web Site: www.gainbase.com
Emp.: 1,800
Printed Circuit Boards Mfr
S.I.C.: 3672
N.A.I.C.S.: 334412
Danny Yip Kar Shun *(Mng Dir)*

Great Wall (Holding) Company Limited **(1)**
Units 1217-1223A 12 /F Trade Square No 681 Cheung Sha Wan Road
Kowloon, New Territories, China (Hong Kong)
Tel.: (852) 23955265
Fax: (852) 7890727
Investment Holding Services
S.I.C.: 6799
N.A.I.C.S.: 523920

Great Wall (Optical) Plastic Works Ltd. **(1)**
Units 1110-1123 11/F Trade Square 681 Cheung Sha Wan Road
Kowloon, China (Hong Kong)
Tel.: (852) 23955265
Fax: (852) 27890727
E-Mail: greatwall@greatwalloptical.com.hk
Web Site: www.greatwalloptical.com.hk
Emp.: 10
Optical Instruments Mfr & Supplier
S.I.C.: 3827
N.A.I.C.S.: 333314
Eddie Chan *(Dir-Sls)*

Karmay Industrial Limited **(1)**
8 Fl Tai Tung Indus Bldg 29-33 Tsing Yi Rd
Tsing Yi, New Territories, China (Hong Kong)
Tel.: (852) 85224312111
Fax: (852) 23759626
E-Mail: cmel@cosmel.com
Web Site: www.cosmel.com
Emp.: 500
Plastic Products Mfr
S.I.C.: 2821
N.A.I.C.S.: 325211
Tang To *(Chm)*

Melco Industrial Supplies Co., Limited **(1)**
1st Fl Cheong Fat Factory Bldg 265-271 Un Chau St
Kowloon, China (Hong Kong)
Tel.: (852) 23610102
Fax: (852) 23861802
E-Mail: melco@melco.com.hk
Web Site: www.melco.com.hk
Fastener Products Distr
S.I.C.: 5072
N.A.I.C.S.: 423710

Ming Sun Enterprises (China) Limited **(1)**
unit 1110 Torade square 681 cheung sha wan road
Kowloon, China (Hong Kong)
Tel.: (852) 24312191
Fax: (852) 24350140
E-Mail: sales1@mingsun.com
Web Site: www.mingsun.com
Emp.: 1,700
Plastic Injection Molding Machinery Mfr
S.I.C.: 3559
N.A.I.C.S.: 333249
Walter Chan *(Mgr)*

Welltec Machinery Limited **(1)**
Units 1110-1123 11/F Trade Square No 681 Cheung Sha Wan Road
Kowloon, China (Hong Kong)
Tel.: (852) 24312198
Fax: (852) 24337060
E-Mail: info@welltec.com.hk
Web Site: www.welltec.com.hk
Injection Molding Machine Mfr
S.I.C.: 3559
N.A.I.C.S.: 333249

Non-U.S. Subsidiaries:

Dongguan Cosmos Plastics Products Company Ltd **(1)**
No 93 Shangye Rd 2 Yuwu Indus Dist
Dongcheng, Dongguan, Guangdong, 523117, China
Tel.: (86) 76922806036
Fax: (86) 76922428296
E-Mail: info_dc@cml.com.cn
Web Site: www.cosmos-plastics.com
Emp.: 120
Blow Molded Plastic Products Mfr
S.I.C.: 3053
N.A.I.C.S.: 339991
Frank Fang *(Mng Dir)*

Guangzhou Melco Industrial Supplies Co,, Ltd. **(1)**
Rm 904-905 9 Fl Newpoly Tower No 2 Zhongshan Liu Rd
Guangzhou, Guangdong, China
Tel.: (86) 2083266170
Fax: (86) 2083266180
E-Mail: gzmelco@melco.com.cn
Industrial Machinery & Tools Mfr & Distr
S.I.C.: 3559
N.A.I.C.S.: 333249

Karmay Plastic Products (Zhuhai) Co., Ltd **(1)**
No 7 Airport N Rd
Sanzao Town Jinwan Dist, Zhuhai, Guangdong, 519040, China
Tel.: (86) 7567630668
Fax: (86) 7567630688
E-Mail: lydia-fang@karmay.com.cn
Web Site: www.karmay.com.cn
Emp.: 400
Plastic Products Mfr
S.I.C.: 2821
N.A.I.C.S.: 325211
Steven Wong *(Mng Dir)*

Melco Industrial Supplies (Shanghai) Co., Ltd **(1)**
Flat B 9 Fl Datong Comml Tower
Shanghai, China
Tel.: (86) 2163201250
E-Mail: shmelco@melco.com.cn
Fastener Products Import & Distr
S.I.C.: 5084
N.A.I.C.S.: 423830

COSMOSTEEL HOLDINGS LIMITED

50 Raffles Place 06-00 Singapore Land Tower
Singapore, 048623, Singapore
Tel.: (65) 68631828
Fax: (65) 68612191
E-Mail: general@cosmosteel.com.sg

CosmoSteel Holdings Limited—(Continued)

Web Site: www.cosmosteel.com
B9S—(SES)
Rev.: $122,736,870
Assets: $151,636,534
Liabilities: $73,314,849
Net Worth: $78,321,686
Earnings: $5,016,296
Fiscal Year-end: 09/30/13
Business Description:
Piping System Components Mfr
S.I.C.: 1629
N.A.I.C.S.: 237110
Personnel:
Chin Sum Ong *(CEO)*
Laura Ying Shu Ng *(CFO)*
Pih Peng Lee *(Sec)*
Board of Directors:
Beng Tin Low
Chin Sum Ong
Geraldine Siew Ting Ong
Tong Hai Ong
Tong Yang Ong
Jovenal R. Santiago
Siok Chin Tan
Legal Counsel:
Lee & Lee
50 Raffles Place 06-00 Singapore Land Tower
Singapore, Singapore
Subsidiary:

Kim Seng Huat Hardware Pte Ltd (1)
14 Lok Yang Way
Singapore, 628633, Singapore
Tel.: (65) 68631828
Fax: (65) 68612191
E-Mail: sales@ksh.com.sg
Web Site: www.ksh.com.sg
Emp.: 100
Hardware Retailer
S.I.C.: 5251
N.A.I.C.S.: 444130

Non-U.S. Subsidiary:

CosmoSteel (Australia) Pty Ltd (1)
Biloela Industrial Estate Building 3 82 Biloela Street
Villawood, NSW, 2163, Australia
Tel.: (61) 2 9726 0115
Fax: (61) 2 9724 7115
E-Mail: salesaustralia@cosmosteel.com
Emp.: 4
Steel Structures Whslr
S.I.C.: 5051
N.A.I.C.S.: 423510
Louis Ferguson *(Mgr)*

COSMUR CONSTRUCTION (LONDON) LTD
Cosmur House 72 Salusbury Road
London, NW6 6NU, United Kingdom
Tel.: (44) 2076042277
Fax: (44) 2076042288
E-Mail: info@cosmur.co.uk
Web Site: www.cosmur.co.uk
Year Founded: 1973
Rev.: $28,131,956
Emp.: 53
Business Description:
Construction Materials Distr
S.I.C.: 5039
N.A.I.C.S.: 423390
Personnel:
Paul Godfrey *(Mng Dir)*

COSSACK ENERGY LIMITED
(Formerly PTO Consolidated Limited)
Level 1 981 Wellington Street
West Perth, WA, 6005, Australia
Mailing Address:
PO Box 1346
West Perth, WA, 6872, Australia
Tel.: (61) 8 9322 9295
Fax: (61) 8 6314 1587
E-Mail: admin@cossackenergy.com
Web Site: www.cossackenergy.com
COD—(ASX)
Rev.: $43,184
Assets: $1,471,634
Liabilities: $144,629
Net Worth: $1,327,005
Earnings: ($355,342)
Fiscal Year-end: 06/30/13
Business Description:
Oil & Gas Exploration
S.I.C.: 1311
N.A.I.C.S.: 211111
Personnel:
Peter Wall *(Chm)*
David King *(Mng Dir)*
Lisa Wynne *(Sec)*
Board of Directors:
Peter Wall
Robert J. Bensh
Stuart Brown
Michael Davy
David King
Igor Soshinsky
Legal Counsel:
Steinepreis Paganin
Level 4 The Read Building 16 Milligan Street
Perth, WA, 6000, Australia
Tel.: (61) 8 9321 4000
Fax: (61) 8 9321 4333

COSTA GROUP OF COMPANIES
275 Robinsons Rd
Ravenhall, VIC, 3023, Australia
Tel.: (61) 386451600
Fax: (61) 386451672
Web Site: www.costagroup.com.au
Business Description:
Holding Company; Produce Distr & Logistics Services
S.I.C.: 6719
N.A.I.C.S.: 551112
Personnel:
Frank A. Costa *(Chm)*
Holding:

CostaExchange Ltd (1)
275 Robinsons Rd
Ravenhall, VIC, 3023, Australia AU
Tel.: (61) 386451600
Fax: (61) 38639099
E-Mail: info@costaexchange.com.au
Web Site: www.costaexchange.com.au
Sales Range: $250-299.9 Million
Emp.: 2,000
Produce Farming, Packing, Marketing & Distr
Export
S.I.C.: 5148
N.A.I.C.S.: 424480
Frank A. Costa *(Chm)*
Harry Debney *(CEO)*
John Harris *(Grp CFO)*

COSTAIN GROUP PLC
Costain House Vanwall Business Park
Maidenhead, Berks, SL6 4UB, United Kingdom
Tel.: (44) 1628842444
Fax: (44) 1628674477
E-Mail: info@costain.com
Web Site: www.costain.com
Year Founded: 1875
COST—(LSE)
Rev.: $1,475,846,505
Assets: $621,766,473
Liabilities: $571,545,051
Net Worth: $50,221,422
Earnings: $38,218,818
Emp.: 4,283
Fiscal Year-end: 12/31/12
Business Description:
Holding Company; Civil Engineering, Commercial & Residential Building Contractor; Property Management
S.I.C.: 6719
N.A.I.C.S.: 551112
Personnel:
Andrew Wyllie *(CEO)*
Tracey Wood *(Sec & Dir-Legal)*
Board of Directors:
David Phillip Allvey
Michael R. Alexander
Anthony O. Bickerstaff
Jane A. Lodge
James Morley
Alison Wood
Andrew Wyllie
Samer G. Younis
Legal Counsel:
Slaughter & May
One Bunhill Row
London, EC1Y 8YY, United Kingdom
Tel.: (44) 20 7600 1200
Fax: (44) 20 7600 0289
Transfer Agent:
Lloyds TSB Registrars
The Causeway
Worthing, W Sussex, BN99 6DA, United Kingdom
Tel.: (44) 870 600 3969
Fax: (44) 870 600 3980
Subsidiaries:

Costain Civil Engineering Ltd. (1)
Costain Ltd Costain House Vanwall Business Park
Maidenhead, Berkshire, SL6 4UP, United Kingdom UK
Tel.: (44) 1628842196 (100%)
Telex: 859375 Coswok G
Fax: (44) 1628674477
E-Mail: mike.napier@costain.com
Web Site: www.costain.com
Sales Range: $25-49.9 Million
Emp.: 1,000
Civil Engineering Contractor
S.I.C.: 8711
N.A.I.C.S.: 541330
Mike Napier *(Mgr-Bus Dev)*

Costain Engineering & Construction Ltd. (1)
111 Westminster Bridge Rd
London, SE1 7UE, United Kingdom (100%)
Tel.: (44) 2077058444
Fax: (44) 2077058599
Emp.: 50
Civil Engineering, Commercial & Residential Building Contractor
S.I.C.: 1629
N.A.I.C.S.: 237990
Andrew Wyllie *(CEO)*

Subsidiaries:

Costain Building & Civil Engineering Ltd. (2)
Costain House Nicholsons Walk
Maidenhead, Berkshire, SL6 1LN, United Kingdom (100%)
Tel.: (44) 628842444
Telex: 849281 Costuk G
Fax: (44) 628674477
Emp.: 200
Civil Engineering, Commercial & Residential Building Contractor
S.I.C.: 1629
N.A.I.C.S.: 237990

Costain Construction Limited (2)
Costain House
Vanwall Bus Pk, Maidenhead, Berks, SL6 4UB, United Kingdom (100%)
Tel.: (44) 1628842444
Telex: 849281 Costuk G
Fax: (44) 1628674477
E-Mail: info@costain.com
Web Site: www.costain.com
Emp.: 110
Commercial & Residential Building Contractor
S.I.C.: 1542
N.A.I.C.S.: 236220
Andrew Wyllie *(CEO)*

Costain International Limited (2)
Costain House
Vanwall Business Park, Maidenhead, Berkshire, SL6 4UB, United Kingdom (100%)
Tel.: (44) 628842444
Telex: 859375 Coswok G
Fax: (44) 628674477
Web Site: www.costain.com
Emp.: 500
Holding Company; Civil Engineering, Commercial & Residential Building Contractor
S.I.C.: 8711
N.A.I.C.S.: 541330
Claud Franks *(Sec)*

Non-U.S. Joint Venture:

NESMA & Partners Contracting Ltd. (2)
PO Box 1498
Al Khobar, 31952, Saudi Arabia
Tel.: (966) 38971050
Fax: (966) 38643121
E-Mail: marketing.np@nesma.com
Web Site: www.nesma.com
Emp.: 600
Provider of Process Engineering, Procurement, Construction & Project Management Services
S.I.C.: 8711
N.A.I.C.S.: 541330
Imad Gholmieh *(CEO)*

Costain Ltd (1)
Costain House Van Wall
Maidenhead, Berkshire, SL6 4UB, United Kingdom
Tel.: (44) 1628842444
Fax: (44) 1628674477
E-Mail: info@costain.com
Emp.: 150
Construction Engineering Services
S.I.C.: 8711
N.A.I.C.S.: 541330

Costain Oil, Gas & Process Ltd (1)
Costain House Styal Road
Manchester, M22 5WN, United Kingdom
Tel.: (44) 1619103444
Fax: (44) 161 910 3399
Web Site: www.costain.com
Emp.: 300
Oil & Natural Gas Plant Construction Services
S.I.C.: 1389
N.A.I.C.S.: 213112
Neil Longfellow *(Dir-Nuclear, Hydrocarbons & Chemicals)*

Division:

Costain Oil, Gas & Process Limited Pipeline & Offshore Division (2)
Costain House Styal Road
Manchester, M22 5WN, United Kingdom (100%)
Tel.: (44) 1619103444
Telex: 629447 Lmbrom G
Fax: (44) 1619103345
E-Mail: marketing@costain.com
Web Site: www.costain-group.com
Emp.: 100
Oil & Gas Industry Construction Services
S.I.C.: 1623
N.A.I.C.S.: 237120

Richard Costain Ltd (1)
Costain House Nicholsons Walk
Maidenhead, Berkshire, SL6 1LN, United Kingdom
Tel.: (44) 1628842444
Fax: (44) 1628 842 554
Construction Engineering Services
S.I.C.: 8711
N.A.I.C.S.: 541330

Non-U.S. Subsidiaries:

Costain Abu Dhabi Company (1)
MN 4 Plot 20 Industrial Area Mussafah
PO Box 3069
Mussafah Industrial Area, Abu Dhabi, United Arab Emirates
Tel.: (971) 25553920
Fax: (971) 25559598
E-Mail: costainad@costain.ae
Web Site: www.costain-abudhabi.ae
Emp.: 40
Oil & Gas Industry Construction Services
S.I.C.: 1629
N.A.I.C.S.: 237120
Mike Thomson *(Gen Mgr)*

Costain (Africa) Limited (1)
87 Plymouth Rd
PO Box ST 197
Southerton, Harare, Zimbabwe (100%)

Tel.: (263) 4663571
Fax: (263) 4668647
E-Mail: costain@costain.co.zw
Web Site: www.costain.co.zw
Emp.: 60
Civil Engineering & Construction Contracting
S.I.C.: 8711
N.A.I.C.S.: 541330

Yahya Costain LLC (1)
PO Box 2282
112 Ruwi, Oman (60%)
Tel.: (968) 4591366
Telex: 5218 Cosdon ON
Fax: (968) 24592627
Web Site: www.costain.com
Civil Engineering & Contract Construction
S.I.C.: 8711
N.A.I.C.S.: 541330

COSTAMARE INC.
60 Zephyrou Street & Syngrou Avenue
17564 Athens, Greece
Tel.: (30) 2109490050
Fax: (30) 2109496454
Web Site: www.costamare.com
CMRE—(NYSE)
Rev.: $414,249,000
Assets: $2,685,842,000
Liabilities: $2,028,893,000
Net Worth: $656,949,000
Earnings: $103,087,000
Emp.: 2,124
Fiscal Year-end: 12/31/13
Business Description:
Container Vessel Transportation
S.I.C.: 4412
N.A.I.C.S.: 483111
Personnel:
Konstantinos Konstantakopoulos *(CEO)*
Gregory Zikos *(CFO)*
Konstantinos Zacharatos *(Gen Counsel & Sec)*
Board of Directors:
Konstantinos Konstantakopoulos
Charlotte Stratos
Konstantinos Zacharatos
Gregory Zikos

COSTIN NEW MATERIALS GROUP LIMITED
(See Under CECEP COSTIN New Materials Group Limited)

COSUMAR SA
8 rue Mouatamid Ibnou Abbad
BP 3098
Roches Noires, Casablanca, Morocco
Tel.: (212) 5 22 67 83 00
Fax: (212) 5 22 24 10 71
Web Site: www.cosumar.co.ma
Year Founded: 1929
CSR—(CAS)
Sales Range: Less than $1 Million
Business Description:
Sugar Mfr
S.I.C.: 2063
N.A.I.C.S.: 311313
Personnel:
Mohammed Fikrat *(Chm & CEO)*
Board of Directors:
Mohammed Fikrat
Abdellazi Abarro
Anass Houir Alami
Mohamed Ramses Arroub
Hicham Belmrah
Jean Luc Robert Bohbot
Khalid Cheddadi
Khoon Hong Kuok
Regis Karim Salamon

COTE RESTAURANTS LTD.
Woolverstone House 61 Berners St
London, W1T 3NJ, United Kingdom
Tel.: (44) 203 2067940
Web Site: www.cote-restaurants.co.uk
Year Founded: 2007
Sales Range: $10-24.9 Million
Emp.: 1,124
Business Description:
Restaurant Operator
S.I.C.: 5812
N.A.I.C.S.: 722511
Personnel:
Harald Samuelsson *(Co-Mng Dir)*
Alex Scrimgeour *(Co-Mng Dir)*

COTEC CONSTRUCTION JOINT STOCK COMPANY
236/6 Dien Bien Phu Street Ward 17
Binh Thanh, Ho Chi Minh City, Vietnam
Tel.: (84) 8 35142255
Fax: (84) 8 35142277
E-Mail: contact@coteccons.vn
Web Site: www.coteccons.vn
Year Founded: 2004
CTD—(HOSE)
Business Description:
Construction Services
S.I.C.: 1629
N.A.I.C.S.: 236210
Personnel:
Ba Duong Nguyen *(Chm & Gen Dir)*
Board of Directors:
Ba Duong Nguyen
Quang Quan Tran
Quang Tuan Tran

COTEMINAS COMPANHIA DE TECIDOS NORTE DE MINAS
Av Magalhaes Pinto 4000
Bairro Planalto, CEP 39404-166
Montes Claros, MG, Brazil
Tel.: (55) 38 3215-7777
Fax: (55) 38 3217 1633
E-Mail: jbomfim@coteminas.com.br
Web Site: www.coteminas.com.br
Year Founded: 1967
Sales Range: $550-599.9 Million
Business Description:
Yarn, Textiles, Knitwear, T-Shirts, Underwear, Bathrobes, Towels & Linens Mfr
S.I.C.: 2269
N.A.I.C.S.: 313310
Personnel:
Josue Christiano Gomes da Silva *(Pres)*
Luiz de Paula Ferreira *(Deputy CEO)*
Joint Venture:

Springs Global Participacoes S.A. (1)
Bairro Planalto Avenida Magalhaes Pinto 4000
39404-166 Montes Claros, Minas Gerais, Brazil BR
Tel.: (55) 553832157777
Sales Range: $900-999.9 Million
Emp.: 23,000
Mfr of Linens, Rugs, Pillows & Window Treatments
S.I.C.: 2299
N.A.I.C.S.: 313210

U.S. Subsidiary:

Springs Global US, Inc. (2)
205 N White St PO Box 70
Fort Mill, SC 29715
Tel.: (803) 547-3775
Fax: (803) 547-1636
Web Site: www.springs.com
Sales Range: $650-699.9 Million
Emp.: 200
Mfr of Home Furnishing Products
S.I.C.: 2299
N.A.I.C.S.: 313210
Edward Cardimona *(Chief Global Creative Officer & Sr VP)*

Non-U.S. Divisions:

Springs Canada, Ltd. (3)
110 Matherson Blvd W Ste 200
Mississauga, ON, L5R 3T4, Canada ON
Tel.: (905) 890-4994
Fax: (905) 507-5070
Sales Range: $10-24.9 Million
Emp.: 70
Marketing of Bed & Bath Products
S.I.C.: 5719
N.A.I.C.S.: 442299

Springs de Mexico, S.A. de C.V. (3)
Carretera Acambaro Jerecuaro No 19
Acambaro Guanajuato, CP 38610 Mexico, Mexico MX
Tel.: (52) 4171727711
Fax: (52) 4171727516
Sales Range: $25-49.9 Million
Emp.: 250
Finished Fabrics, Home Furnishings & Window Treatments Mfr
S.I.C.: 2394
N.A.I.C.S.: 314910

COTT CORPORATION
6525 Viscount Road
Mississauga, ON, L4V 1H6, Canada
Tel.: (905) 672-1900
Fax: (905) 672-5229
E-Mail: public_affairs@cott.com
Web Site: www.cott.com
Year Founded: 1955
COT—(NYSE TSX)
Rev.: $2,094,000,000
Assets: $1,426,100,000
Liabilities: $820,200,000
Net Worth: $605,900,000
Earnings: $22,000,000
Emp.: 3,966
Fiscal Year-end: 12/28/13
Business Description:
Holding Company; Soft Drinks Mfr & Marketer
S.I.C.: 6719
N.A.I.C.S.: 551112
Personnel:
David T. Gibbons *(Chm)*
Jerry S.G. Fowden *(CEO)*
Marni Morgan Poe *(Gen Counsel, Sec & VP)*
Board of Directors:
David T. Gibbons
Mark Benadiba
George A. Burnett
Jerry S.G. Fowden
Stephen H. Halperin
Betty Jane Hess
Gregory Rush Monahan
Mario Pilozzi
Andrew R. Prozes
Eric S. Rosenfeld
Graham W. Savage
Transfer Agent:
Computershare Trust Company
8th Floor 100 University Avenue
Toronto, ON, M5J 2Y1, Canada
Tel.: (416) 263-9701
Co-Headquarters:

Cott USA Corp. (1)
5519 W Idlewild Ave
Tampa, FL 33634 GA
Tel.: (813) 313-1800
Web Site: www.cott.com
Executive Managing Office
S.I.C.: 8741
N.A.I.C.S.: 551114
Steven Kitching *(Pres)*
Jerry S.G. Fowden *(CEO)*
Michael Gibbons *(Chief Comml & Bus Officer)*

Subsidiaries:

Cliffstar LLC (2)
One Cliffstar Ave
Dunkirk, NY 14048 DE
Tel.: (716) 366-6100 (100%)
Toll Free: (800) 777-2389
E-Mail: sales@Cliffstar.com
Web Site: www.cliffstar.com
Sales Range: $650-699.9 Million
Emp.: 1,200
Juice Mfr
S.I.C.: 2037
N.A.I.C.S.: 311411
Leah Hale *(Mgr-HR)*

Cott Beverages Inc. (2)
5519 W Idlewild Ave
Tampa, FL 33634 GA
Tel.: (813) 313-1800 (100%)
Fax: (813) 881-1926
Web Site: www.cott.com
Emp.: 1,500
Bottled & Canned Soft Drinks & Water Mfr
S.I.C.: 2086
N.A.I.C.S.: 312111
Michael Gibbons *(Pres)*

Plants:

Cott Beverages Inc. - Maryland Heights (3)
2525 Schuetz Rd
Maryland Heights, MO 63043-3316
Tel.: (314) 567-1300
Fax: (314) 569-0930
Web Site: www.cott.com
Emp.: 122
Distributer & Retailer of Carbonated Brand Water
S.I.C.: 2086
N.A.I.C.S.: 312111

Cott Beverages Inc. - San Antonio (3)
4238 Director Dr
San Antonio, TX 78219
Tel.: (210) 333-4310
Fax: (210) 333-5826
Web Site: www.cott.com
Emp.: 160
Bottled & Canned Soft Drinks & Water Mfr
S.I.C.: 2086
N.A.I.C.S.: 312111

Cott Beverages Inc. - Sikeston (3)
301 Larcel Dr
Sikeston, MO 63801-9380
Tel.: (573) 471-4445
Fax: (573) 471-1664
Web Site: www.cott.com
Emp.: 120
Bottled & Canned Soft Drinks & Water Mfr
S.I.C.: 2086
N.A.I.C.S.: 312111

Cott U.S. Holdings LLC (2)
5519 W Idlewild Ave
Tampa, FL 33634
Tel.: (813) 313-1781
Fax: (813) 888-1817
Investment Management Services
S.I.C.: 6211
N.A.I.C.S.: 523999

Cott Vending Inc. (2)
10838 Ambassador Blvd
Saint Louis, MO 63132 DE
Tel.: (314) 994-7545
Fax: (314) 994-7221
Web Site: www.cott.com
Emp.: 16
Soft Drink Vending Machine Distr
S.I.C.: 5962
N.A.I.C.S.: 454210
Lisa Judd *(Office Mgr)*

Non-U.S. Division:

Cott Beverages Canada (2)
6525 Viscount Rd
Mississauga, ON, L4V1H6, Canada (100%)
Tel.: (905) 672-1900
Fax: (905) 672-7504
Emp.: 150
S.I.C.: 2086
N.A.I.C.S.: 312112
Jerry S.G. Fowden *(CEO)*

Plants:

Cott Beverages Canada - Calgary (3)
4810 76 Ave Southeast
Calgary, AB, T2C 2V2, Canada (100%)
Tel.: (403) 279-6677
Fax: (403) 279-2260

Cott Corporation—(Continued)

Web Site: www.cotte.com
Emp.: 150
S.I.C.: 2086
N.A.I.C.S.: 312112
Curtis Tetttis *(Plant Mgr)*

Cott Beverages Canada - Montreal (3)
333 Avro Rd Point Clear
Pointe Claire, Montreal, QC, H9R 5W3, Canada (100%)
Tel.: (514) 428-1000
Fax: (514) 428-1001
Web Site: www.cott.com
Emp.: 200
Beverage Bottler
S.I.C.: 2086
N.A.I.C.S.: 312112

Cott Beverages Canada - Scoudouc (3)
4 Eddison Avenue
Scoudouc, NB, E4P 3N4, Canada
Tel.: (506) 532-5157
Fax: (506) 532-8882
E-Mail: industrialrelations@cott.com
Emp.: 75
S.I.C.: 2086
N.A.I.C.S.: 312112
Dave Stewart *(Gen Mgr)*

Cott Beverages Canada - Surrey (3)
15050 54A Ave
Surrey, BC, V3S 5X7, Canada (100%)
Tel.: (604) 574-1970
Fax: (604) 574-8645
Web Site: www.cott.com
Emp.: 75
S.I.C.: 2086
N.A.I.C.S.: 312112

Non-U.S. Subsidiaries:

Cott Beverages UK Ltd. (2)
Citrus Grove
Side Ley, Kegworth, Derbyshire, DE74 2FJ, United Kingdom (100%)
Tel.: (44) 1509674915
Fax: (44) 1509673461
E-Mail: service@cattronuk.com
Web Site: www.cott.co.uk
Emp.: 400
Beverages Whslr
S.I.C.: 2086
N.A.I.C.S.: 312111

Cott Embotelladores de Mexico, S.A. de C.V. (2)
Calle de los Palos No 35
San Pablo Xochimehuacan, Puebla, 72014, Mexico
Tel.: (52) 2223721400
Fax: (52) 22886025
E-Mail: alopes1@cott.com
Web Site: www.cott.com.mx
Emp.: 30
Soft Drink & Bottled Water Mfr
S.I.C.: 2086
N.A.I.C.S.: 312111
Ernesto Contreras *(Gen Mgr)*

Cott Europe Trading Limited (2)
Citrus Grove Sideley
Derby, Derbyshire, DE74 2FJ, United Kingdom
Tel.: (44) 1509 674915
Fax: (44) 509673461
E-Mail: reception@cott.com
Web Site: www.cott.com
Emp.: 100
Beverage Products Distr
S.I.C.: 5182
N.A.I.C.S.: 424820

Cott Limited (2)
Citrus Grove Sideley
Derby, Derbyshire, DE74 2FJ, United Kingdom
Tel.: (44) 1509 674915
Fax: (44) 1509 674683
E-Mail: reception@cott.co.uk
Web Site: www.cott.com
Emp.: 100
Soft Drink Mfr
S.I.C.: 2086
N.A.I.C.S.: 312111

Cott (Nelson) Limited (2)
1 Lindred Road Lomeshaye Industrial Estate
Brierfield, BB9 5SR, United Kingdom
Tel.: (44) 1282690014
Fax: (44) 1282721838
Soft Drink Mfr
S.I.C.: 2086
N.A.I.C.S.: 312111

Cott Private Label Limited (2)
Citrus Grove Sideley
Derby, DE74 2FJ, United Kingdom
Tel.: (44) 1509 674915
Fax: (44) 1509 674683
Emp.: 700
Soft Drink Mfr & Distr
S.I.C.: 2086
N.A.I.C.S.: 312111

Mexico Bottling Services, S.A. de C.V. (2)
Calle De Los Palos 35
San Pablo Xochimehuacan, Puebla, 72014, Mexico
Tel.: (52) 2223721400
Fax: (52) 2222886025
Web Site: www.cott.com.mx
Emp.: 30
Soft Drink Mfr
S.I.C.: 2086
N.A.I.C.S.: 312111
ErnestoContreras *(CEO)*

U.S. Subsidiary:

Caroline LLC (1)
607 Highland Colony Pkwy
Ridgeland, MS 39157
Tel.: (601) 605-4458
Business Support Services
S.I.C.: 7389
N.A.I.C.S.: 561499

Non-U.S. Subsidiaries:

Cott Beverages Limited (1)
Citrus Grove Side Ley
Kegworth, Derby, Derbyshire, DE74 2FJ, United Kingdom
Tel.: (44) 1509674915
Fax: (44) 1509680650
E-Mail: reception@cott.co.uk
Emp.: 1,000
Soft Drink Mftr
S.I.C.: 2086
N.A.I.C.S.: 312111

Cott Maquinaria y Equipo, S.A. de C.V. (1)
Calle De Los Palos No 35
San Pablo Xochimehuacan, Puebla, Mexico
Tel.: (52) 2223721400
Fax: (52) 2222886025
Web Site: www.cott.com.mx
Emp.: 300
Soft Drink Mfr
S.I.C.: 2086
N.A.I.C.S.: 312111
Ernesto Contreras *(Gen Dir)*

COTT OIL AND GAS LIMITED

945 Wellington Street
West Perth, WA, 6005, Australia
Tel.: (61) 8 9322 7600
Fax: (61) 8 9322 7602
Web Site: www.cottoilandgas.com.au
Year Founded: 2012
CMT—(ASX)
Business Description:
Oil & Gas Exploration
S.I.C.: 1311
N.A.I.C.S.: 211111
Personnel:
Stephen Dennis *(Chm)*
Andrew Dimsey *(Mng Dir)*
Board of Directors:
Stephen Dennis
David Bradley
Andrew Dimsey

COUGAR ENERGY LIMITED

(Name Changed to Moreton Resources Limited)

COUGAR LOGISTICS CORPORATION LTD.

(Name Changed to MYP Ltd.)

COUGAR METALS NL

Unit 5/531 Hay Street
Subiaco, WA, 6008, Australia
Mailing Address:
PO Box 1628
Subiaco, WA, 6904, Australia
Tel.: (61) 893811755
Fax: (61) 8 6102 1788
E-Mail: admin@cgm.com.au
Web Site: www.cgm.com.au
CGM—(ASX)
Rev.: $7,668,479
Assets: $5,588,448
Liabilities: $4,360,390
Net Worth: $1,228,058
Earnings: ($14,477,066)
Fiscal Year-end: 06/30/13
Business Description:
Mineral Exploration
S.I.C.: 1481
N.A.I.C.S.: 213115
Personnel:
Randal Swick *(Mng Dir)*
Michael Fry *(CFO & Sec)*
Johan Van De Stricht *(COO)*
Board of Directors:
Roger Hussey
Paul Hardie
Randal Swick
Legal Counsel:
Steinepreis Paganin
Level 4 The Read Building 16 Milligan Street
Perth, WA, 6000, Australia
Tel.: (61) 8 9321 4000
Fax: (61) 8 9321 4333

Hardies Lawyers
45 Ventnor Avenue
West Perth, WA, Australia

COUGAR MINERALS CORP.

201 - 919 Notre Dame Avenue
Winnipeg, MB, R3E 0M8, Canada
Tel.: (204) 989-2434
Fax: (204) 989-2433
E-Mail: info@cougarminerals.com
Web Site: www.cougarminerals.com
Year Founded: 2004
COU—(TSXV)
Assets: $1,331,586
Liabilities: $809,581
Net Worth: $522,006
Earnings: ($1,869,026)
Emp.: 4
Fiscal Year-end: 09/30/13
Business Description:
Gold & Precious Metals Mining & Exploration Services
S.I.C.: 1041
N.A.I.C.S.: 212221
Personnel:
Murray Nye *(Chm, Pres & CEO)*
Max Polinsky *(CFO)*
Megan Francis *(Sec)*
Board of Directors:
Murray Nye
Max Polinsky
Larry Segerstrom
Mark Tommasi
Legal Counsel:
McMillan LLP
Royal Centre 1055 West Georgia Street Suite 1500
PO Box 11117
Vancouver, BC, Canada
Transfer Agent:
Computershare Trust Company of Canada
Vancouver, BC, Canada
Tel.: (604) 661-9400
Fax: (604) 669-1548

COUGAR OIL AND GAS CANADA INC.

833 4th Avenue SW Suite 1120
Calgary, AB, T2P 3T5, Canada
Tel.: (403) 262-8044
Fax: (403) 513-2670
E-Mail: info@cougarenergyinc.com
Web Site: www.cougarenergyinc.com
COUGF—(OTC)
Sales Range: $1-9.9 Million
Emp.: 8
Business Description:
Oil & Gas Exploration
S.I.C.: 1311
N.A.I.C.S.: 211111
Personnel:
William Stewart Tighe *(Chm & CEO)*
Glenn Watt *(Pres & COO)*
Richard D. Carmichael *(CFO & VP-Fin)*
Lee Lischka *(Sec & Treas)*
Board of Directors:
William Stewart Tighe
William E. Brimacombe
Bruce Dowell
Robert Paul Galachiuk
Michael J. Hamilton
Lee Lischka
Glenn Watt

COULSON GROUP OF COMPANIES

4890 Cherry Creek Road
Port Alberni, BC, V9Y 8E9, Canada
Tel.: (250) 723-8118
Fax: (250) 723-7766
Toll Free: (800) 941-9998
Web Site: www.coulsongroup.com
Business Description:
Holding Company; Logging & Forestry Operations; Aircraft Operator
S.I.C.: 6719
N.A.I.C.S.: 551112
Personnel:
Wayne Coulson *(Pres)*
Subsidiaries:

Coulson Aircrane Ltd. (1)
Port Alberni Airport 7500 Airport Rd
Port Alberni, BC, V9Y 7L7, Canada
Tel.: (250) 723-8100
Fax: (250) 723-0608
Aircraft Operator
S.I.C.: 4522
N.A.I.C.S.: 481219

Subsidiary:

Flying Tankers, Inc. (2)
9350 Bomber Base V9Y8Z3
Port Alberni, BC, V9Y 7L7, Canada
Tel.: (250) 723-6225
Fax: (250) 723-6200
E-Mail: flyingtankers@shaw.ca
Web Site: www.martinmars.com
Emp.: 23
Fire Fighting Aircraft Operator
S.I.C.: 4522
N.A.I.C.S.: 481219
Wayne Coulson *(CEO)*
Jim Messer *(COO)*

Coulson Manufacturing Ltd. (1)
100 Seizal Rd
Port Alberni, BC, V9Y 1A1, Canada
Tel.: (250) 723-8118
Wood Product Mfr
S.I.C.: 2421
N.A.I.C.S.: 321912

COUNSEL CORPORATION

1 Toronto Street Suite 700
PO Box 3
Toronto, ON, M5C 2V6, Canada
Tel.: (416) 866-3000
Fax: (416) 866-3061
E-Mail: info@counselcorp.com
Web Site: www.counselcorp.com
Year Founded: 1979
CXS—(TSX)
Rev.: $138,625,035
Assets: $246,135,256
Liabilities: $100,013,322
Net Worth: $146,121,934

Earnings: $10,394,467
Emp.: 193
Fiscal Year-end: 12/31/12

Business Description:
Investment Services
S.I.C.: 6211
N.A.I.C.S.: 523999

Personnel:
Allan C. Silber *(Chm, Pres & CEO)*
Morris Perlis *(Vice Chm)*
Stephen Weintraub *(CFO, Sec & Exec VP)*
Kenney Finkelstein *(Pres/CEO-Merchant Banking)*
Anuja Royan *(Sr VP-Fin)*
Howard Wortzman *(Sr VP-Real Estate Investments)*

Board of Directors:
Allan C. Silber
Ronald Appleby
Tibor Donath
Jonathan Goodman
William H. Lomicka
Philip Reichmann
J. Barry Rotenberg
Paul Vessey

Legal Counsel:
Goodman, Phillips & Vineberg
250 Yonge Street Eaton Tower, Suite 2400
P.O. Box 2400
Toronto, ON, M5B 2M6, Canada
Tel.: (416) 979-2211
Fax: (416) 979-1234

Transfer Agent:
Computershare Investor Services Inc.
Montreal, QC, Canada

Subsidiary:

COUNSEL RB CAPITAL INC. **(1)**
700 1 Toronto St
Toronto, ON, M5C 2V6, Canada FL
Tel.: (416) 866-3000 (77%)
Fax: (416) 866-3090
E-Mail: sweintraub@counselrb.com
Web Site: www.counselrb.com
CRBN—(OTC OTCB)
Rev.: $14,128,000
Assets: $61,310,000
Liabilities: $15,298,000
Net Worth: $46,012,000
Earnings: ($1,813,000)
Emp.: 44
Fiscal Year-end: 12/31/12
Asset Liquidation Services; Patent Licensing Services
S.I.C.: 6211
N.A.I.C.S.: 523999
Allan C. Silber *(Chm & Pres)*
Henry Y.L. Toh *(Vice Chm)*
Adam Marc Reich *(Co-CEO)*
Jonathan Reich *(Co-CEO)*
Stephen A. Weintraub *(CFO, Sec & Exec VP)*

COUNTERPATH CORPORATION

Suite 300 One Bentall Centre 505 Burrard Street
Vancouver, BC, V7X 1M3, Canada
Tel.: (604) 320-3344
Fax: (604) 320-3399
Toll Free: (877) 818-3777
E-Mail: corporate@counterpath.com
Web Site: www.counterpath.com
CPAH—(NASDAQ TSX)
Rev.: $15,239,923
Assets: $25,055,877
Liabilities: $4,128,268
Net Worth: $20,927,609
Earnings: $472,280
Emp.: 86
Fiscal Year-end: 04/30/13

Business Description:
Multimedia Application Software Designer, Developer & Marketer
S.I.C.: 7372
N.A.I.C.S.: 511210

Personnel:
Terence H. Matthews *(Chm)*
Owen Nicholas Matthews *(Vice Chm)*
Donovan R. Jones *(Pres & CEO)*
David Karp *(CFO)*
Nemer D. Abourizk *(Gen Counsel)*

Board of Directors:
Terence H. Matthews
Christopher R. Cooper
Donovan R. Jones
Bruce A. Joyce
Owen Nicholas Matthews
Larry Timlick

Transfer Agent:
Valiant Trust Company
750 Cambie Street, 3rd Floor
Vancouver, BC, Canada

U.S. Subsidiary:

BridgePort Networks, Inc. **(1)**
651 W Washington Blvd Ste 500
Chicago, IL 60661
Tel.: (312) 377-1345
Fax: (312) 463-0390
Emp.: 5
Software Publishers
S.I.C.: 7372
N.A.I.C.S.: 511210
Robert Brown *(VP-Mktg)*

COUNTRY BIRD HOLDINGS LIMITED

Ground Floor 8 Melville Road
Illovo, Johannesburg, 2196, South Africa
Mailing Address:
PO Box 412523
Craighall, 2024, South Africa
Tel.: (27) 11 447 6044
Fax: (27) 11 447 5728
E-Mail: maria.antunes@countrybird.co.az
Web Site: www.cbhltd.co.za
CBH—(JSE)
Rev.: $361,525,539
Assets: $218,433,260
Liabilities: $147,951,230
Net Worth: $70,482,030
Earnings: $6,493,680
Emp.: 5,389
Fiscal Year-end: 06/30/13

Business Description:
Agricultural Business
S.I.C.: 8999
N.A.I.C.S.: 541690

Personnel:
Marthinus Stander *(CEO)*
Maria Jose Camacho Antunes *(Acting CFO & Sec)*

Board of Directors:
Bryan Hugh Kent
Raymond Gibbison
Geoffrey Philip Heath
Ian Wilson Martin Isdale
Kevin William James
Marthinus Stander
Carl Dennis Stein

Transfer Agent:
Computershare Investor Services (Proprietary) Limited
70 Marshall Street
Johannesburg, South Africa

Subsidiaries:

Long Iron Meats (Pty) Limited **(1)**
12 Tjaart Kruger Rd
Randlespark, Klerksdorp, North West, 2570, South Africa
Tel.: (27) 184641001
Fax: (27) 184628090
Web Site: www.longironmeats.com
Emp.: 140
Beef Slaughtering Services
S.I.C.: 2011
N.A.I.C.S.: 311611

Nutri Feeds (Pty) Limited **(1)**
Ofc 203 MooiRivier Mall
Potchefstroom, North West, 2531, South Africa
Tel.: (27) 182930019
Fax: (27) 182930131
E-Mail: sales@nutri.co.za
Web Site: www.nutrifeeds.co.za
Emp.: 11
Animal Feeds Mfr
S.I.C.: 2048
N.A.I.C.S.: 311119
Mario Le Roux *(Mng Dir)*

Plants:

Nutri Feeds (Pty) Limited - Bloemfontein Feed Mill **(2)**
Leon Bartell St 22
Oos Einde, Bloemfontein, Free State, 9301, South Africa
Tel.: (27) 514321313
Fax: (27) 514321064
E-Mail: salesbfn@nutri.co.za
Web Site: www.nutri.co.za
Emp.: 70
Animal Feeds Mfr
S.I.C.: 2048
N.A.I.C.S.: 311119
Johan Anderson *(Gen Mgr)*

Nutri Feeds (Pty) Limited - Mafikeng Feed Mill **(2)**
Agro Road 2 Industrial Area
Mafikeng, North West Region, 2745, South Africa
Tel.: (27) 183810686
Fax: (27) 183810687
Web Site: www.nutrifeeds.co.za
Emp.: 60
Animal Feeds Mfr
S.I.C.: 2048
N.A.I.C.S.: 311119
Tobie Stear *(Gen Mgr)*

Nutri Feeds (Pty) Limited - Viljoenskroon Feed Mill **(2)**
Fortuna Street 18
Viljoenskroon, Free State, 9520, South Africa
Tel.: (27) 563442200
Fax: (27) 563432271
Web Site: www.nutrifeeds.com
Animal Feeds Mfr
S.I.C.: 2048
N.A.I.C.S.: 311119
Johan Anderson *(Gen Mgr)*

Supreme Poultry (Pty) Limited **(1)**
PO Box 6851
Bloemfontein, Free State, South Africa
Tel.: (27) 514486803
Fax: (27) 514471269
Web Site: www.supremechicken.net
Emp.: 40
Poultry Hatcheries & Breeding Services
S.I.C.: 0254
N.A.I.C.S.: 112340
Izaak Breitenbach *(Mng Dir)*

Non-U.S. Subsidiary:

Ross Breeders (Botswana) (Pty) Limited **(1)**
Plot 55 Ntowanie St
Gaborone, Botswana
Tel.: (267) 3161629
Fax: (267) 3161628
E-Mail: kagiso@rossafrica.com
Web Site: www.rossafrica.com
Emp.: 280
Poultry Breeding Services
S.I.C.: 0752
N.A.I.C.S.: 115210
Doug Williams *(Mgr)*

Subsidiary:

OistIns (Pty) Limited **(2)**
PO Box 285
Shashis, Botswana
Tel.: (267) 2484274
Fax: (267) 2484838
Emp.: 120
Broiler Chicken Production Services
S.I.C.: 0251
N.A.I.C.S.: 112320
Michelle Burmester *(Mgr)*

COUNTRY CONDOS LTD

8 2 703 Mahogany Complex Ground Fl Amrutha Valley
Rd No 12 Banjara Hills
500034 Hyderabad, Andhra Pradesh, India
Tel.: (91) 4064541609
Fax: (91) 66833954
E-Mail: info@countrycondos.co.in
Web Site: www.countrycondos.co.in
531624—(BOM)
Sales Range: $1-9.9 Million

Business Description:
Pharmaceuticals Mfr
S.I.C.: 5122
N.A.I.C.S.: 424210

Personnel:
D. Krishna Kumar Raju *(Chm)*

Board of Directors:
D. Krishna Kumar Raju
P. Krupavaram
P. V.V. Prasad
C. H. Srinivas

COUNTRY DEVELOPMENT BANK LIMITED

Banepa 10 Kavre
POB 15111
Kathmandu, Nepal
Tel.: (977) 11 660701
Fax: (977) 11 660733
E-Mail: info@cdbank.com.np
Web Site: www.cdbank.com.np
CNDBL—(NEP)

Business Description:
Banking Services
S.I.C.: 6029
N.A.I.C.S.: 522110

Personnel:
Janardan Psd. Malla *(Chm)*
Uday Lal Raj *(Mng Dir)*

Board of Directors:
Janardan Psd. Malla
Mohan Bdr. Thapa Magar
Raghu Raj Onta
Uday Lal Raj
Bharat Mani Risal
Keshab Shrestha
Samundra Kaji Shrestha

COUNTRY GARDEN HOLDINGS COMPANY LIMITED

Rooms 901-904 9/F Manulife Provident Funds Place 345 Nathan Road
Kowloon, China (Hong Kong)
Tel.: (852) 2782 2881
Web Site: www.countrygarden.com.cn
2007—(HKG OTC)
Rev.: $6,654,382,808
Assets: $21,686,543,210
Liabilities: $15,509,754,999
Net Worth: $6,176,788,211
Earnings: $1,093,612,674
Emp.: 40,243
Fiscal Year-end: 12/31/12

Business Description:
Investment Holding Company; Property Development, Construction & Management
S.I.C.: 6719
N.A.I.C.S.: 551112

Personnel:
Kwok Keung Yeung *(Chm)*
Huiyan Yang *(Vice Chm)*
Bin Mo *(Pres)*
Rongbin Zhu *(Assoc Pres)*
Estella Yi Kum Ng *(CFO)*
Po Wah Huen *(Sec)*

Board of Directors:
Kwok Keung Yeung
Hongyan Huang
Xiao Huang
Joseph Ming Lai
Guokun Liang
Hongyu Liu
Wenjue Mei
Bin Mo

Country Garden Holdings Company Limited—(Continued)

Xueming Ou
Abraham Lai Him Shek
Jun Song
Rubo Su
Ronald Wui Tung Tong
Shutai Xie
Erzhu Yang
Huiyan Yang
Yongchao Yang
Zhicheng Yang
Ziying Yang
Yaoyuan Zhang
Rongbin Zhu

Royal Bank of Canada Trust Company (Cayman) Limited
4th Floor Royal Bank House 24 Shedden Road
Georgetown, Cayman Islands

Transfer Agents:
Tricor Investor Services Limited
26th Floor Tesbury Centre 28 Queens Road East
Wanchai, China (Hong Kong)

Royal Bank of Canada Trust Company (Cayman) Limited
4th Floor Royal Bank House 24 Shedden Road
Georgetown, Cayman Islands

COUNTRY GROUP DEVELOPMENT PUBLIC COMPANY LIMITED

Level 11-03 Q House Lumpini 1
South Sathorn Road
Sathorn, Bangkok, 10120, Thailand
Tel.: (66) 2677 7333
Fax: (66) 2677 7337
Web Site: www.cgd.co.th
Year Founded: 2010
CGD—(THA)
Rev.: $18,370,973
Assets: $27,773,246
Liabilities: $10,853,995
Net Worth: $16,919,250
Earnings: ($2,406,999)
Fiscal Year-end: 12/31/12

Business Description:
Real Estate Development Services
S.I.C.: 6531
N.A.I.C.S.: 531390

Personnel:
Vikrom Koompirochana *(Chm)*
Sadawut Taechaubol *(Vice Chm)*
Ben Taechaubol *(Mng Dir)*
Songwut Vejjanukroh *(Sec)*

Board of Directors:
Vikrom Koompirochana
Gavintorn Atthakor
Subhakorn Bhalakula
Werapong Chuenpagdee
Jrarat Pingclasai
Jirasak Ponghathaikul
Hsu-Feng Shueh
Ben Taechaubol
Sadawut Taechaubol
Songwut Vejjanukroh

Subsidiary:

A-HOST Co., Ltd. **(1)**
SM Tower 21st Floor 979/53-55
Phaholyothin Rd
Samsennai Phyatai, Bangkok, 10400, Thailand
Tel.: (66) 2298 0625
Fax: (66) 2298 0053
Information Technology Consulting Services
S.I.C.: 7373
N.A.I.C.S.: 541512

Subsidiary:

ABCS Co., Ltd. **(2)**
Software Park Building 7 th Floor Unit D
99/28 Chaengwattana Road
Klong Gleua Pak Kret, Nonthaburi, Thailand
Tel.: (66) 2962 0470
Fax: (66) 2962 0471
Software Development Services
S.I.C.: 7371
N.A.I.C.S.: 541511

COUNTRY GROUP SECURITIES PUBLIC COMPANY LIMITED

132 Sindhorn Tower 1 2nd Floor
Wireless Road Lumpini Patumwan
Bangkok, Thailand 10330
Tel.: (66) 2205 7000
Fax: (66) 2205 7171
E-Mail: cgsetrade@countrygroup.co.th
Web Site: www.cgsec.co.th
CGS—(THA)
Rev.: $53,812,817
Assets: $176,773,619
Liabilities: $79,190,554
Net Worth: $97,583,066
Earnings: $10,658,742
Fiscal Year-end: 12/31/12

Business Description:
Financial Services
S.I.C.: 6211
N.A.I.C.S.: 523999

Personnel:
Prayoon Chindaprodist *(Co-Chm)*
Sadawut Taechaubol *(Co-Chm)*
Surabhon Kwunchaithunya *(Vice Chm)*
Dej Namsirikul *(Vice Chm)*
Wattana Sanphanich *(Vice Chm)*
Prasit Srisuwan *(Pres & CEO)*

Board of Directors:
Prayoon Chindaprodist
Sadawut Taechaubol
Totsachai Asvinvichit
Sudthida Chirapatsakul
Litti Kewkacha
Surabhon Kwunchaithunya
Dej Namsirikul
Wattana Sanphanich
Hong Chye Sim
Prasit Srisuwan
Somkad Sueptrakul
Charn Tulyaphisitchai
Somchai Vanichsenee

Legal Counsel:
TVS Law Office Limited
99/168 Moo 11 Phaholyothin Road Soi Senanikom 1 Ladprao
Ladprao, Bangkok, 10230, Thailand

Siam Premier International Law Office Limited
26th Floor The Offices at Central World 999/9 Rama I Road Pathumwan
Bangkok, 10330, Thailand

Samack & Associates Legal Counselor Co Ltd
122 Bunsiri Rd Chao Pho Seua Pranakorn
Bangkok, 10200, Thailand

Chaiyutt Dhan Law Office Co Ltd
61/52 Thaweemit 8 Rama 9 Road Huay Kwang
Bangkok, 10310, Thailand

COUNTRY HEIGHTS HOLDINGS BERHAD

10th Floor Block C Mines Waterfront Business Park
No 3 Jalan Tasik Mines Resort City, 43300 Seri Kembangan, Selangor
Darul Ehsan, Malaysia
Tel.: (60) 389438811
Fax: (60) 389411470
E-Mail: inquiry@countryheights.com.my
Web Site: www.countryheights.com.my
CHHB—(KLS)
Rev.: $83,198,551
Assets: $458,393,138
Liabilities: $201,652,764
Net Worth: $256,740,373
Earnings: $8,446,235
Fiscal Year-end: 12/31/12

Business Description:
Property Development & Investment Services
S.I.C.: 6531
N.A.I.C.S.: 531311

Personnel:
Cheng Wen Lee *(CEO)*
Kok Kee Tan *(CFO & Sec)*
Sow Lin Lee *(CEO-Property Investment Div)*
Yip Chun Mun Ricky *(CEO-Palace Vacation Club Div)*

Board of Directors:
Mohamed Hashim Mohd Ali
Chong Eu Chew
Cheng Wen Lee
Kim Tiong Lee
Hassan Mohd Amin
Soon Hock Ong

COUNTRY STYLE COOKING RESTAURANT CHAIN CO., LTD.

No 1-2 5F Mingyi Floor Junhao
Building No 8 Jianxin North Road
Jiangbei District, Chongqing, China
Tel.: (86) 23 8671 2610
Fax: (86) 2386873700
Web Site: www.csc100.com
CCSC—(NYSE)
Rev.: $188,779,246
Assets: $162,935,463
Liabilities: $24,715,630
Net Worth: $138,219,833
Earnings: $12,014,779
Emp.: 5,280
Fiscal Year-end: 12/31/12

Business Description:
Restaurant Owner & Operator
S.I.C.: 5812
N.A.I.C.S.: 722513

Personnel:
Hong Li *(Chm & CEO)*
Adam J. Zhao *(CFO)*
Chao Sun *(COO)*

Board of Directors:
Hong Li
Li-Lan Cheng
Tim T. Gong
Yue Ji
Jin Li
Zhiyun Peng
Chao Sun
Eric Haibing Wu
Xingqiang Zhang

COUNTRY VIEW BERHAD

Unit 26-01 Level 26 Menara Landmark
Mail Box 261
No 12 Jalan Ngee Heng, 80000
Johor Bahru, Johor, Malaysia
Tel.: (60) 72236799
Fax: (60) 72246557
Web Site: www.countryview.com.my
CVIEW—(KLS)
Rev.: $62,692,074
Assets: $113,202,247
Liabilities: $56,828,864
Net Worth: $56,373,383
Earnings: $12,467,846
Fiscal Year-end: 11/30/12

Business Description:
Property Development & Investment Services
S.I.C.: 6531
N.A.I.C.S.: 531312

Personnel:
Mohamed Al Amin Abdul Majid *(Chm)*
Siow Ping Hung *(Co-Sec)*
Wee Hee Lee *(Co-Sec)*

Board of Directors:
Mohamed Al Amin Abdul Majid
Azhar Azizan
Shiau Yoon Choong
Kee Kong Law
Kit Tat Law
Chee Sean Wong
Joon Chin Wong

COUNTRYSIDE PROPERTIES PLC

Countryside House The Drive
Brentwood, Essex, CM13 3AT, United Kingdom
Tel.: (44) 1277260000
Fax: (44) 1277690690
E-Mail: group@cpplc.com
Web Site: www.countryside-properties.com
Year Founded: 1958
Emp.: 850

Business Description:
Residential & Commercial Property Builder & Developer
S.I.C.: 6552
N.A.I.C.S.: 237210

Personnel:
Andrew C. P. Carr-Locke *(Founder)*
Ian Sutcliffe *(Chm)*
Richard S. Cherry *(Deputy Chm)*
Graham S. Cherry *(CEO)*

Board of Directors:
Richard S. Cherry
Ian Sutcliffe
Andrew C. P. Carr-Locke
Graham S. Cherry
Keith Cushen
Jeremy Miller

Transfer Agent:
Computershare Services plc
PO Box 82 The Pavilions Bridgewater Rd
Bristol, BS99 7NH, United Kingdom
Tel.: (44) 117 930 6666
Fax: (44) 171 930 6509

COUNTY COAL LIMITED

Level 2 27-31 Macquarie Street
Sydney, NSW, 2000, Australia
Tel.: (61) 2 9251 3311
Fax: (61) 2 9251 6550
Web Site: www.countycoal.com
CCJ—(ASX)

Business Description:
Coal Mining
S.I.C.: 1222
N.A.I.C.S.: 212112

Personnel:
Robert G. Cameron *(Chm)*
Terry Flitcroft *(Sec)*

Board of Directors:
Robert G. Cameron
Marcus Boland
David Miller

COUNTY HERITAGE FOREST PRODUCTS LTD.

1275 Hubrey Road
London, ON, N6N 1E2, Canada
Tel.: (519) 686-7573
Fax: (519) 686-8044
Toll Free: (800) 265-7643
E-Mail: sales@countyheritage.com
Web Site: www.countyheritage.com
Year Founded: 1976
Rev.: $26,584,800
Emp.: 75

Business Description:
Doors & Windows Mfr
S.I.C.: 2431
N.A.I.C.S.: 321911

Personnel:
Denis Crane *(Pres)*

COUNTY LINE ENERGY CORPORATION

Ste 530-1015 Fourth St SW
Calgary, AB, T2R 1J4, Canada

Tel.: (403) 200-1033
Web Site: www.countylineenergy.com
G7Q—(DEU)
Business Description:
Oil & Gas Exploration Services
S.I.C.: 1389
N.A.I.C.S.: 213112
Personnel:
Harry Bygdnes *(Pres & CEO)*
Board of Directors:
John Kenney Berscht
Harry Bygdnes

COURAGE MARINE GROUP LIMITED

1801 West Tower Shun Tak Centre
200 Connaught Road
Central, China (Hong Kong)
Tel.: (852) 3184 0755
Fax: (852) 3184 0750
E-Mail: courage@couragemarine.com
Web Site: www.couragemarine.com
1145—(HKG SES)
Rev.: $18,758,000
Assets: $104,631,000
Liabilities: $36,958,000
Net Worth: $67,673,000
Earnings: ($10,677,000)
Fiscal Year-end: 12/31/12
Business Description:
Marine Transportation Services
S.I.C.: 4491
N.A.I.C.S.: 488320
Personnel:
Chao-Huan Wu *(Founder & Mng Dir)*
Chi-Shun Chiu *(Founder & Deputy Gen Mgr-Sys & Standard Compliance)*
Shin-Yung Chen *(Founder & Dir-Technical Repair & Maintenance)*
Tsai-Seng Lin *(Founder & Mgr-Sls & Mktg)*
Chih-Chien Hsu *(Founder)*
Hsien-Long Sun *(Founder)*
Lawrence Kwok-Ping Hon *(Co-Sec & Dir-Fin)*
Pih Peng Lee *(Co-Sec)*
Board of Directors:
Chih-Chien Hsu
James Shun-Chi Chang
Wen Yuan Chu
Gary Chun Kin Liu
Boon Ann Sin
Hsien-Long Sun
Chao-Huan Wu

Codan Services Limited
Clarendon House 2 Church Street
Hamilton, Bermuda

Boardroom Corporate & Advisory Services Pte. Ltd.
50 Raffles Place 32-00 DBS Building Tower Two
Singapore, Singapore

Transfer Agent:
Tricor Investor Services Limited
26th Floor Tesbury Centre 28 Queens Road East
Wanchai, China (Hong Kong)

Subsidiary:

Courage Marine (HK) Company Limited **(1)**
Room 1801 18th Fl Shuntak Ctr W Tower No 200
Connaught Road Sheungaan, Hong Kong, China (Hong Kong)
Tel.: (852) 31840755
Fax: (852) 31840750
E-Mail: courage@couragemarine.com
Web Site: www.couragemarine.com
Emp.: 5
Ship Management Services
S.I.C.: 4412
N.A.I.C.S.: 483111
Wu Chao Huan *(Mng Dir)*

Non-U.S. Subsidiary:

Courage - New Amego Shipping Corp. **(1)**
5/F Transworld Commercial Center 2
Nanking East Road Section 2
Taipei, 10457, Taiwan
Tel.: (886) 2 2542 0122
Fax: (886) 25420121
E-Mail: ops@couragemarine.com
Emp.: 15
Marine Shipping Services
S.I.C.: 4731
N.A.I.C.S.: 488510
Philip Wu *(Gen Mgr)*

Subsidiary:

Courage - New Amego Shipping Agency Co. Ltd. **(2)**
5 F No 2 Nanjing E Road
Jhongstan District, Taipei, 104, Taiwan
Tel.: (886) 2 25420122
Fax: (886) 2 25420121
E-Mail: courage-agency@couragemarine.com
Ship Management Services
S.I.C.: 4412
N.A.I.C.S.: 483111
Chu Wu *(Gen Mgr)*

COURANT SAS

241 Route de Dommartin
Manziat, 01570 Lyon, France
Tel.: (33) 385368800
Fax: (33) 385301082
E-Mail: lm.cognet@courant.fr
Web Site: www.courant.fr
Sales Range: $25-49.9 Million
Emp.: 104
Business Description:
Rubber & Plastic Hoses Mfr
S.I.C.: 3052
N.A.I.C.S.: 326220
Personnel:
Stephanie Bernard *(Dir-Sls, Admin & Comm)*

COURTESY CHEV OLDS LTD.

1635 The Queensway
Toronto, ON, M8Z 1T8, Canada
Tel.: (416) 255-9151
Fax: (416) 255-6258
Toll Free: (888) 309-5084
E-Mail: info@courtesychev.com
Web Site: www.courtesychevrolet.ca
Year Founded: 1968
Rev.: $36,130,457
Emp.: 75
Business Description:
New & Used Car Dealers
S.I.C.: 5511
N.A.I.C.S.: 441110
Personnel:
Don Polyschuk *(Owner & Pres)*

COURTESY FORD LINCOLN SALES

684 Wharncliffe Rd S
London, ON, N6J 2N4, Canada
Tel.: (519) 680-1200
Fax: (519) 680-3222
Web Site: www.courtesyfordlincoln.dealerconnection.com
Year Founded: 1996
Rev.: $35,212,705
Emp.: 70
Business Description:
New & Used Car Dealers
S.I.C.: 5511
N.A.I.C.S.: 441110
Personnel:
Bill Eansor *(Pres)*

COURTIERS EN DOUANES CARSON LIMITEE

700 Leigh Capreol
Dorval, QC, H4Y 1G7, Canada
Tel.: (514) 393-9830
Fax: (514) 633-9670
Toll Free: (800) 390-0039
E-Mail: clearance@carson.ca
Web Site: www.carson.ca
Sales Range: $100-124.9 Million
Emp.: 80
Business Description:
Custom house broker
S.I.C.: 6531
N.A.I.C.S.: 531210
Personnel:
Bob Walker *(Gen Mgr)*

COURTS ASIA LIMITED

50 Tampines North Drive 2
Singapore, 528766, Singapore
Tel.: (65) 63097777
Fax: (65) 67848076
E-Mail: ir@courts.com.sg
Web Site: www.courts.com.sg
RE2—(SES)
Rev.: $642,698,074
Assets: $532,464,191
Liabilities: $298,082,073
Net Worth: $234,382,118
Earnings: $33,524,800
Emp.: 2,021
Fiscal Year-end: 03/31/13
Business Description:
Electrical & Computer Retailer
S.I.C.: 5731
N.A.I.C.S.: 443142
Personnel:
Terence Donald O'Connor *(CEO)*
Kim Eng Kee *(CFO)*
Siew Koon Ang *(Sec)*
Board of Directors:
Jack Hennessy
Adnan Abdulaziz Ahmed AlBahar
Chor Wai Chey
Kim Eng Kee
Kewee Kho
Terence Donald O'Connor
Transfer Agent:
Tricor Barbinder Share Registration Services
80 Robinson Road 02-00
Singapore, Singapore

COURTS (JAMAICA) LIMITED

79-81A Slipe Road
Cross Roads, Kingston, 5, Jamaica
Tel.: (876) 9262110
Fax: (876) 9290887
Web Site: www.courts.com.jm/
CRTS—(JAM)
Business Description:
General Merchandise Retailer
S.I.C.: 5399
N.A.I.C.S.: 452990
Personnel:
Mario Guerrero *(Mng Dir)*

COVALENT MATERIALS CORPORATION

Nissei Bldg 6 3 Ohsaki 1 chome
Shinagawa ku, Tokyo, 141 0032, Japan
Tel.: (81) 354378401
Fax: (81) 354377172
E-Mail: r.yamada@covalent.co.jp
Web Site: www.covalent.co.jp
Sales Range: $350-399.9 Million
Emp.: 1,475
Business Description:
Quartz Glass, Carbon & Silicon Carbide Products, Electric Brushes, Semiconductor Materials, Special Material Products, Formed & Unformed Fire-Resistant Products, Fire-Resistant Clay & Industrial Furnaces Mfr
S.I.C.: 3291
N.A.I.C.S.: 327910
Personnel:
Fujio Owa *(CFO, Sr VP & Gen Mgr-Acctg & Fin)*
Masanori Nishimura *(COO & Exec VP)*
Nobuyuki Toyoda *(CTO, Pres-New Bus Dev Grp & Sr VP)*
Yuji Hayashi *(VP, Chief Product Officer & Gen Mgr-Productivity Plng Grp)*
Kazuo Minagawa *(Pres-Silicon Grp & Sr VP)*
Toshio Nagahama *(Pres-Ceramics Bus Grp & Sr VP)*
Yoichi Nishina *(Sr VP & Gen Mgr)*
Board of Directors:
Tatsuo Kawasaki
Masato Marumo
Masanori Nishimura
Fujio Owa
Kazuhiro Yamada
Osamu Yamamoto

Subsidiaries:

Covalent Machinery Corporation **(1)**
378 Oguni-machi Oaza
Nishitama, Oguni, Yamagata, 999-1351, Japan
Tel.: (81) 238 62 5942
Fax: (81) 238 62 5193
Industrial Machinery Equipment Mfr & Whslr
S.I.C.: 3559
N.A.I.C.S.: 333249

Covalent Materials Nagasaki Corporation **(1)**
296 Kawatana-cho Momozugo
Higashisonogi-gun, Nagasaki, 859-3605, Japan
Tel.: (81) 956 82 3111
Fax: (81) 956 82 3111
Fused Silica Powder Mfr
S.I.C.: 2819
N.A.I.C.S.: 325180

Covalent Materials Tokuyama Corporation **(1)**
2-1-32 Eguchi
Shunan, Yamaguchi, 745-0862, Japan
Tel.: (81) 834 32 3400
Fax: (81) 834 32 3403
Quartz Glass Product Mfr
S.I.C.: 3679
N.A.I.C.S.: 334419

Covalent Sales Corporation **(1)**
Nihonbashi IP Bldg 13-3
Nihonbashikobunecho
Chuo, Tokyo, 103-0024, Japan
Tel.: (81) 3 3662 3371
Fax: (81) 3 3662 3375
Sales Range: $10-24.9 Million
Cinema Projection System Retailer
S.I.C.: 5043
N.A.I.C.S.: 423410

Tokai Ceramics Co., Ltd. **(1)**
308-1 Shidare-cho Yosibora
Tokyo, Aichi, 470-0308, Japan
Tel.: (81) 565 45 0611
Fax: (81) 565 45 8066
Refractory Material Mfr
S.I.C.: 3297
N.A.I.C.S.: 327120

Plants:

Covalent Materials Corporation - Hatano Facility **(1)**
30 Soya
Hadano, Kanagawa, 257-8566, Japan
Tel.: (81) 463 81 1050
Fax: (81) 463 81 1664
Industrial Machinery Equipment Mfr & Whslr
S.I.C.: 3559
N.A.I.C.S.: 333249

Covalent Materials Corporation - Kariya Facility **(1)**
1 Minami-Fuji Ogakie-cho
Kariya, Aichi, 448-8665, Japan
Tel.: (81) 566 21 2851
Fax: (81) 566 21 6365
Industrial Machinery Equipment Mfr & Whslr

Covalent Materials Corporation—(Continued)

S.I.C.: 3559
N.A.I.C.S.: 333249

Covalent Materials Corporation - Oguni Facility (1)
378 Oguni-machi Oaza
Nishi-okitama-gun, Oguni, Yamagata, 999-1351, Japan
Tel.: (81) 238 62 5902
Fax: (81) 238 62 5178
Industrial Machinery Equipment Mfr & Whslr
S.I.C.: 3559
N.A.I.C.S.: 333249

U.S. Subsidiary:

Covalent Materials USA Inc. (1)
2010 N 1st St Ste 400
San Jose, CA 95131-2018
Tel.: (408) 467-0515
Fax: (408) 467-0510
Quartz Glass & Ceramic Product Whslr
S.I.C.: 3679
N.A.I.C.S.: 334419
Tom Mao *(Sr Mgr-Acctg & Admin)*

Non-U.S. Subsidiaries:

Covalent Materials Europe GmbH (1)
Herzog-Heinrich-Strasse 11
80336 Munich, Germany
Tel.: (49) 89 55 14 19 0
Fax: (49) 89 55 14 19 40
Ceramic Product Whslr
S.I.C.: 5032
N.A.I.C.S.: 423320
Jeremy Stevens *(Pres)*

Covalent Materials Korea Ltd. (1)
Rm 1505 Hibrand Bldg 215 YangJae-dong
Seocho-ku, Seoul, Korea (South)
Tel.: (82) 2 2155 2225
Fax: (82) 2 2155 2226
Ceramic Product Whslr
S.I.C.: 5032
N.A.I.C.S.: 423320

Covalent Materials Taiwan Corp. (1)
16F-4 No 295 Sec 2 Kuang-Fu Road
Hsin-chu, 30071, Taiwan
Tel.: (886) 3 575 1238
Fax: (886) 3 575 1633
Ceramic Product Whslr
S.I.C.: 5032
N.A.I.C.S.: 423320

THE COVALI GROUP LLC

309 Q House Furze Road
Sandyford Industrial Estate, Dublin, 18, Ireland
Tel.: (353) 1 293 9302
E-Mail: info@covaligroup.com
Web Site: www.covaligroup.com
Year Founded: 2006
Emp.: 20
Business Description:
Business Data Intelligence Solutions
S.I.C.: 7372
N.A.I.C.S.: 511210
Personnel:
Noel Shannon *(Mng Dir)*

COVALON TECHNOLOGIES LTD.

405 Britannia Road East Suite 106
Mississauga, ON, L4Z 3E6, Canada
Tel.: (905) 568-8400
Fax: (905) 568-5200
E-Mail: office@covalon.com
Web Site: www.covalon.com
COV—(TSXV)
Rev.: $3,770,766
Assets: $5,928,066
Liabilities: $2,712,861
Net Worth: $3,215,204
Earnings: ($3,967,514)
Fiscal Year-end: 09/30/12
Business Description:
Pharmaceutical Products Mfr & Sales
S.I.C.: 2834
N.A.I.C.S.: 325412
Personnel:
Martin Charles Bernholtz *(Chm)*
Abe Schwartz *(Chm)*
Brian Pedlar *(Pres, CEO & Interim CFO)*
Val DiTizio *(Chief Scientific Officer)*
Board of Directors:
Martin Charles Bernholtz
Abe Schwartz
Joseph Cordiano
William Jackson
Jeffrey Mandel
Murray Miller
Brian Pedlar
Transfer Agent:
Equity Financial Trust Company
200 University Avenue Suite 400
Toronto, ON, Canada

Subsidiary:

Covalon Technologies Inc. (1)
405 Britannia Rd E Suite 106
Mississauga, ON, L4Z 3E6, Canada
Tel.: (905) 568-8400
Fax: (416) 944-8520
Surgical & Medical Instrument Mfr
S.I.C.: 3841
N.A.I.C.S.: 339112

COVEA GROUPE S.A.S.

(d/b/a Covea Mutual Insurance Group Company)
7 place des 5 Martyrs du Lycee Buffon
75015 Paris, France
Tel.: (33) 153106600
Web Site: www.covea.eu
Premiums: $19,943,293,163
Assets: $114,712,873,653
Liabilities: $101,660,657,029
Net Worth: $13,052,216,625
Earnings: $856,808,935
Emp.: 25,000
Fiscal Year-end: 12/31/12
Business Description:
Mutual Insurance Holding Company; Reinsurance, Health Insurance, Property & Casualty Insurance Products & Services
S.I.C.: 6719
N.A.I.C.S.: 551112
Personnel:
Thierry Derez *(Chm & CEO)*
Jean-Claude Seys *(Vice Chm & Mng Dir)*
Jean Fleury *(Deputy Mng Dir & Gen Sec)*
Pascal Gueniot *(Deputy Mng Dir-Banking, Participations & Strategy)*
Board of Directors:
Thierry Derez
Bernard Barbottin
Michele Beyt
Daniele Bouchut
Georges Cambour
Alex Capelle
Michel Castagne
Mario Colaiacovo
Michel Coursat
Patrice Daudier de Cassini
Xavier Dejaiffe
Christian Delahaigue
Serge Dussaussois
Marie-France Ferrand
Didier Gardinal
Jean-Philippe Gauduchon
Jean-Pierre Gualezzi
Christophe Guettier
Jean-Marie Iche
Hubert Ivanoff
Gilbert Lebrument
Alexis Lehmann
Michel Radelet
Michel Roux
Jean-Claude Seys
Remy Verges
Pierre Vionnet
Charles Zanoni

Subsidiaries:

GMF Assurances S.A. (1)
76 rue de Prony
75857 Paris, Cedex 17, France FR
Tel.: (33) 147541010
Web Site: www.gmf.fr
Sales Range: $5-14.9 Billion
Emp.: 6,200
Health, Property & Casualty Insurance Products & Services
S.I.C.: 6331
N.A.I.C.S.: 524126
Patrice Forget *(Deputy Mng Dir)*
Laurent Tollie *(Deputy Mng Dir-Insurance)*

MAAF Assurances S.A. (1)
Chaban de Chauray
F-79036 Niort, Cedex 09, France FR
Tel.: (33) 549343536
E-Mail: facteur.maaf@maaf.fr
Web Site: www.maaf.fr
Sales Range: $1-4.9 Billion
Emp.: 7,000
Health, Property & Casualty Insurance Products & Services
S.I.C.: 6351
N.A.I.C.S.: 524126
Thierry Derez *(Chm & Mng Dir)*
Etienne Couturier *(Deputy Mng Dir)*
Joaquim Pinheiro *(Deputy Mng Dir-Resources)*

MMA S.A. (1)
14 Boulevard Marie et Alexandre Oyon
F-72030 Le Mans, Cedex 9, France FR
Tel.: (33) 243417272
Fax: (33) 243417226
E-Mail: recramacions.claims@mmgroupe-mma.fr
Web Site: www.mma.fr
Sales Range: $5-14.9 Billion
Emp.: 11,800
Insurance Services
S.I.C.: 6311
N.A.I.C.S.: 524113
Thierry Derez *(Chm)*
Christian Baudon *(Mng Dir)*
Didier Bazzocchi *(Deputy Mng Dir-Resources)*
Herve Frapsauce *(Deputy Mng Dir-Insurance)*

Non-U.S. Subsidiary:

Swinton Group Ltd. (2)
Swinton House
6 Great Marlborough Street, Manchester, M1 5SW, United Kingdom UK
Tel.: (44) 1612361222
Web Site: www.swinton.co.uk
Emp.: 4,450
Insurance Services
S.I.C.: 6351
N.A.I.C.S.: 524126
Patrick Smith *(CEO)*

Subsidiary:

Equity Insurance Group Ltd. (3)
Library House New Road
Brentwood, Essex, CM14 4GD, United Kingdom
Tel.: (44) 01277200100
E-Mail: info@equitygroup.co.uk
Web Site: www.equitygroup.co.uk
Sales Range: $700-749.9 Million
Emp.: 1,200
Insurance Services
S.I.C.: 6411
N.A.I.C.S.: 524298
Neil Utley *(CEO)*

COVENTRY BUILDING SOCIETY

Economic House High Street
PO Box 9
Coventry, CV1 5QN, United Kingdom
Tel.: (44) 845 7665522
Fax: (44) 2476257593
E-Mail: marketing@thecoventrybuildingsociety.co.uk
Web Site: www.coventrybuildingsociety.co.uk
CVB—(LSE)
Rev.: $1,336,868,985
Assets: $42,536,281,002
Liabilities: $41,270,006,280
Net Worth: $1,266,274,722
Earnings: $106,602,075
Emp.: 1,283
Fiscal Year-end: 12/31/12
Business Description:
Insurance & Financial Services
S.I.C.: 6399
N.A.I.C.S.: 524128
Personnel:
Bridget P. Blow *(Deputy Chm)*
Colin Franklin *(Interim CEO)*
Peter Frost *(COO)*
Board of Directors:
Ian Pickering
Bridget P. Blow
Roger Burnell
Colin Franklin
Peter Frost
Ian Geden
John Lowe
Glyn Smith

Subsidiaries:

Godiva Mortgages Limited (1)
Binley Bus Pk
PO139
CV15WF Coventry, United Kingdom (100%)
Tel.: (44) 8457573612
Fax: (44) 2476431679
E-Mail: documents@thecoventry.co.uk
Web Site: www.coventrybuildingsociety.co.uk/intermediaries/intermediariesnonsecure/aboutgodiva.aspx
Mortgage & Nonmortgage Loan Brokers
S.I.C.: 6163
N.A.I.C.S.: 522310
Colin Franklin *(Mng Dir)*

The Property Directory Limited (1)
Binley Bus Pk
139
CV15WF Coventry, United Kingdom (100%)
Tel.: (44) 2476653517
Fax: (44) 2476431679
Miscellaneous Financial Investment Activities
S.I.C.: 6211
N.A.I.C.S.: 523999
David Stewart *(Mng Dir)*

COVENTRY GROUP LIMITED

525 Great Eastern Highway
Redcliffe, WA, 6104, Australia
Mailing Address:
PO Box 740
Cloverdale, WA, 6985, Australia
Tel.: (61) 894365400
Fax: (61) 894365406
E-Mail: information@cgl.com.au
Web Site: www.cgl.com.au
CYG—(ASX)
Rev.: $246,449,355
Assets: $189,655,947
Liabilities: $31,655,872
Net Worth: $158,000,076
Earnings: $6,131,716
Emp.: 826
Fiscal Year-end: 06/30/13
Business Description:
Industrial & Automotive Products Supplier
Export
S.I.C.: 5085
N.A.I.C.S.: 423840
Personnel:
Roger Baden Flynn *(Chm)*
Keith Smith *(CFO)*
Mark W. Ridley *(CIO)*
John Colli *(Sec)*
Board of Directors:
Roger Baden Flynn
Barry Frederick Nazer

John Harold Nickson
Kenneth Royce Perry

Subsidiaries:

AA Gaskets Pty Ltd (1)
F 4 1730 Hume Hwy
3061 Campbellfield, Victoria, Australia
Tel.: (61) 393554400
Fax: (61) 393591124
E-Mail: sales@aagaskets.com.au
Web Site: www.aagaskets.com.au
Emp.: 60
Automotive Gasket Mfr
S.I.C.: 3053
N.A.I.C.S.: 339991
Michael Callaghan *(Gen Mgr)*

Non-U.S. Subsidiary:

NZ Gaskets Limited (2)
25 Patiki Rd
Avondale, 1026 Auckland, New Zealand
Tel.: (64) 98290047
Fax: (64) 98285212
E-Mail: sales@nzgaskets.co.nz
Web Site: www.nzgaskets.co.nz
Emp.: 10
Automotive Gaskets Mfr
S.I.C.: 3053
N.A.I.C.S.: 339991
Steve Tregoweth *(Mgr)*

Coventry Group Limited Artia Division (1)
34 Mckenzie St
Launceston, Tasmania, 7250, Australia
Tel.: (61) 363343925
Fax: (61) 363267423
E-Mail: launceston@cf.cgl.com.au
Web Site: www.coventrys.com.au/coventry/divisions/industrial/coventry_fasteners_victas/vic_contacts.htm
Emp.: 4
Fasteners Mfr
S.I.C.: 3965
N.A.I.C.S.: 339993
Mathew Godfrey *(Branch Mgr)*

Coventry Group Limited Coventry Fasteners Division (1)
31 Liberty Road
Huntingwood, NSW, 2148, Australia
Tel.: (61) 296166100
Fax: (61) 296166150
E-Mail: wetherillpark@cf.CGL.com.au
Web Site: www.coventryfasteners.com.au
Emp.: 10
Fasteners Whslr
S.I.C.: 5072
N.A.I.C.S.: 423710
Mark Abbott *(Mgr)*

Coventry Group Limited Coventrys Division (1)
525 Great Eastern Hwy
Redcliffe, Western Australia, Australia
Tel.: (61) 892760111
Fax: (61) 894365555
E-Mail: mail@coventrys.cgl.com.au
Web Site: www.coventrys.com.au/coventry/divisions/automotive/coventrys/contacts_locations.htm
Emp.: 300
Automotive Parts & Tools Whslr
S.I.C.: 5013
N.A.I.C.S.: 441310
Harry Philipi *(Mgr-Mktg)*

Coventry Group Limited Drivetrain Division (1)
4 Atlas Ct
Welshpool, Western Australia, 6106, Australia
Tel.: (61) 8 9353 4444
Fax: (61) 8 9356 1429
E-Mail: drivetrain@drivetrain.CGL.com.au
Emp.: 20
Vehicle & Trailing Equipment Mfr
S.I.C.: 5013
N.A.I.C.S.: 423120
Grant Hartfield *(Mgr)*

Non-U.S. Subsidiaries:

Coventry Group Limited Hylton Parker Fasteners Division (1)
17-19 Constellation Dr
Mairangi Bay, Auckland, New Zealand
Tel.: (64) 94770480
Fax: (64) 94785801
E-Mail: sales.auckland@hpfast.co.nz
Emp.: 100
Fasteners Mfr
S.I.C.: 3965
N.A.I.C.S.: 339993
Mike Wansink *(Gen Mgr)*

Coventry Group (NZ) Limited (1)
17-19 Contellation Rd
Mairangi Bay, New Zealand
Tel.: (64) 94796260
Fax: (64) 94785801
E-Mail: sales.auckland@hpfast.co.nz
Web Site: www.coventrys.com.au/coventry/divisions/industrial/hylton_parker_fasteners/contacts_locations.htm
Emp.: 30
Automotive Gasket Mfr
S.I.C.: 3053
N.A.I.C.S.: 339991
Gene Enqiry *(Mgr-Mktg)*

COVENTRY RESOURCES INC.

Suite 1490 - 1075 West Georgia Street
Vancouver, BC, V6E 3C9, Canada
Tel.: (604) 688-9478
Fax: (604) 688-9458
Web Site: www.coventryres.com
Year Founded: 1984
CYY—(ASX TSXV)
Int. Income: $8,996
Assets: $2,322,630
Liabilities: $959,497
Net Worth: $1,363,133
Earnings: ($1,010,552)
Fiscal Year-end: 12/31/12

Business Description:
Mineral Exploration Services
S.I.C.: 1081
N.A.I.C.S.: 213114

Personnel:
Steven Chadwick *(Interim Pres & CEO)*
Nicholas Day *(CFO)*

Board of Directors:
Eric Edwards
Robert Boaz
Steven Chadwick
Nicholas Day
Anthony Goddard
Don Halliday
Michael Haynes

Legal Counsel:
Steinepreis Paganin
Level 4 The Read Buildings 16 Milligan Street
6000 Perth, WA, Australia

Anfield Sujir Kennedy & Durno LLP
609 Granville Street Suite 1600
Vancouver, BC, V7Y 1C3, Canada

Transfer Agent:
Computershare Investor Services Inc.
100 University Ave 9th Floor
Toronto, ON, Canada

Non-U.S. Subsidiary:

Coventry Resources Limited (1)
Suite 9 5 Centro Avenue
Subiaco, WA, 6008, Australia AU
Tel.: (61) 893241266
Fax: (61) 892262027
E-Mail: info@coventryres.com
Web Site: www.coventryres.com
Emp.: 18
Gold Exploration & Mining Services
S.I.C.: 1041
N.A.I.C.S.: 212221
Nicholas Day *(Sec)*

COVER-MORE GROUP LIMITED

Level 10 60 Miller Street
North Sydney, NSW, 2060, Australia
Mailing Address:
Private Bag 913
North Sydney, NSW, 2059, Australia
Tel.: (61) 2 8907 5125
Fax: (61) 2 9202 8001
Web Site: www.covermore.com
Year Founded: 1986
CVO—(ASX)

Business Description:
Travel & Medical Insurance
S.I.C.: 6411
N.A.I.C.S.: 524298

Personnel:
Michael Alscher *(Chm)*
Peter Edwards *(CEO)*
John Murphy *(CFO)*
George Saunders *(COO)*
Sanjeev Gupta *(CIO)*
Steve Rashford *(Chief Medical Officer)*
Michele Grow *(CEO-Employee Assistance)*

Board of Directors:
Michael Alscher
Louis Carroll
Peter Edwards
Stephen Loosely
Trevor John Matthews
Lisa McIntyre
Sam Mostyn

COVIDIEN PLC

20 On Hatch Lower Hatch Street
Dublin, 2, Ireland
Tel.: (353) 1 438 1700
Web Site: www.covidien.com
COV—(NYSE)
Sls.: $10,235,000,000
Assets: $19,918,000,000
Liabilities: $10,676,000,000
Net Worth: $9,242,000,000
Earnings: $1,700,000,000
Emp.: 38,500
Fiscal Year-end: 09/27/13

Business Description:
Holding Company; Pharmaceuticals Mfr
S.I.C.: 6719
N.A.I.C.S.: 551112

Personnel:
Jose E. Almeida *(Chm, Pres & CEO)*
Charles J. Dockendorff *(CFO & Exec VP)*
Richard G. Brown, Jr. *(Chief Acctg Officer, VP & Controller)*
Michael Tarnoff *(Chief Medical Officer)*
Eric C. Green *(Chief Tax Officer & VP)*
James C. Clemmer *(Pres-Medical Supplies & Sr VP)*
Bryan C. Hanson *(Pres-Medical Devices-US & Sr VP)*
Brian Douglas King *(Pres-Emerging Markets)*
Peter L. Wehrly *(Pres-Developed Markets)*
John H. Masterson *(Gen Counsel & Sr VP)*
Gregory S. Andrulonis *(Treas & VP)*
John Wodick Kapples *(Sec)*
Michael P. Dunford *(Sr VP-HR)*
Amy A. McBride-Wendell *(Sr VP-Strategy & Bus Dev)*
Michael Sgrignari *(Sr VP-Quality & Ops)*
Jacqueline F. Strayer *(Sr VP-Corp Comm)*

Board of Directors:
Jose E. Almeida
Joy A. Amundson
Craig Arnold
Robert H. Brust
Christopher J. Coughlin
Randall J. Hogan, III
Martin D. Madaus
Dennis H. Reilley
Stephen H. Rusckowski
Joseph A. Zaccagnino

Transfer Agent:
Mellon Investor Services, LLC
480 Washington Blvd
Jersey City, NJ 07310
Tel.: (201) 680-6610
Toll Free: (888) 581-9376

Corporate Headquarters:

Covidien Inc. (1)
15 Hampshire St
Mansfield, MA 02048 DE
Tel.: (508) 261-8000
Fax: (508) 261-8424
Toll Free: (800) 346-7197
Web Site: www.covidien.com
Emp.: 1,700
Disposable Medical Products, Wound-Care Products, Syringes & Needles, Sutures, Surgical Staplers, Incontinence Products, Electrosurgical Instruments & Laparoscopic Instruments Mfr, Developer & Marketer
Export
S.I.C.: 3842
N.A.I.C.S.: 339113
Jose E. Almeida *(Chm, Pres & CEO)*
Charles J. Dockendorff *(CFO & Exec VP)*
Steven M. McManama *(CIO & VP)*
Richard G. Brown *(Chief Accounting Officer, VP & Controller)*
Eric C. Green *(Chief Tax Officer & VP)*
James C. Clemmer *(Pres-Medical Supplies & Sr VP)*
John H. Masterson *(Gen Counsel & Sr VP)*
Michael P. Dunford *(Sr VP-HR)*
James M. Muse *(Sr VP-Global Supply Chain)*
Amy A. Wendell *(Sr VP-Strategy & Bus Dev)*

Branches:

Covidien (2)
6135 Gunbarrel Ave
Boulder, CO 80301-3214
Tel.: (925) 463-4000
Toll Free: (800) NELLCOR
Web Site: www.nellcor.com
Monitoring Instruments, Sensors, Airway Adapters & Detectors Mfr
Import Export
S.I.C.: 3841
N.A.I.C.S.: 339112
Frank Chan *(VP-R&D)*

Covidien (2)
5920 Longbow Dr
Boulder, CO 80301-3202
Tel.: (303) 530-2300
Fax: (303) 530-6285
Toll Free: (800) 255-8522
E-Mail: valleylab.webmaster@tycohealthcare.com
Web Site: www.valleylab.com
Emp.: 1,600
Medical Products
S.I.C.: 3841
N.A.I.C.S.: 339112
Leah Hoover *(Mgr-Trng)*

Covidien (2)
555 Long Wharf Dr
New Haven, CT 06511
Tel.: (203) 845-1000
Toll Free: (800) 722-8772
Web Site: www.ussurg.com
Emp.: 1,500
Surgical Instruments Mfr
S.I.C.: 3841
N.A.I.C.S.: 339112

Covidien (2)
101A 1st Ave
Waltham, MA 02451
Tel.: (781) 693-2300
Web Site: www.confluentsurgical.com
Sales Range: $25-49.9 Million
Emp.: 106
Surgical Products Mfr
S.I.C.: 3841
N.A.I.C.S.: 339112

Covidien (2)
2 Ludlow Park Dr
Chicopee, MA 01022-1318
Tel.: (413) 593-6400
Web Site: www.covidien.com
Emp.: 700
Medical Products & Supplies
S.I.C.: 5047

Covidien plc—(Continued)

N.A.I.C.S.: 423450
Aaron Gerber *(Mgr-Mktg-Therapy IV)*

Covidien (2)
201 Sabaneta Industrial Pk
Ponce, PR 00716
Tel.: (787) 844-4526
Emp.: 750
Surgical Instruments Mfr
S.I.C.: 3841
N.A.I.C.S.: 339112
Raul Cardona *(Gen Mgr)*

Division:

Covidien GI Solutions (2)
540 Oakmead Pkwy
Sunnyvale, CA 94085 DE
Tel.: (408) 328-7300
Toll Free: (888) 662-2779
Sales Range: $75-99.9 Million
Gastrointestinal Treatment Apparatus Developer & Mfr
S.I.C.: 3845
N.A.I.C.S.: 334510
David S. Utley *(Chief Medical Officer)*

Subsidiaries:

Auto Suture Puerto Rico, Inc. (2)
201 Sabaneta Industrial Park
Mercedita, PR 00715
Tel.: (787) 844-4526
Fax: (787) 259-6583
Surgical & Medical Instrument Mfr
S.I.C.: 3841
N.A.I.C.S.: 339112

Bacchus Vascular Inc. (2)
3110 Coronado Dr.
Santa Clara, CA 95054
Tel.: (408) 980-8300
Web Site: www.bacchus-vascular.com
Emp.: 32
Surgical & Medical Instrument Mfr
S.I.C.: 3841
N.A.I.C.S.: 339112
Scott Cramer *(Pres)*

ev3 Inc. (2)
3033 Campus Dr
Plymouth, MN 55441 DE
Tel.: (763) 398-7000
Fax: (763) 398-7001
Toll Free: (800) 716-6700
E-Mail: ir@ev3.net
Web Site: www.ev3.net
Sales Range: $400-449.9 Million
Emp.: 1,350
Catheter-Based & Endovascular Medical Devices Mfr
S.I.C.: 3841
N.A.I.C.S.: 339112
Stacy Enxing Seng *(Pres-Worldwide Peripheral Vascular & Exec VP)*
Brett A. Wall *(Pres-Intl & Sr VP)*

Divisions:

Micro Therapeutics, Inc. (3)
9775 Toledo Way
Irvine, CA 92618 DE
Tel.: (949) 837-3700
Fax: (949) 837-2044
Toll Free: (800) 684-6733
E-Mail: inquiry@1mti.com
Web Site: www.ev3.net
Medical Device Mfr
S.I.C.: 3841
N.A.I.C.S.: 339112
Earl Slee *(VP-Res & Devel)*

Mallinckrodt Caribe, Inc. (2)
Carr 869 Km 2 0 Bo Palmas
Catano, PR 00962
Tel.: (787) 706-2200
Toll Free: (866) 683-2928
Healthcare Product Developer & Mfr
S.I.C.: 5122
N.A.I.C.S.: 424210

superDimension Inc. (2)
161 Cheshire Ln Ste 100
Minneapolis, MN 55441-5433
Tel.: (763) 210-4000
Fax: (866) 706-9639
Toll Free: (800) 387-9016
E-Mail: info.us@superdimension.com
Web Site: www.superdimension.com
Healthcare Product Developer & Mfr
S.I.C.: 5122
N.A.I.C.S.: 424210
Rick Buchholz *(VP & CFO)*

VNUS Medical Technologies, Inc. (2)
5799 Fontanoso Way
San Jose, CA 95138-1015 CA
Tel.: (408) 473-1100
Fax: (408) 365-8480
Toll Free: (888) 797-8346
E-Mail: info@vnus.com
Web Site: www.vnus.com
Sales Range: $100-124.9 Million
Emp.: 318
Medical Device Mfr
S.I.C.: 3845
N.A.I.C.S.: 334510
Jon Kitahara *(Coord-Media)*

Non-U.S. Subsidiary:

VNUS Medical Technologies GmbH (3)
Wilhelm-Pfitzer-Str. 28
70736 Fellbach, Germany
Tel.: (49) 7117948090
Fax: (49) 7117948093099
Emp.: 12
Medical Device Mfr
S.I.C.: 3845
N.A.I.C.S.: 334510

Plant:

Covidien (2)
5439 State Rte 40
Argyle, NY 12809
Tel.: (518) 638-6101
Fax: (518) 638-8493
Emp.: 220
Mfr of Catheters & Airway Management Products
S.I.C.: 3841
N.A.I.C.S.: 339112

Non-U.S. Branches:

Covidien (2)
Hemsvarnsgatan 9
PO Box 54
17174 Solna, Sweden
Tel.: (46) 858560500
Fax: (46) 851761579
E-Mail: jessica.mohn@covidien.com
Emp.: 200
Medical Products
S.I.C.: 5047
N.A.I.C.S.: 423450
Annica Wefterman *(Mgr-HR)*

Covidien (2)
7F Nippon Brunswick Bldg
5-27-7 Sendagaya Shibuya-Ku, Tokyo, 151-00511, Japan
Tel.: (81) 357171700
Fax: (81) 3 5717 1240
E-Mail: japan.info@covidien.com
Web Site: www.covidien.co.jp
Emp.: 500
Medical Devices
S.I.C.: 3841
N.A.I.C.S.: 339112
Junichi Obata *(Pres)*

Covidien (2)
303 Terry Fox Dr Ste 400
Kanata, ON, K2K 3J1, Canada ON
Tel.: (613) 238-1840
Fax: (613) 238-1291
Toll Free: (800) 663-3336
E-Mail: info@sandmansleep.com
Web Site: www.sandmansleep.com
Emp.: 100
Sleep Diagnostic Software
S.I.C.: 7371
N.A.I.C.S.: 541511
Lee Ann Clare *(Controller)*

Covidien (2)
Ermita Izatapalapa 1514 Col Barrio San Miguel
Mexico, DF, 09360, Mexico
Tel.: (52) 5558041500
Fax: (52) 5558041500
Web Site: www.covidien.com
Emp.: 200
Medical Sensors & Monitors Mfr
S.I.C.: 3841
N.A.I.C.S.: 339113
Jorge Ramirez *(Dir-HR)*

Covidien (2)
Costa del Este Parque Industrial
1st Street 4th Building
Panama, Panama
Tel.: (507) 2647337
Fax: (507) 2717277
E-Mail: silvea.cavallero@covidien.com
Emp.: 31
Medical Supplies
S.I.C.: 3842
N.A.I.C.S.: 339113
R. B. Wong *(Controller)*

Covidien (2)
Westerduinweg 3
PO Box 3
NL 1755 LE Petten, Netherlands
Tel.: (31) 224567890
Telex: 57801
Fax: (31) 224567008
E-Mail: info.nuclear@covidien.com
Web Site: www.covidien.com
Emp.: 300
Medical Products Mfr
Import Export
S.I.C.: 3841
N.A.I.C.S.: 339112
Frank Delange *(Gen Mgr)*

Covidien (2)
Cornamaddy
Athlone, Westmeath, Ireland
Tel.: (353) 906475210
Fax: (353) 906441206
E-Mail: liam.hynes@covidien.com
Emp.: 600
Medical Products
Import Export
S.I.C.: 3841
N.A.I.C.S.: 339112
Liam Hynes *(Mng Dir)*

Covidien (2)
154 Fareham Rd
Gosport, Hampshire, PO13 0AS, United Kingdom
Tel.: (44) 1329224000
Fax: (44) 1329220213
Emp.: 300
Medical Products
S.I.C.: 5047
N.A.I.C.S.: 423450
Bob Stokes *(Mgr-Mktg)*

Covidien (2)
9 Sur 125 Industrial NBA
Tijuana, Baja California, Mexico
Tel.: (52) 6646234200
Fax: (52) 6196908523
E-Mail: lizbeth.juvera@covidien.com
Web Site: www.covidien.com
Emp.: 1,000
Disposable Medical Products Mfr
S.I.C.: 3841
N.A.I.C.S.: 339112
Hector Flores *(Gen Mgr)*

Covidien (2)
Generaal De Wittelaan 9 5
B-2800 Mechelen, Belgium
Tel.: (32) 15294450
Fax: (32) 015294455
E-Mail: covidien.belgium@covidien.com
Emp.: 110
Surgical & Medical Instruments
S.I.C.: 3841
N.A.I.C.S.: 339112

Covidien (2)
2 rue Denis Diderot
78990 Elancourt, France
Tel.: (33) 0130798000
Fax: (33) 0130798030
E-Mail: elancourt.accueilchh@Covidien.com
Web Site: www.covidien.com
Emp.: 350
Medical Monitoring Equipment
S.I.C.: 5047
N.A.I.C.S.: 423450

Covidien (2)
215 Herbert St
Gananoque, ON, K7G 2Y7, Canada ON
Tel.: (613) 382-4733
Fax: (613) 382-7036
Emp.: 440
Medical & Hospital Equipment
S.I.C.: 5047
N.A.I.C.S.: 423450

Covidien (2)
Hogeweg 105
5301 LL Zaltbommel, Netherlands
Tel.: (31) 418576600
Fax: (31) 418576793
E-Mail: infonl@covidien.com
Emp.: 100
Medical Monitoring Equipment
S.I.C.: 5047
N.A.I.C.S.: 423450

Covidien (2)
Chinham Business Park Ashwood
Basingstoke, Hants, RG24 8EH, United Kingdom
Tel.: (44) 1256708880
Fax: (44) 1256372693
Emp.: 100
Medical Supplies
S.I.C.: 3842
N.A.I.C.S.: 339113

Covidien (2)
7300 Trans Canada Hwy
Pointe-Claire, QC, H9R 1C7, Canada
Tel.: (514) 695-1220
Fax: (800) 567-1939
Web Site: www.covidien.com
Emp.: 400
Medical Products Mfr
S.I.C.: 3841
N.A.I.C.S.: 339112
Teresa Mattarelli *(Gen Mgr)*

Subsidiary:

Covidien Ireland Commercial Limited (1)
Block G Ground Floor Cherrywood
Technology Park
Loughlinstown, Dublin, Ireland
Tel.: (353) 14381613
Fax: (353) 14393039
E-Mail: TechnicalServicesIreland@Covidien.com
Healthcare Product Developer & Mfr
S.I.C.: 5122
N.A.I.C.S.: 424210

Non-U.S. Subsidiaries:

A&E Products Guatemala, S.A. (1)
Km 30 5 Carretera CA-9 Sur Amatitlan
Interior Zona France Parque
Industrial Zeta, La Union, 1016, Guatemala
Tel.: (502) 66338240
Fax: (502) 66338244
E-Mail: folatexgt@gmail.com
Emp.: 15
Healthcare Product Developer & Mfr
S.I.C.: 5122
N.A.I.C.S.: 424210
Dong Kim *(Mng Dir)*

Auto Suture U.K. Limited (1)
4500 Parkway Whiteley
Fareham, Hampshire, PO15 7AY, United Kingdom
Tel.: (44) 1329224000
Fax: (44) 1329220213
Emp.: 200
Surgical & Medical Instrument Mfr
S.I.C.: 3841
N.A.I.C.S.: 339112
Debra Reynolds *(Dir-Fin)*

Covidien Austria GmbH (1)
Campus21 Europaring F09402
Brunn am Gebirge, Lower Austria, 2345, Austria
Tel.: (43) 2236378839
Fax: (43) 2236378840
Healthcare Product Developer & Mfr
S.I.C.: 5122
N.A.I.C.S.: 424210

Covidien Danmark A/S (1)
Arne Jacobsens Alle 7 5th Fl
2300 Copenhagen, Denmark
Tel.: (45) 70275350
Fax: (45) 70275650
Emp.: 15
Healthcare Product Developer & Mfr
S.I.C.: 5122
N.A.I.C.S.: 424210
Agnete Holm *(Mgr)*

Covidien Deutschland GmbH (1)
Gewerbepark 1
93333 Neustadt, Germany
Tel.: (49) 94459590
Fax: (49) 9445959155
E-Mail: info.de@covidien.com
Emp.: 500
Medical Supplies
S.I.C.: 5047
N.A.I.C.S.: 423450
Joerg Hirschfeld *(Mgr-Nuclear Energy)*

Covidien Healthcare India Private Limited (1)
Building No 9B 10th Floor Dlf Cyber City Phase-III
Gurgaon, Haryana, 122002, India
Tel.: (91) 1244709800
Fax: (91) 1244206850
Emp.: 150
Healthcare Product Developer & Mfr
S.I.C.: 5122
N.A.I.C.S.: 424210
Mark Rooney *(Gen Mgr)*

Covidien Hellas S.A. (1)
L Kifisias 268 Building Pwc
Halandri, 152 32 Athens, Greece
Tel.: (30) 2106874400
Fax: (30) 2106874444
Surgical & Medical Instrument Mfr
S.I.C.: 3841
N.A.I.C.S.: 339112

Covidien Hong Kong Limited (1)
Unit 12-16 18 Floor Bea Tower Millennium City 5 418 Kwun Tong Road
Kwun Tong, Kowloon, China (Hong Kong)
Tel.: (852) 25743251
Fax: (852) 28380749
Emp.: 40
Healthcare Product Developer & Mfr
S.I.C.: 5122
N.A.I.C.S.: 424210

Covidien (Israel) Ltd. (1)
5 Shacham St
POBox 3069
North Industrial Park, Caesarea, 38900, Israel
Tel.: (972) 46277388
Fax: (972) 46277688
Healthcare Product Developer & Mfr
S.I.C.: 5122
N.A.I.C.S.: 424210

Covidien Italia, S.p.A. (1)
Via Rivoltana 2 d
20090 Segrate, Milan, Italy
Tel.: (39) 02703171
Fax: (39) 0270317284
Healthcare Product Developer & Mfr
S.I.C.: 5122
N.A.I.C.S.: 424210

Covidien Medical Products (Shanghai) Manufacturing L.L.C. (1)
Building 10 No789 Puxing Road Caohejing Export Processing Zone
Pujiang Town Minhang District, Shanghai, 201114, China
Tel.: (86) 2124082408
Surgical & Medical Instrument Mfr
S.I.C.: 3841
N.A.I.C.S.: 339112

Covidien New Zealand Limited (1)
Ground Floor 15B Vestey Drive
Mount Wellington, Auckland, 2140, New Zealand
Tel.: (64) 95736700
Fax: (64) 95736298
Emp.: 20
Healthcare Product Developer & Mfr
S.I.C.: 5122
N.A.I.C.S.: 424210
Philippa Dennis *(Country Mgr)*

Covidien Polska Sp.z.o.o. (1)
Al Jerozolimskie 162
Warsaw, 02 342, Poland
Tel.: (48) 223122000
Fax: (48) 223122020
Healthcare Product Developer & Mfr
S.I.C.: 5122
N.A.I.C.S.: 424210

Covidien Private Limited (1)
103 Penang Road No 10-01 Visioncrest Commercial
Singapore, 238467, Singapore
Tel.: (65) 64820100
Fax: (65) 64820300
Healthcare Product Developer & Mfr
S.I.C.: 5122
N.A.I.C.S.: 424210

Covidien Pty Limited (1)
L 1 Riverview Park 166 Epping Rd
Lane Cove, NSW, 2066, Australia
Tel.: (61) 294189611
Fax: (61) 289048904
Emp.: 150
Healthcare Product Developer & Mfr
S.I.C.: 5122
N.A.I.C.S.: 424210

Covidien Saglik A.S. (1)
Maslak Mahallesi Bilim Sokak No 5 Sun Plaza Kat 2-3
Sisli, Istanbul, 34398, Turkey
Tel.: (90) 2123662000
Fax: (90) 2122763525
Healthcare Product Developer & Mfr
S.I.C.: 5122
N.A.I.C.S.: 424210

Covidien Sendirian Berhad (1)
Level 12 Wisma Kelana Brem Tower 1
Jalan Ss7/15 Jalan Stadium
Kelana Jaya, 47301 Petaling Jaya, Selangor, Malaysia
Tel.: (60) 374911900
Fax: (60) 374919122
Surgical & Medical Instrument Mfr
S.I.C.: 3841
N.A.I.C.S.: 339112

Covidien Spain S.L. (1)
World Trade Center Almeda Park building 7 3rd Fl
8940 Cornella, Barcelona, Spain
Tel.: (34) 934758669
Fax: (34) 934771017
E-Mail: spain.covidien@covidien.com
Emp.: 100
Healthcare Product Developer & Mfr
S.I.C.: 5122
N.A.I.C.S.: 424210

Covidien (Thailand) Limited (1)
319 Chamchuri Square 17th Floor Unit 1-8
Phayathai Road Pathumwan, Bangkok, 10330, Thailand
Tel.: (66) 22073100
Fax: (66) 22073101
Healthcare Product Developer & Mfr
S.I.C.: 5122
N.A.I.C.S.: 424210

Covidien (UK) Commercial Limited (1)
Technical Services & Support Unit 2
Talisman Business Centre
London Road, Bicester, Oxfordshire, OX26 6HR, United Kingdom
Tel.: (44) 1869328092
Fax: (44) 1869327585
Emp.: 40
Medical Device & Hospital Equipment Supplies & Distr
S.I.C.: 5047
N.A.I.C.S.: 423450
Paul Camidge *(Mgr-Tech Svcs)*

Dendron GmbH (1)
Universitatsstr 140 Wiemelhausen
44799 Bochum, North Rhine-Westphal, Germany
Tel.: (49) 234970610
Fax: (49) 23497061640
Healthcare Product Developer & Mfr
S.I.C.: 5122
N.A.I.C.S.: 424210

ev3 Canada Inc. (1)
1920 Yonge St Suite 200
Toronto, ON, M4S 3E2, Canada
Tel.: (416) 572-7692
Fax: (647) 477-6792
Surgical & Medical Instrument Mfr
S.I.C.: 3841
N.A.I.C.S.: 339112

ev3 Europe SAS (1)
106/108 rue La Boetie
75008 Paris, France
Tel.: (33) 156885910
Fax: (33) 156885912
Surgical & Medical Instrument Mfr
S.I.C.: 3841
N.A.I.C.S.: 339112

ev3 Limited (1)
Hadham House 3 -7 Church Street
Bishop's Stortford, Hertfordshire, CM23 2LY, United Kingdom
Tel.: (44) 1279659900
Fax: (44) 1279654900
Emp.: 22
Medical Device & Hospital Equipment Supplies & Distr
S.I.C.: 5047
N.A.I.C.S.: 423450
Elise Ellis *(Office Mgr)*

ev3 Nordic AB (1)
Kanalvagen 1A 2tr
194 61 Upplands Vasby, Sweden
Tel.: (46) 859000950
Fax: (46) 859000959
Surgical & Medical Instrument Mfr
S.I.C.: 3841
N.A.I.C.S.: 339112

ev3 SAS (1)
106/108 rue La Boetie
75008 Paris, France
Tel.: (33) 156883110
Fax: (33) 156885912
Surgical & Medical Instrument Mfr
S.I.C.: 3841
N.A.I.C.S.: 339112
kenny Christofferson *(Gen Mgr)*

ev3 S.r.l. (1)
Piazza Repubblica 32
Milan, 20124, Italy
Tel.: (39) 026797761
Fax: (39) 0266986234
E-Mail: ev3@ev3.net
Emp.: 23
Healthcare Product Developer & Mfr
S.I.C.: 5122
N.A.I.C.S.: 424210
Paola Coscarella *(Office Mgr)*

ev3 Technologies Iberica, S.L. (1)
Avda Castilla de 3
28830 San Fernando de Henares, Madrid, Spain
Tel.: (34) 916567154
Fax: (34) 916567214
E-Mail: ev3spain@ev3.net
Emp.: 20
Healthcare Product Developer & Mfr
S.I.C.: 5122
N.A.I.C.S.: 424210
Esperanza Lazaro *(Gen Mgr)*

Given Imaging Ltd. (1)
Hermon Building New Industrial Park
Yokneam, 20692, Israel II
Mailing Address:
PO Box 258
Yokneam, 20692, Israel
Tel.: (972) 4 909 7777
Fax: (972) 4 959 2466
E-Mail: info@givenimaging.com
Web Site: www.givenimaging.com
Rev.: $180,501,000
Assets: $274,314,000
Liabilities: $51,366,000
Net Worth: $222,948,000
Earnings: $14,257,000
Emp.: 804
Fiscal Year-end: 12/31/12
Medical Diagnostic Imaging Technology
S.I.C.: 5047
N.A.I.C.S.: 423450
Israel Makov *(Chm)*
Nachum Homi Shamir *(Pres & CEO)*
Yuval Yanai *(CFO)*
Kevin Rubey *(COO)*
Thomas Looby *(CMO & Sr VP)*
David H. Mason, Jr. *(Chief Medical Officer & Sr VP)*
Skip Baldino *(Pres-Americas)*
Thomas Pracht *(Pres-Given Imaging-EMEA)*
Ido Warshavski *(Gen Counsel, Sec & Sr VP)*
Ori Braun *(Sr VP-Bus Dev)*
Keith A. Chrzanowski *(Sr VP-HR)*
Steve Murray *(Sr VP-Global Mfg & Ops)*
Kazem Samandari *(Sr VP-Asia Pacific & Japan)*

U.S. Subsidiary:

Given Imaging Inc. (2)
3950 Shackleford Rd Ste 500
Duluth, GA 30096-1852
Tel.: (770) 662-0870
Fax: (770) 662-0510
E-Mail: infousa@givenimaging.com
Web Site: www.givenimaging.com
Emp.: 70
Mfr of Gastrointestinal Diagnosis Products
S.I.C.: 3841
N.A.I.C.S.: 339112

Non-U.S. Subsidiaries:

Given Imaging (Asia Pacific) Pte Ltd. (2)
152 Beach Road
04-07 Gateway East
Singapore, 198721, Singapore
Tel.: (65) 62980200
Fax: (65) 62980100
E-Mail: infoap@givenimaging.com
Web Site: www.givenimaging.com
Emp.: 35
Medical Diagnostic Imaging Technology
S.I.C.: 3841
N.A.I.C.S.: 339112
Andrew Cheung *(Mng Dir)*
Kazem Samandari *(Sr VP-Asia Pacific/ Japan Reg)*

Given Imaging France s.a.s (2)
22 Rue Guynemer
Maison-Laffitte Paris, 78600, France
Tel.: (33) 134938000
Fax: (33) 134938011
E-Mail: infofr@givenimaging.com
Web Site: www.givenimaging.com
Emp.: 21
Medical Diagnostic Imaging Technology
S.I.C.: 5047
N.A.I.C.S.: 423450
Manfred Gehrtz *(Pres-EMEA)*

Given Imaging GmbH (2)
Borsteler Chaussee 47
Hamburg, 22453, Germany
Tel.: (49) 405133000
Fax: (49) 4046069611
E-Mail: infode@givenimaging.com
Web Site: www.givenimaging.com
Emp.: 35
Medical Diagnostic Imaging Technology
S.I.C.: 3841
N.A.I.C.S.: 339112
Thomas Prath *(Pres)*

Given Imaging K.K. (2)
2F KDX Kojimachi Bldg 3-3 Kojimachi
Chiyoda-ku, Tokyo, 102-0083, Japan
Tel.: (81) 352140588
Fax: (81) 352140590
E-Mail: info@givenimaging.com
Web Site: www.givenimaging.com
Emp.: 30
Medical Diagnostic Imaging Technology
S.I.C.: 5047
N.A.I.C.S.: 423450
Kazem Samandari *(Pres-Asia Pacific)*

Given Imaging Pty., Ltd. (2)
Rydelink Business Park Unit 4
277 Lane Cove Road, North Ryde, NSW, 2113, Australia
Tel.: (61) 298893944
Fax: (61) 2 9889 3955
E-Mail: infoaus@givenimaging.com
Web Site: www.givenimaging.com
Medical Diagnostic Imaging Technology
S.I.C.: 5047
N.A.I.C.S.: 423450
Warne Dinjhan *(Pres)*

Kendall-Gammatron Co., Ltd. (1)
117 Moo 2 Petchkasem Road
Sampran, Nagorn Pathom, 73110, Thailand TH
Tel.: (66) 34222792
Fax: (66) 34324462
Web Site: www.gammatron.co.th
Emp.: 430
Medical Device Mfr
S.I.C.: 3842
N.A.I.C.S.: 339113
Lim Thaueane *(Plant Mgr)*

Ludlow Technical Products Canada, Ltd. (1)
215 Herbert Street
Gananoque, ON, K7g 2y7, Canada
Tel.: (613) 382-4733
Surgical & Medical Instrument Mfr
S.I.C.: 3841

Covidien plc—(Continued)

N.A.I.C.S.: 339112

Mallinckrodt DAR Srl (1)
Via G Bove 2/4/6/8
41037 Mirandola, Modena, Italy
Tel.: (39) 0535617901
Fax: (39) 0535617933
E-Mail: mirandolaplant@covidien.com
Emp.: 450
Surgical & Medical Instrument Mfr
S.I.C.: 3841
N.A.I.C.S.: 339112
Stefano Cavaliere *(Plant Mgr)*

Mallinckrodt Switzerland Limited (1)
Roosstrasse 53
8832 Wollerau, Switzerland
Tel.: (41) 442542454
Fax: (41) 442526796
E-Mail: mallswiss@covidien.com
Web Site: www.mallinckrodt.ch
Emp.: 5
Radiopharmaceutical Product Distr
S.I.C.: 2836
N.A.I.C.S.: 325414
Marco Montagnolo *(Dir-Sls & Mktg)*

Mediquip Sdn. Bhd. (1)
Batu 5 Padang Lati Jalan Santan
Kangar, Perlis, 02450, Malaysia
Tel.: (60) 49381411
Fax: (60) 49382150
Healthcare Product Developer & Mfr
S.I.C.: 5122
N.A.I.C.S.: 424210

Nippon Covidien Ltd. (1)
4-10-2 Yoga
Setagaya-Ku, Tokyo, 158-0097, Japan
Tel.: (81) 357170510
Fax: (81) 357101310
Emp.: 600
Healthcare Product Developer & Mfr
S.I.C.: 5122
N.A.I.C.S.: 424210
Ryo Noda *(Pres)*

Polysuture Industria e Comercio Ltda. (1)
Av Gabriel Ramos da Silva 1245 Parque Industrial Joao F Zanin
Sao Sebastiao do Paraiso, 37950-000, Brazil
Tel.: (55) 3535394750
Fax: (55) 3535394774
E-Mail: pedidos.polysuture@covidien.com
Web Site: www.Polysuture.com.br
Emp.: 300
Surgical & Medical Instrument Mfr
S.I.C.: 3841
N.A.I.C.S.: 339112
Jose Roberto Carvalho *(Plant Mgr)*

Tyco Healthcare International Trading Co., Ltd. (1)
Fl 2-4 Tyco Centre 99 Tian Zhou Rd Cao Heijing Hi-Tech Park
Shanghai, 200233, China
Tel.: (86) 2124010200
Fax: (86) 2124010220
Web Site: www.tycohealthcareasia.com
Medical Products Distr
S.I.C.: 5047
N.A.I.C.S.: 423450

Tyco Healthcare Pte. Ltd. (1)
103 Penang Rd Ste 10-01 Visioncrest Commercial
238467 Singapore, Singapore
Tel.: (65) 64820100
Fax: (65) 64820300
E-Mail: info@tycohealth.com.sg
Web Site: www.covidien.com.sg
Emp.: 100
Medical Products Distr
S.I.C.: 5047
N.A.I.C.S.: 423450
Brian King *(Pres-Asia)*

USSC (Deutschland) GmbH (1)
Gewerbepark 1
93333 Neustadt, Rhineland-Palatinate, Germany
Tel.: (49) 9445959177
Fax: (49) 9445959214
Healthcare Product Developer & Mfr
S.I.C.: 5122
N.A.I.C.S.: 424210

COVINGTON CAPITAL CORPORATION

(d/b/a Covington Group of Funds)
87 Front St E Ste 400
Toronto, ON, M5E 1B8, Canada
Tel.: (416) 365-9155
Fax: (416) 365-9822
Toll Free: (866) 244-4714
E-Mail: info@covingtonfunds.com
Web Site: www.covingtonfunds.com
Year Founded: 1994
Sales Range: $75-99.9 Million
Emp.: 20

Business Description:
Private Equity Firm
S.I.C.: 6211
N.A.I.C.S.: 523999

Personnel:
Scott Clark *(Mng Partner)*
Phil Reddon *(Mng Partner)*
Lisa Low *(CFO)*
Wesley Ollson *(Exec VP-Sls & Bus Dev)*
Fiona Robertson *(Exec VP-Sls & Mktg)*
Matthew Hall *(Sr VP-Investments)*
William Jin *(Sr VP-Investments)*

COWELL E HOLDINGS INC.

Suite 3208-9 32/FL The Tower 6 9 Canton Road TST
Kowloon, China (Hong Kong)
Tel.: (852) 23686620
Fax: (852) 23686620
E-Mail: master@cowellkorea.com
Web Site: www.cowellkorea.com
Year Founded: 2006
Sales Range: $300-349.9 Million

Business Description:
Electronic Product Mfr
S.I.C.: 3679
N.A.I.C.S.: 334419

Personnel:
Kab-Cheol Kim *(Chm & CEO)*

COWELL IMPORTS INC.

(d/b/a Land Rover of Richmond)
5660 Parkwood Way
Richmond, BC, V6V 2M4, Canada
Tel.: (604) 273-6068
Fax: (604) 207-1682
E-Mail: sales@landroverofrichmond.com
Web Site: www.landroverofrichmond.com
Year Founded: 1996
Rev.: $12,900,000
Emp.: 25

Business Description:
New & Used Car Dealers
S.I.C.: 5511
N.A.I.C.S.: 441110

Personnel:
Ryan Cowell *(Pres)*

COWON SYSTEMS INC.

Cowon Tower 689-3 YeokSam-Dong Gangnam-Gu
Seoul, 135-080, Korea (South)
Tel.: (82) 269000000
Fax: (82) 234608222
E-Mail: business2@cowon.com
Web Site: www.cowonglobal.com
Year Founded: 1995
056000—(KRS)
Sales Range: $100-124.9 Million
Emp.: 180

Business Description:
Digital Multimedia & Wireless Internet Products
S.I.C.: 3663
N.A.I.C.S.: 334220

Personnel:
Park Namkyu *(Pres)*

Non-U.S. Subsidiary:

Cowon Indonesia (1)
TIFA Bldg 2nd Fl
Jl Kuningan Barat I No 26, Jakarta, 12710, Indonesia
Tel.: (62) 215262409
Fax: (62) 215262410
E-Mail: agustina@cowon.com
Web Site: www.cowon.com
Emp.: 30
Electronic Products Mfr
S.I.C.: 3651
N.A.I.C.S.: 334310
Irma Carolina *(Mgr-Mktg)*

COX & KINGS LIMITED

Turner Morrison Building 16 Bank Street Fort
Mumbai, 400 001, India
Tel.: (91) 2222709100
Fax: (91) 2222709161
E-Mail: contactus@coxandkings.com
Web Site: www.coxandkings.com
533144—(BOM LUX NSE)
Rev.: $3,462,382,080
Assets: $15,484,200,120
Liabilities: $12,020,668,560
Net Worth: $3,463,531,560
Earnings: $282,716,460
Emp.: 700
Fiscal Year-end: 03/31/13

Business Description:
Travel & Tour Services
S.I.C.: 4729
N.A.I.C.S.: 561599

Personnel:
Anil Khandelwal *(CFO)*
Rashmi Jain *(Sec)*

Board of Directors:
A. B. M. Good
Subhash Chandra Bhargava
Ajay Ajit Peter Kerkar
Urrshila Kerkar
Mahalinga Narayanan
Pesi Patel

Transfer Agent:
Karvy Compushare Private Limited
Plot No 17 to 24 Vittalrao Nagar Madhapur
Hyderabad, India

Non-U.S. Subsidiary:

Holidaybreak plc (1)
Hartford Manor
Greenbank Lane, Northwich, Cheshire, CW8 1HW, United Kingdom UK
Tel.: (44) 1606787000
Fax: (44) 1606787001
E-Mail: group@holidaybreak.co.uk
Web Site: www.holidaybreak.co.uk
Sales Range: $750-799.9 Million
Emp.: 3,480
Holding Company; Tour Operator of Self-Drive Camping & Mobile-Home Holidays in Europe
S.I.C.: 4725
N.A.I.C.S.: 561520
Peter Kerkar *(CEO)*
Alex Williamson *(Sec)*

Subsidiaries:

European Study Tours Limited (2)
4 Post Office Walk
Fore Street, Hertford, Hertfordshire, SG14 1DL, United Kingdom
Tel.: (44) 844 576 1960
Fax: (44) 1992 586381
E-Mail: estsales@euro-study-tours.co.uk
Web Site: www.euro-study-tours.co.uk
Emp.: 22
Educational Tour Operating Services
S.I.C.: 4725
N.A.I.C.S.: 561520
Laura Michelson *(Mgr-Ops)*

Explore Worldwide Limited (2)
Nelson House
55 Victoria Road, Farnborough, Hampshire, GU14 7PA, United Kingdom
Tel.: (44) 8450131537
Fax: (44) 1252391110
E-Mail: marketing@explore.co.uk
Web Site: www.explore.co.uk
Emp.: 90
Travel Tour Operating Services
S.I.C.: 4725
N.A.I.C.S.: 561520
Ashley Toft *(Mng Dir)*

Greenbank Holidays Limited (2)
Hartford Manor
Greenbank Lane, Northwich, Cheshire, CW8 1HW, United Kingdom (100%)
Tel.: (44) 8703 667552
Fax: (44) 8703 667640
Web Site: www.eurocamp.co.uk
Ferry & Campsite Booking Services for Self-Drive Camping & Motorhome Holidays in Europe
S.I.C.: 4729
N.A.I.C.S.: 561599

NST Travel Group Limited (2)
Discovery House Brooklands Way
Whitehills Business Park, Blackpool, Lancashire, FY4 5LW, United Kingdom
Tel.: (44) 1253 833 833
Fax: (44) 1253 833 844
E-Mail: info@nstgroup.co.uk
Web Site: www.nstgroup.co.uk
Emp.: 130
School Trips, Tours, Educational Visits & School Group Travel
S.I.C.: 4725
N.A.I.C.S.: 561520
Michelle Evans *(Head-Product & Mktg)*

Own A Holiday Home Limited (2)
Hartford Manor
Greenbank Lane, Northwich, Cheshire, CW8 1HW, United Kingdom
Tel.: (44) 1606787000
Fax: (44) 8444060210
E-Mail: info@ownaholidayhome.com
Web Site: www.ownaholidayhome.com
Emp.: 3
Mobile Home Sales
S.I.C.: 5271
N.A.I.C.S.: 453930
Jez Allen *(Gen Mgr)*

PGL Adventure Limited (2)
Alton Court
Penyard Lane, Ross-on-Wye, Herefordshire, HR9 5GL, United Kingdom
Tel.: (44) 1989764211
Fax: (44) 1989767358
E-Mail: contact@pgl.co.uk
Web Site: www.pgl.co.uk
Emp.: 53
Outdoor Accommodation & Recreational Services
S.I.C.: 7032
N.A.I.C.S.: 721214
Richard Sanders *(Dir-Ops)*

PGL Group Limited (2)
Alton Court
Penyard Lane, Ross-on-Wye, Herefordshire, HR9 5GL, United Kingdom
Tel.: (44) 1989764211
Fax: (44) 1989767358
E-Mail: enquiries@pgl.co.uk
Web Site: www.pgl.co.uk
Emp.: 250
Holding Company; Travel & Tour Operating Agencies
S.I.C.: 6719
N.A.I.C.S.: 551112
Patricia Mary Walker *(Dir-HR)*

PGL Travel Limited (2)
Alton Court
Penyard Lane, Ross-on-Wye, Herefordshire, HR9 5GL, United Kingdom
Tel.: (44) 1989764211
Fax: (44) 8443710102
E-Mail: enquiries@pgl.co.uk
Web Site: www.pgl.co.uk
Emp.: 250
Residential Activity Holidays & Educational Tours for Youth
S.I.C.: 4725
N.A.I.C.S.: 561520
Darren McLean *(Mgr-HR Sys)*

Regal Diving and Tours Limited (2)
58 Lancaster Way
Ely, Cambridgeshire, CB6 3NW, United Kingdom
Tel.: (44) 1353 659 999
Fax: (44) 1353666128

E-Mail: info@regal-diving.co.uk
Web Site: www.regal-diving.co.uk
Emp.: 10
Diving Tour Operating Services
S.I.C.: 8299
N.A.I.C.S.: 611620
Andreas Elia *(Mng Dir)*

Superbreak Mini Holidays Group Ltd. **(2)**
Eboracum Way
York, YO31 7RE, United Kingdom (100%)
Tel.: (44) 1904 420440
Fax: (44) 871 221 3377
E-Mail: admin@superbreak.com
Web Site: www.superbreak.com
Emp.: 200
Tour Operators & Travel Arrangements
S.I.C.: 4725
N.A.I.C.S.: 561520
Jane Atkins *(Sls Dir)*

Superbreak Mini-Holidays Limited **(2)**
Eboracum Way
Heworth Green, York, North Yorkshire, YO31 7RE, United Kingdom
Tel.: (44) 1904 420440
Fax: (44) 871 221 3377
E-Mail: admin@superbreak.com
Web Site: www.superbreak.com
Emp.: 200
Travel Agency Activities
S.I.C.: 4729
N.A.I.C.S.: 561599
Jane Atkins *(Sls Dir)*

Non-U.S. Subsidiaries:

Bookit B.V. **(2)**
Van Heuven Goedhartlaan 935a
1181 LD Amstelveen, North Holland, Netherlands
Tel.: (31) 20 456 42 42
Fax: (31) 20 456 40 50
E-Mail: pr@bookit.nl
Web Site: www.bookit.nl
Emp.: 100
Hotel & Transportation Reservation Services
S.I.C.: 4729
N.A.I.C.S.: 561599
Karel Vos *(Mng Dir)*

Business Reservations Centre Holland B.V. **(2)**
Van Heuven Goedhartlaan 935 A
1181 LD Amstelveen, North Holland, Netherlands
Tel.: (31) 204564035
Fax: (31) 204 56 40 45
E-Mail: info@bookit.nl
Web Site: www.bookit.nl
Emp.: 100
Hotel & Transportation Reservation Services
S.I.C.: 4729
N.A.I.C.S.: 561599
Karel Vos *(Mng Dir)*

B.V. Weekendjeweg.nl **(2)**
Van Heuven Goedhartlaan 935a
1181 LD Amstelveen, North Holland, Netherlands
Tel.: (31) 204564099
Fax: (31) 204564050
E-Mail: info@bookit.com
Web Site: www.weekendjeweg.nl
Hotel Reservation Services
S.I.C.: 4729
N.A.I.C.S.: 561599
Karel Vos *(Mng Dir)*

Camping in Comfort B.V. **(2)**
Zuidsingel 22
3811 HB Amersfoort, Netherlands
Tel.: (31) 334602703
Fax: (31) 334612811
Web Site: www.eurocamp.nl
Emp.: 60
Camping & Touring Services
S.I.C.: 7032
N.A.I.C.S.: 721214

Djoser B.V. **(2)**
Breestraat 125
2311 CM Leiden, South Holland, Netherlands
Tel.: (31) 71 5126400
Fax: (31) 71 5120775
E-Mail: info@djoser.nl
Web Site: www.djoser.nl
Emp.: 40
Travel Tour Operating Services
S.I.C.: 4725
N.A.I.C.S.: 561520
Herman van der Velde *(Founder & Dir)*

Non-U.S. Subsidiary:

Djoser-Divantoura bvba **(3)**
Bagattenstraat 176
9000 Gent, Oost-Vlaanderen, Belgium
Tel.: (32) 92230069
Fax: (32) 92230435
E-Mail: info@djoser.be
Web Site: www.djoser.be
Emp.: 3
Travel & Tour Operating Agencies
S.I.C.: 4724
N.A.I.C.S.: 561510
Dirk Vandewiele *(Mng Dir)*

Easycamp B.V. **(2)**
Zuidsingel 22
3811 HB Amersfoort, Utrecht, Netherlands
Tel.: (31) 334220470
Fax: (31) 334220471
E-Mail: info@ecamp.nl
Web Site: www.ecamp.nl
Emp.: 60
Camping Tour Operators
S.I.C.: 7032
N.A.I.C.S.: 721214
D. M. Poortinga *(Principal)*

Ecamp GmbH **(2)**
Barmbeker Str 10
22303 Hamburg, Germany
Tel.: (49) 408221830
Fax: (49) 40450971
E-Mail: info@ecamp.de
Web Site: www.ecamp.de
Emp.: 13
Recreational Camps & Touring Services
S.I.C.: 7032
N.A.I.C.S.: 721214
Martin Rodenbeck *(Mng Dir)*

Eurocamp Travel B.V. **(2)**
Zuidsingel 22
3811 HB Amersfoort, Utrecht, Netherlands
Tel.: (31) 334602722
Fax: (31) 334612811
E-Mail: info@eurocamp.nl
Web Site: www.eurocamp.nl
Emp.: 60
Transportation & Camps Accommodation Services
S.I.C.: 7032
N.A.I.C.S.: 721214
R. G. Baddeley *(Principal)*

Eurocamp Travel GmbH **(2)**
Barmbeker Str 10
22303 Hamburg, Germany
Tel.: (49) 40450970
Fax: (49) 40450971
E-Mail: info@eurocamp.de
Web Site: www.eurocamp.de
Emp.: 30
Camping Tour Operators
S.I.C.: 4725
N.A.I.C.S.: 561520
Carola Thuering *(Mgr-Online Mktg)*

Eurocamp Travel (Schweiz) AG **(2)**
Max Hoegger-Strasse 6
8048 Zurich, Switzerland
Tel.: (41) 525607000
Fax: (41) 526460100
E-Mail: info@eurocamp.ch
Web Site: www.eurocamp.ch
Emp.: 30
Camping Tour Operators
S.I.C.: 7032
N.A.I.C.S.: 721214
Martin Rodenbeck *(Mng Dir)*

Keycamp Holidays (Ireland) Limited **(2)**
78-80 South Mall
Cork, Munster, Ireland
Tel.: (353) 21 425 2300
Fax: (353) 214252301
E-Mail: kc.cork@keycamp.com
Web Site: www.keycamp.ie
Emp.: 6
Outdoor Accommodation & Management Services
S.I.C.: 7032
N.A.I.C.S.: 721214
Colette Forde *(Mgr)*

Keycamp Holidays Netherlands B.V. **(2)**
Zuidsingel 22
3811 HB Amersfoort, Utrecht, Netherlands
Tel.: (31) 334602775
Fax: (31) 334612811
E-Mail: info@keycamp.nl
Web Site: www.keycamp.nl
Emp.: 60
Holiday Tour Operators
S.I.C.: 4725
N.A.I.C.S.: 561520
Edwin Teepe *(Brand Mgr)*

NST Limited **(2)**
Unit 22 Northwood Court
Swords Road, Dublin, 9, Ireland
Tel.: (353) 1 8940300
Fax: (353) 18523531
E-Mail: info@nst.ie
Web Site: www.nst.ie
Emp.: 16
School & College Tour Operating Agencies
S.I.C.: 4725
N.A.I.C.S.: 561520
Steve Craven *(Mgr-Bus Dev)*

SAS Le Chateau d'Ebblinghem **(2)**
Lieudit Kastel Velt RN 42
59173 Ebblinghem, France FR
Tel.: (33) 328442210 (100%)
Fax: (33) 328442211
Emp.: 20
Residential Hostel
S.I.C.: 7011
N.A.I.C.S.: 721199

Travelplus Group GmbH **(2)**
Munsterstr 111
48155 Munster, Nordrhein-Westfalen, Germany
Tel.: (49) 2506 8303 0
Fax: (49) 2506 8303 230
E-Mail: info@travelplusgroup.de
Web Site: www.travelplusgroup.de
Emp.: 42
Travel Tour Operating Services
S.I.C.: 4725
N.A.I.C.S.: 561520
Thomas Meier *(Chm)*
Peter Churchus *(Mng Dir)*

COXE GLOBAL AGRIBUSINESS INCOME FUND

1 First Canadian Place 3rd Floor Podium
Toronto, ON, M5X 1H3, Canada
Tel.: (416) 359-4597
Fax: (416) 359-5727
Toll Free: (866) 864-7760
E-Mail: gloria.lau@bmo.com
Year Founded: 2011
CAG.UN—(TSX)
Rev.: $1,030,601
Assets: $54,293,742
Liabilities: $1,199,122
Net Worth: $53,094,620
Earnings: ($106,982)
Fiscal Year-end: 12/31/12

Business Description:
Investment Services
S.I.C.: 6211
N.A.I.C.S.: 523999

Personnel:
L. Jacques Menard *(Chm)*
Eric C. Tripp *(Pres)*
Thomas V. Milroy *(CEO)*
Robert Allair *(CFO)*

Board of Directors:
L. Jacques Menard
Charyl Galpin
Peter Hinman
Richard Mills
Thomas V. Milroy
Gilles Ouellette
Connie Stefankiewicz
Eric C. Tripp

Transfer Agent:
CIBC Mellon Trust Company
PO Box 7010
Adelaide Street Postal Station, Toronto, ON, M5C 2W9, Canada
Tel.: (416) 643-5500
Fax: (416) 643-5501
Toll Free: (800) 387-0825

COXON PRECISE INDUSTRIAL CO., LTD.

No 42 Ln 1274 Chung Cheng Rd
320 Chung-li, Taoyuan, Taiwan
Tel.: (886) 34252153
Fax: (886) 34254320
E-Mail: coxon@coxon.com.tw
Web Site: www.coxon.com.tw
3607—(TAI)
Sales Range: $250-299.9 Million

Business Description:
Communication Device Parts Mfr
S.I.C.: 3663
N.A.I.C.S.: 334220

Personnel:
Huan-Ching Hong *(Chm & CEO)*

Subsidiary:

TECKON Industrial Corporation **(1)**
6E06 Taipei World Trade Center 5 Xin Yi Road Section 5
Taipei, 11011, Taiwan
Tel.: (886) 2 2723 5945
Fax: (886) 2 2723 5945
Web Site: www.teckon.com.tw
Molded Plastic Products Mfr
S.I.C.: 3089
N.A.I.C.S.: 326199
Paul Chang *(Gen Mgr)*

Non-U.S. Subsidiaries:

COXON Industrial Ltd. **(1)**
Flat V 10 F Everest Industrial Centre 396 Kwun Tong Road
Kwun Tong, Kowloon, China (Hong Kong)
Tel.: (852) 2 412 0080
Fax: (852) 2 490 5889
E-Mail: info@coxon.com.hk
Web Site: www.coxon.com.hk
Injection Molded Plastic Products Mfr
S.I.C.: 3082
N.A.I.C.S.: 326121
Steve J.C. Lee *(Dir-Mktg)*

Non-U.S. Plant:

COXON Industrial Ltd. - Guangdong Plastic & Mould Plant **(2)**
Zhen An 1st Road 6th Industrial District
Shang Sha Village
Chang An Town, Dongguan, Guangdong, 523859, China
Tel.: (86) 76985070288
Fax: (86) 76985079238
E-Mail: sinyon@sinyon.com.cn
Web Site: www.coxon.com.tw/pge/en/01com_sn.htm
Injection Molded Plastic Products Mfr
S.I.C.: 2679
N.A.I.C.S.: 322299

VASTECH Plastic (Shanghai) Industrial Co., Ltd. **(1)**
No 3 Lane 309 Nanle Road Chedun Town
Songjiang District, Shanghai, 201613, China
Tel.: (86) 2157749216
Fax: (86) 2157749210
Injection Molded Plastic Products Mfr
S.I.C.: 3082
N.A.I.C.S.: 326121

Non-U.S. Plant:

SUN CAN International Ltd. - SINYON Plastic & Mould Factory **(1)**
Industrial Area No 3 Xin Hua Road Wu Sha Jiang Bei Village
Chang An Town, Dongguan, Guangdong, 523859, China
Tel.: (86) 76985548081
Fax: (86) 76985338931
E-Mail: sinyon@sinyon.com.cn
Injection Molded Plastic Products Mfr

COXON Precise Industrial Co., Ltd.—(Continued)

S.I.C.: 3082
N.A.I.C.S.: 326121

COZIRON RESOURCES LIMITED

Level 24 44 St Georges Terrace
Perth, WA, 6000, Australia
Mailing Address:
PO Box 363
Northbridge, Perth, WA, 6865, Australia
Tel.: (61) 8 6211 5099
Fax: (61) 8 9218 8875
E-Mail: info@coziron.com
Web Site: www.coziron.com
CZR—(ASX)
Rev.: $47,943
Assets: $14,363,629
Liabilities: $3,005,305
Net Worth: $11,358,324
Earnings: ($2,925,629)
Fiscal Year-end: 06/30/13
Business Description:
Metal Ore Mining Development Export
S.I.C.: 1081
N.A.I.C.S.: 213114
Personnel:
Stephen Hewitt-Dutton *(Sec)*
Board of Directors:
Adam Sierakowski
Stephen Lowe
Robert Ramsay
Legal Counsel:
Price Sierakowski Corporate
Level 24 44 St George's Terrace
Perth, Australia

C.P. ALL PUBLIC COMPANY LIMITED

283 Sriboonrueng Building 1 Silorn Road
Silorn Bangrak, Bangkok, 10500, Thailand
Tel.: (66) 26779000
Fax: (66) 26790050
E-Mail: info@cpall.co.th
Web Site: www.cpall.co.th
CPALL—(OTC THA)
Rev.: $6,553,630,901
Assets: $2,378,683,147
Liabilities: $1,484,633,910
Net Worth: $894,049,237
Earnings: $366,328,730
Emp.: 35,557
Fiscal Year-end: 12/31/12
Business Description:
Convenience Stores Operator & Franchisor
S.I.C.: 5411
N.A.I.C.S.: 445120
Personnel:
Dhanin Chearavanont *(Chm)*
Korsak Chairasmisak *(Vice Chm & CEO)*
Pittaya Jearavisitkul *(Deputy CEO)*
Piyawat Titasattavorakul *(Mng Dir)*
Suraphan Pussadej *(Asst CEO-HR)*
Supot Shitgasornpongse *(Sec & VP-Fin)*
Tanin Buranamanit *(Exec VP-Operation, Mktg & HR)*
Kosa Pongsupath *(Sr VP-IT)*
Taweesak Kaewrathtanapattama *(Sr VP-Acctg & Fin)*
Suwit Kingkaew *(Sr VP-Gen Mgmt)*
Chuan Nimkittikul *(Sr VP-Pur & Distr)*
Board of Directors:
Dhanin Chearavanont
Komain Bhatarabhirom
Pridi Boonyoung
Tanin Buranamanit
Korsak Chairasmisak
Narong Chearavanont
Soopakij Chearavanont
Prasert Jarupanich
Pittaya Jearavisitkul
Suphachai Phisitvanich
Umroong Sanphasitvong
Adirek Sripratak
Apisak Tantivorawong
Padoong Techasarintr
Piyawat Titasattavorakul

Subsidiaries:

Gosoft (Thailand) Company Limited **(1)**
Cp Twr 1 26th Floor
313 Silom Rd, 10500 Bangkok, Thailand (99.99%)
Tel.: (66) 26779451
Fax: (66) 26779400
E-Mail: suree@gosoft.th
Web Site: www.gosoft.co.th
Emp.: 600
Computer Facilities Management Services
S.I.C.: 7376
N.A.I.C.S.: 541513
Kosa Pongsupath *(COO)*

Siam Makro Public Company Limited **(1)**
3498 2nd Floor Lardprao Road Klongchan
Bangkok, 10240, Thailand TH
Tel.: (66) 2 723 1000
Fax: (66) 27342141
E-Mail:
Web Site: www.siammakro.co.th
MAKRO—(OTC THA)
Rev.: $3,808,487,283
Assets: $1,062,961,533
Liabilities: $709,908,828
Net Worth: $353,052,705
Earnings: $117,807,486
Emp.: 8,545
Fiscal Year-end: 12/31/12
Discount Stores
S.I.C.: 5149
N.A.I.C.S.: 424490
Arsa Sarasin *(Chm)*
Suchada Ithijarukul *(Vice Chm, CEO & Member-Exec Bd)*
Saowaluck Thithapant *(CFO & Member-Exec Bd)*
Thomas Leslie Hammer *(COO)*
Jean-Michel de Geyer *(Chief Comml Officer)*
Chi-Lung Lin *(CEO-Food Svc Bus)*
Stephan Ronald Nanninga *(Member-Exec Bd)*
Willem Hendrikus van Leeuwen *(Member-Exec Bd)*
Nilobon Tangprasit *(Sec)*

Non-U.S. Subsidiaries:

Orkam Asia Holding AG **(2)**
Aspermontstrasse 24
CH 7006 Chur, Switzerland (100%)
Tel.: (41) 813549070
Fax: (41) 813549061
Emp.: 4
Holding Company
S.I.C.: 6719
N.A.I.C.S.: 551112
Matelea Vaselga *(Mgr)*

CP ELECTRONICS LTD.

Brent Crescent
London, NW10 7XR, United Kingdom
Tel.: (44) 333 900 0671
Fax: (44) 333 900 0674
E-Mail: enquiry@cpelectronics.co.uk
Web Site: www.cpelectronics.co.uk
Year Founded: 1970
Sales Range: $10-24.9 Million
Emp.: 65
Business Description:
Energy Saving Electronic Control Mfr
S.I.C.: 3822
N.A.I.C.S.: 334512
Personnel:
Paul Mans *(Mng Dir)*

CP2 GROUP LIMITED

Level 8 Aurora Place 88 Phillip Street
Sydney, NSW, 2000, Australia
Tel.: (61) 282745900
Fax: (61) 282745999
E-Mail: info@cp2.com
Web Site: www.cp2.com
Year Founded: 2007
Business Description:
Investment Holding Company
S.I.C.: 6719
N.A.I.C.S.: 551112
Personnel:
Sally Holloway *(Co-Founder & Chm)*
Bob Officer *(Co-Founder)*
Syd Bone *(Mng Dir)*
Board of Directors:
Sally Holloway
Syd Bone
Bob Officer
Geoffrey R. Phillips
David Taylor

Subsidiary:

CP2 Limited **(1)**
Level 8 Aurora St
88 Phillip St, Sydney, NSW, 2000, Australia AU
Tel.: (61) 282745900
Fax: (61) 282745999
E-Mail: sydney@cp2.com
Web Site: www.cp2.com
Emp.: 35
Investment Management Firm
S.I.C.: 6211
N.A.I.C.S.: 523999
Sally Holloway *(Co-Founder & Chm)*
Syd Bone *(Mng Dir)*

Holding:

ConnectEast Pty. Limited **(2)**
2 Hilcrest Ave
Ringwood, VIC, 3134, Australia AU
Tel.: (61) 399551700
Fax: (61) 399551701
E-Mail: enquiries@connecteast.com.au
Web Site: www.connecteast.com.au
Sales Range: $150-199.9 Million
Emp.: 321
Building Maintaining & Operating Services
S.I.C.: 4789
N.A.I.C.S.: 488490
Dennis Cliche *(Mng Dir & CEO)*
Tony Hudson *(Gen Counsel & Sec)*

Joint Venture:

Airport Link Co. Pty Ltd. **(2)**
Mascot Station
PO Box 604
Cnr Church Ave & Bourke Road, Mascot, NSW, 2020, Australia
Tel.: (61) 0283378412
Fax: (61) 0283378413
E-Mail: marketing@airportlink.com.au
Web Site: www.airportlink.com.au
Emp.: 60
Operation & Management of Railway Stations; Owned 50.1% by Capital Partners & 49.9% by Westpac Banking Corporation
S.I.C.: 4789
N.A.I.C.S.: 488210
Tim Anderson *(CEO)*

CPC CORPORATION

No 3 Sungren Rd Shinyi Chiu
Taipei, 11010, Taiwan
Tel.: (886) 287898989
Fax: (886) 287899000
E-Mail: ir@cpc.com.tw
Web Site: www.cpc.com.tw
Year Founded: 1946
Rev.: $38,855,900,413
Assets: $28,937,628,108
Liabilities: $20,827,073,064
Net Worth: $8,110,555,044
Earnings: ($1,138,944,288)
Emp.: 14,977
Fiscal Year-end: 12/31/12
Business Description:
Petroleum & Natural Gas Exploration & Production Services
S.I.C.: 2911
N.A.I.C.S.: 324110
Personnel:
Sheng-Chung Lin *(Chm)*
Arthur Hsiang-Yun Kung *(Pres)*
Jin-Sie Yang *(CEO-Petrochemical Bus Div & VP)*
Jimmy Chang *(CEO-Solvent & Chemical Bus Div)*
Jei-Yuan Chen *(CEO-Natural Gas Bus Div)*
Ting-Pang Chi *(CEO-Lubricants Bus Div)*
Jung-Lieh Lin *(CEO-LPG Bus Div)*
Cheng-Hsie Liu *(CEO-Mktg Bus Div)*
Ching-Yang Wu *(CEO-Refining Bus Div)*
Jong-Chang Wu *(CEO-Exploration & Production Bus Div)*
Board of Directors:
Sheng-Chung Lin
Chuh-Yung Chen
Yi Chou
Chin-Lai Huang
Mei-Ying Huang
Wang-Hsiang Hwang
Arthur Hsiang-Yun Kung
Tung-Yi Lee
Chi-Yuan Liang
Yaw-chung Liao
Jyh Wei Sun
Kwung-Shing Wu
Shin-Cheng Yeh
Supervisory Board of Directors:
Ter-Shing Chen
Chiao-Tao Hsu
Chi-An Wu

Divisions:

Exploration & Development Research Institute **(1)**
No 1 Ta Yuan Wen Shan
Miao-li, 36010, Taiwan
Tel.: (886) 37356150
Fax: (886) 37357188
E-Mail: 155501@cpc.com.tw
Web Site: www.cpc.com.tw
Emp.: 150
Commercial Petroleum Research
S.I.C.: 8731
N.A.I.C.S.: 541712

Exploration & Production Business Division **(1)**
No 3 Sungren Road Shinyi Chiu
Taipei, 11010, Taiwan
Tel.: (886) 2 8989
Fax: (886) 37271934
Web Site: www.cpc.com.tw
Emp.: 1,400
Commercial Exploration of Oil-Bearing Lands
S.I.C.: 1311
N.A.I.C.S.: 211111
Yong-Yaw Chsu *(Acting CEO)*

Kaohsiung Refinery **(1)**
Tso Ying Nan Road 2
Kaohsiung, 811, Taiwan
Tel.: (886) 75824141
Fax: (886) 75834228
Web Site: www.cpckoa.com.tw
Emp.: 3,000
Petroleum Refinery
S.I.C.: 2911
N.A.I.C.S.: 324110

LNG Project & Construction Division **(1)**
1 20 Shin Shing Rd
Shin Kong Vlg, Kaohsiung, Yong An Hsiang, Taiwan
Tel.: (886) 76911131
Fax: (886) 76914768
Construction of Natural Gas Processing Facilities
S.I.C.: 4924
N.A.I.C.S.: 221210

Northern Project & Construction Division **(1)**
111 Shalung Village Tayuan Town
Taoyuan, Hsien, Taiwan
Tel.: (886) 3 3832 680
Fax: (886) 3 3832 475

E-Mail: npcd0100@ms19.hinet.net
Provider of Petroleum Services
S.I.C.: 2911
N.A.I.C.S.: 324110

Refining & Manufacturing Research Institute (1)
217 Min Sheng South Road
Chiayi, 60036, Taiwan
Tel.: (886) 52224171
Fax: (886) 52285798
E-Mail: e002100@cpc.com.tw
Web Site: www.cpc.com.tw/english/content/index01.asp?sno=275&pno=8
Emp.: 12
Petroleum Manufacturing Research
S.I.C.: 8731
N.A.I.C.S.: 541712
Yen Shiang Shih *(Chm)*

Taiwan Marketing & Transportation Division (1)
No 3 Sungren Rd
Taipei, Shinyi Chu, 11010, Taiwan
Tel.: (886) 287898989
Fax: (886) 287899000
E-Mail: ir@cpctmtd.com.tw
Web Site: www.cpctmtd.com.tw
Emp.: 2,500
Provider of Marketing & Transportation of Petroleum & Petrochemicals
S.I.C.: 4613
N.A.I.C.S.: 486910
Yang King Lee *(Gen Mgr)*

Taoyuan Refinery (1)
50 Min Sheng North Road Sec 1
333 Taoyuan, Taiwan (100%)
Tel.: (886) 33555111
Fax: (886) 33252123
Web Site: www.cpc.com
Emp.: 1,000
Refiner of Petroleum
S.I.C.: 2911
N.A.I.C.S.: 324110
David Yen *(Gen Mgr)*

Subsidiary:

Overseas Petroleum and Investment Corporation (1)
No 3 Sungren Road Shinyi Chiu
11010 Taipei, Taiwan
Tel.: (886) 287898989
Fax: (886) 287899021
E-Mail: opic@cpc.com.tw
Web Site: www.cpc.com.tw/english
Emp.: 1,000
Crude Petroleum & Natural Gas Extraction; Investments
S.I.C.: 1311
N.A.I.C.S.: 211111

Division:

Lubricants Business Division (2)
6th Fl No 15 Cheng Kung 2nd Rd
Kaohsiung, PRC, 11010, Taiwan
Tel.: (886) 75361510
Fax: (886) 75361442
E-Mail: t00@cpc.com.tw
Web Site: www.cpc.com.tw/english/content/index01.asp?sno=275&pno=8
Crude Petroleum & Natural Gas Extraction
S.I.C.: 1311
N.A.I.C.S.: 211111
Tien-Chieh Lee *(CEO)*

U.S. Subsidiary:

Opicoil America, Inc. (1)
3040 Post Oak Blvd Ste 800
Houston, TX 77056
Tel.: (713) 840-7171
Emp.: 11
Crude Petroleum & Natural Gas Extraction
S.I.C.: 1311
N.A.I.C.S.: 211111
Gin Fu Huang *(Pres)*

Division:

Opicoil Houston, Inc. (2)
3040 Post Oak Blvd Ste 800
Houston, TX 77056
Tel.: (713) 840-7171
Fax: (713) 297-8108
Emp.: 15
Crude Petroleum & Natural Gas Extraction
S.I.C.: 1311
N.A.I.C.S.: 211111

CPC INGENIERIA Y CONSTRUCCIONES SA

Av Madero 900
Torre Catalinas Plaza Piso 20,
Buenos Aires, C105 4AAF, Argentina
Tel.: (54) 11 5077 6980
E-Mail: info@cpc-sa.com.ar
Web Site: www.cpc-sa.com.ar
Business Description:
Construction Services
S.I.C.: 1611
N.A.I.C.S.: 237310
Personnel:
Alberto Ealo Artetxe *(Dir-Fin)*

Subsidiary:

Autopista Ezeiza Canuelas, S.A. (1)
Ricchieri Av San Martin
Madero, B1768DJA Buenos Aires, Argentina
Tel.: (54) 1144620661
Fax: (54) 11 44 621242
Civil Engineering Services
S.I.C.: 1629
N.A.I.C.S.: 237990

CPFL ENERGIA S.A.

Rua Gomes de Carvalho 1 510 14th Floor Suite 142 Vila Olimpia
Sao Paulo, SP, 04547-005, Brazil
Tel.: (55) 11 3841 8507
Fax: (55) 1937563756
E-Mail: ri@cpfl.com.br
Web Site: www.cpfl.com.br
CPL—(BRAZ NYSE)
Rev.: $7,405,476,258
Assets: $15,285,819,678
Liabilities: $11,150,470,443
Net Worth: $4,135,349,235
Earnings: $618,174,887
Emp.: 8,477
Fiscal Year-end: 12/31/12
Business Description:
Electricity Distr, Generation & Trading
S.I.C.: 4931
N.A.I.C.S.: 221122
Personnel:
Helio Viana Pereira *(Pres-Piratininga Campinas)*
Board of Directors:
Expedito Afonso Veloso

Subsidiaries:

Campo dos Ventos II Energias Renovaveis S.A. (1)
Avenida Paulista 1842 Set 225 North Tower Room 18
Belavista, Sao Paulo, 01310-200, Brazil
Tel.: (55) 19 3756 8659
Electric Power Generation Services
S.I.C.: 4911
N.A.I.C.S.: 221118

Centrais Eletricas da Paraiba S.A. (1)
Avenida Fernando Simoes Barbosa 266
Boa Viagem, 51020-390 Recife, Pernambuco, Brazil
Tel.: (55) 19 3756 8844
Fax: (55) 19 3756 8040
Thermal Power Plant Construction Services
S.I.C.: 1629
N.A.I.C.S.: 237130

CERAN - Companhia Energetica Rio das Antas (1)
Av Carlos Gomes 300 8 andar
Bairro Boa Vista, Porto Alegre, Rio Grande do Sul, 90480-000, Brazil
Tel.: (55) 51 3025 6700
Fax: (55) 51 3025 6700
E-Mail: ceran@ceran.com.br
Web Site: www.ceran.com.br
Emp.: 65
Power Plant Construction Services
S.I.C.: 1629
N.A.I.C.S.: 237990
Marcelo Wood Chiarello *(Mng Dir)*

Companhia Jaguari de Energia (1)
Rua Vigato 1620
Sao Paulo, Jaguariuna, 13820-000, Brazil
Tel.: (55) 19 3847 5945
Fax: (55) 19 3847 5900
E-Mail: cpfl@cpfl.com.br
Web Site: www.cpfl.com.br/relatorioanual2009/CPFL/tabid/1631/EntryId/31/Informacoes-Corporativas.aspx
Electric Power Distr
S.I.C.: 4911
N.A.I.C.S.: 221122

Companhia Jaguari de Geracao de Energia Ltda. (1)
Rua Vigato 1620 Terreo Sala 2
Jaguariuna, Sao Paulo, 13820-000, Brazil
Tel.: (55) 19 3847 5910
Fax: (55) 19 3837 4567
Electric Power Generation Services
S.I.C.: 4931
N.A.I.C.S.: 221118

Companhia Paulista de Energia Eletrica Ltda. (1)
Rua Vigato 1 620 1 andar sala 1
Jaguariuna, Sao Paulo, 13820-000, Brazil
Tel.: (55) 19 3847 5900
Fax: (55) 19 3847 5900
Web Site: www.cpfl.com.br/relatorioanual2009/CPFL/tabid/1631/EntryId/31/Informacoes-Corporativas.aspx
Electric Power Distr
S.I.C.: 4911
N.A.I.C.S.: 221122

Companhia Sul Paulista de Energia (1)
Rua Vigato 1 620 1 andar sala 2
Jaguariuna, Sao Paulo, 13820-000, Brazil
Tel.: (55) 19 3847 5900
Fax: (55) 19 3847 5900
Web Site: www.cpfl.com.br/relatorioanual2009/CPFL/tabid/1631/EntryId/31/Informacoes-Corporativas.aspx
Electric Power Generation & Distribution Services
S.I.C.: 4939
N.A.I.C.S.: 221118

CPFL Bio Buriti S.A. (1)
Rodovia Campinas-Mogi Mirim Km 2 5
Jardim Santana, Campinas, Sao Paulo, 13088-900, Brazil
Tel.: (55) 19 3847 5910
Fax: (55) 19 3837 4567
Electric Power Generation Services
S.I.C.: 4931
N.A.I.C.S.: 221118

CPFL Bio Formosa S.A. (1)
Rodovia Campinas-Mogi Mirim Km 2 5
Jardim Santana, Campinas, Sao Paulo, 13088-900, Brazil
Tel.: (55) 19 3847 5910
Fax: (55) 19 3837 4567
Electric Power Generation Services
S.I.C.: 4939
N.A.I.C.S.: 221118

CPFL Bio Ipe S.A. (1)
Rodovia Campinas-Mogi Mirim Km 2 5
Jardim Santana, Campinas, Sao Paulo, 13088-900, Brazil
Tel.: (55) 19 3847 5910
Fax: (55) 19 3837 4567
Electric Power Generation Services
S.I.C.: 4939
N.A.I.C.S.: 221118

CPFL Bio Pedra S.A. (1)
Rodovia Campinas-Mogi Mirim Km 2 5
Jardim Santana, Campinas, Sao Paulo, 13088-900, Brazil
Tel.: (55) 19 3847 5910
Fax: (55) 19 3837 4567
Thermal Power Plant Construction Services
S.I.C.: 1623
N.A.I.C.S.: 237130

CPFL Bioenergia S.A. (1)
Rua Gomes de Carvalho n 1510 14 Andar
Conjunto 1402 Sala 04
Vila Olimpia, Sao Paulo, 04547-005, Brazil
Tel.: (55) 11 3841 8507
Fax: (55) 11 3841 8516
Electric Power Generation Services
S.I.C.: 4939
N.A.I.C.S.: 221118

CPFL Comercializacao Cone Sul S.A. (1)
Rua Gomes De Carvalho 1 510 14 Andar
Conjunto 1402 Sala 3
Vila Olimpia, Sao Paulo, 04547-005, Brazil
Tel.: (55) 11 3841 8507
Fax: (55) 11 3841 8516
Web Site: www.cpfl.com.br/relatorioanual2009/CPFL/tabid/1631/EntryId/31/Informacoes-Corporativas.aspx
Electric Power Distr
S.I.C.: 4911
N.A.I.C.S.: 221122

CPFL Energias Renovaveis S.A. (1)
Avenida Dr Cardoso de Melo 1 184 - 7th floor
Vila Olimpia, Sao Paulo, Brazil
04548-004 (58.8%)
Tel.: (55) 11 3157 9300
Fax: (55) 11 3157 9464
E-Mail: ri@cpflrenovaveis.com
Web Site: www.cpflrenovaveis.com.br
CPRE3—(BRAZ)
Electric Power Generation Services
S.I.C.: 4911
N.A.I.C.S.: 221111
Wilson Ferreira, Jr *(Chm)*
Gustavo Estrella *(Vice Chm)*

CPFL Planalto Ltda. (1)
Rua Vigato 1 620 1 Andar Sala 7
Jaguariuna, Sao Paulo, 13820-000, Brazil
Tel.: (55) 19 3847 5910
Fax: (55) 19 3837 4567
Electric Power Distribution Services
S.I.C.: 4939
N.A.I.C.S.: 221122

CPFL Santa Cruz (1)
Rua Gomes de Carvalho 1510
14 der andar Conjunto 02, Vila Olimpia, Sao Paulo, 04547 005, Brazil
Tel.: (55) 1433059100
Fax: (55) 14 3305 9108
Electricity Distr
S.I.C.: 4931
N.A.I.C.S.: 221122
Wilson Pinto Ferreira, Jr. *(CEO)*
Jose Antonio de Almeida Filippo *(CFO & Head-Investor Rels)*

CPFL Servicos, Equipamentos, Industria e Comercio S.A. (1)
Avenida dos Bragheta 364
Sao Jose do Rio Pardo, Sao Paulo, 13720-000, Brazil
Tel.: (55) 19 3687 8200
Electric Power Generation & Distribution Services
S.I.C.: 4931
N.A.I.C.S.: 221118

Eurus VI Energias Renovaveis Ltda. (1)
Rua Gomes de Carvalho n 1510 14 Andar
Conjunto 1402 Sala 11
Vila Olimpia, Sao Paulo, 04547-005, Brazil
Tel.: (55) 11 3841 8507
Fax: (55) 11 3841 8516
Web Site: www.cpfl.com.br/relatorioanual2009/CPFL/tabid/1631/EntryId/31/Informacoes-Corporativas.aspx
Electric Power Generation Services
S.I.C.: 4939
N.A.I.C.S.: 221118

Santa Clara I Energias Renovaveis Ltda. (1)
Rua Gomes de Carvalho n 1510 14 andar
Conjunto 1402 Sala 01
Vila Olimpia, Sao Paulo, 04547-005, Brazil
Tel.: (55) 11 3841 8507
Fax: (55) 11 3841 8516
Web Site: www.cpfl.com.br/relatorioanual2009/CPFL/tabid/1631/EntryId/31/Informacoes-Corporativas.aspx
Electric Power Generation Services
S.I.C.: 4911
N.A.I.C.S.: 221118

Santa Clara II Energias Renovaveis Ltda. (1)
Rua Gomes de Carvalho n 1510 14 Andar
Conjunto 1402 Sala 05
Vila Olimpia, Sao Paulo, 04547-005, Brazil
Tel.: (55) 11 3841 8507
Fax: (55) 11 3841 8516
Web Site: www.cpfl.com.br/relatorioanual2009/CPFL/tabid/1631/EntryId/31/Informacoes-Corporativas.aspx

CPFL Energia S.A.—(Continued)

Electric Power Generation Services
S.I.C.: 4939
N.A.I.C.S.: 221118
Miguel Normando Abdalla Saad *(Mng Dir)*

Santa Clara III Energias Renovaveis Ltda. **(1)**
Rua Gomes de Carvalho n 1510 14 Andar
Conjunto 1402 Sala 07
Vila Olimpia, Sao Paulo, 04547-005, Brazil
Tel.: (55) 11 3841 8507
Fax: (55) 11 3841 8516
Electric Power Generation Services
S.I.C.: 4911
N.A.I.C.S.: 221118

Santa Clara IV Energias Renovaveis Ltda. **(1)**
Rua Gomes de Carvalho n 1510 14 Andar
Conjunto 1402 Sala 07
Vila Olimpia, Sao Paulo, 04547-005, Brazil
Tel.: (55) 11 3841 8507
Fax: (55) 11 3841 8516
Electric Power Generation Services
S.I.C.: 4911
N.A.I.C.S.: 221118

Santa Clara V Energias Renovaveis Ltda. **(1)**
Rua Gomes de Carvalho n 1510 14 Andar
Conjunto 1402 Sala 09
Vila Olimpia, Sao Paulo, 04547-005, Brazil
Tel.: (55) 11 3841 8507
Fax: (55) 11 3841 8516
Electric Power Generation Services
S.I.C.: 4939
N.A.I.C.S.: 221118

Santa Clara VI Energias Renovaveis Ltda. **(1)**
Rua Gomes de Carvalho n 1510 14 andar
Conjunto 1402 Sala 10
Vila Olimpia, Sao Paulo, 04547-005, Brazil
Tel.: (55) 11 3841 8507
Fax: (55) 11 3841 8516
Web Site: www.cpfl.com.br/relatorioanual2009/CPFL/tabid/1631/EntryId/31/Informacoes-Corporativas.aspx
Electric Power Generation Services
S.I.C.: 4911
N.A.I.C.S.: 221118

SPE Alto Irani Energia S.A. **(1)**
Rua Sao Pedro 2987 E
Jardim America, 89803-903 Chapeco, Santa Catarina, Brazil
Tel.: (55) 49 3328 6199
Electric Power Generation Services
S.I.C.: 4911
N.A.I.C.S.: 221118

CPG INTERNATIONAL S.P.A.

Via Martiri d'Italia 26
10014 Caluso, Italy
Tel.: (39) 011 989411
Fax: (39) 011 9894089
E-Mail: sales@cpg-i.com
Web Site: www.cpg-i.com
Emp.: 300
Business Description:
Printer Mfr
S.I.C.: 3555
N.A.I.C.S.: 333244

CPH CHEMIE + PAPIER HOLDING AG

Perlenring 1
6035 Perlen, Switzerland
Tel.: (41) 414558000
Fax: (41) 414558012
E-Mail: info@perlen.ch
Web Site: www.cph.ch
CPHN—(SWX)
Sls.: $527,453,970
Assets: $1,049,510,261
Liabilities: $283,447,780
Net Worth: $766,062,480
Earnings: $8,700,399
Emp.: 849
Fiscal Year-end: 12/31/12
Business Description:
Chemicals Papers & Packaging Films Producer
S.I.C.: 2671
N.A.I.C.S.: 322220
Personnel:
Peter Schaub *(Chm)*
Max Walter *(Vice Chm)*
Peter Schildknecht *(CEO)*
Manfred Haner *(CFO)*
Board of Directors:
Peter Schaub
Franz-Josef Albrecht
Hanspeter Balmer
Mauro Gabella
Tim Talaat
Max Walter
Christian Wipf

Subsidiaries:

CU Agro AG **(1)**
Seestrasse 108
8707 Uetikon, Zurich, Switzerland
Tel.: (41) 449229357
Fax: (41) 449201764
Emp.: 12
Agricultural Chemicals Mfr
S.I.C.: 2879
N.A.I.C.S.: 325320

CU Chemie Uetikon AG **(1)**
Seestrasse 108
Uetikon, Zurich, 8707, Switzerland
Tel.: (41) 449229111
Fax: (41) 449206205
E-Mail: info@zeochem.ch
Web Site: www.zeochem.ch
Emp.: 150
Pharmaceuticals & Fine Chemicals Mfr
S.I.C.: 2834
N.A.I.C.S.: 325412
Luciano Milesi *(Mgr)*

CU Immobilien Lahr AG **(1)**
Seestrasse 108
Uetikon, Zurich, 8707, Switzerland
Tel.: (41) 449229111
Fax: (41) 449209036
E-Mail: info@uition.ch
Web Site: www.uition.ch
Emp.: 10
Real Estate Property Mangement Services
S.I.C.: 6531
N.A.I.C.S.: 531210
Luciano Milesi *(Mng Dir)*

Perlen Converting AG **(1)**
Perlenring 3
6035 Perlen, Switzerland
Tel.: (41) 414558800
Fax: (41) 414558801
E-Mail: perlen-converting@perlen.ch
Web Site: www.perlen.ch
Emp.: 120
Coated Pharma Films Mfr
S.I.C.: 3081
N.A.I.C.S.: 326113
Wolfgang Grimm *(CEO)*

Perlen Immobilien AG **(1)**
Perlenring 1
6035 Perlen, Switzerland
Tel.: (41) 414558950
Fax: (41) 414558037
E-Mail: info@perlen-immobilien.ch
Web Site: www.perlen-immobilien.ch
Emp.: 2
Apartment Rental Services
S.I.C.: 6514
N.A.I.C.S.: 531110

Perlen Papier AG **(1)**
Perlenring 1
6035 Perlen, Switzerland
Tel.: (41) 414558000
Fax: (41) 41 455 80 01
E-Mail: info@perlen.ch
Web Site: www.perlenpapier.ch
Emp.: 450
Magazine & Newsprint Paper Mfr
S.I.C.: 2621
N.A.I.C.S.: 322122
Clemence Gottstein *(CEO)*
Peter Schildknecht *(Mng Dir)*

Zeochem AG **(1)**
Seestrasse 108
8707 Uetikon, Zurich, Switzerland
Tel.: (41) 449229393
Fax: (41) 449202093
E-Mail: info@zeochem.ch
Web Site: www.zeochem.ch
Emp.: 100
Molecular Chemicals Mfr
S.I.C.: 2899
N.A.I.C.S.: 325998
Jonathan Lund *(Dir-Mktg & Sls)*

U.S. Subsidiaries:

Perlen Converting L.L.C. **(1)**
135 Algonquin Pkwy
Whippany, NJ 07981
Tel.: (973) 887-0257
Fax: (973) 887-0258
E-Mail: info@perlenpackaging.com
Web Site: www.perlenpackaging.com
Emp.: 12
Pharmaceuticals Products Distr
S.I.C.: 5122
N.A.I.C.S.: 424210
Douglas Voreis *(Mng Dir & VP)*

Zeochem L.L.C **(1)**
1600 W Hill St
Louisville, KY 40210
Tel.: (502) 634-7600
Fax: (502) 634-8133
E-Mail: info@zeochem.com
Web Site: www.zeochem.com
Emp.: 75
Inorganic Chemicals Mfr
S.I.C.: 2899
N.A.I.C.S.: 325199
Steve Witthoeft *(Pres & Gen Mgr)*

Non-U.S. Subsidiaries:

ac-Folien GmbH **(1)**
Neuenburger Strasse 9
79379 Mullheim, Germany
Tel.: (49) 76318030
Fax: (49) 7631803141
E-Mail: info@ac-folien.com
Web Site: www.ac-folien.com
Emp.: 140
Plastic Mono Films Mfr
S.I.C.: 2671
N.A.I.C.S.: 326112
Roland Bernauer *(Mng Dir)*
Reiner Gerlach *(Mng Dir)*

CPH Chemie + Papier Holding GmbH **(1)**
Neuenburger Strasse 9
D-79379 Mullheim, Germany
Tel.: (49) 7631 803 0
Fax: (49) 7631 803 141
E-Mail: info@uetikon.com
Web Site: www.uetikon.com
Emp.: 115
Investment Holding Services
S.I.C.: 6719
N.A.I.C.S.: 551112
Hienz Seiger *(Gen Mgr)*

Perlen Deutschland GmbH **(1)**
Ranertstrasse 6
81249 Munich, Bavaria, Germany
Tel.: (49) 89 863 893 0
Fax: (49) 89 863 893 10
Paper Products Distr
S.I.C.: 5113
N.A.I.C.S.: 424130
Alexander Wicklein *(Mng Dir)*

Perlen France Sarl **(1)**
1 Ave Sonia Delaunay
94506 Champigny-sur-Marne, France
Tel.: (33) 148811968
Fax: (33) 148811969
E-Mail: info@perlen-france.fr
Paper Products Distr
S.I.C.: 5113
N.A.I.C.S.: 424130
Raoul Gil *(Mng Dir)*

CPI IMMOBILIEN AG

Hahngasse 3
A-1090 Vienna, Austria
Tel.: (43) 40954400
Fax: (43) 409544030
E-Mail: office@cpi.co.at
Web Site: www.cpi.co.at
Year Founded: 1997
Sales Range: $1-9.9 Million
Emp.: 80
Business Description:
Property Developer & Manager
S.I.C.: 6531
N.A.I.C.S.: 531311
Personnel:
Johann Franke *(Member-Mgmt Bd)*
Ernst Kreihsler *(Member-Mgmt Bd)*

Subsidiaries:

CPI Bautrager und Immobilienverwaltung GmbH **(1)**
Hahngasse 3
1090 Vienna, Austria
Tel.: (43) 14095440
Fax: (43) 4314095430
Apartment Building Contractors
S.I.C.: 1522
N.A.I.C.S.: 236116

CPI Marketing GmbH **(1)**
Hahngasse 3
1090 Vienna, Austria
Tel.: (43) 140954400
Fax: (43) 1409544030
E-Mail: office@cpi.co.at
Real Estate Rental Services
S.I.C.: 6531
N.A.I.C.S.: 531390
Ernst Kreihsler *(Gen Mgr)*

CPI Wachstums Immobilien AG **(1)**
Hahngasse 3
1090 Vienna, Austria
Tel.: (43) 14095440
Fax: (43) 1409544030
Real Estate Investment Services
S.I.C.: 6531
N.A.I.C.S.: 531390
Harald Diethard *(Mng Dir)*

CPI Wertpapier Beratung und Vermittlung GmbH **(1)**
Hahngasse 3
1090 Vienna, Austria
Tel.: (43) 14095440
Fax: (43) 1 409544030
Web Site: www.cpi.co.at/index.php?page=24
Real Estate Brokerage Services
S.I.C.: 6531
N.A.I.C.S.: 531390

C.P.L. GROUP PUBLIC COMPANY LIMITED

700 Moo 6 Sukhumvit Rd Bangpoo - Mai Muang
Samut Prakan, 10280, Thailand
Tel.: (66) 2709 5633
Fax: (66) 2709 6033
E-Mail: contact@cpl.co.th
Web Site: www.cpl.co.th
Year Founded: 1989
CPL—(THA)
Rev.: $57,545,775
Assets: $37,329,922
Liabilities: $5,640,034
Net Worth: $31,689,887
Earnings: $1,414,795
Fiscal Year-end: 12/31/12
Business Description:
Leather Mfr & Distr
S.I.C.: 3199
N.A.I.C.S.: 316998
Personnel:
Manoch Wongcharoensin *(Chm)*
Chi Hsiang Lai *(Mng Dir)*
Singha Wongrujipairoj *(CFO)*
Arjaree Suphasinwongchai *(Co-Sec & Mgr-Fin)*
Suwatchai Wongcharoensin *(Co-Sec)*
Board of Directors:
Manoch Wongcharoensin
Shih Lun Kuo
Chi Hsiang Lai
Mongkon Laoworapong
Kamthon Vathanalaoha
Sukho Voddhijoti
Kitichai Wongcharoensin
Puvasith Wongcharoensin

Suwatchai Wongcharoensin

CPL RESOURCES PLC

83 Merrion Square
Dublin, 2, Ireland
Tel.: (353) 16146000
Fax: (353) 016147274
E-Mail: info@cpl.ie
Web Site: www.cpl.ie
DQ5—(ISE)
Rev.: $445,256,497
Assets: $139,911,487
Liabilities: $54,754,119
Net Worth: $85,157,368
Earnings: $14,394,596
Emp.: 520
Fiscal Year-end: 06/30/13

Business Description:
Recruitment Services
S.I.C.: 7361
N.A.I.C.S.: 561311

Personnel:
Anne Heraty *(CEO)*
Mark Buckley *(CFO)*

Board of Directors:
John Hennessy
Breffni Byrne
Paul Carroll
Anne Heraty
Garret John Roche
Oliver Tattan

Legal Counsel:
William Fry Solicitors
Fitzwilton House Wilton Place
Dublin, Ireland

Subsidiaries:

Careers Register Limited (1)
49 Saint Stephen's Green
Dublin, Ireland
Tel.: (353) 1 5005900
Fax: (353) 1 5005999
E-Mail: info@careers-register.com
Web Site: www.careers-register.com
Recruitment Consulting Services
S.I.C.: 8999
N.A.I.C.S.: 541612
Lisa Holt *(Mng Dir)*

Computer Placement Limited (1)
Ross House Merchants Road
Galway, Ireland (100%)
Tel.: (353) 91509740
Fax: (353) 91778588
E-Mail: galwayjobs@cpl.ie
Web Site: www.cpl.com
Emp.: 10
Business Support Services
S.I.C.: 7389
N.A.I.C.S.: 561499
Ronan O. Sullivan *(Mgr)*

CPL Solutions Limited (1)
83 Merrion Square
2 Dublin, Ireland
Tel.: (353) 16146002
Fax: (353) 7067274
E-Mail: info@cpl.ie
Web Site: www.cpl.ie
Emp.: 300
Employment Placement Agencies
S.I.C.: 7361
N.A.I.C.S.: 561311
Edel Murphy *(Office Mgr)*

Cpl Training Limited (1)
83 Merrion Square
Dublin, Ireland
Tel.: (353) 1 614 6000
E-Mail: info@cpl.ie
Human Resource Consulting Services
S.I.C.: 8999
N.A.I.C.S.: 541612

Flexsource Limited (1)
83 Merrion Square
Dublin, Ireland
Tel.: (353) 1 614 6000
Fax: (353) 1 614 7274
E-Mail: info@flexsource.ie
Web Site: www.flexsource.ie
Recruitment Consulting Services
S.I.C.: 8999
N.A.I.C.S.: 541612

Kate Cowhig International Recruitment Limited (1)
49 St. Stephen's Green
Dublin, 2, Ireland
Tel.: (353) 16715557
Fax: (353) 16715965
E-Mail: info@kcr.ie
Web Site: www.kcr.ie
Emp.: 15
Employment Placement Agencies
S.I.C.: 7361
N.A.I.C.S.: 561311
Kate Cowhig *(Mng Dir)*

Medical Recruitment Specialists (1)
84 Merrion Square
Dublin, 2, Ireland
Tel.: (353) 016146063
Fax: (353) 16146041
E-Mail: info@mrs.ie
Web Site: www.mrs.ie
Medical Staffing Services
S.I.C.: 7361
N.A.I.C.S.: 561311
John Hennessy *(Chm)*

Multiflex Limited (1)
3 Main Street
Blanchardstown, Ireland
Tel.: (353) 1 829 5800
Fax: (353) 1 614 7278
Staff Recruitment Consulting Services
S.I.C.: 8999
N.A.I.C.S.: 541612
Garrett Roth *(Gen Mgr)*

Northside Recruitment Services Limited (1)
5 Saint Fintans N St
Dublin, Swoor, Ireland
Tel.: (353) 18346344
Employment Placement Agencies
S.I.C.: 7361
N.A.I.C.S.: 561311

Richmond Recruitment Limited (1)
83 Merrion Square
Dublin, Ireland
Tel.: (353) 1 614 6000
E-Mail: info@cpl.ie
Recruitment Consulting Services
S.I.C.: 8999
N.A.I.C.S.: 541612

Servisource Healthcare Limited (1)
East Mid-Leinster Office International House
Tara Street
Dublin, Ireland
Tel.: (353) 1 473 0474
E-Mail: info@servisource.ie
Health Care Services
S.I.C.: 8099
N.A.I.C.S.: 621999

Servisource Recruitment Limited (1)
East Mid-Leinster Office International House
Tara Street
Dublin, Ireland
Tel.: (353) 1 473 0474
E-Mail: info@servisource.ie
Web Site: www.servisource.ie
Emp.: 1,800
Recruitment Consulting Services
S.I.C.: 8999
N.A.I.C.S.: 541612
Declan Murphy *(Mng Dir)*

Techskills Resources Limited (1)
25 Merrion Sq N
Dublin, 2, Ireland
Tel.: (353) 16390390
Fax: (353) 16147281
E-Mail: resources@techskills.ie
Web Site: www.techskills.ie
Emp.: 15
Engineering Services
S.I.C.: 8711
N.A.I.C.S.: 541330
Des Maguire *(Mng Dir)*

Non-U.S. Subsidiaries:

Cpl Jobs Kft (1)
Teve u 1 a-c
1139 Budapest, Hungary
Tel.: (36) 1 501 54 60
Fax: (36) 1 501 54 61
E-Mail: budapest@cpljobs.hu
Web Site: www.cpljobs.hu
Emp.: 40
Staff Recruitment Consulting Services
S.I.C.: 8999
N.A.I.C.S.: 541612
Beatrrix Forkas *(Gen Mgr)*

Cpl Jobs Sp z.o.o (1)
Al Jerozolimskie 81
02-001 Warsaw, Poland
Tel.: (48) 224886500
Fax: (48) 224886530
E-Mail: warsaw@cpljobs.pl
Web Site: www.cpljobs.pl
Staff Recruitment Consultancy Services
S.I.C.: 8999
N.A.I.C.S.: 541612
Renata Kozlowska *(Office Mgr)*

Cpl Jobs S.r.o. (1)
Burzovni palac Rybna 14
Prague, 110 05, Czech Republic
Tel.: (420) 221773611
Fax: (420) 221773624
E-Mail: praha@cpljobs.cz
Web Site: www.cpljobs.cz
Emp.: 20
Staff Recruitment Consulting Services
S.I.C.: 8999
N.A.I.C.S.: 541612
Brigid Corby *(Mng Dir)*

Cpl Jobs S.r.o. (1)
Vysoka 14
811 06 Bratislava, Slovakia
Tel.: (421) 232191200
Fax: (421) 252 631 587
E-Mail: bratislava@cpljobs.sk
Web Site: www.cpljobs.sk
Staff Recruitment Consultancy Services
S.I.C.: 8999
N.A.I.C.S.: 541612

Cpl (Northern Ireland) Limited (1)
20 Adelaide Street
Belfast, BT2 8GD, United Kingdom
Tel.: (44) 2890725600
E-Mail: info@cpl-ni.com
Web Site: www.cpl-ni.com
Emp.: 12
Staff Recruitment Consulting Services
S.I.C.: 8999
N.A.I.C.S.: 541612
Paul Bacon *(Mng Dir)*

Cpl Recruitment S.L. (1)
Via Augusta 2 bis 50 planta
Barcelona, 8006, Spain
Tel.: (34) 932387134
Fax: (34) 93 4150462
Web Site: www.cplspain.es
Recruitment Consulting Services
S.I.C.: 8999
N.A.I.C.S.: 541612

NurseFindersUK Limited (1)
146A High Street
Tonbridge, Kent, TN9 1BB, United Kingdom
Tel.: (44) 1732355585
Fax: (44) 1732369043
E-Mail: info@nursefindersuk.com
Web Site: www.nursefindersuk.com
Emp.: 3
Nursing Recruiters
S.I.C.: 7361
N.A.I.C.S.: 561311
Gaelle Henderson *(Mgr)*

CPM GROUP LTD.

Mells Road Mells
Frome, Somerset, BA11 3PD, United Kingdom
Tel.: (44) 1179812791
Fax: (44) 1179814511
Web Site: www.cpm-group.com
Sales Range: $25-49.9 Million
Emp.: 150

Business Description:
Concrete Pipes & Drainage Systems Mfr
S.I.C.: 3272
N.A.I.C.S.: 327332

Personnel:
Mike Stacy *(Mng Dir)*

CPMC HOLDINGS LIMITED

160 Wei Ken Street Economic & Development District
Hangzhou, China
Tel.: (86) 571 87388300
Fax: (86) 571 87388199
E-Mail: ir.cpmc@cofco.com
Web Site: www.cofcopack.com
Year Founded: 2000
8C3—(DEU)
Rev.: $801,551,064
Assets: $1,099,090,775
Liabilities: $519,022,678
Net Worth: $580,068,097
Earnings: $52,826,997
Fiscal Year-end: 12/31/12

Business Description:
Metal Packaging Product Mfr
S.I.C.: 3412
N.A.I.C.S.: 332439

Personnel:
Jinchang Wang *(Chm)*
Fan Shing Chan *(Sec & Controller-Fin)*

Board of Directors:
Jinchang Wang
Yuk Wo Cheng
Tingmei Fu
Yonglei Hu
Gaoning Ning
Wanpeng Shi
Xin Zhang
Zheng Zhou

CPPGROUP PLC

Holgate Park
York, YO26 4GA, United Kingdom
Tel.: (44) 1904 544500
Fax: (44) 1904 544933
E-Mail: nick.jones@cpp.co.uk
Web Site: www.cppgroupplc.com
Year Founded: 2010
CPP—(LSE)
Rev.: $426,201,413
Assets: $257,318,458
Liabilities: $241,966,179
Net Worth: $15,352,278
Earnings: ($27,211,167)
Emp.: 1,711
Fiscal Year-end: 12/31/12

Business Description:
Holding Company; Life Assistance Products & Services
S.I.C.: 6719
N.A.I.C.S.: 551112

Personnel:
Brent Escott *(CEO)*
Craig Parsons *(CFO)*
Neil Hamilton *(CIO)*
John Titchener *(Gen Counsel & Sec)*

Board of Directors:
Shaun Astley-Stone
Hamish MacGregor Ogston
Les Owen

Legal Counsel:
Herbert Smith Freehills LLP
Exchange House Primrose Street
London, EC2A 2HS, United Kingdom

Subsidiaries:

Concepts for Travel Limited (1)
M K M House Warwick Road
Manchester, Greater Manchester, United Kingdom M16 0XX
Tel.: (44) 1618771114
Fax: (44) 1618771116
E-Mail: admin@conceptsfortravel.com
Web Site: www.conceptsfortravel.com
Emp.: 5
Travel & Tour Operating Agencies
S.I.C.: 4725
N.A.I.C.S.: 561520
Denis Woodall *(Mgr)*

CPP Holdings Limited (1)
Holgate Park Holgate Road
York, North Yorkshire, YO26 4GA, United Kingdom

CPPGroup Plc—(Continued)

Tel.: (44) 1904544500
Fax: (44) 1904544933
E-Mail: info@cpp.co.uk
Web Site: www.cpp.co.uk
Emp.: 600
Management Services
S.I.C.: 8741
N.A.I.C.S.: 551114
Kim Eyre *(Mng Dir)*

Subsidiary:

CPP Travel Services & Promotional Marketing Limited (2)
Nelson House Park Road
Timperley, Altrincham, Cheshire, WA14 5BZ, United Kingdom UK
Tel.: (44) 161 877 1112
Fax: (44) 161 877 1116
E-Mail: enquiries.timperley@cpp.co.uk
Web Site: www.theleapfroggroup.co.uk
Marketing & Promotional Services
S.I.C.: 8742
N.A.I.C.S.: 541613
Matthew Toynton *(Mng Dir)*

U.S. Subsidiaries:

CPP North America LLC (2)
5100 Gamble Dr Ste 600
Minneapolis, MN 55416
Tel.: (952) 541-5800
Fax: (952) 541-5973
E-Mail: inquiries@cppna.co.uk
Web Site: www.cppnorthamerica.com
Emp.: 190
Electronic Security Systems Mfr & Distr
S.I.C.: 3699
N.A.I.C.S.: 335999

CPP Travel LLC (2)
5100 Gamble Dr Ste 600
Saint Louis Park, MN 55416-1521
Tel.: (952) 541-5891
Fax: (952) 541-5971
Web Site: www.cpptravel.com
Emp.: 3
Liability Insurance Services
S.I.C.: 6331
N.A.I.C.S.: 524126
Eric R Woolley *(Mgr)*

CPP Warranties LLC (2)
5100 Gamble Dr Ste 600
Saint Louis Park, MN 55416
Tel.: (952) 541-5807
Fax: (952) 541-5973
General Insurance Services
S.I.C.: 6311
N.A.I.C.S.: 524113

Non-U.S. Subsidiaries:

CPP Asia Limited (2)
PO Box 12239
Central, China (Hong Kong)
Tel.: (852) 22951828
Fax: (852) 22951825
E-Mail: services@cppasia.com
Web Site: www.cppasia.com.hk
Credit Card Protection Services
S.I.C.: 7299
N.A.I.C.S.: 812990

CPP Assistance Services Private Limited (2)
R89 Greater Kailash I
New Delhi, 110048, India
Tel.: (91) 1160004000
Credit Life Insurance Services
S.I.C.: 6311
N.A.I.C.S.: 524113

CPP France SA (2)
120 rue Jean Jaures
92300 Levallois-Perret, Hauts-de-Seine, France
Tel.: (33) 147305620
Fax: (33) 147305628
E-Mail: contact@cppfrance.fr
Web Site: www.cppfrance.fr
Emp.: 8
Credit Card Protection Services
S.I.C.: 7299
N.A.I.C.S.: 812990
Angel Deleon *(Pres & Gen Dir)*

Non-U.S. Subsidiary:

CPP Creating Profitable Partnerships GmbH (1)
Grosse Elbstr 39
Hamburg, 22767, Germany
Tel.: (49) 407699670
Fax: (49) 40769967111
E-Mail: info@cpp-group.de
Web Site: www.cpp-group.de
Emp.: 75
Bail Bonding Services
S.I.C.: 7299
N.A.I.C.S.: 812990
Soeren Timm *(Mng Dir)*

CPR GOMU INDUSTRIAL PUBLIC COMPANY LIMITED

78 Moo 2 Tambon Sanabthub
Amphur Wangnoi
Ayutthaya, 13170, Thailand
Tel.: (66) 35 723324
Fax: (66) 35 7233323
E-Mail: cprgomu@cprgomu.co.th
Web Site: www.cprgomu.co.th
Year Founded: 1975
CPR—(THA)
Rev.: $16,543,466
Assets: $18,558,432
Liabilities: $3,043,322
Net Worth: $15,515,110
Earnings: $2,145,499
Fiscal Year-end: 12/31/12

Business Description:
Synthetics Rubber Part Mfr
S.I.C.: 2822
N.A.I.C.S.: 325212

Personnel:
Yuji Kyoi *(Chm)*
Aran Sriwongthai *(Vice Chm)*
Noppadol Wanichvisitkul *(Mng Dir)*

Board of Directors:
Yuji Kyoi
Ek-kamol Gangaketu
Naohito Mine
Tomohisa Ohno
Phongdhorn Sae-Oui
Somchai Saisaeng
Shinichi Sampei
Aran Sriwongthai
Takashi Tomomatsu
Tossaphol Wanichvisitgul

CPS COLOR B.V.

Nusterweg 98
6136 KV Sittard, Netherlands
Mailing Address:
PO Box 809
6130 AV Sittard, Netherlands
Tel.: (31) 464570100
Fax: (31) 464570150
E-Mail: info@cpscolor.com
Web Site: www.cpscolor.com
Sales Range: $25-49.9 Million
Emp.: 95

Business Description:
Mfr. of Paints
S.I.C.: 2851
N.A.I.C.S.: 325510

Personnel:
Kaj Brandt *(CEO)*
Stephan Schroeer *(Mng Dir)*

Non-U.S. Subsidiaries:

CPS Color Equipments Oy (1)
Paivolantie 5
28400 Ulvila, Finland
Tel.: (358) 26777700
Fax: (358) 26777701
E-Mail: info@cpscolor.com
Web Site: www.dalkia.com
Sls.: $9,692,800
Emp.: 30
Mfr. of Tinting Machines
S.I.C.: 2851
N.A.I.C.S.: 325510
Eika Makines *(Mgr-Fin)*

U.S. Subsidiary:

CPS Color North America Inc. (2)
7295 W Winds Blvd
Concord, NC 28027
Tel.: (704) 588-8408
Fax: (704) 588-8471
Web Site: www.cpscolor.com
Emp.: 40
Painting Services
S.I.C.: 5084
N.A.I.C.S.: 423830
Daniel Bush *(Pres)*

Non-U.S. Subsidiaries:

CPS Color Equipment S.p.A. (2)
Via Agricoltura 103
I-41038 San Felice sul Panaro, Modena, Italy
Tel.: (39) 0535663111
Fax: (39) 0535663285
E-Mail: info@cpscolor.com
Supplier of Tinting & Colorant Solutions
S.I.C.: 2851
N.A.I.C.S.: 325510

CPS Color S.A. (2)
Local 203 Zonamerica Business & Technology Park
Ruta 8 km 17500, 91600 Montevideo, CP, Uruguay
Tel.: (598) 25185500
E-Mail: info@cpscolor.com
Web Site: www.cpscolor.com
Emp.: 30
Tinting & Colorant Solutions
S.I.C.: 2851
N.A.I.C.S.: 325510

CPS Color (2)
Rm 403 Printing House
6 Duddell St, Central, China (Hong Kong)
Tel.: (852) 25578108
Fax: (852) 25667160
S.I.C.: 2851
N.A.I.C.S.: 325510

CPS Color Ltda. (1)
Av Tambore 1 180 Modulo B-02
Condominio Multiplo I, CEP 06460-000 Sao Paulo, Barueri, Brazil
Tel.: (55) 1136431620
Fax: (55) 1136431639
E-Mail: info@cpscolor.com.br
Web Site: www.cpscolor.com.br
Emp.: 30
S.I.C.: 2851
N.A.I.C.S.: 325510
Hipolito Teixeira *(Mng Dir)*

CPS Color Pte Ltd. (1)
No 3 International Business Park
Unit No 01 17 Nordic European, Singapore, 609927, Singapore
Tel.: (65) 68906060
Fax: (65) 68906066
Web Site: www.cpscolor.com
Emp.: 8
S.I.C.: 2851
N.A.I.C.S.: 325510

Automation Techniques (1)
PO Box 17257
Durban, Congella, 4013, South Africa
Tel.: (27) 86 11 000 55
Fax: (27) 86 519 0833
E-Mail:
Web Site: www.automation.co.za
Emp.: 15
Supplier of Integrated Tinting Solutions
S.I.C.: 2851
N.A.I.C.S.: 325510
Kevin Baltz *(Mgr)*

CPS Color (1)
Kuninkaalantie 3A
PO Box 53
FIN 01301 Vantaa, Finland
Tel.: (358) 9857751
Fax: (358) 985776904
Web Site: www.cpscolor.com
Emp.: 50
S.I.C.: 2851
N.A.I.C.S.: 325510

CPS GMBH

Meisenstr 3
83101 Rohrdorf, Germany
Tel.: (49) 80319011730
Fax: (49) 803190117330
E-Mail: info@cps-gmbh.net
Web Site: www.cps-gmbh.net
Sales Range: $10-24.9 Million
Emp.: 80
Fiscal Year-end: 12/31/12

Business Description:
Mfr of Specialty Plastic Products
S.I.C.: 3089
N.A.I.C.S.: 326199

Personnel:
Karl Hofstaetter *(Mng Dir)*
Adalbert Loidl *(Mng Dir)*

CPS GROUP INVESTMENTS PTY LTD.

Level 4 116 Military Road
Neutral Bay, NSW, 2089, Australia
Tel.: (61) 2 9909 3022

Business Description:
Investment Services
S.I.C.: 6211
N.A.I.C.S.: 523999

Subsidiary:

IMX Software Group Pty Ltd (1)
Level 5 176 Wellington Parade
Melbourne, 3002, Australia
Tel.: (61) 3 9016 4222
E-Mail: johnnewbery@powerlan.com
Web Site: www.imxsoftware.com
Emp.: 30
Financial Software Solutions
S.I.C.: 7373
N.A.I.C.S.: 541512
Jon Newbery *(CEO)*

Non-U.S. Subsidiaries:

IMX Software South Africa (2)
Business Edge Systems 313 Rivonia Road K
Morningside, Gauteng, South Africa
Tel.: (27) 117062930
Fax: (27) 117062991
Web Site: www.businessedge.co.za
Emp.: 60
Financial Software Solutions
S.I.C.: 7373
N.A.I.C.S.: 541512
Bob Stansell *(Mng Dir)*

IMX Software UK Limited (2)
Tower Point 44 North Road
Brighton, BN1 1YR, United Kingdom
Tel.: (44) 845 838 2940
Fax: (44) 1273666887
E-Mail: enquiries@drewberryltd.com
Web Site: www.inxsoftware.com
Financial Software Solutions
S.I.C.: 7373
N.A.I.C.S.: 541512
Andrew P. Buller *(Mng Dir)*

U.S. Subsidiary:

ConverterTechnology Inc. (1)
1 Tara Blvd Ste 301
Nashua, NH 03060
Tel.: (603) 880-9118
Fax: (603) 882-8884
Toll Free: (800) 541-7409
E-Mail: info@convertertechnology.com
Web Site: www.convertertechnology.com
IT Services
S.I.C.: 7379
N.A.I.C.S.: 541519
Larry Nuttall *(Chm)*
Shawn Allaway *(CEO)*

CPT GLOBAL LIMITED

Level 1 4 Riverside Quay
Southbank, VIC, 3006, Australia
Tel.: (61) 396847900
Fax: (61) 396847999
E-Mail: info@cptglobal.com
Web Site: www.cptglobal.com
CGO—(ASX)
Rev.: $36,558,952
Assets: $21,254,672
Liabilities: $7,669,856

Net Worth: $13,584,816
Earnings: $335,556
Emp.: 162
Fiscal Year-end: 06/30/13
Business Description:
IT Consulting Services
S.I.C.: 8999
N.A.I.C.S.: 541690
Personnel:
Gerry Tuddenham *(CEO & Mng Dir)*
Elliot Opolion *(CFO & Sec)*
Kevin Akom *(COO)*
Board of Directors:
Fred S. Grimwade
Alan Baxter
Gerry Tuddenham
Peter Wright

U.S. Subsidiary:

CPT Global Inc (1)
410 Park Ave Fl 15
New York, NY 10022
Tel.: (917) 210-8668
Fax: (917) 210-8182
Web Site: www.cptglobal.com
Emp.: 10
Management Consulting Services
S.I.C.: 8748
N.A.I.C.S.: 541618
Mike Lazorik *(Pres)*

CQV CO., LTD.

450 Songdu-Ri Jincheon-Eup
Jincheon-Gun, Jincheon,
Chungcheong Buk-Do, 365802,
Korea (South)
Tel.: (82) 43 5312500
Fax: (82) 43 5360314
Web Site: www.cqv.co.kr
Year Founded: 2000
101240—(KRS)
Emp.: 100
Business Description:
Chemical Products Mfr
S.I.C.: 2899
N.A.I.C.S.: 325998
Personnel:
K.W. Chang *(Pres & CEO)*

CR CAPITAL REAL ESTATE AG

Fasanenstrasse 77
10623 Berlin, Germany
Tel.: (49) 30 889 26880
Fax: (49) 30 889 268869
E-Mail: info@capital-real-estate-a g.de
Web Site: www.capital-real-estate-a g.de
CRZ—(DEU)
Sales Range: $1-9.9 Million
Emp.: 4
Business Description:
Real Estate Management Services
S.I.C.: 6531
N.A.I.C.S.: 531390
Personnel:
Stefan Krach *(Chm-Supervisory Bd)*
Axel Eggers *(Chm-Mgmt Bd)*

CR2 EMPREENDIMENTOS IMOBILIARIOS S.A.

Av Borges de Medeiros 633 6 andar - sala 604 a 608
Leblon, Rio de Janeiro, RJ, 22430-041, Brazil
Tel.: (55) 21 3095 4600
Fax: (55) 21 3095 4699
E-Mail: ri@cr2.com.br
Web Site: www.cr2.com.br
Year Founded: 2006
CRDE3—(BRAZ)
Business Description:
Real Estate Development Services
S.I.C.: 6531
N.A.I.C.S.: 531390
Personnel:
Rogerio Furtado Moreira *(Chm, CFO & IR Officer)*
Carlos Antonio Guedes Valente *(Vice Chm & CEO)*
Felipe Alves Costa *(Officer)*
Board of Directors:
Rogerio Furtado Moreira
Eduardo Grande Bittencourt
Pedro Cavalcanti Gomes Ferreira
Amin Alves Murad
Luiz Fernando Azevedo Resende
Carlos Antonio Guedes Valente

CRABTREE OF GATESHEAD LTD.

Kingsway Team Valley Trading Estate
Gateshead, Tyne & Wear, NE11 0SU, United Kingdom
Tel.: (44) 191 487 5071
Fax: (44) 191 487 3997
E-Mail: sales@crabpress.co.uk
Web Site: www.crabpress.co.uk
Year Founded: 1849
Sales Range: $25-49.9 Million
Emp.: 249
Business Description:
Printing Machinery Mfr
S.I.C.: 3555
N.A.I.C.S.: 333244
Personnel:
Neil Willcock *(Head-Production)*

CRADLE RESOURCES LIMITED

Suite 23 513 Hay Street
Subiaco, WA, 6008, Australia
Tel.: (61) 8 6143 1869
Fax: (61) 8 9388 8824
E-Mail: admin@cradleresources.co m.au
Web Site: www.cradleresources.co m.au
CXX—(ASX)
Business Description:
Metal Mining
S.I.C.: 1099
N.A.I.C.S.: 212299
Personnel:
Ian Gregory *(Sec)*
Board of Directors:
Craig Burton
Evan Cranston
Didier Murcia

CRAFT PRINT INTERNATIONAL LIMITED

9 Joo Koon Circle Jurong
Singapore, 629041, Singapore
Tel.: (65) 68614040
Fax: (65) 68610530
E-Mail: info@craftprint.com
Web Site: www.craftprint.com
541—(SES)
Rev.: $16,279,970
Assets: $27,467,810
Liabilities: $13,678,816
Net Worth: $13,788,994
Earnings: ($1,576,022)
Fiscal Year-end: 09/30/12
Business Description:
Commercial Printing Services
S.I.C.: 2759
N.A.I.C.S.: 323111
Personnel:
Dora Kwee Cheng Ong *(Founder & Chm)*
Charlie Chan *(Mng Dir)*
Busarakham Kohsikaporn *(Sec)*
Board of Directors:
Dora Kwee Cheng Ong
Charlie Chan
Cher Boon Chan
Boon Tiong Choo
Gim Teik Soh

CRAIG MANUFACTURING LTD.

96 McLean Avenue
Hartland, NB, E7P 2K5, Canada
Tel.: (506) 375-4493
Fax: (506) 375-4848
Toll Free: (800) 565-5007
E-Mail: sales@craigattachments.com
Web Site: www.craig-mfg.com
Year Founded: 1941
Rev.: $13,320,339
Emp.: 85
Business Description:
Heavy Equipment Mfr
S.I.C.: 3559
N.A.I.C.S.: 333249
Personnel:
Colden Wetmore *(Gen Mgr)*

CRAIG WIRELESS SYSTEMS LTD.

30th Floor - 360 Main Street
Winnipeg, MB, R3C 4G1, Canada
Tel.: (204) 925-9125
Fax: (204) 488-2710
E-Mail: craiginfo@craigwireless.com
Web Site: www.craigwireless.com
Year Founded: 2007
CWG—(TSXV)
Rev.: $13,390,794
Assets: $22,225,089
Liabilities: $4,062,298
Net Worth: $18,162,791
Earnings: ($10,629,111)
Emp.: 101
Fiscal Year-end: 08/31/13
Business Description:
Wireless Systems
S.I.C.: 4812
N.A.I.C.S.: 517210
Personnel:
T. Boyd Craig *(Chm, Pres & CEO)*
Richard Coningham *(CFO)*
Board of Directors:
T. Boyd Craig
Brian Collins
David Coriat
Michael Dubois
Transfer Agent:
Equity Financial Trust Company
Toronto, ON, Canada

Subsidiaries:

Craig Wireless Manitoba Inc. (1)
177 Lombard Ave 4th Fl Ste 401
Winnipeg, MB, R3B 0W5, Canada
Tel.: (204) 925-9125
Fax: (204) 488-2710
Toll Free: (888) 244-5544
E-Mail: info@craigwireless.com
Web Site: www.craigwireless.com
Emp.: 2
Wireless Telecommunication Services
S.I.C.: 4812
N.A.I.C.S.: 517210
Cole Cox *(Gen Mgr)*

U.S. Subsidiary:

Craig Wireless Palm Springs Inc. (1)
71713 Hwy 1011
Rancho Mirage, CA 92270
Tel.: (760) 346-3282
Fax: (760) 346-1995
E-Mail: info@craigwireless.com
Web Site: www.craigwireless.com
Emp.: 15
Wireless Broadband Services
S.I.C.: 4812
N.A.I.C.S.: 517210
Gary Birkland *(Pres)*

Non-U.S. Subsidiary:

Craig Wireless Hellas S.A. (1)
76 Kifisias Ave
Neo Psychiko, 15125 Athens, Greece
Tel.: (30) 2108055661
Fax: (30) 2106728546
E-Mail: info@craigwireless.gr
Web Site: www.craigwireless.gr
Emp.: 15
Wireless Telecommunication Services
S.I.C.: 4812
N.A.I.C.S.: 517210
Vassilis Sotiriou *(Gen Mgr)*

CRAILAR TECHNOLOGIES INC.

(Formerly NATURALLY ADVANCED TECHNOLOGIES INC.)
Suite 305 4420 Chatterton Way
Victoria, BC, V8X 5J2, Canada
Tel.: (250) 658-8582
E-Mail: ir@naturallyadvanced.com
Web Site: www.naturallyadvanced. com
CL—(OTC TSXV)
Assets: $20,328,540
Liabilities: $13,426,339
Net Worth: $6,902,201
Earnings: ($9,315,360)
Emp.: 25
Fiscal Year-end: 12/31/12
Business Description:
Fiber Mfr
S.I.C.: 2823
N.A.I.C.S.: 325220
Personnel:
Lesley Hayes *(Chm)*
Jason David Finnis *(Pres & Chief Innovation Officer)*
Kenneth C. Barker *(CEO)*
Theodore R. Sanders, Jr. *(CFO & Treas)*
Thomas C. Robinson *(COO)*
Jay Nalbach *(CMO)*
Larisa Harrison *(Sec)*
Board of Directors:
Lesley Hayes
Kenneth C. Barker
Robert Edmunds
Jason David Finnis
Larisa Harrison
Jeremy K. Jones
Peter C. Moore
Guy Prevost
Transfer Agent:
Computershare Investor Services Inc.
510 Burrard St 2nd Floor
Vancouver, BC, V6C 3B9, Canada
Tel.: (604) 661-9400

U.S. Subsidiary:

Naturally Advanced Technologies US Inc. (1)
696 McVey Ave
Lake Oswego, OR 97034
Tel.: (503) 387-3941
Flax Fiber Products Mfr
S.I.C.: 2299
N.A.I.C.S.: 313110

CRAMO PLC

Kalliosolantie 2
FI-01740 Vantaa, Finland
Tel.: (358) 1066110
Fax: (358) 106611298
Web Site: www.cramo.com
CRA1V—(OMX)
Rev.: $926,691,312
Assets: $1,491,739,439
Liabilities: $774,719,489
Net Worth: $717,019,950
Earnings: $51,881,392
Emp.: 2,555
Fiscal Year-end: 12/31/12
Business Description:
Construction Machinery, Equipment & Modular Space Rental & Leasing Services
S.I.C.: 7359
N.A.I.C.S.: 532412

Cramo Plc—(Continued)

Personnel:
Stig Gustavson *(Chm)*
Eino Halonen *(Deputy Chm)*
Vesa Koivula *(Pres & CEO)*
Martti Ala-Harkonen *(CFO)*
Merja Naumanen *(IR Comm Officer)*
Erik Bengtsson *(Mng Dir-Sweden & Exec VP-Scandinavia)*
Tatu Hauhio *(Mng Dir-Finland & Exec VP-Eastern Europe)*
Dirk Schlitzkus *(Mng Dir-Theisen Group & Exec VP-Central Europe)*
Martin Holmgren *(Sr VP-Fleet Mgmt)*
Per Lundquist *(Sr VP-Ops)*
Petri Moksen *(Sr VP-Modular Space)*
Aku Rumpunen *(Sr VP-Grp Bus Control)*

Board of Directors:
Stig Gustavson
Helene Bistrom
Eino Halonen
Victor Hartwall
Jari Lainio
Esko Makela
Erkki Stenberg

Non-U.S. Subsidiaries:

ALVA Technika, UAB (1)
Metalo g 23
LT 02190 Vilnius, Lithuania
Tel.: (370) 8 52108741
Fax: (370) 8 52108742
E-Mail: info@alvatechnika.lt
Web Site: www.alvatechnika.lt
Emp.: 2
Construction Equipment Rental Services
S.I.C.: 7359
N.A.I.C.S.: 532412
Darius Norkus *(Gen Mgr)*

AS Cramo Estonia (1)
Kadaka Tee 131
Tallinn, 12915, Estonia
Tel.: (372) 6830800
Fax: (372) 6830808
E-Mail: info.ee@cramo.com
Web Site: www.cramo.ee
Emp.: 30
Construction Equipment Rental Services
S.I.C.: 7359
N.A.I.C.S.: 532412
Taivo Sillaste *(Mgr)*

Cramo A/S (1)
Sarverland 7
2600 Glostrup, Denmark
Tel.: (45) 28140604
Fax: (45) 43200570
E-Mail: info@cramo.com
Web Site: www.cramo.dk/
Emp.: 130
Construction Machinery Rental Services
S.I.C.: 7359
N.A.I.C.S.: 532412
Martin Henriksen *(Gen Mgr)*

Cramo AB (1)
Torshamnsgatan 35
164 95 Kista, Sweden
Tel.: (46) 86235400
Fax: (46) 86235410
E-Mail: info.se@cramo.com
Web Site: www.cramo.se
Emp.: 90
Construction Machinery Rental Services
S.I.C.: 7353
N.A.I.C.S.: 532412
Erik Bengtsson *(Mng Dir)*

Cramo AS (1)
Brobekkveien 80C Bygg 8
Postboks 34
Alnabru, 0614 Oslo, Norway
Tel.: (47) 23375560
Fax: (47) 23 37 55 61
E-Mail: info.no@cramo.com
Web Site: www.cramo.no
Emp.: 180
Construction Machinery, Equipment & Modules Rental Services
S.I.C.: 7359
N.A.I.C.S.: 532490

Cramo AS (1)
Kobbervikdalen 75
3036 Drammen, Norway
Mailing Address:
Postboks 503
Brakeroya, Drammen, 3002, Norway
Tel.: (47) 32 23 50 00
Fax: (47) 32 23 50 10
E-Mail: drammen@cramo.com
Web Site: www.cramo.no
Emp.: 4
Construction Machinery Rental Services
S.I.C.: 7359
N.A.I.C.S.: 532412

Cramo Instant AB (1)
Torshamsgatan 35
164 95 Kista, Sweden
Tel.: (46) 86235400
Fax: (46) 86235410
E-Mail: info.se@cramo.com
Web Site: www.cramo.se
Emp.: 90
Construction Machinery Rental Services
S.I.C.: 7353
N.A.I.C.S.: 532412

Cramo Kaliningrad OOO (1)
St 4 Kiev 33
236009 Kaliningrad, Russia
Tel.: (7) 4012776222
Web Site: www.cramo.no/Web/Apps/Downloads/MediaBank.aspx?id=23040&epslanguage=RU
Construction Equipment Rental Services
S.I.C.: 7359
N.A.I.C.S.: 532412

Cramo New Holding AB (1)
Tureberg Rd 11A
19129 Sollentuna, Sweden
Tel.: (46) 86235400
Fax: (46) 86235410
E-Mail: info.se@cramo.com
Web Site: www.cramo.se
Emp.: 90
Construction Machinery Rental Services
S.I.C.: 7359
N.A.I.C.S.: 532412

Cramo S.R.O (1)
Na Petynce 136 120
Prague, 169 00, Czech Republic
Tel.: (420) 220512182
Fax: (420) 220515427
E-Mail: josef.liska@cramo.com
Web Site: www.cramo.cz
Emp.: 30
Construction Machinery Rental Services
S.I.C.: 7359
N.A.I.C.S.: 532412
Josef Liska *(Sls Mgr)*

Cramo Sverige AB (1)
Torshamnsgatan 35
164 95 Kista, Sweden
Tel.: (46) 86235400
Fax: (46) 86235410
E-Mail: info@cramo.com
Web Site: www.cramo.se
Emp.: 90
Construction Machinery Rental Services
S.I.C.: 7353
N.A.I.C.S.: 532412

Cramo (1)
Hasthagsvagen 14
194 52 Upplands Vasby, Stockholm, Sweden
Tel.: (46) 859030390
Fax: (46) 859071105
E-Mail: upplands.vasby@cramo.com
Web Site: www.cramo.se
Emp.: 25
Construction Equipment Rental Services
S.I.C.: 7359
N.A.I.C.S.: 532412
Lasse Hedstrom *(Mgr)*

CRANAB AB

Karlsgardsvagen 56
Vindeln, 922 82, Sweden
Tel.: (46) 93313500
Fax: (46) 93314591
E-Mail: info@cranab.se
Web Site: www.cranab.se
Sales Range: $10-24.9 Million
Emp.: 218

Business Description:
Forestry Equipment Mfr
S.I.C.: 8711
N.A.I.C.S.: 541330

Personnel:
Hans Eliasson *(Chm)*
Fedrick Johnson *(Mng Dir)*

Subsidiary:

Vimek AB (1)
Lidvagen 11
922 31 Vindeln, Sweden
Tel.: (46) 933 135 15
Fax: (46) 56 933 710
E-Mail: info@vimek.se
Web Site: www.vimek.se
Forestry Machinery Mfr
S.I.C.: 3524
N.A.I.C.S.: 333112
Fredrik Lundberg, *(CEO & Mng Dir-Export Sls)*

Units:

Cranab AB - Cranab 1 Factory (1)
Karlsgardsvagen 56
922 32 Vindeln, Sweden
Tel.: (46) 933 145 91
Crane, Grapple & Bushcutter Mfr & Whslr
S.I.C.: 3537
N.A.I.C.S.: 333924

Cranab AB - Cranab 2 Factory (1)
Lidvagen 4
922 31 Vindeln, Sweden
Tel.: (46) 933 145 94
Crane, Grapple & Bushcutter Mfr & Whslr
S.I.C.: 3537
N.A.I.C.S.: 333924

CRANES SOFTWARE INTERNATIONAL LIMITED

2 Tavarekere Bannerghatta Road 1st Phase 1st Stage BTM Layout
Bengaluru, Karnataka, 560 029, India
Tel.: (91) 80 4128 1111
Fax: (91) 80 4128 0203
E-Mail: info@cranessoftware.com
Web Site: www.cranessoftware.com
Year Founded: 1991
512093—(BOM)
Rev.: $61,337,049
Assets: $244,360,263
Liabilities: $230,535,903
Net Worth: $13,824,360
Earnings: ($48,550,978)
Fiscal Year-end: 03/31/13

Business Description:
Software Development Services
S.I.C.: 7371
N.A.I.C.S.: 541511

Personnel:
Asif Khader *(Co-Founder & Mng Dir)*
Mukkaram Jan *(Co-Founder)*
P. Phaneendra *(Compliance Officer & Sec)*

Board of Directors:
Richard Gall
Mukkaram Jan
Asif Khader
Mueed Khader
Peter Ryser

Transfer Agent:
Integrated Enterprises (India) Ltd
30 Ramana Residency 4th Cross Sampige Road Malleswaram
Bengaluru, India

CRANEWARE PLC

1 Tanfield
Edinburgh, EH3 5DA, United Kingdom
Tel.: (44) 131 550 3100
Fax: (44) 131 550 3101
Web Site: www.craneware.com
CRW—(LSE)
Rev.: $41,452,000
Assets: $64,375,000
Liabilities: $23,054,000
Net Worth: $41,321,000
Earnings: $8,296,000
Emp.: 198
Fiscal Year-end: 06/30/13

Business Description:
Supplier of Business Intelligence & Revenue Cycle Software
S.I.C.: 7372
N.A.I.C.S.: 511210

Personnel:
Gordon Craig *(Pres & CTO)*
Keith Neilson *(CEO)*
Craig T. Preston *(CFO & Sec)*
Derek Paterson *(CIO)*
Mark Montgomery *(CMO)*
Karen Bowden *(Exec VP-Revenue Integrity Ops)*
Seth Droe *(Exec VP-Sls)*
Sharon Cuming *(Sr VP-HR)*
Glen Johnson *(Sr VP-Product Mgmt)*

Board of Directors:
George Reginald Elliott
Colleen A. Blye
Neil Philip Lanceley Heywood
Keith Neilson
Craig T. Preston
Ronald Frank Verni

Legal Counsel:
Pinsent Masons
Princes Exchange 1 Earl Grey Street
Edinburgh, EH3 9AQ, United Kingdom

U.S. Subsidiaries:

Craneware, Inc. (1)
3340 Peachtree Rd Ne Ste 850
Atlanta, GA 30326-1072 FL
Tel.: (407) 384-9413
Web Site: www.craneware.com
Emp.: 30
Supplier of Business Intelligence & Revenue Cycle Software
S.I.C.: 7372
N.A.I.C.S.: 511210
Keith Neilson *(Co-Founder & CEO)*

Craneware InSight, Inc. (1)
545 Brandies Cir
Murfreesboro, TN 37128
Tel.: (615) 869-4000
Fax: (615) 869-4099
Toll Free: (866) 745-5500
E-Mail: clientservices@claimtrust.com
Web Site: www.cranewareinsight.com
Emp.: 23
Healthcare Software Development Services
S.I.C.: 7371
N.A.I.C.S.: 541511
Karen Bowden *(Sr VP)*
Glen Johnson *(Sr VP-Product Mgmt)*
Richard Rizza *(Sr VP-Fin)*

CRANEX LIMITED

9 DDA Market Katwaria Sarai Opp Qutub Hotel
New Delhi, 110016, India
Tel.: (91) 11 3240427
Fax: (91) 11 2895761
E-Mail: info@cranexltd.com
Web Site: www.cranexltd.com
522001—(BOM)
Sales Range: $1-9.9 Million

Business Description:
Crane Mfr
S.I.C.: 3536
N.A.I.C.S.: 333923

Personnel:
S. C. Agrawal *(Chm & Mng Dir)*

Board of Directors:
S. C. Agrawal
Piyush Agrawal
Anil Kumar Jain
M. C. Jain
Ashwani Kumar Jindal

CRANSWICK PLC

74 Helsinki Road
Sutton Fields, Hull, HU7 0YW, United Kingdom

Tel.: (44) 1482372000
Fax: (44) 1482876146
Web Site: www.cranswick.plc.uk
CWK—(LSE)
Rev.: $1,382,148,809
Assets: $674,325,244
Liabilities: $242,130,426
Net Worth: $432,194,819
Earnings: $57,235,049
Emp.: 4,402
Fiscal Year-end: 03/31/13
Business Description:
Pig Farming & Feed & Food Mfr
S.I.C.: 2099
N.A.I.C.S.: 311999
Personnel:
Martin Davey *(Chm)*
Adam Couch *(CEO)*
Malcolm Windeatt *(Sec)*
Board of Directors:
Martin Davey
Kate Allum
Mark Bottomley
Jim Brisby
Adam Couch
Steven Esom
Bernard Hoggarth
John Worby
Legal Counsel:
Rollits
Hull, United Kingdom
Subsidiaries:

Delico Limited (1)
Steinbeck Crescent Snelshaw West
Milton Keynes, Buckinghamshire, MK4 4AE, United Kingdom
Tel.: (44) 1908522122
Fax: (44) 1908522111
Emp.: 350
Cooked Meat Products Mfr
S.I.C.: 5147
N.A.I.C.S.: 311612
Trew Drayton *(Mng Dir)*

The Sandwich Factory Holdings Limited (1)
Carlyon Road Industrial Estate
Atherstone, Warwickshire, CV9 1LQ, United Kingdom
Tel.: (44) 1827719100
Fax: (44) 1827719101
E-Mail: info@tsfl.co.uk
Web Site: www.tsfl.co.uk
Emp.: 500
Food Products Mfr
S.I.C.: 2099
N.A.I.C.S.: 311991
Tony Cleaver *(Mng Dir)*

Cranswick Convenience Foods (1)
Valley Park Industrial Estate Meadowgate
Wombwell, Barnsley, South Yorkshire, S73 0UN, United Kingdom
Tel.: (44) 1226344400
Fax: (44) 1226272900
E-Mail: reception@cranswick.plc.uk
Web Site: www.cranswick.plc.uk
Emp.: 600
Fresh Pork Distr
S.I.C.: 5147
N.A.I.C.S.: 424470
Nicholas John Tranfield *(Mng Dir)*

Subsidiary:

Cranswick Country Foods plc (1)
Staithes Road
Preston, Hull, HU12 8TB, United Kingdom
Tel.: (44) 1482891001
Fax: (44) 1482890080
Pork & Pork Products Mfr
S.I.C.: 5147
N.A.I.C.S.: 311612
Bernard Hoggarth *(CEO)*

Subsidiary:

Cranswick Country Foods (Norfolk) Limited (2)
Brandon Road
Thetford, Norfolk, IP25 6LW, United Kingdom
Tel.: (44) 1953881555
Fax: (44) 1953882455
E-Mail: ccfm.reception@cranswick.co.uk
Web Site: www.cranswick.co.uk
Emp.: 800
Fresh Pork Distr
S.I.C.: 5147
N.A.I.C.S.: 424470

CRATER GOLD MINING LIMITED

(Formerly Gold Anomaly Limited)
Level 4 15 17 Young Street
Sydney, NSW, 2001, Australia
Tel.: (61) 2 9241 4224
Fax: (61) 2 9252 2335
E-Mail: info@cratergold.com.au
Web Site: www.cratergold.com.au
CGN—(ASX)
Rev.: $26,623
Assets: $33,909,408
Liabilities: $1,211,459
Net Worth: $32,697,949
Earnings: ($3,072,199)
Fiscal Year-end: 06/30/13
Business Description:
Gold & Other Metal Mining Services
S.I.C.: 1041
N.A.I.C.S.: 212221
Personnel:
Sam Chan *(Chm)*
Greg Barry Starr *(Mng Dir)*
G. R. Boyce *(CFO)*
John Andrew Lemon *(Sec)*
Board of Directors:
Sam Chan
Thomas M. Fermanis
Robert Peter Macnab
Russell Parker
Greg Barry Starr
Desmond Sun
Legal Counsel:
Herbert Geer
Level 12 77 King Street
Sydney, Australia

CRAVATEX LTD.

Sahas 4th Floor 414 / 2 Veer
Savarkar Marg Prabhadevi
Mumbai, 400025, India
Tel.: (91) 22 66667474
Fax: (91) 22 24313210
E-Mail: info@cravatex.com
Web Site: www.cravatex.com
509472—(BOM)
Rev.: $41,514,681
Assets: $26,564,113
Liabilities: $19,403,821
Net Worth: $7,160,292
Earnings: $1,383,049
Fiscal Year-end: 03/31/13
Business Description:
Casual & Sport Wear Mfr
S.I.C.: 3949
N.A.I.C.S.: 339920
Personnel:
Rajesh Batra *(Chm & Mng Dir)*
Sudhanshu Namdeo *(Compliance Officer & Sec)*
Board of Directors:
Rajesh Batra
Rajiv Batra
Arjun Bulchandani
Nabankur Gupta
S. D. Israni
N. R. Mangalingam
N. Santhanam
H. K. Vakharia
Transfer Agent:
Sharepro Services (India) Private Limited
13 AB Samhita Warehousing Complex II Floor
Sakinaka Telephone Lane
Off Andheri Kurla Rd Sakinaka, Mumbai, India

CRAVEN HOUSE CAPITAL

60 Cannon Street
London, EC4N 6NP, United Kingdom
Tel.: (44) 20 7002 1027
Fax: (44) 20 7681 2101
E-Mail: info@cravenhousecapital.com
Web Site: www.cravenhousecapital.com
CRV—(AIM)
Rev.: $549,593
Assets: $7,386,339
Liabilities: $1,318,707
Net Worth: $6,067,632
Earnings: ($704,363)
Fiscal Year-end: 05/31/13
Business Description:
Investment Services
S.I.C.: 6211
N.A.I.C.S.: 523999
Personnel:
Xyras To *(Chief Strategy Officer-Greater China)*
Alexandra Naomi Eavis *(Sec)*
Board of Directors:
Mark J. Pajak
Balbir S. Bindra
Alexandra Naomi Eavis
Legal Counsel:
Field Fisher Waterhouse LLP
35 Vine Street
London, United Kingdom

CRAVEROLANIS

Alicia Moreau de Justo 2050 1Fl
C1107AFP Buenos Aires, Argentina
Tel.: (54) 11 4 314 5050
Fax: (54) 11 4 314 4225
E-Mail: gabriel.manloneay@craverolanis.com
Year Founded: 1974
Emp.: 120
Business Description:
Advertising Agency
S.I.C.: 7311
N.A.I.C.S.: 541810
Personnel:
Juan Cravero *(Pres & Chief Creative Officer)*
Dario Lanis *(Partner & Chief Creative Officer)*
Martin Glucksman *(CFO)*

CRAWFORD HEALTHCARE HOLDINGS LIMITED

Unit 1 Adams Ct Adams Hill
Knutsford, Cheshire, WA16 6BA, United Kingdom
Tel.: (44) 1565654920
Fax: (44) 1565654117
E-Mail: info@crawfordpharma.com
Web Site: www.crawfordpharma.com
Business Description:
Pharmaceutical Mfr
S.I.C.: 2834
N.A.I.C.S.: 325412
Personnel:
Richard Anderson *(CEO)*
Subsidiary:

Patient Plus Limited (1)
79 New Cavendish St
London, W1W 6XB, United Kingdom UK
Tel.: (44) 2073887722
Fax: (44) 2073887805
Emp.: 15
Medicine Research & Development Services
S.I.C.: 8731
N.A.I.C.S.: 541712

CRAWFORD PACKAGING INC.

3036 Page Street
London, ON, N5V 4P2, Canada
Tel.: (519) 659-0909
Fax: (519) 659-9910
Toll Free: (800) 265-4993
E-Mail: info@cpsupplyline.com
Web Site: www.crawfordpackaging.com
Rev.: $26,444,791
Emp.: 100
Business Description:
Packaging Services
S.I.C.: 3565
N.A.I.C.S.: 333993
Personnel:
Clarence A. Covey *(Pres & CEO)*

CRAWSHAW GROUP PLC

Unit 16 Bradmarsh Business Park
Bow Bridge Close
Rotherham, S Yorkshire, S60 1BY, United Kingdom
Tel.: (44) 1709369600
Fax: (44) 1709369988
E-Mail: enquiries@crawshawbutchers.com
Web Site: www.crawshawgroupplc.com
CRAW—(AIM)
Rev.: $29,656,582
Assets: $21,389,408
Liabilities: $5,404,471
Net Worth: $15,984,937
Earnings: $281,865
Emp.: 232
Fiscal Year-end: 01/31/13
Business Description:
Meat Retailer
S.I.C.: 5421
N.A.I.C.S.: 445210
Personnel:
Richard Sidney Rose *(Chm)*
Kevin P. Boyd *(Mng Dir)*
Lynda J. Sherratt *(Sec & Dir-Fin)*
Board of Directors:
Richard Sidney Rose
Kevin P. Boyd
Colin B. Crawshaw
Mark Naughton-Rumbo
Lynda J. Sherratt
Legal Counsel:
Atticus Legal LLP
Castlefield House Liverpool Road Castlefield
Manchester, United Kingdom
Subsidiary:

Crawshaw Butchers Limited (1)
17-25 John Street
Rotherham, South Yorkshire, S60 1EQ, United Kingdom
Tel.: (44) 1709 562 182
Fax: (44) 1709 512 983
Meat Retailer
S.I.C.: 5421
N.A.I.C.S.: 445210

CRAZY HORSE RESOURCES INC.

Suite 800 789 West Pender St
Vancouver, BC, V6C 1H2, Canada
Tel.: (604) 638-8063
Fax: (604) 648-8105
Web Site: www.crazyhorseresources.com
Year Founded: 2007
CZH—(OTC TSXV)
Int. Income: $4,279
Assets: $3,720,581
Liabilities: $133,822
Net Worth: $3,586,759
Earnings: ($29,572,830)
Fiscal Year-end: 07/31/13
Business Description:
Mineral Exploration Services
S.I.C.: 3299
N.A.I.C.S.: 327999
Personnel:
Darryl S. Cardey *(Chm, Acting Pres, Interim CEO & CFO)*
Brian Lueck *(COO)*
Board of Directors:

Crazy Horse Resources Inc.—(Continued)

Darryl S. Cardey
Jose D. Leviste, III
Paul Reynolds
Roderick R. C. Salazar, III

Legal Counsel:
Owen Bird Law Corporation
2900 595 Burrard Street
Vancouver, BC, Canada

Transfer Agent:
Equity Financial Trust Company
200 University Avenue Suite 400
Toronto, ON, Canada

CRAZY INFOTECH LTD.

3/5 Alonkar Aadharsh 7th Avenue
Ashok Nagar
Chennai, 600 083, India
Tel.: (91) 4424716633
Fax: (91) 4424744997
E-Mail: info@crazyinfotech.com
Web Site: www.crazyinfotech.com
524388—(BOM)
Rev.: $16,080
Assets: $2,784,424
Liabilities: $965,908
Net Worth: $1,818,516
Earnings: ($21,603)
Fiscal Year-end: 03/31/13

Business Description:
Information Technology Enabled Services
S.I.C.: 7389
N.A.I.C.S.: 519190

Personnel:
N. Aravind *(Chm & Mng Dir)*
K. N. Anand *(Pres, CEO & Head-Ops, Relationship Mgmt & Co-ordination)*
M. Senthil Kumar *(CTO & Head-Software Dev & Solutions)*
P. Obul Reddy *(Sec & Head-Corp Plng)*

Board of Directors:
N. Aravind
Anitha Anand
T. Rajendran

Transfer Agent:
System Support Services
Gala No 209 Shivai Ind Estate Near Logitech Park 89 Andheri Kurla Road
Sakinaka Andheri (East), Mumbai, 400072, India

CRDB BANK PLC

Office Accommodation Scheme
Azikiwe Street
PO Box 268
Dar es Salaam, Tanzania
Tel.: (255) 222117442
Fax: (255) 222116714
E-Mail: info@crdbbank.com
Web Site: www.crdbbank.com
Year Founded: 1996
CRDB—(DAR)
Rev.: $159,662,010
Assets: $1,875,637,760
Liabilities: $1,682,004,240
Net Worth: $193,633,520
Earnings: $49,131,230
Emp.: 1,898
Fiscal Year-end: 12/31/12

Business Description:
Banking Services
S.I.C.: 6029
N.A.I.C.S.: 522110

Personnel:
Martin J. Mmari *(Chm)*
Charles S. Kimei *(Mng Dir)*
Rachel G. Shambwe *(IR Officer)*
John B. Rugambo *(Sec)*

Board of Directors:
Martin J. Mmari
Juma A. Abdulrahman
Kai Kristoffersen
Ally H. Laay
Joyce W. Luhanga
Bede P. Lyimo
Joseph C. Machange
Boniface C. Muhegi
Joyce N. Nyanza
Frederick T. Sumaye

Legal Counsel:
Abenry& Company
NIC Life House 2nd Floor Ohio St Sokoine Drive
PO Box 3167
Dar es Salaam, Tanzania

CREADES AB

Engelbrektsgatan 5
114 32 Stockholm, Sweden
Tel.: (46) 8 412 011 00
Fax: (46) 8 412 011 11
E-Mail: info@creades.se
Web Site: www.creades.se
CRED A—(OMX)

Business Description:
Investment Services
S.I.C.: 6211
N.A.I.C.S.: 523999

Personnel:
Sven Hagstromer *(Chm)*
Stefan Charette *(CEO)*

CREALOGIX HOLDING AG

(d/b/a Crealogix Gruppe)
Baslerstrasse 60
PO Box 112
8066 Zurich, Switzerland
Tel.: (41) 58 404 80 00
Fax: (41) 58 404 80 90
E-Mail: info@crealogix.com
Web Site: www.crealogix.com
Year Founded: 1996
CLXN—(SWX)
Sls.: $53,181,334
Assets: $53,921,748
Liabilities: $14,432,667
Net Worth: $39,489,081
Earnings: $2,754,425
Emp.: 216
Fiscal Year-end: 06/30/13

Business Description:
IT & Software Consulting Services
S.I.C.: 7371
N.A.I.C.S.: 541511

Personnel:
Bruno Richle *(Chm & CEO)*
Richard Dratva *(Vice Chm & Chief Strategy Officer)*
Rolf Lichtin *(CFO)*
Thomas F. J. Avedik *(CEO-EBanking)*
Werner Truol *(CEO-EPayment)*
Louis-Paul Wicki *(CEO-Education & EBus)*

Board of Directors:
Bruno Richle
Richard Dratva
Jean-Claude Philipona
Beat Schmid
Christoph Schmid

Subsidiaries:

C-Channel AG **(1)**
Bosch 838
6331 Hunenberg, Switzerland
Tel.: (41) 417845555
Fax: (41) 417845566
E-Mail: info@c-channel.ch
Web Site: www.c-channel.ch
Emp.: 25
Internet Banking Services
S.I.C.: 4899
N.A.I.C.S.: 517919
Paul Gnos *(Mng Dir)*

Crealogix AG **(1)**
Rosengartenstrasse 6
8608 Bubikon, Switzerland
Tel.: (41) 552532121
Fax: (41) 552532120
E-Mail: info@crealogix.com
Web Site: www.crealogix.com
IT Solutions
S.I.C.: 4899
N.A.I.C.S.: 517919
Bruno Richle *(Gen Mgr)*

Crealogix E-Banking Solutions AG **(1)**
Hohlstrasse 535
8048 Zurich, Switzerland
Tel.: (41) 444395757
Fax: (41) 44 433 15 17
E-Mail: info@crealogix.com
Internet Banking Services
S.I.C.: 4899
N.A.I.C.S.: 517919

Non-U.S. Subsidiary:

Crealogix AG **(1)**
Mainzer Landstrasse 27-31
D-60329 Frankfurt am Main, Germany
Tel.: (49) 69274015208
Fax: (49) 69274015208111
E-Mail: info@crealogix.com
Web Site: www.crealogix.com
Internet Banking Services
S.I.C.: 4899
N.A.I.C.S.: 517919

CREAM MINERALS LTD.

890-789 West Pender Street
Vancouver, BC, V6C 1H2, Canada
Tel.: (604) 687-4622
Fax: (604) 687-4212
Toll Free: (888) 267-1400
E-Mail: info@creamminerals.com
Web Site: www.creamminerals.com
CMA—(OTC OTCB TSXV)
Rev.: $3,774
Assets: $259,070
Liabilities: $475,682
Net Worth: ($216,612)
Earnings: ($1,783,897)
Emp.: 3
Fiscal Year-end: 03/31/13

Business Description:
Gold, Silver & Base Metal Mining Services
S.I.C.: 1041
N.A.I.C.S.: 212221

Personnel:
Christopher Hebb *(Chm)*
Michael E. O'Connor *(Pres & CEO)*
Angela Yap *(CFO)*

Board of Directors:
Christopher Hebb
Gerald Morris Feldman
Dwayne Larry Melrose
Robin H. Merrifield
Michael E. O'Connor

Legal Counsel:
DuMoulin Black LLP
595 Howe Street 10th Floor
Vancouver, BC, Canada

Transfer Agent:
Computershare Investor Services Inc.
3rd Floor 510 Burrard St
V6C 3B9 Vancouver, BC, Canada

CREAT RESOURCES HOLDINGS LIMITED

262 Main St
PO Box 30
Hobart, TAS, 7469, Australia
Tel.: (61) 36 471 6228
Fax: (61) 36 471 6152
E-Mail: morris.hansen@creatresources.com
Web Site: www.creatresources.com
Year Founded: 1999
CRHL—(AIM)
Rev.: $208,094
Assets: $4,514,694
Liabilities: $42,742,748
Net Worth: ($38,228,054)
Earnings: ($20,954,223)
Emp.: 100
Fiscal Year-end: 06/30/13

Business Description:
Zinc, Lead & Silver Mining Services
S.I.C.: 1031
N.A.I.C.S.: 212231

Personnel:
Derek An Loy Leung *(Chm, CEO & Mng Dir)*
Morris R. Hansen *(Sec & Gen Mgr)*

Board of Directors:
Derek An Loy Leung
Tad Mackay Ballantyne
Morris R. Hansen
Zhi Lin
Phillip Simpson

CREATE MEDIC CO. LTD.

5-25 Chigasaki Minami-2 Tsuzuki-ku
Yokohama, Kanagawa, 224-0037, Japan
Tel.: (81) 459432611
Fax: (81) 459432746
Web Site: www.createmedic.co.jp
5187—(TKS)
Sls.: $102,641,000
Assets: $181,511,000
Liabilities: $55,374,000
Net Worth: $126,137,000
Earnings: $5,632,000
Emp.: 976
Fiscal Year-end: 12/31/12

Business Description:
Medical Appliances Mfr & Sales
S.I.C.: 3845
N.A.I.C.S.: 334510

Personnel:
Masahiro Sato *(Pres)*

Board of Directors:
Sumio Ai
Yozo Akaoka
Shinichi Endo
Masataka Kasahara
Masahiro Sato
Takao Sekido
Ichiro Sugimoto
Hidenori Taniguchi

CREATE RESTAURANTS HOLDINGS INC.

5-10-18 Higashigotanda
Shinagawa-Ku, Tokyo, 141-0002, Japan
Tel.: (81) 357749700
Web Site: www.createrestaurants.com
3387—(TKS)
Sls.: $408,837,000
Assets: $209,517,000
Liabilities: $168,333,000
Net Worth: $41,184,000
Earnings: $14,487,000
Emp.: 1,325
Fiscal Year-end: 02/28/13

Business Description:
Restaurant Management Services
S.I.C.: 5812
N.A.I.C.S.: 722511

Personnel:
Hitoshi Gotoh *(Chm)*
Haruhiko Okamoto *(Pres & CEO)*
Jun Kawai *(Exec Mng Dir & CFO)*

Board of Directors:
Hitoshi Gotoh
Jun Kawai
Haruhiko Okamoto
Akira Shimamura
Takakazu Tanaka

Subsidiaries:

Create Kissho Inc. **(1)**
10th Floor Shibuya Cross Tower 2-15-1 Shibuya
Shibuya-ku, Tokyo, 150-0002, Japan
Tel.: (81) 3 5774 9700
Food Marketing Services
S.I.C.: 7389

N.A.I.C.S.: 561499
Naohiko Harada *(CEO)*

create restaurants inc. (1)
10th Floor Shibuya Cross Tower 2-15-1 Shibuya
Shibuya-ku, Tokyo, 150-0002, Japan
Tel.: (81) 3 5774 9700
Web Site: www.createrestaurants.com
Food Service Shop Operations
S.I.C.: 5812
N.A.I.C.S.: 722511
Hiroshi Ikeda *(CEO)*

CREATE S.D. HOLDINGS CO., LTD.

1 9 15 Edanishi Aoba-ku
Yokohama, 225 0014, Japan
Tel.: (81) 459743161
Fax: (81) 459743155
E-Mail: webmaster@createsdhd.co.jp
Web Site: www.createsdhd.co.jp
3148—(TKS)
Sales Range: $1-4.9 Billion
Emp.: 1,335

Business Description:
Pharmaceuticals, Food Products & Cosmetics Retailer
S.I.C.: 5912
N.A.I.C.S.: 446110

Personnel:
Hisao Yamamoto *(Chm)*
Tetsushiro Wakao *(Pres)*

CREATIVE MASTER BERMUDA LTD.

Yeung Yiu Chung No 8 Industrial Building
20 Wang Hoi Road, Kowloon, China (Hong Kong)
Tel.: (852) 23960147
Fax: (852) 27891737
E-Mail: info@creativemaster.com
Web Site: www.creativemaster.com
Year Founded: 2002
C35—(SES)
Sales Range: Less than $1 Million
Emp.: 25

Business Description:
Holding Company
S.I.C.: 6719
N.A.I.C.S.: 551112

Personnel:
Carl Ka Wing Tong *(CEO)*
Kam Ming Shing *(CFO)*
Gwendolyn Jong Yuh Gn *(Sec)*

Board of Directors:
Yu Meng Chan
Wing Teh Teh
Carl Ka Wing Tong

Transfer Agent:
M & C Services Private Limited
112 Robinson Road 05-01
Singapore, 068902, Singapore

Subsidiaries:

Creative Master L&W Limited (1)
Yeung Yiu Chung No 8 Industrial Building
20 Wang Hoi Road, Kowloon, China (Hong Kong)
Tel.: (852) 23960147
Fax: (852) 27891737
Web Site: www.creativemasterlw.com
Emp.: 20
Die-Cast Plastic Molded Products Mfr
S.I.C.: 3089
N.A.I.C.S.: 326199
Leo Kwok *(Gen Mgr)*

Creative Master Northcord Limited (1)
Yeung Yiu Chung No 8 Industrial Building
20 Wang Hoi Road, Kowloon, China (Hong Kong)
Tel.: (852) 23960147
Fax: (852) 27891737
E-Mail: info@cmn.com.hk
Web Site: www.cmn.com.hk
Emp.: 50
Die-Cast Replica Model Mfr & Distr
S.I.C.: 3364
N.A.I.C.S.: 331523
Danny C. Y. Chan *(Gen Mgr)*

Creative Master Overseas Holdings Limited (1)
Room D 3 F Yeung Yiu Chung No 8 Indl 20 Wang Hoi Road
Hong Kong, China (Hong Kong)
Tel.: (852) 23960147
Die Cast Replicas Mfr
S.I.C.: 3364
N.A.I.C.S.: 331523

Excel Master Limited (1)
Room D 3 F Yeung Yiu Chung No 8 Industrial Building 20 Wang Hoi Road
Kowloon Bay, Kowloon, China (Hong Kong)
Tel.: (852) 23960147
Fax: (852) 27891737
E-Mail: info@creativemaster.com
Emp.: 50
Die Cast Replica Mfr
S.I.C.: 3364
N.A.I.C.S.: 331523
Eric Rowe *(Pres)*

Non-U.S. Subsidiary:

Creative Master L&W Limited (1)
Foreign Economic District
Shang Ling Chun
Heng Li Zhen Dongguan, 523478, China
Tel.: (86) 769 373 2828
Fax: (86) 769 373 2711
Web Site: www.creativemasterlw.com
Die-Cast Plastic Molded Products Mfr
S.I.C.: 3089
N.A.I.C.S.: 326199

CREATIVE SALMON COMPANY LTD.

612 Campbell Street
PO Box 265
Tofino, BC, V0R 2Z0, Canada
Tel.: (250) 725-2884
Fax: (250) 725-2885
E-Mail: info@creativesalmon.com
Web Site: www.creativesalmon.com
Year Founded: 1990
Rev.: $11,209,516
Emp.: 45

Business Description:
Salmon Farming Services
S.I.C.: 5421
N.A.I.C.S.: 445220

Personnel:
Tim Rundle *(Gen Mgr)*

CREATIVE SENSOR INC.

6F Bldg 4 No 128 Ln 235 Pao Chiao Rd
Hsin Tien, Taipei, Taiwan
Tel.: (886) 289121289
Fax: (886) 289121111
Web Site: www.csi-sensor.com.tw
8249—(TAI)
Sales Range: $150-199.9 Million

Business Description:
Image Sensor Mfr
S.I.C.: 3674
N.A.I.C.S.: 334413

Personnel:
Eugene Huang *(Chm)*
Martin Hsieh *(Acting Pres, CEO & Exec VP)*

Non-U.S. Subsidiaries:

NanChang Creative Sensor Technology Co., LTD. (1)
No 36 HuoJu Wu Road Hi Tech Zone
Nanchang, Jiangxi, China
Tel.: (86) 7918851198
Fax: (86) 7918299459
Web Site: www.csi-sensor.com.tw/eng/about.aspx
Image Sensors Mfr
S.I.C.: 3674
N.A.I.C.S.: 334413

Wuxi Creative Sensor Technology Co., LTD (1)
A4 No 93 Wuxi National Hi Tech Industrial Development Zone
New District, Wuxi, Jiangsu, 214028, China
Tel.: (86) 51085342588
Fax: (86) 51085342660
Web Site: www.csi-sensor.com.tw/eng/about.aspx
Sensor Modules Mfr
S.I.C.: 3674
N.A.I.C.S.: 334413

CREATIVE TECHNOLOGY LTD.

31 International Business Park 03-01
Lobby C Creative Resource
Singapore, 609921, Singapore
Tel.: (65) 68954000
Fax: (65) 68954999
E-Mail: press_contact@ctl.creative.com
Web Site: www.creative.com
Year Founded: 1981
C76—(DEU OTC SES)
Sls.: $165,342,000
Assets: $237,206,000
Liabilities: $74,157,000
Net Worth: $163,049,000
Earnings: $16,662,000
Emp.: 1,000
Fiscal Year-end: 06/30/13

Business Description:
Digital Entertainment Products Mfr
S.I.C.: 3575
N.A.I.C.S.: 334118

Personnel:
Wong Hoo Sim *(Chm & CEO)*
Keh Long Ng *(CFO & Sec)*

Board of Directors:
Wong Hoo Sim
Gwong-Yih Lee
Kheng Nam Lee
Kai Wa Ng

Legal Counsel:
Duane Morris & Selvam LLP
16 Collyer Quay 17-00
Singapore, Singapore

Subsidiaries:

Creative Technology Centre Pte Ltd (1)
31 International Business Park Creative Resource
Singapore, 609921, Singapore
Tel.: (65) 68954000
Fax: (65) 68954999
Computer Peripheral Equipment Mfr
S.I.C.: 3575
N.A.I.C.S.: 334118

QMax Communications Pte Ltd. (1)
Creative Resource 31 International Business Park
609921 Singapore, Singapore
Tel.: (65) 6895 4899
E-Mail: enquiries@qmaxcom.com
Web Site: www.qmaxcom.com
Telecommunication Equipment Mfr & Whslr
S.I.C.: 3669
N.A.I.C.S.: 334290

U.S. Subsidiaries:

3D Labs Inc., Ltd. (1)
1901 McCarthy Blvd
Milpitas, CA 95035
Tel.: (408) 432-6700
Fax: (408) 432-6702
E-Mail: info@3dlabs.com
Web Site: www.3dlabs.com
Emp.: 150
Supplier of Integrated Hardware & Software Graphics Accelerator Solutions
S.I.C.: 7374
N.A.I.C.S.: 518210
Jeff Little *(Dir-Mktg)*

Non-U.S. Subsidiary:

3DLabs (2)
Level 16 Shiroyama Hills
4-3-1 Toranomon Minato-Ku, Tokyo, 105, Japan
Tel.: (81) 354034653
Fax: (81) 3 5403 4654
Provider of Electronic Products & Components
S.I.C.: 3679
N.A.I.C.S.: 334419

Broadxent, Inc. (1)
188 Topaz St
Milpitas, CA 95035-5429
Tel.: (408) 719-5100
Fax: (408) 262-1390
E-Mail: info@broadxent.com
Web Site: www.broadxent.com
Emp.: 23
Communications Equipment & Custom Communications Solutions for OEM & PC Vendors
S.I.C.: 3575
N.A.I.C.S.: 334118

Cambridge SoundWorks, Inc. (1)
100 Brickstone Sq
Andover, MA 01810-1428
Tel.: (978) 623-4400
Fax: (978) 475-7219
Toll Free: (800) 367-4434
E-Mail: info@cambridgesoundworks.com
Web Site: www.cambridgesoundworks.com
Emp.: 250
Online Retailer of Consumer Electronics
S.I.C.: 5731
N.A.I.C.S.: 443142
Rob Mainiero *(Gen Mgr)*

Creative Advanced Technology Center (1)
1500 Green Hills Rd Ste 205
Scotts Valley, CA 95066
Tel.: (831) 440-2800
Fax: (831) 440-2882
Web Site: www.atc.creative.com
Emp.: 50
Integrated Circuits for the Multimedia, Storage & Communications Markets
S.I.C.: 8711
N.A.I.C.S.: 541330

Creative Labs, Inc. - Latin America (1)
5200 Blue Lagoon Dr Ste 250
Miami, FL 33126-2034 (100%)
Tel.: (305) 264-7050
Fax: (305) 264-1738
E-Mail: info@creative.com
Emp.: 3
Mfr. & Distributor of Electronics
S.I.C.: 7373
N.A.I.C.S.: 541512
Roger Sanchez *(Mng Dir)*

Creative Labs, Inc. (1)
1901 McCarthy Blvd
Milpitas, CA 95035-7427 (100%)
Tel.: (408) 428-6600
Fax: (408) 428-6611
Web Site: www.creativelabs.com
Emp.: 120
Computer Peripherals, Consumer Electronics & Home Entertainment Devices Mfr
S.I.C.: 5045
N.A.I.C.S.: 423430
Phil O'Shaughnessy *(VP-Corp Comm)*

E-Mu Systems, Inc (1)
1500 Green Hills Rd Ste 205
Scotts Valley, CA 95066-4945 (100%)
Tel.: (831) 438-1921
Fax: (831) 438-8612
E-Mail: service@emu.com
Web Site: www.emu.com
Emp.: 50
Developer of Digital Audio Products Based on Digital Sampling Technology for the Musical Instrument & Computer Controlled Sound Markets
S.I.C.: 3931
N.A.I.C.S.: 339992

Non-U.S. Subsidiaries:

Creative Labs A.S. (1)
Gydevang 39 241
3450 Allerod, Denmark (100%)
Tel.: (45) 48168400
Fax: (45) 48168401
Web Site: www.creative.europe.com
Sales Range: $10-24.9 Million
Emp.: 8
Electronic Products & Components

Creative Technology Ltd.—(Continued)

S.I.C.: 5734
N.A.I.C.S.: 443142

Creative Labs GmbH (1)
Feringastrasse 4
85774 Munich, Germany (100%)
Tel.: (49) 899928710
Fax: (49) 8999287122
Web Site: www.europecreative.com
Emp.: 13
Electronic Products & Components
S.I.C.: 5734
N.A.I.C.S.: 443142

Creative Labs (HK) Limited (1)
Units 2908 29/F, Tower 1, Metroplaza
223 Hing Fong Road, Kwai Fong, China
(Hong Kong) (100%)
Tel.: (852) 23312930
Fax: (852) 23312151
Web Site: www.asia.creative.com
Emp.: 11
Electronic Products & Components
S.I.C.: 5731
N.A.I.C.S.: 443142

Creative Labs, Inc. (1)
703 Evans Avenue Suite 401
Etobicoke, ON, M9C 5E9, Canada
Tel.: (405) 742-6655
Provider of Computer Services
S.I.C.: 7371
N.A.I.C.S.: 541511

Creative Labs Ireland Ltd. (1)
Unit 1 Block 4B Blanchardstown Corporate Park
Blanchardstown, Dublin, 15, Ireland (100%)
Tel.: (353) 18206444
Fax: (353) 18209557
Web Site: en.europe.creative.com
Emp.: 360
Operations & Technical Center
S.I.C.: 5731
N.A.I.C.S.: 443142

Creative Labs N.V. (1)
Royal House Coremansstraat 34
PO Box 2
2600 Berchem, Belgium (100%)
Tel.: (32) 32878777
Fax: (32) 32308550
E-Mail: benelux@cle.creative.com
Web Site: www.europe.creative.com
Emp.: 11
Electronic Products & Components
S.I.C.: 5731
N.A.I.C.S.: 443142

Creative Labs Srl (1)
Strada 4 Palazzo A/2
Assago Milanofiori, 20090 Assago, MI, Italy
Tel.: (39) 02 822 8161
Fax: (39) 02 5750 0768
Web Site: www.creative.com
Electronic Products & Components
S.I.C.: 3679
N.A.I.C.S.: 334419

Creative Labs (Sweden) (1)
Spanga Ctr
P O Box 129
Stormbyvagen 2 4, 16329 Spanga, Sweden (100%)
Tel.: (46) 856472020
Fax: (46) 87957835
E-Mail: info@europe.creative.com
Web Site: www.europe.creative.com
Emp.: 5
Electronic Products & Components
S.I.C.: 5734
N.A.I.C.S.: 443142
Dennis Dress *(Mng Dir)*

Creative Labs (UK) Ltd. (1)
Unit 3 The Pavilions
Ruscombe Business Park, Ruscombe,
Berks, RG10 9NN, United Kingdom (100%)
Tel.: (44) 189344322
Fax: (44) 1189320300
Web Site: www.europe.creative.com
Emp.: 40
Electronic Products & Components
S.I.C.: 5731
N.A.I.C.S.: 443142

Creative Labs (1)
Av Eng Duarte Pacheco
Torre 2 Amoreiras Piso 4
Sala 4, 1070 Lisbon, Portugal
Tel.: (351) 21 383 9720
Fax: (351) 21 383 97 27
Electronic Products & Components
S.I.C.: 5731
N.A.I.C.S.: 443142

Creative Labs (1)
15th Fl No 163 Sec 1 Keelung Rd
11 Taipei, Taiwan
Tel.: (886) 227482988
Fax: (886) 227482989
Web Site: www.taiwan.creative.com
Electronic Products & Components
S.I.C.: 5946
N.A.I.C.S.: 443142

Creative Media K.K. (1)
Kanda 8 Bldg 4th Fl 4-6-7 Soto-Kanda
Tokyo, Chiyoda-Ku, 101 0021,
Japan (100%)
Tel.: (81) 332565577
Fax: (81) 332565221
Web Site: www.jp.creative.com
Emp.: 30
Electronic Products & Components
S.I.C.: 5734
N.A.I.C.S.: 443142
Wong Hoo Sim *(Chm & CEO)*

Creative Technology (China) Co., Ltd. (1)
4-12 Building No 1388 Zhangdong Road
Zhangjiang Hi-tech Park
Pudong New District, Shanghai, 201203, China
Tel.: (86) 21 6100 1100
Fax: (86) 21 6100 1105
Web Site: www.creative.com
Emp.: 50
Electronic Products & Components
S.I.C.: 3679
N.A.I.C.S.: 334419

Branches:

Creative Technology (China) Co., Ltd. (2)
Creative Park 18 Anhuaxili Block 2
Chaoyang District, Beijing, 100011,
China (100%)
Tel.: (86) 10 64257312
Emp.: 20
Electronic Products & Components
S.I.C.: 3577
N.A.I.C.S.: 334118

Creative Technology (China) Co., Ltd. (2)
Room 2001 Eastern Tower Building
No 625 Tianhe Road
Tianhe Entertainment Plaza, Guangzhou,
Guandong, 510630, China
Tel.: (86) 2087540677
Web Site: www.creative.com
Emp.: 6
Electronic Products & Components
S.I.C.: 3679
N.A.I.C.S.: 334419

Cubic Electronics Sdn. Bhd. (1)
1 Jalan TU 43 Taman Tasik Utama
Ayer Keroh, Melaka, 75450,
Malaysia (100%)
Tel.: (60) 62512801
Fax: (60) 62512999
Web Site: www.cubicgrp.com
Emp.: 3,000
Electronic Products & Components
S.I.C.: 5946
N.A.I.C.S.: 443142

JCHyun Systems, Inc. (1)
JCHyun Bldg
6 1 Shingye Dong Yongsan Distr, 140090
Seoul, Korea (South) (100%)
Tel.: (82) 27075044
Fax: (82) 27075086
E-Mail: jchyun@jchyun.com
Web Site: www.jchyun.com
Emp.: 150
Electronic Products & Components
S.I.C.: 3679
N.A.I.C.S.: 334419

CREATIVE VISTAS INC.

2100 Forbes Street Unit 8-10
Whitby, ON, L1N 9T3, Canada
Tel.: (905) 666-8676
Fax: (905) 666-9795
E-Mail: info@creativevistasinc.com
Web Site: www.creativevistasinc.com
Year Founded: 1983
CVAS—(OTC)
Sales Range: $1-9.9 Million
Emp.: 47

Business Description:
Electronic Security & Surveillance Products & Solutions
S.I.C.: 7382
N.A.I.C.S.: 561621

Personnel:
Sayan Navaratnam *(Chm)*
Dominic Burns *(Pres & CEO)*
Heung Hung Lee *(CFO & Sec)*

Board of Directors:
Sayan Navaratnam
Dominic Burns
Heung Hung Lee

Subsidiaries:

9142-2063 Quebec Inc. (1)
1956 B 3e rue.
Saint-Romuald, QC, G6W 5M6, Canada
Tel.: (418) 878-8996
Fax: (418) 683-2030
Web Site: tatexp.com
Emp.: 30
General Freight Trucking Services
S.I.C.: 4213
N.A.I.C.S.: 484121
Regan Bedard *(Pres)*

Creative Vistas Acquisition Corp. (1)
2100 Forbes St
Whitby, ON, L1N 9T3, Canada
Tel.: (905) 666-8676
Fax: (905) 666-9795
Web Site: actechnical.com
Broadband Services
S.I.C.: 4813
N.A.I.C.S.: 517110
Fairy Lee *(CFO)*

Subsidiary:

AC Technical Systems Ltd. (2)
2100 Forbes St Units 8-10
Whitby, ON, L1N 9T3, Canada (100%)
Tel.: (905) 666-8676
Fax: (905) 666-9795
Web Site: www.actechnical.com
Emp.: 50
Security Solutions
S.I.C.: 7382
N.A.I.C.S.: 561621

Dependable HomeTech (1)
2321 Fairview St
Burlington, ON, L7R 2E3, Canada
Tel.: (905) 634-7152
Fax: (905) 634-1156
Toll Free: (877) 226-2225
E-Mail: info@mydh.com
Web Site: www.dependablehometech.com
Electrical Contractors
S.I.C.: 1731
N.A.I.C.S.: 238210
Ross Jepson *(Pres & CEO)*
Catherine Lewis *(CFO)*
Paul Mease *(Sr VP-Field Svcs)*

Subsidiary:

XL Digital Services Inc. (2)
2321 Fairview St
Burlington, ON, L7R 2E3, Canada
Tel.: (905) 634-7152
Fax: (905) 634-1156
Cable Subscription Services
S.I.C.: 4841
N.A.I.C.S.: 515210
Tracy Lee *(Mgr-HR)*

OSS IM View Inc. (1)
2321 Fairview St Ste 200
Burlington, ON, L7R 2E3, Canada
Tel.: (905) 634-2206
Web Site: www.ossimview.com
Software Consulting Services
S.I.C.: 7373
N.A.I.C.S.: 541512

CREATON AG

Dillinger Strasse 60
86637 Wertingen, Germany
Tel.: (49) 827286461
Fax: (49) 827286500
E-Mail: info@creaton.de
Web Site: www.creaton.de
Year Founded: 1992
Sales Range: $150-199.9 Million
Emp.: 1,000

Business Description:
Roofing Tile Mfr
S.I.C.: 3297
N.A.I.C.S.: 327120

Personnel:
Alfons J. Peeters *(Vice Chm-Supervisory Bd)*
Stephan Fuhrling *(CEO)*

Supervisory Board of Directors:
Philippe Coens
Frederic Deslypere
Manfred Kratzer
Andreas Liedel
Alfons J. Peeters

CREATOR CAPITAL LIMITED

Floor Six 65 Front Street
Hamilton, HM 12, Bermuda
Tel.: (441) 295 2244
Fax: (441) 292 8666
E-Mail: info@creatorcapital.com
Web Site: www.creatorcapital.com
CTORF—(OTC)
Rev.: $1,750
Assets: $3,439
Liabilities: $8,315,560
Net Worth: ($8,312,121)
Earnings: ($807,484)
Fiscal Year-end: 12/31/12

Business Description:
Inflight Gaming Software Systems & Services
S.I.C.: 7372
N.A.I.C.S.: 511210

Personnel:
Deborah Fortescue-Merrin *(Pres, CEO & CFO)*

Board of Directors:
Anthony P. Clements
Deborah Fortescue-Merrin
Anastasia Kostoff-Mann

CREDENT CAPITAL CORP.

3rd Floor 120 Lonsdale Avenue
North Vancouver, BC, V7X 1S8, Canada
Tel.: (604) 984-9959
Fax: (604) 983-8056
E-Mail: jav@cabo.ca
Year Founded: 2011
CDT.P—(TSXV)

Business Description:
Investment Services
S.I.C.: 6211
N.A.I.C.S.: 523999

Personnel:
John A. Versfelt *(Pres & CEO)*
Calvin Lucyshyn *(CFO & Sec)*

Board of Directors:
John Bevilacqua
Gong Chen
Calvin Lucyshyn
John A. Versfelt

Transfer Agent:
Valiant Trust Company
750 Cambie St, Ste 600
Vancouver, BC, V6B 0A2, Canada

CREDICORP LTD.

Calle Centenario 156 La Molina
Lima, 12, Peru
Tel.: (51) 13132140
Fax: (51) 13132135
E-Mail: guillermocastillo@bcp.com.pe
Web Site: www.credicorpnet.com
Year Founded: 1995
BAP—(LIM NYSE)

Rev.: $2,310,441,000
Assets: $40,797,121,000
Liabilities: $36,431,786,000
Net Worth: $4,365,335,000
Earnings: $808,227,000
Emp.: 22,538
Fiscal Year-end: 12/31/12

Business Description:
Bank Holding Company
Export
S.I.C.: 6712
N.A.I.C.S.: 551111

Personnel:
Dionisio Romero Paoletti *(Chm & CEO)*
Raimundo Morales *(Vice Chm)*
Fernando Dasso *(CFO)*
Alvaro Correa *(Chief Insurance Officer & CEO-Pacifico Peruano Suiza)*

Board of Directors:
Dionisio Romero Paoletti
Fernando Fort
Reynaldo Llosa
Raimundo Morales
Felipe Ortiz de Zevallos
German Suarez
Juan Carlos Verme
Luis Enrique Yarur

Subsidiaries:

Banco de Credito del Peru SA **(1)**
No 156 Calle Centenario
La Molina 12, Lima, Peru
Tel.: (51) 13119898
Web Site: www.bcp.com.pe
Sales Range: $500-549.9 Million
Emp.: 9,336
Banking Services
S.I.C.: 6029
N.A.I.C.S.: 522110
Fernando Dasso *(CFO)*

Subsidiary:

Empresa Financiera Edyficar S.A. **(2)**
Avenida Paseo De La Republica Nro 3717
3705 Urb Limatambo, San Isidro, Lima, Peru
Tel.: (51) 1 319 5555
Fax: (51) 1 319 1157
Web Site: www.edyficar.com.pe
Emp.: 30
Financial Management Services
S.I.C.: 6211
N.A.I.C.S.: 523999
Ana Maria Zegarra *(Gen Mgr)*

U.S. Subsidiary:

Credicorp Securities Inc. **(1)**
121 Alhambra Plz Ste 1200
Coral Gables, FL 33134
Tel.: (786) 999-1603
Web Site: www.credisec.com
Security Brokerage Services
S.I.C.: 6211
N.A.I.C.S.: 523120

CREDIT AGRICOLE S.A.

12 place des Etats-Unis Montrouge
92545 Paris, Cedex, France
Tel.: (33) 143235202
Telex: 250971 F CAGRJ
Fax: (33) 143233448
E-Mail: relations.investor@credit-agricole-sa.fr
Web Site: www.credit-agricole.com
Year Founded: 1894
ACA—(EUR OTC)
Int. Income: $43,769,371,380
Net Worth: $60,889,961,440
Earnings: ($8,767,605,210)
Emp.: 79,282
Fiscal Year-end: 12/31/12

Business Description:
International Banking Services
S.I.C.: 6029
N.A.I.C.S.: 522110

Personnel:
Jean-Marie Sander *(Chm)*
Philippe Brassac *(Deputy Chm)*
Dominique Lefebvre *(Deputy Chm)*
Jean-Paul Chifflet *(CEO)*
Bruno de Laage *(Deputy CEO & Head-Retail Banking Activities & Payment Sys)*
Jean-Yves Hocher *(Deputy CEO & Head-Corp, Investment & Private Banking)*
Michel Mathieu *(Deputy CEO & Head-Central Functions)*
Xavier Musca *(Deputy CEO-Intl Retail Banking, Asset Mgmt & Insurance)*
Bernard Delpit *(CFO)*
Philippe Dumont *(CEO-Consumer Fin)*
Jerome Grivet *(CEO-Assurances)*
Yves Nanquette *(CEO-LCL)*
Joseph d'Auzay *(Sec)*

Board of Directors:
Jean-Marie Sander
Pascale Berger
Xavier Beulin
Philippe Brassac
Caroline Catoire
Pascal Celerier
Patrick Clavelou
Bernard de Dree
Jean-Louis Delorme
Laurence Meary Dors
Veronique Flachaire
Francoise Gri
Francois Heyman
Dominique Lefebvre
Bernard Paul Constan Lepot
Monica Mondardini
Christian Moueza
Marc Pouzet
Jean-Claude Rigaud
Jean-Louis Roveyaz
Christian Streiff
Christian Jean Marie Talgorn
Francois Thibault
Francois Veverka

Ernst & Young et Autres
1-2 Place des Saisons Paris La Defense 1
92400 Courbevoie, France

Division:

Caisse Nationale de Credit Agricole International Division **(1)**
91 93 Blvd Pasteur
75015 Paris, France (100%)
Tel.: (33) 143235202
Fax: (33) 143235903
Web Site: www.cncas.sn
Emp.: 50
International Banking
S.I.C.: 6159
N.A.I.C.S.: 522293
Carron Rene *(Pres)*

Subsidiaries:

Amundi Group S.A. **(1)**
90 boulevard Pasteur
75015 Paris, France FR
Tel.: (33) 1 7633 3030 (75%)
E-Mail:
Web Site: www.amundi.com
Holding Company; Investment Management Services
S.I.C.: 6719
N.A.I.C.S.: 551112
Yves Perrier *(CEO)*
Patricia Bouchard *(CFO)*
Jean-Paul Mazoyer *(COO & Chm/CEO-Fin Grp)*
Pascal Blanque *(Chief Investment Officer)*
Jean-Philippe Bianquis *(CEO-Investment Solutions)*
Fathi Jerfel *(CEO-Private Equity Funds)*
Nicolas Simon *(CEO-Real Estate)*

Subsidiary:

Amundi SA **(2)**
90 Boulevard Pasteur
75015 Paris, France FR
Tel.: (33) 1 7633 3030 (100%)
Web Site: www.amundi.com
Emp.: 1,100
Investment Management Services
S.I.C.: 6282
N.A.I.C.S.: 523920
Julien Bernard *(Head-Client Svcs)*

U.S. Subsidiaries:

Amundi Investments USA, LLC **(2)**
CAICB Bldg 1301 Ave of the Americas
New York, NY 10019 DE
Tel.: (212) 603-5000 (100%)
Fax: (212) 603-5001
Web Site: www.amundi.com
Emp.: 18
Investment Management Services
S.I.C.: 6282
N.A.I.C.S.: 523920
Joe Morano *(Mng Dir)*

Amundi Smith Breeden **(2)**
(Formerly Smith Breeden Associates Inc.)
280 S Mangum St Ste 301
Durham, NC 27701 (100%)
Tel.: (919) 967-7221
Fax: (919) 933-3157
Toll Free: (800) 268-7151
Web Site: www.smithbreeden.com
Sales Range: $10-24.9 Million
Emp.: 70
Investment Advisory Services
S.I.C.: 6282
N.A.I.C.S.: 523930
Patrick Pagni *(Chm)*
Michael J. Giarla *(CEO)*
Daniel C. Dektar *(Chief Investment Officer & Exec VP)*
Carl D. Bell *(Principal & Sr Portfolio Mgr)*
Stephen A. Eason *(Exec VP & Dir-Separate Acct Mgmt)*
Stanley J. Kon *(Exec VP & Dir-Res)*

Non-U.S. Subsidiary:

Amundi (UK) Limited **(2)**
41 Lothbury
London, EC2R 7HF, United Kingdom UK
Tel.: (44) 20 7074 9300
Fax: (44) 20 7074 9309
Web Site: www.amundi.com
Investment Management Services
S.I.C.: 6282
N.A.I.C.S.: 523920
Ian Milton *(Dir-Institutional Bus Dev-UK & Ireland)*

Credit Lyonnais S.A. **(1)**
19 Boulevard des Italiens
75002 Paris, France FR
Tel.: (33) 1 42 95 7000 (100%)
Telex: 612400
Fax: (33) 1 42 95 9437
Web Site: www.lcl.com
Emp.: 130
International Banking
S.I.C.: 6159
N.A.I.C.S.: 522293
Jean Laurent *(Chm)*

Newedge Group SA **(1)**
52/60 Avenue des Champs Elysees
75008 Paris, France FR
Tel.: (33) 55072020
Fax: (33) 155072001
E-Mail: accueil.paris@newedge.com
Web Site: www.newedge.com
Rev.: $2,441,952,380
Assets: $67,114,651,520
Liabilities: $65,546,363,470
Net Worth: $1,568,288,050
Earnings: $18,846,380
Emp.: 2,707
Fiscal Year-end: 12/31/12
Securities Brokerage; Owned 50% by Societe Generale S.A. & 50% by Credit Agricole S.A.
S.I.C.: 6211
N.A.I.C.S.: 523120
Francis Canterini *(Chm)*
Christophe Mianne *(Vice Chm)*
David Escoffier *(CEO)*
Francoise Guillaume *(Deputy CEO & COO)*
Ghislaine Mattlinger *(CFO)*
Alain Courbebaisse *(CIO)*
Richard Wilson *(CEO-Newedge UK Financial Limited & Chief Admin Officer-EMEA)*
Mathieu Giovachini *(Chief Risk Officer)*
Gerard de Lambilly *(Sec Gen & Head-Legal)*

U.S. Subsidiary:

Newedge USA, LLC **(2)**
550 W Jackson Blvd Ste 500
Chicago, IL 60661 IL
Tel.: (312) 762-1000
Emp.: 54
Brokerage Services
S.I.C.: 6211
N.A.I.C.S.: 523120
Antoine Babule *(CEO)*

Non-U.S. Subsidiary:

Newedge Canada, Inc. **(2)**
1501 McGill College Ave Ste 1930
Montreal, QC, H3A 3M8, Canada Ca
Tel.: (514) 841-6210
Fax: (514) 841-6254
Web Site: www.newedge.com
Emp.: 25
Securities Broker
S.I.C.: 6211
N.A.I.C.S.: 523120

Non-U.S. Subsidiaries:

Credit Agricole Cheuvreux Deutschland GmbH **(1)**
Messe Turm Friedrich Ebert Anlage 49
60308 Frankfurt am Main, Germany (100%)
Tel.: (49) 947897100
Telex: 412 409 CNCA D
Fax: (49) 6947857530
Investment Bank
S.I.C.: 6211
N.A.I.C.S.: 523110

Credit Agricole (CNCA) Luxembourg **(1)**
39 Allee Scheffer
L-2520 Luxembourg, Luxembourg (100%)
Tel.: (352) 24671
Fax: (352) 24678000
E-Mail: info@ca-luxembourg.com
Web Site: www.ca-luxembourg.com
Emp.: 400
Internet & Private Banking Services
S.I.C.: 6159
N.A.I.C.S.: 522298
Jean-Francois Abadie *(Mng Dir)*

Credit Agricole Luxembourg Bank **(1)**
39 Alleescheffer
L 2520 Luxembourg, Luxembourg
Tel.: (352) 4578801
Fax: (352) 24678000
E-Mail: santina.sava@ca-luxemberg.com
Web Site: www.ca-luxembergbank.com
Emp.: 350
Credit & Loan Services
S.I.C.: 6153
N.A.I.C.S.: 522210
Santina Sava *(Sec)*

Credit Agricole (Suisse) S.A. **(1)**
4 Quai General Guisan
PO Box 5260
1211 Geneva, Switzerland (100%)
Tel.: (41) 223199191
Telex: 427 300
Fax: (41) 583219100
E-Mail: info@ca-suisse.com
Web Site: www.ca-suisse.com
Emp.: 1,500
Banking Services
S.I.C.: 6159
N.A.I.C.S.: 522298
Gancel Christophe *(CEO)*

Credit Agricole Van Moer Courtens **(1)**
Dreve du Prieure 19 Priorijdreef
B 1160 Brussels, Belgium
Tel.: (32) 25490320
Fax: (32) 25126085
E-Mail: damien.courtens@cavmc.be
Web Site: www.cavmc.be
Portfolio Asset Management Services
S.I.C.: 6799
N.A.I.C.S.: 523920

Credit Agricole S.A.—(Continued)

Damien Courtens *(Mng Dir)*

CREDIT ANALYSIS & RESEARCH LTD

4th Floor, Godrej Coliseum Somaiya Hospital Road
Off Eastern Express Highway
Sion (East), Mumbai, 400 022, India
Tel.: (91) 22 6754 3456
Fax: (91) 22 6754 3457
E-Mail: care@careratings.com
Web Site: www.careratings.com
Year Founded: 1993
534804—(BOM NSE)
Business Description:
Credit Analysis & Research Services
S.I.C.: 7389
N.A.I.C.S.: 561499
Personnel:
D.R. Dogra *(CEO & Mng Dir)*
Rajesh Mokashi *(Deputy Mng Dir)*
Board of Directors:
A. K. Bansal
D.R. Dogra
Rajesh Mokashi
Bharti Prasad
Nitish Kumar Sengupta
Venkatraman Srinivasan

CREDIT ANDORRA, S.A.

Av Meritxell 80
AD500 Andorra La Vella, Andorra
Tel.: (376) 88 93 00
Fax: (376) 888601
E-Mail: comunicacio@creditandorra.ad
Web Site: www.creditandorra.ad
Int. Income: $92,458,408
Emp.: 250
Business Description:
Banking Services
S.I.C.: 6029
N.A.I.C.S.: 522110
Personnel:
Jaume Casal Mor *(Pres)*
Josep Peralba Duro *(CEO & Sec)*
Board of Directors:
Josep Peralba Duro
Antoni Pintat Mas
Jaume Casal Mor
Josep Marti Vidal

Subsidiaries:

Crediinvest SA (1)
C/Bonaventura Armengol 6-8
Andorra La Vella, Andorra
Tel.: (376) 88 95 10
Investment Management Services
S.I.C.: 6799
N.A.I.C.S.: 523920
Sergi Martin *(Gen Mgr)*

Credit Andorra Private Bankers (1)
Av Meritxell 80
AD500 Andorra La Vella, Andorra
Tel.: (376) 88 86 50
E-Mail: privatebankers@creditandorra.com
Web Site: www.creditandorraprivatebankers.com
Banking & Financial Services
S.I.C.: 6011
N.A.I.C.S.: 521110

Credit Assegurances (1)
C/Bonaventura Armengol 6-8 2n
AD500 Andorra La Vella, Andorra
Tel.: (376) 88 89 00
E-Mail: info@creditassegurances.com
Web Site: www.creditassegurances.ad
Insurance Mamagement Services
S.I.C.: 6411
N.A.I.C.S.: 524298

U.S. Subsidiary:

Beta Capital Managomont LP (1)
777 Brickell Ave Ste 1201
Miami, FL 33131
Tel.: (305) 358-8844
Fax: (305) 358-8864
E-Mail: contact@betacap.com
Web Site: www.betacap.com
Emp.: 22
Investment Management Services
S.I.C.: 6799
N.A.I.C.S.: 523920
Genis Ros-Armengol *(CEO)*
Idelma Hervis *(Chief Compliance Officer)*

Non-U.S. Subsidiaries:

Banco Alcala, SA (1)
Ortega Y Gasset 7 4a planta
28006 Madrid, Spain
Tel.: (34) 91 175 07 00
Fax: (34) 91 575 5251
E-Mail: info@bancoalcala.com
Web Site: www.bancoalcala.com
Emp.: 35
Investment Management Services
S.I.C.: 6799
N.A.I.C.S.: 523920
Diego Fernandez de Henestrosa Arguelles *(Chm)*
Josep Peralba Duro *(Vice Chm)*
Frank Martinez Sanchez *(CEO)*
Xavier Cornella Castel *(Sec)*

Banque de Patrimoines Prives, SA (1)
30 Boulevard Royal
Luxembourg, 2449, Luxembourg
Tel.: (352) 27 207 1
Fax: (352) 26 200 131
E-Mail: contact@bbpp.lu
Web Site: www.bbpp.lu
Emp.: 30
Banking & Financial Services
S.I.C.: 6011
N.A.I.C.S.: 521110

Credit Andorra Panama Securities SA. (1)
Regus Business Centre Torres de las Americas Torre A
Piso 10 Punta Pacifica, Panama, Panama
Tel.: (507) 306 48 00
Securities Brokerage Services
S.I.C.: 6211
N.A.I.C.S.: 523120

Valira Asset Management SL (1)
C/ Goya 23 1
Madrid, 28001, Spain
Tel.: (34) 91 429 08 37
Fax: (34) 91 369 13 03
E-Mail: info@valiraam.com
Web Site: www.valiraam.com
Emp.: 12
Investment Management Services
S.I.C.: 6282
N.A.I.C.S.: 523920

CREDIT BANK OF IRAQ S.A.

(See Under National Bank of Kuwait S.A.K.)

CREDIT CHINA HOLDINGS LIMITED

Rooms 2101-05 21/F Sun Hung Kai Centre 30 Harbour Road
139 Hennessy Road, Wanchai, China (Hong Kong)
Tel.: (852) 31021327
Fax: (852) 31029177
E-Mail: info@creditchina.hk
Web Site: www.creditchina.hk
Year Founded: 2003
8207—(HKG)
Sls.: $48,039,735
Assets: $209,847,204
Liabilities: $89,592,830
Net Worth: $120,254,374
Earnings: $26,094,925
Emp.: 150
Fiscal Year-end: 12/31/12
Business Description:
Financial Consultancy, Pawn Loan, Real Estate Entrusted Loan & Loan Guarantee Services
S.I.C.: 6163
N.A.I.C.S.: 522310
Personnel:
Zhi Jun Shi *(Co-Founder & Deputy Chm)*
Zu Guang Ji *(Co-Founder & Dir-HR Mgmt & Legal Compliance)*
Raymond Pang Wan Ting *(Chm)*
Li Shen *(CEO)*
Belinda Kwan Kuo *(CFO & Sec)*
Ivan Man Chun Leung *(COO)*
James Jun Sun *(Chief Investment Officer)*
Zhen Dong Sun *(Legal Counsel)*
Board of Directors:
Zhi Jun Shi
Raymond Pang Wan Ting
Zu Guang Ji
Reimer Mary Jean Lau
Sze Wai Lee
Poh Kiat Neo
Li Shen

Royal Bank of Canada Trust Company (Cayman) Limited
4th Floor Royal Bank House 24 Shedden Road
Georgetown, Cayman Islands

Transfer Agents:
Tricor Investor Services Limited
26th Floor Tesbury Centre 28 Queens Road East
Wanchai, China (Hong Kong)

Royal Bank of Canada Trust Company (Cayman) Limited
4th Floor Royal Bank House 24 Shedden Road
Georgetown, Cayman Islands

CREDIT CORP GROUP LIMITED

Level 11 10 Barrack Street
Sydney, NSW, 2000, Australia
Mailing Address:
GPO Box 4475
Sydney, NSW, 2001, Australia
Tel.: (61) 293473600
Fax: (61) 2 9347 3650
E-Mail: info@creditcorp.com.au
Web Site: www.creditcorp.com.au
CCP—(ASX)
Rev.: $148,579,492
Assets: $188,649,279
Liabilities: $42,972,036
Net Worth: $145,677,243
Earnings: $33,332,611
Emp.: 1,016
Fiscal Year-end: 06/30/13
Business Description:
Debt Management & Support Services
S.I.C.: 6211
N.A.I.C.S.: 523999
Personnel:
Thomas Beregi *(CEO & Co-Sec)*
Michael Eadie *(CFO & Co-Sec)*
Matthew Angell *(COO)*
Geoffrey Templeton *(Co-Sec)*
Board of Directors:
Donald McLay
Simon Calleia
Eric Dodd
Leslie Martin
Robert Shaw
Richard Thomas

Subsidiaries:

Credit Corp Australia Pty Limited (1)
Level 11 10 Barrack Street
Sydney, NSW, 2000, Australia
Tel.: (61) 293473600
Fax: (61) 292624017
Web Site: www.creditcorp.com.au
Debt Collection Services
S.I.C.: 7322
N.A.I.C.S.: 561440
Amanda Pope *(Mgr-Customer Rels)*

Credit Corp Collections Pty Limited (1)
Level 11 10 Barrack Street
Sydney, NSW, 2001, Australia
Tel.: (61) 293473600
Debt Collection Services
S.I.C.: 7322
N.A.I.C.S.: 561440

Credit Corp Facilities Pty Limited (1)
Level 11 10 Barrack Street
Sydney, NSW, 2000, Australia
Tel.: (61) 293473600
Fax: (61) 293624017
Web Site: creditcorp.com
Debt Collection Services
S.I.C.: 7322
N.A.I.C.S.: 561440

Credit Corp Services Pty Limited (1)
Level 11 10 Barrack Street
Sydney, NSW, 2000, Australia
Tel.: (61) 293473600
Fax: (61) 293473650
E-Mail: info@creditcorp.com.au
Emp.: 360
Debt Collection Services
S.I.C.: 7322
N.A.I.C.S.: 561440
Samantha Kelly *(Mgr-Sls)*

Credit Plan B Pty Limited (1)
PO Box 4491
Sydney, NSW, 2001, Australia
Tel.: (61) 1300663281
Fax: (61) 1300720108
E-Mail: enquiries@creditplanb.com.au
Web Site: www.creditplanb.com.au
Financial Support Services
S.I.C.: 6211
N.A.I.C.S.: 523999

CREDIT MUTUEL-CIC

88-90 Rue Cardinet
F 75847 Paris, Cedex 17, France
Tel.: (33) 144011010
Telex: CCCMU 640 373F
Fax: (33) 144011231
Web Site: www.creditmutuel.com
Year Founded: 1958
Emp.: 35,000
Business Description:
Bank Holding Company
S.I.C.: 6712
N.A.I.C.S.: 551111
Personnel:
Etienne Pflimlin *(Chm & Pres)*
Michel Jean Francis Lucas *(Gen Dir)*

Subsidiaries:

Banque Regionale De L'Ain (1)
14 Pl Des Terreaux
Belley, 01300, France (100%)
Tel.: (33) 479812327
Telex: 330 185
Fax: (33) 479812891
Emp.: 10
Banking & Finance
S.I.C.: 6282
N.A.I.C.S.: 523930

Banque Scalbert Dupont (1)
33 Ave Le Corbusier
BP 322
F 59020 Lille, Cedex, France (100%)
Tel.: (33) 320126464
Telex: 820 680 F
Fax: (33) 320126409
Web Site: www.cic.fr
Emp.: 2,200
Banking & Finance
S.I.C.: 6282
N.A.I.C.S.: 523930
Stelli Premaor *(Pres)*

Banque Transatlantique (1)
26 Ave Franklin D Roosevelt
75008 Paris, France (73.38%)
Tel.: (33) 156887777
Fax: (33) 1568857280
Web Site: www.banquetransatlantique.com
Sales Range: $1-4.9 Billion
Emp.: 250
Commerical Banking
S.I.C.: 6029

N.A.I.C.S.: 522110
Bruno Julin Lafferiere *(CEO)*

Bonnasse Lyonnaise de Banque (1)
448 Ave Du Prado
13008 Marseilles, France (100%)
Tel.: (33) 491236767
Telex: LEBONAS 430 242
Fax: (33) 491236799
E-Mail: lyonnaisedebanque@blb.cic.fr
Web Site: www.blb.cic.fr
Emp.: 100
Banking & Finance
S.I.C.: 6282
N.A.I.C.S.: 523930

Credit Industriel d'Alsace et de Lorraine (1)
31 Rue Jean Wenger Valentin
BP 477
67958 Strasbourg, Cedex 9, France (100%)
Tel.: (33) 388377123
Telex: CREAL 890 167 F
Fax: (33) 388370159
E-Mail: cialin@cial.cic.fr
Web Site: www.banquecial.fr
Emp.: 600
Banking & Finance
S.I.C.: 6282
N.A.I.C.S.: 523930
Phillip Vidal *(Pres)*

Credit Industriel de Normandie (1)
2 bis rue Duguay Trouin
76041 Rouen, Cedex, France (100%)
Tel.: (33) 2 35 08 6400
Telex: 770 950
Fax: (33) 2 35 08 6179
Web Site: www.cic.fr/bsd-cin/fr/
Emp.: 78
Banking & Finance
S.I.C.: 6282
N.A.I.C.S.: 523930
Mederic Monestier *(Reg Dir)*

Credit Industriel et Commercial SA (1)
6 avenue de Provence
75452 Paris, France (90%)
Tel.: (33) 145969696
Fax: (33) 145969666
E-Mail: cicdrhcontact@cic.fr
Web Site: www.cic.fr
CC—(EUR)
Sales Range: $5-14.9 Billion
Emp.: 21,642
Banking, Asset Management, Leasing, Securities & Insurance Services
S.I.C.: 6029
N.A.I.C.S.: 522110
Etienne Pflimlin *(Chm-Supervisory Bd)*
Michel Jean Francis Lucas *(Chm-Mgmt Bd)*
Gerard Cormoreche *(Vice Chm-Supervisory Bd)*
Alain Fradin *(Vice Chm-Mgmt Bd)*
Michel Michenko *(Member-Mgmt Bd)*
Jean-Jacques Tamburini *(Member-Mgmt Bd)*
Philippe Vidal *(Member-Mgmt Bd)*
Remy Weber *(Member-Mgmt Bd)*
Gilles Le Noc *(Sec)*

Subsidiary:

Nerim SAS (2)
19 Rue du Quatre
Paris, 75002, France
Tel.: (33) 0()4 77 26
Fax: (33) 33 9 73 87 00 95
Broadband Services
S.I.C.: 4812
N.A.I.C.S.: 517210
Christophe Carel *(Mng Dir)*

Subsidiary:

Normaction SA (3)
38-42 rue Gallieni
92600 Asnieres-sur-Seine, France
Tel.: (33) 140864190
Fax: (33) 1 40864191
E-Mail: jc.hudo@normaction.com
Web Site: www.normaction.com
Sales Range: $10-24.9 Million
Emp.: 50
Telecommunications & IT System Security Services
S.I.C.: 4899
N.A.I.C.S.: 517919
Jean-Marc Amouroux *(Pres)*

Subsidiaries:

Normaction Centre Pays de Loire Orleans (4)
12 Rue Emile Zola
45000 Orleans, France
Tel.: (33) 238541067
Fax: (33) 238548273
E-Mail: normaction@normaction.com
Emp.: 8
Telecommunication Service Provider
S.I.C.: 4899
N.A.I.C.S.: 517919
Philippe Pierre *(Gen Mgr)*

Normaction Covensys Nimes (4)
Immeuble Ellipsis 125 rue de l Hostellerie
30907 Nimes, France
Tel.: (33) 466299680
Fax: (33) 466299679
Web Site: fr.normaction.be/implantations.php
Emp.: 20
Telecommunication Service Provider
S.I.C.: 4899
N.A.I.C.S.: 517919
Lunrc Dominic *(Mng Dir)*

Normaction Ouest Telecom Evreux (4)
ZAC du Long Buisson 301 rue Clement Ader
27000 Evreux, France
Tel.: (33) 232622525
Fax: (33) 2 32 62 25 26
Web Site: www.normaction.com
Telecommunication Service Provider
S.I.C.: 4899
N.A.I.C.S.: 517919

Normaction Sals Telecom Nimes (4)
Immeuble Ellipsis 125 Rue De l Hostellerie
Nimes, France
Tel.: (33) 466299696
Fax: (33) 466299679
E-Mail: d.renac@normaction.com
Web Site: www.fr.normaction.be/implantations.php
Emp.: 25
Telecommunication Service Provider
S.I.C.: 4899
N.A.I.C.S.: 517919
Dominique Renac *(Mng Dir)*

Normaction Sogetel Aubagne (4)
Techniparc de la Bastidonne Chemin de l Aumone-Vieille 29
13671 Aubagne, France
Tel.: (33) 491272727
Fax: (33) 491270925
E-Mail: fghrciea@fsalstelecom.fr
Web Site: fr.normaction.be
Telecommunication Services Provider
S.I.C.: 4899
N.A.I.C.S.: 517919

Non-U.S. Subsidiary:

Normaction Benelux Belgique (4)
Rue de Stalle 63 - Bte 6
1180 Brussels, Belgium
Tel.: (32) 23337121
Fax: (32) 2 333 71 22
Web Site: fr.normaction.be/implantations.php
Emp.: 7
Telecommunication Service Provider
S.I.C.: 4899
N.A.I.C.S.: 517919

Holding:

IPO SA (2)
32 Avenue Camus
BP 50 416
44004 Nantes, Cedex, 1, France
Tel.: (33) 240357531
Fax: (33) 240352737
E-Mail: ipo@ipo.cic.fr
Web Site: www.ipo.fr
Sales Range: $25-49.9 Million
Emp.: 15
Investment Banking Services
S.I.C.: 6211
N.A.I.C.S.: 523110
Pierre Tiers *(Pres)*

Socapi (1)
42 Rue De Mathurins
75008 Paris, France (100%)
Tel.: (33) 144715200
Fax: (33) 140170233
Web Site: www.socapi.com
Emp.: 100
Insurance
S.I.C.: 6311
N.A.I.C.S.: 524113

Non-U.S. Subsidiaries:

Credit Mutuel Nord Europe Belgium NV (1)
Avenue des Arts 6-9
Brussels, 1210, Belgium
Tel.: (32) 2 289 82 00
Fax: (32) 2 289 89 90
Banking Services
S.I.C.: 6029
N.A.I.C.S.: 522110

Subsidiary:

Citibank Belgium S.A./N.V. (2)
Boulevard General Jacques 263G
Brussels, Belgium BE
Tel.: (32) 22625427 (100%)
Fax: (32) 22625655
E-Mail: meridien@citigroup.com
Web Site: www.citibank.be
Emp.: 15
Commercial Banking Services
S.I.C.: 6029
N.A.I.C.S.: 522110
Jose Penaranda *(CEO)*

CREDIT ORGANIZATION OF SMALL & MEDIUM-SIZED ENTERPRISES CO., LTD.

1-10-7 Ryogoku
Sumida-ku, 130-0026 Tokyo, Japan
Tel.: (81) 356253190
Year Founded: 1974
8489—(JAS)
Sales Range: $10-24.9 Million
Emp.: 105
Business Description:
Financial Business Credit Services
S.I.C.: 6159
N.A.I.C.S.: 522298
Personnel:
Masashi Kamimura *(Pres)*

CREDIT RATING & COLLECTION COMPANY KSCC

(d/b/a TAHSSILAT)
Sharq Ahmad Al-Jaber Street Al-Awadi Towers No 3 1st Floor
PO Box 1432
Safat, Kuwait, 13015, Kuwait
Tel.: (965) 1802230
Fax: (965) 22452590
E-Mail: info@crckt.com
Web Site: www.crckt.com
Year Founded: 1998
TAHSSILAT—(KUW)
Rev.: $2,909,287
Assets: $52,324,650
Liabilities: $1,995,041
Net Worth: $50,329,609
Earnings: ($11,651,324)
Emp.: 50
Fiscal Year-end: 12/31/12
Business Description:
Credit Rating, Risk Management & Debt Recovery Services
S.I.C.: 7323
N.A.I.C.S.: 561450
Personnel:
Abdullah Mushari Ahmad Al-Humadhi *(Chm)*
Ibrahim Abbas Othman Al-Sakhi *(Vice Chm & Mng Dir)*
Board of Directors:
Abdullah Mushari Ahmad Al-Humadhi
Bassam Saleh Al-Msalam
Ibrahim Abbas Othman Al-Sakhi
Saleh Ghaiem Malallah
Abdulrahman Mostafa Mohammad Tahhan

CREDIT SAISON CO., LTD.

Sunshine 60 Bldg 1-1 Higashi-Ikebukuro 3-chome Toshima-ku
Tokyo, 170-6073, Japan
Tel.: (81) 339882111
Fax: (81) 353914392
E-Mail: dept.060@cs.saisoncard.co.jp
Web Site: corporate.saisoncard.co.jp
Year Founded: 1951
8253—(TKS)
Rev.: $2,688,455,000
Assets: $23,559,822,000
Liabilities: $19,216,274,000
Net Worth: $4,343,548,000
Earnings: $360,470,000
Emp.: 3,689
Fiscal Year-end: 03/31/13
Business Description:
Credit Card Issuer
S.I.C.: 6141
N.A.I.C.S.: 522210
Personnel:
Hiroshi Rinno *(Pres, CEO & Head-Audit Office & Credit Card Div)*
Naoki Takahashi *(Sr Mng Dir & Head-Corp Plng Dept & Credit Div & Internet Bus Div)*
Haruhisa Kaneko *(Mng Dir & Head-Overseas Bus Div)*
Hiroshi Yamamoto *(Mng Dir, Head-Customer Satisfaction Promotion office & Fin Div)*
Masahiro Yamashita *(Mng Dir & Head-Sls Dev Div & Alliance Dev Dept)*
Junji Kakusho *(Mng Dir & Gen Mgr-Credit Card Div & Internet Bus Div)*
Teruyuki Maekawa *(Exec VP & Head-PR Office, Gen Affairs Dept & Strategic HR Dept)*
Board of Directors:
Teruhisa Aoyama
Kazuhiro Hirase
Junji Kakusho
Haruhisa Kaneko
Teruyuki Maekawa
Akihiro Matsuda
Katsumi Mizuno
Tatsunari Okamoto
Hiroshi Rinno
Sadamu Shimizu
Naoki Takahashi
Yasuhisa Ueno
Hiroshi Yamamoto
Yoshihisa Yamamoto
Masahiro Yamashita
Subsidiaries:

Saison Information Systems Co., Ltd. (1)
21 F Sunshine 60 3-1-1 Higashi-Ikebukuro
Toshima-ku
Tokyo, 170-6021, Japan
Tel.: (81) 3 3988 2020
E-Mail: mail@saison.co.jp
Web Site: www.saison.co.jp
9640—(JAS)
Sls.: $322,190,000
Assets: $275,726,000
Liabilities: $97,966,000
Net Worth: $177,760,000
Earnings: $18,414,000
Emp.: 1,223
Fiscal Year-end: 03/31/13
Software Development Services
S.I.C.: 7371
N.A.I.C.S.: 541511
Takashi Miyano *(Pres)*

Takashimaya Credit Co. Ltd. (1)
Koueikayabacho Building
Chuo-Ku, Tokyo, Japan
Tel.: (81) 336681700
Fax: (81) 336681690
Web Site: www.t-card.co.jp

Credit Saison Co., Ltd.—(Continued)

Credit Card Issuing
S.I.C.: 6153
N.A.I.C.S.: 522210

CREDIT SUISSE GROUP AG

Paradeplatz 8
8001 Zurich, Switzerland
Tel.: (41) 44 333 6607
Fax: (41) 44 333 1790
Web Site: www.credit-suisse.com
Year Founded: 1856
CS—(NYSE)
Rev.: $23,858,368,600
Assets: $997,593,889,600
Liabilities: $951,955,922,720
Net Worth: $45,637,966,880
Earnings: $1,818,654,200
Emp.: 47,400
Fiscal Year-end: 12/31/12

Business Description:
Holding Company; Private Banking, Investment Banking & Asset Management Services
Export
S.I.C.: 6719
N.A.I.C.S.: 551112

Personnel:
Urs Rohner *(Chm)*
Peter Brabeck-Letmathe *(Vice Chm)*
David R. Mathers *(CFO)*
Pamela A. Thomas-Graham *(Chief Talent, Branding & Comm Officer)*
Tobias Guldimann *(Chief Risk Officer)*
Gael de Boissard *(CEO-EMEA & Co-Head-Investment Banking-Global)*
Hans-Ulrich Meister *(CEO-Switzerland & Co-Head-Private Banking & Wealth Mgmt-Global)*
Robert Shafir *(CEO-Americas & Co-Head-Private Banking & Wealth Mgmt-Global)*
Eric M. Varvel *(CEO-Asia Pacific & Co-Head-Investment Banking-Global)*
Garrett Curran *(CEO-UK)*
Romeo Cerutti *(Gen Counsel)*
Pierre Schreiber *(Sec)*

Board of Directors:
Urs Rohner
Iris Bohnet
Peter Brabeck-Letmathe
Noreen Doyle
Jean-Daniel Gerber
Jassim Hamad Jassim Jabor Al Thani
Walter B. Kielholz
Andreas N. Koopmann
Jean Lanier
Kaikhushru Shiavax Nargolwala
Richard E. Thornburgh
John Tiner
Anton van Rossum

American Stock Transfer & Trust Co
Peck Slip Station P.O. Box 2050
New York, NY 10272-2050

Transfer Agents:
Credit Suisse Group AG
Dept. RXS
Zurich, CH, 8070, Switzerland

American Stock Transfer & Trust Co
Peck Slip Station P.O. Box 2050
New York, NY 10272-2050

Subsidiaries:

BANK-now AG (1)
Neugasse 18
Postfach 852
8810 Horgen, Switzerland
Tel.: (41) 44 657 20 20
Fax: (41) 44 447 12 13
Web Site: www.bank-now.ch
Financial Management Services
S.I.C.: 6211
N.A.I.C.S.: 523999

Credit Suisse AG (1)
Paradeplatz 8
8070 Zurich, Switzerland CH
Tel.: (41) 443331111 (100%)
Fax: (41) 443325555
Web Site: www.credit-suisse.com
Rev.: $11,046,840,200
Assets: $635,787,477,160
Liabilities: $593,685,362,600
Net Worth: $42,102,114,560
Earnings: $197,515,560
Fiscal Year-end: 12/31/12
Private Banking, Investment Banking & Asset Management Services
S.I.C.: 6282
N.A.I.C.S.: 523110
Hans-Ulrich Doerig *(Chm)*
Peter Brabeck-Letmathe *(Vice Chm)*
Brady W. Dougan *(CEO)*
David R. Mathers *(CFO)*
D. Wilson Ervin *(Chief Risk Officer)*

Subsidiaries:

Corner Bank Ltd. (2)
Via Canova 16
Lugano, 6900, Switzerland (100%)
Tel.: (41) 918005111
Fax: (41) 918005349
E-Mail: info@cornerbanka.com
Web Site: www.cornerbanka.com
Emp.: 800
S.I.C.: 6159
N.A.I.C.S.: 522298
Ana Russo *(Mgr-Mktg)*

Credit Suisse Asset Management International Holding Ltd (2)
Uetlibergstrasse 231
8045 Zurich, Switzerland
Tel.: (41) 44333 11 11
Fax: (41) 44333 22 25
Investment Management Services
S.I.C.: 6282
N.A.I.C.S.: 523920
Neil Harvey *(Vice Chm-Asia Pacific)*

Credit Suisse Asset Management (2)
Gieshubelstrasse 40
8045 Zurich, Switzerland (100%)
Tel.: (41) 3351111
Fax: (41) 13332225
E-Mail: info@csam.com
Web Site: www.csam.com
Emp.: 600
Provider of Investment Services
S.I.C.: 6282
N.A.I.C.S.: 523930

Credit Suisse Bank (2)
Saint Alban Graben 13
CH 4002 Basel, Switzerland (100%)
Tel.: (41) 612667711
Fax: (41) 612667733
E-Mail: webmaster@credit-suisse.com
Emp.: 50
Mortgage Banking Services
S.I.C.: 6159
N.A.I.C.S.: 522292
Patrice Kleewein *(Branch Mgr)*

Credit Suisse Bank (2)
Paradeplatz 8
PO Box 100
8070 Zurich, Switzerland (100%)
Tel.: (41) 44 333 11 11
E-Mail: info@credit-suisse.com
Web Site: www.credit-suisse.ch
S.I.C.: 6099
N.A.I.C.S.: 522390

Credit Suisse IT Services AG (2)
Zurichstrasse 8
8600 Dubendorf, Switzerland CH
Mailing Address: (100%)
Postfacht 113
8600 Dubendorf, Switzerland
Tel.: (41) 44 802 92 92
Fax: (41) 44 802 92 93
Web Site: www.credit-suisse.com
Emp.: 120
IT Services
S.I.C.: 7389
N.A.I.C.S.: 519190

Credit Suisse Leasing AG (2)
Thurgauerstrasse 56
Zurich, 8070, Switzerland (100%)
Tel.: (41) 13342800
Fax: (41) 13342144
E-Mail: webmaster@csl.ch
Web Site: www.creditsuisse.com
Emp.: 130
S.I.C.: 7359
N.A.I.C.S.: 532210

Innoventure Capital AG (2)
Bleicherweg 72
CH-8070 Zurich, Switzerland (90%)
Tel.: (41) 13325842
Fax: (41) 13333338
Investments
S.I.C.: 6282
N.A.I.C.S.: 523930

U.S. Subsidiary:

Credit Suisse (USA), Inc. (2)
11 Madison Ave
New York, NY 10010-3629 (100%)
Tel.: (212) 325-2000
Fax: (212) 325-6665
Web Site: www.credit-suisse.com
Emp.: 10,465
Investment & Merchant Banking Services
S.I.C.: 6211
N.A.I.C.S.: 523110
Larry Hamdan *(Vice Chm-Global Mergers & Acq)*
David Mulford *(Vice Chm-Intl)*
James Walker *(Mng Dir & Head-Investment Banking-Americas & Over-The-Counter Ops)*
Anthony DeChellis *(Mng Dir & Head-Private Banking Americas)*
Lara Warner *(CFO)*
D. Wilson Ervin *(Chief Risk Officer)*

Branch:

Credit Suisse (3)
302 Carnegie Ctr Fl 2
Princeton, NJ 08540-6226 NJ
Tel.: (609) 627-5000
Fax: (609) 627-5011
Rev.: $3,500,000
Emp.: 40
Security Brokers & Dealers
S.I.C.: 7374
N.A.I.C.S.: 518210
Rajesh Alva *(Mng Dir & Head-Health Care M&A)*
Jay Kim *(Mng Dir & Head-Securitized Products Asset Fin Grp)*
Amy Cerciello *(Sec & VP)*

Subsidiaries:

Credit Suisse Asset Management, LLC (3)
11 Madison Ave 11th Fl
New York, NY 10010-3629 DE
Tel.: (212) 325-2000 (100%)
Fax: (212) 658-0728
Toll Free: (800) 577-2321
Emp.: 400
Asset Management for Institutional and Individual Investors
S.I.C.: 6282
N.A.I.C.S.: 523930
Robert Parker *(Vice Chm)*
Rob Sharif *(CEO & CEO-Americas Region)*

Credit Suisse Private Equity, LLC (3)
11 Madison Ave
New York, NY 10010
Tel.: (212) 325-2000
Web Site: www.creditsuisse.com
Private Equity Investment Services
S.I.C.: 6211
N.A.I.C.S.: 523999

Credit Suisse Securities (USA) LLC (3)
11 Madison Ave
New York, NY 10010 DE
Tel.: (212) 325-2000 (100%)
Fax: (212) 538-3395
E-Mail: info@credit-suisse.com
Web Site: www.credit-suisse.com
Emp.: 9,050
Investment & Merchant Banking Services
S.I.C.: 6211
N.A.I.C.S.: 523110
Brady Dougan *(CEO)*
Amy Grossman *(Mng Dir)*
Neil Moskowitz *(Mng Dir)*

Subsidiaries:

Autranet Inc. (4)
1 Pershing Plz
Jersey City, NJ 07399-0001 NJ
Tel.: (201) 395-1400
Rev.: $6,200,000
Emp.: 67
Security Brokers
S.I.C.: 6211
N.A.I.C.S.: 523120

Special Situations Holdings, Inc. Westbridge (4)
11 Madison Ave
New York, NY 10010
Tel.: (212) 325-2000
Fax: (212) 325-6665
Holding Company
S.I.C.: 6719
N.A.I.C.S.: 551112

Subsidiary:

USHEALTH Group, Inc. (5)
3100 Burnett Plz 801 Cherry St Unit 33
Fort Worth, TX 76102-7025 DE
Tel.: (817) 878-3300
Fax: (817) 878-3430
Web Site: www.ushealthgroup.com
Emp.: 213
Insurance Services
S.I.C.: 6361
N.A.I.C.S.: 524127
Benjamin M. Cutler *(Chm & CEO)*
Cynthia B. Koenig *(CFO & Sr VP)*
Patrick H. O'Neill *(Gen Counsel, Sec & Exec VP)*

Subsidiaries:

Foundation Financial Services, Inc. (6)
3100 Burnett Plz 801 Cherry St Unit 33
Fort Worth, TX 76102 NV
Tel.: (817) 878-3300 (100%)
Fax: (817) 878-3440
Web Site: www.ushealthgroup.com
Emp.: 10
Insurance Brokerage Services
S.I.C.: 6411
N.A.I.C.S.: 524210
Benjamin Cutler *(Sec & Asst VP)*

Freedom Life Insurance Company (6)
3100 Burnett Plz 801 Cherry St Unit 33
Fort Worth, TX 76102-7025 TX
Tel.: (817) 878-3303 (100%)
Fax: (817) 878-3480
Toll Free: (800) 387-9027
Web Site: www.ushealthgroup.com
Emp.: 145
Health Insurance Services
S.I.C.: 6311
N.A.I.C.S.: 524113
Benjamin M. Cutler *(Chm & CEO)*
Cynthia B. Koenig *(CFO & Sr VP)*

USHEALTH Career (6)
3100 Burnett Plz 801 Cherry St Unit 33
Fort Worth, TX 76102 DE
Tel.: (817) 878-3300 (100%)
Fax: (817) 878-3480
Toll Free: (800) 437-8694
Web Site: www.ushealthgroup.com
Insurance Marketing Services
S.I.C.: 6411
N.A.I.C.S.: 524298
Benjamin M. Cutler *(Chm, Pres & CEO)*
Cynthia B. Koenig *(CFO & Sr VP)*
Patrick H. O'Neill *(Gen Counsel, Sec & Exec VP)*

Subsidiaries:

LifeStyles Marketing Group, Inc. (7)
3100 Burnett Plz 801 Cherry St Unit 33
Fort Worth, TX 76102 DE
Tel.: (817) 878-3300 (100%)
Insurance Marketing Services
S.I.C.: 6411
N.A.I.C.S.: 524298
Benjamin M. Cutler *(Pres)*

Precision Dialing Services, Inc. (7)
1100 E Campbell Rd Ste 150
Richardson, TX 75081 DE
Tel.: (214) 343-7374 (100%)
Fax: (214) 343-3070
Web Site: www.pdsdallas.com
Emp.: 100
Telemarketing Services
S.I.C.: 7889
N.A.I.C.S.: 561422

USHEALTH Funding, Inc. (7)
3100 Burnett Plz 801 Cherry St Unit 33
Fort Worth, TX 76102 DE
Tel.: (817) 878-3307 (100%)
Fax: (817) 885-5500
Financing Services
S.I.C.: 6733
N.A.I.C.S.: 525190
Benjamin M. Cutler *(Pres)*

Sprout Group (4)
11 Madison Ave 13th Fl
New York, NY 10010
Tel.: (212) 538-3600
Fax: (212) 538-8245
Web Site: www.sproutgroup.com
Emp.: 36
Open-End Management Investment Services
S.I.C.: 6722
N.A.I.C.S.: 525910

Stewart Stamping Corp. (4)
45 Old Waterbury Rd
Thomaston, CT 06787-1903
Tel.: (914) 965-0816
Fax: (914) 965-4431
Web Site: www.insilco.com
Metal Stamping & Formed Wire Products
S.I.C.: 3466
N.A.I.C.S.: 332119

DLJ Merchant Banking Partners (3)
11 Madison Ave
New York, NY 10010
Tel.: (212) 325-2000
E-Mail: dljmb-na@credit-suisse.com
Web Site: www.csfb.com
Private Equity Investment Services
S.I.C.: 6211
N.A.I.C.S.: 523999
Charles Pieper *(Vice Chm-Alternative Investments & Mng Dir-Asset Mgmt)*
Susan C. Schnabel *(Mng Dir & Partner)*
Nicole Arnaboldi *(Mng Dir)*
Colin Taylor *(Mng Dir)*
Edward A. Johnson *(Mng Dir)*
Robert Neal Pomroy *(Mng Dir)*

Holdings:

Deffenbaugh Industries Inc. (4)
2601 S 90th St
Kansas City, KS 66111-1760 KS
Tel.: (913) 631-3300
Fax: (913) 631-6647
E-Mail: info@deffenbaughinc.com
Web Site: www.deffenbaughinc.com
Sales Range: $150-199.9 Million
Emp.: 1,500
Waste Disposal Systems
Import Export
S.I.C.: 4953
N.A.I.C.S.: 562212
Ron Anderson *(CFO)*

Merrill Corporation (4)
1 Merrill Cir
Saint Paul, MN 55108 MN
Tel.: (651) 646-4501 (58%)
Fax: (651) 646-5332
Toll Free: (800) 688-4400
E-Mail: info@merrillcorp.com
Web Site: www.merrillcorp.com
Sales Range: $750-799.9 Million
Emp.: 5,000
Business Communication & Information Management Outsourcing Services
S.I.C.: 7389
N.A.I.C.S.: 561410
John W. Castro *(Chm & CEO)*
Robert H. Nazarian *(CFO, Treas & Exec VP)*
Brenda J. Vale *(Chief Admin Officer, Exec VP & Sec)*
Katherine L. Miller *(Chief Acctg Officer, Controller & Sr VP)*
Rick R. Atterbury *(Pres/COO-DataSite & Intl)*
Roy Gross *(Pres-Mktg & Comm Solutions)*
Pat Prozzi *(Pres-Captioning)*
Steven J. Machov *(Gen Counsel, Sec & Exec VP)*
Craig Levinsohn *(Exec VP-Global Mktg)*
Mark Rossi *(Sr VP & Gen Mgr-Sls)*
Jim Garippa *(Sr VP-Sls)*

Branches:

Merrill Corporation (5)
2603 Main St Ste 100
Irvine, CA 92614-4242
Tel.: (949) 252-9449
Web Site: www.merrillcorp.com
Financial, Legal, Commercial, Corporate & DRG Printing
S.I.C.: 2759
N.A.I.C.S.: 323111

Merrill Corporation (5)
16200 Trojan Way
La Mirada, CA 90638-5600
Tel.: (213) 765-7000
Fax: (213) 765-7001
Web Site: www.merrillcorp.com
Financial, Legal, Commercial & Corporate Printing
S.I.C.: 2759
N.A.I.C.S.: 323111

Merrill Corporation (5)
350 S Grand Ave Ste 3000
Los Angeles, CA 90071-3424
Tel.: (213) 253-5900
Web Site: www.merrillcorp.com
Financial, Legal, Commercial, Corporate & DRG Printing
S.I.C.: 2759
N.A.I.C.S.: 323111

Merrill Corporation (5)
1225 17th St Ste 2800
Denver, CO 80202-5599
Tel.: (303) 572-3889
Fax: (303) 573-7566
Web Site: www.merrilldirect.com
Emp.: 50
Provide Financial, Legal, Commercial & Corporate Printing Services
S.I.C.: 7389
N.A.I.C.S.: 323111
Bob Bergstrom *(Gen Mgr)*

Merrill Corporation (5)
100 Pearl St Fl 14
Hartford, CT 06103-4500
Tel.: (860) 249-7220
Web Site: www.merrillntext.com
Emp.: 20
Financial, Legal, Commercial, Corporate & DRG Printing
S.I.C.: 2759
N.A.I.C.S.: 323111

Merrill Corporation (5)
1325 G St NW Ste 200
Washington, DC 20005-3104
Tel.: (202) 879-8400
Fax: (202) 955-6121
Web Site: www.merrillcorp.com
Emp.: 60
Financial Legal Commercial Corporate and DRG Printing
S.I.C.: 2759
N.A.I.C.S.: 323111
Jose Lebron *(Gen Mgr)*

Merrill Corporation (5)
311 S Wacker Dr Ste 1800
Chicago, IL 60606-6620
Tel.: (312) 786-6300
Fax: (312) 786-9900
Web Site: www.merrillcorp.com
Emp.: 3,300
Provider of Financial, Legal, Commercial & Corporate Printing Services
S.I.C.: 2759
N.A.I.C.S.: 323111
John W. Castro *(Chm & CEO)*

Merrill Corporation (5)
111 S Calvert St Ste 2350
Baltimore, MD 21202
Tel.: (410) 625-0400
Fax: (410) 625-0405
Web Site: www.merrillcorp.com
Emp.: 2
Financial, Legal, Commercial, Corporate & DRG Printing
S.I.C.: 2759
N.A.I.C.S.: 323111
John Linden *(Mgr-Mktg)*

Merrill Corporation (5)
4110 Clearwater Rd
Saint Cloud, MN 56301-9634
Tel.: (320) 656-5000
Web Site: www.merrillcorp.com
Financial, Legal, Commercial, Corporate & DRG Printing
S.I.C.: 2759
N.A.I.C.S.: 323111
Brenda Vale *(Chief Admin Officer & Exec VP)*
Katherine Miller *(Chief Acctg Officer, Sr VP & Controller)*
Anne Leonard *(Principal)*
Steve Machov *(Gen Counsel, Sec & Exec VP)*
Tracy S. Kirby *(Sr VP-Sls)*
Amy Reichenbach *(Sr VP-MCS HR)*
Darlene Shay *(Sr VP-Client Svcs)*

Merrill Corporation (5)
225 Varick St
New York, NY 10014-4304
Tel.: (212) 620-5600
Fax: (212) 645-8552
Web Site: www.merrillcorp.com
Emp.: 100
Financial, Legal, Commercial & Corporate Printing
S.I.C.: 5099
N.A.I.C.S.: 423990
Rick Atterbury *(Pres & COO)*
Mike James *(Pres-Sls)*
Brenda Vale *(Exec VP-HR)*

Merrill Corporation (5)
4144 N Central Expy Ste 450
Dallas, TX 75204-3132
Tel.: (214) 698-9777
Fax: (214) 760-9968
E-Mail: dfwcust@merrillcorp.com
Web Site: www.merrillcorp.com
Emp.: 100
Financial, Legal, Commercial, Corporate & DRG Printing Services
S.I.C.: 2759
N.A.I.C.S.: 323111
Jim Buffington *(Gen Mgr)*

Merrill Corporation (5)
Bayou Pl 315 Capitol St Ste 210
Houston, TX 77002
Tel.: (713) 650-9640
Fax: (713) 650-3149
Web Site: www.merrillcorp.com
Emp.: 20
Financial, Legal, Commercial, Corporate & DRG Printing
S.I.C.: 2759
N.A.I.C.S.: 323111
Chris McLean *(Mgr-Sls)*

Merrill Corporation (5)
14640 172nd Dr SE
Monroe, WA 98272-1076
Tel.: (360) 794-3157
Fax: (360) 794-3100
Web Site: www.merrillcorp.com
Emp.: 50
Financial Legal Commercial Corporate and DRG Printing
S.I.C.: 2759
N.A.I.C.S.: 323111
Mike Hatfield *(Gen Mgr)*

Merrill/Daniels, Inc. (5)
40 Commercial St
Everett, MA 02149-5507 (100%)
Tel.: (617) 389-7900
Fax: (617) 389-5520
Web Site: www.danielsprinting.com
Emp.: 270
Commercial & Financial Printing
S.I.C.: 7389
N.A.I.C.S.: 323111

Subsidiary:

Merrill Brink International Corporation (5)
1 Merrill Cir Bldg 1455
Saint Paul, MN 55108-5264 (100%)
Tel.: (651) 646-4501
Toll Free: (800) 688-4400
E-Mail: translations@merrillbrink.com
Web Site: www.merrillcorp.com
Language Solutions Including Translation, Localization, Desktop Publishing & Globalization Services
S.I.C.: 7389
N.A.I.C.S.: 541930
Claes Holm *(Pres)*

Non-U.S. Subsidiaries:

Merrill Corporation Canada (5)
Brookfield Place 161 Bay Street Suite 2410
Toronto, ON, M5J 2S1, Canada
Tel.: (416) 214-2448
Fax: (416) 214-4825
E-Mail: torcust@merrillcorp.com
Web Site: www.merrillcorp.com
Emp.: 40
Printing Services
S.I.C.: 2759
N.A.I.C.S.: 323111
Aivars Beikmanis *(Pres)*

Branches:

Merrill Corporation (6)
1 Place Ville Marie Suite 1505
Montreal, QC, H3B 2B5, Canada (100%)
Tel.: (514) 877-5177
Fax: (514) 954-9736
E-Mail: mtlcust@merrillcorp.com
Web Site: www.merrillcorp.com
Emp.: 7
Financial & Commercial Document Printing Services
S.I.C.: 2759
N.A.I.C.S.: 323111

Merrill Corporation (6)
1111 West Hastings Street Suite 333
Vancouver, BC, V6E 2J3, Canada
Tel.: (604) 682-8594
Fax: (604) 682-8599
E-Mail: vancust@merrillcorp.com
Web Site: www.merrillcorp.com
Emp.: 3
Financial Printing Services
S.I.C.: 2759
N.A.I.C.S.: 323111
Hank Gregery *(Sr VP)*

Merrill Corporation Limited (5)
101 Finsbury Pavement
London, EC2A 1ER, United Kingdom (100%)
Tel.: (44) 2074226100
Fax: (44) 20 7588 7605
E-Mail: datasite.uk@merrillcorp.com
Web Site: www.merrillcorp.com
Emp.: 100
Financial, Legal, Commercial, Corporate & DRG Printing
S.I.C.: 2759
N.A.I.C.S.: 323111
Lorraine Ivory *(Mgr-HR)*

Merrill France S.A.R.L. (5)
11 rue de Teheran
75008 Paris, France
Tel.: (33) 1 40 06 13 00
Fax: (33) 1 40 06 00 55
E-Mail: DataSite.fr@merrillcorp.com
Business Communication & Information Management Outsourcing Services
S.I.C.: 7389
N.A.I.C.S.: 561410

Merrill Germany GmbH (5)
An der Welle 8
D 60322 Frankfurt am Main, Germany De
Tel.: (49) 69 244 321 450 (100%)
E-Mail: fracustomerservice@merrillcorp.com
Business Communication & Information Management Outsourcing Services
S.I.C.: 7389
N.A.I.C.S.: 561410

Affiliate:

Visant Holding Corp. (4)
357 Main St
Armonk, NY 10504 DE
Tel.: (914) 595-8200
Fax: (914) 595-8239
E-Mail: paul.carousso@visant.net
Web Site: www.visant.net
Sales Range: $1-4.9 Billion
Emp.: 5,250
Holding Company; Owned by KKR & Co. L.P. & by DLJ Merchant Banking Partners
S.I.C.: 6719
N.A.I.C.S.: 551112
Marc L. Reisch *(Chm, Pres & CEO)*
Paul B. Carousso *(CFO & Sr VP)*
Marie D. Hlavaty *(Chief Legal Officer, Sr VP & Sec)*

Holding:

Visant Corporation (5)
357 Main St
Armonk, NY 10504 DE
Tel.: (914) 595-8200
Fax: (914) 595-8239

Credit Suisse Group AG—(Continued)

Web Site: www.visant.net
Sls.: $1,155,342,000
Assets: $1,926,406,000
Liabilities: $2,568,959,000
Net Worth: ($642,553,000)
Earnings: ($58,600,000)
Emp.: 4,174
Fiscal Year-end: 12/29/12
Marketing & Publishing Services
S.I.C.: 2741
N.A.I.C.S.: 511199
Marc L. Reisch *(Chm, Pres & CEO)*
Paul B. Carousso *(CFO & Sr VP)*
Marie D. Hlavaty *(Chief Legal Officer, Sec & VP)*

Subsidiaries:

Arcade Marketing, Inc. (6)
1700 Broadway Ste 2500
New York, NY 10019 DE
Tel.: (212) 541-2600
Fax: (212) 489-3026
Web Site: www.arcadeinc.com
Sales Range: $1-9.9 Million
Emp.: 28
Fragrance Sampling, Scent Sampling & Interactive Product Sampling Technologies Import Export
S.I.C.: 2759
N.A.I.C.S.: 323111
Debra Yale-Litman *(Pres)*
Steve Greenland *(Sr VP-R&D)*

Jostens, Inc. (6)
5501 American Blvd W
Minneapolis, MN 55437 MN
Tel.: (952) 830-3300
Fax: (952) 830-3293
E-Mail: info@jostens.com
Web Site: www.jostens.com
Emp.: 6,300
School-Related Affinity Products & Marketing & Photography Services Import Export
S.I.C.: 7335
N.A.I.C.S.: 541922
Charles Mooty *(Pres & CEO)*
James Simpson *(CFO)*
Val Williams *(COO)*
Marjorie J. Brown *(Sr VP-Fin)*

Non-U.S. Subsidiaries:

Clariden Leu Asset Management (Hong Kong) Ltd. (2)
1 Austin Road West International Commerce Centre Level 88
Kowloon, China (Hong Kong) HK (100%)
Tel.: (852) 29137678
Fax: (852) 28455447
Web Site: www.claridenleu.com
Emp.: 20
Investment Banking Services
S.I.C.: 6211
N.A.I.C.S.: 523110

Credit Suisse Asset Management (Deutschland) GmbH (2)
Junghofstrasse 16
Frankfurt am Main, 60311, Germany(100%)
Tel.: (49) 6975381500
Fax: (49) 6975381796
E-Mail: info@csam.com
Web Site: www.credit-suisse.de
Emp.: 130
Investment Banking
S.I.C.: 6211
N.A.I.C.S.: 523110

Credit Suisse Asset Management (France) S.A. (2)
25 Ave Kleber
75008 Paris, France (100%)
Tel.: (33) 170919191
Fax: (33) 170919190
Web Site: www.globalcsamintra.net
Emp.: 50
S.I.C.: 6159
N.A.I.C.S.: 522298

Credit Suisse Asset Management Ltd. (2)
One Cabot Square
London, E14 4QJ, United Kingdom (100%)
Tel.: (44) 2078881000
Fax: (44) 2078881600
Web Site: www.credit-suisse.com
Emp.: 400
Investment Banking
S.I.C.: 6211
N.A.I.C.S.: 523110
Christiana Marran *(Mng Dir & Head-Comm-EMEA-Canary Wharf)*
Gael de Boissard *(CEO-EMEA)*

Credit Suisse Asset Management SIM S.p.A. (2)
Piazza Missori 2
Milan, 20122, Italy (100%)
Tel.: (39) 02724141
Fax: (39) 02866115
Web Site: www.csam-europe.com
Emp.: 55
Asset Management
S.I.C.: 6211
N.A.I.C.S.: 523999

Credit Suisse (Bahamas) Ltd. (2)
Bahamas Financial Ctr Shirley & Charlotte St
Nassau, Bahamas (100%)
Tel.: (242) 3568100
Fax: (242) 3266589
E-Mail: csbahamas@credit-suisse.com
Web Site: www.credit-suisse.com
Emp.: 65
Investment & Private Banking Services
S.I.C.: 6211
N.A.I.C.S.: 523110
Barbara Gardiner *(Mgr-HR)*

Credit Suisse Brasil (2)
Avenida Brigadeiro Faria Lima 3064 13 andar
Itaim Bibi, 01451 000 Sao Paulo, Brazil (100%)
Tel.: (55) 1138416800
Fax: (55) 1138416900
E-Mail: info@csfb.com
Web Site: www.csfb.com.br
Emp.: 300
Investment Banking Services
S.I.C.: 6211
N.A.I.C.S.: 523110

Credit Suisse Consultaciones y Servicios S.A. (2)
Av Luis Alberto de Herrera 1248 Torre B Piso 9
11300 Montevideo, Uruguay (19%)
Tel.: (598) 2 622 9393
Fax: (598) 2 623 2770
Web Site: www.creditsuisse.com
Emp.: 6
Private Banking Services
S.I.C.: 6159
N.A.I.C.S.: 522298

Credit Suisse (Deutschland) Aktiengesellschaft (2)
Messeturm
60327 Frankfurt, Germany (100%)
Tel.: (49) 69974630
Fax: (49) 6997463333
Web Site: www.credit-suisse.de
Investment & Private Banking Services
S.I.C.: 6211
N.A.I.C.S.: 523110

Credit Suisse Equity Fund Management Company SA (2)
5 Rue Jean Monnet
Luxembourg, 2180, Luxembourg (100%)
Tel.: (352) 4361611
Fax: (352) 436161505
E-Mail: mranne.gaubremomg@credit-suissie.com
Web Site: www.creditsussie.com
Sales Range: $1-9.9 Million
Emp.: 100
S.I.C.: 6159
N.A.I.C.S.: 522298

Credit Suisse France (2)
25 Ave Kleber
75009 Paris, France (100%)
Tel.: (33) 149705800
Fax: (33) 149705880
E-Mail: credit-suisse@credit-suisse.com
Web Site: www.credit-suisse.com
Emp.: 120
Investment & Private Banking Services
S.I.C.: 6211
N.A.I.C.S.: 523110

Credit Suisse (Gibraltar) Ltd. (2)
Neptune House
PO Box 556
Marina Bay 1st Floor, Gibraltar, Gibraltar (100%)
Tel.: (350) 20078399
Fax: (350) 20076027
E-Mail: csg.mail@cspb.com
Web Site: www.credit-suisse.com
Sales Range: $1-9.9 Million
Emp.: 50
Private Banking Services
S.I.C.: 6211
N.A.I.C.S.: 523110
Kerry Blight *(CEO)*
Thomas West Olson *(Mng Dir)*

Credit Suisse Group Finance (Guernsey) Limited (2)
Helvetia Court South Esplanade
PO Box 413
Saint Peter Port, GY1 3WF, Guernsey
Tel.: (44) 1481 71908
Fax: (44) 1481 70023
Web Site: www.credit-suisse.com
Financial Planning Services
S.I.C.: 6282
N.A.I.C.S.: 523930

Credit Suisse (Guernsey) Ltd. (2)
Helvetia Court
PO Box 368
South Esplanade, Saint Peter Port, GY1 3YJ, Guernsey (100%)
Tel.: (44) 1481719000
Fax: (44) 1481724676
Web Site: www.credit-suisse.com
Emp.: 250
Investment Banking Services
S.I.C.: 6211
N.A.I.C.S.: 523110

Credit Suisse Holdings (Australia) Limited (2)
Level 31 Gateway 1 Macquarie Place
Sydney, NSW, 2000, Australia
Tel.: (61) 2 8205 4400
Fax: (61) 2 8205 4382
Investment Management Services
S.I.C.: 6282
N.A.I.C.S.: 523920
Rob Stewart *(CEO)*

Credit Suisse Investment Services (Cayman) (2)
802 West Bay Road
PO Box KY1-1104
Georgetown, Grand Cayman, Cayman Islands
Tel.: (345) 949-7942
Web Site: www.credit-suisse.com
Investment Banking Services
S.I.C.: 6211
N.A.I.C.S.: 523110

Credit Suisse (Italy) S.p.A. (2)
Via Mengoni 4
Milan, Italy (100%)
Tel.: (39) 0288550602
Fax: (39) 02 88 550 592
Web Site: www.credit-suisse.it
Emp.: 200
Investment & Private Banking Services
S.I.C.: 6211
N.A.I.C.S.: 523110
Federico Imbert *(CEO)*

Credit Suisse Life & Pensions AG (2)
Pradafant 21
9490 Vaduz, Liechtenstein
Tel.: (423) 230 17 60
Fax: (423) 230 17 62
E-Mail: keyaccount.trust@credit-suisse.com
Web Site: www.credit-suisse.com
General Insurance Services
S.I.C.: 6411
N.A.I.C.S.: 524210

Credit Suisse (Luxembourg) S.A. (2)
56 Grand Rue
2010 Luxembourg, 1660, Luxembourg (100%)
Tel.: (352) 4600111
Fax: (352) 463270
Web Site: www.credit-sussie.com
Rev.: $476,749
Emp.: 150
Private Banking Services
S.I.C.: 6022
N.A.I.C.S.: 522190

Credit Suisse (Monaco) S.A.M. (2)
Le Parc Palace
27 Ave De La Costa, 98000 Monaco, Monaco (100%)
Tel.: (377) 93152727
Fax: (377) 937793252799
Web Site: www.creditsuisse.com
Emp.: 50
Private Banking Services
S.I.C.: 6022
N.A.I.C.S.: 522190

Credit Suisse Securities (Japan) Limited (2)
1-6-1 Roppongi Izumi Garden Tower Level 27
Minatu-ku, Tokyo, 106 6024, Japan
Tel.: (81) 3 4550 9000
Fax: (81) 3 4550 9800
Web Site: www.credit-suisse.com
Investment Banking
S.I.C.: 6211
N.A.I.C.S.: 523110
Martin Keeble *(Pres & CEO)*

Credit Suisse Securities Ltd. (2)
1 Cabot Sq
London, E14 4QJ, United Kingdom (100%)
Tel.: (44) 2078888888
Fax: (44) 2078881600
Web Site: www.credit-suisse.com
Emp.: 100
International Financial Services Company; Provider of Institutional Asset Management & Corporate/Investment Banking Services
S.I.C.: 6282
N.A.I.C.S.: 523930

Credit Suisse (2)
1 Cabot Sq
E144QJ London, United Kingdom (100%)
Tel.: (44) 2078888888
Fax: (44) 2078881600
Emp.: 7,000
Derivative Trading
S.I.C.: 6211
N.A.I.C.S.: 523110
Garrett Curran *(CEO-UK)*

Credit Suisse (2)
Honthorststraat 19
1071 DC Amsterdam, Netherlands (100%)
Tel.: (31) 205754890
Fax: (31) 205754860
Web Site: www.cssb.com
Emp.: 15
S.I.C.: 6159
N.A.I.C.S.: 522298
Willen Bosch *(Mng Dir)*
Thijs Jochems *(Mng Dir)*

Credit Suisse (2)
101 Collins St
41st Fl, Melbourne, VIC, 3000, Australia (100%)
Tel.: (61) 92801666
Fax: (61) 92801890
Web Site: www.creditsuisse.com
Emp.: 80
S.I.C.: 6159
N.A.I.C.S.: 522298
Edward Jewell-Tait *(Mng Dir & Head-Private Banking)*

Credit Suisse (2)
1 Raffles Link #05-02
039393 Singapore, Singapore (100%)
Tel.: (65) 6212 6000
Fax: (65) 6212 6200
E-Mail: askhr.sg@credit-suisse.com
Web Site: www.credit-suisse.com
Emp.: 5,005
Provider of Investment Banking Services
S.I.C.: 6211
N.A.I.C.S.: 523110
Tee Fong Seng *(Vice Chm & Head-Asia Pacific)*
Lim Eng Guan *(Mng Dir)*

SECB Swiss Euro Clearing Bank GmbH (2)
Solmstrasse 18
D 60486 Frankfurt am Main, Germany (25%)
Tel.: (49) 699798980
Fax: (49) 6997989898
E-Mail: mail@secb.de
Web Site: www.secb.de
Emp.: 14

Credit Institution
S.I.C.: 6159
N.A.I.C.S.: 522298
Roland Boeff *(Mng Dir)*

Non-U.S. Affiliate:

McLarens Young International Panama (2)
Tower 50 4th Floor Corner 50th Street & 68th Street
Panama, Panama (12%)
Mailing Address:
PO Box 0816-3120
Panama, Panama
Tel.: (507) 2022222
Fax: (507) 5072023344
E-Mail: Miguel.Franco@McLarensYoung.com
Web Site: www.MclarensYoung.com
Emp.: 12
Financial Services
S.I.C.: 6211
N.A.I.C.S.: 523999
Miguel Franco *(Gen Mgr)*

Credit Suisse (International) Holding AG (1)
Bahnhofstrasse 17
Zurich, 6300, Switzerland
Tel.: (41) 44 212 16 16
Fax: (41) 44 333 25 87
Investment Management Services
S.I.C.: 6282
N.A.I.C.S.: 523920

Fides Treasury Services Ltd. (1)
Badenerstrasse 141
8004 Zurich, Switzerland (100%)
Tel.: (41) 442986580
Fax: (41) 442986581
E-Mail: support@fides.ch
Web Site: www.fides.ch
Emp.: 39
Financial Services & Software
S.I.C.: 3652
N.A.I.C.S.: 334614
Zazenier Cazanier *(Head-Infrastructure Dept)*

Merban Equity AG (1)
Bahnhofstrasse 17
6300 Zug, Switzerland
Tel.: (41) 41 7279922
Fax: (41) 41 7279943
Financial Planning Services
S.I.C.: 6282
N.A.I.C.S.: 523930

Neue Aargauer Bank (1)
Bahnhofstrasse 49
5001 Aarau, Switzerland (98%)
Tel.: (41) 564627100
Fax: (41) 628388280
E-Mail: info@nab.ch
Web Site: www.nab.ch
Emp.: 900
Full Banking Services
S.I.C.: 6099
N.A.I.C.S.: 522320
Peter Buehlmann *(CEO)*

Savoy Hotel Baur en Ville AG (1)
Paradeplatz
8022 Zurich, Switzerland
Tel.: (41) 44 215 25 25
Fax: (41) 44 215 25 00
E-Mail: welcome@savoy-zuerich.ch
Web Site: www.savoy-baurenville.ch
Hotel Management Services
S.I.C.: 7011
N.A.I.C.S.: 721110

Joint Venture:

Swisscard AECS AG (1)
Neugasse 18
8810 Horgen, Switzerland CH
Tel.: (41) 442666767
Fax: (41) 44 266 67 00
E-Mail: medienstelle.info@swisscard.ch
Web Site: www.swisscard.ch
Sales Range: $150-199.9 Million
Emp.: 400
Credit Cards; Owned 50% by Credit Suisse Group & 50% by American Express Travel Related Services Company, Inc.
S.I.C.: 6141
N.A.I.C.S.: 522210
Marcel Buehrer *(CEO)*

U.S. Subsidiaries:

Credit Suisse First Boston Mortgage Capital LLC (1)
11 Madison Ave
New York, NY 10010
Tel.: (212) 325-2000
Mortgage Loan Brokerage Services
S.I.C.: 6163
N.A.I.C.S.: 522310

Credit Suisse Holdings (USA), Inc. (1)
11 Madison Ave
New York, NY 10010-3679
Tel.: (212) 325-2000
Investment Management Services
S.I.C.: 6799
N.A.I.C.S.: 523920

Credit Suisse Management LLC (1)
1 Madison Ave Ste 450
New York, NY 10010
Tel.: (212) 538-6320
Fax: (212) 538-4095
Financial Planning Services
S.I.C.: 6282
N.A.I.C.S.: 523930

Non-U.S. Subsidiaries:

Banco Credit Suisse (Brasil) S.A. (1)
Av Brigadeiro Faria Lima 3064 - 13 Andar Parte
Jardim Paulistano, Sao Paulo, 01451-000, Brazil
Tel.: (55) 11 3841 6000
Web Site: www.credit-suisse.com
Financial Planning Services
S.I.C.: 6282
N.A.I.C.S.: 523930

Banco Credit Suisse (Mexico), S.A. (1)
Paseo de la Reforma 115 - Piso 26 Colonia Lomas de Chapultepec
11000 Mexico, Mexico
Tel.: (52) 55 5283 8900
Fax: (52) 55 5283 8977
Web Site: www.credit-suisse.com
Financial Management Services
S.I.C.: 6211
N.A.I.C.S.: 523999

Casa de Bolsa Credit Suisse (Mexico), S.A. de C.V. (1)
Paseo de la Reforma Num 115 Piso 26 Col Lomas de Chapultepec, Mexico, Mexico
Tel.: (52) 55 5283 8900
Sales Range: $1-9.9 Million
Emp.: 190
Financial Planning Services
S.I.C.: 6282
N.A.I.C.S.: 523930

CJSC Bank Credit Suisse (1)
4 Romanov Pereulok Bldg 2 Fl 6
125009 Moscow, Russia
Tel.: (7) 495 967 8200
Web Site: www.credit-suisse.com
Commercial Banking Services
S.I.C.: 6029
N.A.I.C.S.: 522110

Clariden Leu Financial Products (Guernsey) Ltd (1)
Millcourt La Charroterie
Saint Peter Port, GY1 1EJ, Guernsey
Tel.: (44) 1481 729110
Fax: (44) 1481 724685
Financial Planning Services
S.I.C.: 6282
N.A.I.C.S.: 523930

Credit Suisse Asesoria (Panama) S.A. (1)
Calle 50 con Calle Santo Domingo
Piso 39, Panama, Panama
Tel.: (507) 2941200
Fax: (507) 2941204
Web Site: www.credit-suisse.com
Financial Planning Services
S.I.C.: 6282
N.A.I.C.S.: 523930

Credit Suisse Asia International (Cayman) Limited (1)
No 109 Min-Sheng East Road Section 3 Union
Enterprise Plaza 8/F, 105 Taipei, Taiwan
Tel.: (886) 2 2544 5288
Fax: (886) 2 8712 3956
Web Site: www.credit-suisse.com
Financial Management Services
S.I.C.: 6211
N.A.I.C.S.: 523999

Credit Suisse Asset Management Funds (UK) Limited (1)
One Cabot Square
London, E14 4QJ, United Kingdom
Tel.: (44) 20 7888 1000
Fax: (44) 20 78881600
Asset Management Services
S.I.C.: 6799
N.A.I.C.S.: 523920

Credit Suisse Asset Management Immobilien Kapitalanlagegesellschaft mbH (1)
MesseTurm
60308 Frankfurt am Main, Germany
Tel.: (49) 69 75 38 1111
Fax: (49) 69 75 38 1796
Financial Management Services
S.I.C.: 6211
N.A.I.C.S.: 523999

Credit Suisse (Brasil) Distribuidora de Titulos e Valores Mobiliarios S.A. (1)
Av Brig Faria Lima 3064 - 13 andar
Sao Paulo, 01451-000, Brazil
Tel.: (55) 11 3841 6717
Financial Planning Services
S.I.C.: 6282
N.A.I.C.S.: 523930

Credit Suisse (Brasil) S.A. Corretora de Titulos e Valores Mobiliarios (1)
Av Brig Faria Lima 3064 - 13 floor
Sao Paulo, 01451-000, Brazil
Tel.: (55) 11 3841 6000
Fax: (55) 11 3841 6900
Financial Planning Services
S.I.C.: 6282
N.A.I.C.S.: 523930

Credit Suisse Equities (Australia) Limited (1)
L 31 Gateway 1 Macquarie Pl
Sydney, NSW, 2000, Australia
Tel.: (61) 282054400
Web Site: www.credit-suisse.com
Financial Planning Services
S.I.C.: 6282
N.A.I.C.S.: 523930

Credit Suisse Finance (Guernsey) Limited (1)
Helvetia Court South Esplanade
Saint Peter Port, GY1 3YJ, Guernsey
Tel.: (44) 1481 719 000
Fax: (44) 1481 724 676
E-Mail: guernsey.location@credit-suisse.com
Web Site: www.credit-suisse.com
Financial Management Services
S.I.C.: 6211
N.A.I.C.S.: 523999

Credit Suisse First Boston Finance B.V. (1)
Honthorststraat 19
Amsterdam, 1071 DC, Netherlands
Tel.: (31) 205754890
Fax: (31) 205754860
Financial Management Services
S.I.C.: 6211
N.A.I.C.S.: 523999

Credit Suisse Fund Management S.A. (1)
5 Rue Jean Monne
PO Box 369
2190 Luxembourg, Luxembourg
Tel.: (352) 43 61 61 1
Fax: (352) 43 61 61 405
Fund Management Services
S.I.C.: 6282
N.A.I.C.S.: 523920

Credit Suisse Fund Services (Luxembourg) S.A. (1)
5 Rue Jean Monnet
PO Box 369
2013 Luxembourg, Luxembourg
Tel.: (352) 43 61 61 616
Fax: (352) 43 61 61 605
E-Mail: clientservices.lux@credit-suisse.com
Web Site: www.credit-suisse.com
Emp.: 110
Financial Management Services
S.I.C.: 6211
N.A.I.C.S.: 523999

Credit Suisse International (1)
One Cabot Square
London, E14 4QJ, United Kingdom
Tel.: (44) 20 7888 8888
Fax: (44) 20 7888 1600
Commercial Banking Services
S.I.C.: 6029
N.A.I.C.S.: 522110

Credit Suisse (Investment Banking) (1)
Avenida Ricardo Rivera Navarrete 501
Edificio Capital
Office B 7th Floor, Lima, 27, Peru
Tel.: (51) 1 422 05 00
Fax: (51) 1 422 05 25
Web Site: www.credit-suisse.com
Investment Banking Services
S.I.C.: 6211
N.A.I.C.S.: 523110

Credit Suisse (Lebanon) Finance S.A.L. (1)
Park Avenue BCD Berytus Park Mina'a el Hosn Bloc B 6th Floor
PO Box 11-966
1107-2060 Beirut, Lebanon
Tel.: (961) 1 95 66 00
Fax: (961) 1 95 66 95
Web Site: www.credit-suisse.com
Financial Management Services
S.I.C.: 6211
N.A.I.C.S.: 523999

Credit Suisse Life & Pensions Indonesia (1)
Gedung Asuransi Wahana Tata
Jl HR Rasuna Said Kav C4, Jakarta, 12920, Indonesia (60%)
Tel.: (62) 215221851
Fax: (62) 215206572
Web Site: www.cslife.co.id
Sales Range: $10-24.9 Million
Emp.: 30
S.I.C.: 6399
N.A.I.C.S.: 524128

Credit Suisse Life & Pensions Penzijni Fond A.S. (1)
Starobrnensk 335 8
Brno, 60200, Czech Republic (79%)
Tel.: (420) 531021111
Fax: (420) 531021237
E-Mail: Peter.Zaludava@axa.cz
Web Site: www.axa.cz
Emp.: 10,000
S.I.C.: 6399
N.A.I.C.S.: 524128
Peter Zaludava *(Gen Mgr)*

Credit Suisse Life & Pensions (1)
Rakoczi UT 70 72
Budapest, 1074, Hungary (65%)
Tel.: (36) 014135100
Fax: (36) 14135101
E-Mail: info.axa@axa.hu
Web Site: www.axa.hu
Insurance Provider
S.I.C.: 6399
N.A.I.C.S.: 524128

Credit Suisse Life (Bermuda) Ltd. (1)
5 Park Road
Hamilton, HM 09, Bermuda
Tel.: (441) 3330369
Fax: (441) 2954401
Financial Management Services
S.I.C.: 6211
N.A.I.C.S.: 523999
Tom Coffey *(CEO)*

Credit Suisse Saudi Arabia (1)
Al Jumaiah Center 2nd Floor Office No 1
Hay El Mohamadiah
PO Box 5000
King Fahad Road, Riyadh, 12361-6858, Saudi Arabia
Tel.: (966) 1 203 9700
Fax: (966) 1 203 9791
E-Mail: contact.saudi@credit-suisse.com
Web Site: www.credit-suisse.com
Financial Management Services

Credit Suisse Group AG—(Continued)

S.I.C.: 6211
N.A.I.C.S.: 523999

Credit Suisse Securities (Canada), Inc. **(1)**
1 First Canadian Place 100 King Street West Suite 2900
Toronto, ON, M5X 1C9, Canada
Tel.: (416) 352-4500
Fax: (416) 352-4685
Web Site: www.credit-suisse.com
Securities Brokerage Services
S.I.C.: 6211
N.A.I.C.S.: 523120

Credit Suisse Securities (Hong Kong) Limited **(1)**
Level 88 International Commerce Centre 1 Austin Road West
Central, China (Hong Kong)
Tel.: (852) 3969 5900
Fax: (852) 2101 7990
Investment Banking Services
S.I.C.: 6211
N.A.I.C.S.: 523110
Liping Zhang *(Vice Chm-Global Investment Banking)*
Neil Harvey *(CEO)*
Thomas Wong *(Mng Dir & Head-Res & Sls)*

Credit Suisse Securities (India) Private Limited **(1)**
10th Floor Ceejay House Plot F Shivsagar Estate
Dr Annie Besant Road Worli, Mumbai, 400 018, India
Tel.: (91) 22 6777 3777
Fax: (91) 22 6777 3820
E-Mail: india.info@credit-suisse.com
Web Site: www.credit-suisse.com
Securities Brokerage Services
S.I.C.: 6211
N.A.I.C.S.: 523120

Credit Suisse Securities (Johannesburg) (Proprietary) Limited **(1)**
2nd Floor Building 3 Inanda Greens 54 Wierda Road
Wierda Valley, Sandton, South Africa
Tel.: (27) 11 012 8000
Fax: (27) 11 012 8095
Financial Investment Services
S.I.C.: 6211
N.A.I.C.S.: 523999

Credit Suisse Securities (Thailand) Limited **(1)**
990 Rama IV Road Abdulrahim Place 27th Floor Unit 2701
Bangkok, 10500', Thailand
Tel.: (66) 2614 6000
Fax: (66) 2614 6362
Web Site: www.credit-suisse.com
Emp.: 32
Financial Management Services
S.I.C.: 6211
N.A.I.C.S.: 523999
Pornchai Prasertsintanah *(Gen Mgr)*

Credit Suisse Trust Holdings Ltd. **(1)**
Helvetia Ct S Esplanade
Saint Peter Port, GY1 4EE, Guernsey (100%)
Tel.: (44) 1481719000
Fax: (44) 1481726218
Emp.: 80
International Financial Services Company; Provider of Institutional Asset Management & Corporate Investment Banking Services
S.I.C.: 6211
N.A.I.C.S.: 523110

Credit Suisse (UK) Limited **(1)**
16th Floor 5 Cabot Square
London, E14 4QR, United Kingdom
Tel.: (44) 20 7888 8000
Fax: (44) 20 7888 8641
Web Site: www.credit-suisse.com
Financial Planning Services
S.I.C.: 6282
N.A.I.C.S.: 523930

C.S. Consultaciones y Servicios S.A **(1)**
Av Luis Alberto de Herrera 1248 Torre B Piso 9
11300 Montevideo, Uruguay
Tel.: (598) 2 622 9393
Fax: (598) 2 623 2770
Web Site: www.credit-suisse.com
Financial Management Services
S.I.C.: 6211
N.A.I.C.S.: 523999

CSG Asesoria S.A. **(1)**
Av Victor Andres Belaunde 147 Via Principal 123 Suite 1001 Torre Real 1 San Isidro, Lima, Peru
Tel.: (51) 1 422 05 00
Fax: (51) 1 422 05 25
Web Site: www.credit-suisse.com
Financial Planning Services
S.I.C.: 6282
N.A.I.C.S.: 523930

Limited Liability Partnership "Credit Suisse (Kazakhstan)" **(1)**
77/7 Al-Farabi Avenue Esentai Towers Building Centre 8th Floor
050040 Almaty, Kazakhstan
Tel.: (7) 727 356 2727
Fax: (7) 727 356 2737
Web Site: www.credit-suisse.com
Securities Trading Services
S.I.C.: 6211
N.A.I.C.S.: 523110

LLC Credit Suisse Securities **(1)**
Romanov pereulok 4 Building 2
125009 Moscow, Russia
Tel.: (7) 495 967 8200
Fax: (7) 495 967 8210
E-Mail: moscow.reception@credit-suisse.com
Web Site: www.credit-suisse-securities-moscow.ru/ru/securities_moscow/en/index.jsp
Emp.: 300
Securities Trading Services
S.I.C.: 6211
N.A.I.C.S.: 523110
Nicholas Wilcock *(Pres)*

Oficina de Representacion de Credit Suisse AG **(1)**
Avda Francisco de Miranda Edificio Cavendes Los Palos
Grandes Office 1401 Piso 14, Caracas, 1060, Venezuela
Tel.: (58) 21 2283 6422
Fax: (58) 21 2284 2697
Financial Management Services
S.I.C.: 6211
N.A.I.C.S.: 523999

PT Credit Suisse Securities Indonesia **(1)**
Jalan Jenderal Sudirman Kav 45
Sampoerna Strategic Square
South Tower 23rd floor, Jakarta, 12930, Indonesia
Tel.: (62) 21 2553 7900
Fax: (62) 21 2553 7999
Web Site: www.credit-suisse.com
Financial Planning Services
S.I.C.: 6282
N.A.I.C.S.: 523930

CREDITO EMILIANO S.P.A.

(d/b/a CREDEM)
Via Emilia San Pietro 4
42121 Reggio nell'Emilia, Italy
Tel.: (39) 0522582111
Fax: (39) 0522433969
E-Mail: info@credem.it
Web Site: www.credem.it
Year Founded: 1910
CE—(ITA)
Int. Income: $1,156,035,603
Assets: $41,392,981,518
Liabilities: $36,332,715,026
Net Worth: $5,060,266,492
Earnings: $163,383,307
Emp.: 5,686
Fiscal Year-end: 12/31/12

Business Description:
Bank Holding Company
S.I.C.: 6712
N.A.I.C.S.: 551111

Personnel:
Giorgio Ferrari *(Chm)*
Lucio Zanon di Valgiurata *(Deputy Chm)*
Ignazio Maramotti *(Deputy Chm)*
Ottorino Righetti *(Sec)*

Board of Directors:
Giorgio Ferrari
Romano Alfieri
Enrico Corradi
Guido Corradi
Lucio Zanon di Valgiurata
Giorgia Fontanesi
Ignazio Maramotti
Ugo Medici
Benedetto Renda
Paola Schwizer
Giovanni Viani

Subsidiaries:

Abaxbank SpA **(1)**
Corso Monforte 34
20122 Milan, Italy
Tel.: (39) 0277426I
Fax: (39) 0277426649
E-Mail: info@abaxbank.com
Web Site: www.abaxbank.com
Commercial Banking
S.I.C.: 6029
N.A.I.C.S.: 522110
Gianni Tanturli *(Chm)*

Anteprima Srl **(1)**
Via Che Guevara 4
42100 Modena, Reggio Emilia, Italy
Tel.: (39) 0522285260
Fax: (39) 0522285199
E-Mail: info@agenzia-anteprima.it
Web Site: www.agenzia-anteprima.it
Insurance Agencies & Brokerages
S.I.C.: 6411
N.A.I.C.S.: 524210
Ferdinando Rebecchi *(Pres)*

Banca Euromobiliare SpA **(1)**
Via Santa Margherita 9
20121 Milan, Italy
Tel.: (39) 0263761
Fax: (39) 026376998
E-Mail: info@bancaeuro.it
Web Site: www.bancaeuro.it
Commercial Banking
S.I.C.: 6029
N.A.I.C.S.: 522110
Alberto Milla *(Deputy Chm)*
Matteo Mattei Gentili *(Pres)*

Credem Private Equity Sgr SpA **(1)**
Via Che Guevara 4
42123 Reggio nell'Emilia, Italy
Tel.: (39) 0522582203
Fax: (39) 0522582742
E-Mail: abrale@credem.it
Web Site: www.credempriveq.it
Emp.: 5
Real Estate Investment Trusts
S.I.C.: 6726
N.A.I.C.S.: 525990
Enrico Corradi *(Chm)*
Maurizio Esposito *(Mng Dir)*

Credemassicurazioni SpA **(1)**
Via Mirabello 2
42100 Modena, Reggio Emilia, Italy
Tel.: (39) 0522586050
Fax: (39) 0522442041
E-Mail: assicurazioni@credemassicurazioni.it
Web Site: www.credemassicurazioni.it
Insurance Agencies & Brokerages
S.I.C.: 6411
N.A.I.C.S.: 524210
Giorgio Ferrari *(Chm)*

Credemfactor SpA **(1)**
Via Che Guevara 4-B
42100 Modena, Reggio Emilia, Italy
Tel.: (39) 0522326911
Fax: (39) 0522326000
Web Site: www.credemfactor.it
Business Associations
S.I.C.: 8611
N.A.I.C.S.: 813910
Matteo Mattei Gentili *(Chm)*
Fridmani Lobeco *(Mng Dir)*

Credemleasing S.p.A. **(1)**
Via Mirabello 2
42100 Modena, Reggio Emilia, Italy
Tel.: (39) 0522236511
Fax: (39) 0522 920495
E-Mail: reggioemilia@credemleasing.it
Web Site: www.credemleasing.it
Emp.: 15
Credit Intermediation
S.I.C.: 6099
N.A.I.C.S.: 522390
Franco Terrachini *(Chm)*

Credemtel SpA **(1)**
via P Togliatti 36 1
Montecavolo di Quattro I, 42020 Modena, Reggio Emilia, Italy
Tel.: (39) 0522203040
Fax: (39) 0522203500
E-Mail: amm@credemtel.it
Web Site: www.credemtel.it
Data Processing Hosting & Related Services
S.I.C.: 7374
N.A.I.C.S.: 518210
Tiziano Ferretti *(Dir-Admin)*

Credemvita SpA **(1)**
Via Mirabello 2
42122 Reggio nell'Emilia, Italy
Tel.: (39) 0522 402600
Fax: (39) 0522 430889
E-Mail: vita@credemassicurazioni.it
Web Site: www.credemassicurazioni.it
Emp.: 35
Direct Life Insurance Carriers
S.I.C.: 6311
N.A.I.C.S.: 524113
Rovani Giuseppe *(Chm)*

Credito Emiliano SpA **(1)**
Via Emilia San Pietro 4
42100 Modena, Reggio Emilia, Italy
Tel.: (39) 0522582111
Fax: (39) 0522433969
E-Mail: infocredem@credem.it
Web Site: www.credem.it
Commercial Banking
S.I.C.: 6029
N.A.I.C.S.: 522110
Adolfo Bizzocchi *(Gen Mgr)*

Euromobiliare Alternative Investment Sgr SpA **(1)**
Corso Monforte 34
20121 Milan, Italy
Tel.: (39) 02620841
Fax: (39) 0262084241
E-Mail: alessandro.montmarane@euroaisgr.it
Web Site: www.euroaisgr.it
Emp.: 70
Financial Investment Activities
S.I.C.: 6211
N.A.I.C.S.: 523999
Fulvio Albarelli *(Mng Dir)*

Euromobiliare Asset Management Sgr SpA **(1)**
Corso Monsorpee 34
20122 Milan, Italy
Tel.: (39) 02620841
Fax: (39) 0262084967
E-Mail: amcon@eurosgr.it
Web Site: www.eurosgr.it
Emp.: 16
Open-End Investment Funds
S.I.C.: 6722
N.A.I.C.S.: 525910
Matteo Mattei Gentili *(Chm)*

Euromobiliare Fiduciaria SpA **(1)**
Corso Monforte 34
20122 Milan, Italy
Tel.: (39) 0277426281
Fax: (39) 0277426280
Web Site: www.euromobiliarefiduciaria.it/
Holding Company
S.I.C.: 6719
N.A.I.C.S.: 551112
Emilio Perrone Da Zara *(Chm)*
Sergio Benetti *(Mng Dir)*

Magazzini Generali Delle Tagliate (M.G.T.) SpA **(1)**
Via Togliatti 35-1
Montecavolo di Quattro Castell, Modena, Italy
Tel.: (39) 0522880634
Fax: (39) 0522880845
General Warehousing & Storage
S.I.C.: 4225

N.A.I.C.S.: 493110
Mose Natale Arduini *(Chm)*

Non-U.S. Subsidiary:

Credem International (LUX) S.A. (1)
10 12 Ave Pasteur
2310 Luxembourg, Luxembourg
Tel.: (352) 4759591
Telex: 1533 DIRNAPLU
Fax: (352) 352227614
E-Mail: sso@credem.lu
Emp.: 25
S.I.C.: 6159
N.A.I.C.S.: 522298
Lorenzo Modestini *(Gen Mgr)*

CREDITO VALTELLINESE SOCIETA COOPERATIVA

Piazza Quadrivio 8
23100 Sondrio, Italy
Tel.: (39) 0342522111
Fax: (39) 0342522700
E-Mail: creval@creval.it
Web Site: www.creval.it
Year Founded: 1908
CVAL—(ITA)
Rev.: $1,357,126,478
Assets: $40,245,183,129
Liabilities: $37,570,242,376
Net Worth: $2,674,940,753
Earnings: ($428,251,677)
Emp.: 4,362
Fiscal Year-end: 12/31/12
Business Description:
Bank Holding Company
S.I.C.: 6712
N.A.I.C.S.: 551111
Personnel:
Giovanni De Censi *(Chm)*
Aldo Fumagalli Romario *(Deputy Chm)*
Miro Fiordi *(Mng Dir & Gen Mgr)*
Board of Directors:
Giovanni De Censi
Mario Anolli
Fabio Bresesti
Gabriele Cogliati
Michele Colombo
Paolo De Santis
Miro Fiordi
Isabella Bruno Tolomei Frigerio
Paolo Stefano Giudici
Gian Maria Gros Pietro
Franco Moro
Angelo Maria Palma
Valter Pasqua
Alberto Ribolla
Aldo Fumagalli Romario
Paolo Scarallo

Subsidiaries:

Banca Cattolica S.p.A. (1)
Via Cardinal Salotti 6
01027 Montefiascone, Viterbo, Italy
Tel.: (39) 07618381
Fax: (39) 0761838389
E-Mail: info@bancacattolica.it
Web Site: www.bancacattolica.it
Commercial Banking Services
S.I.C.: 6029
N.A.I.C.S.: 522110

Bancaperta S.p.A. (1)
Via Ragazzi Del 99 12
23100 Sondrio, Italy
Tel.: (39) 0342522111
Fax: (39) 0342522584
Emp.: 100
Commercial Banking Services
S.I.C.: 6029
N.A.I.C.S.: 522110
Norberto Gualteroni *(Pres)*

Bankadati Servizi Informatici S.p.A. (1)
Via Trento 22
23100 Sondrio, Italy
Tel.: (39) 0342522111
Fax: (39) 0342522377
E-Mail: creval@creval.it
Banking Software Development Services
S.I.C.: 7371
N.A.I.C.S.: 541511
Giovanni De Censi *(Pres)*

Cassa di Risparmio di Fano S.p.A. (1)
Piazza Xx Settembre 19
61032 Fano, Pesaro e Urbino, Italy
Tel.: (39) 721886400
Fax: (39) 0721886219
E-Mail: carefano@creval.it
Web Site: www.creval.it
Emp.: 350
Banking Services
S.I.C.: 6029
N.A.I.C.S.: 522110
Francesco Giacobbi *(Pres)*

Credito Artigiano S.p.A. (1)
Piazza San Fedele 4
20121 Milan, Italy
Tel.: (39) 02806371
Fax: (39) 0280637297
E-Mail: creart@creval.it
Web Site: www.creval.it
Sales Range: $1-9.9 Million
Emp.: 70
Banking
S.I.C.: 6211
N.A.I.C.S.: 523110
Angelo Palma *(Chm)*

Credito Piemontese S.p.A. (1)
Corso Re Umberto 21-Bis
10128 Turin, Italy
Tel.: (39) 01119782601
Fax: (39) 0115617673
Banking Services
S.I.C.: 6029
N.A.I.C.S.: 522110

Stelline Servizi Immobiliari S.p.A. (1)
Via Cesura 3
23100 Sondrio, Italy
Tel.: (39) 0342522111
Fax: (39) 0342522332
E-Mail: stelline@creval.it
Web Site: www.creval.it
Emp.: 55
Real Estate Management Services
S.I.C.: 6531
N.A.I.C.S.: 531210
Giovanni Maria Boccardo *(Pres)*
Enzo Rocca *(Gen Dir)*

CREDITWEST FAKTORING A.S.

Buyukdere Cad Enka Binasi No 108
Kat 2-3 Esentepe
34394 Istanbul, Turkey
Tel.: (90) 2123561910
Fax: (90) 2123561911
E-Mail: info@creditwest.com.tr
Web Site: www.creditwest.com.tr
CRDFA—(IST)
Sales Range: $75-99.9 Million
Business Description:
Financial Factoring Services
S.I.C.: 6159
N.A.I.C.S.: 522298
Personnel:
Ali Altinbas *(Chm)*

CREDITWEST FAKTORING HIZMETLERI A.S.

(See Under Creditwest Faktoring A.S.)

CREDO INTERACTIVE INC.

4612 Strathcona Rd
North Vancouver, BC, V7G 1G3, Canada
Tel.: (604) 291-6717
E-Mail: info@charactermotion.com
Web Site: www.charactermotion.com
Rev.: $55,000,000
Emp.: 20
Business Description:
Software & Animation Developers
S.I.C.: 7372
N.A.I.C.S.: 511210
Personnel:
Bart Copeland *(Pres & CEO)*

CREDO RESOURCES LIMITED

Suite 1 245 Churchill Avenue
Subiaco, WA, 6008, Australia
Mailing Address:
PO Box 2025
Subiaco, WA, 6904, Australia
Tel.: (61) 8 9381 4866
Fax: (61) 8 9388 2355
E-Mail: admin@credoresources.com.au
Web Site: www.credoresources.com.au
CRQ—(ASX)
Rev.: $59,626
Assets: $980,463
Liabilities: $114,335
Net Worth: $866,128
Earnings: ($5,206,991)
Emp.: 1
Fiscal Year-end: 06/30/13
Business Description:
Gold Mining Services
S.I.C.: 1041
N.A.I.C.S.: 212221
Personnel:
Lloyd Flint *(Sec)*
Board of Directors:
Riccardo Vittino
William Dix
Robert Kirtlan
Legal Counsel:
Corrs Chambers Westgarth
Level 15 Woodside Plaza 240 Saint Georges Terrace
Perth, WA, 6000, Australia

CREED CORPORATION

9F KN Shinjuku Building 2-6-4
Shinjuku
Shinjuku-ku
Tokyo, Japan
Tel.: (81) 3 5361 8585
Fax: (81) 3 5361 8581
E-Mail: ir@creed.com.jp
Web Site: www.creed.co.jp/english/
Year Founded: 1996
Sales Range: $400-449.9 Million
Emp.: 301
Business Description:
International Real Estate Investments & Management Services
S.I.C.: 6726
N.A.I.C.S.: 525990
Personnel:
Toshihiko Muneyoshi *(Pres & CEO)*
Board of Directors:
Toshihiko Muneyoshi
Kazuhiro Okabe
Takeshi Sugahara

Subsidiaries:

Creed Capital Management and Research, Inc. (1)
Kasumigaseki Building 20th Floor
3-2-5 Kasumigaseki Chiyoda-ku, Tokyo, Japan
Tel.: (81) 335003466
Fax: (81) 335003080
Web Site: www.creed.co.jp/english/
Emp.: 3
Management Consulting Services
S.I.C.: 8748
N.A.I.C.S.: 541618
Toshihiro Hiraoka *(Mng Dir)*

Creed Hotel Management Corporation (1)
Shimbashi 5-chome Building 6th Floor
5-9-1 Shimbashi Minato-ku, 105-0004 Tokyo, Japan
Tel.: (81) 354039600
Fax: (81) 354031201
Web Site: www.creed.co.jp/english/
Management Consulting Services
S.I.C.: 8748
N.A.I.C.S.: 541618
Teruaki Hozumi *(Mng Dir)*

CREGANNA - TACTX MEDICAL

Parkmore West
Galway, Ireland
Tel.: (353) 91 757 801
Fax: (353) 757 850
E-Mail: sales@creganna.com
Web Site: www.creganna.com
Year Founded: 1980
Emp.: 1,000
Business Description:
Medical Device Mfr
S.I.C.: 3841
N.A.I.C.S.: 339112
Personnel:
Ian Quinn *(Founder)*
Scott R. Ward *(Chm)*
Helen Ryan *(CEO)*
Board of Directors:
Scott R. Ward
Ian Quinn

U.S. Plant:

Creganna Tactx Medical Inc. (1)
2495 Xenium Ln N
Minneapolis, MN 55441-3625 (100%)
Tel.: (763) 557-1024
Fax: (763) 557-0920
Web Site: www.tactxmed.com
Sales Range: $25-49.9 Million
Emp.: 150
Custom Design, Development & Manufacturing of Disposable Medical Devices, Primarily Catheters
S.I.C.: 3841
N.A.I.C.S.: 339112
Helen Ryan *(CEO)*

CREIGHTONS PLC

1210 Lincoln Road
Peterborough, Cambs, PE4 6ND, United Kingdom
Tel.: (44) 1733281000
Fax: (44) 1733281028
E-Mail: info@creightons.com
Web Site: www.creightons.com
CRL—(LSE)
Rev.: $27,362,779
Assets: $11,873,102
Liabilities: $5,018,984
Net Worth: $6,854,119
Earnings: $476,946
Emp.: 186
Fiscal Year-end: 03/31/13
Business Description:
Beauty Products Mfr
S.I.C.: 2844
N.A.I.C.S.: 325620
Personnel:
William O. McIlroy *(Chm & CEO)*
Bernard J. M. Johnson *(Mng Dir)*
Nicholas D. J. O'Shea *(Sec)*
Board of Directors:
William O. McIlroy
Mary T. Carney
William T. Glencross
Bernard J. M. Johnson
Nicholas D. J. O'Shea
Legal Counsel:
Coole & Haddock
5 The Steyne
BN11 3DT Worthing, United Kingdom

U.S. Subsidiary:

Potter and Moore International Inc (1)
1140 Bay St Ste 2C
Staten Island, NY 10305-4937
Tel.: (347) 745-2871
Fax: (718) 727-9667
E-Mail: ussales@potterandmoore.com
Web Site: www.potterandmoore.com
Emp.: 1
Toiletries Product Distr

Creightons plc—(Continued)

S.I.C.: 5122
N.A.I.C.S.: 446120
Bernard Johnson *(Pres)*

Subsidiary:

Potter & Moore Innovations Limited **(1)**
1210 Lincoln Rd
Peterborough, Cambridgeshire, PE4 6ND, United Kingdom
Tel.: (44) 1733281000
Fax: (44) 1733281028
E-Mail: info@potterandmoore.com
Web Site: www.potterandmoore.com
Emp.: 200
Cosmetics Mfr & Distr
S.I.C.: 2844
N.A.I.C.S.: 325620
Bernard J Johnson *(Mng Dir)*

CREMONINI S.P.A.

Via Modena 53
Castelvetro, 41014 Modena, Italy
Tel.: (39) 059754611
Fax: (39) 059754699
E-Mail: info@cremonini.com
Web Site: www.cremonini.com
Sales Range: $1-4.9 Billion
Emp.: 1,564
Business Description:
Fresh, Canned & Frozen Beef
S.I.C.: 2033
N.A.I.C.S.: 311421
Personnel:
Paolo Sciume *(Vice Chm)*
Luigi Cremonini *(Pres)*
Vincenzo Cremonini *(CEO)*
Board of Directors:
Luigi Cremonini
Illias Aratri
Paolo Boni
Vincenzo Cremonini
Valentino Fabbian
Giorgio Pedrazzi
Paolo Sciume

Joint Venture:

Montana Alimentari S.p.A. **(1)**
Via Marconi 3
46040 Gazoldo degli Ippoliti, Italy
Tel.: (39) 03766801
Fax: (39) 0376657651
E-Mail: info@montanalimentari.it
Web Site: www.montanafood.it
Meat Processing
S.I.C.: 2013
N.A.I.C.S.: 311613
Giorgio Pedrazzi *(Chm & Mng Dir)*

Non-U.S. Subsidiaries:

Cremonini Rail Iberica s.a. **(1)**
Calle Comercio 12
28045 Madrid, Spain
Tel.: (34) 915064390
Fax: (34) 915398591
Web Site: www.cremonini.it
On-Board Railway Catering Services
S.I.C.: 5812
N.A.I.C.S.: 722511

Frimo S.A.M. **(1)**
1 Rue du Gabian Le Thales
Monte Carlo, Monaco (51%)
Tel.: (377) 93104193
Fax: (377) 93305761
E-Mail: frimo@frimo-mc.com
Emp.: 10
Meat & Meat Product Whslr
S.I.C.: 5147
N.A.I.C.S.: 424470
Mirco Albisecci *(Gen Mgr)*

Subsidiaries:

Cremonini S.p.A. Div. Ristorazione Sede Amministrativa **(1)**
Via Modena 53
41014 Rome, Italy
Tel.: (39) 059754811
Fax: (39) 059754699
E-Mail: info@agape.it
Web Site: www.cremonini.it
Restaurants
S.I.C.: 5812
N.A.I.C.S.: 722511
Valentino Fabbian *(Mng Dir)*

Ges.Car. S.r.l. **(1)**
Viale Europa 10
Ospedaletto Lodigiano, Lodi, 26864, Italy
Tel.: (39) 03779791
Fax: (39) 0377979471
Emp.: 100
Rendering & Meat Byproduct Processing
S.I.C.: 2013
N.A.I.C.S.: 311613
Roberto Canonico *(Mng Dir)*
Gureno Luca *(Mng Dir)*

Inalca S.p.A. **(1)**
Via Spilamberto 30/c
Castelvetro de Modena, 41014 Modena, Italy
Tel.: (39) 059755111
Fax: (39) 059755517
E-Mail: info@inalca.it
Web Site: www.inalca.com
Emp.: 1,000
Meat Processing
S.I.C.: 2013
N.A.I.C.S.: 311613
Paolo Boni *(Mng Dir)*
Luigi P. Scordamaglia *(Mng Dir)*

Marr S.p.A. **(1)**
Via Spagna 20
47921 Rimini, Italy (58.8%)
Tel.: (39) 0541746111
Fax: (39) 0541742422
E-Mail: marr@marr.it
Web Site: www.marr.it
MARR—(ITA)
Rev.: $1,654,141,388
Assets: $1,049,622,211
Liabilities: $739,926,379
Net Worth: $309,695,832
Earnings: $65,830,405
Emp.: 986
Fiscal Year-end: 12/31/12
Food Products Distr to Foodservice Operators
S.I.C.: 5141
N.A.I.C.S.: 424410
Ugo Ravanelli *(Chm)*
Pierpaolo Rossi *(CEO)*
Antonio Tiso *(Chief Acctg Officer)*

Subsidiary:

Sfera S.p.A. **(2)**
Via Della Croseta 51
Arcore, Italy (100%)
Tel.: (39) 0464513114
Grocery & Related Products Whslr
S.I.C.: 5149
N.A.I.C.S.: 424490
Vincenzo Cremonini *(CEO)*

Moto S.p.A. **(1)**
Via V Veneto 9
Introbio, 23815 Lecco, Italy
Tel.: (39) 0341901533
Fax: (39) 0341901457
E-Mail: info@hmmoto.it
Web Site: www.hmmoto.it
Emp.: 35
Miscellaneous Food Mfr
S.I.C.: 2099
N.A.I.C.S.: 311999
Ricci Benedette *(Mng Dir)*

Realfood 3 S.r.l. **(1)**
Via Chiusa Saliceto 5
Cadeo, 29010 Piacenza, Italy
Tel.: (39) 0523502711
Fax: (39) 0523502725
Food Mfr
S.I.C.: 2099
N.A.I.C.S.: 311999

Roadhouse Grill Italia S.r.l. **(1)**
Via Modena 53
Castelvetro Di Modena, Modena, Italy
Tel.: (39) 059754611
Fax: (39) 059754699
Web Site: www.roadhousegrill.it
Drinking Places
S.I.C.: 5813
N.A.I.C.S.: 722410
Vincenzo Cremonini *(CEO)*

Salumi D'Emilia Srl **(1)**
Via Europa 14
43011 Busseto, Parma, Italy
Tel.: (39) 0524930311
Fax: (39) 0524930022
E-Mail: ebis@ebis-salumi.com
Web Site: www.cremonini.it/en/gruppo/page.php?id=3&id_pag=10
Emp.: 125
Mfr. of Prepared Meats
Import Export
S.I.C.: 5147
N.A.I.C.S.: 311612
Fabio Bassi *(Mgr-Export)*

U.S. Subsidiary:

Busseto Foods, Inc. **(2)**
1090 West Church St
Fresno, CA 93706 CA
Tel.: (559) 485-9882
Fax: (559) 237-5745
Toll Free: (800) 628-2633
Web Site: www.busseto.com
Emp.: 50
Mfr. of Salami
S.I.C.: 5147
N.A.I.C.S.: 311612
Mike Grapier *(CEO)*

Tecno-Star Due S.r.l. **(1)**
Via Modena 53
Castelvetro Di Modena, 41014 Modena, Italy
Tel.: (39) 059754901
Fax: (39) 059754900
Food Product Machinery Mfr
S.I.C.: 3556
N.A.I.C.S.: 333241

CREON RESOURCES PLC

205 Temple Chambers 3-7 Temple Avenue
London, EC4Y 0DT, United Kingdom
Tel.: (44) 2072451271
Web Site: www.creoncorporation.com
CRO—(AIM)
Assets: $17,838,081
Liabilities: $132,660
Net Worth: $17,705,420
Earnings: ($1,727,743)
Emp.: 4
Fiscal Year-end: 01/31/13
Business Description:
Real Estate Investment Services
S.I.C.: 6531
N.A.I.C.S.: 531390
Personnel:
Glen Lau *(CEO)*
John Bromley *(Sec)*
Board of Directors:
Ghanim Saad Al Saad Al Kuwari
August Johannes Francisca Maria Berting
Glen Lau
Aamir Ali Quraishi
Legal Counsel:
Ashfords LLP
Tower Wharf,Cheese Lane
Bristol, United Kingdom

CRESCENDAS PTE. LTD.

23 Tai Seng Drive #05-07
Singapore, 534167, Singapore
Tel.: (65) 64884688
Fax: (65) 64884555
Web Site: www.crescendas.com
Year Founded: 1982
Sales Range: $50-74.9 Million
Emp.: 1,600
Business Description:
Holding Company; International Real Estate Development, Manufacturing, Distribution & Technology Services
S.I.C.: 6719
N.A.I.C.S.: 551112
Personnel:
Lawrence Leow *(Chm & CEO)*
Michael Leow *(Deputy CEO)*
Gurdip Singh *(Pres/CEO-Electronics Bus)*

Joint Venture:

Crescendas MEC (S) Pte. Ltd. **(1)**
87 Defu Lane 10
MEC TechnoCentre 06-00, Singapore, 539219, Singapore SG
Tel.: (65) 6282 8222
Fax: (65) 6282 9995
E-Mail: sales@mec.com.sg
Web Site: www.mec.com.sg
Sales Range: $150-199.9 Million
Emp.: 20
Wire & Cable Harness Mfr
S.I.C.: 5065
N.A.I.C.S.: 423690

CRESCENDO CORPORATION BERHAD

Unit No 203 2nd Floor Block C
Damansara Intan No 1 Jalan SS 20/27
47400 Petaling Jaya, Selangor Darul Ehsan, Malaysia
Tel.: (60) 371182688
Fax: (60) 371182693
Web Site: www.crescendo.com.my
CRESNDO—(KLS)
Rev.: $92,662,866
Assets: $257,852,082
Liabilities: $56,300,975
Net Worth: $201,551,106
Earnings: $19,547,915
Fiscal Year-end: 01/31/13
Business Description:
Investment Services; Real Estate & Building
S.I.C.: 6211
N.A.I.C.S.: 523999
Personnel:
Seong Lim Gooi *(Chm & Mng Dir)*
Seong Chneh Gooi *(CEO-Construction Ops)*
Fook Sin Chong *(Co-Sec)*
Yoke Bee Chun *(Co-Sec)*
Chee Jing Kan *(Co-Sec)*
Board of Directors:
Seong Lim Gooi
Kim Guan Gan
Seong Chneh Gooi
Seong Gum Gooi
Seong Heen Gooi
Ah Lai Tan
Jon Tian Yeo

CRESCENDO INDUSTRIES

1030 Avenue Guillibert de la Lauziere
BP 20140
ZI Les Milles, F-13794 Aix-en-Provence, Cedex 03, France
Tel.: (33) 442607000
Fax: (33) 442600026
Web Site: www.crescendo-industries.com
Year Founded: 2004
Business Description:
Holding Company
S.I.C.: 6719
N.A.I.C.S.: 551112
Personnel:
Philippe Vannier *(Pres-Amesys)*

CRESCENT CAPITAL PARTNERS LTD.

Leve 29 farrer Pl.
Sydney, NSW, 2000, Australia
Tel.: (61) 292208100
Fax: (61) 292219650
E-Mail: mail@crescentcap.com.au
Web Site: www.crescentcap.com.au
Emp.: 20
Business Description:
Private Equity Firm
S.I.C.: 6211
N.A.I.C.S.: 523999
Personnel:
David Allen Mortimer *(Chm)*

CRESCENT FIBRES LIMITED
104 Shadman 1
Lahore, 54000, Pakistan
Tel.: (92) 4237598301
Fax: (92) 4237560963
E-Mail: javaidhussain@crescentfibres.com
Web Site: www.crescentfibres.com
Year Founded: 1969
CFL—(KAR)
Sls.: $31,845,175
Assets: $16,381,851
Liabilities: $8,867,627
Net Worth: $7,514,224
Earnings: $2,467,677
Fiscal Year-end: 06/30/13
Business Description:
Paperboard Mill
S.I.C.: 2631
N.A.I.C.S.: 322130
Personnel:
Imran Maqbool *(CEO)*
Kamran Rasheed *(CFO)*
Javaid Hussain *(Sec)*
Board of Directors:
Khawar Maqbool
Jahanzeb Saeed Khan
Humayun Maqbool
Imran Maqbool
Nadeem Maqbool
Naila Humayun Maqbool
Riaz Masood

CRESCENT JUTE PRODUCTS LIMITED
Ste 306 3rd Fl Siddiq Trade Ctr 72-Main Blvd
Gulberg
54000 Lahore, Pakistan
Tel.: (92) 425787592
Fax: (92) 425787594
E-Mail: info@cresjute.com
Web Site: www.cresjute.com
CJPL—(KAR)
Sales Range: $1-9.9 Million
Emp.: 3,000
Business Description:
Jute & Jute Products Mfr
S.I.C.: 2299
N.A.I.C.S.: 313210
Personnel:
Mazhar Karim *(Chm)*
Humayun Mazhar *(CEO)*
Saif Ullah *(CFO)*
Board of Directors:
Mazhar Karim
Khalid Bashir
A. Rashid M. Hanif
Syed Raza Abbas Jaffery
Khurram Mazhar Karim
Humayun Mazhar

CRESCENT POINT ENERGY CORP.
Suite 2800 111 - 5 Avenue SW
Calgary, AB, T2P 3Y6, Canada
Tel.: (403) 693-0020
Fax: (403) 693-0070
Toll Free: (888) 693-0020
E-Mail: info@crescentpointenergy.com
Web Site: www.crescentpointenergy.com
Year Founded: 2003
CPG—(NYSE TSX)
Sls.: $3,171,511,009
Assets: $11,454,834,785
Liabilities: $3,810,294,132
Net Worth: $7,644,540,653
Earnings: $130,294,231
Emp.: 781
Fiscal Year-end: 12/31/13
Business Description:
Petroleum & Natural Gas Services
S.I.C.: 1311
N.A.I.C.S.: 211111
Personnel:
Peter Bannister *(Chm)*
Scott Saxberg *(Pres & CEO)*
Gregory T. Tisdale *(CFO)*
C. Neil Smith *(COO)*
Kenneth R. Lamont *(Treas & VP-Fin)*
Mark G. Eade *(Sec)*
Board of Directors:
Peter Bannister
Kenney F. Cugnet
D. Hugh Gillard
Gerald A. Romanzin
Scott Saxberg
Gregory G. Turnbull
Legal Counsel:
Norton Rose Fulbright Canada LLP
Calgary, AB, Canada
Transfer Agent:
Olympia Trust Company
125 9th Avenue SE Suite 2300
Calgary, AB, T2G 0P6, Canada
Tel.: (403) 261-0900
Subsidiaries:

Crescent Point Resources Inc. (1)
111 5th Avenue Southwest Suite 2800
Calgary, AB, T2P 3Y6, Canada AB
Tel.: (403) 693-0020
Fax: (403) 693-0070
Emp.: 500
Petroleum & Natural Gas Exploration, Drilling & Extraction
S.I.C.: 1311
N.A.I.C.S.: 211111
Scott Saxberg *(Pres & CEO)*
Gregory T. Tisdale *(CFO)*
Ken Lamont *(Treas & Controller)*

U.S. Subsidiaries:

Crescent Point Energy U.S. Corp. (1)
Ste 1800 555 17 St
Denver, CO 80202
Tel.: (720) 880-3610
Fax: (303) 292-1562
Oil & Gas Exploration Services
S.I.C.: 1311
N.A.I.C.S.: 211111

CRESCENT STEEL AND ALLIED PRODUCTS LIMITED
10th Floor BOP Tower 10-B Block
E-2 Main Boulevard
Gulberg III, Lahore, Punjab, Pakistan
Tel.: (92) 42 3578 3801
Fax: (92) 42 3578 3811
E-Mail: mail@crescent.com.pk
Web Site: www.crescent.com.pk
Year Founded: 1987
CSAP—(KAR)
Sls.: $50,666,887
Assets: $58,682,634
Liabilities: $9,230,963
Net Worth: $49,451,672
Earnings: $9,020,755
Emp.: 852
Fiscal Year-end: 06/30/13
Business Description:
Mfr. of Cotton Yarn & Coating of Steel Pipes
S.I.C.: 3317
N.A.I.C.S.: 331210
Personnel:
Ahsan M. Saleem *(CEO & Mng Dir)*
Muhammad Saad Thaniana *(CFO & Sec)*
Board of Directors:
Mazhar Karim
Zahid Bashir
Mahmood Ehtishamullah
Zahid Hussain
Ahsan M. Saleem
Nasir Shafi
Ahmad Waqar
Legal Counsel:
Hassan & Hassan
Lahore, Pakistan
Subsidiary:

Rousch (Pakistan) Power Limited (1)
39-C 4 Block-6 P E C H S
Karachi, 75400, Pakistan
Tel.: (92) 214530642
Fax: (92) 214535484
E-Mail: rousch@cyber.net.pk
Web Site: www.rouschpak.com
Power Generation Services
S.I.C.: 4931
N.A.I.C.S.: 221113

CRESCENT SUGAR MILLS AND DISTILLERY LIMITED
New Lahore Road
Nishatabad, Faisalabad, Pakistan
Tel.: (92) 41 8752111
Fax: (92) 41 8750366
E-Mail: info@crescentsugar.com
Web Site: www.crescentsugar.com
Year Founded: 1959
CSMD—(ISL)
Sales Range: $25-49.9 Million
Business Description:
Sugar Mfr
S.I.C.: 2063
N.A.I.C.S.: 311313
Personnel:
Muhammad Arshad *(Chm & CEO)*
Sami Ullah Chaudhry *(Sec)*
Board of Directors:
Muhammad Arshad
Muhammad Anwar
Shahid Arshad
Khalid Bashir
Naveed Gulzar
Abid Mahmood
Salman Rafi

THE CRESCENT TEXTILE MILLS LIMITED
45-A Off Zafar Ali Road Gulberg V
Lahore, Pakistan
Tel.: (92) 42111245245
Fax: (92) 42111222245
E-Mail: mailho@crescentbahuman.com
Web Site: www.crescenttextile.com
CRTM—(KAR)
Sls.: $134,344,587
Assets: $127,062,748
Liabilities: $75,232,066
Net Worth: $51,830,682
Earnings: $1,133,871
Emp.: 6,052
Fiscal Year-end: 06/30/13
Business Description:
Textile Mill Mfr
S.I.C.: 2299
N.A.I.C.S.: 313210
Personnel:
Muhammad Anwar *(Chm & CEO)*
Sadiq Saleem *(CFO & VP-Fin)*
Naseer Ahmad Chaudhary *(Sec)*
Board of Directors:
Muhammad Anwar
Zeshan Afzal
Muhammad Arshad
Muhammad Asif
Khalid Bashir
Khurram Mazhar Karim
Ahsan Mehanti
Nasir Shafi

CRESCO, LTD.
Shinagawa Intercity A-tower 25th-27th Floor 2-15-1 Kounan Minato-ku
Tokyo, 108-6026, Japan
Tel.: (81) 357698011
Fax: (81) 357698019
E-Mail: ir@cresco.co.jp
Web Site: www.cresco.co.jp
Year Founded: 1988
46740—(TKS)
Sls.: $209,341,000
Assets: $156,750,000
Liabilities: $62,557,000
Net Worth: $94,193,000
Earnings: $8,404,000
Emp.: 1,610
Fiscal Year-end: 03/31/13
Business Description:
Software Developer
S.I.C.: 3652
N.A.I.C.S.: 334614
Personnel:
Toshio Iwasaki *(Chm & Pres)*
Shuuichi Kumazawa *(Sr Mng Dir)*
Hiroyuki Nemoto *(Co-Mng Dir)*
Kurao Niwa *(Co-Mng Dir)*
Kohji Mizuya *(Exec VP)*
Board of Directors:
Toshio Iwasaki
Shuuichi Kumazawa
Kohji Mizuya
Hiroyuki Nemoto
Kurao Niwa
Chihiro Sugawara
Kazuo Sugiyama
Yoshie Taniguchi
Hiroshi Tominaga
Takashi Yamamoto

Subsidiaries:

CRESCO Communications Inc. (1)
TOC Building 10th Floor 7-22-17 Nishi-Gotanda
Shinagawa-ku, Tokyo, 141-0031, Japan
Tel.: (81) 357193418
Fax: (81) 357193428
E-Mail: info@cresco-com.jp
Web Site: www.cresco-com.jp
Website Designing & Hosting Services
S.I.C.: 7379
N.A.I.C.S.: 518210
Shoji Inagaki *(Pres)*

Cresco e-Solution Co. Ltd. (1)
The Tokyo Minato-ku lawn 5
Chome 31-19 Tamati Building 2n, Tokyo, Japan (100%)
Tel.: (81) 354444621
Fax: (81) 354444622
Web Site: www.cresco-es.co.jp
Emp.: 90
Computer Systems Design Services
S.I.C.: 7373
N.A.I.C.S.: 541512

Cresco ID Systems Inc. (1)
Senryudou Bldg 1st Fl 3-6 Hayabusa-cho
Chiyoda-ku, Tokyo, Japan
Tel.: (81) 332217735
Fax: (81) 332217736
E-Mail: ohsaka@cresco-id.com
Web Site: www.cresco-ids.jp
Emp.: 8
Security Locker Installation Services
S.I.C.: 7382
N.A.I.C.S.: 561621
Yasuhiro Osaka *(Gen Mgr)*

Infinide Co., Ltd. (1)
14th Okabe Builing 6th Floor 1-7-22 Hakata Ekimae
Hakata-ku, Fukuoka, Japan
Tel.: (81) 924153540
Fax: (81) 92 415 3541
E-Mail: info@infinide.com
Web Site: www.infinide.com
Business Management Software Development Services
S.I.C.: 7371
N.A.I.C.S.: 541511

IOS Co., Ltd. (1)
Shinagawa Tokyu Building 9th Floor 1-6-31 Kounan
Minato-ku, Tokyo, Japan
Tel.: (81) 364339981
Fax: (81) 364339982
Web Site: www.ios-net.co.jp
Emp.: 200
Financial & Business Software Development Services
S.I.C.: 7371
N.A.I.C.S.: 541511

Cresco, Ltd.—(Continued)

Wireless Technologies, Inc. (1)
Omuri Mitsubishi Bldg 7 Fl
Otaku, Tokyo, 143-0023, Japan
Tel.: (81) 357466800
Fax: (81) 357466801
E-Mail: info@wireless-t.jp
Web Site: www.wireless-t.jp
Emp.: 5
Wireless Devices Retailer
S.I.C.: 4812
N.A.I.C.S.: 517210

CRESO EXPLORATION INC.

600 Maisonneuve Blvd West Suite 2750
Montreal, QC, H3A 3J2, Canada
Tel.: (514) 866-6001
Fax: (514) 866-6193
Web Site: www.creso.ca
Year Founded: 2004
CXT—(CNSX DEU OTC)
Int. Income: $114
Assets: $13,516,359
Liabilities: $511,415
Net Worth: $13,004,944
Earnings: ($2,369,702)
Fiscal Year-end: 12/31/12

Business Description:
Metal Mining Services
S.I.C.: 1099
N.A.I.C.S.: 212299

Personnel:
Pierre R. Gauthier *(Chm, Interim Pres & Interim CEO)*
Vatche Tchakmakian *(CFO)*
Luce Saint-Pierre *(Sec)*

Board of Directors:
Pierre R. Gauthier
Jacques Bouchard, Jr.
Rejean Gosselin
Jean-Guy Lambert
Andre Thibault

Transfer Agent:
Computershare Investor Services Inc
1500 University Ste 700
Montreal, QC, Canada

CREST ANIMATION STUDIOS LTD.

501 Raheja Plaza 1 L B S Marg Ghatkopar W
Mumbai, 400 086, India
Tel.: (91) 2225197600
Fax: (91) 2225197616
Web Site: www.crestindia.com
CRESTANI—(NSE)
Rev.: $4,490,036
Assets: $38,036,942
Liabilities: $19,987,010
Net Worth: $18,049,932
Earnings: ($2,247,252)
Fiscal Year-end: 03/31/13

Business Description:
Motion Picture Production & Distribution Services
S.I.C.: 7819
N.A.I.C.S.: 512191

Personnel:
Seemha Ramanna *(CEO)*
Vijay Paranjpe *(CFO)*
Noah Fogelson *(CEO-Crest Animation Holdings Inc)*

Board of Directors:
Srinivas Chada
Bharat Merchant
K. Nagesh
Prahalad Rao

Chaturvedi & Shah
Mumbai, India

Transfer Agent:
Sharepro Services
13AB Samhita Warehousing Complex Second Floor Sakinaka Telephone
Mumbai, India

CREST BUILDER HOLDINGS BERHAD

Penthouse The Crest 3 Two Square No 2 Jalan 19/1
46300 Petaling Jaya, Selangor Darul Ehsan, Malaysia
Tel.: (60) 378416000
Fax: (60) 378416088
E-Mail: corporate@crestbuilder.com.my
Web Site: www.crestbuilder.com.my
CRESBLD—(KLS)
Rev.: $185,510,033
Assets: $302,065,111
Liabilities: $198,717,326
Net Worth: $103,347,785
Earnings: $12,977,293
Fiscal Year-end: 12/31/12

Business Description:
General Construction, Mechanical & Electrical Engineering Services
S.I.C.: 8711
N.A.I.C.S.: 541330

Personnel:
Soon Chow Yong *(Mng Dir)*
Han Twee Chiam *(Co-Sec)*
Chiang Pooh Heng *(Co-Sec)*

Board of Directors:
Sulaiman Shah Abdul Jalil Shah
Mohd Khasan Ahmad
Yong Kan Kam
Choon Keat Keong
Hua Lan Koh
Shang Ming Yong
Soon Chow Yong

CREST INVESTMENTS CO., LTD.

1-3 Kamiyama-cho
Kita-ku, Osaka, 530-0026, Japan
Tel.: (81) 677327890
Fax: (81) 677327891
E-Mail: info@crest-inv.jp
Web Site: www.crest-inv.jp
Year Founded: 2000
2318—(TKS)
Sales Range: $150-199.9 Million
Emp.: 191

Business Description:
Consulting & Back Office Services to Small & Medium Size Enterprises
S.I.C.: 7389
N.A.I.C.S.: 561499

Personnel:
Akihiro Kurosawa *(Pres)*
Shinji Suzuki *(Mng Dir & Dir-Admin, Investment Mgmt & Bus Plng)*
Masufumi Nakayama *(Mng Exec Officer & Pres-Subsidiaries)*

Board of Directors:
Takahide Kawabata
Yasuhiro Kawase
Akihiro Kurosawa
Tomisaku Miyashiro
Masufumi Nakayama
Shinji Suzuki

Subsidiaries:

Club Nets Corporation (1)
Aqua Dojima NBF Tower 1 4 16
Kita-Ku, Osaka, Japan
Tel.: (81) 335193411
Fax: (81) 335951231
E-Mail: info@clubnets.jp
Web Site: www.clubnets.jp
Emp.: 40
Development & Operation of Point Card System Promotion Programs for Increasing Customers
S.I.C.: 7373
N.A.I.C.S.: 541512
Hitoshi Tomiyasu *(Office Mgr)*

Cube Planning Corporation (1)
Aqua Dojima Building 1 4 16 Dojimahama Kita-ku
Osaka, 530-0004, Japan
Tel.: (81) 677327875
Fax: (81) 6 4797 1402
Web Site: www.cubeplanning.com
Interior Design Services for Stores & Bakeries
S.I.C.: 7389
N.A.I.C.S.: 541410

Yusei Nishi-Kyushu Seika Co.,Ltd. (1)
484 Tasakimachi
860-0058 Kumamoto, Japan
Tel.: (81) 963232611
Fax: (81) 963232570
Web Site: www.b-b-net.com
Nondurable Goods Whslr
S.I.C.: 5199
N.A.I.C.S.: 424990

CREST MINERALS LIMITED

100 King William St
Adelaide, SA, 5000, Australia
Tel.: (61) 8 7324 2987
Fax: (61) 8 8213 2002
E-Mail: admin@crestminerals.com.au
Web Site: www.crestminerals.com.au
CTT—(ASX)

Business Description:
Gold Mining
S.I.C.: 1041
N.A.I.C.S.: 212221

Personnel:
Jonathon Trewartha *(Chm)*
Stephen Jones *(CEO)*
Jaroslaw Kopias *(CFO & Sec)*

Board of Directors:
Jonathon Trewartha
Stephen Jones
Jaroslaw Kopias
Andrew Kuzemko

Legal Counsel:
Steinepreis Paganin
Level 4 The Read Building 16 Milligan Street
Perth, WA, 6000, Australia
Tel.: (61) 8 9321 4000
Fax: (61) 8 9321 4333

CREST NICHOLSON PLC

Pyrcroft Road Crest House
Chertsey, Surrey, KT16 9GN, United Kingdom
Tel.: (44) 1932580555
Fax: (44) 8703363990
E-Mail: info@crestnicholson.com
Web Site: www.crestnicholson.com
Sales Range: $1-4.9 Billion
Emp.: 790

Business Description:
Residential Housing & Mixed-Use Real Estate Developer
S.I.C.: 1531
N.A.I.C.S.: 236117

Personnel:
William Rucker *(Chm)*
Stephen Stone *(CEO)*

Board of Directors:
William Rucker
Andrew Coppel
Malcolm McCaig
Stephen Stone
Chris Tinker

Subsidiaries:

Crest Nicholson (Chiltern) Ltd. (1)
Crest House Progression Centre Mark Rd
Hemel Hempstead, Herts, HP2 7DW, United Kingdom
Tel.: (44) 01442219921
Fax: (44) 01442219829
E-Mail: chilternenquiries@crestnicholson.com
Web Site: www.crestnicholson.com
Emp.: 75
Residential Development Services
S.I.C.: 1531
N.A.I.C.S.: 236117
Greg Ketteridge *(Mng Dir)*

Crest Nicholson (Eastern) Ltd. (1)
1 Myrtle Rd
Brentwood, Essex, CM14 5EG, United Kingdom UK
Tel.: (44) 1277693230
Fax: (44) 1277693277
E-Mail: easternenquiries@crestnicholson.com
Web Site: www.crestnicholson.com
Emp.: 50
Residential Housing & Mixed-Use Real Estate Developer
S.I.C.: 1531
N.A.I.C.S.: 236117
James Moody *(Mng Dir)*

Crest Nicholson (South) Ltd. (1)
Crest House Pyrcroft Rd
Chertsey, Surrey, KT16 9GN, United Kingdom UK
Tel.: (44) 1932580444
Fax: (44) 8703363991
E-Mail: southenquiries@crestnicholson.com
Web Site: www.crestnicholson.com
Emp.: 60
Residential Housing & Mixed-Use Real Estate Developer
S.I.C.: 1531
N.A.I.C.S.: 236117
Dean Cooke *(Mgr-IT)*

Crest Nicholson (South West) Ltd. (1)
Crest House Lime Kiln Close
Bristol, Avon, BS34 8ST, United Kingdom UK
Tel.: (44) 1179236600
Fax: (44) 1179695792
E-Mail: southwestenquiries@crestnicholson.com
Emp.: 41
Residential Housing & Mixed-Use Real Estate Developer
S.I.C.: 1531
N.A.I.C.S.: 236117
Tim Beale *(Mng Dir)*

Crest Partnership Homes Ltd. (1)
Crest House
Pyrcroft Road, Chertsey, Surrey, KT16 9GN, United Kingdom UK
Tel.: (44) 1932580555
Fax: (44) 8703363970
E-Mail: info@crestnicholson.com
Web Site: www.crestnicholson.com
Emp.: 80
Residential Housing & Mixed-Use Real Estate Developer
S.I.C.: 1531
N.A.I.C.S.: 236117
Steven Stone *(CEO)*
Colin Smith *(Mng Dir)*

CREST PETROLEUM CORP.

Suite 800 1199 West Hastings Street
Vancouver, BC, V6E 3T5, Canada
Tel.: (604) 306-0068
Fax: (604) 913-2433
E-Mail: adam.cegielski@me.com
Year Founded: 2012
CTP.P—(TSXV)

Business Description:
Investment Services
S.I.C.: 6211
N.A.I.C.S.: 523999

Personnel:
Adam Cegielski *(CEO)*
Jim Greig *(CFO & Sec)*

Board of Directors:
Adam Cegielski
Jim Greig
Jesse Meidl
Toby Robert Pierce
David Matthew Schmidt

Transfer Agent:
Equity Financial Trust Company
1185 West Georgia Street Suite 1620
Vancouver, BC, Canada

CRESTLINE COACH LTD.

126 Wheeler Street
Saskatoon, SK, S7P 0A9, Canada
Tel.: (306) 934-8844
Fax: (306) 242-5838
Toll Free: (888) 887-6886
Web Site: www.crestlinecoach.com
Year Founded: 1975

Rev.: $20,318,069
Emp.: 140
Business Description:
Ambulance & Emergency Vehicle Mfr
S.I.C.: 3711
N.A.I.C.S.: 336112
Personnel:
Keith Brown *(Chm)*
Steven Hoffrogge *(CEO)*
Board of Directors:
Keith Brown
Jim Doyle

CRESTON PLC

Creston House 10 Great Pulteney Street
London, W1F 9NB, United Kingdom
Tel.: (44) 20 7930 9757
Fax: (44) 20 7930 8727
E-Mail: info@creston.com
Web Site: www.creston.com
CRE—(LSE)
Sls.: $169,123,008
Assets: $235,402,650
Liabilities: $59,141,252
Net Worth: $176,261,398
Earnings: $15,467,566
Emp.: 817
Fiscal Year-end: 03/31/13
Business Description:
Advertising
S.I.C.: 7311
N.A.I.C.S.: 541810
Personnel:
Barrie Brien *(CEO)*
Paul Tullo *(Creative Partner-TMW)*
Tim Bonnet *(Chm-Creston Comm)*
Martin Bostock *(Chm-Nelson Bostock Grp)*
Catherine Warne *(Head-Creston Health)*
Richard Marshall *(CEO-TMW)*
Board of Directors:
David Grigson
Barrie Brien
Andrew J. H. Dougal
Richard Huntingford
David Marshall
Legal Counsel:
Olswang
90 High Holborn
London, WC1V 6XX, United Kingdom
Subsidiaries:

Nelson Bostock Communications Limited (1)
Compass House 22 Redan Pl
London, W2 4SA, United Kingdom
Tel.: (44) 20 7229 4400
Fax: (44) 20 7727 2025
E-Mail: info@nelsonbostock.com
Web Site: www.nelsonbostock.com
Sales Range: $10-24.9 Million
Emp.: 80
Public Relations Services
S.I.C.: 8743
N.A.I.C.S.: 541820
Lee Nugent *(Mng Dir)*
Martin Bostock *(Chm-Nelson Bostock Grp)*

Red Door Communications, Ltd. (1)
South Wing Spencer House
23 Sheen Road, Richmond, Surrey, TW9 1BN, United Kingdom
Tel.: (44) 20 8392 8040
Fax: (44) 20 8392 8050
E-Mail: info@rdcomms.com
Web Site: www.rdcomms.com
Emp.: 45
Healthcare Communications Services
S.I.C.: 7319
N.A.I.C.S.: 541890
Catherine Warne *(Founder & CEO)*
Catherine Devaney *(Mng Dir)*
Nicky Walsby *(Deputy Mng Dir)*

Tullo Marshall Warren Ltd. (1)
81 Kings Rd
London, SW3 4NX, United Kingdom
Tel.: (44) 2073494000
Fax: (44) 2073494001
E-Mail: info@tmw.co.uk
Web Site: www.tmw.co.uk
Emp.: 300
Advertising Services
S.I.C.: 7311
N.A.I.C.S.: 541810
Richard Marshall *(CEO)*
Paul Tullo *(Creative Partner)*
Chris Pearce *(Mng Dir)*
Chris Freeland *(COO)*

U.S. Subsidiary:

Cooney/Waters Group, Inc. (1)
90 5th Ave 8th Fl
New York, NY 10011
Tel.: (212) 886-2200
Fax: (212) 886-2288
E-Mail: business@cooneywaters.com
Web Site: www.cooneywaters.com
Emp.: 12
Corporate Identity, Crisis Communications, Strategic Planning/Research
S.I.C.: 7311
N.A.I.C.S.: 541810
Lenore Cooney *(Founder & Chm)*
Timothy Bird *(Pres & COO)*
Lisa D. Weiss *(Exec VP)*

Subsidiary:

The Corkery Group, Inc. (2)
260 5th Ave Fl 10
New York, NY 10001 NY
Tel.: (212) 584-5021
Web Site: www.corkerygroup.com
Emp.: 24
Public Relations Services
S.I.C.: 8743
N.A.I.C.S.: 541820
David Corkery *(Pres)*

CRESTWELL RESOURCES INC.

Suite 804 750 West Pender St
Vancouver, BC, V6C 2T7, Canada
Tel.: (604) 682-2928
Fax: (604) 685-6905
E-Mail: info@crestwellresources.com
Web Site: www.crestwellresources.com
Year Founded: 2011
CER—(CNSX)
Business Description:
Gold Mining
S.I.C.: 1041
N.A.I.C.S.: 212221
Personnel:
Nelson W. Baker *(Pres & CEO)*
John Morita *(CFO)*
Board of Directors:
Nelson W. Baker
Marshall Bertram
John Morita
Jeff Yenyou Zheng

CRESUD SOCIEDAD ANONIMA COMERCIAL INMOBILIARIA FINANCIERA Y AGROPECUARIA

(d/b/a Cresud Inc.)
Moreno 877 23rd Floor
C1091AAQ Buenos Aires, Argentina
Tel.: (54) 1148147800
Fax: (54) 11 4344 4611
E-Mail: info@cresud.com.ar
Web Site: www.cresud.com.ar
Year Founded: 1972
CRES—(BUE NASDAQ)
Rev.: $710,367,887
Assets: $2,498,527,157
Liabilities: $1,548,484,790
Net Worth: $950,042,367
Earnings: $31,056,227
Emp.: 2,408
Fiscal Year-end: 06/30/13
Business Description:
Real Estate Investment Trust; Beef, Dairy Cattle & Grains Farming
S.I.C.: 6726
N.A.I.C.S.: 525990
Personnel:
Eduardo Sergio Elsztain *(Chm)*
Alejandro Gustavo Elsztain *(Second Vice Chm & CEO)*
Saul Zang *(First Vice Chm)*
David Alberto Perednik *(Chief Admin Officer)*
Carlos Blousson *(CEO-Argentina, Bolivia & Paraguay Ops)*
Board of Directors:
Eduardo Sergio Elsztain
Alejandro Gustavo Casaretto
Alejandro Gustavo Elsztain
Fernando Adrian Elsztain
Jorge Oscar Fernandez
Pedro Damaso Labaqui Palacio
Daniel Elias Mellicovsky
David Alberto Perednik
Gabriel A. G. Reznik
Saul Zang
Transfer Agent:
The Bank of New York Mellon
London, United Kingdom

CRESVAL CAPITAL CORP.

9th Floor - 570 Granville Street
Vancouver, BC, V6C 1T1, Canada
Tel.: (604) 682-3701
Fax: (604) 682-3600
E-Mail: info@cresval.com
Web Site: www.cresval.com
Year Founded: 2004
CRV—(TSXV)
Int. Income: $139
Assets: $1,490,937
Liabilities: $329,877
Net Worth: $1,161,059
Earnings: ($183,612)
Fiscal Year-end: 12/31/12
Business Description:
Metal Mining Services
S.I.C.: 1099
N.A.I.C.S.: 212299
Personnel:
Lou Wolfin *(Founder)*
Lee Ann Wolfin *(Pres)*
Pamela Lynch *(CFO)*
Board of Directors:
Ernest A. Calvert
Dan Gosselin
David Wolfin
Lee Ann Wolfin
Lou Wolfin

CRETA FARM S.A.

15th km Heraklion Hwy
PO Box 115
741 00 Athens, Greece
Tel.: (30) 2831086700
Fax: (30) 2831058035
E-Mail: info@cretafarm.gr
Web Site: www.cretafarm.gr
CRETA—(ATH)
Sales Range: $100-124.9 Million
Emp.: 854
Business Description:
Meat & Meat Products Producer
S.I.C.: 5147
N.A.I.C.S.: 311612
Personnel:
Emmanuel S. Domazakis *(Chm)*
Konstantinos S. Domazakis *(Vice Chm)*
Board of Directors:
Eleni Domazaki
Konstantinos S. Domazakis
Konstantinos Genigiorgis
Emmanuel Kotzambasakis
Emmanuel Tetoros
Vasilios Voumvourakis

Subsidiaries:

Creta Farm S.A. (1)
15th Kilometre Rethymno-Irakleio National Road
Post Box 115
74100 Rethymno, Greece (80%)
Tel.: (30) 2831086700
Fax: (30) 2831058035
E-Mail: info@cretafarm.gr
Emp.: 100
Meat & Meat Product Whslr
S.I.C.: 5147
N.A.I.C.S.: 424470
Ioannis Morakis *(Mng Dir)*

Eurocreta S.A. (1)
15th Klm Rethymno-Iraklio
Rethymno, Greece (100%)
Tel.: (30) 2831086700
Fax: (30) 2831058035
E-Mail: creatafarm@alternate.gr
Web Site: www.creatafarm.gr
Emp.: 2,000
Hotels & Motels
S.I.C.: 7011
N.A.I.C.S.: 721110
Domazakis Manos *(Mgr)*

CRETAN GROUP PLC

Roman House 296 Golders Green Road
London, NW11 9PT, United Kingdom
Tel.: (44) 2084559570
E-Mail: info@cretangroup.com
Web Site: www.cretangroup.com
CGRP—(ISDX)
Business Description:
Real Estate Investment Services
S.I.C.: 6531
N.A.I.C.S.: 531390
Personnel:
Georgios Vlamakis *(Chm & CEO)*
Stavros Stavrinides *(Sec)*
Board of Directors:
Georgios Vlamakis
Georgios Athanasiades
Nikolaos Dialynas
Paraschos Koufos
Stavros Stavrinides

CREW BOS PRODUCTS LTD

304A Jaina Tower 1 District Centre
Janakpuri, New Delhi, New Delhi, 110058, India
Tel.: (91) 1145530149
Fax: (91) 1145530148
E-Mail: communication@crewbos.com
Web Site: www.crewbos.com
532542—(BOM)
Rev.: $54,992,458
Assets: $86,705,944
Liabilities: $98,115,200
Net Worth: ($11,409,256)
Earnings: ($38,983,075)
Emp.: 4,000
Fiscal Year-end: 03/31/13
Business Description:
Home Decoration Products & Fashion Accessories Mfr
S.I.C.: 7389
N.A.I.C.S.: 541490
Personnel:
Tarun Oberoi *(Mng Dir)*
Rakesh Diwan *(CFO)*
Ashish Goel *(Compliance Officer & Sec)*
Board of Directors:
Prasanta Bandyopadhyay
Robin Bartholomew
Tarun Oberoi
Mahavir Singh
Transfer Agent:
Skyline Financial Services Pvt Ltd.
D 153A 1st Floor Okhla Industrial Area Phase 1
New Delhi, India

CREW ENERGY INC.
Suite 800 250 5th Street SW
Calgary, AB, T2P 0R4, Canada
Tel.: (403) 266-2088
Fax: (403) 266-6259
E-Mail: investor@crewenergy.com
Web Site: www.crewenergy.com
Year Founded: 2003
CR—(TSX)
Sls.: $415,264,777
Assets: $1,822,835,864
Liabilities: $646,350,571
Net Worth: $1,176,485,293
Earnings: $21,413,179
Emp.: 137
Fiscal Year-end: 12/31/12

Business Description:
Petroleum & Natural Gas Exploration, Drilling & Extraction
S.I.C.: 1311
N.A.I.C.S.: 211111

Personnel:
John A. Brussa *(Chm)*
Dale O. Shwed *(Pres & CEO)*
John G. Leach *(CFO & Sr VP)*
Rob Morgan *(COO & Sr VP)*
Rosanna Dardano *(Officer Mgr)*
Michael D. Sandrelli *(Sec)*
Ken Truscott *(Sr VP-Land & Bus Dev)*

Board of Directors:
John A. Brussa
Jeffery E. Errico
Dennis L. Nerland
Dale O. Shwed
David G. Smith

Legal Counsel:
Burnet, Duckworth & Palmer LLP
Suite 1400 350 7th Avenue Southwest
Calgary, AB, T2P 3N9, Canada
Tel.: (403) 263-3050

Transfer Agent:
Valiant Trust Company
Calgary, AB, Canada

Subsidiaries:

Crew Resources Inc. **(1)**
425 1 St SW
Calgary, AB, Canada
Tel.: (403) 266-2088
Fax: (403) 266-6259
Oil & Gas Exploration Services
S.I.C.: 1389
N.A.I.C.S.: 213112
Dale O. Shwed *(Pres & CEO)*

CRH MEDICAL CORPORATION
999 Canada Place Suite 522 World Trade Center
Vancouver, BC, V6C 3E1, Canada
Tel.: (604) 633-1440
Fax: (604) 633-1443
Web Site: www.crhsystem.com
Year Founded: 1995
CRH—(TSX)
Rev.: $6,848,643
Assets: $5,888,349
Liabilities: $335,521
Net Worth: $5,552,828
Earnings: $1,331,831
Emp.: 10
Fiscal Year-end: 12/31/12

Business Description:
Medical Products Mfr
S.I.C.: 3841
N.A.I.C.S.: 339112

Personnel:
Anthony F. Holler *(Chm)*
Edward Wright *(CEO)*
Richard Bear *(CFO)*

Board of Directors:
Anthony F. Holler
Iain Cleator
David A. Johnson
Bergein F. Overholt
Todd R. Patrick
Ian A. Webb
Edward Wright

Transfer Agent:
Computershare Investor Services Inc
100 University Avenue 9 Floor North Tower
Toronto, ON, M5J 2Y1, Canada

CRH PLC
Belgard Castle Clondalkin
Dublin, 22, Ireland
Tel.: (353) 1 4041000
Telex: 93881
Fax: (353) 1 4041007
E-Mail: mail@crh.com
Web Site: www.crh.ie
Year Founded: 1970
CRH—(ISE LSE NYSE)
Rev.: $24,764,676,950
Assets: $28,058,210,050
Liabilities: $14,754,973,350
Net Worth: $13,303,236,700
Earnings: ($405,167,750)
Emp.: 75,642
Fiscal Year-end: 12/31/13

Business Description:
Holding Company; Building Materials Mfr & Distr
Import Export
S.I.C.: 6719
N.A.I.C.S.: 551112

Personnel:
Nicky Hartery *(Chm)*
Albert Manifold *(Grp CEO)*

Board of Directors:
Nicky Hartery
Ernst Bartschi
Maeve Carton
J. M. De Jong
William P. Egan
Utz-Hellmuth Felcht
John W. Kennedy
Albert Manifold
Donald A. McGovern, Jr.
Heather Ann McSharry
Dan N. O'Connor
R. Henk Rottinghuis
Mark S. Towe

Subsidiaries:

Clogrennane Lime Limited **(1)**
Clogrennane
Carlow, Ireland
Tel.: (353) 59 9131811
Fax: (353) 59 9131607
E-Mail: office@clogrennane.ie
Web Site: www.irishlime.com
Lime Product Mfr
S.I.C.: 2819
N.A.I.C.S.: 325180

CRH Europe-Materials **(1)**
Shrewsbury House Cabinteely
Dublin, 18, Ireland (100%)
Tel.: (353) 012048200
Fax: (353) 012847075
E-Mail: crheur@crh.com
Web Site: www.crh.com
Emp.: 30
S.I.C.: 3281
N.A.I.C.S.: 327991
Henry Morris *(Mng Dir)*

Irish Cement Ltd. **(1)**
Platin
Drogheda, Co Louth, Ireland (100%)
Tel.: (353) 419876000
Fax: (353) 419876400
E-Mail: info@irishcement.ie
Web Site: www.irishcement.ie
Emp.: 300
Mfr. of Cement Products
Import Export
S.I.C.: 3241
N.A.I.C.S.: 327310
Barry Leonard *(Mng Dir)*

Plaka Ireland Limited **(1)**
Toughers Business Park Newhall
Naas, Kildare, Ireland
Tel.: (353) 45 438691
Fax: (353) 45 438690
E-Mail: sales@plakagroup.ie
Web Site: www.plakagroup.ie
Construction Material Distr
S.I.C.: 5039
N.A.I.C.S.: 423390

Roadstone Wood Limited **(1)**
Fortunestown Tallaght 24
Dublin, Ireland
Tel.: (353) 1 4041200
Fax: (353) 1 4041321
Web Site: www.roadstone.ie
Building Material Mfr & Distr
S.I.C.: 3255
N.A.I.C.S.: 327120

Joint Venture:

Williaam Cox Ireland Ltd. **(1)**
Cloverhill Industrial Estate
22 Clondalkin, Ireland IE
Tel.: (353) 14605400
Fax: (353) 14500481
E-Mail: admin@williaamcox.ie
Web Site: www.williaamcox.ie
Emp.: 15
Architectural Glazing, Coxdome Daylight Products, Smoke & Heat Ventilation & Plastic Distr
S.I.C.: 8712
N.A.I.C.S.: 541310
Pat McCarthy *(Gen Mgr)*

U.S. Group:

Oldcastle, Inc. **(1)**
900 Ashwood Pkwy
Atlanta, GA 30338 (100%)
Tel.: (770) 804-3363
Fax: (770) 673-2400
Toll Free: (800) 899-8455
Web Site: www.oldcastle.com
Sales Range: $5-14.9 Billion
Emp.: 50,000
Holding Company
S.I.C.: 3273
N.A.I.C.S.: 327320
David Clark *(Pres)*
Mark Towe *(CEO)*
Michael O'Driscoll *(CFO)*

Divisions:

Allied Building Products Corporation **(2)**
15 E Union Ave
East Rutherford, NJ 07073-2127 NJ
Tel.: (201) 507-8400 (100%)
Fax: (201) 507-3842
Toll Free: (800) 541-2198
Web Site: www.alliedbuilding.com
Emp.: 3,100
Roofing, Siding, Insulation, Sheet Metal & Waterproofing
S.I.C.: 5031
N.A.I.C.S.: 423310
Robert Feury, Jr. *(CEO)*
Jamie Kutzer *(Chief Admin Officer)*
John McLaughlin *(Pres-Exterior Products)*

Branch:

Allied Building Products Corp.-Ferndale **(3)**
1700 E 9 Mile Rd
Ferndale, MI 48220
Tel.: (248) 398-5005
Fax: (248) 398-5909
Web Site: www.alliedbuilding.com
Sales Range: $10-24.9 Million
Emp.: 12
Lumber, Plywood, Millwork, & Wood Panel Merchant Whslr
S.I.C.: 5031
N.A.I.C.S.: 423310
Eric Beltowski *(Branch Mgr)*

Subsidiaries:

Acoustical Material Services, Inc. **(3)**
6700 E Pacific Coast Hwy Ste 295
Long Beach, CA 90803-4214
Tel.: (562) 431-8470
Web Site: www.a-m-s.com
Emp.: 11
Industrial Construction Supplies & Building Materials Whslr
S.I.C.: 5211
N.A.I.C.S.: 444190
Chuck Lynch *(VP-Door Div)*

A.L.L. Roofing & Building Materials Corp. **(3)**
3645 Long Beach Blvd
Long Beach, CA 90807-4018 CA
Tel.: (562) 595-7531
Fax: (562) 426-8389
Web Site: www.allroofingandbuilding.com
Emp.: 27
Insulation
Import Export
S.I.C.: 5033
N.A.I.C.S.: 423330

A.L.L. Roofing Materials of Los Angeles Inc. **(3)**
1212 W 58th St
Los Angeles, CA 90037-3917
Tel.: (323) 753-1277
Fax: (323) 753-5405
Web Site: www.alliedbuilding.com
Sales Range: $10-24.9 Million
Emp.: 30
Provider of Roofing, Siding & Insulation
Import Export
S.I.C.: 5033
N.A.I.C.S.: 423330
Rick Sasswen *(Gen Mgr)*

A.L.L. Roofing Materials of Van Nuys Inc. **(3)**
15208 Raymer St
Van Nuys, CA 91405-1016
Tel.: (818) 781-3280
Fax: (818) 781-4989
Web Site: www.alliedbuilding.com
Sls.: $17,905,470
Emp.: 15
Roofing Siding & Insulation
Import Export
S.I.C.: 5033
N.A.I.C.S.: 423330
Allen Hopper *(Mgr-Store)*

A.L.L. Roofing Materials of Ventura Inc. **(3)**
1435 Walter St
Ventura, CA 93003-5669 (100%)
Tel.: (805) 656-6319
Fax: (805) 644-4351
Sls.: $5,524,295
Emp.: 25
Roofing & Insulation Services
Import Export
S.I.C.: 5033
N.A.I.C.S.: 423330
Alen Harbour *(Mgr)*

A.L.L. Roofing Supplies of Arizona Inc. **(3)**
1951 Industrial Blvd
Lake Havasu City, AZ 86403-3631 (100%)
Tel.: (928) 453-7080
Fax: (928) 453-3223
Web Site: www.allsupply.com
Sls.: $3,500,000
Emp.: 22
Provider of Roofing, Siding & Insulation
S.I.C.: 5033
N.A.I.C.S.: 423330

Atlantic Building Material Inc. **(3)**
945 Wagner Pl
Fort Pierce, FL 34982 FL
Tel.: (772) 464-6900
Fax: (772) 464-1147
Sales Range: $10-24.9 Million
Emp.: 50
Building Materials Whslr
S.I.C.: 5211
N.A.I.C.S.: 444190
Chris Blount *(Gen Mgr)*

Austin Acoustical Materials, Inc. **(3)**
109 Farley Dr
Austin, TX 78753
Tel.: (512) 339-3006
Fax: (512) 339-4529
Web Site: www.alliedbuildingproducts.com
Emp.: 23
Building Materials Whslr & Distr
S.I.C.: 5211
N.A.I.C.S.: 444190
Mike Smith *(Branch Mgr)*

Builders Gypsum Supply Co., Inc. **(3)**
2015 Pasket Ln
Houston, TX 77092-8409 TX
Mailing Address:
PO Box 223767
Dallas, TX 75222-3767

Tel.: (713) 681-2201
Fax: (713) 681-7802
Emp.: 145
Lumber, Plywood & Millwork Distr
S.I.C.: 5031
N.A.I.C.S.: 423310
Kenneth Haude *(Branch Mgr)*

United Products Corp. **(3)**
200 Sycamore St W
Saint Paul, MN 55117
Tel.: (651) 227-8731
Fax: (651) 227-3699
Toll Free: (800) 879-8626
Web Site: www.unitedproducts.com
Sales Range: $25-49.9 Million
Emp.: 150
Roofing & Siding Materials Mfr
S.I.C.: 5033
N.A.I.C.S.: 423330
M. Allen Hatfield *(Chm)*

MMI Products, Inc. **(2)**
400 N Sam Houston Pkwy E Ste 1200
Houston, TX 77060 DE
Tel.: (281) 876-0080
Fax: (281) 448-6302
Web Site: www.mmiproductsinc.com
Emp.: 2,500
Fencing & Concrete Construction Products
S.I.C.: 3441
N.A.I.C.S.: 332312
Glenn Head *(Mgr-Benefits)*

Subsidiaries:

ADC Manufacturing **(3)**
300 N Industrial Park Rd
Harrison, AR 72601-1197 DE
Tel.: (870) 741-6193
Fax: (870) 741-6163
Toll Free: (800) 258-9576
Web Site: www.adcmanufacturing.com
Emp.: 50
Fence Parts & Castings
S.I.C.: 3496
N.A.I.C.S.: 332618

Meadow Burke **(3)**
531 S Hwy 301
Tampa, FL 33619
Tel.: (813) 248-1944
Fax: (813) 247-1424
Toll Free: (877) 518-7665
E-Mail: info@meadowburke.com
Web Site: www.meadowburke.com
Custom Constuction Reinforcement Products
S.I.C.: 5039
N.A.I.C.S.: 423390
Tab Buckner *(VP-Sls)*

Plant:

Meadow Burke **(4)**
5110 Santa Fe Rd
Tampa, FL 33619 DE
Tel.: (813) 247-3663
Fax: (813) 248-0703
Web Site: www.meadowburke.com
Emp.: 50
Concrete Forming & Reinforcing Products
S.I.C.: 3315
N.A.I.C.S.: 331222

Merchants Metals, Inc. **(3)**
400 N Sam Houston Pkwy E Ste 1200
Houston, TX 77060 DE
Tel.: (281) 372-3800
Fax: (281) 372-3801
Web Site: www.merchantsmetals.com
Emp.: 1,140
Fence & Gate Products Mfr & Distr
S.I.C.: 3496
N.A.I.C.S.: 332618
David Clark *(Pres)*

Oldcastle Architectural, Inc. **(2)**
375 Northridge Rd Ste 250
Atlanta, GA 30350
Tel.: (770) 804-3363
Fax: (770) 804-3369
Toll Free: (800) 899-8455
Web Site: www.oldcastle.com
Emp.: 50
Concrete, Masonry & Brick Products
S.I.C.: 3271
N.A.I.C.S.: 327331
Keith Hass *(CEO-Oldcastle Building Products)*

Subsidiaries:

Anchor Concrete Products Inc. **(3)**
1913 Atlantic Ave
Manasquan, NJ 08736
Tel.: (732) 292-2500
Fax: (732) 292-2650
Toll Free: (800) 682-5625
E-Mail: info@anchorcp.com
Web Site: www.oldcastlemasonry.com
Emp.: 105
Masonry & Landscape Products Mfr
S.I.C.: 3271
N.A.I.C.S.: 327331
John O'Neill *(VP)*

Big River Industries, Inc. **(3)**
3600 Mansell Rd Ste 575
Alpharetta, GA 30022-1512 (100%)
Mailing Address:
PO Box 190
Erwinville, LA 70729-0190
Tel.: (678) 461-2830
Fax: (678) 461-2845
Web Site: www.bigriverind.com
Emp.: 10
Mfr. of Lightweight Aggregates & Fly-Ash
S.I.C.: 3295
N.A.I.C.S.: 327992
Joel Hammond *(Pres)*

Bonsal American, Inc. **(3)**
8201 Arrowridge Blvd
Charlotte, NC 28273-5678 NC
Tel.: (704) 525-1621
Fax: (704) 529-5261
Toll Free: (800) 738-1621
Web Site: www.bonsalamerican.com
Emp.: 700
Packaged Building Materials & Pavement Maintenance Products Mfr
Import Export
S.I.C.: 3272
N.A.I.C.S.: 327390
David Maske *(Pres)*

Subsidiary:

Sakrete of North America, LLC **(4)**
5155 Fisher Ave
Cincinnati, OH 45217
Mailing Address:
PO Box 17087
Saint Bernard, OH 45217-0087
Tel.: (513) 242-3644
Fax: (513) 242-7845
Toll Free: (866) 725-7383
E-Mail: sakrete@oldcastleapg.com
Web Site: www.sakrete.com
Sales Range: $10-24.9 Million
Emp.: 10
Concrete Mix Mfr & Distr
S.I.C.: 3273
N.A.I.C.S.: 327320
Johnsie Beck *(Pres)*

Dixie Distribution **(3)**
6045 Dixie Hwy
Bridgeport, MI 48722
Tel.: (989) 777-0420
Fax: (989) 777-7970
Sls.: $42,399,612
Emp.: 19
Wholesale Stone & Marble Products
S.I.C.: 5032
N.A.I.C.S.: 423320
Craig Belasco *(Pres)*

Glen-Gery Corporation **(3)**
1166 Spring St
Wyomissing, PA 19610-6001 PA
Mailing Address:
PO Box 7001
Wyomissing, PA 19610
Tel.: (610) 374-4011
Fax: (610) 374-1622
E-Mail: gg@glengerybrick.com
Web Site: www.glengerybrick.com
Emp.: 30
Mfr. & Sales of Brick & Concrete Block
Export
S.I.C.: 3255
N.A.I.C.S.: 327120
Stephen G. Matsick *(Pres)*
Craig S. Oberholtzer *(Sec)*

Supreme Concrete Block Inc. **(3)**
396 Tyson Dr
Winchester, VA 22603
Mailing Address:
PO Box 478
Hagerstown, MD 21741
Tel.: (540) 667-4600
Fax: (540) 662-5920
Toll Free: (800) 343-1605
Web Site: www.betcosupreme.com
Sls.: $12,000,000
Emp.: 30
Concrete Products, Nec
S.I.C.: 3272
N.A.I.C.S.: 327332

Trenwyth Industries **(3)**
1 Connelly Rd PO Box 438
Emigsville, PA 17318
Tel.: (717) 767-6868
Fax: (717) 767-4023
Toll Free: (800) 233-1924
Web Site: www.trenwyth.com
Sales Range: $10-24.9 Million
Emp.: 225
Architectural Concrete Masonry Products Mfr
S.I.C.: 3271
N.A.I.C.S.: 327331
Carmen Ginter *(Mgr-Customer Svc)*

Non-U.S. Subsidiary:

APG Canada **(3)**
8145 Bombardier St
Ville d'Anjou, QC, H1J 1A5, Canada
Tel.: (514) 351-2125
Fax: (514) 352-9802
Web Site: www.permacon.ca
Emp.: 200
Concrete Pavers Mfr
S.I.C.: 3271
N.A.I.C.S.: 327331
Gary Belisle *(Pres)*

Oldcastle Glass, Inc. **(2)**
2425 Olympic Blvd Ste 525E
Santa Monica, CA 90404 DE
Tel.: (310) 264-4700
Fax: (310) 264-4703
Toll Free: (866) 653-2278
Web Site: www.oldcastlebe.com
Emp.: 6
Architectural Glass Mfr
S.I.C.: 3211
N.A.I.C.S.: 327211
Edwin B. Hathaway *(CEO)*
Daniel Hamblen *(CFO)*

Subsidiary:

Oldcastle BuildingEnvelope, Inc. **(3)**
2745 Dallas Pkwy Ste 560
Plano, TX 75093-8724 DE
Tel.: (469) 241-3800
Fax: (469) 241-3838
Web Site: www.oldcastlebe.com
Sales Range: $500-549.9 Million
Emp.: 25
Tempered Glass Fabricators
S.I.C.: 3231
N.A.I.C.S.: 327215
Edwin B. Hathaway *(CEO)*
Daniel Hamblen *(CFO)*
Mollie L. Hines *(Sec)*

Plants:

Oldcastle BuildingEnvelope, Inc. - Chandler **(4)**
50 S 56th St
Chandler, AZ 85226 AZ
Tel.: (480) 961-2000
Emp.: 65
Metal Window & Door Mfr
S.I.C.: 3442
N.A.I.C.S.: 332321
Carolyn Popkins *(Sec & VP)*

Oldcastle BuildingEnvelope, Inc. - Dallas **(4)**
10453 Brockwood Rd
Dallas, TX 75238-1651
Tel.: (214) 340-7041
Fax: (214) 348-3684
E-Mail:
Sales Range: $10-24.9 Million
Emp.: 34
Curtain Wall System Mfr
S.I.C.: 3449
N.A.I.C.S.: 332323

Oldcastle Materials, Inc. **(2)**
900 Ashwood Pkwy Ste 700
Atlanta, GA 30338-4780 DE
Tel.: (770) 522-5600
Fax: (770) 522-5608
E-Mail: info@oldcastlematerials.com
Web Site: www.oldcastlematerials.com
Sales Range: $5-14.9 Billion
Emp.: 23,000
Holding Company; Construction Materials & Civil Engineering Construction Services
S.I.C.: 6719
N.A.I.C.S.: 551112
Randy Lake *(CEO)*

Division:

Oldcastle Materials, Inc.-Mid-Atlantic Group **(3)**
2950 Charles Ave
Dunbar, WV 25064
Tel.: (304) 769-9733
Fax: (304) 768-9351
Web Site: www.oldcastlematerials.com
Aggregate, Ready Mixed Concrete & Asphalt Products Mfr
S.I.C.: 3273
N.A.I.C.S.: 327320

Subsidiaries:

Pennsy Supply, Inc. **(4)**
1001 Paxton St
Harrisburg, PA 17105 PA
Tel.: (717) 233-4511
Fax: (717) 238-7312
E-Mail: contact@pennsysupply.com
Web Site: www.oldcastlemidatlantic.com
Emp.: 500
Asphalt & Concrete Mfr; Construction Sand & Crushed Stone Mining
S.I.C.: 2951
N.A.I.C.S.: 324121
Mark Snyder *(Pres)*

Subsidiary:

McMinn, Inc. **(5)**
95 Louise Dr
Warminster, PA 18974
Tel.: (215) 953-5858
Rev.: $1,400,000
Emp.: 15
Radio, Television, & Other Electronics Stores
S.I.C.: 5734
N.A.I.C.S.: 443142
Glenn McMinn *(Pres)*

Subsidiaries:

Binkley & Ober Inc. **(6)**
RR 72
East Petersburg, PA 17520
Tel.: (717) 569-0441
Fax: (717) 569-5066
Web Site: www.binkleyandober.com
Sales Range: $10-24.9 Million
Emp.: 65
Concrete Block & Brick
S.I.C.: 3271
N.A.I.C.S.: 327331
Lee Ober *(Pres)*

McMinn's Asphalt Co., Inc. **(6)**
2743 Lancaster Rd
Manheim, PA 17545 PA
Tel.: (717) 569-2623
Fax: (717) 569-3617
Emp.: 150
Highway Construction Services & Materials
S.I.C.: 1622
N.A.I.C.S.: 237310
Jeffrey Sweigart *(Pres)*

PROSPECT AGGREGATES, INC. **(6)**
1001 Paxton St
Harrisburg, PA 17104 PA
Tel.: (717) 233-4511
Fax: (717) 255-3844
Building Materials & Hardscape Supply Whlsr
S.I.C.: 5211
N.A.I.C.S.: 444190

Pioneer Concrete, Inc. **(4)**
101 Rogers Rd Ste 202
Wilmington, DE 19801
Tel.: (302) 472-7400
E-Mail: contact@pioneerconcrete.net
Web Site: www.pioneerconcrete.net
Concrete Mfr & Whlsr

CRH plc—(Continued)

S.I.C.: 3273
N.A.I.C.S.: 327320

Slusser Brothers, Inc. (4)
125 N Warren St
Wilkes Barre, PA 18202
Tel.: (570) 455-3961
Fax: (570) 459-0322
E-Mail: contact@slusserbrothers.net
Web Site: slusserbrothers.net
Contractor & Construction Material Supplier
S.I.C.: 5032
N.A.I.C.S.: 423320

Subsidiaries:

A.L. Blades & Sons Inc. (3)
7610 County Rte 65
Hornell, NY 14843-9626 NY
Mailing Address:
PO Box 590
Hornell, NY 14843-0590
Tel.: (607) 324-3636
Fax: (607) 324-0998
E-Mail: office@alblades.com
Web Site: www.alblades.com
Emp.: 60
General Contractor & Construction Materials Mfr; Highway & Street Construction
S.I.C.: 1611
N.A.I.C.S.: 237310
Christopher Blades *(Pres)*
Lynn W. Blades *(Treas & Sec)*

Subsidiary:

Blades Construction Products Corp. (4)
7610 County Rte 65
Hornell, NY 14843-9626 NY
Tel.: (607) 324-6600
Fax: (607) 324-0998
E-Mail: office@alblades.com
Web Site: www.alblades.com
Emp.: 37
Bituminous Concrete, Asphalt & Aggregates Mfr & Distr
S.I.C.: 2951
N.A.I.C.S.: 324121
James McGee *(Gen Mgr)*

APAC Mid-South, Inc. (3)
500 Riverhills Park Ste 590
Birmingham, AL 35242 DE
Tel.: (205) 995-5912
Fax: (205) 252-3542
Web Site: apacmidsouth.com
Construction Sand & Crushed Stone Mining
S.I.C.: 1442
N.A.I.C.S.: 212321
Sean O'Sullivan *(Pres)*

APAC-Mississippi, Inc. (3)
5725 Hwy 18 S
Jackson, MS 39209 DE
Tel.: (601) 376-4000
Fax: (601) 376-4099
Web Site: www.oldcastlematerials.com
Emp.: 150
Asphalt Paving & Construction Services
S.I.C.: 2951
N.A.I.C.S.: 324121
Dwayne H. Boyd *(Pres)*

APAC-Missouri, Inc. (3)
1591A E Prathersville Rd
Columbia, MO 65202 DE
Tel.: (573) 449-0886
Fax: (573) 449-8004
Web Site: www.apacmo.com
Asphalt & Construction Services
S.I.C.: 2951
N.A.I.C.S.: 324121
Arlen W. Halvorson *(Pres)*

APAC-Oklahoma, Inc. (3)
4150 S 100th E Ave Cherokee Bldg Ste 300
Tulsa, OK 74146 DE
Mailing Address:
PO Box 580670
Tulsa, OK 74158
Tel.: (918) 438-2020
Fax: (918) 438-5826
Web Site: www.oldcastlematerials.com
Emp.: 130
Asphalt & Concrete Paving & Construction Services
S.I.C.: 1611
N.A.I.C.S.: 237310
Jerry A. Kreymer *(Pres)*

APAC-Tennessee, Inc. (3)
1210 Harbor Ave
Memphis, TN 38113 DE
Mailing Address:
PO Box 13427
Memphis, TN 38113-0427
Tel.: (901) 947-5600
Fax: (901) 947-5699
Web Site: www.apac.com
Emp.: 350
Highway Paving & Heavy Construction Services
S.I.C.: 1429
N.A.I.C.S.: 212319
Nickolas R. Haynes *(Pres)*

Best Masonry & Tool Supply, Inc. (3)
16745 W Hardy Rd
Houston, TX 77060 TX
Tel.: (281) 821-9487
Fax: (281) 821-9572
Web Site: www.isgproducts.com
Brick, Stone & Related Materials Supplier
S.I.C.: 5032
N.A.I.C.S.: 423320

Callanan Industries, Inc. (3)
1245 Kings Rd
Albany, NY 12303-5097 (100%)
Tel.: (518) 374-2222
Fax: (518) 374-1721
Web Site: www.callanan.com
Emp.: 600
Aggregates Asphalt & Related Construction Activities
S.I.C.: 3272
N.A.I.C.S.: 327390
Donald E. Fane *(Pres)*
David Rayno *(CFO)*

Conrad Yelvington Distributors, Inc. (3)
2326 Bellevue Ave PO Box 11637
Daytona Beach, FL 32114-5614 FL
Tel.: (386) 257-5504
Toll Free: (800) GRAVELS
Web Site: www.cydi.com
Emp.: 165
Construction Materials Services
S.I.C.: 5032
N.A.I.C.S.: 423320
Conrad F. Yelvington *(Chm)*
Mark Klebe *(CEO)*

Dolomite Products Company Inc. (3)
1150 Penfield Rd
Rochester, NY 14625 NY
Tel.: (585) 381-7010
Fax: (585) 381-0208
Web Site: www.dolomitegroup.com
Emp.: 30
Asphalt & Ready-Mix Concrete Mfr; Construction Sand, Gravel & Crushed Stone Mining
S.I.C.: 2951
N.A.I.C.S.: 324121
John Siel *(Owner & Pres)*

Don's Building Supply, L.P. (3)
2327 Langford St
Dallas, TX 75208 TX
Tel.: (214) 742-3045
Fax: (214) 742-3304
Emp.: 15
Supplier of Building Materials
S.I.C.: 5039
N.A.I.C.S.: 423390

Eugene Sand & Gravel, Inc. (3)
3000 N Delta Hwy
Eugene, OR 97408
Tel.: (541) 683-6400
Fax: (541) 683-4794
E-Mail: administrator@eugenesand.com
Web Site: www.eugenesand.com
Emp.: 120
Highway & Street Paving Contractor
S.I.C.: 1442
N.A.I.C.S.: 212321
K. C. Klosterman *(Pres)*

Evans Construction Company (3)
7255 S US Hwy 89 PO Box 4309
Jackson, WY 83001-4309 WY
Tel.: (307) 733-3029
Fax: (307) 733-8313
E-Mail: info@evansconstructionwy.com
Web Site: www.evansconstructionwy.com
Emp.: 50
Heavy Civil Construction Services, Asphalt & Ready-Mix Concrete Mfr, Construction Sand & Rock Mining
S.I.C.: 1622
N.A.I.C.S.: 237310
Mitch Lewis *(Pres)*

Four Corners Materials (3)
PO Box 1969
Bayfield, CO 81122
Tel.: (970) 247-2172
Fax: (970) 259-3631
Web Site: www.oldcastlematerials.com
Sls.: $15,000,000
Emp.: 100
Provider of Heavy Construction Services
S.I.C.: 3272
N.A.I.C.S.: 327390
Kyle High *(Pres)*

Helena Sand & Gravel, Inc. (3)
2209 Airport Rd
Helena, MT 59601 DE
Tel.: (406) 442-1185
Fax: (406) 442-1105
Web Site: www.montanamaterials.com
Construction Sand & Gravel Mining
S.I.C.: 1442
N.A.I.C.S.: 212321
Scott Olsen *(Pres)*

Intermountain Construction & Materials, Inc. (3)
209 Limestone Ave
Gillette, WY 82717
Tel.: (307) 682-8407
E-Mail: webmaster@stellarstar.com
Web Site: www.icm.bz
Sls.: $15,000,000
Emp.: 60
Highway Street & Bridge Construction
S.I.C.: 1611
N.A.I.C.S.: 237310
John Kane *(Pres)*

Michigan Paving & Materials Co. (3)
2575 S Hagerty Rd Ste 100
Canton, MI 48188 MI
Tel.: (734) 397-2050
Fax: (734) 397-8480
Web Site: www.michiganpaving.com
Emp.: 700
Paving Services; Ready-Mixed Asphalt & Concrete Mfr
S.I.C.: 1711
N.A.I.C.S.: 238220
Gregg Campbell *(Sec & Controller)*

Subsidiary:

Michigan Materials & Aggregates Company (4)
15203 S Telegraph Rd
Monroe, MI 48161 MI
Tel.: (734) 397-2050
Fax: (734) 241-3636
Web Site: www.stoneco.net
Construction Sand, Gravel & Crushed Limestone Mining
S.I.C.: 1442
N.A.I.C.S.: 212321

Mountain Enterprises, Inc. (3)
2257 Executive Dr
Lexington, KY 40505-4809
Tel.: (859) 299-7001
Fax: (859) 294-4232
E-Mail: arodabaugh@mountaincompanies.com
Web Site: www.mountaincompanies.com
Sls.: $23,300,000
Emp.: 1,500
Highway & Street Paving Contracting Services
S.I.C.: 1611
N.A.I.C.S.: 237310
Phillip Annis *(Pres)*

Subsidiary:

Bizzack, Inc. (4)
3009 Atkinson Ave Ste 400
Lexington, KY 40509 KY
Mailing Address:
PO Box 12530
Lexington, KY 40583-2530
Tel.: (859) 299-8001
Fax: (859) 299-0480
E-Mail: bizzack@mountaincompanies.com
Emp.: 13
Highway Construction Services
S.I.C.: 1611
N.A.I.C.S.: 237310
Lester Wimpy *(Pres)*
James Rodney Martin *(Treas)*

OMG Midwest, Inc. (3)
5550 NE 22nd St Ste 100
Des Moines, IA 50313 DE
Tel.: (515) 263-3860 (100%)
Fax: (515) 263-3878
Web Site: www.omgmidwest.com
Emp.: 100
Holding Company; Asphalt & Ready-Mix Concrete Mfr & Paving Services
S.I.C.: 6719
N.A.I.C.S.: 551112
Craig Lamberty *(Pres)*
Bill Raimer *(CFO)*

Divisions:

American Concrete Products (4)
PO Box 3365
Des Moines, IA 50316
Tel.: (515) 263-3860
Fax: (515) 263-3868
Web Site: www.amerconcrete.com
Emp.: 75
Ready-Mix Concrete Mfr
S.I.C.: 3273
N.A.I.C.S.: 327320
Rodney McCarn *(Gen Mgr)*

Des Moines Asphalt & Paving Co. (4)
2401 SE Tones Dr # 13
Ankeny, IA 50021
Tel.: (515) 262-8296
Fax: (515) 262-5813
Web Site: www.desmoinesasphalt.com
Emp.: 5
Asphalt Mfr & Paving Services
S.I.C.: 2951
N.A.I.C.S.: 324121
James D. Gauger *(Pres)*

Subsidiaries:

Cessford Construction Company (4)
2320 Zeller Ave
Le Grand, IA 50142
Mailing Address:
PO Box 160
Le Grand, IA 50142
Tel.: (641) 479-2695
Web Site: www.cessfordconstruction.com
Emp.: 200
Asphalt & Ready-Mix Concrete Mfr & Paving Services
S.I.C.: 1622
N.A.I.C.S.: 237310
Ted Huisman *(Mgr-Quality Control)*

Hills Materials Company (4)
3975 Sturgis Rd
Rapid City, SD 57702 SD
Mailing Address:
PO Box 2320
Rapid City, SD 57709-2320
Tel.: (605) 394-3300
Fax: (605) 341-3446
E-Mail: info@hillsmaterials.com
Web Site: www.hillsmaterials.com
Emp.: 200
Asphalt & Ready-Mix Concrete Mfr, Paving Services, Construction Sand & Rock Mining
S.I.C.: 3273
N.A.I.C.S.: 327320
William J. Keller *(VP)*

Southern Minnesota Construction Company (4)
1905 3rd Ave
Mankato, MN 56001-2802
Mailing Address:
PO Box 3069
Mankato, MN 56002-3069
Tel.: (507) 625-4848
Fax: (507) 625-4907
Web Site: www.smc-co.com
Paving Services, Asphalt & Ready-Mix Concrete Mfr, Construction Sand & Rock Mining
Import Export

S.I.C.: 1611
N.A.I.C.S.: 237310
Eric W. Leverson *(Gen Mgr)*

Pike Industries, Inc. (3)
3 Eastgate Park Dr
Belmont, NH 03220-3603 DE
Tel.: (603) 527-5100 (100%)
Fax: (603) 527-5101
E-Mail: info@pikeindustries.com
Web Site: www.pikeindustries.com
Emp.: 45
Mfr. of Paving Mixtures, Guardrail & Fencing Highway Contractor
S.I.C.: 1611
N.A.I.C.S.: 237310
Dave Duncan *(VP-Quality Control)*

Unit:

Pike Industries (4)
95 Western Ave
Fairfield, ME 49371-1336
Tel.: (207) 453-9381
Fax: (207) 453-2557
Web Site: www.pikeindustries.com
Sales Range: $10-24.9 Million
Emp.: 40
Bridge Construction
S.I.C.: 1611
N.A.I.C.S.: 237310

P.J. Keating Company (3)
998 Reservoir Rd
Lunenburg, MA 01462
Mailing Address:
PO Box 367
Fitchburg, MA 01462
Tel.: (978) 582-5200
Fax: (978) 582-7130
Toll Free: (800) 441-4119
E-Mail: info@pjkeating.com
Web Site: www.pjkeating.com
Emp.: 100
Hot Mix Asphalt Mfr
S.I.C.: 2951
N.A.I.C.S.: 324121
James Reger *(Pres)*

The Shelly Company (3)
80 Park Dr
Thornville, OH 43076
Tel.: (740) 246-6315
Fax: (740) 246-4715
Toll Free: (888) 743-5590
E-Mail: info@shellyco.com
Web Site: www.shellyco.com
Emp.: 3,000
Sand, Gravel & Limestone Mining, Asphalt Mfr, Road Construction & Paving Services
S.I.C.: 2951
N.A.I.C.S.: 324121
Ty Nofziger *(Pres)*
Doug Radabaugh *(CFO, Sec & Sr VP)*
David Kern *(Gen Counsel & VP)*
Lyn Yost *(Sr VP)*

Divisions:

The Shelly Co. - Columbus Division (4)
1771 Harmon Ave
Columbus, OH 43223
Tel.: (614) 437-2345
Fax: (614) 437-2331
Web Site: www.shellyco.com
Emp.: 800
Sand, Gravel & Limestone Mining, Asphalt Mfr, Road Construction & Paving Services
S.I.C.: 2951
N.A.I.C.S.: 324121
Ted Lemmon *(VP & Gen Mgr)*

The Shelly Co. - Northeast Division (4)
8920 Canyon Falls Blvd Ste 120
Twinsburg, OH 44087
Tel.: (330) 425-7861
Fax: (330) 405-4189
E-Mail: info@shellyco.com
Web Site: www.shellyco.com
Emp.: 356
Sand, Gravel & Limestone Mining, Asphalt Mfr, Road Construction & Paving Services
S.I.C.: 2951
N.A.I.C.S.: 324121
Steve Alex *(VP-Mktg & Coord-Special Project)*

The Shelly Co. - Northwest Division (4)
1700 Fostoria Ave Ste 200
Findlay, OH 45840
Tel.: (419) 422-8854
Fax: (419) 429-3444
Web Site: www.shellyco.com
Sand, Gravel & Limestone Mining, Asphalt Mfr, Road Construction & Paving Services
S.I.C.: 2951
N.A.I.C.S.: 324121
Lyle F. Snyder *(VP-Contracting)*

The Shelly Co. - Southern Division (4)
80 Park Dr
Thornville, OH 43076-0266
Tel.: (740) 246-6315
Fax: (740) 246-4715
Web Site: www.shellyco.com
Emp.: 787
Sand, Gravel & Limestone Mining & Asphalt Mfr
S.I.C.: 2951
N.A.I.C.S.: 324121
Lyn Yost *(VP-Sls)*

Subsidiaries:

All Ohio Ready Mix (4)
7901 Sylvania Ave
Sylvania, OH 43560-9732
Tel.: (419) 841-3838
Fax: (419) 841-4352
Toll Free: (888) OHIOMIX
Web Site: www.shellyco.com
Sales Range: $10-24.9 Million
Emp.: 85
Ready Mix Concrete Mfr
S.I.C.: 3273
N.A.I.C.S.: 327320
Billy Perry *(VP & Gen Mgr)*

Middleport Terminal, Inc. (4)
1400 State Route 7 N
Gallipolis, OH 45631-9475
Tel.: (740) 441-0004
Fax: (740) 441-0028
Emp.: 20
Asphalt Mfr
Import Export
S.I.C.: 2951
N.A.I.C.S.: 324121
Rick Vangundy *(Gen Mgr)*

Shelly Materials, Inc. (4)
80 Park Dr PO Box 266
Thornville, OH 43076-9397
Tel.: (740) 246-6315
Fax: (740) 246-4715
E-Mail: info@shellyco.com
Web Site: www.shellyco.com
Emp.: 200
Sand, Gravel & Limestone Mining
S.I.C.: 1422
N.A.I.C.S.: 212312
Mike Matoszkia *(Mgr-Ops)*

Smith Concrete (4)
26650 SR 7
Marietta, OH 45750
Tel.: (740) 373-7441
Fax: (740) 373-7446
Web Site: www.shellyco.com
Emp.: 80
Ready Mix Concrete Mfr
S.I.C.: 3273
N.A.I.C.S.: 327320

Staker & Parson Companies Inc. (3)
2350 South 1900 W
Ogden, UT 84409 (100%)
Mailing Address:
PO Box 3429
Ogden, UT 84409-1429
Tel.: (801) 731-1111
Fax: (801) 731-8800
Web Site: www.stakerparson.com
Emp.: 225
Asphalt, Gravel, Sand & Concrete Products Mfr
S.I.C.: 1442
N.A.I.C.S.: 212321
Scott Parson *(Pres & CEO)*
Jared Hyde *(CFO)*

Tilcon Connecticut Inc. (3)
642 Black Rock Ave
New Britain, CT 06052 DE
Mailing Address:
PO Box 1357
New Britain, CT 06050-1357
Tel.: (860) 223-3651
Fax: (860) 225-1865
Web Site: www.tilconct.com
Emp.: 1,500
Asphalt Mfr & Paving Services; Construction Sand, Gravel & Crushed Stone Mining
S.I.C.: 2951
N.A.I.C.S.: 324121
Dan Stover *(Exec VP)*

Tilcon New York Inc. (3)
162 Old Mill Rd
West Nyack, NY 10994 DE
Tel.: (845) 358-4500
Fax: (845) 480-3231
Web Site: www.tilconny.com
Asphalt Mfr & Paving Services; Construction Sand, Gravel & Crushed Stone Mining
S.I.C.: 2951
N.A.I.C.S.: 324121
Christopher J. Madden *(Pres & CEO)*
John Cooney, Jr. *(Pres-New York Div)*

Division:

Tilcon New York Inc. - New Jersey (4)
625 Mount Hope Rd
Wharton, NJ 07885-2807
Tel.: (973) 366-7741
Fax: (973) 366-1026
Web Site: www.tilconny.com
Emp.: 500
Asphalt Mfr & Paving Services; Construction Sand, Gravel & Crushed Stone Mining
Import Export
S.I.C.: 2951
N.A.I.C.S.: 324121
George W. Thompson *(Chm)*

United Companies of Mesa County (3)
2273 River Rd
Grand Junction, CO 81505
Tel.: (970) 243-4900
Fax: (970) 243-5945
Web Site: www.united-gj.com
Sales Range: $25-49.9 Million
Emp.: 250
General Contractor, Highway & Street Construction
S.I.C.: 1611
N.A.I.C.S.: 237310
Richard Umbel *(Pres)*

W-L Construction & Paving, Inc. (3)
1484 Hwy 107
Chilhowie, VA 24319 VA
Mailing Address:
PO Drawer 927
Chilhowie, VA 24319
Tel.: (276) 646-3804
Fax: (276) 646-3141
Web Site: www.oldcastlematerials.com
Emp.: 230
Provider of Highway & Street Construction Services
S.I.C.: 1611
N.A.I.C.S.: 237310
Kenneth M. Taylor *(VP)*

West Virginia Paving, Inc. (3)
2950 Charles Ave
Dunbar, WV 25064-2103
Tel.: (304) 768-9733
Fax: (304) 768-9351
Web Site: www.oldcastle.com
Emp.: 32
Highway & Street Construction Services
Import Export
S.I.C.: 1622
N.A.I.C.S.: 237310
Daniel L. Cooperrider *(Pres)*

Subsidiary:

Southern West Virginia Asphalt, Inc. (4)
651 Ewart Ave
Beckley, WV 25801
Mailing Address:
PO Box 7305
Beckley, WV 25801
Tel.: (304) 252-6528
Fax: (304) 252-2123
Web Site: www.asphaltwv.com
Emp.: 8
Highway & Street Construction Services
Import Export
S.I.C.: 2951
N.A.I.C.S.: 324121
Andy Bragg *(Gen Mgr)*

Units:

APAC-Arkansas - Arkhola Division (3)
523 Garrison Ave
Fort Smith, AR 72902
Mailing Address:
PO Box 1627
Fort Smith, AR 72902-1627
Tel.: (479) 785-4271
Fax: (479) 788-6302
Construction Materials
S.I.C.: 3281
N.A.I.C.S.: 327991

APAC-Arkansas - McClinton Anchor Division (3)
755 E Millsap Rd PO Box 9208
Fayetteville, AR 72703
Mailing Address:
PO Box 9208
Fayetteville, AR 72703-0021
Tel.: (479) 587-3300
Fax: (479) 521-2826
Emp.: 50
Hot-Mix Asphalt, Construction Aggregates & Heavy Highway Construction Services
S.I.C.: 2951
N.A.I.C.S.: 324121
Lee S. DuChanois *(Pres)*

APAC-Atlantic - Asheville Division (3)
1188 Smokey Park Hwy
Candler, NC 28715
Tel.: (828) 665-1180
Fax: (828) 665-9345
Web Site: www.apacatlanticinc.com
Emp.: 500
Asphalt Production Services
S.I.C.: 2951
N.A.I.C.S.: 324121

APAC-Atlantic - Harrison Division (3)
226 Gill St
Alcoa, TN 37701
Tel.: (865) 983-3100
Fax: (865) 984-5478
Web Site: www.oldcastlematerials.com
Asphalt Paving & Construction Services
S.I.C.: 2951
N.A.I.C.S.: 324121
William H. Tomlinson *(Pres)*

APAC-Kansas - Kansas City Division (3)
7415 W 130th St Ste 300
Overland Park, KS 66213-2677
Tel.: (913) 814-6700
Fax: (913) 814-6766
Web Site: www.oldcastlematerials.com
Construction Services & Products
S.I.C.: 1611
N.A.I.C.S.: 237310
David Gillialim *(Pres)*

APAC-Kansas - Shears Division (3)
1600 N Lorraine St Ste 1
Hutchinson, KS 67501
Tel.: (620) 662-3307
Fax: (620) 662-3181
Web Site: www.oldcastlematerials.com
Emp.: 500
Asphalt Paving & Construction Materials
S.I.C.: 1622
N.A.I.C.S.: 237310
William C. Girard *(Pres)*

APAC-Southeast - First Coast Division (3)
11482 Columbia Park Dr W Ste 3
Jacksonville, FL 32258
Tel.: (904) 288-6300
Fax: (904) 288-6301
Web Site: www.apac.com
Emp.: 11
Asphalt Paving & Construction Services
S.I.C.: 2951
N.A.I.C.S.: 324121

CRH plc—(Continued)

Timothy G. Mullendore *(Pres)*

APAC-Southeast - Gulf Coast Division (3)
4375 McCoy Dr
Pensacola, FL 32503
Tel.: (850) 433-3001
Fax: (850) 434-8971
Web Site: www.oldcastle.com
Emp.: 50
Asphalt Paving & Construction Services
S.I.C.: 2951
N.A.I.C.S.: 324121

APAC-Southeast, Inc. - Central Florida Division (3)
13101 Telecom Dr Ste 101
Temple Terrace, FL 33637-0936
Tel.: (813) 973-2888
Fax: (813) 971-5317
Web Site: www.oldcastlematerials.com
Asphalt Paving & Construction Services
S.I.C.: 2951
N.A.I.C.S.: 324121
Timothy G. Mullendore *(Pres)*

APAC-Southeast - Southern Florida Division (3)
1451 Myrtle St
Sarasota, FL 34234-4723
Tel.: (941) 355-7178
Fax: (941) 351-4078
Emp.: 60
Asphalt Paving & Construction Services
S.I.C.: 1611
N.A.I.C.S.: 237310

APAC-Texas - Texas Bitulithic Division (3)
2121 Irving Blvd
Dallas, TX 75207
Mailing Address:
PO Box 224048
Dallas, TX 75222-4048
Tel.: (214) 741-3531
Fax: (214) 742-3540
Asphalt Paving & Construction Services
S.I.C.: 2951
N.A.I.C.S.: 324121
Stephen R. Koonce *(Pres)*

APAC-Texas - Trotti & Thomson Division (3)
12907 US Hwy 90
Beaumont, TX 77713
Mailing Address:
PO Box 20779
Beaumont, TX 77720-0779
Tel.: (409) 866-1444
Fax: (409) 866-5541
Web Site: www.apac.com
Emp.: 150
Asphalt Paving & Construction Services
S.I.C.: 2951
N.A.I.C.S.: 324121
Kal A. Kincaid *(Pres)*

Ballenger Paving Division (3)
900 W Lee Rd
Taylors, SC 29687-2521
Mailing Address:
PO Box 127
Taylors, SC 29062
Tel.: (864) 292-9550
Fax: (864) 244-9310
Web Site: www.oldcastlematerials.com
Sls.: $55,000,000
Emp.: 150
Concrete Paving & Construction Services
S.I.C.: 1622
N.A.I.C.S.: 237310
Robert W. Mccord *(VP)*

Thompson-Arthur Paving & Construction (3)
300 S Benbow Rd
Greensboro, NC 27401
Mailing Address:
PO Box 21088
Greensboro, NC 27420-1088
Tel.: (336) 412-6800
Fax: (336) 412-6888
Web Site: www.thompsonarthur.com
Emp.: 400
Asphalt Paving Services; Stone Base, Bridge, Curb & Gutter Construction Services; Site Utilities; Grading & Sand Products
S.I.C.: 2951
N.A.I.C.S.: 324121
Larry Brickey *(Pres)*

Oldcastle Precast, Inc. (2)
1002 15th St SW Ste 110
Auburn, WA 98001
Tel.: (253) 833-2777
Fax: (877) 520-8341
Web Site: www.oldcastleprecast.com
Emp.: 5,000
Precast Concrete & Composite Products Mfr
S.I.C.: 3272
N.A.I.C.S.: 327390
Mark Schack *(CEO)*

Division:

Oldcastle Precast Building Systems (3)
1401 Trimble Rd
Edgewood, MD 21040 MD
Tel.: (410) 612-1213
Fax: (410) 612-1214
Web Site: www.oldcastleprecast.com
Emp.: 180
Concrete Products
Import Export
S.I.C.: 3272
N.A.I.C.S.: 327390
John Jones *(Gen Mgr)*

Subsidiaries:

Amcor, Inc. (3)
333 S Redwood Rd
North Salt Lake, UT 84054-2902 (100%)
Tel.: (801) 936-7628
Fax: (801) 936-5470
Web Site: www.amcormasonry.com
Emp.: 48
Mfr. of Concrete Pipe & Precast Concrete Products
S.I.C.: 3317
N.A.I.C.S.: 331210
Paul Kamnikar *(Gen Mgr)*

Central Precast Concrete, Inc. (3)
3049 Independence Dr Ste A
Livermore, CA 94551 CA
Tel.: (925) 960-8740
Fax: (925) 454-8593
Web Site: www.central-precast.com
Sales Range: $25-49.9 Million
Emp.: 26
Precast Concrete Products & Services
S.I.C.: 3272
N.A.I.C.S.: 327390
Doug McLaughlin *(Pres)*

N.C. Products (3)
920 Withers Rd
Raleigh, NC 27603-6095 NC (100%)
Tel.: (919) 772-6301
Fax: (919) 772-1209
Emp.: 60
Mfr. of Concrete Pipe, Precast Concrete Products & Manholes
S.I.C.: 5039
N.A.I.C.S.: 423390

San Diego Precast Concrete, Inc. (3)
2735 Cactus Rd
Santee, CA 92154
Tel.: (619) 240-8000
Fax: (619) 661-1038
E-Mail: wkeener@sdpc.com
Web Site: www.sdpc.com
Sales Range: $50-74.9 Million
Emp.: 81
Precast Concrete Mfr
S.I.C.: 3272
N.A.I.C.S.: 327390
Bobby Gifford *(Plant Mgr)*

Utility Vault Co., Inc. (3)
2808 A St SE
Auburn, WA 98002 (100%)
Tel.: (253) 839-3500
Fax: (253) 735-4201
Web Site: www.uvauburn.com
Emp.: 80
Mfr. of Precast Concrete, Concrete Pipe, Prestrassed Concrete Piling
S.I.C.: 3272
N.A.I.C.S.: 327390
Gary Venn *(Gen Mgr)*

Subsidiary:

Oldcastle Adams Products Company (2)
5701 McCrimmon Pkwy
Morrisville, NC 27560-8340 NC (100%)
Tel.: (919) 467-2218
Fax: (919) 469-0509
Web Site: www.adamsproducts.com
Emp.: 50
Mfr. of Masonry Block & Pavers
S.I.C.: 3271
N.A.I.C.S.: 327331
Frank Werner *(VP-Mktg)*

U.S. Subsidiaries:

Americas Products & Distribution, Inc. (1)
12811 Commerce Lakes Dr
Fort Myers, FL 33913
Tel.: (239) 204-9063
Fax: (239) 204-9063
Investment Management Services
S.I.C.: 6211
N.A.I.C.S.: 523999

AMS Holdings, Inc. (1)
2608 SW Emerald Creek Pl
Blue Springs, MO 64015
Tel.: (816) 228-7373
Investment Management Services
S.I.C.: 6211
N.A.I.C.S.: 523999

CPM Development Corporation (1)
5111 E Broadway
Spokane, WA 99212
Tel.: (509) 534-6221
Fax: (509) 536-3051
Ready Mix Concrete Mfr
S.I.C.: 3273
N.A.I.C.S.: 327320
Mike Delaney *(VP)*

Eugene Sand Construction, Inc. (1)
3000 Delta Hwy N
Eugene, OR 97408
Tel.: (541) 683-6400
Fax: (541) 683-4794
E-Mail: spriaulx@oldcastlematerials.com
Web Site: www.eugenesand.com
Building Material Distr
S.I.C.: 5039
N.A.I.C.S.: 423390

Mahalo Acquisition Corp. (1)
1081 Makepono St
Honolulu, HI 96819
Tel.: (808) 864-0136
Construction Material Whslr
S.I.C.: 5039
N.A.I.C.S.: 423390

Oldcastle APG Northeast, Inc. (1)
7920 Notes Dr
Manassas, VA 20109
Tel.: (703) 361-2777
Fax: (703) 361-6495
Building Material Distr
S.I.C.: 5032
N.A.I.C.S.: 423320
Peter Kelly *(Pres)*

Oldcastle APG South, Inc. (1)
108 Buchanan Church Rd
Greensboro, NC 27405-8631
Tel.: (336) 375-5656
Building Material Mfr
S.I.C.: 3255
N.A.I.C.S.: 327120
Tracey Griffin *(Office Mgr)*

Oldcastle APG West, Inc. (1)
4720 E Cotton Gin Loop Ste 200
Phoenix, AZ 85040
Tel.: (602) 302-9600
Fax: (602) 273-1079
Building Material Mfr & Distr
S.I.C.: 3259
N.A.I.C.S.: 327120
Cindy Marksberry *(Reg Mgr-Utilities & Procurement)*

Oldcastle Building Products, Inc (1)
375 Northridge Rd Ste 250
Atlanta, GA 30350
Tel.: (800) 899-8455
Fax: (770) 804-3369
Emp.: 7,000
Concrete Block Mfr & Whslr
S.I.C.: 3271
N.A.I.C.S.: 327331

Oldcastle Lawn & Garden, Inc. (1)
481 Spring Water Rd
Poland Spring, ME 04274
Tel.: (207) 998-5580
Fax: (207) 998-5755
Web Site: www.oldcastlelawngarden.com
Garden Supplies Mfr & Distr
S.I.C.: 3999
N.A.I.C.S.: 339999
Eoin Lehane *(Pres)*

Subsidiary:

Jolly Gardener Products Inc. (2)
481 Spring Water Rd
Poland Spring, ME 04274
Tel.: (207) 998-5580
Fax: (207) 998-3192
Web Site: www.jollygardener.com
Sls.: $25,000,000
Emp.: 65
Mulch, Wood & Bark Producer & Distr
S.I.C.: 2499
N.A.I.C.S.: 321999
Richard M. Morrison *(Gen Mgr)*

Oldcastle Southern Group, Inc. (1)
13101 Telecom Dr Ste 101
Tampa, FL 33637
Tel.: (813) 384-3030
Fax: (813) 971-5317
Web Site: www.oldcastlesoutherngroup.com
Asphalt Mix Mfr
S.I.C.: 2951
N.A.I.C.S.: 324121
Kenny Laing *(CFO)*

Oldcastle Surfaces, Inc. (1)
1400 W Marietta St
Atlanta, GA 30318
Tel.: (404) 355-3108
Fax: (404) 355-0560
Web Site: www.oldcastlesurfaces.com
Countertop Mfr
S.I.C.: 2434
N.A.I.C.S.: 337110

Oldcastle SW Group, Inc. (1)
2273 River Rd
Grand Junction, CO 81502
Tel.: (970) 243-4900
Fax: (970) 243-5945
Ready Mix Concrete Mfr
S.I.C.: 3273
N.A.I.C.S.: 327320
Ken W. Nesbitt *(Pres)*

Non-U.S. Subsidiaries:

Adronit GmbH (1)
Oberwengerner Str 204
58300 Wetter, Germany
Tel.: (49) 233597850
Fax: (49) 233572258
E-Mail: info@adronit.de
Web Site: www.adronit.de
Mfr. of Security Systems
S.I.C.: 7382
N.A.I.C.S.: 561621
Simone Diekmann *(Mng Dir & Sec)*
Frank Kuppenbender *(Mng Dir & Dir-Tech)*
Bernd H. Sander *(Mng Dir)*

Aluminium Verkoop Zuid B.V. (1)
Kanaaldijk 11
Postbus 37
Best, 5683 CK, Netherlands
Tel.: (31) 49 932 8600
Fax: (31) 49 939 7640
E-Mail: avz@avz.nl
Web Site: www.avz.nl
Aluminum Component Whslr
S.I.C.: 5211
N.A.I.C.S.: 444190

Arfman Hekwerk B.V. (1)
Ondernemersweg 15
7451 PK Holten, Netherlands
Tel.: (31) 548362948
Fax: (31) 548365042
E-Mail: info@arfman.nl
Web Site: www.arfman.nl
Emp.: 30
Fencing System Mfr
S.I.C.: 3499
N.A.I.C.S.: 332999

Edward Van Veen *(Mng Dir)*

Bauking AG (1)
Buchholzer Str 98
30655 Hannover, Germany
Tel.: (49) 5111232060
Fax: (49) 51112320655
E-Mail: info@bauking.de
Web Site: www.bauking.de
Emp.: 3,500
Manufacture And Distribution of Building Products And Materials
S.I.C.: 5039
N.A.I.C.S.: 423390
Christopher Lehrmann *(Mng Dir)*

Beton Catalan S.A. (1)
Segunda Plt 5 Cantera De La Marqueza
Barcelona, 08028, Spain
Tel.: (34) 934 90 79 79
Fax: (34) 935 05 36 17
E-Mail: comercial@beton.com
Emp.: 60
Ready Mix Concrete Mfr
S.I.C.: 3273
N.A.I.C.S.: 327320
Roger Roic *(Mng Dir)*

Beton Moule Industriel S.A. (1)
47 Ave des Genottes Le Cerame - Bat B
BP 98318
Cergy-Pontoise, 95803, France
Tel.: (33) 1 34 25 55 55
Fax: (33) 1 34 25 55 85
Concrete Block Mfr
S.I.C.: 3271
N.A.I.C.S.: 327331

Betongruppen RBR A/S (1)
Industrivej 8
Varde, 6800, Denmark
Tel.: (45) 76 95 11 22
Fax: (45) 76 95 11 33
E-Mail: rbr@rbr.dk
Web Site: www.rbr.dk
Paving Material Mfr
S.I.C.: 2951
N.A.I.C.S.: 324121
Trine Brinch Sorensen *(Mng Dir)*

Bosta Beton Sp. z o.o. (1)
Ul Ksawerow 30
Warsaw, 02-656, Poland
Tel.: (48) 225 08 09 01
Fax: (48) 225 08 09 09
E-Mail:
Web Site: www.bostabeton.com.pl
Building Material Mfr & Distr
S.I.C.: 3297
N.A.I.C.S.: 327120

BR Bauhandel AG (1)
Riedmattstrasse 2
8153 Rumlang, Switzerland
Tel.: (41) 43 211 21 51
Fax: (41) 43 211 21 69
Web Site: www.baubedarf.ch
Construction Material Distr
S.I.C.: 5039
N.A.I.C.S.: 423390
Yves Helbling *(Partner-Mktg Bus)*
Sibylle Remund *(Partner-HR Bus)*

Broughton Controls Limited (1)
33 Stakehill Industrial Estate Finlan Road
Middleton, Manchester, M24 2RW, United Kingdom
Tel.: (44) 161 655 1020
Fax: (44) 161 655 1021
E-Mail: info@broughton-controls.co.uk
Web Site: www.broughton-controls.co.uk
Emp.: 50
Security Purpose Construction Services
S.I.C.: 1799
N.A.I.C.S.: 238990
Mike Farrall *(Product Mgr)*

Cabi S.A. (1)
Joaquim Molins 5
08028 Barcelona, Spain
Tel.: (34) 93 505 36 00
Fax: (34) 93 505 36 18
Web Site: www.cabi.es
Cement Mfr
S.I.C.: 3241
N.A.I.C.S.: 327310

Calduran Kalkzandsteen B.V. (1)
Einsteinstraat 5
3846 BH Harderwijk, Netherlands
Tel.: (31) 341 464 000
Fax: (31) 341 464 001
E-Mail: info@calduran.nl
Web Site: www.calduran.nl
Emp.: 260
Building Material Mfr
S.I.C.: 3255
N.A.I.C.S.: 327120
Henk Schaap *(Dir-Comml)*

Cantera de Aridos Puig Broca S.A. (1)
Calle Joaquim Molins 5
Barcelona, 08028, Spain
Tel.: (34) 972622362
Building Material Distr
S.I.C.: 5032
N.A.I.C.S.: 423320

Canteras Cerro Negro S.A. (1)
Manuel Belzu 1939-43
Olivos, Buenos Aires, B1636GMI, Argentina
Tel.: (54) 11 4790 0200
Fax: (54) 11 4790 2772
Web Site: www.cerronegro.com.ar
Ceramic Wall & Floor Tile Mfr
S.I.C.: 3297
N.A.I.C.S.: 327120

Cementbouw B.V. (1)
Bennebroekerdijk 244
2142 LE Cruquius, Netherlands
Tel.: (31) 23 548 14 81
Fax: (31) 23 548 16 00
E-Mail:
Web Site: www.cementbouw.nl
Ready Mix Concrete Mfr
S.I.C.: 3273
N.A.I.C.S.: 327320

Comercial Duomo Limitada (1)
Avenue Kennedy 6980 Vitacura
Santiago, 7650672, Chile
Tel.: (56) 2 202 3635
Fax: (56) 2 202 3637
Web Site: www.duomocom.cl
Bathroom Fixture & Fittings Mfr
S.I.C.: 3499
N.A.I.C.S.: 332999

Cormela S.A. (1)
Suipacha 268 Piso 10
Buenos Aires, C1008AAF, Argentina
Tel.: (54) 11 4328 1600
Fax: (54) 11 4328 8324
E-Mail: info@cormela.com.ar
Web Site: www.cormela.com.ar
Emp.: 88
Clay Ceramic & Brick Mfr
S.I.C.: 3259
N.A.I.C.S.: 327120
Federico Ferro *(Gen Mgr)*

CRH Bouwmaten B.V. (1)
Straatweg 62
3621 BR Breukelen, Netherlands
Tel.: (31) 346 259159
Fax: (31) 346 259160
Emp.: 17
Building Material Distr
S.I.C.: 5039
N.A.I.C.S.: 423390

CRH Bouwmaterialenhandel B.V. (1)
Stationsweg 2
4191 KK Geldermalsen, Netherlands
Tel.: (31) 88 6337202
E-Mail: info@crh-bmh.nl
Web Site: www.crh-bouwmaterialen.nl
Construction Material Distr
S.I.C.: 5039
N.A.I.C.S.: 423390

CRH Clay Solutions GmbH (1)
Wellie 65
31595 Steyerberg, Germany
Tel.: (49) 50 23 98 01 10
Fax: (49) 50 23 98 01 99
E-Mail: info@crh-ccs.de
Web Site: www.crh-ccs.de
Emp.: 25
Concrete Brick Mfr
S.I.C.: 3271
N.A.I.C.S.: 327331
Bas Coenen *(Mgr-IT)*

CRH Concrete A/S (1)
Vestergade 25
Seeland, 4130 Viby, Denmark
Tel.: (45) 7010 3510
E-Mail: info@crhconcrete.dk
Web Site: www.crhconcrete.dk
Concrete Product Distr
S.I.C.: 5032
N.A.I.C.S.: 423320
Claus Bering *(CEO)*

CRH Europe (1)
Einsteinlaan 26
2289 CC Rijswijk, Netherlands
Tel.: (31) 704142400
Fax: (31) 104358635
E-Mail: info@crh.com
Emp.: 60
S.I.C.: 3281
N.A.I.C.S.: 327991
Erik Bax *(Mng Dir)*

Division:

CRH Europe - Products & Distribution (2)
Einsteinlaan 26
2289 CC Rijswijk, Netherlands
Tel.: (31) 704142400
Fax: (31) 704142409
E-Mail: infohr@crh-eur.nl
Web Site: www.crh.nl
Emp.: 100
Operating Division
S.I.C.: 3271
N.A.I.C.S.: 327331
Erik Bax *(Mng Dir)*

Non-U.S. Subsidiary:

Ancon Limited (3)
President Way President Pk
Sheffield, S4 7UR, United Kingdom UK
Tel.: (44) 1142755224
Fax: (44) 1142768543
E-Mail: info@ancon.co.uk
Web Site: www.ancon.co.uk
Sales Range: $150-199.9 Million
Emp.: 370
Building Products
S.I.C.: 3441
N.A.I.C.S.: 332312
John Davies *(Project Mgr)*

CRH Fencing Limited (1)
Herons Way Carr Hill
Doncaster, DN4 8WA, United Kingdom
Tel.: (44) 1302 760861
Fax: (44) 1302 327135
E-Mail:
Emp.: 75
Building Material Mfr & Distr
S.I.C.: 3255
N.A.I.C.S.: 327120
Andrew Peach *(Mng Dir)*

CRH Getaz Holding AG (1)
Avenue Reller 14
Vevey, 1800, Switzerland
Tel.: (41) 21 925 08 00
Fax: (41) 21 925 08 02
Web Site: www.getaz-romang.ch
Concrete Block Mfr
S.I.C.: 3271
N.A.I.C.S.: 327331

CRH Ile de France Distribution S.A.S. (1)
69 Blvd De La Republique
Boulogne, 92100, France
Tel.: (33) 1 46 10 48 40
Web Site: www.raboni.fr
Building Material Distr
S.I.C.: 5039
N.A.I.C.S.: 423390

CRH Kleiwaren Beheer B.V. (1)
Engelsmanstraat 56
6086 BD Neer, Netherlands
Tel.: (31) 475 51 81 00
Fax: (31) 475 51 82 00
Building Material Mfr & Distr
S.I.C.: 3255
N.A.I.C.S.: 327120

CRH Klinkier Sp. z o.o. (1)
Ul Pszczynska 309
Gliwice, 44-100, Poland
Tel.: (48) 32 239 4105
Fax: (48) 32 239 4106
E-Mail: crh-klinkier@klinkier.pl
Web Site: www.crh-klinkier.pl
Construction Material Distr
S.I.C.: 5039
N.A.I.C.S.: 423390

CRH Structural Concrete B.V. (1)
Boerdijk 30
7844 TC Veenoord, Netherlands
Tel.: (31) 591 551763
Fax: (31) 320 269200
Emp.: 120
Building Material Distr
S.I.C.: 5032
N.A.I.C.S.: 423320
Maarten Hogervorst *(Mgr-Mktg)*

CRH Structural Concrete SRL (1)
Str Neagoe Basarab Nr 4
Negoiesti, Brazi, Romania
Tel.: (40) 344100240
Fax: (40) 344100247
E-Mail: office@ergon-international.com
Web Site: www.ergon-international.com
Emp.: 74
Building Material Distr
S.I.C.: 5032
N.A.I.C.S.: 423320
Ovidiu Dumitrescu *(Mng Dir)*

CRH Sudamericana S.A. (1)
Manuel Belzu 1939 Olivos
B1636GMI Buenos Aires, Argentina
Tel.: (54) 11 4790 4500
Building Material Mfr & Distr
S.I.C.: 3255
N.A.I.C.S.: 327120

Douterloigne N.V. (1)
Vichtsesteenweg 136
Anzegem, Belgium
Tel.: (32) 56 69 40 40
Fax: (32) 56 68 09 14
Web Site: www.douterloigne.be
Prefabricated Concrete Material Distr
S.I.C.: 5032
N.A.I.C.S.: 423320

Drogomex Sp. Z O.O. (1)
Ul Stefana Bryly 4
05-800 Pruszkow, Poland
Tel.: (48) 22 758 89 81
Fax: (48) 22 758 89 76
E-Mail:
Web Site: www.drogomex.pl
Road Construction Engineering Services
S.I.C.: 1611
N.A.I.C.S.: 237310

Dycore B.V. (1)
Ambachtsweg 16
4906 CH Oosterhout, Netherlands
Tel.: (31) 162 477 477
Fax: (31) 162 477 499
E-Mail: info@dycore.nl
Web Site: www.dycore.nl
Emp.: 100
Concrete Floor System Mfr
S.I.C.: 3272
N.A.I.C.S.: 327390
Daniel D'hondt *(Engr-Product)*

Element AG (1)
Mariahilfstrasse 25
1712 Tafers, Switzerland
Tel.: (41) 26 494 77 77
Fax: (41) 26 494 77 78
E-Mail: info@element.ch
Web Site: www.element.ch
Emp.: 110
Concrete Product Distr
S.I.C.: 5032
N.A.I.C.S.: 423320
Claus Arntjen *(CEO)*
Ralf Grisch *(CFO)*
Steve Hoffer *(CMO)*

Elpreco SA (1)
Calea Severinului Nr 44
Craiova, 200609, Romania
Tel.: (40) 25 130 7700
Fax: (40) 25 159 0225
E-Mail: office@elpreco.ro
Web Site: www.elpreco.ro
Building Material Mfr
S.I.C.: 3297
N.A.I.C.S.: 327120

Ergon N.V. (1)
Marnixdreef 5
Lier, 2500, Belgium
Tel.: (32) 3 490 04 00
Fax: (32) 3 489 23 27
E-Mail: info@ergon.be

CRH plc—(Continued)

Web Site: www.ergon.be
Emp.: 350
Prefabricated Concrete Material Distr
S.I.C.: 5032
N.A.I.C.S.: 423320
Patrick van Dyck *(Head-Plng)*

Ergon Poland Sp. z o.o. (1)
Ul Grojecka 19
Badowo Msciska, 96-320 Mszczonow, Poland
Tel.: (48) 468 58 18 00
Fax: (48) 468 58 18 09
E-Mail: ergon@ergon.pl
Web Site: www.ergon-international.com
Building Material Distr
S.I.C.: 5039
N.A.I.C.S.: 423390
Robert Szymor *(Mng Dir)*

Explotacion de Aridos Calizos S.A. (1)
Cr Comarcal 246 Barcelona Valls Km 23
Garraf Cataluna
08871 Barcelona, Spain
Tel.: (34) 936 653 204
Fax: (34) 934 900 078
Building Material Distr
S.I.C.: 5032
N.A.I.C.S.: 423320

Faelbud Prefabrykaty Sp. z o.o. (1)
Ul Melgiewska 74
20-234 Lublin, Poland
Tel.: (48) 81 710 26 36
Fax: (48) 81 710 26 28
E-Mail: faelbud@faelbud.pl
Web Site: www.faelbud.pl
Emp.: 70
Building Material Mfr & Distr
S.I.C.: 3255
N.A.I.C.S.: 327120
Robert Szymor *(Gen Mgr)*

FCA Wholesalers Limited (1)
Alpha 319 Chobham Business Centre
Chertsey Road
Chobham, Surrey, GU24 8JB, United Kingdom
Tel.: (44) 1276 485450
Fax: (44) 1276 485451
E-Mail: sales@forsite.co.uk
Web Site: www.forsite.co.uk
Building Material Distr
S.I.C.: 5039
N.A.I.C.S.: 423390

Ferrobeton Beton-es Vasbetonelem gyarto Zrt (1)
Papirgyari Ut 18-22
Dunaujvaros, 2400, Hungary
Tel.: (36) 25283346
Concrete Brick Distr
S.I.C.: 5032
N.A.I.C.S.: 423320

Ferrobeton concrete and reinforced concrete producer Public Limited Company (1)
18-22 Papirgyari Street
Dunaujvaros, 2400, Hungary
Tel.: (36) 36 25 284 444
Fax: (36) 36 25 283 031
E-Mail: ferrobeton@ferrobeton.hu
Web Site: www.ferrobeton.hu
Concrete Block & Brick Mfr
S.I.C.: 3271
N.A.I.C.S.: 327331
Peter Juhasz *(Gen Dir)*

Ferrobeton Slovakia, s.r.o. (1)
Sladkovicova 8
943 02 Sturovo, Slovakia
Tel.: (421) 36 751 1150
Fax: (421) 36 752 4750
E-Mail: ferrobeton@ferrobeton.sk
Web Site: www.ferrobeton.sk
Emp.: 20
Building Material Distr
S.I.C.: 5032
N.A.I.C.S.: 423320

Finnsementti Oy (1)
Lars Sonckin Kaari 16
PL 115
02601 Espoo, Finland
Tel.: (358) 201 206 200
Fax: (358) 201 206 202
E-Mail: info@finnsementti.fi
Web Site: www.finnsementti.fi
Cement Mfr & Distr
S.I.C.: 3241
N.A.I.C.S.: 327310

F.J. Aschwanden AG (1)
Grenzstrasse 24
3250 Lyss, Switzerland
Tel.: (41) 323879595
Fax: (41) 323879599
E-Mail: info@aschwanden.com
Web Site: www.aschwanden.com
Emp.: 60
Metal Construction Accessory Mfr
S.I.C.: 3449
N.A.I.C.S.: 332323
Alex Frea *(Gen Mgr)*

Formigons Girona S.A. (1)
Disseminat S/N Vilatenim Figures
17484 Gerona, Spain
Tel.: (34) 972468070
Fax: (34) 972171899
Building Material Distr
S.I.C.: 5039
N.A.I.C.S.: 423390

Geoquip Limited (1)
Units 3 & 4 Duffield Road
Little Eaton, Derbyshire, DE21 5DR, United Kingdom
Tel.: (44) 1629 824891
Fax: (44) 1629 824896
E-Mail: info@geoquip.com
Web Site: www.geoquip.com
Emp.: 40
Electronic Security System Installation Services & Mfr
S.I.C.: 1731
N.A.I.C.S.: 238210
Stephen Midani *(Mng Dir)*

Grupa Ozarow S.A. (1)
Karsy 77
27-530 Ozarow, Poland
Tel.: (48) 158 39 11 00
Fax: (48) 158 39 13 88
E-Mail: marketing@ozarow.com.pl
Web Site: www.ozarow.com.pl
Emp.: 550
Cement Mfr
S.I.C.: 3241
N.A.I.C.S.: 327310
Barbara Sulowska *(Dir-IT)*

Grupa Prefabet S.A. (1)
Swierze Gorne
26-900 Kozienice, Poland
Tel.: (48) 48 330 97 40
Fax: (48) 48 614 37 89
E-Mail: Prefabet@grupa-prefabet.pl
Web Site: www.grupa-prefabet.pl
Emp.: 120
Building Material Mfr
S.I.C.: 3255
N.A.I.C.S.: 327120

Halfen AS (1)
Flintegata 4
4095 Stavanger, Norway
Tel.: (47) 51 82 34 00
Fax: (47) 51 82 34 01
E-Mail: post@halfen-frimeda.no
Web Site: www.halfen.no
Metal Product Distr
S.I.C.: 5051
N.A.I.C.S.: 423510

Halfen GmbH (1)
Liebigstr 14
40764 Langenfeld, Rheinland, Germany
Tel.: (49) 2173 970 0
Fax: (49) 2173 970 123
E-Mail: info@halfen.de
Web Site: www.halfen.com
Construction Fitting Mfr
S.I.C.: 3494
N.A.I.C.S.: 332919

Halfen S.R.L. (1)
Via F lli Bronzetti 28
24124 Bergamo, Italy
Tel.: (39) 035 0760711
Fax: (39) 035 0760799
E-Mail: info@halfen.it
Web Site: www.halfen.it
Emp.: 17
Building Fixture Mfr
S.I.C.: 3499
N.A.I.C.S.: 332999
Marco Bolis *(Gen Mgr)*

Hammerl GmbH & Co. KG (1)
Niedere Klinge 15
74376 Gemmrigheim, Germany
Tel.: (49) 7143 8448 0
Fax: (49) 7143 8448 88
E-Mail: sales@hammerl.de
Web Site: www.hammerl.de
Plastic Product Mfr & Distr
S.I.C.: 3089
N.A.I.C.S.: 326199
Juergen Uherek *(Gen Mgr)*

Heras-Adronit GmbH (1)
Raiffeisenring 44
46395 Bocholt, Germany
Tel.: (49) 2871 24414 0
Fax: (49) 2871 24414 99
E-Mail: info@heras-adronit.de
Web Site: www.heras-adronit.de
Security Fencing Services
S.I.C.: 3315
N.A.I.C.S.: 331222
Marc Peltzer *(Dir-Fin)*

Heras B.V. (1)
Hekdam 1
5688 JE Oirschot, Netherlands
Tel.: (31) 499 55 12 55
Fax: (31) 499 55 17 99
E-Mail: infonl@heras.nl
Web Site: www.heras.com
Emp.: 700
Security Fencing Services
S.I.C.: 3315
N.A.I.C.S.: 331222
Hans Michiels *(Mgr-Pur)*

Heras Cloture S.A.R.L. (1)
Allee des Lilas Les Fenieres-Bat A
01150 Saint-Vulbas, France
Tel.: (33) 4 74 36 67 11
Fax: (33) 4 74 36 69 51
E-Mail: info@heras.fr
Web Site: www.cloture-mobile.fr
Emp.: 10
Security System Services
S.I.C.: 7382
N.A.I.C.S.: 561621
Jerome Lardenois *(Gen Mgr)*

Heras Mobilzaun GmbH (1)
Heinrich-Malina-Str 100
47809 Krefeld, Germany
Tel.: (49) 2151 32 78 274
Fax: (49) 2151 32 78 275
E-Mail: mobilzaun@heras.de
Web Site: www.heras-mobilzaun.de
Emp.: 4
Electronic Security System Services
S.I.C.: 7382
N.A.I.C.S.: 561621
Hans Welding *(Gen Mgr)*

Heras Sks Gmbh (1)
Raiffeisenring 44
Bocholt, 46395, Germany
Tel.: (49) 287124414 0
E-Mail:
Concrete Block & Brick Mfr
S.I.C.: 3271
N.A.I.C.S.: 327331

Hylas B.V. (1)
Nijverheidsweg 3f
6662 NG Elst, Netherlands
Tel.: (31) 481 371948
Fax: (31) 481 373775
E-Mail: info@hylas.nl
Web Site: www.hylas.nl
Emp.: 25
Fabric Screen Mfr
S.I.C.: 3496
N.A.I.C.S.: 332618
Yao-Wen Chang *(Controller)*

Ibstock Brick Limited (1)
Leicester Road
Ibstock, Leicestershire, United Kingdom
Tel.: (44) 1530261999
E-Mail: marketing@ibstock.co.uk
Web Site: www.ibstock.co.uk
Building Products & Materials Mfr
S.I.C.: 3271
N.A.I.C.S.: 327331

Subsidiary:

Kevington Building Products Limited (2)
Hamsey Road
Sharpthorne, RH19 4PB, United Kingdom
Tel.: (44) 1342718899
Fax: (44) 1342718528
Web Site: www.kevington.com
Building Product & Material Mfr
S.I.C.: 3271
N.A.I.C.S.: 327331
Warren Dean *(Dir-Sls & Mktg)*

Subsidiary:

Manchester Brick & Precast Limited (3)
Haigh Avenue Whitehill Ind Est
Stockport, SK4 1NU, United Kingdom
Tel.: (44) 161 480 2621
Fax: (44) 161 480 0108
Web Site: www.manbrick.co.uk
Brick Mfr
S.I.C.: 3271
N.A.I.C.S.: 327331

J. De Saegher Steenhandel N.V. (1)
Engelselei 79
2140 Antwerp, Belgium
Tel.: (32) 3 2310821
Fax: (32) 3 2310282
E-Mail: info@desaegher.be
Web Site: www.desaegher.be
Building Material Distr
S.I.C.: 5039
N.A.I.C.S.: 423390

Jonker Beton B.V. (1)
Panovenweg 15
Postbus 6193
4004 JE Tiel, Netherlands
Tel.: (31) 344 624 488
Fax: (31) 344 624 384
Building Materials Distr
S.I.C.: 5039
N.A.I.C.S.: 423390

JURA-Holding AG (1)
Zurlindeninsel 1
Aarau, 5000, Switzerland
Tel.: (41) 62 838 05 05
Fax: (41) 62 838 05 01
E-Mail:
Investment Management Services
S.I.C.: 6211
N.A.I.C.S.: 523999

Kleiwarenfabriek Buggenum B.V. (1)
Dorpstraat 60
6082 AR Buggenum, Netherlands
Tel.: (31) 475 591666
Fax: (31) 475 518220
E-Mail: Buggenum@crhccs.com
Emp.: 20
Building Material Distr
S.I.C.: 5039
N.A.I.C.S.: 423390
Paul Collard *(Plant Mgr)*

Kooy Baksteencentrum B.V. (1)
Rembrandtlaan 38
3723 BJ Bilthoven, Netherlands
Tel.: (31) 30 22 59 800
Fax: (31) 30 22 59 801
E-Mail: info@kooy.nl
Web Site: www.kooy.nl
Building Material Distr
S.I.C.: 5039
N.A.I.C.S.: 423390
Marcel van Ginkel *(Dir-Fin)*

Laubeuf SAS (1)
5 avenue du General de Gaulle
94160 Saint-Mande, France
Tel.: (33) 141743660
Fax: (33) 148080645
E-Mail: office@laubeuf.com
Web Site: www.laubeuf.com
Roofing System Designer & Mfr
S.I.C.: 3446
N.A.I.C.S.: 332323

Marlux Klaps N.V. (1)
Albertkade 3
3980 Tessenderlo, Belgium
Tel.: (32) 13 67 91 00
Fax: (32) 13 67 91 61
E-Mail: info@marlux.com
Web Site: www.marlux.com

Emp.: 200
Building Material Distr
S.I.C.: 5032
N.A.I.C.S.: 423320
Patrick van der Hoeven *(Gen Mgr)*

Masfalt Sp. z o.o. (1)
Ul Stefana Bryly 4
05-800 Pruszkow, Poland
Tel.: (48) 22 758 89 81
Fax: (48) 22 758 89 76
E-Mail: masfalt@masfalt.pl
Web Site: www.masfalt.pl
Building Material Mfr & Distr
S.I.C.: 3297
N.A.I.C.S.: 327120

Mavotrans B.V. (1)
Storkstraat 25
Postbus 81
2700 AB Zoetermeer, Netherlands
Tel.: (31) 79 344 63 63
Fax: (31) 79 344 63 88
E-Mail: info@mavotrans.nl
Web Site: www.mavotrans.nl
Emp.: 30
Building Material Mfr & Distr
S.I.C.: 3255
N.A.I.C.S.: 327120
Marion Berg-Meere *(Dir-Fin)*

Northstone (NI) Limited (1)
99 Kingsway Dunmurry
Belfast, BT17 9NU, United Kingdom
Tel.: (44) 28 9055 1200
Fax: (44) 28 9060 1930
Web Site: www.northstone-ni.co.uk
Building Material Distr
S.I.C.: 5039
N.A.I.C.S.: 423390
Graham McQuillan *(Mng Dir)*

N.V.B. Ubbens Bouwstoffen B.V. (1)
Slauerhoffweg 6
Postbus 48
8912 BH Leeuwarden, Netherlands
Tel.: (31) 58 2937777
Fax: (31) 58 2122352
E-Mail: leeuwarden@nvbvermeulen.nl
Web Site: www.nvbubbens.nl
Building Materials Distr
S.I.C.: 5039
N.A.I.C.S.: 423390

Oeterbeton N.V. (1)
Hooggeistersveld 15
3680 Maaseik, Belgium
Tel.: (32) 89 86 01 00
Fax: (32) 89 86 37 05
E-Mail: info@oeterbeton.be
Web Site: www.oeterbeton.be
Precast Concrete Mfr
S.I.C.: 3272
N.A.I.C.S.: 327390

O.K.S.M. Sp. z o.o. (1)
ul Budowlana 3
10-424 Olsztyn, Poland
Tel.: (48) 89 521 10 00
Fax: (48) 89 512 26 37
E-Mail:
Web Site: www.oksm.pl
Mineral Mining Services
S.I.C.: 1499
N.A.I.C.S.: 212399
Malgorzata Zydek *(Chm-Mgmt Bd & Dir Gen)*
Krzysztof Starzyk *(Vice Chm-Mgmt Bd)*
Krzysztof Maczka *(Dir-Production)*
Piotr Zelazowski *(Dir-Trade)*

Oldcastle Building Envelop Canada, Inc. (1)
3601 72 Ave SE
Calgary, AB, T2C 2K3, Canada
Tel.: (403) 279-2544
Fax: (403) 279-0070
Building Material Distr
S.I.C.: 5032
N.A.I.C.S.: 423320

Oldcastle Building Products Canada, Inc. (1)
8145 Rue Bombardier
Anjou, QC, H1J 1A5, Canada
Tel.: (514) 351-2120
Fax: (514) 352-9802
Emp.: 200
Concrete Block Mfr & Distr
S.I.C.: 3271
N.A.I.C.S.: 327331
Luc Vaillancourt *(VP-Fin & Dev)*

Division:

Oldcastle Building Products Canada, Inc. - Permacon Division (2)
8140 rue Bombardier
Anjou, QC, H1J 1A4, Canada
Tel.: (888) 737-6226
Fax: (888) 475-8068
Web Site: www.permacon.ca
Emp.: 800
Concrete Paver Mfr
S.I.C.: 3272
N.A.I.C.S.: 327390
Gary Belisle *(Pres)*

Subsidiary:

Expocrete Concrete Products Ltd. (2)
16333-137 Ave
Edmonton, AB, T5V 1N8, Canada
Tel.: (780) 447-2122
Fax: (780) 447-1426
Toll Free: (800) 387-5630
E-Mail: sales_edmont@expocrete.com
Web Site: www.expocrete.com
Sales Range: $25-49.9 Million
Emp.: 100
Concrete Products Mfr
S.I.C.: 3272
N.A.I.C.S.: 327390
Jay Frederickson *(Pres)*
Joseph Concini *(CFO)*
John Heffernan *(Sr VP-Sls & Mktg)*

Plaka Group S.R.L. (1)
Via Camillo Vazzoler
31015 Conegliano, Treviso, Italy
Tel.: (39) 0 438 49 23 37
Fax: (39) 0 438 30 91 20
E-Mail: info@plakagroup.it
Web Site: www.plakagroup.it
Building Material Distr
S.I.C.: 5032
N.A.I.C.S.: 423320

Plakabeton France S.A. (1)
6 Rue de Cabanis L'Union
31240 Toulouse, France
Tel.: (33) 5 34 25 39 25
Fax: (33) 5 34 25 54 85
E-Mail: info@plakagroup.fr
Building Material Retailer
S.I.C.: 5211
N.A.I.C.S.: 444190

Plakabeton N.V. (1)
Industrielaan 2
1740 Ternat, Belgium
Tel.: (32) 2 582 29 45
Fax: (32) 2 582 19 62
E-Mail: info@plakagroup.be
Web Site: en.plakagroup.com
Emp.: 130
Building Material Distr
S.I.C.: 5039
N.A.I.C.S.: 423390
Eef Tuerlinckx *(Dir-Fin)*

Plakabeton S.L.U. (1)
Poligono Industrial Santa Rita C/ Acustica 14
08755 Barcelona, Spain
Tel.: (34) 93 772 31 00
Fax: (34) 93 772 31 03
E-Mail: barcelona@plakagroup.es
Web Site: es.plakagroup.com
Emp.: 24
Building Material Distr
S.I.C.: 5039
N.A.I.C.S.: 423390
Alexandre Damon *(Mng Dir)*

Polbruk S.A. (1)
ul Nowy Swiat 16 c
80-299 Gdansk, Poland
Tel.: (48) 58 554 59 45
Fax: (48) 58 554 59 50
Web Site: www.polbruk.pl
Emp.: 60
Ready Mix Concrete Mfr
S.I.C.: 3273
N.A.I.C.S.: 327320
Czeslaw Pyjaj *(Head-Concrete Laboratory)*

Prefaco N.V. (1)
Hoeksken 5A
9280 Lebbeke, Belgium
Tel.: (32) 5 376 73 73
Fax: (32) 5 379 00 12
E-Mail: info@prefaco.be
Web Site: www.prefaco.be
Concrete Block & Brick Mfr
S.I.C.: 3271
N.A.I.C.S.: 327331

Premac spol. s.r.o. (1)
Stara Vajnorska 25
832 17 Bratislava, Slovakia
Tel.: (421) 2 492 79 111
Fax: (421) 2 492 79 147
E-Mail: Premac@Premac.sk
Web Site: www.Premac.sk
Emp.: 120
Concrete Paving Services
S.I.C.: 1799
N.A.I.C.S.: 238990
Miroslav Lesko *(Mng Dir)*

Premier Cement Limited (1)
Shed E Kings Dock Swansea
SA1 8QT Swansea, United Kingdom
Tel.: (44) 1792645302
Fax: (44) 1792645411
E-Mail: info@premiercement.co.uk
Web Site: www.premiercement.co.uk
Emp.: 5
Cement Mfr
S.I.C.: 3241
N.A.I.C.S.: 327310
Philip Matthews *(Reg Mgr-Sls)*

Quester Baustoffhandel GmbH (1)
Heiligenstadter Strasse 24
Vienna, 1190, Austria
Tel.: (43) 50 1616 710
Fax: (43) 5016169102
E-Mail: info@quester.at
Web Site: www.quester.at
Emp.: 600
Building Material Distr
S.I.C.: 5039
N.A.I.C.S.: 423390
Michael Janisch *(Mgr-IT)*

Regusci S.A. (1)
Via San Gottardo 98
Bellinzona, 6500, Switzerland
Tel.: (41) 91 820 23 23
Fax: (41) 91 820 23 13
E-Mail: info@reguscireco.ch
Web Site: www.regusci.ch
Construction Material Distr
S.I.C.: 5039
N.A.I.C.S.: 423390

Remacle NV/SA. (1)
Rue Sous-la-Ville 8
5150 Floriffoux, Belgium
Tel.: (32) 81 44 88 88
Fax: (32) 81 44 88 99
E-Mail: info@remacle.be
Web Site: www.remacle.be
Building Material Distr
S.I.C.: 5039
N.A.I.C.S.: 423390

Reuss-Seifert GmbH (1)
Wuppertaler Strasse 77
45549 Sprockhovel, Germany
Tel.: (49) 2324 9046 0
Fax: (49) 2324 9046 329
E-Mail: info@reuss-seifert.de
Web Site: www.reuss-seifert.de
Construction Equipment Whslr
S.I.C.: 5082
N.A.I.C.S.: 423810

Royal Roofing Materials B.V. (1)
Bijsterhuizen 24-01
6604 LK Wijchen, Netherlands
Tel.: (31) 24 371 73 91
Fax: (31) 24 378 32 63
E-Mail: info@royalroofingmaterials.com
Web Site: www.royalroofingmaterials.com
Emp.: 170
Roofing Material Distr
S.I.C.: 5039
N.A.I.C.S.: 423390
Jos de Nijs *(Mng Dir)*

Rudus Oy Ab (1)
Pronssitie 1
PO Box 49
FIN-00441 Helsinki, Finland (100%)
Tel.: (358) 20447711
Fax: (358) 204477410
Web Site: www.rudus.fi
Sales Range: $250-299.9 Million
Emp.: 50
Ready-mixed Concrete & Aggregates Mfr
S.I.C.: 3272
N.A.I.C.S.: 327390

Subsidiary:

Lemminkainen Rakennustuotteet Oy (2)
Puusepantie 11
4360 Tuusula, Finland
Tel.: (358) 2071 50100
Fax: (358) 2071 54001
Emp.: 40
Building Materials Mfr & Distr
S.I.C.: 3271
N.A.I.C.S.: 327331

SAX Sanitair N.V. (1)
Autostradeweg 3
9090 Melle, Belgium
Tel.: (32) 9 252 44 00
Fax: (32) 9 252 52 12
E-Mail: info@sax-sanitair.be
Web Site: www.sax-sanitair.be
Sanitary & Plumbing Product Retailer
S.I.C.: 5211
N.A.I.C.S.: 444190

Schelfhout N.V. (1)
Rue de l'Avenir 18
Villers-le-Bouillet, 4530, Belgium
Tel.: (32) 4 228 28 28
Fax: (32) 4 228 28 68
E-Mail: info@schelfhout.com
Web Site: www.schelfhout.com
Emp.: 38
Wall Precast Concrete Mfr
S.I.C.: 3272
N.A.I.C.S.: 327390
Mark Schelfhout *(Mng Dir)*

Schrauwen Sanitair en Verwarming BVBA (1)
Kapelsesteenweg 80
Brasschaat, 2930, Belgium
Tel.: (32) 3 645 24 79
Fax: (32) 3 645 95 05
E-Mail: info@schrauwen.be
Web Site: www.schrauwen.be
Sanitary & Heating Material Sales & Installation Services
S.I.C.: 5074
N.A.I.C.S.: 423720

Stoel van Klaveren Bouwstoffen B.V. (1)
Oud Zaenden 10
1506 PE Zaandam, Netherlands
Tel.: (31) 75 6168851
Fax: (31) 75 6701034
E-Mail: Zaandam@stoelvanklaveren.nl
Web Site: www.stoelvanklaveren.nl
Emp.: 7
Building Material Distr
S.I.C.: 5039
N.A.I.C.S.: 423390
Jan Buiten *(Mgr-Store)*

Stradal Sas (1)
47 Avenue des Genottes
95800 Cergy-Pontoise, France
Tel.: (33) 1 34 25 55 55
Fax: (33) 1 34 25 55 85
Emp.: 1,200
Concrete Product Mfr & Distr
S.I.C.: 3272
N.A.I.C.S.: 327390

Struyk Verwo Groep B.V. (1)
De Waard 9
4906 BC Oosterhout, Netherlands
Tel.: (31) 162 475475
Fax: (31) 162 475499
Web Site: www.struykverwo.nl
Building Material Dealer
S.I.C.: 5211
N.A.I.C.S.: 444190

Superglass S.A. (1)
Marcos Sastre 627 El Talar De Pacheco
Buenos Aires, B1618GSZ, Argentina
Tel.: (54) 1141166400
Fax: (54) 1145132361
E-Mail:
Tempered Glass Product Mfr
S.I.C.: 3231
N.A.I.C.S.: 327215

CRH plc—(Continued)

Supreme Concrete Limited (1)
Coppingford Hall Coppingford Road Sawtry
Huntingdon, PE28 5GP, United Kingdom
Tel.: (44) 1487 833300
Fax: (44) 1487 833348
E-Mail: sales@supremeconcrete.co.uk
Web Site: www.supremeconcrete.co.uk
Emp.: 50
Building Material Mfr
S.I.C.: 3089
N.A.I.C.S.: 326199
Lisa Mackett *(Area Mgr-Sls)*

TangoRail Limited (1)
CRH House Units 1-3 Prothero Industrial Estate
Bilport Lane, Wednesbury, West Midlands, WS10 0NT, United Kingdom
Tel.: (44) 8448 360008
Fax: (44) 8448 360009
E-Mail: info@tangorail.com
Web Site: www.tangorail.com
Emp.: 15
Railway Security System Services
S.I.C.: 7382
N.A.I.C.S.: 561621

ThermiSol Denmark A/S (1)
Lundagervej 20
DK 8722 Hedensted, Denmark (100%)
Tel.: (45) 76741611
Fax: (45) 76741600
E-Mail: thermisol@thermisol.dk
Web Site: www.thermisol.dk
Emp.: 30
Chemicals & Polystryene
S.I.C.: 2899
N.A.I.C.S.: 325998
senn Bauotlos *(Mng Dir)*

ThermiSol Finland Oy (1)
Toravantie 18
FIN 38210 Sastamala, Finland FI
Tel.: (358) 108419200
Telex: 22528 isora fi
Fax: (358) 108419225
E-Mail: info@thermisol.fi
Web Site: www.thermisol.fi
Emp.: 109
Produces & Markets Expanded Polystyrene Products in Finland
S.I.C.: 3086
N.A.I.C.S.: 326140
Veli Ollila *(Mng Dir)*

Transpave, Inc. (1)
500 Rue Saint-Eustache
Saint-Eustache, QC, J7R 7E7, Canada
Tel.: (450) 491-7800
Fax: (450) 491-4600
Toll Free: (800) 363-8099
E-Mail: info@transpave.com
Web Site: www.transpave.com
Emp.: 50
Concrete Block Mfr
S.I.C.: 3271
N.A.I.C.S.: 327331
Richard Caissy *(Mgr-Sls)*

TUVAN-stangsel AB (1)
Knut Pals Vag 1
256 69 Helsingborg, Sweden
Tel.: (46) 42 29 56 50
Fax: (46) 42 29 74 80
E-Mail: info@heras.se
Web Site: www.heras.se
Security System Services
S.I.C.: 7382
N.A.I.C.S.: 561621

Unipol Holland B.V. (1)
Rijnstraat 15a
5347 KL Oss, Netherlands
Tel.: (31) 412 643 243
Fax: (31) 412 636 946
E-Mail: sales@unipol.nl
Web Site: www.unipol.nl
Construction Material Distr
S.I.C.: 5039
N.A.I.C.S.: 423390
Andries van Bergen *(Mng Dir)*

Van Neerbos Belgie N.V. (1)
Koralenhoeve 5
2160 Wommelgem, Belgium
Tel.: (32) 3 355 27 40
Fax: (32) 3 355 27 67
Emp.: 20
Building Material Distr
S.I.C.: 5032
N.A.I.C.S.: 423320

Van Neerbos Bouwmarkten B.V. (1)
Reeuwijkse Poort B5 nr 201
2811 MZ Reeuwijk, Netherlands
Tel.: (31) 182 506000
Fax: (31) 182 506005
E-Mail: info@vnb-diy.com
Web Site: www.vanneerbosbouwmarkten.com
Emp.: 110
Building Material Distr
S.I.C.: 5039
N.A.I.C.S.: 423390
Emiel Hopmans *(Gen Mgr)*

Vidrios Dell Orto, S.A. (1)
Piloto Lazo 419
Cerrillos, Santiago, Chile
Tel.: (56) 2 7511800
Fax: (56) 2 5383385
E-Mail: contacto@dellorto.cl
Web Site: www.dellorto.cl
Tempered Glass Product Mfr
S.I.C.: 3231
N.A.I.C.S.: 327215
Bernardo Alamos *(Gen Mgr)*

VVM N.V. (1)
Kaaistraat 75
8800 Roeselare, Belgium
Tel.: (32) 51 207313
Fax: (32) 51 241310
E-Mail: info@vvmcem.be
Web Site: www.vvmcem.be
Ready Mix Concrete Mfr
S.I.C.: 3273
N.A.I.C.S.: 327320

West Midland Fencing Limited (1)
West Midland House Alma Street
Wednesbury, WS10 0QB, United Kingdom
Tel.: (44) 1215051022
Fax: (44) 1215051027
Security Fencing Services
S.I.C.: 1799
N.A.I.C.S.: 238990

ZPW Trzuskawica S.A. (1)
Sitkowka 1
26-052 Sitkowka-Nowiny, Poland
Tel.: (48) 41 346 91 30
Fax: (48) 41 346 91 30
E-Mail: info@trzuskawica.pl
Web Site: www.trzuskawica.pl
Limestone Mfr
S.I.C.: 1411
N.A.I.C.S.: 212311

CRICKET AUSTRALIA

60 Jolimont Street
Jolimont, VIC, 3002, Australia
Tel.: (61) 396539999
Fax: (61) 396539911
E-Mail: public.enquiries@cricket.com.au
Web Site: www.cricket.com.au
Rev.: $175,482,101
Assets: $124,444,645
Liabilities: $115,954,427
Net Worth: $8,490,218
Earnings: ($36,100,798)
Emp.: 70
Fiscal Year-end: 06/30/13

Business Description:
National Cricket Association
S.I.C.: 7941
N.A.I.C.S.: 711211

Personnel:
Wally Edwards *(Chm)*
James Sutherland *(CEO)*
Dean Kino *(Sec & Gen Mgr-Legal & Bus Affairs)*

Board of Directors:
Wally Edwards
John Bannon
Earl Eddings
Tony Harrison
Jacquie Hey
Michael Kasprowicz
David Peever
Kevin Roberts
Mark Taylor

CRICKET RESOURCES INC.

2630 - 1075 W Georgia Street
Vancouver, BC, V6E 3C9, Canada
Tel.: (604) 661-0742
Fax: (604) 682-1288
Year Founded: 2006
CKC—(TSXV)
Assets: $259,743
Liabilities: $25,643
Net Worth: $234,100
Earnings: ($127,556)
Fiscal Year-end: 09/30/12

Business Description:
Mineral Exploration Services
S.I.C.: 1099
N.A.I.C.S.: 212299

Personnel:
Michael Dake *(Pres, CEO & Sec)*
Joel Dumaresq *(CFO)*

Board of Directors:
Michael Dake
Joel Dumaresq
Stephen B. Jackson

CRIF SPA

Via M Fantin 1-3
Bologna, 40131, Italy
Tel.: (39) 51 4176111
Fax: (39) 51 4176010
E-Mail: info@crif.com
Web Site: www.crif.com
Sales Range: $350-399.9 Million
Emp.: 1,500

Business Description:
Credit Reporting, Business Information & Decision Support Systems Mfr
S.I.C.: 7389
N.A.I.C.S.: 561499

Personnel:
Carlo Gherardi *(Pres & CEO)*

Non-U.S. Subsidiary:

CRIF AG (1)
Riesbachstrasse 61
8008 Zurich, Switzerland
Tel.: (41) 44 9135058
Fax: (41) 44 9135051
E-Mail: info.ch@crif.ch
Web Site: www.crif.ch
Credit Reporting, Business Information & Decision Support Systems Mfr
S.I.C.: 7389
N.A.I.C.S.: 561499
Andreas Dietschweiler *(Mgr-Bus Dev & Risk)*

Subsidiary:

Orell Fussli Wirtschaftsinformationen AG (2)
Hagenholzstrasse 81
8050 Zurich, Switzerland
Tel.: (41) 443051212
Fax: (41) 443051214
E-Mail: info@ofwi.ch
Web Site: www.ofwi.ch
Emp.: 100
Business Support Services
S.I.C.: 7389
N.A.I.C.S.: 561499
Markus Binzegger *(CEO)*

CRIMSON BIOENERGY LTD.

Suite 202 5752 176th Street
Surrey, BC, V3S 4C8, Canada
Tel.: (604) 574-3100
Fax: (604) 576-1208
E-Mail: info@crimsonbioenergy.com
Web Site: www.crimsonbioenergy.com
Year Founded: 2009
CSN—(TSXV)
Rev.: $1,998
Assets: $546,513
Liabilities: $882,019
Net Worth: ($335,506)
Earnings: ($127,284)
Emp.: 2
Fiscal Year-end: 12/31/12

Business Description:
Investment Services
S.I.C.: 6211
N.A.I.C.S.: 523999

Personnel:
Grant Sutherland *(Chm)*
William W. Carr *(Pres & CEO)*
Garry Renwick *(CFO)*

Board of Directors:
Grant Sutherland
William W. Carr
Tom Locke

Transfer Agent:
Valiant Trust Company
750 Cambie St, Ste 600
Vancouver, BC, V6B 0A2, Canada

CRIMSON TIDE PLC

Heathervale House Vale Avenue
Tunbridge Wells, Kent, TN1 1DJ, United Kingdom
Tel.: (44) 1892542444
Fax: (44) 1892510441
E-Mail: info@crimsontide.co.uk
Web Site: www.crimsontide.co.uk
TIDE—(LSE)
Rev.: $1,936,210
Assets: $3,700,276
Liabilities: $901,775
Net Worth: $2,798,502
Earnings: $7,896
Emp.: 13
Fiscal Year-end: 12/31/12

Business Description:
Mobile Data Solution Provider
S.I.C.: 3663
N.A.I.C.S.: 334220

Personnel:
Barrie Reginald John Whipp *(Chm)*
Stephen Keith Goodwin *(CEO & Sec)*

Board of Directors:
Barrie Reginald John Whipp
Rowley Stuart Ager
Graham Basil Ashley
Stephen Keith Goodwin
Luke Anthony Jeffrey
Jeremy Walter Frederick Roth

Legal Counsel:
Gordons Partnership LLP
22 Great James Street
London, WC1N 3ES, United Kingdom

Subsidiary:

Crimson Tide mPro Limited (1)
The Tavern Cellars 39-41 The Pantiles
Tunbridge Wells, Kent, TN2 5TE, United Kingdom
Tel.: (44) 1892542444
Fax: (44) 1892510441
E-Mail: info@crimsontide.co.uk
Web Site: www.crimsontide.co.uk
Emp.: 10
Mobile Data & Software Solutions
S.I.C.: 7374
N.A.I.C.S.: 518210
Keith Knott *(Mng Dir)*
Barrie R Whipp *(Sec)*

CRIMSONLOGIC PTE LTD

31 Science Park Road The Crimson
Singapore, 117611, Singapore
Tel.: (65) 68877888
Fax: (65) 67785277
E-Mail: sales@crimsonlogic.com
Web Site: www.crimsonlogic.com
Rev.: $106,200,000
Emp.: 250

Business Description:
Information Technology Services
S.I.C.: 7379
N.A.I.C.S.: 518210

Personnel:
Leong Peng Kiong *(CEO)*
Chong Kok Keong *(Sr VP)*

CRISTALERIAS DE CHILE S.A.
Ave Apoquindo 3669 16th Fl Las Condes
Santiago, Chile
Tel.: (56) 27878888
Fax: (56) 27878800
Web Site: www.cristalchile.cl
Year Founded: 1904
Sales Range: $300-349.9 Million
Emp.: 710
Business Description:
Glass & Plastic Containers Mfr
S.I.C.: 3221
N.A.I.C.S.: 327213
Personnel:
Baltazar Sanchez Guzman *(Pres)*
Board of Directors:
Joaquin Barros Fontaine
Patricio Claro Grez
Jaime Claro Valdes
Gustavo De La Cerda Acuna
Christian Eyzaguirre Johnston
Juan Augustin Figueroa Yavar
Patricio Garcia Dominguez
Baltazar Sanchez Guzman
Alfonso Swett Saavedra
Subsidiary:

S.A. Vina Santa Rita **(1)**
Avenida Apoquindo 3669 Piso 6
Santiago, Chile (100%)
Tel.: (56) 23622000
Fax: (56) 22062848
E-Mail: remexportaciones@santarita.cl
Web Site: www.santarita.cl
Emp.: 100
Wine & Distilled Alcoholic Beverage Whslr
S.I.C.: 5181
N.A.I.C.S.: 424810
Luis Arturo Valverde *(Gen Mgr)*

CRISTALLERIA ARTISTICA LA PIANA S.P.A.
Localita Catarelli
I 53034 Colle di Val d'Elsa, SI, Italy
Tel.: (39) 0577910111
Fax: (39) 0577910432
E-Mail: mkt@calp.it
Web Site: www.calp.it
Year Founded: 1967
Emp.: 793
Business Description:
Crystal, Glass & Related Products Mfr & Distr
S.I.C.: 3229
N.A.I.C.S.: 327212
Personnel:
Pearucte Roberto *(Mgr-Mktg)*

CRISTIRO S.A.
Str Industriei nr 5
Bistrita, Romania
Tel.: (40) 263 238 066
Fax: (40) 263 234 525
E-Mail: cristiro@cristiro.ro
Web Site: www.romtradeinvest.ro
Year Founded: 1974
CROI—(BUC)
Rev.: $1,933,454
Assets: $2,189,643
Liabilities: $674,761
Net Worth: $1,514,882
Earnings: ($72,041)
Emp.: 121
Fiscal Year-end: 12/31/12
Business Description:
Household Glassware Mfr
S.I.C.: 3229
N.A.I.C.S.: 327212
Personnel:
Maria Balint *(Gen Mgr)*

CRITEO S.A.
32 rue Blanche
75009 Paris, France
Tel.: (33) 1 40 40 22 90
Fax: (33) 1 40 40 22 30
Web Site: www.criteo.com
Year Founded: 2005
CRTO—(NASDAQ)
Rev.: $609,756,862
Assets: $537,170,030
Liabilities: $173,104,144
Net Worth: $364,065,885
Earnings: $1,913,216
Emp.: 810
Fiscal Year-end: 12/31/13
Business Description:
Digital Display Advertising Solutions
S.I.C.: 7319
N.A.I.C.S.: 541890
Personnel:
Jean-Baptiste Rudelle *(Chm & CEO)*
Gregory G. Coleman *(Pres)*
Benoit Fouilland *(CFO)*
Pascal Gauthier *(COO)*
Romain Niccoli *(CTO)*
Franck Le Ouay *(Chief Scientific Officer)*
Eric Eichmann *(Chief Revenue Officer)*
Antoine Mingalon *(Chief Culture Officer)*
Board of Directors:
Jean-Baptiste Rudelle
Hubert de Pesquidoux
Byron B. Deeter
Marie Ekeland
Dana L. Evan
Benoist Grossmann
Dominique Vidal
James A. Warner

CRITES & RIDDELL BASICS
8203 Montreal Toronto Blvd
Montreal, QC, H4X 1N1, Canada
Tel.: (514) 368-8641
Fax: (514) 368-1212
Toll Free: (800) 263-8641
E-Mail: crites@crites-riddell.com
Web Site: www.crites-riddell.com
Year Founded: 1911
Rev.: $10,939,302
Emp.: 47
Business Description:
Office Supplies & Printing Service
S.I.C.: 5112
N.A.I.C.S.: 424120
Personnel:
Peter Lai *(Mng Partner)*

CRITICAL CAPITAL CORPORATION
Suite 1200 999 West Hastings Street
Vancouver, BC, V6C 2W2, Canada
Tel.: (604) 669-5244
Fax: (604) 669-5791
E-Mail: smalley@fraserlaw.com
Year Founded: 2009
CQZ.P—(TSXV)
Business Description:
Investment Services
S.I.C.: 6211
N.A.I.C.S.: 523999
Board of Directors:
Luis Goyzueta
David W. Smalley
Legal Counsel:
Fraser and Company LLP
Vancouver, BC, Canada
Transfer Agent:
Computershare Investor Services inc
3rd Fl 510 Burrard Street
Vancouver, BC, Canada

CRITICAL ELEMENTS CORPORATION
505 boul de Maisonneuve ouest Suite 906
Montreal, QC, H3A 3C2, Canada
Tel.: (514) 904-1496
Fax: (514) 904-1597
Web Site: www.cecorp.ca
CRE—(TSXV)
Rev.: $9,662
Assets: $14,806,726
Liabilities: $1,266,980
Net Worth: $13,539,746
Earnings: ($2,354,057)
Fiscal Year-end: 08/31/13
Business Description:
Metal Exploration Services
S.I.C.: 1081
N.A.I.C.S.: 213114
Personnel:
Jean-Sebastien Lavallee *(Pres & CEO)*
Nathalie Laurin *(CFO & Sec)*
Board of Directors:
Jean-Raymond Lavallee
Jean-Sebastien Lavallee
Jean-Francois Meilleur
Richard Saint-Jean
Marc Simpson
Legal Counsel:
Fasken Martineau DuMoulin S.E.N.C.R.L s.r.l / LLP
800 Place Victoria Suite 3700
Montreal, QC, Canada
Transfer Agent:
Computershare Investor Services Inc
1500 University Ste 700
Montreal, QC, Canada

CRITICAL OUTCOME TECHNOLOGIES INC.
700 Collip Circle Suite 213
London, ON, N6G 4X8, Canada
Tel.: (519) 858-5157
Fax: (519) 858-5179
E-Mail: info@criticaloutcome.com
Web Site: www.criticaloutcome.com
COT—(OTC TSXV)
Int. Income: $5,934
Assets: $2,253,163
Liabilities: $376,250
Net Worth: $1,876,913
Earnings: ($2,610,102)
Emp.: 8
Fiscal Year-end: 04/30/13
Business Description:
Pharmaceutical Product Development Services
S.I.C.: 2834
N.A.I.C.S.: 325412
Personnel:
John C. Drake *(Chm)*
Wayne R. Danter *(Pres & CEO)*
Gene Kelly *(CFO)*
Board of Directors:
John C. Drake
Douglas S. Alexander
Wayne R. Danter
Kathleen A. Ferguson
Bruno Maruzzo
Brent Norton
Murray Wallace
Thomas Wellner
Transfer Agent:
Computershare Investor Services Inc
Suite 600 530 8th Avenue S W
Calgary, AB, Canada

CRITICALCONTROL SOLUTIONS CORP.
840 7th Ave SW Suite 1100
Calgary, AB, T2P 3G2, Canada
Tel.: (403) 705-7500
Fax: (403) 705-7555
Toll Free: (855) 426-6368
E-Mail: info@criticalcontrol.com
Web Site: www.criticalcontrol.com
CCZ—(TSX)
Rev.: $46,542,998
Assets: $40,307,511
Liabilities: $15,031,570
Net Worth: $25,275,941
Earnings: $308,146
Emp.: 359
Fiscal Year-end: 12/31/12
Business Description:
Business Process & Information Control Solutions
S.I.C.: 7389
N.A.I.C.S.: 561499
Personnel:
Alykhan A. Mamdani *(Founder, Pres & CEO)*
George William Watson *(Chm)*
Bruce Byford *(CFO)*
Brenton Lawther *(Pres-Ops-GAS Analytical Service Inc)*
Board of Directors:
George William Watson
Gary L. Bentham
William Hammett
Alykhan A. Mamdani
Dennis L. Nerland
Murray D. Smith
Thomas Ulrich
Transfer Agent:
Computershare Trust Company of Canada
530 8th Ave SW 6th Floor
Calgary, AB, T2P 3S8, Canada
Tel.: (403) 267-6800
Fax: (403) 267-6529
Subsidiaries:

CriticalControl Energy Services **(1)**
1100 840 7th Ave SW
Calgary, AB, T2P 3G2, Canada
Tel.: (403) 705-7500
Fax: (403) 705-7555
Web Site: www.criticalcontrol.com
Emp.: 80
Business Management Services
S.I.C.: 8748
N.A.I.C.S.: 541618
Alykhan Mamdeni *(Pres)*

CriticalControl Solutions Inc **(1)**
10045 111 St NW
Edmonton, AB, T5J 2M5, Canada
Tel.: (780) 423-3100
Fax: (780) 426-3925
Web Site: www.criticalcontrol.com
Emp.: 100
Business Management Services
S.I.C.: 8748
N.A.I.C.S.: 541618

CRITTALL WINDOWS LTD.
Francis House Freebournes Road
Witham, Essex, CM8 3UN, United Kingdom
Tel.: (44) 1376530800
Fax: (44) 1376530801
E-Mail: hq@crittall-windows.co.uk
Web Site: www.crittall-windows.co.uk
Sales Range: $10-24.9 Million
Emp.: 180
Business Description:
Window Mfr
S.I.C.: 3442
N.A.I.C.S.: 332321
Personnel:
John Pyatt *(Mng Dir)*

CRM COMPANY GROUP SA
10 place du General Catroux
75017 Paris, France
Tel.: (33) 1 73 04 60 00
Fax: (33) 1 42 67 13 05
E-Mail: contact@crmcompany.fr
Web Site: www.crmcompany.fr
ALCRM—(EUR)
Sales Range: $10-24.9 Million

CRM Company Group SA—(Continued)

Business Description:
Marketing Consulting Services
S.I.C.: 8742
N.A.I.C.S.: 541613
Personnel:
Bertrand Frey *(Chm-Exec Bd)*
Pascal Josselin *(Member-Exec Bd)*

CROATIA AIRLINES D.D.
Bhni 75b Buzin
10 010 Zagreb, Croatia
Tel.: (385) 16676555
Fax: (385) 16160152
E-Mail: contact@croatiaairlines.hr
Web Site: www.croatiaairlines.hr
CRAL-R-A—(ZAG)
Rev.: $274,896,400
Assets: $201,368,355
Liabilities: $175,247,117
Net Worth: $26,121,237
Earnings: ($86,694,757)
Emp.: 1,128
Fiscal Year-end: 12/31/12
Business Description:
Air Transportation Services
S.I.C.: 4512
N.A.I.C.S.: 481111
Personnel:
Sinisa Petrovic *(Chm-Supervisory Bd)*
Darko Prebezac *(Deputy Chm-Supervisory Bd)*
Kresimir Kucko *(Pres & CEO)*
Damir Sprem *(CFO & Exec VP-Fin)*
Zlatko Sirac *(COO)*
Josip Bilic *(Exec VP-HR, Legal Affairs & IT)*
Nenad Jelavic *(Exec VP-Sls, Mktg, Networking & Revenue Mgmt)*
Alen Kauzlaric *(Exec VP-Maintenance)*
Supervisory Board of Directors:
Sinisa Petrovic
Izidor Alfirevic
Ratimir Andrijanic
Ines Banicek-Vuk
Goran Becker
Marija Cacic
Tihomir Domazet
Josip Horvat
Bozo Jusup
Berislav Matijevic
Stanislav Pavlin
Tonci Peovic
Darko Prebezac
Subsidiaries:

Amadeus Croatia d.d. (1)
Trg kralja Tomislava 9
10000 Zagreb, Croatia (95%)
Tel.: (385) 14839555
Fax: (385) 4839444
E-Mail: amadeus@amadeus.hr
Web Site: www.amadeus.ht
Emp.: 8
Scheduled Passenger Air Transportation
S.I.C.: 4512
N.A.I.C.S.: 481111
Egen Sune *(CEO)*

Obzor putovanja d.o.o (1)
Teslina 5
10000 Zagreb, Croatia (100%)
Tel.: (385) 16160243
Fax: (385) 16160240
E-Mail: obzor@croatiaairlines.hr
Web Site: www.croatia.hr
Emp.: 13
Tour operators
S.I.C.: 4725
N.A.I.C.S.: 561520
Jabranka Skelin *(Gen Mgr)*

Pleso prijevoz d.o.o. (1)
Avenija Marina Drzica bb
10000 Zagreb, Croatia (50%)
Tel.: (385) 16331999
Fax: (385) 16111198
E-Mail: plesoprijevoz@plesoprijevoz.hr
Web Site: www.plesoprijevoz.hr
Emp.: 62
Other Support Activities for Road Transportation
S.I.C.: 4789
N.A.I.C.S.: 488490
Zvonka Zuhec *(Gen Mgr)*

CROATIA LLOYD D.D.
Ulica grada Vukovara 62
PO Box 737
10000 Zagreb, Croatia
Tel.: (385) 16308888
Fax: (385) 16308800
E-Mail: croatia.lloyd@croatialloyd.hr
Web Site: www.croatialloyd.hr
CRLL-R-A—(ZAG)
Sales Range: $25-49.9 Million
Business Description:
Reinsurance Services
S.I.C.: 6399
N.A.I.C.S.: 524130
Personnel:
Zdravko Zrinusic *(Chm-Supervisory Bd)*
Robert Stude *(Chm-Mgmt Bd)*
Silvana Ivancic *(Vice Chm-Supervisory Bd)*
Kitica Mioc *(Member-Mgmt Bd)*
Supervisory Board of Directors:
Zdravko Zrinusic
Silvana Ivancic
Nikola Mijatovic
Ramis Serifovic
Zoran Zaninovic

CROCODILE GARMENTS LIMITED
1/ F Lai Sun Commercial Centre
680 Cheung Sha Wan Road,
Kowloon, China (Hong Kong)
Tel.: (852) 27853898
Fax: (852) 27860190
E-Mail: corpadmin@crocodile.com.hk
Web Site: www.crocodile.com.hk
0122—(HKG)
Rev.: $64,404,206
Assets: $260,622,521
Liabilities: $78,265,558
Net Worth: $182,356,964
Earnings: $30,546,063
Emp.: 778
Fiscal Year-end: 07/31/13
Business Description:
Apparel & Accessories Mfr
S.I.C.: 5699
N.A.I.C.S.: 315220
Personnel:
Kin Ming Lam *(Chm & CEO)*
Vanessa Wai Shan Lam *(Deputy CEO)*
Ming Kin Ko *(CFO & Sec)*
Board of Directors:
Kin Ming Lam
Bing Chiu Chow
Diana Suk Ying Lam
Matthew Kin Hong Lam
Peter Kin Ngok Lam
Vanessa Wai Shan Lam
William Shu Yin Leung
Edward Yee Hwa Wan
Sui Sang Yeung
Legal Counsel:
Vincent T. K. Cheung, Yap & Co.
11th Floor Central Building 1-3 Pedder Street
Central, China (Hong Kong)

Reed Smith Richards Butler
20th Floor Alexandra House 18 Chater Road
Central, China (Hong Kong)

Deacons
5th Floor Alexandra House 18 Chater Road
Central, China (Hong Kong)
Transfer Agent:
Tricor Tengis Limited
26th Floor Tesbury Centre 28 Queen's Road East
Wanchai, China (Hong Kong)
Tel.: (852) 29801333
Fax: (852) 28108185

CROCOTTA ENERGY INC.
639 5 Avenue SW Suite 700
Calgary, AB, T2P OM9, Canada
Tel.: (403) 538-3737
Fax: (403) 538-3735
E-Mail: info@crocotta.ca
Web Site: www.crocotta.ca
CTA—(OTC TSX)
Sls.: $80,036,502
Assets: $299,180,140
Liabilities: $120,364,888
Net Worth: $178,815,252
Earnings: ($5,222,581)
Emp.: 20
Fiscal Year-end: 12/31/12
Business Description:
Oil & Natural Gas Exploration
S.I.C.: 1311
N.A.I.C.S.: 211111
Personnel:
Larry G. Moeller *(Chm)*
Robert J. Zakresky *(Pres & CEO)*
Nolan Chicoine *(CFO & VP-Fin)*
Terry L. Trudeau *(COO & VP-Ops)*
Board of Directors:
Larry G. Moeller
Brian Boulanger
Gary W. Burns
Donald Darrell Copeland
Don Cowie
Daryl Harvey Gilbert
Brian Krausert
Patricia Phillips
Robert J. Zakresky
Legal Counsel:
Gowling Lafleur Henderson LLP
1400 700 2nd St SW
Calgary, AB, Canada
Transfer Agent:
Valiant Trust Company
606 4th Street SW Suite 310
Calgary, AB, T2P 1T1, Canada
Tel.: (403) 233-2801
Fax: (403) 233-2857

CRODA INTERNATIONAL PLC
Cowick Hall
Snaith, Goole, East Yorkshire, DN14 9AA, United Kingdom
Tel.: (44) 1405860551
Fax: (44) 1405861767
E-Mail: enquiries@croda.com
Web Site: www.croda.com
Year Founded: 1925
CRDA—(LSE OTC)
Rev.: $1,661,255,151
Assets: $1,584,817,515
Liabilities: $1,041,067,968
Net Worth: $543,749,547
Earnings: $255,687,051
Emp.: 3,288
Fiscal Year-end: 12/31/12
Business Description:
Specialty Chemicals Mfr
S.I.C.: 2869
N.A.I.C.S.: 325199
Personnel:
Steve E. Foots *(Grp CEO)*
Keith Layden *(CTO)*
Stuart Arnott *(Pres-Global Ops)*
David Barraclough *(Pres-Asia Pacific)*
Sandra Breene *(Pres-Consumer Care-Europe)*
Nick Challoner *(Pres-Latin America)*
Kevin Gallagher *(Pres-North America)*
Maarten Heybroek *(Pres-Performance Technologies & Indus Chemical-Europe)*
Tom Brophy *(Gen Counsel & Sec)*
Graham Myers *(Treas & Controller-Fin Grp)*
Board of Directors:
Martin Flower
Sean Michael Christie
Alan M. Ferguson
Steve E. Foots
Helena Ganczakowski
Keith Layden
Nigel Turner
Steve Williams
Subsidiaries:

Croda Chemicals Europe Ltd (1)
Cowick Hall
Snaith, DN14 9AA Goole, E Yorkshire, United Kingdom UK
Tel.: (44) 1405860551 (100%)
Fax: (44) 1405861767
E-Mail: enquiries@croda.com
Web Site: www.croda.com
Emp.: 300
Mfr of Polymer Additives
S.I.C.: 2899
N.A.I.C.S.: 325998
Michael Humphrey *(CEO)*

Croda Chemicals International Ltd (1)
Cowick Hall
Goole, North Humberside, DN14 9AA, United Kingdom
Tel.: (44) 1405 860 551
Fax: (44) 1405 861 767
Chemical Products Mfr
S.I.C.: 2819
N.A.I.C.S.: 325180
Michael Humphrey *(Grp CEO)*

Croda Overseas Holdings Ltd (1)
Cowick Hall
Goole, East Yorkshire, DN14 9AA, United Kingdom
Tel.: (44) 1405 860551
Investment Management Services
S.I.C.: 6211
N.A.I.C.S.: 523999

John L. Seaton & Co. Ltd (1)
7 Waterside Business Park
Livingstone Rd, HU13 0EG Hessle, Yorkshire, United Kingdom UK
Tel.: (44) 1482579700 (100%)
Fax: (44) 1482647313
E-Mail: sales@seatons-uk.co.uk
Web Site: www.croda.com
Emp.: 20
Vegetable Oil Mfr
S.I.C.: 2079
N.A.I.C.S.: 311225

U.S. Subsidiaries:

Croda Inc. (1)
300-A Columbus Cir
Edison, NJ 08837 (100%)
Tel.: (732) 417-0800
Web Site: www.crodausa.com
Emp.: 4
Specialty Chemicals Distr
S.I.C.: 2899
N.A.I.C.S.: 325998
Kevin Gallagher *(Pres)*

SEDERMA Inc. (1)
300 Columbus Cir
Edison, NJ 08837
Tel.: (732) 692-1652
Fax: (732) 417-0804
E-Mail: sederma-usa@croda.com
Web Site: www.sederma.fr/home.aspx?d=content&s=111&r=158&p=1425
Cosmetic Products Mfr
S.I.C.: 2844
N.A.I.C.S.: 325620

Non-U.S. Subsidiaries:

Croda Argentina SA (1)
Dardo Rocha 2924 Martinez
1640 Buenos Aires, Argentina AR
Tel.: (54) 11 4898 3000 (100%)
Fax: (54) 11 4898 3010
Web Site: www.croda.com
Emp.: 6
Specialty & Oleochemical Distr
S.I.C.: 5169
N.A.I.C.S.: 424690

Croda Canada Ltd. (1)
1700 Langstaff Ste 1000
Vaughan, Toronto, ON, L4k 3S3,

Canada Ca
Tel.: (905) 886-1383 (100%)
Fax: (905) 886-4753
E-Mail: info@croda.com
Emp.: 9
Specialty Chemicals Distr
S.I.C.: 5169
N.A.I.C.S.: 424690

Croda Chemicals International (Moscow) Ltd (1)
Raketnyi Boulevard 16 BC Alekseevskaya Tower
129164 Moscow, Russia
Tel.: (7) 495 660 8898
Fax: (7) 495 660 8898
Web Site: www.croda.com
Healthcare Chemical Products Whslr
S.I.C.: 5169
N.A.I.C.S.: 424690

Croda Chemicals SA Pty Ltd (1)
4 Cover St
PO Box 1641
Kempton Pk, Johannesburg, 1620, South Africa ZA
Tel.: (27) 113972380 (100%)
Fax: (27) 113972442
E-Mail: cridasa@mweb.co.za
Web Site: www.croda.co.za
Emp.: 30
Specialty Chemicals Distr
S.I.C.: 2899
N.A.I.C.S.: 325998
Tony Donoghue *(Mng Dir)*

Croda Chocques SAS (1)
1 Rue De Lapugnoy
Chocques, Pas-de-Calais, 62920, France
Tel.: (33) 321618400
Fax: (33) 321618484
Emp.: 100
Cosmetic Products Mfr
S.I.C.: 2844
N.A.I.C.S.: 325620
Jean Rapp *(Gen Mgr)*

Croda Colombia (1)
Calle 67 No 7-35 Oficina 1101 Edificio Plaza 67
Bogota, Colombia
Tel.: (57) 1 3214230, ext. 110
Fax: (57) 1 321 4230
Web Site: www.croda.com
Personal Care Product Whslr
S.I.C.: 5159
N.A.I.C.S.: 424590

Croda do Brasil Ltda (1)
Rua Croda 580-Distrito Industrial
Campinas, Sao Paulo, Brazil
Tel.: (55) 19 3765 3500
Fax: (55) 19 3765 3536
Web Site: www.croda.com.br
Specialty Chemicals Mfr
S.I.C.: 2899
N.A.I.C.S.: 325998

Croda Europe (1)
Buurtje 1
2802 BE Gouda, Netherlands NL
Tel.: (31) 182542911
Fax: (31) 182542250
Web Site: www.croda.com
Sls.: $791,389,184
Emp.: 400
Oleochemical Developer & Mfr
S.I.C.: 2899
N.A.I.C.S.: 325998
H. Legyus *(Gen Mgr)*

Non-U.S. Subsidiaries:

PT Croda Cikarang (2)
Cikarang Industrial Estate JL Jababeka IV Block V
Kav 74 75, Jakarta, Cikarang Bekasi, 17530, Indonesia Id
Tel.: (62) 218934923 (60%)
Fax: (62) 218934926
Web Site: www.croda.com
Emp.: 40
Mfr & Distr of Oleochemicals
S.I.C.: 2899
N.A.I.C.S.: 325998
Anand Aminbhavi *(Mng Dir)*

Croda France SAS (1)
Immoparc RN 10
PO Box 49
78197 Trappes, France FR
Tel.: (33) 130139430 (100%)
Fax: (33) 130629107
E-Mail: croda@croda.com
Emp.: 43
Specialty Chemicals Distr
S.I.C.: 2899
N.A.I.C.S.: 325998
Nicolas Gadda *(Mgr)*

Croda GmbH (1)
Herrenpfad Sud 33
41334 Nettetal, Germany De
Tel.: (49) 215781730 (100%)
Fax: (49) 21572132350
E-Mail: kontakt@croda.de
Web Site: www.croda.de
Emp.: 45
Specialty Chemicals Distr
S.I.C.: 2899
N.A.I.C.S.: 325998
Klaus L. Helmdach *(Mng Dir)*

Croda Holdings France SAS (1)
Immoparc Route Nationale No 10
78190 Trappes, France
Tel.: (33) 1 30 13 94 30
Fax: (33) 1 30 62 91 07
Emp.: 14
Chemical Products Distr
S.I.C.: 5169
N.A.I.C.S.: 424690
Nicolas Gedda *(Gen Mgr)*

Croda Hungary Ltd. (1)
Sasadi Ut 114
1112 Budapest, Hungary HU
Tel.: (36) 012470910 (100%)
Fax: (36) 12463491
E-Mail: croda.hungary.info@mail.datanet.hu
Web Site: www.corda.com
Emp.: 2
Specialty Chemicals Distr
S.I.C.: 2899
N.A.I.C.S.: 325998
Klaus Helmbech *(Mng Dir)*

Croda Iberica SA (1)
Plaza Francesc Macia 7 7 B
08029 Barcelona, Spain
Tel.: (34) 933 22 11 93
Fax: (34) 933 22 01 69
E-Mail: croda-iberica@croda.com
Web Site: www.croda.com
Specialty Chemicals Mfr & Distr
S.I.C.: 2899
N.A.I.C.S.: 325998

Croda Italiana S.p.A. (1)
Via Petro Grocco 917/919
27036 Mortara, Italy IT
Tel.: (39) 0384205011 (100%)
Fax: (39) 038491973
E-Mail: croda.italiana@croda.com
Web Site: www.croda.com
Emp.: 22
Specialty Chemicals Distr
S.I.C.: 2899
N.A.I.C.S.: 325998
Raffaele Bellasio *(Country Mgr-Sls)*

Croda Mexico, S.A. de C.V. (1)
Hamburgo 213 Piso 10
Parque Indus San Pablo Xalpa T, Chihuahua, Colonia Juarez, 54090, Mexico MX
Tel.: (52) 5553675760 (100%)
Fax: (52) 5553675684
E-Mail: ventas@crodala.com
Web Site: www.crodala.com
Sales Range: $10-24.9 Million
Emp.: 18
Specialty Chemicals Distr
S.I.C.: 5169
N.A.I.C.S.: 424690
Lfelai Gonzalez *(Mgr-Indus)*

Croda Middle East (1)
Office 511 LOB 16 Jebel Ali Free Zone
PO Box 17916
Dubai, United Arab Emirates
Tel.: (971) 4 887 0100
Fax: (971) 4 887 0300
Emp.: 6
Specialty Chemicals Distr
S.I.C.: 5169
N.A.I.C.S.: 424690
Deepak Diddi *(Reg Mgr)*

Croda Nederland B.V. (1)
Gouda Buurtje 1
2802 BE Gouda, Netherlands
Tel.: (31) 182 542911
Fax: (31) 182 542250
Emp.: 300
Chemical Products Mfr
S.I.C.: 2899
N.A.I.C.S.: 325998
Hubert Legius *(Gen Mgr)*

Croda Nordica AB (1)
Krossverksgatan 5C
216 16 Limhamn, Sweden SE
Tel.: (46) 40368550 (100%)
Fax: (46) 40150570
E-Mail: nordica@croda.com
Web Site: www.croda.com
Emp.: 10
Specialty Chemicals Distr
S.I.C.: 2899
N.A.I.C.S.: 325998
Martin Wildt *(Mng Dir)*

Croda Oleochemicals Iberica, S.A. (1)
Plz Francesco Macia 7 7B
08029 Barcelona, Spain ES
Tel.: (34) 933221193 (100%)
Fax: (34) 933220169
Web Site: www.croda-iberica.com
Specialty Chemicals Mfr & Distr
S.I.C.: 2899
N.A.I.C.S.: 325998

Croda Peruana S.A.C (1)
La Encalada 1388 Urb El Polo Hunt
Distrito de Surco, Lima, Peru
Tel.: (51) 1 435 9827
Fax: (51) 1 435 9859
Web Site: www.croda.com
Emp.: 4
Personal Care Product Distr
S.I.C.: 5122
N.A.I.C.S.: 424210
Bercy Vogangel *(Gen Mgr)*

Croda Poland Sp. z o.o. (1)
Wadowicka 6 lok 83A
31-131 Krakow, Poland
Tel.: (48) 12 6331529
Fax: (48) 12 6343742
Web Site: www.croda.com.pl
Emp.: 1
Health Care Products Whslr
S.I.C.: 5122
N.A.I.C.S.: 424210
Moneka Kozdron *(Mng Dir)*

Croda Singapore Pte. Ltd. (1)
30 Seraya Ave
Singapore, 627884, Singapore SG
Tel.: (65) 65519600 (100%)
Fax: (65) 65519550
Web Site: www.croda.com.sg
Emp.: 100
Specialty Chemicals Mfr & Distr
S.I.C.: 2899
N.A.I.C.S.: 325998
Arother Knox *(Mng Dir)*

Non-U.S. Subsidiaries:

Croda Australia (2)
Suite 102 Level 1 447 Victoria Street
Wetherill Park, NSW, 2164, Australia AU
Tel.: (61) 01300667050 (100%)
Fax: (61) 1300667080
E-Mail: customercare@croda.com.au
Web Site: www.croda.com.au
Emp.: 10
Specialty Chemicals Distr
S.I.C.: 2899
N.A.I.C.S.: 325998
Linda Jacob *(Mgr)*

Croda Chemicals (India) Pvt Ltd. (2)
501 Glacis Tower Linking Road
Khar W, Mumbai, 400 052, India In
Tel.: (91) 22 2648 2733 (100%)
Fax: (91) 22 2648 2744
E-Mail: sales@croda.in
Web Site: www.croda.co.in
Emp.: 7
Specialty Chemicals Distr
S.I.C.: 2899
N.A.I.C.S.: 325998
Deenar Khanvilkar *(Head-Sls & Mktg)*

Croda Hong Kong (2)
Rm 806 Tower 2 South Seas St
77 Mody Rd Psin Sha Psui E, Kowloon, China (Hong Kong) HK
Tel.: (852) 25593327 (100%)
Fax: (852) 28586047
E-Mail: sale@croda.com.hk
Emp.: 11
Specialty Chemicals Distr
S.I.C.: 2899
N.A.I.C.S.: 325998
Wang Shui Ling *(Mng Dir)*

Croda Korea Chemical International Ltd. (2)
Rm 704 Yeoam Building 254-4 Seohyun-Dong
Bundang-Ku, Seongnam, Kyunggi-Do, 463 824, Korea (South) Ks
Tel.: (82) 317061756 (100%)
Fax: (82) 317061767
E-Mail: crodakorea@croda.co.kr
Web Site: www.croda.com
Specialty Chemicals Distr
S.I.C.: 2899
N.A.I.C.S.: 325998

Croda Shanghai (2)
Room 531 D5 Building Shanghai Jia Hua Business Center
No 808 Hong Qiao Road, Shanghai, 200030, China CN
Tel.: (86) 2164479516 (100%)
Fax: (86) 2164480322
Emp.: 3
Specialty Chemicals Distr
S.I.C.: 2899
N.A.I.C.S.: 325998

Croda (Thailand) Co., Ltd (1)
319 Chamchuri Square Building 16th Floor
Unit 1613 Payathai Road
Patumwan, Bangkok, 10330, Thailand
Tel.: (66) 2 160 5444
Fax: (66) 2 160 5450
Oleochemical Products Whslr
S.I.C.: 5169
N.A.I.C.S.: 424690

Croda Trading (Shanghai) Co., Ltd (1)
Rm 531 Rm 301 Building D5 Jiahua Business Centre No 808
Shanghai, 200000, China
Tel.: (86) 2164479516
Fax: (86) 2164480322
Emp.: 2
Personal Care Products Distr
S.I.C.: 5122
N.A.I.C.S.: 424210
James Lee *(Gen Mgr)*

Crodarom SAS (1)
Parc d'Activites Les Plaines
48230 Chanac, France
Tel.: (33) 4 66 482 027
Fax: (33) 4 66 482 841
Web Site: www.crodarom.com
Plant Extraction Mfr
S.I.C.: 2836
N.A.I.C.S.: 325414

Crodarom (1)
Herrenpfad Sud 33
41334 Nettetal, Kaldenkirchen, Germany De
Tel.: (49) 215781730 (100%)
Fax: (49) 215713250
E-Mail: info@croda.com
Web Site: www.croda.co.in/home.aspx?d=content&s=1&r=73&p=53
Emp.: 50
Mfr. of Plant Extractss & Additives
S.I.C.: 2899
N.A.I.C.S.: 325998

PT Croda Indonesia Ltd (1)
Cikarang Industrial Estate JL Jababeka IV Block V Kav 74-75
Bekasi, Cikarang, 17530, Indonesia
Tel.: (62) 21 893 4923
Fax: (62) 21 893 4926
Chemical Products Mfr
S.I.C.: 2899
N.A.I.C.S.: 325998

SEDERMA GmbH (1)
Herrenpfad-Sud 33
41334 Nettetal, Germany
Tel.: (49) 21 57 817318
Fax: (49) 21 57 817361
E-Mail: sederma@sederma.de
Web Site: www.sederma.de

Croda International plc—(Continued)

Cosmetic Products Mfr
S.I.C.: 2844
N.A.I.C.S.: 325620
Oliver Reimelt *(Gen Mgr)*

Sederma SA (1)
29 Rue Du Chemin Vert
78612 Yvelines, Cedex, France FR
Tel.: (33) 134841010 (100%)
Fax: (33) 134841130
E-Mail: sederma@sederma.fr
Web Site: www.sederma.fr
Emp.: 130
Specialty Chemical & Toiletries Mfr
S.I.C.: 2899
N.A.I.C.S.: 325998
Arnaud Fournial *(Mng Dir)*

CRODUX PLIN D.O.O.

Kaptol 19
Zagreb, 10000, Croatia
Tel.: (385) 1 60 52 177
Web Site: www.crodux-plin.hr
Business Description:
Natural Gas Distr Services
S.I.C.: 4924
N.A.I.C.S.: 221210
Subsidiary:

Crodux Derivati d.o.o. (1)
Josipa Marohnica 1
Zagreb, 10000, Croatia
Tel.: (385) 1 665 14 00
Fax: (385) 1 665 24 00
Natural Gas Distr Services
S.I.C.: 4924
N.A.I.C.S.: 221210

CROESUS RETAIL TRUST

10 Collyer Quay #40-00 Ocean Financial Centre
Singapore, Singapore
Tel.: (65) 6622 5531
Fax: (65) 6622 5999
E-Mail: ir@croesusretailtrust.com
Web Site: www.croesusretailtrust.com
S6NU—(SES)
Business Description:
Real Estate Investment Services
S.I.C.: 6211
N.A.I.C.S.: 523999
Personnel:
David Teck Leong Lim *(Chm)*
Jim Cheng-Wen Chang *(CEO)*
Hidenori Asai *(CFO)*
Tetsuo Ito *(Deputy CFO)*
Kiyoshi Sato *(Chief Investment Officer)*
Shunji Miyazaki *(Chief Asset Mgmt Officer)*
Board of Directors:
David Teck Leong Lim
Jim Cheng-Wen Chang
Meng Leong Eng
Ban Huat Quah
Jeremy Chao Hsien Yong

CROMA SECURITY SOLUTIONS GROUP PLC

Unit 6 Fulcrum 4 Solent Way
Whiteley, Hampshire, PO15 7FT, United Kingdom
Tel.: (44) 1489 566101
Fax: (44) 1489 565375
E-Mail: info@cssgroupplc.com
Web Site: www.cssgroupplc.com
CSSG—(AIM)
Rev.: $20,926,696
Assets: $17,574,508
Liabilities: $4,063,153
Net Worth: $13,511,355
Earnings: $126,021
Emp.: 393
Fiscal Year-end: 06/30/13
Business Description:
Covert Surveillance Security & Homeland Defense Related Products Designer & Mfr
S.I.C.: 7382
N.A.I.C.S.: 561621
Personnel:
Sebastian Jake Finch Morley *(Chm)*
Roberto Michele Fiorentino *(CEO)*
Board of Directors:
Sebastian Jake Finch Morley
Roberto Michele Fiorentino
Andrew Nicholas Hewson
Charles Neil McMicking
James William Eustace Percy
Legal Counsel:
Shepherd & Wedderburn LLP
1 Exchange Crescent Conference Sq
Edinburgh, United Kingdom
Subsidiaries:

Photobase Limited (1)
Dover Innovation Centre Whitecliff House
Dover, Poulton Close, CT17 0HL, United Kingdom
Tel.: (44) 1843233043
Web Site: www.photobase.co.uk
Biometric Entry Systems Mfr
S.I.C.: 3575
N.A.I.C.S.: 334118
James Sullivan *(Mng Dir)*

R&D Design Services Limited (1)
Star Ln
Margate, Kent, CT9 4NN, United Kingdom
Tel.: (44) 1843233030
Fax: (44) 1843233031
E-Mail: office@rdds.co.uk
Web Site: www.rdds.co.uk
Emp.: 15
Surveillance Equipment Mfr
S.I.C.: 3669
N.A.I.C.S.: 334290
James Sullivan *(Mng Dir)*

Vigilant Security (Scotland) Limited (1)
Security House
23 Loganbarns Rd, Dumfries, DG1 4BZ, United Kingdom
Tel.: (44) 1334834777
Fax: (44) 1387252678
E-Mail: mail@vigilantsecurityservices.com
Web Site: www.vigilantsecurityservices.com
Security Training Services
S.I.C.: 7382
N.A.I.C.S.: 561621

CROMEX S/A

Av Prof Celestino Bourroul 273
Sao Paulo, Brazil 02710-000
Tel.: (55) 11 3856 1000
Fax: (55) 11 3966 0036
E-Mail: atec@cromex.com.br
Web Site: www.cromex.com.br
Business Description:
Color Concentrate Mfr
S.I.C.: 2816
N.A.I.C.S.: 325130
Personnel:
Roberto Jacomini *(CFO)*

CROMPTON CONTROLS LTD.

Monckton Rd
Wakefield, W Yorkshire, WF2 7AL, United Kingdom
Tel.: (44) 1924368251
Fax: (44) 1924367274
E-Mail: sales@cromptoncontrols.co.uk
Web Site: www.cromptoncontrols.co.uk
Emp.: 25
Business Description:
Electric Motor Control Equipment Mfr
S.I.C.: 3699
N.A.I.C.S.: 335999
Personnel:
Brent Mason *(Dir-Sls)*

CROMPTON GREAVES LTD.

CG House 6th Floor Dr Annie Besant Road
Worli, Mumbai, Maharashtra, 400 030, India
Tel.: (91) 2224237777
Fax: (91) 2224237788
Web Site: www.cgglobal.com
500093—(BOM)
Rev.: $2,323,694,214
Assets: $1,882,325,412
Liabilities: $1,220,262,012
Net Worth: $662,063,400
Earnings: ($6,700,356)
Emp.: 9,575
Fiscal Year-end: 03/31/13
Business Description:
Power Distribution & Industrial Equipment Mfr; Household Appliance Mfr
Export
S.I.C.: 3612
N.A.I.C.S.: 335311
Personnel:
Laurent Demortier *(CEO & Mng Dir)*
Madhav Acharya *(CFO, CIO & Exec VP)*
Dileep S. Patil *(CTO & Exec VP)*
Anil Raina *(Pres-Indus Bus Unit, Exec VP & VP-Supply Chain)*
Norberto Santiago Elustondo *(Pres-Automation Bus Unit & Exec VP)*
Ash Gupta *(Pres-Consumer Bus Unit & Exec VP)*
Jayant Kulkarni *(Pres-Power Bus Unit & Exec VP)*
Wilton Henriques *(Compliane Officer, Gen Counsel, Sec & Exec VP)*
Sanjay Jorapur *(Exec VP & Head-HR)*
Board of Directors:
Gautham Thapar
Shirish Apte
Laurent Demortier
Omkar Goswami
B. Hariharan
Sanjay Labroo
Colette Lewiner
Suresh Prabhu
Meher Pudumjee
Sudhir M. Trehan
Valentin von Massow
Legal Counsel:
Crawford Bayley & Co.
State Bank Buildings
NGN Vaidya Marg Fort, Mumbai, 400 023, India
Transfer Agent:
Datamatics Financial Services Ltd
Plot No B 5 Part B Crosslane MIDC Marol
Andheri East
Mumbai, India
Subsidiaries:

CG Capital And Investments Limited (1)
6th Floor CG House
Dr Annie Besant Road Worli, 400030
Mumbai, India (100%)
Tel.: (91) 2224237777
Fax: (91) 2224237788
Miscellaneous Financial Investment Activities
S.I.C.: 6211
N.A.I.C.S.: 523999
S. M. Threhan *(Mng Dir)*

CG Motors Private Ltd (1)
6th Floor CG House
Dr Annie Besant Road Worli, 400030
Mumbai, India (100%)
Tel.: (91) 2224237777
Fax: (91) 2224237788
Web Site: www.cgglobal.com
Emp.: 48
Other Specialized Design Services
S.I.C.: 7389
N.A.I.C.S.: 541490
S. M. Threhan *(Mng Dir)*

CG Ppi Adhesive Products Limited (1)
215 Kundaim Industrial Estate
Kundaim, 403115 Goa, India (100%)
Tel.: (91) 8322395210
Fax: (91) 8322395308
E-Mail: cgptigoa@sancharnet.in
Web Site: www.cgppi.com
Emp.: 80
Adhesive Mfr
S.I.C.: 2891
N.A.I.C.S.: 325520

Malapur Captive Power LTD (1)
Vandana Building 11
Tolstoy Marg, 11001 New Delhi, India (100%)
Tel.: (91) 1130416300
Fax: (91) 1123324360
Web Site: www.cgglobal.com
Computer Systems Design Services
S.I.C.: 7373
N.A.I.C.S.: 541512
Sudhir M. Trehan *(Mng Dir)*

Joint Venture:

CG Lucy Switchgear Ltd. (1)
F-10 MIDC Ambad
422010 Nasik, India
Tel.: (91) 2532381603
Fax: (91) 2532381542
Emp.: 50
On-Line Information Services
S.I.C.: 2741
N.A.I.C.S.: 519130
Nitin Taombie *(CEO)*

U.S. Subsidiaries:

CG Automation Solutions USA Inc. (1)
60 Fadem Rd
Springfield, NJ 07081-3116 NJ
Tel.: (973) 379-7400
Fax: (973) 379-2138
E-Mail: asolus.sales@cgglobal.com
Web Site: www.cgautomationusa.com
Sales Range: $10-24.9 Million
Emp.: 60
Telemetering & Computer Interfacing Equipment Mfr
Import Export
S.I.C.: 3823
N.A.I.C.S.: 334513
Steve Dalyai *(Co-Pres & COO)*
Normand Lavoie *(Co-Pres)*

CG Power Systems USA Inc. (1)
One Pauwels Dr
Washington, MO 63090 (100%)
Tel.: (636) 239-9300
Fax: (636) 239-9398
E-Mail: info@pauwels.com
Web Site: careers.pauwels.com
Emp.: 320
Power Distribution & Specialty Transformer Mfr
S.I.C.: 3612
N.A.I.C.S.: 335311
Bob Winters *(Mgr)*

CG Power Solutions USA Inc. (1)
403 New Karner Rd
Albany, NY 12205
Tel.: (518) 452-7718
Fax: (518) 452-7716
E-Mail: info@cgpowersolutions.com
Emp.: 73
Power Transmission & Distribution Systems Engineering & Construction Services
S.I.C.: 1623
N.A.I.C.S.: 237130
Mark Scher *(Pres)*

Non-U.S. Subsidiaries:

CG Electric Systems Hungary Zrt (1)
Mariassy utca 7
1095 Budapest, Hungary (100%)
Tel.: (36) 1 4836600
Fax: (36) 1 4836862
E-Mail: info.hu@cgglobal.com
Web Site: www.cgglobal.com
Power Distribution & Specialty Transformer Mfr
S.I.C.: 3612
N.A.I.C.S.: 335311

CG Holdings Belgium NV (1)
Antwerpsesteenweg 167
2800 Mechelen, Belgium (100%)
Tel.: (32) 15283333
Fax: (32) 15283300
E-Mail:
Web Site: www.cgglobal.com
Emp.: 1,000
Electrical Transmission & Distribution Equipment Mfr
S.I.C.: 3612
N.A.I.C.S.: 335311
Dhilip Patel *(CTO & Exec VP)*

CG Power Systems Belgium NV (1)
Antwerpsesteenweg 167
2800 Mechelen, Belgium (100%)
Tel.: (32) 15283333
Fax: (32) 15283300
E-Mail: info@cgglobal.com
Emp.: 700
Electronic Coil Transformer & Other Inductor Mfr
S.I.C.: 3677
N.A.I.C.S.: 334416
Dominque Gaul *(Dir-HR)*

CG Power Systems Canada Inc. (1)
101 Rockman Street
Winnipeg, MB, R3T 0L7, Canada (100%)
Tel.: (204) 452-7446
Fax: (204) 453-8644
Web Site: www.cgglobal.com
Emp.: 300
Power Distribution & Specialty Transformer Mfr
S.I.C.: 3612
N.A.I.C.S.: 335311
Ian Harrison *(Gen Mgr)*

CG Power Systems Ireland Ltd. (1)
Dublin Road
Cavan, Ireland (100%)
Tel.: (353) 494331588
Fax: (353) 494332053
E-Mail: info@cgglobal.com
Web Site: www.cgglobal.com
Emp.: 350
Electronic Coil Transformer & Other Inductor Mfr
S.I.C.: 3676
N.A.I.C.S.: 334416
James McMahon *(Mng Dir)*

CG Sales Networks France S.A. (1)
Immeuble Arago 1
41 Boulevard Vauban, F-78280 Guyancourt, France (100%)
Tel.: (33) 134521080
Fax: (33) 134522730
Web Site: www.pauwels.com
Emp.: 4
Electrical Apparatus & Equipment Wiring Supplies & Construction Materials Sales
S.I.C.: 5063
N.A.I.C.S.: 423610
Laurent Demortier *(CEO & Mng Dir)*
Madhav Acharya *(Exec VP & CFO)*
Jayant Kulkarni *(Exec VP & Pres-CG India)*
Dileep Patil *(Exec VP & Pres-Power Bus Unit)*
Anil Raina *(Exec VP & Pres-Indus Bus Unit)*
Manoj Verma *(Exec VP & Pres-Consumer Bus Unit)*
Wilton Henriques *(Exec VP, Sec & Gen Counsel & Head-HR)*

CG Service Systems Curacao NV (1)
Sans Souci 47 C
Willemstad, Curacao (100%)
Tel.: (599) 98883355
Fax: (599) 98883353
E-Mail: pauwcur@fcarlat.an
Web Site: www.cglonline.com
Emp.: 6
Computer Systems Design Services
S.I.C.: 7373
N.A.I.C.S.: 541512
Ruthmila Marthe *(Mgr)*

CROMSOURCE S.R.L.

(d/b/a CROMSOURCE Group)
Via Scuderlando 10
37135 Verona, MI, Italy
Tel.: (39) 045 8222 811
Fax: (39) 045 8222 812
E-Mail: cromsource@cromsource.com
Web Site: www.cromsource.com
Year Founded: 1993
Emp.: 90

Business Description:
Clinical Research & Testing Services
S.I.C.: 8731
N.A.I.C.S.: 541711

Personnel:
Oriana Zerbini *(Pres & CEO)*

U.S. Subsidiary:

CROMSOURCE Inc. (1)
1 Alewife Ctr Ste 120
Cambridge, MA 02140 MA
Tel.: (617) 871-1128
Fax: (617) 871-1129
Web Site: www.cromsource.com
Clinical Research & Testing Services
S.I.C.: 8731
N.A.I.C.S.: 541711
Helen Colquhoun *(Sr VP)*

Non-U.S. Subsidiary:

CROMSOURCE Ltd. (1)
Suite 11 Sabrina Court Longden Coleham
Shrewsbury, SY3 7BF, United Kingdom UK
Tel.: (44) 1743 243 277
Fax: (44) 1743 291 851
Web Site: www.cromsource.com
Clinical Research & Testing Services
S.I.C.: 8731
N.A.I.C.S.: 541711
Kerry Dyson *(Mng Dir)*

CROMWELL PROPERTY GROUP

Level 19 200 Mary Street
Brisbane, QLD, 4000, Australia
Tel.: (61) 7 3225 7777
Fax: (61) 7 3225 7788
E-Mail: cromwell@cromwell.com.au
Web Site: www.cromwell.com.au
CMW—(ASX)
Rev.: $240,219,682
Assets: $2,653,301,231
Liabilities: $1,401,893,362
Net Worth: $1,251,407,869
Earnings: $48,099,168
Emp.: 96
Fiscal Year-end: 06/30/13

Business Description:
Real Estate Investment Trust
S.I.C.: 6726
N.A.I.C.S.: 525990

Personnel:
Paul L. Weightman *(CEO & Mng Dir)*
Nicole Riethmuller *(Gen Counsel & Sec)*

Board of Directors:
Geoffrey Levy
Richard W. Foster
Michelle A. McKellar
Robert J. Pullar
David E. Usasz
Marc Wainer
Michael Watters
Paul L. Weightman
Daryl J. Wilson

Subsidiary:

Cromwell Corporation Limited (1)
Level 19 200 Mary Street
Brisbane, QLD, 4000, Australia
Tel.: (61) 732257777
Fax: (61) 732257788
E-Mail: cromadmin@cromwell.com.au
Web Site: www.cromwell.com.au
Emp.: 60
Property Management Services
S.I.C.: 6531
N.A.I.C.S.: 531312
Paul Weightman *(CEO)*

Subsidiaries:

Cromwell Property Securities Limited (2)
Level 19 200 Mary Street
Brisbane, QLD, 4000, Australia
Tel.: (61) 732257777
Fax: (61) 732257788
E-Mail: invest@cromwell.com.au
Web Site: www.cromwell.com.au
Emp.: 60
Fund Management Services
S.I.C.: 6722
N.A.I.C.S.: 525910
Paul Weight *(CEO)*

Cromwell Property Services Pty. Ltd. (2)
Level 19 200 Mary St
Brisbane, QLD, 4000, Australia
Tel.: (61) 732257777
Fax: (61) 732257788
E-Mail: property@cromwell.com.au
Web Site: www.cromwell.com.au
Emp.: 60
Property Management Services
S.I.C.: 6531
N.A.I.C.S.: 531312
Paul Louis Weightman *(CEO)*

CRONIMET HOLDING GMBH

Sudbeckenstrasse 22
76189 Karlsruhe, Germany
Tel.: (49) 721952250
Fax: (49) 721591086
E-Mail: mail@cronimet.de
Web Site: www.cronimet.de
Year Founded: 1980
Emp.: 180

Business Description:
Holding Company
S.I.C.: 6719
N.A.I.C.S.: 551112

Personnel:
Thomas Heil *(Mng Dir)*
Gunter Pilarsky *(Mng Dir)*
Joachim Pilarsky *(Mng Dir)*
Jurgen Pilarsky *(Mng Dir)*

Subsidiary:

CRONIMET Ferrolegierungen Handelsges. mbH (1)
Sudbeckenstrasse 22
76189 Karlsruhe, Germany
Tel.: (49) 721952250
Fax: (49) 721591086
E-Mail: mail@cronimet.de
Web Site: www.cronimet.de
Sls.: $358,550,000
Emp.: 120
Raw Material & Stainless Steel Recycling Company
S.I.C.: 3312
N.A.I.C.S.: 331110
Thomas Heil *(Mng Dir)*
Jurgen Pilarsky *(Mng Dir)*

Joint Venture:

TSR Recycling GmbH & Co. KG (1)
Hafenstr 98
46242 Bottrop, Germany DE
Tel.: (49) 204170600
Fax: (49) 20417060399
E-Mail: info@tsr.eu
Web Site: www.tsr.eu
Emp.: 2,000
Steel Scrap & Non-Ferrous Metals Recycling
S.I.C.: 5093
N.A.I.C.S.: 423930

Non-U.S. Subsidiary:

HKS Metals BV (2)
Kwadrantweg 2-12
Postbus 8050
1042 AG Amsterdam, Netherlands NL
Mailing Address:
Postbus 5165
NL-3295 ZH 's-Gravendeel, Netherlands
Tel.: (31) 78 673 9200
Fax: (31) 78 673 4060
E-Mail: info@hks.au
Web Site: www.hks.nl
Sales Range: $500-549.9 Million
Emp.: 45
Holding Company; Scrap Metal Recycling
S.I.C.: 6719
N.A.I.C.S.: 551112

Subsidiary:

HKS Scrap Metals BV (3)
Havenweg 1
NL 3295 XZ 's-Gravendeel, Netherlands NL
Tel.: (31) 786739200
Fax: (31) 786734060
E-Mail: receptea@hks.nl
Web Site: www.hks.nl
Emp.: 200
Scrap Metal Recycling
S.I.C.: 4953
N.A.I.C.S.: 562920

CROOKES BROTHERS LIMITED

Renishaw KwaZulu-Natal
Renishaw, 4181, South Africa
Tel.: (27) 399784600
Fax: (27) 399784628
E-Mail: info@cbl.co.za
Web Site: www.cbl.co.za
CKS—(JSE)
Rev.: $43,286,654
Assets: $89,744,583
Liabilities: $24,713,067
Net Worth: $65,031,517
Earnings: $10,440,041
Emp.: 1,979
Fiscal Year-end: 03/31/13

Business Description:
Sugar Products Producers
S.I.C.: 0133
N.A.I.C.S.: 111930

Personnel:
Guy S. Clarke *(Mng Dir)*

Board of Directors:
Guy P. Wayne
Phillip Barker
John Barton
Paul Bhengu
Christopher J. H. Chance
Guy S. Clarke
J. Anthony F. Hewat
Phumla Mnganga
Malcolm T. Rutherford
Rodger E. Stewart
Gary Vaughan-Smith

Transfer Agent:
Computershare Investor Services (Pty) Ltd.
70 Marshall Street
Johannesburg, 2001, South Africa
Tel.: (27) 11 370 5000
Fax: (27) 11 370 5487

Subsidiary:

Mthayiza Farming (Pty) Ltd (1)
Mtata Farm
Malelane, Mpumalanga, 1320, South Africa
Tel.: (27) 137937196
Fax: (27) 137937625
E-Mail: agricmthayiza@telkomsa.net
Web Site: www.crookesbrothers.co.za
Emp.: 250
Citrus Groves Farming Services
S.I.C.: 0721
N.A.I.C.S.: 115112
Elli Erlendsson *(Gen Mgr)*

Non-U.S. Subsidiary:

Crookes Plantations Ltd (1)
PO Box 35
Big Bend, Swaziland
Tel.: (268) 2363 6523
Fax: (268) 2363 6168
E-Mail: cpl@cbl.co.za
Web Site: www.cbl.co.za
Sugarcane Farming Services & Sugar Exports
S.I.C.: 0133
N.A.I.C.S.: 111930
Christo Bothma *(Gen Mgr)*

JAMES CROPPER PLC

Burneside Mills
Kendal, Cumbria, LA9 6PZ, United Kingdom

James Cropper Plc—(Continued)

Tel.: (44) 1539722002
Fax: (44) 1539728088
E-Mail: info@cropper.com
Web Site: www.cropper.com
CRPR—(AIM)
Rev.: $125,144,519
Assets: $80,030,521
Liabilities: $47,912,500
Net Worth: $32,118,021
Earnings: $2,282,074
Emp.: 505
Fiscal Year-end: 03/30/13

Business Description:
Paper Making (Uncoated Paper, Book Binding Papers & Text & Cover Papers), Converting (Display Board & Mount Board) & Manufacture of Technical Fibre Products
S.I.C.: 2679
N.A.I.C.S.: 322299

Personnel:
Philip Ian Wild *(CEO)*
Dave Watson *(COO)*
David R. Carey *(Sec)*

Board of Directors:
Mark A. J. Cropper
John M. Denman
Douglas Mitchell
Nigel A. Read
James E. Sharp
Martin Thompson
Philip Ian Wild
David R. Wilks
Patrick J. Willink

Legal Counsel:
Dickinson Dees
St Anns Wharf 112 Quayside
Newcastle upon Tyne, NE99 1SB, United Kingdom

Subsidiaries:

James Cropper Converting Limited **(1)**
Burneside Mills
LA96PZ Kendal, United Kingdom (100%)
Tel.: (44) 1539818210
Fax: (44) 1539818216
E-Mail: info@cropper.com
Web Site: www.cropper.com
Emp.: 496
Coated & Laminated Packaging Paper & Plastics Film Mfr
S.I.C.: 2672
N.A.I.C.S.: 322220
Alun Lewis *(CEO & Mng Dir)*

James Cropper Speciality Papers Limited **(1)**
Burneside Mills
Kendal, LA9 6PZ, United Kingdom (100%)
Tel.: (44) 1539818240
Fax: (44) 1539818239
E-Mail: info@cropper.com
Web Site: www.jamescropper.com
Emp.: 450
Paperboard Mills
S.I.C.: 2631
N.A.I.C.S.: 322130
Mark Cropper *(Chm)*
Alun Lewis *(CEO & Mng Dir)*

The Paper Mill Shop Company Limited **(1)**
Burneside Mills
LA96PZ Kendal, United Kingdom (100%)
Tel.: (44) 1539818484
Fax: (44) 01539818248
Web Site: papermilldirect.co.uk
Emp.: 500
All Other General Merchandise Stores
S.I.C.: 5399
N.A.I.C.S.: 452990
Alan I. Lewis *(CEO & Mng Dir)*

Papermilldirect.com Limited **(1)**
Burneside Mills
Kendal, LA96PZ, United Kingdom (100%)
Tel.: (44) 1539722002
Fax: (44) 1539818239
E-Mail: info@papermilldirect.co.uk
Web Site: www.papermilldirect.co.uk
Emp.: 4
Other Direct Selling Establishments
S.I.C.: 5963
N.A.I.C.S.: 454390
Alun Lewis *(CEO & Mng Dir)*

Technical Fibre Products Limited **(1)**
Burneside Mills
LA96PZ Kendal, United Kingdom (100%)
Tel.: (44) 1539818264
Fax: (44) 1539733850
E-Mail: marketing@techfibres.com
Web Site: www.techfibres.com
Emp.: 100
Nonwoven Fabric Mills
S.I.C.: 2297
N.A.I.C.S.: 313230
George T. Quayle *(Mng Dir)*

U.S. Joint Venture:

Electro Fiber Technologies LLC **(2)**
611 Access Rd
Stratford, CT 06615
Tel.: (203) 380-1353
Fax: (845) 567-9524
E-Mail: jhaaland@electrofibertechnologies.com
Web Site: www.electrofibertechnologies.com
Emp.: 12
Noncellulosic Organic Fiber Mfr; Owned 50% by Thermion Systems International, Inc. & 50% by James Cropper Plc
S.I.C.: 2823
N.A.I.C.S.: 325220
John Halland *(VP)*

U.S. Subsidiary:

Technical Fiber Products Inc **(1)**
259 Route 17k
Newburgh, NY 12550
Tel.: (845) 567-9066
Fax: (845) 567-9524
E-Mail: usa.sales@techfibres.com
Web Site: www.techfibres.com
Nonwoven Mats Mfr
S.I.C.: 2297
N.A.I.C.S.: 313230

CROPPER MOTORS

Highway 6 North
PO Box 430
Naicam, SK, S0K 2Z0, Canada
Tel.: (306) 874-2011
Fax: (306) 874-2227
Toll Free: (877) 339-9998
E-Mail: info@croppermotors.com
Web Site: www.croppermotors.com
Rev.: $20,605,953
Emp.: 44

Business Description:
New & Used Car & Truck Dealers
S.I.C.: 5511
N.A.I.C.S.: 441110

Personnel:
Kevin Cropper *(Gen Mgr & Mgr-Vehicle & RV Sls)*

CROPS CORPORATION

4-23-9 Meieki Nakamura-ku
Nagoya, 450-0002, Japan
Tel.: (81) 52 5865145
Web Site: www.crops.ne.jp
9428—(NGO TKS)
Emp.: 450

Business Description:
Mobile Communications Retailer
S.I.C.: 5734
N.A.I.C.S.: 443142

Personnel:
Hiroshi Maeda *(Chm)*

CROS NT SRL

Via Germania 2
37136 Verona, Italy
Tel.: (39) 45 820 26 66
Fax: (39) 45 820 58 75
E-Mail: info@crosnt.com
Web Site: www.crosnt.com

Business Description:
Statistical Consultancy, Programming & Analysis, Clinical Data Management; Medical Writing, Pharmacovigilance & Technology Services
S.I.C.: 8748
N.A.I.C.S.: 541618

Personnel:
Paolo Morelli *(Chm)*
Andrew MacGarvey *(Pres & CEO)*
Gianni Saccomani *(CFO)*
Paul Fardy *(COO)*

CROSBY CAPITAL LIMITED

Unit 502 5th Floor AXA Centre
151 Gloucester Road, Wanchai, China (Hong Kong)
Tel.: (852) 3476 2700
Fax: (852) 2169 0008
E-Mail: info@crosby.com
Web Site: www.crosbycapitallimited.com
8088—(DEU HKG)
Rev.: $2,481,000
Assets: $22,093,000
Liabilities: $52,924,000
Net Worth: ($30,831,000)
Earnings: ($5,249,000)
Emp.: 33
Fiscal Year-end: 12/31/12

Business Description:
Asset Management Services
S.I.C.: 6726
N.A.I.C.S.: 525990

Personnel:
Clive Cheang Neng Ng *(Chm)*
Ulric Yuk Lun Leung *(CFO)*
Winnie Wing Hung Sin *(Sec)*

Board of Directors:
Clive Cheang Neng Ng
Raymond Chi Chuen Chan
Johnny Ka Chi Fok
Jeffrey Chun Hung Lau
Ulric Yuk Lun Leung
Guang He Liu
Jinsheng Shi
Stephen Shiu
Hendrick Sin
Nelson Naiyi Tong
Anthony Koon Tung Yuen
Kwok On Yuen

Transfer Agent:
Computershare Hong Kong Investor Services Limited
46th Floor Hopewell Centre 183 Queen's Road East
Wanchai, China (Hong Kong)

CROSBY VOLKSWAGEN INC

1175 Weber Street E
Kitchener, ON, N2A 1C1, Canada
Tel.: (519) 894-9300
Fax: (519) 894-9790
Toll Free: (866) 403-2834
E-Mail: info@crosbyvwaudi.com
Web Site: www.crosbyvw.com
Year Founded: 1937
Rev.: $14,103,200
Emp.: 37

Business Description:
New & Used Car Dealers
S.I.C.: 5511
N.A.I.C.S.: 441110

Personnel:
Michael Crosby *(Gen Mgr)*

CROSS CAT CO., LTD.

NOF Shinagawa Konan Building
1-2-5 Higashi Shinagawa Shinagawa-ku, Tokyo, 140-0002, Japan
Tel.: (81) 3 3474 5251
Fax: (81) 3 3474 5085
Web Site: www.xcat.co.jp
Year Founded: 1973
2307—(JAS)
Sales Range: $75-99.9 Million
Emp.: 541

Business Description:
System Development Services
S.I.C.: 7373
N.A.I.C.S.: 541512

Personnel:
Yutaka Ushijima *(Chm)*
Takanori Inoue *(Pres)*
Koji Maeda *(Exec Operating Officer)*
Taketsugu Sato *(Exec Operating Officer)*
Yutaka Emoto *(Operating Officer & Gen Mgr-Fin)*
Takahiro Iino *(Operating Officer & Gen Mgr-Sls)*
Takashi Ito *(Operating Officer & Gen Mgr-Sendai)*
Masami Masuda *(Operating Officer & Gen Mgr-Fin Bus)*
Masahiko Nakamura *(Operating Officer & Gen Mgr-Admin)*
Mineo Mishima *(Operating Officer)*

Board of Directors:
Yutaka Ushijima
Takanori Inoue
Koji Maeda
Mineo Mishima
Taketsugu Sato

CROSS EQUITY PARTNERS AG

Kreuzstrasse 60
8008 Zurich, Switzerland
Tel.: (41) 44 269 93 93
Fax: (41) 44 269 93 94
E-Mail: info@crossequitypartners.ch
Web Site: www.crossequitypartners.ch
Year Founded: 2008

Business Description:
Private Equity Firm
S.I.C.: 6211
N.A.I.C.S.: 523999

Personnel:
Markus Reich *(Mng Partner)*
Michael Petersen *(Mng Dir)*

Holding:

Spirella S.A. **(1)**
Tannenstrasse 98
8424 Embrach, Switzerland
Tel.: (41) 44 866 24 24
Fax: (41) 44 866 24 90
Sales Range: $50-74.9 Million
Emp.: 180
Shower Curtain & Bathroom Accessory Mfr
S.I.C.: 5023
N.A.I.C.S.: 423220
Ernst Kraft *(CEO)*

Non-U.S. Subsidiaries:

Spirella France s.a.r.l. **(2)**
4 Avenue Gutenberg
31120 Portet-sur-Garonne, France
Tel.: (33) 56220 6560
Fax: (33) 56220 0479
E-Mail: standard.spirella@spirella.fr
Shower Curtain & Bathroom Accessory Mfr
S.I.C.: 5023
N.A.I.C.S.: 423220

Spirella GmbH **(2)**
Burgbergweg 1
56377 Nassau, Germany
Tel.: (49) 260494330
Fax: (49) 2604 9433 20
E-Mail: spinassau@spirella.ch
Web Site: www.spirella.ch
Shower Curtain & Bathroom Accessory Mfr
S.I.C.: 5023
N.A.I.C.S.: 423220

THE CROSS-HARBOUR (HOLDINGS) LIMITED

Rm 3301 07 China Resources Bldg
26 Harbour Rd
Wanchai, China (Hong Kong)

Tel.: (852) 21611888
Fax: (852) 28022080
Web Site: www.crossharbour.com.hk
0032—(HKG)
Sales Range: $25-49.9 Million
Emp.: 476

Business Description:
Transportation Management Services
S.I.C.: 4731
N.A.I.C.S.: 541614

Personnel:
Chung Kiu Cheung *(Chm)*
Hin Chung Yeung *(Mng Dir)*
Shuk Mun Leung *(Sec)*

Board of Directors:
Chung Kiu Cheung
Carmelo Ka Sze Lee
Steven Yu Ming Leung
Wai Fai Leung
James Yu King Luk
Kwok Fu Ng
Wai Lan Tung
Chi Keung Wong
Yat Fai Wong
Hin Chung Yeung
Wing Shing Yuen

Transfer Agent:
Tricor Tengis Limited
26th Floor Tesbury Centre 28 Queen's Road East
Wanchai, China (Hong Kong)
Tel.: (852) 29801333
Fax: (852) 28108185

Subsidiary:

The Hong Kong School of Motoring Limited **(1)**
Ground Fl 138 Sha Tin Wai Rd
Siu Lek Yuen, Sha Tin, New Territories, China (Hong Kong)
Tel.: (852) 26046123
Fax: (852) 26091357
E-Mail: comments@hksm.com.hk
Web Site: www.hksm.com.hk
Emp.: 500
Automobile Driving Training Services
S.I.C.: 8299
N.A.I.C.S.: 611692

CROSS INDUSTRIES AG

Edison Strasse 1
Wels, 4600, Austria
Tel.: (43) 7242 69402
Fax: (43) 724269 402 109
E-Mail: info@crossindustries.at
Web Site: www.cross-ag.com
Rev.: $1,111,466,607
Assets: $1,235,692,520
Liabilities: $810,222,030
Net Worth: $425,470,490
Earnings: $26,292,046
Emp.: 3,131
Fiscal Year-end: 12/31/12

Business Description:
Investment Holding Company
S.I.C.: 6719
N.A.I.C.S.: 551112

Personnel:
Stefan Pierer *(CEO & Member-Mgmt Bd)*
Friedrich Roithner *(CFO & Member-Mgmt Bd)*
Alfred Hortenhuber *(Member-Mgmt Bd)*
Klaus Rinnerberger *(Member-Mgmt Bd)*

Supervisory Board of Directors:
Ernst Chalupsky
Gerald Kiska

Subsidiary:

CROSS Finanzierungs GmbH **(1)**
EdisonStr 1
4600 Wels, Austria (100%)
Tel.: (43) 7242643600
Fax: (43) 724264360109
Emp.: 15
Transaction Financing Services
S.I.C.: 6726
N.A.I.C.S.: 525990
Stefen Pierer *(Mng Dir)*

Holdings:

KTM AG **(1)**
Stallhofnerstrasse 3
5230 Mattighofen, Austria AT
Tel.: (43) 7742 6000 0 (50.1%)
Fax: (43) 7742 6000 303
E-Mail: info@ktm.com
Web Site: www.ktm.com
KTM—(VIE)
Rev.: $823,866,809
Assets: $701,827,076
Liabilities: $359,197,195
Net Worth: $342,629,881
Earnings: $34,080,986
Emp.: 1,702
Fiscal Year-end: 12/31/12
Holding Company; Motorcycle & Other Recreational Vehicle Mfr & Distr
S.I.C.: 6719
N.A.I.C.S.: 551112
Josef Blazicek *(Chm-Supervisory Bd)*
Stefan Pierer *(Chm-Exec Bd & CEO)*
Rudolf Knunz *(Deputy Chm-Supervisory Bd)*
Friedrich Roithner *(Co-CFO & Member-Exec Bd)*
Viktor Sigl *(Co-CFO & Member-Exec Bd)*
Harald Plockinger *(COO & Member-Exec Bd)*
Hubert Trunkenpolz *(Chief Sls Officer & Member-Exec Bd)*

Subsidiary:

KTM-Sportmotorcycle AG **(2)**
Stallhofnerstrasse 3
AT-5230 Mattighofen, Austria AT
Tel.: (43) 7742 6000 0
Fax: (43) 7742 6000 303
E-Mail: info@ktm.com
Web Site: www.ktm.com
Motorcycle & Other Recreational Vehicle Mfr & Distr
S.I.C.: 3751
N.A.I.C.S.: 336991
Stefan Pierer *(CEO & Chm-Exec Bd)*
Harald Plockinger *(Member-Exec Bd-Logistics & Bus Dev)*
Viktor Sigl *(Member-Exec Bd-Fin, Legal, Insurance & HR)*
Hubert Trunkenpolz *(Member-Exec Bd-Sls)*

U.S. Subsidiary:

KTM North America, Inc. **(3)**
1119 Milan Ave
Amherst, OH 44001-1319 OH
Tel.: (440) 985-3553 (100%)
Fax: (440) 985-3060
Web Site: www.ktm.com
Emp.: 60
Motorcycles & Dirt Bikes Distr
S.I.C.: 5012
N.A.I.C.S.: 423110
Brad Hagi *(VP-Sls)*

Pankl Racing Systems AG **(1)**
Industriestrasse West 4
8605 Kapfenberg, Austria (55%)
Tel.: (43) 3862339990
Fax: (43) 386233999181
E-Mail: office@pankl.com
Web Site: www.pankl.com
PARS—(DEU VIE VSE)
Rev.: $171,885,716
Assets: $201,605,112
Liabilities: $107,896,872
Net Worth: $93,708,240
Earnings: $7,998,942
Emp.: 1,142
Fiscal Year-end: 12/31/12
Engine Systems & Components
S.I.C.: 3519
N.A.I.C.S.: 333618
Stefan Pierer *(Chm-Supervisory Bd)*
Josef Blazicek *(Deputy Chm-Supervisory Bd)*
Wolfgang Plasser *(CEO& Member-Exec Bd)*
Josef Faigle *(COO & Member-Exec Bd)*

Subsidiaries:

Pankl Aerospace Systems Europe GmbH **(2)**
Industriestrasse W 4
8605 Kapfenberg, Austria
Tel.: (43) 3862339990
Fax: (43) 386233999860
E-Mail: aerospace@pankl.com
Web Site: www.pankl.com
Emp.: 400
Transportation Equipment & Supplies except Motor Vehicle Whslr
S.I.C.: 5088
N.A.I.C.S.: 423860
Wolfgang Plasser *(CEO)*

Pankl Drivetrain Systems GmbH And Co KG **(2)**
Industriestrasse West 4
Steiermark, 8605 Kapfenberg, Austria
Tel.: (43) 386233999
Fax: (43) 386233999719
E-Mail: drivetrain@pankl.com
Web Site: www.pankl.co.at
Emp.: 420
Other Metalworking Machinery Mfr
S.I.C.: 3547
N.A.I.C.S.: 333519
Wolfgang Plasser *(Pres & CEO)*

Pankl Engine Systems AG **(2)**
Kaltschmidstrasse 2-6
8600 Bruck an der Mur, Austria
Tel.: (43) 3862512500
Fax: (43) 386251250290
E-Mail: engine@pankl.com
Web Site: www.pankl.com
Emp.: 400
Motor & Generator Manufacturing of High Performance Vehicles
S.I.C.: 3621
N.A.I.C.S.: 335312
Wolfgang Plasser *(CEO)*

Pankl High Performance Pistons GmbH **(2)**
Kaltschmidstrasse 2-6
8600 Bruck an der Mur, Austria
Tel.: (43) 3862512500
Fax: (43) 386251250290
E-Mail: engine@pankl.com
Web Site: www.pankl.com
Emp.: 300
Motor & Generator Mfr
S.I.C.: 3621
N.A.I.C.S.: 335312
Wolfgang Plasser *(CEO)*

Pankl Schmiedetechnik GmbH & Co KG **(2)**
Industriestrasse West 2
8605 Kapfenberg, Austria
Tel.: (43) 3862339990
Fax: (43) 386233999910
E-Mail: fortint@pankl.com
Emp.: 400
Aluminum Sheet Plate & Foil Mfr
S.I.C.: 3353
N.A.I.C.S.: 331315
Wolfgang Plasser *(CEO)*

U.S. Subsidiaries:

CP Pistons LLC **(2)**
1902 McGaw Ave
Irvine, CA 62614
Tel.: (949) 567-9000
Fax: (949) 567-9010
E-Mail: sales@cppistons.com
Web Site: www.cppistons.com
Emp.: 100
Carburetor Piston Piston Ring & Valve Mfr
S.I.C.: 3714
N.A.I.C.S.: 336310

Pankl Aerospace Systems Inc. **(2)**
16615 Edwards Rd
Cerritos, CA 90703
Tel.: (562) 207-6300
Fax: (562) 207-6301
E-Mail: sales@pankl.com
Web Site: www.pankl.com
Emp.: 70
Search Detection Navigation Guidance Aeronautical & Nautical System & Instrument Mfr
S.I.C.: 3812
N.A.I.C.S.: 334511
Soniya Clark *(Gen Mgr)*

Pankl Inc **(2)**
16615 Edwards Rd
Cerritos, CA 90703
Tel.: (562) 677-7251
Fax: (562) 677-7298
E-Mail: PanklUSA@earthlink.net
Web Site: www.pankl.com
Emp.: 50
Automotive Parts & Accessories Stores
S.I.C.: 5531
N.A.I.C.S.: 441310

Non-U.S. Subsidiaries:

Pankl Automotive Slovakia s.r.o. **(2)**
Odbojarov 294-10
95588 Tovarniky, Slovakia
Tel.: (421) 385369811
Fax: (421) 385369898
E-Mail: automotive@pankl.com
Web Site: www.pankl.com
Emp.: 150
Other Engine Equipment Mfr
S.I.C.: 3519
N.A.I.C.S.: 333618
Veronica Botkova *(Mng Dir)*

Pankl Japan Inc. **(2)**
301 Storia Shinagawa 2-16-8 Konan
Minato-ku, Tokyo, Japan
Tel.: (81) 357153877
Fax: (81) 357153878
Emp.: 3
Other Engine Equipment Mfr
S.I.C.: 3519
N.A.I.C.S.: 333618

Pankl Racing Systems UK Ltd **(2)**
Telford Road Oxon
OX26 4LD Bicester, United Kingdom
Tel.: (44) 1869243344
Fax: (44) 1869248005
E-Mail: enquiries@pankl.co.uk
Web Site: www.pankl.co.uk
All Other Automotive Repair & Maintenance
S.I.C.: 7549
N.A.I.C.S.: 811198

Joint Venture:

CROSS Informatik GmbH **(1)**
Edisonstrasse 1
A 4600 Wels, Austria AT
Tel.: (43) 7242 69402
Fax: (43) 7242 69402 109
E-Mail: info@crossinformatik.at
Web Site: www.crossinformatik.at
Emp.: 25
Holding Company
S.I.C.: 6719
N.A.I.C.S.: 551112
Santiago Montoya *(Gen Mgr)*

Holding:

Brain Force Holding AG **(2)**
Am Hof 4
1010 Vienna, Austria AT
Tel.: (43) 126309090
Fax: (43) 1263090940
E-Mail: info@brainforce.com
Web Site: www.brainforce.com
BFC—(DEU)
Rev.: $121,387,890
Assets: $58,991,801
Liabilities: $32,579,801
Net Worth: $26,412,000
Earnings: $3,672,821
Emp.: 804
Fiscal Year-end: 09/30/13
Holding Company; Enterprise, Outsourcing & Financial Services
S.I.C.: 6719
N.A.I.C.S.: 551112
Stefan Pierer *(Chm-Supervisory Bd)*
Friedrich Roithner *(Deputy Chm-Supervisory Bd)*
Michael Hofer *(CEO & Member-Mgmt Bd)*
Michaela Friepess *(CFO & Member-Mgmt Bd)*

Subsidiary:

Brain Force Software GmbH **(3)**
IZD Tower Wagramer Strabe 19
1220 Vienna, Austria AT
Tel.: (43) 1599510
Fax: (43) 15995113
E-Mail: info@brainforce.com
Web Site: www.brainforce.com
Software Publishers
S.I.C.: 7372
N.A.I.C.S.: 511210

CROSS Industries AG—(Continued)

Non-U.S. Subsidiaries:

BFS Brain Force Software AG (3)
Zimmermann Balz 7
Balsberg Airport, 8058 Zurich, Switzerland
Tel.: (41) 438133310
Fax: (41) 438133312
E-Mail: karl.haas@brainforce.com
Web Site: www.brainforce.com
Emp.: 4
Software Reproducing
S.I.C.: 3652
N.A.I.C.S.: 334614
Karl Haas *(Mng Dir)*

Brain Force B.V. (3)
Kantorenpark de Vendel
Vendelier 69, 3905 PD Veenendaal, Netherlands
Mailing Address:
Postbus 1020
3900 BA Veenendaal, Netherlands
Tel.: (31) 8560360
Fax: (31) 8560370
E-Mail: info@brainforce.nl
Web Site: www.brainforce.nl
Emp.: 65
Custom Computer Programming Services
S.I.C.: 7371
N.A.I.C.S.: 541511

Brain Force Software GmbH (3)
Wilhelm-Wagenfeld-Strasse 30
D-80807 Munich, Germany De
Tel.: (49) 89748330
Fax: (49) 8974833920
E-Mail: kontakt@brainforce.com
Web Site: www.brainforce.de
Emp.: 90
Computer & Computer Peripheral Equipment & Software Whslr
S.I.C.: 5045
N.A.I.C.S.: 423430
Birgit Marz *(Head-Mktg)*

Subsidiary:

Network Performance Channel GmbH (4)
Ohmstrasse 12
63225 Langen, Germany De
Tel.: (49) 6103906767
Fax: (49) 6103906711
E-Mail: info@np-channel.com
Web Site: www.np-channel.com
Emp.: 20
Other Management Consulting Services
S.I.C.: 8748
N.A.I.C.S.: 541618
Michael Hofer *(CEO & Mng Dir)*

Brain Force Software s.r.o. (3)
Mala Stepanska 1929
12000 Prague, Czech Republic
Tel.: (420) 296331111
Fax: (420) 296331112
E-Mail: info@brainforce.cz
Web Site: www.brainforce.cz
Emp.: 10
Computer & Computer Peripheral Equipment & Software Whslr
S.I.C.: 5045
N.A.I.C.S.: 423430
Brahomir Hruby *(Mng Dir)*

Brain Force S.p.A. (3)
Via Alessandro Volta 16
Cologne Monzese, I-20093 Milan, Italy
Tel.: (39) 02250941
Fax: (39) 0227300901
E-Mail: info@brainforce.it
Web Site: www.brainforce.it/
Emp.: 300
Software Reproducing
S.I.C.: 3652
N.A.I.C.S.: 334614

Non-U.S. Holding:

All for One Steeb AG (2)
(Formerly All for One Midmarket AG)
Gottlieb Manz Strasse 1
70794 Filderstadt, Germany De
Tel.: (49) 711788070
Fax: (49) 71178807699
E-Mail: info@allforone.com
Web Site: www.all-for-one.com
ACV—(DEU)
Rev.: $206,270,937
Assets: $155,469,173
Liabilities: $100,424,282
Net Worth: $55,044,891
Earnings: $5,684,876
Emp.: 649
Fiscal Year-end: 09/30/12
Business Services
S.I.C.: 7372
N.A.I.C.S.: 511210
Peter Brogle *(Chm-Supervisory Bd)*
Josef Blazicek *(Deputy Chm-Supervisory Bd)*
Lars Landwehrkamp *(CEO)*
Stefan Land *(CFO)*
Ralf Linha *(Member-Mgmt Bd)*
Andreas Naunin *(Member-Mgmt Bd)*
Wolfgang Rath *(Member-Mgmt Bd)*
Andree Stachowski *(Member-Mgmt Bd)*

Subsidiary:

Steeb Anwendungssysteme GmbH (3)
Heilbronner Strasse 4
74232 Abstatt, Germany De
Tel.: (49) 70626730
Fax: (49) 7062673164
E-Mail:
Sales Range: $75-99.9 Million
Emp.: 220
Computer Related Services
S.I.C.: 7371
N.A.I.C.S.: 541511
Alexander Arnold *(Mng Dir)*

CROSS MARKETING GROUP INC.

Ginza COM Building 6F 8-15-2 Ginza
Chuo-ku, Tokyo, 104-0061, Japan
Tel.: (81) 335490603
Fax: (81) 335490232
Web Site: group.cross-m.co.jp
Year Founded: 2013
3675—(TKS)
Sales Range: $25-49.9 Million
Emp.: 331
Business Description:
Holding Company; Marketing Research, Consulting & Information Services
S.I.C.: 6719
N.A.I.C.S.: 551112
Personnel:
Tamamatsu Kuwata *(Chm)*
Miki Igarashi *(Pres)*
Shigeki Hitomi *(CFO)*
Board of Directors:
Tamamatsu Kuwata
Shigeki Hitomi
Miki Igarashi

Subsidiary:

Cross Marketing Inc. (1)
Ginza COM Building 6F 8-15-2 Ginza
Chuo-ku, Tokyo, 104-0061, Japan JP
Tel.: (81) 335490603
Fax: (81) 335490232
E-Mail: global-practices@cross-m.co.jp
Web Site: www.cross-m.co.jp
Sales Range: $25-49.9 Million
Emp.: 120
Marketing Research & Consulting Services
S.I.C.: 8732
N.A.I.C.S.: 541910
Miki Igarashi *(Pres)*

Subsidiary:

EC Research Corp. (2)
Ginza COM Building 6F 8-15-2 Ginza
Chuo-ku, Tokyo, 104-0061, Japan JP (100%)
Tel.: (81) 335490262
Fax: (81) 335490221
E-Mail: t_yukishima@cross-m.co.jp
Web Site: www.ec-r.co.jp
Emp.: 280
Information Technology Market Research & Consulting Services
S.I.C.: 8732
N.A.I.C.S.: 541910
Takahiko Umeyama *(Pres & CEO)*

CROSS PLUS INC.

3-9-13 Hananoki Nishi-ku
Nagoya, 451-8560, Japan
Tel.: (81) 525322211
Web Site: www.crossplus.co.jp
Year Founded: 1951
3320—(TKS)
Sales Range: $800-899.9 Million
Emp.: 1,118
Business Description:
Clothing Mfr & Sales
S.I.C.: 5137
N.A.I.C.S.: 424330
Personnel:
Fumio Mori *(Pres & CEO)*

Subsidiary:

Stylink Inc. (1)
3-9-13 Hananoki Nishi-ku
Nagoya, 451-8560, Japan
Tel.: (81) 5253 22211
Womens & Children Clothing Whslr
S.I.C.: 5137
N.A.I.C.S.: 424330

CROSSHAIR ENERGY CORPORATION

(Name Changed to Jet Metal Corp.)

CROSSJECT SA

60L avenue du 14 Julliet
21300 Chenove, France
Tel.: (33) 3 80 54 98 50
Fax: (33) 3 80 54 98 59
E-Mail: info@crossject.com
Web Site: www.crossject.com
ALCJ—(EUR)
Sls.: $486,201
Earnings: ($1,271,815)
Emp.: 20
Fiscal Year-end: 12/31/12
Business Description:
Needle-Free Injection Systems Mfr
S.I.C.: 3841
N.A.I.C.S.: 339112
Personnel:
Philippe Monnot *(Chm-Supervisory Bd)*
Patrick Alexandre *(CEO)*
Tim Muller *(Chief Bus Officer)*
Supervisory Board of Directors:
Philippe Monnot
Francois Micelli
Richard Molay
Eric Nemeth
Jean-Michel Pimont

CROSSLAND URANIUM MINES LIMITED

Level 3 80 Arthur Street
North Sydney, NSW, 2060, Australia
Tel.: (61) 889815911
Fax: (61) 889411364
E-Mail: cux@crosslanduranium.com.au
Web Site: www.crosslanduranium.com.au
CUX—(ASX)
Rev.: $82,250
Assets: $7,067,404
Liabilities: $406,217
Net Worth: $6,661,188
Earnings: ($1,832,331)
Emp.: 20
Fiscal Year-end: 12/31/12
Business Description:
Uranium Mining Services
S.I.C.: 1094
N.A.I.C.S.: 212291
Personnel:
Tony Chamberlain *(COO)*
Malcolm K. Smartt *(Sec & Dir-Fin)*
Board of Directors:
Robert Lewis Richardson
Geoffrey Samuel Eupene
Malcolm K. Smartt
Peter William Walker
Legal Counsel:
O'Loughlins Lawyers
Level 2 55 Hunter Street
Sydney, NSW, Australia

CROWE HORWATH AUSTRALASIA LTD.

(Formerly WHK Group Limited)
Level 9 473 Bourke Street
Melbourne, VIC, 3000, Australia
Tel.: (61) 395220888
Fax: (61) 395220899
E-Mail: info@crowehorwath.com.au
Web Site: www.crowehorwath.net
CRH—(ASX)
Rev.: $422,988,390
Assets: $420,786,433
Liabilities: $144,962,363
Net Worth: $275,824,070
Earnings: $7,305,121
Emp.: 3,000
Fiscal Year-end: 06/30/13
Business Description:
Accounting, Audit, Tax, Business & Financial Services
S.I.C.: 8721
N.A.I.C.S.: 541211
Personnel:
Richard John Grellman *(Chm)*
Peter Hastings Warne *(Deputy Chm)*
John Alexander Lombard *(Mng Dir)*
C. Price *(CFO)*
G. Emsley *(CIO)*
C. Lake *(Chief Risk Officer)*
Bruce Craig Paterson *(Sec)*
Board of Directors:
Richard John Grellman
Peeyush Kumar Gupta
Nancy Jane Milne
Raymond Maxwell Smith
Peter Hastings Warne
Melanie Victoria Rose Willis
Legal Counsel:
Herbert Geer
Level 20 385 Bourke Street
Melbourne, VIC, Australia
Blake Dawson
Level 26 181 William Street
Melbourne, Australia

Subsidiaries:

EIS-One Pty Ltd. (1)
Level 15 309 Kent St
Sydney, NSW, 2000, Australia
Tel.: (61) 733672623
Fax: (61) 0292622190
E-Mail: enquiries@eis-one.com
Web Site: www.eis-one.com
Emp.: 6
Business Management Consulting Services
S.I.C.: 8742
N.A.I.C.S.: 541611
Thomas Thomi *(Principal)*

Horwath (Brisbane) Pty. Ltd. (1)
120 Edward St Level 16
Brisbane, QLD, 4000, Australia AU
Tel.: (61) 7 3233 3555
Fax: (61) 7 3210 6183
E-Mail: brisbane@crowehorwath.com.au
Web Site: www.crowehorwath.net
Financial & Tax Advisory Services
S.I.C.: 7291
N.A.I.C.S.: 541213
Christopher Shay *(CEO)*
Peter Bishop *(Principal-Corp Fin)*
Vanessa de Waal *(Principal-Assurance & Audit)*
Harley Mitchell *(Principal-Corp Fin)*
Ross Patane *(Principal-Corp Fin)*
Frank Ramsey *(Principal-Wealth Mgmt)*
Brendan Worrall *(Principal-Assurance & Audit)*

Michael Templeton and Associates Pty Ltd. (1)
35 Oldaker Street
Devonport, TAS, 7310, Australia

Tel.: (61) 364241172
Fax: (61) 364248224
Emp.: 40
Financial Advisory Services
S.I.C.: 6282
N.A.I.C.S.: 523930

Prescott Securities Limited (1)
245 Fullarton Rd
Eastwood, SA, 5063, Australia
Tel.: (61) 883721300
Fax: (61) 883731710
E-Mail: info@prescottsecurities.com.au
Web Site: www.prescottsecurities.com.au
Emp.: 90
Financial Advisory Services
S.I.C.: 6282
N.A.I.C.S.: 523930

Walker Partners Pty Ltd. (1)
162 Hume St
Toowoomba, QLD, 4350, Australia
Tel.: (61) 746382866
Fax: (61) 746391303
Accounting & Financial Management Services
S.I.C.: 8721
N.A.I.C.S.: 541219

WHK Central West Pty Ltd. (1)
2-4 Commercial Ave
Dubbo, NSW, 2830, Australia
Tel.: (61) 268835600
Fax: (61) 2 6884 2242
Web Site: www.whkcentralwest.com
Emp.: 60
Financial Advisory Services
S.I.C.: 6282
N.A.I.C.S.: 523930

WHK Financial Planning Pty Ltd. (1)
Suite 37 Level 3 799 Springvale Road
Mulgrave, VIC, 3140, Australia
Tel.: (61) 397355133
Fax: (61) 395355399
Financial Planning Services
S.I.C.: 6282
N.A.I.C.S.: 523930
Michael Templeton *(Principal-Fin Svcs)*

WHK Horwath Corporate Finance Limited (1)
Level 1 120 Sussex St
Sydney, NSW, 2000, Australia
Tel.: (61) 292622155
Fax: (61) 292622190
Financial Advisory Services
S.I.C.: 6282
N.A.I.C.S.: 523930
Brad Higgs *(Principal)*
Warren Howe *(Principal)*
Gary McLoughlin *(Principal)*
Ross Patane *(Principal)*

WHK Horwath Securities Limited (1)
Level 16 WHK Horwath Ctr 120 Edward St
Brisbane, QLD, 4000, Australia
Tel.: (61) 732333529
Fax: (61) 732106183
Emp.: 140
Financial Advisory Services
S.I.C.: 6282
N.A.I.C.S.: 523930

Non-U.S. Subsidiaries:

TEO Training Limited (1)
44 York Place Dunedin Center
PO Box 193
Dunedin, 9054, New Zealand
Tel.: (64) 34677000
Fax: (64) 34677009
E-Mail: info@teo.co.nz
Web Site: www.teo.co.nz
Emp.: 2
Professional Training Services
S.I.C.: 8299
N.A.I.C.S.: 611430
Amanda Cookson *(Gen Mgr)*

WHK (NZ) Limited (1)
Level 6 WHK Tower 51-53 Shortland St
Auckland, 1010, New Zealand
Tel.: (64) 93034586
Fax: (64) 93091198
E-Mail: auckland@whk.co.nz
Web Site: www.whk.co.nz
Emp.: 125
Financial Advisory Services
S.I.C.: 6282
N.A.I.C.S.: 523930
Gay Rankin *(CEO)*
Richard Currie *(Principal)*
Glen Gernhoefer *(Principal)*
Heta Hudson *(Principal)*
Catriona Knapp *(Principal)*
Chris Lindsay *(Principal)*
Grant McCurrach *(Principal)*
Gary McLoughlin *(Principal)*
Glenn Nightingale *(Principal)*

CROWN CONFECTIONERY CO., LTD.

131-1 Namyeong-Dong Yongsan-Gu
Seoul, 140-160, Korea (South)
Tel.: (82) 27919103
Telex: 2 973 3303
Fax: (82) 27919119
E-Mail: crown@crown.co.kr
Web Site: www.crown.co.kr
Year Founded: 1968
Emp.: 500

Business Description:
Bakery & Confectionery Products Mfr
Import Export
S.I.C.: 2051
N.A.I.C.S.: 311812

Personnel:
Su Jang Wang *(CEO)*

Divisions:

Crown Confectionery Co., Ltd. (1)
1337 31 Socho Dong
Sucho Gu, Seoul, 137 070, Korea (South) (100%)
Tel.: (82) 27919133
Fax: (82) 234152859
E-Mail: dscho@crown.co.kr
Web Site: www.crown.co.kr/english/contact/01_location.asp
Emp.: 1,000
Import Export
S.I.C.: 2052
N.A.I.C.S.: 311812

Crown Snack Co., Ltd. (1)
131-1 Namyeong-Dong Yongsan-Gu
Seoul, Korea (South)
Tel.: (82) 27919103
E-Mail: juftin@crown.co.kr
Sls.: $33,000,000
Emp.: 200
Bakery & Snack Food Mfr
Import Export
S.I.C.: 2052
N.A.I.C.S.: 311812

CROWN GOLD CORPORATION

130 Adelaide Street West Suite 1010
Toronto, ON, M5H 3P5, Canada
Tel.: (416) 361-2827
Fax: (416) 364-5400
E-Mail: info@crowngoldcorp.com
Web Site: www.crowngoldcorp.com
CWM—(TSXV)
Assets: $374,217
Liabilities: $76,831
Net Worth: $297,386
Earnings: ($1,003,500)
Fiscal Year-end: 12/31/12

Business Description:
Gold Mining Services
S.I.C.: 1041
N.A.I.C.S.: 212221

Personnel:
Stephen Dunn *(Pres & CEO)*
Johnny Oliveira *(CFO)*

Board of Directors:
Stephen Dunn
James Fairbairn
Donald Alexander Sheldon

Legal Counsel:
Sheldon Huxtable Professional Corporation
180 Dundas Street West Suite1801
Toronto, ON, Canada

Transfer Agent:
Computershare Trust Company of Canada
9th Floor 100 University Avenue
Toronto, ON, Canada

CROWN INVESTMENTS CORPORATION OF SASKATCHEWAN

2400 College Avenue Suite 400
Regina, SK, S4P 1C8, Canada
Tel.: (306) 787-6851
Fax: (306) 787-8125
Web Site: www.cicorp.sk.ca
Year Founded: 1947
Rev.: $4,518,780,129
Assets: $13,071,533,971
Liabilities: $8,755,886,799
Net Worth: $4,315,647,172
Earnings: $476,038,166
Emp.: 15,561
Fiscal Year-end: 12/31/12

Business Description:
Holding Company
S.I.C.: 6719
N.A.I.C.S.: 551112

Personnel:
Donna Harpauer *(Chm)*
Don McMorris *(Vice Chm)*
R. W. Carter *(Pres & CEO)*
Blair Swystun *(CFO & Sr VP-Fin & Admin)*
Doug Kosloski *(Gen Counsel & VP-HR Policy, Governance & Legal)*

Board of Directors:
Donna Harpauer
Bill Boyd
Don McMorris
Paul Merriman
Laura Ross

Subsidiaries:

Information Services Corporation (1)
300-10 Research Drive
Regina, SK, S4S 7J7, Canada SK (100%)
Tel.: (306) 787-8179
Fax: (306) 787-9220
Toll Free: (866) 275-4721
E-Mail: ask@isc.ca
Web Site: www.isc.ca/
ISV—(TSX)
Rev.: $76,857,626
Assets: $48,347,145
Liabilities: $26,537,352
Net Worth: $21,809,793
Earnings: $21,112,985
Emp.: 293
Fiscal Year-end: 12/31/12
Saskatchewan Land Registry, Personal Property Registry, Survey Plan Registry & Geomatics Services
S.I.C.: 6531
N.A.I.C.S.: 531390
Joel Douglas Teal *(Chm)*
Jeff Stusek *(Pres & CEO)*
Shawn B. Peters *(CFO, VP-Fin & Tech)*
Kathy Hillman-Weir *(Gen Counsel, Chief Privacy Officer & VP-Corp Affairs)*

Saskatchewan Government Insurance (1)
2260 11th Ave
Regina, SK, S4P 0J9, Canada (100%)
Tel.: (306) 751-1200
Fax: (306) 307-9037
Toll Free: (800) 667-8015
E-Mail: inquirycenter@sgi.sk.ca
Web Site: www.sgi.sk.ca
Sales Range: $500-549.9 Million
Emp.: 1,800
Provider of Propery & Casualty Insurance Products in Saskatchewan
S.I.C.: 6351
N.A.I.C.S.: 524126
Don Thompson *(CFO)*

Subsidiary:

SGI CANADA Insurance Services Ltd. (2)
2260 11th Avenue
Regina, SK, S4P 0J9, Canada SK (83%)
Tel.: (306) 775-6590
E-Mail: sgiinquiries@sgi.sk.ca
Web Site: www.sgi.sk.ca
Emp.: 50
Provider of Property & Casualty Insurance Products Outside Saskatchewan
S.I.C.: 6399
N.A.I.C.S.: 524128
Andrew Cartmell *(Pres & CEO)*

Saskatchewan Power Corporation (1)
2025 Victoria Avenue
Regina, SK, S4P 0S1, Canada (100%)
Tel.: (306) 566-2121
Fax: (306) 566-2548
Toll Free: (888) 757-6937
E-Mail: info@saskpower.com
Web Site: www.saskpower.com
Rev.: $1,850,865,240
Assets: $6,969,074,220
Liabilities: $5,122,185,060
Net Worth: $1,846,889,160
Earnings: $152,085,060
Emp.: 3,419
Fiscal Year-end: 12/31/12
Public Utility & Electricity Supplier
S.I.C.: 4931
N.A.I.C.S.: 221122
Joel Teal *(Chm)*
Bill Wheatley *(Vice Chm)*
Robert Watson *(Pres & CEO)*
Sandeep Kalra *(CFO, VP-Fin)*
Mike Marsh *(COO & VP-Ops)*
Tom Kindred *(CIO & VP-Corp IT)*
Steve Sousa *(Chief Comml Officer)*
Guy Bruce *(Pres/CEO-NorthPoint Energy Solutions & VP-Resource Plng)*
Michael Monea *(Pres-Carbon Capture & Storage Initiatives)*
Rachelle Verret Morphy *(Gen Counsel, VP-Law, Land & Regulatory Affairs & Asst Sec)*
Dale Bloom *(Sec)*

Subsidiary:

SaskPower International (2)
2025 Victoria Ave
Regina, SK, S4P 0S1, Canada (100%)
Tel.: (306) 566-2121
Fax: (306) 566-3034
E-Mail: spi@saskpower.com
Web Site: www.saskpower.com
Emp.: 15
Power Marketing Services
S.I.C.: 4931
N.A.I.C.S.: 221118

Saskatchewan Telecommunications Holdings Corporation (1)
2121 Saskatchewan Drive
Regina, SK, S4P 3Y2, Canada
Tel.: (306) 777-4476
Fax: (306) 565-8717
Toll Free: (800) 727-5835
Web Site: www.sasktel.com
Sales Range: $750-799.9 Million
Emp.: 3,800
Communications Services Including Wireline, Wireless, Internet & Digitial Network E-Business Solutions
S.I.C.: 4812
N.A.I.C.S.: 517210
Grant J. Kook *(Chm)*
Darcy Bear *(Vice Chm)*
Ron Styles *(Pres & CEO)*
Mike Anderson *(CFO)*
John Hill *(CIO)*
Stacey Sandison *(CMO)*
Kym Wittal *(CTO)*
John Meldrum *(Gen Counsel, Chief Privacy Officer & VP-Regulatory Affairs)*

CROWN LIMITED

(Name Changed to Crown Resorts Limited)

CROWN PAINTS KENYA LTD.

Likoni Road Industrial Area
PO Box 78848
00507 Nairobi, Kenya
Tel.: (254) 20 6533604
Fax: (254) 20 6558480
E-Mail: info@crwonpaints.co.ke
Web Site: www.crownpaints.co.ke
CRBG—(NAI)
Sales Range: $25-49.9 Million

Business Description:
Paint & Coating Mfr
S.I.C.: 2851
N.A.I.C.S.: 325510

Crown Paints Kenya Ltd.—(Continued)

Personnel:
Mhamud Charania *(Chm)*
Rakesh K. Rao *(Mng Dir)*
Conrad Nyukuri *(Sec)*

Legal Counsel:
Kairu Mbutina & Kingati Advocates
Penesia Center Ngong Road
Nairobi, Kenya

CROWN POINT ENERGY INC.

Suite 1600 700 Sixth Avenue SW
Calgary, AB, T2P 0T8, Canada
Tel.: (403) 232-1150
Fax: (403) 232-1158
E-Mail: info@crownpointenergy.com
Web Site: www.crownpointenergy.com
Year Founded: 1966
CWV—(OTC TSXV)
Emp.: 7

Business Description:
Oil & Gas Exploration Services
S.I.C.: 1311
N.A.I.C.S.: 211111

Personnel:
Murray D. McCartney *(Pres & CEO)*
Arthur J. G. Madden *(CFO & VP)*
Brian J. Moss *(COO & Exec VP)*
Glenn R. Yeadon *(Sec)*
Daniel Lanussol *(Exec VP-Ops-Argentina)*

Board of Directors:
Gordon Kettleson
John Clark
Denny Deren
Murray D. McCartney
Brian J. Moss
Carlos Olivieri
Keith S. Turnbull

Transfer Agent:
Computershare Trust Company of Canada
9th Floor 100 University Avenue
Toronto, ON, Canada

CROWN PROPERTY BUREAU

173 Ratchasima Road
Dusit, Bangkok, 10300, Thailand
Tel.: (66) 26873379
Fax: (66) 26873006
E-Mail: info@crownproperty.or.th
Web Site: www.crownproperty.or.th
Emp.: 1,000

Business Description:
Financial Services
S.I.C.: 6726
N.A.I.C.S.: 525990

Personnel:
Chirayu Isarangkul Na Ayuthaya *(Dir Gen)*

Subsidiary:

The Deves Insurance Public Company Limted (1)
97 99 Deves Insurance Building
Ratchadamnoen-Klang Road
Pranakorn, Bangkok, 10200, Thailand (86.68%)
Tel.: (66) 26704444
Fax: (66) 22800399
E-Mail: dvsins@deves.co.th
Web Site: www.deves.co.th
Sales Range: $75-99.9 Million
Emp.: 482
Insurance Services
S.I.C.: 6411
N.A.I.C.S.: 524298
Chirayu Isarangkul Na Ayuthaya *(Chm)*
Anant Keskasemsook *(Pres)*
Pawinee Tippetch *(Sec)*
Supradit Ram-Indra *(Sr Exec VP-Bus Dev)*
Chatchai Chinvetkitvanit *(Exec VP-Bus Ops)*
Santi Iamvuthipreecha *(Exec VP-Bus Ops)*
Umnaj Lohsuwan *(Exec VP-Admin)*
Preecha Vitavaskarnvej *(Exec VP-Bus Support)*
Wachira Chuaychoo *(Sr VP-Mktg)*

CROWN RESORTS LIMITED

(Formerly Crown Limited)
Level 3 Crown Towers 8 Whiteman Street
Southbank, VIC, 3006, Australia
Tel.: (61) 3 9292 8888
Fax: (61) 3 9292 8808
Web Site: www.crownresorts.com.au
CWN—(ASX OTC)
Rev.: $3,016,675,248
Assets: $6,262,651,055
Liabilities: $2,456,275,552
Net Worth: $3,806,375,502
Earnings: $571,065,590
Emp.: 11,764
Fiscal Year-end: 06/30/13

Business Description:
Casino Hotels & Gaming Establishments
S.I.C.: 7011
N.A.I.C.S.: 721120

Personnel:
James Douglas Packer *(Chm)*
John Henry Alexander *(Deputy Chm)*
Rowen Bruce Craigie *(CEO & Mng Dir)*
Kenneth M. Barton *(CFO)*
Barry Felstead *(CEO-Australian Resorts)*
Gregory F. Hawkins *(CEO-Melbourne)*
Michael J. Neilson *(Gen Counsel & Sec)*
W. Todd Nisbet *(Exec VP-Design & Strategy)*

Board of Directors:
James Douglas Packer
John Henry Alexander
Benjamin Alexander Brazil
Helen Anne Coonan
Rowen Bruce Craigie
Rowena Danziger
Geoffrey James Dixon
John Stephen Horvath
Ashok P. Jacob
Michael Roy Johnston
Harold Charles Mitchell

Subsidiaries:

Burswood Limited (1)
Great Eastern Hwy
Burswood, WA, 6100, Australia AU
Mailing Address:
PO Box 500
Victoria Park, WA, 6979, Australia
Tel.: (61) 893627777
Fax: (61) 894701789
E-Mail: crownperth@crownperth.com.au
Web Site: www.crownperth.com.au
Emp.: 5,000
Operator of Resort Hotel & Casino
S.I.C.: 7011
N.A.I.C.S.: 721120
Justine Henwood *(CFO)*
Andrew Hill *(COO)*
Michael Egan *(Sec & Gen Mgr-Legal Svcs)*

Crown Melbourne Limited (1)
8 Whiteman Street
Southbank, VIC, 3006, Australia
Tel.: (61) 392928888
Fax: (61) 392926600
Web Site: www.crowncasino.com.au
Emp.: 8,000
Casino Hotel
S.I.C.: 7011
N.A.I.C.S.: 721120
Rowen Craigie *(CEO)*

CROWN TECH ADVANCE PUBLIC COMPANY LIMITED

30/10-14 Moo 5 Soi Tungpattanapisan
Leabklongsiwaphasawat Road
Kokkrabue Muangsamutsakorn,
Samut Sakhon, 74000, Thailand
Tel.: (66) 3449 4900
Fax: (66) 3449 4909
Web Site: www.ajthai.com
AJD—(THA)
Rev.: $53,691,179
Assets: $41,912,833
Liabilities: $32,293,871
Net Worth: $9,618,962
Earnings: $990,625
Fiscal Year-end: 12/31/12

Business Description:
Electric Appliances Importer & Distr
S.I.C.: 5064
N.A.I.C.S.: 423620

Personnel:
Dusit Kruayai *(Chm)*
Amorn Meemano *(Mng Dir)*

Board of Directors:
Dusit Kruayai
Khan Akaworawit
Sompoth Booraphasakul
Kamol Chirapathama
Vacharin Duangdara
Amorn Meemano
Jinda Meemano
Anake Patansarit
Pipat Patiwatephinyo
Pisanu Rienmahasarn
Jitti Rodbangyang

CROWN VAN GELDER N.V.

Eendrachtsstraat 30
1951 AZ Velsen, Netherlands
Tel.: (31) 251262233
Fax: (31) 251262399
E-Mail: info@cvg.nl
Web Site: www.cvg.nl
CVG—(EUR)
Rev.: $224,632,696
Assets: $97,248,667
Liabilities: $32,641,930
Net Worth: $64,606,737
Earnings: ($32,636,545)
Emp.: 282
Fiscal Year-end: 12/31/12

Business Description:
Uncoated & Single-Coated Paper Mfr
S.I.C.: 2672
N.A.I.C.S.: 322220

Personnel:
Miklas Dronkers *(CEO & Member-Mgmt Bd)*
Henk van der Zwaag *(CFO & Member-Mgmt Bd)*

Supervisory Board of Directors:
E. J. L. Bakkar
T. Philippa
J. A. J. M. van den Hoven
H. van Houtum
Han Wagter

Subsidiary:

Inkoopcombinatie De Eendragt B.V (1)
Sluispolderweg 8
1505 HK Zaandam, North Holland, Netherlands
Tel.: (31) 756311425
Fax: (31) 756311104
E-Mail: info@alliancell.com
Web Site: www.alliancell.com
Emp.: 3
Wood Pulp & Filters Procurement Tools Provider
S.I.C.: 2499
N.A.I.C.S.: 321999
Norman Snel *(Gen Mgr)*

CROWN WORLDWIDE HOLDINGS LTD.

(d/b/a Crown Worldwide Group)
Ste 2001 MassMutual Tower 38 Gloucester Rd
Wanchai, China (Hong Kong)
Tel.: (852) 25286111
Fax: (852) 25280177
E-Mail: holdings@crownworldwide.com
Web Site: www.crownworldwide.com
Year Founded: 1965
Sales Range: $550-599.9 Million
Emp.: 5,000

Business Description:
Holding Company; Mobility, Relocation, Record Management, Warehousing, Freight Forwarding & Third-Party Logistics Services
S.I.C.: 6719
N.A.I.C.S.: 551112

Personnel:
James Edward Thompson *(Founder & Chm)*
Ken Madrid *(CFO & CEO-Asia-Pacific)*
David Muir *(CEO-EMEA)*

Board of Directors:
James Edward Thompson
Ken Madrid
David Muir

U.S. Subsidiary:

Crown Relocations (1)
5252 Argosy Ave
Huntington Beach, CA 92649-1074
Mailing Address:
PO Box 2297
Huntington Beach, CA 92647-0297
Tel.: (714) 898-0955
Fax: (714) 898-5640
E-Mail: losangeles@crownrelo.com
Web Site: www.crownrelo.com
Emp.: 35
Freight Transportation Services Import Export
S.I.C.: 4731
N.A.I.C.S.: 488510
James E. Thompson *(Chm)*

CROWSNEST ACQUISITION CORP.

1400 700 2nd Street S.W
Calgary, AB, T2P 4V5, Canada
Tel.: (780) 465-4467
Year Founded: 2012
CAW.P—(TSXV)

Business Description:
Investment Services
S.I.C.: 6211
N.A.I.C.S.: 523999

Personnel:
Gordon McCormack *(Pres & CEO)*
Blair Pennock *(CFO & Sec)*

Board of Directors:
Victor S. Dusik
Paul Folkmann
Gordon McCormack
Blair Pennock

CROYDON CLOCKTOWER

Katharine Street
Croydon, CR9 1ET, United Kingdom
Tel.: (44) 2082531030
Fax: (44) 2082531003
E-Mail: sam.hunt@croydon.gov.uk
Web Site: www.croydon.gov.uk
Emp.: 100

Business Description:
Cultural Services; Exhibitions, Museum, Live Performances, Art House Films, Library, Cinema, Cafe & Tourist Services
S.I.C.: 8299
N.A.I.C.S.: 611620

CRS ELECTRONICS INC.

9120 Leslie Street Suite 102
Richmond Hill, ON, L4B 3J9, Canada
Tel.: (905) 788-9039
Fax: (905) 788-2739
Toll Free: (888) 330-6786
E-Mail: reception@crselectronics.com

Web Site: www.crselectronics.com
LED—(OTC TSXV)
Sls.: $3,070,121
Assets: $6,896,844
Liabilities: $1,926,620
Net Worth: $4,970,224
Earnings: ($5,272,982)
Emp.: 30
Fiscal Year-end: 12/31/12
Business Description:
Light Emitting Diode Mfr
S.I.C.: 3646
N.A.I.C.S.: 335122
Personnel:
Scott Riesebosch *(Founder & CTO)*
Chang Jiang Wu *(Chm)*
Travis Jones *(CEO)*
Matthew Groen *(CFO)*
Jennifer Yan Li *(Chief Admin Officer)*
Kristen Ryan *(Customs Compliance Officer)*
Board of Directors:
Chang Jiang Wu
Bernard J. Erickson
Zheng-Hong Lu
Robert Neill
Scott Riesebosch
Lian Wu
Legal Counsel:
Gowlings LLP
1 First Canadian Place 100 King Street West
Suite 1600
Toronto, ON, Canada
Goodwin Procter LLP
Exchange Pl 53 State St
Boston, MA 02109-2881
Tel.: (617) 570-1000
Transfer Agent:
Equity Transfer & Trust Company
200 University Avenue Ste 400
Toronto, ON, M5H 4H1, Canada
Tel.: (416) 361-0152
Fax: (416) 361-0470

CRS HOLDING AG
Burgstrasse 28
Glarus, GL, 8750, Switzerland
Tel.: (41) 556402147
Year Founded: 1989
Business Description:
Holding Company
S.I.C.: 6719
N.A.I.C.S.: 551112
Subsidiary:

Filtrox AG (1)
Moosmuhlen Strasse 6
Saint Gallen, 9001, Switzerland (100%)
Tel.: (41) 712729111
Fax: (41) 712771284
E-Mail: filtrox@filtrox.ch
Web Site: www.filtrox.ch
Emp.: 100
Mfr of Industrial Machinery
S.I.C.: 3589
N.A.I.C.S.: 333318
Kristen Rusch *(Gen Mgr)*

Subsidiary:

A. Sutter AG (2)
Moosmuhlestrasse 6
CH 9000 Saint Gallen, Switzerland CH (100%)
Tel.: (41) 712729500
Fax: (41) 712729600
E-Mail: info@sutterag.ch
Web Site: www.sutterag.ch
Emp.: 150
Consulting, Designing & Producing Equipment for the Production of Wine & Fruit Juice
S.I.C.: 3556
N.A.I.C.S.: 333241
Patrick Neher *(Product Mgr)*

CRT - CONCESSIONARIA RIO-TERESOPOLIS S/A
Rod Santos Dumont br-116/rj - Km 133 5
25930530 Brasilia, RJ, Brazil
Tel.: (55) 21 2777 8333
Fax: (55) 21 2777 8420
E-Mail: ricrt@crt.com.br
Web Site: www.crt.com.br
Year Founded: 1995
CRTE3B—(BRAZ)
Business Description:
Highway Transportation Management Services
S.I.C.: 4789
N.A.I.C.S.: 488490
Personnel:
Carlos Eduardo Soares de Menezes *(Dir-IR)*

CRT CONSTRUCTION INC.
870 Archimede Street
Levis, QC, G6V 7M5, Canada
Tel.: (418) 833-8073
Fax: (418) 833-9629
E-Mail: levis@crtconstruction.ca
Web Site: www.crtconstruction.ca
Year Founded: 1966
Rev.: $31,726,263
Emp.: 50
Business Description:
Highway Street & Bridge Construction Services
S.I.C.: 1622
N.A.I.C.S.: 237310
Personnel:
Denis Turgeon *(Pres)*

CRUCIALTEC CO., LTD.
165 Secul Baebang
Asan, Chungnam, Korea (South)
Tel.: (82) 419130001
Fax: (82) 419130009
Web Site: www.crucialtec.com
Year Founded: 2001
114120—(KRS)
Sales Range: $150-199.9 Million
Emp.: 1,200
Business Description:
Mobile Device Mfr
S.I.C.: 3663
N.A.I.C.S.: 334220
Personnel:
Charles Keon-Joon Ahn *(CEO)*
Dae-joon Kim *(Exec VP-Strategic Plng)*
Jong-bin Kim *(Exec VP-Mfg & Production)*
Board of Directors:
Charles Keon-Joon Ahn
Jae-hoon Bae
Byung-Cheol Chung
Kyung-lim Kang
Dae-joon Kim
Jong-bin Kim

CRUCIBLE GOLD LIMITED
Level 1 6 Thelma Street
West Perth, 6005, Australia
Tel.: (61) 8 9486 8237
Fax: (61) 8 9226 3764
E-Mail: info@cruciblegold.com.au
Web Site: www.cruciblegold.com.au
O5A—(ASX DEU)
Rev.: $47,209
Assets: $1,173,432
Liabilities: $53,270
Net Worth: $1,120,162
Earnings: ($1,721,285)
Fiscal Year-end: 06/30/13
Business Description:
Gold Exploartion Services
S.I.C.: 1041
N.A.I.C.S.: 212221
Personnel:
Ian Hobson *(Sec)*
Board of Directors:
Tim Fry
Simon Coxhell
Michel Mian
Peter Pawlowitsch
Ken Richards
Legal Counsel:
Nova Legal
Ground Floor 10 Ord Street
West Perth, WA, Australia
Freehills
250 St Georges Terrace
Perth, Australia

CRUDECORP ASA
Skagen 27
Postboks 896
4004 Stavanger, Norway
Tel.: (47) 51 12 30 18
Fax: (47) 51 21 46 39
Web Site: www.crudecorp.no
Year Founded: 2007
Business Description:
Oil Drilling
S.I.C.: 1381
N.A.I.C.S.: 213111
Personnel:
Sigurd Aase *(Chm)*
Gunnar Hviding *(Pres & CEO)*
Anniken Landre Bjerke *(CFO)*
Havard Rod *(COO)*
Board of Directors:
Sigurd Aase
Espen Fjogstad
Sissel K. Hegdal
Stig M. Herbern
Silje Veen

CRUDELI SA
47 Boulevard Des Acieries
13010 Marseille, Bouches-du-Rhone, France
Tel.: (33) 491177070
Web Site: www.crudeli.com
Year Founded: 1965
Sales Range: $25-49.9 Million
Emp.: 160
Business Description:
Plumbing, Heating & Air-Conditioning Services
S.I.C.: 1711
N.A.I.C.S.: 238220
Personnel:
Gregory Frayssinet *(Mgr-DP)*

CRUSADER RESOURCES LIMITED
Suite 1 Level 1 35 Havelock Street
West Perth, WA, 6005, Australia
Mailing Address:
PO Box 692
West Perth, WA, 6872, Australia
Tel.: (61) 893207500
Fax: (61) 893207501
E-Mail: admin@crusaderresources.com
Web Site: www.crusaderresources.com
CAS—(ASX)
Rev.: $2,492,986
Assets: $33,567,356
Liabilities: $7,600,247
Net Worth: $25,967,109
Earnings: ($8,000,922)
Fiscal Year-end: 06/30/13
Business Description:
Mineral Mining Services
S.I.C.: 1041
N.A.I.C.S.: 212221
Personnel:
Robert Smakman *(Mng Dir)*
Andrew Beigel *(CFO & Sec)*
Mike Schmulian *(COO)*
Board of Directors:
Stephen Copulos
John Evans
Mauricio Ferreira
David Netherway
Robert Smakman
Paul Stephen
Legal Counsel:
GTP Legal
Level 1 28 Ord Street
West Perth, Australia

CRUST CRAFT INC.
13211 146 Street
Edmonton, AB, T5L 4S8, Canada
Tel.: (780) 466-1333
Fax: (780) 466-1347
E-Mail: orderdesk@crustcraft.com
Web Site: www.crustcraft.com
Rev.: $10,349,230
Emp.: 70
Business Description:
Flour & Other Grain Products Supplier
S.I.C.: 2041
N.A.I.C.S.: 311211
Personnel:
Paul Flesher *(Pres)*

CRYO-SAVE GROUP N.V.
Piet Heinstraat 11
7204 JN Zutphen, Netherlands
Tel.: (31) 575509100
Fax: (31) 575509130
E-Mail: int@cryo-save.com
Web Site: www.cryo-save.com
CRYO—(AIM EUR)
Rev.: $49,595,595
Assets: $74,875,322
Liabilities: $34,719,070
Net Worth: $40,156,251
Earnings: ($23,023,546)
Emp.: 259
Fiscal Year-end: 12/31/12
Business Description:
Adult Stem Cell Collection & Storage Services
S.I.C.: 8731
N.A.I.C.S.: 541712
Board of Directors:
Walter van Pottelberge
Karin Dorrepaal
Ronald Lorijn
Legal Counsel:
Simmons & Simmons
PO Box 79023
1070 NB Amsterdam, Netherlands
Subsidiary:

Stichting Cryo-Save (1)
Pyet Hein Straat 11
7204 Zutphen, Gelderland, Netherlands
Tel.: (31) 575509100
Fax: (31) 575547424
E-Mail: int@cryo-save.com
Web Site: www.cryo-save.com
Emp.: 20
Stem Cell Storage Services
S.I.C.: 8011
N.A.I.C.S.: 621491
Arnoud Van Tulder *(CEO)*

Non-U.S. Subsidiaries:

Archiv Bunek s.r.o. (1)
Podolske embankment 157/36
Praha 4 Podoli, 147 00 Prague, Czech Republic
Tel.: (420) 241 430 241
Fax: (420) 257 210 126
E-Mail: info@cryo-save.cz
Web Site: www.cryo-save.cz
Emp.: 20
Stem Cell Storage Services
S.I.C.: 8011
N.A.I.C.S.: 621491
Zoltan Merhala *(CEO)*

The Cell-Factory NV (1)
Molenberglei 20
2627 Schelle, Antwerpen, Belgium
Tel.: (32) 38801540
Fax: (32) 38841648
E-Mail: medinfo@cell-factory.com

Cryo-Save Group N.V.—(Continued)

Web Site: www.cell-factory.com
Emp.: 4
Stem Cell Storage Services
S.I.C.: 8011
N.A.I.C.S.: 621491
Marc Waeterschoot *(Mng Dir)*

Cryo-Save AG (1)
Churerstrasse 65B
8808 Pfaffikon, Schwyz, Switzerland
Tel.: (41) 552220255
Fax: (41) 552220257
E-Mail: ch@cryo-save.com
Web Site: www.cryo-save.com
Emp.: 5
Stem Cell Storage Services
S.I.C.: 8011
N.A.I.C.S.: 621491
Evi Mattil *(Chief Comml Officer)*

Cryo-Save Espana S.A. (1)
Josep Argemi 13-15
08950 Esplugues de Llobregat, Barcelona, Spain
Tel.: (34) 934705656
Fax: (34) 934732855
E-Mail: es@cryo-save.com
Web Site: www.2.cryo-save.com
Stem Cell Storage Services
S.I.C.: 8011
N.A.I.C.S.: 621491

Cryo-Save GmbH (1)
Pauwelsstrasse 19
52074 Aachen, Germany
Tel.: (49) 24198092750
Fax: (49) 08003318002
Toll Free: 8003318000
E-Mail: de@cryo-save.com
Web Site: www.cryo-save.com
Stem Cell Storage Services
S.I.C.: 8011
N.A.I.C.S.: 621491
Ria Lindt *(Mgr)*

Cryo-Save (Pty) Ltd. (1)
3rd Fl 13th S Ridge Rd
PO Box 51231
4061 Durban, Kwazulu-Natal, South Africa
Tel.: (27) 312014420
Fax: (27) 312015440
E-Mail: post@cryo-save.co.za
Web Site: www.cryo-sace.co.za
Stem Cell Storage Services
S.I.C.: 8011
N.A.I.C.S.: 621491
Justine Joubert *(Branch Mgr)*

Output Pharma Services GmbH (1)
Pauwelsstrasse 19
52074 Aachen, Germany
Tel.: (49) 2419632680
Fax: (49) 2419632689
E-Mail: contact@output.eu
Web Site: www.output.eu
Emp.: 9
Medicinal Products Trading Services
S.I.C.: 5122
N.A.I.C.S.: 424210
Stephen Heckler *(Mgr)*

CRYO-SAVE (INDIA) PVT. LTD.

No 183 Gayatri Tech Park Rd 1B
EPIP KIADB Whitefield, Bengaluru, Karnataka, 560 066, India
Tel.: (91) 8042430100
Fax: (91) 42430107
E-Mail: in@cryo-save.com
Web Site: www.cryo-save.com
Year Founded: 2008
Business Description:
Stem Cell Storage Services
S.I.C.: 8011
N.A.I.C.S.: 621491
Personnel:
Rajesh Sharma *(Mng Dir)*

CRYOCORD HOLDINGS SDN. BHD.

No 37-3 Jalan PJU 1 41
Block D1 Dataran Prima, 47301
Petaling Jaya, Selangor Darul Ehsan, Malaysia
Tel.: (60) 3 7880 2929
Fax: (60) 3 7880 1919
E-Mail: info@cryocord.com.my
Web Site: cryocord.com.my
Year Founded: 2003
Business Description:
Holding Company; Stem Cell Cryogenic Storage & Services
S.I.C.: 8071
N.A.I.C.S.: 621511
Personnel:
James Khong Lek Then *(Mng Dir)*
Kong Yong Then *(CTO)*

Subsidiary:

CryoCord Sdn. Bhd. (1)
Suite 1-1 1st Floor Bio X Centre Persiaran Cyberpoint Selatan Cyber 8
Block D1 Dataran Prima, 47301 Cyberjaya, Selangor, Malaysia MY
Tel.: (60) 3 7880 2929
Fax: (60) 386898866
E-Mail: info@cryocord.com.my
Web Site: www.cryocord.com.my
Emp.: 320
Stem Cell Crogenic Storage & Services
S.I.C.: 8071
N.A.I.C.S.: 621511
Soon Keng Cheong *(Dir-Medical)*

Subsidiary:

Stemtech International Sdn. Bhd. (2)
UM-PKNS Innotech Park Block E&F Jalan Teknologi 3/4 Selangor Science Park Sec 3 Kota Damansara, 47810
Petaling Jaya, Selangor DE, Malaysia (100%)
Tel.: (60) 361418881
Fax: (60) 361418882
E-Mail: enquiries@stemtech-international.com
Web Site: www.stemtech-international.com
Emp.: 20
Stem Cell Research
S.I.C.: 8071
N.A.I.C.S.: 621511
Khalid Bin Abdul Kadir *(Dir-Medical)*

CRYONIC MEDICAL

6 rue Berthelot
25000 Besancon, France
Tel.: (33) 3 81 54 35 40
Fax: (33) 3 81 48 43 28
E-Mail: cryonic@cryonic-medical.com
Web Site: www.cryonic-medical.com
MLCRY—(EUR)
Business Description:
Medical Equipment Mfr
S.I.C.: 3845
N.A.I.C.S.: 334510
Personnel:
Robert Taub *(Chm)*
Gerald Brothier *(CEO)*
Board of Directors:
Robert Taub
Jean-Pierre Capdevielle

CRYOSITE LIMITED

13a Ferndell Street South
PO Box 324
Granville, NSW, 2142, Australia
Tel.: (61) 2 8865 2000
Fax: (61) 2 8865 2090
E-Mail: corporate@cryosite.com
Web Site: www.cryosite.com
CTE—(ASX)
Rev.: $9,133,443
Assets: $11,840,577
Liabilities: $5,312,625
Net Worth: $6,527,952
Earnings: $1,302,584
Emp.: 35
Fiscal Year-end: 06/30/13
Business Description:
Temperature Critical Biological Products Distribution
S.I.C.: 2834
N.A.I.C.S.: 325412
Personnel:
Gordon Milliken *(Mng Dir)*
Philip Alger *(CFO)*
Bryan Dulhunty *(Sec)*
Board of Directors:
Andrew Kroger
Christina Boyce
Gordon Milliken
Graeme Moore

Subsidiary:

Cryosite Distribution Pty Limited (1)
13A Ferndell St
South Granville, Sydney, New South Wales, 2066, Australia
Tel.: (61) 294201400
Fax: (61) 288652090
E-Mail: store@cryosite.com
Web Site: www.cryosite.com
Logistics Services
S.I.C.: 4731
N.A.I.C.S.: 541614
Grahm Moure *(Mng Dir)*

CRYSTAL AMBER FUND LIMITED

Heritage Hall Le Marchant Street
PO Box 225
Saint Peter Port, GY1 4HY, Guernsey
Tel.: (44) 1481 716000
E-Mail: fund@crystalamber.com
Web Site: www.crystalamber.com
CRS—(LSE)
Rev.: $28,245,483
Assets: $117,011,693
Liabilities: $376,056
Net Worth: $116,635,638
Earnings: $25,242,410
Fiscal Year-end: 06/30/13
Business Description:
Investment Fund Services
S.I.C.: 6722
N.A.I.C.S.: 525910
Personnel:
William Nicholas Collins *(Chm)*
Board of Directors:
William Nicholas Collins
Sarah Evans
John Nigel Ward
Legal Counsel:
Norton Rose LLP
3 More London Riverside
London, SE1 2AQ, United Kingdom
Tel.: (44) 20 7283 6000
Fax: (44) 20 7283 6500

Carey Olsen
Riverside 7 New Street
Saint Peter Port, Guernsey

CRYSTAL CLAIRE COSMETICS INC.

20 Overlea Boulevard
Toronto, ON, M4H 1A4, Canada
Tel.: (416) 421-1882
Fax: (416) 421-5025
E-Mail: sales@crystalclaire.com
Web Site: www.crystalclaire.com
Rev.: $15,642,363
Emp.: 150
Business Description:
Cosmetic Products Mfr
S.I.C.: 5122
N.A.I.C.S.: 446120
Personnel:
Wendy Tung *(Dir-Sls)*

CRYSTALGENOMICS, INC.

5F Tower A Korea Bio Park 694-1 Sampyeong-dong
Bundang-gu, Seongnam, 463-400, Korea (South)
Tel.: (82) 316282700
Fax: (82) 316282701
E-Mail: info@cgxinc.com
Web Site: www.crystalgenomics.com
Year Founded: 2000
083790—(KRS)
Business Description:
Drug Discovery & Development Services
S.I.C.: 2834
N.A.I.C.S.: 325412
Personnel:
Joong Myung Cho *(Pres & CEO)*
Sang-Cheon Ahn *(Exec Mng Dir)*
Seonggu Ro *(CTO & Exec VP)*

U.S. Subsidiary:

CG Pharmaceuticals, Inc. (1)
5890 Horton St Ste 610
Emeryville, CA 94608
Tel.: (510) 594-8200
Fax: (510) 594-8201
E-Mail: info@cgxinc.com
Web Site: www.cgpharma.com
Pharmaceutical Development Services
S.I.C.: 2834
N.A.I.C.S.: 325412
Paul Kim *(Chief Bus Officer & VP)*

CRYSTALLEX INTERNATIONAL CORPORATION

8 King Street East Suite 1201
Toronto, ON, M5C 1B5, Canada
Tel.: (416) 203-2448
Fax: (416) 203-0099
Toll Free: (800) 738-1577
E-Mail: info@crystallex.com
Web Site: www.crystallex.com
Year Founded: 1984
Business Description:
Gold Mining & Exploration Services
S.I.C.: 1041
N.A.I.C.S.: 212221
Personnel:
Robert A. Fung *(Chm & CEO)*
Robert Crombie *(Pres)*
Board of Directors:
Robert A. Fung
David Kay
Harry J. Near
Marc J. Oppenheimer
Robin Rajendra Shah
Transfer Agent:
CIBC Mellon Trust Company
PO Box 7010
Adelaide Street Postal Station, Toronto, ON, M5C 2W9, Canada
Tel.: (416) 643-5500
Fax: (416) 643-5501
Toll Free: (800) 387-0825

Non-U.S. Subsidiary:

CRYSTALLEX de VENEZUELA, C.A (1)
Piso 12 Of AB Urb El Rosal Caracas C/C Carabobo Torre Forum
Caracas, Venezuela
Tel.: (58) 212 9520972
Gold Mining Services
S.I.C.: 1099
N.A.I.C.S.: 212299

C.S. BACHLY BUILDERS LTD.

(d/b/a Bachly Construction)
27 Nixon Road
Bolton, ON, L7E 1J7, Canada
Tel.: (905) 951-3100
Fax: (905) 951-3101
Toll Free: (800) 363-3473
Web Site: www.bachly.com
Year Founded: 1962
Rev.: $14,767,900
Emp.: 47
Business Description:
Building Construction Services
S.I.C.: 1521
N.A.I.C.S.: 236115
Personnel:
Scott Bachly *(Pres)*

CS COMMUNICATION & SYSTEMES SA

22 Avenue Galilee
92350 Le Plessis-Robinson, France
Tel.: (33) 141284000
Fax: (33) 141284040
Web Site: www.c-s.fr
SX—(EUR)
Sls.: $232,610,099
Earnings: $3,417,926
Emp.: 2,000
Fiscal Year-end: 12/31/12

Business Description:
Mission Critical Systems Designer, Integrator & Operator
S.I.C.: 3669
N.A.I.C.S.: 334290

Personnel:
Yazid Sabeg *(Chm)*

Board of Directors:
Yazid Sabeg
Olivier Barre
Francois Davy
Michel Desbard
Laurent Giovachini
Gilles Marchiat
Patrice Mignon
Jean-Pascal Tranie
Antoine Veil

Cabinet Mazars
Paris, France

Non-U.S. Subsidiaries:

BetEire Flow Ltd. (1)
7-A Wilson Terr
Business & Technology Park, Dublin, 2, Ireland
Tel.: (353) 16099500
Fax: (353) 16628290
System Design & Integration Services
S.I.C.: 7373
N.A.I.C.S.: 541512

CS Canada Inc. (1)
6363 Transcanada Hwy Ste 102
Saint Laurent, QC, H4T 1Z9, Canada
Tel.: (514) 748-8258
Fax: (514) 748-8509
Toll Free: (866) 748-8258
E-Mail: info@cscanada.ca
Web Site: www.cscanada.ca
Emp.: 80
System Design & Integration Services
S.I.C.: 7373
N.A.I.C.S.: 541512
Eric Mathieu *(Gen Mgr)*

CS Chile S.A. (1)
Las Torres 1425 A
G.E El Rosal Huechuraba, Santiago, Chile CL
Tel.: (56) 24431666
Fax: (56) 2 4472856
Web Site: uk.c-s.fr/Worldwide_a113.html
Foreign Missions Services
S.I.C.: 9721
N.A.I.C.S.: 928120

CS Romania SA (1)
CS Romania Str Pacii nr 29
200692 Craiova, Dolj, Romania
Tel.: (40) 251412850
Fax: (40) 251417307
E-Mail: office@c-s.ro
Web Site: www.c-s.ro
Emp.: 70
Foreign Missions Services
S.I.C.: 9721
N.A.I.C.S.: 928120
Mircea Grosu *(Gen Mgr)*

Ecsat D.O.O. (1)
Zrinjsko Frankopanska bb
21 000 Split, Croatia
Tel.: (385) 21347700
Fax: (385) 21347700
E-Mail: info@ecsat.hr
Web Site: www.ecsat.hr
Emp.: 40
Computer Software Whslr
S.I.C.: 5045
N.A.I.C.S.: 423430
Branko Vujovic *(Mgr-Bus Dev)*

RTI Systems Ltd. (1)
Unit 11 Swan Business Park
Sandpit Rd, Dartford, DA1 5ED, United Kingdom UK
Tel.: (44) 1322286866
Fax: (44) 1322286867
Emp.: 3
Foreign Missions Services
S.I.C.: 9721
N.A.I.C.S.: 928120
Simon Thime *(Gen Mgr)*

USB GmbH (1)
Beta Str 13 a
85774 Unterfohring, Germany
Tel.: (49) 8999894283
Fax: (49) 899280455
E-Mail: info@usb-muc.com
Web Site: www.usb-muc.com
Emp.: 30
Aeronautics Embedded System Mfr
S.I.C.: 3812
N.A.I.C.S.: 334511
Detlef Haesner *(Gen Mgr)*

CS CORPORATION

CS-Dong Pangyo 7 Venture Valley
625 Sampyung-Dong
Bundang-Gu, Seongnam, Kyunggi-DO, Korea (South)
Tel.: (82) 316223333
Fax: (82) 316223355
Web Site: www.cs-holdings.co.kr
Year Founded: 1999
065770—(KRS)
Emp.: 160

Business Description:
Wireless Telecommunication Components Mfr & Supplier
S.I.C.: 3663
N.A.I.C.S.: 334220

Personnel:
Hong Bae Lee *(CEO)*

Non-U.S. Subsidiary:

CS MACROLITE (1)
8/F Suite 808 West Tower Phillipine Stock Exchange Bldg Exchange Rd
Ortigas Centre, Pasig, 1605, Philippines
Tel.: (63) 2637 1488
Fax: (63) 2632 1245
Web Site: www.macrolite-phil.com
Emp.: 2
Industrial Machinery Distr
S.I.C.: 5084
N.A.I.C.S.: 423830
Mario Jan-Sen T. Coloma *(Bus Mgr)*

CS ELSOLAR CO., LTD.

510-9 Sangdaewon-dong Jungwon-gu
Seongnam-si, Seongnam, Gyeonggi-do, 462-120, Korea (South)
Tel.: (82) 31 7345400
Fax: (82) 31 7331954
E-Mail: info@cselsolar.com
Web Site: www.cselsolar.com
Year Founded: 2006
159910—(KRS)
Sales Range: $1-9.9 Million
Emp.: 60

Business Description:
Organic Dyes Used in Light Emitting Diodes
S.I.C.: 2816
N.A.I.C.S.: 325130

Personnel:
Wu Geun Byun *(CEO)*

CS LOXINFO PUBLIC COMPANY LIMITED

90 Cyber World Tower A 17-20th Floor Ratchadapisek Road
Huai Khwang, Bangkok, 10310, Thailand
Tel.: (66) 2 263 8000
Fax: (66) 2263 8266
E-Mail: support@csloxinfo.com
Web Site: www.csloxinfo.com
CSL—(THA)
Rev.: $97,546,677
Assets: $70,713,423
Liabilities: $33,020,382
Net Worth: $37,693,041
Earnings: $12,690,900
Emp.: 950
Fiscal Year-end: 12/31/12

Business Description:
Internet Services
S.I.C.: 4899
N.A.I.C.S.: 517919

Personnel:
Wongkulpat Snidvongs na Ayudyha *(Chm)*
Anant Kaewruamvongs *(Mng Dir)*
Anuwat Sanguansappayakomn *(CFO)*
Surachart Kugasemrat *(Deputy Mng Dir-Teleinfo Media Public Company Limited)*
Sarisorn Chandraramya *(Sec)*

Board of Directors:
Wongkulpat Snidvongs na Ayudyha
Vuthi Asvasermcharoen
Sitthichai Chantraravadee
Hansa Chevaprke
Hui Beng Gan
Anant Kaewruamvongs
Han Kheng Lee
Pratheuang Sirodbang
Sillapaporn Srijunpetch
Suphajee Suthumpun

Subsidiary:

Teleinfo Media Public Company Limited (1)
1126 2 Vanit Bldg 2 New Psetchaburi Rd
Makkasan Ratchatsewi, 10400 Bangkok, Thailand
Tel.: (66) 22628888
Fax: (66) 22628456
E-Mail: info@teleinfomedia.net
Web Site: www.teleinfomedia.net
Emp.: 500
Telephone Directory Publishing & Advertising Services
S.I.C.: 2741
N.A.I.C.S.: 511140
Rittchart Sirivoncse Naayutsya *(Dir-Online Bus)*

C'S MEN CO., LTD.

13-4 Nihonbashikodenmacho Chuo-ku
Tokyo, 103-0001, Japan
Tel.: (81) 356233781
Fax: (81) 36650098
E-Mail: info@csmen.co.jp
Web Site: www.csmen.co.jp
Year Founded: 1989
3083—(TKS)
Sales Range: $75-99.9 Million
Emp.: 147

Business Description:
Men's Casual Clothing Retailer
S.I.C.: 5611
N.A.I.C.S.: 448110

Personnel:
Shoji Kabashima *(Pres)*

CSA GROUP

178 Rexdale Blvd
Toronto, ON, M9W 1R3, Canada
Tel.: (416) 747-4000
Fax: (416) 747-4149
Toll Free: (866) 797-4272
E-Mail: info@csagroup.org
Web Site: www.csagroup.org
Sales Range: $200-249.9 Million
Emp.: 1,200

Business Description:
Business Services
S.I.C.: 7389
N.A.I.C.S.: 561499

Personnel:
H. Roland Hosein *(Chm)*
Robert A. Cook *(Vice Chm)*
David T. Fung *(Vice Chm)*
Ash K. Sahi *(Pres & CEO)*
Robert J. Falconi *(Gen Counsel, Sec & Exec VP)*
Paul Keane *(Exec VP-HR)*
Helene Vaillancourt *(Exec VP-Science & Engrg)*

Board of Directors:
H. Roland Hosein
Sondra E. Bruni
Robert A. Cook
Kim A. Dunphy
Robert J. Falconi
David T. Fung
Allan S. Gibbins
Jimmy LaValley
Linda Anne Lusby
David C. MacKinnon
Norma McCormick
Malcolm E. O'Hagan
Robert Page
France Pegeot
Jeremy Rakusin
Ash K. Sahi
Gregory M. Thomas
William E. Watchorn
Greg B. Weeres

Subsidiaries:

Canadian Standards Association (1)
5060 Spectrum Way Ste 100
Mississauga, ON, L4W 5N6, Canada
Tel.: (416) 747-4000
Fax: (416) 747-2473
E-Mail: sales@csagroup.com
Web Site: www.csagroup.com
Emp.: 215
Testing Laboratories
S.I.C.: 8734
N.A.I.C.S.: 541380
Suzanne Kiraly *(Pres)*

CSA International (1)
178 Rexdale Blvd
Toronto, ON, M9W 1R3, Canada
Tel.: (416) 747-4000
Fax: (416) 747-4149
E-Mail: susan.pearse@csagroup.org
Web Site: www.csa-international.org
Emp.: 600
Testing Laboratories
S.I.C.: 8734
N.A.I.C.S.: 541380
Bonnie Rose *(Pres-CSA Standards)*

Non-U.S. Subsidiaries:

CSA International - Asia (2)
Room 1604 Concordia Plaza 1 Science Museum Road
Tsimshatsui East, Kowloon, China (Hong Kong)
Tel.: (852) 26642872
Fax: (852) 26645033
E-Mail: csahk@csa-international.org
Web Site: www.csa-international.org
Emp.: 20
Testing Laboratories
S.I.C.: 8734
N.A.I.C.S.: 541380
Randall L. Luecke *(Pres)*

CSA International - Europe (2)
Utrechtseweg 310
6812 AR Arnhem, Netherlands
Tel.: (31) 263562856
Fax: (31) 264453033
E-Mail: csa.europe@csa-international.org
Web Site: www.csa-europe.org
Testing Laboratories
S.I.C.: 8734
N.A.I.C.S.: 541380
Randall L. Luecke *(Pres)*

U.S. Subsidiary:

CSA America, Inc. (1)
8501 E Pleasant Valley Rd
Cleveland, OH 44131-5575
Tel.: (216) 524-4990
Fax: (216) 520-8979
Web Site: www.csa-america.org
Emp.: 50
Holding Company

CSA Group—(Continued)

S.I.C.: 6719
N.A.I.C.S.: 551112
Randall L. Luecke *(Pres)*

Subsidiary:

OnSpeX (2)
8503 E Pleasant Valley Rd
Cleveland, OH 44131-5516
Tel.: (216) 524-4990
Fax: (216) 520-8983
Toll Free: (888) CPE-3335
E-Mail: info@onspex.com
Web Site: www.onspex.com
Emp.: 175
Consumer Product Evaluation, Data Management & Consulting Services
S.I.C.: 8734
N.A.I.C.S.: 541380
Ash Sahi *(CEO)*

CSB-SYSTEM AG

An Furthenrode 9 15
52511 Geilenkirchen, Germany
Tel.: (49) 2451 6250
Fax: (49) 2451 625 291
E-Mail: info@csb-system.com
Web Site: www.csb-system.com
Year Founded: 1977
Sales Range: $75-99.9 Million
Emp.: 450

Business Description:
IT Services
S.I.C.: 7373
N.A.I.C.S.: 541512

Personnel:
Peter Schimitzek *(CEO)*

CSC HOLDINGS LIMITED

No 2 Tanjong Penjuru Crescent
Singapore, 608968, Singapore
Tel.: (65) 63670933
Fax: (65) 63670911
E-Mail: corp@cschl.com.sg
Web Site: www.cschl.com.sg
C06—(SES)
Rev.: $430,196,764
Assets: $409,104,126
Liabilities: $251,322,155
Net Worth: $157,781,972
Earnings: ($605,243)
Emp.: 2,000
Fiscal Year-end: 03/31/13

Business Description:
Civil Engineering Services
S.I.C.: 8711
N.A.I.C.S.: 541330

Personnel:
Yen Tarn See *(CEO)*
Quang Loong Lee *(CFO & Sec)*
Jimmy Chee Eng Lim *(COO)*
Lip Chee Yee *(Gen Dir-L&M Foundation Specialist Vietnam Limited Company)*

Board of Directors:
Patrick Teck Kwong Chee
Roland San Tiong Ng
Yen Tarn See
Ee Ping Tan
Hup Foi Tan
Beng Teck Teo

Transfer Agent:
M & C Services Private Limited
112 Robinson Road 05-01
Singapore, 068902, Singapore

Subsidiaries:

CS Bored Pile System Pte. Ltd. (1)
2 Tanjong Penjuru Crescent
Singapore, 608968, Singapore SG
Tel.: (65) 63627088
Fax: (65) 63627066
Emp.: 200
Bored Piling Contractors
S.I.C.: 1799
N.A.I.C.S.: 238910
Soon Kong Chan *(Gen Mgr)*

CS Construction & Geotechnic Pte. Ltd. (1)
2 Tanjong Penjuru Crescent
Singapore, 608968, Singapore
Tel.: (65) 6367 0933
Fax: (65) 6367 0911
E-Mail: corp@cschl.com.sg
Construction Engineering Services
S.I.C.: 8711
N.A.I.C.S.: 541330
Boon Chong Loh *(Gen Mgr)*

Subsidiary:

CS Geotechnic Pte. Ltd. (2)
2 Tanjong Penjuru Crescent
Singapore, Singapore SG
Tel.: (65) 63626866
Fax: (65) 63626877
E-Mail: corp@cschl.com.sg
Emp.: 300
Geotechnical Engineering Services
S.I.C.: 8711
N.A.I.C.S.: 541330
Poh Chee Kuan *(CEO)*

L&M Foundation Specialist Pte. Ltd. (1)
2 Tanjong Penjuru Crescent
Singapore, Singapore SG
Tel.: (65) 62626266
Fax: (65) 62667791
E-Mail: corp@cschl.com.sg
Emp.: 400
Foundation Engineering Services
S.I.C.: 1771
N.A.I.C.S.: 238140
Yen Tarn See *(Pres & CEO)*

Soil Investigation Pte. Ltd. (1)
14 Little Road 06-01 Tropical Industrial Building
Singapore, Singapore SG
Tel.: (65) 67456765
Fax: (65) 67471733
E-Mail: soil@soilinvestigation.com.sg
Web Site: www.soilinvestigation.com.sg
Geotechnical Engineering Services
S.I.C.: 8734
N.A.I.C.S.: 541380
Hua Keong Ting *(Gen Mgr)*

Subsidiary:

Wisescan Engineering Services Pte. Ltd. (2)
14 Little Road 02-01 Tropical Industrial Building
Singapore, Singapore SG
Tel.: (65) 68410880
Fax: (65) 68410770
E-Mail: enquiry@wisescan.com
Web Site: www.wisescan.com
Land & Tunnel Surveying Services
S.I.C.: 8713
N.A.I.C.S.: 541370
Keng Guan Chua *(Founder & Mng Dir)*

THL Foundation Equipment Pte. Ltd. (1)
18 Sungei Kadut Ave
Singapore, Singapore
Tel.: (65) 68610089
Fax: (65) 68610087
E-Mail: thlfe@singnet.com.sg
Web Site: www.thl.com.sg
Emp.: 55
Foundation & Geotechnical Equipment Rental Services
S.I.C.: 7359
N.A.I.C.S.: 532412
Lawrence Jong An Chong *(Mng Dir)*

Non-U.S. Subsidiary:

Borneo Geotechnic Sdn. Bhd. (1)
B-3-01 B-3A-01 B-5-01 Neo Damansara
Jalan PJU 8/1
Bandar Damansara Perdana, 47820
Petaling Jaya, Selangor, Malaysia MY
Tel.: (60) 377106266
Fax: (60) 377107266
E-Mail: bg@borneogeotechnic.com.my
Emp.: 50
Geotechnical Engineering Services
S.I.C.: 8711
N.A.I.C.S.: 541330
Soon Teck Tee *(Gen Mgr)*

CSC STEEL HOLDINGS BERHAD

180 Kawasan Industri Ayer Keroh
75450 Melaka, Malaysia
Tel.: (60) 62310169
Fax: (60) 62310167
E-Mail: info@cscmalaysia.com
Web Site: www.cscmalaysia.com
CSCSTEL—(KLS)
Rev.: $369,563,739
Assets: $277,937,824
Liabilities: $24,423,570
Net Worth: $253,514,254
Earnings: $9,184,286
Fiscal Year-end: 12/31/12

Business Description:
Steel Mfr
S.I.C.: 3312
N.A.I.C.S.: 331110

Personnel:
High-Pinn Chen *(Mng Dir)*
Sook Ching Lam *(Co-Sec)*
Bee Hwee Tan *(Co-Sec)*

Board of Directors:
High-Pinn Chen
Khim Leong Chong
Mohd Zaaba Daud
Jih-Gang Liu
Lung-Yuan Nee
Fee Yoon Pang
Chin Teng Tan

Legal Counsel:
Koh Kim Leng & Co.
No 5-1 Lorong Hang Jebat
Melaka, Malaysia

CSE GLOBAL LTD.

2 Ubi View 5th Floor
Singapore, 408556, Singapore
Tel.: (65) 65120333
Fax: (65) 67429179
E-Mail: customerservice@cse-global.com
Web Site: www.cse-global.com
544—(OTC SES)
Rev.: $440,845,660
Assets: $382,013,501
Liabilities: $193,582,343
Net Worth: $188,431,159
Earnings: $45,420,619
Emp.: 1,869
Fiscal Year-end: 12/31/12

Business Description:
System Integration Services
S.I.C.: 7373
N.A.I.C.S.: 541512

Personnel:
Rick T. L. Lynn *(Pres/CEO-CSE-W Industries Inc)*
Alan Russell Stubbs *(CEO)*
Boon Kheng Lim *(Interim Grp Mng Dir)*
David W. Chou *(Pres/CEO-CSE Hankin Inc)*
Roy Rowe *(CEO-Ops-Australia & New Zealand)*
Cher Liang Tan *(Co-Sec)*
San-Ju Tan *(Co-Sec)*

Board of Directors:
Ming Seong Lim
Kwok Chong Lam
Richard Last
Phillip Soo Hoon Lee
Boh Soon Lim
Boon Ann Sin
Alan Russell Stubbs
Mok Koon Tan

Subsidiaries:

CSE-EIS Pte Ltd (1)
3 Church Street 08-01 Samsung Hub
Singapore, 049483, Singapore
Tel.: (66) 65120333
Fax: (65) 67429179
Industrial Automation Solutions
S.I.C.: 1731
N.A.I.C.S.: 238210

CSE-IAP Pte Ltd (1)
2 Ubi View 05-00
Singapore, 408556, Singapore
Tel.: (65) 65120333
Fax: (65) 67429179
Industrial Automation Solutions
S.I.C.: 1731
N.A.I.C.S.: 238210

CSE-ITS Pte Ltd (1)
2 Ubi View 05-00 CSE Building
Singapore, 408556, Singapore
Tel.: (65) 65120333
Fax: (65) 67429179
Telecommunication Services
S.I.C.: 4899
N.A.I.C.S.: 517919

TransTel Engineering Pte Ltd. (1)
1 Jalan Kilang
Dynasty Bldg 06-00, Singapore, 159402, Singapore
Tel.: (65) 62767600
Fax: (65) 62767800
E-Mail: transtel@cse-transtelsg.com
Web Site: www.transtel-engineering.com
Emp.: 170
System Integration Services
S.I.C.: 7373
N.A.I.C.S.: 541512
Tan Goh Beng *(Mng Dir)*

Non-U.S. Subsidiaries:

CSE Systems & Engineering (Thailand) Limited (2)
283/46 Unit No 1001-2 Homeplace Office Building 10th Floor
Soi Sukhumvit 55 Khet Wattana, Bangkok, 10110, Thailand
Tel.: (66) 2 7127331
Fax: (66) 2 7127334
Web Site: www.cse-global.com
Emp.: 14
Engineering Services
S.I.C.: 8711
N.A.I.C.S.: 541330
Lee Wahlian *(Mng Dir)*

PT TransTel Engineering (2)
MidPlaza Building I 10th Floor Jl Jend Sudirman Kav 10-11
Jakarta, 10220, Indonesia
Tel.: (62) 2157905515
Fax: (62) 21 5790 5522
Emp.: 26
Telecommunication Services
S.I.C.: 4899
N.A.I.C.S.: 517919

TransTel Engineering Arabia Limited Co (2)
1st Floor Air Line Center Building
PO Box 691
Al Khobar, 31932, Saudi Arabia
Tel.: (966) 38870230
Fax: (966) 38870410
Telecommunication Engineering Services
S.I.C.: 8711
N.A.I.C.S.: 541330

TransTel Engineering PNG Ltd (2)
Waigani
PO Box 981
National Capital District, Port Moresby, Papua New Guinea
Tel.: (675) 3256399
Fax: (675) 3250386
Web Site: www.transtel-engineering.com
Telecommunication Services
S.I.C.: 4899
N.A.I.C.S.: 517919
Chen Wansin *(Bus Mgr)*

TransTel Engineering (Thailand) Co Limited (2)
No 200 Moo 4 12-1201B Jasmine INT L Tower Chaengwatana Road
Pakkred, Nonthaburi, 11120, Thailand
Tel.: (66) 2502 3868
Fax: (66) 2502 3869
Web Site: www.transtelengineering.com
Emp.: 10
Telecommunication Services
S.I.C.: 4899
N.A.I.C.S.: 517919
Parinya Suwanmalee *(Gen Mgr)*

U.S. Subsidiaries:

CSE-Hankin Inc (1)
1 Harvard Way Ste 6
Hillsborough, NJ 08844
Tel.: (908) 722-9595
Fax: (908) 722-9514
E-Mail: hankin@earthlink.net
Web Site: www.hankinenv.com
Emp.: 13
Waste Water Treatment Services
S.I.C.: 4971
N.A.I.C.S.: 221310
David W. Chou *(Pres & CEO)*

CSE Semaphore Inc (1)
1200 Chantry Place
Lake Mary, FL 32746
Tel.: (407) 333-3235
Fax: (407) 386-6284
E-Mail: support.americas@cse-semaphore.com
Web Site: www.cse-semaphore.com
Electronic Component Mfr
S.I.C.: 3679
N.A.I.C.S.: 334419

W-Industries, Inc. (1)
11500 Charles Rd
Houston, TX 77041
Tel.: (713) 466-9463
Fax: (713) 466-7205
Web Site: www.w-industries.com
Emp.: 400
System Integration Services
S.I.C.: 7373
N.A.I.C.S.: 541512
Rick Lynn *(Pres & CEO)*

Subsidiary:

W-Industries - Louisiana LLC (2)
7620 Johnston St
Maurice, LA 70555
Tel.: (337) 233-4537
Fax: (337) 233-6452
Web Site: www.w-industries.com
Emp.: 50
Industrial Control Systems Distr
S.I.C.: 5084
N.A.I.C.S.: 423830

Non-U.S. Subsidiaries:

Astib Group Pty Ltd (1)
2 Sleat Road
Applecross, WA, 6153, Australia
Tel.: (61) 892048000
Fax: (61) 892048080
E-Mail: csiwa@astibgroup.com
Web Site: www.astibgroup.com
Telecommunications Integration Services
S.I.C.: 4899
N.A.I.C.S.: 517919

Subsidiaries:

CSE-Comsource Pty Ltd (2)
2 Sleat Road
Applecross, WA, 6017, Australia
Tel.: (61) 892048000
Fax: (61) 892048080
E-Mail: info@cse-comsource.com
Web Site: www.cse-comsource.com
Emp.: 50
Business Support Services
S.I.C.: 7389
N.A.I.C.S.: 561990

CSE-Transtel Pty Ltd (2)
2 Sleat Road
Applecross, WA, 6153, Australia
Tel.: (61) 892048000
Fax: (61) 892048080
E-Mail: info@cse-transtel.com
Web Site: www.cse-transtel.com
Telecommunication Engineering Services
S.I.C.: 8711
N.A.I.C.S.: 541330
Roy Rowe *(Gen Mgr)*

CSE-EIS (Malaysia) Sdn Bhd (1)
Suite 3.02 3rd Fl Lot 10 Wisma BKA
Jalan Astaka U8/84 Bukit
Jelutong Bus & Tech Ctr, 40150 Shah Alam, Selangor Darul Ehsan, Malaysia
Tel.: (60) 378468580
Fax: (60) 378469580
E-Mail: cse-eis@cse-global.com
Web Site: www.cse-global.com
Emp.: 30
System Integration Services
S.I.C.: 7373
N.A.I.C.S.: 541512
Sunnie Ng *(Country Mgr)*

CSE-Global (Australia), Ltd. (1)
10 Columbia Way
Baulkham Hills, NSW, 2153, Australia
Tel.: (61) 288534200
Fax: (61) 288534260
E-Mail: cse-uniserve@cse-uniserve.com.au
Web Site: www.cse-uniserve.com.au
Emp.: 30
System Integration Services
S.I.C.: 7373
N.A.I.C.S.: 541512
Greg Swinton *(Mng Dir)*

Subsidiary:

CSE-Uniserve Pty Limited (2)
10 Columbia Way
Baulkham Hills, NSW, Australia
Tel.: (61) 288534200
Fax: (61) 0288534260
E-Mail: cse-uniserve@cse-uniserve.com.au
Web Site: www.cse-uniserve.com.au
Emp.: 35
System Integration Services
S.I.C.: 7373
N.A.I.C.S.: 541512

CSE-Global (Australia) Pty Ltd (1)
2 Sleat Road
Applecross, WA, 6153, Australia
Tel.: (61) 892048000
Fax: (61) 892048080
E-Mail: info@cse-globalaus.com
Web Site: www.cse-globalaus.com
Emp.: 50
Industrial Automation & Telecommunication Support Services
S.I.C.: 1731
N.A.I.C.S.: 238210
Roy Row *(CEO)*

CSE-Global (UK) Limited (1)
Rotherside Road
Eckington, Sheffield, S21 4HL, United Kingdom
Tel.: (44) 1246437400
Fax: (44) 1246437401
E-Mail: sales@cse-globaluk.com
Web Site: www.cse-globaluk.com
Business Consultancy Services
S.I.C.: 7389
N.A.I.C.S.: 561499

Subsidiaries:

CSE-Controls Limited (2)
Technology Centre Claymore Drive
Aberdeen, AB23 8GD, United Kingdom
Tel.: (44) 1224707700
Fax: (44) 1224707017
E-Mail: sales@cse-controls.com
Web Site: www.cse-controls.com
Emp.: 40
Oil & Gas Exploration Services
S.I.C.: 1389
N.A.I.C.S.: 213112
Ronald Holden *(Dir-Controls)*

CSE-Healthcare Systems Limited (2)
Rotherside Road
Sheffield, S21 4HL, United Kingdom
Tel.: (44) 1246437500
E-Mail: sales@cse-healthcare.com
Web Site: www.cse-healthcare.com
Health Care Services
S.I.C.: 8099
N.A.I.C.S.: 621999

Non-U.S. Subsidiary:

CSE-Controls s.r.o. (2)
Piaristickai 2
949 01 Nitra, Slovakia
Tel.: (421) 37 6519 529
Fax: (421) 37 7410 021
E-Mail: sales@cse-controls.com
Web Site: www.cse-globaluk.com
Emp.: 37
Industrial Control System Mfr
S.I.C.: 3625
N.A.I.C.S.: 335314
Peter Rozek *(Mng Dir)*

CSE Semaphore Australia Pty Ltd (1)
Unit 8/3-5 Gilda Ct
Mulgrave, VIC, 3170, Australia
Tel.: (61) 385448544
Fax: (61) 385448555
E-Mail: Info.kingfisher@cse-semaphore.com
Web Site: www.cse-semaphore.com
Electronic Component Mfr
S.I.C.: 3679
N.A.I.C.S.: 334419

CSE Semaphore Belgium SA (1)
Waterloo Office Park Building M Dreve Richelle 161
1410 Waterloo, Belgium
Tel.: (32) 2 387 42 59
Fax: (32) 2 387 42 75
E-Mail: support.tbox@cse-semaphore.com
Electronic Component Mfr
S.I.C.: 3679
N.A.I.C.S.: 334419

CSE-Servelec Limited (1)
Rotherside Rd
Eckington, Sheffield, S214HL, United Kingdom
Tel.: (44) 01246433981
Fax: (44) 1246437401
E-Mail: admin@cse-globaluk.com
Web Site: www.cse-servelec.com
Emp.: 200
System Integration Services
S.I.C.: 7373
N.A.I.C.S.: 541512

CSE-Servelec s.r.o. (1)
Piaristicka 2
949 01 Nitra, Slovakia
Tel.: (421) 376519529
Fax: (421) 377410021
Web Site: www.cse-control.sk
Emp.: 48
Pipeline Management Services
S.I.C.: 4619
N.A.I.C.S.: 486990

CSE Systems & Engineering (India) Pvt Limited (1)
No 3 3rd Floor 100ft Road 2nd Stage 1st Phase BTM Layout
Bengaluru, 560 076, India
Tel.: (91) 8026783302
Fax: (91) 80 26783305
Emp.: 20
Industrial Automation Solutions
S.I.C.: 1731
N.A.I.C.S.: 238210
Ravindra D. *(Country Mgr)*

CSE-Uniserve Corporation Pty Ltd (1)
10 Columbia Way
Baulkham Hills, NSW, 2153, Australia
Tel.: (61) 288534200
Fax: (61) 288534260
Emp.: 30
Industrial Automation & Telecommunication Support Services
S.I.C.: 1731
N.A.I.C.S.: 238210

Non-U.S. Subsidiary:

CSE-W Arthur Fisher Limited (2)
15 Polaris Place
East Tamaki, Auckland, New Zealand
Tel.: (64) 92713810
Fax: (64) 9 265 1362
E-Mail: sales@cse-waf.co.nz
Web Site: www.cse-waf.co.nz
Emp.: 25
Instrumentation & Control System Whslr
S.I.C.: 5065
N.A.I.C.S.: 423690
Harry Singh *(Gen Mgr)*

eBworx Berhad (1)
LI A Block B Axis Business Park
No 10 Jalan Bersatu 13/4, Petaling Jaya, Selangor, 200, Malaysia
Tel.: (60) 379569822
Fax: (60) 379572661
E-Mail: contact@ebworx.com
Web Site: www.eBworx.com
Financial System Integration Services
S.I.C.: 7373
N.A.I.C.S.: 541512
Suan Fong Tan *(CEO)*

RTUnet (Australia) Pty Ltd. (1)
Ste 8 3-5 Gilda Court
Mulgrave, VIC, 3170, Australia
Tel.: (61) 385448544
Fax: (61) 385448555
E-Mail: info@cse-semaphore.com
Web Site: www.cse-semaphore.com
Emp.: 50
System Integration Services
S.I.C.: 7373
N.A.I.C.S.: 541512
Acianne Cliuw *(Mgr-Customer Svcs)*

CSEPEL HOLDING PLC

Varrogepgyar ut 1
1211 Budapest, Hungary
Tel.: (36) 1278 58 00
Fax: (36) 1425 76 05
E-Mail: szerviz@excel-csepel.hu
Web Site: www.excel-csepel.hu
CSEPEL—(BUD)
Rev.: $12,375,105
Assets: $12,793,914
Liabilities: $10,963,233
Net Worth: $1,830,681
Earnings: $333,721
Emp.: 121
Fiscal Year-end: 12/31/12

Business Description:
Industrial Machinery Mfr
S.I.C.: 3559
N.A.I.C.S.: 333249

Personnel:
Gusztav Arz *(Chm-Supervisory Bd)*
Zoltan Parkanyi *(Chm-Mgmt Bd)*
Ivan Szomi *(Mng Dir)*
Paul Dan Viorel *(Member-Mgmt Bd)*
R. Kalaichelvan *(Member-Mgmt Bd)*

Supervisory Board of Directors:
Gusztav Arz
Jozsefne Pap
Laszlo Rozsavolgyi

CSF GROUP PLC

CSF Computer Exchanges 5 Jalan Cyber Point 2 Cyber 12
63000 Cyberjaya, Selangor Darul Ehsan, Malaysia
Tel.: (60) 383181313
Fax: (60) 383180303
E-Mail: enquiry@csf-group.com
Web Site: www.csf-group.com
CSFG.GB—(AIM)
Rev.: $46,922,073
Assets: $86,856,498
Liabilities: $27,950,589
Net Worth: $58,905,909
Earnings: ($10,763,974)
Emp.: 206
Fiscal Year-end: 03/31/13

Business Description:
Data Center Design, Construction & Maintenance Services
S.I.C.: 1542
N.A.I.C.S.: 236220

Personnel:
King Loon Lee *(CFO)*

Board of Directors:
Heng Peng Ting
Phil Cartmell
Dennis Jing Ow Kian
Richard King
King Loon Lee

Legal Counsel:
Verras Law
First Floor Pentera Chambers Centruy Buildings
Patriotic Place
Saint Helier, Jersey

Stephenson Harwood
One St. Paul's Churchyard
London, EC4M 85H, United Kingdom
Tel.: (44) 81 329 4422

Raja Darryl & Loh
18th Floor Wisma Sime Darby Jalan Raja Laut
Kuala Lumpur, Malaysia

CSG HOLDINGS LIMITED

(Formerly M&S Holdings Limited)

CSG Holdings Limited—(Continued)

Duncan Manor Suite 4 150 Brooks Street
Brooklyn, Pretoria, 0002, South Africa
Tel.: (27) 12 362 9778
Fax: (27) 12 362 4120
Web Site: www.csgholdings.co.za
Year Founded: 1980
MSA—(JSE)
Rev.: $43,207,124
Assets: $9,688,858
Liabilities: $2,544,526
Net Worth: $7,144,332
Earnings: $2,940,056
Emp.: 137
Fiscal Year-end: 06/30/13

Business Description:
Personnel Management Consulting Services
S.I.C.: 8999
N.A.I.C.S.: 541612

Personnel:
Bulelani Thandabantu Ngcuka *(Chm)*
Petrus Johannes Jacobus Dry *(CEO)*
Jacobus Gerrit Nieuwoudt *(COO)*

Board of Directors:
Bulelani Thandabantu Ngcuka
Pieter Nicolaas de Waal
Petrus Johannes Jacobus Dry
Sarah Liezel Grobler
Judy Malan
Jacobus Gerrit Nieuwoudt
Nona Ndiliseka Sonjani
Nicolaas Godfried Thiart

Transfer Agent:
Link Market Services South Africa (Pty) Limited
13th Floor Rennie House 19 Ameshoff Street
Braamfontein, South Africa

CSG LIMITED

252 Montague Road
West End, QLD, 4101, Australia
Tel.: (61) 7 3840 1234
Fax: (61) 7 3840 1222
E-Mail: info@csg.com.au
Web Site: www.csg.com.au
CSV—(ASX)
Rev.: $192,412,302
Assets: $426,784,760
Liabilities: $157,525,920
Net Worth: $269,258,840
Earnings: $9,083,986
Emp.: 700
Fiscal Year-end: 06/30/13

Business Description:
Holding Company; Information & Communication Technology Services & Consulting
S.I.C.: 6719
N.A.I.C.S.: 551112

Personnel:
Julie-Ann Kerin *(CEO & Mng Dir)*
Neil Lynch *(CFO)*
Duncan Powell *(COO)*
Jillian Bannan *(Gen Counsel & Sec)*

Board of Directors:
Tom Cowan
Philip Bullock
Julie-Ann Kerin
Ian Kew

Legal Counsel:
DLA Phillips Fox
Level 21 140 William St
Melbourne, Australia

Subsidiary:

Connected Services Group Pty. Ltd. **(1)**
Level 8 Jacana House 39 Woods Street
Darwin, NT, 0800, Australia AU
Tel.: (61) 889229000 (100%)
Fax: (61) 889229016
E-Mail: info@csg.com.au
Web Site: www.csg.com.au
Information & Communication Technology Services & Consulting
S.I.C.: 7389
N.A.I.C.S.: 541990
Julie-Ann Kerin *(Mng Dir)*

Subsidiaries:

CSG Communications Pty. Ltd. **(2)**
252 Montague Rd
West End, QLD, 4101, Australia
Tel.: (61) 738401244
Fax: (61) 738401290
E-Mail: comms.sales@csg.com.au
Web Site: www.csg.com.au
Emp.: 100
Communications Equipment Services
S.I.C.: 7389
N.A.I.C.S.: 541990
Julie-Ann Kerin *(Gen Mgr)*

CSG Print Services Pty. Ltd. **(2)**
Level 6 320 Adelaide Street
Brisbane, QLD, 4000, Australia AU
Mailing Address: (100%)
PO Box 10048
Brisbane, QLD, 4000, Australia
Tel.: (61) 7 3840 1244
Fax: (61) 7 3840 1290
E-Mail: printsupport@csg.com.au
Web Site: www.csg.com.au/Print-Services.aspx
Commercial Office Equipment & Telecommunications Network Services
S.I.C.: 7389
N.A.I.C.S.: 541990
Philip Chambers *(Gen Mgr)*

Non-U.S. Subsidiary:

Konica Minolta Business Solutions New Zealand Ltd. **(1)**
Khyber Pass And Nugent St
Graston, Auckland, 1001, New Zealand NZ
Tel.: (64) 956356000 (90%)
Fax: (64) 95735449
Web Site: www.konicaminolta.co.nz
Business Equipment Services
Export
S.I.C.: 5044
N.A.I.C.S.: 423420
Evan Johnson *(CEO)*

CSI-GMBH

Cargo Modul H
85356 Munich, Germany
Tel.: (49) 89973304410
Fax: (49) 89973304412
E-Mail: Verkauf@csi-spedition.de
Web Site: www.csi-spedition.de
Rev.: $21,159,996
Emp.: 28

Business Description:
Transportation Services
S.I.C.: 4789
N.A.I.C.S.: 488999

Personnel:
Martin Brummer *(Co-Mng Dir)*
Peter Grabowski *(Co-Mng Dir)*

CSI PROPERTIES LIMITED

3108 Bank of America Tower 12 Harcourt Road
Central, China (Hong Kong)
Tel.: (852) 28782800
Fax: (852) 28787525
Web Site: www.csigroup.hk
497—(HKG)
Rev.: $149,888,772
Assets: $1,481,591,657
Liabilities: $567,967,754
Net Worth: $913,623,903
Earnings: $119,281,458
Fiscal Year-end: 03/31/13

Business Description:
Financial Investment Services
S.I.C.: 6211
N.A.I.C.S.: 523999

Personnel:
Mico Cho Yee Chung *(Chm)*
Hou Man Chow *(CFO)*
Sze Man Kan *(Gen Counsel & Sec)*

Board of Directors:
Mico Cho Yee Chung
Yuk Wo Cheng
Hou Man Chow
Sze Man Kan
Lee G. Lam
Chung Kwong Wong
Sin Just Wong

Butterfield Fulcrum Group (Bermuda) Limited
26 Burnaby Street
Hamilton, HM 11, Bermuda

THE CSL GROUP INC.

759 Square Victoria 6th Fl
Montreal, QC, H2Y 2K3, Canada
Tel.: (514) 982-3800
Fax: (514) 982-3801
E-Mail: ships@cslmtl.com
Web Site: www.csl.ca
Sales Range: $10-24.9 Million
Emp.: 700

Business Description:
Self Unloading Bulk Freight Carriers
S.I.C.: 4412
N.A.I.C.S.: 483111

Personnel:
Rod Jones *(Pres & CEO)*
Darlene Harvey *(Dir-HR & Partner)*
Pierre Prefontaine *(Sec & Sr VP)*

U.S. Subsidiary:

CSL International, Inc. **(1)**
152 Conant St
Beverly, MA 01915
Tel.: (978) 922-1300
Fax: (978) 922-1772
E-Mail: info@cslint.com
Web Site: www.cslint.com
Emp.: 50
Deep Sea Freight Transportation
S.I.C.: 4412
N.A.I.C.S.: 483111
Sylvie Lafleur *(Dir-Customer Svc)*

Joint Venture:

Marbulk Canada Inc. **(2)**
152 Conant St
Beverly, MA 01915
Tel.: (978) 299-1090
Web Site: www.algonet.com
Holding Company
S.I.C.: 6719
N.A.I.C.S.: 551112

Subsidiary:

Marbulk Shipping Inc. **(3)**
152 Conant St
Beverly, MA 01915 BB
Tel.: (978) 232-4810
Fax: (978) 232-4805
Emp.: 5
Provider of International Dry Bulk Shipping
S.I.C.: 4432
N.A.I.C.S.: 483113
Dave Geiger *(CFO & Treas)*

CSL LIMITED

45 Poplar Rd
Parkville, VIC, 3052, Australia
Tel.: (61) 3 9389 1911
Fax: (61) 3 9389 1434
Web Site: www.csl.com.au
Year Founded: 1916
CSL—(ASX OTC)
Rev.: $4,950,400,000
Assets: $5,975,500,000
Liabilities: $2,968,700,000
Net Worth: $3,006,800,000
Earnings: $1,216,300,000
Emp.: 11,285
Fiscal Year-end: 06/30/13

Business Description:
Vaccines, Pharmaceutical Products & Plasma Protein Biotherapies Developer, Mfr & Marketer
S.I.C.: 2836
N.A.I.C.S.: 325414

Personnel:
Paul R. Perreault *(CEO & Mng Dir)*
Gordon Naylor *(CFO)*
Andrew Cuthbertson *(Chief Scientific Officer & Dir-R&D)*
Gregory Boss *(Gen Counsel & Exec VP-Legal)*
Edward H. Bailey *(Sec)*
Karen Etchberger *(Exec VP-Quality & Bus Svcs)*
Ingolf Sieper *(Exec VP-Comml Ops)*
Mary Sontrop *(Exec VP-Mfg & Plng)*
Jill Lever *(Sr VP-HR)*

Board of Directors:
John Shine
John H. Akehurst
David W. Anstice
Bruce Robert Brook
Marie McDonald
Christine E. O'Reilly
Paul R. Perreault
Maurice A. Renshaw

Division:

CSL Biotherapies Ltd. **(1)**
45 Poplar Road
Parkville, VIC, 3052, Australia AU
Tel.: (61) 393891911 (100%)
Fax: (61) 393891434
Web Site: www.cslbiotherapies.com.au
Emp.: 1,000
Vaccines & Pharmaceutical Products Mfr & Marketer
S.I.C.: 2836
N.A.I.C.S.: 325414
Mary Sontrop *(Exec VP)*

Subsidiaries:

CSL International Pty. Ltd. **(1)**
45 Poplar Rd
Parkville, VIC, 3052, Australia
Tel.: (61) 393891911
Fax: (61) 393891434
Management Services
S.I.C.: 8741
N.A.I.C.S.: 551114
Edd Bailey *(Sec)*

Non-U.S. Subsidiaries:

CSL Behring S.A. **(2)**
Fray Justo Sarmiento 2350
B1636AKJ Buenos Aires, Argentina
Tel.: (54) 1143449550
Fax: (54) 1143449577
Plasmas Distr
S.I.C.: 8099
N.A.I.C.S.: 621991
Juan Juan *(Mng Dir)*

CSL Behring Verwaltungs GmbH **(2)**
Emil von Behring Str 76
Marburg, Hessen, 35041, Germany
Tel.: (49) 6421390
Fax: (49) 6421393985
Pharmaceutical Products Distr
S.I.C.: 5122
N.A.I.C.S.: 424210
Peter Turner *(CEO)*
Roland Martin *(Mng Dir)*

Subsidiary:

CSL Behring Beteiligungs GmbH & Co KG. **(3)**
Emil von Behring Str 76
Marburg, Hessen, 35041, Germany
Tel.: (49) 6421393152
Fax: (49) 6421393620
Emp.: 2,000
Plasmas Mfr & Sales
S.I.C.: 2836
N.A.I.C.S.: 325414
Roland Martin *(Mng Dir)*

CSL Biotherapies Asia Pacific Limited **(2)**
420528 AIA tower 183 Electric rd
North Point, China (Hong Kong)
Tel.: (852) 28805333
Fax: (852) 20085952
E-Mail: sarah.yeung@cslbehring.com
Web Site: www.cslbehring.com
Emp.: 17
Vaccines Whslr

S.I.C.: 5122
N.A.I.C.S.: 424210
Sarah Yeung *(Mgr-Admin)*

U.S. Subsidiaries:

CSL Behring LLC (1)
1020 1st Ave
King of Prussia, PA 19406 DE
Mailing Address:
PO Box 61501
King of Prussia, PA 19406
Tel.: (610) 878-4000
Fax: (610) 878-4009
Toll Free: (800) 394-1290
Web Site: www.cslbehring.com
Emp.: 400
Plasma-Derived & Recombinant Products Mfr
Export
S.I.C.: 2836
N.A.I.C.S.: 325414
Paul R. Perreault *(Pres)*
Peter Turner *(Pres)*
Gordon Naylor *(CIO)*
Greg Boss *(Gen Counsel & Sr VP)*
Karen Etchberger *(Exec VP-Plasma, Supply Chain & IT)*
Wally Casey *(Sr VP & Gen Mgr)*
Randy L. Furby *(Sr VP & Gen Mgr)*
Uwe E. Jocham *(Sr VP & Gen Mgr)*
Roland Martin *(Sr VP & Gen Mgr)*
Dennis Jackman *(Sr VP-Pub Affairs)*
Val Romberg *(Sr VP-R&D)*

Subsidiaries:

CSL Plasma Inc. (2)
5201 Congress Ave Ste 220
Boca Raton, FL 33487
Tel.: (561) 981-3700
Fax: (561) 912-3005
Web Site: www.cslplasma.com
Blood Plasma Collection Services
S.I.C.: 8099
N.A.I.C.S.: 621991

ZLB Bioplasma Inc. (2)
5201 Congress Ave Ste 220
Boca Raton, FL 33487 DE
Tel.: (561) 981-3700 (100%)
Fax: (561) 912-3005
Web Site: www.clsplasma.com
Plasma Collection Services
S.I.C.: 2836
N.A.I.C.S.: 325414

Non-U.S. Subsidiaries:

CSL Behring K.K. (2)
Inui Building Kachidoki 1-13-1 Kachidoki
Tokyo, 104-0054, Japan
Tel.: (81) 335345831
Fax: (81) 0335345937
Web Site: www.cslbehring.co.jp
Pharmaceutical Products Distr
S.I.C.: 5122
N.A.I.C.S.: 424210
Koichi Terakawa *(Mgr)*

CSL Behring S.A. (2)
44 rue Cambronne
75015 Paris, France
Tel.: (33) 153585400
Fax: (33) 1 53 58 54 05
Web Site: www.cslbehring.fr
Emp.: 30
Plasmas Mfr & Sales
S.I.C.: 2836
N.A.I.C.S.: 325414
Alan Anderson *(Pres)*

CSL Biotherapies GmbH. (2)
Emil Von Behring Str 76
Marburg, Hessen, 35041, Germany
Tel.: (49) 6421390
Fax: (49) 64214792
Pharmaceutical Products Mfr & Distr
S.I.C.: 2834
N.A.I.C.S.: 325412

CSL Biotherapies Inc. (1)
1020 First Ave
King of Prussia, PA 19406
Tel.: (610) 290-7499
Fax: (610) 878-4009
Toll Free: (888) 435-8633
E-Mail: info@cslbiotherapies.com
Web Site: www.cslbiotherapies-us.com
Vaccines Distr
S.I.C.: 5122
N.A.I.C.S.: 424210
Paul R. Perreault *(Exec VP)*

Non-U.S. Subsidiaries:

CSL Behring AG (1)
Wankdorfstrasse 10
3000 Bern, Switzerland
Tel.: (41) 313444444
Fax: (41) 313445555
Web Site: www.cslbehring.com
Emp.: 1,200
Plasma Mfr & Distr
S.I.C.: 2836
N.A.I.C.S.: 325414
Uwe E. Jocham *(Sr VP & Gen Mgr)*

CSL Behring Canada Inc. (1)
55 Metcalfe Ste 1460
Ottawa, ON, K1P 6L5, Canada
Tel.: (613) 232-3111
Fax: (613) 232-5031
Toll Free: (866) 773-7721
E-Mail: canadacontactus@cslbehring.com
Web Site: www.cslbehring.ca
Emp.: 30
Pharmaceutical Products Mfr & Distr
S.I.C.: 2834
N.A.I.C.S.: 325412
Joe Farago *(Dir-Sls)*

CSL Behring GmbH (1)
Commercial Development Coagulation Emil von Behring Strasse 76
35041 Marburg, Hessen, Germany
Tel.: (49) 6421394191
Plasmas Retailer
S.I.C.: 5122
N.A.I.C.S.: 424210

Non-U.S. Subsidiaries:

CSL Behring AB (2)
Berga Backe 2
Box 712
182 17 Danderyd, Stockholm, Sweden
Tel.: (46) 854496670
Fax: (46) 86226838
E-Mail: info@cslbehring.se
Web Site: www.cslbehring.se
Emp.: 15
Plasmas Retailer
S.I.C.: 5122
N.A.I.C.S.: 424210
Ulf Hultquist *(Mgr)*

CSL Behring B.V. (2)
Bijster 14
4817 HX Breda, North Brabant, Netherlands
Tel.: (31) 765236045
Fax: (31) 851119960
E-Mail: infonetherlands@cslbehring.com
Web Site: www.cslbehring.com
Emp.: 9
Plasmas Retailer
S.I.C.: 5122
N.A.I.C.S.: 424210
Patrick Reygaert *(Gen Mgr)*

CSL Behring GmbH (2)
Altmannsdorfer Strasse 104
1121 Vienna, Austria
Tel.: (43) 1801012463
Fax: (43) 1801012810
E-Mail: office.vienna@cslbehring.com
Web Site: www.cslbehring.at
Emp.: 16
Plasmas Mfr & Distr
S.I.C.: 2836
N.A.I.C.S.: 325414
Norbert Piana *(Co-Gen Mgr)*

CSL Behring Lda. (2)
Av 5 de Outubro 198 3 Esq
1050-064 Lisbon, Portugal
Tel.: (351) 217826230
Fax: (351) 217826236
Plasmas Mfr & Sales
S.I.C.: 2836
N.A.I.C.S.: 325414
Paulo Roberto Morisson *(Mng Dir)*

CSL Behring MEPE (2)
5 Hatziyianni Mexi Str
Athens, 115 28, Greece
Tel.: (30) 2107255660
Fax: (30) 2107255663
Plasmas Retailer
S.I.C.: 5122
N.A.I.C.S.: 424210

CSL Behring N.V. (2)
Technologielaan 13
3001 Leuven, Flemish Brabant, Belgium
Tel.: (32) 16388080
Fax: (32) 16388089
Web Site: www.cslbehring.com
Emp.: 15
Plasmas Mfr & Distr
S.I.C.: 2836
N.A.I.C.S.: 325414
Patrick Reyaert *(Gen Mgr)*

CSL Behring S.A. (2)
Av dels Paisos Catalans 34 3 Planta
08950 Esplugues de Llobregat, Barcelona, Spain
Tel.: (34) 933671870
Fax: (34) 933671868
Web Site: www.cslbehring.com
Emp.: 12
Plasmas Retailer
S.I.C.: 5122
N.A.I.C.S.: 424210
Alan Anderson *(Pres)*

CSL Behring S.p.A. (2)
Viale del Ghisallo 20
20151 Milan, Italy
Tel.: (39) 02349641
Fax: (39) 02 34964 261
E-Mail: info@cslbehring.com
Web Site: www.cslbehring.it
Plasmas Mfr
S.I.C.: 2836
N.A.I.C.S.: 325414
Thomas Oliver Schmitt *(Pres)*

CSL Behring UK Ltd. (1)
Market Place Hayworth House
Haywards Heath, West Sussex, RH16 1DB, United Kingdom
Tel.: (44) 1444447402
Fax: (44) 1444447403
E-Mail: customerserviceuk@cslbehring.com
Web Site: www.cslbehring.co.uk
Emp.: 30
Plasmas Mfr & Sales
S.I.C.: 2836
N.A.I.C.S.: 325414
Emil von Behring *(Founder)*
Peter Turner *(Pres & CEO)*

CSL Biotherapies (NZ) Limited (1)
666 Great South Road
Penrose, Auckland, 1061, New Zealand
Tel.: (64) 95798105
Fax: (64) 95798106
E-Mail: nzadmin@biocsl.co.nz
Web Site: www.csl.co.nz
Emp.: 19
Pharmaceutical Products Distr
S.I.C.: 5122
N.A.I.C.S.: 424210
Mary Sontrop *(Dir-CSL)*

CSL Plasma GmbH (1)
Emil-von-Behring-Strasse 76
35041 Marburg, Hessen, Germany
Tel.: (49) 91122911
Fax: (49) 911222197
E-Mail: impressum@cslplasma.com
Web Site: www.cslplasma.de
Emp.: 30
Plasmas Mfr & Sales
S.I.C.: 2836
N.A.I.C.S.: 325414
Michael Schroeder *(Mng Dir)*

CSLI CO., LTD.

Rm 303 3/F Daehong Bldg
Seoul, Korea (South)
Tel.: (82) 2 557 6826
Fax: (82) 2 557 9311
Web Site: www.csli.co.kr
Year Founded: 1995

Business Description:
Language Translation Software Products Developer
S.I.C.: 7372
N.A.I.C.S.: 511210

CSM N.V.

(d/b/a Corbion)
Nienoord 13
1112 XE Diemen, Netherlands
Mailing Address:
PO Box 349
1000 AH Amsterdam, Netherlands
Tel.: (31) 205906911
Fax: (31) 206951942
E-Mail: communictions@corbion.com
Web Site: www.corbion.com
Year Founded: 1919
CSM—(EUR OTC)
Sls.: $1,014,608,329
Assets: $2,941,785,301
Liabilities: $1,785,829,122
Net Worth: $1,155,956,179
Earnings: ($85,751,029)
Emp.: 9,650
Fiscal Year-end: 12/31/12

Business Description:
Bakery Products Mfr
Export
S.I.C.: 2051
N.A.I.C.S.: 311812

Personnel:
Rudolph Harold Peter Markham *(Chm-Supervisory Bd)*
Mattheus P. M. de Raad *(Vice Chm-Supervisory Bd)*
Gerard J. Hoetmer *(CEO & Member-Mgmt Bd)*
Peter Hammond *(Mng Dir)*
Koos Kramer *(CFO & Member-Mgmt Bd)*
Fabrizio Rampinelli *(Pres-Purac Div)*
Brigitte de Veld *(Exec Sec)*
Jan W. E. van der Klaauw *(Sec)*

Supervisory Board of Directors:
Rudolph Harold Peter Markham
Jack P. de Kreij
Mattheus P. M. de Raad
R. Pieterse
Werner Spinner
Mathieu Vrijsen

Divisions:

PURAC Division (1)
Arkelsedijk 46
4200 AA Gorinchem, Netherlands
Tel.: (31) 183695695
Fax: (31) 183695602
E-Mail: pnl@purac.com
Web Site: www.purac.com
Sls.: $143,226,000
Emp.: 400
Naturally Fermented Lactic Acid & Derivatives
S.I.C.: 2833
N.A.I.C.S.: 325411
Fabrizei Rampinelle *(CEO)*

Subsidiary:

PURAC Biochem BV (2)
Arkelsedijk 46
PO Box 21
4206 AC Gorinchem, Netherlands (100%)
Tel.: (31) 183695695
Fax: (31) 183695600
E-Mail: pnl@purac.com
Web Site: www.purac.com
Emp.: 450
S.I.C.: 2063
N.A.I.C.S.: 311313
W. De Roy Fooi *(Gen Mgr)*

U.S. Subsidiary:

PURAC America Inc. (2)
111 Barclay Blvd
Lincolnshire, IL 60069-3610 IL
Tel.: (847) 634-6330
Fax: (847) 634-1992
E-Mail: info@purac.com
Web Site: www.purac.com
Emp.: 40
Marketing Company for Lactic Acid & Derivatives
S.I.C.: 5169
N.A.I.C.S.: 424690
Gerry Vreeman *(Pres)*

CSM N.V.—(Continued)

Non-U.S. Subsidiaries:

PURAC Asia Pacific Pte. Ltd. (2)
3 International Business Park #06-19 Nordic European Centre
Singapore, 609927, Singapore SG
Tel.: (65) 63491350
Fax: (65) 62221707
E-Mail: pap@purac.com
Web Site: www.purac.com
Emp.: 20
Marketing Company for Lactic Acid & Additives
S.I.C.: 5169
N.A.I.C.S.: 424690

PURAC Biochem (UK) Limited (2)
50-54 St Pauls Sq Ste 17
Birmingham, B3 1QS, United Kingdom (100%)
Tel.: (44) 1212361828
Fax: (44) 1212361401
E-Mail: admin@purac.com
Web Site: www.purac.com
Emp.: 4
Marketing of Lactic Acid & Derivatives
S.I.C.: 5122
N.A.I.C.S.: 424210

PURAC Bioquimica S.A. (2)
Gran Vial 19 25
08160 Montmelo, Barcelona, Spain ES
Tel.: (34) 935686300 (100%)
Fax: (34) 935683955
E-Mail: psp@purac.com
Web Site: www.purac.com
Emp.: 150
Mfr. of Lactic Acid & Derivatives
S.I.C.: 2833
N.A.I.C.S.: 325411
Agustin Cerda *(Gen Mgr)*

Purac China (2)
Building 3 No 318 Yuanshan Road
Minhang District, Shanghai, 201108, China
Tel.: (86) 21 6887 8755
Fax: (86) 21 6489 7679
E-Mail: pcn@purac.com
Web Site: www.purac.com
Bakery Products Distr
S.I.C.: 5142
N.A.I.C.S.: 424420

Purac Deutschland Gmbh (2)
Mainzer Str 160
55411 Bingen, Germany
Tel.: (49) 672 11 81 74
Fax: (49) 67 21 18 17 50
E-Mail:
Emp.: 10
Specialty Chemicals Distr
S.I.C.: 5169
N.A.I.C.S.: 424690

Purac India Private Limited (2)
Office 5 101 Apeejay Business Centre 1st Floor Apeejay Express
Plot No 87 Sector 17 Vashi, Navi Mumbai, 400 703, India
Tel.: (91) 22 6609 9416
Fax: (91) 22 3918 0614
E-Mail: pin@purac.com
Web Site: www.purac.com
Bakery Products Distr
S.I.C.: 5142
N.A.I.C.S.: 424420

PURAC Japan K.K. (2)
Gluck Daikanyama 4F 2 11 12 Ebisu Nishi
Shibuya Ku, Tokyo, 150 0021, Japan (100%)
Tel.: (81) 357286700
Fax: (81) 357286789
E-Mail: pjk@Corbion.com
Web Site: www.Corbion.com
Emp.: 14
Lactic Acid
S.I.C.: 2869
N.A.I.C.S.: 325199
Koji Nakamura *(Pres)*

Purac Korea (2)
402 Suin Building 23-8 Jamwon-Dong
Seocho-Ku, Seoul, 137-903, Korea (South)
Tel.: (82) 2 532 9623
Fax: (82) 2 532 9624
E-Mail: pkr@purac.com
Web Site: www.purac.com
Bakery Food Products Distr
S.I.C.: 5142
N.A.I.C.S.: 424420

Purac Mexico S de RL de CV (2)
Cadiz 83
3810 Mexico, Mexico
Tel.: (52) 55 9000 4844
Fax: (52) 55 9000 4845
E-Mail: tmx@corbion.com
Web Site: www.corbion.com
Emp.: 13
Bakery Food Products Distr
S.I.C.: 5142
N.A.I.C.S.: 424420
Leonardo Vega *(Gen Mgr)*

Purac Polska Sp. z o.o. (2)
Ul Krakowiakow 103
02-255 Warsaw, Poland
Tel.: (48) 22 575 50 80
Fax: (48) 22 575 50 89
E-Mail: ppl@purac.com
Food Products & Beverage Mfr
S.I.C.: 2099
N.A.I.C.S.: 311999
Beata Popielarz *(Gen Mgr)*

PURAC Sinteses (2)
Ave Rui Barbosa 521
28013-000 Sao Paulo, Brazil BR
Tel.: (55) 2227377200 (100%)
Fax: (55) 2227377210
E-Mail: c.costa@purac.com
Web Site: www.purac.com
Emp.: 200
Naturally Fermented Lactic Acid & Derivatives
S.I.C.: 2833
N.A.I.C.S.: 325411
Paulo Thomazoe *(Mng Dir)*

Purac Thailand Ltd (2)
3 Moo 2 - Asia Industrial Estate
T Banchang A Banchang, Rayong, 21130, Thailand
Tel.: (66) 38 698 800
Fax: (66) 38 698 801
E-Mail: pth@purac.com
Emp.: 25
Bakery Food Products Mfr
S.I.C.: 2053
N.A.I.C.S.: 311813
Stephan Paauwe *(Pres)*

Subsidiaries:

CSM Nederland BV (1)
Neanoord 13
1112XE Diemen, Netherlands (100%)
Tel.: (31) 5906911
Fax: (31) 6951942
Web Site: www.csmglobal.com
Emp.: 250
S.I.C.: 2063
N.A.I.C.S.: 311313

U.S. Subsidiary:

Caravan Ingredients (1)
550 S 18th St
Kansas City, KS 66105-1104
Tel.: (816) 561-9050
Fax: (913) 438-2697
Toll Free: (800) 669-4092
E-Mail: info@caravaningredients.com
Web Site: www.caravaningredients.com
Emp.: 100
Mfr. of Bakery Ingredients & Related Products
S.I.C.: 2099
N.A.I.C.S.: 311999
Bill McGowan *(Pres & CEO)*

Non-U.S. Subsidiaries:

Classic Cakes Ltd (1)
Newton Close Drayton Fields Industrial Estate
Daventry, NN11 8RR, United Kingdom
Tel.: (44) 1327 310993
Fax: (44) 1327 310968
E-Mail: sales@classiccakesltd.co.uk
Web Site: www.classiccakesltd.co.uk
Sales Range: $10-24.9 Million
Emp.: 90
Cake Mfr & Distr
S.I.C.: 2053
N.A.I.C.S.: 311813

CSM Austria GmbH (1)
Feschnigstrasse 221
9020 Klagenfurt, Austria
Tel.: (43) 463 41403 0
Fax: (43) 463 41403 33
E-Mail: info.austria@csmglobal.com
Emp.: 7
Bakery Products Distr
S.I.C.: 5142
N.A.I.C.S.: 424420

CSM Benelux NV (1)
Borrewaterstraat 182
2170 Merksem, Belgium
Tel.: (32) 3 6417100
Fax: (32) 3 6417111
E-Mail: info.benelux@csmglobal.com
Web Site: www.csmglobal.com
Emp.: 60
Bakery Products Mfr & Distr
S.I.C.: 2053
N.A.I.C.S.: 311813
Edwin Wentink *(Gen Mgr)*

CSM Biochem Trading Shanghai Co., Ltd. (1)
Room 601 No 10 Lane 198 Zhang Heng Road
Pudong New District, 201204 Shanghai, China
Tel.: (86) 21 6887 8755
Fax: (86) 21 6887 8098
Specialty Chemicals Distr
S.I.C.: 5169
N.A.I.C.S.: 424690

CSM Deutschland Gmbh (1)
Verwaltung Bremen Theodor-Heuss-Allee 8
28215 Bremen, Germany
Tel.: (49) 421 3502 0
Fax: (49) 421 3502 355
E-Mail: info.deutschland@csmbaking.com
Web Site: www.csmbaking.com
Baked Goods Mfr & Distr
S.I.C.: 2053
N.A.I.C.S.: 311813

CSM Hellas SA (1)
34a Averof
Nea Ionia, Athens, 14232, Greece
Tel.: (30) 210 2589200
Fax: (30) 210 2589210
E-Mail: info.hellas@csmglobal.com
Web Site: www.csmglobal.com
Baked Foods Mfr
S.I.C.: 2053
N.A.I.C.S.: 311813

CSM Iberia S.A. (1)
C/Samonta 21
08970 Sant Joan Despi, Barcelona, Spain
Tel.: (34) 93 477 51 20
Fax: (34) 93 373 01 51
E-Mail: info.iberia@csmglobal.com
Bakery Products Distr
S.I.C.: 5142
N.A.I.C.S.: 424420

CSM Italia Srl (1)
Viale S Maria della Croce 12
26013 Crema, Cremona, Italy
Tel.: (39) 0373 8961
Fax: (39) 0373896524
E-Mail: info.italia@csmglobal.com
Emp.: 20
Bakery Products Mfr
S.I.C.: 2053
N.A.I.C.S.: 311813
Gitietro Ernesgo *(Gen Mgr)*

CSM Magyarorszag Kft (1)
Ocsai Ut 5
Budapest, 1239, Hungary
Tel.: (36) 1 421 2000
Fax: (36) 1 421 2004
E-Mail: info@csmbaking.com
Web Site: www.csmbaking.com
Emp.: 15
Bakery Products Mfr
S.I.C.: 2053
N.A.I.C.S.: 311813
Pyroska Haydu *(Gen Mgr)*

CSM Nordic A/S (1)
Vaerkstedsvej 34
5500 Middelfart, Denmark
Tel.: (45) 63418300
Fax: (45) 63418310
E-Mail: info.nordic@csmglobal.com
Bakery Products Distr
S.I.C.: 5142
N.A.I.C.S.: 424420

CSM Polska Sp. z.o.o (1)
ul Krakowiakow 103
02-255 Warsaw, Poland
Tel.: (48) 22 575 50 00
Fax: (48) 22 575 50 09
E-Mail: biuro@csmpolska.pl
Web Site: www.csmpolska.pl
Emp.: 45
Bakery Products Mfr & Distr
S.I.C.: 2053
N.A.I.C.S.: 311813
Krzysztof Sobocinski *(Gen Mgr)*

CSM Turkey (1)
Ferhatpasa Mah Anadolu Cad G45 Sok No 48
Atasehir, 34858 Istanbul, Turkey
Tel.: (90) 216 661 3838
Fax: (90) 216 661 3323
E-Mail: info.turkey@csmglobal.com
Bakery Food Products Mfr
S.I.C.: 2053
N.A.I.C.S.: 311813

CSM UK Ltd. (1)
Skerton Road
Bromborough, Wirral, CH62 3NU, United Kingdom
Tel.: (44) 151 343 1600
E-Mail: info.uk@csmglobal.com
Web Site: www.bakemark.co.uk
Emp.: 6
Bakery Products Distr
S.I.C.: 5142
N.A.I.C.S.: 424420
David Eckersall *(Gen Mgr)*

Kate's Cakes Ltd (1)
Unit 3 Wiston Business Park London Road A24
Ashington, West Sussex, RH20 3DJ, United Kingdom
Tel.: (44) 1903 891910
Fax: (44) 1903 891935
E-Mail: info@katescakes.com
Web Site: www.katescakes.com
Emp.: 550
Baked Foods Mfr
S.I.C.: 2053
N.A.I.C.S.: 311813
Charles Groves *(Project Mgr)*

MARGO CSM Schweiz AG (1)
Lindenstrasse 16
6340 Baar, Switzerland
Tel.: (41) 41 768 22 22
Fax: (41) 41 768 22 99
E-Mail: info@margo.ch
Web Site: www.margo.ch
Bakery Products Distr
S.I.C.: 5142
N.A.I.C.S.: 424420
Sandra Barmettler *(Acct Mgr)*

CSM SYSTEMS CORP.

8634 - 53 Avenue
Edmonton, AB, T6E 5G2, Canada
Tel.: (780) 425-9460
Fax: (780) 425-9463
Year Founded: 2000
CKX—(TSXV)
Rev.: $347,052
Assets: $141,101
Liabilities: $756,604
Net Worth: ($615,503)
Earnings: ($383,388)
Fiscal Year-end: 09/30/12

Business Description:
Electronic Equipment Mfr
S.I.C.: 3575
N.A.I.C.S.: 334118

Personnel:
John A. Putters *(CEO)*
Randa Kachkar *(CFO)*

CSP CHINA STEEL PLC

Thames House Portsmouth Road
Esher, Surrey, KT10 9AD, United Kingdom
Tel.: (44) 20 341 10465
Fax: (44) 20 341 41465

E-Mail: info@cspchinasteel.com
Web Site: www.cspchinasteel.com
CT4—(DEU)

Business Description:
Steel
S.I.C.: 3312
N.A.I.C.S.: 331110

Personnel:
Hugo Benz *(Dir)*

CSP INTERNATIONAL FASHION GROUP S.P.A.

Via Piubega 5/C
Ceresara Mantova, 46040 Mantua, Italy
Tel.: (39) 03768101
Fax: (39) 0376810573
E-Mail: export.office@cspinternational.it
Web Site: www.cspinternational.it
CSP—(ITA)
Sales Range: $150-199.9 Million
Emp.: 635

Business Description:
Mfr & Distr of Various Hosiery & Underwear Products
Export
S.I.C.: 2252
N.A.I.C.S.: 315110

Personnel:
Francesco Bertoni *(Pres & CEO)*
Carlo Bertoni *(Mng Dir)*

Board of Directors:
Francesco Bertoni
Giorgio Bardini
Luigi Bellavita
Carlo Bertoni
Maria Grazia Bertoni
Arturo Tedeldi

Non-U.S. Subsidiaries:

Le Bourget S.A. **(1)**
68 Rue Henri Matisse
Fresnoy-le-Grand, Le Bourget, 02230, France
Tel.: (33) 323093300
Fax: (33) 323093319
Web Site: www.lebourget.com
Emp.: 150
Sheer Hosiery Mills
S.I.C.: 2252
N.A.I.C.S.: 315110
Chierry Simons *(Mng Dir)*

Sanpellegrino Polska Sp. z o.o. **(1)**
Ul Lodzka 27
Konstantynow Lodzki, 95-050 Pabianice, Poland PL
Tel.: (48) 422111334
Fax: (48) 426892190
E-Mail: mark@sanpellegrino.com.pl
Sheer Hosiery Mills
S.I.C.: 2252
N.A.I.C.S.: 315110

CSP STEEL CENTER PUBLIC COMPANY LIMITED

475 Rama 3 Road Bangklo
Bangkolaem
Bangkok, 10120, Thailand
Tel.: (66) 2291 6314
Fax: (66) 229 13828
E-Mail: info@cspsteel.com
Web Site: www.cspsteel.com
Year Founded: 1987
CSP—(THA)
Rev.: $141,007,095
Assets: $77,715,754
Liabilities: $51,985,282
Net Worth: $25,730,473
Earnings: $3,331,833
Fiscal Year-end: 12/31/12

Business Description:
Rolled Steel Mfr
S.I.C.: 3399
N.A.I.C.S.: 331221

Personnel:
Supachai Chaisupat *(Chm, Pres & CEO)*
Weerasak Chaisupat *(Mng Dir)*
Suppatcha Sansook *(Sec)*
Kritsada Chaisupat *(Exec VP-Gen Mgmt)*
Suwimon Chaisupat *(Exec VP-Fin & Acctg)*
Kanyarach Noppasang *(Exec VP-HR)*
Thanatat Thovanish *(Exec VP-Sls & Mktg)*

Board of Directors:
Supachai Chaisupat
Janram Atthakrisna
Kritsada Chaisupat
Weerasak Chaisupat
Panthipa Chewthanasoontorn
Charus Khanchanakhajit
Surachat Pongpattarrine
Bunjerd Somsem

CSPC PHARMACEUTICAL GROUP LIMITED

(Formerly China Pharmaceutical Group Limited)
Suite 3206 32/F Central Plaza
18 Harbour Road, Wanchai, China (Hong Kong)
Tel.: (852) 2802 3011
Fax: (852) 2802 4552
E-Mail: ir@cspc.hk
Web Site: www.chinapharma.com.hk
1093—(HKG OTC)
Rev.: $534,683,954
Assets: $1,766,448,783
Liabilities: $894,263,866
Net Worth: $872,184,918
Earnings: $279,672,950
Emp.: 10,205
Fiscal Year-end: 12/31/12

Business Description:
Pharmaceutical Mfr
S.I.C.: 2834
N.A.I.C.S.: 325412

Personnel:
Dong Chen Cai *(Chm & CEO)*
Carmelo Ka Sze Lee *(Sec)*

Board of Directors:
Dong Chen Cai
Kin Man Chak
Leonard Siu Keung Chan
Zhenying Feng
Shichang Guo
Zhenxing Huo
Carmelo Ka Sze Lee
Jianmin Lu
Weidong Pan
Moujia Qi
Bo Wang
Huaiyu Wang
Jinxu Wang
Shunlong Wang
Zhenguo Wang
Fawang Zhang
John Huan Zhao

Transfer Agent:
Tricor Secretaries Limited
26th Floor Tesbury Centre 28 Queens Rd E
Hong Kong, China (Hong Kong)

CSR CORPORATION LIMITED

(Formerly China South Locomotive & Rolling Stock Corporation Limited)
No 16-5 Xisihuan Zhonglu
Haidian District, Beijing, 100036, China
Tel.: (86) 10 5186 2093
Fax: (86) 10 6398 4786
E-Mail: csrhw@csrhw.com.cn
Web Site: www.csrgc.com.cn
601766—(HKG OTC SHG)
Rev.: $14,140,739,474
Assets: $16,713,768,264
Liabilities: $10,437,626,844
Net Worth: $6,276,141,420
Earnings: $770,774,353
Emp.: 86,058
Fiscal Year-end: 12/31/12

Business Description:
Rolling Railroad Stock Mfr
S.I.C.: 3743
N.A.I.C.S.: 336510

Personnel:
Changgong Zhen *(Chm)*
Wang Yan *(Chm-Supervisory Bd)*
Hualong Liu *(Pres)*
Yanjing Zhan *(CFO & VP)*
Renqiang Shao *(Sec)*

Board of Directors:
Changgong Zhen
Fayang Chen
Yongkuan Chen
Deming Dai
Hualong Liu
David Tsoi
Yuzhong Yang
Jibin Zhao

Supervisory Board of Directors:
Wang Yan
Sun Ke
Qiu Wei

Ernst & Young
22/ F CITIC Tower 1 Tim Mei Ave
Central, China (Hong Kong)

Legal Counsel:
Jia Yuan Law Firm
F407 Ocean Plaza 158 Fuxing Men Nei Avenue
Beijing, China

Baker & Mckenzie
23rd Floor Pacific Place 88 Queensway
Hong Kong, China (Hong Kong)

Subsidiaries:

Beijing CSR Times Locomotive and Rolling Stock Mechanics Co., Ltd. **(1)**
W Rwy Sta 500 Meters Zhong Guan Cun Hi-Tech Park
Changping, Beijing, China
Tel.: (86) 1060753721
Fax: (86) 1060756553
E-Mail: cpgc@263.net
Web Site: www.teg.cn/en/cyqy.aspx?c=1&articleid=594
Railway Locomotives Mfr
S.I.C.: 4789
N.A.I.C.S.: 488210

CSR Feb. 7th Rolling Stock Co., Ltd **(1)**
No A1 Zhang Guo Zhuang
Fengtai, Beijing, China
Tel.: (86) 1083804132
Fax: (86) 1083876250
E-Mail: market@psreq.com.in
Web Site: www.psreq.com.in
Emp.: 3,500
Rolling Stock Mfr
S.I.C.: 3743
N.A.I.C.S.: 336510
Shuozhi Shi *(Gen Mgr)*

CSR Meishan Rolling Stock Co., Ltd **(1)**
Chongren Town Dongpo
Meishan, Sichuan, 620032, China
Tel.: (86) 2838502013
Fax: (86) 2838502046
E-Mail: marketingl@msrsco.com
Web Site: www.msrsco.com
Emp.: 5,000
Rolling Stock Mfr
S.I.C.: 3743
N.A.I.C.S.: 336510

CSR Qishuyan Locomotive Co., Ltd **(1)**
No 358 Yanling Rd
Changzhou, Jiangsu, China
Tel.: (86) 51985051291
Fax: (86) 51988777844
E-Mail: sale@csrqs.com
Web Site: www.qscn.cn
Emp.: 6,000
Locomotives Mfr
S.I.C.: 4789
N.A.I.C.S.: 488210
Hong Nian Wang *(Gen Mgr)*

CSR Ziyang Locomotive Co., Ltd **(1)**
No 16-5 Xisihuan Zhonglu
Haidan District, Beijing, 100036, China
Tel.: (86) 1051862093
Fax: (86) 1063984786
E-Mail: csrft@csrgc.com.cn
Railway Locomotives Mfr
S.I.C.: 3743
N.A.I.C.S.: 336510

CSR LIMITED

Triniti 3 39 Delhi Road
North Ryde, NSW, 2113, Australia
Tel.: (61) 2 9235 8000
Fax: (61) 2 8362 9013
E-Mail: investorrelations@csr.com.au
Web Site: www.csr.com.au
Year Founded: 1855
CSR—(ASX)
Rev.: $1,753,229,040
Assets: $2,118,276,670
Liabilities: $985,930,810
Net Worth: $1,132,345,860
Earnings: ($142,142,440)
Emp.: 3,218
Fiscal Year-end: 03/31/13

Business Description:
Concrete, Quarrying, Concrete Pipes & Products, Cement, Plasterboard & Accessories, Bricks, Roof Tiles, Insulation Glasswool, Rockwool & Laminated Foil; Investments in Aluminum; Flat Glass Mfr
Export
S.I.C.: 3272
N.A.I.C.S.: 327332

Personnel:
Jeremy L. Sutcliffe *(Chm)*
Rob Sindel *(Mng Dir)*
Greg Barnes *(CFO)*
Debbie Schroeder *(Legal Counsel & Sec)*
Marion Johnstone *(Treas)*

Board of Directors:
Jeremy L. Sutcliffe
Greg Barnes
Kathleen Marie Conlon
Ray Horsburgh
Michael Ihlein
Rebecca McGrath
Debbie Schroeder
Rob Sindel

Subsidiaries:

Burnbridge Glass Pty Limited **(1)**
1 A Pennant Street
Cardiff, New South Wales, 2285, Australia
Tel.: (61) 4956 9811
Fax: (61) 4952 9915
E-Mail: burn@hunterlink.net.au
Web Site: www.burnbridgeglass.com.au
Emp.: 25
Glass Mfr
S.I.C.: 3211
N.A.I.C.S.: 327211
Brian Creek *(Acct Mgr)*

CSR Fricker Ceiling Systems **(1)**
20 Loftus Street
Sydney, NSW, 2000, Australia
Tel.: (61) 2 9247 5333
Fax: (61) 2 9247 4620
Ceiling Tile Mfr
S.I.C.: 2599
N.A.I.C.S.: 337215
Gary May *(Gen Mgr)*

Unit:

CSR Fricker Ceiling Systems QLD **(2)**
Unit 2 151 Robinson Road
Banyo Geebung, Brisbane, QLD, 4034, Australia
Tel.: (61) 736218888
Fax: (61) 7 3621 8800
E-Mail: brisbane@comprador.com.au
Web Site: www.comprador.com.au

CSR Limited—(Continued)

Emp.: 10
Commercial Interior Products Mfr
S.I.C.: 2599
N.A.I.C.S.: 337215

Non-U.S. Subsidiary:

Potter Interior Systems Ltd. (2)
9 McNab St
Penrose, 1061, New Zealand
Mailing Address:
PO Box 13451
Onehunga, 1643, New Zealand
Tel.: (64) 95791338
Fax: (64) 95795661
E-Mail: info@potters.co.nz
Web Site: www.potters.co.nz
Emp.: 45
Interior Partition & Ceiling Tile Mfr
S.I.C.: 2599
N.A.I.C.S.: 337215
Brian Bamforth *(Gen Mgr)*

Viridian (1)
95 Greens Rd
Locked Bag 1350
Dandenong, VIC, 3175, Australia AU
Tel.: (61) 392122222
Fax: (61) 392122112
Web Site: www.viridianglass.com.au
Emp.: 210
Glass Mfr
S.I.C.: 3211
N.A.I.C.S.: 327211
Steve Choat *(Gen Mgr-Primary Products)*

Non-U.S. Division:

Viridian (2)
19 Gabador Place
Mount Wellington, Auckland, 1020, New Zealand
Tel.: (64) 95731427
Telex: 31173
Fax: (64) 95730389
Web Site: www.viridianglass.com.au/About/contact/default.aspx
Glass Mfr
S.I.C.: 3211
N.A.I.C.S.: 327211
Brett Woods *(Gen Mgr)*

CSR PLC

Churchill House Cambridge Business Park Cowley Road
Cambridge, CB4 0WZ, United Kingdom
Tel.: (44) 1223692000
Fax: (44) 1223692001
E-Mail: csr@wordsun.co.uk
Web Site: www.csr.com
CSR.L—(LSE)
Rev.: $960,710,000
Assets: $883,243,000
Liabilities: $253,681,000
Net Worth: $629,562,000
Earnings: ($46,329,000)
Emp.: 2,146
Fiscal Year-end: 12/27/13

Business Description:
Single-Chip Wireless Devices Mfr
S.I.C.: 3674
N.A.I.C.S.: 334413

Personnel:
Ronald W. Mackintosh *(Chm)*
Joep A. J. van Beurden *(CEO)*
Dwight Daniel Willard Gardiner *(CFO)*
Kanwar Chadha *(CMO)*
Jon Hudson *(Sr VP-Programme Mgmt)*
Klaus Buehring *(Sr VP-Product Dev)*
Neil MacMullen *(Sr VP-Convergence Strategic Bus Unit)*
Anthony Murray *(Sr VP-Wireless Audio Strategic Bus Units)*

Board of Directors:
Ronald W. Mackintosh
Walker Boyd
Anthony E.C.G. Carlisle
Dwight Daniel Willard Gardiner
Levy Gerzberg
Sergio Giacoletto-Roggio
Christopher A. Ladas
Chris Stone
Joep A. J. van Beurden
Teresa Vega

Subsidiaries:

APT Licensing Limited (1)
Unit 2 The Legacy Building Northern Ireland Science Park Queen's Road
Queen's Island, Belfast, BT3 9DT, United Kingdom
Tel.: (44) 28 9046 3140
Fax: (44) 28 9046 3141
Web Site: www.aptx.com
Emp.: 14
Audio Compressing Equipment Mfr
S.I.C.: 3651
N.A.I.C.S.: 334310

Cambridge Positioning Systems Limited (1)
Church Hale Road
Cambridge, CB4 0UZ, United Kingdom
Tel.: (44) 1223 326900
Fax: (44) 1223 692001
E-Mail: info@csr.com
Emp.: 60
Wireless Communication Services
S.I.C.: 4812
N.A.I.C.S.: 517210

Cambridge Silicon Radio Limited (1)
Churchill House Cambridge Business Park
Cambridge, CB4 0WZ, United Kingdom (100%)
Tel.: (44) 1223692000
Fax: (44) 1223692001
Web Site: www.csr.com
Emp.: 700
Other Electronic Parts & Equipment Whslr
S.I.C.: 5065
N.A.I.C.S.: 423690
Joep A. J. van Beurden *(CEO)*

UbiNetics VPT Limited (1)
Cambridge Technology Centre
Melbourn, SG8 6DP, United Kingdom
Tel.: (44) 1763 262 222
Fax: (44) 1763 267 320
Emp.: 600
Mobile Communication Services
S.I.C.: 4812
N.A.I.C.S.: 517210
Joep Beurden *(Gen Mgr)*

U.S. Subsidiaries:

CSR Technology Holdings Inc. (1)
217 Devcon Dr
San Jose, CA 95112 DE
Tel.: (408) 467-0410
Fax: (408) 467-0420
Web Site: www.csr.com
Sales Range: $200-249.9 Million
Emp.: 500
Holding Company; Global Positioning System Semiconductor Products Developer & Mfr
S.I.C.: 6719
N.A.I.C.S.: 551112
Ahmet Alpdemir *(Sr VP-Mobile Bus Area)*

Subsidiary:

CSR Technology Inc. (2)
217 Devcon Dr
San Jose, CA 95112 DE
Tel.: (408) 467-0410
Fax: (408) 467-0420
Web Site: www.csr.com
Global Positioning System Semiconductor Products Developer & Mfr
S.I.C.: 3674
N.A.I.C.S.: 334413
Ahmet Alpdemir *(Sr VP-Mobile Bus Area)*

Non-U.S. Subsidiaries:

CSR Technology Singapore Pte. Ltd. (2)
101 Thomson Road No 08-06 United Square
Singapore, 307591, Singapore SG
Tel.: (65) 68270666
Fax: (65) 63544969
Web Site: www.csr.com
Emp.: 9
Global Positioning System Semiconductor Products Mfr
S.I.C.: 3674
N.A.I.C.S.: 334413
Sebastian Koh *(VP-Sls)*

SiRF Technology (India) Pvt. Ltd. (2)
Level 9 10th Floor Tower C IBC Knowledge Park
No 4/1 Bannerghatta Road, Bengaluru, 560029, India In
Tel.: (91) 8041966000
Fax: (91) 8041966099
Web Site: www.csr.com
Global Positioning System Semiconductor Products Developer & Mfr
S.I.C.: 3674
N.A.I.C.S.: 334413

Zoran Corporation (1)
1390 Kifer Rd
Sunnyvale, CA 94086 DE
Tel.: (408) 523-6500
Fax: (408) 523-6501
Sales Range: $350-399.9 Million
Emp.: 1,532
Integrated Circuits Mfr, Developer & Marketer
S.I.C.: 3674
N.A.I.C.S.: 334413
Isaac Shenberg *(Sr VP-Bus & Strategic Dev)*

Subsidiaries:

Microtune, Inc. (2)
2201 10th St
Plano, TX 75074 DE
Tel.: (972) 673-1600
Fax: (972) 673-1602
Sales Range: $50-74.9 Million
Emp.: 276
Radio Frequency Tuners & Transceivers Mfr
S.I.C.: 3679
N.A.I.C.S.: 334419
Justin M. Chapman *(CFO & VP)*

Non-U.S. Subsidiary:

Microtune GmbH & Co. KG. (3)
Marie Curie Strasse 1
85055 Ingolstadt, Germany
Tel.: (49) 8419378011
Fax: (49) 8419378010
E-Mail: info@microtune.com
Web Site: www.microtune.de
Sales Range: $10-24.9 Million
Emp.: 60
Developer of Microelectronics
S.I.C.: 3679
N.A.I.C.S.: 334418
Barry F. Koch *(Mng Dir)*

Zoran Corporation Imaging Division (2)
1 Wall St 3rd Fl
Burlington, MA 01803
Tel.: (781) 791-6000
Fax: (781) 791-6111
E-Mail: imaging_sales@zoran.com
Web Site: www.zoran.com
Sales Range: $50-74.9 Million
Emp.: 100
Digital Imaging
S.I.C.: 3571
N.A.I.C.S.: 334111

Non-U.S. Subsidiaries:

Zoran Digital Technologies (Shenzhen) Limited (2)
5F Block A No 122 Zhenhua Rd
Overseas Decoration Bldg, Shenzhen, Guangdong, 518031, China
Tel.: (86) 75582815777
Fax: (86) 75583220889
E-Mail: nicole.qi@csr.com
Sales Range: $100-124.9 Million
Emp.: 40
Circuit Board Mfr
S.I.C.: 3672
N.A.I.C.S.: 334412
Nicole Qi *(Mgr-Admin)*

Zoran Japan Office (2)
2 2 8 Roppongi
Tokyo, Minato Ku, 106 0032, Japan (100%)
Tel.: (81) 355747081
Fax: (81) 355747156
Web Site: www.zoran.com
Sales Range: $100-124.9 Million
S.I.C.: 3672
N.A.I.C.S.: 334412

Zoran Microelectronics Ltd. (2)
Advanced Technology Ctr
PO Box 15015
Haifa, 31905, Israel (100%)
Tel.: (972) 48545777
Fax: (972) 48551550
E-Mail: zml.lobby@csr.com
Web Site: www.zoran.com
Sales Range: $125-149.9 Million
Emp.: 300
S.I.C.: 3672
N.A.I.C.S.: 334412
Isaac Shenberg *(Gen Mgr)*

Zoran Toronto Labs (2)
2175 Queen St E Ste 302
Toronto, ON, M4E 1E5, Canada (100%)
Tel.: (408) 523-6500
Fax: (416) 690-3363
Web Site: www.zoran.com
Sales Range: $10-24.9 Million
Emp.: 50
Digital Imaging Testing Laboratory
S.I.C.: 3672
N.A.I.C.S.: 334412

Non-U.S. Subsidiaries:

Cambridge Silicon Radio Sarl (1)
Village d'Enterprise Green Side 400 Avenue Roumanille
BP 309
06906 Sophia-Antipolis, France (100%)
Tel.: (33) 492384720
Fax: (33) 492384721
Telecommunications Resellers
S.I.C.: 4813
N.A.I.C.S.: 517911

CSR China (Shanghai) Co. Limited (1)
Room 2201-05 Platinum Building
No 233 Taicang Road Luwan Dist, 200020
Shanghai, China (100%)
Tel.: (86) 2161352100
Fax: (86) 2161352199
E-Mail: hlee@csr.com
Emp.: 15
Semiconductor & Related Device Mfr
S.I.C.: 3674
N.A.I.C.S.: 334413
Helena Lee *(Mng Dir)*

CSR (India) Private Limited (1)
7th floor Wing A Block Technology Park
No 4-1 Bannerghatta Main Rd, 560029
Bengaluru, India In
Tel.: (91) 8025183000 (100%)
Fax: (91) 8025183001
Emp.: 120
General Automotive Repair
S.I.C.: 7538
N.A.I.C.S.: 811111
Prabhakar Shastry *(Gen Mgr)*

CSR KK (1)
Kojimachi KS Square 9th Floor
5-3-3 Kojimachi Chiyoda-ku, Tokyo, 102-0083, Japan (100%)
Tel.: (81) 352762911
Fax: (81) 352762915
Semiconductor Machinery Mfr
S.I.C.: 3291
N.A.I.C.S.: 327910

CSR Korea Limited (1)
15th Floor West wing POSCO center
892 Daichi-Dong Gangnam-Gu, 135-777
Seoul, Korea (South) (100%)
Tel.: (82) 264442000
Fax: (82) 264442001
E-Mail: kay.kim@csr.com
Web Site: www.csr.com
Emp.: 30
Semiconductor & Related Device Mfr
S.I.C.: 3651
N.A.I.C.S.: 334310
Richard Yoo *(Gen Mgr)*

CSR Sweden AB (1)
Emdalav 16
22369 Lund, Sweden (100%)
Tel.: (46) 462881600
Fax: (46) 462881601
Emp.: 34
Custom Computer Programming Services

S.I.C.: 7371
N.A.I.C.S.: 541511
Henry Hedlund *(Mng Dir)*

CSS TECHNERGY LTD.

6-1 85/10 Opp Telephone Bhavan
Saifabad
Hyderabad, Andhra Pradesh, 500
004, India
Tel.: (91) 40 2323 0305
Fax: (91) 40 2323 0313
E-Mail: bd@csstechnergy.com
Web Site: www.csstechnergy.com
590050—(BOM)
Rev.: $4,455,861
Assets: $3,340,082
Liabilities: $1,600,699
Net Worth: $1,739,383
Earnings: ($2,938,290)
Fiscal Year-end: 03/31/13
Business Description:
IT Solutions
S.I.C.: 7371
N.A.I.C.S.: 541511
Personnel:
Ravi Vishnu *(Chm & Mng Dir)*
Aravind Aitipamula *(Sec)*
Board of Directors:
Ravi Vishnu
V. L. Nanda Kumar
Ravi Radha Krishna Murthy
T. Venkateshwara Prasad
Tayi Krishna Rao
Bhopal A. Reddy
Doodipala Vikram Reddy
Transfer Agent:
XL Softech Systems Limited
3 Sagar Society Road No. 2 Banjara Hills
Hyderabad, India

CST MINING GROUP LIMITED

Room 4503-05 45/F China
Resources Building 26 Harbour Road
Wanchai, China (Hong Kong)
Tel.: (852) 28569300
Fax: (852) 28242616
E-Mail: information@cstmining.com
Web Site: www.cstmining.com
0985—(HKG)
Rev.: $172,340,000
Assets: $1,056,831,000
Liabilities: $53,362,000
Net Worth: $1,003,469,000
Earnings: $118,126,000
Emp.: 266
Fiscal Year-end: 03/31/13
Business Description:
Copper Mining Services
S.I.C.: 1021
N.A.I.C.S.: 212234
Personnel:
Tao Chiu *(Chm)*
Ming Tung Lee *(CFO)*
Kim Hang Chow *(Sec)*
Board of Directors:
Tao Chiu
Richard Rui Hui
Jimmy Kam Hung Kwan
Ming Tung Lee
Yin Fan Ma
So Yuet Tong
Ching Hung Tsui
Kwok Yu Yeung
Pan Yu
The R&H Trust Co. Ltd
Windward 1 Regatta Office Park
897
Georgetown, Cayman Islands
Transfer Agents:
Tricor Tengis Limited
26th Floor Tesbury Centre 28 Queen's Road
East
Wanchai, China (Hong Kong)
Tel.: (852) 29801333
Fax: (852) 28108185
The R&H Trust Co. Ltd
Windward 1 Regatta Office Park
897
Georgetown, Cayman Islands
Non-U.S. Subsidiary:

CST Minerals Lady Annie Pty
Limited **(1)**
Mcnamara Road
Mount Isa, QLD, 4825, Australia
Tel.: (61) 7 4748 0000
Fax: (61) 747480066
Emp.: 20
Copper Mining Services
S.I.C.: 1021
N.A.I.C.S.: 212234
Tracey Pile *(Mgr-Tenement)*

CSU CARDSYSTEM S.A.

R Piaui 136 - Bloco A/b
06440-182 Barueri, SP, Brazil
Tel.: (55) 11 3030 3700
Fax: (55) 11 3819 3991
E-Mail: ri@csu.com.br
Web Site: www.csu.com.br
Year Founded: 1992
CARD3—(BRAZ)
Business Description:
Payment Processing Services
S.I.C.: 6099
N.A.I.C.S.: 522320
Personnel:
Marcos Ribeiro Leite *(Founder, Chm & CEO)*
Ricardo Jose Ribeiro Leite *(Legal & IR Officer)*
Board of Directors:
Marcos Ribeiro Leite
Rubens Barbosa
Antonio Fadiga
Ricardo Jose Ribeiro Leite
Jorge Michel Lepeltier

CSUN MFG. LTD.

No 2-1 Kung 8 Rd 2nd Industrial Park
Linkou Hisiang, Taipei, Taiwan
Tel.: (886) 226017706
Fax: (886) 226018854
E-Mail: sale@csun.com.tw
Web Site: www.csun.com.tw
2467—(TAI)
Sales Range: $25-49.9 Million
Business Description:
Printed Circuit Boards Mfr
S.I.C.: 3672
N.A.I.C.S.: 334412
Personnel:
Morrison Liang *(Chm)*
Choung Liang Mao *(Vice Chm)*
Board of Directors:
Morrison Liang
Choung Liang Mao

CT&T CO., LTD.

113-5 Banpo 4-dong
Seocho-gu, Seoul, Korea (South)
Tel.: (82) 15992227
Fax: (82) 25920574
Web Site: www.ctco.lv
Year Founded: 2002
Business Description:
Electric Vehicles Mfr & Sales
S.I.C.: 3711
N.A.I.C.S.: 336211
Personnel:
Young Gi Lee *(CEO)*

CT DEVELOPERS LTD.

155 Vine Avenue
Toronto, ON, M6P 1V9, Canada
Tel.: (416) 604-7620
Fax: (416) 946-1161
E-Mail: n.eyolfson@gmail.com
Year Founded: 2011
DEV.P—(TSXV)
Business Description:
Investment Services
S.I.C.: 6211
N.A.I.C.S.: 523999
Personnel:
Norman Eyolfson *(Pres, CEO & CFO)*
Richard Buzbuzian *(Treas & Sec)*
Board of Directors:
Richard Buzbuzian
Terry Christopher
Jason Monaco
Transfer Agent:
Computershare Investor Services Inc.
3rd Floor 510 Burrard Street
Vancouver, BC, Canada

CT ENVIRONMENTAL GROUP LIMITED

17/F Best Centre Gangkou Road
Xintang Town
Zencheng, Guangzhou, 511340,
China
Tel.: (86) 20 8277 7777
Fax: (86) 20 8260 6177
E-Mail: info@chongto.com
Web Site: www.chongto.com
1363—(HKG)
Emp.: 280
Business Description:
Wastewater & Industrial Water Supply
Services
S.I.C.: 4971
N.A.I.C.S.: 221310
Personnel:
Cham To Tsui *(Chm)*

CT REAL ESTATE INVESTMENT TRUST

2180 Yonge Street
PO Box 770 Station K
Toronto, ON, M4P 2V8, Canada
Tel.: (416) 480-8725
Fax: (416) 480-8763
Year Founded: 2013
CRT.UN—(TSX)
Business Description:
Real Estate Investment Services
S.I.C.: 6211
N.A.I.C.S.: 523999
Personnel:
Kenneth Silver *(Pres & CEO)*
Transfer Agent:
Computershare Trust Company of
Canada
Toronto, ON, Canada

CTA HOLDING

ZA du Caillou 3 rue Jules Verne
69630 Chaponost, France
Tel.: (33) 4 78 56 70 70
Fax: (33) 4 78 56 17 31
Web Site: www.cta.fr
Year Founded: 1987
MLCTA—(EUR)
Sales Range: $1-9.9 Million
Business Description:
Air Compressor Mfr
S.I.C.: 3563
N.A.I.C.S.: 333912
Personnel:
Emmanuel Perez *(Chm & CEO)*
Louis Fillot *(Gen Sec)*

CTAC N.V.

Meerendonkweg 11
5216 TZ 's-Hertogenbosch,
Netherlands
Tel.: (31) 736920692
Fax: (31) 736920688
E-Mail: info@ctac.nl
Web Site: www.ctac.nl
CTAC—(EUR)
Rev.: $107,506,482
Assets: $53,702,760
Liabilities: $44,224,377
Net Worth: $9,478,383
Earnings: $1,083,667
Emp.: 448
Fiscal Year-end: 12/31/12
Business Description:
IT Consulting Services
S.I.C.: 8999
N.A.I.C.S.: 541690
Personnel:
H. G. B. Olde Hartmann *(Chm-Supervisory Bd)*
H. L. J. Hilgerdenaar *(CEO)*
Douwe van der Werf *(CFO)*
Supervisory Board of Directors:
H. G. B. Olde Hartmann
H. P. M. Jagers
E. Kraaijenzank
Subsidiaries:

IFS Probity B.V. **(1)**
Albert Plesmanstraat 2
Barneveld, Netherlands 3772 MN
Tel.: (31) 34 242 0120
E-Mail: info@ifsprobity.nl
Web Site: www.ifsprobity.nl
Emp.: 31
Investment Management Services
S.I.C.: 6282
N.A.I.C.S.: 523920
Rob ten Berge, *(Gen Mgr)*

Persity Resourcing B.V. **(1)**
Minister Hartsenlaan 10
Hilversum, 1217 LS, Netherlands
Tel.: (31) 35 8200988
E-Mail: info@persity.nl
Web Site: www.persity.nl
Human Resources Consulting Services
S.I.C.: 8999
N.A.I.C.S.: 541612
Tesca Dijkstra, *(Office Mgr)*

Non-U.S. Subsidiaries:

Ctac Belgium BVBA **(1)**
Uilenbaan 82
2160 Wommelgem, Belgium
Tel.: (32) 3 354 09 79
Fax: (32) 3 354 07 89
E-Mail: info@ctac.be
Web Site: www.ctac.be
Information Technology Consulting Services
S.I.C.: 7373
N.A.I.C.S.: 541512
Sofie Possson, *(Mgr-Sls)*

Ctac Deutschland GmbH **(1)**
Kaiserswerther Str 115
40880 Ratingen, Germany
Tel.: (49) 2102 420 675
Fax: (49) 2102 420 62
E-Mail: info@ctacpowerhouse.de
Information Technology Consulting Services
S.I.C.: 7373
N.A.I.C.S.: 541512

Ctac France SAS **(1)**
54-56 Avenue Hoche
75008 Paris, France
Tel.: (33) 1 56 60 53 89
Fax: (33) 1 56 60 56 00
E-Mail: info@ctacfrance.fr
Web Site: www.ctacfrance.fr
Information Technology Consulting Services
S.I.C.: 7373
N.A.I.C.S.: 541512
Jean-Claude Gandon *(Mng Dir)*

CTBC FINANCIAL HOLDING CO., LTD.

(Formerly Chinatrust Financial
Holding Co., Ltd.)
17F No3 Sung Shou Road
Taipei, Taiwan
Tel.: (886) 227222002
Fax: (886) 227237883
E-Mail: ir@email.chinatrust.com.tw
Web Site: www.chinatrustgroup.com.tw
Year Founded: 2002

CTBC Financial Holding Co., Ltd.—(Continued)

2891—(TAI)
Int. Income: $1,556,850,909
Assets: $71,463,140,241
Liabilities: $65,694,473,984
Net Worth: $5,768,666,257
Earnings: $717,631,463
Emp.: 10,000
Fiscal Year-end: 12/31/12

Business Description:
Bank Holding Company
S.I.C.: 6712
N.A.I.C.S.: 551111

Personnel:
Wen-Long Yen *(Chm)*
H. Steve Hsieh *(Vice Chm)*
Ruu-Tian Chang *(CIO)*
Elaine Yeh *(Chief Compliance Officer & Head-Legal Dept)*
Jack T. K. Cheng *(Chief Risk Officer)*
Rachael Kao *(Head-Fin Mgmt & Gen Admin Dept)*
Sting Yang *(Acctg Officer)*
Daniel I. K. Wu *(Pres/CEO-Investment Bus)*
Michael B. DeNoma *(CEO-Banking Bus)*
Frank K. Ling *(CEO-Insurance Bus)*
Charles L. F. Lo *(CEO-China Bus)*
Roger Kao *(Gen Sec)*

Board of Directors:
Wen-Long Yen
Thomas K. S. Chen
Yen-Pao Chen
Song-Chi Chien
H. Steve Hsieh
Jie-Haun Lee
Wen-Chih Lee
Chao-Chin Tung
Chung-Yu Wang

Subsidiaries:

CTBC Bank Co., Ltd. **(1)**
(Formerly Chinatrust Commercial Bank Co., Ltd.)
3 Sung Shou Rd
Taipei, Taiwan
Tel.: (886) 227222002
Fax: (886) 227237883
E-Mail: mymail@ctcb.com.tw
Web Site: www.chinatrust.com.tw
Sales Range: $300-349.9 Million
Emp.: 416
National Commercial Banks & Bank Holding Companies
Import Export
S.I.C.: 6712
N.A.I.C.S.: 551111

U.S. Subsidiary:

CTBC Bank Corp. (USA) **(2)**
801 S Figueroa St Ste 2300
Los Angeles, CA 90017
Tel.: (310) 791-2828
Fax: (310) 791-2835
E-Mail: compliance@ctbcbankusa.com
Web Site: www.ctbcbankusa.com
Sls.: $85,327,000
Emp.: 100
Banking Services
Import Export
S.I.C.: 6029
N.A.I.C.S.: 522110
C. C. Tung *(Chm)*
Noor Menai *(Pres & CEO)*
Brian Constable *(Exec VP & Head-Retail Banking Grp)*
Parham Medhat *(Exec VP & Head-Ops)*
Peter Yam *(Exec VP)*

Non-U.S. Subsidiary:

Chinatrust (Philippines) Commercial Bank Corporation **(2)**
16th to 19th Floors Fort Legend Towers
31st Street corner 3rd Avenue
Bonifacio Global City, 1634 Taguig, Philippines (99.41%)
Tel.: (63) 29889287
Fax: (63) 25767935
E-Mail: customercare@chinatrust.com.ph
Web Site: www.chinatrust.com.ph
Sales Range: $25-49.9 Million
Emp.: 575
Commercial Banking Services
S.I.C.: 6029
N.A.I.C.S.: 522110
Jack Weng-Hung Lee *(Chm)*
William B. Go *(Vice Chm)*
Mark Chen *(Pres & CEO)*
Raymundo Martin M. Escalona *(Exec VP & Head-Institutional Banking)*
Victor Q. Lim *(Exec VP & Head-Retail Banking)*
Edgardo A.M. Mendoza, Jr. *(Sr VP & Grp Head-HR & Admin)*
Gretchen S. Macabasco *(Sr VP-Institutional Banking)*
Jimmy Arsenio Y. Samonte *(Sr VP-Internal Audit)*
Cecilia E. Tabuena *(Sr VP-Institutional Banking)*

Chinatrust Insurance Brokers Co., Ltd. **(1)**
13F No 16 Young Ji Road
11070 Taipei, Taiwan
Tel.: (886) 227680505
Fax: (886) 227605379
Web Site: www.chinatrust.com.tw
Emp.: 200,000
Insurance & Brokerage Services
S.I.C.: 6411
N.A.I.C.S.: 524210
Michael DeNoma *(Pres)*

Chinatrust Life Insurance Co., Ltd. **(1)**
8th Floor 1 Sec 5 Nanjing South Rd
Taipei, 105, Taiwan TW
Tel.: (886) 227607988
Fax: (886) 27617868
E-Mail:
Sales Range: $50-74.9 Million
Emp.: 50
Personal & Group Life & Health Insurance, Personal Annuities & Personal & Group Accident Services
S.I.C.: 6411
N.A.I.C.S.: 524298
Frank K. Ling *(CEO)*

Chinatrust Securities Co., Inc. **(1)**
10F 3 Sung Shou Road
Taipei, Taiwan
Tel.: (886) 287808867
Fax: (886) 287808868
Web Site: www.win168.com.tw
Securities Brokerage Services
S.I.C.: 6211
N.A.I.C.S.: 523120

Chinatrust Security Co., Ltd. **(1)**
13F 247 Chi Hsien 3rd Road
Kaohsiung, Taiwan
Tel.: (886) 75311166
Fax: (886) 75619997
Securities Brokerage Services
S.I.C.: 6211
N.A.I.C.S.: 523120
Chee Sung Taek *(Mgr)*

Taiwan Lottery Co., Ltd. **(1)**
9F No 133 Sec 4 Minsheng East Road
10574 Taipei, Taiwan
Tel.: (886) 221751915
Fax: (886) 227170886
Web Site: www.taiwanlottery.com.tw
Emp.: 180
Lottery Operating Services
S.I.C.: 7999
N.A.I.C.S.: 713290
Stebe Hsueh *(Chm)*

CTC AVIATION GROUP LIMITED

Dibden Manor
Dibden, Southampton, SO45 5TD, United Kingdom
Tel.: (44) 23 8084 4000
Fax: (44) 23 8074 2400
E-Mail: clientsupport@ctcaviation.com
Web Site: www.ctcaviation.com
Year Founded: 1995
Sales Range: $25-49.9 Million
Emp.: 344

Business Description:
Investment Management Services
S.I.C.: 6282
N.A.I.C.S.: 523920

Personnel:
Yagnish Chotai *(Chm)*
Chris Clarke *(Pres)*
Rob Clarke *(Grp CEO)*

Board of Directors:
Yagnish Chotai
John Hartz
Martin Hunt
Mike Redrupp
Julian So
Mark Williams

CTC BIO., INC.

93 Ogeum-dong
Songpa-gu, Seoul, Korea (South)
Tel.: (82) 70 4033 0200
Fax: (82) 2 449 3886
Web Site: www.ctcbio.com
Year Founded: 1995
060590—(KRS)
Sls.: $120,698,190
Assets: $116,588,520
Liabilities: $58,556,520
Net Worth: $58,032,000
Earnings: $7,612,980
Emp.: 150
Fiscal Year-end: 12/31/12

Business Description:
Pharmaceutical Product Mfr
S.I.C.: 2834
N.A.I.C.S.: 325412

Personnel:
Ho-Yeon Cho *(Co-CEO)*
Seong-Rin Kim *(Co-CEO)*

CTC MEDIA, INC.

31A Leningradsky Prospekt
125284 Moscow, Russia
Tel.: (7) 495 785 6333
Fax: (7) 495 955 7858
E-Mail: info@ctcmedia.ru
Web Site: www.ctcmedia.ru
Year Founded: 1996
CTCM—(NASDAQ)
Rev.: $832,103,000
Assets: $970,976,000
Liabilities: $236,860,000
Net Worth: $734,116,000
Earnings: $160,161,000
Emp.: 1,129
Fiscal Year-end: 12/31/13

Business Description:
Commercial Television Broadcasting Services
S.I.C.: 4841
N.A.I.C.S.: 515210

Personnel:
Angelo Codignoni *(Co-Chm)*
Lorenzo Grabau *(Co-Chm)*
Yuliana Slashcheva *(CEO)*
Nikolay Surikov *(CFO)*
Elmira Makhmutova *(CMO)*
Yulia Mitrovich *(Chief Strategy Officer & Chief Digital Media Officer)*
Julia Moskvitina *(Chief Comml Officer)*
Vyacheslav Murugov *(Chief Content Officer & Head-CTC Channel)*
Konstantin Khachaturov *(Chief Bus Support Officer)*
Tatyana Korneva *(Chief Mktg Svcs Officer)*
Sergey Petrov *(Chief Brdcst Officer)*
Alexey Shchedrin *(Chief Strategic Comm Officer)*

Board of Directors:
Angelo Codignoni
Lorenzo Grabau
Tamjid Basunia
Irina Gofman
Werner E. Klatten
Jorgen Madsen Lindemann
Jean-Pierre Morel
Alexander Pentya
Timur Weinstein

CTCI CORPORATION

89 Sec 6 Zhongshan N Rd
Taipei, 11155, Taiwan
Tel.: (886) 228339999
Fax: (886) 228338833
E-Mail: hu@ctci.com.tw
Web Site: www.ctci.com.tw
Year Founded: 1979
9933—(TAI)
Rev.: $2,057,224,849
Assets: $1,766,066,915
Liabilities: $1,184,317,997
Net Worth: $581,748,918
Earnings: $94,172,792
Emp.: 7,500
Fiscal Year-end: 12/31/12

Business Description:
Engineering & Construction Services
S.I.C.: 1629
N.A.I.C.S.: 237990

Personnel:
John T. Yu *(Chm & CEO)*
John H. Lin *(Vice Chm)*
Andy Sheu *(Pres)*
Patrick Lin *(CFO & VP)*
Po-Chien Wang *(Chief Legal Officer-Legal & Compliance Div & VP)*
Ike W. Liao *(Chm-Corp Trng)*
Chih Sen Lin *(CEO-CTCI Foundation)*
Pi-Chuan Chen *(Exec VP & Head-Exec Mgmt Office)*
M. H. Wang *(Exec VP & Head-Hydrocarbon Bus Ops)*
Mark W. H. Yang *(Exec VP & Head-EPC Ops & Innovation R&D Center)*
Michael Yang *(Exec VP & Head-Infrastructure, Environment & Power Bus Ops)*
Brad Chen *(Sr VP & Head-Plant Maintenance Bus Ops)*
Tien-Nan Pan *(Sr VP & Head-Tech Dev-Infrastructure Environment & Power Bus Ops)*
Andrew Tsai *(Sr VP & Head-Admin & PR)*
Robert Ming-Cheng Hsiao *(Sr VP & Interim Head-Plng, HR, Strategy & Bus Dev Dept)*
Ching-Lin Hsu *(Sr VP)*

Subsidiaries:

Advanced Control & Systems Inc. **(1)**
5th Fl 52 Sec 3 Nankang Road
Taipei, 115, Taiwan TW
Tel.: (886) 227853839
Fax: (886) 227820180
Web Site: www.acs.com.tw
Emp.: 230
System Integrator of Computer, Communication, Control & Information Technologies
S.I.C.: 7379
N.A.I.C.S.: 541519
Tony Leo *(Pres)*
Chin-Tang Liu *(Pres)*

CTCI Chemicals Corp. **(1)**
5th Floor 132 Xingshan Road
Neihu District, Taipei, Taiwan, 114, Taiwan
Tel.: (886) 221621687
Fax: (886) 226121680
E-Mail: info@ctci.com.tw
Web Site: www.ctci.com
Emp.: 50
Chemicals Mfr & Supplier
S.I.C.: 2899
N.A.I.C.S.: 325998
Robert Li *(pres)*

CTCI Machinery Corporation **(1)**
5 Hsin Kung Rd
Ta-She Hsian, Kaohsiung, 815, Taiwan TW
Tel.: (886) 73512141

Fax: (886) 73512460
E-Mail: hoffnann@ctci.com.tw
Web Site: www.ctcim.com.tw
Emp.: 435
Power Plant Machinery Mfr, Maintenance & Inspection Services
S.I.C.: 3559
N.A.I.C.S.: 333249
Jenny C. L. Wei *(Chm)*
T. J. Huang *(Pres)*

E&C Engineering Corporation (1)
5th Floor 16 Lane 270 Sec 3 Pei Shen Road
Shenkeng, Taipei, 222, Taiwan TW
Tel.: (886) 226625858 (100%)
Fax: (886) 226622814
E-Mail: mail@eandc.com.tw
Web Site: www.eandc.com.tw
Emp.: 650
Engineering & Construction Services
S.I.C.: 8711
N.A.I.C.S.: 541330
H. C. Jen *(Chm)*
Andrew Tsai *(Pres)*

Fortune Energy Corporation (1)
5th Fl 132 Xingshan Road
Neihu District, Taipei, 114, Taiwan TW
Tel.: (886) 2 2612 1689 (75%)
Fax: (886) 2 2612 1680
Waste Treatment Services
S.I.C.: 4953
N.A.I.C.S.: 562219
Donald M. Yu *(Chm)*
F. H. Lee *(Pres)*

KD Holding Corporation (1)
5th Fl 132 Xingshan Road
Neihu District, Taipei, 114, Taiwan TW
Tel.: (886) 2 2612 1689
Fax: (886) 2 2612 1680
Web Site: www.kdhc.com.tw
Sales Range: $100-124.9 Million
Emp.: 8
Holding Company; Professional Investments
S.I.C.: 6719
N.A.I.C.S.: 551112
John T. Yu *(Chm)*
Donald M. Yu *(Pres)*

Subsidiaries:

HD Resources Management Corporation (2)
5th Fl 132 Xingshan Road
Neihu District, Taipei, 114, Taiwan TW
Tel.: (886) 2 2612 1689
Fax: (886) 2 2612 1680
Sales Range: $1-9.9 Million
Emp.: 48
Waste Management Services
S.I.C.: 4212
N.A.I.C.S.: 562119
Donald M. Yu *(Chm)*
Yun-Peng Shih *(Pres)*

Leading Energy Corporation (2)
5th Fl 132 Xingshan Road
Neihu District, Taipei, 114, Taiwan TW
Tel.: (886) 226121689
Fax: (886) 2 2612 1680
Waste Management
S.I.C.: 4953
N.A.I.C.S.: 562213
Donald M. Yu *(Chm)*
Perry Yeh *(Pres)*

Resources Engineering Services Inc. (1)
4th Fl 48 Sec 3 Nankang Road
Taipei, 115, Taiwan TW
Tel.: (886) 227838250
Fax: (886) 227838232
Web Site: www.res.com.tw
Planning, Design, Engineering & Construction Services
S.I.C.: 1629
N.A.I.C.S.: 237990
Judson C. Yen *(Chm)*
Ching-Jenn Yeh *(Pres)*

Sino Environmental Services Corp. (1)
5F No 132 Xingshan Road
Neihu District, Taipei, 114, Taiwan TW
Tel.: (886) 226121688
Fax: (886) 226121681
Web Site: www.sesc.com.tw
Emp.: 580
Waste Management Services
S.I.C.: 4959
N.A.I.C.S.: 562998
Donald M. Yu *(Chm)*
J. J. Liao *(Pres)*

Subsidiary:

Innovest Investment Corp (2)
10 Fl 89 Sec 6 Zhongshan North Rd
Taipei, Taiwan
Tel.: (886) 2 2833 9999
Fax: (886) 2 2835 7531
Investment Management Services
S.I.C.: 6211
N.A.I.C.S.: 523999

U.S. Subsidiary:

CTAS Corporation (1)
11757 Katy Fwy Ste
Houston, TX 77079
Tel.: (281) 870-9998
Fax: (281) 870-9981
Petroleum Refinery Services
S.I.C.: 2911
N.A.I.C.S.: 324110

Non-U.S. Subsidiaries:

Advanced Control & Information Technologies Ltd. (1)
8F No 26 Lane 168 Daduhe Road
Shanghai, Shanghai, 200062, China
Tel.: (86) 21 52519888
Fax: (86) 21 32501013
Computer Software Development Services
S.I.C.: 7371
N.A.I.C.S.: 541511

CINDA Engineering & Construction Pvt. Ltd. (1)
Corenthum 6th Floor Tower-B Plot No A-41
Sector-62
Noida, Uttar Pradesh, 201301, India
Tel.: (91) 120 4722300
Fax: (91) 120 4722399
Construction Engineering Services
S.I.C.: 8711
N.A.I.C.S.: 541330

CTCI Engineering & Construction Sdn Bhd (1)
Suite 22-03B 22nd Fl Menara Tan & Tan 207
Jalan Tun Razak, 50400 Kuala Lumpur, Malaysia MY
Tel.: (60) 321665568
Fax: (60) 321666658
E-Mail: ctcikl@streamyx.com
Emp.: 50
Planning, Design, Procurement, Construction & Maintenance of Refinery, Petrochemical & Power Plants
S.I.C.: 1629
N.A.I.C.S.: 237990
P. C. Chen *(Chm)*
Steven Wu *(Mng Dir)*

CTCI Singapore Pte. Ltd. (1)
1 Sims Lane 06-11
Singapore, 387355, Singapore
Tel.: (65) 6748 4785
Fax: (65) 6746 2713
Petrochemical Refinery Services
S.I.C.: 2911
N.A.I.C.S.: 324110
Steve Wu *(Mng Dir)*

Jingding Engineering & Construction Co., Ltd. (1)
9-11F Building B No 136 Andingmenwai Street
Dongcheng District, Beijing, 100011, China
Tel.: (86) 10 64827878
Fax: (86) 10 64827958
Web Site: www.jdec.com.cn
Emp.: 450
Construction Engineering Services
S.I.C.: 8711
N.A.I.C.S.: 541330

Non-U.S. Joint Ventures:

CIMAS ENGINEERING Co., Ltd. (1)
7th Fl Schmidt Tower 239 Xuan Thuy Road
Cau Giay, Hanoi, Vietnam VN
Tel.: (84) 4 833 5513
Fax: (84) 4 833 7824
Web Site: www.cimas.com.vn/index.php
Emp.: 153
Engineering & Construction Services; Joint Venture Owned 50% by CTCI Corporation, 33% by LILAMA Corporation & 17% by Sincerity Engineering Company
S.I.C.: 8711
N.A.I.C.S.: 541330
Nguyen The Thanh *(Chm)*
Paul Yang *(Gen Dir)*

CTCI (Thailand) Co., Ltd. (1)
17-19th Floor Phairojkijja Tower 400
Bangna-Trad Road
KM 4 Bangna, Bangkok, 10260, Thailand TH
Tel.: (66) 27696888
Fax: (66) 27696820
E-Mail: kun@ctci.co.th
Web Site: www.ctci.co.th
Emp.: 300
Construction & Engineering Services
S.I.C.: 8711
N.A.I.C.S.: 237990
John H. Lin *(Chm)*
John K.C. Yeh *(Mng Dir)*

CTI ENGINEERING CO., LTD.

3-21-1 Nihonbashi Hama-cho
Chuo-ku, Tokyo, 103-8430, Japan
Tel.: (81) 336680451
E-Mail: ctie_hq@ctie.co.jp
Web Site: www.ctie.co.jp
Year Founded: 1945
9621—(TKS)
Sales Range: $300-349.9 Million
Emp.: 1,423

Business Description:
Construction Consulting Services
S.I.C.: 8711
N.A.I.C.S.: 541330

Personnel:
Kazuya Oshima *(Pres)*
Reiichi Abe *(Sr Mng Exec Officer)*
Kunihiko Harada *(Sr Mng Exec Officer)*
Konomu Uchimura *(Sr Mng Exec Officer)*
Tsuneo Uesaka *(Sr Mng Exec Officer)*
Yasuki Komatsu *(Mng Exec Officer)*
Kazuo Murata *(Mng Exec Officer)*
Yoshihito Sabase *(Mng Exec Officer)*

Board of Directors:
Reiichi Abe
Kunihiko Harada
Yasuki Komatsu
Kazuo Murata
Tetsuzo Okada
Kazuya Oshima
Yoshihito Sabase
Konomu Uchimura
Tsuneo Uesaka
Kazunori Yoshioka

Subsidiaries:

CTI AURA Co., Ltd. (1)
Cti Saitama Bldg 1-14-6 Kamikizaki
Urawa, Saitama, 330-0071, Japan
Tel.: (81) 488332049
Fax: (81) 488252665
Environmental Engineering Services
S.I.C.: 8711
N.A.I.C.S.: 541330

CTI Engineering International Co., Ltd. (1)
Tachibana Annex Bldg 2-25-14 Kameido
Koto-ku, Tokyo, 136-0071, Japan
Tel.: (81) 336382561
Fax: (81) 336382560
E-Mail: info@ctii.co.jp
Web Site: www.ctii.co.jp
Emp.: 115
Engineering Consulting Services
S.I.C.: 8711
N.A.I.C.S.: 541330
Yoshiharu Matsumoto *(Chm)*
Toshiki Kawakami *(Mng Exec Officer)*
Kanehiro Morishita *(Exec Officer)*

CTI Ground Planning Co., Ltd. (1)
Cti Fukuoka Bldg 2-4-12 Daimyo
Chuo-Ku, Fukuoka, 810-0041, Japan
Tel.: (81) 927375333
Fax: (81) 927371244
Emp.: 55
Environmental Engineering Services
S.I.C.: 8711
N.A.I.C.S.: 541330
Takahiro Sakata *(Mng Dir)*

CTI LOGISTICS LIMITED

1 Drummond Place
West Perth, WA, 6005, Australia
Mailing Address:
PO Box 400
West Perth, WA, 6872, Australia
Tel.: (61) 8 9422 1100
Fax: (61) 8 9227 8000
E-Mail: corporate@ctilogistics.com
Web Site: www.ctilogistics.com
CLX—(ASX)
Rev.: $132,001,462
Assets: $106,139,814
Liabilities: $57,779,647
Net Worth: $48,360,167
Earnings: $10,237,063
Emp.: 274
Fiscal Year-end: 06/30/13

Business Description:
Transportation & Warehousing Logistics
Import Export
S.I.C.: 4731
N.A.I.C.S.: 488510

Personnel:
David Robert Watson *(Chm)*
David Anderson Mellor *(Co-Mng Dir & Sec)*
Bruce Edmond Saxild *(Co-Mng Dir)*

Board of Directors:
David Robert Watson
Peter James Leonhardt
David Anderson Mellor
Bruce Edmond Saxild
Matthew David Watson

Divisions:

CTI Logistics Ltd - Fleet Management Division (1)
54 Miguel Road
Bibra Lake, WA, 6163, Australia
Tel.: (61) 8 9499 8888
Fax: (61) 8 9434 2242
E-Mail: admin@ctilogistics.com
Web Site: www.ctitaxitrucks.com.au
Emp.: 20
Logistics Services
S.I.C.: 4731
N.A.I.C.S.: 541614
Mark Cameron *(Mng Dir)*

CTI Logistics Ltd - General & Container Transport Division (1)
54 Miguel Road
Bibra Lake, WA, 6163, Australia
Tel.: (61) 894998888
Fax: (61) 894345390
E-Mail: logistics@ctilogistics.com
Web Site: www.ctitaxitrucks.com.au/static/contacts.cfm#fleet
Emp.: 20
Logistics Services
S.I.C.: 4731
N.A.I.C.S.: 541614
Lin Montgomery *(Mgr-Sls)*

Subsidiaries:

Ausplastics Pty Ltd (1)
36 Denninup Way
Malaga, WA, 6090, Australia
Tel.: (61) 892491500
Fax: (61) 892495150
E-Mail: sales@ausplastics.com
Web Site: www.ausplastics.com
Emp.: 25
Plastic Plumbing Fittings Mfr
S.I.C.: 3089
N.A.I.C.S.: 326122
Eddie Baroni *(Gen Mgr)*

Bring Transport Industries Pty Ltd (1)
1 Drummond St
West Perth, WA, 6005, Australia

CTI Logistics Limited—(Continued)

Tel.: (61) 894221100
Fax: (61) 892278000
E-Mail: admin@bringcouriers.com.au
Transportation Services
S.I.C.: 4789
N.A.I.C.S.: 488490
Lin Montgomery *(Mgr-HR)*

Consolidated Transport Industries Pty Ltd (1)
1 Drummond Pl
West Perth, WA, 6005, Australia
Tel.: (61) 894221100
Fax: (61) 892278000
Transportation Services
S.I.C.: 4789
N.A.I.C.S.: 488490
David Watson *(CEO)*

Subsidiary:

Foxline Logistics Pty Ltd (2)
5-7 Eyre Street
Belmont, WA, 6104, Australia
Tel.: (61) 894783088
Fax: (61) 894783575
E-Mail: accounts@foxline.com.au
Web Site: www.foxline.com.au
Courier & Taxi Truck Services
S.I.C.: 4215
N.A.I.C.S.: 492110

CTI Business Investment Company Pty Ltd (1)
1 Drummond Pl
West Perth, WA, 6005, Australia
Tel.: (61) 892276333
Fax: (61) 894221100
E-Mail: admin@bringcouriers.com.au
Transportation Services
S.I.C.: 4789
N.A.I.C.S.: 488490
Lin Montgomery *(Mgr-Sls)*

CTI Couriers Pty Ltd (1)
15 Drummond Pl
West Perth, WA, 6005, Australia
Tel.: (61) 894274700
Fax: (61) 894274789
E-Mail: sales@ctisupercouriers.com.au
Web Site: www.ctisupercouriers.com.au
Courier Services
S.I.C.: 4513
N.A.I.C.S.: 492110

CTI Fleet Management Pty Ltd (1)
328 Aberdeen Street
West Perth, WA, 6005, Australia
Tel.: (61) 893283666
Fax: (61) 892278000
Fleet Leasing Services
S.I.C.: 7515
N.A.I.C.S.: 532112

CTI Freight Systems Pty Ltd (1)
54 Miguel Rd
Bibra Lake, WA, 6163, Australia
Tel.: (61) 894221100
Fax: (61) 94342242
E-Mail: admin@ctilogistics.com
Freight Transportation Services
S.I.C.: 4522
N.A.I.C.S.: 481212
Neil Raspi *(Gen Mgr)*

CTI Management Pty Ltd (1)
54 Miguel Road
1585
Bibra Lake, WA, 6965, Australia
Tel.: (61) 8 9434 3433
Fax: (61) 8 9434 2242
E-Mail: admin@ctitaxitrucks.com.au
Web Site: www.ctitaxitrucks.com.au
Taxi Fleet Operators
S.I.C.: 4121
N.A.I.C.S.: 485310

CTI Records Management Pty Ltd (1)
1 Drummond Place
West Perth, WA, 6005, Australia
Tel.: (61) 894274747
Fax: (61) 8 9227 8000
E-Mail: admin@ctirecordsmgt.com
Web Site: www.ctirecordsmgt.com.au
Emp.: 4
Record Management & Document Storage Services
S.I.C.: 7334
N.A.I.C.S.: 561439

CTI Security Services Pty Ltd (1)
328 Aberdeen Street
West Perth, WA, 6005, Australia
Tel.: (61) 893283666
Fax: (61) 893289980
Security Consulting Services
S.I.C.: 7382
N.A.I.C.S.: 561621

CTI Security Systems Pty Ltd (1)
1 Drummond Pl
West Perth, WA, 6005, Australia
Tel.: (61) 894221111
Fax: (61) 893285260
Security Services
S.I.C.: 7382
N.A.I.C.S.: 561621

CTI Transport Systems Pty Ltd (1)
54 Miguel Rd
Bibra Lake, WA, 6163, Australia
Tel.: (61) 894998888
Web Site: www.ctitaxitrucks.com.au
Emp.: 1,000
Transportation Services
S.I.C.: 4789
N.A.I.C.S.: 488490

CTI Xpress Systems Pty Ltd (1)
50 Railway Parade
Welshpool, WA, 6106, Australia
Tel.: (61) 894513233
Fax: (61) 8 9451 5139
E-Mail: admin@ctixpress.com.au
Web Site: www.ctixpress.com.au
Parcel Delivery Services
S.I.C.: 4215
N.A.I.C.S.: 492110

Mercury Messengers Pty Ltd (1)
1 Drummond Place
West Perth, WA, 6005, Australia
Tel.: (61) 894274777
Fax: (61) 8 9227 6433
E-Mail: admin@mercuryonline.com.au
Web Site: www.mercuryonline.com.au
Courier Services
S.I.C.: 4215
N.A.I.C.S.: 492110

CTIL LIMITED

(Formerly Comp-U-Learn Tech India Ltd.)
4th Floor My Home Tycoon Lifestyle Building
Green Lands Begumpet, Hyderabad, 500016, India
Tel.: (91) 40 23412103
Fax: (91) 40 23414156
E-Mail: info@ctil.co.in
Web Site: www.ctil.co.in
Year Founded: 1997
532363—(BOM)
Sales Range: $1-9.9 Million

Business Description:
Software Development Services
S.I.C.: 7372
N.A.I.C.S.: 511210

Personnel:
P. V. V. Satyanarayana *(Chm)*
A. S. R. Shiva Prasad *(Sr VP)*

Board of Directors:
P. V. V. Satyanarayana
P. Jagadeesh Babu
V. Suresh Babu
P. Gurukrishna
Raj Kosaraju
M. Balarama Krishnaiah
Gottipati S.S. Prasad
K. Ramesh
P. Obul Reddy
William Subba

CTNETWORKS CO., LTD.

12 Shinhawa-gil Ansim-ri Yeonmu-eup
Ch'ung-Nam, Chungcheongnam-do, Korea (South)
Tel.: (82) 41 742 0609
Fax: (82) 41 742 0611
E-Mail: contact@ctnetworks.co.kr
Web Site: www.ctnetworks.co.kr
Year Founded: 2007
189540—(KRS)

Business Description:
Fiber Optic Cable Mfr
S.I.C.: 3357
N.A.I.C.S.: 335921

Personnel:
Jae-Sung Lee *(CEO)*

CTRIP.COM INTERNATIONAL LTD.

99 Fu Quan Road
Shanghai, 200335, China
Tel.: (86) 21 34064880
Fax: (86) 21 52510000
E-Mail: e_service@ctrip.com
Web Site: www.ctrip.com
CTRP—(NASDAQ)
Rev.: $700,400,190
Assets: $1,853,739,948
Liabilities: $807,731,821
Net Worth: $1,046,008,127
Earnings: $109,687,635
Emp.: 19,000
Fiscal Year-end: 12/31/12

Business Description:
Travel Arrangements, Reservations, Lodging Services
S.I.C.: 4724
N.A.I.C.S.: 561510

Personnel:
James Jianzhang Liang *(Co-Founder, Chm & CEO)*
Alfred Min Fan *(Co-Founder, Vice Chm & Pres)*
Qi Ji *(Co-Founder)*
Gabriel Li *(Deputy Chm)*
Jane Jie Sun *(CFO)*

Board of Directors:
James Jianzhang Liang
Alfred Min Fan
Jianping P. Gan
Qi Ji
Gabriel Li
Neil Nanpeng Shen
Suyang Zhang

Transfer Agent:
The Bank of New York
101 Barclay St
New York, NY 10286
Tel.: (212) 815-2321
Toll Free: (800) 524-4458

Divisions:

Ctrip Beijing (1)
9F Juran Building Room 901 A3 South Street Dongzhimen
Dongcheng District, Beijing, 100007, China
Tel.: (86) 1064181616
Fax: (86) 1064185833
Web Site: pages.english.ctrip.com
Travel & Lodging Consolidator
S.I.C.: 4729
N.A.I.C.S.: 561599

Ctrip Guangzhou (1)
24F West Tower Fortune Plaza 116-118 East Tiyu Road
Guangzhou, 510620, China
Tel.: (86) 20 83936393
Fax: (86) 20 38931331
Web Site: english.ctrip.com
Travel & Lodging Consolidator
S.I.C.: 4729
N.A.I.C.S.: 561599

Ctrip.com (1)
20F Tower A Honglong Century Plz 3001 Heping Rd
Luohu District, Shenzhen, 518001, China
Tel.: (86) 75525981699
Fax: (86) 75525981698
Web Site: pages.english.ctrip.com
Travel & Lodging Consolidator
S.I.C.: 4729
N.A.I.C.S.: 561599

Subsidiaries:

Ctrip Computer Technology (Shanghai) Co., Ltd. (1)
No 99 Fuquan Rd
Shanghai, 200335, China
Tel.: (86) 2134064880
Information Technology Consulting Services
S.I.C.: 7373
N.A.I.C.S.: 541512
Min Fan *(Mgr)*

Ctrip Travel Information Technology (Shanghai) Co., Ltd. (1)
No 99 Fuquan Rd
Changning Dist, Shanghai, 200335, China
Tel.: (86) 2134064880
Fax: (86) 2154261600
Online Travel Booking Services
S.I.C.: 4729
N.A.I.C.S.: 561599

Shanghai Ctrip Commerce Co., Ltd. (1)
3F Ctrip Building No 99 Fu Quan Road
Shanghai, 200335, China
Tel.: (86) 2134064880
Tour Operating Services
S.I.C.: 4725
N.A.I.C.S.: 561520

Shanghai Huacheng Southwest Travel Agency Co., Ltd. (1)
No 99 Fuquan Rd
Shanghai, 200335, China
Tel.: (86) 2134064880
Fax: (86) 2154261600
Tour Operating Services
S.I.C.: 4725
N.A.I.C.S.: 561520

Non-U.S. Division:

Ctrip Hong Kong (1)
7/F Paul Y Centre 51 Hung To Rd Kwun Tong
60 Wyndham Street Central, Kowloon, China (Hong Kong)
Tel.: (852) 21690911
Fax: (852) 21690919
Web Site: www.english.ctrip.com
Emp.: 8
Travel & Lodging Consolidator
S.I.C.: 4729
N.A.I.C.S.: 561599
Liu Jeanpaul *(Gen Mgr)*

Non-U.S. Subsidiary:

Ctrip.com (Hong Kong) Limited (1)
Unit 2001 The Centrium 60 Wyndham Street
Central, China (Hong Kong)
Tel.: (852) 2169 0912
Fax: (852) 2169 0919
Tour Operating Services
S.I.C.: 4725
N.A.I.C.S.: 561520

CTS EVENTIM AG

Contrescarpe 75 A
28195 Bremen, Germany
Tel.: (49) 42136660
Fax: (49) 4213666290
E-Mail: investor@eventim.de
Web Site: www.eventim.de
EVD—(DEU)
Rev.: $700,457,648
Assets: $1,091,865,211
Liabilities: $801,867,221
Net Worth: $289,997,990
Earnings: $74,026,104
Emp.: 1,657
Fiscal Year-end: 12/31/12

Business Description:
Ticket Retailer
S.I.C.: 7999
N.A.I.C.S.: 713990

Personnel:
Edmund Hug *(Chm-Supervisory Bd)*
Klaus-Peter Schulenberg *(Chm-Mgmt Bd & CEO)*
Jobst W. Plog *(Vice Chm-Supervisory Bd)*

Volker Bischoff *(CFO & Member-Mgmt Bd)*
Alexander Ruoff *(COO & Member-Mgmt Bd)*
Supervisory Board of Directors:
Edmund Hug
Bernd Kundrun
Jobst W. Plog

Subsidiaries:

CTS Eventim Solutions GmbH (1)
Contrescarpe 75 A
28195 Bremen, Germany
Tel.: (49) 421366600
Fax: (49) 4213666829
Ticketing Software Development Services
S.I.C.: 7371
N.A.I.C.S.: 541511

CTS Eventim Sports GmbH (1)
Hohe Bleichen 11
20354 Hamburg, Germany
Tel.: (49) 40380788599
Fax: (49) 40380788598
E-Mail: info@eventimsports.de
Web Site: www.eventimsports.de
Emp.: 30
Software Solutions & Consulting Services
S.I.C.: 7371
N.A.I.C.S.: 541511

Eventim Sports Consulting GmbH (1)
Hohe Bleichen 11
Hamburg, 20354, Germany
Tel.: (49) 40380788599
Fax: (49) 40380788598
E-Mail: info@eventimsports.de
Web Site: www.eventimsports.de
Emp.: 20
Business Management Services
S.I.C.: 8748
N.A.I.C.S.: 541618
Arndt Scheffler *(Mng Dir)*

Marek Lieberberg Konzertagentur GmbH & Co. KG (1)
Morikestr 14
60320 Frankfurt am Main, Germany
Tel.: (49) 699562020
Fax: (49) 69568199
E-Mail: info@mlk.com
Web Site: www.mlk.com
Emp.: 100
Ticketing & Event Management Services
S.I.C.: 7999
N.A.I.C.S.: 711310

Marek Lieberberg Konzertagentur Holding GmbH (1)
Morikestr 14
DE 60320 Frankfurt am Main, Hessen, Germany
Tel.: (49) 699562020
Fax: (49) 69568199
E-Mail: info@mlk.com
Web Site: www.mlk.com
Emp.: 18
Ticketing & Event Management Services
S.I.C.: 8748
N.A.I.C.S.: 541618
Marek Lieberberg *(Gen Mgr)*

Palazzo Produktionen Berlin GmbH (1)
Grosse Elbstrasse 277-279
22767 Hamburg, Germany
Tel.: (49) 40 853 88 730
Fax: (49) 40 853 88 747
E-Mail: service@palazzo.org
Web Site: www.palazzo.org
Emp.: 25
Dining & Entertainment Services
S.I.C.: 7922
N.A.I.C.S.: 711110
Oliver Jauk *(Mng Dir)*

Palazzo Produktionen GmbH (1)
Grosse Elbstrasse 277-279
22767 Hamburg, Germany
Tel.: (49) 4085388730
Fax: (49) 4085388747
E-Mail: service@palazzo.org
Web Site: www.palazzo.org
Emp.: 50
Dining & Entertainment Services
S.I.C.: 7922
N.A.I.C.S.: 711110
Oliver Jauk *(Mng Dir)*

Peter Rieger Konzertagentur GmbH & Co. KG (1)
Sulzburgstrasse 13
Cologne, 50937, Germany
Tel.: (49) 2219420020
Fax: (49) 22194200220
E-Mail: info@prknet.de
Web Site: www.prknet.de
Entertainment Agency Services
S.I.C.: 4729
N.A.I.C.S.: 561599

Peter Rieger Konzertagentur Holding GmbH (1)
Sulzburgstr 13
North Rhine-Westphalia, 50937 Cologne, Germany
Tel.: (49) 2219420020
Fax: (49) 2219420022
E-Mail: info@prknet.de
Web Site: www.prknet.de
Emp.: 10
Entertainment Agency Services
S.I.C.: 4729
N.A.I.C.S.: 561599
Klaus Matziol *(Mgr)*

Peter Rieger Verwaltungs GmbH (1)
Sulzburgstrasse 13
50937 Cologne, Nordrhein-Westfalen, Germany
Tel.: (49) 2219420020
Fax: (49) 2219420022
E-Mail: info@prknet.de
Web Site: www.prknet.de
Emp.: 15
Entertainment Agency Services
S.I.C.: 4729
N.A.I.C.S.: 561599
Peter Rieger *(CEO)*

PGM Promotors Group Munich Konzertagentur GmbH (1)
Ganghoferstrasse 68a
80339 Munich, Germany
Tel.: (49) 897907800
Fax: (49) 8979078019
E-Mail: info@promoters-group-munich.de
Web Site: www.promoters-group-munich.de
Emp.: 4
Concert Promoter Services
S.I.C.: 7999
N.A.I.C.S.: 711310
Peter Pracht *(Mgr)*

tour-house Veranstaltungs-, Konzert-, TV- und Media-Consulting GmbH (1)
Semmel Concert Hohepleichen 11
20354 Hamburg, Germany
Tel.: (49) 4075118580
Fax: (49) 403807887697
E-Mail: info@tour-house.de
Web Site: www.tour-house.de
Emp.: 5
Ticketing & Entertainment Event Management Services
S.I.C.: 4729
N.A.I.C.S.: 561599
Thomas Tiedemann *(CEO)*

Non-U.S. Subsidiaries:

Act Entertainment AG (1)
Paulusgasse 16
PO Box 4
4011 Basel, Switzerland
Tel.: (41) 612269000
Fax: (41) 612269001
E-Mail: act@actentertainment.ch
Web Site: www.topact.ch
Emp.: 25
Concert Organising Services
S.I.C.: 7999
N.A.I.C.S.: 711310
Thomas Durr *(CEO)*

CTS Eventim Nederland B.V. (1)
PO Box 69507
1060 Amsterdam, Netherlands
Tel.: (31) 206167895
Fax: (31) 206167863
E-Mail: info@eventim.nl
Web Site: www.eventim.nl
Emp.: 25
Ticketing & Entertainment Event Management Services
S.I.C.: 4729
N.A.I.C.S.: 561599
Martin van Moorsel *(Mng Dir)*

CTS Eventim Schweden AB (1)
Arenavagen 41
Stockholm, 12128, Sweden
Tel.: (46) 855668980
Fax: (46) 85568989
Web Site: www.eventim.se
Emp.: 9
Ticketing & Event Management Services
S.I.C.: 8748
N.A.I.C.S.: 541618
Lars Aadde *(CEO)*

Eventim BG o.o.d. (1)
10 Nikola Vaptzapov Blvd
1407 Sofia, Bulgaria
Tel.: (359) 29615370
Fax: (359) 28160927
E-Mail: info@eventim.bg
Web Site: www.eventim.bg
Emp.: 3
Ticketing & Entertainment Event Management Services
S.I.C.: 4729
N.A.I.C.S.: 561599
Mirohlav Enanoilov *(Mgr)*

Eventim d.o.o. (1)
Kupinecka 4
10020 Zagreb, Croatia
Tel.: (385) 16552860
Fax: (385) 16552861
E-Mail: info@eventim.hr
Web Site: www.eventim.hr
Emp.: 4
Ticketing & Entertainment Event Management Services
S.I.C.: 4729
N.A.I.C.S.: 561599
Damir Zigic *(Mng Dir)*

Eventim ru S.R.L. (1)
Polona St No 15
010502 Bucharest, Romania
Tel.: (40) 212501008
Fax: (40) 212501073
E-Mail: contact@eventim.ro
Web Site: www.eventim.ro
Emp.: 25
Ticketing & Event Management Services
S.I.C.: 4729
N.A.I.C.S.: 561599

Eventim SK, s.r.o. (1)
29 Augusta 5
81108 Bratislava, Slovakia
Tel.: (421) 252632425
E-Mail: office@eventim.sk
Web Site: www.eventim.sk
Emp.: 6
Ticketing & Entertainment Event Management Services
S.I.C.: 4729
N.A.I.C.S.: 561599
Ivica Stajkovic *(Gen Mgr)*

OTS Gesellschaft zum Vertrieb elektronischer Eintrittskarten mbH (1)
Brandstrasse 16
8510 Stainz, Styria, Austria
Tel.: (43) 34633323
Fax: (43) 346369580
E-Mail: claudia.sallene@oeticket.com
Web Site: www.oeticket.com
Emp.: 2
Ticketing & Event Management Services
S.I.C.: 4729
N.A.I.C.S.: 561599
Claudia Sallene *(Mgr-Styria)*

Palazzo Producties B.V. (1)
ArenA Blvd 61-75 1101 DL A'dam
Amsterdam, Zuidoost, Netherlands
Tel.: (31) 204353010
Fax: (31) 204353011
E-Mail: info@palazzo.nl
Web Site: www.palazzo.nl
Emp.: 6
Dining & Entertainment Services
S.I.C.: 5812
N.A.I.C.S.: 711110
Michaela Topf *(Mng Dir)*

Show-Factory Entertainment GmbH (1)
Mehrerauerstrabe 3
6900 Bregenz, Austria
Tel.: (43) 557454750
Fax: (43) 55745475015
E-Mail: office@showfactory.at
Web Site: www.showfactory.at
Emp.: 25
Family Entertainment Services
S.I.C.: 7389
N.A.I.C.S.: 711410
Walter Egle *(Mng Dir)*

Ticket Express Hungary Kft. (1)
Andrassy ut 18
H-1061 Budapest, Hungary
Tel.: (36) 303030999
E-Mail: info@tex.hu
Web Site: www.eventim.hu
Ticketing & Entertainment Event Management Services
S.I.C.: 7389
N.A.I.C.S.: 561499
Gyula Kovacska *(Gen Mgr)*

Non-U.S. Joint Venture:

Ticketcorner Holding AG (1)
Riedmatt Center
8153 Rumlang, Switzerland CH
Tel.: (41) 900 800 800
Fax: (41) 44 818 31 10
E-Mail: info@ticketcorner.ch
Web Site: www.ticketcorner.ch
Sales Range: $25-49.9 Million
Emp.: 130
International & Local Ticket & Event Retailer
S.I.C.: 7999
N.A.I.C.S.: 711310
Andreas Angehrn *(CEO)*

CTS INTERNATIONAL LOGISTICS CORPORATION LIMITED

20th Floor Tian An Center No 338
Nanjing Xi Road
Shanghai, 200003, China
Tel.: (86) 21 63580088
Fax: (86) 21 63588801
E-Mail: ird@ctsfreight.com
Web Site: www.ctsfreight.com
Year Founded: 1984
603128—(SHG)
Emp.: 2,033

Business Description:
Logistics Services
S.I.C.: 4731
N.A.I.C.S.: 541614

Personnel:
Fengchun Zhang *(Chm)*
Xuqing Zhou *(Pres)*
Shikuan Lin *(CFO)*
Zhenming Guo *(Exec VP)*

Board of Directors:
Fengchun Zhang
Zhenming Guo
Xiangyun Meng
Yuedong Miao
Jinxin Qiu
Jiaao Wang
Xiaoguang Wang
Denghui Zhang
Xuqing Zhou

CTS SPEDITION GMBH

Industriestrasse 34
Bremen, 28199, Germany
Tel.: (49) 421437 72 87 0
Fax: (49) 421437 72 87 20
E-Mail: info@cts-bremen.de
Web Site: www.cts-bremen.de/
Emp.: 160

Business Description:
Trucking Services
S.I.C.: 4213
N.A.I.C.S.: 484230

Personnel:
Dan Lipson *(Partner)*
Corey Whisner *(Partner)*
Bob Wickham *(Partner)*
Friedrich Jarren *(Mng Dir)*
Wolfgang Weber *(Mng Dir)*

CTS Spedition GmbH—(Continued)

Subsidiary:

EKB Container Logistik GmbH & Co. KG (1)
Industriestrasse 34
28199 Bremen, Germany
Tel.: (49) 42152360
Fax: (49) 4215236159
E-Mail: info@ekb-containerlogistik.com
Web Site: www.ekb-containerlogistik.com
Sales Range: $100-124.9 Million
Emp.: 400
Transportation Services
S.I.C.: 4789
N.A.I.C.S.: 488490
Frank Dreeke *(Mng Dir)*
Hans-Jurgen Sandmann *(Mng Dir)*
Holger Schulz *(Mng Dir)*
Wolfgang Weber *(Mng Dir)*

CTT - CORREIOS DE PORTUGAL SA

Avenida de Joao II
1999-001 Lisbon, Portugal
Tel.: (351) 210 471 857
Fax: (351) 210 471 996
Web Site: www.ctt.pt
CTT—(EUR)
Sls.: $941,419,758
Earnings: $48,417,696
Fiscal Year-end: 12/31/12

Business Description:
Postal Services
S.I.C.: 4311
N.A.I.C.S.: 491110
Personnel:
Francisco Jose Queiroz de Barros de Lacerda *(Chm & CEO)*
Andre Gorjao Costa *(CFO)*

CTT SYSTEMS AB

Box 1042
611 29 Nykoping, Sweden
Tel.: (46) 155205900
Fax: (46) 155205925
E-Mail: ctt@ctt.se
Web Site: www.ctt.se
CTT—(OMX)
Sales Range: $1-9.9 Million
Emp.: 51

Business Description:
Aircraft Humidity Control Systems Mfr
S.I.C.: 3728
N.A.I.C.S.: 336413
Personnel:
Karl-Axel Granlund *(Chm)*
Torbjorn Johansson *(Pres)*
Board of Directors:
Karl-Axel Granlund
Anders Helmner
Lars Lindgren
Johan Lundsgard
Bjorn Ronnqvist

Subsidiary:

Broderna Ingemar och Bo Mekaniska AB (1)
Diabasvagen 1
Nybro, 39222, Sweden
Tel.: (46) 48148280
Fax: (46) 48113865
Web Site: www.bribo.se
Emp.: 9
Machine Tools Mfr
S.I.C.: 3545
N.A.I.C.S.: 333515
Tony Rosendahl *(Mgr)*

CU MEDICAL SYSTEMS INC.

5F Cheonggye Plaza 991-4
Cheonggye-gu, Uiwang, Gyeonggi-do, Korea (South)
Tel.: (82) 31 4219700
Fax: (82) 31 4219911
E-Mail: admin@cu911.com
Web Site: www.cu911.com
Year Founded: 2001
115480—(KRS)
Emp.: 120

Business Description:
Emergency Medical Device Mfr & Sales
S.I.C.: 3841
N.A.I.C.S.: 339112
Personnel:
Harock Na *(CEO)*

CUB ELECPARTS INC.

6 Lane 546 Sec 6 Chang Lu Rd
Fuhsin Hsiang
Changhua, Taipei, Taiwan
Tel.: (886) 47782010
Fax: (886) 47782009
E-Mail: sales@cubelec.com.tw
Web Site: www.cubelec.com.tw
2231—(TAI)
Sales Range: $25-49.9 Million

Business Description:
Electric Automotive Parts Mfr
S.I.C.: 3714
N.A.I.C.S.: 336320
Personnel:
San-Chuan Yu *(Chm)*

Non-U.S. Plant:

Cub Elecparts Inc. - Shanghai Facility (1)
No 51 Jinwen Road Zhuqiao udong New Area
Pudong New Area, Shanghai, 201323, China
Tel.: (86) 2133756999
Fax: (86) 2133756100
Web Site: www.cubelec.com.tw/shanghaisite.php
Automobile Electronic Parts Mfr
S.I.C.: 3711
N.A.I.C.S.: 336111

CUB ENERGY INC.

36 Toronto Street Suite 1000
Toronto, ON, M5C 2C5, Canada
Tel.: (713) 677-0439
Fax: (713) 677-0181
Toll Free: (888) 335-1415
Web Site: www.cubenergyinc.com
KUB—(DEU TSXV)
Rev.: $1,666,000
Assets: $79,266,000
Liabilities: $7,197,000
Net Worth: $72,069,000
Earnings: $2,290,000
Fiscal Year-end: 12/31/12

Business Description:
Oil & Gas Exploration Services
S.I.C.: 1311
N.A.I.C.S.: 211111
Personnel:
Mikhail Afendikov *(Chm & CEO)*
Patrick McGrath *(CFO)*
Cliff West *(COO & Exec VP)*
Rebecca Gottsegen *(Chief Compliance Officer, Gen Counsel & Sec)*
Board of Directors:
Mikhail Afendikov
Gregory M. Cameron
Robert Bruce Hodgins
J. Frank Mermoud
Steve Vansickle
Transfer Agent:
Equity Financial Trust Company
Toronto, ON, Canada

CUBE SYSTEM INC.

Shirakiji Building 1-2-33 Higashi Gotanda
Shinagawa-ku, Tokyo, 141-0022, Japan
Tel.: (81) 3 5447 3350
Web Site: www.cubesystem.co.jp
Year Founded: 1972
2335—(TKS)
Sales Range: $100-124.9 Million
Emp.: 576

Business Description:
Information Technology Services
S.I.C.: 7373
N.A.I.C.S.: 541512
Personnel:
Osamu Sakiyama *(Pres)*
Toshikuni Sato *(Exec Mng Dir)*
Masaki Tochizawa *(Exec Mng Dir)*
Kenkichi Kumagai *(Corp Officer)*
Shin Nakamura *(Corp Officer)*
Hideaki Nishimura *(Corp Officer)*
Minoru Odaka *(Corp Officer)*
Masaaki Saito *(Corp Officer)*
Nobuyoshi Yonemoto *(Corp Officer)*
Board of Directors:
Kenichiro Iida
Kazuki Nakura
Osamu Sakiyama
Toshikuni Sato
Masaki Tochizawa
Toshio Uchida
Kazuhiro Yamaoka

CUBEX TUBINGS LIMITED

1-7-27 to 34 II Floor Shyam Towers
United Building Complex S D Road
Secunderabad, 500 003, India
Tel.: (91) 4027817440
Fax: (91) 4027812569
E-Mail: info@cubextubing.com
Web Site: www.cubextubings.com
CUBEXTUB—(NSE)
Sales Range: $10-24.9 Million

Business Description:
Copper Alloys Products Mfr
S.I.C.: 3351
N.A.I.C.S.: 331420
Personnel:
Pushparaj Bhandari *(Mng Dir)*
Board of Directors:
Pushparaj Bhandari
U. M. Bhandari
Mukun Chand Devada
Balakrishna Karande
K. Venkat Ramani
Mohammed Rajab Syed Ali
Transfer Agent:
Aarthi Consultants Private Limited
1-2-285, Domalguda
Hyderabad, India

CUBIC KOREA INC.

1070-7 Singil Dong
Danwon Gu, Ansan, Kyonggi DO, Korea (South)
Tel.: (82) 31 491 5325
Fax: (82) 31 491 5327
E-Mail: admin@cubic.co.kr
Web Site: www.cubic.co.kr
Year Founded: 1989
021650—(KRS)

Business Description:
Cubic Printing Services
S.I.C.: 2759
N.A.I.C.S.: 323111
Personnel:
Wu Taek Oh *(CEO)*

CUBICAL FINANCIAL SERVICES LIMITED

456 Aggarwal Metro Heights Netaji Subhash Place Pitam Pura
Delhi, 110034, India
Tel.: (91) 11 27351705
E-Mail: cubfinser@yahoo.com
Web Site: www.cubicalrealtors.com
Year Founded: 1990
511710—(BOM)
Sales Range: Less than $1 Million
Emp.: 4

Business Description:
Investment Management Services
S.I.C.: 6211
N.A.I.C.S.: 523999
Personnel:
Ashwani Kr Gupta *(Mng Dir)*
Board of Directors:
Ashish Bhala
Ankur Gupta
Ashwani Kr Gupta
N. S. R. Prasad Raju

CUBO COMMUNICATIONS GROUP PLC

Holden House 57 Rathbone Place
London, W1T 1JU, United Kingdom
Tel.: (44) 20 7637 4198
Fax: (44) 20 7580 2649
Web Site: www.cubogroupplc.com
Rev.: $12,302,669
Assets: $9,360,452
Liabilities: $2,615,304
Net Worth: $6,745,148
Earnings: $773,852
Emp.: 49
Fiscal Year-end: 12/31/12

Business Description:
Marketing Services
S.I.C.: 8742
N.A.I.C.S.: 541613
Personnel:
Kerry Simpson *(CEO)*
Ian Mansel-Thomas *(CFO & Sec)*
Board of Directors:
Andrew Harris
Ian Mansel-Thomas
Kerry Simpson
Legal Counsel:
Lewis Silkin LLP
5 Chancery Lane Cliffords Inn
London, United Kingdom

Subsidiaries:

Cubo Brand Communications Limited (1)
Holden House 57 Rethbone Pl
London, W1T 1JU, United Kingdom
Tel.: (44) 2076121111
E-Mail: hello@cubo.com
Web Site: www.cubo.com
Emp.: 50
Communication Agency
S.I.C.: 4899
N.A.I.C.S.: 517919
Toby Hartwell *(Mng Dir)*

The Media Foundry International Limited (1)
Holden House 57 Rathbone Pl
London, W1T 1JU, United Kingdom
Tel.: (44) 2076121155
Fax: (44) 2076121112
E-Mail: info@themediafoundry.com
Web Site: www.themediafoundry.com
Emp.: 10
Public Relations Consulting Services
S.I.C.: 8743
N.A.I.C.S.: 541820
Neil Foster *(Mng Dir)*

CUBUS LUX PLC

66 Wigmore Street
London, W1 U2SB, United Kingdom
Tel.: (44) 1992149636
Web Site: www.cubuslux.com
CBX—(LSE)
Sales Range: $1-9.9 Million
Emp.: 65

Business Description:
Hotels
S.I.C.: 7011
N.A.I.C.S.: 721110
Personnel:
Christian Kaiser *(CEO)*
Steve McCann *(CFO)*
Board of Directors:
Christian Kaiser
Steve McCann

Non-U.S. Subsidiaries:

Cubus Lux d.o.o (1)
Verudela 17
Pula, Istria, 52100, Croatia
Tel.: (385) 52 380350
Fax: (385) 52 590731
E-Mail: cubus-lux@pu.t-com.hr
Web Site: www.lasvegas.hr
Emp.: 30
Casino Operators
S.I.C.: 7999
N.A.I.C.S.: 713210

Duboko Plavetnilo Ugljan Projektant d.o.o. (1)
Obala kneza Trpimira 33
Zadar, 23000, Croatia
Tel.: (385) 23335811
Fax: (385) 23335828
E-Mail: info@deepbluecroatia.com
Emp.: 1
Real Estate & Development Services
S.I.C.: 6531
N.A.I.C.S.: 531390
Milan Kotur *(Gen Mgr)*

Plava Vala d.o.o (1)
Sutomiscica
Island of Ugljan, Sutomisica, 23273, Croatia
Tel.: (385) 23335809
Fax: (385) 23335810
E-Mail: info@oliveislandmarina.com
Web Site: www.oliveislandmarina.com
Recreational Boating Services
S.I.C.: 4493
N.A.I.C.S.: 713930

CUDECO LTD.

Unit 34 Brickworks Annex 19 Brolga Avenue
Southport, QLD, 4215, Australia
Tel.: (61) 7 55 031955
Fax: (61) 75 50 30288
E-Mail: kaldig@qldnet.com.au
Web Site: www.cudeco.com.au
CDU—(ASX)
Rev.: $3,748,053
Assets: $343,104,005
Liabilities: $7,339,843
Net Worth: $335,764,163
Earnings: ($4,161,302)
Fiscal Year-end: 06/30/13

Business Description:
Copper Exploration
Import
S.I.C.: 3351
N.A.I.C.S.: 331420

Personnel:
Wayne Michael McCrae *(Chm & CEO)*
Bruno Bamonte *(Sec)*

Board of Directors:
Wayne Michael McCrae
Peter Robert Hutchison
Vitie Paul Keran
Gerald Adrian Lambert
Hongwei Liu
Zhijun Ma
David John Edward Taylor
Zhaohui Wu

CUE ENERGY RESOURCES LIMITED

Level 21 114 William Street
Melbourne, VIC, 3000, Australia
Tel.: (61) 396708668
Fax: (61) 396708661
E-Mail: mail@cuenrg.com.au
Web Site: www.cuenrg.com.au
CUE—(ASX OTC)
Rev.: $51,894,496
Assets: $183,656,578
Liabilities: $46,548,523
Net Worth: $137,108,055
Earnings: $6,637,135
Emp.: 11
Fiscal Year-end: 06/30/13

Business Description:
Oil & Gas Exploration
S.I.C.: 1389
N.A.I.C.S.: 213112

Personnel:
David A. J. Biggs *(CEO)*
Andrew M. Knox *(CFO & Co-Sec)*
Pauline M. Moffatt *(Co-Sec)*

Board of Directors:
Geoffrey John King
Paul Derek Moore
Andrew Alexander Young

Legal Counsel:
Bell Gully
171 Featherston Street
PO Box 1291
Wellington, New Zealand

Allens Arthur Robinson
Level 33 530 Collins Street
Melbourne, Australia

Computershare Investor Services Pty Limited
Level 2 Deloitte Tower Douglas Street
PO Box 1141
National Capital District, Port Moresby, Papua New Guinea

Subsidiaries:

Cue Energy Indonesia Pty. Ltd. (1)
Level 21 114 Williams St
Melbourne, Victoria, 3000, Australia
Tel.: (61) 396708668
Fax: (61) 396708661
E-Mail: mail@cuenrg.com.au
Oil & Gas Exploration Services
S.I.C.: 1389
N.A.I.C.S.: 213112

Cue Exploration Pty. Ltd. (1)
Level 21 144 William St
Melbourne, Victoria, 3000, Australia
Tel.: (61) 396708668
Fax: (61) 396708661
E-Mail: mail@cuenrg.com.au
Emp.: 10
Exploration Services
S.I.C.: 1081
N.A.I.C.S.: 213114
Pauline M. Moffatt *(Office Mgr)*

CUERVO RESOURCES INC.

247 Major Street
Toronto, ON, M5S 2L5, Canada
Tel.: (416) 203-3957
Fax: (416) 203-4197
Toll Free: (877) -266-2579
E-Mail: investors@cuervoresources.com
Web Site: www.cuervoresources.com
Year Founded: 2005
FE—(CNSX)
Int. Income: $12,542
Assets: $693,054
Liabilities: $1,244,553
Net Worth: ($551,499)
Earnings: ($4,788,268)
Fiscal Year-end: 03/31/13

Business Description:
Iron Ore Mining & Exploration Services
S.I.C.: 1011
N.A.I.C.S.: 212210

Personnel:
Gordon D. Watts *(Chm)*
Brian Berner *(CEO)*
Timothy M. Nigh *(CFO)*
Velasquez Spring *(COO)*

Board of Directors:
Gordon D. Watts
Brian Berner
Brian M. Cloney
John Gruetzner
William Johnson
Velasquez Spring

Transfer Agent:
Equity Financial Trust Company
200 University Avenue Suite 400
Toronto, ON, M5H 4H1, Canada
Tel.: (416) 361-0152
Fax: (416) 361-0470
Toll Free: (866) 393-4891

Non-U.S. Subsidiary:

Minera Cuervo S.A.C. (1)
Av Jose Galvez Barrenechea No 592 Int 603 Urb Corpac
San Isidro, Lima, Peru
Tel.: (51) 12232119
Fax: (51) 12232115
Emp.: 15
Iron Mining Services
S.I.C.: 1011
N.A.I.C.S.: 212210
John Siriunas *(Pres)*

CUESTA COAL LIMITED

Suite 15.01 Level 15 31 Market St
Sydney, NSW, 2000, Australia
Tel.: (61) 2 9284 5900
Fax: (61) 2 9284 5999
E-Mail: info@cuestacoal.com.au
Web Site: www.cuestacoal.com.au
Year Founded: 2011
CQC—(ASX)

Business Description:
Coal Exploration
S.I.C.: 1222
N.A.I.C.S.: 212112

Personnel:
Matthew Crawford *(Mng Dir)*
Keith McKnight *(COO)*
Megan McPherson *(Sec)*

Board of Directors:
Brian Johnson
Matthew Crawford
Patrick Elliott
Hanping Liu
Keith McKnight
Brice Mutton
Yong Xiao

CUKIERMAN & CO. INVESTMENT HOUSE LTD.

3 Daniel Frish Street
Tel Aviv, 64731, Israel
Tel.: (972) 36950666
Fax: (972) 36950222
E-Mail: info@cukierman.co.il
Web Site: www.cukierman.co.il
Year Founded: 1993

Business Description:
Holding Company; Investment Banking, Real Estate & Private Equity Services
S.I.C.: 6719
N.A.I.C.S.: 551112

Personnel:
Edouard Cukierman *(Chm)*
Guy Ravid *(CEO)*
Peleg Hadar *(Mng Partner & Head-Telecom/IT)*
Alon Michal *(CFO & Partner)*
Eyal Hadas *(Mng Dir & Head-Renewable Energy)*

Board of Directors:
Edouard Cukierman
Roger Cukierman
Luc Muller
Guy Ravid
Dani Weintraub

Subsidiaries:

Catalyst Investments, L.P. (1)
3 Daniel Frish St Fl 11
Tel Aviv, 64731, Israel
Tel.: (972) 36950666
Fax: (972) 36950222
E-Mail: info@catalystfund.co.in
Web Site: www.catalyst-fund.com
Emp.: 50
Private Equity Firm
S.I.C.: 6211
N.A.I.C.S.: 523999
Edouard Cukierman *(Founder, Mng Partner & CEO)*
Yair Shamir *(Founding Partner)*
Vladimir Bernstein *(Mng Partner-CIII)*
Alain Dobkin *(Mng Partner)*
Boaz Harel *(Sr Partner)*
Dorothee Moshevich *(Partner)*
Elena Rogovina *(Partner-Catalyst Russia)*
Amir Sharabi *(CFO)*

Holding:

Onset Technology Inc. (2)
2 Maskit Bldg D 3rd Fl
Herzliya Pituach, 46733, Israel DE
Tel.: (972) 99561615
Fax: (972) 99561610
Web Site: www.onsettechnology.com
Sales Range: $1-9.9 Million
Emp.: 45
Mobile Technologies Software Developer
S.I.C.: 7372
N.A.I.C.S.: 511210
Avi Legmann *(CEO)*
Judit Sharon *(CFO)*

U.S. Holding:

harmon.ie Corporation (2)
1521 California Cir
Milpitas, CA 95035 DE
Tel.: (408) 907-1339
Fax: (408) 351-4984
Toll Free: (800) 624-6946
Web Site: www.harmon.ie
Sales Range: $25-49.9 Million
Interoperable Computer Software Developer, Publisher & Whslr
S.I.C.: 7372
N.A.I.C.S.: 511210
Yaacov Cohen *(Co-Founder, Pres & CEO)*
Roy Sheinfeld *(Co-Founder & VP-R&D)*
Zvika Pakula *(COO)*

Branch:

harmon.ie Corp. - Boston Office (3)
31 Milk St Ste 717
Boston, MA 02109
Toll Free: (800) 624-6946
Web Site: www.harmon.ie
Emp.: 25
Interoperable Computer Software Whslr
S.I.C.: 5045
N.A.I.C.S.: 423430
Tim Bridge *(VP-Sls-Americas)*

Non-U.S. Branch:

harmon.ie Corp. - Israel Office (3)
18 Abba Hillel Silver
North Industrial Area, Lod, 71294, Israel
Tel.: (972) 8 978 1300
Web Site: www.harmon.ie
Interoperable Computer Software Developer, Publisher & Whslr
S.I.C.: 7372
N.A.I.C.S.: 511210
Roy Sheinfeld *(Co-Founder & VP-R&D)*

Cukierman & Co. Life Sciences (1)
3 Daniel Frish St
Tel Aviv, 64731, Israel
Tel.: (972) 36950666
Fax: (972) 36950222
Web Site: www.cukierman.co.il
Emp.: 15
Life Sciences Industry Corporate Intermediation
S.I.C.: 6799
N.A.I.C.S.: 523910
Laurent Choppe *(Mng Partner-Switzerland Office)*
Alexandra Vallon-Eberhard *(Partner & Head-Bus Solution)*

Cukierman & Co. Real Estate Ltd. (1)
3 Daniel Frish St
Tel Aviv, 64731, Israel II
Tel.: (972) 36950666
Fax: (972) 36950222
E-Mail: info@cukierman.co.il
Web Site: www.cukierman.co.il
Emp.: 15
Real Estate Investment Trust
S.I.C.: 6726
N.A.I.C.S.: 525990
Laurent-Darius Salimpour *(Founder)*

Non-U.S. Subsidiary:

Cukierman & Co. S.A. (1)
56 Rue Lafayette
F-75009 Paris, France FR

Cukierman & Co. Investment House Ltd.—(Continued)

Tel.: (33) 147700184
Investment Banking, Real Estate & Private Equity Investment Services
S.I.C.: 6211
N.A.I.C.S.: 523110
Annabelle Cukierman *(CEO)*

CUKUROVA HOLDING A.S.

Buyukdere Caddesi
Yapi Kredi Plaza A Blok K 15, 34330
Istanbul, Turkey
Tel.: (90) 2123701200
Fax: (90) 2123701268
E-Mail: info@cukurovaholding.com.tr
Web Site: www.cukurovaholding.com.tr

Business Description:
Holding Company
S.I.C.: 6719
N.A.I.C.S.: 551112

Personnel:
A. Samsa Karamehmet *(Vice Chm)*

Board of Directors:
H. Yasemin Cetinalp
M. Bulent Ergin
F. Sadi Gucum
A. Samsa Karamehmet
Oner Toker
A. Tugrul Tokgoz

Joint Ventures:

Noksel A.S. **(1)**
Cetin Emec Bulvari 1065 Cad No 10
Ovecler, 06460 Ankara, Turkey
Tel.: (90) 312 472 59 59
Telex: 46408 yins tr
Fax: (90) 312 472 59 60
E-Mail: noksel@noksel.com.tr
Web Site: www.noksel.com.tr
Emp.: 670
Spiral Welded Steel Pipes Mfr
S.I.C.: 3317
N.A.I.C.S.: 331210

Non-U.S. Subsidiary:

Noksel Espana S.A. **(2)**
Complejo Empresarial IMCE Edificio B
Calle Enrique Granados 6 Planta 2
Pozuelo de Alarcon, 28224 Madrid, Spain ES
Tel.: (34) 91 535 17 90
Fax: (34) 91 534 69 42
E-Mail: nokselspain@nokselspain.com
Web Site: www.nokselspain.com
Spiral Welded Steel Pipes Mfr
S.I.C.: 3317
N.A.I.C.S.: 331210

Turkcell Holding AS **(1)**
Turkcell Plaza Mesrutiyet Caddesi 153
Tepebasi, 80050 Istanbul, Turkey
Tel.: (90) 2123131000
Fax: (90) 2123130099
Web Site: www.turkcell.com.tr
Emp.: 50
Holding Company; Communications; Owned by Cukurova Holding A.S. & by TeliaSonera AB
S.I.C.: 4812
N.A.I.C.S.: 517210
Colin J. Williams *(Chm)*
Sureyya Ciliv *(CEO)*
Cenk Bayrakdar *(CIO)*
Lale Saral Develioglu *(CMO)*
Tayfun Cataltepe *(Chief Corp Strategy & Regulations Officer)*
Selen Kocabas *(Chief Bus Support Officer)*
Koray Ozturkler *(Chief Corp Affairs Officer)*
Emre Sayin *(Chief Consumer Sls Officer)*
Ilter Terzioglu *(Chief Network Ops Officer)*
Ekrem Yener *(Chief Corp Bus Officer)*

Subsidiary:

Turkcell Iletisim Hizmetleri A.S. **(2)**
Turkcell Plaza Mesrutiyet Caddesi No 71
Tepebasi, 34430 Istanbul, Turkey TR
Tel.: (90) 2123131000
Fax: (90) 2123130099
E-Mail: corporatecommunications@turkcell.com.tr
Web Site: www.turkcell.com.tr
TKC—(IST NYSE)
Rev.: $5,865,787,000
Assets: $10,483,236,000
Liabilities: $3,323,092,000
Net Worth: $7,160,144,000
Earnings: $1,147,129,000
Emp.: 13,414
Fiscal Year-end: 12/31/12
Communication Services
S.I.C.: 4813
N.A.I.C.S.: 517110
Sureyya Ciliv *(CEO)*
Hulusi Acar *(Chief Consumer Sls Officer)*
Lale Saral Develioglu *(Chief Intl Bus Officer)*
Selen Kocabas *(Chief Corp Bus Unit Officer)*
Ilker Kuruoz *(Chief Info & Comm Technologies Officer)*
Koray Ozturkler *(Chief Corp Affairs Officer)*
Butrak Sevilengul *(Chief Consumer Mktg Officer)*
Ekrem Yener *(Cheif Intl Expansion Officer)*

CULINARY DESTINATIONS LIMITED

35 Jutland Road
Toronto, ON, Canada M8Z 2G6
Tel.: (416) 201-0707
Fax: (416) 201-3014
E-Mail: info@culinarydestinations.com
Web Site: www.culinarydestinations.com
Year Founded: 1997
Rev.: $17,194,390
Emp.: 60

Business Description:
Food Products Mfr
S.I.C.: 5145
N.A.I.C.S.: 424450

Personnel:
Keith Chen *(Pres)*

CULLEN RESOURCES LIMITED

U4/7 Hardy Street
South Perth, WA, 6151, Australia
Tel.: (61) 894745511
Fax: (61) 894745588
E-Mail: cullen@cullenresources.com.au
Web Site: www.cullenresources.com
CUL—(ASX)
Rev.: $51,801
Assets: $6,429,255
Liabilities: $248,838
Net Worth: $6,180,417
Earnings: ($2,166,074)
Emp.: 3
Fiscal Year-end: 06/30/13

Business Description:
Support Activities for Nonmetallic Minerals
Export
S.I.C.: 1499
N.A.I.C.S.: 212399

Personnel:
Chris Ringrose *(Mng Dir)*
Wayne John Kernaghan *(Sec)*

Board of Directors:
Denis Edmund Clarke
Grahame Hamilton
John Robert Horsburgh
Wayne John Kernaghan
Chris Ringrose

Legal Counsel:
McKenzie Moncrieff Lawyers
Level 5 Citibank House 37 St Georges Terrace
Perth, Australia

Subsidiary:

Cullen Exploration Pty Ltd **(1)**
Northern Territory
Saint Leonards, WA, 2065, Australia
Tel.: (61) 894096951
Fax: (61) 893099335
Mineral Exploration Services
S.I.C.: 1481
N.A.I.C.S.: 213115

CULLITON BROTHERS LIMITED

473 Douro St
PO Box 850
Stratford, ON, N5A 6W3, Canada
Tel.: (519) 271-1981
Fax: (519) 273-4885
Web Site: www.cullitonbrothers.com
Year Founded: 1932
Rev.: $23,475,137
Emp.: 120

Business Description:
Multi Trade Contractor Services
S.I.C.: 7629
N.A.I.C.S.: 811219

Personnel:
Tim Culliton *(Pres)*
Ted Lange *(Sr VP)*

CULTURE CONVENIENCE CLUB CO. LTD.

Yebisu Garden Place Tower 21st Floor 4-20-3 Ebisu
Tokyo, Shibuya-ku, 150-6021, Japan
Tel.: (81) 354241600
Fax: (81) 354241701
E-Mail: investor@ccc.co.jp
Web Site: www.ccc.co.jp
Year Founded: 1983
Sales Range: $1-4.9 Billion
Emp.: 2,259

Business Description:
DVDs, CDs, Books, Magazines & Video Games Retailer; E-Commerce; Marketing Services
S.I.C.: 5999
N.A.I.C.S.: 453998

Personnel:
Muneaki Masuda *(Pres & CEO)*
Shinichi Kasuya *(Chief Strategy Officer)*

Board of Directors:
Jhoichi Itou
Masahiko Kamata
Shinichi Kasuya
Kazuhiko Kitamura
Muneaki Masuda
Rie Nakamura
Hideo Shimizu

Transfer Agent:
Mizuho Trust & Banking Co., Ltd.
2-1 Yaesu 1-Chome Chuo-ku
Tokyo, 103 8670, Japan
Tel.: (81) 332788111
Fax: (81) 332816947

Subsidiaries:

Culture Publishers Inc **(1)**
16th Floor Yebisu Garden Place Tower
4-20-3 Ebisu Shibuya-ku, 150-6021 Tokyo, Japan
Tel.: (81) 354756910
Fax: (81) 354756912
Web Site: www.culture-pub.jp
Emp.: 3,000
Music Publishers
S.I.C.: 2741
N.A.I.C.S.: 512230
I. Yoshimu *(Mng Dir)*

Esquire Magazine Japan, Inc. **(1)**
4th Floor SI Bldg
1-3-6 Kita-Aoyama Minato-ku, 107-0061
Tokyo, Japan
Tel.: (81) 357755690
Fax: (81) 357755695
Web Site: www.esquire.co.jp
Emp.: 45
Publishers
S.I.C.: 2741
N.A.I.C.S.: 511199

T Card & Marketing Co., Ltd. **(1)**
24th Floor Yebisu Garden Place Tower
4-20-3 Ebisu Shibuya-ku, 150-6023 Tokyo, Japan
Tel.: (81) 354242361
Fax: (81) 354242362
Web Site: www.tcard.jp
Credit Card Issuing
S.I.C.: 6153
N.A.I.C.S.: 522210
Tsutomu Matsumoto *(Gen Mgr)*

Tsutaya Online Co., Ltd. **(1)**
26th Floor Yebisu Garden Place Tower
4-20-3 Ebisu Shibuya-ku, 150-6021 Tokyo, Japan
Tel.: (81) 354241674
Fax: (81) 354242476
Web Site: www.tsutaya.co.jp/index.html
Emp.: 3,000
Electronic Shopping & Mail-Order Houses
S.I.C.: 5961
N.A.I.C.S.: 454111
Hiroshi Yamaji *(Pres)*

Tsutaya Stores Holdings Co., Ltd **(1)**
7th Floor Shionogi Shibuya Bldg
2-17-5 Shibuya Shibuya-ku, 150-0002
Tokyo, Japan
Tel.: (81) 354594281
Fax: (81) 354594289
Web Site: www.ccc.co.jp/eng/company/profile/connection_group
Prerecorded Compact Disc Tape & Record Reproducing
S.I.C.: 3652
N.A.I.C.S.: 334614
Motoaki Kimura *(CEO)*

CULTURECOM HOLDINGS LTD

Suite 1102 11 Floor Chinachem Tower 34-37
Connaught Road, Hong Kong, China (Hong Kong)
Tel.: (852) 29508888
Fax: (852) 29508838
E-Mail: info@culturecom.com.hk
Web Site: www.culturecom.com.hk
0343—(HKG)
Rev.: $3,457,536
Assets: $75,657,157
Liabilities: $7,616,432
Net Worth: $68,040,725
Earnings: ($38,426,584)
Emp.: 145
Fiscal Year-end: 03/31/13

Business Description:
Printing & Publishing Industry
S.I.C.: 2721
N.A.I.C.S.: 511120

Personnel:
Livia Lai Wah Chow Lee *(Vice Chm)*
Ronnie Cheung *(Pres & CFO)*
Huaguo Yu *(CEO)*
Jennie Wing Shuen Mak Lau *(Deputy CEO)*
Kin Chung Kwan *(Mng Dir)*
Man Lung Chen *(COO)*
U Fai Tang *(CTO)*
Hung Lien Shen *(CEO-Chu Bong Foo Labs)*
Francis Kwok Keung Shiu *(CEO-Culturecom Investments Limited)*
William Kam Biu Tam *(Sec)*

Board of Directors:
Bong Foo Chu
Man Lung Chen
Joseph Lee Chennault
Billy Chung
Kin Chung Kwan
Qiang Lai
Livia Lai Wah Chow Lee
Ying Ng
Kenneth Kwing Chuen Tang
U Fai Tang
Wilfred Wai Wa Tsang
Xiaolin Wan

Butterfield Fulcrum Group (Bermuda) Limited
26 Burnaby Street
Hamilton, HM 11, Bermuda

Subsidiaries:

Citicomics Limited (1)
Rm 610c 12-13 6 F Cyberport 3 100 Cyberport Rd
Pok Fu Lam, China (Hong Kong)
Tel.: (852) 29508888
Fax: (852) 23452500
E-Mail: info@culturecom.com.hk
Emp.: 50
Book Publishing Services
S.I.C.: 2721
N.A.I.C.S.: 511120
Cheung Wai Tung *(Mng Dir)*

Culturecom Centre Limited (1)
Rm 610c 612-613 Level 6 Core D 100 Cyberport Rd
Hong Kong, China (Hong Kong)
Tel.: (852) 29508888
Fax: (852) 29508838
Property Holding Services
S.I.C.: 6531
N.A.I.C.S.: 531312
Chung Billy *(Mgr)*

CULVER HOLDINGS PLC

Llanmaes Saint Fagans
Cardiff, CF5 6DU, United Kingdom
Tel.: (44) 2920675204
Fax: (44) 2920565706
E-Mail: info@culverholdings.com
Web Site: www.culverholdings.com
Sales Range: $350-399.9 Million
Emp.: 30

Business Description:
Insurance, Risk Assessment & Business Services
S.I.C.: 6331
N.A.I.C.S.: 524126

Personnel:
Richard M.H. Read *(Chm)*
Adrian Biles *(Mng Dir)*

Board of Directors:
Richard M.H. Read
Adrian Biles

Subsidiary:

Culver Financial Management Limited (1)
Llanmaes St Fagans
Cardiff, S Glamorgan, CF56DU, United Kingdom (100%)
Tel.: (44) 8705365999
Insurance Services
S.I.C.: 6411
N.A.I.C.S.: 524298

CUMBERLAND BUILDING SOCIETY

Cumberland House Cooper Way
Parkhouse, Carlisle, Cumbria, CA3 0JF, United Kingdom
Tel.: (44) 8456018396
Fax: (44) 1228 525309
E-Mail: customerservice@cumberland.co.uk
Web Site: www.cumberland.co.uk
Rev.: $73,740,209
Assets: $2,453,174,329
Liabilities: $130,809,432
Net Worth: $2,322,364,896
Earnings: $9,731,585
Emp.: 274
Fiscal Year-end: 03/31/13

Business Description:
Mortgage Lending
S.I.C.: 6163
N.A.I.C.S.: 522310

Personnel:
Kevin Parr *(CEO)*
John Leveson *(Deputy CEO)*
John Kidd *(Sec & Dir-Fin)*

Board of Directors:
Michael J. Pratt
Richard Atkinson
David Clarke
Gill Gardner
Trevor Hebdon
Alan Johnston
John Kidd
John Leveson
Kevin Parr
Peter Temple

CUORO RESOURCES CORP.

1305-1090 W Georgia St
Vancouver, BC, V6E 3V7, Canada
Tel.: (604) 315-1237
Fax: (604) 683-1585
E-Mail: info@cuororesources.com
Web Site: www.cuororesources.com
Year Founded: 2007
CUA—(OTC TSXV)
Int. Income: $135,315
Assets: $18,907,874
Liabilities: $413,255
Net Worth: $18,494,619
Earnings: ($3,587,491)
Emp.: 4
Fiscal Year-end: 11/30/12

Business Description:
Copper & Gold Mining Services
S.I.C.: 1021
N.A.I.C.S.: 212234

Personnel:
Marc Cernovitch *(Pres & CEO)*
Nick DeMare *(CFO)*

Board of Directors:
Joseph Belan
Marc Cernovitch
Nick DeMare
Dave Doherty
John Seaman

Transfer Agent:
Valiant Trust Company
600-750 Cambie St
Vancouver, BC, Canada

Non-U.S. Subsidiary:

Minera Cuoro S.A.S. (1)
Cl 7 S 42-70 Int 22
Antioquia, Colombia
Tel.: (57) 4 3131787
Emp.: 12
Mineral Mining Services
S.I.C.: 1499
N.A.I.C.S.: 212399
Pablo Orsolani *(Gen Mgr)*

CUP INTERACTIVE SAS

(Formerly CBS Interactive SAS)
122 rue Edouard Vaillant
92300 Levallois-Perret, France
Tel.: (33) 1 4639 5500
Fax: (33) 1 4639 0208
Web Site: www.cbsinteractive.fr
Sales Range: $10-24.9 Million

Business Description:
Online Media Publisher
S.I.C.: 2741
N.A.I.C.S.: 519130

Personnel:
Emmanuel Parody *(Partner & Gen Mgr-BtoB)*
Matthieu Urruty *(Partner & Gen Mgr-BtoC)*
Jean-Philippe Caste *(Dir Gen)*

CUPID LTD.

103 Sona Chambers 507/509 J S S Road
Mumbai, 400 002, India
Tel.: (91) 22 22037633
Fax: (91) 22 22073416
Web Site: www.cupidltd.com
Year Founded: 1993
530843—(BOM)
Sales Range: $1-9.9 Million

Business Description:
Personal Care Products Mfr
S.I.C.: 5999
N.A.I.C.S.: 446199

Personnel:
Om Prakash Garg *(Chm & Mng Dir)*
Pawan Bansal *(Compliance Officer)*

Board of Directors:
Om Prakash Garg
Pawan Bansal

Transfer Agent:
Bigshare Services Pvt. Ltd.
E-2/3 Ansa Industrial Estate Sakivihar Road
Saki Naka Andheri E
Mumbai, India

CURA TECHNOLOGIES LTD.

12 Software Units Layout Cyberabad
Hyderabad, 500 081, India
Tel.: (91) 40 23111793
Fax: (91) 40 23100385
E-Mail: cura@curatechnologies.co.in
Web Site: www.curatechnologies.co.in
Year Founded: 1994
532332—(BOM)
Rev.: $7,748,181
Assets: $36,715,086
Liabilities: $27,126,594
Net Worth: $9,588,492
Earnings: $22,364
Fiscal Year-end: 03/31/13

Business Description:
Software Development Services
S.I.C.: 7371
N.A.I.C.S.: 541511

Personnel:
G. Bala Reddy *(Chm & Mng Dir)*
J. Ramachandran *(CEO)*
K. S. Ananth Narayanan *(CFO)*
Jyothi Bung *(Compliance Officer & Sec)*

Board of Directors:
G. Bala Reddy
Velangini Mary Gopu
Lalitha Gudimetla
Venkateswara Rao Gudipudi
Venkata Reddy Nalabolu
Avula Venkata Narayana Reddy
Shyam Sunder Reddy Vangala

Transfer Agent:
Venture Capital & Corporate Investments Private Limited
12-10-167 Bharat Nagar
500018 Hyderabad, India

Non-U.S. Subsidiaries:

CURA Risk Management Software (PTY) Limited (1)
Level 10 390 St Kilda Road
Melbourne, VIC, 3004, Australia
Tel.: (61) 3 9948 0020
Fax: (61) 3 9948 0017
E-Mail: info@curasoftware.com.au
Web Site: www.curasoftware.com
Software Development Services
S.I.C.: 7371
N.A.I.C.S.: 541511

Non-U.S. Subsidiary:

CURA Software Solutions UK Limited (2)
Suite 125 Berkeley Square House
London, W1J 6BD, United Kingdom
Tel.: (44) 20 7887 1584
Software Development Services
S.I.C.: 7371
N.A.I.C.S.: 541511

CURA Risk Management Software (PTY) Limited (1)
13 Scott Street Waverly
Johannesburg, 2090, South Africa
Mailing Address:
PO Box 771
Melrose Arch, 2072 Johannesburg, South Africa
Tel.: (27) 11 321 7500
Fax: (27) 86 649 3760
E-Mail: support@curasoftware.com
Web Site: www.curasoftware.com
Emp.: 200
Management Software Publisher
S.I.C.: 7372
N.A.I.C.S.: 511210

CURANUM AG

Engelbertstrasse 23-25
81241 Munich, Bavaria, Germany
Tel.: (49) 892420650
Fax: (49) 8924206510
E-Mail: info@curanum.de
Web Site: www.curanum.de
BHS—(DEU)
Rev.: $388,736,203
Assets: $353,369,625
Liabilities: $278,118,722
Net Worth: $75,250,903
Earnings: $5,622,952
Emp.: 6,919
Fiscal Year-end: 12/31/12

Business Description:
Nursing Care Services
S.I.C.: 8051
N.A.I.C.S.: 623110

Personnel:
Uwe Ganzer *(Chm-Supervisory Bd)*
Walther Wever *(Chm-Mgmt Bd & CEO)*
Dieter Thomae *(Deputy Chm-Supervisory Bd)*
Judith Barth *(CFO & Member-Mgmt Bd)*

Supervisory Board of Directors:
Uwe Ganzer
Martin Hoyos
Norbert Klusen
Peter Oberender
Dieter Thomae
Michael B. Treichl

Subsidiaries:

Alten-und Pflegeheim Sieglar GmbH (1)
Rathausstrasse 1
53844 Troisdorf, Germany
Tel.: (49) 22414940
Fax: (49) 2241494105
E-Mail: sieglar@curanum.de
Nursing Home Services
S.I.C.: 8051
N.A.I.C.S.: 623110

Altenheimbetriebsgesellschaft Sud GmbH (1)
Hirschhalde 1
78073 Bad Durrheim, Baden-Wurttemberg, Germany
Tel.: (49) 772666080
Fax: (49) 77261820
E-Mail: hirschhalde@curanum.de
Nursing Home Services
S.I.C.: 8051
N.A.I.C.S.: 623110

Altenheimbetriebsgesellschaft West GmbH (1)
Westuffler Weg 9
59457 Werl, Germany
Tel.: (49) 292280400
Fax: (49) 29224993
E-Mail: amadeus@curanum.de
Emp.: 70
Nursing Home Services
S.I.C.: 8051
N.A.I.C.S.: 623110
Sabine Weirich *(Mng Dir)*

CURANUM Bad Hersfeld GmbH (1)
Gotzbertstrasse 92
36251 Bad Hersfeld, Germany
Tel.: (49) 66211820
Fax: (49) 662176495
E-Mail: badhersfeld@curanum.de
Nursing Home Services
S.I.C.: 8051
N.A.I.C.S.: 623110

CURANUM Seniorenpflegezentrum Am Spessart (1)
Ludwig-Straub-Str 10
63856 Bessenbach, Bavaria, Germany
Tel.: (49) 6095 998 0
Fax: (49) 6095 998 199
E-Mail: bessenbach@curanum.de

Curanum AG—(Continued)

Web Site: www.curanum-seniorenpflegezentrum-bessenbach.de/kontakt.html
Senior Residential Home Care Services
S.I.C.: 8051
N.A.I.C.S.: 623110
Markus Thumm *(Mgr-Facility Mgmt)*

CURANUM Franziskushaus GmbH (1)
Hagenstrasse 16-18
45894 Gelsenkirchen, Nordrhein-Westfalen, Germany
Tel.: (49) 2099331440
Fax: (49) 20993314433
E-Mail: franziskushaus@curanum.de
Senior Residential Home Care Services
S.I.C.: 8051
N.A.I.C.S.: 623110

CURANUM Holding GmbH (1)
Engelbertstraase 23-25
81241 Munich, Bavaria, Germany
Tel.: (49) 892420650
Fax: (49) 89820859011
E-Mail: info@curanum.de
Emp.: 5,000
Management Services
S.I.C.: 8741
N.A.I.C.S.: 551114
Walter Wever *(CEO)*

CURANUM Westfalen GmbH (1)
Am Ochsenkamp 60
58332 Schwelm, Nordrhein-Westfalen, Germany
Tel.: (49) 2336929100
Fax: (49) 2336929180
E-Mail: Curanum@curanum.de
Web Site: www.Curanum.com
Senior Citizens Nursing Home Services
S.I.C.: 8051
N.A.I.C.S.: 623110

ELISA Seniorenstift GmbH (1)
Maximilianstr 35c
80539 Munich, Bavaria, Germany
Tel.: (49) 892420650
Fax: (49) 8924206510
E-Mail: info@elisa-seniorenstifte.de
Web Site: www.elisa-seniorenstifte.de
Emp.: 5,000
Senior Citizens Residential Homes
S.I.C.: 8361
N.A.I.C.S.: 623312
Bernd Rothe *(Mng Dir)*
Judith Barth *(CFO)*
Sabine Merazzi-Weirich *(COO)*

Subsidiary:

Elisa Seniorenstift Aschaffenburg GmbH (2)
Goldbacher Strasse 13
63739 Aschaffenburg, Bavaria, Germany
Tel.: (49) 60213840
Fax: (49) 6021384100
E-Mail: aschaffenburg@elisa-seniorenstifte.de
Web Site: www.elisa-seniorenstift-aschaffenburg.de
Adult Home Care Services
S.I.C.: 8361
N.A.I.C.S.: 623312
Barbara Ilchmann *(Gen Dir)*

GAP Media Service GmbH (1)
Engelbertstrasse 23-25
81241 Munich, Germany
Tel.: (49) 892420650
Fax: (49) 8924206510
E-Mail: info@curanum.de
Web Site: www.guranum.de
Senior Residential Home Care Services
S.I.C.: 8051
N.A.I.C.S.: 623110

Krankenheim Ruhesitz am Wannsee-Seniorenheimstatt GmbH (1)
Am Sandwerder 43
14109 Berlin, Germany
Tel.: (49) 30 8 04 74 91 0
Fax: (49) 30 8 04 74 91 30
E-Mail: sandwerder@curanum.de
Senior Residential Home Care Services
S.I.C.: 8051
N.A.I.C.S.: 623110

Residenz Lobberich GmbH (1)
Burgstrasse 9
Lobberich, 41334 Nettetal, Nordrhein-Westfalen, Germany
Tel.: (49) 215395730
Fax: (49) 21539573111
E-Mail: lobberich@curanum.de
Emp.: 60
Nursing Homes Management Services
S.I.C.: 8051
N.A.I.C.S.: 623110
Peter Jansen *(Mng Dir)*

Seniorenzentrum Hennef GmbH (1)
Kurhausstrasse 45
53773 Hennef, Germany
Tel.: (49) 22429300
Fax: (49) 2242930999
E-Mail: hennef@curanum.de
Senior Residential Home Care Services
S.I.C.: 8051
N.A.I.C.S.: 623110

Wascherei Ellerich GmbH (1)
Wilhelm-Conrad-Rontgen-Str 1
56759 Kaisersesch, Rhineland-Palatinate, Germany
Tel.: (49) 265398980
Fax: (49) 2653989820
E-Mail: info@waescherei-ellerich.de
Web Site: www.waescherei-ellerich.de
Emp.: 140
Laundry & Dry Cleaning Services
S.I.C.: 7219
N.A.I.C.S.: 812320
Monica Hesse *(Gen Mgr)*

Non-U.S. Subsidiary:

CB Seniorenresidenz Armbrustergasse GmbH (1)
Armbrustergasse 6-8
1190 Vienna, Austria
Tel.: (43) 1379050
Fax: (43) 137905111
E-Mail: info@bonifatius.at
Web Site: www.bonifatius.at
Senior Citizen Homes Operation Services
S.I.C.: 8361
N.A.I.C.S.: 623312

CURASAN AG

Lindigstrasse 4
63801 Kleinostheim, Germany
Tel.: (49) 60 27 40 900 0
Fax: (49) 60 27 40 900 29
E-Mail: info@curasan.de
Web Site: www.curasan.de
CUR—(DEU)
Rev.: $4,342,744
Assets: $12,400,918
Liabilities: $2,464,837
Net Worth: $9,936,081
Earnings: ($4,675,248)
Emp.: 30
Fiscal Year-end: 12/31/12

Business Description:
Regenerative Medicinal Products Mfr
S.I.C.: 2834
N.A.I.C.S.: 325412

Personnel:
Hans Dieter Rossler *(CEO)*

CURCAS OIL N.V.

Haaksbergweg 71
1101 BR Amsterdam, Netherlands
Tel.: (31) 203121212
Fax: (31) 203121210
E-Mail: info@curcas-oil.com
Web Site: www.curcas-oil.com
CCZ—(DEU)

Business Description:
Alternative Energy Services
S.I.C.: 1389
N.A.I.C.S.: 213112

Personnel:
Kurt Stuessi *(Mng Dir)*

Board of Directors:
Katharina Pernilla Dolk
Kurt Stuessi

Non-U.S. Subsidiary:

P.T. Pengembangan Jarak Indonesia (1)
One Pacific Pl 15th Fl Sudirman Central Business District
JL Jend Sudirman Kav 52 53, Jakarta, 12190, Indonesia
Tel.: (62) 2125502473
Fax: (62) 2125502555
E-Mail: info@algae-farming.com
Web Site: www.algae-farming.com
Agricultural Services
S.I.C.: 0181
N.A.I.C.S.: 111422

CURIS RESOURCES LTD.

15th Floor 1040 West Georgia Street
Vancouver, BC, V6E 4H1, Canada
Tel.: (604) 484-6365
Fax: (604) 684-8092
Toll Free: (800) 667-2114
E-Mail: info@curisresources.com
Web Site: www.curisresources.com
Year Founded: 2008
CUV—(TSX)
Rev.: $35,094
Assets: $37,803,553
Liabilities: $25,906,581
Net Worth: $11,896,972
Earnings: ($17,492,998)
Emp.: 12
Fiscal Year-end: 03/31/13

Business Description:
Mineral Exploration & Development Services
S.I.C.: 1499
N.A.I.C.S.: 212399

Personnel:
David Copeland *(Co-Chm)*
Russell Hallbauer *(Co-Chm)*
Michael R. J. McPhie *(Pres & CEO)*
Brian Causey *(CFO)*
Rita P. Maguire *(Gen Counsel & Exec VP)*
Trevor Thomas *(Sec)*

Board of Directors:
Russell Hallbauer
Rene Carrier
David Copeland
Gordon Fretwell
James Douglas Kerr
Michael R. J. McPhie
Robert Schafer

Legal Counsel:
McMillan LLP
1500 1055 West Georgia Street
V6E4N7 Vancouver, BC, Canada

Transfer Agent:
Computershare Investor Services Inc.
510 Burrard Street 2nd Floor
Vancouver, BC, V6C 3B9, Canada

CURLEW LAKE RESOURCES INC.

Suite 303 - 595 Howe Street
Vancouver, BC, Canada
Tel.: (604) 336-8613
Fax: (604) 718-2808
E-Mail: information@curlew-lake.com
Web Site: www.curlew-lake.com
Year Founded: 1987
CWQ—(OTC TSXV)
Assets: $703,810
Liabilities: $119,226
Net Worth: $584,584
Earnings: ($727,943)
Emp.: 2
Fiscal Year-end: 01/31/13

Business Description:
Oil & Gas Exploration & Development Services
S.I.C.: 1311
N.A.I.C.S.: 211111

Personnel:
Jurgen Wolf *(Interim Pres & CEO)*
Robert K. Kramer *(CFO & Sec)*

Board of Directors:
Robert K. Kramer
Harold Noyes
Huitt Tracey
Jurgen Wolf

Legal Counsel:
DuMoulin Black LLP
10th Floor 595 Howe St
Vancouver, BC, Canada

Transfer Agent:
Computershare Trust Company
100 University Avenue 9th Floor
Toronto, ON, Canada

CURO HOLDINGS CO., LTD.

Donwon B/D 4F Teheran-ro 77gil 7
Gangnam-gu, Seoul, 137-877, Korea (South)
Tel.: (82) 2 2141 3000
Fax: (82) 2 2141 3097
E-Mail: curoholdings@curoholdings.com
Web Site: www.curoholdings.com
Year Founded: 1985
051780—(KRS)

Business Description:
Semiconductor Device Mfr & Coffee Distr
S.I.C.: 3674
N.A.I.C.S.: 334413

Personnel:
In-chang Hwang *(CEO)*

Subsidiary:

Curocom Co., Ltd. (1)
Dongwon B/D 4F Teheran-ro 77-gil
Gangnam-gu, Seoul, Korea (South)
Tel.: (82) 2 2141 3000
Fax: (82) 2 2141 3097
E-Mail: curocom@curocom.com
Web Site: www.curocom.com
040350—(KRS)
Financial & Information Technology Services
S.I.C.: 6211
N.A.I.C.S.: 523999
Jung-gee Cho, *(CEO)*

CURRENT TECHNOLOGY CORPORATION

850 West Hastings Street Suite 302
Vancouver, BC, V6C 1E1, Canada
Tel.: (604) 684-2727
Fax: (604) 684-0526
Web Site: www.current-technology.com
CRTCF—(OTC)
Sales Range: Less than $1 Million
Emp.: 4

Business Description:
Applied Research Solutions
S.I.C.: 8999
N.A.I.C.S.: 541690

Personnel:
Robert K. Kramer *(Chm, Pres, CEO & Treas)*

Board of Directors:
Robert K. Kramer
Douglas Beder
Anthony Harrison

Transfer Agent:
Computershare Investor Services Inc.
510 Burrard St 2nd Floor
Vancouver, BC, V6C 3B9, Canada
Tel.: (604) 661-9400

CURRIE ROSE RESOURCES INC.

110-B Hannover Dr Suite 102
Saint Catharines, ON, L2W 1A4, Canada
Tel.: (905) 688-9115
Fax: (905) 688-5615
E-Mail: info@currierose.com
Web Site: www.currierose.com
CUI—(TSXV)
Int. Income: $2,258
Assets: $6,138,925
Liabilities: $73,858
Net Worth: $6,065,068
Earnings: ($859,198)

Emp.: 1
Fiscal Year-end: 12/31/12
Business Description:
Gold Exploration & Mining Services
S.I.C.: 1041
N.A.I.C.S.: 212221
Personnel:
Michael Griffiths *(Pres)*
Harold Smith *(CEO)*
Gael Northey *(CFO)*
Ken Embree *(Sec)*
Board of Directors:
Dwane Brosseau
Michael Griffiths
Shiv Madan
Harold Smith
Legal Counsel:
DuMoulin Black
10th Floor, 595 Howe Street
Vancouver, BC, V6C 2T5, Canada
Transfer Agent:
Valiant Trust Company
606 4th Street SW Suite 310
Calgary, AB, T2P 1T1, Canada
Tel.: (403) 233-2801
Fax: (403) 233-2857

CURRY GOLD CORP.
29 Farmington
Cheltenham, Gloucestershire, GL54 3ND, United Kingdom
Tel.: (44) 1451 860 563
Year Founded: 2009
CURG—(OTC OTCB)
Assets: $625
Liabilities: $33,713
Net Worth: ($33,088)
Earnings: ($50,532)
Fiscal Year-end: 11/30/12
Business Description:
Fast Food Restaurants
S.I.C.: 5812
N.A.I.C.S.: 722513
Personnel:
Daniel M. Ferris *(Pres, CEO, Treas & Sec)*
Steven M. Plumb *(CFO)*
Transfer Agent:
Empire Stock Transfer, Inc.
1859 Whitney Mesa Dr
Henderson, NV 89009

CURT BAUER GMBH
Bahnhofstrasse 16
08280 Aue, Germany
Tel.: (49) 37715000
Fax: (49) 3771500270
E-Mail: info@curt-bauer.de
Web Site: www.curt-bauer.de
Rev.: $18,968,026
Emp.: 123
Business Description:
Broadwoven Fabrics Mfr
S.I.C.: 2299
N.A.I.C.S.: 313210
Personnel:
Gert Bauer *(Co-Mng Dir)*
Michael Bauer *(Co-Mng Dir)*

CURT GEORGI GMBH & CO. KG
Otto-Lilienthal-Str 35-37
71034 Boblingen, Germany
Tel.: (49) 7031640101
Fax: (49) 7031640120
E-Mail: curtgeorgi@curtgeorgi.de
Web Site: www.curtgeorgi.de
Year Founded: 1875
Rev.: $10,544,046
Emp.: 50
Business Description:
Food Products Mfr
S.I.C.: 2099
N.A.I.C.S.: 311999
Personnel:
Andreas Landgraf *(Owner & Co-Mng Dir)*
Melanie Landgraf *(Co-Mng Dir)*

CURTIS INTERNATIONAL LTD.
315 Attwell Dr
Toronto, ON, M9W 5C1, Canada
Tel.: (416) 674-2123
Fax: (416) 674-2135
Toll Free: (800) 968-9853
E-Mail: info@curtisint.com
Web Site: www.curtisint.com
Sales Range: $25-49.9 Million
Emp.: 200
Business Description:
Consumer Electronic Products Mfr & Distr
S.I.C.: 5064
N.A.I.C.S.: 423620
Personnel:
Jacob Herzog *(Chm, CFO, Treas & Sec)*
Aaron Herzog *(Pres & CEO)*

CURTY MATERIELS SA
ZI 40 Rue Roger Salengro
69740 Genas, Rhone, France
Tel.: (33) 478905700
Fax: (33) 478406928
E-Mail: info@curty-materiels.com
Web Site: www.curty-materiels.com
Sls.: $23,500,000
Emp.: 22
Business Description:
Professional Equipment
S.I.C.: 5049
N.A.I.C.S.: 423490
Personnel:
Paerre Derectur *(Mng Dir)*

CUSCAL LTD.
1 Margaret Street
Sydney, NSW, 2000, Australia
Mailing Address:
GPO Box 4720
Sydney, NSW, 2001, Australia
Tel.: (61) 282999000
Fax: (61) 282999600
E-Mail: cilldiract@cuscal.com.au
Web Site: www.cuscal.com.au
Int. Income: $146,936,100
Assets: $3,317,421,140
Liabilities: $3,084,720,210
Net Worth: $232,700,930
Earnings: $9,066,270
Emp.: 284
Fiscal Year-end: 06/30/13
Business Description:
Wholesale & Transactional Banking Services
S.I.C.: 6029
N.A.I.C.S.: 522110
Personnel:
Craig N. Kennedy *(Mng Dir)*
Iain Keddie *(CFO & Gen Mgr-Fin)*
Brian J. Parker *(CIO & Gen Mgr-Tech Svcs)*
Louise Petschler *(CEO-Abacus-Australian Mutuals)*
Diane Osborne *(Gen Counsel & Sec)*
Board of Directors:
William J. Conn
Peter T. Evers
Mark S. Genovese
Craig N. Kennedy
Robert B. Miller
Anne L. Templeman-Jones
Chris M. Whitehead
Subsidiaries:

Credit Union Dispute Resolution Centre Pty Limited **(1)**
1 Margaret Street
2000 Sydney, NSW, Australia (100%)
Tel.: (61) 2 8299 9000
Fax: (61) 2 8299 9600
E-Mail: calldirect@cuscal.com.au
Web Site: www.cuscal.com.au
Trust Fiduciary, Credit Union & Custody Activities
S.I.C.: 6733
N.A.I.C.S.: 523991
Philip Shield *(Mgr-Banking & Fin)*

Credit Union Foundation Australia Pty Limited **(1)**
Level 1 No 1 Margireg St
10 Queen Rd, 3004 Sydney, Australia (100%)
Tel.: (61) 282999059
Fax: (61) 282999606
E-Mail: info@cufa.com.au
Web Site: www.cufa.com.au
Emp.: 25
Trust Fiduciary & Custody Activities
S.I.C.: 6099
N.A.I.C.S.: 523991
Peter Maison *(CEO)*

Cuscal Management Pty Limited **(1)**
1 Margaret St
Sydney, NSW, 2001, Australia
Tel.: (61) 282999000
Fax: (61) 282999610
E-Mail: info@cuscal.com.au
Web Site: www.cuscal.com.au
Trust Fiduciary & Custody Activities
S.I.C.: 6733
N.A.I.C.S.: 523991
Craig Kennedy *(CEO)*

Integris Securitisation Services Pty Limited **(1)**
1 Margaret St Level 1
Sydney, NSW, 2000, Australia
Tel.: (61) 282999000
Fax: (61) 282999600
Web Site: www.cuscal.com.au
Mortgage & Nonmortgage Loan Brokers
S.I.C.: 6163
N.A.I.C.S.: 522310
Craig N. Kennedy *(Mng Dir)*

CUSTOM ELECTRIC LTD.
1725 27th Avenue NE
Calgary, AB, T2E 7E1, Canada
Tel.: (403) 291-3303
Fax: (403) 291-4473
E-Mail: info@customelectric.com
Web Site: www.customelectric.com
Year Founded: 1970
Rev.: $27,058,737
Emp.: 150
Business Description:
Electrical Contractors
S.I.C.: 1731
N.A.I.C.S.: 238210
Personnel:
Stuart Hay *(Pres)*

CUSTOM PLASTICS INTERNATIONAL LTD.
887 D Arcy Street
Cobourg, ON, K9A 4B4, Canada
Tel.: (905) 372-2281
Fax: (905) 372-7378
E-Mail: sales@customplastics.ca
Web Site: www.customplastics.ca
Year Founded: 1965
Rev.: $13,277,500
Emp.: 90
Business Description:
Plastic Injection Molding Material Mfr
S.I.C.: 3559
N.A.I.C.S.: 333249
Personnel:
Richard B. Gadd *(VP-Sls)*

CUSTOM SOLUTIONS S.A.
Zone Industrial Parc Club 496
Avenue Francis Perrin
13790 Rousset, France
Tel.: (33) 486914200
E-Mail: contact@customsolutions.fr
Web Site: www.customsolutions.fr
ALSOL—(EUR)
Sales Range: $1-9.9 Million
Emp.: 60
Business Description:
Marketing Solutions
S.I.C.: 8742
N.A.I.C.S.: 541613
Personnel:
Cedric Reny *(CEO)*

CUTLER FOREST PRODUCTS INC.
1265 Aerowood Drive
Mississauga, ON, L4W 1B9, Canada
Tel.: (416) 622-7321
Fax: (905) 238-5512
Toll Free: (800) 268-2393
E-Mail: sales@cutlerforestproducts.com
Web Site: www.cutlerforestproducts.com
Year Founded: 2001
Rev.: $31,626,797
Emp.: 80
Business Description:
Wood Products Whslr
S.I.C.: 2499
N.A.I.C.S.: 321999
Personnel:
Richard Dreving *(VP)*

CUULONG FISH JOINT STOCK COMPANY
90 Hung Vuong street My Quy industrial zone
Long Xuyen, An Giang, Vietnam
Tel.: (84) 76 931000
Fax: (84) 76 932446
E-Mail: clfish@vnn.vn
Web Site: www.clfish.com
ACL—(HOSE)
Business Description:
Fish Farming Services
S.I.C.: 0921
N.A.I.C.S.: 112511
Personnel:
Thi Van Loan Tran *(Chm & Gen Dir)*
Nguyen Thi Hoang Yen *(Deputy CEO)*
Minh Nhut Tran *(Member-Mgmt Bd)*
Tuan Nam Tran *(Member-Mgmt Bd)*
Van Nhan Tran *(Member-Mgmt Bd)*

CVC CAPITAL PARTNERS GROUP SARL
20 Ave Monterey
L-2163 Luxembourg, Luxembourg
Tel.: (352) 26478368
Fax: (352) 26478367
Web Site: www.cvc.com
Year Founded: 1981
Sales Range: $75-99.9 Billion
Emp.: 270
Business Description:
Holding Company; Private Equity Investment Firms
S.I.C.: 6719
N.A.I.C.S.: 551112
Personnel:
Michael Smith *(Co-Founder & Chm)*
Iain Parham *(Co-Founder & Mng Partner)*
Steve Koltes *(Co-Founder & Mng Partner-German Speaking Countries)*
Fred Watt *(COO & Mng Partner)*
Jonathan Feuer *(Mng Partner & Grp Head-Global Fin Institutions)*
Donald Mackenzie *(Mng Partner & Grp Co-Head-Global Investments)*
Rolly van Rappard *(Mng Partner & Grp Co-Head-Global Investments)*
Bertrand Meunier *(Mng Partner)*

CVC Capital Partners Group Sarl—(Continued)

Mark Grizzelle *(Partner & Grp Dir-Fin)*
Kamil Salame *(Partner & Grp Head-Global Fin Institutions)*

Holding:

Flint Group SA **(1)**
26B Boulevard Royal
2449 Luxembourg, Luxembourg
E-Mail: info@flintgrp.com
Web Site: www.flintgrp.com
Rev.: $3,100,000,000
Emp.: 8,300
Holding Company
S.I.C.: 6719
N.A.I.C.S.: 551112
Charles Knott *(Chm)*
Antoine Fady *(CEO)*
Steve Dryden *(CFO)*

Corporate Headquarters:

Flint Group Germany GmbH **(2)**
Siegle Strasse 25
70469 Stuttgart, Germany DE
Mailing Address:
Postfach 30 02 49
70466 Stuttgart, Germany
Tel.: (49) 7119816230
Telex: 722651 kast d
Fax: (49) 7119816700
E-Mail: info@flintgrp.com
Web Site: www.flintgrp.com
Sales Range: $1-4.9 Billion
Emp.: 1,040
Printing Ink, Plate & Colorant Mfr
S.I.C.: 8741
N.A.I.C.S.: 551114
Howard Poulson *(Chm)*
Leonard D. Frescoln *(Deputy Chm)*
Michael J. Bissell *(CFO & Exec VP)*
Dirk Aulbert *(Pres-Ink-Europe)*

U.S. Subsidiaries:

Day International Group, Inc. **(3)**
130 W 2nd St
Dayton, OH 45402-1500
Mailing Address:
PO Box 338
Dayton, OH 45401-0338
Tel.: (937) 224-4000
Fax: (937) 226-1855
E-Mail: info@day-intl.com
Web Site: www.dayintl.com
Sales Range: $350-399.9 Million
Emp.: 1,465
Engineered Products Mfr for the Printing & Packaging Industries
S.I.C.: 2295
N.A.I.C.S.: 313320
Mike Neroni *(VP-Mktg & Natl Accts)*

Flint Group, Inc. **(3)**
14909 N Beck Rd
Plymouth, MI 48170-2411 MI
Tel.: (734) 781-4600
Fax: (734) 622-6131
E-Mail: info@flintgrp.com
Web Site: www.flintgrp.com
Sales Range: $1-4.9 Billion
Emp.: 150
Ink & Coating Mfr
Export
S.I.C.: 2893
N.A.I.C.S.: 325910
Russell Joyce *(Pres-Narrow Web)*
William B. Miller *(Pres-Americas)*
Thomas Telser *(Pres-Flexographic Products)*
Lawrence E. King *(Gen Counsel, Sec & VP)*

Subsidiary:

CDR Pigments & Dispersions **(4)**
305 Ring Rd
Elizabethtown, KY 42701-9318
Tel.: (270) 737-1700
Fax: (270) 737-0318
Web Site: www.cdrpigments.com
Organic Pigments & Pigment Dispersions Mfr
S.I.C.: 2816
N.A.I.C.S.: 325130
Craig Foster *(Pres)*

U.S. Branch:

CVC Capital Partners (U.S.), Inc. **(1)**
712 5th Ave 43rd Fl
New York, NY 10019 DE
Tel.: (212) 265-6222
Fax: (212) 265-6375
Web Site: www.cvc.com
Emp.: 20
Private Equity Firm
S.I.C.: 6211
N.A.I.C.S.: 523999
Christopher J. Stadler *(Mng Partner)*
Kamil Salame *(Partner & Head-FIG-US)*
Cameron Breitner *(Mng Dir)*
Gijs Vuursteen *(Mng Dir)*

Joint Venture:

Pilot Flying J **(2)**
5508 Lonas Dr
Knoxville, TN 37902
Tel.: (865) 588-7487
Toll Free: (800) 562-6210
Web Site: www.pilotflyingj.com
Sales Range: $1-4.9 Billion
Emp.: 25,000
Travel Centers & Gasoline Stations
S.I.C.: 5541
N.A.I.C.S.: 447110
Jimmy Haslam, II *(Founder)*
Mark Hazelwood *(Pres)*
James A. Haslam, III *(CEO)*
Mitchell D. Steenrod *(CFO, CIO & Sr VP)*
Ken Parent *(Exec VP)*

Subsidiary:

Maxum Petroleum, Inc. **(3)**
20 Horseneck Ln
Greenwich, CT 06830 DE
Tel.: (203) 861-1200
Fax: (203) 661-1865
E-Mail: info@maxumpetroleum.com
Web Site: www.maxumpetroleum.com
Refined Petroleum Products Marketer & Logistics Services
S.I.C.: 5172
N.A.I.C.S.: 424720
George Ristevski *(Pres & COO)*
E. Perot Bissell *(CEO)*
David W. Cummings *(Sr VP & CIO)*
Steven M. Cross *(Sr VP)*
Pat Graney *(Sr VP)*
John C. Vitale *(Sr VP-HR)*

Subsidiaries:

Canyon State Oil Company Inc. **(4)**
2640 N 31st Ave
Phoenix, AZ 85009
Mailing Address:
PO Box 18490
Phoenix, AZ 85005-8988
Tel.: (602) 269-7981
Fax: (602) 269-2936
Toll Free: (800) 894-3304
E-Mail: mgmt@canyonstateoil.com
Web Site: www.canyonstateoil.com
Sales Range: $25-49.9 Million
Emp.: 70
Petroleum Distr
S.I.C.: 5172
N.A.I.C.S.: 424720
Rod Burgett *(Gen Mgr)*

Paulson Oil Company Inc. **(4)**
950 Wabash Ave
Chesterton, IN 46304-2252 IN
Mailing Address:
PO Box 903
Chesterton, IN 46304-0903
Tel.: (219) 926-4379
Fax: (219) 926-9683
Toll Free: (800) 726-7626
E-Mail: info@pocooil.com
Web Site: www.pocooil.com
Emp.: 45
Fuels & Lubricants Distr
S.I.C.: 5172
N.A.I.C.S.: 424720
Peter E. Paulson *(Co-Owner & COO)*

Pecos Inc. **(4)**
19501 S Santa Fe
Rancho Dominguez, CA 90221 DE
Fax: (310) 356-2349
Toll Free: (800) 659-5823
Web Site: www.generalpetroleum.com
Emp.: 200
Petroleum Products Mfr
Import Export
S.I.C.: 5172
N.A.I.C.S.: 424720

Simons Petroleum Inc. **(4)**
210 Park Ave Ste 1800
Oklahoma City, OK 73102 OK
Tel.: (405) 848-3500
Fax: (405) 848-3508
Toll Free: (888) 574-6667
E-Mail: contactus@simonspetroleum.com
Web Site: www.simonspetroleum.com
Sales Range: $25-49.9 Million
Emp.: 200
Petroleum & Petroleum Products Distr
S.I.C.: 5172
N.A.I.C.S.: 424720
Brad Simons *(Pres)*
Roger N. Simons *(CEO)*

Non-U.S. Subsidiaries:

CVC Asia Pacific Ltd. **(1)**
Suite 901-3 ICBC Tower Citibank Plaza
3 Garden Road, Central, China (Hong Kong) HK
Tel.: (852) 35186360
Fax: (852) 35186380
Web Site: www.cvc.com
Emp.: 30
Private Equity Firm
S.I.C.: 6211
N.A.I.C.S.: 523999
Maarten Ruijs *(Chief Investment Officer & Mng Partner)*
Roy Kuan *(Mng Partner-Greater China, Southeast Asia & Korea)*
William Ho *(Partner-Beijing)*
Hans Wang *(Mng Dir)*

Non-U.S. Subsidiaries:

CVC Asia Pacific (Australia) Ltd. **(2)**
Level 45 Citigroup Centre 2 Park St
Sydney, NSW, 2000, Australia
Tel.: (61) 292609800
Fax: (61) 292609820
Web Site: www.cvc.com
Emp.: 4
Private Equity Firm
S.I.C.: 6211
N.A.I.C.S.: 523999
Andrew Cummins *(Chm)*
Adrian MacKenzie *(Mng Partner-Australia & New Zealand)*
Graham Brooke *(Mng Dir)*

Holding:

Stella Group Pty Ltd. **(3)**
77 Berry St Level 3
North Sydney, NSW, 2060, Australia AU
Tel.: (61) 282294000 (65%)
Fax: (61) 289200110
Web Site: www.jetsettravelworld.com.au
Sales Range: $75-99.9 Million
Emp.: 2,200
Travel Agency & Hotel Operator
S.I.C.: 4724
N.A.I.C.S.: 561510
Rob Gurney *(CEO)*

Subsidiaries:

Harvey World Travel Group Pty. Ltd. **(4)**
Level 3 225 Euston Road
Alexandria, NSW, 2015, Australia AU
Tel.: (61) 285655111
Fax: (61) 2 9550 5850
E-Mail: reception@harveyworld.com.au
Web Site: www.harveyworld.com.au
Sales Range: $1-4.9 Billion
Emp.: 1,584
Travel Agencies
S.I.C.: 4724
N.A.I.C.S.: 561510
Chris Scott *(CEO)*

Non-U.S. Subsidiary:

Harvey World Travel (UK) Ltd. **(5)**
Harvey House Lakeside Plaza
Walkmill Lane, Cannock, WS11 OXE, United Kingdom
Tel.: (44) 8712 080 525
Fax: (44) 1922 702 799
E-Mail: franchising@harveyworldtravel.co.uk
Web Site: www.harveyworldtravel.co.uk
Emp.: 25
Travel Agencies
S.I.C.: 4724
N.A.I.C.S.: 561510
John Donnelly *(Mng Dir)*

Stella Travel Services Australia **(4)**
Level 3 77 Berry Street
North Sydney, NSW, 2060, Australia
Tel.: (61) 282294000
Fax: (61) 289200110
Web Site: www.stellatravel.com
Travel Agency
S.I.C.: 4724
N.A.I.C.S.: 561510
Peter Lacaze *(CEO)*

Non-U.S. Subsidiary:

Stella Travel Services UK Limited **(4)**
Glendale House Glendale Business Pk
Glendale Ave Sandycroft, Deeside, CH5 2DL, United Kingdom
Tel.: (44) 8448262600
Fax: (44) 2075612424
E-Mail: enquiries@stellatravelservices.co.uk
Web Site: www.stellatravel.co.uk
Emp.: 300
Travel Services & Support Services for Travel Agencies
S.I.C.: 4724
N.A.I.C.S.: 561510
Andrew Botterill *(CEO)*

CVC Asia Pacific (Japan) Ltd. **(2)**
Kabushiki Kaisha Atago Green Hills MORI Tower 24F 2-5-1 Atago
Minato-ku, Tokyo, 105-6224, Japan
Tel.: (81) 354025300
Fax: (81) 354025301
E-Mail: smiyo@cvc.com
Web Site: www.cvc.com
Emp.: 8
Private Equity Firm
S.I.C.: 6211
N.A.I.C.S.: 523999
Kei Mizukami *(Sr Mng Dir)*
Norimitsu Niwa *(Mng Dir)*
Mamine Soeda *(Sr Exec Officer)*

Non-U.S. Holding:

Asia Timber Products Group **(2)**
9th Floor Shanghai Oriental Centre No 31 Wujiang Road
Jing'an District, Shanghai, 200041, China
Tel.: (86) 21 5200 1188
Fax: (86) 21 5200 1000
Web Site: www.atpgroup.com.cn
Sales Range: $200-249.9 Million
Emp.: 2,800
Lumber & Other Wood Materials Distr
S.I.C.: 5031
N.A.I.C.S.: 423310
Paul Weatherall *(CEO)*

CVC Capital Partners (Benelux) SA/NV **(1)**
Chaussee de la Hulpe 166
BE-1170 Brussels, Belgium
Tel.: (32) 26638090
Fax: (32) 26638099
Web Site: www.cvc.com
Emp.: 10
Private Equity Firm
S.I.C.: 6211
N.A.I.C.S.: 523999
Rolly van Rappard *(Mng Partner & Grp Head-Global Investments)*
Geert Duyck *(Mng Partner-Belgium & France)*
Jean-Remy Roussel *(Partner)*
Steven Buyse *(Mng Dir)*
Jan Reinier Voute *(Mng Dir)*

Holdings:

Betafence NV **(2)**
Deerlijkstraat 58A
8550 Zwevegem, Belgium
Tel.: (32) 56734500
Fax: (32) 56734599
E-Mail: info@betafence.com
Web Site: www.betafence.com
Emp.: 500
Fencing Mfr & Distr
S.I.C.: 3499
N.A.I.C.S.: 332999
Michele Volpi *(CEO)*

Non-U.S. Subsidiaries:

Betafence Deutschland GmbH (3)
Werk Rosler Draht
Postfach 67
41364 Schwalmtal, Germany
Tel.: (49) 21633390
Fax: (49) 2163339120
E-Mail: infogarden.germany@betafence.com
Web Site: www.betafence.com
Sls.: $69,195,112
Emp.: 181
Security Fence Mfr
S.I.C.: 3496
N.A.I.C.S.: 332618
Egon Vonken *(Mng Dir)*

Betafence France SA (3)
Rte Du Guindal 15
BP 20
F 59630 Bourbourg, France
Tel.: (33) 328658300
Fax: (33) 328223210
E-Mail: fencing.bourbourg@betafence.com
Web Site: www.betafence.com
Emp.: 160
Mfr of Security Fencing Systems
S.I.C.: 3496
N.A.I.C.S.: 332618
Koen Debaicker *(Gen Mgr)*

Betafence Sp Zoo (3)
Ul Debowa 4
47 246 Kotlarnia, Poland
Tel.: (48) 774062200
Telex: 39242 beko pl
Fax: (48) 774825000
E-Mail: info.poland@betafence.com
Web Site: www.betafence.com
Sales Range: $25-49.9 Million
Emp.: 180
Fabricated Wire Products
S.I.C.: 3496
N.A.I.C.S.: 332618

Betafence (3)
Shepcote Ln
PO Box 119
Sheffield, S9 1TY, United Kingdom
Tel.: (44) 1142561561
Fax: (44) 1142244550
Web Site: www.betafence.com
Sales Range: $150-199.9 Million
Emp.: 583
Wire & Steel Products
S.I.C.: 3496
N.A.I.C.S.: 332618
Andrea Davies *(Mgr-Fin Acct)*

Werler Drahtwerke GmbH & Co. KG (3)
Runtestrasse 5 9 and 24
D 59457 Werl, Germany
Tel.: (49) 29229890
Fax: (49) 2922989153
E-Mail: info@betafenns-germany.com
Web Site: www.betafenns.com
Sales Range: $50-74.9 Million
Emp.: 112
Building Materials & Products
S.I.C.: 3496
N.A.I.C.S.: 332618
Jurgen Schroyen *(Mgr-Ops)*

De Weide Blik N.V. (2)
Strijbroek 10
B-2860 Saint-Katelijne-Waver, Belgium BE
Tel.: (32) 15324200
Fax: (32) 15324201
E-Mail: info@univeg.com
Web Site: www.univeg.com
Sales Range: $1-4.9 Billion
Emp.: 600
Holding Company; Fruit & Vegetables, Flowers, Prepared Meals & Meal Components Distr
Import Export
S.I.C.: 6719
N.A.I.C.S.: 551112
Hein Deprez *(Founder & Chm)*
Francis Kint *(CEO)*
Koen Sticker *(CFO)*
Jean-Paul Van de Velde *(Sec)*

Division:

Univeg Fruit & Vegetables B.V. (3)
Strijbroek 10
2860 Saint-Katelijne-Waver, Belgium BE
Tel.: (32) 15324200 (100%)
Fax: (32) 15324201
E-Mail: info@univeg.com
Web Site: www.univeg.com
Emp.: 30
Fruit & Vegetables Distr
Import
S.I.C.: 5148
N.A.I.C.S.: 424480
Theo de Kool *(CFO)*

U.S. Subsidiary:

Seald Sweet LLC (4)
1991 74th Ave
Vero Beach, FL 32966-5110 DE
Mailing Address:
PO Box 690152
Vero Beach, FL 32969-0152
Tel.: (772) 569-2244
Fax: (772) 562-9038
E-Mail: info@sealdsweet.com
Web Site: www.sealdsweet.com
Emp.: 40
Citrus Products Marketer & Distr
Import Export
S.I.C.: 5148
N.A.I.C.S.: 424480
Mayda Sotomayor-Kirk *(CEO)*
William Kearney *(COO)*
David Mixon *(CMO)*

Non-U.S. Subsidiary:

Atlanta Aktiengesellschaft (4)
Breitenweg 29- 3
D 28195 Bremen, Germany De
Tel.: (49) 421 30 92 1
Fax: (49) 421 13617
Web Site: www.univeg.de
Fruit & Vegetables Distr
Import
S.I.C.: 5148
N.A.I.C.S.: 424480
Hein Deprez *(Chm)*

CVC Capital Partners (Deutschland) GmbH (1)
WestendDuo Bockenheimer Landstrasse 24
60323 Frankfurt am Main, Germany De
Tel.: (49) 699758350
Fax: (49) 6997583511
Web Site: www.cvc.com
Emp.: 10
Private Equity Firm
S.I.C.: 6211
N.A.I.C.S.: 523999
Steve Koltes *(Mng Partner)*
Marc Strobel *(Partner)*

CVC Capital Partners (Espana) SL (1)
Jose Ortega y Gasset 25 1
ES-28006 Madrid, Spain ES
Tel.: (34) 914364280
Fax: (34) 914364282
Web Site: www.cvc.com
Emp.: 9
Private Equity Firm
S.I.C.: 6211
N.A.I.C.S.: 523999
Javier de Jaime *(Mng Partner)*
Santiago Ramirez *(Partner-Indus)*
Inaki Cobo *(Mng Dir)*
Jose Antonio Torre de Silva *(Mng Dir)*

CVC Capital Partners (France) SA (1)
63 Ave Des Champselysee
75008 Paris, France FR
Tel.: (33) 145022300
Fax: (33) 145022301
Web Site: www.cvc.com
Emp.: 9
Private Equity Firm
S.I.C.: 6211
N.A.I.C.S.: 523999
Geert Duyck *(Mng Partner-Belgium & France)*
Domnin de Kerdaniel *(Sr Mng Dir)*

Holdings:

Delachaux SA (2)
119 ave Louis Roche
BP 152
92231 Gennevilliers, Cedex, France
Tel.: (33) 146881500
Fax: (33) 146881501
E-Mail: delachomgt@delachaux.fr
Web Site: www.delachaux.fr
Sales Range: $1-4.9 Billion
Emp.: 2,500
Industrial Machinery, Railroad, Electricity & Cast Iron Molded Steel Mfr
S.I.C.: 3559
N.A.I.C.S.: 333249
Francois Delachaux *(Chm)*
Jean-Pierre Colliaut *(Mng Dir)*

Subsidiaries:

ETS RAOUL LENOIR SAS (3)
ZI du Bearn
54400 Cosnes-et-Romain, Meurthe-et-Moselle, France
Tel.: (33) 382252300
Fax: (33) 3 82 24 59 19
E-Mail: raoullenoir@wanadoo.fr
Web Site: www.raoul-lenoir.com
Emp.: 100
Magnetic Separation & Lifting Equipments Mfr
S.I.C.: 3569
N.A.I.C.S.: 333999

Non-U.S. Subsidiaries:

MEC DELACHAUX S.R.L. (4)
Via Isorella 5
25010 Visano, Brescia, Italy
Tel.: (39) 030 9958561
Fax: (39) 030 9952321
E-Mail: info@mec-delachaux.it
Web Site: www.mec-delachaux.it
Emp.: 20
Magnetic Separation & Lifting Equipments Mfr
S.I.C.: 3569
N.A.I.C.S.: 333999

FONDERIES NICOLAS SAS (3)
5 Rue de la Haillette
08700 Nouzonville, Ardennes, France
Tel.: (33) 324538210
Fax: (33) 324531625
E-Mail: Fonderie.Nicolas@delachaux.fr
Web Site: www.delachaux.fr/Implantation.aspx?Zone=Annu&Company_Id=55
Emp.: 33
Foundry Machinery Distr
S.I.C.: 5084
N.A.I.C.S.: 423830
Ben Bournane *(Mng Dir)*

TAMARIS INDUSTRIES SAS (3)
212 rue de Pressense
30319 Ales, Gard, France
Tel.: (33) 4 66 54 27 00
Fax: (33) 4 66 54 27 19
E-Mail: tamaris@delachaux.fr
Web Site: www.delachaux.fr/Implantation.aspx?Zone=Europe&Company_Id=62&SessLang=en
Industrial Machinery Mfr
S.I.C.: 3559
N.A.I.C.S.: 333249
Remy Sauron *(Mgr)*

Holding:

Railtech International (3)
205 R De Sin Le Noble
BP 261
59504 Douai, France
Tel.: (33) 327996400
Fax: (33) 327999399
E-Mail: management@railtech.fr
Web Site: www.railtech.fr
Emp.: 100
Railroad & Other Heavy Manufacturing
S.I.C.: 3743
N.A.I.C.S.: 336510
Cocq Alexander *(Gen Mgr)*

Subsidiaries:

Railtech Alu Singen SAS (4)
119 Avenue Louis Roche
BP 152
92231 Gennevilliers, Hauts-de-Seine, France FR
Tel.: (33) 146881772
Fax: (33) 146881740
E-Mail: management@railtech.fr
Web Site: www.railtech.fr
Emp.: 5
Rail Joints & Fastenings Mfr
S.I.C.: 3399
N.A.I.C.S.: 331110
Jean-Pierre Colliaut *(Mng Dir)*

Railtech Schlatter Systems, S.A.S. (4)
119 Ave Louis Roche
PO Box 152
F 92231 Gennevilliers, Cedex, France
Tel.: (33) 146881730
Fax: (33) 146881740
E-Mail: management@railtech.fr
Web Site: www.railtech.fr
Emp.: 5
Railroad Systems; Joint Venture of Railtech International (51%) & Schaltter AG (49%)
S.I.C.: 3548
N.A.I.C.S.: 333992
Seewald Sabrace *(Mng Dir)*

U.S. Subsidiaries:

Railtech Boutet Inc. (4)
25 Interstate Dr
Napoleon, OH 43545
Tel.: (419) 592-5050
Fax: (419) 599-3630
E-Mail: info@railtechboutet.com
Web Site: www.railtechboutet.com
Railway Track Welding Supplies Mfr
S.I.C.: 3544
N.A.I.C.S.: 333514
Hans Dolder *(Pres)*
Oliver Dolder *(COO & Exec VP)*

RT CONTRACTING Corp. (4)
25 Interstate Dr
Napoleon, OH 43545
Tel.: (419) 592-5050
Fax: (419) 599-3630
E-Mail: info@railtechboutet.com
Rail Fastenings Mfr
S.I.C.: 3312
N.A.I.C.S.: 331110

Non-U.S. Subsidiaries:

Les Industries RAILWEL Inc. (4)
175 Rue JF Kennedy
Saint-Jerome, QC, J7Y 4B5, Canada
Tel.: (450) 565-9100
Fax: (450) 432-6985
E-Mail: contact@railwel.com
Emp.: 25
Railway Track Welding Product Mfr
S.I.C.: 3548
N.A.I.C.S.: 333992
Marie-Josee Lelievre *(Controller)*

Railtech Australia Ltd. (4)
52 Lysaght Street
Acacia Ridge, QLD, 4110, Australia AU
Tel.: (61) 733445444
Fax: (61) 733445377
E-Mail: sales@railtech.com.au
Web Site: www.railtech.com.au
Aluminothermic Rail Welding Materials Distr
S.I.C.: 5085
N.A.I.C.S.: 423840
Nathalie Gaveau *(Mgr-Fin & Admin)*

Railtech Calomex S. de R. L. de C. V. (4)
Marconi No 6 Fracc Industrial San Nicolas
Tlalnepantla, 54030, Mexico
Tel.: (52) 5553109371
Fax: (52) 5553109371
E-Mail: contacto@railtech.com.mx
Web Site: www.railtech.com.mx
Emp.: 30
Railway Track Components Mfr
S.I.C.: 3446
N.A.I.C.S.: 332323
Genaro De la Cruz *(Gen Mgr)*

Railtech Pandrol China Ltd. (4)
HanZhengJie Industrial Zone Building A122
21 Jiefang Avenue
Wuhan, Hubei, China
Tel.: (86) 2783499999
Fax: (86) 2783499990
E-Mail: info@railtech.com.cn
Emp.: 200
Rail Fastening Systems Mfr
S.I.C.: 3312
N.A.I.C.S.: 331110

Railtech-Pandrol Italia Srl (4)
Via Facii Zona Industriale le S Atto
64020 Teramo, Italy IT
Tel.: (39) 0861587149
Fax: (39) 0861588590

CVC Capital Partners Group Sarl—(Continued)

Emp.: 15
Rail Joints & Fastenings Mfr
S.I.C.: 3312
N.A.I.C.S.: 331110
Jean-Pierre Colliaut *(Pres)*

Railtech Porsol Lda. (4)
Rua Jose Afonso No 4C 1st Floor
1600-130 Lisbon, Portugal PT
Tel.: (351) 213866234
Fax: (351) 21 386 62 50
E-Mail: railtechporsol@railtechporsol.pt
Rail Joints & Fastenings Mfr
S.I.C.: 3399
N.A.I.C.S.: 331110
Rkuem Amaro *(Mgr)*

U.S. Subsidiaries:

Conductix Inc. (3)
10102 F St
Omaha, NE 68127-1104
Tel.: (402) 339-9300
Fax: (402) 339-9627
Toll Free: (800) 521-4888
E-Mail: info.us@conductix.com
Web Site: www.conductix.us
Emp.: 125
Safety Electrification Products Mfr for Cranes, Monorails, Conveyors, Tools & Transport
Import Export
S.I.C.: 3699
N.A.I.C.S.: 335999
Lon Miller *(CEO)*
Stuart Zastrow *(CFO)*
Chris Michl *(CIO)*

Non-U.S. Subsidiaries:

CONDUCTIX-WAMPFLER Ltd. (4)
1 Michigan Avenue Off-Broadway
Salford, Lancashire, M50 2GY, United Kingdom
Tel.: (44) 1618480161
Fax: (44) 1618737017
E-Mail: info.uk@conductix.com
Web Site: www.conductix.co.uk
Emp.: 30
Power Transmission Equipments Mfr
S.I.C.: 3568
N.A.I.C.S.: 333613
Alen Jones *(Mng Dir)*

CONDUCTIX-WAMPFLER Pty Ltd (4)
14 England Street
Dandenong, VIC, 3175, Australia
Tel.: (61) 397068844
Fax: (61) 3 97 94 92 98
E-Mail: sales-australia@conductix.com
Web Site: www.conductix.com.au
Emp.: 25
Mobile Electrification Systems Mfr
S.I.C.: 3699
N.A.I.C.S.: 335999
Mark Howlett *(Mng Dir)*

CONDUCTIX-WAMPFLER S.de RL de C.V. (4)
Calle Trevino 983-C esquina Reforma Col Centro
66600 Apodaca, Nuevo Leon, Mexico
Tel.: (52) 528110909013
Fax: (52) 8110909014
E-Mail: info.mx@conductix.com
Web Site: www.conductix.mx
Power Transmission Equipments Distr
S.I.C.: 5063
N.A.I.C.S.: 423610
David Vazquez *(Gen Mgr)*

DELACHAUX METAL Inc. (3)
25 Interstate Dr
Napoleon, OH 43545
Tel.: (419) 599-1754
Fax: (419) 599-3630
Web Site: www.delachaux.fr/Implantation.aspx?Zone=Annu&Company_Id=94&SessLang=en
Materials Handling Machinery Distr
S.I.C.: 5084
N.A.I.C.S.: 423830

Non-U.S. Subsidiaries:

CONDUCTIX-WAMPFLER AG (3)
Rheinstrasse 27-33
79576 Weil am Rhein, Baden-Wurttemberg, Germany
Tel.: (49) 76216620
Fax: (49) 7621662144
E-Mail: info.de@conductix.com
Web Site: www.conductix.de
Emp.: 300
Power Transmission Equipments Mfr & Distr
S.I.C.: 3568
N.A.I.C.S.: 333613
Jean-Pierre Colliaut *(Co-CEO)*
Daniel Doerflinger *(Co-CEO)*

Non-U.S. Subsidiaries:

CONDUCTIX-WAMPFLER AB (4)
PO Box 7214
187 13 Taby, Sweden
Tel.: (46) 8 630 12 90
Fax: (46) 8 630 12 91
E-Mail: info.se@conductix.com
Web Site: www.conductix.se
Power Transmission Equipments Distr
S.I.C.: 5065
N.A.I.C.S.: 423690
Anders Wikstron *(Gen Mgr)*

CONDUCTIX-WAMPFLER B.V. (4)
A Hofmanweg 75
2031 BH Haarlem, North Holland, Netherlands
Tel.: (31) 235421200
Fax: (31) 23 532 02 48
E-Mail: info.nl@conductix.com
Web Site: www.conductix.nl
Emp.: 10
Power Transmission Equipments Mfr
S.I.C.: 3566
N.A.I.C.S.: 333612
Jan Soede *(Principal)*

CONDUCTIX-WAMPFLER Ltda (4)
Rua Manoel Silveira de 361 Bairro Jardim Santana
Camargo, Itu, Sao Paulo, Brazil
Tel.: (55) 11 4813 7330
Fax: (55) 11 4813 7330
E-Mail: info.br@conductix.com
Data Transmission Systems Distr
S.I.C.: 5063
N.A.I.C.S.: 423610

CONDUCTIX-WAMPFLER Ltd. (4)
Lathaleere
Baltinglass, Wicklow, Ireland
Tel.: (353) 59 648 12 08
Fax: (353) 59 648 10 06
E-Mail: info.ie@conductix.com
Web Site: www.conductix.ie
Emp.: 42
Energy & Data Transmission Equipments Mfr
S.I.C.: 3441
N.A.I.C.S.: 332312
Marian Roberts *(Gen Mgr)*

CONDUCTIX-WAMPFLER O.O.O. (4)
Tverskaya Street Building 16/1 Office 901 B Floor 7, Moscow, 125009, Russia
Tel.: (7) 499 922 24 06
Fax: (7) 495 935 89 62
E-Mail: info.ru@conductix.com
Web Site: www.conductix.ru
Emp.: 4
Data Transmission System Mfr
S.I.C.: 3661
N.A.I.C.S.: 334210
Borris Moskovskiy *(Gen Mgr)*

CONDUCTIX-WAMPFLER Sdn Bhd (4)
678076 U 28A Jalan SS4C 5
47301 Petaling Jaya, Selangor, Malaysia
Tel.: (60) 378055663
Fax: (60) 378055605
E-Mail: info.my@conductix.com
Web Site: www.conductix.my
Emp.: 9
Data Transmission Equipments Distr
S.I.C.: 4911
N.A.I.C.S.: 221121
Kia Yong Kim *(Gen Mgr)*

CONDUCTIX-WAMPFLER Pvt Ltd (3)
4/24 Goodwill Enclave Road No 9 Kalyani Nagar
Pune, Maharashtra, 411 006, India
Tel.: (91) 2040046409
Fax: (91) 2040046410
E-Mail: info.in@conductix.com
Web Site: www.conductix.com
Data Transmission Equipments Distr
S.I.C.: 5085
N.A.I.C.S.: 423840
Kishor Dagia *(Mng Dir)*

CONDUCTIX-WAMPFLER Pte Ltd (3)
3 Raffles Place 07-01 Baharat Building
Singapore, 048617, Singapore
Tel.: (65) 63296405
Fax: (65) 6329 9699
Web Site: www.conductix.com
Data Transmission Systems Mfr
S.I.C.: 4911
N.A.I.C.S.: 221121

CONDUCTIX-WAMPFLER Srl (3)
Via de Capitani 14/16
Agrate Brianza, Monza e Brianza, Italy
Tel.: (39) 039 60743 1
Fax: (39) 039 60743 292
E-Mail: info.it@conductix.com
Web Site: www.wampfler.it
Emp.: 70
Power Transmission Equipments Distr
S.I.C.: 5065
N.A.I.C.S.: 423690
Jean-Pierre Colliaut *(Pres)*

IAT Ltda (3)
Av Severo Dullius 2015
Porto Alegre, 90200-310, Brazil
Tel.: (55) 5133734300
Fax: (55) 5133712120
E-Mail: iatltda@iatltda.com.br
Web Site: www.iatltda.com.br
Rail Fastening Systems Mfr
S.I.C.: 3312
N.A.I.C.S.: 331110

PANDROL AUSTRALIA Pty Limited (3)
7 Bessemer Street
Blacktown, NSW, 2148, Australia
Tel.: (61) 298522500
Fax: (61) 2 9671 7875
Web Site: www.pandrol.com.au
Emp.: 80
Rail Joints & Fastenings Mfr
S.I.C.: 3499
N.A.I.C.S.: 332999
Justin Taylor *(Controller-Fin)*

PANDROL HOLDINGS LTD. (3)
63 Station Road
Addlestone, Surrey, KT15 2AR, United Kingdom
Tel.: (44) 1932834500
Fax: (44) 1932850858
E-Mail: info@pandroll.com
Web Site: www.pandroll.com
Emp.: 50
Management Services
S.I.C.: 8741
N.A.I.C.S.: 551114

Subsidiaries:

PANDROL Ltd. (4)
63 Station Road
Addlestone, Surrey, KT15 2AR, United Kingdom
Tel.: (44) 1932834500
Fax: (44) 1932 850858
E-Mail: info@pandrol.com
Web Site: www.pandrol.com
Emp.: 36
Rail Joints & Fastenings Mfr
S.I.C.: 3312
N.A.I.C.S.: 331110

PANDROL U.K. Ltd. (4)
Gateford Road
Worksop, Nottinghamshire, S81 7AX, United Kingdom
Tel.: (44) 1909476101
Fax: (44) 1909482989
E-Mail: commercial@pandrol.com
Web Site: www.pandrol.com
Emp.: 130
Rail Joints & Fastenings Distr
S.I.C.: 5051
N.A.I.C.S.: 423510
Donald Webster *(Mng Dir)*

Non-U.S. Subsidiaries:

IAT Fixacoes Elasticas Ltd (4)
IAT Ltda Av Severo Dullius 2015
Porto Alegre, Rio Grande do Sul, 90200-310, Brazil
Tel.: (55) 5133734300
Fax: (55) 51 3371 2110
E-Mail: iatltda@iatltda.com.br
Web Site: www.iatltda.com.br
Emp.: 100
Rail Fastening Systems Mfr
S.I.C.: 3399
N.A.I.C.S.: 331110

PANDROL CANADA Ltd (4)
6910 34th St
Edmonton, AB, T6B 2X2, Canada
Tel.: (780) 413-4281
Fax: (780) 413-4283
E-Mail: info@pandrolcanada.ca
Web Site: www.pandrolcanada.ca
Railway Fastening Systems Mfr
S.I.C.: 3399
N.A.I.C.S.: 331110

PANDROL KOREA Ltd (4)
10 Seoul Ctr Bldg 91-1 Sogong-dong
Jung-Gu, Seoul, 100-094, Korea (South)
Tel.: (82) 27576721
Fax: (82) 27565077
E-Mail: sales@pandrol.co.kr
Web Site: www.pandrol.co.kr
Emp.: 8
Rail Fasteners Mfr
S.I.C.: 3399
N.A.I.C.S.: 331110
S. Jae Lee *(Mng Dir)*

ROSENQVIST RAIL AB (4)
Skordevagen 3
824 34 Hudiksvall, Sweden
Tel.: (46) 65016505
Fax: (46) 65016501
E-Mail: info@rosenqvist-group.se
Web Site: www.rosenqvistrail.se
Emp.: 25
Rail Joints & Fastenings Mfr
S.I.C.: 3312
N.A.I.C.S.: 331110
Anders Rosenqvist *(CEO)*

PT PANDROL INDONESIA (3)
Jalan Abdul Muis No 80A
Jakarta, 10160, Indonesia
Tel.: (62) 21 344 3333
Fax: (62) 21 384 7422
Rail Joints & Fastenings Mfr
S.I.C.: 3312
N.A.I.C.S.: 331110
A. Dirdjaja *(Mng Dir)*

Railtech Deutschland GmbH (3)
Wiesenstrasse 12
51580 Reichshof, Nordrhein-Westfalen, Germany
Tel.: (49) 22619134828
Fax: (49) 2261913489
Emp.: 20
Rail Joints & Fastenings Mfr
S.I.C.: 3312
N.A.I.C.S.: 331110
Robert Ploetz *(Mng Dir)*

Railtech Stedef Ltd (3)
16th Floor Chartered Square Building 152 North Sathorn Road
SILOM, Bangkok, 10500, Thailand
Tel.: (66) 26378127
Fax: (66) 2 637 8129
E-Mail: stedefas@loxinfo.co.th
Rail Fastenings Mfr
S.I.C.: 3312
N.A.I.C.S.: 331110
Stephane Edenwald *(Mng Dir)*

Railtech UK Ltd (3)
Unit 100 Catesby Park Kings Norton
Birmingham, West Midlands, B38 8SE, United Kingdom UK
Tel.: (44) 1214864444
Fax: (44) 1214595551
E-Mail: enquiries@railtech-uk.com
Web Site: www.railtech-uk.com
Emp.: 5
Rail Fastenings Mfr
S.I.C.: 3312
N.A.I.C.S.: 331110
Baptiste Destailleur *(Mng Dir)*

ROLF PLOTZ GmbH & Co. KG (3)
Wiesenstrasse 12
51580 Reichshof, Nordrhein-Westfalen, Germany De
Tel.: (49) 2261913480
Fax: (49) 2261 91348 9

E-Mail: info@ploetz-group.com
Web Site: www.ploetz-group.com
Rail Fastenings Mfr
S.I.C.: 3312
N.A.I.C.S.: 331110
Rolf Plotz *(Founder)*

Non-U.S. Plant:

SUFETRA-TRANOSA SA - Asteasu Plant (3)
Crtra De Asteasu km 22
20150 Cizurquil, Gipuzkoa, Spain
Tel.: (34) 943692680
Fax: (34) 943693453
E-Mail: arobles@sufetra.es
Emp.: 35
Rail Joints & Fastenings Mfr
S.I.C.: 3399
N.A.I.C.S.: 331110
Eusta Urrestarazu *(Mng Dir)*

Lecta S.A. (2)
15 Avenue Galilee
92350 Le Plessis-Robinson, France
Tel.: (33) 146017070
Fax: (33) 146017071
Web Site: www.lecta.com
Sales Range: $1-4.9 Billion
Emp.: 4,000
Coated Woodfree Paper Mfr
S.I.C.: 2672
N.A.I.C.S.: 322220
Santiago Ramirez Larrauri *(Chm & CEO)*

Non-U.S. Subsidiaries:

Polyedra SpA (3)
Via Edison 96
20019 Settimo Milanese, Italy (100%)
Tel.: (39) 02335511
Fax: (39) 0233551555
E-Mail: info@polyedra.com
Web Site: www.polyedra.com
Emp.: 365
Graphics Solutions & Paper Products Distr
S.I.C.: 5113
N.A.I.C.S.: 424130
Claudio Cervellati *(Gen Mgr)*

Subsidiary:

Carthago Srl (4)
Via Quattro Novembre 18
Trecasali, Parma, 43010, Italy
Tel.: (39) 0521372160
Fax: (39) 0521872193
Paper & Cardboard Distr
S.I.C.: 5113
N.A.I.C.S.: 424130

Torraspapel, S.A. (3)
Llull 331
08019 Barcelona, Spain
Tel.: (34) 93 482 10 00
Fax: (34) 93 482 11 70
Sales Range: $1-4.9 Billion
Emp.: 2,600
Paper Mfr
S.I.C.: 2679
N.A.I.C.S.: 322299
Francisco Rudilla *(CEO)*

CVC Capital Partners Limited (1)
111 Strand
London, WC2R OAG, United Kingdom UK
Tel.: (44) 2074204200
Fax: (44) 2074204231
E-Mail: info@cvceurope.com
Web Site: www.cvc.com
Private Equity Firm
S.I.C.: 6211
N.A.I.C.S.: 523999
Robert R. Lucas *(Mng Partner & Head-UK Investments)*
Hardy McLain *(Mng Partner)*
Fred Watt *(COO & Mng Partner)*
Jonathan Feuer *(Mng Partner & Grp Head-FIG)*
Lorne Somerville *(Partner & Head-TMT)*
Nick Archer *(Partner-Fund Admin)*
Istvan Szoke *(Partner)*
Marc St. John *(Partner & Head-IR)*
Nicholas Clarry *(Sr Mng Dir)*
Pev Hooper *(Sr Mng Dir)*

Holdings:

Autobar Group Ltd. (2)
East Wing 14th Floor 389 Chiswick High Road
London, W4 4AJ, United Kingdom
Tel.: (44) 20 8987 6500
Fax: (44) 20 8987 6501
Web Site: www.autobar.com
Sales Range: $900-999.9 Million
Emp.: 4,000
Vending Machine Services
S.I.C.: 5962
N.A.I.C.S.: 454210
Andrew Bristow *(CEO)*

Merlin Entertainments Group Ltd. (2)
3 Market Close
Poole, BH15 1NQ, United Kingdom (50.7%)
Tel.: (44) 1202666900
Fax: (44) 1202661303
E-Mail: enquiries@merlinentertainments.biz
Web Site: www.merlinentertainments.biz
Sales Range: $1-4.9 Billion
Emp.: 13,000
Theme Park Owner & Operator; Owned by The Blackstone Group L.P., Kirkbi A/S & CVC Capital Partners Group Sarl
S.I.C.: 7996
N.A.I.C.S.: 713110
Nicholas J. Varney *(CEO)*
Andrew Carr *(CFO)*

Subsidiary:

Thorpe Park (3)
Staines Road
Chertsey, Surrey, KT16 8PN, United Kingdom
Tel.: (44) 1932 577 130
Fax: (44) 1932566367
E-Mail: events@thorpepark.co.uk
Web Site: www.thorpepark.com
Sales Range: $25-49.9 Million
Amusement Park
S.I.C.: 7996
N.A.I.C.S.: 713110
Jacqui Dixon *(Head-Customer Svc)*

U.S. Subsidiary:

LEGOLAND California LLC (3)
1 Legoland Dr
Carlsbad, CA 92008
Tel.: (760) 918-5346
Fax: (760) 918-8975
Web Site: www.legoland.com
Sales Range: $50-74.9 Million
Emp.: 400
Theme Park Operator
S.I.C.: 7996
N.A.I.C.S.: 713110
Peter Kock *(Dir-Mktg & Sls)*

Non-U.S. Subsidiary:

Living and Leisure Australia Group (3)
Level 3 Northbank Place
525 Flinders Street, Melbourne, VIC, 3000, Australia
Tel.: (61) 3 9415 4000
Fax: (61) 3 9473 2500
Web Site: www.livingandleisure.com.au
Sales Range: $125-149.9 Million
Owns & Operates Leisure Businesses & Assets
S.I.C.: 7999
N.A.I.C.S.: 713990

Subsidiaries:

Oceanis Holdings Ltd. (4)
Cnr King & Flinders Streets
Melbourne, VIC, 3000, Australia
Tel.: (61) 3 9923 5900
Holding Company
S.I.C.: 6719
N.A.I.C.S.: 551112

Subsidiaries:

Melbourne Underwater World Pty Ltd (5)
Melbourne Aquarium
Cnr King & Flinders Streets, Melbourne, VIC, 3000, Australia
Tel.: (61) 396200999
Fax: (61) 396200222
E-Mail: info@melbourneaquarium.com.au
Web Site: www.melbourneaquarium.com.au
Emp.: 150
Aquarium Management Services
S.I.C.: 6531
N.A.I.C.S.: 531312
Ari Brown *(Mgr-Retail Shop)*

Oceanis Australia Pty Ltd (5)
Cnr King & Flinders Streets
Melbourne, VIC, 3000, Australia
Tel.: (61) 3 9923 5900
E-Mail:
Aquarium Construction & Management Services
S.I.C.: 1542
N.A.I.C.S.: 236220

UnderWater World Sunshine Coast Pty Ltd. (5)
Parkyn Parade
Mooloolaba, QLD, 4557, Australia
Tel.: (61) 754586280
Fax: (61) 754448515
E-Mail: shark@underwaterworld.com.au
Web Site: www.underwaterworld.com.au
Emp.: 80
Aquarium Management Services
S.I.C.: 6531
N.A.I.C.S.: 531312
Tina Holmes *(Mng Dir)*

The Otway Fly Pty. Ltd. (4)
360 Phillips Track
Weeaproinah, VIC, 3237, Australia
Tel.: (61) 352359200
Fax: (61) 352359388
E-Mail: elaineburridge@otwayfly.com
Web Site: www.otwayfly.com
Emp.: 10
Rainforest Adventure Activities
S.I.C.: 0851
N.A.I.C.S.: 115310
Daniel Kay *(Mgr)*

Parkthorn Properties Pty Ltd. (4)
Parkyn Dr
Mooloolaba, QLD, 4557, Australia
Tel.: (61) 754448088
Fax: (61) 754440293
Emp.: 12
Real Estate Management Services
S.I.C.: 6531
N.A.I.C.S.: 531390

Skrill Ltd. (2)
(Formerly Moneybookers Ltd.)
Welken House 10 11 Charterhouse Sq
London, EC1M 6EH, United Kingdom
Tel.: (44) 8703830232
Fax: (44) 8709223274
Web Site: www.skrill.com
Sales Range: $300-349.9 Million
Emp.: 700
Online Payment System Operator
S.I.C.: 6099
N.A.I.C.S.: 522320
Nikolai Riesenkampff *(Co-CEO)*
Roland Schaar *(Sr VP-Tech)*

Joint Venture:

Acromas Holdings Ltd. (2)
Enbrook Park
Folkestone, Kent, CT20 3SE, United Kingdom UK
Tel.: (44) 1303771111
Web Site: www.acromas.com
Sls.: $3,551,507,352
Assets: $10,715,166,792
Liabilities: $16,122,497,823
Net Worth: ($5,407,331,031)
Earnings: ($1,001,427,789)
Emp.: 31,302
Fiscal Year-end: 01/31/13
Holding Company; Financial, Insurance, Travel, Healthcare & Lifestyle Products & Services
S.I.C.: 6719
N.A.I.C.S.: 551112
J. Andrew Goodsell *(CEO)*
Stuart M. Howard *(CFO)*
A. P. Stringer *(Sec)*

Subsidiaries:

The Automobile Association Limited (3)
Fanum House Basingview
Basingstoke, Hants, RG21 4EA, United Kingdom UK
Tel.: (44) 8705448866
E-Mail: hr.operations@theaa.com
Web Site: www.theaa.com
Emp.: 1,000
Motoring Assistance; Financial Services; Owned by Permira Advisers Limited & CVC Capital Partners Limited
S.I.C.: 6153
N.A.I.C.S.: 522220
Andrew Strong *(CEO)*

Saga Group Limited (3)
Enbrook Park
Middleburg Square, Folkestone, Kent, CT20 3SE, United Kingdom UK
Tel.: (44) 1303771111
E-Mail: sagazone@saga.co.uk
Web Site: www.saga.co.uk
Emp.: 300
Holding Company; Insurance, Travel, Financial & Lifestyle Products & Services
S.I.C.: 6719
N.A.I.C.S.: 551112
Ros Altmann *(Dir Gen)*
Susan Hooper *(CEO-Saga Holidays)*
Roger Ramsden *(CEO-Saga Svcs)*
Robin Shaw *(CEO-Saga Shipping)*

Subsidiaries:

Acromas Holidays Limited (4)
Enbrook Park
Middleburg Square, Folkestone, Kent, CT20 3SE, United Kingdom UK
Tel.: (44) 1303 771 111 (Switchboard)
E-Mail: reservations@saga.co.uk
Web Site: travel.saga.co.uk
Vacation & Tour Travel Agency
S.I.C.: 4724
N.A.I.C.S.: 561510
Susan Hooper *(CEO)*

Acromas Shipping Limited (4)
Enbrook Park
Middleburg Square, Folkestone, Kent, CT20 1AZ, United Kingdom UK
Tel.: (44) 1303 771 111 (Switchboard)
Web Site: travel.saga.co.uk
Cruise Vacation Travel Agency
S.I.C.: 4724
N.A.I.C.S.: 561510
Robin Shaw *(CEO)*

Nestor Healthcare Group Limited (4)
Beaconsfield Court Beaconsfield Road
Hatfield, Herts, AL10 8HU, United Kingdom UK
Tel.: (44) 8458501435
Fax: (44) 8458501433
E-Mail: homecare.services@saga.co.uk
Web Site: www.saga.co.uk
Sales Range: $200-249.9 Million
Emp.: 991
Holding Company; Health & Social Care Staffing
S.I.C.: 6719
N.A.I.C.S.: 551112
John Rennocks *(Chm)*
John Ivers *(CEO)*

Subsidiary:

Nestor Primecare Services Ltd. (5)
Beaconsfields Court Beaconsfield Road
Hatfield, Herts, AL10 8HU, United Kingdom
Tel.: (44) 1707 286800
Fax: (44) 845 850 1433
Web Site: www.nestor-healthcare.co.uk/
Emp.: 200
Health Care Services
S.I.C.: 8099
N.A.I.C.S.: 621999
David Collison *(Controller)*

Saga Services Limited (4)
Enbrook Park
Middleburg Square, Folkestone, Kent, CT20 1AZ, United Kingdom UK
Tel.: (44) 1303771111
Web Site: www.saga.co.uk
Emp.: 3,000
Financial Information & Advisory Services
S.I.C.: 6726
N.A.I.C.S.: 525990
Andrew Goodsell *(CEO)*

U.S. Subsidiary:

Allied Healthcare International Inc. (4)
245 Park Ave 39th Fl
New York, NY 10167 NY
Tel.: (212) 750-0064
Fax: (212) 750-7221
Web Site: www.alliedhealthcare.com
Sales Range: $250-299.9 Million
Emp.: 1,160
Holding Company; Healthcare Staffing

CVC Capital Partners Group Sarl—(Continued)

S.I.C.: 7363
N.A.I.C.S.: 561320
Leslie J. Levinson *(Sec)*

Non-U.S. Subsidiary:

Allied Healthcare Group Holdings Limited (5)
Stone Business Park
Brooms Road, Stone, Staffs, ST15 0TL, United Kingdom UK
Tel.: (44) 1785810600
Fax: (44) 1785818200
E-Mail: info@alliedhealthcare.com
Web Site: www.alliedhealthcare.co.uk
Holding Company
S.I.C.: 6719
N.A.I.C.S.: 551112
Lisa Mclean *(Dir-Care Delivery)*

Subsidiaries:

Allied Healthcare Holdings Limited (6)
Stone Business Park
Brooms Road, Stone, Staffs, ST15 0TL, United Kingdom UK
Tel.: (44) 1785810600
Fax: (44) 1785818200
E-Mail: info@alliedhealthcare.com
Web Site: www.alliedhealthcare.co.uk
Sales Range: $150-199.9 Million
Emp.: 200
Holding Company; Healthcare Staffing Services
S.I.C.: 6719
N.A.I.C.S.: 551112

Subsidiaries:

Allied Healthcare Group Limited (7)
Stone Business Park
Brooms Road, Stone, Staffordshire, ST15 OTL, United Kingdom UK
Tel.: (44) 1785810600
Fax: (44) 1785288849
Web Site: www.alliedhealthcare.co.uk
Sales Range: $25-49.9 Million
Nursing & Healthcare Services
S.I.C.: 8082
N.A.I.C.S.: 621610

U.S. Holding:

Cunningham Lindsey Group Ltd. (2)
3030 N Rocky Point Dr W Ste 530
Tampa, FL 33607 ON
Tel.: (813) 830-7100
Fax: (813) 830-7121
E-Mail: global@cunninghamlindsey.com
Web Site: www.cunninghamlindsey.com
Sales Range: $350-399.9 Million
Emp.: 3,971
Insurance Claims Services, Adjusting, Appraisal & Risk Management
S.I.C.: 6411
N.A.I.C.S.: 524291
Philippe Bes *(Pres & CEO)*
Ed Mullen *(CFO)*
Harry Patel *(CEO-Americas)*

Subsidiaries:

Cunningham Lindsey U.S. Inc. (3)
405 State Hwy 121 Bypass Bldg A Ste 200
Lewisville, TX 75067
Mailing Address:
PO Box 703689
Dallas, TX 75370-3689
Tel.: (214) 488-5139
Fax: (214) 488-6570
E-Mail: corpservices@na.cunninghamlindsey.com
Web Site: www.cunninghamlindseyus.com
Emp.: 100
Insurance Risk, Claims & Loss Management Services
S.I.C.: 6411
N.A.I.C.S.: 524298
Jim Girard *(Pres & CEO)*
Tina Mallie *(COO)*
Daniel Schulz *(Gen Counsel & VP)*
Dan Daniel *(Sr VP-Centralized Svcs)*
Gail Oliver *(Sr VP-Sls & Client Dev)*

Subsidiary:

Vale National Training Center Inc. (4)
2424 E Randol Mill Rd
Arlington, TX 76011
Tel.: (817) 633-4800
Fax: (817) 633-2922
Toll Free: (800) 860-2230
E-Mail: registrations@vale-ts.com
Web Site: www.valenational.com
Emp.: 6
Insurance Claims Adjusting & Estimation Training
S.I.C.: 9411
N.A.I.C.S.: 923110
Jon McCreath *(Pres)*

EFI Global, Inc. (3)
8811 FM 1960 Bypass Rd W Ste 400
Humble, TX 77338 DE
Tel.: (281) 358-4441 (100%)
Fax: (281) 358-2517
Web Site: www.efiglobal.com
Emp.: 400
Forensic Engineering Services
S.I.C.: 7381
N.A.I.C.S.: 561611
Ron Holt *(Pres & CEO)*

Non-U.S. Subsidiaries:

Cunningham Lindsey Belgium N.V. (3)
Noorderlaan 133 bus 16
2030 Antwerp, Belgium
Tel.: (32) 35414539
Fax: (32) 35414643
E-Mail: info@cl-be.com
Web Site: www.cunninghamlindsey.com
Emp.: 16
Insurance Risk, Claims & Loss Management Services
S.I.C.: 6411
N.A.I.C.S.: 524298
Martine Laureys *(Head-Fin & Admin)*

Cunningham Lindsey Canada Limited (3)
50 Burnhamthorpe Road West Suite 1102
Mississauga, ON, L5B 3C2, Canada
Tel.: (905) 896-8181
Fax: (905) 896-3485
E-Mail: corpservices@cl-na.com
Web Site: www.cunninghamlindsey.com
Emp.: 288
Insurance Risk, Claims & Loss Management Services
S.I.C.: 6411
N.A.I.C.S.: 524298
Rob Seal *(Pres & CEO)*
Gary Dalton *(Sr VP & Exec Dir)*
Lorri Frederick *(Sr VP & Exec Dir-Atlantic Canada & Quebec)*
Albert Poon *(Sr VP & Exec Dir-Western & Central Canada)*
John Mark Laurin *(Sr VP-Quebec Ops)*

Division:

EFI Global (4)
(Formerly Environment Solutions Remediation Services Inc.)
50 Burnhamthorpe Road West Suite 1102
Mississauga, ON, L5B 3C2, Canada
Tel.: (905) 896-8181
Fax: (905) 896-3486
E-Mail: gdalton@cl-na.com
Web Site: www.efiglobal.ca/en-GB/ca/
Emp.: 25
Mould & Chemical Remediation Services
S.I.C.: 1799
N.A.I.C.S.: 562910
Gary Dalton *(Sr VP & Exec Dir)*

Cunningham Lindsey Deutschland GmbH (3)
Montanusstrasse 21a
51429 Bergisch Gladbach, Germany
Tel.: (49) 220457511
Fax: (49) 220456726
Web Site: www.cunninghamlindsey.com
Emp.: 10
Insurance Risk, Claims & Loss Management Services
S.I.C.: 6411
N.A.I.C.S.: 524298
Jens Otto *(Mng Dir)*

Cunningham Lindsey France S.A. (3)
92 Bd de Victor Hugo
92110 Clichy, France
Tel.: (33) 1 4022 8080
Fax: (33) 140228080
E-Mail: info@cl-fr.com
Web Site: www.cunninghamlindsey.com
Emp.: 200
Insurance Risk, Claims & Loss Management Services
S.I.C.: 6411
N.A.I.C.S.: 524298
Pierre Brigadeau *(CEO)*

Cunningham Lindsey International Limited (3)
International House 1 St Katharines Way
London, E1W 1UU, United Kingdom
Tel.: (44) 20 7816 1800
Fax: (44) 20 7816 1816
E-Mail: info@cl-int.com
Web Site: www.cunninghamlindsey.com
Emp.: 100
Insurance Risk, Claims & Loss Management Services
S.I.C.: 6411
N.A.I.C.S.: 524298
Jim Grant *(Chm)*
Liz Tubb *(Gen Counsel-Intl)*

Subsidiary:

Cunningham Lindsey United Kingdom (4)
Apex Plaza
Forbury Road, Reading, Berkshire, RG1 1AX, United Kingdom
Tel.: (44) 118 960 7100
Fax: (44) 118 950 5424
E-Mail: headoffice@cl-uk.com
Web Site: www.cunninghamlindsey.com
Emp.: 70
Insurance Risk, Claims & Loss Management Services
S.I.C.: 6411
N.A.I.C.S.: 524298
Phil McNeilage *(CEO)*

Subsidiary:

Claims International Limited (5)
Oakleigh House
Cardiff, CF11 1HU, United Kingdom
Tel.: (44) 8456049855
Fax: (44) 8456048634
E-Mail: info@cilint.com
Web Site: www.cilint.com
Emp.: 40
Travel Insurance Claims
S.I.C.: 6411
N.A.I.C.S.: 524298
Roger Sims *(Mng Dir)*

Cunningham Lindsey Nederland B.V. (3)
Westerstraat 21
3016 DG Rotterdam, Netherlands
Mailing Address:
PO Box 23212
3001 KE Rotterdam, Netherlands
Tel.: (31) 88 286 64 64
Fax: (31) 88 286 64 65
E-Mail: info@cl-nl.com
Web Site: www.CunninghamLindsey.nl
Emp.: 200
Insurance Risk, Claims & Loss Management Services
S.I.C.: 6411
N.A.I.C.S.: 524298
Jeroen Frohlich *(CEO)*

Non-U.S. Holdings:

Ahlsell AB (2)
Liljeholmsvagen 30
SE-117 98 Stockholm, Sweden SE
Tel.: (46) 86857000
Fax: (46) 86857096
E-Mail: info@ahlsell.com
Web Site: www.ahlsell.com
Sales Range: $1-4.9 Billion
Emp.: 4,500
Holding Company; Installation Products, Tools & Machinery Distr
S.I.C.: 6719
N.A.I.C.S.: 551112
Goran Nasholm *(Pres & CEO)*
Gunnar Haglund *(CFO & VP)*

Subsidiaries:

Gelia Industri AB (3)
Industrigatan
PO Box 214
SE 467 84 Grastorp, Sweden
Tel.: (46) 51458800
Fax: (46) 51458808
E-Mail: info@gelia.se
Web Site: www.gelia.se
Emp.: 50
Tires Mfr
S.I.C.: 3011
N.A.I.C.S.: 326211
Mikael Olsson *(Dir-Sls)*

Non-U.S. Subsidiaries:

Ahlsell Danmark ApS (3)
Abildager 24
PO Box 61
DK 2605 Brondby, Denmark DK
Tel.: (45) 43444299
Fax: (45) 43430094
E-Mail: info@ahlsell.dk
Web Site: www.ahlsell.dk
Emp.: 55
Air Conditioning & Refrigeration Services
S.I.C.: 3585
N.A.I.C.S.: 333415
Henrik Lohse *(Mgr-Sls)*

Ahlsell Norway AS (3)
Kvaenv 4
PO Box 184
Stavanger, 4065, Norway NO
Tel.: (47) 69236150
Fax: (47) 51818600
Web Site: www.ahlsell.no
Emp.: 250
Tire Mfr
S.I.C.: 3011
N.A.I.C.S.: 326211
Helge Holen *(Mng Dir)*

Ahlsell Oy (3)
Ayritie 12C
FI 01510 Vantaa, Finland
Tel.: (358) 205845000
Fax: (358) 205845101
E-Mail: info@ahlsell.fi
Web Site: www.ahlsell.fi
Emp.: 12
Tire Mfr
S.I.C.: 3011
N.A.I.C.S.: 326211
Mika Salokangas *(Mng Dir)*

VVS Trading A/S (3)
Ellegardsvej 30
DK 6400 Sonderborg, Denmark
Tel.: (45) 74430200
Fax: (45) 74428383
E-Mail: info@vvstrading.dk
Web Site: www.vvs-trading.dk
Emp.: 175
Tire Mfr
S.I.C.: 3011
N.A.I.C.S.: 326211

ZAO Ahlsell Spb (3)
Rentgena 5
PO Box 7001
190000 Saint Petersburg, Russia RU
Tel.: (7) 8123252424
Fax: (7) 8123252407
E-Mail: info@ahlsell.ru
Web Site: www.ahlsell.ru
Emp.: 50
Tires Mfr
S.I.C.: 3011
N.A.I.C.S.: 326211
Pavel Almdree *(Mgr-Sls)*

Ortel Mobile Holding B.V. (2)
Rijswijkseweg 66
Hague, 2516 EH, Netherlands
Tel.: (31) 703634565
Fax: (31) 703630812
Investment Management Services
S.I.C.: 6211
N.A.I.C.S.: 523999

Non-U.S. Joint Venture:

Brit Insurance Holdings N.V. (2)
SOM II Claude Debussylaan 11
1082 MC Amsterdam, Netherlands
Tel.: (31) 207191100
Fax: (31) 207191101
E-Mail: britinsenquiries@britinsurance.com
Web Site: www.britinsurance.com
Premiums: $1,545,268,543
Assets: $4,809,192,325
Liabilities: $3,888,277,428
Net Worth: $920,914,897

Earnings: $114,020,599
Emp.: 761
Fiscal Year-end: 12/31/12
Holding Company; Insurance & Reinsurance Services
S.I.C.: 6719
N.A.I.C.S.: 551112
Nicholas Edward Tucker Prettejohn *(Chm)*
Mark Bertrand Cloutier *(CEO)*
Andrew Baddeley *(CFO)*
Nigel Meyer *(COO)*
John Stratton *(Chief Investment Officer)*
Mark Allan *(Chief Risk Officer & Dir-Strategy)*
Peter Burrows *(CEO-UK)*
Ray Cox *(CEO-Strategic Bus Unit-UK)*
Jonathan Turner *(CEO-Reinsurance)*
Matthew Wilson *(CEO-Global Specialty)*

Non-U.S. Subsidiaries:

Brit Group Services Limited **(3)**
55 Bishopsgate 2nd Fl
London, EC2N 3AS, United Kingdom
Tel.: (44) 20 7984 8500
Fax: (44) 20 7984 8501
E-Mail: info@britinsurance.com
Web Site: www.britinsurancc.com
Emp.: 700
Insurance Agencies & Brokerages
S.I.C.: 6411
N.A.I.C.S.: 524210

Brit Syndicates Limited **(3)**
55 Bishopsgate
London, EC2N 3AS, United Kingdom
Tel.: (44) 2079848700
Fax: (44) 2079848701
E-Mail: britinsenquiries@britinsurance.com
Web Site: www.britinsurance.com
Insurance Agencies & Brokerages
S.I.C.: 6411
N.A.I.C.S.: 524210

Brit UW Limited **(3)**
55 Bishopsgate
London, EC2N 3AS, United Kingdom
Tel.: (44) 2079848700
Fax: (44) 2079848701
E-Mail: britinsenquiries@britinsurance.com
Web Site: www.britinsurance.com
Emp.: 750
Insurance Agencies & Brokerages
S.I.C.: 6411
N.A.I.C.S.: 524210

CVC Capital Partners Netherlands **(1)**
World Trade Center Schiphol Airport Twr B
6th Fl Schiphol Boulevard
285 Luchthaven, 1118 BH Amsterdam, Netherlands
Tel.: (31) 203548051
Fax: (31) 203548052
Web Site: www.cvc.com
Emp.: 5
Private Equity Firm
S.I.C.: 6211
N.A.I.C.S.: 523999
Hugo van Berckel *(Partner)*

Holdings:

Acordis BV **(2)**
Westervoortsedijk 73
6827 AV Arnhem, Netherlands
Tel.: (31) 263664444
Fax: (31) 263664692
E-Mail: folkert.blaisse@acordis.com
Web Site: www.acordis.com
Emp.: 400
Fiber & Specialty Material Mfr
S.I.C.: 2823
N.A.I.C.S.: 325220

Non-U.S. Subsidiary:

Acetate Products Ltd. **(3)**
1 Holme Ln
PO Box 5
Spondon, Derby, Ds21 7BP, United Kingdom UK
Tel.: (44) 332661422
Fax: (44) 1332681786
Web Site: www.acetateproducts.com
Emp.: 800
Man-Made Fiber & Specialty Material Mfr
S.I.C.: 2823
N.A.I.C.S.: 325220

Non-U.S. Joint Venture:

Century Enka Ltd. **(3)**
Century Arcade 2nd Floor Narangi Baug Road
Pune, 411 001, India In
Tel.: (91) 202616 6511
Fax: (91) 202616 6511
E-Mail: regdoffice@centuryenka.com
Web Site: www.centuryenka.com
500280—(BOM KOL NSE)
Rev.: $290,024,928
Assets: $205,705,008
Liabilities: $84,484,926
Net Worth: $121,220,082
Earnings: $4,058,406
Emp.: 1,496
Fiscal Year-end: 03/31/13
Synthetic Fibers Mfr
S.I.C.: 2299
N.A.I.C.S.: 314999
C. B. Gagrani *(Sec)*

Raet B.V. **(2)**
Plotterweg 38
3821 BB Amersfoort, Netherlands NL
Mailing Address:
PO Box 1495
3800 BL Amersfoort, Netherlands
Tel.: (31) 33 4506 506
Fax: (31) 33 4506 507
E-Mail: info@raet.com
Web Site: www.raet.nl
Sales Range: $150-199.9 Million
Emp.: 900
Human Resource & Payroll Business Process Outsourcing Services
S.I.C.: 7389
N.A.I.C.S.: 561499
Cees van den Heijkant *(CEO)*
Peter Schrijnemaekers *(CFO)*

Retail Network BV **(2)**
Erasmuslaan 82
3707 ZE Zeist, Netherlands NL
Tel.: (31) 30 234 0490
Emp.: 6
Holding Company; Non-Food Retailer
S.I.C.: 6719
N.A.I.C.S.: 551112
Tom Heidman *(CEO)*

Subsidiaries:

Hans Anders Opticiens **(3)**
Papland 21
4206 CK Gorinchem, Netherlands
Mailing Address:
Postbus 838
4200 AV Gorinchem, Netherlands
Tel.: (31) 183697500
Fax: (31) 183628596
Web Site: www.hansanders.nl
Emp.: 200
Opticians & Retailers of Ophthalmic Goods
S.I.C.: 3851
N.A.I.C.S.: 339115

Het Huis Opticiens **(3)**
Edisonweg 21 Paelan Papland 21
NL 4207 HE Gorinchem, Netherlands
Tel.: (31) 183697588
Fax: (31) 183628596
Web Site: www.hethuisopticiens.nl
Emp.: 170
Opticians
S.I.C.: 3851
N.A.I.C.S.: 339115

Kijkshop BV **(3)**
Schimminck 12
NL 5301 KR Zaltbommel, Netherlands
Tel.: (31) 418512345
Fax: (31) 418515985
E-Mail: orderdesk@kijkshop.nl
Web Site: www.kijkshop.nl
Emp.: 70
Showroom Retailing
S.I.C.: 5399
N.A.I.C.S.: 452990
Frank Pruijn *(Mng Dir)*

Lucardie BV **(3)**
Lauren
NL 2521 DD Hague, Netherlands
Tel.: (31) 573401800
Fax: (31) 573401880
E-Mail: sale@lucardi.nl
Web Site: www.lucardi.com
Emp.: 15
Walk-in Jewelers
S.I.C.: 5944
N.A.I.C.S.: 448310
Andrea Wuestman *(Gen Mgr)*

Perry Sport BV **(3)**
Oosteinderweg 247 B
NL 1432 AT Aalsmeer, Netherlands
Tel.: (31) 297330600
Fax: (31) 297330660
E-Mail: info@perrysport.nl
Web Site: www.perrysport.nl
Emp.: 100
Sportswear & Sports & Camping Equipment Retailer
S.I.C.: 5941
N.A.I.C.S.: 451110
Steve Preston *(Mng Dir)*

Prenatal Moeder En Kind BV **(3)**
Vlotbrugweg 10
NL 1332 AH Almere, Netherlands
Tel.: (31) 365322000
Fax: (31) 365321912
E-Mail: info@prenatal.nl
Web Site: www.prenatal.nl
Emp.: 120
Chain of Retail Shops for Child & Infant Wear; Maternity Ready-to-Wear
S.I.C.: 5641
N.A.I.C.S.: 448130
P. Brussen *(Mng Dir)*

Scapino BV **(3)**
Industrieweg 28
Assen, Drenche, NL 9403 AB, Netherlands
Tel.: (31) 592340042
Fax: (31) 592344904
E-Mail: scapino@scapino.nl
Web Site: www.scapino.nl
Emp.: 200
Shoe Retailer
S.I.C.: 5661
N.A.I.C.S.: 448210
Diederiek Vanderkerckhove *(CEO)*

Siebel BV **(3)**
Cerhaas Kada 197
NL 2521 DD Hague, Netherlands
Tel.: (31) 703766300
Fax: (31) 703766400
Web Site: www.siebel.com
Emp.: 150
Jewelers
S.I.C.: 5944
N.A.I.C.S.: 448310
F. van Loef *(Mng Dir)*

Univar N.V. **(2)**
Blaak 333
3011 GB Rotterdam, Netherlands NL
Tel.: (31) 102757800
Fax: (31) 104146863
E-Mail: univarbenelux@univareurope.com
Web Site: www.univar.com
Sales Range: $5-14.9 Billion
Emp.: 6,900
Holding Company
S.I.C.: 6719
N.A.I.C.S.: 551112
John J. Zillmer *(Pres & CEO)*
Chris Oversby *(Pres-Global Oil & Gas Indus)*
Marco Antonio Quirino *(Pres-Brazil)*

Corporate Headquarters:

Univar Inc. **(3)**
17425 NE Union Hill Rd
Redmond, WA 98052 DE
Mailing Address:
PO Box 34325
Seattle, WA 98124-1325
Tel.: (425) 889-3400
Fax: (425) 889-4100
Web Site: www.univar.com
Sales Range: $1-4.9 Billion
Emp.: 3,950
Holding Company; Chemicals Distr Import Export
S.I.C.: 6719
N.A.I.C.S.: 551112
J. Erik Fyrwald *(Pres & CEO)*
D. Beatty D'Alessandro *(CFO & Exec VP)*
Mark J. Byrne *(COO & Exec VP)*
Edward A. Evans *(Chief HR Officer & Exec VP)*
Terry Hill *(Pres-Emerging Markets & Exec VP-Indus Rels)*
Randy D. Craddock *(Pres-Canada)*

Subsidiaries:

Basic Chemical Solutions, LLC **(4)**
525 Seaport Blvd
Redwood City, CA 94063-2711 MA
Tel.: (650) 261-2010
Fax: (650) 261-2020
Web Site: www.basicchem.com
Sales Range: $800-899.9 Million
Emp.: 200
Commodity Chemical Distr & Trading Import Export
S.I.C.: 5169
N.A.I.C.S.: 424690

Performance Polymers Inc. **(4)**
803R Lancaster St
Leominster, MA 01453
Tel.: (978) 534-8000
Fax: (978) 534-3889
Toll Free: (800) 244-POLY
E-Mail: ppicustomerservice@univarusa.com
Web Site: www.performancepolymers.com
Emp.: 71
Plastics Distr
S.I.C.: 5162
N.A.I.C.S.: 424610
Michael Carota *(Pres)*

Univar USA Inc. **(4)**
17425 NE Union Hill Rd
Redmond, WA 98052 DE
Tel.: (425) 889-3400 (100%)
Fax: (425) 889-4100
Web Site: www.univarusa.com
Sales Range: $1-4.9 Billion
Emp.: 3,950
Chemical Distr
S.I.C.: 5169
N.A.I.C.S.: 424690

Non-U.S. Division:

Univar Europe Holdings B.V. **(4)**
Blvd International 55 Bldg G
1070 Brussels, Belgium (100%)
Tel.: (32) 25250511
Fax: (32) 25201751
Web Site: www.univareurope.com
Sales Range: $1-4.9 Billion
Holding Company; Regional Managing Office
S.I.C.: 6719
N.A.I.C.S.: 551112
John van Osch *(Pres-EMEA)*

Subsidiary:

Univar Benelux **(5)**
Boulevard International 55 Building G
Brussels, 1070, Belgium
Tel.: (32) 25250511
Fax: (32) 25201751
E-Mail: univarbenelux@univareurope.com
Web Site: www.univarbenelux.com
Emp.: 160
Chemicals Distr
S.I.C.: 5169
N.A.I.C.S.: 424690
Tom Berghmans *(Reg Dir)*

Non-U.S. Subsidiaries:

Univar AG **(5)**
Drahtzugstrasse 18
CH-8032 Zurich, Switzerland
Tel.: (41) 443845111
Fax: (41) 444222166
E-Mail: info-ch@univareurope.com
Web Site: www.univareurope.com
Emp.: 60
Chemicals Distr
S.I.C.: 5169
N.A.I.C.S.: 424690
Paul Handerson *(Gen Mgr)*

Univar France **(5)**
17 avenue Louison Bobet
94132 Fontenay-sous-Bois, France
Tel.: (33) 149748080
Fax: (33) 149748111
E-Mail: contact.france@univareurope.com
Web Site: www.univareurope.com
Emp.: 100
Chemicals Distr
S.I.C.: 5169
N.A.I.C.S.: 424690
Christophe Jacob *(Gen Mgr)*

Univar GmbH **(5)**
Hinsbecker Loeh 10c
45257 Essen, Germany

CVC Capital Partners Group Sarl—(Continued)

Tel.: (49) 20189590
Fax: (49) 2018959100
E-Mail: info-de@univareurope.com
Web Site: www.univar.de
Emp.: 75
Chemical, Food Ingredient & Polymer Distr
S.I.C.: 5169
N.A.I.C.S.: 424690
Mirko Schnitzler *(Reg Dir)*

Univar Iberia S.A. (5)
C/Goya 115 Planta 6
28009 Madrid, Spain
Tel.: (34) 913096363
Fax: (34) 913096340
E-Mail: univariberia@univareurope.com
Web Site: www.univariberia.com
Chemicals Distr
S.I.C.: 5169
N.A.I.C.S.: 424690

Univar Ireland (5)
536 Grants Crescent Greenogue Business Park
Rathcoole, Dublin, County Dublin, Ireland
Tel.: (353) 14019800
Fax: (353) 14019142
Web Site: www.univareurope.com
Emp.: 40
Chemicals Distr
S.I.C.: 5169
N.A.I.C.S.: 424690
Nigel Hayes *(Reg Dir)*

Univar Nordic (5)
Marieholmsgatan 56
PO Box 48
SE-401 20 Gothenburg, Sweden
Tel.: (46) 31838000
Fax: (46) 31843980
E-Mail: info.nordic@univareurope.com
Web Site: www.univareurope.com
Emp.: 200
Chemicals Distr
S.I.C.: 5169
N.A.I.C.S.: 424690
Ola Tengroth *(Reg Dir)*

Univar S.p.A. (5)
Via Caldera 21
20153 Milan, Italy
Tel.: (39) 02452771
Fax: (39) 024525810
E-Mail: info@univareurope.com
Web Site: www.univareurope.com
Emp.: 214
Chemicals Distr
S.I.C.: 5169
N.A.I.C.S.: 424690
Silvio Scarpanti *(Reg Dir)*

Univar UK Limited (5)
Argyle House Epsom Avenue
Stanley Green Trading Estate, Wilmslow, Cheshire, SK9 3RN, United Kingdom UK
Tel.: (44) 845 202 6406 (100%)
Fax: (44) 845 602 7234 (Sales)
Web Site: www.univareurope.com
Emp.: 200
Wholesale Chemical Distribution
S.I.C.: 5169
N.A.I.C.S.: 424690
Nigel Hayes *(Reg Dir)*

Non-U.S. Subsidiary:

Univar Canada Ltd. (4)
9800 Van Horne Way
Richmond, BC, V6X 1W5, Canada
Tel.: (604) 273-1441
Fax: (604) 273-2046
Web Site: www.univarcanada.com
Sales Range: $1-4.9 Billion
Emp.: 100
Chemicals Distr
S.I.C.: 5169
N.A.I.C.S.: 424690
Randy D. Craddock *(Pres)*

Joint Ventures:

RBV Leaf bv (2)
PO Box 69
4900 AB Oosterhout, Netherlands
Tel.: (31) 162485485
Fax: (31) 162485562
Web Site: www.leaf.nl
Sales Range: $700-749.9 Million
Emp.: 2,400
Confectionery Mfr
S.I.C.: 2064
N.A.I.C.S.: 311352
Robert-Jan van Ogtrop *(Chm)*
Bengt Baron *(Pres & CEO)*
Danko Maras *(CFO)*
Giorgio Boggero *(Pres-Italy)*
Ewald Frenay *(Pres-Middle)*
Jacqueline Hoogerbrugge *(Pres-Ops)*
David Nuutinen *(Pres-Finland)*
Lars Pahlson *(Pres-Scandinavia)*
Jacob Broberg *(Sr VP-Corp Comm)*
Edwin Kist *(Sr VP-HR)*

Stockholm Headquarters

Leaf AB (3)
Telegrafgatan 6A
Box 4009
SE-169 04 Solna, Sweden
Tel.: (46) 8 5272 8808
Candy Mfr
S.I.C.: 2064
N.A.I.C.S.: 311340

Subsidiaries:

Leaf Eesti AS (3)
Adamsoni 2
10137 Tallinn, Estonia
Tel.: (372) 6691170
Fax: (372) 6691171
E-Mail: leaf@leaf.ee
Web Site: www.leaf.ee
Sales Range: $1-9.9 Million
Emp.: 12
Sugar Products Mfr
S.I.C.: 2063
N.A.I.C.S.: 311313
Dairi Neerot *(Sec)*

Leaf Italia S.r.l. (3)
Milano St 16
26100 Cremona, Italy
Tel.: (39) 372482319
Fax: (39) 037224600
E-Mail: info@sperlari.it
Web Site: www.sperlari.it
Emp.: 350
S.I.C.: 2063
N.A.I.C.S.: 311313

Subsidiary:

Sperlari, S.r.l. (4)
Via Milano 16
26100 Cremona, Italy
Tel.: (39) 03724821
Fax: (39) 0372 24600
Web Site: www.sperlari.it
Confectionery Mfr
S.I.C.: 2064
N.A.I.C.S.: 311340

Leaf Norway (3)
Fjordveien 3
1363 Hovik, Norway
Mailing Address:
PO Box 263
1323 Hovik, Norway
Tel.: (47) 67818100
Fax: (47) 67583601
E-Mail: fornavn.etternavn@leaf.no
Web Site: www.leaf.no
Emp.: 60
S.I.C.: 2063
N.A.I.C.S.: 311313
Lars Pahlson *(Pres-Leaf Scandinavia)*
Kenneth Fradksen *(Mng Dir)*

Malaco K/S (3)
Fabriksvej 6
4200 Slagelse, Denmark
Tel.: (45) 58565555
Fax: (45) 58565556
Web Site: www.malacoleaf.com
Sales Range: $1-9.9 Million
Emp.: 400
Sugar Production
S.I.C.: 2063
N.A.I.C.S.: 311313

MalacoLeaf Denmark A/S (3)
Vallensbokvej 18 D
DK 2605 Brondby, Denmark
Tel.: (45) 43297500
Fax: (45) 43297501
Web Site: www.malacoleaf.com
Sales Range: $1-9.9 Million
Emp.: 35
Sugar Mfr
S.I.C.: 2063
N.A.I.C.S.: 311313

RBV Leaf Belgium N.V. (3)
Everdongenlaan 25
2300 Turnhout, Belgium
Tel.: (32) 14405311
Fax: (32) 14422946
Web Site: www.rbvleaf.com
Emp.: 25
Confectionery
S.I.C.: 5441
N.A.I.C.S.: 445292

Van Gansewinkel Groep B.V. (2)
Flight Forum 240
5657 DH Eindhoven, Netherlands NL
Mailing Address:
Postbus 8785
NL-5605 LT Eindhoven, Netherlands
Tel.: (31) 402944444
Fax: (31) 407514001
E-Mail: info@vangansewinkel.com
Web Site: www.vangansewinkel.com
Sales Range: $1-4.9 Billion
Emp.: 6,500
Holding Company; Owned 38% by CVC Capital Partners Group Sarl & 33% by KKR & Co. L.P.
S.I.C.: 6719
N.A.I.C.S.: 551112
Yves Luca *(Co-COO)*
Frans C.W. van de Noort *(Co-COO)*

Subsidiaries:

Holding AVR-Bedrijven NV (3)
Seattleweg 17
NL-3195 ND Rotterdam, Netherlands NL
Mailing Address: (100%)
Postbus 59144
3008 PC Rotterdam, Netherlands
Tel.: (31) 181275275
Web Site: www.vangansewinkel.eu
Sales Range: $400-449.9 Million
Emp.: 2,200
Holding Company; Waste Management Services
S.I.C.: 6719
N.A.I.C.S.: 551112
Reinhard J. Gorenflos *(Chm-Supervisory Bd)*
Ruud Sondag *(CEO)*
Frans C.W. van de Noort *(COO)*
Paul M. Braams *(Sec)*

Subsidiaries:

AVR-Industrial Services B.V. (4)
Seattleweg 17
NL-3195 ND Rotterdam, Netherlands NL
Tel.: (31) 181273443
Web Site: www.vangansewinkel.eu
Sales Range: $25-49.9 Million
Hazardous Waste Collection & Removal Services
S.I.C.: 4212
N.A.I.C.S.: 562112

Co-Headquarters:

Van Gansewinkel N.V. (3)
Nijverheidsstraat 2
B-2870 Puurs, Belgium BE
Tel.: (32) 70223100 (100%)
Fax: (32) 70223101
E-Mail: info@vangansewinkel.eu
Web Site: www.vangansewinkel.eu
Sales Range: $250-299.9 Million
Emp.: 80
Waste Collection & Processsing Services
S.I.C.: 8741
N.A.I.C.S.: 551114
Yves Luca *(Mng Dir & COO)*

Non-U.S. Holdings:

Sunrise Communications AG (1)
Binzmuhlestrasse 130
8050 Zurich, Switzerland CH
Tel.: (41) 587777777
Fax: (41) 587776167
E-Mail: info@sunrise.net
Web Site: www1.sunrise.ch
Sales Range: $1-4.9 Billion
Emp.: 1,600
Mobile Telecommunications & Internet Services
S.I.C.: 4812
N.A.I.C.S.: 517210
Dominik S. Koechlin *(Chm)*
Lorne Somerville *(Vice Chm)*
Oliver Steil *(CEO)*
Kamran Ziaee *(CTO)*
Andreas Gregori *(Chief Comml Officer-Residential)*

TechnoPro Holdings, Inc. (1)
6-10-1 Roppongi 6-chome
Minato-ku, Tokyo, 106-6135, Japan
Tel.: (81) 3 3405 9229
Fax: (81) 3 3405 9448
E-Mail: pr@technopro.com
Web Site: www.technopro.com
Sales Range: $650-699.9 Million
Emp.: 12,231
Engineering Staffing Services
S.I.C.: 7361
N.A.I.C.S.: 561311
Yasuji Nishio *(CEO)*
Akito Sonohara *(Mng Dir & Gen Mgr-HR & Gen Affairs)*

Subsidiaries:

CSI, Inc. (2)
Tokyo Minato-ku 6-10-1 Roppongi
Roppongi Hills Mori Tower 35F, Tokyo, 106 6135, Japan
Tel.: (81) 354101014
Fax: (81) 354101015
Web Site: www.csicorp.jp
Emp.: 1,395
Software Design Services
S.I.C.: 7373
N.A.I.C.S.: 541512
Kouichirou Asai *(Pres)*

Hitec, Inc. (2)
Tokyo Minato-ku 6-10-1 Roppongi Roppongi Hills Mori Tower 35F
Tokyo, 106 6135, Japan
Tel.: (81) 354101012
Fax: (81) 354101013
Web Site: www.hitec.co.jp
Emp.: 770
Biotechnology Research & Development Company
S.I.C.: 8731
N.A.I.C.S.: 541711
Masami Hayafune *(Pres)*

TechnoPro Smile, Inc. (2)
(Formerly Premier Smile, Inc.)
Minato-ku Roppongi Hills Mori Tower 35F
6-10-1 Roppongi, Tokyo, 106 6135, Japan
Tel.: (81) 363616055
Fax: (81) 363616208
E-Mail:
Web Site: www.technopro-smile.com
Emp.: 30
Staffing Services
S.I.C.: 7363
N.A.I.C.S.: 561330
Akito Sonohara *(Pres)*

TechnoPro Engineering Inc. (2)
Tokyo Minato-ku 6-10-1 Roppongi
Roppongi Hills Mori Tower 35F, Tokyo, 106 6135, Japan
Tel.: (81) 363117924
Fax: (81) 363117921
E-Mail: mspinfo@gweg.co.jp
Web Site: www.technopro-eg.com
Emp.: 2,035
Engineering Services
S.I.C.: 8711
N.A.I.C.S.: 541330
Kouichirou Asai *(Pres)*

CVC CAYMAN VENTURES CORP.

(Name Changed to Discovery Harbour Resources Corp.)

CVC LIMITED

(d/b/a CVC Group)
Level 42 Suncorp Place 259 George Street
Sydney, NSW, 2000, Australia
Tel.: (61) 290878000
Fax: (61) 290878088
E-Mail: cvc@cvc.com.au
Web Site: www.cvc.com.au
Year Founded: 1984
CVC—(ASX)

Rev.: $121,833,561
Assets: $260,822,001
Liabilities: $62,795,163
Net Worth: $198,026,838
Earnings: $11,545,893
Emp.: 10
Fiscal Year-end: 06/30/13
Business Description:
Venture Capital & Investment Management Firm
S.I.C.: 6211
N.A.I.C.S.: 523999
Personnel:
John Douglas Read *(Chm)*
Alexander Damien Harry Beard *(CEO & Co-Sec)*
John Andrew Hunter *(Co-Sec)*
Board of Directors:
John Douglas Read
Alexander Damien Harry Beard
Jason Ters

Subsidiary:

CVC Managers Pty. Limited (1)
Level 42 Suncorp Place
259 George Street, Sydney, NSW, 2000, Australia AU
Tel.: (61) 290878000
Fax: (61) 298078088
Investment Management Services
S.I.C.: 6799
N.A.I.C.S.: 523920
John Andrew Hunter *(Controller-Fin)*

Holding:

CVC Property Fund (1)
Level 42 Suncorp Place 259 George Street
Sydney, NSW, 2000, Australia AU
Tel.: (61) 290878000 (85.26%)
Fax: (61) 290878088
E-Mail:
Web Site: www.cvc.com.au/cvctpf
CJT—(ASX)
Rev.: $4,037,221
Assets: $34,582,057
Liabilities: $22,573,680
Net Worth: $12,008,377
Earnings: $1,277,003
Fiscal Year-end: 06/30/13
Real Estate Investment Trust
S.I.C.: 6726
N.A.I.C.S.: 525990
Vanda Russell Gould *(CEO)*
John Andrew Hunter *(Sec)*

Affiliate:

CVC Private Equity Limited (1)
Level 42 Suncorp Place 259 George Street
Sydney, NSW, 2000, Australia AU
Tel.: (61) 2 9087 8000
Fax: (61) 2 9087 8088
Web Site: www.cvc.com.au/cvcpe
Rev.: $505,885
Assets: $13,662,194
Liabilities: $37,767
Net Worth: $13,624,427
Earnings: ($207,177)
Fiscal Year-end: 06/30/13
Closed-End Venture Capital Private Equity Fund
S.I.C.: 6726
N.A.I.C.S.: 525990
Vanda Russell Gould *(Chm)*
Elliot Grant Kaplan *(Mng Dir)*
Alexander Damien Harry Beard *(Co-Sec)*
John A. H. Hunter *(Co-Sec)*

CVC PROPERTY FUND

(See Under CVC Limited)

CVI ENERGY CORPORATION LIMITED

9th Floor 28 The Esplanade
6000 Perth, WA, Australia
Tel.: (61) 892264788
Fax: (61) 892264799
Sales Range: Less than $1 Million
Business Description:
Energy & Minerals Investments Export
S.I.C.: 6211
N.A.I.C.S.: 523999
Personnel:
Mark Smyth *(CEO & Sec)*
Board of Directors:
Bernard Robert Brady
Philip Graeme Rand
Mark Smyth

Computershare Investor Services
Level 2 45 St Georges Terrace
Perth, Australia

CVIDYA NETWORKS LTD.

3 Sapir Street Ampa Building
PO Box 12003
Herzliyya, 46733, Israel
Tel.: (972) 99734000
Fax: (972) 99734001
E-Mail: info@cvidya.com
Web Site: www.cvidya.com
Business Description:
Revenue Intelligence Solutions
S.I.C.: 7372
N.A.I.C.S.: 511210
Personnel:
Alon Aginsky *(Co-Founder, Pres & CEO)*
Limor Schwartz *(CFO)*
Ronen Tanami *(COO)*
Gadi Solotorevsky *(Chief Scientist)*
Eran Wagner *(Pres-Ops-North America)*
Amit Daniel *(Exec VP-Mktg & Bus Dev)*
Ron Halpern *(Exec VP-Global Sls)*

CVILUX CORPORATION

9F No 9 Ln 3 Sec 1 Chung-Cheng E Rd
Tamsui, Taipei, Taiwan
Tel.: (886) 226201000
Fax: (886) 226282333
E-Mail: cvilux@cvilux.com.tw
Web Site: www.cvilux.com.tw
8103—(TAI)
Sales Range: $25-49.9 Million
Business Description:
Computer Communication Equipment Mfr
S.I.C.: 3678
N.A.I.C.S.: 334417
Personnel:
Chao-Chun Yang *(Chm)*

Non-U.S. Subsidiaries:

CviLux (Singapore) Corporation (1)
Block 52 Ubi Avenue 3 04-36 Froniter
Singapore, Singapore
Tel.: (65) 67420946
Fax: (65) 6 842 5770
E-Mail: cviluxsing@pacific.net.sg
Electronic Components Distr
S.I.C.: 5065
N.A.I.C.S.: 423690

Dongguan Qunhan Electronics Co.,Ltd. (1)
Tai He Road Gao Long Development Zone
Huan Zhu Li Village
Chang Ping Town, Dongguan, Guangdong, 523560, China
Tel.: (86) 769 83397111
Fax: (86) 769 83397900
E-Mail: cvilux.sales@cvilux.com.tw
Connectors Mfr
S.I.C.: 3678
N.A.I.C.S.: 334417

CVM MINERALS LIMITED

3rd Floor Wisma Ho Wah Genting No 35 Jalan Maharajalela
50150 Kuala Lumpur, Malaysia
Tel.: (60) 2148 1088
Fax: (60) 2148 5288
E-Mail: info@cvmminerals.com
Web Site: www.cvmminerals.com
0705—(HKG)
Sls.: $1,873,811
Assets: $129,488,467
Liabilities: $109,458,565
Net Worth: $20,029,902
Earnings: ($85,697,729)
Emp.: 174
Fiscal Year-end: 12/31/12
Business Description:
Magnesium Mining & Exploration Services
S.I.C.: 1099
N.A.I.C.S.: 212299
Personnel:
Kuang Ji *(Chm)*
Aaron Ooi Hong Lim *(Vice Chm)*
Hui Boon Lim *(Pres)*
Wai Kwan Leung *(CEO)*
Keet Loy Wong *(CFO)*
Annie Man Wai Au *(Sec)*
Board of Directors:
Kuang Ji
Lee Chang Chong
Wai Kwan Leung
Zi Cong Ll
Hai Yang Liang
Aaron Ooi Hong Lim
Tony Tan
Choi Kay Wong
Legal Counsel:
Richards Butler
20/F Alexandra House 16-20 Chater Road
Central, China (Hong Kong)
Tel.: (852) 2810 8008
Fax: (852) 2810 0664
Transfer Agent:
Computershare Hong Kong Investor Services Limited
Shops 1712-1716 17th Floor Hopewell Centre
183 Queens Road East
Wanchai, China (Hong Kong)

CVS GROUP PLC

CVS House Vinces Road
Diss, Norfolk, IP22 4AY, United Kingdom
Tel.: (44) 1379644288
Fax: (44) 1379644004
E-Mail: admin@cvsvets.com
Web Site: www.cvsgroupplc.com
CVSG—(LSE)
Rev.: $189,672,729
Assets: $137,872,017
Liabilities: $98,863,554
Net Worth: $39,008,463
Earnings: $6,317,160
Emp.: 2,479
Fiscal Year-end: 06/30/13
Business Description:
Veterinary Services
S.I.C.: 0742
N.A.I.C.S.: 541940
Personnel:
Simon Innes *(CEO)*
Rebecca Cleal *(Sec)*
Board of Directors:
Richard Connell
Simon Innes
Mike McCollum
Nick Perrin
Legal Counsel:
Leathes Prior
74 The Close
Norwich, United Kingdom

DLA Piper UK LLP
3 Noble Street
London, United Kingdom

Subsidiaries:

Axiom Veterinary Laboratories Limited (1)
The Manor House Brunel Rd
Newton Abbot, Devon, TQ12 4PB, United Kingdom
Tel.: (44) 1626355655
Fax: (44) 1626357750
E-Mail: admin@axiomvetlab.co.uk
Web Site: www.axiomvetlab.com
Emp.: 50
Clinical Pathology Services
S.I.C.: 8071
N.A.I.C.S.: 621511
Anne Tiley *(Head-Diagnostic Support)*

CVS (UK) Limited (1)
CVS House Vinces Rd
Diss, Norfolk, IP22 4AY, United Kingdom
Tel.: (44) 1379644288
Fax: (44) 1379644004
E-Mail: admin@cvsvets.com
Web Site: www.cvsukltd.co.uk
Emp.: 45
Veterinary Services
S.I.C.: 0742
N.A.I.C.S.: 541940
Simon Innes *(CEO)*

Rossendale Pet Crematorium Limited (1)
Sunnybank Farm
Crawshawbooth, Rossendale, Lancashire, BB4 8UE, United Kingdom
Tel.: (44) 1706213810
Fax: (44) 1706213610
E-Mail: enquiries@rossendalepetcrem.co.uk
Web Site: www.rossendalepetcrem.co.uk
Emp.: 10
Pet Cremation Services
S.I.C.: 7261
N.A.I.C.S.: 812220
Russell Grey *(Gen Mgr)*

CVTECH GROUP INC.

1975 JB Michaud Street
Drummondville, QC, J2C 0H2, Canada
Tel.: (819) 479-7771
Fax: (819) 479-8887
Web Site: www.cvtech.ca
CVT—(TSX)
Rev.: $247,710,778
Assets: $155,591,963
Liabilities: $74,543,548
Net Worth: $81,048,415
Earnings: $10,117,136
Emp.: 922
Fiscal Year-end: 12/31/12
Business Description:
Continuously Variable Transmission System Mfr; Power Transmission System Construction Services
S.I.C.: 3568
N.A.I.C.S.: 333613
Personnel:
Jacques Joly *(Chm)*
Andrew Laramee *(Pres & CEO)*
Mario Trahan *(CFO)*
Emilie Duguay *(Legal Counsel & Sec)*
Board of Directors:
Jacques Joly
Robert Beaudoin
Serge Chiasson
Andrew Laramee
Andre Lepage
Luc Reny
Jean Rochette
Legal Counsel:
Stein Monast LLP Lawyers
70 Dalhousie Street Suite 300
Quebec, QC, G1K 4B2, Canada
Transfer Agent:
Computershare Investor Services Inc.
1500 University Street Suite 700
Montreal, QC, H3A 3SB, Canada

Subsidiaries:

CVTech-AAB Inc. (1)
3037 Boul Frontenac Est
Thetford Mines, Quebec, QC, G6G 6P6, Canada
Tel.: (418) 335-7220
Fax: (418) 335-5613
Toll Free: (800) 518-7220
E-Mail: info@cvtech-aab.com
Web Site: www.cvtech-aab.com
Emp.: 55
Engine Rebuilding Services
S.I.C.: 5013
N.A.I.C.S.: 423120

CVTech Group Inc.—(Continued)

Michel Bernard *(Gen Mgr)*

Thiro Ltee. (1)
489 Boul Industriel E
C P 458, Victoriaville, QC, G6P 6T3, Canada
Tel.: (819) 752-9741
Fax: (819) 752-4386
E-Mail: info@thiro.com
Web Site: www.thiro.com
Emp.: 200
Power Delivery Contract Services
S.I.C.: 4939
N.A.I.C.S.: 221122

U.S. Subsidiaries:

Riggs Distler & Company Inc. (1)
4 Esterbrook Ln
Cherry Hill, NJ 08003-4002
Tel.: (856) 433-6000
Fax: (856) 433-6035
Web Site: www.riggsdistler.com
Sales Range: $100-124.9 Million
Emp.: 200
Mechanical Contractor
S.I.C.: 1711
N.A.I.C.S.: 238220
Stephen M. Zemaitatis, Jr. *(Pres & Exec VP-Ops)*

Thiro USA Inc. (1)
127 Costello Rd
Newington, CT 06111
Tel.: (860) 667-2163
Fax: (860) 667-3103
Toll Free: (800) 240-4446
E-Mail: thiro@thirousa.com
Web Site: www.thirousa.com
Emp.: 50
Utility Contract Services
S.I.C.: 5571
N.A.I.C.S.: 441228

CVTECH-IBC INC.

300 Labonte St
Drummondville, Quebec, QC, J2C 6X9, Canada
Tel.: (819) 477-3232
Fax: (819) 477-4705
E-Mail: info@cvtech-ibc.com
Web Site: www.cvtech-ibc.com
Emp.: 10
Business Description:
Power Transmission System Mfr
S.I.C.: 3568
N.A.I.C.S.: 333613
Personnel:
Alain Charest *(VP)*

CW GROUP HOLDINGS LIMITED

50 Kallang Avenue #05-01/02
Singapore, 339505, Singapore
Tel.: (65) 6259 2289
Fax: (65) 6259 9829
E-Mail: enquiry@cwgroup-int.com
Web Site: www.cwgroup-int.com
1322—(HKG)
Emp.: 210
Business Description:
Holding Company; Precision Machine Tool Mfr
S.I.C.: 6719
N.A.I.C.S.: 551112
Personnel:
William Wong *(Chm & CEO)*
Suan Ping Foo *(CFO)*
Mun-Sum Wong *(COO)*
Chwee Heng Lim *(CTO)*
Board of Directors:
William Wong
Johnny Hon Chung Chan
Cheng Tuck Kuan
Jeffery Su Aun Ong
Mun-Sum Wong
Sam Wong

Subsidiaries:

CW Advanced Technologies Pte. Ltd. (1)
50 Kallang Avenue 05-01/02
Singapore, 339505, Singapore
Tel.: (65) 6747 3996
Fax: (65) 6747 7976
Industrial Equipment Distr
S.I.C.: 5084
N.A.I.C.S.: 423830

CW Group Pte. Ltd. (1)
50 Kallang Avenue 05-01/02
Singapore, 339505, Singapore
Tel.: (65) 6259 2289
Fax: (65) 6259 9829
Industrial Machinery & Equipment Whslr
S.I.C.: 5084
N.A.I.C.S.: 423830

CW Tech Pte. Ltd. (1)
50 Kallang Avenue 05-01/02
Singapore, 339505, Singapore
Tel.: (65) 6259 2289
Fax: (65) 6259 9829
Emp.: 20
Investment Management Services
S.I.C.: 6799
N.A.I.C.S.: 523920
William Wong, *(CEO)*

SG Tech Holdings Limited (1)
50 Kallang Avenue 05-01/02
Singapore, 339505, Singapore
Tel.: (65) 6259 2289
Fax: (65) 6259 9829
E-Mail: enquiries@sgtechholdings.com
Web Site: www.sgtechholdings.com
Investment Management Services
S.I.C.: 6799
N.A.I.C.S.: 523920
William Wong *(Chm & CEO)*
Lee Tiang Soon *(CFO)*
Lim Chwee Heng *(COO & Exec Dir)*

C.W. MACKIE PLC

No 36 DR Wijewardena Mawatha
Colombo, 10, Sri Lanka
Tel.: (94) 112423554
Fax: (94) 112423554
E-Mail: info@cwmackie.com
Web Site: www.cwmackie.com
CWM—(COL)
Rev.: $60,030,583
Assets: $23,192,597
Liabilities: $9,912,784
Net Worth: $13,279,814
Earnings: $1,283,577
Emp.: 560
Fiscal Year-end: 03/31/13
Business Description:
Latex Crepe Rubber Mfr & Export Services
S.I.C.: 2822
N.A.I.C.S.: 325212
Personnel:
William Tissa Ellawala *(Chm & CEO)*
Asoka I. Piyadigama *(CFO)*
Camani Renuka Ranasinghe *(Sec)*
Board of Directors:
William Tissa Ellawala
Hemaka Devapriya Senarath Amarasuriya
Dhaman Rajendram Arudpragasam
Ajit Mahendra de Silva Jayaratne
Karawa Thanthrige Aruna Mangala Perera
Ranjit Crisantha Peries
Alagarajah Rajaratnam
Anushman Rajaratnam
Camani Renuka Ranasinghe
Thirugnanasambandar Senthilverl

CWC WELL SERVICES CORP.

Bow Valley Square III Suite 755 255 - 5th Ave SW
Calgary, AB, T2P 3G6, Canada
Tel.: (403) 264-2177
Fax: (403) 264-2842
E-Mail: info@cwcwellservices.com
Web Site: www.cwcwellservices.com
Year Founded: 2007
CWC—(TSXV)
Rev.: $111,660,255
Assets: $151,766,974
Liabilities: $55,878,834
Net Worth: $95,888,139
Earnings: $4,754,398
Emp.: 511
Fiscal Year-end: 12/31/12
Business Description:
Oil & Gas Exploration Services
S.I.C.: 1389
N.A.I.C.S.: 213112
Personnel:
Jim Reid *(Chm)*
Duncan T. Au *(Pres & CEO)*
Ryan A. Michaluk *(CFO)*
James L. Kidd *(Sec)*
Board of Directors:
Jim Reid
Duncan T. Au
Gary L. Bentham
Alexander D. Greene
Wade McGowan
Transfer Agent:
Olympia Trust Company
Suite 2300 125 9th Ave SE
Calgary, AB, Canada

CWH RESOURCES LTD.

Suite 1503 Level 15
97 99 Bathurst Street, Sydney, NSW, 2000, Australia
Tel.: (61) 2 9268 0555
Fax: (61) 2 9268 0155
E-Mail: office@cwh.com.au
Web Site: www.cwh.com.au
CWH—(ASX)
Business Description:
Production, Marketing, Research & Development & Investments in Building Materials, Mining & Construction Industries
S.I.C.: 5211
N.A.I.C.S.: 444190
Personnel:
Bao Cheng Luo *(Chm)*
Alistair Mckeough *(Sec)*
Board of Directors:
Bao Cheng Luo
Peter Blair
Shun Ming Li
Charles Sher
Wei Guo Wang

Non-U.S. Subsidiary:

Chongqing Yuao Building Material Co. Ltd. (1)
Shuangshi Town
Yongchuan, Chongqing, 402193, China (100%)
Tel.: (86) 2349301787
Fax: (86) 2349303249
Web Site: www.cwh.com.cn/abtus.htm
Cement & Limestone Production
S.I.C.: 3241
N.A.I.C.S.: 327310
Mengjiao Yang *(Mgr)*

CWN MINING ACQUISITION CORPORATION

Suite 368 1199 West Pender Street
Vancouver, BC, V6E 2R1, Canada
Tel.: (778) 998-9168
E-Mail: terrywong@cwncapital.com
Year Founded: 2012
CWN.P—(TSXV)
Business Description:
Investment Services
S.I.C.: 6211
N.A.I.C.S.: 523999
Personnel:
Joe Kin Foon Tai *(Chm, Pres & CEO)*
Terry Wong *(CFO & Sec)*
Board of Directors:
Joe Kin Foon Tai
William B. Burton
Chi Tung Chan
Transfer Agent:
Equity Financial Trust Company
1185 West Georgia Street Suite 1620
Vancouver, BC, Canada

CX ADVISORS LLP

(d/b/a CX Partners)
D-15 1st Floor Defence Colony
New Delhi, 110024, India
Tel.: (91) 11 4764 0000
Web Site: www.cxpartners.in
Business Description:
Investment Advisory Services
S.I.C.: 6282
N.A.I.C.S.: 523930
Personnel:
Ajay Relan *(Mng Partner)*
Jayanta Kumar Basu *(Partner)*
Amit Bhatiani *(Partner)*
Vivek Chhachhi *(Partner)*
Tarun Khanna *(Principal)*

Subsidiary:

CX Capital Management Limited (1)
D-15 1st Floor Defence Colony
New Delhi, 10024, India In
Tel.: (91) 11 4764 0000
Web Site: www.cxcapital.net
Investment Fund Management Services
S.I.C.: 6282
N.A.I.C.S.: 523920

Holding:

Transaction Solutions International (India) Private Limited (2)
11 A&B 4th Floor D2 Southern Park Saket Place
Saket, New Delhi, 110 017, India In
Tel.: (91) 1142658401 (75%)
Fax: (91) 1142658409
Web Site: www.tsiplc.com
Electronic Transaction Processing Services
S.I.C.: 6099
N.A.I.C.S.: 522320
Mohnish Kumar *(CEO)*

CX TECHNOLOGY CORPORATION

No 33 Ln 433 Chung Cheng Rd
Section 2
320 Chung-li, Taoyuan, Taiwan
Tel.: (886) 34253160
Fax: (886) 34258846
Web Site: www.cxtechnology.com
2415—(TAI)
Sales Range: $10-24.9 Million
Business Description:
Magnetic Induction Speaker Parts Mfr
S.I.C.: 3651
N.A.I.C.S.: 334310
Personnel:
Albert Kwang-Chin Ting *(Chm)*
Board of Directors:
Albert Kwang-Chin Ting
Harvey Chang
Roy Lee
C. Y. Wang
Jay Wu

Non-U.S. Subsidiary:

CX Technology (Shanghai) Corp. (1)
245 Pan Qiao Road Xu Han Town
Jia Ding District, Shanghai, 201809, China
Tel.: (86) 2139533308
Fax: (86) 2139533309
E-Mail: sales_sh@mail.cxtechnology.com
Metal Stampings Mfr
S.I.C.: 3469
N.A.I.C.S.: 332119

CYAN HOLDINGS PLC

Buckingway Business Park Anderson Road
Swavesey, Cambridge, CB24 4UQ, United Kingdom

Tel.: (44) 1954234400
Fax: (44) 1954234405
E-Mail: information@cyantechnology.com
Web Site: www.cyantechnology.com
CYAN—(LSE)
Rev.: $497,783
Assets: $4,713,906
Liabilities: $454,475
Net Worth: $4,259,430
Earnings: ($4,543,257)
Emp.: 23
Fiscal Year-end: 12/31/12

Business Description:
Semiconductor Mfr
S.I.C.: 3674
N.A.I.C.S.: 334413

Personnel:
John James Cronin *(Chm)*
Paul Ruskin *(COO)*
Ken Siegel *(Gen Counsel & VP)*

Board of Directors:
John James Cronin
Stephen Newton
John Read
Simon Smith

Legal Counsel:
Taylor Wessing LLP
24 Hills Road
Cambridge, United Kingdom

Non-U.S. Subsidiary:

Cyan Asia Limited **(1)**
Ste 2012 20 F Paul Y Ctr 51 Hung To Rd
Kwun Tong Dist, Kowloon, China (Hong Kong)
Tel.: (852) 27971900
Fax: (852) 23891956
E-Mail: asiasales@cyantechnology.com
Emp.: 5
Microcontroller Sales & Marketing Services
S.I.C.: 5065
N.A.I.C.S.: 423690

Subsidiary:

Cyan Technology Limited **(1)**
Buckingway Business Park
Swavesey, Cambs, CB24 4UQ, United Kingdom
Tel.: (44) 1954234400
Fax: (44) 1954234405
E-Mail: sales@cyantechnology.com
Web Site: www.cyantechnology.com
Emp.: 25
Microcontroller Chip Mfr
S.I.C.: 3674
N.A.I.C.S.: 334413

CYBA-STEVENS MANAGEMENT GROUP

3016 19 St NE Ste 100
Calgary, AB, T2E 6Y9, Canada
Tel.: (403) 291-3288
Fax: (403) 291-2277
Toll Free: (888) 336-3397
E-Mail: info@cybastevens.com
Web Site: www.cybastevens.com
Sales Range: $400-449.9 Million
Emp.: 50

Business Description:
Grocery Merchant Whslr
S.I.C.: 5141
N.A.I.C.S.: 424410

CYBELE INDUSTRIES LIMITED

138 & 179 Sidco Industrial Estate
Ambattur, Chennai, Tamil Nadu, 600 098, India
Tel.: (91) 44 32958399
Fax: (91) 44 43111117
E-Mail: investor@qflexcable.com
Web Site: www.qflexcable.com
531472—(BOM)
Sls.: $3,069,835
Assets: $6,744,648
Liabilities: $2,136,846
Net Worth: $4,607,802
Earnings: $707,116
Fiscal Year-end: 03/31/13

Business Description:
Electric Cable Mfr
S.I.C.: 3496
N.A.I.C.S.: 332618

Personnel:
P. A. Joykutty *(Chm & Co-Mng Dir)*
Annamma Joy *(Co-Mng Dir)*

Board of Directors:
P. A. Joykutty
George Baby George
Sunny Kutty George
Annamma Joy
Thomas P. Joy
N. Karuppiah

Transfer Agent:
Cameo Corporate Services Limited
Subramanian Building No 1 Club House Road
5th Floor
Chennai, India

CYBER MEDIA INDIA LTD.

Cyber House B-35 Sector-32
Gurgaon, Haryana, 122001, India
Tel.: (91) 1244822222
Fax: (91) 1242380694
Web Site: www.cybermedia.co.in
CYBERMEDIA—(NSE)
Rev.: $13,460,230
Assets: $19,309,915
Liabilities: $12,267,324
Net Worth: $7,042,591
Earnings: ($327,885)
Emp.: 244
Fiscal Year-end: 03/31/13

Business Description:
Magazine Publishing Services
S.I.C.: 2721
N.A.I.C.S.: 511120

Personnel:
Pradeep Gupta *(Chm & Mng Dir)*
Shilpi Gupta *(Compliance Officer & Sec)*

Board of Directors:
Pradeep Gupta
Rohit Asava Chand
Kulmohan Singh Mehta
Krishan Kant Tulshan

Transfer Agent:
Link Intime India Pvt. Ltd.
A-40, Naraina Industrial Area Phase-II
New Delhi, India

CYBER VILLAGE SDN BHD

(Acquired by Silverlake Axis Ltd.)

CYBERAGENT, INC.

1 12 1 Dogenzaka Shibuya ku
Tokyo, 150 0043, Japan
Tel.: (81) 3 54590202
Fax: (81) 3 54590222
Web Site: www.cyberagent.co.jp
Year Founded: 1998
4751—(OTC TKS)
Sls.: $1,585,931,680
Assets: $794,708,000
Liabilities: $300,969,120
Net Worth: $493,738,880
Earnings: $102,519,040
Emp.: 2,089
Fiscal Year-end: 09/30/13

Business Description:
Internet Related Services Including E-Commerce, Online Gaming, Website Development & Advertising
S.I.C.: 2741
N.A.I.C.S.: 519130

Personnel:
Susumu Fujita *(Co-Founder & Pres)*
Yusuke Hidaka *(Co-Founder & VP-Social Game Bus)*
Masato Sato *(CTO-Tech Div & Gen Mgr-R&D)*

Subsidiaries:

AMoAd, Inc. **(1)**
2-11-1 Dogenzaka Shibuya Mark City West 13f
Shibuya-Ku, Tokyo, 150-0043, Japan
Tel.: (81) 3 5459 6760
Web Site: www.amoad.com
Emp.: 5
Mobile Platform Software & Development Services
S.I.C.: 7371
N.A.I.C.S.: 541511
Kazushi Fujita *(Mgr)*

CA Mobile Ltd. **(1)**
Infosstower 6F 20-1 Sakuragaoka
Shibuya-ku, Tokyo, 150-0031, Japan
Tel.: (81) 3 6415 3400
Fax: (81) 3 6415 3401
E-Mail: info@camobile.com
Web Site: www.camobile.com
Emp.: 330
Mobile Marketing Services
S.I.C.: 7389
N.A.I.C.S.: 561422

CyberAgent Ventures Inc. **(1)**
Akasaka DS bldg 3F 8-5-26 Akasaka
Minato-ku, Tokyo, 107-0052, Japan
Tel.: (81) 3 5772 1234
Fax: (81) 3 5772 1233
E-Mail: cav_pub@cyberagent.co.jp
Web Site: www.cyberagentventures.com
Emp.: 1
Venture Capital Services
S.I.C.: 6799
N.A.I.C.S.: 523910
Soichi Tajima *(Chm & CEO)*
Tetsuro Oshita *(Mng Dir)*

CyberZ Inc. **(1)**
1-12-1 Dogenzaka Shibuya Mark City 23f
Shibuya-Ku, Tokyo, 150-0043, Japan
Tel.: (81) 3 5459 6276
Fax: (81) 3 5428 2318
E-Mail: furuichi@cyberz.co.jp
Web Site: www.cyberz.co.jp
Emp.: 45
Internet Service Provider
S.I.C.: 4899
N.A.I.C.S.: 517919
Takahiro Yamauchi *(Mng Dir)*

Newness Inc **(1)**
20-1 Sakuragaoka-cho
Shibuya-ku, Tokyo, 150-0031, Japan
Tel.: (81) 3 6415 3418
Fax: (81) 3 6415 3406
Online Advertising Services
S.I.C.: 7319
N.A.I.C.S.: 541890

Trenders Inc. **(1)**
3-9-19 Higashi Pola Ebisu Bldg 2f
Shibuya-Ku, Tokyo, 150-0011, Japan
Tel.: (81) 3 5774 8871
Fax: (81) 3 5774 8872
E-Mail: Info@trenders.co.jp
Web Site: www.trenders.co.jp
6069—(TKS)
Sls.: $17,776,000
Assets: $19,481,000
Liabilities: $3,388,000
Net Worth: $16,093,000
Earnings: $2,728,000
Emp.: 70
Fiscal Year-end: 03/31/13
Marketing Consulting Services
S.I.C.: 8742
N.A.I.C.S.: 541613
Kahoko Tsunezawa *(CEO)*
Yuji Akao *(Exec Officer)*
Takeshi Igarashi *(Exec Officer)*
Ryoko Kurokawa *(Exec Officer)*
Yosuke Matsumoto *(Exec Officer)*

VOYAGE BB Inc **(1)**
First Place 8-16 Shinsen-Cho Shibuya 7 Floor
Shibuya-Ku, Tokyo, 150-0045, Japan
Tel.: (81) 3 5459 1168
E-Mail: voyagebb@voyagegroup.com
Web Site: www.voyage-bb.com
Internet Application Systems Development Services
S.I.C.: 7371
N.A.I.C.S.: 541511

VOYAGE GROUP Inc. **(1)**
Shibuya First Place Bldg 1F 6F 7F 8F
Shinsen-cho 8-16
Shibuya, Tokyo, 150-0045, Japan
Tel.: (81) 3 5459 1166
Fax: (81) 3 5459 4223
E-Mail: pr-info@voyagegroup.com
Web Site: www.voyagegroup.com
Rev.: $102,937,000
Emp.: 28
Online Media Research Services
S.I.C.: 8731
N.A.I.C.S.: 541712
Shinsuke Usami *(Pres & CEO)*
Hidenori Nagaoka *(CFO)*

Subsidiaries:

adingo, Inc. **(2)**
Shibuya First Place Bldg 8F Shinsen-cho 8-16
Shibuya, Tokyo, 150-0045, Japan
Tel.: (81) 3 5459 1182
Fax: (81) 3 5459 1881
E-Mail: info@adingo.jp
Web Site: www.adingo.jp
Emp.: 5
Online Advertising Services
S.I.C.: 7319
N.A.I.C.S.: 541890
Kazuyuki Furuya *(Gen Dir)*

Flessel, Inc. **(2)**
8-16 Shinsencho Shibuya First Place 8F
Tokyo, 150-0045, Japan
Tel.: (81) 3 5459 1178
Fax: (81) 3 5459 5571
Web Site: www.flessel.co.jp
Emp.: 15
Online Advertising Services
S.I.C.: 7319
N.A.I.C.S.: 541890
Shohei Terada *(Gen Mgr)*

genesix, Inc. **(2)**
8-16 Shinsencho Shibuya First Place 8F
Shibuya-Ku, Tokyo, 150-0045, Japan
Tel.: (81) 3 5459 1167
Fax: (81) 3 5459 5591
E-Mail: genesix@voyagegroup.com
Web Site: www.genesix.co.jp
Emp.: 15
Mobile Application Software Development Services
S.I.C.: 7371
N.A.I.C.S.: 541511
Fumiyasu Mita *(CEO)*

PeX, Inc **(2)**
8-16 Shinsencho Shibuya First Place 8F
Shibuya-Ku, Tokyo, 150-0045, Japan
Tel.: (81) 3 5459 1215
Fax: (81) 3 5459 5571
E-Mail: pex_alliance@voyagegroup.info
Web Site: www.pex.jp
Emp.: 11
Data Processing Services
S.I.C.: 7379
N.A.I.C.S.: 518210
Yasuyuki Tosaki *(Gen Mgr)*

Research Panel Asia Inc. **(2)**
8F First Place Bldg Shinsen-Cho 8-16
Shibuya, Tokyo, 150-0045, Japan
Tel.: (81) 3 5459 1230
E-Mail: contact@researchpanelasia.com
Web Site: www.researchpanelasia.com
Emp.: 8
Online Surveying Services
S.I.C.: 4899
N.A.I.C.S.: 517919
Toshiki Sano *(Pres)*

Research Panel, Inc. **(2)**
8-16 Shinsencho Shibuya First Place 8f
Shibuya-Ku, Tokyo, 150-0045, Japan
Tel.: (81) 3 5459 5562
Web Site: www.research-panel.jp
Information Services
S.I.C.: 7389
N.A.I.C.S.: 519190

VOYAGE Ventures Inc **(2)**
Shibuya First Place Bldg 8F Shinsen-Cho 8-16
Shibuya, Tokyo, 150-0045, Japan
Tel.: (81) 3 5459 1166
Fax: (81) 3 5459 4223
E-Mail: voyage-ventures@voyage.com
Web Site: www.voyage-ventures.com

CyberAgent, Inc.—(Continued)

Emp.: 250
Online Marketing Services
S.I.C.: 8742
N.A.I.C.S.: 541613
Hidenori Nagaoka *(Chm & CEO)*

Zucks Inc (1)
Shibuya First Place Bldg 8F Shinsen-cho 8-16
Shibuya, Tokyo, 150-0045, Japan
Tel.: (81) 3 5459 2061
Fax: (81) 3 54559 1881
E-Mail: zucks_inquiry@voyagegroup.info
Web Site: www.zucks.co.jp
Emp.: 15
Online Advertising Services
S.I.C.: 7319
N.A.I.C.S.: 541890
Masashi Nishizono *(Gen Dir)*

Non-U.S. Subsidiary:

CyberAgent Ventures (Beijing) Co., Ltd (1)
Twin Tower East Room 1023 10th Floor
B-12 Jianguomenwai Avenue
Beijing, 100022, China
Tel.: (86) 10 5123 5061
Fax: (86) 10 5123 5051
E-Mail: cav_pub@cyberagent.co.jp
Emp.: 1
Online Game Software Development Services
S.I.C.: 7371
N.A.I.C.S.: 541511
Nobuaki Kitagawa *(CEO & Mng Dir)*

CYBERCOM GROUP AB

Lindhagensgatan 126
PO Box 7574
103 93 Stockholm, Sweden
Tel.: (46) 857864600
Fax: (46) 857864610
E-Mail: info@cybercom.com
Web Site: www.cybercom.com
Year Founded: 1995
CYBE—(OMX)
Sls.: $204,053,645
Assets: $209,624,587
Liabilities: $84,110,270
Net Worth: $125,514,317
Earnings: ($8,217,868)
Emp.: 1,335
Fiscal Year-end: 12/31/12

Business Description:
IT Consulting Services
S.I.C.: 8999
N.A.I.C.S.: 541690

Personnel:
Hampus Ericsson *(Chm)*
Niklas Flyborg *(Pres & CEO)*
Camilla Oberg *(CFO)*
Helena Borglund *(Gen Counsel)*

Board of Directors:
Hampus Ericsson
Robin Hammarstedt
Nicolas Hassbjer
Jan-Erik Karlsson
Thomas Landberg
Henrik Lundin
Dag Sundman
Cecilia Westin

Non-U.S. Subsidiary:

Plenware Oy (1)
Pakkahuoneenaukio 2
PO Box 13
33201 Tampere, Finland
Tel.: (358) 104364000
Fax: (358) 32302250
E-Mail: info@cybercom.com
Web Site: www.cybercom.fi
Sales Range: $25-49.9 Million
Emp.: 550
Telecommunications Systems & Software Development Services
S.I.C.: 7371
N.A.I.C.S.: 541511
Petteri Puhakka *(CEO)*
Joni Aaltonen *(Sec)*

CYBERDECK SA

7 allee Moulin Berger
69130 Ecully, France
Tel.: (33) 478667400
Fax: (33) 478667401
E-Mail: info@cyberdeck.com
Web Site: www.cyberdeck.com
Year Founded: 1998
CBD—(EUR)
Sales Range: $1-9.9 Million
Emp.: 35

Business Description:
Interactive Kiosks & Associated Software Products Designer, Mfr & Marketer
S.I.C.: 3575
N.A.I.C.S.: 334118

Personnel:
Philippe Dufeutrelle *(Chm & Mng Dir)*

CYBERDYNE INC.

D25-1 Gakuen Minami
Tsukuba-shi, Ibaraki, 305-0818, Japan
Tel.: (81) 29 869 8446
Web Site: www.cyberdyne.jp
Rev.: $2,795,820
Emp.: 70
Fiscal Year-end: 03/31/13

Business Description:
Medical Device Mfr
S.I.C.: 3841
N.A.I.C.S.: 339112

Personnel:
Yoshiyuki Sankai *(CEO)*

CYBERGUN SA

ZI Les Bordes 9-11 Rue Henri Dunant
91070 Bondoufle, Ot, France
Tel.: (33) 1 69 11 71 00
Fax: (33) 1 69 11 71 01
E-Mail: infos@3psa.com
Web Site: www.cybergun.com
ALCYB—(EUR)
Rev.: $93,614,008
Emp.: 160
Fiscal Year-end: 03/31/13

Business Description:
Toy Gun Mfr
S.I.C.: 3942
N.A.I.C.S.: 339930

Personnel:
Jerome Marsac *(Chm-Supervisory Bd)*
Olivier Gualdoni *(CEO)*
Eric Gruau *(CFO)*

CYBERLINK CORP.

15F No 100 Minquan Rd
Xindian Dist, New Taipei City, 231, Taiwan
Tel.: (886) 2 8667 1298
Fax: (886) 2 8667 1385
Web Site: www.cyberlink.com
5203—(TAI)
Emp.: 610

Business Description:
Digital Entertainment & Multimedia Solutions Provider
S.I.C.: 7372
N.A.I.C.S.: 511210

Personnel:
Jau Huang *(Founder & Chm)*
Alice H. Chang *(CEO)*
Hyder Rabbani *(Sr VP & Gen Mgr-North America)*
Richard Carriere *(Sr VP-Global Mktg)*
Johnny Tseng *(Sr VP-R&D)*

Board of Directors:
Jau Huang
Alice H. Chang
Liang-Gee Cheng
Wen-Hsiang Hung
James Lee

Supervisory Board of Directors:
Wen-Chin Chen
Sherry Lin
Yuen-Man Lin

Transfer Agent:
Yuanta Core Pacific Securities
B1 No. 210 Sec. 3 Chengde Rd
Taipei, Taiwan

U.S. Subsidiary:

CyberLink.Com Corp. (1)
46750 Fremont Blvd Ste 200
Fremont, CA 94538-6573
Tel.: (510) 668-0118
Fax: (510) 668-0121
Multimedia Software Retailer
S.I.C.: 5045
N.A.I.C.S.: 423430
Hyder Rabbani *(Sr VP & Gen Mgr)*

Non-U.S. Subsidiaries:

CyberLink Europe B.V. (1)
Tyrellsestraat 2
6291 AL Vaals, Limburg, Netherlands
Tel.: (31) 433060797
Fax: (31) 433063235
E-Mail: info@cyberlink.com
Web Site: www.cyberlink.com
Emp.: 760
Video Playback Software Publishing Services
S.I.C.: 7372
N.A.I.C.S.: 511210
Alice Chang *(CEO)*

CyberLink Inc. (1)
Sigma Building 4F 3-7-12 Shibaura
Minato-ku, Tokyo, 108-0023, Japan
Tel.: (81) 3 5875 6650
Fax: (81) 3 5875 6652
Web Site: jp.cyberlink.com
Multimedia Software Sales & Support Service
S.I.C.: 7371
N.A.I.C.S.: 541511
Kenichi Takimoto *(Pres & Gen Mgr)*

CYBERLINK PACIFIC TELECOMMUNICATIONS LIMITED

202 1128 W Broadway
Vancouver, BC, V6H 1G5, Canada
Tel.: (604) 668-9898
Fax: (604) 668-9899
Year Founded: 1994
Rev.: $27,100,000
Emp.: 140

Business Description:
Communication Services
S.I.C.: 4813
N.A.I.C.S.: 517110

Personnel:
David Lopes *(Pres)*

CYBERLINKS CO., LTD.

849-3 Kimiidera
Wakayama-shi, Wakayama, 641-0012, Japan
Tel.: (81) 73 448 3600
Web Site: www.cyber-l.co.jp
3683—(JAS)
Rev.: $69,353,389
Emp.: 370
Fiscal Year-end: 12/31/12

Business Description:
Cloud-Based Software
S.I.C.: 7372
N.A.I.C.S.: 511210

Personnel:
Tsuneo Murakami *(Pres)*

CYBERMATE INFOTEK LTD.

11 Sripuri Colony Karkhana
Secunderabad, 500015, India
Tel.: (91) 40 6632 6447
Fax: (91) 40 6648 6446
E-Mail: info@cybermateinfotek.com
Web Site: www.cybermateinfotek.com
532271—(BOM)
Rev.: $2,433,615
Assets: $22,749,181
Liabilities: $1,809,028
Net Worth: $20,940,154
Earnings: $10,948
Emp.: 22
Fiscal Year-end: 03/31/13

Business Description:
IT Software Products Distr
S.I.C.: 5045
N.A.I.C.S.: 423430

Personnel:
P. C. Panthulu *(CEO & Mng Dir)*
P. Chandra Sekhar *(CFO & Dir-Fin)*
K. S. Shiva Kumar *(COO)*
R. Venkatakiran *(Compliance Officer & Sec)*

Board of Directors:
Pawan Kumar Kasera
Shankar Khasnis
P. C. Panthulu
K. K. Rao
D. Jayarami Reddy
P. Chandra Sekhar
K. S. Shiva Kumar

Transfer Agent:
Aarthi Consultants Private Limited
1-2-285, Domalguda
Hyderabad, India

CYBERNET SYSTEMS CO., LTD.

Fujisoft Bldg 3 Kanda-Neribeicho
Chiyoda-ku
Tokyo, 101-0022, Japan
Tel.: (81) 352973010
Fax: (81) 352973609
E-Mail: cybernet-products@cybernet.co.jp
Web Site: www.cybernet.co.jp
Year Founded: 1985
4312—(TKS)
Sls.: $149,327,013
Assets: $192,546,189
Liabilities: $46,325,444
Net Worth: $146,220,745
Earnings: $4,184,785
Emp.: 537
Fiscal Year-end: 03/31/13

Business Description:
Computer Aided Engineering Services
S.I.C.: 7373
N.A.I.C.S.: 541512

Personnel:
Kuniaki Tanaka *(Pres & CEO)*
Gun Eki *(Exec Officer)*
Masatake Kagari *(Exec Officer)*
Hiroshi Katou *(Exec Officer)*
Kyuetsu Mihira *(Sr Mng Exec Officer)*
Youichi Mizoguchi *(Exec Officer)*
Emiko Nishigohri *(Exec Officer)*
Hiroshi Takahashi *(Exec Officer)*
Hiroki Yoshinaga *(Mng Exec Officer)*

Board of Directors:
Kiyohito Koyama
Kyuetsu Mihira
Naitou Tatsuya

Non-U.S. Subsidiaries:

CCA Engineering Simulation Software (Shanghai) Co.,Ltd (1)
RM 908 No 777
Zhao Jia Bang Rd, 200032 Shanghai, China (100%)
Tel.: (86) 2164716037
Fax: (86) 2164716050
Web Site: www.cca-es.com
Emp.: 20
Software Reproducing
S.I.C.: 3652
N.A.I.C.S.: 334614

Lifen Mao *(Mng Dir)*

Cybernet CAE Systems (Shanghai) Co.,Ltd (1)
RM 718 Pine City Hotel
777 Zhaojiabang Road, 200032 Shanghai, China
Tel.: (86) 2164227122
Fax: (86) 2164171126
E-Mail: sales@cybernet.sh.cn
Web Site: www.cybernet.sh.cn
Emp.: 40
Software Reproducing
S.I.C.: 3652
N.A.I.C.S.: 334614
Yoichi Nakashima *(Gen Mgr)*

CYBERPLANET INTERACTIVE PUBLIC COMPANY LIMITED

Emporio Place Condominium 93/352
Floor 8 South Tower Soi Sukhumvit 24
Sukhumvit Rd Klongton Klongtoey,
Bangkok, 10110, Thailand
Tel.: (66) 21604248
Fax: (66) 21604249
E-Mail: bd@cpigames.com
Web Site: www.cpigames.com
Year Founded: 2000
CYBER—(THA)
Rev.: $126,888
Assets: $5,208,699
Liabilities: $2,617,933
Net Worth: $2,590,766
Earnings: ($1,893,711)
Fiscal Year-end: 12/31/12
Business Description:
Software Game Developer
S.I.C.: 7372
N.A.I.C.S.: 511210
Personnel:
Chanindej Vanijwongse *(Chm, Pres & CEO)*
Chanin Vanijwongse *(Mng Dir & Dir-Mktg)*
Board of Directors:
Chanindej Vanijwongse
Soraj Asavaprapha
Kittipol Pramoj Na Ayudhya
Anan Leetrakul
Wiluck Lohtong
Parkpoom Pakvisal
Kraipob Pangsapa
Chanin Vanijwongse

CYBERPLEX INC.

(Name Changed to EQ Inc.)

CYBERPORT GMBH

Am Brauhaus 5
D-01099 Dresden, Germany
Mailing Address:
Postfach 10 11 41
D-0108 Dresden, Germany
Tel.: (49) 351 33 95 60
Fax: (49) 351 33 95 699
E-Mail: info@cyberport.de
Web Site: www.cyberport.de
Sls.: $514,784,880
Business Description:
Computer Products Online Retailer
S.I.C.: 5961
N.A.I.C.S.: 454111
Personnel:
Danilo Frasiak *(Member-Mgmt Bd)*
Arnd Muckenberger *(Member-Mgmt Bd)*
Fritz Oidtmann *(Member-Mgmt Bd)*
Olaf Siegel *(Member-Mgmt Bd)*

CYBERPOWER SYSTEMS, INC.

6F 32 Sec 1 Chenggong Rd
Nanggang District, Taipei, 115, Taiwan
Tel.: (886) 226518699
Fax: (886) 226516821
E-Mail: sales@cyberpowersystems.com.tw
Web Site: www.cyberpowersystems.com.tw
3617—(TAI)
Sales Range: $100-124.9 Million
Emp.: 1,800
Business Description:
Power Supply Systems & Computer Peripherals Mfr & Distr
S.I.C.: 3699
N.A.I.C.S.: 335999
Personnel:
Jin Guo *(Chm)*
Lianxun He *(Pres)*

U.S. Subsidiary:

CyberPower Systems (USA), Inc. (1)
4241 12th Ave E Ste 400
Shakopee, MN 55379
Tel.: (952) 403-9500
Fax: (952) 403-0009
E-Mail: sales@cyberpowersystems.com
Web Site: www.cyberpowersystems.com
Emp.: 90
Uninterruptible Power Supply Systems Mfr
S.I.C.: 3699
N.A.I.C.S.: 335999
Dan Ayala *(VP-Worldwide Sls)*

Non-U.S. Subsidiaries:

Cyber Power Systems France (1)
ZI Saint Severin
28220 Cloyes-sur-le-Loir, France
Tel.: (33) 237986150
Fax: (33) 237986004
E-Mail: sales@cpsww.com.fr
Emp.: 14
Power Management Systems Distr
S.I.C.: 5063
N.A.I.C.S.: 423610
Loic Lamirault *(Gen Mgr)*

CyberPower Systems B.V. (1)
Flight Forum 3545
5657DW Eindhoven, Netherlands
Tel.: (31) 402348170
Fax: (31) 402340314
E-Mail: sales@cyberpower-eu.com
Web Site: eu.cyberpowersystems.com
Emp.: 9
Power Management Systems Distr
S.I.C.: 5063
N.A.I.C.S.: 423610
Douglas Wu *(Gen Mgr)*

CyberPower Systems K.K. (1)
9F Cosmo Kourakuen BL 1-3-10 Koishikawa
Bunkyoku, 112-0002 Tokyo, Japan
Tel.: (81) 358405025
Fax: (81) 358405026
E-Mail: sales@cpsww.co.jp
Web Site: www.cpsww.co.jp
Emp.: 3
Power Management Systems Distr
S.I.C.: 5063
N.A.I.C.S.: 423610
Ittoku Yoh *(Pres)*

CYBERSCAPE MULTIMEDIA LTD.

941 21st Main 22nd A Cross Opp BDA Complex
Banashankari 2nd Stage, Bengaluru, 560 070, India
Tel.: (91) 80 26710925
Fax: (91) 80 26714454
E-Mail: info@cyberscapeindia.com
Web Site: cyberscapeindia.com
Year Founded: 1996
532364—(BOM)
Sales Range: Less than $1 Million
Business Description:
Information Technology Service
S.I.C.: 7371
N.A.I.C.S.: 541511
Personnel:
K. Anand *(Mng Dir)*
M. S. Sridhar *(Mng Dir)*
Krishnakant Parashar *(Sec & Mgr-Fin)*

CYBERTAN TECHNOLOGY, INC.

99 Park Ave 3 Science Park
308 Hsin-chu, Taiwan
Tel.: (886) 35777777
Fax: (886) 35777788
E-Mail: info@cybertan.com.tw
Web Site: www.cybertan.com.tw
3062—(TAI)
Sales Range: $200-249.9 Million
Business Description:
Broadband & Wireless Networking Equipment Mfr
S.I.C.: 3661
N.A.I.C.S.: 334210
Personnel:
Gwong-Yih Lee *(Chm, CEO & Pres)*
Wayne Chan *(Vice Chm)*
Board of Directors:
Gwong-Yih Lee
Wayne Chan
Repus Hsiung
Andy Lee
Ching-Kuang C. Tzuang

U.S. Subsidiary:

CyberTAN Corporation (1)
15551 Red Hill Ave Ste B
Tustin, CA 92780
Tel.: (714) 258-2588
Fax: (714) 258-2688
Web Site: www.cybertan.com.tw/contactus.htm
Emp.: 10
Internet Service Provider
S.I.C.: 4899
N.A.I.C.S.: 517919

CYBIO AG

Goeschwitzer Strasse 40
07745 Jena, Thuringia, Germany
Tel.: (49) 36413510
Fax: (49) 3641351409
E-Mail: info@cybio-ag.com
Web Site: www.cybio-ag.com
CQJ—(DEU)
Sales Range: $10-24.9 Million
Emp.: 102
Business Description:
Plate Handling Product Developer
S.I.C.: 3399
N.A.I.C.S.: 331110
Personnel:
Klaus Berka *(Chm-Supervisory Bd)*
Martin Fischer *(Deputy Chm-Supervisory Bd)*
Udo Werner *(CEO & Member-Mgmt Bd)*
Thomas Moore *(CTO & Member-Mgmt Bd-Sls & R&D)*
Supervisory Board of Directors:
Klaus Berka
Martin Fischer
Kurt Ochner

CYBIRD HOLDINGS CO., LTD.

Roppongi Hills Mori Tower 22F 6-10-1 Roppongi
Tokyo, 106-6161, Japan
Tel.: (81) 357856111
Fax: (81) 357859321
Web Site: www.cybird.co.jp
Year Founded: 1998
Sales Range: $150-199.9 Million
Emp.: 670
Business Description:
Holding Company; Mobile Content & Platforms Developer & Marketer
S.I.C.: 4812
N.A.I.C.S.: 517210
Personnel:
Kazutomo Hori *(Pres & Grp CEO)*
Yoko Nakai *(Grp CFO)*
Hideaki Nagamori *(COO & Exec VP)*
Yohei Hosoda *(Exec VP)*
Toshiaki Kawata *(Exec VP)*
Yasuharu Kishitani *(Exec VP)*
Kenichiro Nakajima *(Exec VP)*
Shinichiro Yamashita *(Exec VP)*
Board of Directors:
Michael Alfant
Mark Chiba
Kazutomo Hori
Yohei Hosoda
Toshiaki Kawata
Yoko Nakai
Kenichiro Nakajima
Tomoya Sugimoto
Hiromichi Yoshitake
Masamichi Yoshizawa

Subsidiaries:

Gigaflops Japan Inc. (1)
Roppongi Hills Mori Tower 22nd Floor
Minato-Ku, Tokyo, Japan
Tel.: (81) 357856149
Web Site: www.gigaflops.co.jp
Emp.: 35
Data Processing Services
S.I.C.: 7379
N.A.I.C.S.: 518210

Plus Mobile Communications Co., Ltd. (1)
Roppongi Hills Mori Tower 22nd Floor C-O Cybird Co Ltd
Minato-Ku, Tokyo, Japan
Tel.: (81) 334052510
Advertising Agencies
S.I.C.: 7311
N.A.I.C.S.: 541810

CYBOZU INC.

12 F Karaku Mori Building
1-4-14 Koraku Bunkyo-ku, Tokyo, 112-0004, Japan
Tel.: (81) 358059035
Web Site: www.cybozu.com
Year Founded: 1997
4776—(TKS)
Sales Range: $50-74.9 Million
Emp.: 352
Business Description:
Software Services
S.I.C.: 7372
N.A.I.C.S.: 511210
Personnel:
Yoshihisa Aono *(Pres)*
Osamu Yamada *(Exec VP)*
Hideki Fudatsuji *(Exec Officer)*
Katsuhiko Matsumura *(Exec Officer)*
Hiroyuki Nakahara *(Exec Officer)*
Hirotaka Yamamoto *(Exec Officer)*
Yuji Yamamoto *(Exec Officer)*
Board of Directors:
Yoshihisa Aono
Shinya Hata
Osamu Yamada

Subsidiaries:

BRING UP Co.,Ltd. (1)
2-10-5 Toridoe Paito-ku
Tokyo, Japan
Tel.: (81) 358336322
Fax: (81) 338650216
Web Site: www.bringup.co.jp
Human Resource Development Services
S.I.C.: 8999
N.A.I.C.S.: 541612

Cybozu Media and Technology Co.,Ltd. (1)
7-3-16 Kikunakohoku-ku
Yokohama, 222-0011, Japan
Tel.: (81) 454318951
Fax: (81) 454318954
E-Mail: nishide@tc3.jp
Web Site: www.tc3.jp
Emp.: 10
Computer Servers Mfr

Cybozu Inc.—(Continued)

S.I.C.: 3571
N.A.I.C.S.: 334111

Cybozu Research Institute, Inc. **(1)**
1-4-14 Kouraku Bunkyo-Ku
Tokyo, 112-0004, Japan
Tel.: (81) 363612501
Fax: (81) 363612502
Web Site: www.cybozu-ri.co.jp
Emp.: 30
Business Research Services
S.I.C.: 8732
N.A.I.C.S.: 541720
Hideki Fudasuji *(Pres)*

J-Yado Inc. **(1)**
Shinjuku-ku Yotsuya 2-4-1 Rune Yotuya Bldg 8F
Tokyo, 160-0004, Japan
Tel.: (81) 359191220
Fax: (81) 359191225
E-Mail: info@j-yado.com
Web Site: www.j-yado.com
Emp.: 13
Tour Operating Services
S.I.C.: 4725
N.A.I.C.S.: 561520
Takahashi Hiroyuki *(Pres)*

YMIRLINK Inc. **(1)**
Ebisu East 438 Bldg 4F 4-3-8 Ebisu
Shibuya-ku, Tokyo, 150-0013, Japan
Tel.: (81) 368200088
Fax: (81) 357913262
Web Site: www.ymir.co.jp
Emp.: 57
Software Development Services
S.I.C.: 7371
N.A.I.C.S.: 541511
Wataru Shimizu *(Pres)*

Non-U.S. Subsidiaries:

Cybozu IT Shanghai Inc. **(1)**
Yan An W Rd 726 11th Fl E Room
Shanghai, 200050, China
Tel.: (86) 2152392626
Fax: (86) 2162515398
E-Mail: info@cybozu.net.cn
Web Site: www.cybozu.net.cn
Emp.: 30
Software Development Services
S.I.C.: 7371
N.A.I.C.S.: 541511
Huang Yuan *(Gen Mgr)*

Cybozu Vietnam Co., Ltd. **(1)**
7th Fl E Town 3 Bldg 364 Cong Hoa Ward 13
Tan Binh Dist, Ho Chi Minh City, Vietnam
Tel.: (84) 838131101
Fax: (84) 838131102
E-Mail: contatvo@cybozu.vn
Web Site: www.cybozu.com
Emp.: 24
Software Development Services
S.I.C.: 7371
N.A.I.C.S.: 541511
Huynx Trieu *(Mng Dir)*

CYBRDI INC.

No 29 Chang'An South Road
Xi'an, Shaanxi, China 710061
Tel.: (86) 29 8237 3068
Web Site:
Year Founded: 1966
CYDI.PK—(OTC)
Rev.: $783,175
Assets: $10,551,508
Liabilities: $6,124,658
Net Worth: $4,426,850
Earnings: ($655,640)
Emp.: 37
Fiscal Year-end: 12/31/12
Business Description:
Biological Product Mfr
S.I.C.: 2836
N.A.I.C.S.: 325414
Personnel:
Yanbiao Bai *(Chm, Pres & CEO)*
Yonghong Ren *(COO & Treas)*
Board of Directors:
Yanbiao Bai
Yonghong Ren

Transfer Agent:
Securities Transfer Corporation
2591 Dallas Pkwy Ste 102
Frisco, TX 75034
Tel.: (469) 633-0101
Fax: (469) 633-0088

CYCLE & CARRIAGE BINTANG BERHAD

Level 18 The Gardens North Tower
Mid Valley City
Lingkaran Syed Putra, 59200 Kuala Lumpur, Malaysia
Tel.: (60) 322648888
Fax: (60) 322822733
Web Site: www.ccb.com.my
CCB—(KLS)
Rev.: $215,178,481
Assets: $125,869,797
Liabilities: $62,307,752
Net Worth: $63,562,045
Earnings: $5,300,171
Emp.: 518
Fiscal Year-end: 12/31/12
Business Description:
Motor Vehicles Retailer
S.I.C.: 5013
N.A.I.C.S.: 423120
Personnel:
Kin Foo Wong *(CEO)*
Swee Chin Oh *(Co-Sec)*
Kok Leong Yeap *(Co-Sec)*
Board of Directors:
Alex Newbigging
Kim Teck Cheah
Vimala Menon
Tamim Ansari Mohamed
Sulaiman Sujak

CYCLES LAMBERT INC.

1000 rue des Riveurs
Levis, QC, G6V 9G3, Canada
Tel.: (418) 835-1685
Fax: (418) 835-5322
Toll Free: (800) 463-4452
E-Mail: info@cycleslambert.com
Web Site: www.cycleslambert.com
Year Founded: 1945
Rev.: $12,172,293
Emp.: 70
Business Description:
Cycling Products Distr
S.I.C.: 5091
N.A.I.C.S.: 423910
Personnel:
Tracey Lee Batsford *(Dir-Mktg)*

CYCLON HELLAS S.A.

Megaridos Avenue 124
Aspropyrgos, Attica, 193 00, Greece
Tel.: (30) 210 809 3900
Fax: (30) 210 809 3999
Web Site: www.cyclon.gr
Year Founded: 1974
CYCL—(ATH)
Sls.: $490,481,078
Assets: $129,239,051
Liabilities: $88,832,412
Net Worth: $40,406,639
Earnings: ($1,027,128)
Emp.: 269
Fiscal Year-end: 12/31/12
Business Description:
Lubricant Mfr & Distr
S.I.C.: 2992
N.A.I.C.S.: 324191
Personnel:
Dimitrios P. Kontaxis *(Pres & Mng Dir)*
Board of Directors:
Dimitrios Bartzokas
Evangelos N. Fafoutis
Dimitrios P. Kontaxis
Ioannis E. Papamichali
Nikolaos N. Rebakos
Achilleas Sklivaniotis

CYCLONE INDUSTRIES PTY LTD

317 Abbotts Rd
Dandenong, VIC, 3175, Australia
Tel.: (61) 387919300
Fax: (61) 387919333
E-Mail: customerservice@cyclone.com.au
Web Site: www.cyclone.com.au
Sales Range: $400-449.9 Million
Emp.: 100
Business Description:
Hand & Edge Tools Mfr
S.I.C.: 3425
N.A.I.C.S.: 332216
Personnel:
Alan Mackie *(Gen Mgr)*

CYCLONE MFG. INC.

7300 Rapistan Court
Mississauga, ON, L5N 5S1, Canada
Tel.: (905) 567-5601
Fax: (905) 567-6911
E-Mail: RFQ@cyclonemfg.com
Web Site: www.cyclonemfg.com
Year Founded: 1964
Rev.: $11,965,780
Emp.: 120
Business Description:
Aircraft Parts & Equipment Mfr
S.I.C.: 3728
N.A.I.C.S.: 336413
Personnel:
Andrew Sochaj *(Pres)*
Robert Sochaj *(Exec VP)*

CYCLOPHARM LIMITED

Building 75 Business & Techonology Park New Illawarra Road
Lucas Heights, NSW, 2234, Australia
Mailing Address:
PO Box 350
Menai Central, Sydney, NSW, 2234, Australia
Tel.: (61) 295410411
Fax: (61) 295430960
E-Mail: enquiries@cyclopharm.com.au
Web Site: www.cyclopharm.com
CYC—(ASX)
Rev.: $11,221,088
Assets: $22,568,096
Liabilities: $6,302,548
Net Worth: $16,265,548
Earnings: ($1,088,085)
Emp.: 36
Fiscal Year-end: 12/31/12
Business Description:
Nuclear Medicine Mfr
Import Export
S.I.C.: 8071
N.A.I.C.S.: 621511
Personnel:
James M. McBrayer *(CEO, Mng Dir & Sec)*
Nabil Morcos *(COO & Dir-Science)*
Board of Directors:
Vanda Russell Gould
David J. Heaney
James M. McBrayer
Legal Counsel:
Piper Alderman
Level 24 385 Bourke Street
Melbourne, Australia

Subsidiary:

Cyclomedica Australia Pty Ltd **(1)**
Bldg 75 Bus & Tech Park New Illawarra Rd
Lucas Heights, New South Wales, 2234, Australia
Tel.: (61) 295410411
Fax: (61) 295430960
E-Mail: enquiries@cyclomedica.com.au
Web Site: www.cyclopharm.com
Emp.: 20
Medical Equipment & Pharmaceutical Mfr
S.I.C.: 2834
N.A.I.C.S.: 325412
James McBrayer *(Mng Dir)*

Non-U.S. Subsidiaries:

Cyclomedica Europe Limited **(1)**
Ulysses House Foley St
Dublin, Ireland
Tel.: (353) 18881004
Fax: (353) 18881005
E-Mail: tom.odoherty@cyclomedica.ie
Web Site: www.cyclopharm.com
Emp.: 15
Medical Equipment Mfr
S.I.C.: 3841
N.A.I.C.S.: 339112
Bjorn Altmann *(Gen Mgr)*

Cyclomedica Germany GmbH **(1)**
Geschaftsfuhrer Museumstrasse 69
38229 Salzgitter, Germany
Tel.: (49) 5341550802
Fax: (49) 5341550803
E-Mail: info@technegas.de
Web Site: www.cyclopharm.com
Emp.: 4
Medical Equipment Mfr
S.I.C.: 3841
N.A.I.C.S.: 339112
Bjorn Altmann *(Gen Mgr)*

CYCOS AG

Joseph-von-Fraunhofer-Strasse 5
52477 Alsdorf, Germany
Tel.: (49) 24049010
Fax: (49) 2404901100
E-Mail: info@cycos.com
Web Site: www.cycos.com
YOS—(DEU)
Sls.: $14,673,253
Assets: $16,019,423
Liabilities: $2,288,489
Net Worth: $13,730,934
Earnings: $403,851
Emp.: 137
Fiscal Year-end: 09/30/12
Business Description:
Communication Services
S.I.C.: 4899
N.A.I.C.S.: 517919
Personnel:
Uwe Hermanns *(CEO)*
Rudolf Seeber *(CFO)*

CYDSA S.A. DE C.V.

(d/b/a Grupo Cydsa)
Avenida Ricardo Margain Zozaya 565 B
Garza Garcia, Nuevo Leon, Mexico 66267
Tel.: (52) 8181524500
Fax: (52) 8181524822
E-Mail: cydsa@cydsa.com
Web Site: www.cydsa.com
Year Founded: 1945
CYDSASA—(MEX)
Sls.: $432,582,640
Assets: $847,855,680
Liabilities: $377,349,280
Net Worth: $470,506,400
Earnings: $48,545,560
Emp.: 2,513
Fiscal Year-end: 12/31/12
Business Description:
Chemical Mfr
S.I.C.: 2899
N.A.I.C.S.: 325998
Personnel:
Tomas Gonzalez Sada *(Chm & CEO)*
Jose de Jesus Montemayor Castillo *(CFO)*
Alejandro von Rossum Garza *(COO-Chemical Div)*
Humberto Jasso Barrera *(Chief Corp Officer)*
Board of Directors:

Tomas Gonzalez Sada
Alberto Santos de Hoyos
Jose de Jesus Montemayor Castillo
Adan Elizondo Elizondo
Alvaro Fernandez Garza
Alejandro Garza Laguera
Francisco Garza Zambrano
Laura Gonzalez Casas
Tomas Gonzalez Casas
Pablo Gonzalez Sada
Humberto Jasso Barrera
Mario Laborin Gomez
Antonio Madero Bracho
Fernando Margain Sada
Herminio Blanco Mendoza
Abelardo Morales Puron
Adrian G. Sada Gonzalez
Alejandro von Rossum Garza

Divisions:

Cydsa S.A. Environmental Services Div. (1)
Av Ricardo Margain Zozaya 325 565
Col Valle Del Campestre, 66267 Garza Garcia, NL, Mexico
Tel.: (52) 8181524699
Fax: (52) 81 8152 4822
Web Site: www.cydsa.com
S.I.C.: 2823
N.A.I.C.S.: 325220

Grupo Cydsa S.A. de C.V. - Fibers Division (1)
Av Ricardo Margain Zozaya 565
Col Valle del Campestre, 66265 Monterrey, NL, Mexico
Tel.: (52) 8181524500
Telex: 38-3034
Fax: (52) 8181524822
E-Mail: cydsa@cydsa.com
Web Site: www.cydsa.com
Emp.: 100
Rayon & Acrylic Fibers Mfr
S.I.C.: 2823
N.A.I.C.S.: 325220
Megane Baske *(Mgr)*

Grupo Cydsa S.A. de C.V. - Packaging Division (1)
Av Ricardo Margain Zozaya 325 565
Col Valle del Campestre, 66265 Garza Garcia, NL, Mexico
Tel.: (52) 8181524500
Telex: 38-3034
Fax: (52) 8181524812
E-Mail: cydsa@cydsa.com
Web Site: www.cydsa.com
Emp.: 100
Flexible Packaging Mfr
S.I.C.: 2671
N.A.I.C.S.: 326112
Thomas Gonzales Sada *(Gen Mgr)*

Subsidiaries:

CELULOSA Y DERIVADOS DE MONTERREY, SA (1)
Av Ricardo Margain No 565 Santa Engracia
Garza Garcia, Nuevo Leon, 66265, Mexico
Tel.: (52) 8181524500
Fax: (52) 8181524812
Emp.: 100
Rayon Filament Weaving Mfr
S.I.C.: 2389
N.A.I.C.S.: 314999
Tomas Gonzalez Sada *(Gen Mgr)*

Cydsa S.A. de C.V. - La Presa Plant (1)
Av La Presa 8 Col Lazaro Cardenas
San Juan Ixhuatepec, Tlalnepantla, Mexico 54180
Tel.: (52) 55 5747 5500
Chemical Products Mfr
S.I.C.: 2899
N.A.I.C.S.: 325998

Industria Quimica del Istmo, S.A. de C.V. (1)
Complejo Indus Pajaritos SN
PO Box 850
96400 Coatzacoalcos, Veracruz, Mexico (100%)
Tel.: (52) 9212113400
Telex: 38-3034
Fax: (52) 9212113557
E-Mail: mas@anachemia.com
Web Site: www.asertec.com.mx
Emp.: 300
Mfr. of Chlorine, Caustic Soda & Basic Chemical Products
S.I.C.: 2899
N.A.I.C.S.: 325998

Plants:

INDUSTRIA QUIMICA DEL ISTMO, S.A. de C.V. - COATZACOALCOS PLANT (2)
Complejo Industrial Pajaritos
Coatzacoalcos, Veracruz, 96400, Mexico
Tel.: (52) 9212113400
Web Site: www.cydsa.com
Chlorine & Caustic Soda Mfr
S.I.C.: 2899
N.A.I.C.S.: 325998

INDUSTRIA QUIMICA DEL ISTMO, S.A. de C.V. - HERMOSILLO PLANT (2)
Calle del Plomo 45 Parque Industrial
Hermosillo, Sonora, 83299, Mexico
Tel.: (52) 6622511024
Web Site: www.cydsa.com
Chlorine & Caustic Soda Mfr
S.I.C.: 2899
N.A.I.C.S.: 325998

Industrias Cydsa Bayer, S.A. de C.V. (1)
Rio Becerra 287
Col Napoles Del Benito Juarez, 03810
Mexico, DP, Mexico (60%)
Tel.: (52) 5553401800
Telex: 38-3034
Fax: (52) 15523401827
E-Mail: ramirezb@cydsa.com
Web Site: www.icb.com.mx
Emp.: 70
Mfr. of Toluene Di-Isocyanate
S.I.C.: 2869
N.A.I.C.S.: 325110
Jenea Isgenere *(Mgr)*

INVERSIONES MEXIMEX, S.A. DE C.V (1)
Ricardo Margain Zozaya 325 Valle del Campestre
Garza Garcia, Nuevo Leon, 66220, Mexico
Tel.: (52) 8181524500
Investment Management Services
S.I.C.: 6211
N.A.I.C.S.: 523999

Plasticos Rex S.A. de C.V. (1)
Romulo OFarril 434
Col Olivar De Los Padres, 01780 Mexico, DF, Mexico (100%)
Tel.: (52) 5555953100
Telex: 38-3034
Fax: (52) 5255955673
E-Mail: edramirezr@cydsa.com
Web Site: www.plasticosrex.com.mx
Emp.: 250
PVC & Polyethylene Pipes & Fittings, Drip Irrigation Systems
S.I.C.: 2821
N.A.I.C.S.: 325211
Gloria Ermande *(Mgr)*

Quimica Empresarial De Mexico, SA De CV (1)
Av Ricardo Margain Zozaya No 565-B
Garza Garcia, 66267, Mexico
Tel.: (52) 8181524500
Web Site: www.cydsa.com
Emp.: 20
Chemical Products Distr
S.I.C.: 5169
N.A.I.C.S.: 424690

Quimobasicos, S.A. de C.V. (1)
Ave Ruiz Cortinez 2333 Pte
PO Box 1730
64400 Monterrey, NL, Mexico (60%)
Tel.: (52) 8183054600
Fax: (52) 83054614
E-Mail: selozano@cydsa.com
Web Site: www.quimobasicos.com.mx
Emp.: 200
Refrigeration & Repellent Gases
S.I.C.: 5078
N.A.I.C.S.: 423740

Sales del Istmo, S.A. de C.V. (1)
Rio Becerra 287
Col Napoles Del Benito Juarez, 03810
Mexico, DF, Mexico (100%)
Tel.: (52) 5555433400
Telex: 38-3034
Fax: (52) 5555237203
E-Mail: calcalap@cydsa.com
Web Site: www.salesdelistmo.com.mx
Emp.: 250
Refined Table & Industrial Salt Mfr
S.I.C.: 5169
N.A.I.C.S.: 424690

Plants:

Cydsa S.A. de C.V. - Altamira Plant (1)
Km 32 Carr Tampico-Mante
Altamira, Tamps, Mexico 89600
Tel.: (52) 833 229 1300
Plastic Products Mfr
S.I.C.: 3089
N.A.I.C.S.: 326199

Derivados Acrilicos S.A. de C.V. - AGUASCALIENTES PLANT (1)
Av Adolfo Lopez Mateos 1502 Pte
Col Circunvalacion Pte, Aguascalientes, 20210, Mexico
Tel.: (52) 449 910 3300
Web Site: www.cydsa.com
Synthetic & Natural Fiber Yarn Mfr
S.I.C.: 2299
N.A.I.C.S.: 313110

CYFROWY POLSAT S.A.

ul Lubinowa 4A
03-878 Warsaw, Poland
Tel.: (48) 223566600
Fax: (48) 223566003
E-Mail: cyfrowypolsat@cyfrowypolsat.pl
Web Site: www.cyfrowypolsat.pl
CPS—(WAR)
Rev.: $881,055,323
Assets: $1,763,669,340
Liabilities: $980,864,696
Net Worth: $782,804,643
Earnings: $189,738,245
Emp.: 1,452
Fiscal Year-end: 12/31/12

Business Description:
Satellite Television & Wireless Telecommunications Services
S.I.C.: 4841
N.A.I.C.S.: 515210

Personnel:
Zygmunt Solorz-Zak *(Chm-Supervisory Bd)*
Dominik Libicki *(Chm-Mgmt Bd)*
Dariusz Dzialkowski *(Member-Mgmt Bd-Tech)*
Aneta Jaskolska *(Member-Mgmt Bd-Legal Affairs, Personnel, Admin & Security)*
Tomasz Szelag *(Member-Mgmt Bd-Fin)*

Supervisory Board of Directors:
Zygmunt Solorz-Zak
Robert Gwiazdowski
Andrzej Papis
Leszek Reksa
Heronim Ruta

CYGAM ENERGY INC.

760 340 - 12th Ave SW
Calgary, AB, T2R 1L5, Canada
Tel.: (403) 802-6983
Fax: (403) 802-6984
E-Mail: info@cygamenergy.com
Web Site: www.cygamenergy.com
Year Founded: 2005
CYG—(TSXV)
Rev.: $9,827,917
Assets: $20,282,647
Liabilities: $1,793,895
Net Worth: $18,488,752
Earnings: $1,125,027
Emp.: 6
Fiscal Year-end: 12/31/12

Business Description:
Oil & Natural Gas Exploration Services
S.I.C.: 1389
N.A.I.C.S.: 213112

Personnel:
Giuseppe Rigo *(Chm)*
David Taylor *(Pres & CEO)*
Alastair Robertson *(CFO)*

Board of Directors:
Giuseppe Rigo
Robert B. Carter
Neli da Silva Rigo de Righi
Peter Haverson
David Taylor

Transfer Agent:
Computershare Trust Company of Canada
Calgary, AB, Canada

Non-U.S. Subsidiaries:

Rigo Oil Company Tunisia Ltd (1)
Rue du Lac Turkana - Les Berges du Lac
Immeuble Nour el Bouhaira
App B4, 1053 Tunis, Tunisia
Tel.: (216) 71 962 562
Fax: (216) 71 961 566
Web Site: www.cygamenergy.com
Oil & Gas Exploration Services
S.I.C.: 1389
N.A.I.C.S.: 213112
Giuseppe Rigo *(Chm & Mng Dir)*

Vega Oil S.p.A. (1)
Via Rabirio 1
136 Rome, Italy
Tel.: (39) 06 390 31336
Fax: (39) 06 397 63703
Web Site: www.cygamenergy.com
Emp.: 3
Oil & Gas Exploration Services
S.I.C.: 1389
N.A.I.C.S.: 213112
Giuseppe Rigo *(Chm & Mng Dir)*

CYL CORPORATION BERHAD

Level 18 The Gardens North Tower
Mid Valley City Lingkaran Syed Putra
59200 Kuala Lumpur, Malaysia
Tel.: (60) 32264 8888
Fax: (60) 32282 2733
E-Mail: info@my.tricorglobal.com
Web Site: www.cylcorporation.com
CYL—(KLS)
Rev.: $20,759,531
Assets: $30,504,221
Liabilities: $5,483,109
Net Worth: $25,021,112
Earnings: $1,132,319
Fiscal Year-end: 01/31/13

Business Description:
Plastic Products Mfr
S.I.C.: 1751
N.A.I.C.S.: 238350

Personnel:
Yat Lee Chen *(Mng Dir)*
Hui Fang Kuan *(Co-Sec)*
Wai Ying Tham *(Co-Sec)*

Board of Directors:
Abu Talib Othman
Abd Malik A. Rahman
Wai Ling Chen
Yat Lee Chen
Kim Lian Lau
Nyoke Yoong Seow

CYMAO HOLDINGS BERHAD

MPT 4604 3rd Fl Lot 15-16 Block B
Bandaran Baru Jalan Baru
91000 Tawau, Sabah, Malaysia
Tel.: (60) 89767600
Fax: (60) 89766100
E-Mail: info@cymao.com
Web Site: www.cymao.com
CYMAO—(KLS)

CYMAO HOLDINGS BERHAD—(Continued)

Rev.: $39,460,534
Assets: $40,668,780
Liabilities: $7,119,671
Net Worth: $33,549,109
Earnings: ($6,337,084)
Fiscal Year-end: 12/31/12

Business Description:
Plywood Mfr
S.I.C.: 2435
N.A.I.C.S.: 321211

Personnel:
Tsai-Rong Lin *(Mng Dir)*
Katherine Mei Ling Chung *(Sec)*

Board of Directors:
Mohd Zain Omar
Seng Hiew
Li-Chu Lin Hsu
Kai-Hsuan Lin
Kai-Min Lin
Tsai-Rong Lin

Subsidiaries:

Cymao Plywood Sdn. Bhd. **(1)**
Km 9 1 Jalan Batu Sapi
Locked Bag No 13
90009 Sandakan, Sabah, Malaysia
Tel.: (60) 89612799
Fax: (60) 89612607
E-Mail: info@cymao.com
Web Site: www.cymao.com
Emp.: 1,000
Wood Products Mfr
S.I.C.: 2435
N.A.I.C.S.: 321211
Lin Tsai-Rong *(Mng Dir)*

Poly-Ply Industries Sdn. Bhd. **(1)**
Jalan Kapar Kampung Batu Empat
42100 Kelang, Selangor, Malaysia
Tel.: (60) 193815518
Fax: (60) 332912902
E-Mail: marketing@polyply.com.my
Emp.: 80
Decorative Panels Mfr
S.I.C.: 2431
N.A.I.C.S.: 321918
David Chang *(Acct Mgr)*

CYMAT TECHNOLOGIES LTD.

6320-2 Danville Road
Mississauga, ON, L5T 2L7, Canada
Tel.: (905) 696-9900
Fax: (905) 696-9300
E-Mail: info@cymat.com
Web Site: www.cymat.com
CYM—(TSXV)
Rev.: $919,980
Assets: $1,288,809
Liabilities: $976,205
Net Worth: $312,603
Earnings: $440,788
Emp.: 11
Fiscal Year-end: 04/30/13

Business Description:
Materials Technology Services
S.I.C.: 7389
N.A.I.C.S.: 541990

Personnel:
Michael M. Liik *(Chm & CEO)*
Darryl Kleebaum *(CFO & VP-Fin)*

Board of Directors:
Michael M. Liik
Jon David Gill
Lewis Wharton MacKenzie
Martin J. Mazza
William Pettipas

Transfer Agent:
Equity Transfer Services
200 University Ave, Suite 400
Toronto, ON, Canada

CYMBRIA CORPORATION

150 Bloor Street West Suite 500
Toronto, ON, M5S 2X9, Canada
Tel.: (416) 963-9353
Fax: (416) 963-5060
E-Mail: info@hpointwealth.com
Web Site: www.hpointwealth.com
CYB—(TSX)
Rev.: $7,755,790
Assets: $346,759,702
Liabilities: $7,153,823
Net Worth: $339,605,879
Earnings: $2,260,685
Emp.: 24
Fiscal Year-end: 12/31/12

Business Description:
Investment Services
S.I.C.: 6211
N.A.I.C.S.: 523999

Personnel:
Patrick Farmer *(Chm)*
Tye Bousada *(Co-CEO)*
Geoff MacDonald *(Co-CEO)*
Norman Tang *(CFO)*
Diane Rossi *(Sec)*

Board of Directors:
Patrick Farmer
James S. A. MacDonald
Richard Whiting

Legal Counsel:
Stikeman Elliott LLP
5300 Commerce Court West 199 Bay Street
Toronto, ON, Canada

Transfer Agent:
Computershare Investor Services Inc.
100 University Avenue 8th Floor
Toronto, ON, M5J 2Y1, Canada
Tel.: (514) 982-7555

CYMER, INC.

(Acquired by ASML HOLDING N.V.)

CYMOT (PTY) LTD.

15 Newcastle St
PO Box 726
Windhoek, Namibia
Tel.: (264) 612956000
Fax: (264) 612956100
E-Mail: info@cymot.co
Web Site: www.cymot.com
Year Founded: 1948
Sales Range: $200-249.9 Million
Emp.: 360

Business Description:
Automotive Refinishing Products, Workshop Equipment, Tools, Safety Products & Sports Equipment Distr
S.I.C.: 7389
N.A.I.C.S.: 425120

Personnel:
Axel Theissen *(Mng Dir)*

CYNAPSUS THERAPEUTICS INC.

828 Richmond St W
Toronto, ON, M6J 1C9, Canada
Tel.: (416) 703-2449
Fax: (416) 703-8752
E-Mail: info@cannasat.com
Web Site: www.cynapsus.ca
Year Founded: 2004
CTH—(OTC TSXV)
Assets: $1,161,940
Liabilities: $6,142,180
Net Worth: ($4,980,240)
Earnings: ($3,045,484)
Fiscal Year-end: 12/31/12

Business Description:
Pharmaceutical Products Mfr
S.I.C.: 2834
N.A.I.C.S.: 325412

Personnel:
Rochelle Stenzler *(Chm)*
Anthony J. Giovinazzo *(Pres & CEO)*
Andrew Williams *(CFO & COO)*
Albert Agro *(Chief Medical Officer)*

Board of Directors:
Rochelle Stenzler
Anthony J. Giovinazzo
Ronald Hosking
Nan Hutchinson
Julia G. Levy
Perry Molinoff
Alan D. C. Ryley
Alan Torrie

Transfer Agent:
Equity Financial Trust Company
200 University Avenue Suite 400
Toronto, ON, Canada

CYNOTECH HOLDINGS LIMITED

Level 4 20 Kent St
PO Box 9846
1149 Auckland, New Zealand
Tel.: (64) 95206073
Fax: (64) 95206068
E-Mail: corporate@cynotech.co.nz
Web Site: www.cynotech.co.nz
CYT—(NZE)
Sales Range: $1-9.9 Million
Emp.: 80

Business Description:
Investment Management & Satellite Phones Mfr
S.I.C.: 6282
N.A.I.C.S.: 523920

Personnel:
Allan Hawkins *(Chm)*
Brett Tawse *(Mng Dir)*

Board of Directors:
Allan Hawkins
Paul Hutchinson
Kevin Mcdonald
Brett Tawse

Subsidiary:

Cynotech Finance Group Ltd **(1)**
15 A Saleyards Road Otahuhu
New Market, Auckland, New Zealand
Tel.: (64) 95206073
Fax: (64) 95206068
E-Mail: finance@budgetloans.co.nz
Web Site: www.budgetloans.co.nz
Emp.: 20
Financial Management Services
S.I.C.: 6141
N.A.I.C.S.: 522291
Wayne Hawkins *(Gen Mgr)*

CYNTERGY SERVICES LIMITED

33 Hanworth Road
Sunbury, Middlesex, TW16 5DA, United Kingdom
Tel.: (44) 1932 778000
Fax: (44) 1932 778080
E-Mail: info@cyntergy.co.uk
Web Site: www.cyntergyservicesltd.com
Year Founded: 2003
Emp.: 100

Business Description:
Information Technology Support Services
S.I.C.: 7376
N.A.I.C.S.: 541513

Personnel:
Peter Walker *(CEO)*
Richard Jennings *(CFO)*
Steven Rose *(COO)*

Board of Directors:
Tim Bittleston
Richard Jennings
Steven Rose
Peter Walker

CYOPTICS, INC.

(Acquired by Avago Technologies Limited)

CYPARK RESOURCES BERHAD

13A-09 Block A Phileo Damansara II
No 15 Jalan 16/11
46350 Petaling Jaya, Selangor, Malaysia
Tel.: (60) 376606170
Fax: (60) 376606169
E-Mail: info@crbenv.com
Web Site: www.crbenv.com
CYPARK—(KLS)
Rev.: $64,207,265
Assets: $170,737,279
Liabilities: $120,686,424
Net Worth: $50,050,855
Earnings: $8,387,669
Emp.: 140
Fiscal Year-end: 10/31/12

Business Description:
Landscaping & Engineering Services
S.I.C.: 0781
N.A.I.C.S.: 541320

Personnel:
Razali Ismail *(Chm)*
Daud Ahmad *(CEO)*
Mohammed Faitouri Mohamed *(Sr Quantity Surveyor & Procurement Officer)*
Siew Chuan Chua *(Co-Sec)*
Sze Min Yeow *(Co-Sec)*

Board of Directors:
Razali Ismail
Abdul Malek Abdul Aziz
Abdul Munir Abdullah Rafaie
Daud Ahmad
Freezailah Che Yeom
Headir Mahfidz

Transfer Agent:
Securities Services (Holdings) Sdn Bhd
Level 7 Menara Milenium Jalan Damanlela
Pusat Bandar Damansara
Damansara Heights, Kuala Lumpur, Malaysia

CYPHER SYSTEMS GROUP INC.

3600 Rhodes Drive
Windsor, ON, N8W 5A4, Canada
Tel.: (519) 945-4943
Fax: (519) 974-7290
Toll Free: (800) 396-1986
Web Site: www.cyphersystemsgroup.com
Year Founded: 1983
Rev.: $21,736,238
Emp.: 500

Business Description:
Software Services
S.I.C.: 7371
N.A.I.C.S.: 541511

Personnel:
John Savage *(Founder)*

CYPRESS DEVELOPMENT CORP.

885 West Georgia Street Suite 2230
Vancouver, BC, V6C 3E8, Canada
Tel.: (604) 687-3376
Fax: (604) 687-3119
Toll Free: (800) 567-8181
E-Mail: info@cypressdevelopmentcorp.com
Web Site: www.cypressdevelopmentcorp.com
Year Founded: 1991
CYP—(OTC TSXV)
Int. Income: $6,166
Assets: $2,980,962
Liabilities: $24,670
Net Worth: $2,956,292
Earnings: ($7,717,068)
Emp.: 25
Fiscal Year-end: 12/31/12

Business Description:
Gold, Silver & Base Metal Mining & Exploration Services
S.I.C.: 1041
N.A.I.C.S.: 212221

Personnel:
Donald C. Huston *(Pres & CEO)*
James G. Pettit *(Acting CFO)*

Board of Directors:
Amanda Chow
Donald C. Huston
Donald G. Myers
James G. Pettit
Transfer Agent:
Computershare Trust Company of Canada
100 University Avenue 9th Floor
Toronto, ON, M5J 2Y1, Canada
Tel.: (416) 663-9097
Fax: (416) 263-9694

CYPRESS HILLS RESOURCE CORP.

416 602 - 11th Avenue SW
Calgary, AB, T2R 1J8, Canada
Tel.: (403) 265-7663
Fax: (403) 266-1847
E-Mail: info@cypresshillsresource.com
Web Site: www.cypresshillsresource.co
Year Founded: 1983
CHY—(TSXV)
Rev.: $19,528
Assets: $92,923
Liabilities: $508,045
Net Worth: ($415,122)
Earnings: ($375,461)
Fiscal Year-end: 12/31/12
Business Description:
Oil & Gas Exploration Services
S.I.C.: 1311
N.A.I.C.S.: 211111
Personnel:
Ted Fostey *(Pres & CEO)*
Board of Directors:
Brian Bayley
Tim Collins
Ted Fostey
Michael Thackray

CYPRESS JADE AGRICULTURAL HOLDINGS LIMITED

Units 801-803 8/F Tins Enterprises Centre 777 Lai Chi Kok Road
Cheung Sha Wan, Kowloon, China (Hong Kong)
Tel.: (852) 31226600
Fax: (852) 25369223
E-Mail: info@cyj.hk
Web Site: www.cyj.hk
875—(HKG)
Sls.: $34,548,155
Assets: $40,602,100
Liabilities: $25,356,084
Net Worth: $15,246,016
Earnings: $4,048,901
Emp.: 728
Fiscal Year-end: 12/31/12
Business Description:
Investment Management Services
S.I.C.: 6799
N.A.I.C.S.: 523920
Personnel:
Herbert Ho Ming Hui *(Deputy Chm)*
Lanjiang Shi *(CEO)*
Wai Yee Lee *(Sec)*
Board of Directors:
Michael Wai Chung Wu
Tommy Yu Yan Cheung
Yuet Chung Chu
Herbert Ho Ming Hui
Japhet Sebastian Law
Estella Yi Kum Ng
Lanjiang Shi
Jianzun Yang
Fai San Yau

Appleby Management (Bermuda) Ltd.
Canon's Court 22 Victoria Street
HM 12 Hamilton, Bermuda

Transfer Agent:
Tricor Tengis Limited
26th Floor Tesbury Centre 28 Queen's Road East
Wanchai, China (Hong Kong)
Tel.: (852) 29801333
Fax: (852) 28108185

CYPRINT PLC

Industrial Area Ayios Athanasios
PO Box 58300
3732 Limassol, Cyprus
Tel.: (357) 25 720 035
Fax: (357) 25 720 123
E-Mail: info@cyprint.com.cy
Web Site: www.cyprint.com.cy
Year Founded: 2000
CYP—(CYP)
Emp.: 33
Business Description:
Digital Prinitng Services
S.I.C.: 2759
N.A.I.C.S.: 323111
Personnel:
Theodoros Antoniou *(Chm & Mng Dir)*
Board of Directors:
Theodoros Antoniou
Stella Kyrou Hadgipanagi
Sofoklis Sofokleous
Christakis Christodoulou Xantho
Andreas Christodoulou Xanthos

CYPROTEX PLC

15 Beech Lane
Macclesfield, Cheshire, SK10 2DR, United Kingdom
Tel.: (44) 1625505100
Fax: (44) 1625505199
E-Mail: info@cyprotex.com
Web Site: www.cyprotex.com
Year Founded: 1999
CRX—(AIM)
Rev.: $13,151,181
Assets: $15,150,033
Liabilities: $4,163,332
Net Worth: $10,986,700
Earnings: $319,809
Emp.: 73
Fiscal Year-end: 12/31/12
Business Description:
Pharmaceutical Contract Research Services
S.I.C.: 8731
N.A.I.C.S.: 541712
Personnel:
Anthony D. Baxter *(CEO)*
John Dootson *(CFO)*
Mark C. Warburton *(Sec)*
Board of Directors:
Steve Harris
Anthony D. Baxter
Chris Clothier
John Dootson
Subsidiary:

Cyprotex Discovery Limited (1)
15 Beech Ln
Macclesfield, Cheshire, SK10 2DR, United Kingdom
Tel.: (44) 1625505100
Fax: (44) 1625505199
Web Site: www.cyprotex.com
Pharmaceutical Products Mfr
S.I.C.: 2834
N.A.I.C.S.: 325412
Mark C. Warburton *(Gen Mgr)*

U.S. Subsidiary:

Ceetox, Inc. (1)
4717 Campus Dr
Kalamazoo, MI 49008
Tel.: (269) 353-5555
Fax: (269) 544-1077
E-Mail: info@ceetox.com
Web Site: www.ceetox.com
Sales Range: $1-9.9 Million
Emp.: 13
Research & Development in Biotechnology
S.I.C.: 8731
N.A.I.C.S.: 541711
Timothy M. Mitchell *(Pres)*

CYPRUS AIRWAYS PUBLIC LIMITED

21 Alkeou Street
PO Box 21903
Engomi, 2404 Nicosia, Cyprus
Tel.: (357) 22661800
Fax: (357) 22 663167
E-Mail: webcenter@cyprusairways.com
Web Site: www.cyprusairways.com
CAIR—(CYP)
Sales Range: $300-349.9 Million
Emp.: 1,226
Business Description:
Air Transportation Services
S.I.C.: 4512
N.A.I.C.S.: 481111
Personnel:
George Mavrocostas *(Chm)*
Eleni Kaloyirou *(Deputy CEO)*
George Spyrou *(Sec)*
Board of Directors:
George Mavrocostas
Charalambos Alexandrou
Michalis Antoniou
Andreas Chrysafis
Kypros Ellinas
George Georgiou
Marios Hadjigavriel
George Kallis
Constantinos Lefkaritis
Andreas Philippou
Pavlos Photiades
Subsidiaries:

Cyprus Airways (Duty Free Shops) Ltd. (1)
Larnaca International Airport
PO Box 43020
6650 Larnaca, Cyprus
Tel.: (357) 24841400
Fax: (357) 24643571
Web Site: services.cyprusair.com
Sales Range: $75-99.9 Million
Emp.: 220
General Retailer
S.I.C.: 5399
N.A.I.C.S.: 452990

Eurocypria Airlines Ltd (1)
97 Artemidos Ave Artemis Building
PO Box 40970
6308 Larnaca, Cyprus (100%)
Tel.: (357) 24658005
Fax: (357) 24650568
E-Mail: ecacs@eurocypria.com
Web Site: www.eurocypria.com
Emp.: 180
Charter Flight Operations
S.I.C.: 4522
N.A.I.C.S.: 481211
Panayiotis Neophytou *(Vice Chm)*

ZENON National Distribution Centre Ltd. (1)
Alkaiou 24
PO Box 25326
Engomi, 1308 Nicosia, Cyprus (100%)
Tel.: (357) 22664515
Fax: (357) 22664502
E-Mail: zenonsales@cyprusair.com.cy
Web Site: www.zenonndc.com
Travel Industry Electronic Information Distr
S.I.C.: 4729
N.A.I.C.S.: 561599

CYPRUS FOREST INDUSTRIES PUBLIC LTD

Ayias Sofias1
PO Box 24043
Paliometocho, 2682 Nicosia, Cyprus
Tel.: (357) 22872700
Fax: (357) 22833622
E-Mail: cfi@cfi.com.cy
Web Site: www.cfi.com.cy
Year Founded: 1970
CFI—(CYP)
Emp.: 110
Business Description:
Industrial Wood Panels Mfr
S.I.C.: 2499
N.A.I.C.S.: 321999
Personnel:
Stelios Papadopoulos *(Chm)*
Board of Directors:
Stelios Papadopoulos
Constantinos Chrisodontas
Iosif Constantinides
Pavlos Karydas
Pantelis Ksinisteris
Savvas Neophitou
Vaggelis Sykopetrides

CYPRUS STOCK EXCHANGE

71-73 Lordou Vironos Ave
1096 Nicosia, Cyprus
Tel.: (357) 22712300
Fax: (357) 22570308
E-Mail: info@cse.com.cy
Web Site: www.cse.com.cy
Rev.: $4,713,945
Emp.: 93
Business Description:
Stock Exchange Services
S.I.C.: 6231
N.A.I.C.S.: 523210
Personnel:
George Kousaris *(Chm)*
Demetris Papadopoulos *(Vice Chm)*
Nondas C.I. Metaxas *(CEO & Dir Gen)*
Board of Directors:
Alexis Anninos
Andreas Leonidou
Nondas C.I. Metaxas
Nicos Nicolaou
Demetris Papadopoulos
Marios Pilavakis
Andreas Theodosiou

CYPRUS TELECOMMUNICATIONS AUTHORITY

(d/b/a CYTA)
1 Telecommunications Str
Strovolos, Nicosia, 1396, Cyprus
Mailing Address:
PO Box 24929
Strovolos, Nicosia, 1396, Cyprus
Tel.: (357) 22701000
Fax: (357) 22494940
E-Mail: info@cyta.com.cy
Web Site: www.cyta.com.cy
Sales Range: $400-449.9 Million
Emp.: 2,485
Business Description:
Telecommunications Services Administration Organization
S.I.C.: 9631
N.A.I.C.S.: 926130
Personnel:
Stathis Kittis *(Chm)*
Pavlos Theodotou *(Vice Chm)*
Photios Savvides *(CEO)*
Michael I. Economides *(Deputy CEO)*
Board of Directors:
Gregory Diacou
Takis Fekkos
George Korfiotis
Demetris Phellas
Pavlos Theodotou
Subsidiaries:

Cytacom Solutions Limited (1)
Vision Towers 67 Lemesou Ave
PO Box 24929
6th Fl Aglantzia, 2121 Nicosia, 1396, Cyprus
Mailing Address:
PO Box 24929
CY-1396 Nicosia, Cyprus

Cyprus Telecommunications Authority—(Continued)

Tel.: (357) 70006000
Fax: (357) 22702047
E-Mail: info@cytacom.net
Web Site: www.cytacom.net
Emp.: 20
Telecommunications Equipment & Consulting Services
S.I.C.: 4899
N.A.I.C.S.: 517919
Aggelos Kountouris *(Mng Dir)*

CytaGlobal (1)
Telecommunications Street
PO Box 24929
1396 Nicosia, Cyprus
Tel.: (357) 22702550
Fax: (357) 22494155
E-Mail: global@cyta.com.cy
Web Site: www.cytaglobal.com
Emp.: 35
Electronic Communication Products & Services
S.I.C.: 4899
N.A.I.C.S.: 517919
Yiannis Koulias *(Dir-Natl & Intl Wholesale Market)*

Iris Gateway Satellite Services Limited (1)
Telecommunications Street
PO Box 24929
CY-1396 Nicosia, Cyprus
Tel.: (357) 22701730
Fax: (357) 22701872
E-Mail: sales@irissat.com
Web Site: www.irissat.com
Satellite Turnaround Services
S.I.C.: 4899
N.A.I.C.S.: 517410
Tassos Partzilis *(Mng Dir)*

Non-U.S. Subsidiaries:

Actel Kft. (1)
105-113 Bartok Bela Street
1115 Budapest, Hungary
Tel.: (36) 14814646
Fax: (36) 14814645
E-Mail: office@actel.hu
Web Site: www.actel.hu
Data Transmission, Telephony & Multimedia Services
S.I.C.: 4899
N.A.I.C.S.: 517919
Pal Horvath *(CEO)*
Peter Kis *(CFO)*

CYTA (UK) Ltd (1)
56A Haverstock Hill
London, NW3 2BH, United Kingdom
Tel.: (44) 2074281000
Fax: (44) 2074281005
E-Mail: info@cytauk.com
Web Site: www.cytauk.com
Telecommunications Products & Services
S.I.C.: 4899
N.A.I.C.S.: 517919

CYRELA BRAZIL REALTY S.A.

Av Pres Juscelino Kubitschek 1455-3 Andar
04543-011 Sao Paulo, SP, Brazil
Tel.: (55) 11 4502 3153
Fax: (55) 11 4502 3225
E-Mail: ri@cyrela.com.br
Web Site: www.cyrela.com.br
Year Founded: 1962
CYRE3—(BRAZ)
Emp.: 10,300
Business Description:
Real Estate Development Services
S.I.C.: 6531
N.A.I.C.S.: 531390
Personnel:
Elie Horn *(Chm & CEO)*
Rogerio Jonas Zylbersztajn *(Vice Chm & VP)*
Eric Alencar *(CFO & IR Officer)*
Claudio Carvalho de Lima *(Legal Dept Officer)*
Cassio Mantelmacher *(Heal Estate Dev Officer)*
Board of Directors:
Elie Horn
Vicente Falconi Campos
Joao Cesar de Queiroz Tourinho
Fernando Goldsztein
Sergio Rial
George Zausner
Rogerio Jonas Zylbersztajn

CYRELA COMMERCIAL PROPERTIES S.A.

Pres Juscelino Kubitschek Avenue
1455 5 Floor Itaim Bibi
0453-011 Sao Paulo, Brazil
Tel.: (55) 1130187600
Fax: (55) 1130187680
E-Mail: ccpsa@ccpsa.com.br
Web Site: www.ccpsa.com.br
CCPR3—(BRAZ OTC)
Rev.: $238,515,002
Assets: $914,207,078
Liabilities: $559,513,562
Net Worth: $354,693,517
Earnings: $75,276,386
Fiscal Year-end: 12/31/12
Business Description:
Commercial Real Estate Investment Services
S.I.C.: 6531
N.A.I.C.S.: 531390
Personnel:
Elie Horn *(Chm)*
Leo Krakowiak *(Vice Chm)*
Rafael Novellino *(CEO)*
Dani Ajbeszyc *(Fin & IR Officer)*
Hilton Rejman *(Dev Officer)*
Nessim Daniel Sarfati *(Comml Properties Officer)*
Jose Roberto Voso *(Shopping Malls Officer)*
Board of Directors:
Elie Horn
Marcos Sampaio de Almeida Prado
Ilan Goldfajn
Leo Krakowiak
Rafael Novellino
Pedro Franco Sales
Decio Tenerello
George Zausner

Subsidiary:

BRX Administradora de Shopping malls Ltda. (1)
Endereco Av Industrial 600 Jardim Jardim Sao Judas, Santo Andre, Sao Paulo, 9080 510, Brazil
Tel.: (55) 11 4432 1035
Property Rental Services
S.I.C.: 6512
N.A.I.C.S.: 531120

CYTERRA CAPITAL CORP.

600 999 Hastings Street West
Vancouver, BC, V6C 2W2, Canada
Tel.: (778) 329-9629
E-Mail: craig@urg.ca
Year Founded: 2009
CYC.P—(TSXV)
Sales Range: Less than $1 Million
Business Description:
Investment Services
S.I.C.: 6211
N.A.I.C.S.: 523999
Personnel:
Craig Robson *(Pres & CEO)*
Bill Grossholz *(CFO)*
Board of Directors:
Robert Fraser
Bill Grossholz
Craig Robson
James Ross
Wei Yuan
Transfer Agent:
Computershare Investor Services Inc.
2nd Fl 510 Burrard St
Vancouver, BC, Canada

CYTOS BIOTECHNOLOGY AG

Wagistrasse 25
8952 Schlieren, Switzerland
Tel.: (41) 447334747
Fax: (41) 447334740
E-Mail: info@cytos.com
Web Site: www.cytos.com
CYTN—(SWX)
Rev.: $1,187,252
Assets: $32,801,614
Liabilities: $21,977,114
Net Worth: $10,824,500
Earnings: ($9,947,013)
Emp.: 30
Fiscal Year-end: 12/31/12
Business Description:
Biopharmaceutical Products Mfr
S.I.C.: 2834
N.A.I.C.S.: 325412
Personnel:
Christian Itin *(Chm & CEO)*
John Berriman *(Vice Chm)*
Arthur Krieg *(Vice Chm)*
Harry Welten *(CFO & Exec VP)*
Matthias Alder *(Exec VP-Corp Dev & Legal Affairs)*
Frank Hennecke *(Exec VP-Product Dev)*
Board of Directors:
Christian Itin
Joseph Anderson
John Berriman
Paul A. Brooke
Arthur Krieg
Kurt von Emster

CYTOTOOLS AG

Klappacher Strasse 126
64285 Darmstadt, Germany
Tel.: (49) 6151 9515812
Fax: (49) 6151 9515813
E-Mail: kontakt@cytotools.de
Web Site: www.cytotools.de
T5O—(DEU)
Sls.: $67,309
Assets: $8,480,871
Liabilities: $134,617
Net Worth: $8,346,254
Earnings: ($942,319)
Emp.: 3
Fiscal Year-end: 12/31/12
Business Description:
Medical Devices Mfr
S.I.C.: 3841
N.A.I.C.S.: 339112
Personnel:
Manfred May *(Chm-Supervisory Bd)*
Peter Friedl *(Deputy Chm-Supervisory Bd)*
Mark Andre Freyberg *(Member-Exec Bd-Fin, IR & Mktg)*
Dirk Kaiser *(Member-Exec Bd-Project Controlling, Product Dev & Patents)*
Supervisory Board of Directors:
Manfred May
Peter Friedl
Matthias Hoffmann
Bernhard Seehaus
Dieter Tober
Markus Weissbach

CZECH AIRLINES, A.S.

ul K Letisti
6 16008 Prague, Czech Republic
Tel.: (420) 220104111
Web Site: www.csa.cz
Sales Range: $1-9.9 Million
Emp.: 5,303
Business Description:
Air Transportation
S.I.C.: 4512
N.A.I.C.S.: 481111
Personnel:
Miroslav Dvorak *(Chm & CEO)*
Michal Mejstrik *(Chm-Supervisory Bd)*
Board of Directors:
Miroslav Dvorak
Josef Adam
Jiri Marek
Philippe Moreels
Marek Tybl
Supervisory Board of Directors:
Michal Mejstrik
Miroslav Bernasek
Tomas Brabec
Radomil Kratochvil
Radek Smerda

CZERWONA TOREBKA SA

ul Taczaka 13
61-819 Poznan, Poland
Tel.: (48) 616232800
Fax: (48) 616232852
Web Site: www.czerwonatorebka.pl
CZTA—(WAR)
Business Description:
Shopping Centers & Retail Chain Stores
S.I.C.: 5999
N.A.I.C.S.: 453998
Personnel:
Ireneusz Kazimierczyk *(CEO)*
Pawel Ciszek *(COO)*
Piotr Pecherski *(CIO)*
Maciej Nowak *(Chief Legal Officer)*

D ALEX MACDONALD FORD LINCOLN

25 Water Street
Summerside, PE, C1N 1A3, Canada
Tel.: (902) 436-2138
Fax: (902) 436-0232
E-Mail: sales@dalexmacdonald.com
Web Site: www.dalexmacdonald.com
Rev.: $15,727,375
Emp.: 35
Business Description:
New & Used Car Dealers
S.I.C.: 5511
N.A.I.C.S.: 441110
Personnel:
Rod MacDonald *(Gen Mgr)*

D & H INDIA LIMITED

Plot A Sector A Industrial Area
Sanwer Road
Indore, 452 015, India
Tel.: (91) 731 4273501
Fax: (91) 731 2722447
E-Mail: ho@dnhindia.com
Web Site: www.dnhindia.com
517514—(BOM)
Rev.: $14,327,081
Assets: $8,301,333
Liabilities: $3,235,062
Net Worth: $5,066,271
Earnings: $480,860
Fiscal Year-end: 03/31/13
Business Description:
Welding Electrode & Material Mfr
S.I.C.: 3548
N.A.I.C.S.: 333992
Personnel:
Harsh Kumar Vora *(CEO & Mng Dir)*
Sanat Jain *(CFO & Gen Mgr-Fin)*
Rajesh Sen *(Sec)*
Board of Directors:
Vasudeo S. Bhate
Madhusudan Jain
Basant Singh Johari
Jagdish C. Kapur
Nirmal Lunia
Vimal Lunia
Sushil Rawka
Surjit Singh
Harsh Kumar Vora
Transfer Agent:
Ankit Consultancy Pvt. Ltd
Plot No 60 Electronic Complex Pardeshipura
Indore, India

Unit:

D & H India Limited - Unit II (1)
Village Sejvaya Dhar Road
Ghatabillod, Dhar, Madhya Pradesh, India
Tel.: (91) 7292 277030
Fax: (91) 7292 277930
Welding Consumable Mfr
S.I.C.: 2899
N.A.I.C.S.: 325998

D&M TELEMARKETING PUBLIC COMPANY LTD

101 Grigoriou Afxendiou
Kokkinotrimithia, 2660 Nicosia, Cyprus
Tel.: (357) 22692222
Fax: (357) 22667001
E-Mail: orders@telemarketing.com.cy
Web Site: www.telemarketing.com.cy
Year Founded: 1994
TLM—(CYP)
Business Description:
Telemarketing Services
S.I.C.: 7389
N.A.I.C.S.: 561422
Personnel:
Marios Xinaris *(Mng Dir)*

D & O GREEN TECHNOLOGIES BERHAD

No 15 Bukit Ledang Off Jalan Duta
50480 Kuala Lumpur, Malaysia
Tel.: (60) 3 2094 3268
Fax: (60) 3 2094 3188
E-Mail: corp@do.com.my
Web Site: www.do.com.my
D&O—(KLS)
Rev.: $63,034,422
Assets: $101,270,878
Liabilities: $43,323,151
Net Worth: $57,947,727
Earnings: ($1,240,849)
Fiscal Year-end: 12/31/12
Business Description:
Semiconductor Components Mfr
S.I.C.: 3674
N.A.I.C.S.: 334413
Personnel:
Kheng Chiong Tay *(Mng Dir)*
Pei Choo Tan *(Sec)*
Board of Directors:
Mohammed Azlan Hashim
Dau Peng Cheam
Nam Seng Goh
Nan Yang Goh
Chong Puang Lim
Kheng Chiong Tay
Meng Tak Wong
See Yuen Yeow
Subsidiary:

Omega Semiconductor Sdn. Bhd. (1)
8760 Lot 8 Kawasan Perdagangan Bebas Fasa III Batu Berendam
75350 Melaka, Malaysia
Tel.: (60) 62822672
Fax: (60) 6062839608
E-Mail: corp@omegasemicon.com.my
Web Site: www.omegasemicon.com.my
Emp.: 800
Semiconductor Mfr
S.I.C.: 3674
N.A.I.C.S.: 334413
Dau Peng Cheam *(CEO)*

Subsidiary:

Dominant Opto Technologies Sdn. Bhd. (2)
Lot 6 Batu Berendam FTZ Phase III
75350 Melaka, Malaysia
Tel.: (60) 62833566
Fax: (60) 62830566
E-Mail: sales@dominant-semi.com
Web Site: www.dominant-semi.com
Emp.: 1,000
Opto Semiconductors Mfr
S.I.C.: 3674
N.A.I.C.S.: 334413

Non-U.S. Subsidiaries:

Dominant Semiconductors (Europe GmbH) (3)
Raiffeisenstr 38
74906 Bad Rappenau, Baden-Wurttemberg, Germany
Tel.: (49) 7264890100
Fax: (49) 72648901029
E-Mail: info@dominant-semi.eu
Web Site: www.dominant-semi.com
Light Emitting Diodes Mfr
S.I.C.: 3674
N.A.I.C.S.: 334413
Holger Wagner *(Gen Mgr)*

Dominant Semiconductors Korea Inc. (3)
Room 211 Sunteak City Apartment 513 15 Sangdaewon-dong
Jungwon-gu, Seongnam, Gyeonggi-do, 462 725, Korea (South)
Tel.: (82) 317015203
Fax: (82) 31 701 5204
E-Mail: sales_korea@dominant-semi.co.kr
Web Site: www.dominant-semi.com
Semiconductor Devices Distr
S.I.C.: 5065
N.A.I.C.S.: 423690

D-BOX TECHNOLOGIES INC.

2172 De La Province
Longueuil, QC, J4G 1R7, Canada
Tel.: (450) 442-3003
Fax: (450) 442-3230
Toll Free: (888) 442-3269
E-Mail: info@d-box.com
Web Site: www.d-box.com
DBO—(TSX)
Rev.: $14,167,767
Assets: $24,390,269
Liabilities: $2,515,865
Net Worth: $21,874,404
Earnings: ($2,559,601)
Emp.: 67
Fiscal Year-end: 03/31/13
Business Description:
Motion Simulation System Mfr
S.I.C.: 3679
N.A.I.C.S.: 334419
Personnel:
Louis Brunel *(Chm)*
Claude Mc Master *(Pres & CEO)*
Luc Audet *(CFO)*
Philippe Roy *(Chief Bus Dev Officer)*
Board of Directors:
Louis Brunel
Jean Colbert
Kit Dalaroy
Jean-Pierre Desrosiers
Jean Lamarre
Claude Mc Master
Elaine C. Phenix
Transfer Agent:
Computershare Investor Services Inc.
1500 University Street Suite 700
Montreal, QC, H3A 3SB, Canada

D C SECURITY INC

22 Goodmark Place Unit 20
Etobicoke, ON, M9W 6R2, Canada
Tel.: (416) 213-1995
Fax: (416) 213-1328
E-Mail: info@dc-security.com
Web Site: www.dc-security.com
Rev.: $24,653,724
Emp.: 100
Business Description:
Security Services
S.I.C.: 7381
N.A.I.C.S.: 561612
Personnel:
Clement G. Dennis *(Pres)*

D HLM LES FOYERS

1 Rue Du Houx
35700 Rennes, Ille Et Vilaine, France
Tel.: (33) 299845555
Rev.: $21,100,000
Emp.: 34
Business Description:
Apartment Building Operators
S.I.C.: 6513
N.A.I.C.S.: 531110
Personnel:
Yvon Douard *(Pres)*

D HLM NOTRE LOGIS

1 Place des Bleuets
BP 126
59433 Halluin, Cedex, France
Tel.: (33) 320030201
Fax: (33) 359811622
Web Site: www.notre-logis.fr/
Rev.: $23,900,000
Emp.: 51
Business Description:
Apartment Building Operators
S.I.C.: 6513
N.A.I.C.S.: 531110
Personnel:
Didier Motte *(Chm)*
Board of Directors:
Didier Motte
Alain Leurent

D-LINK CORPORATION, INC.

4th Floor No 289 Sinhu 3rd Road
Neihu Districe, Taipei, Taiwan
Tel.: (886) 266000123
Fax: (886) 266008168
Web Site: www.dlinktw.com.tw/
Year Founded: 1986
2332—(TAI)
Sales Range: $100-124.9 Million
Emp.: 1,898
Business Description:
Data Network Equipment Mfr
S.I.C.: 3661
N.A.I.C.S.: 334210
Personnel:
Roger Kao *(Chm & CEO)*
A. P. Chen *(Pres)*
Board of Directors:
Roger Kao
Charley Chang
A. P. Chen
Joan Chen
Hu Hui-Tzu
John Lee
Victor Lee
Steve S. K. Lin
Mason Liu
Kenneth Tai
Transfer Agent:
China Trust Commercial Bank
5 F 83 Sec 1 Chung-Ching S Road
Taipei, Taiwan
Tel.: (886) 2 2361 3033
Fax: (886) 2 2311 6723

U.S. Subsidiary:

D-Link Systems, Inc. (1)
17595 Mount Herrmann St
Fountain Valley, CA 92708
Tel.: (714) 885-6000
Fax: (866) 743-4905
Toll Free: (800) 326-1688
E-Mail: support@dlink.com
Web Site: www.dlink.com
Emp.: 3,200
Networking Connectivity & Data Communications Products Mfr
S.I.C.: 5045
N.A.I.C.S.: 423430
William Brown *(Assoc VP-Product Dev)*

Non-U.S. Subsidiary:

D-Link (India) Ltd (1)
Kalpataru Square 2nd Floor Unit No 24
Kondivita Lane
Off Andheri Kurla Road Next to VITS hotel
Andheri East, Mumbai, 400059, India (60.37%)
Tel.: (91) 2229215700
Fax: (91) 912228301901
E-Mail: sales@dlink.co.in
Web Site: www.dlink.co.in
533146—(BOM NSE)
Rev.: $65,684,039
Assets: $28,348,209
Liabilities: $11,992,032
Net Worth: $16,356,177
Earnings: $2,285,058
Emp.: 156
Fiscal Year-end: 03/31/13
Telecommunication Equipment Mfr
S.I.C.: 3663
N.A.I.C.S.: 334220
Gary Yang *(Mng Dir)*
C. M. Gaonkar *(CFO)*
Shrinivas Adkesar *(Compliance Officer & Sec)*

D. MEDICAL INDUSTRIES LTD.

3 HaSadna Street
Tirat Karmel, 39026, Israel
Tel.: (972) 4 855 0652
Fax: (972) 4 850 0297
E-Mail: info@dmedicalindustries.com
Web Site: www.dmedicalindustries.com
DMED—(OTC TAE)
Rev.: $246,648
Assets: $915,393
Liabilities: $1,072,033
Net Worth: ($156,640)
Earnings: ($3,807,196)
Emp.: 63
Fiscal Year-end: 12/31/12
Business Description:
Diabetes Medical Device Mfr
S.I.C.: 3841
N.A.I.C.S.: 339112
Personnel:
Meni Mor *(Chm)*
Efraim Argaman *(CEO)*
Amir Loberman *(CFO)*
Hezkiah Tsoory *(COO)*
Board of Directors:
Meni Mor
Shai Beilis
Avi Ben Haim
Zeev Bronfeld
Avraham Eylon
Galia Malka
Eyal Sheratzky
Subsidiary:

NiliMEDIX Ltd. (1)
Hasadna 3 St
Tirat Karmel, 39032, Israel
Tel.: (972) 48550652
Fax: (972) 48500297
E-Mail: info@nilimedix.com
Web Site: www.nilimedix.com
Medical Devices Mfr
S.I.C.: 3845
N.A.I.C.S.: 334510
Efri Argaman *(Chm & CEO)*

D NALOZBE D.D.

Smartinska 52
1000 Ljubljana, Slovenia
Tel.: (386) 31326879
E-Mail: dnalozbe@gmail.com
Web Site: www.dnalozbe.si
DFNR—(LJU)
Business Description:
Investment Fund Services
S.I.C.: 6722
N.A.I.C.S.: 525910
Personnel:
Danilo Peteh *(CEO)*

D P H, S.A.

(d/b/a D.P.H. Lingerie)
59 avenue Victor Hugo
F-75116 Paris, France
Tel.: (33) 149582300
Fax: (33) 149588215
E-Mail: dph@dph-lingerie.com

D P H, S.A.—(Continued)

Web Site: www.hechter-lingerie.com
Year Founded: 1991
Sls.: $21,800,000
Emp.: 63

Business Description:
Women's Lingerie Designer & Distr
S.I.C.: 5137
N.A.I.C.S.: 424330

Personnel:
Firoz Hiridjee *(Founder & CEO)*

D-PHARM LTD.

Kiryat Weizmann Science Park Bldg 7
PO Box 2313
76123 Rehovot, Israel
Tel.: (972) 89385100
Fax: (972) 89300795
E-Mail: aklainer@dpharm.com
Web Site: www.dpharm.com
Year Founded: 1993
DPRM—(TAE)
Sales Range: $25-49.9 Million
Emp.: 90

Business Description:
Pharmaceutical Mfr
S.I.C.: 2834
N.A.I.C.S.: 325412

Personnel:
Ruben Krupik *(Chm)*
Aharon Schwartz *(Chm)*
Alexander Kozak *(Pres & CEO)*

Board of Directors:
Ruben Krupik
Aharon Schwartz
Ofer Goldberg
Alexander Kozak

D. WESTERN THERAPEUTICS INSTITUTE, INC.

7th Floor 18 KT Bldg 1-18-11 Nishiki
Naka-ku
Nagoya, Aichi, 460-0003, Japan
Tel.: (81) 522188785
Fax: (81) 522021866
E-Mail: info@dwti.co.jp
Web Site: www.dwti.co.jp
Year Founded: 1999
4576—(JAS)
Rev.: $1,237,500
Assets: $5,143,776
Liabilities: $167,530
Net Worth: $4,976,246
Earnings: ($2,817,507)
Emp.: 21
Fiscal Year-end: 12/31/12

Business Description:
Pharmaceutical Mfr & Researcher
S.I.C.: 2834
N.A.I.C.S.: 325412

Personnel:
Hiroyoshi Hidaka *(Chm & Co-CEO)*
Yuichi Hidaka *(Pres & Co-CEO)*

Board of Directors:
Hiroyoshi Hidaka
Yuichi Hidaka
Ayako Kamikubo
Masakatsu Nishikawa
Yoshiyuki Yamakawa

DA AN GENE CO., LTD.

80 Xianlie Zhong Road 27th Floor
Huihua Commerce and Trade Building
Guangzhou, 510070, China
Tel.: (86) 2037617457
Fax: (86) 2037617476
Web Site: en.daangene.com
002030—(SSE)

Business Description:
Biological Products Mfr & Distr
S.I.C.: 2836
N.A.I.C.S.: 325414

Personnel:
Yunshao He *(Chm & CEO)*
Cuiling Wu *(Vice Chm)*

Board of Directors:
Yunshao He
Shusong Ba
Cuiling Wu
Shiyou Yu

DA CIN CONSTRUCTION CO., LTD.

9F No 92 Sec 2 Dunhua S Rd Da-an District
Taipei, Taiwan
Tel.: (886) 227062929
Fax: (886) 227081317
E-Mail: cm10023@dacin.com.tw
Web Site: www.dacin.com.tw
2535—(TAI)
Sales Range: $150-199.9 Million

Business Description:
Commercial Construction Services
S.I.C.: 1521
N.A.I.C.S.: 236115

Personnel:
Jen-Jeng Wang *(Chm)*
Tsai-Pin Wang *(Pres)*
Kong-Wah Lu *(Sr VP)*

Board of Directors:
Jen-Jeng Wang
Pao-Shan Ku
Vin-Cent Pan

D.A. CONSORTIUM, INC.

Yebisu Garden Pl Tower 33F
4-20-3 Ebisu Shibuya, Tokyo, 150-6033, Japan
Tel.: (81) 354496295
Fax: (81) 3 5449 6201
Web Site: www.dac.co.jp
4281—(TKS)
Emp.: 938
S.I.C.: 7311
N.A.I.C.S.: 541810

Personnel:
Adeline Chang *(Sr Acct Mgr)*

DA GROUP

70 Mitchell St
Glasgow, G1 3LX, United Kingdom
Tel.: (44) 1415820600
Fax: (44) 1415820699
E-Mail: info@dagroupplc.com
Web Site: www.digital-animations.com
Year Founded: 1990
Sales Range: $10-24.9 Million
Emp.: 40

Business Description:
Computer Software
S.I.C.: 7371
N.A.I.C.S.: 541511

Personnel:
Angie Collins *(Office Mgr)*

DA-LI CONSTRUCTION CO., LTD.

8F No 143 Sec 2 Minsheng East Road
Zongshan District, Taipei, 10483, Taiwan
Tel.: (886) 2 25061966
Fax: (886) 2 25061989
Web Site: www.da-li.com.tw
6177—(TAI)
Rev.: $94,246,018
Fiscal Year-end: 12/31/12

Business Description:
Residential Buildings & Home Construction Services
S.I.C.: 1522
N.A.I.C.S.: 236116

Personnel:
Chi-Chang Hsieh *(Chm & Gen Mgr)*

DA MING INTERNATIONAL HOLDINGS LIMITED

No 1518 Tongjiang Road
Wuxi, Jiangsu, China
Tel.: (86) 510 83859388
Fax: (86) 510 83858001
Web Site: www.dmssc.net
1090—(HKG)
Rev.: $1,857,512,475
Assets: $665,750,199
Liabilities: $401,746,105
Net Worth: $264,004,093
Earnings: $4,774,396
Emp.: 1,510
Fiscal Year-end: 12/31/12

Business Description:
Stainless Steel Processor & Distr
S.I.C.: 3312
N.A.I.C.S.: 331110

Personnel:
Keming Zhou *(Co-Founder, Chm & CEO)*
Xia Xu *(Co-Founder)*
Man Fai Leung *(CFO & Sec)*

Board of Directors:
Keming Zhou
Xuedong Chen
Wa Pang Cheuk
Min Hua
Changhong Jiang
In Soo Kang
Zhonghai Tang
Xia Xu
Xiaoping Zou

Legal Counsel:
Deacons
5th Floor Alexandra House 18 Chater Road
Central, China (Hong Kong)

Conyers Dill & Pearman
Cricket Square Hutchins Drive
PO Box 2681
Georgetown, Grand Cayman, Cayman Islands

DA RETAILGROEP B.V.

Benj Fralklinstraat 2
8013 NC Zwolle, Netherlands
Mailing Address:
Postbus 82
8000 AB Zwolle, Netherlands
Tel.: (31) 384697200
Fax: (31) 384697250
E-Mail: info@da.nl
Web Site: www.da.nl
Year Founded: 1991
Sales Range: $350-399.9 Million
Emp.: 400

Business Description:
Drugstore Supplier & Operator
S.I.C.: 5912
N.A.I.C.S.: 446110

Personnel:
Joaan Boaiganga *(Mng Dir)*

DABBAGH GROUP HOLDING COMPANY LTD.

PO Box 1039
Jeddah, 21431, Saudi Arabia
Tel.: (966) 26697220
Fax: (966) 26696184
E-Mail: info@dabbagh.com
Web Site: www.dabbagh.com
Year Founded: 1962

Business Description:
Diverse Holding Company
S.I.C.: 6719
N.A.I.C.S.: 551112

Personnel:
M. H. Jazeel *(CEO & CFO)*
Waheed A. Shaikh *(COO)*

Board of Directors:
Hussein Abdullah Al-Dabbagh
Jamal Abdullah Al-Dabbagh
Majid Abdullah Al-Kassabi
Marcus Alexander
Tariq L. Ali
M. H. Jazeel
Kamel Lazaar
Waheed A. Shaikh

Subsidiaries:

Advance Petroleum Services Ltd. **(1)**
3rd Floor Adham Center Madinah Road
PO Box 2120
Jeddah, 21451, Saudi Arabia
Tel.: (966) 2 614 2424
Fax: (966) 2 650 0741
E-Mail: info@apsl-ksa.com
Web Site: www.apsl-ksa.com
Petroleum & Lubricants Distr
S.I.C.: 5172
N.A.I.C.S.: 424720
Sajid Saeed *(Gen Mgr)*

Agricultural Development Company Ltd. **(1)**
PO Box 86909
Riyadh, 11632, Saudi Arabia
Tel.: (966) 14775192
Fax: (966) 14792647
E-Mail: adc@adc-ksa.com
Web Site: www.adc-ksa.com
Animal Feeds, Broiler Chicks, Hatching Eggs, Animal Health Products, Livestock Equipment & Technology Producer & Distr
S.I.C.: 0251
N.A.I.C.S.: 112320
Sean Holder *(Mng Dir)*

Al Jazira Oil & Gas Services Company EC **(1)**
PO Box 1039
Jeddah, 21431, Saudi Arabia
Tel.: (966) 26697220
Fax: (966) 26696184
E-Mail: info@al-jazira.com
Web Site: www.al-jazira.com
Oil & Gas Investment Services
S.I.C.: 6211
N.A.I.C.S.: 523999
M. H. Jazeel *(CFO)*

Consulting Engineering Bureau Abdullah Dabbagh Partners **(1)**
PO Box 1039
Jeddah, 21431, Saudi Arabia
Tel.: (966) 26678662
Fax: (966) 26679053
E-Mail: info@dabbaghceb.com
Web Site: www.dabbaghceb.com
Emp.: 10
Engineer Services
S.I.C.: 8711
N.A.I.C.S.: 541330
Hussein Abdullah Al-Dabbagh *(Mng Dir)*

DG International Oil Company Ltd. **(1)**
PO Box 1039
Jeddah, 21431, Saudi Arabia
Tel.: (966) 26697220
Fax: (966) 26696184
E-Mail: info@dgoil.com
Web Site: www.dgoil.com
Emp.: 500
Oil & Gas Investment Services
S.I.C.: 6211
N.A.I.C.S.: 523999
M. H. Jazeel *(CFO)*

DGH Investment Company Ltd. **(1)**
PO Box 1039
Jeddah, 21431, Saudi Arabia
Tel.: (966) 26697220
Fax: (966) 2 6696184
E-Mail: info@dabbagh.com
Web Site: www.dabbagh.com
Investment Services
S.I.C.: 6211
N.A.I.C.S.: 523999
M. H. Jazeel *(CEO & CFO)*

Gulf Co-Operation Insurance Company Ltd., EC **(1)**
PO Box 5248
Jeddah, 21422, Saudi Arabia
Tel.: (966) 26515808
Fax: (966) 26510075
Web Site: www.gci-ksa.com
Emp.: 150
Insurance Services
S.I.C.: 6351
N.A.I.C.S.: 524126

Javed Quraishi *(Gen Mgr)*

Gulf Power International Ltd. (1)
PO Box 1039
Jeddah, 21431, Saudi Arabia
Tel.: (966) 26683407
Fax: (966) 26696184
E-Mail: info@gulf-power-sys.com
Web Site: www.gulf-power-sys.com
Emp.: 500
Power Facilities Construction & Engineering
S.I.C.: 8711
N.A.I.C.S.: 541330
Mohammed Z. Chouayeb *(CEO & Gen Mgr)*

Marketing and Commercial Agencies Company Ltd. (1)
PO Box 5248
Jeddah, 21422, Saudi Arabia
Tel.: (966) 26515808
Fax: (966) 26510075
E-Mail: info@gci-ksa.com
Web Site: www.gci-ksa.com
Emp.: 100
Insurance Services
S.I.C.: 6411
N.A.I.C.S.: 524210
Javed Quraishi *(Gen Mgr)*

National Scientific Company Ltd. (1)
Al-Salam Building Tahlia Street
PO Box 1039
Jeddah, 21431, Saudi Arabia
Tel.: (966) 26644466
Fax: (966) 26696192
E-Mail: info@nsc-ksa.com
Web Site: www.nsc-ksa.com
Industrial Chemicals, Laboratory Equipment & Scientific Instruments Distr
S.I.C.: 5169
N.A.I.C.S.: 424690

Red Sea Housing Services Co. (1)
PO Box 1531
Al Jubayl, 31951, Saudi Arabia
Tel.: (966) 33624544
Fax: (966) 33614490
E-Mail: info@redseahousing.com
Web Site: www.redseahousing.com
4230—(SAU)
Rev.: $230,308,271
Assets: $328,614,089
Liabilities: $111,785,600
Net Worth: $216,828,489
Earnings: $32,121,487
Emp.: 2,374
Fiscal Year-end: 12/31/12
Modular Buildings Mfr
S.I.C.: 2451
N.A.I.C.S.: 321991
Ibrahim Hassan Al-Madhoun *(Chm)*
Don Brown Sumner *(Mng Dir)*

Supreme Foods Processing Company Ltd. (1)
PO Box 86909
Riyadh, 11632, Saudi Arabia
Tel.: (966) 14775192
Fax: (966) 14765865
Web Site: www.sfgarabia.net
Food Processor
S.I.C.: 2099
N.A.I.C.S.: 311999
Robert Morrison *(Gen Mgr)*

Tanmiah Commercial Group Ltd. (1)
PO Box 1039
Jeddah, 21431, Saudi Arabia
Tel.: (966) 26697220
Fax: (966) 26696184
E-Mail: info@dabbagh.com
Web Site: www.tanmiah.com
Emp.: 100
Investment Services
S.I.C.: 6211
N.A.I.C.S.: 523999
M. H. Jazeel *(CFO)*

Joint Venture:

International Project Developers Ltd. (1)
PO Box 1039
Jeddah, 21431, Saudi Arabia
Tel.: (966) 26697220
Fax: (966) 2 6696184
Web Site: www.ipd-intl.com
Turnkey Project Development Services; Owned 51% by Dabbagh Group Holding Company Ltd. & 49% by IPCO International Ltd.
S.I.C.: 1629
N.A.I.C.S.: 237990
Mohammed Z. Chouayeb *(Gen Mgr)*

Non-U.S. Subsidiaries:

Saudi Egyptian Logistics and Electronics Company, S.A.E. (1)
8278th Street
Maadi, Cairo, Egypt
Tel.: (20) 225229222
Fax: (20) 225229223
E-Mail: sales.info@salec.com
Web Site: www.salec.com
Data Network & Telecommunication Infrastructure Designer & Mfr
S.I.C.: 7379
N.A.I.C.S.: 541519
Mahmoud Soliman *(Pres & CEO)*

DABUR INDIA LTD

8/3 Asaf Ali Road
New Delhi, 110 002, India
Tel.: (91) 1123253488
Fax: (91) 1203001000
E-Mail: corpcomm@dabur.com
Web Site: www.dabur.com
500096—(BOM NSE)
Rev.: $1,162,572,948
Assets: $878,130,414
Liabilities: $482,034,438
Net Worth: $396,095,976
Earnings: $141,977,466
Emp.: 6,154
Fiscal Year-end: 03/31/13

Business Description:
Health, Personal Care & Food Products Mfr
S.I.C.: 2844
N.A.I.C.S.: 325620

Personnel:
Sunil Duggal *(CEO)*
Lalit Malik *(CFO)*
Ashok Kumar Jain *(Compliance Officer, Sec & Gen Mgr-Fin)*

Board of Directors:
Anand C. Burman
R. C. Bhargava
Sanjay Kumar Bhattacharyya
Amit Burman
Mohit Burman
Saket Burman
Ajay Dua
Sunil Duggal
P. D. Narang
S. Narayan
Albert Wiseman Paterson
P. N. Vijay

Transfer Agent:
Karvy Computershare Private Limited
Plot No 17 to 24 Vittalrao Nagar Madhapur
Hyderabad, India

Subsidiary:

H&B Stores Ltd. (1)
Hindi Bhavan 11-Rouse Avenue ITO
Near Bal Bhavan, New Delhi, 110002, India
Tel.: (91) 11 42786084
Health Care & Cosmetic Products Distr
S.I.C.: 5122
N.A.I.C.S.: 424210

Units:

Dabur India Ltd - Baddi - Oral Care Unit (1)
601 Malkhumajra Nalagarh Road
Baddi, Himachal Pradesh, India
Tel.: (91) 1795 246363
Fax: (91) 1795 246363
Web Site: www.dabur.com
Oral Care Products Mfr
S.I.C.: 2834
N.A.I.C.S.: 325412

Dabur India Ltd - Jammu Unit I , II & III (1)
Lane No 3 Phase II Sidco Industrial Complex
Bari Brahmana, Jammu and Kashmir, India
Tel.: (91) 1923 220123
Fax: (91) 1923 221970
Personal Care Products Mfr
S.I.C.: 2844
N.A.I.C.S.: 325620

Dabur India Ltd - Nashik Unit (1)
D-55 MIDC Ambad
Nasik, 422 010, India
Tel.: (91) 253 6623222
Fax: (91) 253 2383146
Web Site: www.dabur.com
Pharmaceutical Products Mfr
S.I.C.: 2834
N.A.I.C.S.: 325412

Non-U.S. Subsidiaries:

African Consumer Care Ltd. (1)
18 Burma Road Apapa
Lagos, Nigeria
Tel.: (234) 17902781
Fax: (234) 12712758
Food Products Mfr
S.I.C.: 2099
N.A.I.C.S.: 311999

Dabur Egypt Ltd (1)
2 Saudi Co Bldgs El Nozha St
Heliopolis, Cairo, Egypt
Tel.: (20) 2 22900264
Fax: (20) 2 22901739
Cosmetics Mfr
S.I.C.: 2844
N.A.I.C.S.: 325620

Dabur International Ltd. (1)
PO Box 16944
Jebel Ali, Dubai, United Arab Emirates
Tel.: (971) 4 8817756
Fax: (971) 4 8817734
E-Mail: dabur@emirates.net.ae
Web Site: www.dabur.com
Emp.: 150
Food Products Mfr
S.I.C.: 2099
N.A.I.C.S.: 311999

Non-U.S. Subsidiaries:

Dabur International Limited (2)
2 Gayton Road
Harrow, HA1 2XU, United Kingdom
Tel.: (44) 2089 01 7620
Fax: (44) 2089 01 7472
E-Mail: info@dabur.co.uk
Web Site: www.dabur.co.uk
Personal Care Products Mfr
S.I.C.: 2844
N.A.I.C.S.: 325620
Rahul Chaudhary *(Head-Bus-Europe)*

Dabur Nepal Pvt. Ltd. (2)
TNT Building Tinkune Koteshwor
Kathmandu, 14375, Nepal
Tel.: (977) 12054533
Fax: (977) 712054534
E-Mail: nepal@dabur.wlink.com.np
Emp.: 4,000
Personal Care Products Mfr
S.I.C.: 2844
N.A.I.C.S.: 325620
Rukma Rana *(Mng Dir)*

Hobi Kozmetik Imalat Sanayi Ve Anel Is Merkezi Kat 2-6-A 5-4 Saray Mahallesi (2)
Siteyolu Sokak, Istanbul, Turkey
Tel.: (90) 2166300030
Fax: (90) 2166306807
E-Mail: info@hobikozmetik.com
Web Site: www.hobikozmetik.com
Cosmetic Products Distr
S.I.C.: 5122
N.A.I.C.S.: 424210

DACHA STRATEGIC METALS INC.

212 King Street W Suite 201
Toronto, ON, M5H 1K5, Canada
Tel.: (416) 348-8585
Fax: (416) 861-8165
E-Mail: info@dachacapital.com
Web Site: www.dachacapital.com
Year Founded: 1996
DSM—(TSXV)
Int. Income: $863
Assets: $27,510,710
Liabilities: $1,980,979
Net Worth: $25,529,731
Earnings: ($57,549,264)
Fiscal Year-end: 05/31/13

Business Description:
Industrial Metal Sales
S.I.C.: 1481
N.A.I.C.S.: 213115

Personnel:
Ian W. Delaney *(Chm)*
Peter H. Puccetti *(CEO)*
Graham C. Warren *(CFO)*
Michael D. Woollcombe *(Sec)*

Board of Directors:
Ian W. Delaney
Jorge Bernhard
Tye W. Burt
G. Scott Moore
Alastair S. Neill
Peter H. Puccetti
Timothy E. Thorsteinson

Transfer Agent:
Equity Financial Trust Company
200 University Avenue Suite 300
Toronto, ON, M5H 4H1, Canada

DACHAN FOOD (ASIA) LIMITED

Suite 1806 Tower 1 The Gateway 25 Canton Road Tsimshatsui
Kowloon, China (Hong Kong)
Tel.: (852) 27375300
Fax: (852) 27303773
E-Mail: info@dachanfoodasia.com
Web Site: www.dfa3999.com
3999—(HKG)
Sls.: $1,816,522,027
Assets: $587,040,183
Liabilities: $271,233,992
Net Worth: $315,806,190
Earnings: $17,725,595
Emp.: 14,774
Fiscal Year-end: 12/31/12

Business Description:
Food Industry
S.I.C.: 2015
N.A.I.C.S.: 311615

Personnel:
Mark Jia-Hwan Han *(Chm)*
Chia-Yin Han *(CEO)*
Li-Chin Chen *(Chief Admin Officer)*
Yu-Lung Chang *(COO-Feed Products Bus & Sr VP)*
Jing-Hui Li *(COO-Meat Products Bus & Sr VP)*
Chang-Jou Ou *(COO-Food Products Bus & Sr VP)*
Siu Yin Pang *(Sec)*

Board of Directors:
Mark Jia-Hwan Han
Tien-Shin Chao
Chih Chen
Chia-Yau Han
Chia-Yin Han
Jia-Chen Harn
Fuchun Liu
Nicholas William Rosa
Yung-Do Way

Legal Counsel:
Cheung, Tong & Rosa
Rooms 501, 5/F, Sun Hung Kai Cenre, 30 Harbour Road
Hong Kong, China (Hong Kong)

Butterfield Fulcrum Group (Cayman) Limited
Butterfield House 68 Fort Street 609
Georgetown, Grand Cayman, KY1 1107, Cayman Islands

Transfer Agents:
Tricor Investor Services Limited
26th Floor Tesbury Centre 28 Queens Road East
Wanchai, China (Hong Kong)

Butterfield Fulcrum Group (Cayman) Limited
Butterfield House 68 Fort Street 609

DaChan Food (Asia) Limited—(Continued)

Georgetown, Grand Cayman, KY1 1107, Cayman Islands

DACHSER GMBH & CO.

Memmingerstrasse 140
87439 Kempten, Germany
Tel.: (49) 8315916191
Fax: (49) 8315916910
E-Mail: info@dachser.com
Web Site: www.dachser.com
Year Founded: 1930
Emp.: 12,000

Business Description:
International Freight Forwarding
S.I.C.: 4731
N.A.I.C.S.: 488510

Personnel:
Dieter Bendele *(Mng Dir)*
Ingo Boeckenholt *(Mng Dir)*
Michael Schilling *(Mng Dir)*
Bernhard Simon *(Mng Dir)*

U.S. Subsidiary:

Dachser Transport of America Inc. **(1)**
20 W Lincoln Ave
Valley Stream, NY 11580-5730 (100%)
Tel.: (516) 561-7800
Fax: (516) 561-7834
E-Mail: jfk@dachser.us
Web Site: www.dachser.us
Emp.: 25
Freight Forwarding
S.I.C.: 4731
N.A.I.C.S.: 488510
Frank Guenzerodt *(Pres & CEO)*

DACIAN GOLD LIMITED

Ground Floor 26 Clive Street
West Perth, WA, 6005, Australia
Mailing Address:
PO Box 1123
West Perth, WA, 6872, Australia
Tel.: (61) 8 9226 4622
Fax: (61) 8 9226 2722
E-Mail: info@daciangold.com.au
Web Site: www.daciangold.com.au
Year Founded: 2011
DCN—(ASX)

Business Description:
Gold Mining
S.I.C.: 1041
N.A.I.C.S.: 212221

Personnel:
Rohan Ian Williams *(Chm)*
Paul Payne *(Mng Dir)*
Kevin Hart *(Sec)*

Board of Directors:
Rohan Ian Williams
Barry Patterson
Paul Payne
Rob Reynolds

Legal Counsel:
Mills Oakley Lawyers
Level 12 George Street
Sydney, NSW, 2000, Australia

DACRO INDUSTRIES INC.

9325 51 Ave
Edmonton, AB, T6E 4W8, Canada
Tel.: (780) 434-8900
Fax: (780) 437-6291
Web Site: www.dacro.com
Year Founded: 1974
Rev.: $31,305,192
Emp.: 140

Business Description:
Fabricated Metal Equipment Mfr
S.I.C.: 3448
N.A.I.C.S.: 332311

Personnel:
Marvin Kossowan *(Pres)*

DADABHAI GROUP

Building 600 Road 2808 Seif District
PO Box 20143
Manama, Bahrain
Tel.: (973) 17587575
Fax: (973) 17587500
E-Mail: info@dadabhai.com
Web Site: www.dadabhai.com
Emp.: 500

Business Description:
Construction Services, Travel Services & Neon Sign Mfr & Sales
S.I.C.: 1542
N.A.I.C.S.: 236220

Personnel:
Mohammed Dadabhai *(Chm)*

Subsidiary:

Arabian Neon W.L.L. **(1)**
PO Box 11587
Manama, Bahrain
Tel.: (973) 1746 9999
Fax: (973) 1746 4111
E-Mail: info@pegasusbahrain.com
Web Site: www.arabianneon.com
Neon Signs & Billboards Design & Manufacture
S.I.C.: 3993
N.A.I.C.S.: 339950
Mohammed Dadabhai *(Chm)*

DADCO ALUMINA & CHEMICALS LTD.

Hamilton House Saint Julians Avenue
Saint Peter Port, GY1 1WA, Guernsey
Tel.: (44) 1481740605
Fax: (44) 1481740604
Web Site: www.dadcoalumina.com
Year Founded: 1915

Business Description:
Private Equity Firm; Alumina Refining & Trading
S.I.C.: 6211
N.A.I.C.S.: 523999

Personnel:
Victor Phillip Michael Dahdaleh *(Owner & Chm)*

Non-U.S. Holding:

Aluminium Oxid Stade GmbH **(1)**
Johann Rathjekoeser Str
PO Box 2269
D 21683 Stade, Germany De
Mailing Address: (100%)
Postfach 2269
D-21662 Stade, Germany
Tel.: (49) 4146921
Fax: (49) 414692359
E-Mail: info@aos-stade.de
Web Site: www.aos-stade.de
Emp.: 530
Alumina Refinery
S.I.C.: 3334
N.A.I.C.S.: 331313
Helmuth Buhrfeindt *(Mng Dir)*
Eberhard Guhl *(Mng Dir)*

DADEX ETERNIT LIMITED

34-A/1 Block-6 P E C H S Shahrah-e-Faisal
Karachi, 75400, Pakistan
Tel.: (92) 21 111 000 789
Fax: (92) 21 343 15716
E-Mail: info@dadex.com
Web Site: www.dadex.com
DADX—(KAR)
Sls.: $24,051,315
Assets: $29,185,138
Liabilities: $18,236,553
Net Worth: $10,948,585
Earnings: ($124,700)
Emp.: 555
Fiscal Year-end: 06/30/13

Business Description:
Fibre Cement Sheets, Malidar Beams, Fibre Cement, PVC Pressure Pipes, Building Pipes & Other Related Products Mfr & Distr
S.I.C.: 3241
N.A.I.C.S.: 327310

Personnel:
Sikander Dada *(CEO)*
Shazam Butt *(CFO & Sec)*

Board of Directors:
Abu Talib H. K. Dada
Qazi Sajid Ali
Samad Dada
Sikander Dada
Shahzad M. Hussain
Zulfiqar Ali Lakhani
Maqbool H. H. Rahimtoola

Legal Counsel:
Surridge & Beecheno
3rd Floor Finlay House I.I. Chundrigar Road
Karachi, Pakistan

DAE SUNG MICROBIOLOGICAL LABS. CO., LTD.

293 Sam-Dong
Uiwang, Kyunggi-Do, Korea (South)
Tel.: (82) 31 4617103
Fax: (82) 31 4610599
Web Site: www.dsmbio.com
Year Founded: 1968
036480—(KRS)

Business Description:
Pharmaceutical Preparation Mfr
S.I.C.: 2834
N.A.I.C.S.: 325412

Personnel:
Dong Gyu Lee *(Chm)*

DAEATI CO., LTD.

200-1 Nae-Dong
Ojeong-Gu, Bucheon, Gyeonggi-Do, 421-806, Korea (South)
Tel.: (82) 32 680 0818
Fax: (82) 32 674 2506
E-Mail: daeati@daeati.co.kr
Web Site: www.daeati.co.kr
Year Founded: 1996
045390—(KRS)

Business Description:
Communication Equipment Mfr
S.I.C.: 3669
N.A.I.C.S.: 334290

Personnel:
Jin-Woo Choi *(Pres & CEO)*

DAEBONG LS CO., LTD.

692-8 Kojan-dong
Namdong-ku, Incheon, Korea (South)
Tel.: (82) 32 817 8800
Fax: (82) 32 817 8808
Web Site: www.daebongls.co.kr
Year Founded: 1986
078140—(KRS)

Business Description:
Pharmaceutical Product Mfr
S.I.C.: 2834
N.A.I.C.S.: 325412

Personnel:
Jin-Ho Park *(CEO)*

DAECHANG CO., LTD.

506 4Na Sihwa Industrial Complex
1292-4 Jeongwang-dong
Siheung, Gyeonggi-do, Korea (South)
Tel.: (82) 31 496 3000
Fax: (82) 31 496 2538
Web Site: www.brasone.co.kr
Year Founded: 1974
012800—(KRS)

Business Description:
Metal Product Mfr
S.I.C.: 3339
N.A.I.C.S.: 331410

Personnel:
Si-Young Cho *(CEO)*

DAEDONG GEAR CO., LTD.

71 Yuchun Ri
Sahnam Myun
Gyungsangnam Do, 664940
Sacheon, Korea (South)
Tel.: (82) 558512300
Fax: (82) 558516135
Web Site: www.daedonggear.com
8830—(KRS)
Sales Range: $100-124.9 Million

Business Description:
Axle Assemblies Mfr
S.I.C.: 3714
N.A.I.C.S.: 336350

Personnel:
Jae Hyung Han *(CEO)*

DAEDONG KOREA GINSENG CO., LTD.

586 Gunbuk-ro Gunbuk-myeon
Geumsan-gun
Ch'ung-Nam, Korea (South)
Tel.: (82) 41 7538803
Fax: (82) 41 7539914
Web Site: www.ddkorea.co.kr
Year Founded: 2002
178600—(KRS)

Business Description:
Ginseng Products
S.I.C.: 2833
N.A.I.C.S.: 325411

Personnel:
Sung-Geun Choi *(CEO)*

DAEDUCK ELECTRONICS CO., LTD.

390-1 Mocknae-dong
Danwon-gu, Ansan, Gyeonggi-do, Korea (South) 425-100
Tel.: (82) 315998800
Fax: (82) 314818245
E-Mail: deoffshore@daeduck.com
Web Site: www.daeduck.com
008060—(KRS)

Business Description:
Printed Circuit Board Mfr & Services
S.I.C.: 3672
N.A.I.C.S.: 334412

Personnel:
Gregory Y. J. Kim *(Pres & CEO)*

Plant:

Daeduck Electronics Co., Ltd. - Ansan Plant #1 **(1)**
390-1 Mocknae-dong
Danwon-gu, 425-100 Ansan, Gyeonggi-do, Korea (South)
Tel.: (82) 31 599 8800
Fax: (82) 31 481 8245
E-Mail: deoffshore@daeduck.com
Web Site: www.daeduck.com
Electronic Component Mfr
S.I.C.: 3679
N.A.I.C.S.: 334419

Non-U.S. Subsidiaries:

DAEDUCK PHILLIPINES, INC **(1)**
Phillipines Economic Zone Authority PEZA
Lot 1-13 Block 20 Phase 4
Main Ave, Rosario, Cavite, Philippines
Tel.: (63) 46 437 0741 48
Fax: (63) 46 437 1597
E-Mail: sales@ddpi.com.ph
Web Site: www.ddpi.com.ph
Electronic Component Mfr
S.I.C.: 3679
N.A.I.C.S.: 334419

Nakor Inc. **(1)**
215 Sanders St Suite 202
Kemptville, ON, K0G 1J0, Canada
Tel.: (613) 258-4775
Fax: (613) 258-7936
Electronic Component Mfr
S.I.C.: 3679
N.A.I.C.S.: 334419
Bill Ballantyne *(Gen Mgr)*

DAEDUCK GDS CO LTD

475 Moknae Dong
Danwon Gu
425100 Ansan, Kyonggi Do, Korea (South)

Tel.: (82) 82314818025
Fax: (82) 82314818081
Web Site: www.daeduckgds.co.kr
4130—(KRS)
Sales Range: $25-49.9 Million

Business Description:
Printed Circuit Boards Mfr
S.I.C.: 3672
N.A.I.C.S.: 334412

Personnel:
Young Hoon Yoo *(Pres & CEO)*

DAEHAN FLOUR MILLS CO., LTD

14F KCCI Bldg 45 Namdaemunno 4-ga
Jung-gu, Seoul, Korea (South)
Tel.: (82) 2 3455 0200
Web Site: www.dhflour.co.kr
001130—(KRS)

Business Description:
Flour Product Mfr
S.I.C.: 2041
N.A.I.C.S.: 311211

Personnel:
Jong Gak Lee *(Chm)*

DAEHAN STEEL CO., LTD.

69 Hasin Beonyeong-ro
Saha-gu, Busan, Korea (South)
Tel.: (82) 51 220 3300
Fax: (82) 51 220 3398
Web Site: www.idaehan.com
Year Founded: 1954
084010—(KRS)

Business Description:
Steel Product Mfr
S.I.C.: 3312
N.A.I.C.S.: 331110

Personnel:
Wan-soo Oh *(Pres)*
Hyung-keun Oh *(CEO)*

DAEHO P&C CO., LTD.

328 Sanmak-dong
Yangsan, Gyeongsangnam-do, Korea (South)
Tel.: (82) 553884001
Fax: (82) 553837377
Web Site: www.daehopnc.co.kr
Year Founded: 1988
021040—(KRS)

Business Description:
Automobile Product Mfr
S.I.C.: 3711
N.A.I.C.S.: 336111

Personnel:
Wan-shin Park *(CEO)*

Subsidiaries:

Daeho Co., Ltd (1)
503-2 Gamheon-dong
Sasang-gu, Busan, Korea (South)
Tel.: (82) 51 311 0083
Fax: (82) 51 311 0082
Real Estate Leasing Services & Steel Products Distr
S.I.C.: 6519
N.A.I.C.S.: 531190

DSP Co., Ltd. (1)
725-4 Hakjang-dong
Sasang-gu, Busan, Korea (South)
Tel.: (82) 51 323 3511
Fax: (82) 51 314 3540
Emp.: 300
Steel Products Distr
S.I.C.: 5051
N.A.I.C.S.: 423510
Park Wan Sin *(Gen Mgr)*

Hwaseung Savings Bank (1)
1287-11 Yeonsan 5 dong
Yeonjae-gu, Busan, Korea (South)
Tel.: (82) 51 867 7701
Fax: (82) 51 867 1169
Web Site: www.daehopnc.co.kr/eng/aboutus05.html
Investment Banking Services
S.I.C.: 6211
N.A.I.C.S.: 523110

Mijuland Co., Ltd. (1)
San 27-7 Harim-li Daeshin-meon
Yeoju-gun, Harim, Gyeonggi, Korea (South)
Tel.: (82) 31 881 0714
Fax: (82) 31 881 0707
Landscape Architectural Services
S.I.C.: 0781
N.A.I.C.S.: 541320

Plant:

Daeho P&C Co., Ltd. - Busan Factory (1)
725-4 Hakjang-dong
Sasang-gu, Busan, Korea (South)
Tel.: (82) 51 323 3511
Fax: (82) 51 314 3540
Web Site: www.daehopnc.co.kr/eng/aboutus04.html
Industrial Pipe Mfr
S.I.C.: 3498
N.A.I.C.S.: 332996

DAEHONG COMMUNICATIONS INC.

Yonsei Jaedan Severance Building # 84-11 5KA
Namdaemun-ro
Chung-Ku, Seoul, 100-753, Korea (South)
Tel.: (82) 2 3671 6114
Fax: (82) 2 3671 6770
Web Site: www.daehong.co.kr
Year Founded: 1982
Sales Range: $300-349.9 Million

Business Description:
Advertising
S.I.C.: 7311
N.A.I.C.S.: 541810

Personnel:
Choi Jong-Won *(CEO)*

DAEJAN HOLDINGS PLC

Freshwater House 158-162
Shaftesbury Avenue
London, WC2H 8HR, United Kingdom
Tel.: (44) 2078361555
Fax: (44) 2074978941
E-Mail: Mark.Jenner@highdorn.co.uk
Web Site: www.daejanholdings.com
Year Founded: 1935
DJAN—(LSE)
Rev.: $175,359,624
Assets: $2,405,549,259
Liabilities: $850,022,836
Net Worth: $1,555,526,423
Earnings: $141,757,070
Emp.: 139
Fiscal Year-end: 03/31/13

Business Description:
Holding Company; Property Investment & Trading
S.I.C.: 6719
N.A.I.C.S.: 551112

Personnel:
B. S. E. Freshwater *(Chm & Mng Dir)*
M. R. M. Jenner *(Sec)*

Board of Directors:
B. S. E. Freshwater
D. Davis
A. M. Freshwater
R. E. Freshwater
S. I. Freshwater

Subsidiaries:

Bampton (Redbridge) Limited (1)
158-162 Shattsburry Ave
London, WC2 H8HR, United Kingdom
Tel.: (44) 2078361555
Fax: (44) 20783796365
Property Development Services
S.I.C.: 1542
N.A.I.C.S.: 236220
Benzion Freshwater *(Chm)*

Brickfield Properties Limited (1)
High Holborn House
London, WC1V 6RL, United Kingdom
Tel.: (44) 2078361555
Real Estate Investment Services
S.I.C.: 6211
N.A.I.C.S.: 523999
Benzion S.E. Freshwater *(CEO)*

City and Country Properties (Birmingham) Limited (1)
Freshwater House 158-162 Shaftesbury Ave
London, WC2H 8HR, United Kingdom
Tel.: (44) 2078361555
Fax: (44) 2073796365
Emp.: 130
Property Management Services
S.I.C.: 6531
N.A.I.C.S.: 531312
Benzion Freshwater *(Chm & Mng Dir)*

City and Country Properties (Camberley) Limited (1)
Freshwater House 158-162 Shaftesbury Avenue
London, WC2H 8HR, United Kingdom
Tel.: (44) 2078361555
Fax: (44) 02073796365
Web Site: www.hightorn.co.uk
Property Management Services
S.I.C.: 6531
N.A.I.C.S.: 531312

City and Country Properties (Midlands) Limited (1)
Freshwater House 158-162 Shaftesbury Avenue
London, WC2H 8HR, United Kingdom
Tel.: (44) 2078361555
Fax: (44) 2073796365
Web Site: www.daejanholdings.com
Property Management Services
S.I.C.: 6531
N.A.I.C.S.: 531312
B. Freshwater *(Mng Dir)*

Daejan (Brighton) Limited (1)
Freshwater House 158-162 Shaftesbury Avenue
London, WC2H 8HR, United Kingdom
Tel.: (44) 2078361555
Fax: (44) 2074978941
Property Management Services
S.I.C.: 6531
N.A.I.C.S.: 531312

Daejan (Cambridge) Limited (1)
Freshwater House 158-162 Shaftesbury Avenue
London, WC2H 8HR, United Kingdom
Tel.: (44) 2078361555
Investment Management Services
S.I.C.: 6211
N.A.I.C.S.: 523999

Daejan (Cardiff) Limited (1)
Freshwater House 158-162 Shaftesbury Avenue
London, WC2H 8HR, United Kingdom
Tel.: (44) 2078361555
Residential Real Estate Management Services
S.I.C.: 6531
N.A.I.C.S.: 531311

Daejan Commercial Properties Limited (1)
158/162 Shaftesbury Avenue
London, WC2H 8HR, United Kingdom
Tel.: (44) 2078361555
Commercial Property Management Services
S.I.C.: 6531
N.A.I.C.S.: 531312

Daejan (Dartford) Limited (1)
Freshwater House 158-162 Shaftesbury Avenue
London, WC2H 8HR, United Kingdom
Tel.: (44) 2078361555
Fax: (44) 2074978941
Property Management Services
S.I.C.: 6531
N.A.I.C.S.: 531312

Daejan Developments Limited (1)
High Holborn House
Kingsway, London, WC1V 6RL, United Kingdom
Tel.: (44) 2078361555
Fax: (44) 02073796365
Web Site: www.highdorn.co.uk
Real Estate Investment
S.I.C.: 6531
N.A.I.C.S.: 531390
Benzion S.E. Freshwater *(Chm & Mng Dir)*

Daejan Enterprises Limited (1)
Freshwater House 158-162 Shaftesbury Avenue
London, WC2H 8HR, United Kingdom
Tel.: (44) 2078361555
Fax: (44) 2073796365
Investment Management Services
S.I.C.: 6211
N.A.I.C.S.: 523999

Daejan Estates Limited (1)
High Holborn House
London, WC1V 6RL, United Kingdom
Tel.: (44) 2078361555
Fax: (44) 2078314627
Web Site: www.daejanholdings.com
Emp.: 25
Real Estate Property Lessor
S.I.C.: 6519
N.A.I.C.S.: 531190
Benzion S.E. Freshwater *(CEO)*

Daejan Investments (Grove Hall) Limited (1)
Freshwater House 158/162 Shaftesbury Avenue
London, WC2H 8HR, United Kingdom
Tel.: (44) 2078361555
Fax: (44) 2073796365
Investment Management Services
S.I.C.: 6211
N.A.I.C.S.: 523999

Daejan Investments (Harrow) Limited (1)
162 Shaftesbury Avenue
London, WC2H 8HR, United Kingdom
Tel.: (44) 2078361555
Investment Management Services
S.I.C.: 6211
N.A.I.C.S.: 523999

Daejan Investments Limited (1)
Freshwater House 158-162 Shaftesbury Avenue
London, WC2H 8HR, United Kingdom
Tel.: (44) 2078361555
Fax: (44) 2073796365
Investment Management Services
S.I.C.: 6211
N.A.I.C.S.: 523999

Daejan (Kingston) Limited (1)
Freshwater House 158-162 Shaftesbury Avenue
London, WC2H 8HR, United Kingdom
Tel.: (44) 2078361555
Fax: (44) 2073693695
Investment Management Services
S.I.C.: 6211
N.A.I.C.S.: 523999

Daejan (Lauderdale) Limited (1)
Freshwater House 158-162 Shaftesbury Avenue
London, WC2H 8HR, United Kingdom
Tel.: (44) 2078361555
Fax: (44) 2073796365
Investment Management Services
S.I.C.: 6211
N.A.I.C.S.: 523999

Daejan Properties Limited (1)
Freshwater House 158 162 Shaftesbury Avenue
London, WC2H 8HR, United Kingdom
Tel.: (44) 2078361555
Fax: (44) 2073796365
Web Site: www.daejanholdings.com
Emp.: 100
Investment Management Services
S.I.C.: 6211
N.A.I.C.S.: 523999

Daejan (Reading) Limited (1)
Freshwater House 158-162 Shaftsebury Avenue
London, WC2H 8HR, United Kingdom
Tel.: (44) 2078361555
Fax: (44) 2073796365
Investment Management Services
S.I.C.: 6211
N.A.I.C.S.: 523999

Daejan Holdings PLC—(Continued)

Daejan Retail Properties Limited (1)
158/162 Shaftesbury Avenue
London, WC2H 8HR, United Kingdom
Tel.: (44) 2078361555
Fax: (44) 2073793665
Property Management Services
S.I.C.: 6531
N.A.I.C.S.: 531312

Daejan (Taunton) Limited (1)
Freshwater House 158-162 Shaftesbury Avenue
London, WC2H 8HR, United Kingdom
Tel.: (44) 2078361555
Fax: (44) 2074978941
Investment Management Services
S.I.C.: 6211
N.A.I.C.S.: 523999

Daejan (Traders) Limited (1)
158-162 Shaftesbury Avenue
London, WC2H 8HR, United Kingdom
Tel.: (44) 2078361555
Investment Management Services
S.I.C.: 6211
N.A.I.C.S.: 523999

Daejan (UK) Limited (1)
Freshwater House 158 162 Shaftesbury Avenue
London, WC2H 8HR, United Kingdom
Tel.: (44) 2078361555
Investment Management Services
S.I.C.: 6211
N.A.I.C.S.: 523999

Daejan (US) Limited (1)
Freshwater House 158-162 Shaftesbury Avenue
London, WC2H 8HR, United Kingdom
Tel.: (44) 2078361555
Fax: (44) 20 7497 8941
Property Management Services
S.I.C.: 6531
N.A.I.C.S.: 531312

Daejan (Warwick) Limited (1)
Freshwater House 158-162 Shaftesbury Avenue
London, WC2H 8HR, United Kingdom
Tel.: (44) 2078361555
Fax: (44) 2073796365
Web Site: www.highdorn.co.uk
Emp.: 110
Investment Management Services
S.I.C.: 6211
N.A.I.C.S.: 523999
Benzion Freshwater *(Chm & Mng Dir)*

The Halliard Property Co. Limited (1)
Freshwater House 158-162 Shaftesbury Avenue
London, WC2H 8HR, United Kingdom
Tel.: (44) 2078361555
Fax: (44) 1713796365
Investment Management Services
S.I.C.: 6211
N.A.I.C.S.: 523999

Pegasus Investment Company Limited (1)
13-17 Burlington Place
London, SW6 4NL, United Kingdom
Tel.: (44) 2078361555
Investment Management Services
S.I.C.: 6211
N.A.I.C.S.: 523999

Ponteland Properties Limited (1)
Freshwater House
158-162 Shaftesbury Avenue, London, WC2H 8HR, United Kingdom
Tel.: (44) 2078361555
Fax: (44) 2073796365
Real Estate Investment Services
S.I.C.: 6211
N.A.I.C.S.: 523999

DAEJIN DMP CO., LTD.

316-4 Cheonheung-ri Seonggeo-eup
Seobuk-gu, Cheonan, Chungcheongnam-do, 331-836, Korea (South)
Tel.: (82) 2 3443 5360
Fax: (82) 2 3443 5351
E-Mail: info@daejindmp.co.kr
Web Site: www.daejindmp.com
Year Founded: 1970
065690—(KRS)
Business Description:
Electronic Component & Light Emitting Diode Mfr
S.I.C.: 3861
N.A.I.C.S.: 325992
Personnel:
Chang-sik Park *(CEO)*

DAEJOO ELECTRONIC MATERIALS CO., LTD.

Sihwa Ind Complex 1 Ra 110 1236-10 Jeongwang-Dong
Siheung, Gyunggi-Do, Korea (South) 429-848
Tel.: (82) 31 498 2901
Fax: (82) 31 498 2902
Web Site: www.daejoo.co.kr
Year Founded: 1981
078600—(KRS)
Sales Range: $125-149.9 Million
Emp.: 267
Business Description:
Electronic Material Mfr
S.I.C.: 3676
N.A.I.C.S.: 334416
Personnel:
Moo Hyun Lim *(Chm & CEO)*

DAEJUNG CHEMICALS & METALS CO., LTD.

1235-8 Jeongwang 3-dong
Siheung, Gyeonggi-do, Korea (South)
Tel.: (82) 314888822
Fax: (82) 314888968
E-Mail: daejung@daejung.kr
Web Site: www.daejung.kr
Year Founded: 1968
120240—(KRS)
Sales Range: $10-24.9 Million
Emp.: 100
Business Description:
Chemical Mfr
S.I.C.: 2899
N.A.I.C.S.: 325998
Personnel:
Ki Sup Song *(CEO)*

Subsidiary:

Daejungem Co.,Ltd, (1)
116B 6L Namdong Industrial Complex Gojan-dong
Namdong-gu, Incheon, Korea (South)
Tel.: (82) 12691456
Fax: (82) 32 818 6616
Medicines Mfr & Sales
S.I.C.: 2834
N.A.I.C.S.: 325412

DAEKYO CO LTD

Noonnopi Seocho Center 446-3
Bangbae-2dong Seocho-gu
Seoul, 137-060, Korea (South)
Tel.: (82) 28291114
Fax: (82) 8228290647
Web Site: www.daekyo.com
19680—(KRS)
Sls.: $808,629,433
Assets: $757,125,220
Liabilities: $178,730,741
Net Worth: $578,394,479
Earnings: $19,313,956
Fiscal Year-end: 12/31/12
Business Description:
Educational Service
S.I.C.: 8299
N.A.I.C.S.: 611710
Personnel:
Young-Joong Kang *(Chm)*
Myung-Kyu Park *(Co-CEO)*
Tae-Young Park *(Co-CEO)*
Board of Directors:
Young-Joong Kang
Jeong-Tak Kim
Jung-Kyoo Park
Myung-Kyu Park
Soo-Wan Park
Tae-Young Park
Ja Song
Jong-Cheon Yoon

DAELIM B&CO., LTD.

574 Yanggok-dong
Changwon, Gyeongsangnam-do, Korea (South)
Tel.: (82) 55 280 8400
Fax: (82) 55 286 2630
Web Site: www.daelimbath.com
Year Founded: 1966
005750—(KRS)
Business Description:
Bathroom Product Mfr
S.I.C.: 3999
N.A.I.C.S.: 327110
Personnel:
Hae Yeong Lee *(Pres)*

DAELIM INDUSTRIAL CO., LTD.

146-12 Susong-Dong
Jongno-Gu, Seoul, 110 732, Korea (South)
Tel.: (82) 2 2011 7114
Fax: (82) 220118000
E-Mail: irmaster@dic.co.kr
Web Site: www.daelim.co.kr
Year Founded: 1939
000210—(KRS)
Rev.: $9,518,872,710
Assets: $10,236,016,170
Liabilities: $5,661,770,250
Net Worth: $4,574,245,920
Earnings: $372,732,840
Emp.: 7,910
Fiscal Year-end: 12/31/12
Business Description:
Civil Engineering Construction, Architectural Services & Production of Petrochemical Products
S.I.C.: 8711
N.A.I.C.S.: 541330
Personnel:
Charles Y. Kim *(Vice Chm & Co-CEO)*
Hae-Wook Lee *(Vice Chm & Co-CEO)*
Chul-Kyoon Lee *(Pres/CEO-Plant Bus)*
Chan-Jo Park *(Pres/CEO-Petrochemical Unit)*
Hong-Chun Park *(Pres-Middle East Bus Support-Plant Bus)*
Ho Kim *(CEO-Building & Housing Bus & Sr Exec VP)*
Young-Do Park *(CEO-Pub Bus Office & Exec VP)*
Dong-Su Kim *(CEO-Civil Bus)*
Kil-Su Kim *(Sr Exec VP-Mfg-Petrochemical Unit)*
Ha-Chang Chung *(Exec VP-Overseas Power & Indus Bus-Overseas Bus)*
Un-Il Beak *(Exec VP-Overseas Civil Bus)*
Hyuk Cho *(Exec VP-Bus Support-Building & Housing Bus)*
In-Chan Han *(Exec VP-Plant Engrg-Plant Bus)*
Yong-Cook Kang *(Exec VP-Plng, Tender & Cost Estimation-Plant Bus)*
Yun-Sub Kim *(Exec VP-Domestic & Overseas Execution-Plant Bus)*
Ki-Bae Lee *(Exec VP-Plant Project Execution-Plant Bus)*
Phil-Keun Lee *(Exec VP-Corp Plng-Corp Mgmt)*
Heung-Kyun Park *(Exec VP-Plant Cost Estimation-Plant Bus)*
Hwan-Yong Yoo *(Exec VP-Corp Subcontracts & Procurement-Corp Mgmt)*
Dong-Yeob Choi *(Sr VP-Overseas Execution-Plant Bus)*
Jong-Kee Jang *(Sr VP-Plant Project Conducting-Plant Bus)*
Seon-Yong Bae *(Sr VP-Corp Comm, Safety, Environment & Quality Mgmt)*
Ho-Young Choi *(Sr VP-Overseas Execution-Plant Bus)*
Kyung-Il Kang *(Sr VP-Execution-Civil Bus)*
Yang-Sub Kim *(Sr VP-Architectural Electricity-Building & Housing Bus)*
Sang-Taek Lee *(Sr VP-Saudi JER Site-Plant Bus)*
Hee-Tai Park *(Sr VP-HR Dev-Corp Mgmt)*
Seong-Yoon Park *(Sr VP-Domestic Bus & SOC Bus-Civil Bus)*
Jae-Duk Suk *(Sr VP-Civil Safety & Quality-Civil Bus)*
Jae-Kwan Yoo *(Sr VP-Flim Bus-Petrochemical Unit)*
Tae-Seob Yoon *(Sr VP-Overseas-Civil Div)*

Ahn kwon & Co.
6th Floor, Tae Young Corporation Building, 252-5 Kongdeok-Do, Mapo-Gu
P.O. Box 124, Seoul, Korea (South)
Tel.: (82) 2 3271 3000
Fax: (82) 2 3271 3100

Subsidiaries:

Daelim C&S Co., Ltd. (1)
12 Th FL Hanoe Bldg 70 Da-dong
Chung-Ku, Seoul, Korea (South)
Tel.: (82) 52287938
Fax: (82) 2 311 3355
Web Site: www.daelimcns.co.kr
Concrete Pile Mfr
S.I.C.: 3272
N.A.I.C.S.: 327390
Jae-Sik Namgung *(CEO)*

Plants:

Daelim C&S Co., Ltd. - Bu-yeo Plant (2)
1007 Hapgok-ri Jangam-myun
Buyeo, Chungcheong Nam-do, Korea (South)
Tel.: (82) 02 53 88 99
Fax: (82) 41 837 7934
Concrete Pile Mfr
S.I.C.: 3272
N.A.I.C.S.: 327390

Daelim C&S Co., Ltd. - Chil-seo Plant (2)
Gyeonae-ri Chilseo-myun
Haman-gun, Gyeongnam, Korea (South)
Tel.: (82) 55 587 4890
Fax: (82) 55 587 4894
Concrete Pile Mfr
S.I.C.: 3272
N.A.I.C.S.: 327390

Daelim C&S Co., Ltd. - Yong-in Plant (2)
317-1 Jwahang-ri Wonsam-myun
Yongin, Gyeonggi-do, Korea (South)
Tel.: (82) 31 333 3744
Fax: (82) 31 333 3747
Functional Pile Mfr
S.I.C.: 3312
N.A.I.C.S.: 331221

Daelim Concrete Products Co., Ltd. (1)
15th Fl Donghwa Bldg 5A 7 Seosomun Dong Chung Ku
Chongno Ku, Seoul, 100-814, Korea (South) (100%)
Tel.: (82) 23113300
Fax: (82) 23113377
Web Site: www.dcp.co.kr
Emp.: 50
Mfr. of Concrete Products
S.I.C.: 3272
N.A.I.C.S.: 327332

Daelim Corporation (1)
11th Fl The Korea Chamber of Commerce & Industry Building 45 4-ga

Namdaemunro Jung-gu, Seoul, 100 743, Korea (South) (100%)
Tel.: (82) 237083114
Fax: (82) 27547114
E-Mail: daecoweb@daelimcorp.co.kr
Web Site: www.daelimcorp.co.kr
Emp.: 115
Distr Petrochemical Products
S.I.C.: 2869
N.A.I.C.S.: 325110
Jin Seo Kim *(CEO)*

Daelim Information & Service Co., Ltd. **(1)**
19F KBS Media Center 1652 Sangam-dong
Mapo-gu, Seoul, Korea (South)
Tel.: (82) 2 3704 8400
Fax: (82) 2 3704 8491
Web Site: www.daelimins.com
Emp.: 400
System Integration & Consulting; Software Development & Software Package; Networking & System Management
S.I.C.: 7373
N.A.I.C.S.: 541512

Daelim Motor Co., Ltd. **(1)**
58 Sungsan-Dong
Changwon-si, Changwon, Kyoungnam, Korea (South) (100%)
Tel.: (82) 552397000
Fax: (82) 552397520
E-Mail: enquiries@dmc.co.kr
Web Site: www.dmc.co.kr
Emp.: 800
Motorcycles & Scooters Mfr
S.I.C.: 3751
N.A.I.C.S.: 336991
Kye Soo Kim *(Pres & CEO)*

Korea Development Corporation **(1)**
954-2 Kwanyang 2 Ding
Dongan Gu Anyang St, Seoul, 431 804, Korea (South)
Tel.: (82) 314209000
Fax: (82) 3142090010
Web Site: www.kdc.co.kr
Engineering & Construction
S.I.C.: 8711
N.A.I.C.S.: 541330

Ora Resort Co., Ltd. **(1)**
263 15 Yon Dong
Cheju, 690723, Korea (South) (100%)
Tel.: (82) 647475000
Fax: (82) 647470278
E-Mail: osamaster@grandora.co.kr
Web Site: www.oraresort.com
Emp.: 350
Operation of Hotel & Leisure Facilities
S.I.C.: 7011
N.A.I.C.S.: 721199
Kyounghong Yang *(CEO)*

Joint Venture:

Yeochun NCC Co., Ltd. **(1)**
Korea Chamber of Commerce & Industry Building 2 Chilpae-gil
Namdaemunno 4-ga
Jung-gu, Seoul, 100-743, Korea (South)
Tel.: (82) 260502400
Fax: (82) 260500881
Web Site: www.yncc.co.kr
Sales Range: $1-4.9 Billion
Petrochemical Mfr; Owned 50% by Hanwha Chemical Corporation & 50% by Daelim Industrial Co., Ltd.
S.I.C.: 2869
N.A.I.C.S.: 325110

Non-U.S. Subsidiaries:

Daelim (Malaysia) Sdn. Bhd. **(1)**
9th Fl Menarahapseng Jalan P R, 50250
Kuala Lumpur, Malaysia (100%)
Tel.: (60) 321459911
Fax: (60) 321458877
Web Site: www.daelim.com
Emp.: 4
S.I.C.: 8711
N.A.I.C.S.: 541330
Cheolbok Lee *(Gen Mgr)*

Daelim Saudi Arabia Co., Ltd. **(1)**
Al Raja Tower 1st FL King Abdulaziz Rd
PO Box 2346
Al Khobar, Dammam, 31451, Saudi Arabia (100%)
Tel.: (966) 38879303
Fax: (966) 38878909
Web Site: eng.daelim.co.kr/daelim/oversea s.jsp#7
Emp.: 25
Engineering & Project Management Services
S.I.C.: 8711
N.A.I.C.S.: 541330
Sung In Kin *(Mng Dir)*

PT Daelim Utama Construction **(1)**
Korea Center Building 4th Floor JL Gatot Subroto Kav 58
12950 Jakarta, Selatan, Indonesia
Tel.: (62) 21 5296 1061
Fax: (62) 21 5296 1065
E-Mail:
Web Site: eng.daelim.co.kr
Emp.: 2
Engineering & Construction Services
S.I.C.: 8711
N.A.I.C.S.: 541330

DAELIM PAPER CO., LTD.

7 Nueup-Dong
Osan, Gyeonggi-Do, Korea (South)
Tel.: (82) 31 373 7670
Fax: (82) 31 373 0662
Web Site: www.daelimpaper.co.kr
17650—(KRS)
Sales Range: $25-49.9 Million
Emp.: 80
Business Description:
Corrugated Board Mfr
S.I.C.: 2653
N.A.I.C.S.: 322211
Personnel:
Chang Seung Ryu *(CEO)*

DAELIM TRADING CO., LTD.

Daelim Trading Building 87-9
Yeonhee-dong
Seodaemun-gu, Seoul, 120-712, Korea (South)
Tel.: (82) 2 730 9811
Fax: (82) 2 739 9024
Web Site: www.dltc.co.kr
Year Founded: 1970
006570—(KRS)
Business Description:
Architecture & Interior Material Whslr
S.I.C.: 5039
N.A.I.C.S.: 423390
Personnel:
Jae Man Lee *(CEO)*

DAERYUK CAN CO., LTD.

733-25 Yeoksam-dong
Seoul, Gangnam-gu, Korea (South)
Tel.: (82) 260030600
Fax: (82) 25629912
Web Site: www.drcc.co.kr
Year Founded: 1958
004780—(KRS)
Business Description:
Metal Container Mfr
S.I.C.: 3499
N.A.I.C.S.: 332439
Personnel:
Bong-Joon Park *(CEO)*

U.S. Subsidiary:

Dae Ryuk International Inc **(1)**
140 Rte 70 N 301
Paramus, NJ 07652
Tel.: (201) 655-6337
Fax: (201) 655-6340
Industrial Machinery Distr
S.I.C.: 5084
N.A.I.C.S.: 423830
Don Hee Yeum *(Chm)*

DAESUNG ELTEC CO., LTD.

5F Sj Techno Ville 60-19 Gasan-dong
Geumcheon-gu, Seoul, 153-769, Korea (South)
Tel.: (82) 2 2102 3000
Web Site: www.dseltec.co.kr
Year Founded: 1979
025440—(KRS)
Business Description:
Electronic Product Mfr
S.I.C.: 3679
N.A.I.C.S.: 334419
Personnel:
Jae Bum Park *(Chm)*
Sun-young Kim *(CEO)*
Board of Directors:
Jae Bum Park
Young Im Hwang
Yasuhiro Ikeuchi
Sun-young Kim
Won Ki Pae
Sang Kyu Park
Hee Sik Ro

DAESUNG ENERGY

Namsan-dong 2268-1 Joong-gu
Daegu, 700-725, Korea (South)
Tel.: (82) 536061000
Fax: (82) 536061004
Web Site: ww.daesungenergy.com
117580—(KRS)
Sls.: $911,160,060
Assets: $599,472,420
Liabilities: $349,780,440
Net Worth: $249,691,980
Earnings: $11,899,350
Emp.: 397
Fiscal Year-end: 12/31/12
Business Description:
Natural Gas Distr
S.I.C.: 4924
N.A.I.C.S.: 221210
Personnel:
Sukki Kang *(Pres)*
David Younghoon Kim *(CEO)*

DAESUNG FINE TECH. CO., LTD.

58-17 Seongsan-Dong
Changwon, Gyeongnam, Korea (South)
Tel.: (82) 552894885
Fax: (82) 552894890
Web Site: www.dsfinetec.com
Year Founded: 1988
104040—(KRS)
Business Description:
Automobile Products Mfr
S.I.C.: 3999
N.A.I.C.S.: 339999
Personnel:
Byung jun Kim *(Pres & CEO)*

DAETWYLER HOLDING AG

Gotthardstrasse 31
CH-6460 Altdorf, Switzerland
Tel.: (41) 418751100
Fax: (41) 418751205
E-Mail: info@datwyler.com
Web Site: www.daetwyler.com
DAE—(SWX)
Rev.: $1,526,374,344
Assets: $1,164,586,280
Liabilities: $569,988,892
Net Worth: $594,597,388
Earnings: $137,613,300
Emp.: 6,670
Fiscal Year-end: 12/31/12
Business Description:
Holding Company
S.I.C.: 6719
N.A.I.C.S.: 551112
Personnel:
Ulrich Graf *(Chm)*
Hans R. Rueegg *(Deputy Chm)*
Paul J. Haelg *(CEO)*
Reto Welte *(CFO)*
Board of Directors:
Ulrich Graf
Hanspeter Faessler
Gabi Huber
Werner Inderbitzin
Ernst Lienhard
Ernst Odermatt
Hans R. Rueegg
Subsidiaries:

Alvest AG **(1)**
Gotthardstrasse 31
6460 Altdorf, Switzerland (100%)
Tel.: (41) 418751122
Fax: (41) 418751205
Web Site: www.daetwyler.ch/Medienkontakt.103.0.html
Open-End Investment Funds
S.I.C.: 6722
N.A.I.C.S.: 525910

Daetwyler Switzerland Inc **(1)**
Gotthardstrasse 31
6460 Altdorf, Switzerland (100%)
Tel.: (41) 418751122
Fax: (41) 418751986
E-Mail: info.ch@daetwyler-cables.com
Web Site: www.daetwyler.ch/fileadmin/user_upload/investoren/g-bericht-08/adressen-e.pdf
Emp.: 500
Fabricated Wire Product Mfr
S.I.C.: 3496
N.A.I.C.S.: 332618
Johannes Mueller *(Mng Dir)*

Daetwyler Teco Holding AG **(1)**
Gotthardstrasse 31
6460 Altdorf, Switzerland (100%)
Tel.: (41) 418751122
Fax: (41) 418751870
E-Mail: info.ch@daetwyler-cables.com
Web Site: www.daetwyler-cables.com
Emp.: 300
Industrial Machinery & Equipment Whslr
S.I.C.: 5084
N.A.I.C.S.: 423830
Johannes Mueller *(Mng Dir)*

Kaved AG **(1)**
Gotthardstrasse 31
6460 Altdorf, Switzerland (100%)
Tel.: (41) 418753800
Fax: (41) 418753839
E-Mail: verkauf@kaved.ch
Web Site: www.kaved.ch
Miscellaneous Electrical Equipment & Component Mfr
S.I.C.: 3699
N.A.I.C.S.: 335999
Markus Grueter *(Mng Dir)*

Mader Technic AG **(1)**
Gotthardstrasse 31
6460 Altdorf, Switzerland (100%)
Tel.: (41) 418751122
Fax: (41) 418751870
E-Mail: info.ch@daetwyler-cables.com
Web Site: www.daetwyler-cables.com
Emp.: 700
Refrigeration Equipment & Supplies Whslr
S.I.C.: 5078
N.A.I.C.S.: 423740
Johannes Moaller *(Mng Dir)*

Pohl Immobilien AG **(1)**
Gotthardstrasse 31
6460 Dubendorf, Switzerland (100%)
Tel.: (41) 418751122
Fax: (41) 418751870
E-Mail: info@daetwyler-cables.com
Web Site: www.daetwyler-cables.com
Emp.: 200
Real Estate Agents & Brokers
S.I.C.: 6531
N.A.I.C.S.: 531210
Johannes Miller *(Gen Mgr)*

Proditec AG **(1)**
Grabenstrasse No 6
Naenikon, 8606 Zurich, Switzerland (100%)
Tel.: (41) 448071111
Fax: (41) 448071112
E-Mail: info@proditec.ch
Web Site: www.proditec.ch
Emp.: 50
Electronic Parts & Equipment Whslr
S.I.C.: 5065
N.A.I.C.S.: 423690
Jurg Detzel *(Mng Dir)*

Wachendorf AG **(1)**
Sonnentalstrasse 8
Dubendorf, 8600, Switzerland (100%)

Daetwyler Holding AG—(Continued)

Tel.: (41) 613153030
Fax: (41) 848111334
E-Mail: info@maagtechnic.com
Web Site: www.maagtechnic.ch
Emp.: 250
Plastics Product Mfr
S.I.C.: 3089
N.A.I.C.S.: 326199
Joel Souchon *(Mng Dir)*

Non-U.S. Subsidiaries:

CJSC Daetwyler Rubber Ukraine (1)
2 Nemanykhina Str
Malyn, 11602 Kiev, Ukraine (100%)
Tel.: (380) 4133 32508
Fax: (380) 4133 33008
E-Mail: info@daetwyler-rubber.com
Web Site: www.daetwyler-rubber.com
Fabricated Wire Product Mfr
S.I.C.: 3496
N.A.I.C.S.: 332618
Sergey Orlov *(Gen Dir)*

Daetwyler Cables+Systems (Shanghai) Co. Ltd (1)
Bldg 16 No 1-111 Kang Qiao Dong Rd
Kang Qiao Industrial Zone Pudo, 201319
Shanghai, China (100%)
Tel.: (86) 2168130066
Fax: (86) 2168130298
E-Mail: info@datwyler-china.com
Web Site: www.datwyler-china.com
Emp.: 100
Cable Networks
S.I.C.: 4841
N.A.I.C.S.: 515210
Siaoping Pu *(Mng Dir)*

Daetwyler Inter GmbH (1)
Allerfeldstrasse 5
31832 Springe, Germany (100%)
Tel.: (49) 504591090
Fax: (49) 5045910911
E-Mail: info.de@daetwyler-rubber.com
Web Site: www.daetwyler-rubber.com
Emp.: 30
Industrial Building Construction
S.I.C.: 1541
N.A.I.C.S.: 236210
Rainer Grote *(Mng Dir)*

Daetwyler Kabel+Systeme GmbH (1)
Lilienthalstrasse 7
Hallbergmoos, 85399 Neufahrn, Germany (100%)
Tel.: (49) 816595010
Fax: (49) 81659501130
E-Mail: info.de@daetwyler-cables.com
Emp.: 40
Nonferrous Metal Rolling Drawing & Extruding
S.I.C.: 3356
N.A.I.C.S.: 331491

Daetwyler (Suzhou) Cabling Systems Co. Ltd (1)
Block 31 #15 Dong Fu Road Suzhou
Singapore Industrial Park
215123 Suzhou, China (100%)
Tel.: (86) 51262653600
Fax: (86) 51262653650
E-Mail: sales.harnessing@datwyler-china.com
Web Site: www.datwyler-china.com
Emp.: 100
Fiber Optic Cable Mfr
S.I.C.: 3357
N.A.I.C.S.: 335921
Chen Wei *(Mgr)*

Daetwyler (Thelma) Cables & Systems Pte Ltd (1)
29 Tech Park Crescent
638103 Singapore, Singapore (100%)
Tel.: (65) 68631166
Fax: (65) 68978885
E-Mail: sales@datwyler.com.sg
Web Site: www.daetwyler.ch
Emp.: 21
Fabricated Wire Product Mfr
S.I.C.: 3496
N.A.I.C.S.: 332618
Melva Yue *(CEO)*

Daetwyler (UK) Ltd (1)
Unit B Omega Enterprise Park
Electron Way, Chandlers Ford, Hamps, SO53 4SE, United Kingdom (100%)
Tel.: (44) 2380279999
Fax: (44) 2380279998
E-Mail: info.uk@datwyler.com
Web Site: www.datwyler.com
Emp.: 7
Fabricated Wire Product Mfr
S.I.C.: 3496
N.A.I.C.S.: 332618
Paul Cattell *(Mng Dir)*

Distrelec Gesellschaft mbH (1)
Trestner Strasse 47
1200 Vienna, Austria (100%)
Tel.: (43) 13341010
Fax: (43) 1334101099
E-Mail: info-at@distrelec.com
Web Site: www.daetwyler.ch/fileadmin/user_upload/investoren/g-bericht-08/adresse n-e.pdf
Emp.: 15
Electronic Parts & Equipment Whslr
S.I.C.: 5065
N.A.I.C.S.: 423690
Martein Taesl *(Gen Mgr)*

Distrelec Italia Srl (1)
Via Canova 40-42
20020 Lainate, Italy (100%)
Tel.: (39) 02937551
Fax: (39) 0293755755
E-Mail: info-it@distrelec.com
Web Site: www.distrelec.it
Electronic Parts & Equipment Whslr
S.I.C.: 5065
N.A.I.C.S.: 423690
Dalessa Andro *(Mng Dir)*

Helvoet Pharma N.V. (1)
Industriepark 1519
B 3570 Alken, Belgium (100%)
Tel.: (32) 0011590811
Fax: (32) 11314086
E-Mail: info@helvoetpharma.be
Web Site: www.helvoetpharma.be
Sales Range: $200-249.9 Million
Emp.: 500
Mfr. of Rubber Closures & Aluminum & Plastic Caps for Pharmaceutical Packaging
S.I.C.: 3089
N.A.I.C.S.: 326199
Euido Wallsaff *(Pres)*

U.S. Subsidiary:

Helvoet Pharma Inc. (2)
9012 Pennsuaken Hwy
Pennsauken, NJ 08110 (100%)
Tel.: (856) 663-2202
Fax: (856) 663-2636
Web Site: www.helvoetpharma.com
Emp.: 220
Rubber Product Mfr
S.I.C.: 3069
N.A.I.C.S.: 326299

Non-U.S. Subsidiaries:

Daetwyler Pharma Packaging Italy Srl (2)
Via Bernarde 11
Montegaldella, 36040 Vicenza, Italy (100%)
Tel.: (39) 0444737200
Fax: (39) 0444737221
Web Site: www.helvoetpharma.com
Fabricated Wire Product Mfr
S.I.C.: 3496
N.A.I.C.S.: 332618

Helvoet Pharma Deutschland (2)
Tornadostrasse 4
D-76307 Karlsbad, Ittersbach, Germany DE
Tel.: (49) 72489230
E-Mail: info@helvoetpharma.com
Web Site: www.helvoetpharma.com
Mfr of Rubber Closures & Aluminum & Plastic Caps for Pharmaceutical Packaging
S.I.C.: 3089
N.A.I.C.S.: 326199

Matrijzenmakerij Maro B.V. (1)
Scherpdeel 30
4703RJ Roosendaal, Netherlands (100%)
Tel.: (31) 165553160
Fax: (31) 165558387
Web Site: www.daetwyler.ch/fileadmin/user_upload/investoren/g-bericht-08/adresse n-e.pdf
Emp.: 15
Unclassified Establishments
S.I.C.: 7629
N.A.I.C.S.: 811211
Erik Thielens *(Mng Dir)*

Schuricht Distrelec GmbH (1)
Lise-Meitner-Str 4
28359 Bremen, Germany (100%)
Tel.: (49) 1805223435
Fax: (49) 1805223436
E-Mail: scc@distrelec.de
Web Site: www.distrelec.de
Emp.: 50
Electronic Parts & Equipment Whslr
S.I.C.: 5065
N.A.I.C.S.: 423690
Jorg-Lothar Loch *(Mng Dir)*

Wachendorf GmbH (1)
Engeler Strasse 29
Hannover, Germany (100%)
Tel.: (49) 424793090
Fax: (49) 4247930915
E-Mail: systenhauf@wachendorf.de
Web Site: www.wachendorf.de
Emp.: 10
Custom Computer Programming Services
S.I.C.: 7371
N.A.I.C.S.: 541511
Heinrich Wachendorf *(Mng Dir)*

DAEWON CHEMICAL CO., LTD.

Gungdo Bldg 278-19 Nonhyeon-Dong
Gangnam-Gu, Seoul, Korea (South)
Tel.: (82) 2 2141 3531
Fax: (82) 2 2141 3596
Web Site: www.daewon21.co.kr
Year Founded: 1974
024890—(KRS)
Emp.: 250

Business Description:
Synthetic Leather Mfr & Distr
S.I.C.: 3199
N.A.I.C.S.: 316998

Personnel:
Dong-Yeop Kang *(CEO)*

DAEWON MEDIA CO., LTD.

40-456 Hanganro 3 ga
Yongsan-gu, Seoul, Korea (South) 140-013
Tel.: (82) 2 6373 3000
Fax: (82) 2 6373 3160
Web Site: www.daewonmedia.com
Year Founded: 1973
048910—(KRS)

Business Description:
Animation Services
S.I.C.: 7819
N.A.I.C.S.: 512191

Personnel:
Wook-Ho Ham *(CEO)*

DAEWON PHARMACEUTICAL CO., LTD.

229-3 Yongdap Dong
Seongdong Gu, Seoul, Korea (South)
Tel.: (82) 2 2204 6971
Web Site: www.daewonpharm.com
Year Founded: 1958
003220—(KRS)
Sales Range: $125-149.9 Million
Emp.: 530

Business Description:
Pharmaceutical Product Mfr & Whslr
S.I.C.: 2834
N.A.I.C.S.: 325412

Personnel:
Seung Ho Baek *(Chm & Co-CEO)*
Seung Ryel Baek *(Pres & Co-CEO)*

Board of Directors:
Seung Ho Baek
Seung Ryel Baek
Seo-Young Jung
Hyun-Tae Kim
Jeong-Hui Kim
Hyeong-Ju Lee

DAEWON SANUP CO., LTD.

Wonsi-dong 718
Danwon-gu, Ansan, Gyeonggi-do, Korea (South)
Tel.: (82) 31 495 2301
Fax: (82) 31 491 2701
Web Site: www.dwsu.co.kr
Year Founded: 1968
005710—(KRS)
Sales Range: $200-249.9 Million

Business Description:
Automobile Seat Mfr
S.I.C.: 2396
N.A.I.C.S.: 336360

Personnel:
Jae Geon Huh *(Chm & CEO)*

DAEWON SEMICONDUCTOR PACKAGING INDUSTRIAL CORPORATION

33 622 Beon-gil
Hanam-daero, Hanam, Gyeonggi-do, 465-110, Korea (South)
Tel.: (82) 317942001
Fax: (82) 317947711
E-Mail: sales@daewonspic.com
Web Site: www.daewonspic.com
Emp.: 250

Business Description:
Mfr of Plastic Extrusion & Injection Molded Products
S.I.C.: 3089
N.A.I.C.S.: 326199

Subsidiary:

S&G Company, Ltd. (1)
Unit F 19/F CDW Building
388 Castle Peak Road, Tsuen Wan, China (Hong Kong)
Tel.: (852) 31936000
Fax: (852) 81481872
E-Mail: jess_tang@peak.com.hk
Web Site: www.peakf.com
Emp.: 20
Semiconductor Plastic Extrusion & Thermoform Molded Products
S.I.C.: 3089
N.A.I.C.S.: 326199
Sungyuk Won *(Pres)*

Subsidiary:

Peak International, Inc. (2)
Ste F 19/F CDW Bldg
388 Castle Peak Rd, Tsuen Wan, China (Hong Kong)
Tel.: (852) 31936000
Fax: (852) 24985382
E-Mail: jess_pang@peak.com.hk
Web Site: www.peak.com.hk
Sales Range: $50-74.9 Million
Emp.: 102
Engineered Plastics & Packaging Products Mfr
S.I.C.: 3089
N.A.I.C.S.: 326199
Michael Cho Nae Eul *(Pres)*
Stephen Wong *(CEO)*

U.S. Subsidiary:

Peak International, Inc. (3)
2350 Mission College Blvd Ste 900
Santa Clara, CA 95054-1532
Tel.: (408) 213-6200
Fax: (408) 213-6207
Web Site: www.peakinternational.com
Engineered Plastics & Packaging Mfr
S.I.C.: 3086
N.A.I.C.S.: 326140

Non-U.S. Subsidiary:

Peak International Singapore (3)
150 Kmpong Ampag KA Ctr 0404A
Singapore, 368324, Singapore
Tel.: (65) 68462002
Fax: (65) 68467559
E-Mail: info@peak.com.hk
Web Site: www.peak.com.hk
Sales Range: $10-24.9 Million
Emp.: 10

Semiconductor Precision-Engineered Packaging
S.I.C.: 3089
N.A.I.C.S.: 326199
Hector Coria *(CEO)*

DAEWOO ELECTRONIC COMPONENTS CO, LTD.

19 Mang-je Dong
Jung-eup, Jeonbuk, Korea (South)
Tel.: (82) 63 530 8114
Web Site: www.dwecc.com
Year Founded: 1973
009320—(KRS)

Business Description:
Electronic Component Mfr
S.I.C.: 3679
N.A.I.C.S.: 334419

Personnel:
Jun-Kyoo Seo *(Co-CEO)*
Jung-ho Seo *(Co-CEO)*

DAEWOO MOTOR SALES CORPORATION

426-1 Chongchon-2Dong
Bupyong-gu, Incheon, Korea (South)
Tel.: (82) 32510414
Web Site: www.dm.co.kr
Year Founded: 1993

Business Description:
Automobile Parts Mfr
S.I.C.: 3711
N.A.I.C.S.: 336111

Personnel:
Dongho Lee *(Pres & Co-CEO)*
Yongho Park *(Co-CEO)*
Byunggi Park *(CFO)*

Board of Directors:
Youngkyu Cho
Youngchan Kim
Dongho Lee
Bongsung Oum
Byunggi Park
Yongho Park
Siwang Ryu

DAEWOO SECURITIES CO., LTD.

Daewoo Securities Bldg 34-3 Youido-Dong
Yeongdeungpo-Gu, Seoul, 150-716, Korea (South)
Tel.: (82) 27683355
Telex: DWSECK26332
Fax: (82) 27682119
Web Site: www.bestez.co.kr
Year Founded: 1970
006800—(KRS)
Sales Range: $1-4.9 Billion
Emp.: 3,125

Business Description:
Securities, Investment & Management Services; Owned 39.1% by Korea Development Bank
S.I.C.: 6211
N.A.I.C.S.: 523999

Personnel:
Young Im Kee *(Pres & CEO)*
Hui Hwan Ahn *(Mng Dir)*
Seong Wu Huh *(Mng Dir)*
Hae Geun Jung *(Mng Dir)*
Jong Ok Jung *(Mng Dir)*
Guk Yong Kim *(Mng Dir)*
Jeong-Ja Lee *(Mng Dir)*
Dong Yeong Park *(Mng Dir)*

Board of Directors:
Seok Oh Chan
Sung You Hae
Gyu Park Jin
Ho Kim Jin
Young Im Kee
Ihl Hong Sung

U.S. Subsidiaries:

Daewoo Securities (America) Inc. (1)
600 Lexington Ave Ste 301
New York, NY 10022
Tel.: (212) 407-1000
Telex: 262383
Fax: (212) 407-1010
E-Mail: kelly@dwsusa.com
Sales Range: $1-9.9 Million
Emp.: 12
Brokerage of Korean Stocks, Overseas of Issues of Korean Companies Including CBs, BWs and DRs
S.I.C.: 6211
N.A.I.C.S.: 523120
Jae Ryu *(Pres)*

Non-U.S. Subsidiaries:

Daewoo Leasing (Czech) S.R.O. (1)
Vaclavske Namesti 47
11000 Prague, 1, Czech Republic
Tel.: (420) 221625550
Fax: (420) 221625556
S.I.C.: 6799
N.A.I.C.S.: 523910

Daewoo Securities (Europe) Ltd. (1)
25 Old Broad Street
London, EC2N 1HQ, United Kingdom
Tel.: (44) 2079828000
Telex: 9413098
Fax: (44) 2079828040
E-Mail: hw.kim@dwse.com
Web Site: www.securities.co.kr
Emp.: 10
Full Range of Securities Services Including Brokerage, Dealing and Underwriting
S.I.C.: 6221
N.A.I.C.S.: 523140
H. W. Kim *(Mng Dir)*

Daewoo Securities (Hong Kong) Ltd. (1)
Ste 2005-2012 20 Fl 2 IFC
Central, China (Hong Kong)
Tel.: (852) 28456332
Fax: (852) 28455374
E-Mail: daewoo@dws.com.hk
Emp.: 19
S.I.C.: 6799
N.A.I.C.S.: 523910
Jong Son Kim *(Mgr)*

Uz-Daewoo Bank (1)
1 Pushkin St
700000 Tashkent, Uzbekistan
Tel.: (998) 711320640
Fax: (998) 711320800
E-Mail: assistant@daewoobank.com
Web Site: www.daewoobank.com
Emp.: 50
S.I.C.: 6799
N.A.I.C.S.: 523910
Saida Ganieva *(Head-IOD Dept)*

DAEWOONG PHARMACEUTICAL CO., LTD.

163-3 Samsung-dong
Gangnam-gu, 135-715 Seoul, Korea (South)
Tel.: (82) 2 550 8800
Fax: (82) 2 550 8400
Web Site: www.daewoong.com
Year Founded: 1945
069620—(KRS)
Sls.: $618,078,000
Assets: $443,703,000
Liabilities: $86,025,000
Net Worth: $357,678,000
Earnings: $32,178,000
Emp.: 1,282
Fiscal Year-end: 12/31/12

Business Description:
Pharmaceutical Product Mfr
S.I.C.: 2834
N.A.I.C.S.: 325412

Personnel:
Yeong Hwan Yoon *(Chm)*
Jae Seung Yoon *(Vice Chm & Co-CEO)*
Jong Wook Lee *(Pres & Co-CEO)*

Board of Directors:
Yeong Hwan Yoon
Jong Wook Lee
Gap Yong Noh
Jae Hong Park
Jae Seung Yoon

DAEYANG ELECTRIC CO., LTD.

503 Sinpyong-Dong Saha-Ku
Pusan, 604030, Korea (South)
Tel.: (82) 51 200 5282
Fax: (82) 51 200 5210
Web Site: www.daeyang.co.kr
108380—(KRS)
Emp.: 380

Business Description:
Electrical Lighting, Components & Instruments Mfr
S.I.C.: 3646
N.A.I.C.S.: 335122

Personnel:
Yeung Wu Seo *(CEO)*

Divisions:

Daeyang Electric Co., Ltd. - ELECTRICAL / ELECTRONIC DIVISON (1)
504 Sinpyong-Dong
Saha-Ku, Busan, Korea (South)
Tel.: (82) 51 200 5283
Fax: (82) 51 200 5289
E-Mail: overseas@daeyang.co.kr
Emp.: 40
Communication System Mfr
S.I.C.: 3669
N.A.I.C.S.: 334290

Daeyang Electric Co., Ltd. - LIGHTING DIVISON (1)
503 Shinpyeong-Dong
Saha-Ku, 604-030 Pusan, Korea (South)
Tel.: (82) 51 200 5281
Fax: (82) 51 200 5289
E-Mail: overseas@daeyang.co.kr
Emp.: 40
Electronic Lighting Mfr
S.I.C.: 3648
N.A.I.C.S.: 335129
Young Woo Seo *(Pres)*

Subsidiary:

DAEYANG INSTRUMENT CO., LTD (1)
502 Sinpyong-Dong
Saha-Ku, Busan, Korea (South)
Tel.: (82) 51 200 5284
Fax: (82) 51 200 5249
E-Mail: overseas@daeyang.co.kr
Emp.: 24
Measuring Instrument Mfr
S.I.C.: 3823
N.A.I.C.S.: 334513
Young Woo Seo *(Pres)*

U.S. Subsidiary:

KIMPEX. INC (1)
235 Anthony Trail
Northbrook, IL 60062
Tel.: (847) 412-4600
Fax: (847) 412-4602
E-Mail: info@kimpexUSA.com
Web Site: www.kimpexusa.com
Electronic Component Distr
S.I.C.: 5065
N.A.I.C.S.: 423690

Non-U.S. Subsidiaries:

LEADERS INTERNATIONAL UK LTD (1)
42 Purley Bury Avenue
CR8 1JD Purley, Surrey, United Kingdom
Tel.: (44) 7831 324 625
Fax: (44) 20 8668 0800
Lighting Equipment Mfr
S.I.C.: 3648
N.A.I.C.S.: 335129

ZIRCON ENGINEERING PTE LTD (1)
7 Kaki Bukit Crescent Fullion Building
Singapore, 416239, Singapore
Tel.: (65) 6288 8889
Fax: (65) 6283 8889
E-Mail: zircon@zircon.com.sg
Web Site: www.zircon.com.sg
Marine Equipment Distr
S.I.C.: 5088
N.A.I.C.S.: 423860

DAFFODIL COMPUTERS LIMITED

64/03 Lake Circus Kalabagan 2nd-5th Floor
Dhaka, 1205, Bangladesh
Tel.: (880) 2 8115986
Fax: (880) 2 8116103
E-Mail: Info@daffodil-bd.com
Web Site: www.daffodil-bd.com
Year Founded: 1990
DAFODILCOM—(DHA)
Emp.: 430

Business Description:
Software Development Services
S.I.C.: 7371
N.A.I.C.S.: 541511

Personnel:
Shahana Khan *(Chm)*
Mohammad Sabur Khan *(CEO & Mng Dir)*
Mohammad Monir Hossain *(Sec)*

Board of Directors:
Shahana Khan
Mohammad Emran Hossain
Mohammad Sabur Khan
Mohammad Younus Khan
Mohammad Mahtab Uddin

DAFORA S.A.

P-ta Regele Ferdinand I nr 15 Medias
551002 Sibiu, Romania
Tel.: (40) 269844507
Fax: (40) 269841726
E-Mail: office@dafora.ro
Web Site: www.dafora.ro
DAFR—(BUC)
Sls.: $67,412,901
Assets: $141,971,468
Liabilities: $107,501,643
Net Worth: $34,469,825
Earnings: ($6,974,966)
Emp.: 740
Fiscal Year-end: 12/31/12

Business Description:
Oil, Gas & Geothermal Water Onshore Drilling Services
S.I.C.: 1389
N.A.I.C.S.: 213112

Personnel:
Gheorghe Calburean *(Chm)*
Dan Popovici *(Mng Dir)*
Ligia Marian *(CFO)*

Board of Directors:
Gheorghe Calburean
Livia Calburean
Mircea Calburean
Mihal Eugen Popa
Alexandru-Liviu Tatar

DAGI GIYIM SANAYI VE TICARET A.S.

Birahane Sokak Plaza 3/1
Bomonti Sisli, Istanbul, Turkey
Tel.: (90) 2122404065
Fax: (90) 2122333028
E-Mail: dagi@dagi.com.tr
Web Site: www.dagi.com.tr
Sales Range: $10-24.9 Million
Emp.: 180

Business Description:
Underwear, Nightwear, Sportswear, Maternity & Other Clothing Mfr
S.I.C.: 2259
N.A.I.C.S.: 315190

Personnel:
Mahmut Nedim Koc *(Chm)*

DAH SAN ELECTRIC WIRE & CABLE CO., LTD.

369 Yun-Lin Rd Sec 3
64054 Touliu, Yunlin, Taiwan
Tel.: (886) 55222333
Fax: (886) 55220478
E-Mail: purchase@dahsan.com.tw
Web Site: www.dahsan.com.tw
1615—(TAI)
Sales Range: $50-74.9 Million

Business Description:
Power & Communication Cables Mfr
S.I.C.: 3357
N.A.I.C.S.: 335929

Personnel:
Wen-Bin Su *(Chm)*

Plant:

Dah San Electric Wire & Cable Co., Ltd. - Second Factory (1)
369 Shi Pin Road
Douliou, Yunlin, 64057, Taiwan
Tel.: (886) 55518868
Fax: (886) 55513157
Web Site: www.dahsan.com.tw/english401.html
Electric Cables Mfr
S.I.C.: 3355
N.A.I.C.S.: 331318

DAH SING FINANCIAL HOLDINGS LIMITED

36th Floor Dah Sing Financial Centre
108 Gloucester Road
Hong Kong, China (Hong Kong)
Tel.: (852) 25078866
Fax: (852) 25985052
E-Mail: ops@dahsing.com
Web Site: www.dahsing.com
0440—(HKG OTC)
Int. Income: $534,966,612
Assets: $22,305,891,310
Liabilities: $19,425,593,317
Net Worth: $2,880,297,994
Earnings: $206,170,676
Emp.: 2,451
Fiscal Year-end: 12/31/12

Business Description:
Bank Holding Company
S.I.C.: 6712
N.A.I.C.S.: 551111

Personnel:
David Shou-Yeh Wong *(Chm)*
Hon-Hing Wong *(CEO & Mng Dir)*
Harold Tsu-Hing Wong *(CEO/Mng Dir-Dah Sing Banking Group Limited)*
Eleonore Wing-Kay Chow *(CEO/Dir-Dah Sing Life Assurance Company Limited)*
Doris Wai-Nar Wong *(Sec)*

Board of Directors:
David Shou-Yeh Wong
John Wai-Wai Chow
Lonnie Dounn
Hidekazu Horikoshi
Nicholas John Mayhew
Takashi Morimura
Seiji Nakamura
Yuan Shu
Dennis Tai-Lun Sun
Robert Tsai-To Sze
Gary Pak-Ling Wang
Hon-Hing Wong

Transfer Agent:
Computershare Hong Kong Investor Services Limited
Room 1712-1716 17th Floor Hopewell Centre
183 Queen's Road East
Hong Kong, China (Hong Kong)

Subsidiaries:

Dah Sing Bank Limited (1)
36th Fl Dah Sing Financial Ctr 108 Gooustor Rd
Hong Kong, China (Hong Kong) (100%)
Tel.: (852) 25078866
Telex: 74063 DSB HX
Fax: (852) 25985052
Web Site: www.dahsing.com
Int. Income: $294,879,968
Emp.: 1,000
S.I.C.: 6159
N.A.I.C.S.: 522298
David Shou-Yeh Wong *(Chm)*

Dah Sing Banking Group Limited (1)
36th Floor Dah Sing Financial Centre
108 Gloucester Rd, Wanchai, China (Hong Kong)
Tel.: (852) 25078866
Fax: (852) 25985052
Web Site: www.dahsing.com
Commercial Banking
S.I.C.: 6029
N.A.I.C.S.: 522110
David Shou-Yeh Wong *(Chm)*
Hon-Hing Wong *(Mng Dir)*
Hoi-Lun Soo *(Sec)*

Dah Sing Company Limited (1)
36th Floor Dah Sing Financial Centre
108 Gloucester Rd, Wanchai, China (Hong Kong)
Tel.: (852) 25078866
Fax: (852) 25985052
Holding Company
S.I.C.: 6719
N.A.I.C.S.: 551112
David Shou-Yeh Wong *(Chm)*
Hon-Hing Wong *(Mng Dir)*
Hoi-Lun Soo *(Sec)*

Dah Sing Finance Limited (1)
36th Floor Dah Sing Financial Centre
108 Gloucester Rd, Wanchai, China (Hong Kong)
Tel.: (852) 25078866
Fax: (852) 25985052
Nondepository Credit Intermediation
S.I.C.: 6159
N.A.I.C.S.: 522298
David Shou-Yeh Wong *(Chm)*
Hon-Hing Wong *(Mng Dir)*
Hoi-Lun Soo *(Sec)*

Dah Sing General Insurance Company Limited (1)
13th Fl Island Pl Twr
North Point, China (Hong Kong) (100%)
Tel.: (852) 28085000
Fax: (852) 25988008
Emp.: 30
Insurance Agencies & Brokerages
S.I.C.: 6411
N.A.I.C.S.: 524210
Derek Wong *(Mng Dir & CEO)*

Dah Sing Insurance Services Limited (1)
4th Floor Dah Sing Financial Centre
PO Box 141
108 Gloucester Road, Wanchai, China (Hong Kong) (100%)
Tel.: (852) 25078866
Insurance Agencies & Brokerages
S.I.C.: 6411
N.A.I.C.S.: 524210

Dah Sing Nominees Ltd (1)
36th Floor Dah Sing Financial Centre
108 Gloucester Road, Wanchai, China (Hong Kong)
Tel.: (852) 25078866
Fax: (852) 25985052
Real Estate Investment Trusts
S.I.C.: 6726
N.A.I.C.S.: 525990
David Shou-Yeh Wong *(Chm)*
Hon-Hing Wong *(Mng Dir)*
Hoi-Lun Soo *(Sec)*

Mevas Bank Limited (1)
33rd Floor Dah Sing Financial Centre
PO Box 141
108 Gloucester Road, Wanchai, China (Hong Kong) (74.9%)
Tel.: (852) 31013101
Fax: (852) 31013700
E-Mail: contactuf@mevas.com
Web Site: www.mevas.com
Emp.: 35
Commercial Banking
S.I.C.: 6029
N.A.I.C.S.: 522110
Jeffery Nji *(Gen Mgr-Sls)*

Non-U.S. Subsidiaries:

Macau Insurance Company Limited (1)
Pcm BLd 114
AVisstop TaToaia Goante-594, Macau, China (Macau)
Tel.: (853) 28555078
Fax: (853) 28551074
E-Mail: mic@bcm.com.mo
Web Site: www.macauinsurance.com.mo/en/
Emp.: 60
Insurance Agencies & Brokerages
S.I.C.: 6411
N.A.I.C.S.: 524210
Steven Chik *(Mng Dir)*

Macau Life Insurance Company Limited (1)
Avenida da Praia Grande No 594 Edf BCM 11th Floor
Macau, China (Macau)
Tel.: (853) 28555078
Fax: (853) 28551074
Web Site: www.macauinsurance.com.mo
Direct Life Insurance Carriers
S.I.C.: 6311
N.A.I.C.S.: 524113
Chi Hok Si *(Mng Dir)*

DAHER GROUP

1 allee Maryse Bastie
91325 Wissous, Cedex, France
Tel.: (33) 149759800
Fax: (33) 149759833
E-Mail: standard.orlytech@daher.com
Web Site: www.daher.com
Year Founded: 1863
Sales Range: $750-799.9 Million
Emp.: 5,000

Business Description:
Aerospace Equipment Manufacturing & Services
S.I.C.: 3724
N.A.I.C.S.: 336412

Personnel:
Patrick Daher *(Chm & CEO)*

Divisions:

DAHER Industry & Defence (1)
10 Pl de la Joliette
BP 32312
13567 Marseilles, France
Tel.: (33) 491397500
Fax: (33) 491900437
Emp.: 50
Industrial Parts Mfr
S.I.C.: 3769
N.A.I.C.S.: 336419
Jean-Paul Lafitte *(Pres)*

DAHER-SOCATA (1)
Aeroport de Tarbes-Lourdes-Pyrenees
F-65290 Tarbes, Cedex 9, France
Tel.: (33) 562417300
Fax: (33) 562417355
E-Mail: info@socata.daher.com
Web Site: www.socata.com
Emp.: 1,200
Aircraft & Aircraft Parts Mfr & Distr
S.I.C.: 3721
N.A.I.C.S.: 336411
Francis Lepinoy *(Pres)*
Stephane Mayer *(CEO)*

U.S. Subsidiary:

SOCATA North America, Inc. (2)
N Perry Airport 7501 S Airport Rd
Pembroke Pines, FL 33023-2579
Tel.: (954) 893-1414
Fax: (954) 964-0805
E-Mail: sales@socataaircraft.com
Web Site: www.socatanorthamerica.com
Sales Range: $10-24.9 Million
Emp.: 30
Aircraft Parts Distr
S.I.C.: 3724
N.A.I.C.S.: 336412
Nicolas Chabbert *(Pres)*

DAHER Support Management (1)
10 Place de la Joliette
13567 Marseilles, France
Tel.: (33) 491397500
Fax: (33) 491397537
Support Services
S.I.C.: 7389
N.A.I.C.S.: 561499
Francis Etienne *(Dir-HR)*

DAHUA INC.

8th Floor Officer Tower 3 Henderson Center
18 Jianguomennei Street
Dongcheng District, Beijing, 100005, China
Tel.: (86) 1064801527
Fax: (86) 1064801519
Web Site:
Year Founded: 2002
DHUA—(OTC)
Emp.: 65

Business Description:
Single-Family Home Construction Services
S.I.C.: 1521
N.A.I.C.S.: 236115

Personnel:
Yonglin Du *(Pres & CEO)*
Hua Meng *(CFO)*
Qinna Zeng *(Sec)*

Board of Directors:
Yonglin Du
Wulong Wang

DAI-DAN CO LTD

1-9-25 Edobori Nishi-ku
Osaka, 550-8520, Japan
Tel.: (81) 664418231
Fax: (81) 664477176
Web Site: www.daidan.co.jp
1980—(TKS)
Sls.: $1,341,109,000
Assets: $1,167,705,000
Liabilities: $672,837,000
Net Worth: $494,868,000
Earnings: $17,589,000
Emp.: 1,364
Fiscal Year-end: 03/31/13

Business Description:
Engineering Services
S.I.C.: 1731
N.A.I.C.S.: 238210

Personnel:
Setsu Sugaya *(Chm & CEO)*
Shohei Kitano *(Pres & COO)*

Board of Directors:
Setsu Sugaya
Hirokazu Kawakubo
Shohei Kitano
Kazuya Yoshida

Division:

DAI-DAN Co Ltd - Technical Development Division (1)
390 Kitanagai Miyoshi
Iruma, Saitama, 354-0044, Japan
Tel.: (81) 492581511
Fax: (81) 492581863
Air Conditioner Mfr
S.I.C.: 3585
N.A.I.C.S.: 333415

Subsidiary:

DAI-DAN Service Kanto Co., Ltd. (1)
3rd Fl Fukagawa Hanawa Bldg 1-1-10 Hirano
Koto-ku, Tokyo, 135-0023, Japan
Tel.: (81) 356390721
Fax: (81) 356390727
Web Site: www.daidan.co.jp/english/company/index4.html
Emp.: 14
Air Conditioning Equipments Mfr
S.I.C.: 3585
N.A.I.C.S.: 333415
Hijime Shipazaki *(Office Mgr)*

Non-U.S. Subsidiaries:

Dai-Dan Philippines, Inc. (1)
7th Fl Mobile Entertainment Ctr 104 Rada St
Legaspri Vlg, Makati, Philippines

Tel.: (63) 27522431
Fax: (63) 27522434
Web Site: www.daidan.co.jp/english/company/index4.html
Emp.: 3
Electrical & Plumbing Services
S.I.C.: 1731
N.A.I.C.S.: 238210
Koji Azono *(Mgr)*

Merino-ODD Sdn. Bhd. **(1)**
57-3A Jalan SS 23 15 Taman SEA
47400 Petaling Jaya, Selangor, Malaysia
Tel.: (60) 378048877
Fax: (60) 378051143
Emp.: 12
Air Conditioners Mfr
S.I.C.: 3585
N.A.I.C.S.: 333415
Y. Yamamoto *(Gen Mgr)*

DAI HAN PHARM. CO., LTD.

8-3 4-Ga Yangpyeong-dong
Seoul, Yeongdeungpo-gu, Korea (South)
Tel.: (82) 226788445
Fax: (82) 226719636
Web Site: www.daihan.com
023910—(KRS)

Business Description:
Pharmaceuticals Product Mfr & Sales
S.I.C.: 2834
N.A.I.C.S.: 325412

Personnel:
Yoonwoo Lee *(Chm)*

DAI-ICHI KARKARIA LIMITED

Liberty Building Sir V Thackersey Marg
Mumbai, Maharashtra, 400 020, India
Tel.: (91) 22 2201 5895
Fax: (91) 22 2209 6976
E-Mail: diklbom@dai-ichiindia.com
Web Site: www.dai-ichiindia.com
Year Founded: 1960
526821—(BOM)
Rev.: $20,404,728
Assets: $18,052,625
Liabilities: $4,332,264
Net Worth: $13,720,361
Earnings: $1,219,405
Emp.: 239
Fiscal Year-end: 03/31/13

Business Description:
Specialty Chemical Mfr & Distr
S.I.C.: 2869
N.A.I.C.S.: 325199

Personnel:
S. F. Vakil *(Chm & Mng Dir)*
Kavita Thadeshwar *(Compliance Officer & Sec)*

Board of Directors:
S. F. Vakil
K. R. Bharucha
K. M. Elavia
A. H. Jehangir
J. H. C. Jehangir
A. M. Naik
K. D. Patel

Transfer Agent:
Sharex Dynamic (India) Pvt. Ltd.
Unit-1 Luthra Ind Premises Safed Pool Andheri Kurla Rd Andheri (E)
Mumbai, India

THE DAI-ICHI LIFE INSURANCE COMPANY LIMITED

13-1 Yurakucho 1-chome
Chiyoda-ku, Tokyo, 100-8411, Japan
Tel.: (81) 332161211
Telex: 29848
Fax: (81) 3 5221 4360
Web Site: www.dai-ichi-life.co.jp
Year Founded: 1902
8750—(TKS)
Rev.: $58,123,879,000
Assets: $392,638,521,000
Liabilities: $374,499,301,000
Net Worth: $18,139,220,000
Earnings: $356,697,000
Emp.: 56,976
Fiscal Year-end: 03/31/13

Business Description:
Insurance & Financial Services
S.I.C.: 6311
N.A.I.C.S.: 524113

Personnel:
Katsutoshi Saito *(Chm)*
Koichiro Watanabe *(Pres)*
Hideto Masaki *(Deputy Pres)*
Shinichi Aizawa *(Exec Officer)*
Nobuyuki Akimoto *(Exec Officer)*
Tomoyasu Asano *(Mng Exec Officer)*
Norimitsu Horio *(Sr Mng Exec Officer)*
Kazuma Ishii *(Sr Mng Exec Officer)*
Takehide Itonaga *(Mng Exec Officer)*
Hiroshi Kanai *(Mng Exec Officer)*
Takashi Kawashima *(Mng Exec Officer)*
Morinobu Nagahama *(Mng Exec Officer)*
Atsushi Nagayama *(Exec Officer)*
Masamitsu Nanbu *(Exec Officer)*
Kenji Sakurai *(Mng Exec Officer)*
Satoru Sato *(Exec Officer)*
Atsushi Takahashi *(Exec Officer)*
Masao Taketomi *(Exec Officer)*
Yoshio Takeyama *(Mng Exec Officer)*
Akio Tanaka *(Mng Exec Officer)*
Hideo Teramoto *(Mng Exec Officer)*
Shigeo Tsuyuki *(Sr Mng Exec Officer)*
Satoru Ueno *(Sr Mng Exec Officer)*
Ryoji Yajima *(Sr Mng Exec Officer)*

Board of Directors:
Katsutoshi Saito
Tomoyasu Asano
Haruo Funabashi
Norimitsu Horio
Kazuma Ishii
Hiroshi Kanai
Takashi Kawashima
Hideto Masaki
Michiko Miyamoto
Hideo Teramoto
Shigeo Tsuyuki
Koichiro Watanabe
Ryoji Yajima

Subsidiaries:

The Dai-ichi Life Information Systems Co., Ltd **(1)**
1-9 Nikkocho Daiichiseimei Building Fuchu
Fuchu, Tokyo, 183-0044, Japan
Tel.: (81) 423306500
Fax: (81) 423688024
Insurance Management Services
S.I.C.: 6311
N.A.I.C.S.: 524113

Dai-ichi Life Research Institute Inc., **(1)**
13-1 Yurakucho 1-chome
Chiyoda-ku, Tokyo, 100-0006, Japan
Tel.: (81) 332161211
Fax: (81) 3 5221 4360
Insurance Management Services
S.I.C.: 6411
N.A.I.C.S.: 524298
Masayuki Koyama *(Pres)*

U.S. Subsidiaries:

Dai-ichi Life International (U.S.A.) Inc. **(1)**
1133 Ave of the Americas 28th Fl
New York, NY 10036 (100%)
Tel.: (212) 350-7600
Telex: 23-234201 DAI UR
Fax: (212) 354-1866
E-Mail: postnafger@blusa.com
Web Site: www.dai-ichi-life.co.jp/english/overseas_network.html
Life Insurance Services
S.I.C.: 6311
N.A.I.C.S.: 524113
Toshiya Kaname *(Pres)*

Non-U.S. Subsidiaries:

Dai-ichi Life Insurance Company of Vietnam, Limited **(1)**
3rd Fl Saigon Riverside Office Ctr 2A-4A Ton Duc Thang St
District 1, Ho Chi Minh City, Vietnam
Tel.: (84) 838291919
Fax: (84) 838293131
E-Mail: information@dai-ichi-life.com.vn
Web Site: www.dai-ichi-life.co.jp/english/overseas_network.html#a03
Emp.: 400
Life Insurance Services
S.I.C.: 6311
N.A.I.C.S.: 524113
Takashi Fujii *(Chm & Gen Dir)*

Dai-ichi Life International (AsiaPacific) Limited **(1)**
Suite 6702 Central Plaza 18 Harbour Road
Wanchai, China (Hong Kong) (100%)
Tel.: (852) 25881331
Telex: 802-68686 DISJP-HX
Fax: (852) 25881218
E-Mail: info@dai-ichi-life.co.jp
Web Site: www.dai-ichi-life.co.jp
Emp.: 100
Life Insurance Services
S.I.C.: 6311
N.A.I.C.S.: 524113
Tetsuya Kikuta *(Mng Dir)*

Dai-ichi Life International (Europe) Limited **(1)**
Level 4 155 Bishopsgate
London, EC2M 3XN, United Kingdom (100%)
Tel.: (44) 2074549871
Telex: 51-8954913 DMLIL G
Fax: (44) 2076280074
Web Site: www.dai-ichi-life.co.jp/english/overseas_network.html
Emp.: 14
Life Insurance Services
S.I.C.: 6311
N.A.I.C.S.: 524113
Koichi Kashimoto *(Mng Dir)*
Suguru Nishioka *(Mng Dir)*

Ocean Life Insurance Co., Ltd. **(1)**
170/74-83 Ocean Tower 1 Building Rachadapisek Road
Klongtoey, Bangkok, 10110, Thailand
Tel.: (66) 22612300
Fax: (66) 22613355
E-Mail: uraiwan.ru@Ocean.co.th
Web Site: www.Ocean.co.th
Emp.: 1,000
Life Insurance Services
S.I.C.: 6311
N.A.I.C.S.: 524113
Kirati Assakul *(Chm)*

Star Union Dai-ichi Life Insurance Company Limited **(1)**
Star House 3rd Floor West Wing C-5 G Block Bandra-Kurla Comples
Bandra East, Mumbai, 400 051, India
Tel.: (91) 226639546270
Fax: (91) 2266684591
Web Site: sudlife.in/
Life Insurance Services
S.I.C.: 6311
N.A.I.C.S.: 524113
Mathusamy Balachandran *(Chm)*

TAL Limited **(1)**
80 Alfred Street
Milsons Point, NSW, 2061, Australia (100%)
Mailing Address:
PO Box 142
Milsons Point, NSW, 1565, Australia
Tel.: (61) 294489000
Fax: (61) 2 9448 9100
Web Site: www.tal.com.au
Rev.: $951,657,193
Emp.: 650
Insurance Services
S.I.C.: 6411
N.A.I.C.S.: 524298
Jim Minto *(CEO & Mng Dir)*
Phil Soutter *(CIO)*
Geoff Black *(CEO-Investments)*
Andrew Boldeman *(CEO-Grp Life)*
Brett Clark *(CEO-Retail Life)*

Branch:

TAL Limited-Victoria **(2)**
606 St Kilda Road
PO Box 142
Melbourne, VIC, 1565, Australia
Tel.: (61) 294489000
Telex: 3 3 547 all aa
Fax: (61) 294489100
Web Site: www.toweraustralia.com.au
Sales Range: $10-24.9 Million
Emp.: 5
Provider of Insurance Services
S.I.C.: 6311
N.A.I.C.S.: 524113
Jim Minto *(Mng Dir)*

Subsidiaries:

Beacon Investment Management Services Limited **(2)**
Suite 402 25 Lime Street
Sydney, NSW, 2001, Australia
Tel.: (61) 292793332
Fax: (61) 292793302
E-Mail: info@beaconinvestment.com.au
Web Site: www.beaconinvestment.com.au/index.php?option=com_frontpage&Itemid=1
Emp.: 5
Investment Management Services
S.I.C.: 6211
N.A.I.C.S.: 523999
Kevin Wyld *(Mng Dir)*

TAL Direct Pty Limited **(2)**
L3 / 4 Martin Place
Sydney, NSW, Australia
Tel.: (61) 2 9222 7222
Fax: (61) 2 9222 7299
Web Site: www.insuranceline.com.au
Emp.: 450
General Insurance Services
S.I.C.: 6311
N.A.I.C.S.: 524113
Bradley Goldschmidt *(Co-CEO/Mng Dir)*
Howard Ware *(Co-CEO/Mng Dir)*

Pivotal Financial Advisers Limited **(2)**
Level 13 80 Alfred Street
Milsons Point, NSW, 2061, Australia
Tel.: (61) 2 9954 0325
Fax: (61) 2 9954 3824
E-Mail: enquiries@pivfin.com.au
Web Site: www.pivfin.com.au
Emp.: 15
General Insurance Services
S.I.C.: 6311
N.A.I.C.S.: 524113
Craig Parker *(Gen Mgr)*

DAI-ICHI SEIKO CO., LTD.

12-4 Negoro Momoyama-cho Fushimi-ku
Kyoto, 612-8024, Japan
Tel.: (81) 756117155
Fax: (81) 756117150
Web Site: www.daiichi-seiko.co.jp
Year Founded: 1963
6640—(JAS TKS)
Sales Range: $550-599.9 Million
Emp.: 4,764

Business Description:
Electronic Components
Semiconductor & Industrial Mold Mfr
S.I.C.: 3679
N.A.I.C.S.: 334419

Personnel:
Hideki Konishi *(Pres)*
Tetsumi Fukumoto *(Exec VP)*

Board of Directors:
Takayoshi Endou
Tetsumi Fukumoto
Nobuaki Goto
Takashi Harada
Yoshiaki Hiraoka
Tomio Kakiuchi
Kenjirou Katabuchi
Hideki Konishi
Hitoshi Nakata
Kenji Ogata
Yasutoshi Tagomori

Dai-ichi Seiko Co., Ltd.—(Continued)

Takaharu Tsuchiyama
Munehiro Tsunoda
Kenji Yano

Subsidiaries:

I-PEX Co., Ltd (1)
Machida ST Bldg 1-33-10 Morino
Machida, Tokyo, 194-0022, Japan
Tel.: (81) 42 729 1670
Fax: (81) 42 7291678
Web Site: www.i-pex.com
Emp.: 248
Electronic Component Mfr
S.I.C.: 3679
N.A.I.C.S.: 334419
Takashi Harada *(Sr Mng Dir)*
Yoshi Hiraoka *(Mng Dir)*

Matsue Dai-ichi Seiko Co., Ltd (1)
12 Hokuryo-cho
Matsue, Shimane, 690-0816, Japan
Tel.: (81) 852 60 5710
Fax: (81) 852 60 5750
Electronic Component Mfr
S.I.C.: 3679
N.A.I.C.S.: 334419

Techno Dai-ichi Co., Ltd (1)
12-4 Negoro Momoyama-cho
Fushimi-ku, Kyoto, 612-8024, Japan
Tel.: (81) 75 602 2191
Fax: (81) 75 602 2193
E-Mail: mdd@daiichi-seiko.co.jp
Emp.: 13
Injection Molding Machinery Mfr
S.I.C.: 3559
N.A.I.C.S.: 333249
Ogata Kenji *(Pres)*

Plants:

Dai-ichi Seiko Co., Ltd. - Ogori Plant (1)
863 Mitsusawa
Ogori, Fukuoka, 838-0106, Japan
Tel.: (81) 942 75 5115
Fax: (81) 942 75 2050
Web Site: www.daiichi-seiko.co.jp/english/company/d_works_jpn.html
Electronic Connector Mfr
S.I.C.: 3678
N.A.I.C.S.: 334417

Dai-ichi Seiko Co., Ltd. - Onojo Plant (1)
6-1-8 Mikasagawa
Onojo, Fukuoka, 816-0912, Japan
Tel.: (81) 92 503 0551
Fax: (81) 92 504 0854
Electronic Connector Mfr
S.I.C.: 3678
N.A.I.C.S.: 334417

Dai-ichi Seiko Co., Ltd. - Tachiarai Plant (1)
2455-1 Takata Chikuzen-machi
Asakura, Fukuoka, 838-0814, Japan
Tel.: (81) 946 24 0300
Fax: (81) 946 24 6081
Electronic Connector Mfr
S.I.C.: 3678
N.A.I.C.S.: 334417

Dai-ichi Seiko Co., Ltd. - YAMANASHI PLANT (1)
1816-1 Shotokuji
Yamanashi, 405-0032, Japan
Tel.: (81) 553 23 0450
Fax: (81) 553 23 0390
Electronic Connector Mfr
S.I.C.: 3678
N.A.I.C.S.: 334417

Non-U.S. Subsidiaries:

DONG GUAN DAI-ICHI SEIKO MOLD & PLASTICS CO., LTD. (1)
305 Zhen An West Road Shang Jiao Area
Chang An Town, Dongguan, Guangdong, 523878, China
Tel.: (86) 769 8535 8671
Fax: (86) 769 8535 8677
Web Site: www.daiichi-seiko.co.jp/english/company/iwork010.html
Injection Molded Plastic Products Mfr
S.I.C.: 3089
N.A.I.C.S.: 326199

LAGUNA DAI-ICHI, INC. (1)
103 North Science Avenue Laguna
Tecnopark SEPZ
Binan, Laguna, 4024, Philippines
Tel.: (63) 49 541 2860
Fax: (63) 49 541 2397
Electronic Connector Mfr
S.I.C.: 3678
N.A.I.C.S.: 334417

MDI SDN. BHD. (1)
85 Jalan Tampoi
81200 Johor Bahru, Malaysia
Tel.: (60) 7 236 6851
Fax: (60) 7 236 7211
Web Site: www.daiichi-seiko.co.jp/english/company/iwork010.html
Injection Molded Plastic Products Mfr
S.I.C.: 3089
N.A.I.C.S.: 326199

PT. PERTAMA PRECISION BINTAN (1)
Lot SD26/27 Bintan Industrial Estate Lobam
Pulau Bintan, Tanjunguban, Riau, 29152, Indonesia
Tel.: (62) 770 696 668
Fax: (62) 770 696 670
Injection Molded Plastic Products Mfr
S.I.C.: 3089
N.A.I.C.S.: 326199

Non-U.S. Plants:

Shanghai Dai-Ichi Seiko Mould & Plastics Co., Ltd. - Shanghai Plant 1 (1)
100 Baiyun Road Minhang SMEDZ
Shanghai, 200245, China
Tel.: (86) 21 6430 3470
Fax: (86) 21 6430 3471
Web Site: www.daiichi-seiko.co.jp/english/company/iwork010.html
Injection Molded Plastic Products Mfr
S.I.C.: 3089
N.A.I.C.S.: 326199

Shanghai Dai-Ichi Seiko Mould & Plastics Co., Ltd. - Shanghai Plant 2 (1)
169 Bei Dou Road Minhang SMEDZ
Shanghai, 200245, China
Tel.: (86) 21 6463 6616
Fax: (86) 21 6463 6099
Web Site: www.daiichi-seiko.co.jp/english/company/iwork010.html
Injection Molded Plastic Products Mfr
S.I.C.: 3089
N.A.I.C.S.: 326199

SINGAPORE DAI-ICHI PTE. LTD. - WOODLANDS PLANT (1)
Block 2 Woodlands Sector 1 01-24
Woodlands Spectrum 1
Singapore, 738068, Singapore
Tel.: (65) 6753 8558
Fax: (65) 6483 1673
Injection Molded Plastic Products Mfr
S.I.C.: 3089
N.A.I.C.S.: 326199

THAI DAI-ICHI SEIKO CO., LTD - Thai Plant (1)
700/390 Moo 6 Tambol Donhuaroh
Amphur Muangchonburi, Chon Buri, 20000, Thailand
Tel.: (66) 3846 8316
Fax: (66) 3846 8322
Web Site: www.daiichi-seiko.co.jp/english/company/iwork010.html
Electronic Connector Mfr
S.I.C.: 3678
N.A.I.C.S.: 334417

VIETNAM DAI-ICHI SEIKO CO., LTD. - Vietnam Plant (1)
41 Tu Do Avenue Viet Nam Singapore Industrial Park
Thuan An, Binh Duong, Vietnam
Tel.: (84) 650 3 767744
Fax: (84) 650 3 767745
Web Site: www.daiichi-seiko.co.jp/english/company/iwork010.html
Electronic Connector Mfr
S.I.C.: 3678
N.A.I.C.S.: 334417

DAI NIPPON PRINTING CO., LTD.

1-1-1 Ichigaya Kagacho Shinjuku-ku
Tokyo, 162-8001, Japan
Tel.: (81) 332662111
Telex: J22737
Fax: (81) 352258239
E-Mail: info@mail.dnp.co.jp
Web Site: www.dnp.co.jp
Year Founded: 1876
7912—(TKS)
Sls.: $15,912,677,000
Assets: $17,368,736,000
Liabilities: $7,061,131,000
Net Worth: $10,307,605,000
Earnings: $211,398,000
Emp.: 39,445
Fiscal Year-end: 03/31/13

Business Description:
Printing Materials; Packaging; Interior & Exterior Design; Micro Products; Plastic Processing Services
S.I.C.: 2759
N.A.I.C.S.: 323111

Personnel:
Yoshitoshi Kitajima *(Pres)*
Mitsuhiko Hakii *(Sr Mng Dir)*
Yujiro Kuroda *(Sr Mng Dir)*
Osamu Tsuchida *(Sr Mng Dir)*
Masahiko Wada *(Sr Mng Dir)*
Teruomi Yoshino *(Sr Mng Dir)*
Kunikazu Akishige *(Mng Dir)*
Sakae Hikita *(Mng Dir)*
Kazumasa Hiroki *(Mng Dir)*
Tokuji Kanda *(Mng Dir)*
Motoharu Kitajima *(Mng Dir)*
Tetsuji Morino *(Mng Dir)*
Yoshiki Nozaka *(Mng Dir)*
Takao Shimizu *(Mng Dir)*
Masaki Tsukada *(Mng Dir)*
Fujio Yamazaki *(Mng Dir)*
Shigemi Furuya *(Sr Corp Officer)*
Tatsuro Kitayuguchi *(Sr Corp Officer)*
Masato Koike *(Sr Corp Officer)*
Tatsuo Komaki *(Sr Corp Officer)*
Ryuji Minemura *(Sr Corp Officer)*
Kenji Miya *(Corp Officer)*
Morihiro Muramoto *(Corp Officer)*
Tatsuya Nishimura *(Sr Corp Officer)*
Takashi Saito *(Sr Corp Officer)*
Toshio Sugimoto *(Corp Officer)*
Yasuo Takeda *(Corp Officer)*
Masato Yamaguchi *(Sr Corp Officer)*
Yoshinari Kitajima *(Exec VP)*
Koichi Takanami *(Exec VP)*
Masayoshi Yamada *(Exec VP)*

Board of Directors:
Kunikazu Akishige
Mitsuhiko Hakii
Sakae Hikita
Kazumasa Hiroki
Tokuji Kanda
Motoharu Kitajima
Yoshinari Kitajima
Yoshitoshi Kitajima
Yujiro Kuroda
Tetsuji Morino
Yoshiki Nozaka
Takao Shimizu
Koichi Takanami
Osamu Tsuchida
Masaki Tsukada
Tadao Tsukada
Masahiko Wada
Masayoshi Yamada
Fujio Yamazaki
Teruomi Yoshino

Subsidiaries:

At Table Co., Ltd. (1)
Dnpgotanda Bldg 12f
Shinagawa-ku, Tokyo, 141-0031, Japan
Tel.: (81) 364313636
Management Consulting Services
S.I.C.: 8742
N.A.I.C.S.: 541611

CP Design Consulting Co., Ltd. (1)
3-5-20 Nishi Gotanda DNP Gotanda Building
Shinagawa-ku, Tokyo, 141-0031, Japan
Tel.: (81) 364313640
Web Site: www.cpdc.co.jp
Environmental Consulting Services
S.I.C.: 8999
N.A.I.C.S.: 541620

Dai Nippon Book Binding Co., Ltd. (1)
39 3 2 Chome Kamiya Kita Ku
Tokyo, 115, Japan (100%)
Tel.: (81) 339038806
Emp.: 262
Provider of Binding & Additional Books Processing Services
S.I.C.: 7389
N.A.I.C.S.: 323120

Dai Nippon Shoji Co., Ltd. (1)
Kanaba Jinbo
Chochiyo Daku, Tokyo, 101 8424, Japan (94.3%)
Tel.: (81) 332887630
Fax: (81) 332885956
E-Mail: miyakarah4@mail.dnp.co.jp
Emp.: 240
Wholesaler, Trade & Broker of Materials
S.I.C.: 7389
N.A.I.C.S.: 425120
Masatoshi Omatsu *(Gen Mgr)*

Direc Co., Ltd. (1)
5-6-30 Kojimashimonocho
Kurashiki, Okayama, 711-0906, Japan
Tel.: (81) 864725222
Educational Equipment & Books Distr
S.I.C.: 5192
N.A.I.C.S.: 424920

D.N.K. Co., Ltd. (1)
2-21-8 Kichijoji Honcho Momiji Bldg
Musashino, Tokyo, 180-0004, Japan
Tel.: (81) 422227787
Machine Tools Repair & Maintenance Services
S.I.C.: 7699
N.A.I.C.S.: 811310

DNP AV Center Co., Ltd. (1)
14th Floor DNP Gotanda Building 5-20
3-chome Nishi-Gotanda
Shinagawa-ku, Tokyo, 141-8001, Japan
Tel.: (81) 3 6431 3510
Fax: (81) 3 6431 3502
Graphic Software Development Services
S.I.C.: 7371
N.A.I.C.S.: 541511

DNP Chubu Co., Ltd. (1)
3-902 Seko
Moriyama-ku, Nagoya, Aichi, 463-8543, Japan
Tel.: (81) 52 758 2215
Web Site: www.dnp-chubu.co.jp
Book Publishing Services
S.I.C.: 2731
N.A.I.C.S.: 511130

DNP Color Techno Kameyama Co., Ltd. (1)
464 Shiraki-cho
Kameyama, Mie, 519-0169, Japan
Tel.: (81) 595842650
Color Filters Mfr
S.I.C.: 3679
N.A.I.C.S.: 334419

DNP Corporate History Center Co., Ltd. (1)
3-5-20 Nishi Gotanda DNP Gotanda Building
Shinagawa-ku, Tokyo, 141-0031, Japan
Tel.: (81) 364314800
Web Site: shashinomori.dualchives.jp
Business Support Services
S.I.C.: 7389
N.A.I.C.S.: 561499

DNP Data Techno Co., Ltd. (1)
1650-70 Okubaracho
Ushiku, Ibaraki, 300-1283, Japan
Tel.: (81) 298752211
Plastic Cards Mfr
S.I.C.: 3089
N.A.I.C.S.: 326199

DNP Data Techno Kansai Co., Ltd. (1)
712-10 Toin Kawanishicho
Shiki-gun, Nara, 636-0204, Japan

Tel.: (81) 745441121
Commercial Printing Services
S.I.C.: 2759
N.A.I.C.S.: 323111

DNP Digitalcom Co., Ltd. (1)
DNP Gotanda Bldg 3-5-20 Nishi Gotanda
Shinagawa-ku, Tokyo, 141-8001, Japan
Tel.: (81) 364316000
Fax: (81) 364316195
Web Site: www.dnp-digi.com
Emp.: 436
Web Consulting Services
S.I.C.: 7373
N.A.I.C.S.: 541512
Ryota Chiba *(Pres & CEO)*

DNP Facility Services Co., Ltd. (1)
2-1 Ichigayatakajomachi
Shinjuku-ku, Tokyo, 162-0-848, Japan
Tel.: (81) 332664743
Building Facility Management Services
S.I.C.: 8744
N.A.I.C.S.: 561210

DNP Fine Chemicals Co., Ltd. (1)
450 Aoto-cho
Midori-ku, Yokohama, Kanagawa, 226-0022, Japan
Tel.: (81) 45 932 5121
Fax: (81) 45 932 3242
Chemical Products Mfr
S.I.C.: 2869
N.A.I.C.S.: 325199
Itsuo Totsuka *(Pres)*

DNP Fine Electronics Co., Ltd. (1)
2-2-1 Fukuoka
Fujimino, Saitama, 356-0011, Japan
Tel.: (81) 492782458
Semiconductor Device Mfr
S.I.C.: 3674
N.A.I.C.S.: 334413

DNP Fotolusio Co., Ltd. (1)
3-35-13 Yayoi-cho
Nakano-ku, Tokyo, 164-0013, Japan
Tel.: (81) 367020810
Web Site: www.fotolusio.jp
Commercial Printing Services
S.I.C.: 2759
N.A.I.C.S.: 323111

DNP Graphica Co., Ltd. (1)
1062-8 Honjo Nishikatamachi
Kamitsuga-gun, Tochigi, 322-0606, Japan
Tel.: (81) 282921200
Commercial Printing Services
S.I.C.: 2759
N.A.I.C.S.: 323111

DNP Hokkaido Co., Ltd. (1)
11-1-1 Kita7johigashi
Higashi-Ku, Sapporo, Hokkaido, 065-0007, Japan
Tel.: (81) 11 750 2205
Fax: (81) 11 750 2390
Web Site: www.dnp.co.jp/hokkaido
Packaging Product Mfr & Distr
S.I.C.: 2679
N.A.I.C.S.: 322299

DNP Hoso Co., Ltd. (1)
2-10-25 Akabane-Minami
Kita-ku, Tokyo, 115-0044, Japan
Tel.: (81) 339038900
Packaging Product Distr
S.I.C.: 5085
N.A.I.C.S.: 423840

DNP ID System Co., Ltd. (1)
4-3-17 Shinjuku Davinci Shinjuku 6F
Shinjuku-ku, Tokyo, 160-0022, Japan
Tel.: (81) 333504611
Precision Electronic Component Whslr
S.I.C.: 5084
N.A.I.C.S.: 423830

DNP IMS Odawara Co., Ltd. (1)
28 Horinouchi
Odawara, Kanagawa, 250-0853, Japan
Tel.: (81) 465362222
Photographic Materials Mfr & Whslr
S.I.C.: 3579
N.A.I.C.S.: 333316

DNP Information Systems Co., Ltd. (1)
21-banchi Ichigaya Sanaicho
Shinjuku-ku, Tokyo, 162-0846, Japan
Tel.: (81) 849276639
Fax: (81) 849276737
Web Site: www.dnp-is.co.jp
Computer Software Development Services
S.I.C.: 7371
N.A.I.C.S.: 541511
Tatsuo Komaki *(Pres)*

DNP Logistics Co., Ltd. (1)
2-20-7 Akabaneminami
Kita-ku, Tokyo, 115-0044, Japan
Tel.: (81) 339038940
Web Site: www.dnp.co.jp/logistics/
Warehouse Management Services
S.I.C.: 4225
N.A.I.C.S.: 493110

DNP LSI Design Co., Ltd. (1)
2-2-1 Fukuoka
Fujimino, Saitama, 356-0011, Japan
Tel.: (81) 492781912
Fax: (81) 4922624321
Web Site: www.dnp.co.jp/DLD
Semiconductor Component Mfr
S.I.C.: 3674
N.A.I.C.S.: 334413

DNP Media Art Co., Ltd. (1)
1-1-1 Ichigaya Kaga-cho
Shinjuku-ku, Tokyo, 162-0062, Japan
Tel.: (81) 332663531
Commercial Printing Services
S.I.C.: 2759
N.A.I.C.S.: 323111

DNP Media Create Co., Ltd. (1)
7 Enokicho
Shinjuku-ku, Tokyo, 162-0806, Japan
Tel.: (81) 352616444
Commercial Photography Services
S.I.C.: 7335
N.A.I.C.S.: 541922

DNP Media Techno Kansai Co., Ltd. (1)
1-17-28 Minamihorie Nambass Building 8F
Nishi-ku, Osaka, 550-0015, Japan
Tel.: (81) 661103011
Commercial Printing Services
S.I.C.: 2759
N.A.I.C.S.: 323111

DNP Micro Technica Co., Ltd. (1)
2-2-1 Fukuoka
Fujimino, Saitama, 356-0011, Japan
Tel.: (81) 492781658
Industrial Machinery Mfr
S.I.C.: 3559
N.A.I.C.S.: 333249

DNP Multi Print Co., Ltd. (1)
Ksk Bldg 1f
Shinjuku-ku, Tokyo, 162-0842, Japan
Tel.: (81) 332662930
Commercial Printing Services
S.I.C.: 2759
N.A.I.C.S.: 323111

DNP Nishi Nippon Co., Ltd. (1)
2-16-36 Shimizu
Minami-ku, Fukuoka, 815-0031, Japan
Tel.: (81) 92 553 4144
Packaging Product Mfr & Distr
S.I.C.: 2672
N.A.I.C.S.: 322220

DNP Photo Imaging Co., Ltd. (1)
3-35-13 Yayoi-cho
Nakano-ku, Tokyo, 164-0013, Japan
Tel.: (81) 367020420
Book Publishing Services
S.I.C.: 2731
N.A.I.C.S.: 511130

DNP Precision Devices Co., Ltd. (1)
2-2-1 Fukuoka
Fujimino, Saitama, 356-0011, Japan
Tel.: (81) 492782456
Electronic Component Mfr
S.I.C.: 3679
N.A.I.C.S.: 334419

DNP Shikoku Co., Ltd. (1)
1-15 Nakashimadacho
Tokushima, 770-0052, Japan
Tel.: (81) 886313279
Commercial Printing Services
S.I.C.: 2759
N.A.I.C.S.: 323111

DNP SP Tech Co., Ltd. (1)
3-10-17 Nishigotanda
Shinagawa-ku, Tokyo, 141-0031, Japan
Tel.: (81) 334924825
Web Site: www.dnp.co.jp/sp_tech
Outdoor Advertising Services
S.I.C.: 7312
N.A.I.C.S.: 541850

DNP Techno Polymer Co., Ltd. (1)
409 Toyofuta
Kashiwa, Chiba, 277-0872, Japan
Tel.: (81) 471321731
Web Site: www.dnp.co.jp/techno_polymer
Molded Plastic Products Mfr
S.I.C.: 3089
N.A.I.C.S.: 326199

DNP Technopack Co., Ltd. (1)
2-6-1 Hirosedai
Sayama, Saitama, 350-1328, Japan
Tel.: (81) 429550582
Containers & Packaging Products Mfr & Distr
S.I.C.: 2672
N.A.I.C.S.: 322220

DNP Technopack Tokai Co., Ltd. (1)
1646-39 Nasubigawa
Nakatsugawa, Gifu, 509-9132, Japan
Tel.: (81) 573686122
Packaging Paper Product Mfr
S.I.C.: 2679
N.A.I.C.S.: 322299

DNP Technopack Yokohama Co., Ltd. (1)
3500 Ikonobecho
Tsuzuki-ku, Yokohama, Kanagawa, 224-0053, Japan
Tel.: (81) 459331111
Fax: (81) 459340660
Commercial Printing Services
S.I.C.: 2759
N.A.I.C.S.: 323111

DNP Tohoku Co., Ltd. (1)
3-5-1 Nigatake
Miyagino-ku, Sendai, Miyagi, 983-0036, Japan
Tel.: (81) 22 783 4700
Fax: (81) 22 783 4710
Web Site: www.dnp-tohoku.co.jp
Packaging Product Mfr & Distr
S.I.C.: 2671
N.A.I.C.S.: 322220

DNP Total Process Maebashi Co., Ltd. (1)
1-2-12 Honmachi
Maebashi, Gunma, 371-0023, Japan
Tel.: (81) 272353366
Commercial Printing Services
S.I.C.: 2759
N.A.I.C.S.: 323111

DNP Total Process Nagaoka Co., Ltd. (1)
1-6-22 Fukuzumi
Nagaoka, Niigata, 940-0034, Japan
Tel.: (81) 258325400
Commercial Printing Services
S.I.C.: 2759
N.A.I.C.S.: 323111

DNP Total Process Warabi Co., Ltd. (1)
C/O Ips Jigyobu Warabi Factory
Warabi, Saitama, 335-0005, Japan
Tel.: (81) 484423752
Commercial Printing Services
S.I.C.: 2759
N.A.I.C.S.: 323111

DNP Trading Co., Ltd. (1)
2-1-11 Iidabashi Dmp Logistics Iidabashi Bldg
Chiyoda-ku, Tokyo, 102-0072, Japan
Tel.: (81) 332887630
Paper Products Whslr
S.I.C.: 5113
N.A.I.C.S.: 424130

DNP Uniprocess Co., Ltd. (1)
Dainipponinsatsuhonsha Bldg
Shinjuku-ku, Tokyo, 162-0062, Japan
Tel.: (81) 332663565
Web Site: www.dnp.co.jp/uniprocess
Commercial Printing Services
S.I.C.: 2759
N.A.I.C.S.: 323111

DT Fine Electronics Co., Ltd. (1)
1 Komukai Toshiba-cho
Saiwai-ku, Kawasaki, 212-8583, Japan
Tel.: (81) 44 549 8393
Fax: (81) 44 549 2781
Web Site: www.dtf.co.jp
Semiconductor Component Mfr
S.I.C.: 3674
N.A.I.C.S.: 334413

Hokkaido Coca-Cola Bottling Co., Ltd. (1)
1-2-1 Kiyota Ichijo
Kiyota-ku, Sapporo, Hokkaido, 004-8588, Japan JP
Tel.: (81) 0118882001 (53%)
Fax: (81) 118836143
Web Site: www.hokkaido.ccbc.co.jp
Emp.: 481
Mfr. & Sale of Beverages
S.I.C.: 2087
N.A.I.C.S.: 311930
Kenji Yabuki *(Pres)*

LIFESCAPE MARKETING CORPORATION (1)
1-11-11 Kudan-kita No 2 Funato Bldg
Chiyoda-ku, Tokyo, 102-0073, Japan
Tel.: (81) 335157088
Information Technology Consulting Services
S.I.C.: 7373
N.A.I.C.S.: 541512

Maruzen CHI Holdings Co., Ltd. (1)
3-9-2 Nihonbashi
Chuo-ku, Tokyo, 162-0846, Japan JP
Tel.: (81) 3 32720526 (52.3%)
Web Site: www.maruzen-chi.co.jp
3159—(TKS)
Holding Company
S.I.C.: 6719
N.A.I.C.S.: 551112
Tatsuya Nishimura *(Vice Chm & Pres)*

Subsidiary:

Maruzen Company, Limited (2)
1-9-18 Kaigan
Minato-ku, Tokyo, 105-0022, Japan JP
Tel.: (81) 332727211
Fax: (81) 332727268
E-Mail: webmaster@maruzen.co.jp
Web Site: www.maruzen.co.jp
5982—(TKS)
Emp.: 365
Academic Books, Journals & Online Information Publisher, Importer, Exporter & Sales; Stationery & Apparel Sales; Library Designing & Engineering Services
S.I.C.: 2731
N.A.I.C.S.: 511130
Eisuke Matsuo *(Pres)*

Subsidiaries:

Junkudo Co., Ltd. (3)
1-6-18 Sannomiyacho
Chuo-ku, Kobe, 650-0021, Japan
Tel.: (81) 7 8392 1001
Fax: (81) 7 8392 1024
Web Site: www.junkudo.co.jp
Books & Magazines Retailer
S.I.C.: 5942
N.A.I.C.S.: 451211

Maruzen Bookmates Co., Ltd. (3)
9-2 Nihombashi 3-chome
Chuo-ku, Tokyo, 103 8244, Japan JP
Tel.: (81) 3 3273 3601 (100%)
Fax: (81) 3 3273 3608
E-Mail: export@maruzen.co.jp
Web Site: www.maruzen.co.jp/corp/en/aboutus/contacts.html
Emp.: 200
Import, Export & Domestic Sales of Books, Journals, Stationery, Office Furniture & Sundries
S.I.C.: 5192
N.A.I.C.S.: 424920

Maruzen Bookstores Co., Ltd. (3)
27-5 Sakamachi
Shinjuku-ku, Tokyo, 160-0002, Japan
Tel.: (81) 3 6380 1291
Fax: (81) 3 6380 1295
Books & Magazines Retailer
S.I.C.: 5942
N.A.I.C.S.: 451211

Maruzen Publishing Co., Ltd. (3)
3-10 Nihonbashi 2-Chome
Chuo-ku, Tokyo, Japan
Tel.: (81) 3 6367 6035

Dai Nippon Printing Co., Ltd.—(Continued)

Fax: (81) 3 6367 6156
E-Mail: pub@maruzen.co.jp
Web Site: www.pub.maruzen.co.jp
Book Publishing Services
S.I.C.: 2731
N.A.I.C.S.: 511130

Maruzen System Service Co., Ltd. (3)
2 17 Kandajinbocho
Chiyoda-ku, Tokyo, 105-0022, Japan JP
Tel.: (81) 335123256 (100%)
Fax: (81) 335123270
E-Mail: pub@maruzen.co.jp
Web Site: www.maruzen.co.jp/corp/en/aboutus/contacts.html
Sale, Lease, Service & Customer Support of Computer & Information Technology Equipment; Applications Software Development
S.I.C.: 7359
N.A.I.C.S.: 532420

U.S. Subsidiary:

Maruzen International Co., Ltd. (3)
40 Seaview Dr 2nd Fl
Secaucus, NJ 07094 (100%)
Tel.: (201) 865-4400
Fax: (201) 865-4845
E-Mail: mic@maruzenusa.com
Web Site: www.maruzenusa.com
Emp.: 9
Publishers
S.I.C.: 5192
N.A.I.C.S.: 424920

Non-U.S. Branch:

Maruzen Co., Ltd. - London Office (3)
1st Fl 2 Thayer St
London, W1U 3JB, United Kingdom
Tel.: (44) 2074873865
E-Mail: london-office@maruzen.co.jp
Web Site: www.maruzen.co.jp
Emp.: 3
Publishing Services
S.I.C.: 7389
N.A.I.C.S.: 561410

Non-U.S. Subsidiaries:

Maruzen Kyoei Prince (3)
Wisma Kyoei Prince Bldg 2nd Fl 1 Jalan Jenderal
Sudirman Kav 3-4, Jakarta, Pusat, 10220, Indonesia
Tel.: (62) 215723171
Fax: (62) 215723011
Publishing Services
S.I.C.: 2731
N.A.I.C.S.: 511130

Maruzen Mega Pasaraya (3)
Mega Pasaraya 8th Fl Jalan Iskandarsyah II 2 Blok M
Kebayoran Baru, Jakarta, Selatan, Indonesia
Tel.: (62) 217260170
Fax: (62) 217204890
Web Site: www.pasaraya.co.id
Emp.: 1,000
Provider of Publishing Services
S.I.C.: 7389
N.A.I.C.S.: 561410

Maruzen Pasaraya Manggarai (3)
Pasara Manggarai 6th Fl
Jalan Sultan Agung 1
Manggarai, Jakarta, 12970, Indonesia (100%)
Tel.: (62) 218312510
Fax: (62) 21 83057233
Provider of Publishing Services
S.I.C.: 7389
N.A.I.C.S.: 561410

M's Communicate Co., Ltd (1)
3-5-20 Nishi Gotanda DNP Gotanda Building
Shinagawa-ku, Tokyo, 141-8001, Japan
Tel.: (81) 3 6431 3651
Fax: (81) 3 6431 3650
E-Mail: info@emscom.co.jp
Web Site: www.emscom.co.jp
Customer Relationship Management Services
S.I.C.: 8742
N.A.I.C.S.: 541611

NexantiS Corporation (1)
26-8 Nandomachi Yokoi Bldg 2F
Shinjuku-ku, Tokyo, 115-8001, Japan
Tel.: (81) 352494810
Fax: (81) 352494812
E-Mail: info@nexantis.net
Web Site: www.nexantis.co.jp
Business Software Development Services
S.I.C.: 7371
N.A.I.C.S.: 541511

OGUCHI BOOK BINDING & PRINTING CO., LTD. (1)
3-6 Chikumazawa Miyoshi-cho
Iruma-gun, Saitama, 354-0046, Japan
Tel.: (81) 49 259 7577
Fax: (81) 49 259 7741
E-Mail: info@obp1949.co.jp
Web Site: www.obp1949.co.jp
Books Binding & Printing Services
S.I.C.: 2732
N.A.I.C.S.: 323117

Sagami Yoki Co., Ltd. (1)
1000 Naruda
Odawara, Kanagawa, 250-0862, Japan
Tel.: (81) 465366633
Plastic Products Mfr
S.I.C.: 3089
N.A.I.C.S.: 326199

SHUFUNOTOMO Co., Ltd. (1)
9 Kanda Surugadai 2-chome
Chiyoda-ku, Tokyo, 101-0062, Japan
Tel.: (81) 3 5280 7500
Fax: (81) 3 5280 7568
E-Mail: international@shufunotomo.co.jp
Web Site: www.shufunotomo.co.jp
Women Magazines Publishing Services
S.I.C.: 2721
N.A.I.C.S.: 511120

TRC, Inc. (1)
1-1-25 Shin-Urashimacho Techno Wave 100 Bldg 8F
Kanagawa-ku, Yokohama, Kanagawa, 221-0031, Japan
Tel.: (81) 454503391
Books Distr
S.I.C.: 5192
N.A.I.C.S.: 424920

Uzumine Country Club Co., Ltd. (1)
1 Miyata Shioda
Sukagawa, Fukushima, 962-0711, Japan
Tel.: (81) 248792101
Golf Course Management Services
S.I.C.: 7999
N.A.I.C.S.: 713910

Yushodo Co., Ltd. (1)
27 Sakamachi
Shinjuku-ku, Tokyo, 160-0002, Japan
Tel.: (81) 3 3357 1411
Fax: (81) 3 3356 8730
E-Mail: intl@yushodo.co.jp
Web Site: www.yushodo.co.jp
Industrial Machinery & Equipment Distr
S.I.C.: 2731
N.A.I.C.S.: 511130
Mitsuo Nitta *(CEO)*

Yushodo (Kyoto) CO., Ltd. (1)
Kyoto Asahi Building Oike-dori
Yanaginobamba-kado
Nakagyo-ku, Kyoto, 604-8101, Japan
Tel.: (81) 75 222 0165
Fax: (81) 75 256 2032
E-Mail: kb@yushodo.co.jp
Book Publishing Services
S.I.C.: 2731
N.A.I.C.S.: 511130

U.S. Subsidiaries:

DNP (AMERICA), Inc. (1)
101 Uhland Rd Ste 210
San Marcos, TX 78666 (100%)
Tel.: (512) 753-7280
Fax: (512) 753-7299
E-Mail: customercare@dnpphoto.com
Web Site: www.dnpphoto.com
Emp.: 50
Printing Whslr
S.I.C.: 5111
N.A.I.C.S.: 424110

DNP Corporation USA (1)
335 Madison Ave Lbby 3
New York, NY 10017-4646 (100%)
Tel.: (212) 503-1850
Fax: (212) 286-1493
Web Site: www.dnp.co.jp/international/pack/index.html
Emp.: 14
Printing & Publishing Services
S.I.C.: 5111
N.A.I.C.S.: 424110

Subsidiaries:

DNP America, LLC (2)
335 Madison Ave 3rd Fl
New York, NY 10017
Tel.: (212) 503-1060
Fax: (212) 286-1501
E-Mail: decomaterials@dnpamerica.com
Web Site: www.dnpamerica.com
Precision Electronic Component Whslr
S.I.C.: 5084
N.A.I.C.S.: 423830

DNP Electronics America, LLC (2)
2391 Fenton St
Chula Vista, CA 91914
Tel.: (619) 397-6700
Fax: (619) 397-6739
Web Site: www.dnpamerica.com
Precision Electronic Component Mfr & Whslr
S.I.C.: 3679
N.A.I.C.S.: 334419
Toshiyuki Suzuki *(Pres)*

DNP Holding USA Corporation (1)
335 Madison Ave Fl 3
New York, NY 10017
Tel.: (212) 503-1860
Investment Management Services
S.I.C.: 6211
N.A.I.C.S.: 523999

DNP IMS America Corporation (1)
4524 Enterprise Dr NW
Concord, NC 28027
Tel.: (800) 814-4672
Fax: (704) 784-7196
Web Site: www.dnpribbons.com
Inked Ribbon Mfr
S.I.C.: 3579
N.A.I.C.S.: 339940
Keigo Hayakawa *(Pres)*
Mineo Yamauchi *(Sr VP-Ops)*

Unit:

DNP IMS America Corporation (2)
1001 Technology Dr
Mount Pleasant, PA 15666-1763 PA
Mailing Address:
PO Box 360294
Pittsburgh, PA 15251-6294
Tel.: (724) 696-7500
Fax: (724) 696-7555
Web Site: www.dnp.com
Emp.: 200
Inked Ribbon Mfr
S.I.C.: 3579
N.A.I.C.S.: 339940
Satoshi Kondo *(Sr VP)*

Non-U.S. Subsidiaries:

Dai Nippon Printing Co. (Australia) Pty. Ltd. (1)
Ste 1002 Level 10 St Martins Tower 31 Market St
Sydney, NSW, 2000, Australia (100%)
Tel.: (61) 292678166
Telex: 22151
Fax: (61) 292679533
Web Site: www.dnp.co.jp/international/pack/index.html
Emp.: 3
Sales of Printed Matter
S.I.C.: 7319
N.A.I.C.S.: 541890
Kazunori Daimaru *(Mng Dir)*

Dai Nippon Printing Co. (Hong Kong) Ltd. (1)
2 5/F Tsuen Wan Indus Center 220 248 Texaco Road
Tsuen Wan, NT, China (Hong Kong) (99%)
Tel.: (852) 24080188
Telex: 43801
Fax: (852) 24076201
E-Mail: info@dnp.com.hk
Emp.: 340
Publisher & Printer
S.I.C.: 2731
N.A.I.C.S.: 511130

Dai Nippon Printing Co. (Taiwan), Ltd. (1)
RM D 6F 44 Chung-Shan North Road Section 2
Taipei, 104, Taiwan (100%)
Tel.: (886) 223278311
Fax: (886) 223278283
Web Site: www.dnp.co.jp
Sales of Precision Electronic Components & Information Media Supplies
S.I.C.: 3679
N.A.I.C.S.: 334419

Dai Nippon Printing (Europa) GmbH (1)
Berliner Allee 26
40212 Dusseldorf, Germany (100%)
Tel.: (49) 2118620180
Telex: 8588382
Fax: (49) 21186201892
E-Mail: hossmann@dnpe.jis.de
Web Site: www.dnp.co.jp/international/cardprinter/contact_us/index.html
Emp.: 13
Sales of Printed Matter
S.I.C.: 7319
N.A.I.C.S.: 541890
Wilhelm Prange *(Mng Dir)*
Tadashi Yamazaki *(Mng Dir)*

DNP Denmark A/S (1)
Skruegangen 2
2690 Karlslunde, Denmark
Tel.: (45) 46165100
Fax: (45) 46165200
E-Mail: dnp@dnp.dk
Web Site: www.dnp-screens.com
Emp.: 100
Optical Projection Screens Distr
S.I.C.: 5043
N.A.I.C.S.: 423410
Niels Hermansen *(COO)*

DNP International Trading (Shanghai) Co., Ltd. (1)
603B No 1376 Nanjing West Road
Shanghai, 200040, China
Tel.: (86) 2162798511
Fax: (86) 2162798507
Commercial Printing Services
S.I.C.: 2759
N.A.I.C.S.: 323111

DNP Photo Imaging Europe SAS (1)
Z I Paris Nord II 305 rue de la Belle Etoile
BP 51077
95948 Roissy-en-France, France
Tel.: (33) 1 49 38 65 50
Fax: (33) 1 48 63 80 69
E-Mail: contact@dnpphoto.eu
Web Site: www.dnpphoto.eu
Emp.: 47
Photo Imaging Products Distr
S.I.C.: 5043
N.A.I.C.S.: 423410
Roch Hollande *(Pres)*

DNP Photomask Europe S.p.A. (1)
Via C Olivetti 2/A
20041 Agrate Brianza, Italy
Tel.: (39) 03965493300
E-Mail: dpe_pm_group@fml.micro.dnp.co.jp
Web Site: www.dnp.co.jp/semi/e/mask/contact.html
Photomasks Mfr & Whslr
S.I.C.: 3861
N.A.I.C.S.: 325992

DNP Photomask Technology Taiwan Co., Ltd. (1)
6 Li Hsing 7th Road
Hsin-chu, 30078, Taiwan
Tel.: (886) 36662877
Fax: (886) 36662878
Electronic Device Mfr
S.I.C.: 3679
N.A.I.C.S.: 334419

DNP Plastic Molding (Shanghai) Co., Ltd. (1)
888-2-1-A Taishunlu Anting Zhen Jiading Qu
Shanghai, China
Tel.: (86) 21 3958 7045
Fax: (86) 21 3958 7049
Plastic Products Mfr
S.I.C.: 3089

N.A.I.C.S.: 326199

DNP (Singapore) Pte. Ltd. (1)
4 Pandwan Crescent
Singapore, 128475, Singapore (100%)
Tel.: (65) 64697611
Telex: 37562
Fax: (65) 64668486
Web Site: www.dnp.co.jp/international/cardprinter/products/pdf/pamphlet_product_line_up.pdf
Emp.: 17
Sales of Printed Matter
S.I.C.: 7319
N.A.I.C.S.: 541890
Fengoku Shin *(Mng Dir)*

DNP (UK) Co. Ltd. (1)
4th Fl 27 Throgmorton St
London, EC2N 2AQ, United Kingdom (100%)
Tel.: (44) 2075882088
Telex: 299855
Fax: (44) 2075882089
Web Site: www.dnp.co.jp/eng/corporate/brochure_pdf/dnpall.pdf
Emp.: 3
Sales of Printed Matter
S.I.C.: 7319
N.A.I.C.S.: 541890
Teiuomi Yoshino *(Mng Dir)*

P.T. Dai Nippon Printing Indonesia (1)
Kawasan Industri Pulogadung Jalan Pulogadung Kaveling II
Block H No 2 3, Jakarta, Timur, 13920, Indonesia (51%)
Tel.: (62) 14605790
Telex: 63694
Fax: (62) 14619934
Web Site: www.dnp.co.jp/international/pack/index.html
Emp.: 2,000
Mfr., Printing & Sale of Printed Matter
S.I.C.: 2731
N.A.I.C.S.: 511130

Tien Wah Press (Pte.) Ltd. (1)
4 Pandan Crescent
Singapore, 128475, Singapore (84.6%)
Tel.: (65) 64666222
Telex: 21606
Fax: (65) 64693894
Web Site: www.twpsin.com
Emp.: 850
Mfr. & Sale of Printed Matter; Printing Services
S.I.C.: 2731
N.A.I.C.S.: 511130
Andrew Yo *(Dir-Mktg-Sls)*

TWP Sendirian Berhad (1)
89 Jalan Tampoi
Kawasan Perindustrian Tampoi, 80350
Johor Bahru, Malaysia (100%)
Tel.: (60) 72369899
Fax: (60) 72363148
Web Site: www.twpsip.com
Emp.: 2,000
Provider of Corrugated & Solid Fiber Boxes
S.I.C.: 2653
N.A.I.C.S.: 322211
Makoto Takakura *(Mng Dir)*

DAI NIPPON TORYO CO., LTD.
1-124 Nishikujo 6-chome
Konohana-ku, Osaka, 554-0012, Japan
Tel.: (81) 664666690
Fax: (81) 664667797
Web Site: www.dnt.co.jp
Year Founded: 1929
4611—(TKS)
Sls.: $779,064,000
Assets: $740,168,000
Liabilities: $528,451,000
Net Worth: $211,717,000
Earnings: $13,112,000
Emp.: 665
Fiscal Year-end: 03/31/13
Business Description:
Industrial, Automobile, Refinishing, Marine & Home Paints & Coating Mfr; Paint Creation Machinery Mfr
S.I.C.: 2851
N.A.I.C.S.: 325510
Personnel:
Fumitaka Yamashita *(Chm)*
Toshijiro Iwasa *(Pres)*
Board of Directors:
Fumitaka Yamashita
Toshijiro Iwasa

Subsidiaries:

BO- Chemical Co.,Ltd (1)
142 Tobara Kasuyamachi
Kasuya, Fukuoka, 811-2312, Japan
Tel.: (81) 929382321
Fax: (81) 929386278
Paint Mfr
S.I.C.: 2851
N.A.I.C.S.: 325510

Chiba Kako Co., Ltd. (1)
4-1 Yakoshimmei Sakaemachi
Imba-gun, Chiba, 270-1501, Japan
Tel.: (81) 476957711
Fax: (81) 476957710
Paint & Coating Mfr
S.I.C.: 2851
N.A.I.C.S.: 325510

Dai Nippon Toryo Hanbai Co., Ltd. (1)
6-1-124 Nishikujo
Konohana-Ku, Osaka, 554-0012, Japan
Tel.: (81) 664666653
Fax: (81) 664666654
Paint Sales
S.I.C.: 5198
N.A.I.C.S.: 424950

Daia Keiko Co., Ltd. (1)
1-13-5 Nishigotanda
Shinagawa-Ku, Tokyo, 141-0031, Japan
Tel.: (81) 334924461
Fax: (81) 334926865
Web Site: www.daiakeiko.co.jp
Fluorescent Lamp Mfr
S.I.C.: 3641
N.A.I.C.S.: 335110

DN LIGHTING Co., Ltd. (1)
1-13-5 Nishigotanda
Shinagawaku, Tokyo, 141-0031, Japan
Tel.: (81) 334924323
Fax: (81) 3 3492 7123
E-Mail: info@dnlighting.co.jp
Web Site: www.dnlighting.co.jp
Fluorescent Lamp Sales
S.I.C.: 5063
N.A.I.C.S.: 423610

DNT Business Service Co., Ltd. (1)
6-1-124 Nishikujo
Konohana-ku, Osaka, 554-0012, Japan
Tel.: (81) 664666665
Fax: (81) 664687068
Emp.: 23
Accounting Services
S.I.C.: 8721
N.A.I.C.S.: 541219
Norihiro Nagata *(Gen Mgr)*

DNT Service Co., Ltd. (1)
6-4-37 Kizuri
Higashi-osaka, Osaka, 577-0827, Japan
Tel.: (81) 667272376
Fax: (81) 667200934
Paint Tinting Services
S.I.C.: 7389
N.A.I.C.S.: 561990

Nitto Chemical Co., Ltd. (1)
209-3 Ko Kaminozoki-machi
Nagaoka, Niigata, 940-2033, Japan
Tel.: (81) 258469037
Fax: (81) 258466596
Web Site: www.nitto-c.co.jp
Industrial Chemicals Mfr
S.I.C.: 2899
N.A.I.C.S.: 325998

Nitto Engineering Co., Ltd. (1)
5-13-23 Kamata Tokyu Reit Kamata Building 2F
Ota-Ku, Tokyo, 144-0052, Japan
Tel.: (81) 357100601
Fax: (81) 357100606
Engineering Services
S.I.C.: 8711
N.A.I.C.S.: 541330

Nitto Fudohsan Co., Ltd. (1)
Dai Nippon Toryo Co Limited 6-1-124 Nishikujo
Konohana-ku, Osaka, 554-0012, Japan
Tel.: (81) 664666682
Fax: (81) 664662102
Real Estate Management Services
S.I.C.: 6531
N.A.I.C.S.: 531390

Nitto Sanwa Toryo Co., Ltd. (1)
3-3-1 Ishibeguchi
Konan, Aichi, 520-3114, Japan
Tel.: (81) 748778825
Fax: (81) 748776636
Paint Mfr
S.I.C.: 2851
N.A.I.C.S.: 325510

Nitto Service Co., Ltd (1)
4-12-24 Mokuzaidori Mihara-Ku Osaka Mokuzai Kogyo Danchi
Sakai, Osaka, 587-0042, Japan
Tel.: (81) 723622123
Fax: (81) 723629186
Paint Mfr & Sales
S.I.C.: 2851
N.A.I.C.S.: 325510

Okayama Kako Co., Ltd. (1)
152-6 Omukai Nishi Kibichuocho
Kaga, Okayama, 716-1554, Japan
Tel.: (81) 866556234
Fax: (81) 866556235
Paint Mfr
S.I.C.: 2851
N.A.I.C.S.: 325510

SINLOIHI Co., Ltd. (1)
2-19-2 Dai
Kamakura, Kanagawa, 247-8550, Japan
Tel.: (81) 467432121
Fax: (81) 467 45 4708
E-Mail: info@sinloihi.co.jp
Web Site: www.sinloihi.co.jp
Fluorescent Pigment Mfr
S.I.C.: 2819
N.A.I.C.S.: 325130
Shin Emi *(Pres)*

Sunday Paint Co., Ltd. (1)
6-1-124 Nishikujo
Konohana-Ku, Osaka, 554-0012, Japan
Tel.: (81) 664666700
Fax: (81) 664662751
Paint Sales
S.I.C.: 5198
N.A.I.C.S.: 424950

Non-U.S. Subsidiaries:

AJISCO-DNT (Ningbo) Paint Co.,Ltd. (1)
Building 2 No 25 Gangxi Avenue West Area
Ningbo Free Trade Zone, Ningbo, Zhejiang, 315806, China
Tel.: (86) 57486822006
Paint Mfr & Sales
S.I.C.: 2851
N.A.I.C.S.: 325510

Dai Nippon Toryo Mexicana S. A. DE C. V. (1)
Prol Avenue Juarez Sur No 801 Int 3 Centro
San Francisco de los Romos, Aguascalientes, 20300, Mexico
Tel.: (52) 4659672454
Fax: (52) 4659672458
Paint Mfr & Distr
S.I.C.: 2851
N.A.I.C.S.: 325510
Wataru Fujie *(Gen Mgr)*

DNT (Shanghai) Co.,Ltd. (1)
No 8 Dongye Road Dongjing Town
Songjiang District, Shanghai, 201689, China
Tel.: (86) 2157670682
Fax: (86) 2157670681
Paint Mfr & Sales
S.I.C.: 2851
N.A.I.C.S.: 325510

DNT Singapore Pte. Ltd. (1)
No 48 Tanjong Penjuru
Singapore, 609033, Singapore SG (100%)
Tel.: (65) 62653344
Fax: (65) 62689923
E-Mail: dntsmg@dnt.com.sg
Web Site: www.dnt.com.sg
Emp.: 40
Paints & Coating Mfr; Paint Creation Machinery Mfr
S.I.C.: 2851
N.A.I.C.S.: 325510

Thai DNT Paint Manufacturing Co., Ltd. (1)
38/25 Moo 5 Sukhumvit Road Leam Chabang Industrial Estate
Si Racha, Chon Buri, 20230, Thailand
Tel.: (66) 38494865
Fax: (66) 38494864
Web Site: www.thaidnt.com
Paint & Coating Mfr
S.I.C.: 2851
N.A.I.C.S.: 325510

DAI THIEN LOC CORPORATION
Group A Road 22 Song Than 2 Industrial zone
Di An, Thu Dau Mot, Binh Duong, Vietnam
Tel.: (84) 650 3732 981
Fax: (84) 650 3732 980
Web Site: www.daithienloc.com.vn
Year Founded: 2001
DTL—(HOSE)
Sales Range: $75-99.9 Million
Emp.: 491
Business Description:
Steel Sheet Mfr
S.I.C.: 3399
N.A.I.C.S.: 331110
Personnel:
Thanh Nghia Nguyen *(Pres & Gen Dir)*

DAIBIRU CORPORATION
3-3-23 Nakanoshima
Kita-ku, Osaka, 530-0005, Japan
Tel.: (81) 664411932
Web Site: www.daibiru.co.jp
8806—(TKS)
Rev.: $376,255,000
Assets: $3,438,743,000
Liabilities: $2,048,442,000
Net Worth: $1,390,301,000
Earnings: $53,680,000
Emp.: 2,138
Fiscal Year-end: 03/31/13
Business Description:
Office Building Leasing, Residential Property Planning Services, Real Estate, Design & Supervision for Buildings and Facilities, Building Management, Lease Agreements, Facilities Management, Cleaning & Security Services
S.I.C.: 6512
N.A.I.C.S.: 531120
Personnel:
Takehiko Yamamoto *(Pres)*
Yoichi Hayashi *(Exec Officer)*
Yoichi Ibayashi *(Sr Mng Exec Officer)*
Noboru Kitazawa *(Exec Officer)*
Junichi Narita *(Mng Exec Officer)*
Yoshihiro Nishiguchi *(Mng Exec Officer)*
Katsumi Tamai *(Sr Mng Exec Officer)*
Kensuke Tanaka *(Exec Officer)*
Takeo Yada *(Mng Exec Officer)*
Board of Directors:
Hirokazu Hatta
Yoichi Ibayashi
Junichi Narita
Akira Takamatsu
Katsumi Tamai
Takeo Yada
Takehiko Yamamoto
Transfer Agent:
Sumitomo Mitsui Trust Bank Limited
1-4-1 Marunouchi Chiyoda-ku
Tokyo, Japan

Daibiru Corporation—(Continued)

Subsidiaries:

Daibiru Facility Management Ltd. **(1)**
3-3-23 Nakanoshima Dai Building
Kita-ku, Osaka, 530-0005, Japan
Tel.: (81) 6 6441 6373
Fax: (81) 6 6441 6376
Facility Management Services
S.I.C.: 8744
N.A.I.C.S.: 561210

Mitsui O.S.K. Kosan Co., Ltd **(1)**
Wakamatsu Building
Chuo-Ku, Tokyo, 103-0023, Japan (51%)
Tel.: (81) 335175300
Fax: (81) 335175311
Web Site: www.mo-kosan.co.jp
Emp.: 180
Real Estate Agents & Brokers Offices
S.I.C.: 6531
N.A.I.C.S.: 531210

Subsidiaries:

Kosan Kanri Service Co., Ltd. **(2)**
3-6 Nihonbashihoncho 3-Chome
Chuo-Ku, Tokyo, 103-0023, Japan
Tel.: (81) 335175207
Fax: (81) 335175311
E-Mail: manabu.wada@mo-kosan.co.jp
Office Space Rental & Real Estate Management Services
S.I.C.: 6512
N.A.I.C.S.: 531120

Kosan Kanri Service West Co., Ltd. **(2)**
2-4 Tosabori 2-chomeNishi-ku
Osaka, 550-0001, Japan
Tel.: (81) 664416491
Fax: (81) 664418073
Office Space Rental & Real Estate Management Services
S.I.C.: 6531
N.A.I.C.S.: 531210

Santo Tatemono Service Co., Ltd. **(1)**
Nishiku Posapori 2-4
Osaka, Japan (100%)
Tel.: (81) 664418490
Fax: (81) 66405714
Other Services to Buildings & Dwellings
S.I.C.: 7349
N.A.I.C.S.: 561790
Hiroyuki Sato *(Pres)*

DAIBOCHI PLASTIC AND PACKAGING INDUSTRY BHD.

Kompleks Daibochi Plastic Lot 3 & 7
Air Keroh Indus Estate Phase IV
75450 Melaka, Malaysia
Mailing Address:
PO Box 263
75750 Melaka, Malaysia
Tel.: (60) 62312746
Fax: (60) 62328988
E-Mail: info@daibochiplastic.com
Web Site: www.daibochiplastic.com
DAIBOCI—(KLS)
Rev.: $91,408,356
Assets: $77,134,982
Liabilities: $27,809,256
Net Worth: $49,325,726
Earnings: $8,204,558
Fiscal Year-end: 12/31/12
Business Description:
Plastic Packaging Mfr
S.I.C.: 2671
N.A.I.C.S.: 326112
Personnel:
Soo Koon Lim *(Mng Dir)*
Gaik Hong Tan *(Sec)*
Board of Directors:
P. James Edwin
Caroline Choo Bee Ang
Fu Joe Heng
Soo Koon Lim
Chan Tian Low
Geoff Jin Wei Low
Soon Lim Wong

Subsidiary:

Daibochi Land Sdn. Bhd. **(1)**
D8/08 Plz Jayamuda Jalan Pelanduk Putih
75300 Melaka, Malaysia
Tel.: (60) 62835442
Fax: (60) 62845740
Emp.: 5
Residential Property Development Services
S.I.C.: 6531
N.A.I.C.S.: 531390

Non-U.S. Subsidiary:

Daibochi Australia Pty. Ltd. **(1)**
18 Capital Court
Braeside, VIC, 3195, Australia
Tel.: (61) 385860400
Fax: (61) 395871552
E-Mail: sales@daibochi.com.au
Web Site: www.daibochi.com.au
Emp.: 4
Flexible Packaging Products Mfr
S.I.C.: 2671
N.A.I.C.S.: 326112
Paul Quinn *(Mng Dir)*

DAICEL CORPORATION

Mainichi Intecio 3-4-5 Umeda
Kita-ku, Osaka, 530 0001, Japan
Tel.: (81) 6 6342 6111
Telex: 5374213
Fax: (81) 6 6342 6118
Web Site: www.daicel.com
Year Founded: 1919
4202—(TKS)
Sls.: $3,943,643,000
Assets: $5,076,632,000
Liabilities: $2,582,305,000
Net Worth: $2,494,327,000
Earnings: $169,092,000
Emp.: 9,233
Fiscal Year-end: 03/31/13
Business Description:
Cellulosic Derivatives, Organic Chemicals, Plastics, Films, Membranes, Medical Products & Rocket Propellants Mfr
S.I.C.: 2899
N.A.I.C.S.: 325199
Personnel:
Daisuke Ogawa *(Chm)*
Misao Fudaba *(Pres & CEO)*
Masayuki Mune *(Mng Exec Officer)*
Masumi Fukuda *(Sr Mng Exec Officer)*
Dieter Heckmann *(Exec Officer)*
Yuji Iguchi *(Mng Exec Officer)*
Yasunori Iwai *(Exec Officer)*
Hidekage Kojima *(Exec Officer)*
Tetsuzo Miyazaki *(Sr Mng Exec Officer)*
Hisao Nishimura *(Exec Officer)*
Yoshimi Ogawa *(Exec Officer)*
Board of Directors:
Daisuke Ogawa
Misao Fudaba
Masumi Fukuda
Noboru Goto
Shigetaka Komori
Yuichi Miura
Yoshimi Ogawa
Akishige Okada
Transfer Agent:
The Chuo Mitsui Trust & Banking Company Limited
33-1, Shiba 3-chome
Minato-ku, Tokyo, Japan

Subsidiaries:

Daicel Aboshi Sangyo Co. Ltd. **(1)**
1239 Shinzaike Aboshi Ku Himeji Shi
Hyogo, 671 1281, Japan (45%)
Tel.: (81) 792743621
Fax: (81) 792742097
Web Site: www.daicel.co.jp/group/index_e.html
Mfr. & Distributor of Magnesium Hydroxide
S.I.C.: 2819
N.A.I.C.S.: 325180

Daicel Arai Chemical Ltd. **(1)**
1 1 Shinko Cho Myoko shi
Niigata, 9448550, Japan (100%)
Tel.: (81) 255723123
Fax: (81) 255720388
Web Site: www.daicel.co.jp/group/index_e.html
Emp.: 400
Mfr. of Chlorinated Compounds
S.I.C.: 2819
N.A.I.C.S.: 325180
Mashaho Naito *(Plant Mgr)*

Daicel Chemical Industries Ltd. **(1)**
1 4 Higashisakae 2 Chome
Ohtake Shi, Hiroshima, 739 0695, Japan (100%)
Tel.: (81) 827536721
Fax: (81) 827531839
Web Site: www.daicel.co.jp/group/index_e.html
Emp.: 300
Administrative Operations
S.I.C.: 8741
N.A.I.C.S.: 561110

Plant:

Daicel Chemical Industries, Ltd. - Aboshi Plant **(2)**
1239 Shinzaike
Aboshi-ku, Himeji, Hyogo, 671-1281, Japan
Tel.: (81) 79 273 7001
Fax: (81) 79 273 7661
Specialty Chemicals Mfr
S.I.C.: 2869
N.A.I.C.S.: 325199

Daicel Chemicals Co Ltd **(1)**
1 Teppo Cho Sakai Shi
Osaka, 590 8501, Japan (100%)
Tel.: (81) 722273088
Fax: (81) 722273247
Emp.: 400
Mfr. & Distribution of Oligomer Products, Acryl Resins & Polyesther Resins
S.I.C.: 2821
N.A.I.C.S.: 325211

Daicel-Cytec Company, Ltd. **(1)**
3-5-7 Ariake Toc Ariake E Tower 9f
Koto, Tokyo, 135-0063, Japan
Tel.: (81) 3 3527 7890
Fax: (81) 3 3527 7894
Web Site: www.daicel-cytec.com
Polyester Resin Mfr
S.I.C.: 2821
N.A.I.C.S.: 325211

Daicel Finance Ltd. **(1)**
3 13 Azuchi Machi 2 Chome
Chuo Ku, Osaka, Japan (100%)
Tel.: (81) 662634806
Fax: (81) 662634835
Web Site: www.daicel.co.jp/kaisya/jigyo/osakaeie.htm
Emp.: 3
Fund Manager
S.I.C.: 6799
N.A.I.C.S.: 523920

Daicel FineChem Ltd. **(1)**
Kyobashi 1 Chome Bldg 1-13-1
Tokyo, 1040031, Japan (100%)
Tel.: (81) 335671871
Fax: (81) 335671876
Web Site: www.daicelfinechemicals.jp
Emp.: 60
Mfr. of Resin-Based Construction Materials
S.I.C.: 2821
N.A.I.C.S.: 325211

Daicel Novafoam Ltd. **(1)**
36-1 1 Oaza Karita Obuse Cho
Kamitakai Gun, Nagano, 3810211, Japan (100%)
Tel.: (81) 262472557
Fax: (81) 262472281
E-Mail: naganoba@annexis.ne.jp
Web Site: www.daicel.co.jp/group/index_e.html
Emp.: 80
Mfr. of Foam Packaging Materials
S.I.C.: 3089
N.A.I.C.S.: 326199

Daicel Ohtake Sangyo Co., Ltd. **(1)**
1-4 Higashisakae 2-chome
Otake, Hiroshima, 739-0695, Japan
Tel.: (81) 827536721
Chemical Products Mfr
S.I.C.: 2869
N.A.I.C.S.: 325199

Daicel Pack Systems Ltd. **(1)**
2-8-1 Kandasudacho Sudachomk Bldg 5f
Chiyoda-Ku, Tokyo, 101-0041, Japan
Tel.: (81) 3 5209 7900
Fax: (81) 3 3255 7800
Web Site: www.daicel.com
Emp.: 23
Plastic Molded Products Mfr
S.I.C.: 2671
N.A.I.C.S.: 322220

Daicel Packsystems Ltd. **(1)**
25 Kasumigaseki
3 Chome Chiyoda K, Tokyo, 100 6077, Japan (100%)
Tel.: (81) 335073188
Fax: (81) 335073172
Web Site: www.daicel.co.jp/group/index_e.html
Vacuum & Pressure-Molded Plastic Products Mfr
S.I.C.: 3089
N.A.I.C.S.: 326199

Daicel Polymer Co Ltd **(1)**
East Bldg 2 18 1 Konan
Tokyo, 108 8231, Japan (100%)
Tel.: (81) 367118401
Fax: (81) 367118408
Web Site: www.daicelpolymer.com
Sales Range: $10-24.9 Million
Emp.: 200
Mfr. of ABS Resins
S.I.C.: 2821
N.A.I.C.S.: 325211
Yagi Mikio *(Mgr)*

Daicel Polymer, Ltd. **(1)**
JR Shinagawa East Bldg 14 Fl 2-18-1
Kohnan Minato-Ku
Minato ku, Tokyo, 108 8230, Japan (100%)
Tel.: (81) 367118401
Fax: (81) 367118408
Web Site: www.daicelpolymer.com
Emp.: 160
Mfr & Sales of Polymer Alloys
S.I.C.: 3089
N.A.I.C.S.: 326199
Mikio Yagi *(Pres)*

Daicel Safety Systems, Inc. **(1)**
805 Umaba Ibogawa Cho Ibo Gun
Hyogo, 6711681, Japan (100%)
Tel.: (81) 791725411
Fax: (81) 791725466
Web Site: www.daicel.co.jp/group/index_e.html
Emp.: 1,000
Mfr. of Automobile Airbag Inflators
S.I.C.: 2899
N.A.I.C.S.: 325998
Kawaguchi Naotaka *(Gen Mgr)*

Daicel Sakai Jitsugyo Co. Ltd. **(1)**
1 Teppo Cho Sakai Shi
Osaka, 590 0905, Japan (50%)
Tel.: (81) 22273271
Fax: (81) 722273471
Web Site: www.daicel.co.jp/guj/gujfe.html
Emp.: 100
Administrative Operations & Management of Buildings; Manufacturer and Distribution of Mats.
S.I.C.: 8741
N.A.I.C.S.: 561110

Daicel-UCB Co. Ltd. **(1)**
Ochanomizu Kyoun Bldg 2
Kandasurugadai 2 Chome, Tokyo, 101 0062, Japan (100%)
Tel.: (81) 352824101
Fax: (81) 352824102
Web Site: www.daicel.co.jp/guj/gujfe.html
Mfr. of Ultraviolet & Electron Beam Curable Resins
S.I.C.: 2821
N.A.I.C.S.: 325211

Daicel Value Coating Ltd. **(1)**
12 1 Kanzaki Cho Amagasaki Shi
Hyogo, 6610964, Japan (100%)
Tel.: (81) 664971108
Fax: (81) 664971123
Web Site: www.daicel.co.jp/
Emp.: 180
Mfr. of Industrial Films & Processing of Polystyrene Products

S.I.C.: 3086
N.A.I.C.S.: 326140

Daicen Membrane-Systems Ltd. (1)
Shinjuku Estate Bldg 34 15
Shinjuku 1 Chome, Tokyo, 160 0022, Japan (100%)
Tel.: (81) 333545081
Fax: (81) 333545080
E-Mail: tokyo@daicen.co.jp
Web Site: www.daicen.co.jp
Emp.: 68
Mfr., Processing & Marketing of Separation Membranes
S.I.C.: 2899
N.A.I.C.S.: 325998

Dainichi Chemical Corp. (1)
23-11 Kuidesaku Jobanshimofunaomachi
Iwaki, Fukushima, 972-8312, Japan
Tel.: (81) 246445255
Specialty Chemicals Mfr & Distr
S.I.C.: 2899
N.A.I.C.S.: 325199

Japan Shotshell Ltd. (1)
760 Hamagawa-machi
Takasaki, Gunma, 370 0081, Japan (100%)
Tel.: (81) 27 343 8700
Fax: (81) 273430723
E-Mail: hi_wakita@jp.daicel.com
Web Site: www.daicel.com
Emp.: 60
Mfr & Distr of Shell Cartridges for Hunting
S.I.C.: 3482
N.A.I.C.S.: 332992
Koji Kamimura *(Pres)*

Kyodo Sakusan Co. Ltd. (1)
7-3S Shinbashi 3-chome
Minato-ku, Tokyo, 105 0004, Japan (54%)
Tel.: (81) 335037503
Fax: (81) 335037515
Web Site: www.daicel.co.jp/group/index_e.html
Emp.: 3
Acetic Acid Mfr & Distr
S.I.C.: 2899
N.A.I.C.S.: 325199

Kyoei Shokusan Co. Ltd. (1)
2 15 Kawara Machi 3 Chome
Chuo Ku, Osaka, 541-0048, Japan (45%)
Tel.: (81) 662034770
Fax: (81) 662034611
E-Mail: kyoueishokusanosaka@ganna.ocn.ne.jp
Web Site: www.daicel.co.jp/guj/gujfe.html
Emp.: 10
Insurance & Travel Agency
S.I.C.: 6411
N.A.I.C.S.: 524298

Y.S. Logistics Service Co., Ltd. (1)
13 4 Matsuya Yamatogawa Dori 1 Chome
Sakai Shi, Osaka, 590 0902, Japan (60%)
Tel.: (81) 55370367
Fax: (81) 5537 0376
Web Site: www.ys-butsuyu.co.jp
Emp.: 40
Warehousing Packing & Transporting
S.I.C.: 4226
N.A.I.C.S.: 493190

Joint Ventures:

Daicel-Evonik Ltd. (1)
Shinjuku Monolith 13F 2-3-1 Nishi-shinjuku
Shinjuku-ku, Tokyo, 163-0913, Japan
Tel.: (81) 3 5324 6331
Fax: (81) 3 5324 6335
Web Site: www.daicel-evonik.com
Sales Range: $25-49.9 Million
Emp.: 25
Mfr & Distr of Polymers
S.I.C.: 2821
N.A.I.C.S.: 325211
Ulrich Sieler *(Chm)*
Masanori Sakano *(Pres)*

Polyplastics Co., Ltd. (1)
JR Shinagawa E Bldg 18-1 Konan 2 Chome Minato-Ku
Tokyo, NSW, 2150, Japan
Tel.: (81) 367118600
Fax: (81) 367118606
Web Site: www.polyplastics.com
Sales Range: $1-4.9 Billion
Emp.: 1,500
Mfr. & Distributor of Acetal Polymers & PBT Resins; Joint Venture of Daicel Chemical Industries, Ltd. (55%) & Ticona GmbH (45%)
S.I.C.: 2821
N.A.I.C.S.: 325211
Noboru Goto *(Pres & CEO)*

Joint Venture:

WinTech Polymer Ltd. (2)
JR Shinagawa East Building 18-1 Konan 2-chome Minato-ku
Minato-ku, Tokyo, 108 8280, Japan
Tel.: (81) 367118610
Fax: (81) 367118616
Web Site: www.wintechpolymer.co.jp
Emp.: 150
Mfr. & Distribution of Polymer Plastic Products; Joint Venture Between Polyplastics Co. Ltd. (60%) & (Teijin Ltd. (40%)
S.I.C.: 3089
N.A.I.C.S.: 326199

Non-U.S. Subsidiaries:

Polyplastics Asia Pacific Sdn. Bhd. (2)
50 5 3A 5th Fl Wisma UOA Damansara 50 Jalan D
50490 Kuala Lumpur, Malaysia (100%)
Tel.: (60) 327332599
Fax: (60) 327736700
E-Mail: info@polyplastics.com
Web Site: www.polyplastics.com
Sales Range: $100-124.9 Million
Emp.: 250
Mfr. of Plastic Materials
S.I.C.: 2821
N.A.I.C.S.: 325211
Sideti Nakano *(Gen Mgr)*

Polyplastics Asia Pacific Singapore Pte. Ltd. (2)
6 Temasek Blvd 25 01 Suntec Tower 4
Singapore, 38986, Singapore (100%)
Tel.: (65) 67373693
Fax: (65) 67377823
E-Mail: pauline.khoo@polyplastics.com
Web Site: www.polyplastics.com
Sales Range: $10-24.9 Million
Emp.: 18
Provider of Plastic Materials
S.I.C.: 2821
N.A.I.C.S.: 325211
Jun Uchida *(Mng Dir)*

Polyplastics China Ltd. (2)
17th Fl Soundwill Plz
38 Russell St, Causeway Bay, China (Hong Kong)
Tel.: (852) 28029488
Fax: (852) 28249913
E-Mail: pcl.office@polyplastics.com
Web Site: www.polyplastics.com
Emp.: 30
Provider of Plastic Materials
S.I.C.: 2821
N.A.I.C.S.: 325211
Steve Ma *(Mng Dir)*
Tsuneyasu Nakashima *(Mng Dir)*
Yukiteru Shimura *(Mng Dir)*

Non-U.S. Subsidiary:

Polyplastics Shanghai Ltd. (3)
9th Fl Wheelock Square No 1717 Nan Jing West Rd
Jing'an District, Shanghai, 200040, China
Tel.: (86) 2132568600
Fax: (86) 2132561800
Web Site: www.polyplastics.com
Emp.: 71
Plastic Products Distr
S.I.C.: 5162
N.A.I.C.S.: 424610
Masaaki Nakamura *(Mng Dir)*

Polyplastics Marketing (T) Ltd. (2)
Lake Rajada Office Complex 15th Fl
Bangkok, 10110, Thailand (100%)
Tel.: (66) 22640447
Fax: (66) 22640449
E-Mail: poly@polyplastics.com
Web Site: www.polyplastics.com
Sales Range: Less than $1 Million
Emp.: 39
Provider of POM Products
S.I.C.: 3089
N.A.I.C.S.: 326199
Minoiu Hirose *(Mng Dir)*

Polyplastics Taiwan Co., Ltd. (2)
9th Fl 26 Min Quan E Rd Section 2
Taipei, 104, Taiwan TW
Tel.: (886) 225253116
Fax: (886) 225253116
E-Mail: tim.huang@polyplastics.com
Web Site: www.polyplastics.com
Sales Range: $50-74.9 Million
Emp.: 160
POM Resin Mfr
S.I.C.: 2821
N.A.I.C.S.: 325211
Tim Huang *(Mgr-Sls)*

Polyplastics Trading (Shanghai) Ltd. (2)
9th Fl Wheelock Square No 1717 Nan Jing West Road
Shanghai, Jing'an District, 200040, China (100%)
Tel.: (86) 21 3256 8600
Fax: (86) 21 3256 1800
Web Site: www.polyplastics.com
Sales Range: $25-49.9 Million
Emp.: 10
Importing & Selling Various Engineering Plastics
S.I.C.: 3089
N.A.I.C.S.: 326199

U.S. Subsidiary:

Daicel (U.S.A.) Inc. (1)
1 Parker Plz Sixth Fl 400 Kelby St
Fort Lee, NJ 07024
Tel.: (201) 461-4466
Fax: (201) 461-2776
E-Mail: inquiry@daicel.com
Web Site: www.daicel.com
Emp.: 4
U.S. Marketing Operations
S.I.C.: 5169
N.A.I.C.S.: 424690
Hiroki Takeuchi *(Pres)*

Subsidiaries:

Chiral Technologies Inc. (2)
800 N 5 Points Rd
West Chester, PA 19380 (100%)
Tel.: (610) 594-2100
Fax: (610) 594-2325
E-Mail: chiral@chiraltech.com
Web Site: www.chiraltech.com
Sales Range: $10-24.9 Million
Emp.: 25
Develops & Supplies Bulk Chiral Stationary Phase Media for Process Scale Chromatographic Separations
S.I.C.: 5047
N.A.I.C.S.: 423450
Joseph Barendt *(COO)*

Daicel Safety Systems America LLC (2)
720 Old Liberty Church Rd
Beaver Dam, KY 42320-9130
Tel.: (270) 274-2600
Fax: (270) 274-0750
Web Site: www.daicelssa.com
Automotive Air Bag Inflator Mfr
S.I.C.: 3714
N.A.I.C.S.: 336390
Wayne Thomas *(Pres)*

Special Devices, Incorporated (2)
5898 Condor Dr Ste 200
Moorpark, CA 93021 DE
Tel.: (805) 553-1200
Fax: (805) 553-1201
E-Mail: general.info@sdi.daicel.com
Web Site: www.specialdevices.com
Sales Range: $100-124.9 Million
Emp.: 570
Pyrotechnic Devices Designer & Mfr
S.I.C.: 2899
N.A.I.C.S.: 325998
Christopher Hunter *(Pres & CEO)*
Harry Rector *(CFO & Sec)*
Nicholas J. Bruge *(COO)*

Non-U.S. Subsidiaries:

Daicel Chemical (Asia) Pte. Ltd. (1)
78 Shenton Way 15 01 01B
Singapore, 079120, Singapore (100%)
Tel.: (65) 63272038
Fax: (65) 63272048
Web Site: www.daicel.com
Emp.: 9
Asian Chemical Marketing Operations
S.I.C.: 2899
N.A.I.C.S.: 325998
Yoshiyuki Nogochi *(Mng Dir)*

Daicel Chemical (China) Investment Co., Ltd. (1)
Rm 3004 Shanghai Information Mansion No 211 Shiji Ave
Pudong, Shanghai, 200120, China
Tel.: (86) 2158780737
Fax: (86) 2158780649
Investment Management Services
S.I.C.: 6211
N.A.I.C.S.: 523999

DAICEL CHIRAL TECHNOLOGIES (CHINA) CO., LTD. (1)
Part C Fl 5 The 16th Building No 69 XiYa Rd WaiGaoQiao Free Trade Zone
Shanghai, 200131, China
Tel.: (86) 2150460086
Fax: (86) 21 50462321
E-Mail: chiral@ctc.daicel.com
Web Site: www.daicelchiraltech.cn
Emp.: 32
Medical Equipment Mfr
S.I.C.: 3845
N.A.I.C.S.: 334510

Daicel Chiral Technologies (India) Pvt Ltd. (1)
Lab No 4A Phase III ICICI Knowledge Park Genome Valley
Ranga Reddy Dist, Hyderabad, Andhra Pradesh, 500 078, India
Tel.: (91) 40 2348 0103
Fax: (91) 40 2348 0104
E-Mail: chiral@chiral.daicel.com
Web Site: www.daicelchiral.com
Emp.: 17
Chromatography Analytical Services
S.I.C.: 8734
N.A.I.C.S.: 541380
Lakshmi Narayana *(VP)*

Daicel Europe GmbH (1)
Mergenthalerallee 77
65760 Eschborn, Germany (100%)
Tel.: (49) 6196470350
Fax: (49) 6196470360
Web Site: www.daicel.co.jp/group/index2_e.html
Sales Range: $1-9.9 Million
Emp.: 6
Management of Marketing Operations
S.I.C.: 5169
N.A.I.C.S.: 424690
Ken Bando *(Mgr)*

Daicel (Hong Kong) Ltd. (1)
Ste 2103 21 Fl CMG Asia Tower
The Gtwy, Kowloon, China (Hong Kong) (100%)
Tel.: (852) 27302129
Fax: (852) 323753090
Web Site: www.daicel.co.jp/guw/com_we.html
Emp.: 50
Marketing Offices for Hong Kong & Southern China
S.I.C.: 2899
N.A.I.C.S.: 325998

Daicel International Finance B.V. (1)
Houtplein 47
Haarlem, Netherlands
Tel.: (31) 662634806
Fax: (31) 662634835
Web Site: www.daicel.co.jp/annual/ar2001e/html/corpo.html
Finance & Investment
S.I.C.: 6282
N.A.I.C.S.: 523930

Daicel Nanning Food Ingredients Co., Ltd. (1)
29 Jinkai Road Nanning
Nanning, Guangxi, China
Tel.: (86) 7714810970
Fax: (86) 7714810975
E-Mail: DaicelNanning@gmail.com
Web Site: www.daicelnn.com.cn
Food Ingredient Mfr
S.I.C.: 2099
N.A.I.C.S.: 311999

Daicel Polymer (Hong Kong) Limited. (1)
Suite 23A01 23A/F Tower 2 The Gateway
Harbour City 25 Canton Road
Kowloon, China (Hong Kong)

Daicel Corporation—(Continued)

Tel.: (852) 2730 2129
Fax: (852) 2375 3090
Thermoplastic Resin Mfr
S.I.C.: 2821
N.A.I.C.S.: 325211
Katano Hirotomo *(Gen Mgr)*

Daicel Safety Systems (Thailand) Co.,Ltd. **(1)**
241 Moo 4304 Industrial Park T Thatoom
A Srimahapote, Tambol Dong-Kee-Lek, 25140, Thailand
Tel.: (66) 37270900
Fax: (66) 37274225
Web Site: www.daicelsst-stt.com
Emp.: 800
Automotive Parts Mfr
S.I.C.: 3714
N.A.I.C.S.: 336390
Yoshihiro Yamada *(Pres)*

Daicel Safety Technologies (Thailand) Co., Ltd. **(1)**
241 Moo 4 304 Industrial Park T Thatoom
A Srimahapote, Tambol Dong-Kee-Lek, 25140, Thailand
Tel.: (66) 37270900
Fax: (66) 37274225
Web Site: www.daicelsst-stt.com
Automotive Parts Mfr
S.I.C.: 3714
N.A.I.C.S.: 336390

Polyplastics Marketing (India) Pvt Ltd. **(1)**
No 818 C Wing 215 Atrium Andheri Kurla Rd
Andheri East, Mumbai, 400059, India
Tel.: (91) 2267587668
Fax: (91) 2267258662
Web Site: www.polyplastics.com
Emp.: 6
Poly Plastic Products Distr
S.I.C.: 5162
N.A.I.C.S.: 424610
Jun Uchida *(Mng Dir)*

Non-U.S. Affiliates:

Chiral Technologies-Europe S.A.R.L. **(1)**
Parc d'Innovation Blvd
Gonthier Dandernach, 67400 Illkirch-Graffenstaden, France (100%)
Tel.: (33) 388795200
Fax: (33) 388667166
E-Mail: cte@chiral.fr
Web Site: www.chiral.fr
Emp.: 30
Sale of Optical Separation Columns and Provision of Services Related to the Separation of Optical Active Compounds
S.I.C.: 2899
N.A.I.C.S.: 325998
Dieter Heckmann *(Mng Dir)*

Shanghai Daicel Polymers, Ltd. **(1)**
East Industrial Development Zone
Sijing Town, Shanghai, Songjiang, China
Tel.: (86) 2157619381
Fax: (86) 2157619078
E-Mail: ms-shiba@daicelpolymers.co.jp
Web Site: www.daicelpolymers.cn
Emp.: 200
Mfr. & Sale of Flame-Retardant ABS Resins and ABS Alloy Resin
S.I.C.: 2821
N.A.I.C.S.: 325211

DAIDO GROUP LTD

Unit No 1906 19th Floor West Tower
Shun Tak Centre
168-200 Connaught Road Central,
Hong Kong, China (Hong Kong)
Tel.: (852) 31078600
Fax: (852) 21111438
E-Mail: general@daidohk.com
Web Site: www.daidohk.com
0544—(HKG)
Rev.: $27,684,404
Assets: $54,471,059
Liabilities: $14,621,125
Net Worth: $39,849,934
Earnings: ($23,362,000)
Emp.: 840
Fiscal Year-end: 12/31/12

Business Description:
Construction & Building Material Mfr
S.I.C.: 5039
N.A.I.C.S.: 423390

Personnel:
Tat Wai Au *(CEO)*
Kai Sing Choy *(CFO & Sec)*

Board of Directors:
Wa Ko Fung
Tat Wai Au
Kai Sing Choy
Siu Wah Chung
Ronny Siu Kit Fung
Ivan Hon Chung Ho
Chi Hung Leung
Philip Tang Tsz Man
Yuen Ming Tse

Transfer Agent:
Union Registrars Limited
18/F Fook Lee Commercial Centre Town Place
33 Lockhart Road
Wanchai, China (Hong Kong)

Subsidiaries:

Brilliant Cold Storage Management Limited **(1)**
8 Kwai Hei Street
Kwai Chung, New Territories, China (Hong Kong)
Tel.: (852) 26148383
Fax: (852) 2614 1120
E-Mail: cont-brilliant@b-coldstorage.com.hk
Web Site: www.b-coldstorage.com.hk
Emp.: 300
Refrigerated Warehousing Services
S.I.C.: 4222
N.A.I.C.S.: 493120

Daido Home International Ltd. **(1)**
50 Wang Lee Street
Yuen Long Industrial Estate, Yuen Long, China (Hong Kong)
Tel.: (852) 26673630
Fax: (852) 26648125
E-Mail: general@daidohk.com
Web Site: www.daidohk.com
Construction & Building Materials Mfr
S.I.C.: 5039
N.A.I.C.S.: 423390

Diamond Sparkling Limited **(1)**
Room 1906 19th Floor Shun Tak Center West Twr
Sheung Wan, China (Hong Kong) (100%)
Tel.: (852) 31078600
Fax: (852) 21111438
Emp.: 25
Real Estate Property Lessors
S.I.C.: 6519
N.A.I.C.S.: 531190

DAIDO KOGYO CO., LTD.

I-197 Kumasaka-cho
Kaga, Ishikawa, 922-8686, Japan
Tel.: (81) 761 72 1234
Fax: (81) 761 72 6458
Web Site: www.did-daido.co.jp
Year Founded: 1933
6373—(TKS)
Emp.: 731

Business Description:
Industrial Machinery Mfr
S.I.C.: 3559
N.A.I.C.S.: 333249

Personnel:
Kozo Araya *(Pres)*
Yasuyuki Tatsuta *(Sr Mng Dir)*
Hirofumi Araya *(Co-Mng Dir)*
Shinichi Hirano *(Co-Mng Dir)*
Kinichiro Nakano *(Co-Mng Dir)*

Board of Directors:
Hirofumi Araya
Kozo Araya
Shinichi Hirano
Katsuyuki Kikuchi
Kinichiro Nakano
Toshihiro Shimizu
Yasuyuki Tatsuta

DAIDO METAL CORPORATION

13F Nagoya Hirokonji Bldg 2-3-1
Sake Naka-ku
Nagoya, 460-0008, Japan
Tel.: (81) 522051401
Fax: (81) 522051411
Web Site: www.daidometal.com
Year Founded: 1939
7245—(TKS)
Sales Range: $450-499.9 Million
Emp.: 1,300

Business Description:
Bearings Mfr
S.I.C.: 3562
N.A.I.C.S.: 332991

Personnel:
Seigo Hanji *(Chm & CEO)*
Masaaki Sakamoto *(Pres & COO)*

Division:

Daido Metal Corporation - Bimetal Division **(1)**
Tendoh Shinden Maehara
Inuyama, Aichi, 484-0061, Japan
Tel.: (81) 568611350
Fax: (81) 568611361
Web Site: www.daidometal.com
Automotive Bearing Mfr
S.I.C.: 3562
N.A.I.C.S.: 332991

Subsidiaries:

Asia Kelmet Co., Ltd. **(1)**
3-29-1 Yaguchi
Ohta-ku, Tokyo, 146-0093, Japan
Tel.: (81) 337594571
Fax: (81) 337573088
Web Site: www.daidometal.com
Emp.: 4
Automotive Plain Bearing Mfr
S.I.C.: 3714
N.A.I.C.S.: 336390

Daido Logitech Co., Ltd. **(1)**
Tendoh Shinden Maehara
Inuyama, Aichi, 484-0061, Japan
Tel.: (81) 568611214
Fax: (81) 568 62 6754
Web Site: www.daidometal.com
Warehousing Services
S.I.C.: 4226
N.A.I.C.S.: 493190

Daido Metal Co., Ltd **(1)**
Tendoh Shinden Maehara Inuyama
Nagoya, 484-0061, Japan
Tel.: (81) 568613111
Fax: (81) 568626755
Web Site: www.daidometal.com
Emp.: 1,200
Motor Vehicle Electrical & Electronic Equipment Mfr
S.I.C.: 3714
N.A.I.C.S.: 336320
Tomihifa Nagata *(Mgr-Sls)*

Daido Metal Sales Co., Ltd **(1)**
Tendoh Shinden Maehara Inuyama
484-0061 Nagoya, Japan
Tel.: (81) 568611367
Fax: (81) 568611379
Web Site: www.daidometal.co.jp
Emp.: 25
Ball & Roller Bearing Mfr
S.I.C.: 3562
N.A.I.C.S.: 332991
Yoshitaka Emoto *(Mgr-Bushing & Overseas Sls Dept)*

Daido Plain Bearings Co., Ltd. **(1)**
8-1 Nozomigaoka Seki
Gifu, 501-3219, Japan
Tel.: (81) 575234083
Fax: (81) 575234086
Web Site: www.daidometal.com
Automotive Plain Bearings Mfr
S.I.C.: 3714
N.A.I.C.S.: 336390

NDC Co., Ltd. **(1)**
2-39-1 Mimomi
Narashino, Chiba, 2750002, Japan
Tel.: (81) 474771128
Fax: (81) 474771131
E-Mail: ndc@venus.dti.na.jp
Web Site: www.nds-sales.co.jp
Emp.: 400
Engine Bearings, Bushings & Thrust Washers Mfr & Sales
S.I.C.: 3714
N.A.I.C.S.: 336310
Fumiaki Iwamoto *(Mng Dir)*

U.S. Subsidiary:

NDC OF AMERICA INC. **(2)**
2300 Norman Dr S
Waukegan, IL 60085
Tel.: (847) 578-0251
Fax: (847) 578-0302
E-Mail: ntakahata@peerinc.com
Web Site: www.daidometal.com
Automobile Polymer Bearing Mfr & Distr
S.I.C.: 3562
N.A.I.C.S.: 332991
Noril Takahata *(Mgr)*

NDC Sales Co., Ltd. **(1)**
2-39-1 Mimomi Narashino
Chiba, 275-0002, Japan
Tel.: (81) 474771128
Fax: (81) 474771131
E-Mail: ndc@venus.dti.ne.jp
Web Site: www.ndc-sales.co.jp
Automotive Plain Bearing Distr
S.I.C.: 5013
N.A.I.C.S.: 423120
Iwa Moto *(Pres)*

Plants:

Daido Metal Corporation - Gifu Factory **(1)**
135 Ohara Minami Gujo
Gifu, 501-4107, Japan
Tel.: (81) 575792221
Fax: (81) 575792911
Web Site: www.daidometal.com
Automotive Metal Bearings Mfr
S.I.C.: 3562
N.A.I.C.S.: 332991

Daido Metal Corporation - Inuyama Factory **(1)**
Tendoh Shinden Maehara
Inuyama, Aichi, 484-0061, Japan
Tel.: (81) 568611350
Fax: (81) 568611361
Web Site: www.daidometal.com
Automotive Bearing Mfr
S.I.C.: 3562
N.A.I.C.S.: 332991

Daido Metal Corporation - Maehara Factory **(1)**
Tendoh Shinden Maehara
Inuyama, Aichi, 484-0061, Japan
Tel.: (81) 568613112
Fax: (81) 568611361
Web Site: www.daidometal.com
Emp.: 900
Automotive Bearing Mfr
S.I.C.: 3562
N.A.I.C.S.: 332991

U.S. Subsidiary:

Daido Metal U.S.A. Inc **(1)**
1215 S Greenwood St
Bellefontaine, OH 43311-1628
Tel.: (847) 590-8520
Fax: (847) 590-8630
Web Site: www.daidometal.com
Emp.: 100
Ball & Roller Bearing Mfr
S.I.C.: 3562
N.A.I.C.S.: 332991
Atira Saida *(Office Mgr)*

Non-U.S. Subsidiaries:

Bimetal Bearings Ltd **(1)**
18 Race Course Road
641018 Coimbatore, India
Tel.: (91) 4222220054
Fax: (91) 4222220853
E-Mail: bimite@md2.vsnl.net.in
Web Site: www.bimite.co.in
Emp.: 100
Ball & Roller Bearing Mfr
S.I.C.: 3562
N.A.I.C.S.: 332991
R. K. Moorthi *(Exec Dir-Mktg)*

Daido Industrial Bearings Europe Ltd. **(1)**
Winterhay Lane Ilminster
Somerset, TA19 9PH, United Kingdom

Tel.: (44) 146053221
Fax: (44) 1460257832
E-Mail: sales@daidoeurope.com
Web Site: www.daidometal.com
Emp.: 180
Ball & Roller Bearing Mfr
S.I.C.: 3562
N.A.I.C.S.: 332991
Toshiaki Kawachi *(Mng Dir)*

DAIDO METAL CZECH s.r.o. (1)
Svedske valy 1309/6
627 00 Brno, Czech Republic
Tel.: (420) 545425511
Fax: (420) 545425555
E-Mail: dmc@daidometal.com
Web Site: www.daidometal.cz
Emp.: 80
Automobile Bearings Mfr
S.I.C.: 3562
N.A.I.C.S.: 332991
Nobutaka Hiramatsu *(Gen Mgr)*

Daido Metal Europe GmbH (1)
Solitudestrasse 49
71638 Ludwigsburg, Germany
Tel.: (49) 71416889340
Fax: (49) 71416889350
Motor Vehicle Supplies & New Parts Whslr
S.I.C.: 5013
N.A.I.C.S.: 423120
Michitoshi Inagaki *(Mng Dir)*

DAIDO METAL EUROPE LTD (1)
Winterhay Lane
Ilminster, Somersetshire, TA19 9PH, United Kingdom
Tel.: (44) 146053221
Fax: (44) 1460256217
Web Site: www.daidometal.com
Emp.: 300
Automobile Bearing Distr
S.I.C.: 5085
N.A.I.C.S.: 423840
Keiichi Kogure *(Gen Mgr)*

DAIDO METAL GERMANY GmbH (1)
Solitudestrasse 49
71638 Ludwigsburg, Germany
Tel.: (49) 7141 6889340
Fax: (49) 7141 6889350
Web Site: www.daidometal.com
Plain Bearing Distr
S.I.C.: 5085
N.A.I.C.S.: 423840

DAIDO METAL KOTOR AD (1)
Industrijska Zona bb
85330 Kotor, Montenegro
Tel.: (382) 32 331 513
Fax: (382) 82 331 506
E-Mail: daido@t-com.me
Web Site: www.daidokotor.com
Emp.: 140
Automobile Plain Bearing Mfr & Distr
S.I.C.: 3714
N.A.I.C.S.: 336390
T. Furukawa *(Mng Dir)*

DAIDO METAL RUSSIA LLC (1)
Zavolzhye Sovetskaya st 1A
Nizhniy Novgorod, Russia
Tel.: (7) 83161 2 12 30
Fax: (7) 83161 7 63 25
E-Mail: dmr@daidorussia.com
Web Site: www.daidorussia.ru
Plain Bearings Distr
S.I.C.: 5085
N.A.I.C.S.: 423840
Sorokin Vladimir *(Gen Mgr)*

DAIDO PRECISION METAL (SUZHOU) CO., LTD. (1)
No 246 QingQiu Str Suzhou Industrial Park
Suzhou, China
Tel.: (86) 512 6283 3531
Fax: (86) 512 6283 3003
E-Mail: daido@dpmsz.cn
Web Site: www.dpmsz.cn
Automotive Bearing Mfr & Distr
S.I.C.: 3714
N.A.I.C.S.: 336390

DAIDO REBUILD SERVICES INC. (1)
665 A Bonifacio Street Balintawak
Quezon City, Philippines
Tel.: (63) 23668476
Fax: (63) 23667145
Web Site: www.daidometal.com
Engine Rebuilding Services
S.I.C.: 7539
N.A.I.C.S.: 811118

DONGSUNG METAL CO., LTD. (1)
160 Yongsan-myun
Youngdong-kun, Bekjajun, Chungbuk, 370-912, Korea (South)
Tel.: (82) 5 730 36 88
Fax: (82) 43 742 8448
Emp.: 190
Automobile Plain Bearing Mfr
S.I.C.: 3714
N.A.I.C.S.: 336390
Song Yang Guen *(Mng Dir)*

KOREA DRY BEARING CO., LTD. (1)
163-12 Okcheon-eup
Okcheon-gun, Dongan, Chungcheongbuk-do, 373-800, Korea (South)
Tel.: (82) 97998695
Fax: (82) 43 7339360
Polymer Bearings Mfr & Distr
S.I.C.: 3562
N.A.I.C.S.: 332991
Wan Soo Lin *(Gen Mgr)*

PT. Daido Metal Indonesia (1)
Block M 25-26
Bekasi, Indonesia
Tel.: (62) 218980038
Web Site: www.daidometal.com
Copper Foundries
S.I.C.: 3369
N.A.I.C.S.: 331529

DAIDO SIGNAL CO., LTD.

Shin-Onarimon-Building 6-17-19 Shimbashi
Minato-ku, Tokyo, Japan
Tel.: (81) 3 3438 4111
Fax: (81) 3 3438 4640
Web Site: www.daido-signal.co.jp
Year Founded: 1929
6743—(TKS)
Emp.: 536

Business Description:
Synthetic Resin Mfr & Whslr
S.I.C.: 2821
N.A.I.C.S.: 325211
Personnel:
Fumio Kitahara *(Pres)*

DAIDO STEEL CO., LTD.

1-10 Higashisakura 1-chome Higashi-ku
Nagoya, Aichi, 461-8581, Japan
Tel.: (81) 529637501
Telex: 4422243
Fax: (81) 529634386
E-Mail: d3501@so.daido.co.jp
Web Site: www.daido.co.jp
Year Founded: 1916
5471—(NGO TKS)
Sls.: $4,844,708,000
Assets: $5,622,749,000
Liabilities: $3,291,618,000
Net Worth: $2,331,131,000
Earnings: $120,813,000
Emp.: 10,447
Fiscal Year-end: 03/31/13

Business Description:
Integrated Specialty Steel
S.I.C.: 3325
N.A.I.C.S.: 331513
Personnel:
Masatoshi Ozawa *(Chm)*
Tadashi Shimao *(Pres)*
Takeshi Ishiguro *(Co-Mng Dir)*
Yasuhiro Itazuri *(Co-Mng Dir)*
Akira Miyajima *(Co-Mng Dir)*
Motoshi Shinkai *(Co-Mng Dir)*
Kazuto Tachibana *(Co-Mng Dir)*
Hajime Takahashi *(Co-Mng Dir)*
Hitoshi Horie *(Exec VP)*
Shuichi Nakatsubo *(Exec VP)*
Michio Okabe *(Exec VP)*
Board of Directors:
Masatoshi Ozawa
Hajime Amano
Kazuhiko Hirabayashi
Hitoshi Horie
Takeshi Ishiguro
Yasuhiro Itazuri
Shuji Matsubuchi
Akira Miyajima
Takeshi Muto
Shuichi Nakatsubo
Shinji Naruse
Tsukasa Nishimura
Michio Okabe
Yoshitsugu Sakamoto
Tadashi Shimao
Susumu Shimura
Motoshi Shinkai
Kazuto Tachibana
Hajime Takahashi
Satoshi Tsujimoto

Transfer Agent:
Sumitomo Mitsui Trust Bank, Limited
15-33 Sakae 3-chome Naka-ku
Nagoya, Japan

Subsidiaries:

Daido Amistar Co., Ltd. (1)
152 Hino 3-chome
Daito, Osaka, 574-0062, Japan
Tel.: (81) 728718601
Fax: (81) 728718620
E-Mail: e-help@amistar.co.jp
Web Site: www.amistar.co.jp
Emp.: 100
Metal Stampings Mfr
S.I.C.: 3469
N.A.I.C.S.: 332119
Tsuda Takayoshi *(Pres)*

Daido Bunseki Research Inc. (1)
30 Daido-cho 2-chome
Minami-ku, Nagoya, Aichi, 457-0811, Japan
Tel.: (81) 526119434
Fax: (81) 526119948
Web Site: www.daido.co.jp/dbr/
Emp.: 115
Biotechnology Research & Development Services
S.I.C.: 8731
N.A.I.C.S.: 541712
Hisao Kamiya *(Pres)*

Daido Castings Co., Ltd. (1)
10 Ryugu-cho
Minato-ku, Nagoya, Aichi, 455-0022, Japan
Tel.: (81) 526915191
Fax: (81) 526915190
E-Mail: hiura@d-cast.jp
Web Site: www.d-cast.jp
Emp.: 500
Steel Castings Mfr
S.I.C.: 3325
N.A.I.C.S.: 331513
Kazuhiko Matano *(Pres)*

Daido EcoMet Co., Ltd. (1)
7 Daido-cho 4-chome
Minami-ku, Nagoya, Aichi, 457-0811, Japan
Tel.: (81) 562 33 5946
Fax: (81) 562 33 5947
Web Site: www.d-ecomet.co.jp
Steel Wastes Recycling Services
S.I.C.: 2842
N.A.I.C.S.: 325612

Daido Environment Engineering Co.,Ltd., (1)
9 Takiharu-cho
Minami-ku, Nagoya, Aichi, 457-0819, Japan
Tel.: (81) 52 613 6851
Fax: (81) 52 613 6855
Web Site: www.daido-kankyo.co.jp
Contract Maintenance Services
S.I.C.: 7389
N.A.I.C.S.: 561990

Daido Life Service Co., Ltd. (1)
7 Daido-cho 4-chome
Minami-ku, Nagoya, Aichi, 457-0811, Japan
Tel.: (81) 526118841
Fax: (81) 526118899
Web Site: www.daidolife.co.jp
Apartment Building Construction Services
S.I.C.: 1522
N.A.I.C.S.: 236116

Daido Machinery Co., Ltd. (1)
9 Takiharu-cho
Minami-ku, Nagoya, Aichi, 457-8577, Japan
Tel.: (81) 526117171
Fax: (81) 526117153
Web Site: www.dm-daido.co.jp
Metal Cutting Machinery Mfr
S.I.C.: 3542
N.A.I.C.S.: 333517

Daido Matex Co., Ltd. (1)
16-1 Minami-machi
Kawasaki, Kanagawa, 210-0015, Japan
Tel.: (81) 442211070
Fax: (81) 442211072
Web Site: www.daidomatex.co.jp
Emp.: 70
Steel Products Distr
S.I.C.: 5051
N.A.I.C.S.: 423510
Tokio Miyachi *(Mgr)*

Daido Precision Industries Ltd. (1)
1-15 Nishiikebukuro 3-chome
Toshima-ku, Tokyo, 171-0021, Japan
Tel.: (81) 359569176
Fax: (81) 359569177
E-Mail: sales@daidoseimitu.co.jp
Web Site: www.daidoseimitu.co.jp
Emp.: 200
Precision Machine Parts Mfr & Distr
S.I.C.: 3325
N.A.I.C.S.: 331513
Hiromi Hata *(Pres)*

Daido Shizai Service Co., Ltd. (1)
4-7 Daido Buld 4F Daido Cho
Minami Ku, Nagoya, Aichi, 457-0811, Japan
Tel.: (81) 52 611 8801
Fax: (81) 52 611 8849
Web Site: www.daido.co.jp/dsk/en/index.html
Emp.: 45
Industrial Materials & Equipments Procurement Services
S.I.C.: 6794
N.A.I.C.S.: 533110
Takashi Murase *(Pres)*

Daido Star Techno Co., Ltd. (1)
500 Ishihara
Shibukawa, Gunma, 377-0007, Japan
Tel.: (81) 279 23 1375
Fax: (81) 279 23 1558
Web Site: www.daido.co.jp/en/about/corporate/domestic.html
Steel Products Mfr
S.I.C.: 3325
N.A.I.C.S.: 331513

Daido Technica Co., Ltd. (1)
39 Motohama-machi
Tokai, Aichi, 477-0035, Japan
Tel.: (81) 562331231
Fax: (81) 562 33 1233
Web Site: www.daido-technica.co.jp
Emp.: 500
Stainless Steel Products Mfr
S.I.C.: 3312
N.A.I.C.S.: 331110
Teruyoshi Hotta *(Pres)*

Izumi Denki Kogyo Co., Ltd. (1)
8-1 Narihara 4-chome
Sumida-Ku, Tokyo, 130-0002, Japan
Tel.: (81) 3 3624 8331
Fax: (81) 3 3624 8336
Steel Products Mfr
S.I.C.: 3312
N.A.I.C.S.: 331110

Japan Drop Forge Co., Ltd. (1)
1 Ohama-cho 2-chome
Amagasaki, Hyogo, 660-0095, Japan
Tel.: (81) 6 6416 1051
Fax: (81) 6 6416 3741
Web Site: www.j-d-f.co.jp
Crankshaft Assemblies Mfr
S.I.C.: 3714
N.A.I.C.S.: 336310

Kawaichi Sangyo Co., Ltd. (1)
5-9 Ogi-machi
Kawasaki-ku, Kawasaki, Kanagawa, 210-0867, Japan
Tel.: (81) 443552715
Fax: (81) 44 355 3587
Web Site: www.kawaichi.jp
General Freight Trucking Services
S.I.C.: 4214

Daido Steel Co., Ltd.—(Continued)

N.A.I.C.S.: 484110
Iwata Syuuiti *(Pres)*

Log Transport Co., Ltd. (1)
12-18 Donghae Motohama Town
Nagoya, Aichi, 477-0035, Japan
Tel.: (81) 562 33 2652
Fax: (81) 562 33 3852
Web Site: www.maruta.co.jp
Transportation & Warehousing Services
S.I.C.: 4225
N.A.I.C.S.: 493110

Nissei Seiko Co., Ltd. (1)
1-3 Tango-dori 2-chome
Minami-ku, Nagoya, Aichi, 457-0801, Japan
Tel.: (81) 52 611 6271
Fax: (81) 52 612 6139
Web Site: www.nssy.co.jp
Fasteners Mfr
S.I.C.: 3965
N.A.I.C.S.: 339993

Riken Seiko Co., Ltd. (1)
17-3 Kyobashi 2-chome
Chuo-ku, Tokyo, 104-0031, Japan
Tel.: (81) 351590811
Fax: (81) 351590812
Web Site: www.rkn.co.jp
Emp.: 200
Stainless Steel Products Mfr
S.I.C.: 3545
N.A.I.C.S.: 333515
Yasuaki Sawachika *(Pres)*

Sakurai Kosan Co., Ltd. (1)
3 Tsurumidori 3-chome
Minami-ku, Nagoya, Aichi, 457-0807, Japan
Tel.: (81) 52 611 5151
Fax: (81) 52 611 5142
Web Site: www.sakuraikosan.co.jp
Steel Products Mfr
S.I.C.: 3312
N.A.I.C.S.: 331110

Shimomura Tokushu Seiko Co., Ltd. (1)
3-18 Ichi1-kawa
Ichikawa, Chiba, 272-0034, Japan
Tel.: (81) 473213841
Fax: (81) 473213830
E-Mail: eigyo@sts-shimomura.co.jp
Web Site: www.sts-shimomura.com
Emp.: 200
Steel Products Mfr
S.I.C.: 3325
N.A.I.C.S.: 331513
Mineo Tamai *(Pres)*

Star Info Tech Co., Ltd. (1)
Urban Net Nagoya Building 21 Floor
Higashi-ku Nagoya Higashisakura
Chome 1-10, Nagoya, Aichi, 461-0005, Japan
Tel.: (81) 52 308 5801
Fax: (81) 52 963 4382
Web Site: www.d-sit.co.jp
Sls.: $45,100,000
Emp.: 204
Fiscal Year-end: 12/31/12
Enterprise Management Software Development Services
S.I.C.: 7371
N.A.I.C.S.: 541511
Genki Kusakabe *(Pres)*

Toyo Sangyo Co., Ltd. (1)
30 Daido-cho 2 chome Minami-ku Nagoya Aichi
Nagoya, Hoshizaki, 457-8545, Japan
Tel.: (81) 52 611 2512
Fax: (81) 52 614 2492
Web Site: www.daido.co.jp
Mfr of Automobile & Industrial Equipment Parts
S.I.C.: 3711
N.A.I.C.S.: 336111

Plants:

Daido Steel Co., Ltd. - Chita Plant (1)
39 Motohama-machi
Tokai, Aichi, 477-0035, Japan
Tel.: (81) 562333101
Fax: (81) 562331570
Steel Products Mfr
S.I.C.: 3291
N.A.I.C.S.: 327910

Daido Steel Co., Ltd. - Kawasaki Plant (1)
4-1 Yako 2-chome
Kawasaki-ku, Kawasaki, Kanagawa, 210-0863, Japan
Tel.: (81) 44 266 3760
Fax: (81) 44 266 3768
Web Site: www.daido.co.jp/en/about/corporate/facilities.html
Reinforcing Bars & Rails Mfr
S.I.C.: 3399
N.A.I.C.S.: 331110

Daido Steel Co., Ltd. - Kimitsu Plant (1)
1 Kimitsu
Kimitsu, Chiba, 299-1141, Japan
Tel.: (81) 439521541
Fax: (81) 439541280
Emp.: 3,000
Steel Forgings Mfr
S.I.C.: 3312
N.A.I.C.S.: 331110
Isaki Masahiro *(Project Mgr)*

Daido Steel Co., Ltd. - Oji Plant (1)
9-3 Kamiya 3-chome
Kita-ku, Tokyo, 115-0043, Japan
Tel.: (81) 339014161
Fax: (81) 3 3901 8211
Steel Alloys Mfr
S.I.C.: 3312
N.A.I.C.S.: 331110

Daido Steel Co., Ltd. - Shibukawa Plant (1)
500 Ishihara
Shibukawa, Gunma, 377-0007, Japan
Tel.: (81) 279252000
Fax: (81) 279252040
Web Site: www.daido.co.jp/en/about/corporate/facilities.html
Emp.: 600
Steel Forgings Mfr
S.I.C.: 3462
N.A.I.C.S.: 332111
Hajime Amano *(Pres)*

U.S. Subsidiaries:

Daido Steel (America) Inc (1)
1111 Plz Dr Ste 740
Schaumburg, IL 60173
Tel.: (847) 517-7950
Fax: (847) 517-7951
Web Site: www.daidosteel.com
Emp.: 8
S.I.C.: 2999
N.A.I.C.S.: 324199
Yasushi Kuwayama *(Gen Mgr-Sls & Mktg)*

Ohio Star Forge Co. (1)
4000 Mahonig Ave
Warren, OH 44482-0430 (100%)
Tel.: (330) 847-6360
Fax: (330) 847-6368
E-Mail: info@ohiostar.com
Web Site: www.ohiostar.com
Emp.: 70
Mfr. of Bearing Lace and Automobile Parts by Steel Bar Hot-Forming
S.I.C.: 3463
N.A.I.C.S.: 332112
Jeffrey Downing *(Pres)*

Non-U.S. Subsidiaries:

DAIDO AMISTAR (M) SDN. BHD. (1)
No 8 Jalan Perusahaan Utama Taman Industri Selesa Jaya Off Jalan
43300 Balakong, Selangor, Malaysia
Tel.: (60) 389617566
Fax: (60) 389618566
E-Mail: dam@amistar.com.my
Web Site: www.amistar.com.my
Emp.: 60
Stainless Steel Products Mfr
S.I.C.: 3312
N.A.I.C.S.: 331110
Hiroji Kitada *(Mng Dir)*

DAIDO AMISTAR (S) PTE LTD (1)
21 Senoko South Road Woodlands East
Singapore, Singapore
Tel.: (65) 67581611
Fax: (65) 67529457
Web Site: www.daido.co.jp/en/about/corporate/overseas.html
Emp.: 49
Steel Products Distr
S.I.C.: 5051
N.A.I.C.S.: 423510
Hiroji Kitada *(Mng Dir)*

Daido Electronics (Thailand) Co., Ltd. (1)
43 Moo 9 Rojana Industrial Park Rojana Road Tambol Tanuu
Amphur U-Thai, Ayutthaya, 13210, Thailand
Tel.: (66) 35330734
Fax: (66) 35330737
Web Site: www.daido-electronics.co.jp/english/corporate/foreign/thailand/
Emp.: 450
Spindle Motor Magnets Mfr
S.I.C.: 3499
N.A.I.C.S.: 332999

DAIDO PDM (Thailand) CO., LTD. (1)
120 Moo 5 Wellgrow Industrial Estate
Bangna-Trad Rd KM 36 Bangsamak
Bang Pakong, Chachoengsao, 24180, Thailand
Tel.: (66) 38545999
Fax: (66) 38545911
E-Mail: sales@daidopdm.co.th
Web Site: www.daidopdm.co.th
Emp.: 150
Tool Steels Distr
S.I.C.: 5051
N.A.I.C.S.: 423510
Hiroyuki Sano *(Mng Dir)*

Daido Tienwen Steel Co., Ltd. (1)
No 1 Ta-Chang Rd
Ping Cheng City, Taoyuan, 324, Taiwan
Tel.: (886) 34936622
Fax: (886) 34944801
E-Mail: dts143@daidosteel.com.tw
Web Site: www.daidosteel.com.tw
Tool Steels Mfr
S.I.C.: 3312
N.A.I.C.S.: 331110

DAIDOH LIMITED

3-1-16 Sotokanda
Chiyoda-ku, Tokyo, 101-8619, Japan
Tel.: (81) 3 3257 5050
Fax: (81) 3 3257 5051
Web Site: www.daidoh-limited.com
Year Founded: 1879
3205—(TKS)
Sls.: $304,293,000
Assets: $535,337,000
Liabilities: $251,823,000
Net Worth: $283,514,000
Earnings: $3,982,000
Emp.: 1,714
Fiscal Year-end: 03/31/13

Business Description:
Apparel Mfr & Whslr
S.I.C.: 5699
N.A.I.C.S.: 315220

Personnel:
Shin Okawa *(Pres)*
Kanai Tozawa *(Mng Dir)*
Tsutomu Murao *(Exec Officer)*
Masayuki Taguchi *(Sr Exec Officer)*
Yasuhiko Kawanishi *(Exec VP)*

Board of Directors:
Kiyoshi Fukura
Yasuhiko Kawanishi
Tsutomu Murao
Shin Okawa
Masayuki Taguchi
Kanai Tozawa

THE DAIEI, INC.

4-1-1 Minatojima Nakamachi
Chuo-ku, Kobe, Hyogo, 135-0016, Japan
Tel.: (81) 78 3025 001
Fax: (81) 78 3025572
E-Mail: callcenter@daiei.co.jp
Web Site: www.daiei.co.jp/corporate/index.html
Year Founded: 1957
8263—(FKA NGO SAP TKS)
Sales Range: $75-99.9 Billion
Emp.: 10,476

Business Description:
Food, Clothing, Personal Care Products, Household Items & Other Goods Retailer; Restaurant Operator; Department Stores Operator; Specialty Stores Operator
Import Export
S.I.C.: 5311
N.A.I.C.S.: 452111

Personnel:
Yoshiharu Kawato *(Chm)*
Toru Nishimi *(Pres)*
Yoshiaki Takahashi *(Mng Dir & Chief Compliance Officer)*
Tatsumichi Ishimura *(Mng Dir)*
Toshio Kawamoto *(Mng Dir)*
Akinori Yamashita *(Mng Dir)*
Koji Yamazaki *(Mng Dir)*
Tsuneyuki Mori *(Mng Exec Officer)*
Shinji Ohsumi *(Mng Exec Officer)*

Board of Directors:
Yoshiharu Kawato
Tatsumichi Ishimura
Minoru Mukai
Keiji Nakamae
Toru Nishimi
Hideaki Shiraishi
Yoshiaki Takahashi

Subsidiaries:

Altyfoods Co. Ltd. (1)
2-7-52 Yokoe
Ibaraki, Osaka, Japan
Tel.: (81) 726334830
Perishable Food Processing
S.I.C.: 2099
N.A.I.C.S.: 311991

The Big-A. (1)
Ooyamahigashi 25-13
Itabashi, Tokyo, Japan
Tel.: (81) 359432820
Perishable Food Processor
S.I.C.: 2099
N.A.I.C.S.: 311991
Hiroyoshi Kozima *(Pres)*

The Bonte Inc. (1)
3-39-6 Katsushika 1Tokyo Bldg 3F
Aoto Katsushika, Tokyo, Japan
Tel.: (81) 338381981
Bread, Pastry & Sandwich Distr & Retail Sales
S.I.C.: 5461
N.A.I.C.S.: 445291
Toshio Kawai *(Pres)*

The Consumer Economics Research Institute, Inc (1)
5 Aizumi Plaza 6th Floor
IK-cho Shinjuku-ku, Tokyo, Japan
Tel.: (81) 3 5363 1201
Fax: (81) 3 5363 1210
Web Site: www.syo-k.co.jp
Commodity Inspection, Analysis, Product Development, Quality Management, Consulting Health Market Research , Marketing, & Staffing Services
S.I.C.: 9651
N.A.I.C.S.: 926150
Seiiti Itou *(Pres)*

Kagoshima Sunrise Farm K. K. (1)
1131-1, Kagoshima Prefecture
Kagoshima, Japan
Tel.: (81) 994435588
Beef & Pork Supplier; Cattle & Pig Farming
S.I.C.: 0212
N.A.I.C.S.: 112111
Akira Hiroshi *(Pres)*

OPA Co., Ltd (1)
2-2-20 Toyo Koto
Toyo Ekimae Building, Tokyo, 135-0016, Japan
Tel.: (81) 3 6388 7900
Commercial & Retail Development
S.I.C.: 9532
N.A.I.C.S.: 925120

Orange Food Court (1)
4-17-8 Minamihatiman Cosmos Building 3F
Ichikawa, Japan
Tel.: (81) 473700211
Fax: (81) 47370292
E-Mail: kanrisha@orangefoodcourt.co.jp
Web Site: www.orangefoodcourt.co.jp
Food Court Services
S.I.C.: 5812
N.A.I.C.S.: 722513
Masu Naitou *(Pres)*

U.S. Subsidiaries:

D International Inc. (1)
5558 166th Pl SE
Bellevue, WA 98006-5534 (100%)
Tel.: (206) 243-3888
Telex: 321121 D INTL INC
Fax: (206) 243-3416
Emp.: 4
Exporter of Meat & Food Products
S.I.C.: 5064
N.A.I.C.S.: 423620

Non-U.S. Subsidiaries:

Tianjin Daiei International Trading Co., Ltd. (1)
151 Hami Rd
Heping District, Tianjin, 300020, China (95%)
Tel.: (86) 2227316969
Fax: (86) 2227316969
E-Mail: tjeaiei@tianjin.cngb.com
Emp.: 70
Retailer of Food Products
S.I.C.: 5149
N.A.I.C.S.: 424490

Non-U.S. Joint Venture:

Shanghai Hualian Lawson Co., Ltd. (1)
5/F Beizhong Mansion No 651 Huaihai M Rd
Luwan Dist, Shanghai, 200020, China
Tel.: (86) 2153881500
Fax: (86) 2153065848
Web Site: www.lawson.co.jp
Development of Convenience Store Operations in Shanghai
S.I.C.: 5411
N.A.I.C.S.: 445120

DAIFUKU CO., LTD.

3-2-11 Mitejima Nishiyodogawa-ku
Osaka, 555-0012, Japan
Tel.: (81) 664721261
Fax: (81) 664762561
Web Site: www.daifuku.com
Year Founded: 1937
6383—(TKS)
Sls.: $2,225,707,000
Assets: $2,275,625,000
Liabilities: $1,333,090,000
Net Worth: $942,535,000
Earnings: $48,829,000
Emp.: 6,678
Fiscal Year-end: 03/31/13

Business Description:
Material Handling Systems Mfr
S.I.C.: 3559
N.A.I.C.S.: 333249

Personnel:
Masaki Hojo *(Pres & CEO)*
Mikio Inohara *(Sr Mng Dir, CFO & Chief Risk Officer)*
Akio Tanaka *(Sr Mng Dir & COO-Mfg & Distr Automation)*
Kanji Anno *(Corp Officer-Mfg & Distrubution Automation Production)*
Hiroshi Geshiro *(Corp Officer-Mfg & Distr Automation Sls)*
Toshiaki Hayashi *(Corp Officer-Automotive Automation Production)*
Yoshiyuki Horiba *(Corp Officer-Cleanroom Automation)*
Akira Ikari *(Corp Officer-Lifestyle Products Production)*
Hidenori Iwamoto *(Mng Officer-Automotive Automation Sls)*
Tadashi Kimura *(Corp Officer-Mfg & Distr Automation Svcs)*
Yoshihisa Kimura *(Corp Officer-Acctg & Fin)*
Akihiko Kishida *(Corp Officer)*
Yoshiyuki Nakashima *(Mng Officer)*
Ken Sasaki *(Corp Officer-Tech & Dev)*
Seiji Sato *(Mng Officer-Cleanroom Automation-Semiconductor)*
Naoki Tahara *(Mng Officer-Mfg & Distr Automation)*
Brian G. Stewart *(Pres/CEO-Daifuku Webb Holding Company)*
Fumio Kobayashi *(COO-Sls & Mktg & Exec VP)*

Board of Directors:
Takashi Hiramoto
Masaki Hojo
Mikio Inohara
Masayoshi Inoue
Noboru Kashiwagi
Fumio Kobayashi
Susumu Moriya
Hiroyoshi Takeda
Akio Tanaka

Subsidiaries:

Daifuku Business Service Corporation (1)
3-2-11 Mitejima
Nishiyodogawa-Ku, Osaka, 555-0012, Japan JP
Tel.: (81) 664762661
Security Support Services
S.I.C.: 7382
N.A.I.C.S.: 561621

Daifuku Design & Engineering Co., Ltd. (1)
3-2-11 Mitejima
Nishiyodogawa-Ku, Osaka, 555-0012, Japan JP
Tel.: (81) 664762951
Material Handling System Mfr
S.I.C.: 3559
N.A.I.C.S.: 333249

Daifuku Institute of Technology & Training Co., Ltd. (1)
1225 Nakazaiji Hino-cho
Gamo-gun, Shiga, 529-1692, Japan JP
Tel.: (81) 748 52 5942
Fax: (81) 748 52 5899
Web Site: www.daifuku.co.jp/dit
Emp.: 25
Material Handling Equipment Research & Professional Training Services
S.I.C.: 8731
N.A.I.C.S.: 541712
Tatsuo Inoue *(Chm)*
Yoshitaka Watanabe *(Pres)*

Daifuku Logistic Technology Co., Ltd. (1)
4-103 Komakihara
Komaki, 485-0829, Japan JP
Tel.: (81) 568741558
Material Handling System Mfr
S.I.C.: 3559
N.A.I.C.S.: 333249

Daifuku Manufacturing Technology Co., Ltd. (1)
5-3-50 Ayukawa
Ibaraki, 567-0831, Japan JP
Tel.: (81) 726344341
Fax: (81) 726352761
Web Site: www.daifuku.com
Material Handling System Mfr
S.I.C.: 3559
N.A.I.C.S.: 333249
Ikuo Kajiuchi *(Gen Mgr)*

Daifuku Plusmore Co., Ltd. (1)
2-14-5 Shiba 3-chome
Minato-ku, Tokyo, 105-0014, Japan JP
Tel.: (81) 3 3456 2294
Fax: (81) 3 3456 2313
Web Site: www.daifuku-plusmore.co.jp
Car Wash Machinery Distr
S.I.C.: 5084
N.A.I.C.S.: 423830

Daifuku Software Development Co., Ltd. (1)
3-9-31 Himesato
Nishiyodogawa-Ku, Osaka, 555-0025, Japan JP
Tel.: (81) 664762381
Material Handling Software Development Services
S.I.C.: 7371
N.A.I.C.S.: 541511

Hiniaratakan Corporation (1)
1225 Nakazaiji Hino-cho
Gamo-gun, Shiga, 529-1692, Japan JP
Tel.: (81) 748 53 3970
Fax: (81) 748 53 3921
Web Site: www.daifuku.co.jp
Material Handling Equipment Mfr
S.I.C.: 3559
N.A.I.C.S.: 333249
Kenichi Togami *(Gen Mgr)*

Plant:

Daifuku Co., Ltd. - Shiga Works (1)
1225 Nakazaiji Hino-cho
Gamo-gun, Shiga, 529-1692, Japan
Tel.: (81) 748 53 0321
Fax: (81) 748 52 2963
Web Site: www.daifuku.com
Material Handling Equipment Mfr
S.I.C.: 3559
N.A.I.C.S.: 333249

U.S. Subsidiary:

Daifuku America Corporation (1)
6700 Tussing Rd
Reynoldsburg, OH 43068
Tel.: (614) 863-1888
Fax: (614) 863-0331
Web Site: www.daifukuamerica.com
Manufacturing & Distribution Machinery
S.I.C.: 3559
N.A.I.C.S.: 333249
Aki Nishimura *(Pres)*

Subsidiaries:

Daifuku Webb Holding Company (2)
34375 W 12 Mile Rd
Farmington Hills, MI 48331 DE
Tel.: (248) 553-1000
Fax: (248) 553-1242
E-Mail: info@daifukuwebb.com
Web Site: www.daifukuwebb.com
Holding Company
S.I.C.: 6719
N.A.I.C.S.: 551112
Brian Stewart *(Chm, Pres & CEO)*

Subsidiaries:

Jervis B. Webb Company (3)
34375 W 12 Mi Rd
Farmington Hills, MI 48331 MI
Tel.: (248) 553-1000
Telex: 211892 jwebb ur
Fax: (248) 553-1228
Toll Free: (800) 526-9322
E-Mail: info@jervisbwebb.com
Web Site: www.jervisbwebb.com
Sales Range: $300-349.9 Million
Emp.: 2,000
Material Handling Systems
Import Export
S.I.C.: 3559
N.A.I.C.S.: 333249
Brian G. Stewart *(Pres)*
John S. Doychich *(CFO & Sr VP)*
Timothy Veeser *(Gen Counsel & Sec)*
Kenneth Hamel *(Sr VP-Airport Sys)*

Plants:

Jervis B. Webb Company (4)
8212 M-119
Harbor Springs, MI 49740-9595 MI
Tel.: (231) 347-3931
Fax: (231) 348-7201
Web Site: www.jervisbwebb.com
Emp.: 150
Heavy Duty Roller Conveyors, Gravity Roller, Chain Driven Live Roller, Accumulation Conveyors, Chain Transfer Conveyors
S.I.C.: 3537
N.A.I.C.S.: 333924

Jervis B. Webb Company (4)
156 Webb Forging Rd
Carlisle, SC 29031-0400 SC
Tel.: (864) 427-8421
Fax: (864) 427-8425
E-Mail: info@jervisbwebb.com
Web Site: www.jervisbwebb.com
Emp.: 80
Forgings & Machining
S.I.C.: 3462
N.A.I.C.S.: 332111

Non-U.S. Subsidiaries:

Jervis B. Webb Company Ltd. (4)
Office at Swan Valley 1 Cob Drive
Swan Valley, Northampton, NN4 9BB, United Kingdom UK
Tel.: (44) 1604591104
Fax: (44) 1604594399
E-Mail: sales@jerviswebb.co.uk
Web Site: www.jervisbwebb.com
Emp.: 10
Custom-Designed Material Handling Systems, Conveyors
S.I.C.: 3535
N.A.I.C.S.: 333922
Ian Mole *(Mng Dir)*

Jervis B. Webb Company of Canada Ltd. (4)
1647 Burlington St E
PO Box 3428 Sta C
Hamilton, ON, L8H 7M5, Canada
Tel.: (905) 547-0411
Fax: (905) 549-3798
E-Mail: info@jerviswebb.com
Web Site: www.jervisbwebb.com
Emp.: 200
Custom-designed Material Handling Systems, Conveyors
S.I.C.: 3535
N.A.I.C.S.: 333922
Rob Meijer *(Exec VP & Gen Mgr)*

Jervis Webb China Co., Ltd. (4)
2908 New Town Center 83 Loushanguan Road
Shanghai, 200336, China CN
Tel.: (86) 21 5879 9020
Fax: (86) 21 5879 9027
E-Mail: info@webb-china.com
Web Site: www.webb-china.com
Automotive Spare Parts Distr
S.I.C.: 5013
N.A.I.C.S.: 423120

Wynright Corporation (3)
2500 York Rd
Elk Grove Village, IL 60007
Tel.: (847) 595-9400
Web Site: www.wynright.com
Sales Range: $100-124.9 Million
Emp.: 200
Industrial Machinery & Equipment Merchant Whslr
S.I.C.: 5084
N.A.I.C.S.: 423830
Ken Dickerson *(COO)*
Robert Zaleiski *(CIO & Dir-IT)*
John Dillon *(Pres-Client Care)*
Kevin Ambrose *(CEO-Intralogistics)*
Brigitte Janos Brozenec *(Exec VP-Mktg)*
Gordon Hellberg *(Exec VP)*
Ron Adams *(Sr VP-Software & Controls Solutions)*

Logan Teleflex, Inc. (2)
4620-C Proximity Dr
Louisville, KY 40213 DE
Tel.: (502) 964-4929
Fax: (502) 964-1018
E-Mail: marketing@loganteleflex.com
Web Site: www.loganteleflex.com
Emp.: 14
Airport Baggage Handling Services
S.I.C.: 4581
N.A.I.C.S.: 488119
Mike Prentice *(VP-Ops)*

Non-U.S. Subsidiaries:

ATS Co., Ltd. (1)
678-11 Kojan-dong
Namdong-gu, Incheon, Korea (South)
Tel.: (82) 326650300
Fax: (82) 326650301
E-Mail: wun12345@naveo.com
Web Site: www.daifukukorea.com

Daifuku Co., Ltd.—(Continued)

Emp.: 53
Material Handling Equipment
S.I.C.: 3559
N.A.I.C.S.: 333249
Imasato Tetsushi *(Chm)*

BEIJING CONTEC MICROELECTRONICS CORPORATION (1)
B-806 Huatong Building No B19
Chegongzhuang West Road
Haidian District, Beijing, 100044, China
Tel.: (86) 10 8801 8228
Fax: (86) 10 8801 8209
Web Site: www.daifuku.com
Computer Peripheral Device Distr
S.I.C.: 5045
N.A.I.C.S.: 423430

CLEAN FACTOMATION, INC. (1)
746-8 Banpo-Dong
Seocho-Gu, Seoul, 137810, Korea (South)
Tel.: (82) 415381000
Fax: (82) 415381111
Web Site: www.cfinc.co.kr
Material Handling Equipment Mfr
S.I.C.: 3559
N.A.I.C.S.: 333249

Plant:

CLEAN FACTOMATION, INC. - Asan Plant (2)
168 Wonnam-ri Eumbong-myeon
Asan, Chungnam, 336-864, Korea (South)
Tel.: (82) 41 538 1000
Fax: (82) 41 538 1111
Web Site: www.daifuku.com
Material Handling Equipment Mfr
S.I.C.: 3559
N.A.I.C.S.: 333249

CONTEC SOLUTION CHINA CORPORATION (1)
Room 1002 Qilai Building 889 Yishan Road
Shanghai, 200233, China
Tel.: (86) 21 5401 2288
Fax: (86) 21 5401 2287
Web Site: www.contecsolution.com.cn
Electronic Software Development Services
S.I.C.: 7371
N.A.I.C.S.: 541511

CONTEC SOLUTION CO., LTD. (1)
2FL-3 No 738 Zhongzheng Road
Zhonghe District, Taipei, 23511, Taiwan
Tel.: (886) 2 8227 8669
Fax: (886) 2 8227 2498
E-Mail: info@contecsolution.com
Web Site: www.contec.com
Computer Peripheral Equipment Distr
S.I.C.: 5045
N.A.I.C.S.: 423430
Kris Hsu *(Gen Mgr)*

U.S. Subsidiary:

DTx, Inc. (2)
1800 Penn St Ste 1
Melbourne, FL 32901-2625
Tel.: (321) 728-0172
Fax: (321) 722-2216
Toll Free: (888) 285-0172
Web Site: www.dtx.com
Sales Range: $25-49.9 Million
Emp.: 75
Systems Design, Engineering & Computing Services
Import Export
S.I.C.: 7373
N.A.I.C.S.: 541512
Randall E. Poliner *(Chm)*
Todd E. Stirtzinger *(Pres & CEO)*
Kevin Manuel *(CFO)*
Dan Nelson *(Exec VP-Sls & Mktg)*

Daifuku Automation (Tianjin) Co., Ltd. (1)
Room 31E Block B The Mansion Triumphal Arch
66 Nanjing Road, Tianjin, 300042, China
Tel.: (86) 2223111291
Fax: (86) 2223111292
Web Site: www.daifukutianjin.com
Automotive Assembly Systems
S.I.C.: 3559
N.A.I.C.S.: 333249

Daifuku Canada Inc. (1)
216 Matheson Blvd E
Mississauga, ON, L4Z 1X1, Canada
Tel.: (905) 507-1133
Fax: (905) 507-1715
E-Mail: pmartin@daifukucanada.com
Web Site: www.daifukucanada.com
Rev.: $10,000,000
Emp.: 8
Automotive Assembly Systems
S.I.C.: 3559
N.A.I.C.S.: 333249

DAIFUKU (CHINA) AUTOMATION CO., LTD. (1)
Yushan-zhen
Mocheng District, Changshu, Jiangsu, 215556, China
Tel.: (86) 512 5249 0111
Fax: (86) 512 5249 0133
Web Site: www.daifuku.com
Automobile Spare Parts Mfr
S.I.C.: 3714
N.A.I.C.S.: 336390

Daifuku (China) Co., Ltd. (1)
Room 2401 New Town Center 83
Loushanguan Rd
88 Lou Shan Guan Rd, Shanghai, 200336, China
Tel.: (86) 2162368600
Fax: (86) 2162368200
Web Site: www.daifukushanghai.com
Material Handling Systems
S.I.C.: 3559
N.A.I.C.S.: 333249
Katsutoshi Fujiki *(Chm)*

DAIFUKU (CHINA) MANUFACTURING CO., LTD. (1)
322 Songdong Road Songjiang Industrial Zone
Shanghai, 201613, China
Tel.: (86) 21 6774 2436
Fax: (86) 21 6774 2437
Material Handling Machinery Mfr
S.I.C.: 3559
N.A.I.C.S.: 333249

Daifuku Europe Ltd. (1)
Daifuku House Waterside Dr
Langley Business Park, Langley, Berks, SL3 6EZ, United Kingdom
Tel.: (44) 753581000
Fax: (44) 753582210
Web Site: www.daifukueurope.com
Emp.: 35
Material Handling Systems
S.I.C.: 3559
N.A.I.C.S.: 333249
Tamatsu Yamasaki *(Mng Dir)*

DAIFUKU INDIA PRIVATE LIMITED (1)
18 Ramnath House Community Centre
Yusuf Sarai, New Delhi, 110049, India
Tel.: (91) 11 2651 2970
Fax: (91) 11 2651 2974
E-Mail: daifukuindia@airtelmail.in
Web Site: www.daifukuindia.com
Material Handling Equipment Mfr
S.I.C.: 3559
N.A.I.C.S.: 333249
Tadahisa Tamura *(Co-Mng Dir)*
Katsuo Tsuji *(Co-Mng Dir)*

DAIFUKU KOREA CO., LTD. (1)
88B-12L Namdong Industrial Estate 678-11 Gojan-dong
Namdong-gu, Incheon, 405-819, Korea (South)
Tel.: (82) 32 665 0300
Fax: (82) 32 665 0301
Web Site: www.daifukukorea.com
Material Handling Machinery Mfr & Distr
S.I.C.: 3559
N.A.I.C.S.: 333249
Imasato Tetsushi *(Chm)*

Divisions:

DAIFUKU KOREA CO., LTD. - Carwash Division (2)
5FL Ungjin Bldg 682-2 Deungchon-dong
Gangseo-gu, Seoul, 157-033, Korea (South)
Tel.: (82) 2 3663 1326
Fax: (82) 2 3663 5860
Web Site: www.daifuku.com
Material Handling Machinery Mfr
S.I.C.: 3559
N.A.I.C.S.: 333249

DAIFUKU KOREA CO., LTD. - Overseas Division (2)
114B-2L Namdong Industrial Estate 684-1 Gojan-dong
Namdong-gu, Incheon, 405-820, Korea (South)
Tel.: (82) 32 818 0033
Fax: (82) 32 815 9922
Web Site: www.daifuku.com
Material Handling Machinery Mfr
S.I.C.: 3559
N.A.I.C.S.: 333249

Daifuku (Malaysia) Sdn. Bhd. (1)
27 Jalan PJS 11 14 Bandar Sunway
Petaling Jaya, 46160, Malaysia
Tel.: (60) 356321842
Fax: (60) 60356321843
E-Mail: admin@daifuku.com.my
Web Site: www.daifukumalaysia.com
Emp.: 20
Material Handling Systems
S.I.C.: 3559
N.A.I.C.S.: 333249
Hiroyuki Katsura *(Mng Dir)*

Daifuku Mechatronics (Singapore) Pte. Ltd. (1)
Block 4010 Ang Mo Kio Avenue 10
07-01 Techplace 1, Singapore, 569626, Singapore
Tel.: (65) 65526166
Fax: (65) 65526766
Web Site: www.daifukusingapore.com
Emp.: 70
Material Handling Systems
S.I.C.: 3559
N.A.I.C.S.: 333249
Koji Yamamoto *(Mng Dir)*

Daifuku Pioneer Co., Ltd. (1)
6F 202 Sec 2 Yen Ping North Road
Taipei, Taiwan
Tel.: (886) 225533653
Fax: (886) 2 2557 7073
E-Mail: dpc@dpc.daifuku.co.jp
Web Site: www.taiwandaifuku.com
Material Handling Systems
S.I.C.: 3559
N.A.I.C.S.: 333249

Daifuku (Thailand) Ltd. (1)
35 Moo 4 Chonburi Industrial Estate
Bo-Win Sriracha, Chon Buri, 20230, Thailand
Tel.: (66) 38345481
Fax: (66) 38345479
Web Site: www.daifukuthailand.com
Material Handling Systems
S.I.C.: 3559
N.A.I.C.S.: 333249
Kazunobu Hirotsu *(Pres)*

Jiangsu Daifuku Rixin Automation Co., Ltd. (1)
Changrui Village Mocheng Management Zone Yushan Town
Changshu, 215556, China
Tel.: (86) 51252490198
Fax: (86) 51252490133
Automotive Parts Mfr
S.I.C.: 3714
N.A.I.C.S.: 336390

LOGAN TELEFLEX (FRANCE) S.A. (1)
7 Allee de la Seine
BP 229
94203 Ivry-sur-Seine, France
Tel.: (33) 1 49 597474
Fax: (33) 1 46 713524
E-Mail: systems@loganteleflex.fr
Web Site: www.loganteleflex.com
Emp.: 18
Airport Baggage Handling Services
S.I.C.: 4581
N.A.I.C.S.: 488119
Daniel Bordes *(Gen Mgr)*

LOGAN TELEFLEX (UK) LTD. (1)
Sutton Road
Hull, HU7 0DR, United Kingdom
Tel.: (44) 1482 78 56 00
Fax: (44) 1482 78 56 99
E-Mail: marketing@loganteleflex.co.uk
Web Site: www.loganteleflex.co.uk
Baggage Handling System Mfr
S.I.C.: 3559
N.A.I.C.S.: 333249
Ron Osborne *(Mng Dir)*

P.T. DAIFUKU INDONESIA (1)
Wisma Aldiron Dirgantara 3rd Floor Unit 349 Jl Jend
Gatot Subroto Kav 72, Jakarta, 12780, Indonesia
Tel.: (62) 21 797 5448
Fax: (62) 21 797 5457
Web Site: www.daifukuindonesia.com
Material Handling System Mfr
S.I.C.: 3559
N.A.I.C.S.: 333249
Hiromitsu Yakabe *(Pres)*

TAIWAN CONTEC CO., LTD. (1)
2FL-2 No 186 Jianyi Road
Zhonghe District, Taipei, 23553, Taiwan
Tel.: (886) 2 8227 8669
Fax: (886) 2 8227 2498
Computer Peripheral Device Mfr
S.I.C.: 3575
N.A.I.C.S.: 334118

TAIWAN DAIFUKU CO., LTD. (1)
No 7 Daye 1st Road Tainan Science Park
Sinshih District, T'ainan, 74146, Taiwan
Tel.: (886) 6 505 5993
Web Site: www.taiwandaifuku.com
Material Handling System Mfr & Distr
S.I.C.: 3559
N.A.I.C.S.: 333249
Hideyuki Ikeda *(Chm)*
Tsuneo Sugimoto *(Pres)*

Plant:

TAIWAN DAIFUKU CO., LTD. - Taichung Plant (2)
4 Fl No 46 Keya Road
Daya District, Taichung, 42878, Taiwan
Tel.: (886) 4 2567 5885
Fax: (886) 4 2568 0285
Web Site: www.taiwandaifuku.com
Material Handling Machinery Mfr
S.I.C.: 3559
N.A.I.C.S.: 333249

DAIHAN SCIENTIFIC CO., LTD.

24-4 Daihan Building Sangwolgok-Dong
Sungbuk-Gu, Seoul, 136-120, Korea (South)
Tel.: (82) 2 9675235
Fax: (82) 2 9635231
E-Mail: info@daihansci.co.kr
Web Site: www.daihan-sci.com
Year Founded: 1980
131220—(KRS)
Sales Range: $10-24.9 Million
Emp.: 140

Business Description:
Laboratory Instruments Mfr
S.I.C.: 3826
N.A.I.C.S.: 334516

Personnel:
Eun Taek Shu *(CEO)*

DAIHEN CORPORATION

2-1-11 Tagawa, Yodogawa-ku
Osaka, 532-8512, Japan
Tel.: (81) 663011212
Fax: (81) 663080913
Web Site: www.daihen.co.jp
Emp.: 800

Business Description:
Robotics
S.I.C.: 7389
N.A.I.C.S.: 541490

Personnel:
Masaru Yagyu *(Pres)*

DAIHO CORPORATION

24 4 Shinkawa 1 Chome Chuo ku
1048289 Tokyo, Tokyo, Japan
Tel.: (81) 332977008
Fax: (81) 335536935
Web Site: www.daiho.co.jp

1822—(TKS)
Sales Range: $1-4.9 Billion
Emp.: 924

Business Description:
Construction Services
S.I.C.: 8711
N.A.I.C.S.: 541330

Personnel:
Hisao Mizushima *(CEO)*

DAIICHI CHUO KISEN KAISHA

14-4 Shintomi 2-chome
Chuo-ku, Tokyo, 104-8544, Japan
Tel.: (81) 355401997
Fax: (81) 335238987
Web Site: www.firstship.co.jp
Year Founded: 1892
D5C—(DEU TKS)
Rev.: $1,544,961,000
Assets: $1,531,519,000
Liabilities: $1,396,692,000
Net Worth: $134,827,000
Earnings: ($351,813,000)
Fiscal Year-end: 03/31/13

Business Description:
Deep Sea Freight Transportation Services
S.I.C.: 4412
N.A.I.C.S.: 483111

Personnel:
Masakazu Yakushiji *(Pres)*
Toshihide Egawa *(Exec Officer)*
Kouji Fujita *(Sr Mng Exec Officer)*
Naoki Ishii *(Exec Officer)*
Masahiro Kanno *(Mng Exec Officer)*
Kazuo Kato *(Exec Officer)*
Tadashi Kato *(Assoc Exec Officer)*
Shigeo Kobayashi *(Exec Officer)*
Kosuke Kodaka *(Mng Exec Officer)*
Tetsuya Mera *(Assoc Exec Officer)*
Fumihito Murase *(Assoc Exec Officer)*
Ken Shimizu *(Exec Officer)*
Yasuhiko Tamakoshi *(Sr Mng Exec Officer)*
Shuichi Tomita *(Exec Officer)*
Takami Watanabe *(Mng Exec Officer)*

Board of Directors:
Kouji Fujita
Masahiro Kanno
Kosuke Kodaka
Yasuhiko Tamakoshi
Takami Watanabe
Masakazu Yakushiji

DAIICHI JITSUGYO CO. LTD.

Kowa Nibancho Bldg 11-19 Nibancho
Chiyoda-Ku
Tokyo, 102 0084, Japan
Tel.: (81) 352148500
Fax: (81) 352148501
E-Mail: info@djk.co.jp
Web Site: www.djk.co.jp
Year Founded: 1948
8059—(TKS)
Sls.: $1,410,519,000
Assets: $896,258,000
Liabilities: $577,115,000
Net Worth: $319,143,000
Earnings: $33,561,000
Emp.: 1,043
Fiscal Year-end: 03/31/13

Business Description:
Machinery Distr
S.I.C.: 5084
N.A.I.C.S.: 423830

Personnel:
Koji Yamagata *(Pres & CEO)*
Tohru Tsuda *(Sr Mng Dir & CFO)*
Michiaki Sugiura *(Mng Dir)*
Junzo Takai *(Mng Dir)*
Shigeki Terakawa *(Mng Dir)*
Yoshihide Yamanaka *(Mng Dir)*
Itaru Kage *(Exec Officer-Admin & Acctg Div)*
Akira Kasamatsu *(Mng Exec Officer)*
Hajime Kimoto *(Mng Exec Officer)*
Ryuichi Ninomiya *(Exec Officer-Nagoya Bus Div)*
Takanori Ogura *(Mng Exec Officer)*
Daisuke Ozono *(Exec Officer-Aviation & Indus Machinery Bus Div)*
Hitoshi Takasaki *(Exec Officer)*
Toru Takata *(Mng Exec Officer-Plant & Energy Bus Div)*
Masatoshi Ueno *(Exec Officer-Electronics Sys Bus Div)*
Ichiro Uno *(Exec Officer-Osaka Bus Div)*
Muneo Yamano *(Exec Officer-Plant & Energy Bus Div)*
Hiroshi Yoshida *(Mng Exec Officer)*
Mitsuru Yoshida *(Mng Exec Officer)*

Board of Directors:
Michiaki Sugiura
Junzo Takai
Shigeki Terakawa
Tohru Tsuda
Koji Yamagata
Yoshihide Yamanaka

Transfer Agent:
Tokyo Securities Transfer Agent Co., Ltd.
Togin Bldg 1-4-2 Marunouchi
Chiyoda-ku, Tokyo, 100-0005, Japan
Tel.: (81) 3 3212 4611

Subsidiaries:

DAIICHI ENGINEERING CO., LTD. (1)
Kowa Nibancho Bldg 11-19 Nibancho
Chiyoda-ku, Tokyo, 102-0084, Japan
Tel.: (81) 3 3288 1951
Fax: (81) 3 3288 1955
E-Mail: dekinfo@djkeng.com
Web Site: www.djkeng.com
Industrial Engineering Equipment Mfr
S.I.C.: 3559
N.A.I.C.S.: 333249

DAIICHI JITSUGYO VISWILL CO., LTD. (1)
12-43 Honami-cho
Osaka, 564-0042, Japan
Tel.: (81) 6 6378 6115
Fax: (81) 6 6378 6117
Web Site: www.viswill.jp
Inspection System Mfr
S.I.C.: 3829
N.A.I.C.S.: 334519

Daiichi Mecha-Tech Corporation (1)
8-6 Ryoke 5-chome kayaguchi-city
Kawaguchi, Saitama, 332-0004, Japan (100%)
Tel.: (81) 482221692
Fax: (81) 482221692
Web Site: www.dmt.co.jp
Emp.: 130
Engineering Services
S.I.C.: 8711
N.A.I.C.S.: 541330
Ogura Takanori *(Pres)*

DJK INNOVALUE CORPORATION (1)
Kowa Nibancho Bldg 11-19 Nibancho
Chiyoda-ku, Tokyo, Japan
Tel.: (81) 3 5214 8728
Fax: (81) 3 5214 8508
Industrial Machinery Mfr
S.I.C.: 3559
N.A.I.C.S.: 333249

Djtech Co.,Ltd. (1)
Asahidai 15 Moroyama Town
Iruma-gun, 350-0444 Saitama, Japan (100%)
Tel.: (81) 492954975
Fax: (81) 492954972
Web Site: www.djtech.co.jp
Emp.: 40
Semiconductor & Related Device Mfr
S.I.C.: 3674
N.A.I.C.S.: 334413
Norio Watanabe *(Pres)*

Joint Venture:

Sulzer Daiichi K.K. (1)
TSI Hakozaki Building 20 5 Nihonbashi
Tokyo, 103 0015, Japan
Tel.: (81) 336645721
Fax: (81) 336645737
Web Site: www.sulzerpumps.com
Emp.: 8
Joint Venture of Sulzer Ltd. & Daichi Jitsugyo Co. Ltd.; Pulp & Paper Machinery & Equipment Sales
S.I.C.: 3553
N.A.I.C.S.: 333243
Takumi Seki *(CEO)*

U.S. Subsidiaries:

Daiichi Jitsugyo (America), Inc. (1)
939 AEC Dr
Wood Dale, IL 60191 (100%)
Tel.: (630) 875-0101
Fax: (630) 875-0422
Industrial Machinery & Equipment Whslr
S.I.C.: 5084
N.A.I.C.S.: 423830
Taka Sagawa *(Mgr-Coordination)*

Daiichi Jitsugyo Purerto Rico, Inc (1)
106 Gautier Benitez Ave
Caguas, PR 00725 (100%)
Tel.: (787) 746-5396
Web Site: www.dja-global.com
Industrial Machinery & Equipment Whslr
S.I.C.: 5084
N.A.I.C.S.: 423830

Non-U.S. Subsidiaries:

Dai-Ichi Jitsugyo (Malaysia) Sdn Bhd (1)
Ste 21B 21st Fl UBN Twr
Box No 80
No 10 Jalan P Ramlee, 50250 Kuala Lumpur, Malaysia (100%)
Tel.: (60) 320706913
Fax: (60) 320706912
E-Mail: isa@daichijitsuguio.com
Web Site: www.dja-global.com
Emp.: 20
Industrial Machinery & Equipment Whslr
S.I.C.: 5084
N.A.I.C.S.: 423830
Masahiko Mizumoto *(Mng Dir)*

DAI-ICHI JITSUGYO (THAILAND) CO., LTD. (1)
252/117-8 G-H 23 Rd Floor Rachadaphisek Road
Huaykwang, Bangkok, 10320, Thailand
Tel.: (66) 2 693 2681
Fax: (66) 2 693 2683
Emp.: 35
Steel Products Mfr
S.I.C.: 3312
N.A.I.C.S.: 331110
Shinji Otsuki *(Mng Dir)*

Daiichi Jitsugyo Asia Pte Ltd (1)
31 Kaki Bukit Rd 3 #02-02 Techlink
417818 Singapore, Singapore (100%)
Tel.: (65) 63383732
Fax: (65) 63376761
E-Mail: info@djk-global.com
Web Site: www.djksp.com.sg
Emp.: 36
Industrial Machinery & Equipment Whslr
S.I.C.: 5084
N.A.I.C.S.: 423830

Daiichi Jitsugyo (Guangzhou), Trading Co., Ltd. (1)
Unit 6803A Citic Plz 233 Tianhe N Rd
Guangzhou, China (100%)
Tel.: (86) 2038772405
Fax: (86) 2038772410
Industrial Machinery & Equipment Whslr
S.I.C.: 5084
N.A.I.C.S.: 423830

Daiichi Jitsugyo (Hong Kong), Limited (1)
Ste 1316-16A 13th Fl Ocean Ctr
Harbour City, Kowloon, China (Hong Kong) (100%)
Tel.: (852) 28028233
Fax: (852) 28029734
E-Mail: djk@djk.com.hk
Web Site: www.djk.co.jp/engl/01aboutus/06aboutus_group_aboard.html
Emp.: 30
Industrial Machinery & Equipment Whslr
S.I.C.: 5084
N.A.I.C.S.: 423830

Daiichi Jitsugyo Philippines, Inc. (1)
Unit 2001-2002 Philippines AXA Life Center
Sen Gil Puyat Avenue, 1200 Makati, Philippines (100%)
Tel.: (63) 27596944
Fax: (63) 27596946
Web Site: www.dja-global.com
Emp.: 30
Industrial Machinery & Equipment Whslr
S.I.C.: 5084
N.A.I.C.S.: 423830
Chris Geneciran *(VP)*

DJK EUROPE GMBH (1)
Mergenthalerallee 79-81
65760 Eschborn, Germany
Tel.: (49) 6196 776 1421
Fax: (49) 6196 776 1419
E-Mail: frankfurt@djkeurope.com
Web Site: www.djkeurope.com
Industrial Supplies Distr
S.I.C.: 5085
N.A.I.C.S.: 423840
Shinichiro Masuda *(Mgr-Czech Republic Branch)*

DJK FACTORY SOLUTIONS (PHILIPPINES), INC. (1)
Orient Goldcrest Bldg Lot 32-D Block 2
Phase 5 East Main Avenue
Laguna Techno Park, Binan, Laguna, 4024, Philippines
Tel.: (63) 27596944
Fax: (63) 495023155
Industrial Equipment Repair Services
S.I.C.: 7699
N.A.I.C.S.: 811310
Chris Rey Geneciran *(VP)*

DJK Global Mexico, S.A. de C.V. (1)
Blvd Bellas Artes 17686-114 Fracc
Garita de Otay, 22645 Tijuana, Mexico (99%)
Tel.: (52) 6646478471
Fax: (52) 6646478473
Web Site: www.djk-global.com
Emp.: 150
Industrial Machinery & Equipment Whslr
S.I.C.: 5084
N.A.I.C.S.: 423830

DJK (Taiwan) Corp. (1)
11th Fl-3 23 Sec 1
Chang-An E Road, Taipei, Taiwan (100%)
Tel.: (886) 225371017
Fax: (886) 225216389
Emp.: 14
Industrial Machinery & Equipment Whslr
S.I.C.: 5084
N.A.I.C.S.: 423830

Shanghai Yishi Trading Co., Ltd. (1)
Rm 13th Floor 02-06 Aetna Twr No 107 Zunyi Rd
200051 Shanghai, China (100%)
Tel.: (86) 2162375800
Fax: (86) 2162375258
Web Site: www.djksh.com
Emp.: 100
Industrial Machinery & Equipment Whslr
S.I.C.: 5084
N.A.I.C.S.: 423830
Takehiro Anata *(Gen Mgr)*

DAIICHI KIGENSO KAGAKU KOGYO CO., LTD.

6-38 Hirabayashi Minami 1-chome
Suminoe-ku, Osaka, 559-0025, Japan
Tel.: (81) 666821261
Fax: (81) 666821238
Web Site: www.dkkk.co.jp
Year Founded: 1956
4082—(TKS)
Sales Range: $125-149.9 Million
Emp.: 300

Business Description:
Zirconium Compounds Researcher & Developer
S.I.C.: 2899
N.A.I.C.S.: 325998

Daiichi Kigenso Kagaku Kogyo Co., Ltd.—(Continued)

Personnel:
Hiroshi Sugii *(Pres)*

DAIICHI KOUTSU SANGYO CO., LTD.

2-6-8 Basyaku Kokura-Kita-ku
Kitakyushu City, Fukuoka, 802-8515, Japan
Tel.: (81) 935118811
Fax: (81) 93 511 8812
E-Mail: d_group@daiichi-koutsu.co.jp
Web Site: www.daiichi-koutsu.co.jp/en/index.html
Year Founded: 1960
9035—(FKA)
Sales Range: $800-899.9 Million
Emp.: 10,600

Business Description:
Holding Company; Taxicab Services; Real Estate; Car Sales; Financial Services
S.I.C.: 6719
N.A.I.C.S.: 551112

Personnel:
Hajime Kurotsuchi *(Founder)*
Ryouichirou Tanaka *(Pres)*

Divisions:

Daiichi Koutsu Sangyo Co., Ltd. - Fukuoka Branch (1)
2-17-15 Higashi Hie
Hakata-ku, Fukuoka, 812-0007, Japan
Tel.: (81) 92 475 1567
Taxicab Operating Services
S.I.C.: 4121
N.A.I.C.S.: 485310

Daiichi Koutsu Sangyo Co., Ltd. - Kagoshima Branch (1)
2-11-3 Usuki
Kagoshima, 890-0073, Japan
Tel.: (81) 99 286 5802
Taxicab Operating Services
S.I.C.: 4121
N.A.I.C.S.: 485310

Daiichi Koutsu Sangyo Co., Ltd. - Kitakyushu Headquarters Traffic Enterprise Division (1)
2-6-8 Basyaku
Kokurakita-ku, Kitakyushu, Fukuoka, 802-8515, Japan
Tel.: (81) 93 511 8850
Taxicab Operating Services
S.I.C.: 4121
N.A.I.C.S.: 485310

Daiichi Koutsu Sangyo Co., Ltd. - Miyazaki Banch (1)
4238-1 Ko Minami Hamada
Yoshimura-town, Miyazaki, 880-0841, Japan
Tel.: (81) 985 27 5513
Taxicab Operating Services
S.I.C.: 4121
N.A.I.C.S.: 485310

Subsidiaries:

Ajigaura Daiichi Traffic Ltd. (1)
185-22 Maeyama Aza
Ajigaura-town, 311-1201 Hitachinaka, Ibaraki, Japan
Tel.: (81) 29 265 8545
Web Site: www.daiichi-koutsu.co.jp/en/group/gaiyou/network/net_taxi.html
Taxicab Operating Services
S.I.C.: 4121
N.A.I.C.S.: 485310

Akashina Daiichi Traffic Ltd. (1)
6833 Nakagawate Oaza
Higashi Chikuma-gun, Azumino, Nagano, 399-7102, Japan
Tel.: (81) 263 82 2306
Web Site: www.daiichi-koutsu.co.jp/en/group/gaiyou/network/net_taxi.html
Taxicab Operating Services
S.I.C.: 4121
N.A.I.C.S.: 485310

Atami Daiichi Traffic Co., Ltd. (1)
14 16 Chuo Town
Atami, Shizuoka, Japan
Tel.: (81) 557818285
Fax: (81) 557818286
Web Site: www.daiichi-koutsu.co.jp/en/group/gaiyou/network/net_taxi.html
Emp.: 90
Hired Car Enterprise
S.I.C.: 4121
N.A.I.C.S.: 485310
Daiichi Takshi *(Pres)*

Daiichi Tourism Taxi Co., Ltd. (1)
27 Chikara Town
Iida, Nagano, 395 0032, Japan
Tel.: (81) 265225050
E-Mail: d_group@daiichi-koutsu.co.jp
Web Site: www.daiichi-koutsu.co.jp
Hired Car Enterprise
S.I.C.: 4121
N.A.I.C.S.: 485310

Daishoji Daiichi Traffic Co., Ltd. (1)
I 133 3 Kumasaka
Kaga, Ishikawa, 922 0842, Japan
Tel.: (81) 761731113
Web Site: www.daiichi-koutsu.co.jp/en/group/gaiyou/network/net_taxi.html
Emp.: 53
Hired Car Enterprise
S.I.C.: 4121
N.A.I.C.S.: 485310
Yoshigi Monakata *(Mgr)*

Fuji Daiichi Traffic Co., Ltd. (1)
I-281 Oda
Oda, Shimane, 694-0064, Japan
Tel.: (81) 854 82 0660
Taxicab Operating Services
S.I.C.: 4121
N.A.I.C.S.: 485310

Fukugawa Daiichi Traffic Ltd (1)
3 11 6 Fukugawa
Shunan, Yamaguchi, 746 0038, Japan
Tel.: (81) 834630735
Web Site: www.daiichi-koutsu.co.jp/en/group/gaiyou/network/net_taxi.html
Hired Car Enterprise
S.I.C.: 4121
N.A.I.C.S.: 485310

Fuyo Daiichi Traffic Co., Ltd. (1)
1 16 Minami Rokugo
Ota ku, Tokyo, 144 0045, Japan
Tel.: (81) 337387186
Fax: (81) 337301466
Web Site: www.daiichi-koutsu.co.jp/en/group/gaiyou/network/net_taxi.html
Emp.: 153
Hired Car Enterprise
S.I.C.: 4121
N.A.I.C.S.: 485310
Hiroshi Fujiu *(Mgr)*

Gobo Daiichi Traffic Co., Ltd. (1)
158 Sono
Gobo, Wakayama, 644-0002, Japan
Tel.: (81) 738 22 3366
Taxicab Operating Services
S.I.C.: 4121
N.A.I.C.S.: 485310

Gunhoku Daiichi Traffic Co., Ltd. (1)
1691-6
Shibukawa, Gunma, 377-0000, Japan
Tel.: (81) 279 22 2247
Taxicab Operating Services
S.I.C.: 4121
N.A.I.C.S.: 485310

Higo Daiichi Traffic Ltd (1)
2 17 28 Shimasaki
Kumamoto, Kumamoto, 860 0073, Japan
Tel.: (81) 963542765
Web Site: www.daiichi-koutsu.co.jp/en/group/gaiyou/network/net_taxi.html#fukuoka
Hired Car Enterprise
S.I.C.: 4121
N.A.I.C.S.: 485310

Himeji Daiichi Traffic Co., Ltd. (1)
867 Megakita town
Shikama ku, Himeji, Hyogo, 672 8031, Japan
Tel.: (81) 792452440
Web Site: www.daiichi-koutsu.co.jp/en/group/gaiyou/network/net_taxi.html
Hired Car Enterprise
S.I.C.: 4121
N.A.I.C.S.: 485310

Hiratsuka Daiichi Traffic & Co., Ltd. (1)
1 Kotohira-town
Akune, Kagoshima, 899 1615, Japan
Tel.: (81) 996721135
Web Site: www.daiichi-koutsu.co.jp
Taxi & Car Enterprise
S.I.C.: 4121
N.A.I.C.S.: 485310

Hiroshima Daiichi Traffic Co., Ltd. (1)
1 9 54 Kusatsu port Nishi ku
Hiroshima, Hiroshima, 733 0832, Japan
Tel.: (81) 822785522
Fax: (81) 822784433
E-Mail: hiroshima@daiichi-koutsu.co.jp
Web Site: www.daiichi-koutsu.co.jp
Emp.: 100
Hired Car Enterprise
S.I.C.: 4121
N.A.I.C.S.: 485310
Kazuyuki Noguchi *(Pres)*

Ibaraki Daiichi Traffic Ltd. (1)
1-1233-1 Migawa
Mito, Ibaraki, 310-0912, Japan
Tel.: (81) 29 243 1231
Taxicab Operating Services
S.I.C.: 4121
N.A.I.C.S.: 485310

Idsumo Daiichi Traffic Co., Ltd. (1)
1248 1 Zenkoji Aza
Enya Town, Izumo, Shimane, 693 0021, Japan
Tel.: (81) 853212556
Web Site: www.daiichi-koutsu.co.jp
Hired Car Enterprise
S.I.C.: 4121
N.A.I.C.S.: 485310

Iwakuni Daiichi Traffic Ltd (1)
4 65 28 Minami Iwakuni Town
Iwakuni, Yamaguchi, 740 0034, Japan
Tel.: (81) 827312418
Web Site: www.daiichi-koutsu.co.jp/en/group/gaiyou/network/net_taxi.html
Hired Car Enterprise
S.I.C.: 4121
N.A.I.C.S.: 485310

Izu Daiichi Traffic Co., Ltd. (1)
9 1 B 201 Tawara Hon
Atami, Shizuoka, 413 0011, Japan
Tel.: (81) 557822410
Fax: (81) 557812830
Web Site: www.daiichi-koutsu.co.jp/en/group/gaiyou/network/net_taxi.html
Hired Car Enterprise
S.I.C.: 4121
N.A.I.C.S.: 485310

Kanko Daiichi Traffic Co., Ltd. (1)
1-4002-38 Ishikawa
Mito, Ibaraki, 310-0905, Japan
Tel.: (81) 29 253 1125
Taxicab Operating Services
S.I.C.: 4121
N.A.I.C.S.: 485310

Kento Daiichi Traffic Co., Ltd. (1)
2-4-4 Soja
Maebashi, Gunma, 371-0853, Japan
Tel.: (81) 27 251 4789
Taxicab Operating Services
S.I.C.: 4121
N.A.I.C.S.: 485310

Koa Daiichi Traffic Co., Ltd. (1)
10-1-25 Kita Nijuyonjo Higashi
Higashi-ku, Sapporo, Hokkaido, 065-0024, Japan
Tel.: (81) 11 731 2413
Taxicab Operating Services
S.I.C.: 4121
N.A.I.C.S.: 485310

Kobe Daiichi Traffic Co., Ltd. (1)
80 Fukaehama Higashi Nada ku
Kobe, Hyogo, 658 0023, Japan
Tel.: (81) 78 411 2137
Web Site: www.daiichi-koutsu.co.jp/en/group/gaiyou/network/net_taxi.html
Hired Car Enterprise
S.I.C.: 4121
N.A.I.C.S.: 485310

Koshu Daiichi Traffic Co., Ltd. (1)
3-32-10 Marunouchi
Kofu, Yamanashi, 400-0031, Japan
Tel.: (81) 55 223 0288
Taxicab Operating Services
S.I.C.: 4121
N.A.I.C.S.: 485310

Kumamoto Daiichi Traffic Ltd (1)
2 3421 Yamanokami
Kumamoto, Kumamoto, 862 0915, Japan
Tel.: (81) 963606622
Web Site: www.daiichi-koutsu.co.jp/en/group/gaiyou/network/net_taxi.html
Hired Car Enterprise
S.I.C.: 4121
N.A.I.C.S.: 485310

Kumano Daiichi Traffic Co., Ltd. (1)
3 1 1 Ikeda
Shingu, Wakayama, 647 0021, Japan
Tel.: (81) 735226313
Web Site: www.daiichi-koutsu.co.jp
Hired Car Enterprise
S.I.C.: 4121
N.A.I.C.S.: 485310

Kushikino Daiichi Traffic Co., Ltd. (1)
163 Sakae
Kagoshima, Kushikino, 896 0013, Japan
Tel.: (81) 996322128
Web Site: www.daiichi-koutsu.co.jp
Hired Car Enterprise
S.I.C.: 4121
N.A.I.C.S.: 485310

Kyoe Daiichi Traffic Industrial Ltd (1)
3 2 39 Yatsue
Yahata Nishi ku, Kitakyushu, Fukuoka, 807 0851, Japan
Tel.: (81) 936027200
Web Site: www.daiichi-koutsu.co.jp/en/group/gaiyou/network/net_taxi.html
Hired Car Enterprise
S.I.C.: 4121
N.A.I.C.S.: 485310

(Masuda) Daiichi Traffic Co., Ltd. (1)
1-15 Akebono-Hon
698-0026 Masuda, Shimane, Japan
Tel.: (81) 856 22 1402
Web Site: www.daiichi-koutsu.co.jp/en/group/gaiyou/network/net_taxi.html
Taxicab Operating Services
S.I.C.: 4121
N.A.I.C.S.: 485310

Matsue Daiichi Traffic Ltd (1)
281 Higashi Asahi town
Matsue, Shimane, 690 0001, Japan
Tel.: (81) 852252323
Web Site: www.daiichi-koutsu.co.jp
Hired Car Enterprise
S.I.C.: 4121
N.A.I.C.S.: 485310

(Matsumoto) Daiichi Traffic Co., Ltd. (1)
2-269-1 Nagisa
Matsumoto, Nagano, 390-0841, Japan
Tel.: (81) 263 26 9333
Taxicab Operating Services
S.I.C.: 4121
N.A.I.C.S.: 485310

Matsushima Wakaba Daiichi Traffic Ltd. (1)
6-14 Konashiya Aza
Miyagi-gun, Matsushima, 981-0200, Japan
Tel.: (81) 22 354 2068
Taxicab Operating Services
S.I.C.: 4121
N.A.I.C.S.: 485310

Mikage Daiichi Co., Ltd. (1)
3 1 5 Sumiyoshimiya town
Higashi Nada ku, Kobe, 658 0053, Japan
Tel.: (81) 788111814
Web Site: www.daiichi-koutsu.co.jp/en/group/gaiyou/network/net_taxi.html
Hired Car Enterprise
S.I.C.: 4121
N.A.I.C.S.: 485310
Kawahara Guwoshi *(Mng Dir)*

Minato Daiichi Traffic Co., Ltd. (1)
882 Asai town
Hamada, Shimane, 697 0022, Japan
Tel.: (81) 855226567
Web Site: www.daiichi-koutsu.co.jp
Hired Car Enterprise
S.I.C.: 4121
N.A.I.C.S.: 485310

Nagoya Daiichi Traffic Co., Ltd. (1)
3 6 45 Yanagihara
Kita ku, Nagoya, Aichi, 462 0845, Japan
Tel.: (81) 529131112
Web Site: www.daiichi-koutsu.co.jp/en/grou p/gaiyou/network/net_taxi.html
Hired Car Enterprise
S.I.C.: 4121
N.A.I.C.S.: 485310

Numazu Daiichi Traffic Co., Ltd. (1)
10-9 Shinsawada-town
Numazu, Shizuoka, 410-0003, Japan
Tel.: (81) 559 23 5811
Taxicab Operating Services
S.I.C.: 4121
N.A.I.C.S.: 485310

Okubo Daiichi Traffic Ltd. (1)
2-22-2 Fujimi
350-1306 Sayama, Saitama, Japan
Tel.: (81) 42 959 5161
Web Site: www.daiichi-koutsu.co.jp/en/grou p/gaiyou/network/net_taxi.html
Taxicab Operating Services
S.I.C.: 4121
N.A.I.C.S.: 485310

Osaka Daiichi Traffic Co., Ltd. (1)
1-45-1 Kan-nabe-town
Sakai, Osaka, 590-0984, Japan
Tel.: (81) 72 232 6764
Taxicab Operating Services
S.I.C.: 4121
N.A.I.C.S.: 485310

Saitama Daiichi Traffic Co., Ltd. (1)
1-3-28 Irumagawa
350-1305 Sayama, Saitama, Japan
Tel.: (81) 42 959 5161
Web Site: www.daiichi-koutsu.co.jp/en/grou p/gaiyou/network/net_taxi.html
Taxicab Operating Services
S.I.C.: 4121
N.A.I.C.S.: 485310

Sakai Daiichi Traffic Co., Ltd. (1)
1 45 1 Kan Nabe
Sakai, Osaka, 590 0984, Japan
Tel.: (81) 722326764
Web Site: www.daiichi-koutsu.co.jp
Hired Car Enterprise
S.I.C.: 4121
N.A.I.C.S.: 485310

(Saku) Daiichi Traffic Ltd. (1)
47-1 Atobe Oaza
385-0054 Saku, Nagano, Japan
Tel.: (81) 267 64 0808
Web Site: www.daiichi-koutsu.co.jp/en/grou p/gaiyou/network/net_taxi.html
Taxicab Operating Services
S.I.C.: 4121
N.A.I.C.S.: 485310

San Daiichi Traffic Ltd. (1)
2-22-2 Fujimi
350-1306 Sayama, Saitama, Japan
Tel.: (81) 42 959 5161
Web Site: www.daiichi-koutsu.co.jp/en/grou p/gaiyou/network/net_taxi.html
Taxicab Operating Services
S.I.C.: 4121
N.A.I.C.S.: 485310

Sapporo Daiichi Traffic Co., Ltd. (1)
1-1-1 Ichijo Higashi Sapporo
Shiraishi-ku, 003-0001 Sapporo, Hokkaido, Japan
Tel.: (81) 11 811 6024
Web Site: www.daiichi-koutsu.co.jp/en/grou p/gaiyou/network/net_taxi.html
Taxicab Operating Services
S.I.C.: 4121
N.A.I.C.S.: 485310

Sawara Daiichi Traffic Ltd (1)
3 25 10 Noke
Sawara ku, Fukuoka, Fukuoka, 814 0171, Japan
Tel.: (81) 928745131
Fax: (81) 928745132
Web Site: www.daiichi-koutsu.co.jp
Emp.: 150
Hired Car Enterprise
S.I.C.: 4121
N.A.I.C.S.: 485310
Iwa Moto *(Gen Mgr)*

Sen Nari Daiichi Traffic Co., Ltd. (1)
1-63 Nakagiri cho
Kita-ku, Nagoya, Aichi, 462-0051, Japan
Tel.: (81) 525311126
Web Site: www.daiichi-koutsu.co.jp
Hired Car Enterprise
S.I.C.: 4121
N.A.I.C.S.: 485310

Sendai Daiichi Traffic Co., Ltd. (1)
58 Yomogidamae Aza Gamo
Miyagino-ku, 983-0002 Sendai, Miyagi, Japan
Tel.: (81) 22 254 2224
Web Site: www.daiichi-koutsu.co.jp/en/grou p/gaiyou/network/net_taxi.html
Taxicab Operating Services
S.I.C.: 4121
N.A.I.C.S.: 485310

Shimabara Daiichi Traffic Ltd (1)
18 Shimo Kawashiri
Shimabara, Nagasaki, 855 0861, Japan
Tel.: (81) 957 62 2262
Web Site: www.daiichi-koutsu.co.jp/en/grou p/gaiyou/network/net_taxi.html
Hired Car Enterprise
S.I.C.: 4121
N.A.I.C.S.: 485310

Shirahama Daiichi Traffic Co., Ltd. (1)
3086 Shirahama town
Nishi Muro gun, Wakayama, 649 2211, Japan
Tel.: (81) 739423666
Web Site: www.daiichi-koutsu.co.jp/en/grou p/gaiyou/network/net_taxi.html
Hired Car Enterprise
S.I.C.: 4121
N.A.I.C.S.: 485310

Shunan Daiichi Traffic Co., Ltd. (1)
4 2 4 Nishi Matsubara
Tokuyama, Yamaguchi, 745 0054, Japan
Tel.: (81) 834212288
Web Site: www.daiichi-koutsu.co.jp/en/grou p/gaiyou/network/net_taxi.html
Hired Car Enterprise
S.I.C.: 4121
N.A.I.C.S.: 485310

Suwa Daiichi Traffic Ltd. (1)
2-1249-1 Takashima
Suwa, Nagano, 392-0022, Japan
Tel.: (81) 266 58 5151
Taxicab Operating Services
S.I.C.: 4121
N.A.I.C.S.: 485310

Taiyo Daiichi Traffic Co., Ltd. (1)
4 15 16 Wakunami
Kanazawa, Ishikawa, 920 0953, Japan
Tel.: (81) 76 231 5556
Fax: (81) 76 242 2305
Web Site: www.daiichi-koutsu.co.jp/en/grou p/gaiyou/network/net_taxi.html
Hired Car Enterprise
S.I.C.: 4121
N.A.I.C.S.: 485310
Masanori Ikeda *(Mgr)*

Takasaki Daiichi Traffic Co., Ltd. (1)
1842-2 Shibaduka
Takasaki, Gunma, 370-0064, Japan
Tel.: (81) 27 325 5454
Taxicab Operating Services
S.I.C.: 4121
N.A.I.C.S.: 485310

(Takashima) Daiichi Traffic Ltd. (1)
2-1249-1 Takashima
392-0022 Suwa, Nagano, Japan
Tel.: (81) 266 58 5151
Web Site: www.daiichi-koutsu.co.jp/en/grou p/gaiyou/network/net_taxi.html
Taxicab Operating Services
S.I.C.: 4121
N.A.I.C.S.: 485310

Tobata Daiichi Traffic Industrial Co., Ltd. (1)
2 5 27 Yomiya
Tobata ku, Kitakyushu, Fukuoka, 804 0042, Japan
Tel.: (81) 938814380
Web Site: www.daiichi-koutsu.co.jp/en/grou p/gaiyou/network/net_taxi.html
Hired Car Enterprise
S.I.C.: 4121
N.A.I.C.S.: 485310

Tohoku Daiichi Traffic Co., Ltd. (1)
3-6-14 Ogi-town
Miyagino-ku, Sendai, Miyagi, 983-0034, Japan
Tel.: (81) 22 231 7259
Taxicab Operating Services
S.I.C.: 4121
N.A.I.C.S.: 485310

Tokushima Daiichi Traffic Co., Ltd. (1)
3 36 2 Minamijosanjima
Tokushima, Tokushima, 770 0814, Japan
Tel.: (81) 886547651
Web Site: www.daiichi-koutsu.co.jp
Hired Car Enterprise
S.I.C.: 4121
N.A.I.C.S.: 485310

Tokuyama Daiichi Traffic Ltd (1)
4233 3 Shimo Ogushibara
Yunoaza Oaza, Tokuyama, Yamaguchi, 745-1132, Japan
Tel.: (81) 834 83 3901
Web Site: www.daiichi-koutsu.co.jp
Hired Car Enterprise
S.I.C.: 4121
N.A.I.C.S.: 485310

Tokyo Daiichi Hire(Chauffeur driven hired car) Ltd (1)
1 17 3 Senju Midori Town
Adachi ku, Tokyo, 120 0044, Japan
Tel.: (81) 338707733
Fax: (81) 338707112
Web Site: www.daiichi-koutsu.co.jp/en/grou p/gaiyou/network/net_taxi.html
Emp.: 400
Hired Car Enterprise
S.I.C.: 4121
N.A.I.C.S.: 485310
Kaneko Kogiro *(Mgr)*

Tokyo Daiichi Traffic Co., Ltd. (1)
1 17 3 Senju Midori town
Adachi ku, Tokyo, 120 0044, Japan
Tel.: (81) 338707111
Fax: (81) 338707112
Web Site: www.daiichi-koutsu.co.jp
Emp.: 170
Hired Car Enterprise
S.I.C.: 4121
N.A.I.C.S.: 485310
Hiromi Tagashira *(Pres)*

Tsuwano Daiichi Traffic Co., Ltd. (1)
I 53 1 Ushiroda Oaza Tsuwano town
Kanoashi Gun, Tsuwano, Shimane, 699 5605, Japan
Tel.: (81) 856720400
Web Site: www.daiichi-koutsu.co.jp/en/grou p/gaiyou/network/net_taxi.html
Hired Car Enterprise
S.I.C.: 4121
N.A.I.C.S.: 485310

Yamanaka Daiichi Traffic Co., Ltd. (1)
1 YA 25 Honmachi Yamanaka
Enuma, Kanazawa, Ishikawa, 922 0115, Japan
Tel.: (81) 761781324
Web Site: www.daiichi-koutsu.co.jp/en/grou p/gaiyou/network/net_taxi.html
Hired Car Enterprise
S.I.C.: 4121
N.A.I.C.S.: 485310

Yamanashi Daiichi Traffic Co., Ltd. (1)
3-10-12 Satoyoshi
400-0822 Kofu, Yamanashi, Japan
Tel.: (81) 55 223 0285
Web Site: www.daiichi-koutsu.co.jp/en/grou p/gaiyou/network/net_taxi.html
Taxicab Operating Services
S.I.C.: 4121
N.A.I.C.S.: 485310

Yamashiro Daiichi Traffic Co., Ltd. (1)
2-96-1 Yamashiro Onsen Kikyogaoka
922-0257 Kaga, Ishikawa, Japan
Tel.: (81) 761 76 0111
Web Site: www.daiichi-koutsu.co.jp/en/grou p/gaiyou/network/net_taxi.html
Taxicab Operating Services
S.I.C.: 4121
N.A.I.C.S.: 485310

DAIICHI SANKYO CO., LTD.

3-5-1 Nihombashi Honcho
Chuo-ku, Tokyo, 103-8426, Japan
Tel.: (81) 332436051
Web Site: www.daiichisankyo-ep.co.jp
Year Founded: 2005
4568—(OTC TKS)
Sls.: $10,976,372,000
Assets: $18,084,781,000
Liabilities: $8,011,586,000
Net Worth: $10,073,195,000
Earnings: $732,831,000
Emp.: 32,229
Fiscal Year-end: 03/31/13

Business Description:
Pharmaceutical Product Development & Mfg Services
S.I.C.: 2834
N.A.I.C.S.: 325412

Personnel:
Takashi Shoda *(Chm)*
Joji Nakayama *(Pres & CEO)*
Koichi Akahane *(Corp Officer)*
Katsumi Fujimoto *(Corp Officer)*
Shuji Handa *(Exec Officer)*
Kazunori Hirokawa *(Sr Exec Officer)*
Kenji Inoue *(Corp Officer)*
Norimasa Kamura *(Corp Officer)*
Ryouichi Kibushi *(Sr Exec Officer)*
Junichi Koga *(Corp Officer)*
Satoshi Kunitada *(Corp Officer)*
Sunao Manabe *(Corp Officer)*
Katsuaki Miyoshi *(Corp Officer)*
Ryoji Nagasawa *(Corp Officer)*
Takeshi Ogita *(Sr Exec Officer)*
Toshiaki Sai *(Corp Officer)*
Manabu Sakai *(Sr Exec Officer)*
Kazuo Sato *(Corp Officer)*
Yuki Sato *(Sr Exec Officer)*
Shinichi Terano *(Corp Officer)*
Toshiaki Tojo *(Corp Officer)*
Tomoo Yokoi *(Exec Officer)*
Glenn Gormley *(Pres-Pharma Dev & Global Head-R&D)*

Board of Directors:
Takashi Shoda
Hiroshi Hirabayashi
Kazunori Hirokawa
Kunio Ishihara
Ichiro Kanazawa
Joji Nakayama
Takeshi Ogita
Manabu Sakai
Yuki Sato
Seiji Sugiyama

Subsidiaries:

DAIICHI SANKYO BUSINESS ASSOCIE CO., LTD. (1)
1-8 Nihonbashi Koamicho
Chuo-ku, Tokyo, 103-8541, Japan
Tel.: (81) 3 6744 8500
Web Site: www.daiichisankyo.com
Business Support Services
S.I.C.: 7389
N.A.I.C.S.: 561499

DAIICHI SANKYO CHEMICAL PHARMA CO., LTD. (1)
4-4-8 Nishi-yawata
Hiratsuka, Kanagawa, 254-0073, Japan
Tel.: (81) 463 31 3710
Web Site: www.daiichisankyo.com
Pharmaceutical Ingredients Mfr
S.I.C.: 2834
N.A.I.C.S.: 325412

DAIICHI SANKYO ESPHA CO., LTD. (1)
1-16-13 Kitakasai Daiichisankyo Kasai Kenkyukaihatsu Center Nai
Edogawa-Ku, Tokyo, 134-0081, Japan
Tel.: (81) 356968700
E-Mail: info@daiichisankyo-ep.co.jp
Web Site: www.daiichisankyo-ep.co.jp
Pharmaceutical Products Whslr
S.I.C.: 5122
N.A.I.C.S.: 424210

DAIICHI SANKYO HAPPINESS CO., LTD. (1)
1-12-1 Shinomiya
Hiratsuka, Kanagawa, 254-0014, Japan

Daiichi Sankyo Co., Ltd.—(Continued)

Tel.: (81) 463 31 7194
Web Site: www.daiichisankyo.com
Business Support Services
S.I.C.: 7389
N.A.I.C.S.: 561499

DAIICHI SANKYO HEALTHCARE CO., LTD (1)
1-8 Nihonbashi Koamicho
Chuo-ku, Tokyo, 103-8541, Japan
Tel.: (81) 3 6667 3211
Web Site: www.daiichisankyo-hc.co.jp
Personal Care Products Mfr & Whslr
S.I.C.: 2844
N.A.I.C.S.: 325620

DAIICHI SANKYO LOGISTICS CO., LTD. (1)
1-8 Nihonbashi koamicho
Chuo-ku, Tokyo, 103-8541, Japan
Tel.: (81) 3 3664 0941
Web Site: www.daiichisankyo.com
Pharmaceutical Products Distr
S.I.C.: 5122
N.A.I.C.S.: 424210

DAIICHI SANKYO PROPHARMA CO., LTD. (1)
1-8 Nihonbashi Koamicho
Chuo-ku, Tokyo, 103-8541, Japan
Tel.: (81) 3 3664 0946
Web Site: www.ds-propharma.com
Pharmaceutical Products Mfr
S.I.C.: 2834
N.A.I.C.S.: 325412

DAIICHI SANKYO RD NOVARE CO., LTD. (1)
3-10-2 Kitashinagawa
Shinagawa-Ku, Tokyo, 140-0001, Japan
Tel.: (81) 334746651
Chemical Products Mfr
S.I.C.: 2899
N.A.I.C.S.: 325998

Sankyo Co. Ltd. (1)
3 5 1 Nihonbashi Honcho
Chuo Ku
103-8426 Tokyo, Japan
Tel.: (81) 8135996333
Fax: (81) 81352557035
Web Site: www.sankyo.co.jp
Sales Range: $50-74.9 Million
Pharmaceuticals, Agricultural Chemicals & Specialty Chemical Mfr
S.I.C.: 2834
N.A.I.C.S.: 325412

U.S. Subsidiary:

Sankyo Pharma Inc. (2)
2 Hilton Ct
Parsippany, NJ 07054
Tel.: (973) 359-2600
Fax: (973) 359-2645
Web Site: www.tsi.com
Emp.: 500
Mfr. & Marketer of Pharmaceuticals
S.I.C.: 2834
N.A.I.C.S.: 325412

Non-U.S. Subsidiaries:

Daiichi Sankyo Deutschland GmbH (2)
Zielstattstrasse 48
D 81379 Munich, Germany
Tel.: (49) 8978080
Fax: (49) 897808202
E-Mail: service@daiichi-sankyo.eu
Web Site: www.daiichi-sankyo.de
Emp.: 350
Pharmaceutical Research & Development; Mfr & Marketer of Pharmaceuticals
S.I.C.: 2834
N.A.I.C.S.: 325412
Reanhard Pauer *(CEO)*
Ralf Goeddertz *(Mng Dir)*

Non-U.S. Subsidiaries:

Daiichi Sankyo Altkirch (3)
39 Rue du 3 Eme Zouvaes
F 68130 Altkirch, France
Tel.: (33) 389089632
Fax: (33) 389089631
Web Site: www.daiichisankyo.com
Sales Range: $1-9.9 Million
Emp.: 45
Mfr & Exporter of Raw Materials for Pharmaceuticals
Export
S.I.C.: 2834
N.A.I.C.S.: 325412
Boisivom Friederic *(Mng Dir)*

Daiichi Sankyo Italia S.p.A. (3)
Via Paolo di Dono 73
00142 Rome, Italy
Tel.: (39) 06852551
Fax: (39) 0685255233
E-Mail: sankyo@sankyo-pharma.it
Web Site: www.daiichi-sankyo.it
Emp.: 30
Importer & Marketer of Pharmaceuticals
Import
S.I.C.: 5122
N.A.I.C.S.: 424210

Daiichi Sankyo Nederland B.V. (3)
Wilgenlaan 5
1161 JK Zwanenburg, Netherlands
Tel.: (31) 204072072
Fax: (31) 204072070
E-Mail: info@daiichi-sankyo.nl
Web Site: www.daiichi-sankyo.nl
Emp.: 30
Importer & Marketer of Pharmaceuticals
Import
S.I.C.: 5122
N.A.I.C.S.: 424210
Curd Lejaegere *(Mng Dir)*

Daiichi Sankyo Portugal, Lda. (3)
Lagoas Park Bldg 11
2740 270 Porto Salvo, Portugal
Tel.: (351) 214232010
Fax: (351) 214218305
E-Mail: info@daiichi-sankyo.pt
Web Site: www.daiichi-sankyo.pt
Emp.: 20
Importer & Marketer of Pharmaceuticals
Import
S.I.C.: 5122
N.A.I.C.S.: 424210
Isabel Borges *(Mng Dir)*

Daiichi Sankyo (Schweiz) AG (3)
Gewerbestrasse 16
CH 8800 Thalwil, Switzerland
Tel.: (41) 434333300
Fax: (41) 434333301
E-Mail: info@daiichi-sankyo.ch
Web Site: www.daiichi-sankyo.ch
Importer & Marketer of Pharmaceuticals
Import
S.I.C.: 5122
N.A.I.C.S.: 424210
Ralf Goeddertz *(Mng Dir)*

Oy Sankyo Pharma Finland AB (3)
Salomonkatu 17 B
FIN 00100 Helsinki, Finland
Tel.: (358) 207416888
Fax: (358) 207416889
Web Site: www.sankyo-pharma.com
Emp.: 10
Importer & Marketer of Pharmaceuticals
Import
S.I.C.: 5122
N.A.I.C.S.: 424210

Sankyo Pharma UK Ltd (3)
Tilton Pl Chalfont Pk Derrards Cross
Amersham, Buckinghamshire, SL9 OBD, United Kingdom
Tel.: (44) 494766866
Fax: (44) 1494766557
E-Mail: stephenlightfoot@sankyo.co.uk
Web Site: www.sankyo-pharma.com
Emp.: 40
Importer & Marketer of Pharmaceuticals
Import
S.I.C.: 5122
N.A.I.C.S.: 424210

Sankyo Pharmazeutika Austria GmbH (3)
Effingergasse 21
A 1160 Vienna, Austria
Tel.: (43) 48586420
Fax: (43) 4858642345
E-Mail: info@sankyo-pharma.at
Web Site: www.sankyo-pharma.at
Sales Range: $10-24.9 Million
Emp.: 40
Pharmaceuticals Importer & Marketer
Import
S.I.C.: 5122
N.A.I.C.S.: 424210
Rals Godeertz *(Mgr)*

Ranbaxy Laboratories Limited (2)
Plot 90 Sector 32
Gurgaon, Haryana, 122 001, India (60%)
Tel.: (91) 1244135000
Fax: (91) 1244135001
E-Mail: corporate.communications@ranbaxy.com
Web Site: www.ranbaxy.com
500359—(BOM)
Rev.: $23,639,358,402
Assets: $30,526,478,946
Liabilities: $22,789,221,534
Net Worth: $7,737,257,412
Earnings: $1,710,804,456
Emp.: 14,600
Fiscal Year-end: 12/31/12
Branded Generic Pharmaceuticals & Active Pharmaceutical Ingredients Mfr & Pharmaceutical Researcher
S.I.C.: 2834
N.A.I.C.S.: 325412
Indrajit Banerjee *(Pres & CFO)*
Arun Sawhney *(CEO & Mng Dir)*
David Briskman *(CIO & VP)*
R. S. Bakshi *(Chief Medical Officer-Ranbaxy Community Healthcare Society)*
Sudarshan K. Arora *(Pres-R&D)*
Rajiv Gulati *(Pres-Global Pharmaceuticals Bus)*
Sushil K. Patawari *(Sec & VP-IR)*
Dale Adkisson *(Exec VP & Head-Global Quality)*
Sanjeev I. Dani *(Exec VP & Head-Global Strategy, Corp & Bus Dev)*
Ashwani Kumar Malhotra *(Exec VP-Global Pharma Mfg & Supply Chain)*
Ranjan Chakravarti *(Head-Transformation & Bus Consulting)*
Sandeep Girotra *(Sr VP & Head-Global HR)*
K. Venkatachalam *(Sr VP & Dir-North America & Latam)*
Pradip Bhatnagar *(Sr VP-New Drug Discover Res)*
Jay Deshmukh *(Sr VP-Intellectual Property)*
T. L. Easwar *(Sr VP-API Mfg, Projects & EHS)*

Subsidiary:

Rexcel Pharmaceuticals Limited (3)
12th Floor Devika Tower 6 Nehru Place
New Delhi, 110019, India
Tel.: (91) 1126452666
Fax: (91) 1126225987
Emp.: 12
Pharmaceutical Products Mfr
S.I.C.: 2834
N.A.I.C.S.: 325412

U.S. Subsidiaries:

Ohm Laboratories, Inc. (3)
600 College Rd E
Princeton, NJ 08540
Tel.: (877) 646-5227
Web Site: www.ohmlabs.com
Pharmaceutical Products Testing Services
S.I.C.: 8734
N.A.I.C.S.: 541380
Chuck Caprariello *(VP-Corp Comm & Govt Affairs)*

Ranbaxy Laboratories, Inc. (3)
600 College Rd E Fl 22
Princeton, NJ 08540-6636
Tel.: (609) 720-9200
Fax: (609) 750-1155
Pharmaceutical Products Testing Services
S.I.C.: 8734
N.A.I.C.S.: 541380

Ranbaxy Pharmaceuticals Inc. (3)
600 College Rd E
Princeton, NJ 08540-6636
Tel.: (609) 720-9200
Fax: (609) 720-1155
Web Site: www.ranbaxyusa.com
Emp.: 178
Branded Generic Pharmaceuticals Mfr & Pharmaceutical Researcher
S.I.C.: 2834
N.A.I.C.S.: 325412
Charles M. Caprariello *(VP-Corp Comm & Govt Affairs)*

Ranbaxy USA, Inc. (3)
600 College Rd E Ste 2100
Princeton, NJ 08540-6636
Tel.: (609) 720-9200
Pharmaceutical Products Mfr & Whslr
S.I.C.: 2834
N.A.I.C.S.: 325412

Non-U.S. Subsidiaries:

Basics GmbH (3)
Hemmelrather Weg 201 Gebaude GIZ 1
51377 Leverkusen, Germany
Tel.: (49) 214403990
Fax: (49) 21440399909
E-Mail: info@ranbaxy.de
Web Site: www.basics.de
Emp.: 3
Pharmaceutical Products Mfr
S.I.C.: 2834
N.A.I.C.S.: 325412
Sabine Radl *(Mgr)*

Be-Tabs Pharmaceuticals (Proprietary) Ltd. (3)
14 Loutre Road Stormmill Ext 1
Roodepoort, Gauteng, 1724, South Africa
Tel.: (27) 114950100
Fax: (27) 114950150
E-Mail: infosa@ranbaxy.com
Web Site: www.ranbaxy.com
Pharmaceutical Products Mfr
S.I.C.: 2834
N.A.I.C.S.: 325412

Ranbaxy Australia Pty. Ltd. (3)
Suite 4 02 Building D Level 4 12-24 Talavera Road
2113 North Ryde, NSW, Australia
Tel.: (61) 298872600
Fax: (61) 298870119
E-Mail: customerservice.aus@ranbaxy.com
Emp.: 20
Pharmaceutical Products Mfr
S.I.C.: 2834
N.A.I.C.S.: 325412
Alex Evans *(Gen Mgr)*

Ranbaxy Egypt Limited (3)
3 Ahmed Nessim St
Giza, Egypt
Tel.: (20) 2 37613973
Fax: (20) 2 37614513
Web Site: www.ranbaxy-egypt.com
Emp.: 10
Pharmaceutical Products Mfr
S.I.C.: 2834
N.A.I.C.S.: 325412
Ibrahim Shalaby *(Gen Mgr)*

Ranbaxy Europe Ltd (3)
Building 4 Chiswick Park 566 Chiswick High Road
London, W4 5YE, United Kingdom
Tel.: (44) 208 742 5260
Fax: (44) 208 742 5291
Web Site: www.ranbaxy.com
Pharmaceutical Products Mfr
S.I.C.: 2834
N.A.I.C.S.: 325412

Ranbaxy Italia Spa (3)
Via Ariberto 3
20123 Milan, Italy
Tel.: (39) 02 250661
Fax: (39) 02 89419546
E-Mail: info.italia@ranbaxy.com
Web Site: www.ranbaxy.it
Emp.: 25
Pharmaceutical Products Mfr
S.I.C.: 2834
N.A.I.C.S.: 325412
Neeraj Sharma *(Gen Mgr)*

Ranbaxy Malaysia Sdn. Bhd. (3)
Peti 8 Wisma Selangor Dredging 5th Floor
South Block 142-A
Jalan Ampang, 50450 Kuala Lumpur, Malaysia
Tel.: (60) 3 2161 4181
Fax: (60) 3 2162 7593
Web Site: www.ranbaxy.com
Pharmaceutical Products Mfr
S.I.C.: 2834
N.A.I.C.S.: 325412
T. Jeyabalan *(Mng Dir)*

Ranbaxy Mexico S.A. De C.V. (3)
Boulevard Manuel Avila Camacho 76 9th Floor Col Lomas de Chapultepec
Del Miguel Hidalgo, Mexico, 11000, Mexico

Tel.: (52) 55 9178 7640
Fax: (52) 55 9178 7663
Pharmaceutical Products Distr
S.I.C.: 5122
N.A.I.C.S.: 424210

Ranbaxy Morocco LLC (3)
Zenith Millenium Lotissement Attaoufik
Immeuble 1 Bureau 409
Sidi Maarouf, Casablanca, 20190, Morocco
Tel.: (212) 522879440
Fax: (212) 522879441
Web Site: www.ranbaxy.com
Pharmaceutical Products Mfr
S.I.C.: 2834
N.A.I.C.S.: 325412
Atul Chhabra *(Gen Mgr)*

Ranbaxy Pharmaceuticals Canada INC. (3)
2680 Matheson Blvd E Ste 200
Mississauga, ON, L4W 0A5, Canada
Tel.: (905) 219-8820
Fax: (905) 602-4216
Toll Free: (866) 840-1340
E-Mail: sales.canada@ranbaxy.com
Web Site: www.ranbaxy.ca
Emp.: 22
Pharmaceutical Products Distr
S.I.C.: 5122
N.A.I.C.S.: 424210
Paul Drake *(Gen Mgr)*

Ranbaxy (Poland) Sp. Z o.o. (3)
ul Kubickiego 11
02-954 Warsaw, Poland
Tel.: (48) 22 642 07 75
Fax: (48) 22 642 80 57
E-Mail: ranbaxy@ranbaxy.com.pl
Web Site: www.ranbaxy.com.pl
Pharmaceutical Products Mfr & Distr
S.I.C.: 2834
N.A.I.C.S.: 325412
Monika Wierzbowska-Slawinska *(Mgr-Field Force)*

Ranbaxy Portugal (3)
Rua do Campo Alegre 1306 5 Andar Sala 501
4150-174 Porto, Portugal
Tel.: (351) 226 007 647
Fax: (351) 226 007 649
E-Mail: geral@ranbaxy.com
Web Site: www.ranbaxy.pt
Emp.: 1
Pharmaceutical Products Mfr
S.I.C.: 2834
N.A.I.C.S.: 325412
Octavio Andapia *(CFO)*

Ranbaxy-PRP (Peru) S.A.C (3)
Av Juan de Arona 761-765
San Isidro, Lima, Peru
Tel.: (51) 1 441 4553
Fax: (51) 1 421 1553
Pharmaceutical Products Mfr
S.I.C.: 2834
N.A.I.C.S.: 325412

Ranbaxy South Africa (Proprietary) Limited (3)
Tugela House Riverside Office Park 1303
Heuwel Avenue
Centurion, Gauteng, 157, South Africa
Tel.: (27) 126432000
Fax: (27) 126432001
Emp.: 4
Pharmaceutical Products Mfr & Whslr
S.I.C.: 2834
N.A.I.C.S.: 325412

Ranbaxy (UK) Ltd. (3)
Bldg 4 Chiswick Park 566 Chiswick High Road
London, W4 5YE, United Kingdom UK
Tel.: (44) 2087425250
Fax: (44) 2087425251
E-Mail: nevin.bradford@ranbaxy.com
Web Site: www.ranbaxy.com
Sales Range: $1-4.9 Billion
Emp.: 54
Branded Generic Pharmaceuticals Mfr & Pharmaceutical Researcher
S.I.C.: 2834
N.A.I.C.S.: 325412

Plants:

Daiichi Sankyo Co., Ltd. - Akita Plant (1)
1-10-1 Mukaihama
Akita, 010-1601, Japan
Tel.: (81) 18 863 7701
Web Site: www.daiichisankyo.com
Pharmaceutical Products Mfr
S.I.C.: 2834
N.A.I.C.S.: 325412

Daiichi Sankyo Co., Ltd. - Hiratsuka Plant (1)
1-12-1 Shinomiya
Hiratsuka, Kanagawa, 254-0014, Japan
Tel.: (81) 463 31 6111
Web Site: www.daiichisankyo.com
Pharmaceutical Products Mfr
S.I.C.: 2834
N.A.I.C.S.: 325412

Daiichi Sankyo Co., Ltd. - Odawara Plant (1)
450 Takada
Odawara, Kanagawa, 250-0216, Japan
Tel.: (81) 465 42 4101
Web Site: www.daiichisankyo.com
Pharmaceutical Products Mfr
S.I.C.: 2834
N.A.I.C.S.: 325412

Daiichi Sankyo Co., Ltd. - Onahama Plant (1)
389-4 Izumimachi Shimokawa Aza Otsurugi
Iwaki, Fukushima, 971-8183, Japan
Tel.: (81) 246 56 1981
Web Site: www.daiichisankyo.com
Pharmaceutical Products Mfr
S.I.C.: 2834
N.A.I.C.S.: 325412

Daiichi Sankyo Co., Ltd. - Takatsuki Plant (1)
4-38 Aketacho
Takatsuki, Osaka, 569-0806, Japan
Tel.: (81) 72 682 1181
Pharmaceutical Products Mfr
S.I.C.: 2834
N.A.I.C.S.: 325412

U.S. Subsidiaries:

Asubio Phamaceuticals, Inc. (1)
115 W Century Rd 3rd Fl
Paramus, NJ 07652
Tel.: (201) 368-5020
Fax: (201) 225-1358
E-Mail: info@asubio.com
Web Site: www.asubio.com
Pharmaceutical Products Research & Development Services
S.I.C.: 8731
N.A.I.C.S.: 541712

DAIICHI SANKYO, INC. (1)
Two Hilton Ct
Parsippany, NJ 07054
Tel.: (973) 944-2600
Fax: (973) 944-2645
Toll Free: (877) 482-5378
E-Mail: info@dsi.com
Web Site: www.dsi.com
Pharmaceutical Products Mfr
S.I.C.: 2834
N.A.I.C.S.: 325412
Glenn Gormley *(Chm & Corp Pres)*
Greg Barrett *(Acting Pres-Admin & Comml Ops)*

Plexxikon, Inc. (1)
91 Bolivar Dr
Berkeley, CA 94710 CA
Tel.: (510) 647-4000
E-Mail: info@plexxikon.com
Web Site: www.plexxikon.com
Emp.: 40
Pharmaceutical Research & Development
S.I.C.: 8731
N.A.I.C.S.: 541712
Kathleen Sereda Glaub *(Pres)*
K. Peter Hirth *(CEO)*
Keith B. Nolop *(Chief Medical Officer & Sr VP-Dev)*
Gideon E. Bollag *(Sr VP-Res)*

Non-U.S. Subsidiaries:

DAIICHI SANKYO AUSTRIA GmbH (1)
Effingergasse 21
1160 Vienna, Austria
Tel.: (43) 1 485 86 42 0
Fax: (43) 1 485 86 42 345
E-Mail: info@daiichi-sankyo.at
Web Site: www.daiichi-sankyo.at
Pharmaceutical Products Whslr
S.I.C.: 5122
N.A.I.C.S.: 424210

DAIICHI SANKYO BRASIL FARMACEUTICA LTDA. (1)
Av Dr Chucri Zaidan 920-15th Floor Vila Cordeiro
Sao Paulo, 04583-904, Brazil
Tel.: (55) 11 5186 4500
Web Site: www.daiichisankyo.com.br
Pharmaceutical Products Mfr & Whslr
S.I.C.: 2834
N.A.I.C.S.: 325412

DAIICHI SANKYO DEVELOPMENT LTD. (1)
Chiltern Place Chalfont Park
Gerrards Cross, Buckinghamshire, SL9 0BG, United Kingdom
Tel.: (44) 17 53 89 36 00
Web Site: www.daiichisankyo.com
Pharmaceutical Products Mfr
S.I.C.: 2834
N.A.I.C.S.: 325412

DAIICHI SANKYO ESPANA, S.A. (1)
C/Acanto 22 Planta 12
28045 Madrid, Spain
Tel.: (34) 91 5399911
Fax: (34) 91 5284423
E-Mail: info@daiichi-sankyo.es
Web Site: www.daiichi-sankyo.es
Pharmaceutical Products Whslr
S.I.C.: 5122
N.A.I.C.S.: 424210

DAIICHI SANKYO EUROPE GmbH (1)
Zielstattstrasse 48
81379 Munich, Germany
Tel.: (49) 89 78080
Fax: (49) 897808615
E-Mail: service@daiichi-sankyo.eu
Web Site: www.daiichi-sankyo.eu
Emp.: 30
Pharmaceutical Products Mfr
S.I.C.: 2834
N.A.I.C.S.: 325412
Martin Hesse *(CFO)*

DAIICHI SANKYO FRANCE S.A.S. (1)
Immeuble Le Corosa 1 rue Eugene et Armand Peugeot
92508 Rueil-Malmaison, France
Tel.: (33) 1 55 62 14 60
Fax: (33) 1 55 62 14 61
E-Mail: info@daiichi-sankyo.fr
Web Site: www.daiichi-sankyo.fr
Pharmaceutical Products Whslr
S.I.C.: 5122
N.A.I.C.S.: 424210

DAIICHI SANKYO HONG KONG LIMITED (1)
Suite 2905 29/F Central Plaza 18 Harbour Road
Wanchai, China (Hong Kong)
Tel.: (852) 2868 9072
Fax: (852) 2801 4341
E-Mail: infohk@daiichisankyo.com.hk
Web Site: www.daiichisankyo.com.hk
Pharmaceutical Products Distr
S.I.C.: 5122
N.A.I.C.S.: 424210

DAIICHI SANKYO KOREA CO., LTD. (1)
3rd Floor West Wing Posco Center 892
Daechi 4-Dong
Kangnam-gu, Seoul, Korea (South)
Tel.: (82) 52636557
Web Site: www.daiichisankyo.co.kr
Pharmaceutical Products Distr
S.I.C.: 5122
N.A.I.C.S.: 424210

DAIICHI SANKYO PHARMACEUTICAL (BEIJING) CO., LTD. (1)
No 5 Yong Chang Zhong Lu Beijing
Economic Technological Development
Beijing, China
Tel.: (86) 10 8525 1088
Pharmaceutical Products Mfr & Whslr
S.I.C.: 5122
N.A.I.C.S.: 424210

DAIICHI SANKYO PHARMACEUTICAL (SHANGHAI) CO., LTD. (1)
500 Juli Rd Zhangjiang Hi-Tech Park
Pudong New Area, Shanghai, 201203, China
Tel.: (86) 21 5080 3338
Fax: (86) 21 5080 3102
Web Site: www.daiichisankyo-sh.com.cn
Pharmaceutical Products Mfr & Whslr
S.I.C.: 5122
N.A.I.C.S.: 424210

DAIICHI SANKYO TAIWAN LTD. (1)
7F-1 No 308 Sec 2 Bade Rd
Taipei, Taiwan
Tel.: (886) 2 8772 2250
Fax: (886) 2 8772 2251
Web Site: www.daiichisankyo.com.tw
Pharmaceutical Products Whslr
S.I.C.: 5122
N.A.I.C.S.: 424210

DAIICHI SANKYO (THAILAND) LTD. (1)
138 10th Floor Boonmitr Bldg Silom Rd
Khet Bangrak, Bangkok, 10500, Thailand
Tel.: (66) 2634 3401 6
Fax: (66) 2236 2656
Web Site: www.daiichisankyo.co.th
Pharmaceutical Products Mfr & Distr
S.I.C.: 2834
N.A.I.C.S.: 325412

DAIICHI SANKYO UK LIMITED (1)
Chiltern Place Chalfont Park
Gerrards Cross, Buckinghamshire, SL9 0BG, United Kingdom
Tel.: (44) 1753893600
Fax: (44) 1753893894
Web Site: www.daiichi-sankyo.co.uk
Pharmaceutical Products Whslr
S.I.C.: 5122
N.A.I.C.S.: 424210

U3 Pharma GmbH (1)
Fraunhoferstrasse 22
82152 Martinsried, Germany
Tel.: (49) 89 8103 9100
Fax: (49) 89 8103 9199
E-Mail: info@u3pharma.com
Web Site: www.u3pharma.com
Pharmaceutical Products Research Services
S.I.C.: 8731
N.A.I.C.S.: 541711
Johannes Bange *(CEO)*

DAIICHI SOGYO CO. LTD.

Okigin Kohakura Shiten 3F 3 8 8
Kohakura, Naha, 900 0024, Japan
Tel.: (81) 988535353
Business Description:
Office Equipmemt
S.I.C.: 2522
N.A.I.C.S.: 337214

DAIICHIKOUSHO CO., LTD.

5-5-26 Kitashinagawa Shinagawa-ku
Tokyo, 141-8701, Japan
Tel.: (81) 3 3280 2151
Web Site: www.dkkaraoke.co.jp
Year Founded: 1973
7458—(JAS)
Sls.: $1,417,911,000
Assets: $1,754,269,000
Liabilities: $650,804,000
Net Worth: $1,103,465,000
Earnings: $141,009,000
Emp.: 3,025
Fiscal Year-end: 03/31/13
Business Description:
Music Software Publishers
S.I.C.: 7372
N.A.I.C.S.: 511210
Personnel:
Saburo Hayashi *(Pres)*
Tatsuya Kumagai *(Sr Mng Dir)*
Hiroshi Mitomi *(Sr Mng Dir)*
Kenichi Nemoto *(Sr Mng Dir)*
Tadahiro Hoshi *(Mng Dir)*
Yuichi Murai *(Mng Dir)*

DAIICHIKOUSHO CO., LTD.—(Continued)

Yasutaka Wada *(Mng Dir)*
Shigeki Kobayashi *(Corp Officer)*
Hiroshi Kunitsu *(Corp Officer)*
Akira Miyake *(Corp Officer)*
Ichio Odagiri *(Corp Officer)*
Hisahiro Ogura *(Corp Officer)*
Kenji Otsuka *(Corp Officer)*
Noriyuki Takehana *(Corp Officer)*
Yasuhito Watanabe *(Corp Officer)*
Akihito Yoshizawa *(Corp Officer)*
Board of Directors:
Saburo Hayashi
Tadahiro Hoshi
Tatsuya Kumagai
Hiroshi Mitomi
Akira Miyake
Yuichi Murai
Kenichi Nemoto
Yoshimi Shimizu
Noriyuki Takehana
Yasutaka Wada
Yasuhito Watanabe
Mitsuru Yoshikawa
Transfer Agent:
Mitsubishi UFJ Trust & Banking Corporation
7-10-11 Higashisuna Koto-ku
Tokyo, Japan

Subsidiaries:

DK Music Publishing Co., Ltd. **(1)**
2-5-10 Higashigotanda
Shinagawa-Ku, Tokyo, 141-0022, Japan
Tel.: (81) 363817820
Karaoke Equipment Mfr
S.I.C.: 3651
N.A.I.C.S.: 334310

Nippon Crown Co., Ltd. **(1)**
2-12-19 Shibuya
Shibuya-Ku, Tokyo, 150-0002, Japan
Tel.: (81) 363817732
Karaoke Equipment Mfr & Distr
S.I.C.: 3651
N.A.I.C.S.: 334310

U.S. Subsidiary:

Tri-M, Inc. **(1)**
7542 Darrow Rd
Hudson, OH 44236
Tel.: (330) 342-1400
Karaoke Equipment Mfr & Distr
S.I.C.: 3999
N.A.I.C.S.: 339999

Non-U.S. Subsidiary:

DK KOREA Co., Ltd. **(1)**
Room No 1911 Korea Trade Tower 159-1 Samseong-dong
Gangnam, Seoul, 135-090, Korea (South)
Tel.: (82) 2 6000 4600
Fax: (82) 2 6000 4400
Karaoke Equipment Distr
S.I.C.: 5946
N.A.I.C.S.: 443142

DAIKAFFIL CHEMICALS INDIA LIMITED.

D-13 Everest 5th Floor Tardeo Road
Mumbai, Maharashtra, 400 034, India
Tel.: (91) 2249215555
Fax: (91) 2249215599
E-Mail: info@daikaffil.com
Web Site: www.daikaffil.com
530825—(BOM)
Rev.: $5,934,813
Assets: $3,447,457
Liabilities: $1,675,449
Net Worth: $1,772,008
Earnings: $180,777
Fiscal Year-end: 03/31/13
Business Description:
Specialty Chemicals Mfr
S.I.C.: 2899
N.A.I.C.S.: 325998
Personnel:
Amit J. Patel *(Chm)*
Sishir R. Amin *(Co-Mng Dir)*
Aditya A. Patel *(Co-Mng Dir)*
Devidas N. Tendolkar *(Compliance Officer)*
Board of Directors:
Amit J. Patel
Sishir R. Amin
Aditya A. Patel
Sudhir M. Patel
Giuseppe Seccomandi
Hiroshige Tanaka
Jagdish J. Vasa
Transfer Agent:
Link Intime India Private Limited
C-13 Pannalal Silk Mills Compound L.B.S. Marg Bhandup
Mumbai, India

DAIKEN CORPORATION

22F Dojima Avanza 6-20 Dojima 1-chome Kita-ku
Osaka, 530-8210, Japan
Tel.: (81) 6 6452 6000
Fax: (81) 6 6452 6072
Web Site: www.daiken.jp
Year Founded: 1945
7905—(TKS)
Sls.: $1,739,683,000
Assets: $1,447,798,000
Liabilities: $1,009,228,000
Net Worth: $438,570,000
Earnings: $14,498,000
Emp.: 3,183
Fiscal Year-end: 03/31/13
Business Description:
Residential & Construction Building Materials Mfr
S.I.C.: 1542
N.A.I.C.S.: 236220
Personnel:
Ryoji Sawaki *(Pres & CEO)*
Kazumasa Kanesaka *(Sr Mng Dir)*
Kikuo Imamura *(Mng Exec Officer)*
Katao Kitagawa *(Exec Officer)*
Masanori Okuda *(Sr Exec Officer)*
Mutsuhiro Shimada *(Sr Exec Officer)*
Masami Yatsu *(Mng Exec Officer)*
Katsumi Fujii *(Exec VP)*
Board of Directors:
Katsumi Fujii
Shinichi Iwamoto
Kazumasa Kanesaka
Tomoaki Kato
Masanori Okuda
Ryoji Sawaki
Kenji Yamanaka
Subsidiaries:

Dai-tac Corporation **(1)**
2-5-8 Kaigandori
Minami-ku, Okayama, 702-8045, Japan
Tel.: (81) 862625450
Fax: (81) 862624596
Door & Window Mfr
S.I.C.: 2431
N.A.I.C.S.: 321911

Dai-Wood Corporation **(1)**
2782-23 Saimyoji
Iga, Mie, Japan
Tel.: (81) 595238872
Fax: (81) 595238013
Emp.: 40
Hardwood Veneer & Plywood Mfr
S.I.C.: 2435
N.A.I.C.S.: 321211
Ono Toshio *(Mgr)*

Daifit Co., Ltd **(1)**
776-1 Wada
Kurayoshi, Tottori, 682-0912, Japan
Tel.: (81) 858235155
Fax: (81) 858235166
Door & Window Mfr
S.I.C.: 2431
N.A.I.C.S.: 321911

Daiken Engineering Corporation **(1)**
Doshima Abanza 21th Floor
Osaka, Japan
Tel.: (81) 664523000
Web Site: www.daiken.jp/english/cpdata.html
Special Trade Contractors
S.I.C.: 1799
N.A.I.C.S.: 238990
Minoru Yamada *(Pres)*

Inami Daiken Corporation **(1)**
1-1 Inami Nanto
Toyama, 932-0211, Japan
Tel.: (81) 763825850
Fax: (81) 763 82 5879
E-Mail: csr@daikin.co.jp
Web Site: www.daiken.jp/inami
Door & Window Mfr
S.I.C.: 2431
N.A.I.C.S.: 321911

Inami Daiken Products Corporation **(1)**
1-1 Inami
Nanto, Toyama, Japan
Tel.: (81) 763825850
Fax: (81) 763825879
Web Site: www.daiken.com
Custom Architectural Woodwork & Millwork Mfr
S.I.C.: 2541
N.A.I.C.S.: 337212

Koukou Sangyo Corporation **(1)**
3-12-8 Sotokanda
Sumitomofudosanakihabara Building 5kai
Chiyoda-ku, Tokyo, 101-0021, Japan
Tel.: (81) 362717880
Fax: (81) 352964069
Door & Window Mfr
S.I.C.: 2431
N.A.I.C.S.: 321911

Mie Daiken Corporation **(1)**
930-1 Kitashinden
Kawage-cho, Tsu, Japan
Tel.: (81) 592453811
Fax: (81) 592545656
Web Site: www.daiken.jp
Millwork
S.I.C.: 2426
N.A.I.C.S.: 321918

Okayama Daiken Corporation **(1)**
2-5-8 Kaigandori
Minami-ku, Okayama, 702-8045, Japan
Tel.: (81) 862621137
Web Site: www.daiken.jp/west
Door & Window Mfr
S.I.C.: 2431
N.A.I.C.S.: 321911

Sanki Co Ltd **(1)**
4-18 Higashishimbo
Sanjo, Niigata, 955-0863, Japan
Tel.: (81) 256340209
Industrial Machinery & Equipment Mfr
S.I.C.: 3559
N.A.I.C.S.: 333249

Takahagi Daiken Corporation **(1)**
160-1 Akahama
Takahagi, Ibaraki, 318-0001, Japan
Tel.: (81) 293 23 6511
Fax: (81) 293 23 6331
Fiber Board Mfr
S.I.C.: 2499
N.A.I.C.S.: 321999

Toyama Daiken Corporation **(1)**
6 Horiesengoku
Imazu, Shiga, Japan
Tel.: (81) 766860585
Hardwood Veneer & Plywood Mfr
S.I.C.: 2435
N.A.I.C.S.: 321211

Toyama Juki Co., Ltd. **(1)**
614 Takanami
Tonami, Toyama, 939-1341, Japan
Tel.: (81) 763335523
Wood Household Furniture Mfr
S.I.C.: 2511
N.A.I.C.S.: 337122

Non-U.S. Subsidiaries:

Daiken Industries (Ningbo) Corporation **(1)**
Inside Simen Town Industrial Park
Yuyao, Ningbo, China
Tel.: (86) 57462159777
Custom Architectural Woodwork & Millwork Mfr
S.I.C.: 2541
N.A.I.C.S.: 337212
Satoshi Yoshimi *(CEO)*

Daiken Miri Sdn. Bhd. **(1)**
Lot 191 Block 1 Kuala Baram Industrial Estate
CDT 121, 98009 Miri, Sarawak, Malaysia
Tel.: (60) 85605099
Fax: (60) 85605009
Web Site: www.daiken.com
Emp.: 250
Reconstituted Wood Product Mfr
S.I.C.: 2493
N.A.I.C.S.: 321219
Takashi Nakamichi *(CEO)*

Daiken New Zeland Limited **(1)**
525C Great South Road Penrose
Auckland, 1061, New Zealand
Tel.: (64) 95711101
Fax: (64) 95711109
Web Site: www.daikin.co.nz
Emp.: 14
Air Conditioning Installation Services
S.I.C.: 1711
N.A.I.C.S.: 238220
Mike Meekings *(Mgr)*

Daiken Sarawak Sdn. Bhd. **(1)**
Lot 2069 Block 26
Kidurong Industrial Estate, 97008 Bintulu, Sarawak, Malaysia
Tel.: (60) 86251000
Fax: (60) 86252803
Reconstituted Wood Product Mfr
S.I.C.: 2493
N.A.I.C.S.: 321219
Kazuyoshi Katsumata *(CEO)*

DAIKEN MEDICAL CO., LTD.

2-6-2 Ayumino Izumi-City
Osaka, 594-1157, Japan
Tel.: (81) 725512130
Fax: (81) 725543861
E-Mail: matsui@dainken-iki.co.jp
Web Site: www.daiken-iki.co.jp
7775—(TKS)
Sales Range: $1-4.9 Billion
Emp.: 280
Business Description:
Medical Devices & Equipment Mfr & Distr
S.I.C.: 3841
N.A.I.C.S.: 339112
Personnel:
Mitsuru Yamada *(Chm & CEO)*
Keiichi Yamada *(Pres & COO)*
Masahiko Ohama *(Mng Dir & CFO)*
Masayuki Yamada *(Mng Dir & Chief Comml Officer)*
Board of Directors:
Mitsuru Yamada
Keiichi Yamada

DAIKI ALUMINIUM INDUSTRY CO., LTD.

Nichiei Bldg 4-8 1-chome Tosabori
Nishi-ku, Osaka, 550-0001, Japan
Tel.: (81) 6 6444 2751
Fax: (81) 6 6444 2797
Web Site: www.dik-net.com
Year Founded: 1922
5702—(TKS)
Business Description:
Aluminium Alloy Ingot Mfr
S.I.C.: 3334
N.A.I.C.S.: 331313
Personnel:
Takaaki Yamamoto *(Pres)*

DAIKI ATAKA ENGINEERING CO., LTD

Ninety Bldg 5-3-28 Nishikujo
Konohana-ku, Osaka, 554-0012, Japan
Tel.: (81) 6 6468 9650
Fax: (81) 6 6462 1482

Web Site: www.atk-dk.co.jp
Year Founded: 1967
1978—(TKS)
Emp.: 1,228
Business Description:
Industrial Machinery Mfr
S.I.C.: 3559
N.A.I.C.S.: 333249
Personnel:
Yasuo Ogawa *(Pres)*

DAIKI AXIS CO., LTD.

1-9-1 Misawa Matsuyama
Matsuyama, 791-8022, Japan
Tel.: (81) 89 927 2222
Web Site: www.daiki-axis.com
4245—(TKS)
Rev.: $299,224,651
Emp.: 420
Fiscal Year-end: 12/31/12
Business Description:
Water Treatment Equipment Mfr
S.I.C.: 4971
N.A.I.C.S.: 221310
Personnel:
Yutaka Ohkame *(Chm & Pres)*

DAIKIN INDUSTRIES, LTD.

Umeda Center Building 2-4-12
Nakazaki-Nishi Kita-ku
Osaka, 530-8323, Japan
Tel.: (81) 663734312
Fax: (81) 663734380
Web Site: www.daikin.com
Year Founded: 1924
6367—(FKA NGO SAP TKS)
Sls.: $14,199,933,000
Assets: $19,094,196,000
Liabilities: $12,098,229,000
Net Worth: $6,995,967,000
Earnings: $479,435,000
Emp.: 51,398
Fiscal Year-end: 03/31/13
Business Description:
Air Conditioners & Freezers, Fluorochemical Products & Hydraulic Equipment & Machinery Mfr
S.I.C.: 3585
N.A.I.C.S.: 333415
Personnel:
Noriyuki Inoue *(Chm & CEO)*
Masanori Togawa *(Pres & COO)*
Takeshi Ebisu *(Sr Exec Officer)*
Shigeki Hagiwara *(Sr Exec Officer)*
Yukio Hayashi *(Sr Exec Officer)*
Hitoshi Jinno *(Exec Officer)*
Guntaro Kawamura *(Sr Exec Officer)*
Takashi Matsuzaki *(Sr Exec Officer)*
Masatsugu Minaka *(Sr Exec Officer)*
Yoshihiro Mineno *(Exec Officer)*
Masayuki Moriyama *(Exec Officer)*
Shinya Okada *(Sr Exec Officer)*
Susumu Okano *(Sr Exec Officer)*
Hiroo Sakai *(Exec Officer)*
Junichi Sato *(Sr Exec Officer)*
Katsuyuki Sawai *(Exec Officer)*
Koichi Takahashi *(Exec Officer)*
Osamu Tanaka *(Exec Officer)*
Yoshikazu Tayama *(Exec Officer)*
Ken Tayano *(Sr Exec Officer)*
Jiro Tomita *(Sr Exec Officer)*
Toshitaka Tsubouchi *(Exec Officer)*
Kosei Uematsu *(Sr Exec Officer)*
Yoshiyuki Uemura *(Exec Officer)*
Yasushi Yamada *(Sr Exec Officer)*
Hiroo Yoshioka *(Sr Exec Officer)*
Board of Directors:
Noriyuki Inoue
Takeshi Ebisu
Frans Hoorelbeke
Kosuke Ikebuchi
Guntaro Kawamura
Takashi Matsuzaki
Masatsugu Minaka
Koichi Takahashi
Ken Tayano
Chiyono Terada
Masanori Togawa
Jiro Tomita
Subsidiaries:

Daikin Accounting Solutions Co., Ltd (1)
2-4-12 Nakazakinishi Umeda Center Bldg
Kita-Ku, Osaka, 530-0015, Japan
Tel.: (81) 663734321
Fax: (81) 663734393
Financial Management Services
S.I.C.: 6211
N.A.I.C.S.: 523999
Ikura Keiichi *(Mgr)*

Daikin Applied Systems Co., Ltd. (1)
4-13-23 Shibaura Ms Shibaura Bldg
Minato-Ku, Tokyo, 108-0023, Japan
Tel.: (81) 364145580
Web Site: www.daps.co.jp
Air Conditioning Equipment Mfr
S.I.C.: 3585
N.A.I.C.S.: 333415

Daikin Facilities Co., Ltd. (1)
5-29-3 Toyo Sumitomofudosan No 2 Toyo Bldg 2f
Koto-Ku, Tokyo, 135-0016, Japan
Tel.: (81) 336489531
Fax: (81) 336489630
Web Site: www.daikin-dfc.com
Emp.: 150
Facilities Management Services
S.I.C.: 8744
N.A.I.C.S.: 561210
Shinosuke Kitazawa *(Pres)*

Daikin Fukushi Service Co., Ltd. (1)
2-4-12 Nakazakinishi Umeda Center Bldg 18f
Kita-Ku, Osaka, 530-0015, Japan
Tel.: (81) 663734301
Air Conditioning Equipment Whslr
S.I.C.: 5075
N.A.I.C.S.: 423730

Daikin HVAC Solution Hokkaido Co., Ltd. (1)
19-1-12 Kita16johigashi
Higashi-Ku, Sapporo, Hokkaido, 065-0016, Japan
Tel.: (81) 117846661
Fax: (81) 117846630
Emp.: 3
Air Conditioning Equipment Mfr
S.I.C.: 3585
N.A.I.C.S.: 333415
Hiroki Kasai *(Pres)*

Daikin HVAC Solution Kinki Co., Ltd. (1)
2-10-70 Nambanaka Namba Parks Parks Bldg 12f
Naniwa-Ku, Osaka, 556-0011, Japan
Tel.: (81) 666472355
Chemical Products Mfr
S.I.C.: 2899
N.A.I.C.S.: 325998

Daikin HVAC Solution Kyushu Co., Ltd. (1)
1-10-21 Enokida Daikin Kogyo Fukuoka Bldg
Hakata-Ku, Fukuoka, 812-0004, Japan
Tel.: (81) 924756204
Chemical Products Mfr
S.I.C.: 2899
N.A.I.C.S.: 325998

Daikin HVAC Solution Niigata Co., Ltd. (1)
6-5-27 Meike
Chuo-Ku, Niigata, 950-0941, Japan
Tel.: (81) 252847181
Chemical Products Mfr
S.I.C.: 2899
N.A.I.C.S.: 325998

Daikin HVAC Solution Tohoku Co., Ltd. (1)
3-1-33 Oroshimachihigashi
Wakabayashi-Ku, Sendai, Miyagi, 984-0002, Japan
Tel.: (81) 222880222
Air Conditioning Equipment Whslr
S.I.C.: 5075
N.A.I.C.S.: 423730

Daikin HVAC Solution Tokai Co., Ltd. (1)
1-17 Shirakabe Daikin Kogyo
Higashi-Ku, Nagoya, Aichi, 461-0011, Japan
Tel.: (81) 529550700
Chemical Products Mfr
S.I.C.: 2899
N.A.I.C.S.: 325998

Daikin Hydraulic Engineering Co., Ltd. (1)
4-6-16 Hommachi Torikai
Settsu, Osaka, 566-0052, Japan
Tel.: (81) 72 653 1111
Fax: (81) 72 653 1112
Web Site: www.daikinpmc.com
Hydraulic Equipment Mfr
S.I.C.: 3559
N.A.I.C.S.: 333249

Daikin Information Systems Co., Ltd. (1)
4-5-2 Koraibashi Koraibashi West Bldg
Chuo-Ku, Osaka, 541-0043, Japan
Tel.: (81) 662085130
Fax: (81) 662085129
Web Site: www.dki.co.jp
Information System Development Services
S.I.C.: 7389
N.A.I.C.S.: 519190
Hiroshi Matsuo *(Gen Mgr)*

Daikin Lubrication Products & Engineering Co., Ltd. (1)
Daikin Kogyo Esaka Building 7F 3-21-3 Tarumi-Cho
Suita, Osaka, Japan
Tel.: (81) 6 6337 2123
Fax: (81) 6 6337 2125
E-Mail: admin@daikin-lubrication.co.jp
Web Site: www.daikin-lubrication.com
Industrial Machinery Mfr
S.I.C.: 3559
N.A.I.C.S.: 333249

Daikin MR Engineering Co., Ltd. (1)
Shin Osaka Central-tower 11F 5-5-15 Nishinakajima
Yodogawa-ku, Osaka, 532-0011, Japan
Tel.: (81) 648057298
Fax: (81) 648057321
Web Site: www.daikin.co.jp/group/dmre
Emp.: 100
Marine Air Conditioning Equipment Mfr & Whslr
S.I.C.: 3585
N.A.I.C.S.: 333415
Shoji Harada *(Pres)*

Daikin-Sauer-Danfoss Manufacturing Ltd. (1)
1-1 Nishi Hitotsuya
Settsu, Osaka, 566-0044, Japan
Tel.: (81) 6 6349 7264
Fax: (81) 6 6349 7401
Hydraulic Component Mfr
S.I.C.: 3492
N.A.I.C.S.: 332912

Daikin Sunrise Settsu Co., Ltd. (1)
4-9-9 Higashibefu
Settsu, Osaka, 566-0042, Japan
Tel.: (81) 663493173
Specialty Chemicals Mfr
S.I.C.: 2899
N.A.I.C.S.: 325998

Moritani Daikin Co, Ltd. (1)
1-17-24 Shinkawa Shinkawachuo Bldg 5f
Chuo-Ku, Tokyo, 104-0033, Japan
Tel.: (81) 3 3206 0929
Fax: (81) 3 3206 0931
Web Site: www.gmdk.co.jp
Air Conditioning Equipment Mfr
S.I.C.: 3585
N.A.I.C.S.: 333415

Nippon Muki Co., Ltd. (1)
Nisshin Ueno Bldg 5-1-5 Higashi-ueno
Taito-ku, Tokyo, 110-0015, Japan
Tel.: (81) 3 6860 7500
Fax: (81) 3 6860 7510
E-Mail: info@nipponmuki.co.jp
Web Site: www.nipponmuki.co.jp
Emp.: 223
Fiberglass Mfr & Whslr
S.I.C.: 3089
N.A.I.C.S.: 326199
Michihiro Hiroto *(Pres)*

OK Kizai Co., Ltd. (1)
1-7-4 Higashinodamachi Wakita
Sumitomoseimei Kyobashi Daini Bldg
Miyakojima-Ku, Osaka, 534-0024, Japan
Tel.: (81) 6 6354 3013
Fax: (81) 6 6354 3891
Web Site: www.ok-kizai.co.jp
Air Conditioning Equipment Whslr
S.I.C.: 5075
N.A.I.C.S.: 423730

SEM Daikin Co, Ltd. (1)
3-1-22 Toyosaki Yodogawa67bankan 12f
Kita-Ku, Osaka, 531-0072, Japan
Tel.: (81) 6 6377 6150
Fax: (81) 6 6377 6169
Web Site: www.sem-daikin.co.jp
Air Conditioning Equipment Whslr
S.I.C.: 5075
N.A.I.C.S.: 423730
Shoichi Okuda *(Gen Mgr)*

Toho Kasei Co., Ltd. (1)
6-2 Imago-cho
Yamato-koriyama, Nara, 639-1031, Japan
Tel.: (81) 743 59 2361
Fax: (81) 743 59 2350
E-Mail: info@toho-kasei.co.jp
Web Site: www.toho-kasei.co.jp
Emp.: 200
Semiconductor Equipment Mfr & Distr
S.I.C.: 3674
N.A.I.C.S.: 334413
Satoshi Doi *(Gen Mgr)*

Plants:

Daikin Industries, Ltd. - Kanaoka Factory (1)
1304 Kanaoka-cho
Kita-ku, Sakai, Osaka, 591-8511, Japan
Tel.: (81) 72 252 1151
Fax: (81) 72 252 1326
Air Conditioning & Refrigeration System Mfr
S.I.C.: 3585
N.A.I.C.S.: 333415

Daikin Industries, Ltd. - Kashima Plant (1)
21 Sunayama
Kamisu, Ibaraki, Japan
Tel.: (81) 479 46 2441
Web Site: www.daikin.com
Specialty Chemicals Mfr
S.I.C.: 2819
N.A.I.C.S.: 325180

Daikin Industries, Ltd. - Rinkai Factory (1)
12 Chikko Shin-machi 3-chome
Nishi-ku, Sakai, Osaka, 592-8331, Japan
Tel.: (81) 72 241 1151
Fax: (81) 72 243 2650
Air Conditioning Equipment Mfr
S.I.C.: 3585
N.A.I.C.S.: 333415
Noriyuki Inoue *(Pres)*

Daikin Industries, Ltd. - Shiga Plant (1)
1000-2 Aza-Ohtani Okamoto-cho
Kusatsu, Shiga, 525-8526, Japan
Tel.: (81) 77 563 1151
Web Site: www.daikin.com
Air Conditioning Equipment Mfr
S.I.C.: 3585
N.A.I.C.S.: 333415

Daikin Industries, Ltd. - Yodogawa Plant (1)
1-1 Nishi-Hitotsuya
Settsu, Osaka, 566-8585, Japan
Tel.: (81) 6 6349 7361
Fax: (81) 6 6349 7262
Specialty Chemical Mfr
S.I.C.: 2899
N.A.I.C.S.: 325998

U.S. Subsidiaries:

Cri-Tech Inc. (1)
85 Winter St
Hanover, MA 02339
Tel.: (800) 826-5699
Fax: (781) 826-5770
E-Mail: info@critechinc.com
Web Site: www.critechinc.com
Chemical Products Mfr

Daikin Industries, Ltd.—(Continued)

S.I.C.: 2819
N.A.I.C.S.: 325180
Richard Park *(Dir-Bus Sys)*

DAI Funding Corporation (1)
20 Olympic Dr
Orangeburg, NY 10962
Tel.: (845) 365-9500
Fax: (845) 365-9515
Toll Free: (800) 365-9570
Web Site: www.daikin-america.com
Emp.: 75
Financial Management Services
S.I.C.: 6211
N.A.I.C.S.: 523999
Lisa Strassman *(Mgr)*

Daikin AC (Americas), Inc. (1)
1645 Wallace Dr Ste 100
Carrollton, TX 75006 (100%)
Tel.: (972) 245-1510
Fax: (972) 245-1038
E-Mail: info@daikinac.com
Web Site: www.daikinac.com
Air Conditioning Solutions for Residential, Commercial & Industrial Applications
S.I.C.: 3585
N.A.I.C.S.: 333415
Akinori Atarashi *(Pres)*
Doug Widenmann *(Sr VP-Sls)*

Daikin America, Inc. (1)
20 Olympic Dr
Orangeburg, NY 10962-2511
Tel.: (845) 365-9500
Fax: (845) 365-9515
Toll Free: (800) 365-9570
E-Mail: customerservice@daikin-america.com
Web Site: www.daikin-america.com
Emp.: 60
S.I.C.: 3585
N.A.I.C.S.: 333415
Cliff Adams *(Chm)*

Daikin Holdings (USA), Inc. (1)
475 Fifth Ave 18th Fl
New York, NY 10017
Tel.: (212) 340-7400
Fax: (212) 779-5925
Web Site: www.daikin.com
Air Conditioning Equipment Distr
S.I.C.: 5075
N.A.I.C.S.: 423730
Yukiyoshi Okane *(Pres)*

Daikin U.S. Corporation (1)
Fl 18 475 5th Ave
New York, NY 10017-6220 (100%)
Tel.: (212) 340-7400
Fax: (212) 779-5925
E-Mail: tyagi@daikin.ny.com
Web Site: www.daikin.com
Emp.: 24
Mfr of Air Conditioning Equipment
S.I.C.: 5075
N.A.I.C.S.: 423730
Kelvin Williams *(Gen Counsel & Dir-Gen Affairs)*

Goodman Global, Inc. (1)
5151 San Felipe St Ste 500
Houston, TX 77056 DE
Tel.: (713) 861-2500
Fax: (713) 861-4701
Toll Free: (877) 254-4729
E-Mail: customerservice@goodmanmfg.com
Web Site: www.goodmanmfg.com
Sales Range: $1-4.9 Billion
Emp.: 4,331
Air-Conditioners & Heating Units Mfr
S.I.C.: 3585
N.A.I.C.S.: 333415
David Swift *(Pres & CEO)*
Lawrence M. Blackburn *(CFO & Exec VP)*
Terrance M. Smith *(CIO & Sr VP)*
James L. Mishler *(Pres-Company Owned Distr)*
Ben D. Campbell *(Gen Counsel, Sec & Exec VP)*
Mark M. Dolan *(Treas, VP & Controller)*
Peter H. Alexander *(Sr VP)*
Samuel G. Bikman *(Sr VP-Logistics & Bus Dev)*
Gary L. Clark *(Sr VP-Mktg)*
Karilee A. Durham *(Sr VP-HR)*
William L. Topper *(Sr VP-Ops)*

Subsidiaries:

Goodman Distribution Southeast, Inc. (2)
10000 NW 17th St
Doral, FL 33172
Tel.: (305) 696-0830
Fax: (305) 594-1846
Sales Range: $150-199.9 Million
Emp.: 260
Air Heating & Air Conditioning Equipment Whslr
S.I.C.: 5075
N.A.I.C.S.: 423730

Subsidiaries:

Goodman Distribution (3)
2450 Silver Star Rd
Orlando, FL 32804
Tel.: (407) 296-4499
Fax: (407) 296-4446
Emp.: 15
Air Heating & Air Conditioning Equipment Whslr
S.I.C.: 5075
N.A.I.C.S.: 423730
Jim Weber *(Mgr)*

Goodman Distribution (3)
13200 Automobile Blvd
Clearwater, FL 33762
Tel.: (727) 573-2772
Air Heating & Air Conditioning Equipment Whslr
S.I.C.: 5075
N.A.I.C.S.: 423730
Stacy Redmond *(Mgr)*

Goodman Distribution (3)
2123 Park Central Blvd N
Pompano Beach, FL 33064
Tel.: (954) 984-4848
Emp.: 12
Air Heating & Air Conditioning Equipment Whslr
S.I.C.: 5075
N.A.I.C.S.: 423730
Scott Wallace *(Mgr)*

Goodman Manufacturing Company, L.P. (2)
5151 San Felipe Ste 500
Houston, TX 77056
Tel.: (713) 861-2500
Fax: (713) 861-0772
Web Site: www.goodmanmfg.com
Sls.: $1,320,000,000
Emp.: 4,500
Air-Conditioning, Ventilation & Heating Equipment Mfr
S.I.C.: 3585
N.A.I.C.S.: 333415
David Swift *(Pres & CEO)*
Lawrence M. Blackburn *(CFO & Exec VP)*

Non-U.S. Subsidiaries:

Abbar & Zainy Daikin Airconditioning Company Ltd. (1)
PO Box 5700
Jeddah, 21432, Saudi Arabia
Tel.: (966) 26473367
Fax: (966) 26492368
Web Site: www.daikin.com
Air Conditioning Equipment Installation Services
S.I.C.: 1711
N.A.I.C.S.: 238220
Abdul Najjar *(Gen Mgr)*

Daikin AC Spain, S.A. (1)
C/ Labastida 2
28034 Madrid, Spain
Tel.: (34) 91 334 56 00
Fax: (34) 91 334 56 29
Web Site: www.daikin.es
Air Conditioning Equipment Mfr
S.I.C.: 3585
N.A.I.C.S.: 333415

Daikin Air Conditioning Argentina S.A. (1)
Marcelo T de Alvear 1430 1er Piso
C1060AAB Buenos Aires, Argentina
Tel.: (54) 11 4816 3274
Fax: (54) 11 4375 4280
Web Site: www.daikin-argentina.com
Air Conditioning Equipment Whslr
S.I.C.: 5075
N.A.I.C.S.: 423730

Daikin Air Conditioning (M) Sdn. Bhd. (1)
1 Floor Lot 4 Lorong 191A Seksyen 19
46300 Petaling Jaya, Selangor, Malaysia (100%)
Tel.: (60) 379559090
Fax: (60) 379547722
E-Mail: ngyl@daikin.com.my
Web Site: www.daikin.com
Emp.: 50
Air Conditioning
S.I.C.: 3585
N.A.I.C.S.: 333415

Daikin Air-Conditioning (Shanghai) Co., Ltd. (1)
318 Shen Fu Road
Xin Zhuang Industry Zone, Shanghai, 201108, China
Tel.: (86) 2154421118
Fax: (86) 2154424910
E-Mail: dis@daikin-dis.com
Web Site: www.daikin-dis.com
Air Conditioning Mfr
S.I.C.: 3585
N.A.I.C.S.: 333415

Branch:

Daikin Air-Conditioning (Shanghai) Co., Ltd. - Huizhou Branch (2)
Xinla Industrial Area
Maan Town, Huizhou, Guangdong, 516257, China (100%)
Tel.: (86) 7523619401
Fax: (86) 7523619438
S.I.C.: 3585
N.A.I.C.S.: 333415

Daikin Air Conditioning Singapore Pte. Ltd. (1)
No 10 Ang Mo Kio Industrial Park 2
Singapore, 569501, Singapore
Tel.: (65) 65838888
Telex: 22126
Fax: (65) 63497307
E-Mail: sales@daikin.com.sg
Web Site: www.daikin.com.sg
Emp.: 280
Mfr. of Air Conditioning Products
S.I.C.: 3585
N.A.I.C.S.: 333415
Ching Khim Huat *(Mng Dir)*

Daikin Air-Conditioning Technology (Beijing), Ltd. (1)
20F Tower E3 Oriental Plaza No 1 East Chang An Ave
Dong Cheng District, Beijing, 100738, China
Tel.: (86) 1085182872
Fax: (86) 1085183866
Web Site: www.daikin.com
Air Conditioning Equipment Maintenance Services
S.I.C.: 7699
N.A.I.C.S.: 811310

Daikin Air-Conditioning Technology (Shanghai), Ltd. (1)
United Plz B1F 1468 Nan Jing Rd W
Shanghai, 200040, China
Tel.: (86) 2162897118
Fax: (86) 2164664238
Web Site: www.daikin.com
Air Conditioning Equipment Mfr
S.I.C.: 3585
N.A.I.C.S.: 333415

Daikin Airconditioning Argentina (1)
Marcelo T de Alvear 1430
C1060 AAB Buenos Aires, Argentina
Tel.: (54) 01148163274
Fax: (54) 1143754280
E-Mail: daikin@daikin-argentina.com
Web Site: www.daikin-argentina.com
Emp.: 36
Air Conditioning Equipment & Supplies Sales & Distr
S.I.C.: 5075
N.A.I.C.S.: 423730
Alberto Gustavo Starosta *(Pres)*

Daikin Airconditioning Belgium NV (1)
Ave Franklin 1B
B 1300 Wavre, Belgium (100%)
Tel.: (32) 10237223
Fax: (32) 10244910
E-Mail: info@daikin.de
Web Site: www.daikin.de
Emp.: 59
S.I.C.: 3585
N.A.I.C.S.: 333415
Mark Oosterlinck *(Mng Dir)*

Daikin Airconditioning Central Europe GmbH (1)
Campus 21
Europaring F 12 402, 2345 Brunn am Gebirge, Austria (100%)
Tel.: (43) 223632557
Fax: (43) 223632557900
E-Mail: office@daikin.at
Web Site: www.daikin.at
Rev.: $25,161,860
Emp.: 70
S.I.C.: 3585
N.A.I.C.S.: 333415
Otto Oberhumer *(Gen Mgr)*

Daikin Airconditioning France SAS (1)
ZA du Petit Nanterre 31 rue des Hautes Patures
Le Narval Batiment B, 92737 Nanterre, Cedex, France (100%)
Tel.: (33) 146699569
Fax: (33) 147214160
E-Mail: sdaikin@daikin.fr
Web Site: www.daikin.fr
Emp.: 60
S.I.C.: 3585
N.A.I.C.S.: 333415
Kazuhide Horimoto *(Gen Mgr)*

Daikin Airconditioning Germany GmbH (1)
Inselkammer Strasse 2
82008 Unterhaching, Germany (100%)
Tel.: (49) 8974427210
Fax: (49) 8974427299
E-Mail: info@daikin.de
Web Site: www.daikin.de
Sales Range: $50-74.9 Million
Emp.: 130
S.I.C.: 3585
N.A.I.C.S.: 333415
Gunther Gamst *(Mng Dir)*

Daikin Airconditioning Greece S. A. (1)
50 Ag Konstantinous Str
151 24 Maroussi, Greece
Tel.: (30) 2108761300
Fax: (30) 2108761400
E-Mail: info@daikin.gr
Web Site: www.daikin.gr
Emp.: 21
Air Conditioning Equipment Whslr
S.I.C.: 5075
N.A.I.C.S.: 423730
Ilias Katsoulis *(Gen Mgr)*

Daikin Airconditioning (Hong Kong) Ltd. (1)
74 Futura Plz 111 113 How Ming St
Kwun Tong, Hong Kong, China (Hong Kong) (100%)
Tel.: (852) 25702786
Fax: (852) 28072484
E-Mail: info@daikin.com
Web Site: www.daikin.com.hk
Emp.: 50
S.I.C.: 3585
N.A.I.C.S.: 333415
Y. Watanabe *(Mng Dir)*

Daikin Airconditioning India Private Limited (1)
12th Floor Building No 9 Tower A DLF Cyber City DLF Phase III
Gurgaon, Haryana, 122002, India
Tel.: (91) 124 4555444
Fax: (91) 124 4555333
E-Mail:
Web Site: www.daikinindia.com
Air Conditioning Equipment & Supplies Sales & Distr
S.I.C.: 5075
N.A.I.C.S.: 423730
Sanjay Goyal *(VP-Sls)*

Plant:

Daikin Airconditioning India Pvt. Ltd. - Rajasthan Factory (2)
SP2-12 to SP2-15 & SP2-24 to SP2-27
RIICO New Industrial Complex
Majrajath Neemrana, 301 705 Alwar, Rajasthan, India
Tel.: (91) 1494 229 100
Fax: (91) 1494 229 151
Air Conditioning Equipment Mfr
S.I.C.: 3585
N.A.I.C.S.: 333415

Daikin Airconditioning Italy S.p.A. (1)
Via Milano 6
20097 San Donato Milanese, Milan, Italy
Tel.: (39) 02516191
Fax: (39) 0251619222
E-Mail: info@daikin.it
Web Site: www.daikin.it
Air Conditioning Equipment Mfr
S.I.C.: 3585
N.A.I.C.S.: 333415

Daikin Airconditioning Korea Co., Ltd. (1)
3F Nashil Building 604-1 Yeoksam-dong
Gangnam-gu, Seoul, Korea (South)
Tel.: (82) 2 568 1722
Fax: (82) 2 573 1620
Web Site: www.daikin-korea.co.kr
Air Conditioning Equipment Whslr
S.I.C.: 5075
N.A.I.C.S.: 423730

Daikin Airconditioning (Malaysia) Sdn., Bhd. (1)
1st Floor Lot 4 Lorong 19/1A Seksyen 19
46300 Petaling Jaya, Selangor, Malaysia
Tel.: (60) 3 7955 9090
Fax: (60) 3 7954 7722
E-Mail: sales@daikin.com.my
Web Site: www.daikin.com.my
Air Conditioning Products Distr
S.I.C.: 5075
N.A.I.C.S.: 423730

Daikin Airconditioning Netherlands B.V. (1)
Fascinatio Boulevard 562
2909 VA Capelle aan den IJssel, Netherlands
Tel.: (31) 88 324 54 60
E-Mail: info@daikin.nl
Web Site: www.daikin.nl
Air Conditioning Equipment Mfr
S.I.C.: 3585
N.A.I.C.S.: 333415

Daikin Airconditioning Philippines, Inc. (1)
Unit 801 Sunnymede IT Ctr 1614 Quezon Ave
Quezon City, 1103, Philippines (60%)
Tel.: (63) 29273633
Fax: (63) 29266696
E-Mail: info@daikin.com
Web Site: www.daikin.com
Emp.: 100
Air Conditioning Equipment Mfr
S.I.C.: 3585
N.A.I.C.S.: 333415
Angelito Dizon *(Mgr-Fin)*

Daikin Airconditioning Poland Sp. z o.o. (1)
ul Tasmowa 7
02-677 Warsaw, Poland
Tel.: (48) 223199000
Fax: (48) 224335198
E-Mail: office@daikin.pl
Web Site: www.daikin.pl
Emp.: 45
Air Conditioning Equipment & Supplies Sales & Distr
S.I.C.: 5075
N.A.I.C.S.: 423730
Bernard Dehertogh *(Gen Mgr)*

Daikin Airconditioning Portugal S.A. (1)
Edificio D Maria I Piso 0 ala A/B Quinta da Fonte
Paco de Arcos, 2770-229 Oeiras, Portugal
Tel.: (351) 21 426 87 00
Fax: (351) 21 426 22 94
E-Mail: info@daikin.pt
Web Site: www.daikin.pt
Air Conditioning Equipment Distr
S.I.C.: 5075
N.A.I.C.S.: 423730

Daikin Airconditioning South Africa Pty. Ltd. (1)
Units 1 & 2 Edison Way Century Gate Business Park
Montague Gardens, Cape Town, Century City, 7441, South Africa (100%)
Tel.: (27) 21 528 3500
Fax: (27) 21 551 8434
E-Mail: info@daikin.co.za
Web Site: www.daikin.co.za
Sales Range: $1-9.9 Million
Emp.: 20
Air-Conditioning Mfr & Installer
S.I.C.: 3585
N.A.I.C.S.: 333415

Daikin Airconditioning (Thailand) Ltd. (1)
700/44 Moo 7 Amata Nakorn Industrial Estate Bangna-Trad Rd
Amphur Muang, Chon Buri, 20000, Thailand
Tel.: (66) 3871 7066 70
Fax: (66) 3845 4184
Web Site: www.daikinthai.com
Emp.: 100
Industrial Air Conditioning Mfr
S.I.C.: 3585
N.A.I.C.S.: 333415
Hiroo Yoshioka *(Pres)*

Daikin Airconditioning U.K., Ltd. (1)
The Heights Brooklands
Weybridge, Surrey, KT13 0NY, United Kingdom
Tel.: (44) 845 6419000
Fax: (44) 845 6419009
E-Mail: cservices@daikin.co.uk
Web Site: www.daikin.co.uk
Air Conditioning Mfr & Whslr
S.I.C.: 3585
N.A.I.C.S.: 333415

Daikin Arkema Refrigerants Asia Ltd. (1)
Suite No 4 15/F Sino Plaza 225-257 Gloucester Road
Causeway Bay, Hong Kong, China (Hong Kong)
Tel.: (852) 2295 6608
Specialty Chemicals Mfr
S.I.C.: 2899
N.A.I.C.S.: 325199

Daikin Asia Servicing Pte., Ltd. (1)
19 Loyang Way 02-21 Rear Block Changi Logistics Ctr
Singapore, 508724, Singapore (100%)
Tel.: (65) 65468678
Fax: (65) 65469727
E-Mail: dap.admin@grp.daikin.co.jp
Web Site: www.daikinasia.com.sg
Emp.: 30
S.I.C.: 3585
N.A.I.C.S.: 333415
Kusuo Kitahara *(Pres)*

Daikin Australia Pty. Ltd. (1)
77 83 Alfred Rd Chipping Norton
PO Box 120
Moorebank, NSW, 2170, Australia (100%)
Tel.: (61) 297258888
Fax: (61) 297553450
E-Mail: hr@daikin.com.au
Web Site: www.daikin.com.au
Emp.: 150
S.I.C.: 3585
N.A.I.C.S.: 333415
Robert Woodhouse *(Gen Mgr)*

Daikin Chemical Europe GmbH (1)
Immermannstrasse 65 D
Dusseldorf, 40210, Germany (100%)
Tel.: (49) 2111792250
Fax: (49) 2111640734
E-Mail: sales@daikinchem.de
Web Site: www.daikinchem.de
Emp.: 25
S.I.C.: 3585
N.A.I.C.S.: 333415
Yasuhiko Hiray *(Pres)*

Daikin Chemical France S.A.S. (1)
Chemin de la Volta
BP 52
69492 Pierre-Benite, France
Tel.: (33) 4 7239 4930
Fax: (33) 4 7239 4939
Emp.: 42
Chemical Products Mfr
S.I.C.: 2819
N.A.I.C.S.: 325180
Tetsuia Higuchi *(Gen Mgr)*

Daikin Chemical International Trading (Shanghai) Co., Ltd (1)
7/F City Point No 1600 Zhonghua Road
Shanghai, China
Tel.: (86) 2153514920
Fax: (86) 21 5386 6610
Web Site: www.daikin.com
Specialty Chemicals Distr
S.I.C.: 5169
N.A.I.C.S.: 424690

Daikin Chemical Netherlands B.V. (1)
Maaskade 16
5347 KD Oss, Netherlands
Tel.: (31) 412697580
Fax: (31) 412697589
Web Site: www.daikin.com
Emp.: 15
Chemical Products Mfr
S.I.C.: 2819
N.A.I.C.S.: 325180
Herman Pietersma *(Gen Mgr)*

Daikin (CHINA) Investment Co., Ltd. (1)
20F Tower E3 Oriental Plaza No 1 East Chang An Ave
Dong Cheng District, Beijing, 100738, China
Tel.: (86) 10 8518 1117
Fax: (86) 10 8518 3856
Web Site: www.daikin-china.com.cn
Air Conditioning Equipment Mfr
S.I.C.: 3585
N.A.I.C.S.: 333415

Daikin Compressor Industries, Ltd. (1)
7/202 Moo 6 Tambol Mabyangporn Amphur Pluakdaeng
Rayong, 21140, Thailand
Tel.: (66) 3865 0060, ext. 104
Fax: (66) 3865 0061
E-Mail: dci.info@dci.daikin.co.jp
Web Site: www.daikinthai.com
Air Conditioner Equipment Mfr
S.I.C.: 3585
N.A.I.C.S.: 333415
Sutep R. *(Gen Mgr)*

Daikin Device Czech Republic s.r.o. (1)
Svedske Valy 2
627 00 Brno, Czech Republic
Tel.: (420) 517547310
Fax: (420) 517547340
E-Mail: info@daikinbrno.cz
Web Site: www.daikinbrno.cz
Emp.: 500
Air Conditioning Equipment Mfr
S.I.C.: 3585
N.A.I.C.S.: 333415
Hiroyuki Kubota *(Gen Mgr)*

Daikin Europe Coordination Center NV (1)
Zandvoordestraat 300
Oostende, West Vlaanderen, 8400, Belgium (100%)
Tel.: (32) 59558111
Fax: (32) 59558899
E-Mail: info@daikineurope.com
Web Site: www.daikineurope.com
Emp.: 1,500
S.I.C.: 3585
N.A.I.C.S.: 333415
Frans Hoorelbeke *(Mng Dir)*

Daikin Europe N.V. (1)
Zandvoordestraat 300
B 8400 Oostende, Belgium (100%)
Tel.: (32) 59558111
Fax: (32) 059558899
E-Mail: info@daikineurope.com
Web Site: www.daikineurope.com
Emp.: 1,500
S.I.C.: 3585
N.A.I.C.S.: 333415
Toshiki Hayashi *(Mng Dir)*

Non-U.S. Subsidiary:

Rotex Heating Systems GmbH (2)
Langwiesenstrasse 10
74363 Guglingen, Germany
Tel.: (49) 7135 103 0
Fax: (49) 7135 103 200
E-Mail: info@rotex.de
Web Site: www.rotex-heating.com
Emp.: 350
Heating Equipment Mfr
S.I.C.: 3433
N.A.I.C.S.: 333414
Georg Blumel *(CEO)*
Franz Grammling *(CEO)*
Yasuo Mishiro *(CEO)*

Daikin Fluorochemicals (China) Co., Ltd. (1)
No 8 Jinyu Road West Advanced Materials Industrial Park
215522 Changshu, Jiangsu, China
Tel.: (86) 51252322266
Fax: (86) 51252322366
Web Site: www.daikinchem.com.cn
Air Conditioning Equipment Mfr
S.I.C.: 3585
N.A.I.C.S.: 333415

Daikin Fuoro Coatings (Shanghai) Co., Ltd. (1)
388 Chun Guan Rd Xinzhuang Industry Zone
Shanghai, 201108, China
Tel.: (86) 2154421840
Fax: (86) 2154420654
Web Site: www.daikinchem.com
Emp.: 100
S.I.C.: 3585
N.A.I.C.S.: 333415
Lu Zheng *(Mgr-Sls)*

Daikin Industries (Thailand) Ltd. (1)
700 11 Bangpakong Industrial Estate
Bangna Trad Rd KM 57 Tambol Klongt
Chon Buri, 20000, Thailand (100%)
Tel.: (66) 38213032
Fax: (66) 38213047
E-Mail: info@daikinthai.com
Web Site: www.daikinthai.com
Sales Range: $300-349.9 Million
Emp.: 4,000
S.I.C.: 3585
N.A.I.C.S.: 333415
Satoru Kadoya *(Pres)*

DAIKIN McQUAY AR CONDICIONADO BRASIL LTDA. (1)
Alameda Santos 787-12 Andar
01419 001 Sao Paulo, Brazil
Tel.: (55) 11 3123 2525
Fax: (55) 11 3123 2526
E-Mail: comercial@daikin-mcquay.com.br
Web Site: www.daikin-mcquay.com.br
Air Conditioning Equipment Mfr
S.I.C.: 3585
N.A.I.C.S.: 333415

Daikin McQuay Middle East FZE (1)
Jebel Ali Free Zone
PO Box 18674
Dubai, United Arab Emirates
Tel.: (971) 4 8110300
Fax: (971) 4 8110311
E-Mail: info@daikinmcquayme.com
Web Site: www.daikinmcquayme.com
Airconditioning Equipment Distr
S.I.C.: 5075
N.A.I.C.S.: 423730
Francois Boueri *(Gen Mgr)*

Daikin Sweden A.B. (1)
Bjornstigen 87
170 72 Solna, Sweden
Tel.: (46) 8 564 855 40
Fax: (46) 8 564 855 50
E-Mail: info@daikinsverige.se
Web Site: www.daikinsverige.se
Heat Pump Mfr
S.I.C.: 3561
N.A.I.C.S.: 333911

Daikin Trading (Thailand) Ltd. (1)
283 77 Home Pl Office Bldg 15th Fl
Bangkok, 10110, Thailand (100%)
Tel.: (66) 27127314
Fax: (66) 27127316
Web Site: www.daikinthai.com
Emp.: 40
S.I.C.: 3585
N.A.I.C.S.: 333415
Sajime Iida *(Pres)*

IRS International Pty. Ltd. (1)
30 Burgess Street
Brooklyn, Melbourne, VIC, 3012, Australia

Daikin Industries, Ltd.—(Continued)

Tel.: (61) 3 9314 0577
Fax: (61) 3 9314 5562
E-Mail: melbourne@irsaust.com
Web Site: www.irsaust.com
Refrigerated Container Repair Services
S.I.C.: 7699
N.A.I.C.S.: 811310

O.Y.L. Manufacturing Company Sdn. Bhd. (OYLM) (1)
Lot 60334 Persiaran Bukit Rahman Putra 3
Taman Perindustrian Bukit
Raman Putra, 47000 Sungai Buloh, Selangor Darul Ehsan, Malaysia
Tel.: (60) 361458600
Fax: (60) 361412286
Web Site: www.oyl.com.my
Sales Range: $1-4.9 Billion
Emp.: 1,600
Heating & Air Conditioning Products Mfr
S.I.C.: 3585
N.A.I.C.S.: 333415
Hirokazu Hireo *(Gen Mgr)*

U.S. Subsidiaries:

AAF International (2)
10300 Ormsby Pk Pl Ste 600
Louisville, KY 40223 DE
Mailing Address:
PO Box 35690
Louisville, KY 40232-5690
Tel.: (502) 445-1263
Fax: (502) 637-0452
Web Site: www.aafintl.com
Sls.: $880,000,000
Emp.: 200
Commercial, Industrial & Institutional Heating, Ventilating, Air-Conditioning, Filtration & Air Pollution Control Products, Systems & Controls
Export
S.I.C.: 3585
N.A.I.C.S.: 333415
Rich Lancaster *(CIO)*
Ronald J. Pederson *(Treas)*

Non-U.S. Subsidiaries:

AAF International B.V. (3)
Egelenburg 2
1081 GK Amsterdam, Netherlands
Tel.: (31) 205494411, ext. 591686911
Fax: (31) 205494400
E-Mail: info@nl.aafeurope.com
Web Site: www.aafeurope.com
Emp.: 25
Air Pollution Control Equipment Mfr
S.I.C.: 3564
N.A.I.C.S.: 333413
Quekleng Chan *(Mng Dir)*

McQuay International (2)
13600 Industrial Park Blvd
Minneapolis, MN 55441
Tel.: (763) 553-5330
Fax: (763) 553-5177
Toll Free: (800) 432-1342
Web Site: www.mcquay.com
Emp.: 250
Heating, Ventilating & Air Conditioning Equipment Mfr, Retailer & Servicer
Export
S.I.C.: 3585
N.A.I.C.S.: 333415
Chris Sachrison *(COO)*

Subsidiaries:

McQuay International-Chiller Products (3)
207 Laurellhill Rd
Verona, VA 24482-2510
Mailing Address:
PO Box 2510
Staunton, VA 24402-2510
Tel.: (540) 248-0711
Fax: (540) 248-9412
Web Site: www.mcquay.com
Refrigeration Products
S.I.C.: 3585
N.A.I.C.S.: 333415

ROTEX Polska SP. Z O.O. (1)
ul Tasmowa 7
02-677 Warsaw, Poland
Tel.: (48) 22 319 90 00
Fax: (48) 22 433 51 98
E-Mail: rotex@rotex.com.pl
Web Site: www.rotex.com.pl
Heating Equipment Mfr
S.I.C.: 3433
N.A.I.C.S.: 333414

Siam Daikin Sales Co., Ltd. (1)
22 Soi Onnuch 55/1 Pravet Subdistrict
Pravet District, Bangkok, 10250, Thailand
Tel.: (66) 2 715 3200
Fax: (66) 2 721 7607
E-Mail: coolline@daikin.co.th
Web Site: www.daikin.co.th
Air Conditioning Equipment Distr
S.I.C.: 5075
N.A.I.C.S.: 423730

Xi'an Daikin Qing'an Compressor Co., Ltd. (1)
No 10 Gao Xin Road 2 Hi Tec Industrial Development Area
Xi'an, Shaanxi, 710075, China CN
Tel.: (86) 2988310966
Fax: (86) 2988317543
E-Mail: xadaikin@xadaikin.com
Web Site: www.xadaikin.com
Emp.: 1,000
Commercial Airconditioning Scroll Compressors Mfr
S.I.C.: 3585
N.A.I.C.S.: 333415

Zhuhai Gree Daikin Device Co., Ltd. (1)
No 8 Longshan No 3 Rd Longshan Area
Fushan Industrial Park
Zhuhai, Guangdong, 519110, China
Tel.: (86) 7565790174
Fax: (86) 7565790807
Printed Circuit Board Mfr
S.I.C.: 3672
N.A.I.C.S.: 334412

DAIKO CLEARING SERVICES CORPORATION

13-1 Nihonbashi Kabuto-cho
Chuo-ku, Tokyo, 103 0026, Japan
Tel.: (81) 3 3666 2231
Web Site: www.daiko-sb.co.jp
8692—(TKS)
Rev.: $198,539,000
Assets: $577,874,000
Liabilities: $301,840,000
Net Worth: $276,034,000
Earnings: $9,801,000
Emp.: 656
Fiscal Year-end: 03/31/13

Business Description:
Securities Related Services
S.I.C.: 6211
N.A.I.C.S.: 523120

Personnel:
Akira Yamamoto *(Chm)*
Hitoshi Tada *(Pres & CEO)*
Yoji Furukawa *(Corp Officer)*
Shigeru Inoki *(Corp Officer)*
Fumio Kaneko *(Corp Officer)*
Masami Kobayashi *(Corp Officer)*
Shingo Koike *(Corp Officer)*
Katsuo Narukami *(Mng Exec Officer)*
Masato Wagi *(Corp Officer)*

Board of Directors:
Akira Yamamoto
Hiroshi Funakura
Kozo Kazekami
Hiroyuki Kobayashi
Etsuo Misono
Katsuo Narukami
Yoshiaki Shin
Hitoshi Tada

Subsidiaries:

Fujisoft Dis Co., Ltd. (1)
NK Building 2-7 Kanda-Sudacho
Chiyoda-ku, 101-0041 Tokyo, Japan
Tel.: (81) 352097351
Data Processing Hosting & Related Services
S.I.C.: 7379
N.A.I.C.S.: 518210

KCS Co., Ltd. (1)
(Formerly Fujisoft KCS Co., Ltd.)
2-19-7 Kotobashi
Sumida-ku, Tokyo, 130-0022, Japan
Tel.: (81) 356381300
Fax: (81) 356381377
Web Site: www.kkcs.co.jp
Emp.: 350
Custom Computer Programming Services
S.I.C.: 7371
N.A.I.C.S.: 541511
Taketoshi Takizawa *(Pres)*

DAIKO DENSHI TSUSHIN, LTD.

2-1 Ageba-cho
Shinjuku-ku, Tokyo, 162-8565, Japan
Tel.: (81) 3 3266 8111
Fax: (81) 3 3266 8110
E-Mail: admin@daikodenshi.co.jp
Web Site: www.daikodenshi.jp
Year Founded: 1953
8023—(TKS)
Sales Range: $350-399.9 Million
Emp.: 990

Business Description:
Computer & Computer Related Product Whslr
S.I.C.: 5045
N.A.I.C.S.: 423430

Personnel:
Takahide Tsudama *(Pres)*

DAIKOKU DENKI CO., LTD.

43-5 Nagono 1-chome
Nakamura-ku, Nagoya, 450-8640, Japan
Tel.: (81) 52 581 7111
Fax: (81) 52 581 7135
Web Site: www.daikoku.co.jp
Year Founded: 1964
6430—(TKS)
Sls.: $647,471,000
Assets: $623,766,000
Liabilities: $288,937,000
Net Worth: $334,829,000
Earnings: $45,771,000
Emp.: 603
Fiscal Year-end: 03/31/13

Business Description:
Computer System Mfr & Whslr
S.I.C.: 3571
N.A.I.C.S.: 334111

Personnel:
Masakatsu Kayamori *(Chm)*
Hideyuki Kayamori *(Pres)*

Board of Directors:
Masakatsu Kayamori
Yoshihiro Adachi
Tadami Hashimoto
Setsuo Iwane
Akira Kayamori
Hideyuki Kayamori
Ken Kayamori
Tokumaru Kuniyasu
Masaki Muromachi
Hiroshi Nemoto
Tokishige Niwa
Naoshi Saito
Shingo Sato
Koji Yoshikawa

DAIKOKUTENBUSSAN CO., LTD.

704-5 Horinan
Kurashiki, Okayama, 710-0841, Japan
Tel.: (81) 86 435 1100
Web Site: www.e-dkt.co.jp
Year Founded: 1986
2791—(TKS)
Sales Range: $800-899.9 Million
Emp.: 707

Business Description:
Supermarket Operator
S.I.C.: 5411
N.A.I.C.S.: 445110

Personnel:
Shoji Oga *(Pres & CEO)*

DAIKYO INCORPORATED

Sendagaya No 21 Daikyo Building
24-13 Sendagaya 4-chome Shibuya-ku
Tokyo, 151-8506, Japan
Tel.: (81) 334751111
Fax: (81) 3 3475 3803
E-Mail: info@daikyo.co.jp
Web Site: www.daikyo.co.jp
Year Founded: 1964
8840—(TKS)
Sls.: $3,328,721,000
Assets: $3,029,873,000
Liabilities: $1,585,408,000
Net Worth: $1,444,465,000
Earnings: $170,885,000
Emp.: 3,940
Fiscal Year-end: 03/31/13

Business Description:
Real Estate Leasing & Condominium Developer
Export
S.I.C.: 6519
N.A.I.C.S.: 531190

Personnel:
Yoshiyuki Yoshizumi *(Chm)*
Akira Yamaguchi *(Pres)*
Katsumi Kubota *(Exec Officer)*
Konosuke Miyakawa *(Exec Officer)*
Kunihiko Numanyu *(Exec Officer)*
Yoichi Okada *(Exec Officer)*
Ryuhei Sakamoto *(Exec VP)*
Eiji Ochiai *(Sr VP)*
Joichiro Tsuchida *(Sr VP)*

Board of Directors:
Yoshiyuki Yoshizumi
Toru Hambayashi
Kazuhiko Kaise
Akira Miyahara
Hiroaki Nishina
Teruo Ozaki
Ryuhei Sakamoto
Akira Yamaguchi

Subsidiaries:

Asset Wave Corporation, Inc. (1)
3-10-2 Kandajinbocho
Chiyoda-ku, Tokyo, Japan
Tel.: (81) 352116080
Web Site: www.awave.co.jp
Sls.: $10,168,000
Emp.: 30
Real Estate Services
S.I.C.: 6531
N.A.I.C.S.: 531210
Shigeyuki Takagi *(CEO)*
Masami Hatae *(COO)*

Daikyo L. Design Incorporated (1)
5-25-5 Sendagaya
Shibuya-ku, Tokyo, Japan
Tel.: (81) 353662490
Fax: (81) 352692979
House Remodeling Services
S.I.C.: 1522
N.A.I.C.S.: 236118

Daikyo Life Incorporated (1)
4-8-16 Sendagaya
1510051
Shibuya-Ku, Tokyo, Japan
Tel.: (81) 357755170
Condominiums & Housing Services
S.I.C.: 6531
N.A.I.C.S.: 531311

Daikyo Realdo Incorporated (1)
5-25-5 Sendagaya
Shibuya-ku, 1510051 Tokyo, Japan
Tel.: (81) 353662106
Fax: (81) 352692944
E-Mail: dr-cinfo@grp.daikyo.co.jp
Web Site: www.luxury.daikyo-realdo.co.jp
Real Estate Brokerage & sales
S.I.C.: 6519
N.A.I.C.S.: 531190

DAILY INTERNET PLC
9 Regan Way Chetwynd Business Park
Chilwell, Nottingham, NG9 6RZ, United Kingdom
Tel.: (44) 845 466 2100
Fax: (44) 845 466 0102
E-Mail: helpdesk@daily.co.uk
Web Site: www.daily.co.uk
Year Founded: 2006
DAIP—(AIM)
Rev.: $2,458,955
Assets: $1,806,708
Liabilities: $2,523,705
Net Worth: ($716,998)
Earnings: ($1,421,361)
Emp.: 19
Fiscal Year-end: 03/31/13
Business Description:
Domain Name Registration & Hosting Services
S.I.C.: 7374
N.A.I.C.S.: 518210
Personnel:
Abby Hardoon Adulayavichit *(Mng Dir)*
Clive Maudsley *(Sec)*
Board of Directors:
John Michael Edelson
Abby Hardoon Adulayavichit
Christopher Evans
Julie Ann Joyce
Robert Khalastchy
Legal Counsel:
Kuit Steinart Levy LLP
3 St Mary's Parsonage
Manchester, M3 2RD, United Kingdom

DAILY MAIL & GENERAL TRUST PLC
Northcliffe House 2 Derry Street
London, W8 5TT, United Kingdom
Tel.: (44) 2079386000
Fax: (44) 2079384626
E-Mail: enquiries@dmgt.com
Web Site: www.dmgt.co.uk
Year Founded: 1896
DMGT—(LSE OTC)
Rev.: $2,746,388,832
Assets: $3,413,333,040
Liabilities: $3,010,839,600
Net Worth: $402,493,440
Earnings: $440,069,976
Emp.: 12,130
Fiscal Year-end: 09/30/12
Business Description:
Newspaper & Business-to-Business Information Publisher; Conference & Trade Show Organizer; Radio Station Operator
Import Export
S.I.C.: 2711
N.A.I.C.S.: 511110
Personnel:
Viscount Rothermere *(Chm)*
Claire Chapman *(Gen Counsel & Sec)*
Board of Directors:
Viscount Rothermere
Francisco P. Balsemao
Kevin J. Beatty
Nicholas W. Berry
Claire Chapman
Paul M. Dacre
Stephen W. Daintith
David M. M. Dutton
Tom S. Gillespie
John G. Hemingway
David H. Nelson
Heidi Roizen
Dominique Trempont
David J. Verey

Subsidiaries:

Associated Newspapers Ltd. (1)
Northcliffe House 2 Derry Street
London, Kensington, W8 5TT, United Kingdom UK
Tel.: (44) 2079386000 (100%)
Telex: 884243
Fax: (44) 2079386764
Web Site: www.associatednewspapers.co.uk
Sales Range: $1-4.9 Billion
Emp.: 3,835
Publisher of Newspapers
Import Export
S.I.C.: 2711
N.A.I.C.S.: 511110
Jonathan Harmsworth Rothermere, IV *(Chm)*
Roland Agambar *(CMO)*
Nick Jennings *(Sec)*

Subsidiaries:

This Is London Ltd. (2)
2 Derry Street
London, W8 5TT, United Kingdom
Tel.: (44) 2033677000
E-Mail: editor@thisislondon.com
Web Site: www.thisislondon.com
News & Entertainment Website
S.I.C.: 2741
N.A.I.C.S.: 519130
Sarah Sands *(Editor)*

British Pathe PLC (1)
The Media Centre
3-8 Carburton St, London, W1W 5AJ, United Kingdom (100%)
Tel.: (44) 02076658340
E-Mail: info@britishpathe.com
Web Site: www.britishpathe.com
Newsreel Archive Services
S.I.C.: 2711
N.A.I.C.S.: 511110

Euromoney Institutional Investor PLC (1)
Nestor House Playhouse Yard
London, EC4V 5EX, United Kingdom UK
Tel.: (44) 2077798888 (68%)
Fax: (44) 2077798506
E-Mail: hotline@euromoneyplc.com
Web Site: www.euromoneyplc.com
ERM—(LSE)
Rev.: $672,391,414
Assets: $1,040,980,216
Liabilities: $486,459,663
Net Worth: $554,520,553
Earnings: $121,326,656
Emp.: 2,142
Fiscal Year-end: 09/30/13
Trade Magazine, Newsletter, Journal & Book Publisher; Conference, Seminar & Training Course Organizer
S.I.C.: 2721
N.A.I.C.S.: 511120
P. Richard Ensor *(Chm)*
Patrick Sergeant *(Pres)*
Chris H. C. Fordham *(Mng Dir)*
C. Benn *(Sec)*

Subsidiary:

Metal Bulletin Limited (2)
Nestor house PlayHouse yard
London, Surrey, EC4V 5EX, United Kingdom UK
Tel.: (44) 2078279977
E-Mail: editorial@metalbulletin.com
Web Site: www.metalbulletin.com
Sales Range: $100-124.9 Million
Emp.: 460
Data Management & Publishing Services
S.I.C.: 2741
N.A.I.C.S.: 511140
Alison Ellmann *(Head-Online)*

Division:

World Textile Publications Ltd (3)
Perkin House 1 Longlands St
Bradford, West Yorkshire, BD1 2TP, United Kingdom UK
Tel.: (44) 12743788
Fax: (44) 1274378811
E-Mail: info@worldtextile.net
Web Site: www.wtin.com
Emp.: 30
Data Management & Publishing
S.I.C.: 2741
N.A.I.C.S.: 511140
Mark Jarvis *(Mng Dir)*

U.S. Holdings:

American Metal Market (3)
1 Gateway Ctr Ste 1375
Pittsburgh, PA 15222
Tel.: (412) 765-2580
Fax: (412) 765-3073
E-Mail: subscriptions@amm.com
Web Site: www.amm.com
Emp.: 10
Journal Publisher
S.I.C.: 2721
N.A.I.C.S.: 511120
David Brooks *(Exec VP)*

Non-U.S. Holdings:

Metal Bulletin Japan (3)
Rm 701 Oak Mansions
Negishi 5 16 5
Taito Ku, Tokyo, 1100003, Japan
Tel.: (81) 338765760
Fax: (81) 338765761
E-Mail: mcculloch@metalbulletin.com
Web Site: www.metalbulletin.com
Data Management & Publishing
S.I.C.: 2741
N.A.I.C.S.: 511140

Metal Bulletin Singapore (3)
3 Raffles Pl 08-01
Singapore, 048617, Singapore SG
Tel.: (65) 63335523
Fax: (65) 63335501
E-Mail: martin.ritchie@metalbulletin.com
Web Site: www.metalbulletin.com
Emp.: 10
Data Management & Publishing
S.I.C.: 2741
N.A.I.C.S.: 511140
Martin Ritchie *(Editor)*

U.S. Subsidiaries:

Euromoney Training, Inc. (2)
225 Park Ave S 8th Fl
New York, NY 10003 DE
Tel.: (212) 361-3299 (100%)
Fax: (212) 361-3499
E-Mail: info@euromoneyny.com
Web Site: www.euromoneytraining.com
Legal, Information Technology Audit, Information Security, Banking & Financial Training Services
S.I.C.: 8299
N.A.I.C.S.: 611430

Gulf Publishing Company, Inc. (2)
2 Green Way Plz Ste 1020
Houston, TX 77046 DE
Tel.: (713) 529-4301
Fax: (713) 520-4433
E-Mail: publications@gulfpub.com
Web Site: www.gulfpub.com
Sales Range: $50-74.9 Million
Emp.: 230
Magazine, Catalog & Trade Journal Publishers
S.I.C.: 2721
N.A.I.C.S.: 511120
John T. Royall *(Pres & CEO)*
Bret Ronk *(Publr-Hydrocarbon Processing Magazine)*

Institutional Investor, Inc. (2)
225 Park Ave S 8th Fl
New York, NY 10003-1605
Tel.: (212) 224-3300
Telex: 671391
E-Mail: ideas@institutionalinvestor.com
Web Site: www.institutionalinvestor.com
Emp.: 50
Business Periodicals Publisher
S.I.C.: 2721
N.A.I.C.S.: 511120
Diane Alfano *(Chm)*
Allison Adams *(Mng Dir & Grp Publr)*
Ernest S. McCrary *(Editor & Publr-Special Projects)*
Christine Cavolina *(Publr-Magazine)*

MIS Training Institute, LLC (2)
153 Cordaville Rd
Southborough, MA 01772-1834
Tel.: (508) 879-7999
Fax: (508) 872-1153
Web Site: www.misti.com
Audit & Information Security Training Courses & Services; Conference & Trade Show Organizer
S.I.C.: 8299
N.A.I.C.S.: 611430
Michael I. Sobol *(Founder)*
Linda Burton *(Pres & CEO)*
Mimi Hatch *(Exec VP-In-House Trng & Sls)*

Ned Davis Research Inc. (2)
600 Bird Bay Dr W
Venice, FL 34285
Tel.: (941) 484-6107
Fax: (941) 484-5215
Web Site: www.ndr.com
Sales Range: $10-24.9 Million
Emp.: 90
Investment Research & Advisory Services
S.I.C.: 8732
N.A.I.C.S.: 541910
Nathan E. Davis *(Pres)*
Eric Lankinen *(CEO)*

Hobsons (1)
IDT house
44 Seitherstone Street, London, EC1Y 8RN, United Kingdom
Tel.: (44) 2072506600
Fax: (44) 2072506601
Web Site: www.hobsons.com
Emp.: 50
Publisher of Educational & Career Information
S.I.C.: 2741
N.A.I.C.S.: 511199
Sharon Johnson *(Dir-Fin & HR)*

U.S. Subsidiary:

Intelliworks, Inc. (2)
3033 Wilson Blvd Ste 500
Arlington, VA 22201
Tel.: (240) 238-3210
Fax: (703) 234-5909
Web Site: www.intelliworks.com
Sales Range: $1-9.9 Million
Emp.: 200
Custom Computer Programming Services
S.I.C.: 7371
N.A.I.C.S.: 541511
Rob Riedel *(CFO)*
Chris Beall *(CTO)*

Independent Television News Ltd. (1)
200 Grays Inn Rd
London, WC1X 8XZ, United Kingdom
Tel.: (44) 2078333000
Fax: (44) 2074304305
E-Mail: views@itn.co.uk
Web Site: www.itn.co.uk
Rev.: $171,730,415
Assets: $62,045,566
Liabilities: $157,366,773
Net Worth: ($95,321,207)
Earnings: $1,718,268
Emp.: 707
Fiscal Year-end: 12/31/12
Television Broadcaster
S.I.C.: 4833
N.A.I.C.S.: 515120
Maggie Carver *(Chm)*
John Hardie *(CEO)*
Bryan Martin *(CFO)*

Landmark Information Group (1)
7 Abbey Ct Eagle Way
Sowton Industrial Estate, Exeter, Devon, EX2 7HY, United Kingdom (100%)
Tel.: (44) 392441700
Telex: 135607 Exeter 16
Fax: (44) 392441709
E-Mail: mailbox@landmark.co.uk
Web Site: www.landmark.co.uk
Emp.: 100
Produces Site-Specific Environmental Reports for Firms of Environmental & Geo-Technical Consultants, Civil Engineers & Large Industrial Owners
S.I.C.: 8999
N.A.I.C.S.: 541620
Mark Milner *(CEO)*
Ian Clarke *(CTO)*

Northcliffe Newspapers Group Limited (1)
Northcliffe House 2 Derry Street
London, W8 5TT, United Kingdom (100%)

Daily Mail & General Trust plc—(Continued)

Tel.: (44) 2074001401
Web Site: www.thisisnorthcliffe.co.uk
Sales Range: $800-899.9 Million
Emp.: 6,350
Regional Newspaper Publisher
S.I.C.: 2711
N.A.I.C.S.: 511110
Steven Auckland *(Mng Dir)*

Teletext Limited (1)
10 Chiswick Park
566 Chiswick High Road, London, W4 5TS, United Kingdom (100%)
Tel.: (44) 2083235000
Fax: (44) 8707313200
E-Mail: butyeditor@teletext.co.uk
Web Site: www.teletext.co.uk
Emp.: 200
Television Information Services
S.I.C.: 2741
N.A.I.C.S.: 519130
Victoria Sanders *(Gen Mgr)*

U.S. Subsidiaries:

DMG Events (USA) Inc. (1)
3 Stamford Landing Ste 400 46 Southfield Ave
Stamford, CT 06902 DE
Tel.: (203) 973-2940
Fax: (203) 973-2995
Web Site: www.dmgevents.com
Emp.: 300
Consumer Exhibitions Organizer
S.I.C.: 7389
N.A.I.C.S.: 561920
Suresh Kavan *(Chm)*
Paul Sykes *(CFO)*
Galen Poss *(COO)*
Paul M. Vogt *(Gen Counsel)*

Units:

DMG Events (USA) Inc. - Digital Marketing (2)
221 Main St Ste 920
San Francisco, CA 94105-1923
Tel.: (415) 537-8500
Fax: (415) 537-8530
E-Mail: contactus@dmgdigitalmarketing.com
Web Site: www.dmgdigitalmarketing.com
Emp.: 20
Consumer Exhibitions Organizer & Digital Marketing Services
S.I.C.: 7389
N.A.I.C.S.: 561920
Susan C. MacDermid *(Pres)*

Non-U.S. Subsidiaries:

DMG Events (Canada) Inc. (2)
302 1333 8 Street SW
Calgary, AB, T2R 1M6, Canada ON (100%)
Tel.: (403) 209-3555
Fax: (416) 245-8649
E-Mail: calgarysales@dmgevents.com
Web Site: www.dmgevents.com
Rev.: $1,764,720
Emp.: 35
Consumer Exhibitions Organizer
S.I.C.: 7389
N.A.I.C.S.: 561920
Wes Scott *(VP)*

DMG Events (Dubai) Limited (2)
5th Floor The Palladium Bldg Cluster C
Jumeirah Lakes Towers
PO Box 33817
Dubai, United Arab Emirates AE
Tel.: (971) 4 4380 355
Fax: (971) 4 4380 361
E-Mail: dmgdubai@dmgevents.com
Web Site: www.dmgevents.com
Emp.: 300
Consumer Exhibitions Organizer
S.I.C.: 7389
N.A.I.C.S.: 561920
Galen Poss *(Vice Chm)*
Geoff Dickinson *(CEO)*
Simon Mellor *(Pres-Middle East & Asia)*

DMG Events Limited (2)
Northcliffe House 2 Derry Street
London, W8 5TT, United Kingdom UK (100%)
Tel.: (44) 20 7938 6000
Fax: (44) 20 3180 6550
E-Mail: info@gastech.co.uk
Web Site: www.gastech.co.uk
Sales Range: $300-349.9 Million
Emp.: 813
Consumer Exhibitions Organizer
S.I.C.: 7389
N.A.I.C.S.: 561920
Nick Ratcliffe *(CFO)*
Mark Carr *(Pres-Energy Sector)*

DMG Information US Inc. (1)
46 Southfield Ave
Stamford, CT 06902 DE
Tel.: (203) 973-2940
Fax: (203) 973-2995
E-Mail: info@dmginfo.com
Web Site: www.dmginfo.com
Sales Range: $125-149.9 Million
Emp.: 10
Group Investment Services
S.I.C.: 4899
N.A.I.C.S.: 517919
Suresh Kavan *(CEO)*
Paul Sykes *(CFO)*
Stephen Stout *(CEO-Asia Pacific)*
Paul M. Vogt *(Gen Counsel)*

Environmental Data Resources, Inc. (1)
440 Wheelers Farms Rd
Milford, CT 06461
Tel.: (203) 255-6606
Fax: (203) 782-0305
Toll Free: (800) 352-0050
E-Mail: edr@edrnet.com
Web Site: www.edrnet.com
Emp.: 200
Geographic-Based Information Publishing, Consulting & Analytic Services to the Real Estate, Municipal & Telecommunications Markets
S.I.C.: 8999
N.A.I.C.S.: 541690
Robert Barber *(CEO)*
Jon Walker *(Mng Dir)*
Oreste Petillo *(CFO)*
Jay Gaines *(CMO)*
Gerry Tsui *(CTO)*

Risk Management Solutions Inc. (1)
7575 Gateway Blvd
Newark, CA 94560-1152
Tel.: (510) 505-2500
Fax: (510) 505-2501
E-Mail: info@riskinc.com
Web Site: www.rms.com
Emp.: 200
Risk Management Solutions Provider
S.I.C.: 8748
N.A.I.C.S.: 541618
Hemant H. Shah *(Co-Founder & CEO)*
Weimin Dong *(Co-Founder)*
Paul Dali *(Chm)*
Stephen I. Robertson *(CFO)*
Philippe Stephan *(CTO)*
Paul VanderMarck *(Chief Products Officer)*
John Abraham *(Sr VP-Corp Mktg)*
Paul Winsberg *(Sr VP-Software Dev)*

Branches:

Risk Management Solutions - East Coast US (2)
433 Hackensack Ave Fl 5
Hackensack, NJ 07601
Tel.: (201) 498-8600
Fax: (201) 498-8601
Web Site: www.rms.com
Emp.: 90
Risk Management Solution Providers
S.I.C.: 8748
N.A.I.C.S.: 541618
Hemant H. Shah *(Pres & CEO)*

Risk Management Solutions - Midwest US (2)
621 SW Commercial Alley Ste D
Peoria, IL 61602
Tel.: (309) 637-6350
Fax: (309) 637-6750
Web Site: www.rms.com
Risk Management Solutions
S.I.C.: 6411
N.A.I.C.S.: 524210

Non-U.S. Subsidiaries:

OYO RMS Corporation (2)
Akasaka Kikyo Bldg 4 Fl 11 15 Akasaka 3 Chome
Tokyo, Minato Ku, 107 0052, Japan (50%)
Tel.: (81) 355757189
Fax: (81) 355757197
Web Site: www.oyorms.co.jp
Emp.: 20
Risk Management Solutions Provider
S.I.C.: 7373
N.A.I.C.S.: 541512

RMS Ltd. (2)
Peninsular House 30 Monument St
London, EC3R 8HB, United Kingdom (100%)
Tel.: (44) 2072563800
Fax: (44) 20 7256 3838
Web Site: www.rms.com
Risk Management Solutions Provider
S.I.C.: 7373
N.A.I.C.S.: 541512
Martin Weinthrop *(VP-Client Dev-Europe)*

RMSI Private Limited (2)
A-7 Sector 16
Noida, 201 301, India (100%)
Tel.: (91) 1202511102
Fax: (91) 1202511109
E-Mail: india@rmsi.com
Web Site: www.rms.com
Emp.: 650
Geographical Information Services
S.I.C.: 7373
N.A.I.C.S.: 541512
Rajiv Kapoor *(Mng Dir)*

DAIMAN DEVELOPMENT BERHAD

Level 32 & 33 Menara Landmark No 12 Jalan Ngee Heng
80000 Johor Bahru, Malaysia
Tel.: (60) 72255888
Fax: (60) 72255999
E-Mail: enquiry@daiman.com.my
Web Site: www.daiman.com.my
DAIMAN—(KLS)
Rev.: $62,453,676
Assets: $422,695,110
Liabilities: $84,890,290
Net Worth: $337,804,820
Earnings: $22,580,571
Fiscal Year-end: 06/30/13

Business Description:
Property Development Services
S.I.C.: 6531
N.A.I.C.S.: 531312

Personnel:
Thiam Song Tay *(Mng Dir)*
Min Fong Woo *(Co-Sec)*
Wai Bing Yap *(Co-Sec)*

Board of Directors:
Ahmad Johari Abdul Razak
Eddie Yean Hoe Chan
Sing Ho
Seng Pheow Ong
Thiam Song Tay
Thiam Yew Tay
Tian Liang Tay

Subsidiaries:

Atlantic Dynamics Sdn. Bhd. (1)
Level 32 Menara Landmark No 12 Jalan Ngee Heng
80150 Johor Bahru, Johor, Malaysia
Tel.: (60) 73311366
Fax: (60) 72255999
E-Mail: enquiry@daiman.com.my
Web Site: www.daiman.com.my
Emp.: 100
Property Development Services
S.I.C.: 6531
N.A.I.C.S.: 531390
Siah Chin Leong *(Gen Mgr)*

Daiman Bowl Sdn. Bhd. (1)
No 2 Jalan Dedap 3 Taman Johor Jaya
81100 Johor Bahru, Johor, Malaysia
Tel.: (60) 73513399
Fax: (60) 73519922
E-Mail: daimanbowl@daiman.com.my
Emp.: 21
Ten Pin Bowling Center Operation Services
S.I.C.: 7933
N.A.I.C.S.: 713950
Tay Siowee *(Mgr)*

Daiman Golf Berhad (1)
No 18 Jalan Pesona Taman Johor Jaya
81100 Johor Bahru, Johor, Malaysia
Tel.: (60) 73516813
Fax: (60) 73516823
E-Mail: daiman18@daimangolf.com.my
Emp.: 15
18 Holes Golf Course Operation Services
S.I.C.: 7999
N.A.I.C.S.: 713910
Tay Tian Liang *(Mng Dir)*

Daiman Johor Jaya Sports Complex Berhad (1)
No 1 Jalan Dedap 3 Taman Johor Jaya
81100 Johor Bahru, Johor, Malaysia
Tel.: (60) 73551888
Fax: (60) 73552077
E-Mail: djjsc@daiman.com.my
Emp.: 26
Sports Club Facilities Operation Services
S.I.C.: 7999
N.A.I.C.S.: 713940

Daiman Trading Sdn. Bhd. (1)
Room 601 6th Floor Wisma Daiman No 64
Jalan Sulam Taman Sentosa
80150 Johor Bahru, Johor, Malaysia
Tel.: (60) 73329866
Fax: (60) 73331262
E-Mail: daimantrading@daiman.com.my
Web Site: www.daiman.com.my/trading.html
Building Materials Distr
S.I.C.: 5211
N.A.I.C.S.: 444190
Serene Han *(Mgr-HR)*

DAIMLER AG

Epplestrasse 225
70546 Stuttgart, Germany
Tel.: (49) 711 17 0
Fax: (49) 711 17 22 44
E-Mail: dialog@daimler.com
Web Site: www.daimler.com
Year Founded: 1998
DAI—(DEU EUR OTC STU)
Rev.: $153,863,192,490
Assets: $219,396,094,260
Liabilities: $158,131,897,560
Net Worth: $61,264,196,700
Earnings: $8,743,374,150
Emp.: 275,087
Fiscal Year-end: 12/31/12

Business Description:
Automobiles, Trucks, Electric & Electronics, Aviation, Space Defense Technologies, Propulsion & Financial Services Mfr & Dealer
Import Export
S.I.C.: 3711
N.A.I.C.S.: 336111

Personnel:
Manfred Bischoff *(Chm-Supervisory Bd)*
Dieter Zetsche *(Chm-Mgmt Bd)*
Erich Klemm *(Deputy Chm-Supervisory Bd)*
Herbert Werner *(CFO & VP-South Africa)*
Mike Belk *(Pres/CEO-Middle East & Levant)*
Wolfgang Bernhard *(Member-Mgmt Bd)*
Christine Hohmann-Dennhardt *(Member-Mgmt Bd)*
Wilfried Porth *(Member-Mgmt Bd)*
Andreas Renschler *(Member-Mgmt Bd)*
Hubertus Troska *(Member-Mgmt Bd)*
Bodo Uebber *(Member-Mgmt Bd)*
Thomas Weber *(Member-Mgmt Bd)*
Michael Muhlbayer *(Sr VP & Head-Treasury & IR)*

Supervisory Board of Directors:
Manfred Bischoff
Paul M. L. Achleitner
Sari Maritta Baldauf
Clemens A. H. Boersig
Michael Brecht
Jurgen Hambrecht

Petraea Heynike
Jorg Hofmann
Andrea Jung
Gerard J. Kleisterlee
Erich Klemm
Jurgen Langer
Sabine Maassen
Wolfgang Nieke
Valter Sanches
Jorg Spies
Elke Tonjes-Werner
Lloyd G. Trotter
Bernhard Walter
Frank Markus Weber

Division:

Daimler Financial Services AG **(1)**
Eichhornstrasse 3
10875 Berlin, Germany DE
Tel.: (49) 3025540 (100%)
Fax: (49) 3025541021
E-Mail: laila.krout@daimler.com
Web Site: www.daimlerfinancialservices.com
Sales Range: $5-14.9 Billion
Emp.: 10,718
Financial Services
S.I.C.: 6099
N.A.I.C.S.: 522320
Klaus Entenmann *(Chm)*
David Olsen *(CFO)*
Alwin Epple *(Member-Bd of Mgmt-Europe, Africa & Asia Pacific)*

Subsidiaries:

Daimler Export & Trade Finance GmbH **(2)**
Eichhornstr. 3
10785 Berlin, Germany (100%)
Tel.: (49) 3025541634
Fax: (49) 3025541640
Sales Range: $1-9.9 Million
Emp.: 30
Electric Power Svcs
S.I.C.: 1731
N.A.I.C.S.: 238210

DaimlerChrysler Services Structured Finance GmbH **(2)**
Epplestrasse 225
Stuttgart, 70567, Germany (100%)
Tel.: (49) 7111793103
Fax: (49) 7111794697
E-Mail: structuredfinance@daimlerag.com
Web Site: www.daimlerag.com
Sales Range: $50-74.9 Million
Emp.: 46
Lessors of Real Estate & Real Estate Investment Fund
S.I.C.: 6519
N.A.I.C.S.: 531190
Wilfried Porth *(Dir-HR-Labor Rels)*

Mercedes-Benz Bank AG **(2)**
Seimenstrasse 7
70439 Stuttgart, Germany (100%)
Tel.: (49) 71125740
Fax: (49) 1125748005
E-Mail: dialog@daimler.com
Web Site: www.mercedes-benz-bank.de
Rev.: $163,928,000
Emp.: 250
Automobile Mfr
S.I.C.: 3711
N.A.I.C.S.: 336111

Mercedes-Benz Leasing GmbH **(2)**
Siememstrasse 7
70469 Stuttgart, Germany (100%)
Tel.: (49) 711257401
Fax: (49) 71125748005
E-Mail: kundenservice@mercedes-benz-bank.com
Web Site: www.mercedes-benz-bank.de
Rev.: $34,900,800
Emp.: 1,450
Car Leasing Services
S.I.C.: 7515
N.A.I.C.S.: 532112
Peter Zierenger *(Mng Dir)*

U.S. Subsidiaries:

Daimler Financial Services Americas **(2)**
36455 Corporate Dr
Farmington Hills, MI 48331
Tel.: (248) 991-6700
Fax: (248) 957-2997
Web Site: www.daimlerchrysler-financialservices.com
Emp.: 50
Automotive Financing Services
S.I.C.: 6141
N.A.I.C.S.: 522291
Klaus Entenmann *(Pres & CEO)*

Unit:

DaimlerChrysler Truck Financial **(3)**
1011 Warrenville Rd
Lisle, IL 60532-0903 IL
Mailing Address:
PO Box 901
Roanoke, TX 76262-0901
Tel.: (630) 241-5950
Web Site: www.dctruckfinancial.com
Emp.: 300
Automobile Finance Leasing
S.I.C.: 6141
N.A.I.C.S.: 522220

Non-U.S. Unit:

Mercedes-Benz Financial Services Canada **(3)**
2680 Matheson Blvd E Ste 500
Mississauga, ON, L4W 0A5, Canada ON
Tel.: (905) 813-6900
Fax: (905) 821-7650
Toll Free: (888) 532-7362
Web Site: www.mbfinancial.ca
Sales Range: $10-24.9 Million
Emp.: 70
Automotive Finance
S.I.C.: 6153
N.A.I.C.S.: 522220

Non-U.S. Subsidiaries:

Mercedes-Benz Auto Finance Ltd. **(2)**
Daimler Tower 19F No 8 Wangjing St
Chaoyang District, Beijing, China 100102
Tel.: (86) 4008981888
Fax: (86) 1084174199
E-Mail: MBAFC-CRM@daimler.com
Web Site: www.mercedes-benz-finance.com.cn
Emp.: 100
Automotive Financial Leasing Services
S.I.C.: 6159
N.A.I.C.S.: 522220
Brian D. Fulton *(Pres & CEO)*

Mercedes-Benz Financial Services Australia Pty. Ltd. **(2)**
Level 1 41 Lexia Place
Mulgrave, VIC, 3170, Australia
Tel.: (61) 3 8554 3000
Fax: (61) 3 8554 3022
Commercial Vehicle Financial Services
S.I.C.: 6726
N.A.I.C.S.: 525990
Gero Goetzenberger *(Mng Dir)*

Mercedes-Benz Financial Services New Zealand Ltd. **(2)**
9 Pacific Rise
Mount Wellington, Auckland, 1060, New Zealand
Tel.: (64) 9 573 3500
Fax: (64) 9 573 5116
E-Mail: mbfs_customercare@daimler.com
Emp.: 3
Automotive Financial Services
S.I.C.: 6726
N.A.I.C.S.: 525990
Daniel van Treeck *(Gen Mgr)*

Subsidiaries:

Anota Fahrzeug Service- und Vertriebsgesellschaft mbH **(1)**
Eichhornstr 3
Berlin, 10785, Germany
Tel.: (49) 3026942319
Motor Vehicle Distr
S.I.C.: 5012
N.A.I.C.S.: 423110

Automotive Training GmbH **(1)**
Hauptstrasse 31
70563 Stuttgart, Germany
Tel.: (49) 7111770402
Fax: (49) 7111770403
E-Mail: info@automotive-training-consulting.com
Web Site: www.automotive-training-consulting.com
Emp.: 20
Automotive Training & Consulting Services
S.I.C.: 8748
N.A.I.C.S.: 541618
Walter Konzmann *(CEO & Co-Mng Dir)*
Bettina Schuele *(CFO & Co-Mng Dir)*

car2go GmbH **(1)**
Wilhelm-Runge-Str 11
89081 Ulm, Germany
Tel.: (49) 180 573 11110
Fax: (49) 731 505 6599
E-Mail: ulm@car2go.com
Web Site: www.car2go.com
Car Sharing Services
S.I.C.: 7514
N.A.I.C.S.: 532111

U.S. Subsidiary:

car2go N.A. LLC **(2)**
800 W 5th St Ste 100 B
Austin, TX 78703
Tel.: (512) 480-0813
E-Mail: austin@car2go.com
Web Site: www.car2go.com
Car Sharing Services
S.I.C.: 7514
N.A.I.C.S.: 532111

Non-U.S. Subsidiaries:

car2go Canada Ltd. **(2)**
45 Water Street
Vancouver, BC, V6G 1Z3, Canada
Tel.: (512) 497-5826
E-Mail: vancouver@car2go.com
Web Site: www.car2go.com
Car Rental Services
S.I.C.: 7514
N.A.I.C.S.: 532111
Katie Stafford *(Mgr-Comm-North America)*

car2go France SAS **(2)**
2 Place Francfort
69003 Lyon, France
Tel.: (33) 478186101
Web Site: www.car2go.com
Car Rental Services
S.I.C.: 7514
N.A.I.C.S.: 532111

car2go Osterreich GmbH **(2)**
Hintere Zollamtstrasse 9
1030 Vienna, Austria
Tel.: (43) 820 919199
E-Mail: wien@car2go.com
Web Site: www.car2go.com
Car Rental Services
S.I.C.: 7514
N.A.I.C.S.: 532111

CARS Technik und Logistik GmbH **(1)**
Junkersstrasse 3
4509 Wiedemar, Germany
Tel.: (49) 34207 4066 6352
Fax: (49) 34207 4066 6360
E-Mail: info@cars-gmbh.de
Web Site: www.cars-gmbh.de
Automotive Repair & Logistics Services
S.I.C.: 7539
N.A.I.C.S.: 811198
Marc Stoesser *(Mng Dir & Head-Ops-Vehicle Transport)*

Daimler Aerospace GmbH & Co. KG **(1)**
Epplestr 225
Stuttgart, Baden-Wurttemberg, 70567, Germany
Tel.: (49) 7111776432
Military Aircraft Mfr
S.I.C.: 3721
N.A.I.C.S.: 336411

Daimler-Benz AG & Co. AMICITIA Grundstucksvermietung Potsdamer Platz OHG **(1)**
Lilienthalstr 6
Schonefeld, 12529, Germany
Tel.: (49) 711170
Real Estate Management Services
S.I.C.: 6531
N.A.I.C.S.: 531390

Daimler-Benz AG & Co. EFFICIENTIA Grundstucksvermietung Potsdamer Platz OHG **(1)**
Lilienthalstr 6
Schonefeld, Germany
Tel.: (49) 711170
Real Estate Management Services
S.I.C.: 6531
N.A.I.C.S.: 531390

Daimler-Benz AG & Co. "GENEROSA" Grundstucksvermietung Potsdamer Platz OHG **(1)**
Lilienthalstr 6
Schonefeld, 12529, Germany
Tel.: (49) 306331110
Real Estate Management Services
S.I.C.: 6531
N.A.I.C.S.: 531390

Daimler-Benz AG & Co. LEGITIMA Grundstucksvermietung Potsdamer Platz OHG **(1)**
Lilienthalstr 6
Schonefeld, 12529, Germany
Tel.: (49) 711170
Real Estate Management Services
S.I.C.: 6531
N.A.I.C.S.: 531390

Daimler-Benz AG & Co. NEGOTIA Grundstucksvermietung Potsdamer Platz OHG **(1)**
Albert-Tanneur-Str 25
14974 Ludwigsfelde, Brandenburg, Germany
Tel.: (49) 3378 337 8830
Real Estate Management Services
S.I.C.: 6531
N.A.I.C.S.: 531390

Daimler-Benz AG & Co. NOBILITAS Grundstucksvermietung Potsdamer Platz OHG **(1)**
Lilienthalstr 6
Schonefeld, 12529, Germany
Tel.: (49) 711170
Real Estate Management Services
S.I.C.: 6531
N.A.I.C.S.: 531390

Daimler-Benz AG & Co. PROSPERA Grundstucksvermietung Potsdamer Platz OHG **(1)**
Lilienthalstr 6
Schonefeld, 12529, Germany
Tel.: (49) 306331110
Fax: (49) 30633111120
Real Estate Management Services
S.I.C.: 6531
N.A.I.C.S.: 531390

Daimler Fleet Management GmbH **(1)**
Leitzstrasse 45
Stuttgart, 70469, Germany
Tel.: (49) 711 2574 4010
Fax: (49) 711 2574 8005
Web Site: www.daimler-fleetmanagement.de
Fleet Management Services
S.I.C.: 7515
N.A.I.C.S.: 532112

Daimler FleetBoard GmbH **(1)**
Am Wallgraben 125
Stuttgart, Baden-Wurttemberg, 70565, Germany
Tel.: (49) 7 11 17 9 19 99
Fax: (49) 7 11 17 9 12 11
E-Mail: support@fleetboard.com
Web Site: www.fleetboard.com
Emp.: 800
Transportation Telematic Internet Services
S.I.C.: 4899
N.A.I.C.S.: 517919
Ralf Forcher *(CEO)*
Dietrich Muller *(Mng Dir)*
Patrick Hackenberger *(CFO)*

Non-U.S. Subsidiary:

Daimler FleetBoard UK Ltd. **(2)**
Victoria House Cygnet Drive
Tamworth, Staffs, B79 7RU, United Kingdom
Tel.: (44) 1827 311912
Fax: (44) 1827 311916

Daimler AG—(Continued)

E-Mail: support@fleetboard.co.uk
Web Site: www.fleetboard.com
Emp.: 15
Vehicle & Transportation Management Software Distr
S.I.C.: 5045
N.A.I.C.S.: 423430
Philipp Janya van Witzendorff *(Dir-Vehicle Mgmt & Sls)*

Daimler Insurance Services GmbH (1)
Siemensstrasse 7
Stuttgart, 70469, Germany
Tel.: (49) 3025544600
Fax: (49) 71125748100
E-Mail: versicherungen@daimler.com
Automotive Insurance Services
S.I.C.: 6351
N.A.I.C.S.: 524126
Hanns Martin Schindewolf *(Chm)*

Daimler IT Retail GmbH (1)
Leibnizstrasse 2
71032 Boblingen, Germany
Tel.: (49) 7031 9046354
Fax: (49) 7031 9077971
E-Mail: itr@daimler.com
Web Site: www.daimler-itr.com
Emp.: 16
Information Technology Consulting Services
S.I.C.: 7373
N.A.I.C.S.: 541512
Bettina Grimm *(Mng Dir)*

Daimler Luft- und Raumfahrt Holding AG (1)
Willy-Messerschmitt-Str 1
Ottobrunn, Bayern, 85521, Germany
Tel.: (49) 896070
Fax: (49) 8960734890
Investment Management Services
S.I.C.: 6282
N.A.I.C.S.: 523920

Daimler Mitarbeiter Wohnfinanz GmbH (1)
Karl-Benz-Platz 1
Stuttgart, Baden-Wurttemberg, 70327, Germany
Tel.: (49) 7111776627
Financial Management Services
S.I.C.: 6211
N.A.I.C.S.: 523999

Daimler Parts Brand GmbH (1)
Epplestr 225
Stuttgart, Baden-Wurttemberg, 70567, Germany
Tel.: (49) 711170
Fax: (49) 7111722244
E-Mail: dialog@daimler.com
Automotive Parts Mfr
S.I.C.: 3714
N.A.I.C.S.: 336390

Daimler protics GmbH (1)
Augsburger Str 540
Stuttgart, Baden-Wrttemberg, 70327, Germany
Tel.: (49) 7111759660
Fax: (49) 7111759569
E-Mail: info-daimler-protics@daimler.com
Web Site: www.daimler-protics.de
Emp.: 400
Automotive Data Processing Services
S.I.C.: 7379
N.A.I.C.S.: 518210
Klaus Grebner *(CEO)*
Ralph Krueckel *(CFO)*
Winfried Rembold *(Head-Product Data Mgmt Div)*

Daimler Re Brokers GmbH (1)
Eichhornstr 3
Berlin, 10785, Germany
Tel.: (49) 3025540
Fax: (49) 4215988300
Insurance Brokerage Services
S.I.C.: 6411
N.A.I.C.S.: 524210

Daimler TSS GmbH (1)
Wilhelm-Runge-Strasse 11
89081 Ulm, Germany
Tel.: (49) 7 31 5 05 06
Fax: (49) 7 31 5 05 65 99
E-Mail: tss@daimler.com
Web Site: www.daimler-tss.de
Emp.: 40
Software Development Services
S.I.C.: 7371
N.A.I.C.S.: 541511
Gerhart Streit *(CEO)*
Stefan Eberhardt *(COO)*

Daimler Unterstutzungskasse GmbH (1)
Mercedesstr 137
Stuttgart, 70327, Germany
Tel.: (49) 711170
Fax: (49) 7111722244
E-Mail: dialog@daimler.com
Automobile Mfr
S.I.C.: 3711
N.A.I.C.S.: 336111
Dieter Zetsche *(CEO)*

Daimler Vorsorge und Versicherungsdienst GmbH (1)
Otto-Braun-Str 78
Berlin, 10249, Germany
Tel.: (49) 3025540
Fax: (49) 1803802021
Web Site: www.daimler-vvd.com
Pension Fund & General Insurance Services
S.I.C.: 6371
N.A.I.C.S.: 525110

DC Immobilien Projekt Bad Homburg GmbH (1)
Lilienthalstrasse 6
12529 Schonefeld, Germany
Tel.: (49) 30 25540
Fax: (49) 30 25542460
Real Estate Management Services
S.I.C.: 6531
N.A.I.C.S.: 531390

Deutsche Accumotive Verwaltungs-GmbH (1)
Neue Str 95
Kirchheim, Baden-Wurttemberg, 73230, Germany
Tel.: (49) 7021893546
Fax: (49) 7021892530
Administrative Management Services
S.I.C.: 8742
N.A.I.C.S.: 541611

EHG Elektroholding GmbH (1)
Epplestr 225
Stuttgart, Baden-Wurttemberg, 70567, Germany
Tel.: (49) 711170
Fax: (49) 7111722244
E-Mail: dialog@daimler.com
Emp.: 1
Investment Management Services
S.I.C.: 6211
N.A.I.C.S.: 523999
Dietrich Raepple *(Mng Dir)*

EvoBus GmbH (1)
Vaihinger Strasse 131
70567 Stuttgart, Germany (100%)
Tel.: (49) 7111799014
Fax: (49) 7111799151
E-Mail: info.evobus@daimler.com
Web Site: www.evobus.com
Rev.: $2,218,249,984
Emp.: 8,000
Motor Vehicles & Passenger Car Bodies
S.I.C.: 3711
N.A.I.C.S.: 336211
Hartmut Schick *(Pres)*

Subsidiary:

Mercedes-Benz Minibus GmbH (2)
Niedersachsenweg 20
44309 Dortmund, Germany
Tel.: (49) 231 5182 0
Fax: (49) 231 5182 300
Web Site: www.daimler.com
Emp.: 249
Bus & Coach Mfr
S.I.C.: 3711
N.A.I.C.S.: 336111

Non-U.S. Subsidiaries:

EvoBus Austria GmbH (2)
Industriezentrum No-Sud Strasse 4 Objekt 18
Wiener Neudorf, 2355, Austria
Tel.: (43) 2236 61604 0
Fax: (43) 711 3052188 709
Web Site: www.evobus.com
Emp.: 120
Bus & Coach Mfr & Distr
S.I.C.: 3711
N.A.I.C.S.: 336111
Roman Laczkovich *(CFO)*

EvoBus Portugal, S.A. (2)
Apartado 1 - Abrunheira
2726-911 Mem Martins, Portugal
Tel.: (351) 21 925 7013
Fax: (351) 21 915 4056
E-Mail: evobus_portugal@daimler.com
Web Site: www.evobus.pt
Emp.: 22
Bus & Coach Mfr
S.I.C.: 3711
N.A.I.C.S.: 336111
Gonzalo Rodriguez *(Gen Mgr)*

EvoBus Sverige AB (2)
Avestagatan 61
Spanga, Stockholm, 160 38, Sweden
Tel.: (46) 84 74 52 00
Fax: (46) 84 74 52 51
E-Mail: evobus.sverige@daimler.com
Web Site: www.evobus.se
Bus & Coach Mfr
S.I.C.: 3711
N.A.I.C.S.: 336111
Gunter Klemt *(Mgr)*

Grundstucksverwaltungsgesellschaft Henne- Unimog GmbH & Co. OHG (1)
Lilienthalstr 6
Schonefeld, 12529, Germany
Tel.: (49) 3063313135
Real Estate Management Services
S.I.C.: 6531
N.A.I.C.S.: 531390

Grundstucksverwaltungsgesellschaft Mercedes-Benz AG & Co. OHG (1)
Lilienthalstr 6
Schonefeld, 12529, Germany
Tel.: (49) 306331110
Real Estate Management Services
S.I.C.: 6531
N.A.I.C.S.: 531390

Henne-Unimog GmbH (1)
Landsberger Strasse 382
Munich, 80687, Germany
Tel.: (49) 89 1206 0
Fax: (49) 89 1206 5338
Web Site: www.henne-unimog.de
New Car Dealer
S.I.C.: 5511
N.A.I.C.S.: 441110

MB GTC GmbH Mercedes-Benz Gebrauchtteile Center (1)
Morikestrasse 60-64
Neuhausen, 73765, Germany
Tel.: (49) 711 17 70000
Fax: (49) 711 17 70039
Web Site: www.mbgtc.de
Motor Vehicle Parts Mfr
S.I.C.: 3714
N.A.I.C.S.: 336390
Thomas Lechler *(Mng Dir)*

MDC Technology GmbH (1)
Rudolf-Carracciola-Str 1
Kolleda, Thuringen, 99625, Germany
Tel.: (49) 3635601190
Fax: (49) 3635601102
Motor Vehicle Parts Mfr
S.I.C.: 3714
N.A.I.C.S.: 336390

Mercedes-AMG GmbH (1)
Daimlerstr 1
Affalterbach, 71563, Germany
Tel.: (49) 7144 30 20
Fax: (49) 7144 30 21 20
E-Mail: marketing-amg@daimler.com
Web Site: www.mercedes-amg.com
Car & Engine Parts Mfr
S.I.C.: 3711
N.A.I.C.S.: 336111
Tobias Moers *(CEO)*

Mercedes-Benz Accessories GmbH (1)
Horizont 2 Building Am Wallgraben 125
70565 Stuttgart, Germany
Tel.: (49) 7111795555
Web Site: www.mercedes-benz-accessories.com
Emp.: 20
Motor Vehicle Parts Mfr
S.I.C.: 3714
N.A.I.C.S.: 336390
Christian Boucke *(CEO)*

Mercedes-Benz AG & Co. Grundstucksvermietung Objekte Leipzig und Magdeburg KG (1)
Lilienthalstr 6
Schonefeld, 12529, Germany
Tel.: (49) 306331110
Real Estate Management Services
S.I.C.: 6531
N.A.I.C.S.: 531390

Mercedes-Benz Asia GmbH (1)
Epplestr 225
Stuttgart, 70567, Germany
Tel.: (49) 711170
Automotive Distr
S.I.C.: 5012
N.A.I.C.S.: 423110

Mercedes-Benz Bank Service Center GmbH (1)
Otto-Braun-Strasse 78
Berlin, 10249, Germany
Tel.: (49) 30 868755755
Fax: (49) 30 868755756
Commercial Banking Services
S.I.C.: 6029
N.A.I.C.S.: 522110

Mercedes-Benz Banking Service GmbH (1)
Gewerbepark Eschberger Weg 3
Saarbrucken, Saarland, 66121, Germany
Tel.: (49) 71125740
Fax: (49) 1803883366
Commercial Banking Services
S.I.C.: 6029
N.A.I.C.S.: 522110

Mercedes-Benz CharterWay GmbH (1)
English St 30
10587 Berlin, Germany (100%)
Tel.: (49) 3026945455
Fax: (49) 3026945456
E-Mail: charterway@justcall-19.de
Web Site: www.charterway.de
Emp.: 80
Motor Vehicles Mfr
S.I.C.: 3711
N.A.I.C.S.: 336111
Bern Hard *(Mng Dir)*

Mercedes-Benz Finanzierungsvermittlungs GmbH (1)
Schoemperlenstr 14
Karlsruhe, 76185, Germany
Tel.: (49) 72195650
Fax: (49) 7219565282
E-Mail: info@sug.de
Emp.: 46
Financial Intermediation Services
S.I.C.: 6799
N.A.I.C.S.: 523910
Richard Heckert *(Mng Dir)*

Mercedes-Benz GastroService GmbH (1)
Hauptstrasse 107
76571 Gaggenau, Germany
Tel.: (49) 7225612674
Fax: (49) 7225615203
E-Mail: info@mb-gastro.com
Web Site: www.mb-gastro.com
Catering Services
S.I.C.: 5812
N.A.I.C.S.: 722320
Christina Palma Diaz *(CEO)*

Mercedes-Benz Leasing Treuhand GmbH (1)
Siemensstr 7
Stuttgart, Baden-Wurttemberg, 70469, Germany
Tel.: (49) 71511360
Fax: (49) 71511362880
Automobile Financial Leasing Services
S.I.C.: 6153
N.A.I.C.S.: 522220

Mercedes-Benz Ludwigsfelde GmbH (1)
Zum Industriepark 10
14974 Ludwigsfelde, Germany

Tel.: (49) 3378 830
Fax: (49) 3378 832044
Web Site: www.daimler.com
Emp.: 2,079
Automobile Mfr
S.I.C.: 3711
N.A.I.C.S.: 336111

Mercedes-Benz Mitarbeiter-Fahrzeuge Leasing GmbH (1)
Service Center Berlin
Post Box 110706
10837 Berlin, Germany
Tel.: (49) 711257402
Fax: (49) 30868755405
Passenger Car Rental Services
S.I.C.: 7514
N.A.I.C.S.: 532111
Jurgen Hildebrand *(Mng Dir)*

Mercedes-Benz Museum GmbH (1)
Mercedesstrasse 100
70372 Stuttgart, Germany
Tel.: (49) 711 17 30 000
Fax: (49) 711 17 30 400
E-Mail: classic@daimler.com
Web Site: www.mercedes-benz-classic.com
Museum Operating Services
S.I.C.: 8412
N.A.I.C.S.: 712110
Michael Bock *(Chm)*

Mercedes-Benz Project Consult GmbH (1)
Karl-Benz-Platz 1
Stuttgart, 70327, Germany
Tel.: (49) 7111721652
Fax: (49) 7111755732
Business Management Consulting Services
S.I.C.: 8742
N.A.I.C.S.: 541611
Claus-Peter Willi *(Mng Dir)*

Mercedes-Benz Vertriebsgesellschaft mbH (1)
Potsdamer Str 7
10785 Berlin, Germany
Tel.: (49) 30 2694 0
Fax: (49) 3026943999
Motor Vehicle Distr
S.I.C.: 5012
N.A.I.C.S.: 423110

MercedesService Card Beteiligungsgesellschaft mbH (1)
Mainparkstr 2-4
Kleinostheim, 63801, Germany
Tel.: (49) 60275090
Fax: (49) 6027509599
Credit Card Operating Services
S.I.C.: 6099
N.A.I.C.S.: 522320

MercedesService Card GmbH & Co. KG (1)
Mainparkstrasse 2
63801 Kleinostheim, Germany
Tel.: (49) 6027 50 95 67
Fax: (49) 6027 50 97 75 67
E-Mail: info@mercedesservicecard.de
Web Site: www.msc.mercedes-benz.com
Emp.: 35
Automotive Credit Card Processing Services
S.I.C.: 6099
N.A.I.C.S.: 522320
Juergen Beine *(Mng Dir)*

MILON Grundstucks-Verwaltungsgesellschaft mbH & Co. KG (1)
Tolzer Str 30
82031 Grunwald, Germany
Tel.: (49) 89 641430
Real Estate Management Services
S.I.C.: 6531
N.A.I.C.S.: 531390

NuCellSys GmbH (1)
Neue Strasse 95 Industriepark Nabern
73230 Kirchheim, Germany
Tel.: (49) 7021 89 3666
Fax: (49) 7021 89 4110
E-Mail: info@NuCellSys.com
Web Site: www.NuCellSys.com
Emp.: 200
Automotive Application Fuel Cell System Mfr
S.I.C.: 3674
N.A.I.C.S.: 334413
Massimo Venturi *(Mng Dir)*
Simone Galkowski *(CFO)*

Porcher & Meffert Grundstucks-gesellschaft mbH & Co. Stuttgart OHG (1)
Lilienthalstr 6
Schonefeld, 12529, Germany
Tel.: (49) 306331110
E-Mail: info@daimler.com
Web Site: www.daimler.com
Automotive Parts Mfr
S.I.C.: 3714
N.A.I.C.S.: 336390

proceda Modellbau GmbH (1)
Im Neuenbuhl 23
Weissach, Baden-Wurttemberg, 71287, Germany
Tel.: (49) 7044900740
Fax: (49) 7044900750
E-Mail: info@proceda.de
Web Site: www.proceda.de
Interior Design Services
S.I.C.: 7389
N.A.I.C.S.: 541410

Russ & Janot GmbH (1)
Binderslebener Landstr 92
Erfurt, Thuringen, 99092, Germany
Tel.: (49) 36121500
Fax: (49) 3612150110
E-Mail: gl@russ-janot.de
Web Site: www.russ-janot.de
Automobile Dealer
S.I.C.: 5599
N.A.I.C.S.: 441228

Ruth Verwaltungsgesellschaft mbH (1)
Metternichstr 7
Bochum, 44867, Germany
Tel.: (49) 2327 320414
Fax: (49) 2327 33939
Automotive Parts Mfr
S.I.C.: 3714
N.A.I.C.S.: 336390

Sechste Vermogensverwaltungs-gesellschaft DVB mbH (1)
Epplestr 225
Stuttgart, 70567, Germany
Tel.: (49) 7111795336
Investment Management Services
S.I.C.: 6211
N.A.I.C.S.: 523999

Siebte Vermogensverwaltungs-gesellschaft DVB mbH (1)
Epplestr 225
Stuttgart, 70567, Germany
Tel.: (49) 7111795336
Investment Management Services
S.I.C.: 6282
N.A.I.C.S.: 523920

Smart GmbH (1)
Leivnis Str 2
Postfach 2060
71010 Boblingen, Germany (100%)
Tel.: (49) 18022802
Fax: (49) 1802336655
E-Mail: info@smart.com
Web Site: www.smart.com
Emp.: 50
Mfr. & Dealer of Automobiles
S.I.C.: 3711
N.A.I.C.S.: 336111

smart Vertriebs gmbh (1)
Potsdamer Platz 1
Berlin, 10785, Germany
Tel.: (49) 30390170
New & Used Car Dealer
S.I.C.: 5511
N.A.I.C.S.: 441110

SteloTec GmbH (1)
Rudolf-Diesel-Strasse 48
68169 Mannheim, Germany
Tel.: (49) 621 309 838 0
Fax: (49) 621 309 838 7466
E-Mail: dialog@daimler.com
Web Site: www.stelotec.de
Pipe & Pipe Fitting Mfr
S.I.C.: 3089
N.A.I.C.S.: 326122

System Design GmbH (1)
Robert-Bosch-Str 9
Leonberg, Baden-Wurttemberg, 71229, Germany
Tel.: (49) 715297640
Fax: (49) 7152976440
E-Mail: mail@system-design.com
Web Site: www.system-design.com
Automotive Software Consulting Services
S.I.C.: 7373
N.A.I.C.S.: 541512

Taunus-Auto-Verkaufs GmbH (1)
Mainzer Str 82-92
Wiesbaden, 65189, Germany
Tel.: (49) 6117770
Fax: (49) 611777841
E-Mail: info@taunus-auto.de
Web Site: www.taunus-auto.de
Automotive Dealer
S.I.C.: 5571
N.A.I.C.S.: 441228
Armin Mack *(Mng Dir)*

Vermogensverwaltungsgesellschaft Daimler Atlanta mbH (1)
Epplestr 225
Stuttgart, 70567, Germany
Tel.: (49) 711170
Investment Management Services
S.I.C.: 6799
N.A.I.C.S.: 523920

Joint Venture:

Tognum AG (1)
Maybachplatz 1
88045 Friedrichshafen, Germany
Tel.: (49) 75419091
Fax: (49) 74519050
E-Mail: info@tognum.com
Web Site: www.tognum.com
TGM—(DEU)
Rev.: $4,058,029,465
Assets: $3,943,605,015
Liabilities: $2,833,149,382
Net Worth: $1,110,455,633
Earnings: $244,599,089
Emp.: 10,479
Fiscal Year-end: 12/31/12
Holding Company; Diesel & Gas Engines Mfr
S.I.C.: 3714
N.A.I.C.S.: 336310
John Paul Paterson *(Chm-Supervisory Bd)*
Joachim Coers *(Chm-Exec Bd & CEO)*
Thomas Bittelmeyer *(Deputy Chm-Supervisory Bd)*
Ulrich Dohle *(Deputy Chm-Exec Bd & CTO)*
Dieter Royal *(CFO & Member-Exec Bd)*
Nina Felicitas Ravens *(Press Officer)*
Michael Haidinger *(Member-Exec Bd-Sls)*
Jorg Schwitalla *(Member-Mgmt Bd-HR & Integrity)*

Subsidiaries:

L'Orange GmbH (2)
Porschestr 30
Stuttgart, Baden-Wurttemberg, 70435, Germany
Tel.: (49) 711826090
Fax: (49) 7118260961
E-Mail: info@lorange.com
Web Site: www.lorange.de
Emp.: 900
Engine & Fuel Pumps Mfr
S.I.C.: 3519
N.A.I.C.S.: 333618
Laris Borsum *(Mgr-Sls)*

MTU Friedrichshafen GmbH (2)
Maybachplatz 1
88045 Friedrichshafen, Baden Wurttemberg, Germany
Tel.: (49) 7541900
Fax: (49) 7541905000
E-Mail: info@mtu-online.com
Web Site: www.mtu-online.com
Emp.: 5,000
Mfr of Diesel Engines & Drive Systems
S.I.C.: 3714
N.A.I.C.S.: 336310
Joachim Coers *(Pres, CEO & Dir-Indus Rels)*
Rainer Breidenbach *(Exec VP-Sls)*
Ulreeh Tohle *(Exec VP-Tech)*

Subsidiaries:

MTU DDC International GmbH (3)
Maybachplatz 1
Friedrichshafen, Baden-Wurttemberg, 88045, Germany
Tel.: (49) 7541902208
Fax: (49) 7541902724
Engines & Turbines Mfr
S.I.C.: 3519
N.A.I.C.S.: 333618
Harald Schur *(Mgr)*

MTU Onsite Energy GmbH (3)
Dasinger Str 11
Augsburg, Bayern, 86165, Germany
Tel.: (49) 82174800
Fax: (49) 8217480119
Web Site: www.mtu-online.com
Emp.: 300
Fossil Fuel Power Generation Services
S.I.C.: 4939
N.A.I.C.S.: 221112
Ulrich Kemnitz *(Co-CEO)*
Karl Kiessling *(Co-CEO)*

Non-U.S. Subsidiaries:

MTU Australia Pty. Ltd. (3)
11-13 Garling Rd
Kings Park, NSW, 2148, Australia
Tel.: (61) 288227000
Fax: (61) 88227083
Emp.: 500
Diesel & Gas Engines Distr
S.I.C.: 5013
N.A.I.C.S.: 423120
Greg Dobe *(Office Mgr)*

MTU DD Benelux B.V. (3)
Merwedestraat 86
3313 CS Dordrecht, Netherlands
Tel.: (31) 786395777
Fax: (31) 786148971
E-Mail: info@mtudd-benelux.com
Emp.: 50
Engine Equipment Mfr
S.I.C.: 3519
N.A.I.C.S.: 333618
G. J. Van Erkel *(Mgr)*

MTU Detroit Diesel Israel Ltd. (3)
45 Hamelacha St Poleg South Industrial Zone
42505 Netanya, Israel
Tel.: (972) 98858522
Fax: (972) 98855685
Web Site: www.mtu-online.com
Emp.: 6
Diesel Engines Distr
S.I.C.: 5088
N.A.I.C.S.: 423860
Gabriel Westfried *(Gen Mgr)*

MTU do Brasil Ltda. (3)
Via Anhanguera km 29 203
05276-000 Sao Paulo, Brazil
Tel.: (55) 2125096459
Fax: (55) 11 3915 8901
E-Mail: mtu@mtu.com.br
Web Site: www.mtu.com.br
Marine Engineering Services
S.I.C.: 8711
N.A.I.C.S.: 541330

MTU France SAS (3)
281 Chaussee Jules Cesar
95250 Beauchamp, Val-d'Oise, France
Tel.: (33) 134186060
Fax: (33) 1 34 18 60 61
E-Mail: servicesud.france@mtu-online.com
Web Site: www.mtu-online.fr
Emp.: 65
Marine Engineering Services
S.I.C.: 8711
N.A.I.C.S.: 541330
Christian Courcelles *(Pres)*

MTU Iberica Propulsion y Energia S.L. (3)
Calle Copernico 28
28820 Coslada, Madrid, Spain
Tel.: (34) 914851900
Fax: (34) 916748972
E-Mail: mtu-iberica@mtu-online.com
Web Site: www.mtu-online.com
Emp.: 40
Engines & Turbines Mfr
S.I.C.: 3511
N.A.I.C.S.: 333611
Ramnials Christos *(CEO)*
Schuh Hubert *(Co-CEO)*

MTU Italia S.r.l. (3)
Via Aurelia Nord 328
19021 Arcola, La Spezia, Italy

Daimler AG—(Continued)

Tel.: (39) 0187952601
Fax: (39) 0187954713
E-Mail: martina.koglin@mtu-online.com
Emp.: 80
Marine Engineering Services
S.I.C.: 8711
N.A.I.C.S.: 541330
Emanuela Pagani *(Dir-Mktg)*

MTU Motor Turbin Sanayi ve Ticaret A.S. **(3)**
Omerli Koyo No 5 Omerli Cad
34555 Istanbul, Turkey
Tel.: (90) 2127982710
Fax: (90) 2127982794
E-Mail: info@mtu-online.com
Web Site: www.mtu-online.com
Emp.: 105
Engineering Services
S.I.C.: 8711
N.A.I.C.S.: 541330
Muammer Iyi *(Gen Mgr)*

MTU South Africa Pty. Ltd. **(3)**
Corner Marconi Road & 3rd Street
Cape Town, Western Cape, South Africa
Tel.: (27) 215295760
Fax: (27) 215511970
E-Mail: info@mtu-online.co.za
Web Site: www.mtu-online.co.za
Port Facility Construction & Engineering Services
S.I.C.: 1629
N.A.I.C.S.: 237990
Michael Baumann *(Mng Dir)*

MTU UK Ltd. **(3)**
Unit 29 Birches Industrial Estate
East Grinstead, West Sussex, RH19 1XZ, United Kingdom
Tel.: (44) 1342335450
Fax: (44) 1342335470
Web Site: www.mtu-online.co.uk
Emp.: 60
Diesel & Gas Engines Distr
S.I.C.: 5013
N.A.I.C.S.: 423120
Mike Ferris *(Mng Dir)*

Subsidiary:

MTU Detroit Diesel UK Ltd **(4)**
Unit 29 The Birches Industrial Estate
East Grinstead, West Sussex, RH1 91XZ, United Kingdom
Tel.: (44) 1342335450
Fax: (44) 01302335475
E-Mail: liuoen.wilt@mtu-online.com
Web Site: www.mtu-online.co.uk
Emp.: 50
Engineering Services
S.I.C.: 8711
N.A.I.C.S.: 541330
Michael Ferris *(Mng Dir)*

SKL Motor GmbH **(2)**
Friedrich List Strasse 8
39122 Magdeburg, Germany
Tel.: (49) 39150460
Fax: (49) 3915046500
E-Mail: info@skl-motor.de
Web Site: www.skl-motor.com
Emp.: 196
Engine Systems Mfr
S.I.C.: 3519
N.A.I.C.S.: 333618
Wilfried Probian *(Gen Mgr)*

U.S. Subsidiary:

Tognum America Inc. **(2)**
13400 Outer Dr W
Detroit, MI 48239-4001
Tel.: (313) 592-7000
Fax: (313) 592-5137
E-Mail: regionalcenter3@mtu-online.com
Web Site: www.mtudetroitdiesel.com
Emp.: 400
Diesel Engines Mfr
S.I.C.: 3519
N.A.I.C.S.: 333618
Matthias Vogel *(Pres & CEO)*
Anke Lorscheid *(CFO)*

Subsidiary:

MTU Onsite Energy **(3)**
100 Power Dr
Mankato, MN 56001
Tel.: (507) 625-7973
Fax: (507) 625-2968
Web Site: www.mtuonsiteenergy.com
Sales Range: $125-149.9 Million
Emp.: 340
Mfr of Custom Generators
S.I.C.: 3621
N.A.I.C.S.: 335312
Todd Riemann *(Pres & CEO)*

Non-U.S. Subsidiaries:

Envirovent AG **(2)**
Hauptstrasse 137
8274 Taegerwilen, Thurgau, Switzerland
Tel.: (41) 716667300
Fax: (41) 716667301
Diesel Engines Mfr
S.I.C.: 3519
N.A.I.C.S.: 333618
Christoph Teetz *(Chm)*

Tognum Asia Pte. Ltd. **(2)**
1 Benoi Place
Singapore, 629923, Singapore
Tel.: (65) 68615922
Fax: (65) 6861 3615
E-Mail: regionalcenter2@mtu-online.com
Web Site: www.mtu-online.com
Emp.: 500
Diesel Engines & Drive Systems Distr
S.I.C.: 5088
N.A.I.C.S.: 423860
Chai Chew Phua Chin *(Sr Mgr-Fin)*

Non-U.S. Subsidiaries:

MTU China Co. Ltd. **(3)**
4701-4703 47F Tower 1 Grand Gateway 1
HongQiao Road
Shanghai, 200030, China
Tel.: (86) 2124190500
Fax: (86) 2124190550
E-Mail: mtuchina@mtu-online.com
Web Site: www.mtuonline.com
Diesel Engine Repair & Maintenance Services
S.I.C.: 7539
N.A.I.C.S.: 811198

MTU Engineering (Suzhou) Co. Ltd. **(3)**
9 Long Yun Road Suzhou Industrial Park
Suzhou, Jiangsu, 215024, China
Tel.: (86) 51262850188
Fax: (86) 512 6285 0388
Web Site: www.mtu-online.com.sg/cms/index.php?id=242
Emp.: 200
Diesel Engines Repair & Maintenance Services
S.I.C.: 7539
N.A.I.C.S.: 811198
Tina Chao *(Mgr)*

MTU India Pvt. Ltd. **(3)**
159 / 1 Tathawade
Pune-Mumbai Highway, Pune, Maharashtra, 411 033, India
Tel.: (91) 2067209200
Fax: (91) 2067209299
Web Site: www.mtu-online.com
Emp.: 70
Diesel Engines Distr
S.I.C.: 5088
N.A.I.C.S.: 423860
Prasanth Bhagatt *(Mgr-HR)*

MTU Marubeni Co. Ltd. **(3)**
Yushi Kogyo-Kaikan Bldg 3-13-11
Nihonbashi
Chuo-ku, Tokyo, 103-0027, Japan
Tel.: (81) 352058300
Fax: (81) 335162298
E-Mail: mtu-marubeni@mtu-marubeni.com
Web Site: www.mtu-online.com.sg
Emp.: 6
Diesel Engines Distr
S.I.C.: 5088
N.A.I.C.S.: 423860
Ryoichi Kobatake *(CEO)*

MTU Vietnam Co. Ltd. **(3)**
C/O V-Trac Level 16 106 Hoang Quoc Viet Street
Cau Giay District, Hanoi, Vietnam
Tel.: (84) 4 3755 1100
Fax: (84) 4 3755 7100
Web Site: www.mtu-online.com
Diesel & Gas Engines Distr
S.I.C.: 5013
N.A.I.C.S.: 423120

PT MTU Indonesia **(3)**
Cilandak Commercial Estate Building 109
Jl Cilandak KKO, Jakarta, 12560, Indonesia
Tel.: (62) 21 789 1410
Fax: (62) 21 789 1452
E-Mail: MTU.Jakarta@mtu-online.co.id
Web Site: www.mtu-online.com.sg/cms/index.php?id=229&L=16
Emp.: 50
Diesel Engines Sales & Maintenance Services
S.I.C.: 5013
N.A.I.C.S.: 423120

Plants:

Daimler AG - Mercedes-Benz Berlin Plant **(1)**
Daimlerstrasse 143
12277 Berlin, Germany
Tel.: (49) 30 7491 0
Fax: (49) 30 2491 2849
Emp.: 2,628
Diesel Engine & Fuel System Mfr
S.I.C.: 3519
N.A.I.C.S.: 333618
Hans George Nieser *(Plant Mgr)*

Daimler AG - Mercedes-Benz Bremen Plant **(1)**
Mercedesstrasse 1
28309 Bremen, Germany
Tel.: (49) 421 419 0
Web Site: www.daimler.com
Emp.: 12,843
Automobile Mfr
S.I.C.: 3711
N.A.I.C.S.: 336111
Andreas Kellerman *(Plant Mgr)*

Daimler AG - Mercedes-Benz Gaggenau Plant **(1)**
Hauptstrasse 107
76568 Gaggenau, Germany
Tel.: (49) 722 561 0
Web Site: www.daimler.com
Emp.: 6,212
Automotive Parts Mfr
S.I.C.: 3714
N.A.I.C.S.: 336390

Daimler AG - Mercedes-Benz Hamburg Plant **(1)**
Mercedesstrasse 1
21079 Hamburg, Germany
Tel.: (49) 407 920 0
Fax: (49) 79 20 29 30
Web Site: www.daimler.com
Emp.: 2,609
Axle & Light Weight Structural Component Mfr
S.I.C.: 3714
N.A.I.C.S.: 336350
Werner Schalow *(Mng Dir)*

Daimler AG - Mercedes-Benz Kassel Plant **(1)**
Mercedesplatz 1
34127 Kassel, Germany
Tel.: (49) 561 802 0
Web Site: www.daimler.com
Emp.: 2,893
Axle & Powertrain Component Mfr
S.I.C.: 3714
N.A.I.C.S.: 336350
Ludwig Pauss *(Gen Mgr)*

Daimler AG - Mercedes-Benz Rastatt Plant **(1)**
Mercedesstrasse 1
76437 Rastatt, Germany
Tel.: (49) 722 291 0
Web Site: www.daimler.com
Emp.: 6,168
Automobile Mfr
S.I.C.: 3711
N.A.I.C.S.: 336111

Daimler AG - Mercedes-Benz Sindelfingen Plant **(1)**
Bela-Barenyi-Strasse
71063 Sindelfingen, Germany
Tel.: (49) 7031 90 0
Emp.: 26,414
Commercial Vehicle Mfr
S.I.C.: 3711
N.A.I.C.S.: 336111

Daimler AG - Mercedes-Benz Werk Mannheim Plant **(1)**
Hanns-Martin-Schleyer-Strasse 21-57
68305 Mannheim, Germany
Tel.: (49) 621 393 0
Emp.: 562
Automotive Engine Mfr
S.I.C.: 3519
N.A.I.C.S.: 333618

Daimler AG - Mercedes-Benz Werk Worth Plant **(1)**
Daimlerstrasse 1
76744 Worth, Rheinland-Pfalz, Germany
Tel.: (49) 7271 71 1
Emp.: 11,645
Truck Mfr
S.I.C.: 3711
N.A.I.C.S.: 336120

U.S. Division:

Daimler Trucks North America LLC **(1)**
4747 Channel Ave
Portland, OR 97217
Tel.: (503) 745-8000
Fax: (503) 745-6657
Web Site: www.daimler-trucksnorthamerica.com
Emp.: 25,000
Heavy & Medium Duty Truck & Specialized Commercial Vehicle Mfr
S.I.C.: 3711
N.A.I.C.S.: 336120
Martin Daum *(CEO)*
John O'Leary *(CFO)*
Roger M. Nielsen *(COO)*
Friedrich Baumann *(Sr VP-Svc & Parts)*
Elmar Boeckenhoff *(Sr VP-Engrg & Tech)*
Jack Conlan *(Sr VP-Customer Support)*
Richard Howard *(Sr VP-Sls & Mktg)*

Branch:

Daimler Trucks North America **(2)**
1400 Tulip Dr
Gastonia, NC 28052-1873
Tel.: (704) 868-5700
Fax: (704) 868-5642
Web Site: www.daimler-trucksnorthamerica.com
Sales Range: $50-74.9 Million
Emp.: 1,000
Motor Vehicle Parts & Accessories Mfr
S.I.C.: 3714
N.A.I.C.S.: 336390
Andy Lukacs *(Plant Mgr)*

Subsidiaries:

Detroit Diesel Corporation **(2)**
13400 Outer Dr W
Detroit, MI 48239 DE
Tel.: (313) 592-5001
Fax: (313) 592-7323
Web Site: www.detroitdiesel.com
Emp.: 2,600
Mfr & Designer of Diesel & Alternative Fuel Engines
Export
S.I.C.: 3519
N.A.I.C.S.: 333618
David Siler *(Dir-Mktg)*

Divisions:

Detroit Diesel Corp. - Canton **(3)**
515 11th St SE
Canton, OH 44707-3811
Tel.: (330) 430-4300
Fax: (330) 430-4395
E-Mail: info@detroitdiesel.com
Web Site: www.detroitdiesel.com
Emp.: 190
Distribution Center
S.I.C.: 5084
N.A.I.C.S.: 423830
Jerry Reed *(Plant Mgr)*

Detroit Diesel Overseas Distribution Corp. **(3)**
2277 Northwest 14th St
Miami, FL 33125-2101 FL
Tel.: (305) 637-1555 (100%)
Fax: (305) 637-1580
Web Site: www.detroitdiesel.com
Emp.: 5

Distributors of Diesel Engines & Parts
S.I.C.: 5084
N.A.I.C.S.: 423830
Pete Diaz *(Mgr)*

Detroit Diesel Remanufacturing-East (3)
60703 Country Club Rd
Byesville, OH 43723-9730 OH
Mailing Address:
60703 Country Club Rd
Byesville, OH 43723-9730
Tel.: (740) 439-7701
Fax: (740) 439-1214
Web Site: www.detroitdiesel.com
Emp.: 540
Diesel Engine Rebuilding
S.I.C.: 3519
N.A.I.C.S.: 333618

Detroit Diesel Remanufacturing (3)
4232 Brockton Dr SE
Kentwood, MI 49512 MI
Tel.: (616) 541-1100
Fax: (616) 541-1148
Web Site: www.detroitdiesel.com
Emp.: 150
Remanufacturers of Fuel Injectors
S.I.C.: 3714
N.A.I.C.S.: 336310
Sanjiv Khurana *(Pres)*

Florida Detroit Diesel-Allison (3)
224 SW 52nd Ave
Ocala, FL 34474-9364 FL
Tel.: (352) 237-7977 (100%)
Fax: (352) 237-4566
E-Mail: info@fdda.com
Web Site: www.fdda.com
Emp.: 16
Sales & Services of Diesel Engines & Parts
S.I.C.: 5084
N.A.I.C.S.: 423830

Florida Detroit Diesel-Allison (3)
8411 Adamo Dr
Tampa, FL 33619-3517 FL
Tel.: (813) 621-5651
Fax: (813) 628-0807
Web Site: www.fpda.com
Emp.: 45
Sales of Automotive Parts
S.I.C.: 5013
N.A.I.C.S.: 441310
Marcelo Sanz *(Gen Mgr)*

Subsidiaries:

Detroit Deisel Corporation (3)
13400 W Outer Dr
Detroit, MI 48239-1309 MI
Tel.: (313) 592-5000
Fax: (313) 592-8176
E-Mail: info@detroitdeisel.com
Web Site: www.detroitdeisel.com
Emp.: 2,500
Industrial Machinery & Equipment
S.I.C.: 3519
N.A.I.C.S.: 333618

Detroit Diesel Corp. - Irvine (3)
7700 Irvine Ctr Dr Ste 875
Irvine, CA 92618
Tel.: (949) 753-7710
Fax: (949) 753-7711
Web Site: www.detroitdeisel.com
Emp.: 15
Diesel & Semi-Diesel or Dual-Fuel Engines
S.I.C.: 7538
N.A.I.C.S.: 811111
Glen Nutting *(VP)*

Detroit Diesel Corp. - Laredo (3)
1109 Uniroyal Dr
Laredo, TX 78045-9406
Tel.: (956) 722-0906
Fax: (956) 726-9097
Web Site: www.detroitdiesel.com
Emp.: 4
Diesel Engines & Parts
S.I.C.: 5084
N.A.I.C.S.: 423830

Detroit Diesel Remanufacturing-Central (3)
840 Overlander Rd
Emporia, KS 66801-8900 KS
Tel.: (620) 343-3790
Fax: (620) 343-6781
Web Site: www.detroitdieselreman.com
Emp.: 180
Diesel Engine Rebuilding
S.I.C.: 3519
N.A.I.C.S.: 333618

Detroit Diesel Remanufacturing-West (3)
PO Box 550
Tooele, UT 84074-0550 UT
Tel.: (435) 843-6000
Fax: (435) 843-6061
Web Site: www.detroitdiesel.com
Emp.: 400
Diesel Engine Rebuilding
S.I.C.: 3519
N.A.I.C.S.: 333618
Bruce McCormack *(Engr-Safety & Environmental)*

Florida Detroit Diesel-Allison Inc. (3)
6850 Presidents Dr
Orlando, FL 32809-5699 FL
Tel.: (407) 888-1700
Fax: (407) 888-0100
Web Site: www.fdda.com
Emp.: 50
Diesel Engines & Parts
S.I.C.: 5084
N.A.I.C.S.: 423830

Florida Detroit Diesel-Allison (3)
2277 NW 14th St
Miami, FL 33125-2101 FL
Tel.: (305) 638-5300
Fax: (305) 637-1592
E-Mail: info@fdda.com
Web Site: www.fdda.com
Emp.: 80
Engines & Parts, Diesel
S.I.C.: 5084
N.A.I.C.S.: 423830

Florida Detroit Diesel-Allison (3)
2305 Rockfill Rd
Fort Myers, FL 33916-4819 FL
Tel.: (239) 332-3100
Fax: (239) 332-4857
Web Site: www.fdda.com
Emp.: 11
Engines & Parts Diesel
S.I.C.: 5084
N.A.I.C.S.: 423830
Don Man *(CEO)*

Florida Detroit Diesel-Allison (3)
3885 Selvitz Rd
Fort Pierce, FL 34981 FL
Tel.: (772) 464-6006
Fax: (772) 465-2163
Web Site: www.fdda.com
Emp.: 20
Sales and Services of Diesel Engines
S.I.C.: 5084
N.A.I.C.S.: 423830
Fred Vedder *(Mgr-Svc)*

Outer Drive Holdings Inc. (3)
13400 Outer Dr W
Detroit, MI 48239-1309 MI
Tel.: (313) 592-5000
Web Site: www.detroitdiesel.com
Emp.: 1
Diesel Engines & Parts
S.I.C.: 5084
N.A.I.C.S.: 423830

Subsidiaries:

Atlantic Detroit Diesel-Allison (4)
281 Wolf Rd
Latham, NY 12110-4806
Mailing Address:
PO Box 549
Latham, NY 12110-0549
Tel.: (201) 489-5800
Fax: (518) 951-7158
E-Mail: info@atlanticdda.com
Web Site: www.atlanticdda.com
Emp.: 140
Industrial Equipment
S.I.C.: 5084
N.A.I.C.S.: 423830

Non-U.S. Subsidiary:

Detroit Diesel of Canada Ltd. (3)
150 Dufferin Ave Ste 701
London, ON, N6A 5N6, Canada ON
Mailing Address: (100%)
150 Dufferin Ave. Ste. 70
London, ON, N6A 5N6, Canada
Tel.: (519) 661-0149
Fax: (519) 661-0171
Web Site: www.detroitdiesel.com
Sales Range: $1-9.9 Million
Emp.: 19
Distributor of Diesel Engine
S.I.C.: 3519
N.A.I.C.S.: 333618
Lile Adams *(VP)*

Freightliner LLC (2)
4747 N Channel Ave
Portland, OR 97217-7613 (100%)
Tel.: (503) 745-8000
Fax: (503) 745-8921
E-Mail: webmaster@freightliner.com
Web Site: www.freightliner.com
Diesel Trucks & Tractors Mfr
S.I.C.: 3711
N.A.I.C.S.: 336120
Juergen Kritschgau *(CFO-Fin & Control)*

Subsidiaries:

Commercial Vehicles of South Florida (3)
7528 US Hwy 301 N
Tampa, FL 33637 FL
Tel.: (813) 262-0890
Fax: (813) 714-4139
E-Mail: jmeyer@freightlineroftampa.com
Web Site: www.freightlineroftampa.com
Emp.: 106
New & Used Trucks, Tractors & Trailers Sales
S.I.C.: 5511
N.A.I.C.S.: 441110

Freightliner Custom Chassis (3)
552 Hyatt St
Gaffney, SC 29341-2525 SC
Tel.: (864) 487-1700
Fax: (864) 487-6405
Web Site: www.freightlinerchassis.com
Emp.: 750
Assembly of Truck Tractors for Highway Use
S.I.C.: 3711
N.A.I.C.S.: 336120
Bob Horbin *(Pres)*

Subsidiary:

Houston Freightliner Inc. (4)
9550 N Loop E
Houston, TX 77029-1230 TX
Tel.: (713) 672-4115
Fax: (713) 672-9449
Web Site: www.freightliner.com
Emp.: 300
Commercial Trucks
S.I.C.: 5012
N.A.I.C.S.: 423110
Rick Stuart *(Owner)*

Division:

Beaumont Freightliner, Sterling, Western Star (5)
6975 S Major Dr
Beaumont, TX 77705-7209 TX
Mailing Address:
PO Box 20717
Beaumont, TX 77720-0717
Tel.: (409) 951-8300
Fax: (409) 951-8399
Toll Free: (888) 830-1733
Web Site: www.beaumontfreightliner.com
Emp.: 23
Personal Service Agents, Brokers & Bureaus
S.I.C.: 5012
N.A.I.C.S.: 423110
Rick Stewart *(Pres)*

Freightliner LLC (3)
3025 Evergreen Dr Ste 150
Duluth, GA 30096-2317 GA
Tel.: (770) 623-5300
Web Site: www.freightliner.com
Emp.: 16
Trucks Commercial
S.I.C.: 4225
N.A.I.C.S.: 493110

Freightliner LLC (3)
804 Mittel Dr
Wood Dale, IL 60191-1172 IL
Tel.: (630) 350-3189
Fax: (630) 350-3167
Web Site: www.freightliner.com
Emp.: 60
Automotive Supplies & Parts
S.I.C.: 5013
N.A.I.C.S.: 423120

Freightliner LLC (3)
9225 Indian Creek Pkwy
Overland Park, KS 66210-2009 KS
Tel.: (913) 451-8626
Fax: (913) 451-8662
Web Site: www.freightliner.com
Emp.: 28
North Central Retail Office
S.I.C.: 8741
N.A.I.C.S.: 561110

Freightliner LLC (3)
1800 N Main St
Mount Holly, NC 28120-9141
Tel.: (704) 822-7000
Fax: (704) 822-7300
Web Site: www.freightliner.com
Emp.: 400
Truck Mfr
S.I.C.: 3999
N.A.I.C.S.: 339999
Mark Hernandez *(Pres)*

Freightliner LLC (3)
2078 Ctr Sq Rd
Logan Township, NJ 08085 NJ
Tel.: (856) 467-6000
Fax: (856) 467-6030
Web Site: www.freightliner.com
Emp.: 27
Truck Parts & Accessories
S.I.C.: 5013
N.A.I.C.S.: 423120

Freightliner LLC (3)
5745 Challenge Dr
Memphis, TN 38115-5013 TN
Tel.: (901) 367-8400 (100%)
Fax: (901) 367-8594
E-Mail: pdc@freightliner.com
Web Site: www.freightliner.com
Emp.: 100
Distributor of Motor Vehicle Supplies & New Parts
S.I.C.: 5013
N.A.I.C.S.: 423120

Freightliner of Grand Rapids, Inc. (3)
5285 Clay Ave SW
Grand Rapids, MI 49548-5657
Tel.: (616) 531-6600
Fax: (616) 531-2300
Web Site: www.freightliner.com
Emp.: 140
Sales of Trucks
Import Export
S.I.C.: 5012
N.A.I.C.S.: 423110

Freightliner of Maine Inc. (3)
422 Perry Rd
Bangor, ME 04401-6728 (100%)
Tel.: (207) 945-6451
Fax: (207) 947-6557
E-Mail: mail@freightlinerofmaine.com
Web Site: www.freightlinerofmaine.com
Emp.: 100
Provider of Automotive Goods & Services
S.I.C.: 5013
N.A.I.C.S.: 423120
Thomas E. Thornton, Jr. *(Pres)*

Freightliner of Southern Alabama (3)
1507 Reeves St
Dothan, AL 36303-2843 AL
Mailing Address: (100%)
PO Box 6569
Dothan, AL 36302-6569
Tel.: (334) 793-4455
Fax: (334) 793-1047
Web Site: www.freightliner.com
Emp.: 50
Mfr. of Automotive Supplies and Parts
S.I.C.: 5013
N.A.I.C.S.: 423120
Gary Imdieke *(Gen Mgr)*

Freightliner of Southern Alabama (3)
211 Speigner St
Dothan, AL 36303-2856 AL
Maiiing Address:
PO Box 6526
Dothan, AL 36302-6526

Daimler AG—(Continued)

Tel.: (334) 793-4455
Fax: (334) 793-1047
E-Mail: info@freightliner.com
Web Site: www.freightliner.com
Emp.: 80
Commercial Trucks
S.I.C.: 5531
N.A.I.C.S.: 441310
Gary Imdieke *(Controller)*

Freightliner Trucking L.L.C. (3)
11550 Statesville Blvd
Cleveland, NC 27013 NC
Tel.: (704) 645-5000
Fax: (704) 645-5151
Web Site: www.freightlinertrucks.com
Emp.: 4,300
Training & Development Consultant
S.I.C.: 7538
N.A.I.C.S.: 811111

Kansas City Freightliner Sales Inc. (3)
7800 NE 38th St
Kansas City, MO 64161-9454
Tel.: (816) 453-4400
Fax: (816) 453-8470
E-Mail: info@kcfreightliner.com
Web Site: www.kcfreightliner.com
Emp.: 257
Mfr. of Automobiles & other Motor Vehicles Parts & Accessories
Import Export
S.I.C.: 5511
N.A.I.C.S.: 441110

McCoy Freightliner (3)
2323 NE Columbia Blvd
Portland, OR 97211 OR
Mailing Address:
PO Box 17218
Portland, OR 97217-0218
Tel.: (503) 735-1970
Fax: (503) 735-2145
Web Site: www.freightlinertrucks.com
Emp.: 11
Truck Tractors
S.I.C.: 5511
N.A.I.C.S.: 441110
Robert McCoy *(Owner)*

Peach State Freightliner (3)
5884 Frontage Rd
Forest Park, GA 30297-2882 GA
Mailing Address: (100%)
PO Box 218
Forest Park, GA 30298-0218
Tel.: (404) 366-8044
Fax: (404) 366-8665
Web Site: www.peachstate.com
Emp.: 250
Dealer of New & Used Trucks, Tractors & Trailers
S.I.C.: 5511
N.A.I.C.S.: 441110
Rick Reynolds *(Owner)*

Subsidiaries:

Atlanta Freightliner Truck Sales & Service (4)
333 Industrial Blvd
McDonough, GA 30253 GA
Tel.: (770) 957-1997 (100%)
Fax: (770) 957-6363
Web Site: www.peachstatetrucks.com
Emp.: 33
Dealer of New & Used Trucks, Tractors & Trailers
S.I.C.: 5511
N.A.I.C.S.: 441110
Gary Conleay *(Branch Mgr)*

Freightliner Service Center (4)
11710 Statesville Blvd
Cleveland, NC 27013 NC
Tel.: (704) 278-3193
Fax: (704) 278-4097
Web Site: www.freightliner-pdi.com
Emp.: 80
General Truck Repair
S.I.C.: 7538
N.A.I.C.S.: 811111

Portland Freightliner Inc. (3)
4747 N Channel Ave
Portland, OR 97217-7613 OR
Mailing Address:
PO Box 3849
Portland, OR 97208-3849
Tel.: (503) 745-8000
Fax: (503) 745-8921
Web Site: www.freightliner.com
Emp.: 4
Truck Tractors
S.I.C.: 5012
N.A.I.C.S.: 423110

SelecTrucks of Cleveland L.L.C. (3)
1244 Industrial Pkwy N
Brunswick, OH 44212 OH
Tel.: (330) 273-2142 (100%)
Fax: (330) 225-1526
Toll Free: (866) 815-0160
Web Site: www.selectrucks.com
Emp.: 7
Sales of Trucks
S.I.C.: 5521
N.A.I.C.S.: 441120
Dominic Piazza *(Office Mgr)*

SelecTrucks of the Twin Cities (3)
424 Farwell Ave
South Saint Paul, MN 55075-2427 MN
Tel.: (651) 455-0027
Fax: (651) 455-3939
E-Mail: hmrowam@selectrucks.com
Web Site: www.selectrucks.com
Emp.: 8
Truck Sales
S.I.C.: 5599
N.A.I.C.S.: 441228

Sherwood Freightliner Sterling & Western Star (3)
107 Monahan Ave
Dunmore, PA 18512 PA
Tel.: (570) 343-9747
Fax: (570) 343-0673
E-Mail: info@freightlinertrucks.com
Web Site: www.freightlinertrucks.com
Emp.: 38
Dealers of New & Used Trucks, Tractors & Trailers
S.I.C.: 5511
N.A.I.C.S.: 441110
Don Sherwood *(Pres)*

Thomas Built Buses, Inc. (3)
1408 Courtesy Rd
High Point, NC 27260-7248
Mailing Address:
PO Box 2450
High Point, NC 27261-2450
Tel.: (336) 889-4871
Fax: (336) 881-6509
Web Site: www.thomasbus.com
Emp.: 1,600
Mfr. of School & Commercial Buses
Import Export
S.I.C.: 3711
N.A.I.C.S.: 336211
Kelley Platt *(Pres & CEO)*
Christine Kamps *(CFO)*

Western Star Trucks Inc. (3)
2477 Deerfield Dr
Fort Mill, SC 29715-6942 BC
Tel.: (313) 592-4200 (100%)
Fax: (313) 592-4249
Web Site: www.wstar.com
Emp.: 1,602
Mfr. & Distributor of Truck Parts
S.I.C.: 3714
N.A.I.C.S.: 336340

Non-U.S. Subsidiary:

Western Star Sales Thunder Bay Ltd. (4)
3150 arthur st w
PO Box 10039
Thunder Bay, ON, P7E 3N1, Canada AU
Tel.: (807) 939-2537
Fax: (807) 939-2811
E-Mail: westernstar@tbaytel.net
Rev.: $15,757,354
Emp.: 20
New & Used Car Dealer
S.I.C.: 5511
N.A.I.C.S.: 441110
Lionel Boyer *(Pres)*

Non-U.S. Subsidiaries:

Freightliner of Canada, Ltd. (3)
6733 Mississauga Rd Ste 404
Mississauga, ON, L5N 6J5, Canada (100%)
Tel.: (905) 812-6500
Fax: (905) 812-6507
Web Site: www.freightliner.com
Emp.: 12
Mfr. of Diesel Trucks & Tractors
S.I.C.: 3711
N.A.I.C.S.: 336211
Brad Thiessen *(Gen Mgr)*

Freightliner of Vancouver Ltd. (3)
18688 96th Ave
V4N 3P9 Surrey, BC, Canada BC
Tel.: (604) 888-1424 (100%)
Fax: (604) 888-7693
E-Mail: info@freightliner.bc.ca
Web Site: www.freightliner.bc.ca
Emp.: 100
Freightliners For Heavy Duty Automobiles
S.I.C.: 4213
N.A.I.C.S.: 484230
Roman Tomica *(Gen Mgr)*

Globocam Anjou (3)
8991 Boul Metropolitain E
Anjou, QC, H1J 1K2, Canada QC
Tel.: (514) 353-4000 (100%)
Fax: (514) 353-9600
Web Site: www.globocam.ca
Sales Range: $10-24.9 Million
Emp.: 70
Dealers of Industrial Machinery & Equipments
S.I.C.: 5084
N.A.I.C.S.: 423830
Gilles Beaudoin *(VP-Svcs)*

Harper Truck Centres, Inc. (3)
720 Wilson Rd S
Oshawa, ON, L1H 6E8, Canada ON
Tel.: (905) 432-3838 (100%)
Fax: (905) 434-4553
Web Site: www.harpertruckcentres.com
Emp.: 180
Transportation Services
S.I.C.: 4522
N.A.I.C.S.: 481212
Rick Hoyle *(Gen Mgr)*

Mitsubishi Fuso Truck of America, Inc. (2)
2015 Ctr Square Rd
Logan Township, NJ 08014
Tel.: (856) 467-4500
Fax: (856) 467-4695
Toll Free: (877) 829-3876
Web Site: www.mitfuso.com
Sales Range: $200-249.9 Million
Emp.: 72
Class 3-7, Diesel Powered & Cab-Over Commercial Trucks Mfr
Import
S.I.C.: 5012
N.A.I.C.S.: 423110
Todd Bloom *(Pres & CEO)*
Mutsumi Miwa *(CFO)*

Plant:

Daimler Buses North America - Orinskay - Parts & Service (2)
165 Base Rd
Oriskany, NY 13424-4205 NY
Tel.: (315) 768-8101 (100%)
Fax: (315) 768-3513
Emp.: 480
Bus Parts & Service
S.I.C.: 5013
N.A.I.C.S.: 423120
Harry Rendel *(CFO)*

U.S. Subsidiaries:

Columbia Freightliner, LLC (1)
1450 Bluff Rd
Columbia, SC 29201
Tel.: (803) 376-4455
Fax: (803) 376-1311
Freight Liner Truck Distr
S.I.C.: 5012
N.A.I.C.S.: 423110
Scott Witt *(Gen Mgr)*

Daimler Buses North America Inc. (1)
165 Base Rd
Oriskany, NY 13424
Tel.: (315) 223-5100
Fax: (315) 768-6520
Motor Vehicle Parts Mfr
S.I.C.: 3711
N.A.I.C.S.: 336211

Daimler Buses North Carolina LLC (1)
6012 High Point Rd
Greensboro, NC 27407
Tel.: (336) 878-5400
Fax: (336) 878-5410
Bus & Coach Mfr
S.I.C.: 3711
N.A.I.C.S.: 336111

Daimler Finance North America LLC (1)
1 Mercedes Dr
Montvale, NJ 07645
Tel.: (201) 573-2724
Fax: (201) 573-2300
Financial Management Services
S.I.C.: 6799
N.A.I.C.S.: 523920

Daimler Insurance Agency LLC (1)
36455 Corporate Dr
Farmington Hills, MI 48331
Tel.: (248) 991-6700
Web Site: www.daimlerinsurance.com
Commercial Vehicle Insurance Services
S.I.C.: 6411
N.A.I.C.S.: 524210

Daimler International Assignment Services USA, LLC (1)
36455 Corporate Dr
Farmington Hills, MI 48331
Tel.: (248) 991-6037
Automotive Parts Mfr
S.I.C.: 3714
N.A.I.C.S.: 336390

Daimler Meridian Corporation (1)
36455 Corporate Dr
Farmington Hills, MI 48331
Tel.: (248) 991-6700
Automobile Parts Mfr
S.I.C.: 3714
N.A.I.C.S.: 336390

Daimler Motors Investments LLC (1)
36455 Corporate Dr
Farmington Hills, MI 48331-3552
Tel.: (248) 991-6700
Automobile Mfr
S.I.C.: 3711
N.A.I.C.S.: 336111

Daimler North America Corporation (1)
1 Mercedes Dr
Montvale, NJ 07645
Tel.: (201) 573-2724
Fax: (201) 573-2300
Automobile Mfr
S.I.C.: 3711
N.A.I.C.S.: 336111
Dieter E. Zetsche *(Pres)*

Non-U.S. Subsidiary:

Daimler Canada Finance Inc (2)
1 Place Ville Marie 37th Floor
Montreal, QC, H3B 3P4, Canada
Tel.: (201) 573-0600
Fax: (201) 573-0117
Fund Lending Services
S.I.C.: 6141
N.A.I.C.S.: 522291

Daimler North America Finance Corporation (1)
131 Continental Dr Ste 408
Newark, NJ 19713
Tel.: (302) 292-6840
Fax: (302) 292-6842
Financial Management Services
S.I.C.: 6211
N.A.I.C.S.: 523999

Daimler Purchasing Coordination Corp. (1)
36455 Corporate Dr
Farmington Hills, MI 48331
Tel.: (248) 991-6700
Automobile Distr
S.I.C.: 5012
N.A.I.C.S.: 423110

Daimler Retail Receivables LLC (1)
36455 Corporate Dr
Farmington Hills, MI 84331

Tel.: (248) 991-6700
Automobile Parts Mfr
S.I.C.: 3711
N.A.I.C.S.: 336111

Daimler Trust Holdings LLC (1)
36455 Corporate Dr
Farmington Hills, MI 48331
Tel.: (248) 991-6700
Investment Management Services
S.I.C.: 6282
N.A.I.C.S.: 523920

Daimler Trust Leasing LLC (1)
36455 Corporate Dr
Farmington Hills, MI 48331-3552
Tel.: (248) 991-6700
Automobile Parts Mfr
S.I.C.: 3714
N.A.I.C.S.: 336390

Daimler Vans Manufacturing, LLC (1)
8501 Palmetto Commerce Pkwy
Ladson, SC 29456
Tel.: (843) 695-5000
Fax: (843) 695-5031
Web Site: www.daimler.com
Emp.: 93
Automotive Parts Mfr
S.I.C.: 3714
N.A.I.C.S.: 336390
Marco Writz *(Mgr)*

Daimler Vans USA, LLC (1)
3 Mercedes Dr
Montvale, NJ 07645
Tel.: (877) 762-8267
Web Site: www.freightlinersprinterusa.com
Sprinter Van Mfr
S.I.C.: 3711
N.A.I.C.S.: 336111

Daimler Vehicle Innovations USA, LLC (1)
1 Mercedes Dr
Montvale, NJ 07645
Tel.: (800) 762-7887
Automotive Parts Mfr
S.I.C.: 3714
N.A.I.C.S.: 336390

DCS UTI LLC (1)
36455 Corporate Dr36455 Corporate Dr
Farmington Hills, MI 48331-3552
Tel.: (248) 991-6700
Automobile Mfr
S.I.C.: 3711
N.A.I.C.S.: 336111

Detroit Diesel Overseas Corporation (1)
13400 W Outer Dr
Detroit, MI 48239
Tel.: (313) 592-5000
Engine Equipment Mfr
S.I.C.: 3519
N.A.I.C.S.: 333618

Detroit Diesel Realty, Inc. (1)
13400 W Outer Dr
Detroit, MI 48239
Tel.: (313) 592-5000
Real Estate Financial Services
S.I.C.: 6531
N.A.I.C.S.: 531390

Drivetest, Llc. (1)
812 Surrey Rd
Laredo, TX 78041
Tel.: (956) 725-1636
Sales Range: $1-9.9 Million
Emp.: 60
Automotive Testing Services
S.I.C.: 8734
N.A.I.C.S.: 541380
Arch Deutschman *(Principal)*

Intrepid Insurance Company (1)
36455 Corporate Dr
Farmington Hills, MI 48331
Tel.: (248) 991-6642
General Insurance Services
S.I.C.: 6411
N.A.I.C.S.: 524210

Mercedes-Benz Advanced Design of North America, Inc. (1)
2250 Rutherford Rd
Carlsbad, CA 92008
Tel.: (619) 488-9360
Fax: (619) 488-9388
E-Mail: mbrdna.carlsbad.info@daimler.com
Web Site: www.mbrdna.com
Automotive Research & Development
S.I.C.: 7389
N.A.I.C.S.: 541420

Mercedes-Benz Financial Services USA LLC (1)
36455 Corporate Dr
Farmington Hills, MI 48331
Tel.: (248) 991-6700
Fax: (877) 267-6745
Toll Free: (800) 654-6222
Web Site: www.mbfs.com
Automotive Financial Services
S.I.C.: 6726
N.A.I.C.S.: 525990
Peter Zieringer *(Pres & CEO)*
Stefan Karrenbauer *(Pres & CEO-MBFS-Canada)*
Brian Stevens *(CFO & VP-Fin & Controlling)*
Michelle Spreitzer *(VP-Gen Counsel & Corp Sec)*

Mercedes-Benz Research & Development North America, Inc. (1)
850 Hansen Way
Palo Alto, CA 94304
Tel.: (650) 845-2500
Fax: (650) 845-2555
E-Mail: MBRDNA.PaloAlto.info@daimler.com
Web Site: www.mbrdna.com
Automotive Research & Development Services
S.I.C.: 8731
N.A.I.C.S.: 541712
Johann Jungwirth *(Pres & CEO)*

Mercedes-Benz USA Inc. (1)
1 Mercedes Dr
Montvale, NJ 07645-1815 DE (100%)
Tel.: (201) 573-0600
Fax: (201) 573-4394
Toll Free: (800) FORMERCEDES
Web Site: www.mbusa.com
Emp.: 1,853
Distr of Automobiles Import
S.I.C.: 5012
N.A.I.C.S.: 423110
Steve Cannon *(Pres & CEO)*
Bernhard Glaser *(Mng Dir & VP-Mercedes-Benz Vans USA)*
Harald Henn *(CFO & VP)*

Branch:

Mercedes-Benz USA Los Angeles Regional Corporate Office (2)
650 Town Ctr Dr
Costa Mesa, CA 92626-1989 CA (100%)
Tel.: (714) 435-3100
Fax: (714) 435-3142
Web Site: www.mbusa.com
Emp.: 30
Automobile Services
S.I.C.: 5012
N.A.I.C.S.: 423110

Divisions:

Mercedes-Benz Credit (2)
111 Continental Dr
Newark, DE 19713-4306 DE (100%)
Tel.: (302) 368-2447
Fax: (302) 813-3496
Web Site: www.mbcc.com
Emp.: 28
Car Division
S.I.C.: 5261
N.A.I.C.S.: 444220

Mercedes-Benz Customer Service Corp. (2)
3 Paragon Dr
Montvale, NJ 07645-1725 NJ
Tel.: (201) 476-6200
Fax: (201) 573-0117
Web Site: www.mbusa.com
Emp.: 200
Automotive Maintenance Services
S.I.C.: 7539
N.A.I.C.S.: 811198

Mercedes-Benz Financial (2)
PO Box 685
Roanoke, TX 76262 OR (100%)
Fax: (503) 293-0862
Toll Free: (800) 654-6222
Web Site: www.mbcredit.com
Emp.: 20
Provider of Financing Services of Dealers By Motor Vehicle Manufacturers
S.I.C.: 6159
N.A.I.C.S.: 522298

Mercedes-Benz Manhattan Inc. (2)
536 W 41st St
New York, NY 10036-6201 NY (100%)
Tel.: (212) 629-1600
Fax: (212) 629-1450
E-Mail: info@mb-usa.com
Web Site: www.mercedesbenzmanhattan.com
Emp.: 200
Automobiles New & Used
S.I.C.: 5511
N.A.I.C.S.: 441110

Mercedes-Benz Service Corp. (2)
3953 Research Park Dr
Ann Arbor, MI 48108-2219 MI
Tel.: (734) 995-3066
Fax: (734) 995-1342
Web Site: www.mbusa.com
Emp.: 22
Provider of Automotive Emissions Testing Without Repairs
S.I.C.: 7539
N.A.I.C.S.: 811198
Ernst Leib *(Pres & CEO)*

Mercedes-Benz USA Inc. (2)
14613 Bar Harbor Rd
Fontana, CA 92336-1660 CA
Tel.: (909) 428-4000
Fax: (909) 428-4092
Emp.: 120
Automotive Supplies & Parts
S.I.C.: 5013
N.A.I.C.S.: 423120

Mercedes-Benz USA Inc. (2)
1 Mercedes Dr
Belcamp, MD 21017-1203 MD
Tel.: (410) 272-6900
Fax: (410) 273-1701
Web Site: www.mbusa.com
Emp.: 66
Automobile Body Shop
S.I.C.: 5012
N.A.I.C.S.: 423110

Mercedes-Benz USA Inc. (2)
400 Interpace Pkwy Bldg D
Parsippany, NJ 07054-1120 NJ
Tel.: (973) 331-5400
Fax: (973) 331-5441
Web Site: www.mbusa.com
Emp.: 15
Automobiles Sales
S.I.C.: 5012
N.A.I.C.S.: 423110

Mercedes-Benz USA LLC (2)
8813 Western Way
Jacksonville, FL 32256-0367 FL (100%)
Tel.: (904) 443-2100
Fax: (904) 443-2101
Web Site: www.mbusa.com
Emp.: 60
Administrative Management
S.I.C.: 6153
N.A.I.C.S.: 522220

Mercedes-Benz USA LLC (2)
100 New Canton Way
Trenton, NJ 08691-2345 MD
Tel.: (609) 259-8778
Web Site: www.mbusa.com
Emp.: 70
Mfr. of Automotive Supplies & Parts
S.I.C.: 5013
N.A.I.C.S.: 423120
Niles Barlow *(Gen Mgr-Fleet & Pre-Owned Ops)*

Subsidiaries:

Mercedes-Benz U.S. International, Inc. (2)
1 Mercedes Dr
Tuscaloosa, AL 35490-2900 AL
Mailing Address:
PO Box 100
Tuscaloosa, AL 35403-0100
Tel.: (205) 507-3300
Fax: (205) 507-3700
Toll Free: (888) 286-8762
Web Site: www.mbusi.com
Emp.: 4,000
Motor Vehicles & Car Bodies Mfr
S.I.C.: 3711
N.A.I.C.S.: 336111
Markus Schaefer *(Pres & CEO)*

SelecTrucks of America LLC (1)
4747 N Channel Ave
Portland, OR 97217
Tel.: (503) 745-8000
Automobile Whslr
S.I.C.: 5012
N.A.I.C.S.: 423110

Suffolk Leasing, Inc. (1)
225 High Ridge Rd
Stamford, CT 06905
Tel.: (203) 975-3200
Automobile Leasing Services
S.I.C.: 6153
N.A.I.C.S.: 522220

Western Star Trucks Sales, Inc. (1)
2477 Deerfield Dr
Fort Mill, SC 29715
Tel.: (803) 578-3300
Fax: (803) 578-3702
E-Mail: caccustomer@daimler.com
Web Site: www.westernstartrucks.com
Motor Vehicle Parts Distr
S.I.C.: 3714
N.A.I.C.S.: 336390

Non-U.S. Subsidiaries:

Atlantis Foundries (Pty.) Ltd. (1)
11 William Gourlay Street
PO Box 1701
Dassenberg, 7530 Atlantis, Western Cape, South Africa
Tel.: (27) 215737200
Fax: (27) 215737296
Web Site: www.daimler.com
Emp.: 1,172
Automotive Steel Casting Mfr
S.I.C.: 3321
N.A.I.C.S.: 331511

Circulo Cerrado S.A. de ahorro para fines determinados (1)
Azucena Villaflor 435
Buenos Aires, 1107, Argentina
Tel.: (54) 1148088820
Fax: (54) 1148088121
E-Mail: circulo@mercedes-benz.ar
Web Site: www.circulo.mercedes-benz.com.ar
Emp.: 12
Financial Management Services
S.I.C.: 6211
N.A.I.C.S.: 523999

Daimler Australia/Pacific Pty. Ltd. (1)
44 Lexia Place
Mulgrave, VIC, 3170, Australia
Tel.: (61) 395669266
Fax: (61) 395617088
Passenger Car & Commercial Vehicle Distr
S.I.C.: 5012
N.A.I.C.S.: 423110

Daimler Belgium Financial Company S.A. (1)
Avenue Du Peage 68
1200 Brussels, Belgium
Tel.: (32) 27241211
Fax: (32) 27248897
Emp.: 100
Financial Management Services
S.I.C.: 6211
N.A.I.C.S.: 523999
De Haes Mark *(CEO)*

Daimler Colombia S. A. (1)
Avenida Calle 26 70a 25
Bogota, Colombia
Tel.: (57) 14236700
Fax: (57) 14121664
E-Mail: info@daimler.com.co
Web Site: www.daimler.com.co
Emp.: 30
New Car Dealer
S.I.C.: 5511
N.A.I.C.S.: 441110
Mathias Eduardo Held Kotietzkoc *(Gen Mgr)*

Daimler Espana Gestion Inmobiliaria, S.L. (1)
Avenida De Bruselas 30
Alcobendas, Madrid, 28108, Spain

Daimler AG—(Continued)

Tel.: (34) 914846000
Fax: (34) 914846290
Real Estate Management Services
S.I.C.: 6531
N.A.I.C.S.: 531390

Daimler Financial Services Mexico, S. de R.L. de C.V. (1)
Av Paseo De Los Tamarindos No 90 Piso 16
Mexico, Distrito Federal, 05120, Mexico
Tel.: (52) 5541552000
Web Site: www.daimlerfinancialservices.com.mx
Financial Management Services
S.I.C.: 6211
N.A.I.C.S.: 523999

Daimler Fleet Management Polska Sp. z.o.o. (1)
Ul Gottlieba Daimlera 1
Warsaw, 02-460, Poland
Tel.: (48) 22 312 7900
Fax: (48) 22 312 6700
E-Mail: information@daimler.com
Web Site: www.daimler-fleetmanagement.pl
Emp.: 10
Fleet Management Services
S.I.C.: 7515
N.A.I.C.S.: 532112
David Dyson *(Gen Mgr)*

Daimler Fleet Services A.S. (1)
TEM Otoyolu Hadimkoy Cikisi Mercedes Caddesi
Bahcesehir, 34500 Istanbul, Turkey
Tel.: (90) 212 866 65 65
Fleet Management Services
S.I.C.: 7515
N.A.I.C.S.: 532112

Daimler Group Services Madrid, S.A. (1)
Calle Isla De Graciosa 3 - 3 Planta
San Sebastian de los Reyes, Madrid, 28703, Spain
Tel.: (34) 914545311
Fax: (34) 914545249
Emp.: 300
Financial Management Services
S.I.C.: 6211
N.A.I.C.S.: 523999
Bernd Rumscheid *(Gen Mgr)*

Daimler India Commercial Vehicles Private Limited (1)
Unit 301 & 302 3rd Floor Campus 3B RMZ Millennia Business Park No 143
Dr M G R Road Perungudi, Chennai, 600 096, India
Tel.: (91) 44 45996000
Fax: (91) 4442036836
Web Site: www.daimler-indiacv.com
Emp.: 1,200
Light & Heavy Commercial Vehicles Mfr & Distr
S.I.C.: 3711
N.A.I.C.S.: 336120
Marc Llistosella *(CEO & Mng Dir)*
Sanjiv Khurana *(CFO)*

Daimler Insurance Services UK Limited (1)
Burystead Ct Caldecotte Lake Dr Caldecott
Milton Keynes, Buckinghamshire, MK7 8ND, United Kingdom
Tel.: (44) 8708500845
Fax: (44) 1908557837
General Insurance Services
S.I.C.: 6411
N.A.I.C.S.: 524210

Daimler International Finance B.V. (1)
Van Deventerlaan 50
Utrecht, 3528 AE, Netherlands
Tel.: (31) 306059316
Fax: (31) 306050680
Financial Management Services
S.I.C.: 6211
N.A.I.C.S.: 523999

Daimler Manufactura, S.A. de C.V. (1)
Av Paseo De Los Tamarindos No 90 Piso 16 Bosques De Las Lomas
Cuajimalpa De Morelos, Mexico, Distrito Federal, 05120, Mexico
Tel.: (52) 5541552527
Fax: (52) 5541552527
General Freight Trucking Services
S.I.C.: 4214
N.A.I.C.S.: 484110

Daimler Middle East & Levant FZE (1)
Daimler Chrysler Street
PO Box 17880
Dubai, United Arab Emirates
Tel.: (971) 4 8833200
Fax: (971) 4 8075450
Web Site: www.mideast.mercedes-benz.com
Commercial Vehicle Distr
S.I.C.: 5012
N.A.I.C.S.: 423110
Mike Belk *(Pres & CEO)*

Daimler Northeast Asia Parts Trading and Services Co., Ltd. (1)
Rm 901 9/F Daimler Mansion No 8 Yard Wangjing St
Chaoyang, Beijing, 100102, China
Tel.: (86) 1084173587
Fax: (86) 1084173950
Automobile Parts Whslr
S.I.C.: 5013
N.A.I.C.S.: 423120

Daimler Re Insurance S.A. Luxembourg (1)
Rue De Bitbourg 53
Luxembourg, 1248, Luxembourg
Tel.: (352) 27 12 56 66
General Insurance Services
S.I.C.: 6411
N.A.I.C.S.: 524210

Daimler Servicios Corporativos Mexico S. de R.L. de C.V (1)
Av Paseo De Los Tamarindos No 90 Piso 11
Mexico, 5120, Mexico
Tel.: (52) 5541552000
Business Management Consulting Services
S.I.C.: 8742
N.A.I.C.S.: 541611

Daimler South East Asia Pte. Ltd. (1)
3 Temasek Avenue 29-01 Centennial Tower
Singapore, 39190, Singapore
Tel.: (65) 68 49 8 000
Fax: (65) 68 49 8 480
Emp.: 30
Commercial Vehicle Distr
S.I.C.: 5012
N.A.I.C.S.: 423110
Wolfgang Erhard Huppenbauer *(CEO)*

Daimler Starmark A/S (1)
Adalsvej 54
2970 Horsholm, Denmark
Tel.: (45) 72 116016
Fax: (45) 45 165955
Automotive Parts Mfr
S.I.C.: 3714
N.A.I.C.S.: 336390

Daimler Trucks Canada Ltd. (1)
6733 Mississauga Rd Suite 404
Mississauga, ON, L5N 6J5, Canada
Tel.: (905) 812-6500
Fax: (905) 812-6507
Emp.: 1
Industrial Truck Mfr
S.I.C.: 3537
N.A.I.C.S.: 333924
Brad Thiessen *(Gen Mgr)*

Daimler Trucks Korea Ltd. (1)
9th Fl Seoul Square Building 541 Namdaemunno 5-ga
Jung-gu, Seoul, 100-714, Korea (South)
Tel.: (82) 2 6456 2500
Fax: (82) 2 6456 2626
Web Site: www.daimler.com
Industrial Truck Mfr
S.I.C.: 3537
N.A.I.C.S.: 333924

Daimler UK Ltd (1)
Delaware Drive Tongwell
Milton Keynes, Buckinghamshire, MK15 8BA, United Kingdom
Tel.: (44) 20 7660 9993
Automobile Leasing Services
S.I.C.: 7515
N.A.I.C.S.: 532112

Daimler UK Share Trustee Ltd. (1)
Delaware Drive Tongwell
Milton Keynes, Buckinghamshire, MK15 8BA, United Kingdom
Tel.: (44) 1908 301 570
Emp.: 1,000
Business Support Services
S.I.C.: 7389
N.A.I.C.S.: 561499

Daimler Vehiculos Comerciales Mexico S. de R.L. de C.V. (1)
Av Paseo De Los Tamarindos 90
Bosques de las Lomas, 05120 Mexico, Mexico
Tel.: (52) 55 4155 2000
Fax: (52) 722 279 2400
Web Site: www.daimler.com
Transportation Equipment Mfr
S.I.C.: 3799
N.A.I.C.S.: 336999
Bodo Uebber *(Chm)*
Stefan Kurschner *(Pres & CEO)*

Daiprodco Mexico S. de R.L. de C.V. (1)
Paseo De Los Tamarindos No 90 Torre 2 Piso 8 Bosques De Las Lomas
Cuajimalpa De Morelos, Mexico, 05120, Mexico
Tel.: (52) 5550817000
Business Management Consulting Services
S.I.C.: 8742
N.A.I.C.S.: 541611

Daiya Shoji Co., Ltd. (1)
4-7-12 Nadakitadori
Nada-ku, Kobe, 657-0835, Japan
Tel.: (81) 78 861 1978
Fax: (81) 78 861 1979
Data Processing Services
S.I.C.: 7379
N.A.I.C.S.: 518210

Dasa Aircraft Finance XIV B.V. (1)
Van Deventerlaan 50
Utrecht, 3528 AE, Netherlands
Tel.: (31) 302471945
Aircraft & Industrial Truck Leasing Services
S.I.C.: 7359
N.A.I.C.S.: 532411

Dasa Aircraft Finance XV B.V. (1)
Van Deventerlaan 50
Utrecht, 3528 AE, Netherlands
Tel.: (31) 30 2471945
Aircraft & Industrial Truck Leasing Services
S.I.C.: 7359
N.A.I.C.S.: 532411

Dasa Aircraft Finance XVI B.V. (1)
Van Deventerlaan 50
Utrecht, 3528 AE, Netherlands
Tel.: (31) 302471945
Aircraft & Industrial Truck Leasing Services
S.I.C.: 7359
N.A.I.C.S.: 532411

Detroit Diesel-Allison de Mexico, S.A. de C.V. (1)
Av Santa Rosa No 58
San Juan Ixtacala, Tlalnepantla, Mexico, 54160, Mexico
Tel.: (52) 5553331826
Fax: (52) 5553331826
Diesel Engine & Parts Mfr
S.I.C.: 3519
N.A.I.C.S.: 333618

Detroit Diesel Remanufacturing Mexicana, S de R.L. de C.V. (1)
Carretera Villa Cuauhtemoc S/N Nave 5 Exhacienda Santin
Parque Ind Vesta Park, Toluca, Mexico 50010
Tel.: (52) 7222622700
Fax: (52) 7222492210
Motor Vehicle Parts Mfr
S.I.C.: 3714
N.A.I.C.S.: 336390

Eishin Jidosha Kogyo Co., Ltd. (1)
131-16 Kobukecho
Inage-Ku, Chiba, 263-0003, Japan
Tel.: (81) 432501233
Automobile Mfr
S.I.C.: 3711
N.A.I.C.S.: 336111

EvoBus Belgium N.V. (1)
Z 4 Broekooi 270
Asse, 1730, Belgium
Tel.: (32) 2 454 02 80
Fax: (32) 2 452 46 95
E-Mail: brussels@omniplus.com
Web Site: www.evobus.be
Emp.: 6
Bus & Coach Mfr
S.I.C.: 3711
N.A.I.C.S.: 336111
John Peters *(Mng Dir)*
Hans Smits *(Mng Dir)*

EvoBus Danmark A/S (1)
Centervej 3
Koge, Roskilde, 4600, Denmark
Tel.: (45) 56370000
Fax: (45) 56370001
Web Site: www.evobus.dk
Motor Vehicle Distr
S.I.C.: 5012
N.A.I.C.S.: 423110

EvoBus France SAS (1)
2-6 Rue du Vignolle Zone Industrielle
BP 90134
Sarcelles, 95842 Paris, France
Tel.: (33) 1 39 92 62 00
Fax: (33) 1 39 92 62 04
Web Site: www.evobus.fr
Bus & Coach Mfr
S.I.C.: 3711
N.A.I.C.S.: 336111

EvoBus Hellas A.E.B.E. (1)
27 Archimidous
PO Box 413
Koropi, 19400, Greece
Tel.: (30) 2106687000
Fax: (30) 2106687222
Motor Vehicle Mfr & Distr
S.I.C.: 3711
N.A.I.C.S.: 336111

EvoBus Iberica, S. A. (1)
Poligono Industrial Vallegon Samano
Apartado 610 S/N
Castro Urdiales, 39709, Spain
Tel.: (34) 942859260
Fax: (34) 942859204
Web Site: www.evobus.es
Emp.: 261
Bus & Coach Mfr
S.I.C.: 3711
N.A.I.C.S.: 336111

EvoBus Italia S.p.A. (1)
Via Togliatti 7/11
Bomporto, Modena, 41030, Italy
Tel.: (39) 059810811
Fax: (39) 059810853
Web Site: www.evobus.it
Emp.: 15
Bus & Coach Mfr
S.I.C.: 3711
N.A.I.C.S.: 336111
Holger Suffel *(Pres)*

EvoBus Nederland B.V. (1)
Handelsstraat 25
Nijkerk, 3861 RR, Netherlands
Tel.: (31) 33 247 4247
Fax: (31) 33 247 4200
Web Site: www.evobus.nl
Emp.: 6
Bus & Coach Mfr
S.I.C.: 3711
N.A.I.C.S.: 336111
Raimond Berle *(Mgr-IT & Quality)*

EvoBus Polska Sp. z.o.o. (1)
Al Katowicka 46
Wolica, 05-830, Poland
Tel.: (48) 22 356 0600
Fax: (48) 22 356 0605
E-Mail: ebiuro@evobus.com
Web Site: www.evobus.pl
Emp.: 5
Bus & Coach Mfr
S.I.C.: 3711
N.A.I.C.S.: 336111
Pat Healy *(CEO)*
Frank Koschatzky *(CEO)*

EvoBus Reunion S. A. (1)
72 Rue Paul Verlaine
Le Port, Reunion, 97420, France
Tel.: (33) 262425566
Fax: (33) 262425567

Car Mfr
S.I.C.: 3711
N.A.I.C.S.: 336111

EvoBus Romania SRL (1)
373-377 Sos Odai
Bucharest, 13605, Romania
Tel.: (40) 21 528 66 02
Fax: (40) 21 528 66 26
Web Site: www.evobusromania.ro
Bus & Coach Mfr
S.I.C.: 3711
N.A.I.C.S.: 336111

EvoBus (Schweiz) AG (1)
Steinackerstrasse 19
Kloten, Zurich, 8302, Switzerland
Tel.: (41) 448043535
Fax: (41) 448043555
Web Site: www.evobus.ch
Bus & Coach Mfr
S.I.C.: 3711
N.A.I.C.S.: 336111

EvoBus (UK) Ltd. (1)
Bus World Home Coventry Ashcroft Way
Cross Point Business Park
Coventry, CV2 2TU, United Kingdom
Tel.: (44) 24 76 626000
Fax: (44) 24 76 626020
Web Site: www.evobus.co.uk
Bus & Coach Mfr
S.I.C.: 3711
N.A.I.C.S.: 336111
Jan Aichinger *(CEO & Mng Dir)*
Antoine Habar *(CFO)*
Mike Beagrie *(Dir-Sls-Coach)*
Marcus Watts *(Dir-After Sls)*

Gemini-Tur Excursoes Passagens e Turismo Ltda. (1)
65 Rua da Consolacao
01301-000 Sao Paulo, Brazil
Tel.: (55) 11 21254999
Fax: (55) 11 21254925
Tour Operating Services
S.I.C.: 4725
N.A.I.C.S.: 561520

Ilmore Engineering Ltd. (1)
Quarry Rd
Brixworth, Northampton, NN6 9UB, United Kingdom (100%)
Tel.: (44) 1604 799100
Telex: 317406 ILMOR G
Web Site: www.ilmor.co.uk
Emp.: 70
Automotive Engine Mfr
S.I.C.: 3714
N.A.I.C.S.: 336310
Steve Miller *(Mng Dir)*

Jidosha Yuso Kogyo Co., Ltd. (1)
4-7-2 3jo Kikusuikamimachi
Shiroishi-Ku, Sapporo, Hokkaido, 003-0813, Japan
Tel.: (81) 118213171
Business Support Services
S.I.C.: 7389
N.A.I.C.S.: 561499

Kyushu Fuso Bipros Co., Ltd. (1)
1-3-1 Befunishi Shimemachi
Kasuya-Gun, Fukuoka, 811-2232, Japan
Tel.: (81) 929371145
Automobile Mfr
S.I.C.: 3711
N.A.I.C.S.: 336111

Lapland Car Test Aktiebolag (1)
Skent
930 90 Arjeplog, Norrbotten, Sweden
Tel.: (46) 96013280
Real Estate Management Services
S.I.C.: 6531
N.A.I.C.S.: 531390

Legend Investments Ltd. (1)
Delaware Drive
Milton Keynes, Buckinghamshire, MK15 8BA, United Kingdom
Tel.: (44) 1908 668899
Investment Management Services
S.I.C.: 6799
N.A.I.C.S.: 523920

Mercedes AMG High Performance Powertrains Limited (1)
Morgan Drive
Brixworth, Northamptonshire, NN6 9GZ, United Kingdom
Tel.: (44) 1604 880100
Fax: (44) 1604 882800
E-Mail: publicity@mercedes-amg-hpp.com
Web Site: www.mercedes-amg-hpp.com
Emp.: 40
Automotive Engine Mfr
S.I.C.: 3519
N.A.I.C.S.: 333618

Mercedes-Benz - Aluguer de Veiculos, Unipessoal Lda. (1)
Abrunheira
Sintra, 2710-089, Portugal
Tel.: (351) 219257000
Passenger Car Rental Services
S.I.C.: 7514
N.A.I.C.S.: 532111

Mercedes-Benz Argentina S.A. (1)
Azucena Billaslor 435 Puerto Mabero
1425 Buenos Aires, Argentina (100%)
Tel.: (54) 1148088700
Fax: (54) 1148088701
Web Site: www.mercedes-benz.com.ar
Emp.: 100
Mfr. of Automobiles
S.I.C.: 3711
N.A.I.C.S.: 336111

Mercedes-Benz Australia/Pacific Pty. Ltd. (1)
44 Lexia Place
Mulgrave, VIC, 3170, Australia (100%)
Tel.: (61) 395669266
Fax: (61) 395617088
Web Site: www.daimler.com
Emp.: 400
Mercedes Benz Dealer
S.I.C.: 5511
N.A.I.C.S.: 441110
Horst von Sanden *(Mng Dir)*

Mercedes-Benz Bank Polska S.A. (1)
Ul Gottlieba Daimlera 1
02-460 Warsaw, Poland
Tel.: (48) 22 312 78 00
Fax: (48) 22 312 6740
Web Site: www.daimler.com
Automobile Financial Services
S.I.C.: 6726
N.A.I.C.S.: 525990

Mercedes-Benz Bank Rus OOO (1)
Leningradskij Prospekt 39
125167 Moscow, Russia
Tel.: (7) 495 797 9911
Financial Management Services
S.I.C.: 6211
N.A.I.C.S.: 523999

Mercedes-Benz Belgium Luxembourg S.A. (1)
Avenue du Peage Tollaan 68
B-1200 Brussels, Belgium (100%)
Tel.: (32) 27241211
Telex: 21 020
Fax: (32) 27241459
Web Site: www.daimler.com
Emp.: 350
Automobile Sales & Services
S.I.C.: 5511
N.A.I.C.S.: 441110
Mark De Haes *(Gen Mgr)*

Mercedes-Benz Bordeaux SAS (1)
Parc d'Activites Port Wilson - 1 rue Port Arthur
33130 Begles, Gironde, France
Tel.: (33) 5 56 75 76 00
Fax: (33) 5 56 75 76 42
Web Site: www.bordeaux.mercedes.fr
New & Used Car Dealer
S.I.C.: 5511
N.A.I.C.S.: 441110

Mercedes-Benz Broker Biztositasi Alkusz Hungary Kft. (1)
Karpat U 21
Budapest, 1133, Hungary
Tel.: (36) 18806081
Fax: (36) 18806082
E-Mail: biztosetas@daimler.com
Web Site: www.daimler.com
Emp.: 2
Insurance Brokerage Services
S.I.C.: 6411
N.A.I.C.S.: 524210
Beno Zseni *(Mgr)*

Mercedes-Benz Canada Inc. (1)
98 Vanderhoof Ave
Toronto, ON, M4G 4C9, Canada (100%)
Tel.: (416) 425-3550
Telex: 65-24232
Fax: (416) 423-5027
Toll Free: (800) 387-0100
E-Mail: info@mercedes-benz.ca
Web Site: www.mercedes-benz.ca
Sales Range: $800-899.9 Million
Emp.: 300
Sales & Service Company
S.I.C.: 5511
N.A.I.C.S.: 441110
Christian Spelter *(VP-Fin)*

Subsidiaries:

Mercedes-Benz Canada Inc. (2)
761 Dundas St E
Toronto, ON, M5A 4N5, Canada ON (100%)
Tel.: (416) 947-9000
Fax: (416) 947-9085
E-Mail: info@mercedes.ca
Web Site: www.mercedes.ca
Emp.: 100
Mfr. of Automobiles & Other Motor Vehicles
S.I.C.: 3714
N.A.I.C.S.: 336390
Mark Dube *(Gen Mgr)*

Mercedes-Benz Canada Inc. (2)
1395 W Broadway
Vancouver, BC, V6H 1G9, Canada BC (100%)
Tel.: (604) 736-7411
Fax: (604) 736-0313
Web Site: www.mercedes-benz.ca
Emp.: 70
Automobiles & Other Motor Vehicles
S.I.C.: 3714
N.A.I.C.S.: 336390
Vaughan Urquhart *(Gen Mgr)*

Mercedes Benz Canada Inc. (2)
3650 Charles St
Vancouver, BC, V5K 5A9, Canada BC (100%)
Tel.: (604) 639-3310
Fax: (604) 639-4436
E-Mail: info@mercedes-benz.ca
Web Site: www.mercedes-benz.ca
Emp.: 20
Automobiles & Motor Vehicles
S.I.C.: 3714
N.A.I.C.S.: 336390
Jim Rossitter *(Mgr-Reg)*

Mercedes-Benz Capital Services (Debis) UK Ltd. (1)
Burystead Court 120 Caldecotte Lake Drive
Milton Keynes, Buckinghamshire, MK7 8ND, United Kingdom
Tel.: (44) 8708405000
Fax: (44) 1908620216
Investment Management Services
S.I.C.: 6211
N.A.I.C.S.: 523999

Mercedes-Benz Ceska republika s.r.o. (1)
Daimlerova 2296/2
149 45 Prague, Czech Republic
Tel.: (420) 271077111
Fax: (420) 271077312
Web Site: www.mercedes-benz.cz
Automotive Distr
S.I.C.: 5012
N.A.I.C.S.: 423110
Karel Knap *(Mgr)*

Mercedes-Benz CharterWay Espana, S.A. (1)
Avenida De Bruselas 30
28108 Alcobendas, Spain
Tel.: (34) 914846000
Fax: (34) 914846352
Passenger Car Rental Services
S.I.C.: 7514
N.A.I.C.S.: 532111

Mercedes-Benz CharterWay Ltd. (1)
Delaware Drive
Tongwell, Milton Keynes, Great Britian, MK15 8BA, United Kingdom
Tel.: (44) 8702 403 135
Fax: (44) 1908 632 596
Web Site: www.mbcharterway.co.uk
Automotive Insurance Services
S.I.C.: 6351
N.A.I.C.S.: 524126

Mercedes-Benz CharterWay SAS (1)
Parc De Rocquencourt
Rocquencourt, Yvelines, 78150, France
Tel.: (33) 139235600
Fax: (33) 139235321
Commercial Truck Rental & Leasing Services
S.I.C.: 7519
N.A.I.C.S.: 532120
Jean-Luc Francois *(Pres)*

Mercedes-Benz CharterWay S.p.A. (1)
Via Giulio Vincenzo Bona 110
Rome, 00156, Italy
Tel.: (39) 06415951
Fax: (39) 06412212220
Passenger Car Rental Services
S.I.C.: 7514
N.A.I.C.S.: 532111

Mercedes-Benz (China) Ltd. (1)
16/F Daimler Tower No 8 Wangjing Commercial St
Chaoyang District, Beijing, 100102, China
Tel.: (86) 1084178887
Fax: (86) 1084173911
Web Site: www.mercedes-benz.com.cn
New Car Dealer
S.I.C.: 5511
N.A.I.C.S.: 441110
Klaus Maier *(Pres & CEO)*
Duan Jianjun *(Exec VP-Sls & Mktg)*

Mercedes-Benz Comercial, Lda. (1)
Abrunheira-Sintra Apartado 125
Mem Martins, Sintra, 2726-901, Portugal
Tel.: (351) 21 910 9400
Fax: (351) 21 923 2790
E-Mail: contactcenter-mbc@daimler.com
Web Site: www.comercial.mercedes-benz.pt
Commercial Vehicle Mfr
S.I.C.: 3711
N.A.I.C.S.: 336111

Mercedes-Benz Comercial Valencia, S.A. (1)
Avenida La Pista 50
Massanassa, Valencia, 46470, Spain
Tel.: (34) 961 22 44 00
Fax: (34) 961 25 18 58
E-Mail: mbv@daimler.com
Web Site: www.valencia.mercedes-benz.es
Emp.: 185
New & Used Car Dealer
S.I.C.: 5511
N.A.I.C.S.: 441110
Diego Aznar Rodriguez *(Gen Mgr)*

Mercedes-Benz Compania Financiera Argentina S.A. (1)
Boulevard Azucena Villaflor 435
Puerto Madero, C1107CII Buenos Aires, Argentina
Tel.: (54) 11 4808 8900
Fax: (54) 11 4808 8977
Web Site: www.mbfonline.com.ar
Automotive Financial Leasing Services
S.I.C.: 6153
N.A.I.C.S.: 522220

Mercedes-Benz Consult Graz GmbH (1)
Dr-Auner-Strasse 21
8074 Raaba, Austria
Tel.: (43) 316 4115 0
Fax: (43) 316 4115 701
Web Site: www.mercedes-benz-consult-graz.at
Automotive Repair Services
S.I.C.: 7539
N.A.I.C.S.: 811118

Mercedes-Benz Danmark AS (1)
Digevej 114
2300 Copenhagen, Denmark (100%)
Tel.: (45) 33785656
Fax: (45) 33785855
E-Mail: receptioncph.tool-it@taimler.com
Web Site: www.mercedes-benz.dk
Emp.: 10
Mfr. & Dealer of Automobiles, Trucks, Electric & Electronics, Aviation, Space Defense Technologies, Propulsion & Financial Service
S.I.C.: 3711
N.A.I.C.S.: 336120
Laris Erve *(Dir-Comm)*

Daimler AG—(Continued)

Mercedes-Benz Dealer Bedrijven B.V. (1)
Donau 42
Hague, 2491 BA, Netherlands
Tel.: (31) 70 340 0300
Fax: (31) 70 340 0421
Web Site: www.mbdb.nl
Used Car Dealer
S.I.C.: 5521
N.A.I.C.S.: 441120

Mercedes-Benz Desarrollo de Mercados, S. de R.L. de C.V. (1)
Via Jose Lopez Protillo No 127 Santa Maria Cuautepec
Tultitlan, Hidalgo, 54949, Mexico
Tel.: (52) 5541552566
New Car Dealer
S.I.C.: 5511
N.A.I.C.S.: 441110

Mercedes-Benz do Brasil S.A. (1)
Av Mercedes-Benz 679
13054-750 Campinas, SP, Brazil (100%)
Tel.: (55) 19 3225 5418
Fax: (55) 19 3725 3635
Web Site: www.mercedes-benz.com.br
Mfr. & Assembly of Automobiles
S.I.C.: 3711
N.A.I.C.S.: 336111

Mercedes-Benz Egypt S.A.E. (1)
28th Floor Sofitel Towers Cornich El-Nil
PO Box 1125
Maadi, Cairo, Egypt
Tel.: (20) 2 252 99 100
Fax: (20) 2 252 99 105
Web Site: www.mercedes-benz.com.eg
Emp.: 60
New & Used Car Dealer
S.I.C.: 5511
N.A.I.C.S.: 441110
Mike Nolte *(CEO)*
Joachim Wolf *(CFO)*
Bernhard Buchner *(Dir-After Sls)*
Zakaria Mackary *(Dir-Sls & Mktg)*

Mercedes-Benz Esch S.A. (1)
190 Route de Belvaux
Esch-sur-Alzette, 4026, Luxembourg
Tel.: (352) 552323 1
Fax: (352) 552323 501
New & Used Car Dealer
S.I.C.: 5511
N.A.I.C.S.: 441110

Mercedes-Benz Espana, S.A. (1)
Avenida Bruselas 30
28100 Madrid, Spain (100%)
Tel.: (34) 914846000
Fax: (34) 9144646001
E-Mail: auxiliadora.welte@daimler.com
Web Site: www.mercedes.benz.com
Emp.: 300
Mfr. & Assembly of Automobiles
S.I.C.: 3711
N.A.I.C.S.: 336111

Mercedes-Benz Financial Services Austria GmbH (1)
Himmelreich 1
5020 Salzburg, Austria
Tel.: (43) 662 4666 0
Fax: (43) 662 4666 190
E-Mail: austria@mercedes-benz-fs.com
Web Site: www.mercedes-benz-financial.at
Financial Management Services
S.I.C.: 6211
N.A.I.C.S.: 523999

Mercedes-Benz Financial Services BeLux N.V. (1)
Tollaan 68 Avenue du Peage
1200 Brussels, Belgium
Tel.: (32) 2 254 6811
Fax: (32) 2 254 6812
Web Site: www.daimler.com
Financial Management Services
S.I.C.: 6211
N.A.I.C.S.: 523999

Mercedes-Benz Financial Services Ceska republika s.r.o. (1)
Daimlerova 2
149 45 Prague, Czech Republic
Tel.: (420) 271 077 666
Fax: (420) 271 077 609
E-Mail: mbfs@daimler.com
Web Site: www.mercedes.cz
Emp.: 75
Automotive Financial Leasing Services
S.I.C.: 6141
N.A.I.C.S.: 522220
Ralf Ewald *(CEO)*

Mercedes-Benz Financial Services Espana E. F. C., S.A.U. (1)
Avda de Bruselas 30 Poligono Arroyo de la Vega
28108 Alcobendas, Madrid, Spain
Tel.: (34) 91 484 6000
Web Site: www.daimler.com
Motor Vehicle Financial Services
S.I.C.: 6726
N.A.I.C.S.: 525990

Mercedes-Benz Financial Services France S.A. (1)
ZAC du Cournouiller 9 rue de Chaponval
78870 Bailly, France
Tel.: (33) 1 30 80 84 00
Financial Management Services
S.I.C.: 6211
N.A.I.C.S.: 523999

Mercedes-Benz Financial Services Hellas AE (1)
20 Odos Thivaidos
14564 Kifissia, Greece
Tel.: (30) 210 8188800
Fax: (30) 210 8188880
Emp.: 3
Financial Management Services
S.I.C.: 6211
N.A.I.C.S.: 523999
Stathis Skaris *(Mgr-IT)*

Mercedes-Benz Financial Services Hong Kong Ltd. (1)
59/F Central Plaza 18 Harbour Road
Wanchai, China (Hong Kong)
Tel.: (852) 2594 8780
Fax: (852) 2594 8784
Web Site: www.daimler.com
Emp.: 10
Motor Vehicle Insurance Services
S.I.C.: 6331
N.A.I.C.S.: 524126
Alla Semiletova *(Mng Dir)*

Mercedes-Benz Financial Services Italia S.p.A (1)
Via Giulio Vincenzo Bona 110
156 Rome, Italy
Tel.: (39) 06415951
Fax: (39) 0641595200
Web Site: www.mercedes-benz-financialservices.it
Motor Vehicle Financial Services
S.I.C.: 6726
N.A.I.C.S.: 525990

Mercedes-Benz Financial Services Nederland B.V. (1)
Van Deventerlaan 50
3528 AE Utrecht, Netherlands
Tel.: (31) 30 6079410
Fax: (31) 30 2471600
E-Mail: info@daimler.com
Web Site: www.mercedes-benzfinancialservices.nl
Emp.: 150
Automotive Financial Leasing Services
S.I.C.: 6141
N.A.I.C.S.: 522220
P. J. B. Derks *(Principal)*

Mercedes-Benz Financial Services Portugal - Instituicao Financeira de Credito S.A. (1)
Abrunheira - Apartado 6
2726-901 Mem Martins, Portugal
Tel.: (351) 707210211
Fax: (351) 219257327
E-Mail: mbfinanciamento@daimler.com
Web Site: www.mercedes-benz.pt
Automotive Financial Services
S.I.C.: 6726
N.A.I.C.S.: 525990
Gerd Sailer *(Product Mgr)*

Mercedes-Benz Financial Services Rus OOO (1)
Leningradskij Prospekt 39
125167 Moscow, Russia
Tel.: (7) 495 797 5354
Fax: (7) 495 797 5355
Financial Leasing Services
S.I.C.: 6159
N.A.I.C.S.: 522220

Mercedes-Benz Financial Services Schweiz AG (1)
Bernstrasse 55
8952 Schlieren, Switzerland
Tel.: (41) 44 755 99 99
Fax: (41) 44 755 99 88
Web Site: www.mercedes-benz-financialservices.ch
Automotive Financial Services
S.I.C.: 6726
N.A.I.C.S.: 525990

Mercedes-Benz Financial Services Slovakia s.r.o. (1)
Tuhovska 11
831 07 Bratislava, Slovakia
Tel.: (421) 249 294 600
Fax: (421) 249 294 666
E-Mail: leasing@mbfs.sk
Web Site: www.mbfs.sk
Emp.: 25
Automotive Financial Services
S.I.C.: 6726
N.A.I.C.S.: 525990
Martin Pavelek *(Mng Dir)*

Mercedes-Benz Financial Services South Africa (Pty) Ltd. (1)
123 Wierda Road
Zwartkop, Centurion, 0046, South Africa
Tel.: (27) 861 324653
Fax: (27) 126736059
E-Mail: info@mbfssa.co.za
Web Site: www.mbfssa.co.za
Automotive Financial Services
S.I.C.: 6726
N.A.I.C.S.: 525990
Franz Koller *(CEO)*

Mercedes-Benz Financial Services Taiwan Ltd. (1)
4F No 129 Min-Sheng East Road Sec 3
Taipei, 10596, Taiwan
Tel.: (886) 2 2547 8788
Web Site: www.mercedes-benz-financial.com.tw
Automotive Financial Services
S.I.C.: 6141
N.A.I.C.S.: 522220

Mercedes-Benz Financial Services UK Limited (1)
Delaware Drive
Tongwell, Milton Keynes, MK15 8BA, United Kingdom
Tel.: (44) 870 847 0700
Fax: (44) 870 840 9000
Automotive Financial Services
S.I.C.: 6726
N.A.I.C.S.: 525990

Mercedes-Benz Finans Danmark A/S (1)
Stamholmen 157 1
2650 Hvidovre, Denmark
Tel.: (45) 33788900
Fax: (45) 33789901
E-Mail: bilsalg@daimler.com
Web Site: www.dcsbilsalg.com
Fleet Management Services
S.I.C.: 7515
N.A.I.C.S.: 532112

Mercedes-Benz Finans Sverige AB (1)
Dockgatan 1
211 12 Malmo, Sweden
Tel.: (46) 406609260
Fax: (46) 40305250
E-Mail: info.finans.se@daimler.com
Emp.: 7
Automotive Financial Services
S.I.C.: 6726
N.A.I.C.S.: 525990
Mark Lovely *(CEO)*

Mercedes-Benz Finansal Kiralama Turk A.S. (1)
Tem Otoyolu Hadimkoy Cikisi
34500 Istanbul, Turkey
Tel.: (90) 2128666565
Web Site: www.mercedes-benz-finansalhizmetler.com
Financial Leasing Services
S.I.C.: 6141
N.A.I.C.S.: 522220

Mercedes-Benz Finansman Turk A.S. (1)
TEM Otoyolu Hadimkoy Cikisi Mercedes Caddesi Bahcesehir
34500 Istanbul, Turkey
Tel.: (90) 212 866 6565
Fax: (90) 212 867 45 96
Web Site: www.mercedes-benz-finansalhizmetler.com
Financial Leasing Services
S.I.C.: 6159
N.A.I.C.S.: 522220

Mercedes-Benz Forsaljnings AB (1)
Kottbygatan 4
164 94 Kista, Sweden
Tel.: (46) 8 4772200
Fax: (46) 8 4772235
Web Site: www.mercedes-benz-malmo.se
Motor Vehicle Repair & Maintenance Services
S.I.C.: 7539
N.A.I.C.S.: 811198

Mercedes-Benz France S.A. (1)
11 Rue Mercedes Benz
67129 Molsheim, Cedex, France (100%)
Tel.: (33) 388478800
Fax: (33) 388478801
E-Mail: molsheim@diamler.com
Web Site: www.mercedes-benz.fr
Emp.: 500
Sales & Service of Diesel Trucks & Tractors
S.I.C.: 5084
N.A.I.C.S.: 423830
Klaus Fischenger *(Mng Dir)*

Mercedes-Benz Gent N.V. (1)
Afrikalaan 208
Gent, Oost-Vlaanderen, 9000, Belgium
Tel.: (32) 92500511
Fax: (32) 92500506
E-Mail: info@gent.mercedes-benz.be
Web Site: www.gent.mercedes-benz.be
Emp.: 100
New Car & Used Car Dealer
S.I.C.: 5511
N.A.I.C.S.: 441110
Mijnheer Koen Smet *(Mgr-After Sls)*

Mercedes-Benz Global Training Nederland B.V. (1)
Nijverheidsstraat 55
Nijkerk, 3861 RJ, Netherlands
Tel.: (31) 33 247 3333
Fax: (31) 33 247 3287
Emp.: 17
Automotive Training Services
S.I.C.: 8299
N.A.I.C.S.: 611692
Branko van Eerden *(Principal)*

Mercedes-Benz Grand Prix Ltd. (1)
Operations Centre
Brackley, Northamptonshire, NN13 7BD, United Kingdom
Tel.: (44) 1280 844000
Fax: (44) 1280 840001
Web Site: www.mercedes-amg-f1.com
Emp.: 500
Sporting Goods Retailer
S.I.C.: 5941
N.A.I.C.S.: 451110
Niki Lauda *(Chm)*

Mercedes-Benz Hellas S.A. (1)
20 Thivaidos St
145 64 Nea Kifissia, Greece (100%)
Tel.: (30) 2106296500
Fax: (30) 2106296710
E-Mail: magdalini.agrafioti@daimler.com
Web Site: www.mercedes-benz.gr
Emp.: 220
Motor Vehicles
S.I.C.: 3711
N.A.I.C.S.: 336111
John Kalligeros *(Mng Dir)*

Mercedes-Benz Hong Kong Limited (1)
59th Floor Central Plaza 18 Harbour Road
Wanchai, China (Hong Kong)
Tel.: (852) 25948800
Fax: (852) 25948801
Web Site: www.mercedes-benz.com.hk
New Car Dealer
S.I.C.: 5511

N.A.I.C.S.: 441110
Klaus Maier *(Pres)*

Mercedes-Benz Insurance Broker SRL (1)
Strada Biharia Nr 26 Sector 1
13981 Bucharest, Romania
Tel.: (40) 21 3060 700
Fax: (40) 21 3060 721
E-Mail: info-insurance@daimler.com
Emp.: 2
Insurance Brokerage Services
S.I.C.: 6411
N.A.I.C.S.: 524210
Cristina Staicu *(Gen Mgr)*

Mercedes-Benz Italia S.p.A. (1)
Via Giulio Vincenzo Bona 110
00156 Rome, RM, Italy (97.2%)
Tel.: (39) 0641441
Fax: (39) 0641219088
Web Site: www.mercedesbenz.it
Emp.: 2,000
Sales & Service Company
S.I.C.: 5511
N.A.I.C.S.: 441110

Mercedes-Benz Japan Co., Ltd. (1)
Roppongi First Bldg 9-9 Roppongi 1-chome
Minato-ku, Tokyo, 106-8506, Japan (100%)
Tel.: (81) 355727200
Fax: (81) 355727334
E-Mail: info@mercedes-benz.co.jp
Web Site: www.mercedes-benz.co.jp
Emp.: 457
Automobile & Other Motor Vehicle Mfr & Distr
S.I.C.: 5012
N.A.I.C.S.: 423110
Nicolas Steeks *(Pres & CEO)*

Subsidiary:

Daimler Financial Services Japan Co., Ltd. (2)
Shin-Kawasaki Mitsui Bldg 890-12 Kashimada
Saiwai-ku, Kawasaki, Kanagawa, 212-0058, Japan
Tel.: (81) 44 542 1200
Web Site: www.daimler-financialservices.jp
Emp.: 7
Automotive Financial Leasing Services
S.I.C.: 6141
N.A.I.C.S.: 522220
Hiroshi Hanai *(Pres & CEO)*

Mercedes-Benz Leasing do Brasil Arrendamento Mercantil S.A. (1)
Rio Negro 585
Barueri, Sao Paulo, 06454-000, Brazil
Tel.: (55) 1168585800
Real Estate Leasing Services
S.I.C.: 6519
N.A.I.C.S.: 531190

Mercedes-Benz Leasing Hrvatska d.o.o. (1)
Kovinska 5
10090 Zagreb, Croatia
Tel.: (385) 1 3441 250
Fax: (385) 1 3441 255
E-Mail: dfs875.info@daimler.com
Web Site: www.mercedes-benz-leasing.hr
Emp.: 28
Automobile Financial Leasing Services
S.I.C.: 6159
N.A.I.C.S.: 522220
Krunoslav Pavic *(Pres & Mng Dir)*

Mercedes-Benz Leasing IFN SA (1)
Strada Biharia Nr 267 Sector 1
013981 Bucharest, Romania
Tel.: (40) 21 3060 700
Fax: (40) 21 2004 620
E-Mail: customerservicero@daimler.com
Web Site: www.mercedes-benz-financial-services.ro
Emp.: 30
Automobile Financial Leasing Services
S.I.C.: 6153
N.A.I.C.S.: 522220
Roland Leitner *(CEO)*

Mercedes-Benz Leasing Kft. (1)
Karpat U 21
1133 Budapest, Hungary
Tel.: (36) 1 880 6066
Fax: (36) 1 880 6066
E-Mail: ugyfelszolgalat@daimler.com
Web Site: www.mercedes-benz-credit.hu
Automobile Financial Leasing Services
S.I.C.: 6153
N.A.I.C.S.: 522220
Horst Wohlfart *(Mng Dir)*
Janos Magyar *(CFO)*

Mercedes-Benz Leasing Polska Sp. z.o.o. (1)
Ul Gottlieba Daimlera 1
02-460 Warsaw, Poland
Tel.: (48) 22 312 78 00
Fax: (48) 22 312 68 81
Web Site: www.mercedes-benz-financialservices.pl
Automobile Financial Leasing Services
S.I.C.: 6141
N.A.I.C.S.: 522220

Mercedes-Benz Leasing (Thailand) Co., Ltd. (1)
20th Floor Rajanakarn Building 183 South Sathorn Road
Yannawa Sathorn, Bangkok, 10120, Thailand
Tel.: (66) 2614 8500
Fax: (66) 2676 5949
E-Mail: mblt.customerservice@daimler.com
Web Site: www.mercedes-benz-leasing.co.th
Emp.: 120
Automotive Financial Leasing Services
S.I.C.: 6153
N.A.I.C.S.: 522220
Mike Ponnaz *(Dir-Sls & Mktg)*

Mercedes-Benz Leudelange S.A. (1)
Zone D'Activites Am Bann 16
Leudelange, 3372, Luxembourg
Tel.: (352) 2637261
Fax: (352) 263726306
New & Used Car Dealer
S.I.C.: 5511
N.A.I.C.S.: 441110

Mercedes-Benz Lille SAS (1)
20 Rue Chappe
Villeneuve d'Ascq, Nord, 59650, France
Tel.: (33) 320723939
Fax: (33) 328328828
Web Site: www.lille.mercedes.fr
Emp.: 138
New & Used Car Dealer
S.I.C.: 5511
N.A.I.C.S.: 441110
Gentile Hubert *(Gen Mgr)*

Mercedes-Benz Luxembourg-Centre S.A. (1)
Rue De Bouillon 45
Luxembourg, 1248, Luxembourg
Tel.: (352) 408011
Fax: (352) 408711
Emp.: 20
New & Used Car Dealer
S.I.C.: 5511
N.A.I.C.S.: 441110
Katherine Adt *(Pres)*

Mercedes-Benz Luxembourg S.A. (1)
Rue De Bouillon 45
Luxembourg, 1248, Luxembourg
Tel.: (352) 408011
Fax: (352) 408711
Web Site: www.mercedes-benz.lu
New & Used Car Dealer
S.I.C.: 5511
N.A.I.C.S.: 441110
Katrin Adt *(Pres)*
Justin Mangen *(Mng Dir & Gen Mgr)*

Mercedes-Benz Lyon SAS (1)
89 Rue Marietton
69009 Lyon, Rhone, France
Tel.: (33) 472857800
New & Used Car Dealer
S.I.C.: 5511
N.A.I.C.S.: 441110

Mercedes-Benz Manufacturing Hungary Kft. (1)
Mercedes Ut 1
6000 Kecskemet, Hungary
Tel.: (36) 76 30 1022
Fax: (36) 76 30 1097
Web Site: www.mercedes-benz.hu
Emp.: 250
Automobile Mfr
S.I.C.: 3711
N.A.I.C.S.: 336111

Mercedes-Benz Mexico, S. de R.L. de C.V. (1)
Av Paseo de los Tamarindos 90
Bosques de las Lomas, 05120 Mexico, Mexico
Tel.: (52) 55 4155 2000
Web Site: www.daimler.com
New & Used Car Dealer
S.I.C.: 5511
N.A.I.C.S.: 441110

Mercedes-Benz Milano S.p.A. (1)
Via Gottlieb Wilhelm Daimler 1
Milan, 20151, Italy
Tel.: (39) 0230251
Fax: (39) 0230258201
Web Site: www.milano.mercedes-benz.it
New & Used Car Dealer
S.I.C.: 5511
N.A.I.C.S.: 441110

Mercedes-Benz Molsheim SAS (1)
19 Route Industrielle de la Hardt
67120 Molsheim, France
Tel.: (33) 388 478800
Fax: (33) 388 478801
E-Mail: Molsheim@daimler.com
Web Site: www.daimler.com
Emp.: 560
Automobile Mfr
S.I.C.: 3711
N.A.I.C.S.: 336111
Klaus Fischinger *(Pres)*

Mercedes-Benz Nederland B.V. (1)
Van Deventerlaan 50
PO Box 2088
NL 3528 AE Utrecht, Netherlands (100%)
Tel.: (31) 302471911
Fax: (31) 302471600
E-Mail: info@daimler.com
Web Site: www.mercedes-benz.nl
Emp.: 300
Mfr & Dealer of Automobiles
S.I.C.: 3711
N.A.I.C.S.: 336120

Mercedes-Benz New Zealand Ltd. (1)
9 Pacific Rise
Mount Wellington, 1062 Auckland, New Zealand
Tel.: (64) 9 573 0192
Fax: (64) 95730208
E-Mail: mbnz.enquiriesMBPC@daimler.com
Web Site: www.mercedes-benz.co.nz
Emp.: 6
New & Used Car Dealer
S.I.C.: 5511
N.A.I.C.S.: 441110
Steve MacSween *(Gen Mgr)*

Mercedes-Benz Ninove N.V. (1)
Brakelsesteenweg 398
Ninove, East Flanders, 9406, Belgium
Tel.: (32) 54319229
Fax: (32) 54327449
Web Site: www.ninove.mercedes-benz.be
New & Used Car Dealer
S.I.C.: 5521
N.A.I.C.S.: 441120
Johan de Ninove *(Mgr-After Sls)*

Mercedes-Benz of South Africa (Pty.) Ltd. (1)
123 wierda road zwartkop centurian 0046
P O Box 1717
Pretoria, 0001, South Africa (100%)
Tel.: (27) 126771500
Web Site: www.mercedesbenzsa.co.za
Emp.: 1,100
New Car Dealership
S.I.C.: 5511
N.A.I.C.S.: 441110
Arno van der Merwe *(CEO & VP-Mfg)*

Mercedes-Benz Osterreich Vertriebsgesellschaft mbH (1)
Fasaneriestra 35
5020 Salzburg, Austria (50%)
Tel.: (43) 66244780
Fax: (43) 6624478277
E-Mail: office@mercedes-benz.at
Web Site: www.mercedes-benz.at
Emp.: 130
S.I.C.: 3711
N.A.I.C.S.: 336111
Bernhard Denk *(Mng Dir)*

Mercedes-Benz Paris SAS (1)
10 Avenue De Saint Germain
78560 Le Port-Marly, Yvelines, France
Tel.: (33) 139173117
Fax: (33) 156845102
E-Mail: mbcenter@daimler.com
Web Site: www.paris.mercedes.fr
Used & New Car Dealer
S.I.C.: 5521
N.A.I.C.S.: 441120
Reinhard Lyhs *(Pres)*

Mercedes-Benz Polska Sp. z.o.o. (1)
Ul Gottlieba Daimlera 1
02-460 Warsaw, Poland
Tel.: (48) 22 312 5000
Fax: (48) 22 312 5099
Web Site: www.mercedes-benz.pl
New & Used Car Dealer
S.I.C.: 5511
N.A.I.C.S.: 441110

Mercedes-Benz Portugal-Comercio de Automoveis, S.A. (1)
Industrial Abrunheira Ap 1
2726 911 Abrunheira, Portugal (100%)
Tel.: (351) 219257000
Fax: (351) 219257010
E-Mail: info_mbp@daimler.com
Web Site: www.mercedes-benz.com
Emp.: 200
Motor Vehicles & Passenger Cars
S.I.C.: 3711
N.A.I.C.S.: 336111
Carstan Odar *(Mng Dir)*

Mercedes-Benz Portugal, S.A. (1)
Apartado 1 - Abrunheira
2726-911 Mem Martins, Portugal
Tel.: (351) 21 925 7000
Fax: (351) 21 925 7010
E-Mail: info_mbp@daimler.com
Web Site: www.mercedes-benz.pt
Commercial Vehicle Mfr
S.I.C.: 3711
N.A.I.C.S.: 336111

Mercedes-Benz Renting, S.A. (1)
Avenida De Bruselas 30
28108 Alcobendas, Spain
Tel.: (34) 91 484 60 00
Fax: (34) 91 484 60 01
Web Site: www.mercedes-benz.es
New & Used Car Dealer
S.I.C.: 5511
N.A.I.C.S.: 441110

Mercedes-Benz Research & Development India Pvt Ltd. (1)
Pine Valley 3rd Floor Embassy Golf Links Business Park
Bengaluru, 530 071, India
Tel.: (91) 80 67685000
Emp.: 500
Information Technology Development Services
S.I.C.: 7371
N.A.I.C.S.: 541511
Manu Saale *(CEO & Mng Dir)*

Mercedes-Benz Retail Group UK Limited (1)
Delaware Drive Tongwell
Milton Keynes, Buckinghamshire, MK15 8BA, United Kingdom
Tel.: (44) 1908668899
Web Site: www.mercedes-benzretailgroup.co.uk
Commercial Vehicle Dealer
S.I.C.: 5571
N.A.I.C.S.: 441228
Neil Williamson *(Mng Dir)*

Subsidiary:

Mercedes-Benz Brooklands Limited (2)
Brooklands Drive
Weybridge, KT13 0SL, United Kingdom
Tel.: (44) 8451205637
Fax: (44) 1932373500
E-Mail: internet.enquiries@mercedes.co.uk
Web Site: www.mercedes-benzbrooklands.co.uk
New & Used Car Dealer

Daimler AG—(Continued)

S.I.C.: 5511
N.A.I.C.S.: 441110

Mercedes-Benz Roma S.p.A. (1)
Via Zoe Fontana 220
Rome, 00131, Italy
Tel.: (39) 06451441
Fax: (39) 064191991
Web Site: www.roma.mercedes-benz.it
New Car Dealer
S.I.C.: 5511
N.A.I.C.S.: 441110

Mercedes-Benz Russia SAO (1)
Leningradsky Prospek 39a
125167 Moscow, Russia
Tel.: (7) 495 745 26 00
Fax: (7) 495 783 37 78
E-Mail: mbr@daimler.com
Web Site: www.mercedes-benz.ru
Emp.: 800
New Car Dealer
S.I.C.: 5511
N.A.I.C.S.: 441110
Jan K. Madeja *(Gen Dir)*

Mercedes-Benz Schweiz AG (1)
Bernstrasse 55
Schlieren, Zurich, 8952, Switzerland
Tel.: (41) 44 755 80 00
Fax: (41) 44 755 80 80
Web Site: www.mercedes-benz.ch
Commercial Vehicle Mfr
S.I.C.: 3711
N.A.I.C.S.: 336111

Mercedes-Benz Service Leasing SRL (1)
Strada Biharia Nr 26 Sector 1
13981 Bucharest, Romania
Tel.: (40) 21 3060 700
Fax: (40) 21 3060 707
E-Mail: customerservicebro@daimler.com
Emp.: 3
Passenger Car Leasing Services
S.I.C.: 7515
N.A.I.C.S.: 532112
Roland Leitner *(CEO)*

Mercedes-Benz Services Correduria de Seguros, S.A. (1)
Avenida De Bruselas 30
Alcobendas, Madrid, 28108, Spain
Tel.: (34) 917214540
Fax: (34) 917210665
Web Site: www.mercedes-benzseguros.es
Insurance Brokerage Services
S.I.C.: 6411
N.A.I.C.S.: 524210

Mercedes-Benz Servizi Assicurativi Italia S.p.A. (1)
Via Giulio Vincenzo Bona 110
Rome, 00156, Italy
Tel.: (39) 06 415951
Fax: (39) 06 41595872
Automotive Insurance Services
S.I.C.: 6351
N.A.I.C.S.: 524126

Mercedes-Benz Sigorta Aracilik Hizmetleri A.S. (1)
Tem Otoyolu Hadimkoy Cikisi Mercedes Caddesi Bahcesehir
Istanbul, 34500, Turkey
Tel.: (90) 212 867 30 00
Fax: (90) 212 867 45 96
Insurance Brokerage Services
S.I.C.: 6411
N.A.I.C.S.: 524210

Mercedes-Benz Sosnowiec Sp. z o.o. (1)
St Gottlieb Daimler 1
Sosnowiec, 41-209, Poland
Tel.: (48) 32 368 4500
Fax: (48) 32 368 4510
E-Mail: info-mbs@daimler.com
Web Site: www.sosnowiec.mercedes-benz.pl
Emp.: 200
New & Used Car Dealer
S.I.C.: 5511
N.A.I.C.S.: 441110
Elzbieta Duraj *(Mgr-Local Compliance)*

Mercedes-Benz Srbija i Crna Gora d.o.o. (1)
Omladinskih Brigada 33
Belgrade, 11070, Serbia
Tel.: (381) 11 3019000
Fax: (381) 11 3019035
E-Mail: informacije@daimler.com
Web Site: www.mercedes-benz.rs
Emp.: 25
New & Used Car Dealer
S.I.C.: 5511
N.A.I.C.S.: 441110
Andreas Binder *(CEO & Gen Dir)*

Mercedes-Benz Sverige AB (1)
Dockgatan 1
211 12 Malmo, Sweden
Tel.: (46) 406718484
Fax: (46) 84745655
Web Site: www.mercedes-benz.se
New & Used Car Dealer
S.I.C.: 5511
N.A.I.C.S.: 441110

Mercedes-Benz Taiwan Ltd. (1)
13F No 129 Minsheng E Rd Section 3
Taipei, 10596, Taiwan
Tel.: (886) 2 2719 3488
Fax: (886) 2 2719 3545
E-Mail: csm_crm@daimler.com
Web Site: www.mercedes-benz.com.tw
Automobile Mfr
S.I.C.: 3711
N.A.I.C.S.: 336111

Mercedes-Benz Tasit Ticaret ve Servis A.S. (1)
Akcaburgaz Mahallesi Mercedes Caddesi No 2
Esenyurt, Istanbul, 34500, Turkey
Tel.: (90) 212 867 43 00
Fax: (90) 212 867 45 29
E-Mail: info@mercedes-benz-tasitticaret.com
Web Site: www.mercedes-benz-tasitticaret.com.tr
Emp.: 50
Automotive Repair & Maintenance Services
S.I.C.: 7549
N.A.I.C.S.: 811198
Osman Nuri Aksoy *(Gen Mgr)*

Mercedes-Benz Technical Center Nederland B.V. (1)
Nijverheidsstraat 55
Nijkerk, Gelderland, 3861 RJ, Netherlands
Tel.: (31) 332473333
Automotive Body Repair & Maintenance Services
S.I.C.: 7532
N.A.I.C.S.: 811121

Mercedes-Benz (Thailand) Limited (1)
Rajanakarn Building 19th Floor 183 South Sathorn Road
Yan Nawa Sathorn, Bangkok, Thailand
Tel.: (66) 2 614 8888
Fax: (66) 2 676 6234
Web Site: www.mercedes-benz.co.th
New Car Dealer
S.I.C.: 5511
N.A.I.C.S.: 441110
Alexander Paufler *(Pres & CEO)*

Mercedes-Benz Turk A.S. (1)
Yilanli Ayazma Sok No 12
Davutpasa, Istanbul, 34 020, Turkey (55%)
Tel.: (90) 2124843300
Fax: (90) 2124643300
E-Mail: info@avm.com.tr
Web Site: www.mengarlar.com.tr
Emp.: 150
Mfr & Dealer of Automobiles
S.I.C.: 3711
N.A.I.C.S.: 336111
Hayraten Karaboga *(CEO)*

Mercedes-Benz UK Limited (1)
Tongwell
Tongwell, Milton Keynes, MK15 8BA, United Kingdom (100%)
Tel.: (44) 1908668899
Telex: 826904 MERCMK G
Fax: (44) 1908664351
Web Site: www.mercedes-benz.co.uk
Emp.: 1,500
Car & Commercial Vehicle Importers
S.I.C.: 5511
N.A.I.C.S.: 441110
Marcus Breitschwerdt *(Mng Dir)*

Mercedes-Benz V.I. Lille SAS (1)
4 Rue De Seclin
Vendeville, Nord, 59175, France
Tel.: (33) 320161600
Fax: (33) 320161662
E-Mail: infos@lille.mercedes.fr
Web Site: www.lille.ul.mercedes.fr
Automotive Dealer
S.I.C.: 5511
N.A.I.C.S.: 441110

Mercedes-Benz V.I. Lyon SAS (1)
Zac Les Grandes Terres 530 Rue Antoine Pinay
Genas, Rhone, 69740, France
Tel.: (33) 472473600
Automotive Dealer
S.I.C.: 5599
N.A.I.C.S.: 441228

Mercedes-Benz V.I. Paris Ile de France SAS (1)
Zac Du Vaulorin 17 Rue Marcellin Berthelot
91320 Wissous, Essonne, France
Tel.: (33) 160138000
Fax: (33) 160138002
E-Mail: infos@parissud.mercedes.fr
Web Site: www.parissud.ca.mercedes.fr
Automotive Dealer
S.I.C.: 5599
N.A.I.C.S.: 441228

Mercedes-Benz V.I. Toulouse SAS (1)
65 Route De Paris
31150 Fenouillet, France
Tel.: (33) 5 62 75 82 00
Fax: (33) 5 62 75 82 02
E-Mail: infos@toulouse.mercedes.fr
Web Site: www.toulouse.ul.mercedes.fr
Commercial Vehicle Services
S.I.C.: 7549
N.A.I.C.S.: 488410

Mercedes-Benz Warszawa Sp. z o.o. (1)
Ul Gottlieba Daimlera 1
Warsaw, 02-460, Poland
Tel.: (48) 223127000
Fax: (48) 223126005
E-Mail: info-mbw@daimler.com
Web Site: www.warszawa.mercedes-benz.pl
New & Used Car Dealer
S.I.C.: 5511
N.A.I.C.S.: 441110
Konrad Drzewiecki *(Acct Mgr-Van Center)*

Mercedes-Benz Wavre S.A. (1)
Avenue Lavoisier 10
Wavre, 1300, Belgium
Tel.: (32) 1 022 28 88
Fax: (32) 1 024 11 02
Web Site: www.wavre.mercedes-benz.be
Automotive Repair & Maintenance Services
S.I.C.: 7549
N.A.I.C.S.: 811198
Michel Ateca *(Mgr-After Sls)*

Mitsubishi Fuso Bus Manufacturing Co., Ltd. (1)
1 Dojo Fuchu-machi
Toyama, Japan 939-2757
Tel.: (81) 76 465 2160
Emp.: 600
Motor Vehicle Parts Mfr
S.I.C.: 3711
N.A.I.C.S.: 336211

Mitsubishi Fuso Truck and Bus Australia Pty. Ltd. (1)
Level 1 Macarthur Point Business Centre
25 Solent Circuit
Norwest Business Park, Baulkham Hills, NSW, 2153, Australia
Tel.: (61) 2 8763 8700
Fax: (61) 2 8850 8775
Web Site: www.mitsubishi-trucks.com.au
Truck & Bus Distr
S.I.C.: 5012
N.A.I.C.S.: 423110

Mitsubishi Fuso Truck & Bus Corp. (1)
890 12 Kashimada
Saiwai ku, Kawasaki, 212 0058, Japan
Tel.: (81) 443307700
Fax: (81) 445872211
Web Site: www.mitsubishi-fuso.com
Emp.: 15,400
Commercial Vehicle Mfr
S.I.C.: 3711
N.A.I.C.S.: 336112
Keisuke Egashira *(Chm)*
Harald Boelstler *(Pres & CEO)*
Frank Markus Weber *(CFO & VP-Fin & Controlling)*
Naoya Hasegawa *(Sr VP & Gen Mgr-Quality Mgmt)*
Masayuki Nagano *(Sr VP & Gen Mgr-Sls & Svcs)*
Yoshitaka Taniyama *(Sr VP & Gen Mgr-Production)*
Bert van Dijk *(Sr VP & Gen Mgr-Intl Sls & Svc)*
Dieter Buhl *(Sr VP)*
Sascha Paasche *(Sr VP-R&D)*

Mitsubishi Fuso Truck Europe, S. A. (1)
Tramagal Plant Zona Industrial Casal da Coelheira
2205-644 Tramagal, Portugal
Tel.: (351) 241 899800
Fax: (351) 241 899870
Web Site: www.mitsubishifuso.com.pt
Emp.: 38
Truck Mfr
S.I.C.: 3711
N.A.I.C.S.: 336112
Antonio Jorge Lima Da Silva Rosa *(Pres)*

Monarch Cars (Tamworth) Ltd. (1)
Mile Oak Business Park Hints Road Mile Oak
Tamworth, Staffordshire, B78 3PQ, United Kingdom
Tel.: (44) 1827 284284
Fax: (44) 1827285299
New Car Dealer
S.I.C.: 5511
N.A.I.C.S.: 441110

Nankyu Butsuryu Support Co., Ltd. (1)
2-5-7 Taniyamako
Kagoshima, 891-0131, Japan
Tel.: (81) 992623900
Business Support Services
S.I.C.: 7389
N.A.I.C.S.: 561499

N.V. Mercedes-Benz Aalst (1)
Nachtegaalstraat 6
Aalst, Oost-Vlaanderen, 9320, Belgium
Tel.: (32) 5 385 95 95
Fax: (32) 5 383 20 75
Web Site: www.aalst.mercedes-benz.be
Automotive Repair & Maintenance Services
S.I.C.: 7539
N.A.I.C.S.: 811198
Peter de Jong *(Mgr-After Sls)*

N.V. Mercedes-Benz Mechelen (1)
Brusselsesteenweg 359
Mechelen, Antwerp, 2800, Belgium
Tel.: (32) 15401111
Fax: (32) 15422345
E-Mail: info@mechelen.mercedes-benz.be
Web Site: www.mechelen.mercedes-benz.be
Automotive Repair & Maintenance Services
S.I.C.: 7539
N.A.I.C.S.: 811198
Thomas Riegler *(Chm & Mng Dir)*

PABCO Co., Ltd. (1)
456 Kashiwagaya
Ebina, Kanagawa, 243-0402, Japan
Tel.: (81) 462312211
Fax: (81) 462315718
Web Site: www.pabco.co.jp
Automotive Parts Mfr
S.I.C.: 3714
N.A.I.C.S.: 336390

PABCO Sendai Co., Ltd. (1)
2-4-11 Ogimachi
Miyagino-Ku, Sendai, Miyagi, 983-0034, Japan
Tel.: (81) 222322374
Automobile Mfr
S.I.C.: 3711
N.A.I.C.S.: 336111

P.T. DaimlerChrysler Indonesia (1)
Desa Wanaherang Gunung Putri
Bogor, 16965, Indonesia (33.3%)
Mailing Address:
PO Box 3769
Jakarta, 10002, Indonesia
Tel.: (62) 2186899350
Fax: (62) 2186899103

E-Mail: dcdindonesia@daimlerchrysler.com
Web Site: www.daimlerchrysler.com
Emp.: 100
Mfr. & Assembly Company
S.I.C.: 3711
N.A.I.C.S.: 336111

P.T. Mercedes-Benz Indonesia (1)
Desa Wanaherang Gunung Putri
Bogor, West Java, 16965, Indonesia
Tel.: (62) 21 23519 350
Fax: (62) 21 23519 303
E-Mail: mbindonesia@daimler.com
Web Site: www.mercedes-benz.co.id
New Car Dealer
S.I.C.: 5511
N.A.I.C.S.: 441110
Claus Weidner *(Chm & CEO)*

P.T. Star Engines Indonesia (1)
Desa Wanaherang Gunung Putri
Bogor, 16965, Indonesia
Tel.: (62) 2123519314
Fax: (62) 2123519311
Automobile Parts Mfr
S.I.C.: 3714
N.A.I.C.S.: 336390

Renting del Pacifico S.A.C. (1)
Av Nicolas Arriola 500
Lima, 1313, Peru
Tel.: (51) 17122000
Transportation Equipment Rental Services
S.I.C.: 7359
N.A.I.C.S.: 532490

Ring Garage AG Chur (1)
Ringstrasse 5-9
Chur, Graubunden, 7000, Switzerland
Tel.: (41) 812871111
Fax: (41) 812871100
Web Site: www.ringgarage.mercedes-benz.ch
Passenger Car Rental Services
S.I.C.: 7514
N.A.I.C.S.: 532111

Saitama Rikuso Co., Ltd. (1)
5-23-15 Negishi
Minami-Ku, Saitama, 336-0024, Japan
Tel.: (81) 488611112
Business Support Services
S.I.C.: 7389
N.A.I.C.S.: 561499

Sandown Motor Holdings (Pty.) Ltd. (1)
Block A Library Office Park 14 Pine Rd
Johannesburg, Gauteng, 2021, South Africa
Tel.: (27) 115490200
Fax: (27) 115490220
E-Mail: sandownservice@sandown.co.za
Web Site: www.sandown.co.za
Commercial Vehicle Dealer
S.I.C.: 5571
N.A.I.C.S.: 441228
Roy McAllister *(Mng Dir)*

SelecTrucks of Toronto, Inc. (1)
7020 Pacific Circle
Mississauga, ON, L5T 1S9, Canada
Tel.: (905) 362-1302
Fax: (905) 362-1034
Toll Free: (855) 370-5915
Web Site: www.selectruckstoronto.com
Used Truck Dealer
S.I.C.: 5521
N.A.I.C.S.: 441120

smart France SAS (1)
Europole de Sarreguemines
57913 Hambach, France
Tel.: (33) 387 2820 00
Fax: (33) 387 2820 01
Web Site: www.daimler.com
Emp.: 777
Automobile Mfr
S.I.C.: 3711
N.A.I.C.S.: 336111

T.O.C. (Schweiz) AG (1)
Kohlestrasse 6
8952 Schlieren, Switzerland
Tel.: (41) 44 755 41 41
Fax: (41) 44 755 41 49
E-Mail: toc@toc-online.ch
Web Site: www.toc-online.ch
Commercial Vehicle Dealer
S.I.C.: 5599
N.A.I.C.S.: 441228

Hannelore Kastner *(Mgr-Sls)*

Troia Empreendimentos Imobiliarios Ltda. (1)
R Voluntarios de Sao Paulo 3361 Conj 41
San Jose, Brazil
Tel.: (55) 17 3234 6289
Automobile Leasing Services
S.I.C.: 6159
N.A.I.C.S.: 522220

DAIMYO AS

Molleparken 6
0459 Oslo, Norway
Tel.: (47) 22374300
Fax: (47) 22374301
E-Mail: info@daimyo.no
Web Site: www.daimyo.no
Sales Range: $10-24.9 Million
Emp.: 25

Business Description:
Investment Services
S.I.C.: 6211
N.A.I.C.S.: 523999

Personnel:
Karsten Aubert *(Dir-Project & Chm)*
Espen Aubert *(Mng Dir)*

DAINICHI CO., LTD.

1-33 Himegaoka
Kani, Gifu, 509-0249, Japan
Tel.: (81) 58 265 9124
Fax: (81) 574 63 4681
E-Mail: info@kk-dainichi.co.jp
Web Site: www.kk-dainichi.co.jp
Year Founded: 1948
5951—(TKS)

Business Description:
Fabricated Structural Metal Mfr
S.I.C.: 3441
N.A.I.C.S.: 332312

Personnel:
Hironori Onda *(CEO)*

DAINICHISEIKA COLOR & CHEMICALS MFG. CO., LTD.

1-7-6 Nihonbashi-Bakurocho Chuo-ku
Tokyo, 103-8383, Japan
Tel.: (81) 336627111
Telex: 2523595
Fax: (81) 36693924
E-Mail: koho-nagata@daicolor.co.jp
Web Site: www.daicolor.co.jp
Year Founded: 1931
4116—(TKS)
Sls.: $1,671,934,000
Assets: $1,729,321,000
Liabilities: $1,091,827,000
Net Worth: $637,494,000
Earnings: $62,997,000
Emp.: 3,641
Fiscal Year-end: 03/31/13

Business Description:
Mfr. & Sales of Inorganic & Organic Pigments, Printing Inks, Coloring Agents for Plastics & Synthetic Fibers, Printing Agents for Textile, Synthetic Resin & High Polymer Products
Import Export
S.I.C.: 2821
N.A.I.C.S.: 325211

Personnel:
Koji Takahashi *(Pres)*
Yoshihiko Takeichi *(CFO & Mng Dir-Fin & Acctg Dept)*

Board of Directors:
Kazuyuki Hanada
Yoshihisa Makino
Kengo Nakajo
Kazuo Nakamura
Takanori Sannan
Koji Takahashi
Yoshihiko Takeichi

Non-U.S. Subsidiaries:

Daicolor do Brasil Ind. e Com. Ltda. (1)
Avenida da Piramide 692 Jardim Inamar
Diadema, Sao Paulo, 9970330, Brazil BR
Tel.: (55) 1140435521 (100%)
Fax: (55) 1140435282
Web Site: www.daicolor.com.br
Emp.: 60
S.I.C.: 2821
N.A.I.C.S.: 325211

Daicolor Italy S.R.L. (1)
Via Vittor Pisani 28
Milan, 20124, Italy IT
Tel.: (39) 0267076688 (100%)
Fax: (39) 0267076683
E-Mail: dcli@daicoloritalysrl.it
Web Site: www.daicolor.co.jp
Emp.: 6
Mfr of Inks, Pigments & Other Coloring Agents
S.I.C.: 2893
N.A.I.C.S.: 325910
Isoda Susumu *(Mgr)*

Daicolor Philippines, Inc. (1)
Lot 7 D 8 Silangan Canlubang Industrial Park
Extension Airstrip Canlubang, Calamba, Laguna, 4028, Philippines PH
Tel.: (63) 495491622 (32%)
Fax: (63) 495491596
Web Site: www.daicolor.co.jp
Sales Range: $1-9.9 Million
Emp.: 38
S.I.C.: 2821
N.A.I.C.S.: 325211

Daicolor Shanghai Mfg. Co., Ltd. (1)
125 Chu Hua Road Shanghai Chemical Industrial Zone Feng Xian Sub Zone
Shanghai, China
Tel.: (86) 2157448220
Fax: (86) 2157448290
Specialty Chemicals Mfr
S.I.C.: 2899
N.A.I.C.S.: 325998

Daicolorchem EU, S.A. (1)
Pol Ind Baix Ebre 165
Campredo, 43897 Tortosa, Spain ES
Tel.: (34) 977597453 (100%)
Fax: (34) 977597454
E-Mail: daicolorchem@daicolorchem.com
Web Site: www.daicolorchem.com
Emp.: 30
Plastics
S.I.C.: 2821
N.A.I.C.S.: 325211
Daniel Ymbernon *(Bus Mgr)*

DAINICHI COLOR VIETNAM CO., LTD. (1)
TS5 Tien Son Industrial Zone
Tien Du District, Bac Ninh, Vietnam
Tel.: (84) 2413714800
Fax: (84) 2413714803
Web Site: www.daicolor.co.jp/english/itd/itd_e03.html
Coloring Pigment Mfr
S.I.C.: 2899
N.A.I.C.S.: 325199
Mitsuo Kishimoto *(Gen Mgr)*

Dainichiseika Color & Chemicals S.A. (1)
4 Rue Agrippa Daubigne
78540 Vernouillet, France (100%)
Tel.: (33) 139280956
Fax: (33) 139280957
Emp.: 1
Chemical Mfg
S.I.C.: 2851
N.A.I.C.S.: 325510

Dainichiseika (H.K.) Ltd. (1)
Room 3607 36/F Windsor House Causeway Bay
311 Gloucester Rd, Hong Kong, China (Hong Kong) HK
Tel.: (852) 25778923 (100%)
Fax: (852) 25778961
E-Mail: dnshkltd@dns-hk.com.hk
Web Site: www.dns-hk.com.hk
Sales Range: $1-9.9 Million
Emp.: 360
S.I.C.: 2821
N.A.I.C.S.: 325211
Kenji Uchiba *(Mgr)*

Non-U.S. Subsidiaries:

Dainichiseika Chemical (ShenZhen) Factory Ltd. (2)
55 Tie Zai Road Gongle Industrial District Xi Xian Town
Bao An District, Shenzhen, Guangdong, 518102, China CN
Tel.: (86) 755 791 6111 (100%)
Fax: (86) 755 791 6123
E-Mail: dnssz@public.szptt.net.cn
Web Site: www.dns-hk.com.hk
S.I.C.: 2821
N.A.I.C.S.: 325211

Dong Guan Dainichi Chemical Manufacturing Co., Ltd. (2)
Dabandi Industrial Estate
Daning District Humen Town, Dongguan, Guangdong, China CN
Tel.: (86) 769 8555 6675 (90%)
Fax: (86) 769 8555 6695
E-Mail: dnscol@dns-hk.com.hk
Web Site: www.dns-hk.com.hk
Emp.: 230
Plastic Compounding & Plastics Materials Mfr
S.I.C.: 2821
N.A.I.C.S.: 325211
Shiro Takagi *(Mng Dir)*

Subsidiary:

Dainichiseika (H.K.) Colouring Co., Ltd. (2)
27 Fl Guandgong Investment Twr 148 Connaught Rd
Central, China (Hong Kong) HK
Tel.: (852) 25778923 (100%)
Fax: (852) 25778961
E-Mail: dnscol@dns-hk.com.hk
Web Site: www.dns-hk.com.hk
Emp.: 50
S.I.C.: 2821
N.A.I.C.S.: 325211
Takahiro Shoda *(Mng Dir)*

Dainichiseika Ink (Guangzhou) Ltd. (1)
No 3 Xinye Road Yonghe Economic Zone Getdd
Guangzhou, 511356, China
Tel.: (86) 2082976870
Fax: (86) 2082976875
E-Mail: long@dns-hk.com.hk
Emp.: 3
Printing Ink Mfr
S.I.C.: 2893
N.A.I.C.S.: 325910
Kijiya Tomiyasu *(Mng Dir)*

Dainichiseika (Shanghai) Trading Ltd. (1)
1507 841 Yan An Middle Rd OOCL Plz
Shanghai, 200040, China (100%)
Tel.: (86) 2162792737
Fax: (86) 2162791047
Web Site: www.daicolor.co.jp
Emp.: 20
S.I.C.: 2821
N.A.I.C.S.: 325211
Kevin Sang *(Gen Mgr)*

Dainichiseika (Shenzhen) Trading Ltd. (1)
Rm 2510 25/F Kerry Centre 2008 Ren Min Nan Road
Luohu District, Shenzhen, Guangdong, China
Tel.: (86) 75582145021
Fax: (86) 75582219056
E-Mail: cui@dns-hk.com.hk
Web Site: www.dns-hk.com.hk/eng/p3.htm
Paint Coating Distr
S.I.C.: 5198
N.A.I.C.S.: 424950
Kenji Uchida *(Mng Dir & Gen Mgr)*

Esta Fine Color Corporation (1)
37 Arturo Drive
Taguig, Metro Manila, 1630, Philippines
Tel.: (63) 28661337
Fax: (63) 28370484
E-Mail: sales@esta3d.net
Web Site: www.daicolor.co.jp
Emp.: 43

Dainichiseika Color & Chemicals Mfg. Co., Ltd.—(Continued)

Coloring Pigment Mfr
S.I.C.: 2816
N.A.I.C.S.: 325130
Gerry Qua *(Mgr)*

Hi-Tech Color (Shanghai) Co., Ltd. **(1)**
125 Chu Hua Road Shanghai Chemical Industrial Zone Feng Xian Sub Zone
Shanghai, China
Tel.: (86) 2157448222
Fax: (86) 2157448294
Emp.: 13
Packaging & Building Materials Mfr
S.I.C.: 3089
N.A.I.C.S.: 326199

Plalloy Mtd B.V. **(1)**
6460 Ha Kerkrade Mercuriusstraat 2
6468ER Kerkrade, Netherlands NL
Tel.: (31) 455464653 (60%)
Fax: (31) 455352523
E-Mail: info@plalloy.nl
Web Site: www.plalloy.com
Rev.: $18,871,396
Emp.: 85
S.I.C.: 2821
N.A.I.C.S.: 325211
Jack Zamangelen *(Mng Dir)*

P.T. Hi-Tech Ink Indonesia **(1)**
Delta Silicon Industrial Park Jl Akasia Blok A8 No 2
Lippo Cikarang, Bekasi, 17550, Indonesia Id
Tel.: (62) 218973890 (100%)
Fax: (62) 218973443
E-Mail: hii@cbm.net.id
Web Site: www.daicolor.co.jp
Rev.: $290,000
Emp.: 150
Adhesives & Gravure & Offset Printing Inks Mfr & Sales
S.I.C.: 2891
N.A.I.C.S.: 325520

Sambo Fine Chemicals Mfg. Co., Ltd. **(1)**
628 2 Hakjang Dong Sasang Ku
Pusan, Korea (South) KS
Tel.: (82) 513113001 (100%)
Fax: (82) 513231742
E-Mail: aphoe@sambofine.co.kr
Web Site: www.sambofine.co.kr
Sales Range: $1-9.9 Million
Emp.: 100
Mfr. of C-Acid, Dye Intermediates & Inorganic Pigments
S.I.C.: 2819
N.A.I.C.S.: 325130
Jeung Hee Cho *(Chm)*

Shanghai Daicolor & Fuji Co., Ltd. **(1)**
1033 Xin Miao San Road
Xinqiao Songjiang, Shanghai, China
Tel.: (86) 2157680930
Fax: (86) 2157680770
Emp.: 3
Specialty Chemicals Mfr
S.I.C.: 2899
N.A.I.C.S.: 325998

Shanghai Mitsui Plastic Compounds Ltd. **(1)**
511 Yutang Rd Songjiang Industrial Zone
Shanghai, 201600, China (33%)
Tel.: (86) 2157741111
Fax: (86) 2157740055
E-Mail: general@shmpc.com.cn
Web Site: www.shmpc.com.cn
Sales Range: $1-9.9 Million
Emp.: 150
Plastics Compounding Mfr
S.I.C.: 2821
N.A.I.C.S.: 325211
Keisuke Fukuzawa *(Pres)*

Tai Chin Chemical Industry Co., Ltd. **(1)**
No 402 Feng Jen Rd Jen Wu Shiang Hsin
Kaohsiung, Hsin, 814, Taiwan TW
Tel.: (886) 73711621 (100%)
Fax: (886) 73711911
E-Mail: info@daicolor.co.jp
Web Site: www.taichin.com.tw
Emp.: 90
S.I.C.: 2821
N.A.I.C.S.: 325211
David Wang *(Chm)*

Toyo Dai-Nichi Ink Sdn Bhd **(1)**
Lot 21 Jalan Pahat 16/8A
40000 Shah Alam, Selangor Darul Ehsan, Malaysia MY
Tel.: (60) 3 5510 8991
Fax: (60) 3 5510 7131
Web Site: www.daicolor.co.jp
Mfr of Inks, Pigments & Other Coloring Agents
S.I.C.: 2893
N.A.I.C.S.: 325910

Non-U.S. Subsidiaries:

CWV Group Ltd. **(1)**
1 Beehive Lions Dr
Shadworth Business Park, BB10 2TJ
Blackburn, United Kingdom
Tel.: (44) 0254222800
Fax: (44) 1254222960
Web Site: www.worldpapers-uk.com
Sells Inorganic & Organic Pigments & Printing Inks
S.I.C.: 2821
N.A.I.C.S.: 325211

E & S Home of Color B.V. **(1)**
Ir. E.L.C. Schiffstraat 246
7547 Enschede, Netherlands
Tel.: (31) 53 4601010
Fax: (31) 53 4601009
Sells Inorganic & Organic Pigments & Printing Inks
S.I.C.: 2821
N.A.I.C.S.: 325211

Filpassion SA **(1)**
10 Rue Des Moissons
51110 Caurel, France
Tel.: (33) 326828694
Fax: (33) 326827550
E-Mail: export@filpassion.fr
Web Site: www.filpassion.fr
Emp.: 30
Sells Inorganic & Organic Pigments & Printing Inks
S.I.C.: 2821
N.A.I.C.S.: 325211
Virgile Deghaye *(Gen Mgr)*

Midbec AB **(1)**
Analysvagen 1
43533 Molnlycke, Sweden
Tel.: (46) 31880550
Fax: (46) 31885142
E-Mail: order@midbec.se
Web Site: www.midbec.se
Emp.: 20
Sells Inorganic & Organic Pigments & Printing Inks
S.I.C.: 2821
N.A.I.C.S.: 325211

Oy. Avane Trading Ltd. **(1)**
Kuortaneenkatu 7
00520 Helsinki, Finland
Tel.: (358) 8929509610
Fax: (358) 892952070
E-Mail: avane@kolumbus.fi
Web Site: www.avane.com
Sells Inorganic & Organic Pigments & Printing Inks
S.I.C.: 2821
N.A.I.C.S.: 325211

Puylaert Designs Of The Time N.V. **(1)**
Europapark Zuid 15
St Nicholas, 9100 Brussels, Belgium (100%)
Tel.: (32) 37809470
Fax: (32) 37809479
E-Mail: info@puylaertdesigns.be
Web Site: www.designsofthetime.be
Sells Inorganic & Organic Pigments & Printing Inks
S.I.C.: 2821
N.A.I.C.S.: 325211
Ezan Paylaert *(Gen Mgr)*

Subsidiaries:

Hi-Tech Color, Inc. **(1)**
Midway Industrial Park 1721 Midway Rd
Odenton, MD 21113
Tel.: (410) 551-9871
Fax: (410) 672-3002
E-Mail: info@htcolor.com
Web Site: www.htcolor.com
Emp.: 12
Mfr. of Printing Ink
S.I.C.: 2893
N.A.I.C.S.: 325910
Greg Kersabage *(Office Mgr)*

Kanto Dainichiseika Kogyo Co., Ltd. **(1)**
2-2-1 Furukawa
Kazo, Saitama, 3400113, Japan
Tel.: (81) 480684600
Chemical Products Mfr
S.I.C.: 2899
N.A.I.C.S.: 325998

Kyushu Dainichiseika Kogyo Co., Ltd **(1)**
1-15-50 Nishitsukiguma
Hakata-Ku, Fukuoka, 812-0857, Japan
Tel.: (81) 924112020
Fax: (81) 924112033
Specialty Chemicals Mfr
S.I.C.: 2899
N.A.I.C.S.: 325199

DAINIPPON SCREEN MFG. CO., LTD.

Tenjinkita-machi 1-1 Teranouchi-agaru 4-chome Horikawa-dori
Kamigyo-ku, Kyoto, 602 8585, Japan
Tel.: (81) 754147111
Fax: (81) 75 451 6500
E-Mail: synchronize@screen.co.jp
Web Site: www.screen.co.jp
Year Founded: 1943
7735—(TKS)
Sls.: $2,089,164,000
Assets: $2,585,253,000
Liabilities: $1,691,877,000
Net Worth: $893,376,000
Earnings: ($148,357,000)
Emp.: 4,955
Fiscal Year-end: 03/31/13

Business Description:
Electronic Component & Semiconductor Component & Inspection Systems Developer, Mfr & Whslr
S.I.C.: 3674
N.A.I.C.S.: 334413

Personnel:
Akira Ishida *(Chm & CEO)*
Masahiro Hashimoto *(Pres & COO)*
Osamu Ryonai *(Sr Mng Dir & CFO)*
Yoichi Kondo *(Deputy CFO & Deputy Gen Mgr-Bus Svc Center)*
Soichi Nadahara *(CTO & Gen Mgr-R&D Center)*
Kimito Ando *(Corp Officer)*
Katsuhiko Aoki *(Sr Corp Officer)*
Masato Goto *(Corp Officer)*
Hayato Hayashi *(Corp Exec Officer)*
Eiji Kakiuchi *(Chief Officer-PR, IR, GPS, Imaging & Solutions)*
Tadahiro Suhara *(Sr Corp Exec Officer)*
Yoshinori Tsuruya *(Corp Officer)*
Hirofumi Uchida *(Sr Corp Officer)*
Hitoshi Yamamoto *(Corp Officer)*

Board of Directors:
Akira Ishida
Masahiro Hashimoto
Eiji Kakiuchi
Shin Minamishima
Shosaku Murayama
Katsutoshi Oki
Osamu Ryonai
Shigeru Saito
Yoshio Tateisi

Subsidiaries:

DS Finance Co., Ltd. **(1)**
Tenjinkita-machi 1-1 Teranouchi-agaru 4-chome Horikawa-dori
Kamigyo-ku, Kyoto, 602 8585, Japan
Tel.: (81) 754418131
Accounting & Lease Mediation Services
S.I.C.: 8721
N.A.I.C.S.: 541219

FASSE Co., Ltd. **(1)**
Iwatsubo Industrial Area 23-25 Iwatsubo
Takaoka, Toyama, 933 0974, Japan
Tel.: (81) 766252010
Fax: (81) 766 25 2017
Web Site: www.fasse.co.jp
Assembly, Inspection, Installation & Setup of Semiconductor Manufacturing Equipment
S.I.C.: 3559
N.A.I.C.S.: 333242
Yoshio Wakai *(Pres)*

FEBACS Co., Ltd. **(1)**
Dainippon Screen Gojo Bldg 12-2 Chudoji-Bojo-cho
Shimogyo-ku, Kyoto, 600 8811, Japan
Tel.: (81) 753433201
Fax: (81) 753433208
Web Site: www.febacs.co.jp/en
Emp.: 60
Maintenance for Semiconductor Manufacturing Equipment
S.I.C.: 7699
N.A.I.C.S.: 811310
Minoru Saito *(Pres)*

Gerant Co., Ltd. **(1)**
480-1 Takamiya-cho
Hikone, Shiga, 522 0292, Japan JP
Tel.: (81) 749 24 8303
Facility Management, Including Building & Environmental Control
S.I.C.: 8744
N.A.I.C.S.: 561210

INITOUT Japan Co., Ltd. **(1)**
2nd Floor Keihan Bus Jujo Bldg 5 Minami-Ishida-cho Higashi-Kujo
Minami-ku, Kyoto, 601 8033, Japan JP
Tel.: (81) 75 662 6633
Fax: (81) 75 662 6678
Web Site: www.jp.initout.com
Emp.: 32
Information Technology Services
S.I.C.: 7379
N.A.I.C.S.: 541519
Hirosada Takagi *(Pres)*

MEBACS Co., Ltd. **(1)**
8th Floor Yasukuni-Kudan-Minami Bldg 3-14 Kudan-Minami 2-chome
Chiyoda-ku, Tokyo, 102 0074, Japan JP
Tel.: (81) 3 3237 3117
Fax: (81) 3 3237 3150
Web Site: www.mebacs.co.jp
Maintenance for PCB Production Equipment
S.I.C.: 7699
N.A.I.C.S.: 811310
Akira Izumi *(Pres)*

Media Technology Japan Co., Ltd. **(1)**
8th Floor Yasukuni-Kudan-Minami Bldg 3-14 Kudan-Minami 2-chome
Chiyoda-ku, Tokyo, 102 0074, Japan
Tel.: (81) 332373101
Fax: (81) 332373187
Web Site: www.mtjn.co.jp
Emp.: 120
Domestic Sales of Graphic Arts Equipment
S.I.C.: 5065
N.A.I.C.S.: 423690
Tsuneo Baba *(Pres)*

Miyako LinkRing Co., Ltd. **(1)**
Tenjinkita-machi 1-1 Teranouchi-agaru 4-chome Horikawa-dori
Kamigyo-ku, Kyoto, 602 8585, Japan JP
Tel.: (81) 754143850
Fax: (81) 754143977
E-Mail: info@miyako.co.jp
Web Site: www.miyakolr.co.jp
Personnel Staffing Services
S.I.C.: 7363
N.A.I.C.S.: 561320
Naomichi Suzuka *(Pres)*

MT Service Japan East Co., Ltd. **(1)**
6th Fl Otsuka-Higashiikebukuro Bldg 32-22 Gugasgu-Ikebukuro 2-chome
Toshima-ku, Tokyo, 170 0013, Japan JP
Tel.: (81) 359526011
Fax: (81) 359526729
Web Site: www.mtsej.co.jp
Maintenance for Graphic Arts Equipment

S.I.C.: 7699
N.A.I.C.S.: 811310
Yoshio Sugawara *(Pres)*

MT Service Japan West Co., Ltd. (1)
6th Floor Nihonseimei Sakaisuji-honmachi Bldg 8-12 Honmachi 1-chome
Chuo-ku, Osaka, 541 0053, Japan JP
Tel.: (81) 662686185
Fax: (81) 662686196
Web Site: www.mtswj.co.jp
Maintenance for Graphic Arts Equipment
S.I.C.: 7699
N.A.I.C.S.: 811310
Yoshio Sugawara *(Pres)*

Quartz Lead Co., Ltd. (1)
Koriyuma Seibu Industrial Park 2
1-15-4 Machiikedai, Koriyama, Fukushima, 963 0215, Japan JP
Tel.: (81) 249631711
E-Mail: info@qld.dsg.ne.jp
Web Site: www.qld.co.jp/en
Emp.: 72
Production of Quartz Glass Parts for Semiconductor Equipment
S.I.C.: 3674
N.A.I.C.S.: 334413
Yoshimi Chiba *(Pres)*

ReVersion 65 Co., Ltd. (1)
Tenjinkita-machi 1-1 Teranouchi-agaru 4-chome Horikawa-dori
Kamigyo-ku, Kyoto, Japan
Tel.: (81) 754143300
Web Site: www.screen.co.jp/eng/profile/group/japan.html
Printing Machinery Mfr
S.I.C.: 3555
N.A.I.C.S.: 333244

S. Ten Nines Kyoto Co., Ltd. (1)
13-1 Shinmei-cho Nishikyogoku
Ukyo-ku, Kyoto, 615 0864, Japan JP
Tel.: (81) 75 325 6116
Fax: (81) 75 325 6118
Web Site: www.st-kyoto.co.jp
Software Development for Graphic Arts Equipment
S.I.C.: 7372
N.A.I.C.S.: 511210
Norihiko Nakamura *(Pres)*

Scientific and Semiconductor Manufacturing Equipment Recycling Co., Ltd. (1)
1st Floor Keihan Bus Jujo Building 5 Minami-Ishida-cho
Higashi-Kujo
Minami-ku, Kyoto, 601-8033, Japan
Tel.: (81) 756934630
Fax: (81) 0756934615
Web Site: www.sserc.co.jp
Emp.: 20
Sales & Maintenance of Second-Hand Electronic Equipment
S.I.C.: 5734
N.A.I.C.S.: 443142
Hiro Oka *(Gen Mgr)*

SEBACS Co., Ltd. (1)
13-1 Shinmei-cho Nishikyogoku
Ukyo-ku, Kyoto, 615 0864, Japan
Tel.: (81) 753232080
Fax: (81) 75 323 2098
Web Site: www.sebacs.co.jp
Maintenance for Semiconductor Manufacturing Equipment
S.I.C.: 7699
N.A.I.C.S.: 811310
Kenji Kamei *(Pres)*

Sokudo Co., Ltd. (1)
5th Floor K-I Shijo Building 88 Kankoboko-cho Shimogyo-ku
Shijodori-Muromachi-Higashiiru, Kyoto, 600 8009, Japan (81%)
Tel.: (81) 752568245
Fax: (81) 752568235
E-Mail: info@sokudospeed.com
Web Site: www.sokudo.com
Emp.: 300
Development, Sales & Service Related to Coat/Develop Track Equipment for Semiconductor Production
S.I.C.: 3674
N.A.I.C.S.: 334413
Tadahiro Suhara *(Pres & CEO)*

U.S. Subsidiary:

Sokudo USA, LLC (2)
2841 Scott Blvd M/S 1863
Santa Clara, CA 95050
Tel.: (408) 496-8064
Web Site: www.sokudo.com
Sales Range: $1-9.9 Million
Emp.: 90
Semiconductors & Related Devices Mfr
S.I.C.: 3674
N.A.I.C.S.: 334413

Tec Communications Co., Ltd. (1)
13-1 Shinmei-cho Nishikyogoku
Ukyo-ku, Kyoto, 615 0864, Japan (100%)
Tel.: (81) 753256221
Fax: (81) 75 325 6243
Web Site: www.k-tecs.co.jp
Emp.: 10
Planning & Production of Technical Documents
S.I.C.: 2741
N.A.I.C.S.: 511140

Tech In Tech Co., Ltd. (1)
425 Oyabu-cho Kuze
Minami-ku, Kyoto, 601 8206, Japan (100%)
Tel.: (81) 759317781
Fax: (81) 759317780
Web Site: www.techintech.co.jp/english
Emp.: 110
Development & Production of Semiconductor & Graphic Arts Equipment
S.I.C.: 3674
N.A.I.C.S.: 334413
Toshiyuki Osaki *(Pres)*

TRANSUP Japan Co., Ltd. (1)
Dainippon Screen Gojo Bldg 12-2 Chudoji-Bojo-cho
Shimogyo-ku, Kyoto, 600 8811, Japan JP
Tel.: (81) 753422277
Fax: (81) 75 342 2255
Web Site: www.transup.co.jp
Installation, Transport, Packing, Supply Chain Management & Related Services
S.I.C.: 4783
N.A.I.C.S.: 488991
Takeshi Moriya *(Pres)*

Plants:

Dainippon Screen Mfg. Co., Ltd. - Hikone Plant (1)
Takamiya-cho 480-1
Hikone, Shiga, 522-0292, Japan
Tel.: (81) 749248300
Fax: (81) 749248307
Web Site: www.screen.co.jp/eng/profile/ma p_hikone.html
Printing Machinery Mfr
S.I.C.: 3555
N.A.I.C.S.: 333244

Dainippon Screen Mfg. Co., Ltd. - Kuze Plant (1)
304-1 Shinkaichi Sayama Kumiyamacho
Kuse-Gun, Kyoto, 613-0034, Japan
Tel.: (81) 774467900
Fax: (81) 774431367
Printing Machinery Mfr
S.I.C.: 3555
N.A.I.C.S.: 333244

Dainippon Screen Mfg. Co., Ltd. - Rakusai Plant (1)
Furukawa-cho 322 Hazukashi
Fushimi-ku, Kyoto, 612-8486, Japan
Tel.: (81) 759317771
Fax: (81) 759317661
Semiconductor Machinery Mfr
S.I.C.: 3559
N.A.I.C.S.: 333242

Dainippon Screen Mfg. Co., Ltd. - Taga Plant (1)
Suwa 976-5 Shide Taga-cho
Inugami-gun, Shiga, 522-0314, Japan
Tel.: (81) 749488200
Fax: (81) 749482770
Semiconductor Device Mfr
S.I.C.: 3674
N.A.I.C.S.: 334413

Dainippon Screen Mfg. Co., Ltd. - Yasu Plant (1)
Mikami 2426-1
Yasu, Shiga, 520-2323, Japan
Tel.: (81) 775865111
Fax: (81) 775865011
Semiconductor Device Mfr
S.I.C.: 3674
N.A.I.C.S.: 334413

U.S. Subsidiaries:

Dainippon Screen Graphics (USA), LLC (1)
5110 Tollview Dr
Rolling Meadows, IL 60008
Tel.: (847) 870-7400
Fax: (847) 870-0149
Toll Free: (800) 372-7737
E-Mail: info@screenusa.com
Web Site: www.screenusa.com
Emp.: 45
Electronic Component & Semiconductor Component & Inspection Systems Developer, Mfr & Whslr
S.I.C.: 3674
N.A.I.C.S.: 334413
Sean Dawson *(Product Mgr)*

DNS Electronics, LLC (1)
820 Kifer Rd Ste B
Sunnyvale, CA 94086
Tel.: (408) 523-9140
Fax: (408) 523-9150
E-Mail: sales@dnse.com
Web Site: www.dnse.com
Semiconductor Products Sales, Marketing, Engineering & Service
S.I.C.: 7629
N.A.I.C.S.: 811219
Keith Horiguchi *(Pres)*
Terry Yanagi *(CFO & VP-Fin)*
James Beard *(Sr VP-Sls & Mktg & Field Ops)*

Silicon Light Machines Corp. (1)
3939 N 1st St
San Jose, CA 95134-1506
Tel.: (408) 240-4700
Fax: (408) 456-0708
E-Mail: sales@siliconlight.com
Web Site: www.siliconlight.com
Emp.: 30
Digital Display & Telecommunications Component Mfr
S.I.C.: 3679
N.A.I.C.S.: 334419
Toshio Hiroe *(Pres & CEO)*

Non-U.S. Subsidiaries:

Dainippon Screen (Australia) Pty. Ltd. (1)
Suit11 2 Edenpark Dr Macquaria Park
Sydney, 2113, Australia (100%)
Tel.: (61) 290163400
Fax: (61) 290163425
Web Site: www.screenaust.com.au
Emp.: 11
Sales & Maintenance of Graphic Arts Equipment
S.I.C.: 7629
N.A.I.C.S.: 811211
Peter Scott *(Mng Dir)*

Dainippon Screen (China) Ltd. (1)
Rm 2003 20th Fl Cable Tv Tower 9 Hoi Shing Rd
Tsuen Wan, New Territories, China (Hong Kong) (100%)
Tel.: (852) 29530038
Fax: (852) 27558683
E-Mail: techsup@screen.com.hk
Web Site: www.screen.com.hk
Emp.: 45
Sales & Maintenance of Electronics & Graphic Arts Equipment
S.I.C.: 7629
N.A.I.C.S.: 811211
Masefield Chan *(Gen Mgr)*

Dainippon Screen (Deutschland) GmbH (1)
Mundelheimer Weg 39
40472 Dusseldorf, Germany (100%)
Tel.: (49) 211472701
Fax: (49) 114727199
E-Mail: info@screen-dsd.de
Web Site: www.dainippon-screen.de
Emp.: 30
Sales & Maintenace of Electronics Equipment & Graphic Arts Equipment
S.I.C.: 7622
N.A.I.C.S.: 811211
Satoshi Kitano *(Gen Mgr)*

Dainippon Screen Electronics France Sarl (1)
Rousset Parc Club-Z I Num 205
13106 Rousset, France
Tel.: (33) 442290820
Fax: (33) 442200489
Emp.: 13
Semiconductor Device Mfr
S.I.C.: 3674
N.A.I.C.S.: 334413
Herve Busseire *(Gen Mgr)*

Dainippon Screen Electronics (Shanghai) Co., Ltd (1)
Unit I-J 5F No 1777 Century Ave
Pudong New Area, Shanghai, 200122, China
Tel.: (86) 2158313033
Fax: (86) 2158312722
Web Site: www.dnssh.com.cn
Emp.: 40
Semiconductor Device Mfr
S.I.C.: 3674
N.A.I.C.S.: 334413
Nishita Koi *(Gen Mgr)*

Dainippon Screen Electronics (Taiwan) Co., Ltd (1)
11 Kao-Tsui Rd
Hsin-chu, Taiwan
Tel.: (886) 35631066
Fax: (886) 35631077
Web Site: www.screen.com.tw
Emp.: 150
Printing Machinery Mfr
S.I.C.: 3555
N.A.I.C.S.: 333244
Stepen Huang *(Gen Mgr)*

Dainippon Screen (Korea) Co., Ltd. (1)
10th Fl Yonsei Bongnae B D 48 3 1G A Bongnae Dong Joong Gu, Seoul, 100161, Korea (South) (100%)
Tel.: (82) 27766786
Fax: (82) 27270876
E-Mail: takmitsu@dsk.co.kr
Web Site: www.screenkorea.com
Emp.: 150
Sales & Maintenance of Graphic Arts Equipment
S.I.C.: 7622
N.A.I.C.S.: 811211
Mipsuhashi Takeo *(Mgr)*

Dainippon Screen Mt (Hangzhou) Co., Ltd. (1)
7 Chunhui Road Qiaonan Block Xiaoshan Economic And Technology Development Zone, Hangzhou, Zhejiang, 311231, China
Tel.: (86) 57122861088
Fax: (86) 57122861098
Printing Machinery Mfr
S.I.C.: 3555
N.A.I.C.S.: 333244

Dainippon Screen (Nederland) B.V. (1)
Bouwerij 46
PO Box 9125
Amstelveen, 1180, Netherlands (100%)
Tel.: (31) 204567800
Fax: (31) 204567805
E-Mail: info@screeneurope.com
Web Site: www.screeneurope.com
Emp.: 25
Sales & Maintenance of Graphic Arts Equipment
S.I.C.: 7629
N.A.I.C.S.: 811211
Tim Taylor *(VP-Solution & Tech)*

Dainippon Screen Singapore Pte. Ltd. (1)
29 Kaki Bukit View
Kaki Bukit Techpark II, Singapore, 415963, Singapore (100%)
Tel.: (65) 67493833
Fax: (65) 67499010
E-Mail: gasales@screensg.com.sg
Web Site: www.screensg.com.sg
Sales Range: $75-99.9 Million
Emp.: 84
Sales & Maintenance of Electronics & Graphic Arts Equipment

Dainippon Screen Mfg. Co., Ltd.—(Continued)

S.I.C.: 7622
N.A.I.C.S.: 811211
Lewis Koh *(Gen Mgr)*

Dainippon Screen (Taiwan) Co., Ltd. (1)
4th Fl 126 1
Min Tsu West Rd, Taipei, 103, Taiwan (100%)
Tel.: (886) 225862711
Fax: (886) 225914367
E-Mail: tstw@ms4.hinet
Web Site: www.screen.co.jp/profile/index-E-5-AsiOce.html
Emp.: 11
Sales & Maintenance of Electronics & Graphic Arts Equipment
S.I.C.: 7622
N.A.I.C.S.: 811211
Eric Lee *(Mgr)*

Dainippon Screen (U.K.) Ltd. (1)
Michigan Dr Tongwell
Milton Keynes, MK158HT, United Kingdom (100%)
Tel.: (44) 908848500
Fax: (44) 908848501
E-Mail: service@screen.co.uk
Web Site: www.screeneurope.com
Emp.: 60
Retailer & Maintenance of Graphic Arts Equipment
S.I.C.: 7699
N.A.I.C.S.: 811211
Brian Filler *(Mng Dir)*

Dainippon Screen Unterstuetzungskasse GmbH (1)
Mundelheimer Weg 39
40472 Dusseldorf, Germany
Tel.: (49) 211472701
Fax: (49) 2114727199
Inkjet Printer Mfr
S.I.C.: 3555
N.A.I.C.S.: 333244
Satoshi Kitano *(Co-Mng Dir)*
Junji Otsuka *(Co-Mng Dir)*

DNS Feats (Taiwan) Co., Ltd (1)
2F-1 No 20 Taiyuan St
Jhubei, Hsinchu, 30288, Taiwan
Tel.: (886) 35526288
Fax: (886) 35526100
Printing Machinery Mfr
S.I.C.: 3555
N.A.I.C.S.: 333244

Inca Digital Printers Ltd (1)
511 Coldhams Lane
Cambridge, CB1 3JS, United Kingdom
Tel.: (44) 1223577800
Fax: (44) 1223577801
E-Mail: info@incadigital.com
Web Site: www.incadigital.com
Inkjet Printer Mfr
S.I.C.: 3555
N.A.I.C.S.: 333244

Screen Media Technology Ltd (1)
Unit East 1st Fl Bldg 4 No 799 Tian Shan West Road
Shanghai, 200335, China
Tel.: (86) 2131265122
Fax: (86) 2152182199
Emp.: 2
Inkjet Printer Mfr
S.I.C.: 3555
N.A.I.C.S.: 333244
Kojima Yasuhito *(Gen Mgr)*

DAINIPPON SUMITOMO PHARMA CO., LTD.

6-8 Doshomachi 2-chome
Chuo-ku, Osaka, 541-0045, Japan
Tel.: (81) 6 6203 5321
Fax: (81) 6 6202 6028
E-Mail: pr@ds-pharma.co.jp
Web Site: www.ds-pharma.co.jp
Year Founded: 1897
4506—(TKS)
Sls.: $3,824,964,000
Assets: $6,679,409,000
Liabilities: $2,837,681,000
Net Worth: $3,841,728,000
Earnings: $110,484,000
Emp.: 7,129
Fiscal Year-end: 03/31/13

Business Description:
Pharmaceuticals Preparation & Research & Development
S.I.C.: 2834
N.A.I.C.S.: 325412

Personnel:
Masayo Tada *(Pres & CEO)*
Patricia S. Andrews *(Chief Comml Officer & Exec VP-Boston Biomedical)*
Masaru Ishidahara *(Sr Exec Officer-Corp Comm, Personnel, Gen Affairs & Procurement)*
Chiang J. Li *(Exec Officer)*
Antony Loebel *(Exec Officer)*
Hiroshi Noguchi *(Sr Exec VP & Dir-Drug Res, Global R&D Office & Oncology Office)*
Makoto Hara *(Exec VP-Global Corp Mgmt, Strategy, Legal Affairs, Fin & Acctg)*

Board of Directors:
Makoto Hara
Masaru Ishidahara
Hiroshi Noguchi
Hiroshi Nomura
Tetsuya Oida
Yoshihiro Okada
Hidehiko Sato
Masayo Tada

Subsidiaries:

DS Pharma Animal Health Co., Ltd. (1)
1-5-51 Ebie Fukushima-ku
Osaka City, Osaka, Japan
Tel.: (81) 664548823
Fax: (81) 6 6454 8107
Veterinary Medicines Mfr
S.I.C.: 0741
N.A.I.C.S.: 541940

DS Pharma Biomedical Co., Ltd. (1)
33-94 Enoki-Cho
Suita, Osaka, 564-0053, Japan
Tel.: (81) 663375940
Fax: (81) 663375997
E-Mail: makoto-nishimura@bio.ds-pharma.co.jp
Web Site: www.dspbio.co.jp
Emp.: 90
In-Vitro Diagnostics & Research Materials Research & Development
S.I.C.: 2835
N.A.I.C.S.: 325413
Yukio Takano *(Pres)*

DSP Distribution Service Co., Ltd. (1)
1-5-51 Ebie Fukushima-ku
Osaka City, Osaka, Japan
Tel.: (81) 6 6453 3179
Fax: (81) 6 6453 3866
Pharmaceutical Products Mfr
S.I.C.: 2834
N.A.I.C.S.: 325412

DSP Gokyo Food & Chemical Co., LTD. (1)
1-5-51 Ebie Fukushima-ku
Osaka, Japan
Tel.: (81) 6 6202 7691
Fax: (81) 6 6202 7689
Web Site: www.dsp-gokyo-fc.co.jp
Food Additives & Fine Chemicals Mfr
S.I.C.: 2899
N.A.I.C.S.: 325199

Eiko Service Co., Ltd. (1)
1-33 Nozaki-cho
Kita-ku, Osaka, Japan
Tel.: (81) 6 6314 0795
Fax: (81) 6 6314 1613
Building Management Services
S.I.C.: 8748
N.A.I.C.S.: 541618

Marupi Lifetech Co., Ltd. (1)
103 Fushio-cho
Ikeda City, Osaka, Japan
Tel.: (81) 727530335
Fax: (81) 727542208
Clinical Pathology Testing Services
S.I.C.: 8069
N.A.I.C.S.: 622310

Nichiei Sangyo Co., Ltd. (1)
1-33 Nozaki-cho
Kita-ku, Osaka, Japan
Tel.: (81) 663143455
Insurance Services
S.I.C.: 6411
N.A.I.C.S.: 524298

NS Life Corporation (1)
28F Seiruka Tower 8-1 Akashi-cho
Osaka, Japan
Tel.: (81) 335427666
Fax: (81) 3 3542 7730
Pharmaceutical Product Sales
S.I.C.: 2834
N.A.I.C.S.: 325412

U.S. Subsidiary:

Sunovion Pharmaceuticals Inc. (1)
(Formerly Sepracor, Inc.)
84 Waterford Dr
Marlborough, MA 01752 DE
Tel.: (508) 481-6700
Fax: (508) 357-7490
E-Mail: info@sunovion.com
Web Site: www.sunovion.com
Sales Range: $1-4.9 Billion
Emp.: 2,400
Pharmaceutical & Biopharmaceutical Compounds Mfr
S.I.C.: 2834
N.A.I.C.S.: 325412
Hiroshi Nomura *(Vice Chm, Exec VP & CFO)*
Robert Gregorio *(Exec VP & Chief Admin Officer)*
Matthew D'Ambrosio *(Sr VP, Chief Compliance Officer & Chief Ethics Officer)*
Antony Loebel *(Exec VP & Chief Medical Officer)*
Richard Russell *(Exec VP & Chief Comml Officer)*
Albert P. Parker *(Exec VP, Gen Counsel & Sec)*
Yoshiharu Ikeda *(Exec VP-Corp Strategy)*

Non-U.S. Subsidiary:

Sepracor Canada (Nova Scotia) Ltd. (2)
24 Ivey Lane
PO Box 2880
Windsor, NS, B0 2T0, Canada Ca (100%)
Tel.: (902) 798-4100
Fax: (902) 798-4101
Emp.: 33
Pharmaceutical Preparation Mfr
S.I.C.: 2834
N.A.I.C.S.: 325412
Jerry Aguinaga *(Sr Dir-State)*

Non-U.S. Subsidiaries:

Dainippon Sumitomo Pharma Europe Ltd. (1)
First Fl Southside
97-105 Victoria St, London, SW1E 6QT, United Kingdom
Tel.: (44) 2078212840
Fax: (44) 2078212841
E-Mail: support@dsp-e.com
Web Site: www.dsp-e.com
Emp.: 20
Pharmaceuticals Preparation & Research & Development
S.I.C.: 2834
N.A.I.C.S.: 325412

Sumitomo Pharmaceuticals(Suzhou)Co., Ltd. (1)
Suchun Industrial Estate 22
No 428 Xinglong Street, Suzhou, 215126, China
Tel.: (86) 51262837896
Fax: (86) 51262652606
Pharmaceuticals Preparation & Research & Development
S.I.C.: 2834
N.A.I.C.S.: 325412

DAIO PAPER CORPORATION

2-60 Mishimakamiya-chou
Shikoku Chuo-Ku, Tokyo, 799-0402, Japan
Tel.: (81) 896239006
Fax: (81) 896243860
Web Site: www.daio-paper.co.jp
Year Founded: 1943
3880—(TKS)
Sales Range: $25-49.9 Billion
Emp.: 8,000

Business Description:
Paper, Paperboard, Stationery & Office Supplies Mfr
S.I.C.: 2621
N.A.I.C.S.: 322121

Personnel:
Mototaka Ikawa *(Pres)*

DAIOS PLASTICS S.A

12th klm Veroia
Naousa, 59200, Greece
Tel.: (30) 23320 42 412
Fax: (30) 23320 42 600
E-Mail: info@daiosplastics.com
Web Site: www.daios.gr
Year Founded: 1977
DAIOS—(ATH)
Emp.: 301

Business Description:
Polyethylene Film Mfr
S.I.C.: 3083
N.A.I.C.S.: 326130

Personnel:
Asterios D. Daios *(Founder, Pres & Gen Dir)*
Dimitrios A. Daios *(Member-Exec Bd)*
Stergios N. Georgalis *(Member-Exec Bd)*
Konstantinos N. Koukoutzos *(Member-Exec Bd)*

DAIRY CREST GROUP PLC

Claygate House Littleworth Road
Esher, Surrey, KT10 9PN, United Kingdom
Tel.: (44) 1372472200
Fax: (44) 01372472333
E-Mail: generalenquiries@dairycrest.co.uk
Web Site: www.dairycrest.co.uk
DCG—(LSE OTC)
Rev.: $2,181,947,064
Assets: $1,554,811,005
Liabilities: $1,069,337,259
Net Worth: $485,473,746
Earnings: $86,071,305
Emp.: 5,283
Fiscal Year-end: 03/31/13

Business Description:
Processor of Milk & Other Dairy Products
S.I.C.: 2026
N.A.I.C.S.: 311511

Personnel:
Mark Allen *(CEO)*
Martyn Wilks *(Exec Mng Dir)*
Robin Miller *(Gen Counsel & Sec)*

Board of Directors:
Anthony Fry
Stephen Alexander
Mark Allen
Tom Atherton
Andrew C. P. Carr-Locke
Sue Farr
Richard Macdonald
Martyn Wilks

Subsidiary:

Dairy Crest Limited (1)
Claygate House
Littleworth Rd, Esher, KT109PN, United Kingdom (100%)
Tel.: (44) 1372472200
Fax: (44) 1372472333
Web Site: www.dairycrest.co.uk/our-business/our-locations/head-office/claygate-house.aspx
Emp.: 300
Fluid Milk Mfr

S.I.C.: 2026
N.A.I.C.S.: 311511
Mark Allen *(CEO)*

Subsidiaries:

Fayrefield Foodtec Limited (2)
Gateway Crewe Gates Industrial Estate
Crewe, CW1 6XA, United Kingdom
Tel.: (44) 1270 530750
Fax: (44) 1270 580605
E-Mail: enquiries@fayrefieldfoodtec.com
Web Site: www.fayrefieldfoodtec.com
Food Ingredient Mfr
S.I.C.: 2099
N.A.I.C.S.: 311999

Philpot Dairy Products Limited (2)
Philpot House
Rayleigh, Essex, SS6 7HH, United Kingdom (100%)
Tel.: (44) 1268775522
Fax: (44) 1268747666
E-Mail: info@philpots.co.uk
Web Site: www.philpots.co.uk
Emp.: 5
Dairy Product Whslr
S.I.C.: 5143
N.A.I.C.S.: 424430
Claud Bilbao *(Mng Dir)*

DAIRYGOLD CO-OPERATIVE SOCIETY LIMITED

Clonmel Road
Mitchellstown, Co Cork, Ireland
Tel.: (353) 2524411
Telex: 26033
Fax: (353) 2544135
E-Mail: info@dairygold.ie
Web Site: www.dairygold.ie
Sls.: $984,363,928
Assets: $563,773,304
Liabilities: $225,526,552
Net Worth: $338,246,751
Earnings: $18,515,222
Emp.: 1,099
Fiscal Year-end: 12/31/12

Business Description:
Dairy Products Mfr
S.I.C.: 2023
N.A.I.C.S.: 311514

Personnel:
Bertie O'Leary *(Chm)*
James Lynch *(Vice Chm)*
Jim Woulfe *(CEO)*
Michael Harte *(CFO)*
Eamonn Looney *(Sec)*

Board of Directors:
Bertie O'Leary
Donal Buckley
Thomas Feeney
Dan Flinter
Liam Foley
Richard Hinchion
Edmund Lynch
James Lynch
John Malone
John F. McKeogh
John F. O'Gorman
Patrick O'Keeffe

Subsidiaries:

Dairygold Finance Limited (1)
Clon mel rd
Mitchelstown, Cork, Ireland (100%)
Tel.: (353) 2524411
Fax: (353) 2544189
E-Mail: eugene.connor@dairygold.ie
Web Site: www.dairygold.com
Emp.: 300
Cheese Mfr
S.I.C.: 2022
N.A.I.C.S.: 311513
Eugene O. Connor *(Mgr-Production)*

Dairygold Food Ingredients Limited (1)
Clonmel Rd
Mitchelstown, Cork, Ireland (100%)
Tel.: (353) 2524411
Fax: (353) 2541112
Web Site: www.dairygold.ie/dairygold/dfi/foodInfo_05ireland.html
Emp.: 3,400
Cheese Mfr
S.I.C.: 2022
N.A.I.C.S.: 311513
Blanca Camarasa *(Mgr-Bus Dev-Cheese Solutions)*

Dairygold Trading Limited (1)
Dairygold Trading
Mallow, Ireland (100%)
Tel.: (353) 2221204
Fax: (353) 2221205
Nondurable Goods Whslr
S.I.C.: 5199
N.A.I.C.S.: 424990

Joint Venture:

Co-Operative Animal Health Limited (1)
Indust Est
Tullow, Carlow, Ireland IE
Tel.: (353) 599151251
Fax: (353) 599151856
E-Mail: info@cahl.ie
Web Site: www.cahl.ie
Emp.: 100
Animal Health Products Whlsr; Owned 50% by Glanbia plc & 50% by Dairygold Co-op Society Limited
S.I.C.: 2048
N.A.I.C.S.: 311119
Donald O'Sullivan *(Mng Dir)*
Martin Gillespie *(CFO)*

Non-U.S. Subsidiaries:

Dairygold Food Ingredients (UK) Limited (1)
Lancaster Fields
Crewe Gates Farm, Crewe, CW16FU, United Kingdom (100%)
Tel.: (44) 1270589136
Fax: (44) 1270530726
Emp.: 150
Cheese Mfr
S.I.C.: 2022
N.A.I.C.S.: 311513

Dan Dairies (UK) Limited (1)
19 Astley Way
Swillington, Leeds, West Yorkshire, LS26 8XT, United Kingdom (100%)
Tel.: (44) 1132877788
Fax: (44) 1132877700
E-Mail: info@dairygold.co.uk
Web Site: www.dairygold.co.uk
Emp.: 50
Dairy Product Whslr
S.I.C.: 5143
N.A.I.C.S.: 424430
Simon Sharpe *(Plant Mgr)*

DAIRYTOWN PRODUCTS LIMITED

49 Milk Board Road
Sussex, NB, Canada E4E 5L2
Tel.: (506) 432-1950
Fax: (506) 432-1940
Toll Free: (800) 561-5598
E-Mail: admin@dairytown.com
Web Site: www.dairytown.ca
Rev.: $37,678,660
Emp.: 88

Business Description:
Dairy Products & Butter Mfr
S.I.C.: 2021
N.A.I.C.S.: 311512

Personnel:
Jim Walker *(Chm)*
Wietze Dijkstra *(Second Vice Chm)*
Peter Kaye *(Vice Chm)*
Derek Roberts *(CEO & Gen Mgr)*
Carol Cyr *(Treas)*
Derek Robinson *(Sec)*

Board of Directors:
Jim Walker
Vernon Black
Carol Cyr
Wietze Dijkstra
Leon Gaudet
Alex Henderson
Peter Kaye
Derek Robinson
John Schuttenbeld

THE DAISAN BANK, LTD.

510 Kyo-machi
Matsuzaka, Mie, 515-8530, Japan
Tel.: (81) 598231111
Fax: (81) 598216120
E-Mail: kokusai@daisanbank.co.jp
Web Site: www.daisanbank.co.jp
Year Founded: 1927
8529—(NGO TKS)
Sales Range: $500-549.9 Million
Emp.: 1,600

Business Description:
Banking Services
S.I.C.: 6029
N.A.I.C.S.: 522110

Personnel:
Kenzo Tanikawa *(Chm)*
Hiroshi Iwama *(Pres)*

DAISEKI CO. LTD.

1 86 Funami cho Minato ku
Nagoya, Aichi, 4558505, Japan
Tel.: (81) 526116322
Fax: (81) 526124382
E-Mail: soumu@daiseki.co.jp
Web Site: www.daiseki.co.jp
9793—(TKS)
Sls.: $396,143,000
Assets: $654,148,000
Liabilities: $94,963,000
Net Worth: $559,185,000
Earnings: $33,264,000
Emp.: 770
Fiscal Year-end: 02/28/13

Business Description:
Environmental Service & Petroleum Mfr
S.I.C.: 2911
N.A.I.C.S.: 324110

Personnel:
Hiroyuki Ito *(Pres)*
Michio Fukushima *(Sr Mng Dir)*
Tetsuya Yamamoto *(Sr Mng Dir)*
Kouji Amano *(Mng Dir)*
Kazumi Hirabayashi *(Mng Dir)*
Yasuo Ito *(Mng Dir)*
Hideki Hashira *(Exec VP)*

Board of Directors:
Kouji Amano
Katsuaki Egoshi
Michio Fukushima
Hideki Hashira
Kazumi Hirabayashi
Toshiyasu Isaka
Hiroyuki Ito
Yasuo Ito
Yoshihiro Miyachi
Tetsuya Yamamoto

Subsidiaries:

Daiseki MCR Co., Ltd. (1)
38-25 Hiraide-Kogyo Danchi
Utsunomiya, Tochigi, 321-0905, Japan
Tel.: (81) 286642228
Fax: (81) 286642566
E-Mail: info@daiseki-mcr.com
Web Site: www.daiseki-mcr.com
Emp.: 62
Recyclable Waste Materials Collection & Industrial Waste Processing Services
S.I.C.: 4212
N.A.I.C.S.: 562111
Okada Atsushi *(Pres)*
Ishido Masahiro *(Mng Dir)*
Yamaga Takayuki *(Mng Dir)*

Hokuriku Daiseki Co., Ltd. (1)
302-2 Utsugicho-Higashi
Kanazawa, Ishikawa, 920-0377, Japan
Tel.: (81) 762496363
Fax: (81) 762499337
E-Mail: hokuriku@daiseki.co.jp
Web Site: www.daiseki.co.jp/english/profile/group.html
Emp.: 11
Lubricating Oil Refining Services & Petroleum Products Sales
S.I.C.: 2911
N.A.I.C.S.: 324110

Units:

Daiseki Co. Ltd. - Chiba Unit (1)
23-8 Minamisode
Sodegaura, Chiba, Japan
Tel.: (81) 438628798
Fax: (81) 438640019
E-Mail: chiba@daiseki.co.jp
Industrial Waste & Water Treatment Services
S.I.C.: 4953
N.A.I.C.S.: 562211

Daiseki Co. Ltd. - Hokuriku Unit (1)
631-1 Sougoshinmachi
Hakusan, Ishikawa, 924-0028, Japan
Tel.: (81) 762756585
Fax: (81) 762756791
E-Mail: hokuriku@daiseki.co.jp
Industrial Waste Treatment Services
S.I.C.: 4952
N.A.I.C.S.: 221320
Hiroyuki Ito *(Pres)*

Daiseki Co. Ltd. - Kansai Unit (1)
21-6 Minamifutami Futamicho
Akashi, Hyogo, Japan
Tel.: (81) 789491180
Fax: (81) 789491315
E-Mail: kansai@daiseki.co.jp
Web Site: www.daiseki.co.jp
Emp.: 63
Industrial Wastes Treatment Services
S.I.C.: 4952
N.A.I.C.S.: 221320
Hiroyuki Ito *(Pres)*

Daiseki Co. Ltd. - Kyushu Unit (1)
13-3 Minamifutajima 4-chome
Wakamatsuku, Kitakyushu, Kyushu, Japan
Tel.: (81) 937012016
Fax: (81) 937915219
E-Mail: kyushu@daiseki.co.jp
Industrial Waste Treatment Services
S.I.C.: 4953
N.A.I.C.S.: 562219

Daiseki Co. Ltd. - Nagoya Unit (1)
1-86 Funamicho Minato ku
Nagoya, Aichi, 455-8505, Japan
Tel.: (81) 526116321
Fax: (81) 526110160
E-Mail: recycle@daiseki.co.jp
Web Site: www.daiseki.co.jp
Emp.: 600
Industrial Wastes Treatment Services
S.I.C.: 4952
N.A.I.C.S.: 221320
Hiroyuki Ito *(Pres)*

Plants:

Daiseki Co. Ltd.- Kanto First Plant (1)
14-10 Sakaemachi
Sano, Tochigi, Japan
Tel.: (81) 283248006
Fax: (81) 526110160
E-Mail: kankyo@daiseki.co.jp
Web Site: www.daiseki.co.jp/english/profile/divisions/kanto.html
Emp.: 571
Industrial Wastes Treatment Services
S.I.C.: 4953
N.A.I.C.S.: 562219
Hiroyuki Itou *(Pres)*

Daiseki Co. Ltd. - Kanto Second Plant (1)
3-4 Sakaemachi
Sano, Tochigi, Japan 327-0816
Tel.: (81) 283 22 8862
Web Site: www.daiseki.co.jp/english/profile/divisions/kanto.html
Industrial Wastes Treatment Services
S.I.C.: 4953
N.A.I.C.S.: 562211

Daiseki Co. Ltd. - Kanto Third Plant (1)
570-1 Nishiuracho
Sano, Tochigi, Japan
Tel.: (81) 283248006
Fax: (81) 283227408

Daiseki Co. Ltd.—(Continued)

E-Mail: kanto@daiseki.co.jp
Web Site: www.daiseki.co.jp/english/profile/divisions/kanto.html
Emp.: 500
Industrial Wastes Treatment Services
S.I.C.: 4953
N.A.I.C.S.: 562219
Hiroyuki Ito *(Pres)*

THE DAISHI BANK, LTD.

1071-1 Higashiborimae-dori 7 bancho
Chuo-ku, Niigata, 950-8746, Japan
Tel.: (81) 252224111
Fax: (81) 252252331
Web Site: www.daishi-bank.co.jp
Year Founded: 1873
8324—(TKS)
Rev.: $1,048,366,000
Assets: $53,854,394,000
Liabilities: $50,764,494,000
Net Worth: $3,089,900,000
Earnings: $118,844,000
Fiscal Year-end: 03/31/13

Business Description:
Banking Services
S.I.C.: 6029
N.A.I.C.S.: 522110

Personnel:
Fujio Namiki *(Pres)*
Yoshihito Saito *(Deputy Pres)*
Kousuke Sasaki *(Sr Mng Dir)*
Satoshi Hasegawa *(Mng Dir)*
Seiya Kiguchi *(Mng Dir)*
Akira Sakagami *(Mng Dir)*
Minoru Soyama *(Mng Dir)*

Board of Directors:
Satoshi Hasegawa
Seiya Kiguchi
Akira Kiriyama
Fujio Namiki
Yoshihito Saito
Akira Sakagami
Kousuke Sasaki
Minoru Soyama

Subsidiaries:

The Daishi Business Service Co., Ltd. (1)
9-15 Shichikuyama 3-chome
Chuo-ku, Niigata, 950 0914, Japan (100%)
Tel.: (81) 252857221
Fax: (81) 252857244
Custody & Management of Housing Loan Documents; Assessment of Secured Property
S.I.C.: 6099
N.A.I.C.S.: 523991

The Daishi Cash Business Co., Ltd. (1)
1-20 Horinouchi Minami 3-chome
Niigata, 950 0982, Japan JP (100%)
Tel.: (81) 252818181
Fax: (81) 252818191
Emp.: 100
Cash Settlements & Processing Services
S.I.C.: 6099
N.A.I.C.S.: 522320

The Daishi Staff Service Co., Ltd. (1)
224-1 Honcho-dori 5-bancho
Chuo-ku, Niigata, 951 8067, Japan JP (100%)
Tel.: (81) 252281411
Fax: (81) 252281441
Emp.: 1,000
Temporary Staff for Banking Businesses
S.I.C.: 7363
N.A.I.C.S.: 561320

Affiliates:

The Daishi Computer Service Co., Ltd. (1)
1-17 Abumi 1-chome
Niigata, 950-0913, Japan (5%)
Tel.: (81) 252224111
Computer-Related Services
S.I.C.: 7371
N.A.I.C.S.: 541511

The Daishi DC Card Co., Ltd. (1)
1245 Kamiokawamae-dori 8-Bancho
Chuo-ku, Niigata, 950 8068, Japan (5%)
Tel.: (81) 252254440
Fax: (81) 252254450
Emp.: 20
Credit Card Services
S.I.C.: 6141
N.A.I.C.S.: 522210

The Daishi Guaranty Co., Ltd. (1)
224-1 Honcho-dori 5-Bancho
Chuo-ku, Niigata, 951 8067, Japan (5%)
Tel.: (81) 252224111
Fax: (81) 252256388
Web Site: www.daishibank.co.jp
Credit Guarantee Business
S.I.C.: 6159
N.A.I.C.S.: 522298

The Daishi JCB Card Co., Ltd. (1)
1245 Kamiokawamae-dori 8-bancho
Chuo-ku, Niigata, 950 8068, Japan (5%)
Tel.: (81) 252224111
Credit Card & Credit Guaranty Businesses
S.I.C.: 6141
N.A.I.C.S.: 522210

The Daishi Lease Co., Ltd. (1)
1071-1 Higashiborimae dori 7 Bancho
Chuo-ku
Niigata, 950 8746, Japan (5%)
Tel.: (81) 252224111
Fax: (81) 252252331
General Leasing Business
S.I.C.: 6513
N.A.I.C.S.: 531110

DAISHINKU CORP.

1389 Shinzaike Hiraoka-cho
Kakogawa
Hyogo, 675-0194, Japan
Tel.: (81) 794263211
Fax: (81) 794268618
E-Mail: kouhou602@mail.kds.info
Web Site: www.kds.info
Year Founded: 1959
6962—(TKS)
Sls.: $361,405,000
Assets: $648,780,000
Liabilities: $269,027,000
Net Worth: $379,753,000
Earnings: $11,968,000
Emp.: 748
Fiscal Year-end: 03/31/13

Business Description:
Electronic Components & Equipment Mfr & Sales
S.I.C.: 3679
N.A.I.C.S.: 334419

Personnel:
Sohei Hasegawa *(Pres)*
Norio Doi *(Co-Mng Dir)*
Hideyuki Tanaka *(Co-Mng Dir)*
Hozumi Nakata *(Exec VP)*

Board of Directors:
Norio Doi
Sohei Hasegawa
Takatoshi Ishii
Hiroshi Maeda
Junichi Morikawa
Toshiki Morimoto
Hozumi Nakata
Kenji Nakazawa
Hideyuki Tanaka

Divisions:

Daishinku Corp. - Tokushima Production Division (1)
1939-11 Ushinoshima Kamojima-cho
Yoshinogawa, Tokushima, 776-0001, Japan
Tel.: (81) 883 24 5161
Fax: (81) 883 24 8818
Synthetic Quartz Crystals Mfr
S.I.C.: 3679
N.A.I.C.S.: 334419

Daishinku Corp. - Tottori Production Division (1)
7-3-21 Wakabadai Minami
Tottori, 689-1112, Japan
Tel.: (81) 857524501
Fax: (81) 857524503
Web Site: www.kds.info/html/company_info/service_network/jpn/index_en.htm
Quartz Crystals Mfr
S.I.C.: 3679
N.A.I.C.S.: 334419

Subsidiary:

Kyushu Daishinku Corp (1)
20013-2 Kawaminami Kawaminami-cho
Koyu, Miyazaki, 889-1301, Japan
Tel.: (81) 983 47 0345
Fax: (81) 983 27 4774
Web Site: www.kds.info/html/company_info/service_network/jpn/index_en.htm
Quartz Crystal Mfr
S.I.C.: 3679
N.A.I.C.S.: 334419

Plants:

Daishinku Corp. - Kanzaki Plant (1)
629 Sawa Ichikawa-cho
Kanzaki, Hyogo, 679-23362336, Japan
Tel.: (81) 790281241
Fax: (81) 790 28 1709
Synthetic Quartz Crystals Mfr
S.I.C.: 3679
N.A.I.C.S.: 334419

Daishinku Corp. - Nishiwaki Plant (1)
2082 Maesaka Kurodasho-cho
Nishiwaki, Hyogo, 679-0303, Japan
Tel.: (81) 795282491
Fax: (81) 795 28 4660
Synthetic Quartz Crystals Mfr
S.I.C.: 3679
N.A.I.C.S.: 334419

U.S. Subsidiary:

DAISHINKU (AMERICA) CORP (1)
17835 Newhope St Ste B
Fountain Valley, CA 92708
Tel.: (714) 641-2600
Fax: (714) 641-2606
E-Mail: kdssna@kdsamerica.com
Web Site: www.kds.info/html/company_info/service_network/overseas/index_en.htm
Quartz Crystals Mfr
S.I.C.: 3679
N.A.I.C.S.: 334419
Yoko Kermane *(Gen Mgr)*

Non-U.S. Subsidiaries:

Daishinku (Deutschland) GmbH (1)
Wiesenstrasse 70A2
40549 Dusseldorf, Germany
Tel.: (49) 2115065300
Fax: (49) 211596054
E-Mail: yoshitaka.tokuda@kds.jis.de
Web Site: www.kds.info/html/company_info/service_network/overseas/index_en.htm#e
Emp.: 12
Other Electronic & Precision Equipment Repair & Maintenance
S.I.C.: 7629
N.A.I.C.S.: 811219
Yoshitaka Tokuda *(Mng Dir)*

Daishinku (HK) Ltd (1)
Rm 3501-6 35th Floor
Millennium City 1 Tong Road, Kowloon, China (Hong Kong)
Tel.: (852) 23302541
Fax: (852) 27656673
E-Mail: chinasales220@mail.kds.info
Web Site: www.kds.info
Other Electronic Parts & Equipment Whslr
S.I.C.: 5065
N.A.I.C.S.: 423690
Rock Tsang Kwok Ming *(Chm & CEO)*

Daishinku (Singapore) Pte. Ltd (1)
12 Little Rd 03-01
Lian Cheong Industrial Bldg, 536986
Singapore, Singapore
Tel.: (65) 62867646
Fax: (65) 63825394
E-Mail: aseansales419@mail.kds.info
Web Site: www.kds.info
Emp.: 10
Other Electronic Component Mfr
S.I.C.: 3679
N.A.I.C.S.: 334419
Masatoshi Kato *(Mng Dir)*

DAISHINKU (THAILAND) CO., LTD. (1)
161 Nantawan Building 10th Floor
Ratchadamri Road Lumpinee Pathumwan
Bangkok, 10330, Thailand
Tel.: (66) 26518130
Fax: (66) 2 651 8168
Web Site: www.kds.info/html/company_info/service_network/overseas/index_en.htm
Quartz Crystals Mfr
S.I.C.: 3679
N.A.I.C.S.: 334419

Harmony Electronics Corp (1)
2nd Floor 409 Tiding Blvd
Sec 2 Neihu, Taipei, Taiwan
Tel.: (886) 226588883
Fax: (886) 226588683
E-Mail: kenliu@hele.com.tw
Web Site: www.hele.com.tw
Emp.: 32
Other Electronic Component Mfr
S.I.C.: 3679
N.A.I.C.S.: 334419
Yang Juisyang *(Gen Mgr)*

Harmony Electronics (Thailand) Co Ltd (1)
66 Moo 5 Kaongu- Beokprai Road
T. Beokprai A. Banpong, 70110 Ratchaburi, Thailand
Tel.: (66) 32344467
Fax: (66) 32200742
E-Mail: qa@harmony.co.th
Web Site: www.hele.com.tw
Emp.: 450
Quartz Frequency Component Mfr
S.I.C.: 3679
N.A.I.C.S.: 334419
Yan Yan *(Mng Dir)*

Pt. Kds Indonesia (1)
Blok O-20 O-21
Kawasan Berikat MM2100 Industr, 17520
Bekasi, Jawa Barat, Indonesia
Tel.: (62) 218980120
Fax: (62) 218980045
Other Electronic Parts & Equipment Merchant Whslr
S.I.C.: 5065
N.A.I.C.S.: 423690

Shanghai Daishinku International Trading Co., Ltd (1)
906 1# No. 641 Tianshan Road
Shanghai, 200336, China
Tel.: (86) 2162368701
Fax: (86) 2162368707
E-Mail: s-inoue@kdssh.com.cn
Web Site: www.kds.info/html/company_info/service_network/overseas/index_en.htm
Emp.: 60
Other Electronic Parts & Equipment Merchant Whslr
S.I.C.: 5065
N.A.I.C.S.: 423690

DAISHO CO., LTD.

1-17-3 Kamezawa
Sumida-ku, Tokyo, 130-0014, Japan
Tel.: (81) 3 3626 9321
Web Site: www.daisho.co.jp
Year Founded: 1966
2816—(TKS)

Business Description:
Food Product Mfr & Whslr
S.I.C.: 2035
N.A.I.C.S.: 311941

Personnel:
Yosuke Matsumoto *(Pres & CEO)*

DAISO CO., LTD.

12-18 Awaza 1-chome Nishi-ku
Osaka, 550-0011, Japan
Tel.: (81) 661101560
Fax: (81) 661101603
E-Mail: kanri@daiso.co.jp
Web Site: www.daiso.co.jp
Year Founded: 1915
4046—(TKS)
Sls.: $914,639,000
Assets: $844,844,000
Liabilities: $424,138,000
Net Worth: $420,706,000

Earnings: $31,768,000
Emp.: 798
Fiscal Year-end: 03/31/13
Business Description:
Soda Products, Inorganic Chemical Products, Organic Chemical Products, Synthetic Resins, Fabricated Resin Products, Pharmaceuticals & Other Chemicals Producer, Processor & Sales
S.I.C.: 2819
N.A.I.C.S.: 325180
Personnel:
Tamotsu Sato *(CEO)*
Tetsuo Abe *(Exec Officer)*
Ichiro Baba *(Exec Officer)*
Yoshiro Furukawa *(Exec Officer)*
Tadashi Hirai *(Exec Officer)*
Noboru Hori *(Exec Officer)*
Junichi Kadoya *(Exec Officer)*
Yoshinori Kato *(Exec Officer)*
Ryutaro Matsumoto *(Exec Officer)*
Yujiro Mori *(Exec Officer)*
Yoshiaki Nakashima *(Exec Officer)*
Mltsunobu Nishimoto *(Exec Officer)*
Tetsuyuki Saika *(Exec Officer)*
Michirou Shibano *(Mng Exec Officer)*
Tsuneyuki Takeo *(Exec Officer)*
Hiroyuki Taki *(Exec OFficer)*
Kenshi Terada *(Exec Officer)*
Munetomo Torii *(Exec Officer)*
Koichi Yamashita *(Sr Mng Exec Officer)*
Board of Directors:
Tamotsu Sato
Michirou Shibano
Hiroyuki Taki
Munetomo Torii
Koichi Yamashita

Subsidiaries:

Daiso Chemical Co., Ltd. (1)
Nishi-ku
Osaka, 550-0011, Japan
Tel.: (81) 665393610
Fax: (81) 665393712
E-Mail: sales@daiso-chem.co.jp
Web Site: www.daiso-chem.co.jp
Emp.: 70
Chemicals Products Trading Services
S.I.C.: 5169
N.A.I.C.S.: 424690
Noboru Hori *(Pres)*

Non-U.S. Subsidiary:

Taiwan Daiso Chemical Co., Ltd. (2)
No 96 Section 2 Chung-Shan Rd N
Taipei, Taiwan
Tel.: (886) 225111186
Fax: (886) 225210712
E-Mail: mkyu@daiso-chem.co.jp
Web Site: www.daiso-chem.co.jp/eng/com.html
Emp.: 5
Chemical Products Trading Services
S.I.C.: 5169
N.A.I.C.S.: 424690
Oktsu Seiji *(Mgr)*

DAISO Engineering Co., Ltd. (1)
12-18 Awaza 1-chome
Nishi-ku, Osaka, 5500011, Japan
Tel.: (81) 661101632
Fax: (81) 661101633
Web Site: www.daiso-eng.co.jp
Chemical Plants Design Services
S.I.C.: 1629
N.A.I.C.S.: 236210

Subsidiary:

Japan Material Recycle System (JMR) Co., Ltd. (2)
9-2 Otakasu-cho
Amagasaki, 6600842 Hyogo, Japan
Tel.: (81) 664090252
Fax: (81) 664090195
Web Site: www.jmrsys.co.jp
Emp.: 15
Mercury Lamp Recycling Services
S.I.C.: 4953
N.A.I.C.S.: 562920
Kieamura Takeo *(Gen Mgr)*

DS Logistics Co., Ltd. (1)
11 Otakasu-cho
Amagasaki, 660 0842 Hyogo, Japan
Tel.: (81) 664091588
Fax: (81) 664091573
E-Mail: hshimura@daiso-co.jp
Web Site: www.daiso-co.com
Emp.: 20
Logistics Services
S.I.C.: 4412
N.A.I.C.S.: 483111
Tuneki Takeo *(Mgr)*

DS WELLFOODS CO.,LTD. (1)
12-18 Awaza 1-chome
Nishi-ku, 5500011 Osaka, Japan
Tel.: (81) 661101644
Fax: (81) 661101644
E-Mail: wellfood@daiso.co.jp
Web Site: www.daiso-co.com
Emp.: 75
Health Food Mfr
S.I.C.: 2099
N.A.I.C.S.: 311999
Kenichi Endo *(Pres)*

SANYO FINE CO.,LTD. (1)
12-18 Awaza 1-chome
Nishi-ku, 5500011 Osaka, Japan
Tel.: (81) 661101527
Fax: (81) 661101644
E-Mail: info@sanyofine.co.jp
Web Site: www.sanyofine.co.jp
Emp.: 66
Pharmaceutical Ingredients Mfr
S.I.C.: 2834
N.A.I.C.S.: 325412
Osamu Uede *(Pres)*
Yoshiro Furukawa *(Mng Dir)*
Yuichiro Mori *(Mng Dir)*

U.S. Subsidiary:

DAISO Fine Chem USA,Inc. (1)
275 Saratoga Ave Ste 102
Santa Clara, CA 95050-6664
Tel.: (408) 855-8789
Fax: (408) 855-8784
E-Mail: silica@daiso.us
Web Site: www.daiso-co.com
Emp.: 3
Silica Gel Mfr
S.I.C.: 2819
N.A.I.C.S.: 325180

Non-U.S. Subsidiary:

DAISO Fine Chem GmbH (1)
Immermannstrasse 13
40210 Dusseldorf, Germany
Tel.: (49) 21183025168
Fax: (49) 21183025213
E-Mail: silica@daiso.de
Web Site: www.daiso-co.com
Emp.: 1
Silica Gel Mfr
S.I.C.: 2819
N.A.I.C.S.: 325180
Tomoyuki Kitano *(Mgr)*

DAISY GROUP PLC

Daisy House Lindred Road Business Park
Nelson, Lancs, BB9 5SR, United Kingdom
Tel.: (44) 845 450 4520
Fax: (44) 845 450 4521
E-Mail: ir@daisygroupplc.com
Web Site: www.daisygroupplc.com
DAY—(AIM)
Rev.: $555,095,166
Assets: $663,567,121
Liabilities: $436,250,435
Net Worth: $227,316,685
Earnings: ($25,990,376)
Emp.: 1,391
Fiscal Year-end: 03/31/13
Business Description:
Wireless Communications
S.I.C.: 4812
N.A.I.C.S.: 517210
Personnel:
Peter Dubens *(Chm)*
Matthew Riley *(CEO & Member-Exec Bd)*
Steve Smith *(CFO & Member-Exec Bd)*
Nathan Marke *(CTO)*
David McGlennon *(Member-Exec Bd, Gen Counsel & Sec)*
Board of Directors:
Peter Dubens
Laurence Charles Neil Blackall
Christina Kennedy
Ian McKenzie
Matthew Riley
Steve Smith
Legal Counsel:
Eversheds
Eversheds House 70 Great Bridgewater Street
Manchester, United Kingdom

Addleshaw Goddard LLP
100 Barbirolli Square
Manchester, United Kingdom

Subsidiaries:

Servassure Ltd (1)
Unit 4 Cramond Park
Lovet Road, Harlow, Essex, CM19 5TF, United Kingdom
Tel.: (44) 8700843030
Fax: (44) 1279636491
E-Mail: enquiries@servassure.co.uk
Web Site: www.servassure.co.uk
Emp.: 50
Internet Publishing & Broadcasting
S.I.C.: 2741
N.A.I.C.S.: 519130
Steve Walsh-Hill *(Mng Dir)*

DAISY WHOLESALE LIMITED

4th Floor Eastleigh House
Upper Market Street, Eastleigh, Hants, SO50 9RD, United Kingdom
Tel.: (44) 3301001233
E-Mail: sales@murphx.com
Web Site: www.daisywholesale.com
Year Founded: 2001
Sales Range: $50-74.9 Million
Emp.: 49
Business Description:
Telecommunications Connectivity & Hosting Solutions
S.I.C.: 4899
N.A.I.C.S.: 517919
Personnel:
Richard Jay *(CEO)*

DAITO ELECTRON CO., LTD.

6-11 Miyahara 4-chome
Osaka, Yodogawa-ku, 532-0003, Japan
Tel.: (81) 663995041
Fax: (81) 663996041
Web Site: www.daitron.co.jp
Year Founded: 1952
7609—(TKS)
Sls.: $396,741,851
Assets: $259,849,579
Liabilities: $133,072,203
Net Worth: $126,777,376
Earnings: $2,010,371
Emp.: 384
Fiscal Year-end: 12/31/12
Business Description:
Electronic Components & Semiconductor Equipment Mfr, Sales, Importer & Exporter
S.I.C.: 3674
N.A.I.C.S.: 334413
Personnel:
Kenji Kontani *(Chm & CEO)*
Isayuki Mae *(Pres)*
Tomio Nishida *(Mng Dir)*
Board of Directors:
Kenji Kontani
Yasutoshi Kimura
Isayuki Mae
Noboru Nonaka
Hitoshi Takamoto
Subsidiaries:

Daito Denso Co., Ltd. (1)
689-1 Nogami Iseochi
Ritto, Shiga, 520-3044, Japan
Tel.: (81) 775537600
Fax: (81) 775537877
Web Site: www.daitodenso.co.jp
Electronic Products Mfr & Sales
S.I.C.: 3679
N.A.I.C.S.: 334419

Daitron Technology Co., Ltd. (1)
1-1-3 Shimamachi Chuo-ku
Osaka, 540-0034, Japan (100%)
Tel.: (81) 669431911
Fax: (81) 669422665
Web Site: www.dtc-daitron.com
Emp.: 127
Semiconductor Manufacturing & Inspection Equipment & water Pressure-Resistant Connectors Mfr & Sales
S.I.C.: 3559
N.A.I.C.S.: 333242
Shigeyoshi Kunizane *(Pres)*

Plants:

Daito Electron Co., Ltd. - EM Machida Factory (1)
2-5-6 Oyamagaoka 2 Chome
Machida-City, Tokyo, 194-0215, Japan
Tel.: (81) 42 798 5161
Fax: (81) 42 798 5160
Web Site: www.daitron.co.jp/english/company/network.html
Electronic Components Mfr
S.I.C.: 3679
N.A.I.C.S.: 334419

Daito Electron Co., Ltd. - Machida Factory (1)
2-5-6 Oyamagaoka 2-chome
Machida, Tokyo, 194-0215, Japan
Tel.: (81) 427985161
Fax: (81) 427985160
Emp.: 30
Power Supplies Mfr
S.I.C.: 3699
N.A.I.C.S.: 335999
Ozaki Masahide *(Mgr-Sls)*

U.S. Subsidiary:

Daitron Inc. (1)
27750 SW 95th Ave Ste 100
Wilsonville, OR 97070
Tel.: (503) 682-7560
Fax: (503) 682-2861
Toll Free: (888) 324-8766
E-Mail: dtr@daitron.com
Web Site: www.daitron.com
Emp.: 14
Electronic Component Mfr & Distr
S.I.C.: 3679
N.A.I.C.S.: 334419
Toshi Moritani *(Pres)*

Non-U.S. Subsidiaries:

Daitron (H.K.) Co., Ltd. (1)
Unit 03 13th Floor MirrorTower 61 Mody Road Tsim Sha Tsui
255 257 Gloucester Rd, Kowloon, China (Hong Kong) (100%)
Tel.: (852) 28380682
Fax: (852) 2591 0818
Web Site: www.daitron.com.hk
Semiconductor & Electronic Components & Equipment Mfr, Importer, Exporter & Sales
S.I.C.: 3674
N.A.I.C.S.: 334413

Daitron (Korea) Co., Ltd. (1)
7th Floor E & C Venture Dream Tower 6 Cha Guro-dong
Guro-gu, 152-719 Seoul, Korea (South)
Tel.: (82) 23265151
Fax: (82) 2 6910 3399
E-Mail: abt@daitron.co.kr
Web Site: www.daitron.co.kr
Emp.: 372
Software Development & Electronic Equipment Sales
S.I.C.: 7371
N.A.I.C.S.: 541511

Daito Electron Co., Ltd.—(Continued)

Daitron (Malaysia) Sdn. Bhd. (1)
Suite 808 8th Floor Central Tower Wisma Consplant 1 No 2
Jalan SS16 4, 47500 Subang Jaya, Selangor Darul Ehsan, Malaysia (100%)
Tel.: (60) 358805300
Fax: (60) 358805297
E-Mail:
Web Site: www.daitron.com.my
Emp.: 11
Semiconductor & Electronic Equipment & Components Mfr, Importer, Exporte & Sales
S.I.C.: 3674
N.A.I.C.S.: 334413
Isayuki Mae *(Mng Dir)*

Daitron (Shanghai) Co., Ltd. (1)
Room F 9F Century Ba Shi Building No 398 Huai Hai Zhong Road
Shanghai, 200020, China
Tel.: (86) 2160932193
Fax: (86) 21 6093 2173
Web Site: www.daitron.com.cn
Electronic Components Mfr & Distr
S.I.C.: 3679
N.A.I.C.S.: 334419

Daitron (Thailand) Co., Ltd. (1)
209 K Tower 9th Floor A Tower Sukhumvit 21 Asoke Road
Khlong Toey Nua Wattana, Bangkok, 10110, Thailand
Tel.: (66) 26641366
Fax: (66) 2 664 1368
Electronic Components Sales & Maintenance Services
S.I.C.: 5065
N.A.I.C.S.: 423690

DAITO PHARMACEUTICAL CO., LTD.

326 Yokamachi Toyama City
Toyama, 939-8567, Japan
Tel.: (81) 764215665
Fax: (81) 764216006
E-Mail: takeda@daitonet.co.jp
Web Site: www.daitonet.co.jp
4577—(TKS)
Sls.: $318,516,000
Assets: $382,382,000
Liabilities: $216,579,000
Net Worth: $165,803,000
Earnings: $19,646,000
Emp.: 476
Fiscal Year-end: 05/31/13
Business Description:
Pharmaceutical Mfr
S.I.C.: 2834
N.A.I.C.S.: 325412
Personnel:
Yasunobu Otsuga *(Pres & CEO)*

DAITO TRUST CONSTRUCTION CO., LTD.

2-16-1 Konan Minato-ku
Tokyo, 108-8211, Japan
Tel.: (81) 367189111
Fax: (81) 367189069
Web Site: www.kentaku.co.jp
Year Founded: 1974
1878—(OTC TKS)
Sls.: $12,676,543,000
Assets: $6,795,118,000
Liabilities: $4,742,595,000
Net Worth: $2,052,523,000
Earnings: $568,414,000
Emp.: 14,154
Fiscal Year-end: 03/31/13
Business Description:
Land Developer Specializing in Commerical & Residential Use Properties
S.I.C.: 6552
N.A.I.C.S.: 237210
Personnel:
Naomi Kumakiri *(Pres)*
Akio Inada *(Sr Mng Dir)*
Katsuma Kobayashi *(Sr Mng Dir)*
Shuji Nakada *(Sr Mng Dir)*
Yukio Daimon *(Exec Officer)*
Koichi Ebihara *(Exec Officer)*
Hideo Gorai *(Exec Officer)*
Yoshihiro Hashimoto *(Exec Officer)*
Takuya Ishii *(Exec Officer)*
Naoki Naito *(Exec Officer)*
Takeshi Nakagawa *(Exec Officer)*
Hideyuki Nakaita *(Exec Officer)*
Hiromichi Ono *(Exec Officer)*
Kazuhiko Saito *(Exec Officer)*
Hiroshi Sugiyama *(Exec Officer)*
Kei Takeuchi *(Exec Officer)*
Masayoshi Tanaka *(Exec Officer)*
Hirosuke Tanimichi *(Exec Officer)*
Katsuya Touge *(Exec Officer)*
Kanitsu Uchida *(Exec Officer)*
Hideaki Ueki *(Exec Officer)*
Hitoshi Wada *(Exec Officer)*
Sachio Washi *(Exec Officer)*
Shoji Yamada *(Exec Officer)*
Hitoshi Kadouchi *(Exec VP)*
Board of Directors:
Akio Inada
Hitoshi Kadouchi
Shuji Kawai
Katsuma Kobayashi
Naomi Kumakiri
Marcus Scott Merner
Shuji Nakada
Yujiro Sasamoto
Toshiaki Yamaguchi
Transfer Agent:
Mitsubishi UFJ Trust Bank Limited
Corporate Agency Department 7 10 11 Higashisuna Koto Ku
Tokyo, 137-8081, Japan
Subsidiaries:

Care Partner Co Ltd (1)
2-16-1 Konan Shinagawa East One Tower 3F
Minato-ku, Tokyo, 108-0075, Japan
Tel.: (81) 367189077
Fax: (81) 367189135
Web Site: www.care-partner.com
Emp.: 40
Nursing Homes Operation Services
S.I.C.: 8051
N.A.I.C.S.: 623110
Shuji Nakata *(Pres)*

Daito Building Management Co Ltd (1)
Konan 2-16-1
Minato-ku Shinagawa, Tokyo, 108-8211, Japan
Tel.: (81) 3 6718 9111
Web Site: www.kentaku.co.jp
Sales Range: $1-9.9 Million
Emp.: 420
Building Management & Rental Services
S.I.C.: 8748
N.A.I.C.S.: 541618
Hitoshi Kadouchi *(Pres)*

Daito Construction Co., Ltd. (1)
1-5-11 Omochanomachi Mibumachi
Shimotsuga-Gun, Tochigi, 321-0202, Japan
Tel.: (81) 282862773
Fax: (81) 2 8286 1142
Web Site: www.daito-j.com
Apartment Construction & Rental Services
S.I.C.: 1522
N.A.I.C.S.: 236116

Daito Corporate Service Co., Ltd. (1)
2-16-1 Konan Shinagawa East One Tower 22F
Minato-ku, Tokyo, 108-0075, Japan
Tel.: (81) 354618411
Fax: (81) 3 5461 8412
Physically & Mentally Challenged People Employment Services
S.I.C.: 9441
N.A.I.C.S.: 923130

Daito Steel Co., Ltd. (1)
901-1 Hamatome
Yaizu, Shizuoka, 425-0012, Japan
Tel.: (81) 546284012
Fax: (81) 546284606
Web Site: www.daito-steel.com
Steel Materials Distr
S.I.C.: 5039
N.A.I.C.S.: 423390

Gaspal Co Ltd (1)
Kounan ISUTOWANTAWA 2-16-1
Minato-ku, Shinagawa, Tokyo, 108 0075, Japan
Tel.: (81) 367189080
Fax: (81) 367189131
Web Site: www.gas-pal.com
Emp.: 318
Petroleum Distr
S.I.C.: 5989
N.A.I.C.S.: 454310

Housecom Corporation (1)
2-16-1 Konan Minato-ku
Shinagawa East 5th Floor, Tokyo, 108-0075, Japan
Tel.: (81) 367176900
Fax: (81) 367176901
E-Mail: kojinjyouhou@housecom.co.jp
Web Site: www.housecom.co.jp
3275—(JAS)
Sales Range: $75-99.9 Million
Emp.: 811
Real Estate Brokerage & Rental Management Services
S.I.C.: 6531
N.A.I.C.S.: 531210
Tada Haruhiko *(Pres)*

JUSHII Publishing Corporation (1)
Kounan 2 16 1
Minato ku Shinagawa, 108 0075 Tokyo, Japan
Tel.: (81) 367176922
Fax: (81) 367176923
Web Site: www.jsee.com
Emp.: 12
Magazines Merchant Whslr
S.I.C.: 2741
N.A.I.C.S.: 511199
Koji Takahashi *(Gen Mgr)*

Non-U.S. Subsidiary:

Daito Asia Development (Malaysia) Sdn. Bhd. (1)
7th Floor Le Meridien KL No 2 Jalan Stesen Sentral
50480 Kuala Lumpur, Malaysia
Tel.: (60) 322735387
Fax: (60) 322637222
E-Mail: dadn-admin@arc.net.my
Hotel Operation Services
S.I.C.: 7011
N.A.I.C.S.: 721110
Harvey Thompson *(Gen Mgr)*

DAIWA ASSOCIATE HOLDINGS LIMITED

11/F Block G East Sun Industrial Centre 16 Shing Yip St
Kwun Tong, Kowloon, China (Hong Kong)
Tel.: (852) 2341 3351
Fax: (852) 2797 8275
E-Mail: daiwa@daiwahk.com
Web Site: www.daiwa.com.cn
Year Founded: 1980
1037—(HKG)
Rev.: $70,653,768
Assets: $56,557,212
Liabilities: $29,102,983
Net Worth: $27,454,229
Earnings: ($22,017,181)
Emp.: 800
Fiscal Year-end: 03/31/13
Business Description:
Semiconductor Product Distr
S.I.C.: 5065
N.A.I.C.S.: 423690
Personnel:
Tak Wan Lau *(Pres)*
Wai Chuen Man *(Sec)*
Board of Directors:
Barry John Buttifant
Pinky Yuen Mei Chan
Wai Ho Cheung
Yuk Fan Choi
James Wing Kam Chong
Wai Ching Fung
Tak Wan Lau
Ngai Wing Liu
Chor Fai Wan
Butterfield Fulcrum Group (Bermuda) Limited
26 Burnaby Street
Hamilton, HM 11, Bermuda

DAIWA CAN COMPANY

2-1-10 Nihonbashi
Chuo-ku, Tokyo, 103-8240, Japan
Tel.: (81) 3 3272 0561
Fax: (81) 3 3281 8167
Web Site: www.daiwa-can.com
Year Founded: 1939
Sales Range: $1-4.9 Billion
Emp.: 1,489
Business Description:
Metal & Plastic Cans Mfr
S.I.C.: 3411
N.A.I.C.S.: 332431
Personnel:
Hisakazu Yamaguchi *(Pres)*

DAIWA COMPUTER CO., LTD.

36-18 Wakamatsu-Cho Takatsuki-Shi
Osaka, 5690054, Japan
Tel.: (81) 72 676 2221
Fax: (81) 72 676 2224
Web Site: www.daiwa-computer.co.jp
Year Founded: 1977
3816—(JAS)
Sls.: $21,648,000
Assets: $36,168,000
Liabilities: $9,746,000
Net Worth: $26,422,000
Earnings: $2,024,000
Fiscal Year-end: 07/31/13
Business Description:
Software Development Services
S.I.C.: 7371
N.A.I.C.S.: 541511
Personnel:
Kenji Nakamura *(Pres & CEO)*
Tadashi Hayashi *(Mng Dir)*
Board of Directors:
Tadashi Hayashi
Kenji Nakamura
Yoshihito Suzuki
Mizue Yamane
Subsidiary:

fit.com Co., Ltd. (1)
2-25-7 Shirokanedai
Minato-Ku, Tokyo, 108-0071, Japan
Tel.: (81) 5031627281
Information Technology Consulting Services
S.I.C.: 7373
N.A.I.C.S.: 541512

DAIWA HEAVY INDUSTRY CO,. LTD.

21-23 Kabe 1
Asakita, Hiroshima, Japan
Tel.: (81) 82 814 2101
Fax: (81) 82 814 2109
E-Mail: info@daiwajuko.co.jp
Web Site: www.daiwajuko.co.jp
Year Founded: 1831
5610—(TKS)
Business Description:
Industrial Machinery Mfr
S.I.C.: 3569
N.A.I.C.S.: 333999
Personnel:
Yasuaki Tanaka *(Pres)*

DAIWA HOUSE INDUSTRY CO., LTD.

3-3-5 Umeda Kita-ku
Osaka, 530-8241, Japan
Tel.: (81) 663421369
Telex: 525-5857 HOUSEOJ

Fax: (81) 663421587
E-Mail: zaimu@daimahouse.jp
Web Site: www.daiwahouse.co.jp
Year Founded: 1947
1925—(TKS)
Sls.: $22,087,879,000
Assets: $26,083,618,000
Liabilities: $17,999,894,000
Net Worth: $8,083,724,000
Earnings: $729,014,000
Emp.: 30,361
Fiscal Year-end: 03/31/13

Business Description:
Holding Company; Construction & Real Estate Services
S.I.C.: 6719
N.A.I.C.S.: 551112

Personnel:
Takeo Higuchi *(Chm & CEO)*
Naotake Ohno *(Pres & COO)*
Tetsuji Ogawa *(CFO, Exec VP & Head-Mgmt Admin)*
Tamio Ishibashi *(Exec VP & Head-Info Sys, CSR, Mktg Support & TKC Dept)*

Board of Directors:
Takeo Higuchi
Osamu Fujitani
Takashi Hama
Fukujiro Hori
Takuya Ishibashi
Tamio Ishibashi
Koichi Kamikawa
Katsutomo Kawai
Masahiro Kiguchi
Kazuyoshi Kimura
Takeshi Kousokabe
Tatsushi Nishimura
Shigeru Numata
Tetsuji Ogawa
Naotake Ohno
Yutaka Shigemori
Kazuto Tsuchida
Makoto Yamamoto
Keiichi Yoshii

Subsidiaries:

Daiwa Energy Co., Ltd. **(1)**
Daiwa House Osaka Building 3-3-5 Umeda
Kita-ku, Osaka, 530- 8241, Japan
Tel.: (81) 663421765
Fax: (81) 663421766
Web Site: www.daiwa-energy.com
Emp.: 40
Development of Business & Housing Environmental Products
S.I.C.: 3822
N.A.I.C.S.: 334512
Hidekazu Matsushima *(Pres)*

Daiwa Estate Co., Ltd. **(1)**
Daiwa House Tokyo Building 3-13-1 Iidabashi
Chiyoda-ku, Tokyo, Japan
Tel.: (81) 352142263
Fax: (81) 352142336
Web Site: www.daiwaestate.jp
Sales Range: $1-9.9 Million
Emp.: 35
Real Estate Brokerage
S.I.C.: 6531
N.A.I.C.S.: 531210
Atsushi Kanakubo *(Pres)*

Daiwa House Asset Management Co., Ltd. **(1)**
Nissei Nagatacho Building 7th Floor 4-8 Nagatacho 2-chome
Chiyoda-Ku, Tokyo, 100-0014, Japan
Tel.: (81) 3 3595 1151
Fax: (81) 3 3595 1972
Web Site: www.dh-am.com
Sls.: $12,508,800
Emp.: 37
Asset Management Services
S.I.C.: 6799
N.A.I.C.S.: 523920
Yuji Yamada *(Pres & CEO)*

Daiwa House Financial Co., Ltd. **(1)**
Daiwa House Osaka Building 3-3-5 Umeda
Kita-ku, Osaka, Japan
Tel.: (81) 663421770
Fax: (81) 663421769
Web Site: www.daiwahouse.com
Emp.: 13
Credit Card & Consumer Finance Services
S.I.C.: 6153
N.A.I.C.S.: 522210
Osami Nishikawa *(Pres)*

Daiwa House Insurance Co., Ltd. **(1)**
1-5-2 Bingo-machi
Chuo-ku, Osaka, Japan JP
Tel.: (81) 6 6229 7260
Fax: (81) 6 6229 7266
Web Site: www.daiwahouse-ins.jp
Emp.: 69
Insurance Agency
S.I.C.: 6411
N.A.I.C.S.: 524210
Sigeru Sasashita *(Pres)*

Daiwa House Morimoto Asset Management Co., Ltd. **(1)**
2-4-8 Nagatacyo
Chiyoda-ku, Tokyo, Japan
Tel.: (81) 3 3595 1151
Fax: (81) 3 3595 1972
Web Site: www.daiwahouse-resi-reit.co.jp
Asset Management Services
S.I.C.: 6282
N.A.I.C.S.: 523920
Yuji Yamada *(Pres)*

Daiwa House REIT Management Co., Ltd. **(1)**
2-3-6 Nihombashi Kayabayacho
Chuo-ku, Tokyo, Japan JP
Tel.: (81) 335101561
Fax: (81) 335101562
Web Site: www.daiwahouse.com
Emp.: 7
Investment Trust Management
S.I.C.: 6726
N.A.I.C.S.: 525990
Takeshi Kosokabe *(Pres)*
Kenjiro Kmatsuke *(Mng Dir)*

Daiwa House Renew Co., Ltd. **(1)**
Daiwa House Osaka Building 3-3-5 Umeda
Kita-ku, 530-8241 Osaka, Japan JP
Tel.: (81) 663424410
Fax: (81) 663421838
Web Site: www.daiwahouse-renew.co.jp
Sales Range: $10-24.9 Million
Emp.: 500
Home Renovation
S.I.C.: 1522
N.A.I.C.S.: 236118
Junichi Sugiura *(Pres)*

Daiwa Information Service Co., Ltd. **(1)**
Royment Ueno Building 7-14-4 Ueno
Tokyo, Taito-ku, Japan JP
Tel.: (81) 358288891 (100%)
Fax: (81) 352465870
E-Mail: natakubeo@msn.com
Web Site: www.dis-net.jp
Sales Range: $1-9.9 Million
Emp.: 166
Property Leasing & Shopping Center Operation; Property Management for Commercial Facilities, Office Buildings & Hotels
S.I.C.: 6519
N.A.I.C.S.: 531190
Osao Fukushima *(Pres)*

Daiwa Lantec Co., Ltd. **(1)**
1-5-2 Bingo-machi
Chuo-ku, Osaka, Japan
Tel.: (81) 6 6229 7270
Fax: (81) 6 6229 7287
Web Site: www.daiwalantec.jp
Sls.: $170,536,640
Emp.: 240
Geological Surveying Services
S.I.C.: 8713
N.A.I.C.S.: 541360
Chiyohiro Aoyagi *(Pres)*

Daiwa Lease Co., Ltd. **(1)**
Pippu Building 2-1-36 Noninbashi
Chuo-ku, 540-0011 Osaka, Japan JP
Tel.: (81) 669428011 (100%)
Fax: (81) 669428051
Web Site: www.daiwalease.co.jp
Sales Range: $1-4.9 Billion
Emp.: 2,086
Leasing & Sales of Temporary Housing, Development of Commercial Facilities, Leasing & Sales of Machinery, Equipment & Vehicles
S.I.C.: 7359
N.A.I.C.S.: 532490
Shunsaku Morita *(Pres)*

Daiwa LifeNext Co., Ltd. **(1)**
5-1-33 Akasaka
Minato-Ku, Tokyo, 107-0052, Japan
Tel.: (81) 355497111
Fax: (81) 355497021
Web Site: www.daiwalifenext.co.jp
Emp.: 300
Property Management Services
S.I.C.: 6531
N.A.I.C.S.: 531311

Daiwa Living Co., Ltd. **(1)**
Daiwa House Tokyo Building 3-13-1 Iidabashi
Chiyoda-ku, Tokyo, Japan JP
Tel.: (81) 352142330 (100%)
Fax: (81) 352142333
Web Site: www.daiwaliving.co.jp
Sales Range: $1-4.9 Billion
Emp.: 1,281
Management & Operation of Rental Housing, Subcontractor for Renovation Work & Insurance Services
S.I.C.: 1522
N.A.I.C.S.: 236118
Masaru Akashi *(Pres)*

Daiwa Logistics Co., Ltd. **(1)**
Daiwa Building 1-5-16 Awaza
Nishi-ku, Osaka, Japan JP
Tel.: (81) 649686355 (100%)
Fax: (81) 649686331
Web Site: www.daiwabutsuryu.co.jp
Sales Range: $300-349.9 Million
Emp.: 1,103
Trucking Services, Storage & Packing of Goods
S.I.C.: 4731
N.A.I.C.S.: 541614
Katsuyoshi Tateno *(Pres)*

Daiwa Monthly Co., Ltd. **(1)**
Daiwa House Tokyo Building 3-13-1 Iidabashi
Tokyo, Chiyoda-ku, 1020072, Japan JP
Tel.: (81) 352142706
Fax: (81) 352142791
E-Mail: refer-dm@daiwaliving.co.jp
Web Site: www.daiwamonthly.co.jp
Sales Range: $1-9.9 Million
Emp.: 23
Rental Housing Management; Non-Life Insurance Services
S.I.C.: 6531
N.A.I.C.S.: 531311
Atsushi Kanakubo *(Pres)*

Daiwa Rakuda Industry Co., Ltd. **(1)**
Daiwa Building 1-5-16 Awaza
Nishi-ku, Osaka, Japan JP
Tel.: (81) 665366111 (100%)
Fax: (81) 665366112
Web Site: www.daiwarakuda.co.jp/index.asp
Sales Range: $350-399.9 Million
Emp.: 800
Manufacture, Installation & Sale of Housing Equipment, Metal Housing Materials & Construction Materials; Interior Design; Office Furniture & Equipment Sales & Leasing
S.I.C.: 3448
N.A.I.C.S.: 332311

Daiwa Resort Co., Ltd. **(1)**
Daiwa House Bingomaki Bldg 1-5-2 Bingo-machi
Chuo-ku, Osaka, Japan JP
Tel.: (81) 662297209 (100%)
Fax: (81) 662297202
Web Site: www.daiwaresort.co.jp/english
Emp.: 2,401
Hotel & Resort Operator
S.I.C.: 7011
N.A.I.C.S.: 721110
Seiji Kushida *(Pres)*

Daiwa Royal Co., Ltd. **(1)**
Daiwa House Tokyo Building 11F 3-13-1 Iidabashi
Chiyoda-ku, Tokyo, Japan JP
Tel.: (81) 3 5214 2410 (100%)
Fax: (81) 3 5214 2420
Web Site: www.daiwaroyal.com
Emp.: 179
Real Estate Brokerage & Property Management Services
S.I.C.: 6531
N.A.I.C.S.: 531210
Ken Harada *(Pres)*

Daiwa Royal Golf Co., Ltd. **(1)**
1055 Yamashita-cho
Kameyama, Mie, Japan JP
Tel.: (81) 595832339
Fax: (81) 0595831115
Web Site: www.daiwaroyalgolf.jp
Emp.: 112
Operation & Management of Golf Courses
S.I.C.: 7999
N.A.I.C.S.: 713910
Seishu Umaoka *(Pres)*

Daiwa Service Co., Ltd. **(1)**
Daiwa Building 1-5-16 Awaza
Nishi-ku, Osaka, Japan JP
Tel.: (81) 665366270
Fax: (81) 665366271
Web Site: www.daiwaservice.co.jp
Sales Range: $200-249.9 Million
Emp.: 3,000
Commercial Building Management, Maintenance & Repair Services; Residential Remodeling
S.I.C.: 6531
N.A.I.C.S.: 531312
Yamne Hirme *(CEO)*

Daiyoshi Trust Co., Ltd. **(1)**
2-2-30 Chiyo Hakata-ku Fukuoka-shi
Fukuoka, 812-0044, Japan (94%)
Tel.: (81) 926416333
Fax: (81) 926417733
E-Mail: ir.info@daiyoshi.com
Web Site: www.daiyoshi.com
Sales Range: $25-49.9 Million
Emp.: 30
Parking Facilities & Real Estate Services
S.I.C.: 7521
N.A.I.C.S.: 812930
Yoshihiro Oho *(Pres)*

Eneserve Corporation **(1)**
2-19-6 Tsukinowa
Otsu, Shiga, Japan JP
Tel.: (81) 775436330 (51.4%)
Fax: (81) 775436331
Web Site: www.eneserve.co.jp
Sales Range: $50-74.9 Million
Emp.: 139
Energy Management Services
S.I.C.: 7699
N.A.I.C.S.: 811310
Yoshio Kinoshita *(Pres)*

Fujita Corporation **(1)**
4-25-2 Sendagaya
Shibuya-ku, Tokyo, 151-8570, Japan JP
Tel.: (81) 334021911 (99.17%)
Fax: (81) 337962346
E-Mail: info2@fujita.co.jp
Web Site: www.fujita.co.jp
Sales Range: $1-4.9 Billion
Emp.: 2,238
Construction & Civil Engineering Services
S.I.C.: 1629
N.A.I.C.S.: 237990
Takuji Ueda *(Pres)*

Subsidiaries:

FBS Co., Ltd. **(2)**
4-25-2 Sendagaya
Shibuya-ku, Tokyo, 151-0051, Japan JP
Tel.: (81) 354743273
Fax: (81) 334055125
E-Mail: fbsinfo@1st-lab.net
Web Site: www.fbsys.net
Sales Range: $25-49.9 Million
Emp.: 12
Information Technology Services
S.I.C.: 7379
N.A.I.C.S.: 541519
Kazuo Hiroshi Kimoto *(CEO)*

Fujita BLDG. Maintenance Co., Ltd. **(2)**
5-8-10 Sendagaya
Shibuya-ku, Tokyo, 151-0051, Japan JP
Tel.: (81) 334031500
Fax: (81) 334032500
Sales Range: $75-99.9 Million
Facility Management Services
S.I.C.: 8744

Daiwa House Industry Co., Ltd.—(Continued)

N.A.I.C.S.: 561210

Fujita Road Construction Co., Ltd. (2)
3-15-8 Nihonbashi
Chuo-ku, Tokyo, 103-0027, Japan
Tel.: (81) 332717966
Fax: (81) 339717918
Web Site: www.fujitaroad.co.jp
Sales Range: $200-249.9 Million
Emp.: 250
Road, Bridge & Other Civil Engineering Construction Services
S.I.C.: 1611
N.A.I.C.S.: 237310

Fujita Shoji Co., Ltd. (2)
23-1 Kanda-Higashimatsushita-cho
Chiyoda-ku, Tokyo, 101-0042, Japan
Tel.: (81) 352970181
Fax: (81) 352970180
E-Mail: kuboa@fujitashoji.jp
Sales Range: $100-124.9 Million
Export & Import Trading Services
S.I.C.: 7389
N.A.I.C.S.: 425120

KOKANKYO Engineering Corporation (EAE) (2)
Ozawa Builsing 4-7-13 Sendagaya
Shibuya-ku, Tokyo, 151-0051, Japan
Tel.: (81) 3 5413 6222
Fax: (81) 3 5413 2228
Web Site: www.eae.co.jp
Sales Range: $250-299.9 Million
Environmental Engineering & Technology-Consulting Construction Services
S.I.C.: 1629
N.A.I.C.S.: 237990
Kazuhiro Dasan *(Pres)*

Technomaterial Corporation (2)
23-1 Kanda-Higashimatsushita-cho
Chiyoda-ku, Tokyo, 101-0042, Japan
Tel.: (81) 3 5269 8450
Fax: (81) 3 5269 8454
Sales Range: $100-124.9 Million
Precast Concrete Product Mfr & Contractor Services
S.I.C.: 3272
N.A.I.C.S.: 327390
Takeo Miyatsuka *(Pres)*

U.S. Unit:

Fujita Research (Encino Office) (2)
30340 Olympic St
Castaic, CA 91384
Mailing Address:
PO Box 55545
Valencia, CA 91385-0545
Tel.: (818) 981-2657
Fax: (818) 981-0829
Web Site: www.fujitaresearch.com
Sales Range: $75-99.9 Million
Construction Technology Development & Transfer Services
S.I.C.: 8999
N.A.I.C.S.: 541690
Sam Shunichi Kadota *(CEO)*

Non-U.S. Subsidiaries:

Fujita Philippines Inc. (2)
10th Floor High Rise of the Pacific Star Bldg
Senator Gil J Puyat Avenue, 1226 Makati, Metro Manila, Philippines
Tel.: (63) 28410582
Fax: (63) 28410581
Sales Range: $150-199.9 Million
Construction Contractors
S.I.C.: 1541
N.A.I.C.S.: 236210
Taihei Motoki *(Mng Dir)*

Jukeikai Co., Ltd. (1)
17-2 Izumi
Atami, Shizuoka, 413-0000, Japan
Tel.: (81) 465 63 6432
Fax: (81) 465 63 6438
Web Site: www.neo-summit.com
Sls.: $9,277,360
Emp.: 79
Residential Facility Management Services
S.I.C.: 8744
N.A.I.C.S.: 561210
Toshinori Inaguchi *(Pres)*

Media Tech Inc. (1)
Daiwa Bldg 5th Fl 1-5-16 Awaza
Nishi-ku, Osaka, 550 0011, Japan JP
Tel.: (81) 665376270 (100%)
Fax: (81) 665376271
Web Site: www.mediatech.jp
Sales Range: $1-9.9 Million
Emp.: 21
Information Communications Services
S.I.C.: 7379
N.A.I.C.S.: 541519
Mitsuyoshi Koga *(Pres)*
Mitsuo Adachi *(Exec Mng Dir)*
Koji Uemura *(Exec Mng Dir)*

Nihon Jyutaku Ryutu Co., Ltd. (1)
Osaka Ekimae No 3 Building 1-1-3-800 Umeda
Kita-ku, Osaka, Japan JP
Tel.: (81) 663446356 (100%)
Fax: (81) 663426610
Web Site: www.jyutaku.co.jp
Sales Range: $150-199.9 Million
Emp.: 395
Real Estate Brokerage; Rental Housing
S.I.C.: 6531
N.A.I.C.S.: 531210
Minoru Fujita *(Pres)*

Nippon Athletic Service Co., Ltd. (1)
Chiyoda Building 9F 1-5-18 Sarugaku-cho
Chiyoda-ku, Tokyo, Japan JP
Tel.: (81) 332331531
Fax: (81) 332331618
Web Site: www.nas-club.co.jp
Sales Range: $75-99.9 Million
Emp.: 250
Operation & Management of Sports Facilities
S.I.C.: 7991
N.A.I.C.S.: 713940
Yoshinadi Shibayama *(Pres)*

Osaka Marubiru Co., Ltd. (1)
1-9-20 Umeda
Osaka, Kita-ku, 5300001, Japan JP
Tel.: (81) 663414411
Fax: (81) 663414930
E-Mail: shukuhaku@osakadaiichi.co.jp
Web Site: www.osakadaiichi.co.jp
Sales Range: $25-49.9 Million
Emp.: 70
Operation of Hotels
S.I.C.: 7011
N.A.I.C.S.: 721110
Haruyuki Yoshimoto *(Pres)*

Royal Home Center Co., Ltd. (1)
Daiwa Building 6F 1-5-16 Awaza
Nishi-ku, Osaka, 550 0011, Japan JP
Tel.: (81) 665366921 (100%)
Fax: (81) 665366930
Web Site: www.royal-hc.co.jp
Sales Range: $550-599.9 Million
Emp.: 484
Home Centers
S.I.C.: 5211
N.A.I.C.S.: 444110

Synchroller Co., Ltd. (1)
2056 Taga
Akaiwa, Okayama, 701-2216, Japan
Tel.: (81) 869579000
Construction Engineering Services
S.I.C.: 8711
N.A.I.C.S.: 541330

Non-U.S. Subsidiaries:

Daiwa House (Suzhou) Real Estate Development Co., Ltd. (1)
1902 Zhongyin Huilong Building 8 Suhui Road Suzhou Industrial Park
Suzhou, Jiangsu, China
Tel.: (86) 51288852001
Fax: (86) 51288852005
Emp.: 56
Real Estate Development Services
S.I.C.: 6531
N.A.I.C.S.: 531390
Hiroshi Azuma *(Chm)*

Dalian Acacia Town Villa Co., Ltd. (1)
Longjiang Road Dalian Economy & Technology Development Ward
Dalian, China
Tel.: (86) 41187641171
Fax: (86) 41187640594
Web Site: www.daiwahouse.com
Sales Range: $1-4.9 Billion
Emp.: 100
Management of Rental Housing
S.I.C.: 6531
N.A.I.C.S.: 531311
Haiyang Wang *(Chm)*

Tianjin Jiuhe International Villa Co., Ltd. (1)
140 China Weiguo Road
Tianjin, Hedong, 300161, China
Tel.: (86) 22 2451 4888
Fax: (86) 22 2455 7980
E-Mail: kyuka@public.tpt.tj.cn
Web Site: www.kyuka.net
Emp.: 70
Rental Housing Management
S.I.C.: 6531
N.A.I.C.S.: 531311
Tian Zhaozhen *(Chm)*

Non-U.S. Affiliate:

Shanghai International Realty Co., Ltd. (1)
3081 Hong Mei Rd
Shanghai, 201103, China (30%)
Tel.: (86) 2162759646
Fax: (86) 2162750031
E-Mail: info@hongqiao-villa.cn
Web Site: www.hongqiao-villa.com
Emp.: 30
Management of Rental Housing
S.I.C.: 6531
N.A.I.C.S.: 531311
John Chen *(Mgr-Section)*

DAIWA HOUSE RESIDENTIAL INVESTMENT CORPORATION

7th Floor Nissei Nagatacho Building
2-4-8 Nagatacho
Chiyoda-ku, Tokyo, 100-0014, Japan
Tel.: (81) 3 3595 1265
Web Site: www.daiwahouse-resi-reit.co.jp
Year Founded: 2005
8984—(TKS)

Business Description:
Real Estate Investment Services
S.I.C.: 6531
N.A.I.C.S.: 531390

Personnel:
Michio Taki *(Exec Dir)*

Supervisory Board of Directors:
Tetsuya Iwasaki
Michio Taki
Isamu Yonekawa

DAIWA ODAKYU CONSTRUCTION CO., LTD.

4-32-22 Nishi-Shinjuku
Shinjuku-ku, Tokyo, 160-0023, Japan
Tel.: (81) 333763101
Fax: (81) 333763100
Web Site: www.daiwaodakyu.co.jp
Year Founded: 1939
1834—(TKS)
Sales Range: $650-699.9 Million
Emp.: 829

Business Description:
Construction & Engineering Services
S.I.C.: 8711
N.A.I.C.S.: 541330

Personnel:
Yoshiaki Takamura *(Pres)*

DAIWA SECURITIES GROUP INC.

GranTokyo North Tower 9-1
Marunouchi 1-chome Chiyoda-ku
Tokyo, 100-6751, Japan
Tel.: (81) 355551111
Fax: (81) 355550661
E-Mail: ir-section@dsgi.daiwa.co.jp
Web Site: www.daiwa-grp.jp
Year Founded: 1999
8601—(OTC TKS)
Rev.: $5,779,532,000
Assets: $209,540,089,000
Liabilities: $197,631,852,000
Net Worth: $11,908,237,000
Earnings: $802,010,000
Emp.: 14,432
Fiscal Year-end: 03/31/13

Business Description:
Holding Company; Securities Brokerage, Investment Banking, Portfolio Management & Trust Services
Import Export
S.I.C.: 6719
N.A.I.C.S.: 551112

Personnel:
Shigeharu Suzuki *(Chm & Sr Mng Dir)*
Takashi Hibino *(Pres & CEO)*
Nobuyuki Iwamoto *(COO & Deputy Pres)*
Takashi Fukai *(Deputy Pres)*
Yoriyuki Kusaki *(Deputy Pres)*
Hiroshi Nakamura *(Deputy Pres)*
Makoto Shirakawa *(Deputy Pres)*
Akio Takahashi *(Deputy Pres)*
Mikita Komatsu *(CFO & Exec Mng Dir)*
Saburo Jifuku *(Chief Risk Officer & Exec Mng Dir)*
Tetsuo Akuzawa *(Exec Mng Dir)*
Masaaki Goto *(Exec Mng Dir)*
Toshihiro Matsui *(Exec Mng Dir)*
Koichi Matsushita *(Exec Mng Dir)*
Masahisa Nakagawa *(Exec Mng Dir)*
Toshihiko Onishi *(Exec Mng Dir)*
Keiko Tashiro *(Exec Mng Dir)*
Hiroyuki Inose *(Sr Mng Dir)*
Yoshihisa Kaneko *(Sr Mng Dir)*
Atsushi Mochizuki *(Sr Mng Dir)*
Hironori Oka *(Sr Mng Dir)*
Takayuki Sawano *(Sr Mng Dir)*

Board of Directors:
Shigeharu Suzuki
Takashi Hibino
Kensuke Itoh
Nobuyuki Iwamoto
Saburo Jifuku
Yoriyuki Kusaki
Nobuko Matsubara
Masaru Shirataki
Keiichi Tadaki
Akio Takahashi
Hiroki Tsuda
Ryuji Yasuda

Transfer Agent:
Sumitomo Mitsui Trust Bank Limited
1-4-1 Marunouchi Chiyoda-ku
Tokyo, Japan

Subsidiaries:

Daiwa Asset Management Co. Ltd. (1)
10-5 Nihombashi Kayabacho 2-chome
Chuo-ku, Tokyo, 103-0025, Japan JP
Tel.: (81) 356952111 (88%)
Fax: (81) 356954087
Web Site: www.daiwa-am.co.jp
Sales Range: $200-249.9 Million
Emp.: 500
Investment Trust
S.I.C.: 6722
N.A.I.C.S.: 525910
Toshiro Ishibashi *(Pres)*

Daiwa Corporate Investment Co., Ltd. (1)
Sumitomo Fudosan Kudan Building 12F
8-10 Kudankita 1-chome
Chiyoda-ku, Tokyo, 102-0073, Japan JP
Tel.: (81) 369102600 (100%)
Fax: (81) 332345013
Sales Range: $250-299.9 Million
Emp.: 185
Private Equity Investment Firm
S.I.C.: 6211
N.A.I.C.S.: 523999
Kazuo Ariake *(Pres)*
Kohei Katsukawa *(Deputy Pres)*

Junichiro Wakimizu *(Deputy Pres)*
Yoshio Narukage *(Sr Mng Dir)*
Mamoru Ohtani *(Sr Mng Dir)*

Daiwa Institute of Research Holdings Ltd. **(1)**
15-6 Fuyuki
Koto-ku, Tokyo, 135-8460, Japan
Tel.: (81) 3 5620 5501
Fax: (81) 3 5620 5515
Web Site: www.dir.co.jp
Business Research & Consulting Services
S.I.C.: 8732
N.A.I.C.S.: 541720
Takashi Fukai *(Chm)*
Kazuhiko Akamatsu *(Vice Chm)*
Kazuo Oda *(Sr Mng Dir)*
Tomio Terada *(Sr Mng Dir)*
Tenzan Watanabe *(Sr Mng Dir)*

Subsidiary:

Daiwa Institute of Research Business Innovation Ltd. **(2)**
36-2 Nihonbashi Hakozaki-cho
Chuo-ku, Tokyo, Japan
Tel.: (81) 3 5931 8600
Fax: (81) 3 5644 1551
System Integration & Consulting Services
S.I.C.: 8748
N.A.I.C.S.: 541618
Takashi Fukai *(Chm)*
Kazuhiko Akamatsu *(Deputy Chm)*
Hisanobu Sonoda *(Exec Mng Dir)*
Hirochika Yamashita *(Exec Mng Dir)*
Akira Nagatsuka *(Sr Mng Dir)*
Hiroyuki Nomura *(Sr Mng Dir)*
Yutaka Ouchi *(Sr Mng Dir)*
Tomio Terada *(Sr Mng Dir)*

Daiwa Institute of Research Ltd. **(1)**
Daiwa Soken Bldg 15-6 Fuyuki
Koto Ku, Tokyo, 135-8460, Japan JP
Tel.: (81) 356205100 (100%)
Fax: (81) 56205603
E-Mail: contact@dir.co.jp
Web Site: www.dir.co.jp
Sales Range: $550-599.9 Million
Emp.: 1,500
Research & System Integration Services
S.I.C.: 7373
N.A.I.C.S.: 541512
Takashi Fukai *(Pres)*

U.S. Subsidiary:

Daiwa Institute of Research America Inc. **(2)**
32 Old Slip 11th Fl
New York, NY 10005-3504 NY
Tel.: (212) 612-6100 (100%)
Fax: (212) 612-8417
Web Site: www.dir.co.jp/english/souken/base.html
Rev.: $1,000,000
Emp.: 21
Investment Research
S.I.C.: 6282
N.A.I.C.S.: 523930
Yoshinari Hara *(CEO)*

Non-U.S. Subsidiaries:

Daiwa Institute of Research Europe Ltd. **(2)**
1st Floor 5 King William Street
London, EC4N 7AX, United Kingdom
Tel.: (44) 2075978000
Fax: (44) 2075978600
E-Mail: info@uk.daiwacm.com
Web Site: www.daiwasmbc.uk
Emp.: 500
Research, System Solutions & Consulting Services
S.I.C.: 8742
N.A.I.C.S.: 541611

Daiwa Institute of Research Hong Kong Ltd. **(2)**
One Pacific Place 88 26th Fl
Queensway, Central, China (Hong Kong)
Tel.: (852) 28484970
Fax: (852) 28452190
Web Site: www.daiwast.com
Emp.: 25
Research, System Solutions & Consulting Services
S.I.C.: 8731
N.A.I.C.S.: 541712

Hisao Katsuta *(Mng Dir)*

Daiwa Next Bank, Ltd. **(1)**
Gran Tokyo North Tower 9-1 Marunouchi 1-chome
Chiyoda-ku, Tokyo, 100-6756, Japan
Tel.: (81) 3 5555 6500
Commercial Banking Services
S.I.C.: 6029
N.A.I.C.S.: 522110
Tomiki Koide *(Pres)*

Daiwa PI Partners Co. Ltd **(1)**
1-9-1 Marunouchi
Chiyoda-Ku, Tokyo, 100-6730, Japan
Tel.: (81) 3 5555 6001
Web Site: www.dpipartners.co.jp
Emp.: 30
Investment Management Services
S.I.C.: 6211
N.A.I.C.S.: 523999
Hideki Araki *(Pres)*

Daiwa Property Co., Ltd. **(1)**
Daiwa Yaesu Bldg 1-2-1 Kyobashi
Chuo-ku, Tokyo, 104 0031, Japan (100%)
Tel.: (81) 355554700
Fax: (81) 0352022035
Web Site: www.daiwa-property.co.jp
Emp.: 45
Property Manager for Group Holdings
S.I.C.: 6531
N.A.I.C.S.: 531311
Hiroshi Fujioka *(Pres)*

Daiwa Real Estate Asset Management Co. Ltd **(1)**
6-2-1 Ginza Davinci Ginza 5f
Chuo-Ku, Tokyo, 104-0061, Japan
Tel.: (81) 362159649
Web Site: www.daiwareal.co.jp
Real Estate Management Services
S.I.C.: 6531
N.A.I.C.S.: 531390

Daiwa Securities Business Center Co., Ltd. **(1)**
3-2 Toyo-machi 2-chome
Koto-ku, Tokyo, 135 0016, Japan JP
Tel.: (81) 356336100 (100%)
E-Mail: webmaster@daiwa-dsc.co.jp
Web Site: www.daiwa-dsc.co.jp
Sales Range: $1-9.9 Million
Emp.: 608
Business Services
S.I.C.: 7389
N.A.I.C.S.: 561499
Yoshimi Murakami *(Pres)*

Daiwa Securities Capital Markets Co. Ltd. **(1)**
GranTokyo North Tower 1-9-1 Marunouchi
Chiyoda-ku, Tokyo, 100-6751, Japan JP
Tel.: (81) 355553111 (100%)
Web Site: www.daiwa.jp/houjin
Emp.: 1,886
Investment Banking & Securities Brokerage Services
S.I.C.: 6211
N.A.I.C.S.: 523110
Takashi Hibino *(Pres)*
Akio Takahashi *(Deputy Pres)*
Masaaki Goto *(Exec Mng Dir)*
Kazuho Takahashi *(Exec Mng Dir)*
Yoshio Urata *(Exec Mng Dir)*
Mikita Komatsu *(Sr Mng Dir)*
Wilfried Schmidt *(Sr Mng Dir)*
Toshihiko Onishi *(Exec Officer)*

U.S. Subsidiary:

Daiwa Capital Markets America Holdings Inc. **(2)**
32 Old Slip Financial Sq
New York, NY 10005-3504 DE
Tel.: (212) 612-7000 (100%)
Fax: (212) 612-7100
Emp.: 250
Holding Company; Investment Banking, Securities Brokerage & Trust Services
S.I.C.: 6719
N.A.I.C.S.: 551112
Masaaki Goto *(Chm & CEO)*
Hiroaki Kato *(Pres/CEO-India)*

Subsidiaries:

Daiwa Capital Markets America Inc. **(3)**
Financial Sq 32 Old Slip
New York, NY 10005 NY
Tel.: (212) 612-7000 (100%)
Telex: 420971
Fax: (212) 612-7100
E-Mail: info@daiwausa.com
Web Site: www.us.daiwacm.com
Emp.: 282
Investment Banking & Securities Brokerage Services
S.I.C.: 6211
N.A.I.C.S.: 523110
Masaaki Goto *(Chm & CEO)*
Richard Beggs *(Co-Pres)*
Hironori Oka *(Co-Pres)*
Bill Cook *(Sr VP)*

Division:

Daiwa Finance Corp. **(4)**
32 Old Slip Financial Sq
New York, NY 10005-3504 NY
Tel.: (212) 612-7000 (100%)
Fax: (212) 612-7100
E-Mail: info@daiwausa.com
Web Site: www.daiwausa.com
Emp.: 250
Financial & Real Estate Services
S.I.C.: 6211
N.A.I.C.S.: 523110

Daiwa Securities Trust Company **(3)**
1 Evertrust Plz
Jersey City, NJ 07302-3051 (100%)
Tel.: (201) 333-7300
Telex: 262976
Fax: (201) 333-7726
Web Site: www.daiwast.com
Emp.: 30
Trust Company
S.I.C.: 6029
N.A.I.C.S.: 522110

Non-U.S. Subsidiaries:

Daiwa Capital Markets Australia Limited **(2)**
Level 34 Rialto North Tower 525 Collins Street
Melbourne, VIC, 3000, Australia AU
Tel.: (61) 399161300 (100%)
Telex: 152198
Fax: (61) 399161330
Web Site: www.au.daiwacm.com
Emp.: 20
Investment Banking & Securities Brokerage Services
S.I.C.: 6211
N.A.I.C.S.: 523110

Daiwa Capital Markets Europe Limited **(2)**
5 King William Street
London, EC4N 7AX, United Kingdom UK
Tel.: (44) 2075978000 (100%)
Telex: 884121
Fax: (44) 2075978600
E-Mail: info@ukdaiwacm.com
Web Site: www.uk.daiwacm.com
Sales Range: $150-199.9 Million
Emp.: 435
Investment Banking & Securities Brokerage Services
S.I.C.: 6211
N.A.I.C.S.: 523110
Masami Tada *(Chm)*
Wilfried Schmidt *(Vice Chm)*
Junichi Arihara *(Pres & COO)*
Keith Meekins *(CEO)*
Michael Botevyle *(Mng Dir & Head-HR)*

Daiwa Capital Markets Hong Kong Limited **(2)**
Level 26 One Pacific Pl
88 Queensway, Hong Kong, China (Hong Kong) HK
Tel.: (852) 25250121 (100%)
Telex: 73325 DAIWA HX
Fax: (852) 28451621
E-Mail: generalinfo@hk.daiwacm.com
Web Site: www.hk.daiwacm.com
Emp.: 100
Investment Banking & Securities Brokerage Services
S.I.C.: 6211
N.A.I.C.S.: 523110
Raymond Yin *(Co-Chm-China & Head-Investment Banking-China)*
Victor Zhikai Gao *(Co-Chm-China)*
Akihiko Kanamura *(Chm)*
Hiroyuki Nomura *(Pres)*
Marco Arosti *(Mng Dir & Head-Gen Indus-Investment Banking-Asia Pacific Reg)*
Gerard Gu *(Mng Dir & Head-Consumer Retail-Investment Banking-Asia Pacific)*
Ali Khan *(Mng Dir & Head-Equity Sls-Asia)*

Daiwa Capital Markets India Private Limited **(2)**
10th Floor 3 North Avenue Maker Maxity Bandra East
Mumbai, 400 051, India
Tel.: (91) 22 6622 1000
Fax: (91) 22 6622 1019
Emp.: 5
Financial Management Services
S.I.C.: 6211
N.A.I.C.S.: 523999
Martin Simons *(Pres & CEO)*

Daiwa Capital Markets Philippines, Inc. **(2)**
Citibank Tower 18th Floor Paseo de Roxas
Salcedo Village
8741 Makati, Philippines
Tel.: (63) 2 813 7344
Fax: (63) 2 848 0105
Financial Management Services
S.I.C.: 6211
N.A.I.C.S.: 523999

Daiwa Capital Markets Singapore Limited **(2)**
6 Shenton Way 26-08 DBS Building Tower 2
Singapore, 068809, Singapore SG
Tel.: (65) 62203666 (100%)
Telex: 24408
Fax: (65) 62236198
Web Site: www.sg.daiwacm.com
Emp.: 120
Investment Banking & Securities Brokerage Services
S.I.C.: 6211
N.A.I.C.S.: 523110
Yuichi Akai *(Chm)*
Sung Ho Kang *(Pres)*
Mathew Welch *(Mng Dir & Head-Banks-Fin Institutions Grp-Investment Banking)*

Daiwa-Cathay Capital Markets Co., Ltd. **(2)**
14th Floor 200 Keelung Road Section 1
1071 Taipei, Taiwan TW
Tel.: (886) 227239698 (90%)
Fax: (886) 223453638
Web Site: www.jp.daiwacm.com
Emp.: 110
Investment Banking & Securities Brokerage Services
S.I.C.: 6211
N.A.I.C.S.: 523110
Shin Yoshidome *(Pres)*

DBP-Daiwa Capital Markets Philippines, Inc. **(2)**
18th Fl Citibank Tower 8741 Paseo de Roxas
Salcedo Village, 1226 Makati, Metro Manila, Philippines PH
Tel.: (63) 28137344 (60%)
Fax: (63) 28480105
E-Mail: admin@dbpdaiwacmbc.com
Emp.: 30
Investment Banking & Securities Brokerage Services
S.I.C.: 6211
N.A.I.C.S.: 523110

Daiwa Securities Co. Ltd. **(1)**
GranTokyo North Tower 9-1 Marunouchi 1-chome
Chiyoda-ku, Tokyo, 100-6752, Japan JP
Tel.: (81) 332432111 (100%)
Web Site: www.daiwa.jp
Emp.: 744
Securities Brokerage Services
S.I.C.: 6211
N.A.I.C.S.: 523120
Shigeharu Suzuki *(Chm & Sr Mng Dir)*
Takashi Hibino *(Pres & CEO)*
Makoto Shirakawa *(Co-Deputy Pres)*
Nobuyuki Iwamoto *(Co-Deputy Pres, COO & CFO)*
Takashi Fukai *(Co-Deputy Pres)*
Yoriyuki Kusaki *(Co-Deputy Pres)*
Akio Takahashi *(Co-Deputy Pres)*
Saburo Jifuku *(Exec Mng Dir)*
Noriaki Kusaka *(Exec Mng Dir)*
Toshihiro Matsui *(Exec Mng Dir)*
Koichi Matsushita *(Exec Mng Dir)*

Daiwa Securities Group Inc.—(Continued)

Joint Ventures:

Daiwa SB Investments Ltd. (1)
2-1 Kasumigaseki 3 chrome
Chuo-ku, Tokyo, 100-0013, Japan JP
Tel.: (81) 362050200
Fax: (81) 362050563
Web Site: www.daiwasbi.co.jp
Emp.: 300
Investment Advisory & Trust Management Services; Owned by Daiwa Securities Group Inc. & by Sumitomo Mitsui Financial Group, Inc.
S.I.C.: 6282
N.A.I.C.S.: 523930
Masamichi Yokoi *(CEO & Pres)*

Daiwa Securities SMBC Principal Investments Co. Ltd. (1)
Gran Tokyo N Tower 1-9-1 Marunouchi
Chiyoda-ku, Tokyo, 100-6753, Japan JP
Tel.: (81) 355556111
Fax: (81) 135550880
Web Site: www.daiwasmbcpi.co.jp
Emp.: 65
Private Equity, Real Estate & Other Investment Services; Owned 60% by Daiwa Securities Group Inc. & 40% by Sumitomo Mitsui Financial Group, Inc.
S.I.C.: 6211
N.A.I.C.S.: 523999
Masaki Shimazu *(Chm)*
Kawasaki Kenichi *(Pres)*

DAIWABO CO. LTD.

3 6 8 Kyutaro Machi
Chuo ku Osaka shi, Osaka, 5410056, Japan
Tel.: (81) 662812404
Fax: (81) 662812522
Web Site: www.daiwabo.co.jp
Year Founded: 1941
31070—(TKS)
Emp.: 362
Business Description:
Textile Product Mfr
S.I.C.: 2299
N.A.I.C.S.: 314999
Personnel:
Hajime Kanno *(CEO)*

Subsidiaries:

Asahi Processing Co., Ltd. (1)
8-14-8-1 Minamihonmachi
Chuo-ku, Osaka, Japan
Tel.: (81) 6 6271 2046
Fax: (81) 6 6271 2060
Textile Product Mfr
S.I.C.: 2389
N.A.I.C.S.: 314999

Daiwa Maruesu Inc. (1)
Uozumicho Shimizu
Akashi, Hyogo, Japan
Tel.: (81) 789467501
Fax: (81) 789463532
Web Site: www.daiwa-maruesu.jp
Textile Products Mfr
S.I.C.: 2389
N.A.I.C.S.: 314999

Daiwabo Information System Co., Ltd. (1)
Hommachi DIS Building 3-2-5 Hommachi
Chuo-ku, Osaka, 541-0053, Japan
Tel.: (81) 662811161
Fax: (81) 662811164
Web Site: www.pc-daiwabo.co.jp
Sales Range: $1-4.9 Billion
Emp.: 1,772
Personal Computer & Office Automation Machine Sales
S.I.C.: 5045
N.A.I.C.S.: 423430
Yoshihiro Nogami *(Pres & CEO)*
Tatsuya Yasunaga *(Sr Mng Dir)*
Yoshio Koyama *(Mng Dir)*

Subsidiaries:

DIS Artworks Co., Ltd. (2)
Oi 1-20-10 Sumitomo Oimachibiru South Bldg Shinagawa-ku
140-0014 Tokyo, Japan
Tel.: (81) 3 6429 6069
Fax: (81) 3 5745 015
Web Site: www.disart.co.jp
Commercial Printing & Promotional Products
S.I.C.: 2759
N.A.I.C.S.: 323111
Kaoru Kikui *(Pres)*

DIS Logistics Co., Ltd. (2)
Hommachi Dis Building 7th Floor
Osaka, Japan
Tel.: (81) 662811301
Fax: (81) 662587213
Web Site: www.pc-daiwabo.co.jp
Computer-Controlled Inventory Control & Delivery Systems
S.I.C.: 4225
N.A.I.C.S.: 493110

DIS Solution Co., Ltd. (2)
Sumitomo Oimachi Bldg Minami-Kan 2nd Fl
Shinagawa-Ku, 140-0014 Tokyo, Japan
Tel.: (81) 364296088
Fax: (81) 364296089
Web Site: www.dsol.co.jp
Emp.: 152
Custom Computer Programming Services
S.I.C.: 7371
N.A.I.C.S.: 541511
Sachio Takai *(Pres & CEO)*

DIS Technical Service Co., Ltd. (2)
TMC Building 2F Minami-Senju
Arakawa-ku, Tokyo, 6-44-1, Japan
Tel.: (81) 358118251
Fax: (81) 358118253
Web Site: www.pc-sk.co.jp
IT Services & Support
S.I.C.: 7379
N.A.I.C.S.: 541519
Itou Takashi Humi *(Pres)*

ZOA Corporation (2)
719 Ozuwa
Numazu City, Shizuoka, 410-0873, Japan
Tel.: (81) 559221975
Fax: (81) 5599225950
E-Mail: info@zoa.co.jp
Web Site: www.zoa.co.jp
3375—(JAS)
Emp.: 128
Computer Retail Operations
S.I.C.: 5731
N.A.I.C.S.: 443142
Yutaka Nagashima *(Pres)*

Daiwabo Neu Corporation (1)
Kyutaromachi
Chuo-ku, Osaka, Japan
Tel.: (81) 662812405
Fax: (81) 662812523
Textile Products MfrMfr
S.I.C.: 2399
N.A.I.C.S.: 314999

Daiwabo Rayon Co., Ltd. (1)
11F Sakaisuji Hommachi Bldg 1-8-14 Minamihommachi
Chuo-ku, Osaka, 541-0054, Japan
Tel.: (81) 662658022
Fax: (81) 662658105
Web Site: www.daiwaborayon.co.jp
Emp.: 28
Textile Product Mfr
S.I.C.: 2389
N.A.I.C.S.: 314999
Yujiro Satoh *(Pres)*

Plant:

Daiwabo Rayon Co., Ltd. - Masuda Mill (2)
3-1 Suko-cho
Masuda, Shimane, 698-0036, Japan
Tel.: (81) 856310550
Fax: (81) 856 22 8930
Cotton Yarn Mfr
S.I.C.: 2299
N.A.I.C.S.: 313110

Daiwabo Tex Inc (1)
Nittsu Nigyocho Building 6F 26-5 Nihonbashiningyocho 2-Chome
Chuo-Ku, Tokyo, 103-0013, Japan
Tel.: (81) 3 4332 5226
Fax: (81) 3 4332 5238
E-Mail: sales@daiwabo.net
Web Site: www.daiwabo-tex.co.jp
Textile Products Mfr
S.I.C.: 2389
N.A.I.C.S.: 314999
Ken Hariya *(Mgr)*

Daiwaboadvance co., ltd. (1)
Kyutaromachi
Chuo-ku, Osaka, Japan
Tel.: (81) 662536900
Fax: (81) 6 6253 6948
Web Site: www.daiwaboadvance.co.jp
Innerwear Mfr
S.I.C.: 2389
N.A.I.C.S.: 315990

Daiwabouasoshie Inc. (1)
8-6-3 Kyutaromachi
Chuo-ku, Osaka, Japan
Tel.: (81) 662812512
Fax: (81) 6 6281 2533
Textile Products Mfr
S.I.C.: 2399
N.A.I.C.S.: 314999

Daiwabouporitekku Inc. (1)
8-6-3 Kyutaromachi
Chuo-ku, Osaka, 541-0056, Japan
Tel.: (81) 662812414
Fax: (81) 6 6281 2536
Textile Products Mfr
S.I.C.: 2389
N.A.I.C.S.: 314999

Plants:

Daiwabouporitekku Inc. - Harima Plant (2)
877 Komiya Harima-cho
Kako-gun, Hyogo, Japan
Tel.: (81) 789421521
Fax: (81) 789426251
Emp.: 150
Textile Product Mfr
S.I.C.: 2399
N.A.I.C.S.: 314999
Sano Toyohiko *(Gen Mgr)*

Daiwabouporitekku Inc. - Mikawa Plant (2)
9-9-1 Kashimamachi
Hakusan, 929-0201, Japan
Tel.: (81) 762787820
Fax: (81) 762787811
Textile Product Mfr
S.I.C.: 2299
N.A.I.C.S.: 314999

Daiwabouraifusapoto Inc. (1)
8-14-1 Minamihonmachi
Chuo-ku, Osaka, 541-0054, Japan
Tel.: (81) 662660314
Fax: (81) 662660355
Textile Products Mfr
S.I.C.: 2389
N.A.I.C.S.: 314999

Dienupurodakutsu Inc. (1)
Uozumicho Nishioka
Akashi, 674-0084, Japan
Tel.: (81) 78 944 6753
Fax: (81) 78 944 6763
Textile Products Mfr
S.I.C.: 2389
N.A.I.C.S.: 314999

Kebi Industry Co., Ltd. (1)
1-5-24 Tadaokakita Tadaoka-cho
Senboku-gun, Osaka, Japan
Tel.: (81) 725203151
Fax: (81) 725203150
Textile Products Mfr
S.I.C.: 2389
N.A.I.C.S.: 314999

Non-U.S. Subsidiaries:

DAIWA DO BRASIL TEXTIL LTDA. (1)
Av Jose Andraus Gassani 2215-Distrito Industrial
Uberlandia, Minas Gerais, 38402-322, Brazil
Tel.: (55) 34 3292 6000
Fax: (55) 34 3292 6001
Textile Products Mfr
S.I.C.: 2389
N.A.I.C.S.: 314999
Fernando Ohhira *(Gen Mgr)*

PT DAIWABO INDUSTRIAL FABRICS INDONESIA (1)
Jl Raya Cirebon Bandung Km 12 Desa Plumbon
Kecamatan Plumbon, Cirebon, Jawa Barat, Indonesia
Tel.: (62) 231 324002
Fax: (62) 231 323984
Emp.: 129
Textile Products Mfr
S.I.C.: 2389
N.A.I.C.S.: 314999
Harif Yasuka *(Gen Mgr)*

PT DAYANI GARMENT INDONESIA (DGI) (1)
Jl Raya Narogong Km 11 Bantar Gebang
Bekasi, Indonesia
Tel.: (62) 21 8250092
Fax: (62) 21 8250093
Web Site: www.daiwabo.co.jp/company/grou p.html
Textile Products Mfr
S.I.C.: 2399
N.A.I.C.S.: 314999
Sinada Gorda *(Gen Mgr)*

PT TOKAI TEXPRINT INDONESIA (TTI) (1)
Jl Jababaka Laya B4 10 Cikarang Industrial Estate
Bekasi, West Java, Indonesia 17530
Tel.: (62) 21 893 4142
Fax: (62) 21 893 4801
Textile Products Mfr
S.I.C.: 2299
N.A.I.C.S.: 314999
Masaru Kasai *(Gen Mgr)*

DAIWASYSTEM CO., LTD.

3-6-1 Dosyo-machi Chuo-ku
Osaka, 541-0045, Japan
Tel.: (81) 662057011
Web Site: www.daiwasys.co.jp
Sales Range: $350-399.9 Million
Emp.: 240
Business Description:
Industrial & Commercial Construction Services; Other Real Estate Services
S.I.C.: 1542
N.A.I.C.S.: 236220
Personnel:
Kazuhiko Hiromoto *(Pres)*

DAIYANG METAL CO., LTD.

Star Gallery Bridge B/D 7F 1553-3 Seocho-dong
Seocho-gu, Seoul, Korea (South) 137-806
Tel.: (82) 2 2156 5500
Fax: (82) 2 2156 5563
Web Site: www.daiyangmetal.com
Year Founded: 1973
009190—(KRS)
Sales Range: $150-199.9 Million
Business Description:
Stainless Steel Mfr
S.I.C.: 3312
N.A.I.C.S.: 331110
Personnel:
Chan-ku Kang *(CEO)*

DAJIN HEAVY INDUSTRY CORPORATION

No 155 Xinqiu Street
Fuxin, Liaoning, 123005, China
Tel.: (86) 4186602601
Fax: (86) 4186600000
E-Mail: trade@dhicorp.cn
Web Site: www.djse.com.cn
Year Founded: 2000
002487—(SSE)
Sales Range: $75-99.9 Million
Emp.: 715
Business Description:
Steel Structure Products Mfr & Distr
S.I.C.: 3399
N.A.I.C.S.: 331110
Personnel:
Xin Jin *(CEO)*

DAJIN RESOURCES CORP.

Suite 450 789 West Pender St
Vancouver, BC, V6C 1H2, Canada

Tel.: (604) 681-6151
Fax: (604) 689-7654
E-Mail: info@dajin.ca
Web Site: www.dajin.ca
DJI—(TSXV)
Int. Income: $2,226
Assets: $5,378,927
Liabilities: $934,226
Net Worth: $4,444,701
Earnings: ($406,359)
Fiscal Year-end: 11/30/12
Business Description:
Mineral Exploration Services
S.I.C.: 1081
N.A.I.C.S.: 213114
Personnel:
Stanley Brian Findlay *(Pres & CEO)*
Benjamin Ainsworth *(CFO)*
Board of Directors:
Benjamin Ainsworth
Steven Cozine
Stanley Brian Findlay
Legal Counsel:
Salley Bowes Harwardt
1750 - 1185 West Georgia Street
Vancouver, BC, Canada
Transfer Agent:
Computershare Investor Services Inc.
510 Burrard St
Vancouver, BC, V6C 3B9, Canada

DAKAR RESOURCE CORP.
570 Granville Street Suite 400
Vancouver, BC, V6C 1P1, Canada
Tel.: (604) 681-9588
Fax: (604) 681-4760
E-Mail: renatak@telus.net
Year Founded: 2010
DKR—(TSXV)
Business Description:
Metal Mining
S.I.C.: 1099
N.A.I.C.S.: 212299
Personnel:
Allen Wilson *(Pres & CEO)*
Henry Bromley *(CFO & Sec)*
Board of Directors:
Nicholas W. Baxter
Tim Callaway
Stephen Patrick Kenwood
Allen Wilson
Transfer Agent:
Olympia Trust Company
Suite 1003 750 West Pender Street
Vancouver, BC, V6C 2T8, Canada

DAKERYN INDUSTRIES LTD
Ste 210 233 W 1 st
North Vancouver, BC, V7M 1B3, Canada
Tel.: (604) 986-0323
Fax: (604) 986-3464
Web Site: www.dakeryn.com
Rev.: $85,977,174
Emp.: 14
Business Description:
Dimension Lumber Supplier
S.I.C.: 5031
N.A.I.C.S.: 423310
Personnel:
Rob Chimko *(Pres)*

DALAT REAL ESTATE JOINT STOCK COMPANY
21 Tran Phu Street Phuong 3
Da Lat, Da Lat, Lam Dong, Vietnam
Tel.: (84) 633822243
Fax: (84) 633821433
E-Mail: ctycpdiaocdl@vnn.vn
Web Site: www.dalatreal.com.vn
DLR—(HNX)
Emp.: 180
Business Description:
Construction & Real Estate Services
S.I.C.: 1542
N.A.I.C.S.: 236220
Personnel:
Anh Che *(Chm)*

DALATA HOTEL GROUP LTD
4th Floor Burton Court Burton Hall Drive
Sandyford, Dublin, 18, Ireland
Tel.: (353) 1 206 9400
Fax: (353) 1 206 9401
E-Mail: info@dalatahotelgroup.com
Web Site: www.dalatahotelgroup.com
Emp.: 2,500
Business Description:
Hotel Owner & Operator
S.I.C.: 7011
N.A.I.C.S.: 721110
Personnel:
John Hennessy *(Chm)*
Pat McCann *(CEO)*
Dermot Crowley *(Deputy CEO-Bus Dev & Fin)*
Stephen McNally *(Deputy CEO)*

DALDRUP & SOHNE AG
Ludinghauser Str 42-46
59387 Ascheberg, Germany
Tel.: (49) 25 93 95 93 0
Fax: (49) 25 93 72 70
E-Mail: info@daldrup.eu
Web Site: www.daldrup.eu
4DS—(DEU)
Sls.: $30,544,989
Assets: $136,569,772
Liabilities: $47,556,646
Net Worth: $89,013,126
Earnings: $1,567,439
Emp.: 141
Fiscal Year-end: 12/31/12
Business Description:
Drilling Services
S.I.C.: 1381
N.A.I.C.S.: 213111
Personnel:
Wolfgang Clement *(Chm-Supervisory Bd)*
Josef Daldrup *(CEO & Member-Mgmt Bd)*
Curd Bems *(CFO & Member-Mgmt Bd)*
Andreas Tonies *(COO & Member-Mgmt Bd)*
Peter Maasewerd *(Member-Mgmt Bd)*
Supervisory Board of Directors:
Wolfgang Clement
Wolfgang Quecke
Joachim Rumstadt
Subsidiaries:

GeoEnergie Taufkirchen GmbH & Co. KG (1)
Bavariafilmplatz 7
Geiselgasteig, 82031 Grunwald, Germany
Tel.: (49) 89 452437911
Fax: (49) 89 452437988
E-Mail: info@geoenergie-taufkirchen.de
Web Site: www.exorka.de/geo
Geothermal Energy Drilling Services
S.I.C.: 1629
N.A.I.C.S.: 237110

Geothermie Neuried Verwaltungs GmbH (1)
Kirchstr 21
77743 Neuried, Baden-Wurttemberg, Germany
Tel.: (49) 89 4524379 11
Geothermal Energy Drilling Services
S.I.C.: 1623
N.A.I.C.S.: 237110

DALE CAPITAL GROUP LIMITED
2 River Court Saint Denis Street
Port Louis, Mauritius
Tel.: (230) 212 6946
Fax: (230) 213 0134
E-Mail: enquires@dale-capital.com
Web Site: www.dale-capital.com
Year Founded: 2000
DCPL—(MAU)
Rev.: $2,746,370
Assets: $12,689,699
Liabilities: $11,002,954
Net Worth: $1,686,745
Earnings: ($10,515,105)
Fiscal Year-end: 02/28/13
Business Description:
Investment Management Services
S.I.C.: 6211
N.A.I.C.S.: 523999
Personnel:
Norman Theodore Noland *(Chm & CEO)*
Board of Directors:
Norman Theodore Noland
Nigel McGowan
Jacobus Cornelis Pauw
Sanjeeven Ramasawmy
Transfer Agent:
Mossack Fonseca & Co. (B.V.I) Ltd
Akara Building 24 De Castro Street Wickhams Cay 1 Road Town
Tortola, Virgin Islands (British)

DALE DOWNIE NISSAN INC
1111 Oxford St E
London, ON, N5Y 3C7, Canada
Tel.: (519) 451-4560
Fax: (519) 451-2824
Toll Free: (888) 711-4857
Web Site: www.daledownie.ca
Year Founded: 1995
Rev.: $38,595,829
Emp.: 80
Business Description:
New & Used Car Dealers
S.I.C.: 5511
N.A.I.C.S.: 441110
Personnel:
Dale Downie *(Pres)*

DALEKOVOD D.D.
Marijana Cavica 4
10000 Zagreb, Croatia
Tel.: (385) 12411111
Fax: (385) 16171283
E-Mail: dalekovod@dalekovod.hr
Web Site: www.dalekovod.com
DLKV-R-A—(ZAG)
Sls.: $222,812,620
Assets: $341,294,898
Liabilities: $307,755,157
Net Worth: $33,539,741
Earnings: ($76,476,077)
Emp.: 1,794
Fiscal Year-end: 12/31/12
Business Description:
Engineering, Manufacturing & Construction Services
S.I.C.: 8711
N.A.I.C.S.: 541330
Personnel:
Marijan Pavlovic *(Chm-Supervisory Bd)*
Matjaz Gorjup *(Chm-Mgmt Bd & Mng Dir)*
Kresimir Anusic *(Member-Mgmt Bd)*
Goran Brajdic *(Member-Mgmt Bd)*
Marko Jurkovic *(Member-Mgmt Bd)*
Zeljko Leksic *(Member-Mgmt Bd)*
Zeljka Klipic *(Sec)*
Supervisory Board of Directors:
Marijan Pavlovic
Ante Curkovic
Davor Doko
Natasa Ivanovic
Viktor Miletic
Dubravko Stimac

Subsidiaries:

Dalekovod-Cincaonica d.o.o., (1)
Trnoscica bb
10 370 Dugo Selo, Croatia
Tel.: (385) 12784110
Fax: (385) 12753652
E-Mail: cincaonica@dalekovod.hr
Web Site: www.dalekovod-cincaonica.com
Steel Products Mfr
S.I.C.: 3399
N.A.I.C.S.: 331110

Dalekovod EMU d.o.o. (1)
43 Street no 36
20 270 Vela Luka, Dubrovnik-Neretva, Croatia
Tel.: (385) 20813440
Fax: (385) 20 813 441
E-Mail: emu@dalekovod.hr
Emp.: 6
Electricity Meters Mfr
S.I.C.: 3825
N.A.I.C.S.: 334515
Damir Skansi *(Asst Pres & Mng Dir)*

Dalekovod Professio d.o.o (1)
Marijana Cavica 4
10 000 Zagreb, Croatia
Tel.: (385) 12459708
Fax: (385) 16170450
E-Mail: dalekovod@dalekovod.hr
Web Site: www.dalekovod.com
Real Estate Consulting Services
S.I.C.: 6531
N.A.I.C.S.: 531210

Dalekovod-projekt d.o.o. (1)
Marijana Cavica 4
10 000 Zagreb, Croatia
Tel.: (385) 12411111
Fax: (385) 12411173
E-Mail: dalekovod.projekt@dalekovod.hr
Web Site: www.dalekovod-projekt.com
Emp.: 100
Electrical Engineering Services
S.I.C.: 8711
N.A.I.C.S.: 541330
Davor Durdevic *(Co-Pres)*
Damir Skansi *(Co-Pres)*
Ivo Milicic *(Deputy Pres)*

Plant:

DALEKOVOD d.d. - Velika Gorica Factory (1)
Vukomericka bb
10 410 Velika Gorica, Zagreb, Croatia
Tel.: (385) 16229900
Fax: (385) 16221199
E-Mail: dalekovod@dalekovod.hr
Web Site: www.dalekovod-pro.com
Emp.: 300
Electricity Transmission Equipments Mfr
S.I.C.: 3612
N.A.I.C.S.: 335311
Eivo Malfat *(Mgr-Sls)*

Non-U.S. Subsidiaries:

Dalcom Engineering GmbH (1)
Muenchener Strasse 67 D
83395 Freilassing, Bavaria, Germany
Tel.: (49) 8654608645
Fax: (49) 8654 608 608
E-Mail: dalcom@royce.at
Electric Power Generation Services
S.I.C.: 4931
N.A.I.C.S.: 221111

Dalekovod AG (1)
Muenchener Strasse 67 D
83395 Freilassing, Bavaria, Germany
Tel.: (49) 8654608645
Fax: (49) 8654 608 608
E-Mail: dalcom@royce.at
Web Site: www.dalekovod.com
Electric Power Generation Services
S.I.C.: 4931
N.A.I.C.S.: 221111

Dalekovod d.o.o., Ljubljana (1)
Zavetiska Ulica 1
1000 Ljubljana, Slovenia
Tel.: (386) 12561597
Fax: (386) 1 2561596
Electric Power Generation Services
S.I.C.: 4911
N.A.I.C.S.: 221111

Dalekovod d.d.—(Continued)

Dalekovod Kazakhstan (1)
Prospekt Kabanbay-Batyra 11
010000 Astana, Kazakhstan
Tel.: (7) 7172688894
Fax: (7) 7172688895
Web Site: www.dalekovod.com
Electric Power Generation Services
S.I.C.: 4931
N.A.I.C.S.: 221111

Dalekovod Skopje (1)
Ulica Jani Lukrovski br 8
10 000 Skopje, Macedonia
Tel.: (389) 23228853
Fax: (389) 23 17 15 43
Web Site: www.dalekovod.com
Electric Power Generation Services
S.I.C.: 4931
N.A.I.C.S.: 221111
Zorm Mikolov *(Mgr)*

Dalekovod TKS a.d. (1)
Rudanka 28 PP 246
74000 Doboj, Bosnia & Herzegovina
Tel.: (387) 53288100
Fax: (387) 53287378
E-Mail: tks-doboj@dalekovod.hr
Web Site: www.dalekovod-tks.com
Emp.: 256
Power Transmission Line & Structure Mfr
S.I.C.: 1623
N.A.I.C.S.: 237130
Jurica Prizmic *(Chm-Supervisory Bd)*
Damir Skansi *(Chm-Mgmt Bd)*
Savo Malesevic *(Vice Chm-Mgmt Bd)*
Milan Kovacevic *(Member-Mgmt Bd)*
Marko Kozina *(Member-Mgmt Bd)*
Zdenko Milas *(Member-Mgmt Bd)*

DALET S.A.

16 rue Rivay
92300 Levallois-Perret, France
Tel.: (33) 1 41 27 67 00
Fax: (33) 1 41 27 67 50
E-Mail: ddms@dalet.com
Web Site: www.dalet.com
Year Founded: 1990
DLT—(EUR)
Rev.: $46,308,248
Assets: $37,154,292
Liabilities: $19,923,316
Net Worth: $17,230,976
Earnings: $1,615,404
Fiscal Year-end: 12/31/12

Business Description:
Software Development Services
S.I.C.: 7371
N.A.I.C.S.: 541511

Personnel:
David Lasry *(Chm & CEO)*
Stephane Guez *(Deputy CEO)*
Stephane Schlayen *(Deputy CEO)*
Nicolas Breugnon *(CFO)*

DALETH PARTICIPACOES S.A.

Av Rio Branco 311 - Sala 523
20040903 Rio de Janeiro, Brazil
Tel.: (55) 21 2196 7200
Fax: (55) 21 2196 7201
Year Founded: 1998
OPDL3B—(BRAZ)
Emp.: 6,820

Business Description:
Investment Management Services
S.I.C.: 6282
N.A.I.C.S.: 523920

Personnel:
Alberto Ribeiro Guth *(Dir-IR)*

DALGASGROUP A/S

Klostermarken 12
DK 8800 Viborg, Denmark
Tel.: (45) 87281133
Fax: (45) 87281001
Web Site: www.dalgasgroup.com
Sales Range: $250-299.9 Million
Emp.: 1,100

Business Description:
Holding Company
S.I.C.: 6719
N.A.I.C.S.: 551112

Personnel:
Ove Kloch *(CEO & Mng Dir)*

Subsidiaries:

HedeDanmark a/s (1)
Klostermarken 12
8800 Viborg, Denmark
Tel.: (45) 87281000
Fax: (45) 87281254
E-Mail: info@hededanmark.dk
Web Site: www.hededanmark.com
Sales Range: $200-249.9 Million
Emp.: 1,000
Landscape & Forest Consulting & Management Services
S.I.C.: 0781
N.A.I.C.S.: 541320
Carsten Thygesen *(Mng Dir)*

Orbicon A/S (1)
Ringstedvej 20
Roskilde, 4000, Denmark (100%)
Tel.: (45) 46300310
Fax: (45) 46300311
E-Mail: info@orbicon.dk
Web Site: www.orbicon.com
Sales Range: $75-99.9 Million
Emp.: 400
Environmental Engineering & Consulting Services
S.I.C.: 8999
N.A.I.C.S.: 541620
Jesper Nybo Andersen *(CEO)*

Joint Venture:

Xergi A/S (1)
Hermesvej 1
DK 9530 Stovring, Denmark
Tel.: (45) 99351600
Fax: (45) 99351699
E-Mail: mail@xergi.com
Web Site: www.xergi.com
Sales Range: $10-24.9 Million
Emp.: 70
Turnkey Energy & Environmental System Designer; Joint Venture of Aktieselskabet Schouw & Co. (50%) & Dalgasgroup A/S (50%)
S.I.C.: 8711
N.A.I.C.S.: 541330

DALHOFF LARSEN & HORNEMAN A/S

(d/b/a DLH Group)
Skakensgade 66
2630 Tastrup, Denmark
Tel.: (45) 43500100
Fax: (45) 043500199
E-Mail: dlh@dlh-group.com
Web Site: www.dlh.com
DLH—(CSE)
Sls.: $436,326,912
Assets: $209,758,680
Liabilities: $101,705,004
Net Worth: $108,053,676
Earnings: ($34,791,444)
Emp.: 540
Fiscal Year-end: 12/31/12

Business Description:
Timber & Forest Products Producer
S.I.C.: 2448
N.A.I.C.S.: 321920

Personnel:
Kurt Anker Nielsen *(Chm-Supervisory Bd)*
Kristian Kolding *(Vice Chm-Supervisory Bd)*
Kent Arentoft *(Pres & CEO)*
Michael Skovbo Buhlmann *(Exec VP-Sls-Nordic)*
Martin Grome *(Exec VP-Sls-USA)*
Mette Rubak Kaarsbo *(Exec VP-Product Mgmt & Grp Mktg)*
Jerzy Karpinski *(Exec VP-Sls-Central Eastern Europe & Russia)*
Soren Strand Larsen *(Exec VP-Sls-Western Europe)*
Poul Leineweber *(Exec VP-Global Sls)*
Peter Thostrup *(Exec VP-Fin & IT)*

Supervisory Board of Directors:
Kurt Anker Nielsen
Jesper Birkefeldt
Lene Burup
Lars Green
Peter Hogsted
Ann Hoy-Thomsen
Kristian Kolding
Agnete Raaschou-Nielsen
John Staer

U.S. Subsidiary:

DLH Nordisk Inc (1)
2307 W Cone Blvd
Greensboro, NC 27408
Tel.: (336) 852-8341
Fax: (336) 852-1933
Toll Free: (800) 688-2882
E-Mail: dlhusa@dlh-group.com
Web Site: www.dlhusa.com
Emp.: 50
Timber Products Whslr
S.I.C.: 5099
N.A.I.C.S.: 423990

Non-U.S. Subsidiaries:

DLH Cote d'Ivoire S.A (1)
01 Abidjan 01 Rue Saint Jean
BP 2648
Cocody, Abidjan, Cote d'Ivoire
Tel.: (225) 22 40 47 40
Fax: (225) 22 44 04 96
Web Site: www.dlh.com
Emp.: 17
Wood Panels & Veneer Whslr
S.I.C.: 5031
N.A.I.C.S.: 423310
Antonio Matteo Milocchi *(Gen Mgr)*

DLH Finland OY (1)
Heidehofintie 4
01300 Vantaa, Finland
Tel.: (358) 20 7902770
Fax: (358) 20 7902779
Web Site: www.dlh-finland.fi
Timber Products Mfr & Distr
S.I.C.: 2439
N.A.I.C.S.: 321213

DLH Nederland B.V (1)
Eemweg 8
3742 LB Baarn, Netherlands
Tel.: (31) 356930720
Fax: (31) 3569 13649
E-Mail: info.nederland@dlh-group.com
Web Site: www.dlh-nederland.nl
Emp.: 8
Wood Whslr
S.I.C.: 5031
N.A.I.C.S.: 423310

DLH Norge AS (1)
Hvamveien 4
N-2013 Skjetten, Norway
Tel.: (47) 2207 0550
Fax: (47) 2207 0551
E-Mail: dlhno@dlh-group.com
Web Site: www.dlh-norge.no
Wood Products Whslr
S.I.C.: 5031
N.A.I.C.S.: 423310
Kim Martens Meyer *(Mgr-Sls)*

DLH Poland Sp. z o.o (1)
Ul Sosnkowskiego 1 D
02-495 Warsaw, Poland
Tel.: (48) 22 667 4414
Fax: (48) 22 667 4288
Web Site: www.dlh-poland.com
Wood Whslr
S.I.C.: 5031
N.A.I.C.S.: 423310

DLH Procurement Cameroun S.A.R.L (1)
BP 4385
Douala, Cameroon
Tel.: (237) 999 111 93
Wood Panels & Veneer Whslr
S.I.C.: 5031
N.A.I.C.S.: 423310

DLH Slovakia s.r.o (1)
Logisticke Centrum Priemyselna 1
900 21 Svaty Jur, Slovakia
Tel.: (421) 2 3300 0271
Fax: (421) 2 3300 0278
E-Mail: info@dlhslovakia.sk
Web Site: www.dlh-slovakia.com
Wood Products Whslr
S.I.C.: 5031
N.A.I.C.S.: 423310
Marcel Novak *(Mgr-Country)*

DLH Sverige AB (1)
N Industrigatan
Box 2014
281 02 Hassleholm, Sweden
Tel.: (46) 771 82 83 10
Fax: (46) 771 82 83 11
E-Mail: info-sverige@dlh-group.com
Web Site: www.dlh.se
Wood Products Whslr
S.I.C.: 5031
N.A.I.C.S.: 423310
Kant Arentoft *(Gen Mgr)*

East Asiatic Timber (Holland) B.V. (1)
Amsterdam, Netherlands
S.I.C.: 5084
N.A.I.C.S.: 425120

Indufor N.V. (1)
Noorderlaan 125
Antwerp, 2030, Belgium
Tel.: (32) 35426370
Fax: (32) 35421894
E-Mail: mail@indufor.com
Web Site: www.dlh-belgium.com
Emp.: 15
Industrial Machinery Sls
S.I.C.: 7389
N.A.I.C.S.: 425120

Subsidiaries:

DLH France S.A.S. (1)
Rue de l'Ile Botty Zl de Chevire
44340 Nantes, Bougenais Cedex, 04, France (100%)
Tel.: (33) 240652510
Fax: (33) 240652774
E-Mail: info@dlh-france.com
Web Site: www.dlh.fr
Emp.: 14
Wood Distribution
S.I.C.: 0811
N.A.I.C.S.: 113110
Blred Mechil *(Gen Mgr)*

DLH Nordisk Sp zoo (1)
Kolobrzeska 3
78 230 Karlino, Poland (100%)
Tel.: (48) 943127000
Fax: (48) 943117275
E-Mail: dlh@dlh.pl
Web Site: www.dlh.pl
Sales Range: $10-24.9 Million
Emp.: 72
S.I.C.: 7389
N.A.I.C.S.: 425120

Nordisk Timber Ltda. (1)
565 Trav Dr Moraes 5th Floor
Belem, 66035-080, Brazil (100%)
Tel.: (55) 91 3222 7088
Fax: (55) 91 3222 7088
Web Site: www.dlh.com
Lumber Operations
S.I.C.: 0811
N.A.I.C.S.: 113110

DLH Denmark A/S (1)
Nordkajen 21
6000 Kolding, Denmark (100%)
Tel.: (45) 43500800
Fax: (45) 43500720
E-Mail: dlhdk@dlh-group.com
Web Site: www.dlh.dk
Emp.: 350
Sales of Hardwood & Wood-Based Panel Products
S.I.C.: 2435
N.A.I.C.S.: 321211
Ole Juul Kirkeby *(Country Mgr)*

DALIA LTD.

6 Sazaklyatie Str
Gabrovo, 5300, Bulgaria
Tel.: (359) 888 205 930

E-Mail: daliagb@gmail.com
Web Site: www.dalia.bg
DAD—(BUL)
Business Description:
Woodworking & Furniture Products Mfr
S.I.C.: 5712
N.A.I.C.S.: 442110
Personnel:
Petya Cvyatkova Racheva-Ivanova *(Dir-IR)*

DALIAN EAST NEW ENERGY DEVELOPMENT CO., LTD.

(d/b/a East New Energy)
2-1 Xuezi Street
Hi-Tech Zone, Dalian, 116023, China
Tel.: (86) 411 84732580
Fax: (86) 411 84732586
E-Mail: dlyishida@163.com
Web Site: www.dleast.cc
300125—(CHIN)
Sales Range: $25-49.9 Million
Emp.: 218
Business Description:
Heavy Engineering & Construction Services
S.I.C.: 1629
N.A.I.C.S.: 237990
Personnel:
Qun Liu *(Chm)*
Jinquan Tang *(CTO)*

DALIAN INSULATOR GROUP CO., LTD.

88 Liaohe East Road DD Port
Dalian Econ & Tech Dev Area,
Dalian, 116600, China
Tel.: (86) 411 82168888
Fax: (86) 411 82168008
E-Mail: info@insulators.cn
Web Site: www.insulators.cn
002606—(SSE)
Sales Range: $75-99.9 Million
Emp.: 2,060
Business Description:
Porcelain & Ceramic Insulator Mfr
S.I.C.: 3269
N.A.I.C.S.: 327110
Personnel:
Guixue Liu *(Chm & Gen Mgr)*

DALIAN KEMIAN WOOD INDUSTRY CO., LTD.

Changsheng Industrial Park
Zhuanghe, Dalian, Liaoing, 116400, China
Tel.: (86) 411 89376969
Fax: (86) 411 89376333
Web Site: www.kemianwood.com
Year Founded: 2003
002354—(SSE)
Sales Range: $25-49.9 Million
Emp.: 600
Business Description:
Wooded Floor Boards Mfr & Distr
S.I.C.: 2431
N.A.I.C.S.: 321918
Personnel:
Ping Wei *(Chm)*

DALIAN PORT (PDA) COMPANY LIMITED

No 1 Gangwan Street
Zhongshan District, Dalian, Liaoning, China 116001
Tel.: (86) 41182798566
Fax: (86) 41182798108
E-Mail: ir@dlport.cn
Web Site: www.dlport.cn
2880—(HKG OTC)
Rev.: $737,788,196
Assets: $4,420,601,772
Liabilities: $2,200,674,322
Net Worth: $2,219,927,449
Earnings: $108,774,611
Emp.: 9,454
Fiscal Year-end: 12/31/12
Business Description:
Oil & Chemical Port & Terminal Operations
S.I.C.: 4491
N.A.I.C.S.: 488310
Personnel:
Kai Hui *(Chm)*
Junyou Sun *(Chm-Supervisory Bd)*
Chunhua Su *(CFO)*
Yuchan Gui *(Co-Sec)*
Arthur Kin Yu Lee *(Co-Sec)*
Board of Directors:
Kai Hui
Liyi Gui
Yongze Liu
Chunhua Su
Peter Kam To Wan
Jian Xu
Song Xu
Zuogang Zhang
Shiliang Zhu
Supervisory Board of Directors:
Junyou Sun
Weihong Jiang
Jing Lv
Fangsheng Xu
Guofeng Zhang
Xianzhi Zhang
Legal Counsel:
Morrison & Foerster
33/F Edinburgh Tower The Landmark 15 Queen's Road
Central, China (Hong Kong)
Liaoning Huaxia Law Firm
5th Floor Liyuan Mansion 16 Mingze Street
Dalian, China
Transfer Agent:
Computershare Hong Kong Investor Services Limited
Shops 1712-1716 17th Floor Hopewell Centre
183 Queens Road East
Wanchai, China (Hong Kong)

DALIAN REFRIGERATION CO. LTD.

888 Xinan Rd
Dalian, China 116033
Tel.: (86) 41186641744
Fax: (86) 41186658099
Web Site: en.daleng.cn
000530—(SSE)
Sales Range: $250-299.9 Million
Emp.: 1,306
Business Description:
Refrigeration Equipment Mfr & Whslr
S.I.C.: 3585
N.A.I.C.S.: 333415
Personnel:
He Zhang *(Chm & Gen Mgr)*

DALIAN SHIDE GROUP CO., LTD.

(d/b/a Shide Group)
38 Gao Er Ji Road
XiGang District, Dalian, Liaoning, 116011, China
Tel.: (86) 41183622218
Fax: (86) 008641187602971
E-Mail: kethy_shide@hotmail.com
Web Site: www.shide.com
Year Founded: 1992
Sales Range: $800-899.9 Million
Emp.: 5,500
Business Description:
Holding Company; Chemical Building Materials, Petrochemicals & Home Appliances Mfr & Distr
S.I.C.: 6719
N.A.I.C.S.: 551112
Personnel:
Ming Xu *(Chm)*
Bin Xu *(Vice Chm)*
Chunguo Chen *(Pres)*
Xin Guang Ruan *(Sec)*

Subsidiary:

Dalian Shide Plastics Industry Co., Ltd. **(1)**
38 Gao Er Ji Road
XiGang District, Dalian, Liaoning, 116011, China CN
Tel.: (86) 41183622218
E-Mail: shide@mail.dlptt.ln.cn
Web Site: www.shide-global.com
Chemical & Plastic Building Materials Mfr & Distr
S.I.C.: 2899
N.A.I.C.S.: 325998
Chunguo Chen *(Pres)*

DALIAN SUNLIGHT MACHINERY CO., LTD.

Dalian High-tech Park 39 Qixianling Torch
Dalian, 116024, China
Tel.: (86) 411 84791333
Fax: (86) 411 84799393
E-Mail: sales@slsj.com.cn
Web Site: www.slsj.com.cn
002621—(SSE)
Sales Range: $25-49.9 Million
Emp.: 340
Business Description:
Plastic Pipe Equipment Mfr
S.I.C.: 3559
N.A.I.C.S.: 333249
Personnel:
Jianmo Yu *(Chm)*

DALIAN TONGHAI MACHINERY & ELECTRONIC EQUIPMENT CO., LTD.

38 Anshan Rd
Dalian, Shahekou District, 116022, China
Tel.: (86) 411 844 22299
Fax: (86) 411 836 13962
Web Site:
Year Founded: 1948
Business Description:
Machine Tool Mfr
S.I.C.: 3541
N.A.I.C.S.: 333517

U.S. Subsidiaries:

ICM **(1)**
3505 Centennial Dr
Midland, MI 48642-6940
Tel.: (989) 495-5000
Fax: (989) 495-5001
E-Mail: info@teamicms.com
Web Site: www.teamicms.com
Emp.: 50
S.I.C.: 3541
N.A.I.C.S.: 333517
Brianna Witkowski *(Controller)*

Ingersoll Production Systems **(1)**
1301 Eddy Ave
Rockford, IL 61103-3173
Tel.: (815) 637-8500
Telex: 257427
Fax: (815) 636-1202
E-Mail: Sales@ingersollprodsys.com
Web Site: www.ingersollprodsys.com
Emp.: 60
Machine Tool Services
S.I.C.: 3542
N.A.I.C.S.: 333517
Scott Kuhar *(Engr-Design Controls)*

DALIAN TOP-EASTERN GROUP CO., LTD.

No 218 Zhenxing Road Dalianwan
Ganjingzi District, Dalian, 116113, China
Tel.: (86) 411 8710 3396
Fax: (86) 411 8760 9222
Web Site: www.top-eastern.com
Sales Range: $50-74.9 Million
Emp.: 2,000
Business Description:
Holding Company
S.I.C.: 6719
N.A.I.C.S.: 551112
Personnel:
Shumin Qi *(CEO)*

U.S. Holding:

Greenfield Industries, Inc. **(1)**
2501 Davis Creek Rd
Seneca, SC 29678
Tel.: (706) 863-7708
Fax: (706) 860-8559
E-Mail: greenfield.information@gfii.com
Web Site: www.gfii.com
Emp.: 200
Industrial Cutting Tools Mfr & Supplier
S.I.C.: 3542
N.A.I.C.S.: 333517
Ty Taylor *(Pres & CEO)*

Non-U.S. Subsidiaries:

Greenfield Industries Canada Inc. **(2)**
1305 Meyerside Dr
Mississauga, ON, L5T 1C9, Canada (100%)
Tel.: (905) 696-8561
Telex: 6-989155
Fax: (905) 696-8938
E-Mail: customerservice@gfii.com
Web Site: www.greenfield-industries.com
Sales Range: $25-49.9 Million
Emp.: 12
Cutting Tools Mfr & Whslr
S.I.C.: 3542
N.A.I.C.S.: 333517
Mike Tusch *(Mgr-Sls)*

Herramientas Cleveland, S.A. de C.V. **(2)**
Calz Azcapotzalco La Villa No 1001
Col Industrial Vallejo, Mexico, DF, 02300, Mexico
Tel.: (52) 55 5587 7400
Telex: 17-5516
Fax: (52) 55 5567 7811
E-Mail: info@herramientascleveland.com
Web Site: www.herramientascleveland.com
Emp.: 150
Cutting Tools, Machine Tool Accessories & Machinists Precision Measuring Devices
S.I.C.: 3545
N.A.I.C.S.: 333515
Manuel Barron *(Gen Mgr)*

DALIAN WANDA GROUP CORPORATION LTD.

(d/b/a Wanda Group)
Floor 28 Wanda Mansion No 9 Jiefang Street
Zhongshan District, Dalian, 116001, China
Tel.: (86) 411 8282 2888 (-111)
Fax: (86) 411 8282 0888
Web Site: www.wanda.cn
Year Founded: 1988
Sales Range: $15-24.9 Billion
Emp.: 50,000
Business Description:
Holding Company; Commercial Properties, Luxury Hotels, Tourism Investment, Cultural Industry Investment & Department Stores Owner & Operator
S.I.C.: 6719
N.A.I.C.S.: 551112
Personnel:
Jianlin Wang *(Chm & Pres)*

U.S. Subsidiary:

AMC Entertainment Holdings, Inc. **(1)**
One AMC Way 11500 Ash St
Leawood, KS 66211 DE
Tel.: (913) 213-2000
Web Site: www.amctheatres.com
AMC—(NYSE)

Dalian Wanda Group Corporation Ltd.—(Continued)

Rev.: $2,749,428,000
Assets: $5,046,724,000
Liabilities: $3,539,254,000
Net Worth: $1,507,470,000
Earnings: $364,400,000
Emp.: 900
Fiscal Year-end: 12/31/13
Holding Company; Motion Picture Theaters Owner & Operator
S.I.C.: 6719
N.A.I.C.S.: 551112
Lin Zhang *(Chm)*
Craig R. Ramsey *(CFO & Exec VP)*
Xin He *(Deputy CFO)*
Michael Czinege *(CIO)*
Stephen A. Colanero *(CMO & Exec VP)*
Chris A. Cox *(Chief Acctg Officer & Sr VP)*
Keith P. Wiedenkeller *(Chief People Officer & Sr VP)*
Elizabeth Furst Frank *(Chief Content Officer, Chief Programming Officer & Exec VP)*
Robert J. Lenihan *(Pres-Programming)*
Kevin M. Connor *(Gen Counsel, Sec & Sr VP)*
Terry W. Crawford *(Treas & Sr VP)*
John D. McDonald *(Exec VP-Ops-United States)*
Mark A. McDonald *(Exec VP-Global Dev)*
Christina Sternberg *(Sr VP-Corp Strategy)*
Michael W. Zwonitzer *(Sr VP-Fin)*

Subsidiaries:

AMC Entertainment Inc. **(2)**
1 AMC Way 11500 Ash St
Leawood, KS 66211 DE
Tel.: (913) 213-2000 (100%)
Web Site: www.amctheatres.com
Rev.: $2,749,428,000
Assets: $5,046,724,000
Liabilities: $3,537,785,000
Net Worth: $1,508,939,000
Earnings: $364,400,000
Emp.: 900
Fiscal Year-end: 12/31/13
Motion Picture Theaters Owner & Operator
S.I.C.: 7832
N.A.I.C.S.: 512131
Lin Zhang *(Chm)*
Gerardo I. Lopez *(Pres & CEO)*
Craig R. Ramsey *(CFO & Exec VP)*
Stephen A. Colanero *(CMO & Exec VP)*
Chris A. Cox *(Chief Acctg Officer & Sr VP)*
Elizabeth Furst Frank *(Chief Content Officer, Chief Programming Officer & Exec VP)*
Samuel D. Gourley *(Pres-AMC Film Programming)*
Robert J. Lenihan *(Pres-Programming)*
Kevin M. Connor *(Gen Counsel, Sec & Sr VP)*
Terry W. Crawford *(Treas & Sr VP)*
John D. McDonald *(Exec VP-Ops-United States)*
Mark A. McDonald *(Exec VP-Global Dev)*
Carla Sanders *(Sr VP-HR)*
Christina Sternberg *(Sr VP-Corp Strategy & Comm)*
Michael W. Zwonitzer *(Sr VP-Fin)*

Subsidiaries:

AMC Entertainment International, Inc. **(3)**
920 Main St
Kansas City, MO 64105 DE
Mailing Address:
PO Box 219615
Kansas City, MO 64121-9615
Tel.: (816) 221-4000
Fax: (816) 480-4725
Web Site: www.amctheaters.com
Emp.: 250
Motion Picture Theaters Operator
S.I.C.: 7832
N.A.I.C.S.: 512131
Gerardo I. Lopez *(Pres & CEO)*
Craig R. Ramsey *(CFO & Exec VP)*
Kevin M. Connor *(Gen Counsel, Sec & Sr VP)*

Non-U.S. Subsidiaries:

Cinemark de Mexico, S.A. de C.V. **(1)**
Calderon de La Barca 89 Piso 3 Polanco Chaputepec
Seccion Miguel Hidalgo, Mexico, 11560, Mexico
Tel.: (52) 5552801882
Fax: (52) 5552811240
E-Mail: steier@cemamarq.com
Motion Picture Exhibition Services
S.I.C.: 7832
N.A.I.C.S.: 512131

Wanda Commercial Properties (Group) Co., Ltd. **(1)**
(Formerly Hengli Commercial Properties (Group) Limited)
Unit 3007 30/F Two Exchange Square 8 Connaught Place
Central, China (Hong Kong) BM
Tel.: (852) 2153 3600 (65%)
Fax: (852) 2153 3610
E-Mail: wanda.ir@wanda.com.cn
Web Site: www.wanda-cp.com.hk
0169—(HKG)
Rev.: $357,632,380
Assets: $796,083,399
Liabilities: $693,545,196
Net Worth: $102,538,203
Earnings: $31,381,659
Emp.: 254
Fiscal Year-end: 12/31/12
Real Estate Development Services
S.I.C.: 6531
N.A.I.C.S.: 531312
Benxi Ding *(Chm)*

DALIAN ZHIYUN AUTOMATION CO., LTD.

(d/b/a Zhiyun Automation)
21/F Ning'an Building 17 Huanghe Road
Xigang District, Dalian, 116011, China
Tel.: (86) 41183630388
Fax: (86) 41183612292
Web Site: www.zhiyun-cn.com
Year Founded: 1999
300097—(CHIN)
Business Description:
Automation Equipment Mfr & Sales
S.I.C.: 3823
N.A.I.C.S.: 334513
Personnel:
Tan Yongliang *(Gen Mgr)*

DALLAH AL BARAKA HOLDING COMPANY E.C.

Dallah Tower Palestine St
PO Box 2618
Jeddah, 21461, Saudi Arabia
Tel.: (966) 26710000
Fax: (966) 26713603
Web Site: www.dallah.com
Sales Range: $1-4.9 Billion
Emp.: 38,250
Business Description:
Holding Company; Industrial Investment; Agriculture; Real Estate Development; Tourism; Transportation; Media; Construction; Communications; Finance & Insurance
S.I.C.: 6719
N.A.I.C.S.: 551112
Personnel:
Saleh Abdullah Kamel *(Chm, Pres & CEO)*

Non-U.S. Subsidiary:

Islamic Arab Insurance Co. (P.S.C.) **(1)**
4th Floor Spectrum Building Plot 319-0145
Oud Metha Sheikh Rashid Road
PO Box 10214
Dubai, United Arab Emirates
Tel.: (971) 43577000
Fax: (971) 43577996
E-Mail: Customerservices.gt@salama.ae
Web Site: www.salama.ae
SALAMA—(DFM)
Rev.: $515,087,585
Assets: $1,320,502,228
Liabilities: $976,619,673
Net Worth: $343,882,555
Earnings: ($99,081,958)
Emp.: 350
Fiscal Year-end: 12/31/12
Insurance Services
S.I.C.: 6411
N.A.I.C.S.: 524298
Khaled Zayed Al Nehayan *(Chm)*
Saleh J. Malaikah *(Vice Chm & CEO)*

DALLAH HEALTH SERVICE HOLDING COMPANY

PO Box 87833
11652 Riyadh, Saudi Arabia
Tel.: (966) 12995555
Fax: (966) 14702748
E-Mail: info@dallahhealth.com
Web Site: www.dallahhealth.com
Year Founded: 1987
4004—(SAU)
Business Description:
Hospital Owner & Operator
S.I.C.: 8062
N.A.I.C.S.: 622110
Personnel:
Tariq Osman Alkasabi *(Chm)*

DALLI-WERKE GMBH & CO. KG

(d/b/a Dalli Group)
Zweifaller Strasse 120
D-52220 Stolberg, Germany
Tel.: (49) 24028900
Fax: (49) 2402892222
E-Mail: kontakt@dalli-group.com
Web Site: www.dalli-group.com
Year Founded: 1845
Emp.: 2,000
Business Description:
Private Label Brand Mfr
S.I.C.: 3999
N.A.I.C.S.: 339999
Personnel:
Hermann Wirtz *(Chm-Mgmt Bd)*
Markus Kessler *(Member-Mgmt Bd)*

DALLMEIER ELECTRONIC GMBH & CO. KG

Cranachweg 1
93051 Regensburg, Germany
Tel.: (49) 94187000
Fax: (49) 9418700180
Web Site: www.dallmeier-electronic.com
Year Founded: 1984
Rev.: $29,657,100
Emp.: 108
Business Description:
Software Technology Solution Service
S.I.C.: 7371
N.A.I.C.S.: 541511
Personnel:
Dieter Dallmeier *(Pres & CEO)*

DALLMER GMBH & CO. KG

Wiebelsheidestr 25
D-59757 Arnsberg, Germany
Tel.: (49) 293296160
Fax: (49) 29329616222
E-Mail: info@dallmer.de
Web Site: www.dallmer.de
Year Founded: 1913
Rev.: $19,984,500
Emp.: 170
Business Description:
Sanitary Ware Products Mfr
S.I.C.: 2676
N.A.I.C.S.: 322291
Personnel:
Harry Bauermeister *(Gen Mgr)*

DALMAC ENERGY INC.

4934 - 89 Street
Edmonton, AB, T6E 5K1, Canada
Tel.: (780) 988-8510
Fax: (780) 988-8512
Toll Free: (888) 632-5622
E-Mail: info@dalmacenergy.com
Web Site: www.dalmacenergy.com
DAL—(TSXV)
Rev.: $41,057,264
Assets: $32,935,760
Liabilities: $19,450,827
Net Worth: $13,484,933
Earnings: $1,424,079
Emp.: 180
Fiscal Year-end: 04/30/13
Business Description:
Hot Oiler, Vacuum, Hydro-Vac, Pressure & Tanker Truck Services
S.I.C.: 4789
N.A.I.C.S.: 488999
Personnel:
John Ivan Babic *(Chm, Pres & CEO)*
John Beasley *(CFO)*
Board of Directors:
John Ivan Babic
Steve M. Babic
Derek A. Callfas
Leonard D. Jaroszuk
Shawn T. Szydlowski
Transfer Agent:
Computershare Trust Company of Canada
9th Floor 100 University Avenue
Toronto, ON, Canada

Divisions:

Dalmac Oilfield Services Inc. **(1)**
338 E River Rd
T7V 1T8 Hinton, AB, Canada
Tel.: (780) 817-5286
Fax: (780) 817-3202
E-Mail: hinton@dalmac.ca
Web Site: www.dalmacenergy.com
Emp.: 4
Oil & Gas Operations Services
S.I.C.: 1389
N.A.I.C.S.: 213112
John I. Babic *(Pres & CEO)*

Dalmac Oilfield Services Inc.-Pigeon Lake **(1)**
RR 5
Wetaskiwin, AB, T9A 1X2, Canada (100%)
Tel.: (780) 352-9995
Fax: (780) 352-9449
Web Site: www.dalmacenergy.com
Emp.: 25
Oilfield Transportation Services
S.I.C.: 4612
N.A.I.C.S.: 486110
Don Harink *(Mgr-Div)*

Dalmac Oilfield Services Inc.-Warburg **(1)**
5603 50th St
PO Box 223
Warburg, AB, T0C 2T0, Canada (100%)
Tel.: (780) 848-2225
Fax: (780) 848-2240
E-Mail: warburg@dalmac.ca
Web Site: www.dalmacenergy.com
Emp.: 30
Oilfield Transportation Services
S.I.C.: 4619
N.A.I.C.S.: 486990
Tony Bryant *(Mgr-Warbur)*

Edson (Tinky Trucking) Division **(1)**
Ste 453 431 40th Street
PO Box 6448
Edson, AB, T7E 1T8, Canada (100%)
Tel.: (780) 723-3439
Fax: (780) 723-6420
E-Mail: edson@dalmac.ca
Web Site: www.tinkytanks.ca
Emp.: 8
Tanker Trucks Oil Services
S.I.C.: 4214
N.A.I.C.S.: 484220
James Rukavina *(Mgr-Div)*

Subsidiary:

Dalmac Oilfield Services Inc. (1)
310 2nd Ave
PO Box 1108
Fox Creek, AB, T0H 1P0, Canada
Tel.: (780) 622-3800
Fax: (780) 622-2401
E-Mail: foxcreek@dalmac.ca
Web Site: www.dalmac.ca
Emp.: 80
Tanker Truck Transportation Services
S.I.C.: 1389
N.A.I.C.S.: 213112
Jim Ericson *(Gen Mgr)*

DALMAR MOTORS LTD.

475 Wharncliffe Rd South
London, ON, N6J 2N1, Canada
Tel.: (519) 433-3181
Fax: (519) 672-5975
Web Site: www.dalmar.com
Year Founded: 1953
Rev.: $16,954,265
Emp.: 37
Business Description:
New & Used Car Dealers
S.I.C.: 5511
N.A.I.C.S.: 441110
Personnel:
Michael Dalglish *(Owner)*

DALMIA BHARAT ENTERPRISES LIMITED

(Name Changed to Dalmia Bharat Limited)

DALMIA BHARAT LIMITED

(Formerly Dalmia Bharat Enterprises Limited)
11th & 12th Floor Hansalaya Building
15-Barakhamba Road, New Delhi, 110 001, India
Tel.: (91) 1123310121
Fax: (91) 1123313303
E-Mail: info@dalmiabharat.com
Web Site: www.dalmiabharat.com
DALMIABEL—(NSE)
Rev.: $531,645,624
Assets: $1,482,931,170
Liabilities: $914,136,948
Net Worth: $568,794,222
Earnings: $36,544,194
Emp.: 1,256
Fiscal Year-end: 03/31/13
Business Description:
Cement Mfr
S.I.C.: 3241
N.A.I.C.S.: 327310
Personnel:
Yadu Hari Dalmia *(CEO & Mng Dir)*
Mahendra K. Singhi *(Grp CEO)*
Jai Hari Dalmia *(Mng Dir)*
Jayesh Doshi *(CFO)*
Nidhi Bisaria *(Compliance Officer & Sec)*
Board of Directors:
Pradip Kumar Khaitan
Bharat Anand
Gautam Dalmia
Jai Hari Dalmia
Puneet Yadu Dalmia
Yadu Hari Dalmia
N. Gopalaswamy
V. S. Jain
Donald M. Peck
Transfer Agent:
Karvy Computershare Private Limited
Plot No 17-24 Vittal Rao Nagar Madhapur
Hyderabad, 500 081, India
Tel.: (91) 40 2342 0818
Subsidiaries:

Dalmia Bharat Sugar and Industries Ltd (1)
Hansalaya Building 11th & 12th Floor 15
Barakhamba Road
New Delhi, 110001, India In
Tel.: (91) 1123310121
Fax: (91) 1123313303
E-Mail: corpcomm@dalmiacement.com
Web Site: www.dalmiasugar.com
500097—(BOM NSE)
Rev.: $191,605,338
Assets: $309,638,394
Liabilities: $224,593,560
Net Worth: $85,044,834
Earnings: $3,405,798
Emp.: 1,701
Fiscal Year-end: 03/31/13
Cement & Sugar Mfr
S.I.C.: 3241
N.A.I.C.S.: 327310
Jai Hari Dalmia *(Vice Chm)*
Gautam Dalmia *(CEO & Mng Dir)*
Anil Kataria *(CFO & Asst Exec Dir-Fin & Accts)*
K. V. Mohan *(Compliance Officer & Sec)*
V. Sundararaj *(Compliance Officer & Asst Gen Mgr-Accts)*
B. B. Mehta *(CEO-Bus)*

Dalmia Cement (Bharat) Limited (1)
Hansalaya Bldg 11th & 12th Fl 15
Barakhamba Rd
New Delhi, 110 001, India
Tel.: (91) 1123465100
Fax: (91) 1123313303
E-Mail: info@dalmiacement.com
Web Site: www.dalmiacement.com
Cement Mfr
S.I.C.: 3241
N.A.I.C.S.: 327310
Jai Hari Dalmia *(Vice Chm)*
Yadu Hari Dalmia *(Vice Chm)*
Gautam Dalmia *(Co-Mng Dir)*
Puneet Dalmia *(Co-Mng Dir)*

DALOL OIL SHARE COMPANY

Ethio-China Friendship St (Wollo Sefer)
PO Box 11937
Addis Ababa, Ethiopia
Tel.: (251) 114163838
Fax: (251) 114164002
E-Mail: info@daloloil.com
Web Site: www.daloloil.com
Year Founded: 2009
Emp.: 8
Business Description:
Petroleum Products & Lubricants Supplier; Oil & Gas Exploration Services; Gas Station Owner & Operator
S.I.C.: 5172
N.A.I.C.S.: 424720
Personnel:
Gebreamlak Gebregiorgis *(Sec)*
Board of Directors:
Fisseha Asres
Dereje Belay
Gebreamlak Gebregiorgis
Nebiyat Gezahegn
Dereje Walelign

DALRADIAN RESOURCES INC.

155 Wellington Street West Suite 2920
Toronto, ON, M5V 3H1, Canada
Tel.: (416) 583-5600
E-Mail: info@dalradian.com
Web Site: www.dalradian.com
Year Founded: 2009
DNA—(OTC TSX)
Int. Income: $306,480
Assets: $69,971,419
Liabilities: $1,643,447
Net Worth: $68,327,972
Earnings: ($7,092,252)
Emp.: 34
Fiscal Year-end: 12/31/12
Business Description:
Gold Mining Services
S.I.C.: 1041
N.A.I.C.S.: 212221
Personnel:
Thomas J. Obradovich *(Chm)*
Timothy Warman *(Pres)*
Patrick F. N. Anderson *(CEO)*
Keith D. McKay *(CFO & Sec)*
Board of Directors:
Thomas J. Obradovich
Patrick F. N. Anderson
Colin K. Benner
Ronald P. Gagel
Sean E. O. Roosen
Jonathan Arn Rubenstein
Ari B. Sussman
Grenville Thomas
Transfer Agent:
Valiant Trust Company
130 King Street West Suite 710
34
Toronto, ON, Canada

DALTON TIMMIS INSURANCE GROUP, INC.

35 Stone Church Road 3rd Floor
Ancaster, ON, L8N 3S4, Canada
Tel.: (905) 648-3922
Fax: (905) 648-6980
Toll Free: (888) 385-8466
E-Mail: info@daltontimmis.com
Web Site: www.daltontimmis.com
Year Founded: 1997
Sales Range: $25-49.9 Million
Emp.: 100
Business Description:
Insurance Brokerage Services
S.I.C.: 6411
N.A.I.C.S.: 524210
Personnel:
Greg Padovani *(Co-Owner & Partner)*
Domenic Tesone *(Co-Owner & Partner)*
Brian Timmis *(Co-Owner & Partner)*

DAMAC GROUP

Damac Exec Heights Opp Emmar Bus Park
PO Box 2195
Dubai, United Arab Emirates
Tel.: (971) 43731000
Fax: (971) 43731373
E-Mail: info@damacgroup.com
Web Site: www.damacgroup.com
Sales Range: $150-199.9 Million
Emp.: 5,000
Business Description:
Holding Company; Investments; Fast Food; Industrial Catering; Property Development; & Commercial Trading
S.I.C.: 6719
N.A.I.C.S.: 551112
Personnel:
Hussain Sajwani *(Chm)*
Sofyan Khatib *(Mng Dir-Food Div)*
Subsidiaries:

Blues Seafood Restaurant LLC (1)
Unit 3 Marina Walk
PO Box 2195
Dubai Marina, Dubai, United Arab Emirates
Tel.: (971) 43674747
Fax: (971) 43674797
E-Mail: blues@damacgroup.com
Web Site: www.damacholding.com
Full-Service Restaurants
S.I.C.: 5812
N.A.I.C.S.: 722511

DAMAC Invest Co. LLC (1)
Tecom Executive Heights Damac Building
PO Box 2195
Dubai, United Arab Emirates
Tel.: (971) 43322005
Fax: (971) 43732399
E-Mail: wilson@damacgroup.com
Web Site: www.damacgroup.com
Real Estate Property Lessors
S.I.C.: 6519
N.A.I.C.S.: 531190

DAMAC Securities LLC (1)
PO Box 2195
Dubai, United Arab Emirates
Tel.: (971) 43322005
Web Site: www.damacsecurities.com
Securities Brokerage
S.I.C.: 6211
N.A.I.C.S.: 523120
Adil Taqi *(Mng Dir)*

Non-U.S. Subsidiaries:

Al Amana Building Materials Co. L.L.C (1)
PO Box 1429
Ruwi, Oman
Tel.: (968) 24815080
Fax: (968) 24817554
E-Mail: alamana@alamana-oman.com
Web Site: www.damacholding.com
Emp.: 85
Building Material Dealers
S.I.C.: 5211
N.A.I.C.S.: 444190
R. Murali *(Gen Mgr)*

Al-Jazeira Services Co. SAOG (1)
408 4th Floor International Medical Centre
Near Al Hamriya Roundabout
PO Box 2865, 112 Ruwi, Oman
Tel.: (968) 24706499
Fax: (968) 24703653
E-Mail: general@aljazeiraservices.com
Web Site: www.aljazeiraservices.com
AJSS—(MUS)
Business Services
S.I.C.: 7389
N.A.I.C.S.: 561499
Hussain Ali Habib Sajwani *(Chm)*
Abdulredha Mustafa Sultan *(Deputy Chm)*

Damac Al Jazeera Catering WLL (1)
PO Box 5113
Doha, Qatar
Tel.: (974) 4447387
Fax: (974) 4449022
E-Mail: damac@qatar.net.qa
Web Site: www.dohadamac.qa
Emp.: 50
Caterers
S.I.C.: 5812
N.A.I.C.S.: 722320
Khalid Chihab *(Mgr)*

Draieh Genera Trading Co. WLL (1)
PO Box 2415
Kuwait, Safat, Kuwait
Tel.: (965) 25313860
Fax: (965) 25313855
Web Site: www.damacholding.com
Full-Service Restaurants
S.I.C.: 5812
N.A.I.C.S.: 722511

DAMANSARA REALTY BERHAD

(See Under Johor Corporation)

DAMARTEX SA

25 avenue de la Fosse-aux-Chenes
59100 Roubaix, France
Tel.: (33) 320114500
Fax: (33) 320114500
E-Mail: bdefache@damart.com
Web Site: www.damartex.com
Year Founded: 1953
ALDAR—(EUR)
Emp.: 3,200
Business Description:
Thermal Underwear & Related Cold Weather Clothing Mfr & Marketer
S.I.C.: 2299
N.A.I.C.S.: 313310
Personnel:
Paul Georges Despature *(Chm-Supervisory Bd)*
Jean-Bernard Guillebert *(Vice Chm-Supervisory Bd)*
Patrick Seghin *(Pres & CEO)*
Alain Defossez *(Member-Mgmt Bd)*
Supervisory Board of Directors:
Paul Georges Despature
Martine Charbonnier
Jean Despature
Jean Guillaume Despature
Victor Despature

Damartex SA—(Continued)

Jean-Bernard Guillebert
Wilfrid Le Naour
Xavier Leurent
Anthony Stahl

Ernst & Young et Autres
Paris, France

Subsidiary:

Damart Serviposte S.A. **(1)**
25 Ave De La Fosse Aux Chenes
59100 Roubaix, France FR
Tel.: (33) 320114530 (100%)
Fax: (33) 320114720
E-Mail: info@damart.com
Web Site: www.damart.com
Sls.: $650,176,320
Emp.: 300
Mail Order House
S.I.C.: 5961
N.A.I.C.S.: 454113
Thiery Daijnes *(Chm)*
Claude Bocquet *(Mng Dir)*

Non-U.S. Subsidiary:

Damart **(1)**
Bowling Green Mills
Bingley, West Yorkshire, BD97 1AD, United Kingdom (100%)
Tel.: (44) 1274 510900
Fax: (44) 1274 510 639
E-Mail: infouk@damart.com
Web Site: www.damartonline.co.uk
Emp.: 350
Provider of Clothing by Mail Order
S.I.C.: 2269
N.A.I.C.S.: 313310

DAMEN SHIPYARDS GROUP

PO Box 1
4200 AA Gorinchem, Netherlands
Tel.: (31) 183639922
Fax: (31) 183632189
E-Mail: info@damen.nl
Web Site: www.damen.nl
Year Founded: 1927
Sls.: $1,100,000,000
Emp.: 660

Business Description:
Ship & Shipyards Designing & Construction Services; Maritime Services
S.I.C.: 3731
N.A.I.C.S.: 336611

Personnel:
Kommer Damen *(Chm)*

Non-U.S. Subsidiary:

Gotaverken Cityvarvet AB **(1)**
Anderscarlssonsgata
PO Box 8045
S 402 77 Gothenburg, Sweden (100%)
Tel.: (46) 31502000
Telex: 274 40 CITYARD S
Fax: (46) 31227931
E-Mail: info@damenshiprepair.se
Web Site: www.damenshiprepair.se
Sales Range: $10-24.9 Million
Emp.: 130
Shipbuilding & Repairing
S.I.C.: 3731
N.A.I.C.S.: 336611
Monica Svennes *(Mng Dir)*

Divisions:

Damen Dredging Equipment BV **(1)**
Edisonstraat 32
PO Box 1021
3861 Nijkerk, Netherlands
Tel.: (31) 332474040
Fax: (31) 332474060
E-Mail: info@damendredging.com
Web Site: www.damendredging.com
Emp.: 70
Ship Building & Repairing
S.I.C.: 3731
N.A.I.C.S.: 336611
David Tenwolde *(Mng Dir)*

Damen Marine Components BV **(1)**
Nijverheidsstraat 8
PO Box 96
3371 XE Hardinxveld-Giessendam, 3370 AB, Netherlands
Tel.: (31) 184676262
Fax: (31) 184676267
E-Mail: info@damenmc.nl
Web Site: www.damenmc.nl
Emp.: 25
Ship Building & Repairing
S.I.C.: 3731
N.A.I.C.S.: 336611
Steef Staal *(Gen Mgr)*

Damen Marine Services BV **(1)**
Rivierdijk 561
PO Box 1
3371 Hardinxveld-Giessendam, Netherlands
Tel.: (31) 184616000
Fax: (31) 184611711
E-Mail: info@dms.nl
Web Site: www.dms.nl
Emp.: 11
Inland Water Passenger Transportation
S.I.C.: 4482
N.A.I.C.S.: 483212
Wim Crum *(Mng Dir)*

Damen Shiprepair **(1)**
Adm de Ruyterstraat 24
PO Box 22
3115 Schiedam, Netherlands
Tel.: (31) 102041222
Fax: (31) 102041388
E-Mail: dsr@damenshiprepair.com
Web Site: www.damenshiprepair.com
Emp.: 260
Ship Building & Repairing
S.I.C.: 3731
N.A.I.C.S.: 336611
Monica Svenner *(Mng Dir-Sweden & France)*

Damen Trading & Chartering **(1)**
Avelingen W 20
PO Box 1
4202 Gorinchem, Netherlands
Tel.: (31) 183639522
Fax: (31) 183639440
E-Mail: info@damentrading.nl
Web Site: www.damentrading.nl
Emp.: 3
Management Consulting Services
S.I.C.: 8748
N.A.I.C.S.: 541618
Michel Radjiman *(Sr Mgr-Sls)*

Non-U.S. Divisions:

Damen Shipyards Galati **(1)**
132 Moruzzi St
Galati, 800223 Bucharest, Romania
Tel.: (40) 40236207122
Fax: (40) 236307211
E-Mail: office@damen.ro
Web Site: www.damen.ro
Emp.: 3,000
Ship Building & Repairing
S.I.C.: 3731
N.A.I.C.S.: 336611
Flemmings Florenson *(Gen Mgr)*

Damen Shipyards Kozle Sp Z.o.o. **(1)**
Stoczniowcow 2
Kedzierzyn-Kozle, 47-200 Rybnik, Opolskie, Poland
Tel.: (48) 774825914
Fax: (48) 774825901
E-Mail: sekretariat@damenkozle.po
Web Site: www.damenkozle.eu
Emp.: 200
Boat Building
S.I.C.: 3732
N.A.I.C.S.: 336612
Jausz Bialic *(Mng Dir)*

Damen Shipyards Oostende NV **(1)**
Industrieterrein Plassendale 1
Esperantolaan 10, 8400 Oostende, Belgium
Tel.: (32) 59251898
Fax: (32) 59251901
E-Mail: info@damen-shipyards.be
Web Site: www.damen-shipyards.be
Special Trade Contractors
S.I.C.: 1799
N.A.I.C.S.: 238990

Damen Shipyards Singapore Pte Ltd **(1)**
29 Tuas Crescent
638720 Singapore, Singapore
Tel.: (65) 68614180
Fax: (65) 68614181
E-Mail: info@damen.com.sg
Web Site: www.damen.com.sg
Ship Building & Repairing
S.I.C.: 3731
N.A.I.C.S.: 336611
Maarten Jongen *(Mng Dir)*

Damen Shipyards Yichang **(1)**
14 Heping Rd Xiba
443002 Yichang, Hubei, China
Tel.: (86) 7176271909
Fax: (86) 7176271214
E-Mail: tys@damenyichang.com.cn
Emp.: 200
Ship Building & Repairing
S.I.C.: 3731
N.A.I.C.S.: 336611

DAMEX Shipbuilding & Engineering **(1)**
KM 7 Carretera de Punta Gorda
Santiago de Cuba, Havana, Cuba
Tel.: (53) 22686101
Fax: (53) 22688101
E-Mail: damex@damex.co.cu
Web Site: www.damex.biz
Emp.: 200
Shipbuilding, Engineering & Repairing Services
S.I.C.: 3731
N.A.I.C.S.: 336611
Isidro Campos Castro *(Mng Dir)*

DAMIANI S.P.A.

Piazza Damiano Grassi Damiani 1
15048 Valenza, Italy
Tel.: (39) 0131929611
Fax: (39) 0131941653
Web Site: www.damiani.it
Year Founded: 1924
DMN—(ITA)
Rev.: $185,533,188
Assets: $239,292,487
Liabilities: $103,869,131
Net Worth: $135,423,356
Earnings: ($11,795,142)
Emp.: 567
Fiscal Year-end: 03/31/13

Business Description:
Mfr & Retailer of Luxury Jewelry
S.I.C.: 5944
N.A.I.C.S.: 448310

Personnel:
Guido Grassi Damiani *(Pres & CEO)*

Board of Directors:
Roberta Benaglia
Giorgio Grassi Damiani
Guido Grassi Damiani
Silvia Grassi Damiani
Stefano Graidi
Giancarlo Malerba
Fabrizio Redaelli

Subsidiary:

Rocca S.p.A. **(1)**
Via Pagano Mario 40
20145 Milan, Italy
Tel.: (39) 024677881
Fax: (39) 246778899
Watch Mfr
S.I.C.: 3829
N.A.I.C.S.: 334519

Non-U.S. Subsidiaries:

Damiani International B.V. **(1)**
Via Cantonele Centro Gallerie 3
6928 Manno, Switzerland
Tel.: (41) 916101500
Fax: (41) 916101555
E-Mail: info@damaninternational.ch
Emp.: 30
Jewelry Whslr
S.I.C.: 5094
N.A.I.C.S.: 423940
Fabrizio Giaccon *(Gen Mgr)*

Damiani Japan K.K. **(1)**
Renai Aoyama Bldg 3 FL 3-3-11 Kita aoyoma
Minato-Ku, Tokyo, 107 0061, Japan
Tel.: (81) 3 5785 1080
Fax: (81) 3 5785 1089
Jewellery Distr
S.I.C.: 5094
N.A.I.C.S.: 423940
Asayo Zuber *(Pres)*

Rocca International S.A. **(1)**
Riva Albertolli 1
6900 Lugano, Switzerland
Tel.: (41) 91 922 99 40
Fax: (41) 91 923 36 00
Jewellery Mfr
S.I.C.: 3911
N.A.I.C.S.: 339910

D'AMICO INTERNATIONAL SHIPPING S.A.

Corso d'Italia 35/B
Rome, 00198, Italy
Tel.: (39) 06 845 611
Fax: (39) 06 9896 8082
E-Mail: info@damicoship.com
Web Site: www.damicoship.com
B7C—(DEU ITA)
Rev.: $325,253,000
Assets: $676,895,000
Liabilities: $382,687,000
Net Worth: $294,208,000
Earnings: ($105,994,000)
Emp.: 549
Fiscal Year-end: 12/31/12

Business Description:
Marine Transportation Services
S.I.C.: 4412
N.A.I.C.S.: 483111

Personnel:
Paolo d'Amico *(Chm)*
Cesare d'Amico *(CEO)*
Maurizio Andrea Bergamaschi *(Sec)*

Board of Directors:
Paolo d'Amico
Cesare d'Amico
Roberto Michetti
Giovanni Battista Nunziante
Alfonso Scannapieco

DAMIXA A/S

Ostbirkvej 2
NO 5240 Odense, Denmark
Tel.: (45) 63102210
Fax: (45) 63102209
E-Mail: damixa@damixa.com
Web Site: www.damixa.com
Year Founded: 1932
Sales Range: $75-99.9 Million
Emp.: 200

Business Description:
Faucets Mfr
S.I.C.: 3269
N.A.I.C.S.: 327110

Personnel:
Lars Bladt *(CEO)*

Non-U.S. Subsidiary:

Damixa Armaturen GmbH **(1)**
Kobbingser Muhle 7
58640 Iserlohn, Germany
Tel.: (49) 237194930
Web Site: www.damixa.com
Sales Range: $25-49.9 Million
Emp.: 75
Faucets Mfr
S.I.C.: 3269
N.A.I.C.S.: 327110

Non-U.S. Affiliate:

Rubinetterie Mariani S.p.A. **(1)**
Via Berlino 2/4
24040 Zingonia, Bergamo, Italy (100%)
Tel.: (39) 0354192911
Fax: (39) 0354192925
E-Mail: info@rubinetteriemariani.it
Web Site: www.rubinetteriemariani.it
Sales Range: $300-349.9 Million
Kitchen & Bath Faucets Mfr
S.I.C.: 2434
N.A.I.C.S.: 337110

DAMODAR INDUSTRIES LIMITED
A1202 Centre Point 2nd Floor NM Joshi Marg
Lower Parel E, Mumbai, 400 006, India
Tel.: (91) 22 66610301
Fax: (91) 22 66610308
E-Mail: info@damodargroup.com
Web Site: www.damodargroup.com
Year Founded: 1987
521220—(BOM)
Rev.: $108,222,105
Assets: $38,612,553
Liabilities: $27,397,826
Net Worth: $11,214,727
Earnings: $2,256,696
Fiscal Year-end: 03/31/13
Business Description:
Synthetic Blended Yarn Mfr
S.I.C.: 2299
N.A.I.C.S.: 313110
Personnel:
Arun Kumar Biyani *(Chm)*
Ajay D. Biyani *(Mng Dir)*
Subodh Kumar Jain *(Compliance Officer & Sec)*
Board of Directors:
Arun Kumar Biyani
Ajay D. Biyani
Anil D. Biyani
Girdharlal S. Daga
Ashok Kumar Damani
Rajendra Prasad Khator
Transfer Agent:
Link Intime India Pvt. Ltd
C-13 Pannalal Silk Mills Compound LBS Marg
Bhandup (West)
Mumbai, India

DAMON CAPITAL CORP.
3404 Calder Avenue
North Vancouver, BC, V7N 3R7, Canada
Tel.: (604) 985-9230
E-Mail: charland@shaw.ca
Year Founded: 2011
DAM.P—(TSXV)
Business Description:
Investment Services
S.I.C.: 6211
N.A.I.C.S.: 523999
Personnel:
Joseph Andre Charland *(Pres, CEO & Sec)*
Jeff Yenyou Zheng *(CFO)*
Board of Directors:
Joseph Andre Charland
Joe Edward Robin DeVries
Patrick Edward Power
Transfer Agent:
Olympia Trust Company
1900 925 W Georgia Street
Vancouver, BC, V6C 3L2, Canada

DAMOVO GROUP
Langhurstwood Rd
Horsham, W Sussex, RH12 4QP, United Kingdom
Tel.: (44) 8704206000
Fax: (44) 01403244660
Web Site: www.damovo.com
Sales Range: $1-4.9 Billion
Emp.: 2,200
Business Description:
Communications Solutions & Services
S.I.C.: 7299
N.A.I.C.S.: 812990
Personnel:
Mike Parton *(Chm & CEO)*
Salim Alam *(CFO)*
Joe Boyle *(COO)*
Board of Directors:
Mike Parton
Salim Alam
Andrew Galloway
Colm Smith
Ralph Woodford
Subsidiary:

Damovo UK Ltd. **(1)**
Langhurstwood Road
Horsham, W Sussex, RH12 4QP, United Kingdom
Tel.: (44) 8704206000
Fax: (44) 014030244660
E-Mail: info@damovo.co.uk
Web Site: www.damovo.co.uk
Emp.: 250
Communications Solutions & Services
S.I.C.: 7299
N.A.I.C.S.: 812990
Paul Bucher *(Mng Dir)*

DAMPIER GOLD LIMITED
6 Outram Street
West Perth, WA, 6005, Australia
Mailing Address:
PO Box 1981
West Perth, WA, 6872, Australia
Tel.: (61) 8 6424 9700
Fax: (61) 8 6424 9799
E-Mail: admin@dampiergold.com
Web Site: www.dampiergold.com
DAU—(ASX)
Rev.: $178,212
Assets: $8,991,912
Liabilities: $2,811,903
Net Worth: $6,180,009
Earnings: ($4,546,490)
Fiscal Year-end: 06/30/13
Business Description:
Gold Mining Services
S.I.C.: 1041
N.A.I.C.S.: 212221
Personnel:
Richard Hay *(Mng Dir)*
Susan Patricia Hunter *(Sec)*
Board of Directors:
Ron Hanson
Richard Hay
Ben Loiterton
Peiqi Zhang
Legal Counsel:
Steinepreis Paganin
Level 4 The Read Building 16 Milligan Street
Perth, WA, 6000, Australia
Tel.: (61) 8 9321 4000
Fax: (61) 8 9321 4333

DAMPSKIBSSELSKABET NORDEN A/S
52 Strandvejen
DK-2900 Hellerup, Denmark
Tel.: (45) 33150451
Fax: (45) 33156199
E-Mail: admin@ds-norden.com
Web Site: www.ds-norden.com
DNORD—(CSE)
Rev.: $2,131,439,000
Assets: $2,033,392,000
Liabilities: $346,161,000
Net Worth: $1,687,231,000
Earnings: ($278,849,000)
Emp.: 1,004
Fiscal Year-end: 12/31/12
Business Description:
Cargo Transportation Services
S.I.C.: 4491
N.A.I.C.S.: 488320
Personnel:
Mogens Hugo *(Chm)*
Klaus Nyborg *(Vice Chm)*
Carsten Mortensen *(Pres & CEO)*
Michael Tonnes Jorgensen *(CFO & Exec VP)*
Jacob Bergholdt *(CEO-NORDEN Shipping (Singapore) Pte Ltd & VP)*
Soren Huscher *(CEO-Norient Product Pool)*
Karina Kjerulff Kotchiev *(Sec)*
Martin Badsted *(Exec VP & Head-Corp Secretariat)*
Ejner Bonderup *(Exec VP & Head-Dry Cargo Dept)*
Lars Bagge Christensen *(Exec VP & Head-Tanker Dept)*
Mikkel Fruergaard *(Sr VP & Head-Panamax-Dry Cargo Dept)*
Lars Lundegaard *(Sr VP & Head-Technical Dept)*
Vibeke Schneidermann *(Sr VP & Head-HR)*
Kristian Waerness *(Sr VP & Head-Fin & Acctg Dept)*
Board of Directors:
Mogens Hugo
Ole Clausen
Arvid Grundekjon
Erling Hojsgaard
Karsten Knudsen
Anne-Katrine Nedergaard
Jacob Koch Nielsen
Klaus Nyborg
Alison J. F. Riegels
U.S. Subsidiary:

NORDEN Tankers & Bulkers (USA) Inc. **(1)**
One Park Pl Ste 275
Annapolis, MD 21401
Tel.: (410) 216-9391
Fax: (410) 216-6574
E-Mail: usa@ds-norden.com
Web Site: www.ds-norden.com
Emp.: 15
Shipping Services
S.I.C.: 4491
N.A.I.C.S.: 488320
Mikkel Borresen *(Gen Mgr)*

Non-U.S. Subsidiaries:

NORDEN Shipping (Singapore) Pte. Ltd **(1)**
Suntec City Tower Four 27-05 6 Temasek Boulevard
Singapore, 38986, Singapore
Tel.: (65) 6395 4233
Web Site: www.ds-norden.com
Shipping Services
S.I.C.: 4412
N.A.I.C.S.: 483111

Non-U.S. Subsidiary:

NORDEN Tankers & Bulkers India Pvt. Ltd **(2)**
Office No 12 First Floor Ground Level
Kalpataru Square Off Kurla Road
Kondivita Lane, Mumbai, Maharashtra, 400059, India
Tel.: (91) 2228329188
Fax: (91) 2228329184
E-Mail: india@ds-norden.com
Emp.: 4
Shipping Services
S.I.C.: 4412
N.A.I.C.S.: 483111
Adam Nielsen *(Gen Mgr)*

NORDEN Tankers & Bulkers do Brazil Ltda **(1)**
Edificio Argentina Praia De Botafogo 228-7
Andar-Sala 711 B
22359-900 Rio de Janeiro, Brazil
Tel.: (55) 2125540055
Fax: (55) 2125534478
E-Mail: brazil@ds-norden.com
Emp.: 3
Ship Management Services
S.I.C.: 3731
N.A.I.C.S.: 336611
Mark Neumann *(Mgr)*

DAMS FORD LINCOLN SALES LTD
14530 104th Ave
Surrey, BC, V3R 1L9, Canada
Tel.: (604) 588-9921
Fax: (604) 584-8733
Toll Free: (800) 567-3267
Web Site: www.damsfordloln.dealerconnection.com
Year Founded: 1974
Rev.: $68,530,925
Emp.: 200
Business Description:
New & Used Car Dealers
S.I.C.: 5511
N.A.I.C.S.: 441110
Personnel:
Gordon Dams *(Pres)*

DAN FORM HOLDINGS COMPANY LIMITED
33/F Tower A Billion Centre 1 Wang Kwong Road
Kowloon, China (Hong Kong)
Tel.: (852) 28280288
Fax: (852) 28014975
E-Mail: info@danform.com.hk
Web Site: www.danform.com.hk
271—(HKG)
Emp.: 52
Business Description:
Real Estate Development Services
S.I.C.: 6531
N.A.I.C.S.: 531390
Personnel:
Xiaoming Dai *(Chm & CEO)*
Cynthia Si Ying Chen *(Sec)*
Board of Directors:
Xiaoming Dai
Kenneth Hiu King Kon
Jesse Nai Chau Leung
Edward Shen
Bing Xiang

DAN KANE CHEVROLET CADILLAC
500 Division Rd
PO Box 510
Windsor, ON, N9A 6M9, Canada
Tel.: (519) 969-6000
Fax: (519) 969-2363
Toll Free: (877) 326-5263
E-Mail: info@dankanechev.ca
Web Site: www.dankanechev.com
Rev.: $49,100,000
Emp.: 83
Business Description:
New & Used Car Dealers
S.I.C.: 5511
N.A.I.C.S.: 441110
Personnel:
Dan Kane *(Pres)*

DAN LACHS GMBH
Lise Meithner Str 16
24223 Schwentinental, Germany
Tel.: (49) 43078233382
Fax: (49) 43075420
E-Mail: info@danlachs.de
Web Site: www.danlachs.de
Year Founded: 1973
Rev.: $37,968,389
Emp.: 20
Business Description:
Fish & Seafood Distr
S.I.C.: 5146
N.A.I.C.S.: 424460
Personnel:
Hans Christian Petersen *(Gen Mgr)*

DANA GAS PJSC
PO Box 2011
Sharjah, United Arab Emirates
Tel.: (971) 65569444
Fax: (971) 65566522
E-Mail: mail@danagas.com
Web Site: www.danagas.ae
Year Founded: 2005
DANA—(ABU LSE)

Dana Gas PJSC—(Continued)

Rev.: $634,451,580
Assets: $3,511,938,540
Liabilities: $1,100,695,920
Net Worth: $2,411,242,620
Earnings: $164,668,900
Emp.: 780
Fiscal Year-end: 12/31/12

Business Description:
Natural Gas Pipeline Transportation, Processing & Marketing Services
S.I.C.: 4923
N.A.I.C.S.: 486210

Personnel:
Adel Khalid Al-Sabeeh *(Chm)*
Tawfeeq Abdulrahman Al-Moayed *(Vice Chm)*
Patrick Allman-Ward *(CEO & Gen Mgr-Egypt)*
Majid Jafar *(Mng Dir)*
Mohamed Nour El Din El Taher *(Legal Counsel & Sec)*

Board of Directors:
Adel Khalid Al-Sabeeh
Sultan Ahmed Al-Qasimi
Ahmed Rashid Al-Arbeed
Rashid Saif Al-Jarwan
Abdulaziz Hamad Al-Jomaih
Abdullah Ali Al-Majdouie
Ahmed Al-Midfa
Tawfeeq Abdulrahman Al-Moayed
Nasser Al-Nowais
Salah Al-Qahtani
Khalid Abdulrahman Al-Rajhi
Rashad Al-Zubair
Said Arrata
Ziad Abdullah Galadari
Hamid Dhiya Jafar
Majid Jafar
Varouj Nerguizian

Subsidiary:

United Gas Transmissions Company Limited **(1)**
PO Box 61213
Sharjah, United Arab Emirates
Tel.: (971) 6 5727000
Fax: (971) 6 5568307
E-Mail: mail@ugtc.ae
Oil & Natural Gas Extraction Services
S.I.C.: 1321
N.A.I.C.S.: 211112

Non-U.S. Subsidiary:

Centurion Energy International Inc. **(1)**
Ste 1700 Bow Valley Square II
205 5th Ave SW, Calgary, AB, T2P 2V7, Canada
Tel.: (403) 263-6002
Fax: (403) 263-5998
E-Mail: info@centurionenergy.com
Web Site: www.centurionenergy.com
Sales Range: $75-99.9 Million
Emp.: 140
Petroleum & Natural Gas Exploration, Development, Drilling & Extraction Export
S.I.C.: 1311
N.A.I.C.S.: 211111
Said S. Arrata *(Chm & CEO)*
David H. Thomas *(Pres & COO)*
Barry W. Swan *(CFO & Sr VP)*
Paul McDougall *(Treas & VP-Fin)*

Non-U.S. Subsidiary:

Centurion Petroleum Corporation **(2)**
El Safa Office Towers Lot No 42 6th district
Zahraa El Maadi subdivision, Cairo, Egypt (100%)
Tel.: (20) 2 7545499
Web Site: centurion.stagingserver.co.uk/pages/12/Contacts.stm
Emp.: 75
Petroleum & Natural Gas Exploration, Development, Drilling & Extraction
S.I.C.: 1311
N.A.I.C.S.: 211111
A.R. Elsharkawi *(Gen Mgr)*

DANA-Y STEEL JOINT STOCK COMPANY

No 11B Thanh Vinh Industrial Park
Lien Chieu District, Da Nang, Vietnam
Tel.: (84) 511 3841000
Fax: (84) 511 3730718
E-Mail: dny@thepdana-y.com
Web Site: www.thepdana-y.com
Year Founded: 2008
DNY—(HNX)
Emp.: 400

Business Description:
Iron & Steel Construction Material Mfr
S.I.C.: 3399
N.A.I.C.S.: 331110

Personnel:
Huynh Van Tan *(Chm)*
Thanh Binh Dang *(Vice Chm)*
Nghia Tin Ho *(Gen Dir)*

Board of Directors:
Huynh Van Tan
Thanh Binh Dang
Nghia Tin Ho
Thi Thao Suong Phan

DANABANK JSC

111 Gogol Street
Almaty, 050004, Kazakhstan
Tel.: (7) 327 244 3434
Fax: (7) 327 278 0674
E-Mail: danabank@db.kz
Web Site: www.db.kz
DNBN—(KAZ)
Emp.: 260

Business Description:
Banking Services
S.I.C.: 6029
N.A.I.C.S.: 522110

Personnel:
Sandzhay Kandpal *(Chm-Mgmt Bd)*

DANAL CO., LTD

7F HUMAX Village 11-4 Sunae-dong
Bundang-gu, Seongnam, Gyeonggi-do, 463-825, Korea (South)
Tel.: (82) 31 697 1004
Fax: (82) 31 697 1460
E-Mail: help@danal.co.kr
Web Site: www.danal.co.kr
Year Founded: 1997
064260—(KRS)
Sls.: $94,620,060
Assets: $243,129,900
Liabilities: $180,506,490
Net Worth: $62,623,410
Earnings: ($7,568,340)
Fiscal Year-end: 12/31/12

Business Description:
Mobile Payment Services
S.I.C.: 6099
N.A.I.C.S.: 522320

Personnel:
Ungjun Min *(CEO)*

DANAMECO MEDICAL JOINT STOCK CORPORATION

105 Hung Vuong Street
Hai Chau 1 Ward
Hai Chau District, Da Nang, Vietnam
Tel.: (84) 511 3823951
Fax: (84) 511 3810004
E-Mail: info@danameco.com
Web Site: www.danameco.com
DNM—(HNX)
Sales Range: $10-24.9 Million

Business Description:
Medical Supplies Mfr & Distr
S.I.C.: 3841
N.A.I.C.S.: 339113

Personnel:
Thi Minh Trang Pham *(Chm & Gen Mgr)*

DANANG HOUSING INVESTMENT AND DEVELOPMENT JOINT STOCK COMPANY

186 Tran Phu Street
Hai Chau District, Da Nang, Vietnam
Tel.: (84) 511 3872213
E-Mail: info@ndn.com.vn
Web Site: www.ndn.com.vn
NDN—(HNX)
Emp.: 100

Business Description:
Real Estate Investment Services
S.I.C.: 6531
N.A.I.C.S.: 531390

Personnel:
Trung Quang Nguyen *(Chm)*
Nam Van Nguyen *(Vice Chm)*

Board of Directors:
Trung Quang Nguyen
Tien Phung Lam
Hien Khanh Le
Mai Thi Nhu Nguyen
Nam Van Nguyen

DANANG PLASTIC JOINT-STOCK COMPANY

371 Tran Cao Van st
Da Nang, Vietnam
Tel.: (84) 511 714642
Fax: (84) 511 714561
E-Mail: danaplast@dng.vnn.vn
Web Site: www.danaplast.vn
Year Founded: 1976
DPC—(HNX)
Sales Range: $1-9.9 Million

Business Description:
Plastic Packaging Product Mfr & Distr
S.I.C.: 2671
N.A.I.C.S.: 326112

Personnel:
Quang Dung Tran *(Chm & Mgr)*

DANAOS CORPORATION

c/o Danaos Shipping Co Ltd 14 Akti Kondyli
185 45 Piraeus, Greece
Tel.: (30) 210 419 6480
Fax: (30) 210 411 2340
E-Mail: contact@danaos.com
Web Site: www.danaos.com
Year Founded: 1972
DAC—(NYSE)
Rev.: $588,117,000
Assets: $4,066,552,000
Liabilities: $3,468,076,000
Net Worth: $598,476,000
Earnings: $37,523,000
Emp.: 1,312
Fiscal Year-end: 12/31/13

Business Description:
International Owner of Containerships
S.I.C.: 4412
N.A.I.C.S.: 483111

Personnel:
John Coustas *(Pres & CEO)*
Evangelos Chatzis *(CFO & Sec)*
Iraklis Prokopakis *(COO, Treas & Sr VP)*

Board of Directors:
John Coustas
Andrew B. Fogarty
Myles R. Itkin
Miklos Konkoly-Thege
Robert A. Mundell
Iraklis Prokopakis

Divisions:

Danaos Management Consultants SA **(1)**
14 Akti Kondili Str
18545 Piraeus, Greece
Tel.: (30) 2104196600
Fax: (30) 2104112340
E-Mail: contact@danaos.gr
Web Site: web2.danaos.gr
Emp.: 70
Management Services
S.I.C.: 8742
N.A.I.C.S.: 541611
Dimitris Theodossiou *(Mng Dir)*

Danaos Peripherals S.A. **(1)**
14 Akti Kondyli
18545 Piraeus, Greece
Tel.: (30) 2104196560
Fax: (30) 2104112340
E-Mail: contact@danaos.gr
Web Site: www.danaos.gr
Emp.: 100
Information Systems Management Services
S.I.C.: 7373
N.A.I.C.S.: 541512
Chris Boukas *(Gen Mgr)*

Danaos SeaRoutes Ltd. **(1)**
14 Akti Kondyli
185 45 Piraeus, Greece
Tel.: (30) 2104196600
Fax: (30) 2104112340
Marine Navigation System & Management Services
S.I.C.: 4499
N.A.I.C.S.: 488330

Danaos Shipping Co., Ltd. **(1)**
14 Akti Kondyli
18545 Piraeus, Greece
Tel.: (30) 2104196400
Fax: (30) 2104220855
E-Mail: danship@danaos.gr
Web Site: www.danaosshipping.gr/contact.html
Emp.: 100
Management Services
S.I.C.: 8742
N.A.I.C.S.: 541611

Non-U.S. Subsidiaries:

Danaos Germany **(1)**
Neuer Wall 9
Hamburg, 20354, Germany
Tel.: (49) 4041349718
Fax: (49) 4041349725
Web Site: web2.danaos.gr
Maritime Shipping Management Services
S.I.C.: 4499
N.A.I.C.S.: 488330

Danaos Management Consultants (UK) Ltd. **(1)**
4 Stapple Inn
Holborn, London, WC1V 7QU, United Kingdom
Tel.: (44) 2074042835
Fax: (44) 2074042836
E-Mail: contact@danaos.co.uk
Web Site: www.danaos.gr
Maritime Shipping Management Services
S.I.C.: 4499
N.A.I.C.S.: 488330

Danaos Nordic A.S. **(1)**
PO Box 111
Sagvag, N-5408, Norway
Tel.: (47) 4000 1819
Fax: (47) 4000 1816
Web Site: web2.danaos.gr/danaos/GroupCompanies.aspx
Maritime Navigation Management Services
S.I.C.: 4499
N.A.I.C.S.: 488330

Danaos Software Services Pte Ltd. **(1)**
3 Brady Gladys Plaza
1/447 S.B. Marg
Lower Parel, Mumbai, 400 013, India
Tel.: (91) 2256611439
Fax: (91) 2224948615
E-Mail: contact@danaos.gr
Web Site: web2.danaos.gr/danaos/GroupCompanies.aspx
Maritime Navigation Management Services
S.I.C.: 4499
N.A.I.C.S.: 488330

Danaos Systems (Cyprus) Ltd. **(1)**
145-149 Chr Hadjipavlou Str
Christiel Building, CY3036 Limassol, Cyprus
Tel.: (357) 25889000
Fax: (357) 25745466
Web Site: www.danaoscy.eu

Emp.: 4
Maritime Navigation Management Services
S.I.C.: 4499
N.A.I.C.S.: 488330

DANAWA CO., LTD.

Dream Tower 923-14 Mok 1-dong gu
Seoul, 501, Korea (South)
Tel.: (82) 221662450
Fax: (82) 221662460
E-Mail: webmaster@danawa.com
Web Site: www.danawa.com
119860—(KRS)
Emp.: 180
Business Description:
Online Shopping Services
S.I.C.: 2741
N.A.I.C.S.: 519130
Personnel:
Jang Hyeon Sung *(CEO)*

DANBY PRODUCTS LTD.

5070 Whitelaw Road
Guelph, ON, N1H 6Z9, Canada
Tel.: (519) 837-0920
Fax: (519) 837-9320
E-Mail: CA-Consumers@danby.com
Web Site: www.danby.com
Year Founded: 1947
Emp.: 100
Business Description:
Household Appliance Distr
S.I.C.: 3631
N.A.I.C.S.: 335221
Personnel:
James Lightfoot *(Pres)*
U.S. Subsidiary:

Intirion Corp. (1)
2 Annette Rd
Foxboro, MA 02035
Tel.: (508) 660-9200
Fax: (800) 231-2182
Toll Free: (800) 637-7567
Web Site: www.microfridge.com
Sales Range: $100-124.9 Million
Emp.: 25
Household Appliance Mfr
S.I.C.: 3631
N.A.I.C.S.: 335221
Jim Russo *(Gen Mgr)*

DANDRIT BIOTECH A/S

Fruebjergvej 3
Box 62
2100 Copenhagen, Denmark
Tel.: (45) 39179840
E-Mail: info@dandrit.com
Web Site: www.dandrit.com
Sls.: $62,806
Assets: $362,864
Liabilities: $4,730,695
Net Worth: ($4,367,831)
Earnings: ($2,427,649)
Emp.: 2
Fiscal Year-end: 12/31/12
Business Description:
Pharmaceutical Mfr
S.I.C.: 2834
N.A.I.C.S.: 325412
Personnel:
Niels Erik Nielsen *(Chm)*
Eric Leire *(CEO)*
Robert E. Wolfe *(CFO)*
Board of Directors:
Niels Erik Nielsen
Eric Leire
Aldo Michael Noes Petersen
Jacob Rosenberg

DANESCO INC.

18111 Trans Canada Hwy
Kirkland, QC, H9J 3K1, Canada
Tel.: (514) 694-9111
Fax: (514) 695-5201
Toll Free: (877) 326-3726
Web Site: www.danescoinc.com
Year Founded: 1963
Rev.: $14,962,260
Emp.: 80
Business Description:
Housewares Distr
S.I.C.: 5023
N.A.I.C.S.: 423220
Personnel:
William R. Ferguson *(Chm & Pres)*

DANFOSS A/S

Nordborgvej 81
6430 Nordborg, Denmark
Tel.: (45) 74882222
Telex: 50 599 danfss dk
Fax: (45) 74490949
E-Mail: danfoss@danfoss.com
Web Site: www.danfoss.com
Year Founded: 1933
Sls.: $6,133,502,520
Assets: $5,008,236,480
Liabilities: $2,448,387,000
Net Worth: $2,559,849,480
Earnings: $425,108,520
Emp.: 23,092
Fiscal Year-end: 12/31/12
Business Description:
Holding Company; Heating, Ventilation, Air Conditioning, Refrigeration & Motion Control Systems & Components Mfr
Import Export
S.I.C.: 6719
N.A.I.C.S.: 551112
Personnel:
Jorgen M. Clausen *(Chm)*
Hans Michael Jebsen *(Vice Chm)*
Niels Bjorn Christiansen *(Pres & CEO)*
Kim Fausing *(COO & Exec VP)*
Ravichandran Purushothaman *(Pres-India)*
Board of Directors:
Jorgen M. Clausen
Peter J. Mads Clausen
Svend Aage Hansen
William Ervin Hoover, Jr.
Hans Michael Jebsen
Gunnar Jensen
Jens Peter Nielsen
Kasper Rorsted
Bjorn Rosengren
Divisions:

Danfoss A/S Appliance Controls Div. (1)
Nordborgvej 81
6430 Nordborg, Denmark (100%)
Tel.: (45) 74882222
Fax: (45) 74490949
E-Mail: appliancecontrols@danfoss.com
Web Site: www.bc.danfoss.com
Emp.: 2,500
Mfr. of Appliance Controls
S.I.C.: 3822
N.A.I.C.S.: 334512
Nils P. Christainsn *(Pres & CEO)*

Danfoss A/S Building Controls Div. (1)
Nordborgvej 81
6430 Nordborg, Denmark (100%)
Tel.: (45) 74882222
Fax: (45) 74490949
E-Mail: bc-division@danfoss.com
Web Site: www.bc.danfoss.com
Emp.: 7,000
Mfr. of Regulating Controls
S.I.C.: 3822
N.A.I.C.S.: 334512
Niels Christenson *(CEO)*

Danfoss A/S - Comfort Controls Division (1)
Haarupvaenget 11
Haarup, DK 8600 Silkeborg, Denmark (100%)
Tel.: (45) 74888000
Fax: (45) 74888100
E-Mail: kim_christensen@danfoss.com
Web Site: www.heating.danfoss.com
Emp.: 130
Temperature Controls Mfr
S.I.C.: 3822
N.A.I.C.S.: 334512
Kim Christensen *(Mng Dir)*

Danfoss A/S Flow Div. (1)
Nordborg Vej 81
6430 Nordborg, Denmark (100%)
Tel.: (45) 74882222
Fax: (45) 74880949
E-Mail: danfoss@danfoss.com
Web Site: www.flow.danfoss.com
Emp.: 300
Mfr. of Flowmeter Components
S.I.C.: 3823
N.A.I.C.S.: 334513

Danfoss A/S Industrial Controls Div. (1)
Albuen 29
6000 Kolding, Denmark (100%)
Tel.: (45) 76356565
Fax: (45) 76356598
E-Mail: industrial_controls@danfoss.com
Web Site: www.ic.danfoss.com
Emp.: 550
Mfr. of Industrial Controls
S.I.C.: 3823
N.A.I.C.S.: 334513
Jorgen M. Clausen *(Pres & Mng Dir)*

Danfoss A/S Refrigeration & A/C Controls Division (1)
Nordborgvej 81
6430 Nordborg, Denmark (100%)
Tel.: (45) 74882222
Fax: (45) 74490949
E-Mail: refcon@danfoss.com
Web Site: www.bc.danfoss.com
Emp.: 7,000
Mfr. of Temperature Controls
S.I.C.: 3822
N.A.I.C.S.: 334512
Jorgen M. Clausen *(Chm & CEO)*

Danfoss A/S Water Hydraulics Division (1)
Nordborgvej 81
6430 Nordborg, Denmark (100%)
Tel.: (45) 74882222
Fax: (45) 74490949
E-Mail: pmc@danfoss.com
Web Site: www.danfoss.com
Emp.: 7,000
Supplier of Hydraulic, Humidification, Lumber Drying & Fire Fighting Products
S.I.C.: 3492
N.A.I.C.S.: 332912
Peter Clausen *(Mng Dir)*

Danfoss Drives A/S (1)
Ulsnas 1
6300 Grasten, Denmark (100%)
Tel.: (45) 74882222
Fax: (45) 74652580
E-Mail: drives_info@danfoss.com
Web Site: www.danfoss.com
Emp.: 1,200
Mfr. of Drives for Motors
S.I.C.: 3568
N.A.I.C.S.: 333613
Niels Bjorn Christiansen *(Pres & CEO)*

Danfoss Heating Division (1)
Nordborgvej 81
6430 Nordborg, Denmark
Tel.: (45) 74882222
Fax: (45) 74490949
E-Mail: bc-division@danfoss.com
Web Site: www.heating.danfoss.com
Sls.: $576,300,032
Emp.: 3,500
Mfr of Heating Systems & Components
S.I.C.: 3433
N.A.I.C.S.: 333414
Nis Storgaard *(Pres)*

Division:

Danfoss Burner Components Division (2)
Vej 81
6430 Nordborg, Denmark (100%)
Tel.: (45) 74882222
Fax: (45) 74491669
E-Mail: danfoss@danfoss.com
Web Site: www.danfoss.com
Emp.: 2,000
Mfr of Oil Burner Nozzles, Pumps, Ignition Components, Preheaters, Controls & Thermostats
S.I.C.: 3822
N.A.I.C.S.: 334512

U.S. Subsidiary:

Danfoss Hago Inc. (3)
1120 Globe Ave
Mountainside, NJ 07092
Tel.: (908) 232-8687
Fax: (908) 232-7246
Toll Free: (800) 710-4246
E-Mail: sales@hagonozzles.com
Web Site: www.hago.danfoss.com
Sales Range: $10-24.9 Million
Emp.: 60
Mfr of Oil Burner Nozzles
S.I.C.: 3433
N.A.I.C.S.: 333414

Danfoss Industrial Refrigeration A/S (1)
Stormosevej 10
8361 Hasselager, Denmark DK
Tel.: (45) 87389600 (100%)
Fax: (45) 86280801
E-Mail: dkacd@danfoss.com
Web Site: www.danfoss.com
Emp.: 100
Researcher, Developer, Manufacturer & Marketer of Valves & Components for Industrial Refrigeration
S.I.C.: 3822
N.A.I.C.S.: 334512

Plant:

Danfoss A/S - Glamsbjerg Factory (1)
Bodebjergvej 22
5620 Glamsbjerg, 5620, Denmark DK
Tel.: (45) 74882222 (100%)
Fax: (45) 64723322
E-Mail: jip@danfoss.com
Web Site: www.dh.danfoss.com
Rev.: $2,480,190
Emp.: 70
Mfr of Ball Valves for District Heating Systems
S.I.C.: 3491
N.A.I.C.S.: 332911
Thorbjoern Hoeyer *(Mng Dir)*

U.S. Subsidiaries:

Danfoss Commercial Compressors Ltd. (1)
1775G Mac Leod Dr
Lawrenceville, GA 30043-5718
Tel.: (678) 337-5100
Fax: (770) 442-6501
Web Site: www.danfoss.com
Emp.: 150
Compressors Mfr
S.I.C.: 3585
N.A.I.C.S.: 333415

Danfoss Electronic Drives (1)
4401 N Bell School Rd
Loves Park, IL 61111-5600
Tel.: (815) 639-8600
Fax: (815) 639-8000
Web Site: www.danfossdrives.com
Emp.: 200
Mfr. of Refrigeration Controls
S.I.C.: 3625
N.A.I.C.S.: 335314
Robert Wilkins *(Pres)*

Subsidiary:

Danfoss Graham (2)
8800 W Bradley Rd
Milwaukee, WI 53224-9541 WI
Mailing Address:
PO Box 245041
Milwaukee, WI 53224
Tel.: (414) 355-8800
Fax: (414) 355-6117
Toll Free: (800) 621-8806
E-Mail: namc@danfoss.com
Web Site: www.danfossdrives.com
Emp.: 200
AC Variable Frequency Drives Mfr
S.I.C.: 3625

Danfoss A/S—(Continued)

N.A.I.C.S.: 335314
Arnaldo Ricca *(Pres)*

Danfoss Inc. (1)
11655 Cross Road Cir
Baltimore, MD 21220
Tel.: (410) 931-8250
Fax: (410) 931-8256
E-Mail: balitimore@danfoss.com
Web Site: www.danfoss.com
Emp.: 300
Mfr of Refrigeration & Air Conditioning Compressors & Components, Heating Systems & Components & Motion Control Components
S.I.C.: 3433
N.A.I.C.S.: 333414
John Galyen *(Pres)*
Peter Simson *(Pres-Bus Svcs)*

Danfoss Turbocor Compressors Inc. (1)
1769 E Paul Dirac Dr
Tallahassee, FL 32310
Tel.: (850) 504-4800
Fax: (850) 504-0280
Web Site: www.turbocor.com
Emp.: 185
Compressor Mfr
S.I.C.: 3563
N.A.I.C.S.: 333912
Ricardo Schneider *(Pres & CEO)*

Sauer-Danfoss Inc. (1)
2800 E 13th St
Ames, IA 50010 DE
Tel.: (515) 239-6000 (100%)
E-Mail: info@sauer-danfoss.com
Web Site: www.sauer-danfoss.com
Sls.: $1,916,094,000
Assets: $1,398,959,000
Liabilities: $702,041,000
Net Worth: $696,918,000
Earnings: $212,078,000
Emp.: 6,400
Fiscal Year-end: 12/31/12
Hydraulic, Electronic, Electrical & Mechanical Components & Systems for Mobile Equipment Designer, Mfr & Whslr
S.I.C.: 3594
N.A.I.C.S.: 333996
Jorgen M. Clausen *(Chm)*
Niels Bjorn Christiansen *(Vice Chm)*
Eric Alstrom *(Pres & CEO)*
Jesper V. Christensen *(CFO & Exec VP)*
Marc Weston *(CMO & Exec VP)*
Charles Kells Hall *(CTO & Exec VP)*
Thomas Kaiser *(Pres-Hydrostatics Div & Exec VP)*
Kenneth D. McCuskey *(VP-Fin, Sec & Treas)*
Anne Wilkinson *(Exec VP-HR)*

Subsidiaries:

Hydro-Gear, Inc. (2)
1411 S Hamilton St
Sullivan, IL 61951
Tel.: (217) 728-2581
Fax: (217) 728-7665
E-Mail: Info@Hydro-Gear.com
Web Site: www.hydro-gear.com
Precision Drive System Design & Mfr
S.I.C.: 3714
N.A.I.C.S.: 336310
Ray Hauser *(Pres)*

Sauer-Danfoss (US) Company (2)
2800 E 13th St
Ames, IA 50010
Tel.: (515) 239-6000
Fax: (515) 239-6618
Hydraulic System & Mechanical Component Mfr
S.I.C.: 3714
N.A.I.C.S.: 336390

Non-U.S. Subsidiaries:

Hydro-Gear Europe BVBA (2)
Henisstraat 28
Tongeren, Belgium 3700
Tel.: (32) 12670631
Fax: (32) 12670630
E-Mail: hgeuro@hydro-gear.com
Web Site: www.hydro-gear.com
Precision Drive System Design & Mfr
S.I.C.: 3714
N.A.I.C.S.: 336310

Sauer-Danfoss AB (2)
Vretenvagen 13
171 54 Solna, Sweden
Tel.: (46) 86290730
Fax: (46) 8286595
E-Mail: stoorder@sauer-danfoss.com
Web Site: www.sauer-danfoss.se
Hydraulic Product & Electrical Component Mfr
S.I.C.: 3679
N.A.I.C.S.: 334419
Matt Lindqvist *(CTO)*

Sauer-Danfoss ApS (2)
Nordborgvej 81
6430 Nordborg, Denmark
Tel.: (45) 74884444
Fax: (45) 74884400
Web Site: www.sauer-danfoss.dk
Motors Steering Component & Valve Mfr
S.I.C.: 3679
N.A.I.C.S.: 334419
Sven Ruder, *(Pres & CEO)*

Sauer-Danfoss AS (2)
Arenga 2 1309 Rud
Skui, 1340 Baerum, Norway
Tel.: (47) 67177373
Fax: (47) 67132084
E-Mail: sauer-danfoss-norway@sauer-danfoss.com
Web Site: www.sauer-danfoss.no
Hydraulic System & Electronic Component Mfr
S.I.C.: 3714
N.A.I.C.S.: 336310

Sauer-Danfoss a.s. (2)
Prevadzka Dubnica nad Vahom Areal ZTS 924
018 41 Dubnica nad Vahom, Slovakia
Tel.: (421) 424487557
Fax: (421) 424487556
E-Mail: JSkonieczny@sauer-danfoss.com
Web Site: www.sauer-danfoss.sk
Hydraulic Electrical & Electronic Component Mfr
S.I.C.: 3679
N.A.I.C.S.: 334419

Sauer-Danfoss BVBA (2)
Gossetlaan 28
1740 Groot-Bijgaarden, Belgium BE
Tel.: (32) 25825880
Fax: (32) 25822972
E-Mail: ibaeyens@sauer-danfoss.com
Web Site: www.sauer-danfoss.com
Emp.: 38
Hydraulic, Electronic, Electrical & Mechanical Components & Systems Whslr
S.I.C.: 5013
N.A.I.C.S.: 423120

Sauer-Danfoss China Holding Company ApS (2)
Nordborgvej 81
6430 Nordborg, Denmark
Tel.: (45) 74882222
Investment Management Services
S.I.C.: 6719
N.A.I.C.S.: 551112

Sauer-Danfoss-Daikin Ltd. (2)
Shin-Osaka Terasaki 3rd Bldg 6F 1-5-28 Nishimiyahara
Yodogawa-ku, Osaka, 532-004, Japan
Tel.: (81) 663956066
Fax: (81) 663958585
Mechanical & Electronic Component Mfr
S.I.C.: 3679
N.A.I.C.S.: 334419

Sauer-Danfoss-Daikin Ltd. (2)
401-2 4th FL Korean Judicial Agent Association Bldg
Nonhyeon-dong Gangnam-gu, 151-31
Seoul, Korea (South)
Tel.: (82) 25087834
Fax: (82) 25407857
Web Site: www.sauer-danfoss-daikin.com
Hydraulic Component & System Design & Mfr
S.I.C.: 3714
N.A.I.C.S.: 336390
Joakim Fahlstedt *(Country Mgr)*

Sauer-Danfoss-Daikin Mobile Hydraulics (Shanghai) Co., Ltd. (2)
900 Yishan Road Block C 22F Caohejing Development Zone
Shanghai, 200233, China
Tel.: (86) 2134185200
Fax: (86) 2164952622
Web Site: www.sauer-danfoss-daikin.com
Hydraulic & Electronic Product Mfr
S.I.C.: 3714
N.A.I.C.S.: 336390

Sauer-Danfoss-Daikin Pte. Ltd. (2)
22 Boon Lay Way 01-59 Tradehub 21
609968 Singapore, Singapore
Tel.: (65) 62623833
Fax: (65) 62654836
Web Site: www.sauer-danfoss-daikin.com
Emp.: 15
Mobile Power & Control System Mfr & Supplier
S.I.C.: 3714
N.A.I.C.S.: 336390
Han Nam Siew *(Gen Mgr)*

Sauer-Danfoss Gmbh & Co. OHG (2)
Krokamp 35
D-24539 Neumunster, Germany De
Mailing Address:
Postfach 24 60
D-24531 Neumunster, Germany
Tel.: (49) 43218710
Fax: (49) 4321871355
E-Mail: info@sauer-danfoss.com
Web Site: www.sauer-danfoss.de
Emp.: 900
Electrohydraulic Products, Hydrostatic Transmissions Systems & Components Mfr
S.I.C.: 3594
N.A.I.C.S.: 333996
John N. Langrick *(Dir-Fin)*

Sauer-Danfoss GmbH (2)
Krokamp 35
24539 Neumunster, Germany
Tel.: (49) 43218710
Fax: (49) 4321871355
Hydraulic Component & System Design & Mfr
S.I.C.: 3594
N.A.I.C.S.: 333996
Joachim Hergt *(Portfolio Mgr-Product)*

Sauer-Danfoss Hidraulica Mobil Ltda. (2)
Rua Domingos Chies 973 Bairro Interlagos
Caxias do Sul, Rio Grande do Sul, 95052-160, Brazil
Tel.: (55) 5430259750
Fax: (55) 5430259776
E-Mail: jfonneta@valmova.com
Emp.: 184
Spool Valve Mfr
S.I.C.: 3491
N.A.I.C.S.: 332911
Julio Raul Martinoil, *(Mgr-Ops)*

Sauer-Danfoss LLC (2)
S Pos Pavlo Suburban D Leshkovo 217
Istra, 143581 Moscow, Russia
Tel.: (7) 4957211767
Fax: (7) 4957211766
Web Site: www.sauer-danfoss.ru
Hydraulic System & Electronic Component Mfr
S.I.C.: 3714
N.A.I.C.S.: 336310
Trinity N. Eugene *(CEO)*
David Duvall, *(Mng Dir)*

Sauer-Danfoss SA (2)
C/ de la Forja n 2 Tres Cantos
28760 Madrid, Spain
Tel.: (34) 918063670
Fax: (34) 918042703
Hydraulic System & Electronic Component Mfr
S.I.C.: 3594
N.A.I.C.S.: 333996

Sauer-Danfoss S.A.S. (2)
322 Rue de Seine
F-77190 Dammarie, Cedex, France FR
Tel.: (33) 164379133
Fax: (33) 164374328
E-Mail: mdejong@sauer-danfoss.com
Web Site: www.sauer-danfoss.com
Emp.: 20
Hydraulic, Electronic, Electrical & Mechanical Components & Systems Whslr
S.I.C.: 5013
N.A.I.C.S.: 423120
Marco De Jong *(Gen Mgr)*

Sauer-Danfoss (Shanghai) Co. Ltd. (2)
No 626 Rong Qiao Jin Hai Road Jin Qiao Export Processing Zone
Pudong New District, Shanghai, 201206, China
Tel.: (86) 2120358100
Fax: (86) 2158345748
Hydraulic System & Electronic Component Mfr
S.I.C.: 3714
N.A.I.C.S.: 336390
Martin Nordborg *(Dir-Work Function Div)*

Sauer-Danfoss S.r.l. (2)
Via Villanova 28
Villanova di Castenaso, 40055 Bologna, Italy IT
Tel.: (39) 0113817711
Fax: (39) 011 3817799
E-Mail: sdbologna@sauer-danfoss.com
Web Site: www.sauer-danfoss.com
Open Circuit Gear Pumps & Motors Mfr & Whslr
S.I.C.: 3594
N.A.I.C.S.: 333996

Scroll Technologies (1)
1 Scroll Dr
Arkadelphia, AR 71923-8813
Tel.: (870) 246-0700
Fax: (870) 246-0707
Sales Range: $125-149.9 Million
Emp.: 750
Compressor Mfr
S.I.C.: 3563
N.A.I.C.S.: 333912

Non-U.S. Subsidiaries:

Danfoss AB (1)
Industrigatan 5
58199 Linkoping, Sweden
Tel.: (46) 14288500
Fax: (46) 013130181
E-Mail: danfoss@danfoss.se
Web Site: www.danfoss.se
Emp.: 60
Mfr. of Industrial & Temperature Controls
S.I.C.: 3822
N.A.I.C.S.: 334512
P. Johnson *(Mgr)*

Danfoss Bauer GmbH (1)
Eberhard Bauer Strasse 36 60
PO Box 100208
Esslingen, 73734, Germany (100%)
Tel.: (49) 71135180
Fax: (49) 7113518381
E-Mail: info@danfoss-bauer.de
Web Site: www.danfoss-bauer.com
Emp.: 200
Mfr. of Gear Motors
S.I.C.: 3566
N.A.I.C.S.: 333612
Hanspeteno Simon *(Mgr)*

Danfoss Commercial Compressors S.A. (1)
ZI De Reyrieux
PO Box 331
F 01603 Trevoux, Cedex, France FR
Tel.: (33) 474002829
Fax: (33) 474005244
E-Mail: commun@danfoss.com
Web Site: www.danfoss-maneurop.com
Emp.: 500
Mfr. of Compressors
S.I.C.: 3563
N.A.I.C.S.: 333912
Noel Ryan *(Pres)*

Danfoss d.o.o. (1)
Ulica Jozeta Jame 16
Ljubljana, Sentvid, 1210, Slovenia (100%)
Tel.: (386) 1 582 0200
Fax: (386) 1507 2518
E-Mail: danfoss.si@danfoss.com
Web Site: www.danfoss.com
Emp.: 12
Sales & Servicer of Valves & Controls
S.I.C.: 3494
N.A.I.C.S.: 332919
Norbert Schulter *(Mng Dir)*

Danfoss Industries, SA de CV (1)
Carretera Miguel Aleman 162
66600 Apodaca, NL, Mexico MX
Tel.: (52) 81 8156 5600 (100%)

Fax: (52) 81 8156 5621
E-Mail: mexico@danfoss.com
Web Site: www.danfoss.com
Emp.: 700
Sales & Servicer of Compressors
S.I.C.: 5084
N.A.I.C.S.: 423830
Kim Fausing *(Exec VP & COO)*

Danfoss (Pty) Ltd. (1)
Cambridge Commercial Park
23Trinity Close Paulshof Ext45,
Johannesburg, 2191, South Africa (100%)
Mailing Address:
PO Box 5022
ZA-2128 Rivonia, South Africa
Tel.: (27) 00118038390
Fax: (27) 118038244
E-Mail: danfoss@danfoss.co.za
Web Site: www.danfoss.co.za
Rev.: $15,723,120
Emp.: 22
Sale of Commercial Refrigeration Equipment
S.I.C.: 5078
N.A.I.C.S.: 423740
Maphetha Molala *(Mng Dir)*

Danfoss Randall Limited (1)
Ampthill Road
Bedford, MK42 9ER, United Kingdom UK
Tel.: (44) 01234364621
Fax: (44) 8451217515
E-Mail: danfossrandall@danfoss.com
Web Site: www.danfoss-randall.co.uk
Emp.: 200
Supplier of Domestic & Commercial Heating Controls
S.I.C.: 3822
N.A.I.C.S.: 334512

Danfoss S.a.r.l. (1)
1 Bis Ave Jean Galenbert
78996 Elancourt, Cedex, France FR
Tel.: (33) 130625000 (100%)
Fax: (33) 130697470
E-Mail: danfoss@danfoss.fr
Web Site: www.danfoss.fr
Emp.: 150
Supplier of Industrial Controls
S.I.C.: 3823
N.A.I.C.S.: 334513

Danfoss Silicon Power GmbH (1)
Heinrich Hertz Strasse 2
24837 Schleswig, Schleswig Holstein, Germany DE
Tel.: (49) 462195120 (100%)
Fax: (49) 46219512310
E-Mail: dsp-info@danfoss.com
Web Site: www.siliconpower.danfoss.com
Emp.: 300
Supplier of Industrial Controls
S.I.C.: 3823
N.A.I.C.S.: 334513
Holger Ulrich *(Mng Dir)*

Danfoss Sp. z.o.o. (1)
Ul Chrzanowska 5th St
Grodzisk Mazowiecki, 05825, Poland (100%)
Tel.: (48) 227550700
Fax: (48) 227550701
E-Mail: info@danfoss.com
Web Site: www.danfoss.com.pl
Emp.: 800
Mfr. & Sales of Industrial & Household Controls
S.I.C.: 3823
N.A.I.C.S.: 334513
Adam Jedrzejczak *(Mng Dir)*

Danfoss S.r.l. (1)
Corso Tazzoli 221
10137 Turin, Italy (100%)
Tel.: (39) 0113000511
Fax: (39) 0113000573
E-Mail: info@danfoss.it
Web Site: www.danfoss.it
Emp.: 90
Industrial Controls & Related Products Mfr & Sales
S.I.C.: 3822
N.A.I.C.S.: 334512
Lorenzo Colombo *(Mgr)*

Danfoss (Tianjin) Ltd. (1)
5 Yuan Road Wuqing Development Area
Tianjin, 301700, China (100%)
Tel.: (86) 2227501402
Fax: (86) 2282126416
E-Mail: wuqing@danfoss.com.cn
Web Site: www.danfoss.com.cn
Sls.: $1,812,645
Emp.: 2,000
Sales & Servicer of Valves & Controls
S.I.C.: 5085
N.A.I.C.S.: 423840
Paulsen Morgen *(Gen Mgr)*

ZAO Danfoss (1)
Pavlo-Slobodskoe d Leshkovo 217
Istra District, 143581 Moscow, Russia (100%)
Tel.: (7) 4957925757
Fax: (7) 4957925758
E-Mail: info@danfoss.ru
Web Site: www.danfoss.ru
Emp.: 200
Mfr of Regulators
S.I.C.: 3613
N.A.I.C.S.: 335313
Mikhail Shapiro *(Gen Mgr)*

DANGOTE GROUP LIMITED

Union Marble House 1 Alfred Rewane Road
PMB 40032
Falomo Ikoyi, Lagos, Nigeria
Tel.: (234) 14480815
Fax: (234) 1 270 2983
E-Mail: communications@dangote-group.com
Web Site: www.dangote-group.com
Sales Range: $700-749.9 Million
Emp.: 7,000
Business Description:
Diversified Mfr, Importer & Exporter
S.I.C.: 7389
N.A.I.C.S.: 425120
Personnel:
Aliko Dangote *(Pres & CEO)*
Kuzhyil Ravindran *(CFO)*
Olakunie Alake *(COO)*
Paramjit Pabby *(Chief HR Officer)*

Holding:

Dangote Cement PLC (1)
Union Marble House 1 Alfred Rewane Road
Ikoyi, Lagos, Nigeria
Tel.: (234) 448 0815
Fax: (234) 463 0316
Web Site: www.dangote.com
DANGCEM—(NIGE)
Rev.: $1,877,276,088
Assets: $4,237,360,543
Liabilities: $1,595,548,648
Net Worth: $2,641,811,894
Earnings: $955,659,910
Emp.: 11,000
Fiscal Year-end: 12/31/12
Cement Products Mfr
S.I.C.: 3241
N.A.I.C.S.: 327310
Aliko Dangote *(Chm)*
Devakumar Victor Gnandoss Edwin *(CEO & Grp Mng Dir)*
Kuzhyil Ravindran *(CFO)*
Olakunle Alake *(COO)*
Paramjit Pabby *(Chief HR Officer)*
Ityoyila Ukpi *(Acting Sec)*

DANHUA CHEMICAL TECHNOLOGY CO., LTD.

Room 61 No 788 Hongxu Road
Minhang District, Shanghai, China
Tel.: (86) 2164015596
Fax: (86) 2164016411
900921—(SHG)
Sales Range: $50-74.9 Million
Emp.: 361
Business Description:
Chemical Component Mfr
S.I.C.: 2899
N.A.I.C.S.: 325998
Personnel:
Xiaoning Zeng *(Chm)*

DANIA CAPITAL ADVISORS A/S

Borgergade 111
1300 Copenhagen, Denmark
Tel.: (45) 70116663
Fax: (45) 33476663
E-Mail: info@daniacapital.dk
Web Site: www.daniacapital.dk
Year Founded: 2003
Emp.: 9
Business Description:
Private Equity Firm
S.I.C.: 6211
N.A.I.C.S.: 523999
Personnel:
Thomas Dywremose *(CEO & Partner)*
Anders Bruun-Schmidt *(CFO & Partner)*
Lars Fejer *(Partner)*
Jorgen Jensen *(Partner)*
Supervisory Board of Directors:
Holger Brogaard
Torben Faurby

DANIEL STEWART SECURITIES PLC

Becket House 36 Old Jewry
London, EC2R 8DD, United Kingdom
Tel.: (44) 20 7776 6550
Fax: (44) 20 7796 4648
Web Site: www.danielstewart.co.uk
Year Founded: 1989
DAN—(LSE)
Rev.: $8,210,369
Assets: $9,965,678
Liabilities: $3,974,463
Net Worth: $5,991,215
Earnings: ($4,956,276)
Emp.: 39
Fiscal Year-end: 03/31/13
Business Description:
Investment Banking, Securities Dealing & Brokerage Services
S.I.C.: 6211
N.A.I.C.S.: 523110
Personnel:
Peter Shea *(Chm & CEO)*
John Whitwell *(Sec)*
Board of Directors:
Peter Shea
Peter Dicks
Stuart Lucas
Legal Counsel:
Swan Turton LLP
68a Neal Street Covent Garden
London, United Kingdom

Subsidiary:

Daniel Stewart & Company plc (1)
Becket House 36 Old Jewry
London, EC2R 8DD, United Kingdom
Tel.: (44) 20 7776 6550
Fax: (44) 20 7796 4648
E-Mail: reception@danielstewart.co.uk
Emp.: 50
Investment Banking Services
S.I.C.: 6211
N.A.I.C.S.: 523110
Martin Lampshire *(Head-Corp Broking)*

DANIEL THWAITES PLC

Penny Street
Blackburn, Lancs, BB1 5BU, United Kingdom
Tel.: (44) 1254686868
Fax: (44) 1254681439
E-Mail: info@danielthwaites.com
Web Site: www.danielthwaites.com
Year Founded: 1807
Emp.: 300
Business Description:
Holding Company; Breweries, Retail Pubs & Hotels Owner & Operator
S.I.C.: 6719
N.A.I.C.S.: 551112
Personnel:
John Yerburgh *(Pres)*
Richard Bailey *(CEO)*

Unit:

Daniel Thwaites Brewery (1)
Penny St
Blackburn, Lancs, BB1 6HL, United Kingdom
Tel.: (44) 1254686868
Fax: (44) 1254681439
E-Mail: info@danielthwaites.com
Web Site: www.danielthwaites.com
Emp.: 500
Brewery
S.I.C.: 2082
N.A.I.C.S.: 312120
John Yerburgh *(Pres)*

Subsidiary:

Shire Hotels Limited (1)
The Old Wine Warehouse Larkhill St
Blackburn, Lancs, BB1 5DF, United Kingdom UK
Tel.: (44) 1254267444 (100%)
Fax: (44) 1254267440
E-Mail: info@shirehotels.com
Web Site: www.shirehotels.com
Emp.: 30
Hotel Owner & Operator
S.I.C.: 7011
N.A.I.C.S.: 721110
Antony Spencer *(Mng Dir)*

DANIELI & C. OFFICINE MECCANICHE S.P.A.

Via Nazionale 41
Buttrio, 33042 Udine, Italy
Tel.: (39) 04321958111
Fax: (39) 04321958289
E-Mail: info@danieli.com
Web Site: www.danieli.com
DAN—(ITA)
Rev.: $3,954,634,186
Assets: $7,158,633,210
Liabilities: $5,237,290,539
Net Worth: $1,921,342,671
Earnings: $219,647,828
Emp.: 10,944
Fiscal Year-end: 06/30/13
Business Description:
Machinery & Plants Mfr
S.I.C.: 3547
N.A.I.C.S.: 333519
Personnel:
Gianpietro Benedetti *(Chm & CEO)*
Carla de Colle *(Vice Chm)*
Alessandro Trivillin *(CEO-Steelmaking)*
Franco Alzetta *(Member-Exec Bd & COO-Engrg & Plantmaking)*
Marco Bossi *(Member-Exec Bd-HR)*
Alessandro Brussi *(Member-Exec Bd-Admin)*
Luca Ferraresi *(Member-Exec Bd-Internal Auditing)*
Enrico Parisi *(Member-Exec Bd-Macro-Plng & Costing)*
Luca Tiepolo *(Member-Exec Bd-IT)*
Board of Directors:
Gianpietro Benedetti
Franco Alzetta
Augusto Clerici Bagozzi
Luigi Cappugi
Giacomo Mareschi Danieli
Carla de Colle

U.S. Subsidiary:

Danieli Corporation (1)
600 Cranberry Woods Dr Ste 200
Cranberry Township, PA 16066 (100%)
Tel.: (724) 778-5400
Fax: (724) 778-5401
E-Mail: sales@danielicorp.com
Web Site: www.danielicorp.com
Emp.: 36
Distributor & Service of Custom Steel-Making Equipment
S.I.C.: 3547
N.A.I.C.S.: 333519
Andrew Betts *(CFO)*

Danieli & C. Officine Meccaniche S.p.A.—(Continued)

Non-U.S. Subsidiaries:

Danieli Hi Tech GmbH (1)
Brunsnosstrasse 12
45470 Mulheim an der Ruhr, Germany (100%)
Tel.: (49) 2083780000
Fax: (49) 2083780200
E-Mail: info@danieli.com
Web Site: www.danieli-ht.de
Emp.: 11
S.I.C.: 3547
N.A.I.C.S.: 333519
Joerg Schroeder *(Mng Dir)*

Danieli Morgardshammar SA (1)
Avenida Zugazarte 8 Fl 2 El Abra 4
48930 Las Arenas, Vizcaya, Spain (100%)
Tel.: (34) 944804343
Fax: (34) 944631183
E-Mail: danmhsa@danmhsa.com
Web Site: www.morgardshammar.org
Emp.: 16
S.I.C.: 3547
N.A.I.C.S.: 333519
Anders Eriksson *(Mng Dir)*

Morgardshammar AB (1)
Nya Agatan 23
PO Box 502
SE 777 82 Smedjebacken, Sweden
Tel.: (46) 240668500
Fax: (46) 240668686
E-Mail: anders.eriksson@morgardshammar.se
Web Site: www.morgardshammar.se
Emp.: 250
Mfr. of Hot Rolling Mill Machinery, Mining Equipment & Wire Drawing Equipment
S.I.C.: 3532
N.A.I.C.S.: 333131
Anders Eriksson *(Mng Dir)*
Anders Westberg *(CFO)*

Non-U.S. Joint Venture:

Danieli Corus Technical Services BV (1)
Rooswijkweg 291
NL-1951 ME Velsen, Netherlands
Mailing Address:
Postbus 10000
NL-1970 CA IJmuiden, Netherlands
Tel.: (31) 251500500
Fax: (31) 251500501
E-Mail: info@danieli-corus.com
Web Site: www.danieli-corus.com
Emp.: 180
Engineering Services
S.I.C.: 8711
N.A.I.C.S.: 541330
Paul Strickland *(Chm-Supervisory Bd)*
Peter Zonneveld *(Mng Dir)*

U.S. Subsidiary:

Danieli Corus, Inc. (2)
8300 Mississippi Street
Merrillville, IN 46410
Tel.: (219) 650-5500
Fax: (219) 755-0074
E-Mail: info@danieli-corus.com
Web Site: www.danieli-corus.com
Metals Industry Equipment Mfr
S.I.C.: 8711
N.A.I.C.S.: 541330

DANIER LEATHER, INC.

2650 St Clair Avenue West
Toronto, ON, M6N 1M2, Canada
Tel.: (416) 762-8175
Fax: (416) 762-4570
E-Mail: bryan@danier.com
Web Site: www.danier.com
Year Founded: 1972
DL—(TSX)
Rev.: $154,068,130
Assets: $68,636,087
Liabilities: $13,061,423
Net Worth: $55,574,664
Earnings: $1,402,562
Emp.: 1,247
Fiscal Year-end: 06/30/13

Business Description:
Leather & Suede Garment Designer, Retailer & Mfr
Import Export
S.I.C.: 2389
N.A.I.C.S.: 315280
Personnel:
Edwin F. Hawken *(Chm)*
Jeffrey Wortsman *(Pres & CEO)*
Bryan Tatoff *(CFO, Sec & Exec VP)*
Philip A. Cutter *(CIO & VP-IT)*
Olga E. Koel *(Chief Mdse Officer & Sr VP)*
Guia Lopez *(Chief Sourcing Officer & VP)*
Brian Burgess *(Exec VP-Mdsg, Sourcing & Plng)*
Michael Watson *(Exec VP-Retail Ops)*
Board of Directors:
Edwin F. Hawken
Clare R. Copeland
Thomas Haig
Stephen I. Kahn
Douglas D. Murphy
Jeffrey Wortsman
Legal Counsel:
Davies, Ward, Phillips & Vineberg LLP
Toronto, ON, Canada
Transfer Agent:
Computershare Investor Services Inc
100 University Avenue 8th Fl North Tower
Toronto, ON, Canada

DANIONICS A/S

Sivlandvaenget 3
DK-5260 Odense, S, Denmark
Tel.: (45) 70238130
Fax: (45) 65915130
E-Mail: info@danionics.com
Web Site: www.danionics.com
DANIO—(CSE)
Sales Range: Less than $1 Million
Emp.: 271

Business Description:
Holding Company
S.I.C.: 6719
N.A.I.C.S.: 551112
Board of Directors:
Karsten Borch
Frank Gad
Henrik Ottosen

Non-U.S. Joint Venture:

Danionics Asia Limited (1)
2/F Gold Peak Building
30 Kwai Wing Road, Kwai Chung, NT, China (Hong Kong)
Tel.: (852) 2484 3111
Fax: (852) 2420 3450
E-Mail: info@danionics.dk
Web Site: www.danionics.com
Energy Storage Devices; Owned 50% by Danionics A/S & 50% by GP Batteries International Limited
S.I.C.: 3691
N.A.I.C.S.: 335911
Frank Gad *(Deputy Chm)*

Non-U.S. Subsidiaries:

Danionics China Ltd. (2)
Room 1200 International Trade Building
No 205 Sec 1 Tun Hua S Ro, Taipei, 10647, Taiwan (100%)
Tel.: (886) 87716029
Fax: (886) 87716352
Energy Storage Devices
S.I.C.: 3691
N.A.I.C.S.: 335911

Danionics International A/S (2)
Sivlandvaenget 3
5260 Odense, S, Denmark (100%)
Tel.: (45) 6591 8130
Fax: (45) 6591 5130
E-Mail: info@danionics.dk
Web Site: www.danionics.com
Energy Storage Sales & Development
S.I.C.: 3691
N.A.I.C.S.: 335911

DANISH AEROTECH A/S

Herningvej 30
7470 Karup, Denmark
Tel.: (45) 99626262
Fax: (45) 99626364
E-Mail: info@aerotech.dk
Web Site: www.aerotech.dk
Year Founded: 1992
Emp.: 100

Business Description:
Development, Production, Installation & Support of Electrical, Electronic & Mechanical Components for Aircraft, Helicopters, Missiles & Targeting Systems
S.I.C.: 3728
N.A.I.C.S.: 336413
Personnel:
Jan Jorgensen *(CEO)*

DANISH CROWN AMBA

Marsvej 43
8900 Randers, Denmark
Tel.: (45) 89191919
Fax: (45) 86448066
E-Mail: dc@danishcrown.dk
Web Site: www.danishcrown.com
Year Founded: 1990
Rev.: $10,027,651,200
Assets: $4,532,707,200
Liabilities: $3,503,160,000
Net Worth: $1,029,547,200
Earnings: $307,603,200
Emp.: 23,582
Fiscal Year-end: 09/30/12

Business Description:
Slaughtering, Meat Processing Export
S.I.C.: 2011
N.A.I.C.S.: 311611
Personnel:
Erik Bredholt *(Chm)*
Asger Krogsgaard *(Vice Chm)*
Kjeld Johannesen *(CEO)*
Preben Sunke *(CFO)*
Flemming N. Enevoldsen *(Exec VP-Foods)*
Board of Directors:
Erik Bredholt
Palle Joest Andersen
Soren Bach
Mogens Birch
Niels Daugaard Buhl
Jeff Olsen Gravenhorst
Hans Klejsgaard Hansen
Tom Michael Jensen
Asger Krogsgaard
Erik Larsen
Torben Lyngso
Peder Philipp
Arne Bech Poulsen
Peter Fallesen Ravn
Cay Wulff Sorensen

Subsidiaries:

DAT-Schaub amba (1)
Flaesketorvet 41
1711 Copenhagen, Denmark
Tel.: (45) 33266600
Fax: (45) 33266666
E-Mail: info@dat-schaub.dk
Web Site: www.dat-schaub.com
Sales Range: $250-299.9 Million
Emp.: 40
Hog Casings Producer & Sales
S.I.C.: 0213
N.A.I.C.S.: 112210
Jan Roelsgaard *(CEO & Mng Dir)*

Subsidiaries:

Aktieselskabet DAT-Schaub Danmark A/S (2)
Flaesketorvet 41
1711 Copenhagen, Denmark
Tel.: (45) 33266600
Fax: (45) 33266666
E-Mail: dat-schaub@dat-schaub.dk
Web Site: www.dat-schaub.dk
Emp.: 30
Meat & Meat Product Merchant Whslr
S.I.C.: 5147
N.A.I.C.S.: 424470
Jan Roelsgaard *(Mng Dir)*

DAT-Schaub Holding A/S (2)
Flaesketorvet 41
DK 1711 Copenhagen, Denmark
Tel.: (45) 33266600
Fax: (45) 33266696
E-Mail: info@dat-schaub.dk
Web Site: www.dat-schaub.dk
Holding Company
S.I.C.: 6719
N.A.I.C.S.: 551112
Jan Roelsgaard *(CEO & Mng Dir)*

Non-U.S. Subsidiaries:

Alandal S.A. (2)
Zona Industrial Apartado 7
Alandroal, 7250 Setubal, Portugal
Tel.: (351) 268449224
Fax: (351) 268449515
E-Mail: mmanoel.alandal@sapo.pt
Emp.: 136
Livestock Merchant Whslr
S.I.C.: 5154
N.A.I.C.S.: 424520
Victor Aguiar *(Mng Dir)*

Argental S.A.R.L. (2)
Sortie Sud R N 82
Bourg Alandroal, 42220 Bourg-en-Bresse, France
Tel.: (33) 477391168
Fax: (33) 477396617
Emp.: 20
Hotels & Motels
S.I.C.: 7011
N.A.I.C.S.: 721110
Patrich Vidal *(Mng Dir)*

Arne B. Corneliussen AS (2)
Kabelgata 37
PO Box 424
0513 Oslo, Norway
Tel.: (47) 22884600
Fax: (47) 22884646
E-Mail: office@abcorneliussen.no
Web Site: www.abcorneliussen.no
Emp.: 30
Meat & Meat Product Merchant Whslr
S.I.C.: 5147
N.A.I.C.S.: 424470
Birger Sagernes *(Mgr-Mktg)*

Boyauderie Orleanaise SA (2)
45 rue de Curembourg
BP 92226
45402 Fleury-les-Aubrais, France
Tel.: (33) 238864545
Fax: (33) 238862887
E-Mail: info@boyauderie-du-poitou.fr
Web Site: dat-schaub.net
Holding Company
S.I.C.: 6719
N.A.I.C.S.: 551112

Boyaux Bressans SA (2)
Cenord-10 rue Jacquard
BP 8303, 01008 Bourg-en-Bresse, France
Tel.: (33) 474233432
Fax: (33) 474223890
E-Mail: info@boyaux-bressans.fr
Holding Company
S.I.C.: 6719
N.A.I.C.S.: 551112

CKW Pharma-Extrakt GmbH & Co. KG (2)
Enshedestrasse 12
48529 Nordhorn, Germany
Tel.: (49) 59212011
Fax: (49) 592177736
E-Mail: ckw.pharma@t-online.de
Web Site: www.dif-kuepers.de
Emp.: 12
Pharmaceutical Preparation Mfr
S.I.C.: 2834
N.A.I.C.S.: 325412
Walter Koop *(Mng Dir)*

DAT-Schaub AB (2)
Varnemovagen 6A
43232 Varberg, Sweden

Tel.: (46) 40592170
Fax: (46) 418661204
E-Mail: info@dat-schaub.se
Web Site: www.dat-schaub.se
Grocery & Related Products Merchant Whslr
S.I.C.: 5149
N.A.I.C.S.: 424490
Bengt Landquist *(Mgr)*

DAT-Schaub (Deutschland) GmbH (2)
Fuchtenfelder Stasse 26
Wietmarschen, 49835 Lingen, Germany
Tel.: (49) 594691330
Fax: (49) 5946913369
E-Mail: info@dif-kuepers.de
Web Site: www.dif-kuepers.de
Emp.: 80
Management Consulting Services
S.I.C.: 8748
N.A.I.C.S.: 541618
Walter Koop *(Mng Dir)*

DAT-Schaub (Porto) SA (2)
Rua Do Eirado 350
Arcozelo, 4410-429 Braga, Gaia, Portugal
Tel.: (351) 227537100
Fax: (351) 227537119
E-Mail: dsp@dat-schaub.pt
Web Site: www.dat-schaub.dk
Emp.: 300
Mayonnaise Dressing & Prepared Sauce Mfr
S.I.C.: 2035
N.A.I.C.S.: 311941
Vitor Aguiar *(Mng Dir)*

Dif Organveredlung Gerhard Kupers GmbH & Co. Kg (2)
Fuchtenfelder Stasse 26
Wietmarschen, 49835 Lingen, Germany
Tel.: (49) 594691330
Fax: (49) 5946913369
E-Mail: info@dif-kuepers.de
Web Site: www.dif-kuepers.de
Emp.: 200
Meat & Meat Product Merchant Whslr
S.I.C.: 5147
N.A.I.C.S.: 424470
Walter Koop *(Mng Dir)*

DS-France S.A.S. (2)
13 rue des Alouettes
94320 Thiais, France
Tel.: (33) 149785800
Fax: (33) 149785888
E-Mail: commercial@gs-france.com
Web Site: www.soussana.com
Emp.: 70
Holding Company
S.I.C.: 6719
N.A.I.C.S.: 551112
Patrich Vidal *(Mng Dir)*

EFS Gerhard Kupers GmbH & Co. KG (2)
Fuchtenfelder Stasse 26
Wietmarschen, 49835 Lingen, Germany
Tel.: (49) 594691330
Fax: (49) 5946913369
E-Mail: info@dis-kueper.de
Web Site: www.dis-kueper.de
Emp.: 100
Meat & Meat Product Merchant Whslr
S.I.C.: 5147
N.A.I.C.S.: 424470
Walter Koop *(Mng Dir)*

Orako AS (2)
Rislokkveien 2
PO Box 424
0513 Oslo, Norway
Tel.: (47) 22722231
Fax: (47) 22884646
E-Mail: office@abcorneliussen.no
Web Site: www.abcorneliussen.no
Emp.: 30
Grocery & Related Products Merchant Whslr
S.I.C.: 5149
N.A.I.C.S.: 424490
Arne Olassen *(Gen Mgr)*

Oriental Sino Limited (2)
2802 28th Floor Universal Trade Centre
3 Arbuthnot Road, Central, China (Hong Kong)
Tel.: (852) 28107321
Fax: (852) 28106817
Web Site: www.dat-schaub.dk
Emp.: 4
Holding Company
S.I.C.: 6719
N.A.I.C.S.: 551112

Soussana S.A. (2)
1 route de Gentelles
Boves, 80440 Rouen, France
Tel.: (33) 322090330
Fax: (33) 322093836
Web Site: www.soussana.com
Emp.: 21
Grocery & Related Products Merchant Whslr
S.I.C.: 5149
N.A.I.C.S.: 424490

ESS-Food AmbA (1)
Industrivej 9
DK-2605 Brondby, Denmark (100%)
Tel.: (45) 43469000
Telex: 22948
Fax: (45) 43469097
E-Mail: ess-food@ess-food.com
Web Site: www.ess-food.com
Sales Range: $250-299.9 Million
Emp.: 100
Beef & Pork Distr
Export
S.I.C.: 5421
N.A.I.C.S.: 445210
Morten Holm *(Mng Dir)*

Non-U.S. Subsidiaries:

ESS-FOOD S.A. (2)
1 Pl Jean Monnet
45000 Orleans, France
Tel.: (33) 238432929
Fax: (33) 238432560
E-Mail: info@ess-food.fr
Web Site: www.ess-food.fr
Emp.: 11
Wholesale of Packaged Frozen Meat & Meat Products
S.I.C.: 5147
N.A.I.C.S.: 424470
Tommy Jensen *(Mng Dir)*

Foodane A/S (1)
Denmarkgade 22
7400 Herning, Denmark (100%)
Tel.: (45) 96274800
Telex: 66532 str dk
Fax: (45) 96275703
E-Mail: tdc@danishcrown.com
Web Site: www.danishcrown.dk
Emp.: 15
Export of Meat Products
S.I.C.: 5421
N.A.I.C.S.: 445210

Friland A/S (1)
Marsvej 43
DK-8960 Randers, Denmark
Tel.: (45) 8919 2760
Fax: (45) 8919 2351
E-Mail: frilandinfo@friland.dk
Web Site: www.friland.dk
Organic Meat Producer
S.I.C.: 0212
N.A.I.C.S.: 112130

Tulip Food Company (1)
Tulipvej 1
DK-8900 Randers, Denmark
Tel.: (45) 89105000
Fax: (45) 89105001
E-Mail: tulip@tulip.dk
Web Site: www.tulip.dk
Food Processing Services
S.I.C.: 2099
N.A.I.C.S.: 311999
Kasper Lenbroch *(CEO)*

Non-U.S. Subsidiary:

Tulip Ltd. (2)
Seton House Warwick Technology Park
Gallows Hill, Warwick, CV34 6DA, United Kingdom
Tel.: (44) 1926 475680
Fax: (44) 1926 475688
Web Site: www.tulipltd.co.uk
Food Products Processing Services
S.I.C.: 2099
N.A.I.C.S.: 311999

Flemming Enevoldsen *(Chm)*
Chris Thomas *(CEO)*

U.S. Subsidiary:

Sunhill Food of Vermont, Inc. (1)
14 Jonergin Dr
Swanton, VT 05488-1312
Tel.: (802) 868-7314
Fax: (802) 868-4554
Web Site: www.meltinyourmouthbbqribs.com
Emp.: 70
Processing & Packaging of Meat
S.I.C.: 5147
N.A.I.C.S.: 311612

Non-U.S. Subsidiaries:

Danish Crown GmbH (1)
Waldstrasse 7
49632 Oldenburg, Germany (100%)
Tel.: (49) 4954 34850
Fax: (49) 4954 348533
E-Mail: ger@danishcrown.dk
Web Site: www.danishcrown.de
Emp.: 20
Packaged Frozen Meat & Meat Products Whslr
S.I.C.: 5147
N.A.I.C.S.: 424470

KLS Ugglarps (1)
Sodra vagen 60
392 45 Kalmar, Sweden
Tel.: (46) 480 707000
Fax: (46) 480 707087
E-Mail: info@klsugglarps.se
Web Site: www.klsugglarps.se
Meat Production Services
S.I.C.: 5147
N.A.I.C.S.: 424470

Sokolow (1)
Ul Bukowinska 22b
02-703 Warsaw, Poland
Tel.: (48) 22 525 8250
E-Mail: marketing@sokolow.pl
Web Site: www.sokolow.pl
Food Products Processing Services
S.I.C.: 2099
N.A.I.C.S.: 311999

DANKOTUWA PORCELAIN PLC

283 Galle Road
Colombo, 3, Sri Lanka
Tel.: (94) 112576572
Fax: (94) 112576571
E-Mail: info@dankotuwa.com
Web Site: www.dankotuwa.com
DPL—(COL)
Rev.: $11,999,921
Assets: $10,623,840
Liabilities: $4,139,198
Net Worth: $6,484,642
Earnings: $272,196
Fiscal Year-end: 03/31/13
Business Description:
Porcelain Tableware Mfr
S.I.C.: 3999
N.A.I.C.S.: 327110
Personnel:
Sarath Mallawa Arachchi *(CEO)*
Board of Directors:
Rajan Asirwatham
Mangala Boyagoda
Sitendra Senaratne
Ruwan Sugathadasa
A. G. Weerasinghe
Eric Bird Wikramanayake
Legal Counsel:
F J & G De Saram
216 De Saram Place
Colombo, Sri Lanka

DANKS HOLDINGS LIMITED

414 426 Lower Dandenong Rd
3195 Braeside, Victoria, Australia
Tel.: (61) 392645000
Fax: (61) 395871719
E-Mail: firstpoint@danks.com.au
Web Site: www.danks.com.au
DKS—(ASX)
Sales Range: $350-399.9 Million
Business Description:
Hardware Whslr
S.I.C.: 5251
N.A.I.C.S.: 444130
Personnel:
Peter T. Kempen *(Chm)*
J. Graeme Danks *(Mng Dir)*
Peter M. Cooper *(Sec)*
Board of Directors:
Peter T. Kempen
Mike D. Danks
David G. Hendy

DANMAGI GROUP APS

Ramsingsvej 28A
2500 Valby, Denmark
Tel.: (45) 70 25 26 71
E-Mail: sales@danmagi.com
Web Site: www.danmagi.com
Business Description:
Internet Access Solutions
S.I.C.: 7372
N.A.I.C.S.: 511210
Personnel:
Daniel Lister *(CEO)*

DANMARKS NATIONALBANK

Havnegade 5
1093 Copenhagen, Denmark
Tel.: (45) 33636363
Fax: (45) 33637103
E-Mail: nationalbanken@nationalbanken.dk
Web Site: www.nationalbanken.dk
Int. Income: $749,049,509
Assets: $113,365,078,341
Liabilities: $100,613,181,934
Net Worth: $12,751,896,407
Earnings: $729,073,196
Emp.: 518
Fiscal Year-end: 12/31/12
Business Description:
Central Bank
S.I.C.: 6011
N.A.I.C.S.: 521110
Personnel:
Soren Bjerre-Nielsen *(Chm)*
Helle Bechgaard *(Deputy Chm)*
Lars Rebien Sorensen *(Pres & CEO)*
Peter Bjerregaard *(Mng Dir)*
Board of Directors:
Soren Bjerre-Nielsen
Anne Kristine Axelsson
Helle Bechgaard
Peter Bjerregaard
Niels Boserup
Jonas Dahl
Kristian Thulesen Dahl
Michael Dithmer
Niels Fog
Peter Gaemelke
Magnus Heunicke
Bent Jensen
Hans Jensen
Kjeld Johannesen
Mike Legarth
Michael Moller
Sofie Carsten Nielsen
Kirsten Nissen
Ellen Trane Norby
John Dyrby Paulsen
Anja Philip
Halldor Pall Ragnarsson
Lars Lokke Rasmussen
Lars Rebien Sorensen
Bente Sorgenfrey
KPMG
Copenhagen, Denmark

DANNEMORA MINERAL AB

Storrymningsvagen 7
SE-748 30 Osterbybruk, Sweden

Dannemora Mineral AB—(Continued)

Tel.: (46) 295 244 400
Fax: (46) 295 244 404
E-Mail: info@dannemoramineral.se
Web Site: www.dannemoramineral.se
DMAB—(OMX OSL)
Sls.: $21,252,956
Assets: $213,079,723
Liabilities: $170,708,022
Net Worth: $42,371,701
Earnings: ($37,284,354)
Emp.: 78
Fiscal Year-end: 12/31/12

Business Description:
Iron Ore Mining Services
S.I.C.: 1011
N.A.I.C.S.: 212210

Personnel:
Lennart Falk *(Founder, Chm)*
Ralf Norden *(Pres & CEO)*
Niklas Kihl *(CFO)*
Par Goting *(CEO-Magnetit)*

Board of Directors:
Lennart Falk
Christer Lindberg
Ake Roos

Subsidiaries:

Dannemora Forvaltnings AB **(1)**
Storrymningsvaegen 5
748 30 Osterbybruk, Uppsala, Sweden
Tel.: (46) 29520720
Property Portfolio Management Services
S.I.C.: 6531
N.A.I.C.S.: 531312
Lars Alm *(CEO)*

Dannemora Magnetit AB **(1)**
Svaerdvaegen 13
Danderyd, 182 33 Stockholm, Sweden
Tel.: (46) 295244400
Fax: (46) 295244404
Emp.: 8
Iron Ore Mining Services
S.I.C.: 1011
N.A.I.C.S.: 212210

DANOPTRA HOLDINGS LIMITED

Low Ln
Horsforth, Leeds, LS18 4ER, United Kingdom
Tel.: (44) 1132390001
Fax: (44) 1132590864
Web Site: www.danoptragaminggroup.com
Emp.: 100

Business Description:
Holding Company; Gaming Machine Mfr & Distr
S.I.C.: 6719
N.A.I.C.S.: 551112

Personnel:
Julian Nicholls *(Chm)*

Subsidiary:

Danoptra Gamestec **(1)**
Low Ln
Horsforth, Leeds, LS18 4ER, United Kingdom
Tel.: (44) 132390001
Fax: (44) 132590864
Web Site: www.kunick.com
Emp.: 250
Operator of Amusement Machines
S.I.C.: 3999
N.A.I.C.S.: 339999

DANSK TRAEEMBALLAGE A/S

Banevej 3
5600 Faborg, Denmark
Tel.: (45) 62681323
Fax: (45) 62681443
E-Mail: dte@dte.dk
Web Site: www.dte.dk
Sales Range: $25-49.9 Million
Emp.: 265

Business Description:
Wooden Packaging Mfr
S.I.C.: 2499
N.A.I.C.S.: 321999

Personnel:
Peter Jensen *(Mgr)*

DANSKE ANDELSKASSERS BANK A/S

Baneskellet 1
DK 8830 Hammershoj, Tjele, Denmark
Tel.: (45) 87 99 30 00
Fax: (45) 87 99 30 99
E-Mail: info@dabank.dk
Web Site: www.dabank.dk
Year Founded: 1969
DAB—(CSE)
Sales Range: $25-49.9 Million
Emp.: 93

Business Description:
Banking Services
S.I.C.: 6029
N.A.I.C.S.: 522110

Personnel:
Jakob Fastrup *(Chm)*
Jens Jorgensen Hald *(Deputy Chm)*
Jan Pedersen *(Deputy CEO)*

Board of Directors:
Jakob Fastrup
Preben Arndal
Kenneth Clausen
Jens Jorgensen Hald
Jens Holt Ladefoged
Hans Jorn Madsen
Jens Norvang Madsen
Asger Pedersen
Jan Pedersen
Poul Weber

DANSKE BANK A/S

(d/b/a Danske Bank Group)
Holmens Kanal 2-12
1092 Copenhagen, Denmark
Tel.: (45) 33440000
Fax: (45) 70121080
E-Mail: danskebank@danskebank.com
Web Site: www.danskebank.com
Year Founded: 1871
DANSKE—(CSE)
Int. Income: $14,065,915,680
Assets: $628,587,245,160
Liabilities: $603,655,360,920
Net Worth: $24,931,884,240
Earnings: $856,529,640
Emp.: 20,308
Fiscal Year-end: 12/31/12

Business Description:
Retail & Commercial Banking, Insurance, Mortgage Finance & Asset Management Services
S.I.C.: 6029
N.A.I.C.S.: 522110

Personnel:
Ole Gjesso Andersen *(Chm)*
Niels Bjorn Christiansen *(Vice Chm)*
Thomas F. Borgen *(CEO)*
Mads Jacobsen *(Mng Dir)*
Jim Ditmore *(Grp COO)*
Laerke Bygholm *(Sr IR Officer)*
Claus Jensen *(Chief IR Officer)*
Elisabeth Toftmann Klintholm *(Chief IR Officer)*

Board of Directors:
Ole Gjesso Andersen
Tonny Thierry Andersen
Susanne Arboe
Urban Backstrom
Helle Brondum
Niels Bjorn Christiansen
Jim Ditmore
Carsten Eilertsen
Robert Endersby
Lars Einar Forberg
Charlotte Hoffmann
Jorn Peter Jensen
Lars Stensgaard Morch
Henrik Ramlau-Hansen
Carol Sergeant
Jim Hagemann Snabe
Glenn Soderholm
Per Alling Toubro
Trond O. Westlie

Subsidiaries:

Danica Ejendomsselskab ApS **(1)**
Holmens Kanal 2-12
Copenhagen, 1060, Denmark
Tel.: (45) 70112525
Commercial Banking Services
S.I.C.: 6029
N.A.I.C.S.: 522110

Danica Pension **(1)**
Parallelvej 17
2800 Lyngby, Denmark
Tel.: (45) 70112525
Fax: (45) 232020
E-Mail: servicecentre@danicapension.dk
Web Site: www.danicapension.com
Pension Insurance
S.I.C.: 6371
N.A.I.C.S.: 525110
Peter Lindegaard *(Chief Investment Officer)*

Danske Leasing A/S **(1)**
Lerso Park Alle 100
2100 Copenhagen, Denmark
Tel.: (45) 45121212
Fax: (45) 45149212
Commercial Banking Services
S.I.C.: 6029
N.A.I.C.S.: 522110
Orla Nielsen *(Gen Mgr)*

Danske Private Equity **(1)**
Ny Kongensgade 10
DK-1472 Copenhagen, Denmark
Tel.: (45) 33446300
Fax: (45) 33446301
E-Mail: info@danskeprivateequity.com
Web Site: www.danskeprivateequity.com
Emp.: 15
Private Equity
S.I.C.: 6211
N.A.I.C.S.: 523110
John Danielsen *(Mng Partner)*

Nordania Leasing **(1)**
Bregnerodvej 94
3460 Birkerod, Denmark
Tel.: (45) 45121212
Fax: (45) 45149212
E-Mail: nordania@nordania.dk
Web Site: www.nordania.dk
Business Equipment Leasing
S.I.C.: 7377
N.A.I.C.S.: 532420

Realkredit Danmark A/S **(1)**
Parallel Vej 17
DK-2800 Lyngby, Denmark
Tel.: (45) 70125300
Fax: (45) 45125641
E-Mail: rd@rd.dk
Web Site: www.rd.dk
Rev.: $342,938,528
Emp.: 300
Mortgage Lending
S.I.C.: 6163
N.A.I.C.S.: 522310
Sven Holm *(Chm & CEO)*

Non-U.S. Subsidiaries:

Danica Life Ltd. **(1)**
3rd Floor International House 3
Harbourmaster Place
Dublin, Ireland
Tel.: (353) 1 484 2000
Fax: (353) 1 484 4710
E-Mail: enquiries@danicalife.ie
Web Site: www.danicalife.ie
Emp.: 8
Pension Fund Management Services
S.I.C.: 6282
N.A.I.C.S.: 523920

Danica Pensjonsforsikring AS **(1)**
Nordregate 12
7011 Trondheim, Norway
Tel.: (47) 73563200
Fax: (47) 85407965
E-Mail: danica@danica.no
Web Site: www.danica.no
Emp.: 90
Investment Management Services
S.I.C.: 6211
N.A.I.C.S.: 523999
Jan Peter Opedal *(Mng Dir)*

Danske Bank International S.A. **(1)**
13 Rue Edward Steishen
2011 Luxembourg, Luxembourg
Tel.: (352) 4612751
Fax: (352) 473078
E-Mail: klped@danskebank.lu
Web Site: www.danskebank.lu
Emp.: 95
Commercial Banking
S.I.C.: 6029
N.A.I.C.S.: 522110
Klaus Petersen *(Mng Dir)*

Danske Capital AS **(1)**
Narva mnt 11
15015 Tallinn, Estonia
Tel.: (372) 6752295
Fax: (372) 675 2895
E-Mail: investeerimine@danskecapital.com
Web Site: www.danskecapital.ee
Fund Management Services
S.I.C.: 6722
N.A.I.C.S.: 525910
Silja Saar *(CEO)*

Fokus Bank ASA **(1)**
Vestre Rosten 77
7466 Trondheim, Norway
Tel.: (47) 91585400
Fax: (47) 81000901
E-Mail: fokus@fokus.no
Web Site: www.fokus.no
Sales Range: $650-699.9 Million
Emp.: 1,000
Banking Services
S.I.C.: 6029
N.A.I.C.S.: 522110
Trond Mellingsaeter *(CEO)*

Fokus Krogsveen AS **(1)**
Rortunet 34
Trondheim, Sor-Trondelag, 3470, Norway
Tel.: (47) 73100000
Web Site: www.krogsveen.no
Property Management Services
S.I.C.: 6519
N.A.I.C.S.: 531190

National Irish Bank Limited **(1)**
3 Harbourmaster Place IFSC
Dublin, 1, Ireland IE
Tel.: (353) 14840000
Telex: 933433
E-Mail: info@danskebank.ie
Web Site: www.danskebank.ie
Sales Range: $200-249.9 Million
Emp.: 800
Retail & Commercial Banking & Other Financial Services
S.I.C.: 6029
N.A.I.C.S.: 522110
Andrew Healy *(CEO)*
Jesper Nielsen *(Deputy CEO & Head-Bus Dev)*
Grellan Dunne *(CFO)*

Northern Bank Limited **(1)**
14 Donegal Sq W
Belfast, BT1 6JS, United Kingdom
Tel.: (44) 2890245277
Telex: 747674
Fax: (44) 2890893214
Web Site: www.nbonline.co.uk
Emp.: 2,000
Banking Services
S.I.C.: 6029
N.A.I.C.S.: 522110
Gerry Mallon *(CEO)*

Sampo Bank plc **(1)**
Hiililaiturinkuja 2 1548
00075 Helsinki, Finland FI
Tel.: (358) 105460000
Fax: (358) 105462533
E-Mail: info@sampopankki.fi
Web Site: www.sampopankki.fi
Int. Income: $368,250,240
Emp.: 4,587
Commercial & Investment Banking
S.I.C.: 6211

N.A.I.C.S.: 523110
Ilkka Sakari Hallavo *(CEO)*

Subsidiary:

Sampo Housing Loan Bank plc **(2)**
Hiililaiturinkuja 2 00
100 Helsinki, Finland
Tel.: (358) 10 516 0100
E-Mail: tj.anttila@danskebank.fi
Web Site: www.danskebank.fi
Commercial Banking Services
S.I.C.: 6029
N.A.I.C.S.: 522110
Kirsti Lamminen *(CEO & CFO)*

ZAO Danske Bank **(1)**
Marata Street 69-71 A
191119 Saint Petersburg, Russia
Tel.: (7) 8123327300
Fax: (7) 812 332 73 01
E-Mail: bank@danskebank.ru
Web Site: www.danskebank.ru
Emp.: 45
Commercial Banking Services
S.I.C.: 6029
N.A.I.C.S.: 522110

DANTHERM A/S

Marienlystvej 65
7800 Skive, Denmark
Tel.: (45) 99149000
Fax: (45) 99149015
E-Mail: info@dantherm.com
Web Site: www.dantherm.com
DANTH—(OMX)
Rev.: $86,943,801
Assets: $74,874,290
Liabilities: $54,692,006
Net Worth: $20,182,284
Earnings: ($2,980,088)
Emp.: 548
Fiscal Year-end: 12/31/12

Business Description:
Industrial Air Management Equipment Design, Production & Installation Services
S.I.C.: 3564
N.A.I.C.S.: 333413

Personnel:
Jorgen Moller-Rasmussen *(Chm)*
Preben Tolstrup *(Deputy Chm)*
Torben Duer *(Pres & CEO)*
Bjarke Brons *(CFO)*

Board of Directors:
Jorgen Moller-Rasmussen
Niels Kristian Agner
Soren Ostergaard Hansen
Conni-Dorthe Laursen
Nils Rosenkrands Olsen
Per Friis Pedersen
Preben Tolstrup

Subsidiaries:

Dantherm Air Handling Holding A/S **(1)**
Marienlystvej 65
PO Box 502
DK 7800 Skive, Denmark
Tel.: (45) 96143700
Fax: (45) 96143820
Web Site: www.dantherm-air-handling.com
Sales Range: $125-149.9 Million
Emp.: 900
Holding Company; Air Dehumidification, Heating, Air Conditioning, Ventilation & Electronics Cooling Equipment Design, Manufacturing & Installation Services
S.I.C.: 6719
N.A.I.C.S.: 551112
Jesper Holm Thorstensen *(Mng Dir)*

Subsidiary:

Dantherm Air Handling A/S **(2)**
Marienlystvej 65
PO Box 502
7800 Skive, Denmark
Tel.: (45) 96143700
Fax: (45) 96143800
E-Mail: dantherm.dk@dantherm.com
Web Site: www.dantherm-air-handling.com
Emp.: 200
Climate Control Systems Mfr
S.I.C.: 3585
N.A.I.C.S.: 333415
Soren Ostergaard Hansen *(Gen Mgr-Telecom EMEA)*

U.S. Subsidiary:

Dantherm Air Handling Inc. **(2)**
110 Corporate Dr Ste K
Spartanburg, SC 29303-5038
Tel.: (864) 595-9800
Fax: (864) 595-9810
Toll Free: (877) 597-9800
E-Mail: dantherm.usa@dantherm.com
Web Site: www.dantherm.com
Emp.: 50
Air Dehumidification, Heating, Air conditioning, Ventilation & Electronics Cooling Equipment Design, Manufacturing & Installation Services
S.I.C.: 3585
N.A.I.C.S.: 333415
Rick Schmidt *(Gen Mgr)*

Non-U.S. Subsidiaries:

Dantherm Air Handling AB **(2)**
Virkesgatan 5
614 31 Soderkoping, Sweden
Tel.: (46) 121 130 4040
Fax: (46) 121 133 70
E-Mail: infose@dantherm.com
Web Site: www.dantherm-air-handling.se
Ventilation Equipments Distr
S.I.C.: 5211
N.A.I.C.S.: 444190
Monika Brolin *(Gen Mgr & Mgr-Fin)*

Dantherm Air Handling AS **(2)**
Postboks 4
3101 Tonsberg, Norway
Tel.: (47) 33 35 16 00
Fax: (47) 33 38 51 91
E-Mail: dantherm.no@dantherm.com
Web Site: www.dantherm-air-handling.no
Dehumidifiers & Ventilation Equipments Distr
S.I.C.: 5074
N.A.I.C.S.: 423720

Dantherm Air Handling Ltd. **(2)**
12 Windmill Business Park Windmill Road
Clevedon, North Somerset, BS21 6SR, United Kingdom
Tel.: (44) 1275 87 68 51
Fax: (44) 1275 34 30 86
E-Mail: dantherm.co.uk@dantherm.com
Web Site: www.dantherm-air-handling.co.uk
Emp.: 20
Climate Control & Air Handling Systems Distr
S.I.C.: 5075
N.A.I.C.S.: 423730
Ian K. Furmidge *(Mng Dir)*

Dantherm Power A/S **(1)**
Majsmarken 1
9500 Hobro, Denmark
Tel.: (45) 88435500
Fax: (45) 96143805
E-Mail: power@dantherm.com
Web Site: www.dantherm-power.com
Sales Range: Less than $1 Million
Emp.: 42
Fuel Cell & Hydrogen Technology Developer
S.I.C.: 3621
N.A.I.C.S.: 335312
Per Albk *(CEO)*
Bjarke Brons *(CFO)*
Jesper Themsen *(CTO)*

Non-U.S. Subsidiary:

Dantherm Air Handling (Suzhou) Co. Ltd. **(1)**
No 855 9 Zhu Jiang Rd SND Shi Shan Industrial Belt
Suzhou, Jiangsu, China
Tel.: (86) 51266678500
Fax: (86) 51266678501
E-Mail: dantherm.cn@dantherm.com
Web Site: www.dantherm-air-handling.com.cn
Emp.: 150
Air Control Equipments Mfr
S.I.C.: 3443
N.A.I.C.S.: 332410

DANUBE GROUP AGGREGATES PLC

Beogradski kej 51
21000 Novi Sad, Serbia
Tel.: (381) 21 421 177
Fax: (381) 21 528 323
E-Mail: hpnsdc@EUnet.yu
Web Site: www.dunav-grupa.rs
DNGA—(BEL)

Business Description:
Cargo Transportation Services
S.I.C.: 4491
N.A.I.C.S.: 488320

Personnel:
Masan Ercegovic *(Gen Mgr)*

DANUBIUS HOTEL AND SPA NYRT.

Szent Istvan ter 11
H-1051 Budapest, Hungary
Tel.: (36) 18899999
Fax: (36) 18894111
E-Mail: info@danubiushotels.com
Web Site: www.danubiushotels.com
DANUBIUS—(BUD)
Rev.: $209,804,840
Assets: $388,494,000
Liabilities: $147,465,000
Net Worth: $241,029,000
Earnings: $6,563,040
Emp.: 4,487
Fiscal Year-end: 12/31/12

Business Description:
Hotel Management Services
S.I.C.: 8741
N.A.I.C.S.: 561110

Personnel:
Bernard Schreier *(Chm)*
Gyorgy Mohai *(Chm-Supervisory Bd)*
John E. Smith *(Deputy Chm)*
Imre Deak *(Pres & CEO)*
Janos Tobias *(CFO & Sr VP)*

Board of Directors:
Bernard Schreier
Sandor Betegh
Imre Deak
Istvan Fluck
Iris Gibbor
Jozsef Laszlo
Robert Levy
Lev Novobilsky
Alexei Schreier
John E. Smith
Janos Tobias

Supervisory Board of Directors:
Gyorgy Mohai
Gabor Boer
Andras Galszecsy
Laszlo Polgar

DANZER AG

(d/b/a Danzer Group)
Schutzengelstr 36
PO Box 2461
6342 Baar, Switzerland
Tel.: (41) 417670303
Fax: (41) 417670301
E-Mail: info@danzer.com
Web Site: www.danzergroup.com
Year Founded: 1936
Sales Range: $400-449.9 Million
Emp.: 3,200

Business Description:
Holding Company; Hardwood Veneer, Lumber & Vinterio Products Mfr & Distr
S.I.C.: 6719
N.A.I.C.S.: 551112

Personnel:
Rolf Dorig *(Chm-Supervisory Bd)*
Hans-Joachim Danzer *(CEO & Chm-Exec Bd)*
Marc Dietrich *(CFO)*
Greg Lottes *(Pres/CEO-Veneer-Americas)*
Mark Conolly *(CEO-Lumber-North America)*
Olof Freiherr von Gagern *(CEO-Veneer-Europe)*
Erhard Buhler *(VP-Corp Dev)*
Yves Vandenbussche *(Sr VP-Log Procurement-Europe)*

Supervisory Board of Directors:
Rolf Dorig
Roland Bosch
Scott Clawson
Hans-Joachim Danzer
Karl Heinz Danzer
Stephen Lovett

Co-Headquarters:

Danzer Services Europe GmbH **(1)**
Storlach Str 1
Reutlingen, 72760, Germany De
Mailing Address: (100%)
Postfach 1452
D-72704 Reutlingen, Germany
Tel.: (49) 71213070
Fax: (49) 712130783
E-Mail: services@danzergroup.com
Web Site: www.danzergroup.com
Emp.: 20
Executive & Legislative Office; Hardwood Veneer & Lumber Products Distr
S.I.C.: 9131
N.A.I.C.S.: 921140
Yves Vandenbussche *(Sr VP-Log Procurement-Europe)*

U.S. Group:

Danzer Services, Inc. **(2)**
119 AID Dr
Darlington, PA 16115 DE
Tel.: (724) 827-3700
Fax: (724) 827-3702
E-Mail: info@danzerservices.com
Web Site: www.danzergroup.com
Emp.: 100
Executive Office; Hardwood Veneer & Lumber Products Distr
S.I.C.: 9111
N.A.I.C.S.: 921110
Greg Lottes *(Pres/CEO-Veneer-Americas)*
Mark Conolly *(CEO-Lumber-North America)*

Divisions:

Bradford Forest, Inc. **(3)**
444 High St
Bradford, PA 16701 DE
Mailing Address: (100%)
PO Box 369
Bradford, PA 16701-0369
Tel.: (814) 368-3701
Fax: (814) 368-3720
E-Mail: admin@bradfordforest.com
Web Site: www.bradfordforest.com
Emp.: 130
Lumber Sawmill & Products Distr
S.I.C.: 2421
N.A.I.C.S.: 321113
Mark Conolly *(Pres)*

Danzer Forestland, Inc. **(3)**
119 AID Dr
Darlington, PA 16115 DE
Tel.: (724) 827-3700
Fax: (724) 827-8162
E-Mail: info@danzerforestland.com
Web Site: www.danzerforestland.com
Timberland Acquisition & Management Services
S.I.C.: 0811
N.A.I.C.S.: 113110
Zane T. Brown *(Pres & CEO)*

Danzer Veneer Americas, Inc. **(3)**
119 AID Dr
Darlington, PA 16115 DE
Tel.: (724) 827-8366
Fax: (724) 827-3702
Web Site: www.danzergroup.com
Emp.: 100
Hardwood Veneer Products Mfr & Distr
S.I.C.: 2435
N.A.I.C.S.: 321211
Greg Lottes *(Pres & CEO)*

Subsidiaries:

David R. Webb Company, Inc. **(4)**
206 S Holland St
Edinburgh, IN 46124 NV

Danzer AG—(Continued)

Tel.: (812) 526-2601
Fax: (812) 526-5842
E-Mail: info@davidrwebb.com
Web Site: www.davidrwebb.com
Sales Range: $25-49.9 Million
Emp.: 50
Hardwood Veneer Mfr & Distr
S.I.C.: 2435
N.A.I.C.S.: 321211
Ed Pendleton *(Mgr-HR)*

Non-U.S. Division:

Danzer Europe Veneer AG **(2)**
Schutzengelstr 36
PO Box 2461
6342 Baar, Switzerland CH
Tel.: (41) 415607813 (100%)
Fax: (41) 415607801
E-Mail: info@danzereuropeveneer.com
Web Site: www.danzergroup.com
Emp.: 10
Holding Company; Hardwood Veneer Mfr & Whslr
S.I.C.: 6719
N.A.I.C.S.: 551112
Olof Freiherr von Gagern *(CEO)*

Non-U.S. Subsidiaries:

Danzer Bohemia-Dyharna s.r.o. **(3)**
Krivenice 1
27703 Horni Pocaply, Czech Republic CZ
Tel.: (420) 315630700 (100%)
Fax: (420) 315630730
E-Mail: info@danzer.cz
Web Site: www.danzer.cz
Emp.: 480
Hardwood Veneer Mfr & Distr
S.I.C.: 2435
N.A.I.C.S.: 321211
Radim Vrablik *(Gen Mgr)*

Danzer UK Limited **(3)**
46 Market Hill
Maldon, Essex, CM9 4QA, United Kingdom UK
Tel.: (44) 1621851002 (100%)
Fax: (44) 1621859122
E-Mail: info@danzer.co.uk
Web Site: www.danzer.co.uk
Emp.: 50
Lumber Sawmill & Products Distr
S.I.C.: 2421
N.A.I.C.S.: 321113
Ken Walsh *(Mng Dir)*

Karl Danzer Ges.m.b.H. **(3)**
Gollstrasse 20
AT-5082 Grodig, Austria AT
Tel.: (43) 624672155 (100%)
Fax: (43) 624676182
E-Mail: info@danzer.at
Web Site: www.danzer.at
Emp.: 50
Hardwood Veneer Mfr & Whslr
S.I.C.: 2435
N.A.I.C.S.: 321211
Walter Mooslechner *(Mng Dir)*

Non-U.S. Subsidiary:

Danzer Forestacion S.A. **(2)**
Casilla de Correo 449
3300 WAI Posadas, Misiones, Argentina Ar
Tel.: (54) 3752480295 (100%)
Fax: (54) 3752480557
E-Mail: info@danfor.com.ar
Web Site: www.danfor.com.ar
Emp.: 60
Timberland Management Services
S.I.C.: 0811
N.A.I.C.S.: 113110
Hermann Hampel *(Mng Dir)*

DAOMING OPTICS AND CHEMICAL CO., LTD.

(Formerly Zhejiang Daoming Optics & Chemical Co., Ltd.)
1 Yingbin Rd 3rd Xiangzhu Industrial Zone
Yongkang, Zhejiang, 321313, China
Tel.: (86) 579 87311606
Fax: (86) 579 87311855
Web Site:
002632—(SSE)
Sales Range: $25-49.9 Million
Emp.: 920
Business Description:
Reflective Films, Fabrics, Apparel & Other Reflective Products Mfr
S.I.C.: 2899
N.A.I.C.S.: 325998
Personnel:
Zhibiao Hu *(Chm)*

DAOU DATA CORP.

7th Floor Digital Square 23-7 jukjeon-Dong
Suji-Gu, Yongin, Kyeonggi-Do, Korea (South)
Tel.: (82) 70 8707 3000
Fax: (82) 31 307 4230
Web Site: www.daoudata.co.kr
Year Founded: 1992
032190—(KRS)
Emp.: 85
Business Description:
Software Development Services
S.I.C.: 7371
N.A.I.C.S.: 541511
Personnel:
Dong-chul Chung *(CEO)*

DAOU INCUBE

81 Digital Valley-ro
Suji-gu, Yongin, Gyeonggi-do, Korea (South) 448-547
Tel.: (82) 70 8707 2500
Fax: (82) 31 889 3455
Web Site: www.daouincube.com
Year Founded: 1987
020120—(KRS)
Business Description:
Technology Consulting Services
S.I.C.: 7373
N.A.I.C.S.: 541512
Personnel:
Ye Gu Lee *(CEO)*

DAOU TECHNOLOGY, INC.

6F Digital Square 23-7 Jukjeon-Dong
Yongin, Gyeonggi-do, Korea (South)
Tel.: (82) 70 8707 1000
Web Site: www.daou.co.kr
Year Founded: 1986
023590—(KRS)
Sales Range: $700-749.9 Million
Emp.: 450
Business Description:
IT Solution Development Services
S.I.C.: 7373
N.A.I.C.S.: 541512
Personnel:
Young-Hoon Kim *(CEO)*

DAPAI INTERNATIONAL HOLDINGS CO. LTD.

Chengbei Industrial Zone
Luocheng Town Huian County,
Quanzhou, Fujian, China
Tel.: (86) 59527301555
Fax: (86) 595 87392099
E-Mail: ir@chinazaino.com
Web Site: www.chinazaino.com
Sales Range: $150-199.9 Million
Emp.: 2,800
Business Description:
Backpacks & Luggage Developer, Mfr & Sales
S.I.C.: 3199
N.A.I.C.S.: 316998
Personnel:
Xizhong Chen *(Chm)*
Yong Chen *(CEO)*
Ng Kiat Peen *(CFO)*
Board of Directors:
Xizhong Chen
Yong Chen
Kern Lim
Kok Yin Sam
Hung Khim Wong
Legal Counsel:
Rajah & Tann LLP
9 Battery Road 25-01 Straits Trading Building
049910 Singapore, Singapore
Conyers Dill & Pearman Pte. Ltd.
9 Battery Road 20-01 Straits Trading Building
049910 Singapore, Singapore
Transfer Agent:
B.A.C.S. Private Limited
63 Cantonment Road
Singapore, 089758, Singapore
Tel.: (65) 3236 2000

DAPD MEDIA HOLDING AG

Reinhardtstrasse 52
D-10117 Berlin, Germany
Tel.: (49) 30 23122 0
Fax: (49) 30 23122 1182
Business Description:
Holding Company; News Syndicate & Media Publishing Services
S.I.C.: 6719
N.A.I.C.S.: 551112
Personnel:
Martin Vorderwulbecke *(CEO)*

Subsidiaries:

dapd nachrichtenagentur GmbH **(1)**
Reinhardtstrasse 52
D-10177 Berlin, Germany De
Tel.: (49) 30 23122 0
Fax: (49) 30 23122 1182
E-Mail: info@dapd.de
Web Site: www.dapd.de
Sales Range: $10-24.9 Million
Emp.: 300
News Agency
S.I.C.: 7383
N.A.I.C.S.: 519110
Martin Vorderwuelbecke *(Chm-Mgmt Bd & CEO)*
Cord Dreyer *(Member-Mgmt Bd, Mng Dir & Editor-in-Chief)*

ddp direct GmbH **(1)**
Thomasiusstrasse 31
D-04109 Leipzig, Germany De
Tel.: (49) 341 350 587 0
Fax: (49) 341 350 587 79
Web Site: www.ddpdirect.de
Multimedia Management Services
S.I.C.: 7374
N.A.I.C.S.: 518210
Wolfgang Zehrt *(Mng Dir)*

DAPHNE INTERNATIONAL HOLDINGS LIMITED

17th Floor Fung House 19 20
Connaught Road
Central, China (Hong Kong)
Tel.: (852) 23679021
Fax: (852) 23113170
Web Site: www.daphneholdings.com
0210—(HKG OTC)
Sls.: $1,357,727,445
Assets: $927,722,393
Liabilities: $278,253,339
Net Worth: $649,469,054
Earnings: $125,695,689
Emp.: 27,000
Fiscal Year-end: 12/31/12
Business Description:
Footwear Industry
S.I.C.: 2389
N.A.I.C.S.: 316210
Personnel:
Ying-Chieh Chen *(Chm & CEO)*
Jerry Che Li Lin *(CFO)*
Michael Huan Xin Hu *(COO)*
Michael Hai Xuan Liang *(CIO)*
Louisa Ying Lu *(CMO)*
Johnson Tao Li *(Chief Dev Officer)*
Allen Sheuh Hvei Liang *(Chief Strategy Officer)*
Jonathan Wen Che Shih *(Chief Sls Officer)*
Juliette Hui Chun Huang *(Chief Product Officer)*
Echo Wan Ching Chou *(Chief HR Officer)*
Oi Chu Chan *(Sec)*
Board of Directors:
Ying-Chieh Chen
Chih-Chiao Chang
Chih-Kai Chang
Tommy Yi-Hsun Chen
Shun-Tsai Huang
Jin-Goon Kim
Jung-Cheng Kuo
Ted Tak-Tai Lee
Transfer Agent:
Tricor Secretaries Limited
26th Floor Tesbury Centre 28 Queens Rd E
Hong Kong, China (Hong Kong)

Subsidiary:

Gentlefit Trading Limited **(1)**
17 F Fung House 19-20 Connaught Rd
Central, China (Hong Kong)
Tel.: (852) 23679021
Fax: (852) 23113170
Web Site: www.daphne.com.cn
Emp.: 30
Footwear Distr
S.I.C.: 5139
N.A.I.C.S.: 424340
Hsien Min Chen *(Mng Dir)*

DAQIN RAILWAY CO., LTD.

14 Zhanbei St
Datong, Shanxi, 037005, China
Tel.: (86) 3527121248
Fax: (86) 352 712 1990
E-Mail: web@daqinrailway.com
Web Site: www.daqintielu.com
601006—(SHG)
Sales Range: $1-4.9 Billion
Emp.: 40,388
Business Description:
Railway Transportation & Freight Services
S.I.C.: 4011
N.A.I.C.S.: 482111
Personnel:
Xun Wu *(Chm)*

DAQO NEW ENERGY CORP.

666 Longdu Avenue Wanzhou
Chongqing, 404000, China
Tel.: (86) 23 64866666
Fax: (86) 23 64866688
E-Mail: poly@daqo.com
Web Site: www.dqsolar.com
DQ—(NYSE)
Rev.: $86,858,401
Assets: $816,307,804
Liabilities: $475,430,391
Net Worth: $340,877,413
Earnings: ($115,637,415)
Emp.: 1,545
Fiscal Year-end: 12/31/12
Business Description:
Polysilicon, Silicon Wafer & Solar Module Mfr
S.I.C.: 2899
N.A.I.C.S.: 325998
Personnel:
Guangfu Xu *(Chm)*
Xiang Xu *(Vice Chm)*
Bing Sun *(CFO)*
Gongda Yao *(Acting COO)*
Tracy Tianqun Zhou *(CMO)*
Guoping Zhu *(CTO)*
Board of Directors:
Guangfu Xu
Rongling Chen
Mingsong Liang
Dafeng Shi
Arthur Wong
Xiang Xu

Gongda Yao
Shuming Zhao
Fumin Zhuo

DAR AL ARKAN REAL ESTATE DEVELOPMENT COMPANY

PO Box 105633
Riyadh, 11656, Saudi Arabia
Tel.: (966) 12069888
Fax: (966) 12061616
E-Mail: customercare@alarkan.com
Web Site: www.alarkan.com
4300—(SAU)
Rev.: $947,248,274
Assets: $5,853,350,961
Liabilities: $1,509,636,059
Net Worth: $4,343,714,902
Earnings: $263,247,403
Emp.: 370
Fiscal Year-end: 12/31/12
Business Description:
Real Estate Investment, Management & Development Services
S.I.C.: 6531
N.A.I.C.S.: 531390
Personnel:
Yousef Abdullah Al Shelash *(Chm)*
Abdullatif Abdullah Al Shelash *(Mng Dir)*
Benoit Bellerose *(CFO)*
Board of Directors:
Yousef Abdullah Al Shelash
Abdul Kareem Hamad Al Babtain
Saud Abdul Aziz AL Gusaiyer
Hathloul Saleh Al Hathloul
Abdul Rahman Abdul Aziz AL Hussain
Tariq Mohamed Al Jarallah
Majed Abdul Rahman Al Qasim
Abdul Aziz Abdullah Al Shelash
Abdullatif Abdullah Al Shelash
Khalid Abdullah Al Shelash
Majid Romi Al-Romi

DAR AL DAWA DEVELOPMENT & INVESTMENT CO.

PO Box 9364
Amman, 11191, Jordan
Tel.: (962) 6 5539416
Fax: (962) 6 5533199
E-Mail: admin.dad@dadgroup.com
Web Site: www.dadgroup.com
Year Founded: 1975
DADI—(AMM)
Rev.: $60,027,839
Assets: $122,932,535
Liabilities: $52,990,473
Net Worth: $69,942,062
Earnings: ($5,068,610)
Emp.: 792
Fiscal Year-end: 12/31/12
Business Description:
Pharmaceutical Product Mfr & Whslr
S.I.C.: 2834
N.A.I.C.S.: 325412
Personnel:
Abed Alraheem N. Jardaneh *(Chm)*
Osama M. Yaish *(Vice Chm)*
Amer Al Khatib *(CEO)*
Abdelrahman Al Ghoul *(COO)*
Board of Directors:
Abed Alraheem N. Jardaneh
Munthir N. Al Nabulsi
Lina N. Jardaneh
Akram A. Jerab
Duraid A. Jerab
Zaid Nassif
Ramzi R. Salfiti
Osama M. Yaish

DAR AL-MAAL AL-ISLAMI TRUST

84 Avenue Louis Casai
PO Box 161
1216 Cointrin, Switzerland
Tel.: (41) 22 7917111
Fax: (41) 22 7917298
E-Mail: info@dmisa.com
Web Site: www.dmitrust.com
Year Founded: 1981
Sales Range: $400-449.9 Million
Business Description:
Banking Services
S.I.C.: 6029
N.A.I.C.S.: 522110
Personnel:
Mohamed Al Faisal Al Saud *(Chm)*

Non-U.S. Subsidiary:

Ithmaar Bank B.S.C. **(1)**
Seef Tower
PO Box 2820
Manama, Bahrain (52.6%)
Tel.: (973) 17584000
Fax: (973) 17584017
E-Mail: info@ithmaarbank.com
Web Site: www.ithmaarbank.com
ITHMR—(BAH KUW)
Rev.: $475,306,457
Assets: $7,059,812,576
Liabilities: $4,547,039,352
Net Worth: $2,512,773,224
Earnings: ($26,211,544)
Emp.: 281
Fiscal Year-end: 12/31/12
Banking Services
S.I.C.: 6029
N.A.I.C.S.: 522110
Mohammed Al Faisal *(Chm)*
Ahmed Abdul Rahim *(Acting CEO)*
Basma Ahmed A Rahman Al-Na'ar *(Officer-Legal)*
Fatima Ali A Rahim Abdulla *(Fin Control Officer)*
Ammar Mohammad Abdulraman *(Fin Control Officer)*
Abdulla Hussain Al Rahman *(Fin Control Officer)*
Abdulla Nooraldin Mohammad Saleh *(Sr Officer-Shareholders Affairs)*
Dana Aqeel Mahmood Raees *(Sec, Head-Legal Affairs & Exec Sr Mgr)*

Subsidiaries:

Shamil Bank of Bahrain B.S.C. **(2)**
PO Box 3005
1714 Manama, Bahrain
Tel.: (973) 17585000
Fax: (973) 017585151
E-Mail: alshamil@shamilbank.net
Web Site: www.shamilbank.net
Sales Range: $100-124.9 Million
Emp.: 251
Banking Services
S.I.C.: 6029
N.A.I.C.S.: 522110
Mohammed Al Faisal *(Chm)*
Mohammed A. Rahman Bucheerei *(CEO)*

Non-U.S. Subsidiary:

Faysal Bank Limited **(2)**
Faysal House ST-02 Shahrah-e-Faisal
Karachi, Pakistan PK
Tel.: (92) 111 060 606 (66.94%)
Fax: (92) 21 3279 5234
Web Site: www.faysalbank.com
FABL—(ISL KAR LAH)
Int. Income: $291,765,780
Assets: $3,171,341,683
Liabilities: $2,958,835,516
Net Worth: $212,506,168
Earnings: $14,413,795
Emp.: 6,454
Fiscal Year-end: 12/31/12
Retail, Commercial & Investment Banking Services
S.I.C.: 6029
N.A.I.C.S.: 522110
Naseem Ahmed *(Chm)*
Naved A. Khan *(Pres & CEO)*
Majid Ali *(CFO)*
Nasir Islam *(Acting Sec & Head-Compliance)*

DAR AL TAKAFUL HOUSE PJSC

Al Andalus Building
235353 Dubai, United Arab Emirates
Tel.: (971) 42623240
Fax: (971) 42666036
Web Site: www.takafulhouse.ae
Year Founded: 2008
DARTAKAFUL—(EMI)
Sales Range: $10-24.9 Million
Business Description:
Insurance Services
S.I.C.: 6411
N.A.I.C.S.: 524298
Personnel:
Muhammad Ali Misbah Al-Naimi *(Chm)*
Abdulah Saeed Juma Al Naboodah *(Vice Chm)*
Saleh Al Hashemi *(Mng Dir)*
Abdul Salam Ali *(CFO)*
Ajai Panicker *(Sr VP-Technical)*
Board of Directors:
Muhammad Ali Misbah Al-Naimi
Saleh Al Hashemi
Abdulah Saeed Juma Al Naboodah
Ali Humaid Al Owais
Ali Sultan Abdullah Al Owais
Mohammad Najib Chaharaldin
Salaah Sharaf

DAR ES SALAM INVESTMENT BANK

Al Sadoun Park Section 103 Street
41 Building 3
PO Box 3067
Elawiya, Baghdad, Iraq
Tel.: (964) 1 7196488
E-Mail: info@desiraq.com
Web Site: desiraq.com
Year Founded: 1998
BDSI—(IRAQ)
Sales Range: $10-24.9 Million
Business Description:
Banking Services
S.I.C.: 6029
N.A.I.C.S.: 522110
Personnel:
Asad Mohammed Hassan Al-khudhaity *(Chm)*
Board of Directors:
Asad Mohammed Hassan Al-khudhaity
Atheer Talib Al-Samerraie
Nashwan Hamdi Aqrawi
Zuhair Shamil Abdul Aziz
Muhannad Khatab Eissa
Salah Eldeen Mulla
Reem Munther

DARAT JORDAN HOLDINGS

PO Box 930428
Amman, 11193, Jordan
Tel.: (962) 65656771
Fax: (962) 65653854
E-Mail: info@darat.jo
Web Site: www.darat.jo
Year Founded: 2008
DARA—(AMM)
Sales Range: Less than $1 Million
Emp.: 14
Business Description:
Investment Development Services
S.I.C.: 6211
N.A.I.C.S.: 523999
Personnel:
Khalid Al Wazani *(Chm & CEO)*

DARCL LOGISTICS LIMITED

M-2 Himland House Karampura Commercial Complex
Delhi, 110 015, India
Tel.: (91) 1125920610
Fax: (91) 1125920618
E-Mail: info@darcl.com
Web Site: www.darcl.com
Sales Range: $300-349.9 Million
Emp.: 3,000
Business Description:
Integrated Logistics Services
S.I.C.: 4731
N.A.I.C.S.: 541614
Personnel:
Krishan Kumar Agarwal *(Chm & Mng Dir)*
Apoorva Kumar *(Sec)*
Board of Directors:
Krishan Kumar Agarwal
Darshan Kumar Agarwal
Narender Kumar Agarwal
Roshan Lal Agarwal
Ashok Kumar Bhargava
Narain Dass Gupta
Vijay Kumar Gupta
Arun Kumar Kher
G. Raghuram
Arvind Murlidhar Uplenchwar

DARCO WATER TECHNOLOGIES LIMITED

123 Woodlands Industrial Park E5
E-Terrace
Singapore, 757498, Singapore
Tel.: (65) 63633886
Fax: (65) 63622355
E-Mail: sales@darcowater.com
Web Site: www.darcowater.com
5CB—(SES)
Rev.: $33,514,275
Assets: $44,496,774
Liabilities: $28,889,382
Net Worth: $15,607,392
Earnings: ($4,992,487)
Fiscal Year-end: 12/31/12
Business Description:
Water Treatment & Waste Management Services
S.I.C.: 9511
N.A.I.C.S.: 924110
Personnel:
Kim Meng Thye *(Chm, CEO & Mng Dir)*
Sze Leng Tan *(CFO)*
Nee Fa Fu *(Sec)*
Board of Directors:
Kim Meng Thye
Zee Moey Ngiam
Joshua Chee Keong Siow
Heather Chern Ling Tan
Sin Yng Teo
Zach Ze Pin Thye
Transfer Agent:
Boardroom Corporate & Advisory Services Pte. Ltd.
50 Raffles Place 32-01 Singapore Land Tower
Singapore, Singapore

Subsidiaries:

Darco Engineering Pte Ltd. **(1)**
41 Loyang Drive
Singapore, 508952, Singapore
Tel.: (65) 65453800
Fax: (65) 65453730
E-Mail: sales@darcowater.com
Web Site: www.darcowater.com
Emp.: 100
Water Treatment Services
S.I.C.: 9511
N.A.I.C.S.: 924110
Swee Heng Teh *(Exec Dir)*

Non-U.S. Subsidiaries:

Darco Environmental (Philippines) Inc. **(2)**
Unit 502 Caresma Building No 50 Polaris
No 27 Badajos Street
Corner P Burgos Street, Makati, 1261, Philippines
Tel.: (63) 28969375
Fax: (63) 28969375
E-Mail: office@darcophil.com.ph
Web Site: www.darcophil.com.ph
Emp.: 56
Environmental Engineering Solutions
S.I.C.: 8999
N.A.I.C.S.: 541620

Darco Water Technologies Limited—(Continued)

Bon Guan Lim *(Chm)*

Shanghai Darco Engineering Co. Ltd **(2)**
No 200 Lane 1276 Nanle Road Songjiang Industrial Zone
Shanghai, China
Tel.: (86) 21 5774 9731
Fax: (86) 21 5774 9730
E-Mail: darcosh@sh163.net
Web Site: www.darcowater.com.cn
Emp.: 300
Water Treatment Services
S.I.C.: 4971
N.A.I.C.S.: 221310

Shanghai Darco Envirotech Company Limited **(2)**
No 200 Lane 1276 Nanle Road
Songjiang Industrial Zone, Shanghai, China
Tel.: (86) 2157749731
Fax: (86) 2157749730
E-Mail: carvin@darcowater.com.cn
Web Site: www.darcowater.com.cn
Water & Wastewater Engineering Services & Solutions
S.I.C.: 9511
N.A.I.C.S.: 924110

PV Vacuum Engineering Pte Ltd **(1)**
21 Marsiling Industrial Estate Rd 9
Singapore, 739175, Singapore
Tel.: (65) 67556169
Fax: (65) 67552801
E-Mail: pvvacuum@pvsin.com.sg
Web Site: www.pvsin.com.sg
Total Vacuum Application Solutions
S.I.C.: 3999
N.A.I.C.S.: 335210
K M Thye *(Chm)*

Singaway FluidControls Pte Ltd. **(1)**
41 Loyang Drive
Singapore, 508952, Singapore
Tel.: (65) 6545 0334
Fax: (65) 6545 3132
E-Mail: singaway@darcowater.com
Web Site: www.darcowater.com
Fluid Control Solutions
S.I.C.: 3823
N.A.I.C.S.: 334513

Non-U.S. Subsidiaries:

Darco Engineering (Taiwan) Co., Ltd. **(1)**
3 1 Floor World Trade Empire
1071 Chung Cheng Road, Taoyuan, 330, Taiwan
Tel.: (886) 33266589
Fax: (886) 33267589
E-Mail: darcoty@darcoty.com.tw
Environmental Engineering Solutions
S.I.C.: 8999
N.A.I.C.S.: 541620

Subsidiaries:

Darco Remediation Technologies Inc. **(2)**
3-1 Floor World Trade Empire 1071 Chung Cheng Road
Taoyuan, 330, Taiwan
Tel.: (886) 33266589
Fax: (886) 3 326 7589
E-Mail: darcoty@darcoty.com.tw
Water Treatment Services
S.I.C.: 4941
N.A.I.C.S.: 221310

Darco Wan Yuan Develop Co., Ltd. **(2)**
3-1 Floor World Trade Empire 1071 Chung Cheng Road
Taoyuan, 330, Taiwan
Tel.: (886) 33266589
Fax: (886) 3 326 7589
E-Mail: darcoty@darcoty.com.tw
Water Treatment Services
S.I.C.: 4941
N.A.I.C.S.: 221310

Darco-EnviDan Sdn Bhd **(1)**
Lot 10645 PT 16724 Jalan Permata 1/6
Arab Malaysian Industrial Park
71800 Nilai, Negeri Sembilan, Malaysia
Tel.: (60) 6 799 6773
Fax: (60) 6 799 6772
E-Mail: darcosy@darcowater.com.my
Web Site: www.darcowater.com
Emp.: 6
Water Management Services
S.I.C.: 4941
N.A.I.C.S.: 221310
Thye Kim Sah *(Gen Mgr)*

Darco Industrial Water Sdn. Bhd. **(1)**
Jalan Permata 1 6
Arab Malaysian Industrial Park, Negeri Sembilan, Malaysia MY
Tel.: (60) 67996773
Fax: (60) 67996772
E-Mail: info@darcowaters.com
Web Site: www.darcowaters.com
Emp.: 40
Water Treatment & Waste Management Services
S.I.C.: 9511
N.A.I.C.S.: 924110
Choo Seng Yeoh *(Gen Mgr)*

Darco Water Systems Sdn. Bhd. **(1)**
Lot 10645 PT 16724 Jalan Permata 1 6
Arab Malaysian Industrial Park, Nilai Negeri Sembilan, Darul Khusus, 71800, Malaysia MY
Tel.: (60) 67996773
Fax: (60) 67996772
E-Mail: darcosy@darcowater.com.my
Web Site: www.darcowater.com
Emp.: 91
Water Treatment & Waste Management Services
S.I.C.: 9511
N.A.I.C.S.: 924110
Kim Fah Thye *(Gen Mgr)*

DARCOR LIMITED

7 Staffordshire Place
Toronto, ON, M8W 1T1, Canada
Tel.: (416) 255-8563
Fax: (416) 251-6117
Web Site: www.darcor.com
Year Founded: 1931
Rev.: $17,041,210
Emp.: 95
Business Description:
Office Equipment Mfr
S.I.C.: 3589
N.A.I.C.S.: 333318
Personnel:
Dan Watson *(Controller)*

DARE FOODS LIMITED

2481 Kingsway Dr
PO Box 1058
Kitchener, ON, N2G 4G4, Canada
Tel.: (519) 893-5500
Fax: (519) 893-8369
Toll Free: (800) 668-3273
Web Site: www.darefoods.com
Year Founded: 1892
Sales Range: $150-199.9 Million
Emp.: 300
Business Description:
Biscuits, Candy & Crackers Mfr Export
S.I.C.: 2052
N.A.I.C.S.: 311821
Personnel:
William Farrell *(Chm)*
Peter Luik *(Pres)*

DARI COUSPATE S.A

Quartier Industriel
EzZahra El Oulja Sale, Casablanca, Morocco
Tel.: (212) 537 81 11 15
Fax: (212) 537 80 87 43
E-Mail: info@couscousdari.com
Web Site: www.couscousdari.com
Year Founded: 1995
DARI—(CAS)
Business Description:
Couscous Pasta Mfr
S.I.C.: 2098
N.A.I.C.S.: 311824
Personnel:
Mohammed Khalil *(Chm & Mng Dir)*

DARKOM INVESTMENT CO.

Alshmesani-Against Almeredian hotel - darkom Building-fl 3
PO Box 930419
Amman, 11193, Jordan
Tel.: (962) 6 5604216
Fax: (962) 6 5670964
E-Mail: info@darkom.jo
DRKM—(AMM)
Rev.: $117,391
Assets: $7,944,940
Liabilities: $2,093,981
Net Worth: $5,850,959
Earnings: ($3,103,055)
Emp.: 8
Fiscal Year-end: 12/31/12
Business Description:
Investment Management Services
S.I.C.: 6211
N.A.I.C.S.: 523999
Personnel:
Wasem Wael Zo'rob *(Gen Mgr)*

DARLINGTON BUILDING SOCIETY

Sentinel House Morton Road
Darlington, DL1 4PT, United Kingdom
Tel.: (44) 1325 366366
Fax: (44) 1325741000
E-Mail: sales@darlington.co.uk
Web Site: www.darlington.co.uk
Rev.: $23,520,366
Assets: $807,399,378
Liabilities: $747,967,537
Net Worth: $59,431,841
Earnings: $505,373
Emp.: 79
Fiscal Year-end: 12/31/12
Business Description:
Mortgage Lending & Other Financial Services
S.I.C.: 6163
N.A.I.C.S.: 522310
Personnel:
James D. A. Ramsbotham *(Chm)*
David A. Dodd *(CEO)*
Board of Directors:
James D. A. Ramsbotham
Bob Cuffe
Kate Davies
David A. Dodd
Andrew Gosling
Janice Lincoln
Paul Richardson
Alison Thain
K. Lucy H. Winskell

DARMON IMPRESSIONS

Zac Du Moulin Rue Du Noyer
95700 Roissy-en-France, Val D Oise, France
Tel.: (33) 134293740
Web Site: www.groupe-darmon.com
Rev.: $23,500,000
Emp.: 75
Business Description:
Commercial Printing
S.I.C.: 2759
N.A.I.C.S.: 323111

DARNLEY BAY RESOURCES LIMITED

1103 - 4 King Street West
Toronto, ON, M5H 1B6, Canada
Tel.: (416) 862-7885
Fax: (416) 862-7889
E-Mail: dbr@darnleybay.com
Web Site: www.darnleybay.com
Year Founded: 1993
DBL—(TSXV)
Business Description:
Metal Exploration Services
S.I.C.: 1081
N.A.I.C.S.: 213114
Personnel:
Leon F. La Prairie *(Chm)*
Patricia G. Mannard *(CFO)*
Stephen W. Reford *(CTO)*
Greg O'Halloran *(Corp Sec & VP-Corp Dev)*
Board of Directors:
Leon F. La Prairie
Mark T. Bennett
Kerry J. Knoll
Patricia G. Mannard
Stephen W. Reford
Peter G. Telford
Donald Yamkowy
Legal Counsel:
Allen & Allen
200 - 15 Toronto Street
Toronto, ON, Canada

DAROU PAKHSH PHARMACEUTICAL MFG CO.

Darou Pakhsh St Km 18 Tehran-Karaj highway
Tehran, Iran
Tel.: (98) 44986815
Fax: (98) 44987314
E-Mail: info@dppharma.com
Web Site: www.dppharma.ir
Year Founded: 1956
DPAK—(THE)
Business Description:
Pharmaceutical Product Mfr
S.I.C.: 2834
N.A.I.C.S.: 325412
Personnel:
Hosein Naderi MAnesh *(Chm)*
Ali Asghari *(Vice Chm)*
Nasse Naghdi *(Mng Dir)*
Board of Directors:
Hosein Naderi MAnesh
Ali Almasi
Ali Asghari
Nasse Naghdi
Hamid Reza Rasekh

DART ENERGY LIMITED

Level 9 Waterfront Place1 Eagle Street
Brisbane, QLD, 4000, Australia
Mailing Address:
GPO Box 3120
Brisbane, QLD, 4001, Australia
Tel.: (61) 7 3149 2100
Fax: (61) 7 3149 2101
Web Site: www.dartenergy.com
DTE—(ASX)
Rev.: $2,266,568
Assets: $318,886,768
Liabilities: $85,696,051
Net Worth: $233,190,717
Earnings: ($138,482,585)
Emp.: 72
Fiscal Year-end: 06/30/13
Business Description:
Coal Bed Methane Exploration & Production Services
S.I.C.: 1311
N.A.I.C.S.: 211111
Personnel:
John McGoldrick *(CEO)*
Eytan Uliel *(CFO)*
Justin Walta *(COO)*
Paul Marshall *(Sec)*
Board of Directors:
Robert Charles Neale
Stephen Edward Lonie
Lester Campbell Rathie
Shaun Scott

Co-Headquarters:

Dart Energy Ltd. - Singapore Head Office (1)
152 Beach Rd
No 19-05 The Gateway E, Singapore, 189721, Singapore
Tel.: (65) 65089840
Fax: (65) 62946904
Web Site: www.dartenergy.com.au
Coal Seam Gas Mfr
S.I.C.: 2999
N.A.I.C.S.: 324199

Non-U.S. Subsidiaries:

Apollo Gas Limited (2)
Level 24 Suite 24.03
MLC Centre 19-21 Martin Place, Sydney, NSW, 2000, Australia AU
Tel.: (61) 291466330
Fax: (61) 280887140
Web Site: www.dartenergy.com.au/page/Worldwide/Australia/Apollo_Gas_Limited/
Emp.: 4
Petroleum Exploration Services
S.I.C.: 1311
N.A.I.C.S.: 211111
Robbert de Weijer *(CEO)*

Dart Energy (India) Pte. Ltd. (2)
DLF Cyber City Phase III
Bldg No 9 Tower B 16th Fl, Gurgaon, Haryana, 122002, India SG
Tel.: (91) 1244391200
Fax: (91) 1244391201
E-Mail: info@daitcbm.com
Emp.: 15
Coal Seam Gas Mfr
S.I.C.: 2999
N.A.I.C.S.: 324199
Sudhansu Adihikari *(Country Mgr)*

DART GROUP PLC

Low Fare Finder House Leeds
Bradford International Airport
Leeds, LS19 7TU, United Kingdom
Tel.: (44) 1132387444
Fax: (44) 1132387455
E-Mail: info@dartgroup.co.uk
Web Site: www.dartgroup.co.uk
Year Founded: 1971
DTG—(AIM)
Sls.: $1,372,718,868
Assets: $1,180,519,275
Liabilities: $885,823,761
Net Worth: $294,695,514
Earnings: $49,273,848
Emp.: 3,762
Fiscal Year-end: 03/31/13

Business Description:
Aviation Services & Fresh Food Distr
S.I.C.: 4512
N.A.I.C.S.: 481111

Personnel:
Philip Meeson *(Chm & CEO)*
Gary Brown *(Grp CFO)*
Paul Forster *(Sec)*

Board of Directors:
Philip Meeson
Gary Brown
Stephen Heapy
Mark Laurence

Legal Counsel:
Herbert Smith Freehills LLP
Exchange House Primrose Street
London, EC2A 2HS, United Kingdom

Bird & Bird LLP
15 Fetter Lane
London, EC4A 1JP, United Kingdom

Addleshaw Goddard LLP
150 Aldersgate Street
London, United Kingdom

Subsidiaries:

Channel Express (CI) Limited (1)
Building 470 Bournemouth International Airport
Christchurch, Dorset, BH23 6SE, United Kingdom
Tel.: (44) 1202597676
Fax: (44) 1202593480
Web Site: www.channel-express.co.uk/passenger/contact.html
Air & Sea Freight Services
S.I.C.: 4412
N.A.I.C.S.: 483111

Fowler Welch-Coolchain Limited (1)
West Marsh Road
Spalding, Lincolnshire, PE11 2BB, United Kingdom
Tel.: (44) 01775715700
Fax: (44) 1775715767
E-Mail: getinfo@fwcool.co.uk
Web Site: www.fowler-welch.co.uk
Emp.: 800
Food Transport & Distribution
S.I.C.: 4731
N.A.I.C.S.: 488510
David Inglis *(Co-Mng Dir)*
John Peall *(Co-Mng Dir)*

Non-U.S. Subsidiary:

Fowler Welch-Coolchain BV (1)
Herenlaan 27
3155 DC Maasland, Netherlands
Tel.: (31) 174631888
Fax: (31) 174643387
E-Mail: info@fowler-welch.nl
Web Site: www.fowler-welch.co.uk
Emp.: 4
Food Transport & Distribution
S.I.C.: 4731
N.A.I.C.S.: 488510
Bas de Koning *(Gen Mgr)*

DART MINING NL

Level 2 395 Collins Street
Melbourne, VIC, 3000, Australia
Tel.: (61) 3 9621 1299
Fax: (61) 3 9620 0070
E-Mail: info@dartmining.com.au
Web Site: www.dartmining.com.au
DTM—(ASX)
Rev.: $5,719,906
Assets: $18,366,417
Liabilities: $665,245
Net Worth: $17,701,172
Earnings: $3,650,160
Emp.: 10
Fiscal Year-end: 06/30/13

Business Description:
Gold & Base-Metals Exploration & Development
S.I.C.: 1041
N.A.I.C.S.: 212221

Personnel:
Andrew J. Draffin *(Sec)*

Board of Directors:
Christopher John Bain
Stephen Garry Poke
Dean George Turnbull
Richard Glenn Udovenya

Legal Counsel:
ResourcesLaw International
Melbourne, Australia

DARTY PLC

22-24 Ely Place
London, EC1N 6TE, United Kingdom
Tel.: (44) 2072691400
Fax: (44) 2072691405
E-Mail: annabel.donaldson@kesaelectricals.com
Web Site: www.dartygroup.com
DRTY.L—(LSE)
Rev.: $511,921,528
Assets: $165,700,065
Liabilities: $200,713,947
Net Worth: ($35,013,882)
Earnings: ($14,175,170)
Emp.: 15,669
Fiscal Year-end: 04/30/13

Business Description:
Appliance & Electronics Retailer
S.I.C.: 3999
N.A.I.C.S.: 335210

Personnel:
Regis Schultz *(CEO)*
Simon Enoch *(Sec)*

Board of Directors:
Alan C. Parker
Pascal Bazin
Carlo D'Asaro Biondo
Eric Knight
Michel Leonard
Antoine Metzger
Dominic Platt
Alison Reed
Regis Schultz
Agnes Touraine

Transfer Agent:
Computershare Investor Services PLC
The Pavilions Bridgewater Road
PO Box 82
Bristol, BS13 8AE, United Kingdom
Tel.: (44) 870 702 0000
Fax: (44) 870 703 6119

Non-U.S. Subsidiaries:

Bcc Holding Amstelveen B.V. (1)
Bellsingel 61
1119NT Schiphol-Rijk, Netherlands
Tel.: (31) 206556556
Fax: (31) 206401409
Emp.: 200
Consumer Electricals Whslr
S.I.C.: 5064
N.A.I.C.S.: 423620

Etablissements Darty Et Fils S.A.S. (1)
129 avenue Gallieni
93140 Bondy, France
Tel.: (33) 148023232
Fax: (33) 148023565
E-Mail: admin@darty.com
Web Site: www.darty.com
Electronic Products Sales & Services
S.I.C.: 7389
N.A.I.C.S.: 425110

New Vanden Borre S.A. (1)
Slesbroekstraat 106
1650 Sint-Pieters-Leeuw, Belgium
Tel.: (32) 23340000
Fax: (32) 23310327
E-Mail: info@vandenborre.be
Web Site: www.vandenborre.be
Emp.: 1,000
Consumer Electronics Retailer
S.I.C.: 5064
N.A.I.C.S.: 423620
Vec Regoen *(Gen Mgr)*

DARWIN PRIVATE EQUITY LLP

15 Bedford Street
London, WC2E 9HE, United Kingdom
Tel.: (44) 2074200750
Fax: (44) 2074200799
E-Mail: contact@darwinpe.com
Web Site: www.darwinpe.com
Emp.: 13

Business Description:
Private Equity Firm
S.I.C.: 6211
N.A.I.C.S.: 523999

Personnel:
Derek Eliiott *(Partner)*
Nick Jordan *(Partner)*
Alan Maynard *(Partner)*
Kevin Street *(Partner)*

Holding:

Bromford Industries Limited (1)
Pegasus House 1 Bromford Gate
Birmingham, B24 8DW, United Kingdom
Tel.: (44) 1216836200
Fax: (44) 121 683 6201
E-Mail: info@bromfordindustries.co.uk
Web Site: www.bromfordindustries.co.uk
Sales Range: $25-49.9 Million
Emp.: 300
Precision Machined Metal Component Mfr
S.I.C.: 3499
N.A.I.C.S.: 332999
John Hudson *(Chm)*
Mike Smith *(CEO)*

DARWIN RESOURCES CORP.

1090 West Georgia Street Suite 1305
Vancouver, BC, V6E 3V7, Canada
Tel.: (604) 685-9316
Fax: (604) 683-1585
E-Mail: info@darwinresources.com
Web Site: www.darwinresources.com
Year Founded: 2011
DAR—(TSXV)

Business Description:
Gold & Copper Mining
S.I.C.: 1041
N.A.I.C.S.: 212221

Personnel:
Graham Donald Carman *(Pres & CEO)*
Mariana Bermudez *(Sec)*

Board of Directors:
Graham Donald Carman
Nick DeMare
Michael Robert Hudson
Mark Saxon

Legal Counsel:
Gowlings Lafleur Henderson LLP
Bentall 5 Suite 2300 550 Burrard Street
Vancouver, BC, Canada

Non-U.S. Subsidiary:

Darwin Resources Peru (1)
Malecon Cisneros 738 Suite 501
Miraflores, Lima, 18, Peru
Tel.: (51) 1 241 1928
Web Site: www.darwinresources.com
Emp.: 7
Gold & Copper Mining
S.I.C.: 1041
N.A.I.C.S.: 212221
Georg Winkelmann *(Gen Mgr)*

DASCAN INDUSTRIAL CONTROLS

300 Wildcat Rd
North York, ON, M3J 2N5, Canada
Tel.: (416) 665-1511
Fax: (416) 736-8402
E-Mail: info@dascan.com
Web Site: www.dascan.com
Year Founded: 1982
Sales Range: $10-24.9 Million
Emp.: 35

Business Description:
Industrial Control Apparatus Mfg
S.I.C.: 3625
N.A.I.C.S.: 335314

Personnel:
Shay Friedman *(CFO)*
Anil Seth *(Controller)*

U.S. Subsidiary:

Electrical Design & Control Co. Inc. (1)
2200 Stephenson Hwy
Troy, MI 48083-2153
Tel.: (248) 743-2400
Fax: (248) 743-2401
E-Mail: cad@edandc.com
Web Site: www.edandc.com
Sls.: $12,000,000
Emp.: 30
Mfr. of Switchgear & Switchboard Apparatus Import Export
S.I.C.: 8711
N.A.I.C.S.: 541330
Henry Nivelt *(Mgr-Mktg & Sls)*

DASHANG GROUP CO., LTD.

1 Qingsan St
Dalian, Liaoning, 116001, China
Tel.: (86) 41183643215
Fax: (86) 41183630358
E-Mail: info@dsjt.com
Web Site: www.dsjt.com
Year Founded: 1992
600694—(SHG)
Emp.: 23,288

Business Description:
Department Stores, Supermarkets, Shopping Malls & Specialty Stores Operator
S.I.C.: 5311

Dashang Group Co., Ltd.—(Continued)

N.A.I.C.S.: 452111
Personnel:
Gang Nui *(Chm)*
Weishun Lu *(Pres)*

DASSAS COMMUNICATION

37 rue Pierre L'homme
92411 Courbevoie, Cedex, France
Tel.: (33) 146917000
Fax: (33) 147687540
E-Mail: dassas@dassas.com
Web Site: www.dassas.com
Year Founded: 1980
Billings: $60,000,000
Emp.: 25
Business Description:
Advertising Agency
S.I.C.: 7311
N.A.I.C.S.: 541810
Personnel:
Pierre Dassas *(Pres)*

DASSAULT SYSTEMES S.A.

10 Rue Marcel Dassault
78140 Velizy-Villacoublay, Cedex, France
Tel.: (33) 161626162
Fax: (33) 70 73 43 63
E-Mail: corpinfo@ds-fr.com
Web Site: www.3ds.com
DSY—(EUR OTC)
Rev.: $2,730,493,150
Assets: $4,851,478,217
Liabilities: $1,646,317,448
Net Worth: $3,205,160,769
Earnings: $456,121,435
Emp.: 10,122
Fiscal Year-end: 12/31/12
Business Description:
3D Software for Product Design & Development
S.I.C.: 7372
N.A.I.C.S.: 511210
Personnel:
Charles Edelstenne *(Chm)*
Bernard Charles *(Pres & CEO)*
Etienne Droit *(CEO/Exec VP-CATIA)*
Thibault de Tersant *(CFO & Sr Exec VP)*
Laurence Barthes *(CIO, Chief People Officer & Exec VP)*
Scott Berkey *(CEO-SIMULIA)*
Philippe Charles *(CEO-DELMIA)*
Laurent Couillard *(CEO-EXALEAD)*
Andy Kalambi *(CEO-ENOVIA)*
Sophie Plante *(CEO-3DSwYm)*
Bertrand Sicot *(CEO-SolidWorks)*
Lynne Wilson *(CEO-3DVIA)*
Dominique Florack *(Sr Exec VP-Products, Strategy & R&D)*
Bruno Latchague *(Exec VP-Global Sls, Ops & 3DS Value Solutions & Mng Dir-NA)*
Pascal Daloz *(Exec VP-Strategy & Market Dev)*
Philippe Forestier *(Exec VP-Global Affairs & Communities)*
Sylvain Laurent *(Exec VP-3DS Bus Transformation)*
Monica Menghini *(Exec VP-Indus, Mktg & Corp Comm)*
Board of Directors:
Charles Edelstenne
Jean-Pierre Chahid-Nourai
Bernard Charles
Nicole Dassault
Serge Dassault
Arnoud De Meyer
Thibault de Tersant
Odile Desforges
Toshiko Mori

Ernst & Young et Autres
Paris, France

Subsidiaries:

Dassault Data Services **(1)**
22 Quai Gallieni
92156 Suresnes, France (95%)
Tel.: (33) 141384138
Fax: (33) 141384139
Web Site: www.dassault-data-services.fr
Emp.: 370
Provider of Information Services
S.I.C.: 7389
N.A.I.C.S.: 519190
Samson Khaou *(Dir Gen)*

Dassault Systemes Provence **(1)**
53 Ave De l Europe
13100 Aix-en-Provence, Aix En Provence, France (100%)
Tel.: (33) 442522000
Fax: (33) 4425222199
Web Site: www.dassualt.com
Emp.: 90
Provider of 3D Software for Product Design & Development
S.I.C.: 3652
N.A.I.C.S.: 334614
Thierry Charron *(Dir Gen)*

Exalead S.A. **(1)**
10 place de la Madeleine
75008 Paris, France (69%)
Tel.: (33) 155352626
Fax: (33) 155352627
Web Site: www.exalead.com
Sales Range: $10-24.9 Million
Emp.: 150
Enterprise & Web Search Software & Services
S.I.C.: 7372
N.A.I.C.S.: 511210
Patrice Bertin *(Co-Founder & CTO)*
Francois Bourdoncle *(Co-Founder & Chief Strategy Officer)*
Alain Cotte *(CEO)*
Gregory Grefenstette *(Chief Science Officer)*

U.S. Subsidiary:

Exalead Inc. **(2)**
221 Main St Ste 750
San Francisco, CA 94105
Tel.: (415) 230-3800
Fax: (415) 230-3850
Web Site: www.exalead.com
Enterprise & Web Search Software & Services
S.I.C.: 7372
N.A.I.C.S.: 511210
Paul Doscher *(CEO)*

U.S. Subsidiaries:

Dassault Systemes Americas Corp. **(1)**
175 Wyman St
Waltham, MA 02451 DE
Tel.: (781) 810-3000
E-Mail:
Web Site: www.3ds.com
Emp.: 185
Holding Company; Regional Managing Office
S.I.C.: 6719
N.A.I.C.S.: 551112
Michel Tellier *(CEO-DS Brand-Global Collaborative Lifestyle Mgmt)*

Subsidiaries:

Apriso Corporation **(2)**
301 E Ocean Blvd Ste 1200
Long Beach, CA 90802-4839
Tel.: (562) 951-8000
Fax: (562) 951-9000
Web Site: www.apriso.com
Sales Range: $10-24.9 Million
Emp.: 140
Software Solutions
S.I.C.: 7372
N.A.I.C.S.: 511210
Jim Henderson *(Pres & CEO)*
Chris Will *(CTO-Delmia)*
Tom Comstock *(Exec VP-Mktg, Product Mgmt & Strategy)*

Dassault Systemes DELMIA Corp. **(2)**
900 N Skuirrel
Auburn Hills, MI 48326-2615 (100%)
Tel.: (248) 267-9696
Fax: (248) 267-8585
Web Site: www.delmia.com
Emp.: 200
Provider of Software
S.I.C.: 5045
N.A.I.C.S.: 423430
Philippe Charles *(CEO)*

Dassault Systemes Enovia Corp. **(2)**
900 Chelmsford St Tower 2 Fl 5
Lowell, MA 01851 DE
Tel.: (978) 442-2500
Fax: (978) 442-1000
Web Site: www.3ds.com
Sales Range: $100-124.9 Million
Emp.: 200
Product Lifecycle Management Application Software Mfr
S.I.C.: 3652
N.A.I.C.S.: 334614
Deborah A. Mulryan *(VP)*

Dassault Systemes Simulia Corp. **(2)**
Rising Sun Mills 166 Valley St
Providence, RI 02909-2499
Tel.: (401) 276-4400
Fax: (401) 276-4408
E-Mail: simulia.info@3ds.com
Web Site: www.hks.com
Sls.: $16,500,000
Emp.: 400
Computer Software Development
S.I.C.: 7371
N.A.I.C.S.: 541511
Scott Berkey *(CEO)*
Jim Lambert *(CFO & VP)*
Kevin Rota *(CIO)*
Bruce Engelmann *(CTO & VP)*
Steve Levine *(Chief Strategy Officer)*
Tamblyn Ghanem *(Gen Counsel)*

Dassault Systemes SolidWorks Corp. **(2)**
300 Baker Ave
Concord, MA 01742 DE (100%)
Tel.: (978) 371-5011
Fax: (978) 371-7303
Toll Free: (800) 693-9000
E-Mail: info@solidworks.com
Web Site: www.solidworks.com
Provider of Software
S.I.C.: 7371
N.A.I.C.S.: 541511
Bertrand Sicot *(CEO)*
David Stott *(CFO)*
Mark Neil *(Gen Counsel & VP)*

Spatial Corp. **(2)**
310 Interlocken Parkway Ste 200
Broomfield, CO 80021-3468 DE (100%)
Tel.: (303) 544-2900
Fax: (303) 544-3000
E-Mail: info_spatial@3ds.com
Web Site: www.spatial.com
Emp.: 100
Developer & Retailer of 3D Software Components for Technical Applications
S.I.C.: 7371
N.A.I.C.S.: 541511
Paul Cardosi *(VP-Fin & CFO)*
Jean-Marc Guillard *(COO)*

Unit:

Dassault Systemes Americas - Woodland Hills **(2)**
Trillium E Tower 6320 Canoga Ave Ste 300
Woodland Hills, CA 91367-2402
Tel.: (818) 999-2500
Fax: (818) 999-3535
Emp.: 80
Provider of 3D Software for Product Design & Development
S.I.C.: 7371
N.A.I.C.S.: 541511
Al Bunshaft *(Mng Dir)*
Horace Bill *(CFO)*
Tom Emmrich *(Sr VP-Worldwide Svcs)*

Non-U.S. Subsidiaries:

Dassault Systemes AB **(1)**
Rosenholmvn 25
1410 Kolbotn, Norway
Tel.: (47) 9164 5932
Web Site: www.3ds.com
Software Development Services
S.I.C.: 7371
N.A.I.C.S.: 541511

Dassault Systemes ApS **(1)**
Silkeborgvej 2 Stuen
8000 Arhus, Denmark
Tel.: (45) 40 49 25 62
Emp.: 6
Software Development Services
S.I.C.: 7371
N.A.I.C.S.: 541511
Bjarne Jorgensen *(Gen Mgr)*

Dassault Systemes Austria GmbH **(1)**
Euro Plaza Wienerbergstrasse 51
1120 Vienna, Austria
Tel.: (43) 1 227 07 0
E-Mail: DACH.info@3ds.com
Computer Software Distr
S.I.C.: 5045
N.A.I.C.S.: 423430

Dassault Systemes BV **(1)**
Crosspoint Office Building Safariweg 14-16
3605 MA Maarssen, Netherlands
Tel.: (31) 346 585 710
Fax: (31) 346 585 759
Emp.: 3
Software Development Services
S.I.C.: 7371
N.A.I.C.S.: 541511
Theo Verbruggen *(Dir-Tech)*

Dassault Systemes Canada Innovation Technologies Inc. **(1)**
300-393 Saint-Jacques St
Montreal, QC, H2Y 1N9, Canada
Tel.: (514) 940-2949
Fax: (514) 940-1399
Computer System Designing Services
S.I.C.: 7373
N.A.I.C.S.: 541512

Dassault Systemes China **(1)**
China Central Place Tower 2 Room 707-709 No 79 Jianguo Road
Chaoyang District, Beijing, China
Tel.: (86) 10 6536 2288
Software Development Services
S.I.C.: 7371
N.A.I.C.S.: 541511

Dassault Systemes CZ s.r.o. **(1)**
Praha City Center Klimentska 46
11000 Prague, Czech Republic
Tel.: (420) 222 191 107
Software Development Services
S.I.C.: 7371
N.A.I.C.S.: 541511

Dassault Systemes Deutschland GmbH **(1)**
Meitnerstr 8
70563 Stuttgart, Germany
Tel.: (49) 711 27300 0
Fax: (49) 711 27300 599
E-Mail: dach.Info@3ds.com
Web Site: www.3dsevents.de
Software Development Services
S.I.C.: 7371
N.A.I.C.S.: 541511

Dassault Systemes Inc. **(1)**
393 St-Jacques West Suite 300
Montreal, QC, H2Y 1N9, Canada
Tel.: (514) 940-2949
Fax: (514) 940-1399
Web Site: www.3ds.com
Emp.: 30
Software Development Services
S.I.C.: 7371
N.A.I.C.S.: 541511

Dassault Systemes India Pvt. Ltd **(1)**
12th Floor Building 10 C Cyber City Phase 2
122002 Gurgaon, Haryana, India
Tel.: (91) 124 4577100
Fax: (91) 124 4577101
E-Mail: in.mkt.info@3ds.com
Emp.: 65
Software Development Services
S.I.C.: 7371
N.A.I.C.S.: 541511
Chandan Chowdhury *(Mng Dir)*

Dassault Systemes Israel Ltd. **(1)**
5 HaGavish St
44641 Kfar Saba, Israel

Tel.: (972) 9 764 4000
Fax: (972) 9 764 3901
Web Site: www.3ds.com
Software Development Services
S.I.C.: 7371
N.A.I.C.S.: 541511
Gilad Friedman *(Gen Mgr)*

Dassault Systemes Istanbul IT (1)
Astoria A Tower 8-9-10 Buyukdere Cad No 127
34394 Esentepe, Istanbul, Turkey
Tel.: (90) 212 340 7600
Fax: (90) 212 340 7601
Web Site: www.3ds.com
Software Publishing Services
S.I.C.: 7372
N.A.I.C.S.: 511210

Dassault Systemes Italia Srl (1)
Via Rossini 1/A
20020 Lainate, Milan, Italy
Tel.: (39) 02 3343061
Web Site: www.3ds.com
Emp.: 87
Software Development Services
S.I.C.: 7371
N.A.I.C.S.: 541511
Tsutomu Toyofuku *(Gen Mgr)*

Dassault Systemes Japan (1)
Pier City Shibaura Bldg 3-18-1 Kaigan
Minato-Ku, Tokyo, 108-0022, Japan
Tel.: (81) 3 5442 40 11
Fax: (81) 3 5442 41 33
Web Site: www.3ds.com
Software Development Services
S.I.C.: 7371
N.A.I.C.S.: 541511

Dassault Systemes Korea Corp. (1)
Mapo Tower 15F 418 Mapo-dong
Mapo-ku, 121-734 Seoul, Korea (South)
Tel.: (82) 2 3270 7800
Fax: (82) 7856709
Emp.: 15
Software Development Services
S.I.C.: 7371
N.A.I.C.S.: 541511
Chang Young Joo *(Gen Dir)*

Dassault Systemes Mexico (1)
Av Paseo de la Reforma No 505 Piso 41
Cuauhtemoc, Mexico, 6500, Mexico
Tel.: (52) 5552560780
Software Development Services
S.I.C.: 7371
N.A.I.C.S.: 541511

Dassault Systemes Oy (1)
Falcon Business Park - Lago Vaisalantie 2-8
02130 Espoo, Finland
Tel.: (358) 50 301 6393
Web Site: www.3ds.com
Software Development Services
S.I.C.: 7371
N.A.I.C.S.: 541511

Dassault Systemes Russia Corp. (1)
Leningradskoe Shosse 16 A B 1 Floor 9
Moscow, 125171, Russia
Tel.: (7) 495 935 89 28
Fax: (7) 495 935 89 29
Emp.: 3
Software Development Services
S.I.C.: 7371
N.A.I.C.S.: 541511

Dassault Systemes Schweiz AG (1)
Balz-Zimmermannstrasse 7
8302 Kloten, Switzerland
Tel.: (41) 44 200 367 0
Fax: (41) 44 200 3671
E-Mail: dach.info@3ds.com
Emp.: 8
Software Development Services
S.I.C.: 7371
N.A.I.C.S.: 541511
Daniel Nick *(Mng Dir)*

Dassault Systemes Sp. z o.o. (1)
ul Ilzecka 26
02-135 Warsaw, Poland
Tel.: (48) 22 575 70 00
Web Site: www.3ds.com
Software Development Services
S.I.C.: 7371
N.A.I.C.S.: 541511

Dassault Systemes Taiwan (1)
Room 607 No 205 Tun Hwa North Road
Shunsan District, Taipei, Taiwan 2 2718 6287
Tel.: (886) 2 2718 0286
Fax: (886) 2 2718 6287
Software Development Services
S.I.C.: 7371
N.A.I.C.S.: 541511

Dassault Sytemes Australia Pty Ltd (1)
236A Lennox Street Ground Floor
Richmond, 2121, Australia
Tel.: (61) 3 9421 2900
Web Site: www.3ds.com
Software Development Services
S.I.C.: 7371
N.A.I.C.S.: 541511

Delmia GmbH (1)
Raiffeisenplatz 4
70736 Fellbach, Germany (97%)
Tel.: (49) 711273000
Fax: (49) 71127300599
Web Site: www.delmia.de
Emp.: 150
Provider of Software
S.I.C.: 3652
N.A.I.C.S.: 334614
Gort Sehieeel *(Pres)*

DS Deutschland GmbH (1)
Meitnerstrasse 8
D-70563 Stuttgart, Germany (99%)
Tel.: (49) 711273000
Web Site: www.3ds.com
3D Software for Product Design & Development
S.I.C.: 3652
N.A.I.C.S.: 334614
Lynne Wilson *(CEO)*

Gemcom Software International Inc. (1)
1066 W Hastings St Ste 1100
Vancouver, BC, V6E 3X1, Canada BC (100%)
Tel.: (604) 684-6550
Fax: (604) 684-3541
Toll Free: (866) 560-5846
E-Mail:
Sales Range: $75-99.9 Million
Mining & Mineral Exploration Industry Software Publisher
S.I.C.: 7372
N.A.I.C.S.: 511210
Richard Moignard *(Pres & CEO)*
Eric Palmer *(CFO)*
Allen D. Vaughn *(Exec VP-Enterprise Bus Unit)*

Branch:

Gemcom Software International - Toronto (2)
110 Yonge Street Suite 1400
Toronto, ON, M5C 1T4, Canada
Tel.: (416) 866-8244
Fax: (416) 866-8539
Toll Free: (866) 560-5846
E-Mail: sales-na@gemcomsoftware.com
Web Site: www.gemcomsoftware.com
Sales Range: $25-49.9 Million
Emp.: 9
Software Developer & Marketer for Mining & Mineral Exploration Industry
S.I.C.: 7372
N.A.I.C.S.: 511210
Cameron Reed *(VP)*

Non-U.S. Subsidiaries:

Gemcom Africa (Pty) Ltd (2)
Building 26 90 Bekker Street
Midrand, 1685, South Africa
Tel.: (27) 11 805 0277
Fax: (27) 11 805 0047
E-Mail: sales-af@gemcomsoftware.com
Web Site: www.gemcomsoftware.com
Sales Range: $150-199.9 Million
Emp.: 21
Software Developer for Mining & Mineral Exploration Industry
S.I.C.: 7372
N.A.I.C.S.: 511210
Dave Osborn *(Mng Dir)*

Gemcom do Brasil Ltda (2)
Av Getulio Vargas 1300 Sala 1101
Belo Horizonte, MG, 30112-021, Brazil
Tel.: (55) 31 2128 7800
Fax: (55) 31 2128 7801
E-Mail: sales-br@gemcomsoftware.com
Sales Range: $50-74.9 Million
Emp.: 30
Software Developer & Marketer for Mining & Mineral Exploration Industry
S.I.C.: 7372
N.A.I.C.S.: 511210
Iain McLean *(VP-Americas)*

Gencom Asia Pacific Pty Ltd (2)
Level 8 190 St Georges Terrace
Perth, WA, 6000, Australia
Mailing Address:
PO Box 7495
Cloisters Square, Perth, WA, 6850, Australia
Tel.: (61) 8 9420 1383
Fax: (61) 8 9420 1350
E-Mail: sales-aa@gemcomsoftware.com
Web Site: www.gemcomsoftware.com
Sales Range: $150-199.9 Million
Emp.: 100
Software Developer & Marketer for Mining & Mineral Exploration Industry
S.I.C.: 7372
N.A.I.C.S.: 511210
Andrew Pyne *(Sr VP)*

Safework, Inc. (1)
215th St Goikacques St W Su
393 St Goikacques 300, Montreal, QC, H2Y1M6, Canada (100%)
Tel.: (514) 931-3000
Fax: (514) 940-1399
Web Site: www.safework.com
Emp.: 15
Provider of Software
S.I.C.: 3652
N.A.I.C.S.: 334614
Julie Charland *(Mgr-Mktg)*

SmarTeam Corp (1)
5 Hagavish St Ovadia House
PO Box 7020
44641 Kfar Saba, Israel (84%)
Tel.: (972) 97644000
Fax: (972) 97644001
Web Site: www.smarteam.com
Emp.: 20
Provider of Software
S.I.C.: 3652
N.A.I.C.S.: 334614
Gilad Friedman *(CEO)*

Non-U.S. Joint Venture:

3D PLM Software Solutions Limited (1)
Plant 6 Pirojshanagar
Vikhroli West, Mumbai, 400 079, India In
Tel.: (91) 2267056500
Fax: (91) 2267056891
Web Site: www.3dplmsoftware.com
Sales Range: $10-24.9 Million
Emp.: 200
Product Lifecycle Management Software Developer & Market Support Services
S.I.C.: 7372
N.A.I.C.S.: 511210
Manu Mahmud Parpia *(Chm)*
Shashank Patkar *(CEO)*

DATA APPLICATIONS CO., LTD.

1-3-8 Nihonbashi Ningyocho Chuo-Ku
Tokyo, 103-0013, Japan
Tel.: (81) 356408540
Fax: (81) 356408541
Web Site: www.dal.co.jp
3848—(JAS)
Sales Range: $10-24.9 Million
Emp.: 92

Business Description:
Prepackaged Software
S.I.C.: 3652
N.A.I.C.S.: 334614

Personnel:
Keita Hashimoto *(Pres)*

DATA CENTER DYNAMICS LTD

(d/b/a DatacenterDynamics)
102108 Clifton Street
London, EC28 4HW, United Kingdom
Tel.: (44) 207 377 1907
Fax: (44) 20 7377 9583
E-Mail: info@datacenterdynamics.com
Web Site: www.datacenterdynamics.com
Sales Range: $1-9.9 Million
Emp.: 70

Business Description:
B2B Information Services
S.I.C.: 7389
N.A.I.C.S.: 519190

Personnel:
Dan Scarbrough *(CEO)*
Simon Banham *(COO)*
George Rockett *(CMO)*
Stephen Worn *(CTO & CEO-North America)*
Haroon Malik *(Grp Publr)*

U.S. Subsidiary:

Data Center Dynamics Inc. (1)
The Monadnock Bldg 685 Market St Ste 590
San Francisco, CA 94105
Tel.: (415) 735-2800
Fax: (415) 735-2801
B2B Information Services
S.I.C.: 7389
N.A.I.C.S.: 519190
Stephen Worn *(CEO)*

Non-U.S. Subsidiaries:

Data Center Dynamics Asia Limited (1)
38/F Tower One Lippo Center 89 Queensway
Hong Kong, China (Hong Kong)
Tel.: (852) 8191 0837
B2B Information Services
S.I.C.: 7374
N.A.I.C.S.: 519190
Dedric Lam *(Gen Mgr)*

Data Center Dynamics (Aust) Pty Ltd (1)
Suite 26 103 George Street
Parramatta, NSW, 2150, Australia
Tel.: (61) 2 9186 2531
Fax: (61) 2 9475 4954
B2B Information Services
S.I.C.: 7389
N.A.I.C.S.: 519190

Data Center Dynamics MEA FZ-LLC (1)
1705 Shatha Tower
PO Box 502520
Dubai, United Arab Emirates
Tel.: (971) 4 434 8450
Fax: (971) 4 427 4050
B2B Information Services
S.I.C.: 7389
N.A.I.C.S.: 519190
Praveen Balachandran *(Gen Mgr)*

Data Center Dynamics Sarl (1)
5 rue de Castiglione
75001 Paris, France
Tel.: (33) 805 08 0016
B2B Information Services
S.I.C.: 2741
N.A.I.C.S.: 519190

Data Center Dynamics Shanghai Co. Ltd. (1)
Crystal Century Tower 5/F Suite 5B
567 Weihai Road, Shanghai, 200041, China
Tel.: (86) 21 6170 3777
Fax: (86) 60911171
Web Site: www.datacenterdynamics.com
Emp.: 5
B2B Information Services
S.I.C.: 7374
N.A.I.C.S.: 519190
Dedric Lam *(Gen Mgr)*

Data Centre Dynamics (Holland) BV (1)
Newtonlaan 115
3584 BH Utrecht, Netherlands
Tel.: (31) 30 210 6534

Data Center Dynamics Ltd—(Continued)

B2B Information Services
S.I.C.: 7389
N.A.I.C.S.: 519190

Data Centre Dynamics Spain S.L.U. (1)
Paseo de la Castellana 121 Esc Izq 5oC
28046 Madrid, Spain
Tel.: (34) 911331762
Fax: (34) 917704051
Web Site: www.datacenterdynamics.es
Emp.: 5
B2B Information Services
S.I.C.: 7389
N.A.I.C.S.: 519190
Jose Luis Friebel *(Gen Mgr)*

DATA GROUP INC.

9195 Torbram Road
Brampton, ON, L6S 6H2, Canada
Tel.: (905) 791-3151
Fax: (905) 791-3277
Toll Free: (800) 268-0128
E-Mail: investors@datagroup.ca
Web Site: www.datagroup.ca
DGI—(OTC TSX)
Rev.: $334,303,836
Assets: $223,285,719
Liabilities: $161,543,160
Net Worth: $61,742,558
Earnings: ($36,850,309)
Emp.: 1,832
Fiscal Year-end: 12/31/12
Business Description:
Data Processing Services
S.I.C.: 7379
N.A.I.C.S.: 518210
Personnel:
Derek Ridout *(Chm)*
Michael Suksi *(Pres & CEO)*
Paul O'Shea *(CFO & Sec)*
Stuart Hendrie *(CIO)*
Steven Albert Galarneau *(Pres-Data West)*
Board of Directors:
Derek Ridout
William Albino
Ronald A. Fotheringham
John H. Greenhough
Paul O'Shea
Thomas R. Spencer
Michael Suksi

DATA HORIZON CORPORATION

1-21-35 Kusatsu Shinmachi
Nishi-ku, Hiroshima, 733-0834, Japan
Tel.: (81) 822795716
Fax: (81) 822799090
E-Mail: dh@dhorizon.co.jp
Web Site: www.dhorizon.co.jp
Year Founded: 1982
3628—(TKS)
Sales Range: $10-24.9 Million
Emp.: 80
Business Description:
Communications Services
S.I.C.: 4899
N.A.I.C.S.: 517919
Personnel:
Yoshio Utsumi *(Pres)*

DATA INTEGRITY INC.

810 Steeprock Dr
Toronto, ON, M3J 2X2, Canada
Tel.: (416) 638-0111
Fax: (416) 638-8429
Toll Free: (800) 263-1407
Web Site: www.dataintegrity.ca
Year Founded: 1980
Rev.: $22,208,384
Emp.: 40
Business Description:
IT Services
S.I.C.: 5045
N.A.I.C.S.: 423430
Personnel:
Norm Filicetti *(Pres)*

DATA MODUL AG

Landsberger Str 322
D-80687 Munich, Germany
Tel.: (49) 89560170
Fax: (49) 8956017119
E-Mail: info@data-modul.com
Web Site: www.data-modul.com
DAM—(DEU)
Rev.: $188,793,612
Assets: $100,051,393
Liabilities: $43,816,487
Net Worth: $56,234,906
Earnings: $9,225,303
Emp.: 326
Fiscal Year-end: 12/31/12
Business Description:
Flat Display Monitors Mfr
S.I.C.: 3577
N.A.I.C.S.: 334118
Personnel:
Victoria Hecktor *(Chm-Supervisory Bd)*
Tony Tong Hoo Tsoi *(Vice Chm-Supervisory Bd)*
Peter Hecktor *(CEO & Member-Exec Bd)*
Florian Pesahl *(CFO & Member-Exec Bd)*
Walter King *(COO & Member-Exec Bd)*
Supervisory Board of Directors:
Victoria Hecktor
Petra Ollhoff
Tony Tong Hoo Tsoi

Subsidiary:

Conrac GmbH (1)
Lindenstrasse 8
97990 Weikersheim, Baden-Wurttemberg, Germany
Tel.: (49) 79341010
Fax: (49) 7934101101
E-Mail: conrac@data-modul.de
Web Site: www.conrac.de
Emp.: 196
Flat Panel Displays Mfr
S.I.C.: 3577
N.A.I.C.S.: 334118
Ralf Zimmermann *(Mng Dir)*

Non-U.S. Subsidiaries:

Conrac Asia Display Products PTE Ltd. (2)
82 Genting Ln No 05-04
Singapore, Singapore
Tel.: (65) 67427988
Fax: (65) 67473933
E-Mail: contact_us@conrac-asia.com
Web Site: www.conrac-asia.com
Emp.: 2
Flat Panel Displays Mfr
S.I.C.: 3577
N.A.I.C.S.: 334118
Kee Sek Huat *(Mgr)*

Conrac France S.A.R.L (2)
7 rue Saint Christophe
60300 Baron, Oise, France
Tel.: (33) 344549699
Fax: (33) 344585509
E-Mail:
Web Site: www.data-modul.com
Emp.: 7
Flat Panel Displays Mfr
S.I.C.: 3575
N.A.I.C.S.: 334118
Patrick Heurtaux *(Mgr)*

CONRAC Ltda. (2)
Carrera 16 No 79-76 Officina 702
Bogota, Cundinamarca, Colombia
Tel.: (57) 13465338
Fax: (57) 13465338
E-Mail: info@conrac.com.co
Emp.: 10
Flat Panel Displays Mfr
S.I.C.: 3575
N.A.I.C.S.: 334118
Joaquin Quijano *(Gen Mgr)*

Conrac MENA FZE (2)
Unit WB 03 Block I Warehouse 11 Airport FZE
PO Box 54592
Dubai, United Arab Emirates
Tel.: (971) 42994009
Fax: (971) 42995587
E-Mail: info@conrac.ae
Web Site: www.conrac.ae
Emp.: 20
Flat Panel Displays Mfr
S.I.C.: 3577
N.A.I.C.S.: 334118

Conrac South Africa (Pty) Ltd. (2)
1st Fl Kiepersol House Stone Mill Ofc Park
300 Acacia Rd Darrenwood
Randburg, Johannesburg, Gauteng, 2194, South Africa
Tel.: (27) 836350369
Fax: (27) 866934976
E-Mail: info@conrac.co.za
Web Site: www.conrac.co.za
Flat Panel Displays Mfr
S.I.C.: 3575
N.A.I.C.S.: 334118

U.S. Subsidiary:

Data Modul Inc. (1)
275 Marcus Blvd Unit K
Hauppauge, NY 11788-2022
Tel.: (631) 951-0800
Fax: (631) 951-2121
E-Mail: info@datamodul.com
Web Site: www.datamodul.com
Emp.: 5
Flat Panel Displays Mfr
S.I.C.: 3577
N.A.I.C.S.: 334118
Thomas Klingl *(Exec VP)*

Non-U.S. Subsidiaries:

Data Modul France, S.A.R.L. (1)
Bat B Hall 204 1-3 rue des Campanules
77185 Lognes, Seine-et-Marne, France
Tel.: (33) 160378100
Fax: (33) 160173586
Web Site: www.datamodul.com
Emp.: 3
Electronic Components Distr
S.I.C.: 5065
N.A.I.C.S.: 423690
Jerome Bly *(Gen Mgr)*

Data Modul Iberia S.L. (1)
c Adolfo Perez Esquivel 3 Edificio Las Americas III Oficina 40
28230 Las Rozas, Madrid, Spain
Tel.: (34) 916366458
Fax: (34) 916366462
E-Mail: agutierre@data-modul.com
Web Site: www.data-modul.com
Emp.: 4
Liquid Crystal Display Screens Mfr
S.I.C.: 3679
N.A.I.C.S.: 334419
Alejandro Garcia *(Mgr-Sls)*

Data Modul Ltd. (1)
2nd Fl 3 Brindley Pl
Birmingham, West Midlands, B12JB, United Kingdom
Tel.: (44) 1216988641
Fax: (44) 121 698 8623
E-Mail: myarnall@data-modul.com
Information System Solutions
S.I.C.: 7373
N.A.I.C.S.: 541512

DATA#3 LIMITED

67 High Street
Toowong, QLD, 4066, Australia
Mailing Address:
PO Box 551
Indooroopilly, Brisbane, QLD, 4068, Australia
Tel.: (61) 300 23 28 23
Fax: (61) 300 32 82 32
E-Mail: info@data3.com.au
Web Site: www.data3.com.au
DTL—(ASX)
Rev.: $803,502,868
Assets: $223,886,848
Liabilities: $188,586,753
Net Worth: $35,300,095
Earnings: $12,649,010
Emp.: 641
Fiscal Year-end: 06/30/13
Business Description:
Software Licensing & Software Asset Management
S.I.C.: 7371
N.A.I.C.S.: 541511
Personnel:
John Grant *(Mng Dir)*
Bremner Hill *(CFO & Co-Sec)*
Terence Bonner *(Co-Sec)*
Board of Directors:
Richard Anderson
Glen Boreham
John Grant
Ian Johnston
Terry Powell

Subsidiaries:

Data#3 Business Systems Pty. Ltd. (1)
67 High Street
Toowong, QLD, 4066, Australia
Tel.: (61) 733718088
Fax: (61) 733710188
E-Mail: info@data3.com.au
Web Site: www.data3.com.au
Emp.: 200
Data Processing Services
S.I.C.: 7374
N.A.I.C.S.: 518210
John Grant *(Mng Dir)*

DATA RESPONS ASA

Sandviksveien 26
NO-1363 Oslo, Norway
Tel.: (47) 67112000
Fax: (47) 67112050
E-Mail: info@datarespons.com
Web Site: www.datarespons.com
DAT—(OSL)
Rev.: $152,780,356
Assets: $77,685,976
Liabilities: $31,833,788
Net Worth: $45,852,188
Earnings: $2,317,396
Emp.: 394
Fiscal Year-end: 12/31/12
Business Description:
Embedded Solutions, Real-Time Wireless Applications & Machine-to-Machine Communication for Technology-Based Companies
S.I.C.: 5045
N.A.I.C.S.: 423430
Personnel:
Ole Jorgen Fredriksen *(Chm)*
Kenneth Ragnvaldsen *(CEO)*
Rune Wahl *(CFO)*
Hans Christian Lonstad *(CTO)*
Susan Hagerty *(Exec VP-Sls & Mktg)*
Board of Directors:
Ole Jorgen Fredriksen
Katryn Baker
Ulla-Britt Frajdin-Hellqvist
Asa Grubb-Weinberg
Jarl Guntveit
Erik Langaker

Units:

Data Respons Norge AS (1)
Sandviksveien 26
1363 Hovik, Norway
Tel.: (47) 67112000
E-Mail: info@datarespons.com
Web Site: www.datarespons.com
Emp.: 100
Embedded Solutions Supplier
S.I.C.: 5045
N.A.I.C.S.: 423430
Jorn E. Toppe *(Mng Dir)*

Data Respons Norge AS (1)
Kirkegardsveien 45
PO Box 44
Kokstad, 5863 Kongsberg, Norway
Tel.: (47) 55114780
Fax: (47) 32299440
E-Mail: info@datarespons.no
Web Site: www.datarespons.com
Emp.: 20
Embedded Solutions Supplier
S.I.C.: 5045
N.A.I.C.S.: 423430
Jorn E. Toppe *(Mng Dir)*

Data Respons Norge AS (1)
Technolog Park Kongsberg
PO Box 1022
NO-3601 Kongsberg, Norway
Tel.: (47) 32299400
Fax: (47) 32299440
E-Mail: info@datarespons.no
Emp.: 22
Embedded Solutions Supplier
S.I.C.: 5045
N.A.I.C.S.: 423430
Tom Holtermann Anderson *(Gen Mgr)*

Non-U.S. Subsidiaries:

Data Respons A/S (1)
Elleker 6
2730 Herlev, Denmark
Tel.: (45) 88327500
Fax: (45) 88327501
E-Mail: info@datarespons.com
Emp.: 50
Embedded Solutions Supplier
S.I.C.: 5045
N.A.I.C.S.: 423430

Data Respons AB (1)
Kandlvagen 12
Stinsen 205, SE-194 61 Sollentuna, Sweden
Tel.: (46) 850168800
Fax: (46) 850168801
E-Mail: info@datarespons.se
Web Site: www.datarespons.com
Emp.: 100
Embedded Solutions Supplier
S.I.C.: 5045
N.A.I.C.S.: 423430

Data Respons GmbH (1)
Amalienbadstr 41 Bau 53
76227 Karlsruhe, Germany
Tel.: (49) 72148088710
Fax: (49) 72148088711
E-Mail: info@datarespons.de
Web Site: www.datarespons.de
Emp.: 50
Embedded Solutions Supplier
S.I.C.: 7379
N.A.I.C.S.: 541519

Data Respons Syren AB (1)
Theres Svenssons Gata 10
417 55 Gothenburg, Sweden
Tel.: (46) 317071480
Fax: (46) 850168801
Computer Software Consulting Services
S.I.C.: 7373
N.A.I.C.S.: 541512

Ipcas GmbH (1)
Gundstrasse 15
91056 Erlangen, Germany
Tel.: (49) 913176770
Fax: (49) 9131 7677 78
E-Mail: info@ipcas.de
Web Site: www.ipcas.com
Information Technology Consulting Services
S.I.C.: 7373
N.A.I.C.S.: 541512
Jochen Staeudinger *(Mgr)*

Sylog Sverige AB (1)
Jan Stenbecks Torg 17 3 tr
PO Box 1186
Kista, Sweden
Tel.: (46) 8750490000
Fax: (46) 87504962
E-Mail: sales@sylog.se
Web Site: www.sylog.se
Emp.: 10
Information Technology Consulting Services
S.I.C.: 7373
N.A.I.C.S.: 541512
Anders Floren *(Acct Mgr)*

DATA SYSTEMS CONSULTING CO., LTD.

222 Sec 1 Jungshing Rd
Hsindian, Taipei, 231, Taiwan
Tel.: (886) 289111688
Fax: (886) 229127809
E-Mail: dscweb@dsc.com.tw
Web Site: www.dsc.com.tw
Year Founded: 1982
Sales Range: $100-124.9 Million
Emp.: 1,380

Business Description:
IT Services
S.I.C.: 7374
N.A.I.C.S.: 518210

Personnel:
Sun Ge Bin *(Chm)*

Non-U.S. Joint Venture:

Digital China Management Systems Ltd. (1)
DCMS Mansion No 5 Shangdi East Road
Haidian District, Beijing, 100085, China
Tel.: (86) 1082705888
Fax: (86) 1082705902
Emp.: 700
Computer Services; Owned by Data Systems Consulting Co., Ltd. & Digital China Holdings Limited
S.I.C.: 7379
N.A.I.C.S.: 541519

THE DATABASE GROUP LTD

Colston Tower
Colston Street, Bristol, BS1 4UH, United Kingdom
Tel.: (44) 1179183500
Fax: (44) 1179183501
E-Mail: sales@databasegroup.co.uk
Web Site: www.databasegroup.co.uk
Year Founded: 1987
Sls.: $3,900,000
Emp.: 90

Business Description:
Data Marketing Services
S.I.C.: 8742
N.A.I.C.S.: 541613

Personnel:
Richard Lees *(Chm)*
Brett Isenberg *(CEO)*

DATAC CONTROL INTERNATIONAL LTD.

Unit 19 Trinity Technology enterprises
Banbun Pearse St
Dublin, 2, Ireland
Tel.: (353) 16717377
Fax: (353) 16717470
E-Mail: info@datac-control.com
Web Site: www.dataconline.com
Year Founded: 1981
Sales Range: $1-9.9 Million
Emp.: 30

Business Description:
Mfr. of Computer Peripheral Equipment
S.I.C.: 3575
N.A.I.C.S.: 334118

Personnel:
Cyril Kerr *(Mng Dir)*

U.S. Subsidiary:

Datac Technologies, Ltd. (1)
2218 Northpark Dr Ste 202
Kingwood, TX 77339-1710 (100%)
Tel.: (281) 348-2341
Fax: (281) 348-2340
E-Mail: sales@datac-technologies.com
Web Site: www.dataconline.com
Mfr. of Computer Peripheral Equipment
S.I.C.: 7371
N.A.I.C.S.: 541511
Cyril Kerr *(Chm)*

DATACENTRIX HOLDINGS LIMITED

Sage Corporate Park North 238 Roan Crescent Old Pretoria Rd
1685 Midrand, South Africa
Tel.: (27) 87 741 5000
Fax: (27) 87 741 5100
E-Mail: info@datacentrix.co.za
Web Site: www.datacentrix.co.za
DCT—(JSE)
Rev.: $214,406,698
Assets: $100,310,063
Liabilities: $45,394,992
Net Worth: $54,915,071
Earnings: $8,636,644
Emp.: 1,060
Fiscal Year-end: 02/28/13

Business Description:
Technology Reseller & Solutions Provider
S.I.C.: 7373
N.A.I.C.S.: 541512

Personnel:
Nolitha Victoria Fakude *(Chm)*
Ahmed Mahomed *(CEO)*
Elizabeth Naidoo *(CFO)*
J. Vaughn Parkin *(Sec)*

Board of Directors:
Nolitha Victoria Fakude
Thenjiwe Claudia Pamela Chikane
Joan Joffe
Ahmed Mahomed
Alwyn Reginald Martin
Elizabeth Naidoo
Dudu Nyamane

Transfer Agent:
Computershare Investor Services (Proprietary) Limited
70 Marshall Street
Johannesburg, South Africa

Subsidiaries:

Datacentrix (Proprietary) Limited (1)
379 Queens Crescent
Menlo Park, Pretoria, Gauteng, 0081, South Africa
Tel.: (27) 12 348 7555
Fax: (27) 12 348 7543
Business Software Consulting Services
S.I.C.: 7371
N.A.I.C.S.: 541511
Kenny Nkosi *(Mng Dir)*

Datacentrix Solutions (Proprietary) Limited (1)
7 Wellington Rd
Johannesburg, Gauteng, 2193, South Africa
Tel.: (27) 123487555
Fax: (27) 123487543
Business Management Software Solutions
S.I.C.: 7371
N.A.I.C.S.: 541511

DATACOLOR AG

Waldstatterstrasse 12
CH-6003 Lucerne, Switzerland
Tel.: (41) 44 488 4019
Telex: 862439 bier ch
Fax: (41) 44 488 4011
E-Mail: investorrelations@datacolor.com
Web Site: www.datacolor.com
Year Founded: 1834
DCN—(SWX)
Sls.: $61,483,000
Assets: $54,419,000
Liabilities: $19,876,000
Net Worth: $34,543,000
Earnings: $4,541,000
Emp.: 331
Fiscal Year-end: 09/30/13

Business Description:
Color Measurement Systems Mfr
Import Export
S.I.C.: 7373
N.A.I.C.S.: 541512

Personnel:
Werner Dubach *(Chm)*
Albert Busch *(CEO)*
Mark Leuchtmann *(CFO)*

Board of Directors:
Werner Dubach
Peter Beglinger
Anne Keller Dubach
Fritz Gantert
Hans Peter Wehrli

U.S. Subsidiary:

Datacolor Inc. (1)
5 Princess Rd
Lawrenceville, NJ 08648 (100%)
Tel.: (609) 924-2189
Fax: (609) 895-7472
E-Mail: marketing@datacolor.com
Web Site: www.datacolor.com
Sls.: $72,336,000
Emp.: 100
Mfr. of Color Measuring & Testing Devices
S.I.C.: 3827
N.A.I.C.S.: 333314
Albert Busch *(Pres & CEO)*

Non-U.S. Subsidiary:

Datacolor Asia Pacific (HK) Limited (1)
Rm 4301 43rd Floor Metroplaza Tower 2
223 Hing Fong Road, Kwai Chung, China (Hong Kong) (51%)
Tel.: (852) 24208283
Fax: (852) 24208320
E-Mail: asiamarketing@datacolor.com
Web Site: www.datacolor.com
Emp.: 100
Ink Mfr
S.I.C.: 2893
N.A.I.C.S.: 325910
William Lam *(Dir-Sls & Support)*

DATADOT TECHNOLOGY LTD

9/19 Rodborough Road
French's Forest, NSW, 2086, Australia
Tel.: (61) 289774900
Fax: (61) 299754700
E-Mail: info@datadotdna.com
Web Site: www.datadotdna.com
DDT—(ASX)
Rev.: $7,326,418
Assets: $8,045,172
Liabilities: $1,892,360
Net Worth: $6,152,813
Earnings: ($173,844)
Emp.: 54
Fiscal Year-end: 06/30/13

Business Description:
Asset Identification System Mfr
S.I.C.: 3829
N.A.I.C.S.: 334519

Personnel:
Bruce Rathie *(Chm)*
R. Standen *(CFO)*
Graham J. Loughlin *(Sec & Mgr-Strategic Dev)*

Board of Directors:
Bruce Rathie
Alison Coutts
Gary Flowers

Non-U.S. Subsidiaries:

DataDot Technology - Taiwan (1)
Nanking E Rd 125 No 12 F
Zhongshan Dist, Taipei, Taiwan
Tel.: (886) 225010930
Fax: (886) 225010985
E-Mail: aero@datadot.com.tw
Web Site: www.datadot.com.tw
Emp.: 10
Theft Prevention Systems Mfr
S.I.C.: 7382
N.A.I.C.S.: 561621

DataDot Technology (UK) Ltd. (1)
4 Twickenham Rd
Union Park Indust, Norwich, Norfolk, NR6 6NG, United Kingdom
Tel.: (44) 1603407171
Fax: (44) 1603401005
E-Mail: info@datadotdna.eu
Web Site: www.datadotdna.co.uk
Emp.: 12
Theft Prevention Systems Mfr
S.I.C.: 7382
N.A.I.C.S.: 561621

DataDot Technology Ltd—(Continued)

Andrew Winfield *(Mng Dir)*

Subsidiary:

DataDot Technology (Europe) Ltd. **(2)**
4 Twickenham Rd
Union Park Indust, Norwich, Norfolk, NR6 6NG, United Kingdom
Tel.: (44) 1603407171
Fax: (44) 1603401005
E-Mail: info@datadotdna.eu
Web Site: www.datadotdna.eu
Emp.: 10
Theft Prevention System Mfr
S.I.C.: 7382
N.A.I.C.S.: 561621
Andrew Winfield *(Dir-Sls)*

DATAGROUP AG

Wilhelm-Schickard-Strasse 7
D-72124 Pliezhausen, Germany
Tel.: (49) 7127 9700 00
Fax: (49) 7127 9700 33
E-Mail: kontakt@datagroup.de
Web Site: www.datagroup.de
Year Founded: 2005
D6H—(DEU)
Sales Range: $10-24.9 Million
Emp.: 1,000
Business Description:
Holding Company; Information Technology Services
S.I.C.: 6719
N.A.I.C.S.: 551112
Personnel:
Heinz Hilgert *(Chm-Supervisory Bd)*
Hans-Hermann Schaber *(Chm-Mgmt Bd & CEO)*
Karlheinz Eisemann *(Vice Chm-Supervisory Bd)*
Dirk Peters *(COO & Member-Mgmt Bd)*
Supervisory Board of Directors:
Heinz Hilgert
Karlheinz Eisemann
Volkmar Weckesser

Subsidiary:

Consinto GmbH **(1)**
Auf Den Tongruben 3
53721 Siegburg, Germany
Tel.: (49) 2241 904 0
Fax: (49) 2241 904 909
E-Mail: info@consinto.com
Web Site: www.consinto.com
Sales Range: $50-74.9 Million
Emp.: 35
Information Technology Consulting Services
S.I.C.: 7373
N.A.I.C.S.: 541512
Nils Haase *(Member-Mgmt Bd)*
Henrik Schultz *(Member-Mgmt Bd)*

Subsidiary:

Consinto Beteiligungs GmbH **(2)**
Ludwig-Ganghofer-Str 6
Grunwald, 82031, Germany
Tel.: (49) 895447990
Fax: (49) 8954479955
Investment Management Services
S.I.C.: 6211
N.A.I.C.S.: 523999

DATALAB TEHNOLOGIJE D.D.

Koprska ulica 92
1000 Ljubljana, Slovenia
Tel.: (386) 12528900
Fax: (386) 12528910
E-Mail: info@datalab.si
Web Site: www.datalab.eu
DATR—(LJU)
Sales Range: $1-9.9 Million
Emp.: 249
Business Description:
Software & Computer Operating Systems Designer
S.I.C.: 7372
N.A.I.C.S.: 511210
Personnel:
Lojze Zajc *(Chm-Exec Bd)*
Igor Sigmundovic *(COO & CTO)*
Matt Mayfield *(Member-Exec Bd)*

Subsidiary:

Datalab SI d.o.o. **(1)**
Koprska ulica 92
SI-1000 Ljubljana, Slovenia
Tel.: (386) 1 2528 900
Fax: (386) 1 2528 910
E-Mail: info@datalab.si
Computer Services
S.I.C.: 7379
N.A.I.C.S.: 541519
David Ceplak *(Mng Dir)*

Non-U.S. Subsidiaries:

Datalab Automotive, d.o.o. **(1)**
Bulevar dr Zorana Dindica 4a
Novi Beograd, 11000 Belgrade, Serbia
Tel.: (381) 11 214 6727
Fax: (381) 11 214 0183
E-Mail: info@dl-automotive.rs
Web Site: www.dl-automotive.rs
Computer Services
S.I.C.: 7379
N.A.I.C.S.: 541519
Persida Pandurovic *(Mng Dir)*

Datalab BH, d.o.o. **(1)**
Hamdije Cemerlica 1/16 Energoinvest Building
71000 Sarajevo, Bosnia & Herzegovina
Tel.: (387) 33 652 101
Fax: (387) 33 711 656
E-Mail: info@datalab.ba
Web Site: www.datalab.ba
Computer Services
S.I.C.: 7379
N.A.I.C.S.: 541519
Nedim Pasic *(Mng Dir)*

Datalab Bulgaria, Ltd. **(1)**
13 Tintyava Str
1113 Sofia, Bulgaria
Tel.: (359) 2 9609 750
Fax: (359) 2 9609 797
E-Mail: info@datalab.bg
Web Site: www.datalab.bg
Computer Services
S.I.C.: 7379
N.A.I.C.S.: 541519
Marussia Margaritova *(Mng Dir)*

Datalab MK, d.o.o. **(1)**
Londonska 19 lokal 7
1000 Skopje, Macedonia
Tel.: (389) 2 3079 231
Fax: (389) 2 3079 231
E-Mail: info@datalab.com.mk
Web Site: www.datalab.com.mk
Computer Services
S.I.C.: 7379
N.A.I.C.S.: 541519
Saso Jovanovski *(Mng Dir)*

Datalab SR, d.o.o. **(1)**
Bulevar Mihajla Pupina 10v/115
11000 Belgrade, Serbia
Tel.: (381) 1 311 9439
Fax: (381) 1 311 9439
E-Mail: info@datalab.rs
Web Site: www.datalab.rs
Computer Services
S.I.C.: 7379
N.A.I.C.S.: 541519
Miodrag Ranisavljevic *(Mng Dir)*

Datalab Tehnologije d.o.o. **(1)**
Trg 1 Istarske brigade 6
52100 Pula, Croatia
Tel.: (385) 52 380 147
Fax: (385) 52 500 087
E-Mail: info@datalab.hr
Web Site: www.datalab.hr
Computer Services
S.I.C.: 7379
N.A.I.C.S.: 541519
Tihomir Stricevic *(Mng Dir)*

Datalab.MN, d.o.o. **(1)**
Serdara Jola Piletica 2/A
81000 Podgorica, Montenegro
Tel.: (382) 20 248 901
Fax: (382) 20 248 902
E-Mail: info@datalab.co.me
Web Site: www.datalab.me
Computer Services
S.I.C.: 7379
N.A.I.C.S.: 541519
Danko Obradovic *(Mng Dir)*

DATALEX PLC

Block U East Point Business Park
Dublin, 3, Ireland
Tel.: (353) 18063500
Fax: (353) 18063501
E-Mail: info@datalex.com
Web Site: www.datalex.com
DLE—(ISE)
Rev.: $32,350,000
Assets: $39,025,000
Liabilities: $8,038,000
Net Worth: $30,987,000
Earnings: $1,121,000
Emp.: 171
Fiscal Year-end: 12/31/12
Business Description:
Ecommerce Software Development Services
S.I.C.: 7371
N.A.I.C.S.: 541511
Personnel:
Aidan Brogan *(CEO)*
Padraig O'Neill *(COO)*
Malachi Faughnan *(CIO)*
Alan Dunne *(CTO)*
David Kennedy *(Sec & Dir-Fin)*
Dominic Clarke *(Sr VP-Global Sls)*
Board of Directors:
Paschal Taggart
John Bateson
Aidan Brogan
Roger Conan
David Kennedy
Peter Lennon
Legal Counsel:
McCann FitzGerald
Riverside One Sir John Rogerson's Quay
Dublin, Ireland

Maples & Calder
75 St Stephens Green
Dublin, 2, Ireland

U.S. Subsidiary:

Datalex USA Inc. **(1)**
1105 Sanctuary Pkwy 190
Alpharetta, GA 30009
Tel.: (770) 255-2400
Fax: (770) 255-2500
E-Mail: info@datalex.com
Sales Range: $1-9.9 Million
Emp.: 42
eCommerce Services
S.I.C.: 7371
N.A.I.C.S.: 541511
Gianni Cataldo *(VP & Gen Mgr)*

DATALINER AB

Skoptorstorpsv St 40
SE 63229 Eskilstuna, Sweden
Tel.: (46) 16147140
Telex: 5446128
Fax: (46) 16122871
E-Mail: info@dataliner.se
Web Site: www.dataliner.se
Sales Range: $1-9.9 Million
Emp.: 3
Business Description:
Automotive Dataline Equipment
S.I.C.: 3714
N.A.I.C.S.: 336390
Personnel:
Johnny Carlson *(Mng Dir)*

DATALOG TECHNOLOGY INC.

10707 50th Street SE
Calgary, AB, T2C 3E5, Canada
Tel.: (403) 243-2024
Fax: (403) 287-3110
E-Mail: info@DatalogTechnology.com
Web Site: www.datalogtechnology.com
Rev.: $19,677,774
Emp.: 700
Business Description:
Petroleum Services
S.I.C.: 1389
N.A.I.C.S.: 213112
Personnel:
Ian Underdown *(Founder & CEO)*

DATALOGIC S.P.A.

(d/b/a Datalogic Group)
Via Candini 2 Lippo di Calderara di Reno
40012 Bologna, Italy
Tel.: (39) 0513147011
Fax: (39) 0513147205
E-Mail: corporate@datalogic.com
Web Site: www.datalogic.com
Year Founded: 1972
DAL—(ITA)
Rev.: $622,267,083
Assets: $774,281,984
Liabilities: $540,852,067
Net Worth: $233,429,917
Earnings: $13,378,237
Emp.: 2,384
Fiscal Year-end: 12/31/12
Business Description:
Mfr of Laser-Based Bar Code Readers, Mobile Computers & Warehouse Management Systems
S.I.C.: 3699
N.A.I.C.S.: 335999
Personnel:
Romano Volta *(Chm, CEO)*
Marco Rondelli *(CFO)*
Giovanni Sgalambro *(CIO)*
Pietro Todescato *(CTO)*
Jacopo Mazzolin *(Chief HR Officer & Sr VP)*
Gian Paolo Fedrigo *(CEO-Industrial Automation)*
Bill Parnel *(CEO-Automatic Data Capture)*
Valentina Volta *(CEO-Bus Dev)*
Federica Lolli *(Gen Counsel)*
Lamberto Girolomoni *(Sr VP-Strategic Projects Corp)*
Board of Directors:
Romano Volta
Emanuela Bonadiman
Pier Paolo Caruso
Gianluca Cristofori
Giovanni Tamburi
Filippo Maria Volta
Valentina Volta

Subsidiaries:

Datalogic Automation S.r.l. **(1)**
Via Lavino n 265
Monte San Pietro, 40050 Bologna, Italy
Tel.: (39) 516765611
Fax: (39) 0516759324
E-Mail: info.automation.it@datalogic.com
Web Site: www.datalogic.com
Emp.: 500
Industrial Automation Products Mfr & Marketer
S.I.C.: 3577
N.A.I.C.S.: 334118
G. P. Fedrigo *(CEO)*

Datalogic Mobile S.r.l. **(1)**
Via S Vitalino n 13
Lippo di Calderara di Reno, 40012
Calderara di Reno, Italy
Tel.: (39) 0513147011
Fax: (39) 0513147561
E-Mail: corprate@datalogic.com
Web Site: www.adc.datalogic.com
Emp.: 300
Mobile Computers Mfr & Marketer
S.I.C.: 3575
N.A.I.C.S.: 334118
Bill Parnell *(CEO)*

U.S. Subsidiary:

Datalogic Holdings, Inc. **(1)**
959 Terry St
Eugene, OR 97402

NY

Tel.: (541) 683-5700
Fax: (541) 345-7140
E-Mail: info.adc.us@datalogic.com
Web Site: www.adc.datalogic.com
Sales Range: $150-199.9 Million
Emp.: 740
Holding Company; Automatic Data Collection Systems & Components Mfr
S.I.C.: 6719
N.A.I.C.S.: 551112
William L. Parnell, Jr. *(CEO-ADC)*

Subsidiaries:

Datalogic ADC, Inc. (2)
959 Terry St
Eugene, OR 97402-9150 DE
Tel.: (541) 349-8283
Fax: (541) 687-7998
Toll Free: (800) 695-5700
E-Mail: info.adc.us@datalogic.com
Web Site: www.adc.datalogic.com
Automatic Data Collection Systems & Components Mfr
S.I.C.: 3699
N.A.I.C.S.: 335999
William L. Parnell, Jr. *(Pres & CEO)*
Joe E. Guy *(Sr VP & Gen Mgr-Solutions Bus Unit)*

PPT Vision, Inc. (2)
6301 W Old Shakopee Rd Ste A
Minneapolis, MN 55438-2693 MN
Tel.: (952) 996-9500
Fax: (952) 996-9501
E-Mail: info@pptvision.com
Web Site: www.pptvision.com
Sales Range: $1-9.9 Million
Emp.: 30
Machine Vision-Based Automated Inspection Systems for Manufacturing Applications Designer, Mfr, Marketer & Integrator
S.I.C.: 3823
N.A.I.C.S.: 334513
Robert W. Heller *(Pres & CEO)*

DATAMATICS GLOBAL SERVICES LTD.

Unit 117-120 SDF IV SEEPZ
Andheri East, Mumbai, 400 096, India
Tel.: (91) 2261020501
Fax: (91) 2228291673
Web Site: www.datamatics.com
DATAMATICS—(BOM NSE)
Rev.: $103,632,067
Assets: $81,110,538
Liabilities: $22,702,749
Net Worth: $58,407,789
Earnings: $5,831,884
Emp.: 4,344
Fiscal Year-end: 03/31/13

Business Description:
Information Technology & BPO Services
S.I.C.: 7376
N.A.I.C.S.: 541513

Personnel:
Lalit S. Kanodia *(Founder & Chm)*
Rahul L. Kanodia *(Vice Chm & CEO)*
C. M. Dwivedi *(Pres & Head-Global HR)*
Vidur Bhogilal *(CFO)*
Divya Kumat *(Compliance Officer, Sec & VP-Legal)*
Pradeep Agarwal *(Sr VP-Fin)*

Board of Directors:
Lalit S. Kanodia
Vidur Bhogilal
Dileep Chokshi
Shahzaad S. Dalal
Sudhir C. Deshpande
Rahul L. Kanodia
Sameer L. Kanodia
Habil Khorakiwala
Radhakrishna K. Saraswat

Transfer Agent:
Datamatics Financial Services Limited
Plot No B-5 MIDC Plart B Cross Lane
Andheri E, Mumbai, India

Subsidiary:

Datamatics Limited (1)
Unit No 117-120 SDF4 SEEPZ East
Mumbai, 400 096, India
Tel.: (91) 2261020501
Fax: (91) 2228291673
Web Site: www.datamatics.com
Global Software & IT Solutions
S.I.C.: 7371
N.A.I.C.S.: 541511
L. S. Kanodia *(Founder & Chm)*
Rahul L. Kanodia *(Vice Chm & CEO)*
Arvind Sirrah *(Sr VP & Head-US-Datamatics America)*
Sanjeet Banerji *(Sr VP-Telecom & Embedded Sys)*

U.S. Subsidiaries:

CIGNEX Datamatics Corporation (1)
2350 Mission College Blvd Ste 490
Santa Clara, CA 95054 CA
Tel.: (408) 327-9900
Fax: (408) 273-6785
E-Mail: mktg@cignex.com
Web Site: www.cignex.com
Emp.: 325
Open Source Solutions
S.I.C.: 7373
N.A.I.C.S.: 541512
Paul Anthony *(Pres)*
Jeff Colvin *(CEO)*
Rajesh Devidasani *(CFO & VP-Ops)*
Dave Malhotra *(COO)*
Munwar Shariff *(CTO)*

Non-U.S. Subsidiaries:

Datamatics Technologies GmbH (1)
Wilhelm-Leuschner-St Hessen 8-10
64347 Griesheim, Germany
Tel.: (49) 6155848614
Fax: (49) 6155848615
E-Mail: michael_thuleweit@datamatics.com
Emp.: 30
Business Solutions Provider
S.I.C.: 7389
N.A.I.C.S.: 561499
Michael Thuleweit *(Gen Mgr)*

Datamatics Technologies U.K. Limited (1)
8 The Square Stockley Park
Uxbridge, Middlesex, UB11 1FW, United Kingdom
Tel.: (44) 2086106105
Fax: (44) 2086106870
Web Site: www.datamatics.co.uk
Business Management Services
S.I.C.: 7389
N.A.I.C.S.: 561499
Navin Anand *(Pres-UK & Europe)*

DATANG HUAYIN ELECTRIC POWER CO., LTD.

No 255 3rd Section Furong Road
Changsha, Hunan, 410007, China
Tel.: (86) 7315388028
Fax: (86) 7315510188
Web Site: www.hypower.com.cn
Year Founded: 1993
600744—(SHG)

Business Description:
Electric Power Distribution Services
S.I.C.: 4939
N.A.I.C.S.: 221122

Personnel:
Shunda Liu *(Pres)*

Board of Directors:
Shou Chen
Zhongxin Wu
Yabin Zhang
Shaowen Zhou

Subsidiary:

Dalian University of Technology Science Park Co., Ltd (1)
No 2 Linggong Road
Ganjingzi District, Dalian, Liaoning, China 116024
Tel.: (86) 411 84708320
Fax: (86) 411 84671713
Educational Support Services
S.I.C.: 8299
N.A.I.C.S.: 611710

DATAPLOT GMBH

Gutenbergstrasse 15
24558 Henstedt-Ulzburg, Germany
Tel.: (49) 41939950
Fax: (49) 4193995150
E-Mail: info@dataplot.de
Web Site: www.dataplot.de
Year Founded: 1979
Rev.: $30,002,821
Emp.: 56

Business Description:
Computer Equipment Mfr
S.I.C.: 5045
N.A.I.C.S.: 423430

Personnel:
Norbert Boehme *(Mng Dir & CEO)*

DATAPOINT CUSTOMER SOLUTIONS LTD.

1000 Great West Road
Brentford, Middlesex, TW8 9HH, United Kingdom
Tel.: (44) 845 850 2277
Telex: (851) 923038/923494
Fax: (44) 8458502626
E-Mail: info@datapoint.com
Web Site: www.datapoint.com
Emp.: 200

Business Description:
Call Centre Equipment Design & Distr
S.I.C.: 5045
N.A.I.C.S.: 423430

Personnel:
Jim Kent *(CEO)*

Non-U.S. Subsidiaries:

Datapoint Iberica S.A. (1)
Costa Brava 13 Mirasierra Bldg 2 Fl
Edificio Mirasierra, 28034 Madrid, Spain (100%)
Tel.: (34) 917341011
Telex: 831 45733
Fax: (34) 917340632
Rev.: $91,592
Emp.: 90
Call Centre Equipment Design & Distr
S.I.C.: 5045
N.A.I.C.S.: 423430
Hermoso Enrique *(Dir-Mktg & Comml)*

Datapoint Nederland B.V. (1)
Maliebaan 6
3581 CM Utrecht, Netherlands (100%)
Tel.: (31) 307999010
Telex: 844 20410
Fax: (31) 307999020
E-Mail: enquiries@datapoint.com
Web Site: www.datapoint.com
Rev.: $5,133,396
Emp.: 77
Call Centre Equipment Design & Distr
S.I.C.: 5045
N.A.I.C.S.: 423430
Reinier Brul *(Country Mgr)*

Datapoint France (1)
64 rue de Tiquetonne
75002 Paris, France (100%)
Tel.: (33) 170392950
E-Mail: enquiries@datapoint.com
Web Site: www.datapoint.com
Call Centre Equipment Design & Distr
S.I.C.: 5045
N.A.I.C.S.: 423430

DATAPREP HOLDINGS BERHAD

Suite 5 02 Level 5 Wisma Academy
4A Jalan 19/1
46300 Petaling Jaya, Selangor, Malaysia
Tel.: (60) 378431600
Fax: (60) 379562324
Web Site: www.dp.com.my
DATAPRP—(KLS)
Rev.: $17,511,912
Assets: $18,629,791
Liabilities: $5,409,696
Net Worth: $13,220,095
Earnings: ($1,620,253)
Emp.: 335
Fiscal Year-end: 03/31/13

Business Description:
Software Solutions
S.I.C.: 7372
N.A.I.C.S.: 511210

Personnel:
Ahmad Rizan Ibrahim *(CEO)*
Hock Chye Tan *(COO & Head-Payment Solutions & Svcs)*
Choong Ming Wong *(Co-Sec & Head-Bus Support Svcs)*
Janies Yoong Shyuan Lee *(Co-Sec)*

Board of Directors:
Adzmi Abdul Wahab
Muhammad Fauzi Abd Ghani
Ahmad Rizan Ibrahim
Chee Wah Lim
Michael Kim Shing Yee

DATAPULSE TECHNOLOGY LTD.

15A Tai Seng Drive
Datapulse Industrial Building
Singapore, 535225, Singapore
Tel.: (65) 63827989
Fax: (65) 63828070
E-Mail: dtpulse@datapulse.com.sg
Web Site: www.datapulse.com.sg
D04—(SES)
Sales Range: $25-49.9 Million
Emp.: 485

Business Description:
Computer-Related Storage Products Mfr
S.I.C.: 3572
N.A.I.C.S.: 334112

Personnel:
Cheng Leok Ng *(Mng Dir)*

Non-U.S. Subsidiary:

Datapulse Technology (Taiwan) Inc. (1)
4th Fl No 103
Rui Ho St, 11494 Taipei, Taipei, Taiwan
Tel.: (886) 226597733
Fax: (886) 226597742
Web Site: www.datapulse.com.tw
Emp.: 80
CD ROM Drives Mfr
S.I.C.: 3651
N.A.I.C.S.: 334310
Kelvin Lim *(Gen Mgr)*

DATASONIC GROUP BERHAD

Level 6 Bangunan Setia 1 15 Lorong Dungun
Damansara Heights, Kuala Lumpur, 50490, Malaysia
Tel.: (60) 3 2087 6000
Fax: (60) 3 2094 3600
E-Mail: ir@datasonic.com.my
Web Site: www.datasonic.com.my
DSONIC—(KLS)
Rev.: $58,608,814
Assets: $78,971,006
Liabilities: $42,682,395
Net Worth: $36,288,611
Earnings: $9,220,455
Fiscal Year-end: 12/31/12

Business Description:
Computer Related Services
S.I.C.: 7379
N.A.I.C.S.: 541519

Personnel:
Abu Hanifah Noordin *(Mng Dir)*
Huei Jiun Chuah *(CFO)*
Chi Hong Chew *(COO)*
Ben Ben Chew *(Deputy Mng Dir)*
Lee Wah Choong *(Co-Sec)*
Yit Chan Tai *(Co-Sec)*

Datasonic Group Berhad—(Continued)

Board of Directors:
Mohamed Hashim Mohd Ali
Mohamed Zulkhornain Ab Ranee
Handrianov Abu Hanifah
Ibrahim Ahmad
Ben Ben Chew
Mohd Safiain Hasan
Zaiful Ayu Ibrahim Ibrahim
Aziz Jamaludin Mhd Tahir
Abu Hanifah Noordin
Md Diah Ramli
Raghbir Singh
Kim Shing Yee

DATATEC LIMITED

Ground Floor Sandown Chambers
Sandown Village 16 Maude Street
Sandton, Johannesburg, South Africa
2146
Mailing Address:
PO Box 76226
Wendywood, Johannesburg, 2144,
South Africa
Tel.: (27) 112331000
Fax: (27) 112333300
E-Mail: info@datatec.co.za
Web Site: www.datatec.co.za
DTC—(JSE LSE)
Rev.: $5,246,667,000
Assets: $2,690,064,000
Liabilities: $1,773,053,000
Net Worth: $917,011,000
Earnings: $85,084,000
Emp.: 6,586
Fiscal Year-end: 02/28/13
Business Description:
Networking, Conferencing & IT Services
S.I.C.: 4899
N.A.I.C.S.: 517919
Personnel:
Jens P. Montanana *(CEO)*
Rob P. Evans *(CFO)*
Board of Directors:
Stephen Davidson
Rob P. Evans
Olufunke Ighodaro
John F. McCartney
Jens P. Montanana
L. Wiseman Nkuhlu
Christopher Stefan Seabrooke
Nick J. Temple
Legal Counsel:
Bowman Gilfillan (Pty) Limited
165 West Street
Sandton, 2196, South Africa
Transfer Agents:
Computershare Investor Services (Pty) Limited
Ground Floor 70 Marshall Street
Johannesburg, South Africa
Computershare Investor Services (Channel Islands) Limited
Ordnance House 31 Pier Road
PO Box 83
JE4 8PW Saint Helier, Jersey

Subsidiaries:

Datatec Management Services (Pty) Limited (1)
Ground Floor Sand Own Chamber 16 Maude St
Sandown, Johannesburg, Gauteng, 2146, South Africa
Tel.: (27) 112331221
Fax: (27) 112333300
E-Mail: info@datatec.co.za
Web Site: www.datatec.co.za
Emp.: 1
Information Technology Consulting Services
S.I.C.: 7373
N.A.I.C.S.: 541512
Jens Montanana *(CEO)*

U.S. Subsidiary:

Westcon Group, Inc. (1)
520 White Plains Rd 2 Fl
Tarrytown, NY 10591-5116 NY
Tel.: (914) 829-7000
Fax: (914) 829-7897
Web Site: us.westcon.com
Emp.: 1,000
Networking Equipment Resale Services
Import Export
S.I.C.: 5045
N.A.I.C.S.: 423430
Jens Montanana *(Chm)*
Charles Thropp *(CFO)*
Gino Cotignola *(CIO)*
Steven Bernard *(Sr VP-Convergence)*
Dan Papes *(Sr VP-Emerging Tech & Data Center Practice)*
Lynn Smurthwaite-Murphy *(Sr VP-US & Canada)*

Division:

Westcon Group (2)
3020 Woodcreek Dr Ste E
Downers Grove, IL 60515-5416
Tel.: (630) 355-8200
Fax: (630) 355-0449
Toll Free: (877) 580-8200
E-Mail:
Web Site: www.westcon.com
Emp.: 30
Audio, Video & Web Conferencing Solutions
S.I.C.: 7389
N.A.I.C.S.: 561499

Subsidiaries:

Comstor Corporation (2)
14850 Conference Ctr Dr Ste 200
Chantilly, VA 20151-3805
Tel.: (703) 345-5100
Fax: (703) 345-5582
Web Site: www.comstor.com
Emp.: 130
Computer Networking
S.I.C.: 5045
N.A.I.C.S.: 423430
Jon Pritchard *(Pres)*
Charles Thropp *(CFO)*
Andreas Dohmen *(Exec VP-EMEA)*
Chris Jones *(Sr VP-Sls-Global)*

Non-U.S. Subsidiary:

Comstor Malaysia Sdn Bhd (3)
Block C 33-5-6 Jaya One Section 13 72A
Jalan Universiti
46200 Petaling Jaya, Selangor, Malaysia
Tel.: (60) 379549919
Fax: (60) 379541626
E-Mail: sales@comstor.com.sg
Web Site: www.comstor.com.my
Software Publishing Services
S.I.C.: 7372
N.A.I.C.S.: 511210
Albert Tan *(Mng Dir)*

Westcon Cala, Inc. (2)
5300 NW 33rd Av Ste 218
Fort Lauderdale, FL 33309
Tel.: (954) 485-3900
Fax: (954) 485-4422
E-Mail: sales@westconcala.com
Web Site: www.westcongroup.com
Software Consulting Services
S.I.C.: 7373
N.A.I.C.S.: 541512
Helio Guimaraes *(Gen Mgr-CANSAC)*

Non-U.S. Subsidiaries:

Westcon Africa (Cameroon) Limited (2)
75 Rue de L'Union Francaise 2eme Etage
Immeuble Entrelec Bali
Douala, Cameroon
Tel.: (237) 33 048 500
Web Site: www.westcongroup.com
Information Technology Consulting Services
S.I.C.: 7373
N.A.I.C.S.: 541512
Forkwen Chi *(Reg Mgr-Sls)*

Westcon Africa (SADC) (Pty) Limited (2)
22 Witkoppen Road
Sandton, Gauteng, 2191, South Africa
Tel.: (27) 112333333
Fax: (27) 112333323
Information Technology Consulting Services
S.I.C.: 7373
N.A.I.C.S.: 541512

Westcon Africa (Tz) (2)
Plot No 311 Lugalo Street
East Upanga, Dar es Salaam, Tanzania
Tel.: (255) 22 212 2886
Fax: (255) 22 212 2861
E-Mail: salestanzania@westconafrica.com
Information Technology Consulting Services
S.I.C.: 7373
N.A.I.C.S.: 541512
Alex Kiome *(Reg Mgr-Sls)*

Westcon Africa UK Limited (2)
4 Penta Court Station Road
Borehamwood, Hertfordshire, WD6 1SL, United Kingdom
Tel.: (44) 2082076171
Fax: (44) 2082075604
Web Site: www.westcongroup.com
Emp.: 20
Information Technology Consulting Services
S.I.C.: 7373
N.A.I.C.S.: 541512

Westcon Brasil, Ltda (2)
Rua Alexandre Dumas 1711 - 3 Andar
Edificio Birmann 11
Chacara Santo Antonio, Sao Paulo, 04717-004, Brazil
Tel.: (55) 11 5186 4333
E-Mail: marketing@westcon.com.br
Web Site: br.westcon.com
Security Management Software Distr
S.I.C.: 5045
N.A.I.C.S.: 423430

Westcon Canada Systems Inc (2)
2100 Trans Canada Hwy
Dorval, QC, H9P 2N4, Canada
Tel.: (514) 420-5400
Fax: (514) 420-5450
Toll Free: (800) 667-6769
Web Site: www.westcongroup.com
Networking Component Distr
S.I.C.: 5045
N.A.I.C.S.: 423430

Westcon Group European Operations Limited (2)
210 Bath Rd
Slough, Berkshire, SL1 3XE, United Kingdom
Tel.: (44) 1753797800
Fax: (44) 1753797801
Emp.: 20
Telecommunication Equipment Distr
S.I.C.: 5065
N.A.I.C.S.: 423690
Jeremy Butt *(Exec VP-EMEA)*

Westcon Group Limited (2)
32 Canaveral Drive
Albany, 632 Albany, New Zealand
Tel.: (64) 94156220
E-Mail: sales.amil@westcongroup.co.nz
Web Site: www.westcongroup.com
Software Publishing Services
S.I.C.: 7372
N.A.I.C.S.: 511210

Westcon Group Pty Limited (2)
Unit 4 39 Herbert Street
Saint Leonards, NSW, 2065, Australia
Tel.: (61) 294321000
Fax: (61) 299013003
E-Mail: services@westcongroup.com.au
Web Site: www.lansystems.com.au
Information Technology & Consulting Services
S.I.C.: 7373
N.A.I.C.S.: 541512
Rhys Shannon *(CTO-Asia Pacific)*

Westcon India Pvt Limited (2)
33 & 34 Indiranagar 1st Stage Off 100 Feet Road
Bengaluru, 560 038, India
Tel.: (91) 9379660371
Fax: (91) 8041265152
E-Mail: info@westcon.com
Web Site: www.westcongroup.in
Emp.: 10
Software Development Services
S.I.C.: 7371
N.A.I.C.S.: 541511
Sanjay Rokhade *(Gen Mgr)*

Westcon Mexico S.A. de C.V. (2)
Lago Victoria 74 Piso 7 Col Granada
Mexico, 11520, Mexico
Tel.: (52) 55 5001 4950
E-Mail: marketing@westcon.com.mx
Web Site: www.westcongroup.com
Information Technology Consulting Services
S.I.C.: 7373
N.A.I.C.S.: 541512

Westcon SA (Pty) Limited (2)
9 Cambridge Commercial Office Park 22 Witkoppen Road
Paulshof, 2191 Johannesburg, South Africa
Tel.: (27) 11 233 3333
Fax: (27) 865 44 49 90
E-Mail: marketing@westcon.co.za
Web Site: www.westconsa.co.za
Emp.: 78
Software Consulting Services
S.I.C.: 7373
N.A.I.C.S.: 541512
Paul Conradie *(CEO)*
Keith Rich *(Interim CEO)*

Non-U.S. Subsidiaries:

Analysys Mason Group Limited (1)
Bush House NW Wing Aldwych
London, WC2B 4PJ, United Kingdom
Tel.: (44) 8456005244
Fax: (44) 2073959001
E-Mail: enquiries@analysysmason.com
Web Site: www.analysysmason.com
Emp.: 250
Network Integration Services
S.I.C.: 7373
N.A.I.C.S.: 541512
Larry Goldman *(Partner & Head-Res-Telecoms Software)*
Amrish Kacker *(Partner-Singapore)*
Duncan Swan *(Partner)*
Andrew Wright *(Partner-Dubai)*
Bram Moerman *(Mng Dir)*

Subsidiaries:

Analysys Limited (2)
Saint Giles Court 24 Castle Street
Cambridge, CB3 0AJ, United Kingdom
Tel.: (44) 1223460600
Fax: (44) 8455280760
Emp.: 40
Information Technology Consulting Services
S.I.C.: 7373
N.A.I.C.S.: 541512
Bram Moerman *(Gen Mgr)*

Subsidiary:

Analysys Consulting Limited (3)
Saint Giles Court 24 Castle Street
Cambridge, Cambridgeshire, CB3 0AJ, United Kingdom
Tel.: (44) 1223 460600
Information Technology Consulting Services
S.I.C.: 7373
N.A.I.C.S.: 541512

Mason Group Ltd. (2)
5 Exchange Quay
Manchester, M5 3EF, United Kingdom
Tel.: (44) 01618777808
Fax: (44) 1618777810
E-Mail: marketing@mason.com
Web Site: www.mason.biz
Emp.: 70
Provider of Telecommunications Consulting Services
S.I.C.: 4813
N.A.I.C.S.: 517110
Simon Jones *(Vice Chm-London)*
Bran Moarman *(Mng Dir)*

Non-U.S. Subsidiary:

Analysys Mason Pte Limited (2)
10-02 Robinson Centre 61 Robinson Rd
Singapore, 068893, Singapore
Tel.: (65) 64936038
E-Mail: singapore@analysysmason.com
Web Site: www.analysysmason.com
Telecommunication Consulting Services
S.I.C.: 8742
N.A.I.C.S.: 541611
Y. S. Lee *(Partner)*

Crane Telecommunications Group Limited (1)
Astral Towers Betts Way
Crawley, West Sussex, RH10 9UY, United Kingdom

Tel.: (44) 1444230004
Fax: (44) 1444872593
Web Site: www.uk.convergence.westcon.com
Emp.: 8
Telecommunication Services
S.I.C.: 4899
N.A.I.C.S.: 517919
Mike James *(Gen Mgr)*

Subsidiary:

Crane Telecommunications Limited (2)
Astral Towers Betts Way
Crawley, West Sussex, RH10 9UY, United Kingdom
Tel.: (44) 1444 230004
Fax: (44) 1444 243889
Web Site: uk.convergence.westcon.com
Emp.: 8
Professional Training Services
S.I.C.: 8299
N.A.I.C.S.: 611430
Tim Brooks *(Gen Mgr)*

Inflow Technologies Pvt Limited (1)
Inflow House 33 & 34 Indiranagar 1st Stage
Off 100 Feet Road
Bengaluru, 560038, India
Tel.: (91) 8041265151
Fax: (91) 8041265152
E-Mail: info@inflowtechnologies.com
Web Site: www.inflowtechnologies.com
Information Technology Consulting Services
S.I.C.: 7373
N.A.I.C.S.: 541512
Byju Pillai *(Pres & CEO)*

Non-U.S. Subsidiary:

Inflow Technologies Singapore Pte Limited (2)
1003 Bukit Merah Central 06-46
Technopreneur Centre
Singapore, 159836, Singapore
Tel.: (65) 96534067
Fax: (65) 62739300
Information Technology Consulting Services
S.I.C.: 7373
N.A.I.C.S.: 541512

Intact Integrated Services Limited (1)
Unit C Silwood Park Buckhurst Road
Ascot, Berkshire, SL5 7PW, United Kingdom
Tel.: (44) 1344756600
Fax: (44) 1344756601
E-Mail: info@intact-is.com
Web Site: www.intact-is.com
Emp.: 50
Network Integration Services
S.I.C.: 7373
N.A.I.C.S.: 541512
Tony Butler *(CTO)*
Bob Dalton *(CEO-IIS Group)*

Logicalis Group Ltd. (1)
110 Buckingham Avenue
Slough, Berkshire, SL1 4PF, United Kingdom UK
Tel.: (44) 1753 797100 (100%)
Fax: (44) 1753777203
E-Mail: info@logicalis.com
Web Site: www.logicalis.com
Sales Range: $1-4.9 Billion
Emp.: 3,500
IT Network Integration Services
S.I.C.: 7373
N.A.I.C.S.: 541512
Jens Montanana *(Chm)*
Ian M. Cook *(CEO)*
Mark Starkey *(Mng Dir)*
Nigel Drakeford-Lewis *(CFO)*
Mark Rogers *(COO)*
Chris Gabriel *(CTO)*

Subsidiaries:

Inca Software Limited (2)
110 Buckingham Avenue
Slough, Berkshire, SL1 4PF, United Kingdom UK
Tel.: (44) 1753 491 310
Fax: (44) 1753 777 383
E-Mail:
Software Developer
S.I.C.: 7372
N.A.I.C.S.: 511210

Logicalis UK Limited (2)
110 Buckingham Avenue
Slough, Berkshire, SL1 4PF, United Kingdom
Tel.: (44) 1753 777200
Fax: (44) 1753 777203
E-Mail: info@uk.logicalis.com
Web Site: www.uk.logicalis.com
Emp.: 200
IT Network Integration Services
S.I.C.: 7379
N.A.I.C.S.: 541519
Mark Starkey *(Mng Dir)*

U.S. Subsidiaries:

Logicalis, Inc. (2)
One Penn Plz 51st Fl Ste 5130
New York, NY 10119
Tel.: (212) 596-7160
E-Mail: info@us.logicalis.com
Web Site: www.us.logicalis.com
Information Technology Solutions & Managed Services
S.I.C.: 7373
N.A.I.C.S.: 541512
Vincent DeLuca *(CEO)*
Nathan Fong *(CFO)*
Michael Souders *(COO)*
Eric Tilds *(Exec VP, Gen Counsel & Sec)*
Mike Martin *(Sr VP-Solutions & Svcs)*
Chris Rafter *(Sr VP)*
Dan Sytsma *(Sr VP-Sls)*
Kirk P. Zaranti *(Sr VP-Sls-Western US)*

Branch:

Logicalis US (3)
34505 W Twelve Mile Rd Ste 210
Farmington, MI 48331
Tel.: (248) 957-5600
E-Mail: info@us.logicalis.com
Web Site: www.us.logicalis.com
Emp.: 77
Information Technology Solutions & Managed Services
S.I.C.: 7379
N.A.I.C.S.: 541519
Vincent DeLuca *(CEO)*

Non-U.S. Subsidiaries:

Logicalis Andina S.A.C. (2)
Av La Floresta 497 Of 201
Miraflores, Lima, 41, Peru
Tel.: (51) 16119696
Fax: (51) 16119697
Logistics Consulting Services
S.I.C.: 4731
N.A.I.C.S.: 541614

Logicalis Brasil Importacao Exportacao Ltda (2)
Av Pres Juscelino Kubitschek 1830 1 Piso - Tower 2
Sao Paulo, 04543-900, Brazil
Tel.: (55) 1152134410
Fax: (55) 1152134500
E-Mail: contact-us@br.promonlogicalis.com
Web Site: www.br.promonlogicalis.com
Logistics Consulting Services
S.I.C.: 4731
N.A.I.C.S.: 541614

Logicalis Deutschland GmbH (2)
Max-Planck-Str 35
50858 Cologne, Germany
Tel.: (49) 2234 95418 0
Fax: (49) 2234 95418 779
E-Mail: info@logicalis.de
Web Site: www.de.logicalis.com
Information Technology Consulting Services
S.I.C.: 7373
N.A.I.C.S.: 541512

Logicalis Inc. S.A. (2)
Luis Lecuever 3536 Tower 2 1109
Montevideo, 11300, Uruguay
Tel.: (598) 27113333
Fax: (598) 26229000
Communication Services
S.I.C.: 4899
N.A.I.C.S.: 517919

Logicalis Ireland Limited (2)
(Formerly Morse Computer Group Limited)
62A Heather Road
Sandyford Industrial Estate, Dublin, 18, Ireland IE
Tel.: (353) 1295 8966
Fax: (353) 1295 2920
Web Site: www.appliancetechnology.ie
Emp.: 45
IT & Analytics Services
S.I.C.: 7379
N.A.I.C.S.: 541519

Logicalis-Minters GmbH (2)
Max Planck Strasse 35
50858 Cologne, Germany
Tel.: (49) 22 34 9 54 18 0
Fax: (49) 22 34 9 54 18 7 79
Information Technology Consulting Services
S.I.C.: 7373
N.A.I.C.S.: 541512

Logicalis Spain SL (2)
(Formerly Morse Spain SL)
Avda Diagonal 569 2A Planta
Edificio L'Illa Diagonal, 08029 Barcelona, Spain
Tel.: (34) 93 363 25 90
Fax: (34) 93 321 76 64
Web Site: www.logicalis.com
Emp.: 75
IT & Analytic Services
S.I.C.: 7379
N.A.I.C.S.: 541519
Alex Zaragoza *(Mng Dir)*

Logicalis Uruguay S.A. (2)
Luis E Lecuever 3536 Tower 2
11300 Montevideo, Uruguay
Tel.: (598) 27113333
Fax: (598) 59826225644
Web Site: www.logicalis.com
Emp.: 3
Logistics Consulting Services
S.I.C.: 4731
N.A.I.C.S.: 541614
Alvaro Sbrocca *(Country Mgr)*

NetstarLogicalis Australia Pty Limited (2)
Unit 18 112-118 Talavera Rd
Sydney, NSW, 2113, Australia
Tel.: (61) 298059805
Fax: (61) 298059905
Emp.: 48
Information Technology Consulting Services
S.I.C.: 7373
N.A.I.C.S.: 541512
Chris Meagher *(CEO)*

NetstarLogicalis Hong Kong Limited (2)
Rm 1401 1063 King's Rd
Quarry Bay, Hong Kong, China (Hong Kong)
Tel.: (852) 21728888
Fax: (852) 25906443
Web Site: www.dwin.net
Emp.: 30
Logistics Consulting Services
S.I.C.: 4731
N.A.I.C.S.: 541614
James Tay *(CEO)*

NetstarLogicalis Malaysia Sdn Bhd (2)
Suite 3b-20-6 20th Floor Block 3b Plaza
Sentral Jalan Stesen Sentral 5
Kuala Lumpur, 50470, Malaysia
Tel.: (60) 322723388
Fax: (60) 322722828
Emp.: 15
Information Technology Consulting Services
S.I.C.: 7373
N.A.I.C.S.: 541512
Shi Ming Shum *(Country Mgr)*

NOXS Netherlands BV (1)
Meidoornkade 12
Houten, 3992 AE, Netherlands
Tel.: (31) 306025400
Fax: (31) 184444445
Emp.: 50
Information Technology Consulting Services
S.I.C.: 7373
N.A.I.C.S.: 541512
Willem de Haan *(Gen Mgr)*

Redbox Consulting Services Limited (1)
First Floor Suite Victoria House 49
Clarendon Road
Watford, WD17 1HZ, United Kingdom
Tel.: (44) 8704 455660
Fax: (44) 8704 455661
Web Site: www.redbox-consulting.com
Research & Consulting Services
S.I.C.: 8748
N.A.I.C.S.: 541618

DATECS LTD.

115A Tsarigradsko shosse
1784 Sofia, Bulgaria
Tel.: (359) 29740055
Fax: (359) 29741100
E-Mail: sales@datecs.bg
Web Site: www.datecs.bg
Year Founded: 1990
Emp.: 250
Business Description:
Office Equipment Mfr & Distr
S.I.C.: 3589
N.A.I.C.S.: 333318
Personnel:
Nikolay Iliev *(Pres)*

DATELINE UK LTD.

1 Cooks Barn
Turkey Mill, Maidstone, Kent, ME14 5PP, United Kingdom
Tel.: (44) 1622753311
Fax: (44) 1622764734
Web Site: www.dateline.co.uk
Year Founded: 1967
Sales Range: $10-24.9 Million
Emp.: 80
Business Description:
Online Dating Services
S.I.C.: 7299
N.A.I.C.S.: 812990
Personnel:
Eddy Ankrett *(Chm)*
Conrad Morris *(Mng Dir)*

DATENTECHNIK AG

Richardstraut St 43
Vienna, 1230, Austria
Tel.: (43) 1740700
Fax: (43) 01740702356
E-Mail: info@datentechnik.com
Web Site: www.datentechnik.com
Year Founded: 1979
Sales Range: $150-199.9 Million
Emp.: 600
Business Description:
Computer Peripherals & Software Mfr
S.I.C.: 3577
N.A.I.C.S.: 334118
Personnel:
George Szlatinay *(CEO)*
Non-U.S. Subsidiaries:

Datentechnik d.o.o. (1)
Dinarska 67
10000 Zagreb, Croatia
Tel.: (385) 13014081
Fax: (385) 13014084
E-Mail: info.hr@datentechnik.com
Web Site: www.datentechnik.com
Custom Computer Programming Services
S.I.C.: 7371
N.A.I.C.S.: 541511
Sanjan Ostro *(Mng Dir)*

Datentechnik S.R.L. (1)
Splaiul Independentei Nr 287 Etaj 3
Sector 6, 60028 Bucharest, Romania
Tel.: (40) 728728688
E-Mail: info.ro@datentechnik.com
Web Site: www.datentechnik.com
Custom Computer Programming Services
S.I.C.: 7371
N.A.I.C.S.: 541511
Alexandru Irimia *(Mng Dir)*

DATEV EG

Paumgartnerstrasse 6 14
90429 Nuremberg, Germany
Tel.: (49) 911 319 0
Fax: (49) 911 319 3196
E-Mail: info@datev.com

DATEV eG—(Continued)

Web Site: www.datev.com
Year Founded: 1966
Sales Range: $900-999.9 Million
Emp.: 5,844
Business Description:
Accounting Software Developer
S.I.C.: 7372
N.A.I.C.S.: 511210
Personnel:
Reinhard Verholen *(Chm-Supervisory Bd)*
Dieter Kempf *(Chm-Exec Bd)*
Norbert Krengel *(Deputy Chm-Supervisory Bd)*
Michael Leistenschneider *(Member-Exec Bd)*
Robert Mayr *(Member-Exec Bd)*
Eckhard Schwarzer *(Member-Exec Bd)*
Wolfgang Stegmann *(Member-Exec Bd)*
Supervisory Board of Directors:
Reinhard Verholen
Karl Bergbauer
Joachim M. Clostermann
Manfred Hinzer
Michael Jakel
Norbert Krengel
Andreas Lander
Horst Mailer
Petra Ruck
Dirk Schmale
Klaus Schroder
Antje Toffels

DATON GROUP AUSTRALIA LIMITED
(Name Changed to Australia New Agribusiness & Chemical Group Limited)

DATONG COAL INDUSTRY CO., LTD.
Xin Ping Wang
Kuang District, Datong, Shanxi, 037003, China
Tel.: (86) 352 7010167
Fax: (86) 352 7011070
Web Site: www.dtmy.com.cn
601001—(SHG)
Sales Range: $1-4.9 Billion
Emp.: 22,200
Business Description:
Coal Mining & Production Services
S.I.C.: 1222
N.A.I.C.S.: 212112
Personnel:
Yongping Wu *(Chm)*
Zemin Li *(Vice Chm & Gen Mgr)*

DATONG COAL MINE GROUP CO., LTD.
Xinpingwang
Datong, 037003, China
Tel.: (86) 352 7868200
Fax: (86) 352 7868201
E-Mail: dtmkjt@dtcoalmine.com
Web Site: www.dtcoalmine.com
Year Founded: 1949
Sales Range: $25-49.9 Billion
Business Description:
Coal Product Mfr & Distr
S.I.C.: 2899
N.A.I.C.S.: 325998
Personnel:
Zhang Youxi *(Chm)*
Guo Jinggang *(Vice Chm & Gen Mgr)*
Board of Directors:
Zhang Youxi
Guo Jinggang

DATONG PLC
1 Low Hall Business Park Low Hall Road
Leeds, LS18 4EG, United Kingdom
Tel.: (44) 1132395350
Fax: (44) 1132395360
E-Mail: info@datong.co.uk
Web Site: www.datong.co.uk
Year Founded: 1974
DTE—(AIM)
Rev.: $15,303,320
Assets: $18,525,072
Liabilities: $2,308,922
Net Worth: $16,216,150
Earnings: $641,192
Emp.: 81
Fiscal Year-end: 09/30/12
Business Description:
Electronic Intelligence Gathering, Tracking & Location Equipment Mfr
S.I.C.: 3812
N.A.I.C.S.: 334511
Personnel:
Mark Cook *(CEO)*
Stephen Ayres *(Sec & Dir-Fin)*
Board of Directors:
Paul Lever
Grant Ashley
Stephen Ayres
Richard Brearley
Mark Cook
Brian Smith

U.S. Subsidiary:

Datong Electronics Inc. **(1)**
4451 Brookfield Corp Dr Ste 111
Chantilly, VA 20151-1693
Tel.: (866) 432-8664
Fax: (703) 263-2490
Web Site: www.datongelectronics.com
Emp.: 9
Electronic Equipment Whslr
S.I.C.: 5065
N.A.I.C.S.: 423690
Roy Schwartz *(Gen Mgr)*

DATRON AG
In den Gansackern 5
Muhltal, 64367 Hessen, Germany
Tel.: (49) 6151 1419 0
Fax: (49) 6151 1419 29
E-Mail: info@datron.de
Web Site: www.datron.de
Year Founded: 1969
DAR—(DEU)
Sales Range: $25-49.9 Million
Emp.: 140
Business Description:
Automation Systems & Electronic Component Mfr & Sales
S.I.C.: 3559
N.A.I.C.S.: 333249
Personnel:
Arne Brusch *(Chm-Mgmt Bd)*
Erwin Sowa *(Deputy Chm-Mgmt Bd)*
Thorsten Muller *(Member-Mgmt Bd-Svc & Internal Org)*
Matthias Reck *(Member-Mgmt Bd-Production, R&D)*

DATRONIX HOLDINGS LIMITED
19/Floor 499 King's Road North Point Industrial Building
Hong Kong, China (Hong Kong)
Tel.: (852) 25648477
Fax: (852) 25657214
E-Mail: datronix@datronixhldgs.com.hk
Web Site: www.datronixhldgs.com.hk
0889—(HKG)
Sls.: $33,863,044
Assets: $92,484,101
Liabilities: $7,770,527
Net Worth: $84,713,574
Earnings: $4,268,890
Emp.: 1,146
Fiscal Year-end: 12/31/12
Business Description:
Conglomerates & Holding Companies
S.I.C.: 6719
N.A.I.C.S.: 551112
Personnel:
Paul Yin Tong Siu *(Chm & CEO)*
Wai Mei Shui *(Vice Chm)*
Connie Sau Fong Leung *(Sec)*
Board of Directors:
Paul Yin Tong Siu
Leo Fai Yue Chan
Pui Lam Chung
Kit Wah Lee
Shing Fai Sheung
Wai Mei Shui
Nina Margaret Siu

Butterfield Fulcrum Group (Bermuda) Limited
26 Burnaby Street
Hamilton, HM 11, Bermuda

Transfer Agents:
Hong Kong Registrars Limited
Shops 1712-1716 17/F Hopewell Centre 183 Queen's Road East
Wanchai, China (Hong Kong)

Butterfield Fulcrum Group (Bermuda) Limited
26 Burnaby Street
Hamilton, HM 11, Bermuda

DATUM VENTURES INC.
Suite 3 246 East 1st Street
North Vancouver, BC, V7L 1B3, Canada
Tel.: (778) 340-3899
Fax: (778) 340-3891
E-Mail: DatumVentures@gmail.com
Year Founded: 2011
DAT.P—(TSXV)
Assets: $139,983
Liabilities: $14,376
Net Worth: $125,607
Earnings: ($56,420)
Fiscal Year-end: 03/31/13
Business Description:
Investment Services
S.I.C.: 6211
N.A.I.C.S.: 523999
Personnel:
Dale Wallster *(CEO & Sec)*
Peter de Visser *(CFO)*
Board of Directors:
James T. Gillis
Dale Wallster
Transfer Agent:
Computershare Investor Services Inc.
100 University Ave 9th Floor
Toronto, ON, Canada

DAULTON CAPITAL CORP.
(Name Changed to ARX Gold Corporation)

DAUM COMMUNICATIONS CORPORATION
714 Hannam dong Yongsan gu
Seoul, 140-894, Korea (South)
Tel.: (82) 15773321
E-Mail: info@daumcorp.com
Web Site: www.daumcorp.com
Year Founded: 1995
035720—(KRS)
Rev.: $421,650,595
Assets: $569,038,536
Liabilities: $85,505,605
Net Worth: $483,532,931
Earnings: $71,272,368
Emp.: 954
Fiscal Year-end: 12/31/12
Business Description:
Internet Services Including Communications, Online Shopping, Entertainment & Finance
S.I.C.: 2741
N.A.I.C.S.: 519130
Personnel:
Saehoon Choi *(Chm & CEO)*
Hyoeun Moon *(COO)*
Board of Directors:
Saehoon Choi
Junho Choi
Joseph Fan
Sujung Hahn
David Hoffman
Jaehyuk Lee

DAUN & CIE. AG
Bahnhofstrasse 21
26180 Rastede, Germany
Tel.: (49) 440299800
Fax: (49) 4402998025
Web Site: www.daun-ag.de
Sales Range: $1-4.9 Billion
Emp.: 6
Business Description:
Holding Company; Textile Mfr
S.I.C.: 6719
N.A.I.C.S.: 551112
Personnel:
Claas E. Daun *(Chm)*

DAUNAT BRETAGNE
Parc D Activites Bellevue
22200 Graces, Cotes D Armor, France
Tel.: (33) 296401060
Web Site: www.daunat.com
Sls.: $37,800,000
Emp.: 330
Business Description:
Commercial Bakeries
S.I.C.: 2052
N.A.I.C.S.: 311812
Personnel:
Bruno Merel *(Pres)*
Board of Directors:
Didier Ernest

DAUPHIN HUMANDESIGN GROUP GMBH & CO. KG
Espanstrasse 36
D-91238 Offenhausen, Germany
Tel.: (49) 915817700
Fax: (49) 915817701
Web Site: www.dauphin-group.in
Year Founded: 1992
Sales Range: $150-199.9 Million
Emp.: 800
Business Description:
Holding Company; Office Furniture Mfr
S.I.C.: 6719
N.A.I.C.S.: 551112
Personnel:
Friedrich-Wilhelm Dauphin *(Founder, CEO & Mng Dir)*

Subsidiary:

Burositzmobelfabrik Friedrich- W. Dauphin GmbH & Co. KG **(1)**
Espanstrasse 29
91238 Offenhausen, Germany De (100%)
Tel.: (49) 9158170
Fax: (49) 91581007
E-Mail: info@dauphin.de
Web Site: www.dauphin.de
Emp.: 200
Office Furniture Mfr
S.I.C.: 2521
N.A.I.C.S.: 337211
Friedrich-Wilhelm Dauphin *(Founder & Mng Dir)*
Antje Dauphin *(Mng Dir)*
Elke Dauphin *(Mng Dir)*
Bernd Neubauer *(Mng Dir)*

U.S. Subsidiary:

Dauphin North America **(1)**
300 Myrtle Ave
Boonton, NJ 07005

Tel.: (973) 263-1100
Fax: (973) 263-3551
Toll Free: (800) 995-6500
Web Site: www.dauphin.com
Emp.: 120
Furniture Mfr & Distr
S.I.C.: 5021
N.A.I.C.S.: 423210
Gary Chin *(Pres)*
Nick Bayvel *(CEO)*

Non-U.S. Subsidiaries:

Dauphin Benelux B.V. (1)
Staalweg 1 3
4104 AS Culemborg, Netherlands
Tel.: (31) 345533292
Fax: (31) 345533132
E-Mail: info@dauphin.nl
Web Site: www.dauphin.nl
Emp.: 13
Mfr. of Office Furniture
S.I.C.: 2599
N.A.I.C.S.: 337127

Dauphin Espana S.A. (1)
Galileo Galilei 14
Poligono Industrial La Garena, 28806
Madrid, Alcala de I lenares, Spain
Tel.: (34) 918845555
Fax: (34) 918845389
E-Mail: dauphinmad@jet.es
Web Site: www.wdauphinespanasa.com
Emp.: 22
Mfr. of Office Furniture
S.I.C.: 2599
N.A.I.C.S.: 337127

Dauphin France S. A. (1)
6 Allee Du Parc De Garlande
92220 Bagneux, France
Tel.: (33) 146541590
Fax: (33) 146541599
E-Mail: infos@dauphin-france.com
Web Site: www.dauphin-france.com
Emp.: 10
Mfr. of Office Furniture
S.I.C.: 2599
N.A.I.C.S.: 337127
Christophe Platerier *(Gen Mgr)*

Dauphin HumanDesign AG (1)
Kirschgartenstrasse 7
CH-4051 Basel, Switzerland
Tel.: (41) 612838000
Fax: (41) 612838005
E-Mail: info@dauphin.de
Web Site: www.dauphin.ch
Sales Range: $10-24.9 Million
Emp.: 5
Office Furniture Mfr
S.I.C.: 2599
N.A.I.C.S.: 337127
Claude Frey *(Mgr)*

Dauphin Italia (1)
Gaetano Crespi 12
I 20134 Milan, Italy
Tel.: (39) 0276018394
Fax: (39) 0276021723
E-Mail: info@dauphin.it
Web Site: www.dauphin.it
Emp.: 6
Mfr. of Office Furniture
S.I.C.: 2599
N.A.I.C.S.: 337127
Mohrle Jens *(Mng Dir)*

Dauphin HumanDesign Belgium NV/SA (1)
Terbekehofdreef 46
Wilrijk, Antwerp, B-2610, Belgium
Tel.: (32) 38877850
Fax: (32) 38879019
E-Mail: info@dauphinnv-sa.be
Web Site: www.dauphinnv-sa.be
Sls.: $4,025,898
Emp.: 3
Mfr of Ergonomic Office Furniture
S.I.C.: 2599
N.A.I.C.S.: 337127
Paul Beeckmans *(Gen Mgr)*

Dauphin Office Seating S.A. (Pty) Ltd. (1)
62 Hume Rd Dunkeld
PO Box 55551
Northlands, 2116 Johannesburg, South Africa
Tel.: (27) 114479888
Fax: (27) 114479889
E-Mail: vpersons@dauphin.co.za
Web Site: www.dauphin.co.za
Emp.: 10
Mfr. of Office Furniture
S.I.C.: 2599
N.A.I.C.S.: 337127
Debbie Arnoldi-Radford *(Mng Dir)*

Dauphin-RIM Polska Sp. z o.o. (1)
ulica Walicow 11 (Aurum Building)
PL-00-851 Warsaw, Poland
Tel.: (48) 225839138
Fax: (48) 225839137
E-Mail: dauphin-rim@poczta.onet.pl
Mfr. of Office Furniture
S.I.C.: 2599
N.A.I.C.S.: 337127

Dauphin Scandinavia A/S (1)
Frederikssuntsvej 272
DK 2700 Herlev, Scandinavia, Denmark
Tel.: (45) 44537053
Fax: (45) 44538050
E-Mail: info@dauphin.dk
Web Site: www.dauphin.dk
Mfr. of Office Furniture
S.I.C.: 2599
N.A.I.C.S.: 337127

Dauphin (SEA) Pte. Ltd. (1)
52 Genting Lane
07 02 03 Hiang Kie Complex 1, 349560
Singapore, Singapore
Tel.: (65) 67481600
Fax: (65) 6744 5028
E-Mail: dauphin@pacific.net.sg
Mfr. of Office Furniture
S.I.C.: 2599
N.A.I.C.S.: 337127

Trendline Office Interiors Ltd. (1)
Peter St
Blackburn, Lancashire, BB1 5LH, United Kingdom
Tel.: (44) 25452220
Fax: (44) 254680401
E-Mail: marketing@trendline-interiors.co.uk
Web Site: www.trendline-interiors.co.uk
Emp.: 41
Office Furniture Designer & Mfr
S.I.C.: 2599
N.A.I.C.S.: 337127
Peter Dowdy *(Financial Dir)*

DAVE HITCHCOCK CHEVROLET

224 Talbot St N
Essex, ON, N8M 2C8, Canada
Tel.: (519) 776-4222
Fax: (519) 776-6300
Toll Free: (888) 763-4222
E-Mail: info@davehitchcockchev.com
Web Site: www.headtohitchcocks.com
Rev.: $13,347,016
Emp.: 30
Business Description:
New & Used Car Dealers
S.I.C.: 5511
N.A.I.C.S.: 441110
Personnel:
Dave Hitchcock *(Pres)*
Gail Cogliati *(Treas & Sec)*

DAVIAN CONSTRUCTION LTD.

740 Logan Avenue
Winnipeg, MB, R3E 1M9, Canada
Tel.: (204) 783-7251
Fax: (204) 775-0464
Web Site: www.davianconstruction.com
Year Founded: 1974
Rev.: $10,346,449
Emp.: 36
Business Description:
Building Construction Services
S.I.C.: 1799
N.A.I.C.S.: 238190
Personnel:
Ian A. Balcain *(Owner & Pres)*

DAVICOM SEMICONDUCTOR, INC.

6 Li-Hsin Road VI
Science Park, Hsin-chu, Taiwan
Tel.: (886) 35798797
Fax: (886) 35646929
E-Mail: investor@davicom.com.tw
Web Site: www.davicom.com.tw
Year Founded: 1996
3094—(TAI)
Sales Range: $10-24.9 Million
Emp.: 95
Business Description:
Semiconductor Mfr
S.I.C.: 3674
N.A.I.C.S.: 334413
Personnel:
Ting Herh *(Chm)*
K. R. Pan *(Pres)*

DAVID CHEVROLET CORVETTE BUICK GMC LTD.

915 Niagara St
Welland, ON, L3C 1M4, Canada
Tel.: (905) 735-3690
Fax: (905) 735-0507
E-Mail: info@davidchev.com
Web Site: www.davidchev.com
Year Founded: 1991
Rev.: $24,146,494
Emp.: 50
Business Description:
New Car Dealers
S.I.C.: 5511
N.A.I.C.S.: 441110
Personnel:
David D'Amico *(Pres)*

DAVID JONES LIMITED

86-108 Castlereagh Street
Sydney, NSW, 2000, Australia
Tel.: (61) 292665544
Fax: (61) 292615717
E-Mail: corporateinformation@davidjones.com.au
Web Site: www.davidjones.com.au
Year Founded: 1838
DJS—(ASX)
Rev.: $1,922,687,005
Assets: $1,289,895,749
Liabilities: $455,073,607
Net Worth: $834,822,142
Earnings: $99,191,246
Emp.: 9,000
Fiscal Year-end: 07/27/13
Business Description:
Department Stores
Import
S.I.C.: 5311
N.A.I.C.S.: 452111
Personnel:
Paul Zahra *(CEO)*
Brad Soller *(CFO)*
Paula Bauchinger *(Exec-HR)*
Cate Daniels *(Exec-Ops)*
Matthew Durbin *(Exec-Strategic Plng)*
Antony Karp *(Exec-Retail Svcs)*
Sacha Laing *(Exec-Mktg & Fin Svcs)*
Donna Player *(Exec-Mdse)*
David Robinson *(Exec-Customer Innovation & Growth)*
Susan Leppinus *(Sec)*
Board of Directors:
Gordon McKellar Cairns
Melinda Conrad
Jane Harvey
Philippa Stone
Steve Vamos
Paul Zahra

Subsidiaries:

David Jones (Adelaide) Pty Limited (1)
100 Rundle Mall
Adelaide, SA, Australia (100%)
Tel.: (61) 883053000
Fax: (61) 883053497
Web Site: www.davidjones.com.au
Store Retailers
S.I.C.: 5999
N.A.I.C.S.: 453998

David Jones Employee Share Plan Pty Limited (1)
86-108 Castlereagh Street
Sydney, NSW, Australia (100%)
Tel.: (61) 292665544
Fax: (61) 292677326
E-Mail: corporateinformation@davidjones.com.au
Web Site: www.davidjones.com.au
Emp.: 40
Durable Goods Merchant Whslr
S.I.C.: 5099
N.A.I.C.S.: 423990
Paul Zahra *(CEO)*

David Jones Insurance Pty Limited (1)
65-77 Market Street
Sydney, NSW, 2000, Australia
Tel.: (61) 292665544
Fax: (61) 292666538
E-Mail: corporate.services@davidjones.com.au
Insurance Brokerage Services
S.I.C.: 6411
N.A.I.C.S.: 524210

David Jones Properties Pty Limited (1)
86-108 Castlereagh Street
2000 Sydney, NSW, Australia (100%)
Tel.: (61) 292665544
Fax: (61) 292677326
E-Mail: customerservice@davidjones.com.au
Store Retailers
S.I.C.: 5999
N.A.I.C.S.: 453998
Ben Webster *(Reg Mgr)*

DAVID MORRIS FINE CARS LTD.

17407 111th Ave
Edmonton, AB, T5S 0A1, Canada
Tel.: (780) 484-9000
Fax: (780) 484-8827
Toll Free: (877) 379-1441
E-Mail: info@davidmorrisfinecars.mercedes-benz.ca
Web Site: www.davidmorrisfinecars.mercedes-benz.ca
Year Founded: 1986
Rev.: $19,997,339
Emp.: 42
Business Description:
New & Used Car Dealers
S.I.C.: 5511
N.A.I.C.S.: 441110
Personnel:
David Morris *(Pres)*

DAVID OPPENHEIMER & COMPANY

(d/b/a The Oppenheimer Group)
11 Burbidge St Ste 101
Coquitlam, BC, V3K 7B2, Canada
Tel.: (604) 461-6779
Fax: (604) 468-4780
Toll Free: (888) 321-6779
Web Site: www.oppyproduce.com
Year Founded: 1858
Emp.: 200
Business Description:
Produce Distr
S.I.C.: 5148
N.A.I.C.S.: 424480
Personnel:
John Anderson *(Chm, Pres & CEO)*
Doug Grant *(COO & VP)*
Dawn Gray *(Sr VP-Categories, Mktg & Sls)*

David Oppenheimer & Company—(Continued)

U.S. Branch:

David Oppenheimer & Company I, LLC (1)
180 Nickerson St Ste 211
Seattle, WA 98109 WA
Tel.: (206) 284-1705
Fax: (206) 284-0203
Emp.: 10
Produce Distr
S.I.C.: 5148
N.A.I.C.S.: 424480

DAVIDSON CHRYSLER DODGE INC

4695 Kingston Rd
Scarborough, ON, M1E 2R1, Canada
Tel.: (416) 281-2277
Fax: (416) 282-5722
Rev.: $39,473,007
Emp.: 80
Business Description:
New & Used Car Dealers
S.I.C.: 5511
N.A.I.C.S.: 441110
Personnel:
Roger Davidson *(Owner)*

DAVIDSON ENMAN LUMBER LTD.

452 42 Avenue SE
Calgary, AB, T2G 1Y5, Canada
Tel.: (403) 243-2566
Fax: (403) 243-7958
E-Mail: information@delumber.com
Web Site: www.delumber.com
Year Founded: 1948
Rev.: $14,335,392
Emp.: 75
Business Description:
Lumber & Building Materials Supplier
S.I.C.: 5031
N.A.I.C.S.: 423310
Personnel:
Greg Davidson *(Gen Mgr)*

DAVIE YARDS ASA

Lysaker Torg 12
PO Box 465
1327 Lysaker, Norway
Tel.: (47) 67200300
Fax: (47) 67200302
Web Site: www.davie.ca
Business Description:
Shipyard Owner & Operator; Water Transportation Services
S.I.C.: 3731
N.A.I.C.S.: 336611
Personnel:
Sigurd Lange *(CEO)*
Audun Roneid *(CFO)*

Non-U.S. Subsidiary:

Davie Yards Inc. (1)
22 George D Davie
Levis, QC, G6V 8V5, Canada (100%)
Tel.: (418) 837-5841
Fax: (418) 835-1017
E-Mail: info@davie.ca
Web Site: www.davie.ca
Rev.: $3,185,211
Emp.: 30
Shipyard Owner & Operator
S.I.C.: 3731
N.A.I.C.S.: 336611
Gilles Gagne *(Pres & COO)*
Richard Bertrand *(CEO)*
Marc Veilleux *(Sr VP-Fin)*

DAVIS + HENDERSON CORPORATION

939 Eglinton Avenue East Ste 201
Toronto, ON, M4G 4H7, Canada
Tel.: (416) 696-7700
Fax: (416) 696-8308
Toll Free: (888) 850-6656
E-Mail: investorrelations@dhltd.com
Web Site: www.dhltd.com
Year Founded: 2010
DH—(TSX)
Rev.: $753,132,175
Assets: $1,281,679,448
Liabilities: $583,770,054
Net Worth: $697,909,394
Earnings: $68,723,561
Emp.: 3,800
Fiscal Year-end: 12/31/12
Business Description:
Supply Programs, Technology Solutions & Financial Business Services
S.I.C.: 6282
N.A.I.C.S.: 523930
Personnel:
Paul D. Damp *(Chm)*
Gerrard Schmid *(CEO)*
Brian Kyle *(CFO & Exec VP)*
Young Park *(CIO & Exec VP)*
Carrie Russell *(CMO & Exec VP)*
Duncan Hannay *(Pres-Canada)*
William W. Neville *(Pres-D+H-USA)*
Yves Denomme *(Exec VP-Ops)*
Alfy Louis *(Exec VP-Lending Solutions & Product Mgmt)*
Bob Noftall *(Exec VP-HR)*
Serge Rivest *(Exec VP-Payment Products & Mktg Programs)*
Board of Directors:
Paul D. Damp
Gordon J. Feeney
Michael A. Foulkes
Deborah L. Kerr
Bradley D. Nullmeyer
John E. O'Malley
Gerrard Schmid
Helen K. Sinclair
Transfer Agent:
CIBC Mellon Trust Company
PO Box 7010
Adelaide Street Postal Station, Toronto, ON, M5C 2W9, Canada
Tel.: (416) 643-5500
Fax: (416) 643-5501
Toll Free: (800) 387-0825

U.S. Subsidiaries:

Compushare, Inc. (1)
3 Hutton Cntre Dr Ste 700
Santa Ana, CA 92707 CA
Tel.: (714) 427-1000
Web Site: www.compushare.com
Sales Range: $10-24.9 Million
Emp.: 100
Technology, Consulting & Implementation Solutions
S.I.C.: 7374
N.A.I.C.S.: 518210
Romir Bosu *(Chm & CEO)*
William Neville *(Pres)*
Brian Kyle *(CFO)*
David Gorsuch *(COO)*

Harland Financial Solutions, Inc. (1)
605 Crescent Executive Ct Ste 600
Lake Mary, FL 32746 OR
Tel.: (407) 804-6600
Fax: (407) 829-6702
Toll Free: (800) 778-5667
E-Mail:
Sales Range: $250-299.9 Million
Emp.: 1,350
Banking Software for Financial Institutions
S.I.C.: 7371
N.A.I.C.S.: 541511
Dan Larlee *(CTO)*

Branches:

Harland Financial Solutions (2)
312 Plum St Fl 15
Cincinnati, OH 45202
Tel.: (513) 381-9400
Fax: (513) 381-9666
Sales Range: $25-49.9 Million
Emp.: 100
Data Processing Service
S.I.C.: 7374
N.A.I.C.S.: 518210
Beth Basil *(COO & Gen Counsel)*

Harland Financial Solutions (2)
22722 29th Dr SE Ste 200
Bothell, WA 98021 WA
Tel.: (425) 951-8300
Fax: (425) 827-0927
Web Site: www.harlandfinancialsolutions.com
Sales Range: $10-24.9 Million
Emp.: 70
Information-Intensive Business Transactions & Technology
S.I.C.: 7373
N.A.I.C.S.: 541512

Subsidiary:

Parsam Technologies, LLC (2)
3197 Players Club Pkwy
Memphis, TN 38125
Mailing Address:
PO Box 38118
Memphis, TN 38183
Tel.: (901) 757-1212
Fax: (901) 757-1799
E-Mail: info@umonitor.com
Web Site: www.umonitor.com
Rev.: $6,500,000
Emp.: 34
Self Service & Electronic Payment Software Publishers
S.I.C.: 7372
N.A.I.C.S.: 511210
Pinakini Sheth *(Pres & CFO)*
Dinesh Sheth *(CEO)*
Sanjiv Desai *(CIO & Sr VP)*
Richard Whiddon *(Sr VP-Sls & Mktg)*

DAWN PROPERTIES LIMITED

8th Floor Beverley Court
100 Nelson Mandela Avenue, Harare, Zimbabwe
Mailing Address:
PO Box CY 1618
Causeway, Harare, Zimbabwe
Tel.: (263) 4793326
Fax: (263) 4796172
E-Mail: info@dawnpro.co.zw
Web Site: www.dawnproperties.co.zw
DAWN—(ZIM)
Rev.: $5,711,211
Assets: $87,232,570
Liabilities: $2,745,652
Net Worth: $84,486,918
Earnings: $251,447
Emp.: 136
Fiscal Year-end: 03/31/13
Business Description:
Investment Property Holding Company
S.I.C.: 6719
N.A.I.C.S.: 551112
Personnel:
Justin Dowa *(CEO)*
Nora M. Tome *(Sec, Exec-Fin, Admin & HR)*
Board of Directors:
Phibion Gwatidzo
Justin Dowa
D. Goldwasser
Richard Makoni
George Manyere
Murisi Mukonoweshuro
Bekhithemba Ndebele
Transfer Agent:
Corpserve
2nd Floor Intermarket Centre Kwame Nkrumah First Street
Harare, Zimbabwe

Subsidiary:

CB Richard Ellis (Private) Limited (1)
8th Floor Beverly Court 100 Nelson Mandela Avenue Fourth Street
Harare, Zimbabwe ZW
Tel.: (263) 4707101
Fax: (263) 4706646
E-Mail: admin@cbre.co.zw
Web Site: www.cbre.co.zw
Commercial Real Estate Brokerage, Property Management & Valuation Advisory Services
S.I.C.: 6531
N.A.I.C.S.: 531210
Toendepi Matonda *(Mng Dir)*

Non-U.S. Subsidiary:

CB Richard Ellis (Proprietary) Limited (1)
Broll House 27 Fricker Road
Illovo, Johannesburg, Gauteng, 2196, South Africa
Tel.: (27) 11 441 4800
Fax: (27) 11 441 4860
E-Mail: valuations@broll.co.za
Emp.: 9
Commercial Real Estate Brokerage, Property Management & Valuation Advisory Services
S.I.C.: 6531
N.A.I.C.S.: 531210
Roger Hunting *(Mgr)*

DAWNRAYS PHARMACEUTICAL (HOLDINGS) LTD

Units 3001-02 30/F CNT Tower 338 Hennessy Road
Wanchai, China (Hong Kong)
Tel.: (852) 21119708
E-Mail: ir@dawnrays.com.hk
Web Site: www.dawnrays.com
2348—(HKG)
Rev.: $136,061,220
Assets: $249,337,791
Liabilities: $93,329,299
Net Worth: $156,008,491
Earnings: $18,189,278
Emp.: 1,250
Fiscal Year-end: 12/31/12
Business Description:
Pharmaceutical Industry
S.I.C.: 2834
N.A.I.C.S.: 325412
Personnel:
Kei Ling Li *(Co-Founder & Chm)*
Yung Lai Hung *(Co-Founder)*
Yi Gao *(CEO)*
Kit Ling Pang *(Sec)*
Board of Directors:
Kei Ling Li
Jacky Tat Ying Choi
Yi Gao
Yung Lai Hung
Hong Man Leung
Tung Ming Li
Tony Tung Sing Lo
Xue Tian Pan
HSBC Trustee (Cayman) Limited
HSBC House 68 West Bay Road
PO Box 484
Georgetown, Cayman Islands
Transfer Agents:
Tricor Abacus Limited
26th Floor Tesbury Centre 28 Queen's Road East
Wanchai, China (Hong Kong)
HSBC Trustee (Cayman) Limited
HSBC House 68 West Bay Road
PO Box 484
Georgetown, Cayman Islands

DAWONSYS CO., LTD.

4 BA 5 Shiwa Industrial Complex
Sungkok-Dong Danwon-Gu
Ansan, Kyungki, 425-110, Korea (South)
Tel.: (82) 313199320
Fax: (82) 313193927
E-Mail: webmster@dawonsys.co.kr
Web Site: www.dawonsys.co.kr
Year Founded: 1996
068240—(KRS)
Business Description:
Inductive Heating Systems & Other Power Supply Products Mfr
S.I.C.: 3675

N.A.I.C.S.: 334416
Personnel:
Sun-Soon Park *(CEO)*

DAWOOD CORPORATION (PVT.) LTD.

(d/b/a Dawood Group)
35-A Empress Rd
54000 Lahore, Pakistan
Tel.: (92) 426301601
Fax: (92) 426364316
Web Site:
Business Description:
Holding Company
S.I.C.: 6719
N.A.I.C.S.: 551112
Subsidiaries:

Dawood Hercules Corporation Limited (1)
Dawood Centre MT Khan Road
Karachi, Pakistan
Tel.: (92) 2135686001
Fax: (92) 2135693416
E-Mail: info@dawoodhercules.com
Web Site: www.dawoodhercules.com
DAWH—(ISL KAR LAH)
Sls.: $46,622,504
Assets: $345,521,901
Liabilities: $84,895,964
Net Worth: $260,625,937
Earnings: $9,952,300
Emp.: 469
Fiscal Year-end: 12/31/12
Fertilizer & Anhydrous Ammonia Mfr
S.I.C.: 2875
N.A.I.C.S.: 325314
Hussain Dawood *(Chm)*
Shahid Hamid Pracha *(CEO)*
Ali Aamir *(CFO & Dir-Fin)*
Shafiq Ahmed *(Sec & Gen Mgr-Fin)*

Plant:

Dawood Hercules Chemicals - Sheikhupura (2)
28-KM Lahore Sheikhupura Road
Chichoki Mallian, Sheikhupura, Pakistan
Tel.: (92) 4237352762
Fax: (92) 4237313380
Chemicals Mfr
S.I.C.: 2899
N.A.I.C.S.: 325998

Dawood Lawrencepur Limited (1)
35-A Shahrah-e-Abdul
Hameed Bin Baadees
Empress Road, Lahore, 54000, Pakistan
Tel.: (92) 4263016017
Fax: (92) 4206364316
E-Mail: info.textile@dawoodgroup.com
Web Site: www.dawoodlawrencepur.com
DLL—(KAR)
Sales Range: $1-9.9 Million
Emp.: 2,658
Yarn & Fabric Mfr & Sales
S.I.C.: 2259
N.A.I.C.S.: 313240
Isar Ahmad *(Chm)*
Inam ur Rahman *(CEO)*
Iqbal A. Shaikh *(CFO & Sec)*

DAWOOD EQUITIES LIMITED

1700-A Saima Trade Towers
I I Chundrigar Road, Karachi, 74000, Pakistan
Tel.: (92) 21 3227 1881
Fax: (92) 21 3227 5086
E-Mail: contact@dawoodequities.com
Web Site: www.dawoodequities.com
DEL—(KAR)
Sales Range: Less than $1 Million
Business Description:
Stock Brokerage Services
S.I.C.: 6211
N.A.I.C.S.: 523120
Personnel:
Abdul Ghani Usman *(Chm)*
Abdul Qadir Sakhi *(CEO)*
Nazeer Haider Zaidi *(CFO & Sec)*
Board of Directors:
Abdul Ghani Usman
Junaid Zakaria Dada
Abdul Aziz Habib
Rubina Khanum
Abdul Qadir Sakhi
Akhtar Ali Shah
Asim Iftekhar Yakoob

DAWSON GOLD CORP.

Suite 1200 - 750 West Pender Street
Vancouver, BC, V6C 2T8, Canada
Tel.: (604) 687-2471
Fax: (604) 687-2472
Web Site:
Year Founded: 2006
DYU—(TSXV)
Int. Income: $3,986
Assets: $447
Liabilities: $492,953
Net Worth: ($492,506)
Earnings: ($28,566)
Fiscal Year-end: 06/30/13
Business Description:
Mineral Exploration Services
S.I.C.: 1081
N.A.I.C.S.: 213114
Personnel:
Paul D. Gray *(CEO)*
Simon Anderson *(CFO)*
Board of Directors:
John Anderson
Paul D. Gray
Alan Sexton
Bijay Ram Singh

DAWSON INTERNATIONAL PLC

Burnfoot Industrial Estate
Hawick, Scotland, TD9 8RJ, United Kingdom
Tel.: (44) 1450 365555
Telex: 727158
Fax: (44) 1450 365556
E-Mail: enquiries@dawson-international.co.uk
Web Site: www.dawson-international.co.uk
Year Founded: 1974
Emp.: 623
Business Description:
Holding Company; Specialty Textile Yarns & Apparel Mfr & Distr
Import Export
S.I.C.: 6719
N.A.I.C.S.: 551112
Personnel:
David John Bolton *(Chm)*
Gary Steven Fraser *(Joint Administrator)*
Blair Carnegie Nimmo *(Joint Administrator)*
Legal Counsel:
Dundas & Wilson CS LLP
191 West George Street
Glasgow, G2 2LD, United Kingdom
Tel.: (44) 141 222 2200
Fax: (44) 141 222 2201
Subsidiaries:

Dawson Fabrics Ltd. (1)
Greenside Mills
Saville Rd Skelmanthorpe, Huddersfield, HD8 9EE, United Kingdom UK (100%)
Tel.: (44) 1484868600
Fax: (44) 1484865635
Web Site: www.dawson-fab.co.uk
Sales Range: $50-74.9 Million
Emp.: 200
Fabric Mills
S.I.C.: 2299
N.A.I.C.S.: 313210
Sam Sharma *(Mng Dir)*

Dawson International Holdings (UK) Ltd (1)
Burnfoot Industrial Estate
Hawick, Scotland, TD9 8RJ, United Kingdom
Tel.: (44) 1450365555
Fax: (44) 01450365556
E-Mail: enquiries@dawson-international.co.uk
Emp.: 130
Investment Management Services
S.I.C.: 6211
N.A.I.C.S.: 523999

Dawson International Trading Ltd (1)
Burnfoot industrial Estate
Hawick, Scotland, TD98 RJ, United Kingdom
Tel.: (44) 1450365555
Fax: (44) 1450365556
E-Mail: enquiries@dawson-international.co.uk
Emp.: 130
Cashmere Knitwear Mfr
S.I.C.: 5137
N.A.I.C.S.: 424330
David Cooper *(Dir-Fin)*

U.S. Subsidiary:

Dawson Cashmere LLC (1)
8A Pleasant St
South Natick, MA 01760 MA
Tel.: (508) 651-7910
Fax: (508) 651-8819
Web Site: www.kinrosscashmere.com
Emp.: 11
Cashmere Apparel Whslr
S.I.C.: 5137
N.A.I.C.S.: 424330
James D. Byrnes *(Exec VP)*

DAX-AUTO SA

2034 Avenue De La Resistance
40990 Saint-Paul-les-Dax, Landes, France
Tel.: (33) 558911178
Fax: (33) 558911177
E-Mail: contact@daxauto.fr
Web Site: www.daxauto.peugeot.fr
Sales Range: $25-49.9 Million
Emp.: 60
Business Description:
New Car Dealer
S.I.C.: 5511
N.A.I.C.S.: 441110
Personnel:
Jean-Pierre Menoux *(CHM)*
Board of Directors:
Jean-Pierre Menoux
Nicolas Rougier

DAXIN MATERIALS CORPORATION

15 Keyuan 1st Rd Central Taiwan Science Park
Taichung, Taiwan
Tel.: (886) 4 24608889
Fax: (886) 4 24608896
E-Mail: info@daxinmat.com
Web Site: www.daxinmat.com
5234—(TAI)
Sls.: $110,474,761
Emp.: 280
Fiscal Year-end: 12/31/12
Business Description:
Chemical Mfr
S.I.C.: 2899
N.A.I.C.S.: 325998
Personnel:
Cheng Yih Lin *(Chm)*
Jeremy Kuo *(Pres)*

DAY LEWIS PLC.

Day Lewis House 2 Peterwood Way
Croydon, Surrey, CR0 4UQ, United Kingdom
Tel.: (44) 208 256 6200
E-Mail: help@daylewisplc.co.uk
Web Site: www.daylewisplc.co.uk
Year Founded: 1975
Sales Range: $300-349.9 Million
Emp.: 1,267
Business Description:
Pharmaceutical Product Whslr
S.I.C.: 5122
N.A.I.C.S.: 424210
Personnel:
Alan Greer *(Mgr-Regional)*

DAY4 ENERGY INC.

8168 Glenwood Drive
Burnaby, BC, V3N 5E9, Canada
Tel.: (604) 297-0444
Fax: (604) 297-0445
E-Mail: info@day4energy.com
Web Site: www.day4energy.com
Sales Range: $50-74.9 Million
Emp.: 116
Business Description:
Solar Electric Modules Mfr
S.I.C.: 3646
N.A.I.C.S.: 335122
Personnel:
Doug Keast *(Co-Owner & CFO)*
John S. MacDonald *(Chm)*
Leonid B. Rubin *(CTO & VP)*
Simon Biancardi *(Gen Counsel & Sec)*
John E. Stonier *(Treas & VP-Strategic Plng)*
Board of Directors:
John S. MacDonald
Wolfgang Hengst
Rainer Moeller
Leonid B. Rubin
Wolfgang Schmidt
James Topham
Legal Counsel:
Farris, Vaughan, Wills & Murphy LLP
Pacific Centre South 25th Floor 700 W Georgia St
V7Y 1B3 Vancouver, BC, Canada
Non-U.S. Subsidiaries:

Day4 Energy Italia S.r.l. (1)
Via Provinciale San Magno 1
04020 Monte San Biagio, Latina, Italy
Tel.: (39) 0771 568067
Fax: (39) 0771 200768
E-Mail: italia@day4energy.com
Emp.: 2
Solar Electric Modules Distr
S.I.C.: 5065
N.A.I.C.S.: 423690
Luigi Fusi *(Mgr)*

Day4 Systems GmbH (1)
Albring 18
78658 Zimmern ob Rottweil, Baden-Wurttemberg, Germany
Tel.: (49) 7411752990
Fax: (49) 74117529950
E-Mail: info@aci-group.de
Web Site: www.aci-group.de
Solar Electric Modules Mfr
S.I.C.: 3674
N.A.I.C.S.: 334413
Wolfgang Schmutz *(Pres)*

DAYA MATERIALS BERHAD

Block D5 Level U1 Solaris Dutamas
No 1 Jalan Dutamas 1
50480 Kuala Lumpur, Malaysia
Tel.: (60) 3 6205 3170
Fax: (60) 3 6205 3171
E-Mail: dmbmail@dmb.com.my
Web Site: www.dmb.com.my
DAYA—(KLS)
Rev.: $90,810,678
Assets: $130,911,092
Liabilities: $55,189,830
Net Worth: $75,721,262
Earnings: $6,596,505
Fiscal Year-end: 12/31/12
Business Description:
Oil & Gas Exploration Services
S.I.C.: 1311
N.A.I.C.S.: 211111
Personnel:
Mazlin Md Junid *(Vice Chm, Pres & CEO)*

Daya Materials Berhad—(Continued)

Nathan Jooi Loon Tham *(Mng Dir)*
Bee Ling Chen *(Co-Sec)*
Ngeok Mui Chin *(Co-Sec)*
Board of Directors:
Azmil Khalili Khalid
Kin Lip Koh
Soon Foo Lim
Mazlin Md Junid
Fazrin Azwar Md. Nor
Nathan Jooi Loon Tham

Subsidiaries:

Daya Clarimax Sdn. Bhd. (1)
Lot 38 Jalan Sungai Pinang 5/1 Pulau Indah KS2
Mukim Klang, 42000 Port Klang, Selangor, Malaysia
Tel.: (60) 331013440
Fax: (60) 331013441
Web Site: www.dmb.com.my/index.php/en/contacts/company-directory
Emp.: 15
Tank Cleaning & Repair Services
S.I.C.: 4959
N.A.I.C.S.: 562998

Daya CMT Sdn. Bhd. (1)
Plot 81 Lebuhraya Kampung Jawa
11900 Bayan Lepas, Penang, Malaysia
Tel.: (60) 46422280
Fax: (60) 46422499
E-Mail: enquiries-dcmt@dayagroup.com.my
Emp.: 150
Construction Engineering Services
S.I.C.: 8711
N.A.I.C.S.: 541330
William Tham *(Mng Dir)*

Daya Polymer Sdn. Bhd. (1)
1744 Jalan Industri Dua Taman Industri Bukit Panchor
14300 Nibong Tebal, Penang, Malaysia
Tel.: (60) 45938811
Fax: (60) 45938833
E-Mail: dayacom@dayapolymercom.my
Web Site: www.dmb.com.my
Emp.: 63
Polymer Compounds Mfr
S.I.C.: 3087
N.A.I.C.S.: 325991
Bernard Soon *(Gen Mgr)*

Daya Proffscorp Sdn. Bhd. (1)
Lot 606-A Kawasan Industri Teluk Kalong
24007 Kemaman, Terengganu, Malaysia
Tel.: (60) 98633000
Fax: (60) 98632000
E-Mail: info@proffscorp.com.my
Emp.: 100
Crane & Forklifts Hiring Services
S.I.C.: 1799
N.A.I.C.S.: 238990
Nasir Ismail *(Sr Mgr-Fin & Admin)*

Daya Secadyme Sdn. Bhd. (1)
Lot 5410 Kawasan Industri Teluk Kalong
24007 Kemaman, Terengganu, Malaysia
Tel.: (60) 98635622
Fax: (60) 98635623
Web Site: www.dmb.com.my/index.php/en/contacts/company-directory
Emp.: 8
Chemicals Distr
S.I.C.: 5169
N.A.I.C.S.: 424690
Rayburn Azhar Ali *(CEO)*

Non-U.S. Subsidiaries:

DMB International Limited (1)
Suite 2802 Lippo Centre Tower 2 89 Queensway
Admiralty, Central, China (Hong Kong)
Tel.: (852) 2918 8760
Fax: (852) 2918 9808
E-Mail: dil@dmb.com.my
Building Materials Distr
S.I.C.: 5211
N.A.I.C.S.: 444190

PT Daya Secadyme Indonesia (1)
Kompleks Wijaya Grand Centre Blok H No 12-B Lantai 3 JL Wijawa II
Kebayoran Baru, Jakarta, 12160, Indonesia
Tel.: (62) 217206696
Fax: (62) 217394078
E-Mail: edwin@seca-dyme.com
Emp.: 10
Petrochemicals Distr
S.I.C.: 5169
N.A.I.C.S.: 424690
Advin Karyayan Psobropo *(Mgr)*

DAYANG ENTERPRISE HOLDINGS BERHAD

Sublot 5 10 Lot 46 Block 10 Jalan Taman Raja
PO Box 1134
Miri Concession Land District, Miri, Sarawak, 98000, Malaysia
Tel.: (60) 85420185
Fax: (60) 85421654
E-Mail: inquiry@desb.net
Web Site: www.desb.net
DAYANG—(KLS)
Rev.: $131,566,581
Assets: $242,142,373
Liabilities: $46,272,357
Net Worth: $195,870,017
Earnings: $33,199,380
Emp.: 1,000
Fiscal Year-end: 12/31/12
Business Description:
Holding Company; Marine Vessel Mfr, Maintenance & Chartering Services
S.I.C.: 6719
N.A.I.C.S.: 551112
Personnel:
Hasmi Hasnan *(Chm)*
Suk Kiong Ling *(Deputy Chm)*
Yusof Ahmad Shahruddin *(Mng Dir)*
Joe Siew Loung Ling *(Deputy Mng Dir)*
Bailey Chung Siang Kho *(Co-Sec & Head-Corp Affairs)*
Siu Lian Bong *(Co-Sec)*
Board of Directors:
Hasmi Hasnan
Mohd Ashraf Assai Abdullah
Yusof Ahmad Shahruddin
Chu Fatt Chia
Jeanita Anak Gamang
Polit Hamzah
Abdul Aziz Ishak
Gordon Kab
Joe Siew Loung Ling
Suk Kiong Ling
Legal Counsel:
Alvin Chong & Partners Advocates
Lots 176 & 177 2nd Floor Jalan Song Thian Cheok
93100 Kuching, Malaysia
Subsidiary:

Fortune Triumph Sdn. Bhd. (1)
Sublot 5-10 Lot 46 Block 10
Jalan Taman Raja-Hilltop, Miri, 98000, Malaysia
Tel.: (60) 85420185
Fax: (60) 85421654
E-Mail: inquiry@desb.net
Emp.: 200
Marine Engineering Services
S.I.C.: 8711
N.A.I.C.S.: 541330
Juanita James *(Mgr-HR)*

DAYMEN CANADA

55 Valleywood Dr
Markham, ON, L3R 5L9, Canada
Tel.: (905) 944-9400
Fax: (905) 944-9401
E-Mail: info@daymen.com
Web Site: www.daymen.ca
Year Founded: 1981
Rev.: $15,472,337
Emp.: 90
Business Description:
Photographic & Digital Imaging Products Distr
S.I.C.: 5043
N.A.I.C.S.: 423410
Personnel:
Rick Zebryk *(Controller)*

DAY'S MOTOR GROUP

Swansea Road Garngoch
Swansea, SA4 4LL, United Kingdom
Tel.: (44) 1792 222 111
Web Site: www.days.co.uk
Year Founded: 1926
Sales Range: $250-299.9 Million
Emp.: 525
Business Description:
New & Used Car Dealer
S.I.C.: 5511
N.A.I.C.S.: 441110
Personnel:
Graham M. Day *(Chm & CEO)*

DAYTONA CORPORATION

4805 Ichinomiya Mori-machi Shuchi-gun
Shizuoka, 437-0226, Japan
Tel.: (81) 538 84 2220
Fax: (81) 538 84 2221
E-Mail: info@daytona-azia.co.id
Web Site: www.daytona-global.com
Year Founded: 1972
7228—(JAS)
Sales Range: $75-99.9 Million
Business Description:
Motorcycle Parts Mfr
S.I.C.: 3751
N.A.I.C.S.: 336991
Personnel:
Scott Suzuki *(Pres)*
Non-U.S. Subsidiary:

PT Daytona Azia (1)
Jl Flores III Blok C3-3 Kawasan Industri MM2100 Cikarang Barat
Bekasi, 17845, Indonesia
Tel.: (62) 21 8998 3135
Fax: (62) 21 8998 3136
E-Mail: info@daytona-azia.co.id
Web Site: www.daytona-azia.co.id
Emp.: 8
Motorcycle Parts Mfr
S.I.C.: 3751
N.A.I.C.S.: 336991
Carlos Campos *(Pres)*

DAYTONA HOMES

11504 170 Street
Edmonton, AB, Canada
Tel.: (780) 452-2288
Fax: (780) 452-7146
E-Mail: info@daytonahomes.ca
Web Site: www.daytonahomes.ca
Year Founded: 1993
Rev.: $13,041,743
Emp.: 60
Business Description:
Building Construction Services
S.I.C.: 1531
N.A.I.C.S.: 236117
Personnel:
Tally Hutchinson *(Pres)*

DB BROADCAST LTD.

Sedgeway Business Park Witchford
Ely, Cambridgeshire, CB6 2HY, United Kingdom
Tel.: (44) 1353 661117
Fax: (44) 1353 665617
E-Mail: sales@dbbroadcast.co.uk
Web Site: www.dbbroadcast.co.uk
Year Founded: 1989
Sales Range: $25-49.9 Million
Emp.: 54
Business Description:
Television Broadcasting Services
S.I.C.: 4833
N.A.I.C.S.: 515120
Personnel:
David Bird *(Mng Dir)*
Board of Directors:
Ross Amory
David Bird
Graham Pearl
Tom Swan

DB CORP LIMITED

Plot 280 Sarkhej Gandhi Nagar
Highway Near YMCA Club Makarba
Ahmedabad, Gujarat, 380051, India
Tel.: (91) 7939888850
Fax: (91) 7939814001
E-Mail: investor@bhaskarnet.com
Web Site: www.bhaskarnet.com
DBCORP—(BOM NSE)
Rev.: $299,172,328
Assets: $302,704,049
Liabilities: $111,700,920
Net Worth: $191,003,130
Earnings: $40,442,509
Fiscal Year-end: 03/31/13
Business Description:
Newspaper Publisher; Radio Stations
S.I.C.: 2711
N.A.I.C.S.: 511110
Personnel:
Sudhir Agarwal *(Mng Dir)*
P. G. Mishra *(CFO)*
Anita Gokhale *(Compliance Officer & Sec)*
Pawan Agarwal *(Deputy Mng Dir)*
Board of Directors:
Ramesh Chandra Agarwal
Girish Agarwal
Pawan Agarwal
Sudhir Agarwal
Harish Bijoor
Kailash Chandra Chowdhary
Piyush Pandey
Ashwani Singhal
Transfer Agent:
Karvy Computershare Private Limited
Plot No 17-24 Vittal Rao Nagar Madhapur
Hyderabad, 500 081, India
Tel.: (91) 40 2342 0818
Subsidiary:

I Media Corp Ltd. (1)
D-143 Sector-63
Noida, Uttar Pradesh, 201 301, India
Tel.: (91) 1203341200
Fax: (91) 1204282605
E-Mail: contact@imcl.co.in
Web Site: www.imcl.in
Emp.: 100
Integrated Internet & Mobile Interactive Services
S.I.C.: 2741
N.A.I.C.S.: 519130
Diwaker Chandani *(Head-Content-Indiainfo & Meramobi)*

DB (INTERNATIONAL) STOCK BROKERS LTD.

402 New Delhi House 27
Barakhamba Road
New Delhi, 110001, India
Tel.: (91) 1123353795
Fax: (91) 1123736162
E-Mail: helpdesk@dbonline.in
Web Site: www.dagabusiness.com
Year Founded: 1992
530393—(BOM)
Rev.: $2,615,472
Assets: $6,938,510
Liabilities: $954,118
Net Worth: $5,984,392
Earnings: $1,235,677
Fiscal Year-end: 03/31/13
Business Description:
Financial Services
S.I.C.: 6211
N.A.I.C.S.: 523999
Personnel:
Shiv Narayan Daga *(Mng Dir)*
Yashwant Kumar Gupta *(Sec)*

Board of Directors:
Chandra Mohan Bahety
Shiv Narayan Daga
Sanjay Kumar Mimani
Sachin Rathi
Brajesh Sadani
Transfer Agent:
Abhipra Capital Limited
A-387 Dilkhush Industries Area G.T Kamal Rd
Azadpur
New Delhi, India

DBA TELECOMMUNICATION (ASIA) HOLDINGS LIMITED

Unit 2307 23rd Floor Great Eagle
Centre 23 Harbour Road
Wanchai, China (Hong Kong)
Tel.: (852) 31063068
Fax: (852) 31065533
E-Mail: ir@dba-asia.com
Web Site: www.dba-asia.com
3335—(HKG)
Rev.: $1,200,256,145
Assets: $455,945,725
Liabilities: $90,455,226
Net Worth: $365,490,499
Earnings: $80,500,256
Emp.: 798
Fiscal Year-end: 12/31/12
Business Description:
Telecommunication Equipment Mfr
S.I.C.: 4899
N.A.I.C.S.: 517919
Personnel:
Longrui Yu *(Chm & CEO)*
Stephen Ho-chi Yiu *(CFO)*
Board of Directors:
Longrui Yu
Xiao Chen
Weiliang Jiang
Shing Yeung
Lun Yu
Lok Ming Yun
Feng Zheng
Butterfield Fund Services (Cayman) Limited
Butterfield House 68 Fort Street PO Box 705
Georgetown, Cayman Islands
Transfer Agents:
Tricor Investor Services Limited
26th Floor Tesbury Centre 28 Queens Road East
Wanchai, China (Hong Kong)
Butterfield Fund Services (Cayman) Limited
Butterfield House 68 Fort Street PO Box 705
Georgetown, Cayman Islands

D.B.E. GURNEY RESOURCES BERHAD

Plot 138 Kawasan Perindustrian
Pelabuhan Lumut Kg Acheh
32000 Setiawan, Perak, Malaysia
Tel.: (60) 56922822
Fax: (60) 56928922
Web Site: www.dbegurney.com
DBE—(KLS)
Rev.: $45,617,713
Assets: $44,730,620
Liabilities: $22,591,147
Net Worth: $22,139,474
Earnings: ($5,076,758)
Fiscal Year-end: 12/31/12
Business Description:
Poultry Broiler Farm & Farm Products Producer
S.I.C.: 0251
N.A.I.C.S.: 112320
Personnel:
Chong Chow Ding *(Chm)*
Alex Seng Huat Ding *(Mng Dir)*
Choon Yung Ding *(Deputy Mng Dir)*
Jesslyn Bee Fang Ong *(Co-Sec)*
Eric Chee Seong Toh *(Co-Sec)*
Board of Directors:
Chong Chow Ding
Lay Miew Cheng
Alex Seng Huat Ding
Choon Yung Ding
Weng Keong Fong
Lew Wea Hong
Sing Kiong Ling
Heng Peng Ting
Subsidiary:

D.B.E. Poultry Sdn. Bhd. **(1)**
Plot 138 Kawasan Perindustrian
32000 Setiawan, Perak, Malaysia
Tel.: (60) 56922822
Fax: (60) 56922322
E-Mail: admin@dbegurney.com
Emp.: 25
Poultry Rearing Services
S.I.C.: 0254
N.A.I.C.S.: 112340
Alex Dingseng Huap *(Mng Dir)*

DBG CANADA LIMITED

110 Ambassador Drive
Mississauga, ON, Canada
Tel.: (905) 670-1555
Fax: (905) 362-2315
E-Mail: sales@dbgcanada.com
Web Site: www.debiasi.com
Year Founded: 1976
Rev.: $41,557,856
Emp.: 320
Business Description:
Design Tools Mfr
S.I.C.: 3541
N.A.I.C.S.: 333517
Personnel:
Mike De Biasi *(Pres)*

DBS GROUP HOLDINGS LTD.

Marina Bay Financial Centre Tower 3
12 Marina Boulevard, Singapore, 018982, Singapore
Tel.: (65) 68788888
Fax: (65) 64451267
E-Mail: investor@dbs.com
Web Site: www.dbs.com
D05—(OTC SES)
Rev.: $6,893,615,520
Assets: $285,843,759,440
Liabilities: $256,696,898,800
Net Worth: $29,146,860,640
Earnings: $3,254,103,920
Emp.: 18,000
Fiscal Year-end: 12/31/12
Business Description:
Bank Holding Company
S.I.C.: 6712
N.A.I.C.S.: 551111
Personnel:
Peter Lim Huat Seah *(Chm)*
Piyush Gupta *(CEO)*
Karen Ngui *(Mng Dir & Head-Strategic Mktg & Comm)*
Eric Teik Lim Ang *(Mng Dir & Head-Capital Markets)*
David Gledhill *(Mng Dir & Head-Tech & Ops)*
Yan Hong Lee *(Mng Dir & Head-HR)*
Sim Seng Lim *(Mng Dir & Head-Singapore)*
Sue Koo Lynn *(Mng Dir & Head-Legal, Compliance & Secretariat)*
Jimmy Ng *(Mng Dir & Head-Audit)*
Bernard Tan *(Mng Dir & Head-Strategic Projects)*
Su Shan Tan *(Mng Dir & Head-Consumer Banking & Wealth Mgmt)*
Sok Hui Chng *(CFO)*
Elbert Pattijn *(Chief Risk Officer)*
Melvin Tzai Win Teo *(Pres-Indonesia)*
Sanjiv Bhasin *(CEO/Gen Mgr-India)*
Sebastian Paredes *(CEO-Hong Kong)*
Peng Fong Goh *(Sec)*
Board of Directors:
Peter Lim Huat Seah
Bart Joseph Broadman
Christopher Wai Chee Cheng
Euleen Yiu Kiang Goh
Piyush Gupta
Tian Yee Ho
Nihal Vijaya Devadas Kaviratne
Foong Pheng Ow
Andre Sekulic
Danny Leong Kay Teoh
Holding:

DBS Bank Ltd **(1)**
6 Shenton Way DBS Bldg Tower 1
Singapore, 068809, Singapore SG
Tel.: (65) 68351234
Telex: RS 24455 DBSBANK
Fax: (65) 64451267
E-Mail: dbsbank@dbs.com
Web Site: www.dbs.com
Emp.: 11,454
Banking & Financial Services
S.I.C.: 6029
N.A.I.C.S.: 522110
Rebecca Ang *(VP-Grp Strategy Mktg & Comm)*

Subsidiaries:

DBS Bank Ltd. **(2)**
6 Shenton Way
DBS Bldg Tower 1, Singapore, 68809, Singapore SG
Tel.: (65) 68788888 (100%)
Telex: RS 24455
Web Site: www.dbs.com.sg
Group Financing
S.I.C.: 6141
N.A.I.C.S.: 522210
Peter Lim Huat Seah *(Chm)*
Karen Ngui *(Mng Dir & Head-Strategic Mktg & Comm)*
Prashant Agarwal *(Sr VP-Mktg)*

Subsidiaries:

AXS Pte Ltd **(3)**
19 Leng Kee Road
Singapore, 159093, Singapore
Tel.: (65) 65602727
Fax: (65) 6479 8203
E-Mail: enquiries@axs.com.sg
Web Site: www.axs.com.sg
Emp.: 100
Telecommunication Services
S.I.C.: 4899
N.A.I.C.S.: 517919
Joey Chang *(Founder & CEO)*
Eugene Chan *(Co- Founder & CTO)*
Chin Mun Chung *(Chief Bus Officer)*

DBS Asset Management (United States) Pte Ltd **(3)**
8 Cross Street 08-01 PWC Building
Singapore, 048424, Singapore
Tel.: (65) 65358025
Fax: (65) 65345183
Fund Management Services
S.I.C.: 6371
N.A.I.C.S.: 524292

DBS Vickers Securities Holdings Pte Ltd **(3)**
8 Cross Street 02-01 PWC Building
Singapore, 048424, Singapore
Tel.: (65) 65339688
Fax: (65) 65386276
E-Mail: assistance@dbsvickers.com
Securities Brokerage Services
S.I.C.: 6211
N.A.I.C.S.: 523120

Non-U.S. Subsidiaries:

DBS Vickers Securities (Thailand) Co. Ltd. **(4)**
989 Siam Tower 9th 14th-15th Floor Rama I Road
Pathumwan, Bangkok, 10330, Thailand
Tel.: (66) 2657 7000
Fax: (66) 2657 7777
E-Mail: clientservices@th.dbsvickers.com
Web Site: www.dbsvitrade.com
Securities Brokerage Services
S.I.C.: 6211
N.A.I.C.S.: 523120

DBS Vickers Securities (UK) Ltd **(4)**
4th Floor Paternoster House 65 St Pauls Churchyard
London, EC4M 8AB, United Kingdom
Tel.: (44) 2076181888
Fax: (44) 2076181900
Securities Brokerage Services
S.I.C.: 6211
N.A.I.C.S.: 523120

DBS Vickers Securities Online Holdings Pte Ltd **(3)**
8th Cross St Level 2 Unit 01 PWC Building
Singapore, 048424, Singapore
Tel.: (65) 63272288
Fax: (65) 62268068
Investment Banking Services
S.I.C.: 6211
N.A.I.C.S.: 523110

Non-U.S. Subsidiaries:

DBS Vickers (Hong Kong) Limited **(3)**
18 F Man Yee Building 68 Des Voeux Road Central
Hong Kong, China (Hong Kong)
Tel.: (852) 28204888
Fax: (852) 2523 6055
Web Site: www.dbsvickers.com
Securities Brokerage Services
S.I.C.: 6211
N.A.I.C.S.: 523120

DBS Vickers Securities (Hong Kong) Limited **(3)**
18-19 f Man Yee Bldg 68 Des Voeux Rd
Hong Kong, China (Hong Kong)
Tel.: (852) 28204888
Fax: (852) 25236055
Securities Brokerage Services
S.I.C.: 6211
N.A.I.C.S.: 523120

DBS Card Centre Pte. Ltd. **(2)**
6 Shenton Way DBS Bldg Tower One
Singapore, 068809, Singapore
Tel.: (65) 68788888
Telex: RS 20229; RS20230
Fax: (65) 68341840
E-Mail: customerservice@dbscc.com
Web Site: www.dbs.com
Emp.: 212
Credit & Charge Card Operations
S.I.C.: 6153
N.A.I.C.S.: 522210
Elsie Foh *(Dir)*

DBS Trustee Ltd. **(2)**
6 Shenton Way
DBS Bldg Tower 1, Singapore, 068809, Singapore SG
Tel.: (65) 68788888
Telex: RS 24618
Web Site: www.dbs.com
Trustee Services
S.I.C.: 6211
N.A.I.C.S.: 523999

DBS Vickers Research (Singapore) Pte Ltd **(2)**
8 Cross Street 02-01 Pwc Building
Singapore, 048424, Singapore
Tel.: (65) 65339688
Fax: (65) 62268048
Investment Banking Services
S.I.C.: 6211
N.A.I.C.S.: 523110

DBS Vickers Securities Nominees (Singapore) Pte Ltd **(2)**
6 Shenton Way Tower 1 Dbs Building
Singapore, 068809, Singapore
Tel.: (65) 65339688
Fax: (65) 65357785
Investment Banking Services
S.I.C.: 6211
N.A.I.C.S.: 523110

Joint Venture:

DBS Vickers Securities (Singapore) Pte Ltd **(2)**
8 Cross Street #02-01 PWC Building
Singapore, 048424, Singapore SG
Tel.: (65) 65339688
Telex: rs 26085 DBS
Fax: (65) 65386276
E-Mail: assistance@dbsvickers.com

DBS Group Holdings Ltd.—(Continued)

Web Site: www.dbsvickers.com
Emp.: 100
Futures Trading
S.I.C.: 6221
N.A.I.C.S.: 523140
Edmund Lee *(CEO)*

Non-U.S. Branch:

DBS Bank-London Branch **(2)**
4th Fl Paternoster House 65 St Pauls Church Yard
London, EC4M8AB, United Kingdom UK
Tel.: (44) 2074896550 (100%)
Fax: (44) 2074895850
E-Mail: dbs@dbs.com
Emp.: 55
Banking Services
S.I.C.: 8732
N.A.I.C.S.: 541910

Non-U.S. Subsidiaries:

DBS Asia Ltd. **(2)**
39-41 Des Voeux Rd
Central, Hong Kong, China (Hong Kong) HK
Tel.: (852) 36682080 (100%)
Telex: 75389 DBSHK HX
Web Site: www.dbs.com
Emp.: 20
Selective Financial Services
S.I.C.: 6159
N.A.I.C.S.: 522220

DBS Bank (Hong Kong) Limited **(2)**
11th Floor The Center
99 Queen's Road, Central, China (Hong Kong) (100%)
Tel.: (852) 36682000
Fax: (852) 21678222
Web Site: www.dbs.com
Int. Income: $622,855,936
Emp.: 3,200
Commercial & Retail Banking
S.I.C.: 6029
N.A.I.C.S.: 522110

Subsidiary:

DBS Asia Capital Limited **(3)**
22nd Fl The Center
99 Queens Road, Central, China (Hong Kong) HK
Tel.: (852) 36681148 (100%)
Fax: (852) 28680250
Web Site: www.dbs.com.hk
Emp.: 70
Investment Banking & Corporate Finance
S.I.C.: 6211
N.A.I.C.S.: 523110
Gary Sik *(Mng Dir)*

DBS Thai Danu Bank Public Company Limited **(2)**
393 Silom Rd
Bangrak, Bangkok, 10500, Thailand (51.72%)
Tel.: (66) 26366365
Fax: (66) 26366366
Web Site: www.dbs.com
Emp.: 1,500
Banking Services
S.I.C.: 6029
N.A.I.C.S.: 522110

PT Bank DBS Indonesia **(2)**
Plaza Permata Jalan MH Thamrin Kav 57
Jakarta, 10350, Indonesia ID
Tel.: (62) 213903366 (99%)
Fax: (62) 213908222
Web Site: www.dbs.com
Emp.: 150
Commercial Banking Services
S.I.C.: 6029
N.A.I.C.S.: 522110
Hendra Gunawan *(Pres)*

DBV TECHNOLOGIES

Green Square Batiment D 80/84 rue des Meuniers
92220 Bagneux, France
Tel.: (33) 1 55 42 78 78
Fax: (33) 1 43 26 10 83
Web Site: www.dbv-technologies.com
Year Founded: 2002
DBV—(EUR)
Rev.: $3,737,759
Assets: $57,851,409
Liabilities: $5,117,710
Net Worth: $52,733,699
Earnings: ($17,516,364)
Emp.: 34
Fiscal Year-end: 12/31/12

Business Description:
Pharmaceutical Mfr
S.I.C.: 2834
N.A.I.C.S.: 325412

Personnel:
Pierre-Henri Benhamou *(Co-Founder, Chm & CEO)*
Bertrand Dupont *(Co-Founder & Chief Indus Officer)*
David Schilansky *(CFO)*
Charles Ruban *(Chief Dev Officer)*
Veronique Foutel *(Chief Strategic Mktg Officer)*

Board of Directors:
Pierre-Henri Benhamou
Torbjorn Bjerke
Mailys Ferrere
Didier Hoch
George F. Horner, III
Peter Barton Hutt
Chahra Louafi
Rafaele Tordjman

Chd Audit Et
8 rue Auber
Paris, France

D.C. THOMSON & CO. LTD.

2 Albert Square
Dundee, DD1 9QJ, United Kingdom
Tel.: (44) 1382 223 131
Web Site: www.dcthomson.co.uk
Year Founded: 1905
Sales Range: $400-449.9 Million
Emp.: 2,170

Business Description:
News Publishing Services
S.I.C.: 2711
N.A.I.C.S.: 511110

Personnel:
Tim Collins *(Head-Comml Dev-Children's Entertainment)*

DCC PLC

DCC House Brewery Road Stillorgan
Blackrock, Dublin, Ireland
Tel.: (353) 12799400
Fax: (353) 12831017
E-Mail: info@dcc.ie
Web Site: www.dcc.ie
Year Founded: 1976
DCC—(ISE OTC)
Rev.: $17,454,786,186
Assets: $5,391,246,617
Liabilities: $3,970,664,378
Net Worth: $1,420,582,239
Earnings: $176,045,382
Emp.: 9,153
Fiscal Year-end: 03/31/13

Business Description:
Holding Company; Energy, IT & Entertainment, Healthcare, Environmental, Food & Beverage Products & Services
S.I.C.: 6719
N.A.I.C.S.: 551112

Personnel:
Tommy Breen *(CEO & Mng Dir)*
Fergal O'Dwyer *(CFO)*
Gerard Whyte *(Sec & Head-Enterprise Risk Mgmt)*

Board of Directors:
Michael Donal Buckley
Tommy Breen
Roisin Brennan
David Byrne
Pamela J. Kirby
Jane A. Lodge
Kevin Christopher Melia
John J. Moloney
Donal Murphy
Fergal O'Dwyer
Leslie Van De Walle

Legal Counsel:
William Fry
Fitzwilton House Wilton Place
Dublin, 2, Ireland

Divisions:

DCC Energy **(1)**
DCC House Brewery Rd
Stillorgan Blackrock, CO Dublin, Ireland
Tel.: (353) 12799400
Fax: (353) 12831017
E-Mail: energy@dcc.ie
Web Site: www.dcc.ie/dcc/tools/contact/
Emp.: 35
Holding Company
S.I.C.: 6719
N.A.I.C.S.: 551112
Donal Murphy *(Mng Dir)*
Colman O'Keeffe *(Deputy Mng Dir)*

DCC Environmental **(1)**
DCC House Brewery Road
Stillorgan Blackrock, Dublin, Ireland
Tel.: (353) 12799400
Fax: (353) 12831017
E-Mail: environmental@dcc.ie
Web Site: www.dcc.ie/dcc/tools/contact/
Emp.: 55
Holding Company
S.I.C.: 6719
N.A.I.C.S.: 551112
Tommy Breen *(CEO & Mng Dir)*

DCC Food & Beverage **(1)**
DCC House Brewery Rd
Stillorgan Blackrock, Dublin, Ireland
Tel.: (353) 12799400
Fax: (353) 12831017
E-Mail: foods@dcc.ie
Web Site: www.dcc.ie/dcc/tools/contact/
Emp.: 35
Holding Company
S.I.C.: 6719
N.A.I.C.S.: 551112
Frank Fenn *(Mng Dir)*

DCC Healthcare **(1)**
DCC House Brewery Rd
Stillorgan Blackrock, Dublin, 18, Ireland
Tel.: (353) 12799400
Fax: (353) 12831017
E-Mail: healthcare@dcc.ie
Web Site: www.dcc.ie
Emp.: 44
Drugs & Druggists Sundries Whslr
S.I.C.: 5122
N.A.I.C.S.: 424210
Conor Costigan *(Mng Dir)*

DCC SerCom **(1)**
DCC House Brewery Rd
Stillorgan Blackrock, Dublin, 18, Ireland
Tel.: (353) 12799400
Fax: (353) 12831017
E-Mail: sercom@dcc.ie
Emp.: 35
Computer Related Services
S.I.C.: 7379
N.A.I.C.S.: 541519
Niall Ennis *(Mng Dir)*

Subsidiaries:

Allied Foods Limited **(1)**
Second Ave
Cookstown Industrial Estate, Dublin, Ireland (100%)
Tel.: (353) 14662600
Fax: (353) 14662698
E-Mail: enquiries@alliedfoods.ie
Web Site: www.alliedfoods.ie
Emp.: 350
Frozen & Chilled Foods Distr
S.I.C.: 5142
N.A.I.C.S.: 424420
John Rally *(Mng Dir)*

Broderick Bros. Limited **(1)**
Cloverhill Industrial Estate
Clondalkin, Dublin, Ireland
Tel.: (353) 14291500
Fax: (353) 14509570
E-Mail: info@broderickbros.ie
Web Site: www.broderickbros.ie
Emp.: 30
Caterers
S.I.C.: 5812
N.A.I.C.S.: 722320
Richard Kieran *(Mng Dir)*

Emo Oil Limited **(1)**
Clonminam Indus Est
Portlaoise, Laois, Ireland
Tel.: (353) 578674700
Fax: (353) 578674775
E-Mail: info@emo.ie
Web Site: www.emo.ie
Emp.: 50
Crude Petroleum & Natural Gas Extraction
S.I.C.: 1311
N.A.I.C.S.: 211111
Tom Walsh *(Mng Dir)*

Enva Ireland Limited **(1)**
Clonminam Industrial Estate
Portlaoise, Laois, Ireland
Tel.: (353) 578678600
Fax: (353) 578678699
E-Mail: info@enva.ie
Web Site: www.enva.ie
Emp.: 200
Nonhazardous Waste Treatment & Disposal
S.I.C.: 4953
N.A.I.C.S.: 562219
Declan Ryan *(Mng Dir)*

Fannin Limited **(1)**
Fannin House
South County Business Park Leo, Dublin, 18, Ireland (100%)
Tel.: (353) 12907000
Fax: (353) 12907111
E-Mail: info@fannin.ie
Web Site: www.fannin.com
Emp.: 100
Pharmacies and Drug Stores
S.I.C.: 5912
N.A.I.C.S.: 446110
Andrew Connell *(Mng Dir)*

Flogas Ireland Limited **(1)**
Dublin Road Co Louth
Drogheda, Ireland
Tel.: (353) 419831041
Fax: (353) 419834652
E-Mail: info@flogas.ie
Web Site: www.flogas.ie
Emp.: 65
Liquefied Petroleum Gas Bottled Gas Dealers
S.I.C.: 5989
N.A.I.C.S.: 454310
Richard Martin *(Mng Dir)*

Great Gas Petroleum (Ireland) Limited **(1)**
Market House
Churchtown, Mallow, Cork, Ireland
Tel.: (353) 22 23 989
Fax: (353) 22 23 980
E-Mail: info@greatgas.com
Web Site: www.greatgas.com
Emp.: 1
Petroleum Product Distr
S.I.C.: 5172
N.A.I.C.S.: 424720
Ray O Sullivan *(Mng Dir)*

Kelkin Limited **(1)**
Unit 1 Crosslands Industrial Park
Ballymount Cross, Dublin, Ireland
Tel.: (353) 14600400
Fax: (353) 014600411
E-Mail: info@kelkin.ie
Web Site: www.kelkin.ie
Emp.: 65
Specialty Food Stores
S.I.C.: 5499
N.A.I.C.S.: 445299
Frank Fenn *(Mng Dir)*

Pilton Company Limited **(1)**
Unit 2 Loughlinstown Industrial Estate
Ballybrack, Dublin, Ireland
Tel.: (353) 12826444
Fax: (353) 12826532
Emp.: 25
Electrical Appliance Television & Radio Set Whslr
S.I.C.: 5064
N.A.I.C.S.: 423620
Jim Morgan *(Mng Dir)*

Robert Roberts Limited (1)
79 Broomhill Road Tallaght
Dublin, 24, Ireland
Tel.: (353) 14047300
Fax: (353) 14047311
E-Mail: info@robert-roberts.ie
Web Site: www.robt-roberts.ie
Emp.: 200
Confectionery Whslr
S.I.C.: 5145
N.A.I.C.S.: 424450
Tom Gray *(Mng Dir)*

SerCom Distribution Limited (1)
DCC House Brewery Road
Stillorgan, Dublin, Ireland
Tel.: (353) 1 2799 400
Fax: (353) 1 2831 017
E-Mail: sercom@dcc.ie
Web Site: www.dcc.ie
Emp.: 5
Software & Consumer Electronics Distr
S.I.C.: 5045
N.A.I.C.S.: 423430
Niall Ennis *(Mng Dir)*

SerCom Solutions Limited (1)
M50 Business Park
Ballymount Road Upper, Dublin, 12, Ireland
Tel.: (353) 14056500
Fax: (353) 14056525
E-Mail: info@sercomsolutions.ie
Web Site: www.sercomsolutions.ie
Emp.: 20
Management Consulting Services
S.I.C.: 8748
N.A.I.C.S.: 541618
Kevin Henry *(CEO)*

Sharptext Limited (1)
M50 Business Park
Ballymount Road Upper, Dublin, 12, Ireland
Tel.: (353) 14087171
Fax: (353) 14193111
E-Mail: sharptext@sharptext.com
Web Site: www.sharptext.com
Emp.: 60
Computer Related Services
S.I.C.: 7379
N.A.I.C.S.: 541519
John Dunne *(Mng Dir)*

Joint Venture:

KP (Ireland) Limited (1)
79 Broomhill Road Tallaght
Dublin, 24, Ireland (50%)
Tel.: (353) 14047300
Fax: (353) 14047311
E-Mail: info@robert-roberts.ie
Web Site: www.robert-roberts.ie
Emp.: 200
Snack Food Mfr
S.I.C.: 2052
N.A.I.C.S.: 311919
Thomas Grey *(Mng Dir)*

U.S. Subsidiary:

Virtus Inc. (1)
1896 Lammers Pke
Batesville, IN 47006
Tel.: (812) 933-1121
Fax: (812) 933-0749
Emp.: 100
Mattress Mfr
S.I.C.: 2515
N.A.I.C.S.: 337910
John Miller *(Mng Dir)*

Non-U.S. Subsidiaries:

Advent Data Limited (1)
Unit H4 Premier Way Lowfields Business park
Elland, HX5 9HF, United Kingdom
Tel.: (44) 871 222 3844
Fax: (44) 871 222 3855
E-Mail: sales@adventdata.co.uk
Web Site: www.adventdata.co.uk
Emp.: 11
Printer & Data Storage Media Supplies Distr
S.I.C.: 5045
N.A.I.C.S.: 423430
Raj Advani *(Gen Mgr)*

Auckbritt International Pty Limited (1)
418 Lake Road Takapuna
Auckland, New Zealand
Tel.: (64) 98369974
Fax: (64) 98369914
E-Mail: sales@auckbritt.co.nz
Web Site: www.auckbritt.co.nz
Vocational Rehabilitation Services
S.I.C.: 8331
N.A.I.C.S.: 624310
Jodi Hannan *(Gen Mgr)*

Banque Magnetique SAS (1)
Paris Nord II - 99 Avenue de la Pyramide
BP 64060
95972 Roissy-en-France, France
Tel.: (33) 1 49 90 93 93
Fax: (33) 1 49 90 94 94
Web Site: www.banquemagnetique.fr
Computer Accessories Distr
S.I.C.: 5045
N.A.I.C.S.: 423430

Bottle Green Limited (1)
19 New Street
Leeds, LS18 4BH, United Kingdom
Tel.: (44) 1132054500
Fax: (44) 1132054501
E-Mail: info@bottlegreen.com
Web Site: www.bottlegreen.com
Emp.: 25
Wine & Distilled Alcoholic Beverage Whslr
S.I.C.: 5181
N.A.I.C.S.: 424810
John Eagle *(Mng Dir)*

Comtrade SAS (1)
300 R Du Pdt Salvador Allende
92700 Colombes, Hauts-de-Seine, France
Tel.: (33) 156470593
Emp.: 60
Multimedia Device & Accessories Distr
S.I.C.: 5065
N.A.I.C.S.: 423690
David Garnier *(Mng Dir)*

DCC Energy Limited (1)
40-48 Airport Road West
Sydenham, Belfast, BT3 9ED, United Kingdom
Tel.: (44) 28 9073 2611
Fax: (44) 28 9045 0243
Lubricant Oil Distr
S.I.C.: 5172
N.A.I.C.S.: 424720
Pat O'Neill *(Gen Mgr)*

DCC Health And Beauty Solutions Limited (1)
9-12 Hardwick Road
Astmoor Industrial Estate, Runcorn, Cheshire, WA71PH, United Kingdom
Tel.: (44) 1928573734
Fax: (44) 1928580694
E-Mail: enquiries@dcchealthandbeauty.com
Web Site: www.dcchealthandbeauty.com
Emp.: 160
Pharmaceutical Preparation Mfr
S.I.C.: 2834
N.A.I.C.S.: 325412
Stephen O'connor *(Gen Mgr)*

Energie Direct MineralolhandelsgesmbH (1)
Alte Poststrasse 400
8055 Graz, Austria
Tel.: (43) 316 210
Fax: (43) 316 210 20
E-Mail: info@energiedirect.at
Web Site: www.energiedirect.at
Emp.: 100
Petroleum Products Distr
S.I.C.: 5172
N.A.I.C.S.: 424720
Hans-Peter Hintermayer *(Gen Mgr)*

EuroCaps Limited (1)
Unit B Crown Business Park
Dukes Town Tredegar Wales, Gwent, NP22 4EF, United Kingdom
Tel.: (44) 1495308900
Fax: (44) 1495308990
E-Mail: info@softgels.co.uk
Web Site: www.dcc.co.uk
Emp.: 160
Chemical Product & Preparation Mfr
S.I.C.: 2899
N.A.I.C.S.: 325998
Stephen O'Connor *(Mng Dir)*

Fannin (UK) Limited (1)
42-46 Booth Drive Park Farm South
Wellingborough, Northamptonshire, NN8 6GT, United Kingdom
Tel.: (44) 1189 305333
Fax: (44) 1189 305111
E-Mail: enquiries@fanninuk.com
Web Site: www.fanninuk.com
Emp.: 10
Medical Device Mfr & Distr
S.I.C.: 3845
N.A.I.C.S.: 334510
Andrew O'Connell *(Grp CEO)*

Flogas UK Limited (1)
81 Raynsway Syston
Leicester, LE71PF, United Kingdom
Tel.: (44) 1162649000
Fax: (44) 1162649001
E-Mail: sales@flogas.co.uk
Web Site: www.flogas.co.uk
Emp.: 150
Crude Petroleum & Natural Gas Extraction
S.I.C.: 1311
N.A.I.C.S.: 211111
James Rudman *(Dir-Bus Dev)*

Non-U.S. Subsidiaries:

Benegas B.V. (2)
Zuiderzeestraatweg 1
3882 NC Putten, Netherlands NL
Tel.: (31) 341723350
Fax: (31) 341360216
E-Mail: info@benegas.com
Web Site: www.benegas.com
Emp.: 27
Liquefied Petroleum Gas Distr
S.I.C.: 4924
N.A.I.C.S.: 221210

LP Gas B.V. (2)
Zuiderzeestraatweg 1
3882 Putten, Netherlands NL
Tel.: (31) 341723400
Fax: (31) 341723401
E-Mail: info@lpgas.nl
Web Site: www.lpgas.nl
Emp.: 60
Petroleum & Gas Products Whslr
S.I.C.: 5172
N.A.I.C.S.: 424720
Jan van Dijk *(Gen Mgr)*

Fuel Card Services Limited (1)
Alexandra House Lawnswood Business Park Redvers Close
Leeds, LS16 6QY, United Kingdom
Tel.: (44) 1132390490
Fax: (44) 18448709827
Web Site: www.fuelcardservices.com
Emp.: 48
Fossil Fuel Electric Power Generation
S.I.C.: 4911
N.A.I.C.S.: 221112

GB Oils Limited (1)
Tryst House
Glenbervie Business Park Stirl, Larbert, FK54RB, United Kingdom
Tel.: (44) 1324408000
Fax: (44) 1324408260
E-Mail: info@emooil.co.uk
Web Site: www.gboils.co.uk
Emp.: 200
Coal & Mineral & Ore Whslr
S.I.C.: 5052
N.A.I.C.S.: 423520
Tony Stewart *(Mng Dir)*

Gem Distribution Limited (1)
St George House Parkway
Harlow Business Park Essex, Harlow, CM195QF, United Kingdom
Tel.: (44) 1279822800
Fax: (44) 1279416228
E-Mail: info@gem.co.uk
Web Site: www.gem.co.uk
Emp.: 70
Office Equipment Whslr
S.I.C.: 5044
N.A.I.C.S.: 423420
Chris Peacock *(Mng Dir)*

Laleham Healthcare Limited (1)
Sycamore Park
Mill Lane, Alton, Hampshire, GU34 2PR, United Kingdom
Tel.: (44) 1420566500
Fax: (44) 1420566566
E-Mail: reception@laleham-healthcare.com
Web Site: www.laleham-healthcare.com
Emp.: 200
Pharmaceutical Preparation Mfr
S.I.C.: 2834
N.A.I.C.S.: 325412
Mark Crawley *(Dir-Tech)*

Micro Peripherals Limited (1)
Shorten Brook Way Altham Bus Pk Altham
Accrington, Lancashire, BB5 5YJ, United Kingdom
Tel.: (44) 1282776776
Fax: (44) 1282770001
E-Mail: enquiries@micro-p.com
Web Site: www.micro-p.com
Emp.: 250
Office Equipment Whslr
S.I.C.: 5044
N.A.I.C.S.: 423420

Pace Fuelcare Limited (1)
Hanover House 18 The Avenue
Egham, Surrey, TW20 9AB, United Kingdom
Tel.: (44) 1784 484444
Fax: (44) 1784 486555
E-Mail: enquiries@pacefuelcare.co.uk
Web Site: www.pacefuelcare.co.uk
Fuel Distr
S.I.C.: 5172
N.A.I.C.S.: 424720
Philip Wharton *(Gen Mgr)*

Squadron Medical Limited (1)
Unit 9 Markham Whale Waterloo Court
Donk Mountain
Chesterfield, S44 5FB, United Kingdom
Tel.: (44) 1246 470999
Fax: (44) 1246 284030
E-Mail: orders@squadronmedical.co.uk
Web Site: www.squadronmedical.co.uk
Healthcare Logistics Services
S.I.C.: 4731
N.A.I.C.S.: 541614
Kevin Pritchard *(Gen Mgr)*

Swea Energi AB (1)
Storgatan 35
SE-434 32 Kungsbacka, Sweden SE
Tel.: (46) 3007 5600
E-Mail: info@sweaenergi.se
Web Site: www.sweaenergi.se
Emp.: 54
Heating Oil & Transport Fuels Distr
S.I.C.: 5172
N.A.I.C.S.: 424720
Magnus Nyfjall *(Pres & Sls Mgr)*

Thompson & Capper Limited (1)
9-12 Hardwick Road
Astmoor Industrial Estate, Runcorn, Cheshire, WA7 1PH, United Kingdom
Tel.: (44) 1928573734
Fax: (44) 1928580694
E-Mail: enquiries@thompsonandcapper.com
Web Site: www.thompsonandcapper.com
Emp.: 130
Pharmaceutical Preparation Mfr
S.I.C.: 2834
N.A.I.C.S.: 325412
Stephen O'Connnor *(Gen Mgr)*

The TPS Healthcare Group Limited (1)
27-35 Napier Place Wardpark North
Cumbernauld, G68 0LL, United Kingdom
Tel.: (44) 1236 739 668
Fax: (44) 3761236 738
E-Mail: corporate@tpshealthcare.com
Web Site: www.tpsmedical.co.uk
Emp.: 6
Healthcare Logistics Services
S.I.C.: 4731
N.A.I.C.S.: 541614
Ian McGuire *(Gen Mgr)*

Wastecycle Ltd. (1)
Enviro Bldg Private Rd Number 4
Colwick Industrial Estate, Nottingham, Nottinghamshire, NG4 2JT, United Kingdom
Tel.: (44) 01159403111
Fax: (44) 1159404141
E-Mail: info@wastecycle.co.uk
Web Site: www.wastecycle.co.uk
Sales Range: $1-9.9 Million
Emp.: 200
Recycling & Waste Management Services
S.I.C.: 4959
N.A.I.C.S.: 562998
Paul Needham *(Mng Dir)*

DCC plc—(Continued)

Non-U.S. Joint Venture:

William Tracey Limited (1)
49 Burnbrae Road Linwood
Renfrewshire, Paisley, PA33BD, United Kingdom (50%)
Tel.: (44) 1505321000
Web Site: www.williamtraceygroup.com
Waste Management Services
S.I.C.: 4959
N.A.I.C.S.: 562998

DCD-DORBYL (PTY) LTD.

Ring Road
Duncanville, 1939 Vereeniging, South Africa
Tel.: (27) 164280000
Fax: (27) 164280190
E-Mail: gcolegate@dcd.co.za
Web Site: www.dcd.com
Year Founded: 2002
Sales Range: $25-49.9 Million
Business Description:
Holding Company; Heavy Mechanical Engineering Products & Services
S.I.C.: 6719
N.A.I.C.S.: 551112
Personnel:
Dirk Els *(Exec Dir-Mktg)*

Branches:

DCD-Dorbyl Heavy Engineering Vereeniging (1)
Ring Road
Duncanville, Vereeniging, 1939, South Africa (100%)
Mailing Address:
PO Box 186
Vereeniging, 1930, South Africa
Tel.: (27) 164280000
Telex: 4 21237
Fax: (27) 164280190
E-Mail: gcolegate@dcd-dorbyl.co.za
Web Site: www.dcd-dorbyl.com
Emp.: 503
Mining, Steel & Power Industry Equipment Mfr
S.I.C.: 3532
N.A.I.C.S.: 333131
Gary Colegate *(Gen Mgr)*

DCD-Dorbyl Rolling Stock Division (1)
54 Victor Street Industrial Park
East Rand, Boksburg, 1406, South Africa
Mailing Address:
PO Box 229
Boksburg, 1460, South Africa
Tel.: (27) 119141400
Telex: 4 29576
Fax: (27) 119143885
Web Site: www.dcd-dorbyl.com
Emp.: 200
Railroad Rolling Stock & Specialty Vehicle Designer, Mfr & Refurbishment Services
S.I.C.: 3743
N.A.I.C.S.: 336510
Petrus Mulaudzi *(Gen Mgr)*

DCD MEDIA PLC

Glen House 22 Glenthorne Road
London, W6 0NG, United Kingdom
Tel.: (44) 208 563 9393
Fax: (44) 208 741 7214
E-Mail: info@dcdmedia.co.uk
Web Site: www.dcdmedia.co.uk
DCD—(LSE)
Rev.: $25,401,300
Assets: $24,471,099
Liabilities: $14,641,598
Net Worth: $9,829,501
Earnings: ($2,083,084)
Emp.: 62
Fiscal Year-end: 12/31/12
Business Description:
Arts, Entertainment, Music & Drama TV Programming Producer & Distr
S.I.C.: 7812
N.A.I.C.S.: 512110
Personnel:
David Craven *(Chm & CEO)*
Nicky Davies Williams *(CEO-DCD Rights)*
Board of Directors:
David Craven
David Green
Andrew James Lindley
Neil Armstrong McMyn
Legal Counsel:
Addleshaw Goddard
Milton Gate 60 Chiswell Street
London, United Kingdom

Subsidiaries:

Box TV Limited (1)
151 Wardour Street
London, W1F 8WE, United Kingdom UK
Tel.: (44) 2072978040
Fax: (44) 2072978041
E-Mail: info@box-tv.co.uk
Web Site: www.box-tv.co.uk
Television Program Producers
S.I.C.: 7812
N.A.I.C.S.: 512110

DCD Publishing Limited (1)
Glen House 22 Glenthorne Road
London, W6 0NG, United Kingdom UK
Tel.: (44) 208 563 9393
Fax: (44) 2087417214
E-Mail: dcdpublishing@dcdmedia.co.uk
Web Site: www.dcdpublishing.co.uk
Emp.: 30
Media & Public Relations Agency
S.I.C.: 7319
N.A.I.C.S.: 541830
Adrian Sington *(CEO)*

Prospect Pictures Limited (1)
Glen House
22 Glenthorne Rd, London, W6 0NG, United Kingdom
Tel.: (44) 2076361234
Fax: (44) 2076361236
E-Mail: info@prospect-uk.com
Web Site: www.prospect-uk.com
Motion Picture Production Services
S.I.C.: 7812
N.A.I.C.S.: 512110

September Films Limited (1)
Glen House
22 Glenthorne Rd, London, W6 0NG, United Kingdom UK
Tel.: (44) 2085639393
Fax: (44) 2087417214
E-Mail: reception@septemberfilms.com
Web Site: www.septemberfilms.com
Motion Picture Production Services
S.I.C.: 7812
N.A.I.C.S.: 512110
Sammy Nourmand *(CEO)*

U.S. Subsidiary:

September Films USA, Inc. (2)
Raleigh Studios 650 N Bronson Ave Ste B114
Los Angeles, CA 90004 CA
Tel.: (323) 960-8085
Fax: (323) 960-8086
E-Mail: september@septemberfilms.com
Web Site: www.septemberfilms.com
Motion Picture Production Services
S.I.C.: 7812
N.A.I.C.S.: 512110
Pamela Covais *(VP-Production)*

DCI DATABASE FOR COMMERCE AND INDUSTRY AG

Enzianstrasse 2
82319 Starnberg, Germany
Tel.: (49) 8151 265 0
E-Mail: info@dci.de
Web Site: www.dci.de
DCI—(DEU)
Business Description:
Database & Information Management Services
S.I.C.: 7389
N.A.I.C.S.: 519190
Personnel:
Thomas Friedbichler *(Chm)*
Michael Mohr *(Chm-Mgmt Bd & CEO)*
Thorsten Koster *(Deputy Chm)*
Gerald Mutsch *(CIO)*
Sascha Neubacher *(Chief Sls Officer)*
Board of Directors:
Thomas Friedbichler
Bernd Kollmannsberger
Thorsten Koster

DCK CONCESSIONS LTD.

DCK House Station Court Radford Way
Billericay, Essex, CM12 0DZ, United Kingdom
Tel.: (44) 1277 650655
Web Site: www.dckconcessions.com
Year Founded: 1992
Sales Range: $300-349.9 Million
Emp.: 2,457
Business Description:
Jewellery Product Whslr
S.I.C.: 5094
N.A.I.C.S.: 423940
Personnel:
Alan Witzenfeld *(Founder & CEO)*

DCM DECOMETAL GMBH

Grazerplatz 5
A-8280 Fuerstenfeld, Austria
Tel.: (43) 3382 520 52
Fax: (43) 3382 557 65
E-Mail: info@dcm-vienna.com
Web Site: www.dcm-vienna.com
Business Description:
Metal Ore Mining Services
S.I.C.: 1099
N.A.I.C.S.: 212299
Personnel:
Herbert H. Depisch *(Chm & Founder)*

Non-U.S. Subsidiary:

Stirling Resources Limited (1)
143 Hay Street
PO Box 8116
Subiaco, WA, 6008, Australia (91%)
Tel.: (61) 863896800
Fax: (61) 863896810
E-Mail: admin@stirlingresources.com.au
Web Site: www.stirlingresources.com.au
SRE—(ASX)
Rev.: $432,186
Assets: $11,698,836
Liabilities: $21,852,359
Net Worth: ($10,153,523)
Earnings: ($1,001,700)
Emp.: 40
Fiscal Year-end: 06/30/13
Investment Services
S.I.C.: 6799
N.A.I.C.S.: 523920
Martin Depisch *(Mng Dir)*
Shannon Coates *(Sec)*

DCM HOLDINGS CO., LTD.

6-16-16 Minamiohi Shinagawa-ku
Tokyo, 140-0013, Japan
Tel.: (81) 357645211
Web Site: www.dcm-hldgs.co.jp
3050—(TKS)
Sls.: $4,776,266,000
Assets: $3,365,032,000
Liabilities: $1,764,290,000
Net Worth: $1,600,742,000
Earnings: $116,391,000
Fiscal Year-end: 02/28/13
Business Description:
Household Products Retailer
S.I.C.: 5719
N.A.I.C.S.: 442299
Personnel:
Toshihiro Hisada *(Pres)*
Board of Directors:
Toshihiro Hisada
Yasunori Ishiguro
Tomochika Iwashita
Kiyotaka Kamada
Ichiro Sato
Tsukasa Takahashi
Yoshiyuki Toyoda

DCM LIMITED

6th Floor Vikrant Tower 4 Rajendra Place
New Delhi, 110 008, India
Tel.: (91) 1125719967
Fax: (91) 1125765214
Web Site: www.dcm.in
DCM—(NSE)
Rev.: $151,949,261
Assets: $111,959,593
Liabilities: $69,887,679
Net Worth: $42,071,914
Earnings: $2,889,107
Fiscal Year-end: 03/31/13
Business Description:
Yarn Mfr & Software Development Services
S.I.C.: 2299
N.A.I.C.S.: 313110
Personnel:
Jitendra Tuli *(Chm & Mng Dir)*
Vinay Bharat Ram *(CEO)*
Sumant Bharat Ram *(CFO & COO)*
Hemant Bharat Ram *(Pres-Textiles)*
Mukesh Sharma *(Sec)*
Ashwani Singhal *(Exec VP-Fin & Taxation)*
Board of Directors:
Jitendra Tuli
N. P. Chawla
Ravi Vira Gupta
Sudhir Kumar Jain
Bipin Maira
Surender Nath Pandey
Joginder Singh Sodhi
Transfer Agent:
MCS Limited
F-65 Okhla Industrial Area Phase-I
New Delhi, India

Subsidiary:

DCM Financial Services Ltd. (1)
D7/3 Okhla Ind Area Ph-II
New Delhi, 110020, India
Tel.: (91) 11 26359991
E-Mail: info@dfslonline.com
Web Site: www.dfslonline.com
511611—(BOM)
Rev.: $1,199,798
Assets: $13,171,928
Liabilities: $20,063,562
Net Worth: ($6,891,633)
Earnings: $563,783
Emp.: 9
Fiscal Year-end: 03/31/13
Financial Services
S.I.C.: 6211
N.A.I.C.S.: 523999
S. K. Sharma *(Exec Dir)*

DCM SHRIRAM CONSOLIDATED LIMITED

5th Floor Kanchenjunga Building 18 Barakhamba Road
New Delhi, 110001, India
Tel.: (91) 1123316801
Fax: (91) 1123318072
Web Site: www.dscl.com
DCMSRMCONS—(NSE)
Sls.: $1,069,787,664
Assets: $880,865,064
Liabilities: $603,619,758
Net Worth: $277,245,306
Earnings: $37,615,806
Fiscal Year-end: 03/31/13
Business Description:
Fertiliser, Cement & Sugar Mfr
S.I.C.: 2874
N.A.I.C.S.: 325312
Personnel:
Ajay S. Shriram *(Chm & Sr Mng Dir)*

Vikram S. Shriram *(Vice Chm & Mng Dir)*
J. K. Jain *(Pres & CFO)*
Rajesh Gupta *(Pres & Head-Hariyali)*
Anil Kumar *(Pres & Head-Chemicals)*
Sushil Baveja *(Pres & Head-Corp HR)*
Alex Murphy *(Pres & Head-Fenesta Building Sys)*
Rajiv Sinha *(Mng Dir)*
Sharad Sharma *(Pres-Bioseed-South Asia)*
A. K. Awasthi *(CEO-Hydro)*
Ajit S. Shriram *(Deputy Mng Dir)*
B. L. Sachdeva *(Sec)*
Rajat Mukerjei *(Sr VP & Head-Cement Bus)*

Board of Directors:
Ajay S. Shriram
S. S. Baijal
Vimal M. Bhandari
Pradeep Dinodia
Rajesh Kandwal
Sunil Kant Munjal
Arun Bharat Ram
D. Sengupta
Ajit S. Shriram
Vikram S. Shriram
N. J. Singh
Rajiv Sinha

Transfer Agent:
MCS Limited
F-65 1st Floor Okhla Industrial Area Phase-I
New Delhi, India

Subsidiaries:

Bioseed Research India Private Limited (1)
Plot No 206 Road No 14 Jubilee Hills
Hyderabad, 500 033, India
Tel.: (91) 40 23555801
Fax: (91) 40 23555530
E-Mail: bioseedresearch@shrirambioseed.com
Web Site: www.shrirambioseed.com
Emp.: 150
Seed Breeding Services
S.I.C.: 8999
N.A.I.C.S.: 541690

Hariyali Insurance Broking Limited (1)
LGF A - 6 Sector 16
Noida, 201301, India
Tel.: (91) 1203968500
Web Site: www.dscl.com
Insurance Brokerage Services
S.I.C.: 6411
N.A.I.C.S.: 524210
Prakash Sharma *(Mgr)*

Non-U.S. Subsidiaries:

Bioseed Research Philippines Inc (1)
National Highway Katangawan
General Santos, 9500, Philippines
Tel.: (63) 83 552 9305
Fax: (63) 83 552 5870
E-Mail: bioseed@bioseedph.com
Web Site: www.bioseedph.com
Emp.: 28
Hybrid Seed Mfr
S.I.C.: 0119
N.A.I.C.S.: 111199
Rajeev Nayak *(Gen Mgr)*

Bioseed Vietnam Limited (1)
Room No 348 Binh Minh Hotel 27 Ly Thai To Street
Hoan Kiem, Hanoi, 1000, Vietnam
Tel.: (84) 4 39344625
Fax: (84) 4 39344626
E-Mail: bioseedvietnam@shrirambioseed.com
Web Site: www.bioseedvietnam.com
Emp.: 10
Farm Seed Mfr
S.I.C.: 2075
N.A.I.C.S.: 311224

DCM SHRIRAM INDUSTRIES LIMITED

Kanchenjunga Building 6th Floor 18
Barakhamba Road
New Delhi, 110 001, India
Tel.: (91) 1123759300
Fax: (91) 1123350765
E-Mail: dsil@dcmsr.com
Web Site: www.dcmsr.com
Year Founded: 1990
523369—(BOM)
Rev.: $205,698,649
Assets: $174,227,370
Liabilities: $133,686,304
Net Worth: $40,541,066
Earnings: $1,100,386
Emp.: 2,477
Fiscal Year-end: 03/31/13

Business Description:
Sugar Mfr & Distr
S.I.C.: 2061
N.A.I.C.S.: 311314

Personnel:
Tilak Dhar *(Chm & Mng Dir)*
D. C. Mittal *(Pres)*
N. K. Jain *(CFO)*
B. P. Khandelwal *(Compliance Officer, Sec & Sr Exec Dir)*
Anil Gujral *(CEO-Chemicals & Alcohol)*
K. N. Rao *(CEO-Rayons)*
Alok B. Shriram *(Deputy Mng Dir)*
P. V. Bakre *(Sr VP)*

Board of Directors:
Tilak Dhar
V. L. Dutt
Anil Gujral
P. R. Khanna
S. C. Kumar
S. B. Mathur
Ravinder Narain
Alok B. Shriram
Madhav B. Shriram

Transfer Agent:
Karvy Computershare Private Limited
17-24 Vittal Rao Nagar Madhapur
Hyderabad, India

DCON PRODUCTS PUBLIC COMPANY LIMITED

3300/57 Elephant Building Tower B
8th FL Phaholyotin Road Chatujak
Bangkok, 10900, Thailand
Tel.: (66) 2937 3312
Fax: (66) 2937 3328
Web Site: www.dconproduct.com
DCON—(THA)
Sls.: $34,114,981
Assets: $34,406,401
Liabilities: $7,422,994
Net Worth: $26,983,407
Earnings: $4,836,812
Emp.: 200
Fiscal Year-end: 12/31/12

Business Description:
Construction Products Mfr
S.I.C.: 1442
N.A.I.C.S.: 212321

Personnel:
Tortrakul Yomnak *(Chm)*
Dhanit Charinsarn *(Vice Chm)*
Wittawat Pornkul *(CEO)*
Kawin Worakanchana *(Deputy Mng Dir)*

Board of Directors:
Tortrakul Yomnak
Pisamai Boonyakiat
Dhanit Charinsarn
Tanai Charinsarn
Nirut Intratachang
Wittawat Pornkul
Wanchai Tantikul
Chana Towan
Jeeradej Viratchai
Kawin Worakanchana

Subsidiary:

Rompo Products Co. Ltd. (1)
170 Moo 4 Pasak District A Meaung
Lamphun, Thailand
Tel.: (66) 2 937 3312
Fax: (66) 2 937 4337
Flooring Product Mfr & Distr
S.I.C.: 3259
N.A.I.C.S.: 327120

Plants:

DCON Products Public Company Limited - Lopburi Factory 1 (1)
33 Moo 8 Chongsarika
Phattananikom, Lopburi, 15140, Thailand
Tel.: (66) 36 491 484
Construction Materials Mfr
S.I.C.: 3272
N.A.I.C.S.: 327390

DCON Products Public Company Limited - Lopburi Factory 2 (1)
280 Moo 1 Chongsarika
Phattananikom, Lopburi, 15140, Thailand
Tel.: (66) 36 436 500 1
Construction Materials Mfr
S.I.C.: 3272
N.A.I.C.S.: 327390

DCON Products Public Company Limited - Surat Thani Factory (1)
39/3 Moo 7 Natai Sub-District
Baan Nakhem, Surat Thani, 84240, Thailand
Tel.: (66) 81 822 5972
Construction Material Mfr
S.I.C.: 3272
N.A.I.C.S.: 327390

DCT CHAMBERS TRUCKING LTD.

600 Waddington Drive
Vernon, BC, V1T 8T6, Canada
Tel.: (250) 549-2157
Fax: (250) 549-2537
Web Site: www.dctchambers.com
Year Founded: 1964
Rev.: $774,656,542
Emp.: 85

Business Description:
Transportation Services
S.I.C.: 4789
N.A.I.C.S.: 488999

Personnel:
Art Chambers *(Co-Owner)*
David Chambers *(Co-Owner)*
Mona Chambers *(Co-Owner)*

DCW LIMITED

Nirmal 3rd Floor Nariman Point
Mumbai, 400 021, India
Tel.: (91) 2222871914
Fax: (91) 2222028838
E-Mail: ho@dcwltd.com
Web Site: www.dcwltd.com
DCW—(NSE)
Rev.: $266,476,644
Assets: $287,006,431
Liabilities: $189,146,378
Net Worth: $97,860,053
Earnings: $19,446,328
Emp.: 2,174
Fiscal Year-end: 03/31/13

Business Description:
Speciality Chemical Mfr
S.I.C.: 2819
N.A.I.C.S.: 325180

Personnel:
Shashi Chand Jain *(Chm & Co-Mng Dir)*
Malti Bhindi *(Co-Pres)*
Ashish Jain *(Co-Pres)*
Paulomi Jain *(Co-Pres)*
Vivek Jain *(Sr Pres)*
Bakul Jain *(Co-Mng Dir)*
Pramod Jain *(Co-Mng Dir)*
Chital V. Shah *(Compliance Officer & Deputy Sec)*
B. R. Singhvi *(Exec VP-Works)*
S. Ganapathy *(Sr VP-Mktg-PVC)*
Amitabh Gupta *(Sr VP-Mktg)*
Vimal Jain *(Sr VP-Fin)*

Board of Directors:
Shashi Chand Jain
Berjis Desai
Sodhsal Singh Dev
D. Ganapathy
Bakul Jain
Mudit Jain
Pramod Jain
Salil Kapoor
Sujata Rangnekar

Transfer Agent:
Bigshare Services Private Limited
E 2/3 Ansa Industrial Estate Sakivihar Road
Sakinaka Andheri(E)
Mumbai, India

Unit:

DCW Limited - SAHUPURAM UNIT (1)
Arumuganeri
Thiruchendur, 628 229, India
Tel.: (91) 4639 280231
Fax: (91) 4639 280611
E-Mail: office@shpm.dcwltd.com
Petrochemical Mfr
S.I.C.: 2869
N.A.I.C.S.: 325110

DDD LTD.

94 Rickmansworth Rd
Watford, Herts, WD18 7JJ, United Kingdom
Tel.: (44) 1923229251
Telex: 935610
Fax: (44) 220728
Web Site: www.dddgroup.co.uk
Year Founded: 1912
Sales Range: $10-24.9 Million
Emp.: 250

Business Description:
Mfr & Distr of Pharmaceuticals, Toiletries & Household Products
Import Export
S.I.C.: 2834
N.A.I.C.S.: 325412

Personnel:
Sally Ledger *(Mgr-Mktg)*

Subsidiaries:

Dendron Ltd. (1)
94 Rickmansworth Road
Watford, Herts, WD18 7JJ, United Kingdom
Tel.: (44) 1923229251
Fax: (44) 1923220728
Web Site: www.ddd.co.uk
Emp.: 150
Markets, Sells & Distributes Branded OTC Pharmaceutical & Toiletry
S.I.C.: 2834
N.A.I.C.S.: 325412

Fleet Laboratories Inc. (1)
Caxton Court Caxton Way
Watford Business Park, WG1D 8RH
Watford, Herts, United Kingdom
Tel.: (44) 01923229251
Fax: (44) 1923220728
Web Site: www.fleetlabs.co.uk
Emp.: 220
Pharmaceutical & Toiletry Product Mfr
S.I.C.: 2834
N.A.I.C.S.: 325412

DDOR NOVI SAD A.D.

8 Mihajlo Pupin Blvd
21000 Novi Sad, Serbia
Tel.: (381) 214886000
Fax: (381) 216624831
E-Mail: info@ddor.co.yu
Web Site: www.ddor.co.rs
DDNS—(BEL)
Sales Range: $150-199.9 Million
Emp.: 2,054

Business Description:
Insurance & Reinsurance Services
S.I.C.: 6351

DDOR Novi Sad a.d.—(Continued)

N.A.I.C.S.: 524126
Personnel:
Veroljub Dugalic *(Chm)*
Nikola Pavicic *(Chm-Supervisory Bd)*
Christian Otto Neu *(Chm-Exec Bd, Deputy Chm & CEO)*
Jelena Kocovic *(Deputy Chm-Supervisory Bd)*
Darko Botic *(Exec Dir-Special Projects & Deputy Chm-Exec Bd)*
Board of Directors:
Veroljub Dugalic
Miodrag Babic
Giorgio Bedogni
Stefano Carlino
Fausto Marchionni
Christian Otto Neu
Andrea Novarese
Goran Stanivukovic
Supervisory Board of Directors:
Nikola Pavicic
Mario Bellucci
Jelena Kocovic
Marinko Matijevic
Alessandro Nerdi
Tomislav Robotic

DDS, INC.

DDS bldg 7F 3-6-41 Marunouchi
Naka-ku, Nagoya, 460-0002, Japan
Tel.: (81) 52 955 6600
E-Mail: info@dds.co.jp
Web Site: www.dds.co.jp
Year Founded: 1992
3782—(TKS)
Sales Range: $10-24.9 Million
Business Description:
Computer Peripheral Mfr
S.I.C.: 3577
N.A.I.C.S.: 334118
Personnel:
Kenji Miyoshino *(Pres & CEO)*
Board of Directors:
Shigenori Matsushita
Kenji Miyoshino
Wataru Sadakata
Kenichiro Yuki

DDS WIRELESS INTERNATIONAL INC.

11920 Forge Place
Richmond, BC, V7A 4V9, Canada
Tel.: (604) 241-1441
Fax: (604) 241-1440
E-Mail: webmaster@ddswireless.com
Web Site: www.ddswireless.com
Year Founded: 1987
DD—(TSX)
Rev.: $40,426,793
Assets: $36,252,903
Liabilities: $8,641,016
Net Worth: $27,611,888
Earnings: $1,569,558
Emp.: 204
Fiscal Year-end: 12/31/12
Business Description:
Turnkey Wireless Mobile Data Dispatching Systems Focusing on Real-Time Dispatching, Vehicle Location, Tracking, Computerized Routing & Scheduling
S.I.C.: 4812
N.A.I.C.S.: 517210
Personnel:
Vari Ghai *(Chm & CEO)*
Caroline Dunn *(CFO & Sec)*
Raymond D. Fast *(Pres-DDS eFleet Services Inc)*
Matt Scheuing *(Pres-Stratagen Systems Inc)*
Board of Directors:
Vari Ghai
Mark K. Joseph
Heikki Karintaus
James Topham
Salvatore Visca
Transfer Agent:
Computershare Trust Company of Canada
Vancouver, BC, Canada
Tel.: (604) 661-9400
Fax: (604) 669-1548
Subsidiaries:

DDS eFleet Services Inc (1)
11920 Forge Pl
Richmond, BC, Canada
Tel.: (604) 214-7299
Toll Free: (888) 821-9321
E-Mail: customer.service@efleetservices.com
Web Site: www.efleetservices.com
Mobile Software Development Services
S.I.C.: 7371
N.A.I.C.S.: 541511

Digital Dispatch Limited Partnership (1)
11920 Forge Pl
Richmond, BC, V7A 4V9, Canada
Tel.: (604) 241-1441
Fax: (604) 241-1440
E-Mail: sales@digital-dispatch.com
Application Software Development Services
S.I.C.: 7371
N.A.I.C.S.: 541511

DW Digital Wireless Inc (1)
11920 Forge Pl
Richmond, BC, V7A 4V9, Canada
Tel.: (604) 241-1441
Fax: (604) 241-1440
E-Mail: sales@dw-wireless.com
Web Site: www.dw-wireless.com
Communication Equipment Mfr & Distr
S.I.C.: 3669
N.A.I.C.S.: 334290
Markus Pauli *(Pres)*

U.S. Division:

Digital Dispatch Systems Inc - Stratagen Systems Division (1)
4040 Lake Washington Blvd NE Ste 201
Kirkland, WA 98033
Tel.: (425) 821-8454
Fax: (425) 823-6959
Toll Free: (888) 921-6659
E-Mail: info@stratagen.com
Web Site: www.stratagen.com
Emp.: 35
Transportation System Software Development Services
S.I.C.: 7371
N.A.I.C.S.: 541511
Matt Scheuing *(Pres)*
William Ho *(CTO)*

U.S. Subsidiaries:

Digital Dispatch Ltd (1)
14833 W 95th St
Lenexa, KS 66215 (100%)
Tel.: (913) 599-0419
Fax: (913) 599-3918
E-Mail: info@digitaldispatch.com
Web Site: www.digitaldispatch.com
Sales Range: $10-24.9 Million
Emp.: 10
Wireless Mobile Data Services
S.I.C.: 4812
N.A.I.C.S.: 517210
Vari Ghai *(Chm)*

Strategem Digital Dispatch (1)
4040 Lake Washington Blvd NE Ste 201
Kirkland, WA 98033
Tel.: (425) 823-4143
Fax: (425) 823-6959
Toll Free: (888) 921-6695
E-Mail: sales@strategem.com
Web Site: www.strategem.com
Sales Range: $10-24.9 Million
Wireless Mobile Data Services
S.I.C.: 4812
N.A.I.C.S.: 517210
Vari Ghai *(Chm)*

Non-U.S. Subsidiaries:

Digital Dispatch India Pvt. Ltd (1)
215 2nd floor Sikanderpur
Mahatma Gandhi Rd, Gurgaon, Haryana, 122002, India
Tel.: (91) 9810396658
E-Mail: suneetn@airtel.blackberry.com
Web Site: www.ddswireless.com
Sales Range: $1-9.9 Million
Emp.: 2
Wireless Mobile Data Services
S.I.C.: 4812
N.A.I.C.S.: 517210
Vari Ghai *(Chm)*

Digital Dispatch (Intl) Ltd (1)
Bar Hill Business Park
Saxon Way Bar Hill, Cambridge, CB23 8SL, United Kingdom
Tel.: (44) 01954780888
Fax: (44) 1954781612
E-Mail: support@digital-dispatch.com
Web Site: www.digital-dispatch.com
Sales Range: $1-9.9 Million
Emp.: 8
Wireless Mobile Data Services
S.I.C.: 4812
N.A.I.C.S.: 517210
Vari Ghai *(Pres & CEO)*

Non-U.S. Subsidiary:

MobiSoft Oy (2)
Hatanpaan Valtatie 26
33100 Tampere, Finland
Tel.: (358) 20 700 1000
Fax: (358) 20 700 1099
E-Mail: info@mobisoft.fi
Web Site: www.mobisoft.fi
Mobile Data Software Development Services
S.I.C.: 7371
N.A.I.C.S.: 541511

Digital Dispatch (Itl) Pte Ltd (1)
12 Arumugam Rd Lion Building B
Ste 03-12B, Singapore, 409958, Singapore
Tel.: (65) 64551713
Fax: (65) 64550307
E-Mail: lau@digital-dispatch.com
Web Site: www.digital-dispatch.com
Sales Range: $1-9.9 Million
Emp.: 1
Wireless Mobile Data Services
S.I.C.: 4812
N.A.I.C.S.: 517210
Vari Ghai *(Chm)*

Digital Dispatch Scandinavia AB (1)
Radmansgatan 48
SE-113 57 Stockholm, Sweden
Tel.: (46) 86741250
Fax: (46) 86126535
Web Site: www.digitaldespatch.com
Sales Range: $1-9.9 Million
Emp.: 4
Wireless Mobile Data Services
S.I.C.: 4812
N.A.I.C.S.: 517210
Vari Ghai *(Pres & CEO)*

DE AGOSTINI S.P.A.

Via G Da Verrazzano 15
28100 Novara, Italy
Tel.: (39) 238086321
Fax: (39) 0231471286
E-Mail: deagostini@gruppodeagostini.it
Web Site: www.gruppodeagostini.it
Year Founded: 1901
Sales Range: $5-14.9 Billion
Emp.: 6,427
Business Description:
Holding Company; Publishing, Gaming, Media & Finance Services
S.I.C.: 6719
N.A.I.C.S.: 551112
Personnel:
Marco Drago *(Chm)*
Marco Boroli *(Sr Vice Chm)*
Pietro Boroli *(Vice Chm)*
Roberto Drago *(Vice Chm)*
Lorenzo Pellicioli *(CEO)*
Anna Belfiore *(Treas)*
Board of Directors:
Marco Drago
Carlo Ferrari Ardicini
Lino Benassi
Andrea Boroli
Chiara Boroli
Marco Boroli
Paolo Boroli
Pietro Boroli
Giorgio Drago
Roberto Drago
Lorenzo Pellicioli
Paolo Tacchini
Alberto Toffoletto

Subsidiaries:

De Agostini Communications S.p.A (1)
Via G da Verrazano 15
Novara, Italy
Tel.: (39) 0321.4241
Web Site: www.deagostinigroup.com
Sales Range: $700-749.9 Million
Media Content Production, Broadcasting & Distribution
S.I.C.: 7812
N.A.I.C.S.: 512110
Roberto Drago *(Chm)*
Paolo Ceretti *(CEO)*
Laurent Boissel *(CFO)*

Non-U.S. Subsidiaries:

Zodiak Media Group - London (2)
Gloucester Building Kensington Village
Avonmore Road, London, W14 8RF, United Kingdom
Tel.: (44) 2070134000
Fax: (44) 2070134012
E-Mail: contactus@zodiakmedia.com
Web Site: www.zodiakmedia.com
Sales Range: $700-749.9 Million
Emp.: 511
Producer & Distr of Television Shows
S.I.C.: 7812
N.A.I.C.S.: 512110
Philippe Alessandri *(Founder & CEO-Tele Images)*
Marc-Antoine d'Halluin *(Grp CEO)*
Joely Fether *(COO)*
Steve Macallister *(CEO-Zodiak Rights)*
Jonny Slow *(CEO-Americas)*
Tony Yates *(CEO-Zodiak Los Angeles)*
Ingrid Libercier *(Gen Counsel-Tele Images)*
Brent Burnette *(Sr VP-Dev-New York)*
Gladys Morchoisne *(Sr VP-Animation-Tele Images)*
Neil Regan *(Sr VP-New York)*

Subsidiaries:

The Comedy Unit (3)
53 Bothwell St
6th Floor, Glasgow, G2 6TS, United Kingdom
Tel.: (44) 1412206400
E-Mail: info@comedyunit.co.uk
Web Site: www.comedyunit.co.uk
Emp.: 40
Television Show Production Services
S.I.C.: 7812
N.A.I.C.S.: 512110
April Chamberlain *(Mng Dir)*

The Foundation (3)
The Maidstone Studios
New Cut Road, Maidstone, Kent, ME14 5NZ, United Kingdom
Tel.: (44) 1622524053
Web Site: www.foundationtv.co.uk
Emp.: 50
Televison Show Production Services
S.I.C.: 7812
N.A.I.C.S.: 512110

IWC Media (3)
93-97 St George
Glasgow, G3 6JA, United Kingdom
Tel.: (44) 1413533222
Fax: (44) 1413533221
E-Mail: mailglasgow@iwcmedia.co.uk
Web Site: www.iwcmedia.co.uk
Emp.: 50
Television Show Production Services
S.I.C.: 7812
N.A.I.C.S.: 512110
Hamish Barbour *(Mng Dir)*

Presentable Ltd (3)
46 Cardiff Rd
Llandaff, Cardiff, CF5 2DT, United Kingdom
Tel.: (44) 29 2057 5729

Fax: (44) 29 2057 5605
E-Mail: all@presentable.co.uk
Web Site: www.presentable.co.uk
Emp.: 3
Televsion Show Production Services
S.I.C.: 7812
N.A.I.C.S.: 512110
Claire Griffiths *(Office Mgr)*

Touchpaper Television (3)
3-6 Kenrick Place
London, W1U 6HD, United Kingdom
Tel.: (44) 2073172233
Fax: (44) 2073172232
E-Mail: info@touchpapertv.com
Web Site: www.touchpapertv.com
Emp.: 6
Televion Show Production Services
S.I.C.: 7812
N.A.I.C.S.: 512110
Rob Pursey *(Mng Dir)*

Non-U.S. Subsidiaries:

Magnolia Italy (3)
Via Deruta 20
20132 Milan, Italy
Tel.: (39) 06 367 751
Fax: (39) 02 28187292
Web Site: www.magnoliatv.it
Television Program Production Services
S.I.C.: 4833
N.A.I.C.S.: 515120
Antonello Perricone *(Pres)*
Ilaria Dallatana *(CEO)*

Zodiak Television AB (3)
Magasin 1
Box 27034
Frihamnen, 102 51 Stockholm, Sweden
Tel.: (46) 850307700
Fax: (46) 850307701
E-Mail: info@zodiaktelevision.se
Web Site: www.zodiaktelevision.se
Sales Range: $50-74.9 Million
Emp.: 200
TV Programs Developer, Producer & Seller
S.I.C.: 4833
N.A.I.C.S.: 515120
Mikael Wallen *(VP-Scripted Programming & CEO)*
Lars Schedin *(CFO)*

Subsidiaries:

Jarowskij Sweden (4)
Magasin 1
Box 27034
Frihamnen, 10251 Stockholm, Sweden
Tel.: (46) 850307700
Fax: (46) 850307701
E-Mail: info@jarowskij.se
Web Site: www.jarowskij.se
Emp.: 100
Television Production Company
S.I.C.: 7812
N.A.I.C.S.: 512110
Johannes Jensen *(Gen Mgr)*

Mastiff Sweden (4)
Magasin 1
PO Box 27034
Frihamnen, 10251 Stockholm, Sweden
Tel.: (46) 852727000
Fax: (46) 850307701
E-Mail: info@mastiff.se
Web Site: www.mastiff.se
Emp.: 150
Television Production
S.I.C.: 4833
N.A.I.C.S.: 515120
Johannes Jensen *(VP)*

Non-U.S. Subsidiaries:

Mastiff Media (4)
Vermundsgade 40D
2100 Copenhagen, Denmark
Tel.: (45) 35550550
Fax: (45) 35552554
E-Mail: mail@mastifftv.dk
Web Site: www.mastifftv.dk
Emp.: 100
Television Production
S.I.C.: 7812
N.A.I.C.S.: 512110
Mads Ulrick *(Gen Mgr)*

Zodiak Television Finland Oy (4)
PO Box 28
00241 Helsinki, Finland
Tel.: (358) 207533000
Fax: (358) 207533001
Web Site: www.broadcasters.fi
Emp.: 20
Television Production
S.I.C.: 4833
N.A.I.C.S.: 515120
Teea Hyytia *(Mng Dir)*
Jaana Besmond *(Exec VP)*

Zodiak Media Group - Paris (2)
8 Boulevard des Capucines
75009 Paris, France
Tel.: (33) 1 53 10 70 21
Fax: (33) 1 53 10 94 50
E-Mail: contactus@zodiakmedia.com
Web Site: www.zodiakmedia.com
Sales Range: $500-549.9 Million
Media Content Production Services
S.I.C.: 7812
N.A.I.C.S.: 512110

De Agostini Editore S.p.A. (1)
via G da Verrazano 15
28100 Novara, Italy
Tel.: (39) 03214241
Fax: (39) 0321471286
Web Site: www.deagostinieditore.com
Book, Periodical & Multimedia Publishing
S.I.C.: 2731
N.A.I.C.S.: 511130
Pietro Boroli *(Chm)*
Paolo Boroli *(Vice Chm)*
Giorgio Drago *(Vice Chm)*
Stefano Di Bella *(Mng Dir)*

Non-U.S. Subsidiaries:

Editions Atlas (France) S.A.S. (2)
89 Rue La Boetie
75008 Paris, France (100%)
Tel.: (33) 0140743838
Fax: (33) 145611985
Web Site: www.editionsatlas.fr
Emp.: 200
Publishing & Communications
S.I.C.: 2731
N.A.I.C.S.: 511130
Oliver Ezard *(Pres)*
Joel LeBihan *(Mng Dir-Fin)*

Editorial Planeta de Agostini, SA (2)
Avenida Diagonal 662
Barcelona, 08034, Spain
Tel.: (34) 933440600
Fax: (34) 932000504
Web Site: www.planetadeagostini.es
Emp.: 200
Printing & Publishing
S.I.C.: 2731
N.A.I.C.S.: 511130
Carlos Fernandez Sanchiz *(CEO)*

Non-U.S. Subsidiary:

Editis S.A. (3)
26 Ave Des Chaqmps Elysees
75383 Paris, Cedex, 08, France FR
Tel.: (33) 0153533000
Fax: (33) 0153533737
E-Mail: aurelie.legeai@editis.com
Web Site: www.editis.com
Sales Range: $1-4.9 Billion
Emp.: 2,400
Trade, Education & Reference Books & Periodicals Publisher
S.I.C.: 2731
N.A.I.C.S.: 511130
Alain Kouck *(Chm & CEO)*

Subsidiaries:

Editions Bordas (4)
25 avenue Pierre de Coubertin
75211 Paris, Cedex 13, France
Tel.: (33) 153552627
Web Site: www.editions-bordas.com
Emp.: 100
Educational Texts & Reference Material Publisher
S.I.C.: 2731
N.A.I.C.S.: 511130

Editions Nathan (4)
25 Avenue Pierre de Coubertin
75211 Paris, Cedex 13, France
Tel.: (33) 53552662
Telex: Nataned 204525 F
Fax: (33) 45875343
Web Site: www.nathan.fr
Emp.: 100
Educational Book Publisher
S.I.C.: 2731
N.A.I.C.S.: 511130

Non-U.S. Subsidiary:

Interforum Canada Inc. (4)
1055 bld Rene Levesque Est Bureau 1100
Montreal, QC, H2L 4S5, Canada QC
Tel.: (514) 281-1050 (100%)
Fax: (514) 281-8413
Web Site: www.interforumcanadapresse.qc.ca
Emp.: 10
Publisher
S.I.C.: 2741
N.A.I.C.S.: 511199
Nycole Bisjareims *(Gen Dir)*

DeA Capital SpA (1)
Via Brera 21
20121 Milan, Italy (51%)
Tel.: (39) 026249951
Fax: (39) 0262499599
E-Mail: info@deacapital.it
Web Site: www.deacapital.it
DEA—(ITA)
Rev.: $19,320,232
Assets: $1,517,845,714
Liabilities: $360,883,946
Net Worth: $1,156,961,768
Earnings: ($24,512,410)
Emp.: 207
Fiscal Year-end: 12/31/12
Equity Investment Services
S.I.C.: 6211
N.A.I.C.S.: 523999
Lorenzo Pellicioli *(Chm)*
Paolo Ceretti *(CEO)*
Manolo Santilli *(CFO)*

GTECH S.p.A. (1)
(Formerly Lottomatica Group S.p.A.)
Viale del Campo Boario 56/D
00154 Rome, Italy IT
Tel.: (39) 06518891 (53.7%)
Fax: (39) 0651894205
E-Mail:
Web Site: www.gtech.com
GTK—(ITA)
Rev.: $4,140,394,876
Assets: $9,796,136,975
Liabilities: $6,239,199,100
Net Worth: $3,556,937,875
Earnings: $357,037,938
Emp.: 8,582
Fiscal Year-end: 12/31/12
Gaming Operator & Lottery & Gambling Technology Developer
S.I.C.: 7999
N.A.I.C.S.: 713290
Lorenzo Pellicioli *(Chm)*
Marco Sala *(CEO)*
Tim Simonson *(CEO-Northstar Illinois)*

U.S. Subsidiary:

GTECH Corporation (2)
10 Memorial Blvd
Providence, RI 02903 DE
Tel.: (401) 392-1000 (100%)
Fax: (401) 392-1234
E-Mail: info@gtech.com
Web Site: www.gtech.com
Sales Range: $1-4.9 Billion
Emp.: 5,300
Gaming System Technology & Software Developer
Import Export
S.I.C.: 7371
N.A.I.C.S.: 541511
Donald R. Sweitzer *(Chm)*
Jaymin B. Patel *(Pres & CEO)*
Alan Eland *(COO & Sr VP)*
Cornelia Laverty O'Connor *(CMO & Sr VP)*
Matthew Whalen *(CTO & Sr VP)*
Stefano Bortoli *(CFO-Lottomatica Grp & Sr VP)*
Declan Harkin *(COO-GTECH Intl & Sr VP)*
Michael K. Prescott *(Gen Counsel, Sec & Sr VP)*
Fabio Celadon *(Sr VP-Strategic Plng)*
Ross Dalton *(Sr VP)*
Robert Vincent *(Sr VP-Corp Affairs)*

Subsidiaries:

Atronic Americas, LLC (3)
17550 N Perimeter Dr Ste 360
Scottsdale, AZ 85255-7838
Tel.: (480) 922-0707
Fax: (480) 922-8877
Toll Free: (800) 864-7670
E-Mail: Marketing@atronic.com
Web Site: www.atronic.com
Sls.: $38,538,296
Emp.: 200
Casino Gaming Machine Developer & Mfr
S.I.C.: 7999
N.A.I.C.S.: 713290
Ken Bossingham *(COO)*

GTECH Latin America Corporation (3)
55 Technology Way
West Greenwich, RI 02817
Tel.: (401) 392-1000
Fax: (401) 392-1234
E-Mail: info@gtech.com
Web Site: www.gtech.com
Emp.: 300
Holding Company
S.I.C.: 6719
N.A.I.C.S.: 551112
Christopher Caldwell *(Sr VP-Latin America & Caribbean)*

GTECH Printing Corporation (3)
4100 S Frontage Rd
Lakeland, FL 33815
Tel.: (863) 248-1300
Fax: (813) 659-4800
Web Site: www.gtech.com
Emp.: 50
Ticket Design & Printing Technology Services
S.I.C.: 2759
N.A.I.C.S.: 323111
Ross Dalton *(Sr VP-Printed Products & Licensed Content)*

Non-U.S. Subsidiaries:

Atronic Australia Pty Ltd (3)
3 186 York Street
Melbourne, VIC, Australia
Tel.: (61) 3 9686 1226
Fax: (61) 3 9686 9338
Casino Gaming System Developer & Mfr
S.I.C.: 7999
N.A.I.C.S.: 713290

Atronic Russia, LLC (3)
4 Building 4
Bolshoy Savvinsky Pereulok, Moscow, Russia
Tel.: (7) 495 737 7299
Fax: (7) 495 737 7299
Web Site: www.atronic.com
Casino Gaming System Developer & Mfr
S.I.C.: 7999
N.A.I.C.S.: 713290

Finsoft Ltd. (3)
70 Chancery Ln
London, WC2A 1AF, United Kingdom
Tel.: (44) 2073696800
Fax: (44) 2073696808
Web Site: www.gtechg2.com
Emp.: 70
Gambling Transaction Processing Services
S.I.C.: 6099
N.A.I.C.S.: 522320
Predrag Popovic *(Mng Dir)*

GEMed AB (3)
Honnorsgatan 2
352 36 Vaxjo, Sweden (87.5%)
Tel.: (46) 470 70 30 00
Holding Company
S.I.C.: 6719
N.A.I.C.S.: 551112

Holding:

Boss Media AB (4)
Honnorsgatan 2
PO Box 3243
350 53 Vaxjo, Sweden
Tel.: (46) 470703000
Fax: (46) 470703050
E-Mail: info@bossmedia.se
Web Site: www.bossmedia.se
Sales Range: $25-49.9 Million
Emp.: 203
e-Gaming Software Solutions
S.I.C.: 5045
N.A.I.C.S.: 423430
Michael Telfer *(Mgr-Sls)*

De Agostini S.p.A.—(Continued)

GTECH Australasia (3)
Level 6 26 OConnel St
Sydney, NSW, 2000, Australia
Tel.: (61) 292230000
Fax: (61) 292234160
Web Site: www.gtech.com
Emp.: 12
Developer & Marketer of Gaming Technology & Software
S.I.C.: 7999
N.A.I.C.S.: 713290

GTECH Europe (3)
Terhulpsesteenweg 6D
B 1560 Hoeilaart, Limburg, Belgium
Tel.: (32) 26781311
Fax: (32) 26781345
E-Mail: info@gtech.com
Web Site: www.gtech.com
Sls.: $11,322,837
Emp.: 53
Developer & Marketer of Gaming Technology & Software
S.I.C.: 7999
N.A.I.C.S.: 713290

GTECH Polska Sp.z o.o. (3)
Ul Ksl Klopotowskiego 5
00 807 Warsaw, Poland PL
Tel.: (48) 223366999 (100%)
Fax: (48) 223366900
E-Mail: Jack.Kierat@gtech.com
Web Site: www.gtech.com
Sales Range: $75-99.9 Million
Emp.: 100
Gaming System Technology & Software Developer
S.I.C.: 7999
N.A.I.C.S.: 713290
Kierat Jacek *(Mng Dir)*

GTECH Southern Africa (Pty) Ltd (3)
21st Fl Radio Park Bldg Henley Rd
Sandton, Auckland, 2092, South Africa
Tel.: (27) 117153100
Web Site: www.gtech.com
Emp.: 19
Developer & Marketer of Gaming Technology & Software
S.I.C.: 7999
N.A.I.C.S.: 713290

IGI Europrint (3)
Lancaster House
52 Preston New Road, Blackburn, Lancashire, BB2 6AH, United Kingdom
Tel.: (44) 1254588400
Fax: (44) 1254588401
E-Mail: andew.gray@gtech.com
Web Site: www.europrint-group.com
Emp.: 40
Developer of Interactive & Promotional Games
S.I.C.: 8742
N.A.I.C.S.: 541613
Andrew P. Gray *(Mng Dir)*

SPIELO International Argentina S.R.L. (3)
Soler 5692 3 Of 302
CP 1425 Buenos Aires, Argentina
Tel.: (54) 11 4312 1222
Fax: (54) 11 4312 1222
Casino Gaming Equipment Mfr
S.I.C.: 7999
N.A.I.C.S.: 713290

SPIELO International Austria GmbH (3)
(Formerly Atronic Austria GmbH)
Am Seering 13-14
8141 Unterpremstatten, Austria
Tel.: (43) 3135 55880
Fax: (43) 3135 55880192
E-Mail: info@spielo.om
Web Site: www.spielo.com
Emp.: 175
Casino Gaming System Developer & Mfr
S.I.C.: 7999
N.A.I.C.S.: 713290

SPIELO International Canada ULC (3)
328 Urquhart Avenue
Moncton, NB, E1H 2R6, Canada
Tel.: (506) 859-7598
Fax: (502) 878-6053
Toll Free: (800) 878-6000
Web Site: www.spielo.com
Emp.: 500
Casino Game Mfr
S.I.C.: 7999
N.A.I.C.S.: 713290
Cindy Hovey *(Sr Dir-Mktg Dev)*

SPIELO International Germany GmbH (3)
(Formerly Atronic International GmbH)
Borsigstrasse 22
32312 Lubeck, Germany
Tel.: (49) 5741 24099950
Fax: (49) 5741 24099951
E-Mail:
Web Site: www.spielo.com
Sales Range: $200-249.9 Million
Emp.: 600
Casino Gaming Machine Developer & Mfr
S.I.C.: 7999
N.A.I.C.S.: 713290
Walter Bugno *(Pres & CEO)*
Lavaz Watson *(CFO & VP)*
Victor Duarte *(COO & Sr VP)*

SPIELO International Monaco S.A.M. (3)
(Formerly Atronic Systems SAM)
7 rue du Gabian Office No 822
98000 Monaco, Monaco
Tel.: (377) 92056805
Fax: (377) 92056806
Web Site: www.spielo.com
Emp.: 60
Casino Gaming System Mfr
S.I.C.: 7999
N.A.I.C.S.: 713290
Walter Bugno *(CEO)*

SPIELO International Peru S.A. (3)
(Formerly Atronic Peru S.A.)
Manuel Olguin 501 Office 1001
Monterrico-Surco, Lima, Peru
Tel.: (51) 16183200
Fax: (51) 16183201
Emp.: 30
Casino Gaming System Developer & Mfr
S.I.C.: 7999
N.A.I.C.S.: 713290

St Minver Ltd. (3)
Ste 812 Europort
Gibraltar, Gibraltar
Tel.: (350) 20049552
E-Mail: marketing@stminverltd.com
Web Site: www.stminverltd.com
Online Gambling Services
S.I.C.: 7999
N.A.I.C.S.: 713290
Gary Shaw *(Chm)*
Gail Gleed *(CFO)*

DE&T CO., LTD.

200 Jangsan Li Soosin Myun
Cheonan
330882 Ch'ung-Nam, Korea (South)
Tel.: (82) 415293456
Fax: (82) 415293599
E-Mail: baekee@i-det.com
Web Site: www.i-det.com
079810—(KRS)
Sales Range: $25-49.9 Million
Emp.: 150

Business Description:
Flat Display Panel Mfr
S.I.C.: 3663
N.A.I.C.S.: 334220

Personnel:
Chang Hyun Park *(CEO)*

DE BEERS GROUP OF COMPANIES

9 Rue St Vithe
2763 Luxembourg, Luxembourg
Tel.: (352) 4025051
Fax: (352) 264871303
E-Mail: info@debeersgroup.com
Web Site: www.debeersgroup.com
Year Founded: 1888
Sales Range: $1-4.9 Billion
Emp.: 11

Business Description:
Holding Company
S.I.C.: 6719
N.A.I.C.S.: 551112

Personnel:
Mark Cutifani *(Chm)*
Phillipe Mellier *(CEO)*
Oliver Bernard *(Mng Dir)*
Varda Shine *(Mng Dir)*
Gareth Mostyn *(CFO)*

Board of Directors:
Mark Cutifani
Bruce Cleaver
Kahijoro Kahuure
Rene Medori
Phillipe Mellier
Gareth Mostyn
Boikobo B. Paya
Barend Petersen
Solomon Sekwakwa
Mervyn Walker
Peter Whitcutt

Subsidiary:

Element Six S.A. (1)
rue Sainte Zithe
L 2763 Luxembourg, Luxembourg
Tel.: (352) 26 940 590
Fax: (352) 26 940 300
Diamond Supermaterial Mfr
S.I.C.: 5085
N.A.I.C.S.: 423840
Jonathan M.E. Oppenheimer *(Chm)*
Cyrus Jilla *(CEO)*
Jonathan Aitken *(CFO)*

U.S. Subsidiary:

Element Six U.S. Corporation (2)
35 W 45th St
New York, NY 10036
Tel.: (212) 869-5155
Fax: (212) 764-0349
E-Mail: USAdvancedMaterials@e6.com
Emp.: 8
Industrial Supplies Merchant Whslr
S.I.C.: 5085
N.A.I.C.S.: 423840
Joseph Connolly *(Gen Mgr)*

Non-U.S. Subsidiaries:

De Beers Canada (1)
900-250 Ferrand Drive
Toronto, ON, M3C 3G8, Canada
Tel.: (416) 645-1710
Fax: (416) 429-2462
E-Mail: info@debeerscanada.com
Web Site: www.debeerscanada.com
Diamond Mining
S.I.C.: 1499
N.A.I.C.S.: 212399
Tony Guthrie *(CEO)*

De Beers Consolidated Mines Limited (1)
Private Bag X01
Southdale, 2135, South Africa ZA
Tel.: (27) 113747000 (100%)
Fax: (27) 113747700
E-Mail: info@debeersgroup.com
Web Site: www.debeersgroup.com
Emp.: 500
Miner & Marketer of Gem & Industrial Diamonds; Mfr & Marketer of Synthetic Diamonds & Related Hard Materials for Use in Industry
Export
S.I.C.: 1429
N.A.I.C.S.: 212319
Barend Petersen *(Chm)*
Manne Dipico *(Deputy Chm)*
Philip Barton *(CEO)*
Gareth Mostyn *(CFO)*

Diamond Trading Company (1)
17 Charterhouse Street
London, EC1N 6RA, United Kingdom
Tel.: (44) 2074044444
Fax: (44) 2078310663
Web Site: www.debeersgroup.com
Emp.: 900
Gem & Industrial Diamonds Marketing
S.I.C.: 5085
N.A.I.C.S.: 423840
Nicholas F. Oppenheimer *(Chm)*
Varda Shine *(Mng Dir)*

DE BOERTIEN GROEP B.V.

Scheepmakerij 320
3331 MC Zwijndrecht, Netherlands
Tel.: (31) 786841800
Fax: (31) 786196676
E-Mail: mail@boertiengroep.nl
Web Site: www.boertiengroep.nl
Sales Range: $25-49.9 Million
Emp.: 220

Business Description:
Holding Company
S.I.C.: 6719
N.A.I.C.S.: 551112

Personnel:
Xander Ferdinadusse *(CEO)*

DE CONSTRUCTII NAPOCA S.A.

(d/b/a Napoca)
Str Taberei Nr 4
Cluj-Napoca, Romania
Tel.: (40) 264425860
Fax: (40) 264425053
E-Mail: sccnapoca@sccnapoca.ro
Web Site: sccnapoca.ro
NAPO—(BUC)
Sales Range: $1-9.9 Million
Emp.: 270

Business Description:
Building Construction
S.I.C.: 1542
N.A.I.C.S.: 236220

Personnel:
Stefan Dimitriu *(Chm & Gen Dir)*

DE DIETRICH PROCESS SYSTEMS S.A.

Rue de la Fonderie
BP 8
F-67110 Zinswiller, France
Tel.: (33) 388532300
Fax: (33) 388532399
E-Mail: sales@dedietrich.com
Web Site: www.dedietrichddz.com
Year Founded: 1684
Sales Range: $400-449.9 Million
Emp.: 3,400

Business Description:
Railways, Heating Equipment, Chemical Equipment & Sundries Mfr
S.I.C.: 3433
N.A.I.C.S.: 333414

Personnel:
Daniel Steck *(CEO)*

Unit:

De Dietrich Process Systems S.A.-Courcouronnes Site (1)
8 -10 Ruaduboissaugaga
91055 Evry, France
Tel.: (33) 169470400
Fax: (33) 169470410
E-Mail: eivs@dedietrich.com
Web Site: www.dedietrichddz.com
Emp.: 13
Industrial Supplies Whslr
S.I.C.: 5085
N.A.I.C.S.: 423840
Christian Jiraugon *(Mng Dir)*

U.S. Subsidiary:

De Dietrich Process Systems, Inc. (1)
244 Sheffield St
Mountainside, NJ 07092 NJ
Tel.: (908) 317-2585
Fax: (908) 889-4960
Web Site: www.ddpsinc.com
Rev.: $14,100,000
Emp.: 90
Mfr. of Glass Lined Vessels
S.I.C.: 3559
N.A.I.C.S.: 333249

Don Doell *(Pres & CEO)*
Helen Wilson *(CFO)*

Subsidiary:

De Dietrich Process Systems-Rosenmund Division (2)
9110 Forsyth Park Dr
Charlotte, NC 28273-3881
Tel.: (704) 587-0440
Fax: (704) 588-6866
Web Site: www.ddpsinc.com
Emp.: 20
Mfr. of General Line Industrial Filters
S.I.C.: 3569
N.A.I.C.S.: 333999

Non-U.S. Subsidiaries:

De Dietrich Do Brasil Ltda (1)
Rua Costa Barros n 3000
Vila Alpina, 03210-001 Sao Paulo, SP, Brazil
Tel.: (55) 1127037380
Fax: (55) 1127024284
E-Mail: brasil@dedietrich.com.br
Web Site: www.dedietrichddz.com
Industrial Machinery & Equipment Whslr
S.I.C.: 5084
N.A.I.C.S.: 423830
Flavia Nascimento *(Controller)*

De Dietrich Equipos Quimicos SL (1)
Av Princep dAsturies 43-45-1 5a
8012 Barcelona, Spain
Tel.: (34) 932188613
Fax: (34) 932184709
E-Mail: comercial@dedietrich.es
Web Site: www.dedietrich.es
Emp.: 25
Industrial Machinery & Equipment Whslr
S.I.C.: 5084
N.A.I.C.S.: 423830
Albert Pujol *(Mng Dir)*

De Dietrich Process Systems Ireland Ltd. (1)
Unit 4D Western Bus Pk
Shannon, Ireland
Tel.: (353) 61366925
Fax: (353) 61366854
Web Site: www.dietrich.com
Emp.: 3
Electrical Apparatus & Equipment Wiring Supplies & Construction Material Whslr
S.I.C.: 5063
N.A.I.C.S.: 423610
Martin Corner *(Mng Dir)*

De Dietrich Singapore (Pte) Ltd. (1)
20 Bukit Batok Crescent #03-05, Enterprise Ctr
Singapore, 658080, Singapore
Tel.: (65) 68611232
Fax: (65) 68616112
E-Mail: dedietrichdds@pacific.net.sg
Web Site: www.dedietrich.com
Emp.: 7
Surgical & Medical Instrument Mfr
S.I.C.: 3841
N.A.I.C.S.: 339112
Allan Ong *(Gen Mgr)*

De Dietrich South Africa (Pty) Ltd. (1)
PO Box 6245
1508 Johannesburg, South Africa
Tel.: (27) 119184131
Fax: (27) 119184133
E-Mail: ddsa@iafrica.com
Web Site: www.dietrich.com
Emp.: 11
Surgical & Medical Instrument Mfr
S.I.C.: 3841
N.A.I.C.S.: 339112

QVF Engineering GmbH (1)
Hattenbergstrasse 36
55122 Mainz, Germany
Tel.: (49) 613197040
Fax: (49) 319704500
E-Mail: mail@qvf.de
Web Site: www.qvf.com
Emp.: 260
Industrial Machinery Mfr
S.I.C.: 3559
N.A.I.C.S.: 333249
Manfred Pertlea *(Mgr-Sls)*

QVF Process Systems Ltd. (1)
Tollgate Drive
Tollgate Industrial Estate, Stafford, ST16 3HS, United Kingdom
Tel.: (44) 1785609900
Fax: (44) 1785609899
E-Mail: sales@qvf.co.uk
Web Site: www.qvf.co.uk/contactus.htm
Industrial Machinery Mfr
S.I.C.: 3559
N.A.I.C.S.: 333249

DE GOUDSE N.V.

Bouwmeesterplein 1
2801 BX Gouda, Netherlands
Tel.: (31) 182544544
Fax: (31) 0182544899
E-Mail: info@goudse.com
Web Site: www.goudse.nl
Year Founded: 1924
Emp.: 800
Business Description:
Insurance Services
S.I.C.: 6411
N.A.I.C.S.: 524298
Personnel:
G. W. Bouwmeester *(Dir-Special Distr)*
Subsidiary:

Algemene Zeeuwse Verzekering Maatschappij N.V. (1)
Houtkaai 11
4331 JR Middelburg, Netherlands (100%)
Mailing Address:
P.O. Box 50
4330 AB Middelburg, Netherlands
Tel.: (31) 118683300
Fax: (31) 118683399
E-Mail: info@algemenezeeuwse.nl
Web Site: www.algemenezeeuwse.nl
Emp.: 35
S.I.C.: 6141
N.A.I.C.S.: 522210
Aan Kole *(Mgr-Admin)*

DE GREY MINING LIMITED

Suite 4 100 Hay Street
PO Box 8289
Subiaco, WA, 6008, Australia
Tel.: (61) 892857500
Fax: (61) 892857599
E-Mail: frontdesk@degreymining.com.au
Web Site: www.degreymining.com.au
DEG—(ASX)
Rev.: $41,772
Assets: $390,160
Liabilities: $304,157
Net Worth: $86,003
Earnings: ($3,948,944)
Emp.: 5
Fiscal Year-end: 06/30/13
Business Description:
Mineral Exploration
S.I.C.: 1481
N.A.I.C.S.: 213115
Personnel:
Peter Batten *(Chm)*
Craig Nelmes *(Sec)*
Board of Directors:
Peter Batten
Darren Townsend
Simon Lill
Legal Counsel:
William & Hughes
25 Richardson St
Perth, Australia

DE GRISOGONO SA

Route de Saint Julien 176 bis
CH 1228 Plan-les-Ouates, Switzerland
Tel.: (41) 228178100
Fax: (41) 228178188
E-Mail: info@degrisogono.com
Web Site: www.degrisogono.com
Year Founded: 1995
Sales Range: $100-124.9 Million
Emp.: 160
Business Description:
Watch & Jewelry Mfr
S.I.C.: 3829
N.A.I.C.S.: 334519
Personnel:
Fawaz Gruosi *(Founder & Pres)*

DE LA RUE PLC

Jays Close Viables
Basingstoke, Hampshire, RG22 4BS, United Kingdom
Tel.: (44) 1256605000
Fax: (44) 1256605004
E-Mail: group.communications@uk.delarue.com
Web Site: www.delarue.com
Year Founded: 1813
DLAR—(LSE)
Rev.: $763,902,573
Assets: $701,046,831
Liabilities: $806,227,545
Net Worth: ($105,180,714)
Earnings: $69,646,689
Emp.: 3,953
Fiscal Year-end: 03/31/13
Business Description:
Mfr of Currency Paper, Secure Printed Products & Cash Handling Equipment
Import Export
S.I.C.: 2759
N.A.I.C.S.: 323111
Personnel:
Edward Peppiatt *(Gen Counsel & Sec)*
Board of Directors:
Philip Rogerson
Colin Child
Victoria Jarman
Gill Rider
Andrew J. Stevens

Division:

De La Rue Security Products (1)
De La Rue House Jays Close
Viables, Basingstoke, Hants, RG22 4BS, United Kingdom UK
Tel.: (44) 256605000 (100%)
Telex: 858621 DELARU G
Fax: (44) 256605004
Web Site: www.delarue.com
Emp.: 300
Security Printers
S.I.C.: 2759
N.A.I.C.S.: 323111

Subsidiaries:

De La Rue Currency (Divisional Engineering Unit) (2)
Kingsway S Team Vly Trading Est
Gateshead, NE11 0SQ, United Kingdom (100%)
Tel.: (44) 1914958000
Fax: (44) 1914958001
E-Mail: info@delarue.com
Emp.: 100
Security Printing Equipment Mfr
S.I.C.: 3555
N.A.I.C.S.: 333244
David Deacon *(Mgr)*

De La Rue Security Papers (2)
Bathford Mill
Bath, Avon, BA1 7QG, United Kingdom (100%)
Tel.: (44) 1225859903
Fax: (44) 1225852128
E-Mail: andrew.nash@uk.delarue.com
Web Site: www.delarue.com
Emp.: 80
Mfr of Cotton-Based Banknote Security Papers
S.I.C.: 7382
N.A.I.C.S.: 561621
Andrew Nash *(Gen Mgr)*

De La Rue Security Products (2)
Frenchs Ave
Dunstable, Beds, LU6 1BJ, United Kingdom (100%)
Tel.: (44) 1582679600
Telex: 82438 RUEDUN G
Fax: (44) 1582471132
Emp.: 200
Security Printers
S.I.C.: 2759
N.A.I.C.S.: 323111

De La Rue Security Products (2)
Padholme Rd E
Peterborough, PE1 5XL, United Kingdom (100%)
Tel.: (44) 1733564164
Fax: (44) 1733342499
Web Site: www.delarue.com
Emp.: 145
Security Printers
S.I.C.: 2759
N.A.I.C.S.: 323111

Portals Limited (2)
Overton Mill
Overton, Basingstoke, Hampshire, RG25 3JG, United Kingdom (100%)
Tel.: (44) 1256771990
Telex: 858217
Fax: (44) 1256771738
Web Site: www.delarue.com
Emp.: 700
Mfr. of Cotton-Based Banknote Paper
S.I.C.: 2621
N.A.I.C.S.: 322122

U.S. Subsidiary:

De La Rue Security Print Inc. (2)
100 Powers Ct
Dulles, VA 20166-9321 (100%)
Tel.: (703) 450-1300
Fax: (703) 450-1308
E-Mail: info@delarue.com
Web Site: www.delarue.com
Emp.: 100
Security Printers
S.I.C.: 2759
N.A.I.C.S.: 323111
Tom Santoliquido *(CFO)*

Non-U.S. Subsidiaries:

De La Rue Currency and Security Print Limited (2)
Noordin Rd Off Thika Rd
PO Box 38622
Ruaraka, Nairobi, Kenya (100%)
Tel.: (254) 2860086
Fax: (254) 2860787
Web Site: www.delarue.com
Emp.: 250
Security Printers
S.I.C.: 2759
N.A.I.C.S.: 323111

De La Rue Currency and Security Print (2)
Villa 2178 Road 2755
Adliya, 327, Bahrain
Tel.: (973) 712667
Fax: (973) 717159
Security Printers
S.I.C.: 2759
N.A.I.C.S.: 323111

De La Rue Currency And Security Print (2)
B40 43 Bulebel Industrial Estate
Zejtun, ZTN 3000, Malta (100%)
Tel.: (356) 21693757
Telex: 1358 DELARU MW
Fax: (356) 21693775
E-Mail: mail.malta@mtdelarue.com
Web Site: www.mtdelarue.com
Rev.: $120,000,000
Emp.: 500
Security Printers
S.I.C.: 2759
N.A.I.C.S.: 323111
Mark Jordan *(Gen Mgr)*

De La Rue Ltd. (2)
Hedwig Van Steenhuyze House
Seatown Business Campus, Swords, Co Dublin, Ireland
Tel.: (353) 18907707
Fax: (353) 18907708

De La Rue plc—(Continued)

E-Mail: jackie.ocanna@ie.delarue.com
Web Site: www.delarue.com
Emp.: 20
Cash Handling Equipment Mfr
S.I.C.: 3589
N.A.I.C.S.: 333318
Jackie Ocanna *(Office Mgr)*

De La Rue Malaysia Sdn. Bhd. (2)
3rd Fl Wisma Able Match
Lot 271 Jalan Dua
Off Jalan Chan Sow Lin, 55200 Kuala Lumpur, Malaysia (100%)
Tel.: (60) 392210952
Fax: (60) 392210941
Web Site: www.delarue.com
Emp.: 12
Security Printers
S.I.C.: 2759
N.A.I.C.S.: 323111
Ghansyam Dass *(Reg Dir)*

De La Rue Smurfit Limited (2)
Pinewood Close Boghall Rd
Bray, Co Wicklow, Ireland (50%)
Tel.: (353) 012768600
Fax: (353) 12768666
E-Mail: info@smurfitkappa.ie
Web Site: www.smurfitkappa.ie
Emp.: 100
Security Printers
S.I.C.: 2759
N.A.I.C.S.: 323111
Tom Omahony *(Mng Dir)*

Subsidiaries:

De La Rue Holdings plc (1)
De La Rue House Jays Close
Basingstoke, Hants, RG22 4BS, United Kingdom
Tel.: (44) 1256 329122
Fax: (44) 1256 605004
E-Mail: group.communication@uk.delarue.com
Emp.: 450
Investment Management Services
S.I.C.: 6211
N.A.I.C.S.: 523999

De La Rue International Limited (1)
Frenchs Avenue
Dunstable, Bedfordshire, LU6 1BJ, United Kingdom
Tel.: (44) 1582679600
Fax: (44) 1582471132
Emp.: 70
Commercial Printing Services
S.I.C.: 2759
N.A.I.C.S.: 323111
Louis Benton *(Gen Mgr)*

U.S. Subsidiary:

De La Rue North America Inc. (1)
6401 Commerce Dr
Irving, TX 75063
Tel.: (972) 582-1100
Fax: (972) 580-9072
Web Site: www.delarue.com
Financial Transaction Processing Services
S.I.C.: 6099
N.A.I.C.S.: 522320

Non-U.S. Subsidiaries:

De La Rue BV (1)
Sportlaan 14
4131 NN Vianen, Netherlands
Tel.: (31) 347 329 000
Fax: (31) 347 322 309
Web Site: www.delarue.com
Warm Air Heating & Air Conditioning Equipment Merchant Whslr
S.I.C.: 5075
N.A.I.C.S.: 423730

De La Rue CIS (1)
212v Building 102 Prospect Red Army
Sergiev Posad, 141300 Moscow, Russia
Tel.: (7) 96 547 3745
Fax: (7) 96 547 3745
Web Site: www.delarue.com
Cash Handling Equipment Mfr
S.I.C.: 3589
N.A.I.C.S.: 333318

De La Rue (Malaysia) Sdn. Bhd. (1)
3rd Floor Wisma Able Match Lot 271
Jalan Chan Sow Lin, 55200 Kuala Lumpur, Malaysia
Tel.: (60) 392210952
Fax: (60) 392212794
Web Site: www.delarue.com
Emp.: 9
Cash Handling Equipment Mfr
S.I.C.: 3589
N.A.I.C.S.: 333318
Jamini Shah *(Mgr-Bus Dev)*

De La Rue Mexico, S.A. de C.V (1)
Sanchez Azcona 239 Colonia Narvarte Pte
03020 Mexico, Mexico
Tel.: (52) 55 5286 4190
Fax: (52) 55 5286 4191
Web Site: www.delarue.com
Emp.: 30
Commercial Printing Services
S.I.C.: 2759
N.A.I.C.S.: 323111

De La Rue Systems Limited (1)
Room 1705-6 17/F Tai Yau Building 181
Johnston Road
Wanchai, China (Hong Kong)
Tel.: (852) 2586 1660
Fax: (852) 2511 2760
Web Site: www.delarue.com
Emp.: 20
Currency Counting & Sorting Machines Mfr
S.I.C.: 3589
N.A.I.C.S.: 333318
Dickson Ching *(Mgr-Fin)*

De La Rue (Thailand) Limited (1)
18th Fl Ste B 2 Ploenchit Center Bldg
Sukhumvit Road, Bangkok, 10110, Thailand
Tel.: (66) 265689614
Fax: (66) 26568965
Emp.: 10
Cash Handling Equipment Mfr
S.I.C.: 3589
N.A.I.C.S.: 333318
Steven Hongkong *(Mng Dir)*

DE LICACY INDUSTRIAL CO., LTD.

No 240 San Sheh
Xinshi, Tainan, Taiwan
Tel.: (886) 65011200
Fax: (886) 65996798
E-Mail: taipei@delicacy.com.tw
Web Site: www.delicacy.com.tw
1464—(TAI)
Sales Range: $50-74.9 Million
Business Description:
Yarn Dyed Fabrics Mfr
S.I.C.: 2269
N.A.I.C.S.: 313310
Personnel:
Jeff Su *(Deputy Gen Mgr)*

D.E MASTER BLENDERS 1753 N.V.

(Acquired by Joh. A. Benckiser SE)

DE NEDERLANDSCHE BANK N.V.

Postbus 98
1000 AB Amsterdam, Netherlands
Tel.: (31) 205249111
Fax: (31) 205242500
E-Mail: info@dnb.nl
Web Site: www.dnb.nl
Int. Income: $3,948,316,610
Assets: $342,454,878,640
Liabilities: $331,939,944,770
Net Worth: $10,514,933,870
Earnings: $2,798,687,430
Emp.: 1,725
Fiscal Year-end: 12/31/12
Business Description:
Banking Services
S.I.C.: 6011
N.A.I.C.S.: 521110
Personnel:
Alexander H. G. Rinnooy Kan *(Chm-Supervisory Bd)*
Klaas H. W. Knot *(Chm-Mgmt Bd)*
Annemiek Fentener van Vlissingen *(Vice Chm-Supervisory Bd)*
Frank Elderson *(Member-Mgmt Bd-Corp Support, Payments & Legal Svcs)*
Joanne Kellermann *(Member-Mgmt Bd-Pension & Insurance Supervision)*
Jan Sijbrand *(Member-Mgmt Bd-Banking Supervision & Supervisory Policy)*
Job Swank *(Member-Mgmt Bd-Monetary Affairs & Fin Stability)*
Bert van Delden *(Sec)*
Supervisory Board of Directors:
Alexander H. G. Rinnooy Kan
Kees P. Goudswaard
Wim J. Kuijken
Feike Sijbesma
Bert van Delden
Jaap A. van Manen
Annemiek Fentener van Vlissingen
Helene M. Vletter-van Dort

DE NORA INDIA LIMITED

Plot Nos 184 185 & 189 Kundaim
Industrial Estate Kundaim
Goa, 403 115, India
Tel.: (91) 8323981100
Fax: (91) 8323981101
E-Mail: denoraindia@denora.com
Web Site: www.denoraindia.com
DENORA—(NSE)
Rev.: $12,572,325
Assets: $9,322,540
Liabilities: $3,078,133
Net Worth: $6,244,407
Earnings: $2,467,122
Fiscal Year-end: 12/31/12
Business Description:
Electrolytic Products Mfr
S.I.C.: 3699
N.A.I.C.S.: 335999
Personnel:
S. C. Jain *(Mng Dir)*
Jyoti Bandodkar *(Sec)*
Board of Directors:
Premal N. Kapadia
Luca Buonerba
Giuseppe Cambareri
Angelo Ferrari
S. C. Jain
M. A. Sundaram
Transfer Agent:
Sharepro Services (India) Private Limited
13 AB Samhita Warehousing Complex II Floor
Sakinaka Telephone Lane
Off Andheri Kurla Rd Sakinaka, Mumbai, India

DE PERSGROEP NV

Brusselsesteenweg 347
Kobbegem, 1730, Belgium
Tel.: (32) 2 454 22 11
Fax: (32) 2 454 28 32
Web Site: www.persgroep.be
Year Founded: 1955
Sls.: $1,224,476,232
Assets: $1,007,069,777
Liabilities: $570,102,995
Net Worth: $436,966,782
Earnings: $28,538,804
Emp.: 2,900
Fiscal Year-end: 12/31/12
Business Description:
Periodical Publishers
S.I.C.: 2721
N.A.I.C.S.: 511120
Personnel:
Ludwig Criel *(Chm)*
Christian Van Thillo *(CEO)*
Piet Vroman *(CFO)*
Rudy Bertels *(COO)*
Xavier Verellen *(Chief Comml Officer)*
Christophe Convent *(Sec Gen)*
Board of Directors:
Ludwig Criel
Jan Louis Burggraaf
Christophe Convent
Ieko Sevinga
Leon Seynave
Christian Van Thillo
Emmanuel Van Thillo
Eric Verbeeck

DE POEL

Moseley Hall Farm Chelford Road
Knutsford, Cheshire, WA16 8RB, United Kingdom
Tel.: (44) 1565 682020
Web Site: www.depoel.co.uk
Year Founded: 2001
Sales Range: $10-24.9 Million
Emp.: 83
Business Description:
Non Permanent Staffing Services
S.I.C.: 7363
N.A.I.C.S.: 561320
Personnel:
Matthew Sanders *(CEO)*
Joe Tully *(Mng Dir)*

DE RIGO S.P.A.

Zona Industriale Villanova 12
32013 Longarone, Belluno, Italy
Tel.: (39) 04377777
Fax: (39) 0437573250
E-Mail: info@derigo.com
Web Site: www.derigo.com
Year Founded: 1978
Sales Range: $650-699.9 Million
Emp.: 4,760
Business Description:
Eyeglass & Sunglass Frames Designer, Distr & Mfr
S.I.C.: 3851
N.A.I.C.S.: 339115
Personnel:
Ennio De Rigo *(Chm)*
Massimo De Rigo *(Vice Chm & Head)*
Maurizio Dessolis *(Vice Chm)*
Michele Aracri *(CEO)*
Russel Hardy *(Mng Dir)*
Board of Directors:
Michele Aracri
Transfer Agent:
The Bank of New York
One Wall Street
New York, NY 10286
Tel.: (212) 495-1784
Fax: (212) 571-3050

Subsidiary:

De Rigo Vision S.p.A. (1)
Zona Industriale Villanova 12
Longarone, 32013 Belluno, Italy
Tel.: (39) 04377777
Fax: (39) 0437573250
Web Site: www.derigo.com
Ophthalmic Goods Mfr
S.I.C.: 3851
N.A.I.C.S.: 339115
Michele Aracri *(Mng Dir)*

Non-U.S. Subsidiaries:

De Rigo Asia Ltd (1)
Rm 1311-12 13th-Fl Grand Central Plz Tower
Sha Tin, China (Hong Kong)
Tel.: (852) 23779640
Fax: (852) 23774165
Emp.: 12
Ophthalmic Goods Mfr
S.I.C.: 3851
N.A.I.C.S.: 339115

De Rigo UK Ltd (1)
Unit 7 Tolpits Lane
Century Court, Watford, Hertfordshire, WD18 9RS, United Kingdom
Tel.: (44) 1923249491
Fax: (44) 1923249490
Emp.: 20
Ophthalmic Goods Mfr
S.I.C.: 3851
N.A.I.C.S.: 339115

Paul Clipton *(Gen Mgr)*

General Optica S.A. (1)
Andrade 128
Barcelona, 08020, Spain
Tel.: (34) 933037970
Fax: (34) 933037996
Web Site: www.generaloptica.es
Emp.: 1,000
Optical Goods Stores
S.I.C.: 5995
N.A.I.C.S.: 446130
Jordi Fontcuberta *(Mng Dir)*

DE ROUCK GEOMATICS S.A.

Route de Lennik 451/32 - Parc
Erasmus bur 19
1070 Brussels, Belgium
Tel.: (32) 2 354 69 95
Fax: (32) 2 210 89 15
E-Mail: customer.support@derou ckgeomatics.com
Web Site: www.derouck.com
Year Founded: 1928
ALROU—(EUR)
Sales Range: $1-9.9 Million
Business Description:
Cartographical Database
Development Services
S.I.C.: 7374
N.A.I.C.S.: 518210
Personnel:
Alain van Gelderen *(Chm)*

DE VERE GROUP LIMITED

17 Portland Place
London, W1B 1PU, United Kingdom
Tel.: (44) 844 346 3370 (PR)
Web Site: www.deveregroup.co.uk
Year Founded: 1999
Sales Range: $550-599.9 Million
Emp.: 8,500
Business Description:
Holding Company; Hotel & Resort
Owner & Operator
S.I.C.: 6719
N.A.I.C.S.: 551112
Personnel:
Andrew Coppel *(CEO)*
Robert Barclay Cook *(CEO-Hotels & Village Urban Resorts)*
Tony Dangerfield *(CEO-Venues)*
Sunital Kaushal *(Gen Counsel & Sec)*
Board of Directors:
Nicholas Bull
Gareth Caldecott
Bruce Cave
Robert Barclay Cook
Andrew Coppel
Tony Dangerfield
Colin Rutherford

The Chase Manhattan Bank N.A.
Trinity Tower 9 Thomas More Street
London, E1 9YT, United Kingdom
Transfer Agent:
Northern Registrars Limited
Northern House Woodsome Park
Fenay Bridge, Huddersfield, HD8 0LA, United Kingdom
Tel.: (44) 1484 606 664

DEAG DEUTSCHE ENTERTAINMENT AG

Potsdamer Strasse 58
10785 Berlin, Germany
Tel.: (49) 30810750
Fax: (49) 3081075519
E-Mail: info@deag.de
Web Site: www.deag.de
ERMK—(DEU)
Sls.: $209,632,323
Assets: $133,265,445
Liabilities: $90,441,085
Net Worth: $42,824,360
Earnings: $6,445,462
Emp.: 206
Fiscal Year-end: 12/31/12
Business Description:
Entertainment Services
S.I.C.: 2741
N.A.I.C.S.: 519130
Personnel:
Wolf-D. Gramatke *(Chm-Supervisory Bd)*
Christine Novakovic *(Vice Chm-Supervisory Bd)*
Peter L. H. Schwenkow *(CEO & Member-Mgmt Bd)*
Christian Diekmann *(CFO, COO & Member-Mgmt Bd)*
Supervisory Board of Directors:
Wolf-D. Gramatke
Christian Angermayer
Christine Novakovic

Subsidiaries:

coco tours Veranstaltungs GmbH (1)
Podtagrmm St 58
10785 Berlin, Germany
Tel.: (49) 30810750
Fax: (49) 3081075519
E-Mail: info@deag.com.ge
Emp.: 50
Concert Tour Operation Services
S.I.C.: 7999
N.A.I.C.S.: 711310
Peter Schwenkow *(CEO)*

Concert Concept Veranstaltungs-GmbH (1)
Potsdamer Strasse 58
10785 Berlin, Germany
Tel.: (49) 30810750
Fax: (49) 3081075229
E-Mail: info@concert-concept.de
Web Site: www.concert-concept.de
Emp.: 3
Concert Organizing Services
S.I.C.: 7999
N.A.I.C.S.: 711310
Peter Schwenkow *(Mng Dir)*

DEAG Classics AG (1)
Potsdamer Strasse 58
10785 Berlin, Germany
Tel.: (49) 30810750
Fax: (49) 3081075519
E-Mail: info@deag.de
Emp.: 50
Concerts & Event Organizing Services
S.I.C.: 7999
N.A.I.C.S.: 711310
Peter Schwenkow *(Mng Dir)*

DEAG Concerts GmbH (1)
Potsdamer Str 58
10785 Berlin, Germany
Tel.: (49) 30810750
Fax: (49) 3081075519
E-Mail: info@deag.de
Emp.: 45
Concerts Organizing Services
S.I.C.: 7999
N.A.I.C.S.: 711310
Peter Schwenkow *(Mng Dir)*

DEAG Music GmbH (1)
Potsdamer Strasse 58
10785 Berlin, Germany
Tel.: (49) 3081075537
Fax: (49) 3081075549
E-Mail: info@deag.de
Web Site: www.deag.de
Music Publishing Services
S.I.C.: 2741
N.A.I.C.S.: 512230
Peter Schwenkow *(CEO)*

Friedrichsbau Variete Betriebs- und Verwaltungs GmbH (1)
Friedrichstrasse 24
70174 Stuttgart, Germany
Tel.: (49) 7112257070
Fax: (49) 7112257075
E-Mail: friedrichsbau@deag.de
Web Site: www.friedrichsbau.de
Emp.: 12
Entertainment Ticketing & Marketing Services
S.I.C.: 4729
N.A.I.C.S.: 561599
Gabriele Frenzel *(Mng Dir)*

Global Concerts GmbH (1)
Ramersdorfer Str 1
81669 Munich, Germany
Tel.: (49) 894900940
Fax: (49) 8949009466
E-Mail: info@globalconcerts.de
Web Site: www.globalconcerts.de
Emp.: 6
Concerts Organizing Services
S.I.C.: 7999
N.A.I.C.S.: 711310
Christian Diekmann *(Mng Dir)*

KBK Konzert- und Kunstleragentur GmbH (1)
Prinzregentenstrasse 95
81677 Munich, Germany
Tel.: (49) 894110940
Fax: (49) 8941109433
E-Mail: info@kb-k.com
Web Site: www.kb-k.com
Emp.: 6
Concert Organizing Services
S.I.C.: 7999
N.A.I.C.S.: 711310
Klaus Boenisch *(Owner)*

Kultur- und Kongresszentrum Jahrhunderthalle GmbH (1)
Pfaffenwiese
65929 Frankfurt am Main, Germany
Tel.: (49) 693601236
Fax: (49) 693601222
E-Mail: infp@jahrhunderthalle.com
Web Site: www.jahrhunderthalle.de
Emp.: 18
Concerts & Event Management Services
S.I.C.: 7999
N.A.I.C.S.: 711310
Uschi Ottersberg *(Mng Dir)*

River Concerts GmbH (1)
Johannisbollwerk 20
20459 Hamburg, Germany
Tel.: (49) 4041330180
Fax: (49) 40413301866
E-Mail: info@riverconcerts.de
Web Site: www.riverconcerts.de
Emp.: 5
Concert Organizing Services
S.I.C.: 7999
N.A.I.C.S.: 711310
Moritz Schwenkow *(Mng Dir)*

Subsidiary:

Elbklassik Konzerte GmbH (2)
Feldbrunnenstrasse 8
20148 Hamburg, Germany
Tel.: (49) 40413301830
Fax: (49) 40413301866
E-Mail: info@elbklassik.de
Web Site: www.elbklassik.de
Emp.: 5
Concerts Organizing Services
S.I.C.: 7999
N.A.I.C.S.: 711310
Christian Diekmann *(Mng Dir)*
Moritz Schwenkow *(Mng Dir)*

Non-U.S. Subsidiaries:

EM Event Marketing AG (1)
Thurgauerstrasse 105 Glattpark
8152 Zurich, Switzerland
Tel.: (41) 448096666
Fax: (41) 448096600
E-Mail: info@goodnews.ch
Web Site: www.goodnews.ch
Emp.: 3
Event Management Services
S.I.C.: 7999
N.A.I.C.S.: 711310
Thomas Post *(Mng Dir)*

Raymond Gubbay Ltd (1)
Dickens House 15 Tooks Court
London, EC4A 1LB, United Kingdom
Tel.: (44) 2070253750
Fax: (44) 2070253751
E-Mail: info@raymondgubbay.co.uk
Web Site: www.raymondgubbay.co.uk
Emp.: 16
Opera & Ballet Music Entertainment Services
S.I.C.: 7999
N.A.I.C.S.: 711310
Raymond Gubbay *(Chm)*
Anthony Findlay *(Mng Dir)*
Christian Diekmann *(CFO & COO)*
Cathy Lewis *(Deputy Mng Dir)*

DEALNET CAPITAL CORP.

(Formerly Gamecorp Ltd.)
325 Milner Avenue Suite 300
Toronto, ON, M1B 5N1, Canada
Tel.: (416) 843-2881
Fax: (905) 833-9847
E-Mail: graham@gamecorp.com
Web Site: www.gamecorp.com
Year Founded: 1986
DLS—(CNSX OTC)
Rev.: $721,659
Assets: $3,639,107
Liabilities: $3,862,762
Net Worth: ($223,654)
Earnings: ($1,074,536)
Emp.: 3
Fiscal Year-end: 09/30/12
Business Description:
Customer Relationship Services
S.I.C.: 8742
N.A.I.C.S.: 541611
Personnel:
Robert J. Cariglia *(Pres & CEO)*
Ashish Kapoor *(CFO)*
Michael Hilmer *(COO)*
Carrie J. Weiler *(Sec)*
Board of Directors:
John Graham Simmonds
Pierre Gagnon
Michael Hilmer
Henry J. Kloepper
Neil Romanchych
Carrie J. Weiler
Transfer Agent:
Pacific Corporate Trust Company
625 Howe St
Vancouver, BC, Canada V6C 3B9

DEALOGIC (HOLDINGS) PLC

Thanet House 231-232 Strand
London, WC2R 1DA, United Kingdom
Tel.: (44) 2073795650
Fax: (44) 2074406005
E-Mail: ukinfo@dealogic.com
Web Site: www.dealogic.com
Sales Range: $100-124.9 Million
Emp.: 500
Business Description:
Software Developer
S.I.C.: 7372
N.A.I.C.S.: 511210
Personnel:
Thomas A. Fleming *(CEO)*
Jonathan O. Drulard *(Mng Dir)*
Frederick McHattie *(CFO)*
Toby Haddon *(COO)*
Helen C. Vincent *(Sec)*
Board of Directors:
Peter J. Ogden
Carl J. Anderson
Joan P. Beck
Jonathan O. Drulard
Thomas A. Fleming
Toby Haddon
Philip W. Hulme
Frederick McHattie
Legal Counsel:
Nabarro LLP
Lacon House, 84 Theobald's Road
London, WC1X 8RW, United Kingdom
Tel.: (44) 171 493 9933
Fax: (44) 171 629 7900

Subsidiary:

Dealogic Limited (1)
Thanet House 231-232 Strand
London, WC2R 1DA, United Kingdom
Tel.: (44) 2073795650
Fax: (44) 2074406005
E-Mail: ukinfo@dealogic.com
Web Site: www.dealogic.com
Emp.: 280
Transaction Management Software & Information System Solutions
S.I.C.: 7371
N.A.I.C.S.: 541511

Dealogic (Holdings) plc—(Continued)

U.S. Subsidiary:

Dealogic LLC (1)
120 Broadway 8th Fl
New York, NY 10271-1199
Tel.: (212) 577-4400
Fax: (212) 577-4545
E-Mail: usinfo@dealogic.com
Emp.: 130
Computer Systems Design Services
S.I.C.: 7371
N.A.I.C.S.: 541511
Greg Young *(Mng Dir)*

DEAN COOLEY MOTORS LTD.

1600 Main Street South
PO Box 747
Dauphin, MB, R7N 3B3, Canada
Tel.: (204) 638-4026
Fax: (204) 638-5875
Toll Free: (800) 442-0402
E-Mail: deancooleygm@deancooleygm.ca
Web Site: www.deancooleygm.ca
Rev.: $23,408,000
Emp.: 50
Business Description:
New & Used Car Dealers
S.I.C.: 5511
N.A.I.C.S.: 441110
Personnel:
Bob Murray *(Sec & Mgr-Acctg)*

DEANS KNIGHT INCOME CORPORATION

Suite 1500 999 West Hastings Street
Vancouver, BC, V6C 2W2, Canada
Tel.: (604) 669-0212
Fax: (604) 669-0238
E-Mail: info@dkincomecorp.com
Web Site: www.dkincomecorp.com
Year Founded: 2001
DNC—(TSX)
Rev.: $11,478,688
Assets: $142,133,639
Liabilities: $709,443
Net Worth: $141,424,196
Earnings: $8,058,469
Fiscal Year-end: 12/31/12
Business Description:
Investment Services
S.I.C.: 6211
N.A.I.C.S.: 523999
Personnel:
Wayne Deans *(Chm)*
Craig Langdon *(CEO)*
Mark Myles *(CFO & Sec)*
Dillon Cameron *(Chief Investment Officer)*
Board of Directors:
Wayne Deans
Denyse Chicoyne
Philip Hampson
Craig Langdon
D. Alan Ross

Computershare Trust Company of Canada
Vancouver, BC, Canada
Tel.: (604) 661-9400
Fax: (604) 669-1548

Transfer Agents:
Computershare Trust Company of Canada
Vancouver, BC, Canada
Tel.: (604) 661-9400
Fax: (604) 669-1548

Computershare Trust Company of Canada
Toronto, ON, Canada

DEAP CAPITAL MANAGEMENT & TRUST PLC

14th Floor St Nicholas House
6 Catholic Mission Street, Lagos, Nigeria
Tel.: (234) 1 4751756
Fax: (234) 1 4622533
E-Mail: info@deapcapital.com
Web Site: www.deapcapital.com
DEAPCAP—(NIGE)
Sales Range: $1-9.9 Million
Business Description:
Investment Services
S.I.C.: 6799
N.A.I.C.S.: 523920
Personnel:
Victoria O. Alo *(Chm)*
Vincent Otiono *(Vice Chm)*
Emmanuel Ugboh *(CEO & Mng Dir)*
Board of Directors:
Victoria O. Alo
Treasure-Sam Afolayan
Gordons Ejikeme
Anthony Eze
Sylvanus C. Ezendu
Joe Idudu
Ifeanyi Nwagnu
Gabriel Ifeanyi Ogbeche
Preye Ogriki
Vincent Otiono
Clara A. Rotzler
Emmanuel Ugboh

Subsidiary:

Resort Developers Limited (1)
Second Fl Resort House
12 Boyle St, Lagos, Nigeria
Tel.: (234) 7098141711
Fax: (234) 7098141951
E-Mail: enquiries@rdlng.com
Web Site: www.rdlng.com
Real Estate Services
S.I.C.: 6531
N.A.I.C.S.: 531210
Kayode Kalesanwo *(CEO & Mng Dir)*

DEAR LIFE CO., LTD.

Iidabashi Building 10F 2-4-5 Chiyoda-ku
Tokyo, 102-0072, Japan
Tel.: (81) 352103721
Fax: (81) 352103723
Web Site: www.dear-life.co.jp
Year Founded: 2004
3245—(TKS)
Sales Range: $10-24.9 Million
Emp.: 20
Business Description:
Real Estate Services
S.I.C.: 6531
N.A.I.C.S.: 531390
Personnel:
Yukihiro Abe *(Pres)*

DEARBORN MOTORS LTD.

2555 East Trans Canada Hwy
Kamloops, BC, V2C 4B1, Canada
Tel.: (250) 372-7101
Fax: (250) 314-5151
Toll Free: (877) 278-0042
E-Mail: reception@dearbornford.com
Web Site: www.dearbornford.com
Year Founded: 1923
Rev.: $36,215,968
Emp.: 95
Business Description:
New & Used Car Dealers
S.I.C.: 5511
N.A.I.C.S.: 441110
Personnel:
Michael Bacon *(Gen Mgr)*

DEBAO PROPERTY DEVELOPMENT LTD.

1 Finlayson Green 14-02
Singapore, 049245, Singapore
Tel.: (65) 65133857
Fax: (65) 65125452
Web Site: debao.listedcompany.com
DE7—(DEU)
Rev.: $19,976,499
Assets: $444,310,916
Liabilities: $263,471,152
Net Worth: $180,839,764
Earnings: ($8,983,762)
Fiscal Year-end: 12/31/12
Business Description:
Property Development Services
S.I.C.: 6519
N.A.I.C.S.: 531190
Personnel:
Le Sheng Yuan *(Chm & CEO)*
Tam Kin Bor *(CFO)*
Janet Tan *(Sec)*
Board of Directors:
Le Sheng Yuan
Alfred Keng Chuan Cheong
Guo Quan He
Ke Ping He
Mao Zhang
Li Hua Zheng
Yu Zhao Zhong

DEBENHAMS PLC

1 Welbeck Street
London, W1G 0AA, United Kingdom
Tel.: (44) 2074084444
Fax: (44) 2074083366
E-Mail: investorrelations@debenhams.com
Web Site: www.debenhams.com
Year Founded: 1778
DEB—(AIM)
Emp.: 8,355
Business Description:
Department Stores
S.I.C.: 5311
N.A.I.C.S.: 452111
Personnel:
Nigel Northridge *(Chm)*
Michael Sharp *(CEO)*
Neil Kennedy *(Acting CFO)*
Paul Eardley *(Sec)*
Board of Directors:
Nigel Northridge
Peter Fitzgerald
Suzanne Harlow
Stephen Ingham
Martina King
Sophie Turner Laing
Dennis Henry Millard
Mark Rolfe
Michael Sharp
Legal Counsel:
Freshfields Bruckhaus Deringer
65 Fleet St
London, United Kingdom

Subsidiaries:

Debenhams Group Holdings Limited (1)
109-112 Princes Street
Edinburgh, EH2 3AA, United Kingdom
Tel.: (44) 1823337979
Financial Investment Management Services
S.I.C.: 6211
N.A.I.C.S.: 523999

Debenhams Properties Limited (1)
West Orchard Shopping Centre
Coventry, West Midlands, CV1 1QL, United Kingdom
Tel.: (44) 1823337979
Property Management Services
S.I.C.: 6531
N.A.I.C.S.: 531311

Debenhams Retail plc (1)
1 Welbeck Street
London, W1G 0AA, United Kingdom
Tel.: (44) 1823 337979
Fax: (44) 2074 083366
E-Mail: head.office@debenhams.com
Web Site: www.debenhams.com
Apparel & Accessories Retailer
S.I.C.: 5699
N.A.I.C.S.: 448150
Michael Sharp *(CEO)*

DEBOFFE

Route N 29
80480 Saleux, France
Tel.: (33) 322332470
Fax: (33) 322335981
E-Mail: fdeboffe@deboffe.com
Web Site: www.deboffe.fr
Sls.: $33,800,000
Emp.: 71
Business Description:
Farm Machinery Retailer
S.I.C.: 5083
N.A.I.C.S.: 423820
Personnel:
Francois Deboffe *(Gen Mgr)*

DEBUSCHERE SA

23 Avenue des Temps Modernes ZI
BP 32
86361 Chasseneuil-du-Poitou, France
Tel.: (33) 549528020
Fax: (33) 5 49 52 85 25
Web Site: www.debuschere.fr
Rev.: $23,800,000
Emp.: 216
Business Description:
Painting & Paper Hanging
S.I.C.: 1721
N.A.I.C.S.: 238320
Personnel:
Bruno Davoine *(Chm)*
Board of Directors:
Bruno Davoine
Laurent Trommenschlager

DEBUT DIAMONDS INC.

141 Adelaide Street West Suite 420
Toronto, ON, M5H 3L5, Canada
Tel.: (416) 642-3575
Fax: (416) 644-0592
E-Mail: info@DebutDiamonds.com
Web Site: www.debutdiamonds.com
Year Founded: 2007
DDI—(CNSX)
Rev.: $130,760
Assets: $1,082,673
Liabilities: $1,488,545
Net Worth: ($405,872)
Earnings: ($4,543,320)
Emp.: 5
Fiscal Year-end: 04/30/13
Business Description:
Diamond Exploration Services
S.I.C.: 1499
N.A.I.C.S.: 212399
Personnel:
Christopher W. Meraw *(Pres)*
Frank C. Smeenk *(CEO & Mng Dir)*
Thomas E. Masters *(CFO)*
Sarah Marriott *(Chief Admin Officer)*
Luce Saint Pierre *(Sec)*
Board of Directors:
Martin Doyle
Douglas M. Flett
Bruce Reid
Luce L. Saint-Pierre
Frank C. Smeenk
Legal Counsel:
Sheldon Huxtable Professional Corporation
180 Dundas Street West Suite1801
Toronto, ON, Canada
Transfer Agent:
Capital Transfer Agency
105 Adelaide St West Suite 1101
Toronto, ON, M5H 1P9, Canada

DECA CABLES INC.

150 N Murray St
Trenton, ON, Canada
Tel.: (613) 392-3585
Fax: (613) 392-7908
Toll Free: (800) 263-3322
E-Mail: sales@decacables.com

Web Site: www.decacables.com
Rev.: $35,615,880
Emp.: 90
Business Description:
Wire & Cable Mfr
S.I.C.: 3357
N.A.I.C.S.: 335921
Personnel:
Domenic Di Pietrantonio *(Pres)*

DECADE RESOURCES LTD.

611 - 8th Street
Box 211
Stewart, BC, V0T 1W0, Canada
Tel.: (604) 202-6596
E-Mail: info@decaderesources.ca
Web Site: www.decaderesources.ca
Year Founded: 2006
DEC—(TSXV)
Int. Income: $12
Assets: $11,462,587
Liabilities: $2,328,841
Net Worth: $9,133,747
Earnings: ($883,333)
Fiscal Year-end: 04/30/13
Business Description:
Mineral Exploration Services
S.I.C.: 1081
N.A.I.C.S.: 213114
Personnel:
Edward R. Kruchkowski *(Pres & CEO)*
Randolph Kasum *(CFO)*
Board of Directors:
Randolph Kasum
Edward R. Kruchkowski
Brian Morrison
Lance Robinson
Transfer Agent:
Valiant Trust Company
600-750 Cambie St
Vancouver, BC, Canada

DECCAN CHRONICLE HOLDINGS LTD.

36 Sarojini Devi Road
Secunderabad, 500003, India
Tel.: (91) 40 2780 3930
Fax: (91) 40 2780 3870
Web Site: www.deccanchronicle.in
DCHL—(NSE)
Sales Range: $150-199.9 Million
Business Description:
Daily Magazine Publisher
S.I.C.: 2721
N.A.I.C.S.: 511120
Personnel:
Venkattram Reddy T. *(Chm)*
Board of Directors:
Venkattram Reddy T.
Sanjiv Gupta
Surrinder Lal Kapur
Subsidiaries:

Asian Age Holdings Ltd. (1)
S-7&8 Green Park Main Mkt
New Delhi, 110 016, India
Tel.: (91) 1126530001
Fax: (91) 1126530027
E-Mail: marketing@asianage.com
Web Site: www.asianage.com
Emp.: 250
Newspaper & Magazine Publishing Services
S.I.C.: 2711
N.A.I.C.S.: 511110
Sanjay Basak *(Mng Dir)*

Odyssey India Ltd. (1)
No 45 & 47 Odyssey Tower 3rd Fl First Main Rd Gandhinagar
Adyar, Chennai, Tamil Nadu, 600 020, India
Tel.: (91) 4443910300
Fax: (91) 4442114799
E-Mail: feedback@odyssey.in
Web Site: www.odyssey.in
Emp.: 500
Book Stores Management Services
S.I.C.: 5942
N.A.I.C.S.: 451211
T. S. Ashwin *(Mng Dir)*

DECCAN GOLD MINES LTD.

Raja Ikon Building 89/1 3rd Floor
Marathahalli Outer Ring Road
Bengaluru, 560 037, India
Tel.: (91) 80 40428400
Fax: (91) 80 40428401
E-Mail: info@deccangoldmines.com
Web Site: www.deccangoldmines.com
Year Founded: 2003
512068—(BOM)
Rev.: $29,126
Assets: $528,557
Liabilities: $30,016
Net Worth: $498,541
Earnings: ($192,130)
Fiscal Year-end: 03/31/13
Business Description:
Gold Exploration Services
S.I.C.: 1041
N.A.I.C.S.: 212221
Personnel:
Charles E. E. Devenish *(Chm)*
Sandeep Lakhwara *(Mng Dir)*
S. Subramaniam *(Compliance Officer & Sec)*
Board of Directors:
Charles E. E. Devenish
V. K. Gaur
Sandeep Lakhwara
K. R. Krishna Murthy
M. Ramakrishnan
Legal Counsel:
Crest Law Partners
No. F-3 Ligoury Court 7 Palmgrove Road
Victoria Layout
Bengaluru, India
Transfer Agent:
Link Intime India Private Limited
C-13 Pannalal Silk Mills Compound LBS Road
Bhandup W
Mumbai, India

DECEUNINCK NV

Bruggesteenweg 164
8830 Hooglede, Belgium
Tel.: (32) 51239211
Fax: (32) 51227993
E-Mail: info@deceuninck.com
Web Site: www.deceuninck.com
Year Founded: 1937
DECB—(EUR)
Sls.: $749,700,919
Assets: $588,160,519
Liabilities: $299,831,098
Net Worth: $288,329,421
Earnings: $5,710,453
Emp.: 2,665
Fiscal Year-end: 12/31/12
Business Description:
Mfr., Designer & Extruder of PVC Systems
S.I.C.: 3089
N.A.I.C.S.: 326199
Personnel:
Pierre Alain De Smedt *(Chm)*
Arnold Deceuninck *(Vice Chm)*
Francois Gillet *(Vice Chm)*
Tom Debusschere *(Chm-Executive Team & CEO)*
Philippe Maeckelberghe *(CFO)*
Board of Directors:
Pierre Alain De Smedt
Tom Debusschere
Arnold Deceuninck
Willy Deceuninck
Francois Gillet
Marcel Klepfisch
Paul Thiers
Giulia Van Waeyenberge

Subsidiaries:

Plastics Deceuninck NV (1)
Bruggesteenweg 374
8800 Roeselare, Belgium
Tel.: (32) 51239206
Fax: (32) 51245454
Plastic Door & Window Mfr
S.I.C.: 3089
N.A.I.C.S.: 326199
Tom Debusschere *(Gen Mgr)*

SA Detajoint NV (1)
ZI Barriere De Fer
Avenue Du Bois Jacquet, B 7711
Dottignies, Belgium (75%)
Tel.: (32) 56484461
Fax: (32) 56485054
E-Mail: info@detajoint.be
Web Site: www.detajoint.be
Emp.: 19
Mfr. of Complex Tri-extrusion Profiles
S.I.C.: 3089
N.A.I.C.S.: 326199
Gohan Pauwels *(Gen Mgr)*

U.S. Subsidiary:

Deceuninck North America Inc. (1)
351 N Garver Rd
Monroe, OH 45050
Tel.: (513) 539-4444
Fax: (513) 539-5404
E-Mail: sales@daytech.com
Web Site: www.decena.zb
Emp.: 300
Mfr. of Door & Window Systems; External Building Products; Interior Wall Panelling; Ceiling Systems
S.I.C.: 3082
N.A.I.C.S.: 326121
Filip G. Geeraert *(Pres)*

Subsidiary:

Deceuninck North America LLC (2)
351 N Garver Rd
Monroe, OH 45050
Tel.: (513) 539-4444
Fax: (513) 539-5404
Toll Free: (877) 563-4251
E-Mail: Support@Deceuninck-Info.com
Web Site: www.deceuninck-americas.com
Emp.: 400
Window & Door Mfr
S.I.C.: 3442
N.A.I.C.S.: 332321
Filip Geeraert *(CEO)*

Non-U.S. Subsidiaries:

Deceuninck Baltic UAB (1)
V Kuzmos 6 1
44280 Kaunas, Lithuania
Tel.: (370) 37338844
Fax: (370) 37338845
E-Mail: info@deceuninck.lt
Plastic Profile Systems Mfr
S.I.C.: 3082
N.A.I.C.S.: 326121

Deceuninck Beheer BV (1)
Krekelveen 629
Spijkenisse, Zuid-Holland, 3205 RD, Netherlands
Tel.: (31) 647912727
Fax: (31) 181613911
Plastic Household Products Mfr
S.I.C.: 3089
N.A.I.C.S.: 326199

Non-U.S. Subsidiary:

Deceuninck Holding Germany GmbH (2)
Bayerwaldstr 18
Bogen, 94327, Germany
Tel.: (49) 94228210
E-Mail: info@inoutic.com
Investment Management Services
S.I.C.: 6211
N.A.I.C.S.: 523999
Edgar Freund *(Gen Mgr)*

Deceuninck Bulgaria EOOD (1)
Sankt Peterburg Blvd 41
4000 Plovdiv, Bulgaria
Tel.: (359) 32637295
Fax: (359) 32637296
E-Mail: office@deceuninck.bg
Web Site: www.deceuninck.bg
Plastic Profile Systems Mfr
S.I.C.: 3082
N.A.I.C.S.: 326121
Asparuh Schterev *(Gen Mgr)*

Deceuninck d.o.o. (1)
Industrijska ulica 3
10370 Dugo Selo, Croatia
Tel.: (385) 12781353
Fax: (385) 12781351
Web Site: www.deceuninck.com
Plastic Profile Systems Mfr
S.I.C.: 3082
N.A.I.C.S.: 326121

Deceuninck Holdings UK Ltd (1)
Unit 2 Stanier Road Porte Marsh-Industrial Estate
Calne, Wiltshire, SN11 9PX, United Kingdom
Tel.: (44) 1249 816 969
Fax: (44) 1249 815 234
E-Mail: deceuninck.ltd@deceuninck.com
Web Site: www.deceuninck.com
Emp.: 55
Plastic Profile System Mfr
S.I.C.: 3082
N.A.I.C.S.: 326121
Victoria Gees-Thornton *(Mgr-Sys Support)*

Deceuninck Ireland Unltd (1)
4th Floor 25-28 Adelaide Road
Dublin, Ireland
Tel.: (353) 1 605 3044
Fax: (353) 1 605 3010
Plastic Profile Systems Mfr
S.I.C.: 3082
N.A.I.C.S.: 326121
Edel Dillon *(Acct Mgr)*

DECEUNINCK ITALIA SRL (1)
Piazza della Concordia 6
56025 Pontedera, Pisa, Italy
Tel.: (39) 0587 59920
Fax: (39) 0587 54432
E-Mail: italia@deceuninck.com
Web Site: www.deceuninck.it
Emp.: 6
Plastic Profile Systems Mfr
S.I.C.: 3082
N.A.I.C.S.: 326121
Mirko Anesi *(Gen Mgr)*

Deceuninck Kunststof B.V. (1)
Jeugdland 1A
4851 AT Houten, Netherlands
Mailing Address:
Postbus 36
4850 AA Houten, Netherlands
Tel.: (31) 765617834
Fax: (31) 767502353
E-Mail: deceuninck.kunststof@deceuninck.com
Emp.: 3
Retailer of PVC-U Profiles for the Building Industry
S.I.C.: 3089
N.A.I.C.S.: 326199
Paul Jansen *(Mgr-Comml)*

Deceuninck Ltd. (1)
Unit 2 Stanier Rd
Porte Marsh Industrial Est, Calne, Wiltshire, SN119PX, United Kingdom (100%)
Tel.: (44) 249816969
Fax: (44) 249815234
E-Mail: deceuninck.ltd@deceuninck.com
Web Site: www.deceuninck.co.uk
Emp.: 130
Mfr. of Door & Window Systems; Roofline Products; External Building Products; Interior Wall Panelling; Ceiling Systems
S.I.C.: 3089
N.A.I.C.S.: 326199

Deceuninck NV Sucursal em Portugal (1)
Avenida Da Liberdade 110 Fl 1
1269-046 Lisbon, Portugal (100%)
Tel.: (351) 214160813
Fax: (351) 214160814
E-Mail: deceuninck@deceuninck.pt
Retailer of PVC-U Profiles for the Building Industry
S.I.C.: 3089
N.A.I.C.S.: 326199
Antonio Escobar *(Gen Mgr-Deceunink Spain & Portugal)*

Deceuninck NV—(Continued)

Deceuninck NV Sucursal en Espana (1)
Avda de la Industria 1007 Pol Ind Antonio del Rincon
Borox, 45222 Toledo, Spain (100%)
Tel.: (34) 902209001
Fax: (34) 902209002
E-Mail: info@deceuninck.es
Web Site: www.deceuninck.es
Emp.: 30
Mfr., Designer & Extrudrer of PVC Systems
S.I.C.: 3089
N.A.I.C.S.: 326199

Deceuninck Polska Sp. z o.o. (1)
Jasin ul Poznanska 34
62020 Swarzedz, Poland (100%)
Tel.: (48) 618187000
Fax: (48) 618187001
E-Mail: deceuninck.polska@deceuninck.com
Web Site: www.deceuninck.pl
Emp.: 18
Mfr. & Retailer of PVC-U Profiles for the Building Industry
S.I.C.: 3089
N.A.I.C.S.: 326199

Deceuninck Pty. Ltd. (1)
142 Freight Drive
Somerton, VIC, 3062, Australia
Tel.: (61) 3 93088300
Fax: (61) 3 93037548
E-Mail: australia@deceuninck.com
Web Site: www.deceuninck.com.au
Emp.: 3
Plastic Windows & Door Mfr
S.I.C.: 3089
N.A.I.C.S.: 326199

Deceuninck Romania SRL (1)
Str Traian nr 2 bl F1 sc 4 ap 24 Sector 3
Bucharest, Romania
Tel.: (40) 213274952
Fax: (40) 21 323 52 90
E-Mail: officedeceuninck.ro@deceuninck.com
Plastic Products Mfr
S.I.C.: 3089
N.A.I.C.S.: 326199
Tom Debusschere *(CEO)*

Deceuninck Rus OOO (1)
Krzhizhanovskogo Ul 6
117218 Moscow, Russia
Tel.: (7) 4956428795
Fax: (7) 495 642 87 96
E-Mail: info@deceuninck.ru
Web Site: www.deceuninck.ru
Emp.: 200
Plastic Profile Systems Mfr
S.I.C.: 3082
N.A.I.C.S.: 326121
Volker Guth *(CEO)*

Deceuninck SA (1)
Z I Impasse Des Bleuets
80700 Roye, France (100%)
Tel.: (33) 322876666
Fax: (33) 322876667
E-Mail: deceuninck.sa@deceuninck.com
Web Site: www.deceuninck.com
Mfr. & Retailer of PVC-U Profiles for the Building Industry
S.I.C.: 3089
N.A.I.C.S.: 326199

Deceuninck Spol (1)
Vintrovna 23
Popovky, 66441, Czech Republic (100%)
Tel.: (420) 547427777
Fax: (420) 547427788
E-Mail: deceuninck.spol@deceuninck.com
Web Site: www.deceuninck.com
Emp.: 50
Retailer of Window & Door Systems; Window Boards, Conservatories, Claddings, Fences, Roofline Products; External Building Products; Interior Wall Panelling; Ceiling Systems
S.I.C.: 3089
N.A.I.C.S.: 326199
Radek Slabak *(Gen Mgr)*

Ege Profil AS (1)
10003 Sokak 5
AOSB 35620 Izmir, Turkey (97.16%)
Tel.: (90) 2323767160
Fax: (90) 2323767163
E-Mail: info@egeten.com
Emp.: 250
Mfr. & Retailer of PVC-U Profiles for the Building Industry
S.I.C.: 3089
N.A.I.C.S.: 326199

Inoutic Deceuninck GmbH (1)
Bayerwaldstrasse 18
94327 Bogen, Germany
Tel.: (49) 94228210
Fax: (49) 9422821379
E-Mail: info@inoutic.com
Web Site: www.inoutic.com
Emp.: 500
Plastic Profile Systems Mfr
S.I.C.: 3082
N.A.I.C.S.: 326121
Freund Etgar *(Gen Mgr)*

Non-U.S. Subsidiary:

Deceuninck d.o.o. (2)
Magistralni put bb
75300 Lukavac, Bosnia & Herzegovina
Tel.: (387) 35 55 03 15
Fax: (387) 35 55 03 16
Web Site: www.deceuninck.com
Plastic Profile Systems Mfr
S.I.C.: 3082
N.A.I.C.S.: 326121

Range Valley Extrusions Ltd (1)
Unit 2 Stanier Road Trading Address Porte Marsh Industrial Estate
Calne, Wiltshire, SN11 9PX, United Kingdom
Tel.: (44) 1249 816 969
Fax: (44) 1249 815 234
E-Mail: deceuninck.ltd@deceuninck.com
Emp.: 63
Plastic Profile System Mfr
S.I.C.: 3082
N.A.I.C.S.: 326121

DECHELETTE MALLEVAL SA

Boulevard Jean Monnet
BP 42
69490 Maurepas, France
Tel.: (33) 474057800
Fax: (33) 474059405
E-Mail: info@dechelette-malleval.com
Web Site: www.dechelette-malleval.fr/
Sls.: $23,400,000
Emp.: 115
Business Description:
Textile Goods
S.I.C.: 2299
N.A.I.C.S.: 313110
Personnel:
Olivier Malleval *(Gen Mgr)*

DECHRA PHARMACEUTICALS PLC

24 Cheshire Avenue Cheshire Business Park
Lostock Gralam, Northwich, CW9 7UA, United Kingdom
Tel.: (44) 1606 814 730
Fax: (44) 1606 814 731
E-Mail: corporate.enquiries@dechra.com
Web Site: www.dechraplc.com
Year Founded: 1997
DPH—(LSE)
Rev.: $298,763,765
Assets: $655,604,341
Liabilities: $379,835,038
Net Worth: $275,769,303
Earnings: $28,289,822
Emp.: 1,287
Fiscal Year-end: 06/30/13
Business Description:
Holding Company; Veterinary Pharmaceutical & Supplement Mfr & Distr
S.I.C.: 6719
N.A.I.C.S.: 551112
Personnel:
Ian Page *(CEO)*
Anne-Francoise Nesmes *(CFO)*
Mike Eldred *(Pres-Ops-Dechra Veterinary Products-US)*
Zoe Goulding *(Sec)*
Board of Directors:
Michael Redmond
Tony Griffin
Julian Heslop
Ishbel Macpherson
Anne-Francoise Nesmes
Ian Page
Christopher Richards
Ed Torr
Legal Counsel:
DLA Piper UK LLP
Victoria Square House Victoria Square
Birmingham, United Kingdom
Subsidiary:

Dechra Limited (1)
Unit 4 Jamage Industrial Estate Talke Pits
Stoke-on-Trent, Staffs, ST7 1XW, United Kingdom
Tel.: (44) 1782 771100
Web Site: www.dechra.com
Veterinary Pharmaceutical & Supplement Mfr & Distr; Veterinary Services
S.I.C.: 2834
N.A.I.C.S.: 325412

Units:

Dales Pharmaceuticals (2)
Snaygill Industrial Estate
Keighley Rd, Skipton, North Yorkshire, BD23 2RW, United Kingdom
Tel.: (44) 1756791311
Fax: (44) 1756798604
E-Mail: sales@dechrapharmaceuticals.com
Web Site: www.dechrapharmaceuticals.com
Emp.: 200
Pharmaceutical Mfr
S.I.C.: 2834
N.A.I.C.S.: 325412
Michael Annice *(Mng Dir)*

Dechra Veterinary Products (2)
Sansaw Business Park
Hadnall, Shrewsbury, Shropshire, SY4 4AS, United Kingdom
Tel.: (44) 1939 211 200
Fax: (44) 1939 211 201
E-Mail: info@dechra.com
Web Site: www.dechra.co.uk
Emp.: 50
Veterinary Products Marketer, Distr & Technical Support Services
S.I.C.: 5199
N.A.I.C.S.: 424990
Ed Torr *(Mng Dir-Europe)*

U.S. Subsidiary:

Dechra Veterinary Products, LLC (3)
7015 College Blvd Ste 525
Overland Park, KS 66211 DE
Tel.: (913) 327-0015
Fax: (913) 327-0016
Toll Free: (866) 933-2472
Web Site: www.dechra-us.com
Emp.: 35
Veterinary Products Marketer, Distr & Technical Support Services
S.I.C.: 5199
N.A.I.C.S.: 424990
Mike Eldred *(Pres-Ops)*

Non-U.S. Subsidiaries:

Dechra Veterinary Products AB (3)
Engelbrektsgatan 6 4 tr
702 12 Orebro, Sweden
Tel.: (46) 19 32 33 55
E-Mail: info.se@dechra.com
Web Site: www.dechra.se
Emp.: 212
Veterinary Products Marketer, Distr & Technical Support Services
S.I.C.: 5199
N.A.I.C.S.: 424990

Dechra Veterinary Products AS (3)
Torgbygget Nydalsveien 33
484 Oslo, Norway
Tel.: (47) 21 52 01 10
Fax: (47) 21 52 01 18
E-Mail: info@dechra.no
Web Site: www.dechra.no
Veterinary Products Marketer, Distr & Technical Support Services
S.I.C.: 5199
N.A.I.C.S.: 424990

Dechra Veterinary Products BV (3)
Minervum 7071
4817 ZK Breda, Netherlands
Tel.: (31) 76 579 81 00
Fax: (31) 76 579 81 09
E-Mail: info.nl@dechra.com
Web Site: www.dechra.nl
Emp.: 7
Veterinary Products Marketer, Distr & Technical Support Services
S.I.C.: 5199
N.A.I.C.S.: 424990
Kurt Hayden *(Gen Mgr)*

Dechra Veterinary Products OY (3)
Apilakatu 10
20 740 Turku, Finland
Tel.: (358) 2 2510 500
E-Mail: info.fi@dechra.com
Web Site: www.dechra.fi
Emp.: 212
Veterinary Products Marketer, Distr & Technical Support Services
S.I.C.: 5199
N.A.I.C.S.: 424990

Dechra Veterinary Products SAS (3)
9 rue Benoit Malon
92150 Suresnes, France
Tel.: (33) 1 41 38 37 20
Fax: (33) 1 41 38 24 63
E-Mail: info.fr@dechra.com
Veterinary Products Marketer, Distr & Technical Support Services
S.I.C.: 5199
N.A.I.C.S.: 424990

Dechra Veterinary Products SLU (3)
Blames 202 6a
08006 Barcelona, Spain
Tel.: (34) 93 544 85 07
Fax: (34) 93 544 37 42
E-Mail: info.es@dechra.com
Web Site: www.dechra.es
Veterinary Products Marketer, Distr & Technical Support Services
S.I.C.: 5199
N.A.I.C.S.: 424990

DECIDEBLOOM LTD.

Winterton Road
Scunthorpe, North Lincolnshire, DN15 6AH, United Kingdom
Tel.: (44) 8451 254 848
Web Site: www.stoneacre.co.uk
Year Founded: 1994
Sales Range: $350-399.9 Million
Emp.: 1,155
Business Description:
New & Used Car Dealer
S.I.C.: 5511
N.A.I.C.S.: 441110
Personnel:
Mike Cain *(Gen Mgr-Regional)*

DECIMAL TECHNOLOGIES INC.

841 Jean Paul Vincent Bvld
Longueuil, QC, J4G 1R3, Canada
Tel.: (450) 640-1222
Fax: (450) 646-1223
E-Mail: info@decimal.ca
Web Site: www.decimal.ca
Emp.: 20
Business Description:
Financial Performance Management Services
S.I.C.: 8742
N.A.I.C.S.: 541611
Personnel:
Stephane Gaouette *(Pres)*
Division:

Amadeus (1)
400 Jean Lesage Blvd Ste 38
Quebec, QC, G1K 8W1, Canada QC

Tel.: (418) 525-0606
Fax: (418) 525-0909
E-Mail: info@amadeussolutions.com
Web Site: www.amadeussolutions.com
Sales Range: $1-9.9 Million
Enterprise Quality & Compliance Management Software Solutions
S.I.C.: 7372
N.A.I.C.S.: 511210
James Castomguay *(VP-Quality)*

DECISION TECHNOLOGIES LIMITED

Third Floor High Holborn House 52-54 High Holborn
London, WC1V 6RL, United Kingdom
Tel.: (44) 20 7400 6200
Fax: (44) 2074007400
E-Mail: enquire@consumerchoices.co.uk
Web Site: www.brodbandchoices.co.uk
Year Founded: 2005
Sales Range: $10-24.9 Million
Emp.: 60
Business Description:
Operator of Price Comparison Websites
S.I.C.: 7389
N.A.I.C.S.: 519190
Personnel:
Michael Phillips *(Mng Dir)*

DECISIVE DIVIDEND CORPORATION

301 1665 Ellis Street
Kelowna, BC, V1Y 2B3, Canada
Tel.: (250) 863-8914
Fax: (250) 762-8204
Web Site: www.decisivedividend.com
Year Founded: 2012
DE.P—(TSXV)
Business Description:
Investment Services
S.I.C.: 6211
N.A.I.C.S.: 523999
Personnel:
James Paterson *(Chm & CEO)*
David Redekop *(CFO)*
G. Terrence Edwards *(COO & Sec)*
Board of Directors:
James Paterson
M. Bruce Campbell
Michael Conway
G. Terrence Edwards
Scott Jenkins
Robert Louie
Warren Matheos
Timothy Pirie
David Redekop
Transfer Agent:
Olympia Trust Company
Suite 1003 750 West Pender Street
Vancouver, BC, V6C 2T8, Canada

DECKMA HAMBURG GMBH

Kieler Strasse 316
22525 Hamburg, Germany
Tel.: (49) 405488760
Fax: (49) 4054887610
E-Mail: post@deckma.com
Web Site: www.deckma.com
Rev.: $10,345,500
Emp.: 18
Business Description:
Oil & Water Supplier
S.I.C.: 1389
N.A.I.C.S.: 213112
Personnel:
Gunther Schulze *(Founder & Mng Dir)*
Anke Schulze *(Mng Dir)*

DECLAN RESOURCES INC.

(Formerly Kokanee Minerals Inc.)
Suite 302 1620 West 8th Avenue
Vancouver, BC, V6J 1V4, Canada
Tel.: (604) 639-4457
Fax: (604) 639-4458
Web Site: www.declanresources.com
Year Founded: 2005
LAN—(TSXV)
Int. Income: $15,692
Assets: $2,982,996
Liabilities: $1,018,203
Net Worth: $1,964,794
Earnings: ($3,836,563)
Fiscal Year-end: 09/30/13
Business Description:
Gold Exploration Services
S.I.C.: 1041
N.A.I.C.S.: 212221
Personnel:
Wayne Tisdale *(Pres & CEO)*
Lesia Burianyk *(CFO)*
Jamie Newall *(COO)*
Tyson King *(Sr VP-Ops)*
Board of Directors:
Michelle Gahagan
Garry Clark
Michael Curtis
Gordon King
Craig McLean
Jamie Newall
Wayne Tisdale
Transfer Agent:
Computershare Investor Services Inc.
100 University Ave 9th Floor
Toronto, ON, Canada

DECLOET GREENHOUSE MANUFACTURING LTD.

RR1
Simcoe, ON, Canada
Tel.: (519) 582-3081
Fax: (519) 582-0851
Toll Free: (888) 786-4769
Web Site: www.decloetgreenhouse.com
Year Founded: 1986
Sales Range: $10-24.9 Million
Emp.: 25
Business Description:
Greenhouse Mfr
S.I.C.: 3448
N.A.I.C.S.: 332311
Personnel:
Ben DeCloet *(Pres)*

DECLOUT LIMITED

29 Tai Seng Ave 05-01 Natural Cool Lifestyle Hub
Singapore, 534119, Singapore
Tel.: (65) 6818 1833
Fax: (65) 6341 1123
E-Mail: enquiry@declout.com
Web Site: www.declout.com
5UZ—(CAT)
Sls.: $43,008,582
Assets: $36,493,087
Liabilities: $17,780,573
Net Worth: $18,712,514
Earnings: $388,646
Emp.: 260
Fiscal Year-end: 12/31/12
Business Description:
IT Services & Solutions
S.I.C.: 7379
N.A.I.C.S.: 541519
Personnel:
Vesmond Wong *(Chm & CEO)*
Steven Lwi *(CFO)*
Marcus Cheng *(CEO-Acclivis Technologies & Solutions Pte Ltd)*
Winston Koh *(CEO-Corous 360 Pte Ltd)*
Ya Kow *(CEO-ASVIDA Asia Pte Ltd)*
Joshua Saw *(CEO-Beaqon Pte Ltd)*
Bee Fong Lee *(Co-Sec)*
Sarah Yi Jing Yang *(Co-Sec)*
Board of Directors:
Vesmond Wong
Li-Ling Ch'ng
Koon Chan Hew
Raymond Ho
Winston Koh
Chee Keong Wong

DECMIL GROUP LIMITED

20 Parkland Road
Osborne Park, WA, 6017, Australia
Mailing Address:
PO Box 1233
Osborne Park, WA, 6916, Australia
Tel.: (61) 893688877
Fax: (61) 893688878
Web Site: www.decmilgroup.com.au
DCG—(ASX)
Rev.: $551,047,891
Assets: $457,701,783
Liabilities: $175,088,432
Net Worth: $282,613,352
Earnings: $67,076,851
Emp.: 886
Fiscal Year-end: 06/30/13
Business Description:
Civil Works Industrial & Non Process Infrastructure
S.I.C.: 8711
N.A.I.C.S.: 541330
Personnel:
Scott Criddle *(CEO)*
Craig Amos *(CFO)*
Todd Strathdee *(COO & Chief Strategy Officer)*
Board of Directors:
Giles Everist
Denis Criddle
Scott Criddle
Trevor Davies
William Healy
Lee Verios
Legal Counsel:
Steinepreis Paganin
Level 4 Next Building 16 Milligan St
Perth, Australia
Subsidiaries:

Decmil Australia Pty. Ltd. (1)
Level 6 20 Parkland Rd
PO Box 1233
Osborne Park, WA, 6017, Australia
Tel.: (61) 893688877
Fax: (61) 893688878
E-Mail: enquiries@decmil.com.au
Web Site: www.decmil.com.au
Emp.: 300
Construction Engineering Services
S.I.C.: 8711
N.A.I.C.S.: 541330
Kym Sturmer *(Mgr-HR)*

Matrix Engineers Pty. Ltd. (1)
Level 1 159 Adelaide Ter
PO Box 6073
Perth, Western Australia, 6000, Australia
Tel.: (61) 8 6211 3800
Fax: (61) 8 6211 3850
E-Mail: matrix@matrixengineers.com.au
Web Site: www.matrixengineers.com.au
Emp.: 31
Engineering Consulting Services
S.I.C.: 8711
N.A.I.C.S.: 541330
Ray Muscat *(Mgr-Bus Dev)*

Subsidiary:

Eastman Fort Pty. Ltd. (2)
Level 1 159 Adelaide Ter
Perth, WA, 6000, Australia
Tel.: (61) 8 6211 3800
Fax: (61) 8 6211 3850
Web Site: www.efp.net.au
Emp.: 15
Construction Engineering Services
S.I.C.: 8711
N.A.I.C.S.: 541330
Mike Dwyer *(Mgr-Ops)*

Novacoat (WA) Pty. Ltd. (1)
60 Ofc Rd
Kwinana, Western Australia, 6167, Australia
Tel.: (61) 894392111
Fax: (61) 894392115
E-Mail: info@novacoat.com.au
Web Site: www.novacoat.com.au
Metal Coating Services
S.I.C.: 3479
N.A.I.C.S.: 332812

DECO-MICA LIMITED

306 3rd Floor Iskon Mall Star Bazar Building
Jodhpur Char Rasta, Ahmedabad, 380015, India
Tel.: (91) 7926763691
Fax: (91) 79 40028458
E-Mail: decomicaltd@yahoo.in
Web Site: www.decomicaltd.com
531227—(BOM)
Rev.: $7,150,521
Assets: $4,773,415
Liabilities: $3,162,496
Net Worth: $1,610,919
Earnings: $196,566
Fiscal Year-end: 03/31/13
Business Description:
Decorative Laminated Sheet Mfr & Distr
S.I.C.: 3083
N.A.I.C.S.: 326130
Personnel:
Vijaykumar Agarwal *(Chm, Mng Dir & Compliance Officer)*
Board of Directors:
Vijaykumar Agarwal
Vishal V. Agarwal
Harishbhai Joshi
Udaybhan V. Tripathi
Transfer Agent:
MCS Limited
101 Shatdal Complex Opp Bata Show Room Ashram Rd
Ahmedabad, India

DECOLIGHT CERAMICS LTD.

Old Ghuntu Road B/H Decogold Glazed Tiles Ltd
Morbi, Gujarat, 363 642, India
Tel.: (91) 2822241156
Fax: (91) 2822241225
E-Mail: decolight2004@yahoo.com
Web Site: www.decocovering.com
DECOLIGHT—(BOM NSE)
Rev.: $3,172,764
Assets: $25,270,229
Liabilities: $8,905,429
Net Worth: $16,364,800
Earnings: ($2,677,715)
Fiscal Year-end: 03/31/13
Business Description:
Ceramic Tiles Mfr
S.I.C.: 5211
N.A.I.C.S.: 444190
Personnel:
Girishbhai M. Pethapara *(Chm & Mng Dir)*
Kantibhai M. Pethapara *(CEO, CFO & Mng Dir)*
Suresh S. Dave *(Compliance Officer & Sec)*
Board of Directors:
Girishbhai M. Pethapara
Ashvin H. Bopaliya
Vasant Avachar Kaila
Jayantibhai M. Pethapara
Kantibhai M. Pethapara
Vijay Maganlal Vidja
Transfer Agent:
Bigshare Services Pvt Ltd
E 23 Ansa Industrial Estate Sakivihar Road
Saki Naka Andheri E
Mumbai, 400 072, India

DECOR CABINETS LTD.

239 Mountain St S
PO Box 2110
Morden, MB, Canada R6M 1B8

Decor Cabinets Ltd.—(Continued)

Tel.: (204) 822-6151
Fax: (204) 822-6856
E-Mail: decor@decorcabinets.com
Web Site: www.decorcabinets.com
Year Founded: 1977
Rev.: $10,286,554
Emp.: 23
Business Description:
Cabinet Mfr
S.I.C.: 2499
N.A.I.C.S.: 321999
Personnel:
Larry Dyck *(Pres)*

DECOR PRODUCTS INTERNATIONAL, INC.

6 Economic Zone
Wushaliwu
Chang'an Town, Dongguan, Guangdong, China
Tel.: (86) 76985533948
Web Site: www.decorproductsinternational.com
DCRD—(OTC)
Sales Range: $10-24.9 Million
Emp.: 75
Business Description:
Interior Decorating
S.I.C.: 7389
N.A.I.C.S.: 541410
Personnel:
Rui Sheng Liu *(Chm, Pres & CEO)*
Qing Hua Lin *(CFO)*
Baotang Zhao *(Chief Sls Officer)*
Zhang Xie *(Sec)*
Board of Directors:
Rui Sheng Liu
Qing Hua Lin
Zhang Xie
Transfer Agent:
Globex Transfer, LLC
780 Deltona Blvd Ste 202
Deltona, FL 32725

DECOR-REST FURNITURE LTD.

511 Chrislea Road
Woodbridge, ON, L4L 8N6, Canada
Tel.: (905) 856-5956
Fax: (905) 856-2034
E-Mail: info@decor-rest.com
Web Site: www.decor-rest.com
Year Founded: 1972
Rev.: $27,420,800
Emp.: 265
Business Description:
Furniture Mfr
S.I.C.: 2521
N.A.I.C.S.: 337211
Personnel:
Christina Marzilli *(Founder)*

DECORA S.A.

ul Ignacego Pradzynskiego 24 a
63-000 Sroda Wielkopolska, Poland
Tel.: (48) 612864200
Fax: (48) 612854975
E-Mail: office@decora.pl
Web Site: www.decora.pl
DCR—(WAR)
Sales Range: $50-74.9 Million
Business Description:
Decorating Products & Home Decor Accessories Mfr
S.I.C.: 2591
N.A.I.C.S.: 337920
Personnel:
Wlodzimierz Lesinski *(Chm-Supervisory Bd)*
Waldemar Osuch *(Chm-Mgmt Bd)*
Heinz W. Dusar *(Deputy Chm-Supervisory Bd)*
Supervisory Board of Directors:
Wlodzimierz Lesinski
Heinz W. Dusar
Paul Horstmann-Meyer
Andrzej Tomaszewski
Peter Weigand
Subsidiary:

Trans Sp. z o.o. **(1)**
Aleja Milenijna 21
66-470 Kostrzyn, Lubusz, Poland
Tel.: (48) 957283100
Fax: (48) 957529239
E-Mail: kostrzyn@trans.pl
Web Site: www.decora.pl/pag/e/37.php
Decorating Products Mfr
S.I.C.: 2421
N.A.I.C.S.: 321918

Non-U.S. Subsidiaries:

Decora Balt uab **(1)**
Savanoriu pr 174 A
03153 Vilnius, Lithuania
Tel.: (370) 52040116
Fax: (370) 521 60056
Web Site: www.decora.pl/pag/e/37.php
Emp.: 9
Decorating Products Distr
S.I.C.: 5947
N.A.I.C.S.: 453220
Marius Sudnix *(Mng Dir)*

Decora Hungaria kft **(1)**
Europa u 9 BILK logisztikai koezpont, I epuelet Wegry
1239 Budapest, Hungary
Tel.: (36) 18025555
Fax: (36) 18025550
E-Mail: decora@decora.hu
Web Site: www.decora.pl/pag/e/37.php
Emp.: 30
Decorating Products Distr
S.I.C.: 5947
N.A.I.C.S.: 453220
Peter Kiss *(Mgr)*

Decora Nova s.r.o. **(1)**
Tesinska 288
Senov, 739 34 Frydek-Mistek, Senov, Czech Republic
Tel.: (420) 596 411 890
Fax: (420) 596 411 891
E-Mail: info@decora.cz
Decorating Products Distr
S.I.C.: 5947
N.A.I.C.S.: 453220

Decora Ru ooo **(1)**
ul 4-ta Tverskaya-Yamskaya 2/11 2
125047 Moscow, Russia
Tel.: (7) 4956633369
E-Mail: info@decora.ru
Decorating Products Distr
S.I.C.: 5947
N.A.I.C.S.: 453220

Decora Ukraina TOB **(1)**
Str Kuthozova No 100 134
07400 Brovary, Ukraine
Tel.: (380) 444985890
Fax: (380) 444985891
E-Mail: uaoffice@decora.pl
Web Site: www.decora.pl/pag/e/37.php
Emp.: 60
Decorating Products Distr
S.I.C.: 5199
N.A.I.C.S.: 424990

E. Wicklein GmbH **(1)**
Am Fluegelbahnhof 4
96317 Kronach, Bavaria, Germany
Tel.: (49) 9261 50490 40
Fax: (49) 9261 50490 49
E-Mail: info@ewifoam.com
Web Site: www.ewifoam.com
Acoustic Insulation Materials Distr
S.I.C.: 5033
N.A.I.C.S.: 423330
Joachim Weber *(Mng Dir)*

IP Decora East **(1)**
ul Gorkogo 145/5/1
210604 Vitsyebsk, Belarus
Tel.: (375) 296795570
Fax: (375) 21 23 43 834
E-Mail: decora.east@decora.pl
Web Site: www.decora.pl/pag/e/37.php
Emp.: 52
Decorating Products Mfr
S.I.C.: 2426
N.A.I.C.S.: 321918

DECORINT SA

Take Ionescu nr 77
Cluj-Napoca, Romania
Tel.: (40) 264 406450
Fax: (40) 264 406451
E-Mail: office@decorint.ro
Web Site: www.decorint.ro
Year Founded: 1994
FIMB—(BUC)
Emp.: 50
Business Description:
Real Estate Development
S.I.C.: 6531
N.A.I.C.S.: 531390
Personnel:
Tibor Konti *(CEO)*

DECOTEX JSC

42 Hadji Dimitar blvd
Sliven, 8800, Bulgaria
Tel.: (359) 44 662 382
Fax: (359) 44 662 591
E-Mail: decotex@decotex.org
Web Site: www.decotex.org
Year Founded: 1909
4DE—(BUL)
Business Description:
Textile Products Mfr
S.I.C.: 2273
N.A.I.C.S.: 314110
Personnel:
Mara Pavlova Veleva *(Dir-IR)*

DECTRON INTERNATIONALE INC.

4300 Poirier Boulevard
Montreal, QC, H4R 2C5, Canada
Tel.: (514) 334-9609
Fax: (514) 334-9184
E-Mail: info@dectron.com
Web Site: www.dectron.com
Year Founded: 1976
Sales Range: $50-74.9 Million
Emp.: 390
Business Description:
Dehumidification, Refrigeration, Air Conditioning & Indoor Air Quality Products Mfr & Supplier
Import Export
S.I.C.: 3585
N.A.I.C.S.: 333415
Personnel:
Ness Lakdawala *(Chm, Pres & CEO)*
Mauro Parissi *(COO, Sec & Controller)*
Leena Lakwadala *(Exec VP)*
Board of Directors:
Ness Lakdawala
Serge Beaudet
Dick W. Driggs
Mauro Parissi
Gilles Richard
Legal Counsel:
Shaffer & Associates
4150 Sherbrooke West, 3rd Floor
H3Z 1C2 Montreal, QC, Canada
Gersten, Savage & Kaplowitz, LLP
New York, NY 21202

U.S. Subsidiaries:

Dectron Inc **(1)**
10898 Crabapple Rd Ste 103
Roswell, GA 30075 (100%)
Tel.: (770) 649-0102
Fax: (770) 649-0243
Toll Free: (800) 676-2566
Emp.: 600
Air Conditioning Products
S.I.C.: 5075
N.A.I.C.S.: 423730
Hirry Topikran *(VP)*

Dectron U.S.A. Inc **(1)**
2934 Hearthside Ln
Lancaster, PA 17601-1457
Tel.: (717) 898-3290
Management Consulting Services
S.I.C.: 8748
N.A.I.C.S.: 541618

IPAC, Inc. **(1)**
155 Pineview Dr
Amherst, NY 14228 NY
Tel.: (716) 204-9580
Fax: (716) 204-9593
Toll Free: (800) 388-3211
Web Site: www.ipacinc.com
Emp.: 100
Mfr. of Precision Air Conditioning Systems & Compressed Air & Gas Accessories, Replacement Parts, Sheet Metal Fabrication & Coating
Import Export
S.I.C.: 3565
N.A.I.C.S.: 333993
Brian Costello *(Pres)*

Subsidiaries:

Circul-Aire Inc. **(1)**
3999 Boul De La Cote-Vertu
Saint Laurent, QC, H4R 1R2, Canada
Tel.: (514) 333-4050
Fax: (514) 333-6149
Toll Free: (800) 667-6338
E-Mail: info@dectron.com
Web Site: www.circul-aire.com
Emp.: 50
Industrial & Commercial Fan & Blower Mfr
S.I.C.: 3564
N.A.I.C.S.: 333413
Sham Ahmed *(COO)*

Refplus Inc **(1)**
1385 de Coulomb St
J4B7L8 Boucherville, QC, Canada
Tel.: (450) 641-2665
Fax: (450) 641-4554
E-Mail: info@refplus.com
Web Site: www.refplus.com
Emp.: 52
Air-Conditioning & Warm Air Heating Equipment & Commercial & Industrial Refrigeration Equipment Mfr
S.I.C.: 3585
N.A.I.C.S.: 333415
Mauro Parissi *(COO)*

Tranzmetal Inc. **(1)**
3999 Boul De La Cote-Vertu
H4R 1R2 Saint Laurent, QC, Canada
Tel.: (514) 333-4050
Fax: (514) 333-6149
E-Mail: info@tranzmetal.com
Web Site: www.tranzmetal.com
Emp.: 70
Industrial & Commercial Fan & Blower Mfr
S.I.C.: 3564
N.A.I.C.S.: 333413
Mauro Parissi *(COO)*

DEDALO GRUPO GRAFICO, S.L.

Carretera de Pinto a Fuenlabrada km 20.8
ES-28320 Pinto, Spain
Tel.: (34) 915069300
E-Mail: info@dedalogrupografico.es
Web Site: www.dedalogrupografico.es
Year Founded: 2003
Emp.: 500
Business Description:
Holding Company; Commercial Printing Services
S.I.C.: 6719
N.A.I.C.S.: 551112
Personnel:
Oscar Gomez Barbero *(Pres)*

Subsidiary:

Graficas Integradas S.A. **(1)**
Santa Leonor N 63 2 planta
ES-28037 Madrid, Spain ES
Tel.: (34) 913273695
Fax: (34) 913273150

E-Mail: fotomecanica@dedalogrupografico.es
Web Site: www.dedalogrupografico.es/fotomecanica_contacto.html
Digital Printing Services
S.I.C.: 2759
N.A.I.C.S.: 323111
Luis Lopez Mendiola *(Mng Dir)*

Unit:

Dedalo Heliocolor **(1)**
Pol Ind N1 Francois Marina E Mindosa No 5 & 6
Poligono Cabanillas del Compo, ES-19171 Guadalajara, Spain
Tel.: (34) 94 933 3100
Fax: (34) 94 933 3120
E-Mail: comercial_huecograbado@dedalogrupografico.es
Web Site: www.dedalogrupografico.es/huecograbado_contacto.html
Emp.: 380
Commercial Lithographic & Gravure Printing Services
S.I.C.: 2759
N.A.I.C.S.: 323111
Antonio Hernando Rodriguez *(Comml Dir)*

DEDICARE AB

Kungsholmsstrand 147
112 48 Stockholm, Sweden
Tel.: (46) 8 555 656 00
Fax: (46) 8 555 651 45
E-Mail: dedicare@dedicare.se
Web Site: www.dedicare.se
DEDI—(OMX)
Sales Range: $25-49.9 Million
Emp.: 200
Business Description:
Medical Staffing Services
S.I.C.: 7361
N.A.I.C.S.: 561311
Personnel:
Stig Engcrantz *(CEO)*
Richard Engel *(CFO)*

DEE VALLEY GROUP PLC

Packsaddle Wrexham Road
Packsaddle Rhostyllen
Wrexham, LL14 4EH, United Kingdom
Tel.: (44) 01978846946
Fax: (44) 1978846888
E-Mail: contact@deevalleygroup.com
Web Site: www.deevalleygroup.com
Year Founded: 1994
DVW—(LSE)
Rev.: $36,018,867
Assets: $183,275,025
Liabilities: $142,976,282
Net Worth: $40,298,743
Earnings: $6,361,380
Emp.: 166
Fiscal Year-end: 03/31/13
Business Description:
Holding Company; Water Supply Services
S.I.C.: 6719
N.A.I.C.S.: 551112
Personnel:
Norman Holladay *(Mng Dir)*
Board of Directors:
Graham Scott
Philip Holder
Norman Holladay
Jon Schofield
David Strahan
David Weir
Subsidiaries:

Chester Water Ltd **(1)**
Packsaddle Wrexham Road
Wrexham, Clwyd, LL14 4EH, United Kingdom
Tel.: (44) 1978 846946
Fax: (44) 1978846888
E-Mail: contact@deevalleygroup.com
Web Site: www.deevalleywater.co.uk
Emp.: 150
Water Distribution Services
S.I.C.: 4971
N.A.I.C.S.: 221310
Norman Holladay *(Mng Dir)*

Dee Valley plc **(1)**
Packsaddle Wrexham Road Rhostyllen
Wrexham, Clwyd, LL14 4EH, United Kingdom
Tel.: (44) 1978846946
Fax: (44) 1978846888
E-Mail: contact@deevalleygroup.com
Emp.: 200
Water Distribution Services
S.I.C.: 4941
N.A.I.C.S.: 221310
Norman Holladay *(Mng Dir)*

Dee Valley Water (Holdings) Ltd **(1)**
Packsaddle Wrexham Road
Rhostyllen, Wrexham, LL144EH, United Kingdom (100%)
Tel.: (44) 197884946
Fax: (44) 197884688
E-Mail: contact@deevalleygroup.com
Web Site: www.deevalleywater.co.uk
Emp.: 170
Water Supply & Irrigation Systems
S.I.C.: 4971
N.A.I.C.S.: 221310
Norman Holladay *(Mng Dir)*

Dee Valley Water plc **(1)**
Packsaddle Wrexham Rd
Rhostyllen, Wrexham, LL14 4EH, United Kingdom
Tel.: (44) 1978846946
Fax: (44) 1978846888
E-Mail: info@deevalleygroup.com
Web Site: www.deevalleygroup.com
Water Supply Services
S.I.C.: 4941
N.A.I.C.S.: 221310
Norman Holladay *(Mng Dir)*

DEEP INDUSTRIES LTD

Opp Suryanaryan Bungalows State Highway
Gandhinagar, Motera, Gujarat, 380005, India
Tel.: (91) 7927571128
Fax: (91) 7926862077
E-Mail: info@deepindustries.com
Web Site: www.deepindustries.com
532760—(BOM)
Rev.: $12,438,489
Assets: $55,670,471
Liabilities: $23,785,041
Net Worth: $31,885,430
Earnings: $2,254,512
Fiscal Year-end: 03/31/13
Business Description:
Oil & Gas Exploration Services
S.I.C.: 1311
N.A.I.C.S.: 211111
Personnel:
Paras S. Savla *(Chm & Co-Mng Dir)*
Rupesh K. Savla *(Co-Mng Dir)*
Bhavika Bhatt *(Compliance Officer & Sec)*
Board of Directors:
Paras S. Savla
Harish G. Bhinde
Kirit V. Joshi
Dharen S. Savla
Rupesh K. Savla
Premsingh Sawhney
Vijay R. Shah
Ajay Kumar Singhania
Transfer Agent:
Link Intime India Pvt. Ltd
303 3rd Floor Shopper's Plaza V Opp. Municipal Market
Off. C.G. Road, Ahmedabad, 380009, India

DEEP SEA SUPPLY PLC

John Kennedy Ave Iris House 7th Floor
Office no 740B, Limassol, 3100, Cyprus
Tel.: (357) 25431113
E-Mail: Constantinos@dess.no
Web Site: www.deepseasupply.no
ZUW—(DEU)
Rev.: $124,140,000
Assets: $765,710,000
Liabilities: $608,703,000
Net Worth: $157,007,000
Earnings: ($4,423,000)
Emp.: 55
Fiscal Year-end: 12/31/12
Business Description:
Anchor Handling Tug Supplier
S.I.C.: 3714
N.A.I.C.S.: 336320
Personnel:
Harald Thorstein *(Chm)*
Finn Amund Norbye *(CEO)*
Anders Hall Jomaas *(CFO)*
Board of Directors:
Harald Thorstein
Hans Petter Aas
Frixos Savvides
Subsidiary:

DESS PSV Ltd **(1)**
Deana Beach Apts Promachon Elefterias Street
Limassol, 4103, Cyprus
Tel.: (357) 25431107
Fax: (357) 25431131
Emp.: 51
Offshore Transportation Services
S.I.C.: 4412
N.A.I.C.S.: 483111

Non-U.S. Subsidiaries:

Deep Sea Supply Management AS **(1)**
Tromoyveien 22
4841 Arendal, Norway
Tel.: (47) 37058610
Emp.: 10
Offshore Transportation Services
S.I.C.: 4412
N.A.I.C.S.: 483111
Finn Amund Norbye *(CEO)*
Anders Hall Jomaas *(CFO)*
Olaf J. Hafredal *(COO & Dir-Mktg)*

Deep Sea Supply Management Singapore Pte Ltd **(1)**
10 Hoe Chiang Road 19-03/04/05 Keppel Tower
Singapore, 089315, Singapore
Tel.: (65) 66319831
Offshore Transportation Services
S.I.C.: 4412
N.A.I.C.S.: 483111

DEEP SPACE MEDIA GROUP AG

Im alten Riet 102
FL-9494 Schaan, Liechtenstein
Tel.: (423) 2320295
Fax: (423) 2320296
E-Mail: office@deepspacemedia.com
Web Site: www.deepspacemedia.com
0DS—(DEU)
Emp.: 30
Business Description:
Interactive Media, TV & Mobile Services
S.I.C.: 4899
N.A.I.C.S.: 517919
Personnel:
Oliver M. Brand *(Mng Dir)*

DEEP WELL OIL & GAS, INC.

Suite 700 10150 - 100 Street
Edmonton, AB, T5J 0P6, Canada
Tel.: (780) 409-8144
Fax: (780) 409-8146
E-Mail: info@deepwelloil.com
Web Site: www.deepwelloil.com
DWOG—(DEU OTC)
Int. Income: $21,492
Assets: $24,366,368
Liabilities: $922,057
Net Worth: $23,444,311
Earnings: ($2,463,403)
Emp.: 3
Fiscal Year-end: 09/30/13
Business Description:
Oil & Gas Exploration Services
S.I.C.: 1389
N.A.I.C.S.: 213112
Personnel:
Horst A. Schmid *(Chm, Pres & CEO)*
Curtis James Sparrow *(CFO, Sec & Treas)*
Board of Directors:
Horst A. Schmid
Said Arrata
Satya Brata Das
Pascal Node-Langlois
David Roff
Curtis James Sparrow
Malik Youyou

DEEP YELLOW LIMITED

Level 1 329 Hay Street
Subiaco, WA, 6008, Australia
Mailing Address:
PO Box 1770
Subiaco, WA, 6904, Australia
Tel.: (61) 8 9286 6999
Fax: (61) 8 9286 6969
E-Mail: info@deepyellow.com.au
Web Site: www.deepyellow.com.au
DYL—(ASX)
Rev.: $751,471
Assets: $97,570,985
Liabilities: $570,188
Net Worth: $97,000,797
Earnings: ($9,032,690)
Emp.: 42
Fiscal Year-end: 06/30/13
Business Description:
Mineral Exploration
S.I.C.: 1481
N.A.I.C.S.: 213115
Personnel:
Greg Cochran *(Mng Dir)*
Mark Pitts *(Sec)*
Board of Directors:
Timothy Carl Netscher
Rudolf Brunovs
Greg Cochran
Mervyn Patrick Greene
Gillian Swaby
Christophe Urtel
Subsidiary:

Superior Uranium Pty. Ltd. **(1)**
329 Hay St
Subiaco, WA, 6008, Australia
Tel.: (61) 892866999
Fax: (61) 892866969
E-Mail: admin@deepyellow.com.au
Web Site: www.deepyellow.com.au
Emp.: 2
Uranium Ore Mining Service
S.I.C.: 1094
N.A.I.C.S.: 212291
Greg Cochran *(Mng Dir)*

Non-U.S. Subsidiary:

Reptile Uranium Namibia (Pty.) Ltd. **(1)**
48 Hidipo Hamutenya St
PO Box 2538
Swakopmund, Namibia
Tel.: (264) 64415200
Fax: (264) 64405384
E-Mail: klaus@reptile.com.na
Web Site: www.reptile.com.na
Emp.: 35
Uranium Ore Mining Services
S.I.C.: 1094
N.A.I.C.S.: 212291
Klaus Frielingdors *(Gen Mgr)*

DEEPAK FASTENERS LIMITED

4th Floor 1st Mall
Ludhiana, Punjab, 141 001, India
Tel.: (91) 1613911111
Fax: (91) 161 2447700
E-Mail: sales@deepakfasteners.com
Web Site: www.deepakfasteners.com
Emp.: 5,000
Business Description:
Industrial Fastener Mfr
S.I.C.: 3452
N.A.I.C.S.: 332722
Personnel:
Sanjeev Kalra *(Mng Dir)*
Non-U.S. Subsidiaries:

Deepak Fasteners (Australia) Pty Ltd. **(1)**
67-69 Licola Crescent
Dandenong, VIC, 3175, Australia
Tel.: (61) 398940026
Telex: AA 31083
Fax: (61) 398940038
E-Mail: DFL.sales@unbrako.com.au
Web Site: www.deepakfasteners.com.au
Sales Range: $10-24.9 Million
Emp.: 16
Industrial Fasteners Mfr
S.I.C.: 3965
N.A.I.C.S.: 339993

Deepak Fasteners (Shannon) Ltd. **(1)**
BAYS 25-30 Shannon Industrial Estate
Shannon, County Clare, Ireland (100%)
Tel.: (353) 61716500
Fax: (353) 61716584
E-Mail: sales@deepakfasteners.com
Web Site: www.unvrako.com
Sales Range: $75-99.9 Million
Emp.: 150
Industrial Fastener Mfr
S.I.C.: 3452
N.A.I.C.S.: 332722
Eddie Cahill *(Pres)*

Deepak Fasteners (U.K.) Ltd. **(1)**
12-14 Tower Street Newtown
Birmingham, B19 3RR, United Kingdom
Tel.: (44) 1213334610
Fax: (44) 1213334525
E-Mail: sales@deepakfasteners.com
Web Site: www.deepakfasteners.co.uk
Emp.: 5
Industrial Fastener Mfr
S.I.C.: 3452
N.A.I.C.S.: 332722
Adesh Gupta *(CEO)*

DEEPAK FERTILISERS & PETROCHEMICALS CORPORATION LIMITED

Opp Golf Course Shastri Nagar
Yerwada
Pune, 411 006, India
Tel.: (91) 2066458000
Fax: (91) 2026683727
E-Mail: investorgrievance@dfpcl.com
Web Site: www.dfpcl.com
500645—(BOM)
Rev.: $527,430,277
Assets: $544,631,893
Liabilities: $307,142,076
Net Worth: $237,489,817
Earnings: $23,972,999
Fiscal Year-end: 03/31/13
Business Description:
Chemicals, Petrochemicals & Fertilizers Mfr
S.I.C.: 2899
N.A.I.C.S.: 325998
Personnel:
Sailesh C. Mehta *(Chm & Mng Dir)*
Somnath Patil *(Pres & CFO)*
R. Sriraman *(Compliance Officer, Sec & Exec VP-Legal)*
Rajeev Chemburkar *(Pres-Chemicals)*
Alok Goel *(Pres-Strategy & Bus Dev)*
Guy R. Goves *(Pres-Agribus)*
Pandurang Landge *(Pres-Projects)*
Carl Anders Lindgren *(Pres-TAN)*
Rajendra Sinh *(Pres-HRD & Corp Svcs)*
Ranjan Basu *(Exec VP-Ops)*
R. P. Haran *(Exec VP-Corp Affairs)*
Vivek Y. Kelkar *(Sr VP-Strategic Comm & IR)*
Board of Directors:
Sailesh C. Mehta
D. Basu
Partha Bhattacharyya
S. Rama Iyer
U. P. Jhaveri
Parul S. Mehta
Anil Sachdev
R. A. Shah
N. C. Singhal
Pranay Vakil
S. R. Wadhwa
Legal Counsel:
Crawford Bayley & Co
Mumbai, India
Transfer Agent:
Sharepro Services (India) Pvt Ltd
13AB Samhita Warehousing Complex 2nd Fl
Sakinaka Telephone Exchange Ln
Off Andheri-Kurla Road Sakinaka Andheri East, Mumbai, 400 072, India
Subsidiary:

Smartchem Technologies Limited **(1)**
W-46 M I D C Baramati
Pune, Maharashtra, 413 133, India
Tel.: (91) 2024334654
Fax: (91) 2024352547
Fertilizers Mfr
S.I.C.: 2875
N.A.I.C.S.: 325314

DEEPAK NITRITE LIMITED

9/10 Kunj Society Alkapuri
Vadodara, 390 007, India
Tel.: (91) 265 235 1013
Fax: (91) 265 233 0994
E-Mail: investor@deepaknitrite.com
Web Site: www.deepaknitrite.com
Year Founded: 1970
506401—(BOM)
Rev.: $202,956,842
Assets: $164,761,828
Liabilities: $112,739,070
Net Worth: $52,022,758
Earnings: $7,012,477
Emp.: 1,151
Fiscal Year-end: 03/31/13
Business Description:
Speciality Chemical Mfr
S.I.C.: 2899
N.A.I.C.S.: 325998
Personnel:
C. K. Mehta *(Founder)*
Deepak C. Mehta *(Vice Chm & Co-Mng Dir)*
Ajay C. Mehta *(Co-Mng Dir)*
Sanjay Upadhyay *(Compliance Officer, Sec & Sr VP-Fin)*
Board of Directors:
C. K. Mehta
S. K. Anand
Umesh Asaikar
Sudhin Choksey
Nimesh Kampani
Sudhir Mankad
Ajay C. Mehta
Deepak C. Mehta
Richard H. Rupp
Swaminathan Sivaram
Transfer Agent:
Sharepro Services (I) Pvt. Ltd.
13 A-B Samhita Warehousing Complex 2nd Floor
Near Sakinaka Telephone Exchange Andheri Kurla Road Sakinaka, Mumbai, 400072, India

DEEPOCEAN GROUP HOLDING AS

Karmsundsgt 74
5504 Haugesund, Norway
Tel.: (47) 52 70 04 00
Fax: (47) 52 70 04 01
E-Mail: post@deepoceangroup.com
Web Site: www.deepoceangroup.com
Business Description:
Subsea Construction & Engineering Services
S.I.C.: 8711
N.A.I.C.S.: 541330
Personnel:
Thomas Thune Andersen *(Chm)*
Bart H. Heijermans *(CEO)*
Brett Cenkus *(Gen Counsel)*
Board of Directors:
Thomas Thune Andersen
Joanne Curin
Bart H. Heijermans
Harald Johan Norvik
Arvid Trolle
David N. Weinstein
Subsidiary:

DeepOcean AS **(1)**
Karmsundgt 74
PO Box 2144
5527 Haugesund, Norway NO
Tel.: (47) 52 70 04 00 (100%)
Fax: (47) 52700401
E-Mail: post@deepoceangroup.com
Web Site: www.deepocean.no
Sales Range: $25-49.9 Million
Emp.: 200
Marine Services
S.I.C.: 4491
N.A.I.C.S.: 488320
Mads Bardsen *(Pres)*
Non-U.S. Subsidiary:

DeepOcean UK Ltd. **(1)**
14 Albyn Terrace
Aberdeen, AB10 1YAP, United Kingdom UK
Tel.: (44) 01224633366 (100%)
Fax: (44) 01224647134
E-Mail: krolinson@tricomarine.com
Web Site: www.tricomarine.com
Sales Range: $100-124.9 Million
Emp.: 8
Marine Services
S.I.C.: 4731
N.A.I.C.S.: 488510
Gerry Gray *(Mng Dir)*

DEER BRIDGE PLUMBING & HEATING LTD.

4522 - 112th Ave SE
Calgary, AB, T2C 2K2, Canada
Tel.: (403) 252-1101
Fax: (403) 252-1103
E-Mail: mirat@deerbridgeplumbing.com
Web Site: www.deerbridgeplumbing.com
Year Founded: 1986
Sales Range: $10-24.9 Million
Emp.: 40
Business Description:
Plumbing Contract Services
S.I.C.: 3432
N.A.I.C.S.: 332913
Personnel:
Dan Marsh *(Owner)*

DEER CONSUMER PRODUCTS, INC.

Area 2 1/F Building M-6 Ctr High-Tech Industrial Park
Nanshan, Shenzhen, 518057, China
Tel.: (86) 75586028285
Web Site: www.deerinc.com
Year Founded: 2006
Sales Range: $200-249.9 Million
Emp.: 890
Business Description:
Home & Kitchen Electric Appliances Designer, Mfr & Sales
S.I.C.: 3639
N.A.I.C.S.: 335228
Personnel:
Ying He *(Chm & CEO)*
Yongmei Helen Wang *(Pres)*
Zongshu Nie *(CFO & Controller-Fin)*
Board of Directors:
Ying He
Edward Hua
Zongshu Nie
Qi Hua Xu
Hardy Zhang

DEER HORN METALS INC.

202 4840 Delta Street
Delta, BC, V4K 2T6, Canada
Tel.: (604) 952-7221
Fax: (604) 952-7223
E-Mail: info@deerhornmetals.com
Web Site: www.deerhornmetals.com
Year Founded: 2004
DHM—(TSXV)
Assets: $269,130
Liabilities: $260,524
Net Worth: $8,606
Earnings: ($953,169)
Fiscal Year-end: 07/31/13
Business Description:
Mineral Exploration Services
S.I.C.: 1081
N.A.I.C.S.: 213114
Personnel:
Tyrone Docherty *(Pres & CEO)*
Pamela Saulnier *(CFO)*
Board of Directors:
Tyrone Docherty
Tony Fogarassy
Lindsay Edward Gorrill
Matt Wayrynen
Transfer Agent:
Olympia Trust Company
Suite 1003-750 West Pender Street
Vancouver, BC, Canada

DEERA INVESTMENT & REAL ESTATE DEVELOPMENT CO.

Al-Madina AlMunawra St Noor Building
PO Box 940237
Amman, 11194, Jordan
Tel.: (962) 65544826
Fax: (962) 65544825
E-Mail: info@deera.jo
Web Site: www.deera.jo
DERA—(AMM)
Sales Range: $1-9.9 Million
Emp.: 13
Business Description:
Real Estate Investment Services
S.I.C.: 6531
N.A.I.C.S.: 531390

DEERLAND FARM EQUIPMENT (1985) LTD.

8599 112 Street
Fort Saskatchewan, AB, T8L 3V3, Canada
Tel.: (780) 998-3249
Fax: (780) 998-7075
Toll Free: (888) 350-7278
E-Mail: deerland@deerland.ca
Web Site: www.deerland.ca
Year Founded: 1978
Rev.: $12,630,950
Emp.: 35
Business Description:
Farm Equipment Supplier
S.I.C.: 5083
N.A.I.C.S.: 423820
Personnel:
Dale Stokke *(Owner)*

DEERNS RAADGEVENDE INGENIEURS B.V

Fleminglaan 10
2289 Rijswijk, Netherlands

Tel.: (31) 88 374 0000
Fax: (31) 88 374 0010
E-Mail: contact@deerns.nl
Web Site: www.deerns.com
Business Description:
Engineering Consulting Services
S.I.C.: 8999
N.A.I.C.S.: 541690
Personnel:
Jan Karel Mak *(CEO)*

Non-U.S. Subsidiary:

Deerns Italia SpA **(1)**
(Formerly Hilson Moran Italia S.p.A.)
via Guglielmo Silva 36
20149 Milan, Italy
Tel.: (39) 02 3616 7888
Fax: (39) 02 3616 7801
E-Mail: info@deerns.it
Web Site: www.deerns.com
Engineering Consulting Services
S.I.C.: 8711
N.A.I.C.S.: 541330

DEETHREE EXPLORATION LTD.

Suite 2200 520 3rd Avenue SW
Calgary, AB, T2P 0R3, Canada
Tel.: (403) 767-3060
Fax: (403) 263-9710
E-Mail: info@deethree.ca
Web Site: www.deethree.ca
Year Founded: 2007
DTX—(OTC TSX)
Rev.: $84,603,030
Assets: $327,694,597
Liabilities: $116,872,896
Net Worth: $210,821,702
Earnings: $7,138,058
Emp.: 8
Fiscal Year-end: 12/31/12
Business Description:
Oil & Gas Exploration Services
S.I.C.: 1311
N.A.I.C.S.: 211111
Personnel:
Michael Kabanuk *(Chm)*
Martin Cheyne *(Pres & CEO)*
Gail Hannon *(CFO)*
Daniel Kenney *(Sec)*
Board of Directors:
Michael Kabanuk
Kevin D. Andrus
Brendan Carrigy
Martin Cheyne
Henry Peter Hamm
Dennis Nerland
Bradley B. Porter
Legal Counsel:
Davis LLP
Calgary, AB, Canada
Transfer Agent:
Olympia Trust Corporation of Canada
Calgary, AB, T2G 0P6, Canada

DEFENSE INDUSTRIES INTERNATIONAL, INC.

12 Hamefalsim Street
49514 Petah Tiqwa, Israel
Tel.: (972) 37168383
Fax: (972) 37168484
E-Mail: exportez@zahav.net.il
Web Site: www.defense-industries.com
DFNS—(OTC)
Sales Range: $10-24.9 Million
Emp.: 201
Business Description:
Security & Defense Products Mfr
S.I.C.: 3489
N.A.I.C.S.: 332994
Personnel:
Uri Nissani *(Pres & CEO)*
Rechela Carmeli *(COO & VP-Ops & Resources)*
Board of Directors:
Motti Hassan
Uri Nissani
Legal Counsel:
Carter, Ledyard & Milburn
2 Wall St
New York, NY 10005
Tel.: (212) 732-3200
Fax: (212) 732-3232
Transfer Agent:
OTC Transfer Agent, Inc
231 E 2100 S
Salt Lake City, UT 84115

Subsidiaries:

Achidatex Nazareth Elite (1977) Ltd **(1)**
12 Hamefalsim St
Kiryat Arieh, Petah Tiqwa, 52121, Israel
Tel.: (972) 39213431
Fax: (972) 39213436
E-Mail: achidatex@achidatex.com
Web Site: www.achidatex.com
Emp.: 100
Military Equipment Mfr
S.I.C.: 3795
N.A.I.C.S.: 336992

Export Erez Ltd **(1)**
PO Box 10194
Petah Tiqwa, 49002, Israel
Tel.: (972) 39271911
Fax: (972) 37168484
E-Mail: zarchin@exporterez.co.il
Web Site: www.exporterez.co.il
Emp.: 200
Military Equipment Mfr
S.I.C.: 3795
N.A.I.C.S.: 336992
Eli Asa *(Mgr-Mktg)*

DEFI GROUP SAS

54 56 rue Klock
92586 Clichy, France
Tel.: (33) 1 41 40 42 00
Fax: (33) 1 41 40 42 29
Web Site: www.defi-group.com
Year Founded: 1977
Sales Range: $50-74.9 Million
Emp.: 120
Business Description:
Outdoor Advertising Services
S.I.C.: 7312
N.A.I.C.S.: 541850
Personnel:
Erminio Deodato *(CEO)*

Subsidiary:

DEFI France SAS **(1)**
54/56 rue Klock
92586 Clichy, Cedex, France
Tel.: (33) 1 41 40 42 00
Fax: (33) 1 41 40 42 25
E-Mail: info@defi-group.com
Web Site: www.defi-group.com
Emp.: 15
Outdoor Advertising Services
S.I.C.: 7312
N.A.I.C.S.: 541850
Cyrille Leclerc *(Head-Ops-Western Europe)*

Non-U.S. Subsidiaries:

DEFI Czech s.r.o. **(1)**
Vaclavske namesti 66
110 00 Prague, Czech Republic
Tel.: (420) 296348307
Fax: (420) 296348305
E-Mail: Info@defi-czech.com
Emp.: 3
Outdoor Advertising Services
S.I.C.: 7312
N.A.I.C.S.: 541850
Emmanuel Cassassolles *(Head-Ops)*

DEFI Deutschland GmbH **(1)**
Magdalenenstrasse 8
20148 Hamburg, Germany
Tel.: (49) 403697360
Fax: (49) 4036973636
E-Mail: info@defi-deutschland.de
Web Site: www.defi-group.com
Emp.: 3
Outdoor Advertising Services
S.I.C.: 7312
N.A.I.C.S.: 541850
Ulf-Gunnar Schochow *(Mgr-External Sls)*

DEFI Group Asia Ltd. **(1)**
12/F Ruttonjee House
11 Duddell Street, Central, China (Hong Kong)
Tel.: (852) 25213661
Fax: (852) 28459198
Outdoor Advertising
S.I.C.: 7312
N.A.I.C.S.: 541850
Christophe Thery *(Head-Ops)*

DEFI Hungary Kft **(1)**
Alkotas Ut 50
H 1123 Budapest, Hungary
Tel.: (36) 1 489 52 40
Fax: (36) 1 325 30 24
E-Mail: info@defi-group.com
Emp.: 6
Outdoor Advertising Services
S.I.C.: 7312
N.A.I.C.S.: 541850
Bertalan Hamvai *(Head-Ops)*

DEFI Italia S.p.A. **(1)**
Via lattanzio 77
20137 Milan, Italy
Tel.: (39) 02 551 3722
Fax: (39) 02 551 1651
E-Mail: defiitalia@defi-italia.com
Web Site: www.defi-group.com
Outdoor Advertising
S.I.C.: 7312
N.A.I.C.S.: 541850
Giuseppe Boggio Merlo *(Head-Ops)*

DEFI Neolux **(1)**
Av Casal Ribeiro 18 9 Floor
1000 103 Lisbon, Portugal
Tel.: (351) 21 351 40 10
Fax: (351) 21 315 02 41
Outdoor Advertising
S.I.C.: 7312
N.A.I.C.S.: 541850
Delfim Costa *(Pres)*

DEFI Poland Sp. z o.o. **(1)**
ul Krucza 16/22
00-526 Warsaw, Poland
Tel.: (48) 224342177
Fax: (48) 224342162
E-Mail: info@defi-poland.com
Emp.: 13
Outdoor Advertising Services
S.I.C.: 7312
N.A.I.C.S.: 541850
Ronald Kosnowicz *(Head-Ops)*

Iberdefi **(1)**
Calle Arturo Soria 336 1 Planta
28033 Madrid, Spain
Tel.: (34) 91 716 02 91
Fax: (34) 91 759 40 53
E-Mail: iberdefi@iberdefi.com
Outdoor Advertising Services
S.I.C.: 7312
N.A.I.C.S.: 541850
Cyrille Leclerc *(Head-Ops-Western Europe)*

ZAO DEFI Russie **(1)**
Usacheva Street 62/1 Office 18
119048 Moscow, Russia
Tel.: (7) 495 925 75 70
Fax: (7) 495 933 5212
E-Mail: info@defi-rus.ru
Emp.: 25
Outdoor Advertising Services
S.I.C.: 7312
N.A.I.C.S.: 541850
Sergey Kluchkin *(Pres)*

DEFIANCE SILVER CORP.

Suite 1610-409 Granville Street
Vancouver, BC, V6C 1T2, Canada
Tel.: (778) 729-0333
Fax: (778) 734-0333
E-Mail: info@defiancesilver.com
Web Site: www.defiancesilver.com
Year Founded: 2007
DEF—(TSXV)
Int. Income: $2,112
Assets: $2,178,255
Liabilities: $375,194
Net Worth: $1,803,061
Earnings: ($885,328)
Fiscal Year-end: 06/30/13
Business Description:
Silver Exploration & Development Services
S.I.C.: 1044
N.A.I.C.S.: 212222
Personnel:
W. D. Bruce Winfield *(Pres & CEO)*
Matthew Kavanagh *(CFO)*
Board of Directors:
Christopher A. Bunka
George A. Gorzynski
Darrell A. Rader
W. D. Bruce Winfield
Transfer Agent:
Equity Financial Trust Company
200 University Avenue Suite 400
Toronto, ON, Canada

DEGELMAN INDUSTRIES LTD.

272 Industrial Dr
PO Box 830
Regina, SK, S4P 3B1, Canada
Tel.: (306) 543-4447
Fax: (306) 543-2140
Toll Free: (800) 667-3545
E-Mail: sales@degelman.com
Web Site: www.degelman.com
Year Founded: 1962
Emp.: 125
Business Description:
Farm Equipment
Import Export
S.I.C.: 3523
N.A.I.C.S.: 333111
Personnel:
Wilfred Degelman *(Pres)*

Division:

Hylar Metal Products **(1)**
272 Industrial Dr
PO Box 830
Regina, SK, S4P 3B1, Canada (100%)
Tel.: (306) 543-4447
Fax: (306) 543-2140
Toll Free: (800) 667-3545
E-Mail: info@degelman.com
Web Site: www.degelman.com
Emp.: 10
Custom Machining & Fabrication Metals
S.I.C.: 3559
N.A.I.C.S.: 333249
Roland Degelman *(Mgr-Admin)*

DEGEM BERHAD

No 40-46 Jalan Maarof Bangsar Baru
59100 Kuala Lumpur, Malaysia
Tel.: (60) 3 2282 3618
Fax: (60) 3 2282 4960
E-Mail: info@degembhd.com
Web Site: www.degembhd.com
DEGEM—(KLS)
Rev.: $82,241,388
Assets: $86,293,778
Liabilities: $21,752,554
Net Worth: $64,541,225
Earnings: $7,480,992
Fiscal Year-end: 12/31/12
Business Description:
Jewelry Mfr & Distr
S.I.C.: 3911
N.A.I.C.S.: 339910
Personnel:
Chooi Yoong Chow *(Sec)*
Board of Directors:
Hasan M. Taib
Zainun Aishah Ahmad
Kai Fatt Choong
Kai Soon Choong
Kay Cheong Choong
Khoi Onn Choong
Teong Aung Chuah
Thiam Lai Leou

DeGem Berhad—(Continued)

Legal Counsel:
Nik Hussain & Partners
27th Floor Menara KH Jalan Sultan Ismail
Kuala Lumpur, Malaysia

Chris Koh & Chew
22nd Floor Menara TA One
22 Jalan P Ramlee, 50250 Kuala Lumpur, Malaysia

DEGETEL
46-48 avenue du General Leclerc
92100 Boulogne-Billancourt, France
Tel.: (33) 141860200
Fax: (33) 141860201
E-Mail: contact@degetel.com
Web Site: www.degetel.com
Rev.: $20,300,000
Emp.: 190

Business Description:
Custom Computer Programming Services
S.I.C.: 7371
N.A.I.C.S.: 541511
Personnel:
Denis Klenkle Lallemand *(Pres)*

DEHAIER MEDICAL SYSTEMS LIMITED
Room 501 Jiuzhou Plaza 83 Fuxing Road
Haidian District, Beijing, 100856, China
Tel.: (86) 1051660080
Fax: (86) 1068416311
E-Mail: intl@dehaier.com.cn
Web Site: www.dehaier.com.cn
DHRM—(NASDAQ)
Rev.: $21,370,325
Assets: $38,282,939
Liabilities: $4,214,643
Net Worth: $34,068,296
Earnings: $3,216,352
Emp.: 165
Fiscal Year-end: 12/31/12

Business Description:
Home Respiratory, Oxygen Homecare Products & Other Medical Devices Developer & Marketer
S.I.C.: 3841
N.A.I.C.S.: 339112
Personnel:
Ping Chen *(Chm & CEO)*
Jingli Li *(CFO)*
Fei Dong *(COO)*
Xiaoqing Wang *(CTO)*
Board of Directors:
Ping Chen
Genhui Chen
Yunxiang Fan
Jingli Li
Mingwei Zhang

DEINOVE SA
22 rue Leon Jouhaux
75010 Paris, France
Tel.: (33) 142032737
Fax: (33) 147235403
E-Mail: contact@deinove.com
Web Site: www.deinove.com
Year Founded: 2006
ALDEI—(EUR)
Rev.: $899,242
Assets: $12,550,343
Liabilities: $1,488,864
Net Worth: $11,061,479
Earnings: ($2,664,070)
Emp.: 29
Fiscal Year-end: 12/31/12

Business Description:
Chemicals & Biofuel Developer & Mfr
S.I.C.: 2899
N.A.I.C.S.: 325998

Personnel:
Philippe Pouletty *(Co-Founder & Chm)*
Miroslav Radman *(Co-Founder)*
Emmanuel Petiot *(CEO)*
Alain Chevallier *(CFO)*
Board of Directors:
Philippe Pouletty
Frederic Dardel
Paul-Joel Derian
Philippe Duval
Christian Pierret
Rodney J. Rothstein
Nabil Y. Sakkab
Bruno Weymuller

DEJIN RESOURCES GROUP COMPANY LIMITED
Room 2601-04 and 38-40 26/F Sun Hung Kai Centre 30 Harbour Road
Wanchai, China (Hong Kong)
Tel.: (852) 2984 0888
Fax: (852) 2598 0968
Web Site: www.dejinresources.com
1163—(HKG)
Rev.: $4,626,855
Assets: $386,375,206
Liabilities: $130,822,741
Net Worth: $255,552,465
Earnings: ($543,607,294)
Emp.: 70
Fiscal Year-end: 12/31/12

Business Description:
Gold Mining, Timber-Related Services & Lighting Product Mfr
S.I.C.: 1041
N.A.I.C.S.: 212221
Personnel:
Wilson Wai Yin Cheung *(Chm)*
Hao Tang *(CEO)*
Ka Wing Chan *(CFO & Sec)*
Milton Yan Loy Mow *(CEO-Mining Segment)*
Board of Directors:
Wilson Wai Yin Cheung
Ka Wing Chan
Ewing Wing Kwok Fu
Pierre Chi Yan Lau
Horace Chun Fung Ma
Tai Loy Mow
Christina Yuen Shan Pang
Lidong Tian
Wallen Tsai
Zhibin Zhao

HSBC Securities Services (Bermuda) Limited
Bank of Bermuda Building 6 Front Street
Hamilton, Bermuda

Transfer Agents:
Tricor Tengis Limited
26th Floor Tesbury Centre 28 Queen's Road East
Wanchai, China (Hong Kong)
Tel.: (852) 29801333
Fax: (852) 28108185

HSBC Securities Services (Bermuda) Limited
Bank of Bermuda Building 6 Front Street
Hamilton, Bermuda

Subsidiary:

Whole Bright Industries (HK) Limited (1)
Rm 1909 Block B Ming Pao Indus Ctr 18 Ka Yip St
Chai Wan, China (Hong Kong)
Tel.: (852) 28892013
Fax: (852) 28984122
Emp.: 4
Electric Lighting Products Sales
S.I.C.: 5023
N.A.I.C.S.: 423220
John Pak *(Gen Mgr)*

DEJMARK GROUP S.R.O.
Podebradska 55/88
190 00 Prague, 9, Czech Republic
Tel.: (420) 724 554 417
Fax: (420) 724 375 294
E-Mail: info@dejmarkgroup.com
Web Site: www.dejmark.com
Year Founded: 2012
Sales Range: $10-24.9 Million
Emp.: 70

Business Description:
Decorative Paints & Industrial Coatings Whslr
S.I.C.: 5198
N.A.I.C.S.: 424950

Non-U.S. Subsidiaries:

Dejmark Kft. (1)
Gyali ut 27-29
H 1097 Budapest, Hungary HU
Tel.: (36) 1 348 3040
Fax: (36) 1 348 3070
E-Mail: info.hu@dejmark.com
Web Site: www.dejmark.hu
Emp.: 30
Paint Mfr
S.I.C.: 2851
N.A.I.C.S.: 325510
Tamas Drnecz *(Controller & Mgr-Fin)*

Dejmark Partners SRL (1)
Str Cernat nr 27
525400 Targu Secuiesc, Romania
Tel.: (40) 734 542 253
E-Mail: lehel.nagy@dejmark.com
Web Site: www.dejmark.ro
Paint
S.I.C.: 5198
N.A.I.C.S.: 424950
Nagy Lehel, *(Sls Dir)*

Dejmark spol. s r.o. (1)
Priekopska 3706/104
Priekopa, 036 08 Martin, Slovakia
Tel.: (421) 43 40 100 40
Fax: (421) 43 40 100 50
E-Mail: martin@dejmark.com
Web Site: www.dejmark.sk
Decorative Paints & Industrial Coatings Whslr
S.I.C.: 5198
N.A.I.C.S.: 424950

DEJOUR ENERGY INC.
World Trade Centre 999 Canada Place Suite 598
Vancouver, BC, V6C 3E1, Canada
Tel.: (604) 638-5050
Fax: (604) 638-5051
Toll Free: (866) 888-8230
E-Mail: investor@dejour.com
Web Site: www.dejour.com
Year Founded: 1968
DEJ—(DEU NYSEMKT TSXV)
Rev.: $6,840,673
Assets: $27,408,122
Liabilities: $17,224,206
Net Worth: $10,183,917
Earnings: ($11,682,245)
Emp.: 17
Fiscal Year-end: 12/31/12

Business Description:
Oil & Gas Property Acquisition & Exploration Services
S.I.C.: 1311
N.A.I.C.S.: 211111
Personnel:
Robert Lloyd Hodgkinson *(Co-Chm & CEO)*
Stephen R. Mut *(Co-Chm)*
David Matheson *(CFO)*
Harrison Franklin Blacker *(Pres/COO-Dejour Energy USA Corp)*
Phil Bretzloff *(Gen Counsel & VP)*
Neyeska Mut *(Exec VP-Ops-Dejour Energy USA Corp)*
Board of Directors:
Robert Lloyd Hodgkinson
Stephen R. Mut
Richard A. Bachmann
Harrison Franklin Blacker
Arthur Ross Gorrell
Richard H. Kennedy
Craig C. Sturrock

Legal Counsel:
Patton Boggs
Denver, CO 80012

Farris LLP
Vancouver, BC, Canada

Dorsey & Whitney
Denver, CO 80012

Computershare Trust Company N.A.
Suite 1700 717 17th Street
Denver, CO 80202-3323

Transfer Agents:
Computershare Trust Company of Canada
2nd Floor 510 Burrard Street
V6C3B9 Vancouver, BC, Canada

Computershare Trust Company N.A.
Suite 1700 717 17th Street
Denver, CO 80202-3323

Subsidiary:

Dejour Energy (Alberta) Ltd. (1)
144 4 Ave Sw Ste 2600
Calgary, AB, T2P 3N4, Canada AB
Tel.: (403) 266-3825
Fax: (403) 450-7520
Oil & Gas Exlporation Services
S.I.C.: 1311
N.A.I.C.S.: 211111

U.S. Subsidiary:

Dejour Energy USA, Inc. (1)
1401 17th St Ste 850
Denver, CO 80202 NV
Tel.: (303) 296-3535
Fax: (303) 296-3888
Web Site: www.dejour.com
Emp.: 7
Oil & Gas Exploration Services
S.I.C.: 1311
N.A.I.C.S.: 211111
Harrison Franklin Blacker *(Pres & COO)*

DEKABANK
Mainzer Landstrasse 16
60325 Frankfurt, Germany
Tel.: (49) 6971470
Telex: 414163 DGZA D; 4170691 DGZD
Fax: (49) 6971471376
E-Mail: konzerninfo@deka.de
Web Site: www.dekabank.de
Rev.: $3,676,794,121
Assets: $174,657,480,480
Liabilities: $169,846,941,985
Net Worth: $4,810,538,495
Earnings: $383,119,982
Emp.: 3,190
Fiscal Year-end: 12/31/12

Business Description:
Financial Services
S.I.C.: 6099
N.A.I.C.S.: 522320
Personnel:
Georg Fahrenschon *(Chm)*
Thomas Mang *(Deputy Chm)*
Helmut Schleweis *(Deputy Chm)*
Michael Rudiger *(CEO & Member-Mgmt Bd)*
Oliver Behrens *(Deputy CEO & Member-Mgmt Bd)*
Matthias Danne *(Member-Mgmt Bd)*
Martin K. Muller *(Member-Mgmt Bd)*
Friedrich Oelrich *(Member-Mgmt Bd)*
Georg Stocker *(Member-Mgmt Bd)*
Board of Directors:
Georg Fahrenschon
Stephan Articus
Michael Breuer
Michael Dorr
Johannes Evers
Rolf Gerlach
Volker Goldmann
Gerhard Grandke
Hans-Gunter Hennke
Walter Kleine

Beate Lasch-Weber
Thomas Mang
Harald Menzel
Hans-Werner Sander
Roland Schafer
Eugen Schaufele
Heike Schillo
Siegmund Schiminski
Helmut Schleweis
Peter Schneider
Georg Sellner
Harald Vogelsang
Johannes Werner
Alexander Wuerst
Theo Zellner

Non-U.S. Subsidiaries:

Deka International (Ireland) Ltd. (1)
Fleming Court Fleming Place
Dublin, 4, Ireland (100%)
Tel.: (353) 12815720
Fax: (353) 16608510
Web Site: www.deka.ie
Emp.: 15
International Banking Institution
S.I.C.: 6159
N.A.I.C.S.: 522293
Grainne Walts *(Gen Mgr)*

Deka International SA. (1)
38 Ave John F Kennedy
PO Box 504
L 2015 Luxembourg, 18855, Luxembourg (100%)
Tel.: (352) 340935
Fax: (352) 346605
E-Mail: info@decabank.lu
Web Site: www.decabank.lu
Emp.: 300
Provider of Financial Services
S.I.C.: 6282
N.A.I.C.S.: 523930
Rainer Mach *(Gen Mgr)*

Deka (Swiss) Privatbank AG (1)
Thurgauerstrasse 54
PO Box 8310
CH 8050 Zurich, Switzerland (100%)
Tel.: (41) 443088888
Fax: (41) 443088999
Web Site: www.deka.ch
Sales Range: $100-124.9 Million
Emp.: 60
S.I.C.: 6159
N.A.I.C.S.: 522298
Michael Albanus *(Mgr)*

DekaBank Deutsche Girozentrale Luxembourg S.A. (1)
38 avenue John F Kennedy
1855 Luxembourg, Luxembourg
Tel.: (352) 340935
Fax: (352) 340937
Web Site: www.dekabank.lu
Emp.: 352
Financial Services
S.I.C.: 6282
N.A.I.C.S.: 523930
Rainer Mach *(Mng Dir)*

International Fund Management SA (1)
38 Ave John F Kennedy
PO Box 504
L 2015 Luxembourg, Luxembourg (100%)
Tel.: (352) 340935
Fax: (352) 340937
E-Mail: info@dekabank.lu
Web Site: www.dekabank.lu
Emp.: 415
Provider of Financial Services
S.I.C.: 6282
N.A.I.C.S.: 523930
Rainer Mach *(CEO)*

DEKELOIL PUBLIC LIMITED

First Floor 18-19 Pall Mall
London, SW1Y 5LU, United Kingdom
Tel.: (44) 207 024 8391
E-Mail: info@dekeloil.com
Web Site: www.dekeloil.com
Year Founded: 2007
DKL—(AIM)
Sales Range: Less than $1 Million
Emp.: 52
Business Description:
Oil Palm Production
S.I.C.: 2075
N.A.I.C.S.: 311224
Personnel:
Andrew Tillery *(Chm)*
Youval Rasin *(CEO)*
Yehoshua Shai Kol *(CFO)*
Eyal Timmor *(COO)*
Board of Directors:
Andrew Tillery
Richard Amon
Yehoshua Shai Kol
Lincoln John Moore
Youval Rasin

DEKOMTE DE TEMPLE KOMPENSATOR-TECHNIK GMBH

Walinusstrasse 13
63500 Seligenstadt, Germany
Tel.: (49) 94412005
Fax: (49) 61822101400
E-Mail: info@dekomte.com
Web Site: www.dekomte.com
Rev.: $11,143,136
Emp.: 34
Business Description:
Prefabricated Metal Buildings
S.I.C.: 3448
N.A.I.C.S.: 332311
Personnel:
Ulrich Stohrer *(Mng Dir)*

DEKRA E.V.

Handwerkstrasse 15
70565 Stuttgart, Germany
Tel.: (49) 711 7861 0
Fax: (49) 7117861224
E-Mail: info@dekra.com
Web Site: www.dekra.com
Year Founded: 1925
Sales Range: $1-4.9 Billion
Emp.: 22,000
Business Description:
Automotive, Industrial & Personnel Training Safety, Inspection & Regulation Organization
S.I.C.: 9651
N.A.I.C.S.: 926150
Personnel:
Stefan Kolbl *(Chm-Mgmt Bd)*
Donald O. Nicholson *(Pres & Chief Reg Officer-North America)*
Roland Gerdon *(Member-Mgmt Bd)*

Subsidiary:

DEKRA SE (1)
Handwerkstrasse 15
70565 Stuttgart, Germany De
Tel.: (49) 71178610 (100%)
Fax: (49) 71178612240
E-Mail: info@dekra.com
Web Site: www.dekra.de
Rev.: $2,913,316,498
Assets: $2,074,815,474
Liabilities: $1,595,051,256
Net Worth: $479,764,219
Earnings: $99,076,766
Emp.: 28,340
Fiscal Year-end: 12/31/12
Automotive Testing & Industrial Inspection Services; Personnel Training, Placement & Human Resource Consulting Services
S.I.C.: 4789
N.A.I.C.S.: 488490
Thomas Pleines *(Chm-Supervisory Bd)*
Stefan Kolbl *(Chm-Mgmt Bd)*
Heinrich Breitbach *(Deputy Chm-Supervisory Bd)*
Roland Gerdon *(Member-Mgmt Bd)*
Clemens Klinke *(Member-Mgmt Bd)*
Jorg Mannsperger *(Member-Mgmt Bd)*
Ivo Rauh *(Member-Mgmt Bd)*

Subsidiaries:

DEKRA Akademie GmbH (2)
Handwerkstrasse 15
70565 Stuttgart, Germany De
Tel.: (49) 71178610 (100%)
Fax: (49) 71178612066
E-Mail: service.akademie@dekra.com
Web Site: www.dekra-akademie.de
Professional Training Services
S.I.C.: 8299
N.A.I.C.S.: 611430
Jorg Mannsperger *(Mng Dir)*

DEKRA Arbeit GmbH (2)
Handwerkstrasse 15
D-70565 Stuttgart, Germany De
Tel.: (49) 71178613203 (100%)
Fax: (49) 71178613208
E-Mail: info.arbeit@dekra.com
Web Site: www.dekra-arbeit-gruppe.de
Emp.: 16
Employment Placement Agency
S.I.C.: 7361
N.A.I.C.S.: 561311
Suzana Bernhard *(Mng Dir)*

DEKRA Automobil GmbH (2)
Handwerkstrasse 15
D-70565 Stuttgart, Germany De
Tel.: (49) 71178610 (100%)
Fax: (49) 71178612240
E-Mail: info@dekra.com
Web Site: www.dekra.de/automobil
Emp.: 1,000
Automotive Vehicle Testing & Safety Inspection Services
S.I.C.: 4789
N.A.I.C.S.: 488490
Stefan Kolb *(Mng Dir)*

DEKRA Industrial GmbH (2)
Handwerkstrasse 15
D-70565 Stuttgart, Germany De
Tel.: (49) 71178612631 (100%)
Fax: (49) 71178612240
E-Mail: info@dekra.com
Web Site: www.dekra.de/industrial-gmbh
Industrial Plant Safety, Inspection & Certification Services
S.I.C.: 7389
N.A.I.C.S.: 541350
Lothar Kreutz *(Mng Dir)*

Non-U.S. Subsidiary:

DEKRA Industrial AB (3)
Kvarnbergsgatan 2
SE-411 05 Gothenburg, Sweden SE
Tel.: (46) 104551000 (100%)
E-Mail: info@dekra-industrila.se
Web Site: www.dekra-industrial.se
Sales Range: $50-74.9 Million
Emp.: 450
Industrial Safety Testing & Inspection Services
S.I.C.: 7389
N.A.I.C.S.: 541350
Jorgen Backersgard *(Pres)*

DEKRA International GmbH (2)
Handwerkstrasse 15
D-70565 Stuttgart, Germany De
Tel.: (49) 71178612065 (100%)
Fax: (49) 71178612066
E-Mail: international@dekra.com
Web Site: www.dekra.de/en/international
Holding Company; Automobile Safety Testing & Inspection Services
S.I.C.: 6719
N.A.I.C.S.: 551112
Rolf Krokel *(Mng Dir)*

DEKRA Personaldienste GmbH (2)
Handwerkstrasse 15
D-70565 Stuttgart, Germany De
Tel.: (49) 71178613650 (100%)
Fax: (49) 71178613660
E-Mail: info.pd@dekra.com
Web Site: www.dekra-pd.de
Emp.: 20
Human Resource Consulting Services
S.I.C.: 8999
N.A.I.C.S.: 541612
Thorsten Machner *(Mng Dir)*

DEKRO PAINTS (PTY) LTD

24 Fabriek Street
Kuils River, 7580, South Africa
Mailing Address:
PO Box 131
Kuils River, 7579, South Africa
Tel.: (27) 219033131
Fax: (27) 219032307
E-Mail: info@dekro.co.za
Web Site: www.dekro.co.za
Emp.: 65
Business Description:
Paint & Resin Mfr & Distr
S.I.C.: 2851
N.A.I.C.S.: 325510
Personnel:
Greg Meaker *(Mng Dir)*

DEL GAUDIO

10 Avenue De Bourgogne
Fruileg 565, 91581 Rungis, Cedex, France
Tel.: (33) 146876561
Fax: (33) 149780255
E-Mail: delgaudio@delgaudiofr.com
Web Site: www.delgaudiofr.com
Sls.: $22,200,000
Emp.: 17
Business Description:
Fresh Fruits & Vegetables
S.I.C.: 5148
N.A.I.C.S.: 424480
Personnel:
Sweet Pandae *(Mng Dir)*

DELAGRAVE SA

Espace Lognes 8 rue Sainte Claire Deville
77437 Marne-la-Vallee, Cedex, 2, France
Tel.: (33) 1 60 37 51 31
Web Site: www.delagrave.fr
Sls.: $23,300,000
Emp.: 180
Business Description:
Wood Office Furniture Mfr & Distr
S.I.C.: 2521
N.A.I.C.S.: 337211
Personnel:
Jean Delagrave *(Editor)*

DELANCE LIMITED

(d/b/a ROLF Group of Companies)
31 Altufievskoe Shosse Bldg 7
127410 Moscow, Russia
Tel.: (7) 495 785 1978
Fax: (7) 495 785 1952
E-Mail: reception@rolf.ru
Web Site: www.rolf.ru
Year Founded: 2004
Sales Range: $1-4.9 Billion
Emp.: 5,500
Business Description:
Holding Company; Motor Vehicle Sales & Related Services
S.I.C.: 6719
N.A.I.C.S.: 551112
Personnel:
Igor Salita *(CEO)*
Andrew Simmons *(CFO)*
Board of Directors:
Georgia Kafkalia
Emilios Kallenos
Evi Papageorgiou
Igor Salita

Subsidiaries:

ROLF Import (1)
31 Altufievskoe Shosse Bldg 7
127410 Moscow, Russia (60%)
Tel.: (7) 495 785 1978
Fax: (7) 495 785 1952
Web Site: www.mitsubishi-motors.ru
Imported Motor Vehicle Distr & Dealership Support Services
Import
S.I.C.: 5012
N.A.I.C.S.: 423110

Delance Limited—(Continued)

Robert Law *(CEO)*

ROLF Retail (1)
31 Altufievskoe Shosse Bldg 7
127410 Moscow, Russia
Tel.: (7) 4957851978
Fax: (7) 4957851952
Web Site: www.rolf.ru
New & Used Car Dealerships Operator
S.I.C.: 5511
N.A.I.C.S.: 441110
Sergey Sherbinin *(CEO)*
Tatiana Lukovetskaya *(COO)*

DELANCEY REAL ESTATE ASSET MANAGEMENT LTD.

Lansdowne House Berkeley Square
London, W1J 6ER, United Kingdom
Tel.: (44) 20 7448 1448
Fax: (44) 20 7448 1449
E-Mail: info@delancey.com
Web Site: www.delancey.com
Year Founded: 2003
Emp.: 45
Business Description:
Real Estate Investment Services
S.I.C.: 6211
N.A.I.C.S.: 523999
Personnel:
Jamie Ritblat *(Chm & CEO)*
Colin Wagman *(Deputy Chm & Dir-Fin)*
Paul Goswell *(Mng Dir)*

Holding:

Minerva Ltd. (1)
42 Wigmore Street
London, W1U 2RY, United Kingdom
Tel.: (44) 2075351000
Fax: (44) 2075351001
E-Mail: mail@minervaproperties.co.uk
Web Site: www.minervaproperty.com
Sales Range: $10-24.9 Million
Emp.: 25
Property Investment & Development Services
S.I.C.: 6211
N.A.I.C.S.: 531311
Ivan Ezekiel *(Co-Mng Dir)*
Tim Garnham *(Co-Mng Dir)*

DELATTRE LEVIVIER MAROC

route de Rabat rp 1 Km 9
20250 Casablanca, Morocco
Tel.: (212) 5 22 66 96 00
Fax: (212) 5 22 35 54 65
E-Mail: contact@dlm.ma
Web Site: www.dlm.ma
Year Founded: 1950
DLM—(CAS)
Emp.: 1,100
Business Description:
Steel Pipe & Tube Mfr
S.I.C.: 3317
N.A.I.C.S.: 331210
Personnel:
Jean-Claude Bouveur *(Chm)*
Eric Cecconello *(CEO)*

DELCLIMA S.P.A.

Via LSeitz 47
Treviso, TV, 31100, Italy
Tel.: (39) 0422413212
Fax: (39) 0422414396
Web Site: www.del-clima.com
Year Founded: 2012
DLC—(ITA)
Rev.: $505,231,063
Assets: $628,960,240
Liabilities: $281,922,998
Net Worth: $347,037,241
Earnings: ($23,727,592)
Emp.: 1,880
Fiscal Year-end: 12/31/12
Business Description:
Industrial Refrigeration Equipment Mfr
S.I.C.: 3585
N.A.I.C.S.: 333415
Personnel:
Giuseppe De'Longhi *(Chm)*
Carlo Grossi *(CEO)*
Board of Directors:
Giuseppe De'Longhi
Fabio De'Longhi
Silvia De'Longhi
Carlo Garavaglia
Carlo Grossi
Domenico Guidi
Ramon Marimon

DELECTA LTD.

Level 1 170-180 Buckhurst Street
South Melbourne, VIC, 3205, Australia
Tel.: (61) 3 9695 5858
Fax: (61) 3 9689 8033
Web Site:
DLC—(ASX)
Emp.: 20
Business Description:
Adult Product Sales
S.I.C.: 3942
N.A.I.C.S.: 339930
Personnel:
Malcolm Day *(Mng Dir)*
John Burness *(CFO & Sec)*
Board of Directors:
Bradley Moore
Malcolm Day
Hans Rudolf Moser

Non-U.S. Subsidiary:

Calvista New Zealand Limited (1)
15 Gundry St
Newton, Auckland, New Zealand
Tel.: (64) 93095496
Fax: (64) 93096560
Web Site: www.calvista.co.nz
Emp.: 5
Adult Toys Whslr
S.I.C.: 5092
N.A.I.C.S.: 423920

Subsidiary:

Calvista Australia Pty Ltd. (1)
170-180 Buckhurst Street
South Melbourne, VIC, 3205, Australia
Tel.: (61) 396955858
Fax: (61) 396860644
Web Site: www.calvista.com.au
Emp.: 40
Adult Toys & Videos & Novelties Whslr
S.I.C.: 5092
N.A.I.C.S.: 423920

DELEGAT'S GROUP LIMITED

Level 1 10 Viaduct Harbour Avenue
Auckland, 1010, New Zealand
Mailing Address:
PO Box 91681
Victoria Street West, Auckland, 1142, New Zealand
Tel.: (64) 9359 7300
Fax: (64) 9359 7359
E-Mail: info@delegats.co.nz
Web Site: www.delegats.co.nz
DGL—(NZE)
Rev.: $192,225,420
Assets: $352,248,939
Liabilities: $170,291,835
Net Worth: $181,957,104
Earnings: $34,497,792
Fiscal Year-end: 06/30/13
Business Description:
Wine Producer & Distr
S.I.C.: 2084
N.A.I.C.S.: 312130
Personnel:
Jakov Nikola Delegat *(Mng Dir)*
Board of Directors:
Robert Lawrence Wilton
Jakov Nikola Delegat
Rosemari Suzan Delegat
Jane Lesley Freeman
Alan William Jackson
Legal Counsel:
Jones Young
Level 19 BDO Tower 120 Albert Street
Auckland, New Zealand

Subsidiary:

Delegat's Wine Estate Limited (1)
Level 1 10 Viaduct Harbour Avenue
PO Box 91681
1142 Auckland, New Zealand
Tel.: (64) 93597300
Fax: (64) 93597359
E-Mail: info@delegats.co.nz
Web Site: www.delegatsgroup.co.nz
Sales Range: $1-9.9 Million
Grapes Production & Vineyard Services
S.I.C.: 0711
N.A.I.C.S.: 115112
Samford Maier *(Chm)*
Jakov Delegat *(Mng Dir)*

U.S. Subsidiary:

Oyster Bay Wines USA, Inc (1)
Ste 9-G The Soho Bldg 110 Greene St
New York, NY 10012
Tel.: (877) 613-9858
Fax: (877) 613-9859
E-Mail: infousa@oysterbaywines.com
Web Site: www.oysterbaywines.com
Grape Wine Mfr
S.I.C.: 2084
N.A.I.C.S.: 312130

Non-U.S. Subsidiaries:

Delegat (1)
4th Fl Kenilworth House 79/80 Margaret St
London, W1W 8TA, United Kingdom
Tel.: (44) 2031307050
Fax: (44) 2075802464
E-Mail: info@delegats.co.uk
Web Site: www.delegats.co.uk
Emp.: 8
Wines Mfr
S.I.C.: 2084
N.A.I.C.S.: 312130

Oyster Bay Wines Australia Pty Limited (1)
PO Box 977
Mascot, Sydney, NSW, 1460, Australia
Tel.: (61) 293179800
Fax: (61) 296694677
Web Site: www.oysterbaywines.com
Emp.: 20
Wine Distr
S.I.C.: 5182
N.A.I.C.S.: 424820
John Freeman *(Gen Mgr)*

DELEK GROUP LTD.

7 Giborei Israel Street
PO Box 8464
Netanya, 42504, Israel
Tel.: (972) 98638444
Fax: (972) 98854955
E-Mail: black_d@delek.co.il
Web Site: www.delek-group.com
Year Founded: 1951
DLEKG—(TAE)
Rev.: $19,236,950,640
Assets: $33,170,695,440
Liabilities: $29,770,818,720
Net Worth: $3,399,876,720
Earnings: $256,589,400
Emp.: 2,325
Fiscal Year-end: 12/31/12
Business Description:
Holding Company
S.I.C.: 6719
N.A.I.C.S.: 551112
Personnel:
Gabriel Last *(Chm)*
Elad Sharon Tshuva *(Deputy Chm)*
Asaf Joseph Bartfeld *(Pres & CEO)*
Barak Mashraki *(CFO)*
Yossi Barnea *(Chief Investment Officer)*
Ido Adar *(Treas)*
Leora Pratt Levin *(Chief Legal Counsel, Sec & VP)*
Board of Directors:
Gabriel Last
Moshe Amit
Moshe Bareket
Mazal Bronstain-Maman
Yoseph Dauber
Carmit Elroy
Abraham Harel
Elad Sharon Tshuva
Ben-Zion Zilberfarb

Subsidiaries:

Delek Investments & Properties Ltd. (1)
7 Giborei Israel St
PO Box 8464
Netanya, 42504, Israel
Tel.: (972) 98638444
Fax: (972) 98854955
E-Mail: contact@delek.co.il
Web Site: www.delek-group.com
Emp.: 70
Fuel Dealers & Investments
S.I.C.: 6211
N.A.I.C.S.: 523999
Asaf Joseph Bartfeld *(Mng Dir)*

Subsidiaries:

Delek Automotive Systems, Ltd. (2)
PO Box 200
72905 Moshav Nir Zvi, Israel
Tel.: (972) 89139999
Fax: (972) 89139991
E-Mail: r.bachar@delekmotors.co.il
Web Site: www.delek-group.com
DLEA—(TAE)
Sales Range: $1-4.9 Billion
Automotive Importer
S.I.C.: 5012
N.A.I.C.S.: 423110
Gabriel Last *(Chm)*
Gil Agmon *(CEO)*
Ronit Bachar *(CFO)*

Subsidiary:

Delek Motors Ltd. (3)
PO Box 200
Moshav Nir Zvi, 72905, Israel
Tel.: (972) 89139999
Fax: (972) 89139991
E-Mail: info@delekmotors.co.il
Web Site: www.delekmotors.co.il
Emp.: 150
Automotive Importer
S.I.C.: 5012
N.A.I.C.S.: 423110
Gil Agmon *(Pres)*

Delek Capital Ltd. (2)
Bet Adar Building
Post Office Box 8464
7 Giborei Street, Netanya, 42504, Israel
Tel.: (972) 98638444
Fax: (972) 98854955
Web Site: www.delek-group.com
International Financial Services
S.I.C.: 6211
N.A.I.C.S.: 523999
Danny Guttman *(CEO)*

Subsidiary:

The Phoenix Holdings Ltd. (3)
53 Derech Hashalom Rd.
Givatayim, 53454, Israel
Tel.: (972) 37332222
Fax: (972) 3 733 2222
Web Site: www.fnx.co.il
PHOE—(TAE)
Holding Company
S.I.C.: 6719
N.A.I.C.S.: 551112
Yali Sheffi *(Pres & CEO)*
David David *(CFO & Sr VP)*
Orly Kronman Dagan *(VP, Legal Counsel & Sec)*

Subsidiary:

The Phoenix Insurance Company Ltd. (4)
53 Derech Hashalom
Givatayim, 53454, Israel
Tel.: (972) 3 733 2222
Web Site: www.fnx.co.il

Insurance
S.I.C.: 6311
N.A.I.C.S.: 524113

U.S. Subsidiary:

The Republic Group (3)
5525 LBJ Fwy
Dallas, TX 75240-6241 DE
Tel.: (972) 788-6001
Fax: (972) 788-6099
E-Mail: info@republicgroup.com
Web Site: www.republicgroup.com
Sales Range: $250-299.9 Million
Emp.: 320
Insurance Services
S.I.C.: 6331
N.A.I.C.S.: 524126
Joe Mattingly *(Pres & CEO)*
Thomas M. Greenfield *(Chief Underwriting Officer & Sr VP)*
Michael E. Ditto *(Gen Counsel, Sec & VP)*

Delek Energy Systems, Ltd. (2)
Nolton Building
14 Shenkar St, 46733 Herzliya Pituach, Israel (89%)
Tel.: (972) 99712424
Fax: (972) 99712425
E-Mail: info@delek.co.il
Web Site: www.delekenergy.co.il
DLEN—(TAE)
Rev.: $75,414,724
Assets: $1,253,488,558
Liabilities: $1,101,851,534
Net Worth: $151,637,024
Earnings: ($3,123,372)
Fiscal Year-end: 09/30/12
Oil & Gas Exploration Services
S.I.C.: 1311
N.A.I.C.S.: 211111
Gabriel Last *(Chm)*
Asaf Bartfeld *(CEO)*

Subsidiaries:

Avner Oil Exploration LP (3)
Nolton Building 14 Shenkar St
46733 Herzliya Pituach, Israel
Tel.: (972) 99712424
Fax: (972) 99712425
E-Mail: reichman_ch@delek.co.il
Web Site: www.delek-group.com
AVNR.L—(TAE)
Sales Range: $75-99.9 Million
Emp.: 16
Oil & Gas Exploration Services
S.I.C.: 1311
N.A.I.C.S.: 211111
David Cohen *(Chm)*
Gideon Tadmor *(CEO)*

Delek Drilling LP (3)
7 Giborei Israel Street
PO Box 8464
42504 Netanya, Israel
Tel.: (972) 98638400
Fax: (972) 98638577
E-Mail: millman_e@delek.co.il
Web Site: www.delek-group.com
DEDR.L —(TAE)
Sales Range: $75-99.9 Million
Oil & Gas Exploration Services
S.I.C.: 1311
N.A.I.C.S.: 211111
Gideon Tadmor *(Chm)*
Zvika Greenfield *(CEO)*

Delek Infrastructures Ltd. (2)
14 Shenkar St
Herzliya Pituach, 46733, Israel
Tel.: (972) 99712424
Fax: (972) 99712425
Web Site: www.delek-group.com
Emp.: 4
Electricity Generation, IPP Power Stations, Water Desalination & Sewage Treatment
S.I.C.: 1389
N.A.I.C.S.: 213112
Gabriel Last *(Chm)*
Silvio Wittinig *(CEO)*

Gadot Biochemical Industries Ltd. (2)
117 Hahistadrut Ave
PO Box 10636
26118 Haifa Bay, Israel
Tel.: (972) 48461555
Fax: (972) 48461560
E-Mail: contact@gadotbio.com
Web Site: www.gadotbio.com
GDBC—(TAE)
Sales Range: $125-149.9 Million
Emp.: 180
Food Ingredients & Fine Chemicals
S.I.C.: 2899
N.A.I.C.S.: 325998
Asaf Joseph Bartfeld *(Chm)*
Jacob Zack *(Pres & CEO)*
Shalom Vaknin *(CIO)*

U.S. Subsidiary:

Gadot Bio-Chem (USA) Inc. (3)
1 International Blvd Ste 407
Mahwah, NY 07495
Tel.: (845) 651-4425
Fax: (847) 419-7765
Toll Free: (888) 424-1424
E-Mail: info@gadotbio.com
Web Site: www.gadotbio.com
Emp.: 3
Food Ingredients & Fine Chemicals
S.I.C.: 2899
N.A.I.C.S.: 325998
Antony Hand *(Pres)*

Non-U.S. Subsidiary:

Gadot Bio-Chem (Europe) B.V. (3)
Hoefsmidstraat 41
3194 AA Hoogvliet, Netherlands
Tel.: (31) 102961096
Fax: (31) 105012850
E-Mail: contact@gadotbio.com
Web Site: www.gadotbio.com
Emp.: 4
Food Ingredients & Fine Chemicals
S.I.C.: 2899
N.A.I.C.S.: 325998
Didier Trimbos *(Mng Dir)*

Delek Petroleum Ltd. (1)
Bet Adar Building 7 Giborei Israel St
PO Box 8464
South Industrial Area, Netanya, 42504, Israel
Tel.: (972) 98638444
Fax: (972) 98854955
E-Mail: service@delek.co.il
Web Site: www.delek.co.il
Emp.: 550
Refined Oil Products & Lubricants Sales
S.I.C.: 5172
N.A.I.C.S.: 424720
Gabriel Last *(Chm)*
Asas Bartseld *(Pres & CEO)*
Bark Mashrji *(CFO)*

Subsidiaries:

Delek Europe Holdings Ltd. (2)
Bet Adar Building 7 Giborei Israel Street
Netanya, 42504, Israel
Tel.: (972) 98638680
Fax: (972) 98854955
Investment Management Services
S.I.C.: 6211
N.A.I.C.S.: 523999

Delek The Israel Fuel Corporation Ltd. (2)
Bet Adar Building 7 Giborei Israel St
PO Box 8464
42504 Netanya, Israel
Tel.: (972) 98638531
Fax: (972) 98638621
E-Mail: mashia_m@delek.co.il
Web Site: www.delek-group.com
DLKIS—(TAE)
Sales Range: $1-4.9 Billion
Emp.: 200
Fuel Sales
S.I.C.: 5989
N.A.I.C.S.: 454310
Moshe Amit *(Chm)*
Eyal Lapidot *(CEO)*
Moshe Mashiah *(CFO)*

Subsidiary:

Delek Transportation Ltd. (3)
Neft Street
PO Box 12018
Ashdod, 31600, Israel
Tel.: (972) 8 8534462
Fax: (972) 8 8534467
Emp.: 7
Fuel Transportation Services
S.I.C.: 4789
N.A.I.C.S.: 488999
Yehuda Ochayon *(Gen Mgr)*

U.S. Subsidiary:

Delek US Holdings, Inc. (2)
7102 Commerce Way
Brentwood, TN 37027 DE
Tel.: (615) 771-6701
Fax: (615) 771-8098
Web Site: www.delekus.com
DK—(NYSE)
Sls.: $8,706,800,000
Assets: $2,834,400,000
Liabilities: $1,714,000,000
Net Worth: $1,120,400,000
Earnings: $135,700,000
Emp.: 4,366
Fiscal Year-end: 12/31/13
Holding Company; Petroleum Refining, Marketing & Supply & Convenience Stores
S.I.C.: 6719
N.A.I.C.S.: 551112
Ezra Uzi Yemin *(Chm, Pres & CEO)*
Assaf Ginzburg *(CFO & Exec VP)*
Mark Davison *(CIO & VP)*
Kent B. Thomas *(Gen Counsel & Sec)*
Greg Intemann *(VP & Treas)*
Mark B. Cox *(Exec VP)*
Frederec Green *(Exec VP)*
Lynwood Gregory *(Sr VP)*

Divisions:

Delek Marketing & Supply, Inc. (3)
7102 Commerce Way
Brentwood, TN 37027
Tel.: (615) 771-6701
Web Site: www.delekus.com
Fuel Sales
S.I.C.: 5989
N.A.I.C.S.: 454310
Pete Daily *(COO)*

Delek Refining, Inc. (3)
7102 Commerce Way
Brentwood, TN 37027
Tel.: (615) 771-6701
Fax: (615) 224-1185
Web Site: www.delekgroup.com
Emp.: 271
Fuel Refining Operations
S.I.C.: 2911
N.A.I.C.S.: 324110
Frederec Green *(Pres & COO)*

Subsidiary:

Delek Refining, Ltd. (4)
425 Mcmurrey Dr
Tyler, TX 75702-6326
Tel.: (903) 579-3400
Fax: (903) 596-0103
Oil & Gas Refinery Operator
S.I.C.: 2911
N.A.I.C.S.: 324110
Fred Green *(Pres & COO)*

Subsidiaries:

Delek Crude Logistics, LLC (3)
425 Mcmurrey Dr
Tyler, TX 75702
Tel.: (615) 435-1402
Petroleum Product Transportation Services
S.I.C.: 4613
N.A.I.C.S.: 486910
Les Keith *(Mgr)*

Delek Finance, Inc. (3)
7102 Commerce Way
Brentwood, TN 37027
Tel.: (615) 771-6701
Financial Management Services
S.I.C.: 8742
N.A.I.C.S.: 541611

Delek Logistics Partners, LP (3)
7102 Commerce Way
Brentwood, TN 37027 DE
Tel.: (615) 771-6701 (60.4%)
Web Site: www.delekus.com
DKL—(NYSE)
Sls.: $907,428,000
Assets: $274,804,000
Liabilities: $212,763,000
Net Worth: $62,041,000
Earnings: $40,977,000
Fiscal Year-end: 12/31/13
Crude Petroleum Logistics
S.I.C.: 4612
N.A.I.C.S.: 486110
Ezra Uzi Yemin *(Chm/CEO-Delek Logistics GP, LLC)*
Andrew L. Schwarcz *(Gen Counsel, Sec & Exec VP)*
Frederec Green *(Exec VP & Dir-Delek Logistics GP, LLC)*
Kent B. Thomas *(Exec VP & Asst Sec)*
Mark B. Cox *(Exec VP)*
Assaf Ginzburg *(Exec VP)*

Delek Marketing & Supply, LP (3)
4008 N US Hwy 67
San Angelo, TX 76905
Tel.: (325) 655-2123
Petroleum Product Transportation Services
S.I.C.: 4613
N.A.I.C.S.: 486910
Pete Daily, *(COO)*

Delek Marketing-Big Sandy, LLC (3)
Attn Vanessa Goodspeed 425 Mcmurrey Dr
Tyler, TX 75702
Tel.: (903) 579-3428
Petroleum Product Whslr
S.I.C.: 5172
N.A.I.C.S.: 424720

Delek Renewables, LLC (3)
3102 Windmill Rd
Joshua, TX 76058
Tel.: (817) 558-9255
Biodiesel Refinery Operator
S.I.C.: 2911
N.A.I.C.S.: 324110

Lion Oil Company (3)
1000 McHenry
El Dorado, AR 71731 (100%)
Tel.: (870) 862-8111
Web Site: www.lionoil.com
Refiner of Petroleum & Marketer of Petroleum & Petroleum Products
S.I.C.: 2911
N.A.I.C.S.: 324110
Tommie Crossland *(Mgr-Supply & Distr)*

Subsidiaries:

J. Christy Construction Co., Inc. (4)
1333 Robert E Lee St
El Dorado, AR 71730-6935 AR
Tel.: (870) 862-9348
Fax: (870) 862-4827
Sls.: $6,300,000
Emp.: 177
Industrial Buildings & Warehouses
S.I.C.: 1542
N.A.I.C.S.: 236220

Lion Oil Trading & Transportation, LLC (4)
1001 School St
El Dorado, AR 71730
Tel.: (870) 864-1280
Fax: (870) 864-1341
Emp.: 80
Petroleum Product Transportation Services
S.I.C.: 4613
N.A.I.C.S.: 486910
Lydia Smith *(Div Mgr-Acctg-Order & Crude Oil)*

MAPCO Express, Inc. (3)
7102 Commerce Way
Brentwood, TN 37027 (100%)
Tel.: (615) 771-6701
Web Site: www.mapcoexpress.com
Emp.: 175
Convenience Stores & Gasoline Pumping Stations
S.I.C.: 5541
N.A.I.C.S.: 447110
Igal Zamir *(Pres)*

Paline Pipeline Company, LLC (3)
7636 US Hwy 190
Jasper, TX 75951
Tel.: (409) 331-0611
Petroleum Pipeline Transportation Services
S.I.C.: 4613
N.A.I.C.S.: 486910

Non-U.S. Subsidiary:

Roadchef Motorways Ltd (2)
Roadchef House Norton Canes MSA Bettys Lane
Norton Canes, Cannock, Staffordshire, WS11 9UX, United Kingdom

Delek Group Ltd.—(Continued)

Tel.: (44) 1543 272540
Fax: (44) 1543 272554
E-Mail: coachsupport@roadchef.com
Web Site: www.roadchef.com
Rev.: $314,448,000
Emp.: 2,000
Motorway Restaurant Operating Services
S.I.C.: 5812
N.A.I.C.S.: 722511
Simon Turl *(CEO)*

Delek Pi Glilot - Limited Partnership (1)
Neft St Northern Industrial Zone
PO Box 292
Ashdod, 77102, Israel
Tel.: (972) 8 8513200, ext. 8
Fax: (972) 8 8604742
Web Site: www.delek.co.il
Emp.: 43
Fuel Extraction Storage & Distr
S.I.C.: 2999
N.A.I.C.S.: 324199
Moshe Karadi *(CEO)*

Delek Real Estate Ltd. (1)
Gilbor Sport 7 Menachem Begin St
52117 Ramat Gan, Israel (67.9%)
Tel.: (972) 36112222
Fax: (972) 36122245
DLKR—(TAE)
Real Estate Holding Company
S.I.C.: 6531
N.A.I.C.S.: 531390
Yuval Gavish *(CEO)*

Subsidiaries:

Delek Belron International Ltd. (2)
Gilbor Sport 7 Menachem Begin St
PO Box 1707
Ramat Gan, 52117, Israel
Tel.: (972) 36112222
Fax: (972) 36129754
Real Estate Investments
S.I.C.: 6726
N.A.I.C.S.: 525990

Non-U.S. Subsidiary:

Delek Global Real Estate Ltd. (3)
4 Stratford Place
Saint Helier, W1C 18G, Jersey
Tel.: (44) 1534626004
Fax: (44) 1534785399
E-Mail: lyael@delekgroup.com
Web Site: www.delekgre.com
Emp.: 4
Real Estate Investment Services
S.I.C.: 6726
N.A.I.C.S.: 525990
Miki Naftali *(Chm)*
Eyal Rabinovitz *(Pres & CEO)*

Elad Israel Residence Ltd. (2)
7 Menachem Begin Road
Ramat Gan, 52681, Israel
Tel.: (972) 36791919
Fax: (972) 36791909
Investment Services
S.I.C.: 6282
N.A.I.C.S.: 523930
Ronen Rafo *(CEO)*

Sahar Development & Investments Ltd. (2)
PO Box 222
Netanya, Israel
Tel.: (972) 98634545
Fax: (972) 98634546
Real Estate Development
S.I.C.: 6531
N.A.I.C.S.: 531390

Non-U.S. Subsidiaries:

Delek Benelux BV (1)
Princenhagelaan 9
4813 DA Breda, Netherlands
Tel.: (31) 76 523 94 50
Fuel Station Operating Services
S.I.C.: 5989
N.A.I.C.S.: 454310
Boaz Chechik *(CEO)*
Kobi Shmerler *(Corp Governance Officer & Sec)*

Delek France BV (1)
Princenhagelaan 9
4813 DA Breda, Netherlands
Tel.: (31) 76 523 94 50
Emp.: 117
Fuel Station Operating Services
S.I.C.: 5989
N.A.I.C.S.: 454310
Kobi Shmerler *(Corp Governance Officer & Sec)*

DELEK LOGISTICS PARTNERS, LP

(See Under Delek Group Ltd.)

DELEUM BERHAD

No 2 Jalan Bangsar Utama 9
Bangsar Utama
59000 Kuala Lumpur, Malaysia
Tel.: (60) 322957788
Fax: (60) 322957777
E-Mail: info@deleum.com
Web Site: www.deleum.com
DELEUM—(KLS)
Rev.: $155,184,851
Assets: $135,765,301
Liabilities: $55,000,050
Net Worth: $80,765,251
Earnings: $17,777,936
Emp.: 585
Fiscal Year-end: 12/31/12

Business Description:
Oil & Gas Exploration Services
S.I.C.: 1311
N.A.I.C.S.: 211111

Personnel:
Nan Yusri Nan Rahimy *(Mng Dir)*
Zamani Abd Ghani *(COO)*
Sew Bee Lee *(Co-Sec & Sr Gen Mgr-Corp Svcs)*
Hooi Mooi Lim *(Co-Sec)*

Board of Directors:
Izham Mahmud
Abdul Ghani Abdul Aziz
Kamaruddin Ahmad
Kwai Yoong Chin
Ishak Imam Abas
Nan Yusri Nan Rahimy
M. V. Nathan

Legal Counsel:
Zain & Co
6th & 7th Fl Menara Etiqa 23 Jalan Melaka
Kuala Lumpur, Malaysia

Subsidiaries:

Delcom Oilfield Services Sdn. Bhd. (1)
42 Jalan Bangsar Utama 1 Bangsar Utama
59000 Kuala Lumpur, Malaysia
Tel.: (60) 322827733
Fax: (60) 322826330
Oil & Gas Field Engineering Services
S.I.C.: 1389
N.A.I.C.S.: 213112

Penaga Dresser Sdn. Bhd. (1)
19A-9-1 Level 9 UOA Center No 19 Jalan Pinang
50450 Kuala Lumpur, Malaysia
Tel.: (60) 321632322
Fax: (60) 321618312
E-Mail: sales@penagadresser.com
Web Site: www.penagadresser.com
Emp.: 40
Ball & Safety Valves Distr
S.I.C.: 5085
N.A.I.C.S.: 423840
Abdul Aziz Zain *(Chm)*
Abdul Ghani Aziz *(Mng Dir)*

DELFINGEN INDUSTRY, S.A.

Rue Emile Streit
25340 Anteuil, France
Tel.: (33) 3 81 90 73 00
Fax: (33) 3 81 90 73 19
E-Mail: delfingen@delfingen.com
Web Site: www.delfingen.com
ALDEL—(EUR)
Rev.: $122,549,000
Assets: $85,627,000
Liabilities: $51,685,000
Net Worth: $33,942,000
Earnings: $3,909,000
Emp.: 1,300
Fiscal Year-end: 12/31/12

Business Description:
Automotive Supplier
S.I.C.: 5531
N.A.I.C.S.: 441310

Personnel:
Bernard Striet *(CEO)*

Board of Directors:
Michel de Massougnes des Fontaines
Juan Manuel Diaz
Georges Francois
Danielle Levi-Feunteun
Frederic Magne
Cataldo Mangione
David Streit
Francois Streit
Gerald Streit
Bernard Striet

U.S. Subsidiaries:

Delfingen US, Inc (1)
3985 W Hamil Rd
Rochester, MI 48309 MI
Tel.: (248) 519-0534
Web Site: www.delfingen.com
Emp.: 81
All Other Plastics Product Mfr
S.I.C.: 3089
N.A.I.C.S.: 326199
Bernard Streit *(Pres)*
Mark Blanke *(CFO)*

Subsidiary:

Delfingen US-New York, Inc. (2)
2221 Niagara Falls Blvd Ste 12
Niagara Falls, NY 14304 NY
Tel.: (716) 215-0300
Web Site: www.delfingen.com
Emp.: 40
All Other Miscellaneous Electrical Equipment & Component Mfr
S.I.C.: 3699
N.A.I.C.S.: 335999
Diana Bollinger *(Mgr-HR)*

Hilec, LLC (1)
11 Railroad Ave
Arcade, NY 14009
Tel.: (585) 492-2212
Fax: (800) 450-8193
E-Mail: info@hilec.com
Web Site: www.hilec.com
Emp.: 40
Electrical Apparatus & Equipment, Wiring Supplies & Related Equipment Merchant Whslr
S.I.C.: 5063
N.A.I.C.S.: 423610
Donald Hubert *(Principal)*

DELFONT MACKINTOSH THEATRES LIMITED

Novello Theatre
London, WC2B 4LD, United Kingdom
Tel.: (44) 2073794431
Fax: (44) 2072403831
E-Mail: delfont@delmack.co.uk
Web Site: www.delfontmackintosh.co.uk
Year Founded: 1991
Emp.: 120

Business Description:
Theatre Owners
S.I.C.: 7361
N.A.I.C.S.: 561311

DELFORTGROUP AG

Fabrikstrasse 20
4050 Traun, Austria
Tel.: (43) 7229 776-0
Fax: (43) 7229 77618-100
E-Mail: info@delfortgroup.com
Web Site: www.delfortgroup.com
Emp.: 1,750

Business Description:
Holding Company; Specialty Papers Developer, Mfr & Distr
S.I.C.: 6719
N.A.I.C.S.: 551112

Personnel:
Martin Zahlbruckner *(CEO)*

Subsidiaries:

Dr. Franz Feurstein GmbH (1)
Fabrikstrasse 20
4050 Traun, Austria AT
Tel.: (43) 7229 776-0
Fax: (43) 7229 77618-100
E-Mail: feurstein@delfortgroup.com
Emp.: 250
Specialty Paper Mill
S.I.C.: 2621
N.A.I.C.S.: 322121

Papierfabrik Wattens GmbH & Co. KG (1)
Ludwig-Lassl-Strasse 15
6112 Wattens, Austria AT
Tel.: (43) 5224 595 0
Fax: (43) 5224 595 250
E-Mail: wattenspapier@delfortgroup.com
Specialty Paper Mill
S.I.C.: 2621
N.A.I.C.S.: 322121

Non-U.S. Subsidiaries:

Dunafin Kft. (1)
Papirgyari ut 42-46
2400 Dunaujvaros, Hungary HU
Tel.: (36) 25 511 400
Fax: (36) 25 511 415
E-Mail: dunafin@delfortgroup.com
Specialty Paper Mill
S.I.C.: 2621
N.A.I.C.S.: 322121

OP Papirna, s.r.o. (1)
Olsany 18
78962 Olsany, Czech Republic CZ
Tel.: (420) 583 384 501
Fax: (420) 583 384 802
E-Mail: oppapirna@delfortgroup.com
Specialty Paper Mill
S.I.C.: 2621
N.A.I.C.S.: 322121

Tervakoski Oy (1)
Vahikkalantie 1
12400 Tervakoski, Finland FI
Tel.: (358) 19 771 1
Fax: (358) 19 771 535
E-Mail: tervakoski@delfortgroup.com
Specialty Paper Mill
S.I.C.: 2621
N.A.I.C.S.: 322121

DELHAIZE GROUP S.A.

Square Marie Curie 40
1070 Brussels, Belgium
Tel.: (32) 2 412 22 11
Telex: 2 21976
Fax: (32) 2 412 21 94
E-Mail: investor@delhaizegroup.com
Web Site: www.delhaizegroup.com
Year Founded: 1867
DEG—(EUR NYSE)
Rev.: $30,607,867,290
Assets: $16,067,885,120
Liabilities: $9,077,224,310
Net Worth: $6,990,660,810
Earnings: $138,655,510
Emp.: 77,500
Fiscal Year-end: 12/31/12

Business Description:
Supermarkets Cosmetics, Health & Beauty Care Products Stores, Food Store Chains
S.I.C.: 5122
N.A.I.C.S.: 446120

Personnel:
Mats Jansson *(Chm)*
Frans W. H. Muller *(Pres & CEO)*
Pierre Bruno Charles Bouchut *(CFO & Exec VP)*

Kostas Macheras *(CEO-Southeast Europe & Asia & Exec VP)*
Dirk Van den Berghe *(CEO-Belgium)*
Maura Abeln Smith *(Gen Counsel, Sec & Exec VP)*
Michel Eeckhout *(Exec VP)*
Nicolas Hollanders *(Exec VP-HR, IT & Sustainability)*
Marcus Spurrell *(Sr VP-Digital)*

Board of Directors:
Mats Jansson
Claire H. Babrowski
Shari L. Ballard
Pierre-Olivier Beckers
Jacques M. de Vaucleroy
Elizabeth Doherty
Hugh G. Farrington
William G. McEwan
Didier Smits
Jack L. Stahl
Luc Vansteenkiste

Subsidiaries:

Aniserco S.A. (1)
Bettegemlaan 3
Zellek, 1731 Brussels, Belgium (100%)
Tel.: (32) 24122557
Fax: (32) 24122194
Emp.: 1,500
S.I.C.: 5541
N.A.I.C.S.: 447110

Delhaize The Lion Coordination Center SA (1)
Rue Osseghem 53
Brussels, 1080, Belgium
Tel.: (32) 24122111
Fax: (32) 24122194
Grocery Store Operating Services
S.I.C.: 5411
N.A.I.C.S.: 445110
Dirk Van den Berghe *(Gen Mgr)*

Delhome S.A. (1)
Bld Del Humanite 219 221
1620 Drogenbos, Belgium (100%)
Tel.: (32) 23782296
Fax: (32) 23782032
E-Mail: bureau@caddjhome.be
Web Site: www.caddjhome.be
Emp.: 100
S.I.C.: 5541
N.A.I.C.S.: 447110
Mark Dauwers *(Mng Dir)*

Delimmo S.A. (1)
Rue Osseghem 53
1080 Brussels, Belgium (100%)
Tel.: (32) 24122141
Telex: VAT BE 408 324 369
Fax: (32) 24122194
Emp.: 120
Real Estate Holding Co
S.I.C.: 6719
N.A.I.C.S.: 551112

Huro NV (1)
Sleihagestraat 57
Oostnieuwkerke, 8840 Staden, Belgium
Tel.: (32) 51 22 72 84
Fax: (32) 51 22 99 93
E-Mail: info@huro.be
Web Site: www.huro.be
Asphalt Roof Installation Services
S.I.C.: 1761
N.A.I.C.S.: 238160

Leoburg NV (1)
Lommelsesteenweg 8
Leopoldsburg, 3970, Belgium
Tel.: (32) 11543350
Emp.: 15
Grocery Store Operating Services
S.I.C.: 5411
N.A.I.C.S.: 445110
Chris Janssens *(Mgr-Store)*

Rousseau NV (1)
Kouter 158
Gent, 9000, Belgium
Tel.: (32) 37761264
Fax: (32) 92243714
Emp.: 50
Supermarket Stores Operating Services
S.I.C.: 5411
N.A.I.C.S.: 445110

Smart Food Shopping SA (1)
Chaussee De Wavre 42a
Gembloux, 5030, Belgium
Tel.: (32) 81613844
Supermarket Operating Services
S.I.C.: 5411
N.A.I.C.S.: 445110

Wambacq & Peeters NV (1)
Isidoor Crockaertstraat 25
1731 Asse, Belgium (100%)
Tel.: (32) 24669380
Fax: (32) 24666309
E-Mail: info@liebherr.com
Web Site: www.liebherr.com
Emp.: 50
Transporting Merchandise to Stores From Delhaize Distribution Centers
S.I.C.: 4214
N.A.I.C.S.: 484110

U.S. Subsidiaries:

Delhaize America, Inc. (1)
2110 Exec Dr
Salisbury, NC 28147 NC
Tel.: (704) 633-8250 (100%)
Fax: (704) 630-5024
Web Site: www.delhaizeamerica.com
Sales Range: $1-4.9 Billion
Emp.: 1,200
Supermarket Operator
S.I.C.: 5411
N.A.I.C.S.: 445110
Pierre-Olivier Beckers *(Chm)*
Carol M. Herndon *(Chief Admin Officer)*

Subsidiaries:

Bottom Dollar Food Southeast, LLC (2)
2110 Executive Dr
Salisbury, NC 28147-9007
Tel.: (704) 310-2221
Fax: (704) 797-2309
E-Mail: mediarelations@foodlion.com
Web Site: www.bottomdollarfood.com
Discount Departmental Stores Operating Services
S.I.C.: 5311
N.A.I.C.S.: 452112
Meg Ham *(Pres)*

DZA Brands, LLC (2)
2110 Executive Dr
Salisbury, NC 28147
Tel.: (866) 322-2439
Grocery Products Distr
S.I.C.: 5149
N.A.I.C.S.: 424490
Michael R. Waller *(Mgr)*

Food Lion, LLC (2)
2110 Executive Dr
Salisbury, NC 28147-9007 NC
Mailing Address: (52%)
PO Box 1330
Salisbury, NC 28145-1330
Tel.: (704) 633-8250
Fax: (704) 630-5024
Toll Free: (800) 210-9569
Web Site: www.foodlion.com
Emp.: 7,500
Supermarket Operator
S.I.C.: 5411
N.A.I.C.S.: 445110
Robert Canipe *(Sr VP-Corp Dev)*

Hannaford Bros. Co. (2)
145 Pleasant Hill Rd
Scarborough, ME 04074-9309 ME
Mailing Address:
PO Box 1000
Portland, ME 04104-5005
Tel.: (207) 883-2911
Fax: (207) 885-2859
Toll Free: (800) 341-6393
E-Mail: working@hannaford.com
Web Site: www.hannaford.com
Emp.: 800
Retail Supermarkets
Import
S.I.C.: 5411
N.A.I.C.S.: 445110
Chris Lewis *(CIO & Sr VP-IT)*
Brad Wise *(Pres-Supermarkets)*
Greg Amoroso *(Sr VP-Corp Dev)*

Subsidiaries:

Hannaford Trucking Company (3)
54 Hannaford Rd
Portland, ME 04104
Tel.: (207) 883-2911
Fax: (207) 482-5684
E-Mail: staffing@hannaford.com
General Freight Trucking Services
S.I.C.: 4214
N.A.I.C.S.: 484110
Jim Moody *(Pres)*
Walter Whittier *(Pres)*

Progressive Distributors, Inc. (3)
1245 US Rte 202
Winthrop, ME 04364 ME
Tel.: (207) 377-2251 (100%)
Fax: (207) 377-5722
E-Mail: info@hannaford.com
Web Site: www.hannaford.com
Emp.: 230
Rack Job Wholesaler
S.I.C.: 3399
N.A.I.C.S.: 331110

J.H. Harvey Co., LLC (2)
727 S Davis St
Nashville, GA 31639-2673 GA
Tel.: (229) 686-7654
Fax: (229) 686-2927
E-Mail: info@jh-harvey.com
Web Site: www.jh-harvey.com
Emp.: 2,500
Supermarkets Operator
S.I.C.: 5411
N.A.I.C.S.: 445110
Barry Robinson *(VP-Consumer Affairs)*

Reid's, Inc. (2)
1050 Dunbarton Blvd
Barnwell, SC 29812 SC
Tel.: (803) 259-1777
Toll Free: (800) 210-9569
Web Site: www.reidsgroceries.com
Supermarkets Operator
S.I.C.: 5411
N.A.I.C.S.: 445110
J. Boyleston *(Principal)*

Kash 'n Karry Food Stores, Inc. (2)
3801 Sugar Palm Dr
Tampa, FL 33619-8301 DE
Tel.: (813) 620-1139
Fax: (813) 627-9765
E-Mail: communications@sweetbaysupermarket.com
Web Site: www.sweetbaysupermarket.com
Supermarket Chain; Liquor & Drug Stores
S.I.C.: 5411
N.A.I.C.S.: 445110
Michael Vail *(Pres & COO)*

Victory Distributors, Inc. (2)
624 W 79th St Ste 1
Chicago, IL 60620-1835
Tel.: (773) 874-0162
Household Appliances Whslr
S.I.C.: 5722
N.A.I.C.S.: 443141
Beth Newlands Campbell *(CEO)*

Delhaize US Holding, Inc. (1)
2110 Executive Dr
Salisbury, NC 28147-9007
Tel.: (704) 633-8250, ext. 2529
Fax: (704) 645-4499
Investment Management Services
S.I.C.: 6211
N.A.I.C.S.: 523999

Non-U.S. Subsidiaries:

Alfa-Beta Vassilopoulos S.A. (1)
81 Spaton Ave Gerakas
153 44 Athens, Greece GR
Tel.: (30) 2106608000 (89.56%)
Fax: (30) 2106612675
E-Mail: vrettas@ab.gr
Web Site: www.ab.gr
Emp.: 650
S.I.C.: 5541
N.A.I.C.S.: 447110
Viasalios Vrettas *(Asst Gen Mgr)*

Atlas A/S (1)
11018 Za Panskou Zahradou
25219 Prague, Czech Republic (100%)
Tel.: (420) 311609111
Fax: (420) 311609465
E-Mail: delnemo@delnemo.cz
Web Site: www.delnemoc.cz
Emp.: 300
S.I.C.: 5541
N.A.I.C.S.: 447110

Delhaize BH d.o.o. (1)
Branka Popovica 115
78000 Banja Luka, Bosnia & Herzegovina
Tel.: (387) 51 337 912
Fax: (387) 51 379 610
Emp.: 110
Grocery Stores Operating Services
S.I.C.: 5411
N.A.I.C.S.: 445110
Mirjana Vracar *(Gen Mgr)*

Delhaize Finance B.V. (1)
Martinus Nijhofflaan 2
Delft, Netherlands
Tel.: (31) 152624590
Financial Management Services
S.I.C.: 6211
N.A.I.C.S.: 523999

Delhaize Luxembourg S.A. (1)
51 Rue d
8281 Kehlen, Luxembourg
Tel.: (352) 30 99 11
Fax: (352) 30 99 11 308
Supermarket Stores Operating Services
S.I.C.: 5411
N.A.I.C.S.: 445110

Delhaize Montenegro d.o.o. (1)
Josipa Broza Tita 23a
81000 Podgorica, Montenegro
Tel.: (382) 20 440 800
Fax: (382) 20 440 821
Emp.: 48
Supermarket Stores Operating Services
S.I.C.: 5411
N.A.I.C.S.: 445110
Ivan Rakovic *(Country Mgr)*

Delhaize "The Lion" Nederland B.V. (1)
Martinus Nijhofflaan 2
Delft, 2624 ES, Netherlands
Tel.: (31) 15 262 4590
Supermarket Stores Operating Services
S.I.C.: 5411
N.A.I.C.S.: 445110

ENA SA (1)
10 Ziridi
151 23 Athens, Greece
Tel.: (30) 210 6855511
Fax: (30) 210 6855540
Video Production Services
S.I.C.: 7812
N.A.I.C.S.: 512110
Moschona Vasilia *(Mgr-HR)*

Mega Image (1)
95 Siret Str Sektor 1
012152 Bucharest, Romania RO
Tel.: (40) 212246677 (100%)
Fax: (40) 212246011
E-Mail: info@megaimage.ro
Web Site: www.mega-image.ro
Emp.: 180
Supermarket
S.I.C.: 5411
N.A.I.C.S.: 445110
Xavier Piesvaux *(Gen Mgr)*

Piccadilly AD (1)
Ul Bitolya 1a
9002 Varna, Bulgaria
Tel.: (359) 52 66 34 34
Fax: (359) 52 66 34 56
Frozen Food Mfr & Distr
S.I.C.: 2038
N.A.I.C.S.: 311412

Super Indo (1)
JL Ancol I nr 9-10 Ancol Barat
Jakarta, 14430, Indonesia Id
Tel.: (62) 216905876 (100%)
Fax: (62) 216905877
Supermarket
S.I.C.: 5411
N.A.I.C.S.: 445110

TP Srbija a.d. (1)
Crvenog barjaka bb
Kragujevac, Serbia
Tel.: (381) 34 333 725
Emp.: 14
Grocery Product Distr
S.I.C.: 5141
N.A.I.C.S.: 424410

DELIGNIT AG
Konigswinkel 2-6
Blomberg, 32825, Germany

Delignit AG—(Continued)

Tel.: (49) 5235966100
Fax: (49) 5235966105
Web Site: www.delignit-ag.de
Year Founded: 1799
DLX—(DEU)
Sls.: $45,904,397
Assets: $28,808,038
Liabilities: $14,673,253
Net Worth: $14,134,785
Earnings: $1,615,404
Emp.: 211
Fiscal Year-end: 12/31/12
Business Description:
Wood Products Mfr
S.I.C.: 2499
N.A.I.C.S.: 321999
Personnel:
Christof Nesemeier *(Chm-Supervisory Bd)*
Markus Buscher *(CEO & Member-Exec Bd)*
Thorsten Duray *(Chief Sls Officer & Member-Exec Bd)*
Supervisory Board of Directors:
Christof Nesemeier
Anton Breitkopf
Gert-Maria Freimuth

Subsidiary:

Blomberger Holzindustrie B. Hausmann GmbH & Co. KG **(1)**
Konigswinkel 2
D-32825 Blomberg, Germany
Tel.: (49) 5235 9660
Fax: (49) 5235 966351
E-Mail: info@delignit.de
Plywood Products Mfr
S.I.C.: 2435
N.A.I.C.S.: 321211

DELIVER-NET LIMITED

Snaygill Industrial Estate Healthcare House Keighley Rd
Skipton, N Yorkshire, BD23 2QQR, United Kingdom
Tel.: (44) 1756706050
Fax: (44) 1756706055
Web Site: www.delivernet.co.uk
Year Founded: 2000
Emp.: 50
Business Description:
Healthcare Supplies Online
S.I.C.: 5999
N.A.I.C.S.: 453998
Personnel:
Nigel Myers *(Dir-Ops)*

DELIVERY HERO HOLDING GMBH

Mohrenstrasse 60
10117 Berlin, Germany
Tel.: (49) 30 54 44 59 100
E-Mail: info@deliveryhero.com
Web Site: www.deliveryhero.com
Year Founded: 2010
Sales Range: $400-449.9 Million
Emp.: 600
Business Description:
Online Food Ordering & Delivery Services
S.I.C.: 2741
N.A.I.C.S.: 519130
Personnel:
Niklas Ostberg *(Co-Founder & CEO)*
Nikita Fahrenholz *(Co-Founder & Chief Bus Dev Officer)*
Claude Ritter *(Co-Founder & Chief Product Officer)*
Markus Fuhrmann *(Co-Founder & Head-Special Projects)*
Doreen Huber *(COO)*
Frank Gessner *(CIO)*
Hugo Suidman *(CMO)*

DELKO S.A.

ul Mickiewicza 93
63-100 Srem, Poland
Tel.: (48) 612837731
Fax: (48) 612834015
E-Mail: office@delko.com.pl
Web Site: www.delko.com.pl
Year Founded: 1995
DEL—(WAR)
Sales Range: $150-199.9 Million
Emp.: 379
Business Description:
Cleaning Products & Cosmetics Distr
S.I.C.: 5199
N.A.I.C.S.: 424990
Personnel:
Miroslaw Newel *(Chm-Supervisory Bd)*
Andrzej Worsztynowicz *(Chm-Mgmt Bd)*
Leszek Wojcik *(Vice Chm-Supervisory Bd)*
Dawid Harsze *(Vice Chm-Mgmt Bd)*
Dariusz Smiejkowski *(Vice Chm-Mgmt Bd)*
Supervisory Board of Directors:
Miroslaw Newel
Miroslaw Jan Dabrowski
Dariusz Kawecki
Wojciech Szymon Kowalski
Kazimierz Jan Luberda
Leszek Wojcik

DELLOYD VENTURES BERHAD

52A Lebuh Enggang
41150 Kelang, Selangor Darul Ehsan, Malaysia
Tel.: (60) 333437145
Fax: (60) 333433296
E-Mail: delloyd@tm.net.my
Web Site: www.delloyd.com
DELLOYD—(KLS)
Rev.: $139,259,098
Assets: $184,376,627
Liabilities: $39,720,294
Net Worth: $144,656,333
Earnings: $11,358,165
Fiscal Year-end: 03/31/13
Business Description:
Motor Vehicles & Automotive Parts Distr
S.I.C.: 5014
N.A.I.C.S.: 423130
Personnel:
Soo Seong Chua *(Deputy CEO & Dir-Mfg)*
Boon Kee Tee *(Mng Dir)*
Yoke Hoong Chan *(CFO)*
Boon Keat Tee *(CEO-Delloyd Auto Parts M Sdn Bhd)*
Leon Wee Leng Tee *(Deputy Mng Dir)*
Say Or Ng *(Co-Sec)*
Ing Chuo Yew *(Co-Sec)*
Board of Directors:
Mohamed Hashim Mohd Ali
Mohamed Nizam Abdul Razak
Chee Sun Chung
Geok Siew Chung
Kwan Hoong Eow
Noor Azmi Jaafar
M. Shanmughalingam
Boon Keat Tee
Boon Kee Tee
Leon Wee Leng Tee

Subsidiaries:

Delloyd Industries (M) Sdn Bhd **(1)**
Lot 33004/5 Batu 5 Jalan Kebun Kampung Jawa
42450 Port Klang, Selangor, Malaysia
Tel.: (60) 351612288
Fax: (60) 351613362
E-Mail: hr@delloyd.com
Emp.: 1,000
Automotive Parts & Accessories Mfr
S.I.C.: 2396
N.A.I.C.S.: 336360
Noor Azmi Jaafar *(CEO)*
Tee Boon Kee *(Mng Dir)*

Delloyd Plantation Sdn. Bhd. **(1)**
Sungai Rambai Estate
Batang Berjuntai, Kuala Selangor, Selangor, Malaysia
Tel.: (60) 332719001
Fax: (60) 332716118
Emp.: 120
Oil Palm Cultivation Services
S.I.C.: 0721
N.A.I.C.S.: 115112
Tee Boon Kee *(Mng Dir)*

Premier Asian Auto Publications (M) Sdn Bhd **(1)**
Lot 33004/5 Jalan Kebun
Kampung Jawa, 42450 Kelang, Selangor, Malaysia
Tel.: (60) 351636856
Fax: (60) 351613362
E-Mail: general@asianauto.com
Web Site: www.asianauto.com
Automobile Magazine Publishing Services
S.I.C.: 2721
N.A.I.C.S.: 511120
V. Suresh *(Mgr-Mktg)*

DELMAR COMMODITIES LTD.

915 Navigator Dr
PO Box 1055
Winkler, MB, R6W 4B1, Canada
Tel.: (204) 331-3696
Fax: (204) 331-3704
Toll Free: (888) 974-7246
Web Site: www.delmarcommodities.com
Year Founded: 1995
Rev.: $12,334,319
Emp.: 92
Business Description:
Grain Mfr
S.I.C.: 4221
N.A.I.C.S.: 493130
Personnel:
Dale Heide *(Pres)*

DELMAR PHARMACEUTICALS, INC.

(Formerly Berry Only Inc.)
720-999 West Broadway
Vancouver, BC, V5Z 1K5, Canada
Tel.: (604) 629-5989
Web Site: www.delmarpharma.com
Year Founded: 2009
DMPI—(OTC OTCB)
Int. Income: $2,491
Assets: $4,318,748
Liabilities: $5,136,726
Net Worth: ($817,978)
Earnings: ($8,290,689)
Emp.: 4
Fiscal Year-end: 12/31/13
Business Description:
Pharmaceutical Mfr
S.I.C.: 2834
N.A.I.C.S.: 325412
Personnel:
Jeffrey A. Bacha *(Pres & CEO)*
Scott Praill *(CFO)*
Dennis M. Brown *(Chief Scientific Officer)*
Board of Directors:
Jeffrey A. Bacha
John K. Bell
Dennis M. Brown
William J. Garner
Robert J. Toth, Jr.
Transfer Agent:
Island Stock Transfer
100 2nd Ave S Ste 104N
Saint Petersburg, FL 33701

DELNOR CONSTRUCTION LTD.

3609 74 Avenue
Edmonton, AB, T6B 2T7, Canada
Tel.: (780) 469-1304
Fax: (780) 466-0798
E-Mail: delnor@delnor.ca
Web Site: www.delnor.ca
Year Founded: 1983
Rev.: $40,776,945
Emp.: 70
Business Description:
Building Construction Services
S.I.C.: 1542
N.A.I.C.S.: 236220
Personnel:
Chris Bodnar *(Mgr-HR)*

DELO PRODAJA, D.D.

Dunajska 5
1000 Ljubljana, Slovenia
Tel.: (386) 14738600
Fax: (386) 1 4738604
E-Mail: info@delo-prodaja.si
Web Site: www.delo-prodaja.si
DPRG—(LJU)
Sales Range: $50-74.9 Million
Emp.: 140
Business Description:
General Merchandise Store Owner & Operator
S.I.C.: 5399
N.A.I.C.S.: 452990
Personnel:
Gregor Zupancic *(Chm-Supervisory Bd)*
Branko Bergant *(Chm-Mgmt Bd & CEO)*
Boris Anisic *(Deputy Chm-Supervisory Bd)*
Supervisory Board of Directors:
Milan Maljkovic
Boris Anisic
Gregor Zupancic

DELOITTE LLP

Hill House 1 Little New Street
London, EC4A 3TR, United Kingdom
Tel.: (44) 2079363000
Fax: (44) 2075831198
Web Site: www.deloitte.com
Rev.: $3,971,914,350
Assets: $1,538,228,460
Liabilities: $3,041,712,540
Net Worth: ($1,503,484,080)
Earnings: $693,308,310
Emp.: 14,529
Fiscal Year-end: 05/31/13
Business Description:
Audit, Tax, Consulting & Financial Advisory Services
S.I.C.: 8721
N.A.I.C.S.: 541211
Personnel:
David Cruickshank *(Chm)*
Neville Kahn *(Vice Chm & Mng Partner-Corp Fin)*
Sabri Challah *(Vice Chm & Partner-Partner Matters)*
Ralph Adams *(Vice Chm)*
Carol Arrowsmith *(Vice Chm)*
Richard Buck *(Vice Chm)*
Mike Dobby *(Vice Chm)*
Cahal Dowds *(Vice Chm)*
Mark Fitzpatrick *(Vice Chm)*
John Fotheringham *(Vice Chm)*
Carl Hughes *(Vice Chm)*
Louis Jordan *(Vice Chm)*
Doug King *(Vice Chm)*
Ken McFarlane *(Vice Chm)*
Vassi Naidoo *(Vice Chm)*
Nick Owen *(Vice Chm)*
Ellie Patsalos *(Vice Chm)*
Graham Richardson *(Vice Chm)*

David Sproul *(CEO & Sr Partner)*
Steve Almond *(Mng Partner-Intl Markets)*
David Barnes *(Mng Partner-Pub Policy)*
Emma Codd *(Mng Partner-Talent)*
Vimi Grewal-Carr *(Mng Partner-Delivery Models)*
Stephen Griggs *(Mng Partner-Fin)*
Andrew Hodge *(Mng Partner-Tax)*
Panos Kakoullis *(Mng Partner-Audit)*
Vince Niblett *(Mng Partner-Sr Markets Grp)*
Simon Owen *(Mng Partner-Innovation & New Bus Models)*
Richard Punt *(Mng Partner-Clients & Markets)*
Paul Robinson *(Mng Partner-Consulting)*
Nick Sandall *(Mng Partner-Fin Svcs)*
Sharon Thorne *(Mng Partner-Reg Markets)*
Steve Ward *(Mng Partner-Quality & Risk)*
Martin Jenkins *(Sr Partner-Sls & Mktg-North East)*
Pat Loftus *(Sr Partner-Sls & Mktg-North West)*
Chris Loughran *(Sr Partner-Sls & Mktg-Midlands)*
Graham Pickett *(Sr Partner-Sls & Mktg-South East)*
Ian Steele *(Sr Partner-Sls & Mktg-Scotland & Northern Ireland)*
Denis Woulfe *(Sr Partner-Sls & Mktg-South West)*
David Gill *(Partner-Internal Client Svcs)*
Heather Hancock *(Partner-Client Experience)*
Caryl Longley *(Sec)*
Board of Directors:
David Cruickshank
David Barnes
Zahir Bokhari
John Cullinane
Nick Edwards
Stephen Griggs
Gerry Grimstone
DeAnne Shirley Julius
Chris Loughran
Anna Marks
Nick Owen
Ellie Patsalos
Michael Charles Gerrard Peat
Christopher Powell
Reto Savoia
David Sproul
Ian Steele
Sharon Thorne
Denis Woulfe
Subsidiaries:

Drivers Jonas Deloitte (1)
85 King William St
London, EC4N 7BL, United Kingdom
Tel.: (44) 2078968000
Fax: (44) 2078968002
Web Site: www.driversjonas.com
Sales Range: $125-149.9 Million
Emp.: 650
Commercial Property Consulting Services
S.I.C.: 6531
N.A.I.C.S.: 531390
Alex Bell *(Partner)*
Gary Cardin *(Assoc Partner)*
Tony Guthrie *(Assoc Partner)*
Mark Lethbridge *(Partner)*
Richard Pike *(Assoc Partner)*

DELOITTE TOUCHE TOHMATSU LIMITED

Hill House 1 Little New Street
London, EC4A 3TR, United Kingdom
Tel.: (44) 20 7936 3000
E-Mail: globalcorporatereputation@deloitte.com
Web Site: www.deloitte.com
Sales Range: $25-49.9 Billion
Emp.: 181,566
Business Description:
Accounting, Auditing, Tax Preparation & Management Consulting Services Organization
S.I.C.: 8621
N.A.I.C.S.: 813920
Personnel:
Steve Almond *(Chm)*
Barry Salzberg *(CEO)*

DELON RESOURCES CORP.

(Name Changed to Gener8 Media Corp.)

DELONG HOLDINGS LIMITED

One Finlayson Green 06-03
Singapore, 049246, Singapore
Tel.: (65) 65352510
Fax: (65) 65357505
E-Mail: delong@listedcompany.com
Web Site: www.delong.listedcompany.com
B1N—(OTC SES)
Rev.: $2,109,509,415
Assets: $1,147,384,828
Liabilities: $733,769,610
Net Worth: $413,615,219
Earnings: $35,664,367
Fiscal Year-end: 12/31/12
Business Description:
Coils Mfr
S.I.C.: 3714
N.A.I.C.S.: 336320
Personnel:
Liguo Ding *(Chm)*
Jihong Lan *(CFO)*
Lee Luang Yeo *(Compliance Officer, Sec & Mgr-Accts)*
Board of Directors:
Liguo Ding
Baohua Bai
Theng Fong Hee
Hock Meng Lai
WeiMin Yuan
Shuowen Zuo

DE'LONGHI S.P.A.

Via Lodovico Seitz 47
31100 Treviso, Italy
Tel.: (39) 0422413235
Fax: (39) 0422414346
E-Mail: info@delonghi.it
Web Site: www.delonghi.com
DLG—(ITA)
Rev.: $2,059,781,448
Assets: $2,056,090,250
Liabilities: $1,202,586,162
Net Worth: $853,504,088
Earnings: $158,830,560
Emp.: 5,694
Fiscal Year-end: 12/31/12
Business Description:
Household Appliances Mfr
S.I.C.: 3639
N.A.I.C.S.: 335228
Personnel:
Giuseppe De'Longhi *(Chm)*
Fabio De'Longhi *(Vice Chm & CEO)*
Stefano Beraldo *(Fin Reporting Officer)*
Board of Directors:
Giuseppe De'Longhi
Alberto Clo
Renato Corrada
Fabio De'Longhi
Silvia De'Longhi
Carlo Garavaglia
Dario Melo
Giorgio Sandri
Silvio Sartori
Giovanni Tamburi
U.S. Subsidiary:

De'Longhi America Inc. (1)
Park 80 W Plz 1 Fl 4
Saddle Brook, NJ 07663 (100%)
Tel.: (201) 909-4000
Fax: (201) 909-8550
Web Site: www.delonghiusa.com
Sls.: $95,000,000
Emp.: 65
Electric Household Appliances Mfr
S.I.C.: 5064
N.A.I.C.S.: 423620
Mike Prager *(Pres & CEO)*
Non-U.S. Subsidiaries:

Kenwood Limited (1)
New Ln
Havant, Hamps, PO9 2NH, United Kingdom UK
Tel.: (44) 2392476000 (100%)
Fax: (44) 2392392400
E-Mail: nigel.wainwright@kenwood.co.uk
Web Site: www.kenwood.co.uk
Emp.: 300
Mfr. of Food Mixers, Liquidisers, Waste Disposal Units; Rotary Ironers
S.I.C.: 3639
N.A.I.C.S.: 335210
Helen Feeney *(Sec)*

Non-U.S. Subsidiary:

Kenwood Manufacturing GmbH (2)
12 Sud Strasse 2A
PO Box 55
2355 Wiener Neudorf, Austria (100%)
Tel.: (43) 223664500
Telex: 136492
Fax: (43) 223662121
E-Mail: info@kenwoodaustria.at
Web Site: www.kenwood.at
Sales Range: $10-24.9 Million
Emp.: 16
Food Mixers & Blenders, Waste Disposal Units, Rotary Ironers
S.I.C.: 3999
N.A.I.C.S.: 335210
Michael Frank *(Mng Dir)*

Parex Appliances Ltd (1)
103 Central Park Drive
Henderson, AK, Australia
Tel.: (61) 98366566
Fax: (61) 9 836 6033
E-Mail: info@parex.co.nz
Web Site: www.parex.co.nz
Household Appliance Distr
S.I.C.: 5722
N.A.I.C.S.: 443141
Andy Higgs *(Gen Mgr)*

DELORO RESOURCES LTD.

Suite 900-925 W Georgia Street
Vancouver, BC, Canada V6C 3L2
Tel.: (604) 484-5761
Fax: (604) 484-5760
Web Site: www.deloro.ca
Year Founded: 1996
DLL—(TSXV)
Business Description:
Oil & Natural Gas Exploration Services
S.I.C.: 1389
N.A.I.C.S.: 213112
Personnel:
Reza Mohammed *(Pres & CEO)*
Board of Directors:
Lloyd Bates
Peter Born
Bill Calsbeck
Reza Mohammed
Robert G. Smith
Legal Counsel:
DuMoulin Black
10th Floor, 595 Howe Street
Vancouver, BC, V6C 2T5, Canada
Transfer Agent:
Computershare Trust Company
510 Burrard Street 2nd Floor
Vancouver, BC, Canada

DELPHARM S.A.S.

6-8 rue du Quartre Septembre
92130 Issy-les-Moulineaux, France
Tel.: (33) 1 41 09 19 70
Fax: (33) 1 41 09 19 83
E-Mail: delpharm@delpharm.com
Web Site: www.delpharm.com
Sales Range: $125-149.9 Million
Emp.: 870
Business Description:
Pharmaceuticals & Cosmetics Mfr
S.I.C.: 2834
N.A.I.C.S.: 325412
Personnel:
Sebastien Aguettant *(Pres)*
Subsidiaries:

Delpharm Evreux SAS (1)
5 rue du Guesclin
BP 285
27002 Evreux, Cedex, France
Tel.: (33) 232295800
Fax: (33) 232331248
E-Mail: evreux@delpharm.com
Web Site: www.delpharm.com
Sales Range: $25-49.9 Million
Emp.: 195
Pharmaceuticals & Cosmetics Mfr
S.I.C.: 2833
N.A.I.C.S.: 325411
Christian Cratere *(Gen Mgr)*

Delpharm Tours SAS (1)
rue Paul Langevin La Baraudiere
BP 90241
37170 Tours, Cedex, France
Tel.: (33) 2 47 48 43 00
Fax: (33) 2 47 48 43 14
E-Mail: tours@delpharm.com
Web Site: www.delpharm.com
Sales Range: $25-49.9 Million
Emp.: 200
Pharmaceuticals & Cosmetics Mfr
S.I.C.: 2833
N.A.I.C.S.: 325411
Vincent Declerck *(Gen Mgr)*

DELPHI AUTOMOTIVE PLC

Courtney Road Hoath Way
Gillingham, Kent, ME8 0RU, United Kingdom
Tel.: (44) 163 423 4422
Web Site: www.delphi.com
DLPH—(NYSE)
Sls.: $16,463,000,000
Assets: $11,047,000,000
Liabilities: $7,613,000,000
Net Worth: $3,434,000,000
Earnings: $1,301,000,000
Emp.: 117,000
Fiscal Year-end: 12/31/13
Business Description:
Vehicle Components Mfr
S.I.C.: 3714
N.A.I.C.S.: 336390
Personnel:
John A. Krol *(Chm)*
Rodney O'Neal *(Pres & CEO)*
Kevin P. Clark *(CFO & Sr VP)*
Timothy C. McCabe *(CIO & Sr VP)*
David M. Sherbin *(Chief Compliance Officer, Gen Counsel, Sec & Sr VP)*
Jeffrey J. Owens *(CTO & Exec VP)*
Allan J. Brazier *(Chief Acctg Officer)*
Majdi B. Abulaban *(Pres-Electrical & Electronic Architecture-Asia Pacific & Sr VP)*
Jugal K. Vijayvargiya *(Pres-Electronics & Safety & Sr VP)*
Luiz R. Corrallo *(Pres-Powertrain & Thermal-South America)*
Keith D. Stipp *(Pres-Thermal Sys)*
Kevin M. Butler *(Sr VP-HR Mgmt & Global Bus Svcs)*
Sidney Johnson *(Sr VP-Global Supply Mgmt)*
Eleanor E. Mascheroni *(Sr VP-Corp Comm)*

Delphi Automotive PLC—(Continued)

Board of Directors:
John A. Krol
Gary L. Cowger
Nicholas M. Donofrio
Mark P. Frissora
Rajiv Lochan Gupta
J. Randall MacDonald
Sean O. Mahoney
Rodney O'Neal
Thomas W. Sidlik
Bernd Wiedemann
Lawrence A. Zimmerman

Subsidiary:

Delphi Automotive LLP (1)
Courtney Road
Gillingham, ME8 ORU, United Kingdom
Tel.: (44) 1634 234 422
Automotive Parts Mfr
S.I.C.: 3714
N.A.I.C.S.: 336390

Subsidiaries:

Delphi Automotive Systems UK Limited (2)
Spartan Close
Warwick, Warwickshire, CV34 6AG, United Kingdom
Tel.: (44) 1926 472400
Fax: (44) 1926 472000
Automotive Electronic Parts Distr
S.I.C.: 5065
N.A.I.C.S.: 423690

Subsidiary:

Delphi Lockheed Automotive Limited (3)
Spartan Close
Warwick, CV34 6ZQ, United Kingdom
Tel.: (44) 1926 470000
Fax: (44) 1926 472000
Automobile Distr
S.I.C.: 5012
N.A.I.C.S.: 423110

Delphi Diesel Systems Limited (2)
Spartan Close
Warwick, CV34 6AG, United Kingdom
Tel.: (44) 1926 472 991
Fax: (44) 1926 472 999
Engine Equipment Mfr
S.I.C.: 3519
N.A.I.C.S.: 333618
Jeffrey A. Parsons *(Dir-Fin)*

Subsidiary:

Hartridge Limited (3)
The Hartridge Building Network 421
Radclive Road
Buckingham, MK18 4FD, United Kingdom
Tel.: (44) 1280 825600
Fax: (44) 1280 825601
E-Mail: sales@hartridge.com
Web Site: www.hartridge.com
Emp.: 70
Fuel Injection Test Equipment Mfr
S.I.C.: 3825
N.A.I.C.S.: 334515
George Taylor *(Dir-Distr Dev)*

U.S. Subsidiary:

Monarch Antenna, Inc. (2)
3055 Plymouth Rd Ste 200
Ann Arbor, MI 48105
Tel.: (734) 213-4944
Fax: (734) 661-0159
E-Mail: info@monarchantenna.com
Web Site: www.monarchantenna.com
Antenna Mfr
S.I.C.: 3663
N.A.I.C.S.: 334220
Tayfun Oezdemir *(Co-Founder & CTO)*
Jayson D. Pankin *(Co-Founder)*
Thomas Anderson *(Chm & Treas)*
Timothy Forbes *(Interim Pres)*
Terry Cross *(Sec)*

Non-U.S. Subsidiaries:

Centro Tecnico Herramental, S.A. de C.V. (2)
Km 8 54 Carr Saltillo - Piedras Negras No 8540
Saltillo, 25900, Mexico
Tel.: (52) 8444115500
Motor Vehicle Parts Mfr
S.I.C.: 3714
N.A.I.C.S.: 336390

Delphi Alambrados Automotrices, S.A. de C.V. (2)
Av De Las Fabricas No 5838
Nuevo Laredo, Tamaulipas, 88275, Mexico
Tel.: (52) 8677114900
Motor Vehicle Parts Distr
S.I.C.: 5013
N.A.I.C.S.: 423120

Delphi Automotive Systems Australia Ltd. (2)
86 Peters Ave
Mulgrave, Melbourne, VIC, 3170, Australia
Tel.: (61) 3 95664400
Fax: (61) 3 95664444
Motor Vehicle Parts Mfr
S.I.C.: 3714
N.A.I.C.S.: 336390

Delphi Automotive Systems do Brasil Ltda. (2)
Av Goias 1820/1860 Santa Paula
Sao Caetano do Sul, Sao Paulo, 13422-210, Brazil
Tel.: (55) 11 4234 9500
Fax: (55) 11 4234 9415
Automotive Parts Mfr & Distr
S.I.C.: 3714
N.A.I.C.S.: 336390

Delphi Automotive Systems Luxembourg S.A. (2)
Avenue de Luxembourg
4940 Bascharage, Luxembourg
Tel.: (352) 50 18 10
Fax: (352) 50 18 2560
Automotive Parts Mfr & Distr
S.I.C.: 3714
N.A.I.C.S.: 336390

Delphi Automotive Systems - Portugal S.A. (2)
Estrada Paco Thurs Lumiar Polo Tec De Lisboa Lote 4 Edif Delphi
1600-545 Lisbon, Portugal
Tel.: (351) 217 10 14 00
Fax: (351) 217 10 14 45
Emp.: 100
Automotive Electrical Equipment Mfr
S.I.C.: 3714
N.A.I.C.S.: 336320

Delphi Automotive Systems Singapore Pte Ltd (2)
501 Ang Mo Kio Industrial Park I
Singapore, 569621, Singapore
Tel.: (65) 6453 8544
Fax: (65) 6458 6091
Automotive Parts Mfr
S.I.C.: 3714
N.A.I.C.S.: 336390

Subsidiary:

Delphi Automotive Systems Singapore Investments Pte Ltd (3)
501 Ang Mo Kio Industrial Park 1 Ang Mo Kio
Singapore, 569621, Singapore
Tel.: (65) 64538544
Fax: (65) 64546091
Emp.: 1,000
Motor Vehicle Electrical & Electronic Equipment Mfr
S.I.C.: 3714
N.A.I.C.S.: 336320
Lim Yew Jian *(Gen Mgr)*

U.S. Subsidiary:

Delphi China LLC (3)
5725 Delphi Dr
Troy, MI 48098-2815
Tel.: (248) 813-2000
Fax: (248) 813-2673
Motor Vehicle Parts Mfr
S.I.C.: 3714
N.A.I.C.S.: 336390
Rodney ONeal *(CEO)*

Non-U.S. Subsidiaries:

Delphi Electrical Centers (Shanghai) Co., Ltd. (4)
No 88 Yuan Guo Road Anting
Jiading, Shanghai, 201814, China
Tel.: (86) 2159562200
Fax: (86) 69573306
Electronic Component Mfr
S.I.C.: 3679
N.A.I.C.S.: 334419

Delphi Electronics (Suzhou) Co. Ltd. (4)
No 123 Changyang Street Industrial Park Zone
Suzhou, Jiangsu, 215126, China
Tel.: (86) 512 6283 1888
Fax: (86) 512 6283 6308
Motor Vehicle Electrical Equipment Mfr
S.I.C.: 3714
N.A.I.C.S.: 336320

Delphi Packard Tanger SA (4)
Ilot 53 Lot 1 Tfz
Tangiers, 90000, Morocco
Tel.: (212) 539329801
Motor Vehicle Parts & Accessories Supplier & Mfr
S.I.C.: 3714
N.A.I.C.S.: 336390

Delphi Shanghai Dynamics and Propulsion Systems Co., Ltd (4)
No 150 Xiya Rd Waigaoqiao Free Trade Zone
Pudong New District, Shanghai, 200131, China
Tel.: (86) 21 5046 0940
Fax: (86) 21 5046 1921
Gasoline Spray Injection System Mfr
S.I.C.: 3714
N.A.I.C.S.: 336310

Non-U.S. Subsidiary:

Delphi Automotive Systems (Thailand) Ltd. (3)
64/26 Moo 4 Eastern Seaboard Industrial Estate
Pluakdaeng, Rayong, 21140, Thailand
Tel.: (66) 3865 6100
Fax: (66) 3865 6109
Automotive Parts Mfr
S.I.C.: 3714
N.A.I.C.S.: 336390

Delphi Automotive Systems Sweden AB (2)
Gustaf Larsons vag 18
418 78 Gothenburg, Sweden
Tel.: (46) 31 750 96 00
Motor Vehicle Electrical & Electronic Equipment Mfr
S.I.C.: 3714
N.A.I.C.S.: 336320

Delphi Cableados, S.A. de C.V. (2)
Calle Apozol 101 Col Solidaridad
Fresnillo, Zacatecas, Mexico
Tel.: (52) 493 983 9310
Motor Vehicle Parts Mfr
S.I.C.: 3714
N.A.I.C.S.: 336390

Delphi Deutschland Services GmbH (2)
Delphiplatz 1
42119 Wuppertal, Nordrhein-Westfalen, Germany
Tel.: (49) 202 2910
Fax: (49) 202 2912777
Automotive Electronic Parts Distr
S.I.C.: 5065
N.A.I.C.S.: 423690

Delphi Deutschland Technologies GmbH (2)
Delphiplatz 1
42119 Wuppertal, Germany
Tel.: (49) 202 2910
Fax: (49) 202 2912777
Automotive Parts Distr
S.I.C.: 5013
N.A.I.C.S.: 423120

Delphi Holding GmbH (2)
Industriestrasse 1
Grosspetersdorf, 7503, Austria
Tel.: (43) 3362 4100
Fax: (43) 3362 4100118
Emp.: 200
Investment Management Services
S.I.C.: 6282
N.A.I.C.S.: 523920
Wolfgang Proell *(Mgr-HR)*

Non-U.S. Subsidiary:

Delphi Thermal Hungary KFT (3)
Deli Iparterulet Szugyi Ut
2660 Balassagyarmat, Hungary
Tel.: (36) 35 50 21 00
Fax: (36) 35 50 21 01
Automotive Heating & Cooling Equipment Distr
S.I.C.: 5013
N.A.I.C.S.: 423120

Delphi Insurance Limited (2)
4th Floor 25-28 Adelaide Rd
Dublin, Ireland
Tel.: (353) 16053000
Fax: (353) 16053010
General Insurance Services
S.I.C.: 6411
N.A.I.C.S.: 524210

Delphi Packard Espana, SL (2)
Calle A Pg Ind Landaben S/N
Pamplona, Navarre, 31012, Spain
Tel.: (34) 948179100
Fax: (34) 948179238
Emp.: 96
Automotive Component Distr
S.I.C.: 5013
N.A.I.C.S.: 423120
Fernando Molina Cortes *(Mgr-Pur)*

Delphi Poland S.A. (2)
Ul Podgorki Tynieckie 2
Krakow, 30-399, Poland
Tel.: (48) 12 252 1100
Fax: (48) 12 252 1001
E-Mail: krakow.delphisekretariathq@delphi.com
Web Site: www.delphikrakow.pl
Automotive Component Mfr
S.I.C.: 3714
N.A.I.C.S.: 336390

Delphi Sistemas de Energia, S.A. de C.V. (2)
Calle Alamedas No 750 Fracc Arboledas
Torreon, Coahuila, 27077, Mexico
Tel.: (52) 871 747 6000
Emp.: 500
Motor Vehicle Brake System Mfr
S.I.C.: 3714
N.A.I.C.S.: 336340
Alberto Calderon *(Plant Mgr)*

Delphi Slovensko s.r.o. (2)
Cacovska cesta 1447/1
905 01 Senica, Slovakia
Tel.: (421) 34 6957 111
Fax: (421) 34 6957 823
Automotive Electronic Component Mfr & Distr
S.I.C.: 3714
N.A.I.C.S.: 336320

Electrotecnica Famar S.A.C.I.I.E. (2)
Rodney 70
Buenos Aires, C1427BNB, Argentina
Tel.: (54) 11 4858 8800
Fax: (54) 11 4858 8886
Automotive Repair & Maintenance Services
S.I.C.: 7549
N.A.I.C.S.: 811198
Hugo Pascarelli *(Mng Dir)*

Subsidiary:

Famar Fueguina, S.A. (3)
Rodney 70 1427 Ciudad De
Buenos Aires, C1427BNB, Argentina
Tel.: (54) 1148588800
Motor Vehicle Electrical & Electronic Equipment Mfr
S.I.C.: 3714
N.A.I.C.S.: 336320

Korea Delphi Automotive Systems Corporation (2)
580-1 Buk-Ri Nongong-Eup
Dalseong-Gun, Daegu, 711-712, Korea (South)
Tel.: (82) 53 610 1500
Fax: (82) 53 615 0786
Web Site: www.kdac.co.kr
Emp.: 2,000
Automotive Component Mfr
S.I.C.: 3714
N.A.I.C.S.: 336390
Park Young-Chul *(Mgr-Sls Plng)*

Non-U.S. Subsidiary:

Changshu KDAC Co., Ltd. (3)
No 66 Xiangjiang Road Dongnan Development Zone
Changshu, Jiangsu, 215500, China
Tel.: (86) 51252309222
Fax: (86) 51252309288
Emp.: 120
Automobile Brake System Mfr
S.I.C.: 3714
N.A.I.C.S.: 336340
Myeong-Sik Kim *(Gen Mgr)*

Sistemas Electricos y Conmutadores, S.A. de C.V. (2)
Ave Antonio J Bermudez 1230
Ciudad Juarez, Chihuahua, 32470, Mexico
Tel.: (52) 656 649 2800
Fax: (52) 656 649 2910
Motor Vehicle Parts Mfr
S.I.C.: 3714
N.A.I.C.S.: 336390

TECCOM GmbH (2)
Steinheilstrasse 10
85737 Ismaning, Germany
Tel.: (49) 89 32 12 16 0
Fax: (49) 89 32 12 16 100
E-Mail: teccom@teccom.de
Web Site: www.teccom.de
Software Development Services
S.I.C.: 7371
N.A.I.C.S.: 541511

U.S. Division:

Delphi Automotive PLC - Delphi Packard Electrical/Electronic Architecture Division (1)
5725 Delphi Dr
Troy, MI 48098
Tel.: (248) 813-2334
Fax: (248) 813-2333
Automotive Electrical & Electronic Equipment Mfr
S.I.C.: 3714
N.A.I.C.S.: 336320

U.S. Subsidiaries:

Delphi Automotive LLP (1)
5725 Delphi Dr
Troy, MI 48098-2815 DE
Tel.: (248) 813-2000
Web Site: www.delphi.com
Sales Range: $5-14.9 Billion
Emp.: 12,700
Automotive Parts Distr & Mfr
S.I.C.: 3711
N.A.I.C.S.: 336211
Rodney O'Neal *(Pres & CEO)*
Kevin P. Clark *(CFO)*
Timothy C. McCabe *(CIO & VP)*
David M. Sherbin *(Chief Compliance Officer, Gen Counsel, Sec & Sr VP)*
James A. Bertrand *(Pres-Thermal Sys & VP)*
Jeffrey J. Owens *(Pres-Delphi Electronics & Safety & VP)*
James A. Spencer *(Pres-Delphi Electrical & Electronic & South America & Mexico & VP)*
Keith D. Stipp *(Treas)*

Divisions:

Delphi Electronics & Safety (2)
2151 E Lincoln Rd
Kokomo, IN 46902-9005 (100%)
Mailing Address:
PO Box 9005
Kokomo, IN 46904
Tel.: (765) 451-5011
Fax: (765) 451-0210
Web Site: www.delphi.com
Sales Range: $1-4.9 Billion
Emp.: 7,000
Automotive Control Electronics & Hybrid Circuits Mfr
S.I.C.: 3714
N.A.I.C.S.: 336320
Jeffrey J. Owens *(Pres)*

Non-U.S. Holdings:

Delphi Delco Electronics de Mexico S.A. de C.V. (3)
Avenida Uniones Y Avenida Michigan
Parke Industrial Del Norte, 87310
Matamoros, Tamaulipas, Mexico (100%)
Tel.: (52) 8688111600
Fax: (52) 9562287206
Sales Range: $100-124.9 Million
Assembly of Radio Circuit Boards & Automobile Radios
S.I.C.: 3651
N.A.I.C.S.: 334310

Delphi Delco Electronics Operations Delnosa, S.A. de C.V. (3)
Carretera A Matamoros Km 109
88500 Reynosa, Mexico
Tel.: (52) 8999215000
Sales Range: $150-199.9 Million
Emp.: 700
Electronic Air Controls & Engine Control Computer Assembler
S.I.C.: 3829
N.A.I.C.S.: 334519

Delphi Energy Chassis Systems (2)
5725 Delphi Dr
Troy, MI 48098-2815
Tel.: (765) 451-5011
Fax: (248) 813-2333
Web Site: www.delphiauto.com
Sales Range: $5-14.9 Billion
Emp.: 32,000
Mfr of Automobile Parts
S.I.C.: 5013
N.A.I.C.S.: 423120
Rodney O'Neal *(Pres & CEO)*

Non-U.S. Subsidiaries:

Delphi Diesel Korea Ltd. (3)
851-1 Oe Dong Changwan City Industrial Complex
Kyungnam, Changwon, Kyungsangnam Do, 641 040, Korea (South) (100%)
Tel.: (82) 552823931
Fax: (82) 552830330
Web Site: www.delphi.com
Sales Range: $125-149.9 Million
Emp.: 300
Automotive Parts Manufacturing
S.I.C.: 5013
N.A.I.C.S.: 441310
J. P. Hong *(Mng Dir)*

Delphi Diesel Systems-Barcelona (3)
Avenue Cerdanyola 97-201
08173 Sant Cugat del Valles, Barcelona, Spain ES
Tel.: (34) 935892000 (100%)
Fax: (34) 935892000
Web Site: www.delphi.es
Sales Range: $650-699.9 Million
Emp.: 800
S.I.C.: 5013
N.A.I.C.S.: 441310
Pascal Giraulp *(Mng Dir)*

Delphi Diesel Systems (3)
64 Ave de la Plaine de France
BP 60059
95972 Charles de Gaulle, France (100%)
Tel.: (33) 149904990
Fax: (33) 156486949
E-Mail: info@delphicorporation.com
Sales Range: $150-199.9 Million
Emp.: 300
S.I.C.: 3714
N.A.I.C.S.: 336340

Delphi Energy Chassis Systems, Asia Headquarters (3)
1 1 110 Tsutsujigaoka
Akishima, Tokyo, 196-8668, Japan (100%)
Tel.: (81) 425497200
Fax: (81) 425423018
Sales Range: $150-199.9 Million
S.I.C.: 5531
N.A.I.C.S.: 441310
K. Yoshida *(Mgr-Mktg)*

Delphi Energy Chassis Systems, European Regional Headquarters (3)
64 Ave de la Plaine de France
93290 Charles de Gaulle, Cedex, France
Tel.: (33) 149904990
Fax: (33) 156486949
Sales Range: $150-199.9 Million
S.I.C.: 5013
N.A.I.C.S.: 441310

Delphi Energy Chassis Systems, South American Regional Headquarters (3)
Avenida Goias 1860
Sao Caetano do Sul, SP, 09550 050, Brazil (100%)
Tel.: (55) 1142349500
Fax: (55) 1142349415
E-Mail: delphi.br@delphi.com
Web Site: www.delphiauto.com.br
Sales Range: $125-149.9 Million
Emp.: 300
S.I.C.: 5013
N.A.I.C.S.: 441310
Luiz Corralo *(Mng Dir)*

Delphi Medical Systems Corporation (2)
5725 Delphi Dr
Troy, MI 48098
Tel.: (888) 526-1426
Fax: (248) 813-5008
E-Mail: medical@delphi.com
Web Site: www.delphimedical.com
Sales Range: $100-124.9 Million
Medical Monitoring Device Mfr
S.I.C.: 3845
N.A.I.C.S.: 334510

Delphi Product & Service Solutions (2)
5820 Delphi Dr
Troy, MI 48098-2819
Mailing Address:
PO Box 5045
Troy, MI 48007-5045
Tel.: (248) 267-8800
E-Mail: dpsscustomerservice@delphi.com
Web Site: www.delphi-pss.com
Sales Range: $150-199.9 Million
Aftermarket Automotive Electronics, Replacement Parts & Services
Import Export
S.I.C.: 5013
N.A.I.C.S.: 423120
Craig Barnes *(VP-Global Independent Aftermarket)*

Non-U.S. Subsidiaries:

Customer Technology Center (2)
Rte De Luxembourg
4940 Bascharage, Luxembourg (100%)
Tel.: (352) 501810
Fax: (352) 50182288
E-Mail: delphi@delphi.com
Web Site: www.delphi.com
Sales Range: $150-199.9 Million
Emp.: 700
Automotive Systems Engineering Support
S.I.C.: 8711
N.A.I.C.S.: 541330
Sabastin Sthilling *(Mng Dir)*

Delphi Aftermarket America do Sul (2)
Av Goeas 1860
09550 050 Sao Caetano do Sul, SP, Brazil (50%)
Tel.: (55) 1142349500
Fax: (55) 1142349415
E-Mail: delphi.atende@delphi.com
Web Site: www.delphiauto.com.br
Sales Range: $200-249.9 Million
Emp.: 500
Mfr. of Automotive Components
S.I.C.: 3714
N.A.I.C.S.: 336330

Delphi Energy & Engine Management Systems (2)
Av Goias 1860
Sao Caetano do Sul, Sao Paulo, 09550-050, Brazil
Tel.: (55) 1142349500
Fax: (55) 1142349415
Web Site: www.delphi.com
Sales Range: $600-649.9 Million
Emp.: 2,000
Mfr. of Throttle Body Fuel Injection
S.I.C.: 3714
N.A.I.C.S.: 336310
Gabor Beak *(Pres)*

Delphi Packard Austria Ges.m.b.H. (2)
Industriestr 1
A 7503 Grosspetersdorf, Austria
Tel.: (43) 336241000
Fax: (43) 33624100200
Sales Range: $150-199.9 Million
Automotive Wiring Systems Mfr
S.I.C.: 5013
N.A.I.C.S.: 441310
Frank Kromp *(Mng Dir)*

Delphi Packard Electric Systems (2)
Poligono Ind De Landaben Calle A
31012 Pamplona, Spain (100%)
Tel.: (34) 948179100
Fax: (34) 948179235
E-Mail: info@delphi.com
Web Site: delphi.com
Sales Range: $50-74.9 Million
Emp.: 165
Mfr. of Automotive Power & Signal Distribution Systems
S.I.C.: 3714
N.A.I.C.S.: 336350
Carlos Tainta *(Mng Dir)*

Delphi Packard Electric Vas Kft (2)
Zanati U 29 A
9700 Szombathely, Hungary (100%)
Tel.: (36) 94517800
Fax: (36) 94328838
E-Mail: delphi@delphi.com
Web Site: www.delphiauto.com
Sales Range: $350-399.9 Million
Emp.: 1,000
Mfr. of Automotive Power & Signal Distribution Systems
S.I.C.: 3714
N.A.I.C.S.: 336350
Robert Tansics *(Mgr-Fin)*

Delphi Rimir S.A. de CV (2)
Ave Michigan Y Ohio S/N 87316
Matamoros, Tamaulipas, Mexico (100%)
Tel.: (52) 52503777
Sales Range: $125-149.9 Million
Assembly of Plastic Bumpers; Supported by Fisher Guide Division
S.I.C.: 3089
N.A.I.C.S.: 326199

Delphi Technical Centre Luxembourg (2)
Ave de Luxembourg Bascharage
Luxembourg, L 4940, Luxembourg (100%)
Tel.: (352) 50181
Fax: (352) 35250182288
E-Mail: delphi@delphi.com
Sales Range: $250-299.9 Million
Emp.: 700
Mfr. of Electric Fuel Pumps
S.I.C.: 3714
N.A.I.C.S.: 336320
Sabastain Schilling *(Gen Mgr)*

Delphi (2)
64 Ave de la Plaine de France
PO Box 65059
95972 Charles de Gaulle, Cedex, France (100%)
Tel.: (33) 149904990
Fax: (33) 156486949
Sales Range: $300-349.9 Million
Emp.: 300
Mfr. of Brake Systems, Spark Plugs, Fuel Pumps & Other Automotive Components
S.I.C.: 3714
N.A.I.C.S.: 336340
Isabelle Zagne *(Dir)*

Delphi (2)
Avenida Goias 1860
Sao Caetano do Sul, SP, 9550050, Brazil (100%)
Tel.: (55) 1142349500
Fax: (55) 1142349654
E-Mail: delphi.atende@delphi.com
Web Site: www.delphi.com.br
Sales Range: $1-4.9 Billion
Emp.: 11,000
Batteries, Ignition Coils & Distributors Mfr
S.I.C.: 3714
N.A.I.C.S.: 336320

Mecel AB (2)
Molndalsvagen 36
SE 412 63 Gothenburg, Sweden (100%)
Tel.: (46) 317204400
Fax: (46) 317204490
E-Mail: info@mecel.se
Web Site: www.mecel.se
Sales Range: $10-24.9 Million
Emp.: 100

Delphi Automotive PLC—(Continued)

Motor Vehicle Electronic System & Software Developer
S.I.C.: 3714
N.A.I.C.S.: 336320
Henrik Haggstrom *(Mng Dir)*

Delphi Technologies, Inc. (1)
5725 Delphi Dr
Troy, MI 48098-2815
Tel.: (248) 813-8065
Automotive Components & Systems Mfr
S.I.C.: 3714
N.A.I.C.S.: 336390

Non-U.S. Subsidiaries:

Delphi Automotive Systems Limited Sirketi (1)
Organize Sanayi Bolgesi 1 Cad No15
Yukari Dudullu
Yusufpasa Umraniye, Istanbul, Turkey
Tel.: (90) 2165283000
Fax: (90) 2163130146
Motor Vehicle Electrical & Electronic Equipment Mfr
S.I.C.: 3714
N.A.I.C.S.: 336320

Delphi Deutschland GmbH (1)
Delphiplatz 1
42119 Wuppertal, North Rhine-Westphal, Germany
Tel.: (49) 2022910
Fax: (49) 2022912777
Motor Vehicle Electrical & Electronic Equipment Mfr
S.I.C.: 3714
N.A.I.C.S.: 336320
Thomas Aurich *(Head-Corp Comm)*

Delphi Holdings Luxembourg S.a r.l. (1)
1 route de Luxembourg
Bascharage, 4940, Luxembourg
Tel.: (352) 501810
Fax: (352) 50182560
Investment Management Services
S.I.C.: 6719
N.A.I.C.S.: 551112

Non-U.S. Subsidiary:

Ondas Media, S.A. (2)
Velazquez 157 - 1a Planta
28002 Madrid, Spain
Tel.: (34) 915245725
Fax: (34) 915245819
E-Mail: info@ondasmedia.com
Web Site: www.ondasmedia.com
Communications services
S.I.C.: 4899
N.A.I.C.S.: 517919
David Krueger *(CEO)*
Christoph With *(CFO)*
Benoit Chereau *(COO)*
Jon Filipek *(Sr VP-Regulatory & Government Affairs)*

Delphi Italia Automotive Systems S.r.l. (1)
Via Nobili Efrem 2
Molinella, Bologna, 40062, Italy
Tel.: (39) 0516906310
Fax: (39) 0516906309
Web Site: www.diavia.it
Motor Vehicle Electrical & Electronic Equipment Mfr
S.I.C.: 3714
N.A.I.C.S.: 336320

Delphi Packard Electric Ceska Republika, S.R.O. (1)
Cechova 235
Bakov Nad Jizerou, Mlada Boleslav, 29401, Czech Republic
Tel.: (420) 326370511
Motor Vehicle Electrical & Electronic Equipment Mfr
S.I.C.: 3714
N.A.I.C.S.: 336320

DELPHI ENERGY CORP.

Suite 300 500 - 4 Avenue SW
Calgary, AB, T2P 2V6, Canada
Tel.: (403) 265-6171
Fax: (403) 265-6207
E-Mail: info@delphienergy.ca
Web Site: www.delphienergy.ca
DEE—(OTC TSX)
Sls.: $85,241,191
Assets: $399,247,139
Liabilities: $159,104,829
Net Worth: $240,142,310
Earnings: ($57,682,981)
Emp.: 56
Fiscal Year-end: 12/31/12

Business Description:
Oil & Gas Exploration Services
S.I.C.: 1311
N.A.I.C.S.: 211111

Personnel:
David J. Reid *(Pres & CEO)*
Brian Kohlhammer *(CFO & Sr VP-Fin)*
Tony Angelidis *(Sr VP-Exploration)*
Rod Hume *(Sr VP-Engrg)*

Board of Directors:
Tony Angelidis
Harry S. Campbell
Robert A. Lehodey
Stephen Mulherin
Andrew E. Osis
David J. Reid
David J. Sandmeyer
Lamont C. Tolley

Transfer Agent:
Olympia Trust Company
125 9th Avenue SE Suite 2300
Calgary, AB, T2G 0P6, Canada
Tel.: (403) 261-0900

DELRAND RESOURCES LIMITED

1 First Canadian Place 100 King St West Suite 7070
PO Box 419
Toronto, ON, M5X 1E3, Canada
Tel.: (416) 366-2221
Fax: (416) 366-7722
Toll Free: (800) 714-7938
E-Mail: dmadilo@brc-diamondcore.com
Web Site: www.delrand.com
DRN—(TSX)
Assets: $5,238,077
Liabilities: $559,513
Net Worth: $4,678,564
Earnings: ($282,079)
Emp.: 6
Fiscal Year-end: 06/30/13

Business Description:
Diamond Mining Services
S.I.C.: 1411
N.A.I.C.S.: 212311

Personnel:
Michiel C. J. de Wit *(Pres & CEO)*
Donat K. Madilo *(Treas)*
Geoffrey G. Farr *(Sec)*

Board of Directors:
Maurice John Colson
Michiel C. J. de Wit
Geoffrey G. Farr
Arnold T. Kondrat
Brian P. Scallan
Stephen C. Thomson
William R. Wilson

Legal Counsel:
Norton Rose Canada LLP
TD Centre CN Tower 100 Wellington Street West
PO Box 128
Toronto, ON, Canada M5K 1H1

Computershare Investor Services (Pty) Limited
Johannesburg, South Africa

Transfer Agents:
Equity Financial Trust Company
Toronto, ON, Canada

Computershare Investor Services (Pty) Limited
Johannesburg, South Africa

DELSBO CANDLE AB

Fredriksfors
Delsbo, 82060, Sweden
Tel.: (46) 65323150
Fax: (46) 65323163
E-Mail: info@delsbocandle.se
Web Site: www.delsbocandle.se
Emp.: 20

Business Description:
Candle Mfr
S.I.C.: 3999
N.A.I.C.S.: 339999

Personnel:
Torbjorn Jonsson *(Mng Dir)*

DELTA BANK JSC

73a Tole Bi Street
050000 Almaty, Kazakhstan
Tel.: (7) 7272448541
Fax: (7) 7272448557
E-Mail: info@deltabank.kz
Web Site: www.deltabank.kz
NFBN—(KAZ)
Emp.: 370

Business Description:
Banking Services
S.I.C.: 6029
N.A.I.C.S.: 522110

Personnel:
Kanat Dosmukametov *(Chm-Mgmt Bd)*

DELTA BRAC HOUSING FINANCE CORPORATION LTD.

Landmark Building 9th Floor 12-14
Gulshan North C/A
Gulshan-2, Dhaka, 1212, Bangladesh
Tel.: (880) 28822374
Fax: (880) 29882110
E-Mail: dbh@deltabrac.com
Web Site: www.deltabrac.com
Year Founded: 1997
DBH—(CHT DHA)
Int. Income: $53,630,014
Assets: $408,590,398
Liabilities: $376,791,551
Net Worth: $31,798,847
Earnings: $6,542,622
Emp.: 159
Fiscal Year-end: 06/30/13

Business Description:
Housing Financial Services
S.I.C.: 6163
N.A.I.C.S.: 522310

Personnel:
Faruq A. Choudhury *(Chm)*
Quazi Mohammad Shariful Ala *(CEO & Mng Dir)*
Jashim Uddin *(Sec & Asst VP)*
Tanvir Ahmad *(Exec VP & Head-HR)*
Nasimul Baten *(Exec VP & Head-Ops)*
A. K. M. Tanvir Kamal *(Exec VP & Head-Credit)*
Md. Hassan Iftekhar Yussouf *(Exec VP & Head-IT)*
Aminul Islam *(Sr VP & Head-Fin)*

Board of Directors:
Faruq A. Choudhury
Shameran Bahar Abed
Quazi Mohammad Shariful Ala
Nasir A. Choudhury
Mahibul Islam Chowdhury
Syeda Rizwana Hasan
Mehreen Hassan
A. Z. Mohammad Hossain
Adeeba Rahman
Rajeev Sardana
Swapan Kumar Sarkar

DELTA CEDAR PRODUCTS LTD

10104 River Road
Delta, BC, V4C 2R3, Canada
Tel.: (604) 583-3818
Fax: (604) 583-3813
E-Mail: info@deltacedarproducts.com
Web Site: www.deltacedarproducts.com
Year Founded: 1958
Rev.: $96,484,160
Emp.: 400

Business Description:
Cedar & Sawmills Mfr
S.I.C.: 2421
N.A.I.C.S.: 321113

Personnel:
Brian Dyck *(Pres)*
Rowland Price *(CEO)*

DELTA CORP LTD

109 Bayside Mall 1st Floor Opp Sobo Central Mall Tardeo Road Haji Ali
Mumbai, 400 034, India
Tel.: (91) 2240794700
Fax: (91) 2240794777
Web Site: www.deltacorp.in
DELTACORP—(NSE)
Rev.: $82,304,270
Assets: $284,398,001
Liabilities: $111,091,198
Net Worth: $173,306,803
Earnings: $5,439,321
Emp.: 1,323
Fiscal Year-end: 03/31/13

Business Description:
Textile & Real Estate Development Consultancy Services
S.I.C.: 6531
N.A.I.C.S.: 531390

Personnel:
Neelish A. Shah *(Vice Chm-DCEAL)*
Ashish Kapadia *(Mng Dir)*
Hardik Dhebar *(CFO)*
Hitesh Kanani *(Compliance Officer & Sec)*
Anil Malani *(Pres-Ops-HCEPL)*

Board of Directors:
Jaydev M. Mody
Homi Aibara
Mahesh S. Gupta
Rajesh Jaggi
Rakesh Jhunjhunwala
Ashish Kapadia
Rajeev A. Piramal

Amit Desai & Co
Mumbai, India

Transfer Agent:
Freedom Registry Limited
Plot No 101/102 19th Street MIDC Satpur
Nasik, Maharashtra, 422 007, India
Tel.: (91) 235 4032
Fax: (91) 235 1892

Subsidiaries:

AAA Aviation Private Limited (1)
16 Ali Chambers 2nd Fl Nagindas Master Rd
Fort, Mumbai, Maharastra, 400001, India
Tel.: (91) 22 40794700
Fax: (91) 22 679246
Emp.: 40
Air Freight Services
S.I.C.: 4522
N.A.I.C.S.: 481212
Ashok Masurkar *(Mktg Mgr)*

Highstreet Cruises & Entertainment Private Limited (1)
Peninsula Ctr 850 Off N H 17
Porvorim Bardez, Goa, 403 521, India
Tel.: (91) 8326659400
Fax: (91) 8326659412
E-Mail: info@casinoroyalegoa.com
Web Site: www.casinoroyalegoa.com
Gambling Cruise Management Services
S.I.C.: 7999
N.A.I.C.S.: 713210
Narinder Punj *(Mng Dir)*
Anil Malani *(Pres-Ops)*

DELTA CORPORATION LIMITED

Sable House Northridge Close
Borrowdale
PO BOX BW 294
Harare, Zimbabwe
Tel.: (263) 4883865
Fax: (263) 4883864
Web Site: www.delta.co.zw
DLTA—(ZIM)
Rev.: $631,276,000
Assets: $561,938,000
Liabilities: $214,688,000
Net Worth: $347,250,000
Earnings: $104,123,000
Emp.: 5,000
Fiscal Year-end: 03/31/13

Business Description:
Soft Drink, Beer & Distilled Beverage Mfr & Distr
S.I.C.: 2086
N.A.I.C.S.: 312111

Personnel:
Canaan Dube *(Chm)*
P. Gowero *(CEO)*
A. Makamure *(Sec)*

Board of Directors:
Canaan Dube
M.J. Bowman
P. Gowero
S.J. Hammond
M.P. Karombo
J.A. Kirby
E.R. Mpisaunga
L.E.M. Ngwerume
H.C. Sadza
T.N. Sibanda
M.M. Valela

Subsidiary:

Delta Beverages (Pvt) Limited (1)
39 Telford Rd
Harare, Zimbabwe
Tel.: (263) 4870839
Fax: (263) 4883937
Beer Mfr
S.I.C.: 2082
N.A.I.C.S.: 312120

Subsidiary:

Mega Pak Zimbabwe (Pvt) Ltd (2)
211 Chihombe Rd
PO Box 52
Ruwa, Mashonaland East, Zimbabwe
Tel.: (263) 73 2935 8
E-Mail: sales@megapak.co.zw
Web Site: www.megapak.co.zw
Mfr of Addis Domestic Storage Wares & Plastic Furniture
S.I.C.: 3089
N.A.I.C.S.: 326199

DELTA DRONE SA

12 Rue Ampere Site Cemoi Batiment A
38000 Grenoble, France
Tel.: (33) 4 27 46 51 54
Web Site: www.deltadrone.fr
ALDR—(EUR)

Business Description:
Civilian Drones Mfr
S.I.C.: 3812
N.A.I.C.S.: 334511

Personnel:
Christian Viguie *(Chm-Supervisory Bd)*
Frederic Serre *(Chm-Mgmt Bd)*
Joel Desmaris *(CFO)*

DELTA ELECTRONICS, INC.

186 Ruey Kuang Road
Neihu, Taipei, 11491, Taiwan
Tel.: (886) 287972088
Fax: (886) 287972338
E-Mail: mkt-serv@delta.com.tw
Web Site: www.delta.com.tw
2308—(TAI)
Sls.: $5,745,681,160
Assets: $6,160,566,780
Liabilities: $2,793,759,194
Net Worth: $3,366,807,587
Earnings: $583,156,319
Emp.: 68,000
Fiscal Year-end: 12/31/12

Business Description:
Switching Power Supply Mfr; Visual Displays & Electronic Components Supplier
S.I.C.: 3679
N.A.I.C.S.: 334419

Personnel:
Bruce C. H. Cheng *(Founder)*
Yancey Hai *(Chm)*
Mark Ko *(Vice Chm)*
Johnson Lee *(Pres & COO)*
Ping Cheng *(CEO)*
Judy Wang *(CFO)*

Board of Directors:
Yancey Hai
Bruce C. H. Cheng
Mark Ko
Johnson Lee
Judy Wang

Transfer Agent:
MasterLink Securities Corporation
B1F No35 Lane 11 Guangfu N Rd Songshan Dist
Taipei, Taiwan

Subsidiaries:

Delta Networks, Inc. (1)
186 Ruey Kuang Road
Neihu, Taipei, 114, Taiwan TW
Tel.: (886) 287973250 (59.03%)
Fax: (886) 287972120
E-Mail: dnisales@delta.com.tw
Web Site: www.dninetworks.com
Emp.: 2,400
Networking Systems & Peripherals Mfr
S.I.C.: 3577
N.A.I.C.S.: 334118
Sam Liang *(Chm & CEO)*
Victor Cheng *(Pres)*
Yipin Lee *(CFO)*

Non-U.S. Subsidiaries:

Delta Networks (Dongguan) Co., Ltd. (2)
Delta Industrial Estate
Shijie Town, Dongguan, Guangdong, 523308, China (59.51%)
Tel.: (86) 76986635008
Fax: (86) 769 8663 4479
Manufacturing & Sales of Radio Transmission Apparatus
S.I.C.: 3679
N.A.I.C.S.: 334419
S. K. Chiu *(Head-Ops)*

Delta Networks (Shanghai) Ltd. (2)
No 238 Minxia Road
Pudong New District, Shanghai, China
Tel.: (86) 2168723988
Fax: (86) 02168723996
Web Site: www.deltagreentech.com.ch
Power Supplies & Computer Peripherals Mfr
S.I.C.: 5063
N.A.I.C.S.: 423610

PreOptix Co., Ltd. (1)
8F 428 Tun Hua Road
Taichung, Taiwan
Tel.: (886) 422969779
Fax: (886) 422969770
Emp.: 30
Optical Equipments Mfr
S.I.C.: 3827
N.A.I.C.S.: 333314
Sheng Chu Huang *(Pres)*

Non-U.S. Subsidiary:

PreOptix (Jiang Su) Co., Ltd. (2)
No 35 Huayang North Road Jurong Economic Development Zone
Zhenjiang, Jiangsu, China
Tel.: (86) 51185978455
Fax: (86) 51187278456
Lenses & Optical Engines Mfr & Distr
S.I.C.: 3579
N.A.I.C.S.: 333316

U.S. Subsidiary:

DEI Logistics (USA) Corp. (1)
4405 Cushing Pkwy
Fremont, CA 94538-6475
Tel.: (510) 668-5588
Fax: (510) 668-0680
Warehousing & Logistics Services
S.I.C.: 4225
N.A.I.C.S.: 493110
Elson Chang *(Pres)*
Jean Huang *(CFO)*

Non-U.S. Subsidiaries:

DelSolar (Wujiang) Ltd. (1)
No 1688 Jiangxing East Road Wujiang Economic Deve District
Suzhou, Jiangsu, 215200, China
Tel.: (86) 512 6316 8558
Fax: (86) 512 6397 0558
Solar Cells Mfr
S.I.C.: 3674
N.A.I.C.S.: 334413

Delta Electronics (Hong Kong) Ltd. (1)
21F Prosperity Center 25 Chong Yip Street
Kwun Tong, Kowloon, China (Hong Kong)
Tel.: (852) 23181038
Fax: (852) 27575819
Web Site: www.delta.com.tw/company/about_operations_asia.asp
Power Supply & Computer Peripherals Mfr
S.I.C.: 3572
N.A.I.C.S.: 334112
Teresa Chen *(Mgr)*

Non-U.S. Subsidiaries:

Delta Electronics (Chenzhou) Co., Ltd. (2)
Chenzou Export Processing Zone Bailutang Town
Chenzhou, Hunan, China
Tel.: (86) 7352661008
Fax: (86) 7352661818
Web Site: www.delta.com.tw/company/about_operations_asia.asp
Electronic Component Distr
S.I.C.: 5065
N.A.I.C.S.: 423690
Daniel Liao *(Mgr-Sls)*

Delta Electronics Components (Dongguan) Co., Ltd. (2)
Hetian Zhenxing Road
Shijie Town, Dongguan, Guangdong, 523301, China
Tel.: (86) 76986329008
Fax: (86) 7 6986631589
Electronic Components Mfr
S.I.C.: 3625
N.A.I.C.S.: 335314
Tony Tian *(Mgr-Factory)*

Delta Electronics (Dongguan) Co., Ltd. (2)
Delta Industrial Estate
Shijie Town, Dongguan, Guangdong, 523308, China
Tel.: (86) 76986635008
Fax: (86) 769 8663 4479
Power Supplies Mfr
S.I.C.: 3699
N.A.I.C.S.: 335999

Delta Electronics Power (Dongguan) Co., Ltd. (2)
Delta Industrial Zone
Shijie Town, Dongguan, Guangdong, 523308, China
Tel.: (86) 76986631008
Fax: (86) 76986637012
Power Supplies Mfr
S.I.C.: 3699
N.A.I.C.S.: 335999
Franky Wang *(Mgr-Factory)*

Delta Electronics (Shanghai) Co., Ltd. (2)
No 238 Minxia Road
Pudong New District, Shanghai, 201209, China
Tel.: (86) 21 6872 3988
Fax: (86) 21 6872 3996
Electronic Component Mfr
S.I.C.: 3699
N.A.I.C.S.: 335999

Delta Electronics (Wuhu) Co., Ltd. (2)
68 Jiuhua North Road Wuhu Export Processing Zones
Wuhu, Anhui, 241009, China
Tel.: (86) 5535773008
Fax: (86) 5535773016
Web Site: www.delta.com.tw/company/about_operations_asia.asp
Power Supply & Computer Peripherals Mfr
S.I.C.: 3612
N.A.I.C.S.: 335311
Chong Len Ghong *(Gen Mgr)*

Delta Video Display System (Wujiang) Ltd. (2)
No 1688 Jiangxing East Road Yundong Development Zone
Wujiang, Jiangsu, China
Tel.: (86) 51263403008
Fax: (86) 512 6340 7290
Power Supply & Computer Peripherals Mfr
S.I.C.: 3612
N.A.I.C.S.: 335311
Ping Zheng *(Gen Mgr)*

Delta Electronics International Ltd. (1)
Rm A & R 17 Fl Edif Fu Tat Fa Yuen Alameda Dr Carlos Dassumpcao
Macau, China (Macau)
Tel.: (853) 28755808
Fax: (853) 28755835
Power Supply & Computer Peripherals Mfr
S.I.C.: 3572
N.A.I.C.S.: 334112

Delta Electronics (Japan) Inc. (1)
Delta Shibadaimon Building 2-1-14 Shibadaimon
Minato-ku, Tokyo, 105 0012, Japan JP
Tel.: (81) 357331111 (94%)
Fax: (81) 357331211
Web Site: www.dej.co.jp
Emp.: 120
Electronic Products Sales
S.I.C.: 5065
N.A.I.C.S.: 423690

Non-U.S. Subsidiary:

Delta Electronics (Korea), Inc. (2)
816 Ruey Kuang Rd Neihu
11491 Taipei, Taiwan
Tel.: (886) 287972088
Fax: (886) 287972120
Web Site: www.deltakor.co.kr
Power Supplies & Computer Peripherals Mfr
S.I.C.: 3612
N.A.I.C.S.: 335311
Yancey Hai *(Pres)*

Delta Electronics Mexico S.A. de C.V. (1)
Uno Poniente 19955 Col Cd Industrial Nueva Tijuana
22470 Tijuana, Baja California, Mexico MX
Tel.: (52) 6641039999
Fax: (52) 6641033999
Web Site: www.delta.com.tw/company/about_operations_usa.asp
Computer Peripheral Equipments Distr
S.I.C.: 5045
N.A.I.C.S.: 423430

Delta Greentech SGP Pte. Ltd. (1)
4 Kaki Bukit Avenue 1 05-04
Singapore, 417939, Singapore (54.83%)
Tel.: (65) 674 751 55
Fax: (65) 6744 9228
Emp.: 45
Investment Management Services
S.I.C.: 6211
N.A.I.C.S.: 523999
Patrick Chang *(Mng Dir)*

Delta Power Sharp Ltd. (1)
21F Prosperity Centre 25 Chong Yip Street
Kwun Tong, Kowloon, China (Hong Kong)
Tel.: (852) 23181038
Fax: (852) 27575819
Power Supplies & Computer Peripherals Mfr
S.I.C.: 3572
N.A.I.C.S.: 334112

Delta Electronics, Inc.—(Continued)

Deltronics (Netherlands) B.V. (1)
Zandsteen 15
2132 MZ Hoofddorp, Netherlands
Tel.: (31) 206550900
Fax: (31) 206550999
E-Mail: Component.sales@euro.delta-corp.com
Power Supply & Computer Peripherals Mfr
S.I.C.: 3699
N.A.I.C.S.: 335999

DELTA ELECTRONICS (THAILAND) PUBLIC COMPANY LIMITED

909 Soi 9 Moo 4 EPZ Bangpoo
Industrial Estate Tambon Prakasa
Amphur Muang, Samut Prakan, 10280, Thailand
Tel.: (66) 2 709 2800
Fax: (66) 2 709 2833
E-Mail: info@deltathailand.com
Web Site: www.deltathailand.com
Year Founded: 1988
DELTA—(TAI THA)
Rev.: $1,375,817,906
Assets: $1,095,763,670
Liabilities: $350,450,244
Net Worth: $745,313,426
Earnings: $144,028,817
Emp.: 9,836
Fiscal Year-end: 12/31/12

Business Description:
Switching Power Supply Mfr; Video Displays & Electronic Components Supplier
S.I.C.: 4911
N.A.I.C.S.: 221122

Personnel:
James Kong Meng Ng *(Chm)*
Stronger Ming-Cheng Wang *(Vice Chm & VP)*
Henry Heng-Hsien Hsieh *(Pres)*
Po-Wen Yu *(CFO)*
Chin-Ming Chen *(CIO)*

Board of Directors:
James Kong Meng Ng
Roger Chih-Yuan Chu
Henry Heng-Hsien Hsieh
Ji-Ren Lee
Supat Limpaporn
Anusorn Muttaraid
Supapun Ruttanaporn
Nirmol Tantipuntum
Stronger Ming-Cheng Wang

U.S. Subsidiary:

Delta Energy Systems (Arizona), Inc. (1)
4400 E Broadway Ste 803
Tucson, AZ 85711 (100%)
Tel.: (520) 326-8401
Fax: (520) 326-8366
E-Mail: rompower@aol.com
Web Site: www.delta-es.com
Emp.: 8
Electric Power Generation
S.I.C.: 4911
N.A.I.C.S.: 221118
Dan Jitaru *(Mng Dir)*

Non-U.S. Subsidiaries:

Delta Electronics Europe Ltd (1)
1 Redwood Court
Peel Park Campus, East Kilbride, G745PF, United Kingdom (100%)
Tel.: (44) 1355588888
Fax: (44) 1355588889
Web Site: www.delta-europe.com
Emp.: 50
Electronic Component Mfr
S.I.C.: 3679
N.A.I.C.S.: 334419
Jackie Chang *(Gen Mgr)*

Delta Electronics (Slovakia) s.r.o. (1)
Botanicka 25-A
84104 Bratislava, Slovakia (100%)
Tel.: (421) 265411258
Fax: (421) 265411283
E-Mail: bratislava.slovakrepublic@delta-es.com
Web Site: www.deltaelectronics.sk
Emp.: 3
Electronic Component Mfr
S.I.C.: 3679
N.A.I.C.S.: 334419
Wilhelm Franz Noebauer *(Gen Mgr)*

Delta Energy Systems (Brasil) S/A (1)
1130 Bairro Afonso Pena
Sao Jose Dos Pinhais, 83040-420 Parana, Brazil (100%)
Tel.: (55) 4121416363
Fax: (55) 4121416300
E-Mail: giovanni.ruggiero@delta-es.com
Web Site: www.delta-es.com
Emp.: 150
Electrical Equipment & Component Mfr
S.I.C.: 3699
N.A.I.C.S.: 335999

Delta Energy Systems (Germany) GmbH (1)
Tscheulinstrasse 21
D 79331 Teningen, Germany
Tel.: (49) 76414550
Fax: (49) 7641455485
E-Mail: deltaenergysystems@deltaenergysystems.com
Web Site: www.deltaenergysystems.com
Emp.: 119
Power Supply Systems
S.I.C.: 3443
N.A.I.C.S.: 332410
Matiaz Mann *(Gen Mgr)*

Delta Energy Systems (India) Private Ltd. (1)
Plot No 27 Sector 34
122001 Gurgaon, Haryana, India (100%)
Tel.: (91) 1245169040
Fax: (91) 1245036039
Web Site: www.deltraeclectronicsindia.com
Emp.: 400
Electronic Coil Transformer & Other Inductor Mfr
S.I.C.: 3675
N.A.I.C.S.: 334416
Dalip Sharma *(Mng Dir)*

Delta Energy Systems (Slovakia) s.r.o. (1)
Priemyselna 4600/1
018 41 Dubnica nad Vahom, Slovakia Sk
Tel.: (421) 42 466 1111 (100%)
Fax: (421) 42 466 1130
E-Mail: dubnica.slovakia@delta-es.com
Web Site: www.delta-es.com
Electrical Equipment & Component Mfr
S.I.C.: 3699
N.A.I.C.S.: 335999
Daniel Heri *(Mng Dir)*

Delta Energy Systems (Switzerland) AG (1)
Freiburgstrasse 251
Bern-Bumpliz, 3018 Bern, Switzerland (100%)
Tel.: (41) 319985388
Fax: (41) 319985485
Web Site: www.deltaenergysystems.com
Emp.: 80
Motor & Generator Mfr
S.I.C.: 3621
N.A.I.C.S.: 335312
Peter Hofstetter *(Mng Dir)*

Non-U.S. Subsidiaries:

Delta Energy Systems (Czech Republic) Spol. s.r.o. (2)
Strasnicka 3165 1B
10200 Prague, 10, Czech Republic CZ
Tel.: (420) 271751800
Fax: (420) 271751799
E-Mail: info@ascom.cz
Web Site: www.energysystems.com
Emp.: 30
Communications Holding Company
S.I.C.: 3669
N.A.I.C.S.: 334290

Delta Energy Systems (France) S.A. (2)
Route de Longjumeau
91380 Orly, Chilly-Mazarin, France (100%)
Tel.: (33) 169101805
Fax: (33) 169341019
Web Site: www.delta-es.com
Emp.: 12
Motor & Generator Mfr
S.I.C.: 3621
N.A.I.C.S.: 335312

Delta Energy Systems (Italy) s.r.l. (2)
Via Primo Maggio 6
Anzola dell Emilia, 40011 Bologna, Italy (100%)
Tel.: (39) 051733045
Fax: (39) 051731838
E-Mail: info@delta-es.com
Web Site: www.deltapowersolutions.com
Emp.: 8
Electrical Equipment & Component Mfr
S.I.C.: 3699
N.A.I.C.S.: 335999
Idilio Ciuffarella *(Gen Mgr)*

Delta Energy Systems LLC (2)
Pokrovskij Boulvourd 4-17
Building 4B, 1010000 Moscow, Russia (100%)
Tel.: (7) 495 787 4738
Fax: (7) 495 795 3040
E-Mail: aberra.mithiku@delta-es.com
Web Site: www.delta-es.com
Electrical Equipment & Component Mfr
S.I.C.: 3699
N.A.I.C.S.: 335999

Delta Energy Systems (Poland) Sp. Z.o.o. (2)
Poleczki 23 Street
02-822 Warsaw, Poland (100%)
Tel.: (48) 223352600
Fax: (48) 223352601
E-Mail: delta@delta-es.pl
Web Site: www.delta-es.com
Electrical Equipment & Component Mfr
S.I.C.: 3699
N.A.I.C.S.: 335999

Delta Energy Systems (Spain) S.L. (2)
Calle Luis I n 60 Nave 1a
28031 Madrid, Spain (100%)
Tel.: (34) 912237420
Fax: (34) 913329038
E-Mail: jose.manuel.roldan@delta-es.com
Web Site: www.delta-es.com
Electrical Equipment & Component Mfr
S.I.C.: 3699
N.A.I.C.S.: 335999

Delta Energy Systems (Sweden) AB (2)
Annavagen 3
PO Box 3096
35033 Vaxjo, Sweden (100%)
Tel.: (46) 470706800
Fax: (46) 470706890
E-Mail: info@delta-es.se
Web Site: www.delta-es.com
Emp.: 12
Motor & Generator Mfr
S.I.C.: 3621
N.A.I.C.S.: 335312
Stefan Sjoblum *(Mng Dir)*

Delta Green (Tianjin) Industries Co., Ltd. (1)
168 No 15 Coastal Way
Tianjin Port Free Trade Zone, Tianjin, China (100%)
Tel.: (86) 2225760371
Fax: (86) 2225760480
E-Mail: joanna.ren@deltaww.com.cn
Web Site: www.delta.com.tw/company/about_operations_asia.asp?aid=1&sid=5
Emp.: 1,500
Wireless Communications Equipment Mfr
S.I.C.: 3663
N.A.I.C.S.: 334220
Richard Wang *(Chm)*

Delta Greentech (Netherlands) BV. (1)
Zandsteen 15
Hoofddorp, 2132 MZ, Netherlands
Tel.: (31) 206550900
Fax: (31) 206550999
E-Mail: info@delta-europe.com
Web Site: www.delta-europe.com
Emp.: 4
Electronic Component Distr
S.I.C.: 5065
N.A.I.C.S.: 423690

DELTA FLEISCH HANDELS GMBH

Lagerstrasse 11
20357 Hamburg, Germany
Tel.: (49) 40431610
Fax: (49) 40431616
E-Mail: info@delta-hamburg.de
Web Site: www.delta-fleisch.de
Rev.: $53,106,900
Emp.: 110

Business Description:
Meat Product Whslr
S.I.C.: 5147
N.A.I.C.S.: 424470

Personnel:
Ludmilla Kreuz *(Mng Dir)*

DELTA GOLD CORP.

(Formerly ADR Capital Corp.)
1020-625 Howe Street
Vancouver, BC, V6C 2T6, Canada
Tel.: (604) 681-2020
Fax: (604) 681-1011
E-Mail: info@deltagold.com
Web Site: www.deltagold.com
Year Founded: 2011
DLT—(TSXV)
Int. Income: $44,896
Assets: $9,904,756
Liabilities: $194,948
Net Worth: $9,709,808
Earnings: ($3,028,569)
Fiscal Year-end: 09/30/13

Business Description:
Investment Services
S.I.C.: 6211
N.A.I.C.S.: 523999

Personnel:
John P.A. Budreski *(Chm)*
Marco Romero *(CEO)*
John Purkis *(COO & Sr VP)*

Board of Directors:
John P.A. Budreski
Jill Leversage
Chris Mitchell
William Myckatyn
Ian Reid
Marco Romero
Roman Shklanka

Transfer Agent:
Olympia Trust Company
Suite 1003 750 West Pender Street
Vancouver, BC, V6C 2T8, Canada

DELTA GROUP PTY LTD

577 Plummer St
Port Melbourne, VIC, 3207, Australia
Tel.: (61) 9646 8277
Fax: (61) 9646 6877
E-Mail: delta@deltagroup.com.au
Web Site: www.deltagroup.com.au

Business Description:
Holding Companies; Landscape & Excavation Services
S.I.C.: 6719
N.A.I.C.S.: 551112

Personnel:
Con Petropoulos *(Founder & Mng Dir)*

Holding:

CMA Contracting Pty Limited (1)
Level 5 160 Sussex St
Sydney, New South Wales, 2000, Australia
Tel.: (61) 292003500
Fax: (61) 292003501
E-Mail: info@cmacontracting.com.au
Web Site: www.cmacontracting.com.au
Demolition Contracting Services
S.I.C.: 1799
N.A.I.C.S.: 238910
Karl Virkus *(Gen Mgr)*

DELTA HOLDING
Milentija Popovica 7b
Novi, 11 070 Belgrade, Serbia
Tel.: (381) 112011102
Fax: (381) 112011111
E-Mail: nebojsa.divljan@deltagenerali.rs
Web Site: www.deltaholding.rs
Year Founded: 1991
Emp.: 1,300
Business Description:
Holding Company
S.I.C.: 6719
N.A.I.C.S.: 551112
Personnel:
Dragan Filipovic *(Chm & CEO-Delta Generali Osiguranje)*
Miroslav Miskovic *(Pres)*
Milka Vojvodic *(CFO)*
Goran S. Karic *(CEO-Delta Sport)*
Subsidiaries:

Delta Agrar d.o.o. **(1)**
Milentija Popovica 7b
11070 Belgrade, Serbia
Tel.: (381) 11 201 23 00
Fax: (381) 11 201 24 17
E-Mail: office@deltaagrar.rs
Web Site: www.deltaagrar.rs
Emp.: 1,500
Food Product Mfr
S.I.C.: 2099
N.A.I.C.S.: 311991
Milan Grgurevic, *(CEO)*

Subsidiaries:

DANUBIUS d.o.o. Novi Sad **(2)**
Kanalska 1
21000 Novi Sad, Serbia
Tel.: (381) 21 48 08 900
Fax: (381) 21 48 08 996
E-Mail: office@addanubius.rs
Web Site: www.addanubius.rs
Pasta Mfr
S.I.C.: 2045
N.A.I.C.S.: 311824

Yuhor A.D. **(2)**
Kablovska bb
35000 Jagodina, Serbia
Tel.: (381) 35 200 300
Fax: (381) 35 226 844
E-Mail: office@yuhor.rs
Web Site: www.yuhor.rs
Canned Meat Product Mfr
S.I.C.: 2099
N.A.I.C.S.: 311999

DELTA FASHION **(1)**
Milentija Popovica 7 v
11000 Belgrade, Serbia
Tel.: (381) 11 201 28 00
Fax: (381) 11 201 18 90
Fashion Apparel Retailer
S.I.C.: 5699
N.A.I.C.S.: 448150
Goran Karic, *(CEO)*
Jordan Dzakovic *(Deputy CEO)*

Delta Foundation **(1)**
Milentija Popovica 7 b
11000 Belgrade, Serbia
Tel.: (381) 11 201 26 58
Fax: (381) 11 201 26 57
E-Mail: fondacija@deltaholding.rs
Employee Benefit Services
S.I.C.: 6371
N.A.I.C.S.: 525120

DELTA MOTORS **(1)**
Radnicka 8
11000 Belgrade, Serbia
Tel.: (381) 11 353 99 00
Fax: (381) 11 353 99 04
Web Site: www.deltamotors.rs
Automobile Dealer
S.I.C.: 5511
N.A.I.C.S.: 441110

Delta Real Estate D.O.O. **(1)**
Milentija Popovica 7b
11000 Belgrade, Serbia
Tel.: (381) 11 201 26 00
Fax: (381) 11 201 26 07
E-Mail: info@deltarealestate.rs
Web Site: www.deltarealestate.rs
Real Estate Management Services
S.I.C.: 6531
N.A.I.C.S.: 531390
Vojislav Glavinic, *(VP)*

DELTA INSURANCE COMPANY LTD.
Delta Building -Jabal Amman 3rd Circle - opposite Hyatt Hotel
PO Box 3055
Amman, 11181, Jordan
Tel.: (962) 6 4621562
Fax: (962) 6 4654631
E-Mail: info@delta-ins.com
Web Site: www.delta-ins.com
Year Founded: 1976
DICL—(AMM)
Sales Range: $10-24.9 Million
Emp.: 42
Business Description:
General Insurance Services
S.I.C.: 6411
N.A.I.C.S.: 524298
Personnel:
Elia Costandi Nuqul *(Chm)*
Lucien Lutayf *(Vice Chm)*
Board of Directors:
Elia Costandi Nuqul
George Nicola Abu Khader
Maurice Akkawi
Antoine Elie Jammal
Lucien Lutayf
Zaki Beni Noursi
Ghassan Elia Nuqul
Nabil Yacoub Rabah
Nader Michael Sindaha

DELTA LLOYD NV
(d/b/a Delta Lloyd Group)
Amstelplein 6
1096 BC Amsterdam, Netherlands
Mailing Address:
PO Box 1000
1000 BA Amsterdam, Netherlands
Tel.: (31) 20 594 91 11
Fax: (31) 20 693 79 68
E-Mail: info@deltalloyd.nl
Web Site: www.deltalloydgroep.com
DL—(EUR OTC)
Rev.: $14,865,216,842
Assets: $107,687,676,852
Liabilities: $104,170,403,876
Net Worth: $3,517,272,976
Earnings: ($1,972,677,518)
Emp.: 5,276
Fiscal Year-end: 12/31/12
Business Description:
Financial Holding Company; Insurance & Pension, Asset Management & Banking Products & Services
S.I.C.: 6712
N.A.I.C.S.: 551111
Personnel:
Rene H. P. W. Kottman *(Chm-Supervisory Bd)*
Niek W. Hoek *(Chm-Exec Bd)*
Eric J. Fischer *(Vice Chm-Supervisory Bd)*
Emiel A. A. Roozen *(CFO & Member-Exec Bd)*
Alex Otto *(Mng Dir/CIO-Delta Lloyd Asset Mgmt)*
Anne Romagnoli *(CIO-Delta Lloyd Life)*
Peter Brewee *(Chief Risk Officer-Delta Lloyd Life)*
Hugo De Cupere *(Chief Comml Officer-Delta Lloyd Life)*
Hans Duine *(IR Officer)*
Paul K. Medendorp *(Member-Exec Bd)*
Onno W. Verstegen *(Member-Exec Bd)*
Caroline van Reedt Dortland *(Sec)*
Supervisory Board of Directors:
Rene H. P. W. Kottman
Eric J. Fischer
Jean M. G. Frijns
Jan G. Haars
Peter Frans Hartman
Patrick Regan
Fieke van der Lecq
Division:

Delta Lloyd Asset Management N.V. **(1)**
Amstelplein 6
1096 BC Amsterdam, Netherlands NL
Mailing Address:
PO Box 1000
1000 BA Amsterdam, Netherlands
Tel.: (31) 205942118
Fax: (31) 205942706
Web Site: www.deltalloydassetmanagement.nl
Rev.: $161,148,350
Emp.: 170
Asset Management Services
S.I.C.: 6799
N.A.I.C.S.: 523920
Peter A. Knoeff *(CFO)*

Subsidiary:

Cyrte Investments BV **(2)**
Flevolaan 41 A
NL-1411 KC Naarden, Netherlands NL
Mailing Address:
Postboks 5081
NL-1410 AB Naarden, Netherlands
Tel.: (31) 356959090
Fax: (31) 356959044
E-Mail: info@cyrte.com
Web Site: www.cyrte.com
Emp.: 30
Equity Investment Firm
S.I.C.: 6211
N.A.I.C.S.: 523999
Frank Botman *(Mng Dir & Head-Investment Team)*

Joint Venture:

Endemol N.V. **(3)**
Berweg 70
Postbus 678
1217 SC Hilversum, Netherlands NL
Tel.: (31) 355399999
Fax: (31) 355399982
Web Site: www.endemol.com
Sales Range: $1-4.9 Billion
Emp.: 5,000
Holding Company; Television & Other Audiovisual Entertainment Programming & Production Services
S.I.C.: 6719
N.A.I.C.S.: 551112
Just Spee *(CEO)*
Edwin van Es *(CFO)*
Martha Brass *(COO)*
David Flynn *(Chief Creative Officer-UK)*
Tom Toumazis *(Chief Comml Officer)*
Deepak Dhar *(CEO-India)*
Arjen van Mierlo *(CEO-Asia)*

Subsidiary:

Endemol Nederland, B.V. **(4)**
MediArena 1
1099 CZ Amsterdam, Duivendrecht, Netherlands NL
Tel.: (31) 297351711
E-Mail: peter.adrichem@endemol.nl
Web Site: www.endemol.com
Sales Range: $50-74.9 Million
Emp.: 300
Television & Other Audiovisual Entertainment Programming Services
S.I.C.: 4841
N.A.I.C.S.: 515210
Peter Adrichem *(Chm-Mgmt Bd & Mng Dir)*

U.S. Division:

Endemol USA Inc. **(4)**
9255 W Sunset Blvd Ste 1100
West Hollywood, CA 90069 CA
Tel.: (310) 860-9914
Fax: (310) 860-0073
Web Site: www.endemolusa.tv
Sls.: $47,000,000
Emp.: 30
Holding Company; Television & Other Audiovisual Entertainment Programming & Production Services
S.I.C.: 6719
N.A.I.C.S.: 551112
David Goldberg *(Chm & CEO)*
Cris Abrego *(Co-Chm/Co-CEO-North America)*
Charlie Corwin *(Co-Chm/Co-CEO-North America)*
Will Keenan *(Pres-Endemol Beyond USA)*
Caroline Baumgard *(Sr VP-Dev)*
Laurens Drillich *(Sr VP-Latino Ops)*
Stephanie Fisch *(Sr VP-US-Based Latin Div)*
Jeremy Gold *(Sr VP-Scripted Programming)*
A. Ron Milkes *(Sr VP-Corp Dev)*
John P. Roberts *(Sr VP-Digital Media & Comml Affairs-Beverly Hills)*
Rob Smith *(Sr VP-Programming)*

Subsidiaries:

Authentic Entertainment, Inc. **(5)**
2860 N Naomi St
Burbank, CA 91504 CA
Tel.: (323) 644-6144
Fax: (323) 644-7266
E-Mail: info@authentictv.com
Web Site: www.authentictv.com
Sales Range: $1-9.9 Million
Emp.: 20
Television Production
S.I.C.: 7812
N.A.I.C.S.: 512110
Lauren Lexton *(Co-Founder)*
Tom Rogan *(Co-Founder)*

True Entertainment LLC **(5)**
601 W 26th St Ste 1336
New York, NY 10001-1103
Tel.: (212) 763-3600
Fax: (212) 763-3700
E-Mail: mail@trueentertainment.net
Web Site: www.trueentertainment.net
Sls.: $14,600,000
Emp.: 60
Television Programming & Production Services
S.I.C.: 7819
N.A.I.C.S.: 512191
Steven Weinstock *(Co-Founder & Pres)*
Glenda Hersh *(Co-Founder)*
Brenda Hurley *(Sr VP & Gen Mgr)*

Subsidiaries:

Delta Lloyd Bankengroep NV **(1)**
Joan Muyskenweg 4
PO Box 231
NL-1096 CJ Amsterdam, Netherlands NL
Mailing Address: (100%)
Postboks 231
NL-1000 AE Amsterdam, Netherlands
Tel.: (31) 205976208
Fax: (31) 205976308
E-Mail: deltalloyd_ftarpn@ahroa.nl
Web Site: www.deltalloyd.nl
Rev.: $417,329,640
Emp.: 1,198
Bank Holding Company; Personal & Commercial Banking & Lending Services
S.I.C.: 6712
N.A.I.C.S.: 551111
Joost L. Melis *(Chm-Exec Bd)*
Gilbert T. Pluym *(CFO)*
Piet A.J.M. Verbrugge *(Member-Exec Bd-Belgium)*

Division:

Delta Lloyd Bank NV **(2)**
Joan Muyskenweg 4
NL-1096 CJ Amsterdam, Netherlands NL
Mailing Address: (100%)
Postbus 231
NL-1000 AE Amsterdam, Netherlands
Tel.: (31) 205976208
Fax: (31) 205976308
E-Mail: info@deltalloydbank.nl
Web Site: www.deltalloyd.nl/bank
Emp.: 200
Personal & Commercial Banking & Lending Services
S.I.C.: 6029
N.A.I.C.S.: 522110
Gilbert T. Pluym *(CFO)*
Erica Blom-Groenink *(Member-Exec Bd)*
Hans R. Cohen *(Member-Exec Bd)*

Delta Lloyd NV—(Continued)

Non-U.S. Subsidiary:

Delta Lloyd Bank NV (2)
Sterrenkundelaan 23
1210 Brussels, Belgium (100%)
Tel.: (32) 22297600
Fax: (32) 22297699
E-Mail: info@dlbank.be
Web Site: www.deltalloydbank.be
Emp.: 550
Personal & Commercial Banking & Lending Services
S.I.C.: 6029
N.A.I.C.S.: 522110
Filip de Campenaere *(CFO)*
Aymon J. Detroch *(COO)*
Piet A.J.M. Verbrugge *(Pres-Commity)*

Delta Lloyd Verzekeringen NV (1)
Spaklerweg 4
NL-1096 BA Amsterdam, Netherlands NL
Mailing Address:
Postboks 1000
NL-1000 BA Amsterdam, Netherlands
Tel.: (31) 205949111
Fax: (31) 206937968
E-Mail: info@deltalloyd.nl
Web Site: www.deltalloyd.nl
Sales Range: $5-14.9 Billion
Emp.: 1,789
Life & General Insurance Products & Services; Pension Management Services
S.I.C.: 6411
N.A.I.C.S.: 524298
Niek Hoek *(Chm-Exec Bd)*

Non-U.S. Subsidiaries:

Delta Lloyd Deutschland AG (1)
Abraham-Lincoln-Park 1
D-65189 Wiesbaden, Germany De
Tel.: (49) 180 5 32 55 322
Fax: (49) 611 773 2664
E-Mail: info@deltalloyd.de
Web Site: www.deltalloyd.de
Sales Range: $650-699.9 Million
Emp.: 738
Life Insurance, Pension, Investment Banking & Mortgage Products & Services
S.I.C.: 6411
N.A.I.C.S.: 524298
Paul K. Medendorp *(Chm)*

Delta Lloyd Life NV (1)
Fonsnylaan 38
BE-1060 Brussels, Belgium BE
Tel.: (32) 2 238 88 11
Fax: (32) 2 238 88 99
E-Mail: laurent.winnock@deltalloydlife.be
Web Site: www.deltalloydlife.be
Sales Range: $750-799.9 Million
Emp.: 589
Life Insurance Products & Services
S.I.C.: 6311
N.A.I.C.S.: 524113
Onno Versteghen *(Chm)*
Jan Van Autreve *(CEO & Member-Exec Bd)*
Bruno Moors *(CFO)*
Peter Brewee *(Chief Risk Officer)*
Hugo De Cupere *(Chief Comml Officer)*

DELTA MAGNETS LTD.

B-87 MIDC Ambad
Nashik, 422 010, India
Tel.: (91) 253 2382238
Fax: (91) 253 2382926
E-Mail: sales@deltamagnets.com
Web Site: www.deltamagnets.com
504286—(BOM NSE)
Business Description:
Magnet Mfr
S.I.C.: 3312
N.A.I.C.S.: 331110
Personnel:
Jaydev Mody *(Chm)*

Subsidiary:

MMG India Pvt Ltd (1)
144 Seevaram
Thoraipakkam, Chennai, 600 096, India (100%)
Tel.: (91) 44 24968000
Fax: (91) 44 24960986
E-Mail: sales@mmg-india.com
Web Site: www.mmg-india.com
Emp.: 200
Electronic Components Mfr
S.I.C.: 3699
N.A.I.C.S.: 335999
S. P. Annamalai *(Gen Mgr)*

Non-U.S. Subsidiary:

MagDev Limited (1)
Unit 23 Ash Industrial Estate Kembrey Park
Swindon, SN2 8UN, United Kingdom (100%)
Tel.: (44) 1793425600
Fax: (44) 1793524357
E-Mail: info@magdev.co.uk
Web Site: www.magdev.co.uk
Emp.: 20
Magnetic Materials Distr
S.I.C.: 5065
N.A.I.C.S.: 423690
Yvonne Mills *(Gen Mgr & Dir-Fin)*

DELTA N.V.

Poelendaelesingel 10
4335 JA Middelburg, Netherlands
Tel.: (31) 118882000
Fax: (31) 118882100
E-Mail: info@DELTA.nl
Web Site: www.delta.nl
Rev.: $2,923,602,583
Assets: $4,124,520,840
Liabilities: $2,525,452,613
Net Worth: $1,599,068,227
Earnings: $118,390,267
Emp.: 2,954
Fiscal Year-end: 12/31/12
Business Description:
Utilities Operator
S.I.C.: 4931
N.A.I.C.S.: 221122
Personnel:
D. van Doorn *(Chm-Supervisory Bd)*
J. G. van der Werf *(Vice Chm-Supervisory Bd)*
R. J. Frohn *(CEO & Member-Exec Bd)*
Frank Verhagen *(CFO & Member-Exec Bd)*
A. S. Louter *(COO)*
Jaap J. Rieter *(Chief Comml Officer)*
Colin Lustenhouwer *(Gen Counsel)*
Supervisory Board of Directors:
D. van Doorn
J. Bout
B. P. T. de Wit
J. G. van der Werf

Subsidiaries:

DELTA Energy B.V. (1)
Poelendaelesingel 10
Middelburg, Zeeland, 4335 JA , Netherlands
Tel.: (31) 118 883 883
Fax: (31) 118 882 994
Emp.: 700
Electric Power Generation Services
S.I.C.: 4939
N.A.I.C.S.: 221118
Rob Frohn, *(Gen Mgr)*

Subsidiaries:

Deltius B.V. (2)
Europaweg Zuid Haven 9890
4389 PD Ritthem, Zeeland, Netherlands
Mailing Address:
Postbus 23
4380 AA Vlissingen, Netherlands
Tel.: (31) 113 741900
Waste Management Services
S.I.C.: 9511
N.A.I.C.S.: 924110

Litro Energie Nederland B.V. (2)
Poelendaelesingel 10
4335 JA Middelburg, Netherlands
Tel.: (31) 30 2903840
Waste Management Services
S.I.C.: 9511
N.A.I.C.S.: 924110

DELTA Industriele Reiniging B.V. (1)
Poelendaelesingel 10
Middelburg, Zeeland, 4335 JA, Netherlands
Tel.: (31) 118882942
Waste Management Services
S.I.C.: 9511
N.A.I.C.S.: 924110

DELTA Infra B.V. (1)
Anthony Fokkerstraat 8
4462 ET Goes, Netherlands
Tel.: (31) 113741902
Fax: (31) 113941909
E-Mail: info@delta.nl
Emp.: 250
Waste Management Services
S.I.C.: 9511
N.A.I.C.S.: 924110
Erik Duim, *(Bus Dir)*

DELTA Investerings Maatschappij B.V. (1)
Poelendaelesingel 10
Middelburg, Zeeland, 4335 JA, Netherlands
Tel.: (31) 118 616888
Waste Management Services
S.I.C.: 9511
N.A.I.C.S.: 924110

DELTA Milieu Composteren B.V. (1)
De Schans 41
2408 ZA Alphen aan den Rijn, Netherlands
Tel.: (31) 115 678 800
Fax: (31) 115 678880
Waste Management Services
S.I.C.: 9511
N.A.I.C.S.: 924110

DELTA Milieu Groencompost B.V. (1)
IJslandweg 6
4455 SR Nieuwdorp, Netherlands
Tel.: (31) 113613960
Waste Management Services
S.I.C.: 9511
N.A.I.C.S.: 924110

DELTA Milieu Recycling B.V. (1)
Deltastraat 47
4301 RC Zierikzee, Zeeland, Netherlands
Tel.: (31) 111 412051
Waste Management Services
S.I.C.: 9511
N.A.I.C.S.: 924110

DELTA Netwerkbedrijf B.V. (1)
Stationspark 28
4462 DZ Goes, Netherlands
Mailing Address:
Postbus 5013
4330 KA Middelburg, Netherlands
Tel.: (31) 113 74 11 00
Fax: (31) 113 74 11 14
E-Mail: info@dnwb.nl
Web Site: www.deltanetwerkbedrijf.nl
Electric Power Distr
S.I.C.: 4931
N.A.I.C.S.: 221122

Derde Merwedehaven B.V. (1)
Baanhoekweg 92A
3313 LP Dordrecht, Zuid-Holland, Netherlands
Tel.: (31) 78 6306711
Fax: (31) 78 6306764
Emp.: 40
Waste Management Services
S.I.C.: 9511
N.A.I.C.S.: 924110
Wim Schmetz, *(Mng Dir)*

Internetplatform Zeeland B.V. (1)
Het Rip 9
4493 RL Kamperland, Zeeland, Netherlands
Tel.: (31) 113 377778
Fax: (31) 113 372292
Waste Management Services
S.I.C.: 9511
N.A.I.C.S.: 924110

Stichting DELTA Zeeland Fonds (1)
Poelendaelesingel 10
4335 JA Middelburg, Netherlands
Tel.: (31) 118 88 30 96
Fax: (31) 118 88 28 72
E-Mail: info@DELTAZeelandFonds.nl
Web Site: www.deltazeelandfonds.nl
Investment Management Services
S.I.C.: 6799
N.A.I.C.S.: 523920

Stortplaats Koegorspolder B.V. (1)
Finlandweg 19
4538 BL Terneuzen, Netherlands
Tel.: (31) 115 678800
Fax: (31) 113 676760
Waste Management Services
S.I.C.: 9511
N.A.I.C.S.: 924110

Stortplaats Noord en Midden Zeeland B.V. (1)
Frankrijkweg 2
4455 TR Nieuwdorp, Zeeland, Netherlands
Tel.: (31) 113 676791
Real Estate Management Services
S.I.C.: 6531
N.A.I.C.S.: 531390

Windpark Kreekraksluis B.V. (1)
Poelendaelesingel 10
4335 JA Middelburg, Netherlands
Tel.: (31) 118 882000
E-Mail: purchasing@windparkkreekraksluis.nl
Web Site: www.windparkkreekraksluis.nl
Electric Power Generation Services
S.I.C.: 4911
N.A.I.C.S.: 221115

ZeelandNet B.V. (1)
Het Rip 9
4493 RL Kamperland, Netherlands
Tel.: (31) 113 377 778
Fax: (31) 118 88 2100
Web Site: www.zeelandnet.nl
Internet Portal Operator
S.I.C.: 2741
N.A.I.C.S.: 519130

Non-U.S. Subsidiary:

SAV Zweite Beteiligungs GmbH & Co. KG (1)
Waldstr 11
64584 Biebesheim am Rhein, Hessen, Germany
Tel.: (49) 6258 8950
Fax: (49) 6258 8953333
Investment Management Services
S.I.C.: 6799
N.A.I.C.S.: 523920

DELTA OIL & GAS, INC.

Suite 604 700 West Pender Street
Vancouver, BC, V6C 1G8, Canada
Tel.: (866) 355-3644
Fax: (604) 602-1625
Toll Free: (866) 355-3644
E-Mail: IR@deltaoilandgas.com
Web Site: www.deltaoilandgas.com
Year Founded: 2001
DLTA—(OTC OTCB)
Sls.: $528,991
Assets: $1,766,545
Liabilities: $75,105
Net Worth: $1,691,440
Earnings: ($480,254)
Fiscal Year-end: 12/31/12
Business Description:
Oil & Gas Exploration
S.I.C.: 1311
N.A.I.C.S.: 211111
Personnel:
Douglas N. Bolen *(Chm & Pres)*
Christopher Paton-Gay *(CEO)*
Kulwant Sandher *(CFO, Chief Acctg Officer, Treas & Sec)*
Board of Directors:
Douglas N. Bolen
Christopher Paton-Gay
Kulwant Sandher
Christopher Tate

DELTA PLUS GROUP

ZAC La Peyroliere
BP 140
84405 Apt, Cedex, France
Tel.: (33) 490742033
Fax: (33) 490743259
E-Mail: information@deltaplus.eu
Web Site: www.deltaplus.fr
DLTA—(EUR)
Sales Range: $200-249.9 Million

Business Description:
Protection Equipment Designer & Mfr
S.I.C.: 3699
N.A.I.C.S.: 335999
Personnel:
Jerome Benoit *(Chm & CEO)*
Ivo Boscardin *(COO)*

Non-U.S. Subsidiaries:

Delta Plus Ceska Republika S.r.o. (1)
Vrsovika 9
101 00 Prague, 10, Czech Republic
Tel.: (420) 267 227 241
Fax: (420) 267 227 242
E-Mail: info@delta-plus.cz
Protection Equipment Mfr
S.I.C.: 3679
N.A.I.C.S.: 334419

Delta Plus Croatia d.o.o. (1)
Poslovni centar Zitnjak Slavonska avenija 24/6
10000 Zagreb, Croatia
Tel.: (385) 1 2929 111
Fax: (385) 1 2929 222
E-Mail: info.croatia@deltaplus.eu
Protection Equipment Mfr
S.I.C.: 3679
N.A.I.C.S.: 334419

Delta Plus-E SA (1)
Poligono Industrial IN-2C/Mecanicos 39
Santa Pola, 03130 Alicante, Spain
Tel.: (34) 96 541 5011
Fax: (34) 96 541 6358
E-Mail: deltaplus@deltaplus.es
Web Site: www.deltaplus.es
Protective Products Mfr
S.I.C.: 3679
N.A.I.C.S.: 334419

Delta Plus Hellas SRL (1)
34 KM Athinon Lavriou Avenue
19003 Markopoulon, Attikis, Greece
Tel.: (30) 22 990 26001
Fax: (30) 22 990 26003
E-Mail: dphellas@deltaplus.eu
Protection Equipment Mfr
S.I.C.: 3679
N.A.I.C.S.: 334419

Delta Plus Magyarorszag Kft (1)
Illatos ut 38
H-1097 Budapest, Hungary
Tel.: (36) 1 377 8124
Fax: (36) 1 280 3738
E-Mail: deltaplus@deltaplus.hu
Web Site: www.deltaplus.hu
Protection Equipment Mfr
S.I.C.: 3699
N.A.I.C.S.: 335999

Delta Plus Middle East FZE (1)
A2 50/51 SAIF Zone
PO Box 121220
Sharjah, United Arab Emirates
Tel.: (971) 6 5575 004
Fax: (971) 6 5575 006
E-Mail: middle.east@deltaplus.eu
Web Site: www.deltaplus.eu
Emp.: 15
Protection Equipment Mfr
S.I.C.: 3699
N.A.I.C.S.: 335999
Arun Parasnis *(Mng Dir)*

Delta Plus Peru SAC (1)
Los Eucaliptos 371 Avenue
Surquillo, Lima, Lima, 16, Peru
Tel.: (51) 1 225 4114
E-Mail: deltaplusperu@deltaplus.eu
Web Site: www.deltaplus.eu
Protection Equipment Mfr
S.I.C.: 3699
N.A.I.C.S.: 335999
Antonio Dulong *(Office Mgr)*

Delta Plus Polska SP zo.o (1)
Ul Sokolska 68B
41-219 Sosnowiec, Poland
Tel.: (48) 3229 64750
Fax: (48) 3229 64769
E-Mail: biuro@deltaplus.com.pl
Web Site: www.deltaplus.com.pl
Protective Equipment Mfr
S.I.C.: 3679
N.A.I.C.S.: 334419

Delta Plus Romania SRL (1)
Str Lt Ionescu Baican nr 24
Sector 2, Bucharest, 21838, Romania
Tel.: (40) 21 250 0556
Fax: (40) 21 250 0553
E-Mail: orders.romania@deltaplus.eu
Protection Equipment Mfr
S.I.C.: 3699
N.A.I.C.S.: 335999

Delta Plus Sicurex SRL (1)
Via E Fermi 265
36100 Vicenza, Italy
Tel.: (39) 0 444 822 822
Fax: (39) 0 444 822 800
E-Mail: vendite@deltaplus.it
Web Site: www.deltaplus.it
Protection Equipment Mfr
S.I.C.: 3679
N.A.I.C.S.: 334419

Delta Plus Slovensko SRO (1)
Mlynske Nivy 71
82105 Bratislava, Slovakia
Tel.: (421) 2 3266 2611
Fax: (421) 2 5341 7702
E-Mail: office@delta-plus.sk
Web Site: www.delta-plus.sk
Protective Equipment Mfr
S.I.C.: 3679
N.A.I.C.S.: 334419
Ivan Zemko *(Mng Dir)*

Suzhou Delta Plus Personal Protection (1)
Zhonglu Ecologic Park Pingwang Town
Wujiang, Jiangsu, 215221, China
Tel.: (86) 512 67 128700
Fax: (86) 512 67 128716
E-Mail: liuyigin@deltaplus.com.cn
Web Site: www.deltaplus.com.cn
Protection Equipment Mfr
S.I.C.: 3679
N.A.I.C.S.: 334419

DELTA RECYCLAGE

576 Rue De La Liberation
Lansargues, 34130 Montpellier, France
Tel.: (33) 467867150
Fax: (33) 467867112
Web Site: www.delta-recyclage.fr
Sls.: $20,100,000
Emp.: 183
Business Description:
Scrap & Waste Mats
S.I.C.: 5093
N.A.I.C.S.: 423930
Personnel:
Raymond Delmas *(Mng Dir)*
Board of Directors:
Dimitri Brousse
Raymond Delmas

DELTA SBD LIMITED

Suite 220 Centric 4 Hyde Parade
Campbelltown, NSW, 2560, Australia
Tel.: (61) 2 4629 0300
Fax: (61) 2 4629 0399
E-Mail: office@deltasbd.com.au
Web Site: www.deltasbd.com.au
Year Founded: 2007
DSB—(ASX)
Rev.: $151,223,299
Assets: $116,684,979
Liabilities: $54,856,144
Net Worth: $61,828,835
Earnings: $7,369,731
Emp.: 540
Fiscal Year-end: 06/30/13
Business Description:
Coal Mining Services
S.I.C.: 1222
N.A.I.C.S.: 212112
Personnel:
Stephen Bizzaca *(CEO & Mng Dir)*
Tony McFadden *(CFO & Sec)*
Board of Directors:
Gordon Thomas Galt
Stephen Bizzaca
Glyn Dawkins
Geoff Garside
Legal Counsel:
McCullough Robertson
Level 12 Central Plaza Two 66 Eagle Street
4000 Brisbane, QLD, Australia

DELTA URANIUM INC.

130 King Street West Suite 720
Toronto, ON, M5X 1A6, Canada
Tel.: (416) 363-3582
Fax: (866) 288-3582
Web Site: www.deltauranium.com
Year Founded: 1988
DUR—(TSXV)
Assets: $169,540
Liabilities: $2,067,138
Net Worth: ($1,897,598)
Earnings: ($444,294)
Fiscal Year-end: 02/28/13
Business Description:
Uranium Mining Services
S.I.C.: 1094
N.A.I.C.S.: 212291
Personnel:
Wayne V. Isaacs *(CEO)*
John V. Tokarsky *(CFO)*
Board of Directors:
Wayne V. Isaacs
Colin Bowdidge
John V. Tokarsky
Legal Counsel:
Fogler, Rubinoff LLP
95 Wellington Street West, Suite 1200
Toronto, ON, Canada
Transfer Agent:
Equity Transfer & Trust Company
200 University Avenue Ste 400
Toronto, ON, M5H 4H1, Canada
Tel.: (416) 361-0152
Fax: (416) 361-0470

DELTA WIRE & MFG.

29 Delta Drive
Harrow, ON, Canada N0R 1G0
Tel.: (519) 738-3514
Fax: (519) 738-3468
E-Mail: contact@deltawire.com
Web Site: www.deltawire.com
Rev.: $20,372,500
Emp.: 80
Business Description:
Fabricated Wire Products Mfr
S.I.C.: 3496
N.A.I.C.S.: 332618
Personnel:
Kerry J. Stomp *(VP-Mfg)*

DELTACO AB

Alfred Nobels Alle 109
146 48 Tullinge, Sweden
Tel.: (46) 8 555 762 00
Fax: (46) 8 555 762 19
E-Mail: siamak.alian@deltaco.se
Web Site: www.deltacoab.se
Year Founded: 1991
DELT—(OMX)
Business Description:
IT Products Distr
S.I.C.: 5045
N.A.I.C.S.: 423430
Personnel:
Arne Myhrman *(Chm)*
Siamak Alian *(CEO & Mng Dir)*
Connie Yau *(CFO & Fin Dir)*
Board of Directors:
Arne Myhrman
Bjorn Abild
Jonas Martensson

Subsidiary:

SweDeltaco AB (1)
Alfred Noble Alle 109
SE 146 48 Stockholm, Tullinge, Sweden
Tel.: (46) 855576200
Fax: (46) 855576219
E-Mail: data@deltaco.se
Web Site: www.deltaco.se
Emp.: 65
Computer Products & Accessories
S.I.C.: 7379
N.A.I.C.S.: 541519
Ali Motazedi *(Mng Dir)*
Claes Eriksson *(Deputy Mng Dir)*

DELTAFORM LTD.

Brue Avenue Colley Lane Industrial Estate
Bridgwater, Somerset, TA6 5YE, United Kingdom
Tel.: (44) 1278 410160
Fax: (44) 1278 410161
E-Mail: sales@deltaform.co.uk
Web Site: www.deltaform.co.uk
Year Founded: 1992
Sales Range: $25-49.9 Million
Emp.: 223
Business Description:
Plastic Packaging Product Mfr
S.I.C.: 3089
N.A.I.C.S.: 326199
Personnel:
Richard Adams *(Co-Founder)*
Stephen Jones *(Co-Founder)*

DELTEX MEDICAL GROUP PLC

Terminus Road
Chichester, West Sussex, PO19 8TX, United Kingdom
Tel.: (44) 1243774837
Fax: (44) 1243532534
E-Mail: info@deltexmedical.com
Web Site: www.deltexmedical.com
DEMG—(LSE)
Rev.: $10,702,848
Assets: $9,878,459
Liabilities: $6,554,054
Net Worth: $3,324,405
Earnings: ($3,305,454)
Emp.: 75
Fiscal Year-end: 12/31/12
Business Description:
Medical Devices
S.I.C.: 3841
N.A.I.C.S.: 339112
Personnel:
Ewan Phillips *(CEO)*
Paul Mitchell *(Sec & Dir-Fin)*
Board of Directors:
Nigel Keen
Julian Cazalet
Paul Mitchell
Duncan Nichol
Ewan Phillips
Edwin Snape
Legal Counsel:
Laytons
Carmelite 50 Victoria Embankment Blackfriars
London, United Kingdom

Subsidiary:

Deltex Medical Limited (1)
Terminus Rd
Chichester, West Sussex, PO19 8TX, United Kingdom
Tel.: (44) 1243774837
Fax: (44) 1243532534
E-Mail: info@deltexmedical.com
Web Site: www.deltexmedical.com
Emp.: 60
Medical Equipments Mfr
S.I.C.: 3841
N.A.I.C.S.: 339112
Ewan Phillips *(CEO)*

U.S. Subsidiary:

Deltex Medical SC Inc. (1)
330 E Coffee St
Greenville, SC 29601
Tel.: (864) 527-5913
Fax: (864) 527-5914
E-Mail: ussales@deltexmedical.com

Deltex Medical Group plc—(Continued)

Web Site: www.deltexmedical.com
Emp.: 25
Medical Equipments Mfr
S.I.C.: 3841
N.A.I.C.S.: 339112
Ana Fowler *(Office Mgr)*

Non-U.S. Subsidiary:

Deltex Medical Espana **(1)**
C Dr Casals 32
Santa Cristina d Aro, 17246 Gerona, Spain
Tel.: (34) 972835954
Fax: (34) 972835952
E-Mail: sales@deltexmedical.com
Emp.: 3
Medical Equipments Mfr
S.I.C.: 3841
N.A.I.C.S.: 339112

DELTICOM AG

Bruhl Strasse 11
30169 Hannover, Germany
Tel.: (49) 1805335842
Fax: (49) 208080810
E-Mail: info@delti.com
Web Site: www.delti.com
DEX—(DEU)
Rev.: $619,417,241
Assets: $210,505,988
Liabilities: $126,187,283
Net Worth: $84,318,704
Earnings: $29,827,089
Emp.: 144
Fiscal Year-end: 12/31/12
Business Description:
Tire Retailer
S.I.C.: 5014
N.A.I.C.S.: 423130
Personnel:
Andreas Pruefer *(Chm-Supervisory Bd)*
Michael Thone-Floge *(Deputy Chm-Supervisory Bd)*
Rainer Binder *(CEO & Member-Mgmt Bd-Procurement)*
Susann Dorsel-Muller *(Member-Mgmt Bd-Wholesale, Ops-Center & B2B)*
Sascha Jurgensen *(Member-Mgmt Bd-Logistics & Staffing)*
Frank Schuhardt *(Member-Mgmt Bd-Fin, Law & IT)*
Philip von Grolman *(Member-Mgmt Bd-B2C & Mktg-North America)*
Supervisory Board of Directors:
Andreas Pruefer
Alan Revie
Michael Thone-Floge

Non-U.S. Subsidiary:

Netix S.R.L. **(1)**
Str Izlaz Nr 103 Ap Camera 5
Timisoara, Timis, 300299, Romania
Tel.: (40) 256270016
Fax: (40) 256306294
E-Mail: office@netix.ro
Web Site: www.netix.ro
Emp.: 372
Online Tire Sales
S.I.C.: 5014
N.A.I.C.S.: 423130
Freumzache Leonpin *(Mng Dir)*

DELTON AG

Gunther Quandt Haus Seedammweg 55
61352 Bad Homburg, Germany
Tel.: (49) 61724040
Fax: (49) 6172404333
E-Mail: pr@delton.de
Web Site: www.delton.de
Sales Range: $1-4.9 Billion
Emp.: 30,077
Business Description:
Diversified Holding Company
S.I.C.: 6719
N.A.I.C.S.: 551112
Personnel:
Stefan Quandt *(Chm-Supervisory Bd)*
Franz Marcus Haniel *(Deputy Chm-Supervisory Bd)*
Ursula Karius *(Deputy Chm-Supervisory Bd)*
Berndt-Michael Winter *(CEO)*
Antonius Wagner *(CFO)*
Supervisory Board of Directors:
Stefan Quandt
Klaus Boos
Marc Anton Deschler
Peter Diesch
Franz Marcus Haniel
Michael Hoffmann-Becking
Heinz K. Junker
Ursula Karius
Martin Kohler
Hans-Peter Konrad
Georg Liebl
Gunther Pfirrmann

Subsidiary:

Biologische Heilmittel Heel GmbH **(1)**
Dr Reckeweg Strasse 2-4
76532 Baden-Baden, Germany De
Tel.: (49) 772150100
Fax: (49) 7221501210
E-Mail: info@heel.de
Web Site: www.heel.de
Mfr of Homeopathic Medications
S.I.C.: 2834
N.A.I.C.S.: 325412
Ralph Schmidt *(CEO & Chm-Mgmt Bd)*
Rainer Hopfgarten *(CFO & Member-Mgmt Bd)*

Non-U.S. Subsidiary:

Heel Biologische Geneesmiddelen B.V. **(2)**
Wilhelmina Straase 5456
4571 JN Axel, Netherlands NL
Tel.: (31) 115 563 200 (100%)
Telex: 42672
Fax: (31) 115564774
E-Mail: info@heelbv.nl
Web Site: www.heelbv.nl
Emp.: 20
Homeopathic Medicines Distr
S.I.C.: 5122
N.A.I.C.S.: 424210

Non-U.S. Subsidiary:

Logwin AG **(1)**
ZIR Potaschberg 5 an de Langten
L-6776 Grevenmacher, Luxembourg (66.8%)
Tel.: (352) 7196900
Fax: (352) 7196901359
E-Mail: info@logwin-logistics.com
Web Site: www.logwin-logistics.com
TGH—(DEU)
Sls.: $1,783,127,359
Assets: $533,594,865
Liabilities: $401,462,894
Net Worth: $132,131,970
Earnings: ($92,375,532)
Emp.: 5,505
Fiscal Year-end: 12/31/12
Logistics & Service Solutions for Trade & Industry
S.I.C.: 7389
N.A.I.C.S.: 561499
Berndt-Michael Winter *(Chm & CEO)*
Antonius Wagner *(Deputy Chm & CFO)*
Thomas Eisen *(Member-Exec Bd)*
Hauke Muller *(Member-Exec Bd)*

DELTON CABLES LIMITED

Delton House 4801 Bharat Ram Road 24 Daryaganj
New Delhi, 110002, India
Tel.: (91) 11 23273905
Fax: (91) 11 23280375
E-Mail: Info@deltoncables.com
Web Site: www.deltoncables.com
Year Founded: 1948
504240—(BOM)
Rev.: $21,532,356
Assets: $17,296,559
Liabilities: $12,936,433
Net Worth: $4,360,126
Earnings: ($520,974)
Fiscal Year-end: 03/31/13
Business Description:
Telecom Cables Distr
S.I.C.: 4813
N.A.I.C.S.: 517110
Personnel:
Vivek K. Gupta *(Chm & Mng Dir)*
Prakash Singh *(Pres)*
Rakesh Verma *(CFO)*
Jitender Kumar *(Sec)*
Board of Directors:
Vivek K. Gupta
B. B. Chadha
Vijay Kumar Goel
A. Karati
M. P. Mehrotra
Rakesh Verma
Transfer Agent:
Beetal Financial & Computer Services Pvt. Ltd
Beetal House 3rd Floor 99 Madangir Behind L S C Near Dada Harsukh Dass
New Delhi, India

Subsidiary:

Delton Cables Limited - DHARUHERA WORKS **(1)**
70th Milestone Delhi-Jaipur Highway
Dharuhera, Haryana, 122106, India
Tel.: (91) 1274 242229
Fax: (91) 1274 242294
Electronic & Electrical Product Mfr
S.I.C.: 3699
N.A.I.C.S.: 335999

Units:

Delton Cables Limited - FARIDABAD WORKS **(1)**
17/4 Mathura Road
Faridabad, Haryana, India
Tel.: (91) 129 2288225
Fax: (91) 129 2223998
Electrical & Electronic Component Mfr
S.I.C.: 3699
N.A.I.C.S.: 335999

Delton Cables Limited - NEW DELHI WORKS **(1)**
24 Shivaji Marg
New Delhi, 110 015, India
Tel.: (91) 11 25928280
Fax: (91) 11 25928037
Electrical & Electronic Product Mfr
S.I.C.: 3699
N.A.I.C.S.: 335999

DEM. TH. BERTZELETOS & BROS. SA

(d/b/a Bertzeletos & Bros. SA)
22 Fleming Street
182 33 Agios Ioannis Rentis, Greece
Tel.: (30) 210 4832 466
Fax: (30) 210 4829 242
E-Mail: perla@hol.gr
Web Site: www.dtb.gr
Year Founded: 1893
Emp.: 300
Business Description:
Holding Company
S.I.C.: 6719
N.A.I.C.S.: 551112
Personnel:
Theodoros Bertzeletos *(Chm & CEO)*

Joint Venture:

Perla Greek Salt Ltd. **(1)**
22 Fleming Street
182 33 Agios Ioannis Rentis, Greece GR
Mailing Address:
PO Box 80145
18510 Piraeus, Greece
Tel.: (30) 2104832466
Telex: 212121
Fax: (30) 2104829242
E-Mail: perlagsalt@tee.gr
Web Site: www.perlasalt.gr
Emp.: 30
Salt Producer
S.I.C.: 2899
N.A.I.C.S.: 325998
Theodoros Bertzeletos *(Mng Dir)*

DEMARAIS INDUSTRIES

6 Rue Honore De Balzac
Montoire Sur Le Loir, 41800 Tours, France
Tel.: (33) 254864440
Web Site: www.demarais.com
Sales Range: $10-24.9 Million
Emp.: 159
Business Description:
Motor Vehicles & Car Bodies
S.I.C.: 3711
N.A.I.C.S.: 336111
Personnel:
Pierre Masson *(Mng Dir)*

DEMCO PUBLIC COMPANY LIMITED

59 Moo 1 Suanphrikthai Muang Pathumthani
Pathumthani, 12000, Thailand
Tel.: (66) 2959 5811
Fax: (66) 2959 5820
E-Mail: info@demco.co.th
Web Site: www.demco.co.th
Year Founded: 1992
DEMCO—(THA)
Rev.: $199,110,671
Assets: $147,051,312
Liabilities: $89,166,931
Net Worth: $57,884,381
Earnings: $13,772,011
Fiscal Year-end: 12/31/12
Business Description:
Engineering Services
S.I.C.: 8711
N.A.I.C.S.: 541330
Personnel:
Praphee Puipunthavong *(Chm & Pres)*
Pradej Kitti-itsaranon *(Mng Dir)*
Suwat Choradol *(Deputy Mng Dir)*
Phumchai Hirunchai *(Asst Mng Dir)*
Arkom Manakaew *(Asst Mng Dir)*
Phongsak Siricupta *(Deputy Mng Dir)*
Board of Directors:
Praphee Puipunthavong
Thien Chonmitree
Suwat Choradol
Phumchai Hirunchai
Pradej Kitti-itsaranon
Arkom Manakaew
Phongsak Siricupta
Sa-nguan Tangdechahirun

DEMERARA DISTILLERS LTD.

Plantation Diamond E Bank
Demerara, Guyana
Tel.: (592) 2655019
Fax: (592) 2652015
E-Mail: ypersaud@demrum.com
Web Site: www.demrum.com
Year Founded: 1952
Sales Range: $600-649.9 Million
Emp.: 1,200
Business Description:
Distilled Liquors & Soft Drinks Mfr
S.I.C.: 2085
N.A.I.C.S.: 312140
Personnel:
Y. Persaud *(Chm & Pres)*
K. R. Samaroo *(Exec VP-Intl Mktg)*
Board of Directors:
Y. Persaud
C. Bisheswar
Egbert A. Carter
Rudolph Collins
L. Nathoo
Lalta Ramgopal
K. R. Samaroo
David R. Spence

U.S. Subsidiary:

Demerara Distillers (USA) Inc. **(1)**
499 NW 70th Ave Ste 120
Plantation, FL 33317
Tel.: (786) 275-0253
Fax: (786) 275-0256
E-Mail: demdus@bellsouth.net
Web Site: www.theeldoradorum.com
Emp.: 2
Rum & Beverage Sales
S.I.C.: 5181
N.A.I.C.S.: 424810
Yesu Persaud *(Pres)*

Non-U.S. Subsidiary:

Demerara Distillers Europe BV **(1)**
Peperstraat 147
1502 E Zaandam, Netherlands
Mailing Address:
PO Box 1262
1500 AG Zaandam, Netherlands
Tel.: (31) 756700575
Fax: (31) 756703395
E-Mail: info@del-europe.nl
Web Site: www.del-europe.nl
Rum & Beverage Sales
S.I.C.: 5181
N.A.I.C.S.: 424810

DEMERS, MANUFACTURIER D'AMBULANCES INC.

(d/b/a Demers Ambulances)
28 Richelieu
Beloeil, QC, J3G 4N5, Canada
Tel.: (450) 467-4683
Fax: (450) 467-6526
Toll Free: (800) 363-7591
E-Mail: info@demers-ambulances.com
Web Site: www.demers-ambulances.com
Year Founded: 1960
Sales Range: $10-24.9 Million
Emp.: 180
Business Description:
Ambulances Design & Mfr
S.I.C.: 3711
N.A.I.C.S.: 336211
Personnel:
Alain Brunelle *(Pres & Gen Mgr)*
Benoit R. Lafortune *(Exec VP)*

DEMERS, PAUL & FILS, INC.

(See Under Demers, Manufacturier d'Ambulances Inc.)

DEMETRA INVESTMENT PUBLIC LIMITED

Demosthenis Severis 34 4th Fl
PO Box 23582
1684 Nicosia, Cyprus
Tel.: (357) 22818222
Fax: (357) 22818223
E-Mail: mailbox@demetra.com.cy
Web Site: www.demetra.com.cy
DEM—(CYP)
Sales Range: $10-24.9 Million
Emp.: 9
Business Description:
Investment Banking Services
S.I.C.: 6211
N.A.I.C.S.: 523110
Personnel:
Demetrios Stavrou *(Chm)*
Lefteris Christoforou *(Vice Chm)*
Nearchos Ioannou *(Vice Chm)*
Nicos Michaelas *(Sec)*
Board of Directors:
Demetrios Stavrou
Lefteris Christoforou
Photis Demetriades
Kriton Georgiades
Evangelos Georgiou
Nearchos Ioannou
Maria Ioannou Theodorou

DEMMEL AG

Gruntenweg 14
D-88175 Lindau, Germany
Tel.: (49) 838191900
Fax: (49) 8381919191
E-Mail: info@demmel.de
Web Site: www.demmel.ag
Sales Range: $10-24.9 Million
Emp.: 400
Business Description:
Industrial Electronics Manufacturing
S.I.C.: 3699
N.A.I.C.S.: 335999
Personnel:
Hansjorg Holderried *(Chm)*
Thomas Holderried *(Chm-Mgmt Bd)*

Joint Venture:

Angell-Demmel Europe GmbH **(1)**
Zechwaldstrasse 1
88131 Lindau, Germany
Tel.: (49) 8382963512
Fax: (49) 8382963544
E-Mail: info@angell-demmel.de
Web Site: www.angell-demmel.de
Sales Range: $25-49.9 Million
Emp.: 500
Automotive Parts Mfr
S.I.C.: 3714
N.A.I.C.S.: 336390

DEMOS LLC

6 1 Ovchinnikovskaya Nab
113035 Moscow, Russia
Tel.: (7) 0959566080
Fax: (7) 0959565042
E-Mail: info@demos.su
Web Site: www.demos.su
Emp.: 250
Business Description:
Holding Company; Internet Services, Corporate Information Solutions, Information Security & Computer Products
S.I.C.: 6719
N.A.I.C.S.: 551112

Subsidiary:

Demos-Internet **(1)**
Lower Krasnoselskay 35 Block 50
Moscow, 105066, Russia
Tel.: (7) 4957370400
Fax: (7) 4957370402
E-Mail: info@demos.ru
Web Site: www.demos-internet.ru
Emp.: 100
Internet Web Hosting
S.I.C.: 7374
N.A.I.C.S.: 518210
Zoudto Victor Genrihovich *(Gen Mgr)*

DEMOS S.A.

20 rue de l'Arcade
75008 Paris, France
Tel.: (33) 1 44 94 16 16
Fax: (33) 1 44 94 16 39
E-Mail: contact@demos.fr
Web Site: www.demosgroup.com
Year Founded: 1972
ALDMO—(EUR)
Emp.: 800
Business Description:
Professional Training Services
S.I.C.: 8299
N.A.I.C.S.: 611430
Personnel:
Jean Wemaere *(Chm & CEO)*
Franck Lebouchard *(COO)*
Jean-Christophe Desire *(CIO)*

DEMPSEY MINERALS LTD.

Level 2 38 Richardson Street
West Perth, WA, 6005, Australia
Tel.: (61) 8 9322 6283
Fax: (61) 8 9322 6398
E-Mail: admin@dempseyminerals.com.au
Web Site: www.dempseyminerals.com.au
DMI—(ASX)
Business Description:
Phosphate & Mineral Sands Exploration Services
S.I.C.: 1475
N.A.I.C.S.: 212392
Personnel:
Nathan Bruce McMahon *(Chm)*
Julie Hill *(Sec)*
Board of Directors:
Nathan Bruce McMahon
Christopher William Chalwell
Lisa Wynne

DEN NETWORKS LIMITED

236 Okhla Industrial Estate Phase III
New Delhi, 110020, India
Tel.: (91) 1140522200
Fax: (91) 1140522203
E-Mail: query@denonline.in
Web Site: www.dennetworks.com
DEN—(BOM NSE)
Rev.: $173,282,998
Assets: $422,902,591
Liabilities: $242,238,449
Net Worth: $180,664,142
Earnings: $11,550,605
Emp.: 550
Fiscal Year-end: 03/31/13
Business Description:
Cable Television
S.I.C.: 4813
N.A.I.C.S.: 517110
Personnel:
Sameer Manchanda *(Chm & Mng Dir)*
Shailender Nath Sharma *(CEO)*
Rajesh Kaushal *(CFO)*
Mohammad Ghulam Azhar *(COO)*
Navroz Behramfram *(CTO)*
Jatin Mahajan *(Compliance Officer & Sec)*
Board of Directors:
Sameer Manchanda
Ajaya Chand
Shahzaad Siraj Dalal
Ankur Sahu
Atul Sharma
Robindra Sharma
Transfer Agent:
Karvy Computershare Private Limited
Karvy House 46 Avenue 4 Street No 1
500034 Hyderabad, India

DENA BANK

Dena Corporate Centre C 10 G Block
Bandra-Kurla Complex Bandra E
Mumbai, 400 051, India
Tel.: (91) 2226545000
Fax: (91) 2226545035
Web Site: www.denabank.com
532121—(BOM)
Rev.: $1,771,469,672
Assets: $21,031,854,610
Liabilities: $19,963,206,803
Net Worth: $1,068,647,806
Earnings: $150,244,897
Emp.: 11,093
Fiscal Year-end: 03/31/13
Business Description:
Banking Services
S.I.C.: 6029
N.A.I.C.S.: 522110
Personnel:
Ashwani Kumar *(Chm & Mng Dir)*
Ramesh Singh Bora *(Chief Vigilance Officer & Gen Mgr)*
Board of Directors:
Ashwani Kumar
J. Balasubramanian
Rohit M. Desai
A. K. Dutt
Rakesh Goel
Trishna Guha
Mohan Lal Gupta
Sanjeev Jindal
Vijay Kapoor
Mukesh Mohan
S. P. Sharma
V. Vasanthan
S C Bapna & Associates
Mumbai, India
P K Chopra & Co
Mumbai, India
Gandhi Minocha & Co
Mumbai, India
B. K. Khare & Co
Mumbai, India
Avanish K Rastogi & Associates
Mumbai, India
Transfer Agent:
Sharepro Services (India) Private Limited
13 AB Samhita Warehousing Complex II Floor
Sakinaka Telephone Lane
Off Andheri Kurla Rd Sakinaka, Mumbai, India

Division:

Dena Bank - International Division **(1)**
5th Fl Dena Corporate Ctr C 10 G Block
Bandra Kurla Complex
Bandra, Maharashtra, 400 051, India
Tel.: (91) 2226545576
Fax: (91) 2226545581
E-Mail: intldiv@denabank.co.in
Web Site: www.denabank.com
Emp.: 10
Banking Services
S.I.C.: 6029
N.A.I.C.S.: 522110
Chitra Krithivasan *(Asst Gen Mgr)*

DENA CO., LTD.

Shibuya Hikarie 2-21-1 Shibuya
Shibuya-ku, Tokyo, 150-8510, Japan
Tel.: (81) 3 5304 1701
E-Mail: info@dena.jp
Web Site: www.dena.com
Year Founded: 1999
2432—(TKS)
Sls.: $2,227,137,000
Assets: $2,142,624,000
Liabilities: $782,188,000
Net Worth: $1,360,436,000
Earnings: $514,085,000
Emp.: 2,108
Fiscal Year-end: 03/31/13
Business Description:
Online Advertising, e-Commerce & Mobile Portal Services
S.I.C.: 7319
N.A.I.C.S.: 541890
Personnel:
Tomoko Namba *(Founder)*
Makoto Haruta *(Chm)*
Isao Moriyasu *(Pres & CEO)*
Shuhei Kawasaki *(CTO)*
Junichi Akagawa *(Sr VP)*
Mitsuhiro Hayashi *(Sr VP)*
Hideo Kimura *(Sr VP)*
Takeshi Matsui *(Sr VP)*
Hiroshi Nakajima *(Sr VP)*
Tomoya Ogawa *(Sr VP)*
Daisuke Shibata *(Sr VP)*
Yoshiki Watabe *(Sr VP)*
Yasuhiro Yano *(Sr VP)*
Board of Directors:
Makoto Haruta
Rehito Hatoyama
Shuhei Kawasaki
Kenji Kobayashi
Isao Moriyasu
Tomoko Namba
Transfer Agent:
Mitsubishi UFJ Trust & Banking Corporation
10-11 Higashisuna 1-chome Koto-ku
Tokyo, Japan

DeNA Co., Ltd.—(Continued)

Subsidiaries:

Mobaoku Co., Ltd. (1)
4-30-3 Yoyogi Shinjuku Midwest Building
Shibuya-ku, Tokyo, 151-0053, Japan
Tel.: (81) 358430584
Web Site: www.mbok.co.jp
Online Auction Services
S.I.C.: 5961
N.A.I.C.S.: 454112

PAYGENT Co., Ltd. (1)
4-30-3 Yoyogi Shinjuku Midwest Building
Shibuya-ku, Tokyo, 151-0053, Japan
Tel.: (81) 353041801
Fax: (81) 333201229
E-Mail: suzuki.naoko@paygent.co.jp
Web Site: www.paygent.co.jp
Emp.: 60
Online Payment Gateway Services
S.I.C.: 6099
N.A.I.C.S.: 522320
Yasushi kanbayashi *(CEO)*

The Yokohama BayStars Baseball Club, Inc. (1)
Kannai Arai Bldg 18 Onoe-cho
Naka-ku, Yokohama, 2310015, Japan JP
Tel.: (81) 456810811 (66.92%)
Fax: (81) 456612500
Web Site: www.baystars.co.jp
Emp.: 80
Professional Baseball Team
S.I.C.: 7941
N.A.I.C.S.: 711211

U.S. Subsidiaries:

DeNA Global, Inc. (1)
1 Waters Park Dr Ste 165
San Mateo, CA 94403
Tel.: (650) 638-1026
E-Mail: info@denaglobal.com
Web Site: www.denaglobal.com
Emp.: 10
Mobile Entertainment & Mobile Social Networking Services
S.I.C.: 7372
N.A.I.C.S.: 511210
Dai Watanabe *(Pres)*

ngmoco Inc. (1)
475 Brannan St Ste 420
San Francisco, CA 94107
Tel.: (415) 375-3170
E-Mail: information@ngmoco.com
Web Site: www.ngmoco.com
Mobile Device Application Developer
S.I.C.: 7372
N.A.I.C.S.: 511210
Bob Stevenson *(Co-Founder)*
Neil Young *(Co-Founder)*
Joanna Drake Earl *(COO)*

DENCO LTD.

Dolphin House Moreton Business Park Morton on Lugg
PO Box 11
Hereford, HR4 8DS, United Kingdom
Tel.: (44) 432277277
Telex: 35144
Fax: (44) 432268005
Web Site: www.denco.co.uk
Emp.: 300
Business Description:
Design & Manufacture of Close Control Air Conditioning for Computer Rooms, Clean Rooms & Compressed Air Dryers & Components; Centralized Lubricating Systems
S.I.C.: 3564
N.A.I.C.S.: 333413
Personnel:
John Tandy *(Mng Dir)*

DENEL (PTY) LTD.

Denel Building Nellmapius Drive
Irene, Gauteng, South Africa
Mailing Address:
PO Box 8322
Centurion, 0046, South Africa
Tel.: (27) 126712700
Fax: (27) 126712793
Web Site: www.denel.co.za
Year Founded: 1992
Sales Range: $400-449.9 Million
Emp.: 4,716
Business Description:
Holding Company; Military Aircraft Components, Munitions & Other Defense Equipment Mfr & Support Services
S.I.C.: 6719
N.A.I.C.S.: 551112
Personnel:
Riaz Saloojee *(Grp CEO)*
J. V. Morris *(Grp Exec-Strategy & Comml)*
T. Patience Mushungwa *(Grp Exec-HR & Transformation)*
Zwelakhe N. Ntshepe *(Grp Exec-Bus Dev & Corp Affairs)*
O. A. Schur *(Grp Exec-Technical)*
A. S. Burger *(CEO-Land Sys)*
I. Dockrat *(CEO-SAAB Aerostructures (Pty) Ltd)*
B. P. E. Garcia *(CEO-Turbomeca Africa (Pty) Ltd)*
M. L. Kgobe *(CEO-Aviation)*
R. Mills *(CEO-Integrated Sys Solutions)*
N. Schulze *(CEO-Rheinmetall Denel Munition (Pty) Ltd)*
A. J. van der Walt *(CEO-Overberg Test Range)*
J. M. Wessels *(CEO-Dynamics)*
A. Williams *(CEO-Mechem (Pty) Ltd)*
C. P. Wolhuter *(CEO-Pretoria Metal Pressings)*
Board of Directors:
Sibusisu P. Sibisi
S. H. Chaba
G. C. Cruywagen
Alan Hirsch
Llewellyn C. Jones
N. R. Kunene
T. Marwala
F. Mhlontlo
B. Paledi
M. J. Janse van Rensburg

Division:

Denel Aviation (1)
Atlas Road Bonaero Park
Kempton Park, Gauteng, 1619, South Africa
Mailing Address:
PO Box 7246
Kempton Park, 1622, South Africa
Tel.: (27) 119272620
E-Mail: marketing@denelaviation.co.za
Web Site: www.denelaviation.co.za
Aircraft Maintenance, Repair & Overhaul Services
S.I.C.: 7699
N.A.I.C.S.: 811310
Ismail Dockrat *(CEO)*
Abdul Karim *(CFO)*
Mike Kgobe *(COO)*

Joint Venture:

Rheinmetall Denel Munition (Pty.) Ltd. (1)
Reeb Road Firgrove
Somerset West, Cape Town, 7130, South Africa
Tel.: (27) 21 850 2911
Fax: (27) 21 850 2011
E-Mail: marketing@rheinmetall-denelmunition.com
Emp.: 700
Ammunition Mfr
S.I.C.: 3483
N.A.I.C.S.: 332993
Norbert Shculze *(Gen Mgr)*

DENHAM FORD SALES LTD.

45th Avenue & 56th Street
Wetaskiwin, AB, T9A 2G2, Canada
Tel.: (780) 352-6043
Fax: (780) 352-0986
Toll Free: (800) 232-7255
Web Site: www.denhamford.com
Year Founded: 1960
Rev.: $40,435,200
Emp.: 55
Business Description:
New & Used Car Dealers
S.I.C.: 5511
N.A.I.C.S.: 441110
Personnel:
John Denham *(Founder & Pres)*

DENIR

ZA Les Crozes
26270 Loriol-sur-Drome, Drome, France
Tel.: (33) 475611320
Fax: (33) 475611333
Sls.: $44,800,000
Emp.: 50
Business Description:
Building Materials Sales
S.I.C.: 5211
N.A.I.C.S.: 444190
Personnel:
Christian Delaye *(Personnel Dir)*

DENISON MINES CORP.

Atrium on Bay 595 Bay Street Suite 402
Toronto, ON, M5G 2C2, Canada
Tel.: (416) 979-1991
Fax: (416) 979-5893
E-Mail: info@denisonmines.com
Web Site: www.denisonmines.com
DNN—(NYSEMKT TSX)
Rev.: $10,407,000
Assets: $330,969,000
Liabilities: $53,829,000
Net Worth: $277,140,000
Earnings: ($83,835,000)
Emp.: 130
Fiscal Year-end: 12/31/13
Business Description:
Uranium Exploration & Mining Services
S.I.C.: 1094
N.A.I.C.S.: 212291
Personnel:
Lukas H. Lundin *(Chm)*
Ronald F. Hochstein *(Pres & CEO)*
David D. Cates *(CFO & VP-Fin & Tax)*
Sheila Colman *(Corp Counsel & Sec)*
Board of Directors:
Lukas H. Lundin
John Hunter Craig
W. Robert Dengler
Brian D. Edgar
Ronald F. Hochstein
Tae-hwan Kim
William A. Rand
Catherine J.G. Stefan
Transfer Agent:
Computershare Investor Services Inc.
100 University Ave 9th Floor
Toronto, ON, Canada

Branch:

Denison Mines Corp. - Vancouver Office (1)
885 West Georgia Street Suite 2000
Vancouver, BC, V6C 3E8, Canada
Tel.: (604) 689-7842
Fax: (604) 689-4250
Toll Free: (888) 689-7842
E-Mail: info@denisonmines.com
Web Site: www.denisonmines.com
Emp.: 40
Uranium Exploration & Mining Services
S.I.C.: 1094
N.A.I.C.S.: 212291
Sheila Colman *(Corp Counsel & Sec)*

U.S. Subsidiary:

Denison Services USA Corp. (1)
445 Union Blvd Ste 121
Lakewood, CO 80228 CO
Tel.: (303) 658-0775
Web Site: www.denisonmines.com
Uranium Exploration & Mining Services
S.I.C.: 1081
N.A.I.C.S.: 213114
Terry V. Wetz *(Grp VP-Project Dev)*

DENKI KAGAKU KOGYO KABUSHIKI KAISHA

(d/b/a DENKA Group)
Nihonbashi Mitsui Tower
2-1-1 Nihonbashi Muromachi
Chuo-ku, Tokyo, 103-8338, Japan
Tel.: (81) 352905055
Telex: 22647
Fax: (81) 352905059
Web Site: www.denka.co.jp
Year Founded: 1915
4061—(TKS)
Sales Range: $1-4.9 Billion
Emp.: 2,800
Business Description:
Chemical Products Mfr
S.I.C.: 2869
N.A.I.C.S.: 325199
Personnel:
Shinsuke Yoshitaka *(Pres & CEO)*
Tetsuro Maeda *(COO)*
Mamoru Hoshi *(Sr Exec Officer)*
Koji Minai *(Sr Mng Exec Officer)*
Kenichi Ono *(Sr Exec Officer)*
Noboyoshi Sakuma *(Sr Exec Officer)*
Shigetoshi Toyooka *(Mng Exec Officer)*
Daiichiro Uematsu *(Sr Exec Officer)*
Hitoshi Watanabe *(Sr Exec Officer)*
Board of Directors:
Tadasu Horikoshi
Mamoru Hoshi
Tetsuro Maeda
Koji Minai
Kenichi Ono
Kozo Tanaka
Shigetoshi Toyooka
Shinsuke Yoshitaka

Subsidiaries:

Denka Seiken Co., Ltd. (1)
3-4-2 Nihonbashi Kayabacho Chuo-ku
Tokyo, 103-0025, Japan (100%)
Tel.: (81) 336699091
Fax: (81) 33699390
E-Mail: seiken@denka-seiken.co.jp
Web Site: www.denka-seiken.co.jp
4561—(JAS)
Sales Range: $100-124.9 Million
Emp.: 377
Human Vaccines & Diagnostic Reagents Mfr, Importer, Exporter & Marketer
S.I.C.: 2835
N.A.I.C.S.: 325413
Kevin Mangan *(Gen Mgr-DENKA SEIKEN USA Inc)*

Non-U.S. Subsidiary:

Denka Seiken UK Limited (2)
The Yard The Square Oakthorpe
Swadlincote, Derbyshire, DE12 7QY, United Kingdom
Tel.: (44) 530270010
Fax: (44) 1530 272009
Pharmaceutical Sales & Distr
S.I.C.: 5912
N.A.I.C.S.: 446110

Hissan Trading Co., Ltd. (1)
14th Floor B Wing Shiba Park Building 2 4 1 Shiba koen
Minato-ku, Tokyo, 105-8568, Japan
Tel.: (81) 3 5405 6105
Fax: (81) 3 5405 6106
Web Site: www.hissan.co.jp
Chemical Products Mfr
S.I.C.: 2899
N.A.I.C.S.: 325199

Toyo Adtec Co., Ltd. (1)
6-16-12 Ginza
Chuo-Ku, Tokyo, Japan
Tel.: (81) 335421331
Fax: (81) 351481682

Web Site: www.toyo-adtec.co.jp
Semiconductor Equipment Import & Distr
S.I.C.: 5065
N.A.I.C.S.: 423690
Manabu Yamamoto *(Pres)*
Tetsuya Tsushima *(Gen Dir-Sls Div)*

U.S. Subsidiary:

Denka Corporation (1)
780 3rd Ave 15th Fl
New York, NY 10017
Tel.: (212) 688-8700
Fax: (212) 688-8727
E-Mail: info@denkany.com
Web Site: www.denka.co.jp/eng/html/co_05.html
Emp.: 6
Chemical & Allied Products Merchant Whslr
S.I.C.: 5169
N.A.I.C.S.: 424690

Non-U.S. Subsidiaries:

Denka Advanced Materials (Suzhou) Co. Ltd. (1)
Unit 9B Modern Indus Sq
No 333 Xingpu Rd Suzhou Indu, Suzhou, China
Tel.: (86) 51262871088
Fax: (86) 51262871066
E-Mail: ttsushima@denka.com.cn
Web Site: www.denka.co.jp/eng/html/co_05.html
Emp.: 60
Organic Chemical Mfr
S.I.C.: 2869
N.A.I.C.S.: 325199
Kamioka Masaki *(Gen Mgr)*

Denka Advantech Private Limited (1)
4 Shenton Way 29-02 SGX Centre 2
068807 Singapore, Singapore
Tel.: (65) 68610004
Fax: (65) 62243840
Web Site: www.dspl.com.sg
Emp.: 150
Organic Chemical Mfr
S.I.C.: 2869
N.A.I.C.S.: 325199
Masaharu Suzuki *(Mng Dir)*

Denka Chemicals GmbH (1)
Wehrhahn-Center Cantadorstr 3
40211 Dusseldorf, Germany
Tel.: (49) 211130990
Fax: (49) 211329942
E-Mail: info@denkagermany.de
Web Site: www.denka.co.jp/eng/html/co_05.html
Emp.: 8
Industrial Supplies Whslr
S.I.C.: 5085
N.A.I.C.S.: 423840
Koyama Tatsuya *(Mng Dir)*

Denka Chemicals Holdings Asia Pacific Pte. Ltd (1)
4 Shenton Way Unit 21-29-02 SGX Ctr 2
068807 Singapore, Singapore
Tel.: (65) 62241305
Fax: (65) 62243840
Web Site: www.denka.co.jp/eng/sitemap/index.htm
Emp.: 20
Chemical Products Mfr
S.I.C.: 2899
N.A.I.C.S.: 325998
Masaharu Suzuki *(Chm)*

Denka Chemicals Hong Kong Ltd. (1)
Unit 1010 East Wing Tsim Sha Tsui Centre
66 Mody Rd
1 Science Museum Road, Kowloon, China (Hong Kong)
Tel.: (852) 36918636
Fax: (852) 3527 0604
Industrial Supplies Whslr
S.I.C.: 5085
N.A.I.C.S.: 423840

Denka Chemicals Shanghai Co., Ltd. (1)
Room 3308 New Hongqiao Center Bldg
No:83 Loushanguan Rd, Shanghai, 200336, China
Tel.: (86) 2162369090
Fax: (86) 21 62 36 8770
Web Site: www.denka.se/eng/html/co_f05.html
Industrial Supplies Whslr
S.I.C.: 5085
N.A.I.C.S.: 423840

Denka Singapore Private Limited (1)
Hong Leong Building 16 Raffles Quay #18-03
048581 Singapore, Singapore
Tel.: (65) 62241305
Fax: (65) 62243840
Web Site: www.denka.com.sg
Industrial Gas Mfr
S.I.C.: 2813
N.A.I.C.S.: 325120
Mitsukuni Ayabe *(Mng Dir)*

DENKI KOGYO CO., LTD.

Shin-Tokyo Building 7th Floor 3-3-1 Marunouchi
Chiyoda-ku, Tokyo, 100-0005, Japan
Tel.: (81) 332161671
Fax: (81) 332161669
Web Site: www.denkikogyo.co.jp
67060—(TKS)
Sls.: $449,559,000
Earnings: $16,456,000
Emp.: 507
Fiscal Year-end: 03/31/13

Business Description:
Communication Equipment Mfr
S.I.C.: 3669
N.A.I.C.S.: 334290

Personnel:
Mikio Matsuzawa *(Pres)*
Takashi Fujisaku *(Sr Exec Mng Officer)*
Atsushi Hasegawa *(Mng Officer)*
Katsuaki Kasai *(Sr Exec Mng Officer)*
Toshikazu Makino *(Mng Officer)*
Kazunori Nonaka *(Mng Officer)*
Tsuyoshi Shimodo *(Mng Officer)*
Masami Yamaguchi *(Mng Officer)*

Board of Directors:
Takashi Fujisaku
Atsushi Hasegawa
Katsuaki Kasai
Toshikazu Makino
Mikio Matsuzawa
Kazunori Nonaka
Yo Ota
Tsuyoshi Shimodo
Shuichi Shindo
Masami Yamaguchi

Transfer Agent:
The Chuo Mitsui Trust & Banking Company Limited
3-33-1 Shiba Minato-ku
Tokyo, Japan

Subsidiaries:

Denko Co., Ltd. (1)
2-8-76 Yoshinodai
Kawagoe, Saitama, 350-0833, Japan
Tel.: (81) 49 225 5100
Web Site: www.denkikogyo.co.jp/en/corporate/company.html
Steel Tower Mfr & Distr
S.I.C.: 3441
N.A.I.C.S.: 332312

Denko Seisakusho Co., Ltd. (1)
637-1 Moro
Kanuma, Tochigi, 322-0026, Japan
Tel.: (81) 289 76 2258
Web Site: www.denkikogyo.co.jp/en/corporate/company.html
Antenna Peripheral Equipment Mfr
S.I.C.: 3663
N.A.I.C.S.: 334220

DKC Co., Ltd. (1)
1-1-1 Nishi Tsurugaoka
Fujimino, Saitama, 356-0044, Japan
Tel.: (81) 49 262 3113
Telecommunication & Engineering Services
S.I.C.: 4899
N.A.I.C.S.: 517919

Fukoku Denko Co., Ltd. (1)
1-15-8 Sanno
Hakata-ku, Fukuoka, 812-0015, Japan
Tel.: (81) 92 452 5311
Web Site: www.fukokud.co.jp
Telecommunication Equipment Distr
S.I.C.: 5065
N.A.I.C.S.: 423690

Koshuha Co., Ltd. (1)
4052-1 Nakatsu
Aikou Gun, Aikawa, Kanagawa, Japan 243-0303
Tel.: (81) 46 286 8175
Fax: (81) 46 286 1065
Web Site: www.e-kkk.jp/outline/index_e.html
Emp.: 200
Induction Heating Equipment Mfr
S.I.C.: 3567
N.A.I.C.S.: 333994
Atsushi Hasegawa *(Pres)*

Plants:

Denki Kogyo Co., Ltd. - Atsugi Plant (1)
Nairiku Industrial Park 4052-1 Nakatsu
Aikawa-machi
Aiko-gun, Koza, 243-0303, Japan
Tel.: (81) 46 285 1411
Fax: (81) 46 285 2298
Web Site: www.denkikogyo.co.jp/en/corporate/atsugi.html
Induction Heating Equipment Mfr
S.I.C.: 3567
N.A.I.C.S.: 333994

Denki Kogyo Co., Ltd. - Kanuma Plant (1)
Kanuma Industrial Park 13-4 Satsuki-cho
Kanuma, Tochigi, 322-0014, Japan
Tel.: (81) 289 76 2275
Fax: (81) 289 72 1522
Web Site: www.denkikogyo.co.jp/en/corporate/kanuma.html
Telecommunication Antenna Mfr
S.I.C.: 3663
N.A.I.C.S.: 334220

Denki Kogyo Co., Ltd. - Kawagoe Plant (1)
2-8-76 Yoshinodai
Kawagoe, Saitama, 350-0833, Japan
Tel.: (81) 49 225 5100
Fax: (81) 49 229 1253
Web Site: www.denkikogyo.co.jp/en/corporate/kawagoe_f.html
Emp.: 50
Telecommunication Steel Tower Mfr
S.I.C.: 3441
N.A.I.C.S.: 332312
Shuichi Shindo *(Mng Dir)*

Denki Kogyo Co., Ltd. - Suzuka Plant (1)
1820-39 Mikkaichi-cho
Suzuka, Mie, 513-0803, Japan
Tel.: (81) 59 382 1829
Induction Heating Equipment Mfr
S.I.C.: 3567
N.A.I.C.S.: 333994

Denko Techno Heat Co., Ltd. - Hamamatsu Plant (1)
170 Tsumori-cho
Minami-ku, Hamamatsu, Shizuoka, 430-0815, Japan
Tel.: (81) 53 441 8451
Fax: (81) 53 441 8896
Web Site: www.denkikogyo.co.jp/en/corporate/company.html
Induction Heating Equipment Mfr
S.I.C.: 3567
N.A.I.C.S.: 333994

U.S. Subsidiary:

DKK of America, Inc. (1)
6345 S Inwood Dr
Columbus, IN 47201
Tel.: (812) 342-1700
Fax: (812) 342-1600
Web Site: www.dkkusa.com
Induction Heating Equipment Mfr
S.I.C.: 3567
N.A.I.C.S.: 333994

Non-U.S. Subsidiary:

DKK (THAILAND) Co., Ltd. (1)
151/6-9 Moo 6 Lam Ta Sao Sub-District
Wang Noi District, Phra Nakhon Si Ayutthaya, 13170, Thailand
Tel.: (66) 35 272 325
E-Mail: dse@dkksinothai.com
Web Site: www.denkikogyo.co.jp/en/business/hf/network/global.html
Induction Heating Equipment Mfr
S.I.C.: 3567
N.A.I.C.S.: 333994

DENKIRO SERVICE CO., LTD.

Shimizu Bldg 3f
Chiyoda-Ku, Tokyo, 101 0033, Japan
Tel.: (81) 332545626
Web Site: www.denkiro.co.jp

Business Description:
Industrial Furnace Mfr
S.I.C.: 3567
N.A.I.C.S.: 333994

Subsidiary:

Yamazaki Denki Co., Ltd. (1)
123 Koyama Sakado
Saitama, 350 0257, Japan
Tel.: (81) 492833511
Fax: (81) 492833520
E-Mail: ydk@yamazaki-denki.co.jp
Web Site: www.yamazaki-denki.co.jp
Emp.: 60
Electric Furnaces Mfr
S.I.C.: 3567
N.A.I.C.S.: 333994
Kazuo Yoshida *(Pres)*

DENKO INDUSTRIAL CORPORATION BERHAD

No 20 Jalan Hasil Dua Kawasan Perindustrian Jalan Hasil
Tampoi
81200 Johor Bahru, Johor, Malaysia
Tel.: (60) 72385888
Fax: (60) 72389993
E-Mail: enquiry@denko.com.my
Web Site: www.denko.com.my
DENKO—(KLS)
Sales Range: $25-49.9 Million

Business Description:
Industrial Products Mfr
S.I.C.: 3823
N.A.I.C.S.: 334513

Personnel:
Boon Cheong Yong *(Chm & Mng Dir)*
Michelle Mui Lean Siow *(Grp CFO)*
Chee Yin Wong *(Co-Sec)*
Min Fong Wong *(Co-Sec)*
Wai Bing Yap *(Co-Sec)*

Board of Directors:
Boon Cheong Yong
Hut Hoo Chong
Yan Teo Huang
Thoolasy Das Ponniah
Kok Swee Teoh

Subsidiaries:

Lean Teik Soon Sdn. Bhd. (1)
No 1589 Lorong Perusahaan Utama 2 Plot P 112B MK 11
14000 Bukit Mertajam, Penang, Malaysia
Tel.: (60) 45072288
Fax: (60) 45079288
E-Mail: sales@leanteiksoon.com.my
Emp.: 27
Convenience Foods Mfr
S.I.C.: 2043
N.A.I.C.S.: 311230
Siak Keng Ng *(CEO)*
Michelle Mui Lean Siow *(CFO)*

Winsheng Plastic Industry Sdn. Bhd. (1)
No 16 Jalan Hasil Dua Kawasan Perindustrian Jalan Hasil
Tampoi, 81200 Johor Bahru, Johor, Malaysia
Tel.: (60) 72385888
Fax: (60) 70233333
Web Site: www.winsheng.com.my
Emp.: 910
Plastic Components Mfr
S.I.C.: 2389
N.A.I.C.S.: 316210

Denko Industrial Corporation Berhad—(Continued)

Yong Boon Cheong *(CEO)*
Michelle Mui Lean Siow *(CFO)*
Liew Young Choong *(COO)*

DENNIS JONSSON MOTOR PRODUCTS LTD.

(See Under Pacific Chevrolet Buick GMC Ltd)

DENNIS PUBLISHING LTD.

30 Cleveland St
London, W1T 4JD, United Kingdom
Tel.: (44) 2079076000
Fax: (44) 2079076020
E-Mail: theboard@dennis.co.uk
Web Site: www.dennis.co.uk
Year Founded: 1974
Emp.: 350
Business Description:
Magazine Publisher & Website Operator
S.I.C.: 2721
N.A.I.C.S.: 511120
Personnel:
Felix Dennis *(Founder & Chm)*
James Tye *(CEO)*
Brett Reynolds *(COO)*
Paul Lomax *(CTO)*
Board of Directors:
Felix Dennis
Ian Leggett
Julian Lloyd-Evans
Kerin O'Connor
Dick Pountain
Alistair Ramsay
Brett Reynolds
James Tye
Ian Westwood
Pete Wootton
Subsidiary:

The Week Ltd. (1)
6th Fl Compass 22 Redan Pl
London, W2 4SA, United Kingdom
Tel.: (44) 2079076180
Fax: (44) 2070340478
E-Mail: editorialadmin@theweek.co.uk
Web Site: www.theweek.co.uk
Emp.: 15
Weekly Magazine Publisher
S.I.C.: 2721
N.A.I.C.S.: 511120
Jolyon Connell *(Founder & Dir-Editorial)*
Jessica Sibley *(Publr)*

DENNY ANDREWS FORD SALES INC.

18208 Stony Plain Road
Edmonton, AB, T5S 1A7, Canada
Tel.: (780) 489-9999
Fax: (780) 930-3191
Toll Free: (800) 252-9303
Web Site: www.dennyandrewsford.com
Rev.: $95,204,720
Emp.: 180
Business Description:
New & Used Car Dealers
S.I.C.: 5511
N.A.I.C.S.: 441110
Personnel:
Dan Wagner *(Controller)*

DENSAN CO., LTD.

451 Minaminagano Agata-Machi
Nagano, 380-0838, Japan
Tel.: (81) 26 234 0151
Fax: (81) 26 233 1139
Web Site: www.ndensan.co.jp
Year Founded: 1966
3640—(TKS)
Sales Range: $125-149.9 Million
Emp.: 730
Business Description:
Data Processing Services
S.I.C.: 7379
N.A.I.C.S.: 518210
Personnel:
Noriyasu Kurosaka *(Pres)*

DENSAN SYSTEM CO., LTD.

1-58 Hikie
Gifu-shi, Gifu, 501-6196, Japan
Tel.: (81) 582793456
Fax: (81) 582795848
E-Mail: info@densan-s.co.jp
Web Site: www.densan-s.co.jp
Year Founded: 1967
3630—(NGO TKS)
Sls.: $257,059,000
Assets: $264,121,000
Liabilities: $195,844,000
Net Worth: $68,277,000
Earnings: $5,676,000
Emp.: 671
Fiscal Year-end: 12/31/12
Business Description:
Computer System Integration & Data Services
S.I.C.: 7373
N.A.I.C.S.: 541512
Personnel:
Masanao Miyachi *(Chm & CEO)*
Yasunori Tanaka *(Pres & COO)*
Yuichi Asano *(Exec Officer)*
Board of Directors:
Masanao Miyachi
Yuichi Asano
Yasunori Tanaka
Subsidiaries:

NetWork And System Fabricative Agency Inc. (1)
Meisan Shinkawa City Building 9th Floor
Shinakawa Chuo-ku, Tokyo, 104-0033, Japan
Tel.: (81) 3 3537 6980
E-Mail: info@neasf.co.jp
Web Site: www.neasf.co.jp
Computer System Maintenance Services
S.I.C.: 7699
N.A.I.C.S.: 811212
Toshihiko Imai *(Pres)*

System Ic Co., Ltd. (1)
1-58 Hikie
Gifu, 501-6133, Japan
Tel.: (81) 58 270 0270
Fax: (81) 58 279 2266
E-Mail: info@system-ic.co.jp
Web Site: www.system-ic.co.jp
Software Development Services
S.I.C.: 7371
N.A.I.C.S.: 541511

DENSITRON TECHNOLOGIES PLC

4th Floor 72 Cannon Street
London, EC4N 6AE, United Kingdom
Tel.: (44) 2076484200
Fax: (44) 2076484201
E-Mail: sales@densitron.co.uk
Web Site: www.densitron.com
Year Founded: 1985
DSN—(LSE)
Rev.: $35,710,905
Assets: $15,012,731
Liabilities: $9,068,283
Net Worth: $5,944,448
Earnings: $385,347
Emp.: 64
Fiscal Year-end: 12/31/12
Business Description:
Designer & Mfr of Information Display Systems
S.I.C.: 3577
N.A.I.C.S.: 334118
Personnel:
Grahame R. Falconer *(CEO)*
Tim Pearson *(Sec & Dir-Fin)*
Board of Directors:
Jan Gustav Lennart Holmstrom
Grahame R. Falconer
John Farrell
Richard Lane
Tim Pearson
Legal Counsel:
K&L Gates LLP
One New Change
London, United Kingdom
Subsidiary:

Densitron Europe Ltd. (1)
72 Cannon St 4th Floor
London, EC4N 6AE, United Kingdom
Tel.: (44) 2076484200
Fax: (44) 2076484201
E-Mail: sales@densitron.co.uk
Web Site: www.densitron.co.uk
Emp.: 15
Information Display Systems Designer, Mfr & Marketer
S.I.C.: 3577
N.A.I.C.S.: 334118
Grahame R. Falconer *(Mng Dir)*

U.S. Subsidiary:

Densitron Corporation (1)
2330 Pomona Rincon Rd
Corona, CA 92880
Tel.: (951) 284-7600
Fax: (951) 284-7699
E-Mail: dcawebsales@densitron.com
Web Site: www.densitron.com
Information Display Systems Design & Marketing
S.I.C.: 5045
N.A.I.C.S.: 423430
Gregory Hayes *(Pres)*

Non-U.S. Subsidiaries:

Densitron Asia Ltd. (1)
5F No 77 Section 1 Sintai 5th Road
Sijhih, Taipei, Taiwan
Tel.: (886) 226981266
Fax: (886) 226982236
E-Mail: sales@densitron.com.tw
Web Site: www.densitron.com.tw
Emp.: 8
Information Display Systems Sales & Customer Support Services
S.I.C.: 5045
N.A.I.C.S.: 423430
Vincent Lin *(Gen Mgr)*

Densitron Corporation (1)
K2 Building 6F 3-4-4 Omori-Kita
Ota-ku, Tokyo, 143 0016, Japan
Tel.: (81) 337679701
Fax: (81) 337679709
E-Mail: sales@densitron.co.jp
Web Site: www.densitron.co.jp
Information Display Systems Sales & Customer Support Services
S.I.C.: 5045
N.A.I.C.S.: 423430
Takashi Kashiwagi *(Mng Dir)*

Densitron Deutschland GmbH (1)
Airport Business Centre
Am Soldnermoos 17, 85399 Hallbergmoos, Germany
Tel.: (49) 8115505949
Fax: (49) 8115505972
E-Mail: info@densitron.de
Web Site: www.densitron.de
Emp.: 5
Information Display Systems Sales & Customer Support Services
S.I.C.: 5045
N.A.I.C.S.: 423430
Grahame R. Falconer *(Mng Dir)*

Densitron Frances SA (1)
24 rue de L'atlantique
44115 Basse-Goulaine, France
Tel.: (33) 251710158
Fax: (33) 251713452
E-Mail: france.sales@densitron.fr
Web Site: www.densitron.com
Emp.: 5
Information Display Systems Sales & Customer Support Services
S.I.C.: 5045
N.A.I.C.S.: 423430
Christophe Desage *(Dir-Sls)*

Densitron Nordic Oy (1)
Niittylantie 5
00620 Helsinki, Finland
Tel.: (358) 927093010
Fax: (358) 97544300
E-Mail: sales@densitron.fi
Web Site: www.densitron.fi
Emp.: 10
Information Display Systems Sales & Customer Support Services
S.I.C.: 5045
N.A.I.C.S.: 423430
Jukka-Pekka Paakkonen *(Mng Dir)*

DENSO CORPORATION

1-1 Showa-cho
Kariya, Aichi, 488-8661, Japan
Tel.: (81) 566255511
Web Site: www.denso.co.jp/ja/
Year Founded: 1949
6902—(OTC TKS)
Sls.: $39,390,153,000
Assets: $43,770,023,000
Liabilities: $17,074,552,000
Net Worth: $26,695,471,000
Earnings: $1,998,502,000
Emp.: 132,276
Fiscal Year-end: 03/31/13
Business Description:
Advanced Automotive Technologies, Systems & Components
Import Export
S.I.C.: 3714
N.A.I.C.S.: 336390
Personnel:
Nobuaki Katoh *(Pres & CEO)*
Koji Arima *(Mng Officer)*
Jiro Ebihara *(Mng Officer)*
Kazuaki Fujitani *(Mng Officer)*
Yasuhiro Iida *(Mng Officer)*
Hiroyuki Ina *(Mng Officer)*
Kenichiro Ito *(Mng Officer)*
Masahiko Ito *(Mng Officer)*
Yoshitaka Kajita *(Mng Officer)*
Kenichiro Kamai *(Mng Officer)*
Toshiyuki Kato *(Mng Officer)*
Yoshifumi Kato *(Mng Officer)*
Yukihiro Kato *(Mng Officer)*
Kazumasa Kimura *(Mng Officer)*
Bunichi Kondo *(Mng Officer)*
Shingo Kuwamura *(Mng Officer)*
Yoshikazu Makino *(Mng Officer)*
Hideaki Matsuki *(Mng Officer)*
Masanari Murakami *(Mng Officer)*
Yukihiko Murakami *(Mng Officer)*
Manfredo Nicolelli *(Mng Officer)*
Hiroaki Okuchi *(Mng Officer)*
Katsuhisa Shimokawa *(Mng Officer)*
Yukihiro Shinohara *(Mng Officer)*
Tatsuya Toyoda *(Mng Officer)*
Masanori Tsuruta *(Mng Officer)*
Shoji Tsuzuki *(Mng Officer)*
Sadahiro Usui *(Mng Officer)*
Noboru Yamada *(Mng Officer)*
Shinsuke Yamaguchi *(Mng Officer)*
Yasushi Yamanaka *(Mng Officer)*
Koji Kobayashi *(Exec VP)*
Masahiko Miyaki *(Exec VP)*
Hikaru Sugi *(Exec VP)*
Hiromi Tokuda *(Exec VP)*
Board of Directors:
Michio Adachi
Kazuo Hironaka
Satoshi Iwata
Nobuaki Katoh
Koji Kobayashi
Haruya Maruyama
Masahiko Miyaki
Akio Shikamura
Shinji Shirasaki
Hikaru Sugi
Akio Tajima
Hiromi Tokuda
Shoichiro Toyoda
Hiroyuki Wakabayashi

Transfer Agent:
Mitsubishi UFJ Trust & Banking Corporation
4-5 Marunouchi 1-Chome Chiyoda-ku
Tokyo, 100-8212, Japan
Tel.: (81) 3 3212 1211

Subsidiaries:

ANDEN CO., LTD. **(1)**
1-10 Sasamecho
Anjo, Aichi, 446-0073, Japan
Tel.: (81) 566730022
Fax: (81) 566730029
Web Site: www.anden.jp
Emp.: 1,516
Electronic Products Mfr & Distr
S.I.C.: 3679
N.A.I.C.S.: 334419

ASAHI MANUFACTURING CO., LTD. **(1)**
5-120 Toshincho
Kariya, Aichi, 448-0031, Japan
Tel.: (81) 566 21 5861
Fax: (81) 566 21 5867
Web Site: www.kk-asahi-ss.co.jp
Wiper Linkage Mfr
S.I.C.: 3714
N.A.I.C.S.: 336390

ASMO CO., LTD **(1)**
390 Umeda
Kosai, Shizuoka, 431-0493, Japan
Tel.: (81) 535723311
Fax: (81) 535723575
E-Mail: saiyo-postbox@asmo.co.jp
Web Site: www.asmo.co.jp
Sls.: $3,343,968,000
Emp.: 11,792
Automobile Motor System Mfr & Distr
S.I.C.: 3714
N.A.I.C.S.: 336390
Kenji Ohya *(Pres)*

DAISHINSEIKI CO., LTD. **(1)**
200 Ohayashi Kume
Tokoname, Aichi, 479-0002, Japan
Tel.: (81) 569440077
Fax: (81) 569440088
E-Mail: jinji@daishinseiki.co.jp
Web Site: www.daishinseiki.co.jp
Emp.: 745
Fuel Injection System Mfr
S.I.C.: 3714
N.A.I.C.S.: 336310

DENSO ABASHIRI TEST CENTER CORPORATION **(1)**
708 Katayama
Abashiri, Hokkaido, 093-0133, Japan
Tel.: (81) 152 61 8700
Fax: (81) 152 61 8713
Emp.: 7
Product Testing Services
S.I.C.: 8734
N.A.I.C.S.: 541380

DENSO ACE CORPORATION **(1)**
2-15-13 Shoto Denso Shibuya Bldg 4f
Shibuya-Ku, Tokyo, 150-0046, Japan
Tel.: (81) 363673810
Fax: (81) 363673820
Web Site: www.denso-ace.com
Emp.: 99
Air Conditioner Distr
S.I.C.: 5075
N.A.I.C.S.: 423730

DENSO AIR SYSTEMS CORPORATION **(1)**
89-8 Hoden Noderacho
Anjo, Aichi, 444-1165, Japan
Tel.: (81) 566 99 0101
Fax: (81) 566 99 4641
Emp.: 983
Air Conditioning Parts Mfr
S.I.C.: 3822
N.A.I.C.S.: 334512

U.S. Subsidiary:

DENSO AIR SYSTEMS MICHIGAN, INC. **(2)**
300 Fritz Keiper Blvd
Battle Creek, MI 49037
Tel.: (269) 962-9676
Fax: (269) 962-4975
E-Mail: info@denso-asmi.com
Web Site: www.denso-asmi.com
Emp.: 229
Automotive Air Conditioning Parts Mfr
S.I.C.: 3585
N.A.I.C.S.: 333415
Jerry McGuire *(Pres)*
Katsuaki Kawai *(Exec VP)*

DENSO AIR SYSTEMS TOYOSHINA CORPORATION **(1)**
1086-1 Toyoshinatakibe
Azumino, Nagano, 399-8204, Japan
Tel.: (81) 263 72 8870
Fax: (81) 263 71 1051
Emp.: 137
Automotive Air Conditioner Mfr
S.I.C.: 3585
N.A.I.C.S.: 333415

DENSO AIR SYSTEMS YASAKA CORPORATION **(1)**
707 Yasaka
Omachi, Nagano, 399-7301, Japan
Tel.: (81) 261 26 2007
Fax: (81) 261 26 2006
Emp.: 57
Automotive Air Conditioning Parts Mfr
S.I.C.: 3714
N.A.I.C.S.: 336390

DENSO CHUBU CORPORATION **(1)**
4-30 Hoshocho
Minami-ku, Nagoya, Aichi, 457-0828, Japan
Tel.: (81) 526191777
Fax: (81) 526191425
Web Site: www.denso-sales.co.jp
Emp.: 346
Automotive Repair & Maintenance Services
S.I.C.: 7539
N.A.I.C.S.: 811198
Masaki Takashima *(Mng Dir)*

DENSO CHUGOKU CORPORATION **(1)**
4-21 Higashihiratsukacho
Naka-Ku, Hiroshima, 730-0025, Japan
Tel.: (81) 822425210
E-Mail: info@denso-chugoku.com
Web Site: www.denso-chugoku.com
Emp.: 84
Automotive Distr & Repair Services
S.I.C.: 5012
N.A.I.C.S.: 423110

DENSO COMMUNICATIONS CORPORATION **(1)**
1-1 Showa-cho
Kariya, Aichi, Japan
Tel.: (81) 566 25 6447
Fax: (81) 566 28 4158
E-Mail: contact@d-coms.co.jp
Web Site: www.d-coms.co.jp
Emp.: 5
Travel Information Services
S.I.C.: 4729
N.A.I.C.S.: 561599

DENSO CREATE INC. **(1)**
3-1-1 Sakae
Naka-Ku, Nagoya, 460-0008, Japan
Tel.: (81) 522380460
Fax: (81) 522380461
Web Site: www.denso-create.jp
Emp.: 208
Software Development Services
S.I.C.: 7371
N.A.I.C.S.: 541511

DENSO E & TS TRAINING CENTER CORPORATION **(1)**
1 Shinmichi Takatana-cho
Anjo, Aichi, 446-8507, Japan
Tel.: (81) 566 73 2612
Fax: (81) 566 73 2965
E-Mail: denso-ets@denso.co.jp
Web Site: www.denso-ets.com
Emp.: 174
Industrial Training Services
S.I.C.: 8299
N.A.I.C.S.: 611430
Koichi Hagino *(Pres)*

DENSO ELECTRONICS CORPORATION **(1)**
1007-195 Izumisawa
Chitose, Hokkaido, 066-0051, Japan
Tel.: (81) 123 47 8800
Fax: (81) 123 48 5200
Web Site: www.denso-electronics.co.jp
Emp.: 298
Automotive Semiconductor Product Mfr
S.I.C.: 3674
N.A.I.C.S.: 334413

DENSO EMC ENGINEERING SERVICE CORPORATION **(1)**
1-1 Showa-cho
Kariya, Aichi, 448-8661, Japan
Tel.: (81) 566 63 1873
Fax: (81) 566 25 4813
E-Mail: info@emces.co.jp
Web Site: www.emces.co.jp
Emp.: 52
Electromagnetic Compatibility Testing Services
S.I.C.: 8734
N.A.I.C.S.: 541380

DENSO FACILITIES CORPORATION **(1)**
2-1 Marutacho
Kariya, Aichi, 448-0033, Japan
Tel.: (81) 566 25 7511
Fax: (81) 566 25 4531
Web Site: www.densofacilities.co.jp
Emp.: 504
Power Plant Construction & Management Services
S.I.C.: 1623
N.A.I.C.S.: 237130

DENSO FINANCE & ACCOUNTING CENTER CO., LTD. **(1)**
1-1 Showacho Kk Denso Honshanai
Kariya, Aichi, 448-0029, Japan
Tel.: (81) 566 25 6775
Fax: (81) 566 25 4538
Emp.: 9
Financial Management Services
S.I.C.: 6211
N.A.I.C.S.: 523999

DENSO HOKKAIDO CORPORATION **(1)**
7-2-27 2jo Yamanote
Nishi-Ku, Sapporo, Hokkaido, 063-0002, Japan
Tel.: (81) 11 614 3511
Fax: (81) 11 614 3522
Emp.: 156
Automotive Repair & Maintenance Services
S.I.C.: 7539
N.A.I.C.S.: 811198

Denso IT Laboratory, Inc. **(1)**
Shibuya Cross Tower 28th Floor 2 15 1 Shibuya
Shibuya ku, Tokyo, 150-0002, Japan (100%)
Tel.: (81) 364192300
Fax: (81) 364192319
Web Site: www.d-itlab.co.jp
IT Services
S.I.C.: 7379
N.A.I.C.S.: 541519
Takeshi Matsui *(Pres)*

DENSO IT SOLUTIONS CORPORATION **(1)**
1-2-7 Sasashimacho
Nakamura-ku, Nagoya, Aichi, 450-0003, Japan
Tel.: (81) 566 25 5600
Fax: (81) 566 25 4558
Web Site: www.dnitsol.com
Emp.: 322
Information Technology Consulting Services
S.I.C.: 7373
N.A.I.C.S.: 541512

DENSO KANSAI CORPORATION **(1)**
1-7-19 Higashitemma Denso Osaka Shiten 3f
Kita-Ku, Osaka, 530-0044, Japan
Tel.: (81) 6 6355 3800
Fax: (81) 6 6355 3899
Web Site: www.denso-kansai.com
Emp.: 147
Automotive Repair Services
S.I.C.: 7539
N.A.I.C.S.: 811198

DENSO KATSUYAMA CO., LTD. **(1)**
220 Sanden
Maniwa, Okayama, 717-0022, Japan
Tel.: (81) 867 44 2653
Fax: (81) 867 44 2654
Emp.: 157
Molded Plastic Product Mfr
S.I.C.: 3089
N.A.I.C.S.: 326199

DENSO KIKO CO., LTD. **(1)**
5-1-5 Shindencho
Takahama, Aichi, 444-1301, Japan
Tel.: (81) 566 53 5115
Fax: (81) 566 53 5112
Web Site: www.denso-kiko.co.jp
Emp.: 196
Car Air Conditioning Prototype Mfr
S.I.C.: 3714
N.A.I.C.S.: 336390

DENSO KYUSHU CORPORATION **(1)**
2-6-35 Sanno
Hakata-Ku, Fukuoka, 812-0015, Japan
Tel.: (81) 924121177
Fax: (81) 92 412 1191
Web Site: www.denso-kyushu.com
Emp.: 161
Automotive Repair & Maintenance Services
S.I.C.: 7549
N.A.I.C.S.: 811198

DENSO LOGITEM CORPORATION **(1)**
1 Sumisaki Shimohasumicho Kk Denso Nishio Seisakusho Nai
Nishio, Aichi, 445-0012, Japan
Tel.: (81) 563 55 1201
Fax: (81) 563 55 1206
Emp.: 183
Cargo Handling Services
S.I.C.: 4491
N.A.I.C.S.: 488320

DENSO MANUFACTURING KITAKYUSHU CO.,LTD. **(1)**
5-4-1 Honjo
Yahatanishi-Ku, Kitakyushu, Fukuoka, 807-0801, Japan
Tel.: (81) 93 693 1111
Fax: (81) 93 693 1445
E-Mail: info@denso-kitakyushu.jp
Web Site: www.denso-kitakyushu.jp
Emp.: 894
Automotive Parts Mfr
S.I.C.: 3714
N.A.I.C.S.: 336310

DENSO PREAS CO., LTD. **(1)**
2-58 Nishisakuragicho
Toyokawa, Aichi, 442-0063, Japan
Tel.: (81) 533862181
Fax: (81) 533845786
Web Site: www.densopreas.co.jp
Emp.: 131
Automotive Parts Mfr & Whslr
S.I.C.: 3714
N.A.I.C.S.: 336390

DENSO REMANI CORPORATION **(1)**
2-1 Nagane Sato-cho
Anjo, Aichi, 446-8511, Japan
Tel.: (81) 566960295
Fax: (81) 566960297
Web Site: www.densoremani.co.jp
Emp.: 50
Automotive Parts Mfr & Whslr
S.I.C.: 3714
N.A.I.C.S.: 336390
Takao Yamaguchi *(Pres)*

DENSO SEIBI CO., LTD. **(1)**
12 Kawarazaki Shimoaonocho
Okazaki, Aichi, 444-0244, Japan
Tel.: (81) 564 43 1945
Fax: (81) 564 43 1925
Emp.: 53
Waste Material Recycling Services
S.I.C.: 4953
N.A.I.C.S.: 562920

DENSO SERVICE NISHISAITAMA CO., LTD. **(1)**
295-2 Higashiaraicho
Tokorozawa, Saitama, 359-0034, Japan
Tel.: (81) 42 992 0275
Fax: (81) 42 992 0276
Emp.: 15
Automotive Repair Services
S.I.C.: 7539
N.A.I.C.S.: 811198

Denso Corporation—(Continued)

DENSO SERVICE OKINAWA CO., LTD. (1)
409 Minatogawa
Urasoe, Okinawa, 901-2134, Japan
Tel.: (81) 98 877 4655
Fax: (81) 98 877 1173
Web Site: www.ds-okinawa.com
Emp.: 34
Automotive Parts Repair Services
S.I.C.: 7539
N.A.I.C.S.: 811198

DENSO SI CORPORATION (1)
1-11-9 Mikawaanjominamimachi
Anjo, Aichi, 446-0058, Japan
Tel.: (81) 566 75 7500
Fax: (81) 566 75 7502
Web Site: www.denso-si.jp
Emp.: 80
Information Technology Consulting Services
S.I.C.: 7373
N.A.I.C.S.: 541512

DENSO TAIYO CO., LTD. (1)
28-1 Kitahama Katahara-cho
Gamagori, Aichi, 443-0103, Japan
Tel.: (81) 533 57 1636
Fax: (81) 533 57 1351
Emp.: 189
Instrument Cluster Mfr & Whslr
S.I.C.: 3714
N.A.I.C.S.: 336390

DENSO TECHNO CO., LTD. (1)
1-714 Taisho-machi
Obu, 448-0855, Japan
Tel.: (81) 562 44 1111
Fax: (81) 562 44 1101
Web Site: www.densotechno.co.jp
Emp.: 2,239
Software Development Services
S.I.C.: 7371
N.A.I.C.S.: 541511

DENSO TOHOKU CORPORATION (1)
2-6-1 Nigatake
Miyagino-Ku, Sendai, Miyagi, 983-0036, Japan
Tel.: (81) 22 238 9911
Fax: (81) 22 238 9923
Web Site: www.denso-tohoku.com
Emp.: 96
Automotive Repair Services
S.I.C.: 7549
N.A.I.C.S.: 811198

DENSO TOKYO CORPORATION (1)
2-15-13 Shoto
Shibuya-Ku, Tokyo, 150-0046, Japan
Tel.: (81) 3 5478 7555
Fax: (81) 3 5487 7559
Web Site: www.denso-tokyo.com
Emp.: 365
Automotive Repair Services
S.I.C.: 7549
N.A.I.C.S.: 811198

DENSO UNITY SERVICE CORPORATION (1)
1-1 Showacho
Kariya, Aichi, 448-0029, Japan
Tel.: (81) 566 25 9860
Fax: (81) 566 25 4963
Web Site: www.denso-unity.co.jp
Emp.: 572
Security Consulting Services
S.I.C.: 7381
N.A.I.C.S.: 561612

Denso Wave Inc. (1)
MT Bldg Hall 2 4 2 12 Toranomon
Minato-ku, Tokyo, 105-0001, Japan (75%)
Tel.: (81) 354726931
Fax: (81) 354726869
Web Site: www.denso-wave.com
Emp.: 491
Automatic Data Capture Equipment, Industrial Robots, Programmable Controllers & Other Apparatus & Systems Developer, Mfr & Sales
S.I.C.: 3822
N.A.I.C.S.: 334512

DENSO WELL CORPORATION (1)
1-1 Showacho
Kariya, Aichi, 448-0029, Japan
Tel.: (81) 566 25 5660
Fax: (81) 566 25 4516
Emp.: 232
Payroll Management Services
S.I.C.: 8721
N.A.I.C.S.: 541214

DENSO YUSEN TRAVEL CORPORATION (1)
1-1 Showacho Denso 2gokan
Kariya, Aichi, 448-0029, Japan
Tel.: (81) 566258520
Fax: (81) 566259974
E-Mail: npl@ytk.co.jp
Web Site: www.denso-yusen.co.jp
Emp.: 10
Travel Arrangement Services
S.I.C.: 4729
N.A.I.C.S.: 561599
Hiroaki Nomura *(Mgr)*

DENSOTRIM CO., LTD. (1)
2460 Akasaka Aza Ogohara Komonocho
Mie, 510-1222, Japan
Tel.: (81) 59 391 0011
Fax: (81) 593 91 0050
Web Site: www.densotrim.co.jp
Emp.: 526
Automotive Spare Parts Mfr
S.I.C.: 3751
N.A.I.C.S.: 336991

GAC CORPORATION (1)
1000 Toyoshina
Azumino, Nagano-ken, Japan
Tel.: (81) 263 73 8000
Fax: (81) 263 73 8015
Web Site: www.gacjp.com
Emp.: 620
Air Conditioner & Heat Exchanger Mfr
S.I.C.: 3585
N.A.I.C.S.: 333415
Akitoshi Sugiura *(Pres)*

Plant:

GAC CORPORATION - Anjo Plant (2)
60 Thouhai Nesaki-cho
Anjo, Aichi-ken, Japan
Tel.: (81) 566 73 8681
Fax: (81) 566 73 8682
Emp.: 1
Air Conditioner Mfr
S.I.C.: 3585
N.A.I.C.S.: 333415

HAMADEN P & S CO., LTD. (1)
136 Washizu
Kosai, Shizuoka, 431-0431, Japan
Tel.: (81) 53 576 1331
Fax: (81) 53 575 0066
Emp.: 56
Petroleum Products Distr
S.I.C.: 5172
N.A.I.C.S.: 424720

IPICS CORPORATION (1)
2-13-19 Nishiki Naka-Ku Takitei Bldg 6f
Nagoya, Aichi, 460-0003, Japan
Tel.: (81) 522201100
Fax: (81) 522201110
Web Site: www.ipics.jp
Emp.: 59
Patent Application Filing Services
S.I.C.: 7389
N.A.I.C.S.: 541199

KYOSAN DENKI CO., LTD. (1)
11-3 Okazato
Koga, Ibaraki, 306-0206, Japan
Tel.: (81) 280 98 3370
Fax: (81) 280 98 3876
Web Site: www.kyosan-denki.co.jp
Sls.: $862,920,000
Emp.: 1,677
Mechanical Fuel Pump Mfr
S.I.C.: 3561
N.A.I.C.S.: 333911
Minoru Ohta *(Pres)*
Hitoshi Iwai *(Sr Mng Dir)*
Masami Naoi *(Sr Mng Dir)*
Yukio Mori *(Mng Dir)*

Plants:

KYOSAN DENKI CO., LTD. - Plant 2 (2)
12-1 Okazato
Koga, Ibaraki, 306-0206, Japan
Tel.: (81) 280 98 1531
Fax: (81) 280 98 4279
Web Site: www.kyosan-denki.co.jp/english/company07_3.htm#2
Diesel Fuel Filter Mfr
S.I.C.: 3714
N.A.I.C.S.: 336390

KYOSAN DENKI CO., LTD - Yuki Plant (2)
8-36 Wakamiya
Yuki, Ibaraki, 307-0017, Japan
Tel.: (81) 296 34 0500
Fax: (81) 296 34 0520
Fuel Injection Control System Mfr
S.I.C.: 3714
N.A.I.C.S.: 336310

KYOSAN SERVICE CORPORATION (1)
11-3 Okasato
Koga, Ibaraki, 306-0206, Japan
Tel.: (81) 280 98 2342
Fax: (81) 280 98 2463
Emp.: 2
Consumer Goods Distr
S.I.C.: 5199
N.A.I.C.S.: 424990

MARCON DENSO CO., LTD. (1)
3893-1 Oka Hagyu Idemachi Nishi
Okitama-Gun, Yamagata, 999-0602, Japan
Tel.: (81) 238 72 2290
Fax: (81) 238 72 2292
Emp.: 128
Electronic Component Mfr
S.I.C.: 3679
N.A.I.C.S.: 334419

MAULTECH CORPORATION (1)
4978-1 Kamitonno
Nogata, Fukuoka, 822-0003, Japan
Tel.: (81) 9492 6 8333
Fax: (81) 9492 6 8335
Emp.: 55
Automotive Air Conditioning Equipment Mfr
S.I.C.: 3585
N.A.I.C.S.: 333415

MIYAZAKI ASMO CO., LTD. (1)
4188 Kiwaki Kunitomi-Cho
Higashimorokata, Miyazaki, 880-1113, Japan
Tel.: (81) 985 75 1236
Fax: (81) 985 75 1226
Web Site: www.m-asmo.co.jp
Emp.: 38
Automotive Parts Mfr
S.I.C.: 3714
N.A.I.C.S.: 336390

MOBILE MEDIANET INC. (1)
1-21-2 Dogenzaka Shinnampeidaitokyu Bldg 6f
Shibuya-Ku, Tokyo, 150-0043, Japan
Tel.: (81) 454707330
Fax: (81) 454708541
Web Site: www.mmnet.co.jp
Satellite Communications Services
S.I.C.: 4899
N.A.I.C.S.: 517410

Nippon Wiper Blade Co., Ltd. (1)
311 Shimo Takayanagi
Kazo, Saitama, 347 8585, Japan (70%)
Tel.: (81) 480671100
Fax: (81) 480671106
Web Site: www.nwb.co.jp
Wiper Blades Mfr & Sales
S.I.C.: 3714
N.A.I.C.S.: 336390

OTARI GAC CO., LTD (1)
1480 Chikuniotsu Otarimura
Kitaazumi-gun, Nagano, Japan
Tel.: (81) 261833051
Fax: (81) 261833053
Emp.: 2
Sheet Metal Mfr
S.I.C.: 3444
N.A.I.C.S.: 332322

Sankyo Radiator Co., Ltd. (1)
102 Omuracho
Toyohashi, Aichi, 440-0081, Japan
Tel.: (81) 532 53 4301
Fax: (81) 532 52 1378
E Mail: info@sankyo-radiator.co.jp
Web Site: www.sankyo-radiator.co.jp
Emp.: 351
Automobile Radiator Mfr
S.I.C.: 3714
N.A.I.C.S.: 336390

SHIMIZU INDUSTRY CO., LTD (1)
1 Chasenboshita Hitotsugicho
Kariya, Aichi, 448-0003, Japan
Tel.: (81) 566232335
Fax: (81) 566228019
E-Mail:
Web Site: www.shimizu-industry.co.jp
Emp.: 642
Automotive Parts Mfr
S.I.C.: 3714
N.A.I.C.S.: 336390

SUAB CO., LTD. (1)
390 Umeda
Kosai, Shizuoka, 431-0425, Japan
Tel.: (81) 53 577 2626
Fax: (81) 53 577 2626
Emp.: 26
Automotive Parts Mfr
S.I.C.: 3714
N.A.I.C.S.: 336390

SYSTEX JAPAN INC. (1)
5-16 Akemicho
Toyohashi, Aichi, 441-8074, Japan
Tel.: (81) 532 23 3355
Fax: (81) 532 23 5180
Emp.: 41
Automotive Plastic Parts Mfr
S.I.C.: 3089
N.A.I.C.S.: 326199

TECHMA CORPORATION (1)
3-1 Himegaoka
Kani, Gifu, 509-0249, Japan
Tel.: (81) 574 60 5220
Fax: (81) 574 60 5238
Web Site: www.techma.co.jp
Emp.: 450
Electronic Component Mfr
S.I.C.: 3679
N.A.I.C.S.: 334419

Yasaka GAC Co., Ltd. (1)
Kanote Yasaka
Omachi, Nagano, Japan
Tel.: (81) 261262007
Web Site: www.gacjp.com
Emp.: 50
Automotive Air Conditioner Mfr
S.I.C.: 3714
N.A.I.C.S.: 336390

Joint Venture:

Nippon Soken, Inc. (1)
14 Iwaya Shimohasumi-cho
Nishio, 445-0012, Japan
Tel.: (81) 563551800
Fax: (81) 563551849
Web Site: www.nipponsoken.com
Emp.: 400
Vehicle Safety & Pollution Prevention; Owned 75% by Denso Corporation & 25% by Toyota Motor Corporation
S.I.C.: 8731
N.A.I.C.S.: 541712
Hiromi Tokuda *(Pres)*

U.S. Subsidiaries:

AMERICAN INDUSTRIAL MANUFACTURING SERVICES, INC. (1)
41673 Corning Pl
Murrieta, CA 92562
Tel.: (951) 698-3379
Fax: (951) 698-1379
Web Site: www.globaldenso.com
Emp.: 100
Automotive Electrical Component Mfr
S.I.C.: 3714
N.A.I.C.S.: 336390
Jim Lewis *(Mgr-Ops)*

ASMO DETROIT, INC (1)
39575 Lewis Dr Ste 800
Novi, MI 48377
Tel.: (248) 359-4440
Fax: (248) 324-0348
Web Site: www.globaldenso.com
Emp.: 38
Automotive Engineering Services
S.I.C.: 8711
N.A.I.C.S.: 541330

ASMO GREENVILLE OF NORTH CAROLINA, INC. (1)
1125 Sugg Pkwy
Greenville, NC 27834
Tel.: (252) 754-1000
Fax: (252) 754-1036
Web Site: www.globaldenso.com
Emp.: 425
Automotive Parts Mfr
S.I.C.: 3714
N.A.I.C.S.: 336390
Jesse Wigent *(Mgr-Production)*

ASMO NORTH CAROLINA, INC. (1)
470 Crawford Rd
Statesville, NC 28625-8504
Tel.: (704) 878-6663
Fax: (704) 872-9786
Web Site: www.globaldenso.com
Emp.: 370
Electric Motor Mfr
S.I.C.: 3621
N.A.I.C.S.: 335312
David Clifton *(VP)*

Denso International America (1)
24777 Denso Dr
Southfield, MI 48033
Tel.: (248) 350 7500
Fax: (248) 213-2337
Web Site: www.densocorp-na.com
Emp.: 1,000
Supplier of Automotive Technology, Systems and Components
S.I.C.: 5013
N.A.I.C.S.: 423120
Koichi Fukaya *(Chm)*
Hikaru Sugi *(Pres & CEO)*
Kazumasa Kimura *(COO)*
Terry Helgesen *(Sr VP-Mktg & Sls)*

Subsidiaries:

DENSO MANUFACTURING ARKANSAS, INC. (2)
100 Denso Rd
Osceola, AR 72370
Tel.: (870) 622-9500
Fax: (870) 622-9563
Web Site: www.densocorp-na.com
Emp.: 414
Automotive Parts Mfr
S.I.C.: 3714
N.A.I.C.S.: 336390
Joe Stich *(Pres)*

DENSO MANUFACTURING MICHIGAN, INC. (2)
One Denso Rd
Battle Creek, MI 49037
Tel.: (269) 965-3322
Fax: (269) 965-8399
E-Mail: dmmi_purchasing@denso-diam.com
Web Site: www.densocorp-na-dmmi.com
Emp.: 1,797
Car Air Conditioner Mfr
S.I.C.: 3714
N.A.I.C.S.: 336390
Akeshi Kumagai *(Pres)*

Joint Venture:

Associated Fuel Pump Systems Corp. (2)
110 Scotts Br Rd
Anderson, SC 29622
Tel.: (864) 224-0012
Fax: (864) 224-2927
Web Site: www.afco.com
Emp.: 350
Automotive Gasoline Pumps Mfr
S.I.C.: 3586
N.A.I.C.S.: 333913
Katrina Beasley *(Supvr-Quality)*

DENSO MANUFACTURING ATHENS TENNESSEE, INC. (1)
2400 Denso Dr
Athens, TN 37303
Tel.: (423) 746-0000
Fax: (423) 746-1088
E-Mail: dmat_purchasing@DENSO-diam.com
Web Site: www.densocorp-na-dmat.com
Emp.: 900
Hydraulic Component Mfr
S.I.C.: 3492
N.A.I.C.S.: 332912
Hugh Cantrell *(Sr Mgr-HR)*

DENSO MANUFACTURING TENNESSEE, INC. (1)
1720 Robert C Jackson Dr
Maryville, TN 37801
Tel.: (865) 982-7000
Fax: (865) 981-5262
Web Site: www.densocorp-na-dmtn.com
Emp.: 2,500
Automotive Component Mfr
S.I.C.: 3714
N.A.I.C.S.: 336390
Jack Helmboldt *(Pres)*

Denso Sales California, Inc. (1)
3900 Via Oro Ave
Long Beach, CA 90810-1868
Tel.: (310) 834-6352
Fax: (310) 513-7319
Toll Free: (800) 222-6352
Web Site: www.denso-dsca.com
Sales Range: $500-549.9 Million
Emp.: 213
Automotive Parts Distr
Import Export
S.I.C.: 5013
N.A.I.C.S.: 423120
Max Adachi *(Pres)*

DENSO WIRELESS SYSTEMS AMERICA, INC. (1)
3250 Business Park Dr
Vista, CA 92081
Tel.: (760) 734-4600
Fax: (760) 734-4685
Emp.: 154
Car Navigation System Mfr
S.I.C.: 3714
N.A.I.C.S.: 336390

KYOSAN DENKI AMERICA, INC. (1)
65 Clarence Dr Mt
Mount Sterling, KY 40353
Tel.: (859) 497-2040
Fax: (859) 497-2050
Web Site: www.globaldenso.com
Emp.: 400
Fuel Pump Module Mfr
S.I.C.: 3714
N.A.I.C.S.: 336390
Mary Grider *(Mgr-HR & IT)*

KYOSAN DENSO MANUFACTURING KENTUCKY, LLC. (1)
65 Clarence Dr Mt
Mount Sterling, KY 40353
Tel.: (859) 497-2040
Fax: (859) 497-2050
Web Site: www.kdmk.com
Emp.: 324
Injection Molding Machinery Mfr
S.I.C.: 3559
N.A.I.C.S.: 333249
Toshiharu Shikata *(Pres)*

SYSTEX PRODUCTS ARKANSAS COMPANY (1)
101 Denso Rd
Osceola, AR 72370
Tel.: (870) 563-7950
Fax: (870) 563-6479
Web Site: www.densocorp-na.com
Emp.: 52
Car Air Conditioner Plastics Mfr
S.I.C.: 3089
N.A.I.C.S.: 326199
Tokue Yamamoto *(Pres)*

Non-U.S. Subsidiaries:

Anden (Thailand) Co., Ltd. (1)
700/87 Moo 1 Amata Nakorn Industrial Estate
Bangna-Trdad KM 57 T Bankao
A Panthon, Chon Buri, 20160, Thailand TH
Tel.: (66) 38214649 (100%)
Fax: (66) 38743872
Web Site: www.denso.co.th
Sales Range: $25-49.9 Million
Emp.: 232
Relays & Flashers Mfr
S.I.C.: 3714
N.A.I.C.S.: 336350
Tsutomu Aoki *(Mng Dir)*

Asmo Czech S.R.O. (1)
Modra 1080
Zruc nad Sazavou, Czech Republic
Tel.: (420) 327533711
Fax: (420) 327533740
E-Mail: recepce@asmo.cz
Web Site: www.asmo.cz
Emp.: 250
Automotive Parts Mfr
S.I.C.: 3714
N.A.I.C.S.: 336390
Tetsu Ono *(Pres)*

CTR S.R.L. (1)
Via Tito ed Ettore Manzini 9
43126 Parma, Italy
Tel.: (39) 0521 957611
Fax: (39) 0521 957677
E-Mail: info@ctrgroup.it
Web Site: www.ctrgroup.it
Emp.: 24
Heat Exchanger Mfr
S.I.C.: 3559
N.A.I.C.S.: 332410
Aldo Adamo *(Gen Mgr)*

DENSO AIR SYSTEMS CZECH s.r.o (1)
Newtonova 484 Zona Liberec Jih
462 02 Liberec, Czech Republic
Tel.: (420) 488 100 100
Fax: (420) 488 100 111
Emp.: 243
Car Air Conditioning Component Mfr
S.I.C.: 3585
N.A.I.C.S.: 333415
Makoto Morimoto *(Gen Mgr)*

DENSO AUTOMOTIVE SYSTEMS AUSTRALIA PTY. LTD. (1)
2-46 Merrindale Drive
Croydon, VIC, 3136, Australia
Tel.: (61) 3 8761 1100
Fax: (61) 3 8761 1501
E-Mail: reception@denso.com.au
Web Site: www.denso.com.au
Emp.: 400
Automotive Cooling System Mfr
S.I.C.: 3714
N.A.I.C.S.: 336390
Russell Pettis *(Mng Dir)*

DENSO (CHANGZHOU) FUEL INJECTION SYSTEM CO., LTD. (1)
No 301 West Hehai Road
Xinbei District, Changzhou, Jiangsu, China
Tel.: (86) 519 8515 2130
Fax: (86) 519 8512 7857
Web Site: www.globaldenso.com
Emp.: 369
Automotive Parts Mfr & Distr
S.I.C.: 3714
N.A.I.C.S.: 336390

DENSO (CHINA) INVESTMENT CO., LTD. (1)
Room No 518 Beijing Fortune Building No 5 Dong San Huan Bei Lu
Chaoyang District, Beijing, 100004, China
Tel.: (86) 1065908337
Fax: (86) 10 6590 9044
Web Site: www.globaldenso.com
Emp.: 582
Automotive Component Distr
S.I.C.: 5013
N.A.I.C.S.: 423120

DENSO DO BRASIL LTDA. (1)
Rua Joao Chede No 891 Cidade Industrial de Curitiba
Caixa Postal 6501
81170-220 Curitiba, Parana, Brazil
Tel.: (55) 41 2141 4300
Fax: (55) 41 2141 4500
Web Site: www.denso.com.br
Emp.: 1,654
Bus Air Conditioner Mfr
S.I.C.: 3714
N.A.I.C.S.: 336390

Denso Europe B.V. (1)
Hogeweyselaan 1651
1382 JL Weesp, Netherlands
Tel.: (31) 294493493
Fax: (31) 294417122
E-Mail: reception@denso.nl
Web Site: www.denso-europe.com
Emp.: 300
Automotive Products Supplier
S.I.C.: 5013
N.A.I.C.S.: 423120
Shigehiro Nishimura *(Pres & CEO)*

Non-U.S. Subsidiaries:

Denso Automotive Deutschland GmbH (2)
Freisinger Str 21
85386 Eching, Germany
Tel.: (49) 81659440
Fax: (49) 8165944800
E-Mail: jobs@denso-auto.de
Web Site: www.denso.com
Emp.: 260
Motor Vehicle Parts & Supplies Whslr
S.I.C.: 5013
N.A.I.C.S.: 423120

Denso Barcelona S.A. (2)
Calle Sakura 1 Poligono Industrial Pla de Santa Anna Sant Fruitos de B
8272 Barcelona, Spain
Tel.: (34) 938777900
Fax: (34) 938788666
Web Site: www.denso.com.es
Emp.: 600
Electronic Control Unit & Engine Management System Components Mfr
S.I.C.: 3519
N.A.I.C.S.: 333618
Masati Ito *(Pres)*

Denso Manufacturing Czech s.r.o. (2)
Heyrovskeho 476
462 07 Liberec, Czech Republic
Tel.: (420) 488101111
Fax: (420) 488101000
E-Mail: info@denso.cz
Web Site: www.denso.cz
Emp.: 1,500
HVAC Units, Evaporators, Condensors & Radiators Mfr
S.I.C.: 3585
N.A.I.C.S.: 333415
Karel Balatka *(Pres)*

Denso Manufacturing Hungary Ltd. (2)
Holland Fasor 14
8000 Szekesfehervar, Hungary
Tel.: (36) 22552000
Fax: (36) 22552099
Web Site: www.denso.com
Emp.: 3,500
Diesel Injection Pumps & System Control Panel Products Mfr
S.I.C.: 3594
N.A.I.C.S.: 333996
Y. Ohoka *(Pres)*

Denso Manufacturing Italia SpA (2)
Viale Marisa Bellisario 75
66050 San Salvo, Chieti, Italy
Tel.: (39) 0873388311
Fax: (39) 0873388613
Web Site: www.denso-europe.com
Emp.: 1,630
Starters, Alternators, Blowers, Fans & Wipers Mfr & Sales
S.I.C.: 5013
N.A.I.C.S.: 423120

Denso Manufacturing Midlands Ltd. (2)
Unit 1 Maybrook Road
Maybrook Business Park
Minworth, Sutton Coldfield, B76 1AL, United Kingdom
Tel.: (44) 1213136900
Fax: (44) 3603222
Web Site: www.denso-midlands.co.uk
Emp.: 445
Starters & Alternators Mfr
S.I.C.: 3714
N.A.I.C.S.: 336390

Denso Manufacturing UK Ltd. (2)
Queensway Campus Hortonwood
Telford, Salop, TF1 7FS, United Kingdom
Tel.: (44) 1952608400
Fax: (44) 1952675222
Web Site: www.globaldenso.com
Emp.: 700
Air Conditioners, Heaters, Blowers & Panels Mfr
S.I.C.: 3714
N.A.I.C.S.: 336390
Mark Hayward *(Mng Dir)*

Denso Marston Ltd. (2)
Marston House Otley Rd
Shipley, W Yorkshire, BD17 7JR, United Kingdom

Denso Corporation—(Continued)

Tel.: (44) 274582266
Fax: (44) 1274597165
Web Site: www.aftermarket.denso-europe.com
Emp.: 939
Radiators, Oil Coolers & Inter-Coolers Mfr & Sales
S.I.C.: 3714
N.A.I.C.S.: 336390
Makoto Inoue *(Mng Dir)*

Denso Otomotiv Parcalari Sanayi A.S. (2)
TSOB-TAYSAD Organize Sanayi Bolgesi 5 Cadde No 1 41480
Sekerpinar/GEBZE, 41480 Istanbul, Turkey
Tel.: (90) 2626795700
Fax: (90) 2626795757
Web Site: www.globaldenso.com
Emp.: 136
Automotive Air Conditioners & Heaters Mfr
S.I.C.: 3714
N.A.I.C.S.: 336390
Mahmut Hocaoglu *(Pres)*

Denso Sales Belgium N.V. (2)
Medialaan 50
1800 Vilvoorde, Belgium
Tel.: (32) 22578900
Fax: (32) 22578800
E-Mail: info@denso.com
Web Site: www.denso.com
Emp.: 45
Air Conditioners, Radiators, Meters & Electric Parts Sales
S.I.C.: 5075
N.A.I.C.S.: 423730
H. Shinomiya *(Mng Dir)*

Denso Sales Italia Srl (2)
Frazione Masio 24
10046 Turin, Italy
Tel.: (39) 0119458811
Fax: (39) 0119458833
Web Site: www.aftermarket.denso-europe.com
Emp.: 26
Automotive Components Sales & Marketer
S.I.C.: 5013
N.A.I.C.S.: 423120
Gianluca Mrostica *(Pres)*

Denso Sales Sweden AB (2)
Gotavertksgatan 6A
SE-41755 Gothenburg, Sweden
Tel.: (46) 317011890
Fax: (46) 317011898
E-Mail: info@denso.se
Web Site: www.denso-europe.com
Emp.: 5
Original Equipment Sales & Engineering Services
S.I.C.: 5013
N.A.I.C.S.: 423120
Philip de Wolf *(Mng Dir)*

Denso Sales UK Ltd. (2)
1 Bishop Sq
Hatfield, Herts, United Kingdom
Tel.: (44) 2476842500
Fax: (44) 1707282450
E-Mail: cvadmin@denso-sales.co.uk
Web Site: www.denso-europe.com
Emp.: 50
Automotive Products Sales
S.I.C.: 5013
N.A.I.C.S.: 423120
Alan Richard *(Mng Dir)*
Shiro Shimada *(Mng Dir)*

Denso Thermal Systems Polska Sp.z.o.o. (2)
Ul Turynska 100
43-100 Tychy, Poland
Tel.: (48) 322179611
Fax: (48) 322179610
E-Mail: sekretariat.tychy@denso-ts.it
Web Site: www.globaldenso.com
Emp.: 206
HVAC, Heaters, Heater Cores & Cockpit Modules Mfr
S.I.C.: 3585
N.A.I.C.S.: 333415

Denso Thermal Systems SpA (2)
Frazione Masio 24
10046 Poirino, Italy
Tel.: (39) 0119417111
Fax: (39) 0119417403
E-Mail: anna.pessuto@benso-ts.it
Web Site: www.benso-ts.com
Emp.: 2,000
Air Conditioners, Heaters, Radiators, Charge Coolers, Front-End Modules & Cockpit Modules Mfr & Sales
S.I.C.: 3714
N.A.I.C.S.: 336390

Joao de Deus & Filhos S.A. (2)
Estrada Nacional N 10 Km 107 Arados
Arados Samora Correja, 2135 Lisbon, Portugal
Tel.: (351) 263650240
E-Mail: info@denso-europe.com
Web Site: www.jdeus.com
Emp.: 375
Radiators, Inter-Coolers & Heater Cores Mfr & Sales
S.I.C.: 3585
N.A.I.C.S.: 333415
Paolo Etzid *(Gen Mgr)*

Non-U.S. Joint Venture:

TBMECA Poland Sp. z o.o. (2)
ul Jaworzynska 291 a
59-220 Legnica, Poland
Tel.: (48) 768508120
Fax: (48) 768660301
Web Site: www.tbmeca.pl
Emp.: 100
Automotive Component Mfr
S.I.C.: 3714
N.A.I.C.S.: 336390
Tetsuya Kuno *(Pres)*

DENSO FINANCE HOLLAND B.V. (1)
Hogeweyselaan 165
1382 JL Weesp, Netherlands
Tel.: (31) 294493493
Fax: (31) 294417122
Web Site: www.globaldenso.com
Financial Management Services
S.I.C.: 6211
N.A.I.C.S.: 523999

DENSO (GUANGZHOU NANSHA) CO., LTD (1)
No 33 Shinandadao Huanggezhen Nanshaqu
Guangzhou, China
Tel.: (86) 2034685598
Fax: (86) 2034685590
Web Site: www.globaldenso.com
Emp.: 1,358
Fuel Injection System Mfr & Distr
S.I.C.: 3714
N.A.I.C.S.: 336390

DENSO HARYANA PVT. LTD. (1)
Plot No 3 Sector-3 IMT-Manesar
Gurgaon, Haryana, 122050, India
Tel.: (91) 124 4871888
Fax: (91) 124 4871899
Web Site: www.globaldenso.com
Emp.: 545
Fuel Pump Mfr & Distr
S.I.C.: 3714
N.A.I.C.S.: 336310
Masaru Tomimoto *(Gen Mgr)*

DENSO INDUSTRIAL DA AMAZONIA LTDA. (1)
Polo Industrial de Manaus Avenida Buriti No 3600
Distrito Industrial, Manaus, Amazonas, 69075-000, Brazil
Tel.: (55) 92 2121 4200
Fax: (55) 92 2121 4201
Web Site: www.denso-dnaz.com.br
Emp.: 334
Automotive Parts Mfr & Distr
S.I.C.: 3714
N.A.I.C.S.: 336390

Denso International Asia Pte. Ltd. (1)
Science Park Road No 01-19 The Aries
Science Park II, 117586 Singapore, Singapore SG
Tel.: (65) 67768286 (100%)
Fax: (65) 67768698
E-Mail: audrey@denso.com.sg
Web Site: www.denso.com.sg
Emp.: 77
Holding Company-Sales of Aftermarket Products
S.I.C.: 6719
N.A.I.C.S.: 551112
Bruce Eng *(Gen Mgr)*

Denso International Australia Pty. Ltd. (1)
2-46 Merrindale Dr
Croydon, VIC, 3136, Australia AU
Tel.: (61) 387611400 (100%)
Fax: (61) 387611505
E-Mail: reception@denso.com.au
Web Site: www.denso.com.au
Sales Range: $50-74.9 Million
Emp.: 420
Holding Company-Aftermarket Sales & Services
S.I.C.: 6719
N.A.I.C.S.: 551112

Subsidiary:

DENSO Australian Automotive Air Pty. Ltd. (2)
2-46 Merrindale Dr
3136 Croydon, VIC, Australia AU
Tel.: (61) 387611100 (100%)
Fax: (61) 387611501
E-Mail: reception@denso.com.au
Web Site: www.globaldenso.com
Sales Range: $10-24.9 Million
Emp.: 400
Automotive Air Conditioners, Radiators & Instrument Clusters Mfr
S.I.C.: 3519
N.A.I.C.S.: 333618

DENSO INTERNATIONAL EUROPE B.V. (1)
Hogeweyselaan 165
1382 JL Weesp, Netherlands
Tel.: (31) 294493493
Fax: (31) 294417122
Automotive Component Mfr
S.I.C.: 3714
N.A.I.C.S.: 336390

DENSO INTERNATIONAL INDIA PVT. LTD. (1)
Plot No 3 Sector-3 IMT-Manesar
Gurgaon, Haryana, 122003, India
Tel.: (91) 124 4803200
Fax: (91) 124 4803201
Web Site: www.globaldenso.com
Emp.: 180
Automotive Parts Distr
S.I.C.: 5013
N.A.I.C.S.: 423120
Yoshitaka Kajita *(Mng Dir)*

DENSO INTERNATIONAL UK LTD. (1)
1 Bishop Square
Hatfield, Herts, AL10 9NE, United Kingdom
Tel.: (44) 1707282400
Fax: (44) 1707282450
E-Mail: covadmin@denso-sales.co.uk
Web Site: www.globaldenso.com
Emp.: 50
Automotive Parts Distr
S.I.C.: 5013
N.A.I.C.S.: 423120
Alan William Richards *(Gen Mgr)*

DENSO MANUFACTURING ARGENTINA S.A. (1)
Avenida Las Malvinas Km 4 5 5012
Cordoba, Argentina
Tel.: (54) 351 496 8500
Fax: (54) 351 496 1091
Web Site: www.globaldenso.com
Emp.: 237
Car Air Conditioner Mfr
S.I.C.: 3714
N.A.I.C.S.: 336390

DENSO MANUFACTURING CANADA, INC (1)
900 Southgate Dr
Guelph, ON, N1L 1K1, Canada
Tel.: (519) 837-6600
E-Mail: dmcn_purchasing@DENSO-diam.com
Web Site: www.densocorp-na-dmcn.com
Emp.: 315
Automotive Parts Mfr
S.I.C.: 3714
N.A.I.C.S.: 336390
Dave Grimmer *(Pres)*

DENSO MAQUINAS ROTANTES do BRASIL LTDA. (1)
Avenida Campo de Ourique No 401 Jardin das Alterosas
Betim, Minas Gerais, Brazil
Tel.: (55) 3121911410
Fax: (55) 3121911401
Web Site: www.denso-dmbr.com.br
Emp.: 27
Motor Mfr & Distr
S.I.C.: 3621
N.A.I.C.S.: 335312

DENSO MEXICO S.A. DE C.V (1)
Boulevard Parque Industrial Monterrey No 502
Apodaca, Nuevo Leon, 66600, Mexico
Tel.: (52) 8181567000
Fax: (52) 8181567090
Web Site: www.globaldenso.com
Emp.: 3,487
Automotive Cluster & Valves Mfr
S.I.C.: 3714
N.A.I.C.S.: 336390

DENSO OTOMOTIV PARCALARI SANAYI ANONIM SIRKET (1)
Tsob-Taysad Organize Sanayi Bolgesi 5 Cadde No 1
Sekerpinar, 41480 Gebze, Turkey
Tel.: (90) 2626795700
Fax: (90) 2626795757
Emp.: 127
Car Air Conditioner Mfr
S.I.C.: 3714
N.A.I.C.S.: 336390

DENSO PS CORPORATION (1)
47 Sungsan-Dong Sungsangu
Changwon, Kyungnam, Korea (South)
Tel.: (82) 556009510
Fax: (82) 556009787
Web Site: www.densops.co.kr
Rev.: $438,480,000
Emp.: 1,238
Automotive Electrical Component Mfr
S.I.C.: 3714
N.A.I.C.S.: 336390
Hwang Suntae *(Chm)*
Okuda Fusaji *(Pres)*

Plant:

DENSO PS CORPORATION - Hongseong Factory (2)
524 Gyunguk-lee Eunha-myeon
Hoengseong, chungcheongnam-do, Korea (South)
Tel.: (82) 56428795
Fax: (82) 41 642 0183
Automotive Component Mfr
S.I.C.: 3714
N.A.I.C.S.: 336390

DENSO SALES CANADA, INC. (1)
195 Brunel Rd
Mississauga, ON, L4Z 1X3, Canada
Tel.: (905) 890-0890
Fax: (905) 890-8474
Emp.: 30
Automotive Parts Distr
S.I.C.: 5013
N.A.I.C.S.: 423120
Hikaru Sugi *(Pres)*

DENSO SALES FRANCE S.A.R.L. (1)
Immeuble Selene 12 Parc Ariane
78280 Guyancourt, France
Tel.: (33) 161372222
Fax: (33) 161372200
Web Site: www.denso-europe.com
Emp.: 46
Automotive Component Distr
S.I.C.: 5013
N.A.I.C.S.: 423120
Y. Kano *(Mng Dir)*

DENSO SALES RUS L.L.C. (1)
4th Street of 8th March 6A
125167 Moscow, Russia
Tel.: (7) 495 645 68 11
Fax: (7) 495 645 68 22
Web Site: www.globaldenso.com
Emp.: 11
Automotive Products Distr
S.I.C.: 5013
N.A.I.C.S.: 423120
Kenji Horibe *(Gen Mgr)*

DENSO SISTEMAS TERMICOS ESPANA S.A. (1)
Parque Tecnologico y Logistico de Vigo
Calle 1 Parcela 7, 36312 Vigo, Spain
Tel.: (34) 986247222
Fax: (34) 986247223
Web Site: www.denso-europe.com
Emp.: 218
Heaters & Cooling Modules Mfr & Distr
S.I.C.: 3433
N.A.I.C.S.: 333414
Roberto Cavallo *(Gen Mgr)*

DENSO SOFTWARE SHANGHAI CO., LTD. (1)
18401-18404 Room 498 Guoshoujing Road
Pudong New Area, Shanghai, China
Tel.: (86) 21 5131 4061
Fax: (86) 21 5131 4315
Web Site: www.globaldenso.com
Emp.: 116
Software Development Services
S.I.C.: 7371
N.A.I.C.S.: 541511

DENSO TAIWAN CORP. (1)
525 Sec 2 Mei Su Road
Yang Mei Town, Taoyuan, Taiwan
Tel.: (886) 34828001
Fax: (886) 34828003
E-Mail: yuwen.chen@denso.com.tw
Web Site: www.denso.com.tw
Emp.: 417
Automotive Electrical Component Mfr & Whslr
S.I.C.: 3714
N.A.I.C.S.: 336390

DENSO TECHNO PHILIPPINES, INC. (1)
25/F BPI Buendia Center Sen Gil Puyat Ave
Makati, Philippines
Tel.: (63) 27519663
Fax: (63) 27519661
Web Site: www.globaldenso.com
Software Development Services
S.I.C.: 7371
N.A.I.C.S.: 541511

DENSO THERMAL SYSTEMS PUNE PVT. LTD. (1)
No 116 Gat No 1228/2 Sanaswadi Nagar Road
Taluka-Shirur, 412208 Pune, Maharashtra, India
Tel.: (91) 2137 618 901
Emp.: 44
Automotive Air Conditioner Mfr & Distr
S.I.C.: 3714
N.A.I.C.S.: 336390

DENSO (TIANJIN) THERMAL PRODUCTS CO., LTD. (1)
No 15 Saida 2nd Street Xiqing Economic Development Area
Tianjin, China
Tel.: (86) 2223889288
Fax: (86) 2223889628
Emp.: 803
Car Air Conditioner Mfr & Distr
S.I.C.: 3714
N.A.I.C.S.: 336390

Denso Tool And Die (Thailand) Co., Ltd. (1)
369 Moo 3 Teparak Road T Teparak
A Muang, Samut Prakan, 10270, Thailand TH
Tel.: (66) 23843501 (100%)
Fax: (66) 27583450
E-Mail: satoiu.znowa@denso.co.th
Web Site: www.denso.co.th
Sales Range: $1-9.9 Million
Emp.: 138
Mfr & Sales of Dyes & Jigs for Automotive Equipment
S.I.C.: 3711
N.A.I.C.S.: 336111
Satoiu Znowa *(Mng Dir)*

GUANGZHOU DENSO CO., LTD. (1)
Guangzhou Auto Parts Industry Town
Yonghe Town
Zhengchen, Guangzhou, 511356, China
Tel.: (86) 2082981155
Fax: (86) 2092970955
Web Site: www.globaldenso.com
Emp.: 814
Car Air Conditioner Mfr & Distr
S.I.C.: 3714
N.A.I.C.S.: 336390

LIPLASTEC s.r.o (1)
Newtonova 478
462 01 Liberec, Czech Republic
Tel.: (420) 488019412
Fax: (420) 488019421
E-Mail: info@liplastec.com
Web Site: www.liplastec.com
Emp.: 183
Automotive Plastic Products Mfr
S.I.C.: 3089
N.A.I.C.S.: 326199
David Vopravil *(Gen Mgr)*

PHILIPPINE AUTO COMPONENTS, INC. (1)
109 Unity Avenue Carmelray Industrial Park 1
PO Box 109
Canlubang, 4037 Calamba, Laguna, Philippines
Tel.: (63) 495493030
Fax: (63) 495493089
Web Site: www.denso.com.ph
Car Air Conditioner Mfr
S.I.C.: 3714
N.A.I.C.S.: 336390
Satoshi Sugiura *(Pres)*

PT. HAMADEN INDONESIA MANUFACTURING (1)
JL Gaya Motor 1/6 Sunter 2
Jakarta, 14330, Indonesia
Tel.: (62) 21 652 1206
Fax: (62) 21 652 2710
Web Site: www.globaldenso.com
Emp.: 300
Horns Mfr
S.I.C.: 3714
N.A.I.C.S.: 336390
Yasuyuki Takai *(Pres)*

Siam Denso Manufacturing Co., Ltd. (1)
Amata Nakorn Industrial Estate 700/618
Moo 4 Bangna-Trad Rd
T Bankao A Panthong, Chon Buri, 20160, Thailand TH
Tel.: (66) 38210100 (100%)
Fax: (66) 38210116
E-Mail: motomikato@sdm.denso.co.th
Web Site: www.denso.co.th
Sales Range: $650-699.9 Million
Emp.: 2,665
Fuel Injection System Products Mfr
S.I.C.: 3594
N.A.I.C.S.: 333996
Motomi Kato *(Pres)*

TIANJIN ASMO AUTOMOTIVE SMALL MOTOR CO., LTD. (1)
No 2 Saida 4th Road Xiqing Economic Development Area
Tianjin, China
Tel.: (86) 2283961808
Fax: (86) 2283961718
Web Site: www.globaldenso.com
Emp.: 905
Windshield Wiper System Mfr & Distr
S.I.C.: 3714
N.A.I.C.S.: 336320

TIANJIN DENSO AIR-CONDITIONER CO., LTD. (1)
Qiansang Yuan Yangliu Qing
Xiqing Ward, Tianjin, 300800, China
Tel.: (86) 2287992171
Fax: (86) 2227994347
Web Site: www.globaldenso.com
Emp.: 128
Automotive Air Conditioner Mfr
S.I.C.: 3714
N.A.I.C.S.: 336390

TIANJIN DENSO ENGINE ELECTRICAL PRODUCTS CO., LTD (1)
No3 Liujing Road Dongli Economic Development District
Tianjin, 300300, China
Tel.: (86) 2258885600
Fax: (86) 2258885618
Web Site: www.globaldenso.com
Emp.: 942
Automotive Electrical Parts Mfr & Distr
S.I.C.: 3714
N.A.I.C.S.: 336320

TIANJIN FAWER DENSO AIR-CONDITIONER CO., LTD. (1)
No 22 Saida Shiji Dadao Xiqing Economic Development Area
Tianjin, China
Tel.: (86) 2223889188
Fax: (86) 2223389199
Web Site: www.globaldenso.com
Emp.: 499
Automotive Air Conditioner Mfr & Distr
S.I.C.: 3714
N.A.I.C.S.: 336390

TIANJIN POON SUNG ELECTRONICS CO., LTD. (1)
Yat Sen Scientific Industrial Park
Wuqing, Tianjin, China
Tel.: (86) 2282172680
Fax: (86) 2282172683
Web Site: www.globaldenso.com
Emp.: 93
Automotive Parts Mfr & Distr
S.I.C.: 3714
N.A.I.C.S.: 336390

Toyota Boshoku Filtration System (Thailand) Co., Ltd. (1)
Eastern Seaboard Indus Estate 64/42 Moo 4 Hemaraj Rd Tumbol
Amphur Pluak Daeng, Rayong, 21140, Thailand TH
Tel.: (66) 38955618 (100%)
Fax: (66) 38955623
Web Site: www.tbfst.co.th
Sales Range: $75-99.9 Million
Emp.: 817
Oil Filter Mfr
S.I.C.: 7549
N.A.I.C.S.: 811191
Tadahiro Inoue *(Pres)*

Non-U.S. Plant:

DENSO (THAILAND) CO., LTD - Wellgrow Plant (1)
Wellgrow Industrial Estate 85 Moo 9
Bangna Trad Rd KM 36
T Bangwua A Bangpakong, Chachoengsao, 24180, Thailand
Tel.: (66) 3857 1717
Fax: (66) 3857 1710
Emp.: 2,987
Automotive Parts Mfr
S.I.C.: 3714
N.A.I.C.S.: 336390

DENT STEEL SERVICES LTD

Low Moor Steel Works New Works Road
Bradford, BD12 0QN, United Kingdom
Tel.: (44) 1274420200
Fax: (44) 1274672979
E-Mail: enquiries@dentsteel.co.uk
Web Site: www.dentsteel.co.uk
Year Founded: 1977
Rev.: $44,151,877
Emp.: 4,347
Business Description:
Steel Supplier
S.I.C.: 1791
N.A.I.C.S.: 238120
Personnel:
Mark Stafford *(Office Mgr-Sls-Bradford)*

DENTATUS AB

Bromstensvagen 172
163 08 Spanga, Sweden
Tel.: (46) 854650900
Fax: (46) 854650901
E-Mail: info@dentatus.se
Web Site: www.dentatus.com
Emp.: 40
Business Description:
Dental Equipment Mfr
S.I.C.: 3843
N.A.I.C.S.: 339114
Personnel:
Bernard Weissman *(Owner)*

U.S. Subsidiary:

Dentatus USA, Ltd. (1)
54 W 39th St # 5
New York, NY 10018 NY
Tel.: (212) 481-1010
E-Mail: dentatus@dentatus.com
Web Site: www.dentatus.com
Emp.: 12
S.I.C.: 5047
N.A.I.C.S.: 423450
Thomas J. Murphy *(CEO)*

DENTELLE SOPHIE HALLETTE

2 rue Melayers
BP 80082
59542 Caudry, France
Tel.: (33) 327765576
Fax: (33) 327765577
Web Site: www.sophiehallette.fr/eng/main.html
Sales Range: $25-49.9 Million
Emp.: 270
Business Description:
Lace Mfr
S.I.C.: 2259
N.A.I.C.S.: 313240
Personnel:
Bruno Lescroart *(Mng Dir)*

DENTONIA RESOURCES, LTD.

Suite 204 837 W Hastings Street
Vancouver, BC, V6C 3N6, Canada
Tel.: (604) 632-0085
Fax: (604) 605-0009
E-Mail: dentonia@telus.net
Web Site: www.dentonia.net
DTA—(TSXV)
Business Description:
Mineral Exploration & Development
S.I.C.: 1499
N.A.I.C.S.: 212399
Personnel:
John R. Chalcraft *(Chm, Interim Pres & CEO)*
Bob Anderson *(CFO & Sec)*
Board of Directors:
John R. Chalcraft
Bob Anderson
Ed Banas
Adolf A. Petancic

DENTONS PENSION MANAGEMENT LTD.

Sutton House Weyside Park
Catteshall Lane, Godalming, GU7 1XE, United Kingdom
Tel.: (44) 1483 521 521
Fax: (44) 1483 521 515
E-Mail: enquiries@dentonspensions.co.uk
Web Site: www.dentonspensions.co.uk
Year Founded: 1989
Sales Range: $10-24.9 Million
Business Description:
Pension Management Services
S.I.C.: 6371
N.A.I.C.S.: 524292
Personnel:
Martyn Rose *(Chm)*
Derrick Fowler *(Co-Mng Dir)*
Ian Stewart *(Co-Mng Dir)*

DENTSU INC.

1-8-1 Higashi-shimbashi Minato-ku
Tokyo, 105-7001, Japan
Tel.: (81) 3 6216 5111
Fax: (81) 3 6217 5515
Web Site: www.dentsu.com
Year Founded: 1901
4324—(NGO TKS)

Dentsu Inc.—(Continued)

Sls.: $21,353,453,000
Assets: $24,261,259,000
Liabilities: $17,566,252,000
Net Worth: $6,695,007,000
Earnings: $399,696,000
Emp.: 37,450
Fiscal Year-end: 03/31/13

Business Description:
Holding Company; Advertising Agencies
S.I.C.: 6719
N.A.I.C.S.: 551112

Personnel:
Tadashi Ishii *(Pres & CEO)*
Shoichi Nakamoto *(Sr Exec VP)*
Akira Sugimoto *(Sr VP)*
Norihisa Awa *(Exec Officer)*
Jerry Buhlmann *(Exec Officer)*
Kazufumi Hattori *(Exec Officer)*
Toru Hirano *(Exec Officer)*
Kazumichi Iwagami *(Exec Officer)*
Tsuyoshi Iwashita *(Exec Officer)*
Kenichi Kato *(Exec Officer)*
Fumiharu Kobayashi *(Exec Officer)*
Tsuneo Ogasawara *(Exec Officer)*
Yuichi Okubo *(Exec Officer)*
Naoki Tani *(Exec Officer)*
Akira Tonouchi *(Exec Officer)*
Nobuyuki Toya *(Exec Officer)*
Toshihiro Yamamoto *(Exec Officer)*
Timothy Paul Andree *(Exec VP)*
Yuzuru Kato *(Exec VP)*
Ryuhei Akiyama *(Sr VP)*
Kunihiro Matsushima *(Sr VP)*
Yoshio Takada *(Sr VP)*

Board of Directors:
Ryuhei Akiyama
Timothy Paul Andree
Kazufumi Hattori
Tadashi Ishii
Satoshi Ishikawa
Yuzuru Kato
Kunihiro Matsushima
Yasuo Motoi
Shoichi Nakamoto
Yutaka Nishizawa
Akira Sugimoto
Yoshio Takada
Akira Tonouchi

Transfer Agent:
Mitsubishi UFJ Trust & Banking Corporation
7-10-11 Higashisuna Koto-ku
Tokyo, Japan

Subsidiaries:

3P Corp. (1)
7th Floor Ginza SC Bldg 8-18-11 Ginza
Chuo-ku, Tokyo, 104-0061, Japan
Tel.: (81) 3 3545 3931
Web Site: www.dentsu.com
Sales Promotion Services
S.I.C.: 7389
N.A.I.C.S.: 561990

Action Click Co., Ltd. (1)
5F TKK Dai2 Shimbashi Bldg 3-15-4 Shimbashi
Minato-ku, Tokyo, 105-0004, Japan
Tel.: (81) 3 5408 5901
Fax: (81) 3 5408 5903
E-Mail: info@actionclick.net
Web Site: www.actionclick.net
S.I.C.: 7311
N.A.I.C.S.: 541810
Takuya Matsumoto *(CEO)*

Ad Area Co., Ltd. (1)
1st Floor Niban-cho Sankyo Bldg 6-3 Niban-cho
Chiyoda-ku, Tokyo, 102-0084, Japan
Tel.: (81) 3 5211 7160
Fax: (81) 3 3264 2602
E-Mail: info@ad-area.jp
Web Site: www.ad-area.jp
Internet Advertising Services
S.I.C.: 2741
N.A.I.C.S.: 519130

Ishida Takashi *(Pres)*

Ad Dentsu Osaka Inc. (1)
Shinfujita Bldg 2-4-27 Dojima
Kita-ku, Osaka, 530-0003, Japan
Tel.: (81) 6 6347 4821
Fax: (81) 6 6347 4836
Web Site: www.addentsu-osaka.co.jp
Emp.: 63
Advertising Services
S.I.C.: 7311
N.A.I.C.S.: 541810
Suehiro Toshihiko *(Pres)*

bless you inc. (1)
Nishirei Higashi Ginza Residence 1907 6-19-21 Tsukiji
Chuo-ku, Tokyo, 104-0045, Japan
Tel.: (81) 3 3545 1081
Fax: (81) 335451082
E-Mail: nobuo.hirano@ers.dentsu.co.jp
S.I.C.: 7311
N.A.I.C.S.: 541810
Nobuo Hirano *(Mgr)*

Boardwalk Inc. (1)
1-4-2 Shibuya
Shibuya-ku, Tokyo, 150-0002, Japan
Tel.: (81) 3 3498 3380
E-Mail: sales@boardwalk-inc.jp
Web Site: www.boardwalk-inc.jp
Entertainment Ticket Booking Services
S.I.C.: 7999
N.A.I.C.S.: 711320

BUILD creativehaus inc. (1)
9F Hamamatsucho DS Bldg 1-27-16 Hamamatsucho
Minato-ku, Tokyo, Minato-ku, 105-0013, Japan
Tel.: (81) 3 5733 5461
Fax: (81) 3 5733 5474
Emp.: 6
S.I.C.: 7311
N.A.I.C.S.: 541810
Keita Yamada *(Dir-Creative)*

Creative Associates Ltd. (1)
Ginza-Showadouri Building 5th Floor 8-14-14 Ginza
Cyuo-ku, Tokyo, Japan
Tel.: (81) 3 3545 2911
Fax: (81) 3 3545 3475
E-Mail: cal.info@cal-pro.jp
Web Site: www.cal-net.co.jp
Emp.: 30
Television Program Production Services
S.I.C.: 7812
N.A.I.C.S.: 512110
Jun Yamasaki *(Pres)*

cyber communications inc. (1)
7F Comodio Shiodome 2-14-1 Higashi-shimbashi
Minato-ku, Tokyo, 105-0021, Japan
Tel.: (81) 3 5425 6111
Fax: (81) 3 5425 6110
Web Site: www.cci.co.jp
Rev.: $21,312,331
S.I.C.: 7311
N.A.I.C.S.: 541810
Hideyuki Nagasawa *(Pres & CEO)*
Katja Baumgartner *(Mng Dir)*
Akio Niizawa *(COO, VP & Exec Officer)*

Dentsu Ad-Gear Inc. (1)
5th Floor Sumitomo Fudosan Shiodome Hamarikyu Bldg 8-21-1 Ginza
Chuo-ku, Tokyo, 104-0061, Japan
Tel.: (81) 3 5565 5510
Fax: (81) 3 5565 5517
Web Site: www.dentsu-adgear.co.jp
Media Advertising Services
S.I.C.: 7319
N.A.I.C.S.: 541890

Dentsu Casting and Entertainment Inc. (1)
8th Floor Shiodome Annex Bldg 1-8-3 Higashi-shimbashi
Minato-ku, Tokyo, 105-0021, Japan
Tel.: (81) 3 6217 1501
Web Site: www.dentsu.com
Advertising Consulting Services
S.I.C.: 7319
N.A.I.C.S.: 541890

Dentsu Communication Institute Inc. (1)
1-8-1 Higashi-Shinbashi
Minato-ku, Tokyo, 105-7001, Japan
Tel.: (81) 3 6217 6111
Fax: (81) 3 6217 6191
E-Mail: info@dci.dentsu.co.jp
Emp.: 24
S.I.C.: 7311
N.A.I.C.S.: 541810
Yutaka Narita *(Chm)*
Masahi Wada *(Pres & CEO)*
Ko Matsumoto *(Exec VP)*

Dentsu Consulting Inc. (1)
11F Jiji Tsushin Bldg 5-15-8 Ginza
Chuo-ku, Tokyo, 104-0061, Japan
Tel.: (81) 3 6226 3265
Fax: (81) 3 6226 3266
Web Site: www.dentsuconsulting.com
Emp.: 30
Management Strategy Consulting Services
S.I.C.: 8748
N.A.I.C.S.: 541618
Naohiko Oikawa *(Pres & CEO)*

Dentsu Creative Force Inc. (1)
4th Floor Renai Partire Shiodome 2-18-3 Higashi-shimbashi
Minato-ku, Tokyo, 105-0021, Japan
Tel.: (81) 3 5408 4422
E-Mail: info@dcf-d.co.jp
Web Site: www.dcf-d.co.jp
Creative Production Services
S.I.C.: 7319
N.A.I.C.S.: 541890

Dentsu Creative X Inc. (1)
10F Hamarikyu Parkside Place 5-6-10 Tsukiji
Chuo-ku, Tokyo, 104-0045, Japan
Tel.: (81) 3 5551 9933
E-Mail: info@dentsu-crx.co.jp
Web Site: www.dentsu-crx.co.jp
Graphic Design Services
S.I.C.: 7336
N.A.I.C.S.: 541430

Dentsu Customer Access Center Inc (1)
Ginza Building MTR 6-18-2 Ginza
Chuo-ku, Tokyo, 104-0061, Japan
Tel.: (81) 3 5551 8855
Web Site: www.dentsucac.co.jp
Customer Relationship Management Services
S.I.C.: 8748
N.A.I.C.S.: 541618
Yasuaki Minegishi *(Pres & CEO)*

Dentsu Digital Holdings Inc. (1)
1-8-1 Higashi Shimbashi
Minato-ku, Tokyo, 105-7001, Japan
Tel.: (81) 3 6252 1703
Fax: (81) 3 6252 1705
E-Mail: info@dentsu-digital.co.jp
Web Site: www.dentsu-digital.co.jp
Digital Communication Services
S.I.C.: 4899
N.A.I.C.S.: 517919
Ryuhei Akiyama *(Pres & CEO)*
Katsuhiko Okubo *(VP & CFO)*
Nobuyuki Tohya *(COO)*
Akihisa Fujita *(Exec VP)*

Dentsu e-marketing One Inc. (1)
5F Hamarikyu Kensetsu Plz 5-5-12 Tsukiji
Chuo-ku, Tokyo, 104-0045, Japan
Tel.: (81) 3 5551 1030
E-Mail: info@dentsu-em1.co.jp
Web Site: www.dentsu-em1.co.jp
S.I.C.: 7311
N.A.I.C.S.: 541810
Nagahama Kaoru *(Pres & CEO)*

Dentsu East Japan Inc. (1)
4-21-3 Shimbashi
Minato-ku, Tokyo, 105-0004, Japan
Tel.: (81) 3 5402 9555
Fax: (81) 354029641
Web Site: www.dentsu-east.co.jp
Billings: $170,000,000
Emp.: 320
S.I.C.: 7311
N.A.I.C.S.: 541810
Hiroshi Hirakawa *(Gen Mgr-Media Div)*

Dentsu Facility Management Inc. (1)
Dentsukosan No3 Bldg
Chuo-Ku, Tokyo, 104-0061, Japan
Tel.: (81) 355518111
Facility Management Services
S.I.C.: 8744
N.A.I.C.S.: 561210

Dentsu Hokkaido Inc. (1)
Nishi 5-11-1 Odori
Chuo-ku, Sapporo, 060-8545, Japan
Tel.: (81) 11 214 5111
Fax: (81) 11 231 4003
Web Site: www.dentsu-hokkaido.jp
Billings: $130,500,000
Emp.: 100
S.I.C.: 7311
N.A.I.C.S.: 541810

Dentsu Kyushu Inc. (1)
1-16-10 Akasaka
Fukuoka, Chuo-ku, 810-8675, Japan JP
Tel.: (81) 92 713 2555
Fax: (81) 92 771 8098
Web Site: www.dentsu-kyu.co.jp
Billings: $275,690,800
Emp.: 212
S.I.C.: 7311
N.A.I.C.S.: 541810

Dentsu Management Services Inc. (1)
Dentsu Tsukiji Bldg 2 1-7-11 Tsukiji
Chuo-ku, Tokyo, 104-0045, Japan
Tel.: (81) 3 5551 8702
Web Site: www.dentsu-ms.co.jp
Payroll Management Services
S.I.C.: 8721
N.A.I.C.S.: 541214

Dentsu Marketing East Asia Inc. (1)
2nd Floor Creglanz Shimbashi III 3-4-8 Shimbashi
Minato-ku, Tokyo, 105-0004, Japan
Tel.: (81) 3 3539 3188
Fax: (81) 3 3539 3788
Web Site: www.dentsumarketing.com
Marketing Research Services
S.I.C.: 8732
N.A.I.C.S.: 541910

Dentsu Meitetsu Communications Inc. (1)
6F, Nissay Nagoyaekinishi Bldg 6-9, Tsubaki-cho
Nakamura-ku, Nagoya, Aichi, 453-0015, Japan
Tel.: (81) 52 459 0555
Fax: (81) 052 459 5508
Web Site: www.dm-c.co.jp
Emp.: 200
S.I.C.: 7311
N.A.I.C.S.: 541810
Tateo Egawa *(Pres & CEO)*

Dentsu Music and Entertainment Inc. (1)
East 17th Floor East Tower Toranomon Twin Bldg 20-10-1 Toranomon
Minato-ku, Tokyo, 105-0001, Japan
Tel.: (81) 3 5575 5712
Fax: (81) 3 5575 5718
E-Mail: info@dentsumusic.co.jp
Web Site: www.dentsumusic.co.jp
Emp.: 35
Music Production Services
S.I.C.: 7929
N.A.I.C.S.: 711130
Shinki Miura *(Pres)*

Dentsu Okinawa Inc. (1)
Kokuba Bldg 3-21-1 Kumoji
Naha, Okinawa, 900-0015, Japan
Tel.: (81) 98 862 0012
Web Site: www.dentsu.com
Motion Picture & Video Advertising Services
S.I.C.: 7812
N.A.I.C.S.: 512110

Dentsu On-Demand Graphics Inc. (1)
1-8-3 Higashi-shimbashi
Minato-ku, Tokyo, 105-0021, Japan
Tel.: (81) 3 6217 1270
Fax: (81) 3 6217 4771
E-Mail: info@dodg.co.jp
Web Site: www.dodg.co.jp
Graphic Production Services
S.I.C.: 7336
N.A.I.C.S.: 541430

Dentsu Operations Development Inc. (1)
Dentsu Tsukiji Bldg 2 1-7-11 Tsukiji
Chuo-ku, Tokyo, 104-0045, Japan
Tel.: (81) 3 6226 2760
Business Support Services

S.I.C.: 7389
N.A.I.C.S.: 561499

Dentsu Public Relations Inc. (1)
2-16-7 Ginza
Chuo-ku, Tokyo, 104-8210, Japan JP
Tel.: (81) 3 5565 8430
Fax: (81) 3 3546 2017
E-Mail: info@dentsu-pr.co.jp
Web Site: www.dentsu-pr.com
Emp.: 210
Public Relations Agency
S.I.C.: 8743
N.A.I.C.S.: 541820
Ishimatu Shigeki *(Pres)*

Dentsu Razorfish Inc. (1)
14F Hamarikyu Parkside Place 5-6-10 Tsukiji
14F Hamarikyu Parkside Place 5, Tokyo, 104-0045, Japan
Tel.: (81) 3 5551 9885
Fax: (81) 3 5551 9978
E-Mail: contact@dentsu-razorfish.com
Web Site: www.dentsu-razorfish.com
Emp.: 211
Online Advertising Services
S.I.C.: 7319
N.A.I.C.S.: 541890
Hidetoshi Tokumaru *(Pres & CEO)*

Dentsu Research Inc. (1)
Dentsu Ginza Bldg 7-4-17 Ginza
Chuo-ku, Tokyo, 104-8171, Japan
Tel.: (81) 3 3289 6711
Fax: (81) 3 3575 1382
E-Mail: info@dentsuresearch.co.jp
Web Site: www.dentsuresearch.co.jp
S.I.C.: 7311
N.A.I.C.S.: 541810
Nomura Kiyoshi *(Pres)*
Andrew Powell *(Mng Dir)*

Dentsu Sports Partners Inc. (1)
Tsukiji Eto Building 8th Floor 1-12-6 Tsukiji
Chuo-ku, Tokyo, 104-0045, Japan
Tel.: (81) 3 6278 1580
Fax: (81) 3 6278 1594
Web Site: www.dentsu-sp.co.jp
Sporting Events Operation Services
S.I.C.: 7999
N.A.I.C.S.: 711310
Tatsuo Tachikawa *(Pres & CEO)*

Dentsu Table Media Communications Inc (1)
6th Floor Table Media Center 2-21 Ichigaya Honmura-cho
Shinjuku-ku, Tokyo, 162-0845, Japan
Tel.: (81) 3 5227 5450
Web Site: www.dentsu.com
Advertising Consulting Services
S.I.C.: 7319
N.A.I.C.S.: 541890

DENTSU TEC INC. (1)
1-11-10 Tsukiji
Chuo-ku, Tokyo, 104-8411, Japan
Tel.: (81) 3 5551 8888
E-Mail: webmaster@dentsutec.co.jp
Web Site: www.dentsutec.co.jp
Rev.: $23,720,150
Emp.: 1,252
S.I.C.: 7311
N.A.I.C.S.: 541810
Tatsuji Matsui *(Pres)*

Dentsu West Japan Inc. (1)
2-3-5 Dojima
Kita-ku, Osaka, 530-8228, Japan
Tel.: (81) 6 6342 3211
Fax: (81) 6 6342 3215
Web Site: www.dentsu.co.jp
S.I.C.: 7311
N.A.I.C.S.: 541810
Isao Maruyama *(Mng Dir & Exec VP)*

Dentsu Works Inc. (1)
4th Floor Dentsu Kosan Bldg 3 2-16-7 Ginza
Chuo-ku, Tokyo, 104-8106, Japan
Tel.: (81) 3 5551 8111
Fax: (81) 3 5551 8181
Web Site: www.dentsu-works.co.jp
Real Estate Management Services
S.I.C.: 6531
N.A.I.C.S.: 531390

dof inc. (1)
6F Kitagawa Bldg 1-9-1 Shimbashi
Minato-ku, Tokyo, 105-0004, Japan
Tel.: (81) 3 5537 5125
Fax: (81) 355375126
E-Mail: info@dof.jp
Web Site: www.dof.jp
Emp.: 4
S.I.C.: 7311
N.A.I.C.S.: 541810
Yukio Ohshima *(Dir-Creative)*

Drill Inc. (1)
1F Yamate Mansion 19-5 Udagawacho
Tokyo, Shibuya-ku, 150-0042, Japan
Tel.: (81) 3 5428 8771
Fax: (81) 354288772
E-Mail: info@drill-inc.jp
Web Site: www.drill-inc.jp
S.I.C.: 7311
N.A.I.C.S.: 541810
Akira Kagami *(Pres & Exec Dir-Creative)*

The Goal Inc. (1)
8-11-11 TK Ginza
Chuo-ku, Tokyo, 104-0061, Japan
Tel.: (81) 3 5537 5006
Fax: (81) 3 3289 3550
E-Mail: info@thegoal.jp
Web Site: www.thegoal.jp
S.I.C.: 7311
N.A.I.C.S.: 541810
Toshiro Kawashima *(Pres)*
Zenta Horiuchi *(CEO)*

Information Services International-Dentsu, Ltd. (1)
2-17-1 Konan Minato-ku
Tokyo, 108-0075, Japan
Tel.: (81) 367136111
Fax: (81) 367139928
Web Site: www.isid.co.jp
4812—(TKS)
Sls.: $800,404,000
Assets: $646,778,000
Liabilities: $229,845,000
Net Worth: $416,933,000
Earnings: $28,842,000
Emp.: 2,295
Fiscal Year-end: 03/31/13
Information Technology Consulting Services
S.I.C.: 7373
N.A.I.C.S.: 541512
Setsuo Kamai *(Pres, CEO & COO)*

Subsidiaries:

ISID Advanced Outsourcing, Ltd. (2)
2-17-1 Konan
Minato-ku, Tokyo, 108-0075, Japan
Tel.: (81) 3 6713 5900
E-Mail: sales-info@group.isid-ao.co.jp
Web Site: www.isid-ao.co.jp
Business Process Outsourcing Services
S.I.C.: 7389
N.A.I.C.S.: 561990

ISID Assist, Ltd. (2)
Keio Shinagawa Bldg 2-17-1 Konan
Minato-ku, Tokyo, 108-0075, Japan
Tel.: (81) 3 6713 9800
Fax: (81) 3 6713 9801
Web Site: www.dentsu.com
Business Support Services
S.I.C.: 7389
N.A.I.C.S.: 561499

ISID Fairness, Ltd. (2)
1st Floor Nittobo Bldg 2-8-1 Yaesu
Chuo-ku, Tokyo, 104-0028, Japan
Tel.: (81) 3 5202 1010
Fax: (81) 3 5201 7774
Web Site: www.dentsu.com
Online Financial Information Services
S.I.C.: 2741
N.A.I.C.S.: 519130

ISID InterTechnologies, Ltd. (2)
6th Floor Keio Shinagawa Bldg 2-17-1 Konan
Minato-ku, Tokyo, 108-0075, Japan
Tel.: (81) 3 6713 5111
Fax: (81) 3 6713 5099
E-Mail: personnel@isid-intertech.co.jp
Web Site: www.isid-intertech.co.jp
Software Development Services
S.I.C.: 7371
N.A.I.C.S.: 541511

iTiD Consulting, Ltd. (2)
2-17-1 Konan
Minato-ku, Tokyo, 108-0075, Japan
Tel.: (81) 3 6713 5700
Fax: (81) 3 6713 5899
E-Mail: g-info@itid.co.jp
Web Site: www.itid.co.jp
Information Technology Consulting Services
S.I.C.: 7373
N.A.I.C.S.: 541512
Atsushi Yoshimoto *(Pres & CEO)*

Non-U.S. Subsidiaries:

ISI-Dentsu of Europe, Ltd. (2)
5th Floor Epworth House 25 City Road
London, EC1Y 1AA, United Kingdom
Tel.: (44) 20 72568369
Fax: (44) 20 72568369
E-Mail: info@iside.co.uk
Web Site: www.iside.co.uk
Financial Software Development Services
S.I.C.: 7371
N.A.I.C.S.: 541511

ISI-Dentsu of Hong Kong, Ltd. (2)
Suite 1505 Central Plaza 18 Harbour Road
Wanchai, China (Hong Kong)
Tel.: (852) 2829 0829
Fax: (852) 2802 8477
E-Mail: isid@isid.hk
Web Site: www.isid.hk
Emp.: 20
Information Technology Consulting Services
S.I.C.: 7389
N.A.I.C.S.: 519190
Carrine Wong *(Gen Mgr)*

ISI-Dentsu Shanghai Co., Ltd (2)
Room 1101-1106 Hongyi Plaza 288 Jiujiang Road
Shanghai, 200001, China
Tel.: (86) 21 6360 0216
Fax: (86) 21 6360 0217
E-Mail: isid@isidsz.com.cn
Web Site: www.isid.com.cn
Computer Software Distr
S.I.C.: 5045
N.A.I.C.S.: 423430
Izumi Hiroyuki *(Gen Mgr)*

ISI-Dentsu South East Asia Pte. Ltd. (2)
1 Raffles Place 23-02 One Raffles Place
Singapore, 048616, Singapore
Tel.: (65) 6511 7088
Fax: (65) 6511 7066
E-Mail: support@isidsea.com
Web Site: www.isidsea.com
Emp.: 15
Information Technology Consulting Services
S.I.C.: 7373
N.A.I.C.S.: 541512
Mitsuhiro Arase *(Mng Dir)*

Interlogics, Inc. (1)
4th Floor Hamarikyu Kensetsu Plaza 5-5-12 Tsukiji
Chuo-ku, Tokyo, 104-0045, Japan
Tel.: (81) 3 3544 0931
Fax: (81) 3 3544 0935
E-Mail: sales@interlogics.co.jp
Web Site: www.interlogics.co.jp
Marketing Information Technology Consulting Services
S.I.C.: 7373
N.A.I.C.S.: 541512

JEB Co., Ltd. (1)
3rd Floor Matsuoka Ginnana Bldg 7-17-14 Ginza
Chuo-ku, Tokyo, 104-0061, Japan
Tel.: (81) 3 3545 2417
Fax: (81) 3 3545 2418
E-Mail: info@jeb.co.jp
Web Site: www.jeb.co.jp
Emp.: 5
Entertainment Event Planning Services
S.I.C.: 7999
N.A.I.C.S.: 711310
Shuji Komori *(CEO)*

Nakahata Inc. (1)
602 ARK Hills Front Tower Rop 2-23-1 Akasaka
Minato-ku, Tokyo, 107-0052, Japan
Tel.: (81) 3 3587 2008
Web Site: www.dentsu.com
Advertising Services
S.I.C.: 7311
N.A.I.C.S.: 541810

One Sky Inc. (1)
Root Azabujuban 902 1-4-1 Azabujuban
Minato-ku, Tokyo, 106-0045, Japan
Tel.: (81) 3 6913 3130
E-Mail: contact@oneskyinc.com
Web Site: www.oneskyinc.com
S.I.C.: 7311
N.A.I.C.S.: 541810

OOH Media Solution, Inc. (1)
4th Floor Four Seasons Ebisu Bldg 1-2-11 Ebisu-minami
Shibuya-ku, Tokyo, 150-0002, Japan
Tel.: (81) 3 5720 2700
Web Site: www.ooh-ms.co.jp
Outdoor Advertising Services
S.I.C.: 7312
N.A.I.C.S.: 541850
Brendon Cook *(CEO)*
Peter McClelland *(COO)*

Pict Inc. (1)
Shiodome Eastside Bldg 8F 5-4-18 Tsukiji
Chuo-ku, Tokyo, 104-0045, Japan
Tel.: (81) 3 5551 9250
Fax: (81) 3 5551 9052
E-Mail: id@pict-inc.co.jp
Web Site: www.pict-inc.co.jp
Motion Picture & Video Production Services
S.I.C.: 7812
N.A.I.C.S.: 512110

REWIND INC. (1)
Azabu KF Bldg 1-9-7 Azabu Juban
Minato-ku, Tokyo, 106 0045, Japan
Tel.: (81) 3 5574 8531
Fax: (81) 55702815
Emp.: 5
S.I.C.: 7311
N.A.I.C.S.: 541810
Takuya Tomohara *(Pres & CEO)*
Helen Brown *(Chief Talent Officer)*
Mick Mernagh *(Chief Insight Officer)*

Shingata Inc. (1)
5F Minami Aoyama Building 6-12-1 Minami-aoyama
Minato-ku, Tokyo, 107-0062, Japan
Tel.: (81) 3 3407 3261
E-Mail: bokura@shingata.co.jp
Graphic Design, Production
S.I.C.: 7311
N.A.I.C.S.: 541810
Hiroshi Sasaki *(Pres)*

Watson-Crick Inc. (1)
4-14-12 Nishi-azabu
Minato-ku, Tokyo, 106-0031, Japan
Tel.: (81) 3 6419 1958
Web Site: www.dentsu.com
Advertising Campaign Planning Services
S.I.C.: 7319
N.A.I.C.S.: 541890

Wunderman Dentsu Inc. (1)
San Marino Shiodome 2-4-1 Higashi-shimbashi Minataku
Minato-ku, Tokyo, 105-0021, Japan
Tel.: (81) 3 6430 8000
Fax: (81) 364308002
Web Site: www.wunderman-d.com
Emp.: 40
Direct & Relationship Marketing Services
S.I.C.: 8742
N.A.I.C.S.: 541613
Kensuke Noguchi *(Pres)*

Yokohama Super Factory Co., Ltd. (1)
1-11 Suehiro-cho
Tsurumi-ku, Yokohama, Kanagawa, 230-0045, Japan
Tel.: (81) 45 506 8181
Fax: (81) 45 506 8185
Web Site: www.y-s-f.co.jp
Film Studio Operating Services
S.I.C.: 7221
N.A.I.C.S.: 541921

Joint Venture:

Dentsu, Sudler & Hennessey Inc. (1)
Tsukiji Eto Bldg 1-12-6 Tsukiji
Chuo-ku, Tokyo, 104-8427, Japan JP
Tel.: (81) 335460463
Fax: (81) 335467462
E-Mail: contact@dsh.co.jp
Web Site: www.dsh.co.jp
Billings: $98,000,000
Emp.: 77
S.I.C.: 7311
N.A.I.C.S.: 541810

Dentsu Inc.—(Continued)

Yasushi Fukai *(Pres & CEO)*

Non-U.S. Subsidiary:

Dentsu Aegis Network Ltd. **(1)**
(Formerly Aegis Group plc)
10 Triton Street
Regent's Place, London, NW1 3BF, United Kingdom UK
Tel.: (44) 2070707700
Fax: (44) 2070707800
E-Mail:
Web Site: www.dentsuaegisnetwork.com
Sales Range: $15-24.9 Billion
Emp.: 16,500
Holding Company; Media Buying & Advertising Agencies
S.I.C.: 6719
N.A.I.C.S.: 551112
Tim Andree *(Chm)*
Kunihiro Matsushima *(Vice Chm)*
Jerry Buhlmann *(CEO)*
Nick Priday *(CFO & CFO-Aegis Media)*
Martyn Rattle *(Chief Client Officer-Aegis Media)*
Andreas Bolte *(CEO-Aegis Media Central & Eastern Europe)*
Mark Cranmer *(CEO-Isobar)*
Nigel Morris *(CEO-Aegis Media-North America & EMEA)*
Nigel Sharrocks *(CEO-Global Brands-Aegis Media)*
Andrew Moberly *(Sec)*

Subsidiaries:

Aegis International Limited **(2)**
180 Great Portland St
London, W1W 5QZ, United Kingdom UK
Tel.: (44) 70707700 (100%)
Fax: (44) 20 7070 7800
E-Mail: mail@aegisplc.com
Web Site: www.aegisplc.com
Holding Company
S.I.C.: 6719
N.A.I.C.S.: 551112
Michael Thew *(Dir-Client Svcs)*

Aegis Media Limited **(2)**
43-49 Parker Street
London, W1H 6LY, United Kingdom UK
Tel.: (44) 207 405 1050 (100%)
Fax: (44) 207 430 6319
E-Mail: carat.reception@carat.com
Web Site: www.aemedia.com
Emp.: 400
Provider of Media Services to Advertisers
S.I.C.: 7319
N.A.I.C.S.: 541830
Jerry Buhlmann *(CEO)*
Caroline Gianias *(Chief Trading Officer-Canada)*
Jim Marshall *(Chief Client Officer)*
Freda Shao *(Chief Digital Officer-Taiwan)*
Nigel Sharrocks *(Chm-UK & CEO-Global Brands)*
Robert Harvey *(CEO-New Zealand)*
Robert Horler *(CEO-UK)*
Michael Nederlof *(CEO-Middle East & North Africa)*
Vichai Suphasomboon *(CEO-Thailand)*
Ann Yang *(CEO-Taiwan)*
Sara Ye *(CEO-Amnet China)*

Subsidiaries:

Aegis Information Services Limited **(3)**
Parker Tower 43-49 Parker St
London, WC2B 5PS, United Kingdom UK
Tel.: (44) 207 430 6000
Fax: (44) 207 430 6299
E-Mail: stephen_white@carat.com
Web Site: www.carat.com
Emp.: 700
Advertising Agency
S.I.C.: 7311
N.A.I.C.S.: 541810
Susannah Outfin *(CEO)*
Tracy De Groose *(Mng Dir)*
Sue Frogley *(CFO)*
Richard Morris *(Deputy Mng Dir)*

Aegis Media Global Brand Management Limited **(3)**
10 Triton Street Regents Place
London, MW1 3BF, United Kingdom UK
Tel.: (44) 20 7430 6000
Fax: (44) 20 7430 6319
E-Mail: contact@aemedia.com
Web Site: www.aemedia.com
Media Communication & Digital Network Services
S.I.C.: 7313
N.A.I.C.S.: 541840

Carat Business Ltd. **(3)**
Parker Tower
43 49 Parker St, London, WC2B 5PS, United Kingdom (100%)
Tel.: (44) 74306399
Fax: (44) 74306299
E-Mail: carat.reception@cart.com
Web Site: www.carat.co.uk
Emp.: 400
Business Consulting
S.I.C.: 7311
N.A.I.C.S.: 541810
Tracy De Goose *(CEO)*
Matthew Hook *(Mng Dir)*
Sanjay Nazerali *(Global Chief Strategy Officer)*
Gavin Ashcroft *(Chief Strategy Officer-Australia & New Zealand)*
Dan Hagen *(Chief Strategy Officer)*
Jo Allan *(Chief Client Officer)*
Simon Ryan *(CEO-Australia & New Zealand)*

Carat Insight Ltd. **(3)**
Parker Tower 43 49 Parker St
London, WC2B 5PS, United Kingdom UK
Tel.: (44) 2074306000
Fax: (44) 20 7430 6299
E-Mail: nick.gracie@carat.com
Web Site: www.carat.co.uk
Emp.: 600
Media Buying Agency
S.I.C.: 7319
N.A.I.C.S.: 541830
Michael Nederlof *(Interim CEO-Middle East & North Africa)*
Michelle Lynn *(Sr VP & Dir)*

Feather Brooksbank Limited **(3)**
Raeburn House
32 York Pl, Edinburgh, EH1 3HU, United Kingdom UK
Tel.: (44) 131 555 2554
Fax: (44) 131 555 2556
E-Mail: contact@featherbrooksbank.co.uk
Web Site: www.featherbrooksbank.co.uk
Billings: $198,351,700
Emp.: 100
Media Buying Agency
S.I.C.: 7319
N.A.I.C.S.: 541830
Stuart Feather *(Mng Dir)*

Branches:

Feather Brooksbank Ltd. - Manchester **(4)**
Cardinal House 8th Fl
820 St Mary's Parsonage, Manchester, M3 2LY, United Kingdom
Tel.: (44) 161 834 9793
Fax: (44) 161 835 1363
E-Mail: contact@featherbrooksbank.co.uk
Web Site: www.featherbrooksbank.co.uk
Sales Range: $10-24.9 Million
Media Buying Services
S.I.C.: 7319
N.A.I.C.S.: 541830
Stuart Feather *(Mng Dir)*
Michel Pepin *(CFO & Sr VP)*
Brian Patreau *(CIO & Sr VP)*
Martha Barss *(Sr VP-Client Svcs)*
Stephen Fraser *(Sr VP-Client Strategy)*
Cam Thomson *(Sr VP-Enhancement Svcs)*

glue London Ltd. **(3)**
10 Triton Street Regents Place
London, NW1 3BF, United Kingdom
Tel.: (44) 20 7739 2345
Fax: (44) 20 7920 7381
E-Mail: hi@isobar.com
Web Site: www.isobar.com
Emp.: 150
Advertising Agency
S.I.C.: 7311
N.A.I.C.S.: 541810
Mark Cridge *(CEO)*
Wayne Brown *(Mng Dir)*
Jo Hagger *(Mng Dir)*

Unit:

Glue Isobar **(4)**
31 Old Nichol Street
Shoreditch, London, E2 7HR, United Kingdom
Tel.: (44) 20 7739 2345
Fax: (44) 20 7920 7381
Web Site: www.isobar.com
S.I.C.: 7311
N.A.I.C.S.: 541810
Penny Herriman *(CEO)*
Rick Williams *(CTO)*
Jo Hagger *(Chief Integration Officer)*

Posterscope Ltd. **(3)**
4th S Fl
55 Baker St, London, W1U 8EW, United Kingdom UK
Tel.: (44) 20 733 66 363
Fax: (44) 20 749 04 030
E-Mail: office@posterscope.com
Web Site: www.posterscope.co.uk
Emp.: 500
Media Buying Agency
S.I.C.: 7319
N.A.I.C.S.: 541830
Annie Rickard *(CEO)*
Glen Wilson *(Mng Dir)*
Brian Beck *(CFO)*
David Liu *(Chm/CEO-China & Taiwan)*
Ashish Bhasin *(Chm-Asia Pacific)*
James Davies *(Exec VP-Strategic Dev-America & Head-Hyperspace Innovations Div)*

U.S. Branches:

Posterscope **(4)**
2700 Pennsylvania Ave 2nd Fl
Santa Monica, CA 90404
Tel.: (415) 541-2900
Fax: (415) 975-0850
Web Site: www.posterscopeusa.com
S.I.C.: 7311
N.A.I.C.S.: 541810
Connie Garrido *(CEO)*
Ray Rotolo *(COO)*
James Davies *(Chief Strategy Officer)*
Jason Newport *(Sr VP & Dir-Tech)*

Posterscope **(4)**
2 Park Ave., 24th Fl
New York, NY 10016
Tel.: (917) 621-3250
Fax: (562) 695-1310
E-Mail: connie.garrido@posterscope.com
Web Site: www.posterscopeusa.com
Emp.: 16
S.I.C.: 7319
N.A.I.C.S.: 541830
Connie Garrido *(CEO)*
Dale Tesmond *(Mng Dir & Chief Experience Officer-The Brand Experience)*
Chris Bagen *(Sr VP & Mng Dir)*
Ray Rotolo *(COO)*
James Davies *(Chief Strategy Officer)*
Brigg Hyland *(Chief Client Officer)*
Natalie Payne *(Sr VP & Dir-West)*

Vizeum UK Ltd. **(3)**
90 Whitfield St
London, W1 T4EZ, United Kingdom
Tel.: (44) 2073799000
Fax: (44) 2075707415
E-Mail: generalenquiries@vizeum.com
Web Site: www.vizeum.co.uk
Billings: $331,901,900
Emp.: 130
Media Buying Agency
S.I.C.: 7319
N.A.I.C.S.: 541830
Ben Wood *(Mng Partner)*
Paul Hutchi *(Mng Partner-Plng)*
Richard Morris *(Mng Dir)*
Martyn Rattle *(COO)*
Manas Mishra *(Exec VP & Dir-Natl Strategy-India)*

Aegis Media Pacific Limited **(2)**
43-49 Parker Street Parker Tower
London, WC2B 5P5, United Kingdom
Tel.: (44) 20 7430 6300
Fax: (44) 20 7430 6319
Marketing Consulting Services
S.I.C.: 8742
N.A.I.C.S.: 541613

U.S. Group:

Dentsu Network **(2)**
32 Ave of the Americas 25th Fl
New York, NY 10013
Tel.: (212) 397-3333
Web Site: www.dentsunetwork.com
Advertising Agency Managing Office
S.I.C.: 8741
N.A.I.C.S.: 551114
Kunihiro Matsushima *(Vice Chm)*
Tim Andree *(Pres & CEO)*
Nicholas Rey *(CFO)*
Dick van Motman *(Chm/CEO-Asia)*
Aki Kakegawa *(Sr VP-Asia & Dir-Multinational Clients-Asia)*

Subsidiary:

Dentsu America LLC **(3)**
32 Ave of the Americas 16th Fl
New York, NY 10013 DE
Tel.: (212) 397-3333
Fax: (212) 397-3322
Web Site: www.dentsuamerica.com
Billings: $122,000,000
Emp.: 120
S.I.C.: 7311
N.A.I.C.S.: 541810
Mike Rogers *(Vice Chm)*
Doug Fidoten *(Pres)*
David Cameron *(CEO)*
Vincent Legg *(COO)*
Tim Andree *(Pres/CEO-Dentsu Network)*
Valerie Heine *(Exec VP & Grp Acct Dir)*
Scott Daly *(Exec VP & Exec Media Dir)*

Subsidiaries:

Dentsu Holdings USA, Inc. **(4)**
32 Ave of the Americas 16th Fl
New York, NY 10013 NY
Tel.: (212) 829-5120
Fax: (212) 829-0009
E-Mail: eeldred@dentsuamerica.com
Web Site: www.dentsuamerica.com
Holding Company
S.I.C.: 6719
N.A.I.C.S.: 551112
Doug Fidoten *(Pres)*
Richard Summo *(CFO & Exec VP)*

Subsidiaries:

Dentsu Attik, LLC **(5)**
85 2nd St 6th Fl
San Francisco, CA 94105
Tel.: (415) 284-2600
Fax: (415) 284-2650
E-Mail: ric@attik.com
Web Site: www.attik.com
Billings: $22,000,000
Advertising
S.I.C.: 7311
N.A.I.C.S.: 541810
Ric Peralta *(CEO)*

Non-U.S. Branch:

Attik **(6)**
10 Hills Pl
London, W1F 7SD, United Kingdom
Tel.: (44) 1132 0215 30
Fax: (44) 1132 4532 51
E-Mail: james@attik.com
Web Site: www.attik.com
Emp.: 11
Full Service
S.I.C.: 7311
N.A.I.C.S.: 541810
Emma Barker *(Dir-Client Svcs)*

Dentsu Communications, Inc. **(5)**
32 Ave of Americas 16th Fl
New York, NY 10013 NY
Tel.: (212) 660-6785
Fax: (212) 660-6797
E-Mail: info@dentsucommunications.com
Web Site: www.dentsucommunications.com
Emp.: 9
Communications, Event Planning & Marketing, Public Relations, Publicity/Promotions
S.I.C.: 7311
N.A.I.C.S.: 541810

Dentsu Entertainment USA, Inc. **(5)**
2001 Wilshire Blvd Ste 600
Santa Monica, CA 90403
Tel.: (310) 586-5677

Fax: (310) 586-5898
E-Mail: info@dci-la.com
Web Site: www.dci-la.com
Animation Picture Production Services
S.I.C.: 7812
N.A.I.C.S.: 512110

Dentsu Innovation Interactive, LLC (5)
32 Avenue Of The Americas
New York, NY 10013
Tel.: (212) 703-7200
Fax: (212) 703-7276
E-Mail: info@innovationinteractive.com
Web Site: www.36pi.com
Emp.: 300
Digital Marketing Services
S.I.C.: 7336
N.A.I.C.S.: 541430
Bryan Wiener *(CEO)*

Unit:

360i LLC (6)
32 Ave of the Americas 6th Fl
New York, NY 10013
Tel.: (212) 703-7201
Fax: (212) 703-7276
Toll Free: (888) 360-9360
E-Mail: press@360i.com
Web Site: www.360i.com
Sales Range: $25-49.9 Million
Emp.: 425
Digital/Interactive, Media Planning, Search Engine Optimization, Strategic Planning/ Research
S.I.C.: 7311
N.A.I.C.S.: 541810
Bryan Wiener *(Chm)*
Sarah Hofstetter *(Global CEO)*
Jonathan Ragals *(COO)*
Adam Kerj *(Chief Creative Officer)*
Craig Pohan *(CTO)*
Eric M. Bacolas *(Chief Talent Officer)*
Jared Belsky *(Pres-US)*
David Levin *(Pres-Creative & Tech)*
Rob Connolly *(CEO-London)*
Richard Mass *(Chief Privacy Officer & Gen Counsel)*
Laura Mete Frizzle *(Sr VP-Media Svcs)*

Branch:

360i (7)
1545 Peachtree St Ste 450
Atlanta, GA 30309
Tel.: (404) 876-6007
Fax: (404) 876-9097
Toll Free: (888) 360-9630
Emp.: 110
S.I.C.: 7311
N.A.I.C.S.: 541810
Jared Belsky *(Mng Dir)*
Craig Pohan *(CTO)*
Laura Mete Frizzell *(Sr VP-Media Svcs)*

Dentsu McGarry Bowen LLC (5)
601 W 26th St Ste 1150
New York, NY 10001 NY
Tel.: (212) 598-2900
Fax: (212) 598-2996
E-Mail: info@mcgarrybowen.com
Web Site: www.mcgarrybowen.com
Sales Range: $10-24.9 Million
Emp.: 300
Full Service
S.I.C.: 7311
N.A.I.C.S.: 541810
Gordon Bowen *(Chief Creative Officer & co-founder)*
John P. McGarry *(CEO)*
Eric Vukmirovich *(CFO)*
Jonathan Buckley *(COO)*
Brandon Cooke *(Global CMO)*
Stewart Owen *(Chief Strategic Officer)*

Branch:

Dentsu McGarry Bowen LLC - Chicago Office (6)
515 N State St 29th Fl
Chicago, IL 60654
Tel.: (312) 239-6370
Fax: (312) 840-8396
E-Mail: info@mcgarrybowen.com
Web Site: www.mcgarrybowen.com
Emp.: 50
S.I.C.: 7311
N.A.I.C.S.: 541810
Timothy Scott *(Pres)*

Non-U.S. Subsidiaries:

Dentsu McGarry Bowen GmbH (6)
(Formerly Dentsu Dusseldorf GmbH)
Rheinallee 9
40549 Dusseldorf, Germany De
Tel.: (49) 211 977 69 0
Fax: (49) 211 977 69 40
E-Mail:
Web Site: www.mcgarrybowen.de
Billings: $236,684,155
Emp.: 75
Advertising Agency
S.I.C.: 7311
N.A.I.C.S.: 541810
Wilfried Klanke *(Pres)*

Dentsu McGarryBowen UK Ltd. (6)
10 Hills Place
London, W1F 7SD, United Kingdom UK
Tel.: (44) 20 7529 9000
Fax: (44) 20 7529 9099
E-Mail:
Web Site: www.mcgarrybowen.com
Advertising Agency Services
S.I.C.: 7311
N.A.I.C.S.: 541810
Simon North *(CEO)*
Ida Rezvani *(Mng Dir)*

Dentsu Sports America, Inc (5)
32 Ave of the Americas 16th Fl
New York, NY 10013
Tel.: (212) 500-5690
Web Site: www.dentsu.com
Sports Marketing Services
S.I.C.: 8742
N.A.I.C.S.: 541613

Firstborn (5)
630 9th Ave Ste 910
New York, NY 10036
Tel.: (212) 581-1100
Fax: (212) 765-7605
E-Mail: info@firstbornmultimedia.com
Web Site: www.firstbornmultimedia.com
Advertising
S.I.C.: 7311
N.A.I.C.S.: 541810
Michael Ferdman *(Founder & CEO)*
Dan LaCivita *(Pres)*
Kevin Arthur *(COO)*
Joon Yong Park *(Chief Creative Officer)*

Non-U.S. Subsidiaries:

Beijing Dentsu Advertising Co., Ltd. (3)
F7-F11 Tower C Beijing Global Trade Center 36 North Third Ring Road
East Dongcheng District, Beijing, 100013, China
Tel.: (86) 10 5953 3737
Fax: (86) 10 6554 2098
Web Site: www.beijing-dentsu.com.cn
Emp.: 125
S.I.C.: 7311
N.A.I.C.S.: 541810
Yukiyasu Nagasaki *(Pres)*
Mikio Shiba *(Mng Dir)*
Yiming Wang *(CEO-Dentsu Media Palette China)*

Beijing Dentsu Advertising Co., Ltd. (3)
21st Floor Novel Plaza 128 Nanjing Road West
Shanghai, 200003, China
Tel.: (86) 21 6350 1660
Fax: (86) 21 6350 8552
Web Site: www.beijingdentsu.com.cn
Emp.: 100
S.I.C.: 7311
N.A.I.C.S.: 541810
Cissy Xu *(Sr Mgr)*

Beijing Dentsu Advertising Co., Ltd. (3)
Room 2906 Guangzhou Exchange Square
268 Dongfeng Zhong Road
Guangzhou, 510030, China
Tel.: (86) 20 8351 1998
Fax: (86) 20 8351 1339
Web Site: www.beijing-dentsu.com.cn
S.I.C.: 7311
N.A.I.C.S.: 541810
Yagi Akii *(Mng Dir)*

Beijing Dentsu Qingdao (3)
Room 1302 Building A Fulai Mansion No 18
Xiang Gang Zhong Road
Qingdao, Shandong, 266071, China
Tel.: (86) 8532 5761 227
Fax: (86) 8532 5762 655
Web Site: www.beijing-dentsu.com.cn
S.I.C.: 7311
N.A.I.C.S.: 541810
Kiko Tokizawa *(Gen Mgr)*

Beijing Oriental Rihai Advertising Co., Ltd. (3)
2003 Phoenix Place No A5 Shuguang Xi Li
Chaoyang District, Beijing, 100028, China
Tel.: (86) 10 5805 3600
Emp.: 80
S.I.C.: 7311
N.A.I.C.S.: 541810
Huang Feng *(Chm)*

BlueChip Agentur for Public Relations & Strategy GmbH (3)
Wilhelm-Beckmann-Str 6
45327 Essen, Germany De
Tel.: (49) 201 83012 4
Fax: (49) 201 83012 60
E-Mail: welcome@bluechip-pr.de
Web Site: www.bluechip-pr.de
Sales Range: $10-24.9 Million
Emp.: 14
S.I.C.: 8743
N.A.I.C.S.: 541820
Suleyman Ucar *(Owner)*
Ulrich Herzog *(Mng Dir & Partner)*

C & Marketing Services Inc. (3)
25th Floor Glass Tower 946-1 Daechi-Dong
Gangnam-Gu, Seoul, 135-798, Korea (South)
Tel.: (82) 2 3404 2800
Fax: (82) 2 548 1577
Web Site: www.cnms.co.kr
Marketing Consulting Services
S.I.C.: 8742
N.A.I.C.S.: 541613

Cayenne S.R.L. (3)
Via Volturno 46
20124 Milan, MI, Italy
Tel.: (39) 02 72 53 31
Fax: (39) 02 86 46 17 78
E-Mail: info@cayenne.it
Web Site: www.cayenne.it
Emp.: 50
S.I.C.: 7311
N.A.I.C.S.: 541810
Peter Grosser *(Mng Dir)*

Dentsu 24/7 Search Holdings B.V. (3)
Weena 327
3013 AL Rotterdam, Netherlands
Tel.: (31) 102064600
Fax: (31) 102064601
Advertising Services
S.I.C.: 7319
N.A.I.C.S.: 541890

Dentsu Alpha Limited (3)
Suite 4-03 4th Fl HCO Bldg 44B Ly Thuong Kiet Street
Hoan Kiem District, Hanoi, Vietnam
Tel.: (84) 4 3934 3388
Fax: (84) 4 834 2034
Web Site: www.dentsu.com
Emp.: 24
S.I.C.: 7311
N.A.I.C.S.: 541810

Dentsu Argentina S.A. (3)
Vuelta de Obligado 1947 Piso 5
Belgrano, C1428ADC Buenos Aires, Argentina
Tel.: (54) 1157774900
Fax: (54) 1157774904
E-Mail: info@dentsu-ar.com.ar
Web Site: www.dentsu-ar.com.ar
Emp.: 38
Advertising Agency Services
S.I.C.: 7311
N.A.I.C.S.: 541810
Guillermo Munro *(Gen Mgr)*

Dentsu Asia Pte. Ltd. (3)
77 Robinson Road 24-01 Robinson 77
Singapore, 068896, Singapore
Tel.: (65) 683722
Fax: (65) 68372262
Web Site: www.dentsuasia.net
Emp.: 200
Regional Administration Management Services
S.I.C.: 9532
N.A.I.C.S.: 925120
Dick van Motman *(Chm & CEO)*
Theodore Lau *(Reg CFO)*
Ted Lim *(Chief Creative Officer)*
Aki Kakegawa *(Sr VP & Dir-Multinational Clients)*

Dentsu Australia Pty Ltd (3)
47 Ridge St
North Sydney, NSW, 2060, Australia
Tel.: (61) 2 9923 3091
Web Site: www.dentsu.com
Advertising Agency Services
S.I.C.: 7311
N.A.I.C.S.: 541810
Mike Thomas *(Exec Dir-Creative)*

Dentsu Brussels Group (3)
Rue Fourmois 15
1050 Brussels, Belgium
Tel.: (32) 2 543 3900
Fax: (32) 2 537 4100
E-Mail: info@dentsubrussels.com
Web Site: www.dentsubrusselsgroup.com
Emp.: 35
S.I.C.: 7311
N.A.I.C.S.: 541810
Patricia Vancraenbroeck *(Mgr-Fin)*

Dentsu China Limited (3)
Room 1A-10A Island Place Tower
510 King's Road, North Point, China (Hong Kong)
Tel.: (852) 2102 3333
Fax: (852) 2104 0111
Web Site: www.dentsu.com.jp
Emp.: 60
S.I.C.: 7311
N.A.I.C.S.: 541810
Iso Mura *(Pres)*

Dentsu Communications Pvt. Ltd. (3)
8 Vittal Mallya Road
Bengaluru, 560 001, India
Tel.: (91) 80 511 20 444
Fax: (91) 80 511 20 404
Web Site: www.dentsu.com
Emp.: 23
S.I.C.: 7311
N.A.I.C.S.: 541810
Sandeep Goyal *(Chm)*
Simi Sabhaney *(CEO)*
Ruchira Raina *(Mng Dir)*
Norimichi Uno *(Exec VP)*
Rajesh Mathew *(Sr VP-Mumbai)*

Dentsu Creative Impact Pvt. Ltd. (3)
Rz-1 Bhwani Kunji
Vasant Kunji, New Delhi, 110070, India
Tel.: (91) 11 4604 7666
Fax: (91) 11 4605 7600
Web Site: www.dentsu.in
Advertising Agency Services
S.I.C.: 7311
N.A.I.C.S.: 541810

Dentsu Holdings CIS B.V. (3)
Prins Bernhardplein 200
1097JB Amsterdam, Netherlands
Tel.: (31) 20 521 4777
Advertising Services
S.I.C.: 7311
N.A.I.C.S.: 541810

Dentsu Holdings Philippines Inc. (3)
7th Fl 111 Paseo de Roxas St
Makati, 1200, Philippines
Tel.: (63) 2 884 8060
Fax: (63) 2 884 8066
Emp.: 40
Advertising Services
S.I.C.: 7311
N.A.I.C.S.: 541810
Nonna Nanagas *(Pres)*

Dentsu Holdings (Thailand) Ltd. (3)
27th Floor U-Chu Liang Bldg 968 Rama IV Road Silom
Bangrak, Bangkok, 10500, Thailand
Tel.: (66) 26324555
Fax: (66) 26324343
Web Site: www.dentsu.co.th
Emp.: 230
Investment Management Services

Dentsu Inc.—(Continued)

S.I.C.: 6211
N.A.I.C.S.: 523999
Kitti Phan *(Gen Mgr)*

Dentsu Hong Kong Ltd. (3)
Room 1A-10A 7/F Island Place Tower
Island Place 510 Kings Road
North Point, China (Hong Kong)
Tel.: (852) 2102 3333
Fax: (852) 2529 5114
Emp.: 55
Telecommunications Network Services
S.I.C.: 4813
N.A.I.C.S.: 517110
Yoshiharu Isomura *(Gen Mgr)*

Dentsu Korea Inc (3)
35th Floor Asem Tower 159-1 Samsung-Dong
Gangnam-Gu, Seoul, 135-798, Korea (South)
Tel.: (82) 12270270
E-Mail: dentsuseminar@dentsukorea.com
Advertising Services
S.I.C.: 7311
N.A.I.C.S.: 541810

Dentsu Kuohua (3)
13F 188 Sec 5 Nanjing East Road
Taipei, 105, Taiwan
Tel.: (886) 2 2747 9494
Fax: (886) 2 2528 5997
E-Mail: services@kuohua-ad.com.tw
Web Site: www.dentsu-kuohua.com
Emp.: 100
S.I.C.: 7311
N.A.I.C.S.: 541810
Emoto Yuichiro *(Chm & Pres)*

Dentsu Latin America Propaganda Ltda. (3)
Rua Joaquim Floriano 413 6 Andar
Itaim Bibi, 04534-011 Sao Paulo, Brazil
Tel.: (55) 11 3528 5333
E-Mail: falecom@dentsu-lat.com.br
Web Site: www.dentsu-lat.com.br
Advertising Agency Services
S.I.C.: 7311
N.A.I.C.S.: 541810
Renato Loes *(CEO)*
Denise Millan *(COO)*
Naoyuki Tsuji *(Exec VP)*

Dentsu (Malaysia) Sdn. Bhd. (3)
45-24 Plaza Level Block C Plaza
Damansara Jalan Medan Setia 1
Damansara Heights, 50490 Kuala Lumpur, Malaysia
Tel.: (60) 3 2711 5555
Fax: (60) 3 2711 5556
Web Site: www.dentsu.com
Emp.: 50
S.I.C.: 7311
N.A.I.C.S.: 541810
S.P. Lee *(Mng Dir & Exec Dir-Creative)*

Dentsu Marcom Pvt. Ltd. (3)
7A Khullar Farms New Mangla Puri
Maandi Road Mehrauli, New Delhi, 110030, India
Tel.: (91) 11 2612 2938
Fax: (91) 11 4185 8055
S.I.C.: 7311
N.A.I.C.S.: 541810
Rajesh Aggarwal *(Pres)*
Gullu Sen *(Exec Vice Chm & Chief Creative Officer-India)*

Dentsu Media Hong Kong Ltd. (3)
Suite 701 7/F 625 King's Road
North Point, Hong Kong, China (Hong Kong)
Tel.: (852) 3971 8500
Fax: (852) 2155 0622
Web Site: www.dentsu.com
Emp.: 20
Media Advertising Services
S.I.C.: 7319
N.A.I.C.S.: 541890
Alice Lam *(Mng Partner)*

Dentsu Media Korea Inc. (3)
20th Floor Glass Tower 946-1 Daechi-Dong
Gangnam-Gu, Seoul, 135-708, Korea (South)
Tel.: (82) 2 3011 2500
Fax: (82) 2 3011 2509
Web Site: www.dentsu.com
Media Advertising Services
S.I.C.: 7311
N.A.I.C.S.: 541810

Dentsu New Ideas LLC (3)
9th Floor 23 Osenny Blvd
Moscow, 121609, Russia
Tel.: (7) 495 781 0068
Fax: (7) 495 781 8817
E-Mail: sales@de-n-i.ru
Web Site: www.de-n-i.ru
Emp.: 25
Advertising Agency Services
S.I.C.: 7311
N.A.I.C.S.: 541810
Alexander Romanov *(Pres)*

Dentsu Philippines Inc. (3)
7th Floor 111 Paseo de Roxas Building
Paseo de Roxas St
Makati, 1200, Philippines
Tel.: (63) 2 884 8060
Web Site: www.dentsu.com
Integrated Marketing Services
S.I.C.: 8742
N.A.I.C.S.: 541613

Dentsu Plus Co., Ltd (3)
323 United Center Bldg 14th Floor Unit
1401 Silom Road Silom
Bangrak, Bangkok, 10500, Thailand
Tel.: (66) 2 234 3535
Web Site: www.dentsu.com
Advertising Services
S.I.C.: 7311
N.A.I.C.S.: 541810

Dentsu Singapore Pvt. Ltd. (3)
77 Robinson Road X25-00
Singapore, 068896, Singapore SG
Tel.: (65) 6734 0110
Fax: (65) 6835 1588
E-Mail: contact@dentsu.com.sg
Web Site: www.dentsu.com.sg
Emp.: 87
S.I.C.: 7311
N.A.I.C.S.: 541810
Rosalynn Tay *(CEO)*
Hiroshi Harada *(Sr Exec VP, Acct Dir & Global Acct Dir)*
Yasushi Itakura *(Exec VP)*

Dentsu-Smart LLC (3)
11 Osennyaya Str 6th Floor
121609 Moscow, Russia
Tel.: (7) 495 781 88 18
Fax: (7) 495 781 88 17
Web Site: www.dentsusmart.ru
Emp.: 20
Advertising Agency Services
S.I.C.: 7311
N.A.I.C.S.: 541810

Dentsu Sports Asia, Pte. Ltd. (3)
77 Robinson Road 24-01 Robinson 77
Singapore, 068896, Singapore
Tel.: (65) 6438 4729
Fax: (65) 6438 4725
Web Site: www.dentsu.com
Sports Event Operating Services
S.I.C.: 7999
N.A.I.C.S.: 711310

Dentsu Sports Europe, Ltd. (3)
Berger House 1st Floor 38
Berkeley Square, London, W1J 5AH, United Kingdom
Tel.: (44) 2074999124
Fax: (44) 2076291482
Global Sports Consulting Services
S.I.C.: 8748
N.A.I.C.S.: 541618

Dentsu (Taiwan) Inc. (3)
13F 68 Sec 3 Nanjing East Road
Taipei, 104, Taiwan
Tel.: (886) 2 2506 9201
Fax: (886) 2 2507 9244
Web Site: www.dentsu.com.tw
Emp.: 170
S.I.C.: 7311
N.A.I.C.S.: 541810
Yoshiharu Isomura *(Chm)*
Gentaro Komiya *(Pres)*
Tetsu Chang *(Exec VP)*
Romie Chen *(Sr VP)*

Dentsu (Thailand) Ltd. (3)
27th Fl U-Chu Liang Bldg 968 Rama IV Rd
Silom Bangrak, Bangkok, 10500, Thailand
Tel.: (66) 2 632 4555
Fax: (66) 2 632 4343
E-Mail: infocenter@dentsu.co.th
Web Site: www.dentsu.co.th
Emp.: 229
S.I.C.: 7311
N.A.I.C.S.: 541810
Amornsak Sakpuaram *(Pres & CEO)*
Takayuki Yamomoto *(Mng Dir)*
Maki Ono *(COO & Exec VP)*

Subsidiary:

Dentsu Media (Thailand) Ltd. (4)
15th Floor U-Chu Liang Bldg 968 Rama IV Road Silom
Bangrak, Bangkok, 10500, Thailand
Tel.: (66) 2 632 4020
Web Site: www.dentsu.com
Emp.: 60
Media Advertising Agency Services
S.I.C.: 7311
N.A.I.C.S.: 541810

Dentsu TOP Co., Ltd. (3)
Room 4E3-F 4th Floor Shi Ye Building 18
Cao Xi Road
Shanghai, 200030, China
Tel.: (86) 21 64271008
Fax: (86) 21 64272466
E-Mail: contact@dentsutop.com
Web Site: www.dentsutop.com
Advertising Services
S.I.C.: 7311
N.A.I.C.S.: 541810

Dentsu Utama Sdn. Bhd. (3)
Unit 1-1 Level 1 Block B Plaza Damansara
45 Medan Setia 1
Bukit Damansara, 50490 Kuala Lumpur, Malaysia
Tel.: (60) 3 2096 2212
Fax: (60) 3 2096 2213
E-Mail: info@dentsutama.com.my
Web Site: www.dentsutama.com.my
Integrated Communications Services
S.I.C.: 4899
N.A.I.C.S.: 517919
Hideo Katakura *(Vice Chm)*
Omar Shaari *(CEO)*

Dentsu Vietnam Ltd. (3)
14F Sun Wah Tower 115 Nguyen Hue Boulevard
District 1, Ho Chi Minh City, Vietnam VN
Tel.: (84) 8 821 9003
Fax: (84) 8 821 9002
Web Site: www.dentsu.com
Emp.: 25
S.I.C.: 7311
N.A.I.C.S.: 541810
Gaku Shinoda *(Gen Dir)*

DentsuBos (3)
276 King St W
Toronto, ON, M5V 1J2, Canada ON
Tel.: (416) 929-9700
Fax: (416) 929-0128
E-Mail: info@dentsubos.com
Web Site: www.dentsubos.com
Emp.: 200
S.I.C.: 7311
N.A.I.C.S.: 541810
Claude Carrier *(Pres)*
Michel Ostiguy *(CEO)*
Annie M. Rizen *(Sr VP & CFO)*

Branch:

DentusBos Montreal (4)
3970 Saint-Ambroise street
Montreal, QC, H4C 2C7, Canada
Tel.: (514) 848-0010
Fax: (514) 373-2992
E-Mail:
Web Site: www.dentsubos.com
Sales Range: $10-24.9 Million
Advertising Agency
S.I.C.: 7311
N.A.I.C.S.: 541810
Michel Ostiguy *(Pres)*
Roger Gariepy *(Chief Creative Officer)*

Division:

DentsuBos - Antibody Healthcare Communications Division (4)
276 King St W Ste 300
Toronto, ON, M5V 1J2, Canada
Tel.: (416) 929-0528
Fax: (416) 929-0128
E-Mail: info@antibodycommunications.com
Web Site: www.antibodycommunications.com
Emp.: 50
Healthcare Advertising & Marketing Services
S.I.C.: 7319
N.A.I.C.S.: 541890
James Cran *(Co-Founder & Pres)*

Indigo Werbeagentur GmbH (3)
Rheinallee 9
40549 Dusseldorf, Germany
Tel.: (49) 211 506538 0
Fax: (49) 213 299281 0
E-Mail: info@indigo-dusseldorf.de
Web Site: www.indigo-wa.de
Advertising & Communication Services
S.I.C.: 7311
N.A.I.C.S.: 541810

KTmhows Co., Ltd. (3)
195-1 Asem Tower 35F Samsung-Dong
Kangnam-Gu, Seoul, 135-798, Korea (South)
Tel.: (82) 2 2189 7000
Fax: (82) 2 508 5335
E-Mail: ksw1687@mhows.com
Web Site: www.mhows.com
Mobile Marketing Services
S.I.C.: 8742
N.A.I.C.S.: 541613

Media Palette (Taiwan) Inc. (3)
4F No 10 Section 3
Minsheng East Road, Taipei, 104, Taiwan
Tel.: (886) 2 2517 8866
Fax: (886) 2 509 5561
Web Site: www.media-palette.com.tw
Emp.: 82
Media Buying Services, Merchandising, Planning & Consultation, Sports Marketing
S.I.C.: 7311
N.A.I.C.S.: 541810
Tsuyoshi Suganami *(Pres & CEO)*

Phoenix Communications Inc. (3)
27F Glass Tower 946-1 Daechi-Dong
Gangnam-Gu, Seoul, 135-846, Korea (South)
Tel.: (82) 2 5600 600
Fax: (82) 2 5600 629
E-Mail: jnahn@pci.co.kr
Web Site: www.pci.co.kr
037270—(KRS)
Sales Range: $25-49.9 Million
Emp.: 181
Advertising Agency
S.I.C.: 7311
N.A.I.C.S.: 541810
Seok-Kyu Hong *(Chm)*
Ryuichi Irisawa *(Co-CEO)*
Duk-Young Kim *(Co-CEO)*

PT. Dentsu Consultants Indonesia (3)
22nd Floor Graha Niaga Jl Jenderal
Sudirman Kav 58
Jakarta, 12190, Indonesia
Tel.: (62) 21 250 5020
Web Site: www.dentsu.com
Management Consulting Services
S.I.C.: 8748
N.A.I.C.S.: 541618

PT. Dentsu Indonesia Inter Admark (3)
22nd Fl Graha Niaga JL
Jenderal Sudirman Kav 58, Jakarta, 12190, Indonesia
Tel.: (62) 21 250 5020
Fax: (62) 21 250 5010
E-Mail: info@dentsu.co.id
Web Site: www.dentsu.co.id
Communications, Consumer Marketing, Direct Marketing, Event Marketing
S.I.C.: 7311
N.A.I.C.S.: 541810
Harris Thajeb *(Pres)*
Yasuyuki Ikegami *(CTO)*

PT Dentsu Media Indonesia (3)
Graha Niaga 22nd Floor Jl Jendral
Sudirman Kav 58
Jakarta, 12190, Indonesia
Tel.: (62) 2505020
Fax: (62) 2505010
Web Site: www.dentsumedia.co.id

Media Communication Services
S.I.C.: 7313
N.A.I.C.S.: 541840
Rudy Mulyadi *(COO)*

PT. Dentsu Strat (3)
Bapindo Plaza 12th Floor Citibank Tower Jl
Jend Sudirman Kav 54-55
Jakarta, 12190, Indonesia
Tel.: (62) 21 5273844
Fax: (62) 21 5273955
Web Site: www.dentsustrat.com
Advertising Agency Services
S.I.C.: 7311
N.A.I.C.S.: 541810
Janoe Arijanto *(Pres)*

RPM Radar Reklam Pazarlama Musavirlik A.S. (3)
Suleyman Seba Caddesi BJK Plaza Blok
No 48 Kat 7 Besiktas
34357 Istanbul, Turkey
Tel.: (90) 212 227 97 77
Fax: (90) 212 227 97 57
E-Mail: rpm@rpm.com.tr
Web Site: www.rpm.com.tr
Emp.: 50
S.I.C.: 7311
N.A.I.C.S.: 541810
Paul McMillen *(CEO)*

Shanghai Oriental Partner Advertising Co., Ltd. (3)
Room 4E3-F 4th Fl Shi Ye Building 18
Caoxi Road North
Shanghai, 200030, China CN
Tel.: (86) 21 6427 2468
Fax: (86) 21 6427 2467
Web Site: www.dentsu.com
S.I.C.: 7311
N.A.I.C.S.: 541810

Steak Group Ltd. (3)
62-70 Shorts Gardens
Covent Garden, London, WC2H 9AH, United Kingdom
Tel.: (44) 20 7420 3500
Fax: (44) 20 7420 3518
E-Mail: moo@steakdigital.co.uk
Web Site: www.steakdigital.co.uk
Digital Marketing Services
S.I.C.: 8742
N.A.I.C.S.: 541613
Duncan Parry *(Co-Founder & Head-Paid Search)*
Rob Connolly *(CEO)*

TUP-NA Ltd. (3)
9th Fl Boonmitr Bldg 138 Silom Rd
Bangkok, 10500, Thailand
Tel.: (66) 2 634 0305
Fax: (66) 2 634 0308
E-Mail: panya@pro-q.co.th
Web Site: www.pro-q.co.th
Emp.: 35
S.I.C.: 7311
N.A.I.C.S.: 541810
Panya Kaiartid *(Mng Dir)*

X-Line Hypermedia Ltd. (3)
3rd Floor 26 Section 3 Nanjing East Road
Taipei, 10489, Taiwan
Tel.: (886) 2 2509 0577
Web Site: www.dentsu.com
Advertising Agency Services
S.I.C.: 7311
N.A.I.C.S.: 541810

Zhongying Dentsu Tec Advertising Co., Ltd. (3)
100027 Room B Floor 13 Tower F Fuhua
Tower No 8 Chaoyangmen Beidajie
Dongcheng District, Beijing, China
Tel.: (86) 10 6554 5354
Fax: (86) 10 6554 5370
Web Site: www.zydentsutec.com
Advertising Services
S.I.C.: 7311
N.A.I.C.S.: 541810
Kexi Le *(Chm)*
Hisashi Shono *(Vice Chm)*
Sheng Xuan *(CEO)*

U.S. Subsidiary:

Aegis Group, LLC (2)
150 E 42nd St
New York, NY 10017 NY
Tel.: (212) 591-9122
Fax: (212) 252-1250
E-Mail: fahmida.aguayo@aemedia.com
Web Site: www.aemedia.com
Emp.: 2,000
Media Buying Agency
S.I.C.: 7319
N.A.I.C.S.: 541830
Angela Courtin *(Pres)*
Nigel Morris *(CEO)*
Donna Wiederkehr *(CMO)*
Simon Zinger *(Gen Counsel)*

Subsidiaries:

Ammo Marketing (3)
475 Brannan St Ste 410
San Francisco, CA 94107
Tel.: (415) 541-2720
Fax: (415) 975-0849
E-Mail: fahmida.aguayo@aemedia.com
Web Site: www.ammomarketing.com
Advertising, Brand Development & Integration, Branded Entertainment, Guerilla Marketing, Logo & Package Design
S.I.C.: 7311
N.A.I.C.S.: 541810

Bluestreak (3)
343 Arsenal St
Watertown, MA 02472
Tel.: (617) 218-0700
Fax: (617) 218-6502
E-Mail: info@bluestreak.com
Web Site: www.bluestreak.com
Rev.: $6,000,000
Emp.: 28
S.I.C.: 7311
N.A.I.C.S.: 541810
Alison Kuryta *(Gen Mgr)*

Carat Brand Experience (3)
201 E 5th St Fl 11
Cincinnati, OH 45202-4187
Tel.: (513) 322-3892
Fax: (513) 255-9831
Web Site: www.caratbrandexperience.com
Emp.: 20
S.I.C.: 7311
N.A.I.C.S.: 541810
Geoff Thatcher *(Exec Dir-Creative)*

Carat North America Inc. (3)
150 E 52nd St
New York, NY 10017 (100%)
Tel.: (212) 252-0050
Fax: (212) 252-1250
E-Mail: info@carat.com
Web Site: www.carat.com
Emp.: 17
Marketing Consulting Services
S.I.C.: 8742
N.A.I.C.S.: 541613
Alex Crowther *(Global Pres-Client)*

Carat Trade (3)
150 E 42nd St
New York, NY 10017
Tel.: (212) 591-9175
Fax: (310) 907-1315
E-Mail: kathy.kladopoulos@carat.com
Web Site: www.carat.com
S.I.C.: 7311
N.A.I.C.S.: 541810
Todd Heligman *(Mng Dir & Exec VP)*

Carat (3)
2450 Colorado Blvd Ste 300 E
Santa Monica, CA 90404
Tel.: (310) 255-1000
Fax: (310) 255-1021
E-Mail: john.cate@carat.com
Web Site: www.carat.com
Emp.: 100
Advertising, Digital/Interactive, Media Buying Services, Media Planning
S.I.C.: 7311
N.A.I.C.S.: 541810

Carat (3)
875 Howard St 64
San Francisco, CA 94107
Tel.: (415) 541-2700
Fax: (415) 975-0850
Web Site: www.carat.com
Sales Range: $100-124.9 Million
Emp.: 30
Advertising, Digital/Interactive, Media Buying Services, Media Planning
S.I.C.: 7311
N.A.I.C.S.: 541810
Susan Taylor *(Exec VP & Mng Dir-Carat West)*

Carat (3)
3390 Peachtree Rd NE Ste 700
Atlanta, GA 30326-2819
Tel.: (404) 231-1232
Fax: (404) 239-9755
Web Site: www.carat.com
Emp.: 33
Digital/Interactive, Media Buying Services, Media Planning
S.I.C.: 7311
N.A.I.C.S.: 541810
Rick Vosk *(Sr VP & Grp Client Dir)*

Carat (3)
401 N Michigan Ave 14th Fl
Chicago, IL 60611-4255
Tel.: (312) 384-4500
Fax: (312) 384-5100
Web Site: www.carat.com
Advertising, Digital/Interactive, Media Buying Services, Media Planning
S.I.C.: 7311
N.A.I.C.S.: 541810
Mark Hodor *(VP-Direct Response)*

Carat (3)
200 Clarendon St 23rd Fl
Boston, MA 02116
Tel.: (617) 449-4100
Fax: (617) 449-4200
E-Mail:
Web Site: www.aegisplc.com
Emp.: 20
Advertising, Integrated Marketing, Media Buying Services, Media Planning
S.I.C.: 7311
N.A.I.C.S.: 541810

Carat (3)
150 E 42nd St
New York, NY 10017
Tel.: (212) 689-6800
Fax: (212) 689-6005
Web Site: www.carat.com
Emp.: 640
Digital/Interactive, Media Buying Services, Media Planning
S.I.C.: 7319
N.A.I.C.S.: 541830
Doug Ray *(Global Pres)*
Rose Zory *(Chief People Officer)*
Walt Cheruk *(Exec VP-Digital Media)*
Mike Hess *(Exec VP-Res, Mktg Sci & Consumer Insights)*
Michelle Lynn *(Sr VP-Carat Insight)*

Carat (3)
3333 Lee Pkwy Ste 400
Dallas, TX 75219
Tel.: (972) 715-1200
Fax: (972) 716-9935
Web Site: www.carat.com
Emp.: 20
Advertising, Digital/Interactive, Media Buying Services, Media Planning
S.I.C.: 7311
N.A.I.C.S.: 541810

Copernicus Marketing Consulting (3)
200 Clarendon St, 23rd Fl
Boston, MA 02116
Tel.: (617) 449-4200
Fax: (310) 255-7402
E-Mail: ami.bowen@copernicusmarketing.com
Web Site: www.copernicusmarketing.com
Business-To-Business, Consumer Marketing, Consumer Publications, Planning & Consultation, Strategic Planning/Research
S.I.C.: 7311
N.A.I.C.S.: 541810
Kevin J. Clancy *(Co-Founder & Chm)*
Peter C. Krieg *(Pres & CEO)*

Freestyle Interactive (3)
475 Brannon St
San Francisco, CA 94107
Tel.: (415) 541-2700
E-Mail: info@freestyleinteractive.com
Web Site: www.freestyleinteractive.com
Emp.: 45
S.I.C.: 7319
N.A.I.C.S.: 541830

Hyperspace (3)
2 Pk F
New York, NY 10006
Tel.: (212) 889-7752
Emp.: 2
S.I.C.: 7311
N.A.I.C.S.: 541810
James Davies *(Exec VP-Strategic Dev)*

iProspect (3)
200 Clarendon St 23rd Fl
Boston, MA 02116
Tel.: (617) 449-4300
Fax: (617) 923-7004
Toll Free: (800) 522-1152
E-Mail: interest@iprospect.com
Web Site: www.iprospect.com
Emp.: 1,300
Advertising Agency
S.I.C.: 7311
N.A.I.C.S.: 541810
Shenda Loughnane *(CEO)*
Francis M. Ferrara, Jr. *(CFO)*
J.B. Brokaw *(Chief Client Officer)*
Ruth Stubbs *(CEO-APAC)*
Sara Ye *(CEO-China)*
Ian Cohen *(Exec VP-Client Ops)*

Subsidiary:

Range Online Media (4)
131 E Exchange Ave Ste 216
Fort Worth, TX 76164
Tel.: (817) 625-4157
Fax: (817) 625-4167
Web Site: www.rangeonlinemedia.com
Emp.: 50
Advertising Agency
S.I.C.: 7311
N.A.I.C.S.: 541810
Cheryl Pingel *(CEO)*
Misty Locke *(Pres-Range Online Media & Chief Strategy Officer-iProspect)*
Ray White *(COO-Range Online Media, Exec VP & Mng Dir-iProspect-Dallas)*

Branches

Range Online Media (5)
150 E 42nd St Fl 13
New York, NY 10017-5609
Tel.: (212) 981-6799
Fax: (817) 665-1327
E-Mail: info@rangeonlinemedia.com
Web Site: www.rangeonlinemedia.com
Emp.: 20
S.I.C.: 7311
N.A.I.C.S.: 541810
Vic Drabicky *(Search Strategist)*

Range Online Media (5)
2245 Sego Lily Dr
Sandy, UT 84092
Tel.: (310) 944-0782
Web Site: www.rangeonlinemedia.com
S.I.C.: 7311
N.A.I.C.S.: 541810
Misty Locke *(Pres & Chief Strategy Officer)*
Ray White *(Mng Dir, COO & Exec VP)*

MMA (3)
15 River Rd
Wilton, CT 06897
Tel.: (203) 834-3300
Fax: (203) 834-3333
E-Mail: info@mma.com
Web Site: www.mma.com
Emp.: 100
S.I.C.: 7311
N.A.I.C.S.: 541810
Randolph Stone *(CEO)*
Jeff Faenza *(CFO)*
Sheila Baker *(Sr VP-Ops)*

Molecular (3)
475 Bannon St Ste 420
San Francisco, CA 94107
Tel.: (415) 541-2700
Fax: (415) 975-0851
E-Mail: melanie.lowe@molecular.com
Web Site: www.molecular.com
Emp.: 10
S.I.C.: 7311
N.A.I.C.S.: 541810

Molecular (3)
The Arsenal of the Charles 343 Arsenal St
Watertown, MA 02472
Tel.: (617) 218-6500
Fax: (617) 218-6700
E-Mail: rfolz@molecular.com
Web Site: www.molecular.com
S.I.C.: 7319

Dentsu Inc.—(Continued)

N.A.I.C.S.: 541830
Scott Savitt *(Sr VP-Sls & Mktg)*

Molecular (3)
150 E 42nd St
New York, NY 10017
Tel.: (646) 742-5000
Fax: (646) 742-5001
Web Site: www.molecular.com
Emp.: 20
S.I.C.: 7311
N.A.I.C.S.: 541810
Scott Savitt *(Sr VP-Sls & Mktg)*

Roundarch Isobar (3)
(Formerly Roundarch Incorporated)
300 E Randolph St Ste 4000
Chicago, IL 60601
Tel.: (312) 529-3500
Toll Free: (800) 700-0098
E-Mail: info@roundarchisobar.com
Web Site: www.roundarchisobar.com
Sales Range: $25-49.9 Million
Emp.: 450
Digital Marketing Agency
S.I.C.: 7311
N.A.I.C.S.: 541810
Jim Butler *(Pres)*
Geoff Cubitt *(Co-CEO)*
Jeff Maling *(Co-CEO)*
Bruce Posner *(CFO)*
Steven Moy *(Chief Commerce Officer)*

Branches:

Roundarch Isobar - Boston (4)
(Formerly Isobar US)
200 Clarendon St 23rd Fl
Boston, MA 02116
Tel.: (617) 936-1600
E-Mail: fahmida.aguayo@aemedia.com
Web Site: www.isobar.net
Emp.: 700
Digital Marketing Agency
S.I.C.: 7311
N.A.I.C.S.: 541810
Darryl Gehly *(Pres)*
Max Fresen *(Sr VP & Exec Dir-Creative)*

Roundarch Isobar - New York (4)
(Formerly Roundarch Inc. - New York)
140 Broadway Ste 4520
New York, NY 10005
Tel.: (212) 909-2300
Fax: (212) 909-2301
E-Mail: info@roundarchisobar.com
Web Site: www.roundarchisobar.com
Emp.: 150
Digital Marketing Agency
S.I.C.: 7311
N.A.I.C.S.: 541810
Todd Healy *(Dir-User Experience)*

Velocity Sports & Entertainment LLC (3)
230 E Ave 3rd Fl
Norwalk, CT 06855
Tel.: (203) 831-2000
Fax: (203) 831-2300
E-Mail: reisman@teamvelocity.com
Web Site: www.teamvelocity.com
Emp.: 125
Brand Development, Entertainment, Event Marketing, Government/Political/Public Affairs, Retail, Sports Marketing, Strategic Planning/Research
S.I.C.: 7311
N.A.I.C.S.: 541810
David Grant *(Principal)*
Alex Nieroth *(Principal)*
Bob Wilhelmy *(Principal)*

Vivid Marketing (3)
5080-B Highlands Pkwy
Smyrna, GA 30082
Tel.: (404) 591-5523
Fax: (404) 159-1553
E-Mail: info@vivdsport.com
Web Site: www.makeitvivid.com
Emp.: 70
S.I.C.: 7311
N.A.I.C.S.: 541810
Erik S. Peterson *(Founder & Pres)*
Andy Cook *(Chief Creative Officer & Principal)*
Kara W. Peterson *(Principal-Culture & Community Outreach)*

Vizeum USA (3)
150 E 42nd St
New York, NY 10017
Tel.: (212) 591-9120
Fax: (310) 907-1311
Web Site: www.vizeum-us.com
Emp.: 5
S.I.C.: 7311
N.A.I.C.S.: 541810
Catherine Davis *(Pres)*
Marc Hamelin *(Mng Dir)*

Non-U.S. Subsidiaries:

Aegis International Holding Company BV (2)
Piet Heinkade 55
1019 GM Amsterdam, Netherlands (100%)
Tel.: (31) 205304500
Fax: (31) 205304530
E-Mail: info.nld@carat.com
Web Site: www.carat.com
Emp.: 80
Holding Company
S.I.C.: 6719
N.A.I.C.S.: 551112
Arjan Ponper *(CEO)*

Aegis Media Australia (2)
105 York Street
Melbourne, VIC, 3205, Australia AU
Tel.: (61) 3 9690 5544
Fax: (61) 3 9690 9318
Web Site: www.aegismedia.com.au
Sales Range: $200-249.9 Million
Emp.: 320
Direct Response Marketing, Media Buying Services, Media Planning, Public Relations, Sports Marketing
S.I.C.: 7311
N.A.I.C.S.: 541810
Matthew Crook *(Chief Digital Officer-Australia & New Zealand)*
Luke Littlefield *(CEO-Australia & New Zealand)*
David Stephenson *(CEO-Creative Svcs Bus-Australia & New Zealand)*

Unit:

emitch (3)
Level 18
456 Kent St
Sydney, NSW, 2000, Australia
Tel.: (61) 2 9266 0777
Fax: (61) 02 9266 0799
E-Mail: john.murray@emitch.com.au
Web Site: www.emitch.com.au
S.I.C.: 7311
N.A.I.C.S.: 541810
John Murray *(Mng Dir)*
Matthew Crook *(Mng Dir)*

Aegis Media (Deutschland) GmbH (2)
Kreuzberger Ring 19
Wiesbaden, 65205, Germany
Tel.: (49) 61197880
Fax: (49) 6119788500
Web Site: www.aemedia.com
Marketing Consulting Services
S.I.C.: 8742
N.A.I.C.S.: 541613
Andreas Bolte *(CEO)*
Katja Anette Brandt *(Mng Dir)*
Marco Bergmann *(Mng Dir)*

Aegis Media France S.A.S. (2)
4 Place de Saverne
92400 Courbevoie, France
Tel.: (33) 141161718
Fax: (33) 141166584
Web Site: www.carat.fr
Emp.: 25
Media Services
S.I.C.: 7319
N.A.I.C.S.: 541830
Michel Teuliere *(Mng Dir)*
Guillaume Multrier *(Mng Dir)*

Subsidiary:

Aposition (3)
4 pl de Saverne
92400 Courbevoie, France
Tel.: (33) 1 44 26 27 00
Fax: (33) 1 44 26 27 01
E-Mail: infos@aposition.com
Web Site: www.aposition.com
Emp.: 50
Search Engine Optimization
S.I.C.: 7319
N.A.I.C.S.: 541890
Sebastien Langlois *(Partner)*

Aegis Media Group Asia Pacific (2)
152 Beach Rd Ste 36-01 Gateway E
Singapore, 189721, Singapore (100%)
Tel.: (65) 63965280
Fax: (65) 65014901
E-Mail: patrick.stahle@aemedia.com
Web Site: www.aemedia.com
Emp.: 20
Media Buying Services
S.I.C.: 7319
N.A.I.C.S.: 541830
Nick Waters *(CEO)*
Sean O'Brien *(Chief Client Officer)*
Ashish Bhasin *(Chm-India & CEO-South East Asia)*
Blaire Currie *(CEO-North Asia)*
K. F. Lee *(CEO-Greater China)*

Aegis Media Iberia S.L (2)
Julian Hernandez 15
Madrid, 28043, Spain
Tel.: (34) 91 353 62 00
Fax: (34) 91 350 12 50
Emp.: 300
Media Communication & Marketing Research Services
S.I.C.: 4899
N.A.I.C.S.: 517919
Andre Andrade *(Gen Mgr)*

Aegis Media Italia Srl (2)
Via Durini 28
Milan, 20122, Italy
Tel.: (39) 02776961
Fax: (39) 0277696259
Advertising Agency Services
S.I.C.: 7311
N.A.I.C.S.: 541810

Age (2)
Av Chedid Jafet 222 Bloco A-1
Andar, Sao Paulo, SP, Brazil
Tel.: (55) 11 2173 0333
Emp.: 60
S.I.C.: 7311
N.A.I.C.S.: 541810
Carlos Domingos *(Exec Dir-Creative)*

Carat Argentina S.A. (2)
Ave L N Alem 986 Piso 6
Buenos Aires, CF, C1001AAR, Argentina
Tel.: (54) 11 4576 7373
Fax: (54) 11 4576 7373, ext. 160
E-Mail: info.argentina@carat.com
Web Site: www.carat.com
Emp.: 44
Media Buying Services
S.I.C.: 7319
N.A.I.C.S.: 541830
Miguel A. Reca *(Pres & CEO)*
Norberto E. Patrici *(CFO)*

Carat Asia Pacific (2)
30/F Cambridge House Taikoo Place
979 King's Road, Quarry Bay, China (Hong Kong)
Tel.: (852) 2523 4222
Fax: (852) 2523 2380
Web Site: www.carat-asiapacific.com
S.I.C.: 7319
N.A.I.C.S.: 541830
Sean O'Brien *(CEO)*
Kym Pfitzner *(CFO)*
Gilad Coppersmith *(Pres-Intl Client-General Motors Acct-Singapore)*
Kate Williams *(Pres-Intl Client-Singapore)*
Patrick Stahle *(CEO-APAC)*
Rob Kabus *(Exec VP & Dir-Comm Plng)*

Carat Austria GmbH (2)
Ares Tower 12 Fl Stock Donau City St 11
Vienna, A 1220, Austria
Tel.: (43) 193435000
Fax: (43) 1 934 3500 299
E-Mail: post@aemedia.com
Web Site: www.aemedia.com
Emp.: 50
Advertising Agencies
S.I.C.: 7311
N.A.I.C.S.: 541810
Dirk Heumann *(Mng Dir)*

Carat Beijing (2)
Level 21 Office Tower E2 The Towers
Oriental Plaza No 1
East Chang An Ave
Dong Cheng District, Beijing, 100738, China
Tel.: (86) 10 8500 2800
Fax: (86) 10 8518 2135
E-Mail: Seth.Grossman@carat.com
Web Site: www.carat.com
Emp.: 150
S.I.C.: 7319
N.A.I.C.S.: 541870
Michelle Lau *(Mng Dir)*
Chen Warren *(Chief Strategy Officer & CEO-Master Kong Bus Acct)*

Carat Belgium (2)
Rue du Moulin a Papier 55
Papiermolenstraat 55, Brussels, 1160, Belgium
Tel.: (32) 26635111
Fax: (32) 26638989
E-Mail: webinfo.belgium@aemedia.com
Web Site: www.carat.be
Emp.: 140
Advertising Agencies
S.I.C.: 7311
N.A.I.C.S.: 541810
Anne Bataille *(CEO)*
Anny Schmit *(CEO)*

Carat Canada (2)
4446 Saint Laurent Blvd Ste 500
Montreal, QC, H2W 1Z5, Canada
Mailing Address:
116 Spaduba Ave Ste 600
Toronto, ON, MSV ZK6, Canada
Tel.: (416) 507-4170
Fax: (416) 804-3945
Web Site: www.caratcanada.com
Emp.: 104
S.I.C.: 7311
N.A.I.C.S.: 541810
Tankut Karahan *(Pres)*
Jacques Dorion *(CEO)*
Patricia Heckman *(Mng Dir-Montreal & Exec VP)*
Louise Gauthier *(CFO)*

Carat Expert - Milan (2)
Via Durini 28
Milan, 20122, Italy
Tel.: (39) 02 77 69 61
Fax: (39) 02 77 69 63 01
E-Mail: norina.buscone@carat.com
Advertising Agencies
S.I.C.: 7311
N.A.I.C.S.: 541810
Walter Hartsarich *(Pres & CEO)*

Carat France (2)
4 Place De Saverne
92400 Courbevoie, Cedex 106, France
Tel.: (33) 141161718
Fax: (33) 141166546
E-Mail: yael.chatelus-kusch@carat.fr
Web Site: www.carat.fr
Emp.: 20
Business-To-Business, Consumer Marketing, Media Buying Services
S.I.C.: 7311
N.A.I.C.S.: 541810
Thomas le Thierry *(Pres)*
William Multrier *(CEO)*

Carat Guangzhou (2)
Room 2501-2502 Dongshan Plaza
69 Xian Lie Road, Guangzhou, 510095, China
Tel.: (86) 20 8732 1091
Fax: (86) 20 8732 4825
E-Mail: michelle.lau@carat.com
Web Site: www.carat.com
S.I.C.: 7319
N.A.I.C.S.: 541870
Dasseux Pascal *(CEO)*
Michelle Lau *(Mng Dir)*

Carat Hong Kong (2)
164633 Kings Rd,
North Point, China (Hong Kong)
Tel.: (852) 2523 4222
Fax: (852) 2523 2380
Web Site: www.carat.com.hk
Emp.: 40
Business-To-Business, Consumer Marketing, Media Buying Services
S.I.C.: 7319
N.A.I.C.S.: 541870
Yves Del Frate *(CEO)*

Carat International Hellas (2)
392 Mesogion Ave
Agia Paraskevi, 153 41 Athens, Greece

Tel.: (30) 2106008200
Fax: (30) 2106008500
E-Mail: info.hellas@aemedia.com
Web Site: www.carat.com
Emp.: 50
Advertising Agencies
S.I.C.: 7311
N.A.I.C.S.: 541810
Elizabeth Zobakou *(Sec)*

Carat International Wiesbaden **(2)**
Kreuzberger Ring 19
65205 Wiesbaden, Germany
Tel.: (49) 61197880
Fax: (49) 6119788500
Web Site: www.caratgermany.de
Emp.: 400
S.I.C.: 7319
N.A.I.C.S.: 541870
Andreas Bolte *(CEO & CFO)*
Willibald Muller *(Mng Dir)*

Carat Ireland **(2)**
16 A The Crescent Monkstown
Dublin, Ireland
Tel.: (353) 12712100
Fax: (353) 2712112
E-Mail: claran@carat.com
Web Site: www.carat.ie
Sales Range: $200-249.9 Million
Emp.: 50
Advertising Agencies
S.I.C.: 7311
N.A.I.C.S.: 541810
Liam McDonell *(CEO)*

Carat Italia-Florence **(2)**
Via L Il Magnifico 10
50129 Florence, Italy
Tel.: (39) 055 46 22 31
Fax: (39) 055 49 66 12
E-Mail: silvana.lavacchielli@carat.com
Advertising Agencies
S.I.C.: 7311
N.A.I.C.S.: 541810
Silvana Lavacchielli *(Dir-Client Svcs)*

Carat Italia-Rome **(2)**
Via Trinita Dei Pellegrini 12
Rome, 00186, Italy
Tel.: (39) 06 68 89 97 1
Fax: (39) 06 68 89 97 36
E-Mail: maurizio.bergami@carat.com
Web Site: www.aegisgroup.co.uk
Advertising Agencies
S.I.C.: 7311
N.A.I.C.S.: 541810

Carat Italia-Turin **(2)**
Via De Sonnaz 14
Turin, 10121, Italy
Tel.: (39) 011 56366 1
Fax: (39) 011 54484 7
E-Mail: info.italia@carat.com
Advertising Agencies
S.I.C.: 7311
N.A.I.C.S.: 541810

Carat Korea **(2)**
5th Fl Dongnam Bldg 997-11 Daechi-Dong
Gangnam-Gu, Seoul, 135-502, Korea (South)
Tel.: (82) 2 2017 9200
Fax: (82) 2 2017 9299
E-Mail: KiHoon.Han@carat.com
Web Site: www.carat.com
Media Buying Services
S.I.C.: 7319
N.A.I.C.S.: 541830
Woohyun Nam *(CEO)*
Blair Currie *(CEO-Japan & South Korea)*

Carat Mexicana **(2)**
Arquimedes 130 Piso 5
Col Polanco, Mexico, DF, C.P. 11000, Mexico
Tel.: (52) 55 5249 7100
Fax: (52) 55 5202 7881
E-Mail: carat.mexicana@carat.com
Web Site: www.carat.com
Emp.: 133
Media Buying Services
S.I.C.: 7319
N.A.I.C.S.: 541830
Martin Loret de Mola *(Pres)*

Carat Mumbai **(2)**
12 Mittal Chambers
228 Nariman Point, Mumbai, 400021, India
Tel.: (91) 22 5660 8088
Fax: (91) 22 5660 8089
E-Mail: Ashish.Bhasin@aemedia.com
Media Buying Services
S.I.C.: 7319
N.A.I.C.S.: 541830
PV Narayanamoorthy *(Mng Dir)*
Ashish Bhasin *(CEO-Aegis Media South Asia)*

Carat New Delhi **(2)**
465 Udyog Vihar
Phase V, Gurgaon, Haryana, 122 016, India
Tel.: (91) 11 2629 4212
Fax: (91) 11 2629 3680
E-Mail: kartik.iyer@carat.com
Web Site: www.carat.com
Billings: $32,031,296
Media Buying Services
S.I.C.: 7319
N.A.I.C.S.: 541830
Karthik Iyer *(Mng Dir-Carat India)*

Carat Nordic AB **(2)**
Asogatan 108
Stockholm, 118 29, Sweden
Tel.: (46) 86986800
Financial Management Services
S.I.C.: 6211
N.A.I.C.S.: 523999

Carat Norge AS **(2)**
Pilestredet 8
0180 Oslo, Norway
Tel.: (47) 22828282
Fax: (47) 22828280
E-Mail: carat.no@carat.com
Web Site: www.carat.no
Emp.: 100
Provider of Media Services to Advertisers
S.I.C.: 7319
N.A.I.C.S.: 541830
Nick Stravs *(Exec VP)*

Carat Shanghai **(2)**
5/F Huai Hai Plaza
1045 Huaihai Zhong Rd, Shanghai, 200030, China
Tel.: (86) 21 2412 1800
Fax: (86) 21 2412 1818
E-Mail: Seth.Grossman@carat.com
Web Site: www.carat.com
Emp.: 241
S.I.C.: 7319
N.A.I.C.S.: 541870
Seth Grossman *(CEO)*
Kitty Leung *(Mng Dir)*
Adil Zaim *(CEO-China)*

Carat Sweden AB **(2)**
Asogatan 108
Box 4125
102 63 Stockholm, Sweden
Tel.: (46) 8698 6800
Fax: (46) 8522 20700
E-Mail: info@carat.se
Web Site: www.carat.se
Emp.: 60
Provider of Media Services to Advertisers
S.I.C.: 7319
N.A.I.C.S.: 541830
Henrik Hannemann *(Mng Dir)*

Dr. Pichutta GmbH And Co KG **(2)**
Kreuzberger Ring 17
D-65205 Wiesbaden, Hessen, Germany De
Tel.: (49) 61150650
Fax: (49) 611506530
E-Mail: info@dr-pichutta.de
Web Site: www.dr-pichutta.de
Emp.: 17
Independent Media Agency
Export
S.I.C.: 7319
N.A.I.C.S.: 541830
Cornelia Baumgartner *(Mng Dir)*

Iprospect **(2)**
Beim Alten Gaswerk 5
D-22761 Hamburg, Germany
Tel.: (49) 40 484 01 98 0
Fax: (49) 40 484 01 98 99
E-Mail: contact@rmsarcar.com
Web Site: www.iprospect.de/index.html
S.I.C.: 7311
N.A.I.C.S.: 541810

Isobar Australia **(2)**
Bond 1, Level 3, 26 Hickson Rd
Walsh Bay, NSW, 2000, Australia
Tel.: (61) 2 9218 8900
Fax: (61) 292114232
E-Mail: contactus@isobaraustralia.com.au
Web Site: www.isobaraustralia.com.au/
Emp.: 100
Advertising, Interactive, Internet/Web Design, Multimedia, Viral/Buzz/Word of Mouth, Web (Banner Ads, Pop-ups, etc.)
S.I.C.: 7311
N.A.I.C.S.: 541810
Cormac Loughran *(CMO-UK)*
Nilesh Pathak *(CTO)*

Isobar Hong Kong **(2)**
16/F 633 King's Rd
North Point, China (Hong Kong)
Tel.: (852) 39624500
Fax: (852) 39624567
E-Mail: dwanye.serjeantx@isobar.com
Web Site: www.wwwins.com
S.I.C.: 7311
N.A.I.C.S.: 541810
Mark Cranmer *(Chm)*
Jean Lin *(Global CEO)*
Dwayne Serjeant *(Mng Dir)*

Isosbar **(2)**
Suite 103-106
Block G Red Town
570 Huai Hai West Road, Shanghai, 200052, China
S.I.C.: 7319
N.A.I.C.S.: 541830
Jean Lin *(Chief Strategy Officer-Global)*

Division:

wwwins Isobar **(3)**
Suite 103 1st Floor
Block G Huai Hai Xi Road, Shanghai, 200052, China
Tel.: (86) 21 5238 1333
Fax: (86) 21 5238 6873
E-Mail: hello.shanghai@wwwins.com
Web Site: www.wwwins.com
Emp.: 300
Advertising, Digital/Interactive, Local Marketing, Media Buying Services, Media Planning, Strategic Planning/Research
S.I.C.: 7311
N.A.I.C.S.: 541810
Deirdre McGlashan *(CEO)*
Jean Lin *(CEO-Asia/Pacific & Chief Strategy Officer-Global)*
Peter Shen *(Chief Creative Officer)*

Kirowski Zrt. **(2)**
Kasca Utca 15-23
1027 Budapest, Hungary HU
Tel.: (36) 1 4112200
Fax: (36) 1 4112299
E-Mail: contact@kirowski.com
Web Site: www.kirowski.hu
Emp.: 100
Advertising Agency
S.I.C.: 7311
N.A.I.C.S.: 541810
Zoltan Kovacs *(CEO)*

Mindblossom **(2)**
116 Spadina Ave Ste 100
Toronto, ON, M5V 2K6, Canada
Tel.: (416) 203-2224
Fax: (416) 203-4024
E-Mail: victoria.tilon@isobar.com
Web Site: www.isobar.com
Emp.: 30
S.I.C.: 7311
N.A.I.C.S.: 541810
Annette Warring *(Pres)*

Planete Interactive **(2)**
4 Place de Saverne
La Defense, Courbevoie, 92 971, France (100%)
Tel.: (33) 141166769
Fax: (33) 141165989
Web Site: www.planete-interactive.com
Interactive Marketing Services
S.I.C.: 7319
N.A.I.C.S.: 541830
Jean-Sebastien Hongre *(Mng Dir)*

Vizeum Canada Inc. **(2)**
22 St Claire Ave E Ste 500
Toronto, ON, M4T 2S5, Canada
Tel.: (416) 967-7282
Fax: (416) 967-1395
E-Mail: vizeum@vizeum.com
Web Site: www.vizeum.com
Emp.: 24
Advertising Services
S.I.C.: 7311
N.A.I.C.S.: 541810
Annette Warring *(Pres)*
Micheal Bispo *(Sr VP & Mng Dir)*
Lulu Phongmany *(VP-Bus & Publr Dev)*

Branches:

Vizeum Canada Inc. - Vancouver **(3)**
1066 W Hastings St
Vancouver, BC, V6E 3X1, Canada
Tel.: (604) 646-7282
Fax: (604) 646-7299
E-Mail: hello.canada@vizeum.com
Emp.: 25
Advertising Services
S.I.C.: 7311
N.A.I.C.S.: 541810
Jim Gordon *(Mng Dir & Sr VP)*

DENYO CO., LTD.

2-8-5 Nihonbashi-horidomecho Chuo-ku
Tokyo, 103-8566, Japan
Tel.: (81) 368611111
Fax: (81) 368611181
E-Mail: s-kato@denyo.co.jp
Web Site: www.denyo.co.jp
Year Founded: 1948
6517—(TKS)
Sls.: $524,381,000
Assets: $612,865,000
Liabilities: $171,193,000
Net Worth: $441,672,000
Earnings: $37,378,000
Emp.: 753
Fiscal Year-end: 03/31/13

Business Description:
Engine-Driven Generators, Welders & Air Compressors Mfr & Sales
S.I.C.: 3621
N.A.I.C.S.: 335312

Personnel:
Hideaki Kuboyama *(Chm & CEO)*
Shigeru Koga *(Pres)*

Board of Directors:
Hideaki Kuboyama
Makoto Harada
Kenji Hasegawa
Shigeru Koga
Toru Masui
Shoichi Shiratori
Yoshio Tsuji

Transfer Agent:
Tokyo Securities Transfer Agent Co., Ltd.
Togin Bldg 1-4-2 Marunouchi
Chiyoda-ku, Tokyo, 100-0005, Japan
Tel.: (81) 3 3212 4611

Subsidiaries:

Denyo Kosan Co., Ltd. **(1)**
2-8-5 Nihombashi Horidome-cho
Chuo-Ku, Tokyo, 103-0012, Japan
Tel.: (81) 368610011
Fax: (81) 368611223
Industrial Machinery Distr
S.I.C.: 5084
N.A.I.C.S.: 423830

Denyo Trading Co Ltd **(1)**
2-8-5 Nihonbashi-horidomecho
Chuo-ku, 103-0012 Tokyo, Japan (100%)
Tel.: (81) 368610055
Fax: (81) 0368611188
E-Mail: s-wakas@denyo.co.jp
Web Site: www.denyo.co.jp
Emp.: 200
Electrical Apparatus & Equipment Wiring Supplies & Construction Material Whslr
S.I.C.: 5063
N.A.I.C.S.: 423610
Mitsura Sakai *(Chm)*

New Japan Machinery Co. Ltd. **(1)**
Daiichi-Seimei Building 7th Floor 3-6-5 Shin-Yokohama
Kouhoku-ku, Yokohama, Kanagawa, 222-0033, Japan
Tel.: (81) 454734011

Denyo Co., Ltd.—(Continued)

Fax: (81) 454736406
Emp.: 200
Sales & Rental Service of Industrial Electrical Machinery
S.I.C.: 7359
N.A.I.C.S.: 532490
Yoshihito Hagino *(Pres)*

Nishinihon Generator Mfg. Co., Ltd. (1)
140 Chichika
Karatsu, 847-0831, Japan
Tel.: (81) 955781115
Fax: (81) 955781616
E-Mail: higuchi@nishihatsu.co.jp
Web Site: www.nishihatsu.co.jp
Emp.: 140
Industrial Electrical Machinery Mfr & Distr
S.I.C.: 3559
N.A.I.C.S.: 333249

U.S. Subsidiaries:

Denyo America Corporation (1)
18111 Santafay Ave
Compton, CA 90221
Tel.: (310) 631-3489
Web Site: www.denyo.co.jp/english/group/group.html
Other Holding Companies Offices
S.I.C.: 6719
N.A.I.C.S.: 551112

Denyo Manufacturing Corporation (1)
1450 Minor Rd
Danville, KY 40422
Tel.: (859) 236-3405
Fax: (859) 236-3423
E-Mail: denyo@denyo.us
Web Site: www.denyo.co.jp/english/group/group.html
Emp.: 65
Motor & Generator Mfr
S.I.C.: 3621
N.A.I.C.S.: 335312
Yoshihiro Inaba *(Pres)*
Tetsuo Kawanishi *(CEO)*

Non-U.S. Subsidiaries:

Denyo United Machinery Pte Ltd. (1)
27 Pioneer Sector 1
Jurong, Singapore
Tel.: (65) 68622301
Fax: (65) 67969069
E-Mail: sales@sg.denyogroup.com
Web Site: www.sg.denyogroup.com
Emp.: 30
Industrial Machinery Whslr
S.I.C.: 5084
N.A.I.C.S.: 423830
Sebastian Koh *(Gen Mgr)*

United Machinery Services Pte Ltd (1)
27 Pioneer Sector 1 Jurong
628433 Singapore, Singapore
Tel.: (65) 68622301
Fax: (65) 67969069
E-Mail: sales@ums.com.sg
Web Site: www.ums.com.sg
Emp.: 35
Construction Machinery Mfr
S.I.C.: 3531
N.A.I.C.S.: 333120
Lee Kuang *(Mng Dir & Gen Mgr)*

DEOLEO, S.A.

Parque Empresarial Rivas Futura C/ Marie Curie 7 4 plta Edificio Beta
28521 Madrid, Spain
Tel.: (34) 915589505
Fax: (34) 913197071
Web Site: www.gruposos.com
OLE—(BAR BIL MAD VAL)
Rev.: $1,115,797,236
Assets: $2,243,866,157
Liabilities: $1,489,135,946
Net Worth: $754,730,211
Earnings: ($330,572,236)
Emp.: 863
Fiscal Year-end: 12/31/12

Business Description:
Olive Oil, Biscuits, Rice, Confectionery & Condiment Producer
S.I.C.: 2075
N.A.I.C.S.: 311224

Personnel:
Oscar Fanjul Martin *(Chm)*
Manuel Atencia Robledo *(Vice Chm)*
Luis Gonzalez Ruiz *(Vice Chm)*
Jaime Carbo Fernandez *(Mng Dir)*
David Moreno Utrilla *(Sec)*

Board of Directors:
Oscar Fanjul Martin
Gonzalo Alcubilla Povedano
Manuel Atencia Robledo
Manuel Azuaga Moreno
Jose Barreiro Seoane
Jaime Carbo Fernandez
Jose Maria de Leon Molinari
Manuel Galarza Pont
Luis Gonzalez Ruiz
Antonio Hernandez Callejas
Antonio Lopez Lopez
Antonio Luque Luque
Jose Moreno Moreno
Antonio Pulido Gutierrez
Jose Ramon Nunez
Antonio San Segundo Hernandez
Carlos Stilianopoulos Ridruejo

U.S. Subsidiary:

American Rice, Inc. (1)
10700 N Fwy Ste 800
Houston, TX 77037-1158 TX
Mailing Address:
PO Box 2587
Houston, TX 77252-2587
Tel.: (281) 272-8800
Telex: 77-5839 ARI HOU
Fax: (281) 272-9707
E-Mail: info@amrice.com
Web Site: www.amrice.com
Emp.: 360
Rice Producer
S.I.C.: 2044
N.A.I.C.S.: 311212
John Akeson *(CEO)*
Rick Arredondo *(CFO)*

Plants:

American Rice, Inc.-Freeport (2)
505 Port Rd
Freeport, TX 77541
Tel.: (979) 233-8248
Fax: (979) 233-4456
Web Site: www.amrice.com
Emp.: 200
Rice Processor
S.I.C.: 2044
N.A.I.C.S.: 311212
Dick Schneider *(Plant Mgr)*

DEP DISTRIBUTION EXCLUSIVE LTEE

6255 rue Hutchison Suite 103
Montreal, QC, H2V 4C7, Canada
Tel.: (514) 274-2040
Fax: (514) 274-2045
E-Mail: info@dep.ca
Web Site: www.dep.ca

Business Description:
Compact Discs, Cassettes, Videos & DVDs Distr
S.I.C.: 5099
N.A.I.C.S.: 423990

Personnel:
Maurice Courtois *(Pres)*
Georges Tremblay *(Sr VP)*

DEPA LTD.

Al Reem Tower 18th Floor
PO Box 56338
Dubai, United Arab Emirates
Tel.: (971) 42243800
Fax: (971) 42243700
E-Mail: info@depa.com
Web Site: www.depa.com
Year Founded: 1996
DEPA—(DFM)
Rev.: $529,753,758
Assets: $855,544,592
Liabilities: $416,468,088
Net Worth: $439,076,504
Earnings: ($50,171,069)
Emp.: 7,237
Fiscal Year-end: 12/31/12

Business Description:
Interior Design Services
S.I.C.: 7389
N.A.I.C.S.: 541410

Personnel:
Mohannad Izzat Sweid *(Founder)*
Hasan Abdullah Ismaik *(Chm)*
Nadim Akhrass *(Acting CEO)*
Umar Saleem *(CFO)*
Bernard Lim *(CEO-Asia)*

Board of Directors:
Hasan Abdullah Ismaik
Mohammed Al Fahim
Abdullah M. Al Mazrui
Fahad Al Nabet
Wassel Fakhouri
Roderick Maciver
Eyad Abdel Rahim
Marwan Shehadeh
Khaldoun Rashid Tabari

Subsidiaries:

Deco Emirates Company LLC (1)
PO Box 19238
Dubai, United Arab Emirates
Mailing Address:
PO Box 19238
Dubai, United Arab Emirates
Tel.: (971) 4 885 4660
Fax: (971) 4 885 4305
E-Mail: info@decoemirates.com
Web Site: www.decoemirates.com
Emp.: 30
Interior Contracting Services & Furniture Mfr
S.I.C.: 7389
N.A.I.C.S.: 541410
Hugh Bigley *(Mgr)*

Decolight Trading Co. LLC (1)
PO Box 62162
Dubai, United Arab Emirates
Tel.: (971) 4 2834346
Fax: (971) 4 2834349
E-Mail: decolite@emirates.net.ae
Web Site: www.decolightllc.com
Emp.: 5
Lighting Fixture Supplier
S.I.C.: 5023
N.A.I.C.S.: 423220
Samer Sawaf *(Mng Dir)*

Depa Al Barakah L.L.C. (1)
5th Floor NASA Bldg Al Maktoum St
PO Box 117357
Dubai, United Arab Emirates
Tel.: (971) 4 222 2259
Fax: (971) 4 222 2318
E-Mail: info.dbrk.dxb@depa.com
Emp.: 40
Interior Designing Services
S.I.C.: 7389
N.A.I.C.S.: 541410
Yasser Abdel Azeem *(Gen Mgr)*

Depa Interiors L.L.C. (1)
1604 16th Floor Al Reem Tower Al Maktoum Street
Dubai, United Arab Emirates
Tel.: (971) 42243800
Fax: (971) 42243700
E-Mail: info@depa.com
Web Site: www.depa.com
Emp.: 20
Interior Design Services
S.I.C.: 7389
N.A.I.C.S.: 541410
Mohannad Sweid *(CEO)*

Eldiar Furniture Manufacturing and Decoration L.L.C. (1)
Mussafah Industrial Area
PO Box 6687
Abu Dhabi, United Arab Emirates
Tel.: (971) 2 5555656
Fax: (971) 2 5555985
E-Mail: eldiar@depa.com
Web Site: www.eldiarfurniture.com
Emp.: 50
Wooden Furniture Mfr
S.I.C.: 2511
N.A.I.C.S.: 337122
James Foster *(Dir-Ops)*

Mivan Depa Contracting L.L.C. (1)
306-310 Wing A Dubai Silicon Oasis Headquarters Bldg Nad Al Sheeba
PO Box 182605
Dubai, United Arab Emirates
Tel.: (971) 4 3724085
Fax: (971) 4 3724105
E-Mail: mivan@depa.com
Web Site: www.depa.com
Interior Designing Services
S.I.C.: 7389
N.A.I.C.S.: 541410

Non-U.S. Subsidiaries:

Depa Egypt (1)
2 W El Mosheer Ahmed Ismail St 1158
Sheraton Heliopolis
Cairo, Egypt
Tel.: (20) 2 2268 6770
Fax: (20) 2 2268 6773
E-Mail: info.depa.egy@depa.com
Emp.: 4
Interior Designing Services
S.I.C.: 7389
N.A.I.C.S.: 541410
Somesh Ganeriwal *(Gen Mgr)*

Depa India Pvt. Ltd. (1)
Sagar Tech Plaza 6th Floor A Wing Andheri Kurla Rd Sakinaka Junction
Andheri E, Mumbai, 400 072, India
Tel.: (91) 22 4052 1234
Fax: (91) 22 4052 1235
E-Mail: info.depa.ind@depa.com
Emp.: 25
Interior Designing Services
S.I.C.: 7389
N.A.I.C.S.: 541410
Ali Malas *(Mng Dir)*

Depa Jordan (1)
3rd Floor 165 Abu Tawileh Plaza Mecca St
PO Box 3233
Amman, 11953, Jordan
Tel.: (962) 6 551 6511
Fax: (962) 6 551 6533
E-Mail: info.depa.jo@depa.com
Emp.: 6
Interior Designing Services
S.I.C.: 7389
N.A.I.C.S.: 541410
Fuad Azab *(Gen Mgr)*

Depa Qatar Co. W.L.L. (1)
Al Jassim Commercial Tower 7th Floor
Suhaim Bin Hamad Street
C Ring Road, Doha, Qatar
Tel.: (974) 4443 6759
Fax: (974) 4431 2502
E-Mail: depaqa.admin@depa.com
Web Site: www.depa.com
Emp.: 310
Interior Designing Services
S.I.C.: 7389
N.A.I.C.S.: 541410
Ibrahim Moussa *(Mgr-Ops)*

Depa Saudi Arabia (1)
Hail Street Abu ALHasan Building 2nd Floor
PO Box 136528
Jeddah, 21313, Saudi Arabia
Tel.: (966) 2 614 5866
Fax: (966) 2 614 5865
E-Mail: info.depa.ksa@depa.com
Emp.: 25
Interior Designing Services
S.I.C.: 7389
N.A.I.C.S.: 541410
Amer Rihawi *(Gen Mgr)*

Depa UK Limited (1)
4 River Court Brighouse Business Village
River Park Industrial Estate
Middlesbrough, TS2 1RT, United Kingdom
Tel.: (44) 1642243857
E-Mail: depa.uk@depa.com
Web Site: www.depa.com
Interior Designing Services
S.I.C.: 7389
N.A.I.C.S.: 541410
Paul Austin *(CEO)*

Vedder GmbH (1)
Industriestr 3
59348 Ludinghausen, Germany

Tel.: (49) 2591 929 0
Fax: (49) 2591929198
E-Mail: vedder@vedder.net
Web Site: www.vedder.net
Interior Designing Services
S.I.C.: 7389
N.A.I.C.S.: 541410
Ludger Dohm *(Mng Dir)*
Nicolas Held *(Mng Dir)*
Stefan Radau *(Mng Dir)*

DEPLOY TECHNOLOGIES INC.

19011- 1153 56th Street
Delta, BC, V4L 2A2, Canada
Tel.: (604) 781-1773
Fax: (888) 777-8099
Toll Free: (888) 213-3888
E-Mail: info@deploy.ca
Web Site: www.deploy.ca
DEP—(CNSX)
Rev.: $3,181
Assets: $120,375
Liabilities: $715,838
Net Worth: ($595,463)
Earnings: ($434,889)
Emp.: 3
Fiscal Year-end: 07/31/13
Business Description:
Fleet Data Management & Weighing Solutions
S.I.C.: 7372
N.A.I.C.S.: 511210
Personnel:
David Eppert *(Pres & CEO)*
Andre Thompson *(CFO & VP-Ops)*
Board of Directors:
Harold Dunnigan
David Eppert
Harjit Grewal
Andre Thompson
Legal Counsel:
Bacchus Law Corporation
Suite 1820 925 Georgia St W
Vancouver, BC, Canada
Transfer Agents:
Valiant Trust
710 130 King Street West
Toronto, ON, Canada

Securities Transfer Corp
2591 Dallas Pky
Frisco, TX 75034

DEPOSIT INSURANCE CORPORATION OF JAPAN

Shin-Yurakucho Bldg 9F Yurakucho
1-12-1 Chiyoda-ku, Tokyo, 100-0006, Japan
Tel.: (81) 332126030
Fax: (81) 332126085
E-Mail: inter-info@dic.go.jp
Web Site: www.dic.go.jp
Year Founded: 1971
Sales Range: $5-14.9 Billion
Emp.: 360
Business Description:
Banking Services
S.I.C.: 6011
N.A.I.C.S.: 521110
Personnel:
Masanori Tanabe *(Deputy Governor)*

DEPOTS PETROLIERS DE FOS

Z I Secteur 81 818 l'Audience
13270 Fos-sur-Mer, France
Tel.: (33) 442476577
Fax: (33) 442051154
Sls.: $21,600,000
Emp.: 70
Business Description:
General Warehousing & Storage
S.I.C.: 4225
N.A.I.C.S.: 493110
Personnel:
Philippe Mazenog *(Mng Dir)*

DEQ SYSTEMS CORP.

1840 1st Street Suite 103 A
Levis, QC, G6W 5M6, Canada
Tel.: (418) 839-3012
Fax: (418) 839-5956
E-Mail: info@deq.com
Web Site: www.deq.com
DEQ—(TSXV)
Rev.: $5,571,266
Assets: $11,449,135
Liabilities: $1,270,753
Net Worth: $10,178,382
Earnings: ($3,316,053)
Emp.: 30
Fiscal Year-end: 11/30/12
Business Description:
Electronic Gaming Systems Mfr
S.I.C.: 7993
N.A.I.C.S.: 713120
Personnel:
Mike Telesmanic *(Chm)*
Francois Proulx *(Interim CEO)*
Mike Poulin *(CMO)*
Genevieve Cossette *(Chief Legal Officer)*
David Jacques *(CTO)*
Real Berube *(Chief Innovation Officer)*
Board of Directors:
Mike Telesmanic
Herve Eschasseriau
Earle G. Hall
Alexandre Lattes
Jean-Claude Vachon
Transfer Agent:
CIBC Mellon Trust Company
320 Bay Street Banking Hall
Toronto, ON, Canada

U.S. Subsidiary:

DP Stud, Inc. **(1)**
2325 Western Ave Ste 6
Las Vegas, NV 89102
Tel.: (702) 383-5959
Fax: (702) 383-3351
E-Mail: infodp@dpstud.com
Web Site: www.dpstud.com
Proprietary Casino Table Games Developer & Marketer
S.I.C.: 7999
N.A.I.C.S.: 713290
David Pokorny *(VP-Customer Svc)*

DER INTERNATIONAL HOME FURNISHING CO., LTD.

Wu Sheng Zebin International Building 28th floor
Wujiang, Suzhou, Jiangsu, 215 228, China
Tel.: (86) 512 63591111
E-Mail: admin@der.com.cn
Web Site: www.der.com.cn
Year Founded: 2004
002631—(SSE)
Emp.: 470
Business Description:
Wood Floor Products
S.I.C.: 2426
N.A.I.C.S.: 321918
Personnel:
Jiyong Ru *(Chm)*

DEREK OIL & GAS CORPORATION

(Name Changed to Newcastle Energy Corp,)

DEREK POBJOY INVESTMENTS LTD.

Millennia House Kingswood Park Bonsor Dr
Kingswood, Surrey, KT20 6AY, United Kingdom
Tel.: (44) 737818181
Fax: (44) 737818199
E-Mail: mint@pobjoy.com
Web Site: www.pobjoy.com
Emp.: 45
Business Description:
Holding Company
S.I.C.: 6719
N.A.I.C.S.: 551112
Personnel:
Derek Pobjoy *(Chm)*

Subsidiary:

Pobjoy Mint Ltd. **(1)**
Millennia House Kingswood Pk Bonsor Dr
Kingswood, Surrey, KT20 6AY, United Kingdom UK
Tel.: (44) 1737818181
Fax: (44) 1737818199
E-Mail: sales@pobjoy.com
Web Site: www.pobjoy.com
Emp.: 40
Mfr. of Precious Metal Jewelry
S.I.C.: 3914
N.A.I.C.S.: 339910
Derek Pobjoy *(Chm)*
Taya Pobjoy *(Mng Dir)*

DERICHEBOURG S.A.

119 avenue du General Michel Bizot
75012 Paris, France
Tel.: (33) 144754040
Fax: (33) 144754322
E-Mail: communication@derichebourg.com
Web Site: www.derichebourg.com
DBG—(EUR)
Sales Range: $1-4.9 Billion
Emp.: 40,052
Business Description:
Environmental & Recycling Services; Airport Support Services; Facilities Management Services
S.I.C.: 4959
N.A.I.C.S.: 562998
Personnel:
Daniel Derichebourg *(Chm & CEO)*
Bernard Regis *(CFO & Deputy Mng Dir)*
Board of Directors:
Daniel Derichebourg
Boris Derichebourg
Thomas Derichebourg
Matthieu Pigasse
Bernard Val

Ernst & Young Audit S.A.S.
Faubourg de l'Arche 11, allee de l'Arche
Paris, France

Divisions:

Derichebourg Environnement **(1)**
119 Ave du General Michel Bizot
75579 Paris, Cedex 12, France
Tel.: (33) 144754040
Fax: (33) 144754322
E-Mail: communication@derichebourg.com
Web Site: www.derichebourg.com
Sales Range: $1-4.9 Billion
Emp.: 4,575
Scrap Metal Collector & Recycling Services
S.I.C.: 4959
N.A.I.C.S.: 562998
Daniel Derichebourg *(Chm)*

Subsidiaries:

AFM Recyclage S.A. **(2)**
Siege Social Prairies de Courrejean
BP 8
Chemin de Guitteronde, 33886 Villenave-d'Ornon, France FR
Tel.: (33) 5 56 87 73 20 (99.81%)
Fax: (33) 5 56 75 84 15
Scrap Metal Collector & Recycling Services
S.I.C.: 4959
N.A.I.C.S.: 562998

Subsidiaries:

AFM Transport S.A. **(3)**
ZI dEn Jacca 27 Chemin de la Menude
BP 96
31772 Colomiers, France FR
Tel.: (33) 5 62 74 87 27 (99.81%)
Fax: (33) 5 62 74 87 36
Web Site: www.derichebourg.com
Scrap Metal Collector & Recycling Services
S.I.C.: 4959
N.A.I.C.S.: 562998

Ibex S.A. **(3)**
3 Av Marcellin Berthelot
92390 Villeneuve-la-Garenne, France FR
Tel.: (33) 147993495 (49.89%)
Fax: (33) 147993924
Scrap Metal Collector & Recycling Services
S.I.C.: 4959
N.A.I.C.S.: 562998

Eco - PHU Holding **(2)**
119 Avenue Bizot
75012 Paris, France
Tel.: (33) 144754040
E-Mail: accueil.paris@derichebourg.com
Web Site: www.derichebourg.com
Holding Company
S.I.C.: 6719
N.A.I.C.S.: 551112
Daniel Derichebourg *(Chm)*

Subsidiaries:

Eco - PHU SAS **(3)**
84 BOULEVARD DE L EUROPE
69310 Lyon, France
Tel.: (33) 472768930
Fax: (33) 478728341
Scrap Metal Collector & Recycling Services
S.I.C.: 4959
N.A.I.C.S.: 562998

Eska S.A.S **(2)**
Siege Social - 56 rue de Metz
57130 Metz, France FR
Tel.: (33) 387604222
Fax: (33) 387608150
Emp.: 318
Scrap Metal Recycling
S.I.C.: 4959
N.A.I.C.S.: 562998
Salton Francois *(Gen Mgr)*

Subsidiaries:

Alsafer Environment SA **(3)**
8 rue Gustave Goldenberg
Saverne, 67700, France FR
Tel.: (33) 388712075 (50%)
Fax: (33) 3 88 03 10 54
Scrap Metal Collection Services
S.I.C.: 4959
N.A.I.C.S.: 562998

Marx Spaenlin SA **(3)**
42 Avenue de Suisse
BP 283
Illzach, Cedex, 68316, France FR
Tel.: (33) 389310202 (100%)
Fax: (33) 389619131
Emp.: 40
Scrap Metal Collection
S.I.C.: 4959
N.A.I.C.S.: 562998
Thierry Konzem *(Mng Dir)*

Rohr SA **(3)**
172 rue du Ladhof
BP 1305
Colmar, Cedex, 68013, France (50%)
Tel.: (33) 389210950
Fax: (33) 3 89 21 09 51
Scrap Metal Collection Services
S.I.C.: 4959
N.A.I.C.S.: 562998

Ferrotrade Sas **(2)**
Siege Social - 56 rue de Metz
Metz, 57130, France FR
Tel.: (33) 387604222 (100%)
Fax: (33) 387608150
Scrap Metal Collection Services
S.I.C.: 4959
N.A.I.C.S.: 562998

Fricom Recycling **(2)**
26-28 Chemin Pave
95340 Bernes-sur-Oise, France
Tel.: (33) 134700320
Fax: (33) 134700320
Scrap Metal Collector & Recycling Services; Owned 50% by Oeko-Service SA & 50% by Derichebourg Environment
S.I.C.: 4959

Derichebourg S.A.—(Continued)

N.A.I.C.S.: 562998

Inorec S.A.S. (2)
54 Rue Ernest Macarez
Valenciennes, 59300, France
Tel.: (33) 327303437
Fax: (33) 327412802
Scrap Metal Collector & Recycling Services
S.I.C.: 4959
N.A.I.C.S.: 562998

Plastic Recycling SA (2)
ZA du Monay
71210 Saint-Eusebe, France
Tel.: (33) 385739060
Fax: (33) 385780347
E-Mail: jquessard@plasticomnium.com
Web Site: www.plasticomnium.com
Emp.: 35
Plastics Product Mfr
S.I.C.: 3089
N.A.I.C.S.: 326199
Quessard Jean Michel *(Gen Mgr)*

Purfer S.A.S (2)
Route Departmentale 147
Saint Pierre De Chandieu Rd
Quartier De La Gare, 69780 Lyon, France FR
Tel.: (33) 472481250 (99.89%)
Fax: (33) 472481277
Scrap Metal & Car Recycling Services
S.I.C.: 5051
N.A.I.C.S.: 423510

Subsidiaries:

Etablissements Russo S.A.S. (3)
62 avenue Denis Semeria
06300 Nice, France FR
Tel.: (33) 493894097 (99.89%)
Fax: (33) 492048080
Scrap Metal Collector & Recycling Services
S.I.C.: 4959
N.A.I.C.S.: 562998
Philip Morrison *(Gen Mgr)*

Purfer Transport S.A. (3)
Quartier De La Gare
Route Departmentale 147, 69780 Mions, Lyons, France FR
Tel.: (33) 472148833 (99.69%)
Fax: (33) 472148837
Metal Scrap & Car Recycling Transport Services
S.I.C.: 4789
N.A.I.C.S.: 488999

Purmet Transport S.A. (3)
Quartier Le Beausset CD 9
13724 Marignane, Cedex, France FR
Tel.: (33) 442094407 (99.89%)
Fax: (33) 442314263
Scrap Metal Recycling & Transport
S.I.C.: 5051
N.A.I.C.S.: 423510

Soper S.A.S (3)
Rue Georges Latil
Espace Polygone Nord, 66000 Perpignan, France FR
Tel.: (33) 468529578 (99.77%)
Fax: (33) 4 68 52 95 79
Scrap Metal Recycling Services
S.I.C.: 5051
N.A.I.C.S.: 423510

ETS Maiarelli (3)
36 Route du Plan
Grasse, 06130, France FR
Tel.: (33) 4 97 01 13 00 (99.89%)
Fax: (33) 4 93 42 01 27
Web Site: www.derichebourg.com
Scrap Metal Recycling Services
S.I.C.: 3499
N.A.I.C.S.: 332999

Revival S.A.S. (2)
3 Av Marcellin Berthelot
ZI du Val de Seine, 92390 Villeneuve-la-Garenne, France
Tel.: (33) 140857700
Fax: (33) 1 47 94 16 40
Scrap Metal Collector & Recycling Services
S.I.C.: 4959
N.A.I.C.S.: 562998

Subsidiaries:

Bolton SARL (3)
90 Rue Des Rosiers
93400 Paris, France
Tel.: (33) 1 401154 05
Scrap Metal Collector & Recycling Services
S.I.C.: 4959
N.A.I.C.S.: 562998

Corepa S.N.C. (3)
119 Avenue Du Generale
75579 Paris, France
Tel.: (33) 144754040
Fax: (33) 1 44 75 43 40
Scrap Metal Collector & Recycling Services
S.I.C.: 4959
N.A.I.C.S.: 562998

Fradena Transport SAS (3)
3 Avenue Marcellin Berthelot
92390 Villeneuve-la-Garenne, France
Tel.: (33) 147984859
Fax: (33) 147982926
E-Mail: splanning.revival@derichebourg.com
Emp.: 6
Transportation Support Services
S.I.C.: 4789
N.A.I.C.S.: 488999
Alain Siebert *(Mgr)*

Sas Du Petit Lac (3)
65 Boulevard Marechal Foch
Saint Gratien, France
Tel.: (33) 391 923 356
Scrap Metal Collector & Recycling Services
S.I.C.: 4959
N.A.I.C.S.: 562998

Valme Technologies SAS (3)
Z I Route de la Hoguette
Falaise, 14700 Caen, France
Tel.: (33) 231903040
Fax: (33) 231400370
Waste Management Services
S.I.C.: 4959
N.A.I.C.S.: 562998
Bertrand Bony *(Mng Dir)*

SCI Quai De Norvege (2)
Activites Immobilieres
D'Autres Biens immobiliers, 59880 Valenciennes, France
Tel.: (33) 327228402
Fax: (33) 3 203 826 00024
Scrap Metal Collector & Recycling Services
S.I.C.: 4959
N.A.I.C.S.: 562998

Strap Transport S.A.S. (2)
BP 8 Zone Industrielle No 4
Rue President Lecuyer, Valenciennes, 59880, France
Tel.: (33) 327228400
Fax: (33) 327461367
Emp.: 200
Scrap Metal Collector & Recycling Services
S.I.C.: 4959
N.A.I.C.S.: 562998

Derichebourg Multiservices SAS (1)
6 allee des Coquelicots
94478 Boissy-Saint Leger, Cedex, France (100%)
Tel.: (33) 145106400
Fax: (33) 145106439
E-Mail: communication-multiservices@derichebourg.com
Web Site: www.derichebourg.com
Sales Range: $700-749.9 Million
Emp.: 20,700
Holding Company; Cleaning, Temporary Staffing & Business Support Services
S.I.C.: 6719
N.A.I.C.S.: 551112
Daniel Derichebourg *(Chm)*

Subsidiaries:

Derichebourg Atis Aeronautique SAS (2)
17 Ave Didier Daurat
D'Activite De L'Aeroport, 31700 Blagnac, France
Tel.: (33) 534606140
Fax: (33) 534606150
Web Site: www.derichebourg-atis.com
Emp.: 1,200
Aircraft Construction Process Services; Manufacturing Preparation, Construction, Assembly, Logistics, Quality Control, & Technical Assistance
S.I.C.: 3721
N.A.I.C.S.: 336411
Pascal Lannette *(Mng Dir)*

Non-U.S. Subsidiary:

Derichebourg Atis GmbH (3)
Klosterstrasse 22
40211 Dusseldorf, Germany
Tel.: (49) 21 11 64 11 44
Temp Services
S.I.C.: 7363
N.A.I.C.S.: 561320

Derichebourg Energie SA (2)
2-4 rue des Sarrazins
Creteil, 94047, Cedex, France FR
Tel.: (33) 145134200 (99.8%)
Fax: (33) 1 4 5 13 42 10
Emp.: 140
Electrical Engineering & Air Conditioning Engineering
S.I.C.: 8711
N.A.I.C.S.: 541330
Boris Derichebourg *(Chm & CEO)*

Derichebourg Entreprises-Valerco - Valren - Ecoval (2)
15 Blvd Yves Farge BP 57401
69347 Lyon, France
Tel.: (33) 472768930
Fax: (33) 478728341
Web Site: www.derichebourg.com
Metal Container Mfr
S.I.C.: 3412
N.A.I.C.S.: 332439

Derichebourg Proprete SAS (2)
6 allee des Coquelicots
Boissy-Saint Leger, F-94478, Cedex, France FR
Tel.: (33) 145106400 (100%)
Fax: (33) 145106421
E-Mail: contact.agence.idnord@derichebourg.com
Emp.: 19,200
Cleaning Services; Hospital & Nuclear Facility Sanitation, Hotel, Transport, & Workshops Cleaning & Waste Collection & Sorting
S.I.C.: 8744
N.A.I.C.S.: 561210
Boris Derichebourg *(Chm)*

Subsidiaries:

Derichebourg Espaces Verts SAS (3)
Hameau de Saulxier 36-38 Grande Rue
91160 Paris, France FR
Tel.: (33) 144926740 (100%)
Fax: (33) 144926750
Landscaping Services
S.I.C.: 0783
N.A.I.C.S.: 561730
Boris Derichebourg *(Mgr)*

Derichebourg Interim SAS (3)
41 rue La Fayette
75009 Paris, France FR
Tel.: (33) 1 4 2 85 18 02 (100%)
Fax: (33) 1 4 0 82 91 53
Holding Company; Aeronautic Industry Temporary Help Services
S.I.C.: 7363
N.A.I.C.S.: 561320
Boris Derichebourg *(Chm)*

Subsidiary:

Derichebourg Interim Aeronautique SAS (4)
Immeuble Perisud II 13 rue Andre Villet
31400 Toulouse, France
Tel.: (33) 5 62 71 51 80
Fax: (33) 5 61 54 38 50
Web Site: www.derichebourg.com
Aeronautic Industry Temporary Help Services
S.I.C.: 7363
N.A.I.C.S.: 561320
Boris Derichebourg *(Chm)*

ULTEAM Sarl (3)
33 Boulevard des Batignolles
75008 Paris, France FR
Tel.: (33) 153268340 (99.98%)
Public & Private Reception Services; Switchboard & Mail Management
S.I.C.: 8744
N.A.I.C.S.: 561210
Boris Derichebourg *(Mgr)*

Servisair S.A.S. (1)
119 Ave du General Michel Bizot
F 75012 Paris, France
Tel.: (33) 144754040
E-Mail: accueil@derichebourg.com
Rev.: $746,494,056
Emp.: 13,666
Aviation Ground Services
S.I.C.: 4581
N.A.I.C.S.: 488190
Daniel Derichebourg *(Chm)*

U.S. Subsidiary:

Servisair USA Inc. (2)
151 Northpoint Dr
Houston, TX 77060
Tel.: (281) 260-3900
Fax: (281) 999-3740
E-Mail: business.development@servisair.com
Web Site: www.servisair.com
Emp.: 70
Aviation Ground Services
S.I.C.: 4581
N.A.I.C.S.: 488190
Dave Finch *(VP)*

Non-U.S. Subsidiary:

Servisair North America Inc. (Canada) (3)
100 Alexis Nihon Ste 400
Ville Saint Laurent, QC, H4M 2N9, Canada
Tel.: (514) 748-2277
Fax: (514) 748-2281
Web Site: www.servisair.com
Emp.: 25
Aviation Ground Services
S.I.C.: 4581
N.A.I.C.S.: 488190
Audery Laurin *(Mgr)*

Non-U.S. Subsidiaries:

Servisair Amsterdam B.V. (2)
Havenmeesterweg 21
1118 CB Schiphol, Netherlands
Tel.: (31) 207952400
Fax: (31) 207952401
E-Mail: patricia.nijholt@servisair.com
Web Site: www.servisair.com
Emp.: 650
Aviation Ground Services
S.I.C.: 4581
N.A.I.C.S.: 488119
Menno Biersma *(Mng Dir)*

Servisair Chile S.A. (2)
1850 Manuel Avalos Prado Aeropuerto Internacional A Merino Benitez
PO Box 4
Pudahuel, Santiago, Chile
Tel.: (56) 2 799 2145
Fax: (56) 2 601 9525
Web Site: www.servisair.com
Aviation Ground Services
S.I.C.: 4581
N.A.I.C.S.: 488190
Renzo Pontiggia *(Mgr)*

Non-U.S. Subsidiary:

Servisair Peru SAC (3)
Julian Arias Araguez N 250
Miraflores, Peru
Tel.: (51) 1 517 3127
Fax: (51) 1 517 3109
Aviation Ground Services
S.I.C.: 4581
N.A.I.C.S.: 488190
Ricardo Salazar *(Mgr)*

Servisair Denmark SAS (2)
Copenhagen Airport Terminal 2
DK 2770 Kastrup, Denmark
Tel.: (45) 32314047
Fax: (45) 32314347
Web Site: www.servisair.com
Emp.: 5
Aviation Ground Services
S.I.C.: 4581
N.A.I.C.S.: 488190
Atilla Meulenbelt *(Mgr)*

Servisair Finland Oy (2)
Rahtikuja 1
01530 Vantaa, Finland
Tel.: (358) 10 230 4121
Fax: (358) 10 230 4123

E-Mail: operations@servisair.fi
Web Site: www.servisair.com
Aviation Ground Services
S.I.C.: 4581
N.A.I.C.S.: 488190
Veijo Karosvuo *(Gen Mgr)*

Servisair Iberica S.A. (2)
C Valentin Beato 11 4 A
28037 Madrid, Spain
Tel.: (34) 915550524
Fax: (34) 915556615
Web Site: www.servisair.com
Emp.: 8
Aviation Ground Services
S.I.C.: 4581
N.A.I.C.S.: 488190
Juan Antonio Alamo *(Gen Mgr)*

Servisair Portugal Lda. (2)
Aeroporto de Lisboa Edificio Principal
Gab 6143 6 Piso, Lisbon, 1700 007, Portugal
Tel.: (351) 939495362
E-Mail: lisbon@servisair.com
Aviation Ground Services
S.I.C.: 4581
N.A.I.C.S.: 488190

Servisair Trinidad & Tobago Ltd. (2)
Piarco International Airport
Piarco, Trinidad & Tobago
Tel.: (868) 6692636
Fax: (868) 6692633
Aviation Ground Services
S.I.C.: 4581
N.A.I.C.S.: 488190
Eugene Shairsingh *(Mgr)*

Servisair UK Ltd. (2)
Servisair House Hampton Court Manor Park
Runcorn, Cheshire, WA7 1TT, United Kingdom
Tel.: (44) 1928570120
Fax: (44) 1928570220
Web Site: www.servisair.com
Airport & Aircraft Services
S.I.C.: 4581
N.A.I.C.S.: 488119
Darren Harding *(VP-Sls)*

Servisair Venzuela CA (2)
Rampa 31 Aeropuerto Simon Bolivar Catia La Mar Vargas
Caracas, Venezuela
Tel.: (58) 4143188016
Aviation Ground Services
S.I.C.: 4581
N.A.I.C.S.: 488190
Gustavo Faria *(Gen Mgr)*

DERWENT LONDON PLC

25 Savile Row
London, W1S 2ER, United Kingdom
Tel.: (44) 2076593000
Fax: (44) 012076593100
E-Mail: mail@derwentlondon.com
Web Site: www.derwentlondon.com
DLN—(LSE)
Sales Range: $600-649.9 Million
Emp.: 77

Business Description:
Commercial Real Estate Investment & Development Services
S.I.C.: 6531
N.A.I.C.S.: 531390

Personnel:
John D. Burns *(CEO)*
Tim J. Kite *(Sec)*

Board of Directors:
Robert A. Rayne
John D. Burns
Stuart A. Corbyn
Richard Dakin
June de Moller
Robert A. Farnes
Simon Fraser
Nigel Q. George
Simon J. Neathercoat
Simon P. Silver
David Silverman
Paul M. Williams
Damian Wisniewski
Stephen G. Young

Legal Counsel:
Slaughter & May
35 Basinghall St
London, EC2V 5DB, United Kingdom
Tel.: (44) 207 600 1200
Telex: 883486
Fax: (44) 207 726 0038

Subsidiaries:

Caledonian Properties Limited (1)
Caledonian Property Letting
20 Melville Terr, Stirling, FK8 2NQ, United Kingdom
Tel.: (44) 1786461117
E-Mail: mail@caledonianletting.com
Web Site: www.caledonianproperty.co.uk
Emp.: 3
Real Estate Mortgage Consulting Services
S.I.C.: 6531
N.A.I.C.S.: 531390

Caledonian Property Investments Limited (1)
2 The Cross Ct Bishopbriggs
Glasgow, G64 2RD, United Kingdom
Tel.: (44) 1417611200
Fax: (44) 1417625600
Property Investment Services
S.I.C.: 6211
N.A.I.C.S.: 523999

The New River Company Limited (1)
25 Savile Row
London, W1S 2ER, United Kingdom
Tel.: (44) 2076593000
Fax: (44) 2076593001
E-Mail: info@derwentlondon.com
Property Development Services
S.I.C.: 6519
N.A.I.C.S.: 531190

DESAILLY SA

Min 6 Rue De Strasbourg
94150 Rungis, Val De Marne, France
Tel.: (33) 146872445
Sls.: $30,700,000
Emp.: 48
S.I.C.: 5143
N.A.I.C.S.: 424430

Personnel:
Maurice Desailly *(Pres)*

DESANE GROUP HOLDINGS LTD

68-72 Lilyfield Road
Rozelle, NSW, 2039, Australia

Mailing Address:
PO Box 331
Leichhardt, NSW, 2040, Australia
Tel.: (61) 2 9555 9922
Fax: (61) 2 9555 9944
E-Mail: info@desane.com.au
Web Site: www.desane.com.au
DGH—(ASX)
Rev.: $3,208,626
Assets: $49,228,804
Liabilities: $22,677,138
Net Worth: $26,551,666
Earnings: $1,350,562
Emp.: 5
Fiscal Year-end: 06/30/13

Business Description:
Investment Services
S.I.C.: 8742
N.A.I.C.S.: 541611

Personnel:
Phil Montrone *(CEO & Mng Dir)*
Jack Sciara *(CFO)*
John William Bartholomew *(Sec)*

Board of Directors:
John Blair Sheehan
John William Bartholomew
Phil Montrone

Legal Counsel:
Cordato Partners
Level 5 49 York St
Sydney, Australia

Subsidiary:

Desane Properties Pty. Ltd. (1)
PO Box 331
Leichhardt, NSW, 2040, Australia
Tel.: (61) 295690344
Fax: (61) 295509363
E-Mail: info@desane.com.au
Web Site: www.desane.com.au
Real Estate Management Services
S.I.C.: 6531
N.A.I.C.S.: 531390
Phil Montrone *(Mng Dir)*

DESARROLLADORA HOMEX, S.A. DE C.V.

Boulevard Alfonso Zaragoza M 2204
Fracc Bonanza
80020 Culiacan, Sinaloa, Mexico
Tel.: (52) 6677585800
Fax: (52) 6677585800
E-Mail: investor.relations@homex.com.mx
Web Site: www.homex.com.mx
Year Founded: 1989
HXM—(MEX NYSE)
Rev.: $2,262,003,028
Assets: $4,039,901,628
Liabilities: $2,879,636,937
Net Worth: $1,160,264,691
Earnings: $125,843,231
Emp.: 9,975
Fiscal Year-end: 12/31/12

Business Description:
Low & Middle-Income Housing Developer
S.I.C.: 1521
N.A.I.C.S.: 236115

Personnel:
Eustaquio Tomas De Nicolas Gutierrez *(Chm)*
Gerardo De Nicolas Gutierrez *(CEO)*
Carlos J. Moctezuma *(CFO)*

Board of Directors:
Eustaquio Tomas De Nicolas Gutierrez
Z. Jamie Behar
Gerardo De Nicolas Gutierrez
Jose Ignacio de Nicolas Gutierrez
Luis Alberto Harvey McKissack
Edward Lowenthal
Wilfrido Castillo Sanchez-Mejorada

Subsidiaries:

Administradora Picsa, S.A. de C.V. (1)
Heroe De Nacataz No 3419
Nuevo Laredo, Tamaulipas, 88040, Mexico
Tel.: (52) 8677154249
Administrative Management Consulting Services
S.I.C.: 8742
N.A.I.C.S.: 541611

Aerohomex, S.A. de C.V. (1)
Andador Javier Mina 891-B
Col Centro Sinaloa, Culiacan, 80200, Mexico (100%)
Tel.: (52) 6677585800
E-Mail: gdenicalos@homex.com.mx
Web Site: www.homex.com.mx/_HOMEXWEBv2/_Ingles/info_I.php?p=atencion_clientes_I.php
Emp.: 50
Air Transportation
S.I.C.: 4522
N.A.I.C.S.: 481219
Gerardo Denicalos *(CEO)*

Altos Mandos de Negocios, S.A. de C.V. (1)
Bulevar Alfonso Zaragoza No 2204 Norte
Culiacan, 80020, Mexico (100%)
Tel.: (52) 6677585800
Fax: (52) 6677585801
E-Mail: lgracia@homex.com.mx
Emp.: 800
Management Consulting Services
S.I.C.: 8748
N.A.I.C.S.: 541618
Gerardo Denicalos *(CEO)*

Casas Beta Del Centro, S De R L De C V (1)
Blvd Alfonso Zaragoza Maytorena No 2204
Culiacan, Mexico (100%)
Tel.: (52) 6677585800
Fax: (52) 667758811
Web Site: www.homex.mx
Emp.: 800
New Single-Family Housing Construction
S.I.C.: 1521
N.A.I.C.S.: 236115
Gerardo Denicalos *(CEO)*

Subsidiary:

Super Abastos Centrales y Comerciales, S.A. de C.V. (2)
Quinana Roo No 3 Int 303 Roma Sur Cuauhtemoc
Mexico, 06760, Mexico
Tel.: (52) 6677585800
Real Estate Development Services
S.I.C.: 6531
N.A.I.C.S.: 531390

Casas Beta Del Noroeste, S.A. de C.V. (1)
Blvd Alfonso Zaragoza Maytorena No 2204
Culiacan, Mexico (100%)
Tel.: (52) 6677585800
New Single-Family Housing Construction
S.I.C.: 1521
N.A.I.C.S.: 236115
Gerardo Denicalos *(CEO)*

Casas Beta Del Norte, S.A. de C.V. (1)
Blvd Alfonso Zaragoza Maytorena No 2204
Culiacan, Mexico (100%)
Tel.: (52) 6677585800
New Single-Family Housing Construction
S.I.C.: 1521
N.A.I.C.S.: 236115
Gerardo Denicalos *(CEO)*

Desarrolladora De Casas Del Noroeste, S.A. de C.V. (1)
Alfonso Zaragoza Maytorena 2204 Bonanza
Culiacan, Mexico (100%)
Tel.: (52) 6677585800
Fax: (52) 6677585811
Emp.: 500
Engineering Services
S.I.C.: 8711
N.A.I.C.S.: 541330
Gerardo Denicalos *(CEO)*

Homex Atizapan, S.A. de C.V. (1)
Blvd Alfonso Zaragoza Maytorena No 2204
Culiacan, Sinaloa, 80020, Mexico
Tel.: (52) 6677585800
Fax: (52) 6677585801
Emp.: 1,000
Construction Engineering Services
S.I.C.: 8711
N.A.I.C.S.: 541330
Gerardo de Nicolas Gutierrez *(Gen Mgr)*

Homex Central Marcaria, S.A. de C.V. (1)
Alfonso Zaragoza Maytorena 2204 Bonanza
Culiacan, Sinaloa, 80020, Mexico
Tel.: (52) 6 677585800
Emp.: 2,000
Intellectual Property Management Services
S.I.C.: 8748
N.A.I.C.S.: 541618
Carlos Moctezuma *(CFO)*

Homex Infraestructura Obras, S.A. de C.V. (1)
Boulevard Alfonzo Zaragoza Maytorena 2204 Bonanza
80020 Culiacan, Sinaloa, Mexico
Tel.: (52) 667 7585800
Fax: (52) 667 7585811
Construction Engineering Services
S.I.C.: 8711
N.A.I.C.S.: 541330
Gerardo de Nicolas Gutierrez *(Mng Dir)*

Homex Infraestructura, S.A. de C.V. (1)
Alfonso Zaragoza Maytorena 2204
Culiacan, Sinaloa, 25050, Mexico
Tel.: (52) 667 7585800
Construction Engineering Services
S.I.C.: 8711
N.A.I.C.S.: 541330

HXMTD, S.A. de C.V. (1)
435319 La Joya No Sn
San Jose del Cabo, 23429, Mexico
Tel.: (52) 624 1636500
Emp.: 50

Desarrolladora Homex, S.A. de C.V.—(Continued)

Commercial Building Construction Services
S.I.C.: 1542
N.A.I.C.S.: 236220
Claudio Sanchez *(Mgr-Branch)*

DESARROLLOS ESPECIALES DE SISTEMAS DE ANCLAJE, S.A.

Viladecans Business Park c / Antonio Machado 78-80 1st floor
08840 Viladecans, Spain
Tel.: (34) 93 630 53 00
E-Mail: desa@desa.es
Web Site: www.desa.es
Year Founded: 1956
DES—(MAD)
Sales Range: Less than $1 Million
Business Description:
Anchors & Fastening Product Mfr
S.I.C.: 3452
N.A.I.C.S.: 332722
Personnel:
Enrique Morera Guajardo *(Pres)*

THE DESCARTES SYSTEMS GROUP INC.

120 Randall Drive
Waterloo, ON, N2V 1C6, Canada
Tel.: (519) 746-8110
Fax: (519) 747-0082
Toll Free: (800) 419-8495
E-Mail: info@descartes.com
Web Site: www.descartes.com
Year Founded: 1981
DSGX—(NASDAQ TSX)
Rev.: $126,883,000
Assets: $274,910,000
Liabilities: $37,868,000
Net Worth: $237,042,000
Earnings: $15,996,000
Emp.: 639
Fiscal Year-end: 01/31/13
Business Description:
Integrated Logistics, Supply Chain & Compliance Software Applications & Services
S.I.C.: 7372
N.A.I.C.S.: 511210
Personnel:
J. Scott Pagan *(Pres & COO)*
Edward J. Ryan *(CEO)*
Stephanie Ratza *(CFO)*
Raimond Diederik *(Exec VP-Info Svcs)*
Chris Jones *(Exec VP-Mktg & Svcs)*
Board of Directors:
David L. Anderson
David I. Beatson
Eric A. Demirian
Chris Hewat
Stephen Watt
Transfer Agents:
Computershare Trust Company
12039 W. Alameda Pkwy., Ste. Z2
Lakewood, CO 80228
Tel.: (303) 986-5400
Fax: (303) 986-2444

Computershare Investor Services Inc
100 University Avenue
Toronto, ON, Canada

U.S. Subsidiary:

Descartes Systems (USA) LLC (1)
200 Hightower Blvd
Pittsburgh, PA 15205-1123 DE (100%)
Tel.: (412) 788-2466
Fax: (412) 788-4821
Toll Free: (800) 394-0020
E-Mail: info@descartes.com
Web Site: www.descartes.com
Software Publisher & Distr
S.I.C.: 7372
N.A.I.C.S.: 511210
Cindy Yamamoto *(VP-Product Dev)*

DESCENTE LTD.

4-2-16 Hirano-machi Chuo-ku
Osaka, 541-0046, Japan
Tel.: (81) 6 6774 0365
Telex: 63681 DESANT J
Fax: (81) 6 6774 0367
E-Mail: info@descente.co.jp
Web Site: www.descente.co.jp/en/company/index.html
Year Founded: 1935
8114—(TKS)
Sales Range: $5-14.9 Billion
Emp.: 730
Business Description:
Active Sportswear & Sports Related Products Mfr & Distr
Import Export
S.I.C.: 5699
N.A.I.C.S.: 315220
Personnel:
Etsuro Nakanishi *(Pres)*
Isao Hoshida *(Sr Mng Dir)*
Masahiro Sawai *(Sr Mng Dir)*
Legal Counsel:
M. Takagi Law Office
1-6-16 Dojima
Kita-ku, Osaka, Japan

Subsidiaries:

Descente Apparel Ltd. (1)
4-2-16 Hiranomachi
Chuo-ku, Osaka, 5410046, Japan (100%)
Tel.: (81) 667740365
Fax: (81) 667740367
E-Mail: info@descente.co.jp
Web Site: www.descente.co.jp
Emp.: 600
Mfr. of General Sportswear
S.I.C.: 5611
N.A.I.C.S.: 448110
Epsurou Nakanishi *(Pres)*

U.S. Affiliate:

Descente North America, Inc. (1)
334 Marshall Way Ste A
Layton, UT 84041-7346 CO (41%)
Tel.: (801) 317-0017
Fax: (801) 317-0020
Toll Free: (800) 999-0475
E-Mail: info@descente.com
Web Site: www.descente.com
Emp.: 12
Ski Apparel Mfr & Distr
Import
S.I.C.: 5136
N.A.I.C.S.: 424320
Kiyoshige Higeo *(VP)*

Non-U.S. Subsidiaries:

Descente Korea, Ltd. (1)
16th Fl Hyundai Insurance Bldg 646 Yuksantong
Seoul, Kangnam Gu, 135080, Korea (South) (100%)
Tel.: (82) 220073300
Fax: (82) 220073399
E-Mail: chpark@descente.co.kr
Web Site: www.descente.co.kr
Emp.: 40
Sales of Descente Sportswear
S.I.C.: 5136
N.A.I.C.S.: 424320

Descente North America, Inc. (1)
1445 Charles St
Vancouver, BC, V5L2S7, Canada BC (100%)
Tel.: (604) 254-9100
Fax: (604) 254-9121
E-Mail: info@descente.ca
Web Site: www.descente.net
Sales Range: $25-49.9 Million
Emp.: 6
Wholesaler of Descente Sportswear
S.I.C.: 5136
N.A.I.C.S.: 424320
Hideo Kiyoshige *(Pres)*

Hong Kong Descente Trading Ltd. (1)
0120305 25F Enterprise Square 3 39 Wang Chu Rd Kowloon bay
Tsim Sha Tsui, Kowloon, China (Hong Kong)
Tel.: (852) 2175 5809
Fax: (852) 2175 5837
E-Mail: info@descente.com.hk
Web Site: www.descente.com.hk
Emp.: 30
Sportswear Sales
S.I.C.: 5136
N.A.I.C.S.: 424320
Kenneth Lee *(Pres)*

Non-U.S. Joint Venture:

Beijing Descente Co., Ltd. (1)
19 Changping Shisanling Shuiku Yangshan Xi Rd, Beijing, 102200, China (63%)
Tel.: (86) 10 6071 3541
Fax: (86) 106713533
Emp.: 175
General Sportswear Mfr & Sales
S.I.C.: 2329
N.A.I.C.S.: 315220

DESCO RESOURCES INC.

Suite 1000 400 Third Avenue Southwest
Calgary, AB, T2P 4H2, Canada
Tel.: (403) 690-3884
Fax: (403) 266-1395
Year Founded: 2009
DSR.P—(TSXV)
Business Description:
Investment Services
S.I.C.: 6211
N.A.I.C.S.: 523999
Personnel:
Neil G. Sinclair *(CFO & VP-Fin)*
William C. Guinan *(Sec)*
Board of Directors:
Massimo Geremia
William C. Guinan
Gregory E. Peterson
James W. Surbey

DESCON CHEMICALS LIMITED

Building 04 18 km Ferozepur Road
Lahore, 54000, Pakistan
Tel.: (92) 42 35923721
Fax: (92) 42 35923749
E-Mail: info@desconchemicals.com
Web Site: www.desconchemicals.com
DCH—(KAR)
Sales Range: $10-24.9 Million
Business Description:
Paints, Coatings & Resins Mfr
S.I.C.: 2821
N.A.I.C.S.: 325211
Personnel:
Abdul Razak Dawood *(Chm)*
Abdul Sohail *(Sec)*

Corplink (Pvt.) Limited
Wings Arcade 1-K Commercial Model Town
Lahore, Pakistan
Tel.: (92) 42 3583 9182
Fax: (92) 42 3586 9037

Subsidiaries:

Descon Chemicals (Pvt) Limited (1)
18-KM Ferozepur Road
Lahore, Pakistan
Tel.: (92) 42 35923721
Fax: (92) 42 35923749
E-Mail: info@desconchemicals.com
Web Site: www.desconchemicals.com
Chemical Mfr & Distr
S.I.C.: 2819
N.A.I.C.S.: 325180
Taimur Saeed *(CEO)*

Descon Engineering Limited Pakistan (1)
9th Floor Business Avenue 26-A Block-6
PECHS Main Shahrah-e-Faisal
Karachi, 75400, Pakistan
Tel.: (92) 21 3454 4481 4
Fax: (92) 21 3454 4480
E-Mail: descon.karachi@descon.com
Web Site: www.descon.com.pk/engineering.php
Emp.: 1,500
Engineering Services
S.I.C.: 8711
N.A.I.C.S.: 541330
Salman Zakaria *(CEO)*
Syed Zamanat Abbas *(CFO)*

Rousch Pakistan Limited (1)
Corporate Office 43-5-E Block-6
Pechs, Karachi, Pakistan
Tel.: (92) 21 34530641
Synthetic Resins Mfr
S.I.C.: 2821
N.A.I.C.S.: 325211

Non-U.S. Subsidiary:

Descon Engineering Abu Dhabi (1)
Mussafah Industrial Area ME-14 United Bank Limited Building
PO Box 46821
Abu Dhabi, United Arab Emirates
Tel.: (971) 25555807
Fax: (971) 2 5555784
E-Mail: descon@emirates.net.ae
Web Site: www.descon.com
Construction Engineering Services
S.I.C.: 8711
N.A.I.C.S.: 541330
Ahson Atta *(Gen Mgr)*

DESCOURS & CABAUD SA

10 rue General Plessier
BP 2437
69219 Lyon, Cedex 2, France
Tel.: (33) 472408585
Fax: (33) 472408541
Web Site: www.descours-cabaud.com
Year Founded: 1782
Sales Range: $1-4.9 Billion
Emp.: 11,600
Business Description:
Holding Company; Iron & Steel Products Mfr & Whslr
S.I.C.: 3312
N.A.I.C.S.: 331110
Personnel:
Pyeffz Delimayraz *(Chm)*

Subsidiary:

Dillon Supply Company (1)
440 Civic Blvd
Raleigh, NC 27610-2967 NC
Mailing Address:
PO Box 1111
Raleigh, NC 27602-1111
Tel.: (919) 838-4200
Fax: (919) 838-4352
E-Mail: edillon@dillonsupply.com
Web Site: www.dillonsupply.com
Emp.: 370
Industrial Supplies, Steel, Safety Equipment & Materials Handling Equipment Mfr & Distr
S.I.C.: 5084
N.A.I.C.S.: 423830
Dean Wagoner *(Pres & CEO)*

Subsidiaries:

Brammer Safety Supply Inc. (2)
3826 Old Forest Rd
Lynchburg, VA 24501
Tel.: (434) 385-6577
Fax: (434) 385-7929
Emp.: 15
Safety Supplies Sls
S.I.C.: 5084
N.A.I.C.S.: 423830
Jim Brammer *(Owner)*

DESENVIX ENERGIAS RENOVAVEIS S.A.

Alameda Araguaia 3571 Conj 2001
Centro Empresarial Tambore
Barueri, Sao Paulo, Brazil 06455-000
Tel.: (55) 11 2106 0100
Fax: (55) 11 2106 0101
E-Mail: ri@desenvix.com.br
Web Site: www.desenvix.com.br
Year Founded: 1995
DVIX3—(BRAZ)

Rev.: $84,329,730
Assets: $828,240,839
Liabilities: $535,779,904
Net Worth: $292,460,935
Earnings: $13,452,631
Emp.: 328
Fiscal Year-end: 12/31/12
Business Description:
Electric Power Generation & Distribution Services
S.I.C.: 4911
N.A.I.C.S.: 221118
Personnel:
Torger Nils Lien *(Chm)*
Joao Robert Coas *(CEO)*
Jan Erik Felle *(CFO & Head-Investor)*
Ming Liu *(Member-Exec Bd)*
Darico Pedro Livi *(Member-Exec Bd)*
Paulo Marcelo Goncalves Margarido *(Member-Exec Bd)*
Alvaro Eduardo Sardinha *(Member-Exec Bd)*
Paulo Roberto Fraga Zuch *(Member-Exec Bd)*
Board of Directors:
Torger Nils Lien
Geraldo Aparecido da Silva
Gerson de Mello Almada
Joakim Johnsen
Cristiano Kok
Ruy Nagano
Austin Laine Powell
Jose Antunes Sobrinho

DESERT EAGLE RESOURCES LTD.
65 Queen Street West Suite 805
PO Box 71
Toronto, ON, M5H 2M5, Canada
Tel.: (416) 524-8150
Fax: (416) 924-8759
E-Mail: info@deserteagleresources.com
Web Site: www.deserteagleresources.com
DER—(TSXV)
Business Description:
Mineral Exploration Services
S.I.C.: 1081
N.A.I.C.S.: 213114
Personnel:
Blair Krueger *(Pres & CEO)*
Anthony Bainbridge *(CFO)*
Board of Directors:
Jules Brossard
Blair Krueger
Paul C. M. Roberts
Legal Counsel:
Ormston List Frawley LLP
Toronto, ON, Canada
Transfer Agent:
Equity Transfer & Trust Company
200 University Avenue Ste 400
Toronto, ON, M5H 4H1, Canada
Tel.: (416) 361-0152
Fax: (416) 361-0470

DESERT GOLD VENTURES INC.
1250 West Hastings Street
Vancouver, BC, V6E 2M4, Canada
Tel.: (604) 566-9240
Fax: (604) 408-9301
Web Site: www.desertgold.ca
Year Founded: 2003
DAU—(TSXV)
Assets: $3,985,251
Liabilities: $516,648
Net Worth: $3,468,603
Earnings: ($2,772,068)
Fiscal Year-end: 12/31/12
Business Description:
Mineral Exploration Services
S.I.C.: 1081
N.A.I.C.S.: 213114
Personnel:
Roeland van Kerckhoven *(Pres & CEO)*
Jared Scharf *(CFO & Sec)*
Board of Directors:
Ayub Khan
Theo Christodoulou
Sonny Janda
Thomas Robert Tough
Roeland van Kerckhoven
Louw van Schalkwyk
Transfer Agent:
Computershare Trust Company of Canada
510 Burrard St 3rd Fl
Vancouver, BC, V6C 3B9, Canada

DESERT MINES AND METALS LIMITED
271 Great Eastern Highway
Belmont, WA, 6104, Australia
Mailing Address:
PO Box 707
Belmont, WA, 6984, Australia
Tel.: (61) 8 6143 1840
Fax: (61) 8 6162 9079
E-Mail: contact@desertminesandmetals.com.au
Web Site: www.desertminesandmetals.com.au
DSN—(ASX)
Rev.: $96,534
Assets: $1,694,834
Liabilities: $290,405
Net Worth: $1,404,429
Earnings: ($1,635,435)
Emp.: 2
Fiscal Year-end: 06/30/13
Business Description:
Uranium Exploration Services
S.I.C.: 1094
N.A.I.C.S.: 212291
Personnel:
Chris Rashleigh *(Mng Dir)*
Eric G. Moore *(Sec & Gen Mgr)*
Board of Directors:
Phillip Sidney Redmond Jackson
Sang Bom Hong
Martin James Pyle
Chris Rashleigh

DESERT STAR RESOURCES LTD.
(Formerly First Graphite Corp.)
Suite 918 1030 West Georgia Street
Vancouver, BC, V6E2Y3, Canada
Tel.: (604) 688-5623
E-Mail: info@desertstar.ca
Web Site: www.desertstar.ca
DSR—(TSXV)
Assets: $2,225,495
Liabilities: $450,243
Net Worth: $1,775,252
Earnings: ($917,680)
Fiscal Year-end: 04/30/13
Business Description:
Mineral Exploration Services
S.I.C.: 1081
N.A.I.C.S.: 213114
Personnel:
Vincenzo Marco Sorace *(Pres & CEO)*
Gavin Cooper *(CFO)*
Alan J. Wainwright *(Chief Geologist)*
Emily Davis *(Sec)*
Board of Directors:
Martin Bajic
Keith Henderson
Vincenzo Marco Sorace
Chris Taylor
Legal Counsel:
Getz Prince Wells LLP
Suite 1810 1111 West Georgia Street
Vancouver, BC, Canada
Transfer Agent:
Computershare
200 - 510 Burrard Street
Vancouver, BC, Canada

DESERTOAK LTD
Unit 7 Briar Close Business Park
Evesham, Worcs, WR11 4JT, United Kingdom
Tel.: (44) 1386765451
Fax: (44) 1386765055
E-Mail: enquiries@desetoak.co.uk
Web Site: www.desertoak.co.uk
Year Founded: 1986
Rev.: $12,236,543
Emp.: 30
Business Description:
Refurbishment Services
S.I.C.: 1799
N.A.I.C.S.: 238390
Personnel:
Jum Ditchfield *(Founder & Chm)*

DESH GARMENTS LIMITED
Awal Centre 7th Floor 34 Kemal Ataturk Avenue Banani C/A
Dhaka, 1213, Bangladesh
Tel.: (880) 2 8828505
Fax: (880) 2 8826049
E-Mail: desh@deshgroup.com
Web Site: www.deshgroup.com
Year Founded: 1977
DSHGARME—(DHA)
Sales Range: $1-9.9 Million
Emp.: 760
Business Description:
Garment Mfr
S.I.C.: 2399
N.A.I.C.S.: 314999
Personnel:
Rokeya Quader *(Chm)*
Omar Quader Khan *(Mng Dir)*
Habibur Rahman *(Sec)*

DESH RAKSHAK AUSHDHALAYA LIMITED
Bhagwant Kuti
Kankhal, Haridwar, Uttarakhand, 249408, India
Tel.: (91) 1334 243833
Fax: (91) 1334 245866
E-Mail: dral95@yahoo.com
Web Site: www.deshrakshak.com
Year Founded: 1901
531521—(BOM)
Rev.: $712,163
Assets: $1,724,370
Liabilities: $477,692
Net Worth: $1,246,678
Earnings: ($657)
Fiscal Year-end: 03/31/13
Business Description:
Pharmaceutical Product Mfr & Distr
S.I.C.: 2834
N.A.I.C.S.: 325412
Personnel:
Paras Kumar Jain *(Chm & Mng Dir)*
Tosh Kumar Jain *(CFO)*
Board of Directors:
Paras Kumar Jain
Monika Jain
Sudesh Jain
Tosh Kumar Jain
Transfer Agent:
Mas Services Limited
T-34 IInd Floor Okhla Phase-II
New Delhi, India

DESHBANDHU POLYMER LIMITED
Mostafa Center House No 59 Road No 27 Block K Banani
Dhaka, 1213, Bangladesh
Tel.: (880) 2 8816731
Fax: (880) 2 9891456
E-Mail: dpl@deshbandhugroup.com.bd
Web Site: www.dbg.com.bd
Year Founded: 2006
DESHBANDHU—(DHA)
Business Description:
Woven Bag Mfr
S.I.C.: 3999
N.A.I.C.S.: 339999
Personnel:
Golam Rahman *(Mng Dir)*
Gobinda Chandra Das *(CFO)*
Mohammad Liakat Ali Khan *(Sec)*

DESIGN HOTELS AG
Stralauer Allee 2c
10245 Berlin, Germany
Tel.: (49) 30 88 494 00 01
Fax: (49) 30 259 330 17
E-Mail: ir@designhotels.com
Web Site: www.corporate.designhotels.com
LBA—(DEU)
Business Description:
Hotel Marketing Services
S.I.C.: 7319
N.A.I.C.S.: 541890
Personnel:
Claus Sendlinger *(Founder & CEO)*
Holger Peres *(Chm)*
Juergen Buellesbach *(Deputy Chm)*
Supervisory Board of Directors:
Holger Peres
Juergen Buellesbach
Bernhard Taubenberger
Axel Weber
Reinhold Weise

DESIGN STUDIO FURNITURE MANUFACTURER LTD.
8 Sungei Kadut Cresent
Singapore, 728682, Singapore
Tel.: (65) 63670133
Fax: (65) 63662612
E-Mail: corpcommunications@designstudio.com.sg
Web Site: www.designstudio.com.sg
D11—(SES)
Rev.: $130,059,708
Assets: $117,427,890
Liabilities: $34,475,365
Net Worth: $82,952,526
Earnings: $9,156,671
Emp.: 5,629
Fiscal Year-end: 12/31/12
Business Description:
Furniture Mfr
S.I.C.: 2599
N.A.I.C.S.: 337127
Personnel:
Bernard Leng Foo Lim *(CEO)*
Helen Campos *(Co-Sec)*
Kelly Chai Choey Ng *(Co-Sec)*
Board of Directors:
Siok Chin Tan
Bernard Leng Foo Lim
Kelly Chai Choey Ng
Tiew Siam Ong
Muhammad Umar Saleem
Mohannad Izzat Sweid

DESIGNCAPITAL PLC
634 Linen Hall 162 168 Regent Street
London, W1B 5TB, United Kingdom
Tel.: (44) 2075548555
Fax: (44) 2075548556
E-Mail: contact@designcapitalplc.com
Web Site: www.designcapitalplc.com
DESC—(AIM)
Sales Range: $10-24.9 Million

designcapital plc—(Continued)

Business Description:
Investment Services
S.I.C.: 6211
N.A.I.C.S.: 523999
Personnel:
Frederic Bobo *(Chm & CEO)*
Michael Hosie *(CFO)*
G. Ashworth *(Sec)*
Board of Directors:
Frederic Bobo
Michael Hosie
Helen Mary Kennedy Lambert
Frederic Michel-Verdier
Legal Counsel:
Matthew Arnold & Baldwin LLP
London, United Kingdom

DESIGNER BLINDS OMAHA INC.

(Acquired & Absorbed by Hunter Douglas N.V.)

DESIRE PETROLEUM PLC

(Acquired by Falkland Oil and Gas Limited)

DESLAURIER CUSTOM CABINETS INC.

773451 Highway 59
Renfrew, ON, K7C 2S9, Canada
Tel.: (613) 432-5431
Fax: (613) 432-0666
Toll Free: (800) 267-8815
E-Mail: info@deslaurier.ca
Web Site: www.deslaurier.ca
Year Founded: 1979
Rev.: $12,020,360
Emp.: 125
Business Description:
Cabinet Mfr
S.I.C.: 2434
N.A.I.C.S.: 337110
Personnel:
Denis Staples *(Co-Owner & Pres)*
Jim Deslaurier *(Co-Owner & VP)*

DESMARAIS ENERGY CORPORATION

751 815 - 8th Avenue SW
Calgary, AB, T2P 3P2, Canada
Tel.: (403) 265-8007
Fax: (403) 264-7076
Web Site: www.desmaraisenergy.com
Year Founded: 1994
DES—(TSXV)
Sls.: $622,732
Assets: $2,825,678
Liabilities: $3,689,591
Net Worth: ($863,913)
Earnings: ($1,538,143)
Fiscal Year-end: 12/31/12
Business Description:
Oil & Natural Gas Exploration Services
S.I.C.: 1389
N.A.I.C.S.: 213112
Personnel:
Douglas F. Robinson *(Interim Pres, CEO & Acting CFO)*
R. Bruce Allford *(Sec)*
Board of Directors:
David Eastham
James G. Feeney
James G. Long
Douglas F. Robinson

DESMAZIERES SA

2 rue du Petit Quinquin
59816 Lesquin, Cedex, France
Tel.: (33) 3 20 87 70 05
E-Mail: contact-client@desmazieres.tm.fr
Web Site: www.chaussures-desmazieres.fr
Sales Range: $125-149.9 Million
Emp.: 750
Business Description:
Shoe Retailer, Mail Order & Internet Sales
S.I.C.: 5661
N.A.I.C.S.: 448210
Personnel:
Guy Serge Desmazieres *(CEO)*

DESON DEVELOPMENT INTERNATIONAL HOLDINGS LTD

11th Floor Nanyang Plz 57 Hung To Road
Kwun Tong, China (Hong Kong)
Tel.: (852) 25701118
E-Mail: deson@deson.com
Web Site: www.deson.com
0262—(HKG)
Rev.: $101,624,850
Assets: $217,125,623
Liabilities: $107,710,646
Net Worth: $109,414,978
Earnings: $6,291,342
Emp.: 128
Fiscal Year-end: 03/31/13
Business Description:
Real Estate Industry
S.I.C.: 6552
N.A.I.C.S.: 237210
Personnel:
Boen Sien Tjia *(Founder, Deputy Chm & Mng Dir)*
Quanzhang Lu *(Chm)*
Angus Wing Wai Lam *(Sec & Asst Controller-Fin)*
Board of Directors:
Quanzhang Lu
Raymond Chung-Tai Ho
Kwok Cheung Keung
Man Po Siu
Boen Sien Tjia
Jing Ning Wang
Oliver Shing Kay Wong
HSBC Bank Bermuda Limited
6 Front Street
Hamilton, Bermuda
Transfer Agents:
Tricor Tengis Limited
26/F Tesbury Centre, 28 Queens Road East
Hong Kong, China (Hong Kong)
HSBC Bank Bermuda Limited
6 Front Street
Hamilton, Bermuda

DESPEC GROUP B.V.

Smidsstraat 2
8601 WB Sneek, Netherlands
Tel.: (31) 515438200
Fax: (31) 515424234
E-Mail: info@despec.com
Web Site: www.despec.com
Sales Range: $900-999.9 Million
Emp.: 650
Business Description:
IT Consumer Products Distr
S.I.C.: 5045
N.A.I.C.S.: 423430
Non-U.S. Subsidiaries:

Despec Denmark A/S (1)
Vassingerodvej 25
2970 Lynge, Denmark
Tel.: (45) 45764700
Fax: (45) 45764701
E-Mail: info@despec.dk
Web Site: www.despec.dk
Emp.: 60
IT Consumer Products Distr
S.I.C.: 5045
N.A.I.C.S.: 423430
Michael Voll *(CEO)*

Despec Doo (1)
Strahinica Bana 1
11000 Belgrade, Serbia
Tel.: (381) 113284979
E-Mail: office@despec-yu.com
Web Site: www.despec-yu.com
IT Consumer Products Distr
S.I.C.: 5045
N.A.I.C.S.: 423430
Branko Salzberger *(Pres)*

Despec Mera Ltd. (1)
PO Box 61050
Jebel Ali Free Zone, Dubai, United Arab Emirates
Tel.: (971) 48811191
Fax: (971) 48811180
E-Mail: info@despecme.ae
Web Site: www.despecmera.com
Emp.: 40
IT Consumer Products Distr
S.I.C.: 5045
N.A.I.C.S.: 423430
Riyaz Jamal *(Mng Dir)*

Despec Supplies BVBA (1)
Dok Noord 4 C103
9000 Gentbrugge, Belgium
Tel.: (32) 92442030
Fax: (32) 92442048
E-Mail: info@despec.be
Web Site: www.despec.be
Emp.: 9
IT Consumer Products Distr
S.I.C.: 5045
N.A.I.C.S.: 423430

Despec Supplies Utibu A Islandi AS (1)
Dalvegur 16A
IS-200 Kopavogur, Iceland
Tel.: (354) 5445533
Fax: (354) 5445534
E-Mail: info@despec.is
Web Site: www.despec.is
Emp.: 4
IT Consumer Products Distr
S.I.C.: 5045
N.A.I.C.S.: 423430
Karl Brynaolssson *(Gen Mgr)*

Despec Sweden AB (1)
Pyramidbacken 6
PO Box 5049
14 105 Huddinge, Sweden
Tel.: (46) 84495900
Fax: (46) 84495929
E-Mail: info@despec.se
Web Site: www.despec.se
Emp.: 40
IT Consumer Products Distr
S.I.C.: 5045
N.A.I.C.S.: 423430
Christer Unnermark *(Mng Dir)*

DESPRED PLC

84 Veslec street
1202 Sofia, Bulgaria
Tel.: (359) 2 931 39 50
Fax: (359) 2 931 39 52
E-Mail: info@despred.com
Web Site: www.despred.com
Year Founded: 1947
4DP—(BUL)
Business Description:
Transportation Arrangement Services
S.I.C.: 4731
N.A.I.C.S.: 488510
Personnel:
Vasia Stefanova Tzvetkova *(Dir-IR)*

DESSAU INC.

1200 Saint Martin Boulevard West Ste 300
Laval, QC, H7S 2E4, Canada
Tel.: (514) 281-1010
Fax: (450) 668-8232
Web Site: www.dessau.com
Year Founded: 1957
Sales Range: $600-649.9 Milllon
Emp.: 4,300
Business Description:
Engineering Services
S.I.C.: 8711
N.A.I.C.S.: 541330
Personnel:
Marc Verreault *(Acting Pres, Acting CEO & VP-Major Projects Construction)*
Subsidiary:

Simo Management Inc. (1)
1200 Blvd St-Martin Ouest Bureau 300
Laval, QC, H7S 2E4, Canada QC
Tel.: (514) 281-6525
Fax: (450) 668-8232
E-Mail: info@proserco.qc.ca
Emp.: 60
Water Treatment Facilities
S.I.C.: 3589
N.A.I.C.S.: 333318

DESTAMPES EMBALLAGES

BP 27
Etagnac, 16150 Limoges, France
Tel.: (33) 545890203
Fax: (33) 545891499
E-Mail: accueil@destampes.fr
Web Site: www.destampes-emballages.fr
Sales Range: $10-24.9 Million
Emp.: 123
Business Description:
Designer, Mfr & Recycler of Wood Packaging
S.I.C.: 2449
N.A.I.C.S.: 321920
Personnel:
Nathalie Mandoux *(Dir-Admin)*

DESTICON TRANSPORTATION SERVICES INC

678 2397 King George Highway
Surrey, BC, V4A 9N3, Canada
Tel.: (604) 244-7244
Fax: (604) 244-7464
Toll Free: (800) 663-4885
Web Site: www.desticon.com
Rev.: $27,387,659
Emp.: 76
Business Description:
Logistics Services
S.I.C.: 4731
N.A.I.C.S.: 488510
Personnel:
Jade Stevenson *(Pres)*

DESTINATION AUTO VENTURES INC

(d/b/a Destination Chrysler Jeep Dodge Northshore)
1600 Marine Drive
North Vancouver, BC, V7P 1T9, Canada
Tel.: (604) 980-8501
Fax: (604) 980-8528
Toll Free: (888) 789-0222
E-Mail: chryslerinfo@destinationauto.ca
Web Site: www.destinationchrysler.ca
Year Founded: 1984
Rev.: $51,558,355
Emp.: 100
Business Description:
New & Used Car Dealers
S.I.C.: 5511
N.A.I.C.S.: 441110
Personnel:
Aziz Ahamed *(Pres)*
John Giuliano *(VP & CFO)*

DESTINY MEDIA TECHNOLOGIES, INC.

Suite 750 650 West Georgia Street
PO Box 11527
Vancouver, BC, V6B 4N7, Canada

Tel.: (604) 609-7736
Fax: (604) 609-0611
Toll Free: (800) 833-7846
E-Mail: steve@dsny.com
Web Site: www.dsny.com
DSY—(DEU OTC TSXV)
Rev.: $3,679,029
Assets: $3,657,656
Liabilities: $374,649
Net Worth: $3,283,007
Earnings: $226,014
Emp.: 23
Fiscal Year-end: 08/31/13

Business Description:
Digital Content Distribution Solutions Including Audio & Video Streaming Solutions
S.I.C.: 7372
N.A.I.C.S.: 511210

Personnel:
Steven E. Vestergaard *(Chm, Pres & CEO)*
Frederick Vandenberg *(CFO & Sec)*

Board of Directors:
Steven E. Vestergaard
Edward Kolic
Yoshitaro Kumagai
Lawrence Jeffrey Langs

DESWELL INDUSTRIES, INC.

17B Edificio Comercial Rodrigues
599 Avenida da Praia Grande
Macau, China (Macau)
Tel.: (853) 322096
Fax: (853) 323265
E-Mail: jnesbett@institutionalms.com
Web Site: www.deswell.com
Year Founded: 1987
DSWL—(NASDAQ)
Sls.: $54,074,000
Assets: $112,565,000
Liabilities: $10,989,000
Net Worth: $101,576,000
Earnings: ($1,991,000)
Emp.: 1,638
Fiscal Year-end: 03/31/13

Business Description:
Injection-Molded Plastic Parts & Components, Electronic Products & Sub-Assemblies, Metallic Molds & Accessory Parts Mfr
S.I.C.: 3089
N.A.I.C.S.: 326199

Personnel:
Lau Pui Hon *(Chm)*
Edward Kin Chung So *(CEO)*
Herman C. W. Wong *(CFO)*

Board of Directors:
Lau Pui Hon
Allen Yau Nam Cham
Wing-Ki Hui
Hung-Hum Leung
Chin Pang Li

Non-U.S. Subsidiaries:

Dongguan Jetcrown Technology Limited (1)
Huangang Industrial Estate Houjie Town
Dongguan, Guangdong, 523946, China
Tel.: (86) 769 83086666
Fax: (86) 769 85820407
Liquid Crystal Display Monitor Mfr
S.I.C.: 3679
N.A.I.C.S.: 334419
Peter Zhang *(Supvr-Sls)*

Dongguan Kwan Hong Electronics Co. Ltd. (1)
Xiaobian 2nd Industrial Zone
Dongguan, Guangdong, 523840, China
Tel.: (86) 769 88619858
Fax: (86) 769 89990501
E-Mail: admin@kwanasia.com
Web Site: www.deswell.com
Vending Machine Mfr
S.I.C.: 3589
N.A.I.C.S.: 333318

Jetcrown Industrial (Dongguan) Limited (1)
Huangang Industrial Estate Houjie Town
523946 Dongguan, China
Tel.: (86) 769 83086666
Fax: (86) 769 85967234
E-Mail: admin@jetcrown.net
Emp.: 200
Injection Molding Plastic Products Mfr
S.I.C.: 3089
N.A.I.C.S.: 326199
Weiye Gan *(Gen Mgr)*

DET DANSKE FILMINSTITUT

(d/b/a Danish Film Institute)
55 Gothersgade
1123 Copenhagen, Denmark
Tel.: (45) 33743400
Fax: (45) 33743401
E-Mail: dfi@dfi.dk
Web Site: www.dfi.dk
Emp.: 150

Business Description:
Film Promoter
S.I.C.: 7819
N.A.I.C.S.: 512199

Personnel:
Henrik Bo Nielsen *(CEO)*

Board of Directors:
Ulla Brockenhuus-Schack
Martin Dahl Pedersen
Torben Krough
Prami Larsen
Birgit Nordsmark Henriksen

DET NORSKE VERITAS AS

(d/b/a DNV)
Veritasveien 1
1322 Hovik, Norway
Tel.: (47) 67579900
Telex: Veritas Oslo
Fax: (47) 67579911
E-Mail: peterrodholm@dnv.com
Web Site: www.dnv.com
Year Founded: 1864
Sales Range: $750-799.9 Million
Emp.: 3,000

Business Description:
Quality, Safety & Environmental Control Services
S.I.C.: 7389
N.A.I.C.S.: 561499

Personnel:
Leif Arne Langoy *(Chm)*
Morten Ulstein *(Vice Chm)*
Tor E. Svensen *(Pres)*
Henrik O. Madsen *(CEO)*
Bjorn K. Haugland *(Chief Tech and Sustainability Officer)*

Board of Directors:
Sille Grjotheim
Leif Arne Langoy
Henrik O. Madsen
Frances Morris-Jones
Thomas Rehder
Odd Sund
Hilde M. Tonne
Morten Ulstein
John H. Wiik

Divisions:

Bomek Consulting AS (1)
Tollbugata 9
8006 Bodo, Norway
Tel.: (47) 75548630
Fax: (47) 75548631
Web Site: www.dnv.no/
S.I.C.: 4432
N.A.I.C.S.: 483113

Det Norske Veritas Eiendom AS - Harstad (1)
Maries vei 20
Hovik, Oslo, 1363, Norway (100%)
Tel.: (47) 4767579900
Fax: (47) 4767579911
Web Site: www.dnv.com
Emp.: 1,500
Risk Management & Management System Certification
S.I.C.: 8748
N.A.I.C.S.: 541618

Det Norske Veritas Eiendom AS - Trondheim (1)
Hovakm 1322
Trondheim, 1322, Norway (100%)
Tel.: (47) 67579900
Fax: (47) 67579945
E-Mail: tnd@dvn.com
Web Site: www.dnya.com
Emp.: 2,000
S.I.C.: 4424
N.A.I.C.S.: 483113
Henrick Magsen *(CEO)*

Det Norske Veritas Eiendom AS (1)
Veritasveien 1
Hovik, 1369, Norway (100%)
Tel.: (47) 67579900
Telex: 76 192 verit n
Fax: (47) 67579911
E-Mail: dnv.cooperate@dnv.com
Web Site: www.dnv.no
Emp.: 2,000
Services to Shipping, Offshore & Land Based Process Industry, Management & Operation
S.I.C.: 4424
N.A.I.C.S.: 483113
Hendric Madsen *(Mng Dir)*

Det Norske Veritas Technology Services (1)
Veritasveien 1
1322 Hovik, Norway (100%)
Tel.: (47) 67579900
Fax: (47) 67579911
Web Site: www.veritas.com
Emp.: 2,500
S.I.C.: 4424
N.A.I.C.S.: 483113
Henrick O. Matson *(CEO)*

DNV Alesund (1)
Nedre Strandgate 29
N 6002 Alesund, Norway (100%)
Tel.: (47) 70115110
E-Mail: alesund.maritime@dnv.com
Emp.: 35
S.I.C.: 4424
N.A.I.C.S.: 483113
Magnes Elbervik *(Mgr-Station)*

DNV Bergen (1)
Johan Berentsensvei 109 111
PO Box 7400
N 5020 Bergen, Norway (100%)
Mailing Address:
PO Box 6005
Bergen, Norway
Tel.: (47) 55943600
E-Mail: bergin.maritime@dnv.com
Web Site: www.dnv.com
Rev.: $5,765,160
Emp.: 140
S.I.C.: 4424
N.A.I.C.S.: 483113
Kore Samnaoy *(Mng Dir)*

DNV Floro (1)
Kolkaia 1
N 6900 Floro, Norway
Tel.: (47) 57745590
Fax: (47) 57742810
Web Site: www.dnv.com
Emp.: 4
S.I.C.: 4424
N.A.I.C.S.: 483113
Nina Kraakenef *(Mng Dir)*

DNV Forde (1)
Fordetunet AS
Hafstadvegen 23, N 6800 Forde, Norway (100%)
Tel.: (47) 57745590
Fax: (47) 57742810
E-Mail: maritime.norway@dnv.com
Emp.: 1
S.I.C.: 4432
N.A.I.C.S.: 483113
Erling Daniel *(Gen Mgr)*

DNV Fredrikstad (1)
KG Meldahls Vei 9
PO Box 304
1610 Fredrikstad, Norway (100%)
Tel.: (47) 69355850
Fax: (47) 69355870
Web Site: www.dnv.com
Emp.: 5
S.I.C.: 4432
N.A.I.C.S.: 483113
Anita Hjerpetjonn *(Gen Mgr)*

DNV Haugesund (1)
Flathauggt 12
5523 Haugesund, Norway (100%)
Mailing Address:
PO Box 400
N-5501 Haugesund, Norway
Tel.: (47) 52703640
Fax: (47) 52711323
Web Site: www.dnv.dk/find_us/findus_more details.asp?id=0362
Emp.: 12
S.I.C.: 4432
N.A.I.C.S.: 483113
Olejohan Harnen *(Mgr)*

DNV Kristiansand S (1)
Kansgaarb Alle 53
PO Box 1652
4688 Kristiansand, 4632, Norway (100%)
Mailing Address:
PO Box 99
N-4601 Kristiansand, Norway
Tel.: (47) 38127800
Fax: (47) 38104730
E-Mail: kristiansandmaritime@dnv.com
Web Site: www.dnv.in
Emp.: 16
S.I.C.: 4432
N.A.I.C.S.: 483113
Alf Haaland *(Mgr)*

DNV Kristiansund N (1)
Verksted 11
N 6517 Kristiansund, Norway (100%)
Tel.: (47) 71588150
Fax: (47) 71585001
E-Mail: kristiansund.maritime@dnv.com
Web Site: www.dnv.com
Emp.: 10
S.I.C.: 4424
N.A.I.C.S.: 483113

DNV Petroleum Services (1)
Veritasveien 1
N-1322 Hovik, Norway
Tel.: (47) 67579900
E-Mail: mpsno@dnv.com
Emp.: 8,000
S.I.C.: 4424
N.A.I.C.S.: 483113

DNV Porsgrunn (1)
Leif Weldingsvei 12
3208 Sandefjord, Norway (100%)
Tel.: (47) 33485550
Fax: (47) 33485560
E-Mail: maritina@dvn.com
Web Site: www.dnv.com
S.I.C.: 4424
N.A.I.C.S.: 483113
Nils Boe *(Gen Mgr)*

DNV Region Norge AS (1)
Nessevegen 2 B
N 9411 Harstad, Norway (100%)
Tel.: (47) 77016550
Fax: (47) 77005220
E-Mail: harstad.maritime@dnv.com
Web Site: www.dnv.in/findus/findus_result.asp?CountryCode=NOR
Emp.: 10
S.I.C.: 4432
N.A.I.C.S.: 483113
Jan Oddvar Olsen *(Gen Mgr)*

DNV Region Norge AS (1)
Professor Brochs gate 2
N 7030 Trondheim, Norway
Tel.: (47) 73903500
Fax: (47) 73903544
E-Mail: asd@dnv.com
Emp.: 40
S.I.C.: 4424
N.A.I.C.S.: 483113
Kent-Age Solem *(Mng Dir)*

DNV Stavanger (1)
Rosenbergace 99
N 4007 Stavanger, Norway (100%)
Mailing Address:
PO Box 788
N-4001 Stavanger, Norway
Tel.: (47) 51506000

Det Norske Veritas AS—(Continued)

E-Mail: eirik.jacobsen@dnv.com
Web Site: www.dnv.no
Emp.: 120
S.I.C.: 4432
N.A.I.C.S.: 483113
Hanrek Matsen *(Gen Mgr)*

DNV Stord (1)
Torget 10 235
N-5402 Stord, Norway
Tel.: (47) 53402900
Fax: (47) 53413449
E-Mail: stord.maritima@dnv.com
Web Site: www.dnv.com
Emp.: 7
S.I.C.: 4424
N.A.I.C.S.: 483113

DNV Tromso (1)
Strandveien 106
9006 Tromso, Norway (100%)
Mailing Address:
PO Box 2193
9002 Tromso, Norway
Tel.: (47) 77016550
Fax: (47) 77 00 5220
E-Mail: harstad.maritime@dnv.com
Web Site: www.dnv.com
Emp.: 1
Shipping Logistics
S.I.C.: 4424
N.A.I.C.S.: 483113

DNV Ulsteinvik (1)
Sjogata 45
N 6065 Ulsteinvik, Norway (100%)
Mailing Address:
PO Box 173
N-6065 Ulsteinvik, Norway
Tel.: (47) 70015200
Fax: (47) 70015201
E-Mail: ulsteinvik.maritime@dnv.com
Web Site: www.dnv.no/finn_oss/findus_more details.asp?IdOrgUnit=0369
Emp.: 11
Transportation
S.I.C.: 4424
N.A.I.C.S.: 483113
Onuj Gaege *(Mng Dir)*

Mo i Rana (1)
PO Box 149
N 8601 Mo i Rana, Norway (100%)
Tel.: (47) 75160175
E-Mail: mor@dnv.com
Emp.: 2
S.I.C.: 4432
N.A.I.C.S.: 483113
Kent Age Solem *(Office Mgr)*

U.S. Subsidiaries:

Det Norske Veritas Holding USA Inc. (1)
1400 Rivallo Dr
Houston, TX 77449 DE
Tel.: (281) 721-6600
Fax: (281) 721-6900
Toll Free: (800) 638-9003
Web Site: www.dnv.com
Emp.: 450
Business Services
Import Export
S.I.C.: 7371
N.A.I.C.S.: 541511
Kenneth Vareide *(Reg Mgr)*

Subsidiaries:

Det Norske Veritas Certification Inc. (2)
1400 Ravello Dr
Katy, TX 77449-5164 TX
Tel.: (281) 396-1000 (100%)
Fax: (281) 721-6600
Toll Free: (800) 638-9003
Web Site: www.dnvcert.com
Emp.: 215
Business Services
Import Export
S.I.C.: 7389
N.A.I.C.S.: 541990

Det Norske Veritas USA Inc. (2)
1400 Ravelo Dr
Katy, TX 77449 TX
Tel.: (281) 721-6600 (100%)
Fax: (281) 396-1900
Emp.: 200
Business Services
Import Export
S.I.C.: 7371
N.A.I.C.S.: 541511
Yehuda Dror *(Mgr)*

Det Norske Veritas-North & Central America (1)
1 International Blvd Ste 1200
Mahwah, NJ 07495 (100%)
Tel.: (201) 512-8900
Telex: 139072(WV) Veritas NYK
Fax: (201) 512-8901
Web Site: www.wwww.dnv.com
Emp.: 30
Clearing & Forwarding Agents
S.I.C.: 8611
N.A.I.C.S.: 813910
Blaine Collins *(Reg Mgr)*

Det Norske Veritas (1)
Cond Playa Serena Apt 605
Carolina, PR 00979
Tel.: (787) 399-5634
Telex: 23 7607747
Fax: (787) 791-3319
E-Mail: sanjuan@dnv.com
Web Site: www.dnv.com
Emp.: 1
S.I.C.: 4432
N.A.I.C.S.: 483113
Knut Lindalen *(Mgr-Ops)*

DNV Certification (1)
3805 Crestwood Pkwy NW Ste 200
Duluth, GA 30096-7145
Tel.: (770) 279-0001
Fax: (770) 279-0282
Web Site: www.dnvtraining.com
Emp.: 16
S.I.C.: 4432
N.A.I.C.S.: 483113

DNV Inc. (1)
1400 Ravello Dri
Katy, TX 77449
Tel.: (281) 396-1000
Fax: (721) 396-1900
Web Site: www.dnvda.com
Emp.: 300
Mfr. of Industrial Machinery
S.I.C.: 7371
N.A.I.C.S.: 541511

DNV Software USA (1)
1400 Ravello Dr
Katy, TX 77449 (100%)
Tel.: (281) 721-6600
Fax: (281) 721-6900
Web Site: www.dnv.com
Emp.: 570
Software Development Services
S.I.C.: 7371
N.A.I.C.S.: 541511

Maritime North America (1)
Corp Ctr Ste 1200 1 Intl Blvd
Mahwah, NJ 07495
Tel.: (201) 512-8900
Fax: (201) 512-8902
Web Site: www.maritime.com
Emp.: 30
S.I.C.: 4424
N.A.I.C.S.: 483113

Divisions:

Det Norske Veritas Certification (2)
3800 Kilroy Airport Way Ste 410
Long Beach, CA 90806 (100%)
Tel.: (562) 426-0500
Fax: (562) 426-0065
E-Mail: manuelmarco@dnv.com
Web Site: www.dnvcert.com
Emp.: 7
Quality Systems Certification for Manufacturing Industries
S.I.C.: 7389
N.A.I.C.S.: 541990
Henrik Madsen *(CEO)*

DNV Maritime North America New Orleans (2)
3445 N Causeway Blvd
Metairie, LA 70002
Tel.: (504) 835-7334
Fax: (504) 835-1735
Web Site: www.dnv.com
Emp.: 7
S.I.C.: 4424
N.A.I.C.S.: 483113

Maritime North America Jacksonville (2)
496 Crosswinds Dr
Fernandina Beach, FL 32034-4545 (100%)
Tel.: (904) 277-1606
Fax: (904) 277-2883
E-Mail: jacksonville@dandb.com
S.I.C.: 4432
N.A.I.C.S.: 483113

Maritime North America Seattle (2)
14450 NE 29th Pl Ste 217
Bellevue, WA 98007-3697
Tel.: (425) 861-7977
Fax: (425) 861-0423
E-Mail: seattle@dnb.com
Web Site: www.dnb.com
Emp.: 3
Marine Investigation Services
S.I.C.: 7812
N.A.I.C.S.: 512110

Non-U.S. Subsidiary:

KEMA N.V. (1)
Utrechtseweg 310
NL-6812 AR Arnhem, Netherlands NL
Mailing Address:
PO Box 9035
NL-6800 ET Arnhem, Netherlands
Tel.: (31) 263569111
Fax: (31) 26 4 42 97 81
E-Mail: contact@kema.com
Web Site: www.kema.com
Emp.: 1,720
Holding Company; Energy Industry Technical & Management Consulting, Inspection, Certification & Operational Support Services
S.I.C.: 6719
N.A.I.C.S.: 551112
Jeroen F. J. M. de Haas *(Vice Chm-Supervisory Bd)*
David Walker *(CEO)*
Aad van den Bos *(CFO)*
J. W. J. van Haarst *(COO & Acting Dir-Transportation Sys)*
S. A. M. van der Weegen *(Gen Counsel & Sec)*

Subsidiary:

KEMA Nederland N.V. (2)
Utrechtseweg 310
NL-6812 AR Arnhem, Netherlands NL
Tel.: (31) 263569111
Fax: (31) 264429781
Web Site: www.kema.com
Energy Industry Technical & Management Consulting, Inspection, Certification & Operational Support Services
S.I.C.: 7389
N.A.I.C.S.: 561990
Jacob P. Fontijne *(Mng Dir)*

U.S. Subsidiary:

KEMA Inc. (2)
67 S Bedford St Ste 201 E
Burlington, MA 01803-5108 VA
Tel.: (781) 273-5700 (100%)
Web Site: www.kema.com
Holding Company; Regional Managing Office
S.I.C.: 6719
N.A.I.C.S.: 551112
Hugo K. van Nispen *(Pres & CEO)*

Subsidiary:

KEMA Services Inc. (3)
67 S Bedford St
Burlington, MA 01803 MA
Tel.: (781) 273-5700
Fax: (781) 229-4867
Web Site: www.kema.com
Sales Range: $400-449.9 Million
Emp.: 60
Energy Industry Technical & Management Consulting, Inspection, Certification & Operational Support Services
S.I.C.: 7389
N.A.I.C.S.: 561990
Hugo K. van Nispen *(Pres & CEO)*

Branches:

KEMA Services Inc. - Anaheim (4)
1440 S State College Blvd Unit 2 F
Anaheim, CA 92806
Tel.: (714) 939-9020
Fax: (714) 939-9022
Web Site: www.kema.com
Emp.: 10
Energy Industry Technical & Management Consulting, Inspection, Certification & Operational Support Services
S.I.C.: 7389
N.A.I.C.S.: 561990
Javier Chaves *(Gen Mgr)*

KEMA Services Inc. - Madison (4)
122 W Washington Ave Ste 1000
Madison, WI 53703-2366
Tel.: (608) 259-9152
Fax: (608) 259-9170
Web Site: www.kema.com
Emp.: 15
Energy Industry Technical & Management Consulting, Inspection, Certification & Operational Support Services
S.I.C.: 7389
N.A.I.C.S.: 561990
Mimi Goldberg *(Sr VP)*

KEMA Services Inc. - Oakland (4)
155 Grand Ave Ste 500
Oakland, CA 94612
Tel.: (510) 891-0446
Fax: (510) 891-0440
Web Site: www.kema.com
Emp.: 30
Energy Industry Technical & Management Consulting, Inspection, Certification & Operational Support Services
S.I.C.: 7389
N.A.I.C.S.: 561990
Rich Barnes *(Pres)*

DETEAM COMPANY LIMITED

Suite 3 31st Floor Sino Plaza 255-257 Gloucester Road
Hong Kong, China (Hong Kong)
Tel.: (852) 2831 9905
Fax: (852) 2838 0866
Web Site: www.irasia.com
0065—(HKG)
Sls.: $55,513,749
Assets: $127,696,219
Liabilities: $50,862,651
Net Worth: $76,833,568
Earnings: ($8,215,276)
Emp.: 705
Fiscal Year-end: 12/31/12

Business Description:
Holding Company; Plastic Woven Bag Mfr; Coal Distr
S.I.C.: 6719
N.A.I.C.S.: 551112

Personnel:
Godfrey Shiu Chung Mak *(Co-Chm & Compliance Officer)*
Bin Xu *(Co-Chm)*
Choi Chak Wong *(Controller-Fin & Sec)*

Board of Directors:
Godfrey Shiu Chung Mak
Bin Xu
Shao Ru Huang
Chi Shing Kwok
Wai Sum Tsang
Hon Chen Wang
Yang Yu
Chao Liang Zhang

Royal Bank of Canada Trust Company (Cayman) Limited
4th Floor Royal Bank House 24 Shedden Road
Georgetown, Cayman Islands

Transfer Agents:
Tricor Abacus Limited
26th Floor Tesbury Centre 28 Queen's Road East
Wanchai, China (Hong Kong)

Royal Bank of Canada Trust Company (Cayman) Limited
4th Floor Royal Bank House 24 Shedden Road
Georgetown, Cayman Islands

DETECTOR EXPLORATION LTD.

1100 540-5th Ave SW
Calgary, AB, T2P 0M2, Canada

Tel.: (403) 264-1880
Fax: (403) 264-7401
Year Founded: 1991
DEX—(TSXV)
Rev.: $909,493
Assets: $906,265
Liabilities: $1,323,045
Net Worth: ($416,780)
Earnings: $92,902
Fiscal Year-end: 12/31/12
Business Description:
Oil & Natural Gas Exploration Services
S.I.C.: 1389
N.A.I.C.S.: 213112
Personnel:
Ronald E. Alexander *(Pres)*
Edward A. James *(CFO)*
Barry Holizki *(COO & VP-Engrg)*
Board of Directors:
Ronald E. Alexander
Stephen N. Ewaskiw
Edward A. James

DETOUR GOLD CORPORATION

Royal Bank Plaza South Tower 200
Bay Street Suite 2200
PO Box 23
Toronto, ON, M5J 2J1, Canada
Tel.: (416) 304-0800
Fax: (416) 304-0184
E-Mail: info@detourgold.com
Web Site: www.detourgold.com
DGC—(OTC TSX)
Assets: $2,353,243,000
Liabilities: $712,069,000
Net Worth: $1,641,174,000
Earnings: ($38,510,000)
Emp.: 510
Fiscal Year-end: 12/31/12
Business Description:
Gold Exploration & Development
S.I.C.: 1041
N.A.I.C.S.: 212221
Personnel:
Gerald S. Panneton *(Founder)*
Michael Kenyon *(Chm)*
Paul Martin *(Pres & CEO)*
James Mavor *(CFO)*
Pierre Beaudoin *(COO & Sr VP)*
Julie Galloway *(Gen Counsel, Sec & Sr VP)*
Derek Teevan *(Sr VP-Aboriginal & Governmental Affairs)*
Board of Directors:
Michael Kenyon
Louis Dionne
Robert Emmet Doyle
Andre Roger Falzon
Ingrid J. Hibbard
Paul Martin
Alexander G. Morrison
Jonathan Arn Rubenstein
Graham Wozniak
Legal Counsel:
McMillan LLP
BCE Place, Suite 4400 Bay Wellington Tower
181 Bay Street
Toronto, ON, Canada
Transfer Agent:
Computershare Trust Company of Canada
Toronto, ON, Canada

DETRON ICT SOLUTIONS BV

Traverse 1
3905 NL Veenendaal, Netherlands
Tel.: (31) 88 44 60 000
E-Mail: ict@detron.nl
Web Site: www.detron.nl
Business Description:
IT & Telecom Services
S.I.C.: 7389
N.A.I.C.S.: 541990
Personnel:
George Banks *(CEO)*

DEUFOL SE

Johannes Gutenberg Strasse 3-5
D-65719 Hofheim, Wallau, Germany
Tel.: (49) 6122 5000
Fax: (49) 6122 501300
E-Mail: info@deufol.com
Web Site: www.deufol.com
LOI—(DEU)
Sls.: $448,274,610
Assets: $297,368,953
Liabilities: $167,194,314
Net Worth: $130,174,639
Earnings: $1,346,170
Emp.: 2,764
Fiscal Year-end: 12/31/12
Business Description:
Packaging & Logistics Services
S.I.C.: 7389
N.A.I.C.S.: 561910
Personnel:
Helmut Olivier *(Chm-Supervisory Bd)*
Detlef W. Hubner *(Chm-Mgmt Bd & Mng Dir)*
Wolfgang Konig *(Deputy Chm-Supervisory Bd)*
Tillmann Blaschke *(Mng Dir)*
Jens Hoff *(Mng Dir)*
Jurgen Schmid *(Mng Dir)*
Manfred Weirich *(Mng Dir)*
Supervisory Board of Directors:
Helmut Olivier
Helmut Gorling
Wolfgang Konig
Wulf Matthias
Subsidiaries:

Aircon Airfreight Container Maintenance GmbH (1)
Dieselstr 5
64546, Morfelden, Hesse, Germany(56.7%)
Tel.: (49) 610524455
Fax: (49) 610525521
E-Mail: aircon@dlogistics.com
Emp.: 16
Air Freight Services
S.I.C.: 4522
N.A.I.C.S.: 481212
Peter Duis *(Mng Dir)*
Heiko Wedmann *(Mng Dir)*

Deufol Tailleur GmbH (1)
Essener Strasse 2-24
46047 Oberhausen, Nordrhein-Westfalen, Germany
Tel.: (49) 2088596100
Fax: (49) 2088596952
Emp.: 10
Packaging Services
S.I.C.: 7389
N.A.I.C.S.: 561910
Andreas Bargende *(Mng Dir)*

Subsidiaries:

Deufol Berlin GmbH (2)
Piesporter Strasse 50-52
13088 Berlin, Germany
Tel.: (49) 3092403590
Fax: (49) 30924035919
E-Mail: r.rahm@tailleur.de
Web Site: www.deufol.de
Emp.: 50
Packaging Services
S.I.C.: 7389
N.A.I.C.S.: 561910
Mark Agatz *(CEO)*

Deufol Bochum GmbH (2)
Arnoldschacht 11
44894 Bochum, Nordrhein-Westfalen, Germany
Tel.: (49) 23423960
Fax: (49) 2342396501
E-Mail: info@dtg-eggemann.de
Web Site: www.dtg-gruppe.de
Emp.: 50
Packaging Services
S.I.C.: 7389
N.A.I.C.S.: 561910
Roland Baumann *(Mgr)*

Deufol Frankfurt GmbH (2)
Cargo City Sud Gebaude 638 E
60549 Frankfurt am Main, Hesse, Germany
Tel.: (49) 696380940
Fax: (49) 6963809499
E-Mail: frankfurt.flughasen@deufol.com
Web Site: www.technopack.de
Emp.: 10
Packaging Services
S.I.C.: 7389
N.A.I.C.S.: 561910
Stefen Tjaden *(Mng Dir)*

Deufol Hamburg GmbH (2)
Ellerholzdamm 16-20
20457 Hamburg, Germany
Tel.: (49) 403197510
Fax: (49) 4031975110
Emp.: 5
Packaging Services
S.I.C.: 7389
N.A.I.C.S.: 561910

Deufol Munchen GmbH (2)
Lichtlocherberg 40
06333 Hettstedt, Saxony-Anhalt, Germany
Tel.: (49) 3476893020
Fax: (49) 34 76 89 30 21
E-Mail: info@ias-hettstedt.de
Web Site: www.ias-hettstedt.de
Packaging Services
S.I.C.: 7389
N.A.I.C.S.: 561910

Deufol Nord GmbH (2)
Vohrumer Str 40
31228 Peine, Germany
Tel.: (49) 51712960
Fax: (49) 417129635
Emp.: 250
Packaging Services
S.I.C.: 7389
N.A.I.C.S.: 561910
Detlef W. Hubnir *(CEO)*

Deufol Nurnberg GmbH (2)
Rotterdamer Strasse 130
90451 Nuremberg, Bavaria, Germany
Tel.: (49) 9119686890
Fax: (49) 91196868955
E-Mail: info@deufol.de
Web Site: www.deufol.de
Emp.: 50
Packaging Services
S.I.C.: 7389
N.A.I.C.S.: 561910
Jurgen Schmid *(Mgr)*

Deufol Sud GmbH (2)
Neugablonzer Str 1
93073 Neutraubling, Germany
Tel.: (49) 9401 607655
Packaging Services
S.I.C.: 7389
N.A.I.C.S.: 561910
Jurgen Schmid *(Mgr)*

Deufol West GmbH (2)
Essener Strasse 2-24
46047 Oberhausen, Nordrhein-Westfalen, Germany
Tel.: (49) 20885 96100
Fax: (49) 20885 96952
E-Mail: info@deufol.de
Packaging Services
S.I.C.: 7389
N.A.I.C.S.: 561910

DTG Verpackungslogistik GmbH (2)
Ringstrasse 71-73
70736 Fellbach, Germany
Tel.: (49) 7113426680
Fax: (49) 71134266850
E-Mail: info@deufol-tailleur.de
Web Site: www.dtg-verpackungslogistik.com
Emp.: 33
Logistics & Packaging Services
S.I.C.: 4731
N.A.I.C.S.: 541614
Herr Ziegler *(Mgr)*

Deufol Remscheid GmbH (2)
Essener Strasse 2-24
46047 Oberhausen, Germany
Tel.: (49) 2088596200
E-Mail:
Emp.: 60
Packaging & Freight Transportation Services
S.I.C.: 4522
N.A.I.C.S.: 481212
Mark Agas *(Mng Dir)*

Horst Lange GmbH (2)
Schlossstrasse 112
22041 Hamburg, Germany
Tel.: (49) 404191940
Packaging Services
S.I.C.: 7389
N.A.I.C.S.: 561910

IAD Industrieanlagen-Dienst GmbH (2)
Lemgostr 21
80935 Munich, Bavaria, Germany
Tel.: (49) 89 3515081
Fax: (49) 89 3544661
E-Mail: iad-muenchen@t-online.de
Web Site: www.iad-muenchen.de
Emp.: 15
Packaging Wooden Boxes Mfr & Distr
S.I.C.: 2449
N.A.I.C.S.: 321920
Jurgen Schmid *(Mng Dir)*

Walpa Gesellschaft fur Ubersee- und Spezialverpackung mbH (2)
Daimlerstrasse 38a
69190 Walldorf, Germany
Tel.: (49) 622782600
Fax: (49) 62274473
E-Mail: info@walpa.de
Web Site: www.walpa.de
Emp.: 45
Packaging Services
S.I.C.: 7389
N.A.I.C.S.: 561910
Friedbert Doll *(Mgr)*

Non-U.S. Subsidiaries:

Deufol Slovensko s.r.o. (2)
Bedzianska cesta 667
956 31 Krusovce, Slovakia
Tel.: (421) 385328403
Fax: (421) 385328404
Web Site: www.logis.sk
Emp.: 25
Logistics & Packaging Services
S.I.C.: 4731
N.A.I.C.S.: 541614
Peter Petras *(Mng Dir)*

Logis Industriedienstleistung GmbH (2)
Jahnstrasse 45
3430 Tulln, Austria
Tel.: (43) 2272 8173520
Fax: (43) 2272 8173590
E-Mail: office@logis-group.eu
Web Site: www.logis-group.eu
Emp.: 30
Logistics & Packaging Services
S.I.C.: 4731
N.A.I.C.S.: 541614
Nickl Johann *(Mgr-Sls & Project)*

Logis prumyslove obaly a.s. (2)
Za Mostem 303 8
664 91 Ivancice, Czech Republic
Tel.: (420) 546 451 101
Fax: (420) 546 418 532
E-Mail: info@deufol.com
Web Site: www.deufol.com
Emp.: 20
Logistics & Packaging Services
S.I.C.: 4731
N.A.I.C.S.: 541614
Pavel Broza *(COO)*

U.S. Subsidiary:

Deufol Sunman Inc. (1)
924 S Meridian St
Sunman, IN 47041-8498
Tel.: (812) 623-1140
Fax: (812) 623-1167
Toll Free: (800) 446-4844
E-Mail: contact@jjpackaging.com
Web Site: www.deufol.com
Emp.: 500
Packaging Services
S.I.C.: 7389
N.A.I.C.S.: 561910
Lisa Nichols *(Dir-HR)*

Non-U.S. Subsidiaries:

Deufol Belgie N.V. (1)
Industriepark 16 2
3300 Tienen, Belgium

Deufol SE—(Continued)

Tel.: (32) 16801011
Fax: (32) 16801090
E-Mail: info@dlogistics.be
Web Site: www.dlogistics.be
Emp.: 300
Packaging & Warehousing Services
S.I.C.: 4225
N.A.I.C.S.: 493110
Olaf Fait *(Mgr)*

Subsidiaries:

Arcus Installation N.V. (2)
Centrum-Zuid 1611
3530 Houthalen, Limburg, Belgium
Tel.: (32) 11606399
Fax: (32) 11606398
Emp.: 20
Logistics Services
S.I.C.: 4731
N.A.I.C.S.: 541614
Olaf Fait *(Mng Dir)*

AT+S N.V. (2)
Centrum Zuid 1611
3530 Houthalen, Limburg, Belgium
Tel.: (32) 11606400
Fax: (32) 11606398
E-Mail: ats@dlogistics.be
Emp.: 20
Transportation Services
S.I.C.: 4212
N.A.I.C.S.: 484220
Olaf Fait *(Mng Dir)*

Deufol Waremme S.A. (2)
Rue du Parc Industriel 29
4300 Waremme, Liege, Belgium
Tel.: (32) 19339730
Fax: (32) 19339749
E-Mail: info@deufol.com
Emp.: 6
Logistics Services
S.I.C.: 4731
N.A.I.C.S.: 541614
Ronald Schrooten *(Gen Mgr)*

Deufol Italia S.p.A. (1)
via Magellano 22
21054 Fagnano Olona, Italy
Tel.: (39) 331613721
Packaging Material Mfr & Related Services
S.I.C.: 2672
N.A.I.C.S.: 322220
Elio Guffanti *(Dir-Ops)*

Deufol Packaging Tienen N.V. (1)
Industriepark 16
Box 3
3300 Tienen, Flemish Brabant, Belgium
Tel.: (32) 16801011
Fax: (32) 16801090
E-Mail: info@deufol.com
Emp.: 150
Packaging & Warehousing Services
S.I.C.: 4225
N.A.I.C.S.: 493110
Olaf Fait *(Mng Dir)*

DEUTA-WERKE GMBH

Paffrather Str 140
51465 Bergisch Gladbach, Germany
Tel.: (49) 2202958100
Fax: (49) 2202958145
E-Mail: support@deuta.de
Web Site: www.deuta.de
Year Founded: 1905
Rev.: $34,527,750
Emp.: 143

Business Description:
Automobile Product Mfr
S.I.C.: 3711
N.A.I.C.S.: 336111

Personnel:
Thomas Blau *(Mng Dir)*
Fabian Rensch *(Mng Dir)*

DEUTRUCK GMBH

Ahrwaldstrasse 7
21376 Garlstorf, Germany
Tel.: (49) 41726647
Fax: (49) 41726059
E-Mail: deutruck@deutruck.com
Web Site: www.deutruck.de
Rev.: $16,222,256
Emp.: 14

Business Description:
Forklift Truck Mfr
S.I.C.: 3537
N.A.I.C.S.: 333924

Personnel:
Georg Grochutek *(Mng Dir)*

DEUTSCHE APOTHEKER- UND ARZTEBANK EG

(d/b/a apoBank Gruppe)
Richard-Oskar-Mattern-Strasse 6
40547 Dusseldorf, Germany
Tel.: (49) 21159980
Fax: (49) 211593877
E-Mail: info@apobank.de
Web Site: www.apobank.de
Year Founded: 1902
Int. Income: $1,799,185,202
Assets: $51,004,082,833
Liabilities: $48,683,387,794
Net Worth: $2,320,695,039
Earnings: $61,073,772
Emp.: 2,360
Fiscal Year-end: 12/31/12

Business Description:
Financial & Banking Services
S.I.C.: 6029
N.A.I.C.S.: 522110

Personnel:
Hermann Stefan Keller *(Chm-Supervisory Bd)*
Wolfgang Hack *(Deputy Chm-Supervisory Bd)*
Harald Felzen *(Member-Mgmt Bd)*
Eckhard Ludering *(Member-Mgmt Bd)*
Herbert Pfennig *(Member-Mgmt Bd)*
Thomas Siekmann *(Member-Mgmt Bd)*
Ulrich Sommer *(Member-Mgmt Bd)*

Supervisory Board of Directors:
Hermann Stefan Keller
Ralph Baumann
Martina Burkard
Mechthild Coordt
Peter Engel
Sven Franke
Eberhard Gramsch
Wolfgang Hack
Klaus Holz
Andreas Kohler
Walter Kollbach
Ulrice Kruger
Frank Ulrich Montgomery
Sigrid Muller-Emsters
Helmut Pfeffer
Karl-Georg Pochhammer
Christian Scherer
Friedemann Schmidt
Ute Szameitat
Heinz-Gunter Wolf

Subsidiaries:

Apo Asset Management GmbH (1)
Richard-Oskar-Mattern-Strasse 6
40547 Dusseldorf, Germany
Tel.: (49) 2118632310
Fax: (49) 21186323150
E-Mail: u.noetges@apoasset.de
Web Site: www.apoasset.de/cgi-bin/htsearch?words=oskar
Emp.: 18
Direct Property & Casualty Insurance Carriers
S.I.C.: 6331
N.A.I.C.S.: 524126
Ulrich Noetges *(Mgr-Mktg)*

Apo Immobilien-KAG (1)
Richard-Oskar-Mattern-Str 6
40547 Dusseldorf, Germany
Tel.: (49) 2115374200
Fax: (49) 211537420290
E-Mail: info@aik-invest.de
Web Site: www.aik-invest.de
Emp.: 50
Real Estate Agents & Brokers Offices
S.I.C.: 6531
N.A.I.C.S.: 531210
Stephen Hinsche *(Mng Dir)*

ApoFinanz GmbH (1)
Bachstr 7
March, 79232 Bremen, Germany
Tel.: (49) 7618859124
Fax: (49) 7618859111
E-Mail: ralf.weckwerth@apofinanz.de
Web Site: www.apofinanz.de
Financial Transactions Processing Reserve & Clearinghouse Activities
S.I.C.: 6099
N.A.I.C.S.: 522320
Ralf Weckwerth *(Gen Mgr)*

DGN Service GmbH (1)
Niederkasseler Lohweg 181-183
40547 Dusseldorf, Germany
Tel.: (49) 211770080
Fax: (49) 21177008500
E-Mail: infoline@dgnservice.de
Web Site: www.dgnservice.de
Emp.: 35
International Trade Financing
S.I.C.: 6159
N.A.I.C.S.: 522293
Armin Flender *(Mng Dir & Gen Mgr)*

medisign GmbH (1)
Richard-Oskar-Mattern-Strasse 6
40547 Dusseldorf, Germany
Tel.: (49) 2115382230
Fax: (49) 2115382232
E-Mail: hotline@medisign.de
Web Site: www.medisign.de
Digital Security Services
S.I.C.: 7379
N.A.I.C.S.: 541519
Peter Gabriel *(Mng Dir)*

DEUTSCHE BAHN AG

Potsdamer Platz 2
10785 Berlin, Germany
Tel.: (49) 302970
Fax: (49) 3029762120
E-Mail: reiseportal@bahn.de
Web Site: www.deutschebahn.com
Year Founded: 1994
Rev.: $52,899,096,320
Assets: $70,660,463,300
Liabilities: $49,210,590,520
Net Worth: $21,449,872,780
Earnings: $1,988,293,090
Emp.: 287,508
Fiscal Year-end: 12/31/12

Business Description:
Holding Company; Passenger & Freight Transportation & Logistics Services
S.I.C.: 6719
N.A.I.C.S.: 551112

Personnel:
Utz-Hellmuth Felcht *(Chm-Supervisory Bd)*
Rudiger Grube *(Chm-Mgmt Bd & CEO)*
Alexander Kirchner *(Deputy Chm-Supervisory Bd)*
Stefan Vogelsang *(Deputy Chief Compliance Officer & Head-Compliance Mgmt I Unit)*
Werner Grebe *(Chief Compliance Officer)*
Gerd Becht *(Member-Mgmt Bd-Compliance, Privacy & Legal Affairs)*
Volker Kefer *(Member-Mgmt Bd-Tech & Infrastructure)*
Richard Lutz *(Member-Mgmt Bd-Fin & Controlling)*
Ulrich Weber *(Member-Mgmt Bd-HR)*

Supervisory Board of Directors:
Utz-Hellmuth Felcht
Hans Bernhard Beus
Christoph Danzer-Vanotti
Patrick Doring
Jurgen Grossmann
Bernhard Heitzer
Jorg Hensel
Klaus-Dieter Hommel
Wolfgang Joosten
Alexander Kirchner
Jurgen Krumnow
Knut Loschke
Vitus Miller
Fred Nowka
Michael Odenwald
Ute Plambeck
Mario Reiss
Regina Rusch-Ziemba
Jens Schwarz
Heinrich Weiss

Groups:

DB Mobility Logistics AG (1)
Potsdamer Platz 3
10785 Berlin, Germany De
Tel.: (49) 3029754855 (100%)
Fax: (49) 3029754029
Sales Range: $25-49.9 Billion
Emp.: 174,988
Holding Company; Passenger & Freight Transportation & Logistics Services
Import Export
S.I.C.: 6719
N.A.I.C.S.: 551112
Werner Muller *(Chm-Supervisory Bd)*
Ruediger Grube *(Chm-Mgmt Bd & CEO)*
Wolfgang Zell *(Deputy Chm-Supervisory Bd)*
Diethelm Sack *(CFO)*
Ulrich Homburg *(Member-Mgmt Bd-Passenger Transport)*
Volker Kefer *(Member Mgmt-Bd-Tech, Integrated Sys Rails & Svcs)*
Walther Otremba *(Integrated Sys Rails & Svcs)*
Karl-Friedrich Rausch *(Member-Mgmt Bd-Transport & Logistics)*
Ulrich Weber *(Member-Mgmt Bd-HR & Svcs)*

Subsidiaries:

Baustoff Union GmbH & Co. KG (2)
Hamburger Strasse 98
D 90451 Nuremberg, Germany (100%)
Tel.: (49) 91164250
Fax: (49) 9116425100
E-Mail: info@baustoffunionfranken.de
Web Site: www.baustoff-union-franken.de/11.html
Emp.: 100
Construction Materials
S.I.C.: 5031
N.A.I.C.S.: 423310
Otto Fortsch *(Mng Dir)*

Ferrocarbon GmbH (2)
Westuferstrasse 10
Postfach 45356
43000 Essen, Germany
Tel.: (49) 201364070
Telex: 8579099 feca d
Fax: (49) 2013640730
Emp.: 36
Steel Foundrie
S.I.C.: 3325
N.A.I.C.S.: 331513

Hotel Nassauer Hof GmbH (2)
Kaiser Friedrich Platz 3 4
65183 Wiesbaden, Germany (100%)
Tel.: (49) 6111330
Telex: 4186847
Fax: (49) 611133643
E-Mail: info@nassauer-hof.de
Web Site: www.nassauerhof.de
Emp.: 150
Hotel, Catering & Conferences
S.I.C.: 7011
N.A.I.C.S.: 721110
Karl Nueser *(Mng Dir)*

Saxonia Baustoffe GmbH (2)
Fritz Reuter Str 56
1097 Dresden, Germany (100%)
Tel.: (49) 35185170
Fax: (49) 18517122
E-Mail: rkb.dresden@raabkarcher.de
Web Site: www.saxonia-baustoffe.de
Emp.: 4,000
Building Materials
S.I.C.: 2452
N.A.I.C.S.: 321992
Sascha Grafe *(Gen Mgr)*

Schenker AG (2)
Alfredstrasse 81
D 45130 Essen, Germany (100%)
Tel.: (49) 20187810
Telex: 41528-0
Fax: (49) 20187818334
E-Mail: info@schenker.com
Web Site: www.schenker.com
Emp.: 225
Freight Forwarding, Fairs in Foreign Countries, Travel Agencies & Railroad Traffic to the Far East
S.I.C.: 4731
N.A.I.C.S.: 488510

Subsidiaries:

Intertec GmbH (3)
Klaus-von-Klitzing-Strasse 2
D-76829 Landau in der Pfalz, Germany De
Tel.: (49) 63412840
Telex: 856200 stb d
Fax: (49) 634120413
E-Mail: info@inter-union.de
Web Site: www.inter-union.de
Sales Range: $250-299.9 Million
Emp.: 500
Holding Company; Motor Vehicle Accessories & Maintenance Products Distr
S.I.C.: 6719
N.A.I.C.S.: 551112
Andreas Koring *(Mng Dir)*

Subsidiaries:

Eisen Lothringen Stahlhandel GmbH (SSH) (4)
Zementstrasse 144
59269 Beckum, Germany (100%)
Tel.: (49) 2521829110
Telex: 89498
Fax: (49) 25218291130
Web Site: www.els.com
Emp.: 100
Oil & Gas Industry Services
S.I.C.: 1389
N.A.I.C.S.: 213112

Inter-Union Technohandel GmbH (4)
Klaus-von-Klitzing-Strasse 2
D-76829 Landau in der Pfalz, Germany De
Tel.: (49) 63412840 (100%)
Fax: (49) 634120413
E-Mail: info@inter-union.de
Web Site: www.inter-union.de
Emp.: 200
Automotive Accessories & Maintenance Products Distr
S.I.C.: 5013
N.A.I.C.S.: 423120
Andreas Koring *(Mng Dir)*

Schenker Deutschland AG (3)
Feimeisenstrasse 4
Dortmund, 44339, Germany (100%)
Tel.: (49) 2319635444
Fax: (49) 2319635119
E-Mail: geschaeftsstelle.dortmund@schenker.com
Web Site: www.schenker.de
Emp.: 7,000
Freight Forwarding Agents
S.I.C.: 4731
N.A.I.C.S.: 488510
Klaus Lesselt *(Mng Dir)*

Non-U.S. Subsidiaries:

Schenker AB (3)
3 Lella Bonnen
S 412 97 Gothenburg, Sweden SE
Tel.: (46) 317038000 (100%)
Fax: (46) 317038924
E-Mail: info.swe@schenker.com
Web Site: www.schenker.se
Sls.: $1,287,769,472
Emp.: 350
Road Haulage, Freight Forwarding, General Warehousing & Storage, Air & Railway Transport, & Logistics Services
S.I.C.: 4213
N.A.I.C.S.: 484122
Ingvar Nilsson *(Mng Dir)*
Karsten Keller *(CFO)*

Schenker & Co AG (3)
Stella-Klein-Low Weg 11
A-1020 Vienna, Austria (100%)
Tel.: (43) 57686210900
Fax: (43) 57686211608
E-Mail: wien@schenker.at
Web Site: www.schenker.at
Emp.: 150
Freight Forwarding, Fairs in Foreign Countries, Travel Agencies & Railroad Traffic to the Far East
S.I.C.: 4731
N.A.I.C.S.: 488510
Elmar Wielend *(Gen Mgr)*

Stinnes Data Service GmbH (2)
Stinnes Plant 1
PO Box 55
45472 Mullheim, Germany (100%)
Tel.: (49) 208494332
Telex: 856200
Fax: (49) 208494388
E-Mail: info@sds-bs.de
Web Site: www.stinnes.de
Emp.: 160
Data Processing Services
S.I.C.: 7379
N.A.I.C.S.: 518210
Bodo Roiko *(Mng Dir)*

Stinnes Freight Logistics (2)
Leipziger Platz 9
D 10117 Berlin, Germany (100%)
Tel.: (49) 40339640
Telex: 2 11 78 60
Fax: (49) 4033964272
Web Site: www.stinnes.de
Oil Dealer
S.I.C.: 1389
N.A.I.C.S.: 213112

Stinnes Immobiliendienst Verwaltungsgesellschaft mbH (2)
Humboldtring 15
45472 Mullheim, Germany
Tel.: (49) 2084940
Fax: (49) 208494698
Real Estate Management
S.I.C.: 6531
N.A.I.C.S.: 531210

Stinnes Technohandel GmbH (2)
Humboldtring 15
4330 Mullheim, Germany (100%)
Tel.: (49) 63412840
Telex: 856200 stb d
Fax: (49) 2084947277
E-Mail: info@interunion.de
Web Site: www.schencker.com
Emp.: 120
Trade in Technical Products, Auto Products, Photography Products, & Home Electronics
S.I.C.: 3651
N.A.I.C.S.: 334310

Wambesco Rohstoffhandelsges. mbH (2)
Am Parallel Hafen 14
47059 Duisburg, Germany (100%)
Tel.: (49) 203932870
Telex: 8551410
Fax: (49) 2039328787
Emp.: 120
Industrial Chemical Products
S.I.C.: 2899
N.A.I.C.S.: 325998

U.S. Subsidiaries:

Schenker, Inc. (2)
150 Albany Ave
Freeport, NY 11520-4702 NY
Tel.: (516) 377-3000
Fax: (516) 377-3133
Toll Free: (800) 225-5229
Web Site: www.dbschenkerusa.com
Insurance, Logistics and Foreign Freight Forwarding
S.I.C.: 4731
N.A.I.C.S.: 488510
Heiner Murmann *(Pres & CEO)*
Eric Dewey *(Exec VP-Logistics)*
Malcolm Heath *(Exec VP-Intl)*

Branch:

DB Schenker USA - Regional Office (3)
440 Exchange
Irvine, CA 92602-4936
Tel.: (714) 442-4500
Fax: (714) 442-2900
Toll Free: (800) 225-5229
Web Site: www.dbschenkerusa.com
Freight Transportation Services
Import Export
S.I.C.: 4731
N.A.I.C.S.: 488510
Stephen Mattessich *(CFO & VP)*
Doris Hall *(CIO & Sr VP)*
Jay Arnold *(Sr VP-HR & Admin)*
Jeffrey Barrie *(Sr VP-Global Sls & Key Acct Mgmt)*

Non-U.S. Subsidiaries:

BAX Global Services Chile Ltda. (4)
Las Urbinas #53 Suite 103
Providencia, Santiago, Chile
Tel.: (56) 2 471 5400
Fax: (56) 2 232 5832
Freight Transportation Services
S.I.C.: 4731
N.A.I.C.S.: 488510

BAX Global S.r.l. (4)
Via Quintiliano 11
20138 Milan, Italy
Tel.: (39) 02506761
Fax: (39) 0258012009
Airfreight & Transportation Services
S.I.C.: 4731
N.A.I.C.S.: 488510

BAX Global (Thailand) Ltd. (4)
Kluaynamthai 5th 42 Twr
Klongtoey, Bangkok, 10110, Thailand
Tel.: (66) 27122593
Fax: (66) 27122602
Web Site: www.baxglobal.com
Transportation & Shipping Services
S.I.C.: 4731
N.A.I.C.S.: 488510

BAX Global (UK) Limited (4)
Schenker House Great Southwest Rd
Feltham, Mddx, TW14 8NT, United Kingdom
Tel.: (44) 2088908899
Fax: (44) 2088906300
Web Site: www.schenker.co.uk
Freight Transportation Services
S.I.C.: 4731
N.A.I.C.S.: 488510
Helgi Ingolfsson *(CEO)*

Schenker Argentina (4)
Tucuman 117 Piso 6
Capital Federal, Buenos Aires, C1049AAC, Argentina
Tel.: (54) 11 4310 1200
Fax: (54) 11 4315 7755
E-Mail: info.argentina@dbschenker.com
Web Site: www.dbschenker.com.ar
Freight Shipping Services
S.I.C.: 4731
N.A.I.C.S.: 488510
Enrique Valera Holthus *(CEO)*

Schenker do Brasil Transportes Internacionais Ltda. (4)
Rua Geraldo Flausino Gomes 78 12th Fl
04575 060 Sao Paulo, SP, Brazil
Tel.: (55) 11 3318 9200
Fax: (55) 11 3318 9203
E-Mail: schenkerdobrasil@dbschenker.com
Web Site: www.dbschenker.com.br
Shipping & Transportation Services
S.I.C.: 4731
N.A.I.C.S.: 488510

Schenker International HK Limited (4)
Fl 35 Skyline Twr 39 Wang Kwong Road
Kowloon Bay, Kowloon, China (Hong Kong)
Tel.: (852) 23799280
Fax: (852) 23799289
E-Mail: marketing@dbschenker.com
Web Site: www.schenker.com
Emp.: 300
Freight Transportation Services
S.I.C.: 4731
N.A.I.C.S.: 488510
Soren Poulsen *(Mng Dir)*

Schenker Philippines, Inc. (4)
44th Floor PBCom Tower 6795 Ayala Avenue
cor VA Rufino Street, Makati, 1200, Philippines
Tel.: (63) 28196033
Fax: (63) 28196020
E-Mail: business-development.ph@schenker.com
Web Site: www.schenker.com.ph
Freight Transportation Services
S.I.C.: 4731
N.A.I.C.S.: 488510
Reiner Allgeier *(Mng Dir)*

Schenker Singapore (Pte) Ltd. (4)
17 Changi South Street 2
Singapore, 486129, Singapore
Tel.: (65) 459788
Fax: (65) 456788
E-Mail: info.singapore@dbschenker.com
Web Site: www.dbschenker.com
Emp.: 1,000
Freight Transportation Services
S.I.C.: 4731
N.A.I.C.S.: 488510
Yuit Oon Chong *(Head-IT)*

Non-U.S. Subsidiary:

Schenker of Canada Limited (3)
6525 Northwest Drive
Mississauga, ON, L4V 1K2, Canada ON
Tel.: (905) 676-0676 (10%)
Fax: (905) 673-3142
Web Site: www.schenker.ca
Sales Range: $25-49.9 Million
Emp.: 120
Freight Transportation Arrangement
S.I.C.: 4731
N.A.I.C.S.: 488510
Heiner Murmann *(Grp CEO)*
Petra Kuester *(CFO)*

Stinnes Corporation (2)
120 White Plains Rd
Tarrytown, NY 10591-5526 DE
Tel.: (914) 366-7200 (100%)
Fax: (914) 366-8226
E-Mail: stinnes@stinnesusa.com
Web Site: www.stinnesusa.com
Sales Range: $900-999.9 Million
Emp.: 20
International & Domestic Trading & Distribution of Chemicals, Coal, Metals, Petroleum Products, Steel & Minerals & Alloys; Remanufacturing & Distribution of Crankshafts & Liners
S.I.C.: 4731
N.A.I.C.S.: 488510

Non-U.S. Subsidiaries:

Frank & Schulte (France) S.A.R.L. (2)
3 Allee des Aulnes
78000 Trappes, France (100%)
Tel.: (33) 139441342
Telex: 42/695706 franshu
Fax: (33) 139441348
E-Mail: febrice.vincent@frank.com
Web Site: www.frank-schulte.com
Emp.: 3
Oil & Gas Services
S.I.C.: 1389
N.A.I.C.S.: 213112
Fabrice Vincent *(CEO)*

Frank & Schulte In Austria Ges. mbH (2)
Paulanergasse 10
PO Box 18
1040 Vienna, Austria (100%)
Tel.: (43) 22258755110, ext. 15875510
Telex: 47/112731 fus a
Fax: (43) 2225875148, ext. 15875148
E-Mail: office@fus.at
Sales Range: $10-24.9 Million
Emp.: 5
S.I.C.: 1389
N.A.I.C.S.: 213112

DB Schenker Rail Deutschland AG (1)
Rheinstrasse 2
D-55116 Mainz, Germany De
Tel.: (49) 6131159 (92%)
Web Site: www.rail.dbschenker.de
Sales Range: $5-14.9 Billion
Emp.: 29,242
Rail Freight Carrier & Logistics
S.I.C.: 4011
N.A.I.C.S.: 482111
Alexander Hedderich *(CEO)*
Michael Anslinger *(Member-Mgmt Bd)*
Christian Kuhn *(Member-Mgmt Bd)*
Rudolf Muller *(Member-Mgmt Bd)*
Karsten Sachsenroder *(Member-Mgmt Bd)*

Deutsche Bahn AG—(Continued)

Subsidiary:

RBH Logistics GmbH (2)
Talstrasse 7
45966 Gladbeck, Germany
Tel.: (49) 2043501320
Fax: (49) 2043501411
Web Site: www.rbh-logistics.com
Emp.: 800
Logistics Services
S.I.C.: 4731
N.A.I.C.S.: 541614
Norbert Gawlik *(Mgr-Sls)*

Non-U.S. Subsidiaries:

DB Schenker Rail Italia S.r.l. (2)
Via Umberto Giordano
I-15100 Alessandria, Italy (100%)
Tel.: (39) 0131218788
Fax: (39) 131240700
E-Mail: info@railion.it
Web Site: www.rail.dbschenker.it
Freight Rail Carrier
S.I.C.: 4011
N.A.I.C.S.: 482111
Hans-Anton Meier *(CEO & COO)*
Olaf Muller *(CFO)*
Marcus Ringeisen *(CMO)*

Subsidiary:

NORDCARGO S.R.L. (3)
Via Spadolini 12
Novate Milanese, 20026 Milan, Italy (60%)
Tel.: (39) 0285113800
Fax: (39) 0285113801
Web Site: www.nordcargo.it
Emp.: 300
Rail Freight Carrier Services
S.I.C.: 4011
N.A.I.C.S.: 482111
Giorgio Spadi *(CEO)*

DB Schenker Rail (UK) Limited (2)
Lakeside Business Park Carolina Way
Doncaster, DN4 5PN, United Kingdom UK
Tel.: (44) 8701405000
Fax: (44) 8701408014
Web Site: www.railwaydbschenker.co.uk
Sales Range: $1-4.9 Billion
Emp.: 500
Holding Company; Railroad Freight Transportation Services
S.I.C.: 6719
N.A.I.C.S.: 551112
Keith Heller *(CEO)*
Michael Lawrence *(CFO)*
Guy Mason *(CIO)*

Divisions:

EWS Construction Limited (3)
Station Road
Stapleford, Notts, NG10 1HA, United Kingdom UK
Tel.: (44) 870 140 7601 (Sales)
Web Site: www.rail.dbschenker.co.uk/services/construction/index.html
Construction & Waste Industries Railway Freight Transportation Services
S.I.C.: 4731
N.A.I.C.S.: 488510
Nigel Smith *(Mng Dir)*

EWS Industrial Limited (3)
National Business Centre Carr Hill
Doncaster, DN4 8DE, United Kingdom UK
Tel.: (44) 870 140 5038 (Sales)
Web Site: www.ews-industrial.co.uk
Industrial Market Railway Freight Transportation Services
S.I.C.: 4731
N.A.I.C.S.: 488510
Neil McDonald *(Mng Dir)*

EWS Network Limited (3)
National Business Centre Carolina Way
Doncaster, DN4 5PN, United Kingdom UK
Tel.: (44) 870 140 5039 (Sales)
Web Site: www.rail.dbschenker.co.uk/services/network/index.html
Railroad Infrastructure, Intermodal & Logistics Rail Freight Transportation & Support Services
S.I.C.: 4731
N.A.I.C.S.: 488510
Stuart Boner *(Mng Dir)*

Subsidiary:

Axiom Rail Limited (3)
Lakeside Business Park Carolina Way
Doncaster, DN4 5PN, United Kingdom UK (100%)
Tel.: (44) 870 140 5330
Fax: (44) 870 140 5009
E-Mail: sales@axiomrail.com
Web Site: www.axiomrail.com
Railway Rolling Stock Maintenance & Support Services
S.I.C.: 4789
N.A.I.C.S.: 488210
Paul McKeown *(Mng Dir)*

Subsidiaries:

Axiom Rail (Stoke) Limited (4)
Whieldon Rd
Stoke-on-Trent, ST4 4HP, United Kingdom UK (100%)
Tel.: (44) 1782844075
Telex: 858829
Fax: (44) 1782843579
Web Site: www.axiomrail.com
Emp.: 200
Railroad Rolling Stock Rental & Management
S.I.C.: 7359
N.A.I.C.S.: 532411
Zrey Finley *(Dir-Engrg)*

Subsidiary:

DB Netz AG (1)
Potsdamerplatz 2
D-10785 Berlin, Germany De (100%)
Tel.: (49) 302970
Fax: (49) 30 297 40197
Web Site: www.dbnetze.com
Railway Infrastructure Support Services
S.I.C.: 4789
N.A.I.C.S.: 488210
Stefan Garber *(Mng Dir)*

Joint Venture:

DVA - Deutsche Verkehrs-Assekuranz-Vermittlungs GmbH (1)
Norsk Data Strasse 3
61352 Bad Homburg, Germany
Tel.: (49) 617248680
Fax: (49) 6172486868
Web Site: www.dva-assekuranz.de
Sales Range: $10-24.9 Million
Emp.: 120
Insurance Services; Owned 65% by Deutsche Bahn AG, 20% by DEVK Service GmbH & 15% by Marsh GmbH
S.I.C.: 6411
N.A.I.C.S.: 524210
Hans Juergen Allerdissen *(Co-Mng Dir)*
Peter Hoechst *(Co-Mng Dir)*

Non-U.S. Subsidiary:

Arriva plc (1)
Admiral Way
Doxford Intl Business Park, Sunderland, SR3 3XP, United Kingdom UK
Tel.: (44) 1915204000
Telex: 68754 Sunderland 3
Fax: (44) 1915204001
E-Mail: enquiries@arriva.co.uk
Web Site: www.arriva.co.uk
Sales Range: $1-4.9 Billion
Emp.: 170
Bus, Train & Coach Transportation Services
S.I.C.: 4111
N.A.I.C.S.: 485113
David Martin *(CEO)*
David Turner *(Sec)*

Subsidiaries:

Arriva Bus & Coach Ltd. (2)
Lodge Garage Whitehall Rd W
Gomersal, Cleckheaton, West Yorkshire, BD19 4BJ, United Kingdom (100%)
Tel.: (44) 1274681144
Fax: (44) 1274651198
E-Mail: busandcoachsales@arriva.co.uk
Web Site: www.arrivabusandcoach.co.uk
Emp.: 45
Leasing & Distribution of Buses & Coaches
S.I.C.: 7359
N.A.I.C.S.: 532411
Steve Hodkinson *(Mng Dir)*

Arriva London Ltd (2)
16 Watsons Rd
Wood Green, London, N22 7TZ, United Kingdom (100%)
Tel.: (44) 2082710101
Fax: (44) 2082710120
E-Mail: yexleym.london@arriva.co.uk
Web Site: www.arriva.co.uk/london
Emp.: 400
Bus Operator
S.I.C.: 4111
N.A.I.C.S.: 485113
Mark Yexley *(Mng Dir & Dir-Bus Ops)*

Arriva Midlands (2)
Unit 5 Norman Rd
PO Box 613
Leicester, Leicestershire, LE4 8EL, United Kingdom (100%)
Tel.: (44) 1162640400
Fax: (44) 1162608620
Web Site: www.arrivabus.co.uk
Emp.: 300
Bus Operator
S.I.C.: 4111
N.A.I.C.S.: 485113
Bob Hind *(Mng Dir)*

Arriva North East (2)
Admiral Way
Doxford International Business, Sunderland, SR3 3XP, United Kingdom (100%)
Tel.: (44) 1915204000
Fax: (44) 1915204001
E-Mail: enquiries@arriva.co.uk
Web Site: www.arriva.co.uk/northeast
Emp.: 200
Bus Operator
S.I.C.: 4111
N.A.I.C.S.: 485113
David Martin *(CEO)*

Arriva North West & Wales (2)
73 Ormskirk Rd
Aintree, Liverpool, Merseyside, L9 5AE, United Kingdom (100%)
Tel.: (44) 1515222800
Fax: (44) 1515236134
Web Site: www.arriva.co.uk
Emp.: 40
Bus Operator
S.I.C.: 4111
N.A.I.C.S.: 485113
Debra Mercer *(Mgr-Mktg & Comm)*

Arriva Northeast (2)
33 Portland Ter
Jesmond, Newcastle upon Tyne, NE2 1QS, United Kingdom (100%)
Tel.: (44) 1912811313
Fax: (44) 1912814829
Web Site: www.arriva.co.uk/northeast
Bus Operator
S.I.C.: 4111
N.A.I.C.S.: 485113

Arriva Passenger Services Ltd. (2)
5 Dominus Way
Meridian Business Park, Leicester, LE3 2RP, United Kingdom (100%)
Tel.: (44) 1162405500
Fax: (44) 1162405516
E-Mail: info@arriva.co.uk
Web Site: www.arriva.co.uk/arriva/en/business_activities/transport_services/uk
Emp.: 20
Bus, Train & Coach Transportation Services
S.I.C.: 4111
N.A.I.C.S.: 485113

Arriva Southern Counties (2)
1 Admiral Way Doxford International Business Park
Sunderland, SR3 3XP, United Kingdom (100%)
Tel.: (44) 191 520 4000
Fax: (44) 191 520 4001
Web Site: www.arriva.co.uk
Emp.: 150
Bus & Tour Operations
S.I.C.: 4111
N.A.I.C.S.: 485113
Michael Cooper *(Mng Dir)*

Arriva The Shires (2)
487 Dunstable Rd
Luton, LU4 8DS, United Kingdom (100%)
Tel.: (44) 1582587000
Fax: (44) 1582587111
Web Site: www.arriva.co.uk
Emp.: 300
Bus Operator
S.I.C.: 4111
N.A.I.C.S.: 485113
Heat Williams *(Mng Dir)*

Arriva Yorkshire (2)
24 Barnsley Rd
Wakefield, WF1 5JX, United Kingdom (100%)
Tel.: (44) 1924375521
Fax: (44) 1924200106
Web Site: www.arriva.co.uk
Emp.: 375
Bus Operator
S.I.C.: 4111
N.A.I.C.S.: 485113

The Original London Sightseeing Tour Ltd. (2)
Jews Row
London, SW18 1TB, United Kingdom (100%)
Tel.: (44) 2088771722
Fax: (44) 2088771968
E-Mail: info@theoriginaltour.com
Web Site: www.theoriginaltour.com
Emp.: 156
Sight-Seeing Bus Operator
S.I.C.: 4111
N.A.I.C.S.: 485999

Non-U.S. Subsidiaries:

Arriva Danmark A/S (2)
Skojtevej 26
2770 Kastrup, Denmark (100%)
Tel.: (45) 72302500
Fax: (45) 72302501
E-Mail: info@arriva.dk
Web Site: www.arriva.dk
Sales Range: $1-4.9 Billion
Emp.: 100
Bus, Train & Water Transportation Service Provider
S.I.C.: 4111
N.A.I.C.S.: 485113
Thomas Oster *(Mng Dir)*

Arriva Nederland B.V. (2)
Trambaan 3
PO Box 626
8440 AP Heerenveen, Netherlands (100%)
Tel.: (31) 513655855
Fax: (31) 513655809
E-Mail: servicekamtoor@arriva.nl
Web Site: www.arriva.nl
Emp.: 150
Bus, Train & Coach Service Provider
S.I.C.: 4111
N.A.I.C.S.: 485113
Anne Hettinga *(Mng Dir)*

Arriva Noroeste SL (2)
Paseo de la Estacion s/n
15405 El Ferrol, Spain (100%)
Tel.: (34) 981330046
Fax: (34) 981 330 047
E-Mail: arriva@arriva.es
Web Site: www.arriva.es
Emp.: 450
Bus Operator
S.I.C.: 4111
N.A.I.C.S.: 485113

Arriva Sverige AB (2)
Dasaltgiaten 15
25468 Helsingborg, Sweden (100%)
Tel.: (46) 42168271
Fax: (46) 42168270
E-Mail: info@arriva.se
Web Site: www.arriva.se
Emp.: 350
Bus, Train & Coach Service Provider
S.I.C.: 4111
N.A.I.C.S.: 485113
Johnny Borge Hansen *(Mng Dir)*

DEUTSCHE BANK AKTIENGESELLSCHAFT

Taunusanlage 12
60325 Frankfurt am Main, Germany
Tel.: (49) 69 910 00
Telex: 41730 0 fn d
Fax: (49) 69 910 34225
E-Mail: db.ir@db.com
Web Site: www.db.com
Year Founded: 1870

DB—(DEU NYSE)
Rev.: $45,421,121,970
Net Worth: $73,164,339,500
Earnings: $391,735,470
Emp.: 98,219
Fiscal Year-end: 12/31/12

Business Description:
Financial Services
S.I.C.: 6029
N.A.I.C.S.: 522110

Personnel:
Jurgen Fitschen *(Co-Chm-Mgmt Bd & Co-CEO)*
Anshuman Jain *(Co-Chm-Mgmt Bd & Co-CEO)*
Paul M. L. Achleitner *(Chm-Supervisory Bd)*
Karin Ruck *(Deputy Chm-Supervisory Bd)*
Stefan Krause *(CFO)*
Henry Ritchotte *(COO)*
Stuart Lewis *(Chief Risk Officer)*
Stephan Leithner *(CEO-HR, Legal & Compliance, Govt & Regulatory Affairs-Europe & Me)*
Jacques Brand *(CEO-North America)*
Richard H. Walker *(Gen Counsel)*

Supervisory Board of Directors:
Paul M. L. Achleitner
Wolfgang Bohr
Karl-Gerhard Eick
Katherine Garrett-Cox
Alfred Herling
Henning Kagermann
Martina Klee
Suzanne B. Labarge
Peter H. Loscher
Henriette Mark
Gabriele Platscher
Karin Ruck
Rudolf Stockem
Johannes Teyssen
Marlehn Thieme
Tilman Todenhofer

Subsidiaries:

ADD ONE GmbH & Co. KG **(1)**
Elsa-Brandstrom-Str 10-12
Cologne, Nordrhein-Westfalen, 50668, Germany
Tel.: (49) 221 14501
Business Management Consulting Services
S.I.C.: 8742
N.A.I.C.S.: 541611

AheadCom Beteiligungs-GmbH **(1)**
Taunusanlage 12
Frankfurt am Main, 60325, Germany
Tel.: (49) 69 910 00
Financial Management Consulting Services
S.I.C.: 8742
N.A.I.C.S.: 541611

Airport Club fur International Executives GmbH **(1)**
Frankfurt Airport Center I Hugo-Eckener-Ring
60549 Frankfurt am Main, Germany
Tel.: (49) 69 69707 0
Fax: (49) 69 69707 400
E-Mail: info@airportclub.de
Web Site: www.airportclub.de
Emp.: 30
Club Operator
S.I.C.: 7999
N.A.I.C.S.: 713910
Roland Ross *(Mng Dir)*

Alfred Herrhausen Gesellschaft - Das internationale Forum der Deutschen Bank - mbH **(1)**
Unter den Linden 13/15
10117 Berlin, Germany (56.5%)
Tel.: (49) 30 3407 4206
Fax: (49) 30 3407 4209
Web Site: www.alfred-herrhausen-gesellschaft.de
Commercial Banking Services
S.I.C.: 6029
N.A.I.C.S.: 522110

America/Asia Private Equity Portfolio (PE-US/ASIA) GmbH & Co. KG **(1)**
Max-Weber-Platz 11
81675 Munich, Germany
Tel.: (49) 89 411894 0
Financial Management Consulting Services
S.I.C.: 8742
N.A.I.C.S.: 541611

AXOS Beteiligungs- und Verwaltungs-GmbH **(1)**
Unter Sachsenhausen 4
Cologne, Nordrhein-Westfalen, 50667, Germany
Tel.: (49) 221 14501
Investment Management Services
S.I.C.: 6799
N.A.I.C.S.: 523920

Benefit Trust GmbH **(1)**
Stosswitzer Strasse 5
Lutzen, Sachsen-Anhalt, 06686, Germany
Tel.: (49) 34444901061
Investment Management Services
S.I.C.: 6799
N.A.I.C.S.: 523920

Berliner Bank AG & Co. KG **(1)**
Pieodor-Heuss-Allee 72
60486 Frankfurt am Main, Germany
Tel.: (49) 3031090
Telex: 182010
Fax: (49) 3031092165
E-Mail: info@berliner-bank.de
Web Site: www.berliner-bank.de
Emp.: 1,100
International Banking
S.I.C.: 6029
N.A.I.C.S.: 522110
Oliver Bortz *(Mng Dir)*

Bfl-Beteiligungsgesellschaft fur Industriewerte mbH **(1)**
Bockenheimer Landstr 10
60323 Frankfurt am Main, Germany
Tel.: (49) 69 718 0
Investment Management Services
S.I.C.: 6211
N.A.I.C.S.: 523999

BHF PEP I Beteiligungsgesellschaft mbH **(1)**
Elsa-Brandstrom-Str 10-12
Cologne, 50668, Germany
Tel.: (49) 2219370850
Investment Management Services
S.I.C.: 6282
N.A.I.C.S.: 523920
Andreas Schmidt *(Mgr)*

BHF PEP III Beteiligungsgesellschaft mbH **(1)**
Elsa-Brandstrom-Str 10-12
Cologne, Nordrhein-Westfalen, 50668, Germany
Tel.: (49) 2219370850
Fax: (49) 22193708519
Emp.: 1
Investment Management Services
S.I.C.: 6282
N.A.I.C.S.: 523920
Andreas Schmidt *(Gen Mgr)*

BHF Private Equity Portfolio GmbH & Co. Beteiligungs KG Nr. 1 **(1)**
Max-Joseph-Str 7
80333 Munich, Germany
Tel.: (49) 2219370850
Investment Management Services
S.I.C.: 6799
N.A.I.C.S.: 523920

BHW - Gesellschaft fur Wohnungswirtschaft mbH & Co. Immobilienverwaltungs KG **(1)**
Lubahnstr 2
Hameln, Niedersachsen, 31789, Germany
Tel.: (49) 515 1180
Investment Management Services
S.I.C.: 6799
N.A.I.C.S.: 523920

BHW - Gesellschaft fur Wohnungswirtschaft mbH **(1)**
Lubahnstrasse 2
31789 Hameln, Niedersachsen, Germany
Tel.: (49) 5151 180
Investment Management Services
S.I.C.: 6282
N.A.I.C.S.: 523920

Bolsena Holding GmbH & Co. KG **(1)**
Grosse Gallusstrasse 10-14
60311 Frankfurt am Main, Germany
Tel.: (49) 69 910 00
Fax: (49) 69 910 34225
Investment Management Services
S.I.C.: 6211
N.A.I.C.S.: 523999

BT Muritz GmbH **(1)**
Alfred-Herrhausen-Allee 16-24
65760 Eschborn, Hessen, Germany
Tel.: (49) 69 910 33974
Fax: (49) 69 910 38077
Financial Management Services
S.I.C.: 6211
N.A.I.C.S.: 523999

BT Vordertaunus Verwaltungs- und Beteiligungsgesellschaft mbH **(1)**
Alfred-Herrhausen-Allee 16-24
65760 Eschborn, Germany
Tel.: (49) 6196 9960
Fax: (49) 6196 996 550
Financial Management Services
S.I.C.: 6211
N.A.I.C.S.: 523999
Philipp Turowski *(Gen Mgr)*

CAM DREI Initiator GmbH & Co. KG **(1)**
Elsa-Brandstrom-Str 10-12
50668 Cologne, Nordrhein-Westfalen, Germany
Tel.: (49) 2219370850
Investment Management Services
S.I.C.: 6799
N.A.I.C.S.: 523920

CAM Initiator Treuhand GmbH & Co. KG **(1)**
Elsa-Brandstrom-Str 10-12
50668 Cologne, Germany
Tel.: (49) 221 937085 0
Fax: (49) 221 937085 19
E-Mail: cologne@cam-pe.com
Investment Management Services
S.I.C.: 6282
N.A.I.C.S.: 523920

CAM Private Equity Nominee GmbH & Co. KG **(1)**
Zeppelinstrasse 4
Cologne, 50667, Germany
Tel.: (49) 2219370850
Fax: (49) 22193708519
Financial Management Services
S.I.C.: 6211
N.A.I.C.S.: 523999

CAM Private Equity Verwaltungs-GmbH **(1)**
Elsa-Brandstrom-Str 10-12
50668 Cologne, Germany
Tel.: (49) 221 9370850
Fax: (49) 221 93708519
Financial Management Services
S.I.C.: 6211
N.A.I.C.S.: 523999

CAM Secondary Select I Beteiligungs GmbH **(1)**
Elsa-Brandstrom-Str 10-12
50668 Cologne, Germany
Tel.: (49) 221 937085 0
Fax: (49) 221 937085 19
Emp.: 80
Financial Management Services
S.I.C.: 8742
N.A.I.C.S.: 541611
Andreas Schmidt *(Gen Mgr)*

CAM Secondary Select I GmbH & Co. KG **(1)**
Elsa-Brandstrom-Str 10-12
Cologne, Nordrhein-Westfalen, 50668, Germany
Tel.: (49) 2219370850
Financial Management Services
S.I.C.: 8742
N.A.I.C.S.: 541611

CAM Select II Beteiligungs GmbH **(1)**
Elsa-Brandstrom-Str 10-12
Cologne, Nordrhein-Westfalen, 50668, Germany
Tel.: (49) 2219370850
Investment Management Services
S.I.C.: 6282
N.A.I.C.S.: 523920
Andreas Smith *(Gen Mgr)*

CAM Select II GmbH & Co. KG **(1)**
Elsa-Brandstrom-Str 10-12
Cologne, Nordrhein-Westfalen, 50668, Germany
Tel.: (49) 2219370850
Investment Management Services
S.I.C.: 6282
N.A.I.C.S.: 523920

CELENA Beteiligungs- und Verwaltungs GmbH **(1)**
Unter Sachsenhausen 4
Cologne, Nordrhein-Westfalen, 50667, Germany
Tel.: (49) 221 14501
Fax: (49) 221 1451454
Investment Management Services
S.I.C.: 6282
N.A.I.C.S.: 523920

Clark GmbH & Co. KG **(1)**
Grosse Gallusstr 10-14
Frankfurt am Main, Hessen, 60311, Germany
Tel.: (49) 699 1000
Investment Management Services
S.I.C.: 6282
N.A.I.C.S.: 523920

DAHOC Beteiligungsgesellschaft mbH **(1)**
Taunusanlage 12
60325 Frankfurt am Main, Hessen, Germany
Tel.: (49) 69 91000
Financial Management Services
S.I.C.: 6211
N.A.I.C.S.: 523999

DB Broker GmbH **(1)**
Grosse Gallusstr 10-14
Frankfurt, Hessen, Germany
Tel.: (49) 69 91000
Real Estate Agency Services
S.I.C.: 6531
N.A.I.C.S.: 531210

DB Capital Markets Asset Management Holding GmbH **(1)**
Taunusanlage 12
Frankfurt am Main, Hessen, 60325, Germany
Tel.: (49) 699 1000
Investment Management Services
S.I.C.: 6799
N.A.I.C.S.: 523920

DB Capital Markets (Deutschland) GmbH **(1)**
Taunusanlage 12
Frankfurt, 60325, Germany
Tel.: (49) 69 910 00
Fax: (49) 69 91034225
Securities Brokerage Services
S.I.C.: 6211
N.A.I.C.S.: 523120

DB Enterprise GmbH **(1)**
Scharnhorststr 40
06686 Sossen, Germany
Tel.: (49) 344 44 41 70
Investment Banking Services
S.I.C.: 6211
N.A.I.C.S.: 523110

DB Export-Leasing GmbH **(1)**
Bockenheimer Landstrasse 42
60323 Frankfurt am Main, Germany De
Tel.: (49) 699100 (100%)
Telex: 41730 601 fm d
Fax: (49) 6991033682
Emp.: 50
International Aircraft Leasing Services
S.I.C.: 7359
N.A.I.C.S.: 532411

DB Finance International GmbH **(1)**
Elisabethenstr 2
Eschborn, Hessen, 65760, Germany
Tel.: (49) 61964960
Commercial Banking Services
S.I.C.: 6029
N.A.I.C.S.: 522110

Deutsche Bank Aktiengesellschaft—(Continued)

DB Finanz-Holding GmbH (1)
Taunusanlage 12
60325 Frankfurt am Main, Germany
Tel.: (49) 6991000
Investment Management Services
S.I.C.: 6799
N.A.I.C.S.: 523920

DB GIF GmbH & Co. KG (1)
Elsa-Brandstrom-Str 10-12
50668 Cologne, Nordrhein-Westfalen, Germany
Tel.: (49) 2219370850
Fax: (49) 22193708519
Emp.: 80
Investment Management Services
S.I.C.: 6282
N.A.I.C.S.: 523920
Andreas Schmidt *(Gen Mgr)*

DB HR Solutions GmbH (1)
Alfred-Herrhausen-Allee 16-24
65760 Eschborn, Hessen, Germany
Tel.: (49) 69 91000
Business Management Consulting Services
S.I.C.: 8742
N.A.I.C.S.: 541611

DB Industrial Holdings Beteiligungs GmbH & Co. KG (1)
Taunusanlage 12
60325 Frankfurt am Main, Germany
Tel.: (49) 69 91 00 0
Fax: (49) 69 91 03 42 27
Investment Management Services
S.I.C.: 6799
N.A.I.C.S.: 523920

DB Industrial Holdings GmbH (1)
Taunusanlage 12
Frankfurt am Main, 60325, Germany
Tel.: (49) 69 9 10 00
Fax: (49) 69 9 10 43583
Investment Management Services
S.I.C.: 6282
N.A.I.C.S.: 523920

DB Investment Services GmbH (1)
(Formerly Xchanging Transaction Bank GmbH)
Wilhelm Fay St 31 - 37
65936 Frankfurt, Germany (51%)
Tel.: (49) 69120120
Fax: (49) 691201269966
E-Mail: info@xchanging.com
Web Site: www.xchanging.com
Emp.: 700
Business Processing Services
S.I.C.: 7334
N.A.I.C.S.: 561439

DB Management Support GmbH (1)
Junghofstr 5-9
60311 Frankfurt, Germany
Tel.: (49) 69 910 34050
Web Site: www.dbms-online.de
Business Management Consulting Services
S.I.C.: 8742
N.A.I.C.S.: 541611

DB PEP V Europe Parallel GmbH & Co. KG (1)
Elsa-Brandstrom-Str 10-12
Cologne, Nordrhein-Westfalen, 50668, Germany
Tel.: (49) 2219370850
Investment Management Services
S.I.C.: 6799
N.A.I.C.S.: 523920

DB Print GmbH (1)
Friedrich-Kahl-Str 10
60489 Frankfurt, Germany
Tel.: (49) 69 91 08 65 23
Fax: (49) 69 91 08 65 59
Commercial Printing Services
S.I.C.: 2759
N.A.I.C.S.: 323111

DB Private Equity GmbH (1)
Elsa-Brandstrom-Str 10-12
50668 Cologne, Germany
Tel.: (49) 221 937085 0
Fax: (49) 221 937085 19
Web Site: www.dbpe.com
Financial Investment Services
S.I.C.: 6211
N.A.I.C.S.: 523999
Rolf Wickenkamp *(Vice Chm & Head-Institutional Client Rels)*
Eberhard Witt *(COO)*
Charles Smith *(CIO & Head-Secondaries)*
Andreas Schmidt *(Head-Primary Private Equity)*
Juergen Borchers *(Member-Exec Bd)*
Bryan DeJonge *(Member-Exec Bd)*
Colleen Sellers *(Member-Exec Bd)*

DBG Vermogensverwaltungsgesellschaft mbH (1)
Taunusanlage 10-12
60329 Frankfurt am Main, Hessen, Germany
Tel.: (49) 69 910 00
Investment Management Services
S.I.C.: 6282
N.A.I.C.S.: 523920

DEBEKO Immobilien GmbH & Co Grundbesitz OHG (1)
Alfred-Herrhausen-Allee 16-24
65760 Eschborn, Germany
Tel.: (49) 6971704841
Fax: (49) 6971704959
Real Estate Advisory Services
S.I.C.: 6531
N.A.I.C.S.: 531390

DEGRU Erste Beteiligungsgesellschaft mbH (1)
Alfred-Herrhausen-Allee 16-24
Eschborn, Hessen, 65760, Germany
Tel.: (49) 697170400
Financial Management Services
S.I.C.: 6211
N.A.I.C.S.: 523999

DEMOS Beteiligungs- und Verwaltungs GmbH (1)
Unter Sachsenhausen 4
50667 Cologne, Nordrhein-Westfalen, Germany
Tel.: (49) 221 14501
Financial Management Services
S.I.C.: 6211
N.A.I.C.S.: 523999

DEUFRAN Beteiligungs GmbH (1)
Taunusanlage 12
60325 Frankfurt, Germany
Tel.: (49) 69 91030111
Fax: (49) 69 91043933
Investment Management Services
S.I.C.: 6282
N.A.I.C.S.: 523920

DEUKONA Versicherungs-Vermittlungs-GmbH (1)
Taunusanlage 12
60325 Frankfurt, Germany
Tel.: (49) 69 91008
Fax: (49) 69 91038792
Investment Management Services
S.I.C.: 6799
N.A.I.C.S.: 523920

Deutsche Asset Management GmbH (1)
Mainzer Landstrasse 178 190
60327 Frankfurt, Germany (100%)
Mailing Address:
Postfach 20 01 11
60605 Frankfurt, Germany
Tel.: (49) 180310111011
Telex: 4170319 dbcm
Fax: (49) 180310111050
E-Mail: info@deam-global.com
Web Site: www.deam-global.com
Investment Banking
S.I.C.: 6211
N.A.I.C.S.: 523110

Subsidiaries:

DB Real Estate Investment GmbH (2)
Mergenthaleralle 73 75
65760 Eschborn, Germany
Tel.: (49) 697170400
Fax: (49) 6971704959
E-Mail: db-real-estate.germany@db.com
Web Site: www.rreef.com
Emp.: 200
Real Estate Investment Trust
S.I.C.: 6726
N.A.I.C.S.: 525990

Non-U.S. Joint Venture:

La Rinascente s.r.l. (3)
via Washington 70
20146 Milan, Italy
Tel.: (39) 02467711
Fax: (39) 0246771387
E-Mail: centralino.sede@rinascente.it
Web Site: www.larinascente.it/
Emp.: 200
Department Store Owner & Operator; Joint Venture by Pirelli & C. Real Estate S.p.A. (20%); Deutsche Bank Real Estate Investment GmbH (30%); Investitori Associati (46%); Other Investors (4%)
S.I.C.: 5311
N.A.I.C.S.: 452111
Victoria Radice *(Pres)*

Deutsche Asset Management International GmbH (2)
Mainzer Landstrasse 178-190
Frankfurt, Germany
Tel.: (49) 69 71404 4001
Fax: (49) 69 71404 3000
Investment Management Services
S.I.C.: 6282
N.A.I.C.S.: 523920

Deutsche Asset Management Investmentgesellschaft mbH (2)
Mainzer Landstr 178-190
60327 Frankfurt am Main, Hessen, Germany De
Tel.: (49) 69 7 17 06 00
Fax: (49) 69 7 17 06 3000
Investment Management Services
S.I.C.: 6282
N.A.I.C.S.: 523920

Deutsche Bank AG-Berlin (1)
Otto Suhr Allee 6 16
10585 Berlin, Germany (100%)
Mailing Address:
Postfach 110165
10585 Berlin, Germany
Tel.: (49) 3034070
Fax: (49) 3034072196
E-Mail: deutsche-bank@db.com
Web Site: www.db.de
Emp.: 100
International Banking Services
S.I.C.: 6211
N.A.I.C.S.: 523110
Ruediger Sandkoetter *(Mng Dir)*

Deutsche Bank Bauspar-Aktiengesellschaft (1)
Niddagaustrasse 42
60489 Frankfurt am Main, Germany
Tel.: (49) 69 910 50500
Fax: (49) 69 910 50555
E-Mail: bauspar.line@db.com
Web Site: www.deutsche-bank-bauspar.de
Commercial Banking Services
S.I.C.: 6029
N.A.I.C.S.: 522110

Deutsche Bank Europe GmbH (1)
Taunusanlage 12
Frankfurt am Main, Hessen, 60325, Germany
Tel.: (49) 699 1000
Commercial Banking Services
S.I.C.: 6029
N.A.I.C.S.: 522110
Karl-Georg Altenburg *(Head-Investment Banking & Corp Fin-EMEA)*

Deutsche Bank Privat und Geschaftskunden AG (1)
Kohlmarkt 7 15
23552 Lubeck, Germany (100%)
Mailing Address:
Postfach 2082
23552 Lubeck, Germany
Tel.: (49) 4511492179
Telex: 26809
Fax: (49) 4511492368
E-Mail: burkhrd.schrager@db.com
Emp.: 60
S.I.C.: 6159
N.A.I.C.S.: 522298
Michael East *(Mktg Dir)*

Deutsche Bank Saar AG (1)
Kaiserstrasse 29 31
66111 Saarbrucken, Germany (100%)
Tel.: (49) 68130020
Telex: 4421243
Fax: (49) 6813002402
E-Mail: juergen.kalmes@db.com
Web Site: www.db.com
Emp.: 400
International Banking Services
S.I.C.: 6211
N.A.I.C.S.: 523110

Deutsche Card Services GmbH (1)
Kaltenbornweg 1-3
50679 Cologne, Germany
Tel.: (49) 221 99577 0
Fax: (49) 221 99577 720
E-Mail: info.deucs@db.com
Web Site: www.deutsche-card-services.com
Cash Management Services
S.I.C.: 6099
N.A.I.C.S.: 522320
Jens Mahlke *(Co-Mng Dir)*
Jens Mikolajczak *(Co-Mng Dir)*

Deutsche Grundbesitz-Anlagegesellschaft mbH & Co Lowenstein Palais (1)
Alfred-Herrhausen-Allee 16-24
Eschborn, 65760, Germany
Tel.: (49) 69 7 17 04 403
Fax: (49) 69 7 17 04 993
Investment Management Services
S.I.C.: 6799
N.A.I.C.S.: 523920

Deutsche Grundbesitz-Anlagegesellschaft mit beschrankter Haftung (1)
Mergenthaleralle 73-75
65760 Eschborn, Hessen, Germany
Tel.: (49) 6971704 831
Fax: (49) 6971704969
Investment Management Services
S.I.C.: 6799
N.A.I.C.S.: 523920

Deutsche Grundbesitz Beteiligungsgesellschaft mbH (1)
Mergenthaleralle 73-76
65760 Eschborn, Germany
Tel.: (49) 69 7170402
Fax: (49) 6971704959
Investment Management Services
S.I.C.: 6282
N.A.I.C.S.: 523920

Deutsche IT License GmbH (1)
Alfred-Herrhausen-Allee 16-24
65760 Eschborn, Germany
Tel.: (49) 69 91000
Commercial Banking Services
S.I.C.: 6029
N.A.I.C.S.: 522110
Dirk Stermann, *(Mng Dir)*
Kai Zeiske *(Mng Dir)*

Deutsche StiftungsTrust GmbH (1)
Taunusanlage 12
60325 Frankfurt am Main, Germany
Tel.: (49) 69 910 47800
Fax: (49) 69 910 85976
E-Mail: info.dstt@db.com
Web Site: www.dstt.de
Trust Management Services
S.I.C.: 6091
N.A.I.C.S.: 523991

DI Deutsche Immobilien Baugesellschaft mbH (1)
Mergenthaleralle 73-75
65760 Eschborn, Germany
Tel.: (49) 697 17 04 00
Real Estate Development Services
S.I.C.: 6531
N.A.I.C.S.: 531390
Andrea Fritzsche *(Mng Dir)*
Alexander Kuhnl, *(Mng Dir)*

DI Deutsche Immobilien Treuhandgesellschaft mbH (1)
Mainzer Landstr 178-190
60327 Frankfurt, Hessen, Germany
Tel.: (49) 69 7170400
Fax: (49) 69 71704959
Real Estate Development Services
S.I.C.: 6531
N.A.I.C.S.: 531390
Thomas Schneider *(Mng Dir)*

DIL Europa-Beteiligungsgesellschaft mbH i.L. (1)
Konigsallee 106
40215 Dusseldorf, Nordrhein-Westfalen, Germany

Tel.: (49) 211 770 80
Investment Management Services
S.I.C.: 6799
N.A.I.C.S.: 523920

DIL Fonds-Beteiligungsgesellschaft mbH (1)
Konigsallee 106
40215 Dusseldorf, Nordrhein-Westfalen, Germany
Tel.: (49) 21199460
Fax: (49) 211 9946400
Financial Management Services
S.I.C.: 6211
N.A.I.C.S.: 523999

DISCA Beteiligungsgesellschaft mbH (1)
Konigsallee 106
40215 Dusseldorf, Nordrhein-Westfalen, Germany
Tel.: (49) 211 99460
Fax: (49) 211 9946400
Investment Management Services
S.I.C.: 6282
N.A.I.C.S.: 523920

Drolla GmbH (1)
Grosse Gallusstr 10-14
Frankfurt am Main, Hessen, 60311, Germany
Tel.: (49) 69 910 00
Fax: (49) 69 910 34225
Business Management Consulting Services
S.I.C.: 8742
N.A.I.C.S.: 541611

DWS Finanz-Service GmbH (1)
Mainzer Landstr 178-190
60327 Frankfurt am Main, Germany
Tel.: (49) 69 71909 2371
Fax: (49) 69 71909 9090
E-Mail: info@dws.com
Web Site: www.dws.de
Financial Management Services
S.I.C.: 6211
N.A.I.C.S.: 523999

DWS Holding & Service GmbH (1)
Mainzer Landstr 178-190
60327 Frankfurt, Hessen, Germany
Tel.: (49) 69 719090
Investment Management Services
S.I.C.: 6282
N.A.I.C.S.: 523920

EC EUROPA IMMOBILIEN FONDS NR. 3 GmbH & CO. KG (1)
Bleichenbrucke 9
20354 Hamburg, Germany
Tel.: (49) 40 376690
Fax: (49) 40 37669188
Investment Management Services
S.I.C.: 6211
N.A.I.C.S.: 523999
Ivo Goessler *(Gen Mgr)*

Elmo Leasing Achte GmbH (1)
Alfr-Herrhausen-Allee 16-24
65760 Eschborn, Germany
Tel.: (49) 69 91000
Financial Leasing Services
S.I.C.: 6153
N.A.I.C.S.: 522220

Elmo Leasing Dreiundzwanzigste GmbH (1)
Alfr-Herrhausen-Allee 16-24
65760 Eschborn, Germany
Tel.: (49) 69 91000
Financial Leasing Services
S.I.C.: 6211
N.A.I.C.S.: 523999

Elmo Leasing Elfte GmbH (1)
Mergenthalerallee 77
Eschborn, Germany
Tel.: (49) 6196 96732 0
Financial Leasing Services
S.I.C.: 6211
N.A.I.C.S.: 523999

Elmo Leasing Sechste GmbH (1)
Alfr-Herrhausen-Allee 16-24
65760 Eschborn, Germany
Tel.: (49) 69 91000
Financial Leasing Services
S.I.C.: 6211
N.A.I.C.S.: 523999

Elmo Leasing Siebte GmbH (1)
Alfr-Herrhausen-Allee 16-24
65760 Eschborn, Germany
Tel.: (49) 69 91000
Financial Leasing Services
S.I.C.: 6211
N.A.I.C.S.: 523999

Elmo Leasing Zwolfte GmbH (1)
Alfred-Herrhausen-Allee 16-24
65760 Eschborn, Germany
Tel.: (49) 69 91000
Financial Leasing Services
S.I.C.: 6211
N.A.I.C.S.: 523999

Erda Funding GmbH (1)
Alfr-Herrhausen-Allee 16-24
65760 Eschborn, Germany
Tel.: (49) 69 91000
Venture Capital Funding Services
S.I.C.: 6799
N.A.I.C.S.: 523910

Erste Frankfurter Hoist GmbH (1)
Steinweg 3-5
60313 Frankfurt, Germany
Tel.: (49) 69 29925385
Financial Management Services
S.I.C.: 6211
N.A.I.C.S.: 523999

EUROKNIGHTS IV GmbH & Co. Beteiligungs KG (1)
Max-Joseph-Strabe 7
80333 Munich, Germany
Tel.: (49) 89 5459640
Investment Management Services
S.I.C.: 6799
N.A.I.C.S.: 523920

Exporterra GmbH (1)
Bockenheimer Landstrasse 1
60323 Frankfurt am Main, Germany
Tel.: (49) 69 7183306
Fax: (49) 69 7182035
Financial Management Services
S.I.C.: 6211
N.A.I.C.S.: 523999

EXTOREL Private Equity Advisers GmbH (1)
Nuffbeum St
80336 Munich, Germany
Tel.: (49) 89207 030
Fax: (49) 89207 033 98
Investment Management Services
S.I.C.: 6211
N.A.I.C.S.: 523999

Frankfurter Vermogens-Treuhand Gesellschaft mit beschrankter Haftung (1)
Bockenheimer Landstr 10
60323 Frankfurt, Germany
Tel.: (49) 69 7180
Investment Management Services
S.I.C.: 6211
N.A.I.C.S.: 523999

Funfte SAB Treuhand und Verwaltung GmbH & Co. Suhl Rimbachzentrum KG (1)
Kaiser-Friedrich Promenade 61a
61348 Bad Homburg, Hessen, Germany
Tel.: (49) 3641 537310
Fax: (49) 3641 537313
Financial Management Services
S.I.C.: 6211
N.A.I.C.S.: 523999

GAVDOS GmbH (1)
Stackenbergstr 34
42329 Wuppertal, Germany
Tel.: (49) 202 7880
Fax: (49) 202 788242
Investment Management Services
S.I.C.: 6799
N.A.I.C.S.: 523920

KEBA Gesellschaft fur interne Services mbH (1)
Theodor-Heuss-Allee 72
Frankfurt am Main, 60486, Germany
Tel.: (49) 6991000
Fax: (49) 69 91039805
Investment Management Services
S.I.C.: 6282
N.A.I.C.S.: 523920

KHP Knuppe, Huntebrinker & Co. GmbH (1)
Lortzingstrasse 2
49074 Osnabruck, Germany
Tel.: (49) 5 41 600 300
Fax: (49) 5 41 600 3030
E-Mail: office@khp-vermoegensverwaltung.de
Web Site: www.khp-vermoegensverwaltung.de
Asset Management Services
S.I.C.: 6282
N.A.I.C.S.: 523920

Klockner Industriebeteiligungsgesellschaft mbH (1)
Taunusanlage 12
Frankfurt am Main, 60325, Germany
Tel.: (49) 6991000
Investment Management Services
S.I.C.: 6799
N.A.I.C.S.: 523920

Matura Vermogensverwaltung mit beschrankter Haftung (1)
Junghofstr 5-9
Frankfurt am Main, 60311, Germany
Tel.: (49) 6991000
Investment Management Services
S.I.C.: 6282
N.A.I.C.S.: 523920

Media Entertainment Filmmanagement GmbH (1)
Erlenstr 4
Pullach, 82049, Germany
Tel.: (49) 89211040
Private Banking Services
S.I.C.: 6022
N.A.I.C.S.: 522190

Mira GmbH & Co. KG (1)
Genslerweg 7
Buxtehude, 21614, Germany
Tel.: (49) 41 61 59 33 10
Fax: (49) 41 61 59 33 33
E-Mail: mira@mira-anlagen.de
Web Site: www.mira-anlagen.de
Investment Advisory Services
S.I.C.: 6282
N.A.I.C.S.: 523930

MPP Beteiligungsgesellschaft mbH (1)
Junghofstr 5-9
Frankfurt am Main, 60311, Germany
Tel.: (49) 699100
Investment Management Services
S.I.C.: 6282
N.A.I.C.S.: 523920

NIDDA Grundstucks- und Beteiligungs-Gesellschaft mit beschrankter Haftung (1)
Bockenheimer Landstr 10
Frankfurt am Main, 60323, Germany
Tel.: (49) 697180
Real Estate Management Services
S.I.C.: 6531
N.A.I.C.S.: 531390

Nordwestdeutscher Wohnungsbautrager Gesellschaft mit beschrankter Haftung (1)
Taunusanlage 12
60325 Frankfurt am Main, Germany
Tel.: (49) 69 91000
Fax: (49) 69 91034225
Investment Management Services
S.I.C.: 6282
N.A.I.C.S.: 523920

Norisbank GmbH (1)
Rathenauplatz 12 18
90489 Nuremberg, Germany
Tel.: (49) 91153900
Telex: 623061
Fax: (49) 911 5390 2222
Web Site: www.norisbank.de
Emp.: 1,073
Banking
S.I.C.: 6159
N.A.I.C.S.: 522298

OPB-Nona GmbH (1)
Bockenheimer Landstr 23
Frankfurt am Main, 60325, Germany
Tel.: (49) 6971340

Investment Advisory Services
S.I.C.: 6282
N.A.I.C.S.: 523930

OPB Verwaltungs- und Treuhand GmbH (1)
Unter Sachsenhausen 4
Cologne, 50667, Germany
Tel.: (49) 22114501
Fax: (49) 221 1451512
Financial Management Services
S.I.C.: 6211
N.A.I.C.S.: 523999

OPPENHEIM Capital Advisory GmbH (1)
Unter Sachsenhausen 4
Cologne, 50667, Germany
Tel.: (49) 22114501
Fax: (49) 221 145 1512
Investment Advisory Services
S.I.C.: 6282
N.A.I.C.S.: 523930
Daniela Schafer *(Mng Dir)*

OPPENHEIM Immobilien Dachfonds III GmbH & Co. KG (1)
Unter Sachsenhausen 4
Cologne, 50667, Germany
Tel.: (49) 221 14501
Fax: (49) 221 1451512
E-Mail: info@oppenheim.de
Emp.: 300
Commercial Banking Services
S.I.C.: 6029
N.A.I.C.S.: 522110

OPPENHEIM Mezzanine GmbH & Co. KG (1)
Untermainanlage 1
Frankfurt am Main, 60329, Germany
Tel.: (49) 6971340
Financial Management Services
S.I.C.: 6211
N.A.I.C.S.: 523999

OPPENHEIM Portfolio Advisors VI GmbH & Co. KG (1)
Unter Sachsenhausen 4
Cologne, 50667, Germany
Tel.: (49) 221 145 01
Fax: (49) 221 145 1512
Investment Management Services
S.I.C.: 6211
N.A.I.C.S.: 523999

OPPENHEIM PRIVATE EQUITY Verwaltungsgesellschaft mbH (1)
Unter Sachsenhausen 4
Cologne, 50667, Germany
Tel.: (49) 2212582010
Fax: (49) 221 145 1512
Administrative Management Services
S.I.C.: 8741
N.A.I.C.S.: 561110

PADUS Grundstucks-Vermietungsgesellschaft mbH (1)
Konigsallee 106
Dusseldorf, 40215, Germany
Tel.: (49) 21199460
Fax: (49) 211 99 46 400
Administrative Management Services
S.I.C.: 8741
N.A.I.C.S.: 561110

PBC Services GmbH der Deutschen Bank (1)
Theodor-Heuss-Allee 72
60486 Frankfurt am Main, Germany
Tel.: (49) 69 91000
Financial Investment Services
S.I.C.: 6211
N.A.I.C.S.: 523999
Thomas Langer *(Mng Dir)*

POSEIDON Vermogensverwaltungsgesellschaft mbH (1)
Unter Sachsenhausen 4
Cologne, 50667, Germany
Tel.: (49) 221 14501
Fax: (49) 221 1451512
Commercial Banking Services
S.I.C.: 6029
N.A.I.C.S.: 522110

PS plus Portfolio Software + Consulting GmbH (1)
Albert-Einstein-Strasse 34
63322 Rodermark, Germany

Deutsche Bank Aktiengesellschaft—(Continued)

Tel.: (49) 6074 91063 5
Fax: (49) 6074 91063 70
Web Site: www.psplus.de
Software Development Services
S.I.C.: 7371
N.A.I.C.S.: 541511
Peter Dobler *(Mng Dir)*

RREEF Investment GmbH (1)
Mainzer Landstrasse
60327 Frankfurt am Main, Germany
Tel.: (49) 69 7 17 04 0
Fax: (49) 69 7 17 04 6959
E-Mail: info.germany@rreef.com
Web Site: www.rreef.com
Investment Management Services
S.I.C.: 6282
N.A.I.C.S.: 523920
Georg Allendorf *(Mgr)*

RREEF Management GmbH (1)
Mainzer Landstrasse 178-190
60327 Frankfurt am Main, Germany
Tel.: (49) 697170400
Fax: (49) 69 7 17 04 6959
E-Mail: info.germany@rreef.com
Web Site: www.rreef.com
Real Estate Management Services
S.I.C.: 6531
N.A.I.C.S.: 531390
Georg Allendorf *(Mng Dir)*

RREEF Spezial Invest GmbH (1)
Mainzer Landstrasse 178-190
60327 Frankfurt am Main, Germany
Tel.: (49) 69 7 17 04 0
Fax: (49) 69 7 17 04 6909
E-Mail: info.germany@rreef.com
Web Site: www.rreef.com
Investment Management Services
S.I.C.: 6211
N.A.I.C.S.: 523999
Georg Allendorf *(Mng Dir)*

SAGITA Grundstucks-Vermietungsgesellschaft mbH (1)
Konigsallee 106
Dusseldorf, 40215, Germany
Tel.: (49) 211 99460
Fax: (49) 211 9946400
Real Estate Management Services
S.I.C.: 6531
N.A.I.C.S.: 531390

Sal. Oppenheim Global Invest GmbH (1)
Unter Sachsenhausen 4
Cologne, 50667, Germany
Tel.: (49) 22114501
Investment Advisory Services
S.I.C.: 6282
N.A.I.C.S.: 523930

Sal. Oppenheim jr. & Cie. AG & Co. KGaA (1)
Unter Sachsenhausen 4
50667 Cologne, Germany
Tel.: (49) 22114501
Fax: (49) 2211451512
E-Mail: info@oppenheim.de
Web Site: www.oppenheim.de
Emp.: 350
Asset Management & Investment Banking Services
S.I.C.: 6211
N.A.I.C.S.: 523110
Henning Heuerding *(Vice Chm-Supervisory Bd)*
Carsten Schildknecht *(Vice Chm-Supervisory Bd)*
Wilhelm Freiherr Haller von Hallerstein *(CEO)*
Gregor Broschinski *(Member-Mgmt Bd)*
Jurgen Dobritzsch *(Member-Mgmt Bd)*
Jurgen Fiedler *(Member-Mgmt Bd)*
Wolfgang Leoni *(Member-Mgmt Bd)*
Francois Pauly *(Member-Mgmt Bd)*

Subsidiaries:

BHF-Bank AG (2)
Bockenheimer Landstrasse 10
D-60323 Frankfurt am Main, Germany De
Tel.: (49) 697180
Telex: 411026
Fax: (49) 697182296
E-Mail: corp-comm@bhf-bank.com
Web Site: www.bhf-bank.com
Emp.: 1,500
Merchant & Commercial Bank
S.I.C.: 6029
N.A.I.C.S.: 522110
Stefan Krause *(Chm-Supervisory Bd)*
Friedrich Carl Freiherr von Oppenheim *(Deputy Chm-Supervisory Bd)*
Franz Herrlein *(CFO)*

Subsidiaries:

BHF Asset Servicing GmbH (3)
Bockenheimer Landstrasse 10
60323 Frankfurt am Main, Germany
Tel.: (49) 6966774400
Fax: (49) 697102296
Web Site: www.bhfbank.com
Emp.: 1,400
Merchant & Commercial Bank
S.I.C.: 6029
N.A.I.C.S.: 522110
Bjorn Robens *(Mng Dir)*

BHF-Betriebsservice GmbH (3)
Bockenheimer Landstr 10
60323 Frankfurt, Hesse, Germany
Tel.: (49) 697180
Fax: (49) 697182296
E-Mail: info@bhf-bank.com
Web Site: www.bhf-bank.com
Emp.: 1,600
Monetary Authorities - Central Bank
S.I.C.: 6011
N.A.I.C.S.: 521110

BHF Club Deal GmbH (3)
Bockenheimer Landstr 10
60323 Frankfurt, Germany De
Tel.: (49) 697180
Fax: (49) 7182296
Emp.: 1,600
Investment Advice
S.I.C.: 6282
N.A.I.C.S.: 523930

BHF Grundbesitz-Verwaltungsgesellschaft mbH & Co am Kaiserlei OHG (3)
Bockenheimer Landstr 10
60302 Frankfurt, Germany
Tel.: (49) 697180
Fax: (49) 697182296
E-Mail: corp-comm@bhf-bank.com
Web Site: www.bhf-bank.com
Emp.: 1,600
Investment Banking & Securities Dealing
S.I.C.: 6211
N.A.I.C.S.: 523110
Bjorn H. Robens *(Mng Dir)*

BHF Immobilien-GmbH (3)
Bockenheimer Landstrasse 10
60323 Frankfurt am Main, Germany
Tel.: (49) 697183285
Fax: (49) 697182408
E-Mail: corp-comm@bhf-bank.com
Web Site: www.bhf-bank.com
Emp.: 1,600
Institutional Asset Management & Real Estate Services
S.I.C.: 6726
N.A.I.C.S.: 525990
Eorn Roeens *(Mng Dir)*

BHF Private Equity Management GmbH (3)
Bockenheimer Landstrasse 10
60323 Frankfurt am Main, Germany
Tel.: (49) 697183621
Fax: (49) 697182408
Merchant & Commercial Bank
S.I.C.: 6029
N.A.I.C.S.: 522110
Thomas Etzel *(Mng Dir)*

BHF Private Equity Treuhand- und Beratungsgesellschaft mbH (3)
Bockenheimer Landstr 10
60323 Frankfurt, Germany
Tel.: (49) 69 718 3621
Fax: (49) 69 718 2408
Emp.: 2,000
Investment Banking & Securities Dealing Services
S.I.C.: 6211
N.A.I.C.S.: 523110

BHF Trust Management Gesellschaft fur Vermogensverwaltung mbH (3)
Neue Mainzer Str 80
60311 Frankfurt, Germany
Tel.: (49) 697182130
Telex: 411 026
Fax: (49) 697183224
E-Mail: ing-bhf-trust@bhf.ing.com
Web Site: www.ing-bhf-bank.de
Emp.: 18
Trust Services, Private Banking, Institutional Asset Management Services
S.I.C.: 6282
N.A.I.C.S.: 523930

Frankfurt-Trust Investment GmbH (3)
Neue Mainzer Strasse
60311 Frankfurt am Main, Germany
Tel.: (49) 69920500
Fax: (49) 6992153132
E-Mail: info@frankfurt-trust.de
Web Site: www.frankfurt-trust.de
Emp.: 100
Employee Benefits, Trust Services, Institutional Asset Mannagement, Saving & Investing Services
S.I.C.: 6722
N.A.I.C.S.: 525910

Non-U.S. Subsidiary:

Frankfurt Trust Invest Luxembourg AG (4)
534 Rue De Neunorf
2220 Luxembourg, Luxembourg
Tel.: (352) 4576761
Fax: (352) 458324
E-Mail: ftlux@bhf.lu
Web Site: www.frankfurt-trust.de
Emp.: 12
Portfolio Management Services
S.I.C.: 6799
N.A.I.C.S.: 523920
Monika Anell *(Mng Dir)*

Frankfurter Service Kapitalanlage-Gesellschaft mbH (3)
Neue Mainzer Strasse 80
60311 Frankfurt am Main, Germany
Tel.: (49) 697953380
Merchant & Commercial Banking Services
S.I.C.: 6029
N.A.I.C.S.: 522110

Non-U.S. Subsidiaries:

BHF-Bank International (3)
534 Rue De Neudors
2220 Luxembourg, Luxembourg
Tel.: (352) 4576761
Telex: 3181
Fax: (352) 458320
E-Mail: sekretariat@bhf.lu
Web Site: www.bhf-bank.com
Emp.: 30
Commercial Bank
S.I.C.: 6029
N.A.I.C.S.: 522110
Roland Scharff *(Chm)*

BHF-Bank (Schweiz) AG (3)
Schulhausstrasse 6
8002 Zurich, Switzerland CH
Mailing Address:
Postfach 25
8027 Zurich, Switzerland
Tel.: (41) 44 209 7511
Fax: (41) 44 202 5606
E-Mail: info@bhf-bank.ch
Web Site: www.bhf-bank.ch
Emp.: 58
Investment Advisory, Securities Dealing & Portfolio Management Services
S.I.C.: 6282
N.A.I.C.S.: 523930
Bjorn Robens *(Chm)*
Franz A. Blankart *(Vice Chm)*
Joachim Kunzi *(CEO)*
Hans-Peter Fornoff *(Mng Dir)*
Udo Schaberle *(Mng Dir)*

Subsidiary:

BHF Zurich Family Office AG (4)
Schulhausstrasse 6
8002 Zurich, Switzerland
Tel.: (41) 44 2097816
Fax: (41) 44 2097916
E-Mail: familyoffice@bhf.ch
Web Site: www.bhf-bank.com
Fund Management Services
S.I.C.: 6799
N.A.I.C.S.: 523920

Collineo Asset Management GmbH (2)
Brinkhoffstr 4
D-44137 Dortmund, Germany
Tel.: (49) 23110821
Fax: (49) 2311082468
E-Mail: service@collineo-am.com
Web Site: www.collineo-am.com
Emp.: 100
Financial Management Services
S.I.C.: 6726
N.A.I.C.S.: 525990

Frankfurt Family Office GmbH (2)
Bockenheimer Landstr 10
60323 Frankfurt, Germany
Tel.: (49) 697180
Fax: (49) 697186900
Web Site: www.bhf-bank.com
Investment Banking & Securities Dealing
S.I.C.: 6211
N.A.I.C.S.: 523110
Markus Jesberger *(Mgr)*

Frankfurter Beteiligungs-Treuhand GmbH (2)
Bockenheimer Landstr 10
60323 Frankfurt, Germany
Tel.: (49) 697180
Fax: (49) 697182296
Web Site: www.bhs-bank.com
Personal Care Services
S.I.C.: 7299
N.A.I.C.S.: 812199

Industrie-Beteiligungs-Gesellschaft mbH (2)
Bockenheimer Landstr 10
60323 Frankfurt, Hesse, Germany
Tel.: (49) 697183210
Fax: (49) 697183206
Bank Holding Companies Office
S.I.C.: 6712
N.A.I.C.S.: 551111

Neptuno Verwaltungs- und Treuhand-Gesellschaft mbH (2)
Unter Sachsenhausen 4
50667 Cologne, Germany
Tel.: (49) 22114501
Fax: (49) 2211451512
Investment Banking & Securities Dealing Services
S.I.C.: 6211
N.A.I.C.S.: 523110

OPB-Structuring GmbH (2)
Unter Sachsenhausen 4
50667 Cologne, Germany
Tel.: (49) 2211451043
Fax: (49) 2211451932
Investment Banking & Securities Dealing
S.I.C.: 6211
N.A.I.C.S.: 523110

Oppenheim Beteiligungs-AG (2)
Stackenbergstrasse 10
42329 Wuppertal, Germany
Tel.: (49) 2211451989
Fax: (49) 22114591989
Web Site: www.oppenheim.de/gb2005en/03_oppenheim_group/05_locations_and_adresses/03_05_01.htm
Investment Banking & Securities Dealing Services
S.I.C.: 6211
N.A.I.C.S.: 523110

Oppenheim Beteiligungs-Treuhand GmbH (2)
Unter Sachsenhausen 4
50667 Cologne, Germany
Tel.: (49) 22114501
Fax: (49) 2211451512
E-Mail: info@oppenheim.de
Web Site: www.oppenheim.de
Emp.: 800
Commercial Banking Services
S.I.C.: 6029
N.A.I.C.S.: 522110

Oppenheim Capital Management GmbH (2)
Unter Sachsenhausen 4
50667 Cologne, Germany
Tel.: (49) 22114501
Fax: (49) 2211451918

E-Mail: info@oppenheim.de
Web Site: www.oppenheim.de
Management Consulting Services
S.I.C.: 8748
N.A.I.C.S.: 541618

Oppenheim-Esch Holding GbR (2)
Christian-Esch-Strasse 2-4
53844 Troisdorf, Germany
Tel.: (49) 22419870
Fax: (49) 2241987196
Commercial Banking Services
S.I.C.: 6029
N.A.I.C.S.: 522110

Oppenheim Fonds Trust GmbH (2)
Unter Sachsenhausen 4
50667 Cologne, Germany
Tel.: (49) 22114502
Fax: (49) 2211452911
E-Mail: info@oppenheim.de
Web Site: www.oppenheim.de
Portfolio Management Services
S.I.C.: 6799
N.A.I.C.S.: 523920
Wilhelm Haller *(Gen Mgr)*

Oppenheim Kapitalanlagegesellschaft mbH (2)
Unter Sachsenhausen 4
50667 Cologne, Germany
Tel.: (49) 22114503
Fax: (49) 2211451512
E-Mail: info@oppenheim.de
Web Site: www.oppenheim.de
Emp.: 800
Investment Funds Services
S.I.C.: 6722
N.A.I.C.S.: 525910
Holger Sepp *(COO-Asset Management)*

Subsidiary:

Oppenheim VAM Kapitalanlagegesellschaft mbH (3)
Clever Str 13 15
Cologne, 50668, Germany (100%)
Tel.: (49) 22177520
Fax: (49) 22177521007
E-Mail: marketing@genrecapital.com
Web Site: www.oppenheim-ovam.de
Sales Range: $1-9.9 Million
Emp.: 55
Insurance Related Services
S.I.C.: 6411
N.A.I.C.S.: 524298
John Connolly *(Mng Dir)*
Susanne Fromme *(Mng Dir)*
Andrea Simokat *(Mng Dir)*

Oppenheim Pramerica Fonds Trust GmbH (2)
Unter Sachsenhausen 4
50667 Cologne, Germany
Tel.: (49) 22114505
Fax: (49) 2211452900
E-Mail: fonds@oppenheim.de
Web Site: www.oppenheimpramerica.de
Trusts, Estates & Agency Account Services
S.I.C.: 6733
N.A.I.C.S.: 525920

Oppenheim Research GmbH (2)
Unter Sachsenhausen 4
50667 Cologne, Germany
Tel.: (49) 6971345651
Fax: (49) 22114502
E-Mail: research@oppenheim.de
Educational Support Services
S.I.C.: 8299
N.A.I.C.S.: 611710
Baerbel Boesner *(Mgr)*

Oppenheim VAM Kapitalanlagegesellschaft mbH (2)
Elsa-Brandstrom-Strasse 10-12
50668 Cologne, Germany
Tel.: (49) 22114507
Fax: (49) 22113981270
Web Site: www.insuranceam.db.com
Emp.: 32
Trusts, Estates & Agency Accounts
S.I.C.: 6733
N.A.I.C.S.: 525920
Christian Finke *(Gen Mgr)*

Oppenheim Vermogenstreuhand GmbH (2)
Oppenheimstrasse 11
50667 Cologne, Germany
Tel.: (49) 2211452400
Fax: (49) 2211452409
E-Mail: info@oppenheim.de
Web Site: www.oppenheim.de/gb2006en/02_sal_oppenheim_group/04_locations_and_adresses/02_04_01.htm
Emp.: 50
Trusts Estates & Agency Accounts
S.I.C.: 6733
N.A.I.C.S.: 525920
Andreas Pithner *(Gen Mgr)*

Oppenheim Verwaltung von Immobilienvermogen GmbH (2)
Unter Sachsenhausen 4
50667 Cologne, Germany
Tel.: (49) 22114501
Fax: (49) 221451512
E-Mail: info@oppenheim.de
Web Site: www.oppenheim.de
Real Estate Agents & Brokers Offices
S.I.C.: 6531
N.A.I.C.S.: 531210

Sal. Oppenheim Alternative Investments GmbH (2)
Unter Sachsenhausen 4
50667 Cologne, Germany
Tel.: (49) 22114501
Fax: (49) 2211451512
E-Mail: info@oppenheim.de
Web Site: www.oppenheim.de
Asset Management & Investment Banking Services
S.I.C.: 6211
N.A.I.C.S.: 523110

Sal. Oppenheim Investments GmbH (2)
Unter Sachsenhausen 4
50667 Cologne, Germany
Tel.: (49) 22114501
Fax: (49) 2211451454
E-Mail: info@oppenheim.de
Web Site: www.oppenheim.de
Emp.: 700
Asset Management & Investment Banking Services
S.I.C.: 6211
N.A.I.C.S.: 523110
Wilhelm Haller *(Gen Mgr)*

Salomon Oppenheim GmbH (2)
Unter Sachsenhausen 4
50667 Cologne, Germany
Tel.: (49) 22114501
Fax: (49) 2211451512
E-Mail: info@oppenheim.de
Web Site: www.oppenheim.de
Emp.: 800
Asset Management & Investment Banking Services
S.I.C.: 6211
N.A.I.C.S.: 523110
Wilhelm Hallerstein *(Mng Dir)*

TILOS Vermogensverwaltungs GmbH (2)
Unter Sachsenhausen 4
50667 Cologne, Germany
Tel.: (49) 22114501
Trusts, Estates & Agency Accounts Services
S.I.C.: 6733
N.A.I.C.S.: 525920

Non-U.S. Subsidiaries:

Bank Sal. Oppenheim jr. & Cie. (Luxembourg) S.A. (2)
4 rue Jean Monnet
2180 Luxembourg, Luxembourg
Tel.: (352) 2215221
Fax: (352) 221522 690
E-Mail: info@oppenheim.lu
Web Site: www.oppenheim.lu
Commercial Banking
S.I.C.: 6029
N.A.I.C.S.: 522110
Dirk von Manikowsky *(Press Rels Officer)*

Deutsche Bank Osterreich AG (2)
Stock im Eisen-Platz 3
1010 Vienna, Austria
Tel.: (43) 1518660
Fax: (43) 1518669000
E-Mail: pwm.austria@db.com
Web Site: www.db.com
Emp.: 80
Commercial Banking
S.I.C.: 6029
N.A.I.C.S.: 522110
Bernard Ramsauer *(CEO)*
Ulrich Kallausch *(Deputy CEO/COO)*

Oppenheim Asset Management Services S.a.r.l. (2)
4 rue Jean Monnet
2180 Luxembourg, Luxembourg
Mailing Address:
Boite Postale 714
2017 Luxembourg, Luxembourg
Tel.: (352) 221 522 297
Fax: (352) 221 522 500
E-Mail: clientrelationship@oppenheim.lu
Web Site: www.oppenheim.lu
Asset Management & Investment Banking Services
S.I.C.: 6211
N.A.I.C.S.: 523110
Marco Schmitz *(Mng Dir)*

Oppenheim Landert Family Office AG (2)
Alte Landstrasse 102
Zollikon, 8702, Switzerland
Tel.: (41) 443963300
Fax: (41) 443963303
Asset Management & Investment Banking Services
S.I.C.: 6211
N.A.I.C.S.: 523110

Oppenheim Pramerica Asset Management S.a r.l. (2)
Rue Jean Monnet 4
2180 Luxembourg, Luxembourg
Tel.: (352) 221522610
Fax: (352) 221522690
E-Mail: fonds@oppenheim.lu
Web Site: www.oppenheim.lu
Emp.: 54
Open-End Investment Funds
S.I.C.: 6722
N.A.I.C.S.: 525910
Andreas Sotkel *(Mng Dir)*

Sal Oppenheim France (2)
4 Place Verdome
75001 Paris, France
Tel.: (33) 144508888
Fax: (33) 1 44 50 88 65
E-Mail: info@oppenheim-france.fr
Web Site: www.oppenheim-france.fr/
Fund & Portfolio Management Services for Institutional & Private Investors
S.I.C.: 6282
N.A.I.C.S.: 523920

Sal. Oppenheim (Hong Kong) Limited (2)
Ste 3408 Two Exchange Square
34th floor 8 Connaught Place, Hong Kong, China (Hong Kong)
Tel.: (852) 37933890
Fax: (852) 3101 9606
Asset Management & Investment Banking Services
S.I.C.: 6211
N.A.I.C.S.: 523110

Sal. Oppenheim jr. & Cie. (Switzerland) Ltd. (2)
Prime Tower Hardstrasse 201
8022 Zurich, Switzerland
Tel.: (41) 442142214
Fax: (41) 442111085
E-Mail: bank@oppenheim.ch
Web Site: www.oppenheim.ch
Emp.: 150
Investment Banking & Securities Dealing
S.I.C.: 6211
N.A.I.C.S.: 523110
Ronald Seuser *(Chm)*

SAMOS Vermogensverwaltungs GmbH (1)
Unter Sachsenhausen 4
Cologne, 50667, Germany
Tel.: (49) 221 14501
Fax: (49) 221 1451512
Administrative Management Services
S.I.C.: 8741
N.A.I.C.S.: 561110

Schiffsbetriebsgesellschaft Brunswik mit beschrankter Haftung (1)
Ludwig-Erhard-Str 1
Hamburg, 20459, Germany
Tel.: (49) 4037010
Investment Management Services
S.I.C.: 6282
N.A.I.C.S.: 523920

Schiffsbetriebsgesellschaft GRIMA mbH (1)
Ludwig-Erhard-Strasse 1
20459 Hamburg, Germany
Tel.: (49) 40 3701 0
Investment Management Services
S.I.C.: 6799
N.A.I.C.S.: 523920

SCUDO Grundstucks-Vermietungsgesellschaft mbH & Co. Objekt Kleine Alexanderstrasse KG (1)
Konigsallee 106
40215 Dusseldorf, Germany
Tel.: (49) 211 99460
Fax: (49) 211 9946400
Real Estate Management Services
S.I.C.: 6531
N.A.I.C.S.: 531390

SEDO Grundstucks-Vermietungsgesellschaft mbH (1)
Konigsallee 106
Dusseldorf, 40215, Germany
Tel.: (49) 21199460
Fax: (49) 211 9946400
Real Estate Management Services
S.I.C.: 6531
N.A.I.C.S.: 531390

SIMA Private Equity 1 Beteiligungs GmbH (1)
Kapstadtring 8
Hamburg, 22297, Germany
Tel.: (49) 2219370850
Financial Management Services
S.I.C.: 6211
N.A.I.C.S.: 523999

SIMA Private Equity 1 GmbH & Co. KG (1)
Kapstadtring 8
Hamburg, 22297, Germany
Tel.: (49) 40300570
Financial Management Services
S.I.C.: 6211
N.A.I.C.S.: 523999

STUPA Heizwerk Frankfurt (Oder) Nord Beteiligungsgesellschaft mbH (1)
Berliner Str 1
Schonefeld, 12529, Germany
Tel.: (49) 33555330
Commercial Banking Services
S.I.C.: 6029
N.A.I.C.S.: 522110

Suddeutsche Vermogensverwaltung Gesellschaft mit beschrankter Haftung (1)
Taunusanlage 12
Frankfurt am Main, 60325, Germany
Tel.: (49) 6991034838
Fax: (49) 69 9 10 22516
Wealth Management Services
S.I.C.: 8742
N.A.I.C.S.: 541611

TAKIR Grundstucks-Vermietungsgesellschaft mbH (1)
Konigsallee 106
Dusseldorf, 40215, Germany
Tel.: (49) 21199460
Fax: (49) 211 9946400
Real Estate Management Services
S.I.C.: 6531
N.A.I.C.S.: 531390

Telefon-Servicegesellschaft der Deutschen Bank mbH (1)
Theodor-Heuss-Allee 72
Frankfurt am Main, 60486, Germany
Tel.: (49) 6991000
Fax: (49) 69 91024031
Web Site: www.dbdirektjobs.de
Telecommunication Services
S.I.C.: 4899
N.A.I.C.S.: 517919

TERGO Grundstucks-Vermietungsgesellschaft mbH (1)
Konigsallee 106
Dusseldorf, 40215, Germany

Deutsche Bank Aktiengesellschaft—(Continued)

Tel.: (49) 211 99460
Fax: (49) 211 9946400
Real Estate Management Services
S.I.C.: 6531
N.A.I.C.S.: 531390

TERRUS Grundstucks-Vermietungsgesellschaft mbH & Co. Objekt Bernbach KG (1)
Konigsallee 106
Dusseldorf, 40215, Germany
Tel.: (49) 211 99460
Fax: (49) 211 9946400
Real Estate Management Services
S.I.C.: 6531
N.A.I.C.S.: 531390

TERRUS Grundstucks-Vermietungsgesellschaft mbH (1)
Konigsallee 106
Dusseldorf, 40215, Germany
Tel.: (49) 211 99460
Fax: (49) 211 9946400
Real Estate Management Services
S.I.C.: 6531
N.A.I.C.S.: 531390

TOSSA Grundstucks-Vermietungsgesellschaft mbH (1)
Konigsallee 106
Dusseldorf, 40215, Germany
Tel.: (49) 21199460
Fax: (49) 211 9946400
Property Leasing Services
S.I.C.: 6519
N.A.I.C.S.: 531190
Klaus Lamers *(Mng Dir)*

Treuinvest Service GmbH (1)
Mainzer Landstr 178-190
Frankfurt am Main, 60327, Germany
Tel.: (49) 6991000
Financial Planning Services
S.I.C.: 6282
N.A.I.C.S.: 523930

TRIPLA Grundstucks-Vermietungsgesellschaft mbH (1)
Konigsallee 106
Dusseldorf, 40215, Germany
Tel.: (49) 211 99460
Fax: (49) 211 9946400
Real Estate Property Leasing Services
S.I.C.: 6519
N.A.I.C.S.: 531190

Vertriebsgesellschaft mbH der Deutschen Bank Privat- und Geschaftskunden (1)
Hardenbergstr 32
Berlin, 10623, Germany
Tel.: (49) 3031088551
Investment Banking Services
S.I.C.: 6211
N.A.I.C.S.: 523110
Bernd Schulte *(Mng Dir)*

VOB-ZVD Processing GmbH (1)
Eckenheimer Landstrasse 242
60320 Frankfurt, Germany
Tel.: (49) 69 95 90 92 0
Fax: (49) 69 95 90 92 200
E-Mail: info@voeb-zvd.de
Web Site: www.voeb-zvd.de
Commercial Banking Services
S.I.C.: 6029
N.A.I.C.S.: 522110

Wilhelm von Finck Deutsche Family Office AG (1)
Keferloh 1a
Grasbrunn, 85630, Germany
Tel.: (49) 89 45 69 16 0
Fax: (49) 89 45 69 16 99
E-Mail: info@wvf-dfo.de
Web Site: www.wvf-dfo.de
Asset Management Services
S.I.C.: 6282
N.A.I.C.S.: 523920
Klaus Kuder *(Mgr)*

ZARAT Beteiligungsgesellschaft mbH & Co. Objekt Leben II KG (1)
Konigsallee 106
Dusseldorf, 40215, Germany
Tel.: (49) 21199460
Fax: (49) 211 9946400
General Insurance Services
S.I.C.: 6411
N.A.I.C.S.: 524210

ZELAS Beteiligungsgesellschaft mbH & Co. Leben I KG (1)
Konigsallee 106
Dusseldorf, 40215, Germany
Tel.: (49) 211 99460
Fax: (49) 211 9946400
Administrative Management Services
S.I.C.: 8741
N.A.I.C.S.: 561110
Helmut Schumacher *(Mng Dir)*

U.S. Subsidiaries:

Alex. Brown Management Services, Inc. (1)
1 South St
Baltimore, MD 21202
Tel.: (410) 727-1700
Business Management Consulting Services
S.I.C.: 8742
N.A.I.C.S.: 541611

Apex Fleet Inc. (1)
2036 Washington St
Hanover, MA 02339
Tel.: (617) 217-6100
Investment Management Services
S.I.C.: 6282
N.A.I.C.S.: 523920

BAL Servicing Corporation (1)
1011 Centre Rd Ste 200
Wilmington, DE 19805
Tel.: (302) 636-3301
Fax: (302) 636-3333
Financial Management Services
S.I.C.: 6211
N.A.I.C.S.: 523999

Bankers International Corporation (1)
1011 Center Rd Ste 200
Wilmington, DE 19805-1266
Tel.: (302) 636-3363
Investment Management Services
S.I.C.: 6799
N.A.I.C.S.: 523920

Beachwood Properties Corp. (1)
1011 Centre Rd
Wilmington, DE 19805-1266
Tel.: (302) 636-3301
Real Estate Development Services
S.I.C.: 6531
N.A.I.C.S.: 531390

Blue Ridge CLO Holding Company LLC (1)
60 Wall St Lbby 1
New York, NY 10005-2880
Tel.: (212) 250-2500
Investment Management Services
S.I.C.: 6799
N.A.I.C.S.: 523920

Bluewater Creek Management Co. (1)
1011 Centre Rd Ste 200
Wilmington, DE 19805
Tel.: (302) 636-3301
Fax: (302) 636-3333
Financial Management Services
S.I.C.: 6211
N.A.I.C.S.: 523999

BT Sable, L.L.C. (1)
2711 Centerville Rd Ste 400
Wilmington, DE 19808
Tel.: (302) 636-3301
Fax: (302) 636-3333
Investment Management Services
S.I.C.: 6799
N.A.I.C.S.: 523920

BT Services Tennessee Inc. (1)
648 Grassmere Park
Nashville, TN 37211-3658 TN
Tel.: (615) 835-3100
Fax: (615) 835-2930
Web Site: www.deutschebank.com
Sales Range: $10-24.9 Million
Emp.: 600
Backoffice Operations
S.I.C.: 6029
N.A.I.C.S.: 522110

Cape Acquisition Corp. (1)
9696 Bonita Beach Rd Se Ste 206
Bonita Springs, FL 34135-8502
Tel.: (239) 495-8200
Financial Management Services
S.I.C.: 6211
N.A.I.C.S.: 523999

Career Blazers Consulting Services, Inc. (1)
5 W 37th St Fl 5
New York, NY 10018-5384
Tel.: (212) 719-3232
Recruitment Services
S.I.C.: 7361
N.A.I.C.S.: 561311

Career Blazers Learning Center of Los Angeles, Inc. (1)
3500 Wilshire Blvd 2nd Fl
Los Angeles, CA 90010
Tel.: (213) 620-8200
Training Center Operating Services
S.I.C.: 8299
N.A.I.C.S.: 611430

Career Blazers Management Company, Inc. (1)
5 W 37th St Fl 5
New York, NY 10018-5384
Tel.: (212) 719-3232
Human Resource Consulting Services
S.I.C.: 8999
N.A.I.C.S.: 541612

Career Blazers New York, Inc. (1)
5 W 37th St 5th Fl
New York, NY 10018
Tel.: (212) 719-3232
Professional Employment Services
S.I.C.: 7361
N.A.I.C.S.: 561311

Career Blazers Personnel Services, Inc. (1)
5 W 37th St Fl 5
New York, NY 10018-5384
Tel.: (212) 719-3232
Human Resource Consulting Services
S.I.C.: 8999
N.A.I.C.S.: 541612

Career Blazers Personnel Services of Washington, D.C., Inc. (1)
5 W 37th St Fl 5
New York, NY 10018-5384
Tel.: (212) 719-3232
Human Resource Consulting Services
S.I.C.: 8999
N.A.I.C.S.: 541612

Career Blazers Service Company, Inc. (1)
590 5th Av Fl 6
New York, NY 10036-4702
Tel.: (212) 719-3232
Professional Employment Services
S.I.C.: 7361
N.A.I.C.S.: 561311

China Recovery Fund LLC (1)
60 Wall St Lbby 1
New York, NY 10005-2880
Tel.: (212) 250-2500
Business Management Consulting Services
S.I.C.: 8742
N.A.I.C.S.: 541611

Cinda - DB NPL Securitization Trust 2003-1 (1)
60 Wall St Lbby 1
New York, NY 10005-2880
Tel.: (212) 250-2500
Business Management Consulting Services
S.I.C.: 8742
N.A.I.C.S.: 541611

Dawn-BV LLC (1)
4425 Ponce Deleon Blvd 5th Fl
Coral Gables, FL 33146
Tel.: (561) 659-8820
Real Estate Management Services
S.I.C.: 6531
N.A.I.C.S.: 531390

DB Alex. Brown Holdings Incorporated (1)
1011 Centre Rd Ste 200
Wilmington, DE 19805
Tel.: (302) 636-3290
Investment Management Services
S.I.C.: 6799
N.A.I.C.S.: 523920

DB Alternative Trading Inc. (1)
280 Park Ave
New York, NY 10017
Tel.: (212) 454-3600
Financial Management Services
S.I.C.: 6211
N.A.I.C.S.: 523999

DB Capital, Inc. (1)
4018 Calgary Ave
San Diego, CA 92122-2507
Tel.: (858) 453-6126
Investment Management Services
S.I.C.: 6282
N.A.I.C.S.: 523920

DB Commodity Services LLC (1)
60 Wall St
New York, NY 10005
Tel.: (212) 250-5883
Fax: (877) 369-4617
Web Site: www.dbfunds.db.com
Fund Management Services
S.I.C.: 6799
N.A.I.C.S.: 523920

DB Delaware Holdings (Europe) Limited (1)
1209 Orange St
Wilmington, DE 19801
Tel.: (302) 636-3301
Fax: (302) 636-3301
Investment Management Services
S.I.C.: 6799
N.A.I.C.S.: 523920

DB Depositor Inc. (1)
1011 Centre Rd Ste 200
Wilmington, DE 19805-1266
Tel.: (302) 636-3301
Fax: (302) 636-3333
Commercial Banking Services
S.I.C.: 6029
N.A.I.C.S.: 522110

DB Global Technology, Inc. (1)
3000 Centre Green Way
Cary, NC 27513-5775
Tel.: (919) 481-7900
Commercial Banking Services
S.I.C.: 6029
N.A.I.C.S.: 522110

DB Green Holdings Corp. (1)
60 Wall St
New York, NY 10005
Tel.: (212) 250-2500
Investment Management Services
S.I.C.: 6282
N.A.I.C.S.: 523920

DB Green, Inc. (1)
60 Wall St
New York, NY 10005
Tel.: (212) 250-2500
Commercial Banking Services
S.I.C.: 6029
N.A.I.C.S.: 522110

DB Holdings (New York), Inc. (1)
60 Wall St
New York, NY 10005
Tel.: (212) 250-2500
Investment Management Services
S.I.C.: 6282
N.A.I.C.S.: 523920

db home lending holdings llc (1)
60 Wall St
New York, NY 10005
Tel.: (212) 250-0382
Investment Management Services
S.I.C.: 6799
N.A.I.C.S.: 523920

D.B. International Delaware, Inc. (1)
1011 Centre Rd
Wilmington, DE 19805
Tel.: (302) 636-3290
Financial Management Services
S.I.C.: 6211
N.A.I.C.S.: 523999

DB Investment Management, Inc. (1)
652 Marsten Green Ct
Ambler, PA 19002

Tel.: (215) 646-6762
Business Management Consulting Services
S.I.C.: 8742
N.A.I.C.S.: 541611

DB Investment Resources Holdings Corp. (1)
60 Wall St Lbby 1
New York, NY 10005-2880
Tel.: (212) 250-2500
Investment Management Services
S.I.C.: 6211
N.A.I.C.S.: 523999

DB Investment Resources (US) Corporation (1)
60 Wall St
New York, NY 10005
Tel.: (212) 250-2500
Investment Management Services
S.I.C.: 6799
N.A.I.C.S.: 523920

DB Io LP (1)
60 Wall St Lbby 1
New York, NY 10005-2880
Tel.: (212) 250-2500
Securities Brokerage Services
S.I.C.: 6211
N.A.I.C.S.: 523120

DB IROC Leasing Corp. (1)
60 Wall St Lbby 1
New York, NY 10005-2880
Tel.: (212) 250-2500
Securities Brokerage Services
S.I.C.: 6211
N.A.I.C.S.: 523120

DB Maia LLC (1)
60 Wall St Lbby 1
New York, NY 10005-2880
Tel.: (212) 250-2500
Business Management Consulting Services
S.I.C.: 8742
N.A.I.C.S.: 541611

DB Management Partners, L.P. (1)
60 Wall St Frnt 1
New York, NY 10005-2836
Tel.: (212) 250-2500
Securities Brokerage Services
S.I.C.: 6211
N.A.I.C.S.: 523120

DB Mortgage Investment Inc. (1)
60 Wall St Lbby 1
New York, NY 10001
Tel.: (212) 250-2500
Investment Management Services
S.I.C.: 6211
N.A.I.C.S.: 523999

DB Mortgage Services, LLC (1)
1 Beacon St Fl 14
Boston, MA 02108
Tel.: (617) 722-5000
Securities Brokerage Services
S.I.C.: 6211
N.A.I.C.S.: 523120

DB Partnership Management II, LLC (1)
60 Wall St Lbby 1
New York, NY 10005-2880
Tel.: (212) 250-2500
Business Management Consulting Services
S.I.C.: 8742
N.A.I.C.S.: 541611

DB Partnership Management Ltd. (1)
1011 Centre Rd
Wilmington, DE 19805-1267
Tel.: (302) 636-3290
Fax: (302) 636-3333
Commercial Banking Services
S.I.C.: 6029
N.A.I.C.S.: 522110

DB Perry Investments Limited (1)
60 Wall St Lbby 1
New York, NY 10005-2880
Tel.: (212) 250-2500
Business Management Consulting Services
S.I.C.: 8742
N.A.I.C.S.: 541611

DB Petri LLC (1)
60 Wall St Lbby 1
New York, NY 10005-2880
Tel.: (212) 250-2500
Administrative Management and General Management Consulting Services
S.I.C.: 8742
N.A.I.C.S.: 541611

DB Private Clients Corp. (1)
345 Park Ave
New York, NY 10154
Tel.: (212) 454-3600
Financial Management Services
S.I.C.: 6211
N.A.I.C.S.: 523999

DB Private Wealth Mortgage Ltd. (1)
60 Wall St
New York, NY 10005
Tel.: (212) 250-8174
Mortgage Loan Brokerage Services
S.I.C.: 6163
N.A.I.C.S.: 522310

DB Securities Services NJ Inc. (1)
5022 Gate Pkwy
Jacksonville, FL 32256
Tel.: (212) 250-7936
Securities Brokerage Services
S.I.C.: 6211
N.A.I.C.S.: 523120

DB Services Americas, Inc. (1)
60 Wall St
New York, NY 10005
Tel.: (212) 250-2500
Financial Management Services
S.I.C.: 6211
N.A.I.C.S.: 523999

DBAH Capital, LLC (1)
60 Wall St
New York, NY 10005
Tel.: (212) 250-2500
Investment Management Services
S.I.C.: 6282
N.A.I.C.S.: 523920

DBD Pilgrim America Corp. (1)
1011 Centre Rd
Wilmington, DE 19805
Tel.: (302) 636-3290
Investment Management Services
S.I.C.: 6211
N.A.I.C.S.: 523999

DBUSBZ2, LLC (1)
1011 Centre Rd Ste 200
Wilmington, DE 19805
Tel.: (302) 636-3290
Financial Management Services
S.I.C.: 6211
N.A.I.C.S.: 523999

DBX Advisors LLC (1)
60 Wall St
New York, NY 10005-2836
Tel.: (212) 250-5883
Financial Management Services
S.I.C.: 6211
N.A.I.C.S.: 523999

Deutsche Alt-A Securities, Inc. (1)
60 Wall St
New York, NY 10005-2836
Tel.: (212) 250-5000
Securities Brokerage Services
S.I.C.: 6211
N.A.I.C.S.: 523120

Deutsche Asset & Wealth Management (1)
345 Park Ave
New York, NY 10154-0004 DE
Tel.: (212) 250-2500 (80%)
Fax: (212) 797-4664
Web Site: www.db.com
Emp.: 2,300
Investment Counseling Firm
S.I.C.: 8741
N.A.I.C.S.: 561110
Felipe Godard *(Mng Dir & Head-Wealth Mgmt-Latin America)*
Matt Montana *(Mng Dir & Head-Equity Trading-Americas)*
Brian Binder *(Mng Dir & Head-Fund Admin)*
Juan Landazabal *(Mng Dir & Global Head-Fixed Income Trading)*
Simon Mendelson *(Mng Dir & Head-Product Mgmt & Dev-Americas)*
Philip Poole *(Mng Dir & Head-Res-London)*
Vincenzo Vedda *(Mng Dir & Deputy Global Head-Equity Trading)*
Brandt Daniel *(Mng Dir)*
Randy Brown *(Co-Chief Investment Officer)*
Asoka Woehrmann *(Co-Chief Investment Officer)*

Subsidiary:

RREEF Management LLC (2)
875 N Michigan Ave 41st Fl
Chicago, IL 60611 DE
Tel.: (312) 266-9300
Fax: (312) 266-9346
E-Mail: info@rreef.com
Web Site: www.rreef.com
Sales Range: $25-49.9 Billion
Emp.: 100
Financial Management & Investment Services
S.I.C.: 6211
N.A.I.C.S.: 523999
Mike Nigro *(Mng Dir)*

Branches:

RREEF Management LLC (3)
101 California St FL 26
San Francisco, CA 94111
Tel.: (415) 781-3300
Fax: (415) 392-4648
Web Site: www.rreef.com
Real Estate & Infrastructure Investment Services
S.I.C.: 6282
N.A.I.C.S.: 523930
Maura Hooper *(Dir-Global Mktg & Comm)*

RREEF Management LLC (3)
280 Park Ave 23rd Fl
New York, NY 10017
Tel.: (212) 454-3900
Fax: (212) 454-6606
E-Mail: info@rreef.com
Web Site: www.rreef.com
Financial Management & Investment Services
S.I.C.: 6211
N.A.I.C.S.: 523999
Mark Roberts *(Mng Dir & Head-Global Res)*
Kurt Roeloffs *(Global Chief Investment Officer)*

Holdings:

Maher Terminals, LLC (3)
1210 Corbin St
Port Elizabeth, NJ 07201 NJ
Tel.: (908) 527-8200
Fax: (908) 436-4812
Web Site: www.maherterminals.com
Emp.: 150
Marine Container Terminal Services
S.I.C.: 4491
N.A.I.C.S.: 488320
Gary Cross *(Pres & CEO)*
Jay Ruble *(Gen Counsel & Sec)*
Paul Shahbazian *(Treas & VP)*
Gerard Crotty *(Sr VP-Ops)*
Leroy Luft *(Sr VP & Chief Engr)*
Anthony Ray *(Sr VP-Ops)*
Frans van Riemsdyk *(Sr VP-Sls & Mktg)*

Winridge Apartments (3)
2075 S Paris Way
Aurora, CO 80014-1173
Tel.: (303) 337-9102
Fax: (303) 750-5479
E-Mail: winridge@sares-regis.com
Web Site: www.srgliving.com
Emp.: 4
Apartment Building Operator
Import Export
S.I.C.: 6513
N.A.I.C.S.: 531110
Allyse McKenner *(Office Mgr)*

Non-U.S. Subsidiary:

RREEF China REIT Management Limited (3)
Level 52 International Commerce Centre 1
Austin Road West
Kowloon, China (Hong Kong)
Tel.: (852) 2203 7872
Fax: (852) 2203 7995
E-Mail: enquiry@rreefchinatrust.com
Web Site: www.rreef.com
Investment Management Services
S.I.C.: 6282
N.A.I.C.S.: 523920

Non-U.S. Joint Venture:

Bahia de Bizkaia Gas, S.L. (3)
Explanda de Punta Ceballos 2
Atraque De Punta Lucero, 48508 Zierbena, Spain ES
Tel.: (34) 946366020
Fax: (34) 946366150
E-Mail: info@bbg.es
Web Site: www.bbg.es
Emp.: 71
Natural Gas Distr
S.I.C.: 4924
N.A.I.C.S.: 221210
Guillermo Gonzalez *(Gen Mgr)*

Affiliates:

RREEF North American Infrastructure Onshore Fund A, L.P. (2)
114 W 47th St
New York, NY 10036
Tel.: (212) 454-6619
Fund Management Services
S.I.C.: 6282
N.A.I.C.S.: 523920

RREEF Property Trust, Inc. (2)
(Formerly RREEF America Property Income Trust, Inc.)
345 Park Ave 24th Fl
New York, NY 10154 MD
Tel.: (212) 454-6260
Fax: (212) 454-6616
Web Site: www.rreefpropertytrust.com
Rev.: $857,705
Assets: $32,692,034
Liabilities: $12,516,962
Net Worth: $20,175,072
Earnings: ($1,981,203)
Fiscal Year-end: 12/31/13
Real Estate Investment Services
S.I.C.: 6211
N.A.I.C.S.: 523999
W. Todd Henderson *(Chm)*
James N. Carbone *(CEO)*
Julianna S. Ingersoll *(CFO & Principal Acctg Officer)*

Deutsche Bank AG (New York) (1)
60 Wall St
New York, NY 10005-2858
Mailing Address:
PO Box 890
New York, NY 10101-0890
Tel.: (212) 250-2500
Web Site: www.db.com
Emp.: 5,000
Commercial Banking
S.I.C.: 6029
N.A.I.C.S.: 522110
John Utendahl *(Vice Chm)*
James Kenny *(Mng Dir & Co-Head-Investment Grade Credit-Markets-North America)*
Carlos A. Rodriguez *(Mng Dir & Head-Municipal Derivatives)*
Don Birchenough *(Mng Dir & Head-Media, Telecom Mergers & Acq-Americas)*
Scott Carter *(Mng Dir & Head-Global Prime Fin Sls-North America)*
Dushyant Chadha *(Mng Dir & Head-Equity Derivatives-Americas)*
Marc Fratepietro *(Mng Dir & Head-Indus Origination-Debt Capital Markets Grp)*
Clark Hutchison *(Mng Dir & Head-Listed Derivatives)*
Lou Jaffe *(Mng Dir & Head-Institutional Client Grp-Debt-Americas)*
Tom Jarck *(Mng Dir & Head-Index Flow Trading-Global Equity Derivatives-US)*
Doug Kline *(Mng Dir & Head-Hedge Fund Consulting-Global Prime Fin Bus)*
Nick Pappas *(Mng Dir & Co-Head-Flow Credit Trading-North America)*
Marcelo Pizzimbono *(Mng Dir & Head-Res Sls-Markets Div)*
Andre Silva *(Mng Dir & Co-Head-Dept Capital Markets-Latin America)*
Venkat Badinehal *(Mng Dir)*
David Heaton *(Mng Dir)*
Seth Heaton *(Mng Dir)*
Pam Kiernan *(Mng Dir & Global Head-Bus Dev)*
Ajay Singh *(Mng Dir & Global Head-Listed Derivatives)*

Deutsche Bank Aktiengesellschaft—(Continued)

Subsidiaries:

Sharps Pixley Brokers Incorporated (2)
200 Park Ave Fl 25
New York, NY 10166-2599
Tel.: (212) 351-5780
Fax: (212) 972-6574
Future Commission Merchant
S.I.C.: 6221
N.A.I.C.S.: 523130

Deutsche Bank Americas Finance LLC (1)
60 Wall St Lbby 1
New York, NY 10005-2880
Tel.: (212) 250-2500
Financial Management Services
S.I.C.: 6211
N.A.I.C.S.: 523999

Deutsche Bank Berkshire Mortgage, Inc. (1)
1 Beacon St 14th Fl
Boston, MA 02108
Tel.: (212) 250-2500
Fax: (617) 722-5090
Toll Free: (877) 526-3562
Web Site: www.dbberkshiremortgage.com
Commercial Mortgage Services
S.I.C.: 6163
N.A.I.C.S.: 522310
Alan Reese *(CFO & Exec VP-Corp Ops)*

Deutsche Bank Capital Corporation (1)
60 Wall St
New York, NY 10005-2836 (100%)
Tel.: (212) 250-2500
Web Site: www.db.com
Investment Banking
S.I.C.: 6141
N.A.I.C.S.: 522291

Deutsche Bank Capital Finance Trust I (1)
60 Wall St
New York, NY 10005
Tel.: (212) 250-2500
Investment Management Services
S.I.C.: 6799
N.A.I.C.S.: 523920

Deutsche Bank Capital Funding LLC IV (1)
60 Wall St Lbby 1
New York, NY 10005-2880
Tel.: (212) 250-2500
Investment Banking Services
S.I.C.: 6211
N.A.I.C.S.: 523110

Deutsche Bank Capital Funding LLC IX (1)
60 Wall St Lbby 1
New York, NY 10005
Tel.: (212) 250-8024
Venture Capital Funding Services
S.I.C.: 6799
N.A.I.C.S.: 523910

Deutsche Bank Capital Funding LLC V (1)
60 Wall St Lbby 1
New York, NY 10005-2880
Tel.: (212) 250-2500
Venture Capital Funding Services
S.I.C.: 6799
N.A.I.C.S.: 523910

Deutsche Bank Capital Funding LLC VI (1)
60 Wall St Lbby 1
New York, NY 10005-2880
Tel.: (212) 250-2500
Venture Capital Funding Services
S.I.C.: 6799
N.A.I.C.S.: 523910

Deutsche Bank Capital Funding LLC VII (1)
60 Wall St Lbby 1
New York, NY 10005-2880
Tel.: (212) 250-2500
Venture Capital Funding Services
S.I.C.: 6799
N.A.I.C.S.: 523910

Deutsche Bank Capital Funding LLC X (1)
60 Wall St Frnt 1
New York, NY 10005-2836
Tel.: (212) 250-8024
Venture Capital Funding Services
S.I.C.: 6799
N.A.I.C.S.: 523910

Deutsche Bank Capital Funding LLC XI (1)
60 Wall St Lbby 1
New York, NY 10005-2880
Tel.: (212) 250-2500
Venture Capital Funding Services
S.I.C.: 6799
N.A.I.C.S.: 523910

Deutsche Bank Capital Funding Trust I (1)
60 Wall St
New York, NY 10005
Tel.: (212) 250-8024
Trust Management Services
S.I.C.: 6091
N.A.I.C.S.: 523991

Deutsche Bank Capital Funding Trust IV (1)
60 Wall St
New York, NY 10005
Tel.: (212) 250-8024
Trust Management Services
S.I.C.: 6733
N.A.I.C.S.: 523991

Deutsche Bank Capital Funding Trust IX (1)
60 Wall St
New York, NY 10005
Tel.: (212) 250-8024
Trust Management Services
S.I.C.: 6091
N.A.I.C.S.: 523991

Deutsche Bank Capital Funding Trust V (1)
60 Wall St Frnt 1
New York, NY 10005
Tel.: (212) 250-8024
Trust Management Services
S.I.C.: 6091
N.A.I.C.S.: 523991

Deutsche Bank Capital Funding Trust VI (1)
60 Wall St
New York, NY 10005
Tel.: (212) 250-2428
Financial Management Services
S.I.C.: 6211
N.A.I.C.S.: 523999

Deutsche Bank Capital Funding Trust VII (1)
1011 Centre Rd Ste 200
Wilmington, DE 19805
Tel.: (302) 636-3301
Commercial Banking Services
S.I.C.: 6029
N.A.I.C.S.: 522110

Deutsche Bank Capital Funding Trust X (1)
60 Wall St
New York, NY 10005
Tel.: (212) 250-8024
Trust Management Services
S.I.C.: 6091
N.A.I.C.S.: 523991

Deutsche Bank Capital LLC I (1)
60 Wall St Lbby 1
New York, NY 10005-2880
Tel.: (212) 250-2500
Financial Management Services
S.I.C.: 6211
N.A.I.C.S.: 523999

Deutsche Bank Capital LLC II (1)
60 Wall St Lbby 1
New York, NY 10005-2880
Tel.: (212) 250-2500
Business Management Consulting Services
S.I.C.: 8742
N.A.I.C.S.: 541611

Deutsche Bank Capital LLC III (1)
60 Wall St Lbby 1
New York, NY 10005-2880
Tel.: (212) 250-2500
Business Management Consulting Services
S.I.C.: 8742
N.A.I.C.S.: 541611

Deutsche Bank Capital LLC IV (1)
60 Wall St Lbby 1
New York, NY 10005-2880
Tel.: (212) 250-2500
Investment Banking Services
S.I.C.: 6211
N.A.I.C.S.: 523110

Deutsche Bank Capital LLC V (1)
60 Wall St Lbby 1
New York, NY 10005-2880
Tel.: (212) 250-2500
Business Management Consulting Services
S.I.C.: 8742
N.A.I.C.S.: 541611

Deutsche Bank Capital Trust I (1)
60 Wall St
New York, NY 10005
Tel.: (212) 250-2500
Trust Management Services
S.I.C.: 6091
N.A.I.C.S.: 523991

Deutsche Bank Capital Trust II (1)
31 W 52nd St
New York, NY 10019
Tel.: (212) 474-7000
Trust Management Services
S.I.C.: 6733
N.A.I.C.S.: 523991

Deutsche Bank Capital Trust III (1)
60 Wall St
New York, NY 10005
Tel.: (212) 250-2500
Trust Management Services
S.I.C.: 6099
N.A.I.C.S.: 523991

Deutsche Bank Capital Trust IV (1)
60 Wall St
New York, NY 10005
Tel.: (212) 250-2500
Trust Management Services
S.I.C.: 6091
N.A.I.C.S.: 523991

Deutsche Bank Contingent Capital Trust I (1)
60 Wall St
New York, NY 10005
Tel.: (212) 250-8024
Trust Management Services
S.I.C.: 6091
N.A.I.C.S.: 523991

Deutsche Bank Contingent Capital Trust II (1)
60 Wall St
New York, NY 10005
Tel.: (212) 250-8024
Trust Management Services
S.I.C.: 6733
N.A.I.C.S.: 523991

Deutsche Bank Contingent Capital Trust III (1)
60 Wall St
New York, NY 10005
Tel.: (212) 250-8024
Trust Management Services
S.I.C.: 6733
N.A.I.C.S.: 523991

Deutsche Bank Government Securities, Inc. (1)
60 Wall St
New York, NY 10005-2858
Tel.: (212) 250-2500
Web Site: www.db.com
Government Bond Trading
S.I.C.: 6211
N.A.I.C.S.: 523120

Deutsche Bank Holdings, Inc. (1)
1011 Centre Rd Ste 200
Wilmington, DE 19805-1266
Tel.: (302) 636-3299
Investment Management Services
S.I.C.: 6282
N.A.I.C.S.: 523920

Deutsche Bank Insurance Agency of Delaware, Inc. (1)
1011 Centre Rd Ste 200
Wilmington, DE 19805
Tel.: (302) 636-3300
General Insurance Services
S.I.C.: 6411
N.A.I.C.S.: 524210

Deutsche Bank International (1)
1 Biscayne Tower Ste 1820 2 S Biscayne Blvd
Miami, FL 33131-1806 FL
Tel.: (305) 577-6600 (100%)
Fax: (305) 329-2211
Web Site: www.db.com
Sales Range: $10-24.9 Million
Emp.: 30
Foreign Trade & International Banks
S.I.C.: 6159
N.A.I.C.S.: 522298

Deutsche Bank Realty Advisors, Inc. (1)
1168 Wantagh Ave
Wantagh, NY 11793
Tel.: (516) 826-1111
Real Estate Advisory Services
S.I.C.: 6531
N.A.I.C.S.: 531390

Deutsche Bank Securities Inc. (1)
60 Wall St
New York, NY 10005
Tel.: (212) 250-2500
Fax: (212) 797-8718
Web Site: www.db.com
Emp.: 800
Financial Services
S.I.C.: 6211
N.A.I.C.S.: 523999
Andrew Safran *(Vice Chm & Mng Dir-Natural Resources Coverage Grp)*
Derek Davies *(Mng Dir & Head-Commodities-Canada)*
Greg Sommer *(Mng Dir-Mergers & Acq Grp & Head-Energy Mergers & Acq-Americas)*
William Curley *(Mng Dir-Global Banking Div)*
Michael Linenberg *(Mng Dir-Global Markets Div)*
Anthony Viscardi *(Mng Dir-Global Banking Div)*
Kevin Harrison *(Mng Dir & Head-Financing)*
Jose Marques *(Mng Dir & Head-Equity Electronic Trading-Global Market Div)*
Douglas Runte *(Mng Dir & Head-Aviation Debt Res-Markets Div)*
Jonathan Arnold *(Mng Dir)*

Division:

Deutsche Bank Alex. Brown Incorporated (2)
1 S St 28th Fl
Baltimore, MD 21202
Tel.: (410) 727-1700
Fax: (410) 895-3950
Toll Free: (800) 638-2596
Web Site: www.alexbrown.db.com
Private Client Financial Services
S.I.C.: 6211
N.A.I.C.S.: 523999
Fred Crozier *(CEO)*
Karl Hahn *(Mng Dir & Client Adviser-Boston)*

Deutsche Bank Trust Company Delaware (1)
1011 Centre Rd Ste 200
Wilmington, DE 19805
Tel.: (302) 636-3354
Fax: (302) 636-3333
Commercial Banking Services
S.I.C.: 6029
N.A.I.C.S.: 522110
Rae Perry *(Asst VP)*

Deutsche Bank Trust Company, National Association (1)
280 Park Ave
New York, NY 10017
Tel.: (212) 454-3600
Trust Management Services
S.I.C.: 6091
N.A.I.C.S.: 523991

Deutsche Bank Trust Company New Jersey Ltd. (1)
100 Plaza One
Jersey City, NJ 07311
Tel.: (212) 602-1764
Fax: (212) 797-0868

Trust Management Services
S.I.C.: 6733
N.A.I.C.S.: 523991

Deutsche Bank Trust Corporation (1)
60 Wall St 40th Fl
New York, NY 10005-2836
Tel.: (212) 250-2500
Trust Management Services
S.I.C.: 6099
N.A.I.C.S.: 523991

Deutsche Bank (1)
2000 Ave of The Stars Fl 9
Los Angeles, CA 90067 CA
Tel.: (213) 620-8200
Fax: (310) 788-6222
Web Site: www.db.com
Emp.: 100
National Consumer Cooperative Bank
S.I.C.: 6029
N.A.I.C.S.: 522110

Deutsche Climate Change Fixed Income QP Trust (1)
11 Northeastern Blvd
Salem, NH 03079
Tel.: (212) 250-7228
Fund Management Services
S.I.C.: 6799
N.A.I.C.S.: 523920

Deutsche Fund Management Inc. (1)
60 Wall St
New York, NY 10005 NY
Tel.: (212) 250-2500
Web Site: www.db.com
Sales of Mutual Funds by Independent Salespersons
S.I.C.: 6211
N.A.I.C.S.: 523110

Deutsche Mortgage Securities, Inc. (1)
60 Wall St Lbby 1
New York, NY 10005-2880
Tel.: (212) 250-2500
Securities Brokerage Services
S.I.C.: 6211
N.A.I.C.S.: 523120

DFC Residual Corp. (1)
101 Convention Ctr Dr
Las Vegas, NV 89109-2001
Tel.: (702) 380-4928
Investment Banking Services
S.I.C.: 6211
N.A.I.C.S.: 523110

DWS Investments Distributors, Inc. (1)
222 S Riverside Plz
Chicago, IL 60606-5808 DE
Tel.: (212) 454-6778
Web Site: www.dws-investments.com
Emp.: 500
Investment Management Services
S.I.C.: 6211
N.A.I.C.S.: 523120
Greg Kiesel *(Mng Dir & Head-Equity Sls)*
Brian Binder *(Pres-Fund)*

Non-U.S. Subsidiaries:

DWS (Austria) Investmentgesellschaft mbH (2)
Hohenstaufengasse 4 5 11
1010 Vienna, Austria
Tel.: (43) 1531810
Fax: (43) 153181114
Emp.: 100
Investment Management Services
S.I.C.: 6211
N.A.I.C.S.: 523120
Rainer Polster *(Gen Mgr)*

DWS Investment GmbH (2)
Mainzer Landstr 178-190
60327 Frankfurt am Main, Germany
Tel.: (49) 180310111011
Investment Management Services
S.I.C.: 6211
N.A.I.C.S.: 523120

DWS Investment S.A. Luxembourg (2)
2 Blvd Konrad Adenauer
2017 Luxembourg, Luxembourg (100%)
Mailing Address:
Boite Postale 1733
1017 Luxembourg, Luxembourg
Tel.: (352) 421011
Fax: (352) 42101900
E-Mail: dws.lu@db.com
Web Site: www.dws.de
Emp.: 130
Investment Banking Services
S.I.C.: 6799
N.A.I.C.S.: 523910
Doris Marx *(Mng Dir)*

DWS Investments S.G.I.I.C. (2)
Paseo de la Castellana 18
28046 Madrid, Spain
Tel.: (34) 913351179
Fax: (34) 913351124
E-Mail: dw.es@db.com
Web Site: www.dws.com
Emp.: 40
Investment Management Services
S.I.C.: 6211
N.A.I.C.S.: 523120
Pedro Danobeitia *(Mgr)*

DWS Polska TFI S.A. (2)
Budynek FOCUS 10 pitro
Armii Ludowej 26, 00 609 Warsaw, Poland
Tel.: (48) 22 5 79 97 00
Investment Management Services
S.I.C.: 6211
N.A.I.C.S.: 523120

DWS Schweiz GmbH (2)
Uraniastrasse 9
8021 Zurich, Switzerland
Tel.: (41) 442247700
Fax: (41) 2247800
Web Site: www.dws.com
Emp.: 15
Investment Management Services
S.I.C.: 6211
N.A.I.C.S.: 523120
Harald Reczek *(Mng Dir)*

DWS Investments Service Company (1)
210 W 10th St
Kansas City, MO 64105-1614
Tel.: (800) 621-1148
Investment Management Services
S.I.C.: 6799
N.A.I.C.S.: 523920

ECT Holdings Corp. (1)
1011 Centre Rd
Wilmington, DE 19805
Tel.: (302) 636-3290
Investment Management Services
S.I.C.: 6799
N.A.I.C.S.: 523920

Enterprise Fleet Management Exchange, Inc. (1)
600 Corporate Park Dr
Saint Louis, MO 63105-4204
Tel.: (314) 512-5000
Fax: (314) 512-5930
Financial Management Services
S.I.C.: 6211
N.A.I.C.S.: 523999

GAFCo Funding Corp. (1)
Corporation Trust Center 1209 Orange St
Wilmington, DE 19801
Tel.: (302) 658-7581
Financial Management Services
S.I.C.: 6211
N.A.I.C.S.: 523999

GWC-GAC Corp. (1)
Corporation Trust Center 1209 Orange St
Wilmington, DE 19801
Tel.: (302) 658-7581
Investment Management Services
S.I.C.: 6282
N.A.I.C.S.: 523920

Kingfisher Canada Holdings LLC (1)
2711 Centerville Rd Ste 400
Wilmington, DE 19808
Tel.: (302) 636-5401
Investment Management Services
S.I.C.: 6282
N.A.I.C.S.: 523920

Mayfair Center, Inc. (1)
100 Baldwin Rd
Hempstead, NY 11550
Tel.: (516) 538-7171
Commercial Banking Services
S.I.C.: 6029
N.A.I.C.S.: 522110

Nevada Property 1 LLC (1)
3708 Las Vegas Blvd S
Las Vegas, NV 89109
Tel.: (702) 698-7000
Rev.: $595,171,000
Assets: $3,320,932,000
Liabilities: $3,651,273,000
Net Worth: ($330,341,000)
Earnings: ($106,571,000)
Emp.: 4,300
Fiscal Year-end: 12/31/12
Resort Management Services
S.I.C.: 7011
N.A.I.C.S.: 721120

Newport Harbor Corporation (1)
366 Thames St
Newport, RI 02840
Tel.: (401) 848-7010
Fax: (401) 847-0560
Web Site: www.newportharbor.com
Hotel Management Services
S.I.C.: 7011
N.A.I.C.S.: 721110
Paul O'Reilly *(Pres)*

Northern Pines Funding, LLC (1)
48 Wall St
New York, NY 10005
Tel.: (212) 346-9008
Financial Planning Services
S.I.C.: 6282
N.A.I.C.S.: 523930

PARTS Student Loan Trust 2007-CT1 (1)
1011 Centre Rd Ste 200
Wilmington, DE 19805
Tel.: (302) 636-3390
Trust Management Services
S.I.C.: 6091
N.A.I.C.S.: 523991

RoCalwest, Inc. (1)
60 Wall St Lbby 1
New York, NY 10005
Tel.: (212) 250-2500
Business Management Consulting Services
S.I.C.: 8742
N.A.I.C.S.: 541611

Stoneridge Apartments, Inc. (1)
930 N Maple Grove Rd
Boise, ID 83704
Tel.: (208) 375-3800
Residential & Commercial Building Leasing Services
S.I.C.: 6512
N.A.I.C.S.: 531120

Structured Finance Americas, LLC (1)
60 Wall St 4th Fl
New York, NY 10005
Tel.: (212) 250-6340
Fax: (212) 797-9358
Financial Planning Services
S.I.C.: 6282
N.A.I.C.S.: 523930

TQI Exchange, LLC (1)
2711 Centerville Rd Ste 400
Wilmington, DE 19808
Tel.: (302) 636-5401
Investment Management Services
S.I.C.: 6282
N.A.I.C.S.: 523920

TRS 1 LLC (1)
60 Wall St Lbby 1
New York, NY 10005
Tel.: (212) 250-2500
Commercial Banking Services
S.I.C.: 6029
N.A.I.C.S.: 522110

TRS Babson I LLC (1)
60 Wall St Lbby 1
New York, NY 10005
Tel.: (212) 250-2500
Commercial Banking Services
S.I.C.: 6029
N.A.I.C.S.: 522110

TRS Bruin LLC (1)
1209 Orange St
Wilmington, DE 19801
Tel.: (302) 658-7581
Commercial Banking Services
S.I.C.: 6029
N.A.I.C.S.: 522110

TRS Camulos LLC (1)
60 Wall St Lbby 1
New York, NY 10005
Tel.: (212) 250-2500
Commercial Banking Services
S.I.C.: 6029
N.A.I.C.S.: 522110

TRS Cypress LLC (1)
60 Wall St Lbby 1
New York, NY 10005
Tel.: (212) 250-2500
Commercial Banking Services
S.I.C.: 6029
N.A.I.C.S.: 522110

TRS DB OH CC Fund Financing LLC (1)
60 Wall St Lbby 1
New York, NY 10005
Tel.: (212) 250-2500
Commercial Banking Services
S.I.C.: 6029
N.A.I.C.S.: 522110

TRS Eclipse LLC (1)
60 Wall St Lbby 1
New York, NY 10005
Tel.: (212) 250-2500
Commercial Banking Services
S.I.C.: 6029
N.A.I.C.S.: 522110

TRS Elgin LLC (1)
60 Wall St Lbby 1
New York, NY 10005
Tel.: (212) 250-2500
Commercial Banking Services
S.I.C.: 6029
N.A.I.C.S.: 522110

TRS Elm LLC (1)
60 Wall St Lbby 1
New York, NY 10005
Tel.: (212) 250-2500
Business Management Consulting Services
S.I.C.: 8742
N.A.I.C.S.: 541611

TRS Fore LLC (1)
60 Wall St Lbby 1
New York, NY 10005
Tel.: (212) 250-2500
Business Management Consulting Services
S.I.C.: 8742
N.A.I.C.S.: 541611

TRS GSC Credit Strategies LLC (1)
60 Wall St Lbby 1
New York, NY 10005
Tel.: (212) 250-2500
Business Management Consulting Services
S.I.C.: 8742
N.A.I.C.S.: 541611

TRS Haka LLC (1)
60 Wall St Lbby 1
New York, NY 10005
Tel.: (212) 250-2500
Business Management Consulting Services
S.I.C.: 8742
N.A.I.C.S.: 541611

TRS HY FNDS LLC (1)
60 Wall St Lbby 1
New York, NY 10005
Tel.: (212) 250-2500
Business Management Consulting Services
S.I.C.: 8742
N.A.I.C.S.: 541611

TRS Landsbanki Islands LLC (1)
60 Wall St Lbby 1
New York, NY 10005
Tel.: (212) 250-2500
Business Management Consulting Services
S.I.C.: 8742
N.A.I.C.S.: 541611

TRS Metis LLC (1)
60 Wall St Fl 40
New York, NY 10005
Tel.: (212) 250-7125
Business Management Consulting Services
S.I.C.: 8742
N.A.I.C.S.: 541611

Deutsche Bank Aktiengesellschaft—(Continued)

TRS Plainfield LLC (1)
60 Wall St Fl 40
New York, NY 10005
Tel.: (212) 250-7125
Business Management Consulting Services
S.I.C.: 8742
N.A.I.C.S.: 541611

TRS Poplar LLC (1)
60 Wall St Fl 40
New York, NY 10005
Tel.: (212) 250-7125
Business Management Consulting Services
S.I.C.: 8742
N.A.I.C.S.: 541611

TRS Quogue LLC (1)
60 Wall St Fl 40
New York, NY 10005
Tel.: (212) 250-7125
Business Management Consulting Services
S.I.C.: 8742
N.A.I.C.S.: 541611

TRS Scorpio LLC (1)
60 Wall St Fl 40
New York, NY 10005
Tel.: (212) 250-7125
Business Management Consulting Services
S.I.C.: 8742
N.A.I.C.S.: 541611

TRS Stag LLC (1)
60 Wall St Fl 40
New York, NY 10005
Tel.: (212) 250-7125
Business Management Consulting Services
S.I.C.: 8742
N.A.I.C.S.: 541611

TRS Stark LLC (1)
60 Wall St Fl 40
New York, NY 10005
Tel.: (212) 250-7125
Business Management Consulting Services
S.I.C.: 8742
N.A.I.C.S.: 541611

TRS SVCO LLC (1)
60 Wall St Fl 40
New York, NY 10005
Tel.: (212) 250-7125
Business Management Consulting Services
S.I.C.: 8742
N.A.I.C.S.: 541611

TRS Sycamore LLC (1)
60 Wall St Fl 40
New York, NY 10005
Tel.: (212) 250-7125
Business Management Consulting Services
S.I.C.: 8742
N.A.I.C.S.: 541611

TRS Tupelo LLC (1)
60 Wall St Lbby 1
New York, NY 10005
Tel.: (212) 250-2500
Business Management Consulting Services
S.I.C.: 8742
N.A.I.C.S.: 541611

TRS Venor LLC (1)
60 Wall St Lbby 1
New York, NY 10005
Tel.: (212) 250-2500
Business Management Consulting Services
S.I.C.: 8742
N.A.I.C.S.: 541611

TRS Watermill LLC (1)
60 Wall St Lbby 1
New York, NY 10005
Tel.: (212) 250-2500
Business Management Consulting Services
S.I.C.: 8742
N.A.I.C.S.: 541611

Village Hospitality LLC (1)
1610 Lake Las Vegas Pkwy
Henderson, NV 89011
Tel.: (702) 567-4700
Sales Range: $1-9.9 Million
Emp.: 50
Hotel Management Services
S.I.C.: 7011
N.A.I.C.S.: 721110
Anna Lam *(Principal)*

Whispering Woods LLC (1)
120 Garden Dr Ofc A
Martinsburg, WV 25404-7530
Tel.: (301) 365-9314
Residential Building Leasing Services
S.I.C.: 6513
N.A.I.C.S.: 531110

World Trading (Delaware) Inc. (1)
1011 Centre Rd Ste 200
Wilmington, DE 19805
Tel.: (302) 636-3290
Investment Advisory Services
S.I.C.: 6282
N.A.I.C.S.: 523930

Young America Corporation (1)
18671 Lake Dr E
Chanhassen, MN 55317 MN
Tel.: (952) 693-4800
Fax: (952) 294-8497
Toll Free: (800) 533-4529
E-Mail: infoya@young-america.com
Web Site: www.young-america.com
Sales Range: $75-99.9 Million
Emp.: 1,500
Business Services
S.I.C.: 7389
N.A.I.C.S.: 561990
Joe Custer *(Pres)*
Patrick Feit *(Sr VP-Sls)*

Non-U.S. Subsidiaries:

3160343 Canada Inc. (1)
199 Bay Street Suite 4700
Box 263
Commerce Court West, Toronto, ON, Canada
Tel.: (416) 682-8000
Investment Management Services
S.I.C.: 6282
N.A.I.C.S.: 523920

Abbey Life Trustee Services Limited (1)
100 Holdenhurst Road
Bournemouth, BH8 8ZQ, United Kingdom
Tel.: (44) 1202 550440
Life Insurance Services
S.I.C.: 6311
N.A.I.C.S.: 524113

Antelope Pension Trustee Services Limited (1)
1 Great Winchester Street
London, EC2N 2DB, United Kingdom
Tel.: (44) 845 600 5405
Business Management Consulting Services
S.I.C.: 8742
N.A.I.C.S.: 541611

Aqueduct Capital S.a r.l. (1)
Boulevard Konrad
1115 Luxembourg, Luxembourg
Tel.: (352) 42122 1
Investment Management Services
S.I.C.: 6799
N.A.I.C.S.: 523920

Arche Investments Limited (1)
8 Salisbury Square
London, EC4Y 8BB, United Kingdom
Tel.: (44) 207 54 58000
Investment Management Services
S.I.C.: 6282
N.A.I.C.S.: 523920

Asian Hybrid Investments LLP (1)
1 Raffles Quay
Singapore, Singapore
Tel.: (65) 6538 7011
Investment Management Services
S.I.C.: 6282
N.A.I.C.S.: 523920

Autumn Leasing Limited (1)
1 Great Winchester Street
London, EC2N 2DB, United Kingdom
Tel.: (44) 207 54 58000
Financial Leasing Services
S.I.C.: 6211
N.A.I.C.S.: 523999

Baincor Nominees Pty. Limited (1)
L 18 Grosvenor Place
Sydney, NSW, 2000, Australia
Tel.: (61) 2 8258 1974
Investment Management Services
S.I.C.: 6282
N.A.I.C.S.: 523920

Bainsec Nominees Pty. Limited (1)
Level 19 225 George St
Sydney, NSW, 2000, Australia
Tel.: (61) 292581234
Investment Management Services
S.I.C.: 6282
N.A.I.C.S.: 523920

Bankers International Corporation (Brasil) Ltda. (1)
Av Brg Faria Lima 3900
Sao Paulo, 04538-133, Brazil
Tel.: (55) 11 2113 5000
Commercial Banking Services
S.I.C.: 6029
N.A.I.C.S.: 522110

Bankers Trust Investments Limited (1)
1 Appold Street
London, EC2A 2AA, United Kingdom
Tel.: (44) 207 54 58000
Investment Management Services
S.I.C.: 6799
N.A.I.C.S.: 523920

Bankers Trust Nominees Limited (1)
1 Great Winchester Street
London, EC2N 2DB, United Kingdom
Tel.: (44) 207 54 58000
Fax: (44) 207 54 56155
Investment Management Services
S.I.C.: 6799
N.A.I.C.S.: 523920

Barkly Investments Ltd. (1)
St Paul's Gate New Street
JE4 8ZB Saint Helier, Jersey
Tel.: (44) 1534 889 900
Investment Management Services
S.I.C.: 6799
N.A.I.C.S.: 523920

Bebek Varlik Yonetym A.S. (1)
Eski Buyukdere Cad Tekfen Tower No 209
Kat 17-18-3 Podium
34394 Istanbul, Turkey
Tel.: (90) 212 317 01 00
Real Estate Development Services
S.I.C.: 6531
N.A.I.C.S.: 531390

Beta DB Lindsell Limited S.C.S. (1)
Boulevard Konrad Adenauer 2
Luxembourg, Luxembourg
Tel.: (352) 42122 1
Investment Management Services
S.I.C.: 6282
N.A.I.C.S.: 523920

Biomass Holdings S.a r.l. (1)
Boulevard Konrad Adenauer 2
Luxembourg, Luxembourg
Tel.: (352) 42122 1
Fax: (352) 42122 346
Investment Management Services
S.I.C.: 6282
N.A.I.C.S.: 523920

BNA Nominees Pty. Limited (1)
L 18 Grosvenor Place
Sydney, NSW, 2000, Australia
Tel.: (61) 2 8258 1974
Investment Management Services
S.I.C.: 6282
N.A.I.C.S.: 523920

Bonsai Investment AG (1)
Oberstadtstrasse 4
8500 Frauenfeld, Switzerland
Tel.: (41) 52 730 18 80
Fax: (41) 52 730 18 88
Fund Management Services
S.I.C.: 6799
N.A.I.C.S.: 523920

BRIMCO, S. de R.L. de C.V. (1)
Tampico No 42 Int 3
Mexico, 06700, Mexico
Tel.: (52) 5513278730
Financial Management Services
S.I.C.: 6211
N.A.I.C.S.: 523999

Britannia Limited (1)
Regis House 45 King William Street
London, EC4R 9AN, United Kingdom
Tel.: (44) 20 7407 3588
Fax: (44) 20 7403 3942
Financial Management Services
S.I.C.: 6211
N.A.I.C.S.: 523999

BT Globenet Nominees Limited (1)
1 Appold St
London, EC2A 2AA, United Kingdom
Tel.: (44) 207 54 58000
Fax: (44) 207 54 56155
Financial Management Services
S.I.C.: 6211
N.A.I.C.S.: 523999

B.T. Vordertaunus (Luxembourg), S.a r.l. (1)
67 Haaptstrooss
9806 Hosingen, Luxembourg
Tel.: (352) 92 341 6
Fax: (352) 26 910 809
Investment Management Services
S.I.C.: 6282
N.A.I.C.S.: 523920

BTD Nominees Pty. Limited (1)
L 18 Grosvenor Place
Sydney, NSW, Australia
Tel.: (61) 2 8258 1974
Investment Management Services
S.I.C.: 6799
N.A.I.C.S.: 523920

BTFIC - Portugal, Gestao e Investimentos (Sociedade Unipessoal) S.A. (1)
Rua dos Murcas 88 - 3
9000-058 Funchal, Portugal
Tel.: (351) 291215700
Investment Management Services
S.I.C.: 6282
N.A.I.C.S.: 523920

B.T.I. Investments INC. (1)
Winchester House 1 Great Winchester Street
London, EC2N 2DB, United Kingdom
Tel.: (44) 2075456000
Investment Management Services
S.I.C.: 6282
N.A.I.C.S.: 523920

B.V. Matura Handelmaatschappij (1)
Herengracht 450
1017 CA Amsterdam, Netherlands
Tel.: (31) 205554911
Investment Management Services
S.I.C.: 6799
N.A.I.C.S.: 523920

Cardales UK Limited (1)
1 Great Winchester Street
London, EC2N 2DB, United Kingdom
Tel.: (44) 207 54 58000
Fax: (44) 207 54 56155
Real Estate Advisory Services
S.I.C.: 6531
N.A.I.C.S.: 531390

Cashforce International Credit Support B.V. (1)
Lichtenauerlaan 142
Rotterdam, 3062 ME, Netherlands
Tel.: (31) 10 2535557
E-Mail: info@cashforce.nl
Financial Management Services
S.I.C.: 6211
N.A.I.C.S.: 523999

Cathay Asset Management Company Limited (1)
Court Twentyeight Cybercity
Port Louis, Mauritius
Tel.: (230) 212 9800
Financial Management Services
S.I.C.: 6211
N.A.I.C.S.: 523999

Cathay Capital Company (No 2) Limited (1)
29 Sir William Newton
Port Louis, Mauritius
Tel.: (230) 212 8585
Financial Investment Services
S.I.C.: 6211
N.A.I.C.S.: 523999

City Leasing and Partners Limited (1)
23 Great Winchester Street
London, EC2P 2AX, United Kingdom
Tel.: (44) 207 54 58000

Fax: (44) 207 54 56155
Financial Leasing Services
S.I.C.: 6211
N.A.I.C.S.: 523999

City Leasing (Donside) Limited (1)
23 Great Winchester Street
London, EC2P 2AX, United Kingdom
Tel.: (44) 207 54 58000
Fax: (44) 207 54 56155
Financial Leasing Services
S.I.C.: 6211
N.A.I.C.S.: 523999

City Leasing Limited (1)
23 Great Winchester Street
London, EC2P 2AX, United Kingdom
Tel.: (44) 20 7545 8000
Fax: (44) 20 7545 7130
Financial Leasing Services
S.I.C.: 6211
N.A.I.C.S.: 523999

City Leasing (Thameside) Limited (1)
23 Great Winchester Street
London, EC2P 2AX, United Kingdom
Tel.: (44) 207 54 58000
Fax: (44) 207 54 56155
Financial Leasing Services
S.I.C.: 6211
N.A.I.C.S.: 523999

City Leasing (Wearside) Limited (1)
23 Great Winchester Street
London, EC2P 2AX, United Kingdom
Tel.: (44) 20 7545 8000
Financial Leasing Services
S.I.C.: 6211
N.A.I.C.S.: 523999

Custom Leasing Limited (1)
23 Grt Winchester Street
London, EC2N 2DB, United Kingdom
Tel.: (44) 207 5458000
Financial Leasing Services
S.I.C.: 6211
N.A.I.C.S.: 523999

D B Rail Holdings (UK) No. 1 Limited (1)
1 Great Winchester Street
London, EC2N 2DB, United Kingdom
Tel.: (44) 207 54 58000
Fax: (44) 207 54 56155
Investment Management Services
S.I.C.: 6282
N.A.I.C.S.: 523920

DAHOC (UK) Limited (1)
1 Great Winchester Street
London, EC2N 2DB, United Kingdom
Tel.: (44) 207 54 58000
Fax: (44) 207 54 56155
Commercial Banking Services
S.I.C.: 6029
N.A.I.C.S.: 522110

DB Advisors SICAV (1)
Rue de Bitbourg 2
Luxembourg, Luxembourg
Tel.: (352) 273321
Financial Advisory Services
S.I.C.: 6282
N.A.I.C.S.: 523930

DB Akela, S.a r.l. (1)
2 boulevard Konrad Adenauer
Luxembourg, 1115, Luxembourg
Tel.: (352) 42122 1
Fax: (352) 42122 346
Commercial Banking Services
S.I.C.: 6029
N.A.I.C.S.: 522110

DB Alternative Strategies Limited (1)
Boundary Hall Cricket Sq 171 Elgin Ave
PO Box 1984
KY1-1104 Georgetown, Grand Cayman, Cayman Islands
Tel.: (345) 949 8244
Fax: (345) 946 3733
Financial Management Services
S.I.C.: 6211
N.A.I.C.S.: 523999

DB Aotearoa Investments Limited (1)
Elizabethan Square
Georgetown, Grand Cayman, Cayman Islands
Tel.: (345) 949 8244
Fax: (345) 949 8178
Investment Management Services
S.I.C.: 6799
N.A.I.C.S.: 523920

DB Bagheera, S.a r.l. (1)
2 Boulevard Konrad Adenauer
1115 Luxembourg, Luxembourg
Tel.: (352) 42122 1
Financial Management Services
S.I.C.: 6211
N.A.I.C.S.: 523999

DB Bluebell Investments (Cayman) Partnership (1)
171 Elgin Avenue
Georgetown, Grand Cayman, Cayman Islands
Tel.: (345) 949 8244
Commercial Banking Services
S.I.C.: 6029
N.A.I.C.S.: 522110

DB Capital Partners General Partner Limited (1)
1 Great Winchester Street
London, EC2N 2DB, United Kingdom
Tel.: (44) 207 54 58000
Fax: (44) 207 54 56155
Financial Management Services
S.I.C.: 6211
N.A.I.C.S.: 523999

DB Chestnut Holdings Limited (1)
171 Elgin Avenue
KY1-1104 Georgetown, Grand Cayman, Cayman Islands
Tel.: (345) 949 8244
Fax: (345) 949 8178
Investment Management Services
S.I.C.: 6282
N.A.I.C.S.: 523920

DB Commodities Canada Ltd. (1)
199 Bay St Suite 4700
Toronto, ON, M5L 1E9, Canada
Tel.: (416) 682-8422
Financial Management Services
S.I.C.: 6211
N.A.I.C.S.: 523999

DB Concerto Limited (1)
171 Elgin Avenue
KY1-1104 Georgetown, Grand Cayman, Cayman Islands
Tel.: (345) 949 8244
Investment Management Services
S.I.C.: 6282
N.A.I.C.S.: 523920

DB Consorzio S. Cons. a r. l. (1)
Piazza Del Calendario 3
Milan, 20126, Italy
Tel.: (39) 024 0241
Financial Management Services
S.I.C.: 6211
N.A.I.C.S.: 523999

DB Crest Limited (1)
St Paul's Gate New Street
JE4 8ZB Saint Helier, Jersey
Tel.: (44) 1534 889 900
Fax: (44) 1534 889 911
Financial Management Services
S.I.C.: 6211
N.A.I.C.S.: 523999

DB Delaware Holdings (UK) Limited (1)
Winchester House
London, EC2N 2DB, United Kingdom
Tel.: (44) 20 7545 8000
Investment Management Services
S.I.C.: 6799
N.A.I.C.S.: 523920

DB Energy Commodities Limited (1)
1 Great Winchester Street
London, EC2N 2DB, United Kingdom
Tel.: (44) 207 54 58000
Fax: (44) 207 54 56155
Electrical License Reissuance Services
S.I.C.: 7389
N.A.I.C.S.: 561990

DB Enfield Infrastructure Holdings Limited (1)
St Paul's Gate New Street
PO Box 272
Saint Helier, JE4 8WQ, Jersey
Tel.: (44) 1534 889 900
Fax: (44) 1534 889 911
Investment Management Services
S.I.C.: 6282
N.A.I.C.S.: 523920

DB Enfield Infrastructure Investments Limited (1)
St Paul's Gate New Street
PO Box 727
Saint Helier, JE4 8ZB, Jersey
Tel.: (44) 1534 889 900
Fax: (44) 1534 889 911
Investment Management Services
S.I.C.: 6282
N.A.I.C.S.: 523920

DB Equity Limited (1)
Winchester House 1 Great Winchester Street
London, EC2N 2DB, United Kingdom
Tel.: (44) 207 54 58000
Fax: (44) 207 54 56155
Commercial Banking Services
S.I.C.: 6029
N.A.I.C.S.: 522110

DB Equity S.a r.l. (1)
6 Avenue Pasteur
2310 Luxembourg, Luxembourg
Tel.: (352) 26 20 27 80
Commercial Banking Services
S.I.C.: 6029
N.A.I.C.S.: 522110

DB Group Services (UK) Limited (1)
Winchester House 1 Great Winchester Street
EC2N 2DB London, United Kingdom
Tel.: (44) 2075 45 80 00
Emp.: 1,000
Commercial Banking Services
S.I.C.: 6029
N.A.I.C.S.: 522110

DB iCON Investments Limited (1)
1 Great Winchester Street
London, EC2N 2DB, United Kingdom
Tel.: (44) 207 54 58000
Fax: (44) 207 54 56155
Investment Management Services
S.I.C.: 6799
N.A.I.C.S.: 523920

DB Impact Investment (GP) Limited (1)
1 Great Winchester Street
EC2N 2DB London, United Kingdom
Tel.: (44) 207 54 58000
Fax: (44) 207 54 56155
Investment Management Services
S.I.C.: 6211
N.A.I.C.S.: 523999

DB Infrastructure Holdings (UK) No.1 Limited (1)
1 Great Winchester Street
London, EC2N 2DB, United Kingdom
Tel.: (44) 207 54 58000
Fax: (44) 207 54 58000
Investment Management Services
S.I.C.: 6799
N.A.I.C.S.: 523920

DB Infrastructure Holdings (UK) No.2 Limited (1)
1 Great Winchester Street
London, EC2N 2DB, United Kingdom
Tel.: (44) 207 54 58000
Fax: (44) 207 54 56155
Investment Management Services
S.I.C.: 6282
N.A.I.C.S.: 523920

DB International Investments Limited (1)
23 Great Winchester Street
London, EC2P 2AX, United Kingdom
Tel.: (44) 207 54 58000
Fax: (44) 207 54 56155
Investment Management Services
S.I.C.: 6282
N.A.I.C.S.: 523920

DB Investments (GB) Limited (1)
6 Bishopsgate
London, EC2P 2AT, United Kingdom
Tel.: (44) 2075458000
Commercial Banking Services
S.I.C.: 6029
N.A.I.C.S.: 522110

DB Jasmine Holdings Limited (1)
1 Great Winchester Street
London, EC2N 2DB, United Kingdom
Tel.: (44) 207 54 58000
Fax: (44) 207 54 56155
Investment Management Services
S.I.C.: 6799
N.A.I.C.S.: 523920

DB Nexus American Investments (UK) Limited (1)
Winchester House 1 Great Winchester Street
London, EC2N 2DB, United Kingdom
Tel.: (44) 2075456000
Investment Management Services
S.I.C.: 6282
N.A.I.C.S.: 523920

DB Nexus Investments (UK) Limited (1)
1 Great Winchester Street
London, EC2N 2DB, United Kingdom
Tel.: (44) 207 54 58000
Fax: (44) 207 54 56155
Investment Management Services
S.I.C.: 6282
N.A.I.C.S.: 523920

DB Overseas Holdings Limited (1)
1 Great Winchester Street
London, EC2N 2DB, United Kingdom
Tel.: (44) 207 54 58000
Fax: (44) 207 54 56155
Investment Management Services
S.I.C.: 6282
N.A.I.C.S.: 523920

DB Platinum Advisors S.A. (1)
Boulevard Konrad Adenauer 2
1115 Luxembourg, Luxembourg
Tel.: (352) 42122 1
Fax: (352) 42122 346
Investment Management Services
S.I.C.: 6799
N.A.I.C.S.: 523920

DB Rail Trading (UK) Limited (1)
1 Great Winchester Street
London, EC2N 2DB, United Kingdom
Tel.: (44) 207 54 58000
Fax: (44) 207 54 56155
Investment Management Services
S.I.C.: 6799
N.A.I.C.S.: 523920

DB Safe Harbour Investment Projects Limited (1)
1 Great Winchester Street
London, EC2N 2DB, United Kingdom
Tel.: (44) 2075456000
Investment Management Services
S.I.C.: 6282
N.A.I.C.S.: 523920

DB Securities S.A. (1)
Al Armii Ludowej 26
00-609 Warsaw, Poland
Tel.: (48) 22 579 87 00
Fax: (48) 22 579 87 01
E-Mail: dbsecurities@db.com
Web Site: www.dbsecurities.pl
Emp.: 30
Securities Brokerage Services
S.I.C.: 6211
N.A.I.C.S.: 523120
Waldemar Markiewicz *(CEO)*

DB Service Centre Limited (1)
Block D Abbey Ct Irish Life Centre Abbey Street
Dublin, Ireland
Tel.: (353) 18051000
Fax: (353) 18051107
Credit Intermediation Services
S.I.C.: 6159
N.A.I.C.S.: 522298

DB Servicios Mexico, S.A. de C.V. (1)
Bvd Manuel Avila Camacho No 40 Lomas de Chapultepec Piso 17
Miguel Hidalgo, Mexico, 11000, Mexico
Tel.: (52) 5552018000
Fax: (52) 5552018001
Commercial Banking Services
S.I.C.: 6029
N.A.I.C.S.: 522110

Deutsche Bank Aktiengesellschaft—(Continued)

DB Strategic Advisors, Inc. (1)
Unit 17E Petron MegaPlaza Sen Gil Puyat Avenue
Makati, 1200, Philippines
Tel.: (63) 28565984
Fax: (63) 28565985
Commercial Banking Services
S.I.C.: 6029
N.A.I.C.S.: 522110

DB Trust Company Limited Japan (1)
Sanno Park Tower Nagatacho 2-11-1
Chiyoda-ku, Tokyo, Japan
Tel.: (81) 3 5156 7704
Trust Management Services
S.I.C.: 6091
N.A.I.C.S.: 523991

DB Trustee Services Limited (1)
23 Great Winchester Street
London, EC2P 2AX, United Kingdom
Tel.: (44) 207 54 58000
Fax: (44) 207 54 56155
Trust Management Services
S.I.C.: 6099
N.A.I.C.S.: 523991

DB Trustees (Hong Kong) Limited (1)
Level 52 International Commerce Centre 1 Austin Road West
Hong Kong, China (Hong Kong)
Tel.: (852) 2203 8888
Fax: (852) 2203 7320
Trust Management Services
S.I.C.: 6733
N.A.I.C.S.: 523991

DB UK Australia Holdings Limited (1)
1 Great Winchester Street
London, EC2N 2DB, United Kingdom
Tel.: (44) 207 54 58000
Fax: (44) 207 54 56155
Investment Management Services
S.I.C.: 6282
N.A.I.C.S.: 523920

DB UK Bank Limited (1)
6 Bishopsgate 1 Great Winchester St
London, EC2N 4DA, United Kingdom
Tel.: (44) 17 15 45 80 00
Fax: (44) 17 15 45 61 80
Commercial Banking Services
S.I.C.: 6029
N.A.I.C.S.: 522110

DB UK Holdings Limited (1)
23 Great Winchester Street
London, EC2P 2AX, United Kingdom
Tel.: (44) 207 54 58000
Fax: (44) 207 54 56155
Investment Management Services
S.I.C.: 6282
N.A.I.C.S.: 523920

DB U.K. Nominees Limited (1)
1 Great Winchester Street
London, EC2N 2DB, United Kingdom
Tel.: (44) 207 54 58000
Fax: (44) 207 54 56155
Financial Management Services
S.I.C.: 6211
N.A.I.C.S.: 523999

DB UK PCAM Holdings Limited (1)
Winchester House
London, EC2N 2DB, United Kingdom
Tel.: (44) 20 7545 8000
Investment Management Services
S.I.C.: 6282
N.A.I.C.S.: 523920

DB Vanquish (UK) Limited (1)
1 Great Winchester Street
London, EC2N 2DB, United Kingdom
Tel.: (44) 207 54 58000
Fax: (44) 207 54 56155
Investment Management Services
S.I.C.: 6799
N.A.I.C.S.: 523920

DB Vantage No.2 (UK) Limited (1)
1 Great Winchester Street
London, EC2N 2DB, United Kingdom
Tel.: (44) 207 54 58000
Fax: (44) 207 54 56155
Commercial Banking Services
S.I.C.: 6029
N.A.I.C.S.: 522110

DB Vantage (UK) Limited (1)
1 Great Winchester Street
London, EC2N 2DB, United Kingdom
Tel.: (44) 207 54 58000
Fax: (44) 207 54 56155
Commercial Banking Services
S.I.C.: 6029
N.A.I.C.S.: 522110

DB Vita S.A. (1)
2 Boulevard Konrad Adenauer
1115 Luxembourg, Luxembourg
Tel.: (352) 26422 9300
Fax: (352) 26422 9400
E-Mail: dbvita.info@db.com
Web Site: www.db-vita.de
General Insurance Services
S.I.C.: 6411
N.A.I.C.S.: 524210

db x-trackers (Proprietary) Limited (1)
Private Bag X9933
Sandton, South Africa 2146
Tel.: (27) 11 775 7076
Fax: (27) 11 775 7611
E-Mail: dbxtrackers@xclients.co.za
Fund Management Services
S.I.C.: 6282
N.A.I.C.S.: 523920

DBC Continuance Inc. (1)
199 Bay Street Suite 4700 Commerce Court West
Box 263
M5L 1E9 Toronto, ON, Canada
Tel.: (416) 682-8000
Fax: (416) 682-8383
Commercial Banking Services
S.I.C.: 6029
N.A.I.C.S.: 522110

DBIGB Finance (No. 2) Limited (1)
1 Great Winchester Street
London, EC2N 2DB, United Kingdom
Tel.: (44) 2075458000
Fax: (44) 2075456155
Financial Management Services
S.I.C.: 6211
N.A.I.C.S.: 523999

DBOI Global Services Private Limited (1)
Logitech Park Tower 2 Sir MV Road Saki Naka
Andheri East, Mumbai, 400 072, India
Tel.: (91) 2267113000
Financial Management Services
S.I.C.: 6211
N.A.I.C.S.: 523999

Non-U.S. Subsidiaries:

Deutsche Asset Management (Asia) Limited (2)
One Raffles Quay 15-00 South Tower
Singapore, 048583, Singapore (100%)
Tel.: (65) 65387011
Telex: RS 23147 MGASIA
Fax: (65) 65383171
Web Site: www.db.com
Emp.: 150
Securities Dealers
S.I.C.: 6211
N.A.I.C.S.: 523110
Ed Peter *(CEO)*

Deutsche Bank AG-Singapore (2)
1 Raffles Quay South Tower Level 17
Singapore, 048583, Singapore (100%)
Mailing Address:
Robinson Road
PO Box 7
Singapore, 900007, Singapore
Tel.: (65) 64238001
Fax: (65) 62259442
Web Site: www.db.com
Emp.: 900
Corporate & Investment Banking Services
S.I.C.: 6211
N.A.I.C.S.: 523110
Klaus Michalak *(Global Head-Structured Trade & Export Fin-Asia Pacific Reg)*
Stuart Smith *(Mng Dir & Head-Corp Commodity Sls-Asia)*
Robert John Rankin *(CEO-Asia Pacific)*

DBOI Global Services (UK) Limited (1)
Winchester House 1 Great Winchester Street
London, EC2N 2DB, United Kingdom
Tel.: (44) 207 54 58000
Fax: (44) 207 54 56155
Business Management Consulting Services
S.I.C.: 8742
N.A.I.C.S.: 541611

DBUKH Finance Limited (1)
1 Great Winchester Street
London, EC2N 2DB, United Kingdom
Tel.: (44) 2075458000
Fax: (44) 2075456155
Commercial Banking Services
S.I.C.: 6029
N.A.I.C.S.: 522110

DeAM Infrastructure Limited (1)
1 Great Winchester Street
London, EC2N 2DB, United Kingdom
Tel.: (44) 207 54 58000
Commercial Banking Services
S.I.C.: 6029
N.A.I.C.S.: 522110

Deutsche Alternative Asset Management (Global) Limited (1)
1 Appold Street
London, EC2A 2UU, United Kingdom
Tel.: (44) 2075456853
Investment Management Services
S.I.C.: 6799
N.A.I.C.S.: 523920

Deutsche Asia Pacific Holdings Pte Ltd. (1)
1 Raffles Quay 17-00 South Tower
38985 Singapore, Singapore (100%)
Mailing Address:
P.O. Box 2103
Singapore, 9059, Singapore
Tel.: (65) 64238001
Fax: (65) 68831615
E-Mail: info@db.com.sg
Web Site: www.db.com
Emp.: 900
Financial Holding Company
S.I.C.: 6712
N.A.I.C.S.: 551111
Gunit Chadha *(CEO)*

Deutsche Asset Management Canada Limited (1)
199 Bay Street Suite 4700 Commerce Court West
Box 263
M5L 1E9 Toronto, ON, Canada
Tel.: (416) 682-8000
Fax: (416) 682-8383
Investment Management Services
S.I.C.: 6282
N.A.I.C.S.: 523920

Deutsche Asset Management (India) Private Limited (1)
Kodak House 2nd Floor 222 Dr D N Road
Mumbai, Maharashtra, 400 001, India
Tel.: (91) 22 7158 4350
Fax: (91) 22 7158 4310
E-Mail: dws.mutual@db.com
Web Site: www.dws-india.com
Emp.: 250
Asset Management Services
S.I.C.: 6282
N.A.I.C.S.: 523920
Suresh Soni *(CEO & Mng Dir)*
Kiran Deshpande *(COO)*
Aniket Inamdar *(Chief Investment Officer)*
Vikram Kotak *(Chief Investment Officer-Equity)*
Nehal Shah *(Compliance Officer)*

Deutsche Asset Management (Japan) Limited (1)
Sanno Park Tower 2 11 1 Nagatacho
Chiyoda-ku, Tokyo, 100 6173, Japan (100%)
Tel.: (81) 351565000
Fax: (81) 351565001
Web Site: www.db.co.jp
Securities Dealers
S.I.C.: 6211
N.A.I.C.S.: 523110
Tim Hudson *(Pres)*

Deutsche Asset Management (Korea) Company Limited (1)
33 Seorin-Dong
Jongno-Gu, Seoul, 110-752, Korea (South)
Tel.: (82) 2 724 7400
Fax: (82) 2 724 7474
Web Site: www.dws-korea.com
Investment Management Services
S.I.C.: 6799
N.A.I.C.S.: 523920

Deutsche Asset Management Schweiz (1)
Prime Tower Hardstrasse 201
8005 Zurich, Switzerland (100%)
Tel.: (41) 581110111
Telex: 423441 MGS CH
Fax: (41) 581115050
Sales Range: $1-9.9 Million
Emp.: 70
Asset Management
S.I.C.: 6531
N.A.I.C.S.: 531390
Phillip Hensler *(COO)*

Deutsche Asset Management Switzerland (1)
Urania Strasse 9
Hardstrasse 201 8005, 8021 Zurich, Switzerland (100%)
Tel.: (41) 442247272
Fax: (41) 0041581117200
E-Mail: info@dws.ch
Web Site: www.dws.ch
Emp.: 60
Asset Management
S.I.C.: 6531
N.A.I.C.S.: 531390
Sven Rump *(CEO)*

Deutsche Australia Limited (1)
Level 16 Deutsche Bank Place Corner of Hunter and Phillip Streets
Sydney, NSW, 2000, Australia
Tel.: (61) 2 8258 1234
Fax: (61) 2 8258 1400
Web Site: www.australia.db.com
Commercial Banking Services
S.I.C.: 6029
N.A.I.C.S.: 522110
John Cincotta *(DIR)*

Deutsche Bank AG-Amsterdam (1)
Entree
1101 HA Amsterdam, Netherlands (100%)
Mailing Address:
Postbus 268
1000 Amsterdam, Netherlands
Tel.: (31) 205554911
Fax: (31) 205554428
E-Mail: info@db.com
Web Site: www.db.com
Emp.: 210
International Banking
S.I.C.: 6159
N.A.I.C.S.: 522298
Maarten Berckel *(Mng Dir-Global Banking Bus)*
Leon Degle *(Mng Dir)*

Deutsche Bank AG (Bombay) (1)
Hazarimal Somani Marg Fort
Mumbai, 400 001, India (100%)
Tel.: (91) 2222074720
Fax: (91) 2222075047
E-Mail: sunher.phanawalla@db.com
Web Site: www.db.com
International Banking
S.I.C.: 6159
N.A.I.C.S.: 522298
Ravneet Gill *(CEO)*
Sanjay Sharma *(Mng Dir & Head-Equity Capital Markets)*

Deutsche Bank AG Canada (1)
199 Bay St Ste 4700
Toronto, ON, M5L 1E9, Canada ON
Mailing Address: (100%)
Box 263
Toronto, ON, M5L 1E9, Canada
Tel.: (416) 682-8000
Fax: (416) 682-8383
E-Mail: info@db.com
Web Site: www.db.com
Sales Range: $125-149.9 Million
Emp.: 100
Security Brokers & Dealers
S.I.C.: 6211
N.A.I.C.S.: 523120

Paul Jurist *(Pres & CEO)*
David Gynn *(CFO)*

Deutsche Bank AG (Hong Kong) (1)
52 Fl International Commerce Ctr 1 Austin Rd W
Kowloon, China (Hong Kong) (100%)
Mailing Address:
GPO Box 3193
Hong Kong, China (Hong Kong)
Tel.: (852) 22038888
Fax: (852) 22037300
E-Mail: info@db.com
Web Site: www.db.com
Emp.: 2,000
Branch of Foriegn Bank
S.I.C.: 6159
N.A.I.C.S.: 522298
Ajay Kapur *(Mng Dir & Head-Equity Strategy-Asia)*

Deutsche Bank AG (Istanbul) (1)
Swiss Hotel Residence 9th Fl Macka
Bebek, Istanbul, 34357, Turkey (100%)
Mailing Address:
PK 194
Sisli, 80222 Istanbul, Turkey
Tel.: (90) 2123278700
Fax: (90) 2123278774
Web Site: www.db.com
Emp.: 4
Representative Office
S.I.C.: 6211
N.A.I.C.S.: 523110

Deutsche Bank AG Johannesburg (1)
3 Exchange Sq 87 Maude St
2196 Sandton, South Africa (100%)
Mailing Address:
P.O. Box 7736
Johannesburg, 2000, South Africa
Tel.: (27) 0117757000
Fax: (27) 0117757449
E-Mail: kevin.latter@db.com
Web Site: www.db.com
Emp.: 187
Representative Office; International Banking
S.I.C.: 6159
N.A.I.C.S.: 522298
Rafik Nayed *(Vice Chm-Middle East & North Africa)*
Kevin Latter *(Mng Dir)*
Ashok Aram *(CEO-Middle East & North Africa)*

Deutsche Bank AG-London (1)
1 Great Winchester St
London, EC2N 2DB, United Kingdom UK
Tel.: (44) 2075458000 (100%)
Telex: 851-895311 MG LDN G
Fax: (44) 2075456155
E-Mail: Anthony.Parsons@db.com
Web Site: www.deutsche-bank.com
Emp.: 7,000
International Investment Banking
S.I.C.: 6159
N.A.I.C.S.: 522298
Anthony Parsons *(Mng Dir)*
Richard Slimmon *(Mng Dir)*
Kim Hammonds *(CIO & Global Head-Grp Tech & Ops)*

Subsidiaries:

Abbey Life Assurance Company Limited (2)
100 Holdenhurst Rd
Bournemouth, Dorset, BH8 8AL, United Kingdom
Tel.: (44) 1202292373
Fax: (44) 1202551236
Web Site: www.abbeylife.co.uk
Sales Range: $450-499.9 Million
Emp.: 200
Life Insurance
S.I.C.: 6311
N.A.I.C.S.: 524113
Neil Tointon *(CEO)*
Claire Kybert *(Sec)*

Deutsche Asset Management (UK) Ltd. (2)
1 Appold St
London, EC2A 2HE, United Kingdom UK
Tel.: (44) 2075456000 (100%)
Web Site: www.deam.co.uk
Asset Management
S.I.C.: 6531
N.A.I.C.S.: 531390
Kevin Parker *(Gen Mgr)*

Non-U.S. Subsidiary:

Deutsche Asset Management Italy S.p.A. (3)
Via Melchiorre Gioia 8
20126 Milan, Italy
Tel.: (39) 0262994212
Web Site: www.db.com
Private Equity Fund
S.I.C.: 6719
N.A.I.C.S.: 551112

Deutsche Bank Group Services Ltd. (2)
6 8 Bishopsgate
London, EC2N 4DA, United Kingdom (100%)
Tel.: (44) 02075458000
Fax: (44) 02075456155
E-Mail: hr.direct@db.com
Web Site: www.db.com
Emp.: 1,000
Commercial Banking
S.I.C.: 6029
N.A.I.C.S.: 522110

Deutsche Bank AG (Macau) (1)
99 Avenida Almeida Ribeiro 7/F
Nam Wah Commercial Edificio, Macau, China (Macau)
Tel.: (853) 3356200
Fax: (853) 3304939
Web Site: www.db.com
International Banking
S.I.C.: 6159
N.A.I.C.S.: 522298

Deutsche Bank AG (Manila) (1)
Ayala Tower 1 Ayala Triangle
Makati, Manila, 1226, Philippines (100%)
Tel.: (63) 28946900
Fax: (63) 28946901
E-Mail: ams.manila@db.com
Web Site: www.db.com
Emp.: 100
International Banking
S.I.C.: 6159
N.A.I.C.S.: 522298
Enrico Cruz *(Gen Mgr)*

Deutsche Bank AG (New Delhi) (1)
Tolstoy House 15-17 Tolstoy Marg
New Delhi, 110 001, India
Mailing Address:
Post Bag 33
110001 New Delhi, India
Tel.: (91) 113721154
Fax: (91) 11 3316237
Web Site: www.db.com
International Banking
S.I.C.: 6159
N.A.I.C.S.: 522298
Ravneet Gill *(CEO)*

Deutsche Bank AG-Paris (1)
3 Ave de Friedland
F-75008 Paris, France (100%)
Mailing Address:
Boite Postale 466
75026 Paris, France
Tel.: (33) 144956400
Fax: (33) 153750701
Web Site: www.db.com
Emp.: 350
Corporate & Investment Banking Services
S.I.C.: 6211
N.A.I.C.S.: 523110
Marc Pandraud *(Chief Country Officer-France)*

Deutsche Bank AG (Prague) (1)
Jungmannova 34 750
110 21 Prague, Czech Republic (100%)
Tel.: (420) 221191111
Fax: (420) 221191411
E-Mail: info@db.com
Web Site: www.db.com
Emp.: 75
Full Banking Services
S.I.C.: 6159
N.A.I.C.S.: 522298
Valbimir Solc *(Mng Dir)*

Deutsche Bank AG (Seoul) (1)
33 SeoRin-dong Chongro-gu 16th Floor
Chongro Ku, 110 752 Seoul, Korea (South) (100%)
Mailing Address:
CPO Box 8904
Seoul, 100-689, Korea (South)
Tel.: (82) 27244500
Fax: (82) 27363871
Web Site: www.db.com
Emp.: 300
International Banking
S.I.C.: 6159
N.A.I.C.S.: 522298
Jeffrey Chung *(Head-Global Markets)*

Deutsche Bank AG (Taipei) (1)
296 Jen-Ai Road Sec 4 Taipei 106
10th Floor, Taipei, ROC, 106, Taiwan (100%)
Mailing Address:
PO Box 87-340
Taipei, 10650, Taiwan
Tel.: (886) 221924666
Fax: (886) 221924370
Web Site: www.db.com
Emp.: 130
International Banking
S.I.C.: 6159
N.A.I.C.S.: 522298

Deutsche Bank AG (Tehran) (1)
Valiasr Ave No 1409 Sayeh Twr
14th Floor Apt No 5
Tehran, Iran
Tel.: (98) 122046575
Fax: (98) 2122051029
Web Site: www.db.com
Representative Office
S.I.C.: 6159
N.A.I.C.S.: 522298

Deutsche Bank AG (Tokyo) (1)
Sanno Park Tower 2 11 1
Tokyo, 100 6170, Japan (100%)
Mailing Address:
CPO Box 1430
Tokyo, 100-8693, Japan
Tel.: (81) 351564000
Fax: (81) 351564001
Web Site: www.db.com
Emp.: 100
International Banking
S.I.C.: 6159
N.A.I.C.S.: 522298
Yasukazu Aiuchi *(Branch Mgr)*

DEUTSCHE BANK A.S. (1)
Eski Buyukdere Caddesi Tekfen Tower No 209 K 17-18 4 Levent
Istanbul, 34394, Turkey
Tel.: (90) 212 317 0100
Fax: (90) 212 317 0105
Commercial Banking Services
S.I.C.: 6029
N.A.I.C.S.: 522110

Deutsche Bank Australia (1)
126 philip st
cnr Hunter & Phillip Streets, Sydney, NSW, 2000, Australia
Tel.: (61) 282581234
Fax: (61) 282581400
Web Site: www.deutschebank.com.au
Sales Range: $25-49.9 Billion
Emp.: 800
Corporate & Investment Banking
S.I.C.: 6211
N.A.I.C.S.: 523110
James McMurdo *(CEO-Australia & New Zealand)*

Branch:

Deutsche Bank AG-Melbourne (2)
Level 23 333 Collins St
Melbourne, VIC, 3000, Australia (100%)
Mailing Address:
GPO Box 2239 T
Melbourne, VIC, 3001, Australia
Tel.: (61) 392704141
Fax: (61) 392704399
Web Site: www.deutschebank.com.au
Emp.: 50
Corporate & Investment Banking Services
S.I.C.: 6211
N.A.I.C.S.: 523110
Scott Perkins *(Head-Global Banking)*

Deutsche Bank Capital Markets S.r.l. (1)
Piazza Del Calendario 3
Milan, 20126, Italy
Tel.: (39) 024 0241
Investment Management Services
S.I.C.: 6799
N.A.I.C.S.: 523920

Deutsche Bank (Cayman) Limited (1)
Boundary Hall Cricket Square 171 Elgin Avenue
PO Box 1984
Georgetown, KY1-1104, Cayman Islands
Tel.: (345) 949 8244
Fax: (345) 949 8178
Web Site: www.dboffshore.com
Commercial Banking Services
S.I.C.: 6029
N.A.I.C.S.: 522110
Janet Hislop *(Chief Country Officer)*

Deutsche Bank (Chile) S.A. (1)
Ave El Bosque Sur 130 Piso 5
Las Condes, Santiago, 7550-0288, Chile
Mailing Address:
Casilla de Correo 3897
Santiago, Chile
Tel.: (56) 23377700
Fax: (56) 2031331
E-Mail: vanessa.benavides@db.com
Web Site: www.db.com
Emp.: 52
Asset Management & Investment Banking Services
S.I.C.: 6211
N.A.I.C.S.: 523110
Jose Alcalde *(Mng Dir)*
Manuel Irarrazaval *(Chief Country Officer & Head-Investment Banking)*

Deutsche Bank (China) Co., Ltd. (1)
Deutsche Bank Tower No 81 China Central Place No 81 Jianguo Avenue
Chaoyang District, Beijing, 100025, China CN
Tel.: (86) 1059698888 (100%)
Fax: (86) 1059695689
Web Site: www.db.com
Asset Management, Corporate & Investment Banking Services
S.I.C.: 6211
N.A.I.C.S.: 523110
Lee Zhang *(Chm)*
Charlie Ye *(Mng Dir & Head-Global Rates Trading)*

Deutsche Bank Corretora de Valores S.A. (1)
Rua Alexandre Dumas 2200
Sao Paulo, 04717-004, Brazil
Tel.: (55) 1151895492
Securities Brokerage Services
S.I.C.: 6211
N.A.I.C.S.: 523120

Deutsche Bank Factoring S.p.A. (1)
Piazza del Calendario 3
20126 Milan, Italy
Tel.: (39) 0240241
Factoring
S.I.C.: 6159
N.A.I.C.S.: 522298

Deutsche Bank Finance N.V. (1)
Pietermaai 17
PO Box 4905
Willemstad, Curacao
Tel.: (599) 94612369
Fax: (599) 94652212
International Financing Company
S.I.C.: 6159
N.A.I.C.S.: 522298

Deutsche Bank International Trust Co. (Cayman) Limited (1)
PO Box 1984
Georgetown, Grand Cayman, Cayman Islands
Tel.: (345) 9498244
Fax: (345) 9498178
Commercial Trust Services
S.I.C.: 6099
N.A.I.C.S.: 523991

Deutsche Bank International Trust Co. (Jersey) Limited (1)
Dumaresq Street
Saint Helier, Jersey JE2 3WP
Tel.: (44) 20 7545 8000
Trust Management Services
S.I.C.: 6733
N.A.I.C.S.: 523991

Deutsche Bank Aktiengesellschaft—(Continued)

Deutsche Bank International Trust Co. Limited (1)
Lefebvre Court Lefebvre Street
PO Box 523
Saint Peter Port, Guernsey GY1 6EJ
Tel.: (44) 1481 702000
Fax: (44) 1481 702003
E-Mail: db.offshore@db.com
Trust Management Services
S.I.C.: 6099
N.A.I.C.S.: 523991

Deutsche Bank Investments (Guernsey) Limited (1)
Lefebvre Court Lefebvre Street
PO Box 523
Saint Peter Port, Guernsey GY1 6EJ
Tel.: (44) 1481 702000
Fax: (44) 1481 702002
Investment Banking Services
S.I.C.: 6211
N.A.I.C.S.: 523110
Andreas Tautscher *(Mng Dir)*

Deutsche Bank Ltd. (1)
Ul Shepkina 4
129090 Moscow, Russia (100%)
Tel.: (7) 957975000
Fax: (7) 957975017
Web Site: www.deutsche-bank.ru
Emp.: 150
Provider of Corporate Banking Services
S.I.C.: 6159
N.A.I.C.S.: 522298
Pavel Teplukhin *(Chief Country Officer)*

Deutsche Bank Luxembourg S.A. (1)
2 Boulevard Konrad Adenauer
L-1115 Luxembourg, Luxembourg LU
Mailing Address: (100%)
Boite Postale 2221
1022 Luxembourg, Luxembourg
Tel.: (352) 421221
Fax: (352) 42122449
E-Mail: contact-pbglobal.luxembourg@db.com
Web Site: www.db.com
Sales Range: $1-4.9 Billion
Emp.: 359
Asset Management, Corporate & Investment Banking Services
S.I.C.: 6211
N.A.I.C.S.: 523110
Boris Liedtke *(CEO & Chief Country Officer)*
Sunke Christian *(Mng Dir)*
Klaus-Michael Vogel *(Mng Dir-Treasury & Global Markets/Intl Loans/Corp Svcs)*

Deutsche Bank (Malaysia) Berhad (1)
Level 18 20 Menara IMC 8
Jalan Sultan Ismail, 50250 Kuala Lumpur, Malaysia
Tel.: (60) 320536788
Fax: (60) 320319822
E-Mail: ams.kualalumpur@db.com
Web Site: www.db.com
Emp.: 250
Corporate & Institutional Banking Services
S.I.C.: 6159
N.A.I.C.S.: 522298
Raymond Yeoh *(CEO)*
Yusof Yaacob *(Chief Country Officer & Head-Corp Banking & Securities)*

Deutsche Bank (Malta) Ltd (1)
Portomaso Business Tower Level 10
San Giljan, Malta
Tel.: (356) 2137 3666
Fax: (356) 2137 7741
Commercial Banking Services
S.I.C.: 6029
N.A.I.C.S.: 522110
Thomas Haag *(CEO)*

Deutsche Bank (Mauritius) Limited (1)
4th Floor Barkly Wharf East
PO Box 615
Le Caudan Waterfront, Port Louis, Mauritius
Tel.: (230) 202 7878
Fax: (230) 202 7898
Web Site: www.db.com
Emp.: 200
Commercial Banking Services
S.I.C.: 6029
N.A.I.C.S.: 522110

Deutsche Bank Mexico S.A. De C.V. (1)
Blvd Manuel Avila Camacho No 40 Colonia Lomas
Lomas de Chapultepec Piso 17, 11000
Mexico, Mexico (100%)
Mailing Address:
Apartado Postal 14 Bis
06000 Mexico, Mexico
Tel.: (52) 5552018000
Fax: (52) 5552018106
Web Site: www.db.com
DBMBF—(OTC)
Emp.: 100
Representative Office; International Banking
S.I.C.: 6159
N.A.I.C.S.: 522298
Jorge Arce *(Chief Country Officer)*
Bernardo Parnes *(CEO-Latin America)*

Deutsche Bank Nederland N.V. (1)
De Entree 99-197
1101 HE Amsterdam, Netherlands
Tel.: (31) 20 555 49 11
Fax: (31) 20 555 44 85
E-Mail: db.public@db.com
Web Site: www.deutschebank.nl
Commercial Banking Services
S.I.C.: 6029
N.A.I.C.S.: 522110
Gerard Zwartkruis *(CEO)*

Deutsche Bank Nominees (Jersey) Limited (1)
St Paul's Gate New Street
Saint Helier, Jersey JE2 3WP
Tel.: (44) 1534 889336
Fax: (44) 1534 889881
Commercial Banking Services
S.I.C.: 6029
N.A.I.C.S.: 522110

Deutsche Bank (Peru) S.A. (1)
Miguel Dasso 104 - 8th Floor
San Isidro, Lima, Peru
Tel.: (51) 1 219 6800
Fax: (51) 1 222 3330
Web Site: www.db.com
Emp.: 28
Commercial Banking Services
S.I.C.: 6029
N.A.I.C.S.: 522110

Deutsche Bank Polska S.A. (1)
Al Armii Ludowej 26
PL 00-609 Warsaw, Poland PL
Tel.: (48) 225799000 (100%)
Fax: (48) 225799001
E-Mail: ala.glowma@db.com
Web Site: www.db-polska.pl
Emp.: 200
Corporate & Investment Banking Services
S.I.C.: 6211
N.A.I.C.S.: 523110
Krzysztof Kalicki *(Chm-Exec Bd)*

Deutsche Bank (Portugal) SA (1)
Rua Castilho No 20
1250 069 Lisbon, Portugal (100%)
Tel.: (351) 213111200
Fax: (351) 213535241
E-Mail: carriers@db.com
Web Site: www.deutschebank.com
Emp.: 200
Investment Bank
S.I.C.: 6799
N.A.I.C.S.: 523910

Deutsche Bank Real Estate (Japan) Y.K. (1)
2-11-1 Nagatacho
Chiyoda-Ku, Tokyo, 100-6171, Japan
Tel.: (81) 351566513
Fax: (81) 351567910
Emp.: 800
Real Estate Development Services
S.I.C.: 6531
N.A.I.C.S.: 531390
Mitchell Mason *(Pres)*

Deutsche Bank RT (1)
Hold Utca 27
H 1054 Budapest, Hungary (100%)
Tel.: (36) 013013700
Fax: (36) 12693239
E-Mail: db.rt@db.com
Web Site: www.db.com
Emp.: 70
Provider of Corporate & Real Estate Banking Services
S.I.C.: 6159
N.A.I.C.S.: 522298

Deutsche Bank S.A.-Banco Alemao (1)
Av Brigadeiro Faria Lima 3900
13 14 15 Andar, Sao Paulo, CEP 04538-132, Brazil (100%)
Mailing Address:
Caixa Postal 1691
13001 Campinas, SP, Brazil
Tel.: (55) 51895000
Web Site: www.db.com
Emp.: 100
Global Corporate & Institutional Banking Services
S.I.C.: 6159
N.A.I.C.S.: 522298

Deutsche Bank S.A. (Buenos Aires) (1)
Fl 14
Tucuman 1, C1049AAA Buenos Aires, Argentina (98%)
Mailing Address:
PO Box 995
1000 Buenos Aires, Argentina
Tel.: (54) 1145902932
Fax: (54) 1145902882
E-Mail: monica.leguizamon@db.com
Web Site: www.db.com
Emp.: 100
Global Corporate and Institutional Banking Services
S.I.C.: 6159
N.A.I.C.S.: 522298
Marcela Pineyro *(Mgr-Mktg)*

Deutsche Bank S.A.E. (1)
Paseo de La Castellana 18
28046 Madrid, Spain (100%)
Mailing Address:
Apartado 221
28080 Madrid, Spain
Tel.: (34) 913355800
Fax: (34) 913355807
E-Mail: info@deutsche-bank.es
Web Site: www.db.com
Emp.: 300
Head Branch & Main Branch; International Banking
S.I.C.: 6211
N.A.I.C.S.: 523110
Antonio Rodriguez Pina *(CEO)*

Deutsche Bank S.A.E. (1)
Avenida Diagonal 446
8006 Barcelona, Spain (100%)
Mailing Address:
Apartado 416
08080 Barcelona, Spain
Tel.: (34) 934042102, ext. 902240010
Fax: (34) 32381911
Web Site: www.db.com
Head Office & Main Branch; International Banking
S.I.C.: 6159
N.A.I.C.S.: 522298

Deutsche Bank Sao Paulo (1)
Av Brigadeiro Faria Lima
3 900 13 ba 15 Andares, 04538 132 Sao Paulo, Brazil (100%)
Mailing Address:
PO Box 55192
04799970 Sao Paulo, Brazil
Tel.: (55) 1121135000
Fax: (55) 1121135100
E-Mail: client.center@db.com
Web Site: www.db.com
Emp.: 400
International Banking
S.I.C.: 6159
N.A.I.C.S.: 522298

Deutsche Bank (Schweiz) AG (1)
Bahnhofquai 9 11
PO Box 7381
8001 Zurich, Switzerland (100%)
Mailing Address:
Postfach 978
CH-8039 Zurich, Switzerland
Tel.: (41) 12245000
Fax: (41) 12245050
Web Site: www.db.com
Emp.: 200
International Banking
S.I.C.: 6159
N.A.I.C.S.: 522298

Deutsche Bank Securities Limited (1)
199 Bay Street Suite 4700 Commerce Court West
Box 263
Toronto, ON, M5L 1E9, Canada
Tel.: (416) 682-8000
Fax: (416) 682-8383
Web Site: www.db.com
Investment Banking Services
S.I.C.: 6211
N.A.I.C.S.: 523110

Deutsche Bank Services (Jersey) Limited (1)
St Paul's Gate New Street
Saint Helier, Jersey JE2 3WP
Tel.: (44) 1534 889 900
Commercial Banking Services
S.I.C.: 6029
N.A.I.C.S.: 522110
Kelly Gouveia *(VP-Fund Svcs)*

Deutsche Bank S.p.A. (1)
Piazza del Calendario 3
20126 Milan, Italy (100%)
Tel.: (39) 02 4024 1
Web Site: www.db.com
Emp.: 200
International Banking
S.I.C.: 6029
N.A.I.C.S.: 522110
Juergen Fitschen *(Chm-Supervisory Bd)*
Flavio Valeri *(Chm-Mgmt Bd & CEO)*

Branch:

DWS Sim S.p.A. (2)
Via Melchiorre Gioia 8
20122 Milan, Italy
Tel.: (39) 02 4024 2375
Fax: (39) 02 4024 2072
Web Site: www.db.com
Investment Management Services
S.I.C.: 6211
N.A.I.C.S.: 523120

Deutsche Bank (Suisse) S.A. (1)
Pl Des Bergues 3
1201 Geneva, Switzerland (100%)
Mailing Address:
Case postale 1416
1211 Geneva, Switzerland
Tel.: (41) 227390111
Fax: (41) 227390700
Web Site: www.db.com
Emp.: 600
International Banking
S.I.C.: 6159
N.A.I.C.S.: 522298
Bob Keller *(Mng Dir)*

Deutsche Bank (Svizzera) S.A. (1)
Via Ferruccio Pelli 1
6901 Lugano, Switzerland (100%)
Mailing Address:
Casella Postale 2783
6901 Lugano, Switzerland
Tel.: (41) 919103838
Fax: (41) 919103939
Web Site: www.pwm.db.com
Rev.: $7,008,500
Emp.: 26
International Banking
S.I.C.: 6159
N.A.I.C.S.: 522298

Deutsche Bank Trustee Services (Guernsey) Limited (1)
Lefebvre Court Lefebvre Street
PO Box 523
Saint Peter Port, Guernsey GY1 6EJ
Tel.: (44) 1481 702000
Fax: (44) 1481 702003
Commercial Banking Services
S.I.C.: 6029
N.A.I.C.S.: 522110
Aaron Mullins *(Head-Sls)*

Deutsche Bank (Uruguay) S.A.I.F.E. (1)
World Trade Ctr Av Luis
Alberto De Herrera Piso 19, Montevideo, 1248, Uruguay (100%)
Mailing Address:
Casilla de Correo 612
Montevideo, Uruguay

Tel.: (598) 26222950
Fax: (598) 6225276
E-Mail: lucia.delcampo@db.com
Web Site: www.db.com
International Banking
S.I.C.: 6159
N.A.I.C.S.: 522298

Deutsche Berri (1)
3 avenue de Friedland
75008 Paris, France
Tel.: (33) 1 44 95 93 93
Fax: (33) 1 42 56 28 71
Trust Management Services
S.I.C.: 6091
N.A.I.C.S.: 523991

Deutsche Capital Hong Kong Limited (1)
55th Floor Cheung Kong Centre 2 Queen's Road
Central, China (Hong Kong)
Tel.: (852) 22038888
Fax: (852) 22037300
Commercial Banking Services
S.I.C.: 6029
N.A.I.C.S.: 522110

Deutsche Capital Markets Australia Limited (1)
L 16 Deutsche Bank Pl Corner Of Hunter St & Phillip St
Sydney, NSW, 2000, Australia
Tel.: (61) 2 8258 1234
Securities Brokerage Services
S.I.C.: 6211
N.A.I.C.S.: 523120
Ian Thompson *(Sec)*

Deutsche Colombia S.A. (1)
Cl 67 7 35 Of 1204
Bogota, Colombia
Tel.: (57) 1 3192900
Investment Management Services
S.I.C.: 6799
N.A.I.C.S.: 523920

Deutsche Custody N.V. (1)
Herengracht 450
Amsterdam, 1017 CA, Netherlands
Tel.: (31) 205554351
Commercial Banking Services
S.I.C.: 6029
N.A.I.C.S.: 522110

Deutsche Fiduciary Services (Suisse) SA (1)
Place des Bergues 3
1201 Geneva, Switzerland
Tel.: (41) 22 739 0664
Fax: (41) 22 739 0665
Web Site: www.db.com
Commercial Trust Services
S.I.C.: 6733
N.A.I.C.S.: 523991
Peter Moorhouse *(Mgr)*

Deutsche Finance No. 1 Limited (1)
Winchester House
London, EC2N 2DB, United Kingdom
Tel.: (44) 20 7545 3499
Financial Management Services
S.I.C.: 6211
N.A.I.C.S.: 523999

Deutsche Finance No. 2 (UK) Limited (1)
Winchester House 1 Great Winchester Street Liverpool Street
London, EC2N 2DB, United Kingdom
Tel.: (44) 20 7545 3499
Financial Management Services
S.I.C.: 6211
N.A.I.C.S.: 523999

Deutsche Finance No. 4 (UK) Limited (1)
Winchester House 1 Great Winchester Street Liverpool Street
London, EC2N 2DB, United Kingdom
Tel.: (44) 20 7545 3499
Financial Management Services
S.I.C.: 6211
N.A.I.C.S.: 523999

Deutsche Finance No. 6 (UK) Limited (1)
Winchester House
London, EC2N 2DB, United Kingdom
Tel.: (44) 20 7545 3499
Financial Management Services
S.I.C.: 6211
N.A.I.C.S.: 523999

Deutsche Futures Singapore Pte Ltd (1)
One Raffles Quay 17-10 South Tower
Singapore, 048583, Singapore
Tel.: (65) 64238001
Fax: (65) 6837 2609
Web Site: www.db.com
Investment Management Services
S.I.C.: 6282
N.A.I.C.S.: 523920

Deutsche Group Services Pty Limited (1)
L 16 Deutsche Bank Pl Corner Of Hunter St And Phillip St
Sydney, NSW, 2000, Australia
Tel.: (61) 2 8258 1234
Financial Management Services
S.I.C.: 6211
N.A.I.C.S.: 523999

Deutsche Holdings (BTI) Limited (1)
Winchester House 1 Great Winchester Street Liverpool Street
London, EC2N 2DB, United Kingdom
Tel.: (44) 207 54 58000
Fax: (44) 207 54 56155
Investment Management Services
S.I.C.: 6282
N.A.I.C.S.: 523920

Deutsche Holdings Limited (1)
Winchester House
London, EC2N 2DB, United Kingdom
Tel.: (44) 2075453499
Investment Management Services
S.I.C.: 6211
N.A.I.C.S.: 523999

Deutsche Holdings (Malta) Ltd. (1)
Portomaso Business Tower
San Giljan, Malta
Tel.: (356) 21373666
Investment Management Services
S.I.C.: 6211
N.A.I.C.S.: 523999
Thomas Haag *(CEO)*

Deutsche Holdings No. 2 Limited (1)
Winchester House
London, EC2N 2DB, United Kingdom
Tel.: (44) 20 7545 8000
Investment Management Services
S.I.C.: 6282
N.A.I.C.S.: 523920

Deutsche International Corporate Services (Ireland) Ltd. (1)
5 Harbourmaster Place International Financial Services Centre 3rd Fl
Dublin, 1, Ireland
Tel.: (353) 16806000
Fax: (353) 16806050
E-Mail: admin@db.com
Emp.: 40
Banking & Securities
S.I.C.: 6211
N.A.I.C.S.: 523110
Mike Hughes *(VP)*

Deutsche International Corporate Services Limited (1)
St Paul's Gate New Street
PO Box 727
Saint Helier, Jersey JE4 8ZB
Tel.: (44) 1534 889900
Financial Management Services
S.I.C.: 6211
N.A.I.C.S.: 523999

Deutsche International Finance (Ireland) Limited (1)
5 Harbourmaster Place
Dublin, Ireland
Tel.: (353) 1 6806000
Fax: (353) 1 6806050
Emp.: 65
Business Management Consulting Services
S.I.C.: 8748
N.A.I.C.S.: 541618
Michael Whelan *(Gen Mgr)*

Deutsche International Holdings (UK) Limited (1)
Winchester House
London, EC2N 2DB, United Kingdom
Tel.: (44) 20 7545 8000
Investment Management Services
S.I.C.: 6282
N.A.I.C.S.: 523920

Deutsche International Trust Corporation (CI) Limited (1)
St Pauls Gate New Street
PO Box 727
JE4 8ZB Saint Helier, Jersey (100%)
Tel.: (44) 534889900
Telex: 4192007 MG JSY G
Fax: (44) 534889911
Web Site: www.deutsche-bank.com
Banking, Investment Management & Company Management
S.I.C.: 6159
N.A.I.C.S.: 522298

Deutsche Inversiones Limitada (1)
Avenida El Bosque Sur 130 Piso 5
Las Condes, Santiago, Chile
Tel.: (56) 2 3377710
Investment Management Services
S.I.C.: 6799
N.A.I.C.S.: 523920

Deutsche Investments Australia Limited (1)
L 16 Deutsche Bank Pl
Sydney, NSW, 2000, Australia
Tel.: (61) 2 9249 9000
Investment Management Services
S.I.C.: 6282
N.A.I.C.S.: 523920

Deutsche Investments India Private Limited (1)
Nirlon Knowledge Park Block B1 Western Express Highway
Mumbai, 400 063, India
Tel.: (91) 22 71806145
Investment Management Services
S.I.C.: 6282
N.A.I.C.S.: 523920

Deutsche Investor Services Private Limited (1)
Nirlon Knowledge Park Block 4th Floor B1 Western Express Highway
Goregaon E, Mumbai, 400 063, India
Tel.: (91) 22 71806145
Fax: (91) 22 71806901
Web Site: www.displ.co.in
Investment Management Services
S.I.C.: 6282
N.A.I.C.S.: 523920
Mrugank Paranjape *(Head-TAS & Cash Mgmt-Fin Institutions-Asia Pacific)*

Deutsche Managed Investments Limited (1)
Deutsche Bank Place Level 16 Cnr Hunter and Phillip Streets
Sydney, NSW, 2000, Australia
Tel.: (61) 2 8258 2515
E-Mail: enquiries.dmil@list.db.com
Web Site: www.dbaccess.db.com
Investment Management Services
S.I.C.: 6799
N.A.I.C.S.: 523920

Deutsche New Zealand Limited (1)
Level 36-48 Shortland Street Vero Centre
Auckland, 1010, New Zealand
Tel.: (64) 9 351 1000
Fax: (64) 9 351 1001
Commercial Banking Services
S.I.C.: 6029
N.A.I.C.S.: 522110

Deutsche Nominees Limited (1)
23 Great Winchester Street
London, EC 2P2AX, United Kingdom
Tel.: (44) 207 54 58000
Fax: (44) 207 54 56155
Commercial Banking Services
S.I.C.: 6029
N.A.I.C.S.: 522110

Deutsche Private Asset Management Limited (1)
1 Appold Street Broadgate
London, EC2A 2UU, United Kingdom
Tel.: (44) 207 54 58000
Fax: (44) 207 54 56155
Financial Management Services
S.I.C.: 6211
N.A.I.C.S.: 523999

Deutsche Securities Asia Limited (1)
Level 55 Cheung Kong Center 2 Queen's Road
Central, China (Hong Kong)
Tel.: (852) 2203 8888
Fax: (852) 2203 7230
E-Mail: info@db.com
Securities Brokerage Services
S.I.C.: 6211
N.A.I.C.S.: 523120

Deutsche Securities Australia Limited (1)
L 16 Deutsche Bank Pl Cnr Hunter & Phillip St
Sydney, NSW, 2000, Australia
Tel.: (61) 2 8258 1234
Securities Brokerage Services
S.I.C.: 6211
N.A.I.C.S.: 523120

Deutsche Securities Corredores de Bolsa Ltda. (1)
Avda el Bosque Sur 130 P 5
Santiago, Chile
Tel.: (56) 2 337 7700
Fax: (56) 2 2031331
Securities Brokerage Services
S.I.C.: 6211
N.A.I.C.S.: 523120

Deutsche Securities (India) Private Limited (1)
5th Floor Nirlon Knowledge Park Block 1 Western Express Highway
Goregaon, Mumbai, 400 063, India
Tel.: (91) 22 6670 3066
Fax: (91) 22 6670 3070
Securities Brokerage Services
S.I.C.: 6211
N.A.I.C.S.: 523120

Deutsche Securities Israel Ltd. (1)
46 Rothschild Blvd
Tel Aviv, Israel
Tel.: (972) 37102000
Securities Brokerage Services
S.I.C.: 6211
N.A.I.C.S.: 523120

Deutsche Securities Korea Co (1)
41 Cheonggyecheon-ro Jongno-gu
Seoul, 110-752, Korea (South)
Tel.: (82) 2 316 8888
Fax: (82) 2 316 8999
Web Site: www.db.com
Securities Brokerage Services
S.I.C.: 6211
N.A.I.C.S.: 523120

Deutsche Securities Limited (1)
Level 52 International Commerce Centre 1 Austin Road West
Kowloon, China (Hong Kong) HK
Tel.: (852) 22038888 (100%)
Fax: (852) 22037300
E-Mail: info@db.com
Web Site: www.db.com
Emp.: 100
Investment Banking
S.I.C.: 6211
N.A.I.C.S.: 523110

Non-U.S. Subsidiary:

Deutsche Securities Inc. (2)
Sanno Park Tower 2 11 1 Nagatacho
Chiyoda-ku, Tokyo, 100 6171, Japan JP
Tel.: (81) 351566000 (100%)
Fax: (81) 351566001
Web Site: www.japan.db.com
Investment Company
S.I.C.: 6211
N.A.I.C.S.: 523110
Shunichi Maeda *(Vice Chm-Global Banking & Mng Dir)*
David Hatt *(Pres & CEO)*
Orlando Faulks *(Mng Dir & Head-Global Markets Res)*
Marzio Keiling *(Mng Dir & Head-Global Markets-Japan)*
Naoki Kamiyama *(Mng Dir)*
Yoshinobu Yamada *(Mng Dir)*

Deutsche Securities (Proprietary) Limited (1)
3 Exchange Square 87 Maude Street
Sandton, 2196, South Africa
Tel.: (27) 11 775 7000

Deutsche Bank Aktiengesellschaft—(Continued)

Fax: (27) 11 775 7635
Emp.: 300
Securities Brokerage Services
S.I.C.: 6211
N.A.I.C.S.: 523120
Sharlene Rajah *(Compliance Officer)*

Deutsche Securities, S.A. de C.V. (1)
Blvd Manuel Avila Camacho No 40 Colonia Lomas de Chapultepec Piso 17
Mexico, 11000, Mexico
Tel.: (52) 55 5201 8000
Fax: (52) 55 5201 8097
Securities Brokerage Services
S.I.C.: 6211
N.A.I.C.S.: 523120

Deutsche Securitisation Australia Pty Ltd (1)
L 16 Deutsche Bank Pl Cnr Hunter & Phillip St
Sydney, NSW, 2000, Australia
Tel.: (61) 2 82581234
Securities Brokerage Services
S.I.C.: 6211
N.A.I.C.S.: 523120

Deutsche Trustee Company Limited (1)
Winchester House 1 Great Winchester Street Liverpool Street
London, EC2N 2DB, United Kingdom
Tel.: (44) 20 7545 8000
Fax: (44) 20 7547 6149
Trust Management Services
S.I.C.: 6099
N.A.I.C.S.: 523991

Deutsche Trustee Services (India) Private Limited (1)
2nd Floor 222 Kodak House Dr D N Road
Mumbai, 400 001, India
Tel.: (91) 22 2207 1050
Trust Management Services
S.I.C.: 6099
N.A.I.C.S.: 523991

DTS Nominees Pty. Limited (1)
L 18 Grosvenor Place
Sydney, NSW, 2000, Australia
Tel.: (61) 2 8258 1974
Investment Management Services
S.I.C.: 6799
N.A.I.C.S.: 523920

Elizabethan Holdings Limited (1)
235 Broadway Newmarket
Auckland, New Zealand
Tel.: (64) 95290071
Investment Management Services
S.I.C.: 6282
N.A.I.C.S.: 523920

GUO Mao International Hotels B.V. (1)
Herengracht 450
1017 CA Amsterdam, Netherlands
Tel.: (31) 206 29 35 96
Hotel Management Services
S.I.C.: 7011
N.A.I.C.S.: 721110

IFN Finance B.V. (1)
Lichtenauerlaan 150
3062 ME Rotterdam, Netherlands
Tel.: (31) 10 253 5353
Fax: (31) 10 253 5455
E-Mail: info@ifn.nl
Web Site: www.ifnfinance.nl
Financial Management Services
S.I.C.: 6211
N.A.I.C.S.: 523999
Enrico Bravenboer *(Mgr-Intl)*

IFN Finance N.V. (1)
Pelikaanstraat 70-76
Antwerp, 2018, Belgium
Tel.: (32) 32321264
Fax: (32) 32326036
Financial Management Services
S.I.C.: 6211
N.A.I.C.S.: 523999

IOS Finance EFC, S.A. (1)
C/Manila 57-59 Bajos B
08034 Barcelona, Spain
Tel.: (34) 93 511 40 25
Fax: (34) 93 511 40 28
E-Mail: iosfinance@iosfinance.es
Web Site: www.iosfinance.es
Emp.: 17
Financial Management Services
S.I.C.: 6211
N.A.I.C.S.: 523999
Alfredo Balcells *(CEO)*
Jordi Fontbute *(CFO)*

London Industrial Leasing Limited (1)
23 Great Winchester Street
London, EC2P 2AX, United Kingdom
Tel.: (44) 2075458000
Fax: (44) 20 75456018
Financial Leasing Services
S.I.C.: 6211
N.A.I.C.S.: 523999

Luxembourg Family Office S.A. (1)
534 Rue de Neudorf
2220 Luxembourg, Luxembourg
Tel.: (352) 457676 1
Fax: (352) 458320
E-Mail: direktion@bhf.lu
Commercial Banking Services
S.I.C.: 6029
N.A.I.C.S.: 522110

Moon Leasing Limited (1)
Winchester House 1 Great Winchester Street
London, EC2N 2DB, United Kingdom
Tel.: (44) 2075455337
Financial Leasing Services
S.I.C.: 6211
N.A.I.C.S.: 523999

Navegator - SGFTC, S.A. (1)
Rua Castilho 20
Lisbon, 1250-069, Portugal
Tel.: (351) 213111215
Fax: (351) 213535241
Financial Management Services
S.I.C.: 6211
N.A.I.C.S.: 523999
Bernardo Meyrelles *(CEO)*

New Prestitempo S.p.A. (1)
Piazza del Calendario 1
20126 Milan, Italy
Tel.: (39) 02 4024 2417
Fax: (39) 02 4024 2422
Commercial Banking Services
S.I.C.: 6029
N.A.I.C.S.: 522110

Oppenheim Asset Management GmbH (1)
Seilergasse 3
1010 Vienna, Austria
Tel.: (43) 1 51866 2510
Fax: (43) 1 51866 9210
E-Mail: asset.management@oppenheim.at
Web Site: www.oppenheim.at
Asset Management Services
S.I.C.: 6799
N.A.I.C.S.: 523920

Plinius Verwaltungs AG (1)
Schulhausstrasse 6
Zurich, 8002, Switzerland
Tel.: (41) 442097511
Financial Management Services
S.I.C.: 6211
N.A.I.C.S.: 523999

Primelux Insurance S.A. (1)
2 Boulevard Konrad Adenauer
1115 Luxembourg, Luxembourg
Tel.: (352) 42 12 25 50
Fax: (352) 42 12 25 86
General Insurance Services
S.I.C.: 6411
N.A.I.C.S.: 524298
Ernst Wilhelm Contzen *(Chm)*
Marleen van Malderen *(CEO)*

Pt Deutsche Securities Indonesia (1)
Deutsche Bank Building Lt 9 Jl Imam Bonjol No 80 6th Floor
Jakarta, 10310, Indonesia
Tel.: (62) 21 318 9545
Fax: (62) 21 318 9076
Securities Brokerage Services
S.I.C.: 6211
N.A.I.C.S.: 523120

Public Joint Stock Company Deutsche Bank DBU (1)
Lavrska Street 20
01015 Kiev, Ukraine
Tel.: (380) 44 495 92 00
Fax: (380) 44 494 44 13
Web Site: www.db.com
Commercial Banking Services
S.I.C.: 6029
N.A.I.C.S.: 522110
Kostyantin Viktorovich Sirogin *(Mgr)*

Reference Capital Investments Limited (1)
Winchester House Mailstop 428 1 Great Winchester Street
London, EC2N 2DB, United Kingdom
Tel.: (44) 2075456000
Financial Management Services
S.I.C.: 6211
N.A.I.C.S.: 523999

REIB Europe Investments Limited (1)
Winchester House 1 Great Winchester Street
London, EC2N 2DB, United Kingdom
Tel.: (44) 2075456000
Financial Planning Services
S.I.C.: 6282
N.A.I.C.S.: 523930

Sal. Oppenheim jr. & Cie. Luxembourg S.A. (1)
4 Rue Jean Monnet
2180 Luxembourg, Luxembourg
Tel.: (352) 221522 1
Fax: (352) 221522 690
E-Mail: info@oppenheim.lu
Web Site: www.oppenheim.lu
Commercial Banking Services
S.I.C.: 6029
N.A.I.C.S.: 522110
Wilhelm Haller von Hallerstein *(Chm)*
Alfons Klein *(CEO)*
Alexander Smyk *(Member-Mgmt Bd)*

Sixco Leasing Limited (1)
160 Northolt Road
Harrow, HA2 0EG, United Kingdom
Tel.: (44) 2076238000
Financial Leasing Services
S.I.C.: 6211
N.A.I.C.S.: 523999

Tagus - Sociedade de Titularizacao de Creditos, S.A. (1)
Rua Castilho 20
Lisbon, 1250-069, Portugal
Tel.: (351) 213111200
Commercial Banking Services
S.I.C.: 6029
N.A.I.C.S.: 522110

Thai Asset Enforcement and Recovery Asset Management Company Limited (1)
999/9 Ramai Road
10330 Bangkok, Thailand
Tel.: (66) 23818188
Asset Management Services
S.I.C.: 6799
N.A.I.C.S.: 523920

Tilney Group Ltd. (1)
Royal Liver Buildings Pier Head
Liverpool, L3 1NY, United Kingdom
Tel.: (44) 01512553000
Web Site: www.tilney.com
Emp.: 330
Holding Company; Investment Management Services
S.I.C.: 6719
N.A.I.C.S.: 551112

Subsidiaries:

DB PWM Collective Management Limited (2)
Royal Liver Building Pier Head
Liverpool, Merseyside, L3 1NY, United Kingdom
Tel.: (44) 151 255 3000
Fax: (44) 151 236 1252
Financial Management Services
S.I.C.: 6211
N.A.I.C.S.: 523999

Tilney Investment Management (2)
Royal Liver Building Pier Head
Liverpool, L3 1NY, United Kingdom
Tel.: (44) 151 236 6000
Fax: (44) 151 236 1252
Web Site: www.tilney.com
Fund Management Services
S.I.C.: 6282
N.A.I.C.S.: 523920

Subsidiary:

TIM (London) Limited (3)
Royal Liver Building Pier Head
Liverpool, L3 1NY, United Kingdom
Tel.: (44) 151 236 6000
Fax: (44) 151 236 1252
Investment Management Services
S.I.C.: 6799
N.A.I.C.S.: 523920

ZAO Deutsche Securities (1)
82 Sadovnicheskaya Street Building 2
115035 Moscow, Russia
Tel.: (7) 495 797 5000
Fax: (7) 495 797 5017
E-Mail: db.moscow@db.com
Web Site: www.deutsche-bank.ru
Securities Brokerage Services
S.I.C.: 6211
N.A.I.C.S.: 523120

ZAO UFG Invest (1)
Petrovka Ul 5
107031 Moscow, Russia
Tel.: (7) 495 721 1212
Fax: (7) 495 721 1210
E-Mail: ufginvest@ufgam.ru
Investment Management Services
S.I.C.: 6799
N.A.I.C.S.: 523920

Non-U.S. Representative Offices:

Deutsche Bank AG-Bangkok (1)
Athenee Tower Level 27-29
63 Wireless Road
Lumpini Pathumwan, Bangkok, 10330, Thailand (100%)
Mailing Address:
GPO Box 1237
Bangkok, 10501, Thailand
Tel.: (66) 2646515000
Web Site: www.db.com
Emp.: 143
Asset Management, Corporate & Investment Banking Services
S.I.C.: 6211
N.A.I.C.S.: 523110
Vikas Arora *(Head-Global Transaction Banking)*

Deutsche Bank AG-Cairo (1)
6 Boulos Hanna St 1st Fl
Doki, Giza, 123111, Egypt (100%)
Mailing Address:
PO Box 2306
Cairo, 11511, Egypt
Tel.: (20) 233336358
Fax: (20) 233336341
E-Mail: yasmine.hesham@db.com
Web Site: www.db.com
Emp.: 10
Asset Management, Corporate & Investment Banking Services
S.I.C.: 6211
N.A.I.C.S.: 523110

Deutsche Bank AG-Colombo (1)
86 Galle Road
PO Box 314
Colombo, 3, Sri Lanka (100%)
Tel.: (94) 112447 062
Fax: (94) 11 2447067
Web Site: www.db.com
Emp.: 60
Asset Management, Corporate & Investment Banking Services
S.I.C.: 6211
N.A.I.C.S.: 523110

Deutsche Bank AG-Jakarta (1)
Deutsche Bank Building No 80 Jalan Imam Bonjol
Jakarta, 10310, Indonesia
Tel.: (62) 2131931092
Fax: (62) 2131935252
Web Site: www.db.com
Emp.: 300
Asset Management, Corporate & Investment Banking Services
S.I.C.: 6211
N.A.I.C.S.: 523110

Deutsche Bank AG-Karachi (1)
Unitowers Unicentre I I
PO Box 4925
Karachi, Pakistan (100%)

Mailing Address:
P.O. Box 4925
Karachi, Pakistan
Tel.: (92) 2111555777
Fax: (92) 215658320
Web Site: www.db.com
Emp.: 55
Asset Management, Corporate & Investment Banking Services
S.I.C.: 6211
N.A.I.C.S.: 523110

Deutsche Bank AG-Lahore (1)
307 Upper Mall
Lahore, 42000, Pakistan (100%)
Mailing Address:
PO Box 1651
Lahore, Pakistan
Tel.: (92) 42111555777
Fax: (92) 5789354
Web Site: www.db.com
Emp.: 21
Asset Management, Corporate & Investment Banking Services
S.I.C.: 6211
N.A.I.C.S.: 523110

Deutsche Bank AG-Manama (1)
Manama Ctr 6th Floor Entrance 1
Government Road
PO Box 20619
Manama, Bahrain (100%)
Tel.: (973) 17218222
Fax: (973) 17224437
Web Site: www.db.com
Emp.: 16
Asset Management, Corporate & Investment Banking Services
S.I.C.: 6211
N.A.I.C.S.: 523110

Deutsche Bank AG-Surabaya (1)
Wisma Dharmala Lt 7 Suite 6
Jalan Panglima
Sudirman 101-103, Surabaya, 60271, Indonesia (100%)
Mailing Address:
P.O. Box 456
60001 Surabaya, Indonesia
Tel.: (62) 315311822
Fax: (62) 315316272
E-Mail: amsjakarta@db.com
Web Site: www.db.com
Emp.: 15
Asset Management, Corporate & Investment Banking Services
S.I.C.: 6211
N.A.I.C.S.: 523110
Mohammad Taufan *(Branch Mgr)*

Deutsche Bank AG-Vienna (1)
Fleischmarkt 1
1010 Vienna, Austria (100%)
Mailing Address:
Postfach 8
1010 Vienna, Austria
Tel.: (43) 1531810
Fax: (43) 153181114
Web Site: www.db.com
Rev.: $37,148,760
Emp.: 50
International Banking
S.I.C.: 6211
N.A.I.C.S.: 523110
Rhina Polster *(Pres)*

DEUTSCHE BETEILIGUNGS AG

Borsenstrasse 1
60313 Frankfurt, Germany
Tel.: (49) 699578701
Fax: (49) 6995787199
E-Mail: ir@deutsche-beteiligung.de
Web Site: www.deutsche-beteiligu ng.de
Year Founded: 1984
DBA—(DEU DUS STU)
Rev.: $69,115,060
Assets: $402,495,407
Liabilities: $44,138,222
Net Worth: $358,357,185
Earnings: $59,837,257
Emp.: 54
Fiscal Year-end: 12/31/12
Business Description:
Private Equity Firm
S.I.C.: 6211
N.A.I.C.S.: 523999
Personnel:
Andrew Richards *(Chm-Supervisory Bd)*
Torsten Grede *(Member-Mgmt Bd)*
Rolf Scheffels *(Member-Mgmt Bd)*
Susanne Zeidler *(Menber-Mgmt Bd)*
Tom Alzin *(Sr VP)*
Jochem Baumann *(Sr VP)*
Volker Bonsels *(Sr VP)*
Gundel Clouth *(Sr VP-Legal)*
Gustav Egger *(Sr VP)*
Jens Holscher *(Sr VP)*
Jannick Hunecke *(Sr VP)*
Gerard Lindgren *(Sr VP)*
Christian Pfirrman *(Sr VP)*
Jarno Schafermann *(Sr VP)*
Bernd Sexauer *(Sr VP)*
Kai Wiesenbach *(Sr VP)*
Supervisory Board of Directors:
Andrew Richards
Roland Norbert Frobel
Philipp Moller
Hendrik Otto
Gerhard Roggemann
Wiltken Freiherr von Hodenberg

Subsidiaries:

DBG Alpha 9 GmbH (1)
Kleine Wiesenau 1
60323 Frankfurt am Main, Germany
Tel.: (49) 69 957870
Fax: (49) 995787199
E-Mail: welcome@deutsche-beteiligungs.de
Web Site: www.deutsche-beteiligungs.de
Emp.: 55
Financial Management Services
S.I.C.: 6211
N.A.I.C.S.: 523999
Torsten Grede *(Gen Mgr)*

DBG Beteiligungsgesellschaft mbH (1)
Borsenstr 1
60313 Frankfurt, Hessen, Germany
Tel.: (49) 69 9578703
Fax: (49) 95787391
E-Mail: welcome@deutsche-beteiligungs.de
Web Site: www.deutsche-beteiligungs.de
Emp.: 5
Investment Management Services
S.I.C.: 6211
N.A.I.C.S.: 523999

DBG Fourth Equity International GmbH (1)
Borsenstr 1
Frankfurt am Main, 60313, Germany
Tel.: (49) 69 9578703
Fax: (49) 69 95787390
Financial Management Services
S.I.C.: 6211
N.A.I.C.S.: 523999

DBG Fourth Equity Team GmbH & Co. KGaA (1)
Borsenstr 1
Frankfurt am Main, Hessen, 60313, Germany
Tel.: (49) 69957870
Fax: (49) 6995787199
E-Mail: welcome@deutsche-beteiligung.de
Web Site: www.deutsche-beteiligung.de
Emp.: 6
Financial Management Services
S.I.C.: 6211
N.A.I.C.S.: 523999
Torsten Grede *(Gen Mgr)*

DBG Lambda GmbH (1)
Borsenstr 1
Frankfurt am Main, Hessen, 60313, Germany
Tel.: (49) 699578701
Financial Management Services
S.I.C.: 6211
N.A.I.C.S.: 523999

DBG My GmbH (1)
Borsenstr 1
Frankfurt am Main, Hessen, 60313, Germany
Tel.: (49) 69 9578701
Fax: (49) 69 95787199
Investment Management Services
S.I.C.: 6211
N.A.I.C.S.: 523999

DBG New Fund Management GmbH & Co. KG (1)
Borsenstr 1
Frankfurt am Main, Hessen, 60313, Germany
Tel.: (49) 69 9578703
Fax: (49) 69 95787390
Investment Management Services
S.I.C.: 6211
N.A.I.C.S.: 523999

DBV Drehbogen GmbH (1)
Borsenstr 1
Frankfurt am Main, Hessen, 60313, Germany
Tel.: (49) 699578701
Fax: (49) 496995787199
Emp.: 53
Financial Management Services
S.I.C.: 6211
N.A.I.C.S.: 523999

Gizeh Verpackungen Beteiligungs-GmbH (1)
Breiter Weg 40
51702 Bergneustadt, Germany
Tel.: (49) 2261 401 0
Fax: (49) 2261 401 401
E-Mail: info@gizeh.de
Web Site: www.gizeh.com
Packaging Plastic Container Mfr
S.I.C.: 2672
N.A.I.C.S.: 322220
Birgit Klein-Neumann *(Editor)*

Holdings:

Romaco Pharmatechnik GmbH (1)
Am Heegwald 11
76227 Karlsruhe, Germany De
Tel.: (49) 721 4804 0
Fax: (49) 721 4804 225
E-Mail: ptckarlsruhe@romaco.com
Web Site: www.romaco.com
Sales Range: $125-149.9 Million
Emp.: 450
Pharmaceutical Packaging Services
S.I.C.: 3565
N.A.I.C.S.: 333993
Paulo Alexandre *(CEO)*

Subsidiary:

Romaco FrymaKoruma (2)
Fischerstrasse 10
79395 Neuenburg, Germany
Tel.: (49) 763170670
Fax: (49) 7631706729
E-Mail: frymakoruma@romaco.com
Web Site: www.frymakoruma.com
Sales Range: $50-74.9 Million
Emp.: 40
Process & Packaging Solutions
S.I.C.: 3565
N.A.I.C.S.: 333993
Arthur Sarmeeki *(Mng Dir)*

Non-U.S. Subsidiaries:

Romaco do Brazil Ltda. (2)
Rua Engenheiro Mesquita Sampaio 137
Chacara Santo Antonio, Sao Paulo, SP, 04711-000, Brazil
Tel.: (55) 11 3168 7992
Fax: (55) 11 3078 7549
Pharmaceutical Packaging Machinery Sales & Service
S.I.C.: 5084
N.A.I.C.S.: 423830
Marcello Valente, *(Mgr)*

Romaco S.r.l. (2)
Via Marzabotto 5
Rastignano, 40067 Bologna, BO, Italy IT
Tel.: (39) 051744817
Fax: (39) 0516202600
E-Mail: info@promatic.romaco.com
Web Site: www.romaco.com
Sales Range: $125-149.9 Million
Emp.: 110
Printing, Packaging & Filling Services for the Pharmaceutical Industry
S.I.C.: 3565
N.A.I.C.S.: 333993
Paolo Naldi *(Gen Mgr)*

Non-U.S. Affiliate:

IPM Technologies (2)
Z I Le Treil
47520 Le Passage, d'Agen, France
Tel.: (33) 553685386
Fax: (33) 553685349
Web Site: www.ipm-pharma.fr
Sales Range: $125-149.9 Million
Process & Packaging Solutions
S.I.C.: 3565
N.A.I.C.S.: 333993

DEUTSCHE BORSE AG

Mergenthalerallee 61
65760 Eschborn, Germany
Tel.: (49) 692110
Fax: (49) 6921112005
E-Mail: info@deutsche-boerse.com
Web Site: www.deutsche-boerse.com
Year Founded: 1993
DB1—(DEU)
Rev.: $2,973,689,530
Assets: $291,483,363,143
Liabilities: $287,216,542,711
Net Worth: $4,266,820,432
Earnings: $901,664,666
Emp.: 3,704
Fiscal Year-end: 12/31/12
Business Description:
Stock Exchange Services
S.I.C.: 6231
N.A.I.C.S.: 523210
Personnel:
Joachim Faber *(Chm-Supervisory Bd)*
Gerhard Roggemann *(Deputy Chm-Supervisory Bd)*
Reto Francioni *(CEO & Member-Exec Bd)*
Andreas Preuss *(Deputy CEO & Member-Exec Bd)*
Gregor Pottmeyer *(CFO & Member-Exec Bd)*
Hauke Stars *(CIO & Member-Exec Bd)*
James H. Freis, Jr. *(Chief Compliance Officer)*
Jeffrey Tessler *(Member-Exec Bd-Clearstream Div)*
Supervisory Board of Directors:
Joachim Faber
Richard Berliand
Irmtraud Busch
Karl-Heinz Floether
Marion Fornoff
Hans-Peter Gabe
Richard M. Hayden
Craig F. Heimark
David Krell
Monica Machler
Friedrich Merz
Thomas Neisse
Heinz-Joachim Neuburger
Gerhard Roggemann
Erhard W. Schipporeit
Jutta Stuhlfauth
Martin Ulrici
Johannes Witt

Subsidiaries:

Clearstream Holding AG (1)
Clearstream Banking AG
60485 Frankfurt, Germany
Tel.: (49) 69 2 110
Fax: (49) 69 2 11 1 20 05
E-Mail: ClearstreamHolding@clearstream.com
Investment Management Services
S.I.C.: 6211
N.A.I.C.S.: 523999
Jeffrey Tessler *(CEO)*
Yves Baguet *(Member-Exec Bd)*
Stefan Lepp *(Member-Exec Bd)*
Marcus Thompson *(Member-Exec Bd)*

Deutsche Borse IT-Holding GmbH (1)
Neue Borsenstr 1
60485 Frankfurt am Main, Germany (100%)

Deutsche Borse AG—(Continued)

Tel.: (49) 692110
E-Mail: info@deutsche-borse.com
Web Site: www.deutscheborse.com
Emp.: 3,000
Holding Company; IT Services
S.I.C.: 6719
N.A.I.C.S.: 551112

Tradegate Exchange GmbH (1)
Kurfurstendamm 119
10711 Berlin, Germany
Tel.: (49) 30 89 021 145
Fax: (49) 30 89 021 134
E-Mail: info@tradegate.de
Web Site: www.tradegate.de
Stock Exchange Operating Services
S.I.C.: 6231
N.A.I.C.S.: 523210
Thorsten Commichau *(Member-Mgmt Bd)*
Jochen Thiel *(Member-Mgmt Bd)*

U.S. Subsidiaries:

Market News International Inc. (1)
40 Fulton St Fl 5
New York, NY 10038
Tel.: (212) 669-6400
Fax: (212) 608-3024
Toll Free: (800) 284-1401
E-Mail: ussales@marketnews.com
Web Site: www.deutsche-boerse.com
Newspaper Publishing Services
S.I.C.: 2711
N.A.I.C.S.: 511110
Kim Shannon *(Asst VP)*

Subsidiary:

Need to Know News, LLC (2)
529 14th St NW Ste 1100
Washington, DC 20045
Tel.: (312) 663-7176
E-Mail: alphaflashtrader@ntkn.com
Web Site: www.ntkn.com
Financial News Agency Services
S.I.C.: 7383
N.A.I.C.S.: 519110

Non-U.S. Subsidiaries:

Clearstream International S.A. (1)
42 Ave JF Kennedy
1855 Luxembourg, Luxembourg (100%)
Tel.: (352) 2430
Fax: (352) 24338000
E-Mail: info@clearstream.com
Web Site: www.clearstream.com
Emp.: 1,000
Settlement & Custody Services
S.I.C.: 6231
N.A.I.C.S.: 523210
Reto Francioni *(Chm)*
Jeffrey Tessler *(CEO)*

Subsidiaries:

Clearstream Banking S.A. (2)
42 Ave JF Kennedy
1855 Luxembourg, Luxembourg (100%)
Tel.: (352) 2430
Fax: (352) 24338000
Web Site: www.clearstream.com
Emp.: 1,100
Banking Services
S.I.C.: 6211
N.A.I.C.S.: 523110
Jeffrey Tessler *(CEO)*

Clearstream Services S.A. (2)
42 Avenue JF Kennedy
1855 Luxembourg, Luxembourg
Tel.: (352) 243 0
Fax: (352) 243 38000
E-Mail: web@clearstream.com
Emp.: 100
Information Technology Consulting Services
S.I.C.: 7373
N.A.I.C.S.: 541512
Jeffrey Tessler *(CEO)*
Mathias Papenfuss *(Member-Exec Bd)*

Non-U.S. Subsidiaries:

Clearstream Banking AG (2)
Neue Borsenstrasse 1
D-60487 Frankfurt am Main, Germany (100%)
Tel.: (49) 692110
E-Mail: info@deutsche-borse.com
Web Site: www.clearstream.com
Banking Services
S.I.C.: 6211
N.A.I.C.S.: 523110
Andreas Wolf *(CEO)*

Clearstream Operations Prague s.r.o (2)
Futurama Business Park Sokolovska 136 B
186 00 Prague, Czech Republic
Tel.: (420) 29 64 2 91 11
Fax: (420) 29 64 2 93 05
Data Processing Services
S.I.C.: 7379
N.A.I.C.S.: 518210

Deutsche Borse Services s.r.o (1)
Futurama Business Park Sokolovska 136 B
186 00 Prague, Czech Republic
Tel.: (420) 29 64 2 91 11
Fax: (420) 29 64 2 93 05
Emp.: 40
Financial Management Services
S.I.C.: 6211
N.A.I.C.S.: 523999
Mats Andersson *(Gen Mgr)*

Eurex Global Derivatives AG (1)
Loewenstrasse 3
8021 Zurich, Switzerland
Tel.: (41) 43 430 72 00
Fax: (41) 43 430 72 90
E-Mail: info@eurexzurichag.com
Web Site: www.eurexchange.com
Emp.: 3
Derivatives Exchange Services
S.I.C.: 6231
N.A.I.C.S.: 523210
Markus-Alexander Flesch *(Gen Mgr)*

Eurex Zurich AG (1)
Selnaustrasse 30
CH-8021 Zurich, Switzerland CH
Tel.: (41) 588542942 (100%)
Fax: (41) 584992466
E-Mail: communications@eurexchange.com
Web Site: www.eurexchange.com
Emp.: 40
Futures & Options Exchange; Owned 50% by Deutsche Borse AG & 50% by SWX Swiss Exchange
S.I.C.: 6231
N.A.I.C.S.: 523210
Peter Gomez *(Chm-Supervisory Bd)*
Andreas Preuss *(CEO)*
Jurg Spillmann *(Deputy CEO)*
Thomas Book *(Member-Exec Bd)*
Gary Katz *(Member-Exec Bd)*
Michael Peters *(Member-Exec Bd)*
Peter Reitz *(Member-Exec Bd)*

Non-U.S. Subsidiary:

Eurex Frankfurt AG (2)
Mergenthalerallee 61
65760 Eschborn, Germany
Tel.: (49) 69 211 1 1700
Fax: (49) 69 211 1 1701
E-Mail: info@eurexchange.com
Web Site: www.eurexchange.com
Emp.: 355
Futures & Options Exchange
S.I.C.: 6231
N.A.I.C.S.: 523210
Thomas Book *(Member-Exec Bd)*
Gary Katz *(Member-Exec Bd)*
Michael Petes *(Member-Exec Bd)*
Peter Reitz *(Member-Exec Bd)*

U.S. Subsidiaries:

International Securities Exchange Holdings, Inc. (3)
60 Broad St
New York, NY 10004 DE
Tel.: (212) 943-2400
Fax: (212) 425-4926
E-Mail: mail@iseoptions.com
Web Site: www.ise.com
Sales Range: $200-249.9 Million
Emp.: 216
Equity Options Exchange
S.I.C.: 6231
N.A.I.C.S.: 523210
Gary Katz *(Pres & CEO)*
Robert J. Cornish *(CTO)*
Michael J. Simon *(Gen Counsel, Chief Regulatory Officer & Sec)*

Subsidiaries:

International Securities Exchange LLC (4)
60 Broad St
New York, NY 10004
Tel.: (212) 943-2400
Fax: (212) 425-4926
Web Site: www.ise.com
Equity Options Exchange
S.I.C.: 6231
N.A.I.C.S.: 523210
David Krell *(Chm)*
Andreas Preuss *(Vice Chm)*
Gary Katz *(Pres & CEO)*
Daniel P. Friel *(CIO)*
Thomas Ascher *(Head-Corp Initiatives & Chief Strategy Officer)*
Lawrence P. Campbell *(CTO)*
Alex Jacobson *(Education Officer)*
Gregory J. Maynard *(System & Product Strategy Officer)*
Thomas Reina *(Software Dev Officer)*
James O. Sampson, III *(Trading & Market Ops Officer)*
Michael J. Simon *(Gen Counsel/Sec & Chief Regulatory Officer)*

Subsidiary:

ISE Stock Exchange LLC (5)
60 Broad St
New York, NY 10004
Tel.: (212) 943-2400
Fax: (212) 425-4926
Web Site: www.ise.com
Stock Exchange
S.I.C.: 6231
N.A.I.C.S.: 523210
Gary Katz *(Pres & CEO)*

ISE Ventures LLC (4)
60 Broad St
New York, NY 10004
Tel.: (212) 943-2400
Fax: (212) 425-4926
Web Site: www.ise.com
Emp.: 200
Holding Company
S.I.C.: 6719
N.A.I.C.S.: 551112
Gary Katz *(Pres & CEO)*

Longitude LLC (4)
60 Broad St
New York, NY 10004
Tel.: (212) 943-2400
Fax: (212) 425-4926
Web Site: www.ise.com
Emp.: 250
Alternative Markets Trading Services
S.I.C.: 6231
N.A.I.C.S.: 523210
Gary Katz *(Pres & CEO)*

U.S. Exchange Holdings, Inc. (3)
141 W Jackson Blvd Lbby 14
Chicago, IL 60604-3136
Tel.: (312) 544-1100
Web Site: www.eurexchange.com
Holding Company
S.I.C.: 6719
N.A.I.C.S.: 551112

Non-U.S. Joint Venture:

STOXX Ltd. (1)
Selnaustrasse 30
CH 8021 Zurich, Switzerland
Tel.: (41) 588545400
Fax: (41) 588545401
E-Mail: stoxx@stoxx.com
Web Site: www.stoxx.com
Sales Range: $100-124.9 Million
Emp.: 70
Stock Market Index Services; Owned by Deutsche Borse AG & SIX Group Ltd.
S.I.C.: 7389
N.A.I.C.S.: 519190
Holger Wohlenberg *(Chm)*
Werner Burki *(Vice Chm)*
Hartmut Graf *(CEO)*
Patrick Valovic *(CFO)*

DEUTSCHE BUNDESBANK

Wilhelm Epstein Strasse 14
60431 Frankfurt, Germany

Mailing Address:
Postfach 10 06 02
60006 Frankfurt, Germany
Tel.: (49) 6995660
Fax: (49) 6995663077
E-Mail: presse-information@bundesbank.de
Web Site: www.bundesbank.de
Int. Income: $14,809,216,170
Net Worth: $7,624,706,880
Earnings: $893,856,880
Emp.: 9,560
Fiscal Year-end: 12/31/12

Business Description:
Banking Services
S.I.C.: 6141
N.A.I.C.S.: 522210

Personnel:
Jens Weidmann *(Pres & Member-Exec Bd)*
Sabine Lautenschlager *(Deputy Pres & Member-Exec Bd)*
Ute Bremers *(Press Officer)*
Claus Brumberg *(Press Officer)*
Dorit Feldbrugge *(Press Officer)*
Ina Kirsch *(Press Officer)*
Moritz August Raasch *(Press Officer)*
Rudolf Bohmler *(Member-Exec Bd-Controlling, Acctg, Org & Economic Education)*
Andreas Dombret *(Member-Exec Bd-Fin Stability, Statistics & Risk Controlling)*
Joachim Nagel *(Member-Exec Bd-IT & Markets)*
Carl-Ludwig Thiele *(Member-Exec Bd-Cash Mgmt, Payment & Settlement Sys)*

Branches:

Deutsche Bundesbank Hauptverwaltung Berlin (1)
Postfach 12 01 63
10591 Berlin, Germany
Tel.: (49) 3034750
Fax: (49) 3034751990
E-Mail: pressestelle.hv-berlin@bundesbank.de
Banking Services
S.I.C.: 6029
N.A.I.C.S.: 522110
Claus Tigges *(Pres)*

Deutsche Bundesbank Hauptverwaltung Dusseldorf (1)
Berliner Allee 14
40212 Dusseldorf, Germany
Tel.: (49) 2118740
Fax: (49) 2118742632
E-Mail: ftab.hv-dusseldorf@bundesbank.de
Web Site: www.bundesbank.de
Emp.: 800
Banking Services
S.I.C.: 6029
N.A.I.C.S.: 522110
Norbert Matysik *(Pres)*
Hans Peter Weser *(Pres)*

Deutsche Bundesbank Hauptverwaltung Frankfurt (1)
Postfach 11 12 32
60047 Frankfurt, Germany
Tel.: (49) 6923880
Fax: (49) 6923881044
E-Mail: presse-information.hv-frankfurt@bundesbank.de
Web Site: www.deutschebundesbank.de
Banking Services
S.I.C.: 6029
N.A.I.C.S.: 522110
Jens Waidman *(Gen Mgr)*

Deutsche Bundesbank Hauptverwaltung Hamburg (1)
Welly-brantt-str 73
Postfach 57 03 48
22772 Hamburg, Germany
Tel.: (49) 4037070
Fax: (49) 4037077371
E-Mail: feleale-hamburg@bundesbank.de
Web Site: www.bundesbank.de
Emp.: 500

Banking Services
S.I.C.: 6029
N.A.I.C.S.: 522110
Adalhaid Sailea-Schufter *(Pres)*

Deutsche Bundesbank Hauptverwaltung Hannover (1)
Georgf Patz 5
Postfach 245
30002 Hannover, 30159, Germany
Tel.: (49) 51130330
Fax: (49) 51130332500
E-Mail: pressestelle.hv-hannover@bundesbank.de
Web Site: www.bundesbank.de
Emp.: 500
Banking Services
S.I.C.: 6029
N.A.I.C.S.: 522110
Werner Ehlers *(Pres)*

Deutsche Bundesbank Hauptverwaltung Leipzig (1)
Postfach 90 11 21
04358 Leipzig, Germany
Tel.: (49) 3418600
Fax: (49) 3418602389
E-Mail: oeffentlichkeitsarbeit.hv-leipzig@bundesbank.de
Web Site: www.bundesbank.com
Emp.: 200
Banking Services
S.I.C.: 6029
N.A.I.C.S.: 522110
Christopher Poppe *(Pres)*

Deutsche Bundesbank Hauptverwaltung Mainz (1)
Hegelstrasse 59
Postfach 30 09
55020 Mainz, Germany
Tel.: (49) 61313770
Fax: (49) 61313103
E-Mail: volkswirtschaft.hv-mainz@bundesbank.de
Web Site: www.bundesbank.de
Emp.: 500
Banking Services
S.I.C.: 6029
N.A.I.C.S.: 522110
Stefan Hardt *(Pres)*

DEUTSCHE EFFECTEN- UND WECHSEL-BETEILIGUNGSGESELLSCHAFT AG.

Leutragraben 1
07743 Jena, Thuringia, Germany
Tel.: (49) 36415733600
Fax: (49) 36415733610
E-Mail: info@dewb-vc.com
Web Site: www.dewb-vc.com
EFF—(DEU)
Sales Range: Less than $1 Million
Business Description:
Bank Independent Investment Company
S.I.C.: 6282
N.A.I.C.S.: 523920
Personnel:
Falk Nuber *(Vice Chm)*
Board of Directors:
Bertram Kohler
Mirko Wackerle

Subsidiaries:

DEWB-IT Beteiligungsgesellschaft mbH (1)
Leutragraben 1
07743 Jena, Thuringia, Germany
Tel.: (49) 3641 5733600
Fax: (49) 3641 5733610
E-Mail: info@dewb-vc.com
Investment Management Services
S.I.C.: 6211
N.A.I.C.S.: 523999

KSW Microtec Holding AG (1)
Leutragraben 1
07743 Jena, Thuringia, Germany
Tel.: (49) 36415733600
Fax: (49) 3641 57 33 610
Management Services
S.I.C.: 8741
N.A.I.C.S.: 551114

DEUTSCHE EUROSHOP AG

Heegbarg 36
22391 Hamburg, Germany
Tel.: (49) 404135790
Fax: (49) 4041357929
E-Mail: info@deutsche-euroshop.de
Web Site: www.deutsche-euroshop.de
DEQ—(DEU)
Rev.: $284,352,835
Assets: $4,777,360,789
Liabilities: $2,997,839,820
Net Worth: $1,779,520,969
Earnings: $164,884,286
Emp.: 4
Fiscal Year-end: 12/31/12
Business Description:
Shopping Malls & Shopping Centers Investment Services
S.I.C.: 1542
N.A.I.C.S.: 236220
Personnel:
Manfred Zass *(Chm-Supervisory Bd)*
Michael Gellen *(Deputy Chm-Supervisory Bd)*
Claus-Matthias Boge *(CEO & Member-Exec Bd)*
Olaf G. Borkers *(CFO & Member-Exec Bd)*
Supervisory Board of Directors:
Manfred Zass
Thomas Armbrust
Karin Dohm
Michael Gellen
Jorn Kreke
Alexander Otto
Reiner Strecker
Klaus Striebich
Bernd Thiemann

Subsidiaries:

Allee-Center Hamm KG (1)
Richard-Matthaei-Platz 1
59065 Hamm, Germany
Tel.: (49) 2381498110
Fax: (49) 2381161405
E-Mail: info@allee-center-hamm.de
Web Site: www.allee-center-hamm.de
Emp.: 14
Shopping Mall Management Services
S.I.C.: 6512
N.A.I.C.S.: 531120
Monika Block *(Mgr)*

City-Arkaden Wuppertal KG (1)
Alte Freiheit 9
42103 Wuppertal, Germany
Tel.: (49) 202946460
Fax: (49) 2029464620
E-Mail: info@city-arkaden-wuppertal.de
Web Site: www.city-arkaden-wuppertal.com
Shopping Mall Management Services
S.I.C.: 5411
N.A.I.C.S.: 445110
Katrin Becker *(Mgr)*

City-Galerie Wolfsburg KG (1)
Porschestrasse 45
38440 Wolfsburg, Germany
Tel.: (49) 53616000
Fax: (49) 5361 600 150
E-Mail: info@city-galerie-wolfsburg.de
Web Site: www.city-galerie-wolfsburg.de
Shopping Mall Management Services
S.I.C.: 6512
N.A.I.C.S.: 531120

Deutsche EuroShop Management GmbH (1)
Oderfelder Str 23
20149 Hamburg, Germany
Tel.: (49) 404135790
Fax: (49) 4041357929
E-Mail: info@des.ag
Web Site: www.des.ag
Emp.: 6
Asset Management Services
S.I.C.: 6531
N.A.I.C.S.: 531390
Claus Matthias Boge *(Mng Dir)*

Forum Wetzlar KG (1)
Am Forum 1
35576 Wetzlar, Germany
Tel.: (49) 6441381970
Fax: (49) 64413819799
E-Mail: info@forum-wetzlar.de
Web Site: www.forum-wetzlar.de
Emp.: 700
Shopping Mall Management Services
S.I.C.: 5411
N.A.I.C.S.: 445110
Sven Martens *(Mgr)*

Stadt-Galerie Hameln KG (1)
Pferdemarkt 1
31785 Hameln, Germany
Tel.: (49) 5151822270
Fax: (49) 51518222799
E-Mail: info@stadt-galerie-hameln.de
Web Site: www.stadt-galerie-hameln.de
Emp.: 14
Shopping Mall Management Services
S.I.C.: 6512
N.A.I.C.S.: 531120
Susanne Schubert *(Gen Mgr)*

Stadt-Galerie Passau KG (1)
Bahnhofstrasse 1
94032 Passau, Germany
Tel.: (49) 8518517970
Fax: (49) 85185179799
E-Mail: info@stadt-galerie-passau.de
Web Site: www.stadtgalerie-passau.de
Shopping Mall Management Services
S.I.C.: 6512
N.A.I.C.S.: 531120
Tanja Popp *(Mgr)*

DEUTSCHE HYPOTHEKENBANK (ACTIEN-GESELLSCHAFT)

(d/b/a Deutsche Hypo)
Georgsplatz 8
30159 Hannover, Germany
Tel.: (49) 51130450
Fax: (49) 511305459
E-Mail: mail@deutsche-hypo.de
Web Site: www.deutsche-hypo.com
Year Founded: 1872
Emp.: 200
Business Description:
Mortgage Bank; Owned 25% BHF-Bank, 25% M.M. Warburg & Co. Kommanditgesellschaft Auf Aktien, 25% Sal. Oppenheimer Jr & Cie KGaA
S.I.C.: 6163
N.A.I.C.S.: 522310
Personnel:
Jurgen Allerkamp *(Chm)*
Board of Directors:
Jurgen Allerkamp
Andreas Pohl

DEUTSCHE LAND PLC

15-19 Athol Street
Douglas, IM1 1LB, Isle of Man
Tel.: (44) 7711670320
Fax: (44) 1624638333
Web Site: www.deutscheland.co.im
Sales Range: $50-74.9 Million
Business Description:
Property Management Services
S.I.C.: 6531
N.A.I.C.S.: 531312
Personnel:
Stephen Dickinson *(Chm)*
David Maxwell *(CEO)*
Board of Directors:
Stephen Dickinson
Tony Ciochetti
Adrian John Reginald Collins
Martin Leitinger
Obie Moore
Christopher Pemberton
Ulrich Rucker

DEUTSCHE LUFTHANSA AG

Lufthansa Aviation Center Airportring
60546 Frankfurt am Main, Germany
Tel.: (49) 69 696 28008
Telex: 887 3531
Fax: (49) 69 696 90990
E-Mail: investor.relations@dlh.de
Web Site: www.lufthansagroup.com
Year Founded: 1926
LHA—(BER DEU OTC)
Rev.: $40,566,832,950
Assets: $38,256,805,230
Liabilities: $27,086,286,570
Net Worth: $11,170,518,660
Earnings: $1,350,208,510
Emp.: 116,957
Fiscal Year-end: 12/31/12
Business Description:
Holding Company; Airline Operations & Support Services
S.I.C.: 6719
N.A.I.C.S.: 551112
Personnel:
Wolfgang Mayrhuber *(Chm-Supervisory Bd)*
Christoph Franz *(Chm-Exec Bd & CEO)*
Christine Behle *(Deputy Chm-Supervisory Bd)*
Simone Menne *(CFO & Member-Exec Bd)*
Carsten Spohr *(Chief Officer-Lufthansa German Airlines & Member-Exec Bd)*
Harry Hohmeister *(CEO-Swiss International Air Lines Ltd & Member-Exec Bd)*
Bettina Volkens *(Dir-Indus Rels Grp & Member-Exec Bd)*
Supervisory Board of Directors:
Wolfgang Mayrhuber
Jacques Aigrain
Christine Behle
Werner Brandt
Herbert Hainer
Jurgen Hambrecht
Uwe Hien
Robert M. Kimmitt
Karl-Ludwig Kley
Martin Koehler
Doris Kruger
Nicola Leibinger-Kammuller
Eckhard Lieb
Ralf Muller
Ilona Ritter
Andreas Strache
Christina Weber
Birgit Weinreich
Matthias Wissmann
Stefan Ziegler

Division:

Lufthansa Passenger Airlines (1)
Lufthansa Aviation Center
Airportring, 60546 Frankfurt, Germany
Tel.: (49) 69 696 0
Fax: (49) 69 696 33022
Web Site: www.lufthansagroup.com
Sales Range: $25-49.9 Billion
Emp.: 55,236
Passenger Air Transportation Services
S.I.C.: 4512
N.A.I.C.S.: 481111

Subsidiaries:

Eurowings Luftverkehrs AG (2)
Flugplatz 21
44319 Dortmund, Germany De
Tel.: (49) 23192450
Fax: (49) 23192457303
E-Mail: kommunikation@eurowings.com
Web Site: www.eurowings.com
Sales Range: $1-4.9 Billion
Emp.: 1,330
Passenger Airline
S.I.C.: 4512
N.A.I.C.S.: 481111
Albrecht Knauf *(Chm-Supervisory Bd)*
Friedrich-Wilhem Weitholz *(Chm-Mgmt Bd)*
Joachim Klein *(Member-Mgmt Bd)*
Peter Kranich *(Deputy Member-Mgmt Bd)*

Deutsche Lufthansa AG—(Continued)

GOAL Verwaltungsgesellschaft mbH & Co. Projekt Nr. 5 KG (2)
Tolzer Str 15
Grunwald, 82031, Germany
Tel.: (49) 8964143149
Fax: (49) 8964143611
Engineering Services
S.I.C.: 8711
N.A.I.C.S.: 541330

Lufthansa AG (2)
Lh Basis
60456 Frankfurt, Germany (100%)
Tel.: (49) 696960
Fax: (49) 6969633022
Web Site: www.lufthansa.com
Emp.: 250
Non-Scheduled Cargo Airline; Domestic & International Flights
Import Export
S.I.C.: 4512
N.A.I.C.S.: 481111
Stephan Gemkow *(CFO)*

U.S. Unit:

Lufthansa German Airlines (3)
1640 Hempstead Tpke
East Meadow, NY 11554
Tel.: (516) 296-9671
Fax: (516) 296-9678
E-Mail: americaspr@dlh.de
Web Site: www.lufthansa.com
Emp.: 100
Passenger Air Transportation Services
S.I.C.: 4512
N.A.I.C.S.: 481111
Nils Haupt *(Dir-Corp Comm)*

Non-U.S. Subsidiary:

Delvag Luftfahrtversicherungs-AG (4)
Von-Gablenz-Strasse 2-6
50679 Cologne, Germany
Tel.: (49) 221 8292 001
Fax: (49) 221 8292 250
E-Mail: marketing@delvag.de
Web Site: www.delvag.de
Emp.: 114
Insurance Management Services
S.I.C.: 6411
N.A.I.C.S.: 524298
Stephan Gemkow *(Chm-Supervisory Bd)*
Peter Metzler *(Member-Exec Bd)*
Reiner Siebert *(Member-Exec Bd)*

Lufthansa WorldShop GmbH (2)
MAC Main Airport Center
Unterschweinstiege 8
60549 Frankfurt, Germany
Tel.: (49) 1803 967537467
Fax: (49) 1803 329 967537467
E-Mail: worldshop@dlh.de
Web Site: www.worldshop.eu
Online Marketing Services
S.I.C.: 8742
N.A.I.C.S.: 541613
Peter Pullem *(Mng Dir)*

Miles & More International GmbH (2)
Dornhofstrasse 100
63263 Neu-Isenburg, Germany
Tel.: (49) 61 02 24 93 500
Fax: (49) 61 02 24 93 101
E-Mail: impressum@milesandmore.com
Emp.: 7
Advertising Agency Services
S.I.C.: 7311
N.A.I.C.S.: 541810
Juergen Weber *(Chm-Supervisory Bd)*
Christoph Franz *(Chm-Exec Bd)*
Stephan Gemkow *(Member-Exec Bd)*
Stefan H. Lauer *(Member-Exec Bd)*
Carsten Spohr *(Member-Exec Bd)*

Non-U.S. Subsidiaries:

Air Dolomiti S.p.A. (2)
Via Bembo 70
Villa Franca, 37062 Verona, Italy IT
Tel.: (39) 0481477711 (100%)
Fax: (39) 00390452886119
Web Site: www.airdolomiti.it
Emp.: 250
Regional Passenger Air Transportation Services
S.I.C.: 4512
N.A.I.C.S.: 481111
Michael Krauss *(Mng Dir)*

AUA Beteiligungen Gesellschaft m.b.H. (2)
Office Park 2
Wien-Flughafen, Vienna, 1300, Austria
Tel.: (43) 517661000
Fax: (43) 517665000
Investment Management Services
S.I.C.: 6211
N.A.I.C.S.: 523999
Jaan Albrecht *(CEO)*

Austrian Airlines AG (2)
Office Pk 2
PO Box 100
1300 Vienna, Austria AT
Tel.: (43) 517660 (95.4%)
Fax: (43) 5176613899
E-Mail: public.relations@austrian.com
Web Site: www.austrian.com
Sales Range: $1-4.9 Billion
Emp.: 7,914
Air Transportation Services
S.I.C.: 4512
N.A.I.C.S.: 481111
Harry Hohmeister *(Chm-Supervisory Bd)*
Jaan Albrecht *(CEO)*
Karsten Benz *(Chief Comml Officer)*

Subsidiaries:

Lauda Air Luftfahrt GmbH (3)
Office Park 2
PO Box 56
1300 Vienna, Austria AT
Tel.: (43) 5176673800 (100%)
E-Mail: charter.myholiday@austrian.com
Web Site: www.austrian.com
Emp.: 27
Passenger Airline Services
S.I.C.: 4512
N.A.I.C.S.: 481111
Doris Kopf-Szankovich *(Mng Dir)*

SCA - Schedule Coordination Austria GmbH (3)
Office Park I Top B 08-04
1300 Vienna, Austria AT
Tel.: (43) 1700723600 (54%)
Fax: (43) 1700723615
Web Site: www.slots-austria.com
Emp.: 100
Commercial Air Transportation Coordination & Scheduling Services
S.I.C.: 9621
N.A.I.C.S.: 926120
Friedrich Lehr *(Chm)*
W. Gallinstl *(Mng Dir)*

Tyrolean Airways Tiroler Luftfahrt GmbH (3)
Furstenweg 176
A-6026 Innsbruck, Austria AT
Tel.: (43) 517663000 (100%)
Web Site: www.tyrolean.at
Passenger Airline Services
S.I.C.: 4512
N.A.I.C.S.: 481111

Non-U.S. Subsidiaries:

Austrian Airlines Technik-Bratislava, s.r.o. (3)
Letisko M R Stefanika Hangar C
820 01 Bratislava, Slovakia
Tel.: (421) 911 487 038
Fax: (421) 248 207 620
E-Mail: customers@atb.sk
Emp.: 16
Aircraft Maintenance Services
S.I.C.: 7539
N.A.I.C.S.: 811198
Konstantin Essler *(Mng Dir, Mgr-Accountable & Dir-Technical)*
Pavol Hamsik *(Deputy Mng Dir & Head-Fin Dept)*
Vladimir Stulancak *(Deputy Mng Dir & Head-Logistics Dept)*
Iveta Nemcikova *(Deputy Mng Dir-HR)*

Lufthansa Malta Holding Ltd (2)
Aragon House Level 4 Dragonara Road
San Giljan, Malta
Tel.: (356) 21383843
Fax: (356) 20107417
Investment Management Services
S.I.C.: 6211
N.A.I.C.S.: 523999
Stefan Mast *(Gen Mgr)*

Swiss International Air Lines AG (2)
Aeschenvorstadt 4
401 Basel, Switzerland
Tel.: (41) 615820000
Fax: (41) 615823333
E-Mail: communications@swiss.com
Web Site: www.swiss.com
Sales Range: $1-4.9 Billion
Emp.: 6,026
Passenger Air Transportation Services
S.I.C.: 4512
N.A.I.C.S.: 481111
Bruno Gehrig *(Chm)*
Walter Bosch *(Vice Chm)*
Reto Schmid *(Mng Dir, Gen Counsel & Head-HR)*
Marcel Klaus *(CFO & Exec VP)*
Rainer Hiltebrand *(COO)*
Peter Wojahn *(CTO)*
Oliver Evans *(Chief Logistic Officer)*

Subsidiaries:

Edelweiss Air AG (3)
Edelweiss Air Operation Ctr Zurich Airport
8058 Zurich, Switzerland
Tel.: (41) 438165060
Fax: (41) 438165061
E-Mail: info@edelweissair.ch
Web Site: www.edelweissair.ch
Rev.: $410,851,300
Emp.: 260
Fiscal Year-end: 12/31/12
Airline
S.I.C.: 4512
N.A.I.C.S.: 481111
Karl Kistler *(CEO)*
Christian Gfeller *(Deputy CEO & Head-Ground Ops)*
Alain Chisari *(Chief Comml Officer)*
Zoltan Horvath *(Flight Safety Officer)*

Swiss Aviation Software AG (3)
Spalenring 150
4002 Basel, Switzerland
Tel.: (41) 61 582 72 94
Fax: (41) 61 582 70 17
E-Mail: marketing@swiss-as.com
Web Site: www.swiss-as.com
Emp.: 95
Aviation Maintenance Software Development Services
S.I.C.: 7371
N.A.I.C.S.: 541511
Ronald Schauffele *(CEO)*

Swiss Aviation Training Ltd. (3)
Balz-Zimmermann-Str 38
Zurich-Airport, 8058 Zurich, Switzerland
Tel.: (41) 44 564 59 00
Fax: (41) 44 564 57 00
E-Mail: info@swiss-aviation-training.com
Web Site: www.swiss-aviation-training.com
Emp.: 300
Aviation Training Services
S.I.C.: 8249
N.A.I.C.S.: 611512
Manfred Brennwald *(Pres & CEO)*

Swiss European Air Lines AG (3)
Zurich Airport
8058 Zurich, Switzerland
Tel.: (41) 44 564 00 00
Fax: (41) 44 564 42 85
E-Mail: europeanfleet@swiss.com
Web Site: www.swiss.com
Emp.: 233
Airline Transportation Services
S.I.C.: 4581
N.A.I.C.S.: 488190
Rainer Hiltebrand *(Chm)*
Maya Adriano *(Sec)*

Non-U.S. Subsidiary:

Swiss WorldCargo (India) Private Limited (3)
501 Solitaire Corporate Park 167 Guru HarGovindji Marg
Andheri East, Mumbai, 400 093, India
Tel.: (91) 22 6177 4687
Fax: (91) 22 6177 4666
E-Mail: cargo.india@swiss.com
Emp.: 8
General Airfreight Cargo Handling Services
S.I.C.: 4581
N.A.I.C.S.: 488119
Shankar Iyer *(Mng Dir)*

TRAVIAUSTRIA Datenservice fur Reise und Touristik Gesellschaft m.b.H. & Co NFG. KG (2)
Dresdner Strasse 81 - 85
1200 Vienna, Austria
Tel.: (43) 1 33733 0
Fax: (43) 1 33733 733
E-Mail: info@travi.com
Web Site: www.travi.com
Emp.: 65
Travel Agencies
S.I.C.: 4724
N.A.I.C.S.: 561510
Rudolf Mertl *(Mng Dir)*
Hans Wildauer *(CIO)*

Subsidiaries:

Airport Services Dresden GmbH (1)
Wilhelmine-Reichhard-Ring 1
1109 Dresden, Germany
Tel.: (49) 351 8814010
Fax: (49) 351 8814015
E-Mail: info@handling-drs.com
Web Site: www.airport-services-dresden.de
Emp.: 14
Airport Baggage Handling Services
S.I.C.: 4581
N.A.I.C.S.: 488119
Stephan J. Weinmann *(Mng Dir)*

Airport Services Leipzig GmbH (1)
PO Box 1122
PO Box 1122
4029 Leipzig, Germany
Tel.: (49) 341 2241601
Fax: (49) 341 2241620
E-Mail: info@handling-lej.de
Web Site: www.handling-lej.de
Emp.: 135
Airport Handling Services
S.I.C.: 4581
N.A.I.C.S.: 488190
Felix Redeker *(Mng Dir & Gen Mgr)*

Albatraos Versicherungsdienste GmbH (1)
Von-Gablenz-Strasse 2-6
50679 Cologne, Germany
Tel.: (49) 221 8292 002
Fax: (49) 221 8292 246
E-Mail: zentrale@albatros.de
Web Site: www.albatros.de
Emp.: 148
Insurance Management Services
S.I.C.: 6411
N.A.I.C.S.: 524298
Walter N. Gehl *(Chm-Supervisory Bd)*
Peter Hoffmann *(Mng Dir)*
Peter Metzler *(Mng Dir)*
Reiner Siebert *(Mng Dir)*

Albatros Service Center GmbH (1)
Gebaude 1335 A
Hahn-Flughafen, 55483 Buchenbeuren, Germany
Tel.: (49) 6543 502 224
Fax: (49) 6543 502 223
E-Mail: service-center@albatros.de
Web Site: www.albatros-service-center.de
Airport Call Center Services
S.I.C.: 7389
N.A.I.C.S.: 561421

AS InPro GmbH (1)
Industriehof 5
Oldenburg, 26133, Germany
Tel.: (49) 441944180
Fax: (49) 4419441899
Information Technology Consulting Services
S.I.C.: 7373
N.A.I.C.S.: 541512

DLH Fuel Company mbH (1)
Weg Beim Jager 193
Hamburg, 22335, Germany
Tel.: (49) 4050700
Airline Transportation Services
S.I.C.: 4581
N.A.I.C.S.: 488190

LH Cargo Holding GmbH (1)
Langer Kornweg 34i
Kelsterbach, 65451, Germany
Tel.: (49) 6107 777666
Fax: (49) 6107 777881
Investment Management Services

S.I.C.: 6211
N.A.I.C.S.: 523999

LSG Lufthansa Service Holding AG (1)
Dornhofstrasse 38
63263 Neu-Isenburg, Germany De
Tel.: (49) 61022400 (100%)
Fax: (49) 6102240999
E-Mail: info@lsgskychefs.com
Web Site: www.lsgskychefs.com
Sales Range: $1-4.9 Billion
Emp.: 30,000
Holding Company; Airline Catering & Airport Contract Food Services
S.I.C.: 6719
N.A.I.C.S.: 551112
Walter Gehl *(Chm-Exec Bd & CEO)*
Jens Theuerkorn *(CFO & Member-Exec Bd)*
Erdmann F. Rauer *(Chief Sls Officer & Member-Exec Bd)*
Jochen Muller *(Member-Exec Bd)*
Josefine Corsten *(Sr VP-Comm)*

Subsidiaries:

LSG Lufthansa Service Catering- und Dienstleistungsgesellschaft mbH (2)
Dornhofstr 40
Neu-Isenburg, 63263, Germany
Tel.: (49) 61022400
Fax: (49) 6102240999
Emp.: 10
Airline Catering Services
S.I.C.: 5812
N.A.I.C.S.: 722320
Gert Schnicke *(Gen Mgr)*

LSG Lufthansa Service Europa/Afrika GmbH (2)
Dornhofstrasse 38
D-63263 Neu-Isenburg, Germany De
Tel.: (49) 6102240999 (100%)
Fax: (49) 6102240999
Holding Company; Airline Catering & Food Service Contractor
S.I.C.: 6719
N.A.I.C.S.: 551112
Alfred Rigler *(COO)*

Non-U.S. Subsidiary:

LSG Sky Chefs South Africa (Pty) Ltd. (3)
Corner Jones & Springbok Road
PO Box 26840
East Rand, Johannesburg, Boksburg, 1462, South Africa ZA
Tel.: (27) 112810000 (100%)
Fax: (27) 113971820
E-Mail: lsg.sa@lsgskychefs.com
Web Site: www.lsgskychefs.com
Airline Catering, Food Service Contractor & Laundry Services
S.I.C.: 5812
N.A.I.C.S.: 722320
Johan Oosthuizen *(Mng Dir)*

LSG Sky Chefs Deutschland GmbH (2)
Dornhofstrasse 38
D-63263 Neu-Isenburg, Germany De
Tel.: (49) 61022400 (100%)
Telex: SITA FRAZDLH
Fax: (49) 6102240999
Web Site: www.lsgskychefs.com
Emp.: 1,400
Airline Catering & Food Service Contractor
S.I.C.: 5812
N.A.I.C.S.: 722320

Subsidiaries:

LSG-Food & Nonfood Handel GmbH (3)
Dornhofstrasse 38
D-63263 Neu-Isenburg, Germany De
Tel.: (49) 6 102 240 790 (100%)
Fax: (49) 6 102 240 799
E-Mail: ringeltaube.neu-isenburg@lsgskychefs.com
Web Site: www.ringeltaube.de
Emp.: 28
Airport Gift Shops & Duty Free Shopping
S.I.C.: 5947
N.A.I.C.S.: 453220
Katja Stahlhacke *(Mng Dir)*

LSG Sky Chefs Catering Logistics GmbH (3)
Dornhofstrasse 40
D-63263 Neu-Isenburg, Germany De
Tel.: (49) 6102240607 (100%)
Web Site: www.lsgskychefs.com
Airline In-Flight Equipment & Logistics Services
S.I.C.: 4731
N.A.I.C.S.: 541614

LSG Sky Chefs Lounge GmbH (3)
Dornhofstr 38
Neu-Isenburg, 63263, Germany
Tel.: (49) 61022400
Fax: (49) 6102240111
Airline Catering Services
S.I.C.: 5812
N.A.I.C.S.: 722320

LSG-Sky Food GmbH (3)
Otto-Lilienthal-Strasse 6-8
D-55232 Alzey, Germany De
Tel.: (49) 67319090 (100%)
Fax: (49) 6731909111
E-Mail: lsg-skyfood@lsgskychefs.com
Web Site: www.lsgskychefs.com
Emp.: 400
Commercial Airline Frozen Meals Mfr
S.I.C.: 2038
N.A.I.C.S.: 311412
Alexander Thies *(Mng Dir)*

LZ-Catering GmbH (2)
Sportallee 54b
22335 Hamburg, Germany
Tel.: (49) 40 5070 5373
Fax: (49) 40 5070 5377
E-Mail: info@lz-catering.de
Web Site: www.lz-catering.de
Emp.: 43
Restaurant Operating Services
S.I.C.: 5812
N.A.I.C.S.: 722511
Joachim Plass *(Gen Mgr)*

U.S. Subsidiaries:

LSG Sky Chefs North America Solutions, Inc. (2)
6191 N State Hwy 161
Irving, TX 75038-2246 DE
Tel.: (972) 793-9000 (100%)
Web Site: www.lsgskychefs.com
Holding Company; Regional Managing Office; Airline Catering & Food Service Contractor
S.I.C.: 6719
N.A.I.C.S.: 551112
Sondra Lehman *(COO)*
Dennis Sadlowski *(Reg COO)*

Subsidiary:

LSG Sky Chefs USA, Inc. (3)
6191 N State Hwy 161
Irving, TX 75038-2246 DE
Tel.: (972) 793-9000 (100%)
Web Site: www.lsgskychefs.com
Airline Catering & Food Service Contractor
S.I.C.: 5812
N.A.I.C.S.: 722320
Sondra Lehman *(Pres & COO)*

Non-U.S. Subsidiary:

CLS Catering Services Ltd. (3)
3560 Jericho Rd Vancouver International Airport
Richmond, BC, V7B 1C2, Canada Ca
Tel.: (604) 273-4438 (70%)
Fax: (604) 270-6538
E-Mail: mfowler@clfcatering.com
Web Site: www.clscater.com
Sales Range: $1-9.9 Million
Emp.: 200
Airline Catering Services
S.I.C.: 5812
N.A.I.C.S.: 722320
David Wainman *(Gen Mgr)*

LSG Sky Chefs Supply Chain Solutions, Inc. (2)
6191 N State Hwy 161 100
Irving, TX 75038-2246
Tel.: (972) 793-9000
Catering Services
S.I.C.: 5812
N.A.I.C.S.: 722320

SCIS Air Security Corporation (2)
1521 N Cooper St Ste 300 SkyMark Bldg
Arlington, TX 76011
Tel.: (817) 792-4500
Fax: (817) 792-4511
Toll Free: (888) 540-0899
Web Site: www.scisairsecurity.com
Emp.: 53
Airline Security Consulting Services
S.I.C.: 4581
N.A.I.C.S.: 488119
Joe Hailey *(Program Mgr)*

Non-U.S. Subsidiaries:

AIRO Catering Services Eesti OU (2)
Kesk-Sojamae 26
Tallinn, 11415, Estonia
Tel.: (372) 6058230
Fax: (372) 6058232
E-Mail: info@airo.com
Emp.: 50
Inflight Catering Services
S.I.C.: 5812
N.A.I.C.S.: 722320
Rita Pappa *(Mgr-Catering)*

Airo Catering Services Latvija SIA (2)
International Airport Riga
Marupe, 1053, Latvia
Tel.: (371) 67207201
Fax: (371) 67207083
E-Mail: info@airo.lv
Web Site: www.lsgskychefs.com
Emp.: 13
Airline Catering Services
S.I.C.: 5812
N.A.I.C.S.: 722320
Andris Balickis *(Gen Mgr)*

AIRO Catering Services - Ukraine (2)
Airport Boryspil-7
Kiev, v, Ukraine
Tel.: (380) 44 230 00 23
Fax: (380) 44 230 00 24
Airline Catering Services
S.I.C.: 5812
N.A.I.C.S.: 722320
Sergey Anfinogenov *(Gen Mgr)*

Caterair Servicos de Bordo e Hotelaria S.A. (2)
Estrada do Galeao s/n
Cacuia, Rio de Janeiro, 21941-570, Brazil
Tel.: (55) 21 2468 6000
Fax: (55) 21 2468 6054
Emp.: 100
Food Processing Machinery Mfr
S.I.C.: 5084
N.A.I.C.S.: 423830
Simone Okazawa *(Mgr)*

Comisariato de Baja California, S.A. de C.V (2)
Calle Uno Norte No 114 Nueva Tijuana
Tijuana, Baja California, 22500, Mexico
Tel.: (52) 6646235427
Fax: (52) 6646233278
Catering Services
S.I.C.: 5812
N.A.I.C.S.: 722320

Finnair Catering Oy (2)
Teknikontie 1
PO Box 41
01053 Vantaa, Finland
Tel.: (358) 9818 5025
Fax: (358) 9818 5599
Web Site: www.finnairgroup.com
Catering Services
S.I.C.: 5812
N.A.I.C.S.: 722320

Inflight Catering Services Limited (2)
PO Box 76070
Dar es Salaam, Tanzania
Tel.: (255) 22 284 3541
Fax: (255) 22 284 439
E-Mail: john.deneys@lsg.co.tz
Web Site: www.lsgskychefs.com
Emp.: 19
Flight Catering Services
S.I.C.: 5812
N.A.I.C.S.: 722320
Thomas Cheah *(Gen Mgr)*

LSG Catering China Ltd (2)
No 6 Catering Road West Hong Kong International Airport
Chek Lap Kok, Hong Kong, China (Hong Kong)
Tel.: (852) 2767 5318
Fax: (852) 2949 8442
E-Mail: gcatering.hkg.group@lsgskychefs.com
Web Site: www.gcateringhk.lsgskychefs.com
General Catering Services
S.I.C.: 5812
N.A.I.C.S.: 722320
Yau Sam *(Gen Mgr)*

LSG Lufthansa Service Asia Ltd. (2)
Suite 1704 Island Place Tower
510 Kings Road, North Point, China (Hong Kong) (100%)
Tel.: (852) 29636388
Fax: (852) 27742874
E-Mail: info@lsg-skychefs.com
Web Site: www.lsg-skychefs.com
Emp.: 30
Air Transportation Svcs
S.I.C.: 4512
N.A.I.C.S.: 481111
Hing Kai Cheung *(COO)*

Subsidiaries:

LSG Holding Asia Ltd. (3)
1704-1706 Island Place Tower
510 Kings Road
North Point, China (Hong Kong) (100%)
Tel.: (852) 29636388
Fax: (852) 25650022
Web Site: www.lsg-skychefs.com
Emp.: 20
Air Transportation Catering Svcs
S.I.C.: 5812
N.A.I.C.S.: 722320

Holding:

LSG Lufthansa Service Hong Kong Ltd. (4)
No 6 Catering Road West Hong Kong International Airport
Chek Lap Kok, Hong Kong, China (Hong Kong) HK
Tel.: (852) 2769 8211 (47.9%)
Fax: (852) 2363 9511
Sales Range: $75-99.9 Million
Emp.: 800
Airline Catering, Cleaning, Laundry & Food Service Contractor
S.I.C.: 5812
N.A.I.C.S.: 722320
Eddy Yung *(Gen Mgr)*

Non-U.S. Subsidiaries:

LSG Sky Chefs (India) Pvt. Ltd. (3)
Begaluru International Airport
Devanahalli, Bengaluru, 560 300, India In
Tel.: (91) 8022018701 (100%)
Fax: (91) 8022018733
E-Mail: info@lsgskychefs.com
Web Site: www.lsgskychefs.com
Emp.: 200
Airline Catering & Food Service Contractor
S.I.C.: 5812
N.A.I.C.S.: 722320
Anup Sahu *(Dir-Ops-India)*

LSG Sky Chefs (Thailand) Ltd. (3)
999 Moo 1 Nong Prue
Bang Phli, 10540 Samut Prakan, Thailand TH
Tel.: (66) 21311900
Fax: (66) 21311998
E-Mail: customerservices.bkk@lsgskychefs.com
Web Site: www.lsgskychefs.com
Holding Company; Airline Catering & Laundry Services
S.I.C.: 6719
N.A.I.C.S.: 551112

Subsidiary:

LSG Catering (Thailand) Ltd. (4)
999 Moo 1 Nong Prue
Bang Phli, 10540 Samut Prakan, Thailand TH
Tel.: (66) 2 131 1900 (100%)
Fax: (66) 2 131 1998

Deutsche Lufthansa AG—(Continued)

E-Mail: customerservices.bkk@lsgskychefs.com
Web Site: www.lsgskychefs.com
Emp.: 35
Airline Catering Services
S.I.C.: 5812
N.A.I.C.S.: 722320

Holding:

Siam Flight Services Ltd. (4)
Bangkok International Airport
Vipavadee-Rangsit Road, 10210 Bangkok, Donmuang, Thailand TH
Tel.: (66) 2 996 8890 (66.67%)
Fax: (66) 2 996 8885
E-Mail: customerservice@siamflight.com
Web Site: www.siamflight.com
Airline Food Service Contractor
S.I.C.: 5812
N.A.I.C.S.: 722310

LSG Lufthansa Service Cape Town (Pty) Ltd (2)
Madrid Street Airport Industry 2
Cape Town, 8001, South Africa
Tel.: (27) 213864093
Fax: (27) 213864097
E-Mail: salesmarketing@lsgskycheff.com
Web Site: www.lsgskycheff.com
Emp.: 7
Airline Catering Services
S.I.C.: 5812
N.A.I.C.S.: 722320
Karin Zimmermann *(Gen Mgr)*

LSG Sky Chefs Belgium N.V. (2)
Gebouw 53 Luchthaven
Zaventem, 1930, Belgium
Tel.: (32) 27237240
Fax: (32) 27237290
Catering Services
S.I.C.: 5812
N.A.I.C.S.: 722320

LSG Sky Chefs de Venezuela C.A. (2)
Aeropuerto Intl Simon Bolivar Sector Tiyuca Alcabala Cojedes Catia
La Mar Edo Vargas Apdo 165, Caracas, Vargas, Venezuela VE
Tel.: (58) 2123552861 (99.9%)
Fax: (58) 2123552741
Web Site: www.lsgskychefs.com
Airline Catering & Food Service Contractor
S.I.C.: 5812
N.A.I.C.S.: 722320

LSG Sky Chefs Havacilik Hizmetleri A.S. (2)
Ataturk Hava Limani Ozel Hangarlar Bolgesi
Istanbul, Turkey
Tel.: (90) 2125929800
Fax: (90) 2125929809
Catering Services
S.I.C.: 5812
N.A.I.C.S.: 722320

LSG Sky Chefs Korea Co Ltd. (2)
2840 Wunseo-Dong
Jung-Gu, Incheon, 400340, Korea (South)
Tel.: (82) 327445222
Fax: (82) 327445219
E-Mail: imchul.kim@lsgskychefs.com
Web Site: www.lsgskychefs.com
Emp.: 3
Flight Catering Services
S.I.C.: 5812
N.A.I.C.S.: 722320

LSG Sky Chefs New Zealand Limited (2)
1 Laurence Stevens Drive Auckland International Airport
Auckland, 2022, New Zealand
Tel.: (64) 9 255 0700
Fax: (64) 9 255 0730
Web Site: www.lsgskychefs.com
Emp.: 60
Catering Services
S.I.C.: 5812
N.A.I.C.S.: 722320

LSG Sky Chefs Norge AS (2)
Roald Amundsensvei
PO Box 16
NO-2061 Gardermoen, Norway NO
Tel.: (47) 64815800 (100%)
Fax: (47) 64815819
E-Mail: dl.bistapch.osl@lsgskychefs.com
Web Site: www.lsgskychefs.com
Emp.: 40
Airline Catering & Food Service Contractor
S.I.C.: 5812
N.A.I.C.S.: 722320
Fredrik Karl Heinrici *(Mng Dir)*

LSG Sky Chefs Schweiz AG (2)
Hofwisenstrasse 48
CH-8153 Rumlang, Switzerland CH
Tel.: (41) 44 818 7571 (100%)
Fax: (41) 44 818 7576
Web Site: www.lsgskychefs.com
Airline Catering & Food Service Contractor
S.I.C.: 5812
N.A.I.C.S.: 722320
Silvio Canettoli *(Chm & COO)*

LSG Sky Chefs Solutions Asia Limited (2)
Rm 2703-6a 27/F Exchange Twr 33 Wang Chiu Rd
Kowloon Bay, Kowloon, China (Hong Kong)
Tel.: (852) 29636388
Fax: (852) 25650022
Web Site: www.lsgskychefs.com
Emp.: 800
Airline Catering Services
S.I.C.: 5812
N.A.I.C.S.: 722320
Angie Fung *(Mng Dir)*

LSG Sky Chefs S.p.A. (2)
Palazzina 80 Terminal 2
PO Box 16 Airport Malpenza
2000, IT-21010 Somma Lombardo, VA, Italy IT
Tel.: (39) 02 58588 434 (100%)
Fax: (39) 02 58588 413
Web Site: www.lsgskychefs.com
Airline Catering & Food Service Contractor
S.I.C.: 5812
N.A.I.C.S.: 722320

Subsidiary:

Starfood S.r.l. (3)
Via Francesco de Pinedo
IT-00054 Fiumicino, Rome, Italy IT
Tel.: (39) 0660234328 (51%)
Telex: FCOVE7X
Airline Catering Services
S.I.C.: 5812
N.A.I.C.S.: 722320
Giovanni Corbelli *(Gen Mgr)*

LSG Sky Chefs Sverige AB (2)
Skogsvagen 2
PO Box 188
190 46 Stockholm, Sweden SE
Tel.: (46) 8 5220 6000 (100%)
Fax: (46) 8 5220 6025
Airline Catering & Food Service Contractor
S.I.C.: 5812
N.A.I.C.S.: 722320
Henrik Lindh *(Mng Dir)*

Subsidiary:

LSG Sky Chefs Building AB (3)
Arlanda Flygplats
190 60 Stockholm, Sweden SE
Mailing Address: (100%)
PO Box 188
190 46 Stockholm, Sweden
Tel.: (46) 87970900
Lessors of Other Real Estate Property
S.I.C.: 6519
N.A.I.C.S.: 531190
Gustaf Henrik Lindh *(Chm)*

LSG Sky Chefs UK Ltd. (2)
Faraday Road
Crawley, W Sussex, RH10 9JX, United Kingdom UK
Tel.: (44) 1293404810 (100%)
Fax: (44) 1293 401 814
Web Site: www.lsgskychefs.com
Emp.: 500
Airline Catering & Food Service Contractor
S.I.C.: 5812
N.A.I.C.S.: 722320
Dale Easdon *(COO)*

Subsidiary:

LSG/Sky Chefs Europe Holdings Ltd. (3)
Faraday Road
Crawley, W Sussex, RH10 9JX, United Kingdom UK
Tel.: (44) 1293 404 810 (100%)
Web Site: www.lsgskychefs.com
Emp.: 400
Holding Company; Airline Catering & Food Service Contractor
S.I.C.: 6719
N.A.I.C.S.: 551112

Affiliate:

LSG Sky Chefs/GCC Ltd. (4)
27 Central Way
Feltham, Mddx, TW14 0UU, United Kingdom UK
Tel.: (44) 2088448000 (50%)
Fax: (44) 208 751 8711
Web Site: www.lsgskychefs.com
Emp.: 500
Airline Catering Services
S.I.C.: 5812
N.A.I.C.S.: 722320

ServCater Internacional Ltda (2)
Rodovia Helio Smidt - Setor 1 - Base A
Guarulhos, 07190-100, Brazil
Tel.: (55) 1121492300
Fax: (55) 1121492326
Processed Food Mfr
S.I.C.: 2099
N.A.I.C.S.: 311999

Sky Chefs De Mexico, S.A. de C.V. (2)
Francisco Sarabia No 15 Penos De Los Banos Venustiano Carranza
Mexico, 15520, Mexico
Tel.: (52) 5557850360
Fax: (52) 5557855607
Catering Services
S.I.C.: 5812
N.A.I.C.S.: 722320

Sky Chefs de Panama, S.A. (2)
Aeropuerto Internacional De Tocumen
Panama, Panama
Tel.: (507) 2384010
Fax: (507) 5072384083
Web Site: www.lsgskychefs.com
Catering Services
S.I.C.: 5812
N.A.I.C.S.: 722320
Rolando Kourany *(Office Mgr)*

Starfood Antalya Gida Sanayi ve Ticaret A.S. (2)
Senlikkoy Mah Yesilkoy Cad No 17/A Kat 2
Istanbul, Turkey
Tel.: (90) 2123766400
Fax: (90) 2123766464
Catering Services
S.I.C.: 5812
N.A.I.C.S.: 722320
Merve Oral *(Mgr-Bus Dev)*

UAB Airo Catering Services Lietuva (2)
Rodunios Kelias 2
Vilnius, 2189, Lithuania
Tel.: (370) 5 230 62 42
Fax: (370) 5 232 07 43
E-Mail: info@airo.lt
Web Site: www.airo.lt
Emp.: 4
Inflight Catering Services
S.I.C.: 5812
N.A.I.C.S.: 722320
Zileinas Karaleicius *(Gen Mgr)*

Non-U.S. Joint Venture:

ZAO Aeromar (2)
31 Sheremetyevskoe Shosse
141426 Moscow, Khimki, Russia RU
Tel.: (7) 95 730 25 50
E-Mail: Dzao@aeromar.ru
Web Site: www.aeromar.ru
Emp.: 1,353
Airline Catering Services; Owned 51% by Aeroflot Russian Airlines & 49% by Deutsche Lufthansa AG
S.I.C.: 5812
N.A.I.C.S.: 722320

Lufthansa AirPlus Servicekarten GmbH (1)
Hans-Bockler-Str 7
63263 Neu-Isenburg, Germany
Tel.: (49) 61 02 204 0
Fax: (49) 61 02 204 349
E-Mail: info@airplus.com
Web Site: www.airplus.com
Travel Payment Data Management Services
S.I.C.: 7379
N.A.I.C.S.: 518210
Patrick W. Diemer *(Chm & Co-Mng Dir)*
Stephan Gemkow *(Chm-Supervisory Bd)*
Klaus Busch *(Co-Mng Dir)*

U.S. Subsidiary:

AirPlus International, Inc. (2)
225 Reinekers Ln Ste 500
Alexandria, VA 22314
Tel.: (703) 373-0940
Fax: (703) 373-0941
E-Mail: usa@airplus.com
Web Site: www.airplus.com
Emp.: 15
Travel Payment Processing Services
S.I.C.: 6099
N.A.I.C.S.: 522320
Michael Boult *(Exec VP-Global Sls-North America)*

Non-U.S. Subsidiaries:

AirPlus Air Travel Card Vertriebsgesellschaft mbH (2)
Rainergasse 1
1041 Vienna, Austria
Tel.: (43) 1 50 135 0
Fax: (43) 1 50 135 111
E-Mail: marketing@airplus.at
Emp.: 80
Tour Operating Services
S.I.C.: 4725
N.A.I.C.S.: 561520
Wolfgang Schneider *(Gen Mgr)*

AirPlus Holding GmbH (2)
Rainergasse 1
Vienna, 1041, Austria
Tel.: (43) 150135
Fax: (43) 15045627
Emp.: 75
Investment Management Services
S.I.C.: 6211
N.A.I.C.S.: 523999
Karl Kainzer *(Gen Mgr)*

AirPlus International Limited (2)
Building 4 Chiswick Park 566 Chiswick High Road
London, W4 5YE, United Kingdom
Tel.: (44) 20 8994 4725
Fax: (44) 20 8987 6113
E-Mail: london@airplus.com
Web Site: www.airplus.com
Emp.: 30
Travel Payment Management Services
S.I.C.: 6099
N.A.I.C.S.: 522320
Yael Klein *(Mng Dir)*

AirPlus International S.r.l. (2)
Via Della Salute 14/2
Bologna, Italy
Tel.: (39) 051 64 15 416
E-Mail: inside@airplus.com
Travel Management Services
S.I.C.: 4724
N.A.I.C.S.: 561510

Lufthansa Cargo AG (1)
Flughafenbereich West Tor 25 Gebaude 451
D 60546 Frankfurt am Main, Germany
Tel.: (49) 69 696 0
Fax: (49) 69 696 91185
E-Mail: lhcargo@dlh.de
Web Site: www.lufthansa-cargo.com
Sales Range: $1-4.9 Billion
Emp.: 4,600
Freight Air Transportation Services
S.I.C.: 4512
N.A.I.C.S.: 481112
Karl Ulrich Garnadt *(Chm-Exec Bd)*

Subsidiaries:

Jettainer GmbH (2)
Am Prime Parc 17
65479 Raunheim, Germany
Tel.: (49) 6142 1770 0
Fax: (49) 6142 1770 420
E-Mail: info@jettainer.com
Web Site: www.jottainer.com
Emp.: 38

Unit Load Device Management Consulting Services
S.I.C.: 8999
N.A.I.C.S.: 541690
Carsten Hernig *(Mng Dir)*
Ingeborg Manz Maier *(Dir-Fin)*
Dirk Thorwirth *(Dir-Sls)*

Lufthansa Leasing GmbH & Co. Echo-Zulu oHG (2)
Tolzer Str 15
Grunwald, 82031, Germany
Tel.: (49) 89 641430
Aircraft Leasing Services
S.I.C.: 7359
N.A.I.C.S.: 532411

U.S. Subsidiaries:

Lufthansa Cargo (2)
5721 West Imperial Hwy
Los Angeles, CA 90045
Tel.: (310) 242-2590
Fax: (310) 649-0204
Toll Free: (800) 542-2746
Web Site: www.lufthansa-cargo.com
Emp.: 20
Freight Air Transportation Services
S.I.C.: 4512
N.A.I.C.S.: 481112
Robyn Gering *(Controller)*

Lufthansa Cargo (2)
Bldg 23
Jamaica, NY 11430
Tel.: (718) 289-7259
Emp.: 100
Freight Air Transportation Services
S.I.C.: 4512
N.A.I.C.S.: 481112
Karl Ulrich Garnadt *(Chm-Supervisory Bd & CEO)*

Non-U.S. Subsidiary:

Lufthansa Cargo India (Priv) Ltd. (2)
2nd Floor 55 J L Nehru Road
Kolkata, West Bengal, 700 071, India
Tel.: (91) 3322821812
Fax: (91) 3322821691
Air Cargo Handling Services
S.I.C.: 4581
N.A.I.C.S.: 488119

Lufthansa CityLine GmbH (1)
Waldstreet 247
Cologne Airport, 51147 Cologne, Germany De
Tel.: (49) 2203 596 0 (100%)
Fax: (49) 2203 596 801
E-Mail: lh-cityline@dlh.de
Web Site: www.lufthansacityline.com
Sales Range: $650-699.9 Million
Emp.: 2,301
Regional Passenger Air Transportation Services
S.I.C.: 4512
N.A.I.C.S.: 481111
Klaus Froese *(Mng Dir & Member-Mgmt Bd)*
Christian Tillmans *(Gen Mgr & Member-Mgmt Bd)*

Lufthansa Commercial Holding GmbH (1)
Von Gablenz St 26
50679 Cologne, Germany De
Tel.: (49) 2218262242 (100%)
Fax: (49) 2218262764
Holding Company
S.I.C.: 6719
N.A.I.C.S.: 551112
Nicolai Von Ruckteschell *(Mng Dir)*
Henning Zur Hausen *(Mng Dir)*

Subsidiary:

LRS Lufthansa Revenue Services GmbH (2)
Schutzenwall 1
22844 Norderstedt, Germany
Tel.: (49) 40 5070 7303
Fax: (49) 40 5070 7810
Web Site: www.revenue-accounting.com
Emp.: 450
Revenue Accounting Services
S.I.C.: 6099
N.A.I.C.S.: 522320
Klaus Furck *(Chm-Supervisory Bd)*
Reinhard Schafer *(Mng Dir)*

Non-U.S. Subsidiaries:

Airline Accounting Center de Mexico S.A. de C.V. (2)
Avenida Ejercito Nacional 418 Piso 11
11570 Mexico, Mexico
Tel.: (52) 55 52 54 83 00
Fax: (52) 55 52 54 83 36
Web Site: www.airline-accounting-center.com
Emp.: 170
Airline Accounting Services
S.I.C.: 8721
N.A.I.C.S.: 541219
Ivonne Romero *(Mgr-HR)*

Airline Accounting Center Sp. z o.o (2)
Al Pokoju 78
31-564 Krakow, Poland
Tel.: (48) 12 6460 801
Fax: (48) 12 6460 888
E-Mail: aac-krakow@dlh.de
Web Site: www.airline-accounting-center.com
Emp.: 200
Airline Accounting & Administrative Services
S.I.C.: 4581
N.A.I.C.S.: 488119
Marc Ammelung *(Gen Mgr)*

Global Tele Sales Brno s.r.o. (2)
Spielberk Office Centre Holandska 1
639 00 Brno, Czech Republic
Tel.: (420) 515 503 100
Fax: (420) 515 503 109
E-Mail: info@globaltelesales.cz
Web Site: www.globaltelesales.cz
Emp.: 230
Flight Reservation Services
S.I.C.: 4729
N.A.I.C.S.: 561599
Roman Tesar *(Mng Dir)*

Global Tele Sales (PTY) Ltd. (2)
9th Floor Picbel Parkade Strand Street
Cape Town, 8001, South Africa
Tel.: (27) 21 415 3550
Fax: (27) 21 415 3569
E-Mail: info@globaltelesales.co.za
Web Site: www.globaltelesales.co.za
Emp.: 50
Customer Care Services
S.I.C.: 7389
N.A.I.C.S.: 561421
Will Schnabel *(Mng Dir)*
Birgit Thuemecke *(Mng Dir)*

Global Tele Sales Pty Limited (2)
Level 2 600 Collins Street
Melbourne, VIC, 3000, Australia
Tel.: (61) 3 8623 6051
Fax: (61) 3 8623 6169
E-Mail: info@globaltelesales.com.au
Web Site: www.globaltelesales.com.au
Emp.: 100
Airline Call Center Services
S.I.C.: 7389
N.A.I.C.S.: 561421

Global Telesales of Canada, Inc. (2)
1900 Fisher Drive
Peterborough, ON, K9J 6X6, Canada
Tel.: (705) 872-3021
Fax: (705) 755-1172
E-Mail: YPQXRCEN@dlh.de
Web Site: www.globaltelesales.ca
Emp.: 23
Flight Reservation Services
S.I.C.: 4729
N.A.I.C.S.: 561599

Lufthansa Consulting GmbH (1)
Von-Gablenz-Str 2-6
50679 Cologne, Germany
Tel.: (49) 221 826 8109
Fax: (49) 221 826 8260
E-Mail: mail@lhconsulting.com
Web Site: www.lhconsulting.com
Emp.: 90
Aviation Management Consulting Services
S.I.C.: 8999
N.A.I.C.S.: 541690
Andreas Jahnke *(Mng Dir)*
Marco Villa *(Principal-Airport Div)*
Christina Schimpf *(Corp Counsel)*

Lufthansa Flight Training GmbH (1)
Airportring Tor 24
60549 Frankfurt am Main, Germany
Tel.: (49) 69 696 724 44
Fax: (49) 69 696 939 50
E-Mail: sales@lufthansa-flight-training.com
Web Site: www.lufthansa-flight-training.com
Flight Training Services
S.I.C.: 8249
N.A.I.C.S.: 611512
Florian Hamm *(Co-Mng Dir)*
Ludwig Merkel *(Co-Mng Dir)*

Subsidiaries:

Aviation Quality Services GmbH (2)
Main Airport Center Unterschweinstiege 10
60549 Frankfurt am Main, Germany
Tel.: (49) 69 696 81739
Fax: (49) 69 696 94160
E-Mail: contact@aviation-quality-services.com
Web Site: www.aviation-quality-services.com
Aviation Management Consulting Services
S.I.C.: 8748
N.A.I.C.S.: 541618
Andreas Dietrich *(Mng Dir)*

Lufthansa Flight Training Berlin GmbH (2)
Schutzenstrasse 10
12526 Berlin, Germany
Tel.: (49) 30 8875 5770
Fax: (49) 30 8875 5778
Web Site: www.lufthansa-flight-training.com
Flight Training Services
S.I.C.: 8249
N.A.I.C.S.: 611512
Stefan Wendrich *(Mng Dir)*

Lufthansa Flight Training - CST GmbH (2)
Schutzenstr 10
Berlin, Germany
Tel.: (49) 30 8875 5761
Fax: (49) 30 8875 5764
E-Mail: customer-service@cstberlin.de
Web Site: www.cstberlin.de
Emp.: 15
Aviation Training Services
S.I.C.: 8249
N.A.I.C.S.: 611512
Christian Korherr *(Co-Mng Dir)*

Pilot Training Network GmbH (2)
Airportring Gate 24 Bldg 392
60549 Frankfurt am Main, Germany
Tel.: (49) 69 696 96290
Fax: (49) 69 696 96407
E-Mail: info@pilottraining-network.com
Web Site: www.pilottraining-network.de
Emp.: 38
Flight Training Services
S.I.C.: 8249
N.A.I.C.S.: 611512
Karsten El-Nemr *(Co-Mng Dir)*
Holger Hoffmann *(Co-Mng Dir)*

U.S. Subsidiary:

Airline Training Center Arizona Inc (2)
1658 S Litchfield Rd 104
Goodyear, AZ 85338-1509
Tel.: (623) 932-1600
Fax: (623) 925-4078
Web Site: www.lufthansa-flight-training.com
Emp.: 150
Flight Training Services
S.I.C.: 8249
N.A.I.C.S.: 611512
Matthias Kippenberg *(Pres)*

Non-U.S. Subsidiary:

Lufthansa Flight Training Vienna GmbH (2)
Austrian Airlines Basis Vienna Airport
1300 Vienna, Austria
Tel.: (43) 1 7007 361 06
Fax: (43) 1 7007 361 05
Web Site: www.lufthansa-flight-training.com
Emp.: 13
Flight Training Services
S.I.C.: 8249
N.A.I.C.S.: 611512
Christian Korherr *(Mng Dir)*

Lufthansa Global Tele Sales GmbH (1)
Rudower Chaussee 12
12489 Berlin, Germany
Tel.: (49) 30 50 57 01 00
Fax: (49) 30 50 57 01 09
E-Mail: info@lufthansagts.de
Airline Travel Information Services
S.I.C.: 7389
N.A.I.C.S.: 519190

Lufthansa Systems AG (1)
Am Weiher 24
65451 Kelsterbach, Germany De
Tel.: (49) 6969690000 (100%)
Fax: (49) 6969695959
E-Mail: info@lhsystems.com
Web Site: www.lhsystems.com
Sales Range: $800-899.9 Million
Emp.: 2,800
Information Technology Consulting & Support Services
S.I.C.: 7379
N.A.I.C.S.: 541519
Stefan Hansen *(Chm & CEO)*

Subsidiaries:

Cargo Future Communications (CFC) GmbH (2)
Gebaude 1335 Hahn-Flughafen
55483 Buchenbeuren, Germany
Tel.: (49) 65 43 983 103
Fax: (49) 65 43 983 160
E-Mail: infomail@cfc-callcenter.de
Web Site: www.cfc-callcenter.de
Emp.: 112
Airline Call Center Services
S.I.C.: 7389
N.A.I.C.S.: 561421
Fredrik Famm *(Gen Mgr)*

Lufthansa Systems AS GmbH (2)
Schutzenwall 1
Norderstedt, 22844, Germany
Tel.: (49) 4050707086
Fax: (49) 4050707880
Web Site: www.lhsystems.com
Information Technology Consulting Services
S.I.C.: 7373
N.A.I.C.S.: 541512
Bernd Appel *(Gen Mgr)*

Lufthansa Systems Berlin GmbH (2)
Salzufer 8
10585 Berlin, Germany
Tel.: (49) 30 34 00 72 00
Fax: (49) 30 34 00 72 02
Web Site: www.lhsystems.com
Emp.: 200
Data Processing Services
S.I.C.: 7374
N.A.I.C.S.: 518210
Stefan Auerbach *(Sr VP)*

Lufthansa Systems Business Solutions GmbH (2)
Am Prime-Parc 1
Raunheim, 65479, Germany
Tel.: (49) 6969690000
Fax: (49) 6969692000
Information Technology Consulting Services
S.I.C.: 7373
N.A.I.C.S.: 541512

Lufthansa Systems Infratec GmbH (2)
Am Weiher 24
Kelsterbach, Hesse, Germany
Tel.: (49) 69 69690000
Fax: (49) 69 69626980
Web Site: www.lhsystems.com
Information Technology Consulting Services
S.I.C.: 7373
N.A.I.C.S.: 541512

Lufthansa Systems IS Consulting GmbH (2)
Schutzenwall 1
Norderstedt, 22844, Germany
Tel.: (49) 40 507060666
Information Technology Consulting Services
S.I.C.: 7373
N.A.I.C.S.: 541512

Lufthansa Systems Network GmbH (2)
Schutzenwall 1
Norderstedt, Germany
Tel.: (49) 40507060666
Fax: (49) 40507060522
Emp.: 5
Information Technology Consulting Services

Deutsche Lufthansa AG—(Continued)

S.I.C.: 7373
N.A.I.C.S.: 541512

Lufthansa Systems Network Services GmbH (2)
Schutzenwall 1
Norderstedt, 22844, Germany
Tel.: (49) 40507060666
Fax: (49) 40507060522
Information Technology Consulting Services
S.I.C.: 7373
N.A.I.C.S.: 541512

Lufthansa Systems Passenger Services GmbH (2)
Am Weiher 24
65451 Kelsterbach, Hesse, Germany
Tel.: (49) 69 69690000
Fax: (49) 6969692000
Airline Ticket Management Services
S.I.C.: 4729
N.A.I.C.S.: 561599

U.S. Subsidiaries:

Lufthansa Systems Americas, Inc. (2)
801 Brickell Ave Ste 520
Miami, FL 33131
Tel.: (305) 536-8938
Fax: (305) 536-8908
Airline Software Development Services
S.I.C.: 7371
N.A.I.C.S.: 541511

Maptext, Inc. (2)
1100 Cornwall Rd
Monmouth Junction, NJ 08852
Tel.: (732) 940-7100
Fax: (732) 940-7101
E-Mail: sales@maptext.com
Web Site: www.maptext.com
Software Development Services
S.I.C.: 7371
N.A.I.C.S.: 541511
Rishi Mehra *(Dir-Sls & Bus Dev)*

Non-U.S. Subsidiaries:

Lufthansa Systems Asia Pacific Pte. Ltd. (2)
390 Orchard Road 07-03/04 Palais Renaissance Orchard
Singapore, 238871, Singapore
Tel.: (65) 65141330
Fax: (65) 67361755
Information Technology Consulting Services
S.I.C.: 7373
N.A.I.C.S.: 541512
Olivier Krueger *(CEO)*

Lufthansa Systems FlightNav AG (2)
Stelzenstrasse 6
Opfikon, Zurich, 8152, Switzerland
Tel.: (41) 448286511
Fax: (41) 448286599
Aviation Information Technology Consulting Services
S.I.C.: 7373
N.A.I.C.S.: 541512

Lufthansa Systems Hungaria Kft (2)
Infopark Building E Neumann Janos u 1/E
1117 Budapest, Hungary
Tel.: (36) 1 8824 900
Fax: (36) 1 8824 977
E-Mail: marketing@lhsystems.com
Emp.: 50
Information Technology Consulting Services
S.I.C.: 7373
N.A.I.C.S.: 541512
Monika Houck *(Mng Dir)*

Lufthansa Systems Poland Sp. z o.o. (2)
Ul Dlugie Ogrody 8
80-765 Gdansk, Poland
Tel.: (48) 58 3265 400
Fax: (48) 58 3265 599
E-Mail: service_pl@lhsystems.com
Information Technology Consulting Services
S.I.C.: 7373
N.A.I.C.S.: 541512

Lufthansa Technical Training GmbH (1)
Unterschweinstiege 12
60549 Frankfurt am Main, Germany
Tel.: (49) 69 696 2751
Fax: (49) 69 696 98 2751
E-Mail: Info@ltt.dlh.de
Web Site: www.ltt.aero
Emp.: 500
Aviation Technology Training Services
S.I.C.: 8249
N.A.I.C.S.: 611512
Andreas Kaden *(CEO)*
Ullrich Geidel *(CFO)*
Karsten Schmidt *(COO)*
Holger Beck *(Chief Comml Officer-Mktg, Sls & Product Mgmt)*

Lufthansa Technik AG (1)
Weg Beim Jaeger 193
22335 Hamburg, Germany De
Tel.: (49) 4050700 (100%)
Fax: (49) 4050704401
E-Mail: press.tr@lht.dlh.de
Web Site: www.lufthansa-technik.com
Sales Range: $5-14.9 Billion
Emp.: 20,300
Aircraft Maintenance, Repair & Overhaul Services
S.I.C.: 4581
N.A.I.C.S.: 488190
August Wilhem Henningsen *(Chm)*
Mark Johnson *(CEO)*
Burkhard Andrich *(Pres/CEO-Philippines)*
Stephan Drewes *(CEO-Malta)*
Johannes Bussmann *(Sr VP-Engine Svcs)*
Holger Dietsch *(Sr VP-Aircraft Maintenance)*

Subsidiaries:

Hamburger Gesellschaft fur Flughafenanlagen mbH (2)
Sportallee 54b
22335 Hamburg, Germany
Tel.: (49) 40 50703081
Fax: (49) 40 50751234
Aircraft Equipment Leasing Services
S.I.C.: 7359
N.A.I.C.S.: 532411

JASEN Grundstucksgesellschaft mbH & Co. oHG (2)
Tolzer Str 15
82031 Grunwald, Germany
Tel.: (49) 89 641430
Real Estate Management Services
S.I.C.: 6531
N.A.I.C.S.: 531390

Lufthansa Engineering and Operational Services GmbH (2)
Lufthansa-Basis
60546 Frankfurt am Main, Germany
Tel.: (49) 69 696 2522
Fax: (49) 69 696 93888
E-Mail: lufthansa.leos@dlh.de
Web Site: www.lufthansa-leos.com
Emp.: 350
Airport Ground Handling Services
S.I.C.: 4581
N.A.I.C.S.: 488119
Alexander Stern *(Mng Dir)*

Lufthansa Technik AERO Alzey GmbH (2)
Rudolf-Diesel-Strasse 10
55232 Alzey, Germany
Tel.: (49) 67 31 4 97 0
Fax: (49) 6731497377
E-Mail: lhaero@lhaero.com
Web Site: www.lhaero.com
Aircraft Repair & Maintenance Services
S.I.C.: 7549
N.A.I.C.S.: 811198
Mark Johnson *(CEO)*
Martin Hach *(COO)*

Lufthansa Technik Immobilien- und Verwaltungsgesellschaft mbH (2)
Sportallee 54b
Hamburg, 22335, Germany
Tel.: (49) 4050700
Fax: (49) 4050704401
Property Management Services
S.I.C.: 6531
N.A.I.C.S.: 531311
August-Wilhelm Henningsen *(Mng Dir)*

Lufthansa Technik Maintenance International GmbH (2)
Frankfurt International Airport South
Frankfurt, 60549, Germany
Tel.: (49) 69 696 69660
Fax: (49) 69 696 69666
Aircraft Repair & Maintenance Services
S.I.C.: 7549
N.A.I.C.S.: 811198
Alexander Heilmann *(COO)*

Lufthansa Technik Objekt- und Verwaltungsgesellschaft mbH (2)
Sportallee 54b
Hamburg, 22335, Germany
Tel.: (49) 40 50700
Fax: (49) 40 50704401
Web Site: www.Lufthansa.com
Property Management Services
S.I.C.: 6531
N.A.I.C.S.: 531312

U.S. Subsidiaries:

BizJet International Sales & Support, Inc. (2)
3515 N Sheridan Rd
Tulsa, OK 74115
Tel.: (918) 832-7733
Fax: (918) 832-8627
Toll Free: (888) 388-4858
E-Mail: bizjet@bizjet.com
Web Site: www.bizjet.com
Emp.: 300
Aircraft Engine Repair & Maintenance Services
S.I.C.: 7539
N.A.I.C.S.: 811118
Manfred Gaertner *(Pres & CEO)*

Hawker Pacific Aerospace (2)
11240 Sherman Way
Sun Valley, CA 91352-4942 CA
Tel.: (818) 765-6201 (72.7%)
Fax: (818) 765-8073
Toll Free: (800) 788-7496
E-Mail: info@hawker.com
Web Site: www.hawker.com
Emp.: 500
Aircraft Repair & Overhaul Services & Parts
S.I.C.: 4581
N.A.I.C.S.: 488119

Lufthansa Technik Component Services LLC (2)
11240 Sherman Way
Sun Valley, CA 91352
Tel.: (818) 765-6201
Fax: (818) 765-7023
E-Mail: sales@ltcs.aero
Emp.: 70
Aircraft Component Repair & Maintenance Services
S.I.C.: 7539
N.A.I.C.S.: 811198

Lufthansa Technik Logistik of America LLC (2)
Cargo Bldg 23 N Door 3738
Jamaica, NY 11430
Tel.: (718) 289-7272
Fax: (718) 289-7095
Emp.: 14
Freight Transportation Services
S.I.C.: 4731
N.A.I.C.S.: 488510
Stephen Fondell *(Mng Dir)*

Non-U.S. Subsidiaries:

Lufthansa Technik Airmotive Ireland Holdings Ltd. (2)
Naas Rd
Rathcoole, Dublin, Ireland
Tel.: (353) 1 4011111
Investment Management Services
S.I.C.: 6211
N.A.I.C.S.: 523999

Lufthansa Technik Airmotive Ireland Leasing Ltd (2)
Naas Rd
Rathcoole, Dublin, Ireland
Tel.: (353) 14011111
Fax: (353) 14011300
Emp.: 480
Automotive Leasing Services
S.I.C.: 6153
N.A.I.C.S.: 522220
Wolfgang Moerig *(Mng Dir)*

Lufthansa Technik Airmotive Ireland Ltd. (2)
Naas Road
Rathcoole, Dublin, Ireland
Tel.: (353) 1 401 1111
Fax: (353) 1 401 1300
E-Mail: info@ltai.ie
Web Site: www.lufthansatechnikairmotiveireland.com
Emp.: 480
Aircraft Repair & Maintenance Services
S.I.C.: 7549
N.A.I.C.S.: 811198
Wolfgang Moerig *(Mng Dir)*
John Lambert *(Sec)*

Lufthansa Technik Brussels N.V. (2)
Vliegveld 117 D
Melsbroek, 1820 Steenokkerzeel, Belgium
Tel.: (32) 2 752 8660
Fax: (32) 2 752 8673
E-Mail: sales.bruub@lht.dlh.de
Emp.: 85
Aircraft Repair & Maintenance Services
S.I.C.: 7539
N.A.I.C.S.: 811198
Christoph Plaha *(Gen Mgr)*

Lufthansa Technik Services India Private Limited (2)
Menzies Aviation Bobba Cargo Ter New Bangalore International Airport
Devanahalli, 560 300 Bengaluru, India
Tel.: (91) 22 3953 7405
Fax: (91) 22 3953 7200
E-Mail: sales@lht-services-india.com
Aircraft Repair & Maintenance Services
S.I.C.: 7549
N.A.I.C.S.: 811198

Lufthansa Technik Switzerland GmbH (2)
C/O Kilian Wunder Steinenschanze 6
4002 Basel, Switzerland
Tel.: (41) 61 568 3000
Fax: (41) 61 568 3009
E-Mail: info@lht-switzerland.com
Web Site: www.lht-switzerland.com
Aircraft Repair & Maintenance Services
S.I.C.: 7549
N.A.I.C.S.: 811198
Thomas Foth *(Head-Mktg & Sls)*

Lufthansa Technik Turbine Shannon Limited (2)
World Aviation Park
Shannon, Co Clare, Ireland
Tel.: (353) 61 360512
Fax: (353) 61 360513
E-Mail: info@ltts.ie
Web Site: www.ltts.ie
Emp.: 184
Aircraft Engine Component Repair Services
S.I.C.: 7532
N.A.I.C.S.: 811121
Aloisio Oliveira *(CEO)*

Shannon Aerospace Ltd. (2)
Shannon Airport
Shannon, Co Clare, Ireland IE
Tel.: (353) 61370000 (100%)
Fax: (353) 61361100
E-Mail: marie.shortt@sal.ie
Web Site: www.shannonaerospace.com
Emp.: 700
Aircraft Maintenance, Repair & Overhaul Services
S.I.C.: 4581
N.A.I.C.S.: 488190
Patrick Shine *(Deputy CEO & Head-Fin)*
Martin Kaiser *(CEO & Mng Dir)*

Non-U.S. Joint Venture:

Aircraft Maintenance & Engineering Corp. (2)
Beijing Capital International Airport
Beijing, 100621, China
Tel.: (86) 10645611224
Fax: (86) 1064561517
Web Site: www.ameco.com.cn
Emp.: 3,600
Aircraft Maintenance, Repair & Overhaul Services; Owned 60% by China National Aviation Holding Company & 40% by Deutsche Lufthansa AG
S.I.C.: 4581
N.A.I.C.S.: 488190
Chai Weixi *(CEO)*

Lufthansa Training & Conference Center GmbH (1)
Lufthansaring 1
64342 Seeheim-Jugenheim, Germany

Tel.: (49) 69 696 131000
Fax: (49) 69 696 131015
E-Mail: lh-seeheim@dlh.de
Web Site: www.lh-seeheim.de
Emp.: 27
Conference Hotel Operating Services
S.I.C.: 7011
N.A.I.C.S.: 721110
Gerald Scholzel *(Mng Dir)*

Passage Services Holding GmbH (1)
Terminalstrasse Sud 1
Munich, 85325, Germany
Tel.: (49) 8997572001
Fax: (49) 8997571099
E-Mail: musec@dlh.de
Web Site: www.lufthansa.com
Investment Management Services
S.I.C.: 6211
N.A.I.C.S.: 523999
Burkhard Feuge *(VP)*

TATS - Travel Agency Technologies & Services GmbH (1)
Hahnstrasse 70
60528 Frankfurt am Main, Germany
Tel.: (49) 69 6 63 77 150
Fax: (49) 69 6 63 77 160
E-Mail: info@ta-ts.de
Emp.: 70
Travel Agency Data Processing Services
S.I.C.: 7374
N.A.I.C.S.: 518210
Rainer Burghardt *(Gen Mgr)*

TRAINICO Training und Ausbildung Cooperation in Berlin Brandenburg GmbH (1)
Schutzenstrasse 10
12526 Berlin, Germany
Tel.: (49) 30 8875 5050
Fax: (49) 30 8875 5051
E-Mail: training@trainico.de
Staffing Agency & Technical Training Services
S.I.C.: 7361
N.A.I.C.S.: 561311

Joint Ventures:

Global Logistics System Europe Company for Cargo Information Services GmbH (1)
Lyoner St 36
60528 Frankfurt am Main, Germany (50%)
Tel.: (49) 69669060
Fax: (49) 6966906231
E-Mail: info@traxon.com
Web Site: www.traxon.com
Emp.: 30
Support Activities for Air Transportation; Owned by Air France-KLM Group & by Deutsche Lufthansa AG
S.I.C.: 4581
N.A.I.C.S.: 488190
Felix Keck *(Mng Dir)*

GOAL German Operating Aircraft Leasing GmbH (1)
Tolzer Str 15
Grunwald, 82031 Munich, Germany De
Tel.: (49) 8964143152
Fax: (49) 8964143611
Web Site: www.goal-leasing.de
Aircraft Leasing Services; Owned 60% by Commerzbank AG & 40% by Deutsche Lufthansa AG
S.I.C.: 7359
N.A.I.C.S.: 532411
Michael Radunz *(Mng Dir)*
Christian Schloemann *(Mng Dir)*

Lufthansa Leasing GmbH (1)
Toelzer Strasse 15
82031 Grunwald, Germany De
Tel.: (49) 8964143203
Fax: (49) 8964143611
Emp.: 10
Aircraft Leasing Services; Owned 51% by Commerzbank AG & 49% by Deutsche Lufthansa AG
S.I.C.: 7359
N.A.I.C.S.: 532411
Jochen Hoerger *(Mng Dir)*
Markus Ott *(Mng Dir)*

U.S. Subsidiary:

Star Risk Services Inc. (1)
536 Silicon Dr Ste 103
Southlake, TX 76092
Tel.: (817) 552-6207
Fax: (817) 552-3125
E-Mail: administrator@starrisk.com
Web Site: www.starrisk.com
Emp.: 4
General Insurance Services
S.I.C.: 6411
N.A.I.C.S.: 524210

Non-U.S. Subsidiaries:

ACS Aircontainer Services Gesellschaft m.b.H (1)
Berggasse 16
2401 Fischamend Dorf, Austria
Tel.: (43) 2232 77878
Fax: (43) 2232 77333
E-Mail: office@aircontainer.eu
Emp.: 50
Air Container Repair & Maintenance Services
S.I.C.: 7699
N.A.I.C.S.: 811310
Andreas Wanko *(Gen Mgr)*

Lufthansa Malta Pension Holding Ltd. (1)
Ana Capri Court Spinola Road
San Giljan, STJ 3012, Malta
Tel.: (356) 2010 7411
Fax: (356) 2010 7415
E-Mail: info@lmp.com.mt
Web Site: www.lmp.com.mt
Investment Management Services
S.I.C.: 6211
N.A.I.C.S.: 523999

Lufthansa Services (Thailand) Ltd. (1)
Suvarnabhumi International Airport Room A4-091a 4th Floor 999 Moo 1
Bangna-Trad Rachathewa, Bang Phli, Samutprakarn, 10540, Thailand
Tel.: (66) 2 134 2210
Fax: (66) 2 134 2219
E-Mail: info@1st-thai.com
Web Site: www.joinlst.com
Airport Ground Handling Services
S.I.C.: 4581
N.A.I.C.S.: 488119

Lufthansa Shenzhen Management Company Limited (1)
Logistics Building Shenzhen Airport
Shenzhen, 518128, China
Tel.: (86) 75527771469
Emp.: 100
Air Cargo Handling Services
S.I.C.: 4512
N.A.I.C.S.: 481112

Swiss Private Aviation AG (1)
Obstgartenstrasse 25
Kloten, Zurich, 8302, Switzerland
Tel.: (41) 43 255 50 70
Fax: (41) 43 255 50 71
Web Site: www.swiss-private-aviation.com
Aircraft Management & Flight Chartering Services
S.I.C.: 4581
N.A.I.C.S.: 488119

TRAVI Holding GmbH (1)
Dresdner Str 81-85
1200 Vienna, Austria
Tel.: (43) 1 33733 0
Fax: (43) 1 33733733
Emp.: 65
Investment Management Services
S.I.C.: 6211
N.A.I.C.S.: 523999

DEUTSCHE MESSE AG

Messegelande
30521 Hannover, Germany
Tel.: (49) 511 89 0
Fax: (49) 511 89 32626
E-Mail: incoming@messe.de
Web Site: www.messe.de
Year Founded: 1947
Sales Range: $350-399.9 Million
Emp.: 930

Business Description:
Trade Shows, Events & Conventions
S.I.C.: 7389
N.A.I.C.S.: 561920

Personnel:
Wolfram V. Fritsch *(Chm-Mgmt Bd)*
Andreas Gruchow *(Member-Mgmt Bd)*
Jochen Kockler *(Member-Mgmt Bd)*
Frank Porschmann *(Member-Mgmt Bd)*

U.S. Subsidiary:

Hannover Fairs USA Inc. (1)
2 Research Way
Princeton, NJ 08540
Tel.: (609) 987-1202
Fax: (609) 987-0092
E-Mail: info@hfusa.com
Web Site: www.hfusa.com
Trade Show & Event Management & Marketing
S.I.C.: 7389
N.A.I.C.S.: 561920
Larry Turner *(CEO)*
Bill Rooney *(Sr VP-Fin & Ops)*

DEUTSCHE NICKEL GMBH

Rosenweg 15
58239 Schwerte, Germany
Tel.: (49) 23041080
Fax: (49) 2304108435
E-Mail: postmaster@deutsche-nickel.de
Web Site: www.deutsche-nickel.de
Year Founded: 1994
Emp.: 200

Business Description:
Provider of Metals Services
Import Export
S.I.C.: 3479
N.A.I.C.S.: 332812

Personnel:
Dirk Kebekus *(CEO)*

Subsidiary:

Deutsche Nickel America Inc. (1)
70 Industrial Rd
Cumberland, RI 02864-1905
Tel.: (401) 721-2158
Fax: (401) 721-2171
Web Site: www.dn-america.com
Emp.: 13
Providers of Nickel Services
Import Export
S.I.C.: 5051
N.A.I.C.S.: 423510
Ed Morrow *(Product Mgr-Bar Sls)*

DEUTSCHE POST AG

Charles-de-Gaulle-Strasse 20
53113 Bonn, Germany
Tel.: (49) 2281820
Fax: (49) 2281827099
Web Site: www.dp-dhl.com
DPW—(DEU)
Rev.: $77,647,085,600
Assets: $45,932,666,570
Liabilities: $29,557,854,690
Net Worth: $16,374,811,880
Earnings: $2,396,182,600
Emp.: 428,129
Fiscal Year-end: 12/31/12

Business Description:
Express Delivery & Logistics Services
Import Export
S.I.C.: 4513
N.A.I.C.S.: 492110

Personnel:
Wulf von Schimmelmann *(Chm-Supervisory Bd)*
Frank Appel *(CEO & Member-Mgmt Bd)*
Ken Allen *(Member-Mgmt Bd-Express Div)*
Juergen Gerdes *(Member-Mgmt Bd-Mail Div)*
Lawrence A. Rosen *(Member-Mgmt Bd-Fin & Global Bus Svcs)*
Angela Titzrath *(Member-Mgmt Bd-HR)*

Supervisory Board of Directors:
Wulf von Schimmelmann
Hero Brahms
Werner Gatzer
Henning Kagermann
Thomas Kunz
Roland Oetker
Ulrich Schroder
Stefan Schulte
Elmar Toime
Katja Windt

Subsidiaries:

ABIS GmbH (1)
Lyoner Str 20
60528 Frankfurt, Germany
Tel.: (49) 697920090
Fax: (49) 6979200920
E-Mail: info@abis-online.net
Web Site: www.abis-online.net
Online Information Updating Services
S.I.C.: 7389
N.A.I.C.S.: 519190

Adcloud Gmbh (1)
Venloer Strasse 25-27
50672 Cologne, Germany
Tel.: (49) 2212920950
Fax: (49) 22129209599
E-Mail: info@adcloud.com
Web Site: www.adcloud.com
Emp.: 45
Advertising Agencies
S.I.C.: 7311
N.A.I.C.S.: 541810

Agheera GmbH (1)
Junkersring 63
53844 Troisdorf, Germany
Tel.: (49) 2241 25284 0
Fax: (49) 412528410
E-Mail: info@agheera.com
Web Site: www.agheera.com
Emp.: 4
Logistics Consulting Services
S.I.C.: 4731
N.A.I.C.S.: 541614
Christoph P. H. Keisers *(Co-Mng Dir)*

Albert Scheid GmbH (1)
Marktstrasse 10
50968 Cologne, Germany
Tel.: (49) 221 376 3771
Fax: (49) 221 376 3773
E-Mail: info@spedition-scheid.com
Web Site: www.spedition-scheid.com
Container Logistics Services
S.I.C.: 4731
N.A.I.C.S.: 541614
Dieter Gerfer *(Mng Dir)*

Danzas Deutschland Holding GmbH (1)
Obenhauptstrasse 9
22335 Hamburg, Germany
Tel.: (49) 405002330
Fax: (49) 702996100
Emp.: 7
Investment Management Services
S.I.C.: 6211
N.A.I.C.S.: 523999
Andreas Oetzel *(Gen Mgr)*

Danzas Grundstucksverwaltung Gross-Gerau GmbH (1)
Andreas-Meyer-Strasse 45
22113 Hamburg, Germany
Tel.: (49) 4038605114
Real Estate Management Services
S.I.C.: 6531
N.A.I.C.S.: 531390

Deutsche Post Adress Geschaftsfuhrungs GmbH (1)
Heinrich-Von-Stephan-Str 1
53175 Bonn, Germany
Tel.: (49) 22852890
Courier Services
S.I.C.: 4513
N.A.I.C.S.: 492110

Deutsche Post Adress GmbH (1)
Am Anger 33
33332 Gutersloh, Germany
Mailing Address:
PO Box 410
33311 Gutersloh, Germany

Deutsche Post AG—(Continued)

Tel.: (49) 524153930
Fax: (49) 5241539349
Web Site: www.deutschepost.de
Address Correction Services
S.I.C.: 4731
N.A.I.C.S.: 541614

Deutsche Post Beteiligungen Holding GmbH (1)
Straesschensweg 10
Bonn, 53113, Germany
Tel.: (49) 228 18264800
Fax: (49) 228 18264399
Investment Management Services
S.I.C.: 6799
N.A.I.C.S.: 523920

Deutsche Post Com GmbH (1)
Tulpenfeld 9
53113 Bonn, Germany
Mailing Address:
Postfach 44 55
53244 Bonn, Germany
Tel.: (49) 22890860
Fax: (49) 2289086109
E-Mail: info@dpcom.de
Web Site: www.dpcom.de
Emp.: 120
Electronic Transaction Services
S.I.C.: 7389
N.A.I.C.S.: 561499
Rudiger Haase *(Mng Dir)*

Deutsche Post Customer Service Center GmbH (1)
Heinestrasse 3-7
40789 Monheim, Nordrhein-Westfalen, Germany
Tel.: (49) 21733900
Business Support Services
S.I.C.: 7389
N.A.I.C.S.: 561499

Deutsche Post DHL Beteiligungen GmbH (1)
Charles-de-Gaulle-Str 20
53113 Bonn, Germany
Tel.: (49) 228 1820
Financial Management Services
S.I.C.: 6211
N.A.I.C.S.: 523999

Deutsche Post DHL Corporate Real Estate Management GmbH & Co. Objekt WeiBenhorn KG (1)
Fritz-Erler-Str 5
Bonn, Nordrhein-Westfalen, 53113, Germany
Tel.: (49) 22852890
Fax: (49) 228528990
Real Estate Management Services
S.I.C.: 6531
N.A.I.C.S.: 531390

Deutsche Post DHL Corporate Real Estate Management GmbH (1)
Godesberger Allee 157
53175 Bonn, Germany
Tel.: (49) 228 5289 0
Fax: (49) 228 5289900
Emp.: 120
Real Estate Management Services
S.I.C.: 6531
N.A.I.C.S.: 531390
Georg Behrens *(Mgr)*

Deutsche Post DHL Inhouse Consulting GmbH (1)
Tulpenfeld 1
Bonn, Nordrhein-Westfalen, 53113, Germany
Tel.: (49) 22824350
Fax: (49) 2282435201
Information Technology Consulting Services
S.I.C.: 7373
N.A.I.C.S.: 541512
Sabine Mueller *(Exec VP)*

Deutsche Post DHL Research and Innovation GmbH (1)
Tulpenfeld Haus 2
53113 Bonn, Germany
Tel.: (49) 228 2435700
Fax: (49) 228 2435799
Emp.: 28
Marketing Research Services
S.I.C.: 8732
N.A.I.C.S.: 541910
Doris Sibum *(VP)*

Deutsche Post Direkt GmbH (1)
Strasschensweg 10
53113 Bonn, Germany
Tel.: (49) 22818257111
Fax: (49) 22818257139
E-Mail: info@postdirekt.de
Web Site: www.postdirekt.de
Emp.: 400
Address & Document Management Services
S.I.C.: 7389
N.A.I.C.S.: 561499
Oliver Reinke *(Mgr)*

Deutsche Post gemeinnutzige Gesellschaft fur sichere und vertrauliche Kommunikation im Internet mbH (1)
Charles-de-Gaulle-Strasse 20
53113 Bonn, Germany
Tel.: (49) 228 182 9944
Fax: (49) 228 182 9880
Software Developmlent Services
S.I.C.: 7371
N.A.I.C.S.: 541511

Deutsche Post Global Mail GmbH (1)
Charles-de-Gaulle-Strasse 20
53113 Bonn, Germany
Tel.: (49) 2281820
Fax: (49) 2281827099
E-Mail: info@deutschepost.de
Web Site: www.dhl.com
Mail Delivery Services
S.I.C.: 4215
N.A.I.C.S.: 492110
Frank Appel *(Chm)*

U.S. Subsidiary:

Deutsche Post Global Mail Ltd. (2)
22560 Glenn Dr
Sterling, VA 20164
Fax: (703) 450-7638
Toll Free: (800) 805-9306
Web Site: www.globalmail.com
Express Mail Services
S.I.C.: 4513
N.A.I.C.S.: 492110

Non-U.S. Subsidiaries:

Deutsche Post Global Mail (Belgium) N.V./S.A. (2)
Avenue R Vandendriesschelaan 18
1150 Brussels, Belgium
Tel.: (32) 27771555
Fax: (32) 27771566
E-Mail: info@dhl-globalmail.be
Web Site: www.dhl-globalmail.be
Emp.: 4
Mail Services
S.I.C.: 4215
N.A.I.C.S.: 492110
Eric Kuhn *(Mng Dir)*

Deutsche Post Global Mail B.V. (2)
Reactorweg 25
3542 AD Utrecht, Netherlands
Tel.: (31) 306008494
Fax: (31) 6008495
E-Mail: service@dhl-globalmail.nl
Web Site: www.dhl-globalmail.nl
Emp.: 20
Mail Services
S.I.C.: 4513
N.A.I.C.S.: 492110

Deutsche Post Global Mail (Switzerland) AG (2)
Peter-Merian-Strasse 88
4002 Basel, Switzerland
E-Mail: service@dhl-globalmail.ch
Web Site: www.dhl-globalmail.ch
Mail Services
S.I.C.: 4215
N.A.I.C.S.: 492110

Deutsche Post Global Mail (UK) Ltd. (2)
4-8 Queensway
Croydon, CRO4BD, United Kingdom
Tel.: (44) 808 100 7678
Fax: (44) 845 600 7679
E-Mail: sales@dhlglobalmail.co.uk
Web Site: www.dhlglobalmail.co.uk
Mail Services
S.I.C.: 4215
N.A.I.C.S.: 492110

Global Mail (Austria) Ges. m.b.H. (2)
Landstrasser Hauptstr 1 3
1030 Vienna, Austria
Tel.: (43) 017064616
Fax: (43) 01706461620
E-Mail: info@dhl.at
Web Site: www.dhl.at
Emp.: 15
Express Mail Services
S.I.C.: 4513
N.A.I.C.S.: 492110
Robert Feichtenschlager *(Mng Dir)*

Deutsche Post Grundstucks-Vermietungsgesellschaft beta mbH (1)
Charles-de-Gaulle-Strasse 20
53113 Bonn, Nordrhein-Westfalen, Germany
Tel.: (49) 228 52890
Fax: (49) 228 1825966
Real Estate Management Services
S.I.C.: 6531
N.A.I.C.S.: 531390

Deutsche Post Immobilien GmbH (1)
Charles-de-Gaulle-Str 20
Bonn, 53113, Germany
Tel.: (49) 22 81 82 59 550
Fax: (49) 22 81 82 70 99
Real Estate Management Services
S.I.C.: 6531
N.A.I.C.S.: 531390

Deutsche Post Investments GmbH (1)
Charles-De-Gaulle-Str 20
53113 Bonn, Germany
Tel.: (49) 2281820
Financial Investment Services
S.I.C.: 6211
N.A.I.C.S.: 523999

Deutsche Post IT BRIEF GmbH (1)
Hullerser Str 20
37574 Einbeck, Germany
Tel.: (49) 5561 314 131
Fax: (49) 5561 314 531 85
Information Technology Consulting Services
S.I.C.: 7373
N.A.I.C.S.: 541512

Deutsche Post IT Services GmbH (1)
Hilpertstrasse 31
64295 Darmstadt, Germany
Tel.: (49) 6151 957 3535
Information Technology Consulting Services
S.I.C.: 7373
N.A.I.C.S.: 541512

Deutsche Post Pensions-Treuhand GmbH & Co. KG (1)
Charles-de-Gaulle-Str 20
53113 Bonn, Germany
Tel.: (49) 2289200
Pension Fund Services
S.I.C.: 6371
N.A.I.C.S.: 525110

Deutsche Post Pensionsfonds AG (1)
Charles-de-Gaulle-Str 20
53113 Bonn, Germany
Tel.: (49) 2281820
Fax: (49) 2281827099
Pension Fund Services
S.I.C.: 6371
N.A.I.C.S.: 525110

Deutsche Post Real Estate Germany GmbH (1)
Godesberger Allee 157
Bonn, 53113, Germany
Tel.: (49) 228 5289 3011
Fax: (49) 2285289900
Customary Property & Facility Management Services
S.I.C.: 8744
N.A.I.C.S.: 561210
Berk Hout *(Gen Mgr)*

Deutsche Post Shop Hannover GmbH (1)
Davenstedter Str 80
Hannover, 30453, Germany
Tel.: (49) 511 9239930
Fax: (49) 511 2123300
Postal Delivery Services
S.I.C.: 4311
N.A.I.C.S.: 491110

Deutsche Post Zahlungsdienste GmbH (1)
fritzschreffer str 729
53113 Bonn, Germany
Tel.: (49) 228 18254280
Fax: (49) 228 18254290
E-Mail: info@dpzahlungsdienste.de
Web Site: www.dpzahlungsdienste.de
Emp.: 3
Postal Delivery Services
S.I.C.: 4311
N.A.I.C.S.: 491110
Bernd Kierdorf *(Gen Mgr)*

Subsidiaries:

BHW Bausparkasse AG (2)
Lubahnstrasse 2
31789 Hameln, Germany
Tel.: (49) 5151183555
Fax: (49) 5151183001
Web Site: www.bhw.de
Emp.: 3,735
Home-Savings Bank Services
S.I.C.: 6035
N.A.I.C.S.: 522120
Michael Meyer *(Chm-Supervisory Bd)*
Dieter Pfeiffenberger *(Chm-Mgmt Bd)*
Lars Stoy *(CFO & Head-Corp Fin)*
Hans-Joachim Neumann *(Head-Corp Resources & Dir-Admin)*
Dietmar Konig *(Head-Corp Credit Svcs)*

Subsidiary:

BHW Immobilien GmbH (3)
Lubahnstrasse 2
31789 Hameln, Germany
Tel.: (49) 5151180
Fax: (49) 5151183001
Web Site: www.bhw.de
Real Estate Services
S.I.C.: 6531
N.A.I.C.S.: 531210

Deutsche Postbank AG (1)
Friedrich-Ebert-Allee 114-126
53113 Bonn, Germany (50%)
Tel.: (49) 2289200
Fax: (49) 22892018009
Web Site: www.postbank.com
DPB—(DEU)
Int. Income: $8,211,637,000
Assets: $260,917,361,740
Liabilities: $252,424,375,210
Net Worth: $8,492,986,530
Earnings: $375,581,430
Emp.: 18,599
Fiscal Year-end: 12/31/12
Private & Commercial Banking Services
S.I.C.: 6029
N.A.I.C.S.: 522110
Rainer Neske *(Chm-Supervisory Bd)*
Frank Strauss *(Chm-Mgmt Bd)*
Marc Hess *(CFO & Member-Mgmt Bd)*
Ralph Muller *(COO, Member-Mgmt Bd & Gen Mgr)*
Hanns-Peter Storr *(Chief Risk Officer & member-Mgmt Bd)*
Susanne Kloss *(Member-Mgmt Bd & Gen Mgr-Product)*
Hans-Peter Schmid *(Member-Mgmt Bd-Retail Outlets)*
Ralf Stemmer *(Member-Mgmt Bd-Resources & Lending)*

DHL Bwlog GmbH (1)
Regioparkring 26
Monchengladbach, Nordrhein-Westfalen, 41199, Germany
Tel.: (49) 2281820
Logistics Consulting Services
S.I.C.: 4731
N.A.I.C.S.: 541614

DHL Freight Germany Holding GmbH (1)
Godesberger Allee 102-104
53175 Bonn, Germany
Tel.: (49) 228 3 77 88 0
E-Mail: freight.de@dhl.com
Freight Forwarding Services
S.I.C.: 4731

N.A.I.C.S.: 488510
Jutta Rawe-Baumer *(Chm-Supervisory Bd)*
Amadou Diallo *(Global CEO)*
Jeroen Eijsink *(CEO)*
Martina Fohr *(Mng Dir)*
Karin Lorenz *(Mng Dir)*
Pieter van Holten *(Mng Dir)*
Bernhard Wirth *(Mng Dir)*

DHL Global Forwarding Management GmbH (1)
Johanniterstr 1
Bonn, Nordrhein-Westfalen, 53113, Germany
Tel.: (49) 22818264800
Freight Traffic Consulting Services
S.I.C.: 4731
N.A.I.C.S.: 541614
Roger Crook *(CEO-Freight)*
Rajeev Singh-Molares *(CEO-EMEA)*

DHL Global Management GmbH (1)
Kurt-Schumacher-Str 28
53113 Bonn, Nordrhein-Westfalen, Germany
Tel.: (49) 228 182 0
Fax: (49) 228 1827099
Financial Investment Management Services
S.I.C.: 6211
N.A.I.C.S.: 523999

DHL International GmbH (1)
Charles-de-Gaulle-Strasse 20
Bonn, 53113, Germany
Tel.: (49) 228 18 20
Courier Services
S.I.C.: 4215
N.A.I.C.S.: 492110

DHL Supply Chain Management GmbH (1)
Charles-De-Gaulle-Str 20
Bonn, Nordrhein-Westfalen, 53113, Germany
Tel.: (49) 228 1820
Logistics Consulting Services
S.I.C.: 4731
N.A.I.C.S.: 541614

DHL Vertriebs GmbH & Co. OHG (1)
Charles-de-Gaulle-Strasse 20
53113 Bonn, Germany
Tel.: (49) 228 18 20
Logistics Consulting Services
S.I.C.: 4731
N.A.I.C.S.: 541614
Andrej Busch *(Mng Dir)*
Norman Chmiel *(Mng Dir)*
Katja Herbst *(Mng Dir)*

Gerlach Zolldienste GmbH (1)
Im Freihafen 6
47138 Duisburg, Germany
Tel.: (49) 203 348 599 0
Fax: (49) 203 348 599 11
E-Mail: gerlach.duisburg@de.gerlachcs.com
Web Site: www.gerlachcs.de
Emp.: 6
Customs Consulting Services
S.I.C.: 4731
N.A.I.C.S.: 541614

Gull GmbH (1)
Heuriedweg 19
88131 Lindau, Germany
Tel.: (49) 83 82 96 310
Fax: (49) 83 82 96 318 61
E-Mail: info@guell.de
Web Site: www.guell-presseservice.de
Emp.: 118
Magazine Publishing Services
S.I.C.: 5192
N.A.I.C.S.: 424920
Ernst G. Wallaschek *(CEO)*

interServ Gesellschaft fur Personalund Beraterdienstleistungen mbH (1)
Charles-de-Gaulle-Str 20
53113 Bonn, Nordrhein-Westfalen, Germany
Tel.: (49) 228 182 0
Logistics Consulting Services
S.I.C.: 4731
N.A.I.C.S.: 541614

it4logistics AG (1)
Am Luftschiffhafen 1
14471 Potsdam, Germany
Tel.: (49) 331 2002 0
Fax: (49) 331 2002 111
E-Mail: info@it4logistics.de
Web Site: www.it4logistics.de
Logistics Consulting Services
S.I.C.: 4731
N.A.I.C.S.: 541614

ITG GmbH Internationale Spedition und Logistik (1)
Eichenstrasse 2
Oberding, 85445 Schwaig, Germany De
Tel.: (49) 8122 567 0
Fax: (49) 8122 567 1001
E-Mail: info@itg.de
Web Site: www.itg.de
Emp.: 100
Logistics & Freight Forwarding Services
S.I.C.: 4731
N.A.I.C.S.: 488510
Andreas Weiss *(CEO & Mng Dir)*

nugg.ad AG predictive behavioral targeting (1)
Rotherstr - 16
10245 Berlin, Germany
Tel.: (49) 30 29 38 19 990
Fax: (49) 30 29 38 19 999
E-Mail: welcome@nugg.ad
Web Site: www.nugg.ad
Emp.: 56
Digital Media Advertising Services
S.I.C.: 7311
N.A.I.C.S.: 541810
Ingo Bohlken *(Chm-Supervisory Bd)*
Stephan Noller *(CEO)*
Klaus Koegler *(CFO)*
Richard Hutton *(CTO)*
Karim H. Attia *(Chief Bus Dev Officer)*

Scherbauer Spedition GmbH (1)
Oberheisinger Strasse 7
93073 Neutraubling, Germany
Tel.: (49) 940152260
Fax: (49) 94015226139
E-Mail: info@scherbauer.de
Web Site: www.scherbauer.de
Freight Forwarding Services
S.I.C.: 4731
N.A.I.C.S.: 488510

Siegfried Vogele Institut (SVI) - Internationale Gesellschaft fur Dialogmarketing mbH (1)
Olmuhlweg 12
61462 Konigstein, Germany
Tel.: (49) 6174 20170
Fax: (49) 6174 201719
E-Mail: info@sv-institut.de
Web Site: www.sv-institut.de
Educational Consulting Services
S.I.C.: 8299
N.A.I.C.S.: 611710

U.S. Subsidiaries:

Advance Logistics Inc. (1)
3301 NW 97th Ave
Doral, FL 33172
Tel.: (305) 718-4160
Fax: (305) 718-6661
E-Mail: inquiries@advanced-logistics.net
Web Site: www.advanced-logistics.net
Logistics Consulting Services
S.I.C.: 4731
N.A.I.C.S.: 541614
Ricardo Castillo *(Pres)*

AEI Drawback Services Inc. (1)
22210 Highland Knolls Dr
Katy, TX 77450-5868
Tel.: (281) 578-9605
Fax: (281) 578-9607
Logistics Consulting Services
S.I.C.: 4731
N.A.I.C.S.: 541614

Air Express International USA, Inc. (1)
1 Slater Dr Ste 8
Elizabeth, NJ 07206-2138
Tel.: (908) 289-6006
Logistics Consulting Services
S.I.C.: 4731
N.A.I.C.S.: 541614

Compass Logistics Inc. (1)
570 Polaris Pkwy Ste 140
Westerville, OH 43082-7902
Tel.: (614) 865-8500
Emp.: 4
Logistics Consulting Services
S.I.C.: 4731
N.A.I.C.S.: 541614
Blake Fleming *(Pres & CEO)*

DHL Network Operations (usa), Inc. (1)
1210 S Pine Island Rd 1st Fl Legal Dept
Plantation, FL 33324
Tel.: (954) 888-7000
Logistics Consulting Services
S.I.C.: 4731
N.A.I.C.S.: 541614

DHL Worldwide Express, Inc (1)
50 California St
San Francisco, CA 94111
Tel.: (415) 677-6800
Logistics Consulting Services
S.I.C.: 4731
N.A.I.C.S.: 541614

Dimalsa Logistics Inc. (1)
Km 1/5 Bo Palmas Rr 869
Catano, PR 00962
Tel.: (787) 788-3935
Fax: (787) 275-0495
Emp.: 16
Logistics Consulting Services
S.I.C.: 4731
N.A.I.C.S.: 541614
Ewar Rivera *(Pres)*

DPWN Holdings (USA), Inc. (1)
1200 S Pine Island Rd Ste 600
Plantation, FL 33324
Tel.: (954) 888-7000
Fax: (954) 888-7310
Logistics Consulting Services
S.I.C.: 4731
N.A.I.C.S.: 541614

Exel Direct Inc. (1)
570 Polaris Pkwy Dept 280
Westerville, OH 43082
Tel.: (614) 865-8500
Fax: (614) 865-8875
Toll Free: (877) 272-1054
Logistics Consulting Services
S.I.C.: 4731
N.A.I.C.S.: 541614
David Vieira *(Pres)*

Exel Investments Inc. (1)
1105 N Market St Ste 1300
Wilmington, DE 19801
Tel.: (302) 427-3547
Financial Investment Services
S.I.C.: 6211
N.A.I.C.S.: 523999

Galaxy Logistics Inc. (1)
15 Independence Blvd
Nashville, TN 37229-2161
Tel.: (615) 479-0112
Logistics Consulting Services
S.I.C.: 4731
N.A.I.C.S.: 541614

Giorgio Gori USA, Inc. (1)
80 River St
Hoboken, NJ 07030
Tel.: (201) 653-6800
Fax: (201) 653-9042
E-Mail: info@goriusa.com
Logistics Consulting Services
S.I.C.: 4731
N.A.I.C.S.: 541614

Global Mail, Inc. (1)
72 Van Reipen Ave
Jersey City, NJ 07306-2806
Tel.: (201) 222-8800
Fax: (201) 792-4230
Parcel & Courier Services
S.I.C.: 4215
N.A.I.C.S.: 492210

ITG International Transports, Inc. (1)
440 William F McClellan Hwy
East Boston, MA 02128
Tel.: (617) 455-6020
Fax: (617) 455-6015
Toll Free: (800) 414-9856
E-Mail: info.bos@itgboston.com
Web Site: www.itg.de/en/boston.html
Emp.: 9
Logistics Consulting Services
S.I.C.: 4731
N.A.I.C.S.: 541614
Guido Voss *(Branch Mgr)*

Radix Group International, Inc. (1)
9543 Heinrch Hrtz Dr
San Diego, CA 92154-7921
Tel.: (619) 661-8057
Freight Forwarding Services
S.I.C.: 4731
N.A.I.C.S.: 488510

Sky Courier, Inc. (1)
21240 Ridgetop Cir
Sterling, VA 20166
Tel.: (703) 433-2800
Fax: (703) 433-2839
Toll Free: (800) 336-3344
E-Mail: sameday_info@dhl.com
Web Site: www.skycourier.com
Emp.: 200
Air Express Services
S.I.C.: 4215
N.A.I.C.S.: 492110
Debra Gruen *(Controller)*

USC Distribution Services LLC (1)
3015 Ana St
Rancho Dominguez, CA 90221
Tel.: (310) 609-1153
Web Site: www.uscds.com
Logistics Distribution Services
S.I.C.: 4731
N.A.I.C.S.: 541614

Non-U.S. Subsidiaries:

Adcloud Operations Spain S.L. (1)
Paseo De Las Castellana 140 Floor 18
28046 Madrid, Spain
Tel.: (34) 638 262 462
E-Mail: spain@adcloud.com
Web Site: www.adcloud.com
Emp.: 6
Online Advertising Services
S.I.C.: 7319
N.A.I.C.S.: 541890
Henrik Varga *(Country Mgr)*

Aero Express del Ecuador TransAm Cia Ltd. (1)
Avenida El Dorado No 106-81 Bodega DHL
Aeropuerto el Dorado
Nuevo Terminal de Carga, Bogota, Colombia
Tel.: (57) 1 7457666
E-Mail: cargo.salesbog@dhl.com
Air Freight Transportation Services
S.I.C.: 4512
N.A.I.C.S.: 481112

Aero Express del Ecuador (TransAm) Ltda. (1)
Av de Las Americas Entre Puerta B
Aeropuerto Jose Joaquin de Olmedo
Guayaquil, Ecuador
Tel.: (593) 4 2282510
Fax: (593) 4 2396478
Emp.: 39
Air Cargo Handling Services
S.I.C.: 4581
N.A.I.C.S.: 488119
Luigi Grudena *(Gen Mgr)*

Aerocar B.V. (1)
Freight Terminal 207 / Schillingweg 60
2153PL Nieuw-Vennep, Netherlands
Tel.: (31) 252 361 300
Fax: (31) 252 361 301
E-Mail: info@aerocar.nl
Web Site: www.aerocar.nl
Air & Marine Cargo Handling Services
S.I.C.: 4581
N.A.I.C.S.: 488119
Guy Hachey *(Mng Dir)*

Agencia de Aduanas dhl Express Colombia Ltda. (1)
Carrera 106 No 15-25 - Manzana 9 - Bodega 12 Zona Franca de Bogota
Bogota, Colombia
Tel.: (57) 1 4227800
Logistics Consulting Services
S.I.C.: 4731
N.A.I.C.S.: 541614

AGENCIA DE ADUANAS DHL GLOBAL FORWARDING (COLOMBIA) S.A. (1)
Popa Cl 30 18 A-226 P-2
Cartagena, Colombia

Deutsche Post AG—(Continued)

Tel.: (57) 5 6723920
Logistics Consulting Services
S.I.C.: 4731
N.A.I.C.S.: 541614

Asia-Pacific Information Services Sdn. Bhd. (1)
No 3509-3511 Jalan Teknokrat 5
Cyberjaya, 63000, Malaysia
Tel.: (60) 383158000
Fax: (60) 83158100
Web Site: www.dhl.com
Emp.: 100
Business Process Outsourcing Services
S.I.C.: 7389
N.A.I.C.S.: 561499

Blue Dart Aviation Ltd. (1)
88-89 Old International Terminal Building
Meenambakkam Airport
Chennai, 600 027, India
Tel.: (91) 44 2256 8200
Fax: (91) 44 2256 8385
E-Mail: bda.groundops@bluedartaviation.com
Web Site: www.bluedartaviation.com
Emp.: 150
Logistics Consulting Services
S.I.C.: 4731
N.A.I.C.S.: 541614
Tushar Jani *(Chm)*
Tulsi N. Mirchandaney *(Mng Dir)*

Cargus International S.R.L. (1)
Calea Bucuresti Nr 169A Cladirea A Etaj 8
Sector 1
Bucharest, 014459, Romania
Tel.: (40) 21 933 00 00
Fax: (40) 21 100 20 15
E-Mail: cargus@cargus.ro
Courier Services
S.I.C.: 4215
N.A.I.C.S.: 492210

Circuit Logistics Inc. (1)
8 Burford Rd
Hamilton, ON, L8E 5B1, Canada
Tel.: (905) 561-5848
Fax: (905) 561-6911
Warehousing & Storage Services
S.I.C.: 4226
N.A.I.C.S.: 493190
Mark Evans *(Gen Mgr)*

Concorde Air Logistics Ltd. (1)
17 Adarsh Industrial Estate Sahar Road
Chakala
Andheri East, Mumbai, 400099, India
Tel.: (91) 22 2837 7431
Fax: (91) 22 836 6268
Air Cargo Handling Services
S.I.C.: 4581
N.A.I.C.S.: 488119

DANMAR LINES AG (1)
Peter Merian-Strasse 88
Basel, 4002, Switzerland
Tel.: (41) 61274 74 74
Fax: (41) 61274 74 75
E-Mail: reception.management.dh@dhl.com
Web Site: www.dhl.com
Emp.: 3
Electronic Data Processing Services
S.I.C.: 7374
N.A.I.C.S.: 518210

Danzas Abu Dhabi LLC (1)
Mezzanine Fl Mafco Bldg Muroor E Rd
Abu Dhabi, United Arab Emirates
Tel.: (971) 2 4452788
Fax: (971) 2 4463702
Freight Forwarding Services
S.I.C.: 4731
N.A.I.C.S.: 488510

Danzas Bahrain WLL (1)
PO Box 56
Manama, Bahrain
Tel.: (973) 17728151
Fax: (973) 17728187
Web Site: www.dhl.com.bh/en/contact_center/contact_global_forwarding.html
Freight Forwarding Services
S.I.C.: 4731
N.A.I.C.S.: 488510

Danzas Fashion NV (1)
Square de l'Atomium
1020 Brussels, Belgium
Tel.: (32) 2 478 17 77
Fax: (32) 2 478 17 53
Logistics Consulting Services
S.I.C.: 4731
N.A.I.C.S.: 541614

Danzas Fashion Service Centers B.V. (1)
Industrieweg 55
5145 PD Waalwijk, Netherlands
Tel.: (31) 41656 55 20
Fax: (31) 41656 55 75
Emp.: 2
Air Freight Transportation Services
S.I.C.: 4731
N.A.I.C.S.: 488510

Danzas Holding AG (1)
Peter Merian-Strasse 88
Basel, 4002, Switzerland
Tel.: (41) 61 274 74 74
Fax: (41) 61 274 74 75
Investment Management Services
S.I.C.: 6799
N.A.I.C.S.: 523920

Danzas Kiev Ltd. (1)
3 Hrinchenka Building Office 3A
Kiev, 3680, Ukraine
Tel.: (380) 442466046
Fax: (380) 442466045
E-Mail: ievglobalforwarding@dhl.com
Emp.: 7
Air & Marine Cargo Handling Services
S.I.C.: 4581
N.A.I.C.S.: 488119
Aleksandra Matvienko *(Gen Mgr)*

Deutsche Post Finance B.V. (1)
Pierre de Coubertinweg 5
Maastricht, 6225 XT, Netherlands
Tel.: (31) 43 356 4000
Fax: (31) 43 356 4099
Financial Investment Services
S.I.C.: 6211
N.A.I.C.S.: 523999
Didier Staquet *(Gen Mgr)*

Deutsche Post Global Mail (Australia) Pty Ltd. (1)
1/55 Kent Rd
Mascot, 2020, Australia
Tel.: (61) 1800 688 280
Air Freight Transportation Services
S.I.C.: 4512
N.A.I.C.S.: 481112

Deutsche Post Global Mail (France) SAS (1)
143 Bis Avenue De Verdun
92130 Issy-les-Moulineaux, France
Tel.: (33) 141083170
Fax: (33) 141083179
E-Mail: akoemaru@dhlglobalmail.fr
Web Site: www.dhlglobalmail.fr
Emp.: 2
Air Freight Transportation Services
S.I.C.: 4512
N.A.I.C.S.: 481112
Marcel Bassant *(Gen Mgr)*

Deutsche Post International B.V. (1)
Jozef Israelskade 48-G
Amsterdam, 1072 SB, Netherlands
Tel.: (31) 20 578 8500
Logistics Consulting Services
S.I.C.: 4731
N.A.I.C.S.: 541614

Deutsche Post Reinsurance S.A. (1)
Rue De Merl 74
Luxembourg, 2146, Luxembourg
Tel.: (352) 496951
Fax: (352) 496936
Emp.: 23
Insurance Management Services
S.I.C.: 6411
N.A.I.C.S.: 524298
Claude Weber *(Mng Dir)*

DHL Aviation (France) SAS (1)
Zone Industrielle Paris Nord li 241 Rue De La Belle Etoile
Roissy-en-France, 95700, France
Tel.: (33) 1 55 30 71 03
Air Freight Transportation Services
S.I.C.: 4512
N.A.I.C.S.: 481112

DHL Aviation (Nigeria) Ltd. (1)
Cargo Terminal MM International Airport
Lagos, Nigeria
Tel.: (234) 12700719
Air Freight Transportation Services
S.I.C.: 4512
N.A.I.C.S.: 481112

DHL (Bolivia) SRL (1)
Av Mcal Santa Cruz 1282 Edf Seguros
La Paz, Bolivia
Tel.: (591) 2 2116161
Web Site: www.dhl.com.bo
Emp.: 130
Logistics Consulting Services
S.I.C.: 4731
N.A.I.C.S.: 541614

DHL (BVI) Ltd. (1)
Wickhams Cay 1
PO Box 3255
Road Town, Virgin Islands (British)
Tel.: (284) 494 4659
Web Site: www.dhl.vg
Emp.: 15
Logistics Consulting Services
S.I.C.: 4731
N.A.I.C.S.: 541614

DHL Corporate Services SC Mexico (1)
Autopista Mexico-Queretaro Km 34 5 Nave 1
Cuautitlan, 54740, Mexico
Tel.: (52) 5530032600
Administrative Management Services
S.I.C.: 8742
N.A.I.C.S.: 541611

DHL Elancourt SARL (1)
65 avenue Georges Politzer Z A de Trappes Elancourt
78190 Trappes, France
Tel.: (33) 820 20 25 25
Fax: (33) 1 30 13 06 76
Logistics Consulting Services
S.I.C.: 4731
N.A.I.C.S.: 541614

DHL Exel Slovakia, s.r.o. (1)
Dialnicna 2/4149
Senec, 90301, Slovakia
Tel.: (421) 232161111
Logistics Consulting Services
S.I.C.: 4731
N.A.I.C.S.: 541614

DHL Exel Supply Chain Portugal, S.A. (1)
Quinta Da Verdelha Corpo B Fraccao 5
Alverca do Ribatejo, Vila Franca De Xira, 2619-501, Portugal
Tel.: (351) 263659000
Logistics Consulting Services
S.I.C.: 4731
N.A.I.C.S.: 541614

DHL Global Forwarding (Argentina) S.A. (1)
Bernardo De Irigoyen 308 1 Piso
Buenos Aires, C1072AAH, Argentina
Tel.: (54) 11 4344 4000
Fax: (54) 11 4343 8805
Freight Forwarding Services
S.I.C.: 4731
N.A.I.C.S.: 488510

DHL Global Forwarding (Cameroon) PLC (1)
22 Rue Pierre Loti
BP 625
Douala, Cameroon
Tel.: (237) 33423872
Fax: (237) 33423854
Freight Forwarding Services
S.I.C.: 4731
N.A.I.C.S.: 488510

DHL global forwarding cote d'ivoire SA (1)
Immeuble Le Massai 1er etage lot 86
Boulevard VGE Marcory 01
BP 2069
Abidjan, 01, Cote d'Ivoire
Tel.: (225) 21 21 28 80
Fax: (225) 21 21 28 81
Freight Forwarding Services
S.I.C.: 4731
N.A.I.C.S.: 488510

DHL Global Forwarding Nigeria Limited (1)
Oregun Business Park 2 Billingsway
Oregun, Lagos, Nigeria
Tel.: (234) 80 250 11806
Fax: (234) 1 493 1094
Freight Forwarding Services
S.I.C.: 4731
N.A.I.C.S.: 488510

DHL Global Forwarding (Thailand) Limited (1)
209 K Tower A 12th-12Ath Floor Sukhumvit
21 Road Asoke Klongtoey-Nua
Watthana, Bangkok, 10110, Thailand
Tel.: (66) 2 791 8000
Freight Forwarding Services
S.I.C.: 4731
N.A.I.C.S.: 488510

DHL Global Mail Nordic AB (1)
Bjornstigen 85
Solna, Stockholm, 170 72, Sweden
Tel.: (46) 854345405
Courier Services
S.I.C.: 4215
N.A.I.C.S.: 492110

DHL Group Services NV/SA (1)
Gebouw 3 Luchthaven
Zaventem, Vlaams Brabant, 1930, Belgium BE
Tel.: (32) 27181211
Fax: (32) 27211751
Logistics Consulting Services
S.I.C.: 4731
N.A.I.C.S.: 541614

DHL International Botswana (Pty) Ltd. (1)
Broadhurst Industrial Western By-pass
PO Box 1077
Gaborone, Botswana
Tel.: (267) 391 2000
Fax: (267) 397 4168
Courier Services
S.I.C.: 4215
N.A.I.C.S.: 492110

DHL International Mauritanie SARL (1)
Avenue Mamadou Konate ILot A 639
PO Box 1996
Nouakchott, Mauritania
Tel.: (222) 254706
Courier Services
S.I.C.: 4215
N.A.I.C.S.: 492110

DHL International Reunion SARL (1)
Za St Exupery Zone Aeropor
Sainte-Marie, 97438, Reunion
Tel.: (262) 262295776
Courier Services
S.I.C.: 4215
N.A.I.C.S.: 492110

DHL International S.A./N.V. (1)
Avenue R Vandendriesschelaan 18
003227155050, 1150 Brussels, Belgium (100%)
Tel.: (32) 27771555
Fax: (32) 27771566
Web Site: www.dhl.be
Sales Range: $25-49.9 Billion
Emp.: 1,500
Express & Global Mail Deliveries & Logistics Services
S.I.C.: 4215
N.A.I.C.S.: 492110
Frank Appel *(CEO)*

Subsidiaries:

DHL Aviation NV / SA (2)
Gebouw Drie Brussel Nationale Luchthaven
Bldg 3
1930 Zaventem, Belgium
Tel.: (32) 2 718 12 11
Fax: (32) 2 718 59 57
Air Freight Transportation Services
S.I.C.: 4512
N.A.I.C.S.: 481112

DHL Employee Benefit Fund ASBL/VZW (2)
De Kleetlaan 1
1831 Machelen, Belgium
Tel.: (32) 2 713 40 00
Fax: (32) 2 713 40 00
E-Mail: dhl.ebf@dhl.com
Web Site: www.dhlebf.be
Pension Fund Services
S.I.C.: 6371

N.A.I.C.S.: 525110
Gilbert McArthy *(Mgr)*

DHL Freight (Belgium) NV (2)
Eppegemsesteenweg 31-33
Grimbergen, 1850, Belgium
Tel.: (32) 2 255 11 24
Fax: (32) 2 255 11 77
Web Site: www.dhl.be
Emp.: 490
Freight Transportation Services
S.I.C.: 4731
N.A.I.C.S.: 488510
Tom De Vleeschauwer *(Pres)*

DHL Global Forwarding (Belgium) NV (2)
Building 720
1931 Brussels, Belgium
Tel.: (32) 27520211
Fax: (32) 27519383
E-Mail: info.dhlglobalforwarding@dhl.com
Emp.: 560
Freight Forwarding Services
S.I.C.: 4731
N.A.I.C.S.: 488510
David Bellon *(Dir-Air Freight)*

DHL Solutions (Belgium) NV (2)
Zandvoortstraat 3
2800 Mechelen, Belgium
Tel.: (32) 15299111
Fax: (32) 15210127
Emp.: 150
Logistics Consulting Services
S.I.C.: 4731
N.A.I.C.S.: 541614
Eddy de Timmerman *(CFO)*

DHL Supply Chain (Belgium) NV (2)
Zandvoortstraat 3
2800 Mechelen, Belgium
Tel.: (32) 15299111
Fax: (32) 15210127
Emp.: 100
Freight Transportation Services
S.I.C.: 4731
N.A.I.C.S.: 488510
Kevin Burrell *(Mgr-Thailand)*

U.S. Subsidiaries:

DHL Holdings (USA), Inc. (2)
1200 S Pine Island Rd Ste 600
Plantation, FL 33324
Tel.: (954) 888-7000
Telex: 261208
Fax: (954) 888-7330
Toll Free: (800) 225-5345
E-Mail: general@wkrn.com
Web Site: www.dhl-usa.com
Emp.: 20,000
Express Delivery & Logistics Services
Export
S.I.C.: 4513
N.A.I.C.S.: 492110
Stephen Fenwick *(CEO-Americas Reg)*

Non-U.S. Subsidiaries:

DHL de El Salvador S.A. de C.V. (3)
47 Av Norte 104
San Salvador, CA, El Salvador
Tel.: (503) 22607722
Fax: (503) 22396551
Web Site: www.dhl.com.sv
Emp.: 150
Express Mail Services
S.I.C.: 4215
N.A.I.C.S.: 492110

DHL Dominicana S.A. (3)
Avenida Sarasota No 26
Santo Domingo, Dominican Republic
Tel.: (809) 534 7888
Web Site: www.dhl.com.do
Emp.: 60
Express Mail Services
S.I.C.: 4215
N.A.I.C.S.: 492110

DHL, S.A. (3)
7A Avenida 2-42 Zona 9
Guatemala, Guatemala
Tel.: (502) 23323023
Web Site: www.dhl.com.gt
Emp.: 144
Express Mail Services
S.I.C.: 4513
N.A.I.C.S.: 492110

DHL Smart & Global Mail (2)
2700 S Commerce Pkwy Ste 400
Weston, FL 33331
Tel.: (954) 903-6300
Fax: (954) 903-6310
Toll Free: (866) 546-5200
E-Mail: contact@globalmail.com
Web Site: www.globalmail.com
Sales Range: $100-124.9 Million
Emp.: 100
Global Mail Delivery Network
S.I.C.: 4311
N.A.I.C.S.: 491110
S. David Fineman *(Chm-Americas)*
Lee Spratt *(CEO-Americas Div)*

DHL Solutions (USA), Inc. (2)
1 Carr 869 Bldg C
Catano, PR 00962-5880
Tel.: (787) 788-3888
Logistics Consulting Services
S.I.C.: 4731
N.A.I.C.S.: 541614

Non-U.S. Division:

DHL Express Germany GmbH (2)
Heinrich-Bruening-Strasse 5
Bonn, 53113, Germany
Tel.: (49) 180 5 345300 1
Web Site: www.dhl.de/en/express/kurierdienst.html
Express Parcel Services
S.I.C.: 4513
N.A.I.C.S.: 492110

U.S. Subsidiary:

DHL Express (USA), Inc. (3)
1210 S Pine Island Rd 4th Fl
Plantation, FL 33324
Tel.: (954) 888-7000
Fax: (888) 221-6211
Toll Free: (800) 225-5345
Web Site: www.dhl-usa.com
Parcel & Courier Delivery Services
S.I.C.: 4215
N.A.I.C.S.: 492210
Mike Parra *(CEO)*
Pablo Ciano *(CIO-Americas)*

Non-U.S. Subsidiaries:

DHL Express A/S (3)
Jydekrogen 14
2625 Vallensbaek, Denmark
Tel.: (45) 70345346
Fax: (45) 70132132
E-Mail: info@dhl.dk
Web Site: www.dhl.dk
Emp.: 100
Express Mail Services
S.I.C.: 4215
N.A.I.C.S.: 492110
Ken Allen *(CEO)*

DHL Express Aduanas Peru S.A.C. (3)
Calle Uno Mz A Lt 6 Bocanegra
Lima, Peru
Tel.: (51) 15172500
Fax: (51) 15754433
Customs Consulting Services
S.I.C.: 4731
N.A.I.C.S.: 541614

DHL Express Aduanas Venezuela C.A. (3)
Edificio DHL La California Sur
Caracas, 1060, Venezuela
Tel.: (58) 212 6206000
Logistics Consulting Services
S.I.C.: 4731
N.A.I.C.S.: 541614

DHL Express (Argentina) S.A. (3)
Larrazabal 2255 Between San Pedro and Bilbao Mataderos
Buenos Aires, CVB1440, Argentina
Tel.: (54) 11 5670 1100
Fax: (54) 11 5670 1036
E-Mail: bueinternet@dhl.com
Web Site: www.dhl.com.ar
Emp.: 40
Logistics Consulting Services
S.I.C.: 4731
N.A.I.C.S.: 541614
Sergio del Casale *(Dir-South Zone)*

DHL Express (Australia) Pty Ltd. (3)
Sydney Airport Cte
Level 5 15 Bourke Rd, Mascot, NSW, 2020, Australia
Tel.: (61) 293178300
Fax: (61) 293173820
E-Mail: info@dhl.com.au
Web Site: www.dhl.com.au
Emp.: 1,010
Express Mail Services
S.I.C.: 4513
N.A.I.C.S.: 492110
Gary Wayne Edstein *(VP-Oceania)*

DHL Express (Austria) GmbH (3)
Viaduktstrasse 20
2353 Guntramsdorf, Austria
Tel.: (43) 73237357700
Fax: (43) 73237365099
E-Mail: relationdesk.at@dhl.com
Web Site: www.dhl.at
Logistics Consulting Services
S.I.C.: 4731
N.A.I.C.S.: 541614
Joanna Krop *(CFO)*

DHL Express Barcelona Spain S.L. (3)
Poligono Industrial Les Minetes 2 - 3 Par
Santa Perpetua de Mogoda, Barcelona, 8130, Spain
Tel.: (34) 935656664
Fax: (34) 935656570
Logistics Consulting Services
S.I.C.: 4731
N.A.I.C.S.: 541614
Juan Sabanes *(Gen Mgr)*

DHL Express (Brazil) Ltda. (3)
Av. Santa Marina 1660/1666-Lapa
Sao Paulo, 05036-001, Brazil
Tel.: (55) 11 3611 2994
Logistics Consulting Services
S.I.C.: 4731
N.A.I.C.S.: 541614

DHL Express (Brunei) Sdn. Bhd. (3)
Ground Floor Unit 4 5 & 6 Bgn Pg Hj Md Daud Simpang 18
Jln Gadong, Bandar Seri Begawan, BE3919, Brunei Darussalam
Tel.: (673) 2444991
Fax: (673) 2444997
Web Site: www.dhl.com.bn/en/express/shipping/find_dhl_locations.html
Emp.: 32
Air Freight Transportation Services
S.I.C.: 4512
N.A.I.C.S.: 481112
Christopher Ong *(Mng Dir-Malaysia & Brunei)*

DHL Express Bulgaria EOOD (3)
10 Prodan Tarakchiev Str
Sofia, 1528, Bulgaria
Tel.: (359) 700 17 700
Fax: (359) 29734808
E-Mail: csasos@dhl.com
Web Site: www.dhl.bg
Emp.: 30
Logistics Consulting Services
S.I.C.: 4731
N.A.I.C.S.: 541614
Biliana Stoyanova *(Mgr-Ops)*

DHL Express (Cambodia) Ltd. (3)
353 St 110 Sk Sras Chark
Phnom Penh, Cambodia
Tel.: (855) 23 427726
Fax: (855) 23 990726
E-Mail: csinfo@dhl.com
Web Site: www.dhl.com.kh/en/contact_center/contact_express.html#local_contact
Logistics Consulting Services
S.I.C.: 4731
N.A.I.C.S.: 541614

DHL Express (Chile) Ltda. (3)
San Francisco 301
Santiago, Chile
Tel.: (56) 22802000
Web Site: www.dhl.cl/en/contact_center/contact_express.html
Logistics Consulting Services
S.I.C.: 4731
N.A.I.C.S.: 541614

DHL Express Cyprus (3)
64 Bethleem Stovlos
2033 Nicosia, Cyprus
Tel.: (357) 22799000
Fax: (357) 22799251
E-Mail: dhl.cyprus@dhl.com
Web Site: www.dhl.com.cy
Emp.: 56
Express Mail Services
S.I.C.: 4215
N.A.I.C.S.: 492110
Dinos Ioannides *(Branch Mgr)*

DHL Express (Czech Republic) s.r.o. (3)
Nam Sv Cecha 3 516
702 00 Ostrava, Privoz, Czech Republic
Tel.: (420) 596279211
Fax: (420) 0042596279260
E-Mail: zuzana.pszczolkova@dhl.com
Web Site: www.dhl.cz
Emp.: 1,700
Express Mail Services
S.I.C.: 4215
N.A.I.C.S.: 492110
Jiri Stojar *(Mng Dir)*

DHL Express (El Salvador) S.A.de C.V. (3)
Col Y Pje Las Terrazas Edif Dhl No 2505
San Salvador, El Salvador
Tel.: (503) 2239 6500
Fax: (503) 2239 6551
Logistics Consulting Services
S.I.C.: 4731
N.A.I.C.S.: 541614

DHL Express (Fiji) Ltd. (3)
Grantham Rd Raiwaqa
Box 13036
Suva, Fiji
Tel.: (679) 3372766
Fax: (679) 3372760
E-Mail: fj.customerservice@dhl.com
Web Site: www.dhl.com
Emp.: 5
Logistics Consulting Services
S.I.C.: 4731
N.A.I.C.S.: 541614

DHL Express (France) SAS (3)
241 Rue de la Belle Etoile ZI Paris Nord 2
95700 Roissy-en-France, France
Tel.: (33) 1 49 38 70 70
Logistics Consulting Services
S.I.C.: 4731
N.A.I.C.S.: 541614

DHL Express (Hellas) S.A. (3)
44 Alimou Ave & Rwma 17
Alimos, 17455 Athens, Greece
Tel.: (30) 210 9890000
Fax: (30) 210 9840041
E-Mail: athservedesk@dhl.com
Emp.: 20
Logistics Consulting Services
S.I.C.: 4731
N.A.I.C.S.: 541614
Pellie Houtas *(Mgr-Import & Export)*

DHL Express (Hong Kong) Ltd (3)
Shop 56 Ho Chuck Center G/F
New Kwai Fong Gardens
2-10 Kwai Yi Road, Kowloon, China (Hong Kong) (100%)
Tel.: (852) 2423 8283
Fax: (852) 22186388
E-Mail: bosco.yeung@dhl.com
Web Site: www.dhl.com.hk
Emp.: 215
Freight Forwarding & Transportation Services
S.I.C.: 4215
N.A.I.C.S.: 492110
Peter Landsiedel *(Sr VP)*

DHL Express Hungary Forwarding and Services LLC (3)
Feherakac U 3
Budapest, 1097, Hungary
Tel.: (36) 13 82 32 00
Fax: (36) 1204 66 66
Postal Services
S.I.C.: 4311
N.A.I.C.S.: 491110

DHL Express Hungary Ltd. (3)
Feheakas 3
1097 Budapest, Hungary
Tel.: (36) 13823222
Fax: (36) 13823348
E-Mail: customerservice.hu@dhl.com
Web Site: www.dhl.hu
Emp.: 330
Express Mail Services
S.I.C.: 4215
N.A.I.C.S.: 492110

Deutsche Post AG—(Continued)

John Lucas *(Gen Mgr)*

DHL Express Iberia S.L. (3)
Paseo Mikeletegi 65
San Sebastian, 20009, Spain
Tel.: (34) 943 37 66 00
Fax: (34) 943 30 80 30
Courier & Parcel Services
S.I.C.: 4215
N.A.I.C.S.: 492210

DHL Express (Iceland) EHF (3)
Skutuvogur 1d
104 Reykjavik, Iceland
Tel.: (354) 535 1100
Fax: (354) 535 1141
E-Mail: rektu@dhl.com
Web Site: www.dhl.is
Emp.: 5
Logistics Consulting Services
S.I.C.: 4731
N.A.I.C.S.: 541614
Freyr Einarsson *(Mng Dir)*

DHL Express (India) Pvt. Ltd. (3)
7th Fl Dheeraj Arma A K Marg Bandra E
Mumbai, 400051, India
Tel.: (91) 22 6741 2615
E-Mail: expressbombco@dhl.com
Web Site: www.dhl.co.in/en/about_us/express.html
Emp.: 1,500
Logistics Consulting Services
S.I.C.: 4731
N.A.I.C.S.: 541614
Jerry Hsu *(CEO-Asia Pacific)*

DHL Express International (Thailand) Ltd. (3)
Sathorn City Tower Fl 7 1 8 1175 South
Sathorn Road Thungmahamek S
10120 Bangkok, Thailand
Tel.: (66) 23455000
Fax: (66) 26346830
E-Mail:
Web Site: www.dhl.com.th
Emp.: 600
Express Mail Services
S.I.C.: 4215
N.A.I.C.S.: 492110
Boonkerd Silpavechkul *(Controller)*

DHL Express (Ireland) Ltd. (3)
Unit 3 Elm Rd Dublin Airport Logistics Pk
St Margaret's Rd, Swords, Co Dublin, Ireland
Tel.: (353) 18700700
Fax: (353) 14569250
E-Mail: info@dhl.com
Web Site: www.dhl.com
Emp.: 350
Express Mail Services
S.I.C.: 4215
N.A.I.C.S.: 492110
Dernart McCarthy *(Mng Dir)*

DHL Express Lda (3)
Rua do Barreiro 300
Crestins, 4470- 573 Maia, Portugal
Tel.: (351) 229 43 05 00
Fax: (351) 229 43 06 02
Web Site: www.dhl.pt/en/country_profile/office_express.html
Logistics Consulting Services
S.I.C.: 4731
N.A.I.C.S.: 541614

DHL Express (Luxembourg) S.A. (3)
11a Rue Edmond Reuter Z A E
Weiergewan
5326 Contern, Luxembourg
Tel.: (352) 35 09 09
Fax: (352) 35 09 09 433
E-Mail: luxinfo@dhl.com
Web Site: www.dhl.lu/en/express.html
Emp.: 135
Air Freight Services
S.I.C.: 4512
N.A.I.C.S.: 481112
Erik Hermans *(Gen Mgr)*

DHL Express (Macau) Ltd. (3)
Avenipapo Conselheiro Ferreira de Almeita 106-122
Macau, China (Macau)
Tel.: (853) 28372828
Fax: (853) 28752010
E-Mail: mcatrc@dhl.com
Web Site: www.dhl.com
Logistics Consulting Services
S.I.C.: 4731
N.A.I.C.S.: 541614

DHL Express Maroc S.A. (3)
114 Lotissement la colline Oulad Haddou
Casablanca, 20190, Morocco
Tel.: (212) 522 972 020
Logistics Consulting Services
S.I.C.: 4731
N.A.I.C.S.: 541614

DHL Express Mexico, S.A. de C.V. (3)
Ave Fuerza Aerea Mexicana #540
15700 Mexico, DF, Mexico
Tel.: (52) 5553452000
Fax: (52) 5553452281
Web Site: www.dhl.com.mx
Express Mail Services
S.I.C.: 4215
N.A.I.C.S.: 492110
Luis Erana *(CEO)*

DHL Express Navarra Spain, S.L. (3)
Poligono Ciudad Del Transporte Cl
Alemania Nave 5c
Navarra, 31119, Spain
Tel.: (34) 948368245
Fax: (34) 948368244
Logistics Consulting Services
S.I.C.: 4731
N.A.I.C.S.: 541614

DHL Express Nepal Pvt. Ltd. (3)
KUK Building Sinamangal Chowk Near
Tribhuvan International Airport
GPO Box 21841
Kathmandu, Nepal
Tel.: (977) 1 4481303
Fax: (977) 1 4481198
Web Site: www.dhl.com
Emp.: 55
Logistics Consulting Services
S.I.C.: 4731
N.A.I.C.S.: 541614
Gagan Mukhia *(Country Mgr)*

DHL Express (Netherlands) B.V. (3)
Anchoragelaan 32
PO Box 7549
1118 LD Schiphol, Netherlands
Tel.: (31) 20 655 5555
E-Mail: inkoop@dhl.com
Web Site: www.dhl.nl/en/country_profile/office_express.html
Emp.: 100
Logistics Consulting Services
S.I.C.: 4731
N.A.I.C.S.: 541614

DHL Express (Norway) AS (3)
Gneisveien 3
2020 Skedsmokorset, Norway
Tel.: (47) 66 92 80 00
Emp.: 70
Logistics Consulting Services
S.I.C.: 4731
N.A.I.C.S.: 541614
Nina Bjorlo *(Mgr-Customer Svcs)*

DHL Express Peru S.A.C. (3)
Calle Uno Mz A Lote 6 Fundo Bocanegra
Etapa I
Lima, Peru
Tel.: (51) 1 517 2500
Logistics Consulting Services
S.I.C.: 4731
N.A.I.C.S.: 541614

DHL Express (Philippines) Corp. (3)
2306 Chino Roces Avenue Pasong Tamo
Extension Kayamanan
Makati, 1231, Philippines
Tel.: (63) 2 811 7100
Fax: (63) 2 811 7000
E-Mail: mnl.customercare@dhl.com
Emp.: 50
Air Freight Services
S.I.C.: 4512
N.A.I.C.S.: 481112
Ken Allen *(CEO)*

DHL Express (Poland) Sp.zo.o. (3)
Osmanska 2 Str
02-823 Warsaw, Poland
Tel.: (48) 225650000
Fax: (48) 225464401
Web Site: www.dhl.com.pl/
Emp.: 750
Express Mail Services
S.I.C.: 4215
N.A.I.C.S.: 492110

DHL Express Portugal, Lda. (3)
Av D Joao II lote 1 18 01 Bloco B 3 Parque das Nacoes
1990-085 Lisbon, Portugal
Tel.: (351) 707 505 606
Fax: (351) 707 505 123
E-Mail: info.portugal@dhl.com
Logistics Consulting Services
S.I.C.: 4731
N.A.I.C.S.: 541614

DHL Express (Schweiz) AG (3)
Pumpwerkstrasse 51
8105 Regensdorf, Switzerland
Tel.: (41) 848 711 711
Fax: (41) 848 712 712
E-Mail: webzust@dhl.com
Emp.: 20
Freight Forwarding Services
S.I.C.: 4731
N.A.I.C.S.: 488510
Chris Hillis *(CEO)*

DHL Express Services (France) SAS (3)
241 Rue de la Belle Etoile ZI Paris Nord 2
95952 Roissy-en-France, France
Tel.: (33) 1 49 38 70 70
E-Mail: cdg.accuail@dhl.com
Web Site: www.dhl.fr
Emp.: 20
Logistics Consulting Services
S.I.C.: 4731
N.A.I.C.S.: 541614
Michel Akavi *(Mng Dir)*

DHL Express (Singapore) Pte Ltd. (3)
DHL Air Express Centre No 1 Tai Seng Dr
535215 Singapore, Singapore
Tel.: (65) 68806060
Web Site: www.dhl.com.sg
Emp.: 1,100
Express Mail Services
S.I.C.: 4513
N.A.I.C.S.: 492110
Sean Wall *(Sr VP-Network Ops & Aviation-Asia Pacific)*

DHL Express (Slovakia), spol. s r. o. (3)
Letisko M R Stefanika 65
820 01 Bratislava, Slovakia
Tel.: (421) 2 48 22 92 29
Fax: (421) 248229408
Emp.: 20
Logistics Consulting Services
S.I.C.: 4731
N.A.I.C.S.: 541614
Daniela Misurova *(Gen Mgr)*

DHL Express S.r.l. (3)
Viale Milanofiori
Palazzo U3 Strada 5
20089 Rozzano, MI, Italy
Tel.: (39) 024677871
Fax: (39) 02 8920 099
Web Site: www.dhl.it
Emp.: 2,192
Express Mail Services
S.I.C.: 4513
N.A.I.C.S.: 492110

DHL Express (Sweden) AB (3)
Bjornstigen 85
PO Box 23260
17072 Stockholm, Sweden
Tel.: (46) 854345000
Fax: (46) 854345851
Web Site: www.dhl.com
Emp.: 2,248
Express Mail Services
S.I.C.: 4215
N.A.I.C.S.: 492110
Ted Soderholm *(CEO)*

DHL Express (Taiwan) Corp. (3)
1st Fl No 82 Chien Kuo N Rd Section 2
10416 Taipei, Taiwan
Tel.: (886) 225036858
Fax: (886) 225032781
E-Mail: tpedhlcare@dhl.com
Web Site: www.dhl.com.tw
Express Mail Services
S.I.C.: 4215
N.A.I.C.S.: 492110

DHL Express (Thailand) Limited (3)
175 Sathorn City Tower 7/1 and 8/1 Floor
South Sathorn Rd Thungmahamek
Sathorn, Bangkok, 10120, Thailand
Tel.: (66) 23455000
Courier Delivery Services
S.I.C.: 4513
N.A.I.C.S.: 492110
Suraphong Suwannatip *(Mgr-Sls Plng & Dev)*

DHL Express (uk) Limited (3)
Orbital Park 178-188 Great South West Road
Hounslow, TW4 6JS, United Kingdom
Tel.: (44) 844 248 0844
Fax: (44) 20 8831 5399
Web Site: www.dhl.co.uk/en/contact_centre/contact_express.html
Air & Ocean Freight Transportation Services
S.I.C.: 4512
N.A.I.C.S.: 481112

DHL Express Valencia Spain S.L. (3)
Paseo De Mikeletegi 65
San Sebastian, Guipuzcoa, 20009, Spain
Tel.: (34) 961368484
Fax: (34) 961341285
Courier Delivery Services
S.I.C.: 4215
N.A.I.C.S.: 492110

Non-U.S. Subsidiaries:

DHL Air Limited (2)
EMA Cargo West East Midlands Airport
Derby, Castle Donington, DE74 2TR, United Kingdom
Tel.: (44) 1332 857815
Fax: (44) 1332 857463
Air Freight Services
S.I.C.: 4512
N.A.I.C.S.: 481112

DHL AirWays GmbH (2)
Flughafen 1
51147 Cologne, Germany
Tel.: (49) 2203 4790
Air Freight Transportation Services
S.I.C.: 4512
N.A.I.C.S.: 481112

DHL Arwest de Mexico S.A. de C.V. (2)
Poniente 140 No 789 Industrial Vallejo
Azcapotzalco
Mexico, 02300, Mexico
Tel.: (52) 55 5078 1999
Fax: (52) 55 5078 1998
E-Mail: soluciones.logisticasmx@dhl.com
Freight Transportation Services
S.I.C.: 4731
N.A.I.C.S.: 488510

Non-U.S. Subsidiaries:

DHL Arwest (Guatemala) S.A. (3)
Ave Hincapie 25-10 Zona 13
Guatemala, Guatemala
Tel.: (502) 2379 1111
Fax: (502) 2379 5002
Web Site: www.dhl.com.gt
Road Transportation Services
S.I.C.: 4789
N.A.I.C.S.: 488490

DHL Arwest (Panama) S.A. (3)
Ave Principal Costa del Este
Panama, Panama
Tel.: (507) 271 34511
Road Transportation Services
S.I.C.: 4789
N.A.I.C.S.: 488490

DHL Asia Pacific Shared Services Sdn. Bhd. (2)
Level 11 Menara Axis No 2 Jalan 51A/223
Petaling Jaya, Selangor, 46100, Malaysia
Tel.: (60) 37948 4848
Courier Services
S.I.C.: 4215
N.A.I.C.S.: 492110

DHL Automotive GmbH (2)
Rungedamm 32
Hamburg, 21035, Germany

Tel.: (49) 4073450
Fax: (49) 4073459199
Automotive Parts Logistics Services
S.I.C.: 4731
N.A.I.C.S.: 541614
Christian Huber *(Gen Mgr)*

DHL Aviation (Netherlands) B.V. (2)
Anchoragelaan 32
1118 LD Schiphol, Netherlands
Tel.: (31) 20 6582300
Fax: (31) 20 6736166
Logistics Distribution Services
S.I.C.: 4731
N.A.I.C.S.: 541614

DHL Aviation (UK) Limited (2)
Building 559 Shoreham Road West London Heathrow Airport
London, TW6 3SJ, United Kingdom
Tel.: (44) 20 8283 4000
Fax: (44) 20 8283 4181
Web Site: www.dhl.co.uk
Emp.: 40
Parcel & Courier Services
S.I.C.: 4215
N.A.I.C.S.: 492210

DHL (Chengdu) Service Ltd. (2)
6 7/F Bldg 6 Area C Tianfu Software Park No 81 Tuoxin E
Chengdu, Sichuan, 610041, China
Tel.: (86) 2865512397
Logistics Consulting Services
S.I.C.: 4731
N.A.I.C.S.: 541614

DHL (Costa Rica) S.A. (2)
600 Metros Noreste De La Interseccion Real Cariari
Heredia, Costa Rica
Tel.: (506) 22090000
Fax: (506) 22096174
E-Mail:
Emp.: 21
Freight Forwarding Services
S.I.C.: 4731
N.A.I.C.S.: 488510

DHL Customs Brokerage Ltd. (2)
3950 Malden Road Suite 6
Windsor, ON, N9C 2G4, Canada
Tel.: (519) 972-1994
Fax: (519) 972-5614
Toll Free: (866) 671-1164
E-Mail: windsor.pars@dhl.com
Web Site: www.dhl.com
Emp.: 15
Customs Brokerage Services
S.I.C.: 4731
N.A.I.C.S.: 488510
Jan Trapmen *(Office Mgr)*

DHL Danzas Air & Ocean (2)
Peter Merian Str 88
CH 4002 Basel, Switzerland (100%)
Tel.: (41) 612747474
Fax: (41) 612747475
Web Site: www.dhl.com
Emp.: 100
Freight Forwarding & Transportation Services
S.I.C.: 4731
N.A.I.C.S.: 488510

U.S. Subsidiary:

DHL Danzas Air & Ocean North America (3)
1200 S Pine Is Rd Fl 6
Plantation, FL 33324
Tel.: (954) 888-7000
Fax: (954) 888-7301
E-Mail: tasso.flath@dhl-us.com
Web Site: www.us.danzas.com
Freight Forwarding & Transportation Services
S.I.C.: 4513
N.A.I.C.S.: 492110
Tasso Flath *(CFO & Controller)*

Non-U.S. Subsidiaries:

Danzas AEI S.A. de C.V. (3)
Fundidora Monterrey 97
15520 Mexico, Mexico
Tel.: (52) 5551331700
Fax: (52) 5551331701
E-Mail: alex.granwitz@dhl.com
Web Site: www.dhl.com
Emp.: 350
Marine Cargo Handler; Freight Forwarding & Transportation Services
S.I.C.: 4491
N.A.I.C.S.: 488320
Alex Granwitz *(Gen Mgr)*

Danzas Ecuador S.A. (3)
Eloy Alfaro y de los Juncos
Lote 113-A, Quito, Ecuador
Tel.: (593) 22485100
Web Site: www.dhl.com.ec
Emp.: 30
Freight Forwarding & Transportation Services
S.I.C.: 4731
N.A.I.C.S.: 488510

Danzas S.A. (3)
15 rue de Nancy
75010 Paris, France
Tel.: (33) 144526666
Fax: (33) 144526790
Web Site: www.dhl.de
Emp.: 100
Freight Forwarding & Transportation Services
S.I.C.: 4731
N.A.I.C.S.: 488510

Danzas S.A. (3)
Rumania 2 4
Centro Transportes De Coslada, 28820
Coslada, Spain (100%)
Tel.: (34) 916604300
Fax: (34) 916604366
E-Mail: info@dhl.com
Web Site: www.dhl.com
Emp.: 150
Freight Forwarding & Transportation Services
S.I.C.: 4731
N.A.I.C.S.: 488510

DHL Danzas Air & Ocean (Belgium) NV/SA (3)
Antwerpsebaan 56 Tov Kaai 730
B-2040 Antwerp, Belgium
Tel.: (32) 35610300
Telex: 61685
Fax: (32) 35610338
Web Site: www.dp-dhl.com
Emp.: 85
Freight Forwarding & Transportation Services
S.I.C.: 4731
N.A.I.C.S.: 488510
Johan Vissers *(Gen Mgr)*

DHL Danzas Air & Ocean (Canada) Inc. (3)
100 World Dr
Mississauga, ON, L5T 3A2, Canada
Tel.: (905) 405-9300
Fax: (905) 405-9301
E-Mail: info@ca.danzas.com
Web Site: www.ca.danzas.com
Emp.: 210
Freight Forwarding & Transportation Services
S.I.C.: 4731
N.A.I.C.S.: 488510
Donna Letterio *(Pres)*

DHL Finland (3)
Tullimiehentie 10
01530 Vantaa, Finland
Tel.: (358) 205333
Fax: (358) 205332580
E-Mail: pressfindland@dhl.com
Web Site: www.dhl.fi
Emp.: 120
Freight Forwarding & Transportation Services
S.I.C.: 4731
N.A.I.C.S.: 488510

DHL Distribution Holdings (UK) Limited (2)
178-188 Great South West Road Orbital Park
Hounslow, TW4 6JS, United Kingdom
Tel.: (44) 20 8818 8000
Investment Management Services
S.I.C.: 6282
N.A.I.C.S.: 523920

DHL Egypt W.L.L. (2)
El Mona Towers
16 Lebanon Street
Mohandessin, Cairo, Egypt
Tel.: (20) 2 302 9801
Fax: (20) 2 305 8858
Web Site: www.dhl.com
Express Mail Services
S.I.C.: 4215
N.A.I.C.S.: 492110

DHL Ekspres (Slovenija), d.o.o. (2)
Spruha 19
Trzin, 1236, Slovenia
Tel.: (386) 1 588 78 00
Fax: (386) 1 588 78 88
E-Mail: si.info@dhl.com
Web Site: www.dhl.com
Emp.: 4
Freight Forwarding Services
S.I.C.: 4731
N.A.I.C.S.: 488510
Amatjaz Sirk *(Gen Mgr)*

DHL Estonia AS (2)
Betooni 6
11415 Tallinn, Estonia
Tel.: (372) 6 808 400
Fax: (372) 6 808 406
E-Mail: estonia@dhl.com
Web Site: www.dhl.ee
Logistics Consulting Services
S.I.C.: 4731
N.A.I.C.S.: 541614

DHL Exel Supply Chain Euskal-Log, S.L.U. (2)
Poligono Industrial Agurain 7 - Par
Salvatierra, Alava, 1200, Spain
Tel.: (34) 945301900
Fax: (34) 945301914
Logistics Consulting Services
S.I.C.: 4731
N.A.I.C.S.: 541614

DHL Exel Supply Chain Hungary Limited (2)
Zoldmezo street 1
2225 Ullo, Hungary
Tel.: (36) 29 523 100
Fax: (36) 29 523 200
E-Mail: sales.ullo@dhl.com
Logistics Consulting Services
S.I.C.: 4731
N.A.I.C.S.: 541614

DHL Exel Supply Chain Phils., Inc. (2)
Km 17 West Service Road South Super Highway Bicutan
Paranaque, 1704, Philippines
Tel.: (63) 2 8584600
Fax: (63) 2 8210752
Web Site: www.dhl.com.ph
Logistics Consulting Services
S.I.C.: 4731
N.A.I.C.S.: 541614
Olive Ramos *(Mng Dir)*

DHL Exel Supply Chain (Spain), S.L.U. (2)
Centro de Transportes de Coslada Calle Rumania 1
28820 Coslada, Madrid, Spain
Tel.: (34) 91 670 75 95
Fax: (34) 91 670 87 27
Logistics Consulting Services
S.I.C.: 4731
N.A.I.C.S.: 541614

DHL Exel Supply Chain (Sweden) AB (2)
Bjornstigen 85
170 87 Stockholm, Sweden
Tel.: (46) 8 543 450 00
Web Site: www.dhl.se/en/contact_center/contact_supplychain.html
Logistics Consulting Services
S.I.C.: 4731
N.A.I.C.S.: 541614

DHL Exel Supply Chain Trade (Poland) Sp.Z.O.O. (2)
Bokserska 66
02-690 Warsaw, Poland
Tel.: (48) 22455 76 55
Fax: (48) 22455 76 56
Logistics Consulting Services
S.I.C.: 4731
N.A.I.C.S.: 541614

DHL Finance Services B.V. (2)
Gaetano Martinolaan 63a
Maastricht, 6229 GS, Netherlands
Tel.: (31) 433564000
Financial Management Services
S.I.C.: 6211
N.A.I.C.S.: 523999

DHL Fletes Aereos, C.A. (2)
Avenida Chicago con Calle Milan
Edificio DHL
Urb la California Sur, Caracas, Venezuela
Tel.: (58) 212 205 6340
Web Site: www.dhl.com.ve
Emp.: 450
Express Mail Services
S.I.C.: 4513
N.A.I.C.S.: 492110

DHL Food Services GmbH (2)
Marktstr 10
50968 Cologne, Germany
Tel.: (49) 2 213 76 90 31
Fax: (49) 2 213 76 90 16
Logistic Consulting Services
S.I.C.: 4731
N.A.I.C.S.: 541614
Dieter Gerfer *(Gen Mgr)*

DHL Freight Finland OY (2)
Katriinantie 14-16
1530 Vantaa, Finland
Tel.: (358) 20 5333
Fax: (358) 20 533 2121
Air & Road Transportation Services
S.I.C.: 4581
N.A.I.C.S.: 488190

DHL Freight GmbH (2)
Godesberger Allee 102-104
53175 Bonn, Germany
Tel.: (49) 228 3 77 88 0
E-Mail: freight.de@dhl.com
Web Site: www.dhl.de/en/toolbar/footer/impressum/dhl-logistics.html
Freight Forwarding Services
S.I.C.: 4731
N.A.I.C.S.: 488510
Jutta Rawe-Baumer *(Chm-Supervisory Bd)*
Birgit Krieger *(Mng Dir)*
Pieter van Holten *(Mng Dir)*
Bernhard Wirth *(Mng Dir)*

DHL Freight Hungary Forwarding and Logistics Ltd. (2)
Utinjska 40 Kesmark U 20-22
Budapest, 1158, Hungary
Tel.: (36) 29 556 000
Fax: (36) 14142504
E-Mail: freight@dhl.com
Web Site: www.dhl.com
Emp.: 7
Freight Transportation & Logistics Consulting Services
S.I.C.: 4731
N.A.I.C.S.: 488510
Attila Kulcsar *(Gen Mgr)*

DHL Freight (Netherlands) B.V. (2)
Achtseweg Noord 20 Haven M397
Eindhoven, 5651 GG, Netherlands
Tel.: (31) 402905555
Web Site: www.dhl.nl/en/about_us/forwarding_freight.html
Freight Transportation Services
S.I.C.: 4731
N.A.I.C.S.: 488510

DHL Freight Services (Netherlands) B.V. (2)
De Riemsdijk 1
4004 LC Tiel, Netherlands
Tel.: (31) 344609300
Fax: (31) 344609499
Freight Transportation Services
S.I.C.: 4731
N.A.I.C.S.: 488510
Linda Truijen *(Mgr-Bus Support)*

DHL Freight Spain, S.L. (2)
Centro de Transportes de Coslada C/ Rumania 4
28821 Coslada, Madrid, Spain
Tel.: (34) 91 660 43 00
E-Mail: Freightsales.spain@dhl.com
Freight Transportation Services
S.I.C.: 4731
N.A.I.C.S.: 488510

DHL Freight (Sweden) AB (2)
Bjornstigen 85
170 87 Stockholm, Sweden
Tel.: (46) 771345345

Deutsche Post AG—(Continued)

Fax: (46) 854345801
Freight Forwarding Services
S.I.C.: 4731
N.A.I.C.S.: 488510
Peter A. Hesslin *(CEO)*

DHL GBS (uk) Limited (2)
Solstice House 251 Midsummer Boulevard
Milton Keynes, Buckinghamshire, MK9
1EQ, United Kingdom
Tel.: (44) 1908 244180
Fax: (44) 1908 244 165
Web Site: www.dhl.com
Logistics Consulting Services
S.I.C.: 4731
N.A.I.C.S.: 541614

DHL (Ghana) Limited (2)
C913/3 North Ridge Crescent Rd North Ridge
PO Box 207
Accra, Ghana
Tel.: (233) 302 21 30907
Fax: (233) 302 21 225237
E-Mail: accwebcust@dhl.com
Web Site: www.dhl.com.gh
Logistics Consulting Services
S.I.C.: 4731
N.A.I.C.S.: 541614
Kader Coulibaly *(Country Mgr-DHL Express)*

DHL Global Forwarding Aduanas Peru S.A. (2)
Calle 1 Mz F Lte 2 B
Callao, Peru
Tel.: (51) 14401936
Fax: (51) 14409893
Freight Forwarding Services
S.I.C.: 4731
N.A.I.C.S.: 488510

DHL Global Forwarding & Co. LLC (2)
Al Khuwair
PO Box 730
133 Muscat, Oman
Tel.: (968) 244 70300
Fax: (968) 244 80830
Emp.: 15
Freight Forwarding Services
S.I.C.: 4731
N.A.I.C.S.: 488510
Chinkwoo Chang *(Supvr-Ops)*

DHL Global Forwarding (Australia) Pty Ltd. (2)
96 - 106 Link Road Melbourne Airport
Melbourne, VIC, 3045, Australia
Tel.: (61) 3 9344 8888
Fax: (61) 3 9344 8998
Web Site: www.dhl.com
Emp.: 30
Freight Forwarding Services
S.I.C.: 4731
N.A.I.C.S.: 488510
Mark Butcher *(Mgr-Security)*

DHL Global Forwarding (Austria) GmbH (2)
Freudenauer Hafenstrasse 20-22
1020 Vienna, Austria
Tel.: (43) 50 345
Fax: (43) 50 345 2398
E-Mail: austria.logistics@dhl.com
Air & Ocean Freight Services
S.I.C.: 4512
N.A.I.C.S.: 481112
Andrew Wingfield *(Gen Mgr)*

DHL Global Forwarding (Canada) Inc. (2)
6200 Edwards Boulevard
Mississauga, ON, L5T 2V7, Canada
Tel.: (289) 562-6500
Fax: (905) 405-9301
E-Mail: sales.dgf.ca@dhl.com
Web Site: www.dhl-dgf.com
Emp.: 260
Freight Forwarding Services
S.I.C.: 4731
N.A.I.C.S.: 488510

DHL Global Forwarding (Chile) S.A. (2)
Avenida Del Parque 4161 Oficina 203
Santiago, Chile
Tel.: (56) 2 4737100
Web Site: www.dhl.cl
Freight Forwarding Services
S.I.C.: 4731
N.A.I.C.S.: 488510

DHL Global Forwarding (Colombia) Ltda. (2)
Av Cl 26 No 85 B 09
Bogota, Colombia
Tel.: (57) 1 4292900
Web Site: www.dhl.com.co/en/contact_center/contact_global_forwarding.html#office_finder
Freight Forwarding Services
S.I.C.: 4731
N.A.I.C.S.: 488510

DHL Global Forwarding (CZ) s. r. o. (2)
Na Strzi 65/1702
140 62 Prague, Czech Republic
Tel.: (420) 261 198 735
Fax: (420) 261 198 729
E-Mail: cz.sales@dhl.com
Web Site: www.dhlgf.cz
Emp.: 5
Freight Forwarding Services
S.I.C.: 4731
N.A.I.C.S.: 488510
Alain Grenon *(Gen Mgr)*

DHL Global Forwarding (Denmark) A / S (2)
Kirstinehoej 42
PO Box 61
2770 Kastrup, Denmark
Tel.: (45) 3690 5500
Fax: (45) 3250 1820
Emp.: 15
Freight Forwarding Services
S.I.C.: 4731
N.A.I.C.S.: 488510
Christoffer Kronborg Hagen *(Mgr-HR)*

DHL Global Forwarding (Ecuador) S.A. (2)
Centro de Convenciones Guayaquil Centro Empresarial Oficina 3 Av De
las Americas No 406, Guayaquil, Ecuador
Tel.: (593) 4 2597666
Fax: (593) 4 2597668
Web Site: www.dhl.com.ec
Emp.: 16
Freight Forwarding Services
S.I.C.: 4731
N.A.I.C.S.: 488510

DHL Global Forwarding Egypt S.A.E. (2)
Building 19 District 7 Sheraton Buildings
Heliopolis
Cairo, 11361, Egypt
Tel.: (20) 226969800
Fax: (20) 226969900
Emp.: 10
Freight Forwarding Services
S.I.C.: 4731
N.A.I.C.S.: 488510
Wilfried Hugebaert *(Country Mgr)*

DHL Global Forwarding (Finland) OY (2)
Katriinantie 14-16
1530 Vantaa, Finland
Tel.: (358) 20 533 11
Fax: (358) 20 533 7200
Emp.: 50
Freight Forwarding Services
S.I.C.: 4731
N.A.I.C.S.: 488510
Ben Angelvirta *(Dir-Mktg & Sls)*

DHL Global Forwarding (Gabon) SA (2)
PO Box 736
Libreville, Gabon
Tel.: (241) 1442972
Fax: (241) 442987
Emp.: 18
Freight Forwarding Services
S.I.C.: 4731
N.A.I.C.S.: 488510
Marc Moreira *(Gen Mgr)*

DHL Global Forwarding GmbH (2)
Cargo City Sued Gebaude 573
60549 Frankfurt, Germany
Tel.: (49) 691301 6
Fax: (49) 691301 7999
E-Mail: globalforwarding.de@dhl.com
Freight Forwarding Services
S.I.C.: 4731
N.A.I.C.S.: 488510
Volker Oesau *(Chm & Mng Dir)*
Frank Appel *(Chm-Supervisory Bd & Mng Dir)*

DHL Global Forwarding (Guatemala) S.A. (2)
46 Calle 24-30 Zona 12
Guatemala, Guatemala
Tel.: (502) 2440 8440
Fax: (502) 24775753
Web Site: www.dhl.com.gt
Emp.: 20
Freight Forwarding Services
S.I.C.: 4731
N.A.I.C.S.: 488510

DHL Global Forwarding Hellas S.A. (2)
Agiou Dimitriou 41
185 46 Piraeus, Greece
Tel.: (30) 210 4062744
Fax: (30) 210 4615188
E-Mail: grinfo.dgf@dhl.com
Web Site: www.dhl.gr
Emp.: 8
Freight Forwarding Services
S.I.C.: 4731
N.A.I.C.S.: 488510
Panagiotis Pertsas *(Mng Dir)*

DHL Global Forwarding (Hong Kong) Limited (2)
Tower 1 Kowloon Commerce Centre 51
Kwai Cheong Road
Kwai Chung, New Territories, China (Hong Kong)
Tel.: (852) 2218 6888
Fax: (852) 2218 6388
Emp.: 60
Freight Forwarding Services
S.I.C.: 4731
N.A.I.C.S.: 488510
Edward Hui *(CEO & Mng Dir)*

DHL Global Forwarding Hungary Kft. (2)
Airport Business Park C6 Lorinci Str 59
Vecses, 2220, Hungary
Tel.: (36) 29 556 000
Fax: (36) 29 556 001
E-Mail: sales.budapest@dhl.com
Web Site: www.dhl.hu/en/country_profile/locations_global_forwarding.html
Freight Forwarding Services
S.I.C.: 4731
N.A.I.C.S.: 488510
Viktor Arany Szabo *(Project Mgr-Indus)*

DHL Global Forwarding (Ireland) Limited (2)
Cedar Drive Dublin Airport Logistics Park St Margaret s
Dublin, Ireland
Tel.: (353) 1 816 1000
Fax: (353) 1 816 1094
Freight Forwarding Services
S.I.C.: 4731
N.A.I.C.S.: 488510
Dermot Walsh *(Dir-Ops-EMEA)*

DHL Global Forwarding (Italy) S. p. A. (2)
Via delle Industrie 1
20060 Pozzuolo Martesana, Milan, Italy
Tel.: (39) 02 95252 1
Fax: (39) 02 95252407
Emp.: 11,000
Freight Forwarding Services
S.I.C.: 4731
N.A.I.C.S.: 488510
Marco Chiodi *(Head-Trade Lane Sls Mgmt)*

DHL Global Forwarding (Kuwait) Company WLL (2)
Block 1 Plot 16 Ardiya Industrial Area
PO Box 2358
Kuwait, 13024, Kuwait
Tel.: (965) 24346300
Fax: (965) 24346335
Web Site: www.dhl.com.kw/en/contact_center/contact_global_forwarding.html
Freight Forwarding Services
S.I.C.: 4731
N.A.I.C.S.: 488510

DHL Global Forwarding Lanka (Private) Limited (2)
8th Floor Setmil Complex 256 Srimath
Ramanathan Mawatha
Colombo, 1500, Sri Lanka
Tel.: (94) 117321321
Fax: (94) 117321258
Web Site: www.dhl.com
Emp.: 135
Freight Forwarding Services
S.I.C.: 4731
N.A.I.C.S.: 488510
Jonathan O'Leary *(COO)*

DHL Global Forwarding Lebanon S.A.L. (2)
490 Harbour Drive Saifi
PO Box 175772
Beirut, Lebanon
Tel.: (961) 1 564789
Fax: (961) 9611565268
Emp.: 44
Freight Forwarding Services
S.I.C.: 4731
N.A.I.C.S.: 488510

DHL Global Forwarding (Luxembourg) S.A. (2)
Room F 2036-F2039 Cargo Centre
Luxembourg Airport
1360 Luxembourg, Luxembourg
Tel.: (352) 34640 9450
Fax: (352) 34640 9457
Web Site: www.dhl.lu/en/about_us/forwarding_freight.html
Emp.: 15
Freight Forwarding Services
S.I.C.: 4731
N.A.I.C.S.: 488510
Schanet Steve *(Mgr-Sls)*

DHL Global Forwarding Management (Asia Pacific) Pte. Ltd. (2)
150 Beach Rd 04-01/04 Gateway W
Singapore, 189720, Singapore
Tel.: (65) 6879 8000
Fax: (65) 6292 2195
Freight Forwarding Services
S.I.C.: 4731
N.A.I.C.S.: 488510
Samar Nath *(CEO & Mgr-India)*
Kelvin Leung *(CEO)*

DHL Global Forwarding (Mexico) S.A. de C.V. (2)
De Cv Fundidora Monterrey 97 Col Penon De Los Banos
15520 Mexico, Mexico
Tel.: (52) 55 5133 1700
Fax: (52) 55 5133 1701
Emp.: 300
Freight Forwarding Services
S.I.C.: 4731
N.A.I.C.S.: 488510

DHL Global Forwarding (Netherlands) B.V. (2)
Prestwickweg 1 Schiphol Airport
1118 ZG Amsterdam, Netherlands
Tel.: (31) 20 3169000
Fax: (31) 20 3169568
Emp.: 60
Air & Ocean Freight Services
S.I.C.: 4512
N.A.I.C.S.: 481112
Suresh Ramlal *(Acct Mgr-Payable)*

DHL Global Forwarding (New Zealand) Limited (2)
Cnr Ron Guthrie & Bolt Drive Christchurch Airport
PO Box 14033
Christchurch, 8544, New Zealand
Tel.: (64) 3940 4044
Fax: (64) 3940 4045
Freight Forwarding Services
S.I.C.: 4731
N.A.I.C.S.: 488510

DHL Global Forwarding (Nicaragua) S.A. (2)
edificio U Camino de Oriente Frente Gimnasio Vally
Ruben Dario 600 Mts East, Managua, Nicaragua
Tel.: (505) 2255 8700
Web Site: www.dhl.com
Emp.: 99

Freight Forwarding Services
S.I.C.: 4731
N.A.I.C.S.: 488510
Gloria Whitlock *(Office Mgr)*

DHL Global Forwarding Pakistan (Private) Limited (2)
187/1/E PECHS Block II Shahrah-e-Quaideen
Karachi, 75400, Pakistan
Tel.: (92) 21 34315041 5
Fax: (92) 21 34533300
E-Mail: sales.khi@dhl.com
Web Site: www.dhl.com.pk/en/contact_center/contact_global_forwarding.html
Emp.: 200
Freight Forwarding Services
S.I.C.: 4731
N.A.I.C.S.: 488510
M. Umair Alam *(COO)*

DHL Global Forwarding Peru S.A. (2)
Victor Maurtua 153
San Isidro, Lima, Peru
Tel.: (51) 14401 936
Fax: (51) 14409 893
Web Site: www.dhl.com.pe/en/about_us/forwarding_freight.html
Freight Forwarding Services
S.I.C.: 4731
N.A.I.C.S.: 488510

DHL Global Forwarding (Philippines) Inc. (2)
8/F Star Cruises Center 100 Andrews Avenue Newport Cybertourism Zone
Pasay, Philippines 1309
Tel.: (63) 2902 3345
Fax: (63) 2902 7600
Web Site: www.dhl.com.ph/en/contact_center/contact_global_forwarding.html
Emp.: 480
Freight Forwarding Services
S.I.C.: 4731
N.A.I.C.S.: 488510
Stephen Ly *(Mng Dir)*

DHL Global Forwarding Portugal, Lda. (2)
Aeroporto De Lisboa Edificio 124 2 Gab 1A
1700-008 Lisbon, Portugal
Tel.: (351) 21 8438930
Fax: (351) 21 8485759
E-Mail: Isabel.Neves@dhl.com
Web Site: www.dhl.pt
Emp.: 1
Freight Forwarding Services
S.I.C.: 4731
N.A.I.C.S.: 488510
Pushpan Murugiah *(Branch Mgr)*

DHL Global Forwarding (Senegal) S.A. (2)
KM 3 5 Boulevard du Centenaire de la Commune de Dakar
BP 16840
Dakar, Senegal
Tel.: (221) 33 859 09 00
Fax: (221) 33 832 66 67
Freight Forwarding Services
S.I.C.: 4731
N.A.I.C.S.: 488510

DHL Global Forwarding Sp. Z.O.O. (2)
ul 17 Stycznia 56
02-146 Warsaw, Poland
Tel.: (48) 22 7037500
Fax: (48) 22 7037528
Web Site: www.dhlgf.pl
Emp.: 5
Freight Forwarding Services
S.I.C.: 4731
N.A.I.C.S.: 488510
Rafal Paliwoda *(Coord-Project)*

DHL Global Forwarding (sweden) AB (2)
Molndalsvagen 30B
400 22 Gothenburg, Sweden
Tel.: (46) 771400 400
Fax: (46) 317994494
Web Site: www.dhl.se/en/contact_center/contact_global_forwarding.html#office_finder
Freight Forwarding Services
S.I.C.: 4731
N.A.I.C.S.: 488510

DHL Global Forwarding Tasimacilik A.S. (2)
Fatih Caddesi Fulya Sokak No 37
B Halkali, 34303 Istanbul, Turkey
Tel.: (90) 2126925050
Fax: (90) 2126933772
Emp.: 30
Freight Forwarding Services
S.I.C.: 4731
N.A.I.C.S.: 488510
Selvi Kirci *(Controller-Fin)*

DHL Global Forwarding (Uganda) Limited (2)
Plot M248 Ntinda Industrial Area Kyambogo Off Jinja
PO Box 72085
Kampala, Uganda
Tel.: (256) 312265722
Fax: (256) 312265647
Freight Forwarding Services
S.I.C.: 4731
N.A.I.C.S.: 488510
Stephen Wanyama *(Controller-Fin)*

DHL Global Forwarding (uk) Limited (2)
Danzas House Kestrel Way Dawley Park
Hayes, UB3 1HJ, United Kingdom
Tel.: (44) 208 754 5000
Fax: (44) 208 754 5110
Web Site: www.dhl.com
Emp.: 30
Freight Forwarding Services
S.I.C.: 4731
N.A.I.C.S.: 488510
Steve Barker *(CEO)*

DHL Global Forwarding Venezuela, C.A. (2)
Av San Francisco Cruce Con Palmarito Edif Parmalat - Piso 6
Estado Miranda Municipio Sucre, Caracas, Venezuela
Tel.: (58) 212205 02 00
Fax: (58) 212202 02 01
Web Site: www.dhl.com.ve/en/contact_center/contact_global_forwarding.html#office_finder
Freight Transportation Services
S.I.C.: 4731
N.A.I.C.S.: 488510

DHL Global Mail (Japan) k. k. (2)
1-37-8 Higashi-Shinagawa
Tokyo, 140-0002, Japan
Tel.: (81) 34332 4668
Fax: (81) 354795847
Emp.: 5
Courier Delivery Services
S.I.C.: 4513
N.A.I.C.S.: 492110
Patrick Martin *(Mng Dir)*

DHL Global Mail (Singapore) Pte. Ltd. (2)
80 Alps Ave 03-07
Singapore, 498792, Singapore
Tel.: (65) 6883 0771
Fax: (65) 6883 0772
E-Mail: sin.service@dhl.com
Emp.: 10
Courier Delivery Services
S.I.C.: 4513
N.A.I.C.S.: 492110
Carl Hemus *(COO)*

DHL Holding (France) SAS (2)
Zone Industrielle Paris Nord Ii 241 Rue De La Belle Etoile
95700 Roissy-en-France, France
Tel.: (33) 149387070
Emp.: 18
Investment Management Services
S.I.C.: 6799
N.A.I.C.S.: 523920
Michel Akavi *(Mgr)*

DHL Home Delivery GmbH (2)
Rungedamm 37 B
21035 Hamburg, Germany
Tel.: (49) 40 73459010
Fax: (49) 4073465701
Web Site: www.dhl.com
Emp.: 2
Courier Delivery Services
S.I.C.: 4215
N.A.I.C.S.: 492210
Patrick Gruen *(Mng Dir)*

DHL Hradflutningar EHF (2)
Skutuvogi 1 D
104 Reykjavik, Iceland
Tel.: (354) 5351100
Fax: (354) 5351111
E-Mail: info@dhl.com
Web Site: www.dhl.is
Emp.: 60
Express Mail Services
S.I.C.: 4215
N.A.I.C.S.: 492110
Atli Einarsson *(Gen Mgr)*

DHL Hub Leipzig GmbH (2)
Hermann-Kohl-Str 1
Flughafen, 4435 Leipzig, Germany
Tel.: (49) 34144990
Fax: (49) 341 5898
Freight Transportation Services
S.I.C.: 4731
N.A.I.C.S.: 488510

DHL Information Services (Europe) S.R.O. (2)
V Parku 2308/10
Prague, 14800, Czech Republic
Tel.: (420) 28 8800000
Fax: (420) 27080439
E-Mail: receptionitseurope@dhl.com
Web Site: www.dhl.com
Emp.: 130
Software Development & Data Processing Services
S.I.C.: 7371
N.A.I.C.S.: 541511
Andy Laurence *(Gen Mgr)*

DHL International (Algerie) S.A.R.L (2)
7 Ave Blaise Pascal
16000 Algiers, Algeria
Tel.: (213) 21230101
Fax: (213) 21239555
Web Site: www.dhl.com
Express Mail Services
S.I.C.: 4513
N.A.I.C.S.: 492110

DHL International (Beograde) d.o.o. (2)
Omladinskih Brigada 86
11070 Belgrade, Serbia
Tel.: (381) 0113105500
Fax: (381) 113105510
E-Mail: darko.dadic@dhl.com
Web Site: www.dhl.com
Express Mail Services
S.I.C.: 4215
N.A.I.C.S.: 492110

DHL International (Brunei) Sdn Bhd (2)
Unit 05 & 06 Ground Fl Bgh Pg Hj Mohd Daud Jalan Gadong
Bandar Seri Begawan, BE3919, Brunei Darussalam
Tel.: (673) 244 4991 2
Fax: (673) 244 4997
Emp.: 45
Logistics Consulting Services
S.I.C.: 4731
N.A.I.C.S.: 541614
Muhammad Ridwan *(Branch Mgr)*

DHL International B.S.C. (C) (2)
Block 224 Bulding 342 Bahrain Regional Distribution Centre
PO Box 5741
Muharraq, Bahrain
Mailing Address:
PO Box 5741
Muharraq, Bahrain
Tel.: (973) 17335005
Fax: (973) 17323301
Web Site: www.dhl.com.bh
Logistics Consulting & Courier Distribution Services
S.I.C.: 4731
N.A.I.C.S.: 541614
Nour Suliman *(CEO)*

DHL International B.V. (2)
Terminalweg 36
PB 2717
3821 AJ Amersfoort, Netherlands
Tel.: (31) 33257 77 77
Web Site: www.dhl.nl
Courier Delivery Services
S.I.C.: 4215

N.A.I.C.S.: 492110

DHL International Cameroon SARL (2)
244 Boulevard De La Liberte
BP 3582
3582 Douala, Cameroon
Tel.: (237) 33423636
Fax: (237) 33428626
Emp.: 80
Logistics Consulting Services
S.I.C.: 4731
N.A.I.C.S.: 541614
Djibril Gaye *(Country Mgr)*

DHL International (Congo) SPRL (2)
180 Avenue du Marche
Gombe, Congo, Democratic Republic of
Tel.: (243) 817888810
Web Site: www.dhl.com
Courier Delivery Services
S.I.C.: 4215
N.A.I.C.S.: 492210

DHL International Cote D'Ivoire SARL (2)
Immeuble Le Massai 1er Etage Lot 86
Boulevard VGE Marcory
BP 2069
Abidjan, Cote d'Ivoire
Tel.: (225) 21 21 99 98
Fax: (225) 21 35 01 26
Web Site: www.dhl.ci
Logistics Consulting Services
S.I.C.: 4731
N.A.I.C.S.: 541614
Patrick Assi *(Area Mng Dir-DHL Express)*

DHL International d.o.o. (2)
Turinina 3
10020 Zagreb, Croatia
Tel.: (385) 016651111
Fax: (385) 016651120
E-Mail: srebrenka.saks@dhl.com
Web Site: www.dhl.hr
Emp.: 200
Express Mail Services
S.I.C.: 4513
N.A.I.C.S.: 492110
Srebrenka Saks *(Country Mgr)*

DHL International Express (France) SAS (2)
241 Rue de la Belle Etoile
95957 Roissy-en-France, France
Tel.: (33) 1 49 38 72 35
Fax: (33) 1 49 38 70 01
Emp.: 20
Logistics Consulting & Courier Distribution Services
S.I.C.: 4731
N.A.I.C.S.: 541614
Florence Noblot *(Head-Global Comml Project)*

DHL International (Gambia) Ltd. (2)
59 Mamadi Maniyang Highway Kanifing Industrial Estate
Banjul, Gambia
Tel.: (220) 4396658
E-Mail: gmhtt@dhl.com
Web Site: www.dhl.com
Emp.: 13
Freight Transportation Services
S.I.C.: 4412
N.A.I.C.S.: 483111

DHL International Hellas S.A. (2)
44 Alimou & 17 Roma Strs
174 55 Athens, Greece
Tel.: (30) 2109890800
Fax: (30) 2109841044
E-Mail: dhlgr@dhl.com
Web Site: www.dhl.gr
Emp.: 450
Express Mail Services
S.I.C.: 4215
N.A.I.C.S.: 492110

DHL International Kazakhstan, TOO (2)
1/1 Dzhandosov Str
Almaty, 50008, Kazakhstan
Tel.: (7) 7272588588
Fax: (7) 7272584358
E-Mail: alacs@dhl.com
Web Site: www.dhl.kz
Emp.: 30
Logistics Consulting Services

Deutsche Post AG—(Continued)

S.I.C.: 4731
N.A.I.C.S.: 541614
Ken Robertson *(Country Mgr-DHL Express)*

DHL International Ltd. (2)
MIA Cargo Village
Luqa, LQA 3290, Malta
Tel.: (356) 21800148
Fax: (356) 23986206
Web Site: www.dhl.com.mt
Logistics Consulting & Courier Distribution Services
S.I.C.: 4731
N.A.I.C.S.: 541614

DHL International Ltd. (2)
Phan Thuc Duyen Street Tan Binh District 4
Ho Chi Minh City, Vietnam
Tel.: (84) 8 3844 6203
Fax: (84) 8 3845 6841
Web Site: www.dhl.com.vn
Emp.: 670
Express Mail Services
S.I.C.: 4513
N.A.I.C.S.: 492110

DHL International Madagascar SA (2)
Lot II J 181 F Bis Ivandry
Antananarivo, 101, Madagascar
Tel.: (261) 20 22 428 39
Fax: (261) 20 22 428 55
E-Mail: mgsales.mg@dhl.com
Logistics Consulting Services
S.I.C.: 4731
N.A.I.C.S.: 541614
Andry Ramarijaona *(Project Mgr)*

DHL International Malawi Ltd. (2)
Masauko Chipembere Highway Kristwick
PO Box 1762
Blantyre, Malawi
Tel.: (265) 1 870 688
Web Site: www.dhl.co.mw
Emp.: 20
Logistics Consulting & Courier Distribution Services
S.I.C.: 4731
N.A.I.C.S.: 541614
Jessie Ndisale *(Head-Customer Svc)*

DHL International (Nigeria) Ltd. (2)
DHL House Isolo Expressway
New Airport Road Junction
Isolo, Lagos, Nigeria
Tel.: (234) 14527086
Fax: (234) 1 450 1222
Web Site: www.dhl.com.ng
Emp.: 700
Express Mail Services
S.I.C.: 4513
N.A.I.C.S.: 492110

DHL International (Pty) Ltd. (2)
Old Mutual Business Park South
Gewel Street
1600 Isando, South Africa
Tel.: (27) 0119213812
Fax: (27) 0119282514
Web Site: www.dhl.com
Emp.: 700
Express Mail Services
S.I.C.: 4215
N.A.I.C.S.: 492110

DHL International Romania SRL (2)
Emanoil Porumbaru Str 85-87
Sector 1
11424 Bucharest, Romania
Tel.: (40) 21 2221469
Fax: (40) 21 2221469
Web Site: www.dhl.ro
Express Mail Services
S.I.C.: 4215
N.A.I.C.S.: 492110

DHL International-Sarajevo D.O.O. (2)
Dzemala Bijedica 166a
71000 Sarajevo, Bosnia & Herzegovina
Tel.: (387) 33 774000
Fax: (387) 33 473646
Emp.: 5
Logistics Consulting & Courier Services
S.I.C.: 4731
N.A.I.C.S.: 541614
Djenan Dzumhur *(Mgr-Comml)*

DHL International Senegal SARL (2)
Rue Leon Gontran Damas X Rue F Fann Residence
BP 3554
Dakar, Senegal
Tel.: (221) 338691111
Fax: (221) 338640236
Parcel & Courier Services
S.I.C.: 4215
N.A.I.C.S.: 492210
Desire Vakta *(Gen Mgr)*

DHL International S.R.L. (2)
Calle 1 Manzana A Lote 6 Fundo
Bocanegra Callao 1
Lima, Peru
Tel.: (51) 1 575 4433
Fax: (51) 1 575 6451
Web Site: www.dhl.com.pe
Emp.: 400
Express Mail Services
S.I.C.: 4215
N.A.I.C.S.: 492110

DHL International (Uganda) Ltd. (2)
Green Summer Building Plot 28 Stroke 30
Jinja, Uganda
Tel.: (256) 3 3226 0062
E-Mail: dhlug.jinja@dhl.com
Web Site: www.dhl.co.ug
Emp.: 3
Logistics Consulting & Courier Distribution Services
S.I.C.: 4731
N.A.I.C.S.: 541614
Baguma Jessica Mawata *(Gen Mgr)*

DHL International (UK) Ltd. (2)
Orbital Park
178-188 Great South West Road
Hounslow, Mddx, TW4 6JS, United Kingdom
Tel.: (44) 8703 661217
Fax: (44) 2088 188149
Web Site: www.dhl.co.uk
Emp.: 17,000
Express Mail Services
S.I.C.: 4215
N.A.I.C.S.: 492110

DHL Intl (Bulgaria) E.O.O.D. (2)
10 Prodan Tarakchiev str
1528 Sofia, Bulgaria
Tel.: (359) 293094
Fax: (359) 29731551
Web Site: www.dhl.bg
Emp.: 300
Express Mail Services
S.I.C.: 4215
N.A.I.C.S.: 492110
Snejina Kazakova *(Gen Mgr)*

DHL Intl (Slovakia) spol. s r.o. (2)
Letisko MR Stefanika 65
82001 Bratislava, Slovakia
Tel.: (421) 800100300
Web Site: www.dhl.sk
Emp.: 175
Express Mail Services
S.I.C.: 4513
N.A.I.C.S.: 492110

DHL ISC (Hong Kong) Limited (2)
21/F Tower 5 China Hong Kong City 33 Canton Road
Tsim Sha Tsui, Kowloon, China (Hong Kong)
Tel.: (852) 29763668
Fax: (852) 23773958
Logistics Consulting Services
S.I.C.: 4731
N.A.I.C.S.: 541614

DHL (Israel) Ltd. (2)
Ben Gurion Airport Maman Building Suite 807
Lod, 71100, Israel
Tel.: (972) 3 9722233
Fax: (972) 3 9791089
Web Site: www.dhl.co.il
Logistics Consulting Services
S.I.C.: 4731
N.A.I.C.S.: 541614

DHL (Jamaica) Ltd (2)
19 Haining Road Kgn 5
Kingston, Jamaica
Tel.: (876) 920 0010
Fax: (876) 920 0088
Web Site: www.dhl.com.jm
Logistics Consulting Services
S.I.C.: 4731
N.A.I.C.S.: 541614

DHL Japan, Inc. (2)
37-8 Higashi-Shinagawa 1-chome
Shinagawa-ku, 140-0002 Tokyo, Japan
Tel.: (81) 354792276
Fax: (81) 3 5479 2274
Web Site: www.dhl.co.jp
Emp.: 138
Express Mail Services
S.I.C.: 4513
N.A.I.C.S.: 492110

DHL Keells (Private) Limited (2)
148 Vauxhall Street
Colombo, 200, Sri Lanka
Tel.: (94) 112304304
Fax: (94) 114717177
E-Mail: customerfeedback@dhl.com
Web Site: www.dhl.com
Emp.: 25
Parcel & Courier Services
S.I.C.: 4215
N.A.I.C.S.: 492210

DHL Korea Ltd. (2)
Ilyang Bldg 164-6 Yeomri-dong Mapo-ku
121-090 Seoul, Korea (South)
Tel.: (82) 27108213
Fax: (82) 27108234
Web Site: www.dhl.co.kr
Emp.: 1,200
Express Mail Services
S.I.C.: 4215
N.A.I.C.S.: 492110
Byung Koo Han *(Country Mgr)*

DHL Kuwait Co. Ltd (2)
Ardiyah Industrial Area Behind SONY Workshop Safat
13126 Kuwait, Kuwait
Tel.: (965) 4318300
Fax: (965) 4317120
Web Site: www.dhl.com
Emp.: 200
Express Mail Services
S.I.C.: 4215
N.A.I.C.S.: 492110

DHL Lao Limited (2)
031 Nongno St Ban Wattaynoy Thong
PO Box 7083
Vientiane, Laos
Tel.: (856) 21 214 868
Fax: (856) 21 214 869
Web Site: www.fastforward.dhl.com
Logistics Consulting Services
S.I.C.: 4731
N.A.I.C.S.: 541614

DHL (Latvia) SIA (2)
International Airport Riga
1053 Riga, Latvia
Tel.: (371) 7802555
Fax: (371) 7802777
Web Site: www.dhl.lv
Emp.: 53
Express Mail Services
S.I.C.: 4215
N.A.I.C.S.: 492110

DHL Lesotho (Proprietary) Ltd. (2)
1st Floor Options Building Pioneer Road
Maseru, 100, Lesotho
Tel.: (266) 22 311082
Fax: (266) 22 310405
Web Site: www.dhl.com
Emp.: 15
Real Estate Management Services
S.I.C.: 6531
N.A.I.C.S.: 531390
Moloko Simon Pholosi *(Supvr-Ops)*

DHL Logistica D.O.O. (2)
Vojkovo Nabrezje 30/A
6000 Koper, Slovenia
Tel.: (386) 5 600 9943
Fax: (386) 5 600 9945
Web Site: www.dhl.com
Emp.: 18
Logistics Consulting Services
S.I.C.: 4731
N.A.I.C.S.: 541614
Zdenka Dodic *(Gen Mgr)*

DHL Logistics (Cambodia) Ltd. (2)
Regency Complex A 1st Fl No 8A/298 Mao Tse Toung Blvd St 245 Sangkat Tomnoubteouk Khan Chamkamon, Phnom Penh, Cambodia
Tel.: (855) 5 23 885968
Fax: (855) 5 23 885967
Freight Forwarding Services
S.I.C.: 4731
N.A.I.C.S.: 488510

DHL Logistics OOO (2)
Leningradskoye Highway 39 Bldg 5 Khimki Business Park 10th Floor
141400 Khimki, Russia
Tel.: (7) 495933 22 00
Fax: (7) 495933 22 02
E-Mail: dgfrussia.mou@dhl.com
Web Site: www.dhl.com
Emp.: 13
Logistics Consulting Services
S.I.C.: 4731
N.A.I.C.S.: 541614
Gapova Elmira *(Mgr-HR)*

DHL Logistics (Schweiz) AG (2)
St Jakobs-Strasse 224
PO Box 2664
4002 Basel, Switzerland
Tel.: (41) 61 315 92 59
Fax: (41) 61 315 91 40
Web Site: external.dhl.ch/mycontacts/karte_global_e.asp#
Freight Forwarding Services
S.I.C.: 4731
N.A.I.C.S.: 488510
Thomas Christ *(Mng Dir)*
Oliver Fitze *(CFO & Head-Bus Controlling)*

DHL Logistics (Slovakia), spol. s r. o. (2)
Letisko M R Stefanika
821 04 Bratislava, Slovakia
Tel.: (421) 2 43426651
Fax: (421) 2 48700490
E-Mail: skdgssales@dhl.com
Logistics Consulting Services
S.I.C.: 4731
N.A.I.C.S.: 541614
Miroslava Rothova *(Mgr-Fin)*

DHL Logistics Tanzania Limited (2)
Capri Point Station Road
PO Box 1904
Mwanza, Tanzania
Tel.: (255) 28 2500800
Fax: (255) 28 2500005
Web Site: www.dhl.com
Logistics Consulting Services
S.I.C.: 4731
N.A.I.C.S.: 541614
Jan Larsen *(Country Mgr)*

DHL Logistics (Ukraine) Ltd. (2)
11 Polskiy Spusk
65026 Odessa, Ukraine
Tel.: (380) 48 7341134
E-Mail: odessa.globalforwarding@dhl.com
Web Site: www.dhl.com.ua/en/logistics.html
Emp.: 9
Logistics Consulting Services
S.I.C.: 4731
N.A.I.C.S.: 541614

DHL Lojistik Hizmetleri A.S. (2)
Kocadag Plaza Kat 3 9 Cubuklu Mahallesi
Orhan Veli Kanik Caddesi
34810 Istanbul, Turkey
Tel.: (90) 2165370707
Fax: (90) 2166801818
Logistics Consulting Services
S.I.C.: 4731
N.A.I.C.S.: 541614

DHL Management (Schweiz) AG (2)
Peter Merian-Strasse 88
Postfach 4002
4052 Basel, Switzerland
Tel.: (41) 612747474
Fax: (41) 612747475
E-Mail: receptionmanagement.ch@dhl.com
Web Site: www.dhl.com
Emp.: 3
Real Estate Investment Services
S.I.C.: 6726
N.A.I.C.S.: 525990
Andreas Sahli *(Head-Lifesciences & Heathcare EMEA & VP)*

DHL (Mauritius) Ltd. (2)
Cnr Mgr Gonin/Sir Virgil Naz Street
Port Louis, Mauritius
Tel.: (230) 2087711
Fax: (230) 2085330
E-Mail: dhl.mu@dhl.com

Web Site: www.dhl.co.mu
Emp.: 150
Express Mail Services
S.I.C.: 4513
N.A.I.C.S.: 492110
Rahman Bholah *(Mng Dir)*

DHL Mozambique Lda. (2)
Cnr Ave 24 de Julho & Av Da Tanzania Nbr 147
Maputo, Mozambique
Tel.: (258) 21 225 300
Fax: (258) 21 425 313
Web Site: www.dhl.co.mz
Emp.: 8
Logistics Consulting & Courier Distribution Services
S.I.C.: 4731
N.A.I.C.S.: 541614
Arash Adilipour *(Acct Mgr)*

DHL (Namibia) (Pty) Ltd. (2)
14 Ongoporo Street Prosperita
Windhoek, Namibia
Tel.: (264) 61 378300
Parcel & Courier Services
S.I.C.: 4215
N.A.I.C.S.: 492210

DHL Pakistan (Private) Limited (2)
Survey Number 137 Jinnah International Airport
Karachi, 74500, Pakistan
Tel.: (92) 21111345111
Fax: (92) 4586312
Web Site: www.dhl.com.pk
Emp.: 60
Air Freight Transportation Services
S.I.C.: 4512
N.A.I.C.S.: 481112
Sarfaraz Siddiqui *(Mng Dir & Country Mgr)*

DHL Panama S.A. (2)
Ave Principal Costa Del Este Edificio Dhl - Apdo 8-400
Panama, Panama
Tel.: (507) 2713400
Fax: (507) 2713480
Web Site: www.dhl.com.pa
Parcel & Courier Services
S.I.C.: 4215
N.A.I.C.S.: 492210

DHL (Paraguay) S.R.L. (2)
Gral Santos 1170 c/ Concoria
Asuncion, 7000, Paraguay
Tel.: (595) 21 21 62000
Fax: (595) 21 21 2543
E-Mail: asucs@dhl.com
Web Site: www.dhl.com.py
Emp.: 10
Logistics Consulting Services
S.I.C.: 4731
N.A.I.C.S.: 541614
Milva Bogado *(Country Mgr)*

DHL Pensions Investment Fund Limited (2)
The Marton Center
Bedford, MK40 2UB, United Kingdom
Tel.: (44) 1234 273727
Fax: (44) 1234 267519
E-Mail: dhl.uk.Pensions@dhl.com
Emp.: 20
Pension Fund Services
S.I.C.: 6371
N.A.I.C.S.: 525110
Robert Sharratt *(Gen Mgr)*

DHL Pipelife Logistik GmbH (2)
IZ NO Sudstrasse 14 Objekt 24
2355 Wiener Neudorf, Austria
Tel.: (43) 2732 855020
Fax: (43) 2732 8550281
Web Site: www.dhl.com
Emp.: 4
Logistics Consulting Services
S.I.C.: 4731
N.A.I.C.S.: 541614
Erich Spreitzenbart *(Gen Mgr)*

DHL Quality Cargo AS (2)
Gladengveien 17
661 Oslo, Norway
Tel.: (47) 23243600
Fax: (47) 23243601
Cargo Handling Services
S.I.C.: 4491
N.A.I.C.S.: 488320

DHL Rail AB (2)
Algatan 27
Box 57
Trelleborg, 231 42, Sweden
Tel.: (46) 410740600
Fax: (46) 410740680
Web Site: www.dhl.com
Emp.: 14
Logistics Consulting Services
S.I.C.: 4731
N.A.I.C.S.: 541614
Anders Hakansson *(Mgr)*

DHL Sainghin SARL (2)
Rue Des Hauts De Sainghin Centre De Gros N 3
59262 Sainghin-en-Melantois, France
Tel.: (33) 320904610
Logistics Consulting Services
S.I.C.: 4731
N.A.I.C.S.: 541614

DHL SCM K. K. (2)
Gotenyama Trust Tower 8F 4-7-35 Kita-Shinagawa
Shinagawa-ku, Tokyo, 140-0001, Japan
Tel.: (81) 357929001
Freight Forwarding Services
S.I.C.: 4731
N.A.I.C.S.: 488510

DHL Services Limited (2)
45 St Peters Street
Bedford, Bedfordshire, MK40 2PN, United Kingdom
Tel.: (44) 1234 273 727
Logistics Consulting Services
S.I.C.: 4731
N.A.I.C.S.: 541614

DHL Services Logistiques SAS (2)
Quais Atlantique Port Ouest Dunkerque Route Ameriques
Loon-Plage, 59279, France
Tel.: (33) 3 28 66 06 66
Fax: (33) 3 28 66 65 66
Logistics Consulting Services
S.I.C.: 4731
N.A.I.C.S.: 541614

DHL Solutions Fashion GmbH (2)
Hafenstr 70
45356 Essen, Germany
Tel.: (49) 201 80601
Transportation Services
S.I.C.: 4789
N.A.I.C.S.: 488999

DHL Solutions GmbH (2)
Hammerbrookstr 94
21035 Hamburg, Germany
Tel.: (49) 40 7345 0
Fax: (49) 40 7345 9098
E-Mail: supplychain.de@dhl.com
Emp.: 10
Logistics Consulting Services
S.I.C.: 4731
N.A.I.C.S.: 541614
Christian Huber *(Co-Mng Dir)*
Michael Rolle *(Co-Mng Dir)*

DHL Solutions Grossgut GmbH (2)
Keine Strasse Angegeben
56477 Rennerod, Germany
Tel.: (49) 26 64 50 83 00
Logistics Consulting Services
S.I.C.: 4731
N.A.I.C.S.: 541614

DHL Solutions Retail GmbH (2)
Giesserstrasse 5
59425 Unna, Nordrhein-Westfalen, Germany
Tel.: (49) 2303 6780
Fax: (49) 6782292
E-Mail: info@dhl.com
Web Site: www.dhl.com
Freight Transportation Services
S.I.C.: 4731
N.A.I.C.S.: 488510

DHL Supply Chain (Australia) Pty Limited (2)
Rhodes Corporate Park L 3 Building A 1 Homebush Bay Dr
Rhodes, Sydney, NSW, 2138, Australia
Tel.: (61) 2 8759 7000
Fax: (61) 2 8759 7190
E-Mail: rhodes.reception@dhl.com
Web Site: www.dhl.com.au
Emp.: 14
Freight Forwarding Services
S.I.C.: 4731
N.A.I.C.S.: 488510
Michael Goldberg *(Gen Mgr-Animal Health & Production)*

DHL Supply Chain (Chile) S.A. (2)
Panamericana Norte 19001 - Km 19
Colina, Santiago, Chile
Tel.: (56) 2 5805700
Web Site: www.dhl.cl
Emp.: 91
Freight Forwarding Services
S.I.C.: 4731
N.A.I.C.S.: 488510
Agustin Croche *(Country Mgr)*

DHL Supply Chain (Finland) Oy (2)
Katriinantie 14-16
1530 Vantaa, Finland
Tel.: (358) 20 5333
Fax: (358) 20 533 2121
Emp.: 33
Logistics Consulting Services
S.I.C.: 4731
N.A.I.C.S.: 541614
Magnus Nordberg *(Mng Dir)*

DHL Supply Chain (Ireland) Limited (2)
Oak Road Western Business Park
Dublin, 12, Ireland
Tel.: (353) 1 405 0800
Fax: (353) 1 405 0802
Web Site: www.dhl.ie/en
Emp.: 20
Freight Forwarding Services
S.I.C.: 4731
N.A.I.C.S.: 488510
David Handcock *(Gen Mgr)*

DHL Supply Chain K. K. (2)
Gotenyama Trust Tower 8F 4-7-35 Kita-Shinagawa
Shinagawa-ku, Tokyo, 140-0001, Japan
Tel.: (81) 357929001
Freight Forwarding Services
S.I.C.: 4731
N.A.I.C.S.: 488510

DHL Supply Chain (Korea) Ltd. (2)
4 5F Yonsei Building 84-11 Namdaemunro 5ga
Jung-gu, Seoul, 100-753, Korea (South)
Tel.: (82) 2 6220 1500
Web Site: www.dhl.co.kr/en/logistics/supply_chain_solutions.html
Logistics & Freight Forwarding Services
S.I.C.: 4731
N.A.I.C.S.: 541614

DHL Supply Chain (New Zealand) Limited (2)
7-9 Burgess Road Mt Wellington
Auckland, 1051, New Zealand
Tel.: (64) 9 574 1450
Fax: (64) 9 574 1460
Web Site: www.dhl.com
Emp.: 60
Logistics Consulting Services
S.I.C.: 4731
N.A.I.C.S.: 541614
Ronald du Plessis *(Dir-Ops)*

DHL Supply Chain (Norway) AS (2)
Ulvenveien 111
665 Oslo, Norway
Tel.: (47) 66 92 96 48
Fax: (47) 22 65 0191
Emp.: 20
Freight Forwarding Services
S.I.C.: 4731
N.A.I.C.S.: 488510

DHL Supply Chain (Poland) Sp. z o.o. (2)
66 Bokserska
02-690 Warsaw, Poland
Tel.: (48) 22 455 76 55
Fax: (48) 22 455 76 56
Emp.: 100
Logistics Consulting Services
S.I.C.: 4731
N.A.I.C.S.: 541614
Pawel Gierszewski *(Project Mgr)*

DHL Supply Chain Singapore Pte. Ltd. (2)
600 North Bridge Road 23-01 Parkview Square
Singapore, 188778, Singapore
Tel.: (65) 6372 8200
Emp.: 50
Freight Forwarding Services
S.I.C.: 4731
N.A.I.C.S.: 488510
Steven Kok Wha Sim *(Sr Mgr-Logistics)*

DHL Swaziland (Proprietary) Ltd. (2)
Karlyn Centre Cooper Lane
Mbabane, 8100, Swaziland
Tel.: (268) 2404 5829
Fax: (268) 2404 5440
Real Estate Management Services
S.I.C.: 6531
N.A.I.C.S.: 531390
Wayne Van Rensburg *(Gen Mgr)*

DHL Trade Fairs and Events (uk) Limited (2)
Unit 17 & 21 2nd Exhibition Avenue
Birmingham, B40 1PJ, United Kingdom
Tel.: (44) 121 782 4626
Fax: (44) 121 782 4680
E-Mail: info@dhl-exh.com
Web Site: www.dhl-exh.com
Emp.: 6
Event Management & Logistics Services
S.I.C.: 8748
N.A.I.C.S.: 541618
Horst Froehling *(Mng Dir)*

DHL-Transportadores Rapidos Internacionais Lda. (2)
Rua Cidade de Liverpool 16
1199 Lisbon, Portugal
Tel.: (351) 218100080
Fax: (351) 21 815 4213
Web Site: www.dhl.pt
Express Mail Services
S.I.C.: 4215
N.A.I.C.S.: 492110
Luis Gonzaga *(Dir-Mktg)*

DHL (Uruguay) S.R.L. (2)
Av de las Americas 7777 BIS
Canelones, 15000, Uruguay
Tel.: (598) 2 6041331
Fax: (598) 9826041333
E-Mail: rrhh@dhl.com
Web Site: www.dhl.com.uy
Emp.: 135
Logistics Consulting Services
S.I.C.: 4731
N.A.I.C.S.: 541614
Rino Chiu *(Country Mgr)*

DHL Verwaltungs GmbH (2)
Charles de Gaulle Strasse 20
53113 Bonn, Germany
Tel.: (49) 2281820
Fax: (49) 2281827099
Web Site: www.deutschepost.de
Emp.: 8,000
Holding Company
S.I.C.: 6719
N.A.I.C.S.: 551112
Christof Ehrhart *(Head-Corp Comm)*

DHL-VNPT Express Ltd. (2)
4 Phan Thuc Duyen
Tan Binh, Ho Chi Minh City, Vietnam
Tel.: (84) 8 3844 6203
Fax: (84) 8 3845 6841
Emp.: 50
Logistics Consulting Services
S.I.C.: 4731
N.A.I.C.S.: 541614
Andrew Bonica *(Gen Mgr)*

DHL Voigt International GmbH (2)
Krokamp 87
24539 Neumunster, Germany
Tel.: (49) 4321 8730
Fax: (49) 4321 873170
Logistics Consulting Services
S.I.C.: 4731
N.A.I.C.S.: 541614

DHL Wahl International GmbH (2)
Gildemeisterstrasse 150
33689 Bielefeld, Germany
Tel.: (49) 5205 755 0
Fax: (49) 5205 755 125
Logistics Consulting Services
S.I.C.: 4731
N.A.I.C.S.: 541614

Deutsche Post AG—(Continued)

DHL Worldwide Express (Bangladesh) Private Limited (2)
Molly Capita Centre Level 4 & 5 76 Bir Uttam Mir
Showket Road Gulshan Avenue, Dhaka, 1212, Bangladesh
Tel.: (880) 298817037
Fax: (880) 28823248
Courier Delivery Services
S.I.C.: 4513
N.A.I.C.S.: 492110

DHL Worldwide Express Cambodia Ltd (2)
353 St 110 Sangkat Sras Chark
Khan Daun Penh, Phnom Penh, 12201, Cambodia
Tel.: (855) 23 427 726
Fax: (855) 23 427 680
E-Mail: csinfo@dhl.com
Web Site: www.dhl.com
Emp.: 5
Logistics Consulting Services
S.I.C.: 4731
N.A.I.C.S.: 541614
Jonty Edgar *(Country Mgr)*

DHL Worldwide Express Cargo LLC (2)
PO Box 6252
Dubai, United Arab Emirates
Tel.: (971) 4 2995333
Fax: (971) 4 2995116
Courier Delivery Services
S.I.C.: 4513
N.A.I.C.S.: 492110

DHL Worldwide Express Kenya Ltd. (2)
DHL House Corner Lusaka Road & Wilu Road
Nyayo Stadium Roundabout
PO Box 67577, Nairobi, Kenya
Tel.: (254) 206925120
E-Mail: nbocustomercare@dhl.com
Web Site: www.dhl.com
Emp.: 130
Express Mail Services
S.I.C.: 4215
N.A.I.C.S.: 492110
Alastair Donald Russel *(Mng Dir)*

DHL Worldwide Express (PH) Corp. (2)
DHL House 2306 Chino Roces Avenue
Pasong Tamo Extension Kayamanan C
1231 Makati, Philippines
Tel.: (63) 28117100
Fax: (63) 28117271
Web Site: www.dhl.com.ph
Emp.: 900
Express Mail Services
S.I.C.: 4513
N.A.I.C.S.: 492110
Rodolfo Feliciano *(Chm)*

DHL Worldwide Express (PNG) Ltd. (2)
PO Box 1775
Port Moresby, Papua New Guinea
Tel.: (675) 325 9866
Fax: (675) 323 0142
Web Site: www.fastforward.dhl.com
Courier Services
S.I.C.: 4215
N.A.I.C.S.: 492110

DHL Worldwide Express Tasimacilik ve Ticaret A.S. (2)
20 Bagcilar Mahallesi Yalcin Kores Caddesi
Istanbul, 34209, Turkey
Tel.: (90) 2124781100
Fax: (90) 2124781400
Courier Services
S.I.C.: 4513
N.A.I.C.S.: 492110

DHL Yemen Ltd. (2)
100 Haddah St
PO Box 19600
Sana'a, Yemen
Tel.: (967) 1441096
Fax: (967) 1441095
Web Site: www.ye.dhl.com
Express Mail Services
S.I.C.: 4513
N.A.I.C.S.: 492110

Dongguan DHL Supply Chain Co., Ltd. (2)
Industrial Park Metro Avenue 4 First Floor
Southern District, Dongguan, 523808, China
Tel.: (86) 13798943525
Fax: (86) 76923831822
Freight Forwarding Services
S.I.C.: 4731
N.A.I.C.S.: 488510

LLC DHL Express (2)
8 Marta Street 14
127 083 Moscow, Russia
Tel.: (7) 495 956 1000
Web Site: www.dhl.ru
Parcel & Courier Services
S.I.C.: 4215
N.A.I.C.S.: 492210

LLC DHL International Kazakhstan (2)
1/1 Dzhandosova str
50009 Almaty, Kazakhstan
Tel.: (7) 3272588588
Fax: (7) 3272584358
Web Site: www.dhl.kz
Emp.: 80
Express Mail Services
S.I.C.: 4215
N.A.I.C.S.: 492110

PT DHL Global Forwarding Indonesia (2)
Lot 8 Block A Soewarna Business Park
Soekarna Hatta Intl Airport
Jakarta, 19110, Indonesia
Tel.: (62) 21 55913161
Fax: (62) 21 55913164
Freight Forwarding Services
S.I.C.: 4731
N.A.I.C.S.: 488510

UAB DHL Lietuva (2)
S Darius Ir S Gireno Str 81
2189 Vilnius, Lithuania
Tel.: (370) 5 236 07 00
Fax: (370) 5 216 77 40
E-Mail: ltinfo@dhl.com
Web Site: www.dhl.lt
Emp.: 10
Logistics Consulting Services
S.I.C.: 4731
N.A.I.C.S.: 541614
Mindaugas Pivoriunas *(Gen Mgr)*

ZAO DHL International Russia (2)
8th Marta St 14
127083 Moscow, Russia
Tel.: (7) 4959561000
Fax: (7) 4952323107
Web Site: www.dhl.ru
Sales Range: $1-9.9 Million
Emp.: 495
Express Mail Services
S.I.C.: 4215
N.A.I.C.S.: 492110
Garry Kemp *(Reg Dir)*

Non-U.S. Joint Ventures:

DHL-Sinotrans International Air Courier Ltd. (2)
No 18 Ronghua Nanlu
BDA, 100176 Beijing, China
Tel.: (86) 10 8785 2000
Fax: (86) 10 6780 5799
Web Site: www.cn.dhl.com
Emp.: 160
Express Mail Services
S.I.C.: 4215
N.A.I.C.S.: 492110
Dongming Wu *(Gen Mgr)*

Myanmar DHL Limited (2)
Bldg 4 Hotel Yangon Corner of Tyay
Kabaye Bagoda Rd Mayangone Township
11061 Yangon, Myanmar
Tel.: (95) 1664423
Fax: (95) 1651394
E-Mail: info@dhl.com
Web Site: www.dhl.com
Emp.: 58
Express Mail Services
S.I.C.: 4513
N.A.I.C.S.: 492110

P.T. Birotika Semesta/DHL (2)
Siemens Business Park Building F Jalan
MT Haryono Kav 58-60
12780 Jakarta, Indonesia
Tel.: (62) 2179173333
Fax: (62) 2179196688
E-Mail: info@dhl.co.id
Web Site: www.dhl.co.id
Emp.: 350
Express Mail Services
S.I.C.: 4513
N.A.I.C.S.: 492110
Rudy J. Pesik *(Chm)*

Tradeteam Limited (2)
Edison Road Hams Hall
National Distribution Park, Coleshill, B46 1TT, United Kingdom (100%)
Tel.: (44) 1675468500
E-Mail: tradeteam.general@dhl.com
Web Site: www.tradeteam.com
Emp.: 1,700
Beverage Transportation & Logistics Services
S.I.C.: 4731
N.A.I.C.S.: 541614
Gavin Murdoch *(Mng Dir)*

DHL International (Thailand) Ltd. (1)
Grand Amarin Tower Floor 22 1550 New Petchburi Road
Makasan Khet Rachatevee, Bangkok, 10400, Thailand
Tel.: (66) 2 658 8000
Fax: (66) 2 207 0630
Courier Services
S.I.C.: 4215
N.A.I.C.S.: 492110

DHL Logistics Ghana Ltd. (1)
18 Kwame Nkruma Avenue Ridge
Accra, Ghana
Tel.: (233) 247935760
Logistics Consulting Services
S.I.C.: 4731
N.A.I.C.S.: 541614

DHL Logistik Service GmbH (1)
IZ NO SUD Strasse 14 Objekt 24
2355 Wiener Neudorf, Austria
Tel.: (43) 22366030
E-Mail: dhlat@dhl.com
Logistics Consulting Services
S.I.C.: 4731
N.A.I.C.S.: 541614

DHL Management Services Limited (1)
178-188 Great South West Road
Hounslow, Middlesex, TW4 6JS, United Kingdom
Tel.: (44) 20 8818 8000
Fax: (44) 20 8818 8925
Financial Investment Management Services
S.I.C.: 6211
N.A.I.C.S.: 523999

DHL Metropolitan Logistics sc Mexico S.A. de C.V. (1)
Autopista Mexico-Queretaro Km 34 5 Nave 1
Cuautitlan, 54740, Mexico
Tel.: (52) 5530032600
Logistics Consulting Services
S.I.C.: 4731
N.A.I.C.S.: 541614

DHL of Curacao N.V. (1)
Handelskade 6
Willemstad, Curacao
Tel.: (599) 9 737 0122
Courier Services
S.I.C.: 4513
N.A.I.C.S.: 492110

DHL Sandouville SARL (1)
266 Avenue Du President Wilson
Saint Denis, 93200, France
Tel.: (33) 1 46 88 89 02
Logistics Consulting Services
S.I.C.: 4731
N.A.I.C.S.: 541614

DHL SC Transport SASU (1)
ZA Trappes Elancourt 2-4 Avenue Enrico Fermi
78190 Trappes, France
Tel.: (33) 1 30 16 20 23
Fax: (33) 1 30 16 20 25
Logistics Consulting Services
S.I.C.: 4731
N.A.I.C.S.: 541614

DHL Stock Express SAS (1)
241 Rue De La Belle Etoile
95700 Roissy-en-France, France
Tel.: (33) 1 49 38 70 70
Logistics Consulting Services
S.I.C.: 4731
N.A.I.C.S.: 541614

DHL Supply Chain (Denmark) A / S (1)
Moenten 7
6000 Kolding, Denmark
Tel.: (45) 7634 3666
Fax: (45) 7634 3669
Logistics Consulting Services
S.I.C.: 4731
N.A.I.C.S.: 541614

DHL Supply Chain (South Africa) (Pty) Ltd. (1)
110 South Coast Road
Congella, 4000, South Africa
Tel.: (27) 312047600
Logistics Consulting Services
S.I.C.: 4731
N.A.I.C.S.: 541614

DHL Supply Chain (Vietnam) Limited (1)
364 Cong Hoa Street 11F eTown 2 Building
Tan Binh, Ho Chi Minh City, Vietnam
Tel.: (84) 8 3812 3888
Fax: (84) 8 3812 5695
Logistics Consulting Services
S.I.C.: 4731
N.A.I.C.S.: 541614

DHL Worldwide Express Logistics NV /SA (1)
De Kleetlaan 1
1831 Diegem, Belgium
Tel.: (32) 27 13 40 00
Fax: (32) 27 18 57 48
Logistics Consulting Services
S.I.C.: 4731
N.A.I.C.S.: 541614

DZ Specialties B.V. (1)
Jozef Israelskade 48 g
1072 SB Amsterdam, Netherlands
Tel.: (31) 20 5788500
Logistics Consulting Services
S.I.C.: 4731
N.A.I.C.S.: 541614

Eurodifarm S.r.l. (1)
Strada Provinciale 159 Km 1 400
26831 Casalmaiocco, Lodi, Italy
Tel.: (39) 029810991
Fax: (39) 0298109948
E-Mail: info@eurodifarm.com
Web Site: www.eurodifarm.com
Pharmaceutical & Diagnostic Products Distr
S.I.C.: 5122
N.A.I.C.S.: 424210

Exel Automocion S.A. de C.V. (1)
Autopista Mexico Puebla Km 117 Nave 4a
Cuautlancingo, Puebla, 72710, Mexico
Tel.: (52) 2223034400
Fax: (52) 2223034448
E-Mail: goadalope.vazillordonec@vhl.com
Freight Trucking Services
S.I.C.: 4213
N.A.I.C.S.: 484122

Exel Canada Ltd. (1)
90 Matheson Blvd W
Etobicoke, ON, L5R 3R3, Canada
Tel.: (905) 366-7700
Fax: (905) 366-7701
Emp.: 7
Logistics Consulting Services
S.I.C.: 4731
N.A.I.C.S.: 541614
Ross Weber *(Dir-Ops)*

Exel Distribution (Thailand) Ltd. (1)
76/1 Moo 6 Talingchan-Bangbuathong Rd
Bangrakpatana
Bang Bua Thong, Nonthaburi, 11110, Thailand
Tel.: (66) 2925 3291
Fax: (66) 2925 3292
Logistics Consulting Services
S.I.C.: 4731
N.A.I.C.S.: 541614

Exel Global Logistics do Brasil S.A. (1)
Av Djalma Batista 735 sl 214
Manaus, Amapa, Brazil
Tel.: (55) 92 3236 7760

Logistics Consulting Services
S.I.C.: 4731
N.A.I.C.S.: 541614

Exel Group Holdings (Nederland) B.V. (1)
Huygensweg 10
Postbus 100
5466AN Veghel, Netherlands
Tel.: (31) 413 347911
Logistics Consulting Services
S.I.C.: 4731
N.A.I.C.S.: 541614

Exel International Holdings (Netherlands 1) B.V. (1)
Huygensweg 10
5466AN Veghel, Netherlands
Tel.: (31) 413347911
Logistics Consulting Services
S.I.C.: 4731
N.A.I.C.S.: 541614

Exel International Holdings (Netherlands 2) B.V. (1)
Huygensweg 10
Postbus 100, 5466 AN Veghel, Netherlands
Tel.: (31) 413 347911
Logistics Consulting Services
S.I.C.: 4731
N.A.I.C.S.: 541614

Exel Supply Chain Services de Mexico, S.A. de C.V. (1)
Autopista Mexico-Queretaro Km 34 5 Nave 1
Cuautitlan Izcalli, 54740, Mexico
Tel.: (52) 5530032600
Logistics Consulting Services
S.I.C.: 4731
N.A.I.C.S.: 541614

Exel Supply Chain Services (South Africa) (Pty) Ltd. (1)
107 Andre Greyvenstein St Isando
1600 Kempton Park, Gauteng, South Africa
Tel.: (27) 11 9237767
Logistics Consulting Services
S.I.C.: 4731
N.A.I.C.S.: 541614

Exel Supply Chain Solutions Ltd. (1)
Unit D 1 & 2 Airport Business Pk Swords Rd
Dublin, Ireland
Tel.: (353) 1844 55 45
Freight Forwarding Services
S.I.C.: 4731
N.A.I.C.S.: 488510

FACT Denmark A / S (1)
Kirstinehoj 50
Kastrup, 2770 Arhus, Denmark
Tel.: (45) 32464600
Fax: (45) 32461656
Logistics Consulting Services
S.I.C.: 4731
N.A.I.C.S.: 541614

F.C. (Flying Cargo) International Transportation Ltd. (1)
4 Ha Melacha st North Industrial Zone
Lod, 71520, Israel
Tel.: (972) 8 9144444
Fax: (972) 8 9243024
E-Mail: onecall@flying-cargo.com
Web Site: www.flying-cargo.com
Air Freight Transportation Services
S.I.C.: 4512
N.A.I.C.S.: 481112

Gerlach AG (1)
Niederstr 5
PO Box 2647
4002 Pratteln, Switzerland
Tel.: (41) 61 315 96 96
Fax: (41) 61 315 96 10
E-Mail: sales.gerlach@ch.gerlachcs.com
Web Site: www.gerlachcs.ch
Customs Consulting Services
S.I.C.: 4731
N.A.I.C.S.: 541614

Gerlach & Co Internationale Expediteurs B.V. (1)
Heemskerckweg of 6
5928 LL Venlo, Netherlands
Tel.: (31) 773246500
Fax: (31) 7732465559
E-Mail: info@nl.gerlachcs.com
Web Site: www.gerlachcs.com
Emp.: 6
Customs Consulting Services
S.I.C.: 4731
N.A.I.C.S.: 541614
Jean-Marc Guyot *(Gen Mgr)*

Gerlach & Co. nv (1)
Schouwkensstraat 7 Haven 200
2030 Antwerp, Belgium
Tel.: (32) 3 545 0220
Fax: (32) 3 545 0229
E-Mail: antwerpen@be.gerlachcs.com
Web Site: www.gerlachcs.be
Emp.: 2
Customs Consulting Services
S.I.C.: 4731
N.A.I.C.S.: 541614
Johan Raats *(Gen Mgr)*

Gerlach Customs Services EOOD (1)
Iztochna Tangenta 94 SPZ Slatina Sever 1
1528 Sofia, Bulgaria
Tel.: (359) 29 70 80 27
Fax: (359) 29 73 88 24
E-Mail: info@bg.gerlachcs.com
Web Site: www.gerlachcs.bg
Emp.: 5
Customs Consulting Services
S.I.C.: 4731
N.A.I.C.S.: 541614
Ruslan Hristov *(Mgr)*

Gerlach European Customs Services, spol. s.r.o. (1)
Horarska 12
821 09 Bratislava, Slovakia
Tel.: (421) 2 5363 5361
Logistics Consulting Services
S.I.C.: 4731
N.A.I.C.S.: 541614

Gerlach Spol s.r.o. (1)
K Vypichu 1086
252 19 Rudna, Czech Republic
Tel.: (420) 311 690 013 015
Fax: (420) 311 690 058
E-Mail: obchod@gerlach.cz
Web Site: www.gerlachcs.cz
Emp.: 12
Customs Consulting Services
S.I.C.: 4731
N.A.I.C.S.: 541614

Giorgio Gori International Freight Forwards (Pty) Ltd. (1)
12th Fl Ernst and Young House
Johannesburg, Gauteng, South Africa
Tel.: (27) 21 880 1680
Freight Forwarding Services
S.I.C.: 4731
N.A.I.C.S.: 488510

Giorgio Gori S.r.l. (1)
Via Lepori 9
57017 Livorno, Italy
Tel.: (39) 0586 967 001
Fax: (39) 0586 941 440
E-Mail: info@it.ggori.com
Web Site: www.ggori.com
Alcoholic Beverage Transportation Service
S.I.C.: 4789
N.A.I.C.S.: 488999

Non-U.S. Subsidiaries:

Giorgio Gori (France) sas (2)
9 Rue de Guerlande Zone Verte
71880 Chatenoy-le-Royal, France
Tel.: (33) 3 85 97 20 60
Fax: (33) 3 85 97 20 61
E-Mail: info@fr.ggori.com
Alcoholic Beverage Transportation Service
S.I.C.: 4789
N.A.I.C.S.: 488999

Gori Argentina S.A. (2)
Ruta Panamericana 2650 Office B/D
Palmares Open Mall - Bureau
5501 Godoy Cruz, Mendoza, Argentina
Tel.: (54) 261 442 9000
Fax: (54) 261 442 9010
E-Mail: info@ar.ggori.com
Alcoholic Beverage Transportation Service
S.I.C.: 4789
N.A.I.C.S.: 488999

Gori Australia Pty Ltd. (2)
3C / 34 MacMahon Street
Hurstville, NSW, 2220, Australia
Tel.: (61) 2 95700000
Fax: (61) 2 95804948
E-Mail: info@au.ggori.com
Web Site: www2.ggori.com
Alcoholic Beverage Transportation Service
S.I.C.: 4789
N.A.I.C.S.: 488999

Gori Iberia S.L. (2)
Passeig del Ferrocarril 335 2 Planta
8860 Castelldefels, Barcelona, Spain
Tel.: (34) 936 342 636
Fax: (34) 936455166
E-Mail: info@es.ggori.com
Alcoholic Beverage Transportation Service
S.I.C.: 4789
N.A.I.C.S.: 488999
Simone Giusti *(Mng Dir)*

Gori Iberia Transitarios, Limitada (2)
AV Dr Antunes Guimaraes Nr 505 6 Floor
Leca Da Palmeira, Matosinhos, 4450-621, Portugal
Tel.: (351) 229 982 080
Fax: (351) 229 982 089
E-Mail: info@pt.ggori.com
Web Site: www.ggori.com
Emp.: 8
Alcoholic Beverage Transportation Service
S.I.C.: 4789
N.A.I.C.S.: 488999

Higgs International Limited (1)
Q E D Distribution Park Purfleet By Pass
Purfleet, Essex, RM19 1NA, United Kingdom
Tel.: (44) 1708 892 800
Fax: (44) 1708 892 801
E-Mail: Export-Sales@higgs.co.uk
Web Site: www.higgs.co.uk
Emp.: 9
Logistics Consulting Services
S.I.C.: 4731
N.A.I.C.S.: 541614
Darren Starkey *(Mng Dir)*

Higgs International Publishing Logistics Ltd (1)
Unit D Q E D Distribution Park
Purfleet, RM19 1NA, United Kingdom
Tel.: (44) 1708 892 800
Fax: (44) 1708 892 801
E-Mail: Export-Sales@higgs.co.uk
Web Site: www.higgs.co.uk
Emp.: 9
Newspaper & Book Publishing Services
S.I.C.: 2711
N.A.I.C.S.: 511110
Ron Kelly *(Head-Sls-Media)*

Hull Blyth & Co Ltd (1)
10 Coldbath Square
London, EC1R 5HL, United Kingdom
Tel.: (44) 7709 483429
E-Mail: enquiries@hull-blyth.com
Web Site: www.hull-blyth.com
Emp.: 4
Marine Shipping Services
S.I.C.: 4412
N.A.I.C.S.: 483111
Peter Carter James *(Mgr-Bus Dev)*

Non-U.S. Subsidiaries:

Hull Blyth Ghana Ltd (2)
Seatec House Akosombo Road
PO Box 214
Tema, Ghana
Tel.: (233) 303 300894
Fax: (233) 303 300916
E-Mail: enquiriesghana@hull-blyth.com
Freight Transportation Services
S.I.C.: 4731
N.A.I.C.S.: 488510
Caroline Baldwin *(Mng Dir)*

Hull Blyth Nigeria Ltd. (2)
34 Wharf Rd
Apapa, Logas, Nigeria
Tel.: (234) 1 764 4914
E-Mail: enquiriesnigeria@hull-blyth.com
Logistics Consulting Services
S.I.C.: 4731
N.A.I.C.S.: 541614
Christian Holm *(Mng Dir)*

Hull Blyth South Africa Pty Ltd (2)
Suite 850 Mansion House 12 Field Street 8th Fl
Durban, 4001, South Africa
Tel.: (27) 31 360 0700
Fax: (27) 31 304 9544
E-Mail: enquiriessa@hull-blyth.com
Web Site: www.hull-blyth.com
Emp.: 4
Ocean Freight Transportation Services
S.I.C.: 4731
N.A.I.C.S.: 488510
Leigh Walker *(Mng Dir)*

Hyperion Inmobilaria S.A. de C.V. (1)
Carr Mexico-Queretaro Km 34 5 Nave 1
Rancho San Isidro, 54740 Cuautitlan Izcalli, Mexico
Tel.: (52) 55 3003 2600
Real Estate Management Services
S.I.C.: 6531
N.A.I.C.S.: 531390

ITG Global Logistics B.V. (1)
Van Weerden Poelmanweg 10
3088 EB Rotterdam, Netherlands
Tel.: (31) 10 8511 600
Fax: (31) 10 8511 601
E-Mail: info@itg.nl
Emp.: 7
Logistics Consulting Services
S.I.C.: 4731
N.A.I.C.S.: 541614
Ron Bothof *(Country Mgr)*

ITG Internationale Spedition GmbH (1)
Objekt 262 Stiege 7 Zimmer A02 067
1300 Vienna, Austria
Tel.: (43) 1 7007 32946
Fax: (43) 1 7007 33457
E-Mail: info.vie@itgvie.at
Emp.: 3
Air & Sea Freight Transportation Services
S.I.C.: 4512
N.A.I.C.S.: 481112
Tamara Grill *(Office Mgr)*

Joint Retail Logistics Limited (1)
Hyde Park Indstl Est
Newtownabbey, BT36 4PP, United Kingdom
Tel.: (44) 28 9083 3671
Fax: (44) 28 9083 3637
Emp.: 200
Freight Trucking Services
S.I.C.: 4213
N.A.I.C.S.: 484122
Una Doherty *(Gen Mgr)*

LLC Williams Lea (1)
2 Paveletskaya Sq Bl 2
115 054 Moscow, Russia
Tel.: (7) 495 258 55 58
Fax: (7) 495 258 55 59
Business Process Outsourcing Services
S.I.C.: 7389
N.A.I.C.S.: 561499

Matrix Logistics Services Ltd. (1)
6941 Kennedy Road
Mississauga, ON, L5T 2R6, Canada
Tel.: (905) 795-2200
Fax: (905) 564-7582
Logistics Consulting Services
S.I.C.: 4731
N.A.I.C.S.: 541614

NFC International Holdings (Ireland) (1)
Oak Road
Dublin, Ireland
Tel.: (353) 14050800
Fax: (353) 14050802
Emp.: 200
Investment Management Services
S.I.C.: 6211
N.A.I.C.S.: 523999
Mark Taylor *(Gen Mgr)*

Ocean Group Investments Limited (1)
Ocean House The Ring
Bracknell, Berkshire, RG12 1AN, United Kingdom
Tel.: (44) 1344 302000
Fax: (44) 1344 301193
Web Site: www.dhl.com
Emp.: 30
Financial Investment Services
S.I.C.: 6211
N.A.I.C.S.: 523999

Deutsche Post AG—(Continued)

Ocean Overseas Holdings Limited (1)
Ocean Ho The Ring
Bracknell, Berkshire, RG12 1AN, United Kingdom
Tel.: (44) 1344302000
Investment Management Services
S.I.C.: 6282
N.A.I.C.S.: 523920

Pharma Logistics NV (1)
Gustave Demeurslaan 71
1654 Huizingen, Belgium
Tel.: (32) 2 363 15 70
E-Mail: info@pharma-logistics.com
Web Site: www.pharma-logistics.com
Healthcare Logistics Services
S.I.C.: 4731
N.A.I.C.S.: 541614

PPL CZ s. r. o. (1)
U Vozovny 658/8
Malesice, Prague, 108 00, Czech Republic
Tel.: (420) 844 775 775
Fax: (420) 225 331 200
E-Mail: info@ppl.cz
Web Site: www.ppl.cz
Parcel & Courier Services
S.I.C.: 4215
N.A.I.C.S.: 492210
Miroslav Mares *(Mgr-Sls & Mktg)*

Presse-Service Gull GmbH (1)
Gaiserwaldstrasse 14
9015 Saint Gallen, Switzerland
Tel.: (41) 713 14 0606
Fax: (41) 713 14 0600
E-Mail: info@guell.de
Web Site: www.guell-presseservice.de
Emp.: 50
Magazine Publishing Services
S.I.C.: 2721
N.A.I.C.S.: 511120
Christine Leuders *(Gen Mgr)*

PT DANZAS SARANA PERKASA (1)
Soekarno-Hatta Int I Airport Wisma Soewarna
19110 Jakarta, Indonesia
Tel.: (62) 21 5591 2930
Fax: (62) 21 5591 3157
Freight Forwarding Services
S.I.C.: 4731
N.A.I.C.S.: 488510

Saturn Integrated Logistics Inc. (1)
100 Disco Rd
Etobicoke, ON, M9W 1M1, Canada
Tel.: (416) 798-0258
Logistics Consulting Services
S.I.C.: 4731
N.A.I.C.S.: 541614

SCM Supply Chain Management Inc. (1)
6800 Maritz Drive
Mississauga, ON, L5W 1W2, Canada
Tel.: (905) 670-9966
Fax: (905) 670-5226
Web Site: www.scm3pl.com
Emp.: 1,100
Logistics Consulting Services
S.I.C.: 4731
N.A.I.C.S.: 541614
Pierre Corbeil *(Dir-Ops)*

Selektvracht B.V. (1)
Atoomweg 30
3542 AB Utrecht, Netherlands (100%)
Mailing Address:
Postbus 40229
3504 AA Utrecht, Netherlands
Tel.: (31) 302477999
Fax: (31) 302477900
E-Mail: info@selektvracht.nl
Web Site: www.selektvracht.nl
Rev.: $35,000,000
Emp.: 150
Mail Delivering Services
S.I.C.: 7331
N.A.I.C.S.: 541860
Hans Kraaijenbrink *(Mng Dir)*

Smoke and Mirrors Productions Limited (1)
57/59 Beak Street
London, W1F 9SJ, United Kingdom
Tel.: (44) 20 74681000
Fax: (44) 20 74681001
E-Mail: production@smoke-mirrors.com
Web Site: www.smoke-mirrors.co.uk
Emp.: 7
Video Production Services
S.I.C.: 7812
N.A.I.C.S.: 512110
Penny Verbe *(Dir-Facility)*

Non-U.S. Unit:

Smoke and Mirrors Productions Limited - Shanghai Unit (2)
201-202 Red Town Building D 570 Huai Hai Xi Road
Chang Ning District, Shanghai, 200052, China
Tel.: (86) 2152580928
Fax: (86) 682152540168
Emp.: 1
Video Production Services
S.I.C.: 7812
N.A.I.C.S.: 512110
Nic George *(Gen Mgr)*

SNAS Lebanon SARL (1)
Airport Road DHL Building 1Floor Aster Libanpost Building
PO Box 166-439
Beirut, Lebanon
Tel.: (961) 1629700
Fax: (961) 1629701
Logistics Consulting Services
S.I.C.: 4731
N.A.I.C.S.: 541614
John Chedid *(Gen Mgr)*

StarBroker AG (1)
Peter Merian-Strasse 88
4002 Basel, Switzerland
Tel.: (41) 612747474
Fax: (41) 612747475
E-Mail: reception.management.dh@dhl.com
Web Site: www.dhl.com
Emp.: 2
Transportation Services
S.I.C.: 4789
N.A.I.C.S.: 488999
Peter Karreman *(VP)*

The Stationery Office Enterprises Limited (1)
Mandela Way
London, SE1 5SS, United Kingdom
Tel.: (44) 20 7394 4200
Fax: (44) 8706005533
E-Mail: customer.services@tso.co.uk
Web Site: www.tso.co.uk
Emp.: 12
Online Book Publishing Services
S.I.C.: 2741
N.A.I.C.S.: 519130
Marco Pierleoni *(CEO)*

SW Post Beheer B.V. (1)
Reactorweg 25
3542 AD Utrecht, Netherlands
Tel.: (31) 302149500
Fax: (31) 302149590
Financial Investment Management Services
S.I.C.: 6211
N.A.I.C.S.: 523999

T & B Whitwood Holdings Limited (1)
Ocean House The Ring
Bracknell, Berkshire, RG12 1AN, United Kingdom
Tel.: (44) 1344 302000
Fax: (44) 1344 301193
Investment Management Services
S.I.C.: 6211
N.A.I.C.S.: 523999

Tag Pac Limited (1)
29 Clerkenwell Road
London, EC1M 5TA, United Kingdom
Tel.: (44) 20 7251 4571
Fax: (44) 113 205 1414
E-Mail: hello@tag-pac.com
Web Site: www.tag-pac.com
Graphic Design Services
S.I.C.: 7336
N.A.I.C.S.: 541430

TEDI Translogic Express Dedicated Inc. (1)
420 Ambassdor Dr 2nd Fl
Mississauga, ON, L5T 2R5, Canada
Tel.: (905) 451-3033
Fax: (888) 363-8387
Freight Trucking Services
S.I.C.: 4213
N.A.I.C.S.: 484121
Kevin Devine *(Pres)*

TheNetherlands622009 b. v. (1)
Reactorweg 25
3542 AD Utrecht, Netherlands
Tel.: (31) 30 2149500
Logistics Consulting Services
S.I.C.: 4731
N.A.I.C.S.: 541614

Tracker Logistics Inc. (1)
3905 81 Ave
Leduc, AB, T9E 8S6, Canada
Tel.: (780) 980-8900
Fax: (809) 860-680
Emp.: 17
Logistics Consulting Services
S.I.C.: 4731
N.A.I.C.S.: 541614

Transcare Supply Chain Management Inc. (1)
7491 Jane St Unit 3
Concord, ON, L4K 2M7, Canada
Tel.: (905) 660-4477
Logistics Warehousing & Storage Services
S.I.C.: 4225
N.A.I.C.S.: 493110

TSO Holdings A Limited (1)
St Crispins House
Norwich, NR3 1PD, United Kingdom
Tel.: (44) 1603 622211
Book Publishing Services
S.I.C.: 2731
N.A.I.C.S.: 511130

TSO Holdings B Limited (1)
St Crispins
Norwich, NR3 1PD, United Kingdom
Tel.: (44) 1603 622211
Book Publishing Services
S.I.C.: 2731
N.A.I.C.S.: 511130

TSO Property Limited (1)
St Crispins House Duke Street
Norwich, NR3 1PD, United Kingdom
Tel.: (44) 1603 622 211
Fax: (44) 8706005533
E-Mail: executiveoffice@tso.co.uk
Web Site: www.tso.co.uk
Emp.: 20
Real Estate Management Services
S.I.C.: 6531
N.A.I.C.S.: 531390
Georg Behrens *(CEO)*

Van Gend & Loos - Euro Express NV (1)
Essenestraat 26
1740 Ternat, Belgium
Tel.: (32) 2 5834209
Fax: (32) 2 582 53 00
Freight Forwarding Services
S.I.C.: 4731
N.A.I.C.S.: 488510

Venture Logistics S.A. de C.V. (1)
Av De Los Tejocotes S/N
Cuautitlan Izcalli, 54769, Mexico
Tel.: (52) 5519402000
Logistics Consulting Services
S.I.C.: 4731
N.A.I.C.S.: 541614

Veron Grauer AG (1)
Halle de Fret 4 Geneva 5 Airport
PO Box 1047
1211 Geneva, Switzerland
Tel.: (41) 22 709 51 93
Fax: (41) 22 709 51 39
E-Mail: verongrauer@dhl.com
Web Site: www.verongrauer.ch
Freight Transportation Services
S.I.C.: 4731
N.A.I.C.S.: 488510

Vetsch AG, Internationale Transporte (1)
Technikumstrasse 20
9471 Buchs, Switzerland
Tel.: (41) 81 354 25 00
Fax: (41) 81 354 25 64
Web Site: www.vetsch.net
Freight Forwarding Services
S.I.C.: 4731
N.A.I.C.S.: 488510

Vetsch Internationale Transporte GmbH (1)
Senderstrasse 30
6960 Wolfurt, Austria
Tel.: (43) 5574 64 8 44
Fax: (43) 5574 64 8 44 4
Web Site: www.vetsch.net
Emp.: 2
Transportation Services
S.I.C.: 4789
N.A.I.C.S.: 488999
Jiri Stastny *(Gen Mgr)*

Williams Lea Group Limited (1)
125 Poland Street
London, EC2A 2EJ, United Kingdom (75%)
Tel.: (44) 2077724200
Fax: (44) 2077724646
E-Mail: info@williamslea.com
Web Site: www.williamslea.com
Emp.: 300
Corporate Information Management Services
S.I.C.: 8742
N.A.I.C.S.: 541611
Conor Davey *(CEO)*
Lesley Lindberg *(CMO)*
Todd Handcock *(CEO-Asia Pacific)*

Subsidiaries:

The Stationery Office Group Limited (2)
St Crispins Ho Duke St
Norwich, Norfolk, NR3 1PD, United Kingdom
Tel.: (44) 1603 622211
Fax: (44) 8706005533
Emp.: 20
Online Book Publishing Services
S.I.C.: 2741
N.A.I.C.S.: 519130

The Stationery Office Limited (2)
St Crispins Duke Street
Norwich, NR3 1PD, United Kingdom
Tel.: (44) 1603 622211
Fax: (44) 8706005533
E-Mail: customer.services@tso.co.uk
Web Site: www.tso.co.uk
Emp.: 20
Online Book Publishing Services
S.I.C.: 2741
N.A.I.C.S.: 519130
Miles Toulson-Clarke *(Chm)*
Elisabetta Beretta *(CEO)*

Tag Worldwide Group Limited (2)
29 Clerkenwell Road
London, EC1M 5TA, United Kingdom
Tel.: (44) 20 7251 4571
Fax: (44) 20 7253 5355
E-Mail: info@tagworldwide.com
Web Site: www.tagworldwide.com
Emp.: 40
Software Development Services
S.I.C.: 7371
N.A.I.C.S.: 541511
Mark Grosvenor *(Gen Mgr)*

Subsidiaries:

Tag Creative Limited (3)
Ground Floor 44 Pear Tree Street
London, EC1V 3SF, United Kingdom
Tel.: (44) 20 3217 2325
E-Mail: contactus@tagcreative.com
Web Site: www.tagcreative.com
Emp.: 2
Advertising Agencies
S.I.C.: 7311
N.A.I.C.S.: 541810
Liam Church *(Mng Dir)*

Tag Europe Limited (3)
29 Clerkenwell Road
London, EC1M 5TA, United Kingdom
Tel.: (44) 20 7251 4571
Fax: (44) 20 7253 5355
E-Mail: reception@tagworldwide.com
Emp.: 200
Production & Design Agency Services
S.I.C.: 7389
N.A.I.C.S.: 541490

Tag NewCo Limited (3)
29 Clerkenwell Rd
London, EC1M 5TA, United Kingdom
Tel.: (44) 20 7251 4571
Fax: (44) 20 7253 5355
E-Mail: info@tagworldwide.com
Web Site: www.tagworldwide.com
Financial Investment Services
S.I.C.: 6211
N.A.I.C.S.: 523999

Tag Print Services Limited (3)
3-4 Bakers Yard Baker's Row
London, EC1R 3DD, United Kingdom
Tel.: (44) 20 7837 0123
Graphic Design Services
S.I.C.: 7336
N.A.I.C.S.: 541430

Tag Response Limited (3)
The Smokery 2 Greenhill Rents
London, EC1M 6BN, United Kingdom
Tel.: (44) 20 7833 6370
Web Site: www.tag-response.com
Emp.: 48
Production Design Agency Services
S.I.C.: 7389
N.A.I.C.S.: 541490
Mikael Pasco *(Mng Dir)*

Tag Worldwide Holdings Limited (3)
82 St John Street
London, EC1M 4JN, United Kingdom
Tel.: (44) 20 7336 6316
Investment Management Services
S.I.C.: 6799
N.A.I.C.S.: 523920

World Writers Limited (3)
29 Clerkenwell Road
London, EC1M 5TA, United Kingdom
Tel.: (44) 20 3217 2220
Fax: (44) 20 7253 5355
E-Mail: info@tagworldwide.com
Web Site: www.worldwriters.com
Emp.: 100
Advertising Agencies
S.I.C.: 7311
N.A.I.C.S.: 541810
Hannah Collyer-Braham *(Dir-Ops)*

U.S. Subsidiary:

Tag Worldwide (USA) Inc. (3)
75 Spring St 3nd Fl
New York, NY 10012
Tel.: (212) 625-6250
Fax: (212) 625-6260
Web Site: www.tagworldwide.com
Emp.: 200
Production & Design Agency Services
S.I.C.: 7389
N.A.I.C.S.: 541490
Peter Kuhn *(Pres)*

Non-U.S. Subsidiaries:

Tag Germany GmbH (3)
Ganghofer Strasse 66e
80339 Munich, Germany
Tel.: (49) 89 309 075 725
Web Site: www.tagworldwide.com
Emp.: 30
Video Production Services
S.I.C.: 7819
N.A.I.C.S.: 512199
Mark McGwire *(Gen Mgr)*

Tag India Private Limited (3)
6th Floor DLF Plaza Tower DLF Phase 1
Gurgaon, 122002, India
Tel.: (91) 124 484 3950
Fax: (91) 124 484 3999
Emp.: 80
Video Production Services
S.I.C.: 7819
N.A.I.C.S.: 512199

Tag MENA FZE (3)
Units No 2702 & 2703 Tiffany Tower Plot
No W2 Jum00eirah Lake Towers
PO Box 211274
Dubai, United Arab Emirates
Tel.: (971) 4 4214602
Fax: (971) 4 4214614
Advertising Agencies
S.I.C.: 7311
N.A.I.C.S.: 541810

Tag Sao Paulo Servico de Consultoria Ltda. (3)
Rua Fidalga 593 - cj 4 e 6 Vila Madalena
Sao Paulo, 05432-070, Brazil
Tel.: (55) 11 3093 8040
Fax: (55) 1147208500, ext. 127
E-Mail: tagsp@tagworldwide.com
Web Site: www.tagworlwide.com
Emp.: 13
Graphical Design Services
S.I.C.: 7336
N.A.I.C.S.: 541430
Juliana d'Alambert *(Dir-Client Svcs)*

Tag Worldwide Australia Pty Ltd. (3)
Level 1 4 Bank Place
Melbourne, VIC, Australia
Tel.: (61) 3 9822 3091
Advertising Agencies
S.I.C.: 7311
N.A.I.C.S.: 541810

Tag Worldwide (Shanghai) Co Ltd. (3)
Unit 201-202 Building D Red Town 570
Huai Hai Xi Road
Shanghai, 200052, China
Tel.: (86) 21 5254 0158
Fax: (86) 21 5254 0168
Emp.: 3
Advertising Agencies
S.I.C.: 7311
N.A.I.C.S.: 541810

Tag Worldwide (Singapore) Pte. Ltd. (3)
51 Cantonment Road
Singapore, 89752, Singapore
Tel.: (65) 6227 9177
Fax: (65) 6227 9848
Web Site: www.tagworlwide.com
Emp.: 6
Video Production Services
S.I.C.: 7819
N.A.I.C.S.: 512199
Melissa Chan *(Grp Acct Dir)*

Williams Lea Group Management Services Limited (2)
1-5 Pearlin Street
London, W1F 8PR, United Kingdom
Tel.: (44) 20 7772 4200
E-Mail: marketing@williamslea.com
Web Site: www.williamslea.com
Real Estate Management Services
S.I.C.: 6531
N.A.I.C.S.: 531390

Williams Lea Holdings PLC (2)
10 Eastbourne Terrace
London, W2 6LG, United Kingdom
Tel.: (44) 20 7394 4200
E-Mail: marketing@williamslea.com
Emp.: 100
Business Process Outsourcing Services
S.I.C.: 7389
N.A.I.C.S.: 561499
Peter Heyden *(Gen Mgr)*

Williams Lea Limited (2)
1-5 poland street
London, W1F 8PR, United Kingdom
Tel.: (44) 20 7772 4200
E-Mail: marketing@williamslea.com
Web Site: www.williamslea.com
Business Process Outsourcing Services
S.I.C.: 7389
N.A.I.C.S.: 561499

Williams Lea UK Limited (2)
McIntosh House Foxbridge Way Normanton Industrial Estate
Normanton, WF6 1TN, United Kingdom
Tel.: (44) 1924 890 000
Fax: (44) 1924 245 444
E-Mail: customer.services@williamslea.com
Web Site: www.williamslea.com
Emp.: 15
Business Process Outsourcing Services
S.I.C.: 7389
N.A.I.C.S.: 561499
Carol Lister *(Accountant)*

Williams Lea (US Acquisitions) Limited (2)
68 Saint Johns Street Clerkenwell
London, EC1M 1DT, United Kingdom
Tel.: (44) 20 7772 4200
E-Mail: marketing@williamslea.com
Web Site: www.williamslea.com
Business Process Outsourcing Services
S.I.C.: 7389
N.A.I.C.S.: 561499

U.S. Subsidiary:

Williams Lea (2)
500 W Madison St Ste 650
Chicago, IL 60661-4524 DE
Tel.: (312) 681-6400
Fax: (312) 681-6363
Toll Free: (888) 309-9393
Web Site: www.williamslea.com
Emp.: 1,800
Document & Facilities Management
Import Export
S.I.C.: 8748
N.A.I.C.S.: 541618
David Ritter *(CIO)*
John Paulson *(CEO-Americas)*

Non-U.S. Subsidiaries:

Williams Lea Argentina S.A. (2)
Arias 3751 15th fl nw sector
Buenos Aires, C1003ABH, Argentina
Tel.: (54) 11 4124 8052
Fax: (54) 11 4124 8000
Web Site: www.williamslea.com
Emp.: 1
Business Process Outsourcing Services
S.I.C.: 7389
N.A.I.C.S.: 561499
Aucan Czackis *(Acct Mgr)*

Williams Lea (Beijing) Limited (2)
Room 1201I 12/F Excel Centre No 6
Wudinghou Street
Xicheng District, Beijing, 100140, China
Tel.: (86) 10 8800 3796
Fax: (86) 10 8800 3819
Emp.: 10
Business Process Outsourcing Sercices
S.I.C.: 7389
N.A.I.C.S.: 561499
Richard Cook *(Gen Mgr)*

Williams Lea (Brazil) Assessoria Em Solucoes Empresariais Ltda. (2)
Alameda Araguaia 1293 Sala 107 Ed Eagle
Point Alphaville
Barueri, Sao Paulo, 06455 000, Brazil
Tel.: (55) 11 4193 6308
Fax: (55) 11 4193 6482
Web Site: www.tagworldwide.com
Emp.: 2
Business Process Outsourcing Services
S.I.C.: 7389
N.A.I.C.S.: 561499
George Schurmann *(Office Mgr)*

Williams Lea (Canada), Inc. (2)
1101 Rene-Levesque Blvd West
Montreal, QC, H3B 5H5, Canada
Tel.: (514) 940-7399
Fax: (514) 940-7344
Emp.: 1
Business Process Outsourcing Services
S.I.C.: 7389
N.A.I.C.S.: 561499
Linda Lebeault *(Sr Acct Mgr)*

Williams Lea France SAS (2)
31/33 Avenue Aristide Briand
Arcueil, 91400 Paris, France
Tel.: (33) 1 45 36 80 30
Fax: (33) 1 46 74 85 86
Business Process Outsourcing Services
S.I.C.: 7389
N.A.I.C.S.: 561499

Williams Lea GmbH (2)
Menuhinstrasse 6
53113 Bonn, Nordrhein-Westfalen, Germany
Tel.: (49) 228249830
Fax: (49) 22834983909
Emp.: 2
Business Process Outsourcing Services
S.I.C.: 7389
N.A.I.C.S.: 561499
Marc Daleiden *(Mng Dir)*
Roni Drori *(Mng Dir)*

Williams Lea India Private Limited (2)
Module 0308 D Block Third Floor Tidel Park
Taramani
Chennai, India 600113
Tel.: (91) 44 3068 5000
Web Site: www.williamslea.com
Emp.: 2,500
Business Process Outsourcing Services
S.I.C.: 7389
N.A.I.C.S.: 561499
Meenakshi Sundaram *(Gen Mgr)*

Williams Lea Ireland Limited (2)
Block 10-3 Blanchardstown Corporate Park
Dublin, 15, Ireland
Tel.: (353) 1 886 5010
Business Process Outsourcing Services
S.I.C.: 7389
N.A.I.C.S.: 561499

Williams Lea Japan Limited (2)
4-3-20 Toranomon Kamiyachomt Bldg 14f
Minato-Ku, Tokyo, 105-0001, Japan
Tel.: (81) 354043801
Fax: (81) 354043577
Web Site: www.williamslea.jpn.com
Business Process Outsourcing Services
S.I.C.: 7389
N.A.I.C.S.: 561499

Williams Lea Private Limited (2)
9 Raffles Place Level 58 Republic Plaza
Singapore, 048619, Singapore
Tel.: (65) 6823 1318
Fax: (65) 6823 1377
Web Site: www.williamslea.com
Business Process Outsourcing Services
S.I.C.: 7389
N.A.I.C.S.: 561499
Joseph Seetoh *(Country Mgr)*

Williams Lea Pty Limited (2)
Level 4 139 Macquarie Street
Sydney, NSW, 2000, Australia
Tel.: (61) 2 9641 2300
Fax: (61) 2 9252 7224
Emp.: 20
Business Process Outsourcing Services
S.I.C.: 7389
N.A.I.C.S.: 561499
Lesley Leech *(Mng Dir)*

Williams Lea S.L. (2)
Rambla Catalunya 62 - Pp Pta 1
Barcelona, 08007, Spain
Tel.: (34) 932155224
Fax: (34) 932155079
Business Process Outsourcing Services
S.I.C.: 7389
N.A.I.C.S.: 561499
Kamyar Arfa Zanganeh *(Gen Mgr)*

Williams Lea Sweden AB (2)
Box 547
611 10 Nykoping, Sweden
Tel.: (46) 155 293350
Business Process Outsourcing Services
S.I.C.: 7389
N.A.I.C.S.: 561499

Zenith Logistics Inc. (1)
1 Boudreau Rd
Saint Albert, AB, T8N 5A6, Canada
Tel.: (780) 458-2898
Fax: (780) 458-5135
Logistics Warehousing & Storage Services
S.I.C.: 4225
N.A.I.C.S.: 493110
Rick Bouk *(Gen Mgr)*

DEUTSCHE ROHSTOFF AG

Friedrich Ebert Anlage 24
69117 Heidelberg, Germany
Tel.: (49) 622187100
Fax: (49) 622187100, ext. 22
E-Mail: info@rohstoff.de
Web Site: www.rohstoff.de
DR0—(DEU)
Rev.: $4,166,990
Assets: $85,415,569
Liabilities: $19,536,044
Net Worth: $65,879,524
Earnings: $3,068,658
Emp.: 74
Fiscal Year-end: 12/31/12

Business Description:
Metal Mining Services
S.I.C.: 1099
N.A.I.C.S.: 212299

Personnel:
Martin Billhardt *(Chm-Supervisory Bd)*
Titus Gebel *(CEO & Member-Exec Bd)*
Thomas Gultschlag *(CFO & Member-Exec Bd)*

Deutsche Rohstoff AG—(Continued)

Supervisory Board of Directors:
Martin Billhardt
Gregor Borg
Wolfgang Seybold

DEUTSCHE RUCKVERSICHERUNG AG

Hansaallee 177
40549 Dusseldorf, Germany
Tel.: (49) 211455401
Fax: (49) 2114554199
E-Mail: info@deutscherueck.de
Web Site: www.deutscherueck.de
Year Founded: 1951
Rev.: $1,161,791,519
Emp.: 85
Business Description:
Insurance Services
S.I.C.: 6411
N.A.I.C.S.: 524210
Personnel:
Arno Junke *(CEO)*
Frank Schaar *(Deputy CEO)*

DEUTSCHE STEINZEUG CREMER & BREUER AG

Servaisstrasse
53347 Bonn, Germany
Mailing Address:
PO Box 2540
53015 Bonn, Germany
Tel.: (49) 2283910
Fax: (49) 228391301006
E-Mail: info@deutsche-steinzeug.de
Web Site: www.deutsche-steinzeu g.de
DSK1—(DEU)
Sls.: $225,079,624
Assets: $177,963,674
Liabilities: $157,367,273
Net Worth: $20,596,401
Earnings: ($6,326,999)
Emp.: 1,255
Fiscal Year-end: 12/31/12
Business Description:
Ceramic Products Mfr
S.I.C.: 3269
N.A.I.C.S.: 327110
Personnel:
Wilfried Delker *(Chm-Supervisory Bd)*
Dieter Schafer *(Chm-Mgmt Bd)*
Stephan Schelo *(Deputy Chm-Supervisory Bd)*
Joachim Ehlers-Nuwenhof *(Member-Mgmt Bd)*
Supervisory Board of Directors:
Wilfried Delker
Brian M. Cook
Frank Kernenbach
Hans-Peter Kohlhammer
Karl Mailbeck
Stephan Schelo
Subsidiaries:

Deutsche Steinzeug Immobilien Verwaltungs-GmbH **(1)**
Servaisstrasse 9
53347 Bonn, Germany
Tel.: (49) 2283910
Fax: (49) 2283911163
E-Mail: info@deutsche-steinzeug.de
Emp.: 400
Ceramic Products Mfr
S.I.C.: 3259
N.A.I.C.S.: 327120
Dieter Schaefer *(CEO)*

Jasba Mosaik GmbH **(1)**
Im Petersborn 2
56244 Otzingen, Germany
Tel.: (49) 26026820
Fax: (49) 26026821506
E-Mail: info@jasba.de
Web Site: www.jasba.de
Emp.: 200
Ceramic Products Mfr
S.I.C.: 3255
N.A.I.C.S.: 327120
Alexandra Schmidt *(Mng Dir)*

Meissen Keramik Vertriebs GmbH & Co. KG **(1)**
Wulffshof Wandweg 3
44149 Dortmund, Germany
Tel.: (49) 231187500
Fax: (49) 231 187 50 29 90
E-Mail: info@meissen-keramik.de
Web Site: www.meissen-keramik.de
Ceramic Products Mfr
S.I.C.: 3255
N.A.I.C.S.: 327120

Non-U.S. Subsidiary:

Archi-Ro Kft. **(2)**
Amade Laszlo St 1 Lukacs S U20
9022 Gyor, Hungary
Tel.: (36) 96517017
Fax: (36) 96 517 019
Emp.: 4
Ceramic Products Mfr
S.I.C.: 3255
N.A.I.C.S.: 327120
Fekete Roland *(Mng Dir)*

Staloton Klinker Vertriebs GmbH **(1)**
Buchtal
Schwarzenfeld, Bavaria, 92521, Germany
Tel.: (49) 943539100
Bricks Whslr
S.I.C.: 5032
N.A.I.C.S.: 423320

Non-U.S. Subsidiary:

Deutsche Steinzeug Italia s.r.l. **(1)**
Strada Statale 467 nr 134
Veggia, 42010 Casalgrande, Reggio Emilia, Italy
Tel.: (39) 0536990288
Fax: (39) 05 36 99 04 17
E-Mail: info@deutsche-steinzeug.it
Web Site: www.deutsche-steinzeug.it
Ceramic Products Sales
S.I.C.: 3255
N.A.I.C.S.: 327120
Beels Dirk *(Mgr)*

U.S. Subsidiary:

Deutsche Steinzeug America Inc. **(1)**
367 Curie Dr
Alpharetta, GA 30005
Tel.: (770) 442-5500
Fax: (770) 442-5502
Toll Free: (800) 584-5501
E-Mail: info@dsa-ceramics.com
Web Site: www.deutsche-steinzeug.de /dscb_usa_site
Emp.: 10
Ceramic Products Mfr
S.I.C.: 3259
N.A.I.C.S.: 327120
Chris McMahan *(Project Mgr)*

DEUTSCHE TELEKOM AG

Friedrich-Ebert-Allee 140
53113 Bonn, Germany
Mailing Address:
Postfach 2000
D 53105 Bonn, Germany
Tel.: (49) 228 181 0
Fax: (49) 228 181 8872
E-Mail: info@telekom.de
Web Site: www.telekom.com
Year Founded: 1995
DTE—(BER DEU OTC)
Rev.: $78,305,362,730
Assets: $145,308,282,140
Liabilities: $104,192,211,830
Net Worth: $41,116,070,310
Earnings: ($6,403,730,690)
Emp.: 229,686
Fiscal Year-end: 12/31/12
Business Description:
Telecommunications Services
S.I.C.: 4813
N.A.I.C.S.: 517110
Personnel:
Ulrich Lehner *(Chm-Supervisory Bd)*
Lothar Schroder *(Deputy Chm-Supervisory Bd)*
Timotheus Hottges *(CEO)*
Thomas Dannenfeldt *(CFO)*
Marion Schick *(Chief HR Officer, Member-Mgmt Bd & Dir-Labor)*
Niek Jan van Damme *(Member-Mgmt Bd-Germany & Mng Dir-Telekom Deutschland GmbH)*
Reinhard Clemens *(Member-Mgmt Bd-T-Systems)*
Thomas Kremer *(Member-Mgmt Bd-Data Privacy, Legal Affairs & Compliance)*
Claudia Nemat *(Member-Mgmt Bd-Europe & Tech)*
Philipp Schindera *(Sr VP-Comm)*
Supervisory Board of Directors:
Ulrich Lehner
Sari Maritta Baldauf
Wulf H. Bernotat
Hans Bernhard Beus
Monika Brandl
Lawrence H. Guffey
Klaus-Dieter Hanas
Sylvia Hauke
Lothar Holzwarth
Hans-Jurgen Kallmeier
Dagmar P. Kollmann
Petra Steffi Kreusel
Waltraud Litzenberger
Ulrich Middelmann
Lothar Schroder
Ulrich Schroder
Michael Sommer
Sibylle Spoo
Hubertus von Grunberg
Bernhard Walter

Subsidiaries:

Atrada Trading Network AG **(1)**
Hugo-Junkers-Strasse 9
D-90461 Nuremberg, Germany
Tel.: (49) 9115205100
Fax: (49) 9115205111
E-Mail: info@atrada.net
Web Site: www.atrada.net
Emp.: 30
E-Commerce Services
S.I.C.: 4899
N.A.I.C.S.: 517919
Konstantin Waldau *(CEO)*

congster GmbH **(1)**
Julius-Reiber-Strasse 37
64293 Darmstadt, Germany
Tel.: (49) 1805324444
Fax: (49) 1805221777
E-Mail: info@congster.de
Web Site: www.congster.de
Internet Services
S.I.C.: 7379
N.A.I.C.S.: 541519

DeTeMedien, Deutsche Telekom Medien GmbH **(1)**
Wiesenhuettenstr 18
60329 Frankfurt, Germany De
Tel.: (49) 6926820 (100%)
Telex: 416272
Fax: (49) 6926821101
E-Mail: info@detemedien.de
Web Site: www.detemedien.de
Emp.: 120
Publicity Production & Execution
S.I.C.: 2721
N.A.I.C.S.: 511120
Spethan Smith *(Mng Dir)*

Interactive Media CCSP GmbH **(1)**
T-Online-Allee 1
64295 Darmstadt, Germany
Mailing Address:
Postfach 10 07 43
64207 Darmstadt, Germany
Tel.: (49) 61515002100
Fax: (49) 61515002101
E-Mail: euido.sazhs@interactivemedia.net
Web Site: www.interactivemedia.net
Emp.: 150
Interactive Media Services
S.I.C.: 7379
N.A.I.C.S.: 541519
Euido Sazhs *(Mng Dir)*

STRATO AG **(1)**
Pascalstrasse 10
10587 Berlin, Germany (100%)
Tel.: (49) 3088615262
Fax: (49) 3088615260
E-Mail: presse@strato.de
Web Site: www.strato.de
Emp.: 500
Web Hosting Services
S.I.C.: 7376
N.A.I.C.S.: 541513
Christoph Steffens *(CFO)*
Rene Wienholtz *(CIO)*

T-Mobile International AG & Co. KG **(1)**
Landgrabenweg 151
53227 Bonn, Germany (100%)
Tel.: (49) 2289360
Fax: (49) 93639360
E-Mail: media@telekom.de
Web Site: www.tmobile.de
Sales Range: $25-49.9 Billion
Emp.: 44,592
Telecommunications Services
S.I.C.: 4812
N.A.I.C.S.: 517210
Hamid Akhavan *(Chm & CEO)*
Katharina Hollender *(CFO)*
Christopher Schlaefser *(CMO)*

Subsidiaries:

Scout24 GmbH **(2)**
Rosenheimer Strasse 143b
81671 Munich, Germany
Tel.: (49) 894902670
Fax: (49) 8949026711
E-Mail: webmaster@scout24.com
Web Site: www.scout24.com
Emp.: 500
Online Services
S.I.C.: 7379
N.A.I.C.S.: 541519

Subsidiaries:

Autoscout24 Deutschland GmbH **(3)**
Rosenheimer Strasse 143b
81671 Munich, Germany
Tel.: (49) 8945099060
Fax: (49) 89490267701
E-Mail: info@autoscout24.com
Web Site: www.autoscout24.de
Emp.: 200
Auto Sales Website Operator
S.I.C.: 5961
N.A.I.C.S.: 454111

ElectronicScout24 **(3)**
Rosenheimerstr 143b
81671 Munich, Germany
Tel.: (49) 89 490 26749
Web Site: www.electronicscout24.de
Online Services
S.I.C.: 7379
N.A.I.C.S.: 541519

FinanceScout24 AG **(3)**
Rosenheimerstr 143b
81671 Munich, Germany
Tel.: (49) 89189690100
Fax: (49) 89189690199
E-Mail: antje.wolter@fscout24.com
Web Site: www.financescout24.de
Emp.: 53
Online Services
S.I.C.: 7379
N.A.I.C.S.: 541519
Erret Schlossberger *(CEO)*

FriendScout24 GmbH **(3)**
Rosenheimer Strasse 143b
81671 Munich, Germany
Tel.: (49) 089490267704
Fax: (49) 089490267701
E-Mail: office-management@friendscout24.de
Web Site: www.friendscout24.de
Emp.: 60
Online Services
S.I.C.: 7379
N.A.I.C.S.: 541519
Martina Bindar *(CEO)*
Andreas Bindar *(COO)*

ImmobilienScout24 GmbH **(3)**
Andreas st 10
10243 Berlin, Germany

Tel.: (49) 30243011100
Fax: (49) 303024301
E-Mail: info@immobilienscout24.de
Web Site: www.immobilienscout24.de
Online Services
S.I.C.: 7379
N.A.I.C.S.: 541519

TravelScout24 (3)
Rosenheimer Strasse 143b
81671 Munich, Germany
Tel.: (49) 69698628574
Fax: (49) 8949026711
E-Mail: info@travelscout24.de
Web Site: www.travelscout24.de
Online Services
S.I.C.: 7379
N.A.I.C.S.: 541519

Telekom Deutschland GmbH (2)
Landgrabenweg 151
D-53227 Bonn, Germany De
Tel.: (49) 228 181 0
E-Mail: impressum@telekom.de
Web Site: www.t-mobile.de
Wireless Telecommunications Services
S.I.C.: 4812
N.A.I.C.S.: 517210
Niek Jan van Damme *(Chm-Mgmt Bd)*
Bruno Jacobfeuerborn *(CTO & Member-Mgmt Bd)*
Thomas Freude *(Member-Mgmt Bd-Technical Svcs)*
Michael Hagspihl *(Member-Mgmt Bd-Mktg)*
Dietmar Welslau *(Member-Mgmt Bd-HR)*
Dirk Wossner *(Member-Mgmt Bd-Sls)*

U.S. Subsidiary:

T-Mobile US, Inc. (2)
(Formerly MetroPCS Communications, Inc.)
12920 SE 38th St
Bellevue, WA 98006-1350 DE
Tel.: (425) 378-4000 (74%)
Fax: (425) 378-4040
E-Mail: investor.relations@t-mobile.com
Web Site: investor.t-mobile.com
TMUS—(NYSE)
Rev.: $24,420,000,000
Assets: $49,953,000,000
Liabilities: $35,708,000,000
Net Worth: $14,245,000,000
Earnings: $35,000,000
Emp.: 40,000
Fiscal Year-end: 12/31/13
Holding Company; Wireless Telecommunications Services
S.I.C.: 6719
N.A.I.C.S.: 551112
Timotheus Hottges *(Chm)*
John J. Legere *(Pres & CEO)*
J. Braxton Carter, II *(CFO & Exec VP)*
Gary A. King *(CIO)*
G. Michael Sievert *(CMO & Exec VP)*
Neville R. Ray *(CTO & Exec VP)*
Michael James Morgan *(Chief Acctg Officer & Sr VP)*
James C. Alling *(COO-T-Mobile Bus & Exec VP)*
David A. Miller *(Gen Counsel, Sec & Exec VP)*
David R. Carey *(Exec VP-Corp Svcs)*
Peter A. Ewens *(Exec VP-Corp Strategy)*
Alexander Andrew Kelton *(Exec VP-Business-to-Business)*
Thomas C. Keys *(Exec VP)*
Larry L. Myers *(Exec VP-HR)*

Subsidiaries:

MetroPCS Wireless, Inc. (3)
2250 Lakeside Blvd
Richardson, TX 75082-4304 DE
Tel.: (214) 570-5800
Fax: (214) 570-5859
Web Site: www.metropcs.com
Wireless Telecommunications Services
S.I.C.: 4812
N.A.I.C.S.: 517210
Thomas C. Keys *(COO)*

T-Mobile USA, Inc. (3)
12920 SE 38th St
Bellevue, WA 98006-1350 DE
Tel.: (425) 378-4000
Fax: (425) 378-4040
Toll Free: (800) 866-2453
E-Mail: mediarelations@t-mobile.com
Web Site: www.t-mobile.com
Wireless Telecommunications Services
S.I.C.: 4812
N.A.I.C.S.: 517210
John J. Legere *(Pres & CEO)*
James C. Alling *(COO & Exec VP)*
G. Michael Sievert *(CMO & Exec VP)*
Neville R. Ray *(CTO & Exec VP)*
David A. Miller *(Gen Counsel, Sec & Exec VP)*
Alexander Andrew Kelton *(Exec VP-Bus-to-Bus)*
Larry L. Myers *(Exec VP-HR)*
Andrew Sherrard *(Sr VP-Mktg-Contract Bus)*

Non-U.S. Subsidiaries:

T-Mobile Austria GmbH (2)
Rennweg 97 99
1030 Vienna, Austria (100%)
Tel.: (43) 1795850
Web Site: www.t-mobile.at
Emp.: 2,000
Wireless Telecommunications Services
S.I.C.: 4812
N.A.I.C.S.: 517210
Andreas Bierwirth *(CEO)*

T-Mobile Czech Republic a.s. (2)
Tomickova 2144/1
149 00 Prague, Czech Republic
Tel.: (420) 603603603
Fax: (420) 603604606
E-Mail: info@t-mobile.cz
Web Site: www.t-mobile.cz
Telecommunication Services
S.I.C.: 4812
N.A.I.C.S.: 517210
Rolad Mahler *(Chm)*

T-Mobile Netherlands BV (2)
Waldorpstraat 60
2521 CC Hague, Netherlands (100%)
Mailing Address:
PO Box 16272
2500BG Hague, Netherlands
Tel.: (31) 614095000
Fax: (31) 703055024
E-Mail: info@t-mobile.nl
Web Site: www.t-mobile.nl
Emp.: 500
Provider of Digital Wireless Communications
S.I.C.: 4812
N.A.I.C.S.: 517210
Reinoud Meijerman *(Mgr-Direct & Indirect Sls)*

T-Online International AG (1)
T Online Allee 1
64295 Darmstadt, Germany (100%)
Mailing Address:
PO Box 10 11 52
64221 Darmstadt, Germany
Tel.: (49) 61516800
Fax: (49) 61516802219
E-Mail: hotline@t-online.de
Web Site: www.t-online.com
Emp.: 3,000
Internet Service Provider
S.I.C.: 4899
N.A.I.C.S.: 517919

Joint Venture:

Bild.T-Online.de AG & Co. KG (2)
Axel-Springer-Strasse 65
10888 Berlin, Germany
Tel.: (49) 30259179000
Fax: (49) 30259179006
E-Mail: info@bild.t-online.de
Web Site: www.bild.t-online.de
Online Investment Services; Owned by Axel Springer Verlag AG & Deutsche Telekom AG
S.I.C.: 7379
N.A.I.C.S.: 541519

T-Systems Enterprise Services GmbH (1)
Hahnstrasse 43
60528 Frankfurt, Germany (100%)
Tel.: (49) 69665310
Fax: (49) 6966531499
E-Mail: info@t-systems.com
Web Site: www.t-systems.com
Emp.: 4,000
Digital Wireless Communications
S.I.C.: 4812
N.A.I.C.S.: 517210
Clemens Reinhard *(CEO)*

Subsidiaries:

T-Systems Business Services (2)
Mainzer Landstrasse 50
60325 Frankfurt, Germany
Tel.: (49) 69665310
Fax: (49) 6966531499
E-Mail: info@t-systems.com
Web Site: www.t-systems.com
Emp.: 1,000
Digital Wireless Communication Services
S.I.C.: 4812
N.A.I.C.S.: 517210
Reinhart Clemens *(CEO)*

Subsidiary:

gedas AG (3)
Dernburgstrasse 44 50 54
14057 Berlin, Germany
Tel.: (49) 30303920
Web Site: www.t-systems.de
Sales Range: $750-799.9 Million
Emp.: 5,504
Information Technology Service Provider
S.I.C.: 7373
N.A.I.C.S.: 541512

U.S. Subsidiary:

T-Systems North America Inc. (4)
755 W Big Beaver Rd Ste 1700
Troy, MI 48084
Tel.: (630) 493-6100
Fax: (248) 754-3065
Toll Free: (866) 704-3327
Web Site: www.t-systemsus.com
Emp.: 302
Information Technology Service Provider
S.I.C.: 7373
N.A.I.C.S.: 541512
Heike Auerbach *(Mng Dir)*
David Andrews *(Member-Mgmt Bd & VP-ICT Ops)*

Non-U.S. Subsidiaries:

gedas Argentina, S.A. (4)
Delcasse Y Av Henry Ford
PO Box B1610BKK
Gral Pacheco, Buenos Aires, B1610, Argentina
Tel.: (54) 43179555
Fax: (54) 43179554
E-Mail: info@gedas.com.ar
Web Site: www.gedas.com.ar
Emp.: 260
Information Technology Service Provider
S.I.C.: 7373
N.A.I.C.S.: 541512

gedas CR s.r.o. (4)
TGM 840
293 01 Mlada Boleslav, Czech Republic
Tel.: (420) 326711411
Fax: (420) 326711420
E-Mail: info@gedas.cz
Web Site: www.gedas.cz
Sls.: $8,788,111
Emp.: 140
Information Technology Service Provider
S.I.C.: 7373
N.A.I.C.S.: 541512

gedas Mexico, S.A. de C.V. (4)
Km 117 Autopista Mexico Puebla Parque Indus
Finsa Nave 1, CP 72710 Puebla, Mexico
Tel.: (52) 2222234000
Fax: (52) 222 223 4018
Web Site: www.gedas.com.mx
Emp.: 613
Information Technology Service Provider
S.I.C.: 7373
N.A.I.C.S.: 541512

gedas (Shanghai) Information Technology Co., Ltd. (4)
Units 2701 2703 Financial Square 333 Jiujiang Road
Huangpu District, Shanghai, China
Tel.: (86) 2161339000
Fax: (86) 2161339001
Web Site: www.t-systems.com
Emp.: 30
Information Technology Service
S.I.C.: 7373
N.A.I.C.S.: 541512

gedas United Kingdom Ltd. (4)
Futura House
Bradbourne Drive
Tilbrook, Milton Keynes, Buckinghamshire, MK7 8AZ, United Kingdom
Tel.: (44) 364656
Fax: (44) 8701212751
E-Mail: info@gedas.co.uk
Web Site: www.gedas.co.uk
Emp.: 309
Information Technology Service
S.I.C.: 7373
N.A.I.C.S.: 541512
Anthony Feeney *(Mng Dir)*

T-Systems (4)
18 Place des Nympheas
BP 55341
Immeuble Le Tropical, 95941 Villepinte, Roissy Ch De Gaulle, France
Tel.: (33) 149908600
Fax: (33) 149908606
Web Site: www.t-systems.fr
Emp.: 500
Information Technology Services
S.I.C.: 7373
N.A.I.C.S.: 541512
Werner Rolf *(Pres)*

T-Systems debis Systemhaus (2)
Dachauer Str 651
80995 Munich, Germany (100%)
Tel.: (49) 8910110
Fax: (49) 8910116176
E-Mail: rh-muenchen-empfang@telekom.de
Web Site: www.t-systems.telekom.de
Rev.: $79,704,384
Emp.: 5
Software Services
S.I.C.: 3652
N.A.I.C.S.: 334614
Bolbeth Andrea *(Gen Mgr)*

U.S. Subsidiary:

T-Systems North America Inc. (2)
1901 Butterfield Rd Ste 700
Downers Grove, IL 60515
Tel.: (630) 493-6100
Fax: (630) 493-6111
E-Mail: info@t-systemsus.com
Web Site: www.t-systemsus.com
Emp.: 350
Communication Technology Solutions
S.I.C.: 4899
N.A.I.C.S.: 517919
Heike Auerbach *(Mng Dir & Member-Mgmt Bd)*
Joachim Langmack *(Chief Sls Officer)*
Jeff Siansky *(Chief Sls & Svc Officer)*
Jordan Kanfer *(VP, Gen Counsel-HR & Member-Mgmt Board)*
Arrie Redelinghuys *(VP-ICT Ops & Member-Mgmt Bd)*

Non-U.S. Subsidiaries:

T-Systems Austria Ges.m.b.H (2)
Rennweg 97-99
1030 Vienna, Austria
Tel.: (43) 570570
Fax: (43) 57057954390
E-Mail: info@t-systems.at
Web Site: www.t-systems.at
Emp.: 647
Telecommunication Services
S.I.C.: 4899
N.A.I.C.S.: 517919
Martin Katzer *(Mng Dir)*

T-Systems Belgium S.A. (2)
't Hofveld 8
1702 Groot-Bijgaarden, Belgium
Tel.: (32) 23009111
Fax: (32) 23009112
E-Mail: admin@t-systems.be
Web Site: www.t-systems.be
Emp.: 75
Communications Technology Solutions
S.I.C.: 4899
N.A.I.C.S.: 517919
Jerry Boezel *(Mng Dir)*

T-Systems China Ltd. (2)
50/F Ste 5008
Central Plz 18 Harbour Rd, Wanchai, China (Hong Kong)
Tel.: (852) 25935300
Fax: (852) 25935397
Web Site: www.t-systems.cn

Deutsche Telekom AG—(Continued)

Emp.: 30
Communication Technology Solutions
S.I.C.: 4899
N.A.I.C.S.: 517919

T-Systems Czech s.r.o. (2)
Kloboucnicka 1435/24
140 00 Prague, Czech Republic
Tel.: (420) 236099444
Fax: (420) 236099999
E-Mail: peter.angelovit@t-systems.co.z
Web Site: www.t-systems.com
Emp.: 670
Communication Technology Solutions
S.I.C.: 4899
N.A.I.C.S.: 517919
Peter Angelovit *(Mgr-HR)*

T-Systems Danmark AS (2)
Lautrupvang 8
3520 Ballerup, Denmark
Tel.: (45) 70122626
Fax: (45) 70122625
E-Mail: t-systems@t-systems.dk
Web Site: www.t-systems.dk
Emp.: 150
Communication Technology Solutions
S.I.C.: 4899
N.A.I.C.S.: 517919
Jens Tiedemann *(Mng Dir)*

T-Systems do Brasil Ltda. (2)
Rua Olimpiadas 205 Vila Olimpia
04551-000 Sao Paulo, SP, Brazil
Tel.: (55) 1121842544
Fax: (55) 1121842919
E-Mail: t-systems@t-systems.com.br
Web Site: www.t-systems.com.br
Emp.: 2,300
Communication Technology Solutions
S.I.C.: 4899
N.A.I.C.S.: 517919
Ideval Munhoz *(Mng Dir)*

T-Systems Hungary Kft. (2)
Krisztina Krt 55
1013 Budapest, Hungary
Tel.: (36) 14587000
Fax: (36) 14587177
E-Mail: info@t-systems.hu
Web Site: www.t-systems.com
Emp.: 200
Communication Technology Solutions
S.I.C.: 4899
N.A.I.C.S.: 517919
Chrestopher Mattheisem *(Mng Dir)*

T-Systems Italia S.p.A. (2)
Strada 2 Palazzo D3
20090 Assago, MI, Italy
Tel.: (39) 0289241
Fax: (39) 0444559352
E-Mail: info@t-systems.com
Web Site: www.t-systems.it
Communication Technology Solutions
S.I.C.: 4899
N.A.I.C.S.: 517919

T-Systems Japan K.K. (2)
Bancho House 29-1 Ichibancho
Chiyoda-ku, Tokyo, 102-0082, Japan
Tel.: (81) 352130080
Fax: (81) 0352767637
E-Mail: info@t-systems.com
Web Site: www.t-systems.jp
Communication Technology Solutions
S.I.C.: 4899
N.A.I.C.S.: 517919

T-Systems Ltd. (2)
21st Floor Euston Tower 286 Euston Road
London, NW1 3DP, United Kingdom
Tel.: (44) 2071213900
Fax: (44) 2071213950
E-Mail: ukwebsite.enquiry@t-systems.co.uk
Web Site: www.t-systems.co.uk
Communications Technology Solutions
S.I.C.: 4899
N.A.I.C.S.: 517919
Sam Kingston *(Mng Dir)*

T-Systems Luxemburg S.A. (2)
117 Route d'Arlon
8009 Strassen, Luxembourg
Tel.: (352) 26119121
Fax: (352) 26402817
E-Mail: info@t-systems.lu
Web Site: www.t-systems.lu

Emp.: 8
Communication Technology Solutions
S.I.C.: 4899
N.A.I.C.S.: 517919
Ralf Beyer *(Mng Dir)*

T-Systems Nederland B.V. (2)
Lage Biezenweg 3
4131 LV Vianen, Netherlands
Mailing Address:
Postbus 65
4131 LV Vianen, Netherlands
Tel.: (31) 347327327
Fax: (31) 347327100
E-Mail: info@t-systems.com
Web Site: www.t-systems.nl
Emp.: 250
Communication Technology Services
S.I.C.: 4899
N.A.I.C.S.: 517919
Jerry Boezel *(Dir-Sls)*

T-Systems Polska Sp. z o.o. (2)
Ul Sw Antoniego 7
50-073 Wroclaw, Poland
Tel.: (48) 713751224
Fax: (48) 713751111
E-Mail: marketing@t-systems.com.pl
Web Site: www.t-systems.pl
Emp.: 100
Communication Technology Solutions
S.I.C.: 4899
N.A.I.C.S.: 517919

T-Systems Singapore Pte. Ltd. (2)
8 Shenton Way 10-01
Singapore, 068811, Singapore
Tel.: (65) 63170700
Fax: (65) 63170707
E-Mail: info@t-systems.com
Web Site: www.t-systems.com.sg
Emp.: 190
Communication Technology Solutions
S.I.C.: 4899
N.A.I.C.S.: 517919
Thomas Jakob *(CEO)*

T-Systems South Africa (Pty) Ltd. (2)
International Business Gateway
PO Box 2496
1685 Gauteng, South Africa
Tel.: (27) 112547400
Fax: (27) 113183458
E-Mail: communications@t-systems.co.za
Web Site: www.t-systems.co.za
Emp.: 300
Communication Technology Solutions
S.I.C.: 4899
N.A.I.C.S.: 517919
Mardia van der Walt Korsten *(CEO, Mng Dir & VP-Corp Customers)*

T-Systems Switzerland Ltd. (2)
Industriestrasse 21
3052 Zollikofen, Switzerland
Tel.: (41) 848112211
Fax: (41) 848112212
E-Mail: contact@t-systems.com
Web Site: www.t-systems.ch
Emp.: 600
Communication Technology Solutions
S.I.C.: 4899
N.A.I.C.S.: 517919
Klatt Pierre *(CEO)*

T-Venture Holding GmbH (1)
Gotenstrasse 156
53175 Bonn, Germany
Tel.: (49) 228308480
Fax: (49) 228308480
E-Mail: t-venture@telekom.de
Web Site: www.t-venture.de
Emp.: 25
Venture Capital Services
S.I.C.: 6211
N.A.I.C.S.: 523999
Patrick Meisberger *(CEO & Mng Dir)*

U.S. Subsidiary:

T-Venture of America, Inc. (2)
Metro Tower Ctr 950 Tower Ln Ste 1600
Foster City, CA 94404
Tel.: (650) 358-2011
Fax: (650) 292-8353
Web Site: www.t-venture.de/en/Contact/USA/index.html
Venture Capital Services
S.I.C.: 6211

N.A.I.C.S.: 523999
Sebastian Blum *(Mgr)*

Non-U.S. Subsidiaries:

Deutsche Telecom AG (1)
Ul Metschnikow 3
01023 Kiev, Ukraine (100%)
Tel.: (380) 442302669
Fax: (380) 442272434
Web Site: www.telekom.com
Provider of Digital Wireless Communications
S.I.C.: 4812
N.A.I.C.S.: 517210

Deutsche Telekom France (1)
30 Rue Galilee
75116 Paris, France (100%)
Tel.: (33) 00144430000
Fax: (33) 144430010
E-Mail: info@telekom.de
Web Site: www.telekom.de
Emp.: 20
Provider of Digital Wireless Communications
S.I.C.: 4812
N.A.I.C.S.: 517210
Nikolai Beckers *(Pres)*

Deutsche Telekom (1)
Av Des Arts House No 53
1000 Brussels, Belgium (100%)
Tel.: (32) 27750500
Fax: (32) 27750509
Web Site: www.telekom.de
Emp.: 5
Provider of Digital Wireless Communications
S.I.C.: 4812
N.A.I.C.S.: 517210
Joachim Hoenig *(Mng Dir)*

Hrvatski Telekom d.d. (1)
Savska cesta 32
10 000 Zagreb, Croatia HR
Tel.: (385) 14911000 (51%)
Fax: (385) 14911011
E-Mail: info@t.ht.hr
Web Site: www.t.ht.hr
THTC—(LSE)
Rev.: $1,325,005,760
Assets: $2,330,311,230
Liabilities: $393,449,940
Net Worth: $1,936,861,290
Earnings: $301,396,160
Emp.: 5,780
Fiscal Year-end: 12/31/12
Telecommunication Services
S.I.C.: 4899
N.A.I.C.S.: 517919
Mark Klein *(Chm-Supervisory Bd)*
Ivica Mudrinic *(Chm-Mgmt Bd & CEO)*
Ivica Misetic *(Vice Chm-Supervisory Bd)*
Dino Dogan *(CFO & Member-Mgmt Bd)*
Norbert Hentges *(COO & Member-Mgmt Bd)*
Bozidar Poldrugac *(CTO, CIO & Member-Mgmt Bd)*
Irena Jolic Simovic *(Chief HR Officer & Member-Mgmt Bd)*
Jens Hartmann *(Member-Mgmt Bd & COO-Bus)*
Natasa Rapaic *(Member-Mgmt Bd & COO-Residential)*

MagyarCom Holding GmbH (1)
Krisztina Krt 55
Budapest, 1013, Hungary (100%)
Tel.: (36) 228 181 0
Holding Company
S.I.C.: 6719
N.A.I.C.S.: 551112

Subsidiary:

Magyar Telekom Telecommunications plc (2)
Krisztina Krt 55
1013 Budapest, Hungary HU
Tel.: (36) 1457 4000 (59.21%)
Fax: (36) 1 458 7105
E-Mail: info@matav.hu
Web Site: www.telekom.hu
MTELEKOM—(BUD OTC)
Rev.: $2,744,218,560
Assets: $4,781,454,880
Liabilities: $2,421,639,720
Net Worth: $2,359,815,160

Earnings: $207,264,600
Emp.: 11,653
Fiscal Year-end: 12/31/12
Telecommunication Services
S.I.C.: 4812
N.A.I.C.S.: 517210
Christopher Mattheisen *(Chm & CEO)*
Laszlo Pap *(Chm-Supervisory Bd)*
Janos Szabo *(CFO)*
Walter Goldenits *(CTO & Chief IT Officer)*
Balazs Mathe *(Chief Legal Officer & Chief Corp Affairs Officer)*
Eva Somorjai *(Chief HR Officer)*
Peter Lakatos *(Chief Comml Officer-SMB)*
Robert Budafoki *(Chief Comml Officer-Enterprise)*
Attila Keszeg *(Chief Comml Officer-Residential)*
Robert Pataki *(Chief Bus Dev Officer)*

Non-U.S. Affiliates:

Asiacom Philippines, Inc. (1)
Makati, Manila, Philippines (49.88%)
Provider of Digital Wireless Communications
S.I.C.: 4812
N.A.I.C.S.: 517210

Isla Communications Co., Inc. (1)
12/F Trafalgar Plaza H.V. dela Costa
Makati, Manila, Philippines (10.42%)
Tel.: (63) 6328140332
S.I.C.: 1731
N.A.I.C.S.: 238210

PT Satelit Palapa Indonesia Satelindo (1)
J Daan Mogot Km 11
Jakarta, Jakarta Barat, 11710, Indonesia (25%)
Tel.: (62) 215451745
Fax: (62) 215451748
Web Site: www.satelindo.co.id
Sales Range: Less than $1 Million
Emp.: 50
Telecommunications & Satellite Svcs
S.I.C.: 4899
N.A.I.C.S.: 517410

Non-U.S. Joint Venture:

Everything Everywhere Limited (1)
Hatfield Business Park
Hatfield, AL10 9BW, United Kingdom
Tel.: (44) 1707 315 000
Web Site: www.explore.ee.co.uk
Sales Range: $5-14.9 Billion
Emp.: 16,500
Wireless Telecommunications Services
S.I.C.: 4812
N.A.I.C.S.: 517210
Timotheus Hottges *(Chm)*
Olaf Swantee *(CEO)*
Neal Milsom *(CFO)*
Pippa Dunn *(CMO-Consumer)*
Gerry McQuade *(CMO-Non-Consumer Mobile)*
Steven Day *(Chief Brand & Comm Officer)*
Marc Allera *(Chief Sls Officer)*
Fotis Karonis *(CTO)*
Francoise Clemes *(Chief HR Officer)*
Ralf Brandmeier *(Chief Performance Officer)*
Stephen Harris *(Chief of Staff)*
Jackie O'Leary *(Chief Customer Officer)*

Subsidiaries:

Orange Plc (2)
50-52 George Street
London, W1U 7DZ, United Kingdom
Tel.: (44) 8703768888
Fax: (44) 8703731601
Web Site: www.orange.co.uk
Mobile Communications Services
S.I.C.: 4812
N.A.I.C.S.: 517210
Martin Stiven *(VP-Bus)*

Subsidiary:

Orange 3G Ltd (3)
St James Court Great Park Road
Bristol, BS32 4QJ, United Kingdom
Tel.: (44) 8703 768888
Fax: (44) 1454618501
Telecommunication Services
S.I.C.: 4899
N.A.I.C.S.: 517919

T-Mobile Limited (2)
Hatfield Business Park
Hatfield, Herts, AL109BW, United Kingdom UK
Tel.: (44) 1707315000
Fax: (44) 1707319001
E-Mail:
Web Site: www.t-mobile.co.uk
Emp.: 6,100
Telecommunications Services
S.I.C.: 4812
N.A.I.C.S.: 517210

DEUTSCHE TRANSPORT-COMPAGNIE ERICH BOGDAN GMBH & CO. KG

Donaustr 126
90451 Nuremberg, Germany
Tel.: (49) 91199620
Fax: (49) 9119962309
E-Mail: info@dtc.de
Web Site: www.dtc.de
Year Founded: 1946
Rev.: $49,007,323
Emp.: 270

Business Description:
Logistics Services
S.I.C.: 4522
N.A.I.C.S.: 481212

Personnel:
Manfred Heuer *(Co-Mng Dir)*
Roland Kuhn *(Co-Mng Dir)*

DEUTSCHE WOHNEN AG

Pfaffenwiese 300
65929 Frankfurt am Main, Germany
Tel.: (49) 69 976 970 0
Fax: (49) 69 976 970 4980
E-Mail: ir@deutsche-wohnen.com
Web Site: www.deutsche-wohnen.com
Year Founded: 1998
DWNI—(DEU)
Rev.: $323,153,493
Assets: $6,606,745,242
Liabilities: $4,439,855,778
Net Worth: $2,166,889,464
Earnings: $195,885,235
Emp.: 1,417
Fiscal Year-end: 12/31/12

Business Description:
Holding Company; Property Management
S.I.C.: 6719
N.A.I.C.S.: 551112

Personnel:
Uwe E. Flach *(Chm-Supervisory Bd)*
Andreas Kretschmer *(Deputy Chm-Supervisory Bd)*
Michael Zahn *(CEO & Member-Mgmt Bd)*
Lars Wittan *(CFO & Member-Mgmt Bd)*

Supervisory Board of Directors:
Uwe E. Flach
Wolfgang Clement
Matthias Hunlein
Andreas Kretschmer
Michael Leinwand
Florian Stetter

Subsidiaries:

Deutsche Wohnen Management GmbH (1)
Mecklenburgische Strasse 57
14197 Berlin, Germany
Tel.: (49) 30897860
Fax: (49) 3089786100
E-Mail: info@deutsche-wohnen.com
Web Site: www.deutsche-wohnen.com
Emp.: 226
Residential Properties Management & Development
S.I.C.: 6531
N.A.I.C.S.: 531311
Tanja Bentin *(Mng Dir)*
Lars Dormeyer *(Mng Dir)*
Kathrin Wolff *(Mng Dir)*

KATHARINENHOF Seniorehwohn- und Pflegeanlage Betriebs-GmbH (1)
Mecklenburgische Strasse 57
14197 Berlin, Germany
Tel.: (49) 30 847 151 902
Fax: (49) 30 847 151 990
E-Mail: info@katharinenhof.net
Web Site: www.katharinenhof.net
Nursing & Residential Care Homes Management
S.I.C.: 8051
N.A.I.C.S.: 623110
Gerald Klinck *(Mng Dir)*
Jochen Schellenberg *(Mng Dir)*

DEUTSCHER SPARKASSEN- UND GIROVERBAND E.V.

Charlottenstrasse 47
10117 Berlin, Germany
Tel.: (49) 30202250
Fax: (49) 3020225250
E-Mail: info@dsgv.de
Web Site: www.dsgv.de
Emp.: 150

Business Description:
Bank Holding Company
S.I.C.: 6712
N.A.I.C.S.: 551111

Personnel:
Heinrich Haasis *(Chm & Pres)*
Roland Schafer *(VP & Fourth Deputy Chm-Mgmt Bd)*

Subsidiary:

Landesbank Berlin Holding AG (1)
Alexanderplatz 2
D 10178 Berlin, Germany De
Mailing Address:
PO Box 110801
D 10838 Berlin Berlin, Germany
Tel.: (49) 30869801
Fax: (49) 3086983074
E-Mail: information@lbb.de
Web Site: www.lbb-holding.de
Int. Income: $5,069,676,220
Assets: $159,249,218,660
Liabilities: $155,637,444,550
Net Worth: $3,611,774,110
Earnings: $133,270,830
Emp.: 5,802
Fiscal Year-end: 12/31/12
Bank Holding Company
S.I.C.: 6712
N.A.I.C.S.: 551111
Georg Fahrenschon *(Chm-Supervisory Bd)*
Johannes Evers *(Chm-Mgmt Bd)*
Barbel Wulff *(Deputy Chm-Supervisory Bd)*
Martin K. Muller *(Member-Mgmt Bd)*

Subsidiaries:

Landesbank Berlin AG (2)
Alexanderplatz 2
Berlin, 10178, Germany
Tel.: (49) 30245 500
Fax: (49) 30245 69 50200
E-Mail: information@lbb.de
Web Site: www.lbb.de
Emp.: 5,000
Banking Services
S.I.C.: 6159
N.A.I.C.S.: 522298
Johannes Evers *(Chm-Mgmt Bd)*

Subsidiaries:

BankenService GmbH (3)
Brunnenstrasse 111
13355 Berlin, Germany
Tel.: (49) 3024557301
Fax: (49) 302456941350
E-Mail: kundenbetreuung@bankenservice.de
Web Site: www.bankenservice.de
Emp.: 800
Banking
S.I.C.: 6029
N.A.I.C.S.: 522110
Martin K. Muller *(Chm-Supervisory Bd)*
Stefan Haemmerling *(Chm-Mgmt Bd)*
Ronald Berentin *(Member-Mgmt Bd)*
Sandro Schurig *(Member-Mgmt Bd)*

Berlin-Hannoversche Hypothekenbank Aktiengesellschaft (3)
Budapester Strasse 1
D 10787 Berlin, Germany (90.4%)
Tel.: (49) 30259990
Fax: (49) 3025999131
E-Mail: ywvonne.sterkopf@berlinhyp.de
Web Site: www.berlinhyp.de
Int. Income: $1,154,039,253
Assets: $46,045,514,135
Liabilities: $44,926,977,232
Net Worth: $1,118,536,903
Earnings: $2,927,910
Emp.: 402
Fiscal Year-end: 12/31/12
Real Estate Financing Bank
S.I.C.: 6159
N.A.I.C.S.: 522292
Jan Bettink *(Chm-Supervisory Bd)*
Johannes Evers *(Deputy Chm-Supervisory Bd)*
Rene Wulff *(Deputy Chm-Supervisory Bd)*
Gero Bergmann *(Member-Mgmt Bd)*
Roman Berninger *(Member-Mgmt Bd)*
Bernd Morgenschweis *(Member-Mgmt Bd)*

Subsidiaries:

Berlin Hyp (4)
Landschaftstrasse 2
30159 Hannover, Germany
Tel.: (49) 5113011233
Fax: (49) 511301115233
Web Site: www.berlinhyp.de
Emp.: 334
Banking Services
S.I.C.: 6159
N.A.I.C.S.: 522298

Berliner Immobilien Holding GmbH (4)
Hallesches Ufer 74 76
10963 Berlin, Germany
Tel.: (49) 30254411900
Fax: (49) 30254411662
E-Mail: info@bih-holding.de
Web Site: www.bih-holding.de
Emp.: 460
Real Estate Management Services
S.I.C.: 6531
N.A.I.C.S.: 531390
Werner Furnkranz *(Member-Mgmt Bd)*

Non-U.S. Subsidiaries:

Berlin Hyp (4)
1 Crown Court 66 Cheapside
London, EC2V 6LR, United Kingdom
Tel.: (44) 2075726493
Fax: (44) 2075726219
Web Site: www.lbb.de
Emp.: 200
S.I.C.: 6159
N.A.I.C.S.: 522298
T. Revers *(Mng Dir)*

Berlin Hyp (4)
ul Widok 8
00 023 Warsaw, Poland
Tel.: (48) 226906566
Fax: (48) 2266906569
Web Site: www.berlinhyp.de
Emp.: 3
Commercial Banking Services
S.I.C.: 6159
N.A.I.C.S.: 522298
Popko Radoslaw *(Pres)*

Landesbank Berlin Investment GmbH (2)
Kurfurstendamm 201
PO Box 110809
10719 Berlin, Germany
Tel.: (49) 3024564500
Fax: (49) 3024564650
E-Mail: direct@lbb-invest.de
Web Site: www.lbb-invest.de
Emp.: 100
Banking Services
S.I.C.: 6159
N.A.I.C.S.: 522298
Serge Demoliere *(Chm-Supervisory Bd)*
Joachim F. Madler *(Chm-Mgmt Bd)*
Dyrk Vieten *(Member-Mgmt Bd)*

DEUTZ AG

Ottostr 1
Koln-Porz, 51149 Cologne, Germany
Tel.: (49) 2218220
Fax: (49) 2218225850
E-Mail: info@deutz.com
Web Site: www.deutz.com
Year Founded: 1864
DEZ—(DEU)
Rev.: $1,739,117,023
Assets: $1,381,708,888
Liabilities: $735,412,671
Net Worth: $646,296,217
Earnings: $28,269,570
Emp.: 3,991
Fiscal Year-end: 12/31/12

Business Description:
Diesel Engine Mfr
Import Export
S.I.C.: 3714
N.A.I.C.S.: 336310

Personnel:
Lars-Goran Moberg *(Chm-Supervisory Bd)*
Helmut Leube *(Chm-Mgmt Bd-Market, Technical & Central Functions)*
Werner Scherer *(Vice Chm-Supervisory Bd)*
Margarete Haase *(Member-Mgmt Bd-Fin, HR & IR)*
Michael Wellenzohn *(Member-Mgmt Bd-Sls, Svc & Mktg)*
Christian Krupp *(Sr VP-Corp Fin & IR)*

Supervisory Board of Directors:
Lars-Goran Moberg
Lodovico Bussolati
Francesco Carozza
Sofia Frandberg
Michael Haupt
Torbjorn Holmstrom
Helmut Lerchner
Michael Lichtenauer
Caterina Messina
Karl-Heinz Muller
Witich Rossmann
Werner Scherer
Herbert Vossel
Egbert Zieher

Subsidiaries:

DEUTZ Beteiligung GmbH (1)
Ottostr 1
51149 Cologne, Nordrhein-Westfalen, Germany
Tel.: (49) 221 8220
Fax: (49) 221 8225 850
E-Mail: info@deutz.com
Web Site: www.deutz.com
Emp.: 4,000
Automobile Engine Mfr
S.I.C.: 3519
N.A.I.C.S.: 333618
Helmut Leube *(Mng Dir)*

DEUTZ SICHERHEIT Gesellschaft fur Industrieservice mbH (1)
Wiersbergstrasse 43
51103 Cologne, Nordrhein-Westfalen, Germany
Tel.: (49) 2218226744
Fax: (49) 2218226848
E-Mail: deutz-sicherheit@deutz.com
Web Site: www.deutz-sicherheit.com
Safety Consulting Services
S.I.C.: 8999
N.A.I.C.S.: 541690
Margarete Haase *(Gen Mgr)*

HGS Henkelhausen G.A.S. Service GmbH & Co. KG (1)
Hafenstrasse 51
47809 Krefeld, Germany (99.7%)
Tel.: (49) 21515255600
Fax: (49) 21515255590
E-Mail: anfrage@hgspartner.de
Web Site: www.hgspartner.de
Sales Range: $25-49.9 Million
Emp.: 17
Construction & Building Services
S.I.C.: 7349
N.A.I.C.S.: 561790

DEUTZ AG—(Continued)

Unterstutzungsgesellschaft mbH der Deutz Aktiengesellschaft (1)
Wiersbergstrasse 01
Cologne, Nordrhein-Westfalen, 51149, Germany
Tel.: (49) 2218226744
Fax: (49) 221822156702
E-Mail: deutz-sicherheit@deutz.com
Industrial Fire Safety & Maintenance Services
S.I.C.: 7389
N.A.I.C.S.: 561990
Werner Becker *(Member-Mgmt Bd)*

U.S. Subsidiaries:

DEUTZ Corporation (1)
3883 Steve Reynolds Blvd
Norcross, GA 30093-3051
Tel.: (770) 564-7100
Fax: (770) 564-7272
E-Mail: engines@deutzusa.com
Web Site: www.deutzusa.com
Sales Range: $125-149.9 Million
Emp.: 100
Air Cooled Diesel Engines & Spare Parts Distr
S.I.C.: 5084
N.A.I.C.S.: 423830
Alex Croxton *(Product Dir-IT Ops & Dev)*

Non-U.S. Subsidiaries:

Deutz Asia-Pacific (Pte) Ltd. (1)
11 Kian Teck Road
Singapore, 628768, Singapore
Tel.: (65) 626 853 11
Fax: (65) 626 417 79
Web Site: www.deutzasia.com.sg
Diesel Engine Sales & Services
S.I.C.: 5088
N.A.I.C.S.: 423860

DEUTZ DITER S.A. (1)
Carretera Badajoz Granada Km 74 6 Zafra
06300 Badajoz, Spain
Tel.: (34) 924565100
Fax: (34) 924 56 5131
Web Site: www.deutzditer.com
Components Machining & Assembling Services
S.I.C.: 7389
N.A.I.C.S.: 561990
Alejandro Castilla *(Mgr)*

DEUTZ FRANCE S.A. (1)
115 Rue du Fosse Blanc
92230 Gennevilliers, Hauts-de-Seine, France
Tel.: (33) 146138787
Fax: (33) 1 46 13 87 67
Web Site: www.deutz.fr
Emp.: 40
Diesel Engines Maintenance & Sales
S.I.C.: 7539
N.A.I.C.S.: 811198
A. Reiter *(Pres & Gen Dir)*

DEUTZ UK Ltd. (1)
Deutz House Willow Park Burdock Close
Cannock, Staffordshire, WS11 7FQ, United Kingdom
Tel.: (44) 1543 438 9
Fax: (44) 1543 438 9
E-Mail: info@deutzuk.com
Web Site: www.deutzuk.com
Emp.: 75
Diesel Engines Mfr
S.I.C.: 3519
N.A.I.C.S.: 333618
Mike Nugent *(Gen Mgr)*

Nouvelle Societe MAGIDEUTZ S.A. (1)
Rue Sergent Khalich Mohamed 6
BP 13024
20300 Casablanca, Morocco
Tel.: (212) 5 22 30 3023
Fax: (212) 5 22 30 39 61
E-Mail: magid@menara.ma
Web Site: www.deutz.ma
Emp.: 48
Diesel Engine Sales & Maintenance Services
S.I.C.: 5084
N.A.I.C.S.: 423830
Andreas Reiter *(Pres)*
Bernd Breves *(Dir Gen)*

DEV INFORMATION TECHNOLOGY PVT. LTD.

14 Aaryans Corporate Park
Thaltej Shilaj Road, 380059
Ahmedabad, Gujarat, India
Tel.: (91) 79 26304241
Web Site: www.devitpl.com
Year Founded: 1997

Business Description:
IT Services
S.I.C.: 7389
N.A.I.C.S.: 519190

Personnel:
Jaimin Shah *(Mng Dir)*

Non-U.S. Subsidiary:

DRS Technologies Canada Ltd. (1)
115 Emily St
Carleton Place, ON, K7C 4J5, Canada ON
Tel.: (613) 253-3020
Fax: (613) 253-3033
E-Mail: info@drs.com
Web Site: www.drs.com
Emp.: 355
Provider of Flight Safety Systems for Military & Commercial Aircraft; Crash Locator Beacons & Shipboard Communications Systems
S.I.C.: 3812
N.A.I.C.S.: 334511
David W. Stapley *(Pres)*

DEVCORP CAPITAL INC.

1200 700 2nd Street SW
Calgary, AB, T2P 4V5, Canada
Tel.: (403) 292-9812
Fax: (403) 695-3522
E-Mail: greg.peterson@gowlings.com
Year Founded: 2011
DCC.P—(TSXV)

Business Description:
Investment Services
S.I.C.: 6211
N.A.I.C.S.: 523999

Personnel:
Sidney Dutchak *(Pres, CEO & CFO)*
Frank Sur *(Sec)*

Board of Directors:
Chris Doll
Sidney Dutchak
Greg Fisher
Robert Jepson
Michael Kohut
Sean Monaghan
Gregory Peterson
James Riddell

Transfer Agent:
Olympia Trust Company
Calgary, AB, Canada

DEVELCON

155 Champagne Dr Ste 7
Toronto, ON, Canada
Tel.: (416) 385-1390
Fax: (416) 385-1610
E-Mail: info@develcon.com
Web Site: www.develcon.com
Year Founded: 1974
Rev.: $18,713,958
Emp.: 130

Business Description:
Wireless Products Supplier
S.I.C.: 4812
N.A.I.C.S.: 517210

Personnel:
Geoffrey Bennett *(Pres)*

DEVELICA DEUTSCHLAND LIMITED

1st Floor Royal Chambers Saint Julian's Avenue
PO Box 650
Saint Peter Port, GY1 3JX, Guernsey
Tel.: (44) 1481715601
Fax: (44) 1481715602
E-Mail: info@develica.com
Web Site: www.develicadeutschland.com
Sales Range: $100-124.9 Million

Business Description:
Investment Services
S.I.C.: 6799
N.A.I.C.S.: 523920

Personnel:
Derek Butler *(Chm)*

Board of Directors:
Derek Butler
John Hallam
Peter Le Cheminant
Quentin Spicer

Legal Counsel:
Stephenson Harwood
One St. Paul's Churchyard
London, EC4M 85H, United Kingdom
Tel.: (44) 81 329 4422

Mourant Ozannes
Saint Peter Port, Guernsey

K&L Gates LLP
Markgrafenstrasse 42
Berlin, Germany

DEVELOPMENT BANK OF JAPAN, INC.

South Tower Otemachi Financial City
9-6 Otemachi 1-chome
Chiyoda-ku, Tokyo, 100-8178, Japan
Tel.: (81) 3 3270 3211
Fax: (81) 3 3271 8472
Web Site: www.dbj.jp
Year Founded: 1999
Rev.: $3,752,199,000
Assets: $178,735,832,000
Liabilities: $150,811,496,000
Net Worth: $27,924,336,000
Earnings: $784,707,000
Emp.: 1,168
Fiscal Year-end: 03/31/13

Business Description:
International Banking Services
S.I.C.: 6159
N.A.I.C.S.: 522293

Personnel:
Toru Hashimoto *(Pres & CEO)*
Hideto Fujii *(Deputy Pres)*
Masanori Yanagi *(Deputy Pres)*
Masafumi Aizawa *(Exec Officer-Fin Institution)*
Tetsumi Hashimoto *(Mng Exec Officer)*
Masahiko Ichie *(Mng Exec Officer)*
Toshiaki Ido *(Mng Exec Officer)*
Hideyuki Kadono *(Mng Exec Officer)*
Shin Kikuchi *(Mng Exec Officer)*
Masaaki Komiya *(Mng Exec Officer)*
Susumu Kusano *(Mng Exec Officer)*
Hisato Nagao *(Mng Exec Officer)*
Hideo Oishi *(Mng Exec Officer)*
Takahiro Suzuki *(Mng Exec Officer)*
Satoshi Tomii *(Mng Exec Officer)*
Satoshi Tomizuka *(Exec Officer-Internal Audit)*
Hajime Watanabe *(Mng Exec Officer)*

Board of Directors:
Hideto Fujii
Toru Hashimoto
Toshiaki Ido
Masaaki Komiya
Susumu Kusano
Akio Mimura
Kazuo Ueda
Hajime Watanabe
Masanori Yanagi

Holding:

Dexerials Corporation (1)
(Formerly Sony Chemical & Information Device Corporation)
Gate City Osaki East Tower 8th Floor
1-11-2 Osaki
Shinagawa-ku, Tokyo, 141-0032, Japan JP
Tel.: (81) 3 5435 3941
Fax: (81) 3 5435 3074
Web Site: www.dexerials.jp
Emp.: 2,911
Chemical & Recording Media Components Mfr & Distr
S.I.C.: 2899
N.A.I.C.S.: 325998
Takashi Ichinose *(Chm & Pres)*
Tetsuji Ishikawa *(Exec Officer-Advanced Process Device Div)*
Soichiro Kishimoto *(Exec Officer-Advanced Matl Div)*
Akira Nozawa *(Exec Officer-Procurement & Corp Plng Div)*
Naoyuki Sanada *(Exec Officer-Global Sls & Mktg Div)*
Masao Wakai *(Exec Officer-Strategic Alliance Div)*
Yukio Yamada *(Exec Officer-Optical Solution Products Div)*

U.S. Subsidiary:

Dexerials America Corporation (2)
215 Satellite Blvd NE Ste 400
Suwanee, GA 30024
Tel.: (770) 945-3845
Fax: (770) 945-8265
UV Curing Resins Mfr
S.I.C.: 2899
N.A.I.C.S.: 325998
Breck Barnes *(Mgr-IT & Compliance)*

Non-U.S. Subsidiaries:

Dexerials Europe B.V. (2)
Singaporestraat 9-11
1175 RA Lijnden, Netherlands
Tel.: (31) 20 4499 700
Fax: (31) 20 4499 726
Web Site: www.dexerials.jp/en/profile/o_office.html#o4
UV Curing Resins Mfr
S.I.C.: 2899
N.A.I.C.S.: 325998

Dexerials Hong Kong Limited (2)
Suites 1913-14 19F The Gateway
Prudential Tower 21 Canton Road
Tsim Sha Tsui, Kowloon, China (Hong Kong)
Tel.: (852) 2156 0505
Fax: (852) 2156 1577
Web Site: www.dexerials.jp/en/profile/o_office.html#o4
Sales of Electronic Parts, Adhesive Materials, Optical Materials
S.I.C.: 5065
N.A.I.C.S.: 423690

Dexerials Korea Corporation (2)
19F Two IFC 10 Gukjegeumyung-ro
Yeoungdeungpo-gu, Seoul, 150-945, Korea (South)
Tel.: (82) 2 6137 9400
Fax: (82) 2 6137 9429
Web Site: www.dexerials.jp/en/profile/o_office.html#o4
Sales of Electronic Parts, Adhesive Materials, Optical Materials
S.I.C.: 5065
N.A.I.C.S.: 423690

Dexerials (Shenzhen) Corporation (2)
2F Excellence Logistics Center Building No 18 Shihua Road
Futian Free Trade Zone, Shenzhen, Guangdong, China
Tel.: (86) 755 8373 8880
Fax: (86) 755 8295 8005
Web Site: www.dexerials.jp/en/profile/o_office.html#o4
Mfr of Anisotropic Conductive Film (ACF)
S.I.C.: 3695
N.A.I.C.S.: 334613

Dexerials Singapore Pte. Ltd. (2)
3A International Business Park #08-03
Tower A Icon@IBP
Singapore, 609935, Singapore
Tel.: (65) 6933 1968
Fax: (65) 6933 1969
Web Site: www.dexerials.jp/en/profile/o_office.html#o4
Sales of Electronic Parts, Adhesive Materials, Optical Materials
S.I.C.: 5065
N.A.I.C.S.: 423690

Dexerials (Suzhou) Co., Ltd. **(2)**
No 19 Zhuyuan Road
New District, Suzhou, Jiangsu, 215011, China
Tel.: (86) 512 6825 2005
Fax: (86) 512 6825 2571
Web Site: www.dexerials.jp/en/profile/o_office.html#o4
Mfr of Anisotropic Conductive Film (ACF), Touch Panels & Thermal Conductive Sheets
S.I.C.: 3695
N.A.I.C.S.: 334613

Dexerials Taiwan Corporation **(2)**
3F No 167 Sec 2 Nanjing E Road
Zhongshan District, Taipei, 104, Taiwan
Tel.: (886) 2 2515 2585
Fax: (886) 2 2515 2567
Sales of Electronic Parts, Adhesive Materials, Optical Materials
S.I.C.: 5065
N.A.I.C.S.: 423690

Non-U.S. Joint Venture:

Grohe AG **(1)**
Feldmuhleplatz 15
40545 Dusseldorf, Germany
Tel.: (49) 21191303000
Fax: (49) 2119130303924
E-Mail: info@grohe.com
Web Site: www.grohe.com
Sales Range: $1-4.9 Billion
Emp.: 5,100
Faucets, Shower Heads & Fittings Mfr & Exporter
Export
S.I.C.: 3432
N.A.I.C.S.: 332913
David J. Haines *(Chm & CEO)*

Subsidiaries:

AQERO Vertriebs GmbH **(2)**
Parkstr 1 5
1335
14974 Ludwigsfelde, Germany
Tel.: (49) 33788180
Fax: (49) 3378818100
Web Site: www.grohe.de
Mfr. of Faucets, Shower Heads & Fittings
S.I.C.: 3432
N.A.I.C.S.: 332913

Dal-Georg Rost & Sohne Sanitar-Armaturen Gmbh **(2)**
Zur Porta 8 12
32457 Porta Westfalica, Germany
Tel.: (49) 57179510
Fax: (49) 57171571
Web Site: www.grohe.de
Emp.: 100
Shower Heads & Fittings
S.I.C.: 3432
N.A.I.C.S.: 332913
Jorguwe Ramaker *(Gen Mgr)*

Grohe Deutschland Vertriebs GmbH **(2)**
Zur Porta 9
32457 Porta Westfalica, Germany
Tel.: (49) 5713989333
Fax: (49) 5713989999
E-Mail: info@grohe.de
Web Site: www.grohe.de
Emp.: 120
Mfr. of Faucets, Shower Heads & Fittings
S.I.C.: 3432
N.A.I.C.S.: 332913
Michael Rauterkus *(Mgr-Sls)*

Grohe Water Technology AG & Co. Kg **(2)**
Industriepark Edelburg
58675 Hemer, Germany
Tel.: (49) 2372930
Fax: (49) 23729301322
E-Mail: info@grohe.com
Web Site: www.grohe.com
Emp.: 1,500
Mfr. of Faucets, Shower Heads & Fittings
S.I.C.: 3432
N.A.I.C.S.: 332913
David Haines *(CEO)*

GROHEDAL Sanitarsysteme GmbH & Co. KG **(2)**
Zur Porta 8 12
32457 Porta Westfalica, Germany
Tel.: (49) 57179510
Fax: (49) 57171571
E-Mail: info@grohe.com
Web Site: www.grohe.com
Emp.: 300
Mfr. of Faucets, Shower Heads & Fittings
S.I.C.: 3432
N.A.I.C.S.: 332913
Andreas Steffan *(Mgr-Personnel)*

H.D. Eichelberg & Co. GmbH **(2)**
Werler Str 3
58706 Menden, Germany
Tel.: (49) 2372930
Fax: (49) 2372931322
E-Mail: info@eichelberg-armaturen.de
Web Site: www.eichelberg-armaturen.de/t/22_3.html
Mfr. of Faucets, Shower Heads & Fittings
S.I.C.: 3432
N.A.I.C.S.: 332913

Joyou AG **(2)**
Winterstrasse 4-8
22765 Hamburg, Germany De
Tel.: (49) 69710456346
Fax: (49) 69710456348
E-Mail: jin.zhao@joyou.net
Web Site: www.joyou.com
JY8—(DEU)
Rev.: $443,716,478
Assets: $607,467,290
Liabilities: $147,686,965
Net Worth: $459,780,325
Earnings: $53,570,835
Emp.: 3,379
Fiscal Year-end: 12/31/12
Bathroom & Kitchen Plumbing Fixture & Accessories Mfr
S.I.C.: 3432
N.A.I.C.S.: 332913
Jianshe Cai *(Founder, Chm-Mgmt Bd & CEO)*
Rainer Simon *(Chm-Supervisory Bd)*
Johnny Chen *(Deputy Chm-Supervisory Bd)*
Zufang Li *(CFO, Chief Acctg Officer & Member-Mgmt Bd)*
Jilin Cai *(COO & Member-Mgmt Bd)*
Gerry Mulvin *(Corp Dev Officer & Member-Mgmt Bd)*
Ian M. Oades *(Member-Mgmt Bd & VP-Fin & Head-IR)*

Non-U.S. Subsidiary:

Joyou Group Building Materials Co., Ltd. **(3)**
Zhongyu Indus Zone
Luncang Town, Quanzhou, Fujian, 362304, China
Tel.: (86) 59586146222
Fax: (86) 595 86187886
Bathroom & Kitchen Plumbing Fixture & Accessories Mfr
S.I.C.: 3432
N.A.I.C.S.: 332913

U.S. Subsidiary:

Grohe America, Inc. **(2)**
241 Covington Dr
Bloomingdale, IL 60108-3109
Tel.: (630) 582-7711
Fax: (630) 582-7722
E-Mail: info@groheamerica.com
Web Site: www.groheamerica.com
Emp.: 100
Distributor of Faucets & Shower Heads
S.I.C.: 3432
N.A.I.C.S.: 332913
Alex Davidkhanian *(Pres-North America)*

Non-U.S. Subsidiaries:

Grohe A/S **(2)**
Walgerholm 9 11
DK 3500 Vaerlose, Denmark
Tel.: (45) 44656800
Fax: (45) 44650252
E-Mail: grohe@grohe.dk
Web Site: www.grohe.dk
Emp.: 42
Mfr. of Faucets, Shower Heads & Fittings
S.I.C.: 3432
N.A.I.C.S.: 332913
Hans Ronnow *(Mgr-Mktg)*

Grohe AS **(2)**
Nils Hansens vei 20
0667 Oslo, Norway
Tel.: (47) 22072070
Fax: (47) 22072071
E-Mail: grohe@grohe.no
Web Site: www.grohe.no
Sales Range: Less than $1 Million
Emp.: 8
Mfr of Faucets, Shower Heads & Fittings
S.I.C.: 3432
N.A.I.C.S.: 332913

Grohe Canada, Inc. **(2)**
1226 Lakeshore Rd E
Mississauga, ON, L5E 1E9, Canada
Tel.: (905) 271-2929
Fax: (905) 271-9494
E-Mail: info@groheamerica.com
Web Site: www.grohe.com
Sales Range: $10-24.9 Million
Emp.: 12
Mfr. of Plumbing Fixtures
S.I.C.: 3432
N.A.I.C.S.: 332913
Bill McLean *(Pres)*

Grohe Espana, S.A. **(2)**
Botanica 78 88
Poligono Pedrosa, E 08908 Hospitalet, Spain
Tel.: (34) 933368850
Fax: (34) 933368851
E-Mail: recepcio@grohe.es
Web Site: www.grohe.es
Emp.: 40
Mfr. of Faucets, Shower Heads & Fittings
S.I.C.: 3432
N.A.I.C.S.: 332913
Miguel Rubio *(Mng Dir)*

Grohe GmbH **(2)**
Wienerbergstrasse 11/A7
1100 Vienna, Austria
Tel.: (43) 1 680 60
Fax: (43) 1 688 45 35
E-Mail: info-at@grohe.com
Web Site: www.grohe.at
Emp.: 45
Mfr of Plumbing Fixtures
S.I.C.: 3432
N.A.I.C.S.: 332913
Robert H. Friedl *(Mng Dir)*

Grohe Japan Ltd. **(2)**
TRC Building 3F
1 1 Heiwajima 6 Chome Ota Ku, Tokyo, 143-0006, Japan
Tel.: (81) 332989730
Fax: (81) 337673811
E-Mail: info@grohe.co.jp
Web Site: www.grohe.co.jp
Sales Range: Less than $1 Million
Emp.: 40
Mfr. of Faucets, Shower Heads & Fittings
S.I.C.: 3432
N.A.I.C.S.: 332913
Kazuyuki Mori *(Gen Mgr)*

Grohe Limited **(2)**
Blays House Wick Road
Englefield Green, Egham, Surrey, TW20 0HJ, United Kingdom
Tel.: (44) 8712003414
Fax: (44) 871 200 3415
E-Mail: info-uk@grohe.co.uk
Web Site: www.grohe.co.uk
Mfr of Faucets, Shower Heads & Fittings
S.I.C.: 3432
N.A.I.C.S.: 332913

Grohe Nederland B.V. **(2)**
Metaalstraat 2
2718 SW Zoetermeer, Netherlands
Tel.: (31) 793680133
Fax: (31) 793615129
E-Mail: grohe@grohe.nl
Web Site: www.grohe.nl
Sls.: $72,696,000
Emp.: 75
Mfr. of Faucets, Shower Heads & Fittings
S.I.C.: 3432
N.A.I.C.S.: 332913
Loprop Maageun *(Mng Dir)*

Grohe N.V. S.A. **(2)**
Diependaalweg 4 A
3020 Winksele, Belgium
Tel.: (32) 16230660
Fax: (32) 16239070
E-Mail: info@grohe.be
Web Site: www.grohe.be
Emp.: 34
Mfr. of Faucets, Shower Heads & Fittings
S.I.C.: 3432
N.A.I.C.S.: 332913
Daniel Dusart *(Mng Dir)*

Grohe Pacific Pte. Ltd. **(2)**
180 Clemenceau Ave
01-01/02 Haw Par Centre, Singapore, 239922, Singapore
Tel.: (65) 63113611
Fax: (65) 67380855
E-Mail: singapore@grohe.com
Web Site: www.grohe.sg
Emp.: 17
Mfr of Faucets, Shower Heads & Fittings
S.I.C.: 3432
N.A.I.C.S.: 332913

Grohe Polska Sp. zo.o. **(2)**
Ul Migdalowa 4
PL 02 796 Warsaw, Poland
Tel.: (48) 22645125557
Fax: (48) 226451258
E-Mail: biuro@grohe.pl
Web Site: www.grohe.pl
Emp.: 10
Provider of Plumbing Fixtures
S.I.C.: 3432
N.A.I.C.S.: 332913

Grohe S.a.r.l. **(2)**
60 boulevard de la Mission Marchand
92400 Courbevoie, La Defense, France
Tel.: (33) 149972900
Fax: (33) 1 55 70 20 38
E-Mail: marketing-fr@grohe.fr
Web Site: www.grohe.fr
Emp.: 150
Mfr of Faucets, Shower Heads & Fittings
S.I.C.: 3432
N.A.I.C.S.: 332913

Grohe S.p.A. **(2)**
Crocesisso 19
20040 Milano, Milan, Italy
Tel.: (39) 02959401
Fax: (39) 0295940263
E-Mail: info-it@grohe.com
Web Site: www.grohe.it
Emp.: 50
Mfr of Faucets, Shower Heads & Fittings
S.I.C.: 3432
N.A.I.C.S.: 332913

DEVELOPMENT BANK OF KAZAKHSTAN JSC

Left Bank of the Ishim River Street N 35 6 Kazyna Tower
010000 Astana, Kazakhstan
Tel.: (7) 7172792600
Fax: (7) 7172 792638
E-Mail: info@kdb.kz
Web Site: www.kdb.kz
Year Founded: 2001
BRKZ—(KAZ)
Sales Range: $150-199.9 Million
Emp.: 291

Business Description:
Banking Services
S.I.C.: 6029
N.A.I.C.S.: 522110

Personnel:
Aset Isekeshev *(Chm)*
Kussainov Nurlan Zhetpisovich *(Chm-Mgmt Bd)*
Marat Duisenbekovich Aitenov *(Mng Dir)*
Seydimbek Zere Akseleukyzy *(Mng Dir)*
Kunanbayev Yerden Ashirbekovich *(Mng Dir)*
Imasheva Aizhan Yessbolatovna *(Mng Dir)*
Nurali Rahatovich Aliyev *(Member-Mgmt Bd)*
Mirzhan Eldesovich Karakulov *(Member-Mgmt Bd)*
Zhaslan Hasenovich Madiyev *(Member-Mgmt Bd)*
Ardak Siyazbekovich Orumbayev *(Member-Mgmt Bd)*

Board of Directors:
Aset Isekeshev

Development Bank of Kazakhstan JSC—(Continued)

Kairat Aytekenov
Jacek Brzezinski
Azat Peruashev
Ulf Wokurka
Sabr Yessimbekov
Kay Zwingenberger

DEVELOPMENT CREDIT BANK, LTD.

6th Floor Tower A Peninsula Business Park Senapati Bapat Marg
Lower Parel, Mumbai, 400013, India
Tel.: (91) 22 6618 7000
Fax: (91) 2266589970
E-Mail: dcbipo@dcbl.com
Web Site: www.dcbbank.com
DCB—(NSE)
Rev.: $191,540,874
Assets: $2,091,093,951
Liabilities: $1,905,126,757
Net Worth: $185,967,194
Earnings: $18,922,369
Emp.: 8
Fiscal Year-end: 03/31/13

Business Description:
Commercial Banking Services
S.I.C.: 6029
N.A.I.C.S.: 522110

Personnel:
Murali M. Natrajan *(CEO & Mng Dir)*
Bharat Laxmidas Sampat *(CFO & Exec VP)*
Sachin Shamkant Patange *(Chief Compliance Officer)*
Jayaraman K. Vishwanath *(Chief Credit Officer)*
H. V. Barve *(Compliance Officer, Sec & VP)*

Board of Directors:
Nasser Munjee
Imran Contractor
Keki Elavia
Altaf Jiwani
Amin Manekia
Chakrapany Narasimhan
Suhail Nathani
Murali M. Natrajan
Sukh Dev Nayyar
Jamal Pradhan
Nalin Shah
S. Sridhar
Darius E. Udwadia

Transfer Agent:
Link Intime India Pvt. Ltd
C-13 Pannalal Silk Mills Compound LBS Marg
Bhandup (West)
Mumbai, India

DEVELOPMENT INVESTMENT CONSTRUCTION JSC

(d/b/a DIC Group)
265 Le Hong Phong Ward 8
Vung Tau, Vietnam
Tel.: (84) 643859248
Fax: (84) 643560712
E-Mail: info@dic.vn
Web Site: www.dic.vn
DIG—(HOSE)

Business Description:
Real Estate Development, Investment & Construction Services
S.I.C.: 1542
N.A.I.C.S.: 236220

Personnel:
Tuan Thien Nguyen *(Chm)*

Affiliate:

Development Investment Construction Number 2 JSC **(1)**
5 Street 6 Thang Nhat Ward
Vung Tau, Vietnam
Tel.: (84) 643613944
Fax: (84) 643582017
Web Site: www.dic-2.com.vn/dic/
DC2—(HNX)
Construction Services
S.I.C.: 1542
N.A.I.C.S.: 236220
Du Van Tuyen *(Chm)*

DEVELOPMENT SECURITIES PLC

Portland House Bressenden Place
London, SW1E 5DS, United Kingdom
Tel.: (44) 2078284777
Fax: (44) 2078284999
E-Mail: sarah.thomas@devsecs.co.uk
Web Site: www.developmentsecurities.com
DSC—(LSE)
Rev.: $157,404,676
Assets: $859,454,356
Liabilities: $375,139,809
Net Worth: $484,314,547
Earnings: $3,705,014
Emp.: 78
Fiscal Year-end: 02/28/13

Business Description:
Commercial Real Estate Development & Investment
S.I.C.: 6531
N.A.I.C.S.: 531390

Personnel:
Michael Marx *(CEO)*
Helen M. Ratsey *(Sec)*

Board of Directors:
David Jenkins
Julian Barwick
Sarah Bates
Michael Marx
Marcus Shepherd
Nick Thomlinson
Matthew Weiner

Transfer Agent:
Capita Registrars
The Registry 34 Beckenham Road
Beckenham, United Kingdom

Subsidiaries:

Development Securities Estates PLC **(1)**
Portland House Bressenden Place
London, SW1E 5DS, United Kingdom
Tel.: (44) 2078284777
Fax: (44) 278284999
Web Site: www.developmentsecurities.co.uk
Emp.: 45
Management & Investment Services
S.I.C.: 8741
N.A.I.C.S.: 561110
David Jenkins *(Chm)*

Development Securities (Investments) PLC **(1)**
Portland House Bressenden Place
London, SW1E 5DS, United Kingdom
Tel.: (44) 2078284777
Emp.: 40
Management & Investment Services
S.I.C.: 8741
N.A.I.C.S.: 561110

Development Securities (Paddington) Limited **(1)**
Portland House Bressenden Pl
London, SW1E 5DS, United Kingdom
Tel.: (44) 2078284777
Fax: (44) 2078284999
Web Site: www.developmentsecurities.co.uk
Emp.: 40
Investment Services
S.I.C.: 6211
N.A.I.C.S.: 523999
Julianna Barwick *(Mng Dir)*

Development Securities (Southampton A) Limited **(1)**
Portland House Bressenden Pl
London, SW1E 5DS, United Kingdom
Tel.: (44) 2078284777
Fax: (44) 2078284999
Web Site: www.developmentsecurities.co.uk
Investment Services
S.I.C.: 6211
N.A.I.C.S.: 523110

DS Property Developments Limited **(1)**
140 Nottingham Rd Burton Joyce
Nottingham, NG14 5AU, United Kingdom
Tel.: (44) 7973 897933
Roofing Services
S.I.C.: 3444
N.A.I.C.S.: 332322

DEVERON RESOURCES LTD.

330 Bay Street Suite 1208
Toronto, ON, M5H 2S8, Canada
Tel.: (416) 367-4571
Fax: (416) 367-5269
E-Mail: info@deveronresources.com
Web Site: www.deveronresources.com
Year Founded: 2011
DVR—(TSXV)

Business Description:
Gold Mining
S.I.C.: 1041
N.A.I.C.S.: 212221

Personnel:
James Pirie *(CEO)*
Carmelo Marrelli *(CFO)*

Board of Directors:
Christopher O. Irwin
David MacMillan
James Pirie
Michael Power

DEVIL AG

Kocherstrasse 2
38120 Braunschweig, Germany
Tel.: (49) 531 21540 0
Fax: (49) 531 21540 999
E-Mail: info@devil.de
Web Site: www.devil.de
Year Founded: 1994
Sales Range: $350-399.9 Million
Emp.: 240

Business Description:
Information Technology Distr
S.I.C.: 5045
N.A.I.C.S.: 423430

Personnel:
Axel Grotjahn *(CEO & Member-Mgmt Bd)*

DEVINE LIMITED

Level 1 KSD1 485 Kingsford Smith Drive
Hamilton, QLD, 4007, Australia
Tel.: (61) 736086300
Fax: (61) 736086333
Web Site: www.devine.com.au
DVN—(ASX)
Rev.: $324,169,173
Assets: $567,284,851
Liabilities: $236,412,890
Net Worth: $330,871,961
Earnings: ($582,534)
Emp.: 221
Fiscal Year-end: 06/30/13

Business Description:
Land Development
S.I.C.: 1531
N.A.I.C.S.: 236117

Personnel:
David B. Keir *(CEO & Mng Dir)*
Paul V. Cochrane *(CFO)*
Viv N. Grayson *(Sec)*

Board of Directors:
Peter J. Dransfield
Judith S. Downes
David B. Keir
Terence M. Mackenroth
Graeme E. McOrist
Rick W. Parris
Vyril A. Vella
Travis G. Young

Legal Counsel:
McCullough Robertson
Level 11 66 Eagle Street
Brisbane, QLD, 4000, Australia

Subsidiaries:

Devine Civil Contracting Pty Ltd. **(1)**
Level 18 175 Eagle St
Brisbane, Queensland, 4001, Australia
Tel.: (61) 733802500
Fax: (61) 732331440
Web Site: www.divine.com.au
Emp.: 150
Construction Management Services
S.I.C.: 5039
N.A.I.C.S.: 423390
David Keir *(Mng Dir)*

Pioneer Homes Australia Pty Ltd **(1)**
3 Westmoreland Blvd
Springwood, Logan, QLD, 4127, Australia
Mailing Address:
PO Box 780
Hamilton, QLD, 4007, Australia
Tel.: (61) 733802500
Fax: (61) 33802501
E-Mail: reception@devine.com.au
Emp.: 50
Construction Management Services
S.I.C.: 1629
N.A.I.C.S.: 237990

DEVITT & FORAND CONTRACTORS INC.

5716 Burbank Cr SE
Calgary, AB, T2H 1Z6, Canada
Tel.: (403) 255-8565
Fax: (403) 255-8501
E-Mail: info@devitt-forand.com
Web Site: www.devitt-forand.com
Year Founded: 1964
Rev.: $29,605,010
Emp.: 45

Business Description:
General Contract Services
S.I.C.: 1796
N.A.I.C.S.: 238290

Personnel:
Garry Boan *(Pres)*
Al Brunette *(CEO)*
Brenda Brunette *(CFO)*

DEVJO INDUSTRIES, INC.

375 Steelcase Rd E
Markham, ON, L3R 1G3, Canada
Tel.: (905) 477-7689
Web Site: www.devjo.com
Year Founded: 1986
Emp.: 50

Business Description:
Holding Company; Mechanical Engineered & Specialty Chemical Products Mfr & Sales
Export
S.I.C.: 2899
N.A.I.C.S.: 325998

Personnel:
Joseph A. Devine *(CEO)*
G. Michael Devine *(Pres & COO)*

Legal Counsel:
Blake, Cassels & Graydon
Commerce Ct. W.
P.O. Box 25
Toronto, ON, M5L 1A9, Canada
Tel.: (416) 863-2400

Divisions:

Elasto Valve Rubber Products Inc. **(1)**
1691 Pioneer Rd
Sudbury, ON, T3G1B2, Canada (100%)
Tel.: (705) 523-2026
Fax: (705) 523-2033
Toll Free: (800) 461-6331
E-Mail: info@evrproducts.com
Web Site: www.evrproducts.com
Emp.: 40
Distributor of A Full Range of Elastomeric Piping Products
S.I.C.: 3089

N.A.I.C.S.: 326122
Gary Waldick *(Pres & Gen Mgr)*

Sluyter Company Ltd. (1)
375 Steelcase Road East
Markham, ON, L3R 1G3, Canada (50%)
Tel.: (905) 475-6011
Fax: (905) 475-3119
E-Mail: info@sluyter.com
Web Site: www.sluyter.com
Emp.: 25
Mfr. of Proprietary Specialty Chemicals & Adhesive Type Products Related to the Plumbing and Heating, Automotive Care, Shoe Care, Furniture and Upholstery, and Janitorial Chemical Fields
S.I.C.: 2891
N.A.I.C.S.: 325520
Sol Buck *(Pres)*

DEVK SERVICE GMBH

Riehler Strasse 190
50735 Cologne, Germany
Tel.: (49) 2217570
Fax: (49) 2217572233
E-Mail: info@devk.de
Web Site: www.devk.de
Emp.: 1,500

Business Description:
Insurance Services
S.I.C.: 6411
N.A.I.C.S.: 524210

Personnel:
Wilhelm Hulfmann *(CEO)*
Bernd Oppermanm *(Mng Dir)*
Reinhard Schmalstieg *(Mng Dir)*

Joint Venture:

DVA - Deutsche Verkehrs-Assekuranz-Vermittlungs GmbH (1)
Norsk Data Strasse 3
61352 Bad Homburg, Germany
Tel.: (49) 617248680
Fax: (49) 6172486868
Web Site: www.dva-assekuranz.de
Sales Range: $10-24.9 Million
Emp.: 120
Insurance Services; Owned 65% by Deutsche Bahn AG, 20% by DEVK Service GmbH & 15% by Marsh GmbH
S.I.C.: 6411
N.A.I.C.S.: 524210
Hans Juergen Allerdissen *(Co-Mng Dir)*
Peter Hoechst *(Co-Mng Dir)*

DEVLIN ELECTRONICS LIMITED

Unit D 1 Grafton Way
Basingstoke, Hants, RG22 6HZ, United Kingdom
Tel.: (44) 256467367
Fax: (44) 256840048
E-Mail: sales@devlin.co.uk
Web Site: www.devlin.co.uk
Sales Range: $1-9.9 Million
Emp.: 40

Business Description:
Keyboards & Accessories Designer, Mfr & Distr
Import Export
S.I.C.: 3575
N.A.I.C.S.: 334118

DEVONSHIRE INDUSTRIES LIMITED

Brighton Hill 9 Watlington Road
Devonshire, DV 06, Bermuda
Tel.: (441) 2364662
Fax: (441) 2368351
DEVON—(BERM)
Sales Range: $1-9.9 Million

Business Description:
Consumable Products Supplier & Mfr
S.I.C.: 7299
N.A.I.C.S.: 812990

Personnel:
Barry Hanson *(Pres & CEO)*

Subsidiary:

Bermuda Paint Company Limited (1)
Brighton Hill 9 Watlington Road
Devonshire, DV 06, Bermuda
Tel.: (441) 2364662
Fax: (441) 2368351
E-Mail: info@bermudapaint.bm
Web Site: www.bermudapaint.bm
Paints & Coatings Mfr
S.I.C.: 2851
N.A.I.C.S.: 325510

DEVOTEAM SA

73 Rue Anatole France
92300 Levallois-Perret, France
Tel.: (33) 41494848
Fax: (33) 3141486070
E-Mail: support@devoteam.com
Web Site: www.devoteam.com
Year Founded: 1995
DVT—(EUR)
Sls.: $693,371,782
Assets: $454,633,917
Liabilities: $282,478,967
Net Worth: $172,154,950
Earnings: ($4,870,443)
Emp.: 4,664
Fiscal Year-end: 12/31/12

Business Description:
Information Technology Consulting
S.I.C.: 8299
N.A.I.C.S.: 611710

Personnel:
Michel Bon *(Chm-Supervisory Bd)*
Stanislas de Bentzmann *(CEO)*
Gregoire Cayatte *(CFO)*
Godefroy de Bentzmann *(CEO-Innovation & Offer Dev & Member-Mgmt Bd)*
Roland de Laage de Meux *(Sec)*
Sebastien Chevrel *(Exec VP-France Expertise, Belgium & Luxemburg)*
Marie-Odile Crinon *(Exec VP-France Solutions, Consulting & North Africa)*
Osama Ghoul *(Exec VP-Middle East)*
Jurgen Hatzipantelis *(Exec VP-Central Europe)*
Regis Tatala *(Exec VP-France Solutions, Consulting & North Africa)*

Supervisory Board of Directors:
Michel Bon
Bertrand de Bentzmann
Roland de Laage de Meux
Elisabeth de Maulde
Patrice de Talhouet
Yves de Talhouet
Vincent Montagne
Philippe Tassin

Non-U.S. Subsidiaries:

DaVinci Consulting AS (1)
Hoffsveien 21-23
Oslo, Norway
Tel.: (47) 23253300
Fax: (47) 23253301
E-Mail: leo@davinci.no
Web Site: www.davinci.no
Emp.: 100
Other Management Consulting Services
S.I.C.: 8748
N.A.I.C.S.: 541618

Devoteam Belgium SA/NV (1)
Heysel Esplanade B62
1020 Brussels, Belgium
Tel.: (32) 22177017
Fax: (32) 024740519
E-Mail: infobe@devoteam.com
Web Site: www.devoteam.be
Emp.: 70
Other Computer Related Services
S.I.C.: 7379
N.A.I.C.S.: 541519
Geert Stragier *(Gen Mgr)*

Devoteam Consulting GmbH (1)
Palais der Schonen Kunste Lowengasse 47
1030 Vienna, Austria
Tel.: (43) 1 715 0000 0
Fax: (43) 1 715 0000 150
E-Mail: office@devoteam.at
Web Site: www.devoteam.at
Emp.: 28
Information Technology Consulting Services
S.I.C.: 7373
N.A.I.C.S.: 541512
Gerald Aster *(Mng Dir)*

Devoteam Danet GmbH (1)
Gutenbergstrasse 10
64331 Weiterstadt, Germany (90%)
Tel.: (49) 61518680
Fax: (49) 61518687131
E-Mail: marketing@danet.com
Web Site: www.danet.com
Sales Range: $50-74.9 Million
Emp.: 400
Telecommunications Information Technology Consulting, Software Development, Systems Integration & Products
S.I.C.: 3669
N.A.I.C.S.: 334290
Jurgen Hatzipantelis *(CEO)*

Devoteam Davinci AS (1)
Hoffsveien 21-23
275 Oslo, Norway
Tel.: (47) 23 25 33 00
Fax: (47) 23 25 33 01
Web Site: www.davinci.no
Information Technology Consulting Services
S.I.C.: 7373
N.A.I.C.S.: 541512
Allan Jensen *(CEO)*
Terje Pettersen *(CFO)*

Devoteam Genesis AG (1)
Bernstrasse 34
3072 Ostermundigen, Switzerland
Tel.: (41) 31 560 35 35
Fax: (41) 31 560 35 45
E-Mail: info@devoteam.ch
Web Site: www.devoteam.ch
Information Technology Consulting Services
S.I.C.: 7373
N.A.I.C.S.: 541512
Thomas Lack *(Founder)*
Urs Zumstein *(Founder)*

Devoteam Guidance S.A. (1)
Route des 3 Cantons 7
8399 Windhof, Luxembourg
Tel.: (352) 31 37 36
Fax: (352) 31 46 47
E-Mail: info@devoteam.lu
Web Site: www.devoteam.lu
Emp.: 70
Computer Software Consulting Services
S.I.C.: 7373
N.A.I.C.S.: 541512

Devoteam Integra (1)
Buyukdere Caddesi Cem Is Merkezi No 23/2
Sisli, 34381 Istanbul, Turkey
Tel.: (90) 212 373 93 93
Fax: (90) 212 373 93 73
E-Mail: tr.info@devoteam.com
Web Site: www.devoteam.com.tr
Information Technology Consulting Services
S.I.C.: 7373
N.A.I.C.S.: 541512

Devoteam Italia S.r.l. (1)
Via Eustachi 7
20129 Milan, Italy (20%)
Tel.: (39) 0245491078
Fax: (39) 0297387276
E-Mail: info@devoteam.it
Web Site: www.devoteam.it
Emp.: 41
Other Management Consulting Services
S.I.C.: 8748
N.A.I.C.S.: 541618
Nicola Bonavita *(Mng Dir)*

Devoteam Middle East (1)
Bldg 17 Office 369 Dubai Internet City
PO Box 500612
Dubai, United Arab Emirates
Tel.: (971) 4 3912943
Fax: (971) 4 3911403
E-Mail: info@devoteamme.com
Web Site: www.me.devoteam.com
Emp.: 150
Information Technology Consulting Services
S.I.C.: 7373
N.A.I.C.S.: 541512
Osama Ghoul *(Mng Partner)*

Devoteam Morocco (1)
7 rue Mariniyine
Hassan, 10000 Rabat, Morocco
Tel.: (212) 5 37 70 59 62
Fax: (212) 5 37 70 59 56
Web Site: www.devoteam.ma
Information Technology Consulting Services
S.I.C.: 7373
N.A.I.C.S.: 541512

Devoteam Nederland BV (1)
Wisselwerking 42
1112 XR Diemen, Netherlands
Tel.: (31) 20 630 47 50
Fax: (31) 20 630 47 51
E-Mail: nl.info@devoteam.com
Web Site: www.devoteam.nl
Emp.: 150
Information Technology Consulting Services
S.I.C.: 7373
N.A.I.C.S.: 541512
Sean Bijallaar *(Gen Mgr)*

Devoteam OSIconsult GmbH (1)
Palais der Schonen Kunste
Lowengasse 47, Vienna, 1030, Austria
Tel.: (43) 171500000
Fax: (43) 17150000150
E-Mail: office.at@devoteam.com
Web Site: www.devoteam.at
Emp.: 27
Other Management Consulting Services
S.I.C.: 8748
N.A.I.C.S.: 541618
Gerald Aster *(Mng Dir)*

Devoteam Polska Sp. z o.o. (1)
Ul Marszalkowska 68-70 l 29
Warsaw, 02-699, Poland
Tel.: (48) 224318794
Fax: (48) 224318401
E-Mail: devoteam.pl@devoteam.com
Web Site: www.devoteam.pl
Emp.: 200
Educational Support Services
S.I.C.: 8299
N.A.I.C.S.: 611710
Jack Rico *(Pres)*

Devoteam Quaint AB (1)
Barnhusgatan 20
111 23 Stockholm, Sweden
Tel.: (46) 8 212125
Fax: (46) 8 212135
E-Mail: info@devoteam.com
Web Site: www.devoteam.se
Emp.: 40
Information Technology Consulting Services
S.I.C.: 7371
N.A.I.C.S.: 541511
Roger Andersson *(Mng Dir)*
Anders Hammar *(CTO)*

Devoteam Secura (1)
Buyukdere Caddesi Cem Is Merkezi No 23 Kat 2
Sisli, 34381 Istanbul, Turkey
Tel.: (90) 212 373 93 93
Fax: (90) 212 373 93 73
Information Technology Consulting Services
S.I.C.: 7373
N.A.I.C.S.: 541512

Devoteam Spain (1)
C/Antracita n 7 4 Planta
28045 Madrid, Spain
Tel.: (34) 902 430 677
Fax: (34) 91 178 77 59
E-Mail: es.info@devoteam.com
Web Site: www.devoteam.es
Information Technology Consulting Services
S.I.C.: 7373
N.A.I.C.S.: 541512
Frederic Rouaud *(Gen Mgr)*

Devoteam s.r.o. (1)
Klimentska 10
110 00 Prague, Czech Republic
Tel.: (420) 296 578 120
Fax: (420) 296 578 125
Web Site: www.devoteam.cz
Emp.: 12
Information Technology Consulting Services
S.I.C.: 7373
N.A.I.C.S.: 541512
Sylvain Bernolle *(Gen Mgr)*

Devoteam Telecom AS (1)
Televeien 1
N-4898 Grimstad, Norway NO
Tel.: (47) 37800000 (100%)

Devoteam SA—(Continued)

Fax: (47) 37800101
E-Mail: joran.boch@devoteam.com
Web Site: www.devoteam.no
Emp.: 100
Telecommunications & Data Communications Accessories & Equipment Mfr
S.I.C.: 5045
N.A.I.C.S.: 423430
Joran Boch *(Mng Dir)*

Devoteam Teligent (1)
33 bld 1 Prospekt Mira
129110 Moscow, Russia
Tel.: (7) 495 514 05 78
Fax: (7) 495 514 05 79
E-Mail: info@teligent.ru
Web Site: www.teligent.ru
Information Technology Consulting Services
S.I.C.: 7373
N.A.I.C.S.: 541512

Devoteam UK Ltd. (1)
Suncourt House 18-26 Essex Road
London, N1 8LN, United Kingdom
Tel.: (44) 20 7288 2800
Fax: (44) 20 7288 2801
Web Site: www.devoteam.co.uk
Information Technology Consulting Services
S.I.C.: 7373
N.A.I.C.S.: 541512
Godefroy de Bentzmann *(Co-CEO)*
Stanislas de Bentzmann *(Co-CEO)*
Roland de Laage *(Gen Sec)*

Genesis Communications AG (1)
18 Binzstrasse
8045 Zurich, Switzerland (100%)
Tel.: (41) 447383000
Fax: (41) 444556085
E-Mail: info@GenesisCom.ch
Web Site: www.GenesisCom.ch
Emp.: 30
Other Management Consulting Services
S.I.C.: 8748
N.A.I.C.S.: 541618
Kurt Bartsch *(CEO & Mng Dir)*

DEVOTION ENERGY GROUP LIMITED

47 Hill Street 06 04 SCCCI Building
Singapore, 179365, Singapore
Tel.: (65) 62200100
Fax: (65) 62230100
E-Mail: devotiongroup@fingnet.com.sg
Web Site: www.devotionenergy.com
Year Founded: 1993
Rev.: $82,665,381
Assets: $81,217,146
Liabilities: $43,600,195
Net Worth: $37,616,951
Earnings: $5,617,571
Fiscal Year-end: 12/31/12

Business Description:
Central Heating Infrastructure Services & Thermal Equipment
S.I.C.: 1711
N.A.I.C.S.: 238220

Personnel:
Zuqin Li *(CEO)*
Beng Hong Ong *(Sec)*

Non-U.S. Subsidiaries:

Guangzhou Devotion Domestic Boilers Manufacturing Co. Ltd. (1)
Devotion Industry Park East Section of GETDD
Hongming Road, Guangzhou, 510760, China (100%)
Tel.: (86) 2082268411
Fax: (86) 2082268590
E-Mail: sales@devotionboilers.com
Web Site: www.squirrelboilers.com
Emp.: 300
Heating Equipment Mfr
S.I.C.: 3433
N.A.I.C.S.: 333414
Hans Johansson *(Mgr)*

Guangzhou Devotion Thermal Facility Co., Ltd. (1)
No 3 Canglian 2nd Road Economic & Technological Development Zone
Guangzhou, Guangdong, 510760, China
Tel.: (86) 2082268372
Fax: (86) 2082269137
Web Site: www.devotionboiler.com
1523—(SES)
Emp.: 1,000
Central Heating Equipment Mfr
S.I.C.: 3433
N.A.I.C.S.: 333414
Shengbin Geng *(Gen Mgr)*

DEVRO PLC

Moodiesburn
Chryston, G69 0JE, United Kingdom
Tel.: (44) 1236879191
Fax: (44) 1236811005
E-Mail: enquiries@devro.plc.uk
Web Site: www.devro.com
DVO—(LSE OTC)
Rev.: $380,717,861
Assets: $461,980,228
Liabilities: $229,941,465
Net Worth: $232,038,763
Earnings: $52,283,975
Emp.: 2,220
Fiscal Year-end: 12/31/12

Business Description:
Sausage Casing Mfr
S.I.C.: 2099
N.A.I.C.S.: 311999

Personnel:
Peter W. B. Page *(CEO)*
J. Meredith *(Sec)*

Board of Directors:
Steve Hannam
Gerard Hoetmer
Jane A. Lodge
Paul Neep
Peter W. B. Page
Simon C. Webb
Paul Withers

Legal Counsel:
Clydesdale Bank PLC
Clydesdale Bank Plaza 50 Lothian Road
Edinburgh, EH3 9BY, United Kingdom

Clifford Chance LLP
10 Upper Bank Street
London, E14 5JJ, United Kingdom
Tel.: (44) 20 7006 1000
Fax: (44) 20 7006 5555

Subsidiaries:

Devro Medical Limited (1)
3 Robroyston Oval Nova Technology Park
Glasgow, G33 1AP, United Kingdom
Tel.: (44) 141 558 9838
E-Mail: enquiries@devromedical.com
Web Site: www.devromedical.com
Emp.: 10
Pharmaceutical Products Mfr
S.I.C.: 2834
N.A.I.C.S.: 325412

Devro New Holdings Limited (1)
Gartferry Rd
Glasgow, Lanarkshire, G69 0JE, United Kingdom
Tel.: (44) 1236872261
Fax: (44) 1236811005
Food Product Mfr
S.I.C.: 2099
N.A.I.C.S.: 311999

Devro (Scotland) Ltd. (1)
Gartferry Rd Moodiesburn
Chryston, Lanarkshire, G69 0JE, United Kingdom (100%)
Tel.: (44) 236872261
Fax: (44) 1236878268
Web Site: www.devro.plc.uk/global_contacts/
Emp.: 500
Sausage Casing Mfr
S.I.C.: 5147
N.A.I.C.S.: 311612

U.S. Subsidiary:

Devro Inc. (1)
785 Old Swamp Rd
Swansea, SC 29160
Tel.: (803) 796-9730
Fax: (803) 796-1636
Web Site: www.devro.plc.uk/global_contacts/
Emp.: 380
Sausage Casing Mfr
S.I.C.: 2823
N.A.I.C.S.: 325220
Eugene Hibshman *(Dir-Sls & Product Dev)*

Non-U.S. Subsidiaries:

Cutisin A.S. (1)
Dedanska 29
CZ 162200 Prague, Czech Republic (100%)
Tel.: (420) 220516767
Fax: (420) 203166220
Web Site: www.cutisin.cz
Emp.: 1,000
Sausage Casing Mfr
S.I.C.: 5147
N.A.I.C.S.: 311612
Mechal Spock *(Gen Mgr)*

Devro Asia Ltd. (1)
7/F CKK Commercial Ctr 289 Hennessy Rd
Wanchai, China (Hong Kong) (100%)
Tel.: (852) 25721998
Fax: (852) 25722313
Emp.: 35
Sausage Casing Mfr
S.I.C.: 5147
N.A.I.C.S.: 311612

Devro K.K. (1)
Takeda Edobashi Bldg 3 14 3 Nihonbashi
Chuo-ku, Tokyo, 103, Japan (100%)
Tel.: (81) 332782871
Fax: (81) 332782873
Web Site: www.devro.plc.uk/global_contacts/
Emp.: 6
Sausage Casing Mfr
S.I.C.: 5147
N.A.I.C.S.: 311612
Ken Tanaka *(Pres)*

Devro Ltd. (1)
Postfach 54 02 44
22502 Hamburg, Germany (100%)
Tel.: (49) 405400030
Fax: (49) 4054000321
Web Site: www.devro.com
Emp.: 45
Sausage Casing Mfr
S.I.C.: 5147
N.A.I.C.S.: 311612
Felix Engler *(Gen Mgr)*

Devro Pty. Ltd. (1)
Unit 3 17 Joval Pl
2104 Manukau, Auckland, New Zealand (100%)
Tel.: (64) 92622523
Fax: (64) 92622496
E-Mail: devro@extra.co.nz
Web Site: www.devro.plc.uk/global_contacts/
Emp.: 6
Sausage Casing Mfr
S.I.C.: 5147
N.A.I.C.S.: 311612
Brian Tilbrook *(Gen Mgr)*

Devro Pty. Ltd. (1)
Sydney Rd
PO Box 659
Kelso, Bathurst, New South Wales, 2795, Australia (100%)
Tel.: (61) 263308200
Fax: (61) 263308261
Web Site: www.devro.plc.uk.com
Emp.: 170
Sausage Casing Mfr
S.I.C.: 5147
N.A.I.C.S.: 311612
Beverley Munro *(Mng Dir)*

Devro s.r.o. (1)
Vichovska 830
CZ-514 19 Jilemnice, Czech Republic
Tel.: (420) 481563111
Fax: (420) 481563232
Web Site: www.cutisin.cz/article.asp?nArticleID=77&nDepartmentID=64&nLanguageID=2
Sausage Casing Mfr
S.I.C.: 5147
N.A.I.C.S.: 311612
Jaroslav Novosad *(Mgr-Sls)*

DEWAN HOUSING FINANCE CORPORATION LIMITED

6th Floor HDIL Towers Anant Kanekar Road Bandra E Station Road
Mumbai, 400 051, India
Tel.: (91) 22 2658 3333
Fax: (91) 22 2658 3344
E-Mail: info@dhfl.com
Web Site: www.dhfl.com
Year Founded: 1984
511072—(BOM NSE)
Rev.: $767,622,744
Assets: $6,637,883,616
Liabilities: $6,037,727,130
Net Worth: $600,156,486
Earnings: $83,772,990
Emp.: 1,736
Fiscal Year-end: 03/31/13

Business Description:
Housing Finance Services
S.I.C.: 6163
N.A.I.C.S.: 522310

Personnel:
Kapil Wadhawan *(Chm & Mng Dir)*
Anoop Pabby *(Co-Pres)*
Anil Sachidanand *(Co-Pres)*
Rajeev Sathe *(COO)*
S. Y. Sankhe *(Compliance Officer & Sec)*

Board of Directors:
Kapil Wadhawan
V. K. Chopra
Anthony Hambro
R. P. Khosla
G. P. Kohli
Ajay Vazirani
M. Venugopalan
Dheeraj Wadhawan

Link Intime India Pvt. Ltd
C-13 Pannalal Silk Mills Compound LBS Marg
Bhandup (West)
Mumbai, India

Transfer Agents:
System Support Services
209 Shivam Industrial Estate Andheri Kurla Road Sakina Andheri East
Mumbai, 400 072i, India

Link Intime India Pvt. Ltd
C-13 Pannalal Silk Mills Compound LBS Marg
Bhandup (West)
Mumbai, India

Subsidiary:

DHFL Vysya Housing Finance Ltd. (DVHFL) (1)
No 3 8 A Main Rd JVT Tower
Sampangi Ramnagar, Bengaluru, Karnataka, 560027, India
Tel.: (91) 8022217637
Fax: (91) 8022290568
E-Mail: info@dvhousing.com
Web Site: www.dvhousing.com
Emp.: 24
Housing Loan Services
S.I.C.: 9311
N.A.I.C.S.: 921130
R. Nambirajan *(Mng Dir)*

DEWAN SALMAN FIBRE LIMITED

Financial Trade Center 2nd Fl Block A
Shahrah-e-Faisal
74000 Karachi, Pakistan
Tel.: (92) 21111313786
Fax: (92) 215611353
Web Site: www.dewansalmanfibre.com
DSFL—(KAR)
Sales Range: $1-9.9 Million

Business Description:
Polyester Staple Fiber Mfr
S.I.C.: 2823
N.A.I.C.S.: 325220

Personnel:
Dewan Muhammad Yousuf Farooqui *(Chm, Pres & CEO)*

Dewan Asim Mushfiq Farooqui *(Mng Dir)*
Muhammad Salahuddin *(Sec)*

Faruq Ali & Co
222A Karachi Memon Cooperative Housing Society Justice Inaumullah Road
Karachi, Pakistan

Transfer Agent:
BMF Consultants Pakistan (Pvt) Limited
Anum Estate Room No 310 & 311 3rd Fl 49 Darul Aman Society
Karachi, Pakistan

DEWAN TEXTILE MILL LIMITED

Fin Trade Ctr 2nd Fl Block A
Shahrah-e-Faisal
74900 Karachi, Pakistan
Tel.: (92) 21111313786
Fax: (92) 215611353
Web Site: www.dewangroup.com.pk
DWTM—(KAR)
Sales Range: $25-49.9 Million

Business Description:
Textile Mills
S.I.C.: 2299
N.A.I.C.S.: 313210

Personnel:
Mohammad Yousuf Farooqui *(Chm)*
Abdul Baqi Farooqui *(CEO)*
Mehmood ul Hassan Asghar *(CFO)*
Syed Muhammad Salahuddin *(Sec)*

Board of Directors:
Mohammad Yousuf Farooqui
Abdul Baqi Farooqui
Abdul Rehman Farooqui
Asim Mushfiq Farooqui
Mohammad Hamza Farooqui
Haroon Iqbal
M. A. Lodhi

Transfer Agent:
BMF Consultants Pakistan (Pvt) Ltd
A-14 4th Floor Block 7 K.C.H.S. Main Shahrah-e-Faisal
Karachi, Pakistan

DEWAVRIN GROUPE

29 Avenue De La Marne
59290 Wasquehal, Cedex, France
Tel.: (33) 320692828
Fax: (33) 320692855
E-Mail: adf@dewavrin.com
Web Site: www.dewavrin.com
Emp.: 200

Business Description:
Holding Company; Wood Trade & Topmaking
S.I.C.: 6712
N.A.I.C.S.: 551111

Personnel:
Christian Dewavrin *(CEO)*

Non-U.S. Subsidiary:

British Mohair Spinners Limited (1)
Lowr Holme Mills
Baildon, Shipley, W Yorkshire, BD1 7EU, United Kingdom
Tel.: (44) 274583111
Telex: 51195
Fax: (44) 274203014
Web Site: www.dewavrin.com
Emp.: 2
Yarn, Worsted Spinners, Synthetic Yarn Processors & Textile Machinery Accessories Mfr
Import Export
S.I.C.: 2299
N.A.I.C.S.: 313210

DEWHURST PLC

Unit 9 Hampton Business Park
Hampton Road West
Hanworth, Middlesex, TW13 6DB, United Kingdom
Tel.: (44) 2087448200
Fax: (44) 2087448299
E-Mail: info@dewhurst.co.uk
Web Site: www.dewhurst.co.uk
Year Founded: 1919
DWHT—(LSE)
Rev.: $81,056,833
Assets: $62,512,262
Liabilities: $28,608,479
Net Worth: $33,903,783
Earnings: $5,902,189
Emp.: 357
Fiscal Year-end: 09/30/12

Business Description:
Push Buttons & Keypads Mfr
S.I.C.: 3699
N.A.I.C.S.: 335999

Personnel:
Richard M. Dewhurst *(Chm)*
David Dewhurst *(Mng Dir)*
Jared Sinclair *(Sec & Dir-Fin)*

Board of Directors:
Richard M. Dewhurst
John Bailey
David Dewhurst
Jared Sinclair
Peter Tett
Richard Young

Legal Counsel:
Keystone Law
53 Davies Street
London, United Kingdom

Subsidiaries:

Cortest Ltd (1)
Unit 7 Gatwick Distribution Point Church Rd
Lowfield Heath, Crawley, West Sussex, RH11 0PJ, United Kingdom
Tel.: (44) 8456 808044
Fax: (44) 8456 808055
E-Mail: sales@cortest.co.uk
Web Site: www.cortest.co.uk
Emp.: 12
Electrical Testing Services
S.I.C.: 8734
N.A.I.C.S.: 541380

Dewhurst UK Manufacturing Ltd (1)
Inverness Rd
Hounslow, TW3 3LT, United Kingdom
Tel.: (44) 20 8607 7300
Fax: (44) 20 8572 5986
E-Mail: info@dewhurst.co.uk
Emp.: 10
Electrical Component Mfr
S.I.C.: 3699
N.A.I.C.S.: 335999
Richard Dewhurst *(Chm)*

LiftStore Ltd. (1)
Inverness Rd
Hounslow, Middlesex, TW3 3LT, United Kingdom
Tel.: (44) 2085381770
Fax: (44) 2085381771
E-Mail: info@liftstore.com
Web Site: www.liftstore.com
Emp.: 30
Development & Marketing of Elevator Products
S.I.C.: 3699
N.A.I.C.S.: 335999
Eamonn Reid *(Dir-Sls)*

U.S. Subsidiaries:

The Fixture Company (1)
8770 W Bryn Mawr Ave Ste 1300
Chicago, IL 60631-3557
Tel.: (847) 214-3100
Fax: (847) 214-2771
Toll Free: (877) 537-8753
E-Mail: info@thefixture.com
Web Site: www.thefixtureco.com
Standard, Modified & Custom Signal Fixtures Mfr
S.I.C.: 3699
N.A.I.C.S.: 335999

Winter & Bain Manufacturing, Inc. (1)
1417 Elwood St
Los Angeles, CA 90021 CA
Tel.: (213) 749-3561
Fax: (213) 749-1355
Web Site: www.elevatorresearch.com
Emp.: 22
Elevator Equipment Mfr
S.I.C.: 3534
N.A.I.C.S.: 333921
Barnet Rogers *(Gen Mgr)*

Non-U.S. Subsidiaries:

Australian Lift Components Pty. Ltd. (1)
5 Saggartfield Rd
Minto, NSW, 2566, Australia
Tel.: (61) 296030200
Fax: (61) 96032700
E-Mail: info@alc.au.com
Web Site: www.alc.au.com
Emp.: 100
Elevator Products Mfr
S.I.C.: 3699
N.A.I.C.S.: 335999
Chris Carroll *(Mng Dir)*

Dewhurst (Hong Kong) Ltd (1)
Ste 19 7 F Block A Hoi Luen Industrial Ctr
55 Hoi Yuen Rd
Hong Kong, China (Hong Kong)
Tel.: (852) 3523 1563
Fax: (852) 3909 1434
Electrical Component Mfr
S.I.C.: 3699
N.A.I.C.S.: 335999

Dewhurst (Hungary) Kft (1)
HRSZ 3518/8
Soskut, 2038, Hungary
Tel.: (36) 23560551
Fax: (36) 14892022
Electrical Component Mfr
S.I.C.: 3699
N.A.I.C.S.: 335999

Dupar Controls Inc. (1)
1751 Bishop St
Cambridge, ON, N1T 1N5, Canada
Tel.: (888) 629-6279
Fax: (519) 624-2524
E-Mail: info@dupar.com
Web Site: www.dupar.com
Emp.: 50
Elevator Push Button Mfr & Distr
S.I.C.: 3679
N.A.I.C.S.: 334419
George Foleanu *(Gen Mgr)*

Lift Material Australia Pty Ltd (1)
Unit 1 17-21 Bowden Street
Alexandria, NSW, 2015, Australia
Tel.: (61) 2 9310 4288
Fax: (61) 2 9698 4990
E-Mail: info@liftmaterial.com
Web Site: www.liftmaterial.com
Emp.: 6
Lift Materials Distr
S.I.C.: 5084
N.A.I.C.S.: 423830
Tony Pegg *(Gen Mgr)*

Lift Materials Australia (1)
17-21 Bowden Street Unit 1
Sydney, NSW, 2015, Australia
Tel.: (61) 293104288
Fax: (61) 296984990
E-Mail: info@liftmaterial.com
Web Site: www.liftmaterial.com
Emp.: 4
Elevator Products Mfr & Sales
S.I.C.: 3699
N.A.I.C.S.: 335999
Tony Tejj *(Gen Mgr)*

DEWILDT CAR SALES LIMITED

(d/b/a DeWildt Chrysler Dodge Jeep Ram)
1600 Main St E
Hamilton, ON, L8K 1E7, Canada
Tel.: (905) 312-0090
Fax: (905) 312-8827
E-Mail: reception@dewildtchrysler.com
Web Site: www.dewildtchrysler.com
Year Founded: 1960
Rev.: $21,678,274
Emp.: 47

Business Description:
New Car Dealers
S.I.C.: 5511
N.A.I.C.S.: 441110

Personnel:
Ted Dewildt *(Pres)*

DEXIA SA

Place du Champ de Mars 5
1050 Brussels, Belgium
Tel.: (32) 22135700
E-Mail: pressdexia@dexia.be
Web Site: www.dexia.com
Year Founded: 1996
DEXB—(EUR OTC)
Int. Income: $23,125,854,430
Assets: $480,865,385,700
Liabilities: $476,409,563,000
Net Worth: $4,455,822,700
Earnings: ($3,886,392,790)
Emp.: 2,429
Fiscal Year-end: 12/31/12

Business Description:
Bank Holding Company
S.I.C.: 6712
N.A.I.C.S.: 551111

Personnel:
Karel De Boeck *(Chm-Mgmt Bd & CEO)*
Pierre Vergnes *(CFO)*
Christine Lensel-Martinat *(COO)*
Marc Brugiere *(Chief Risk Officer)*
Hakan Ates *(CEO-DenizBank AS)*
Claude Edgar L.G. Piret *(Exec VP-Dexia Credit Local SA)*
Philippe Rucheton *(Exec VP-Dexia Credit Local SA)*

Board of Directors:
Robert de Metz
Paul Bodart
Bart Bronselaer
Delphine d'Amarzit
Karel De Boeck
Alexandre De Geest
Thierry Francq
Philippe Rucheton
Koen Van Loo

Subsidiaries:

Centrabail SA (1)
Blvd Pacheco 44
1000 Brussels, Belgium (100%)
Tel.: (32) 222211111
Fax: (32) 022221122
E-Mail: pierre.maoiani@dexia.com
Emp.: 50
Banking Services
S.I.C.: 6099
N.A.I.C.S.: 522320
Maoiani Pierre *(Pres)*

Corona Direct (1)
Metrologielaan 2
Brussels, 1130, Belgium (100%)
Tel.: (32) 2 244 23 23
Fax: (32) 22458890
E-Mail: info@corona.be
Web Site: www.coronadirect.be
Premiums: $1,933,842
Emp.: 180
Insurance Services
S.I.C.: 6311
N.A.I.C.S.: 524113
Yvon Cestrique *(Mng Dir)*

Dexia Employee Benefits N.V. (1)
Avenue Pacheco 44
1000 Brussels, Belgium
Tel.: (32) 2 222 09 13
Fax: (32) 2 222 09 14
Web Site: www.dexia-eb.com
Emp.: 6,000
Employee Fund & Benefit Services
S.I.C.: 6371
N.A.I.C.S.: 525110
Ludovic Wolff *(Mng Dir)*

Dexia Societe de Credit SA (1)
Rue des Clarisses 38
4000 Liege, Belgium
Tel.: (32) 4 232 45 45
Fax: (32) 4 232 45 01
Web Site: www.dexia-societedecredit.be
Emp.: 90

Dexia SA—(Continued)

Credit Management Services
S.I.C.: 6159
N.A.I.C.S.: 522298

Fonds Mercator (1)
Rue du Midi 2
1000 Brussels, Belgium (100%)
Tel.: (32) 25482535
Fax: (32) 25021628
E-Mail: livresdart@fondsmercator.be
Web Site: www.mercatorfonds.be
Sales Range: $1-9.9 Million
Emp.: 4
Book Publishing & Printing
S.I.C.: 2731
N.A.I.C.S.: 511130
Bernard Steyaert *(Mng Dir & Publr)*

U.S. Subsidiary:

Dexia Credit Local (1)
445 Park Ave
New York, NY 10022
Tel.: (212) 515-7000
Fax: (212) 753-5522
Web Site: www.dexia-americas.com
Emp.: 130
Credit Management Services
S.I.C.: 6159
N.A.I.C.S.: 522298
Guy Cools *(Gen Mgr)*

Subsidiary:

Dexia Real Estate Capital Markets (2)
1180 NW Maple St Ste 202
Issaquah, WA 98027-8106
Tel.: (425) 313-4600
Fax: (425) 313-1005
E-Mail: webmaster@dexia-cmbs.com
Web Site: www.dexia-cmbs.com
Emp.: 17
Securities Mortgages
S.I.C.: 6799
N.A.I.C.S.: 523910
Diana Kelsey Kutas *(Mng Dir-Asset Mgmt)*

Non-U.S. Subsidiaries:

Ausbil Dexia Ltd. (1)
Level 23 Symintec 207 Kent St
Sydney, NSW, 2000, Australia (51%)
Mailing Address:
GPO Box 2525
Sydney, NSW, 2001, Australia
Tel.: (61) 292590200
Fax: (61) 292590222
E-Mail: ausbildexia@ausbil.com.au
Web Site: www.ausbil.com.au
Emp.: 38
Equities Trading Services
S.I.C.: 6211
N.A.I.C.S.: 523120
Paul Xiradis *(CEO & Head-Equities)*
Mark Reilly *(COO)*

Dexia Bank Denmark A/S (1)
Gronningen 17
1270 Copenhagen, Denmark
Tel.: (45) 33 46 11 00
Fax: (45) 33 32 42 01
E-Mail: kontakt@dexia.dk
Web Site: www.dexia.jobs/EN/whoweare/Pages/intheworld.aspx
Commercial Banking Services
S.I.C.: 6029
N.A.I.C.S.: 522110

Dexia Bank Nederland N.V. (1)
Piet Heinkade 55
1019 GM Amsterdam, Netherlands (100%)
Mailing Address:
PO Box 808
Amsterdam, 1000 AV, Netherlands
Tel.: (31) 203485000
Fax: (31) 203485555
E-Mail: info@dexia.nl
Web Site: www.dexia.nl
Emp.: 300
Short-Term Business Credit
S.I.C.: 6159
N.A.I.C.S.: 522298
Dirk Bruneel *(Mng Dir)*

Dexia Crediop S.p.A. (1)
30 Via Viente Settembre
I 00187 Rome, Italy (70%)
Tel.: (39) 0647711
Fax: (39) 0647715952
E-Mail: internet@dexia.com
Web Site: www.dexia-crediop.it
Rev.: $1,368,455,532
Assets: $66,588,813,576
Liabilities: $65,059,123,434
Net Worth: $1,529,690,143
Earnings: ($4,541,545)
Emp.: 192
Fiscal Year-end: 12/31/12
Banking Services
S.I.C.: 6029
N.A.I.C.S.: 522110
Mario Sarcinelli *(Chm)*
Claude Piret *(Deputy Chm)*
Jean Le Naour *(CEO)*
Edoardo Baratella *(Sec & Head-Legal Dept)*

Non-U.S. Subsidiary:

Crediop Overseas Bank Ltd. (2)
West Bay Road
PO Box 707
Georgetown, Cayman Islands
Tel.: (345) 9474777
Fax: (345) 94 74799
Provider of Financial Services
S.I.C.: 6211
N.A.I.C.S.: 523999

Dexia Credit Local SA (1)
1 Passerelle des Reflets La Defense 2
92913 Paris, France
Tel.: (33) 1 58 58 77 77
Fax: (33) 1 58 58 70 00
Credit Card Management Services
S.I.C.: 6159
N.A.I.C.S.: 522298

Subsidiary:

Dexia CLF Banque S.A (2)
1 Passerelle des Reflets Tour Dexia La Defense 2 TSA 72200
La Defense, 92919 Paris, France
Tel.: (33) 1 58 58 88 02
Fax: (33) 1 58 58 88 10
Web Site: www.dexia.jobs/EN/whoweare/Pages/intheworld.aspx
Commercial Banking Services
S.I.C.: 6029
N.A.I.C.S.: 522110

U.S. Subsidiary:

Dexia Delaware LLC (2)
445 Park Ave Fl 7
New York, NY 10022-2606
Tel.: (212) 515-7000
Fax: (212) 753-5522
Web Site: www.dexia.jobs/EN/whoweare/Pages/intheworld.aspx
Financial Management Services
S.I.C.: 6211
N.A.I.C.S.: 523999

Non-U.S. Subsidiaries:

Dexia Kommunalbank Deutschland AG (2)
Charlottenstrasse 82
10969 Berlin, Germany De (100%)
Tel.: (49) 30255980
Fax: (49) 25598206
E-Mail: kommunalkredit@dexia.de
Web Site: www.dexia.de
Emp.: 72
Public Finance Services
S.I.C.: 9311
N.A.I.C.S.: 921130
Stephane Vermeire *(Chm-Supervisory Bd)*
Friedrich Munsberg *(Chm-Mgmt Bd)*
Laurent Fritsch *(Member-Mgmt Bd)*

Dexia Kommunalkredit Bank AG (2)
Fischhof 3
Vienna, 1010, Austria
Tel.: (43) 174 040 35 40
Fax: (43) 1 174 040 35 49
Web Site: www.dexia.com
Commercial Banking Services
S.I.C.: 6029
N.A.I.C.S.: 522110
Pierre Verot *(Mng Dir)*

Non-U.S. Subsidiaries:

Dexia Kommunalkredit Bulgaria EOOD (3)
19 Karnigradska
1000 Sofia, Bulgaria
Tel.: (359) 897 886 761
Financial Management Services
S.I.C.: 6211
N.A.I.C.S.: 523999

Dexia Sabadell Banco Local SA (2)
Paseo de las Doce Estrellas 4 Campo de las Naciones
Madrid, 28043, Spain
Tel.: (34) 917213310
Fax: (34) 917213320
Web Site: www.dexiasabadell.es
Emp.: 50
Financial Management Services
S.I.C.: 6211
N.A.I.C.S.: 523999

Dexia Credit Local (1)
800 Square Victoria Suite 1620
CP 201
Montreal, QC, H4Z 1 E3, Canada
Tel.: (514) 868-1200
Fax: (514) 868-1840
Web Site: www.dexia.jobs/EN/whoweare/Pages/intheworld.aspx
Emp.: 3
Credit Management Services
S.I.C.: 6159
N.A.I.C.S.: 522298

Dexia Epargne Pension SA (1)
65 Rue de la Victoire
75009 Paris, France
Tel.: (33) 1 55 50 15 15
Fax: (33) 1 45 26 34 20
Web Site: www.dexia.jobs/EN/whoweare/Pages/intheworld.aspx
Insurance Management Services
S.I.C.: 6411
N.A.I.C.S.: 524298

Dexia Finance SA (1)
1 Passerelle des Reflets Tour Dexia La Defense 2 TSA 92202
La Defense, 92919 Paris, France
Tel.: (33) 1 58 58 77 77
Fax: (33) 1 58 58 70 00
Web Site: www.dexia.jobs/EN/whoweare/Pages/intheworld.aspx
Financial Management Services
S.I.C.: 6211
N.A.I.C.S.: 523999

Dexia Ingenierie Sociale S.A (1)
13 Rue Croquechataigne
PB 30064
45380 La Chapelle-Saint-Mesmin, France
Tel.: (33) 2 36 56 00 00
Fax: (33) 2 36 56 00 01
E-Mail: assurance@dexia-prevoyance.com
Web Site: www.dexia-is.com
Financial Management Services
S.I.C.: 6211
N.A.I.C.S.: 523999

REKORD Versicherungvermittlungs- und Betreuungsgesellschaft fur Selbstandige mbH & Co. KG (1)
Grafenberger Allee 277 287
D 40237 Dusseldorf, Germany (100%)
Tel.: (49) 211914801
Fax: (49) 2119148224
E-Mail: maininfo@rekord.ag
Web Site: www.rekord.ag
Emp.: 60
Insurance Agents, Brokers & Service
S.I.C.: 6411
N.A.I.C.S.: 524298

DEXION EQUITY ALTERNATIVE LIMITED

3rd Fl 1 Le Truchot
Saint Peter Port, GY1 3SZ, Guernsey
Tel.: (44) 1481743940
Fax: (44) 1481743941
E-Mail: investor.services@dexioncapital.com
Web Site: www.dexioncapital.com
DEA—(LSE)
Sales Range: $10-24.9 Million

Business Description:
Investment Services
S.I.C.: 6799
N.A.I.C.S.: 523920

Personnel:
John Hawkins *(Chm)*

Board of Directors:
John Hawkins
Robin Bowie
Charles Parkinson
Christopher Sherwell

Legal Counsel:
Bingham McCutchen (London) LLP
41 Lothbury
London, United Kingdom

DEXTERITY VENTURES INC.

(d/b/a Dexterity Consulting)
Suite 200 3505 14th Street Northwest
Calgary, AB, T2T 3W2, Canada
Tel.: (403) 860-7572
Toll Free: (866) 963-4483
E-Mail: info@dexterityconsulting.ca
Web Site: www.dexterityconsulting.ca
Sales Range: $1-9.9 Million

Business Description:
Charity Consulting Services
S.I.C.: 8742
N.A.I.C.S.: 541611

Personnel:
Gena Rotstein *(CEO)*

DEXTON BUSINESS SOLUTIONS

Rivium 1e straat 35
2909 LE Capelle aan den IJssel, Netherlands
Tel.: (31) 102885020
Fax: (31) 102885021
E-Mail: info@dexton.nl
Web Site: www.dexton.nl
Sales Range: $1-9.9 Million
Emp.: 22

Business Description:
Customer Relationship Management Software
S.I.C.: 3652
N.A.I.C.S.: 334614

Personnel:
Jos Halkus *(Owner, CEO & Mng Dir)*

DEXUS PROPERTY GROUP

Level 25 Australia Square 264-278 George Street
Sydney, NSW, 2000, Australia
Mailing Address:
PO Box R1822
Royal Exchange, Sydney, NSW, 1225, Australia
Tel.: (61) 2 9017 1100
Fax: (61) 2 9017 1101
E-Mail: ir@dexus.com
Web Site: www.dexus.com
DXS—(ASX OTC)
Rev.: $646,831,470
Assets: $8,078,984,460
Liabilities: $2,668,713,890
Net Worth: $5,410,270,570
Earnings: $536,160,450
Fiscal Year-end: 06/30/13

Business Description:
Real Estate Development Services
S.I.C.: 6531
N.A.I.C.S.: 531390

Personnel:
Christopher T. Beare *(Chm)*
Darren J. Steinberg *(CEO)*
Craig D. Mitchell *(CFO)*
Tanya L. Cox *(COO & Gen Mgr-Property Svcs)*
John C. Easy *(Gen Counsel & Sec)*

Board of Directors:
Christopher T. Beare
Elizabeth A. Alexander
Barry R. Brownjohn
John C. Conde
Tonianne Dwyer
Stewart F. Ewen
Craig D. Mitchell
Richard Sheppard

Peter B. St George
Darren J. Steinberg

DEXXON GROUP

79 Ave Louis Roche
F 92238 Gennevilliers, Cedex, France
Tel.: (33) 141322121
Fax: (33) 141322122
E-Mail: info@dexxon.com
Web Site: www.dexxon.com
Sales Range: $700-749.9 Million
Emp.: 550

Business Description:
IT & Office Products Distr
S.I.C.: 5731
N.A.I.C.S.: 443142

U.S. Subsidiary:

Digital Storage Incorporated (1)
7611 Green Meadows Dr
Lewis Center, OH 43035-9445
Tel.: (740) 548-7179
Fax: (740) 548-7978
Toll Free: (800) 232-3475
E-Mail: sales@digitalstorage.com
Web Site: www.digitalstorage.com
Emp.: 50
Computer Media, Hardware & Supplies Distr
Import Export
S.I.C.: 5112
N.A.I.C.S.: 424120
Simon N. Garneau *(Pres)*
Dave Burke *(Exec VP-Fin)*
Bev Fekete *(Exec VP-Sls)*

Non-U.S. Subsidiary:

Dexxon GmbH (1)
Peter Sander Strasse 13
55252 Mainz-Kastel, Germany
Tel.: (49) 61345670
Telex: 462023 basma d
Fax: (49) 6134567555
E-Mail: hilfe@emtec-international.com
Web Site: www.emtec-international.com
Sales Range: $750-799.9 Million
Emp.: 35
Audio & Video Magnetic Recording Media; Data Storage Media
S.I.C.: 3651
N.A.I.C.S.: 334310

Subsidiaries:

EMTEC International Holding GmbH (2)
Kaiser Wilhelm Strasse 52
67059 Ludwigshafen, Germany
Tel.: (49) 62159200
Fax: (49) 6215920395
E-Mail: contact@emtec-group.com
Web Site: www.emtec-group.com
Emp.: 160
Holding Company
S.I.C.: 6719
N.A.I.C.S.: 551112

Non-U.S. Subsidiaries:

Dexxon Belgium S.A. (2)
Pegasuslaan 5
1831 Diegem, Belgium
Tel.: (32) 2 333 7333
Fax: (32) 2 333 7334
Web Site: www.dexxon.eu
Emp.: 15
Audio & Video Magnetic Recording Media
S.I.C.: 3695
N.A.I.C.S.: 334613

Dexxon Italia Spa (2)
Piazza Don Mapelli 75
20099 Sesto San Giovanni, MI, Italy
Tel.: (39) 0224416592
Fax: (39) 02 24 41 66 66
Web Site: www.dexxon.eu/eu/worldwide.php
Emp.: 100
Audio & Video Magnetic Recording Media
S.I.C.: 3695
N.A.I.C.S.: 334613

Dexxon Singapore Pty. Ltd. (2)
371 Beach Rd Keypoint Ste 10-11
Singapore, 199597, Singapore
Tel.: (65) 62950118
Fax: (65) 62950379
Web Site: www.dexxon.eu/eu/worldwide.php
Sales Range: $1-9.9 Million
Emp.: 4
Audio & Video Magnetic Recording Media
S.I.C.: 3695
N.A.I.C.S.: 334613
Lee Suhdin *(Gen Mgr)*

EMTEC Magnetics Australia Pty. Ltd. (2)
700 Springvale Rd 4th Fl
PO Box 4099
Mulgrave, VIC, 3170, Australia
Tel.: (61) 395622255
Fax: (61) 3 9562 2190
E-Mail: service@emtec-austalia.com
Web Site: www.emtec-group.com
Audio & Video Magnetic Recording Media
S.I.C.: 3695
N.A.I.C.S.: 334613

EMTEC Magnetics Iberica S.A. (2)
Paseo De La Castellana 143
E 28046 Madrid, Spain
Tel.: (34) 912108080
Fax: (34) 915710155
E-Mail: emtec_iberica@emtecgroup.com
Web Site: www.emtec.es
Emp.: 100
Audio & Video Magnetic Recording Media
S.I.C.: 3695
N.A.I.C.S.: 334613

EMTEC Magnetics Polska Sp. z.o.o. (2)
Ul Wschodnia 5a
PL 05 090 Warsaw, Poland
Tel.: (48) 227115100
Fax: (48) 227115101
E-Mail: kontakt@emtec-group.pl
Web Site: www.emtec-group.com
Emp.: 14
Audio & Video Magnetic Recording Media
S.I.C.: 3695
N.A.I.C.S.: 334613

EMTEC Magnetics (Schweiz) GmbH (2)
Appital
Postfach 99
CH-8820 Wadenswil, Switzerland
Tel.: (41) 17819511
Fax: (41) 17819512
Web Site: www.emtec-group.ch
Emp.: 8
Audio & Video Magnetic Recording Media
S.I.C.: 3695
N.A.I.C.S.: 334613

DEYAAR DEVELOPMENT PJSC

Deyaar Building Level 5 Beside Mall of the Emirates Al Barsha
PO Box 30833
Dubai, United Arab Emirates
Tel.: (971) 43957700
Fax: (971) 43957711
E-Mail: info@deyaar.ae
Web Site: www.deyaar.ae
Year Founded: 2002
DEYAAR—(DFM)
Rev.: $150,311,405
Assets: $1,787,766,426
Liabilities: $724,941,359
Net Worth: $1,062,825,067
Earnings: $10,507,509
Emp.: 200
Fiscal Year-end: 12/31/12

Business Description:
Real Estate Services
S.I.C.: 6531
N.A.I.C.S.: 531390

Personnel:
Abdullah Ali Obaid AlHamli *(Chm)*
Abdullah Ebrahim Lootah *(Vice Chm)*
Saeed Al Qatami *(CEO)*
S. Krishnamurthy *(CFO)*
Richard Imran Ding *(Gen Counsel & VP-Legal)*

Board of Directors:
Abdullah Ali Obaid AlHamli
Saif Al Khatiri
Mohammed Al Nahdi
Mohammed Al Sharif
Saif Al Yarabi
Khalifa Suhail Juma Al Zaffin
Adnan Chilwan
Abdullah Ebrahim Lootah
Obaid Lootah

Non-U.S. Subsidiary:

Beirut Bay SAL (1)
Ibisa Bldg Verdun St
Beirut, Lebanon
Tel.: (961) 1 809350
Fax: (961) 1 809351
Real Estate Agencies
S.I.C.: 6531
N.A.I.C.S.: 531210

DEYU AGRICULTURE CORP.

Unit 1010 Block B Huizhi Building 9 Xueqing Road
Haidian District, Beijing, China 100085
Tel.: (86) 1082732870
Fax: (86) 1062668580
E-Mail: jimmy@china-deyu.com
Web Site: www.china-deyu.com
Year Founded: 2008
DEYU—(OTC OTCB)
Rev.: $254,046,098
Assets: $113,907,391
Liabilities: $27,448,998
Net Worth: $86,458,393
Earnings: $16,408,819
Emp.: 490
Fiscal Year-end: 12/31/12

Business Description:
Grains, Cereals, Corn & Wheat Producer & Marketer
S.I.C.: 0119
N.A.I.C.S.: 111199

Personnel:
Hong Wang *(Chm)*
Jan Poulsen *(Pres)*
Greg Chen *(CEO)*
Amy He *(CFO)*
Emma Wan *(Sec)*

Board of Directors:
Hong Wang
Adolfo Carmona
Greg Chen
Xinli Li
Timothy C. Stevens

Legal Counsel:
K&L Gates LLP
Boston, MA 02111

DF DEUTSCHE FORFAIT AG

Kattenbug 18-24
50667 Cologne, Germany
Tel.: (49) 221973760
Fax: (49) 2219737676
E-Mail: dfag@dfag.de
Web Site: www.dfag.de
Year Founded: 2003
DE6—(DEU)
Rev.: $41,067,344
Assets: $130,445,763
Liabilities: $94,625,058
Net Worth: $35,820,705
Earnings: $3,349,704
Emp.: 61
Fiscal Year-end: 12/31/12

Business Description:
Financial & Foreign Trade Services
S.I.C.: 8742
N.A.I.C.S.: 541611

Personnel:
Hans-Detlef Bosel *(Chm-Supervisory Bd)*
Christoph Freiherr von Hammerstein-Loxten *(Vice Chm-Supervisory Bd)*
Frank Hock *(CFO & Member-Mgmt Bd)*
Marina Attawar *(Member-Mgmt Bd)*
Ulrich Wippermann *(Member-Mgmt Bd)*

Supervisory Board of Directors:
Hans-Detlef Bosel
Florian Becker
Christoph Freiherr von Hammerstein-Loxten
Ludolf-Georg von Wartenberg
Clemens von Weichs

Non-U.S. Subsidiaries:

DF Deutsche Forfait AG Pakistan (PVT.) LTD. (1)
Ste No 307 3rd Fl Siddiq Trade Ctr 72 Main Blvd
Gulberg, Lahore, Punjab, 54660, Pakistan
Tel.: (92) 42111332433
Fax: (92) 425781700
E-Mail: dfag@dfag.de
Emp.: 10
Forfaiting Business Services
S.I.C.: 6159
N.A.I.C.S.: 522298
Salman Mamoon Ahmad *(CEO)*

DF Deutsche Forfait s.r.o (1)
Panska 894 4
11000 Prague, Czech Republic
Tel.: (420) 221014620
Fax: (420) 221014619
E-Mail: dalibor.hanka@dfag.de
Emp.: 2
Forfaiting Business Services
S.I.C.: 6159
N.A.I.C.S.: 522298
Dalibor Hanka *(Mgr)*

U.S. Subsidiary:

DF Deutsche Forfait Americas Inc. (1)
9045 SW 64th Ct
Miami, FL 33156-1824
Tel.: (305) 377-2688
Fax: (305) 377-2887
Forfaiting & Financial Services
S.I.C.: 6159
N.A.I.C.S.: 522298

DFCC BANK

DFCC Building 73/5 Galle Rd
PO Box 1397
Colombo, 3, Sri Lanka
Tel.: (94) 112442442
Fax: (94) 112440376
E-Mail: info@dfccbank.com
Web Site: www.dfcc.lk
DFCC—(COL)
Rev.: $140,218,105
Assets: $1,167,423,607
Liabilities: $881,948,630
Net Worth: $285,474,976
Earnings: $26,771,145
Emp.: 1,262
Fiscal Year-end: 03/31/13

Business Description:
Banking Services
S.I.C.: 6211
N.A.I.C.S.: 523110

Personnel:
Arjun Rishya Fernando *(CEO & Gen Mgr)*
Dinesh Fernandopulle *(CIO & Sr VP)*
Trevine Fernandopulle *(Chief Risk Officer & Exec VP)*
Lakshman Silva *(CEO-DFCC Vardhana Bank PLC & Exec VP)*
Tyrone De Silva *(Exec VP-Lending)*
Palitha Gamage *(Exec VP-Plng & Ops)*
S. Nagarajah *(Exec VP)*
Anomie Withana *(Exec VP-Fin)*
Nandasiri Bandara *(Sr VP-Internal Audit)*
Manohari Gunawardhena *(Sr VP-Corp Banking & Resource Mobilisation)*
Ananda Kumaradasa *(Sr VP-Rehabilitation & Recoveries)*

DFCC Bank—(Continued)

Kapila Nanayakkara *(Sr VP-Treasury)*
Dharmasiri Wickramatilaka *(Sr VP-Branch Banking)*
Board of Directors:
J. M. S. Brito
A. S. Abeyewardene
L. P. Chandradasa
G. K. Dayasri
Arjun Rishya Fernando
P. M. Bandula Fernando
Hettiarachchige Marie Niranjala Shamalie Gunawardana
Cedric Royle Jansz
J. E. A. Perumal
Ravindra Balakantha Thambiayah

Subsidiaries:

DFCC Consulting (Pvt) Limited **(1)**
No 73 5 Galle Road
Colombo, 00300, Sri Lanka
Tel.: (94) 112442442
Fax: (94) 11 2440376
E-Mail: consulting@dfccbank.com
Business Consulting Services
S.I.C.: 8742
N.A.I.C.S.: 541611

DFCC Vardhana Bank Limited **(1)**
73 W A D Ramanayake
Mawatha, Colombo, 00200, Sri Lanka
Tel.: (94) 112371371
Fax: (94) 112371372
E-Mail: info@dfccvardhanabank.com
Web Site: www.dfccvardhanabank.com
Commercial Banking Services
S.I.C.: 6029
N.A.I.C.S.: 522110
J. M. S. Brito *(Chm)*
Lakshman Silva *(CEO & Mng Dir)*

Lanka Industrial Estates Limited **(1)**
Pattiwila Road
Sapugaskanda, Makola, 11640, Sri Lanka
Tel.: (94) 11 2400318
Fax: (94) 11 2400321
E-Mail: lindel@itmin.net
Web Site: www.lindel.com.lk
Emp.: 14
Industrial Estate Operation Services
S.I.C.: 6531
N.A.I.C.S.: 531390
A N Fonseka *(Chm)*
H A Samarakoon *(CEO)*

DFDS A/S

Sundkrogsgade 11
2100 Copenhagen, Denmark
Tel.: (45) 3342 3342
Fax: (45) 3342 3341
Web Site: www.dfdsgroup.com
DFDS—(CSE)
Rev.: $21,101,984,730
Assets: $2,218,403,110
Liabilities: $961,522,968
Net Worth: $1,256,880,143
Earnings: $26,747,027
Emp.: 5,239
Fiscal Year-end: 12/31/12
Business Description:
Freight & Passenger Transportation Services
S.I.C.: 4412
N.A.I.C.S.: 483111
Personnel:
Bent Ostergaard *(Chm)*
Claus Hemmingsen *(Vice Chm)*
Vagn Ove Sorensen *(Vice Chm)*
Niels Smedegaard *(Pres & CEO)*
Torben Carlsen *(CFO & Exec VP)*
Eddie Green *(Exec VP-Logistics Div)*
Henrik Holck *(Exec VP-People & Ships)*
Peder Gellert Pedersen *(Exec VP-Shipping Div)*
Board of Directors:
Bent Ostergaard
Annette Bjerre Bjerregaard
Claus Hemmingsen
Jens Otto Knudsen
Jill Lauritzen Melby
Ingar Skaug
Lars Skjold-Hansen
Lene Skole
Vagn Ove Sorensen
Kent Vildbaek

Non-U.S. Subsidiary:

Norfolkline B.V. **(1)**
Kranenburgweg 180
NL 2583 ER Hague, Netherlands (100%)
Tel.: (31) 703527400
Fax: (31) 703527435
E-Mail: info@norfolkline.com
Web Site: www.norfolkline.com
Emp.: 1,500
Channel Ferry Services
S.I.C.: 4481
N.A.I.C.S.: 483112

DFI INC.

100 Huanhe St
22154 Sijhih, Taipei, Taiwan
Tel.: (886) 226942986
Fax: (886) 226943226
Web Site: www.dfi.com.tw
2397—(TAI)
Sales Range: $25-49.9 Million
Business Description:
Computer Motherboard & Embedded Board Mfr
S.I.C.: 3575
N.A.I.C.S.: 334118
Personnel:
Y. C. Lu *(Chm & Gen Mgr)*

U.S. Subsidiary:

ITOX, LLC **(1)**
8 Elkins Rd
East Brunswick, NJ 08816
Tel.: (732) 390-2815
Fax: (732) 390-2817
E-Mail: techsupport@dfiweb.com
Web Site: www.dfi/itox.com
Emp.: 20
Computer Peripheral Equipments Distr
S.I.C.: 5045
N.A.I.C.S.: 423430
Robert Liao *(Sr VP)*

Non-U.S. Subsidiaries:

DFI Co.,LTD. **(1)**
542 1 Daman Ri Jinrye Myun
Kimhae, Gyeongsangnam-do, 621 881, Korea (South)
Tel.: (82) 553461882
Fax: (82) 553461883
E-Mail: sales@cybow.com
Web Site: www.cybow.com
Emp.: 60
Medical Device Mfr & Distr
S.I.C.: 3845
N.A.I.C.S.: 334510
Geon Yun Jung *(Pres)*

Diamond Flower Information (NL) B.V. **(1)**
Shannonweg 11
Botlek, 3197 LG Rotterdam, South Holland, Netherlands
Tel.: (31) 102961840
Fax: (31) 102961849
E-Mail: sales@dfi-europe.nl
Emp.: 6
Computer Mother Boards Distr
S.I.C.: 5045
N.A.I.C.S.: 423430
Y. Liao Liao *(Gen Mgr)*

DFL HOLDINGS PTY LTD

Upper Ground Level Queen Adelaide Building
90-112 Queen Street, Brisbane, QLD, 4000, Australia
Tel.: (61) 7 3229 2999
Fax: (61) 7 3221 0292
Business Description:
Holding Company
S.I.C.: 6719
N.A.I.C.S.: 551112
Personnel:
Lina Wood *(Founder)*

Holding:

Premier Fasteners Pty Limited **(1)**
1 & 3 Ladbroke Street
Milperra, NSW, 2214, Australia
Tel.: (61) 297721888
Fax: (61) 297716182
E-Mail: premfast@bigpond.net.au
Web Site: www.Premierfasteners.com.au
Sales Range: $1-9.9 Million
Emp.: 25
Fasteners Mfr & Sales
S.I.C.: 3965
N.A.I.C.S.: 339993
Ivan James Mikkelsen *(Gen Mgr)*

DFL INFRASTRUCTURE FINANCE LIMITED

14 Ramakrishna Street T Nagar
Chennai, Tamil Nadu, 600 017, India
Tel.: (91) 4428141778
Fax: (91) 4428141612
E-Mail: dflinfra@dfl.co.in
Web Site: www.dflfinance.com
511393—(BOM)
Rev.: $640,446
Assets: $21,935,990
Liabilities: $31,519,891
Net Worth: ($9,583,901)
Earnings: ($2,896,615)
Fiscal Year-end: 03/31/13
Business Description:
Commercial Vehicle Finance
S.I.C.: 6153
N.A.I.C.S.: 522291
Personnel:
S. Balachander *(Mng Dir)*
Chandramohan Ikkurthi *(Sec)*
Board of Directors:
V. Sambamoorthy
S. Balachander
R. Baskaran
G. S. Gusain
S. Mahadevan
S. Mythili
B. Prakash
Krithika Sambamoorthy
Transfer Agent:
Cameo Corporate Services Limited
No 1 Club House Road
Chennai, India

DFM FOODS LIMITED

8377 Roshanara Road
Delhi, 110007, India
Tel.: (91) 11 23826445
Fax: (91) 11 23822409
E-Mail: info@dfmfoods.com
Web Site: www.dfmfoods.com
Year Founded: 1983
519588—(BOM)
Rev.: $42,247,098
Assets: $25,650,090
Liabilities: $19,429,920
Net Worth: $6,220,170
Earnings: $1,169,874
Emp.: 390
Fiscal Year-end: 03/31/13
Business Description:
Corn Chips Mfr & Whlsr
S.I.C.: 2096
N.A.I.C.S.: 311919
Personnel:
R. P. Jain *(Chm)*
Mohit Jain *(Vice Chm & Mng Dir)*
Rajiv Bhambri *(CFO)*
Arjun Sahu *(Compliance Officer & Asst Sec)*
N. K. Arora *(Sec)*
Board of Directors:
R. P. Jain
Pradeep Dinodia
Mohit Jain
Rohan Jain
S. C. Nanda
Mohit Satyanand
Sandeep Singhal
Transfer Agent:
MCS Limited
F-65 1st Floor Okhla Industrial Area Phase-I
New Delhi, India

DFNN, INC.

3rd Floor Bonifacio Technology Center 31st St corner 2nd Avenue
E-Square Bonifacio Global City, Taguig, Metro Manila, Philippines
Tel.: (63) 28180973
Fax: (63) 28180998
Web Site: www.dfnn.com
DFNN—(PHI)
Rev.: $1,962,459
Assets: $9,041,783
Liabilities: $8,855,616
Net Worth: $186,167
Earnings: ($3,408,475)
Emp.: 65
Fiscal Year-end: 12/31/12
Business Description:
Information Technology Services
S.I.C.: 7371
N.A.I.C.S.: 541511
Personnel:
Antonio A. Lopa *(Chm)*
Ramon C. Garcia, Jr. *(Pres & CEO)*
Dickson B. Co *(CFO)*
Czarina G. Turla *(Asst Officer-Corp Info & Head-Fin)*
Patricia P. de las Cagigas *(Corp Info Officer)*
Edwin B. Villanueva *(Treas)*
Manuel Z. Gonzalez *(Sec)*
Board of Directors:
Antonio A. Lopa
Ronald A. Arambulo
Roberto F. de Ocampo
Ramon C. Garcia, Jr.
Monico V. Jacob
Jean Henri D. Lhuillier
Miguel R. Manzano
Eric Francis P. Ongkauko
Joseph Peter Y. T. Roxas
Marco Antonio R. Urera
Edwin B. Villanueva

DFS FURNITURE LTD.

1 Rockingham Way Redhouse Interchange
Doncaster, S Yorkshire, DN6 7NA, United Kingdom
Tel.: (44) 1302330365
Fax: (44) 1302330880
E-Mail: contactus@dfs.co.uk
Web Site: www.dfs.co.uk
Year Founded: 1969
Sales Range: $900-999.9 Million
Emp.: 600
Business Description:
Upholstered Furniture Mfr & Retailer
S.I.C.: 2512
N.A.I.C.S.: 337121
Personnel:
Richard Baker *(Chm)*
Jon Massey *(COO)*
Paul Walker *(Sec)*
Transfer Agent:
Deutsche Bank AG London
Winchester House 1 Great Winchester Street
London, WC2N 6NN, United Kingdom

DGB FINANCIAL GROUP CO., LTD.

10F Daegu Bank Head Office Bldg 118
Daegu, 706712, Korea (South)
Tel.: (82) 53 7407900
Fax: (82) 53 7407999
Web Site: www.dgbfg.co.kr

139130—(KRS)
Business Description:
Bank Holding Company
S.I.C.: 6712
N.A.I.C.S.: 551111
Personnel:
Chun-Soo Ha *(CEO)*

Subsidiaries:

The Daegu Bank, Ltd. (1)
118 Su-sung dong 2-ga
Daegu, 706-712, Korea (South)
Tel.: (82) 537562001
Fax: (82) 537559677
E-Mail: sustainability@dgb.co.kr
Web Site: www.daegubank.co.kr
Sales Range: $1-4.9 Billion
Emp.: 2,793
Banking Services
S.I.C.: 6029
N.A.I.C.S.: 522110
Chun-Soo Ha *(Chm & CEO)*
Byung-yong Jin *(Sr Exec VP-Economic Res Div)*
Hee-cheol Kim *(Exec VP-Mktg Plng Div)*
Kwang-su Kim *(Exec VP-Retail Banking Fin Div)*
In-gyu Park *(Exec VP-Strategic Fin Div)*
Jung-won Seo *(Exec VP-Mgmt Plng Div)*

Daegu Credit Information Co. Ltd. (1)
527-4 Bisan-dong Seo-gu
703-040 Daegu, Korea (South)
Tel.: (82) 535737700
Fax: (82) 536081400
Web Site: www.daegucredit.co.kr/
Commercial Banking
S.I.C.: 6029
N.A.I.C.S.: 522110
Cho Seung-woong *(Pres)*

Korea Lease Financing Co., Ltd. (1)
15th Fl Seorin Bldg 88 Seorin-dong
Jongno-gu, Seoul, Korea (South)
Tel.: (82) 23984114
Fax: (82) 2 398 4119
Financial Leasing Services
S.I.C.: 6159
N.A.I.C.S.: 522220
Sejun Ko *(Sr Mgr)*

Korea Non-Bank Lease Financing Co. Ltd (1)
Seolin Bldg 15th Floor
Seolin-dong 88 Jongro-gu, Seoul, Korea (South)
Tel.: (82) 23984113
Fax: (82) 23984198
Financial Investment Activities
S.I.C.: 6211
N.A.I.C.S.: 523999
Jae Chul-chang *(Pres)*

DGE, INC.
(Acquired by FEV GmbH)

DGENX CO., LTD.
288-7 Yeonamyulgeum-ro Eumbong-myeon
Asan-si, Asan, Chungnam, 336-864, Korea (South)
Tel.: (82) 41 530 3200
Fax: (82) 41 546 4736
Web Site: www.dwtechno.com
113810—(KRS)
Business Description:
Automobile Exhaust Systems Mfr
S.I.C.: 3714
N.A.I.C.S.: 336390
Personnel:
Suk Woo Lee *(CEO)*

DGI HOLDINGS LIMITED
100-102 Cavan Road Dry Creek
Adelaide, SA, 5094, Australia
Tel.: (61) 8 8342 3316
Fax: (61) 8 8342 2848
E-Mail: admin@digislide.com.au
Web Site: www.digislide.com.au
DGI—(ASX)
Sales Range: Less than $1 Million
Emp.: 11
Business Description:
Video Projection & Projector Peripherals Researcher, Developer, Mfr & Marketer
S.I.C.: 3651
N.A.I.C.S.: 334310
Personnel:
Kevin Soper *(Founder)*
Luceille Outhred *(CEO)*
Peter Rubinshtein *(Chief Technologist)*
Board of Directors:
Marc Robert McNicol
Luceille Outhred
Legal Counsel:
HWL Ebsworth Lawyers
Level 14 Australia Sq 264 278 George St
Sydney, Australia

DGM MINERALS CORP.
13584 26th Ave
Surrey, BC, V4P 1Z6, Canada
Tel.: (778) 999-7030
Fax: (604) 357-1030
E-Mail: ifgsmith@yahoo.ca
Year Founded: 2010
DGM—(TSXV)
Business Description:
Metal Mining
S.I.C.: 1099
N.A.I.C.S.: 212299
Personnel:
Peter Smith *(Pres & CEO)*
Douglas Smith *(CFO)*
Michael Raven *(Sec)*
Board of Directors:
Nick Houghton
Thomas Lamb
Douglas Smith
Peter Smith
Transfer Agent:
Computershare Investor Services Inc.
510 Burrard St 2nd Floor
Vancouver, BC, V6C 3B9, Canada
Tel.: (604) 661-9400

DGR GLOBAL LIMITED
Level 27 111 Eagle Street
Brisbane, QLD, 4000, Australia
Mailing Address:
PO Box 5261
Brisbane, QLD, 4001, Australia
Tel.: (61) 7 3303 0680
Fax: (61) 7 3303 0681
Web Site: www.dgrglobal.com.au
DGR—(ASX)
Rev.: $9,557,283
Assets: $34,718,600
Liabilities: $2,574,410
Net Worth: $32,144,190
Earnings: ($4,505,550)
Emp.: 50
Fiscal Year-end: 06/30/13
Business Description:
Mineral Exploration Services
S.I.C.: 1041
N.A.I.C.S.: 212221
Personnel:
Nicholas Mather *(Mng Dir)*
Priy Jayasuriya *(CFO)*
Karl Schlobohm *(Sec)*
Board of Directors:
William Stubbs
Vincent Mascolo
Nicholas Mather
Brian Moller
Legal Counsel:
Hopgood Ganim
Level 8 Waterfront Place 1 Eagle Street
Brisbane, QLD, 4000, Australia
Subsidiaries:

AusNiCo Limited (1)
Level 27 111 Eagle Street
Brisbane, QLD, 4000, Australia (53.4%)
Tel.: (61) 7 3303 0611
Fax: (61) 7 3303 0681
E-Mail: info@ausnico.com.au
Web Site: www.ausnico.com.au
ANW—(ASX)
Rev.: $32,921
Assets: $9,580,704
Liabilities: $1,186,699
Net Worth: $8,394,005
Earnings: ($1,898,364)
Fiscal Year-end: 06/30/13
Nickel Mining Services
S.I.C.: 1021
N.A.I.C.S.: 212234
Peter Williams *(CEO)*
Priy Jayasuriya *(CFO)*
Karl Schlobohm *(Sec)*

Eastern Exploration Pty Ltd (1)
14 Harris Place
Kalgoorlie, WA, 6430, Australia
Tel.: (61) 8 9091 3730
Gold Exploration Services
S.I.C.: 1041
N.A.I.C.S.: 212221

Orbis Gold Limited (1)
Level 32 AMP Place 10 Eagle Street
Brisbane, QLD, 4000, Australia (72.7%)
Tel.: (61) 7 3198 3040
Fax: (61) 7 3236 5036
E-Mail: info@mtisametals.com.au
Web Site: www.mtisametals.com.au
OBS—(ASX)
Rev.: $517,419
Assets: $43,261,958
Liabilities: $2,709,760
Net Worth: $40,552,198
Earnings: ($2,933,616)
Emp.: 5
Fiscal Year-end: 06/30/13
Mineral Deposit Exploration & Development Services
S.I.C.: 1099
N.A.I.C.S.: 212299
Peter Spiers *(Mng Dir)*
Peter Harding-Smith *(CFO & Sec)*

Navaho Gold Limited (1)
Level 5 Santos House 60 Edward Street
Brisbane, QLD, 4000, Australia
Tel.: (61) 7 3303 0624
Fax: (61) 7 3303 0681
E-Mail: info@navahogold.com
Web Site: www.navahogold.com
NVG—(ASX)
Rev.: $19,718
Assets: $5,220,368
Liabilities: $343,449
Net Worth: $4,876,919
Earnings: ($3,717,170)
Fiscal Year-end: 06/30/13
Gold Mining Services
S.I.C.: 1041
N.A.I.C.S.: 212221
Priy Jayasuriya *(CFO)*
Karl Schlobohm *(Sec)*

D.G.S. CONSTRUCTION COMPANY LTD.
A101 13761 116th Avenue
Surrey, BC, V3R 0T2, Canada
Tel.: (604) 584-2214
Fax: (604) 588-1703
Web Site: www.dgsconstruction.com
Year Founded: 1983
Rev.: $51,947,320
Emp.: 30
Business Description:
Building Construction Services
S.I.C.: 1542
N.A.I.C.S.: 236220
Personnel:
George Rossi *(Pres)*
Dennis Rossi *(Partner)*

DGS DRUCKGUSS SYSTEME AG
Industriestrasse 10
CH 9015 Saint Gallen, Switzerland
Tel.: (41) 713138888
Fax: (41) 713138800
E-Mail: info@dgs-druckguss.com
Web Site: www.dgs-druckguss.com
Emp.: 650
Business Description:
Industry Castings (Ferrous Metals)
S.I.C.: 3322
N.A.I.C.S.: 331511
Personnel:
Alfred Viaten Steiger *(Gen Mgr)*

Non-U.S. Subsidiary:

DGS Druckguss Systeme s.r.o (1)
Volgogradska 89
460 10 Liberec, Czech Republic
Tel.: (420) 482429710
Fax: (420) 485151064
E-Mail: recepce@dgs-druckguss.com
Emp.: 300
Steel Foundry
S.I.C.: 3325
N.A.I.C.S.: 331513
Pfogl Lubos *(Mng Dir)*

DH HOLDINGS CO., LTD.
Donghee Bldg 705-32 Yeoksam-dong
Gangnam-gu, Seoul, Korea (South)
Tel.: (82) 2 2016 2000
Fax: (82) 2 2016 2009
E-Mail: donghee@donghee.co.kr
Web Site: www.donghee.co.kr
Year Founded: 1972
Business Description:
Holding Company; Motor Vehicle Suspension, Fuel Tank, Pedal, Roof System & Body Mfr
S.I.C.: 6719
N.A.I.C.S.: 551112
Personnel:
Dong-ho Lee *(CEO)*

Joint Venture:

Webasto Donghee Co., Ltd. (1)
579 9 Yong Yeon Dong Nam Gu
680 150 Ulsan, Korea (South) Ks
Tel.: (82) 522594500
Fax: (82) 522570171
Web Site: www.webasto-korea.com
Emp.: 220
Motor Vehicle Sunroof Developer & Mfr; Owned by Webasto AG & by DH Holdings Co., Ltd.
S.I.C.: 3714
N.A.I.C.S.: 336390

DHAKA BANK LIMITED
Biman Bhaban 1st Floor 100
Motijheel C/A
Dhaka, 1000, Bangladesh
Tel.: (880) 29554514
Fax: (880) 29556584
E-Mail: info@dhakabank.com.bd
Web Site: www.dhakabankltd.com
DHAKABANK—(DHA)
Int. Income: $165,506,531
Assets: $1,654,167,441
Liabilities: $1,533,012,908
Net Worth: $121,154,532
Earnings: $28,465,016
Emp.: 1,455
Fiscal Year-end: 12/31/12
Business Description:
Banking Services
S.I.C.: 6211
N.A.I.C.S.: 523110
Personnel:
Abdul Hai Sarker *(Chm)*
Rokshana Zaman *(Vice Chm)*
Niaz Habib *(Mng Dir)*
Khondker Fazle Rashid *(Mng Dir)*
Emranul Huq *(Deputy Mng Dir)*
Sajjad Hussain *(Deputy Mng Dir-Ops)*
Neaz Mohammad Khan *(Deputy Mng Dir-RM)*
Arham Masudul Huq *(Sec & Sr Exec VP)*
Shamshad Begum *(Sr Exec VP)*
Asadul Azim *(Exec VP & Head-Credit)*

Dhaka Bank Limited—(Continued)

Sirajul Hoque *(Exec VP & Head-Islamic Banking Div)*
S. A. F. A. Musabbir *(Exec VP & Head-Legal & Recovery)*
Azad Shamsi *(Exec VP & Head-Retail Banking Div)*
Fakhrul Islam *(Sr VP & Head-Ops)*
Darashiko Khasru *(Sr VP & Head-Fin & Accts)*
Mujib A. Siddiqui *(Sr VP & Head-HR)*
Board of Directors:
Abdul Hai Sarker
Mirza Yaseer Abbas
Abu Naser Bukhtear Ahmed
Mirza Abbas Uddin Ahmed
Abdullah Al Ahsan
Md. Amirullah
Tahidul Hossain Chowdhury
Mohammed Hanif
Suez Islam
Reshadur Rahman
Khondker Fazle Rashid
Altaf Hossain Sarker
Amanullah Sarker
Jashim Uddin
Khondoker Jamil Uddin
Khondoker Monir Uddin
Rokshana Zaman

DHAKA ELECTRIC SUPPLY COMPANY LIMITED

22/B Faruque Sarani Nikunja-2
Dhaka, 1219, Bangladesh
Tel.: (880) 2 8900110
Fax: (880) 2 8900100
E-Mail: info@desco.org.bd
Web Site: www.desco.org.bd
DESCO—(DHA)
Rev.: $275,358,513
Assets: $419,167,917
Liabilities: $285,883,164
Net Worth: $133,284,754
Earnings: $9,961,529
Emp.: 993
Fiscal Year-end: 06/30/13
Business Description:
Electric Power Distribution Services
S.I.C.: 4931
N.A.I.C.S.: 221122
Personnel:
Md. Mofazzel Hossain *(Chm)*
Md. Arjad Hossain *(Mng Dir)*
Md. Shofiqul Islam *(Sec)*
Board of Directors:
Md. Mofazzel Hossain
S. R. Akter
Md. Nurul Alam
Mohammad Harun
Md. Nazrul Hasan
Md. Fazlul Hoque
Md. Arjad Hossain
M. Mahfuzul Islam
A. K. M. Humayun Kabir
Salma Benthe Kadir
Shah Khaled Reza

DHAKA INSURANCE LIMITED

Amin Court 8th Floor 31 Bir Uttam Shahid
Ashfaqueus Samad Road, Dhaka, 1000, Bangladesh
Tel.: (880) 2 9571482
Fax: (880) 2 9554950
E-Mail: contact@dhakainsurancebd.com
Web Site: www.dhakainsurancebd.com
Year Founded: 2000
DHAKAINS—(DHA)
Business Description:
Insurance Services
S.I.C.: 6411
N.A.I.C.S.: 524298
Personnel:
Fazlur Rahman *(Founder)*
Mohammad Hasan *(Chm)*
Farzana Rahman *(Vice Chm)*
A. Q. M. Wazed Ali *(Mng Dir)*
Mohammad Abul Hashim *(CFO, Sec & Deputy Mng Dir)*
Aminul Islam *(Deputy Mng Dir-Dev)*
Syed Farid Uddin Masud *(Deputy Mng Dir)*
Bayazid Muztaba Siddiqui *(Deputy Mng Dir)*
Board of Directors:
Mohammad Hasan
A. Q. M. Wazed Ali
S. K. Basak
M. Mofizul Islam
A. B. M. Kamal
A. K. M. Kamruzzaman
Prodip Karan
Mohammad Masum
Farzana Rahman
Fazlur Rahman
Hamida Rahman
Biswajit Saha
Md. Sahabuddin
Md. Rayhan Uddin

DHAKA STOCK EXCHANGE LTD.

Stock Exchange Building 9 F
Motijheel C A
Dhaka, 1000, Bangladesh
Tel.: (880) 029564601
Fax: (880) 0297175703
E-Mail: dse@bol-online.com
Web Site: www.dsebd.org
Sales Range: $1-4.9 Billion
Emp.: 300
Business Description:
Stock Exchange Services
S.I.C.: 6231
N.A.I.C.S.: 523210
Personnel:
Shakil Rizvi *(Pres)*
Satipati Moitra *(CEO)*
A. S.M. Khairuzzaman *(CTO)*
Shaikh Mohammadullah *(Sec & Gen Mgr)*
Ahsanul Islam Titu *(Sr VP)*
Board of Directors:
Hanif Bhuiya
Abdullah Bokhari
Abdul Haque
N.U.M. Oliullah
M. A. Quayum
Rakibur Rahman
Sharif Ataur Rahman
Kazi Firoz Rashid
Khwaja Ghulam Rasul

DHAMECHA GROUP, INC.

First Way
Wembley, HA9 0TU, United Kingdom
Tel.: (44) 20 8903 8181
Fax: (44) 20 8902 4420
Web Site: www.dhamecha.com
Year Founded: 1976
Sales Range: $800-899.9 Million
Emp.: 432
Business Description:
Grocery Store Operator
S.I.C.: 5411
N.A.I.C.S.: 445110
Personnel:
Rupen Dhamecha *(Owner)*

DHAMPUR SUGAR MILLS LIMITED

241 Okhla Industrial Estate Phase-III
New Delhi, 110020, India
Tel.: (91) 1130659400
Fax: (91) 1126935697
E-Mail: corporateoffice@dhampur.com
Web Site: www.dhampur.com
500119—(BOM NSE)
Rev.: $284,194,098
Assets: $492,585,552
Liabilities: $402,284,628
Net Worth: $90,300,924
Earnings: $4,210,434
Fiscal Year-end: 03/31/13
Business Description:
Sugar Mfr
S.I.C.: 2062
N.A.I.C.S.: 311314
Personnel:
V. K. Goel *(Chm)*
Ashok K. Goel *(Vice Chm)*
Gaurav Goel *(Mng Dir)*
Gautam Goel *(Mng Dir)*
Arhant Jain *(Pres-Fin, Compliance Officer & Sec)*
Board of Directors:
V. K. Goel
Rahul Bedi
Priya Brat
Ashok K. Goel
Gaurav Goel
Gautam Goel
Ashwani K. Gupta
M. K. Jain
M. P. Mehrotra
Harish Saluja
J. P. Sharma
B. B. Tandon
S. K. Wadhwa

Mittal Gupta & Company
Kanpur, India
Transfer Agent:
Alankit Assignments Ltd
Alankit House 2E/21, Jhandewalan Extension
New Delhi, India

DHAMPURE SPECIALTY SUGARS LTD

24 School Lane Opp WTC
New Delhi, 110 001, India
Tel.: (91) 11 23711223
Fax: (91) 11 23352591
E-Mail: info@sugarindia.com
Web Site: www.sugarindia.com
531923—(BOM)
Rev.: $8,443,654
Assets: $4,269,169
Liabilities: $898,244
Net Worth: $3,370,924
Earnings: $143,518
Emp.: 100
Fiscal Year-end: 03/31/13
Business Description:
Sugar Mfr
S.I.C.: 2063
N.A.I.C.S.: 311313
Personnel:
Sorabh Gupta *(Mng Dir)*
Ziaul Hasan Khan *(Sec)*
Board of Directors:
N. K. Gupta
Sorabh Gupta
Murli Manohar
Deshraj Singh
Transfer Agent:
MAS Services Limited
T-34 2nd Floor Okhla Industrial Area Phase - II
New Delhi, India

DHANADA CORPORATION LIMITED

Dhanada 16/6 Erandwane Hsg Soc
Plot No 8 Patwardhan Baug
Pune, Maharashtra, 411 004, India
Tel.: (91) 20 25462408
Fax: (91) 20 25460661
E-Mail: dhanada@dhanadacorp.com
Web Site: www.dhanadacorp.com
Year Founded: 1986
531198—(BOM)
Rev.: $2,089,689
Assets: $9,778,975
Liabilities: $3,662,792
Net Worth: $6,116,183
Earnings: ($208,580)
Emp.: 100
Fiscal Year-end: 03/31/13
Business Description:
Hotel Management Services
S.I.C.: 7011
N.A.I.C.S.: 721110
Personnel:
Ramesh R. Havele *(Chm & Mng Dir)*
Sanjana M. Joshi *(Compliance Officer & Sec)*
Board of Directors:
Ramesh R. Havele
Gajanan M. Deshpande
Veena R. Havele
Shreeniwas G. Kale
Transfer Agent:
LINK INTIME INDIA PVT. LTD.
Block No 202 2nd Floor Akshay Complex Near Ganesh Temple
Off Dhole Patil Road, Pune, 411001, India

DHANALAXMI ROTO SPINNERS LTD.

No 15-9-56 Inani House Mahahraj Gunj
Hyderabad, Andhra Pradesh, 500012, India
Tel.: (91) 7819871367
Fax: (91) 4027847960
Web Site: drsl.tradeindia.com
521216—(BOM)
Rev.: $4,819,658
Assets: $2,079,947
Liabilities: $926,722
Net Worth: $1,153,225
Earnings: $76,793
Fiscal Year-end: 03/31/13
Business Description:
Wood Pulp Mfr
S.I.C.: 2448
N.A.I.C.S.: 321920
Personnel:
Narayan Inani *(Exec Dir)*
Board of Directors:
Simanth Roy Chowdhury
Narayan Inani
Rajkumar Inani
Shyam Sunder Jakhotia
K. N. Prasad
Transfer Agent:
CIL Securities Ltd
214 Raghava Ratna Towers Chirag Ali Lane Abids
Hyderabad, India

DHANLAXMI BANK LTD.

Dhanalakshmi Buildings Naickanal
Thrissur, Kerala, 680 001, India
Tel.: (91) 4876617000
Fax: (91) 4876617222
Web Site: www.dhanbank.com
Year Founded: 1927
DHANBANK—(NSE)
Rev.: $263,693,864
Assets: $2,562,133,038
Liabilities: $2,420,117,046
Net Worth: $142,015,992
Earnings: $486,212
Emp.: 2,601
Fiscal Year-end: 03/31/13
Business Description:
Commercial Banking Services
S.I.C.: 6029
N.A.I.C.S.: 522110
Personnel:
Tekkar Yashwanth Prabhu *(Chm)*
P. G. Jayakumar *(CEO & Mng Dir)*
K. S. Krishnan *(CFO)*

P. S. Ravikumar *(Chief Credit Officer & Chief Compliance Officer)*
Ravindran K. Warrier *(Sec)*
Board of Directors:
Tekkar Yashwanth Prabhu
K. Jayakumar
P. G. Jayakumar
P. Mohanan
S. Raja
K. Srikanth Reddy
Raja Selvaraj
Chella K. Srinivasan
K. Vijayaraghavan
Transfer Agent:
Karvy Compushare Private Limited
Plot No 17 to 24 Vittalrao Nagar Madhapur
Hyderabad, India

DHANLAXMI FABRICS LTD.

Manpada Road
Dombivli E, Thane, Maharashtra, 421 204, India
Tel.: (91) 251 2870589
Fax: (91) 251 2870545
E-Mail: info@dfl.net.in
Web Site: www.dfl.net.in
Year Founded: 1994
521151—(BOM)
Sales Range: $1-9.9 Million
Business Description:
Textile Fabric Mfr & Distr
S.I.C.: 2269
N.A.I.C.S.: 313310
Personnel:
Ramautar S. Jhawar *(Chm)*
Vinod S. Jhawar *(Mng Dir)*
Board of Directors:
Ramautar S. Jhawar
Mahesh S. Jhawar
Vinod S. Jhawar
Durgesh Kabra
Mihir Mehta
N. C. Sharma
S. Sivaswami

DHANUKA AGRITECH LIMITED

14th Floor Building 5A DLF Cyber Terrace Cyber City DLF Phase III
Gurgaon, Haryana, 122002, India
Tel.: (91) 124 3838500
Fax: (91) 124 3838888
E-Mail: headoffice@dhanuka.com
Web Site: www.dhanuka.com
DHANUKA—(BOM NSE)
Rev.: $119,842,653
Assets: $77,957,734
Liabilities: $29,240,435
Net Worth: $48,717,298
Earnings: $11,948,733
Emp.: 500
Fiscal Year-end: 03/31/13
Business Description:
Agro-Chemicals, Fertilizers & Seeds
S.I.C.: 2879
N.A.I.C.S.: 325320
Personnel:
Ram Gopal Agarwal *(Chm)*
V. K. Bansal *(Co-Pres & CFO)*
P. K. Kanodia *(Co-Pres)*
R. K. Kanodia *(Co-Pres)*
K. B. Kejariwal *(Co-Pres)*
Mahendra Kumar Dhanuka *(Mng Dir)*
Shubha Singh *(Compliance Officer & Sec)*
C. M. Gupta *(Pres-Procurement)*
G. D. Gupta *(Pres-Gen Admin)*
O. P. Singh *(Pres-R&D)*
Board of Directors:
Ram Gopal Agarwal
Sachin Bhartiya
Priya Brat
Arun Kumar Dhanuka
Mahendra Kumar Dhanuka
Mridul Dhanuka
Rahul Dhanuka
Subash Chander Gupta
Vinod Jain
Shrikrishna Khetan
Subhash Chandra Lakhotia
Indresh Narain
Transfer Agent:
Abhipra Capital Limited
Ground Fl Abhipra Complex Dilkhush Industrial Area A-387 GT Karnal Rd
Delhi, India

DHANUS TECHNOLOGIES LTD

New No 20 Old No 6 First Floor
Sengunthar Street
Shenoy Nagar, Chennai, Tamil Nadu, 600 030, India
Tel.: (91) 4428151135
Fax: (91) 4439180789
E-Mail: info@dhanus.net
Web Site: www.dhanus.net
DHANUS—(BOM)
Sales Range: $10-24.9 Million
Business Description:
Communications Services
S.I.C.: 8748
N.A.I.C.S.: 541618
Personnel:
D. S. Srinivasan *(Mng Dir)*
R. Ramnath *(CFO, Pres-Corp Affairs & Sec)*
Board of Directors:
A. D. Sudhindra
S. Kalyanam
Kumar Raichand Madan
U. Parthasarathy
D. S. Srinivasan
S. Sriram
Transfer Agent:
Cameo Corporate Services Limited
Subramanian Bldg No 1 Club House Road
Chennai, 600 002, India
Tel.: (91) 44 2846 0390
Fax: (91) 44 2846 0129

THE DHARAMSI MORARJI CHEMICAL CO. LTD.

317 21 Dr. Dadabhoy Naoroji Road
Mumbai, 400 001, India
Tel.: (91) 22 22048881
Fax: (91) 22 22813657
Web Site: www.dmcc.com
506405—(BOM)
Rev.: $15,966,129
Earnings: $6,165,255
Fiscal Year-end: 03/31/13
Business Description:
Chemical Products Mfr
S.I.C.: 2875
N.A.I.C.S.: 325314
Personnel:
B. L. Goculdas *(CEO)*
D. N. Vaze *(CFO)*

DHARANI FINANCE LIMITED

57 Sterling Road
Nungambakkam, Chennai, 600 034, India
Tel.: (91) 44 28311313
Fax: (91) 44 28232074
E-Mail: secretarial@dharanifinance.in
Web Site: www.dharanifinance.in
Year Founded: 1990
511451—(BOM)
Rev.: $552,807
Assets: $1,294,830
Liabilities: $108,322
Net Worth: $1,186,507
Earnings: ($5,315)
Fiscal Year-end: 03/31/13
Business Description:
Financial Management Services
S.I.C.: 6211
N.A.I.C.S.: 523999
Personnel:
K. Kandasamy *(Mng Dir)*
N. Subramanian *(Compliance Officer, Pres-Corp Affairs & Sec)*
Board of Directors:
Palani G. Periasamy
M. Ganapathy
K. Kandasamy
S. Muthu
Visalakshi Periasamy
R. K. Viswanathan
Transfer Agent:
Cameo Corporate Services Limited
Subramanian Building No 1 Club House Road 5th Floor
Chennai, India

DHARANI SUGARS & CHEMICALS LIMITED

57 Sterling Road
Nungambakkam, Chennai, 600 034, India
Tel.: (91) 44 28311313
Fax: (91) 44 28232074
E-Mail: secretarial@dharanisugars-pgp.com
Web Site: www.dharanisugars.in
Year Founded: 1987
507442—(BOM)
Rev.: $107,600,542
Assets: $153,368,498
Liabilities: $129,970,943
Net Worth: $23,397,554
Earnings: $2,264,364
Emp.: 1,076
Fiscal Year-end: 03/31/13
Business Description:
Sugar Mfr
S.I.C.: 2062
N.A.I.C.S.: 311314
Personnel:
Palani G. Periasamy *(Chm)*
M. Ramalingam *(Mng Dir)*
E. P. Sakthivel *(Compliance Officer & Sec)*
Board of Directors:
Palani G. Periasamy
P. S. Gopalakrishnan
M. Ramalingam
K. C. Reddy
A. Sennimalai
K. N. Sivasubramanian
Pitchandi T.
Transfer Agent:
Cameo Corporate Services Limited
Subramanian Building V Floor 1 Club House Road
Chennai, India

DHB INDUSTRIA E COMERCIO S.A.

Av Das Industrias 864
90200290 Porto Alegre, RS, Brazil
Tel.: (55) 51 2121 1297
Fax: (55) 51 2121 1420
Year Founded: 1967
DHBI3—(BRAZ)
Sales Range: $75-99.9 Million
Emp.: 947
Business Description:
Automobile Parts Mfr & Whslr
S.I.C.: 3714
N.A.I.C.S.: 336330
Personnel:
Giancarlo Mandelli *(Dir-IR)*

DHC CORPORATION

2 7 1 Minamiazabu
Minato ku, Tokyo, 106-8571, Japan
Tel.: (81) 334575311
Fax: (81) 34575315
Web Site: www.dhc.co.jp
Emp.: 2,500
Business Description:
Mail Order Services
S.I.C.: 5961
N.A.I.C.S.: 454113
Personnel:
Yoshiaka Yoshida *(Pres)*
U.S. Subsidiary:

DHC USA Inc. (1)
115 Sansome St Ste 400
San Francisco, CA 94104
Tel.: (415) 908-1400
Fax: (888) 650-7118
Toll Free: (800) 342-2273
E-Mail: help@dhccare.com
Web Site: www.dhccare.com
Emp.: 30
Skincare Product Whslr
S.I.C.: 5961
N.A.I.C.S.: 454113
Gary Gauntt *(Pres)*

DHENU BUILDCON INFRA LIMITED

Basement Commercial Union House
9 Wallace Street
Fort, Mumbai, 400 001, India
Tel.: (91) 22 2207 2311
Fax: (91) 22 2207 1494
Web Site: www.hingirrampur.com
Year Founded: 1909
501945—(BOM)
Rev.: $19,245
Assets: $2,168,049
Liabilities: $230,434
Net Worth: $1,937,615
Earnings: $9,826
Fiscal Year-end: 03/31/13
Business Description:
Investment Management Services
S.I.C.: 6211
N.A.I.C.S.: 523110
Personnel:
Shivanand Rama Hemmady *(Compliance Officer)*
Board of Directors:
Haresh A. Bhojwani
Shivanand Rama Hemmady
Pramod D. Rssam

DHOFAR BEVERAGE AND FOOD STUFF COMPANY S.A.O.G

PO Box 390
Muscat, 211, Oman
Tel.: (968) 23225705
Fax: (968) 23225706
Web Site: www.dhofarbeverages.com
Year Founded: 1978
DBCI—(MUS)
Rev.: $11,301,176
Assets: $16,291,739
Liabilities: $4,727,154
Net Worth: $11,564,585
Earnings: $440,678
Fiscal Year-end: 12/31/12
Business Description:
Soft Drink & Beverage Mfr
S.I.C.: 2086
N.A.I.C.S.: 312111
Personnel:
Mohamed Awfait Al Shanfari *(Chm)*
Mustafa Abdul Qader Al Ghassani *(Vice Chm)*
Ghazi Taher Mahmoud Jaber *(Mng Dir)*
Board of Directors:
Mohamed Awfait Al Shanfari
Mustafa Abdul Qader Al Ghassani
Azzan Ahmad Mohammed Al Shanfari
Ahmed Ali Salem Qatan
Ghazi Taher Mahmoud Jaber
Salem Mubarak Salem Al Shanfari
Omer Salem Abdullah Al Dahab
Minakshi Sundra Srinivas
Ahmad Suhail Ahmad Al Hadri

DHOFAR INSURANCE COMPANY S.A.O.G

PO Box 1002
112 Ruwi, Oman

Dhofar Insurance Company S.A.O.G—(Continued)

Tel.: (968) 24 705 305
Fax: (968) 24 782 801
E-Mail: dhofar@dhofarinsurance.com
Web Site: www.eng2.dhofarinsurance.com
Year Founded: 1989
DICS—(MUS)
Premiums: $140,488,256
Assets: $298,928,860
Liabilities: $212,137,257
Net Worth: $86,791,603
Earnings: $15,140,739
Fiscal Year-end: 12/31/12
Business Description:
Insurance Management Services
S.I.C.: 6411
N.A.I.C.S.: 524298
Personnel:
Qais Mustahil Ahmed Al-Mashani *(Chm)*
Abdul Alim Mustahil Naseeb Rakhyoot *(Vice Chm)*
Taher Taleb Al Heraki *(Mng Dir)*
Board of Directors:
Qais Mustahil Ahmed Al-Mashani
Abdul Salam Mohamed Abdula Aziz Al Rawas
Omar Ahmed Abdullah Al-Shaikh
Abdul Alim Mustahil Naseeb Rakhyoot
Taher Taleb Al Heraki

DHOFAR INTERNATIONAL DEVELOPMENT & INVESTMENT HOLDING COMPANY S.A.O.G

23rd July Street DIDIC Building
Salalah, Oman
Tel.: (968) 23295400
Fax: (968) 23291500
E-Mail: didico@omantel.net.om
Web Site: www.didic.net
Year Founded: 1987
DIDI—(MUS)
Sales Range: $1-9.9 Million
Business Description:
Banking & Invetsment Management Services
S.I.C.: 6029
N.A.I.C.S.: 522110
Personnel:
Khalid Mustahail Ahmed Al Mashani *(Chm)*
Sheikh Ahmed Abdullah Sulaiman Muqaibel *(Vice Chm)*
Board of Directors:
Khalid Mustahail Ahmed Al Mashani
Hamood Ibrahim Somar Al Zadjali
Anwar Mohamed Abdul Aziz Al Rawas
Ahmed Mohamed Al Kaf
Salem Mubarak Salem Al Shanfari
Qais Mustahail Ahmed Al Mashani
Salim Taman Al Mashani

DHOLLANDIA FRANCE

13 rue de Gode
95100 Argenteuil, France
Tel.: (33) 134117400
Web Site: www.dhollandia.be/en/service.asp
Sls.: $40,800,000
Emp.: 45
Business Description:
Hydraulic Lifts for Motor Vehicles
S.I.C.: 5013
N.A.I.C.S.: 423120
Personnel:
Marc Gamblin *(Mng Dir)*
Board of Directors:
Marc Gamblin
Thierry Mascort

DHOOT INDUSTRIAL FINANCE LIMITED

504 Raheja Centre 214 Nariman Point
Mumbai, 400 021, India
Tel.: (91) 2222845050
Fax: (91) 2222871155
Web Site: www.dhootfinance.com
526971—(BOM)
Rev.: $16,030,574
Assets: $10,251,534
Liabilities: $3,816,926
Net Worth: $6,434,608
Earnings: $327,644
Fiscal Year-end: 03/31/13
Business Description:
Trading & Distribution
S.I.C.: 1799
N.A.I.C.S.: 238990
Personnel:
Rajgopal Dhoot *(Chm)*
Rohit Kumar Dhoot *(Mng Dir)*
Bharat C. Mistry *(Compliance Officer)*
Board of Directors:
Rajgopal Dhoot
Girish C. Choksey
Rohit Kumar Dhoot
Abhay Firodia
Rajesh M. Loya
Transfer Agent:
Sharepro Services (India) Private Limited
13 AB Samhita Warehousing Complex II Floor
Sakinaka Telephone Lane
Off Andheri Kurla Rd Sakinaka, Mumbai, India

Division:

Dhoot Industrial Finance Limited - SAMPOORNA TRADERS Division **(1)**
504 Raheja Centre 214 Nariman Point
Mumbai, 400 021, India
Tel.: (91) 22 2284 5050
Fax: (91) 22 2287 1155
E-Mail: samptrade@gmail.com
Emp.: 15
Financial Management Services
S.I.C.: 6211
N.A.I.C.S.: 523999

DHOOT INDUSTRIES LIMITED

4 Prathamesh Leela Opp Don Bosco School New Link Road
Borivali west, Mumbai, 400 092, India
Tel.: (91) 66970245
E-Mail: dhoot_2000@rediffmail.com
Web Site: www.dhootindustriesltd.com
Year Founded: 1985
523862—(BOM)
Sls.: $32,464
Assets: $1,975,196
Liabilities: $1,166,555
Net Worth: $808,641
Earnings: $8,065
Fiscal Year-end: 03/31/13
Business Description:
Real Estate Development Services
S.I.C.: 6531
N.A.I.C.S.: 531390
Personnel:
Padamchand Dhoot *(Chm & Mng Dir)*
Pankaj Dhoot *(CFO)*
K. S. V. N. S. Kameswara *(Sec)*
Board of Directors:
Padamchand Dhoot
Nitin Agarwal
Pushpadevi Dhoot
Ramesh Khetan
Jugalkishor Tapadia
Transfer Agent:
Link Intime India Pvt. Ltd
C-13 Pannalal Silk Mills Compound LBS Marg
Bhandup (West)
Mumbai, India

DHP INDIA LIMITED.

10 Middleton Row
Kolkata, 700 071, India
Tel.: (91) 3322295735
Fax: (91) 3322172751
E-Mail: info@dhpindia.com
Web Site: www.dhpindia.com
531306—(BOM)
Rev.: $4,775,538
Assets: $4,557,203
Liabilities: $938,476
Net Worth: $3,618,727
Earnings: $617,558
Fiscal Year-end: 03/31/13
Business Description:
Industrial Machinery
S.I.C.: 3559
N.A.I.C.S.: 333249
Personnel:
Asheesh Dabriwal *(CEO & Mng Dir)*
Ashok Kumar Singh *(CFO)*
Janak Bhardwaj *(COO)*
Adinath Banerjee *(Sec)*
Board of Directors:
Buddhadeb Basu
Janak Bhardwaj
Asheesh Dabriwal
Anjum Dhandhania
Subrata Haldar
Vijay Swaminathan
Transfer Agent:
Niche Technologies Private Limited
D-511 Bagree Market 71 B. R. B. Basu Road
Kolkata, India

DHRUV ESTATES LIMITED

B/709 Sagar Tech Plaza Sakinaka Junction Andheri Kurla Road
Andheri E, Mumbai, 400 072, India
Tel.: (91) 22 28500081
Fax: (91) 22 28500084
E-Mail: dhruvestatesltd@gmail.com
Web Site: www.dhruvestates.com
Year Founded: 1983
507886—(BOM)
Rev.: $14,072
Assets: $282,957
Liabilities: $11,013
Net Worth: $271,945
Earnings: $3,893
Fiscal Year-end: 03/31/13
Business Description:
Real Estate Development Services
S.I.C.: 6531
N.A.I.C.S.: 531390
Personnel:
Kishore Kanungo *(Chm)*
Sanjay Kanungo *(Mng Dir)*
Board of Directors:
Kishore Kanungo
Sanjay Kanungo
Mehboob Pradhan
Jagdish Vora
Transfer Agent:
TSR Darashaw Ltd.
6-10 Haji Moosa Patrawala Industrial Estate 20
Dr E Moses Road
Near Famous Studio Mahalaxmi, Mumbai, India

DHT HOLDINGS, INC.

Clarendon House 2 Church Street
Hamilton, HM 11, Bermuda
Tel.: (441) 299 4912
E-Mail: info@dhtankers.com
Web Site: www.dhtholdings.com
DHT—(NYSE)
Rev.: $87,012,000
Assets: $446,599,000
Liabilities: $161,846,000
Net Worth: $284,753,000
Earnings: ($4,126,000)
Emp.: 8
Fiscal Year-end: 12/31/13
Business Description:
Bulk Shipping Services
S.I.C.: 4412
N.A.I.C.S.: 483111
Personnel:
Svein Moxnes Harfjeld *(Pres & CEO)*
Trygve P. Munthe *(Pres)*
Erik Uboe *(CFO)*
Board of Directors:
Robert N. Cowen
Randee E. Day
Mark Adrian McComiskey
Einar Michael Steimler
Rolf A. Wikborg
Legal Counsel:
Cravath, Swaine & Moore LLP
825 8th Ave
New York, NY 10019
Tel.: (212) 474-1000

DHUNSERI INVESTMENTS LIMITED

Dhunseri House 4A Woodburn Park
Kolkata, 700 020, India
Tel.: (91) 33 22801950
Fax: (91) 22 22878350
E-Mail: mail@dhunseriinvestments.com
Web Site: www.dhunseriinvestments.com
Year Founded: 1997
533336—(BOM)
Rev.: $1,549,684
Assets: $34,534,718
Liabilities: $410,791
Net Worth: $34,123,927
Earnings: $1,286,973
Fiscal Year-end: 03/31/13
Business Description:
Financial Investment Services
S.I.C.: 6211
N.A.I.C.S.: 523999
Personnel:
Chandra Kumar Dhanuka *(Chm, CEO & Mng Dir)*
Ramchandran Mahadevan Iyer *(CFO, Compliance Officer & Sec)*
Board of Directors:
Chandra Kumar Dhanuka
P. L. Agarwal
Basudeo D. Beriwala
Brijesh Kumar Biyani
Aruna Dhanuka
Mrigank Dhanuka
Adarsh Garodia
Ashok Kumar Lohia
Transfer Agent:
Maheshwari Datamatics Pvt Ltd
6 Mangoe Lane 2nd Floor
Kolkata, India

DHUNSERI PETROCHEM & TEA LIMITED

Dhunseri House 4A Woodburn Park
Kolkata, 700 020, India
Tel.: (91) 3322801950
Fax: (91) 3322408995
E-Mail: dhunseri@vsnl.com
Web Site: www.dhunseritea.com
523736—(BOM)
Rev.: $482,345,910
Assets: $613,748,160
Liabilities: $456,399,180
Net Worth: $157,348,980
Earnings: $21,076,272
Emp.: 5,610
Fiscal Year-end: 03/31/13
Business Description:
Resin & Tea Producer; Information Technology Infrastructure Development Services
S.I.C.: 2095
N.A.I.C.S.: 311920
Personnel:
Chandra Kumar Dhanuka *(Chm)*
Mrigank Dhanuka *(Vice Chm & Mng Dir)*

Biswanath Chattopadhyay *(CEO & Mng Dir)*
V. Goel *(CFO)*
P. C. Dhandhania *(COO & Sr VP-Tea Div)*
K. V. Balan *(Compliance Officer & Sec)*
K. K. Tibrewalla *(Sr VP-IT Sez)*
Board of Directors:
Chandra Kumar Dhanuka
Anurag Bagaria
Bharat Bajoria
Raj Narain Bhardwaj
Biswanath Chattopadhyay
Mrigank Dhanuka
Dharam Pal Jindal
Pradip Kumar Khaitan
Joginder Pal Kundra
Yves F. Lombard
Basudeb Sen
Rajiv Kumar Sharma
Transfer Agent:
Maheshwari Datamatics Pvt. Ltd.
6 Mangoe Lane 2nd Fl
Kolkata, 700 001, India
Tel.: (91) 33 22435029
Fax: (91) 913322484787

DHX MEDIA LTD.

1478 Queen Street
Halifax, NS, B3J 2H7, Canada
Tel.: (902) 423-0260
Fax: (902) 422-0752
E-Mail: halifax@dhxmedia.com
Web Site: www.dhxmedia.com
DHX—(TSX)
Rev.: $96,681,367
Assets: $322,457,106
Liabilities: $160,556,098
Net Worth: $161,901,008
Earnings: $1,848,877
Emp.: 212
Fiscal Year-end: 06/30/13
Business Description:
Family Television Programming Services
S.I.C.: 7819
N.A.I.C.S.: 512191
Personnel:
Michael Hirsh *(Chm)*
Steven Graham DeNure *(Pres & COO)*
Michael Patrick Donovan *(CEO)*
Dana Sean Landry *(CFO)*
Peter Byrne *(CEO-Copyright Promos Licensing Grp)*
Mark Gregory Gosine *(Gen Counsel, Sec & Exec VP-Legal Affairs)*
David Andrew Regan *(Exec VP-Corp Dev & IR)*
Josh Scherba *(Sr VP-Distr)*
Board of Directors:
Michael Hirsh
Judson Graham Day
Michael Patrick Donovan
John Loh
John William Ritchie
Michael Salamon
Robert G. C. Sobey
Donald Arthur Wright
Transfer Agent:
Computershare Investor Services Inc
100 University Avenue 8th Floor
Toronto, ON, Canada
Subsidiaries:

Decode Entertainment Inc. **(1)**
235 Carlaw Ave 5th Fl
Toronto, ON, M4M 2S1, Canada
Tel.: (416) 363-8034
Fax: (416) 363-8919
E-Mail: decode@decode-ent.com
Web Site: www.decode.tv
Emp.: 50
Television Programming Services
S.I.C.: 7812
N.A.I.C.S.: 512110

The Family Channel, Inc. **(1)**
181 Bay St Ste 100
PO Box 787
Toronto, ON, M5J 2T3, Canada
Tel.: (416) 956-2010
Fax: (416) 956-2035
E-Mail: info@astro.com
Web Site: www.astro.com
Emp.: 150
National Pay Television Service
S.I.C.: 4841
N.A.I.C.S.: 515210
John Riley *(Pres)*

Halifax Film **(1)**
1478 Queen St 2nd Fl
Halifax, NS, B3J 2H7, Canada
Tel.: (902) 423-0260
Fax: (902) 422-0752
E-Mail: info@dhxmedia.com
Web Site: www.dhxmedia.com
Emp.: 25
Television Programming Services
S.I.C.: 7812
N.A.I.C.S.: 512110
Michael Donovan *(CEO)*

Studio B **(1)**
6th Fl 190 Alexander St
Vancouver, BC, Canada
Tel.: (604) 684-2363
Fax: (604) 602-0208
Web Site: www.studiobproductions.com
Emp.: 150
Animation Production Services
S.I.C.: 7812
N.A.I.C.S.: 512110
Kasey Harris *(Mgr)*

DI CORP.

58-6 Nonhyeon-dong
Gangnam-gu, Seoul, Korea (South)
Tel.: (82) 2 546 5501
Fax: (82) 2 541 3695
Web Site: www.di.co.kr
Year Founded: 1955
003160—(KRS)
Business Description:
Semiconductor Product Mfr
S.I.C.: 3674
N.A.I.C.S.: 334413
Personnel:
Il-sun Jang *(CEO)*

DIA BRAS EXPLORATION INC.

(Name Changed to Sierra Metals Inc.)

DIA DENTAL AESTHETICS INTERNATIONAL INC.

Lindenmattstrasse 13
5616 Meisterschwanden, Switzerland
Tel.: (41) 56 664 53 93
Fax: (41) 56 664 53 92
E-Mail: info@dental-aesthetics.net
Web Site: www.dental-aesthetics.net
14D—(DEU)
Business Description:
Dental Products
S.I.C.: 3843
N.A.I.C.S.: 339114
Personnel:
Heinz Giesswein *(Mng Dir)*
Drew Reid *(Mng Dir)*

DIADEM RESOURCES LTD.

One University Avenue Ste 401
Toronto, ON, M5J 2P1, Canada
Tel.: (416) 369-6080
Fax: (416) 369-6088
E-Mail: paul.carroll@diademresources.com
Web Site: www.diademresources.com
DRL—(TSXV)
Sales Range: Less than $1 Million
Business Description:
Diamond Mining & Exploration Services
S.I.C.: 1499
N.A.I.C.S.: 212399
Personnel:
Aime Bertrand *(Chm & CEO)*
Lina Noble *(Sec)*
Board of Directors:
Aime Bertrand
A. Lee Barker
Thomas Skimming

DIADORA INVICTA

Montello 80 Caerano San Marco
31031 Treviso, Italy
Tel.: (39) 04236581
Fax: (39) 0423858512
E-Mail: infodiadora@diadora.it
Web Site: www.diadora.it
Sales Range: $300-349.9 Million
Emp.: 400
Business Description:
Mfr. of Footwear
S.I.C.: 2389
N.A.I.C.S.: 316210
U.S. Subsidiary:

Diadora America, Inc. **(1)**
6102 S 225th St 21929 67thave
Kent, WA 98032-1874 WA
Tel.: (253) 520-8868
Fax: (253) 520-6333
Toll Free: (800) 423-9958
E-Mail: customerservice@diadoraamerica.com
Web Site: www.diadorasoccer.com
Emp.: 550
Athletic Footwear & Apparel Distr & Mfr Import Export
S.I.C.: 5139
N.A.I.C.S.: 424340
Linda Walker *(COO)*

DIAGEO PLC

Lakeside Drive Park Royal
London, NW10 7HQ, United Kingdom
Tel.: (44) 20 8978 6000
Fax: (44) 20 7927 4600
E-Mail: information@diageo.com
Web Site: www.diageo.com
Year Founded: 1997
DEO—(EUR LSE NYSE)
Sls.: $24,458,464,230
Assets: $39,603,855,330
Liabilities: $26,800,551,300
Net Worth: $12,803,304,030
Earnings: $4,096,678,260
Emp.: 28,410
Fiscal Year-end: 06/30/13
Business Description:
Alcoholic Beverages Mfr
S.I.C.: 2085
N.A.I.C.S.: 312140
Personnel:
Franz B. Humer *(Chm)*
Ivan M. Menezes *(CEO)*
Deirdre A. Mahlan *(CFO)*
Syl Saller *(Global CMO)*
Andrew Fennell *(Pres/COO-Africa)*
Nick Blazquez *(Pres-Africa, Eastern Europe & Turkey)*
Alberto Gavazzi *(Pres-Latin America & Caribbean)*
Gilbert Ghostine *(Pres-Asia Pacific)*
David Gosnell *(Pres-Global Supply & Procurement)*
John Kennedy *(Pres-Western Europe)*
John R. Millian *(Pres-Latin America & Caribbean)*
Andrew Morgan *(Pres-New Bus)*
Larry Schwartz *(Pres-North America)*
Timothy D. Proctor *(Gen Counsel)*
Paul D. Tunnacliffe *(Sec)*
Board of Directors:
Franz B. Humer
Peggy B. Bruzelius
Laurence M. Danon
E. Mervyn Davies
Betsy D. Holden
Deirdre A. Mahlan
Ivan M. Menezes
Philip Gordon Scott
Subsidiaries:

Diageo Capital Plc **(1)**
Edinburg Park 5 Lochside Way
EH12 9DT Edinburgh, United Kingdom
Tel.: (44) 1315192090
Fax: (44) 0131519011
E-Mail: the.registrar@diageo.com
Web Site: www.diageo.com
Emp.: 200
Holding Company
S.I.C.: 6719
N.A.I.C.S.: 551112
Ian Scott *(CEO)*

Diageo Great Britain Limited **(1)**
8 Henrietta Place
W1G0NB London, United Kingdom
Tel.: (44) 2079275200
Fax: (44) 2079274600
E-Mail: global.general.information@diageo.com
Sales Range: $1-4.9 Billion
Emp.: 1,483
Production, Marketing & Distribution of Premium Drinks
S.I.C.: 5181
N.A.I.C.S.: 424810
Philip Gladman *(Dir-Mktg)*

Diageo Holdings Ltd. **(1)**
8 Henrietta Pl
London, W1G ONB, United Kingdom UK
Tel.: (44) 2079275200 (100%)
Telex: 261161
Fax: (44) 2079274894
E-Mail: global.general.informaiton@diageo.com
Web Site: www.diageo.com
Emp.: 250
Holding Company
S.I.C.: 5921
N.A.I.C.S.: 445310

Units:

Diageo Northern Ireland **(2)**
Gilbey House 58 Boucher Rd
Belfast, BT12 6HR, United Kingdom (100%)
Tel.: (44) 2890682021
Telex: 74432 GILBEY G
Fax: (44) 2890660767
E-Mail: andrew.cowan@diageo.com
Web Site: www.Diageo.com
Emp.: 50
Brewer & Distiller
S.I.C.: 2082
N.A.I.C.S.: 312120

Diageo UK **(2)**
8 Henrietta Place
London, W1G 0NB, United Kingdom (100%)
Tel.: (44) 2079275200
Telex: 261161 INDIST G
Web Site: www.diageo.com
Mfr. & Distributor of Alcoholic Beverages
S.I.C.: 2084
N.A.I.C.S.: 312130

Justerini & Brooks Ltd. **(2)**
8 Henrietta Pl
London, W1G ONB, United Kingdom (100%)
Tel.: (44) 2079275200
Telex: 27732 JANDBG
Fax: (44) 2079274641
Web Site: www.justerinis.com
Emp.: 100
Distills, Blends & Markets Scotch Whiskies; Marketer of Wines & Gin
S.I.C.: 2084
N.A.I.C.S.: 312130
Nick Hyde *(Mng Dir)*

Non-U.S. Subsidiaries:

Croft Jerez SA **(2)**
Rancho Croft
PO Box 414
11407 Jerez de la Frontera, Cadiz, Spain

Diageo plc—(Continued)

Tel.: (34) 956306600
Telex: 75041
Fax: (34) 956303707
Emp.: 100
Produces & Markets Premium Sherries
S.I.C.: 2084
N.A.I.C.S.: 312130

Diageo Ireland (2)
Saint James Gate
Dublin, 8, Ireland IE
Tel.: (353) 14536700 (100%)
Fax: (353) 14084804
Web Site: www.diageo.ie
Emp.: 700
Brewing, Marketing & Distribution of Beer
S.I.C.: 2082
N.A.I.C.S.: 312120
John Kennedy *(Pres & CEO-Ireland)*

Diageo Japan KK (2)
Roppongi Bldg 1 2nd Fl 1 9 9 Roppongi
Tokyo, 106 0032, Japan (100%)
Tel.: (81) 355498151
Telex: 2425130
Fax: (81) 355498152
Web Site: www.diageoinjapan.com
Emp.: 60
Oversees Distributor of Liquors & Other Spirits in Japan
S.I.C.: 5921
N.A.I.C.S.: 445310

International Distillers South Asia (2)
50 Raffles Place
230 Orchard Road
Singapore, 0923, Singapore
Tel.: (65) 6534 5315
Telex: INTGIN RS 39106
Manufacturing, Marketing & Sales Organizations
S.I.C.: 5921
N.A.I.C.S.: 445310

W & A Gilbey SA (2)
PO Box 137 16 Stellentia Avenue
Stellenbosch, Cape Province, 7600, South Africa
Tel.: (27) 21 808 6911
Fax: (27) 22 808 6000
Produces, Imports, Markets & Distributes Alcoholic & Non-Alcoholic Beverages in South Africa
S.I.C.: 2084
N.A.I.C.S.: 312130

Diageo Scotland Limited (1)
5 Lochside Way
Edinburgh Park, Edinburgh, United Kingdom
Tel.: (44) 2079275480
Fax: (44) 1315192001
Web Site: www.diageo.com
Sales Range: $1-4.9 Billion
Emp.: 2,585
Production, Marketing & Distribution of Premium Drinks
S.I.C.: 5182
N.A.I.C.S.: 424820
Roger Hugh Myddelton *(CEO)*

The Gleneagles Hotel (1)
Auchterarder
Perth, Perthshire, PH3 1NF, United Kingdom UK
Tel.: (44) 1764662231 (100%)
Fax: (44) 1764662134
E-Mail: resort.sales@gleneagles.com
Web Site: www.gleneagles.com
Emp.: 800
Hotel
S.I.C.: 7011
N.A.I.C.S.: 721199
Peter J. Lederer *(Chm)*

U.S. Subsidiaries:

Diageo Investment Corporation (1)
801 Main Ave
Norwalk, CT 06851-1127
Tel.: (203) 229-2100
Investment Management Services
S.I.C.: 6211
N.A.I.C.S.: 523999

Diageo North America, Inc. (1)
801 Main Ave
Norwalk, CT 06851 CT
Tel.: (203) 229-2100 (100%)
Fax: (203) 229-8901
Web Site: www.diageo.com
Sales Range: $1-4.9 Billion
Emp.: 1,000
Spirits & Wines Producer, Importer & Marketer
Import Export
S.I.C.: 5182
N.A.I.C.S.: 424820
Ivan M. Menezes *(Pres & CEO)*
Peter McDonough *(Pres & Chief Mktg & Innovation Officer)*
Greg Kryder *(CFO)*
Jon Potter *(CMO-North America)*
Pete Carr *(Pres-Sls-USA)*
Guy L. Smith *(Exec VP)*
Mark Hubler *(Sr VP & Gen Mgr)*

Divisions:

Diageo North America Inc. (2)
333 W Wacker Dr Ste 1100
Chicago, IL 60606
Tel.: (312) 279-3400
Fax: (312) 279-3535
Web Site: www.diageo.com
Emp.: 50
Beverage Producer
S.I.C.: 5182
N.A.I.C.S.: 424820
Ivan M. Menezes *(Pres & CEO)*

Diageo North America Inc. (2)
530 5th Ave
New York, NY 10036
Tel.: (646) 223-2000
Fax: (646) 223-2001
E-Mail: aisa.aiyer@diageo.com
Web Site: www.diageo.com
Spirits & Wines Producer, Importer & Marketer
S.I.C.: 5181
N.A.I.C.S.: 424810
Simon Burch *(Sr VP-Mktg)*
Rob Warren *(Sr VP-Global Tequilas)*

Diageo North America (2)
5301 Blue Lagoon Dr
Miami, FL 33126-2097 FL
Tel.: (305) 269-4500
Fax: (305) 269-5005
Web Site: www.whfreeman.com
Emp.: 180
Spirits & Wines Marketing & Distr
S.I.C.: 8741
N.A.I.C.S.: 561110
Jonathan Tepper *(Gen Mgr)*

Diageo North America (2)
24440 W 143rd St
Plainfield, IL 60544-8555 IL
Mailing Address:
PO Box 305
Plainfield, IL 60544-0305
Tel.: (815) 267-4400
Emp.: 90
Alcoholic Beverages
S.I.C.: 2085
N.A.I.C.S.: 312140

Diageo North America (2)
5080 Spectrum Dr Ste 1200
Addison, TX 75001-4648 CO
Tel.: (972) 716-7700
Fax: (972) 716-7799
E-Mail: info@diageo.com
Emp.: 100
Mfr. & Supplier of Alcoholic Beverages
S.I.C.: 5182
N.A.I.C.S.: 424820

Subsidiaries:

Beaulieu Vineyard (2)
1960 St Helena Hwy
Rutherford, CA 94573 CA
Tel.: (707) 967-5200
Fax: (707) 963-5920
Toll Free: (800) 264-6918
E-Mail: bvinfo@bvwines.com
Web Site: www.bvwines.com
Emp.: 80
Mfr. of Premium Wines
Export
S.I.C.: 2085
N.A.I.C.S.: 312140
Jeffrey Stambor *(Dir-Wine Making)*

The Chalone Wine Group, Ltd. (2)
621 Airpark Rd
Napa, CA 94558-6272
Tel.: (707) 254-4200
Fax: (707) 254-4201
Wineries
S.I.C.: 2084
N.A.I.C.S.: 312130

Diageo Chateau & Estate Wines Co. (2)
240 Gateway Rd W
Napa, CA 94558
Tel.: (707) 299-2600
Fax: (707) 299-2777
Toll Free: (800) 373-5896
Web Site: www.diageowines.com
Emp.: 122
Wine Mfr
S.I.C.: 2084
N.A.I.C.S.: 312130
Claudia Schubert *(Pres)*

Subsidiaries:

Rosenblum Cellars, Inc. (3)
2900 Main St
Alameda, CA 94501 CA
Tel.: (510) 865-7007
Fax: (510) 995-4230
Web Site: www.rosenblumcellars.com
Emp.: 52
Wine Mfr
S.I.C.: 2084
N.A.I.C.S.: 312130
Kent Rosenblum *(Founder)*

Sterling Vineyards Inc. (3)
1111 Dunaweal Ln
Calistoga, CA 94515
Tel.: (707) 942-3300
Fax: (707) 942-3467
Toll Free: (800) 726-6136
E-Mail: servicedesk.na@diageo.com
Web Site: www.sterlingvineyards.com
Sls.: $198,789,000
Emp.: 50
Wine Mfr
S.I.C.: 2084
N.A.I.C.S.: 312130
Mike Westrick *(VP-Winemaking)*

George A. Dickel & Co. (2)
1950 Cascade Hollow Rd
Tullahoma, TN 37388
Tel.: (931) 857-3124
Fax: (931) 857-9313
Web Site: www.dickel.com
Emp.: 26
Distilling, Bottling & Warehousing Alcoholic Beverages
S.I.C.: 2085
N.A.I.C.S.: 312140
John R. Lunn *(Pres)*

Non-U.S. Subsidiaries:

Diageo Brands BV (1)
Molenwerf 10-12
1014BG Amsterdam, Netherlands
Tel.: (31) 205814242
Web Site: www.diageo.com
Emp.: 100
Wholesale Grocery Services
S.I.C.: 5141
N.A.I.C.S.: 424410
Edward P. Demery *(CEO)*

Diageo Canada, Inc. (1)
401 The W Mall Ste 800
Toronto, ON, M9C 5P8, Canada
Tel.: (416) 626-2000
Fax: (416) 626-2688
E-Mail: info@diageo.com
Web Site: www.diageo.com
Sales Range: $150-199.9 Million
Emp.: 1,400
Distilled Spirits & Wines, Fruit Juices & Juice Beverages Mfr & Marketer
Export
S.I.C.: 2084
N.A.I.C.S.: 312130
Maggie Lapcewich *(Pres)*

Divisions:

Diageo Canada Inc. (2)
9523 41 Ave NW
Edmonton, AB, T6E 5X7, Canada AB
Tel.: (780) 451-5566 (100%)
Fax: (780) 451-3701
Web Site: www.diageo.com
Emp.: 15
Distilled & Blended Liquors
S.I.C.: 2085
N.A.I.C.S.: 312140

Diageo Canada Inc. (2)
5 A Unit 1080 Waverly st
Winnipeg, MB, R3T 4J6, Canada MB
Tel.: (204) 453-7447 (100%)
Fax: (204) 453-7368
Web Site: www.diageo.com
Emp.: 6
Distilled & Blended Liquors
S.I.C.: 2085
N.A.I.C.S.: 312140

Diageo Capital BV (1)
Molenwerf 10-12
Amsterdam, 1014 BG, Netherlands
Tel.: (31) 207745000
Fax: (31) 207745001
Financial Management Services
S.I.C.: 6211
N.A.I.C.S.: 523999

East African Breweries Limited (1)
PO Box 30161
Ruaraka, 00100 Nairobi, Kenya
Tel.: (254) 20 864 4000
Fax: (254) 20 8561090
E-Mail: eabl.info@eabl.com
Web Site: www.eabl.com
EABL—(NAI)
Rev.: $663,264,856
Assets: $657,584,475
Liabilities: $562,868,521
Net Worth: $94,715,954
Earnings: $77,989,486
Emp.: 1,700
Fiscal Year-end: 06/30/13
Beer Brewery
S.I.C.: 5921
N.A.I.C.S.: 445310
Charles Ireland *(CEO & Mng Dir)*
James Edmunds *(Legal Counsel)*
Alison Kariuki-Mbuthia *(Legal Counsel-KBL)*
Ruth Ngobi *(Sec)*

Subsidiaries:

Central Glass Industries Ltd (2)
PO Box 49835
Nairobi, Kenya
Tel.: (254) 803681
Web Site: www.eabl.com
Glass Mfr
S.I.C.: 3221
N.A.I.C.S.: 327213
James Karegi *(Mng Dir)*

Non-U.S. Subsidiary:

Uganda Breweries Ltd (2)
PO Box 7130
PortBell, Kampala, Luzira, Uganda
Tel.: (256) 312 210 011
Fax: (256) 312 233 277
Web Site: www.eabl.com
Beer & Spirits
S.I.C.: 2082
N.A.I.C.S.: 312120
Alasdair Musselwhite *(Mng Dir)*

Guinness Ghana Breweries Limited (1)
Kaasi Industrial Area
PO Box 1536
Kumasi, Ghana
Tel.: (233) 5126301
Fax: (233) 5183521
Web Site: www.guinness.com
GGBL—(GHA)
Emp.: 560
Beer & Malt Liquor Mfr & Sales
S.I.C.: 2082
N.A.I.C.S.: 312120
Peter Ndegwa *(Mng Dir)*

Mey Icki Sanayi ve Ticaret A.S. (1)
Abide-i Hurriyet Cad 211 Bolkan Center B Blok
Sisli, 34381 Istanbul, Turkey
Tel.: (90) 2123734400
Fax: (90) 2123734404
E-Mail: info@mey.com.tr
Web Site: www.mey.com.tr
Sales Range: $350-399.9 Million
Emp.: 200
Wine & Spirit Mfr & Distr
S.I.C.: 2085
N.A.I.C.S.: 312140

Galip Yorgancioglu *(CEO)*

R&A Bailey & Co. (1)
Nangor House Nangor Rd
Dublin, 12, Ireland (100%)
Tel.: (353) 014051300
Telex: 90948 BALY EI
Fax: (353) 4051222
Web Site: www.bailey.com
Emp.: 200
Mfr. & Marketing of Original Irish Cream
S.I.C.: 5499
N.A.I.C.S.: 445299
John Miller *(Mng Dir)*

DIAGNOCURE INC.

4535 Wilfrid Hamel Blvd Suite 250
Quebec, QC, G1P 2J7, Canada
Tel.: (418) 527-6100
Fax: (418) 527-0240
Toll Free: (888) 900-6626
E-Mail: communications@diagnocure.com
Web Site: www.diagnocure.com
CUR—(OTC TSX)
Rev.: $2,466,501
Assets: $11,231,155
Liabilities: $806,472
Net Worth: $10,424,683
Earnings: ($3,671,082)
Emp.: 13
Fiscal Year-end: 10/31/12
Business Description:
High-Value Diagnostics Developer
S.I.C.: 2835
N.A.I.C.S.: 325413
Personnel:
Yves Fradet *(Chm, Pres & Chief Medical Officer)*
Board of Directors:
Yves Fradet
Danielle Allard
Louise Proulx
Andrew J. Sheldon
Jacques Simoneau
Vincent R. Zurawski, Jr.
Transfer Agent:
Computershare Trust Company of Canada
1500 University St 7th Floor
Montreal, QC, Canada
U.S. Subsidiary:

DiagnoCure Oncology Laboratories (1)
1045A Andrew Dr
West Chester, PA 19380
Tel.: (610) 701-9007
Fax: (610) 701-9009
Toll Free: (877) 701-9007
Web Site: www.diagnocure.com
Emp.: 20
Cancer Diagnostic Testing & Laboratory Services
S.I.C.: 8071
N.A.I.C.S.: 621511
Phillip Wells *(VP-Mktg)*

DIAGNOS INC.

7005 Taschereau Boulevard Suite 340
Brossard, QC, J4Z 1A7, Canada
Tel.: (450) 678-8882
Fax: (450) 678-8119
Toll Free: (877) 678-8882
E-Mail: info@diagnos.com
Web Site: www.diagnos.com
Year Founded: 1998
ADK—(TSXV)
Rev.: $1,499,884
Assets: $2,208,462
Liabilities: $472,960
Net Worth: $1,735,502
Earnings: ($2,031,496)
Fiscal Year-end: 03/31/13
Business Description:
Data Extraction Services
S.I.C.: 7373
N.A.I.C.S.: 541512
Personnel:
Philip Renaud *(Chm)*
Andre Larente *(Pres & CEO)*
Board of Directors:
Philip Renaud
Richard Baxter
Andre Larente
Olivier Lerolle
Bruno Maruzzo
Legal Counsel:
Borden Ladner Gervais s.e.n.c.r.l.
1000 de la Gauchetiere St. West Suite 900
Montreal, QC, Canada
Transfer Agent:
Computershare Trust Company of Canada
1500 University Street Suite 7001
Montreal, QC, H3A 3S8, Canada

DIAGNOSTIC AND THERAPEUTIC CENTER OF ATHENS-HYGEIA S.A.

4 Erythrou Stavrou Str & Kifisias Av
Marousi, 15123 Athens, Greece
Tel.: (30) 2106867000
Fax: (30) 2106845089
E-Mail: info@hygeia.gr
Web Site: www.hygeia.gr
HYGEIA—(ATH)
Sls.: $326,487,956
Assets: $794,510,880
Liabilities: $506,192,228
Net Worth: $288,318,652
Earnings: ($187,105,514)
Emp.: 3,404
Fiscal Year-end: 12/31/12
Business Description:
Medical Services
S.I.C.: 8062
N.A.I.C.S.: 622110
Personnel:
Areti G. Souvatzoglou *(CEO)*
Spyros Kosmas *(Deputy CFO)*
Dimitris Mantzavinos *(CFO)*
Marina Mantzourani *(IR Officer)*
Board of Directors:
Andreas Evangelou Vgenopoulos
Ioannis Andreou
Evaggelos Dedoulis
Alexandros Edipides
George Efstratiadis
Sotirios Gougoulakis
Andreas Kartapanis
Anastasios Kyprianidis
Christos Maroudis
Meletios Moustakas
George Politis
Areti G. Souvatzoglou
George Zacharopoulos
Subsidiaries:

ALPHA LAB A.E. (1)
11 Anastasiou Str
115 24 Athens, Greece
Tel.: (30) 2106984174
Fax: (30) 2106902083
E-Mail: alab@leto.gr
Web Site: www.alphalab.gr
Emp.: 20
Molecular Biology Research & Development Services
S.I.C.: 8731
N.A.I.C.S.: 541711

LETO S.A. (1)
7-13 Mousson
11524 Athens, Greece
Tel.: (30) 2106902000
Fax: (30) 2106902429
E-Mail: info@leto.gr
Web Site: www.leto.gr
Emp.: 250
Health Care Services
S.I.C.: 8011
N.A.I.C.S.: 621491
L. Papadopoulos *(CEO)*

Y-PHARMA S.A. (1)
13th Klm Athens-Lamia National Road
Metamorfosi, Athens, 14451, Greece
Tel.: (30) 2108991626
Fax: (30) 2102841201
E-Mail: info@y-pharma.gr
Web Site: www.y-pharma.gr
Emp.: 19
Health Care Services
S.I.C.: 8099
N.A.I.C.S.: 621999
Michael Staurou *(Gen Mgr)*

MITERA S.A. (1)
Kifissias Avenue & 6 Erythrou Stavrou Str
Maroussi, Athens, 15123, Greece
Tel.: (30) 2106869000
Fax: (30) 2106840894
E-Mail: info@mitera.gr
Web Site: www.mitera.gr
Health Care Services
S.I.C.: 8011
N.A.I.C.S.: 621491
Giorgios Kallipolitis *(Chm-Scientific Council)*
Konstantinos Stavrou *(Chm)*
Areti Sovatzoglou *(Pres)*
Alexios Komninos *(Mng Dir)*
Theophanis Stathis *(VP & Gen Sec)*

Non-U.S. Subsidiaries:

CHRYSSAFILIOTISSA PUBLIC LTD (1)
9 Stygos Street
CY-3117 Limassol, Cyprus
Tel.: (357) 25200000
Fax: (357) 25200001
E-Mail: info@achilionhospital.com
Hospital Management Services
S.I.C.: 8062
N.A.I.C.S.: 622110
Notis Zannetos *(Mng Dir)*

LIMASSOL MEDICAL CENTRE 'ACHILLION' LTD (1)
9 Stygos Street
CY-3117 Limassol, Cyprus
Tel.: (357) 25200000
Fax: (357) 25200145
Health Care Services
S.I.C.: 8011
N.A.I.C.S.: 621491

DIAGNOSTIC MEDICAL SYSTEMS S.A.

Parc de la Mediterranee
Perols, 34470 Montpellier, France
Tel.: (33) 467504900
Fax: (33) 467504909
E-Mail: dms@dms.com
Web Site: www.dms.com
DGM—(EUR)
Sls.: $37,644,298
Earnings: ($628,661)
Emp.: 130
Fiscal Year-end: 12/31/12
Business Description:
Medical Imaging Equipment Designer, Mfr & Marketer
S.I.C.: 3841
N.A.I.C.S.: 339112
Personnel:
Gerard Daguise *(Chm)*
Jean-Paul Ansel *(CEO & Dir Gen)*
Samuel Sacerni *(Mng Dir)*
Subsidiary:

Apelem SAS (1)
Parc Scientifique Georges Besse
175 allee Von Neumann, 30035 Nimes, France
Tel.: (33) 466290907
Fax: (33) 466297123
Web Site: www.dms.com
Emp.: 50
Medical Diagnostic Services
S.I.C.: 8071
N.A.I.C.S.: 621512
Anses Jean Paul *(Mgr)*

DIAGNOSTICA STAGO S.A.S.

9 Rue des Freres Chausson
92600 Asnieres-sur-Seine, France
Tel.: (33) 146882020
Fax: (33) 147910891
E-Mail: webmaster@stago.com
Web Site: www.stago.com
Emp.: 1,500
Business Description:
Hemostasis Instrumentation & Reagent Kit Mfr
S.I.C.: 3826
N.A.I.C.S.: 334516
Personnel:
Lionel Viret *(Pres)*
U.S. Subsidiary:

Diagnostica Stago, Inc. (1)
5 Century Dr
Parsippany, NJ 07054
Tel.: (973) 631-1200
Fax: (973) 631-1618
E-Mail: general.info@stago-us.com
Web Site: www.stago-us.com
Emp.: 200
Hemostasis Instrumentation & Reagent Kit Mfr
S.I.C.: 3826
N.A.I.C.S.: 334516
Stephane Zamia *(CEO)*

DIAGNOSTICOS DA AMERICA S.A.

Av Jurua 434
Alphaville, Barueri, SP, 06455-010, Brazil
Tel.: (55) 11 4197 5410
Fax: (55) 11 4197 5516
E-Mail: ir@dasa.com.br
Web Site: www.diagnosticosdaamerica.com.br
DASA3—(BRAZ)
Rev.: $1,113,708,808
Assets: $2,101,440,161
Liabilities: $818,988,488
Net Worth: $1,282,451,673
Earnings: $41,676,856
Emp.: 18,910
Fiscal Year-end: 12/31/12
Business Description:
Medical Diagnostic Services
S.I.C.: 8071
N.A.I.C.S.: 621511
Personnel:
Romeu Cortes Domingues *(Chm)*
Oscar de Paula Bernardes Neto *(Vice Chm)*
Dickson Esteves Tangerino *(CEO)*
Cynthia May Hobbs *(CFO & VP)*
Paulo Bokel Catta-Preta *(IR Officer)*
Carlos Elder Maciel de Aquino *(Acctg & Infrastructure Officer)*
Antonio Carlos Gaeta *(Exec VP-Bus)*
Board of Directors:
Romeu Cortes Domingues
Carlos Fernando Costa
Oscar de Paula Bernardes Neto
Dickson Esteves Tangerino

DIAL ONE WOLFEDALE ELECTRIC LTD.

415 Ambassador Dr
Mississauga, ON, L5T 2J3, Canada
Tel.: (905) 564-8999
Fax: (905) 564-5677
Toll Free: (800) 303-7568
E-Mail: info@dialonewolfedale.com
Web Site: www.dialonewolfedale.com
Rev.: $16,337,906
Emp.: 120
Business Description:
Electrical-Product Distr
S.I.C.: 5064
N.A.I.C.S.: 423620
Personnel:
Jackie Strachan *(Pres)*

DIALECT SOLUTIONS HOLDINGS PTY LTD.

Level 2 116 Miller St
Sydney, NSW, 2000, Australia
Tel.: (61) 290040600
Fax: (61) 0290040640
Web Site: www.dialectpayments.com
Emp.: 40

Business Description:
Payment Processing Services for Financial Institutions
S.I.C.: 6099
N.A.I.C.S.: 522320

Personnel:
Martin A. Reeves *(VP-Global Bus Dev)*

Subsidiary:

Dialect Interactive (1)
Level 17 100 Arthur Street
Sydney, NSW, 2060, Australia
Tel.: (61) 290040600
Fax: (61) 99286652
E-Mail: info@salmat.com.au
Web Site: www.salmat.com.au
Emp.: 30
Interactive & Consultancy Services
S.I.C.: 8742
N.A.I.C.S.: 541613
Grant Harrod *(Mgr)*

DIALIGHT PLC

Exning Road
Newmarket, Suffolk, CB8 0AX, United Kingdom
Tel.: (44) 1638665161
Fax: (44) 1638660718
E-Mail: dialight@dialight.com
Web Site: www.dialight.com
Year Founded: 1990
DIA—(LSE)
Rev.: $181,823,658
Assets: $145,728,985
Liabilities: $46,236,873
Net Worth: $99,492,111
Earnings: $21,231,975
Emp.: 1,626
Fiscal Year-end: 12/31/12

Business Description:
Mfr of Light Emitting Diode (LED) Indicators, Traffic Signals, Beacons & Vehicle Lighting
Import Export
S.I.C.: 3679
N.A.I.C.S.: 334419

Personnel:
Bill Ronald *(Chm)*
Roy Burton *(Grp CEO)*
Kevin Higginson *(Interim CFO)*
Dan Doxsee *(Chief Comml Officer)*
Nick Giles *(Sec)*

Board of Directors:
Bill Ronald
Stephen Bird
Roy Burton
Mark Fryer
Tracey Graham
Robert Lambourne
Richard Stuckes

Legal Counsel:
Slaughter & May
One Bunhill Row
London, EC1Y 8YY, United Kingdom
Tel.: (44) 20 7600 1200
Fax: (44) 20 7600 0289

Butzel Long
380 Madison Avenue, 22nd Floor, New York, NY 10017

Subsidiaries:

Dialight BLP Ltd (1)
Exning Rd
Newmarket, CB8 0AX, United Kingdom UK
Tel.: (44) 1638665161 (100%)
Fax: (44) 1638660718
E-Mail: sales@blpcomp.com
Web Site: www.blpcomp.com
Emp.: 100
Electro-Mechanical & Electrical Components Mfr
S.I.C.: 3699
N.A.I.C.S.: 335999
Nick Rowland *(Dir-Fin)*

U.S. Division:

BLP Components (2)
1501 Route 34 S
Farmingdale, NJ 07727 (100%)
Tel.: (732) 751-5851
Fax: (732) 751-5779
E-Mail: sales@blpcomp.com
Web Site: www.blpcomp.com
Measurement & Control Equipment Distr
S.I.C.: 3679
N.A.I.C.S.: 334419

Dialight Europe Limited (1)
Exning Road
Newmarket, Suffolk, CB8 0AX, United Kingdom
Tel.: (44) 1638666541
Fax: (44) 1638 660718
Lighting Fixtures Distr
S.I.C.: 5063
N.A.I.C.S.: 423610

U.S. Subsidiary:

Dialight Corporation (1)
1501 Route 34 S
Farmingdale, NJ 07727 (100%)
Tel.: (732) 919-3119
Fax: (732) 751-5778
Toll Free: (800) 835-2870
E-Mail: info@dialight.com
Web Site: www.dialight.com
Emp.: 100
Mfr of LED Products
Import Export
S.I.C.: 3679
N.A.I.C.S.: 334419

Non-U.S. Subsidiary:

BTI Light Systems A/S (1)
Bygmestervej 6
2400 Copenhagen, Denmark
Tel.: (45) 35815800
Fax: (45) 35820099
E-Mail: info@btilight.com
Web Site: www.btilight.com
Emp.: 20
Navigational Lights Distr
S.I.C.: 5063
N.A.I.C.S.: 423610
Jesper Engesgaard *(Gen Mgr)*

DIALOG GROUP BERHAD

109 Block G Phileo Damansara 1 No 9 Jalan 16/11
46350 Petaling Jaya, Selangor Darul Ehsan, Malaysia
Tel.: (60) 379551199
Fax: (60) 379558989
Web Site: www.dialogasia.com
DIALOG—(KLS)
Rev.: $733,616,066
Assets: $930,399,218
Liabilities: $474,285,780
Net Worth: $456,113,438
Earnings: $60,765,871
Emp.: 2,659
Fiscal Year-end: 06/30/13

Business Description:
Oil, Gas & Petrochemical Products Services
S.I.C.: 2911
N.A.I.C.S.: 324110

Personnel:
Boon Keat Ngau *(Chm)*
Yew Kai Chan *(Pres & COO)*
Zainab Mohd Salleh *(CFO, Co-Sec & Controller-Fin)*
Abdul Rahim *(CEO/Gen Mgr-Pengerang Marine Operations Sdn Bhd)*
Richard Ellis *(CEO-Fabrication)*
Jamal Kamaludin *(CEO-Logistic)*
Siew Kim Chay *(Co-Sec)*
Hooi Mooi Lim *(Co-Sec)*
Chee Seng Toh *(Sr VP-Specialist Products & Svcs Div)*

Board of Directors:
Boon Keat Ngau
Yew Kai Chan
Eng Kar Chew
Kamariyah Hamdan
Zainab Mohd Salleh
Chong Peng Oh
Ja'afar Rihan
Khairon Shariff

Legal Counsel:
Mah-Kamariyah & Philip Koh
3A07 Block B Phileo Damansara II No 15 Jalan 16/11
Petaling Jaya, Malaysia

Subsidiaries:

Cendana Sutera Sdn. Bhd. (1)
Projet Jalan Klang banting
41200 Kelang, Selangor, Malaysia
Tel.: (60) 333234928
Petroleum Retailer
S.I.C.: 5171
N.A.I.C.S.: 424710

Dialog E & C Sdn. Bhd. (1)
109 Block G Phileo Damansara 1 No 9 Jalan 16/11
Petaling Jaya, Selangor, 46350, Malaysia
Tel.: (60) 379551199
Fax: (60) 379558989
Emp.: 300
Construction Engineering Services
S.I.C.: 8711
N.A.I.C.S.: 541330
Jamal Kamaludin *(CEO)*

U.S. Subsidiary:

Dialog Services, Inc. (1)
1311 C Avenue A
South Houston, TX 77587
Tel.: (832) 668-5726
Fax: (281) 501-2741
E-Mail: raymond.alamos@dialogasia.com
Web Site: www.dialogasia.com
Emp.: 54
Catalyst Handling Services
S.I.C.: 4491
N.A.I.C.S.: 488320
Raymond Alamos *(Gen Mgr)*

Non-U.S. Subsidiaries:

Dialog International (L) Ltd. (1)
No 10 Tuas Avenue 16
Singapore, Singapore
Tel.: (65) 63363377
Fax: (65) 6338 9929
Petrochemical Products Distr
S.I.C.: 5169
N.A.I.C.S.: 424690
Steven Teow *(Mgr-Mktg)*

Dialog Services Europe Ltd. (1)
Unit 5 Raven Close Bridgend Industrial Estate
Bridgend, Mid Glamorgan, CF31 3RF, United Kingdom
Tel.: (44) 1656645856
Fax: (44) 1656646541
Emp.: 25
Management Services
S.I.C.: 8741
N.A.I.C.S.: 551114
David Morgan *(Gen Mgr)*

Dialog Services Pty. Ltd. (1)
7 Burgay Court
Osborne Park, Perth, WA, 6017, Australia
Tel.: (61) 892449899
Fax: (61) 892449866
Web Site: www.dialogasia.com
Catalyst Handling Services
S.I.C.: 8999
N.A.I.C.S.: 541690
Andy Copland *(Gen Mgr)*

Dialog Systems (Asia) Pte. Ltd. (1)
10 Taus Avenue 16
Singapore, 638931, Singapore
Tel.: (65) 63363377
Fax: (65) 63389929
E-Mail: dspl@dialogasia.com
Web Site: www.dialogasia.com.my
Emp.: 50
Management Services
S.I.C.: 8741
N.A.I.C.S.: 551114
Loy Ah Wei *(Country Mgr)*

Non-U.S. Subsidiaries:

Dialog Services Saudi Arabia Company Ltd. (2)
Jubail Industrial City
PO Box 10990
31961 Al Jubayl, Eastern Province, Saudi Arabia
Tel.: (966) 3340 7740
Fax: (966) 3340 7741
E-Mail: dialog.ksa@dialogasia.com
Web Site: www.dialogasia.com
Emp.: 120
Engineering Consulting Services
S.I.C.: 8711
N.A.I.C.S.: 541330
Tan Ngee Meng *(Country Mgr)*

Dialog Systems (Thailand) Ltd. (2)
No 9A Century Industrial Park 450 Sukhumvit Road
Huaypong Muang, Rayong, 21000, Thailand
Tel.: (66) 38692672
Fax: (66) 38692670
E-Mail: kanyarag.c@dialogasia.com
Emp.: 150
Oil & Gas & Chemical Engineering Services
S.I.C.: 1389
N.A.I.C.S.: 213112
Channnarong Missita *(Gen Mgr)*

P.T. Dialog Sistemindo (2)
Gedung Graha Pratama 11th Floor JL M T Haryono Kav 15
South Jakarta, Jakarta, 12810, Indonesia
Tel.: (62) 2183790625
Fax: (62) 218370739
E-Mail: marketing@dialogsistemindo.com.id
Chemical Engineering Services
S.I.C.: 8711
N.A.I.C.S.: 541330
Edison Sinaga *(Mgr)*

Overseas Technical Engineering and Construction Pte. Ltd. (1)
10 Tuas Ave 16
Singapore, Singapore
Tel.: (65) 67786300
Fax: (65) 67792463
Web Site: www.otec.com.sg
Emp.: 100
Construction Engineering Services
S.I.C.: 8711
N.A.I.C.S.: 541330
Yoshiyuki Hiraoka *(Mgr)*

DIALOG SEMICONDUCTOR PLC

Neue Strasse 95
D-73230 Kirchheim, Germany
Tel.: (49) 70218050
Fax: (49) 7021805100
E-Mail: dialog.nabern@diasemi.com
Web Site: www.dialog-semiconductor.com
DLG—(DEU)
Rev.: $773,583,000
Assets: $708,140,000
Liabilities: $325,549,000
Net Worth: $382,591,000
Earnings: $62,513,000
Emp.: 806
Fiscal Year-end: 12/31/12

Business Description:
Mixed Signal Semiconductors for Wireless Devices Mfr
S.I.C.: 3674
N.A.I.C.S.: 334413

Personnel:
Richard M. Beyer *(Chm)*
Jalal Bagherli *(CEO)*
Jean-Michel Richard *(CFO & VP-Fin)*
Tim Anderson *(Sec)*
Udo Kratz *(Sr VP & Gen Mgr-Mobile Sys Bus Grp)*

Board of Directors:
Richard M. Beyer

Jalal Bagherli
Chris Burke
Michael Cannon
Aidan Hughes
John McMonigall
Eamonn O'Hare
Gregorio Reyes, Sr.
Russell Shaw
Peter Weber

Legal Counsel:
Reynolds Porter Chamberlain LLP
Tower Bridge House St Katherines Way
London, United Kingdom

Subsidiary:

Dialog Semiconductor GmbH (1)
Neue Strasse 95
73230 Kirchheim, Germany (100%)
Tel.: (49) 70218050
Fax: (49) 7021805100
E-Mail: dialog.nabern@diasemi.com
Web Site: www.dialog-semiconductor.com
Emp.: 100
Other Electronic Component Mfr
S.I.C.: 3679
N.A.I.C.S.: 334419
Jalal Bagherli *(CEO)*

U.S. Subsidiaries:

Dialog Semiconductor Inc (1)
16870 W Bernardo Dr
San Diego, CA 92127-1677 (100%)
Tel.: (858) 674-6990
E-Mail: NA_sales_enquiries@diasemi.com
Other Electronic Parts & Equipment Whslr
S.I.C.: 5065
N.A.I.C.S.: 423690

iWatt, Inc. (1)
675 Campbell Technology Pkwy Ste 150
Campbell, CA 95008 CA
Tel.: (408) 374-4200
Fax: (408) 341-0455
E-Mail: sales@iwatt.com
Web Site: www.iwatt.com
Sales Range: $50-74.9 Million
Emp.: 147
Digital-Centric Power Management Integrated Circuits Mfr
S.I.C.: 3674
N.A.I.C.S.: 334413
Ron Edgerton *(Pres & CEO)*
James V. McCanna *(CFO & VP)*
Scott Brown *(Sr VP-Mktg)*
Paul Chu *(Sr VP-Sls)*
Alex Sinar *(Sr VP-Ops)*
Gyanendra Tiwary *(Sr VP-Strategic Mktg)*

Non-U.S. Subsidiary:

iWatt Integrated Circuits (Shenzhen) Limited Company (2)
Rooms 1009-1011 Chang Hong Science & Technology Building
South 12 Road Southern District High Tech Park, Shenzhen, China
Tel.: (86) 755 2981 3669
Fax: (86) 755 8175 1496
Semiconducter Mfr
S.I.C.: 3674
N.A.I.C.S.: 334413
Marco Cheng, *(Mgr-Sls)*

Branch:

iWatt Integrated Circuits (Shenzhen) Limited Company - Shanghai (3)
Room 406 Building 1 No 1535 Hongmei Road
200233 Shanghai, China
Tel.: (86) 21 5178 2561
Fax: (86) 21 5178 2562
Semiconductor Mfr
S.I.C.: 3674
N.A.I.C.S.: 334413

Non-U.S. Subsidiaries:

Dialog Semiconductor KK (1)
Mita Kokusai Bldg 16F 1-4-28 Mita
Tokyo, Minato-ku, 108 0073, Japan (100%)
Tel.: (81) 337698123
Fax: (81) 337698124
E-Mail: dialog.tokyo@diasemi.com
Web Site: www.diasemi.com
Emp.: 13
Other Electronic Component Mfr
S.I.C.: 3679
N.A.I.C.S.: 334419
Toshihiro Watanabe *(Pres)*

Dialog Semiconductor (UK) Limited (1)
Delta 200 Delta Business Park Welton Road
SN5 7XB Swindon, United Kingdom (100%)
Tel.: (44) 1793757700
Fax: (44) 1793757800
E-Mail: mixed-signal@diasemi.com
Web Site: www.dialog-semiconductor.com
Emp.: 82
Semiconductor & Related Device Mfr
S.I.C.: 3674
N.A.I.C.S.: 334413
Jalal Bagherli *(CEO)*

DIAMANT INFRASTRUCTURE LIMITED

9 Beaumoon Chambers 27/33 N M Road Fort
Mumbai, Maharashtra, 400023, India
Tel.: (91) 22 66156606
Fax: (91) 22 66156607
E-Mail: diamant123@gmail.com
Web Site: www.diamantinfra.com
Year Founded: 1980
508860—(BOM)
Rev.: $16,931,544
Assets: $11,105,312
Liabilities: $6,651,614
Net Worth: $4,453,697
Earnings: $230,730
Fiscal Year-end: 03/31/13
Business Description:
Construction & Engineering Services
S.I.C.: 1629
N.A.I.C.S.: 237990
Personnel:
Naresh S. Saboo *(Mng Dir)*
Board of Directors:
Kamlesh Prasad
Ashok Kumar Shukla
Transfer Agent:
Purva Sharegistry (I) Pvt. Ltd.
9 Shiv Shakti Industrial Estate J.R. Boricha Marg Opp. Kasturba Hosp
Mumbai, India

DIAMCOR MINING INC.

630 1620 Dickson Avenue
Kelowna, BC, V1Y 9Y2, Canada
Tel.: (250) 862-3212
Fax: (250) 862-3214
E-Mail: info@diamcormining.com
Web Site: www.diamcormining.com
DMI—(OTC TSXV)
Business Description:
Diamond Mining Services
S.I.C.: 1411
N.A.I.C.S.: 212311
Personnel:
Dean H. Taylor *(Chm & CEO)*
Darren Vucurevich *(CFO)*
Board of Directors:
Dean H. Taylor
Stephen E. Haggerty
Sheldon B. Nelson
Darren Vucurevich

DIAMEDICA INC.

135 Innovation Drive Suite 200
Winnipeg, MB, R3T 6A8, Canada
Tel.: (204) 478-5605
E-Mail: info@diamedica.com
Web Site: www.diamedica.com
DMA—(TSXV)
Rev.: $40,576
Assets: $3,804,423
Liabilities: $1,564,839
Net Worth: $2,239,584
Earnings: ($9,939,842)
Fiscal Year-end: 12/31/12
Business Description:
Pharmaceutical Preparation Mfr
S.I.C.: 2834
N.A.I.C.S.: 325412
Personnel:
Rick Pauls *(Chm, Pres & CEO)*
Dennis D. Kim *(Chief Medical Officer)*
Board of Directors:
Rick Pauls
Michael Giuffre
Richard Pilnik
Thomas Wellner
Transfer Agent:
CIBC Mellon Trust Company
PO Box 721
Agincourt, ON, Canada

DIAMINES AND CHEMICALS LIMITED

Plot No 13 PCC Area P O Petrochemicals
Vadodara, 391346, India
Tel.: (91) 265 2230305
Fax: (91) 265 2230218
E-Mail: info@dacl.co.in
Web Site: www.dacl.co.in
Year Founded: 1976
500120—(BOM)
Rev.: $11,843,963
Assets: $12,321,653
Liabilities: $6,012,580
Net Worth: $6,309,072
Earnings: $249,897
Fiscal Year-end: 03/31/13
Business Description:
Ethylene Amines Mfr
S.I.C.: 2869
N.A.I.C.S.: 325199
Personnel:
Dimple Mehta *(Compliance Officer & Asst Sec)*
Board of Directors:
Yogesh M. Kothari
G. G. Chendwankar
Rajendra S. Chhabra
Ambrish Dalal
Dhruv Kaji
Amit M. Mehta
Shreyas Mehta
Kirat M. Patel
Girish R. Satarkar
G. S. Venkatachalam
Transfer Agent:
MCS Limited
Neelam Apartment 1st Floor 88 Sampatrao Colony Productivity Road
Vadodara, India

DIAMOND AIRCRAFT INDUSTRIES GMBH

NA Ottostrasse 5
Wiener Neustadt, 2700, Austria
Tel.: (43) 262226700
Fax: (43) 262226780
E-Mail: office@diamond-air.at
Web Site: www.diamond-air.at
Emp.: 500
Business Description:
Aircraft Mfr
S.I.C.: 3721
N.A.I.C.S.: 336411
Personnel:
Christian Pries *(Mgr)*

Non-U.S. Subsidiary:

Diamond Aircraft Industries Inc. (1)
1560 Crumlin Sideroad
London, ON, N5V 1S2, Canada
Tel.: (519) 457-4000
Fax: (519) 457-4021
Web Site: www.diamondaircraft.com
Emp.: 600
Aircraft Mfr
S.I.C.: 3721
N.A.I.C.S.: 336411
Peter Maurer *(Pres)*

DIAMOND BUILDING PRODUCTS PUBLIC COMPANY LIMITED

69-70 Moo 1 Mitraphap Rd Km 115
Talingchan Amphur Muang
Saraburi, 18000, Thailand
Tel.: (66) 36224001
Fax: (66) 36224016
E-Mail: corpcenter@dbp.co.th
Web Site: www.dbp.co.th
Year Founded: 1985
DRT—(THA)
Rev.: $128,662,988
Assets: $120,747,732
Liabilities: $47,390,173
Net Worth: $73,357,559
Earnings: $18,086,016
Emp.: 711
Fiscal Year-end: 12/31/12
Business Description:
Roofing Tiles, Siding Boards & Other Roofing Equipment Mfr & Distr
S.I.C.: 3255
N.A.I.C.S.: 327120
Personnel:
Prakit Pradipasen *(Chm)*
Asanee Chantong *(Mng Dir)*
Thanakarn Phanthapirat *(Asst Mng Dir-Acctg & Fin & Sec)*
Suwit Kaewamphunsawat *(Asst Mng Dir-Sls & Mktg)*
Satid Sudbuntad *(Deputy Mng Dir-Sls & Mktg)*
Maitree Tawonatiwasna *(Deputy Mng Dir-Production & Engrg)*
Board of Directors:
Prakit Pradipasen
Asanee Chantong
Phaithoon Kijsamrej
Anun Louharanoo
Sakda Maneeratchatchai
Krit Phanratanamala
Somboon Phuvoravan
James Patrick Rooney
Woodthikrai Soatthiyanon
Chaiyut Srivikorn
Satid Sudbuntad
Maitree Tawonatiwasna

DIAMOND COMPANY OF ARMENIA

1 Sovkhozyan Street
375082 Yerevan, Armenia
Tel.: (374) 1589993
Fax: (374) 1543916
E-Mail: dca@arminco.com
Web Site: www.dca.nt.am
Emp.: 1,000
Business Description:
Diamonds & Other Jewelry Mfr
S.I.C.: 3911
N.A.I.C.S.: 339910

DIAMOND DINING CO., LTD.

1-1-21 Higashi-Shinbashi
Minato-ku, Tokyo, Japan
Tel.: (81) 355375650
Fax: (81) 355375658
E-Mail: info@diamond-dining.com
Web Site: www.diamond-dining.com
Year Founded: 1996
3073—(TKS)
Sales Range: $75-99.9 Million
Emp.: 477
Business Description:
Restaurant Owner & Operator
S.I.C.: 5812
N.A.I.C.S.: 722511
Personnel:
Atsuhisa Matsumura *(Pres)*

DIAMOND FIELDS INTERNATIONAL LTD.

Suite 303 - 595 Howe Street
Box 4
Vancouver, BC, V6C 2T5, Canada
Tel.: (604) 685-9911
Fax: (604) 718-2808
E-Mail: enquire@diamondfields.com
Web Site: www.diamondfields.com
Year Founded: 1996
DFI—(TSXV)
Assets: $152,146
Liabilities: $1,002,433
Net Worth: ($850,287)
Earnings: ($91,934)
Emp.: 2
Fiscal Year-end: 06/30/13

Business Description:
Diamond Mining & Exploration Export
S.I.C.: 1429
N.A.I.C.S.: 212319

Personnel:
Michael Cuthbert *(Chm)*
Ian Ransome *(Pres, CEO & COO)*
Earl V. Young *(CFO & Sec)*

Board of Directors:
Michael Cuthbert
Norman Roderic Baker
Warner Bruckmann
Ian Ransome
Gregg J. Sedun
Earl V. Young

Legal Counsel:
Davis LLP
2800 Park Place 666 Burrard Street
Vancouver, BC, Canada

Transfer Agent:
Computershare Trust Company of Canada
9th Floor 100 University Avenue
Toronto, ON, Canada

Non-U.S. Subsidiary:

Diamond Fields Namibia (Pty) Ltd. **(1)**
76 Plato St
Academia, Namibia (100%)
Tel.: (264) 61372180
Fax: (264) 61372181
Web Site: www.diamondfields.com
Emp.: 35
Diamond Mining
S.I.C.: 1429
N.A.I.C.S.: 212319

DIAMOND GAME ENTERPRISES, INC.

(Acquired by Amaya Gaming Group Inc.)

DIAMOND INFOSYSTEMS LTD

ESSEN Info-Park 5/9-10 BIDC
Gorwa, Baroda, Gujarat, 390016, India
Tel.: (91) 265 2283969
Fax: (91) 265 2284328
E-Mail: sales@diinsy.com
Web Site: www.diinsy.com
Year Founded: 1993
530801—(BOM)
Sls.: $53,180,155
Assets: $9,614,102
Liabilities: $6,014,802
Net Worth: $3,599,300
Earnings: $415,463
Fiscal Year-end: 03/31/13

Business Description:
Information Technology Consulting Services
S.I.C.: 7373
N.A.I.C.S.: 541512

Personnel:
Suresh Naraian Bhatnagar *(Founder & Chm)*
Amit Suresh Bhatnagar *(Vice Chm)*
Sumit Suresh Bhatnagar *(Mng Dir)*
Fatima Dharmajwala *(Compliance Officer & Asst Sec)*

Board of Directors:
Suresh Naraian Bhatnagar
Amit Suresh Bhatnagar
N. N. Bhatnagar
Sumit Suresh Bhatnagar
Triloki Narayan Bhatnagar
Prakash Sinha
Gajendra Narayan Verma

Transfer Agent:
Karvy Computershare Pvt. Ltd.
Plot No.17-24 Vittal Rao Nagar Madhurapur
Hyderabad, India

DIAMOND OGILVY

27-8 KCC Bldg
Seocho-Ku, Seoul, 137-903, Korea (South)
Tel.: (82) 2 513 1114
Fax: (82) 2 3672 0019
E-Mail: webmaster.korea@ogilvy.com
Web Site: www.diamondogilvygroup.com
Year Founded: 1983
Billings: $400,000,000
Emp.: 200

Business Description:
Advertising Services
S.I.C.: 7311
N.A.I.C.S.: 541810

Personnel:
Jay Paik *(Pres)*

DIAMOND POWER INFRASTRUCTURE LTD.

Village Vadadala Phase II Ta-Savli
Vadodara District, Baroda, Gujarat, 391 520, India
Tel.: (91) 2667 251516
Fax: (91) 2667 251202
Web Site: www.dicabs.com
522163—(BOM)
Rev.: $481,347,142
Assets: $465,018,018
Liabilities: $325,451,030
Net Worth: $139,566,988
Earnings: $19,293,280
Emp.: 3,000
Fiscal Year-end: 03/31/13

Business Description:
Power Transmission Equipment Mfr
S.I.C.: 3568
N.A.I.C.S.: 333613

Personnel:
S. N. Bhatnagar *(Chm)*
Amit Bhatnagar *(Co-Mng Dir)*
Sumit Bhatnagar *(Co-Mng Dir)*
Nishant Javlekar *(Costing Officer & Sec)*
Kirit S. Dave *(Sr VP-EPC Div)*

Board of Directors:
S. N. Bhatnagar
Karthik Athreya
Amit Bhatnagar
Sumit Bhatnagar
Aswini Kumar Sahoo
Bhavin Shah
Ranvir Singh Shekhawat
Kirit Vyas

Transfer Agent:
Karvy Computershare Private Limited
Plot No 17 to 24 Vittalrao Nagar Madhapur
Hyderabad, India

DIAMOND TRUST BANK KENYA LIMITED

Nation Centre Kimathi Street
00200 Nairobi, Kenya
Tel.: (254) 202849000
Fax: (254) 202214525
E-Mail: care@dtbuganda.co.ug
Web Site: www.diamondtrust-bank.com
DTK—(NAI)
Int. Income: $186,182,327
Assets: $1,521,231,657
Liabilities: $1,312,051,334
Net Worth: $209,180,323
Earnings: $45,683,393
Emp.: 1,514
Fiscal Year-end: 12/31/12

Business Description:
Personal Banking Services
S.I.C.: 6141
N.A.I.C.S.: 522291

Personnel:
Abdul Samji *(Chm)*
Nasim Devji *(CEO & Mng Dir)*
Stephen Kodumbe *(Sec & Head-Legal)*

Board of Directors:
Abdul Samji
Pamela Ager
Nasim Devji
Moez Jamal
Nizar Juma
Irfan Keshavjee
Rafiuddin Zakir Mahmood
Amin Merali
Mwaghazi Mwachofi
Jamaludin Shamji

Non-U.S. Subsidiaries:

Diamond Trust Bank Burundi S.A. **(1)**
14 Chaussee Prince Louis Rwagasore
Bujumbura, Burundi
Tel.: (257) 22 25 99 88
Fax: (257) 22 25 99 65
Commercial Banking Services
S.I.C.: 6029
N.A.I.C.S.: 522110

Diamond Trust Bank Uganda Limited **(1)**
Diamond Trust Building Plot 17/19 Kampala Road
PO Box 7155
Kampala, Uganda
Tel.: (256) 414387000
Fax: (256) 414342286
Banking Services
S.I.C.: 6029
N.A.I.C.S.: 522110

DIAMONDCORP PLC

Third Floor 48 Gresham Street
London, EC2V 7AY, United Kingdom
Tel.: (44) 20 3151 0970
Fax: (44) 20 3151 0971
E-Mail: info@diamondcorp.plc.uk
Web Site: www.diamondcorp.plc.uk
DCP—(LSE)
Rev.: $40,408
Assets: $28,734,514
Liabilities: $8,088,904
Net Worth: $20,645,610
Earnings: ($5,582,695)
Emp.: 70
Fiscal Year-end: 12/31/12

Business Description:
Diamond Producer
S.I.C.: 5094
N.A.I.C.S.: 423940

Personnel:
Euan Worthington *(Chm)*
Paul Loudon *(CEO)*
John C. Forrest *(CFO)*

Board of Directors:
Euan Worthington
Nicholas Allen
Paul Loudon
John Hulme Scholes
Michael Toxvaerd
Jonathan Willis-Richards

Deloitte & Touche
Johannesburg, South Africa
Tel.: (27) 11 806 5000

Legal Counsel:
Werksmans Inc.
155 5th Street
Sandton, 2196, South Africa

Gowling Lafleur Henderson LLP
15th Floor 125 Old Broad Street
London, EC2N 1AR, United Kingdom

Non-U.S. Subsidiary:

Lace Diamond Mines (Pty) Limited **(1)**
PO Box 6016
Kroonheuwel, 9501 Kroonstad, Free State, South Africa
Tel.: (27) 562122308
Fax: (27) 562122318
E-Mail: lace@telkom.sa.net
Web Site: www.diamondcorp.plc.uk
Emp.: 73
Diamond & Kimberlite Mining Services
S.I.C.: 1499
N.A.I.C.S.: 212399
Paul Loudon *(Mng Dir)*

DIAMONEX LIMITED

1 349 Coronation Drive
PO Box 1357
Milton, QLD, 4064, Australia
Tel.: (61) 737208944
Fax: (61) 7 3720 8988
E-Mail: diamonex@diamonex.com.au
Web Site: www.diamonex.com.au
DON—(AIM ASX BOT)
Sales Range: Less than $1 Million

Business Description:
Mineral Exploration
S.I.C.: 1481
N.A.I.C.S.: 213115

Personnel:
Gregory M. King *(Chm)*
Dennis C. O'Neill *(Mng Dir)*
Hugh Lennerts *(Sec)*

Board of Directors:
Gregory M. King
David N. Magang
Dennis C. O'Neill

Hayes Knight Audit (QLD) Pty Ltd.
Level 4 127 Creek Street
Brisbane, QLD, 4000, Australia

Legal Counsel:
Watson, Farley & Williams
15 Appold Street
London, EC2A 2HB, United Kingdom

Hynes Lawyers
178 Montpelier Road
Bowen Hills, QLD, 4006, Australia

Hemming+Hart Lawyers
2nd Floor 307 Queen Street
Brisbane, QLD, 4000, Australia
Tel.: (61) 7 30028700

Armstrongs
Level 5 Barclays House
Gaborone, Botswana

Computershare Investor Services Pty. Ltd.
GPO Box 523
Brisbane, QLD, 4001, Australia
Tel.: (61) 7 3237 2173
Fax: (61) 7 3237 2152

DIAMYD MEDICAL AB

Kungsatan 29
SE-111 56 Stockholm, Sweden
Tel.: (46) 8 661 00 26
Fax: (46) 8 661 63 68
E-Mail: info@diamyd.com
Web Site: www.diamyd.com
Year Founded: 1994
DMYD B—(OMX)
Rev.: $15,309
Assets: $10,382,105
Liabilities: $1,151,849
Net Worth: $9,230,255
Earnings: ($1,933,986)
Emp.: 7
Fiscal Year-end: 08/31/13

Business Description:
Diabetes Vaccine Mfr
S.I.C.: 2834

N.A.I.C.S.: 325412
Personnel:
Anders Essen-Moller *(Chm)*
Peter Zerhouni *(Pres & CEO)*
Anna Styrud *(CFO)*
Board of Directors:
Anders Essen-Moller
Maria-Teresa Essen-Moller
Erik Nerpin

DIANA CONTAINERSHIPS INC.

Pendelis 16
Palaio Faliro, 175 64 Athens, Greece
Tel.: (30) 210 9470000
Fax: (30) 210 9424975
E-Mail: izafirakis@dcontainerships.com
Web Site: www.dcontainerships.com
Year Founded: 2010
DCIX—(NASDAQ)
Rev.: $56,631,000
Assets: $337,045,000
Liabilities: $98,287,000
Net Worth: $238,758,000
Earnings: $5,969,000
Fiscal Year-end: 12/31/12
Business Description:
Freight Transportation Services
S.I.C.: 4412
N.A.I.C.S.: 483111
Personnel:
Symeon Palios *(Chm & CEO)*
Anastasios Margaronis *(Pres)*
Andreas Michalopoulos *(CFO & Treas)*
Ioannis G. Zafirakis *(COO & Sec)*
Board of Directors:
Symeon Palios
Reidar Brekke
Giannakis Evangelou
Antonios Karavias
Anastasios Margaronis
Nikolaos Petmezas
Ioannis G. Zafirakis

DIANA DOLLS FASHIONS INC

(d/b/a Kushies Baby)
555 Barton Street
Stoney Creek, ON, L8E 5S1, Canada
Tel.: (905) 643-9118
Fax: (905) 643-2102
E-Mail: customerservice@kushies.com
Web Site: www.kushies.com
Year Founded: 1953
Rev.: $34,169,365
Emp.: 160
Business Description:
Baby Products & Accessories Mfr
S.I.C.: 5641
N.A.I.C.S.: 448130
Personnel:
Sam Perez *(Pres & CEO)*
David Swan *(CFO)*

DIANA SHIPPING INC.

Pendelis 16
Palaio Faliro, 175 64 Athens, Greece
Tel.: (30) 210 947 0100
Fax: (30) 210 9470 101
E-Mail: ir@dianashippinginc.com
Web Site: www.dianashippinginc.com
DSX—(NYSE)
Rev.: $220,785,000
Assets: $1,742,802,000
Liabilities: $476,378,000
Net Worth: $1,266,424,000
Earnings: $54,639,000
Emp.: 640
Fiscal Year-end: 12/31/12
Business Description:
Cargo Transport Services
S.I.C.: 4412
N.A.I.C.S.: 483111
Personnel:
Simeon P. Palios *(Chm & CEO)*
Anastassis C. Margaronis *(Pres)*
Andreas Michalopoulos *(CFO & Treas)*
Maria Dede *(Chief Acctg Officer)*
Ioannis G. Zafirakis *(Sec & Exec VP)*
Board of Directors:
Simeon P. Palios
Apostolos Kontoyannis
William Lawes
Anastassis C. Margaronis
Boris Nachamkin
Konstantinos Psaltis
Ioannis G. Zafirakis

Non-U.S. Subsidiary:

Diana Shipping Services S.A. (1)
C/O Chen Estrada And Wong
P H Bonanza Plaza 41 ST, Panama, Panama (100%)
Tel.: (507) 2251228
Fax: (507) 2270403
E-Mail: chestwon@cwpanama.net
Emp.: 10
All Other Legal Services
S.I.C.: 7389
N.A.I.C.S.: 541199
Luis Carlos Chen *(Mng Dir)*

DIANA TEA COMPANY LIMITED

Sir RNM House 4th Floor 3/B Lal Bazar Street
Kolkata, 700 001, India
Tel.: (91) 33 22488672
Fax: (91) 33 22487571
E-Mail: contactus@dianatea.in
Web Site: www.dianateacompany.com
Year Founded: 1911
530959—(BOM)
Rev.: $8,601,466
Assets: $19,620,863
Liabilities: $4,886,013
Net Worth: $14,734,850
Earnings: $495,704
Fiscal Year-end: 12/31/12
Business Description:
Tea & Coffee Mfr
S.I.C.: 2095
N.A.I.C.S.: 311920
Personnel:
Sandeep Singhania *(Mng Dir)*
Manoj Agarwala *(CFO, Compliance Officer & Sec)*
Board of Directors:
Neem Chand Mitruka
Naresh Pachisia
Harish Parekh
Sandeep Singhania
Sarita Singhania
Transfer Agent:
Maheshwari Datamatics Pvt. Ltd.
6 Mangoe Lane 2nd Fl
Kolkata, 700 001, India
Tel.: (91) 33 22435029
Fax: (91) 913322484787

DIANOR RESOURCES INC.

649 3rd Avenue 2nd Floor
Val d'Or, QC, J9P 1S7, Canada
Tel.: (819) 825-7090
Fax: (819) 825-7545
E-Mail: info@dianor.com
Web Site: www.dianor.com
DOR—(TSXV)
Sales Range: Less than $1 Million
Emp.: 10
Business Description:
Diamond Exploration & Mining Services
S.I.C.: 1499
N.A.I.C.S.: 212399
Personnel:
Daniel Duval *(Chm & CFO)*
John Ryder *(Pres)*
Board of Directors:
Daniel Duval
Nicholas Houghton
Lawrence C. Kozak
Pierre Paquet
John Ryder
Octavio Soares
Jim Steel
Me Neil Wiener
Werner Frank Zapfe
Legal Counsel:
Heenan Blaikie LLP
1250 Rene Levesque Blvd W Ste 2500
Montreal, QC, H3B 4Y1, Canada
Tel.: (514) 846-1212
Transfer Agent:
Computershare Investor Services Inc.
1500 University Street Suite 700
Montreal, QC, H3A 3SB, Canada

Subsidiary:

Threegold Resources Inc. (1)
649 3rd Ave 2nd Fl
Val d'Or, QC, J9P 4G8, Canada
Tel.: (819) 825-3883
Fax: (819) 825-3835
E-Mail: info@threegold.ca
Web Site: www.threegold.ca
Emp.: 6
Mineral Exploration Services
S.I.C.: 1389
N.A.I.C.S.: 213112
Richard Tanguay *(Chm)*
Victor Goncalves *(Pres & CEO)*

DIAS AQUACULTURE S.A.

54 Elaion St
14564 Kifissia, Greece
Tel.: (30) 2106251565
Fax: (30) 2106251910
E-Mail: gramatia@diassa.gr
Web Site: www.diassa.gr
DIFF—(ATH)
Sales Range: $150-199.9 Million
Emp.: 465
Business Description:
Fish Feed Mfr
S.I.C.: 2048
N.A.I.C.S.: 311119
Personnel:
Stelios Pitakas *(Chm & Mng Dir)*
Stephanos N. Manellis *(Vice Chm)*
Board of Directors:
Stelios Pitakas
Vadim Doubrovin
Anita Subba Hamilton
Karamouzis Haralampos
Stephanos N. Manellis
George Pitakas

Subsidiaries:

Merkos S.A. (1)
1st Km Attiki Odos
19600 Mandra-Attikis, Greece
Tel.: (30) 2105517900
Fax: (30) 2105517920
E-Mail: info@diassa.gr
Web Site: www.diassa.gr
Emp.: 80
Finfish & Shellfish Fishing & Distr
S.I.C.: 0912
N.A.I.C.S.: 114111
Elena Moutzouri *(Mgr-Export)*

DIASORIN S.P.A.

Via Crescentino
13040 Saluggia, Italy
Tel.: (39) 0161 487 526
Telex: 200064 SORIN I
Fax: (39) 0161 487 670
Web Site: www.diasorin.com
DIA—(ITA)
Rev.: $583,918,738
Assets: $706,766,173
Liabilities: $211,266,573
Net Worth: $495,499,600
Earnings: $118,037,570
Emp.: 1,553
Fiscal Year-end: 12/31/12
Business Description:
Bioengineering Products
S.I.C.: 2835
N.A.I.C.S.: 325413
Personnel:
Carroll E. Streetman, Jr. *(Pres)*
Carlo Rosa *(CEO & Gen Mgr)*
Pier Luigi De Angelis *(CFO)*
Francesco Colotta *(Chief Medical Officer & Sr VP)*
John Eskdale *(Pres-DiaSorin Inc)*
Chen Menachem Even *(Sr VP-Comml Ops)*
Stefano Ronchi *(Sr VP-HR)*
Board of Directors:
Gustavo Denegri
Giuseppe Alessandria
Enrico Mario Amo
Antonio Boniolo
Michele Denegri
Eva Desana
Chen Menachem Even
Ezio Garibaldi
Maria Paola Landini
Franco Moscetti
Carlo Rosa
Gian Alberto Saporiti
Roberta Somati

Non-U.S. Subsidiary:

Biofin Holding International BV (1)
Rokin 55
1012 KK Amsterdam, Netherlands (100%)
Tel.: (31) 205214713
Fax: (31) 205214827
Emp.: 638
Bioengineering
S.I.C.: 8711
N.A.I.C.S.: 541330

U.S. Subsidiary:

DiaSorin Inc. (2)
1951 Northwestern Ave
Stillwater, MN 55082-7536 MN
Mailing Address:
PO Box 285
Stillwater, MN 55082-0285
Tel.: (651) 439-9710
Fax: (651) 351-5669
Toll Free: (800) 328-1482
E-Mail: info@diasorin.com
Web Site: www.diasorin.com
Emp.: 160
In-Vitro Diagnostics Mfr
Import Export
S.I.C.: 2835
N.A.I.C.S.: 325413
Carroll Streetman *(Pres)*

Non-U.S. Holdings:

DiaSorin Ltd. (3)
1st Floor Richmond House
Oldbury, Bracknell, Berks, RG12 8TQ, United Kingdom (100%)
Tel.: (44) 1344401430
Telex: 851 846 934
Fax: (44) 1344401431
E-Mail: info@diasorin.ltd.uk
Emp.: 19
Mfr. & Marketing of Diagnostic Products
S.I.C.: 2834
N.A.I.C.S.: 325412
Steve Swanscott *(Dir-Comml)*

DiaSorin AB (3)
Lofstroms Allen 7
PO Box 1300
172 26 Sundbyberg, Sweden (100%)
Tel.: (46) 855520300
Fax: (46) 855520329
E-Mail: info@diasorin.se
Emp.: 9
Diagnostic Products Mfr.
S.I.C.: 2834
N.A.I.C.S.: 325412
Anne Peterson *(Mgr-HR)*

DiaSorin Deutschland GmbH (3)
Von Hevesy Strasse 3
63128 Dietzenbach, Germany
Tel.: (49) 60744010

DiaSorin S.p.A.—(Continued)

Fax: (49) 60744010
E-Mail: info@diasorin.de
Web Site: www.diasorin.de
Emp.: 100
In-Vitro Diagnostics Mfr
S.I.C.: 2835
N.A.I.C.S.: 325413
Marcus Segal *(Mgr)*

DIATEC S.R.L.

Strada Statale 151 km 13
Collecorvino, 65013, Italy
Tel.: (39) 085 82060 1
Fax: (39) 085 82060 22
E-Mail: staff@diatec.it
Web Site: www.diatec.it
Year Founded: 1992

Business Description:
Industrial Machinery Mfr
S.I.C.: 3559
N.A.I.C.S.: 333249

U.S. Subsidiaries:

Arkwright Advanced Coating, Inc. **(1)**
538 Main St
Fiskeville, RI 02823
Tel.: (401) 821-1000
Web Site: www.arkwright.com
Coated Paper Mfr
S.I.C.: 2672
N.A.I.C.S.: 322220
Michael Collins *(Project Dir-Mgmt)*

SIHL LLC **(1)**
713 Fenway Ave Ste B
Chesapeake, VA 23323
Tel.: (757) 966-7180
Web Site: www.sihlusa.com
Printing Material Mfr
S.I.C.: 2893
N.A.I.C.S.: 325910
Phil Hursh *(CEO)*

DIATREME RESOURCES LIMITED

Level 2 87 Wickham Terrace
Spring Hill, QLD, 4000, Australia
Tel.: (61) 738325666
Fax: (61) 738325300
E-Mail: manager@diatreme.com.au
Web Site: www.diatreme.com.au
DRX—(ASX)
Rev.: $232,674
Assets: $24,035,580
Liabilities: $463,573
Net Worth: $23,572,007
Earnings: ($5,115,115)
Emp.: 5
Fiscal Year-end: 12/31/12

Business Description:
Mineral Mining Services
S.I.C.: 1481
N.A.I.C.S.: 213115

Personnel:
Anthony John Fawdon *(Chm & CEO)*
Tuan Quy Do *(Co-Sec)*
Leni Pia Stanley *(Co-Sec)*

Board of Directors:
Anthony John Fawdon
David Hugh Hall
Neil McIntyre
Andrew Tsang
William Cheng Wang
George Henry White

Legal Counsel:
Quinert Rodda & Associates
Level 19 500 Collins St
Melbourne, Australia

Subsidiaries:

Lost Sands Pty Ltd **(1)**
Level 2 87 Wickham Terr
Spring Hill, QLD, 4000, Australia
Tel.: (61) 738325666
Fax: (61) 738325300
E-Mail: manager@diatreme.com
Web Site: www.diatreme.com
Emp.: 10
Mineral Exploration Services
S.I.C.: 1099
N.A.I.C.S.: 212299
David Hall *(Mng Dir)*

Regional Exploration Management Pty Ltd **(1)**
Level 1 47 McKenzie St
Ceduna, SA, 5690, Australia
Tel.: (61) 886253567
Mineral Exploration Services
S.I.C.: 1481
N.A.I.C.S.: 213115

DIAXONHIT SA

(Formerly ExonHit Therapeutics SA)
65 Boulevard Massena
75013 Paris, France
Tel.: (33) 1 53 94 77 00
Fax: (33) 1 53 94 77 07
E-Mail: Pleaseforward@diaxonhit.com
Web Site: www.diaxonhit.com
Year Founded: 1997
ALEHT—(EUR)

Business Description:
Diagnostic Equipmentt Distr
S.I.C.: 5047
N.A.I.C.S.: 423450

Personnel:
Laurent Condomine *(Chm-Supervisory Bd)*
Loic Maurel *(Chm-Mgmt Bd)*
Patrick Langlois *(Vice Chm-Supervisory Bd)*
Herve Duchesne de Lamotte *(CFO)*
Matthew Pando *(Chief Scientific Officer & VP-R&D)*

Supervisory Board of Directors:
Laurent Condomine
Jean-Jacques De Jaegher
Jean-Pierre Hermet
Christophe Jean
Patrick Langlois
Michel Picot
Deborah Smeltzer

DIAZ RESOURCES LTD.

(Acquired & Absorbed by Tuscany Energy Ltd.)

DIC ASSET AG

Gruenhof Eschersheimer Landstrasse 223
60320 Frankfurt am Main, Germany
Tel.: (49) 6994548580
Fax: (49) 69945485899
E-Mail: info@dic-asset.de
Web Site: www.dic-asset.de
DAZ—(DEU)
Rev.: $308,391,393
Assets: $2,975,267,241
Liabilities: $2,148,285,395
Net Worth: $826,981,847
Earnings: $15,925,191
Emp.: 140
Fiscal Year-end: 12/31/12

Business Description:
Real Estate Services
S.I.C.: 6513
N.A.I.C.S.: 531110

Personnel:
Gerhard Schmidt *(Chm-Supervisory Bd)*
Ulrich Holler *(Chm-Mgmt Bd & CEO)*
Klaus-Jurgen Sontowsk *(Vice Chm-Supervisory Bd)*
Sonja Warntges *(CFO & Member-Mgmt Bd)*
Rainer Pillmayer *(COO & Member-Mgmt Bd)*

Supervisory Board of Directors:
Gerhard Schmidt
Michael Bock
Russell Platt
Michael Peter Solf
Klaus-Jurgen Sontowsk
Bernd Wegener

DIC CORPORATION

Waterras Tower 101 Kanda Awajicho
2-chome Chiyoda-ku
Tokyo, 101-0063, Japan
Mailing Address:
35-38 Sakashita 3-Chome
Itabashi-Ku, Tokyo, 174 8520, Japan
Tel.: (81) 3 6733 3000
Fax: (81) 3 3278 8558
E-Mail: ir@ma.dic.co.jp
Web Site: www.dic-global.com
Year Founded: 1908
4631—(TKS)
Sls.: $7,741,591,000
Assets: $7,622,901,000
Liabilities: $5,854,860,000
Net Worth: $1,768,041,000
Earnings: $209,704,000
Emp.: 20,273
Fiscal Year-end: 03/31/13

Business Description:
Specialty Chemicals & Printing Inks Mfr & Sales
Import Export
S.I.C.: 2893
N.A.I.C.S.: 325910

Personnel:
Kazuo Sugie *(Chm)*
Yoshiyuki Nakanishi *(Pres & CEO)*
Toshio Hasumi *(Mng Exec Officer)*
Hideki Inouchi *(Exec Officer-Gen Affairs & Legal Div)*
Toshio Kanbe *(Exec Officer)*
Yoshihisa Kawamura *(Mng Exec Officer-Bus Coordination & Support Div)*
Kazuo Kudo *(Mng Exec Officer-Corp Strategy Div)*
Rudi Lenz *(Exec Officer)*
Yoshiaki Masuda *(Mng Exec Officer)*
Masayuki Saito *(Sr Mng Exec Officer-Fin & Acctg)*
Eiji Takizawa *(Exec Officer)*

Board of Directors:
Kazuo Sugie
Tetsuro Agawa
Yoshihisa Kawamura
Akira Konishi
Eiko Kono
Yoshiyuki Nakanishi
Masayuki Saito
Takao Suzuki

Transfer Agent:
Mitsubishi UFJ Trust & Banking Corporation
7-10-11 Higashisuna Koto-ku
Tokyo, Japan

Subsidiaries:

DIC Color Design, Inc. **(1)**
No 2 DIC Bldg 16-2 Sotokanda 2-chome
Chiyoda-Ku, Tokyo, 101-0021, Japan
Tel.: (81) 3 5256 3246
Fax: (81) 3 5256 3245
E-Mail: dcdshopping@dic-color.com
Web Site: www.dic-color.com
Emp.: 53
Graphic Design Services
S.I.C.: 7336
N.A.I.C.S.: 541430
Wataru Toriumi *(Pres)*

DIC Decor, Inc. **(1)**
2-20 Akabori
Okegawa, Saitama-ken, 363-0002, Japan
Tel.: (81) 48 728 8741
Fax: (81) 48 728 8742
Web Site: www.dic-decor.co.jp
Emp.: 10
Poly Vinyl Chloride Sheet Mfr & Distr
S.I.C.: 2821
N.A.I.C.S.: 325211
Hitoshi Sumi *(Pres & CEO)*
Shoji Inomata *(Pres)*

DIC EP Corp. **(1)**
11-5 Kitasode
Sodegaura, Chiba, 299-0266, Japan
Tel.: (81) 438 63 0070
Fax: (81) 438 63 0072
Polymer Resin Mfr
S.I.C.: 2821
N.A.I.C.S.: 325211

DIC Estate Co., Ltd. **(1)**
3-7-20 Nihombashi
Chuo-Ku, Tokyo, 103-0027, Japan
Tel.: (81) 352037814
Real Estate Leasing Services
S.I.C.: 6519
N.A.I.C.S.: 531190

DIC Filtec, Inc. **(1)**
2100-28 Kamiyoshiba
Satte, Saitama, 340-0121, Japan
Tel.: (81) 480 48 1670
Fax: (81) 480 48 1679
Plastic Film Mfr & Distr
S.I.C.: 3081
N.A.I.C.S.: 326113

DIC Graphics Corporation **(1)**
DIC Building 7-20 Nihonbashi 3-chome
Chuo-ku, Tokyo, 103-8233, Japan
Tel.: (81) 3 3278 0620
Fax: (81) 3 3274 0868
Web Site: www.dic-graphics.co.jp
Emp.: 900
Printing Ink Mfr & Distr
S.I.C.: 2893
N.A.I.C.S.: 325910
Toshio Hasumi *(Pres)*

Plants:

DIC Graphics Corporation - Chiba Plant **(2)**
12 Yawatakaigandori
Ichihara, Chiba, 290-8585, Japan
Tel.: (81) 436 41 4121
Web Site: www.dic-graphics.co.jp/en/company/index.html#
Printing Ink Mfr
S.I.C.: 2893
N.A.I.C.S.: 325910

DIC Graphics Corporation - Gunma Plant **(2)**
Ooazasyowa-1banchi Chiyoda-machi
Oura-gun, Gunma, 370-0723, Japan
Tel.: (81) 276 86 5811
Web Site: www.dic-graphics.co.jp/en/company/index.html#
Printing Ink Mfr
S.I.C.: 2893
N.A.I.C.S.: 325910

DIC Graphics Corporation - Hokuriku Plant **(2)**
64-2 Minatomachi-So
Hakusan, Ishikawa, 929-0296, Japan
Tel.: (81) 76 278 2332
Fax: (81) 76 278 5354
Printing Ink Mfr
S.I.C.: 2893
N.A.I.C.S.: 325910

DIC Graphics Corporation - Kansai Plant **(2)**
1-33-1 Kasugakita-cho
Hirakata, Oosaka, 573-0137, Japan
Tel.: (81) 72 859 1171
Web Site: www.dic-graphics.co.jp/en/company/index.html#
Printing Ink Mfr
S.I.C.: 2893
N.A.I.C.S.: 325910

DIC Graphics Corporation - Kashima Plant **(2)**
18 Higashifukashiba
Kamisu, Ibaraki, 314-0193, Japan
Tel.: (81) 299 93 8141
Printing Ink Mfr
S.I.C.: 2893
N.A.I.C.S.: 325910

DIC Graphics Corporation - Komaki Plant **(2)**
151-1 Aza Nagare Oaza Shimosue
Komaki, Aichi, 485-0825, Japan
Tel.: (81) 568 75 2751
Fax: (81) 568 73 4120
Printing Ink Mfr & Distr

S.I.C.: 2893
N.A.I.C.S.: 325910

DIC Graphics Corporation - Tokyo Plant (2)
35-58 Sakashita 3-chome
Itabashi-ku, Tokyo, 174-8520, Japan
Tel.: (81) 3 3966 2111
Fax: (81) 3 3965 4320
Printing Ink Mfr
S.I.C.: 2893
N.A.I.C.S.: 325910

DIC Graphics Corporation - Utunomiya Plant (2)
1062-16 Oaza Honjo Nishikata
Kamitsuga, Tochigi, 322-0606, Japan
Tel.: (81) 282 91 1171
Web Site: www.dic-graphics.co.jp/en/company/index.html#
Printing Ink Mfr
S.I.C.: 2893
N.A.I.C.S.: 325910

DIC Interior Co., Ltd. (1)
270-8 Odate Komagata Hiratamura
Ishikawa, Fukushima, 963-8113, Japan
Tel.: (81) 247542990
Interior Housing Design Material Mfr
S.I.C.: 2541
N.A.I.C.S.: 337212

DIC Kako, Inc. (1)
373 Kojibukuro
Konan, Aichi, 520-3233, Japan
Tel.: (81) 748724918
Web Site: www.dic-kako.co.jp
Laminated Plastic Plate & Sheet Mfr
S.I.C.: 3083
N.A.I.C.S.: 326130

DIC Kitanihon Polymer Co., Ltd. (1)
56 Shinoyoke Miya Zaomachi
Katta, Miyagi, 989-0701, Japan
Tel.: (81) 224322226
Fax: (81) 224323515
Emp.: 6
Synthetic Resin Mfr
S.I.C.: 2821
N.A.I.C.S.: 325211

DIC Kyushu Polymer Co., Ltd. (1)
2680-1 Tajiri
Nakatsu, Oita, 879-0123, Japan
Tel.: (81) 979325370
Synthetic Resin Mfr
S.I.C.: 2821
N.A.I.C.S.: 325211

DIC Lifetec Co., Ltd. (1)
Wakamatsu Building 1F 3-6 Nihonbashi-Honcho 3-chome
Chuo-ku, Tokyo, 103-0023, Japan
Tel.: (81) 3 5203 7878
Fax: (81) 3 3281 8610
Web Site: www.dlt-spl.co.jp
Emp.: 68
Nutritional Food Supplements Mfr & Distr
S.I.C.: 2099
N.A.I.C.S.: 311999
Atsushi Egashira *(Pres)*
Amha Belay *(CTO & Sr VP)*

DIC Machinery & Printer's Supplies, Inc. (1)
3-35-58 Sakashita
Itabashi-Ku, Tokyo, 174-0043, Japan
Tel.: (81) 353925387
Printing Ink Distr
S.I.C.: 5085
N.A.I.C.S.: 423840

DIC Molding, Inc. (1)
4429-14 Shiku Komuro Ina-Machi
Kita Adachi-Gun, Saitama, 362-0806, Japan
Tel.: (81) 487230611
Injection Molded Plastic Products Mfr
S.I.C.: 3089
N.A.I.C.S.: 326199

DIC Plastics, Inc. (1)
1-7-5 Sakuragicho Sonic City Bldg 20f
Omiya-Ku, Saitama, 330-0854, Japan
Tel.: (81) 48 658 8855
Fax: (81) 48 643 8891
Web Site: www.dic-plas.co.jp
Injection Molded Plastic Products Mfr
S.I.C.: 3089
N.A.I.C.S.: 326199

Fuji Label Co., Ltd. (1)
1-331-8 Hayashi
Tokorozawa, Saitama, 359-1167, Japan
Tel.: (81) 4 2938 7670
Fax: (81) 4 2938 7676
Web Site: www.fuji-label.co.jp
Labelling Machinery Mfr
S.I.C.: 3565
N.A.I.C.S.: 333993

Nihon Packaging Material Co., Ltd. (1)
2100-30 Kamiyoshiba
Satte, Saitama, 340-0121, Japan
Tel.: (81) 480480681
Packaging Paper Materials Mfr
S.I.C.: 2672
N.A.I.C.S.: 322220

Topic Co., Ltd. (1)
1-7-36 Kamiaoki
Kawaguchi, Saitama, 333-0844, Japan
Tel.: (81) 482412211
Fax: (81) 482412200
Web Site: www.topic-dic.com
Emp.: 89
Printed Circuit Board Photomask Mfr
S.I.C.: 3861
N.A.I.C.S.: 325992
Mitsu Yokoga *(Mgr-Sls)*

U.S. Subsidiaries:

DIC Imaging Products USA Inc. (1)
7300 S 10th St
Oak Creek, WI 53154-1906 WI
Tel.: (414) 764-5100
Fax: (414) 764-5032
Web Site: www.dic.co.jp/en/company/group/america.html
Rev.: $6,700,000
Emp.: 48
Plastic Materials & Resins
S.I.C.: 2821
N.A.I.C.S.: 325211
Lee Rundell *(Plant Mgr)*

DIC International (USA), LLC (1)
35 Waterview Blvd
Parsippany, NJ 07054
Tel.: (973) 404-6600
Fax: (973) 404-6601
Emp.: 11
Retailer of Ink & Chemicals
S.I.C.: 5169
N.A.I.C.S.: 424690

Earthrise Nutritional LLC (1)
2151 Michelson Dr Ste 258
Irvine, CA 92612
Tel.: (949) 623-0980
Fax: (949) 623-0990
Toll Free: (800) 949-7473
E-Mail: info@earthrise.com
Web Site: www.earthrise.com
Emp.: 54
Mfr. of Edible Alga Spirulina
S.I.C.: 0191
N.A.I.C.S.: 111998
Chris Sekiguchi *(Controller)*

Earthrise Nutritionals, LLC. (1)
2151 Michelson Dr Ste 258
Irvine, CA 92612
Tel.: (949) 623-0980
Fax: (949) 623-0990
Toll Free: (800) 949-7473
E-Mail: info@earthrise.com
Web Site: www.earthrise.com
Emp.: 60
Nutritional Supplements Mfr
S.I.C.: 2099
N.A.I.C.S.: 311999
Eiichi Kato *(Pres)*
Amha Belay *(CTO & VP)*

Sun Chemical Corporation (1)
35 Waterview Blvd
Parsippany, NJ 07054-1285
Tel.: (973) 404-6000
Fax: (973) 404-6001
Web Site: www.sunchemical.com
Sales Range: $1-4.9 Billion
Emp.: 200
Mfr of Printing Inks & Organic Pigments & Dispersions
S.I.C.: 2893
N.A.I.C.S.: 325910
Rudi Lenz *(Pres & CEO)*
Gerry Brady *(CFO)*
Felipe Mellado *(CMO)*
Russell Schwartz *(CTO)*
Edward Pruitt *(Chief Procurement Officer)*
Greg Lawson *(Pres-Latin America)*
Charles Murray *(Pres-Inks-North America)*
Myron Petruch *(Pres-Performance Pigments)*
James R. Van Horn *(Gen Counsel & Sec)*
John L. McKeown *(Chief Admin & Sr VP)*

Divisions:

Coates Electrographics Inc. (2)
Country Club Rd
Dallas, PA 18612 PA
Mailing Address:
411 Country Club Rd
Dallas, PA 18612-9170
Tel.: (570) 675-1131
Fax: (570) 675-0415
Emp.: 55
Chemical Preparations
S.I.C.: 2893
N.A.I.C.S.: 325910

Kohl & Madden Printing Ink Corp. Div. (2)
651 Garden St
Carlstadt, NJ 07072
Tel.: (201) 933-4500
Fax: (201) 933-2441
Web Site: www.kohlmadden.com
Emp.: 20
Mfr. of Printing Ink
S.I.C.: 2893
N.A.I.C.S.: 325910
Carolyn Lanz *(Controller-MRP)*

KVK USA Inc. (2)
19 A Home News Row
New Brunswick, NJ 08901-3601 NJ
Tel.: (732) 846-2355
Rev.: $1,200,000
Emp.: 10
Inorganic Pigments
S.I.C.: 2819
N.A.I.C.S.: 325130

Sun Chemical Corporation of Michigan (2)
4925 Evanston Ave
Muskegon, MI 49442-4827
Tel.: (231) 788-2371
Fax: (231) 788-2618
Web Site: www.sunchemical.com
Emp.: 300
Pigment Mfr for Printing Ink
S.I.C.: 2816
N.A.I.C.S.: 325130
Scott Hendryx *(Dir-Ops)*

Sun Chemical Corporation, Pigments Division (2)
5020 Spring Grove Ave
Cincinnati, OH 45232-1926
Tel.: (513) 681-5950
Fax: (513) 681-3419
E-Mail: info@sunpigments.com
Web Site: www.sunpigments.com
Emp.: 5,600
Mfr. of Pigments for Printing Inks, Paints & Plastics
S.I.C.: 2819
N.A.I.C.S.: 325130
Brian Leen *(Pres)*

Sun Chemical Ink (2)
135 W Lake St
Northlake, IL 60164
Tel.: (708) 562-0550
Fax: (708) 562-0580
Toll Free: (800) 933-7863
Web Site: www.sunchemicalink.com
Emp.: 4,000
General Printing Inks Mfr
S.I.C.: 2893
N.A.I.C.S.: 325910
Greg Lawson *(Pres-Publication & Commercial Printing Inks)*

US Ink Corporation (2)
651 Garden St
Carlstadt, NJ 07072-1609 (100%)
Tel.: (201) 935-8666
Fax: (201) 933-3728
Web Site: www.usink.com
Emp.: 60
Mfr. of Ink
S.I.C.: 2893
N.A.I.C.S.: 325910
John Corcoran *(VP-Sls)*

Divisions:

US Ink Corporation, Eastern Region (3)
343 Murray Hill Pkwy
East Rutherford, NJ 07073-2110
Tel.: (201) 933-7100
Fax: (201) 935-3277
Toll Free: (800) 223-0717
E-Mail: vcisales@cashco.com
Web Site: www.usink.com
Emp.: 15
Mfr. of Printing Ink
S.I.C.: 2893
N.A.I.C.S.: 325910
Mike Dodd *(Pres)*

US Ink Corporation, Midwest Region (3)
600 Redna Ter
Cincinnati, OH 45215-1108
Tel.: (513) 771-4030
Fax: (513) 771-1399
Toll Free: (800) 543-1822
E-Mail: info@usink.com
Web Site: www.usink.com
Emp.: 30
Mfr. of Printing Ink
S.I.C.: 2893
N.A.I.C.S.: 325910
Steve Cornwell *(Plant Mgr)*

US Ink Corporation, Southern Region (3)
5200 Shawland Rd
Jacksonville, FL 32254-1651
Tel.: (904) 786-1474
Fax: (904) 786-1476
Toll Free: (800) 874-7950
Web Site: www.usink.com
Emp.: 40
Mfr. of Printing Ink
S.I.C.: 2893
N.A.I.C.S.: 325910

US Ink Corporation, Southwest Region (3)
12010 Corp Dr
Dallas, TX 75228-8102
Fax: (972) 613-6716
Toll Free: (800) 445-7549
Web Site: www.usink.com
Emp.: 50
Ink Mfr
S.I.C.: 2893
N.A.I.C.S.: 325910

US Ink Corporation, Western Region (3)
14465 Griffith St
San Leandro, CA 94577
Tel.: (510) 357-5200
Fax: (510) 352-1776
Toll Free: (800) 222-7709
Web Site: www.usink.com
Emp.: 35
Mfr. of Printing Ink
S.I.C.: 2893
N.A.I.C.S.: 325910

Non-U.S. Subsidiaries:

Benda-Lutz Werke GmbH (2)
Ferdinand-Lutz-Strasse 8
3134 Nussdorf ob der Traisen, Austria AT
Tel.: (43) 278362020
Fax: (43) 2783620224
E-Mail: office@benda-lutz.com
Web Site: www.benda-lutz.com
Emp.: 113
Metal Powders & Pigments Mfr
S.I.C.: 2851
N.A.I.C.S.: 325510
Dieter Lutz *(Mng Dir)*
Martin Lutz *(Mng Dir)*

U.S. Subsidiary:

Benda-Lutz Corporation (3)
10500 Toebben Dr
Independence, KY 41051
Tel.: (859) 746-0392
Fax: (859) 525-3012
E-Mail: office@benda-lutz.net
Web Site: www.benda-lutz.com
Sales Range: $1-9.9 Million
Emp.: 34
Metal Powders & Pigments Mfr
S.I.C.: 2851

DIC Corporation—(Continued)

N.A.I.C.S.: 325510
Matthew Pilon *(Gen Mgr)*

Non-U.S. Joint Venture:

Benda-Lutz-Alpoco Sp.z o.o. (3)
ul Pilsudskiego 23
32 050 Skawina, Poland
Tel.: (48) 122761110
Fax: (48) 122763661
E-Mail: office@benda-lutz.com.pl
Web Site: www.benda-lutz.com
Emp.: 15
Metal Powders & Pigments Mfr
S.I.C.: 2851
N.A.I.C.S.: 325510
Janusz Jedrusik *(Gen Mgr)*

Coates Brothers (Caribbean) Ltd. (2)
12 Label Blvd
Trincity, Trinidad & Tobago
Tel.: (868) 640 9835
Fax: (868) 640 3112
E-Mail: Suzetta.Ali,li@sunchemical.com
Web Site: www.sunchemical.com
Emp.: 11
Printing Ink Mfr
S.I.C.: 2893
N.A.I.C.S.: 325910
Suzetta Ali *(Gen Mgr)*

Coates Brothers (Zambia) Ltd. (2)
Ulengo Road No 3291
Ndola, 230025, Zambia
Tel.: (260) 212650945
Fax: (260) 212650141
E-Mail: coates@coppernet.zm
Emp.: 18
Printing Ink Mfr
S.I.C.: 2893
N.A.I.C.S.: 325910
Edson Kalunga *(Chm)*

Coates Screen Inks GmbH (2)
Wiederholdplatz 1
90451 Nuremberg, Germany
Tel.: (49) 911 6422 0
Fax: (49) 911 6422 200
E-Mail: info@coates.de
Web Site: www.coates.de
Emp.: 10
Printing Ink & Coating Mfr
S.I.C.: 2893
N.A.I.C.S.: 325910
Jean Paul Muller *(Mgr-Sls-Export)*

IMS Concepts S.A./N.V. (2)
Avenue Fleming 2
Wavre, Brabant Wallon, 1300, Belgium
Tel.: (32) 87340153
Printing Ink Mfr
S.I.C.: 2893
N.A.I.C.S.: 325910

Parker Williams Design Ltd. (2)
3rd Floor Voysey House Barley Mow Passage
London, W4 4PH, United Kingdom
Tel.: (44) 20 8995 6411
E-Mail: reception@parkerwilliams.co.uk
Web Site: www.parkerwilliams.co.uk
Emp.: 2
Packaging Design Services
S.I.C.: 7389
N.A.I.C.S.: 541490
Kate Bradford *(Mng Dir)*

Sun Branding Solutions Ltd. (2)
Albion Mills Albion Rd Greengates
Bradford, West Yorkshire, United Kingdom BD10 9TQ
Tel.: (44) 1274 200 700
Fax: (44) 1274 202 425
E-Mail: info@sunbrandingsolutions.com
Web Site: www.sunbrandingsolutions.com
Brand Design Consulting Services
S.I.C.: 8742
N.A.I.C.S.: 541613

Sun Chemical A/S (2)
Kobenhavnsvej 112
4600 Koge, Denmark
Tel.: (45) 56 67 75 85
Fax: (45) 56677693
Web Site: www.sunchemical.com
Emp.: 14
Printing Ink & Organic Pigment Mfr
S.I.C.: 2893
N.A.I.C.S.: 325910
Nobuhisa Hosokawa *(Dir-Fin)*

Sun Chemical A/S (2)
Stlfjaera 1
PO Box 164
NO-0975 Oslo, Norway NO
Tel.: (47) 22975100 (100%)
Fax: (47) 22975120
E-Mail: lars.doresyus@sunchemical.com
Web Site: www.suneurope.com
Emp.: 13
Mfr. of Printing Inks
S.I.C.: 2893
N.A.I.C.S.: 325910
Lars Doresyus *(Controller)*

Sun Chemical AB (2)
Malaxgatan 1
PO Box 16
164 93 Kista, Sweden SE
Tel.: (46) 87950700 (100%)
Fax: (46) 41820507
Web Site: www.sunchemical.com
Emp.: 30
Mfr. of Printing Inks
S.I.C.: 2893
N.A.I.C.S.: 325910

Sun Chemical AG (2)
Perfektastrasse 82
A 1230 Vienna, Austria AT
Tel.: (43) 018697606 (100%)
Fax: (43) 18652731
E-Mail: cornelia.rathmanner@sunchemical.com
Web Site: www.sunchemical.com
Sls.: $8,000,000
Emp.: 150
Mfr. & Sales of Printing Inks
S.I.C.: 2893
N.A.I.C.S.: 325910
Robert Fitzka *(Mng Dir)*

Sun Chemical AG (2)
Grindlenstrasse 3
8954 Geroldswil, Switzerland CH
Tel.: (41) 447495050 (100%)
Fax: (41) 447495055
E-Mail: switzerland@sunchemical.com
Web Site: www.suneurope.com
Emp.: 150
Printing Ink Mfr
S.I.C.: 2893
N.A.I.C.S.: 325910
Robert Fitzka *(Mng Dir)*

Sun Chemical Albania SHPK (2)
Rr Kavajes Ish Kombinati Misto Mame
Tirana, Albania
Tel.: (355) 42255464
Printing Ink & Organic Pigment Mfr
S.I.C.: 2893
N.A.I.C.S.: 325910

Sun Chemical B.V. (2)
Leeuwenveldseweg 3t
Weesp, North Holland, 1382 LV, Netherlands
Tel.: (31) 294492100
Fax: (31) 294492119
E-Mail: info@sunchemical.com
Emp.: 12
Printing Ink Mfr
S.I.C.: 2893
N.A.I.C.S.: 325910
Robert Fitzka *(Mng Dir)*
Gideon Jurgens *(Principal)*

Sun Chemical Canada (2)
10 West Drive
Brampton, ON, L6T 4Y4, Canada
Tel.: (905) 696-2222
Fax: (905) 976-7716
Web Site: www.sunchemical.com
Mfr. of Inks
S.I.C.: 2893
N.A.I.C.S.: 325910

Sun Chemical Chile S.A. (2)
Vicuna MacKenna 4815
Santiago, 10018, Chile CL
Tel.: (56) 25102000 (100%)
Fax: (56) 25523525
E-Mail: Jpauliac@sunchemicalchiles.cl
Web Site: www.sunchemicals.com
Emp.: 220
Mfr. of Printing Inks
S.I.C.: 2893
N.A.I.C.S.: 325910

Sun Chemical de Centro America, S.A. de C.V. (2)
Boulevard Del Ejercito National Km 4 1/2
PO Box 2108
San Salvador, El Salvador SV
Tel.: (503) 22776999 (50%)
Fax: (503) 22274864
E-Mail: sunchemicals@sunchem.com.smv
Web Site: www.sunchemical.com
Emp.: 99
Mfr. of Printing Inks
S.I.C.: 2893
N.A.I.C.S.: 325910
Michael Wager *(Mgr)*

Sun Chemical de Panama, S.A. (2)
Trasistmita Des Nacones Ave 85
PO Box 0819-09350
El Dorado, Panama, 0819-09350, Panama Pa
Tel.: (507) 2315438 (100%)
Fax: (507) 2314571
E-Mail: panama.info@sunchemical.com
Web Site: www.tintas.com
Sales Range: $1-9.9 Million
Emp.: 25
Printing Inks Mfr
S.I.C.: 2893
N.A.I.C.S.: 325910
Guillermo Fernandes *(Gen Mgr)*

Sun Chemical do Brasil Ltda. (2)
Av Justino De Maio 100
Guarulhos, Sao Paulo, 07222-000, Brazil
Tel.: (55) 1124622500
Fax: (55) 1124622520
Printing Ink Mfr
S.I.C.: 2893
N.A.I.C.S.: 325910

Sun Chemical, d.o.o. (2)
Kovinska 4a
Zagreb, 10000, Croatia
Tel.: (385) 12406609
Fax: (385) 12406632
E-Mail: Igor.belosic@sunchemical.com
Web Site: www.sunchemical.com
Emp.: 2
Organic Pigment & Printing Ink Mfr
S.I.C.: 2819
N.A.I.C.S.: 325130
Igor Belosic *(Gen Mgr)*

Sun Chemical Druckfarben GmbH (2)
Rolandsweg 22 24
37520 Osterode am Hartz, Germany De
Tel.: (49) 552286060 (100%)
Fax: (49) 5522860646
Web Site: www.suneurope.com
Emp.: 125
Mfr. of Printing Inks
S.I.C.: 2893
N.A.I.C.S.: 325910
Sontag Karl *(Mng Dir)*

Sun Chemical ECP S.A./N.V. (2)
Ave Fleming 2
B 1300 Wavre, Belgium BE
Tel.: (32) 010231500 (100%)
Fax: (32) 10231600
E-Mail: gerald.davignon@sunchemical.com
Web Site: www.sunchemical.com
Emp.: 70
Mfr. of Printing Inks
S.I.C.: 2893
N.A.I.C.S.: 325910
Gerald Davignon *(Mng Dir)*

Sun Chemical Group S.p.A. (2)
Via Achille Grandi 3/6
Settala, Milan, 20090, Italy
Tel.: (39) 02957901
Fax: (39) 0295307133
E-Mail: infosunchem@sunchemical.com
Web Site: www.sunchemical.com
Emp.: 30
Printing Ink & Organic Pigment Mfr
S.I.C.: 2893
N.A.I.C.S.: 325910
Carlo Musso *(Pres)*

Branch:

Sun Chemical S.p.A. (3)
Via Delle Due Case 2
50127 Florence, Italy IT
Tel.: (39) 05542591 (100%)
Fax: (39) 0554250179
Web Site: www.sunchemical.com
Emp.: 100
Mfr. of Printing Inks
S.I.C.: 2893
N.A.I.C.S.: 325910

Sun Chemical, Inc. S.A. (2)
Zabaleta 699
C1437EYM San Martin, Buenos Aires, Argentina Ar
Tel.: (54) 49114200 (100%)
Fax: (54) 119091001
E-Mail: info@sunchem.com.ar
Web Site: www.sunchemicals.com.ar
Emp.: 90
Mfr. of Printing Inks
S.I.C.: 2893
N.A.I.C.S.: 325910
Guftavo Ponce *(Mng Dir)*

Sun Chemical, Inc. S.A. (2)
Zavaleta 699
1437 Buenos Aires, Argentina Ar
Tel.: (54) 49091000 (100%)
Fax: (54) 114909 1001
E-Mail: info@sunchem.com.ar
Web Site: www.tintas.com
Emp.: 70
Printing Inks Mfr
S.I.C.: 2893
N.A.I.C.S.: 325910

Sun Chemical Inks A/S (2)
Meterbuen 3
Skovlunde, 2740, Denmark
Tel.: (45) 44949122
Fax: (45) 44947292
Emp.: 30
Printing Ink Mfr
S.I.C.: 2893
N.A.I.C.S.: 325910
Jan Lundin *(Mgr)*

Sun Chemical Inks Ltd. (2)
Glenside Words Mill
Palmerstown, Ireland
Tel.: (353) 16206868
Fax: (353) 16262573
Printing Ink Mfr
S.I.C.: 2893
N.A.I.C.S.: 325910
Mark Sedgwick *(Mgr)*

Sun Chemical Inks S.A. (2)
Zavaleta 699
Buenos Aires, 1437, Argentina
Tel.: (54) 1149091000
Fax: (54) 1149091001
E-Mail: argentina_marioinfo@sunchemical.com
Printing Ink Mfr
S.I.C.: 2893
N.A.I.C.S.: 325910

Sun Chemical Lasfelde GmbH (2)
Rolandsweg 26
Osterode am Hartz, 37520, Germany
Tel.: (49) 5522507240
Fax: (49) 5522507270
Web Site: www.sunchemical.com
Emp.: 33
Printing Ink & Pigment Mfr
S.I.C.: 2893
N.A.I.C.S.: 325910
Niels G. Johansen *(Mng Dir)*

Sun Chemical Ltd. (2)
Wexham Springs
Framewood Rd, Slough, SL3 6PJ, United Kingdom (100%)
Tel.: (44) 203 139 0000
Web Site: www.sunchemical.com
Sales Range: $1-9.9 Million
Emp.: 8
Mfr of Printing Ink
S.I.C.: 2893
N.A.I.C.S.: 325910
Greg Hayes *(Grp Mng Dir-Northern Europe)*

Non-U.S. Subsidiaries:

Hartmann Druckfarben GmbH (3)
Borsigallee 13
PO Box 600349
D 60388 Frankfurt am Main, Germany De
Tel.: (49) 6940000 (100%)
Fax: (49) 694000286
E-Mail: info@sunchemical.com
Web Site: www.sunchemical.com
Emp.: 150

Mfr. of Printing Inks
S.I.C.: 2893
N.A.I.C.S.: 325910
Stefan Bridemann *(Gen Mgr)*

Hartmann-Sun Chemical EOOD **(3)**
Tzarigradsko Chaussee 117 A
1184 Sofia, Bulgaria BG
Tel.: (359) 29753218 (100%)
Fax: (359) 29753639
E-Mail: iota.konstantinova@eu-sunchem.com
Web Site: www.suneurope.com
Emp.: 2
Mfr. of Printing Inks & Coatings
S.I.C.: 2893
N.A.I.C.S.: 325910
Iota Konstantinova *(Mgr-Sls)*

SUN Chemical Ltd. **(2)**
Wexham Springs
Framewood Road, Slough, SL3 6PJ, United Kingdom UK
Tel.: (44) 2031390000 (100%)
Fax: (44) 2031390001
Web Site: www.sunchemical.com
Emp.: 50
Mfr of Printing Inks & Coatings
S.I.C.: 2893
N.A.I.C.S.: 325910
Charles Murry *(Mng Dir)*

Sun Chemical Limited **(2)**
10 W Dr
Brampton, ON, L6T 4Y4, Canada ON
Tel.: (905) 796-2222 (100%)
Fax: (905) 796-7716
Web Site: www.sunchemical.com
Emp.: 250
Mfr. of Printing Ink
S.I.C.: 2893
N.A.I.C.S.: 325910
Felipe Mellado *(CMO)*

Sun Chemical Matbaa Murekkepleri Ve Gerecleri Sanayii Ve Ticaret A.S. **(2)**
4 Ataturk Organize Sanayi Bolgesi 10037 Sokak
Izmir, 35620, Turkey
Tel.: (90) 2323768890
Fax: (90) 2323768897
Emp.: 100
Printing Ink Mfr
S.I.C.: 2893
N.A.I.C.S.: 325910
Carlo Musso *(Mng Dir)*

Sun Chemical Moscow Printing Ink **(2)**
35 Volnaya St
105187 Moscow, Russia (98.1%)
Tel.: (7) 4959331303
Fax: (7) 4959331309
E-Mail: mpi@sunchem.ru
Web Site: www.sunchemical.com
Emp.: 80
Mfr. & Sales of Printing Inks & Coatings
S.I.C.: 2893
N.A.I.C.S.: 325910
Andrey Ivanov *(Gen Mgr)*

Sun Chemical N.V./S.A. **(2)**
Donkerstraat 63
Ternat, Vlaams Brabant, 1740, Belgium
Tel.: (32) 25833511
Fax: (32) 25827479
Printing Ink & Organic Pigment Mfr
S.I.C.: 2893
N.A.I.C.S.: 325910

Sun Chemical Nyomdafestek Kereskedelmi Es Gyarto KFT **(2)**
Telek Utca 7-9
Budapest, 1152, Hungary
Tel.: (36) 13061410
Fax: (36) 13061403
Web Site: www.sunchemical.com
Emp.: 13
Printing Ink & Coating Mfr
S.I.C.: 2893
N.A.I.C.S.: 325910
Tabor Istvan *(Mng Dir)*

Sun Chemical Osterode Druckfarben GmbH **(2)**
Rolandsweg 22-24
Osterode am Hartz, 37520, Germany
Tel.: (49) 552286060
Fax: (49) 5522860646
Printing Ink Mfr
S.I.C.: 2893
N.A.I.C.S.: 325910

Sun Chemical Oy **(2)**
Pieni Teollisuuskatu 2
Espoo, Uusimaa, 2920, Finland
Tel.: (358) 207 509 700
Web Site: www.sunchemical.com
Emp.: 7
Printing Ink & Paint Mfr
S.I.C.: 2893
N.A.I.C.S.: 325910
Tapani Arila *(Mgr-Fin)*

Sun Chemical Pigments S.L. **(2)**
Calle Occitania 75
Badalona, Barcelona, 8911, Spain
Tel.: (34) 933893600
Fax: (34) 934640427
Web Site: www.sunchemical.com
Emp.: 35
Printing Ink Mfr
S.I.C.: 2893
N.A.I.C.S.: 325910
Melissa Pavetich *(Gen Mgr)*

Sun Chemical Portugal Tintas Graficas Unipessoal, Ltda. **(2)**
Rua Caminho do Senhor 380
4410-083 Serzedo, Portugal PT
Tel.: (351) 227300100 (100%)
Fax: (351) 227 300 105
E-Mail: sunportugal@sunchemical.com
Web Site: www.sunchemical.com
Mfr of Printing Inks
S.I.C.: 2893
N.A.I.C.S.: 325910

Sun Chemical Printing Ink d.o.o. **(2)**
64 Vitezova Karadordeve Zvezde
Belgrade, 11000, Serbia
Tel.: (381) 113343350
Fax: (381) 113343370
Emp.: 4
Printing Ink & Organic Pigment Mfr
S.I.C.: 2893
N.A.I.C.S.: 325910
Novica Milic *(Mng Dir)*

Sun Chemical S.A. de C.V. **(2)**
Alce Blanco No 20
PO Box 7186
53370 Naucalpan, Mexico MX
Tel.: (52) 5553732000 (100%)
Fax: (52) 5553730862
E-Mail: arturo.medina@chemical.com
Web Site: www.chemical.com.mx
Emp.: 400
Mfr. of Printing Inks
S.I.C.: 2893
N.A.I.C.S.: 325910
Fernando Davara *(Gen Mgr)*

Sun Chemical S.A. **(2)**
Ctra De La Cantera S N
48950 Asua, Vizcaya, Spain ES
Tel.: (34) 944022747 (100%)
Fax: (34) 944711182
E-Mail: sunbilbao@eu.sunchem.com
Web Site: www.suneurope.com
Emp.: 95
Mfr. of Printing Inks
S.I.C.: 2893
N.A.I.C.S.: 325910
Carlo Musso *(Mng Dir)*

Sun Chemical S.A.S. **(2)**
89/91 Avenue du Marechal Joffre Cedex
Nanterre, 92000, France
Tel.: (33) 3 44 90 60 00
Fax: (33) 1 55 47 71 30
Printing Ink & Organic Pigment Mfr
S.I.C.: 2893
N.A.I.C.S.: 325910
Robert Fitzka *(Mng Dir)*

Sun Chemical Sp. zo.o. **(2)**
Wal Miedzeszynski 646
03-994 Warsaw, Poland PL
Tel.: (48) 226713361 (100%)
Fax: (48) 226163749
Web Site: www.suneurope.com
Mfr. of Printing Inks & Coatings
S.I.C.: 2893
N.A.I.C.S.: 325910

Sun Chemical s.r.l. **(2)**
Nr Ap Camera 10 19 Somesului Rm201
Sibiu, 550003, Romania
Tel.: (40) 369436928
Fax: (40) 269213210
Web Site: www.sunchemical.com
Emp.: 2
Printing Ink & Organic Pigment Mfr
S.I.C.: 2893
N.A.I.C.S.: 325910
Geza Kovacs *(Gen Mgr)*

Sun Chemical s.r.o. **(2)**
Udolni 527/27
CZ 602 00 Brno, Czech Republic CZ
Tel.: (420) 542422731 (100%)
Fax: (420) 542422740
E-Mail: sunchemical@sunchemical.cz
Web Site: www.sunchemical.com
Emp.: 17
Mfr of Printing Inks & Coatings
S.I.C.: 2893
N.A.I.C.S.: 325910
Andreas Lackner *(Gen Mgr)*

Sun Chemical s.r.o. **(2)**
Ul SNP 264/3
SK-05921 Svit, Slovakia Sk
Tel.: (421) 52 77 152 425 (100%)
Fax: (421) 52 77 571 92
Web Site: www.suneurope.com
Mfr. of Printing Inks & Coatings
S.I.C.: 2893
N.A.I.C.S.: 325910

Sun Chemical ZAO **(2)**
Luzhnetskaya naberezhnaya Bldg 2
119270 Moscow, Russia
Tel.: (7) 495 933 13 03
Fax: (7) 495 933 13 09
Emp.: 50
Printing Ink & Organic Pigment Mfr
S.I.C.: 2893
N.A.I.C.S.: 325910
Robert Fitzka *(Mng Dir)*

Sun Chemicals S.A.-Pigments International **(2)**
Parc Industrielle de la Noire Epine
Ave Fleming 2, 1300 Wavre, Belgium (100%)
Tel.: (32) 10231500
Fax: (32) 10231600
Web Site: www.sunchemical.com
Emp.: 70
Sales of Printing Inks
S.I.C.: 5085
N.A.I.C.S.: 423840
Gerald d'Avignon *(Mng Dir)*

Sun Chemicals **(2)**
Cray Ave
Saint Mary Cray, Kent, BR5 3PP, United Kingdom (100%)
Tel.: (44) 1689894000
Fax: (44) 689894020
Web Site: www.coates.com
Emp.: 100
Mfr. of Printing Inks
S.I.C.: 2893
N.A.I.C.S.: 325910
Sharadan Milsom *(Mgr-Site)*

Non-U.S. Subsidiaries:

Changzhou Huari New Material Co., Ltd. **(1)**
No 3 Donggang 3 Road
Changzhou, Jinangsu, China 213022
Tel.: (86) 519 85212688
Fax: (86) 519 85212332
E-Mail: hrserver@czdic.com.cn
Web Site: www.czdic.com.cn
Polyester Resin Mfr
S.I.C.: 2821
N.A.I.C.S.: 325211

Chia Lung Chemical Industrial Corp. **(1)**
10th Floor Chang An Building No 18 Chang An East Road
Section 1, Taipei, Taiwan CN
Tel.: (886) 225677071 (100%)
Fax: (886) 225675445
Web Site: www.dic.co.jp
Emp.: 87
Mfr. & Sales of Plastic Colorants, Compounds & Printing Inks
S.I.C.: 2821
N.A.I.C.S.: 325211

Coates Brothers (South Africa) (Pty). Ltd. **(1)**
7 18 Ave Maitland
PO Box 1057
Cape Town, 7405, South Africa ZA
Tel.: (27) 215905100 (100%)
Fax: (27) 215930604
E-Mail: stacy.botes@coates.com
Web Site: www.sunchemical.com
Emp.: 180
Sales of Chemicals
Import Export
S.I.C.: 2899
N.A.I.C.S.: 325998
John Bisset *(Mng Dir)*

Dainippon Ink & Chemicals (HK) Ltd. **(1)**
Rm 1304 13th Fl E Ocean Ctr 98 Granville Rd Tsim Sha Tsui E
Kowloon, China (Hong Kong) (100%)
Tel.: (852) 27236111
Fax: (852) 27234607
Web Site: www.dic.co.jp
Emp.: 35
Inks Mfr
S.I.C.: 2893
N.A.I.C.S.: 325910
Pani Gawa *(Mng Dir)*

Dainippon Ink & Chemicals, Inc. **(1)**
Beijing Fortune Bldg Rm 902 5 Dong San Huan Bei Lu
Chaoyang District, Beijing, 100004, China (100%)
Tel.: (86) 1065908461
Fax: (86) 1065908460
Web Site: www.dic.co.jp
Representative Office; Printing Ink & Resins
S.I.C.: 2893
N.A.I.C.S.: 325910
Yang Jan Jhong *(Gen Mgr)*

Dainippon Ink & Chemicals (Philippines), Inc. **(1)**
26 1st Ave Bo Bagumbayan Tanyag Taguig
Manila, NCR, 1631, Philippines PH
Tel.: (63) 028388888 (99%)
Fax: (63) 028385721
E-Mail: accounting@dic.com.ph
Web Site: www.dic.co.jp
Emp.: 59
Mfr. & Sales of Printing Inks
S.I.C.: 2893
N.A.I.C.S.: 325910
Hideki Ogawa *(Pres & Gen Mgr)*

Dainippon Ink & Chemicals (Singapore) Pte., Ltd. **(1)**
19 International Rd
Jurong, Singapore, 619623, Singapore (100%)
Tel.: (65) 62610644
Fax: (65) 62655256
E-Mail: dicap.sg@dic.com.sg
Web Site: www.dic.com.sg
Emp.: 80
Mfr. of Printing Inks; Sales of Printing Supplies, Pigment Preparations & Chemicals
S.I.C.: 2893
N.A.I.C.S.: 325910
George Teng *(Gen Mgr)*

Deqing DIC Synthetic Resins, Ltd. **(1)**
245 Chaoyang Road West
Deqing County, Zhaoqing, Guangdong, 526600, China
Tel.: (86) 758 777 1878
Fax: (86) 758 777 1848
Web Site: www.dic.co.at/en/index.php?menu=2,3
Emp.: 106
Synthetic Resin Mfr
S.I.C.: 2821
N.A.I.C.S.: 325211
Ma Zuhua *(Chm)*

DIC Alkylphenol Singapore Pte., Ltd. **(1)**
60 Sakra Road Jurong Island
Singapore, 627835, Singapore
Tel.: (65) 6268 1305
Fax: (65) 6268 2012
Web Site: www.dic-global.com
Emp.: 24
Alkyl Phenol Mfr
S.I.C.: 2869
N.A.I.C.S.: 325199
Satoshi Hashi *(Mng Dir)*

DIC Corporation—(Continued)

DIC Asia Pacific Pte Ltd. (1)
78 Shenton Way Floor 16 Unit 1
Singapore, 079120, Singapore SG
Tel.: (65) 62240600 (100%)
Fax: (65) 62243313
Web Site: www.dic.com.jp
Emp.: 22
Administration of Graphic Arts Materials Operations in Asia & Oceania; Investment in Related Subsidiaries; Sales, Export & Import of Related Products
S.I.C.: 2893
N.A.I.C.S.: 325910
Kazuo Kudo *(Mng Dir)*

DIC Australia Pty Ltd. (1)
323 Chisholm Road
Auburn, Sydney, NSW, 2144, Australia
Tel.: (61) 2 9752 1200
Fax: (61) 2 9645 1513
E-Mail: orders@dic.com.au
Web Site: www.dic.com.au
Rev.: $159,750,000
Emp.: 19
Printing Ink Mfr & Distr
S.I.C.: 2893
N.A.I.C.S.: 325910
Ian Johns *(Mng Dir)*

DIC Berlin GmbH R & D Laboratory (1)
Otisstra 39
D 13403 Berlin, Germany De
Tel.: (49) 304357900 (100%)
Fax: (49) 3043579010
E-Mail: mailbox@dic-berlin.de
Web Site: www.dic-berlin.de
Emp.: 25
Research of Polymers
S.I.C.: 2821
N.A.I.C.S.: 325211
Arthur Lachowicz *(Gen Mgr)*

DIC (China) Co., Ltd. (1)
12/F Changfang International No 555 Loushanguan Rd Changnin
Shanghai, 200051, China
Tel.: (86) 21 6228 9922
Fax: (86) 21 6241 9221
Web Site: www.dic.com.cn
Emp.: 10
Printing Ink Mfr & Distr
S.I.C.: 2893
N.A.I.C.S.: 325910
Billy Dong *(CFO)*

DIC Coatings, S.L. (1)
Pol Ind el Campillo Parcela 5 Gallarta Vizcaya
48500 Bilbao, Spain (100%)
Tel.: (34) 9463619999
Fax: (34) 946363451
E-Mail: j-alsalo@diccoatings.com
Web Site: www.sunchemical.com
Emp.: 70
Mfg. & Sales of Can Coatings & Metal-Decorating Inks
S.I.C.: 2851
N.A.I.C.S.: 325510
Inaki Llona *(Branch Mgr)*

DIC Colorants Taiwan Co., Ltd. (1)
No 15 Ching Chien 6th Road Kuan Yin Industrial Park
Kuan Yin Hsiang, Taoyuan, 32853, Taiwan
Tel.: (886) 3 483 3311
Fax: (886) 3 483 3322
Paint & Coating Mfr
S.I.C.: 2851
N.A.I.C.S.: 325510

DIC Compounds (Malaysia) Sdn. Bhd. (1)
Plot 481 Lorong Perusahaan Baru 2 Kawasan Perindustrian Perai
Butterworth, 13600 Perai, Penang, Malaysia MY
Tel.: (60) 43902311 (100%)
Fax: (60) 43900124
E-Mail: sklee@dcm-dic.com.my
Web Site: www.dcm-dic.com.my
Emp.: 150
Mfr. & Sales of Plastic Colorants & Compounds
S.I.C.: 2821
N.A.I.C.S.: 325211
Takehiro Ichinotsubo *(Mng Dir)*

DIC Epoxy (Malaysia) Sdn. Bhd. (1)
Plot 408 Jalan Pekeliling
Pasir Gudang, Johor, 81700, Malaysia
Tel.: (60) 7 2551558
Fax: (60) 7 2542859
Emp.: 6
Epoxy Resin Mfr & Distr
S.I.C.: 2821
N.A.I.C.S.: 325211
Y. K. Tay *(Mgr)*

DIC Europe GmbH (1)
Immermann Strasse 65D
D 40210 Dusseldorf, Germany (100%)
Tel.: (49) 21116430
Fax: (49) 211164388
E-Mail: info@dic-europe.de
Web Site: www.dic-europe.de
Emp.: 25
Mfr. of Inks
S.I.C.: 2893
N.A.I.C.S.: 325910

DIC Graphics Chia Lung Corp. (1)
No 12 Ting-Fu 1st Street Kwei-Shan Hsiang Taoyuan Hsien
Ta-Hua Village, Taoyuan, 33378, Taiwan
Tel.: (886) 3 3283301
Fax: (886) 3 3284131
Emp.: 105
Printing Ink Mfr
S.I.C.: 2893
N.A.I.C.S.: 325910
Hsing-Chung Lue *(Gen Mgr)*

DIC Graphics (Guangzhou) Ltd. (1)
No 77 Xingzhuang Er Road Yonghe Subzone
Guangzhou, 510000, China
Tel.: (86) 2032223200
Fax: (86) 2032223201
Web Site: www.dicgz.com
Printing Ink Mfr & Distr
S.I.C.: 2893
N.A.I.C.S.: 325910

DIC Graphics (Hong Kong) Ltd. (1)
18 Dai Fu Street Tai Po Industrial Estate
Tai Po, China (Hong Kong) HK
Tel.: (852) 26650280 (100%)
Fax: (852) 26678107
E-Mail: willy@dic.com.hk
Web Site: www.dic.co.jp
Emp.: 30
Mfr & Sales of Printing Ink
S.I.C.: 2893
N.A.I.C.S.: 325910
Pilly Lan *(Gen Mgr)*

DIC Graphics Taiyuan Co., Ltd. (1)
No 230 Donggang Rd
Taiyuan, Shanxi, 030012, China
Tel.: (86) 3514292184
Fax: (86) 3514292539
Emp.: 300
Printing Ink Mfr & Distr
S.I.C.: 2893
N.A.I.C.S.: 325910
Zuhua Ma *(Mgr)*

DIC (Guangzhou) Co., Ltd. (1)
Room 1801 Peace World Plaza 366 Huan Shi Dong Road
Guangzhou, 510060, China
Tel.: (86) 20 8384 9737
Fax: (86) 20 8384 8283
E-Mail: mailbox@dic.com.cn
Emp.: 27
Printing Ink Distr
S.I.C.: 5085
N.A.I.C.S.: 423840
Fukui Terumi *(Gen Mgr)*

DIC International Australia Pty. Ltd. (1)
323 Chisholm Road
Auburn, NSW, 2144, Australia AU
Tel.: (61) 297521200 (100%)
Fax: (61) 296454889
Emp.: 100
Sales of Printing Inks
S.I.C.: 5085
N.A.I.C.S.: 423840

DIC International (Thailand) Co., Ltd. (1)
21st Fl Sermmit Tower 159 Soi Asoke Sukhumvit 21 Rd Kwaeng N Klongtoey
Bangkok, 10110, Thailand TH
Tel.: (66) 22606630 (50%)
Fax: (66) 22606642
E-Mail: info@dic.co.th
Web Site: www.dic.co.th
Emp.: 200
Sales of Printing Inks & Resins
S.I.C.: 5085
N.A.I.C.S.: 423840
Shinji Yanauchi *(Mng Dir)*
Shunichi Morishi *(Mng Dir)*
Shichai Yamaughi *(Mng Dir)*

DIC KOREA Corp. (1)
6th Fl S1 Bldg 168 Soonhwa-Dong Jung-gu
Seoul, 100-773, Korea (South) (100%)
Tel.: (82) 2 757 0481
Fax: (82) 2 752 1059
Web Site: www.dic-global.com
Emp.: 13
Sales of Inks, Printing Supplies, Synthetic Resins, Chemicals & Neo-Graphic Arts
S.I.C.: 2893
N.A.I.C.S.: 325910

DIC Lanka (Private) Ltd. (1)
147 Katuwana Industrial Estate
10200 Homagama, Sri Lanka
Tel.: (94) 11 285 5513
Fax: (94) 112857711
E-Mail: coadsinks@dic.com.lk
Web Site: www.dic-global.com
Emp.: 7
Printing Ink Mfr & Distr
S.I.C.: 2893
N.A.I.C.S.: 325910
Kenji Yokoo *(Gen Mgr)*

DIC (Malaysia) Sdn. Bhd. (1)
PT 501 & 502 Persiaran Sabak Bernam Seksyen 26 Kawasan Hicom
40400 Shah Alam, Selangor, Malaysia MY
Tel.: (60) 351910033 (95%)
Fax: (60) 351917199
Web Site: www.dic.co.jp
Emp.: 200
Sales of Printing Inks, Synthetic Resins & Chemicals
S.I.C.: 5085
N.A.I.C.S.: 423840
Cy Ng *(Mng Dir)*

DIC Performance Resins GmbH (1)
Breitenleer Strasse 97-99
1220 Vienna, Austria
Tel.: (43) 1 20110 0
Fax: (43) 1 20110 288
E-Mail: info@denios.at
Web Site: www.dic.co.at
Emp.: 6
Synthetic Resin Mfr
S.I.C.: 2821
N.A.I.C.S.: 325211
Otto Stift *(Mng Dir)*

DIC Philippines, Inc. (1)
No 26 1st Avenue Bo Bagumbayan Tanyag
1631 Taguig, Metro Manila, Philippines
Tel.: (63) 2 838 8888
Fax: (63) 2 838 5721
E-Mail: sales@dic.com.ph
Emp.: 50
Printing Ink Mfr & Distr
S.I.C.: 2893
N.A.I.C.S.: 325910
Jet Labao *(Mgr-Sls)*

DIC (Shanghai) Co., Ltd. (1)
12/F Changfang International Plaza No 555 Loushanguan Rd
Shanghai, 200051, China
Tel.: (86) 21 6228 9911
Fax: (86) 21 6241 9221
Web Site: www.dic.com.cn
Printing Ink Distr
S.I.C.: 5085
N.A.I.C.S.: 423840

DIC Synthetic Resins (Zhongshan) Co., Ltd. (1)
No 18 Danli Road Concentrated Constructed Area
Zhongshan, Guangdong, 528437, China
Tel.: (86) 760 338 1491
Fax: (86) 760 338 1482
Synthetic Resin Mfr
S.I.C.: 2821
N.A.I.C.S.: 325211

DIC (Taiwan) Ltd. (1)
8th Fl Chang An Bldg No 18 Chang An E Rd Section 1
Taipei, 104, Taiwan TW
Tel.: (886) 225518620 (100%)
Fax: (886) 225629240
E-Mail: info@dic.com
Emp.: 20
Sales of Printing Inks & Resins
S.I.C.: 5085
N.A.I.C.S.: 423840
Kikuchi Masahiro *(Pres)*

DIC Trading (HK) Ltd. (1)
Rm 1304 13/F East Ocean Ctr 98 Granville Rd
Tsim Tsa Tsui, Kowloon, China (Hong Kong)
Tel.: (852) 2723 6111
Fax: (852) 2723 4607
E-Mail: chemical@dichk.com.hk
Web Site: www.dic-global.com
Emp.: 7
Printing Ink Distr
S.I.C.: 5085
N.A.I.C.S.: 423840
Allan Perera *(Mng Dir)*

DIC (UK) Ltd. (1)
Park House 643 651 Staines Road
Feltham, Middlesex, TW1 8PA, United Kingdom UK
Tel.: (44) 2088442777 (100%)
Fax: (44) 2088442707
Web Site: www.dic.co.jp
Emp.: 3
Sales of Pigments & Raw Materials for Printing Inks
S.I.C.: 5198
N.A.I.C.S.: 424950

DIC (Vietnam) Co., Ltd. (1)
31 VSIP Street 6 Vietnam Singapore Industrial Park
District, Thuan An, Binh Duong, Vietnam
Tel.: (84) 650 3767357
Fax: (84) 650 3767356
Web Site: www.dic-global.com
Emp.: 3
Printing Ink & Resin Mfr
S.I.C.: 2893
N.A.I.C.S.: 325910
Hideki Hira *(Gen Dir)*

DIC Zhangjiagang Chemicals Co., Ltd. (1)
18-Changjiang Easter Road Jiangsu Yangtze River
Jingang Town, 215635 Zhangjiagang, Jiangsu, China
Tel.: (86) 512 58937600
Fax: (86) 512 58937612
Web Site: en.dzc-dic.com.cn
Emp.: 100
Plastic Materials & Synthetic Resin Mfr
S.I.C.: 2821
N.A.I.C.S.: 325211
Kazuo Kuba *(Gen Mgr)*

Gunong Printing Ink (M) Sdn. Bhd. (1)
PT 501 and 502 Persiaran Sabak Bernam Seksyen 26 Kawasan Hicom, 400000 Shah Alam, Selangor, Malaysia (100%)
Tel.: (60) 351913049
Fax: (60) 351913048
Web Site: www.dic.jp.com.my
Sales Range: $10-24.9 Million
Emp.: 300
Mfg. & Sales of Printing Inks
S.I.C.: 2893
N.A.I.C.S.: 325910
Ng Csewying *(Mng Dir)*

Kangnam Chemical Co., Ltd. (1)
9th Fl Kangnam Bldg
Seocho Dong Seocho Ku, 1355 21 Seoul, Korea (South) KS
Tel.: (82) 234158000 (50%)
Fax: (82) 234733262
E-Mail: kangnam@kangnam.co.kr
Web Site: www.kangnam.co.kr
Emp.: 270
Mfr. & Sales of Synthetic Resins
S.I.C.: 2821
N.A.I.C.S.: 325211
Ha Young Chung *(CEO)*

Lianyungang DIC Color Co., Ltd. (1)
Chemical Industry Park
222523 Lianyungang, Jiangsu, China
Tel.: (86) 518 8361 8888
Fax: (86) 518 8361 8866

Organic Pigment Mfr & Distr
S.I.C.: 5198
N.A.I.C.S.: 424950

Nantong DIC Color Co., Ltd. (1)
No 11 Zhongyang Road Economic Development Zone
Nantong, 226009, China
Tel.: (86) 513 8592 8600
Fax: (86) 513 8592 8601
Organic Pigment & Printing Ink Mfr
S.I.C.: 2816
N.A.I.C.S.: 325130

PT Coates Indonesia (1)
Jl H Baping 108
Ciracas, Jakarta, 13740, Indonesia Id
Tel.: (62) 218712690 (90%)
Fax: (62) 218712695
Web Site: www.dic.co.id
Emp.: 125
Mfr. & Sales of Printing Inks
S.I.C.: 2893
N.A.I.C.S.: 325910

PT DIC Astra Chemicals (1)
Jl Pulobuaran Raya Blok III DD 5 10
Kawasan Industri
Pulogadung, Jakarta, Timur, 13012, Indonesia Id
Tel.: (62) 214603255 (75%)
Fax: (62) 214605557
Web Site: www.dic.co.jp
Emp.: 220
Mfr. & Sales of Plastic Compounds & Plastics, Fiber & Textile Colorants
S.I.C.: 2821
N.A.I.C.S.: 325211

PT DIC Graphics (1)
Jl Rawagelam III Blok II L Kav 8 9
Kawasan Industri Pulogadung, Jakarta, 13012, Indonesia Id
Tel.: (62) 214613525 (98.5%)
Fax: (62) 214613529
E-Mail: eko@dic-jka.co.id
Web Site: www.dic.co.id
Emp.: 100
Mfr. & Sales of Printing Inks
S.I.C.: 2893
N.A.I.C.S.: 325910
Reanna Hasun *(Mgr-Mktg)*

P.T. Pardic Jaya Chemicals (1)
Jalan Gatot Subroto Km 1 Kel Cibodas
Kota Tangerang, Jakarta, Banten, 15138, Indonesia Id
Tel.: (62) 215707330 (93.7%)
Fax: (62) 215523753
Web Site: www.dic.co.jp/en/company/group/asia_oceania.html
Emp.: 300
Mfr & Sales of Synthetic Resins
S.I.C.: 2821
N.A.I.C.S.: 325211
Alina Sution *(Mng Dir)*

Qingdao DIC Finechemicals Co., Ltd. (1)
Hit Industrial City 177 Zhuzhou Rd
Qingdao, 266101, China
Tel.: (86) 532 88701763
Fax: (86) 532 88702454
E-Mail: analyze@qdic.com
Web Site: www.qdic.com
Emp.: 13
Chemical Products Research & Development Services
S.I.C.: 8731
N.A.I.C.S.: 541712
Qiang Gong *(Co-Chm)*
Yutaka Hashimoto *(Co-Chm)*

Shanghai DIC Ink Co., Inc. (1)
No 3888 Humin Road
Minhang District, Shanghai, China CN
Tel.: (86) 2164890888 (65%)
Fax: (86) 2164890688
Web Site: www.dic.co.jp
Mfr. & Sales of Printing Inks
S.I.C.: 2893
N.A.I.C.S.: 325910

Shanghai Long Feng Food Additives Co., Ltd. (1)
Sheshan Town
Song Jiang County, Shanghai, 201602, China CN
Tel.: (86) 2157652271 (35%)
Fax: (86) 2157656351
Web Site: www.dic.co.jp/en/company/group/china.html
Mfr. of Food Additives
S.I.C.: 5169
N.A.I.C.S.: 424690

Shenzhen DIC Chemicals Co., Ltd. (1)
No 300 Huilong Rd Center City
Longgang Dist, Shenzhen, 518172, China
Tel.: (86) 75528941170
Fax: (86) 75528941099
Printing Ink Mfr & Distr
S.I.C.: 2893
N.A.I.C.S.: 325910

Shenzhen-DIC Co., Ltd. (1)
Nanshan Rd 1035
518052 Shenzhen, China CN
Tel.: (86) 75526432333 (90%)
Fax: (86) 75526640133
Web Site: www.dicsz.com
Emp.: 200
Mfr. & Sales of Printing Inks
S.I.C.: 2893
N.A.I.C.S.: 325910
Connie Want *(Mgr-Fin)*

Siam Chemical Industry Co., Ltd. (1)
17th Fl Nantawan Bldg 161 Rajdamri Rd
Bangkok, 10330, Thailand TH
Tel.: (66) 22529521 (50%)
Fax: (66) 22533926
E-Mail: webmaster@siamchem.com
Web Site: www.siamchem.com
Emp.: 300
Mfr. & Sales of Synthetic Resins
S.I.C.: 2821
N.A.I.C.S.: 325211
Somsak Sarautviai *(Mng Dir)*

Sun Chemical Group Cooperatief U.A. (1)
Leeuwenveldseweg 3-t
1382 LV Weesp, Netherlands
Tel.: (31) 294 492 100
Fax: (31) 294 492 119
Web Site: www.sunchemical.com
Printing Ink & Organic Pigment Mfr
S.I.C.: 2893
N.A.I.C.S.: 325910

Tien Lee Hong Co., Ltd. (1)
Ste 222 China Chen Golden Pl Mody Rd
Kowloon, China (Hong Kong) HK
Tel.: (852) 23953217 (100%)
Fax: (852) 27893904
E-Mail: tlhk@hknet.com
Web Site: www.dic.co.jp
Sales Range: Less than $1 Million
Emp.: 20
Sales of Synthetic Resins, Printing Inks, Supplies & Chemicals
S.I.C.: 5085
N.A.I.C.S.: 423840
David Chan *(Mng Dir)*

Zhongshan DIC Colour Co., Ltd. (1)
No 1 Zhenxing North Road No 2 Industrial Zone
Tanzhou Town, Zhongshan, Guangdong, 528467, China
Tel.: (86) 760 8665 5822
Fax: (86) 760 8665 5824
E-Mail: zsdic@zsdic.com.cn
Web Site: www.zsdic.com.cn
Plastic & Leather Colorant Mfr & Distr
S.I.C.: 2851
N.A.I.C.S.: 325510

Non-U.S. Joint Ventures:

Aekyung Chemical Co., Ltd. (1)
5th Fl 2nd Misung Bldg 106-5 Guro 5 Dong
Guro Ku, Seoul, 152842, Korea (South) KS
Tel.: (82) 28607503
Fax: (82) 28607599
Web Site: www.akc.co.kr
Emp.: 192
Mfr. & Sales of Synthetic Resins
S.I.C.: 2821
N.A.I.C.S.: 325211

Lidye Chemical Co., Ltd. (1)
10th Floor The Lidye Commercial Building 22
Nanking West Road, Taipei, 103, Taiwan CN
Tel.: (886) 225553271
Fax: (886) 225553015
Web Site: www.lidyechemical.com.tw
Emp.: 150
Synthetic Resins Mfr & Sales; Owned 50% by Lidye Co., Ltd. & 50% by Dainippon Ink and Chemicals, Incorporated
S.I.C.: 2821
N.A.I.C.S.: 325211

DIC - DONG TIEN JOINT STOCK COMPANY

Lot 17 25B Street Nhon Trach II Industrial Part
Dong Nai, Vietnam
Tel.: (84) 61352 1752
Fax: (84) 61352 1953
Web Site: www.dicdongtien.vn
DID—(HNX)

Business Description:
Readymix Concrete Mfr
S.I.C.: 3273
N.A.I.C.S.: 327320

Personnel:
Thai Hoc Nguyen *(Chm & Dir Gen)*
Minh Vu *(Deputy CEO)*

Board of Directors:
Thai Hoc Nguyen
Thi Anh Vinh Bui
Quyen Nguyen Van
Hung Cuong Nguyen
Luc Ich Nguyen
Thi Dinh Nguyen
Thanh PhamVan

DIC INDIA LTD

Transport Depot Road
Kolkata, 700 088, India
Tel.: (91) 3324496591
Fax: (91) 3324495267
E-Mail: coi@dicindialtd.com
Web Site: www.dicindialtd.com
DICIND—(NSE)
Rev.: $147,073,927
Assets: $84,334,381
Liabilities: $31,841,152
Net Worth: $52,493,229
Earnings: $3,985,173
Emp.: 603
Fiscal Year-end: 12/31/12

Business Description:
Industrial Coatings Mfr
S.I.C.: 2851
N.A.I.C.S.: 325510

Personnel:
Samir Bhaumik *(Mng Dir)*
Sandip Chatterjee *(CFO)*
Timir Baran Chatterjee *(Compliance Officer, Sec & Sr Exec VP-Corp Affairs & Legal)*

Board of Directors:
Prabir Kumar Dutt
Dipak Banerjee
Samir Bhaumik
Subir Bose
Bhaskar Nath Ghosh
Paul Koek
Yoshiaki Masuda
Utpal Sengupta

Transfer Agent:
CB Management Services (P) Limited
P22 Bondel Road
Kolkata, India

DIC INVESTMENT AND TRADING JOINT STOCK COMPANY

13bis Ky Dong Ward 9 District 3
Ho Chi Minh City, Vietnam
Tel.: (84) 8 5262089
Fax: (84) 8 8439279
E-Mail: info@dic-intraco.vn
Web Site: dicintraco.vn
Year Founded: 2005
DIC—(HOSE)

Business Description:
Cement Clinker Mfr
S.I.C.: 3241
N.A.I.C.S.: 327310

Personnel:
Manhy Chien Nguyen *(Deputy Gen Dir)*

DICKER DATA LIMITED

230 Captain Cook Drive
Kurnell, NSW, 2231, Australia
Tel.: (61) 2 9589 8400
Fax: (61) 2 9525 0481
E-Mail: sales@dickerdata.com.au
Web Site: www.dickerdata.com.au
Year Founded: 1978
DDR—(ASX)
Rev.: $470,593,602
Assets: $140,837,731
Liabilities: $119,842,542
Net Worth: $20,995,189
Earnings: $9,635,257
Fiscal Year-end: 06/30/13

Business Description:
Computer Hardware Distr
S.I.C.: 5045
N.A.I.C.S.: 423430

Personnel:
David Dicker *(Chm & CEO)*
Mary Stojcevski *(CFO)*
Leanne Ralph *(Sec)*

Board of Directors:
David Dicker
Fiona Brown
Michael Demetre
Chris Price
Mary Stojcevski

DICKSON CONCEPTS (INTERNATIONAL) LIMITED

4th Floor East Ocean Centre 98
Granville Road Tsimshatsui East
Kowloon, China (Hong Kong)
Tel.: (852) 23113888
Fax: (852) 23113323
Web Site: www.dickson.com.hk
0113—(HKG OTC)
Sls.: $532,075,682
Assets: $447,069,134
Liabilities: $128,578,624
Net Worth: $318,490,510
Earnings: $29,565,269
Emp.: 2,882
Fiscal Year-end: 03/31/13

Business Description:
Jewelry Products Sales
S.I.C.: 5944
N.A.I.C.S.: 448310

Personnel:
Dickson Poon *(Chm)*
Raymond Lee *(Deputy Chm & CEO)*
Nelson Tsang Wing Chan *(COO)*
Stella Suk Ying Or *(Sec)*

Board of Directors:
Dickson Poon
Bhanusak Asvaintra
Johnny Pollux Hon Chung Chan
Nelson Tsang Wing Chan
Nicholas Peter Etches
Christopher Patrick Langley
Gary Yu Hee Lau
Raymond Lee
Chan Lam Ng

Codan Services Limited
Clarendon House 2 Church Street
Hamilton, Bermuda

Subsidiaries:

Ambrose China Limited (1)
98 Granville Road Tsimshatsui East
Kowloon, China (Hong Kong)
Tel.: (852) 2268 8864
Fax: (852) 2268 8860
Watch Distr
S.I.C.: 5094

Dickson Concepts (International) Limited—(Continued)

N.A.I.C.S.: 423940

China Tone Limited (1)
4/F E Ocean Ctr 98 Granville Rd
Tsim Sha Tsui, Kowloon, China (Hong Kong)
Tel.: (852) 23113888
Fax: (852) 23112333
Emp.: 200
Fashion Products Distr
S.I.C.: 5199
N.A.I.C.S.: 424990

Dickson Concepts Limited (1)
4th Floor East Ocean Centre 98 Granville Road
Tsimshatsui East, Kowloon, China (Hong Kong)
Tel.: (852) 2311 3888
Fax: (852) 2311 3323
Investment Management Services
S.I.C.: 6211
N.A.I.C.S.: 523999

Dickson Concepts (Retail) Limited (1)
12B Des Voeux Road G/F The Landmark
Central, China (Hong Kong)
Tel.: (852) 25214245
Fax: (852) 25238677
Watch Distr
S.I.C.: 5094
N.A.I.C.S.: 423940

Dickson Express Company Limited (1)
4/F E Ocean Ctr 98 Granville Rd
Tsim Sha Tsui E, Kowloon, China (Hong Kong)
Tel.: (852) 23113888
Fax: (852) 23113323
Fashion Apparel Distr
S.I.C.: 5131
N.A.I.C.S.: 424310

Dickson Interior Design Limited (1)
4/F E Ocean Ctr 98 Granville Rd
Tsim Sha Tsui E, Kowloon, China (Hong Kong)
Tel.: (852) 23113888
Fax: (852) 23113323
Interior Design Services
S.I.C.: 7389
N.A.I.C.S.: 541410

Dickson Investments (H.K.) Limited (1)
4/F E Ocean Ctr 98 Granville Rd
Tsim Sha Tsui, Kowloon, China (Hong Kong)
Tel.: (852) 23113888
Fax: (852) 23113323
Investment Management Services
S.I.C.: 6211
N.A.I.C.S.: 523999

Dickson Warehousing Limited (1)
9/F Ever Gain Ctr 28 On Muk St
Sha Tin, New Territories, China (Hong Kong)
Tel.: (852) 26351383
Fax: (852) 26351383
Emp.: 12
Warehouse Operating Services
S.I.C.: 4225
N.A.I.C.S.: 493110
Jackson Yam *(Mgr)*

Hong Kong Seibu Enterprise Company Limited (1)
Rm A 21/F Manulife Twr 169 Electric Rd
North Point, China (Hong Kong)
Tel.: (852) 28773627
Fax: (852) 28456533
Fashion Apparel Retailer
S.I.C.: 5131
N.A.I.C.S.: 424310

Tommy Hilfiger Marketing Limited (1)
Rm 804 8/F Skyway House S Block 3
Sham Mong Rd
Tai Kok Tsui, Kowloon, China (Hong Kong)
Tel.: (852) 23011288
Fax: (852) 23126366
Fashion Apparel Retailer
S.I.C.: 5131
N.A.I.C.S.: 424310
Christine Shen *(Reg Mgr)*

Top Creation Limited (1)
Unit 4 8/F Skyway House South Block No 3
Sham Mong Road
Tai Kok Tsui, Kowloon, China (Hong Kong)
Tel.: (852) 23011288
Fax: (852) 23126366
Fashion Product Whslr
S.I.C.: 5122
N.A.I.C.S.: 446120

Non-U.S. Subsidiaries:

Dickson (Shanghai) Company Limited (1)
Room F 6/F No 1358 Yan'an West Rd
Changning, Shanghai, 200052, China
Tel.: (86) 2162820366
Watch Distr
S.I.C.: 5094
N.A.I.C.S.: 423940

The Dickson Shop Sdn. Bhd. (1)
7K Jalan 1/57D Off Jalan Segambut
51200 Kuala Lumpur, Malaysia
Tel.: (60) 3 62580122
Fax: (60) 3 62512145
Fashion Products Retailer
S.I.C.: 5122
N.A.I.C.S.: 446120

The Dickson Trading (Taiwan) Co., Ltd. (1)
11F-12F No 156 Jiankang Road
Songshan District, Taipei, 105, Taiwan
Tel.: (886) 2 3766 3388
Watch Distr
S.I.C.: 5094
N.A.I.C.S.: 423940

Leading Way Apparel Shanghai Limited (1)
Rm 201c International Commercial Trading Mansion No 118
Shanghai, 200131, China
Tel.: (86) 2150462328
Cosmetics Goods Distr
S.I.C.: 5122
N.A.I.C.S.: 446120

Raglan Resources Limited (1)
Offshore Incorporations Centre
Road Town, Virgin Islands (British)
Tel.: (284) 494 8184
Fax: (284) 494 5132
Investment Management Services
S.I.C.: 6211
N.A.I.C.S.: 523999

Tommy Hilfiger Asia-Pacific Limited (1)
No 156 Jiankang Road 11-12th Floor
Songshan District, Taipei, 10586, Taiwan
Tel.: (886) 2 2546 7316
Fax: (886) 2 2546 7223
Apparel & Accessories Retailer
S.I.C.: 5699
N.A.I.C.S.: 448150

DIE SCHWEIZERISCHE POST

(d/b/a Swiss Post)
Viktoriatstrasse 21
3030 Bern, Switzerland
Tel.: (41) 313381289
Fax: (41) 313381311
E-Mail: info@post.ch
Web Site: www.post.ch
Year Founded: 1998
Rev.: $9,262,724,240
Assets: $129,535,669,120
Liabilities: $123,464,494,120
Net Worth: $6,071,175,000
Earnings: $927,135,880
Emp.: 44,605
Fiscal Year-end: 12/31/12

Business Description:
Postal Services; Public Bus Transport Services, Goods & Logistics & Financial Services
S.I.C.: 4311
N.A.I.C.S.: 491110

Personnel:
Peter Hasler *(Chm)*
Dominique Freymond *(Vice Chm)*
Andreas Schlapfer *(Vice Chm)*
Susanne Ruoff *(CEO)*
Ulrich Hurni *(Deputy CEO & Head-PostMail)*
Kerstin Buchel *(Gen Sec)*

Board of Directors:
Peter Hasler
Susanne Blank
Marco Durrer
Dominique Freymond
Michel Gobet
Philippe Milliet
Andreas Schlapfer
Adriano P. Vassalli

Subsidiaries:

Debitoren Service AG (1)
Engehaldenstrasse 26
3030 Bern, Switzerland
Tel.: (41) 848 22 44 44
Fax: (41) 86 179 541 4374
E-Mail: factoringplus@postfinance.ch
Emp.: 6
Debt Collection Services
S.I.C.: 7322
N.A.I.C.S.: 561440
Beat Witschi, *(Chm)*

Direct Mail Company AG (1)
Reinacherstrasse 131
4018 Basel, Switzerland
Tel.: (41) 61 337 87 87
Fax: (41) 61 337 87 71
E-Mail: info@direct-mail-company.com
Web Site: www.direct-mail-company.com
Emp.: 50
Information Processing Services
S.I.C.: 7379
N.A.I.C.S.: 518210
Carlo Leone *(CEO)*
Martin Keller *(COO)*

Subsidiaries:

Direct Mail Logistik AG (2)
Reinacherstrasse 131
4018 Basel, Switzerland
Tel.: (41) 61 337 83 50
Fax: (41) 61 337 83 51
E-Mail: info@direct-mail-logistik.com
Web Site: www.direct-mail-logistik.com
Logistics Consulting Services
S.I.C.: 4731
N.A.I.C.S.: 541614
Armin Camenzind, *(Mng Dir)*

DMB Direct Mail Biel-Bienne AG (2)
Johann-Renfer-Strasse 62
2504 Biel, Switzerland
Tel.: (41) 32 343 30 30
Fax: (41) 32 343 30 31
Direct Marketing Services
S.I.C.: 8742
N.A.I.C.S.: 541613
Ralph Hugelshofer, *(Gen Mgr)*

Epsilon SA (1)
Route Des Jeunes 95
Case Postale 1169
1211 Geneva, Switzerland
Tel.: (41) 22 343 01 00
Fax: (41) 22 343 88 21
E-Mail: info@epsilon-sa.ch
Web Site: www.epsilon-sa.ch
Letter, Parcel & Express Delivery Services
S.I.C.: 4513
N.A.I.C.S.: 492110

IN-Media AG (1)
Reinacherstrasse 131
4018 Basel, Switzerland
Tel.: (41) 61 338 98 98
Fax: (41) 61 338 98 99
E-Mail: info@in-media.ch
Web Site: www.in-media.ch
Magazine Publisher
S.I.C.: 2721
N.A.I.C.S.: 511120
Patrick Flad, *(Mng Dir)*

InfraPost AG (1)
Viktoriastrasse 72
3030 Bern, Switzerland
Tel.: (41) 58 338 94 04
Fax: (41) 58 667 38 42
E-Mail: infrapost@post.ch
Sls.: $155,422,080
Emp.: 1,711
Facility Management Services
S.I.C.: 8744
N.A.I.C.S.: 561210
Patrick Bovigny *(Head-West Reg)*

Mobility Solutions AG (1)
Stockackerstrasse 50
3030 Bern, Switzerland
Tel.: (41) 58 338 55 00
Fax: (41) 58 667 45 19
E-Mail: mobilitysolutions@post.ch
Web Site: www.mobilitysolutions.ch
Emp.: 100
Fleet Management Services
S.I.C.: 7515
N.A.I.C.S.: 532112
Patrick Ineichen *(CEO)*

Mobility Solutions Management AG (1)
Stockackerstrasse 50
3030 Bern, Switzerland
Tel.: (41) 31 338 55 00
Fleet Management Services
S.I.C.: 7515
N.A.I.C.S.: 532112

PostFinance AG (1)
Nordring 8
3030 Bern, Switzerland
Tel.: (41) 84 888 89 00
Fax: (41) 58 667 44 40
Web Site: www.postfinance.ch
Emp.: 3,473
Payment Transaction Services
S.I.C.: 6099
N.A.I.C.S.: 522320
Nathalie Bourquenoud *(Head-HR & Logistics)*

PostLogistics AG (1)
Lagerstrasse 12
Dintikon, 5606, Switzerland
Tel.: (41) 58 448 64 00
Fax: (41) 58 667 31 27
E-Mail:
Logistics Consulting Services
S.I.C.: 4731
N.A.I.C.S.: 541614

PostMail AG (1)
Viktoriastrasse 21
Bern, 3030, Switzerland
Tel.: (41) 31 338 11 11
Fax: (41) 31 338 53 59
Information Processing Services
S.I.C.: 7374
N.A.I.C.S.: 518210

Presto Presse-Vertriebs AG (1)
Zentweg 5
3006 Bern, Switzerland
Tel.: (41) 58 448 07 07
Fax: (41) 58 667 59 13
E-Mail: christo.be@post.ch
Newspaper Publisher
S.I.C.: 2711
N.A.I.C.S.: 511110
Daniel Hugi, *(Mng Dir)*

Swiss Post International Holding AG (1)
Viktoriastrasse 21
Bern, 3030, Switzerland
Tel.: (41) 84 888 88 88
Fax: (41) 84 488 88 88
Logistics Consulting Services
S.I.C.: 4731
N.A.I.C.S.: 541614

Swiss Post International Logistics AG (1)
Via Maestri Comacini 7
6830 Chiasso, Switzerland
Tel.: (41) 91 695 80 30
Fax: (41) 91 682 97 51
E-Mail: teceno@swisspost.com
Logistics Consulting Services
S.I.C.: 4731
N.A.I.C.S.: 541614
Patrik Sarros *(Head-Fin)*

Swiss Post International Management AG (1)
Viktoriastrasse 21
Bern, 3030, Switzerland
Tel.: (41) 313381111
Information Processing Services

S.I.C.: 7379
N.A.I.C.S.: 518210
Davide Boeri *(Product Mgr)*

Swiss Post Solutions AG (1)
Pfingstweidstrasse 60B
8080 Zurich, Switzerland
Tel.: (41) 58 338 20 40
E-Mail: sps_marketing@swisspost.com
Web Site: www.swisspostsolutions.com
Information Processing Services
S.I.C.: 7374
N.A.I.C.S.: 518210

SwissSign AG (1)
Sagereistrasse 25
8152 Glattbrugg, Switzerland
Tel.: (41) 44 838 36 00
Fax: (41) 43 344 88 10
E-Mail:
Web Site: swisssign.com
Software Development Services
S.I.C.: 7371
N.A.I.C.S.: 541511
Urs Fischer *(CEO)*
Gerhard Koch *(CTO)*
Christoph Graf *(Chief Operation Officer)*

velopass SARL (1)
Rue de la Tour 5
1004 Lausanne, Switzerland
Tel.: (41) 21 533 10 10
E-Mail: info@velopass.ch
Web Site: www.velopass.ch
Bicycle Rental Services
S.I.C.: 7999
N.A.I.C.S.: 532292

U.S. Subsidiaries:

Swiss Post Solutions Inc. (1)
10 E 40th St 9th Fl
New York, NY 10016
Tel.: (212) 204-0777
Web Site: www.swisspostsolutions.com
Rev.: $7,500,000
Emp.: 147
Information Processing Services
S.I.C.: 7374
N.A.I.C.S.: 518210
Mitchell D. Weiner *(CEO)*
Baiju Coilparampil *(CFO)*
Mike Mannix *(Chief Sls Officer-North America)*
Dan Moscatiello *(CEO-North America)*
Karen Cumming *(Exec VP-Sls & Mktg)*

Swiss Post US Holding Inc. (1)
10 E 40th St 9th Fl
New York, NY 10016
Tel.: (212) 204-0900
Information Processing Services
S.I.C.: 7374
N.A.I.C.S.: 518210
D. Mitchell *(Principal)*

Non-U.S. Subsidiaries:

Caporin Voyages SARL (1)
1 Boulevard Etivalliere
42000 Saint Etienne, France
Tel.: (33) 9 61 40 72 19
Bus Transportation Services
S.I.C.: 4119
N.A.I.C.S.: 487110

CarPostal Agde SAS (1)
1 B Quai Du Commandant Reveille
34300 Agde, France
Tel.: (33) 800350310
Bus Transportation Services
S.I.C.: 4119
N.A.I.C.S.: 487110

CarPostal Dole SAS (1)
39 rue Macedonio Melloni
39100 Dole, France
Tel.: (33) 3 84 72 98 36
Bus Transportation Services
S.I.C.: 4119
N.A.I.C.S.: 487110

CarPostal Macon SAS (1)
9029 Rue Lavoisier
71000 Macon, France
Tel.: (33) 3 85 21 98 70
Bus Transportation Services
S.I.C.: 4119
N.A.I.C.S.: 487110

CarPostal Mediterranee SAS (1)
9061 Route De Guiraudette
34300 Agde, France
Tel.: (33) 4 67 01 22 24
Fax: (33) 4 67 21 04 61
Bus Transportation Services
S.I.C.: 4119
N.A.I.C.S.: 487110

CF Card Factory GmbH (1)
Im Tal 10
37235 Hessisch Lichtenau, Germany
Tel.: (49) 56 02 91 74 0
Fax: (49) 56 02 91 74 45
E-Mail: info@cardfactory-gmbh.de
Web Site: www.cardfactory-gmbh.de
Smart Card Mfr
S.I.C.: 2679
N.A.I.C.S.: 322299

FMC Insights Limited (1)
Briarslea House Kilgobbin Road
Dublin, Ireland
Tel.: (353) 1 294 4584
Letter, Parcel & Express Delivery Services
S.I.C.: 4513
N.A.I.C.S.: 492110

Fortuna Beteiligungs GmbH (1)
Kronacher Str 70-80
Bamberg, 96052, Germany
Tel.: (49) 95194260
Bus Transportation Services
S.I.C.: 4119
N.A.I.C.S.: 487110

GHP Far East Co. Ltd. (1)
8th Floor Saigon ICT Tower Quang Trung Software City
District 12, Ho Chi Minh City, Vietnam
Tel.: (84) 8 3715 5359
Fax: (84) 8 3715 5391
E-Mail: sales@ghp-fareast.vn
Web Site: www.ghp-fareast.com.vn
Emp.: 1,000
Software Development Services
S.I.C.: 7371
N.A.I.C.S.: 541511
Frank Schellenberg, *(CEO)*
Hua Viet Minh *(CFO)*
Tran Thi Dieu Thuan *(COO)*
Tran Dai Long *(CTO)*
Nguyen Thi Diep *(Chief People Officer)*

PostAuto Liechtenstein Anstalt (1)
Wuhrstrasse 25
PO Box 575
9490 Vaduz, Liechtenstein
Tel.: (423) 388 29 89
Fax: (423) 388 29 80
E-Mail: fl@postauto.ch
Web Site: www.postauto.ch
Sls.: $17,269,120
Emp.: 95
Bus Transportation Services
S.I.C.: 4111
N.A.I.C.S.: 485113

Societe d'Affretement et de Transit S.A.T. SAS (1)
6 Rue Robert Schuman
68870 Bartenheim, France
Tel.: (33) 3 89 69 14 00
Fax: (33) 3 89 69 42 33
Bus Transportation Services
S.I.C.: 4119
N.A.I.C.S.: 487110

Swiss Post Solutions GmbH, Prien (1)
Systemformstr 5
83209 Prien am Chiemsee, Germany
Tel.: (49) 8051 602 0
Fax: (49) 8051 602224
Information Processing Services
S.I.C.: 7379
N.A.I.C.S.: 518210

Swiss Post Solutions GmbH, Pulsnitz (1)
Geothestr 6
01896 Pulsnitz, Germany
Tel.: (49) 35955 7150
Information Processing Services
S.I.C.: 7379
N.A.I.C.S.: 518210

Swiss Post Solutions GmbH (1)
Linzer Strabe 221/4 Stock
1140 Vienna, Austria
Tel.: (43) 1 8904052 0
Fax: (43) 1 8904052 11
E-Mail: office-at@swisspost.com
Web Site: www.swisspostsolutions.com
Emp.: 32
Information Processing Services
S.I.C.: 7374
N.A.I.C.S.: 518210
Olivier Fuchs *(Head-Document Solutions-Central & Eastern Europe)*

Swiss Post Solutions GmbH (1)
Kronacher Strabe 70-80
96052 Bamberg, Germany
Tel.: (49) 951 94 26 0
Fax: (49) 951 94 26 33 99
E-Mail: sps.de@swisspost.com
Web Site: www.swisspostsolutions.com
Emp.: 300
Information Processing Services
S.I.C.: 7374
N.A.I.C.S.: 518210
Walter Gerdes, *(CEO)*
Frank Michael Pacser *(Chief Sls Officer)*
Gerhard Schwab *(CEO-Global Svcs)*

Swiss Post Solutions Ltd (1)
Richmond Place 15 Petersham Road
Richmond upon Thames, London, Surrey, TW10 6TP, United Kingdom UK
Tel.: (44) 845 301 3708
E-Mail: media@swisspost.co.uk
Web Site: www.swisspostsolutions.com
Information Processing Services
S.I.C.: 7374
N.A.I.C.S.: 518210
Jonathan King *(CEO)*
Gary Harrold *(COO)*

Swiss Post Solutions SAS (1)
60-62 rue de Wattignies
75012 Paris, France
Tel.: (33) 1 44 74 35 15
Fax: (33) 1 44 74 24 75
E-Mail: infofrance@gbsplus.eu
Web Site: www.swisspostsolutions.com
Information Processing Services
S.I.C.: 7379
N.A.I.C.S.: 518210
Alexander Valkenberg *(Corp Officer)*

Swiss Post Solutions Singapore (1)
41 Changi South Avenue 2 1st Floor Ghim Li Building
Singapore, 486153, Singapore
Tel.: (65) 6748 44 84
Fax: (65) 6748 40 05
E-Mail: info@swisspost.com.sg
Web Site: www.swisspostsolutions.com
Emp.: 3
Information Processing Services
S.I.C.: 7374
N.A.I.C.S.: 518210
Dimitri Getsios, *(Gen Mgr-Asia)*

Swiss Post Solutions S.p.A. (1)
Via 25 Aprile 11
20097 San Donato Milanese, Milano, Italy
Tel.: (39) 02 4549 1102
E-Mail: info@swisspost.com
Web Site: www.swisspostsolutions.it
Information Processing Services
S.I.C.: 7374
N.A.I.C.S.: 518210
Mauro Succi *(CTO & Dir-Ops)*
Anna Fornara, *(Gen Dir)*

Swiss Post Solutions s.r.o (1)
Puchovska 16
PO Box 70
Bratislava, Slovakia
Tel.: (421) 249277 411
Fax: (421) 249277 419
E-Mail: info.sk@swisspost.com
Web Site: www.swisspostsolutions.com
Emp.: 200
Information Processing Services
S.I.C.: 7379
N.A.I.C.S.: 518210
Matus Gerek *(Mgr-Compliance)*

DIEFFENBACHER GMBH & CO. KG

(See Under Dieffenbacher Holding GmbH & Co. KG)

DIEFFENBACHER HOLDING GMBH & CO. KG

Heilbronner Strasse 20
D 75031 Eppingen, Germany
Tel.: (49) 7262 65 0
Fax: (49) 7262 65 420
E-Mail: dse@dieffenbacher.de
Web Site: www.dieffenbacher.de
Year Founded: 1873
Sales Range: $500-549.9 Million
Emp.: 1,780

Business Description:
Hydraulic Press Production Systems Engineer & Supplier
Import Export
S.I.C.: 3541
N.A.I.C.S.: 333517

Personnel:
Wolf-Gerd Dieffenbacher *(Chm-Mgmt Bd, Pres & CEO)*
Volker Kitzelmann *(CFO & Member-Mgmt Bd)*
Heiko Heitlinger *(COO & Member-Mgmt Bd)*
Gunter Kuhn *(Mng Dir-Tech & Member-Mgmt Bd)*
Ralph Weber *(Dir-HR & Member-Mgmt Bd)*

Subsidiaries:

B. Maier Zerkleinerungstechnik GmbH (1)
Schweriner Strasse 1
33605 Bielefeld, Germany
Tel.: (49) 521 584943 20
Fax: (49) 521 584943 21
E-Mail: mzb@dieffenbacher.de
Web Site: www.maier-dieffenbacher.com
Engineering, Chipping Technology, Conveying & Cleaning Technology
S.I.C.: 8711
N.A.I.C.S.: 541330
Alexander Hoffmann, *(Mng Dir)*

Dieffenbacher Maschinenfabrik GmbH (1)
Gewerbestrasse 29
75059 Zaisenhausen, Germany
Tel.: (49) 7258 609 0
Fax: (49) 7258 8751
E-Mail: info@dm-z.de
Web Site: www.dieffenbacher-zaisenhausen.de
Emp.: 115
Industrial Machinery Mfr
S.I.C.: 3559
N.A.I.C.S.: 333249
Ralf Hagner *(Head-Sls)*

Dieffenbacher Schenck Panel GmbH (1)
Werner Von Siemens Strasse 2
D 64319 Pfungstadt, Baden Wurttemberg, Germany (100%)
Tel.: (49) 61578030
Fax: (49) 6157803109
E-Mail: dsp@dieffenbacher.de
Web Site: www.dieffenbacher.com
Emp.: 30
Metal Tools
S.I.C.: 3541
N.A.I.C.S.: 333517
H. J. Schieber *(Mng Dir)*
Volker Kitzelmann *(CFO)*

Dieffenbacher System-Automation GmbH (1)
Jakob-Dieffenbacher-Str 4
75031 Eppingen, Germany (100%)
Tel.: (49) 72626550-00
Fax: (49) 72626550-11
E-Mail: dsa@dieffenbacher.de
Web Site: www.dieffenbacher.com
Emp.: 40
Metal Tools
S.I.C.: 3542
N.A.I.C.S.: 333517

Karle und Jung GmbH (1)
Heinrich-Hertz-Strasse 3
76470 Oetigheim, Germany (100%)
Tel.: (49) 7222 40 655 0
Fax: (49) 7222 40 655 51
E-Mail: info@karle-jung.de
Web Site: www.karle-jung.de
Emp.: 35
Tool & Mechanical Engineering
S.I.C.: 3541

Dieffenbacher Holding GmbH & Co. KG—(Continued)

N.A.I.C.S.: 333517
Klaus-Juergen Pahl *(Gen Mgr)*

Maertiens Robotec GmbH (1)
Zum Haug 10
76646 Bruchsal, Germany
Tel.: (49) 7251 9573 0
Fax: (49) 7251 9573 25
E-Mail: info@maertiens.de
Web Site: www.maertiens.de
Mfr of Industrial Machinery for Automotive Industry
S.I.C.: 3559
N.A.I.C.S.: 333249
Steffen Maertiens *(CEO)*

U.S. Subsidiaries:

Dieffenbacher Customer Support, LLC (1)
795 Branch Dr
Alpharetta, GA 30004
Tel.: (770) 663-4383
Fax: (770) 663-8411
E-Mail: service@dieffenbacher.com
Web Site: www.dieffenbacher.com
Services & Spare Parts for Wood Panel Manufacturing Machinery
S.I.C.: 5084
N.A.I.C.S.: 423830
Marc Keller *(CFO & Sec)*

Dieffenbacher USA, Inc. (1)
2000 McFarland 400 Blvd
Alpharetta, GA 30004 (100%)
Tel.: (770) 226-6394
Fax: (770) 226-6397
E-Mail: mail@dieffenbacheratl.com
Web Site: www.dieffenbacher.com
Emp.: 50
Industrial Machinery & Equipment Sales
S.I.C.: 5084
N.A.I.C.S.: 423830
Larry Frazier *(CEO)*
Marc Keller *(CFO & Sec)*

Non-U.S. Subsidiaries:

Dieffenbacher Asia Pacific Sdn. Bhd. (1)
Unit#11-02 11th Floor Menara Multi-Purpose Capital Square
No 8 Jalan Munshi Abdullah, Kuala Lumpur, 50100, Malaysia
Tel.: (60) 3 7490 0183
Fax: (60) 3 7490 0184
E-Mail: dap@dieffenbacher.com.my
Industrial Machinery Sales & Service
S.I.C.: 5084
N.A.I.C.S.: 423830

Dieffenbacher Australasia Pty. Ltd. (1)
3 Lauren Court
PO Box 279
Lilydale, VIC, 3140, Australia
Tel.: (61) 3 9735 2537
Fax: (61) 77 6743344
E-Mail: alan.mckinna@dieffenbacher.com
Industrial Machinery Sales & Service
S.I.C.: 5084
N.A.I.C.S.: 423830
Alan McKinna, *(Mgr)*

Dieffenbacher CZ hydraulicke lisy, s.r.o (1)
Ripska 15
627 00 Brno, Czech Republic (98%)
Tel.: (420) 548423111
Fax: (420) 548217087
E-Mail: dcz@dieffenbacher.cz
Web Site: www.dieffenbacher.cz
Emp.: 40
Hydraulic Presses Mfr
S.I.C.: 3559
N.A.I.C.S.: 333249
Miroslav Jopek *(Mng Dir)*

Dieffenbacher do Brasil Construcao de Maquinas e Instalacoes Ltda. (1)
Cyro Correia Pereira Street 667 Block 02-C Neighborhood Cidade Industrial de Curitiba, Curitiba, Parana, 81 170 230, Brazil (100%)
Tel.: (55) 41 3268 4205
E-Mail: service@inserco.com.br
Industrial Machinery Sales & Service
S.I.C.: 5084
N.A.I.C.S.: 423830

Dieffenbacher India Pvt. Ltd. (1)
Unit 105 First Floor Prestige Towers
99 Residency Road, Bengaluru, 560 025, India
Tel.: (91) 80 4151 0060
Fax: (91) 80 4151 0062
E-Mail: info@dieffenbacherindia.in
Industrial Machinery Sales & Service
S.I.C.: 5084
N.A.I.C.S.: 423830

Dieffenbacher Machinery Services (Beijing) Co., Ltd. (1)
Scitech Tower Unit 1305
22 Jianguomen Wai Dajie, Beijing, 100004, China
Tel.: (86) 10 6522 0935
Fax: (86) 10 6522 0936
E-Mail: dboshirley@dieffenbacher.com.cn
Web Site: www.dieffenbacher.cn
Industrial Machinery Sales & Service
S.I.C.: 5084
N.A.I.C.S.: 423830
Shouhua Liu, *(Mgr-Sls & Svc)*

Dieffenbacher North America, Inc. (1)
9495 Twin Oaks Drive
Windsor, ON, N8N 5B8, Canada (100%)
Tel.: (519) 979-6937
Fax: (519) 979-6803
E-Mail: dna@dieffenbacher.ca
Web Site: www.dieffenbacher.ca
Emp.: 65
Press & Forming Machinery Mfr
S.I.C.: 3559
N.A.I.C.S.: 333249
Coloin Folco *(Gen Mgr)*

Dieffenbacher Panelboard Oy (1)
Wipaktie 1
15560 Nastola, Finland
Tel.: (358) 10 572 9000
Fax: (358) 10 572 9001
E-Mail: dpf@dieffenbacher.com
Supplies Production Lines, Single Machines & After-Market Services to Fiberboard & Particleboard Industries
S.I.C.: 5084
N.A.I.C.S.: 423830

OOO Dieffenbacher Moscow (1)
Barklay Street 6 Building 9
121087 Moscow, Russia
Tel.: (7) 495 215 22 57
Fax: (7) 495 215 22 67
E-Mail: dieffenbacher@ttc-net.ru
Industrial Machinery Sales & Service
S.I.C.: 5084
N.A.I.C.S.: 423830

Shanghai Wood Based Panel Machinery Co., Ltd. (1)
No 299 Hejing Road
Anting, Shanghai, 201805, China
Tel.: (86) 21 5957 7480
Fax: (86) 21 5957 2568
E-Mail: customersupport@shbanji.com
Web Site: www.shbanji.com
Supplier of Industrial Machinery for Wood Panel Production Plants
S.I.C.: 5084
N.A.I.C.S.: 423830
Jinxing Wang, *(Mng Dir)*

Sunds MDF Technologies AB (1)
Universitetsallen 32
85171 Sundsvall, Sweden
Tel.: (46) 60 524 200
Fax: (46) 60 524 299
E-Mail: info@sunds-mdf.com
Web Site: www.sunds-mdf.com
Engineering & Supply of Front-End Systems for Fiberboard Plants
S.I.C.: 3559
N.A.I.C.S.: 333249
Kenth Eklund, *(Mng Dir)*

DIEHL STIFTUNG & CO. KG

Stephanstrasse 49
D 90478 Nuremberg, Germany
Tel.: (49) 9119470
Fax: (49) 9119473429
E-Mail: info@diehl.de
Web Site: www.diehl.com
Sales Range: $1-4.9 Billion
Emp.: 13,569

Business Description:
Holding Company
S.I.C.: 6719
N.A.I.C.S.: 551112

Personnel:
Peter A. Diehl *(Vice Chm-Supervisory Bd)*
Thomas Diehl *(Pres & CEO)*
Claus Gunther *(Member-Exec Bd-Defense Div)*
Dieter Neugebauer *(Member-Exec Bd-Controls Div)*
Heiner Otten *(Member-Exec Bd-Metal Div)*
Johannes Sappa *(Member-Exec Bd-Metering Div)*
Martin Sommer *(Member-Exec Bd-Corp Personnel & Welfare)*
Rainer von Borstel *(Member-Exec Bd-Aerosystems Div)*
Wolfgang Weggen *(Exec VP-Fin & Controlling Dept)*

Supervisory Board of Directors:
Peter A. Diehl
Thomas Diehl
Karlhermann Jung

Divisions:

Diehl AKO Stiftung & Co. KG (1)
Pfannerstrasse 75
PO Box 1163
88239 Wangen, Germany De
Tel.: (49) 7522730 (100%)
Fax: (49) 752273250
E-Mail: info@diehlako.de
Web Site: www.diehlako.com
Emp.: 250
Electromechanical & Electronic Controls for Washing Machines, Dryers & Dishwashers; Radiant Heating Systems
S.I.C.: 3823
N.A.I.C.S.: 334513

Diehl Metall Stiftung & Co. KG (1)
Heinrich Diehl Strasse 9
90552 Rothenbach, Pegnitz, Germany (100%)
Tel.: (49) 91157040
Fax: (49) 9115704481
E-Mail: info@diehlmetall.de
Web Site: www.diehlmetall.com
Emp.: 1,200
Mfr. of Rods, Tubes & Brass Forged Parts
S.I.C.: 3317
N.A.I.C.S.: 331210
Heiner Otten *(CEO)*

U.S. Subsidiary:

The Miller Co., Inc. (2)
275 Pratt St
Meriden, CT 06450-8600 CT
Tel.: (203) 235-4474
Fax: (203) 634-6926
Toll Free: (800) 243-3120
E-Mail: sales@themillerco.com
Web Site: www.themillerco.com
Emp.: 100
Mfr. of Strip & Coil Brass Phosphor Bronze Nickel Silver
Export
S.I.C.: 3351
N.A.I.C.S.: 331420
Richard M. Archambault *(VP-Sls & Mktg)*

Diehl Remscheid GmbH & Co (1)
Vieringhausen 118
42857 Remscheid, Germany (100%)
Tel.: (49) 21919760
Fax: (49) 2191976208
Web Site: www.diehlremscheid.de
Sales Range: $75-99.9 Million
Emp.: 400
Production of Tracks for Tanks & Armored Vehicles
S.I.C.: 3795
N.A.I.C.S.: 336992

Joint Ventures:

Diehl Aerospace GmbH (1)
An der Sanelmuhle 13
60439 Frankfurt, Germany
Tel.: (49) 6958050
Fax: (49) 6958051399
E-Mail: marketing@diehl-aerospace.de
Web Site: www.diehl-aerospace.de
Emp.: 400
Development of Missiles, Flight Training Systems & Munitions: Joint Venture of Thales Avionics SA (49%) & Diehl VA Systeme GmbH
S.I.C.: 3761
N.A.I.C.S.: 336414
Gerardo Walle *(Pres & Mng Dir)*

Diehl Aerospace GmbH (1)
Alte Nussdorfer Strasse 23
D 88662 Uberlingen, Germany
Tel.: (49) 75518902
Fax: (49) 7551896001
E-Mail: marketing@diehlavionik.de
Web Site: www.diehl-aerospace.de
Sls.: $147,063,968
Emp.: 425
Development of Missiles, Flight Training Systems & Munitions: Joint Venture of Thales Avionics SA (49%) & Diehl VA Systeme GmbH
S.I.C.: 3761
N.A.I.C.S.: 336414
Manfred Kennel *(Co-Pres)*
V. Rainer Ott *(Co-Pres)*
Markus Marshall *(CFO)*

DIESEL & MOTOR ENGINEERING PLC

65 Jetawana Road
PO Box 339
Colombo, 14, Sri Lanka
Tel.: (94) 112449797
Fax: (94) 112449080
E-Mail: dimo@dimolanka.com
Web Site: www.dimolanka.com
DIMO—(COL)
Rev.: $217,536,091
Assets: $101,267,975
Liabilities: $41,363,314
Net Worth: $59,904,661
Earnings: $3,627,877
Emp.: 1,521
Fiscal Year-end: 03/31/13

Business Description:
Agricultural Machinery Sales & Services
S.I.C.: 5083
N.A.I.C.S.: 423820

Personnel:
A. R. Pandithage *(Chm & Mng Dir)*
A. G. Pandithage *(CEO)*
B. C. S. A. P. Gooneratne *(CFO & Sec)*

Board of Directors:
A. R. Pandithage
A. N. Algama
S. C. Algama
H. Cabral
B. C. S. A. P. Gooneratne
U. P. Liyanage
A. G. Pandithage
A. M. Pandithage
T. G. H. Peries
R. Seevaratnam
R. C. Weerawardane

Legal Counsel:
F.J. & G. De Saram & Company
No. 216 De Saram Place
Colombo, Sri Lanka

Subsidiaries:

Dimo (Pvt) Ltd. (1)
No 65 Jetawana Road
Colombo, Western Province, 01400, Sri Lanka
Tel.: (94) 112449797
Fax: (94) 11 2449080
E-Mail: dimo@dimolanka.com
Emp.: 864
Automotive Components Mfr
S.I.C.: 3519
N.A.I.C.S.: 333618
A. R. Pandithage *(Chm)*
Ranjith Pandithage *(CEO)*
S. C. Algama *(Mng Dir)*

DIESEL SPA

Via dell Industria 4-6
Breganze, Vicenza, 36042, Italy
Tel.: (39) 242409555
Fax: (39) 0424411955
E-Mail: dieselhq_info@diesel.com
Web Site: www.diesel.com
Year Founded: 1978
Sales Range: $1-4.9 Billion
Emp.: 330

Business Description:
Casual Clothing & Accessory Mfr
S.I.C.: 5699
N.A.I.C.S.: 448150

Personnel:
Renzo Rosso *(Founder & Pres)*
Marina Tosin *(Mng Dir)*

DIESELEC THISTLE GENERATORS LIMITED

Cadder House Cloberfield Milngavie
Glasgow, G62 7LN, United Kingdom
Tel.: (44) 141 956 7764
Fax: (44) 141 955 0642
E-Mail: sales@dieselecthistle.co.uk
Web Site: www.dieselecthistle.co.uk
Year Founded: 2004
Sales Range: $25-49.9 Million
Emp.: 49

Business Description:
Generator Distribution Services
S.I.C.: 5063
N.A.I.C.S.: 423610

Personnel:
Paul Moore *(Mng Dir)*

Board of Directors:
Brian Aitken
David Bell
Ian Buchan
Pat Malcolmson
James Pirrie
John Pirrie

DIESSE SRL

Via Cavicchione di Sopra 88-90
Calcinato, 25010, Italy
Tel.: (39) 30 9964552
Fax: (39) 91 8665695
E-Mail: info@diessesrl.com
Web Site: www.diessesrl.com

Business Description:
Polystyrene Packaging Products Mfr
S.I.C.: 2671
N.A.I.C.S.: 326112

Personnel:
Vincenzo Di Massa *(Head-R&D)*

Subsidiary:

Huhtamaki SpA (1)
Via XXV Aprile Ovest 16
42049 Enza, Italy (100%)
Tel.: (39) 0522903411
Fax: (39) 0522671278
E-Mail: huhtamaki.it@huhtamaki.com
Web Site: www.huhtamaki.com
Emp.: 200
Food Packaging & Disposable Dishes Mfr
S.I.C.: 2652
N.A.I.C.S.: 322219
Roberto Morellini *(Gen Mgr)*

DIETHELM KELLER HOLDING LIMITED

(d/b/a Diethelm Keller Group)
Muhlebachstrasse 20
CH-8008 Zurich, Switzerland
Tel.: (41) 442653300
Fax: (41) 442653399
Web Site: www.diethelmkeller.com
Year Founded: 1865
Sales Range: $5-14.9 Billion
Emp.: 24,000

Business Description:
Holding Company; International Trade, Proprietary Brand Management & Travel Services
S.I.C.: 6719
N.A.I.C.S.: 551112

Personnel:
Andreas W. Keller *(Chm)*
Adrian T. Keller *(Vice Chm)*
Markus Braun *(CEO & Head-Corp Office)*

Board of Directors:
Andreas W. Keller
Jean-Daniel de Schaller
Walter Ehrbar
Adrian T. Keller
Joerg W. Wolle

Group:

DKSH Holding Limited (1)
Wiesenstrasse 8
PO Box 888
8034 Zurich, Switzerland CH
Tel.: (41) 443867272 (48.11%)
Fax: (41) 443867282
E-Mail: info@dksh.com
Web Site: www.dksh.com
DKSH—(SWX)
Sls.: $9,534,820,812
Assets: $3,621,118,000
Liabilities: $2,321,185,592
Net Worth: $1,299,933,008
Earnings: $226,009,608
Emp.: 25,882
Fiscal Year-end: 12/31/12
Holding Company; Commercial Sourcing, Marketing, Logistics & Distribution Support Services
S.I.C.: 6719
N.A.I.C.S.: 551112
Adrian T. Keller *(Chm)*
Joerg W. Wolle *(Pres & CEO)*
Bernhard Schmitt *(CFO)*
Bruno Sidler *(COO)*
Sebastian Heuer *(Legal Counsel-Europe & Americas)*

Subsidiaries:

DKSH Management Ltd. (2)
Wiesenstrasse 8
CH-8034 Zurich, Switzerland CH
Tel.: (41) 443867272 (100%)
Fax: (41) 443867282
E-Mail: info.dksh@dksh.com
Web Site: www.dksh.com
Corporate Legislative Services
S.I.C.: 9131
N.A.I.C.S.: 921140
Joerg W. Wolle *(Pres & CEO)*
Gonpo Tsering *(Sr Exec VP-Ops & Bus Support)*
Alexander Stuart Davy *(Exec VP-Fin & Admin)*
Marcel W. Schmid *(Exec VP-Governance, Compliance & Resources)*
Bernhard Schmitt *(Exec VP-Country Ops & Bus Processes)*

DKSH Switzerland Ltd. (2)
Wiesenstrasse 8
CH-8034 Zurich, Switzerland CH
Tel.: (41) 443867272
Fax: (41) 443867282
E-Mail: info@dksh.com
Web Site: www.dksh.com
Emp.: 100
Commercial Sourcing, Marketing, Logistics & Distribution Support Services
S.I.C.: 7389
N.A.I.C.S.: 425120
Robert Koller *(Mng Dir)*

Non-U.S. Subsidiaries:

Diethelm Limited (2)
2535 Sukhumvit Road Bangchack
Prakhanong, Bangkok, 10260, Thailand TH
Tel.: (66) 27908000
Web Site: www.dksh.com
Emp.: 2,000
Commercial Sourcing, Marketing, Logistics & Distribution Support Services
S.I.C.: 7389
N.A.I.C.S.: 425120
Somboon Prasitjutrakul *(Pres & Grp Head-Consumer Goods Div)*

DKSH Australia Pty. Ltd. (2)
14-17 Dansu Ct
Hallam, VIC, 3803, Australia AU
Tel.: (61) 395546666
Fax: (61) 395546677
Web Site: www.dksh.com
Sales Range: $25-49.9 Million
Emp.: 130
Commercial Sourcing, Marketing, Logistics & Distribution Support Services
S.I.C.: 7389
N.A.I.C.S.: 425120

DKSH (China) Co., Ltd. (2)
3/F Tomson Commercial Building 710 Dong Fang Road
Pudong, Shanghai, 200122, China CN
Tel.: (86) 2158300518
Fax: (86) 2158300519
Web Site: www.dksh.com
Sales Range: $125-149.9 Million
Emp.: 1,000
Commercial Sourcing, Marketing, Logistics & Distribution Support Services
S.I.C.: 7389
N.A.I.C.S.: 425120
Johan Woo *(Global Head-Performance Matls Div & Country Mgr)*

DKSH Holdings (Malaysia) Berhad (2)
74 Jalan University
46200 Petaling Jaya, Selangor Darul Ehsan, Malaysia MY
Tel.: (60) 379660288
Fax: (60) 379560401
Web Site: www.dksh.com
5908—(KLS)
Rev.: $1,556,152,230
Assets: $420,875,154
Liabilities: $319,592,144
Net Worth: $101,283,011
Earnings: $26,827,135
Emp.: 2,200
Fiscal Year-end: 12/31/12
Holding Company; Commercial Sourcing, Marketing, Logistics & Distribution Support Services
S.I.C.: 6719
N.A.I.C.S.: 551112
Andre' P'o-Lieng Chai *(Co-Sec)*
Wai Sin Kwan *(Co-Sec)*

Subsidiaries:

DKSH Malaysia Sdn. Bhd. (3)
74 Jalan University
PO Box 77
46700 Petaling Jaya, Selangor Darul Ehsan, Malaysia MY
Tel.: (60) 379660288 (100%)
Fax: (60) 379570829
Web Site: www.dksh.com
Emp.: 3,000
Commercial Sourcing, Marketing, Logistics & Distribution Support Services
S.I.C.: 7389
N.A.I.C.S.: 425120
Niels Johan Holm *(Mng Dir)*
Andre Eugen Hagi *(Grp Dir-Fin)*

DKSH Japan K.K. (2)
DKSH Mita Building 3-4-19 Mita
Minato-ku, Tokyo, 108-8360, Japan JP
Tel.: (81) 354414511
Fax: (81) 354414599
E-Mail: info.jp@dksh.com
Web Site: www.dksh.jp
Sales Range: $350-399.9 Million
Emp.: 300
Commercial Sourcing, Marketing, Logistics & Distribution Support Services
S.I.C.: 7389
N.A.I.C.S.: 425120
Armin Radzwill *(Mng Dir & Gen Mgr-Tech Div-Japan)*

DKSH Korea Ltd. (2)
4-7 Floor SeungHewan Bldg 546-11
DoGok-dong
GangNam-gu, 135-858 Seoul, Korea (South) Ks
Tel.: (82) 221929500
Fax: (82) 221929590
E-Mail:
Web Site: www.dksh.com
Sales Range: $25-49.9 Million
Emp.: 400
Commercial Sourcing, Marketing, Logistics & Distribution Support Services
S.I.C.: 7389
N.A.I.C.S.: 425120
Matthew Beebar *(Country Mgr)*

DKSH Netherlands B.V. (2)
Vogelaarsweg 23
NL-3313 LL Dordrecht, Netherlands NL
Tel.: (31) 786220622
Fax: (31) 786220608
E-Mail: info.netherlands@dksh.com
Web Site: www.dksh.com
Emp.: 200
Commercial Sourcing, Marketing, Logistics & Distribution Support Services
S.I.C.: 7389
N.A.I.C.S.: 425120
Freek Klijnsma *(Mng Dir)*

DKSH Taiwan Ltd. (2)
10F Hannover High-Tech Square No 22
Lane 407
Ti Ding Boulevard Section 2
Neihu Technology Park, Taipei, 114, Taiwan TW
Tel.: (886) 287526666
Fax: (886) 287526000
Web Site: www.dksh.com
Sales Range: $250-299.9 Million
Emp.: 550
Commercial Sourcing, Marketing, Logistics & Distribution Support Services
S.I.C.: 7389
N.A.I.C.S.: 425120
Adrian Eberle *(Mng Dir & Gen Mgr-Tech Div)*

Non-U.S. Group:

STA Travel (Holdings) Pte Ltd (1)
400 Orchard Road 07-02 Orchard Towers
Singapore, 178901, Singapore
Tel.: (65) 67377188
Fax: (65) 67372591
E-Mail: sales@statravel.sg
Web Site: www.statravel.sg
Sales Range: $125-149.9 Million
Emp.: 30
Holding Company; Travel Services
S.I.C.: 6719
N.A.I.C.S.: 551112

Co-Headquarters:

STA Travel Ltd. (2)
Priory House
6 Wrights Lane, London, W8 6TA, United Kingdom UK
Tel.: (44) 2073616100
Fax: (44) 2073686493
E-Mail: marketingteam@statravel.co.uk
Web Site: www.statravelgroup.com
Emp.: 150
Travel Agencies & Services
S.I.C.: 4724
N.A.I.C.S.: 561510
John Constable *(CEO)*
Steve Jenkins *(CFO)*

U.S. Subsidiary:

STA Travel, Inc (3)
750 State Hwy 121 Ste 250
Lewisville, TX 75067
Tel.: (972) 538-8843
Fax: (972) 315-9578
Toll Free: (800) 781-4040
E-Mail: info@statravel.com
Web Site: www.statravel.com
Emp.: 70
Travel Agencies
S.I.C.: 4724
N.A.I.C.S.: 561510
Jane Armstrong *(Controller)*

Non-U.S. Subsidiary:

STA Travel Pty Ltd (3)
Level 3 6 Riverside Quay
Abbotsford, Southbank, VIC, 3067, Australia
Tel.: (61) 384176911
Fax: (61) 384151690
E-Mail: humanresourcesdivision@statravel.com.au
Web Site: www.statravel.com.au
Emp.: 70
Travel Services
S.I.C.: 4724
N.A.I.C.S.: 561510
Friedhelm Schwan *(Chm & Mng Dir)*

DIETSWELL S.A.

Parc Ariane 3 Immeuble Le Naiade 1 rue Alfred Kastler
78284 Guyancourt, France

Dietswell S.A.—(Continued)

Tel.: (33) 139302160
Fax: (33) 139304722
E-Mail: contact@dietswell.com
Web Site: www.dietswell.com
ALDIE—(EUR)
Sls.: $21,391,987
Assets: $35,085,229
Liabilities: $9,144,533
Net Worth: $25,940,696
Earnings: $445,582
Emp.: 72
Fiscal Year-end: 12/31/12
Business Description:
Engineering & Drilling Services
S.I.C.: 1629
N.A.I.C.S.: 237990
Personnel:
Pierre Laborie *(Chm)*
Jean-Claude Bourdon *(CEO)*
Fabian Simonet *(CFO)*
Dominique Michel *(Exec VP)*
Board of Directors:
Pierre Laborie
Jean-Claude Bourdon
Jean-Francois Fourt
Jean-Rene Grignon
Dominique Michel
Daniel L. Valot

Subsidiary:

FACT-O-RIG **(1)**
Parc Ariane 3 Immeuble Le Naiade 1 rue Alfred Kastler
78284 Guyancourt, France
Tel.: (33) 139 302 160
Fax: (33) 139 302 161
Web Site: www.factorig.com
Drilling Rig Inspection & Auditing Services
S.I.C.: 1389
N.A.I.C.S.: 213112
Nicolas Chevalier *(Mgr)*

DIETZEL GMBH

1 Haidequerstrasse 3-5
Vienna, 1110, Austria
Tel.: (43) 1760760
Fax: (43) 176076500
E-Mail: export@dietzel-univolt.com
Web Site: www.dietzel-univolt.com
Year Founded: 1938
Rev.: $50,500,000
Emp.: 210
Business Description:
Plastics and Metal Products Mfr
S.I.C.: 3089
N.A.I.C.S.: 326199
Personnel:
Michael Pocksteiner *(Owner & Co-Mng Dir)*
Peter Steigenberger *(Co-Mng Dir)*

DIEVINI HOPP BIOTECH HOLDING GMBH & CO. KG

Johann-Jakob-Astor-Strasse 57
69190 Walldorf, Germany
Tel.: (49) 62022048945
Fax: (49) 62022048946
E-Mail: contact@dievini.com
Web Site: www.dievini.com
Business Description:
Life & Health Sciences Equity Investment Firm
S.I.C.: 6211
N.A.I.C.S.: 523999
Personnel:
Dietmar Hopp *(Owner)*
Christof Hettich *(Mng Dir)*
Friedrich von Bohlen und Halbach *(Mng Dir)*

DIFC INVESTMENTS LLC

The Gate Level 15
PO Box 74777
Dubai, United Arab Emirates
Tel.: (971) 43622222
Fax: (971) 043622333
E-Mail: info@difc.ae
Web Site: www.difc.ae
Business Description:
Investment Holding Company
S.I.C.: 6211
N.A.I.C.S.: 523999

Subsidiary:

D-Clear LLC **(1)**
Level 15 Business Centre The Gate
PO Box 74777
Dubai, United Arab Emirates
Tel.: (971) 4 3622222
Investment Services
S.I.C.: 6211
N.A.I.C.S.: 523999
Philippe Chambadal *(CEO)*

Non-U.S. Holding:

SmartStream Technologies Ltd. **(2)**
St Helens
1 Undershaft, London, EC3A 8EE, United Kingdom
Tel.: (44) 20 7898 0600
Web Site: www.smartstream-stp.com
Sales Range: $75-99.9 Million
Software Publisher
S.I.C.: 7372
N.A.I.C.S.: 511210
Philippe Chambadal *(CEO)*
Graham Muir *(CFO)*
Mark Roth *(CMO)*
Richard Bemindt *(CTO)*
David Porter *(Dir-HR)*
Katharina Zimmermann *(Gen Counsel & Sec)*
Paul Hansford *(Exec VP-Prof Svcs)*
Alastair McGill *(Exec VP-Bus Dev & Alliances)*
David Penney *(Exec VP-Strategy & Product Mgmt)*
Christian Schiebl *(Exec VP)*

Non-U.S. Holding:

Villa Moda Lifestyle Company K.S.C.C. **(1)**
Commercial Free Zone Shuwaikh Port
PO Box 12112
Shamiya, Kuwait, 71652, Kuwait (70%)
Tel.: (965) 24827004
Fax: (965) 24610261
E-Mail: pr@villa-moda.com
Web Site: www.villa-moda.com
Sales Range: $25-49.9 Million
Clothing Store Owner & Operator
S.I.C.: 5699
N.A.I.C.S.: 448190
Abdullah Bin Hamad Bin Soqat *(Chm)*
Bisher Marwan Al-Barazi *(Vice Chm & CEO)*

DIFFER GROUP HOLDING CO., LTD.

33rd Floor Tower 11 166 Tapu East Road
Xiamen, China
Tel.: (86) 592 8396999
Fax: (86) 592 8806999
Web Site: www.dingfeng-cn.com
8056—(HKG)
Sales Range: $1-9.9 Million
Emp.: 100
Business Description:
Diversified Financial Holding Company
S.I.C.: 6719
N.A.I.C.S.: 551112
Personnel:
Mingxian Hong *(Chm)*
Chung Chi Ng *(CEO)*

DIFFERENCE CAPITAL FINANCIAL INC.

The Exchange Tower 130 King Street Suite 2950
Toronto, ON, M5X 2A2, Canada
Tel.: (416) 649-5085
E-Mail: info@differencecapital.com
Web Site: www.differencecapital.com
Year Founded: 1972
DCF—(TSX)
Rev.: $7,757,192
Assets: $92,783,540
Liabilities: $3,466,153
Net Worth: $89,317,388
Earnings: $4,249,959
Emp.: 4
Fiscal Year-end: 12/31/12
Business Description:
Investment & Financial Services
S.I.C.: 6211
N.A.I.C.S.: 523999
Personnel:
Michael Wekerle *(Chm)*
Paul Sparks *(Vice Chm)*
Neil Johnson *(CEO)*
Jeff Kehoe *(Mng Partner & Gen Counsel)*
Jamie M. Brown *(Partner)*
Henry Knies *(CFO, COO & Sec)*
Board of Directors:
Michael Wekerle
John Albright
Ivan Fecan
Riyaz Lalani
Paul Sparks
Transfer Agent:
Computershare Trust Company of Canada
100 University Ave
Toronto, ON, Canada

DIFFERENCE CAPITAL FINANCIAL INC.

(See Under Difference Capital Financial Inc.)

DIFFUSION AUTOMOBILE CLERMONTAISE

24 Route De Montpellier
34800 Clermont, France
Tel.: (33) 467960342
Sales Range: $10-24.9 Million
Emp.: 49
Business Description:
New & Used Car Dealers
S.I.C.: 5511
N.A.I.C.S.: 441110
Personnel:
Philippe Mazzucchetti *(Dir-Fin)*

DIG FOR FIRE

Players House 300 Attercliffe Common
Sheffield, S9 2AG, United Kingdom
Tel.: (44) 114 281 1200
Fax: (44) 114 281 0055
E-Mail: info@jaywing.com
Web Site: www.jaywingplc.com
Year Founded: 2003
Billings: $54,516,000
Emp.: 100
Business Description:
Advertising Agency
S.I.C.: 7311
N.A.I.C.S.: 541810
Personnel:
Sue Miller *(Mng Dir)*
Charles Buddery *(COO)*

DIGIA PLC

Valimotie 21
FI-00380 Helsinki, Finland
Tel.: (358) 103133000
Fax: (358) 103133700
E-Mail: info@digia.com
Web Site: www.digia.com
Year Founded: 1997
DIG1V—(HEL)
Rev.: $135,220,361
Assets: $124,353,400
Liabilities: $67,729,364
Net Worth: $56,624,036
Earnings: $5,417,407
Emp.: 1,025
Fiscal Year-end: 12/31/12
Business Description:
Information & Communication Technology Services
S.I.C.: 7389
N.A.I.C.S.: 519190
Personnel:
Pertti Kyttala *(Chm)*
Robert Ingman *(Vice Chm)*
Juha Varelius *(Pres & CEO)*
Anja Wasenius *(CFO)*
Mika Palsi *(Gen Counsel)*
Tommi Laitinen *(Sr VP-Industry Verticals & Intl Product)*
Harri Paani *(Sr VP-Indus Verticals)*
Tom Puusola *(Sr VP-Strategy & Bus Dev)*
Kimmo Vainikainen *(Sr VP-Solutions & Svcs Bus)*
Board of Directors:
Pertti Kyttala
Paivi Hokkanen
Robert Ingman
Kari Karvinen
Seppo Ruotsalainen
Tommi Uhari

Subsidiaries:

Digia Finland Oy **(1)**
Valimotie 21
Helsinki, 00380, Finland
Tel.: (358) 103133000
Fax: (358) 103133700
Information Technology Consulting Services
S.I.C.: 7373
N.A.I.C.S.: 541512

Digia Service Oy **(1)**
Valimotie 21
Helsinki, 00380, Finland
Tel.: (358) 103133000
Information Technology Consulting Services
S.I.C.: 7373
N.A.I.C.S.: 541512

Non-U.S. Subsidiaries:

Digia Sweden AB **(1)**
Kungsgatan 8
Stockholm, 111 43, Sweden
Tel.: (46) 857236400
E-Mail: info@digia.com
Computer Software Development Services
S.I.C.: 7371
N.A.I.C.S.: 541511

DIGICEL GROUP LTD.

Dyoll Building 40 Knutsford Boulevard
Kingston, 5, Jamaica
Tel.: (876) 9350000
Fax: (876) 920 4626
Web Site: www.digicelgroup.com
Emp.: 5,500
Business Description:
Wireless Telecommunications Services
S.I.C.: 4812
N.A.I.C.S.: 517210
Personnel:
Colm Delves *(CEO)*
Lawrence Hickey *(CFO)*
Mario Assaad *(CTO)*
Brian Finn *(CEO-Central America)*
Jan Tjernell *(Gen Counsel)*
Board of Directors:
Leslie Buckley
Colm Delves
Lucy Gaffney
Julian Michael Horn-Smith
Seamus Lynch
P. J. Mara
Denis O'Brien
Greg Sparks
David Sykes

DIGI.COM BERHAD
Lot 10 Jalan Delima 1 1 Subang Hi Tech Industrial Park
40000 Shah Alam, Selangor, Malaysia
Tel.: (60) 357211800
Fax: (60) 357211857
Web Site: www.digi.com.my
DIG—(KLS)
Rev.: $2,085,870,591
Assets: $1,316,243,991
Liabilities: $1,230,551,608
Net Worth: $85,692,382
Earnings: $395,378,063
Fiscal Year-end: 12/31/12
Business Description:
Wireless Telecommunication Services
S.I.C.: 4812
N.A.I.C.S.: 517210
Personnel:
Henrik Clausen *(CEO)*
Karl Erik Broten *(CFO)*
Albern Murty *(CMO)*
Christian Trane *(Chief Strategy & Corp Affairs Officer)*
Ole Martin Gunhildsbu *(CTO)*
Mun Lai Choo *(Co-Sec)*
Irene Liew *(Co-Sec)*
Yit Chan Tai *(Co-Sec)*
Board of Directors:
Sigve Brekke
Tore Johnsen
Hakon Bruaset Kjol
Halim Mohyiddin
Choo Boon Saw
Morten Karlsen Sorby

DIGICORE HOLDINGS LIMITED
DigiCore Building Regency Office Park 9 Regency Drive
Route 21 Corporate Park Irene Ext 30, Centurion, South Africa
Tel.: (27) 124502222
Fax: (27) 124502497
E-Mail: info@digicore.co.za
Web Site: www.digicore.com
DGC—(JSE)
Rev.: $96,351,080
Assets: $98,289,410
Liabilities: $25,826,269
Net Worth: $72,463,141
Earnings: ($5,822,586)
Emp.: 1,000
Fiscal Year-end: 06/30/13
Business Description:
Fleet Management & Vehicle Tracking Solutions Provider
S.I.C.: 7373
N.A.I.C.S.: 541512
Personnel:
N. H. Vlok *(Chm)*
P. J. Grove *(CFO)*
M. D. Rousseau *(COO)*
D. du Rand *(CTO & CIO)*
Donald A. Nieuwoudt *(Sec)*
Board of Directors:
N. H. Vlok
D. du Rand
P. J. Grove
B. Marx
S. S. Ntsaluba
G. Pretorius
M. D. Rousseau
J. D. Wiese
Transfer Agent:
Computershare Investor Services (Pty) Ltd
70 Marshall Street
Johannesburg, South Africa
Subsidiaries:

C-track (SA) (Pty) Limited **(1)**
Regency Ofc Park 9 Regency Dr Rte 21 Corp Park
Irene, Pretoria, Gauteng, 0157, South Africa
Tel.: (27) 124502222
Fax: (27) 124502323
E-Mail: info@digicore.co.za
Web Site: www.ctrack.co.za
Emp.: 500
Vehicle Tracking & Fleet Management Solutions
S.I.C.: 4899
N.A.I.C.S.: 517919
Nick Vlok *(CEO)*

DigiCore Electronics (Pty) Limited **(1)**
37 Hillclimb Rd
Pinetown, Kwazulu-Natal, 3610, South Africa
Tel.: (27) 317006133
Fax: (27) 317006143
E-Mail: info@ctrack.co.za
Web Site: www.ctrack.com
Emp.: 100
Printed Circuit Boards Mfr
S.I.C.: 3672
N.A.I.C.S.: 334412
Stuart Aberdein *(Mng Dir)*

DigiCore Fleet Management (SA) (Pty) Limited **(1)**
13 Steventon St
Anderbolt, Boksburg, Gauteng, 1459, South Africa
Tel.: (27) 124502222
Fax: (27) 118944318
Emp.: 100
Fleet Leasing & Management Services
S.I.C.: 7515
N.A.I.C.S.: 532112

Non-U.S. Subsidiary:

DigiCore Europe BV **(1)**
Ketelweg 44
3356 LE Papendrecht, Netherlands
Tel.: (31) 786414478
Fax: (31) 786150676
E-Mail: info@digicore.com
Emp.: 40
Vehicle Tracking & Fleet Services
S.I.C.: 4121
N.A.I.C.S.: 485310
Van Dam *(Gen Mgr)*

Subsidiary:

C-track Benelux BV **(2)**
Ketelweg 44
3356 LE Papendrecht, Netherlands
Tel.: (31) 786449334
Fax: (31) 786449335
E-Mail: info@ctrack.nl
Web Site: www.ctrack.nl
Emp.: 40
Fleet Management Services
S.I.C.: 4121
N.A.I.C.S.: 485310
Hilger Van Dam *(Mng Dir)*

Non-U.S. Subsidiaries:

C-track Belgium bvba **(2)**
Mechelsesteenweg 277
1800 Vilvoorde, Belgium
Tel.: (32) 22548557
Fax: (32) 22525338
E-Mail: info@ctrack.be
Web Site: www.ctrack.be
Emp.: 6
Vehicle Tracking & Fleet Management Services
S.I.C.: 4899
N.A.I.C.S.: 517919
Olivier van Houcke *(Mng Dir)*

C-track France sarl **(2)**
Centre d affaires Ave de l Europe
94320 Thiais, France
Tel.: (33) 141737629
Fax: (33) 1 468 716 17
E-Mail: info@ctrack.fr
Web Site: www.ctrack.fr
Fleet Leasing & Management Services
S.I.C.: 4121
N.A.I.C.S.: 485310
Sipco Broekhuizen *(Mng Dir)*

DigiCore Deutschland GmbH **(2)**
Gewerbepark 19
Bissendorf, 49143 Osnabruck, Lower Saxony, Germany
Tel.: (49) 5402702800
Fax: (49) 5402702828
E-Mail: info@c-track.de
Web Site: www.c-track.de
Emp.: 30
Fleet Management Services
S.I.C.: 7515
N.A.I.C.S.: 532112
Ralph Firman *(Mng Dir)*

DIGILAND INTERNATIONAL LIMITED
21 Serangoon North Avenue 5 Ban Teck Han Building 05-02
Singapore, 554864, Singapore
Tel.: (65) 66039898
Fax: (65) 66039896
Web Site: www.digiland.com.sg
G77—(SES)
Rev.: $54,109,109
Assets: $33,766,498
Liabilities: $13,657,801
Net Worth: $20,108,697
Earnings: ($1,670,878)
Fiscal Year-end: 06/30/13
Business Description:
Information & Communications Technology Products Distr
S.I.C.: 5064
N.A.I.C.S.: 423620
Personnel:
Sui Xin Cai *(Chm)*
Yu Lau *(Vice Chm)*
Chee Hong Teo *(CEO)*
Koon Hock Lim *(CFO & Sec)*
Edwin Ming Fai Long *(Pres-IT Bus)*
Board of Directors:
Sui Xin Cai
Yu Lau
Chee Hong Teo
Tat Hei Wong
XiaoPing Wu
Frank Yu
Subsidiary:

Infonet Systems and Services Pte Ltd **(1)**
21 Serangoon North Ave 5 Ban Teck Han Building #05-02
Singapore, 554864, Singapore
Tel.: (65) 66039877
Fax: (65) 66039897
E-Mail: enquiry@infonet.com.sg
Web Site: www.infonet.com.sg
IT Solution & Services
S.I.C.: 7371
N.A.I.C.S.: 541511

DIGITAL ARIA CO., LTD.
22nd Fl Parkview Office Tower 6 Jeongja-dong
Bundang-gu, Seongnam, Kyunggi-do, Korea (South) 463-811
Tel.: (82) 317867800
Fax: (82) 317867801
E-Mail: marketing@digitalaria.com
Web Site: www.digitalaria.com
Year Founded: 2000
115450—(KRS)
Sales Range: $10-24.9 Million
Emp.: 137
Business Description:
Software Development Services
S.I.C.: 7371
N.A.I.C.S.: 541511
Personnel:
Sung-Ho Song *(CEO)*

DIGITAL ARTS INC.
Otemachi First Square West Tower 14F 1-5-1 Otemachi
Chiyoda-ku, Tokyo, Japan
Tel.: (81) 3 5220 1110
E-Mail: investor@daj.co.jp
Web Site: www.daj.jp
Year Founded: 1995
2326—(TKS)
Sales Range: $25-49.9 Million
Business Description:
Internet Security Software & Appliances
S.I.C.: 7372
N.A.I.C.S.: 511210
Personnel:
Toshio Dogu *(CEO)*

DIGITAL BARRIERS PLC
Enterprise House 1-2 Hatfields
London, SE1 9PG, United Kingdom
Tel.: (44) 2079404740
Fax: (44) 2079404746
E-Mail: info@digitalbarriers.com
Web Site: www.digitalbarriers.com
DGB—(AIM)
Business Description:
Security Products Mfr
S.I.C.: 7382
N.A.I.C.S.: 561621
Personnel:
Thomas Joseph Black *(Chm)*
Colin Michael Evans *(Mng Dir)*
Richard Hird *(Sr VP-Middle East)*
Manuel Magalhaes *(Sr VP)*
Board of Directors:
Thomas Joseph Black
Paul Taylor
Bernie Waldron
Legal Counsel:
Osborne Clarke
One London Wall
London, United Kingdom
Subsidiary:

COE Limited **(1)**
Photon House Percy Street
Leeds, LS12 1EG, United Kingdom
Tel.: (44) 1132308800
Fax: (44) 1132799229
E-Mail: sales@digitalbarriers.com
Web Site: www.coe.co.uk
Sales Range: $1-9.9 Million
Emp.: 10
Surveillance System Designer & Mfr
S.I.C.: 3812
N.A.I.C.S.: 334511
Mark Marriage *(Dir-Technical)*

DIGITAL BROS SPA
Via Tortona 37
20144 Milan, Italy
Tel.: (39) 02413031
Fax: (39) 024130399
E-Mail: info@digital-bros.net
Web Site: www.digital-bros.net
DIB—(ITA)
Emp.: 84
Business Description:
Video Games Distr
S.I.C.: 7841
N.A.I.C.S.: 532230
Personnel:
Abramo Galante *(Chm, Co-CEO & Mng Dir)*
Raffaele Galante *(Co-CEO)*
Stefano Salbe *(CFO & Fin Reporting Officer)*
Board of Directors:
Abramo Galante
Davide Galante
Raffaele Galante
Guido Guetta
Stefano Salbe
Dani Schaumann
Bruno Soresina
Dario Treves
Subsidiaries:

505 Games S.r.l **(1)**
Via Tortona 37
Milan, 20144, Italy
Tel.: (39) 2413031
Fax: (39) 024130399
E-Mail: support@505games.com
Web Site: www.505games.com
Emp.: 6

Digital Bros SpA—(Continued)

Video Games Distr
S.I.C.: 5045
N.A.I.C.S.: 423430
Abramo Galente *(Gen Mgr)*

Non-U.S. Subsidiaries:

505 Games GmbH (2)
Brunnfeld 2-6
93133 Burglengenfeld, Germany
Tel.: (49) 9471 308879 1
Fax: (49) 9471 308879 9
Video Games Distr
S.I.C.: 5045
N.A.I.C.S.: 423430

505 Games Ltd (2)
402-420 Silbury Court Silbury Boulevard
Milton Keynes, MK9 2AF, United Kingdom
Tel.: (44) 1908607772
Fax: (44) 1908546470
E-Mail: info@505games.co.uk
Web Site: www.505games.co.uk
Emp.: 25
Video Game Publishers
S.I.C.: 7372
N.A.I.C.S.: 511210
Ron Scott *(Mng Dir)*

Game Service S.r.l. (1)
Via Leonardo Da Vinci Snc
Marostica, 36063, Italy
Tel.: (39) 042477777
Fax: (39) 424474035
E-Mail: info@gamesservicesrl.it
Web Site: www.games-service.it/
Emp.: 15
Video Games Distr
S.I.C.: 5045
N.A.I.C.S.: 423430

Non-U.S. Subsidiaries:

Digital Bros France S.a.r.l. (1)
2 Chemin de la Chauderaie
Francheville, 69340, France
Tel.: (33) 456384520
Fax: (33) 478348105
E-Mail: info@digital-bros.fr
Web Site: www.digital-bros.fr
Emp.: 8
Video Games Distr
S.I.C.: 5045
N.A.I.C.S.: 423430
Dupon Tloue *(Mgr-Mktg)*

Digital Bros Iberia S.L. (1)
c/ Londres 38 Oficina 105
Las Rozas, Madrid, 28230, Spain
Tel.: (34) 916409518
Fax: (34) 916409481
E-Mail: info@digital-bros.net
Web Site: www.digital-bros.net
Video Game Publishers
S.I.C.: 7372
N.A.I.C.S.: 511210

DIGITAL CHINA HOLDINGS LIMITED

Suite 2008 20/F Devon House Taikoo Place 979 King's Road
Hong Kong, China (Hong Kong)
Tel.: (852) 34168000
Fax: (852) 28055991
E-Mail: info@digitalchina.com
Web Site: www.digitalchina.com.hk
Year Founded: 1984
861—(HKG OTC)
Rev.: $9,477,684,831
Assets: $3,663,194,837
Liabilities: $2,545,052,107
Net Worth: $1,118,142,729
Earnings: $195,894,650
Emp.: 10,600
Fiscal Year-end: 03/31/13

Business Description:
Information Technology Solutions & Service
S.I.C.: 5045
N.A.I.C.S.: 423430

Personnel:
Wei Guo *(Chm)*
Guorong Yan *(Pres)*
Yang Lin *(CEO)*
Lanqing Bai *(Asst Pres)*
Weijun Fei *(Asst Pres)*
Dong Jiang *(Asst Pres)*
Jiangying Li *(Asst Pres)*
Guanhua Wang *(Asst Pres)*
Jing Zhang *(Asst Pres)*
Yunfei Zhang *(Asst Pres)*
Lida Zhou *(Asst Pres)*
Chi Keung Wong *(Sec)*

Board of Directors:
Wei Guo
Zhaoguang Hu
Yang Lin
Hong Ni
Peter Ka Lueng Ong
Francis Man Chung Wong
Andrew Y. Yan
Guorong Yan

Appleby Management (Bermuda) Ltd.
Canon's Court 22 Victoria Street
HM 12 Hamilton, Bermuda

Transfer Agents:
Tricor Abacus Limited
26th Floor Tesbury Centre 28 Queen's Road East
Wanchai, China (Hong Kong)

Appleby Management (Bermuda) Ltd.
Canon's Court 22 Victoria Street
HM 12 Hamilton, Bermuda

Subsidiaries:

Beijing Digital China Limited (1)
Digital China Building 16 Suzhou Street
Haidian District, Beijing, China 100080
Tel.: (86) 10 62694338
Fax: (86) 10 62693493
Information Technology Management Services
S.I.C.: 8741
N.A.I.C.S.: 561110

Changsha Digital China Company Limited (1)
Room 1601-1603 Hunan Cultural Building
139 North Shaoshan Road
Changsha, Hunan, 410001, China
Tel.: (86) 73184161486
Fax: (86) 731 84129058
Information Technology Products Distr
S.I.C.: 5045
N.A.I.C.S.: 423430

Chengdu Digital China Limited (1)
40 Wuqing South Road Wuhou District
Chengdu, Sichuan, China 610045
Tel.: (86) 28 2885003399
Fax: (86) 2885459888
Information Technology Management Services
S.I.C.: 7379
N.A.I.C.S.: 541519

Digital China (China) Limited (1)
Digital Technology Plaza 9 Shangdi 9th Street
PO Box 8608
Haidian District, Beijing, China 100085
Tel.: (86) 10 82707777
Fax: (86) 10 82707776
Information Technology Products Distr
S.I.C.: 5045
N.A.I.C.S.: 423430

Digital China (Hefei) Company Limited (1)
14 F Jincheng Building 436 Changjiang Middle Road
Hefei, Anhui, 230061, China
Tel.: (86) 5512834200
Fax: (86) 551 2834010
Information Technology Products Distr
S.I.C.: 5045
N.A.I.C.S.: 423430

Digital China Limited (1)
9/F Digital China Building 16 Suzhou Street
Haidian District, Beijing, 100080, China
Tel.: (86) 10 62693333
Fax: (86) 10 62693374
Information Technology Products Mfr & Sales
S.I.C.: 3571
N.A.I.C.S.: 334111

Digital China Networks (Beijing) Limited (1)
Third Floor Digital China Plaza No 9 Ninth Street Shangdi
Haidian District, Beijing, China 100085
Tel.: (86) 10 82707777
Fax: (86) 10 82707717
Networking Products Mfr & Distr
S.I.C.: 3661
N.A.I.C.S.: 334210

Digital China (Shenzhen) Limited (1)
11 F United Cdef Building 1 Finance Base
No 8 Knife Road Science Park
Futian District, Shenzhen, Guangdong, 518057, China
Tel.: (86) 75582966699
Fax: (86) 75582966660
Information Technology Products Mfr & Distr
S.I.C.: 3571
N.A.I.C.S.: 334111

Digital China (Zhengzhou) Limited (1)
18 F Block D Building 2 Jincheng International Plaza 68 Jingsan Road
Zhengzhou, Henan, China
Tel.: (86) 371 69508188
Fax: (86) 371 69508199
Information Technology Products Distr
S.I.C.: 5045
N.A.I.C.S.: 423430

Fuzhou Digital China Company Limited (1)
8/F Chuangye Center Building 318 Wushan West Road
Gulou District, Fuzhou, Fujian, 350002, China
Tel.: (86) 591 83306330
Fax: (86) 591 83306322
Information Technology Production Distr
S.I.C.: 5045
N.A.I.C.S.: 423430

Guangzhou Digital China Limited (1)
31-32 F Xinyuan Mansion 898 Tianhebei Road
Guangzhou, Guangdong, 510898, China
Tel.: (86) 20 87582246
Fax: (86) 20 87543458
Information Technology Products Mfr & Distr
S.I.C.: 3571
N.A.I.C.S.: 334111

Hangzhou Digital China Limited (1)
Room 518 East Software Park 90 Wensan Road
Hangzhou, Zhejiang, 310012, China
Tel.: (86) 571 87362221
Fax: (86) 571 87362154
Computer Systems Network Intergration Services
S.I.C.: 7373
N.A.I.C.S.: 541512

Jinan Digital China Limited (1)
2F Block A Seven Star Auspicious Building
29 Wenhua East Road
Jinan, Shandong, 250014, China
Tel.: (86) 531 82382000
Fax: (86) 531 82382013
Information Technology Products Mfr & Distr
S.I.C.: 3571
N.A.I.C.S.: 334111

Nanjing Digital China Limited (1)
10/f Huijie Mansion No 268 Zhongshan Road
Xuanwu Dist, Nanjing, Jiangsu, 210008, China
Tel.: (86) 2583351122
Fax: (86) 2583351122
Computer Network System Integration Services
S.I.C.: 7373
N.A.I.C.S.: 541512

Navimentum Information System Limited (1)
22/F Block B Zhong Shang Plaza 9 Zhongnan Road
Wuchang District, Wuhan, Hubei, 430071, China
Tel.: (86) 27 87312266
Fax: (86) 27 87222999
Information Technology Consulting Services
S.I.C.: 7373
N.A.I.C.S.: 541512

Shanghai Digital China Information Technology Service Co., Ltd. (1)
No 111 Fuquan Road
Shanghai, China 200335
Tel.: (86) 2122019375
Fax: (86) 2122019415
Computer Systems Network Intergration Services
S.I.C.: 7373
N.A.I.C.S.: 541512
Peng Wu *(Mgr)*

Shanghai Digital China Limited (1)
No 111 Fuquan Road
Changning District, Shanghai, 200335, China
Tel.: (86) 21 220 19999
Fax: (86) 21 220 19198
Information Technology Products Mfr & Distr
S.I.C.: 3571
N.A.I.C.S.: 334111

Shenyang Digital China Limited (1)
6F Chengda Technology Building 63 South Sanhao Street
Heping District, Shenyang, Liaoning, 110004, China
Tel.: (86) 24 23582588
Fax: (86) 24 23969054
Computer Network System Integration Services
S.I.C.: 7373
N.A.I.C.S.: 541512

Non-U.S. Subsidiaries:

Digital China Advanced Systems Limited (1)
Room 2008 20 F Devon Hse Taikoo Place
979 Kings Road
Quarry Bay, China (Hong Kong)
Tel.: (852) 34168000
Fax: (852) 28055991
Information Technology Management Services
S.I.C.: 7373
N.A.I.C.S.: 541512

Digital China (BVI) Limited (1)
C/O Offshore Incorporations Limited
Road Town, Tortola, Virgin Islands (British)
Tel.: (284) 4948184
Investment Management Services
S.I.C.: 8741
N.A.I.C.S.: 551114

Digital China (HK) Limited (1)
Room 2008 20 F Devon House Taikoo Place 979 Kings Road
Quarry Bay, China (Hong Kong)
Tel.: (852) 34168000
Fax: (852) 28055991
Computer Peripheral Distr
S.I.C.: 5045
N.A.I.C.S.: 423430

Digital China Macao Commercial Offshore Limited (1)
Room D 14/F Edi China Plaza 730 Avenue da Praia Grande
Macau, China (Macau)
Tel.: (853) 28717039
Fax: (853) 28717038
Information Technology Consulting Services
S.I.C.: 7373
N.A.I.C.S.: 541512

Digital China Technology Limited (1)
Suite 2008 Devon House Taikoo Place 979 Kings Road
Quarry Bay, China (Hong Kong)
Tel.: (852) 34168000
Fax: (852) 2805 5991
Computer Peripheral Equipment Mfr
S.I.C.: 3575
N.A.I.C.S.: 334118

Non-U.S. Joint Venture:

Digital China Management Systems Ltd. (1)
DCMS Mansion No 5 Shangdi East Road
Haidian District, Beijing, 100085, China
Tel.: (86) 1082705888
Fax: (86) 1082705902
Emp.: 700
Computer Services; Owned by Data Systems Consulting Co., Ltd. & Digital China Holdings Limited
S.I.C.: 7379

N.A.I.C.S.: 541519

DIGITAL DESIGN
33 Smolenka River Embankment
Saint Petersburg, 199178, Russia
Tel.: (7) 8123465835
E-Mail: sales.int@digdes.com
Web Site: www.digdes.com
DDJ—(DEU)

Business Description:
Custom Software Programming Services
S.I.C.: 7371
N.A.I.C.S.: 541511

Personnel:
Andrew Fedorov *(CEO)*

DIGITAL GARAGE, INC.
Daikanyama DG Bldg 3-5-7 Ebisu
Minami Shibuya-ku
Tokyo, 150-0022, Japan
Tel.: (81) 3 6367 1111
Fax: (81) 3 6367 1119
E-Mail: info@garage.co.jp
Web Site: www.garage.co.jp
Year Founded: 1995
4819—(JAS TKS)
Sls.: $307,604,000
Assets: $616,110,000
Liabilities: $316,272,000
Net Worth: $299,838,000
Earnings: $29,865,000
Fiscal Year-end: 06/30/13

Business Description:
Information Technology Services
S.I.C.: 7379
N.A.I.C.S.: 541519

Personnel:
Kaoru Hayashi *(Pres & CEO)*
Yasuyuki Rokuyata *(COO)*

Board of Directors:
Kenji Fujiwara
Kaoru Hayashi
Joichi Ito
Naohiko Iwai
Keizo Odori
Joi Okada
Susumu Okamoto
Yasuyuki Rokuyata
Makoto Soda
Masashi Tanaka

Subsidiaries:

CGM Marketing Inc. **(1)**
3-5-7 Ebisuminami Daikanyamadg Building
Shibuya-ku, Tokyo, 150-0022, Japan
Tel.: (81) 363671200
Fax: (81) 363671119
Web Site: www.cgmm.co.jp
Emp.: 270
Marketing Consulting Services
S.I.C.: 8742
N.A.I.C.S.: 541613
Kaoru Hayashi *(Pres)*

DG Communications, Inc. **(1)**
1-15-7 Tsukishima
Chuo-ku, Tokyo, 104, Japan
Tel.: (81) 3 3532 6351
Telex: 3 3532 6380
Fax: (81) 3 3532 6380
E-Mail: info@sogei.co.jp
Web Site: www.sogei.co.jp
Billings: $301,800,000
Emp.: 437
Advertising Agency
S.I.C.: 7311
N.A.I.C.S.: 541810
Iku Hayasi *(Chm)*
Hideo Edashaa *(CEO)*
Nishimoto Yutaka *(CEO)*

Branches

Sogei do Brasil Publicidade Ltda. **(2)**
Alameda Campinas 529 Jardim Paulista
CEP 01404 Sao Paulo, SP, Brazil
Tel.: (55) 11 251 1600
Fax: (55) 11 284 5421
E-Mail: sogei@uol.com.br
Web Site: www.sogei.co.jp
Advertising Agency
S.I.C.: 7311
N.A.I.C.S.: 541810

Sogei Inc.-Sapporo Branch **(2)**
Kitasanjyou-Mitsui Building 3-1-4 Nishi Kitajyou
Chou-Ku, Sapporo, 060-0003, Japan JP
Tel.: (81) 112216881
Fax: (81) 11 231 4358
Web Site: www.sogei.co.jp
Advertising Agency
S.I.C.: 7311
N.A.I.C.S.: 541810

Sogei Inc.-Sendai Branch **(2)**
Lunar Sendai Building 2-15-1 Honcho
Aoba-Ku, Sendai, 980-0014, Japan JP
Tel.: (81) 222620235
Fax: (81) 222621864
E-Mail: abe_r@dg-c.co.jp
Web Site: www.sogei.co.jp
Advertising Agency
S.I.C.: 7311
N.A.I.C.S.: 541810

DG Mobile, Inc. **(1)**
3-5-7 Ebisuminami Daikanyamadg Building
Shibuya-ku, Tokyo, 150-0022, Japan
Tel.: (81) 363671300
Fax: (81) 363671270
Web Site: www.dgmobile.co.jp
Mobile Software Development Services
S.I.C.: 7371
N.A.I.C.S.: 541511

SBI VeriTrans Co., Ltd. **(1)**
3-5-7 Ebisu Minami Daikanyama DG Building 5F
Shibuya-ku, Tokyo, Japan (41.6%)
Tel.: (81) 3 1500 6367
Fax: (81) 3 6367 1230
Web Site: www.veritrans.co.jp/
3749—(TKS)
Electronic Payment Settlements for E-Commerce Businesses
S.I.C.: 7379
N.A.I.C.S.: 541519
Takashi Okita *(CEO)*
Hiroshi Shino *(Exec Officer & Dir-Bus Dev)*

Wheel, Inc. **(1)**
3-5-7 Ebisu Minami
Shibuya-ku, Tokyo, 150-0022, Japan
Tel.: (81) 354657747
Smartphones Content Distr
S.I.C.: 7379
N.A.I.C.S.: 541519
Kaoru Hayashi *(Pres & CEO)*

DIGITAL IDENTIFICATION SOLUTIONS AG
Teckstrasse 52
73734 Esslingen, Germany
Tel.: (49) 71 1341 6890
Fax: (49) 711 3416 89550
E-Mail: mail@digital-identification.com
Web Site: www.edisecure.com
D7S—(DEU)
Sales Range: $25-49.9 Million
Emp.: 95

Business Description:
Security Identification Solutions
S.I.C.: 7382
N.A.I.C.S.: 561621

Personnel:
Lukas Metzler *(Chm-Supervisory Bd)*
Sandro Camilleri *(CEO)*
Fabrizio Armone *(CFO)*

Supervisory Board of Directors:
Lukas Metzler
Francesco Fabiani
Giorgio Magnoni

DIGITAL LEARNING MARKETPLACE PLC
Livingston House
2 Queens Road
Teddington, Mddx, TW11 0LB, United Kingdom
Tel.: (44) 8450583960
Fax: (44) 2089777587
E-Mail: info@intellego.co.uk
Web Site: www.intellego.co.uk
DLM—(LSE)
Sales Range: $1-9.9 Million
Emp.: 23

Business Description:
Software Publishing & E-Learning
S.I.C.: 7372
N.A.I.C.S.: 511210

Personnel:
Angus Forrest *(Chm)*

Board of Directors:
Angus Forrest
Andrew Hasoon
Bruce H. Leith

Legal Counsel:
Vizards Tweedie
Barnards Inn, 86 Fetter Lane
EC4A 1AD London, United Kingdom

Subsidiaries:

Zenosis Limited **(1)**
Livingston House 2 Queens Rd
Teddington, Middlesex, TW110LB, United Kingdom
Tel.: (44) 845 058 3960
Fax: (44) 208 977 7587
E-Mail: healthcare@intellego.co.uk
Web Site: www.zenosis.com
Emp.: 20
Online Educational Support Services
S.I.C.: 8299
N.A.I.C.S.: 611710
Angus Forrest *(CEO)*
Christine Morris *(Sec)*

DIGITAL MAGICS S.P.A.
Via B Quaranta 40
20139 Milan, Italy
Tel.: (39) 02 52505 1
Fax: (39) 02 36598 402
E-Mail: info@digitalmagics.com
Web Site: www.digitalmagics.com
Year Founded: 2004
DM—(ITA)

Business Description:
Investment Services
S.I.C.: 6211
N.A.I.C.S.: 523999

Personnel:
Enrico Gasperini *(Co-Founder & Chm)*
Alberto Fioravanti *(Co-Founder, Venture Partner & CIO)*
Gabriele Ronchini *(Co-Founder & Venture Partner)*
Gabriele Gresta *(Co-Founder)*
Alessandro Malacart *(CEO & Partner)*
Massimiliano Benci *(CFO & Partner)*
Giandomenico Sica *(Partner & Head-IR)*
Edmondo Sparano *(Partner & Head-R&D)*

Board of Directors:
Enrico Gasperini
Massimiliano Benci
Alberto Fioravanti
Luca Fabio Giacometti
Gabriele Gresta
Alessandro Malacart
Gabriele Ronchini

DIGITAL MEDIA PROFESSIONALS INC.
7F Mitaka Takagi Building 1-15-5 Nakacho
Musashino-shi, Tokyo, 180-0006, Japan
Tel.: (81) 422 603480
Fax: (81) 422 603479
Web Site: www.dmprof.com
Year Founded: 2002
3652—(TKS)
Sales Range: $10-24.9 Million
Emp.: 23

Business Description:
Graphics Processor, 3D Graphics Software & Consulting Services
S.I.C.: 3577
N.A.I.C.S.: 334118

Personnel:
Tatsuo Yamamoto *(Pres & CEO)*
Sei Furukawa *(CFO)*

Board of Directors:
Sei Furukawa
Shigeto Iwata
Eisaku Ohbuchi
Shinichi Okamoto
Tatsuo Yamamoto

DIGITAL MULTIMEDIA TECHNOLOGY CO., LTD.
2nd Fl 926 Gwanyang-dong Dongan-gu
Anyang, Gyeonggi-do, 431-060, Korea (South)
Tel.: (82) 31 420 7500
Fax: (82) 31 400 7501
E-Mail: admin@dmt.kr
Web Site: www.dmtsat.com
Year Founded: 2007
134580—(KRS)
Sls.: $83,979,000
Assets: $43,875,540
Liabilities: $13,979,760
Net Worth: $29,895,780
Earnings: $7,572,990
Fiscal Year-end: 12/31/12

Business Description:
Wireless Technology Products
S.I.C.: 3663
N.A.I.C.S.: 334220

Personnel:
Hee-Kee Lee *(CEO)*

DIGITAL ONLINE MEDIA GMBH
Bismarckstrasse 60
50672 Cologne, Germany
Tel.: (49) 221951680
Fax: (49) 221951688
E-Mail: info@dom.de
Web Site: www.dom.de
Year Founded: 1995

Business Description:
E Commerce & Online Marketing Solutions
S.I.C.: 2741
N.A.I.C.S.: 519130

Personnel:
Markus Schulte *(Mng Dir)*

DIGITAL PAYMENT TECHNOLOGIES CORP.
4105 Grandview Hwy
Burnaby, BC, Canada
Tel.: (604) 688-1959
Fax: (604) 629-1867
Toll Free: (888) 687-6822
Web Site: www.digitalpaytech.com
Year Founded: 1997
Rev.: $11,020,000
Emp.: 75

Business Description:
Automated Payment Processing Solutions
S.I.C.: 7389
N.A.I.C.S.: 561499

Personnel:
Andrew Scott *(CEO)*
Laura Colwill *(CFO)*
Christopher MacPhail *(CTO)*

DIGITAL PERFORMANCE GROUP LTD.
Ground Floor 33-35 Saunders Street
Pyrmont, NSW, 2009, Australia

Digital Performance Group Ltd.—(Continued)

Mailing Address:
PO Box 727
North Sydney, NSW, 2059, Australia
Tel.: (61) 2 8569 0000
Fax: (61) 2 8205 8476
E-Mail: enquiries@dpgmedia.com.au
Web Site: www.dpgmedia.com.au
DIG—(ASX)
Rev.: $31,112,938
Assets: $15,956,635
Liabilities: $9,620,667
Net Worth: $6,335,968
Earnings: ($393,914)
Fiscal Year-end: 06/30/13
Business Description:
Holding Company; Digital Media Services
S.I.C.: 6719
N.A.I.C.S.: 551112
Personnel:
Peter Hynd *(Chm)*
Campbell Nicholas *(CFO & Sec)*
Shaun McNamara *(COO)*
Board of Directors:
Peter Hynd
Fionn Hyndman
Roger Sharp
David Sweet
Legal Counsel:
Middletons
Level 26 52 Martin Place
Sydney, NSW, 2000, Australia
Tel.: (61) 2 9513 2300
Fax: (61) 2 9513 2399
Subsidiaries:

Deal Group Media Pty Limited **(1)**
200 Harris St Pyrmont
Sydney, New South Wales, 2009, Australia
Tel.: (61) 285690000
Fax: (61) 285690001
E-Mail: info@dgm-au.com
Web Site: www.dgm-au.com
Emp.: 30
Online Marketing Services
S.I.C.: 8742
N.A.I.C.S.: 541613
Craig Ellis *(Mng Dir)*

Empowered Communications Pty Ltd **(1)**
Ground Fl 102 York Street
South Melbourne, VIC, 3205, Australia
Tel.: (61) 399401600
Fax: (61) 399401653
E-Mail: sales@empoweredcomms.com.au
Web Site: www.empoweredcomms.com.au
Emp.: 12
Online Marketing Solutions
S.I.C.: 8742
N.A.I.C.S.: 541613
Shaun McNamara *(Gen Mgr)*

Reward Mobile Pty Ltd **(1)**
Locked Bag 100
Southport, QLD, 4215, Australia
Tel.: (61) 7 5630 3005
Fax: (61) 7 5630 3030
E-Mail: support@rewardmobile.com.au
Web Site: www.rewardmobile.com.au
Mobile Communication Services
S.I.C.: 4812
N.A.I.C.S.: 517210

DIGITAL PUBLISHING INITIATIVES JAPAN CO., LTD.

3rd Floor Fusanbo Building
1-3 Kandajinbou-chou, Tokyo, Chiyoda-ku, 101-0051, Japan
Tel.: (81) 3 3518 9750
Fax: (81) 3 3518 9760
Web Site: www.pubridge.jp/
Business Description:
Publishing Services
S.I.C.: 2731
N.A.I.C.S.: 511130
Personnel:
Akihiko Takano *(CTO)*

DIGITAL SHELF SPACE CORP.

214-1847 West Broadway Street
Vancouver, BC, V6J 1Y6, Canada
Tel.: (604) 736-7977
Fax: (604) 736-7944
E-Mail: tlamb2@gmail.com
Web Site: www.digitalshelfspace.com
Year Founded: 2009
DSS—(OTC TSXV)
Rev.: $1,637,219
Assets: $2,404,893
Liabilities: $716,649
Net Worth: $1,688,244
Earnings: ($1,977,278)
Fiscal Year-end: 12/31/12
Business Description:
Home Entertainment Creator & Producer
S.I.C.: 7812
N.A.I.C.S.: 512110
Personnel:
Jeffrey N. Sharpe *(Pres & CEO)*
Thomas D. Lamb *(CFO)*
Board of Directors:
Thomas D. Lamb
R. Hector MacKay-Dunn
Jeffrey Sackman
Jeffrey N. Sharpe
Jason P. Sparaga
John J. Sutherland
Legal Counsel:
Farris & Company
Pacific Centre South 25th Floor, 700 W Georgia St
PO Box 10026
Vancouver, BC, Canada
Transfer Agent:
Computershare
200 - 510 Burrard Street
Vancouver, BC, Canada

DIGITAL SKY TECHNOLOGIES LIMITED

(d/b/a DST)
Presnenskaya nab 10 Block C 57th Fl
123317 Moscow, Russia
Tel.: (7) 4953631368
Fax: (7) 0073631364
E-Mail: info@dst-global.com
Web Site: www.dst-global.com
Year Founded: 2005
Emp.: 60
Business Description:
Internet-Related Investment Services
S.I.C.: 6211
N.A.I.C.S.: 523999
Personnel:
Gregory Finger *(Pres & Founding Partner)*
Yuri Milner *(CEO & Founding Partner)*
Verdi Israelian *(Partner)*
Alexander Tamas *(Partner)*
Non-U.S. Holding:

ICQ Inc. **(1)**
Kiriat Atidim Bldg #7
Tel Aviv, Israel
Mailing Address:
PO Box 58161
Tel Aviv, Israel
Tel.: (972) 37665555
Fax: (972) 37665566
Web Site: www.icq.com
Sales Range: $25-49.9 Million
Communication Tools, Content, & Services to Online Communities
S.I.C.: 7372
N.A.I.C.S.: 511210
Alexander Groni *(VP)*

DIGITAL UNITED, INC.

220 Gangqien Road Neihu District
Taipei, 114, Taiwan
Tel.: (886) 2 449 5000
Fax: (886) 2 2659 6655
E-Mail: service@seed.net.tw
Web Site: www.digitalunited.com
Year Founded: 1998
Sales Range: $50-74.9 Million
Emp.: 540
Business Description:
Dial-up & Broadband Internet Services
S.I.C.: 4899
N.A.I.C.S.: 517919
Personnel:
Jyh Jong Fu *(Sr VP-Bus Dev)*

DIGITECH SYSTEMS CO., LTD.

Seonyu Industry Complex 701-3
Hyangyang-ri Paju-eup
Hwasun, Gyeonggi-do, Korea (South)
Tel.: (82) 319503000
Fax: (82) 319503098
E-Mail: sjnam@digitechsys.co.kr
Web Site: www.digitechsys.co.kr
Year Founded: 2000
091690—(KRS)
Sls.: $220,247,250
Assets: $255,326,850
Liabilities: $130,757,070
Net Worth: $124,569,780
Earnings: $9,566,910
Emp.: 180
Fiscal Year-end: 12/31/12
Business Description:
Touch Screen Solution Developer & Mfr
S.I.C.: 3575
N.A.I.C.S.: 334118
Personnel:
Tommy Hwan Yong Lee *(CEO)*

DIGITEST ELEKTRONIK SERVICE GMBH

Im Justus 1
Postfach 1471
76829 Landau, Rhineland-Palatinate, Germany
Tel.: (49) 63419354321
Fax: (49) 634130354
E-Mail: info@digitest.de
Web Site: www.digitest.de
Year Founded: 1991
Emp.: 50
Business Description:
Computer Equipment Repair & Maintenance Services
S.I.C.: 7378
N.A.I.C.S.: 811212
Personnel:
Rainer Saborowski *(Mng Dir)*
Heinz Neumann *(CFO)*

DIGITRONIC GMBH

Carl-Spitzweg-Strasse 33
D-50127 Bergheim, Germany
Tel.: (49) 22717910
Fax: (49) 2271791200
E-Mail: info@digitronic-gmbh.de
Web Site: www.digitronic-gmbh.de
Year Founded: 1977
Rev.: $12,438,419
Emp.: 106
Business Description:
Electronic Components Mfr
S.I.C.: 3679
N.A.I.C.S.: 334419
Personnel:
Gerd Franken *(Head-Quality Control & Quality Mgmt)*

DIGJAM LIMITED

ECE House 2nd Floor 28-A Kasturba Gandhi Marg
New Delhi, 110 001, India
Tel.: (91) 1123765301
Fax: (91) 1123711446
E-Mail: corporate@digjam.co.in
Web Site: www.digjam.co.in
DIGJAM—(NSE)
Rev.: $28,589,849
Assets: $25,205,989
Liabilities: $23,003,338
Net Worth: $2,202,652
Earnings: $824,122
Fiscal Year-end: 03/31/13
Business Description:
Fabrics Mfr
S.I.C.: 3999
N.A.I.C.S.: 339999
Personnel:
R. K. Kedia *(Pres & COO)*
C. Bhaskar *(CEO & Mng Dir)*
G. K. Sureka *(Compliance Officer, Sec & Exec VP-Legal)*
Board of Directors:
Sidharth Birla
Bharat Anand
Meenakshi Bangur
C. Bhaskar
G. Momen
A. C. Mukherji
S. Ragothaman
C. L. Rathi
Transfer Agent:
MCS Share Transfer Agent Limited
12/1/5 Monoharpukur Road
Kolkata, 700026, India

DIGNE DISTRIBUTION

8 avenue du 8 Mai 1945
04000 Digne-les-Bains, France
Tel.: (33) 492314916
Sls.: $23,500,000
Emp.: 53
Business Description:
Miscellaneous General Merchandise Stores
S.I.C.: 5211
N.A.I.C.S.: 444190
Personnel:
Katie Fourneau *(Dir-Admin)*
Board of Directors:
Laurent Renard

DIGNITY PLC

4 King Edwards Court King Edward Square
Sutton Coldfield, West Midlands, B73 6AP, United Kingdom
Tel.: (44) 1213541557
Fax: (44) 1213215644
E-Mail: company.secretary@dignityuk.co.uk
Web Site: www.dignityfunerals.co.uk
DTY—(LSE)
Rev.: $362,604,984
Assets: $729,631,980
Liabilities: $659,195,646
Net Worth: $70,436,334
Earnings: $56,380,653
Emp.: 2,543
Fiscal Year-end: 12/28/12
Business Description:
Funeral Services, Cremations & Prearranged Funeral Plans
S.I.C.: 7261
N.A.I.C.S.: 812210
Personnel:
Mike McCollum *(CEO)*
Richard Portman *(Sec & Dir-Corp Svcs)*
Board of Directors:
Peter Hindley
Andrew Davies
Ishbel Macpherson
Mike McCollum
Alan McWalter
Richard Portman
Steve Whittern
Legal Counsel:
DLA Piper UK LLP
Victoria Square House
Birmingham, United Kingdom

Subsidiaries:

Advance Planning Limited (1)
4 King Edwards Ct King Edwards Sq
Sutton Coldfield, West Midlands, B73 6AP, United Kingdom
Tel.: (44) 1213215592
Fax: (44) 1213215643
Emp.: 25
Funeral Insurance Services
S.I.C.: 6399
N.A.I.C.S.: 524128
Steve Wallis *(Mgr)*

Dignity Crematoria Limited (1)
Westhampnett Rd
Chichester, West Sussex, PO19 7UH, United Kingdom
Tel.: (44) 1243 536 267
Fax: (44) 1243 536 267
Crematories
S.I.C.: 7261
N.A.I.C.S.: 812220

Dignity Funerals Limited (1)
Harrowby Rd
Grantham, Lincolnshire, NG31 9DT, United Kingdom
Tel.: (44) 1476590905
Fax: (44) 1213213762
Toll Free: 8004561047
E-Mail: grantham.crematorium@dignityuk.co.uk
Web Site: www.dignityfunerals.co.uk
Emp.: 10
Funeral Services
S.I.C.: 7261
N.A.I.C.S.: 812210
Delia Bachelor *(Mgr)*

Dignity Pre Arrangement Limited (1)
4 King Edwards Square
Sutton Coldfield, W Midlands, B73 6AP, United Kingdom
Tel.: (44) 1213215272
Fax: (44) 1213555559
E-Mail: stevewallis@dignityuk.co.uk
Web Site: www.dignityfuneralplans.co.uk/funeralplans/contact.jsp
Funeral Services
S.I.C.: 7261
N.A.I.C.S.: 812210
Steve Wallis *(Gen Mgr)*

Dignity Securities Limited (1)
4 King Edward Square
Sutton Coldfield, West Midlands, B73 6AP, United Kingdom
Tel.: (44) 1213541557
Funeral Services
S.I.C.: 7261
N.A.I.C.S.: 812210

Non-U.S. Subsidiary:

Pitcher and Le Quesne Limited (1)
59 Kensington Pl
Saint Helier, Jersey
Tel.: (44) 1534733330
Fax: (44) 1534780708
E-Mail: pitcherandlequesnefd@dignityuk.co.uk
Web Site: www.dignityuk.co.uk
Emp.: 10
Funeral Services
S.I.C.: 7261
N.A.I.C.S.: 812210
Paul Battrick *(Mng Dir)*

DIHAG AG

Altendorfer Strasse 44
D-45127 Essen, Germany
Tel.: (49) 201872450
Fax: (49) 2018724533
E-Mail: info@dihag.com
Web Site: www.dihag.com
Rev.: $240,996,243
Emp.: 1,208
Business Description:
Cast Iron & Steel Supply Services
S.I.C.: 5051
N.A.I.C.S.: 423510
Personnel:
Ralf Schmitz *(Chm)*
Board of Directors:
Ralf Schmitz
Matthias Pampus-Meder
Wilfried Pfaffe
Herbert Werner

DIJET INDUSTRIAL CO., LTD

2-1-18 Kami-Higashi
Hirano-ku, Osaka, 547-0002, Japan
Tel.: (81) 6 6791 6781
Fax: (81) 6 6793 1221
Web Site: www.dijet.co.jp
Year Founded: 1938
6138—(TKS)
Sales Range: $100-124.9 Million
Emp.: 577
Business Description:
Carbide Tool Mfr
S.I.C.: 3541
N.A.I.C.S.: 333517
Personnel:
Ayumu Ikezumi *(Pres)*

DIL LTD.

DIL Complex Ghodbunder Road
Majiwada, Thane, 400610, India
Tel.: (91) 22679808888
Fax: (91) 2267980899
E-Mail: contact@dil.net
Web Site: www.dil.net
Year Founded: 1951
506414—(BOM)
Rev.: $21,941,163
Assets: $41,843,371
Liabilities: $14,492,811
Net Worth: $27,350,560
Earnings: $771,097
Emp.: 215
Fiscal Year-end: 03/31/13
Business Description:
Organic Chemical Mfrs
S.I.C.: 2899
N.A.I.C.S.: 325199
Personnel:
Krishna Datla *(Mng Dir)*
K. H. Kashid *(CFO)*
Srikant N. Sharma *(Compliance Officer & Sec)*
Board of Directors:
G. G. Desai
Sanjay Buch
Krishna Datla
Rajeshwari Datla
Vinayak Hajare
Satish Varma
Transfer Agent:
Link Intime India Private Limited
C-13 Pannalal Silk Mills Compound L.B.S. Marg Bhandup
Mumbai, India

DILLI INCORPORATED

(d/b/a Digital Illustrate)
542-2 Dongducheon-Dong
Dongducheon, Kyunggi-do, 483-080, Korea (South)
Tel.: (82) 31 8605500
Fax: (82) 31 8605590
E-Mail: dilli@dilli.co.kr
Web Site: www.dilli.co.kr
Year Founded: 1975
131180—(KRS)
Sales Range: $10-24.9 Million
Emp.: 70
Business Description:
Printers, Printing Ink & Drawing Instruments Mfr
S.I.C.: 3555
N.A.I.C.S.: 333244
Personnel:
Geon Soo Choi *(Pres)*

DILLISTONE GROUP PLC

50-52 Paul Street
London, EC2A 4LB, United Kingdom
Tel.: (44) 2077496100
Fax: (44) 2077296108
E-Mail: info@dillistonegroup.com
Web Site: www.dillistone.com
DSG—(AIM)
Rev.: $11,137,153
Assets: $14,343,112
Liabilities: $7,277,368
Net Worth: $7,065,743
Earnings: $1,950,423
Emp.: 85
Fiscal Year-end: 12/31/12
Business Description:
Developer of Recruitment Software
S.I.C.: 7372
N.A.I.C.S.: 511210
Personnel:
Jason S. Starr *(CEO)*
Julie P. Pomeroy *(Sec & Dir-Fin)*
Board of Directors:
Mike D. Love
Giles Fearnley
Rory Howard
Alex D. James
Alistair F. Milne
Julie P. Pomeroy
Jason S. Starr
Legal Counsel:
Ashfords LLP
Tower Wharf,Cheese Lane
Bristol, United Kingdom

Subsidiary:

Dillistone Solutions Limited (1)
50-52 Paul St 3rd Fl
London, EC2A 4LB, United Kingdom
Tel.: (44) 2077496100
Computer Software Support Services
S.I.C.: 7371
N.A.I.C.S.: 541511

U.S. Subsidiary:

Dillistone Systems (US) Inc. (1)
50 Harrison St Ste 201A
Hoboken, NJ 07030
Tel.: (201) 653-0013
Fax: (201) 221-7518
Emp.: 6
Computer Software Support Services
S.I.C.: 7371
N.A.I.C.S.: 541511
Jason Starr *(Pres)*

Non-U.S. Subsidiary:

Dillistone Systems (Australia) Pty. Limited (1)
Level 14 309 Kent St
Sydney, New South Wales, 2000, Australia
Tel.: (61) 282218860
Fax: (61) 282125818
E-Mail: sales@dillistone.com
Emp.: 10
Computer Software Support Services
S.I.C.: 7371
N.A.I.C.S.: 541511

DIMARK LTD

(d/b/a Garden Foods)
Unit D1 Stonehill Business Park
Harbet Road, London, N18 3Qp, United Kingdom
Tel.: (44) 8700 61 66 61
Fax: (44) 208 887 9686
E-Mail: info@dimarkltd.co.uk
Web Site: www.gardenfoods.co.uk
Sales Range: $1-9.9 Million
Emp.: 20
Business Description:
Polish & Eastern European Food & Drink Distr
S.I.C.: 5149
N.A.I.C.S.: 424490
Personnel:
Ali Caktu *(Mng Dir)*

DIMCO PLC

47 Kennedy Av
1076 Nicosia, Cyprus
Tel.: (357) 22 446565
Fax: (357) 22 497192
E-Mail: one@1-light.eu
Web Site: www.1-light.eu
Year Founded: 1966
DES—(CYP)
Emp.: 110
Business Description:
Lighting Products Mfr
S.I.C.: 3646
N.A.I.C.S.: 335122
Personnel:
Michalakis Demetriou *(Chm)*
Panayiotis Demetriou *(Gen Dir)*
Board of Directors:
Michalakis Demetriou
Alexis Demetriou
Marios Demetriou
Panayiotis Demetriou

DIMED S.A. DISTRIBUIDORA DE MEDICAMENTOS

R Gomes Jardim 253 - 2 Floor
90620130 Porto Alegre, RS, Brazil
Tel.: (55) 51 3218 9500
Fax: (55) 51 3218 9598
E-Mail: dimed@dimed.com.br
Web Site: www.dimed.com.br
Year Founded: 1968
PNVL3—(BRAZ)
Sales Range: $600-649.9 Million
Emp.: 4,494
Business Description:
Drug Whslr
S.I.C.: 5122
N.A.I.C.S.: 424210
Personnel:
Roberto Coimbra Santos *(Dir-IR)*

DIMENSIONS JORDAN & EMIRATES COMMERCIAL INVESTMENTS CORPORATION

Mecca Street Abu Al Dahab Building
5th Floor
PO Box 2412
Amman, 11821, Jordan
Tel.: (962) 6 581 0196
Fax: (962) 6 581 2936
E-Mail: info@dimensions-inv.com
Web Site: www.dimensions-inv.com
Year Founded: 2007
JEDI—(AMM)
Rev.: $16,642
Assets: $12,362,419
Liabilities: $110,445
Net Worth: $12,251,974
Earnings: ($307,494)
Emp.: 8
Fiscal Year-end: 12/31/12
Business Description:
Investment Management Services
S.I.C.: 6211
N.A.I.C.S.: 523999
Personnel:
Bassam Obaid *(Chm)*
Imad Y. Abdel Hadi *(Deputy Chm & CEO)*
Board of Directors:
Bassam Obaid
Abdel Muttaleb F. Abu Hejleh
Mohammed Omar Ali Binhaider
Imad Y. Abdel Hadi
Hakam Mahmoud Khalil
Mohammad A. Quraan
Jamal Saad

DIMERCO EXPRESS (TAIWAN) CORPORATION

11/12 F No 160 Min Chuan East Road Sec 6
Taipei, Taiwan
Tel.: (886) 227963660
Fax: (886) 227927052
E-Mail: joey_chou@dimerco.com

Dimerco Express (Taiwan) Corporation—(Continued)

Web Site: www.dimerco.com
5609—(TAI)
Rev.: $510,290,000
Assets: $118,930,000
Liabilities: $55,290,000
Net Worth: $63,640,000
Earnings: $473,000,000
Fiscal Year-end: 12/31/12
Business Description:
Freight Transportation Services
S.I.C.: 4731
N.A.I.C.S.: 488510
Personnel:
Paul Chien *(Chm & CEO)*
Edward Lin *(COO)*
Board of Directors:
Paul Chien
Roy Chen
Dionisio Lee
Edward Lin
Jack Ruan
Robert Yang
Supervisory Board of Directors:
John Hah
Mathew Ho
Joe Jwu
Transfer Agent:
YuanTa Securities Co., Ltd.
B1F No 210 Sec 3 Chengde Rd
Taipei, Taiwan

Subsidiaries:

Dimerco Express (Taiwan) Corporation **(1)**
No 52 Ln 90
Chung Hwa N Rd Sec 2, T'ainan, 704, Taiwan (100%)
Tel.: (886) 62502942
Fax: (886) 62502944
Web Site: www.dimerco.com
Arrangement of Freight Transportation
S.I.C.: 4731
N.A.I.C.S.: 488510

Dimerco Express (Taiwan) Corporation **(1)**
7F No 38 Tai Yuen St Chupei
Hsien, Hsin-chu, 302, Taiwan (100%)
Tel.: (886) 35600608
Fax: (886) 35600667
E-Mail: Andy_Cheng@dimerco.com
Web Site: www.dimerco.com
Emp.: 9
Arrangement of Freight Transportation
S.I.C.: 4731
N.A.I.C.S.: 488510
Peggy Chu *(Branch Mgr)*

Dimerco Express (Taiwan) Corporation **(1)**
Rm 506 5F No 306 Sec 1 Wen Hsing Rd
Taichung, 408, Taiwan (100%)
Tel.: (886) 423196721
Fax: (886) 423196724
E-Mail: amy_hung@dimerco.com
Web Site: www.dimerco.com
Emp.: 1,947
Arrangement of Freight Transportation
S.I.C.: 4731
N.A.I.C.S.: 488510

Dimerco Express (Taiwan) Corporation **(1)**
10F 4 No 412 Chung Shan 2nd Rd
Kaohsiung, 802, Taiwan (100%)
Tel.: (886) 73350078
Fax: (886) 73327877
Web Site: www.dimerco.com
Emp.: 15
Arrangement of Freight Transportation
S.I.C.: 4731
N.A.I.C.S.: 488510

Diversified Freight System Corporation **(1)**
11th Fl 1 160 Sec 6
Nin Chuan E Rd, Taipei, 114, Taiwan (100%)
Tel.: (886) 227916455
Fax: (886) 227940698
E-Mail: info@dimerco.com
Web Site: www.dimerco.com
Emp.: 24
Arrangement of Freight Transportation
S.I.C.: 4731
N.A.I.C.S.: 488510
Kimber Lee *(Gen Mgr)*

U.S. Subsidiary:

Dimerco Express USA Corp. **(1)**
430 W Merrick Rd Ste 1
Valley Stream, NY 11580 (100%)
Tel.: (516) 708-4500
Fax: (516) 872-8550
Web Site: www.dimerco.com
Emp.: 7
Freight Transportation Arrangement Import Export
S.I.C.: 4731
N.A.I.C.S.: 488510
Mickle Shea *(Gen Mgr)*

DIMET (SIAM) PUBLIC COMPANY LIMITED

602 Moo 2 Bangpoo Industrial Estate
Bangpoomai Muang, Samut Prakan, 10280, Thailand
Tel.: (66) 2 323 2800
Fax: (66) 2 323 2807
E-Mail: contact@dimetsiam.com
Web Site: www.dimetsiam.com
Year Founded: 1982
DIMET—(THA)
Sales Range: $10-24.9 Million
Business Description:
Coating Product Mfr
S.I.C.: 2851
N.A.I.C.S.: 325510
Personnel:
Suraphol Rujikarnchana *(Chm)*
Saovaluck Chokearpornchai *(Vice Chm)*
Jarintorn Udompipat *(Sec)*
Board of Directors:
Suraphol Rujikarnchana
Chatchaval Asavakanoksilp
Krairit Boonyakiat
Sayomporn Buapoom
Achara Chandrachai
Saovaluck Chokearpornchai
Tumnong Dasri
Achara Momin
Vudichai Neeranartvong
Chokchai Niamratana

DIMOS

648 rue du Tertre
BP 80029
44151 Ancenis, Cedex, France
Tel.: (33) 240832501
Fax: (33) 240832575
E-Mail: world@dimos.fr
Web Site: www.dimos.fr
Sls.: $20,400,000
Emp.: 62
Business Description:
Professional Equipment
S.I.C.: 5049
N.A.I.C.S.: 423490
Personnel:
Michel Goubaud *(Chm)*

DIMUS PARTNERS, INC.

(See Under China Xibolun Technology Holdings Corporation)

DIN TEXTILE MILLS LTD.

35-A/1 Lalazar Area Opp Beach Luxury Hotel
PO Box 4696
Karachi, 74000, Pakistan
Tel.: (92) 21 3561 0001
Fax: (92) 21 3561 0009
E-Mail: textile@dingroup.com
Web Site: www.dingroup.com.pk
Year Founded: 1987
DINT—(KAR)
Sls.: $84,153,688
Assets: $64,588,671
Liabilities: $42,245,603
Net Worth: $22,343,069
Earnings: $6,473,347
Emp.: 3,066
Fiscal Year-end: 06/30/13
Business Description:
Knitting & Weaving Yarn Mfr
S.I.C.: 2299
N.A.I.C.S.: 313110
Personnel:
Mohammad Tanveer *(CEO)*
Shaukat Hussain Ch. *(CFO)*
Islam Ahmed *(Sec)*
Board of Directors:
Shaikh Mohammad Muneer
Faisal Jawed
Farhad Shaikh Mohammad
Shaikh Mohammad Naveed
Shaikh Mohammad Pervez
Mohammad Tanveer
Abdul Razzak Tarmuhammad

Subsidiary:

Din Leather(Pvt) Ltd. **(1)**
Din House 35-A/1 Lalazar Area
Opp Beach Luxury Hotel
PO Box No 4696, Karachi, 74000, Pakistan
Tel.: (92) 21 561 0001
Fax: (92) 21 561 0455
E-Mail: dingroup@dingroup.com
Web Site: www.dingroup.com
Sales Range: $50-74.9 Million
Emp.: 600
Leather Mfr
S.I.C.: 2389
N.A.I.C.S.: 315280
Shaikh Mohammad Muneer *(Chm & CEO)*
Islam Ahmed *(Sec)*

DINAMIA CAPITAL PRIVADO, SOCIEDAD DE CAPITAL RIESGO S.A.

Padilla 17 4th
28006 Madrid, Spain
Tel.: (34) 917458484
Fax: (34) 914313812
E-Mail: infodinamia@dinamia.es
Web Site: www.dinamia.es
Year Founded: 1997
DIN—(MAD)
Sales Range: $10-24.9 Million
Emp.: 2,000
Business Description:
Private Equity Investment Services
S.I.C.: 6211
N.A.I.C.S.: 523999
Personnel:
Santiago Bergareche Busquet *(Chm)*
Joaquin Garcia-Quiros Rodriguez *(Vice Chm)*
Luis de Carlos Bertran *(Sec)*
Marta Rios Estrella *(Vice Sec)*
Board of Directors:
Santiago Bergareche Busquet
Francisco Tomas Bellido
Emilio Carvajal y Ballester
Juan Arena de la Mora
Rafael Jimenez Lopez
Jose Javier Carretero Manzano
Joaquin Garcia-Quiros Rodriguez
Juan Oderiz San Martin
Alfred Merton Vinton

DINAMO CORP.

35 Frensham Walk Farnham Common
Slough, Buckinghamshire, SL2 3QF, United Kingdom
Tel.: (44) 161 2983401
E-Mail: dinamocorp@gmail.com
Year Founded: 2013
Business Description:
Redemption Machine Distr
S.I.C.: 7993
N.A.I.C.S.: 713120
Personnel:
Jolanta Gajdzis *(Pres & Treas)*
Board of Directors:
Jolanta Gajdzis

DINE S.A.B. DE C.V.

Paseo de los Tamarindos 400 B piso 29
Bosques de las Lomas, 05120
Mexico, Mexico
Tel.: (52) 5552618282
Fax: (52) 5552618096
E-Mail: ir@dine.com.mx
Web Site: www.dine.com.mx
DINEB—(MEX)
Sales Range: $50-74.9 Million
Business Description:
Construction & Property Development Services
S.I.C.: 1531
N.A.I.C.S.: 236117
Personnel:
Fernando Senderos Mestre *(Chm)*
Andres Banos Samblancat *(CEO)*
Eduardo Philibert Garza *(Dir-Fin & Admin)*
Alfonso Pasquel Barcenas *(COO)*
Board of Directors:
Fernando Senderos Mestre
Ruben Aguilar Monteverde
Alberto Bailleres Gonzalez
Andres Banos Samblancat
Jose Manuel Canal Hernando
Valentin Diez Morodo
Federico Fernandez Senderos
Carlos Gomez y Gomez
Juan Marco Gutierrez Wanless
Prudencio Lopez Martinez
Victor Rivero Martin
Ernesto Vega Velasco

DINEEN CONSTRUCTION CORPORATION

70 Disco Road Suite 300
Toronto, ON, M9W 1L9, Canada
Tel.: (416) 675-7676
Fax: (416) 675-6987
Web Site: www.dineen.com
Year Founded: 1927
Rev.: $18,258,440
Emp.: 75
Business Description:
General Building Construction Services
S.I.C.: 1542
N.A.I.C.S.: 236220
Personnel:
Peter J. Clarke *(Pres & CEO)*
Paul G. Clarke *(Corp Sec)*
William E. Love *(Exec VP)*

DINEOUT SA LTD.

145-157 St. John St
London, EC1V 4PY, United Kingdom
Tel.: (44) 2032952050
Fax: (44) 7043662463
E-Mail: dineoutsa@gmail.com
Web Site: www.dineoutsa.com
DOGD—(DEU)
Sales Range: $10-24.9 Million
Emp.: 3
Business Description:
Franchise Restaurant Owner & Operator
S.I.C.: 5812
N.A.I.C.S.: 722511
Personnel:
Michael D. Pruitt *(Pres & CEO)*
Spencer Shaw *(Mng Dir)*
Board of Directors:
Paul I. Moskowitz
Michael D. Pruitt

DINGLI COMMUNICATIONS CORP. LTD.
8 The Fifth Technology Road
Gangwan Avenue
Zhuhai, 519085, China
Tel.: (86) 756 3391933
Fax: (86) 756 3391900
E-Mail: ir@dinglicom.com
Web Site: www.dinglicom.com
300050—(CHIN)
Sales Range: $25-49.9 Million
Emp.: 400
Business Description:
Wireless Communication Network Optimization Testing Systems & Software Mfr
S.I.C.: 3669
N.A.I.C.S.: 334290
Personnel:
Joe Yun Wang *(Chm & CEO)*
Eric Ye *(Mng Dir-Overseas Sls & Mktg)*

DINGWALL FORD SALES
Highway 17 East
Kenora, ON, P9N3X3, Canada
Tel.: (807) 468-6443
Fax: (807) 468-4259
Toll Free: (877) 515-3673
E-Mail: info@dingwallford.com
Web Site: www.dingwallford.com
Rev.: $29,039,613
Emp.: 60
Business Description:
New & Used Car Dealers
S.I.C.: 5511
N.A.I.C.S.: 441110
Personnel:
George Krisko *(Office Mgr)*

DINGYI GROUP INVESTMENT LIMITED
Units 2703-06 27/F Convention Plaza-Office Tower 1 Harbour Road
Wanchai, China (Hong Kong)
Tel.: (852) 2845 5188
Fax: (852) 2824 3188
E-Mail: info@dingyi.hk
Web Site: www.dingyi.hk
Year Founded: 1970
0508—(HKG)
Rev.: $8,645,840
Assets: $35,448,871
Liabilities: $10,920,904
Net Worth: $24,527,966
Earnings: ($4,024,916)
Emp.: 77
Fiscal Year-end: 03/31/13
Business Description:
Holding Company; Restaurant & Food Kiosk Owner & Operator
S.I.C.: 6719
N.A.I.C.S.: 551112
Personnel:
Kwong Yuk Li *(Chm)*
Xiaonong Su *(CEO)*
Sze Ming Cheung *(CFO)*
Lavender Tsz Sai Man *(Sec)*
Board of Directors:
Kwong Yuk Li
Sze Ming Cheung
Xiusheng Cheung
Shiu Ki Chow
Xiaonong Su
Dongsheng Sun
Butterfield Fulcrum Group (Bermuda) Limited
26 Burnaby Street
Hamilton, HM 11, Bermuda
Transfer Agents:
Tricor Standard Limited
26/F Tesbury Centre 28 Queens Road East
Hong Kong, China (Hong Kong)
Butterfield Fulcrum Group (Bermuda) Limited
26 Burnaby Street
Hamilton, HM 11, Bermuda

DINO ENERGY CORPORATION
(Formerly Gysan Holdings, Inc.)
Unit 7 833 1st Avenue NW
Calgary, AB, T2N 0A4, Canada
Tel.: (403) 229-2351
DINO—(OTC OTCB)
Assets: $5,585
Liabilities: $486,329
Net Worth: ($480,744)
Earnings: ($427,769)
Fiscal Year-end: 10/31/13
Business Description:
Investment Services
S.I.C.: 6211
N.A.I.C.S.: 523999
Personnel:
Eric David Lawson *(Pres & CEO)*
Vanleo Y.W. Fung *(CFO, Treas & Sec)*
Board of Directors:
Solomon Auyeung
Vanleo Y.W. Fung
Eric David Lawson
Trent Sittler
Transfer Agent:
Action Stock Transfer Corp.
2469 E Fort Union Blvd Ste 214
Salt Lake City, UT 84121

DIO CORPORATION
66 W Sentum Road
Haeundae-gu, Busan, Korea (South)
Tel.: (82) 51 745 7777
Fax: (82) 51 745 7778
E-Mail: dio@dio.co.kr
Web Site: www.dio.co.kr
039840—(KRS)
Business Description:
Medical Instrument Mfr & Whslr
S.I.C.: 3843
N.A.I.C.S.: 339114
Personnel:
J. C. Kim *(CEO)*

DIOKI D.D.
Zitnjak Bb
10000 Zagreb, Croatia
Tel.: (385) 12483000
Fax: (385) 12407364
E-Mail: dioki@dioki.hr
Web Site: www.dioki.hr
Year Founded: 1995
Emp.: 540
Business Description:
Organic Petrochemicals
S.I.C.: 2869
N.A.I.C.S.: 325110
Personnel:
Zdenko Belosevic *(Pres)*
Board of Directors:
Leo Dolezil

DION GLOBAL SOLUTIONS LIMITED
A-3/4/5 4th Floor GYS Global Tower-A Sector-125
Noida, Uttar Pradesh, 201301, India
Tel.: (91) 120 6172065
E-Mail: connect@dionglobal.com
Web Site: www.dionglobal.com
526927—(BOM)
Rev.: $48,325,584
Assets: $112,832,893
Liabilities: $66,736,564
Net Worth: $46,096,329
Earnings: ($4,488,092)
Emp.: 600
Fiscal Year-end: 03/31/13
Business Description:
Financial Services
S.I.C.: 6099
N.A.I.C.S.: 522320
Personnel:
Ralph James Horne *(CEO & Mng Dir)*
Tanmaya Das *(CFO)*
Tarun Rastogi *(Compliance Officer, Sec & VP)*
Board of Directors:
Malvinder Mohan Singh
Padam Bahl
Maninder Singh Grewal
C. P. Gurnani
Ralph James Horne
Preetinder Singh Joshi
Shachindra Nath
Pradeep Ratilal Raniga
Vikram Sahgal
Rama Krishna Shetty
Transfer Agent:
Karvy Computershare Private Limited
Plot No 17 to 24 Vittalrao Nagar Madhapur
Hyderabad, India

Non-U.S. Subsidiaries:

Consort Securities Systems Limited **(1)**
5 Granville Road
Leicester, LE1 7RU, United Kingdom
Tel.: (44) 1162335050
Fax: (44) 1162550822
Software Development Services
S.I.C.: 7371
N.A.I.C.S.: 541511

Dion Global Solutions (Asia Pacific) Pty Ltd. **(1)**
Level 1 55 Southbank Boulevard
Southbank, VIC, 3006, Australia
Tel.: (61) 3 9674 9900
Fax: (61) 3 9674 9901
Emp.: 30
Software Development Services
S.I.C.: 7371
N.A.I.C.S.: 541511
Rudi Pecker *(Mng Dir)*

Dion Global Solutions Gmbh **(1)**
Holzhausenstrasse 44
60322 Frankfurt am Main, Germany
Tel.: (49) 69 50 952 0
Fax: (49) 69 50 952 333
E-Mail: connect.de@dionglobal.com
Web Site: www.dionglobal.com
Banking Software Development Services
S.I.C.: 7371
N.A.I.C.S.: 541511
Jurgen Dahmen *(Mng Dir)*
Ralph James Horne *(Mng Dir)*
Joseph Nash *(Mng Dir)*
Andreas Wagner *(Mng Dir)*

Dion Global Solutions (NZ) Ltd. **(1)**
Level 7 214 Queen Street
Auckland, 1010, New Zealand
Tel.: (64) 9 309 3988
Fax: (64) 9 309 6288
Software Development Services
S.I.C.: 7379
N.A.I.C.S.: 541519
Rudi Pecker *(Mng Dir)*

DIONIC INDUSTRIAL & TRADING S.A
95 Aristotelous Str
13674 Acharnes, Greece
Tel.: (30) 210 2419600
Fax: (30) 210 2404510
E-Mail: info@dionic.gr
Web Site: www.dionicgroup.com
Year Founded: 1995
DION—(ATH)
Sales Range: $75-99.9 Million
Emp.: 465
Business Description:
Consumer Product Distr
S.I.C.: 5137
N.A.I.C.S.: 424330
Personnel:
Thomas Roumpas *(Chm)*
Dimosthenis Vatikiotis *(Mng Dir)*
Board of Directors:
Thomas Roumpas
Christos Bizoumis
Venetis Ioannis
Alexandros Lavranos
Pantelis Pastianidis
Konstantinos Theotokas
Dimosthenis Vatikiotis

DIOS EXPLORATION INC.
Marie-Jose Girard Pres 1000 St Antoine Street W Suite 711
Montreal, QC, H3C 3R7, Canada
Tel.: (514) 483-5149
Fax: (514) 510-7964
Web Site: www.diosexplo.com
DOS—(TSXV)
Rev.: $25,290
Assets: $10,366,269
Liabilities: $151,120
Net Worth: $10,215,149
Earnings: ($445,986)
Fiscal Year-end: 12/31/12
Business Description:
Mineral Exploration Services
S.I.C.: 1081
N.A.I.C.S.: 213114
Personnel:
Marie-Jose Girard *(Pres & CEO)*
Rene Lacroix *(CFO)*
Board of Directors:
Harold Desbiens
Marie-Jose Girard
Rene Lacroix
Aline Leclerc
Normand Payette
Transfer Agent:
Equity Transfer & Trust Company
200 University Avenue Ste 400
Toronto, ON, M5H 4H1, Canada
Tel.: (416) 361-0152
Fax: (416) 361-0470

DIOTEK CO., LTD.
14th FL Baeksang Star Tower 1
Gasan-dong 60-17
Geumcheon-gu, Seoul, Korea (South)
Tel.: (82) 263336999
Fax: (82) 263336888
Web Site: www.diotek.com
Year Founded: 1999
108860—(KRS)
Emp.: 140
Business Description:
Software Development Services
S.I.C.: 7371
N.A.I.C.S.: 541511
Personnel:
Jeong In Doh *(CEO)*

DIP CORPORATION
32nd Floor Izumi Garden Tower 1-6-1 Roppongi
Minato-ku, Tokyo, 106-6032, Japan
Tel.: (81) 3 5114 1177
Fax: (81) 3 5114 1182
E-Mail: info@dip-net.co.jp
Web Site: www.dip-net.co.jp
Year Founded: 1997
2379—(TKS)
Sls.: $100,565,630
Assets: $64,132,332
Liabilities: $26,079,702
Net Worth: $38,052,630
Earnings: $678,546
Emp.: 730
Fiscal Year-end: 02/28/13
Business Description:
Online Job Portal Services
S.I.C.: 2741
N.A.I.C.S.: 519130

Dip Corporation—(Continued)

Personnel:
Hideki Tomita *(Pres & CEO)*
Board of Directors:
Katsunori Fujimoto
Kazuhisa Iwata
Kenichi Kito
Tsuneyo Ohtomo
Hidekazu Suzuki
Katsumi Ueki

DIPL. ING. K. DIETZEL GMBH

Windmuhlenstrasse 6
04626 Beerwalde, Germany
Tel.: (49) 366021400
Fax: (49) 3660234727
E-Mail: info@dietzel-hydraulik.de
Web Site: www.dietzel-hydraulik.de
Rev.: $12,690,480
Emp.: 300
Business Description:
Pipe Fitting Equipment Mfr
S.I.C.: 3498
N.A.I.C.S.: 332996
Personnel:
Uwe Hassler *(Co-Mng Dir)*
Bertram Wossner *(Co-Mng Dir)*

DIPLOMA GROUP LIMITED

First Floor 140 Abernethy Road
Belmont, WA, 6104, Australia
Tel.: (61) 894753500
Fax: (61) 894753501
E-Mail: info@diploma.com.au
Web Site: www.diploma.com.au
DGX—(ASX)
Rev.: $170,293,729
Assets: $78,031,406
Liabilities: $74,588,308
Net Worth: $3,443,098
Earnings: $1,618,381
Emp.: 100
Fiscal Year-end: 06/30/13
Business Description:
Construction & Property Development
S.I.C.: 1442
N.A.I.C.S.: 212321
Personnel:
Nick D. Di Latte *(CEO & Mng Dir)*
Simon A. Oaten *(CFO & Sec)*
Board of Directors:
Ian Peter Olson
Nick D. Di Latte
Carl Lancaster

Subsidiary:

Diploma Properties Pty. Ltd. (1)
PO Box 91
Belmont, Western Australia, 6984, Australia
Tel.: (61) 892213674
Fax: (61) 894783133
E-Mail: sales@allegrorealty.com.au
Web Site: www.diplomaproperties.com.au
Emp.: 160
Luxury Apartments Construction Services
S.I.C.: 1522
N.A.I.C.S.: 236116

DIPLOMA PLC

12 Charterhouse Square
London, EC1M 6AX, United Kingdom
Tel.: (44) 2075495700
Fax: (44) 2075495715
E-Mail: investors@diplomaplc.com
Web Site: www.diplomaplc.com
DPLM—(LSE)
Rev.: $474,341,120
Assets: $384,623,360
Liabilities: $88,388,608
Net Worth: $296,234,752
Earnings: $57,818,112
Emp.: 1,159
Fiscal Year-end: 09/30/13
Business Description:
Hydraulic Seal & Cylinder Components; Consumable Laboratory Items & Instrumentation; Wiring, Connectors & Heat-Shrink Fit Components
S.I.C.: 3593
N.A.I.C.S.: 333995
Personnel:
Bruce M. Thompson *(CEO)*
Iain Henderson *(COO)*
Anthony J. Gallagher *(Sec)*
Board of Directors:
John L. Rennocks
Marie-Louise Clayton
Iain Henderson
Nigel P. Lingwood
John Nicholas
Charles Packshaw
Bruce M. Thompson
Legal Counsel:
Ashurst
Broadwalk House 5 Appold Street
London, United Kingdom
Subsidiaries:

a1-envirosciences Limited (1)
2 Silverton Court Northumberland Business Park
Cramlington, Northumberland, NE23 7RY, United Kingdom
Tel.: (44) 191 5004101
E-Mail: uksales@a1-envirosciences.co.uk
Web Site: www.a1-envirosciences.com
Emp.: 9
Environmental Consulting Services
S.I.C.: 8999
N.A.I.C.S.: 541620
Mark Montague *(Country Mgr)*

Cabletec Interconnect Components Systems Limited (1)
Sunnyside Road
Weston-super-Mare, North Somerset, United Kingdom BS23 3PZ
Tel.: (44) 1934 424900
Fax: (44) 1934 636632
E-Mail: sales@cabletec.com
Web Site: www.cabletec.com
Emp.: 70
Metal Braid & Cables Mfr
S.I.C.: 3499
N.A.I.C.S.: 332999
Karen French *(Mng Dir)*

Clarendon Engineering Supplies Limited (1)
2 Westmead
Swindon, Wiltshire, SN5 7SY, United Kingdom (100%)
Tel.: (44) 1793616700
Fax: (44) 1793644304
E-Mail: sales@clarendoneng.co.uk
Web Site: www.clarendoneng.co.uk
Emp.: 5
Distr of Fasteners, Components & Seals
S.I.C.: 5084
N.A.I.C.S.: 423830
Paul Saunders *(Mgr)*

FPE Limited (1)
2 Kellaw Rd
Yarm Road Industrial Estate, Darlington, Durham, DL1 4YA, United Kingdom (100%)
Tel.: (44) 1325282732
Fax: (44) 1325381815
E-Mail: sales@fpe-ltd.co.uk
Web Site: www.fpe-ltd.co.uk
Emp.: 30
Seals, Seal Kits, Cylinder Parts & Sealants Supplier
S.I.C.: 5084
N.A.I.C.S.: 423830
Philip Kelly *(Mng Dir)*

HA Wainwright (Group) Limited (1)
Wharf Abbey Mill Business Park
Lower Eashing, Godalming, Surrey, GU7 2QN, United Kingdom
Tel.: (44) 1483 869000
Fax: (44) 1483 869001
E-Mail: sales@hawco.co.uk
Web Site: www.hawco.co.uk
Emp.: 70
Electronic Components Distr
S.I.C.: 5084
N.A.I.C.S.: 423830
Gary Bennet *(Mng Dir)*

Hawco Ltd. (1)
The Wharf Abbey Mill Business Park
Lower Eashing, Godalming, Surrey, GU7 2QN, United Kingdom (100%)
Tel.: (44) 1483869000
Fax: (44) 1483869001
E-Mail: sales@hawco.co.uk
Web Site: www.hawco.co.uk
Emp.: 50
Distr of Control Devices Used in Sensing, Measurement & Control of Temperature & Pressure
S.I.C.: 3823
N.A.I.C.S.: 334513
Gary Bennett *(Mng Dir)*

Hitek Limited (1)
Foundry Lane
Horsham, West Sussex, RH13 5PY, United Kingdom
Tel.: (44) 1403 243
Fax: (44) 1403 243536
E-Mail: sales@hitek.co.uk
Web Site: www.hitek.co.uk
Emp.: 10
Instruments Distr & Maintenance Services
S.I.C.: 5084
N.A.I.C.S.: 423830
Solomon Alexander *(Gen Mgr)*

IS Rayfast Limited (1)
2 Westmead
Swindon, Wiltshire, SN5 7SY, United Kingdom (100%)
Tel.: (44) 1793616700
Fax: (44) 1793644304
E-Mail: export@israyfast.com
Web Site: www.israyfast.com
Emp.: 45
Electrical Apparatus & Equipment, Wiring, Interconnect & Fastener Products Distr
S.I.C.: 5063
N.A.I.C.S.: 423610
Karen French *(CEO)*
James Leonard *(Mng Dir)*

U.S. Subsidiaries:

All Seals, Inc. (1)
2110 S Yale St
Santa Ana, CA 92704 CA
Tel.: (714) 556-4931
Fax: (714) 557-3257
Toll Free: (800) 553-5054
E-Mail: sales@allsealsinc.com
Web Site: www.allsealsinc.com
Emp.: 25
Design, Engineering & Distribution of Seals, Packings & Gaskets
S.I.C.: 5085
N.A.I.C.S.: 423840
Jerry Barnett *(Pres)*

Hercules Sealing Products Inc. (1)
1016 N Belcher Rd
Clearwater, FL 33765 (100%)
Tel.: (727) 796-1300
Fax: (727) 797-8849
E-Mail: info@herculesus.com
Web Site: www.herculesus.com
Emp.: 150
Hydraulic & Pneumatic Seals, Seal Kits & Cylinders Distr
S.I.C.: 5084
N.A.I.C.S.: 423830
Andres Echeverri *(Mgr-Intl Sls)*

HKX Inc. (1)
16761 146th St SE Ste 115
Monroe, WA 98272 (100%)
Tel.: (360) 805-8600
Fax: (360) 805-0718
E-Mail: hkx@hkx.com
Web Site: www.hkx.com
Emp.: 40
Supplier of Auxiliary Hydraulic Kits for Excavators
S.I.C.: 5084
N.A.I.C.S.: 423830
Lee Keddie *(Gen Mgr)*

J. Royal Co. Inc. (1)
3720 Stanford Way
Clemmons, NC 27012
Tel.: (336) 794-0400
Fax: (336) 794-0401
Web Site: www.jroyal.com
Sales Range: $10-24.9 Million
Emp.: 25
O-Rings, Industrial Seals & Gaskets Supplier
S.I.C.: 5085
N.A.I.C.S.: 423840
Russel Vroom *(Pres)*

Branch:

J Royal Co. Inc.-Barrington (2)
40 Bay Spring Ave
Barrington, RI 02806
Tel.: (401) 246-0600
Fax: (401) 246-1482
Web Site: www.jroyal.com
Sales Range: $1-9.9 Million
Emp.: 11
O-Rings, Industrial Seals & Gaskets Supplier
S.I.C.: 5085
N.A.I.C.S.: 423840
Russel Vroom *(Pres)*

Non-U.S. Subsidiaries:

a1-envirosciences GmbH (1)
Eichsfelder Str 1
40595 Dusseldorf, Germany
Tel.: (49) 2 11 75 84 83 0
Fax: (49) 2 11 75 84 83 22
E-Mail: sales@a1-envirotech.de
Web Site: www.a1-envirotech.de
Emp.: 2
Environmental Consulting Services
S.I.C.: 8999
N.A.I.C.S.: 541620
Olaf Wolf *(Gen Mgr)*

Big Green Surgical Company Pty Limited (1)
Channel Corporate Centre Unit 1 8 Channel Road
Mayfield, NSW, 2304, Australia
Tel.: (61) 2 4967 6650
Fax: (61) 2 4967 6680
E-Mail: customerservice@biggreen.com.au
Web Site: www.biggreen.com.au
Emp.: 4
Surgical Equipment Supplies & Distr
S.I.C.: 5047
N.A.I.C.S.: 423450
Antony Finlay Bennett *(Mng Dir)*

Carsen Medical Inc. (1)
14-151 Amber Street
Markham, ON, L3R 3B3, Canada
Tel.: (866) 677-4121
Fax: (866) 677-4122
Web Site: www.carsenmedical.com
Emp.: 25
Medical Devices Mfr
S.I.C.: 3845
N.A.I.C.S.: 334510
Michael McGrath *(Gen Mgr)*

Hercules Europe BV (1)
Elftweg 38
4941 VP Raamsdonksveer, Netherlands
Tel.: (31) 162 521422
Fax: (31) 162 522858
E-Mail: info@herculeseu.com
Web Site: www.herculeseu.com
Emp.: 9
Sealing Product Distr
S.I.C.: 5084
N.A.I.C.S.: 423830

M Seals A/S (1)
Bybjergvej 13
3060 Espergaerde, Denmark
Tel.: (45) 49 13 02 05
Fax: (45) 49 13 01 41
E-Mail: sales@m-seals.dk
Web Site: www.m-seals.dk
Emp.: 28
Seal Products Mfr
S.I.C.: 3053
N.A.I.C.S.: 339991
Thomas Petersen *(CEO)*

Sommer GmbH (1)
Kraichgaustrasse 5
73765 Neuhausen, Germany (100%)
Tel.: (49) 7158981270
Fax: (49) 71589812799
E-Mail: info@sommerelectronic.com
Web Site: www.sommerelectronic.com
Emp.: 28

Heatshrink Products, Wire & Wire Associated Accessories Distr
S.I.C.: 5063
N.A.I.C.S.: 423610
Karen French *(Gen Mgr)*

DIRECIONAL ENGENHARIA S.A.

R Grao Para 466
30150-340 Belo Horizonte, MG, Brazil
Tel.: (55) 31 3132 1462
Fax: (55) 31 3132 3546
E-Mail: ri@direcional.com.br
Web Site: www.bmfbovespa.com.br
Year Founded: 1981
DIRR3—(BRAZ)

Business Description:
Real Estate Development & Construction Services
S.I.C.: 6531
N.A.I.C.S.: 531390

Personnel:
Ricardo Valadares Gontijo *(Founder, Chm & CEO)*
Carlos Wollenweber Filho *(CFO & IR Officer)*
Ricardo Ribeiro Valadares Gontijo *(Comml Officer & VP)*
Jose Lucas Dutra Rocha *(Engrg Officer)*

Board of Directors:
Ricardo Valadares Gontijo
Wilson Nelson Brumer
Paulo Nobrega Frade
Ana Lucia Ribeiro Valadares Gontijo
Ricardo Ribeiro Valadares Gontijo
Luiz Andre Rico Vicente

DIRECT HEALTHCARE LTD

(d/b/a Chemist Direct)
Unit 8 Demuth Way
Oldbury, B69 4LT, United Kingdom
Tel.: (44) 121 541 1800
Fax: (44) 1215444740
E-Mail: customercare@chemistdirect.co.uk
Web Site: www.chemistdirect.co.uk
Year Founded: 2007
Sales Range: $1-9.9 Million

Business Description:
Online Pharmaceutical Retailer
S.I.C.: 5961
N.A.I.C.S.: 454111

Personnel:
Mitesh Soma *(CEO)*

DIRECT IT CANADA INC.

675 Cochrane Dr East Tower 6th Floor
Markham, ON, L3R 0B8, Canada
Tel.: (905) 530-2373
Fax: (905) 530-2219
Toll Free: (866) 821-3643
E-Mail: contactus@directitcanada.com
Web Site: www.directitcanada.com
Year Founded: 2001
Sales Range: Less than $1 Million
Emp.: 6

Business Description:
Infrastucture Assets, Planning & Development Management Software
S.I.C.: 7371
N.A.I.C.S.: 541511

Personnel:
George Lykoudis *(Pres, CEO & VP-Tech-Customer Svcs)*

DIRECT LINE INSURANCE GROUP PLC

Churchill Court Westmoreland Road
Bromley, Kent, BR1 1DP, United Kingdom
Tel.: (44) 2083133030
Fax: (44) 2082858846
E-Mail: hrmatters@directlinegroup.co.uk
Web Site: www.directlinegroup.com
Year Founded: 1985
DLG—(LSE OTC)
Rev.: $6,636,966,225
Assets: $20,053,666,491
Liabilities: $15,581,748,927
Net Worth: $4,471,917,564
Earnings: $291,063,147
Emp.: 15,000
Fiscal Year-end: 12/31/12

Business Description:
Insurance Holding Company
S.I.C.: 6719
N.A.I.C.S.: 551112

Personnel:
Michael N. Biggs *(Chm)*
Paul Geddes *(CEO)*
Anthony Jonathan Reizenstein *(CFO)*
Angela Morrison *(CIO)*
Jose Vazquez *(Chief Risk Officer)*
Humphrey Tomlinson *(Gen Counsel & Sec)*

Board of Directors:
Michael N. Biggs
Paul Geddes
Jane Carolyn Hanson
Glyn P. Jones
Andrew William Palmer
Anthony Jonathan Reizenstein
Clare Thompson
Priscilla A. Vacassin
Bruce W. Van Saun

Subsidiaries:

Churchill Insurance Company Limited (1)
Churchill Ct Westmoreland Rd
Bromley, Kent, BR1 1DP, United Kingdom UK
Tel.: (44) 2083133030 (100%)
Fax: (44) 2083135768
E-Mail: enquiries@churchill.com
Web Site: www.churchill.com
Emp.: 3,200
Automobile & Homeowners Insurance
S.I.C.: 6351
N.A.I.C.S.: 524126
Paul Geddes *(CEO)*

Direct Line Insurance plc (1)
Direct Line House 3 Edridge Rd
Croydon, Surrey, CR9 1AG, United Kingdom UK
Tel.: (44) 2086863313 (100%)
Fax: (44) 2086810512
E-Mail: info@directline.com
Web Site: www.directline.com
Emp.: 500
Insurance
S.I.C.: 6399
N.A.I.C.S.: 524128
Chris Moat *(Mng Dir)*

Subsidiary:

Green Flag Limited (2)
The Wharf Neville Street
Leeds, LS1 4AZ, United Kingdom
Tel.: (44) 845 246 2766
Web Site: www.greenflag.com
Breakdown & Roadside Assistance Insurance
S.I.C.: 6411
N.A.I.C.S.: 524298
Mike Bowman *(Mng Dir)*

National Insurance and Guarantee Corporation Limited (1)
Crown House 145 City Road
London, EC1V 1LP, United Kingdom
Tel.: (44) 2076566000
Fax: (44) 2072510345
E-Mail: information@nig-uk.com
Web Site: www.nig-uk.com
Emp.: 400
Vehicle, Home & Business Insurance Products
S.I.C.: 6399
N.A.I.C.S.: 524128
Jonathan Greenwood *(Mng Dir)*

DIRECT NICKEL LIMITED

Level 10 15-17 Young Street
Sydney, NSW, 2000, Australia
Tel.: (61) 2 8014 7780
Fax: (61) 2 8324 6366
E-Mail: info@directnickel.com
Web Site: www.directnickel.com
Year Founded: 2005
DIR—(ASX)
Rev.: $25,047
Assets: $8,228,210
Liabilities: $7,180,899
Net Worth: $1,047,311
Earnings: ($5,678,726)
Fiscal Year-end: 06/30/13

Business Description:
Nickel Extraction Services
S.I.C.: 1021
N.A.I.C.S.: 212234

Personnel:
Vincent Sweeney *(Chm & Sec)*
Russell Debney *(CEO & Mng Dir)*
Richard Carlton *(COO)*
Graham Brock *(CTO, Dir-Technical & Project Mgr)*

Board of Directors:
Vincent Sweeney
Graham Brock
Russell Debney
William Drinkard
Christopher Gower

DIRECT SOURCE SPECIAL PRODUCTS, INC.

2695 Dollard St
La Salle, QC, H8N 2J8, Canada
Tel.: (514) 363-8882
Fax: (514) 368-4555
E-Mail: info@dsspinc.com
Web Site: www.dsspinc.com
Emp.: 15

Business Description:
Compact Disc & DVD Direct Marketing
S.I.C.: 5734
N.A.I.C.S.: 443142

Personnel:
Bill Shannon *(Pres)*

DIRECT WINES LIMITED

New Aquitaine House Exeter Way
Theale, Reading, Berkshire, RG7 4PL, United Kingdom
Tel.: (44) 8704448383
Fax: (44) 8704448182
E-Mail: customerservices@laithwaites.co.uk
Web Site: www.laithwaites.co.uk
Sls.: $492,500,000
Earnings: $13,100,000
Emp.: 891

Business Description:
Wine & Alcoholic Beverages Distr
S.I.C.: 5182
N.A.I.C.S.: 424820

Personnel:
Barbara Laithwaite *(Co-Chm)*
Tony Laithwaite *(Co-Chm)*
Glenn Caton *(Mng Dir)*

Subsidiary:

Virgin Wines Ltd. (1)
St James Mill
Whitefriars, Norwich, NR3 1TN, United Kingdom
Tel.: (44) 8455438864
Fax: (44) 1603619277
E-Mail: help@virginwines.com
Web Site: www.virginwines.com
Online Wine Distr
S.I.C.: 5182
N.A.I.C.S.: 424820
Jay Wright *(Mng Dir)*

DIRECT WONEN N V

Nieuwe Duinweg 24
2501 CV Hague, Netherlands
Tel.: (31) 707115000
Fax: (31) 707115555
E-Mail: info@directwonencorporate.com
Web Site: www.directwonen.nl
Sales Range: $25-49.9 Million
Emp.: 303

Business Description:
Housing & Financial Services
S.I.C.: 6141
N.A.I.C.S.: 522291

Personnel:
Richard Westerhuis *(Chm)*
Yvonne Swaans *(CEO)*
Jan-Peter Duijvestijn *(CFO)*
Ihab el Sayed *(COO)*

Board of Directors:
Richard Westerhuis
Kees Beuving
Jan-Peter Duijvestijn
Ihab el Sayed
Yvonne Swaans

DIRECTCASH PAYMENTS, INC.

Bay 6 1420 - 28th St NE
Calgary, AB, T2A 7W6, Canada
Tel.: (403) 387-2188
Fax: (403) 451-3003
Toll Free: (888) 777-5519
Web Site: www.directcash.net
DCI—(TSX)
Rev.: $190,971,122
Assets: $440,090,427
Liabilities: $297,331,262
Net Worth: $142,759,164
Earnings: $6,290,159
Emp.: 297
Fiscal Year-end: 12/31/12

Business Description:
ATM Services
S.I.C.: 6029
N.A.I.C.S.: 522110

Personnel:
Jeffrey J. Smith *(Pres & CEO)*
Brenda G. Hughes *(CFO & Sec)*
Todd M. Schneider *(COO)*
Joseph Xu *(CTO)*

Board of Directors:
Gary Dundas
Susan M. Gallacher
R. Bradley Hurtubise
Jeffrey J. Smith
Leroy E. Thiessen
Kevin Wolfe

Transfer Agent:
Valiant Trust Company
310 606 4th St SW
Calgary, AB, Canada

Subsidiary:

Threshold Financial Technologies Inc. (1)
3269 American Drive
Mississauga, ON, L4V 1V4, Canada
Tel.: (905) 678-7373
Fax: (905) 678-6800
E-Mail: info@threshold-fti.com
Web Site: www.threshold-fti.com
Electronic Payment Processing Services
S.I.C.: 6099
N.A.I.C.S.: 522320
Matthew McIver *(Pres)*

Non-U.S. Subsidiary:

Customers Limited (1)
Building 2 148 Chesterville Road
Cheltenham, VIC, 3192, Australia
Tel.: (61) 3 9090 4800
Fax: (61) 3 9090 4700
E-Mail: info@customersatm.com.au
Web Site: www.customers.com.au
Sales Range: $125-149.9 Million
Emp.: 140

DirectCash Payments, Inc.—(Continued)

Electronic Payment System Services & Solutions
S.I.C.: 6099
N.A.I.C.S.: 522320
Stephen Allanson *(Gen Mgr-Ops)*

Subsidiary:

Customers ATM Pty Limited **(2)**
87 Corporate Drive
Heatherton, VIC, 3202, Australia
Tel.: (61) 1300305600
Fax: (61) 1300721883
E-Mail: info@dcpayments.com.au
Web Site: www.dcpayments.com.au
Emp.: 70
Automatic Teller Machine Supplier
S.I.C.: 3589
N.A.I.C.S.: 333318

DIRECTEL HOLDINGS LIMITED

Rooms 01 02 14 & 15 37/F Hong Kong Plaza 188 Connaught Road West
Hong Kong, China (Hong Kong)
Tel.: (852) 28599388
Fax: (852) 28599088
E-Mail: info@directel.hk
Web Site: www.directel.hk
8337—(HKG)
Sls.: $9,256,031
Assets: $21,187,259
Liabilities: $1,506,652
Net Worth: $19,680,607
Earnings: $2,853,664
Emp.: 12
Fiscal Year-end: 12/31/12

Business Description:
Mobile Virtual Network Operator
S.I.C.: 4812
N.A.I.C.S.: 517210

Personnel:
Kwok Chau Pang *(CEO & Compliance Officer)*
Wai Ching Chan *(Sec)*

Board of Directors:
Kin Shing Li
Xue Dao Chen
Howard Ho Hwa Chu
Maggie Man Yee Lee
Wang Li
Kwok Chau Pang
Kin Wa Wong

Appleby Trust (Cayman) Ltd.
Clifton House 75 Fort Street
PO Box 1350
Grand Cayman, Cayman Islands

Transfer Agents:
Tricor Investor Services Limited
26th Floor Tesbury Centre 28 Queens Road East
Wanchai, China (Hong Kong)

Appleby Trust (Cayman) Ltd.
Clifton House 75 Fort Street
PO Box 1350
Grand Cayman, Cayman Islands

DIRECTI GROUP

Directiplex Next to Adheri Subway
Old Nagardas Road
Adheri East, Mumbai, Maharashtra, 400069, India
Tel.: (91) 22 30797500
Fax: (91) 22 30797508
Web Site: www.directi.com
Year Founded: 1998
Sales Range: $350-399.9 Million
Emp.: 1,000

Business Description:
Internet Solutions
S.I.C.: 2741
N.A.I.C.S.: 519130

Personnel:
Divyank Turakhia *(Co-Founder & Pres)*
Bhavin Turakhia *(Co-Founder & CEO)*

DIRHAM CONSTRUCTION LTD

PO Box 351
Grande Prairie, AB, T8V 3A5, Canada
Tel.: (780) 532-4094
Fax: (780) 532-9733
Web Site: www.dirhamhomes.com
Year Founded: 1976
Rev.: $34,271,882
Emp.: 41

Business Description:
Home Building Contractors
S.I.C.: 1522
N.A.I.C.S.: 236116

Personnel:
Henry Hamm *(Pres)*

DIRTT ENVIRONMENTAL SOLUTIONS LTD.

7303 30th Street Southeast
Calgary, AB, T2C 1N6, Canada
Tel.: (403) 723-5000
Fax: (403) 723-6644
E-Mail: ir@dirtt.net
Web Site: www.dirtt.net
Year Founded: 2012
DRT—(TSX)

Business Description:
Environmental Software; Interior Construction Services
S.I.C.: 7372
N.A.I.C.S.: 511210

Personnel:
Steve Parry *(Chm)*
Scott Jenkins *(Pres)*
Mogens Smed *(CEO)*
Derek Payne *(CFO & Sec)*
Tracy Baker *(COO)*

Board of Directors:
Steve Parry
Gregory Burke
Lawrence D. Fairholm
Rowland Fleming
James A. Gosling
Scott Jenkins
Christine McGinley
Diana Propper de Callejon
Mogens Smed

DISA INDIA LTD

5th Floor Kushal Garden Arcade 1A
Peenya Industrial Area
Peenya II Phase, Bengaluru, Karnataka, 560058, India
Tel.: (91) 8040201400
Fax: (91) 8028391661
E-Mail: bangalore@noricangoup.com
Web Site: www.disagroup.com
500068—(BOM)
Rev.: $30,902,204
Assets: $22,831,081
Liabilities: $11,420,150
Net Worth: $11,410,931
Earnings: $3,492,511
Fiscal Year-end: 12/31/12

Business Description:
Industrial Machinery Mfr
S.I.C.: 3559
N.A.I.C.S.: 333249

Personnel:
Peter Holm Larsen *(Pres & COO)*
Viraj Naidu *(Mng Dir)*
S. Mohan *(CFO & Compliance Officer)*

Board of Directors:
Sanjay Arte
Andrew T. Carmichael
Deepa Hingorani
Jan Johansen
Robert E. Joyce
Viraj Naidu

Legal Counsel:
Chander Kumar & Associates
Bengaluru, India

Transfer Agent:
Integrated Enterprises (India) Ltd.
No 30 Ramana Residency Ground Floor 4th Cross Sampige Road Malleswaram
Bengaluru, India

DISASTER PREPAREDNESS SYSTEMS, INC.

3531 Commercial Street
Vancouver, BC, V5N 4E8, Canada
Tel.: (604) 785-0184
Fax: (604) 676-2821
E-Mail: info@dpsyinc.com
Web Site: www.dpsyinc.com
Year Founded: 2004
DPSY—(OTC)
Emp.: 5

Business Description:
Homeland Security, Disaster Response & Emergency Preparedness Equipment & Technologies Designer & Marketer
S.I.C.: 7382
N.A.I.C.S.: 561621

Personnel:
Mark J. Henrickson *(Chm, Pres & CTO)*
Fredric W. D. Juzda *(CFO)*
Ronald R. Rogers *(COO & Sec)*

Board of Directors:
Mark J. Henrickson
Fredric W. D. Juzda
Ralph Maddeaux
Ronald L. Rennie
Ronald R. Rogers

DISBROWE CHEVROLET BUICK GMC CADILLAC

116 Edward St
Saint Thomas, ON, N5P 4E6, Canada
Tel.: (519) 631-7960
Fax: (519) 631-9113
Toll Free: (888) 648-3602
E-Mail: info@disbrowe.com
Web Site: www.disbrowe.ca
Year Founded: 1923
Rev.: $25,424,880
Emp.: 55

Business Description:
New & Used Car Dealers
S.I.C.: 5511
N.A.I.C.S.: 441110

Personnel:
Carl Ansingh *(Pres)*

DISCO CORPORATION

13-11 Omori Kita 2-Chome
Ota-Ku, Tokyo, 143 8580, Japan
Tel.: (81) 345901111
Fax: (81) 345901188
E-Mail: cvoice@disco.co.jp
Web Site: www.disco.co.jp
Year Founded: 1937
6146—(TKS)
Sls.: $1,030,788,000
Assets: $1,712,337,000
Liabilities: $496,221,000
Net Worth: $1,216,116,000
Earnings: $82,203,000
Emp.: 4,123
Fiscal Year-end: 03/31/13

Business Description:
Machine Tool Mfr
Export
S.I.C.: 3542
N.A.I.C.S.: 333517

Personnel:
Hitoshi Mizorogi *(Chm & CEO)*
Kazuma Sekiya *(Pres, COO, CIO & Gen Mgr-Engrg R&D Div)*
Takao Tamura *(CFO, Chief Privacy Officer & Gen Mgr-Corp Support Div)*
Hideyuki Sekiya *(Chief Safety Officer & Gen Mgr-Hiroshima Works)*

Board of Directors:
Hitoshi Mizorogi
Ichiro Inasaki
Hideyuki Sekiya
Kazuma Sekiya
Keizo Sekiya
Takao Tamura

Affiliates:

DSD, Ltd. **(1)**
2 15 Minami Shinagawa 2 Chome
Shinagawa Ku, Tokyo, 1400004, Japan (86%)
Tel.: (81) 334509919
Fax: (81) 354610994
E-Mail: info@dsd.co.jp
Web Site: www.dsd.co.jp
Emp.: 10
Designs, Develops & Manufactures Communication Networks & Control Boards for Application & Semiconductor Control Systems
S.I.C.: 3679
N.A.I.C.S.: 334418

Tecnisco Ltd. **(1)**
2 15 Minami Shinagawa 2 Chome
Shinagawa Ku, Tokyo, 140 004, Japan (100%)
Tel.: (81) 334584561
Fax: (81) 334584562
E-Mail: o-sales@tecnisco.co.jp
Web Site: www.tecnisco.co.jp
Emp.: 120
Assembly & Marketing of Electronic Components
S.I.C.: 3679
N.A.I.C.S.: 334419

Plants:

Disco Corporation - Chino Plant **(1)**
480 Toyohira
Chino, Nagano, 391-0294, Japan
Tel.: (81) 266722111
Fax: (81) 266821587
Web Site: www.disco.co.jp/eg/support/network/japan/chino.html
Cutting Tool Mfr
S.I.C.: 3545
N.A.I.C.S.: 333515

Disco Corporation - Kure Plant **(1)**
1-23 Hiro Bunka-cho
Kure, Hiroshima, 737-0198, Japan
Tel.: (81) 823722211
Fax: (81) 823720059
Web Site: www.disco.co.jp/eg/support/network/japan/kure.html
Cutting Tool Mfr
S.I.C.: 3545
N.A.I.C.S.: 333515

Disco Corporation - Kuwabata Plant **(1)**
4010-1 Gohara-cho
Kure, Hiroshima, 737-0161, Japan
Tel.: (81) 823771010
Fax: (81) 823771067
Cutting Tool Mfr
S.I.C.: 3545
N.A.I.C.S.: 333515

U.S. Subsidiary:

Disco Hi-Tec America, Inc. **(1)**
3270 Scott Blvd
Santa Clara, CA 95054-3011 CA
Tel.: (408) 987-3776 (100%)
Fax: (408) 987-3785
Web Site: www.discousa.com
Emp.: 40
Marketer of Disco-Produced Equipment
S.I.C.: 5084
N.A.I.C.S.: 423830
Shinji Ueno *(Exec VP)*

Non-U.S. Subsidiaries:

DISCO HI-TEC CHINA CO., LTD. **(1)**
1F Building 5 No 690 Bi-Bo Rd ZhangJiang High-Tech Park
Shanghai, 201203, China
Tel.: (86) 21 50278018
Fax: (86) 21 50278178
Web Site: www.disco.co.jp/eg/support/network/asia.html

Cutting Tool Sales & Maintenance Services
S.I.C.: 5084
N.A.I.C.S.: 423830

Disco Hi-Tec Europe GmbH (1)
Liebigstrasse 8
Kirchheim, 85551, Germany (100%)
Tel.: (49) 89909030
Fax: (49) 8990903199
Web Site: www.discoeurope.com
Sales Range: $50-74.9 Million
Emp.: 50
Marketer of Industrial Diamond Tools
S.I.C.: 5084
N.A.I.C.S.: 423830

Non-U.S. Subsidiaries:

Disco Hi-Tec France Sarl (2)
Espace Beauvalle C 6 Rue Mahatma Gandhi
13090 Aix-en-Provence, France (100%)
Tel.: (33) 442910020
Telex: 270-105-TX/FRA (REF 696)
Fax: (33) 442910029
E-Mail: s.seror@discoeurope.com
Web Site: www.discoeurope.com
Sls.: $1,091,058
Emp.: 4
Marketer of Industrial Diamond Tools
S.I.C.: 5084
N.A.I.C.S.: 423830

Disco Hi-Tec UK Ltd. (2)
151 London Road
East Grinstead, West Sussex, RH19 1ET, United Kingdom (100%)
Tel.: (44) 1342313165
Telex: 87323 FSI G
Fax: (44) 1342313177
Web Site: www.discoeurope.com
Emp.: 4
Marketer of Industrial Diamond Tools
S.I.C.: 5084
N.A.I.C.S.: 423830
Noboru Yoshinaga *(Pres & Gen Mgr-Sls Div)*

Disco Hi-Tec (Singapore) Pte. Ltd. (1)
Blk 2 Kaki Bukit Ave 1 03-06-08 Kaki Bukit Industrial Est
Singapore, 417938, Singapore (100%)
Tel.: (65) 67473737
Telex: DISCOS RS 26761
Fax: (65) 67450266
E-Mail: dhssales@discosin.com.sg
Web Site: www.discosin.com.sg
Emp.: 79
Marketer of Industrial Diamond Tools
S.I.C.: 5084
N.A.I.C.S.: 423830
Makoto Oyama *(VP)*

Non-U.S. Subsidiaries:

Disco Hi-Tec (Malaysia) Sdn. Bhd. (2)
Suite 13A 03 Level 13 Menara Summit
Persiaran Kewajipan
47620 Subang Jaya, Selangor Darul Ehsan, Malaysia (100%)
Tel.: (60) 380246588
Fax: (60) 380241311
E-Mail: info@disco.co.jp
Emp.: 17
Marketer of Disco-Produced Equipment
S.I.C.: 3674
N.A.I.C.S.: 334413
Tsomaslim Lim *(Gen Mgr)*

Disco Hi-Tec (Thailand) Co., Ltd. (2)
16F Lao Peng Nguan Tower 1 333
Viphavadi Rangsit Rd
Lard Yao Chatuchak, Bangkok, 10900, Thailand (100%)
Tel.: (66) 26188441
Fax: (66) 26188440
E-Mail: taweet@discosin.com.th
Web Site: www.discosin.com.sg/
Sls.: $5,000,000
Emp.: 18
Marketer of Disco-Produced Equipment
S.I.C.: 3674
N.A.I.C.S.: 334413
Hiroyuki Kashiwagi *(Mgr)*

Disco Hi-Tec Taiwan Co., Ltd. (1)
188 Baoqiao Road
Xindian, Taipei, 231, Taiwan
Tel.: (886) 229138877
Fax: (886) 229132525
Web Site: www.disco.co.jp
Sales Support & Maintenance of Dicing/ Cutting Saws, Grinders, Blades/Wheels, Related Machines & Applications Support
S.I.C.: 5084
N.A.I.C.S.: 423830

DISCO HI-TEC (VIETNAM) CO., LTD. (1)
7th Floor Saigonland Building 7 Ly Tu Trong Street
Ben Nghe Ward District 1, Ho Chi Minh City, Vietnam
Tel.: (84) 8 3822 3832
Fax: (84) 8 3822 2613
Emp.: 3
Cutting Tool Repair & Maintenance Services
S.I.C.: 7699
N.A.I.C.S.: 811310
Mikoto Oyimi *(Mng Dir)*

Disco Technology (Shanghai) Co., Ltd. (1)
1F Bldg 5 No 690 Bi-Bo Rd
Zhang Jiang High Tech Pk, Shanghai, 201203, China (100%)
Tel.: (86) 2150278018
Fax: (86) 2150278178
Web Site: www.disco.co.jp/eg/support/network/asia.html
Emp.: 50
Marketer of Disco-Produced Equipment
S.I.C.: 3674
N.A.I.C.S.: 334413

Non-U.S. Affiliates:

DD Diamond Corporation (1)
381 5 Gaehwa Ry Sungju Myeon
Boryung City, Ch'onan, Choongnam, Korea (South)
Tel.: (82) 529348454
Fax: (82) 4529348456
Web Site: www.disco.co.jp/eg/corporate/outline/foreign.html
Producer & Marketer of Industrial Diamond Tools
S.I.C.: 3423
N.A.I.C.S.: 332216

Disco-Sea Europe S.R.L. (1)
Via Augera
Cadelbosco Sopra, 42023 Reggio nell'Emilia, Italy (25%)
Tel.: (39) 0522915251
Fax: (39) 0522915258
E-Mail: disco-seaeurope@sedia.com
Web Site: www.sedia.com
Marketer of Industrial Diamond Tools
S.I.C.: 3544
N.A.I.C.S.: 333514

DISCOUNT CAR & TRUCK RENTALS LTD.

720 Arrow Rd
Toronto, ON, M9M2M1, Canada
Tel.: (416) 744-0123
Fax: (416) 744-0624
Toll Free: (800) 263-2355
E-Mail: privacy@discountcar.com
Web Site: www.discountcar.com
Year Founded: 1980
Emp.: 750
Business Description:
Car & Truck Rentals
S.I.C.: 7514
N.A.I.C.S.: 532111
Personnel:
Herb Singer *(Co-Founder)*
Rhoda Singer *(Co-Founder)*

DISCOVERY AIR INC.

126 Bristol Avenue
PO Box 1530
Yellowknife, NT, X1A 2P2, Canada
Tel.: (867) 873-5350
Fax: (867) 873-5351
Web Site: www.discoveryair.com
DAA—(TSX)
Rev.: $227,981,469
Assets: $304,392,780
Liabilities: $210,330,656
Net Worth: $94,062,125
Earnings: $495,022
Emp.: 850
Fiscal Year-end: 01/31/13
Business Description:
Aviation & Aviation Related Services
S.I.C.: 4581
N.A.I.C.S.: 488119
Personnel:
Brian J. Semkowski *(Chm)*
Jacob Shavit *(Pres & CEO)*
Paul A. Bernards *(CFO)*
Jean Genest *(CTO & Exec VP)*
Adam Bembridge *(Pres-Northern Svcs)*
Paul Bouchard *(Pres-Discovery Air Defence Svcs)*
Jeff Denomme *(Pres-Great Slave Helicopters)*
Mark Hill *(Pres-Discovery Air Fire Svcs)*
Andy Young *(Pres-Discovery Mining Svcs)*
Dennis Lopes *(Gen Counsel, Sec & VP)*
Charles Parker *(Exec VP-Northern Svcs)*
Board of Directors:
Brian J. Semkowski
James L. Goodfellow
Michael Grasty
Raymond R. Henault
G. John Krediet
Kenneth B. Rotman
Legal Counsel:
Aird & Berlis
Toronto, ON, Canada
Transfer Agent:
Computershare Investor Services Inc
100 University Avenue
Toronto, ON, Canada

Subsidiaries:

Air Tindi Ltd. (1)
23 Mitchell Dr
PO Box 1693
Yellowknife, NT, X1A 2H5, Canada
Tel.: (867) 669-8200
Fax: (867) 669-8210
Toll Free: (888) 545-6794
E-Mail: reservations@airtindi.com
Web Site: www.airtindi.com
Emp.: 160
Aircraft Charter Services
S.I.C.: 4522
N.A.I.C.S.: 481219
Kelly Brengon *(VP-Ops)*

Discovery Air Defence Services Inc. (1)
(Formerly Top Aces Inc.)
52 Hymus Boulevard Suite 200
Pointe-Claire, QC, H9R 1C9, Canada
Tel.: (514) 694-5565
Fax: (514) 694-3580
Toll Free: (866) 694-5565
E-Mail:
Web Site: www.discoveryair-ds.com
Military Air Combat Training Services
S.I.C.: 8249
N.A.I.C.S.: 611512
Paul Bouchard *(Pres)*

U.S. Subsidiary:

Advanced Training Systems International, Inc. (2)
6355 S Sossaman Rd Bldg A
Mesa, AZ 85212 AZ
Tel.: (480) 792-6200
Fax: (480) 792-6201
E-Mail: executiveoffice@atsifightertraining.com
Web Site: www.atsifightertraining.com
Sales Range: $1-9.9 Million
Military Air Combat & Maintenance Training Services
S.I.C.: 8249
N.A.I.C.S.: 611512
Mitchell Moore *(Mgr)*

Discovery Air Fire Services Inc. (1)
1012 Hwy 601
PO Box 400
Dryden, ON, P8N 2Z1, Canada
Tel.: (807) 937-5544
Fax: (807) 937-2464
Toll Free: (866) 990-0091
Web Site: www.discoveryair-fs.com
Emp.: 40
Aerial Fire Management & Fire Transport Services
S.I.C.: 9224
N.A.I.C.S.: 922160
Mark Hill *(Mgr-Ops)*

Discovery Mining Services Ltd. (1)
101-487 Range Lk Rd
Yellowknife, NT, X1A 2P7, Canada
Tel.: (867) 920-4600
Fax: (867) 873-8332
E-Mail: info@discoverymining.ca
Web Site: www.discoverymining.ca
Emp.: 70
Mining Support Services
S.I.C.: 1481
N.A.I.C.S.: 213115
Andy Young *(Pres)*

Great Slave Helicopters Ltd. (1)
106 Dickens St
Yellowknife, NT, X1A 2R3, Canada
Tel.: (867) 873-2081
Fax: (867) 873-6087
E-Mail: info@greatslaveheli.com
Web Site: www.greatslaveheli.com
Emp.: 200
Helicopter Operation Services
S.I.C.: 4512
N.A.I.C.S.: 481111
Jeff Denomme *(Pres)*
Lindberg Paul *(CFO & VP)*

DISCOVERY CAPITAL CORPORATION

Ste 570 1285 W Pender St
Vancouver, BC, V6E 4B1, Canada
Tel.: (604) 683-3000
Fax: (604) 662-3457
E-Mail: info@discoverycapital.com
Web Site: www.discoverycapital.com
Year Founded: 1986
Sales Range: $10-24.9 Million
Emp.: 8
Business Description:
Venture Capital Financial Services
S.I.C.: 6221
N.A.I.C.S.: 523130
Personnel:
Harry A. Jaako *(Chm & Co-CEO)*
John McEwen *(Pres & Co-CEO)*
Charles Cook *(CFO & VP)*
Patricia Parisotto *(Sec)*
Board of Directors:
Harry A. Jaako
Bruce Chapman
Jim Fletcher
Randy Garg
Scot Martin
John McEwen
Transfer Agent:
CIBC Mellon Trust Company
1177 W Hastings St - Mall Level
Vancouver, BC, V6E 3XI, Canada
Tel.: (604) 891-3024
Toll Free: (800) 387-0825

DISCOVERY COMPUTERS & WIRELESS INC.

200 3301 Douglas St
Victoria, BC, V8Z 3L2, Canada
Tel.: (250) 382-0499
Toll Free: (888) 313-4726
E-Mail: info@discoverycomputers.com
Web Site: www.discoverycomputers.com
Year Founded: 1997
Sales Range: $1-9.9 Million
Emp.: 25

Discovery Computers & Wireless Inc.—(Continued)

Business Description:
Western Canada Computer & Wireless Store Operators & Franchises
S.I.C.: 5946
N.A.I.C.S.: 443142

DISCOVERY-CORP ENTERPRISES INC.

193 Aquarius Mews Suite 1108
Vancouver, BC, V6Z 2Z2, Canada
Tel.: (778) 371-9936
Fax: (778) 329-3520
Web Site: www.discovery-corp.com
Year Founded: 1986
DCY—(TSXV)
Int. Income: $3,501
Assets: $453,472
Liabilities: $18,719
Net Worth: $434,753
Earnings: ($494,669)
Fiscal Year-end: 07/31/13

Business Description:
Mineral Exploration Services
S.I.C.: 1081
N.A.I.C.S.: 213114

Personnel:
Alex Pannu *(Pres & CEO)*
Iain Brown *(CFO & Sec)*

Board of Directors:
Iain Brown
Thomas Gregory Hawkins
Scott Yonggi Lee
Alex Pannu

DISCOVERY FOODS LTD.

Nimbus House Maidstone Rd
Kingston, Milton Keynes, Bucks, MK10 0BD, United Kingdom
Tel.: (44) 1908933000
Fax: (44) 1908933074
E-Mail: info@discoveryfoods.co.uk
Web Site: www.discoveryfoods.co.uk
Sales Range: $50-74.9 Million
Emp.: 32

Business Description:
Food Products Mfr
S.I.C.: 2099
N.A.I.C.S.: 311999

DISCOVERY FORD BURLINGTON LTD.

850 Brant Street
Burlington, ON, L7R 2J5, Canada
Tel.: (905) 632-8696
Fax: (905) 632-0914
E-Mail: sales@discoveryford.com
Web Site: www.discoveryford.com
Year Founded: 1961
Rev.: $51,558,355
Emp.: 100

Business Description:
New & Used Car Dealers
S.I.C.: 5511
N.A.I.C.S.: 441110

Personnel:
Allan Pearson *(Pres)*

DISCOVERY HARBOUR RESOURCES CORP.

(Formerly CVC Cayman Ventures Corp.)
Suite 1818 701 West Georgia Street
Vancouver, BC, V7Y 1C6, Canada
Tel.: (604) 689-1799
Fax: (604) 689-8199
E-Mail: info@discoveryharbour.com
Web Site: www.discoveryharbour.com
Year Founded: 2009
DHR—(TSXV)
Int. Income: $1,913
Assets: $258,759
Liabilities: $16,223
Net Worth: $242,536
Earnings: ($78,706)
Fiscal Year-end: 01/31/13

Business Description:
Investment Services
S.I.C.: 6211
N.A.I.C.S.: 523999

Personnel:
Frank D. Hegner *(Pres & CEO)*
Binny Jassal *(CFO)*
Michael J. Senn *(Exec VP)*

Board of Directors:
Mark Fields
Richard B. Gilliam
Andrew Hancharyk
Frank D. Hegner
Michael J. Senn
Jorge Patricio Varas

Legal Counsel:
Clark Wilson LLP
800-885 West Georgia Street
Vancouver, BC, Canada V6C 3H1

Transfer Agent:
Computershare Investor Services Inc.
3rd Floor 510 Burrard Street
Vancouver, BC, Canada

DISCOVERY HOLDINGS LIMITED

(Name Changed to Discovery Limited)

DISCOVERY LIMITED

(Formerly Discovery Holdings Limited)
155 West Street
PO Box 786722
Sandton, 2146, South Africa
Tel.: (27) 11 529 2888
Fax: (27) 11 539 8003
E-Mail: askthecfo@discovery.co.za
Web Site: www.discovery.co.za
DSY—(JSE OTC)
Rev.: $2,776,973,700
Earnings: $238,032,700
Emp.: 8,220
Fiscal Year-end: 06/30/13

Business Description:
Holding Company; Insurance Services
S.I.C.: 6719
N.A.I.C.S.: 551112

Personnel:
Monty Hilkowitz *(Chm)*
Adrian Gore *(CEO)*
Richard Farber *(CFO & Dir-Fin)*
John Robertson *(CIO)*
Hylton Kallner *(CMO)*
Jonathan Broomberg *(CEO-Discovery Health)*
Neville Koopowitz *(CEO-PruHealth)*
Herschel Mayers *(CEO-Discovery Life, Discovery Invest & PruProtect)*
Alan Pollard *(CEO-The Vitality Grp)*
M. J. Botha *(Sec)*

Board of Directors:
Monty Hilkowitz
Brian Brink
Peter Cooper
Jannie Jonathan Durand
Steven B. Epstein
Richard Farber
Adrian Gore
Hylton Kallner
Neville Koopowitz
Vincent Maphai
Herschel Mayers
Ayanda Nstaluba
Les Owen
Alan Pollard
John Robertson
Sonja Sebotsa
Tania Slabbert
Barry Swartzberg
Sindi Zilwa

Legal Counsel:
Edward Nathan Sonnenbergs
150 West Street
Sandton, South Africa

Transfer Agent:
Computershare Investor Services (Proprietary) Limited
Ground Floor 70 Marshall St
Johannesburg, South Africa

Subsidiary:

Discovery Health (Proprietary) Limited **(1)**
155 West St
Sandton, Gauteng, 2196, South Africa
Tel.: (27) 115292888
Fax: (27) 115397274
Emp.: 10,000
Health Insurance Services
S.I.C.: 6321
N.A.I.C.S.: 524114
Barry Swartzberg *(Mng Dir)*

U.S. Subsidiary:

The Vitality Group Inc **(1)**
200 W Monroe St
Chicago, IL 60606-5075
Tel.: (312) 224-7100
Web Site: www.thevitalitygroup.com
Health Insurance Services
S.I.C.: 6321
N.A.I.C.S.: 524114
Arthur C. Carlos *(CEO)*
Alan Pollard *(CEO)*
Derek Yach *(Sr VP)*

Non-U.S. Holding:

Prudential Health Holdings Limited **(1)**
Laurence Pountney Hill
London, EC4R 0HH, United Kingdom UK
Tel.: (44) 1202 447 208 (75%)
Holding Company; Health Insurance
S.I.C.: 6719
N.A.I.C.S.: 551112

Holdings:

Prudential Health Insurance Ltd **(2)**
Laurence Pountney Hill
London, EC4R 0HH, United Kingdom UK
Tel.: (44) 1202 447 208
Web Site: www.pruhealth.co.uk
Health Insurance
S.I.C.: 6321
N.A.I.C.S.: 524114
Neville Koopowitz *(CEO)*

DISCOVERY METALS LIMITED

Level 20 333 Ann Street
Brisbane, QLD, 4000, Australia
Mailing Address:
GPO Box 3261
Brisbane, QLD, 4001, Australia
Tel.: (61) 732180222
Fax: (61) 732180233
E-Mail: info@discoverymetals.com
Web Site: www.discoverymetals.com
Year Founded: 2003
DML—(ASX BOT)
Int. Income: $89,000
Assets: $254,214,000
Liabilities: $186,452,000
Net Worth: $67,762,000
Earnings: ($224,280,000)
Emp.: 635
Fiscal Year-end: 06/30/13

Business Description:
Mineral Exploration Services
S.I.C.: 1481
N.A.I.C.S.: 213115

Personnel:
Bob Fulker *(Acting CEO & COO)*
Paul Frederiks *(CFO & Sec)*
Ross Gibbins *(Exec-Project Dev)*

Board of Directors:
Jeremy Read
Ribson Gabonowe
Russell Luxford

Legal Counsel:
GRT Lawyers
Level 1 400 Queen St
Brisbane, QLD, 4000, Australia

Computershare Investor Services Pty Ltd
GPO Box 2975
Melbourne, VIC, Australia VIC

Non-U.S. Subsidiaries:

Discovery Copper Botswana Proprietary Ltd **(1)**
Plot 21314 Phakalane
Gaborone, Botswana
Tel.: (267) 3180751
Fax: (267) 3180752
Web Site: www.discoverymetals.com.au
Emp.: 20
Copper Ore Mining Services
S.I.C.: 1021
N.A.I.C.S.: 212234

Discovery Metals Botswana Proprietary Ltd **(1)**
Plot 21314 Sebele Station Road Phakalane
Gaborone, Botswana
Tel.: (267) 318 0751
Fax: (267) 318 0752
E-Mail: info@discoverymetals.com.au
Web Site: www.discoverymetals.com
Metal Mining Services
S.I.C.: 1099
N.A.I.C.S.: 212299

DISCOVERY MOTORS LTD.

(d/b/a Discovery Honda)
6466 Bell McKinnon Rd
Duncan, BC, V9L 6C1, Canada
Tel.: (250) 748-5814
Fax: (250) 748-2812
Toll Free: (888) 296-9358
Web Site: www.discoveryhonda.com
Year Founded: 1991
Rev.: $10,796,631
Emp.: 24

Business Description:
New & Used Car Dealers
S.I.C.: 5511
N.A.I.C.S.: 441110

Personnel:
Ian Lepper *(Mgr-Sls)*

DISCOVERY RESOURCES LIMITED

Level 9 105 St Georges Terrace
Perth, WA, 6000, Australia
Tel.: (61) 8 9226 0326
Fax: (61) 8 9226 0327
E-Mail: info@discoveryresources.com.au
Web Site: www.discoveryresources.com.au
Year Founded: 2010
DIS—(ASX)

Business Description:
Rare Earth Mineral Mining
S.I.C.: 1099
N.A.I.C.S.: 212299

Personnel:
Josh Puckridge *(Sec)*

Board of Directors:
Peter Wall
Tony Adcock
Josh Puckridge

Legal Counsel:
Steinepreis Paganin
Level 4 The Read Building 16 Milligan Street
Perth, WA, 6000, Australia
Tel.: (61) 8 9321 4000
Fax: (61) 8 9321 4333

DISCOVERY RIDGE RESOURCES, INC.

Suite 1250 639 5th Avenue Southwest
Calgary, AB, T2P 0M9, Canada

Toll Free: (866) 387-3472
Year Founded: 2008
Business Description:
Oil & Gas Exploration Services
S.I.C.: 1311
N.A.I.C.S.: 211111
Personnel:
Will Wagner *(Pres, CFO & Chief Acctg Officer)*
Board of Directors:
Will Wagner

DISCOVERY VENTURES INC.

900-570 Granville St
Vancouver, BC, V6C 3P1, Canada
Tel.: (604) 818-1706
Fax: (604) 926-4232
E-Mail: info@discoveryventuresinc.com
Web Site: www.discoveryventuresinc.com
Year Founded: 1999
DVN—(TSXV)
Int. Income: $2,656
Assets: $3,630,175
Liabilities: $39,345
Net Worth: $3,590,830
Earnings: ($477,972)
Fiscal Year-end: 12/31/12
Business Description:
Gold & Other Metal Mining Services
S.I.C.: 1099
N.A.I.C.S.: 212299
Personnel:
Akash Patel *(Pres & CEO)*
Kenneth C. Phillippe *(CFO & Sec)*
Board of Directors:
Walter A. Marting, Jr.
Neil Hill Morgan
Akash Patel
Kenneth C. Phillippe
Matt Wayrynen
Legal Counsel:
Richards Buell Sutton LLP
700 401 West Georgia Street
Vancouver, BC, Canada
Transfer Agent:
Computershare Inc
510 Burrard Street
Vancouver, BC, Canada

DISCRETIX TECHNOLOGIES LTD.

Grand Netter Industrial Zone Delta Bldg
POB 3641
40593 Kfar Netter, Israel
Tel.: (972) 732558800
Fax: (972) 732558808
Web Site: www.discretix.com
Sales Range: $10-24.9 Million
Emp.: 90
Business Description:
Embedded Security Platform Mfr
S.I.C.: 3674
N.A.I.C.S.: 334413
Personnel:
Gal Salomon *(Founder & Chm)*
Coby Sella *(CEO)*
Hagai Barel *(CTO)*
Edo Ganot *(Exec VP-Sls & Bus Dev)*
Board of Directors:
Gal Salomon
Randy L. Ditzler
Martin Gibson
Isaac Hillel
Yair Shoham

U.S. Subsidiary:

Discretix, Inc. (1)
1521 California Cir 2nd Fl
Milpitas, CA 95035
Tel.: (408) 969-9991
Fax: (408) 969-9994
Web Site: www.discretix.com
Sales Range: $1-9.9 Million
Emp.: 61
Designs & Licenses Processors for Mobile Devices & Flash Memory Data Security
S.I.C.: 3575
N.A.I.C.S.: 334118
Gal Salomon *(Founder & CEO)*
David Deitcher *(CTO)*
Edo Ganot *(Exec VP-Sls & Bus Dev)*

Non-U.S. Branches:

Discretix Technologies Ltd. (1)
4F No 58 Jhouzih Street
Neihu District Taipei, 11493, Taiwan
Tel.: (886) 287523367
Fax: (886) 226580386
Web Site: www.discretix.com
Embedded Security Platform Mfr
S.I.C.: 3674
N.A.I.C.S.: 334413

Non-U.S. Subsidiaries:

Commtone Solution Co. Ltd (1)
Room 4107 580 Nanjing Road W
Shanghai, China
Tel.: (86) 2129264120
Fax: (86) 2153068222
Web Site: www.discretix.com
Embedded Security Platform Mfr
S.I.C.: 3674
N.A.I.C.S.: 334413

Discretix Technologies K.K. (1)
Tukiji Akashicho Duplex Rs 702 6-23-702 Akashi-cho
Chuo-ku, Tokyo, 104-0044, Japan JP
Tel.: (81) 351482053
Fax: (81) 351482054
Web Site: www.discretix.com
Embedded Security Platform Mfr
S.I.C.: 3674
N.A.I.C.S.: 334413

DISH TV INDIA LTD

FC - 19 Sector 16 A Film City
Noida, Uttar Pradesh, 201 301, India
Tel.: (91) 1202599555
Fax: (91) 1204357078
E-Mail: customercare@dishtv.in
Web Site: www.dishtv.in
532839—(BOM)
Rev.: $411,206,076
Assets: $584,892,504
Liabilities: $613,737,036
Net Worth: ($28,844,532)
Earnings: $12,236,400
Fiscal Year-end: 03/31/13
Business Description:
Entertainment Services
S.I.C.: 4833
N.A.I.C.S.: 515120
Personnel:
R. C. Venkateish *(CEO)*
Jawahar Lal Goel *(Mng Dir)*
Rajeev Kumar Dalmia *(CFO)*
V. K. Gupta *(Co-COO)*
Salil Kapoor *(Co-COO)*
Rajiv Khattar *(Pres-Projects)*
Amitabh Kumar *(Pres-Tech)*
Ranjit Singh *(Sec)*
Abhay S. Metkar *(Sr VP-Sls)*
Board of Directors:
Subhash Chandra
Mintoo Bhandari
Lakshmi Chand
Arun Duggal
Jawahar Lal Goel
Ashok Kurien
Bhagwan Dass Narang
Eric Louis Zinterhofer
Transfer Agent:
Sharepro Services (India) Pvt Ltd
13AB Samhita Warehousing Complex 2nd Fl Off Andheri Kurla Rd Sakinaka
Sakinaka Telephone Exchange Lane Andheri East, Mumbai, 400 072, India

DISHMAN PHARMACEUTICALS & CHEMICALS LTD.

Bhadr-Raj Chambers Swastik Cross Road Navrangpura
Ahmedabad, 380 009, India
Tel.: (91) 7926443053
Fax: (91) 7926420198
E-Mail: dishman@dishmangroup.com
Web Site: www.dishmangroup.com
532526—(BOM)
Rev.: $239,173,546
Assets: $424,772,109
Liabilities: $232,978,794
Net Worth: $191,793,315
Earnings: $18,594,489
Emp.: 1,055
Fiscal Year-end: 03/31/13
Business Description:
Pharmaceuticals & Chemicals Mfr
S.I.C.: 2834
N.A.I.C.S.: 325412
Personnel:
Janmejay R. Vyas *(Chm & Mng Dir)*
Mark Griffiths *(CEO)*
Arpit J. Vyas *(Mng Dir)*
Ravi Raval *(COO)*
Rajiv A. Desai *(Pres-QA, QC, RA & ADI)*
Himani Dhotre *(Sr VP-Project Coordination)*
Board of Directors:
Janmejay R. Vyas
Yagneshkumar B. Desai
Ashok C. Gandhi
Sanjay S. Majmudar
Arpit J. Vyas
Deohooti J. Vyas
Transfer Agent:
Link Intime India Pvt. Ltd
C-13 Pannalal Silk Mills Compound LBS Marg
Bhandup (West)
Mumbai, India

Subsidiary:

CarboGen Amcis AG (1)
Hauptstrasse 171
4416 Bubendorf, Switzerland
Tel.: (41) 619355353
Fax: (41) 619355300
E-Mail: info@carbogen-amcis.com
Web Site: www.carbogen.com
Emp.: 180
Specialty Chemical Products
S.I.C.: 2899
N.A.I.C.S.: 325998
Mark Griffiths *(CEO)*
Gaudenz von Capeller *(Mng Dir)*

U.S. Subsidiary:

Dishman USA Inc. (1)
550 Union Ave Ste 9
Middlesex, NJ 08846
Tel.: (732) 560-4300
Fax: (732) 560-4343
Web Site: www.dishmangroup.com
Pharmaceutical Products Mfr
S.I.C.: 2834
N.A.I.C.S.: 325412

Non-U.S. Subsidiaries:

Carbogen Amcis Ltd. (U.K.) (1)
303 Clayton Lane
Manchester, M11 4SX, United Kingdom
Tel.: (44) 161 223 33 44
Fax: (44) 161 220 87 78
Web Site: www.carbogen-amcis.com
Emp.: 30
Pharmaceutical Products Mfr
S.I.C.: 2834
N.A.I.C.S.: 325412
Stephan Fritschi *(Mng Dir)*

Dishman Europe Limited (1)
85 New Cavendish Street
London, W1W6XD, United Kingdom
Tel.: (44) 2073230608
Fax: (44) 2073230609
E-Mail: info@dishman-europe.com
Web Site: www.dishman-europe.com
Emp.: 7
Pharmaceutical Preparation Mfr
S.I.C.: 2834
N.A.I.C.S.: 325412
Janmejay R. Vyas *(Mng Dir)*

Dishman International Trade (Shanghai) Co., Ltd. (1)
Room 1101 Times Building
655# Hubing Road Wuxi, 214071 Nanjing, China
Tel.: (86) 51085840486
Fax: (86) 51085841845
E-Mail: sales@dishman.net.cn
Web Site: www.dishmangroup.com
Emp.: 10
Pharmaceutical Preparation Mfr
S.I.C.: 2834
N.A.I.C.S.: 325412
Tracy Tsui *(Gen Mgr)*

Dishman Japan Ltd. (1)
1-1-8 Hirakawa-cho Chiyoda-ku
3-19 Hayabusa-cho Chiyoda-ku, Tokyo, 102-0093, Japan
Tel.: (81) 332217571
Fax: (81) 332217572
E-Mail: sales@dishman-japan.com
Web Site: www.dishman-japan.com
Emp.: 7
Pharmaceutical Preparation Mfr
S.I.C.: 2834
N.A.I.C.S.: 325412
Takashi Yokouchi *(Mng Dir)*

Dishman Netherlands B.V. (1)
Nieuweweg 2a 3901 BE Veenendaal
PO Box 70
3900 AB Veenendaal, Utrecht, Netherlands
Tel.: (31) 318 545 754
Fax: (31) 8 529 374
E-Mail: info@dishman-netherlands.com
Web Site: www.dishman-netherlands.com
Emp.: 75
Pharmaceutical Products Mfr & Sales
S.I.C.: 5122
N.A.I.C.S.: 424210
Rob Eigkman *(Gen Mgr)*

Dishman Pharma Solutions AG. (1)
Hauptstrasse 171
Bubendorf, Basel-Landschaft, 4416, Switzerland
Tel.: (41) 619355353
Fax: (41) 619355300
Web Site: www.dishman.net.cn/en/group.asp
Pharmaceutical Products Distr
S.I.C.: 5122
N.A.I.C.S.: 424210
Arpit Vyas *(Gen Mgr)*

Dishman Pharmaceuticals & Chemicals (Shanghai) Co. Ltd. (1)
No 69 Shungong Road Shanghai Chemical Industry Park
Shanghai, 201507, China
Tel.: (86) 21 6712 1166
Fax: (86) 21 6712 0811
E-Mail: sales@dishman.net.cn
Web Site: www.dishmangroup.com
Pharmaceutical Products Distr
S.I.C.: 5122
N.A.I.C.S.: 424210

Dishman Switzerland Ltd. (1)
1 Av De Longueville
2013 Colombier, Vaud, Switzerland
Tel.: (41) 328416870
Fax: (41) 32 84168 72
Pharmaceutical Products Mfr
S.I.C.: 2834
N.A.I.C.S.: 325412

DISKUS WERKE AG

Gutleutstr 175
D-60327 Frankfurt am Main, Germany
Tel.: (49) 69 2400 0858
Fax: (49) 69 2400 0849
Web Site: www.diskus-werke.ag
DIS—(DEU)
Sls.: $223,329,603
Assets: $284,041,870
Liabilities: $142,559,403
Net Worth: $141,482,467
Earnings: $8,884,722

DISKUS WERKE AG—(Continued)

Emp.: 931
Fiscal Year-end: 12/31/12
Business Description:
Industrial Machinery Mfr
S.I.C.: 3559
N.A.I.C.S.: 333249
Personnel:
Peter Heinz *(Vice Chm-Supervisory Bd)*
Josef Preis *(CEO)*
Axel Loehr *(CFO)*
Bernd Rothenberger *(Chief Scientific Officer)*
Supervisory Board of Directors:
Meinert Hahnemann
Rolf Hartmann
Peter Heinz
Steen Rothenberger

DISMO

Rue De Poitiers
79700 Mauleon, Deux-Sevres, France
Tel.: (33) 549814301
Sales Range: $25-49.9 Million
Emp.: 66
Business Description:
Supermarket
S.I.C.: 5411
N.A.I.C.S.: 445110
Personnel:
Franck Couprie *(Pres)*

DISPLAY ART PLC

23 Tefkrou Anthia Street Idalion Industrial Zone
PO Box 27108
1642 Nicosia, Cyprus
Tel.: (357) 22 485 420
Fax: (357) 22 485 933
E-Mail: info@displayartgroup.com
Web Site: www.displayartgroup.com
Year Founded: 1982
DISP—(CYP)
Business Description:
Digital Printing Services
S.I.C.: 2759
N.A.I.C.S.: 323111
Personnel:
Paul Nicolaou *(Gen Dir)*
Christina Nicolaou *(Sec)*
Board of Directors:
Michael Antoniades
Marios Cambanella
Panayiotis Kallis
Andis Nathanael
Panayiotis Neofitou
Paul Nicolaou
Savvas Nicolaou

DISTECH CONTROLS, INC.

4005-B Matte Blvd
Brossard, QC, J4Y 2P4, Canada
Tel.: (450) 444-9898
Fax: (450) 444-0770
Toll Free: (800) 404-0043
Web Site: www.distech-controls.com
Year Founded: 1995
Sales Range: $10-24.9 Million
Business Description:
Building Automation Systems Mfr
S.I.C.: 1629
N.A.I.C.S.: 236210
Non-U.S. Subsidiary:

Distech Controls Europe B.V. (1)
Raam 16A
Gemert, 5422 WX Gemert, Netherlands
Mailing Address:
Postbus 206
5420 AE Gemert, Netherlands
Tel.: (31) 492390341
Fax: (31) 492390342
E-Mail: info@distech-controls.eu
Web Site: www.distech-controls.eu
Emp.: 15
Building Automation Systems Mfr
S.I.C.: 1799
N.A.I.C.S.: 238290
Johan Schackenraad *(Pres)*

DISTELL GROUP LIMITED

Aan-de-Wagenweg
Stellenbosch, 7600, South Africa
Mailing Address:
PO Box 184
Stellenbosch, 7599, South Africa
Tel.: (27) 218097000
Fax: (27) 218864611
E-Mail: info@distell.co.za
Web Site: www.distell.co.za
DST—(JSE)
Rev.: $1,771,356,249
Assets: $1,591,332,486
Liabilities: $778,095,051
Net Worth: $813,237,435
Earnings: $122,040,516
Emp.: 5,160
Fiscal Year-end: 06/30/13
Business Description:
Producer & Marketer of Fine Wines, Spirits, Ciders & Ready-to-Drinks (RTDs)
S.I.C.: 2084
N.A.I.C.S.: 312130
Personnel:
Piet E. Beyers *(Chm)*
Richard Rushton *(Mng Dir)*
Wim Buhrmann *(CEO-Southern Africa)*
Stoffel Cronje *(Sec)*
Board of Directors:
Piet E. Beyers
Merwe Botha
Johan Carinus
Gugu Dingaan
Jannie Jonathan Durand
Edwin Hertzog
Joe Madungandaba
Louisa Mojela
David Morris Nurek
Chris Otto
Andre Parker
Richard Rushton
Jan Scannell
Catharina Sevillano-Barredo
Ben van der Ross
Lucas C. Verwey
Transfer Agent:
Computershare Investor Services (Proprietary) Limited
70 Marshall Street
Johannesburg, South Africa

Subsidiaries:

Nederburg Wines (Proprietary) Limited (1)
Sonstraal Rd Daljosafat
Paarl, Western Cape, South Africa
Tel.: (27) 2721862
Fax: (27) 218624887
Emp.: 71
Wine Mfr
S.I.C.: 5182
N.A.I.C.S.: 424820
Sunette Rust *(Controller)*

South African Distilleries and Wines (SA) Limited (1)
Ann-Den-Wagen Rd
Stellenbosch, Western Cape, 7600, South Africa
Tel.: (27) 218098103
Fax: (27) 218864611
E-Mail: info@distell.co.za
Emp.: 4,500
Alcoholic Beverages & Wines Mfr
S.I.C.: 5182
N.A.I.C.S.: 424820
Jan Scannell *(CEO)*

Stellenbosch Farmers Winery Limited (1)
Aan-de-Wagenweg
Stellenbosch, 7600, South Africa
Tel.: (27) 21 809 7000
Fax: (27) 21 886 4611
E-Mail: info@distell.co.za
Web Site: www.distell.co.za
Wines Mfr & Distr
S.I.C.: 5182
N.A.I.C.S.: 424820
Pieter Carolin *(Dir-Distr)*

Non-U.S. Subsidiaries:

Burn Stewart Distillers Ltd. (1)
8 Milton Road
College Milton North, East Kilbride, Scotland, G74 5BU, United Kingdom UK
Tel.: (44) 1355 260999
Fax: (44) 1355 264355
E-Mail: enquiries@burnstewartdistillers.com
Web Site: www.burnstewartdistillers.com
Emp.: 150
Scotch Whiskey Distiller
S.I.C.: 5182
N.A.I.C.S.: 424820
Fraser Thornton *(Mng Dir)*
Campbell Stirrat *(Sec & Dir-Comml)*

Distell Namibia Limited (1)
4 Sollingen St
Windhoek, Namibia
Tel.: (264) 61277038
Fax: (264) 612263412
Emp.: 115
Beverages & Wines Mfr
S.I.C.: 5182
N.A.I.C.S.: 424820
Leon Souche *(Mng Dir)*

Distell Swaziland Limited (1)
Cnr 7th St & 1st Ave
140
Matsapha, 0200, Swaziland
Tel.: (268) 5184107518
Fax: (268) 5184106
E-Mail: sld@realnet.co.sz
Web Site: www.distell.co.za/runtime/popcontentrun.aspx?pageidref=2349
Emp.: 20
Liquor Distr
S.I.C.: 5182
N.A.I.C.S.: 424820
Michelle Lloyd *(Branch Mgr)*

DISTILLERIE MERLET ET FILS SARL

Lieu Dit Chevessac
17610 Poitiers, France
Tel.: (33) 546914781
E-Mail: info@merlet.fr
Web Site: www.merlet.fr
Sls.: $23,700,000
Emp.: 44
Business Description:
Wines, Brandy & Brandy Spirits
S.I.C.: 2084
N.A.I.C.S.: 312130
Personnel:
Emmanuel Rottaro *(Mgr-DP)*
Board of Directors:
Gilles Merlet

DISTILLERIES COMPANY OF SRI LANKA PLC

110 Norris Canal Road
Colombo, 10, Sri Lanka
Tel.: (94) 112695295
Fax: (94) 112696360
E-Mail: info@dcslgroup.com
Web Site: www.dcslgroup.com
DIST—(COL)
Rev.: $516,455,111
Assets: $614,222,104
Liabilities: $200,427,275
Net Worth: $413,794,828
Earnings: $41,276,635
Emp.: 18,674
Fiscal Year-end: 03/31/13
Business Description:
Liquor Distillation
S.I.C.: 2085
N.A.I.C.S.: 312140
Personnel:
D. H. S. Jayawardena *(Chm & Mng Dir)*
Maximus R. Perles *(CEO)*
V. J. Senaratne *(Chief Legal Officer & Sec)*
Ajith Kumara de Silva *(Exec-Distribution & Acting Mgr-Warehouse-Kalutara)*
P. G. A. Dharmapriya *(Asst Warehouse Officer-Mirishena)*
P. Disna Kumara *(Asst Warehouse Officer-Badulla)*
D. H. L. Nissanka *(Asst Warehouse Officer-Teak Store)*
Tharanga Palamakumbura *(Asst Warehouse Officer-Badulla)*
Lalith Obeyesekere *(CEO-Balangoda Plantations Plc & Madulsima Plantations Plc)*
Pushpaka Ranasinghe *(Treas)*
Board of Directors:
D. H. S. Jayawardena
A. Naomal Balasuriya
Niranjan de S. Deva Aditya
C. F. Fernando
C. R. Jansz
K. J. Kahanda
R. K. Obeyesekere
Legal Counsel:
Prasanna Goonewardene & Company
No 26 1 Colonel T.G.Jayawardena Mawatha
Colombo, Sri Lanka

DISTIMO HOLDING B.V.

Plompetorengracht 17
3512 CB Utrecht, Netherlands
Tel.: (31) 30 82 00 567
Fax: (31) 848 35 97 46
Web Site: www.distimo.com
Sales Range: $1-9.9 Million
Business Description:
Mobile Analytics Software
S.I.C.: 7372
N.A.I.C.S.: 511210
Personnel:
Vincent Hoogsteder *(Co-Founder & CEO)*
Ruben Heerdink *(Co-Founder & COO)*
Tom Jansen *(Co-Founder & CTO)*
Remco van den Elzen *(Co-Founder & Chief Comml Officer)*

DISTINCTIVE DESIGNS FURNITURE, INC.

600 Clayson Road
North York, ON, M9M 2H2, Canada
Tel.: (416) 740-7773
Fax: (416) 740-7776
E-Mail: info@ddfi.com
Web Site: www.distinctivedesignsfurniture.com
Emp.: 80
Business Description:
Furniture Mfr
S.I.C.: 2512
N.A.I.C.S.: 337121
Personnel:
Alan Kornblum *(Pres)*

DISTRIBUTEL COMMUNICATIONS LIMITED

300 177 Nepean St
Ottawa, ON, K2P 0B4, Canada
Tel.: (613) 237-7055
Fax: (613) 237-7014
Toll Free: (866) 872-2800
Web Site: www.distributel.ca
Year Founded: 1988
Business Description:
Wired Telecommunication & Internet Services

S.I.C.: 4813
N.A.I.C.S.: 517110
Personnel:
Mel Cohen *(Founder & Pres)*

DISTRIBUTION AND WAREHOUSING NETWORK LIMITED

Cnr Barlow Road & Cavaleros Drive
Jupiter Ext 3
Germiston, 1401, South Africa
Mailing Address:
Postnet Suit No 100
Private Bag X1037, Germiston, 1400, South Africa
Tel.: (27) 113230450
Fax: (27) 113230466
E-Mail: info@dawnltd.co.za
Web Site: www.dawnltd.co.za
DAW—(JSE)
Rev.: $512,518,025
Assets: $344,364,510
Liabilities: $180,457,605
Net Worth: $163,906,905
Earnings: $17,786,550
Emp.: 3,668
Fiscal Year-end: 06/30/13
Business Description:
Hardware, Sanitary Ware Mfr & Whslr
S.I.C.: 3499
N.A.I.C.S.: 332999
Personnel:
Derek A. Tod *(CEO)*
Collin J. Bishop *(COO)*
Jan A. Beukes *(Risk & Internal Audit Officer & Sec)*
R. P. Haynes *(Exec-Brands)*
M. Coetzee *(CEO-Sanitaryware Cluster)*
Gerhard D. Kotzee *(CEO-Infrastructure Cluster)*
R. D. Roos *(CEO-DAWN Solutions)*
Pieter J. van Niekerk *(CEO-Intl Cluster)*
Board of Directors:
R. L. Hiemstra
M. Akoojee
Lou M. Alberts
Osman S. Arbee
Jan A. Beukes
J. A. I. Ferreira
Veli J. Mokoena
R. D. Roos
Derek A. Tod
Transfer Agent:
Computershare Investor Services (Pty) Limited
70 Marshall Street
PO Box 61051
2107 Marshalltown, South Africa
Subsidiaries:

Africa Swiss Trading (Proprietary) Limited **(1)**
C/O Barlow & Caveleros Dr Jupiter Ext 3
Germiston, Johannesburg, Gauteng, 1401, South Africa
Tel.: (27) 113230000
Fax: (27) 113230343
E-Mail: info@africaswisstrading.co.za
Web Site: www.africaswisstrading.com
Kitchen & Bathroom Accessories Supplier
S.I.C.: 5023
N.A.I.C.S.: 423220

Cobra Watertech (Proprietary) Limited **(1)**
18 Ealing Crescent
Bryanston, Johannesburg, Gauteng, 2194, South Africa
Tel.: (27) 118757400
Fax: (27) 118757401
E-Mail: enquires@cobrataps.co.za
Web Site: www.cobra.co.za
Emp.: 20
Taps Mfr
S.I.C.: 3643
N.A.I.C.S.: 335931
Ken Kearns *(Gen Mgr)*

Dawn Kitchen Fittings (Proprietary) Limited **(1)**
6 Barlinka Rd Saxon Bldg
Johannesburg, Gauteng, 2195, South Africa
Tel.: (27) 219051225
Fax: (27) 219052446
E-Mail: orderscpt@affgroup.co.za
Web Site: www.roco.co.za
Emp.: 50
Kitchen Fittings Whslr
S.I.C.: 5719
N.A.I.C.S.: 442299
Christophe Pichon *(Mgr-Bus Dev)*

DPI Holdings (Proprietary) Limited **(1)**
1 Setchell Rd
Roodekop, Germiston, Gauteng, 1401, South Africa
Tel.: (27) 113455600
Fax: (27) 1134555655
Web Site: www.dpiplastics.co.za
Emp.: 240
Polyvinyl Chloride Pipes Mfr & Distr
S.I.C.: 3084
N.A.I.C.S.: 326122
Renier Snyman *(Mgr-Tech)*

DPI Plastics (Proprietary) Limited **(1)**
Setchell Rd
Roodekop, Gauteng, 1401, South Africa
Tel.: (27) 113455600
Fax: (27) 113455780
E-Mail: headoffice@dpiplastics.co.za
Web Site: www.dpiplastics.co.za
Emp.: 250
Polyvinyl Chloride Pipes Mfr
S.I.C.: 3084
N.A.I.C.S.: 326122
Japie Bester *(Mng Dir)*

Isca (Proprietary) Limited **(1)**
131 10th Rd
Kew, Johannesburg, Gauteng, 2090, South Africa
Tel.: (27) 118829100
Fax: (27) 118828321
E-Mail: info@isca.co.za
Web Site: www.isca.co.za
Emp.: 200
Brass Taps & Mixers Mfr
S.I.C.: 3643
N.A.I.C.S.: 335931
Brett Solomon *(Mng Dir)*

Vaal Sanitaryware (Proprietary) Limited **(1)**
Corner Morris & Lilly Rd
Meyerton, Gauteng, 1961, South Africa
Tel.: (27) 163606000
Fax: (27) 163621167
E-Mail: vaalsan@dawnltd.co.za
Web Site: www.vaalsan.co.za
Emp.: 500
Sanitary Ware Mfr & Sales
S.I.C.: 3499
N.A.I.C.S.: 332999
Herman Breytenbach *(Mng Dir)*
Martin Coetzee *(CEO-Dawn Sanitaryware Div)*

Non-U.S. Subsidiaries:

Africa Swiss Trading (Mauritius) Limited **(1)**
3rd Fl Aisha Bldg 25 27 Louis Pasteur St
Port Louis, Mauritius
Tel.: (230) 217 3643
Fax: (230) 217 3642
E-Mail: info@astmauritius.com
Building Materials Whslr
S.I.C.: 5039
N.A.I.C.S.: 423390
Dominique Edmond *(Mng Dir)*

Africa Swiss Trading (Zambia) Limited **(1)**
Plot 7305 Kambala Rd Indus Area
Lusaka, Zambia
Tel.: (260) 211287230
Fax: (260) 211287235
Emp.: 12
Kitchen & Bathroom Accessories Distr
S.I.C.: 5023
N.A.I.C.S.: 423220
Ivan Botha *(Mng Dir)*

DISTRIBUTION MARCEL DION INC.

1660 boul Industriel
Farnham, QC, J2N 2X8, Canada
Tel.: (450) 293-3909
Fax: (450) 293-2998
Toll Free: (888) 273-3909
E-Mail: support@dmdion.com
Web Site: www.dmdion.com
Year Founded: 1948
Rev.: $20,124,345
Emp.: 70
Business Description:
Truck Transportation Services
S.I.C.: 4214
N.A.I.C.S.: 484110
Personnel:
Sylvain Dion *(Pres)*

DISTRIBUTION TECHNOLOGY LTD.

Sovereign House Vastern Road
Reading, RG1 8BT, United Kingdom
Tel.: (44) 118 903 5850
Fax: (44) 118 950 3765
E-Mail: info@distribution-technology.com
Web Site: www1.distribution-technology.com
Year Founded: 2003
Sales Range: $10-24.9 Million
Emp.: 71
Business Description:
Financial Planning Software & Solutions
S.I.C.: 7372
N.A.I.C.S.: 511210
Personnel:
Ben Goss *(CEO)*
Board of Directors:
Ges Whitmore
Neil Brown
Ben Goss
David Wadsworth

DISTRIBUTIONS JRV INC.

5 Rue Regnault
Sept-Iles, QC, G4R 3R4, Canada
Tel.: (418) 962-9457
Fax: (418) 962-9461
E-Mail: jrv@jrv.com
Web Site: www.jrv.com
Year Founded: 1946
Rev.: $10,804,892
Emp.: 100
Business Description:
Industrial Equipment Distr
S.I.C.: 5085
N.A.I.C.S.: 423840
Personnel:
Daniel Larouche *(Pres)*

DITEM EXPLORATIONS INC.

1155 University Street Suite 1308
Montreal, QC, H3B 3A7, Canada
Tel.: (514) 706-1006
Fax: (514) 878-3041
E-Mail: david.vincent@ditem.com
Web Site: www.ditem.com
DIT—(DEU OTC TSXV)
Sales Range: Less than $1 Million
Business Description:
Uranium Exploration Services
S.I.C.: 1094
N.A.I.C.S.: 212291
Personnel:
Raymond Savoie *(Chm & CEO)*
Mario Joly *(Pres)*
Richard-Marc Lacasse *(CFO & VP-Fin)*
Anik Fontaine *(Legal Counsel & Sec)*
Estelle Dufresne *(Sec)*
Board of Directors:
Raymond Savoie
Raymond Davies
Nicholas Di Perno
Lo-Sun Jen
Richard-Marc Lacasse
Transfer Agent:
Computershare Investor Services Inc.
Montreal, QC, Canada

DIVA CORPORATION

(Name Changed to Avant Corporation)

DIVCOM LIGHTING INC.

939 Selkirk Avenue
Pointe-Claire, QC, H9R 4S4, Canada
Tel.: (514) 693-2117
Fax: (514) 693-2177
Toll Free: (877) 693-2117
Year Founded: 1999
DVQ—(TSXV)
Sales Range: $25-49.9 Million
Emp.: 185
Business Description:
Electric Lighting Equipment Mfr
S.I.C.: 3646
N.A.I.C.S.: 335122
Subsidiaries:

Diversified Architectural Lighting Inc. **(1)**
30 Rolland Briere, Suite 104
Blainville, QC, J7C 5R8, Canada
Tel.: (450) 430-1818
Fax: (450) 430-1850
E-Mail: info@dalslighting.com
Web Site: www.dalslighting.com
Emp.: 45
Architectural Lighting Products Designer & Mfr
S.I.C.: 3646
N.A.I.C.S.: 335122
Aslam Khatri *(CEO)*

SNOC Inc. **(1)**
17200 Centrale
Saint-Hyacinthe, QC, J2T 4J7, Canada
Tel.: (450) 774-5823
Fax: (450) 774-3874
E-Mail: info@snoc.net
Web Site: www.snoc.net
Emp.: 100
Cast Aluminum Residential Outdoor Lighting Fixtures Mfr
S.I.C.: 3645
N.A.I.C.S.: 335121

DIVERSA LIMITED

Level 9 Waterfront Place 1 Eagle Street
Brisbane, QLD, 4000, Australia
Mailing Address:
GPO Box 836
Brisbane, QLD, 4001, Australia
Tel.: (61) 7 3212 9250
Fax: (61) 7 3211 8307
E-Mail: mail@diversa.com.au
Web Site: www.diversa.com.au
Year Founded: 2009
DVA—(ASX DEU)
Rev.: $4,758,602
Assets: $7,840,526
Liabilities: $8,124,863
Net Worth: ($284,337)
Earnings: ($2,935,247)
Emp.: 24
Fiscal Year-end: 06/30/13
Business Description:
Investment Management Services
S.I.C.: 6799
N.A.I.C.S.: 523920
Personnel:
Vincent Parrott *(CEO & Head-Funds Mgmt & Trustee Svcs)*
Angus Craig *(CFO & Sec)*
Board of Directors:
Stuart Korchinski
Stephen Bizzell

Diversa Limited—(Continued)

Garry Crole
Matthew Morgan

DIVERSCO SUPPLY INC.
495 Conestoga Blvd
Cambridge, ON, N1R 7P4, Canada
Tel.: (519) 740-1210
Fax: (519) 740-7303
Toll Free: (800) 661-9955
Web Site: www.diverscosupply.com
Year Founded: 1986
Rev.: $24,931,116
Emp.: 50
Business Description:
Propane Equipment Whslr
S.I.C.: 1389
N.A.I.C.S.: 213112
Personnel:
Jon Huddle *(Co-Founder)*
Bob Statham *(Co-Founder)*

DIVERSIFIED ALPHA FUND II
161 Bay Street 27th Floor
Toronto, ON, M5J 2S1, Canada
Tel.: (416) 285-0050
E-Mail: kmatheson@propelcapital.ca
AFT.UN—(TSX)
Business Description:
Investment Services
S.I.C.: 6211
N.A.I.C.S.: 523999
Personnel:
Michael Simonetta *(Chm)*
Raj Lala *(Pres & CEO)*
Krista Matheson *(CFO, Chief Compliance Officer & Sr VP)*
Board of Directors:
Michael Simonetta
Raj Lala
Krista Matheson
Transfer Agent:
Computershare Investor Services Inc.
Montreal, QC, Canada

DIVERSIFIED UNITED INVESTMENT LIMITED
Level 20 101 Collins Street
Melbourne, VIC, 3000, Australia
Tel.: (61) 3 9654 0499
Fax: (61) 3 9654 3499
E-Mail: info@dui.com.au
Web Site: www.dui.com.au
Year Founded: 1991
DUI—(ASX)
Rev.: $29,331,989
Assets: $646,488,619
Liabilities: $133,775,419
Net Worth: $512,713,200
Earnings: $24,634,202
Fiscal Year-end: 06/30/13
Business Description:
Investment Management Services
S.I.C.: 6211
N.A.I.C.S.: 523999
Personnel:
Charles Barrington Goode *(Chm)*
Andrew J. Hancock *(Sec)*
Board of Directors:
Charles Barrington Goode
Anthony R. Burgess
Stephen G. Hiscock
Pierre R. Prentice

DIVESTCO INC.
300 520 3rd Avenue SW
Calgary, AB, T2P 0R3, Canada
Tel.: (587) 952-8000
Fax: (587) 952-8370
Toll Free: (888) 294-0081
E-Mail: info@divestco.com
Web Site: www.divestco.com
DVT—(OTC TSXV)
Rev.: $39,391,025
Assets: $41,694,169
Liabilities: $25,473,751
Net Worth: $16,220,418
Earnings: $1,265,387
Emp.: 500
Fiscal Year-end: 12/31/12
Business Description:
Oil & Gas Industry Software Developer, Data Integration & Consulting Services
S.I.C.: 7379
N.A.I.C.S.: 541519
Personnel:
Edward L. Molnar *(Chm)*
Stephen Popadynetz *(Pres, CEO & CFO)*
Steve Sinclair-Smith *(COO)*
Faralee A. Chanin *(Sec)*
Lonn Hornsby *(Sr VP-Ops-Divestco Seismic LP)*
Board of Directors:
Edward L. Molnar
Wade Brillon
Brent Gough
Stephen Popadynetz
William Tobman
Transfer Agent:
Canadian Stock Transfer Company Inc
PO Box 721
Agincourt, ON, MIS 0AI, Canada

U.S. Subsidiary:

Divertco USA Inc. (1)
1900 Grant St Ste 850
Denver, CO 80203
Tel.: (303) 571-1942
Fax: (909) 860-0066
Toll Free: (800) 900-5737
Web Site: www.divestco.com
Software Developer for the Oil & Gas Industry; Data, Seismic Brokerage & Technical Services
S.I.C.: 7379
N.A.I.C.S.: 541519

DIVI ARUBA BEACH RESORT
JE Irausquin Blvd 41
Oranjestad, Aruba
Tel.: (297) 5255200
Fax: (297) 5255209
Toll Free: 8005542008
E-Mail: reservation@magaresorgs.com
Web Site: www.diviaruba.com
Emp.: 1,000
Business Description:
Resort & Hotel
S.I.C.: 7011
N.A.I.C.S.: 721110
Personnel:
Alex Nieuwmeyer *(Mng Dir)*

DIVIDEND GROWTH SPLIT CORP.
Suite 2930 Bay Wellington Tower 181 Bay Street
PO Box 793
Toronto, ON, M5J 2T3, Canada
Tel.: (416) 642-9050
Fax: (416) 642-0001
Year Founded: 2007
DGS—(TSX)
Rev.: $4,741,470
Assets: $107,159,833
Liabilities: $64,555,046
Net Worth: $42,604,787
Earnings: $308,088
Fiscal Year-end: 12/31/12
Business Description:
Financial Investment Services
S.I.C.: 6211
N.A.I.C.S.: 523999
Personnel:
Mark A. Caranci *(Pres & CEO)*
Transfer Agent:
Equity Financial Trust Company
Toronto, ON, Canada

DIVIS LABORATORIES LIMITED
Divi Towers 7-1-77E/1/303 Dharam Karan Road Ameerpet
Hyderabad, Andhra Pradesh, 500 016, India
Tel.: (91) 40 2378 6300
Fax: (91) 40 2378 6460
E-Mail: mail@divislaboratories.com
Web Site: www.divislaboratories.com
Year Founded: 1990
532488—(BOM NSE)
Rev.: $405,961,073
Assets: $581,926,957
Liabilities: $118,316,347
Net Worth: $463,610,610
Earnings: $111,613,210
Emp.: 4,000
Fiscal Year-end: 03/31/13
Business Description:
Chemical Compound Mfr
S.I.C.: 2899
N.A.I.C.S.: 325998
Personnel:
Murali K. Divi *(Chm & Mng Dir)*
L. Kishore Babu *(CFO)*
P. V. Lakshmi Rajani *(Compliance Officer & Sec)*
Board of Directors:
Murali K. Divi
Kiran S. Divi
Madhusudana Rao Divi
G. Suresh Kumar
N. V. Ramana
Ravipati Ranga Rao
K. Satyanarayana
S. Vasudev
Transfer Agent:
Karvy Computershare Private Limited
Plot No 17 to 24 Vittalrao Nagar Madhapur
Hyderabad, India

DIVYA JYOTI INDUSTRIES LIMITED
Plot No M 19-39 Sector-III Industrial Area
Pithampur, MP, 454 775, India
Tel.: (91) 7292 421900
Fax: (91) 7292 421947
E-Mail: works@divyajyoti.net
Web Site: www.divyajyoti.net
526285—(BOM)
Rev.: $72,811,269
Assets: $10,931,497
Liabilities: $7,561,704
Net Worth: $3,369,793
Earnings: $263,778
Fiscal Year-end: 03/31/13
Business Description:
Edible Oils Refining
S.I.C.: 2079
N.A.I.C.S.: 311225
Personnel:
Sanjay Bawej *(CEO)*
Mala Rohara *(CFO)*
Anirudh Nyati *(COO)*
Sweety Rai *(Sec)*
Board of Directors:
Rangnath Nyat
Girdhari R. Nyati
Gopal Nyati
Sudarshan Shastri
Shriniwas Soni
Transfer Agent:
Link Intime India Private Limited
C-13 Pannalal Silk Mills Compound L.B.S. Marg Bhandup
Mumbai, India

DIVYASHAKTI GRANITES LIMITED
1-304 3rd Floor Divyashakti Complex
Ameerpet, Hyderabad, Andhra Pradesh, 500 628, India
Tel.: (91) 40 2373 0240
Fax: (91) 40 2373 0013
E-Mail: info@divyashakti.com
Web Site: www.divyashakti.com
Year Founded: 1993
526315—(BOM)
Sales Range: $1-9.9 Million
Business Description:
Polished Granite Mfr & Distr
S.I.C.: 3281
N.A.I.C.S.: 327991
Personnel:
D. N. Satyanarayana *(Compliance Officer)*

DIXIE ELECTRIC LTD.
517 Basaltic Road
Concord, ON, L4K 4W8, Canada
Tel.: (905) 879-0533
Fax: (905) 879-0532
E-Mail: sales@dixie-electric.com
Web Site: www.dixie-electric.com
Year Founded: 1968
Rev.: $55,818,658
Emp.: 600
Business Description:
Automotive Repair & Services
S.I.C.: 7539
N.A.I.C.S.: 811118
Personnel:
Angelo Bucciol *(Founder & Co-Pres)*
Voiko Loukanov *(Co-Pres & Gen Mgr)*

DIXIE ENERGY TRUST
620 12th Avenue SW Suite 400
Calgary, AB, T2R 0H5, Canada
Tel.: (403) 232-1010
Fax: (403) 266-8886
Web Site: www.dixieenergytrust.com
Year Founded: 2012
Assets: $7,267,656
Liabilities: $649,056
Net Worth: $6,618,600
Earnings: ($1,107,085)
Fiscal Year-end: 12/31/12
Business Description:
Oil & Gas Real Estate Investment Trust
S.I.C.: 6726
N.A.I.C.S.: 525990
Personnel:
David G. Anderson *(Pres)*
Kevin D. Dumba *(CFO)*
Board of Directors:
Ian Atkinson
David G. Anderson
Earl Fawcett
Rick Fletcher
Jeff Oke

DIXON ELECTRIC
1158 Lorne Street
Sudbury, ON, P3C 4S9, Canada
Tel.: (705) 674-1981
Fax: (705) 674-2428
Toll Free: (800) 461-1132
Web Site: www.dixonelectric.ca
Rev.: $13,355,955
Emp.: 40
Business Description:
Electrical Contractors
S.I.C.: 1731
N.A.I.C.S.: 238210
Personnel:
Steve St Marseille *(VP & Gen Mgr)*

DIXON NETWORKS CORPORATION
7782 Progress Way
Delta, BC, Canada V4G 1A4

Tel.: (604) 940-8817
Fax: (604) 940-8827
Toll Free: (866) 940-8817
E-Mail: info@dixonnetworks.com
Web Site: www.dixonnetworks.com
Year Founded: 1966
Rev.: $49,732,511
Emp.: 300
Business Description:
Engineering Services
S.I.C.: 8711
N.A.I.C.S.: 541330
Personnel:
Steve V. Sanders *(Chm)*
Brian Dixon *(Pres)*
David Baird *(CEO)*
Glen Hawker *(Exec VP)*

DIXON, R B HOLDINGS LTD.
(d/b/a Regina Mazda Sales)
600 Broad St
Regina, SK, S4R 8H8, Canada
Tel.: (306) 543-3345
Fax: (306) 949-4744
Toll Free: (888) 832-2777
E-Mail: jhardy@reginamazda.ca
Web Site: www.reginamazda.ca
Rev.: $10,397,709
Emp.: 19
Business Description:
New & Used Car Dealers
S.I.C.: 5511
N.A.I.C.S.: 441110
Personnel:
Barry Dixon *(Pres & Gen Mgr)*

DIXONS RETAIL PLC
Maylands Avenue
Hemel Hempstead, Herts, HP2 7TG, United Kingdom
Tel.: (44) 844 800 2030
Fax: (44) 1442 233 218
E-Mail: customer.services@dixonsretail.com
Web Site: www.dsgiplc.com
Year Founded: 1937
DXNS—(LSE)
Rev.: $13,328,102,097
Assets: $4,745,292,663
Liabilities: $4,512,663,246
Net Worth: $232,629,417
Earnings: ($265,478,649)
Emp.: 35,892
Fiscal Year-end: 04/30/13
Business Description:
Holding Company; Electronic Retail Services
Import
S.I.C.: 6719
N.A.I.C.S.: 551112
Personnel:
John Allan *(Chm)*
Sebastian James *(CEO)*
Gary Booker *(CMO-UK & Ireland)*
Katie Bickerstaffe *(CEO-UK & Ireland)*
Helen Grantham *(Gen Counsel & Sec)*
Board of Directors:
John Allan
Katie Bickerstaffe
Utho Creusen
Tim How
Sebastian James
Andrea Gisle Joosen
Jock Fyfe Lennox
Dharmash Mistry
Humphrey Singer
Transfer Agent:
Capita Registrars
Northern House Woodsome Park Fenay Bridge
Huddersfield, United Kingdom
Subsidiaries:

Currys Group Ltd. **(1)**
Maylands Avenue
Hemel Hempstead, Herts, HP2 7TG, United Kingdom UK
Tel.: (44) 1442353000 (100%)
Fax: (44) 144233218
Web Site: www.currys.co.uk
Electrical Appliance Retailer
S.I.C.: 5734
N.A.I.C.S.: 443142

Dixons Stores Group Ltd. **(1)**
Maylands Ave
Hemel Hempstead, Herts, HP2 7TG, United Kingdom (100%)
Tel.: (44) 8458500545
Telex: 934594
Web Site: www.dixons.co.uk
Consumer Electronics Retailer
S.I.C.: 5734
N.A.I.C.S.: 443142

DIZUN INTERNATIONAL ENTERPRISES INC.
Suite 605 6068 3 Road
Richmond, BC, V6Y 4M7, Canada
Tel.: (604) 721-1883
Fax: (778) 234-0223
E-Mail: info@dizuntea.ca
Web Site: www.dizuntea.ca
KDZ—(CNSX)
Business Description:
Tea & Tea Products
S.I.C.: 2099
N.A.I.C.S.: 311920
Personnel:
Shaohui Kang *(Pres & CEO)*
Board of Directors:
Shaohui Kang
Susanna Leung

DJERRIWARRH INVESTMENTS LIMITED
Level 21 101 Collins Street
Melbourne, VIC, 3000, Australia
Tel.: (61) 396509911
Fax: (61) 396509100
E-Mail: invest@djerri.com.au
Web Site: www.djerri.com.au
DJW—(ASX)
Sales Range: $25-49.9 Million
Business Description:
Investment Management
S.I.C.: 6282
N.A.I.C.S.: 523920
Personnel:
Ross E. Barker *(Mng Dir)*
Andrew J. B. Porter *(CFO & Co-Sec)*
R. Mark Freeman *(Chief Investment Officer)*
Simon M. Pordage *(Co-Sec)*
Board of Directors:
John Paterson
Ross E. Barker
Peter C. Barnett
Graham B. Goldsmith
Andrew F. Guy
Graham J. Kraehe
Bruce B. Teele
Alice J. M. Williams

DK AZTEC CO., LTD.
459-19 Jimun-ro Wongok-myeon
Anseong, Korea (South)
Tel.: (82) 70 7731 4617
Fax: (82) 31 652 4798
Web Site: www.dkaztec.com
Business Description:
Crystal Material Mfr
S.I.C.: 3299
N.A.I.C.S.: 327999
Personnel:
Seonggyun Kim *(CEO)*

DK FORD SALES LTD
6559 Sparrow Drive
Leduc, AB, T9E 7L1, Canada
Tel.: (780) 986-2929
Fax: (780) 986-9639
Toll Free: (866) 986-2929
E-Mail: info@dkford.com
Web Site: www.dkford.com
Year Founded: 1993
Rev.: $26,076,800
Emp.: 35
Business Description:
New & Used Car Dealers
S.I.C.: 5511
N.A.I.C.S.: 441110
Personnel:
Lisa MacKenzie *(Controller)*

DK SINOPHARMA, INC.
Dongxing Building 4th Floor 1 Xinke Road
Xi'an, 710043, China
Tel.: (86) 2982247500
Fax: (86) 2982214688
E-Mail: dkmds@dkmds.com
Web Site: www.dkmds.com
Year Founded: 2008
DKSP—(OTC)
Business Description:
Pharmaceutical Mfr
S.I.C.: 2834
N.A.I.C.S.: 325412
Personnel:
Dongke Zhao *(Chm, Pres & CEO)*
Yanhong Ren *(CFO)*
Board of Directors:
Dongke Zhao
Yanhong Ren

DK-SPEC INC.
1060 chemin Olivier
Saint-Nicolas, QC, G7A 2M8, Canada
Tel.: (418) 831-3333
Fax: (418) 831-0201
Toll Free: (888) 686-3847
E-Mail: info@dkspec.com
Web Site: www.dkspec.com
Rev.: $14,718,407
Emp.: 100
Business Description:
Hand & Edge Tool Mfr
S.I.C.: 3423
N.A.I.C.S.: 332216
Personnel:
Clermont Levasseur *(Pres)*

DK TECH CORPORATION
826 Naesam-Ri Juchon-Myeon
Gimhae City, Gyeongnam, 621-841, Korea (South)
Tel.: (82) 553380114
Fax: (82) 553386746
Web Site: www.dklok.com
Year Founded: 1986
105740—(KRS)
Emp.: 180
Business Description:
Tube Fittings & Valves Mfr & Sales
S.I.C.: 3492
N.A.I.C.S.: 332912
Personnel:
Eun-Sik Noh *(Pres)*

DKK-TOA CORPORATION
29-10 1-Chome Takadanobaba
Shinjuku-ku, Tokyo, 169-8648, Japan
Tel.: (81) 3 3202 0211
Fax: (81) 3 3202 0220
Web Site: www.toadkk.co.jp
Year Founded: 1944
6848—(TKS)
Emp.: 403
Business Description:
Measuring Instrument Mfr & Whslr
S.I.C.: 3823
N.A.I.C.S.: 334513
Personnel:
Yasuo Yamamori *(Chm)*
Teruo Sasaki *(Pres)*
Toshio Takahashi *(Sr Mng Dir)*
Akio Tamai *(Sr Mng Dir)*
Morizo Nakamura *(Mng Dir)*
Board of Directors:
Yasuo Yamamori
Shinichi Akazawa
Jonathan O. Clark
Tomoo Matsuno
Hiromitsu Moridera
Morizo Nakamura
Teruo Sasaki
Toshio Takahashi
Akio Tamai
Takashi Ueno
Kazuto Yamashita

DKLS INDUSTRIES BERHAD
16th Floor & Penthouse Ipoh Tower
Jalan Dato Seri Ahmad Said
30450 Ipoh, Perak Darul Ridzuan, Malaysia
Tel.: (60) 52532688
Fax: (60) 52532701
Web Site: www.dkls.com.my
DKLS—(KLS)
Rev.: $70,113,570
Assets: $149,627,089
Liabilities: $54,448,056
Net Worth: $95,179,033
Earnings: $5,324,311
Fiscal Year-end: 12/31/12
Business Description:
Construction & Property Management Services
S.I.C.: 6531
N.A.I.C.S.: 531311
Personnel:
Pei Chai Ding *(Chm)*
Poi Bor Ding *(Mng Dir)*
May Yoke Chan *(Co-Sec)*
Weng Hoong Cheai *(Co-Sec)*
Board of Directors:
Pei Chai Ding
Omar Ahmad
Poi Bor Ding
Soo King Ding
Choo Boon Lim
Tuck Wah Sam
Yoke Yan Soh
Subsidiaries:

DKLS Construction Sdn Bhd **(1)**
16th Floor & Penthouse Ipoh Tower Jalan Dato Seri Ahmad Said
30450 Ipoh, Perak, Malaysia
Tel.: (60) 52532688
Fax: (60) 52532701
E-Mail: enquiry@dkls.com.my
Emp.: 30
Property Development & Construction Services
S.I.C.: 6531
N.A.I.C.S.: 531390
Ding Poibor *(Mgr)*

DKLS Development Sdn. Bhd. **(1)**
51E First Floor Jalan Raja Omar
32000 Sitiawan, Perak, Malaysia
Tel.: (60) 56925531
Fax: (60) 5 6925 535
E-Mail: development@dkls.com.my
Property Construction Services
S.I.C.: 1522
N.A.I.C.S.: 236116
Julia Koo *(Mgr)*

DKLS Energy Sdn. Bhd. **(1)**
16th Floor & Penthouse Ipoh Tower Jalan Dato Seri Ahmad Said
30450 Ipoh, Perak, Malaysia
Tel.: (60) 52532688
Fax: (60) 52532701

DKLS Industries Berhad—(Continued)

E-Mail: enquiry@dkls.com.my
Web Site: www.dkls.com.my/energy/
Hydroelectric Power Generation Services
S.I.C.: 4931
N.A.I.C.S.: 221111
Kong Aheoon *(Mgr-Contract)*

DKLS Precast System Sdn Bhd (1)
16th Floor & Penthouse Ipoh Tower Jln Dato Seri Ahmad Said
30450 Ipoh, Perak, Malaysia
Tel.: (60) 56833146
Fax: (60) 52532701
E-Mail: precast@dkls.com.my
Emp.: 150
Precast Concrete Mfr & Distr
S.I.C.: 3272
N.A.I.C.S.: 327390
Julia Koo *(Mgr)*

DKLS Quarry & Premix Sdn. Bhd. (1)
51E 1st Floor Jalan Raja Omar Sitiawan
32000 Sitiawan, Perak, Malaysia
Tel.: (60) 56914660
Fax: (60) 56914910
Emp.: 30
Sand Quarrying Services
S.I.C.: 1442
N.A.I.C.S.: 212321
Lawrence Ling *(Mgr-Quarry)*

DKS CO. LTD.

5 Ogawara-cho Kisshoin
Minami-ku, Kyoto, 601-8391, Japan
Tel.: (81) 75 323 5911
Fax: (81) 75 326 7356
Web Site: www.dks-web.jp
Year Founded: 1909
4461—(TKS)
Sales Range: $550-599.9 Million
Emp.: 861

Business Description:
Surfactant Mfr & Distr
S.I.C.: 2899
N.A.I.C.S.: 325998

Personnel:
Masatoshi Oyanagi *(Pres)*

DL SOFTWARE

50 rue de Monceau
75008 Paris, France
Tel.: (33) 158572294
Fax: (33) 158572289
E-Mail: info@dlsoftware.fr
Web Site: www.dlsoftware.fr
ALSDL—(EUR)
Sales Range: $25-49.9 Million
Emp.: 330

Business Description:
Software Products
S.I.C.: 7372
N.A.I.C.S.: 511210

Personnel:
Jean-Noel Drouin *(Pres)*
Patrick Lemaire *(Dir Gen)*

DLALA BROKERAGE AND INVESTMENTS HOLDING COMPANY Q.S.C

PO Box 24571
Doha, Qatar
Tel.: (974) 4284443
Web Site: www.dlalaholding.com
Year Founded: 2005
DBIS—(QE)
Rev.: $10,072,341
Assets: $160,487,035
Liabilities: $101,154,242
Net Worth: $59,332,793
Earnings: $6,977,453
Fiscal Year-end: 12/31/12

Business Description:
Brokerage Services
S.I.C.: 6411
N.A.I.C.S.: 524210

Personnel:
Mohamed Nasser Al Qahtani *(Chm)*
Nasser Hamad Al Sulaiti *(Vice Chm)*
Abdulhameed Sultan J. M. Al-Jaber *(CEO)*
Ahmad Mohamed Al Asmakh *(Mng Dir)*

Board of Directors:
Mohamed Nasser Al Qahtani
Ahmad Mohamed Al Asmakh
AbdulRahman Ahmed Al Mana
Moza Mohamed Al Sulaiti
Nasser Hamad Al Sulaiti
Waleed Raslan Al-Abdulla
Ali Hussain Al-Sada
Suhaim Khalid Al-Thani

Subsidiaries:

Dlala Islamic Brokerage Company (W.L.L) (1)
PO Box 24571
Doha, Qatar
Tel.: (974) 44285444
Fax: (974) 44285333
E-Mail: info@dlalaislamic.com
Web Site: www.dlalaislamic.com
Securities Brokerage Services
S.I.C.: 6211
N.A.I.C.S.: 523120

Dlala Real Estate S.P.C. (1)
PO Box 24571
Doha, Qatar
Tel.: (974) 44286660
Fax: (974) 44285220
E-Mail: realestate@dlalaholding.com
Web Site: www.dlalarealestate.com
Real Estate Management Services
S.I.C.: 6531
N.A.I.C.S.: 531390
Ahmad Al Asmakh *(Mng Dir)*

DLE INC.

7F KDX Kojimachi Building 3-3-4 Koji-machi
Chiyoda-ku, Tokyo, 102-0083, Japan
Tel.: (81) 3 3221 3990
Web Site: www.dle.jp/jp/
Rev.: $9,202,226
Emp.: 50
Fiscal Year-end: 06/30/13

Business Description:
Movie & Video Production
S.I.C.: 7812
N.A.I.C.S.: 512110

Personnel:
Ryuta Shiiki *(CEO)*

DLF AMBA

Ny Ostergade 9
4000 Roskilde, Denmark
Tel.: (45) 46 33 03 00
Fax: (45) 46 33 08 30
Web Site: www.dlf.dk

Business Description:
Grass & Clover Seed Producer & Whlsr
S.I.C.: 0119
N.A.I.C.S.: 111199

Personnel:
Stig Pddershede *(Chief Comm Officer)*

DLF LIMITED

DLF Shopping Mall 3rd Floor Arjun Marg DLF City Phase-I
Gurgaon, 122002, India
Tel.: (91) 1244334200
Fax: (91) 1244334405
Web Site: www.dlf.in
DLF—(NSE)
Rev.: $1,686,350,789
Assets: $11,981,802,991
Liabilities: $6,803,634,182
Net Worth: $5,178,168,809
Earnings: $131,989,801
Emp.: 2,600
Fiscal Year-end: 03/31/13

Business Description:
Real Estate Services
S.I.C.: 6514
N.A.I.C.S.: 531110

Personnel:
Kushal Pal Singh *(Chm)*
Rajiv Singh *(Vice Chm)*
T. C. Goyal *(Mng Dir)*
Ashok Kumar Tyagi *(CFO)*
Subhash Setia *(Compliance Officer & Sec)*

Board of Directors:
Kushal Pal Singh
Pramod Bhasin
Brijendra Bhushan
T. C. Goyal
Dharam Vir Kapur
Rajiv Krishan Luthra
K. N. Memani
Narendra Pal Singh
Pia Singh
Rajiv Singh
G. S. Talwar

Transfer Agent:
Karvy Computershare Private Limited
Plot No 17-24 Vittal Rao Nagar Madhapur
Hyderabad, 500 081, India
Tel.: (91) 40 2342 0818

Subsidiaries:

DLF Akruti Info Parks (Pune) Limited (1)
Akruti Trade Ctr 6th Fl Rd No 7 Marol M I D C
Andheri E, Mumbai, Maharashtra, 400093, India
Tel.: (91) 2266772301
Fax: (91) 2228218230
Special Economic Zone Development Services
S.I.C.: 1542
N.A.I.C.S.: 236220

DLF Cyber City Developers Limited (1)
1-E Jhandewalan Extn 3rd Fl D-wing
Near Naaz Cinema Complex, New Delhi, 110 055, India
Tel.: (91) 1143013248
Fax: (91) 1143516537
Property Development Services
S.I.C.: 6531
N.A.I.C.S.: 531311

DLF Estate Developers Limited (1)
Shopping Mall Arjun Marg
DLF City Phase I, Gurgaon, Haryana, 122 002, India
Tel.: (91) 1242350418, ext. 1244334200
Fax: (91) 1242351011
Real Estate Property Development Services
S.I.C.: 6531
N.A.I.C.S.: 531390

DLF Financial Services Limited (1)
DLF Centre Sansad Marg
New Delhi, 110 001, India
Tel.: (91) 1123719300
Fax: (91) 1123719344
E-Mail: hrd@dlf.in
Real Estate Investment Services
S.I.C.: 6514
N.A.I.C.S.: 531110

DLF Golf Resort Limited (1)
DLF City Phase V
Gurgaon, Haryana, 122 009, India
Tel.: (91) 1244525274
Fax: (91) 1244525282
E-Mail: contact-golf@dlf.in
Web Site: www.dlfgolfresort.com
Emp.: 300
Golf Course Development & Management Services
S.I.C.: 1629
N.A.I.C.S.: 237990
Akash Ohri *(Mgr)*

DLF Home Developers Limited (1)
DLF Ctr Ground Fl
Sansad Marg, New Delhi, 110 001, India
Tel.: (91) 1142102030
Fax: (91) 1123719344
Residential Property Development Services
S.I.C.: 1522
N.A.I.C.S.: 236116

DLF Info City Developers (Chennai) Ltd. (1)
No 1 124 Shivaji Garden
Manapakkam Ramapuram, Chennai, Tamil Nadu, 600089, India
Tel.: (91) 4445497001
Fax: (91) 4445497001
Property Development Services
S.I.C.: 6531
N.A.I.C.S.: 531311

DLF Projects Limited (1)
DLF Cyber Greens Tower-C 17th Fl
DLF City Phase-111, Gurgaon, Haryana, 122002, India
Tel.: (91) 1244769000
Fax: (91) 1244769192
Emp.: 5,000
Real Estate Management Services
S.I.C.: 6531
N.A.I.C.S.: 531390

DLF Recreational Foundation Limited (1)
DLF City Club Opp Galleria Market
DLF City Phase IV, Gurgaon, Haryana, 122002, India
Tel.: (91) 1244129100
Fax: (91) 124 4050759
Real Estate Management Services
S.I.C.: 6531
N.A.I.C.S.: 531210

DLF Retail Developers Limited (1)
DLF Ctr Sansad Marg
New Delhi, 110 017, India
Tel.: (91) 1123719300
Fax: (91) 1123719344
Emp.: 12
Property Development & Management Services
S.I.C.: 6531
N.A.I.C.S.: 531312

DLF Services Limited (1)
DLF City Phase 1
Sector 55 56 Rd, Gurgaon, Haryana, 122002, India
Tel.: (91) 124 4108816
Fax: (91) 124 4108816
Air Cleaning Equipments Mfr & Sls
S.I.C.: 3822
N.A.I.C.S.: 334512

DLF Universal Limited (1)
DLF Ctr Sansad Marg
New Delhi, 110001, India
Tel.: (91) 1123719300
Fax: (91) 1123719344
Real Estate Development & Management Services
S.I.C.: 6531
N.A.I.C.S.: 531311

DLF Utilities Limited (1)
7th Fl Gateway Tower
Dlf City Phase III, Gurgaon, Haryana, 122002, India
Tel.: (91) 1244778718
Fax: (91) 1244376973
Project Construction Services
S.I.C.: 1623
N.A.I.C.S.: 237110

Shivajimarg Properties Limited (1)
1-E Jhandewalan Extn 3rd Fl D Wing
Near Naaz Cinema Complex, New Delhi, 110 055, India
Tel.: (91) 1143013248
Fax: (91) 1143516537
Real Estate Development Services
S.I.C.: 6531
N.A.I.C.S.: 531210

Non-U.S. Subsidiaries:

Amancruises Company Limited (1)
PO Box 292
Muang Phuket, Phuket, 83000, Thailand
Tel.: (66) 76271162
Fax: (66) 76270161
E-Mail: amancruises@amanpuri.th.com
Web Site: www.amanpuri.th.com
Emp.: 500
Boat & Yacht Rental Services
S.I.C.: 7999

N.A.I.C.S.: 532292
Frederic Varnier *(Gen Mgr)*

Amanresorts International Private Limited (1)
1 Orchard Spring Ln No 05-01 Tourism Ct
Singapore, 247729, Singapore
Tel.: (65) 6883 2555
Fax: (65) 6883 0555
E-Mail: info@amanresorts.com
Web Site: www.amanresorts.com
Resort Operation & Maintenance Services
S.I.C.: 8742
N.A.I.C.S.: 541611

Amanresorts IPR B.V. (1)
Naritaweg 165 Telestone 8
1043 BW Amsterdam, Netherlands
Tel.: (31) 20 5722300
Fax: (31) 205722653
Resort Management Services
S.I.C.: 7011
N.A.I.C.S.: 721110

Amanresorts Limited (1)
12th Fl Friendship Comml Bldg 105
Hollywood Rd
Central, China (Hong Kong)
Tel.: (852) 28685005
Fax: (852) 28685007
E-Mail: info@amanresorts.com
Emp.: 10
Hotel & Motel Management Services
S.I.C.: 7011
N.A.I.C.S.: 721110

DLF International Holdings Pte Limited (1)
9 Temasek Blvd
Singapore, Singapore 038989
Tel.: (65) 6305 2819
Fax: (65) 6305 2829
Emp.: 2
Property Management Services
S.I.C.: 6531
N.A.I.C.S.: 531312
Ee Ping Kho *(VP-Fin)*

P.T. Amanresorts Indonesia (1)
Jalan Nusa Dua Selatan
PO Box 33
Nusa Dua, Bali, 80361, Indonesia
Tel.: (62) 361772333
Fax: (62) 361772335
E-Mail: amanresorts@amanresorts.com
Web Site: www.amanresorts.com
Emp.: 175
Hotel Management Services
S.I.C.: 7011
N.A.I.C.S.: 721110
Monty Brown *(Mgr)*

Silverlink Holdings Limited (1)
Stockbridge House Trinity Gardens
Newcastle upon Tyne, Tyne And Wear, NE1 2HJ, United Kingdom
Tel.: (44) 1912220607
Fax: (44) 1912220506
E-Mail: info@silverlink-uk.com
Web Site: www.silverlink-uk.com
Emp.: 9
Property Development Services
S.I.C.: 6531
N.A.I.C.S.: 531312
David Clouston *(Mng Dir)*

D.L.G.L. LTD.

850 Michele Bohec
Blainville, QC, J7C 5E2, Canada
Tel.: (450) 979-4646
Fax: (450) 979-4650
E-Mail: info@dlgl.com
Web Site: www.dlgl.com
Year Founded: 1980
Rev.: $13,700,000
Emp.: 95
Business Description:
Computer Software Programming Services
S.I.C.: 7371
N.A.I.C.S.: 541511
Personnel:
Jacques Guenette *(Pres)*

DLS LAND UND SEE SPEDITIONSGESELLSCHAFT MBH

Jacobsrade 1
22962 Stormarn, Germany
Tel.: (49) 41073333
Fax: (49) 4107333100
E-Mail: Info@dls-Deutschland.de
Web Site: www.dls-deutschland.de
Year Founded: 1986
Rev.: $81,961,441
Emp.: 200
Business Description:
Transport & Logistic Solution Services
S.I.C.: 4499
N.A.I.C.S.: 488390
Personnel:
Bodo Engler *(CEO)*

DLSA AUTOMOBILES

29-31 Rue de Paris
95310 Saint-Ouen-l'Aumone, France
Tel.: (33) 134485656
Fax: (33) 134485666
Web Site: www.dlsaauto.com
Sls.: $21,900,000
Emp.: 30
Business Description:
New & Used Car Dealers
S.I.C.: 5511
N.A.I.C.S.: 441110
Personnel:
Patrick Paquis *(Dir-Pur)*
Board of Directors:
Roger Mancel

DM-DROGERIE MARKT GMBH & CO. KG

Carl Metz Str 1
76185 Karlsruhe, Germany
Tel.: (49) 72155920
Fax: (49) 721552213
E-Mail: servicecenter@dm-drogeriemarkt.de
Web Site: www.dm-drogeriemarkt.de
Year Founded: 1973
Sales Range: $1-4.9 Billion
Emp.: 21,000
Business Description:
Drug Stores
S.I.C.: 5912
N.A.I.C.S.: 446110
Personnel:
Erich Harsch *(CEO)*

DM HEALTHCARE MANAGEMENT SERVICES LLC

(d/b/a Moopen Group)
702-703 Khalid Bin Al Walid Street
PO Box 8703
Dubai, United Arab Emirates
Tel.: (971) 4 3933033
Fax: (971) 4 3933936
E-Mail: relations@drmoopensgroup.com
Web Site: www.dmghealthcare.com
Year Founded: 1987
Business Description:
Specialty Hospitals, Diagnostic Centers, Medical Clinics & Pharmacies Owner & Operator
S.I.C.: 8069
N.A.I.C.S.: 622310
Personnel:
Azad Moopen *(Chm)*

DM PLC

Green Heys Walford Road
Ross-on-Wye, Herefordshire, HR9 5DB, United Kingdom
Tel.: (44) 1989769292
Fax: (44) 1989 769054
E-Mail: info@dmplc.com
Web Site: www.dmplc.com
Sales Range: $25-49.9 Million
Emp.: 120
Business Description:
Holding Company; Directory Database Management & Home Gaming Direct Marketer
S.I.C.: 6719
N.A.I.C.S.: 551112
Personnel:
Adrian John Williams *(Owner)*
Thomas Brennan *(Sec)*
Legal Counsel:
Davies & Partners
135 Aztec West
Almondsbury, Bristol, BS32 4UB, United Kingdom
Subsidiaries:

Data Locator Group Limited (1)
64 Clarendon Rd
Watford, Hertfordshire, WD17 1DA, United Kingdom
Tel.: (44) 1923281700
Fax: (44) 1923281723
E-Mail: info@dlg.co.uk
Web Site: www.dlg.co.uk
Sales Range: $25-49.9 Million
Emp.: 80
Consumer Data Collection & Analysis Services
S.I.C.: 8732
N.A.I.C.S.: 541910
Sarah Cheeseman *(Head-Key Accts)*

McIntyre Dodd Marketing Ltd (1)
Green Heys Walford Road
Ross-on-Wye, Herefordshire, HR9 5DB, United Kingdom
Tel.: (44) 1989769797
E-Mail: enquiries@mcintyreanddodd.com
Web Site: www.mcintyreanddodd.com
Home Gaming & Competition Operation Services
S.I.C.: 7999
N.A.I.C.S.: 713290

PDV Ltd (1)
3rd Floor 64 Clarendon Road
Watford, Hertfordshire, WD17 1DA, United Kingdom
Tel.: (44) 1923478060
Fax: (44) 1923478070
E-Mail: enquiries@pdvltd.com
Web Site: www.pdvltd.com
Emp.: 20
Online Marketing Services
S.I.C.: 8742
N.A.I.C.S.: 541613
Nigel Goldthorpe *(Gen Mgr)*

Strike Lucky Games Ltd (1)
Green Heys Walford Road
Ross-on-Wye, Herefordshire, HR9 5DB, United Kingdom
Tel.: (44) 1989769292
Fax: (44) 1989767047
E-Mail: enquiries@strikelucky.com
Web Site: www.strikelucky.com
Casino Operation Services
S.I.C.: 7999
N.A.I.C.S.: 713210
Adrian Williams *(Chm)*

Subsidiary:

Purely Creative Ltd (2)
1 Mannin Way Lancaster Business Park
Caton Road
Lancaster, Lancashire, LA1 3SU, United Kingdom
Tel.: (44) 8700 500 755
Fax: (44) 152444020
Web Site: www.purelycreative.co.uk
Emp.: 35
Promotional Marketing Services
S.I.C.: 8742
N.A.I.C.S.: 541613
Catherine Cummings *(Mng Dir)*

D.M. TEXTILE MILLS LIMITED

Industrial Area Westridge
Rawalpindi, Pakistan
Tel.: (92) 51 5181981
Fax: (92) 51 5181979
E-Mail: dmtm@dmtextile.com.pk
Web Site: www.dmtextile.com.pk
Year Founded: 1958
DMTX—(ISL)
Sls.: $449,226
Assets: $9,140,269
Liabilities: $5,462,195
Net Worth: $3,678,074
Earnings: ($341,299)
Fiscal Year-end: 06/30/13
Business Description:
Textile Products Mfr
S.I.C.: 2299
N.A.I.C.S.: 314999
Personnel:
Habib Ulla *(Chm & CEO)*
M. F. Zaman Qureshi *(CFO, Sec & Dir-Fin)*
Board of Directors:
Habib Ulla
Shahid Aziz
Hussain Ahmad Ozgen
Rao Khalid Pervaiz
Hussain Ahmad Qureshi
Obaid ul Haq
Ch. Mohammad Yasin
Legal Counsel:
Hassan & Hassan
PAAF Building 7-D Kashmir/Egerton Road
Lahore, Pakistan
Tel.: (92) 42 3636 0800
Fax: (92) 42 3636 0811

DMAIL GROUP S.P.A.

Corso Vittorio Emanuele II n 15
20122 Milan, Italy
Tel.: (39) 025522941
Fax: (39) 0255229463
Web Site: www.dmailgroup.it
DMA—(ITA)
Sales Range: $75-99.9 Million
Emp.: 272
Business Description:
Media Commerce Services
S.I.C.: 7379
N.A.I.C.S.: 518210
Personnel:
Angelo Rodolfi *(Chm)*
Emilio Sorgi *(Mng Dir)*
Board of Directors:
Angelo Rodolfi
Barbara Bergamaschi
Beniamino Lo Presti
Marzio Carlo Schintu
Emilio Sorgi
Subsidiaries:

DMedia Commerce Spa (1)
Via Aretina 25
50069 Pontassieve, Florence, Italy
Tel.: (39) 558363040
Fax: (39) 0558363057
Web Site: www.dmail.it
Online Business & Trading Services
S.I.C.: 5961
N.A.I.C.S.: 454111

Non-U.S. Subsidiaries:

D-Mail Direct S.r.l. (2)
Bd Natiunile Unite Nr 4 Bl 106 Parter Sector 5
Bucharest, 050122, Romania
Tel.: (40) 213360444
Fax: (40) 213360413
Web Site: www.dmail.ro
Online Business & Trading Services
S.I.C.: 5961
N.A.I.C.S.: 454111
Corbu Dragos *(Mgr)*

D-Mail s.r.o. (2)
Piaristicka 22/8
370 01 Ceske Budejovice, Czech Republic
Tel.: (420) 389139139
Fax: (420) 389139132
E-Mail: info@dmail.cz
Web Site: www.dmail.cz

Dmail Group S.p.A.—(Continued)

Household Products Online Sales
S.I.C.: 5722
N.A.I.C.S.: 443141
Zdenka Kourilka Vranovska *(Gen Mgr)*

D-Mail Venda Directa s.a. **(2)**
Av Dr Luis SA Parque Monserrate Pavilhao C Zona Industrial da
Abrunheira, 2710-022 Sintra, Portugal
Tel.: (351) 21 915 6560
Fax: (351) 21 915 6569
E-Mail: assistencia@dmail.pt
Web Site: www.dmail.pt
Household Products Online Sales
S.I.C.: 5722
N.A.I.C.S.: 443141
Jorge Manuel Almeida da Conceicao Bernardo *(Pres & Mgr-HR)*

DMedia Group S.p.A. **(1)**
Via Campi 29/L
23807 Merate, Lecco, Italy
Tel.: (39) 399989206
Fax: (39) 0399270924
E-Mail: info@dmediagroup.it
Web Site: www.dmediagroup.it
Emp.: 30
Magazine Publishing Services
S.I.C.: 2741
N.A.I.C.S.: 511199
Gianluigi Vigano *(Pres & CEO)*
Mauro Albani *(Mng Dir)*

Subsidiaries:

Editoriale La Cronaca S.r.l **(2)**
Corso Vittorio Emanuele II 52
46100 Mantua, Italy
Tel.: (39) 0376321989
Fax: (39) 0376321183
E-Mail: promotion@nextweek.et
Web Site: www.dmediagroup.et
Online Publishing Services
S.I.C.: 5961
N.A.I.C.S.: 454111
Mauro Albani *(Co-CEO)*
Francesca Porcelli *(Co-CEO)*

Editrice Vimercatese S.r.l. **(2)**
Via Camillo Benso Conte Di Cavour 59
Vimercate, Milan, 2871, Italy
Tel.: (39) 39625151
Fax: (39) 0396853349
Scientific Book Publishing Services
S.I.C.: 2741
N.A.I.C.S.: 511199

Giornale di Merate S.r.l **(2)**
Via Campi 29/L
23807 Merate, Lecco, Italy
Tel.: (39) 03999891
Fax: (39) 0399908028
E-Mail: giornale.merate@giornaledimerate.it
Web Site: www.giornaledimerate.it
Emp.: 35
Online Newspaper Publishing Services
S.I.C.: 2741
N.A.I.C.S.: 519130
Giancarlo Ferrario *(Pres)*

Publisette s.r.l. **(2)**
Via Fiorenza 34
20017 Rho, Milan, Italy
Tel.: (39) 02 93508007
Fax: (39) 02 93505356
E-Mail: publisette@promo.it
Advertising Agencies
S.I.C.: 7311
N.A.I.C.S.: 541810

Promotion Lecco S.r.l. **(1)**
Via Aspromonte 52
23900 Lecco, Italy
Tel.: (39) 0341285875
Fax: (39) 0341286321
E-Mail: promotion.lecco@netweek.it
Web Site: www.giornaledilecco.it
Advertising Agencies
S.I.C.: 7311
N.A.I.C.S.: 541810
Gianluigi Vigano *(CEO)*

DMC EDUCATION LIMITED

H-108 New Asiatic Building
Connaught Place
Delhi, 110001, India
Tel.: (91) 11 43694444
Fax: (91) 11 43694455
E-Mail: info@dmceducation.com
Web Site: www.dmceducation.com
517973—(BOM)
Sales Range: $1-9.9 Million

Business Description:
Educational Training Services
S.I.C.: 8299
N.A.I.C.S.: 611710

Personnel:
Sham Sunder Gupta *(Mng Dir)*

Transfer Agent:
Alankit Assignments Limited
Alankit House 2E/21 Jhandewalan Extension
New Delhi, India

D.M.C. ROCHE

14 Rue De Lyon
75012 Paris, France
Tel.: (33) 153461000
Fax: (33) 146289375
Sls.: $20,500,000
Emp.: 47

Business Description:
Furniture Stores
S.I.C.: 5712
N.A.I.C.S.: 442110

Personnel:
Francois Roche *(Pres)*

Board of Directors:
Francois Jullien

DMCI HOLDINGS, INC.

3rd Floor Dacon Building 2281 Don Chino Roces Avenue
Makati, 1231, Philippines
Tel.: (63) 2 888 3000
Fax: (63) 2 816 7362
E-Mail: investors.dmciholdings@gmail.com
Web Site: www.dmciholdings.com
DMC—(OTC PHI)
Rev.: $1,267,109,637
Assets: $2,332,792,183
Liabilities: $1,157,493,621
Net Worth: $1,175,298,561
Earnings: $307,293,810
Fiscal Year-end: 12/31/12

Business Description:
Investment Holding Company
S.I.C.: 6719
N.A.I.C.S.: 551112

Personnel:
David M. Consunji *(Founder & Chm)*
Cesar A. Buenaventura *(Vice Chm)*
Victor S. Limlingan *(Mng Dir)*
Edwina C. Laperal *(Treas)*
Noel A. Laman *(Sec)*

Board of Directors:
David M. Consunji
Cesar A. Buenaventura
Herbert M. Consunji
Jorge A. Consunji
Victor A. Consunji
Isidro A. Counsunji
Cristina C. Gotianun
Noel A. Laman
Edwina C. Laperal
Victor S. Limlingan
Antonio Jose U. Periquet
Honorio O. Reyes-Lao

Subsidiaries:

DMCI Mining Corporation **(1)**
3rd Floor Dacon Bldg 2281 Don Chino Roces Avenue
Makati, 1231, Philippines PH
Tel.: (63) 2888 3238 (78%)
Fax: (63) 2888 3787
Nickel & Other Metal Ore & Mineral Exploration & Mining
S.I.C.: 1021
N.A.I.C.S.: 212234

Non-U.S. Holding:

Toledo Mining Corporation plc **(2)**
First Floor 10 Dover Street
London, W1S 4LQ, United Kingdom UK
Tel.: (44) 20 7290 3100 (66.52%)
Fax: (44) 20 7290 3109
E-Mail: info@toledomining.com
Web Site: www.toledomining.com
Sales Range: Less than $1 Million
Emp.: 2
Nickel Mining Services
S.I.C.: 1021
N.A.I.C.S.: 212234
Victor Kolesnikov *(CEO)*
Adrian Harvey *(CFO & Sec)*
Pierre Charlent *(COO)*
Marissa S. Nicdao *(Chief Acctg Officer)*

Semirara Mining Corporation **(1)**
2nd Floor DMCI Plaza 2281 Chino Roces Avenue Extension
Makati, 1231, Philippines (56.32%)
Tel.: (63) 2867 3377
Fax: (63) 2816 7185
Web Site: www.semiraramining.com
SCC—(PHI)
Rev.: $591,439,562
Assets: $886,198,103
Liabilities: $472,517,391
Net Worth: $413,680,712
Earnings: $155,714,323
Emp.: 2,195
Fiscal Year-end: 12/31/12
Coal Producer
S.I.C.: 1221
N.A.I.C.S.: 212111
David M. Consunji *(Chm)*
Isidro A. Consunji *(Vice Chm & CEO)*
Victor A. Consunji *(Pres & COO)*
Junalina S. Tabor *(CFO)*
Ma. Cristina C. Gotianun *(Compliance Officer & VP-HR & Admin)*
Sharade E. Padilla *(IR & Bus Dev Officer)*
Melinda V. Reyes *(Risk & Sys Control Officer)*
John R. Sadullo *(Legal Counsel & Sec)*

Non-U.S. Holding:

ENK PLC **(1)**
6th Floor Kildare House 3 Dorset Rise
London, EC4Y 8EN, United Kingdom UK
Tel.: (44) 2072903130 (50%)
Fax: (44) 2072903149
E-Mail: info@enickel.co.uk
Web Site: www.enk.co.uk
Emp.: 228
Nickel Mining Services
S.I.C.: 1021
N.A.I.C.S.: 212234
Mark Hanlon *(Sec & Dir-Fin)*

Non-U.S. Branches:

ENK PLC Australian Regional Office **(2)**
Level 1 83 Havelock Street
West Perth, WA, 6005, Australia
Tel.: (61) 8 9226 1111
Fax: (61) 8 9226 1011
Mineral Exploration Services
S.I.C.: 1479
N.A.I.C.S.: 212393
Robert Gordon Gregory *(CEO & Mng Dir)*
Timothy Marcus Stephen Hanlon *(CFO & Sec)*

ENK PLC Philippines Regional Office **(2)**
4th Floor Pilgrim Building
111 Aguirre Street
Legaspi Village, Makati, 1229, Philippines
Tel.: (63) 2 8151656
Fax: (63) 2 8151655
Emp.: 50
Mineral Exploration Services
S.I.C.: 1481
N.A.I.C.S.: 213115
Ian Moller *(Country Mgr)*

Non-U.S. Subsidiary:

Sardes Nikel Madencilik A.S **(2)**
Akdeniz Caddesi No 14 Birsel Is Merkezi Kat 5 D 502
Konak, 35210 Izmir, Turkey
Tel.: (90) 2324550030
Fax: (90) 2324898060
E-Mail:
Emp.: 30
Mining & Exploration Services
S.I.C.: 1499
N.A.I.C.S.: 212399
Cevat Er *(Mgr)*

DMI UK LTD.

(d/b/a DMI Group)
Gloucester Road
West Chirton Industrial Estate, North Shields, Tyne & Wear, NE29 8RQ, United Kingdom
Tel.: (44) 1912575577
Fax: (44) 1912586398
E-Mail: sales@dmiuk.co.uk
Web Site: www.dmiglobal.com
Emp.: 75

Business Description:
Treatment & Coatings of Metals
S.I.C.: 3479
N.A.I.C.S.: 332812

Personnel:
Peter L. Jackson *(Chm)*

Subsidiaries:

AMI Exchangers Ltd. **(1)**
Apex Workshops
Graythorp Industrial Estate, Hartlepool, TS25 2DF, United Kingdom
Tel.: (44) 1429 860187
Fax: (44) 1429 860673
E-Mail: sales@ami-exchangers.co.uk
Web Site: www.ami-exchangers.co.uk
Emp.: 20
Marine & Industrial Heat Exchangers Mfr
S.I.C.: 3443
N.A.I.C.S.: 332410
John Wiffen *(Mng Dir)*

DMI Young & Cunningham Ltd. **(1)**
Gloucester Road
West Chirton Industrial Estate, North Shields, Tyne and Wear, NE29 8RQ, United Kingdom
Tel.: (44) 191 270 4690
Fax: (44) 191 270 4691
E-Mail: sales@yandc.co.uk
Web Site: www.yandc.co.uk
Taps & Valves Mfr
S.I.C.: 3491
N.A.I.C.S.: 332911
George Wood, *(Gen Mgr)*

Highland Electroplaters Ltd. **(1)**
Howe Moss Drive
Kirkhill Industrial Estate, Dyce, Aberdeen, AB21 0GL, United Kingdom
Tel.: (44) 1224 725581
Fax: (44) 1224 725591
E-Mail: aberdeen@hiplaters.co.uk
Web Site: www.hiplaters.co.uk
Surface Coatings Mfr
S.I.C.: 2851
N.A.I.C.S.: 325510
Norrie Jerrard, *(Mng Dir)*

U.S. Subsidiary:

DMI Automotive Inc. **(1)**
1200 Durant Dr
Howell, MI 48843
Tel.: (517) 548-1414
E-Mail: dmichrome@sbcglobal.net
Web Site: www.dmiautomotive.com
Emp.: 18
Die Chrome Plating
S.I.C.: 3471
N.A.I.C.S.: 332813
Dieter Schormann *(Pres)*
Alan Gray *(Sec & Treas)*

Non-U.S. Subsidiary:

DMI Wolfgang Drechsler GmbH **(1)**
Hohe-Schaar-Strasse 40-42
21107 Hamburg, Germany
Tel.: (49) 40 284 110 0
Fax: (49) 40 284 110 10
E-Mail: info@dmi-drechsler.de
Web Site: www.dmi-drechsler.de
Steel Construction & Machinery, Welding & Metal Spraying; Reconditioning of Engine Components
S.I.C.: 3599
N.A.I.C.S.: 332710

Peter L. Jackson, *(Mng Dir)*

Non-U.S. Affiliate:

Diesel Marine International Dubai L.L.C. **(1)**
Road 120 28A Plot No 364-0376 B562
Near 3rd Interchange Sheikh Zayed
PO Box 8807
Road Al Quoz Indus Area, Dubai, United Arab Emirates
Tel.: (971) 4 339 2219
Fax: (971) 4 339 1952
E-Mail: dmidubai@trinityholdings.com
Web Site: www.dmiuk.co.uk/?q=directoryentry/dmi-dubai-llc
Marine Reconditioning Services
S.I.C.: 3479
N.A.I.C.S.: 332812
Ram K. Shringi, *(Mgr)*

DMK DEUTSCHES MILCHKONTOR GMBH

Industriestrasse 27
27404 Zeven, Germany
Tel.: (49) 4281 72 0
Fax: (49) 4281 72 297
E-Mail: info@dmk.de
Web Site: www.dmk.de
Sales Range: $5-14.9 Billion
Emp.: 5,700
Business Description:
Dairy Products Mfr & Distr
S.I.C.: 2026
N.A.I.C.S.: 311511
Personnel:
Otto Lattwesen *(Chm-Supervisory Bd)*
Adolf Oehlmann *(Vice Chm-Supervisory Bd)*
Josef Schwaiger *(CEO)*
Dirk Gloy *(Member-Mgmt Bd & Head-Ops)*
Ingo Muller *(Member-Mgmt Bd & Head-Quality Mgmt & R&D)*
Volkmar Taucher *(Member-Mgmt Bd & Head-Fin)*
Sonke Voss *(Member-Mgmt Bd & Head-Logistics & Pur)*
Supervisory Board of Directors:
Otto Lattwesen
Dirk Baus
Mohamed Boudih
Uwe Boye
Udo Eckhoff
Herbert Grimberg
Benedikt Langemeyer
Franz Morgret
Bernd Nix
Adolf Oehlmann
Frerk Osterndorff
Josef Veit

Subsidiaries:

DMK Eis GmbH **(1)**
Munsterstrasse 31
48351 Everswinkel, Germany De (100%)
Tel.: (49) 2582 77 0
Fax: (49) 2582 77 60 125
E-Mail: info@dmk-eis.de
Web Site: www.dmk-eis.de
Emp.: 270
Ice Cream Mfr
S.I.C.: 2024
N.A.I.C.S.: 311520
Frank Forstmann *(Mng Dir)*
Stefan A. M. Scherer *(CFO & COO)*

Subsidiary:

Rosen Eiskrem GmbH **(2)**
Brauereistrasse 17
D 52525 Heinsberg, Germany
Tel.: (49) 2452 9977 0
Fax: (49) 2452 9977 40
E-Mail: info@roseneis.de
Web Site: www.roseneis.de
Sales Range: $200-249.9 Million
Emp.: 500
Ice Cream Mfr & Distr
S.I.C.: 2024
N.A.I.C.S.: 311520
Frank Forstmann *(Mng Dir)*
Stefan A. M. Scherer *(CFO & COO)*

Plant:

Rosen Eiskrem Sud GmbH - Prenzlau **(3)**
Brussower Allee 85
17291 Prenzlau, Germany
Tel.: (49) 3984 8504 02
Fax: (49) 3984 8504 44
E-Mail: info@roseneis.de
Web Site: www.roseneis.de
Emp.: 200
Ice Cream Mfr
S.I.C.: 2024
N.A.I.C.S.: 311520
Jens Nitsch *(Plant Mgr)*

NORLAC GmbH **(1)**
Industriestrasse 27
D 27404 Zeven, Germany (100%)
Tel.: (49) 4281 72 2226
Fax: (49) 4281 72 433
Web Site: www.norlac.de
Milk Substitute Products for Calf Rearing
S.I.C.: 2048
N.A.I.C.S.: 311119
Marco Schmidt *(Mng Dir)*

DMK DRILLING FLUIDS LTD.

400 525 8th Avenue SW
Calgary, AB, T2P 1G1, Canada
Tel.: (403) 232-8883
Fax: (403) 234-9369
E-Mail: dmktrk@dmkdrillingfluids.com
Web Site: www.dmkdrillingfluids.com
Year Founded: 1985
Rev.: $33,318,656
Emp.: 40
Business Description:
Chemical Products Supplier
S.I.C.: 5169
N.A.I.C.S.: 424690
Personnel:
Dennis Kostiuk *(Owner & Pres)*

DMSS SOFTWARE LTDA.

Rua Arandu 281 7th andar
Brooklin Novo, CEP 04562030 Sao Paulo, Brazil
Tel.: (55) 1155053644
Fax: (55) 1155051977
E-Mail: dmss@dmss.com.br
Web Site: www.dmss.com.br
Year Founded: 1990
Sales Range: $10-24.9 Million
Emp.: 50
Business Description:
Predictive Analytics & Data Mining Software Distr & Technical Consulting Services
S.I.C.: 5045
N.A.I.C.S.: 423430
Personnel:
Ricardo Ventura *(CEO)*

DMT DEMMINER MASCHINENBAU TECHNIK GMBH

Woldeforster Strasse 5
17109 Demmin, Germany
Tel.: (49) 39984350
Fax: (49) 3998435235
E-Mail: info@dmt-demmin.de
Web Site: www.dmt-demmin.de
Rev.: $11,283,492
Emp.: 130
Business Description:
Industrial Machines Mfr
S.I.C.: 3559
N.A.I.C.S.: 333249
Personnel:
Johann Erich Wilms *(Mng Dir)*

DMW CORPORATION

5-1 Omori Kita 1-Chome
Ota-ku, Tokyo, 143-8558, Japan
Tel.: (81) 332985123
Fax: (81) 332985146
E-Mail: e-info@dmw.co.jp
Web Site: www.dmw.co.jp
Year Founded: 1910
6365—(TKS)
Sales Range: $125-149.9 Million
Emp.: 600
Business Description:
Pumps, Fans, Blowers, Ventilators, Turbo-Compressors, Valves, Water Treatment Systems, Electric Control Panels & Other Machinery Mfr & Sales
S.I.C.: 3441
N.A.I.C.S.: 332312
Personnel:
Masanobu Watanabe *(Chm)*
Nobuhiro Yanase *(Pres & CEO)*
Board of Directors:
Masanobu Watanabe
Tsuneya Sugiya
Tadahiro Tsuchiya
Noboru Yamamoto
Nobuhiro Yanase

DMW ELECTRICAL INSTRUMENTATION INC.

227 Confederation Street
Sarnia, ON, N7T 1Z9, Canada
Tel.: (519) 336-3003, ext. 21
Fax: (519) 336-3995
E-Mail: info@dmwelectrical.com
Web Site: www.dmwelectrical.com
Year Founded: 1984
Rev.: $19,388,724
Emp.: 160
Business Description:
Electrical Contractors
S.I.C.: 1731
N.A.I.C.S.: 238210
Personnel:
Carlo Maola *(Pres)*

DMX TECHNOLOGIES GROUP LIMITED

4303 43/F 100 How Ming Street
Kwun Tong
Kowloon, China (Hong Kong)
Tel.: (852) 25202660
Fax: (852) 28022062
E-Mail: enquiry@dmxtechnologies.com
Web Site: www.dmxtechnologies.com
5CH—(SES)
Rev.: $379,592,000
Assets: $464,953,000
Liabilities: $79,657,000
Net Worth: $385,296,000
Earnings: $21,918,000
Fiscal Year-end: 12/31/12
Business Description:
Software Solution Services
S.I.C.: 7371
N.A.I.C.S.: 541511
Personnel:
Emmy Wu *(Chm)*
Iwao Oishi *(Vice Chm)*
Jismyl Chor Khin Teo *(CEO)*
Skip Tang *(CFO)*
Mun Young Lee *(Chm-SE Asia & Korea)*
Yan Yan Fu *(CEO-China)*
Siew Tian Low *(Sec)*
Board of Directors:
Emmy Wu
Takuro Awazu
Meng Tong Foo
Tajima Hidehiko
Daniel Kung
Kazuo Miwa
Iwao Oishi
Shinichi Suzukawa
Jismyl Chor Khin Teo
Nie Khian Thian
Kenichiro Uchimura
Mark Yat-Yee Wang
Transfer Agent:
Boardroom Corporate & Advisory Services Pte. Ltd.
50 Raffles Place 32-01 Singapore Land Tower
Singapore, Singapore

DNA 2002 PUBLIC COMPANY LIMITED

19 Ramkhamhaeng 22 Kwaeng Huamark Khet
Bangkapi, Bangkok, Thailand
Tel.: (66) 27162233
Fax: (66) 27187026
Web Site: www.dna2002.com
DNA—(THA)
Sales Range: $25-49.9 Million
Business Description:
DVDs, CDs & Games Retailer
S.I.C.: 5999
N.A.I.C.S.: 453998
Personnel:
Lattasanya Plansomparn *(Chm)*
Samart Chuasiriphattana *(Mng Dir)*

DNA CHIP RESEARCH INC.

1-1-43 Suehirocho
Tsurumi-ku, Yokohama, Kanagawa, 230-0045, Japan
Tel.: (81) 45 500 5218
E-Mail: marketing@dna-chip.co.jp
Web Site: www.dna-chip.co.jp
Year Founded: 1999
2397—(TKS)
Business Description:
Deoxyribonucleic Acid Research Services
S.I.C.: 8731
N.A.I.C.S.: 541711
Personnel:
Ryo Matoba *(Pres)*

DNA LINK INC.

12F Asan Institute for Life Sciences 1
88 Olympic-ro 43-gil
Songpa-gu, Seoul, 138-736, Korea (South)
Tel.: (82) 2 3153 1500
Fax: (82) 2 364 4778
E-Mail: office@dnalink.com
Web Site: www.dnalink.com
Year Founded: 2000
127120—(KRS)
Emp.: 30
Business Description:
Biotechnology Research & Development
S.I.C.: 8731
N.A.I.C.S.: 541711
Personnel:
Jong-eun Lee *(CEO)*

DNA OY

Lakkisepantie 21
00620 Helsinki, Finland
Tel.: (358) 44 0440
Web Site: www.dna.fi
Sls.: $1,035,473,964
Assets: $1,340,295,314
Liabilities: $628,163,307
Net Worth: $712,132,007
Earnings: $48,645,199
Emp.: 1,427
Fiscal Year-end: 12/31/12
Business Description:
Mobile Telecommunications Services
S.I.C.: 4812
N.A.I.C.S.: 517210
Personnel:
Leino Jarmo *(Chm)*
Riitta Tiuraniemi *(CEO)*
Timo Karppinen *(CFO)*

DNA Oy—(Continued)

Board of Directors:
Leino Jarmo
Soila Anssi
Isotalo Hannu
Ala-Mursula Juha
Ottela Jukka
Soanjarvi Tuija

DNA PRECIOUS METALS, INC.

9125 rue Pascal Gagnon Suite 204
Saint Leonard, QC, H1P 1Z4, Canada
Tel.: (514) 852-2111
Fax: (514) 852-2221
E-Mail: info@dnapreciousmetals.com
Web Site: www.dnapreciousmetals.com
Year Founded: 2006
DNAP—(OTC OTCB)
Rev.: $101,333
Assets: $1,936,703
Liabilities: $813,334
Net Worth: $1,123,369
Earnings: ($797,126)
Emp.: 4
Fiscal Year-end: 12/31/12
Business Description:
Gold & Silver Mining Services
S.I.C.: 1041
N.A.I.C.S.: 212221
Personnel:
Tony J. Giuliano *(Interim Pres, Interim CEO & CFO)*
James T. Chandik *(COO & Exec VP)*
Board of Directors:
James T. Chandik
Yves Gagnon
Tony J. Giuliano
Transfer Agent:
Olde Monmouth Stock Transfer Co., Inc.
200 Memorial Pkwy
Atlantic Highlands, NJ 07716-1655
Tel.: (732) 872-2727

DNB NOR A.S.A.

Dronning Eufemias gate 30
0191 Oslo, Norway
Mailing Address:
Postboks 1600
Sentrum, 0021 Oslo, Norway
Tel.: (47) 91503000
Fax: (47) 24025300
Web Site: www.dnbnor.com
Year Founded: 2003
DNBNOR—(OSL)
Sales Range: $75-99.9 Million
Emp.: 13,021
Business Description:
Financial Services
S.I.C.: 6099
N.A.I.C.S.: 522320
Personnel:
Anne Carine Tanum *(Chm)*
Tore Olaf Rimmereid *(Vice Chm)*
Rune Bjerke *(Grp CEO)*
Bjorn Erik Naess *(CFO)*
Trond Bentestuen *(Exec VP-Personal Banking-Norway)*
Kjestin Braathen *(Exec VP-Corp Banking-Norway)*
Ottar Ertzeid *(Exec VP-Markets)*
Liv Fiksdahl *(Exec VP-IT & Ops)*
Solveig Hellebust *(Exec VP-HR)*
Thomas Midteide *(Exec VP-Corp Comm)*
Kari Olrud Moen *(Exec VP-Products)*
Tom Rathke *(Exec VP-Wealth Mgmt)*
Harald Serck-Hanssen *(Exec VP-Corp & Intl Banking)*
Trygve Young *(Exec VP-Risk Mgmt)*
Board of Directors:
Anne Carine Tanum
Jarle Bergo
Bente Brevik
Sverre Finstad
Carl A. Lovvik
Vigdis Mathisen
Tore Olaf Rimmereid
Berit Svendsen

Subsidiaries:

DnB NOR Boligkreditt AS **(1)**
Torgallmenningen 2
NO-5020 Bergen, Norway
Tel.: (47) 55211000
Financial Services
S.I.C.: 6029
N.A.I.C.S.: 522110

DnB NOR Eiendom AS **(1)**
Eufemiasgt 30
Oslo, Norway
Tel.: (47) 91503000
Web Site: www.dnbnor.no
Emp.: 4,000
Banking Services
S.I.C.: 6029
N.A.I.C.S.: 522110
Rune Bjerke *(Grp CEO)*

DnB NOR Hypotek AS **(1)**
PO Box 1167
Sentrum, NO-0021 Oslo, Norway
Tel.: (47) 91503000
Web Site: www.dnbnor.no
Financial Services
S.I.C.: 6029
N.A.I.C.S.: 522110
Gunnar H. Gabrielsen *(Mng Dir)*

DnB NOR Kapitalforvaltning ASA **(1)**
Ovre Slottsgate 3
0021 Oslo, Norway
Tel.: (47) 91503000
Fax: (47) 22319543
E-Mail: kapitalforvaltning@dnbnor.no
Web Site: www.dnbnor.no
Emp.: 200
Financial Services
S.I.C.: 6211
N.A.I.C.S.: 523999
Porkile Varran *(Mng Dir)*

DnB NOR Markets **(1)**
Standen 21
NO-0021 Oslo, Norway
Tel.: (47) 91503000
E-Mail: info@dnbnor.no
Web Site: www.dnbnor.no
Emp.: 30
Financial Services
S.I.C.: 6029
N.A.I.C.S.: 522110
Ottar Ertzeid *(Mng Dir)*

DnB NOR Meglerservice AS **(1)**
Kirkegata 21 5etg
0021 Oslo, Norway
Tel.: (47) 24045926
Fax: (47) 22 00 88 66
Financial Management Services
S.I.C.: 6211
N.A.I.C.S.: 523999
Lars Magnus Savang *(Gen Mgr)*

DnB NOR Naeringsmegling AS **(1)**
Standen 21
NO-0021 Oslo, Norway
Tel.: (47) 22948660
Fax: (47) 22948663
E-Mail: maringsmegling@dnb.no
Web Site: www.dnb.no
Emp.: 45
Financial Services
S.I.C.: 6029
N.A.I.C.S.: 522110
Knut Efskin *(Pres)*

Nordlandsbanken ASA **(1)**
Moloveien 16
NO-8002 Bodo, Norway NO (100%)
Tel.: (47) 91508900
Fax: (47) 75558789
E-Mail: Post@nordlandsbanken.no
Web Site: www.nordlandsbanken.no
Emp.: 237
Retail & Commercial Banking Services
S.I.C.: 6029
N.A.I.C.S.: 522110
Morten Stover *(Mng Dir)*

Postbanken **(1)**
Kirkegata 21
NO-0021 Oslo, Norway
Tel.: (47) 91503800
Web Site: www.postbanken.no
Banking Services
S.I.C.: 6029
N.A.I.C.S.: 522110

Vital Eiendom AS **(1)**
Rosenkrantzgate 3
Postboks 7505
Bergen, 5020, Norway
Tel.: (47) 81 54 41 00
Fax: (47) 55 32 61 85
Web Site: www.vital.no/eiendom
Real Estate Development Services
S.I.C.: 6531
N.A.I.C.S.: 531390
Gro Boge *(Mgr-Comml)*

U.S. Subsidiary:

DnB NOR Markets Inc **(1)**
200 Park Ave 31st Fl
New York, NY 10166-0396
Tel.: (212) 681-3800
Fax: (212) 681-4121
Web Site: www.dnb.com
Emp.: 20
Securities Brokerage Services
S.I.C.: 6211
N.A.I.C.S.: 523120
Ted Jadick *(Pres & CEO)*

Non-U.S. Subsidiaries:

Den Norske Syndicates Ltd **(1)**
20 Saint Dunstan Hill
London, EC3R 8HY, United Kingdom
Tel.: (44) 20 7621 1111
Fax: (44) 20 7626 7200
Financial Management Services
S.I.C.: 6211
N.A.I.C.S.: 523999

DNB Nor Asia Ltd **(1)**
8 Shenton Way 48-02 Temasek Tower
Singapore, 068811, Singapore
Tel.: (65) 62206144
Fax: (65) 62249743
Emp.: 100
Commercial Banking Services
S.I.C.: 6029
N.A.I.C.S.: 522110
Omar Sekkat *(Sr VP-Energy)*

DnB NOR Luxembourg SA **(1)**
13 rue Goethe
1637 Luxembourg, Luxembourg
Tel.: (352) 4549451
Fax: (352) 454945200
E-Mail: privatebanking@dnbgroup.lu
Web Site: www.dnb.no/lu
Emp.: 30
Commercial Banking Services
S.I.C.: 6029
N.A.I.C.S.: 522110
Haakon Hansen *(Gen Mgr)*

Dnb Nor Reinsurance SA **(1)**
Rue De Bitbourg 19
Luxembourg, 1273, Luxembourg
Tel.: (352) 4549451
Fax: (352) 45445200
General Insurance Services
S.I.C.: 6411
N.A.I.C.S.: 524210

Svensk Fastighetsformedling AB **(1)**
Arstaangsvagen 11
PO Box 47106
100 74 Stockholm, Sweden
Tel.: (46) 850535800
Fax: (46) 850535899
E-Mail: sf@hk.svenskfast.se
Web Site: www.svenskfast.se
Real Estate Management Services
S.I.C.: 6531
N.A.I.C.S.: 531390

DNF CO., LTD.

Shintanjin 3 gongdon Moonpyung dong
49 9 Daeduk
306220 Daejeon, Korea (South)
Tel.: (82) 429327939
Fax: (82) 429327947
Web Site: www.dnfsolution.com
Year Founded: 2001
092070—(KRS)
Sales Range: $10-24.9 Million
Emp.: 100
Business Description:
Chemical Compounds & Catalysts Mfr
S.I.C.: 2899
N.A.I.C.S.: 325998
Personnel:
Myong-Woon Kim *(Pres & CEO)*
Divisions:

DNF Co Ltd - Electronic Material Division **(1)**
49-9 Muntyeong-Tong
Paepeok-Gu, Daejeon, South Chungcheong, 306-220, Korea (South)
Tel.: (82) 10 4919 7050
Fax: (82) 42 932 7947
E-Mail: dnf@dnfsolution.com
Web Site: www.dnfsolution.com
Emp.: 150
Electronic Materials Mfr
S.I.C.: 3548
N.A.I.C.S.: 333992
Charles Song *(Gen Mgr)*

DNF Co Ltd - Fine Chemical Division **(1)**
49-9 Muntyeong-Tong Paepeok-Gu
Daejeon, 306-220, Korea (South)
Tel.: (82) 42 932 7939
Fax: (82) 42 932 7947
E-Mail: dnf@dnfsolution.com
Web Site: www.dnfsolution.com
Emp.: 150
Chemical Materials Mfr
S.I.C.: 2869
N.A.I.C.S.: 325199
Kim Mong Yoon *(Pres)*

Plant:

DNF Co., Ltd - DNF Ulsan Plant **(1)**
Wonsan-ri 916-6 Onsan-Eup
Ulju-Gun, Ulsan, 689 892, Korea (South)
Tel.: (82) 52 239 7939
Fax: (82) 52 239 7980
Web Site: www.dnfsolution.com
Electronic Component Mfr
S.I.C.: 3679
N.A.I.C.S.: 334419

DNI METALS INC.

Suite 1711 25 Adelaide Street East
Toronto, ON, M5C 3A1, Canada
Tel.: (416) 595-1195
Fax: (416) 595-5458
E-Mail: info@dnimetals.com
Web Site: www.dnimetals.com
Year Founded: 1954
DNI—(OTC TSXV)
Assets: $7,833,321
Liabilities: $97,002
Net Worth: $7,736,318
Earnings: ($793,471)
Fiscal Year-end: 03/31/13
Business Description:
Mineral Exploration Services
S.I.C.: 1081
N.A.I.C.S.: 213114
Personnel:
Denis A. Clement *(Chm)*
Shahe F. Sabag *(Pres, CEO & Acting Sec)*
Colin A. Grant *(CFO)*
Board of Directors:
Denis A. Clement
Michael G. Butler
Justin R. Fogarty
Raymond E. Mitchell
Shahe F. Sabag
Legal Counsel:
Parsons Behle & Latimer
Salt Lake City, UT 84111
Lavery de Billy
Montreal, QC, Canada

Transfer Agent:
Equity Financial Trust Company
Toronto, ON, Canada

DNO INTERNATIONAL ASA

Bryggegata 9
0250 Oslo, Norway
Tel.: (47) 23 23 84 80
Fax: (47) 23 23 84 81
E-Mail: dno@dno.no
Web Site: www.dno.no
DNO—(OSL OTC)
Sls.: $514,337,382
Assets: $1,328,991,471
Liabilities: $602,624,304
Net Worth: $726,367,167
Earnings: $188,157,204
Fiscal Year-end: 12/31/12
Business Description:
Oil & Gas Exploration Services
S.I.C.: 1311
N.A.I.C.S.: 211111
Personnel:
Bijan Mossavar-Rahmani *(Chm)*
Lars Arne Takla *(Deputy Chm)*
Bjorn Dale *(Acting Pres & Mng Dir)*
Haakon Sandborg *(CFO & VP)*
Magne Normann *(Sr VP-Dev)*
Board of Directors:
Bijan Mossavar-Rahmani
Ellen K. Dyvik
Gunnar Hirsti
Lars Arne Takla
Shelley Watson

Non-U.S. Subsidiary:

DNO Yemen AS (1)
Street No 8 Off Damaskus Street
Sana'a, Yemen
Tel.: (967) 1428230
Fax: (967) 1 428 240
Oil & Gas Exploration Services
S.I.C.: 1311
N.A.I.C.S.: 211111

D'NONCE TECHNOLOGY BHD.

51-14-B&C Menara BHL Jalan Sultan Ahmad Shah
10050 Penang, Malaysia
Tel.: (60) 42281198
Fax: (60) 42283016
Web Site: www.dnoncetech.com
DNONCE—(KLS)
Rev.: $58,306,595
Assets: $39,691,055
Liabilities: $24,039,190
Net Worth: $15,651,865
Earnings: ($3,208,732)
Fiscal Year-end: 08/31/13
Business Description:
Electronic Components Mfr
S.I.C.: 3678
N.A.I.C.S.: 334417
Personnel:
Kim Choon Law *(CEO & Mng Dir)*
Siew Cheng Chew *(Co-Sec)*
Chit Geok Gunn *(Co-Sec)*
Board of Directors:
Ahmad Ibnihajar
Kim Choon Law
Kah Choon Lee
Teik Hoe Lim
Choo Eng Oon
Thai Sun Wong
Legal Counsel:
Zaid Ibrahim & Co
51-22 B&C Menara BHL Jalan Sultan Ahmad Shah
Penang, Malaysia
Subsidiaries:

Attractive Venture (JB) Sdn. Bhd. (1)
1218-1220 Jalan Sri Putri 3/4 Taman Putri Kulai
81000 Kulai, Johor, Malaysia
Tel.: (60) 76638200
Fax: (60) 76637200
Web Site: www.attractivepackaging.com.my
Emp.: 90
Industrial Packaging Material Mfr
S.I.C.: 2672
N.A.I.C.S.: 322220
Peter Lim *(Exec Dir)*

Attractive Venture (KL) Sdn. Bhd. (1)
Lot 20 Jalan CJ1/1 Kawasan Perindustrian Cheras Jaya
43200 Cheras, Selangor, Malaysia
Tel.: (60) 390748646
Fax: (60) 390748676
Web Site: www.dnoncetech.com.my
Emp.: 30
Industrial Packaging Materials Mfr
S.I.C.: 2672
N.A.I.C.S.: 322220
Chee Min Low *(Gen Mgr)*

Attractive Venture Sdn. Bhd. (1)
Plot 425 Mukim 1 Tingkat Perusahaan 6A Prai Free Trade Zone
13600 Prai, Penang, Malaysia
Tel.: (60) 43997968
Fax: (60) 43997970
Web Site: www.attractivepackaging.com.my
Emp.: 200
Industrial Packaging Material Mfr
S.I.C.: 2672
N.A.I.C.S.: 322220
K. S. Hong *(Gen Mgr)*

AV Plastics Sdn. Bhd. (1)
No 137 & 138 Jalan Suasa 7 Taman Suasa
09000 Kulim, Kedah, Malaysia
Tel.: (60) 44892255
Fax: (60) 44891166
E-Mail: avplas@dnoncetech.com
Web Site: www.dnoncetech.com
Emp.: 70
Plastic Products Mfr & Whslr
S.I.C.: 3089
N.A.I.C.S.: 326199
Kenneth Kok *(Mgr)*

D'nonce Biofoods Sdn. Bhd. (1)
51-14 B C Menara BHL Jalan Sultan Ahmad Shah
10050 George Town, Penang, Malaysia
Tel.: (60) 42281198
Fax: (60) 42283016
E-Mail: biofoods@dnoncetech.com
Web Site: www.dnoncebiofoods.com
Emp.: 30
Health Beverages Mfr & Distr
S.I.C.: 2099
N.A.I.C.S.: 311999
Roslant Abu *(Grp Gen Mgr)*

D'nonce (Johore) Sdn. Bhd. (1)
1218-1220 Jalan Sri Putri 3/4 Taman Putri Kulai
Kulai, Johor, Malaysia
Tel.: (60) 7 355 7969
Fax: (60) 7 663 7200
Emp.: 100
Security Control Equipment Mfr
S.I.C.: 3679
N.A.I.C.S.: 334419
Peter Lim *(Mng Dir)*

D'nonce (Kelantan) Sdn. Bhd. (1)
PT 4110 A B Kawasan Perindustrian Pengkalan Chepa 2
Padang Tembak, 16100 Kota Baharu, Kelantan, Malaysia
Tel.: (60) 97743312
Fax: (60) 97743313
Emp.: 50
Adhesive Tapes Mfr
S.I.C.: 2678
N.A.I.C.S.: 322230

D'nonce (K.L) Sdn. Bhd. (1)
Lot 20 Jln CJ 1/1 Kawasan Perusahaan Cheras Jaya
Batu 11, Cheras, Kuala Lumpur, 43200, Malaysia
Tel.: (60) 123583011
Fax: (60) 6043997970
Adhesive Tapes Mfr
S.I.C.: 2678
N.A.I.C.S.: 322230

D'nonce (M) Sdn. Bhd. (1)
Lot 1 Puncak Perusahaan 1 Kawasan MIEL
13600 Prai, Penang, Malaysia
Tel.: (60) 43987090
Fax: (60) 43997970
Emp.: 20
Adhesive Tapes Mfr
S.I.C.: 2678
N.A.I.C.S.: 322230

Richmond Technology Sdn. Bhd. (1)
PT 4110 A & B Kaw Perindustrian Pengkalan Chepa
Padang Tembak, 16100 Kota Baharu, Kelantan, Malaysia
Tel.: (60) 97743312
Fax: (60) 9 7743313
Web Site: www.attractivepackaging.com.my
Emp.: 35
Industrial Packaging Material Mfr
S.I.C.: 2671
N.A.I.C.S.: 326112

Non-U.S. Subsidiary:

ISCM Technology (Thailand) Co., Ltd. (1)
101/47/20 Navanakorn Industrial Estate
Klongnueng, Pathumthani, 12120, Thailand
Tel.: (66) 25292180
Fax: (66) 2 529 2179
Web Site: www.iscmtechnology.com
Disk Drives Mfr
S.I.C.: 3572
N.A.I.C.S.: 334112

DO ALL INDUSTRIES LTD.

501 6th St
Estevan, SK, S4A 1A5, Canada
Tel.: (306) 634-8388
Fax: (306) 634-8389
E-Mail: info@doallind.com
Web Site: www.doallmetal.com
Year Founded: 2000
Sales Range: $200-249.9 Million
Emp.: 125
Business Description:
Oil & Gas Machinery Mfr
S.I.C.: 3533
N.A.I.C.S.: 333132
Personnel:
Kordel Korf *(Pres)*

DO & CO AKTIENGESELLSCHAFT

Stephansplatz 12
1010 Vienna, Austria
Tel.: (43) 1740000
Fax: (43) 17400 1029
E-Mail: investor.relations@doco.com
Web Site: www.doco.com
Year Founded: 1981
DOCO—(VIE)
Sales Range: $550-599.9 Million
Emp.: 4,166
Business Description:
Restaurant & Catering Services
S.I.C.: 5812
N.A.I.C.S.: 722320
Personnel:
Waldemar Jud *(Chm-Supervisory Bd)*
Attila Dogudan *(Chm-Mgmt Bd)*
Werner Sporn *(Deputy Chm-Supervisory Bd)*
Michael Dobersberger *(Member-Mgmt Bd)*
Supervisory Board of Directors:
Waldemar Jud
Christian Konrad
Werner Sporn
Georg Thurn-Vrints

Subsidiaries:

DO & CO Airline Catering Austria GmbH (1)
Dampfmuhlg 5
1110 Vienna, Austria
Tel.: (43) 1740000
Fax: (43) 1740001515
E-Mail: Purchase@doco.com
Web Site: www.doco.com
Catering Services
S.I.C.: 5812
N.A.I.C.S.: 722320
Harald Hrastnig *(Gen Mgr)*

DO & CO Catering & Logistics Austria GmbH (1)
Stephansplatz 12
A 1010 Vienna, Austria
Tel.: (43) 1740000
Catering & Logistics Services
S.I.C.: 5812
N.A.I.C.S.: 722320

DO & CO Catering-Consult & Beteiligungs GmbH (1)
Stephanspl 12
1010 Vienna, Austria
Tel.: (43) 1740001010
Fax: (43) 1740001029
Web Site: www.doco.com
Catering Services
S.I.C.: 5812
N.A.I.C.S.: 722320
Akila Togean *(Gen Mgr)*

Subsidiaries:

K.u.K. Hofzuckerbacker Ch. Demel (2)
Kohlmarkt 14
1010 Vienna, Austria
Tel.: (43) 153517170
Fax: (43) 1535171726
E-Mail: wien@demel.at
Web Site: www.demel.at/en/frames/inde x_wien.htm
Baked Food Products Mfr
S.I.C.: 2099
N.A.I.C.S.: 311999
Rose Mary Zechmeister *(Gen Mgr)*

Sky Gourmet - airline catering and logistics GmbH (2)
Postfach 22
Flughafen, A 1300 Schwechat, Austria
Tel.: (43) 1700731300
Fax: (43) 1700731209
E-Mail: office@sky-gourmet.com
Web Site: www.sky-gourmet.com
Airline Catering Services
S.I.C.: 5812
N.A.I.C.S.: 722320
Eric Seiser *(Mgr)*

DO & CO Event Austria GmbH (1)
Stephansplatz 12
1010 Vienna, Austria
Tel.: (43) 174000191
Fax: (43) 174000194
E-Mail: office@doco.com
Emp.: 3,000
Catering Services
S.I.C.: 5812
N.A.I.C.S.: 722320
Attila Dogudan *(Gen Mgr)*

DO & CO Party-Service & Catering GmbH (1)
Dampfmuhlgasse 5
1110 Vienna, Austria
Tel.: (43) 1740001101
Fax: (43) 1740001149
E-Mail: partyservice@doco.com
Web Site: www.doco.com
Emp.: 1,000
Party & Catering Services
S.I.C.: 5812
N.A.I.C.S.: 722320
Dougus Dan *(Mng Dir)*

DO & CO Salzburg Restaurants & Betriebs GmbH (1)
Wilhelm Spazier St 8
5020 Salzburg, Austria
Tel.: (43) 66283990
Fax: (43) 66283990660
E-Mail: dispatch.salzburg@doco.com
Emp.: 40
Catering Services
S.I.C.: 5812
N.A.I.C.S.: 722320
Dogudan Attila *(CEO)*
Hrastnig Harald *(Co-CEO)*

U.S. Subsidiary:

DO & CO New York Catering, Inc. (1)
149-32 132nd St
Jamaica, NY 11430

DO & CO Aktiengesellschaft—(Continued)

Tel.: (718) 529-4570
Fax: (718) 529-4560
E-Mail: newyork@doco.com
Web Site: www.doco.com
Emp.: 250
Catering Services
S.I.C.: 5812
N.A.I.C.S.: 722320
Joerg Wurmitzer *(Controller-North America)*

Non-U.S. Subsidiaries:

DO & CO Berlin GmbH (1)
An der Spreeschanze 2
13599 Berlin, Germany
Tel.: (49) 303377300
Fax: (49) 431740001559
E-Mail: berlin@doco.com
Web Site: www.doco.com
Emp.: 30
Catering Services
S.I.C.: 5812
N.A.I.C.S.: 722320
Mike Kalp *(Mng Dir)*

DO & CO Event & Airline Catering Ltd (1)
Unit 2 Girling Way
Great S W Rd, Feltham, Middlesex, TW14 0PH, United Kingdom
Tel.: (44) 2085870000
Fax: (44) 2085870080
E-Mail: reception.lhr@doco.com
Catering Services
S.I.C.: 5812
N.A.I.C.S.: 722320
Mike Winner *(Mgr)*

DO & CO Frankfurt GmbH (1)
Langer Kornweg 38
Kelsterbach, Germany
Tel.: (49) 610798570
Fax: (49) 6107985750
E-Mail: frankfurt@doco.com
Web Site: www.doco.com
Emp.: 100
Catering Services
S.I.C.: 5812
N.A.I.C.S.: 722320
Alexandera Gereal *(Mgr)*

DO & CO International Catering Ltd (1)
Unit 2 Girling Way
Great S W Rd, Feltham, Middlesex, TW14 0BH, United Kingdom
Tel.: (44) 2085870000
Fax: (44) 2085870080
E-Mail: london@doco.com
Web Site: www.doco.com
Catering Services
S.I.C.: 5812
N.A.I.C.S.: 722320
Mike Winner *(Mgr)*

DO & CO Munchen GmbH (1)
Lohstrasse 36
85445 Schwaig, Germany
Tel.: (49) 8122909980
Fax: (49) 81229099880
E-Mail: munich@doco.com
Web Site: www.doco.com
Emp.: 30
Catering Services
S.I.C.: 5812
N.A.I.C.S.: 722320
Harald Hrastnig *(Gen Mgr)*

DO & CO Museum Catering Ltd (1)
Great Russell St
London, WC1B 3DG, United Kingdom
Tel.: (44) 2077238000
Fax: (44) 2085870080
E-Mail: london@doco.com
Web Site: www.doco.com
Catering Services
S.I.C.: 5812
N.A.I.C.S.: 722320
Mike Winner *(Mgr-Unit)*

DO & CO Olympiapark Munchen Restaurant GmbH (1)
Am Olympiapark 1
80809 Munich, Germany
Tel.: (49) 89358274910
Fax: (49) 89358274920
E-Mail: doco.resturantinternational@doco.com
Web Site: www.doco.com
Emp.: 30
Catering Services
S.I.C.: 5812
N.A.I.C.S.: 722320

DO-FLUORIDE CHEMICALS CO., LTD.

(d/b/a DFD)
Jiaoke Road
Zhongzhan District, Jiaozuo, Henan, 454191, China
Tel.: (86) 391 2802285
Fax: (86) 391 2802927
Web Site: www.chinacryolite.com
Year Founded: 1999
002407—(SSE)
Sales Range: $100-124.9 Million
Emp.: 1,000
Business Description:
Fluoride Chemical Products Mfr
S.I.C.: 2899
N.A.I.C.S.: 325998
Personnel:
Shijiang Li *(Pres)*

DOCA CAPITAL CORP.

(Name Changed to Great Northern Gold Exploration Corporation)

DOCCHECK AG

Vogelsanger Str 66
50823 Cologne, Germany
Tel.: (49) 221 92053 100
Fax: (49) 221 92053 133
E-Mail: presse@doccheck.com
Web Site: www.doccheck.ag
AJ91—(DEU)
Business Description:
Marketing Consulting Services
S.I.C.: 8742
N.A.I.C.S.: 541613
Personnel:
Michael Thiess *(Chm-Supervisory Bd)*
Frank Antwerpes *(CEO)*
Supervisory Board of Directors:
Michael Thiess
Winfried Leimeister
Joachim Pietzko

Subsidiaries:

antwerpes ag (1)
Vogelsanger Strasse 66
50823 Cologne, Germany
Tel.: (49) 221 92053 0
Fax: (49) 221 92053 133
E-Mail: info@antwerpes.de
Web Site: www.antwerpes.de
Healthcare Marketing Services
S.I.C.: 8742
N.A.I.C.S.: 541613
Frank Antwerpes *(CEO)*

DocCheck Medizinbedarf & Logistik GmbH (1)
Carl-Zeiss-Str 3
71093 Weil im Schonbuch, Germany
Tel.: (49) 7157 56 56 50
Fax: (49) 7157 56 56 550
E-Mail: info@doccheckshop.de
Web Site: www.doccheckshop.de
Electronic Shopping & Logistics Consulting Services
S.I.C.: 5961
N.A.I.C.S.: 454111

DOCDATA N.V.

Energieweg 2
5145 NW Waalwijk, Netherlands
Tel.: (31) 416631100
Fax: (31) 416631111
E-Mail: corporate@docdata.com
Web Site: www.docdatanv.com
DOCD—(EUR)
Rev.: $205,743,238
Assets: $111,885,573
Liabilities: $61,362,467
Net Worth: $50,523,106
Earnings: $10,224,161
Emp.: 1,129
Fiscal Year-end: 12/31/12
Business Description:
CD's, DVD's & Audio Cassettes Mfr
S.I.C.: 3651
N.A.I.C.S.: 334310
Personnel:
Jacobus A. de Vreeze *(Chm-Supervisory Bd)*
Adriaan Schouwenaar *(Vice Chm-Supervisory Bd)*
Michiel Alting von Geusau *(CEO)*
Marc E. T. Verstraeten *(CFO)*
Supervisory Board of Directors:
Jacobus A. de Vreeze
Johannes V. Elsendoorn
Dirk Lindenbergh
Adriaan Schouwenaar

Subsidiaries:

Best2Serve B.V (1)
Energieweg 2
Waalwijk, 5145 NW, Netherlands
Tel.: (31) 416674150
Fax: (31) 416674159
E-Mail: helpdesk@best2serve.com
Web Site: www.best2serve.com
Emp.: 30
Payment Software Development Services
S.I.C.: 7371
N.A.I.C.S.: 541511
Joras Ezendak *(Mng Dir)*

Docdata Benelux B.V. (1)
Energieweg 2
5145NW Waalwijk, Netherlands
Tel.: (31) 416631100
Fax: (31) 416631111
E-Mail: info@docdata.nl
Web Site: www.docdata.nl
Emp.: 500
Freight Transportation Arrangement
S.I.C.: 4731
N.A.I.C.S.: 488510
Michiel Alting von Geusau *(Mng Dir)*

Docdata Distributie Benelux B.V. (1)
Energieweg 2
5145 NW Waalwijk, Netherlands
Tel.: (31) 416631100
Fax: (31) 416631111
E-Mail: info@docdata.nl
Web Site: www.docdata.nl
Emp.: 500
Freight Transportation Arrangement
S.I.C.: 4731
N.A.I.C.S.: 488510
Michiel Alting von Geusau *(Mng Dir)*

Docdata Distribution Services B.V. (1)
Energieweg 2
5145NW Waalwijk, Netherlands
Tel.: (31) 416631100
Fax: (31) 416631111
E-Mail: info@docdata.nl
Web Site: www.docdata.nl
Emp.: 1,000
Employment Placement Agencies
S.I.C.: 7361
N.A.I.C.S.: 561311
Michiel Alting von Geusau *(Mng Dir)*

Docdata E-Commerce Solutions B.V. (1)
Energieweg 2
5145 NW Waalwijk, Netherlands
Tel.: (31) 416631100
Fax: (31) 416631111
E-Mail: corporate@docdata.com
Web Site: www.docdata.nl
Advertising Agencies
S.I.C.: 7311
N.A.I.C.S.: 541810
Michiel Alting von Geusau *(CEO)*

Docdata International B.V. (1)
Energieweg 2
5145NW Waalwijk, Netherlands
Tel.: (31) 416631100
Fax: (31) 416674100
E-Mail: info@docdata.nl
Web Site: www.docdata.nl
Emp.: 500
Trusts Estates & Agency Accounts
S.I.C.: 6733
N.A.I.C.S.: 525920
Michiel Alting von Geusau *(Mng Dir)*

Subsidiary:

IAI excimer systems B.V (2)
De Run 5406
Veldhoven, Noord-Brabant, 5504 DE, Netherlands
Tel.: (31) 402542445
Fax: (31) 402545635
Web Site: www.iai.nl
Emp.: 50
Security System Services
S.I.C.: 7382
N.A.I.C.S.: 561621
J. Cobben *(Mng Dir)*

Non-U.S. Subsidiary:

IAI industrial systems GmbH (2)
Am Wall 21
14979 Grossbeeren, Germany
Tel.: (49) 3370174710
Fax: (49) 7017471699
E-Mail: hschmidt@docdata.de
Web Site: www.docdata.de
Emp.: 2
Industrial Machinery Equipment Mfr
S.I.C.: 3559
N.A.I.C.S.: 333249
Nis Weibels *(Gen Mgr)*

Docdata Nederland B.V. (1)
Energieweg 2
5145NW Waalwijk, Netherlands
Tel.: (31) 416631100
Fax: (31) 416631111
E-Mail: info@docdata.nl
Web Site: www.docdata.nl
Emp.: 100
Trusts Estates & Agency Accounts
S.I.C.: 6733
N.A.I.C.S.: 525920
Michiel Alting von Geusau *(Mng Dir)*

Subsidiaries:

Docdata commerce B.V. (2)
Energieweg 2
5145 NW Waalwijk, Netherlands
Tel.: (31) 416674150
Fax: (31) 416674159
E-Mail: commerce.nl@docdata.com
Web Site: www.docdatacommerce.com
Emp.: 25
Payment Software Development Services
S.I.C.: 7371
N.A.I.C.S.: 541511

Docdata fulfilment B.V (2)
Energieweg 2
5145 NW Waalwijk, Netherlands
Tel.: (31) 416674111
Fax: (31) 416674100
E-Mail: fulfilment.nl@docdata.com
Payment Software Development Services
S.I.C.: 7371
N.A.I.C.S.: 541511
Michael Vongaseaw *(Gen Mgr)*

docdata payments B.V (2)
Hoofdstraat 82
3972 LB Driebergen, Netherlands
Tel.: (31) 343530000
Fax: (31) 343530001
E-Mail: support@docdatapayments.com
Web Site: www.docdatapayments.com
Emp.: 40
Online Payment Service Provider
S.I.C.: 6099
N.A.I.C.S.: 522320

Main Capital B.V (2)
Paleisstraat 6
Hague, 2514 JA, Netherlands
Tel.: (31) 70 324 34 33
Fax: (31) 70 324 30 93
E-Mail: pieterv@main.nl
Web Site: www.main.nl
Emp.: 6
Portfolio Management & Software Services
S.I.C.: 6282
N.A.I.C.S.: 523920
Lars van 't Hoenderdaal *(Co-Partner)*
Pieter van Bodegraven *(Partner)*
Charly Zwemstra *(Co-Partner)*

DOCdata-Veldhoven (1)
Energieweg 2
5145 Waalwijk, Netherlands (100%)
Mailing Address:
P.O. Box 200
5500 AE Veldhoven, Netherlands
Tel.: (31) 416674111
Fax: (31) 416674100
E-Mail: info@DOCdata.com
Web Site: www.iai.com
Emp.: 150
Provider of Computer Services
S.I.C.: 7373
N.A.I.C.S.: 541512
Michiel Alting von Geusau *(Mng Dir)*

IAI industrial systems B.V (1)
De Run 5406
5504 DE Veldhoven, Netherlands
Tel.: (31) 402542445
Fax: (31) 402545635
E-Mail: info@iai.nl
Web Site: www.iai.nl
Optical & Laser Industrial Systems Distr
S.I.C.: 5084
N.A.I.C.S.: 423830

Industrial Automation Integrators (IAI) B.V. (1)
De Run 5406
PO Box 200
5504 Veldhoven, Netherlands (100%)
Tel.: (31) 402542445
Fax: (31) 402545635
E-Mail: info@iai.nl
Web Site: www.iai.nl
Emp.: 50
Engineering Services
S.I.C.: 8711
N.A.I.C.S.: 541330
Jan Cobben *(Mng Dir)*

Non-U.S. Subsidiaries:

Docdata commerce Limited (1)
4th Floor 20 Margaret Street
London, W1W8RS, United Kingdom
Tel.: (44) 2075802880
Fax: (44) 2075802844
E-Mail: sales@docdatacommerce.co.uk
Web Site: www.docdatacommerce.co.uk
Emp.: 10
Electronic Commerce Solutions
S.I.C.: 7374
N.A.I.C.S.: 518210
John Van Heumen *(Mng Dir)*

Docdata E-Commerce Fulfilment GmbH (1)
Am Wall 21
Grossbeeren, 14979 Brandenburg, Germany
Tel.: (49) 3370174710
Fax: (49) 337017471699
E-Mail: hschmit@doctata.te
Web Site: www.docdata-ecf.de
Emp.: 20
Business Support Services
S.I.C.: 7389
N.A.I.C.S.: 561499
Volker Weiss *(Gen Mgr)*

Docdata fulfilment Limited (1)
Windrush Industrial Park Burford Road
Witney, OX29 7EW, United Kingdom
Tel.: (44) 1993770600
Fax: (44) 1993779002
E-Mail: fulfilment.uk@docdata.com
Web Site: www.docdatafulfilment.com
Payment Software Development Services
S.I.C.: 7371
N.A.I.C.S.: 541511

Docdata Germany GmbH (1)
Gustav-Meyer-Allee 25
13355 Berlin, Germany (100%)
Tel.: (49) 304670840
Fax: (49) 304638626
E-Mail: sales@docdata.de
Web Site: www.docdata.de
Emp.: 70
Prerecorded Compact Disc Tape & Record Reproducing
S.I.C.: 3652
N.A.I.C.S.: 334614
Antje Engelmann *(Mng Dir)*

Subsidiaries:

Docdata e-business GmbH (2)
Munsterstrabe 111
48155 Munster, Germany
Tel.: (49) 251 620 60 100
Fax: (49) 251 620 60 109
Software Development Services
S.I.C.: 7371
N.A.I.C.S.: 541511

Subsidiary:

Docdata Document Services GmbH (3)
Munsterstr 111
Munster, 48155, Germany
Tel.: (49) 250630793161
Fax: (49) 250630793149
Document Processing Services
S.I.C.: 7389
N.A.I.C.S.: 561410
Mario Stiebner *(Gen Mgr)*

Docdata Fashion Services GmbH (2)
Robert-bosch-str 21-23
Munich, 85748, Germany
Tel.: (49) 3370174710
Fax: (49) 337017471699
Software Development Services
S.I.C.: 7371
N.A.I.C.S.: 541511

Docdata fulfilment GmbH (2)
Am Wall 21
14979 Berlin, Germany
Tel.: (49) 3370174710
Fax: (49) 33701 7471 699
E-Mail: fulfilment.de@docdata.com
Web Site: www.docdatafulfilment.com
Software Development Services
S.I.C.: 7371
N.A.I.C.S.: 541511
Stephen Van Hoof *(Gen Mgr)*

Docdata payments GmbH (1)
Gustav-meyer-allee 25
13355 Berlin, Germany
Tel.: (49) 33701747176
Fax: (49) 33701 7471 699
Financial Management Consulting Services
S.I.C.: 8742
N.A.I.C.S.: 541611

Docdata payments (response) Limited (1)
Windrush Industrial Park Burford Road
Witney, OX29 7EW, United Kingdom
Tel.: (44) 1993770600
Fax: (44) 1993779002
E-Mail: info@docdataresponse.co.uk
Web Site: www.docdataresponse.co.uk
Payment Software Development Services
S.I.C.: 7371
N.A.I.C.S.: 541511

Emedia Spot Exchange (EMX) GmbH (1)
Gustav-Meyer-Allee 25
13355 Berlin, Germany
Tel.: (49) 30726114115
Business Support Services
S.I.C.: 7389
N.A.I.C.S.: 561499

DOCKWISE LTD.
(Acquired by Royal Boskalis Westminster N.V.)

DODGE CITY AUTO (1984) LTD.
2200 Eighth Street East
Saskatoon, SK, S7H 0V3, Canada
Tel.: (306) 374-2120
Toll Free: (800) 667-4755
Web Site: www.dodgecityautodealer.com
Rev.: $40,721,150
Emp.: 84
Business Description:
New & Used Car Dealers
S.I.C.: 5511
N.A.I.C.S.: 441110
Personnel:
Kevin Strunk *(Gen Mgr)*

DODS (GROUP) PLC
21 Dartmouth Street
Westminster, London, SW1H 9BP, United Kingdom
Tel.: (44) 20 7593 5500
Fax: (44) 20 7593 5794
E-Mail: info@dodsgroupplc.com
Web Site: www.dodsgroupplc.com
Year Founded: 2001
DODS—(AIM)
Rev.: $29,648,011
Assets: $60,785,293
Liabilities: $12,425,854
Net Worth: $48,359,439
Earnings: ($16,173,509)
Emp.: 239
Fiscal Year-end: 03/31/13
Business Description:
Global Political Information, Publishing, Training, Events & Communications Services
S.I.C.: 2721
N.A.I.C.S.: 511120
Personnel:
Andrew Wilson *(Interim Chm)*
Keith Sadler *(CEO, Sec & Dir-Fin)*
Board of Directors:
Andrew Wilson
Lord Adonls
Martin Beck
Henrietta Marsh
Keith Sadler
William Wells
Legal Counsel:
Brabners LLP
Manchester Office 55 King Street
Manchester, M2 4LQ, United Kingdom

Subsidiary:

Fenman Limited (1)
Unit 2 e-space North
181 Wisbech Road, Littleport, Cambridgeshire, CB6 1RA, United Kingdom
Tel.: (44) 1353 865350
Fax: (44) 1353 865351
E-Mail: service@fenman.co.uk
Web Site: www.fenman.co.uk
Emp.: 3
Materials & Information for Employee Training & Related Personnel Matters
S.I.C.: 2741
N.A.I.C.S.: 511199
Guy Cleaver *(Mng Dir)*

Division:

Lonsdale (1)
Westerhill Road Bishopbriggs
Elmsfield Pk Holme, Glasgow, G64 2QT, United Kingdom
Tel.: (44) 1539565921
Fax: (44) 8445768131
E-Mail: enquiries@harpercollins.co.uk
Web Site: www.harpercollins.co.uk
Emp.: 100
Publisher of Revision Guides & Workbooks for School Pupils
S.I.C.: 2741
N.A.I.C.S.: 511199
Victoria Barnsley *(Mng Dir)*

THE DODSAL GROUP
Third Fl DNI Bldg Sheikh Zayed Rd
PO Box 8034
Dubai, United Arab Emirates
Tel.: (971) 43431515
Fax: (971) 43434757
E-Mail: coffice@dodsaldxb.ae
Web Site: www.dodsal.com
Year Founded: 1948
Sales Range: $1-4.9 Billion
Emp.: 17,500
Business Description:
Holding Company
S.I.C.: 6719
N.A.I.C.S.: 551112
Personnel:
Rajen A. Kilachand *(Chm & Pres)*

Division:

Dodsal Engineering & Construction Pte. Limited (1)
Third Floor DNI Building Sheikh Zayed Road
PO Box 8034
Dubai, United Arab Emirates
Tel.: (971) 43431515
Fax: (971) 43434757
E-Mail: mail@dodsal.ae
Web Site: www.dodsal.com
Emp.: 220
Engineering, Procurement & Construction Services
S.I.C.: 1629
N.A.I.C.S.: 236210
R. A. Kilachand *(Chm & Pres)*

Non-U.S. Subsidiary:

AE&E I.D.E.A. India Pvt. Ltd. (2)
No 32 A & B Ambit IT Park 7th Fl Ambattur Industrial Estate
Chennai, 600058, India In
Tel.: (91) 4466455200 (100%)
Fax: (91) 4466455330
E-Mail: mail@aee-idea.in
Web Site: www.dodsal.com
Emp.: 350
Energy & Industrial Sector Construction & Engineering Services
S.I.C.: 1629
N.A.I.C.S.: 236210
Pawan Kumar *(Mng Dir)*

DOEDIJNS GROUP INTERNATIONAL B.V.
(See Under IK Investment Partners AB)

DOEPKER INDUSTRIES LTD.
300 Doepker Ave
Annaheim, SK, S0K 0G0, Canada
Tel.: (306) 598-2171
Fax: (306) 598-2028
E-Mail: marketing@doepker.com
Web Site: www.doepker.com
Year Founded: 1963
Rev.: $41,672,562
Emp.: 525
Business Description:
Trailers Equipment Mfr
S.I.C.: 3537
N.A.I.C.S.: 333924
Personnel:
Dave Doepker *(Chm & VP-Intl Mktg)*
Gurcan Kocdag *(Pres)*
Lionel Doepker *(Chief Customer Officer)*

DOF ASA
Alfabygget
5392 Storebo, Norway
Tel.: (47) 56181000
Fax: (47) 56181006
E-Mail: management@dof.no
Web Site: www.dof.no
Year Founded: 1981
DOF—(OSL)
Rev.: $1,472,534,640
Assets: $5,747,156,460
Liabilities: $4,525,654,950
Net Worth: $1,221,501,510
Earnings: $63,346,500
Emp.: 4,306
Fiscal Year-end: 12/31/12
Business Description:
Offshore & Subsea Vessel Owner & Operator
S.I.C.: 4412
N.A.I.C.S.: 483111
Personnel:
Helge Singelstad *(Chm)*
Mons S. Aase *(CEO)*
Hilde Dronen *(CFO)*
Gary Kennedy *(COO)*
Arnstein Klovrud *(CTO)*
Eirik Torressen *(CEO-Norskan Offshore Ltda)*
Anders A. Waage *(CEO-DOF Mgmt AS)*
Mons Melingen *(Exec VP-Marine)*
Board of Directors:

DOF ASA—(Continued)

Helge Singelstad
Wenche Kjolas
Helge Mogster
Karoline Mogster
Oddvar Strangeland

DOGA

ZA Pariwest 8 avenue Gutenberg
78310 Maurepas, Yvelines, France
Tel.: (33) 130664141
Fax: (33) 130664199
E-Mail: export@doga.fr
Web Site: www.dogassembly.com
Sls.: $20,400,000
Emp.: 132

Business Description:
Industrial Machinery & Equipment
S.I.C.: 5084
N.A.I.C.S.: 423830

Personnel:
Jean Augsburger *(Chm)*

Board of Directors:
Jean Augsburger

DOGAN YAYIN HOLDING A.S.

Burhaniye Mah Kisukli Cad No 65
Uskuda
Istanbul, Turkey
Tel.: (90) 216 556 90 00
Fax: (90) 216 556 92 00
Web Site: www.dyh.com.tr
DYHOL—(IST OTC)
Sls.: $1,427,286,112
Assets: $2,225,020,229
Liabilities: $1,422,271,713
Net Worth: $802,748,516
Earnings: $154,060,654
Emp.: 10,302
Fiscal Year-end: 12/31/12

Business Description:
Book Publishing & Radio Broadcasting Services
S.I.C.: 4832
N.A.I.C.S.: 515111

Personnel:
Begumhan Dogan Faralyali *(Chm)*
Soner Gedik *(Vice Chm)*
Yahya Uzdiyen *(Pres & CEO)*
Ahmet Toksoy *(CFO)*
Erem Turgut Yucel *(Chief Legal Officer)*

Board of Directors:
Begumhan Dogan Faralyali
Soner Gedik
Haci Ahmet Kilicoglu
Ahmet Toksoy
Ertugrul Feyzi Tuncer
Yahya Uzdiyen

Subsidiary:

Hurriyet Gazetecilik ve Matbaacilik A.S. **(1)**
Hurriyet Dunyasi 100 Yil Mahallesi
Matbaacilar Caddesi No 78
34214 Istanbul, Turkey
Tel.: (90) 2126770000
Fax: (90) 2126770182
Web Site: www.hurriyetkurumsal.com
HURGZ—(IST)
Sls.: $482,127,945
Assets: $877,561,808
Liabilities: $455,029,221
Net Worth: $422,532,587
Earnings: $83,559,046
Emp.: 7,198
Fiscal Year-end: 12/31/12
Newspaper Publishing Services
S.I.C.: 2741
N.A.I.C.S.: 519130
Vuslat Dogan Sabanci *(Chm)*
Yahya Uzdiyen *(Vice Chm)*
Dursun Ali Yilmaz *(CFO)*

DOGI INTERNATIONAL FABRICS, S.A

C/ Mlg s/n
El Masnou, 08320 Barcelona, Spain
Tel.: (34) 934628000
Fax: (34) 93 116 52 04
E-Mail: info@dogi.com
Web Site: www.dogi.com
DGI—(MAD)
Sales Range: $125-149.9 Million
Emp.: 1,500

Business Description:
Lingerie, Swimwear, Active Wear & Outerwear Mfr & Sales
S.I.C.: 2389
N.A.I.C.S.: 315240

Personnel:
Josep Domenech Gimenez *(Chm)*
Jordi Torras Torras *(CEO)*
Antonio Augustin Penarroja Castell *(Sec)*

Board of Directors:
Josep Domenech Gimenez
Eduardo Domenech Alvaro
Sergi Domenech Alvaro
Carlos Franques Ribera
Antonio Augustin Penarroja Castell
Jordi Torras Torras

Non-U.S. Subsidiary:

Penn Elastic Gmbh **(1)**
Ab Der Talle 20
33102 Paderborn, Germany
Tel.: (49) 525140080
Fax: (49) 5251408590
E-Mail: info@penn-ts.com
Web Site: www.penn-ts.com
Emp.: 200
Fabrics Mfr
S.I.C.: 3499
N.A.I.C.S.: 332999
Markus Regenstein *(Mng Dir)*

U.S. Subsidiary:

EFA, Inc. **(1)**
3112 Pleasant Garden Rd
Greensboro, NC 27406
Tel.: (510) 430-8404
Web Site: www.efainc.com
Building Construction & Remodeling Services
S.I.C.: 1542
N.A.I.C.S.: 236220

DOGINN INC.

1380 Lougar Ave
Sarnia, ON, N7S 5N7, Canada
Tel.: (519) 381-7086
Web Site: www.doginn.com
Year Founded: 2010
DOGI—(OTC)
Liabilities: $10,195
Net Worth: ($10,195)
Earnings: ($25,314)
Fiscal Year-end: 12/31/12

Business Description:
Travel-Related Pet Friendly Accommodation, Services & Products
S.I.C.: 7011
N.A.I.C.S.: 721199

Personnel:
Gary Jacob Perlingos *(Pres & CTO)*
Kyle Winther *(CEO)*
Lori Winther *(CFO, Treas & Sec)*

Board of Directors:
Gary Jacob Perlingos
Kyle Winther
Lori Winther
Niels Winther

Transfer Agent:
Island Stock Transfer
15500 Roosevelt Blvd Ste 301
Clearwater, FL 33760

DOGUS HOLDING AS

Eski Buyukdere Cad 15
Oycan Plaza, 34392 Maslak, Istanbul, Turkey
Tel.: (90) 2123353232
Fax: (90) 2123353090
E-Mail: dmail@dogusholding.com.tr
Web Site: www.dogusholding.com.tr
Emp.: 25,000

Business Description:
Holding Company
S.I.C.: 6719
N.A.I.C.S.: 551112

Personnel:
Ferit F. Sahenk *(Chm)*
Husnu Akhan *(CEO)*

Board of Directors:
Ferit F. Sahenk
Aclan Acar
Husnu Akhan
Yucel Celik
Sadi Gogdun
Sadan Gurtas
Ahmet Kurutluoglu
Muhsin Menguturk
Gonul Talu
Erman Yerdelen

DOGUS OTOMOTIV SERVIS VE TICARET A.S.

Sekerpinar Mah Anadolu Cad No 22
41490 Kocaeli, Turkey
Tel.: (90) 2626769090
Web Site: www.dogusotomotiv.com.tr
OS8—(DEU)
Rev.: $2,900,439,869
Assets: $1,256,200,351
Liabilities: $585,451,510
Net Worth: $670,748,841
Earnings: $144,923,633
Emp.: 1,980
Fiscal Year-end: 12/31/12

Business Description:
Automobile Spare Parts Sales
S.I.C.: 5012
N.A.I.C.S.: 423110

Personnel:
Aclan Acar *(Chm)*
Emir Ali Bilaloglu *(Chm-Exec Bd & CEO)*
Suleyman Kadir Tugtekin *(Vice Chm)*
Giovanni Gino Bottaro *(Member-Exec Bd & Gen Mgr-Audi, Bentley & Lamborghini Brands)*
Berk Cagdas *(Member-Exec Bd & Gen Mgr-Fin, Budget Plng, Risk Mgmt & IR)*
Ilhami Eksin *(Member-Exec Bd & Gen Mgr-Scania Krone Meiller Brands)*
Anil Gursoy *(Member-Exec Bd & Gen Mgr-Seat, Porsche & DOD Brand)*
Kerem Galip Guven *(Member-Exec Bd & Gen Mgr-VW Commercial Vehicle Brand)*
Mustafa Karabayir *(Member-Exec Bd & Gen Mgr-Logistic Svs)*
Tolga Senyucel *(Member-Exec Bd & Gen Mgr-Skoda Brands)*
Vedat Uygun *(Member-Exec Bd & Gen Mgr-VW Passenger Vehicle Brand)*

Board of Directors:
Aclan Acar
H. Murat Aka
Yilmaz Arguden
Emir Ali Bilaloglu
Ferruh Eker
Ozlem Denizmen Kocatepe
Nevzat Oztangut
Suleyman Kadir Tugtekin

DOHA BANK Q.S.C.

Head Office Tower Corniche Street
West Bay
PO Box 3818
Doha, Qatar
Tel.: (974) 44456600
Fax: (974) 4416631
E-Mail: hellodoha@dohabank.com.qa
Web Site: www.dohabank.com.qa
Year Founded: 1978
DHBK—(QE)
Int. Income: $607,897,965
Assets: $14,747,249,134
Liabilities: $12,730,332,963
Net Worth: $2,016,916,172
Earnings: $348,558,021
Fiscal Year-end: 12/31/12

Business Description:
Banking Services
S.I.C.: 6029
N.A.I.C.S.: 522110

Personnel:
Fahad Mohammad Jabor Al Thani *(Chm)*
Ahmed Abdul Rahman Yousuf Obaidan Fakhroo *(Vice Chm)*
Ragavan Seetharaman *(CEO)*
Abdul Rehman Mohammed Jabor Al Thani *(Mng Dir)*

Board of Directors:
Fahad Mohammad Jabor Al Thani
Hamad Mohammad Hamad Abdulla Almana
Jabar Sultan Twar Al Kuwari
Ahmed Abdul Rahman Yousuf Obaidan Fakhroo
Abdul Rehman Mohammed Jabor Al Thani
Abdulla Mohammad Jabor Al Thani
Falah Jassim Jabor Mohammad Al-Thani

Subsidiary:

Doha Bank Assurance Company W.L.L **(1)**
C Ring Rd
Doha, Qatar
Tel.: (974) 4257576
Fax: (974) 44357582
E-Mail: dbac@dohabank.com.qa
Web Site: www.dohabankinsurance.com
Emp.: 50
General Insurance Services
S.I.C.: 6411
N.A.I.C.S.: 524210
Clive R. Weatherley *(Mgr)*

DOHA INSURANCE COMPANY QSC

207 C Ring Road
PO Box 7171
Doha, Qatar
Tel.: (974) 44292777
Fax: (974) 44657777
E-Mail: dohainsco@qatar.net.qa
Web Site: www.dicqatar.com
Year Founded: 2000
DOHI—(QE)
Rev.: $125,233,068
Assets: $368,062,982
Liabilities: $239,446,473
Net Worth: $128,616,510
Earnings: $16,102,373
Fiscal Year-end: 12/31/12

Business Description:
Insurance & Reinsurance Services
S.I.C.: 6411
N.A.I.C.S.: 524298

Personnel:
Nawaf Nasser Khaled Al-Thani *(Chm)*
Khalifa Jassim Mohammed Al-Thani *(Vice Chm)*
Bassam Hussein *(CEO)*
Adel Ali Ali *(Mng Dir)*

Board of Directors:
Nawaf Nasser Khaled Al-Thani
Victor Nazeem Reda Agha
Hitmi Ali Al Hitmi
Jaber Hamad Jassem Jaber Al Thani
Dahlan Jamaan Basheer Al-Hamad
Saud Omer Hamad Abdullah Al-Mana
Ali Nasser Abdullah Al Ahmed Al-Thani
Khalifa Jassim Mohammed Al-Thani
Adel Ali Ali
Hussam Abdul Salam Mohammed Abu Essa

Hassan Jassem Darwish Fakroo

DOHLE HANDELSGRUPPE HOLDING GMBH & CO. KG

(d/b/a Dohle Gruppe/Group)
Alte Lohmarer Strasse 59
53721 Siegburg, Germany
Tel.: (49) 22411220
Fax: (49) 2241122479
Web Site:
Year Founded: 1928
Emp.: 8,000
Business Description:
Holding Company; Grocery Wholesale Trade Distr; Supermarket Franchisor, Owner & Operator Import
S.I.C.: 6719
N.A.I.C.S.: 551112
Personnel:
Klaus Dohle *(Owner & CEO)*

Subsidiary:

HIT Handelsgruppe GmbH & Co. KG (1)
Alte Lohmarer Strasse 59
D-53721 Siegburg, Germany De
Tel.: (49) 22411220
Fax: (49) 2241122479
Web Site: www.hit.de
Supermarket Franchisor & Operator
S.I.C.: 5411
N.A.I.C.S.: 445110
Klaus Dohle *(CEO & Chm-Mgmt Bd)*
Carl Bauerschmitz *(Member-Mgmt Bd)*
Lothar Klopsch *(Member-Mgmt Bd)*
Ulrich Naujoks *(Member-Mgmt Bd)*

Non-U.S. Subsidiary:

HIT Frische GmbH & Co. KG (2)
Alte Lohmarer Strasse 59
53721 Siegburg, Germany De
Tel.: (49) 2241 122 0
Fax: (49) 2241 122 479
Emp.: 260
Supermarket Produce Management
S.I.C.: 7389
N.A.I.C.S.: 425120
Kurt Bohr *(Gen Mgr)*

DOHLER GMBH

Riedstrasse
64295 Darmstadt, Germany
Tel.: (49) 6151 306 0
Fax: (49) 6151 306 278
E-Mail: info@doehler.com
Web Site: www.doehler.com
Sales Range: $10-24.9 Million
Emp.: 3,000
Business Description:
Food & Beverage Ingredient Mfr & Marketer
S.I.C.: 2869
N.A.I.C.S.: 325199
Personnel:
Kurt Hufnagel *(Member-Exec Bd)*
Andreas Klein *(Member-Exec Bd)*

U.S. Joint Venture:

Dohler-Milne Aseptics LLC (1)
804 Bennett Ave
Prosser, WA 99350 WA
Tel.: (509) 786-2240
Fax: (509) 786-4915
Web Site: www.doehler-milne.com
Fruit Juice Blending & Compounding; Owned by Wyckoff Farms, Incorporated & by Dohler GmbH
S.I.C.: 2037
N.A.I.C.S.: 311411
David Wyckoff *(Mng Partner)*

DOHWA CONSULTING ENGINGEERS CO., LTD.

736-6 Yeoksam-Dong
Gangnam-Gu, Seoul, 135-080, Korea (South)
Tel.: (82) 220506000
Fax: (82) 25456050
Web Site: www.dohwa.co.kr
002150—(KRS)
Business Description:
Civil Engineering Services
S.I.C.: 1629
N.A.I.C.S.: 237990
Personnel:
Young Yoon Kim *(Chm & CEO)*
Byung Kwon Moon *(Vice Chm-Intl Construction)*
Hee Uk Moon *(Vice Chm-Intl Construction)*
Se Ung Chang *(Pres-Water)*
Yoon Han Lee *(Pres-Design)*
Kyoung Youl Min *(Pres-Urban Engrg)*
Jin Myung Ro *(Pres-Supervision)*
Board of Directors:
Young Yoon Kim
Se Ung Chang
Yoon Han Lee
Kyoung Youl Min
Byung Kwon Moon
Hee Uk Moon

DOLAT INVESTMENTS LTD.

203 City Center 186 Purswakkam High Road Keleeys
Chennai, 600010, India
Tel.: (91) 22 2673 2603
Fax: (91) 22 2673 2642
E-Mail: post@dolatinvest.com
Web Site: www.dolatinvest.com
505526—(BOM)
Rev.: $40,181,922
Assets: $17,583,661
Liabilities: $500,637
Net Worth: $17,083,024
Earnings: $1,466,739
Fiscal Year-end: 03/31/13
Business Description:
Securities Trading Services
S.I.C.: 6211
N.A.I.C.S.: 523120
Personnel:
Rajendra D. Shah *(Chm & Mng Dir)*
Umesh V. Moolya *(Sec)*
Board of Directors:
Rajendra D. Shah
Shashikant H. Gosalia
Harendra D. Shah
Sunil P. Shah
Transfer Agent:
Purva Sharegistry (India) Pvt. Ltd.
9 Shiv Shakti Industrial Estate Ground Floor
Sitaram Mill Compound
Mumbai, India

DOLCE & GABBANA S.R.L.

Via 20 Settembre 123
Milan, 20025, Italy
Tel.: (39) 2774271
Fax: (39) 0331409220
E-Mail: legano@dolcegabbana.it
Web Site: www.dolcegabbana.it
Emp.: 900
Business Description:
Mfr. & Distributor of Apparel
S.I.C.: 2389
N.A.I.C.S.: 315990
Personnel:
Domenico Dolce *(Chm & CEO)*
Stefano Gabbano *(Pres)*

U.S. Subsidiary:

Dolce & Gabbana USA, Inc. (1)
148 Lafayette St
New York, NY 10013
Tel.: (212) 750-0055
Fax: (212) 750-2750
E-Mail: info@dolcegabbana.it
Web Site: www.dolcegabbana.it/
Emp.: 100
Distr of Men's & Women's Apparel Import
S.I.C.: 5136
N.A.I.C.S.: 424320
Michel Brouillard *(Dir-Retail Visual-Dolce & Gabbana)*

DOLLAR SWEETS COMPANY PTY LTD

22 Purton Road
Pakenham, Vic, 3810, Australia
Tel.: (61) 0359413866
Fax: (61) 0359413607
E-Mail: info@dollarsweets.com.au
Web Site: www.dollarsweets.com.au
Year Founded: 1947
Sales Range: $25-49.9 Million
Emp.: 35
Business Description:
Chocolate & Sugar Confectionery Mfr
S.I.C.: 2066
N.A.I.C.S.: 311352
Personnel:
Neil Higgins *(CEO)*
Dianne Higgins *(Sec)*

DOLLARAMA INC.

5805 Royalmount Avenue
Montreal, QC, H4P 0A1, Canada
Tel.: (514) 737-1006
Fax: (514) 940-6169
E-Mail: contactus@dollarama.com
Web Site: www.dollarama.com
DOL—(TSX)
Sls.: $1,847,702,268
Assets: $1,444,998,922
Liabilities: $519,079,232
Net Worth: $925,919,690
Earnings: $219,663,510
Emp.: 17,428
Fiscal Year-end: 02/03/13
Business Description:
General Merchandise Stores
S.I.C.: 5399
N.A.I.C.S.: 452990
Personnel:
Larry Rossy *(Chm & CEO)*
Michael Ross *(CFO & Sec)*
Neil Rossy *(Chief Mdsg Officer)*
Leonard Assaly *(Sr VP)*
Geoffrey Robillard *(Sr VP-Import)*
Board of Directors:
Larry Rossy
Joshua Bekenstein
Gregory David
Stephen Gunn
Nicholas Nomicos
Neil Rossy
Richard G. Roy
John J. Swidler
J. Huw Thomas
Transfer Agent:
Computershare Investor Services Inc.
Montreal, QC, Canada

DOLLEX INDUSTIRES LIMITED

502 Dheeraj Swapna B Wing Pali Road Pali Naka
Bandra W, Mumbai, 400050, India
Tel.: (91) 22 26555005
Fax: (91) 22 26425005
E-Mail: info@dollexindustries.com
Web Site: www.dollexindustries.com
Year Founded: 1994
531367—(BOM)
Business Description:
Sugar Mfr
S.I.C.: 2063
N.A.I.C.S.: 311313
Personnel:
Mehmood Khan *(CFO)*
Board of Directors:
Radhakrishna Desraju
Nadeem Khan
K. G. Mittal
Ruchi Sogani
Sanjay Tiwari

DOLLY VARDEN SILVER CORPORATION

910 355 Burrard Street
Vancouver, BC, V6C 2G8, Canada
Tel.: (604) 398-4350
Fax: (604) 683-2965
Web Site: www.dollyvardensilver.com
Year Founded: 2012
DV—(OTC TSXV)
Business Description:
Silver & Gold Mining
S.I.C.: 1044
N.A.I.C.S.: 212222
Personnel:
John King Burns *(Chm)*
George Warren Heard *(Pres & CEO)*
Keith Margetson *(CFO)*
Board of Directors:
John King Burns
Allen Ambrose
George Warren Heard
Paul McGuigan
Theo Sanidas

DOLNOSLASKIE SUROWCE SKALNE S.A.

Rondo ONZ 1 33 Floor
00-124 Warsaw, Poland
Tel.: (48) 22 354 93 20
Fax: (48) 22 354 93 30
E-Mail: biuro@dss.pl
Web Site: www.dss.pl
DSS—(WAR)
Sales Range: $25-49.9 Million
Business Description:
Crushed Aggregate Supplier
S.I.C.: 5032
N.A.I.C.S.: 423320
Personnel:
Marek Gluchowski *(Chm-Supervisory Bd)*
Jan Luczak *(Chm-Mgmt Bd & CEO)*
Marcin Jezewski *(Vice Chm-Mgmt Bd)*
Malgorzata Then *(Member-Mgmt Bd)*
Supervisory Board of Directors:
Marek Gluchowski
Adam Budnikowski
Krzysztof Galos
Lukasz Halazinski
Rafal Juszczak
Maksymilian Kostrzewa
Danuta Luczak
Tomasz Siemiatkowski

DOLOMATRIX PHILIPPINES INC.

102 E Rodriguez Jr Ave
Bo Ugong, Pasig, Philippines
Tel.: (63) 26719086
Fax: (63) 26715925
E-Mail: info@dolomatrix.com.ph
Web Site: www.dolomatrix.com.ph
Year Founded: 2001
Business Description:
Toxic & Hazard Waste Treatment Services
S.I.C.: 4953
N.A.I.C.S.: 562211
Personnel:
Arsenio N. Valdes *(Pres & CEO)*

DOLOMITE CORPORATION BERHAD

19 Dolomite Park Avenue Jalan Batu Caves
68100 Batu Caves, Selangor, Malaysia
Tel.: (60) 3619560000
Fax: (60) 361872310
E-Mail: business@dolomite.com.my
Web Site: www.dolomite.com.my
DOLMITE—(KLS)

Dolomite Corporation Berhad—(Continued)

Rev.: $31,808,896
Assets: $142,385,159
Liabilities: $97,794,598
Net Worth: $44,590,562
Earnings: $653,545
Fiscal Year-end: 12/31/12

Business Description:
Construction & Property Development Services
S.I.C.: 1521
N.A.I.C.S.: 236115

Personnel:
Choong Keong Lew *(Mng Dir)*
Su San Chan *(Sec)*
Sze Min Lo *(Sec)*
Yit Chan Tai *(Sec)*

Board of Directors:
Mohd Jamil Johari
Dominic Kian-Wee Aw
Jeffrey Gerard Gomez
Jen Soong Huang
Choong Keong Lew
Beng Keat Lim

Subsidiary:

Dolomite Berhad **(1)**
19 Dolomite Park Avenue Jalan
68100 Batu Caves, Selangor, Malaysia
Tel.: (60) 361860000
Fax: (60) 361888651
E-Mail: business@dolomite.com.my
Emp.: 30
Building Construction Products Mfr
S.I.C.: 3271
N.A.I.C.S.: 327331
Lew Choong Keong *(Mng Dir)*

Subsidiaries:

Dolomite Industries Company Sdn. Bhd. **(2)**
11 3/4 Miles Sungai Serai
Hulu Langat, Selangor, Malaysia
Tel.: (60) 390211600
Fax: (60) 390212610
E-Mail: business@dolomite.com.my
Residential Property Development Services
S.I.C.: 6531
N.A.I.C.S.: 531390
Baldesh Singh *(Asst Gen Mgr)*

Subsidiary:

Dolomite Properties Sdn. Bhd. **(3)**
19 Dolomite Pk Ave Jalan Batu Caves
68100 Batu Caves, Selangor, Malaysia
Tel.: (60) 361861000
Fax: (60) 361857911
E-Mail: bussiness@dolomite.com.my
Residential Property Development Services
S.I.C.: 6531
N.A.I.C.S.: 531390

Dolomite Readymixed Concrete Sdn. Bhd. **(2)**
11 3/4 Miles Sungai Serai
43100 Hulu Langat, Selangor, Malaysia
Tel.: (60) 390211621
Fax: (60) 361872310
Emp.: 90
Readymixed Concrete Mfr
S.I.C.: 3273
N.A.I.C.S.: 327320
Chow Weng Kee *(Gen Mgr)*

DOLPHIN CAPITAL INVESTORS LIMITED

Vanterpool Plaza 2nd Floor Wickams Cay 1
Road Town, Tortola, Virgin Islands (British)
E-Mail: miltos@dolphincp.com
Web Site: www.dolphinci.com
DCI—(AIM OTC)
Rev.: $1,185,976
Assets: $1,224,651,234
Liabilities: $325,713,909
Net Worth: $898,937,326
Earnings: ($57,501,652)
Emp.: 361
Fiscal Year-end: 12/31/12

Business Description:
Real Estate Investment Services
S.I.C.: 6531
N.A.I.C.S.: 531390

Board of Directors:
Andreas Papageorghiou
Antonios Achilleoudis
Cem Duna
David B. Heller
Miltos Kambourides
Roger Lane-Smith
Christopher Pissarides

Legal Counsel:
Lawrence Graham LLP
4 More London Riverside
London, England, SE1 2AU, United Kingdom

DOLPHIN DELIVERY LTD.

4201 Lozells Avenue
Burnaby, BC, V5A 2Z4, Canada
Tel.: (604) 421-7059
Fax: (604) 421-8446
E-Mail: info@dolphindelivery.ca
Web Site: www.dolphindelivery.ca
Year Founded: 1968
Rev.: $44,412,050
Emp.: 500

Business Description:
Logistics & Transportation Services Provider
S.I.C.: 4214
N.A.I.C.S.: 484110

Personnel:
William Morris Peter *(Pres)*

DOLPHIN INTEGRATION S.A.

39 avenue du Granier
BP 65
Inovallee, F-38242 Meylan, France
Tel.: (33) 476411096
Fax: (33) 476902965
E-Mail: myd@dolphin.fr
Web Site: www.dolphin.fr
Year Founded: 1985
ALDOL—(EUR)
Emp.: 194

Business Description:
Semiconductor Mfr
S.I.C.: 3674
N.A.I.C.S.: 334413

Personnel:
Michel Depeyrot *(Chm & Pres)*
Agnes Venet *(CFO & COO)*

Board of Directors:
Michel Depeyrot
Severine Loarne
Viviane Neiter
Jean-Francois Pollet
Alban Richard
Agnes Venet
Louis Zangara
GianCarlo Zanni
Gunter Zimmer

Non-U.S. Subsidiaries:

DOLPHIN Integration GmbH **(1)**
Bismarckstrasse 142a
47057 Duisburg, Germany
Tel.: (49) 2033062250
Fax: (49) 2033062269
Web Site: www.dolphin.fr/corporate/contact/contact.php?version=html
Emp.: 5
Integrated Circuits Design Services
S.I.C.: 3674
N.A.I.C.S.: 334413
Laas Boskanper *(Mgr)*

DOLPHIN Integration Inc. **(1)**
2525 Bd Daniel Johnson
Chomedey, Laval, QC, H7T 1S9, Canada
Tel.: (450) 978-8885
Fax: (450) 978-8800
E-Mail: abl.di-inc@dolphin-integration.com
Web Site: www.dolphin.fr
Emp.: 8
Data Processing Services
S.I.C.: 7374
N.A.I.C.S.: 518210
Michel Depeyrot *(CEO)*

DOLPHIN INTERCONNECT SOLUTIONS ASA

Innspurten 15
Skullerud, 0694 Oslo, Norway
Tel.: (47) 23167000
Fax: (47) 23167180
E-Mail: info@dolphinics.com
Web Site: www.dolphinics.com
Emp.: 5

Business Description:
Develops, Manufactures & Markets High-Speed, High-Bandwidth Interconnect Products
S.I.C.: 7371
N.A.I.C.S.: 541511

Personnel:
Atle Jacobsen *(CEO)*
Hugo Kohmann *(COO)*

Board of Directors:
Anne-Grete Ellingsen
Marit Elisabeth Doving
Ole Henrik Eide
Hege Eikeland
Terje Rogne
Simen Thoresen

U.S. Subsidiary:

Dolphin Interconnect Solutions NA Inc. **(1)**
7 Boomhower Rd
Woodsville, NH 03785
Tel.: (603) 747-4100
Fax: (603) 747-4101
E-Mail: info@dolphinics.com
Web Site: www.dolphinics.com
Emp.: 22
Interconnect Software & Hardware Products
S.I.C.: 5045
N.A.I.C.S.: 423430

DOLPHIN MEDICAL SERVICES LTD.

417 Sanali Heavens Ameerpet
Hyderabad, AP, 500 073, India
Tel.: (91) 40 65889357
Fax: (91) 40 23738877
E-Mail: dolphinmedicalindia@gmail.com
Web Site: www.dolphinmedicalindia.com
Year Founded: 1994
526504—(BOM)
Rev.: $212,040
Assets: $4,307,196
Liabilities: $1,666,554
Net Worth: $2,640,642
Earnings: ($366,710)
Fiscal Year-end: 03/31/13

Business Description:
Healthcare Services
S.I.C.: 8082
N.A.I.C.S.: 621610

Personnel:
G. V. Mohan Prasad *(Mng Dir)*

Board of Directors:
Narendra Seena Karkera
Manikyam Hemanth Kumar
Vinay Vishnuraj Nayak
G. V. Mohan Prasad
M. Lakshmi Sudha

Transfer Agent:
XL Softech Systems Limited
3 Sagar Society Road No. 2 Banjara Hills
Hyderabad, India

DOLPHIN OFFSHORE ENTERPRISES (INDIA) LTD

LIC Building Plot No 54 Sector 11
CBD Belapur East
Navi Mumbai, 400 614, India
Tel.: (91) 2266026602
Fax: (91) 2266026603
E-Mail: contactus@dolphinoffshore.com
Web Site: www.dolphinoffshore.com
DOLPHINOFF—(NSE)
Rev.: $79,856,063
Assets: $115,122,573
Liabilities: $64,020,659
Net Worth: $51,101,913
Earnings: $8,733,656
Fiscal Year-end: 03/31/13

Business Description:
Oil & Gas Offshore Services
S.I.C.: 1311
N.A.I.C.S.: 211111

Personnel:
Kirpal Singh *(Chm)*
Navpreet Singh *(Mng Dir)*
Satpal Singh *(Mng Dir)*
Tapan Banik *(Co-COO & VP-Ops)*
Shashank Karnik *(Co-COO & VP-Projects)*
V. Surendran *(Sec)*

Board of Directors:
Kirpal Singh
Sabyasachi Hajara
J. Jayaraman
Faqir Chand Kohli
Harisimran Singh Malhi
Arvind K. Parikh
Robert D. Petty
Bipin R. Shah
Navpreet Singh
Satpal Singh
S. Sundar

Transfer Agent:
Sharepro Services (India) Pvt Ltd
13AB Samitha Warehousing Complex 2nd Fl
Sakinaka Telephone Exchange Ln
Saki Naka Andheri East, Mumbai, 400 072, India

DOM DEVELOPMENT S.A.

The Metropolitan Building 3
Pilsudskiego Square
Warsaw, 00-078, Poland
Tel.: (48) 223516633
Fax: (48) 223516889
E-Mail: finanse@domdevelopment.com.pl
Web Site: www.domdevelopment.com.pl
DOM—(WAR)
Rev.: $270,008,605
Assets: $558,050,490
Liabilities: $275,043,361
Net Worth: $283,007,129
Earnings: $28,932,721
Emp.: 153
Fiscal Year-end: 12/31/12

Business Description:
Real Estate & Property Development Services
S.I.C.: 6531
N.A.I.C.S.: 531311

Personnel:
Grzegorz Kielpsz *(Chm-Supervisory Bd)*
Jaroslaw Szanajca *(Chm-Mgmt Bd & CEO)*
Janusz Zalewski *(Vice Chm-Mgmt Bd & CFO)*
Jerzy Robert Slusarski *(Vice Chm-Mgmt Bd & COO)*
Markham Dumas *(Vice Chm-Supervisory Bd)*
Marek Moczulski *(Vice Chm-Supervisory Bd)*
Janusz Stolarczyk *(Member-Mgmt Bd & Dir-Bus Dev)*
Terry Roydon *(Member-Mgmt Bd)*

Supervisory Board of Directors:
Grzegorz Kielpsz
Wlodzimierz Bogucki
Michael Cronk
Markham Dumas

Krzysztof Grzylinski
Marek Moczulski
Mark Spiteri

DOM MAKLERSKI WDM S.A.

ul Kielbasnicza 28
50-109 Wroclaw, Poland
Tel.: (48) 71 79 11 555
Fax: (48) 71 79 11 556
E-Mail: biuro@wdmsa.pl
Web Site: www.wdmsa.pl
WDM—(WAR)
Business Description:
Financial Services
S.I.C.: 6726
N.A.I.C.S.: 525990
Personnel:
Wojciech Gudaszewski *(Chm-Mgmt Bd)*
Subsidiaries:

WDM Autoryzowany Doradca sp. z.o.o (1)
Plac Powstancow Slaskich 1 lok 201
53-329 Wroclaw, Poland
Tel.: (48) 71 79 11 555
Fax: (48) 71 79 11 556
E-Mail: biuro@wdmad.pl
Web Site: www.wdmad.pl
Investment Advisory Services
S.I.C.: 6282
N.A.I.C.S.: 523930

WDM Capital SA (1)
Powstancow Slaskich 1
Wroclaw, 53-329, Poland
Tel.: (48) 717911555
Fax: (48) 717911556
Private Equity Fund Investment Services
S.I.C.: 6722
N.A.I.C.S.: 525910

DOM VILLE SERVICES

N 12 14 12 Rue De La Verrerie
44100 Nantes, Loire Atlantique, France
Tel.: (33) 240699480
Rev.: $21,400,000
Emp.: 51
Business Description:
Hotels & Motels
S.I.C.: 7011
N.A.I.C.S.: 721110
Personnel:
Gerard Menguy *(Chm)*
Board of Directors:
Gerard Menguy
Claude Jendron

DOMAIN EXTREMES, INC.

602 Nan Fung Tower Suite 6/F
173 Des Voeux Road, Central, China (Hong Kong)
Tel.: (852) 2868 0668
Fax: (852) 2877 5021
E-Mail: admin@domainextremes.com
Web Site: www.domainextremes.com
Year Founded: 2006
DNME—(OTC)
Sls.: $16,423
Assets: $70,837
Liabilities: $142,917
Net Worth: ($72,080)
Earnings: ($96,264)
Emp.: 1
Fiscal Year-end: 12/31/12
Business Description:
Internet Websites & Applications on Mobile Platforms
S.I.C.: 2741
N.A.I.C.S.: 519130
Personnel:
Francis Bok *(Chm, Pres & CEO)*
Stephen Tang *(CFO, Chief Acctg Officer & Treas)*
Board of Directors:
Francis Bok
Huang Run Peng
Stephen Tang
Wu Cai Xia

DOME GOLD MINES LIMITED

Level 7 71 Macquarie Street
Sydney, NSW, 2000, Australia
Mailing Address:
GPO Box 1759
Sydney, NSW, 2001, Australia
Tel.: (61) 2 8203 5620
Fax: (61) 2 9241 2013
E-Mail: info@domegoldmines.com.au
Web Site: www.domegoldmines.com.au
Year Founded: 2011
DME—(ASX)
Int. Income: $1,456
Assets: $2,021,996
Liabilities: $737,865
Net Worth: $1,284,131
Earnings: ($1,241,942)
Fiscal Year-end: 06/30/13
Business Description:
Gold, Silver & Copper Mining
S.I.C.: 1041
N.A.I.C.S.: 212221
Personnel:
Garry Lowder *(Chm)*
Board of Directors:
Garry Lowder
Allen Jay
Andrew Skinner
Tadao Tsubata

DOME INVESTMENTS PUBLIC COMPANY LTD

PO Box 30198
Makronissos, 5341 Ayia Napa, Cyprus
Tel.: (357) 23 721006
Fax: (357) 23 721010
E-Mail: info@domehotel.com.cy
Web Site: www.domehotel.com.cy
DOME—(CYP)
Business Description:
Hotel Management Services
S.I.C.: 7011
N.A.I.C.S.: 721110
Personnel:
Demetris Papaevelthontos *(Sec)*
Board of Directors:
Antonis Andreou
Vasos Hadjitheodosiou
Nicos Michaelas
Alexis Photiades
Andreas Tsokkos
Anastasia Tsokkou

DOMESCO MEDICAL IMPORT EXPORT JOINT STOCK CORPORATION

66 Highway 30 My Phu Ward
Cao Lanh, Dong Thap, Vietnam
Tel.: (84) 67 3 852 278
Fax: (84) 67 3 851 270
E-Mail: domesco@domesco.com
Web Site: www.domesco.com
Year Founded: 1989
DMC—(HOSE)
Rev.: $68,534,987
Assets: $42,447,389
Liabilities: $13,891,309
Net Worth: $28,556,080
Earnings: $4,506,190
Emp.: 1,285
Fiscal Year-end: 12/31/12
Business Description:
Pharmaceutical Products Mfr & Whslr
S.I.C.: 2834
N.A.I.C.S.: 325412
Personnel:
Nguyen Chi Thanh *(Chm)*
Huynh Trung Chanh *(Vice Chm, Mng Dir & Gen Dir)*
Board of Directors:
Nguyen Chi Thanh
Huynh Trung Chanh
Jose Guillermo Frugone Domke
Luong Thi Huong Giang
Alejandro Esteban Weinstein Manieu
Tran Thanh Phong
Nguyen Thi Tien

DOMETIC INTERNATIONAL AB

Torggatan 8
171 54 Solna, Sweden
Tel.: (46) 850102500
Fax: (46) 850102599
E-Mail: info@dometic.se
Web Site: www.dometic.com
Year Founded: 1922
Sales Range: $150-199.9 Million
Emp.: 6,000
Business Description:
Refrigeration Products Mfr
S.I.C.: 3585
N.A.I.C.S.: 333415
Personnel:
Robert Mackenzie *(Chm)*
Fredrik Moller *(CEO)*
Jan Lindstedt *(CFO)*
Joachim Kinscher *(Pres-EMEA)*
Anne-Marie Davis *(Gen Counsel)*
Hakan Soderstrom *(Exec VP-Ops)*
Rutger Wachtmeister *(Exec VP-Mktg)*
Board of Directors:
Robert Mackenzie
John Leach
Jan Lindstedt
Fredrik Moller
Arne Vraalsen
U.S. Subsidiaries:

Dometic Corporation (1)
2320 Industrial Pkwy
Elkhart, IN 46515 IN
Mailing Address:
PO Box 490
Elkhart, IN 46515-0490
Tel.: (574) 294-2511
Fax: (574) 293-9686
E-Mail: dometic@usa.com
Web Site: www.dometicusa.com
Emp.: 1,500
Air Conditioners Mfr, Refrigeration Products & Awnings Mfr
S.I.C.: 3585
N.A.I.C.S.: 333415
Doug Whyte *(Pres)*
Rutger Wachtmeister *(Exec VP-Mktg & Sls)*

Dometic Sanitation Corporation (1)
13128 State Rd 226
Big Prairie, OH 44611
Mailing Address:
PO Box 38
Big Prairie, OH 44611-0038
Tel.: (330) 496-3211
Fax: (330) 496-3097
Toll Free: (800) 321-9886
E-Mail: sealand@dometicusa.com
Web Site: www.dometicsanitation.com
Emp.: 4,400
Marine & Recreation Vehicle Sanitation Systems Mfr
S.I.C.: 3089
N.A.I.C.S.: 326199

Non-U.S. Subsidiaries:

Dometic GmbH (1)
Ln Der Steinwiese 16
57074 Siegen, Germany
Tel.: (49) 2716920
Fax: (49) 271692300
E-Mail: info@dometic.de
Web Site: www.dometic.de
Emp.: 200
Air Conditioners, Refrigerators, Awnings, Cookers, Sanitation Systems, Lighting, Windows & Doors Mfr
S.I.C.: 3639
N.A.I.C.S.: 335228
Joaghim Kimscher *(COO)*

Dometic S.a.r.L. (1)
17 Op Der Hei
9809 Hosingen, Luxembourg
Tel.: (352) 9207311
Fax: (352) 920731300
E-Mail: info@dometic.lu
Web Site: www.dometic.lu
Emp.: 150
Air Conditioners, Refrigerators, Awnings, Cookers, Sanitation Systems, Lighting, Windows & Doors Mfr
S.I.C.: 3639
N.A.I.C.S.: 335228
Anders Sernell *(Mng Dir)*

DOMEXPORT INC.

8255 boul Henri Bourassa Bureau 260
Quebec, QC, G1G 4C8, Canada
Tel.: (418) 627-0160
Fax: (418) 627-3586
E-Mail: domexport@domexport.com
Web Site: www.domexport.com
Year Founded: 1992
Rev.: $16,816,000
Emp.: 7
Business Description:
Lumber Products Whslr
S.I.C.: 5031
N.A.I.C.S.: 423310
Personnel:

DOMIKI KRITIS S.A.

14 Koroneou str
PO Box 71202
Iraklion, Greece
Tel.: (30) 2810 288287
Fax: (30) 2810 341156
E-Mail: info@domik.gr
Web Site: www.domik.gr
Year Founded: 1985
DOMIK—(ATH)
Rev.: $11,711,679
Assets: $37,558,143
Liabilities: $22,615,656
Net Worth: $14,942,487
Earnings: ($9,019,339)
Emp.: 47
Fiscal Year-end: 12/31/12
Business Description:
Civil Engineering Construction Services
S.I.C.: 1629
N.A.I.C.S.: 237990
Personnel:
Georgios Sinatsakis *(Chm & Mng Dir)*
Board of Directors:
Georgios Sinatsakis
Konstantinos Bakogianakis
Georgios Fournaris
Konstantinos Kritzas
Ioanis Lemonakis
Stilianos Papoutsakis
Asimina Skabavia

DOMINANT ENTERPRISE BERHAD

Suite 1301 13th Floor City Plaza
Jalan Tebrau
80300 Johor Bahru, Johor, Malaysia
Tel.: (60) 73554988
Fax: (60) 73354977
E-Mail: debgroup@dominant.com.my
Web Site: www.dominant.com.my
DOMINAN—(KLS)
Rev.: $137,001,456
Assets: $91,190,889
Liabilities: $38,715,782
Net Worth: $52,475,107
Earnings: ($4,602,671)
Fiscal Year-end: 03/31/13
Business Description:
Laminated Wood Products Mfr & Distr
S.I.C.: 2439
N.A.I.C.S.: 321213
Personnel:
Aku Wai Cha *(Co-Founder & Mng Dir)*

Dominant Enterprise Berhad—(Continued)

Ah Bah Teo *(Co-Founder)*
Ing Yen Chin *(COO)*
Geok Choon Owee *(Deputy Mng Dir)*
May Li Yong *(Sec)*
Board of Directors:
Ah Bah Teo
Aku Wai Cha
Soon Too Chai
Waldersee Chung Ching Chan
Mohd Khalid Idris
Johnson Kandasamy
Kwai Yoke Kuah
Geok Choon Owee
Meng Poo Tan
Yu Chin Teo

DOMINION CITRUS INCOME FUND

165 The Queensway Suite 308
Toronto, ON, M8Y 1H8, Canada
Tel.: (416) 242-8341
Fax: (416) 242-4591
E-Mail: t.atkinson@dominioncitrus.com
Web Site: www.dominioncitrus.com
DOM.UN—(TSX)
Rev.: $70,698,678
Assets: $12,927,230
Liabilities: $10,794,063
Net Worth: $2,133,167
Earnings: $732,593
Emp.: 132
Fiscal Year-end: 12/31/12
Business Description:
Fresh Produce Wholesaling & Food Processing
S.I.C.: 5431
N.A.I.C.S.: 445230
Personnel:
R. Peter McLaughlin *(Chm)*
Ernie Collinson *(CFO, Sec & VP-Fin-Dominion Citrus Limited)*
Jason A. Fielden *(Pres/CEO-Dominion Citrus Limited)*
Legal Counsel:
Sheldon Huxtable
Toronto, ON, Canada
Transfer Agent:
Computershare Investor Services Inc.
100 University Ave 9th Floor
Toronto, ON, Canada
Divisions:

Country Fresh Packaging (1)
51 Kelfield St
Toronto, ON, M8W 1T2, Canada (100%)
Tel.: (416) 252-5801
Fax: (416) 253-1018
Web Site: www.dominioncitrus.com
Emp.: 17
Packaging of Fresh Fruits & Vegetables
S.I.C.: 0723
N.A.I.C.S.: 115114

Dominion Citrus Income Fund - Dominion Citrus Distribution (1)
Ontario Food Terminal Division 165 The Queensway Suite 304
Toronto, ON, M8Y 1H8, Canada
Tel.: (416) 259-6328
Fax: (416) 259-1731
Web Site: www.dominioncitrus.com
Fresh Fruits & Vegetables Distr
S.I.C.: 5148
N.A.I.C.S.: 424480

Dominion Farm Produce Company (1)
215 Dissette St
Bradford, ON, L3Z 2B3, Canada (100%)
Tel.: (416) 798-7741
Fax: (905) 775-4707
E-Mail: dominion@bellnet.ca
Web Site: www.bellnet.ca
Emp.: 50
S.I.C.: 5431
N.A.I.C.S.: 445230
Tony Tomizza *(Gen Mgr)*

Subsidiaries:

Dominion Citrus Limited (1)
165 The Queensway Suite 302
Toronto, ON, M8Y 1H8, Canada
Tel.: (416) 521-6260
Fax: (416) 259-1731
DMN—(TSX)
Rev.: $70,698,700
Assets: $12,915,302
Liabilities: $31,979,612
Net Worth: ($19,064,310)
Earnings: ($247,511)
Fiscal Year-end: 12/31/12
Fruit & Vegetable Distr
S.I.C.: 5148
N.A.I.C.S.: 424480
Winston Ash *(Chm)*
Jason A. Fielden *(Pres & CEO)*
Ernie Collinson *(CFO, Sec & VP-Fin)*

Les Aliments Dominion Citrus Limitee (Bo-Fruits) (1)
1767 Rte De Aeroport L
L'Ancienne-Lorette, QC, G2G 2P5, Canada
Tel.: (418) 877-9908
Fax: (418) 877-9907
Web Site: www.dominioncitrus.com
Fresh Fruit Distr
S.I.C.: 5499
N.A.I.C.S.: 445299

Meschino Banana Co., Ltd. (1)
1613 St Clair Ave W
Toronto, ON, M6E 1C9, Canada
Tel.: (416) 654-7133
Fax: (416) 654-3131
Web Site: www.dominioncitrus.com
Fresh Foods Whslr
S.I.C.: 5148
N.A.I.C.S.: 424480

DOMINION DIAMOND CORPORATION

(Formerly Harry Winston Diamond Corporation)
PO Box 4569
Station A, Toronto, ON, M5C 2C5, Canada
Tel.: (416) 362-2237
Fax: (416) 362-2230
E-Mail: info@ddcorp.ca
Web Site: www.ddcorp.ca
Year Founded: 1978
DDC—(NYSE TSX)
Rev.: $345,411,000
Assets: $1,710,456,000
Liabilities: $879,204,000
Net Worth: $831,252,000
Earnings: $35,218,000
Emp.: 863
Fiscal Year-end: 01/31/13
Business Description:
Diamond Exploration & Mining
S.I.C.: 1499
N.A.I.C.S.: 212399
Personnel:
Robert A. Gannicott *(Chm & CEO)*
Lyle R. Hepburn *(Sec)*
Raymond N. Simpson *(Exec VP)*
Board of Directors:
Robert A. Gannicott
Graham G. Clow
Noel Harwerth
Daniel Jarvis
Tom Kenny
Ollie Olieira
Chuck Strahl
Legal Counsel:
Stikeman Elliott
Commerce Court West
199 Bay Street Suite 5300, Toronto, ON, M5L 1B9, Canada
Transfer Agent:
CIBC Mellon Trust Company
320 Bay Street
PO Box 1
Toronto, ON, M5H 2A6, Canada
Tel.: (416) 643-5500
Fax: (416) 643-5570
Toll Free: (800) 387-0825

Non-U.S. Subsidiary:

Dominion Diamond (India) Private Limited (1)
(Formerly Harry Winston Diamond (India) Private Limited)
9010 Bharat Diamond Bourse Bandra Kurla Complex
Bandra E, 400051 Mumbai, India In
Tel.: (91) 2223699004
Fax: (91) 2223692299
E-Mail: skumaran@harrywinston.com
Web Site: www.harrywinston.co.in
Emp.: 15
Jewelry Watch Precious Stone & Precious Metal Whslr
S.I.C.: 5094
N.A.I.C.S.: 423940
Senthil Kumaran *(Country Mgr)*

DOMINION MOTORS LIMITED

882 Copper Crescent
Thunder Bay, ON, P7B 6C9, Canada
Tel.: (807) 343-2277
Fax: (807) 345-3576
Toll Free: (877) 587-9489
Web Site: www.dominionmotors.com
Rev.: $26,344,320
Emp.: 55
Business Description:
New & Used Car Dealers
S.I.C.: 5511
N.A.I.C.S.: 441110
Personnel:
Tyler Dolcetti *(Owner)*

DOMINION NICKEL ALLOYS LTD.

834 Appleby Line
Burlington, ON, L7L 2Y7, Canada
Tel.: (905) 639-9939
Fax: (905) 639-3788
E-Mail: dna@domnickel.com
Web Site: www.domnickel.com
Year Founded: 1969
Rev.: $99,302,431
Emp.: 25
Business Description:
Stainless Steel & Nickel Alloys Distr
S.I.C.: 5093
N.A.I.C.S.: 423930
Personnel:
Frank Fleisher *(Founder & Pres)*

DOMINION SURE SEAL LIMITED

6175 Danville Rd
Mississauga, ON, L5T 2H7, Canada
Tel.: (905) 670-5411
Fax: (905) 670-5174
Toll Free: (800) 265-0790
Web Site: www.dominionsureseal.com
Year Founded: 1972
Rev.: $11,492,057
Emp.: 45
Business Description:
Adhesives & Other Plastic Products Mfr
S.I.C.: 2891
N.A.I.C.S.: 325520
Personnel:
Ronald B. Morton *(Pres & CEO)*

DOMINION WAREHOUSING & DISTRIBUTION SERVICES LTD.

1920 Albion Road
Toronto, ON, M9W 5T2, Canada
Tel.: (416) 744-2438
Fax: (416) 213-9398
Toll Free: (800) 990-0391
E-Mail: hr@godominion.com
Web Site: www.godominion.com
Rev.: $13,006,965
Emp.: 102
Business Description:
Warehousing & Storage Services
S.I.C.: 4225
N.A.I.C.S.: 493110
Personnel:
D. Robert Dineen *(Pres & Gen Mgr)*
D. Ross Dineen *(Exec VP)*

DOMINIQUE DUTSCHER SAS

30 rue de l'Industrie
BP 62
67172 Brumath, Cedex, France
Tel.: (33) 388593390
Fax: (33) 388593399
E-Mail: info@dutscher.com
Web Site: www.dutscher.com
Emp.: 100
Business Description:
Laboratory Equipment & Supplies Distr
S.I.C.: 5047
N.A.I.C.S.: 423450
Non-U.S. Subsidiary:

Biosigma S.r.l. (1)
Via Valetta 6
Cantarana, 30010 Cona, VE, Italy IT
Tel.: (39) 0426302224
Fax: (39) 0426302228
E-Mail: export@biosigma.com
Web Site: www.biosigma.com
Sales Range: $1-9.9 Million
Disposable Analytical Laboratory Supplies Mfr & Whslr
S.I.C.: 3826
N.A.I.C.S.: 334516
Martino Marcolin *(Pres)*

DOMINIQUE PRUDENT SAS

Bois De Chize
Branges, 71500 Chanlon-sur-Saone, Saone Et Loire, France
Tel.: (33) 385764411
Fax: (33) 3 85 76 44 19
E-Mail: accueil@transportsprudent.fr
Web Site: www.transportprudent.fr/entre_vous-et_nous/contact.php
Sls.: $23,500,000
Emp.: 294
Business Description:
Local Trucking & Freight Transportation Services
S.I.C.: 4212
N.A.I.C.S.: 484110
Personnel:
Maurice Prudent *(CHM)*
Board of Directors:
Maurice Prudent
Jacky Bourlionne

DOMINO PRINTING SCIENCES PLC

Trafalgar Way Bar Hill
Cambridge, CB23 8TU, United Kingdom
Tel.: (44) 1954782551
Fax: (44) 1954782874
E-Mail: info@domino-uk.com
Web Site: www.domino-printing-sciences.com
Year Founded: 1978
DNO—(LSE OTC)
Rev.: $492,836,396
Assets: $510,516,548
Liabilities: $174,863,727
Net Worth: $335,652,821
Earnings: $64,275,524
Emp.: 2,270
Fiscal Year-end: 10/31/12
Business Description:
Commercial Inkjet & Laser Printers Designer, Mfr & Distr
S.I.C.: 3577
N.A.I.C.S.: 334118
Personnel:
Nigel R. Bond *(Mng Dir)*

Garry Havens *(Pres-North America & Dir-Comml)*
Richard J. Pryn *(Sec)*
Board of Directors:
Peter J. Byrom
Nigel R. Bond
Christopher Brinsmead
David Brown
Garry Havens
Andrew C. Herbert
Philip Ruffles
Legal Counsel:
Simmons & Simmons
London, United Kingdom
Ashurst
London, United Kingdom
Subsidiaries:

Domino UK Ltd. (1)
Bar Hill
Cambridge, CB3 8TU, United Kingdom
Tel.: (44) 1954782056
Fax: (44) 1954782874
E-Mail: info@alphadot.com
Web Site: www.alphadot.co.uk
Ink Jet Printing Systems
S.I.C.: 3577
N.A.I.C.S.: 334118

Purex International Limited (1)
Purex House Farfield Park Manvers
Rotherham, South Yorkshire, S63 5DB, United Kingdom
Tel.: (44) 1709763000
Fax: (44) 1709763001
E-Mail: purex@purex.co.uk
Web Site: www.purex.co.uk
Emp.: 35
Fume Extraction Equipment Mfr & Distr
S.I.C.: 3569
N.A.I.C.S.: 333999
Paul Priestley *(Mng Dir)*

U.S. Subsidiaries:

Citronix LP (1)
3030 SE Loop 820
Fort Worth, TX 76140
Tel.: (817) 568-9800
Fax: (817) 568-1970
E-Mail: info@citronix.com
Web Site: www.citronix.com
Inkjet Printing Systems Mfr
S.I.C.: 3575
N.A.I.C.S.: 334118
Richard Fox *(Pres)*

Domino Amjet Inc. (1)
1290 Lakeside Dr
Gurnee, IL 60031
Tel.: (847) 244-2501
Fax: (847) 244-1421
Industrial Coding & Printing Machinery Distr
S.I.C.: 5084
N.A.I.C.S.: 423830
Matthew Condon *(Mgr-Digital Print Product)*

Non-U.S. Subsidiaries:

Alternative Printing Services GmbH (1)
Behringstr 7
71083 Herrenberg, Baden-Wurttemberg, Germany
Tel.: (49) 7032916401
Fax: (49) 7032 9164 03
E-Mail: info@aps-direct.de
Web Site: www.aps-direct.de
Coding & Printing Machinery Distr
S.I.C.: 5045
N.A.I.C.S.: 423430
Werner Schaeffer *(Mng Dir)*

APS Asia-Pacific Pty. Ltd. (1)
Unit 2/34 Collinsvale Street
Rocklea, QLD, 4106, Australia
Tel.: (61) 732744495
Fax: (61) 732744493
Emp.: 7
Coding & Printing Machinery Distr
S.I.C.: 5045
N.A.I.C.S.: 423430
Simon Higgins *(Gen Mgr)*

APS France S.a.r.l. (1)
ZA La Pimpie
26120 Montelier, Drome, France
Tel.: (33) 475602155
Fax: (33) 475596842
E-Mail: info@aps-direct.fr
Web Site: www.aps-direct.fr
Emp.: 8
Coding & Printing Machinery Distr
S.I.C.: 5046
N.A.I.C.S.: 423440
Yann Gorrity *(Gen Mgr)*

Domino Amjet BV (1)
Hoofdveste 11a
Houten, Utrecht, 3992 DH, Netherlands
Tel.: (31) 306363333
Fax: (31) 306363344
E-Mail: info@dominobenelux.com
Web Site: www.dominobenelux.com
Emp.: 40
Coding & Printing Machinery Mfr & Distr
S.I.C.: 5045
N.A.I.C.S.: 423430
Peter van Riel *(Principal)*

Domino Amjet Iberica SA (1)
Avenida De La Fuente Nueva 14 San Sebastian De Los Reye
28703 Madrid, Spain
Tel.: (34) 916542141
Fax: (34) 916239444
Web Site: www.domino-printing.com
Emp.: 50
Coding & Printing Machinery Distr
S.I.C.: 5045
N.A.I.C.S.: 423430
Antonio Gutierrez *(Pres)*
Robert Bond Nigel *(Pres)*

Domino China Limited (1)
No 1150 Yun Qiao Rd Jin Qiao Export Processing Zone
Pudong New Area, Shanghai, 201206, China
Tel.: (86) 2150509999
Fax: (86) 2150329901
E-Mail: marketing@domino.com.cn
Web Site: www.domino.com.cn
Emp.: 200
Industrial Coding & Printing Machinery Mfr & Distr
S.I.C.: 3559
N.A.I.C.S.: 333249
Henrik Lundsgaard *(Chm)*

Domino Holdings Deutschland GmbH (1)
Lorenz- Schott-Str 3
Mainz-Kastel, 55252, Germany
Tel.: (49) 613425050
Fax: (49) 613425055
E-Mail: info@derschlag.com
Web Site: www.derschlag.com
Emp.: 140
Investment Management Services
S.I.C.: 6211
N.A.I.C.S.: 523110
Erich Jax *(Gen Mgr)*

Domino Korea Pte Limited (1)
Star Tower Bldg 2nd Fl 223-25 Sangtaewon-tong
Seongnam, Gyeonggi-do, 462-807, Korea (South)
Tel.: (82) 27971811
Fax: (82) 27968817
E-Mail: domino@dominokorea.com
Web Site: www.dominokorea.com
Emp.: 39
Industrial Coding & Printing Machinery Distr
S.I.C.: 5084
N.A.I.C.S.: 423830
Kwan Ho Kim *(Gen Mgr)*

Domino Printech India Private Limited (1)
167 HSIDC Udyog Vihar Phase-1
Gurgaon, Haryana, 122016, India
Tel.: (91) 1244886100
Fax: (91) 1242347408
E-Mail: marketing@dominoindia.com
Emp.: 200
Industrial Coding & Printing Machinery Distr
S.I.C.: 5084
N.A.I.C.S.: 423830
Mukesh Khanna *(VP-Customer Support)*

Domino Printing Mexico, S.A. de C.V. (1)
Calle 3 No 47 Local F-6 Col Industrial Naucalpan
53370 Naucalpan, Mexico
Tel.: (52) 5555767979
Fax: (52) 5555760185
E-Mail: ventas@domino-mexico.com.mx
Web Site: www.domino-mexico.com.mx
Industrial Coding & Printing Machinery Distr
S.I.C.: 5084
N.A.I.C.S.: 423830
Constantino de Llano *(Gen Mgr)*

Domino Printing Solutions Inc. (1)
2751 Coventry Rd
Oakville, ON, L6H 5V9, Canada
Tel.: (905) 829-2430
Fax: (905) 829-1842
Web Site: www.domino-na.com
Emp.: 32
Industrial Coding & Printing Machinery Distr
S.I.C.: 5084
N.A.I.C.S.: 423830
Savio Martins *(Mgr-Comml Svcs)*

Domino SAS (1)
Za Du Bel Air 2 Rue Hippolyte Mege Mouries
BP 31
78511 Rambouillet, Yvelines, France
Tel.: (33) 130465678
Fax: (33) 130465679
Emp.: 96
Coding & Printing Machinery Distr
S.I.C.: 5045
N.A.I.C.S.: 423430

Labeljet - Comercio e Industria de Etiquetas, S.A. (1)
Zona Industrial da Maia I Sector X Armazem L
4475-249 Maia, Portugal
Tel.: (351) 229866660
Fax: (351) 229866669
Emp.: 3
Industrial Labelling Machinery Mfr
S.I.C.: 3579
N.A.I.C.S.: 339940
Hanretoa Gonsalves *(Mgr)*

Subsidiary:

Marque TDI - Technologias de Codificacao S.A. (2)
Nucleo Empresarial I Bairro da Junqueira Rua de Entremuros N 54
Bloco 1 Armazem H, 2660-395 Sao Juliao do Tojal, Portugal
Tel.: (351) 219427025
Fax: (351) 219427044
E-Mail: mail@marquetdi.pt
Web Site: www.marquetdi.pt
Coding & Printing Machinery Mfr
S.I.C.: 3589
N.A.I.C.S.: 333318
Nigel Bond *(Mng Dir)*

Mectec Elektronik AB (1)
Agnesfridsvagen 189
213 75 Malmo, Scania, Sweden
Tel.: (46) 406892500
Fax: (46) 406892525
E-Mail: info@mectec.se
Web Site: www.mectec.com
Emp.: 65
Industrial Labelling Machinery Mfr
S.I.C.: 3565
N.A.I.C.S.: 333993
Patrik Jenemark *(Mng Dir)*

Pri-Ma-Tech Verwaltungs GmbH (1)
Pastorstrasse 16
56751 Polch, Rhineland-Palatinate, Germany
Tel.: (49) 265496440
Fax: (49) 2654964420
E-Mail: info@primatech.de
Web Site: www.primatech.de
Emp.: 7
Coding & Printing Machinery Distr
S.I.C.: 5046
N.A.I.C.S.: 423440
Hans Robert Dapprich *(Mng Dir)*

Sator Laser GmbH (1)
Fangdieckstrasse 75a
22547 Hamburg, Germany
Tel.: (49) 40888880
Fax: (49) 4088888199
E-Mail: info@dominolaser.com
Web Site: www.dominolaser.com
Emp.: 65
Laser Marking Systems
S.I.C.: 3575
N.A.I.C.S.: 334118
Hans-Robert Dapprich *(Gen Mgr)*

Wiedenbach Apparatebau GmbH (1)
Gewerbestrasse 13
78345 Moos, Germany De
Tel.: (49) 773299440
Fax: (49) 773252438
E-Mail: infoservice@wiedenbach.com
Web Site: www.wiedenbach.com
Emp.: 73
Ink Jet Printers & Applications Solutions
S.I.C.: 3575
N.A.I.C.S.: 334118
Robert van der Most *(Mng Dir)*

U.S. Subsidiary:

Wiedenbach Company L.P. (2)
1290 Lakeside Dr
Gurnee, IL 60031-2400
Tel.: (704) 684-0237
Fax: (704) 684-0262
E-Mail: andy.captain@wiedenbach.com
Web Site: www.wiedenbach.com
Emp.: 6
Ink Jet Printers & Applications Solutions
S.I.C.: 5045
N.A.I.C.S.: 423430

Non-U.S. Subsidiary:

Wiedenbach Apparatebau GmbH (2)
51-52 Victoria Rd
Old Town, Swindon, SN1 3AY, United Kingdom
Tel.: (44) 01793495015
Fax: (44) 1793481990
Web Site: www.wiedenbach.com
Emp.: 6
Ink Jet Printers & Applications Solutions
S.I.C.: 5045
N.A.I.C.S.: 423430

DOMINO'S PIZZA ENTERPRISES LTD.

Level 5 KSD1 485 Kingsford Smith Drive
Hamilton, QLD, 4007, Australia
Tel.: (61) 7 3633 3333
Fax: (61) 7 3633 3399
Web Site: www.dominos.com.au
DMP—(ASX)
Rev.: $196,572,365
Assets: $197,739,517
Liabilities: $90,838,815
Net Worth: $106,900,702
Earnings: $29,863,460
Fiscal Year-end: 06/30/13
Business Description:
Franchise Restaurant Operator
S.I.C.: 5812
N.A.I.C.S.: 722513
Personnel:
Don Meij *(CEO & Mng Dir)*
Richard Coney *(CFO)*
Wayne McMahon *(CIO)*
Allan Collins *(CMO)*
Pat McMichael *(Chief Dev & Franchising Officer)*
John Harney *(Chief Procurement Officer)*
Andrew Megson *(CEO-Australia & New Zealand)*
Andrew Rennie *(CEO-Europe)*
Craig Ryan *(Gen Counsel & Sec)*
Board of Directors:
Ross Adler
Barry Alty
Grant Bourke
Paul Cave
Don Meij
Legal Counsel:
Thomsons Lawyers
Level 16 Waterfront Place 1 Eagle Street
Brisbane, Australia
DLA Piper Australia
Level 28 Waterfront Place 1 Eagle Street
Brisbane, Australia

Domino's Pizza Enterprises Ltd.—(Continued)

Non-U.S. Subsidiaries:

Dominos Pizza Belgium S.P.R.L. **(1)**
Bastion Tower Etage 20 Place du Champ de Mars 5
1050 Brussels, Belgium
Tel.: (32) 25503892
Fax: (32) 25503893
E-Mail: contact@dominospizza.be
Web Site: www.dominospizza.be
Emp.: 168
Pizza Mfr
S.I.C.: 2099
N.A.I.C.S.: 311991
Rowan Hogge *(Mng Dir)*

Domino's Pizza Nederland B.V. **(1)**
Franklinweg 33
Postbus 112
4200 AC Gorinchem, Netherlands
Tel.: (31) 183696300
Fax: (31) 183696302
E-Mail: info@dominos.nl
Web Site: www.dominos.nl
Emp.: 70
Pizza Stores Operator
S.I.C.: 5812
N.A.I.C.S.: 722513

Domino's Pizza New Zealand Limited **(1)**
PO Box 27213
Mt Roskill, Auckland, 1041, New Zealand NZ
Tel.: (64) 9 962 1091
Web Site: www.dominospizza.co.nz
Emp.: 6
Pizza Mfr
S.I.C.: 2099
N.A.I.C.S.: 311991
Josh Kilimnik *(Gen Mgr)*

DPFC S.A.R.L. **(1)**
7 rue de Margnolles
Caluire-et-Cuire, Lyon, Rhone, 69300, France
Tel.: (33) 437920101
Fastfood Restaurant Operators
S.I.C.: 5812
N.A.I.C.S.: 722513

DOMINO'S PIZZA GROUP PLC

1 Thornbury West Ashland
Milton Keynes, MK6 4BB, United Kingdom
Tel.: (44) 1908 580 000
Fax: (44) 1908 588 000
E-Mail: comments@dominos.co.uk
Web Site: www.dominos.co.uk
DOM—(LSE OTC)
Rev.: $379,857,148
Assets: $287,077,019
Liabilities: $176,008,712
Net Worth: $111,068,307
Earnings: $47,863,542
Emp.: 1,002
Fiscal Year-end: 12/30/12

Business Description:
Holding Company; Pizzeria Restaurants Owner, Operator & Franchisor
S.I.C.: 6719
N.A.I.C.S.: 551112

Personnel:
Lee Ginsberg *(CFO)*
Mark Millar *(Gen Counsel & Sec)*

Board of Directors:
Stephen J. Hemsley
Lee Ginsberg
Colin Halpern
John Hodson
Helen Keays
Syl Saller
Michael Shallow
Nigel William Wray

Legal Counsel:
Norton Rose LLP
More London Riverside
London, SE1 2AQ, United Kingdom

Subsidiary:

Domino's Pizza Group Limited **(1)**
1 Thornbury West Ashland
Milton Keynes, MK6 4BB, United Kingdom UK
Tel.: (44) 1908 580 000
Fax: (44) 1908 588 000
Web Site: www.dominos.co.uk
Emp.: 250
Pizzeria Restaurants Operator & Franchisor
S.I.C.: 5812
N.A.I.C.S.: 722513
Stephen J. Hemsley *(CEO)*

Subsidiaries:

Domino's Pizza (Isle of Man) Limited **(2)**
Dominos Pizza Halfords Retail Park
Wellington Road
Aberdeen, AB11 8HX T, United Kingdom IM
Tel.: (44) 1908 580 000
Holding Company; Pizzeria Restaurants Operator & Franchisor
S.I.C.: 6719
N.A.I.C.S.: 551112

DP Realty Limited **(2)**
1 Thornbury West Ashland
Milton Keynes, MK6 4BB, United Kingdom UK
Tel.: (44) 1908 580 000
Commercial Property Investment & Management Services
S.I.C.: 6531
N.A.I.C.S.: 531312

DOMTAR CORPORATION

395 de Maisonneuve Boulevard West
Montreal, QC, H3A 1L6, Canada
Tel.: (514) 848-5555
Telex: 5560625
Fax: (514) 848-5638
Toll Free: (800) 267-2040
E-Mail: ir@domtar.com
Web Site: www.domtar.com
Year Founded: 1929
UFS—(NYSE TSX)
Sls.: $5,391,000,000
Assets: $6,278,000,000
Liabilities: $3,496,000,000
Net Worth: $2,782,000,000
Earnings: $91,000,000
Emp.: 9,400
Fiscal Year-end: 12/31/13

Business Description:
Pulp & Paper Products Mfr
Export
S.I.C.: 2621
N.A.I.C.S.: 322121

Personnel:
Harold H. MacKay *(Chm)*
John D. Williams *(Pres & CEO)*
Daniel Buron *(CFO & Sr VP)*
Melissa Anderson *(Sr VP-HR)*
Steven A. Barker *(Sr VP-Mktg)*
Roger H. Brear *(Sr VP-Southern Reg Mills)*
Michel Dagenais *(Sr VP-HR)*
Ghislain Dinel *(Sr VP-Northern Region Mills)*
Michael Fagan *(Sr VP-Personal Care)*
Zygmunt Jablonski *(Sr VP-Law & Corp Affairs)*
James F. Lenhoff *(Sr VP-Distr)*
Patrick Loulou *(Sr VP-Corp Dev)*
Bart Nicholson *(Sr VP-Specialty Mills & Converting Ops)*
Richard L. Thomas *(Sr VP-Sls & Mktg)*
Mark Ushpol *(Sr VP-Distr)*

Board of Directors:
Harold H. MacKay
Giannella Alvarez
Robert E. Apple
Louis-Pierre Gignac
David J. Illingworth
Brian Michael Levitt
David G. Maffucci
Robert J. Steacy
Pamela B. Strobel
Denis Andre Turcotte
John D. Williams

Legal Counsel:
Ogilvy Renault
1981 Ave. McGill College
Montreal, QC, H3A 3C1, Canada
Tel.: (514) 847-4747
Telex: 525362
Fax: (514) 286-5474

Transfer Agents:
ComputershareTrust Company of Canada
151 King Street West
Toronto, ON, M5J 2N1, Canada
Tel.: (416) 981-9633

The Bank of New York
1 Wall St
New York, NY 10286
Tel.: (212) 815-6436
Fax: (212) 815-3201
Toll Free: (800) 524-4458

Subsidiaries:

Domtar, Inc. **(1)**
PO Box 3521
Station C, Ottawa, ON, K1Y 4L5, Canada (100%)
Tel.: (613) 725-6700
Fax: (613) 725-6759
Web Site: www.domtar.com
Emp.: 17
Mfr. of Paper Products
S.I.C.: 2653
N.A.I.C.S.: 322211
Doc Miorino *(VP)*

Domtar Pacific Papers ULC **(1)**
395 Boul De Maisonneuve O
Montreal, QC, H3A 1L6, Canada
Tel.: (514) 848-5555
Web Site: www.domtar.com
Emp.: 500
Paper Pulp Mills
S.I.C.: 2611
N.A.I.C.S.: 322110
John Williams *(CEO)*

Joint Ventures:

Anthony-Domtar Inc. **(1)**
1195 Peoples Rd
Sault Sainte Marie, ON, P6C 3W7, Canada
Tel.: (705) 254-7597
Fax: (705) 254-1879
Toll Free: (800) 856-2372
E-Mail:
Web Site: www.eacom.ca
Sales Range: $1-9.9 Million
Emp.: 40
Lumber & Wood Chip Mills; Owned 50% by Domtar & 50% by Anthony Forest Products
S.I.C.: 2621
N.A.I.C.S.: 322121
Russ Anthony *(Pres)*

Nabakatuk Forest Products Inc. **(1)**
19 Rue Poplar
Quebec, QC, J0Y 3C0, Canada
Tel.: (819) 753-2995
Fax: (819) 753-2854
Emp.: 50
Lumber Exporting; Owned 45% by Domtar & 55% by Mishtuk Corporation
S.I.C.: 2421
N.A.I.C.S.: 321912
Alfred Jolly *(Pres)*

Plants:

Domtar Corporation - Kamloops Mill **(1)**
2005 Mission Flats Road
Kamloops, BC, V2C 1A9, Canada
Tel.: (250) 434-6000
Web Site: www.domtar.com
Pulp Products Mfr
S.I.C.: 2611
N.A.I.C.S.: 322110

Domtar Corporation - Windsor Mill **(1)**
609 Rang 12
PO Box 1010
Windsor, QC, J1S 2L9, Canada
Tel.: (800) 263-8366
Fax: (819) 845-8230
Emp.: 800
Paper & Pulp Mfr
S.I.C.: 2621
N.A.I.C.S.: 322121
Eric Ashby *(Mng Dir)*

U.S. Subsidiaries:

Associated Hygienic Products LLC **(1)**
3400 River Green Ct Ste 600
Duluth, GA 30096-8334
Tel.: (770) 497-9800
Fax: (770) 623-8679
Web Site: www.ahp-dsg.com
Sales Range: $300-349.9 Million
Emp.: 621
Disposable Diapers Mfr
Export
S.I.C.: 2676
N.A.I.C.S.: 322291

Attends Healthcare Products, Inc. **(1)**
1029 Old Creek Rd
Greenville, NC 27834-8178
Tel.: (252) 752-1100
Fax: (252) 752-7577
Toll Free: (800) 428-8363
E-Mail: info@attends.com
Web Site: www.attends.us
Sales Range: $200-249.9 Million
Emp.: 330
Incontinence Products Mfr & Distr
S.I.C.: 2676
N.A.I.C.S.: 322291
Michael Fagan *(Pres & CEO)*

Subsidiary:

Attends Healthcare Products, Inc. **(2)**
1941 White Ave
La Verne, CA 91750
Tel.: (252) 752-1100
Fax: (909) 971-5627
E-Mail: info@attends.com
Web Site: www.attends.com
Incontinence Products Mfr & Distr
S.I.C.: 2676
N.A.I.C.S.: 322291
Michael E. Fagan *(CEO)*

Domtar A.W. LLC **(1)**
285 Hwy 71 S
Ashdown, AR 71822
Tel.: (870) 898-2711
Fax: (870) 898-4724
Uncoated Freesheet Paper Mfr
S.I.C.: 2671
N.A.I.C.S.: 322220

Domtar Paper Company, LLC **(1)**
100 Kingsley Park Dr
Fort Mill, SC 29715 DE
Tel.: (803) 802-7500
Web Site: www.domtar.com
Paper Mfr & Distr
S.I.C.: 2679
N.A.I.C.S.: 322299

Group:

Domtar Distribution Group **(2)**
50 E Rivercenter Blvd Ste 500
Covington, KY 41011-1661
Tel.: (859) 292-5000
Fax: (859) 261-9777
Web Site: www.domtardistgroup.com
Paper Distr
S.I.C.: 5113
N.A.I.C.S.: 424130

Branch:

Domtar Distribution Group **(3)**
9435 Waterstone Blvd Ste 360
Cincinnati, OH 45249 KY
Tel.: (513) 583-5200
Fax: (513) 583-1888
Web Site: www.domtardistributiongroup.com
Emp.: 500
Fine Paper Distribution
S.I.C.: 5111
N.A.I.C.S.: 424110

Plants:

Domtar-Hawesville **(2)**
Hwy 1406 58 Wescor Rd
Hawesville, KY 42348

Tel.: (270) 927-6961
E-Mail: info@domtar.com
Web Site: www.domtar.com
Emp.: 450
Paper & Pulp Mill
S.I.C.: 2621
N.A.I.C.S.: 322121

Domtar Industries-Ashdown Mill (2)
285 Hwy 71 S
Ashdown, AR 71822 (100%)
Tel.: (870) 898-2711
Fax: (870) 898-3632
E-Mail: domtar@domtar.com
Web Site: www.domtar.com
Emp.: 1,260
Paper Mills
S.I.C.: 2611
N.A.I.C.S.: 322110

Domtar Industries (2)
301 Point Basse Ave
Nekoosa, WI 54457-1422
Tel.: (715) 887-5111
Fax: (715) 887-5555
Emp.: 1,100
Paper Mill
S.I.C.: 2679
N.A.I.C.S.: 322299
Ross Stairs *(Gen Mgr)*

Domtar-Johnsonburg (2)
100 Center St
Johnsonburg, PA 15845
Tel.: (814) 965-2521
Fax: (814) 965-6231
E-Mail: info@domtor.com
Web Site: www.domtor.com
Emp.: 400
Paper Mill
S.I.C.: 2621
N.A.I.C.S.: 322121
Grant Forrest *(Gen Mgr)*

Domtar-Kingsport (2)
100 Clinchfield St
Kingsport, TN 37660
Tel.: (423) 247-7111
Fax: (423) 247-7100
Web Site: www.domtar.com
Emp.: 332
Paper Mill
S.I.C.: 2621
N.A.I.C.S.: 322121
Charlie Floyd *(Gen Mgr & VP)*

Domtar-Marlboro (2)
585 Willamette Rd
Bennettsville, SC 29512
Tel.: (843) 479-0200
Fax: (843) 479-0299
Web Site: www.domtar.com
Emp.: 300
Paper & Pulp Mill
S.I.C.: 2621
N.A.I.C.S.: 322121

Domtar-Plymouth (2)
Highway 149 N
Plymouth, NC 27962
Tel.: (252) 793-8111
Web Site: www.domtar.com
Paper & Pulp Mill
S.I.C.: 2621
N.A.I.C.S.: 322121

Domtar-Rothschild (2)
200 N Grand Ave
Rothschild, WI 54474
Tel.: (715) 359-3101
Fax: (715) 355-6347
Web Site: www.domtar.com
Emp.: 400
Paper Mill
S.I.C.: 2621
N.A.I.C.S.: 322121
Terry Charles *(Plant Mgr)*

EAM Corporation (1)
2075 Sunset Blvd
Jesup, GA 31545 DE
Tel.: (912) 588-2600 (100%)
Fax: (912) 588-2699
Toll Free: (866) 296-1808
E-Mail: info@novaschin.com
Web Site: www.novaschin.com
Sales Range: $10-24.9 Million
Emp.: 60
Absorbent Material for Diapers Mfr
S.I.C.: 2676
N.A.I.C.S.: 322291
Frank Lezzi *(Mng Dir)*

Ris Paper Company, Inc. (1)
1900 River Rd
Cincinnati, OH 45204-1396
Tel.: (513) 244-2300
Printing & Writing Paper Merchant Whlsr
S.I.C.: 5111
N.A.I.C.S.: 424110

U.S. Plants:

Domtar Corporation - Johnsonburg Mill (1)
100 Ctr St
Johnsonburg, PA 15845
Tel.: (814) 965-2521
Fax: (814) 965-6231
Web Site: www.domtar.com
Paper Products Mfr
S.I.C.: 2621
N.A.I.C.S.: 322121

Domtar Corporation - Rothschild Mill (1)
200 N Grand Ave
Rothschild, WI 54474
Tel.: (715) 359-3101
Fax: (715) 355-6347
Web Site: www.domtar.com
Paper & Pulp Mfr
S.I.C.: 2621
N.A.I.C.S.: 322121

Non-U.S. Subsidiaries:

Attends Healthcare Group Ltd. (1)
The Old Post Office 3rd Fl Saint Nicholas St
Newcastle upon Tyne, NE1 1RH, United Kingdom UK
Tel.: (44) 01912427128
Fax: (44) 1912427126
E-Mail: info@attendshealthcare.com
Web Site: www.attendshealthcare.com
Emp.: 413
Incontinence Products Mfr & Distr
S.I.C.: 2676
N.A.I.C.S.: 322291
James Steele *(CEO)*

Domtar Asia Limited (1)
Millennium City Kwun Tong
Hong Kong, China (Hong Kong)
Tel.: (852) 37176888
Fax: (852) 22672188
Pulp Mills
S.I.C.: 2611
N.A.I.C.S.: 322110

DOMTECH, INC.

40 E Davis St
Trenton, ON, K8V 6S4, Canada
Tel.: (613) 394-4884
Fax: (613) 394-0108
Toll Free: (888) BST-VALU
E-Mail: sales@domtech.net
Web Site: www.domtech.net
Sales Range: $1-9.9 Million
Emp.: 150
Business Description:
Electrical Wire & Cable
S.I.C.: 3496
N.A.I.C.S.: 332618
Personnel:
Timothy Bannon *(Co-Pres)*
Jag Singh *(Co-Pres)*

DOMUS FIN S.A.

(d/b/a Gruppo Zunino/Zunino Group)
Via Bagutta 20
20121 Milan, Italy
Tel.: (39) 02 4547 5531
Fax: (39) 02 4547 5532
Web Site: www.gruppozunino.it
Business Description:
Holding Company; Real Estate Investment Services
S.I.C.: 6719
N.A.I.C.S.: 551112
Personnel:
Luigi Zunino *(Founder)*

Holding:

Risanamento S.p.A. (1)
Via Bonfadini 148
20138 Milan, Italy IT
Tel.: (39) 02 454 7551
Fax: (39) 02 454 75532
E-Mail: info@risanamentospa.com
Web Site: www.risanamentospa.com
RN—(ITA)
Rev.: $88,529,524
Assets: $2,558,455,316
Liabilities: $2,857,886,602
Net Worth: ($299,431,285)
Earnings: ($152,385,098)
Fiscal Year-end: 12/31/12
Holding Company; Real Estate Investment, Management & Brokerage Services
S.I.C.: 6719
N.A.I.C.S.: 551112
Daniele G. Discepolo *(Chm)*
Mario Massari *(Vice Chm)*
Claudio Calabi *(CEO)*
Gaetano Casertano *(Dir Gen-Staff & Admin)*
Davide Albertini Petroni *(Dir Gen-Ops)*

Subsidiary:

Tradital S.p.A. (2)
Via Bagutta 148
Milan, 20138, Italy IT
Tel.: (39) 024547551 (100%)
Real Estate Agents & Brokers Offices
S.I.C.: 6531
N.A.I.C.S.: 531210

DON-BUR (BODIES & TRAILERS) LTD

Mossfield Road Adderley Green
Stoke-on-Trent, Staffordshire, ST3 5BW, United Kingdom
Tel.: (44) 1782599666
E-Mail: sales@donbur.co.uk
Web Site: www.donbur.co.uk
Rev.: $57,862,519
Emp.: 374
Business Description:
Vehicle Trailer Mfr
S.I.C.: 3711
N.A.I.C.S.: 336211
Personnel:
Steve Bridgwood *(Mgr-Curtains & Cargo Control)*

DON DOCKSTEADER MOTORS LTD

8530 Cambie Street
Vancouver, BC, V6P-6N6, Canada
Tel.: (604) 325-1000
Fax: (604) 325-7121
Toll Free: (800) 663-3359
E-Mail: inquiries@dondocksteader.com
Web Site: www.dondocksteader.com
Year Founded: 1948
Rev.: $52,601,695
Emp.: 105
Business Description:
New & Used Car Dealers
S.I.C.: 5511
N.A.I.C.S.: 441110
Personnel:
Paul Docksteader *(Pres)*

DON FOLK CHEVROLET KELOWNA

2350 Highway 97 N
Kelowna, BC, V1X 4H8, Canada
Tel.: (250) 860-6000
Fax: (250) 860-8120
Toll Free: (800) 265-3655
E-Mail: davehuber@donfolkchev.com
Web Site: www.donfolkchev.com
Year Founded: 1975
Sales Range: $25-49.9 Million
Emp.: 62
Business Description:
New & Used Car Dealers
S.I.C.: 5511
N.A.I.C.S.: 441110
Personnel:
Jason Jones *(Controller)*

DON QUIJOTE CO., LTD.

(Name Changed to Don Quijote Holdings Co., Ltd.)

DON QUIJOTE HOLDINGS CO., LTD.

(Formerly Don Quijote Co., Ltd.)
2-19-10 Aobadai Meguro-ku
Tokyo, 153-0042, Japan
Tel.: (81) 357257532
Fax: (81) 357257322
Web Site: www.donki.com
Year Founded: 1980
7532—(TKS)
Sls.: $6,252,147,000
Assets: $4,252,842,000
Liabilities: $2,380,884,000
Net Worth: $1,871,958,000
Earnings: $232,551,000
Emp.: 4,391
Fiscal Year-end: 06/30/13
Business Description:
Home Electrical Appliances, Miscellaneous Household Goods, Food, Watches, Fashion-Related Merchandise, Sporting Goods & Leisure Products Sales
S.I.C.: 5064
N.A.I.C.S.: 423620
Personnel:
Takao Yasuda *(Chm, Pres & CEO)*
Mitsuo Takahashi *(Sr Mng Dir & CFO)*
Naoki Yoshida *(Sr Mng Dir)*
Koji Oohara *(COO & Sr Exec VP)*
Board of Directors:
Takao Yasuda
Koji Oohara
Kenji Sekiguchi
Mitsuo Takahashi
Naoki Yoshida
Transfer Agent:
Mitsubishi UFJ Trust & Banking Corporation
1 4 5 Marunouchi Chiyoda ku
Tokyo, 1008212, Japan
Subsidiaries:

D-ONE Co., Ltd. (1)
2-19-10 Aobadai
Meguro-ku, Tokyo, 3 5725 7537, Japan
Tel.: (81) 357257537
Fax: (81) 357257000
Web Site: www.d-one.co.jp
Emp.: 1,000
Real Estate Property Development Services
S.I.C.: 6531
N.A.I.C.S.: 531210
Junji Narusawa *(Pres)*

Doit Co., Ltd. (1)
1-6-18 Hachioji
Chuo-ku, Saitama, 338-0006, Japan
Tel.: (81) 488539700
Fax: (81) 488551577
Web Site: www.doit.co.jp
Emp.: 50
Household Products Retailer
S.I.C.: 5722
N.A.I.C.S.: 443141
Nobuaki Miyata *(Pres & CEO)*

Donki Johokan Co., Ltd. (1)
1-40-2 Kameido Koto-ku
Tokyo, 136 0071, Japan (51%)
Tel.: (81) 357257666
Web Site: www.donkigroup.jp
Cellular Phone Sales
S.I.C.: 5999
N.A.I.C.S.: 453998
Tadahuro Shimadu *(Pres & CEO)*

Japan Commercial Establishment Co., Ltd. (1)
4-14-1 Kitakasai
Edogawa-ku, Tokyo, 134-0081, Japan

Don Quijote Holdings Co., Ltd.—(Continued)

Tel.: (81) 356677657
Fax: (81) 356677739
Web Site: www.j-ce.co.jp
Facility Management Services
S.I.C.: 8744
N.A.I.C.S.: 561210

Nagasakiya Co., LTD. **(1)**
2-19-10 Aobadai
Meguro-ku, Tokyo, 153-0042, Japan
Tel.: (81) 477002100
Fax: (81) 47 378 3824
Web Site: www.nagasakiya.co.jp
Retail Stores Operation Services
S.I.C.: 5712
N.A.I.C.S.: 442110

U.S. Subsidiaries:

Don Quijote USA Co., Ltd. **(1)**
801 Kaheka St
Honolulu, HI 96814-3725
Tel.: (808) 973-6600
Fax: (808) 973-4844
Emp.: 350
Retailer of Food Products
S.I.C.: 5411
N.A.I.C.S.: 445110
Herb Gushikuma *(Sr VP)*

Oriental Seafoods, Inc. **(1)**
801 Kaheka St
Honolulu, HI 96814-3725 (100%)
Tel.: (808) 973-4800
Emp.: 17
Fish & Seafood Whslr
S.I.C.: 5146
N.A.I.C.S.: 424460
Ed Sawai *(Gen Mgr)*

DON VALLEY VOLKSWAGEN LTD.

1695 Eglinton Avenue East
Toronto, ON, M4A 1J6, Canada
Tel.: (416) 751-3131
Fax: (416) 751-3051
Toll Free: (888) 387-4511
E-Mail: sales@donvalleyvw.com
Web Site: www.donvalleyvw.com
Year Founded: 1966
Rev.: $23,735,971
Emp.: 50

Business Description:
New & Used Car Dealers
S.I.C.: 5511
N.A.I.C.S.: 441110

Personnel:
Michael Martan *(Pres & CEO)*

DONACO INTERNATIONAL LIMITED

(Formerly Two Way Ltd.)
Suite 2.02 55 Miller Street
Pyrmont, NSW, 2009, Australia
Tel.: (61) 290177000
Fax: (61) 290177001
E-Mail: enquiries@donacointernational.com
Web Site: www.donacointernational.com
DNA—(ASX)
Rev.: $16,331,540
Assets: $72,086,188
Liabilities: $17,894,427
Net Worth: $54,191,760
Earnings: $9,423,956
Fiscal Year-end: 06/30/13

Business Description:
Casino & Gaming Software
S.I.C.: 7011
N.A.I.C.S.: 721120

Personnel:
Stuart James McGregor *(Chm)*
Joey Keong Yew Lim *(CEO & Mng Dir)*
Ben P. Reichel *(Sec)*

Board of Directors:
Stuart James McGregor
Benjamin Keong Hoe Lim
Joey Keong Yew Lim
Siew Wei Mak
Ben P. Reichel
Gerald Nicholas Eng Hoe Tan

DONALD WARD LIMITED

Quarry Hill Industrial Estate
Ilkeston, Derbyshire, DE7 4RF, United Kingdom
Tel.: (44) 115 930 5899
Fax: (44) 115 930 4788
E-Mail: enquiries@wardrecycling.com
Web Site: www.wardrecycling.com
Year Founded: 1944
Sales Range: $150-199.9 Million
Emp.: 168

Business Description:
Recyclable Metal Whslr
S.I.C.: 5093
N.A.I.C.S.: 423930

Personnel:
David Ward *(Owner & Mng Dir)*

DONE & DUSTED GROUP LIMITED

3rd Floor 6 Ramilies Street
London, W1F 7TY, United Kingdom
Tel.: (44) 207 479 4343
E-Mail: info@doneanddusted.com
Web Site: www.doneanddusted.com
Year Founded: 1998

Business Description:
Events Staging & Television Production Services
S.I.C.: 7999
N.A.I.C.S.: 711320

Personnel:
Hamish Hamilton *(Co-Founder)*
Ian Stewart *(Co-Founder)*
Simon Pizey *(Mng Dir)*

U.S. Subsidiary:

Done & Dusted Productions, Inc. **(1)**
The India Bldg 146 W 29th St 4th Fl
New York, NY 10001 CA
Tel.: (212) 366-6904
Fax: (212) 564-9348
E-Mail: info@doneanddusted.com
Web Site: www.doneanddusted.com
Events Staging & Television Production Services
S.I.C.: 7999
N.A.I.C.S.: 711320
Ian Stewart *(Co-Founder & CEO)*

DONEAR INDUSTRIES LTD

210 Key Tuo Industrial Estate
Kondivita Lane
Near MIDC Andheri E
Mumbai, 400 059, India
Tel.: (91) 2230813591
Fax: (91) 2228370041
E-Mail: info@donear.com
Web Site: www.donear.com
DONEAR—(NSE)
Sales Range: $50-74.9 Million

Business Description:
Textile Products Mfr
S.I.C.: 2399
N.A.I.C.S.: 314999

Personnel:
Rajendra V. Agarwal *(Mng Dir)*
H. Sreedhar *(Compliance Officer & Sec)*

Board of Directors:
Vishwanath L. Agarwal
Ajay V. Agarwal
Durga Prasad C. Agarwal
Rajendra V. Agarwal
Santkumar B. Agarwal

Transfer Agent:
Link Intime India Private Limited
C-13 Pannalal Silk Mills Compound LBS Road
Bhandup W
Mumbai, India

DONEGAL CREAMERIES PLC

Ballyraine
Letterkenny, Co Donegal, Ireland
Tel.: (353) 749121766
Fax: (353) 749124823
E-Mail: james@donegal-creameries.ie
Web Site: www.donegal-creameries.ie
Year Founded: 1985
Rev.: $108,412,455
Assets: $151,157,391
Liabilities: $71,776,438
Net Worth: $79,380,953
Earnings: $10,735,706
Emp.: 225
Fiscal Year-end: 12/31/12

Business Description:
Milk & Agricultural Products Production
S.I.C.: 0241
N.A.I.C.S.: 112120

Personnel:
Ian Ireland *(Mng Dir & Sec)*

Board of Directors:
Geoffrey Vance
Frank Browne
Francis Devenny
Michael Griffin
Ian Ireland
Patrick J. Kelly
Geoffrey McClay
Matt McNulty
Marshall Robinson
Norman Witherow

Legal Counsel:
V.P. McMullin & Son
Letterkenny, Co Donegal, Ireland

Subsidiaries:

An Grianan Grain Company Limited **(1)**
Ballyraine
Letterkenny, Donegal, Ireland
Tel.: (353) 74 91 21766
Fax: (353) 9124823
Web Site: www.donegalcreameries.ir
Emp.: 40
Agricultural Products Distr
S.I.C.: 5191
N.A.I.C.S.: 424910

The Different Dairy Company Limited **(1)**
Crossroads Killygordon
Lifford, Donegal, Ulster, Ireland
Tel.: (353) 749149678
Fax: (353) 749149989
Emp.: 40
Dairy Products Mfr
S.I.C.: 2023
N.A.I.C.S.: 311514
Alan Cunningham *(Gen Mgr)*

Donegal Potatoes Limited **(1)**
Colehill
Newtowncunningham, Donegal, Ireland
Tel.: (353) 749156155
Fax: (353) 749156318
E-Mail: info@donegalpotatoes.ie
Emp.: 4
Potatoes Whslr
S.I.C.: 5148
N.A.I.C.S.: 424480
Neill Mcbride *(Gen Mgr)*

Donra Dairies Limited **(1)**
Princes Street
Tralee, Munster, Ireland
Tel.: (353) 667119850
Dairy Products Mfr
S.I.C.: 2023
N.A.I.C.S.: 311514

Glenveagh Agricultural Co-Operative Society Limited **(1)**
Ballyraine
Letterkenny, Donegal, Ireland
Tel.: (353) 74 9121766
Fax: (353) 74 9124823
E-Mail: donegal@creameries.ie
Dairy Products Mfr
S.I.C.: 2023
N.A.I.C.S.: 311514

Irish Potato Marketing Limited **(1)**
Unit 412 Q House 76 Furze Road
Sandyford Industrial Estate
Dublin, 18, Ireland
Tel.: (353) 1 2135410
Fax: (353) 1 2958035
E-Mail: info@ipm.ie
Web Site: www.ipm.ie
Emp.: 8
Potato Seed Production & Sales
S.I.C.: 0139
N.A.I.C.S.: 111211
Marcel de Sousa *(Gen Mgr)*

Milburn Dairy Limited **(1)**
Milburn
Castlefinn, Donegal, Ulster, Ireland
Tel.: (353) 74 9146631
Fax: (353) 74 9149560
Dairy Products Mfr
S.I.C.: 2023
N.A.I.C.S.: 311514
Alan Cunningham *(Mgr-Site)*

Robert Smyth & Sons (Strabane & Donegal) Limited **(1)**
Daleside Mill Ballindrait
Lifford, Donegal, Ulster, Ireland
Tel.: (353) 74 9171300
Fax: (353) 74 9171321
E-Mail: info@smythfeeds.com
Web Site: www.smythfeeds.com
Emp.: 70
Animal Feeds Mfr & Distr
S.I.C.: 2048
N.A.I.C.S.: 311119
Ray Wanters *(Gen Mgr)*

Zopitar Limited **(1)**
Ballyraine
Letterkenny, Donegal, Ireland
Tel.: (353) 749 12 20 11
Fax: (353) 749 12 47 96
Dairy Products Whslr
S.I.C.: 5143
N.A.I.C.S.: 424430

Non-U.S. Subsidiaries:

Chef in a Box Limited **(1)**
762a-763a Henley Road
Slough, West Berkshire, SL1 4JW, United Kingdom
Tel.: (44) 1753686844
Fax: (44) 1753 681200
E-Mail: info@chefinabox.co.uk
Web Site: www.chefinabox.co.uk
Emp.: 40
Packaged Food Distr
S.I.C.: 5142
N.A.I.C.S.: 424420

IPM Holland B.V. **(1)**
Marssumerdyk 1
9033 WD Deinum, Friesland, Netherlands
Tel.: (31) 582991672
Fax: (31) 582991673
E-Mail: info@ipmholland.nl
Emp.: 4
Seed Production & Sales
S.I.C.: 0119
N.A.I.C.S.: 111199
Eric Apeldoorn *(Gen Mgr)*

IPM Perth Limited **(1)**
E Den Brae
Letham, Forfar, Angus, DD8 2PJ, United Kingdom
Tel.: (44) 1307818121
Fax: (44) 1307818131
Potato Whslr
S.I.C.: 5148
N.A.I.C.S.: 424480

Maybrook Dairy Limited **(1)**
14A Dromore Road
Omagh, Co Tyrone, BT78 1QZ, United Kingdom
Tel.: (44) 2882244184
Dairy Products
S.I.C.: 0241
N.A.I.C.S.: 112120
Ian Ireland *(Chm)*

DONG-A HWASUNG CO., LTD.

334-1 Yuha-ri Jangyu-myun
Kimhae, Gyungnam, 621-384, Korea (South)

Tel.: (82) 55 313 1800
Fax: (82) 55 313 1177
Web Site: www.dacm.com
Year Founded: 1974
041930—(KRS)
Business Description:
Rubber Product Mfr
S.I.C.: 3069
N.A.I.C.S.: 326299
Personnel:
Kyung Sik Lim *(Pres)*

DONG-A PHARMACEUTICAL CO., LTD.
(See Under Dong-A Socio Holdings Co., Ltd.)

DONG-A SOCIO HOLDINGS CO., LTD.
(Formerly Dong-A Pharmaceutical Co., Ltd.)
252 Yongdu-dong Dongdaemun-gu
Seoul, Korea (South)
Tel.: (82) 29208114
Fax: (82) 29269400
Web Site: www.donga.co.kr
000640—(KRS)
Rev.: $865,810,942
Assets: $1,325,951,479
Liabilities: $631,927,434
Net Worth: $694,024,045
Earnings: $63,003,981
Emp.: 2,365
Fiscal Year-end: 12/31/12
Business Description:
Pharmaceutical Products Mfr & Sales
S.I.C.: 2834
N.A.I.C.S.: 325412
Personnel:
Shin-Ho Kang *(Chm)*
Jung-Seok Kang *(Pres & Co-CEO)*
Dong-Hoon Lee *(Co-CEO & Exec VP)*
Soo-Hyung Kang *(Sr Mng Dir)*
Board of Directors:
Shin-Ho Kang
Hong-Ki Chae
Bong-Soo Cho
Jung-Seok Kang
Kyung-Bo Kang
Soo-Hyung Kang
Jin-Ho Kim
Dong-Hoon Lee

Subsidiaries:

DA INFORMATION CO., LTD. (1)
Gyeongui-ro
Ilsandong-gu, Goyang-ri, Gyeonggi-do, Korea (South)
Tel.: (82) 70 8636 3800
Pharmaceutical Information Technology Consulting Services
S.I.C.: 7373
N.A.I.C.S.: 541512

KOREA SHINTO CO., LTD. (1)
434-5 Moknae-dong
Danwon-gu, Ansan, Gyeonggi-do, Korea (South)
Tel.: (82) 31 491 8121
Web Site: en.donga.co.kr/ocp/ocp06.jsp
Industrial Machinery Mfr
S.I.C.: 3559
N.A.I.C.S.: 333249

SOOSEOK CO., LTD. (1)
620-5 Bakdal 2-dong
Manan-gu, Anyang, Gyeonggi-do, Korea (South)
Tel.: (82) 31 449 6151
Glass Container Mfr
S.I.C.: 3221
N.A.I.C.S.: 327213

ST Pharm Co., Ltd. (1)
7F MSA Bldg Daechi-dong
Gangnam-gu, Seoul, 135-840, Korea (South)
Tel.: (82) 2 527 6300
Fax: (82) 2 561 6006
E-Mail: info@scp.co.kr
Web Site: www.stpharm.co.kr
Emp.: 20
Pharmaceutical Ingredient Mfr
S.I.C.: 2834
N.A.I.C.S.: 325412
Geun-Jho Lim *(Pres)*

Yongma Logis Co., Ltd. (1)
249-9 Yongdu-dong Dongdaemun-gu
Seoul, Korea (South)
Tel.: (82) 2 3290 6400
Fax: (82) 2 3290 6464
E-Mail: aya6490@yongmalogis.co.kr
Web Site: www.yongmalogis.co.kr
Warehousing & Logistics Services
S.I.C.: 4225
N.A.I.C.S.: 493110
Dong-Yon Cho *(Mng Partner-Parcel Delivery & Total Logistics Consultation)*
Yong-Rok Kim *(Mng Partner-Transportation Consultation)*

U.S. Subsidiary:

DONG-A AMERICA CORP (1)
17215 Studebaker Rd Ste 335
Cerritos, CA 90703
Tel.: (562) 860-3153
Fax: (562) 860-3241
Web Site: en.donga.co.kr/ocp/ocp06.jsp
Emp.: 1
Health Care Products Distr
S.I.C.: 5122
N.A.I.C.S.: 424210
Kim Chong *(CEO)*

DONG-A STEEL TECHNOLOGY CO., LTD.
1039-1 Unnong-ri Dong-myeon
Hwasun-gun
Hwasun, Jelloanamdo, Korea (South)
Tel.: (82) 613702114
Fax: (82) 613738195
Web Site: www.dast.co.kr
Year Founded: 1996
058730—(KRS)
Emp.: 129
Business Description:
Steel Frameworks Mfr
S.I.C.: 3999
N.A.I.C.S.: 339999
Personnel:
Sang-won Han *(Pres)*

DONG AH TIRE & RUBBER CO., LTD.
90 Yusan-Dong
Yangsan, Kyongnam, Korea (South)
Tel.: (82) 55 389 0011
Fax: (82) 55 382 7736
Web Site: www.dongahtire.co.kr
Year Founded: 1971
007340—(KRS)
Business Description:
Automobile Product Mfr
S.I.C.: 3011
N.A.I.C.S.: 326211
Personnel:
Man Su Kim *(Chm & CEO)*

DONG BANG TRANSPORT LOGISTICS CO., LTD.
23Fl Marine Center 118
Namdaemunro 2ga
Jung-gu, Seoul, 100-770, Korea (South)
Tel.: (82) 2 2190 8100
E-Mail: Seoul@dongbang.co.kr
Web Site: www.dongbang.co.kr
Year Founded: 1965
004140—(KRS)
Business Description:
Freight Transportation Services
S.I.C.: 4731
N.A.I.C.S.: 488510
Personnel:
Jin Gon Kim *(CEO)*

DONG DO MARINE JOINT STOCK COMPANY
Floor 19 Hoa Binh Tower 106 Hoang Quoc Viet Street
Cau Giay, Hanoi, Vietnam
Tel.: (84) 4 3755 6140
Fax: (84) 4 3755 6149
E-Mail: dongdo@dongdomarine.com.vn
Web Site: www.dongdomarine.com.vn
Year Founded: 1985
DDM—(HOSE)
Business Description:
Maritime Transport Services
S.I.C.: 4491
N.A.I.C.S.: 488320
Personnel:
Hoa Binh Ta *(Pres)*
Binh Hung Bui *(Gen Dir)*
Board of Directors:
Binh Hung Bui
Tien Dung Cao
Duy Luan Nguyen
Thanh Tinh Nguyen
Hoa Binh Ta
Van Nghi Tran

DONG ENERGY A/S
Agern Alle 24-26
2970 Horsholm, Denmark
Tel.: (45) 45171022
Fax: (45) 45171044
E-Mail: dong@dongenergy.dk
Web Site: www.dongenergy.dk
Year Founded: 1972
Sales Range: $1-4.9 Billion
Emp.: 1,100
Business Description:
Natural Gas & Energy; Transporter of Oil
S.I.C.: 4924
N.A.I.C.S.: 221210
Personnel:
Henrik Poulsen *(CEO)*
Marianne Wiinholt *(CFO)*
Tomas Lykke Nielsen *(Chief Customer Officer)*
Morten H. Buchgreitz *(Exec VP-Energy Markets)*
Lars Clausen *(Exec VP-Sls & Distr)*
Thomas Dalsgaard *(Exec VP-Skaerbaek)*
Soren Gath Hansen *(Exec VP)*
Kurt Bligaard Pedersen *(Exec VP)*
Supervisory Board of Directors:
Hanne Sten Andersen
Jakob Brogaard
Poul Dreyer
Jorgen Peter Jensen
Poul Arne Nielsen
Kresten Phillipsen
Jens Nybo Stilling Sorensen

Subsidiary:

Elsam A/S (1)
Kraftvaerksvej 53
DK 7000 Fredericia, Denmark (65%)
Tel.: (45) 99551111
Fax: (45) 72102401
E-Mail: dongenergy@dongenergy.dk
Web Site: www.dongenergy.com
Producer & Distr of Electricity & Heat; Waste Incineration Services
S.I.C.: 4939
N.A.I.C.S.: 221122

Non-U.S. Subsidiary:

DONG Energy Sales (UK) Ltd. (1)
Grand Buildings 1-3 Strand
London, WC2N 5EJ, United Kingdom UK
Tel.: (44) 2072570100
Fax: (44) 2072570101
E-Mail: sgd-enquiries@shell.com
Emp.: 100
Natural Gas Marketer & Whslr
S.I.C.: 4924
N.A.I.C.S.: 221210
Benj Sykes *(Country Manager-Wind Power Bus)*

DONG NAI PAINT CORPORATION
Road 7 Bien Hoa 1 Industrial Zone
Bien Hoa, Dong Nai, Vietnam
Tel.: (84) 61 393 1355
Fax: (84) 61 383 6091
E-Mail: visitsdn@hcm.vnn.vn
Web Site: www.dongnaipaint.com.vn
Year Founded: 1987
SDN—(HNX)
Business Description:
Paint Products Mfr
S.I.C.: 2851
N.A.I.C.S.: 325510
Personnel:
Duc Dan Vu *(Chm & Mgr)*

DONG NAI PORT
Long Binh Tan Ward
Bien Hoa, Dong Nai, Vietnam
Tel.: (84) 613832225
Fax: (84) 613831259
E-Mail: dongnaiport@vnn.vn
Web Site: www.dongnai-port.com
Emp.: 250
Business Description:
Port Operations
S.I.C.: 4491
N.A.I.C.S.: 488310
Personnel:
Sam Van Do *(Chm & Deputy Gen Dir-Technical)*
Mai Thi Bach Nguyen *(Vice Chm & Gen Dir)*

DONG PHU RUBBER JOINT STOCK COMPANY
Thuan Phu Ward
Dong Phu Dist, Ho Chi Minh City, Binh Phuoc, Vietnam
Tel.: (84) 651 3819 786
Fax: (84) 651 3819 620
E-Mail: doruco_bpc@hcm.vnn.vn
Web Site: www.doruco.com.vn
DPR—(HOSE)
Business Description:
Rubber Product Mfr
S.I.C.: 3069
N.A.I.C.S.: 326299
Personnel:
Thanh Hai Nguyen *(Dir Gen)*

DONG SUH COMPANIES INC.
10th Fl Dongseo Bldg 546 Dohwa-dong
121-040 Seoul, Korea (South)
Tel.: (82) 27015050
Fax: (82) 7182259
E-Mail: info@dongsuh.com
Web Site: www.dongsuh.com
Year Founded: 1975
Sales Range: $200-249.9 Million
Emp.: 250
Business Description:
Packaged Material & Food Distributor
S.I.C.: 4222
N.A.I.C.S.: 493120
Personnel:
Jong Won Kim *(Pres)*

DONG SUNG PHARMACEUTICAL COMPANY LTD.
703-14 Banghak-dong
Dobon-Ku, Seoul, Korea (South)
Tel.: (82) 2 6911 3600

Dong Sung Pharmaceutical Company Ltd.—(Continued)

Fax: (82) 2 3492 0231
E-Mail: mkt@dongsung-pharm.co.kr
Web Site: www.dongsung-pharm.co.kr
Year Founded: 1957
002210—(KRS)
Emp.: 500

Business Description:
Pharmaceutical Product Mfr & Distr
S.I.C.: 2834
N.A.I.C.S.: 325412

Personnel:
Sun-Kyu Lee *(Founder & Chm)*

DONG WHA PHARM CO., LTD.

5 Soonwha-dong
Joong-gu, Seoul, Korea (South)
Tel.: (82) 220219300
Fax: (82) 27767873
E-Mail: dongwha@dong-wha.co.kr
Web Site: www.dong-wha.co.kr
Year Founded: 1897
000020—(KRS)

Business Description:
Pharmaceutical Product Mfr & Supplier
S.I.C.: 2834
N.A.I.C.S.: 325412

Personnel:
Doh Joon Yoon *(Chm)*
Chang-Soo Cho *(Pres)*

Subsidiary:

Dong Wha G&P Corporation (1)
678 Seonggok-dong
Danwon-gu, 425-836 Ansan, Gyeonggi-Do, Korea (South)
Tel.: (82) 31 499 8574
Fax: (82) 425110
Web Site: www.dong-wha.co.kr/english/company/company07_01.asp
Glass Container Mfr
S.I.C.: 3221
N.A.I.C.S.: 327213
Chang-Hoon Yoon *(Gen Mgr)*

DONG YANG P&F CO., LTD

17th 18th FL IT Premier Tower 345-50 Gasan-dong
Geumcheon-gu, Seoul, Korea (South)
Tel.: (82) 2 2106 8000
Fax: (82) 2 2106 8100
Web Site: www.dypnf.com
Year Founded: 1996
104460—(KRS)
Sls.: $51,851,220
Assets: $69,357,540
Liabilities: $20,378,160
Net Worth: $48,979,380
Earnings: $1,641,450
Fiscal Year-end: 12/31/12

Business Description:
General Purpose Machinery Mfr
S.I.C.: 3569
N.A.I.C.S.: 333999

Personnel:
Jwa Jin Cho *(CEO)*

DONGA ONE CORPORATION

60 63B/D 54F Yeouido-dong
Yeongdeungpo-gu, 150-763 Seoul, Korea (South)
Tel.: (82) 27895022
Fax: (82) 27895109
Web Site: www.dongaone.com
Year Founded: 2002
008040—(KRS)

Business Description:
Food Products Mfr
S.I.C.: 2099
N.A.I.C.S.: 311999

Personnel:
Chang Shik Rhee *(CEO)*

Subsidiaries:

Daesan & Co. Ltd (1)
Woonsan Bldg 18-4 Nonhyeon-dong
Gangnam-gu, 135-010 Seoul, Korea (South)
Tel.: (82) 2 548 8186
Fax: (82) 2 548 1072
Emp.: 10
Pet Food Mfr
S.I.C.: 2047
N.A.I.C.S.: 311111

Dana Cellars Corporation (1)
62 Munjeong-dong
Songpa-gu, Seoul, Korea (South)
Tel.: (82) 2 405 4300
Fax: (82) 2 405 4301
Wine Import & Distr
S.I.C.: 5182
N.A.I.C.S.: 424820

DongA Food Co., Ltd. (1)
Woonsan Bldg 18-4 Nonhyun-dong
Gangnam-gu, Seoul, 135-010, Korea (South)
Tel.: (82) 2 514 3176
Fax: (82) 2 514 5482
Web Site: www.dongahfood.com
Emp.: 2
Meat Import & Whslr
S.I.C.: 5147
N.A.I.C.S.: 424470
Young Kim *(Gen Mgr)*

Forza Motors Korea Corporation (1)
Sincheonji Building 588-16 Sinsa-dong
Gangnam-gu, Seoul, Korea (South)
Tel.: (82) 2 3433 0808
Fax: (82) 2 3433 0899
New Car Dealer
S.I.C.: 5511
N.A.I.C.S.: 441110
In Su Jo *(CEO)*

Korea Industry (1)
631-3 Wanjeon-ri Gwangseok-myeon
Nonsan, Chungnam, Korea (South)
Tel.: (82) 41 732 8200
Fax: (82) 41 733 5639
Rice & Wheat Grain Milling Services
S.I.C.: 2044
N.A.I.C.S.: 311212

PDP Wine Corporation (1)
Podoplaza 634-1 Sinsa-dong
Gangnam-gu, Seoul, 135895, Korea (South)
Tel.: (82) 2 548 3720
Fax: (82) 6 912 7599
E-Mail: yjy@winetine.co.kr
Web Site: www.naracellar.com
Wine Retailer
S.I.C.: 5921
N.A.I.C.S.: 445310
Young Kim *(Gen Mgr)*

Plants:

DongA One Corporation - Busan Factory (1)
601-837 1165-1 Jwacheon-dong
Dong-gu, Busan, Korea (South)
Tel.: (82) 51 630 3100
Fax: (82) 51 632 1180
Web Site: www.dongaone.com
Flour Mfr
S.I.C.: 2041
N.A.I.C.S.: 311211

DongA One Corporation - Incheon Factory (1)
32 Manseok-dong
Dong-gu, Incheon, 401-010, Korea (South)
Tel.: (82) 32 763 6331 3
Fax: (82) 32 763 6314
Web Site: www.dongaone.com
Flour Mfr
S.I.C.: 2041
N.A.I.C.S.: 311211

DongA One Corporation - Wonju Factory (1)
333-3 Usan-dong
Wonju, Gangwon, 220-955, Korea (South)
Tel.: (82) 33 742 8941
Fax: (82) 33 748 6623
E-Mail: leesy@kodoco.com
Emp.: 26
Animal Feed Mfr
S.I.C.: 2048
N.A.I.C.S.: 311119
Joseph L. Herring *(CEO)*

DONGAH GEOLOGICAL ENGINEERING CO., LTD.

1033-2 Guseo 2-dong
Geumjeong-gu, Busan, Korea (South)
Tel.: (82) 515805500
Web Site: www.dage.co.kr
Year Founded: 1971
028100—(KRS)

Business Description:
Construction Engineering Services
S.I.C.: 8711
N.A.I.C.S.: 541330

Personnel:
Jung-woo Lee *(Chm)*

Plant:

DongAh Geological Engineering Co., Ltd. - EUMSEONG PLANT (1)
113-1 2 3 Munchon-ri Gamgok-Myeon
Eumseong, Chungbuk, Korea (South)
Tel.: (82) 43 882 0283
Geological Surveying Equipment Mfr
S.I.C.: 3559
N.A.I.C.S.: 333249

Non-U.S. Subsidiary:

Dongah Geological Engineering India Private Ltd. (1)
329 3rd Floor Tower-B Spazedge Sector-47
Gurgaon-Sohna Road
Gurgaon, Haryana, 122 002, India
Tel.: (91) 124 473 8604
Fax: (91) 124 473 8610
Emp.: 6
Geological Engineering Services
S.I.C.: 8711
N.A.I.C.S.: 541330
Deepak Gupta *(Mgr)*

DONGBANG SHIP MACHINERY CO., LTD.

414-2 Jukgok-Dong
Jinhae, Kyungnam, Korea (South)
Tel.: (82) 555450882
Fax: (82) 555450883
Web Site: www.dongbangsm.co.kr
Year Founded: 1994
099410—(KRS)

Business Description:
Ship Equipment Mfr
S.I.C.: 3999
N.A.I.C.S.: 339999

Personnel:
Sung Ho Kim *(CEO)*

DONGBU GROUP

Dongbu Financial Center 891-10 Daechi-dong
Gangnam-gu, Seoul, 135-523, Korea (South)
Tel.: (82) 2 1588 0100
Web Site: www.dongbu.com
Year Founded: 1969
Sales Range: $25-49.9 Billion
Emp.: 37,000

Business Description:
Holding Company
S.I.C.: 6719
N.A.I.C.S.: 551112

Personnel:
Jun-ki Kim *(Founder, Chm & CEO)*

Subsidiaries:

Daewoo Electronics Corporation (1)
1-dong-dong 1-2 Eastern Daewoo Electronics
Jung-gu, Seoul, 121709, Korea (South)
Tel.: (82) 23607114
Telex: Dwelec K28177/8
Fax: (82) 2 360 7700
Web Site: www.dwe.co.kr
Sales Range: $1-4.9 Billion
Emp.: 8,600
Television Sets, Microwave Ovens, Refrigerators, Air Conditioners, Vacuum Cleaners, Personal Computers & Peripherals Mfr, Distr & Sales
S.I.C.: 3651
N.A.I.C.S.: 334310
Jae-Hyeong Lee *(CEO)*

U.S. Subsidiary:

Daewoo Electronics America, Inc. (2)
120 Chubb Ave
Lyndhurst, NJ 07071
Tel.: (201) 460-2000
Fax: (201) 935-5004
E-Mail: DaewooElectronics@e-daewoo.com
Web Site: www.e-daewoo.com
Electronic Products Mfr & Sales
S.I.C.: 3651
N.A.I.C.S.: 334310

Non-U.S. Subsidiaries:

Daewoo Electronics Europe GmbH (2)
Otto-Hahn-Strasse 21
D-35510 Butzbach, Germany
Tel.: (49) 603396910
Fax: (49) 6033969159
E-Mail: info@daewoo-electronics.com
Web Site: www.daewoo-electronics.com
Emp.: 60
Electronic Products Mfr & Sales
S.I.C.: 3651
N.A.I.C.S.: 334310
Gye-chun Chu *(Pres & CEO)*
Inbo Kong *(Mng Dir)*

Non-U.S. Subsidiaries:

DAEWOO Electronics Deme Fze. (3)
Akademika Kapitsy Street 34/121
117647 Moscow, Russia
Tel.: (7) 0957452018
Fax: (7) 0957452021
E-Mail: info@dwec.ru
Web Site: www.dwec.ru
Electronic Products Distr & Sales
S.I.C.: 5065
N.A.I.C.S.: 423690

Daewoo Electronics Manufacturing Poland Sp. z o.o. (3)
Ul Bokserska 66
02-690 Warsaw, Poland
Tel.: (48) 224550900
Fax: (48) 224550958
E-Mail: info@dempol.com
Web Site: www.d-e.pl
Electronic Products Mfr, Distr & Sales
S.I.C.: 5065
N.A.I.C.S.: 423690

Daewoo Electronics S.A. (3)
Paris Nord II 277 rue de la Belle Etoile
BP 50068
95947 Roissy-en-France, CDG, France
Tel.: (33) 141599200
Fax: (33) 141599201
E-Mail: service-conso@daewoo.fr
Web Site: www.daewoo.fr
Electronic Products Distr & Sales
S.I.C.: 5065
N.A.I.C.S.: 423690

Daewoo Electronics Sales UK Ltd. (3)
640 Wharfedale Road
Winnersh Triangle, Wokingham, Berks, RG41 5TP, United Kingdom
Tel.: (44) 1189252500
Fax: (44) 1189256772
E-Mail: information@desuk.co.uk
Web Site: www.daewoo-electronics.co.uk
Emp.: 20
Electronic Products Distr & Sales
S.I.C.: 5065
N.A.I.C.S.: 423690
S. Chae *(Mng Dir)*

Daewoo Electronics Japan Co., Ltd. (2)
Akihabara Shinko Daiichi Seimei Building
1-2 Ueno 3-chome Taito-ku, Tokyo, 110-0005, Japan
Tel.: (81) 338343177
Fax: (81) 338343188

Web Site: www.daewooelectronics.com.pe/solida_red.htm
Electronic Products Distr
S.I.C.: 5065
N.A.I.C.S.: 423690

Daewoo Electronics (M) Sdn. Bhd. (2)
Lot 8 Sungai Petani Industrial Estate
Sungai Petani, Kedah Darul Aman, Malaysia
Tel.: (60) 44416216
Fax: (60) 44417070
Web Site: www.daewooelectronics.com.pe/solida_red.htm
Emp.: 50
Electronic Products Mfr & Sales
S.I.C.: 3651
N.A.I.C.S.: 334310
Yoo Youngjae *(Mng Dir)*

Daewoo Electronics Middle East FZE Ltd. (2)
PO Box 61163
Dubai, United Arab Emirates
Tel.: (971) 48838349
Fax: (971) 48838302
E-Mail: daewoo@dwe.ae
Web Site: www.daewooelectronics.com.pe/solida_red.htm
Emp.: 22
Electronic Products Distr
S.I.C.: 5065
N.A.I.C.S.: 423690
Dong Cho Lim *(Gen Mgr)*

Daewoo Electronics (Panama) S.A. (2)
Via Espana y Calle Elvira Mendez
Torre Bank Boston Piso 19
Apartado 0816-01094 Zona 5, Panama, Panama
Tel.: (507) 3052000
Fax: (507) 3010112
E-Mail: servicio@decpanama.com
Web Site: www.decpanama.com
Electronic Products Mfr & Sales
S.I.C.: 3651
N.A.I.C.S.: 334310
Tae Hee Lim *(Pres)*

Daewoo Electronics UK Ltd. (2)
Rathenraw Industrial Estate
62/82 Greystone Road, Antrim, N Ireland, BT41 1NU, United Kingdom
Tel.: (44) 2894425000
Fax: (44) 2894425100
E-Mail: info@deuk.co.uk
Web Site: www.deuk.co.uk
Electronic Products Mfr
S.I.C.: 3651
N.A.I.C.S.: 334310

Dongbu Robot Co., Ltd. (1)
11th floor Bucheon Techno Park Bldg 401
Yakdae-dong
Wonmi-gu, Bucheon, Gyeonggi-do, Korea (South)
Tel.: (82) 32 329 5551
Fax: (82) 32 329 5569
E-Mail: robotir@dongbu.com
Web Site: www.dongburobot.com
090710—(KRS)
Robot Mfr
S.I.C.: 3559
N.A.I.C.S.: 333249
Suk Hee Kang *(Co-CEO)*
Il Soon Kwak *(Co-CEO)*

Affiliates:

Agriculture Technology Research Institute (1)
175-1 Botong-ri Jeongnam-myun
Hwasung-gun, Suwon, Korea (South)
Tel.: (82) 31 354 6810
Fax: (82) 31 354 6820
Agricultural Research Services
S.I.C.: 8731
N.A.I.C.S.: 541712

Breeding Research Institute (1)
481-3 Deogbong-ri
Yangseong-myun Ansung City, Suwon, Korea (South)
Tel.: (82) 3167469115
Fax: (82) 316746916
E-Mail: breed@dongbuchem.com
Web Site: www.dongbuchem.com
Emp.: 50
Breeding Research Services
S.I.C.: 8731
N.A.I.C.S.: 541712
Sung Soonti *(Mng Dir)*

Dongbu Advanced Research Institute (1)
103-2 Moonji-dong
Daeduck Science Town
D05708 Daejeon, Korea (South)
Tel.: (82) 428668114
Fax: (82) 82428611583
E-Mail: jsyeo@dongubu.com
Web Site: www.dongbuhitek.co.kr
Emp.: 45
Business Support Services
S.I.C.: 8731
N.A.I.C.S.: 541712
Kmjeyeon Heo *(Gen Mgr)*

Dongbu Asset Management Co., Ltd. (1)
Dongbu Securities Building 36-5 Youido-dong
Youngdungpo-gu, Seoul, Korea (South)
Tel.: (82) 27873700
Fax: (82) 2 787 3719
Web Site: www.dongbuam.co.kr
Managed Assets: $1,069,000,000
Emp.: 47
Investment Management Services
S.I.C.: 6211
N.A.I.C.S.: 523999
D. J. Han *(CEO)*

Dongbu Capital Co., Ltd. (1)
6F Dongbu Da-dong Bldg 103 Da-dong
Chung-gu, Seoul, 100-180, Korea (South) Ks
Tel.: (82) 2 2264 7000
Fax: (82) 2 776 1500
E-Mail: webmaster@dbcap.co.kr
Web Site: www.dongbucapital.co.kr
Sales Range: $10-24.9 Million
Commercial Capital Funding Services
S.I.C.: 6099
N.A.I.C.S.: 522390
Young-Mahn Roh *(Pres & CEO)*

Dongbu CNI Co., Ltd (1)
Anam Semiconductor Bldg 154-17
Samseong-dong
Gangnam-gu, Seoul, Korea (South)
Tel.: (82) 2 3449 2323
Fax: (82) 2 3449-2399
Web Site: www.dongbucni.com
Sales Range: $150-199.9 Million
Emp.: 600
System Integration, IT Consulting & Outsourcing Services
S.I.C.: 7373
N.A.I.C.S.: 541512
Young Cheol Cho *(CEO)*

Dongbu Corporation (1)
Dongbu Financial Center Building
890-10 Daechi-dong Gangnam-gu, Seoul, 135-523, Korea (South)
Tel.: (82) 234842114
Fax: (82) 234842361
E-Mail: dbcom@dongbu.co.kr
Web Site: www.dongbu.co.kr
Sales Range: $1-4.9 Billion
Emp.: 1,700
Construction & Engineering Services
S.I.C.: 8711
N.A.I.C.S.: 541330
Jun-Ki Kim *(Founder & Chm)*
Soon-Byung Lee *(CEO)*

Divisions:

Dongbu Corp - Construction (2)
Dongbu Financial Center Building 890-10
Daechi-dong
Gangnam-gu, Seoul, Korea (South)
Tel.: (82) 234842114
E-Mail: dbcon@dongbu.co.kr
Web Site: dbcon.dongbu.co.kr/english/main.jsp
Business Support Services
S.I.C.: 7389
N.A.I.C.S.: 561499

Dongbu Corp - Logistics (2)
Dongbu Financial Center Building 890-10
Daechi-dong
Gangnam-gu, Seoul, Korea (South)
Tel.: (82) 234842624
Fax: (82) 234842625
Web Site: www.dongbulogis.co.kr
Business Support Services
S.I.C.: 4731
N.A.I.C.S.: 541614

Dongbu Engineering Co., Ltd . (1)
4 Jung Gu Inheyun Pong 2nd Ga
73/1 Pung Jeon Bldg 5th Fl, Seoul, 140709, Korea (South)
Tel.: (82) 221226700
Fax: (82) 22122 6920
Web Site: www.dbeng.co.kr
Emp.: 500
Engineering Contractor & Consulting Services
S.I.C.: 8711
N.A.I.C.S.: 541330
Mun Gyu Lee *(Pres & CEO)*

Dongbu Express Co., Ltd. (1)
135-080 Dongbu Financial Center
891-10 Daechi-dong, Gangnam-gu Seoul, Korea (South)
Tel.: (82) 234842600
Fax: (82) 234842720
Web Site: www.dongbuexpress.com
Sales Range: $350-399.9 Million
Emp.: 1,100
Cargo & Transportation Logistics Services
S.I.C.: 4491
N.A.I.C.S.: 488320
Heon Ki Choi *(Pres)*
Joo Sup Jung *(CEO)*

Dongbu Farm Biotec Co., Ltd. (1)
Dongbu Finance Center
891-10 Daechi-Dong Gangnam-gu, Seoul, Korea (South)
Tel.: (82) 234841500
Fertilizers, Seeds, Veterinary Pharamaceuticals, Environment-Friendly Agricultural Materials Mfr & Distr
S.I.C.: 2873
N.A.I.C.S.: 325311

Dongbu Farm Hannong Co., Ltd. (1)
19 20F Dongbu Financial Center 432
Teheran ro
Gangnam-gu, Seoul, 135-523, Korea (South) Ks
Tel.: (82) 2 3484 1500
Fax: (82) 2 562 8531
E-Mail:
Web Site: www.agriculture.co.kr
Sales Range: Less than $1 Million
Emp.: 2,000
Fiscal Year-end: 12/31/12
Crop Protection Products, Fertilizers, Agrochemicals & Petrochemicals Mfr
S.I.C.: 2879
N.A.I.C.S.: 325320
Sukwon Choi *(CEO)*

Subsidiaries:

Dongbu Hannong Chemical Co., Ltd. (2)
Dongbu Financial Center 891-10 Daechi-dong
Gangnam-gu, Seoul, 135-280, Korea (South) Ks
Tel.: (82) 2 3484 1665
Fax: (82) 2 562 7962
Web Site: www.dongbuchem.com
Sales Range: $800-899.9 Million
Emp.: 1,200
Agrochemical, Petrochemical & Ferro Alloy Mfr
S.I.C.: 2869
N.A.I.C.S.: 325110
Youngkyun Shin *(Pres)*

Monsanto Korea, Inc. (2)
5/13F Gwang-Hui Building 216
Gwanghuidong 1-Ga
Jung-Gu, Seoul, 100-710, Korea (South)
Tel.: (82) 2 3393 3700
Fax: (82) 2 3393 3800
Web Site: www.monsanto.com
Agricultural Chemicals Mfr
S.I.C.: 2879
N.A.I.C.S.: 325320
Hugh Grant *(Chm & CEO)*

Dongbu Fine Chemical Co., Ltd. (1)
Dongbu Financial Center Building
890-10 Daechi-dong Gangnam-gu, Seoul, 135-523, Korea (South)
Tel.: (82) 234841600
Fax: (82) 25627962
Web Site: www.dongbufinechemical.com
Sales Range: $150-199.9 Million
Emp.: 300
Pesticide Raw Materials, Adhesives, Pesticides, Information & Communications Material Mfr
S.I.C.: 2899
N.A.I.C.S.: 325998
Jaekwan Lee *(CEO)*

Dongbu HiTek Co., Ltd. (1)
Dongbu Financial Center 891-10 Daechi-dong
Gangnam-gu, Seoul, 135523, Korea (South)
Tel.: (82) 234842863
Fax: (82) 234842851
E-Mail: daekyeun.kin@dongbu.com
Web Site: www.dongbuhitek.com
Sales Range: $250-299.9 Million
Emp.: 1,800
Semiconductor Materials Mfr
S.I.C.: 3674
N.A.I.C.S.: 334413
D.G. Yoon *(Vice Chm)*
Hwan Oh Young *(CEO)*
Lou N. Hutter *(Sr VP & Gen Mgr-Analog Semiconductor Div)*

Dongbu Insurance Co., Ltd. (1)
Dongbu Financial Center 891 10 Daechi-dong
Gangnam-gu, Seoul, 135 523, Korea (South) Ks
Tel.: (82) 230113144
Fax: (82) 5051812016
E-Mail: webmaster@idongbu.com
Web Site: www.idongbu.com
005830—(KRS)
Sales Range: $5-14.9 Billion
Insurance Services
S.I.C.: 6411
N.A.I.C.S.: 524298
Jeong-Nam Kim *(Pres & CEO)*
Duck-Hwan Ahn *(Sr Exec VP)*
Jae-Dong Kwak *(Sr Exec VP)*
Jong-Yong Choi *(Exec VP)*
Se-Hun Park *(Exec VP)*
Yun-Sik Park *(Exec VP)*
Chi-Hyung Youn *(Exec VP)*
Ho-Tak Jeon *(Sr VP & Dir-Comml Lines Div)*
Chang-Seob Kim *(Sr VP)*
Yeong-Mann Kim *(Sr VP)*
Ki-Moo Lee *(Sr VP)*
Tae-Oon Lee *(Sr VP)*
Kyoung-Il Lim *(Sr VP)*
Jin-Young Mok *(Sr VP)*
Byung-Hoi Yoo *(Sr VP)*

Subsidiary:

Dongbu Life Insurance Co., Ltd. (2)
7F Dongbu Financial Center 891-10
Deachi-dong
Kangnam-gu, Seoul, 135-523, Korea (South) Ks (39.49%)
Tel.: (82) 2 1588 4028
Fax: (82) 2 3011 4000
E-Mail: webmaster@dongbulife.co.kr
Web Site: www.dongbulife.com
Sales Range: $550-599.9 Million
Emp.: 300
Life Insurance Products & Services
S.I.C.: 6311
N.A.I.C.S.: 524113
Jae Hong Cho *(CEO)*

Dongbu Savings Bank Co., Ltd. (1)
Dongbu Da-dong Bldg
103 Da-dong, Seoul, Korea (South)
Tel.: (82) 237051700
Fax: (82) 237051800
Sales Range: $25-49.9 Million
Emp.: 103
Banking Services
S.I.C.: 6029
N.A.I.C.S.: 522110
Ha-Joong Kim *(Pres & CEO)*
Myung-Gyu Oh *(CFO)*

Dongbu Steel Co.,Ltd. (1)
891-10 Daechi-dong
Gangnam-gu, Seoul, Korea (South)
Tel.: (82) 234508114
Fax: (82) 234507418
Web Site: www.edongbusteel.com
Sales Range: $1-4.9 Billion
Emp.: 2,000
Steel Products Mfg

Dongbu Group—(Continued)

S.I.C.: 3399
N.A.I.C.S.: 331110

Dongbu Technology Institute (1)
103-2 Munji-dong
Yuseong-gu, Daejeon, Korea (South)
Tel.: (82) 428668019
Fax: (82) 428611583
Web Site: www.dongbuchem.com
Emp.: 100
Business Support Services
S.I.C.: 7389
N.A.I.C.S.: 561499

DONGBU LIGHTEC CO., LTD.

Ojeong-dong 739-8
Ojeong-gu, 421-170 Bucheon,
Gyeonggi-do, Korea (South)
Tel.: (82) 32 670 3239
Fax: (82) 32 670 3101
E-Mail: dongbulightec@dongbulightec.co.kr
Web Site: www.dongbulightec.co.kr
Year Founded: 1989
045890—(KRS)
Sales Range: $50-74.9 Million
Emp.: 238

Business Description:
Electric Lamp Mfr
S.I.C.: 3641
N.A.I.C.S.: 335110

Personnel:
Jae Hyeong Lee *(CEO)*

DONGFANG ELECTRIC CORPORATION LIMITED

333 Shuhan Avenue
Chengdu, Sichuan, 610036, China
Tel.: (86) 28 87583000
E-Mail: email@dongfang.com.cn
Web Site: www.dongfang.com.cn
600875—(HKG SHG)
Sales Range: $1-4.9 Billion
Emp.: 19,461

Business Description:
Electric Power Generating Equipment Mfr
S.I.C.: 3511
N.A.I.C.S.: 333611

Personnel:
Zefu Si *(Chm)*

DONGFANG SHIPBUILDING (GROUP) COMPANY LIMITED

53 UBI Avenue 1 #03-37 Paya UBI Industrial Park
Singapore, 408934, Singapore
Tel.: (65) 6648 6569
Web Site: www.dongfangship.com.cn
Year Founded: 1986
DFS—(AIM)

Business Description:
Ship Building & Repairing
S.I.C.: 3731
N.A.I.C.S.: 336611

Personnel:
Tong Kao Chen *(CEO)*
Xiaomin Sun *(COO)*

Board of Directors:
Tong Kao Chen
Xiu Dan Chen
Zhiping Hu
A.K.M. Ismael
Grace Shi
Xiaomin Sun
Gong Cheng Wu

DONGFENG AUTOMOBILE CO., LTD.

136 Chuangye Road Economic & Technical Development Zone
Wuhan, Hebei, 430056, China
Tel.: (86) 27 84287900
Fax: (86) 27 84287918
E-Mail: lihua@dfac.com
Web Site: www.dfac.com
600006—(SHG)
Sales Range: $1-4.9 Billion

Business Description:
Light Duty Commercial Vehicles Mfr & Sales
S.I.C.: 3711
N.A.I.C.S.: 336112

Personnel:
Ping Xu *(Chm)*

Joint Venture:

Dongfeng Iseki Agricultural Machinery (Hubei) Co., Ltd. (1)
No 8 Xinguang Road
Hi-Tech Development Zone, Xiangfan,
Hubei, 441000, China CN
Tel.: (86) 710 338 7579
Fax: (86) 710 338 7581
Agricultural Machinery Mfr
S.I.C.: 3523
N.A.I.C.S.: 333111

DONGFENG MOTOR CORPORATION

1 Dongfeng Road
Wuhan, Hubei, 430056, China
Tel.: (86) 27 8428 50041
Web Site: www.dfmc.com.cn/contactUs_en.aspx
Year Founded: 1969
Sales Range: $5-14.9 Billion
Emp.: 121,000

Business Description:
Automobile Mfr
S.I.C.: 3711
N.A.I.C.S.: 336111

Personnel:
Ping Xu *(Chm)*

Subsidiary:

Dongfeng Motor Group Co. Ltd. (1)
Wuhan Economic & Technology Development Zone
Special No 1 Dongfeng Road, Wuhan,
Hubei, 430056, China (66.86%)
Tel.: (86) 2784285000
Fax: (86) 2784285057
E-Mail: ir@dfmg.com.cn
Web Site: www.dfmg.com.cn/en/
0489—(HKG OTC)
Rev.: $19,703,118,600
Assets: $18,237,568,500
Liabilities: $9,082,566,450
Net Worth: $9,155,002,050
Earnings: $1,553,394,150
Emp.: 109,963
Fiscal Year-end: 12/31/12
Commercial Vehicles, Passenger Cars & Automotive Components Mfr
S.I.C.: 3711
N.A.I.C.S.: 336111
Ping Xu *(Chm)*
Liangjie Ma *(Chm-Supervisory Bd)*
Fushou Zhu *(Pres)*
Xindong Hu *(Co-Sec)*
Susan Yee Har Lo *(Co-Sec)*

Joint Ventures:

Dongfeng Peugeot Citroen Automobile Company Ltd. (2)
Wuhan Economic & Technological Development Zone
165 Shenlong Avenue
Wuhan, China
Tel.: (86) 27 6885 2945
Fax: (86) 27 6885 2951
Web Site: www.dpca.com.cn/publish/index.jsp
Automobile Mfr; Owned 50% by Dongfeng Motor Group Co. Ltd. & 50% by PSA Peugeot Citroen S.A.
S.I.C.: 3711
N.A.I.C.S.: 336111
Weidong Liu *(Gen Mgr & Deputy Sec)*

Dongfeng Cummins Engine Co., Ltd. (2)
Automobile Industry Development Zone
Xiangcheng, 441004, China
Tel.: (86) 7103320888
Web Site: www.dfac.com
Sales Range: $500-549.9 Million
Emp.: 2,400
Engine Mfr
S.I.C.: 3519
N.A.I.C.S.: 333618

DONGGUAN EONTEC CO., LTD.

Yinquan Industrial Park
Qingxi Town, Dongguan, Guangdong, 523662, China
Tel.: (86) 769 8733 7777
Fax: (86) 769 87367777
E-Mail: sales@e-ande.com
Web Site: www.e-ande.com
Year Founded: 1993
300328—(CHIN)
Sales Range: $50-74.9 Million
Emp.: 1,400

Business Description:
Aluminum & Magnesium Alloy Die Castings
S.I.C.: 3364
N.A.I.C.S.: 331523

Personnel:
Yangde Li *(Chm)*

DONGGUAN KINGSUN OPTOELECTRONIC CO., LTD.

(d/b/a Kingsun)
Hengjiangxia Administration Zone
Changping Town, Dongguan,
Guangdong, 523565, China
Tel.: (86) 769 83395678
Fax: (86) 769 83395679
E-Mail: sales@kslights.com
Web Site: www.kingsunlights.com
002638—(SSE)
Sales Range: $75-99.9 Million
Emp.: 3,000

Business Description:
LED Street Lighting Mfr
S.I.C.: 3646
N.A.I.C.S.: 335122

Personnel:
Xuliang Li *(CEO)*

DONGHUA TESTING TECHNOLOGY CO., LTD.

Building 4 Northeast of Luojiagang Bridge
Jingjiang City, Taizhou, 214500, China
Tel.: (86) 523 84908559
Fax: (86) 523 84892079
E-Mail: qxs@dhtest.com
Web Site: www.dhtest.com
300354—(CHIN)
Sales Range: $10-24.9 Million
Emp.: 380

Business Description:
Structural Mechanical Performance Testing Equipment Mfr
S.I.C.: 3825
N.A.I.C.S.: 334515

Personnel:
Shigang Liu *(Chm)*

DONGIL METAL CO., LTD.

327 Duksung-Ri Kumho-Eup
Yeongcheon, Gyungsangbuk-Do,
Korea (South) 700-802
Tel.: (82) 54 333 5501
Fax: (82) 54 334 1585
E-Mail: sales@dongilmetal.co.kr
Web Site: www.dongilmetal.co.kr
Year Founded: 1966
109860—(KRS)

Business Description:
Steel Casting Mfr
S.I.C.: 3325
N.A.I.C.S.: 331513

Personnel:
Kilbong Oh *(CEO)*

DONGIL STEEL CO., LTD.

716-1 Hakjang-dong Sasang-gu
Busan, 617843, Korea (South)
Tel.: (82) 513165341
Fax: (82) 513265655
Web Site: www.dongilsteel.com
Year Founded: 1967
023790—(KRS)
Sales Range: $10-24.9 Million
Emp.: 50

Business Description:
Steel Products Mfr
S.I.C.: 3312
N.A.I.C.S.: 331110

Personnel:
In-Hwa Jang *(CEO)*

DONGIL TECHNOLOGY LTD.

215-6 Bugyang-dong
Hwaseong, Gyeonggi-do, 445-040,
Korea (South)
Tel.: (82) 31 356 7114
Fax: (82) 31 357 2610
Web Site: www.dongiltech.co.kr
Year Founded: 1986
032960—(KRS)

Business Description:
Sensor Mfr
S.I.C.: 3823
N.A.I.C.S.: 334513

Personnel:
Dong-Joon Sohn *(Pres & CEO)*

DONGJIANG ENVIRONMENTAL COMPANY LIMITED

Dongjiang Environmental Building 9
Langshan Road
High-tech Industrial Park
Nanshan District, Shenzhen, 518057, China
Tel.: (86) 755 86676186
Fax: (86) 755 86676006
E-Mail: office@dongjiang.com.cn
Web Site: www.szdongjiang.com
Year Founded: 1999
002672—(HKG SSE)
Sales Range: $150-199.9 Million
Emp.: 2,200

Business Description:
Waste Treatment, Recycling, Facility Construction & Management
S.I.C.: 4953
N.A.I.C.S.: 562211

Personnel:
Wei Yang Zhang *(Chm)*
Chen Shu Sheng *(CEO)*

Board of Directors:
Wei Yang Zhang
Yong Peng Li
Chen Shu Sheng

Subsidiaries:

Beijing Novel Environmental Protection Co Limited (1)
8/F Tower A Xue Yan Building Tsinghua University
Haidian District, Beijing, 100084, China
Tel.: (86) 1062770877
Fax: (86) 1062787884
E-Mail: eeplan@e-e.com.cn
Web Site: www.e-e.com.cn
Environmental Consulting Services
S.I.C.: 8999
N.A.I.C.S.: 541620

Huizhou Dongjiang Environment Technology Co. Limited (1)
39 Tongqiao Industrial Park
Tongqiao Town, Huizhou, Guangdong, China
Tel.: (86) 7523796392
Fax: (86) 7523795713

Environmental Consulting Services
S.I.C.: 8999
N.A.I.C.S.: 541620

Kunshan Kunpeng Environmental and Technology Co. Limited (1)
Qiandeng Developing Area
Kunshan, Jiangsu, 215341, China
Tel.: (86) 51257461796
Fax: (86) 51257469599
E-Mail: Ks-kp@ks-kunpeng.com.cn
Waste Collection & Treatment Services
S.I.C.: 4212
N.A.I.C.S.: 562112

Qingdao Dongjiang Environmental Recycled Power Limited (1)
1812 Unit 1 Building 3 Huanyukangting
Shangdong Road No 118
Qingdao, Shandong, China
Tel.: (86) 53280862027
Fax: (86) 53280862027
Electric Power Generation Services
S.I.C.: 4911
N.A.I.C.S.: 221118

Qingyuan Dongjiang Environmental Technologies Company Limited (1)
No 13 Taiji Industrial Park High-tech Zone
Qingyuan, China
Tel.: (86) 7636861628
Fax: (86) 7636861098
Waste Treatment & Disposal Services
S.I.C.: 4953
N.A.I.C.S.: 562211

Shaoguan Green Recycling Resource Development Co Limited (1)
Jiangjun Tuen Tielong Town
Wengyuan County, Shaoguan, Guangdong, 512629, China
Tel.: (86) 7512663228
Fax: (86) 7512663228
E-Mail: sg_office@163.com
Waste Treatment & Disposal Services
S.I.C.: 4953
N.A.I.C.S.: 562211

Shenzhen Huabao Technology Limited (1)
Gonghe Village Shajing Town
BaoAn District, Shenzhen, 518104, China
Tel.: (86) 755 26510878
Fax: (86) 755 26510878
E-Mail: shifeiyan@163.com
Environmental Consulting Services
S.I.C.: 8999
N.A.I.C.S.: 541620

DONGJIN SEMICHEM CO., LTD.

KGIT Center 1601 Sangam-Dong
Mapo-Gu
Seoul, 121 270, Korea (South)
Tel.: (82) 23259451
Fax: (82) 23259459
E-Mail: Trade@dongjinsemichem.com
Web Site: www.dongjin.com
Sales Range: $150-199.9 Million
Emp.: 1,000
Fiscal Year-end: 12/31/12

Business Description:
Mfr. of Semiconductors
S.I.C.: 3674
N.A.I.C.S.: 334413

Personnel:
Boo-Sup Lee *(CEO)*

U.S. Subsidiary:

Dongjin (USA) Inc. (1)
37 Appleby Close 33
Bretton Woods, NH 03575
Tel.: (212) 760-1766
Sls.: $11,410,881
Emp.: 5
Chemicals & Allied Products, Nec
S.I.C.: 5169
N.A.I.C.S.: 424690
Chong P. Kim *(COO)*

Non-U.S. Subsidiary:

Taiwan Dongjin Semichem Co., Ltd. (1)
No 21 Hsiengong North 1st Road
Changbin Ind Complex, Taichung, Taiwan
Tel.: (886) 47580475
Fax: (886) 47580473
Web Site: www.dongjin.com
Semiconductor & Related Device Mfr
S.I.C.: 3674
N.A.I.C.S.: 334413

DONGKUK S&C CO., LTD.

547-3 Jangheung-dong
Nam-ku, Pohang, Kyungsangbuk-do, Korea (South)
Tel.: (82) 542710508
Fax: (82) 542710700
Web Site: www.dongkuksnc.co.kr
Year Founded: 2001
100130—(KRS)

Business Description:
Steel Structures Mfr
S.I.C.: 3999
N.A.I.C.S.: 339999

Personnel:
Kee Hyung Jang *(CEO)*

Subsidiaries:

Hallyeo Energy Resource (1)
Manheung-dong 855
Yeosu, Jeollanam-do, Korea (South)
Tel.: (82) 61 654 3945
Fax: (82) 61 654 3948
Electric Power Generation Services
S.I.C.: 4931
N.A.I.C.S.: 221118

Shinan Wind Power Generation Co (1)
Gurim-ri 175 Bigum-myun
Gurim, Jeollanam, Korea (South)
Tel.: (82) 61 275 4777
Fax: (82) 61 275 4777
Electric Power Generation Services
S.I.C.: 4939
N.A.I.C.S.: 221118

Plant:

Dongkuk S&C Co., Ltd. - DK Wind Power Plant (1)
547-3 Jangheung-Dong
Nam-Gu, Pohang, Gyeong Puk, Korea (South)
Tel.: (82) 54 271 0520
Fax: (82) 54 271 0700
Web Site: www.dongkuksnc.co.kr
Emp.: 9
Electric Power Generation Services
S.I.C.: 4931
N.A.I.C.S.: 221118

DONGKUK STEEL MILL CO., LTD.

Chungu Suhatong 66
Ferrem Tower, Seoul, 100-210, Korea (South)
Tel.: (82) 23171114
Fax: (82) 23171391
Web Site: www.dongkuk.co.kr
Year Founded: 1954
001230—(KRS)
Sales Range: $1-4.9 Billion
Emp.: 1,754

Business Description:
Steel Producer
S.I.C.: 3312
N.A.I.C.S.: 331110

Personnel:
Sae-joo Chang *(Chm & CEO)*
Young Chul Kim *(Pres)*
Ja Hong Park *(Mng Dir)*

Subsidiary:

DK UNC Co., Ltd. (1)
913 Hanshin IT Tower 235 Guro-dong
Guro-gu, Seoul, 152-848, Korea (South)
Tel.: (82) 221088787
Fax: (82) 37898790
Web Site: www.dkunc.co.kr
Emp.: 500
Information Technology Consulting Services
S.I.C.: 7373
N.A.I.C.S.: 541512
Jeong Nam-Gyun *(CEO)*

Units:

Dongkuk Steel Mill Co., Ltd. - Busan Works (1)
370-97 Shinpyeong-dong Saha-gu
Busan, 604-836, Korea (South)
Tel.: (82) 51 294 2133
Fax: (82) 51 220 3010
Steel Products Mfr
S.I.C.: 3399
N.A.I.C.S.: 331110

Dongkuk Steel Mill Co., Ltd. - Dangjin Works (1)
400 Hanjin-ri Songak-myeon
Dangjin, Chungnam, 343-823, Korea (South)
Tel.: (82) 41 351 4984
Fax: (82) 41 351 4691
Web Site: www.dongkuk.co.kr/eng/customer/biz_network.asp#t3
Steel Product Mfr
S.I.C.: 3312
N.A.I.C.S.: 331110

Dongkuk Steel Mill Co., Ltd. - Incheon Works (1)
1 Songhyeon-dong Dong-gu
Incheon, 401-712, Korea (South)
Tel.: (82) 328306216
Fax: (82) 328306902
Web Site: www.dongkuk.com
Emp.: 500
Steel Products Mfr
S.I.C.: 3312
N.A.I.C.S.: 331110
Dooho Kim *(Mgr)*

Dongkuk Steel Mill Co., Ltd. - Pohang Works (1)
880 Songdong-ru Daesong-myeon
Namgu, Pohang, Gyeongsangbuk-do, 790-841, Korea (South)
Tel.: (82) 542786111
Fax: (82) 542715314
Emp.: 1,000
Steel Products Mfr
S.I.C.: 3399
N.A.I.C.S.: 331110
Junghwan Shin *(Mgr-Factory)*

U.S. Subsidiaries:

Branson Machinery LLC (1)
2100 Cedartown Hwy SW
Rome, GA 30161-9565
Tel.: (706) 290-2500
Fax: (877) 734-0637
Web Site: www.bransontractor.com
Emp.: 20
Industrial Machinery Distr
S.I.C.: 5084
N.A.I.C.S.: 423830
Ted Kim *(Pres)*

Dongkuk International, Inc. (1)
19750 Magellan Dr
Torrance, CA 90502 (100%)
Tel.: (310) 523-9595
Fax: (310) 523-9599
E-Mail: info@dongkuk.com
Web Site: www.dongkuk.com
Emp.: 70
Steel Products Mfr
S.I.C.: 3312
N.A.I.C.S.: 331110
Yung Il Mun *(Pres)*

Non-U.S. Subsidiaries:

DK UIL(Tianjin) Electronics Co., Ltd (1)
No 18 Xin Yuan Dao Xiqing Economic Development Area
Tianjin, 300400, China
Tel.: (86) 2283968735
Fax: (86) 22 8396 8737
Steel Products Mfr
S.I.C.: 3312
N.A.I.C.S.: 331110

Dongkuk Corporation (1)
7-6 Nihonbashi Kayaba-cho 2-chome
Chuo-ku, Tokyo, 103-0025, Japan
Tel.: (81) 3 5623 5723
Fax: (81) 3 5623 5722
Structured Steel Products Mfr
S.I.C.: 3312
N.A.I.C.S.: 331110

DONGNAM CHEMICAL CO., LTD.

Cheongcheon-dong 385-1
Bupyeong-gu, Incheon, Korea (South)
Tel.: (82) 32 450 3700
Fax: (82) 32 525 0104
Web Site: www.dongnamchem.com
Year Founded: 1965
023450—(KRS)

Business Description:
Agricultural Chemical Mfr
S.I.C.: 2899
N.A.I.C.S.: 325998

Personnel:
Jang Hoon Rhee *(CEO)*

DONGNAM MARINE CRANE CO., LTD

1196 Myeongdong-ri Hanrim-myeon
Kimhae, South Gyeongsang, Korea (South)
Tel.: (82) 55 720 3000
Fax: (82) 55 720 3019
E-Mail: dongnam@dongnam-crane.co.kr
Web Site: www.dongnam-crane.co.kr
Year Founded: 1988
101000—(KRS)
Emp.: 135

Business Description:
Marine Crane Mfr
S.I.C.: 3536
N.A.I.C.S.: 333923

Personnel:
Eui Youl Lee *(CEO)*

DONGSHENG PHARMACEUTICAL INTERNATIONAL CO., LTD.

China Bing'qi Plaza Floor 17 No 69
Zi Zhu Yuan Road
Haidian District, Beijing, China
Tel.: (86) 10 8858 0708
Year Founded: 2008
DNGH—(OTC)
Sales Range: $10-24.9 Million
Emp.: 69

Business Description:
Pharmaceutical Mfr
S.I.C.: 2834
N.A.I.C.S.: 325412

Personnel:
Xiaodong Zhu *(Chm, Pres & CEO)*
Di Wu *(Chief Dev Officer)*

Board of Directors:
Xiaodong Zhu
Jie Du

Transfer Agent:
American Registrar & Transfer Co.
342 E 900 S
Salt Lake City, UT 84111

DONGSUNG CHEMICAL CO., LTD.

472 Sinpyeong-Dong
Saha-gu, Busan, Korea (South)
Tel.: (82) 51 604 1147
Fax: (82) 51 201 3050
Web Site: www.dschem.co.kr
Year Founded: 1959
005190—(KRS)
Sales Range: $75-99.9 Million

Business Description:
Plastic Adhesive Mfr
S.I.C.: 2821
N.A.I.C.S.: 325211

Personnel:
Heung-Sik Bae *(Mgr-Tech-PU Shoes, Elastomer, NEOSOLE, Paints & Toner)*

DONGSUNG HIGHCHEM CO., LTD.

135 283 9F Shinan Bldg 943 19
Daechi Gangnam
Seoul, Korea (South)
Tel.: (82) 234504200
Fax: (82) 25535922
Web Site: www.dshighchem.com
13450—(KRS)
Sales Range: $150-199.9 Million

Business Description:
Chemicals Mfr
S.I.C.: 2869
N.A.I.C.S.: 325199

Personnel:
S. M. Yang *(CEO)*

DONGSUNG NSC COMPANY LTD.

472 Shinpyung Dongo
Saha Ku, Pusan, 604-030, Korea (South)
Tel.: (82) 512004800
Fax: (82) 512935047
Web Site: www.dongsungnsc.com
Emp.: 100

Business Description:
Adhesives Mfr.
S.I.C.: 2891
N.A.I.C.S.: 325520

Personnel:
Jae Cho *(Pres & CEO)*

Non-U.S. Subsidiary:

Dongsung NSC Vietnam Company Ltd. **(1)**
No 7 9A St Bien Hoa II Industrial Zones
Bien Hoa, Dong Nai, Vietnam
Tel.: (84) 61835461
Fax: (84) 61835463
Emp.: 68
Adhesives Mfr.
S.I.C.: 2891
N.A.I.C.S.: 325520

DONGWHA HOLDINGS CO., LTD.

26-3 Yeouido-dong
Yeongdeungpo-gu, Seoul, Korea (South)
Tel.: (82) 2 2122 0680
Fax: (82) 2 784 8829
Web Site: www.dongwha.co.kr
Year Founded: 1948
025900—(KRS)

Business Description:
Investment Management Services
S.I.C.: 6211
N.A.I.C.S.: 523999

Personnel:
Myung-ho Seung *(CEO)*

DONGWON ENTERPRISE CO., LTD.

275 Yangjae Dong
Seocho Gu, Seoul, Korea (South)
Tel.: (82) 25893032
Fax: (82) 25893292
Web Site: www.dongwon.com
Sales Range: $1-4.9 Billion
Emp.: 10,000
Fiscal Year-end: 12/31/12

Business Description:
Holding Company
S.I.C.: 6719
N.A.I.C.S.: 551112

Personnel:
J.C. Kim *(Chm)*

Subsidiaries:

Dongwon F&B Co., Ltd. **(1)**
275 Yangjae-dong
Seocho-gu, Seoul, 137-717, Korea (South) Ks (45%)
Tel.: (82) 25893000
Fax: (82) 25893190
Web Site: www.dw.co.kr
049770—(KRS)
Sales Range: $450-499.9 Million
Emp.: 1,800
Processed Foods Mfr & Distr
S.I.C.: 5146
N.A.I.C.S.: 424460
Hae Gwan Kim *(Pres & CEO)*

U.S. Subsidiary:

StarKist Foods Inc. **(2)**
323 North Shore Dr Ste 600
Pittsburgh, PA 15212
Tel.: (412) 222-2200
Fax: (412) 222-4050
Toll Free: (800) 732-8812
Web Site: www.starkist.com
Sales Range: $550-599.9 Million
Emp.: 5,000
Tuna, Sardines, Mackerel, Canned Cat Foods, Dry Cat Food, Soft Moist Cat Food, Dry Dog Food, Dog Snacks Mfr
S.I.C.: 2092
N.A.I.C.S.: 311710

Dongwon Industries Co., Ltd. **(1)**
275 Yangjae-Dong
Seocho-Gu, Seoul, 137-717, Korea (South) Ks
Tel.: (82) 25893455
Fax: (82) 2 589 3286
Web Site: www.dwml.co.kr
006040—(KRS)
Sales Range: $250-299.9 Million
Emp.: 771
Catching, Processing, Transporting & Distributing of Marine Products, Including Mackerel & Tuna
S.I.C.: 0919
N.A.I.C.S.: 114119
Jae Chul Kim *(Chm)*
Bu Yin Park *(CEO)*
Jin Geun Hong *(Asst Mng Dir)*
Sang Seon Lee *(Asst Mng Dir)*
Jong Gu Lee *(Mng Dir)*

DONGWON METAL CO., LTD.

330-1 Yanggi-ri Jilyang-eup
Gyeongsan, Gyongbuk, Korea (South)
Tel.: (82) 538592311
Fax: (82) 538532319
Web Site: www.dwmic.co.kr
Year Founded: 1971
018500—(KRS)

Business Description:
Automotive Parts Mfr & Sales
S.I.C.: 3711
N.A.I.C.S.: 336111

Personnel:
Eun-woo Lee *(CEO)*

Subsidiary:

DAK Co., Ltd **(1)**
644-7 Jang bang-ri Hal lim-myun
Kimhae, Gyeong Nam, Korea (South)
Tel.: (82) 55 343 9883
Fax: (82) 55 343 9884
Automotive Exterior Parts Mfr
S.I.C.: 3714
N.A.I.C.S.: 336390

Plants:

Dongwon Metal Co., Ltd. - ASAN PLANT **(1)**
12-6 So dong-ri Eum bong-myun
336864 Asan, Chung Nam, Korea (South)
Tel.: (82) 41 530 3100
Fax: (82) 41 530 3180
Emp.: 50
Automotive Exterior Parts Mfr
S.I.C.: 3714
N.A.I.C.S.: 336390
Eun-Woo Lee *(CEO)*

Dongwon Metal Co., Ltd. - KYUNGSAN PLANT **(1)**
330-1 Yang gi-ri Jil yang-eup
Gyeongsan, Gyong buk, 712835, Korea (South)
Tel.: (82) 53 859 2311
Fax: (82) 53 859 2319
Emp.: 500
Automotive Exterior Parts Mfr
S.I.C.: 3714
N.A.I.C.S.: 336390
Jung-Deok Seo *(Mng Dir)*

U.S. Subsidiary:

Dongwon Autopart Technology Alabama L.L.C **(1)**
12970 Montgomery Hwy
Luverne, AL 36049
Tel.: (334) 537-5000
Fax: (334) 537-9300
Web Site: www.dwautoal.com
Automotive Parts Mfr
S.I.C.: 3714
N.A.I.C.S.: 336390
Charlie Kim *(Pres)*

DONGWU CEMENT INTERNATIONAL LIMITED

Unit 8505B-06A Level 85
International Commerce Centre
1 Austin Road West, Kowloon, China (Hong Kong)
Tel.: (852) 25200978
Fax: (852) 25200696
E-Mail: admin@dongwucement.com
Web Site: www.dongwucement.com
Year Founded: 2011
0695—(HKG)
Rev.: $51,009,594
Assets: $65,622,206
Liabilities: $15,912,005
Net Worth: $49,710,201
Earnings: $164,886
Emp.: 258
Fiscal Year-end: 12/31/12

Business Description:
Investment Management Services
S.I.C.: 6282
N.A.I.C.S.: 523920

Personnel:
Yingxia Xie *(Chm)*
Chungen Jin *(CEO)*
Qiwei Zhu *(CFO)*
Keith Chin Wang Chan *(Co-Sec)*
Xin Sun *(Co-Sec)*

Board of Directors:
Yingxia Xie
Guoqi Cao
Kuangyu Cao
Chungen Jin
Thomas Ho Yiu Lee
Hok Ming Tseung
Bin Yang

Legal Counsel:
Li & Partners
22/F World-Wide House
Central, China (Hong Kong)

Deheng Law Offices
11/F Block B Allianz Building 4018 Gold Fields Road
Futian District, Shenzhen, China

Conyers Dill & Pearman (Cayman) Limited
Cricket Square Hutchins Drive PO Box 2681
Georgetown, Cayman Islands

DONGYANG ENGINEERING & CONSTRUCTION CORP.

Lexus NT bldg 1009 Daechi-dong
Gangnam-gu, Seoul, 135-080, Korea (South)
Tel.: (82) 2 3420 8000
Fax: (82) 2 553 1051
Web Site: www.dongyangex.co.kr
Year Founded: 1968
005900—(KRS)
Sales Range: $1-9.9 Million

Business Description:
Construction Services
S.I.C.: 1542
N.A.I.C.S.: 236220

Personnel:
Kil-jae Lee *(CEO)*

DONGYANG GANGCHUL CO., LTD

275-2 Daehwa-dong
Daedeuk-gu, Daejeon, Korea (South)
Tel.: (82) 42 605 8200
Fax: (82) 42 622 9967
Web Site: www.alusash.co.kr
Year Founded: 1956
001780—(KRS)

Business Description:
Aluminum Product Mfr
S.I.C.: 3353
N.A.I.C.S.: 331315

Personnel:
Do Bong Park *(Chm)*

DONGYANG MECHATRONICS

185-090 Haeam-Building 407
Nambusunhwan-ro
Yangcheon-gu, Seoul, Korea (South)
Tel.: (82) 2 2600 4300
Fax: (82) 2 2607 0220
Web Site: www.dy.co.kr
Year Founded: 1978
013570—(KRS)
Sales Range: $650-699.9 Million

Business Description:
Crane Mfr
S.I.C.: 3536
N.A.I.C.S.: 333923

Personnel:
Byeong Ho Cho *(Chm & CEO)*

DONGYUE GROUP LIMITED

Dongyue International Fluoro Silicone Material Industry Park
Zibo, Shandong, China
Tel.: (86) 53 3851 0072
Fax: (86) 53 3852 0204
Web Site: www.dongyuechem.com
Year Founded: 2006
4D3—(DEU OTC)
Rev.: $1,120,023,075
Assets: $1,394,383,553
Liabilities: $564,097,159
Net Worth: $830,286,393
Earnings: $112,316,958
Emp.: 5,887
Fiscal Year-end: 12/31/12

Business Description:
Chemical Products Mfr
S.I.C.: 2899
N.A.I.C.S.: 325998

Personnel:
Jianhong Zhang *(Chm & CEO)*
Chuanqi Liu *(Pres)*
Guangsheng Zhou *(Deputy Pres)*
Tongzheng Cui *(CFO & VP)*
Kwok Choi Ng *(Sec)*

Board of Directors:
Jianhong Zhang
Tongzheng Cui
Kwan Fu
Chuanqi Liu
Yi Liu
Stephen Leung Huel Ting
Jianhua Yan
Run Dong Yue
Jian Zhang

Royal Bank of Canada Trust Company (Cayman) Limited
4th Floor Royal Bank House 24 Shedden Road
Georgetown, Cayman Islands

Transfer Agents:
Tricor Investor Services Limited
26th Floor Tesbury Centre 28 Queens Road East
Wanchai, China (Hong Kong)

Royal Bank of Canada Trust Company (Cayman) Limited
4th Floor Royal Bank House 24 Shedden Road
Georgetown, Cayman Islands

Subsidiaries:

Shandong Dongyue Chemical Co., Ltd. **(1)**
Dongyue international fluorine silicon material industry zone
Zibo, Shandong, China
Tel.: (86) 533 8220867
E-Mail: info@dongyuechem.com
Fluoride Product Mfr
S.I.C.: 2819
N.A.I.C.S.: 325180

Shandong Dongyue Polymer Material Co., Ltd **(1)**
8th floor Industrial & Commerical Bank Building Xinghuan street
Zibo, 256400, China
Tel.: (86) 53 3822 2259
Fax: (86) 53 3822 0509
Emp.: 100
Fluorpolymer Product Mfr
S.I.C.: 2899
N.A.I.C.S.: 325998

Zibo Dongyue Lvyuan Co., Ltd. **(1)**
Fluorine and Silicon Industry Park
Tangshan, Zibo, Huantai, 256400, China
Tel.: (86) 53 3852 0361
Liquid Chlorine & Alkali Mfr & Whslr
S.I.C.: 2819
N.A.I.C.S.: 325180

DONMAR CAR SALES LTD

(d/b/a Sundance Mazda)
17990 102 Ave Nw
Edmonton, AB, T5S 1M9, Canada
Tel.: (780) 454-0422
Fax: (780) 451-0346
Toll Free: (877) 777-2659
E-Mail: Reception@SundanceMazda.com
Web Site: www.sundancemazda.com
Year Founded: 1975
Rev.: $16,550,000
Emp.: 25
Business Description:
New & Used Car Dealers
S.I.C.: 5511
N.A.I.C.S.: 441110
Personnel:
Brad Miller *(Gen Mgr)*

DONNER METALS LTD.

Suite 2480 1055 West Georgia Street
Vancouver, BC, V6E 0B6, Canada
Tel.: (604) 683-0564
Fax: (604) 602-9311
Toll Free: (800) 909-8311
E-Mail: donner@bed-rock.com
Web Site: www.donnermetals.com
Year Founded: 2005
DON—(DEU OTC TSXV)
Int. Income: $135,434
Assets: $63,047,298
Liabilities: $38,860,331
Net Worth: $24,186,967
Earnings: ($5,189,591)
Fiscal Year-end: 02/28/13
Business Description:
Zinc, Copper & Nickel Mining Services
S.I.C.: 1031
N.A.I.C.S.: 212231
Personnel:
David Patterson *(Chm)*
Normand Champigny *(Pres & CFO)*
Harvey Keats *(CEO)*
Board of Directors:
David Patterson
Harvey Keats
Laurie W. Sadler
Kerry Sparkes
Kenneth R. Thorsen

DONNYBROOK ENERGY INC.

5704 Balsam Street Suite 300
Vancouver, BC, V6M 4B9, Canada
Mailing Address:
700-717 7th Avenue SW
Calgary, AB, T2P 0Z3, Canada
Tel.: (604) 684-2356
Fax: (604) 684-4265
E-Mail: info@donnybrookenergy.ca
Web Site: www.donnybrookenergy.ca
DEI—(TSXV)
Rev.: $2,273,266
Assets: $29,117,824
Liabilities: $2,243,809
Net Worth: $26,874,015
Earnings: ($7,413,783)
Emp.: 5
Fiscal Year-end: 12/31/12
Business Description:
Oil & Natural Gas Exploration & Production
S.I.C.: 1311
N.A.I.C.S.: 211111
Personnel:
David Patterson *(Chm)*
Malcolm Todd *(Pres & CEO)*
Robert Todd *(CFO)*
Murray Scalf *(COO)*
Board of Directors:
David Patterson
Randy Kwasnicia
Murray Scalf
Kenneth Munro Stephenson
Malcolm Todd
Colin Watt
Transfer Agent:
Computershare Trust Company of Canada
Vancouver, BC, Canada
Tel.: (604) 661-9400
Fax: (604) 669-1548

DONNYCREEK ENERGY INC.

Suite 300 5704 Balsam Street
Vancouver, BC, V6M 4B9, Canada
Tel.: (604) 684-2356
Fax: (604) 684-4265
E-Mail: info@donnybrookenergy.ca
Web Site: www.donnycreekenergy.com
Year Founded: 2011
DCK—(OTC TSXV)
Business Description:
Oil & Gas Exploration
S.I.C.: 1311
N.A.I.C.S.: 211111
Personnel:
Malcolm F.W. Todd *(CEO)*
John Marsh *(COO)*
Murray Scalf *(Exec VP)*

DON'S PHOTO SHOP LTD.

1839 Main Street
Winnipeg, MB, R2V 2A4, Canada
Tel.: (204) 942-8335
Fax: (204) 956-0289
Toll Free: (800) 561-6403
E-Mail: sales@donsphoto.ca
Web Site: www.donsphoto.com
Year Founded: 1979
Rev.: $12,811,200
Emp.: 120
Business Description:
Camera & Accessories Supplier
S.I.C.: 5734
N.A.I.C.S.: 443142
Personnel:
Don Godfrey *(Pres)*
Mike Godfrey *(COO)*

DONWAY FORD SALES LTD.

1975 Eglinton Avenue East
Scarborough, ON, M1L 2N1, Canada
Tel.: (416) 751-2200
Fax: (416) 751-9301
Toll Free: (888) 214-8377
E-Mail: reception@donwayford.com
Web Site: www.donwayford.com
Rev.: $44,086,090
Emp.: 90
Business Description:
New & Used Car Dealers
S.I.C.: 5511
N.A.I.C.S.: 441110
Personnel:
Kim Williams *(Dir-Sls)*

DOOSAN CORPORATION

Doosan Tower 18-12 6th Street Euljiro
Jung-gu, 100 730 Seoul, Korea (South)
Tel.: (82) 233980114
Fax: (82) 233985188
E-Mail: press@doosan.com
Web Site: www.doosan.com
Year Founded: 1896
000150—(KRS)
Sls.: $3,565,456,323
Assets: $5,534,123,794
Liabilities: $2,555,254,687
Net Worth: $2,978,869,107
Earnings: $102,116,842
Emp.: 42,000
Fiscal Year-end: 12/31/12
Business Description:
Holding Company
S.I.C.: 6719
N.A.I.C.S.: 551112
Personnel:
Jeong won Park *(Chm)*
Geewon Park *(Vice Chm & COO)*
James B. Bemowski *(Vice Chm)*
Jae Kyung Lee *(Vice Chm)*
Board of Directors:
Jeong won Park
Kim Chang-hwan
Song Gwang-su
Junki Kim
Jae Kyung Lee
Ic-hyun Nam
Yongmann Park
Daewon Seo
Hi-Taek Shin

Subsidiaries:

Doosan Dong-A Co., Ltd. **(1)**
Yonkang Bldg 270 Yeon-ji-dong
Jongno-gu, Seoul, Korea (South)
Tel.: (82) 2 3670 5000
Fax: (82) 2 3670 5002
Online Education Services
S.I.C.: 8299
N.A.I.C.S.: 611710

Doosan DST Co., Ltd. **(1)**
Changwondaero 1144-gil 33 Sungju-dong
Sungsan-gu, Changwon, Gyeongsangnam-do, Korea (South)
Tel.: (82) 55 280 6114
Fax: (82) 55 280 6118
Web Site: www.doosandst.com
Industrial Defense Services
S.I.C.: 7389
N.A.I.C.S.: 561499
Hang Seok Um *(CEO)*

Doosan Feed & Livestock Corporation **(1)**
15-6 Samjeong-dong
Ojeong-gu, Bucheon, Gyeonggi-do, Korea (South)
Tel.: (82) 326803114
Fax: (82) 326810104
E-Mail: kwangtaek@doosan.com
Web Site: www.doosanfeed.com
Emp.: 100
Livestock Feeds Mfr
S.I.C.: 2048
N.A.I.C.S.: 311119
Joen Yunk Yung *(Sec)*

Doosan Heavy Industries & Construction Co., Ltd. **(1)**
555 Guygok Dong
Changwon, Gyeongsangnam, 641792, Korea (South) (100%)
Tel.: (82) 552786114
Fax: (82) 552645551
Web Site: www.doosanheavy.com
Sls.: $1,983,000,064
Emp.: 5,000
Thermal Power, Hydro Power, Nuclear Power, Iron & Steel & Chemical Plants; Civil Engineering & Construction; Diesel Engines; Castings & Forgings; Cement Plants; Material Handling Facilities & Desalination Plants Mfr
S.I.C.: 1623
N.A.I.C.S.: 237120
Yong Sung Park *(Chm)*
J. Taik Chung *(Vice Chm & Co-Pres)*
Geewon Park *(Co-Pres & CEO)*

Subsidiary:

Doosan Engine Co., Ltd. **(2)**
69-3 Shinchon-dong Seongsan-gu
Changwon-si Gyeongsangnam-do
Seoul, 642-370, Korea (South) (100%)
Tel.: (82) 552606000
Fax: (82) 552832233
E-Mail: info@doosanengine.com
Web Site: ww.doosan.com
082740—(KRS)
Sls.: $1,282,263,385
Assets: $1,661,168,594
Liabilities: $965,741,143
Net Worth: $695,427,451
Earnings: $177,052,989
Emp.: 1,200
Fiscal Year-end: 12/31/12
Marine Diesel Engines Mfr
S.I.C.: 3519
N.A.I.C.S.: 333618
Dong-chul Kim *(CEO)*
Nam-suk Cho *(CFO)*

U.S. Subsidiary:

HFControls **(2)**
1624 W Crosby Ste 124
Carrollton, TX 75006
Tel.: (469) 568-6500
Fax: (469) 568-6599
Toll Free: (866) 501-9954
Web Site: www.hfcontrols.com
Emp.: 70
Mfr. of High-Quality Control Systems for Power Plants & Industrial Plants
S.I.C.: 3491
N.A.I.C.S.: 332911

Non-U.S. Subsidiaries:

Doosan Babcock Energy Limited **(2)**
Doosan House Crawely Busniess Quarter
Crawley, W Sussex, RH10 9AD, United Kingdom
Tel.: (44) 1293612888
Fax: (44) 1293584321
E-Mail: jlucasr@doosanbabcock.com
Web Site: www.doosanbabcock.com
Sales Range: $750-799.9 Million
Emp.: 4,000
Thermal Power, Nuclear, Petrochemical, Oil & Gas & Pharmaceutical Industries Energy Services
S.I.C.: 8999
N.A.I.C.S.: 541690
G. W. Park *(Chm)*
Iain Miller *(CEO)*

Co-Headquarters:

Doosan Babcock Energy Limited **(3)**
Porterfield Road
Renfrew, PA4 8DJ, United Kingdom UK
Tel.: (44) 1418864141
Telex: 779027 BABRES G
Fax: (44) 1418853338
Web Site: www.doosanbabcock.com
Engineering Services
S.I.C.: 8711
N.A.I.C.S.: 541330

Doosan Vina Haiphong Co., Ltd. **(2)**
Km 92 No 5 Highway So Dau Ward
Hong Bang District, Haiphong, Vietnam
Tel.: (84) 313712705
Fax: (84) 31 3712714
E-Mail: hoa.damthivu@doosan.com
Web Site: www.hanvico.com
Sales Range: $10-24.9 Million
Emp.: 450
Specialists in Oversized & Overweighted Steel Structures, Boilers, Pressure Vessels, Storage Tanks, Steel Fabrication & Piping Works

Doosan Corporation—(Continued)

S.I.C.: 3559
N.A.I.C.S.: 332410
Hyokil Choi *(Gen Dir)*

Doosan Industrial Development Co., Ltd. (1)
105-7 Nonhyeon-dong Gangnam-gu
Seoul, Korea (South)
Tel.: (82) 25103114
Fax: (82) 25405221
Web Site: www.hdkid.com
Emp.: 890
Construction Services
S.I.C.: 1629
N.A.I.C.S.: 236210

Doosan Infracore Co., Ltd. (1)
27/F Doosan Tower 18 12 Euljiro 6Ga Jung Gu
Seoul, 100-730, Korea (South)
Tel.: (82) 233988114
Fax: (82) 233988117
Web Site: www.doosaninfracore.co.kr
042670—(KRS)
Sls.: $7,587,266,393
Assets: $10,744,141,780
Liabilities: $7,957,199,128
Net Worth: $2,786,942,652
Earnings: $375,738,577
Fiscal Year-end: 12/31/12
Construction Machinery Mfr
S.I.C.: 3531
N.A.I.C.S.: 333120
Jeongwon Park *(Co-Chm)*
Yongmaan Park *(Co-Chm)*
Yongsung Kim *(Co-Pres & CEO)*
Anthony C. Helsham *(Co-Pres)*

U.S. Subsidiaries:

Doosan Infracore America Corporation (2)
2905 Shawnee Industrial Way
Suwanee, GA 30024 NY
Tel.: (770) 831-2200
Web Site: usa.doosaninfracore.co.kr
Construction Equipment Mfr
S.I.C.: 3531
N.A.I.C.S.: 333120
J. Y. Lee *(Pres & COO-Machine Tool Div)*
Stephen Yeongsu Yoon *(CFO)*

Subsidiary:

Bobcat Company (3)
250 E Beaton Dr PO Box 6000
West Fargo, ND 58078-6000
Tel.: (701) 241-8700
Fax: (701) 241-8704
Web Site: www.bobcat.com
Sales Range: $1-4.9 Billion
Farm & Industrial Equipment Mfr
S.I.C.: 3523
N.A.I.C.S.: 333111
Scott R. Nelson *(Pres)*

Non-U.S. Subsidiaries:

Doosan Infracore Belgium S.A (2)
Europark 36A 9100
9100 Saint-Nicolas, Belgium
Tel.: (32) 3 760 0987
Fax: (32) 3 760 0989
Forklift Mfr
S.I.C.: 3537
N.A.I.C.S.: 333924
Martin Knoetgen *(Pres-EMEA)*

Doosan Infracore Germany GmbH (2)
Hans-Boeckler-Strasse 27-29
40764 Langenfeld, Germany
Tel.: (49) 2173 85090
Fax: (49) 2173 850970
Industrial Machinery Mfr
S.I.C.: 3559
N.A.I.C.S.: 333249
Jaejin Ju *(Pres)*

Doosan Infracore India Private Co., Ltd. (2)
No 67 3RD Floor Tnpl Building
Guindy, Chennai, 600032, India
Tel.: (91) 42223900
Fax: (91) 4442223905
Construction Equipment Mfr
S.I.C.: 3531
N.A.I.C.S.: 333120

Doosan Infracore Japan Corp. (2)
2402 Mita Kokusai Bldg 1-4-28 Mita
Minato-Ku, Tokyo, 108-0073, Japan
Tel.: (81) 3 5730 9011
Construction Machinery Mfr
S.I.C.: 3531
N.A.I.C.S.: 333120

Doosan Infracore Norway A.S (2)
Varhol
6440 Elnesvagen, More og Romsdal, Norway
Tel.: (47) 71 26 85 00
Fax: (47) 71 26 85 50
Emp.: 150
Construction Equipment Mfr
S.I.C.: 3531
N.A.I.C.S.: 333120
Stefan Brosick *(Gen Mgr)*

Doosan Infracore U.K. Ltd. (2)
Unit 6 3 Natgarw Park
Cardiff, CF15 7QU, United Kingdom
Tel.: (44) 1443 842273
Fax: (44) 1443 841933
Emp.: 25
Construction Equipment Whslr
S.I.C.: 5082
N.A.I.C.S.: 423810
Kevin Zimmer *(Gen Mgr)*

Doosan Infracore XinJiang Machinery Co., Ltd. (2)
No 178 Hetanbei Road
Wurumuqi, Xinjiang, China
Tel.: (86) 9914697217
Fax: (86) 9914698641
Forklift Mfr
S.I.C.: 3537
N.A.I.C.S.: 333924

Geith International Ltd (2)
Geith Works Grangegeith Slane
Meath, Ireland
Tel.: (353) 419824143
Fax: (353) 419824478
E-Mail: info@geith.com
Web Site: www.geith.com
Sales Range: $50-74.9 Million
Emp.: 140
Construction & Excavation Attachment Mfr
S.I.C.: 3531
N.A.I.C.S.: 333120
Gustavo Otero *(Mng Dir)*

U.S. Subsidiary:

Geith Inc. (3)
1293 Glenway Dr
Statesville, NC 28625
Tel.: (866) 472-4373
Fax: (866) 472-4950
Toll Free: (800) 762-4090
E-Mail: ussales@geith.com
Web Site: www.geith.com
Heavy Equipment Attachment Mfr
S.I.C.: 3531
N.A.I.C.S.: 333120
Joe Forth *(Gen Mgr)*

Non-U.S. Subsidiaries:

Agent Commercial France de Geith International Ltd. (3)
11 Rue Champ Lyon
69800 Saint Priest, Dolin, France
Tel.: (33) 800916626
Fax: (33) 472793269
E-Mail: frsales@geith.com
Web Site: www.geith.com
Heavy Equipment Attachment Mfr
S.I.C.: 3531
N.A.I.C.S.: 333120

Geith International Ltd. (3)
Unit 6 3 Heol Y Gamlas
Parc Nantgarw, Cardiff, CF15 7QU, United Kingdom
Tel.: (44) 1443845666
Fax: (44) 1443844192
E-Mail: uksales@geith.com
Web Site: www.geith.com
Emp.: 4
Heavy Equipment Attachment Mfr
S.I.C.: 3531
N.A.I.C.S.: 333120
Robert Welsh *(Mgr-Sls)*

Global Parts, S.r.l (3)
Via Lamarmora 12
Livorno, Italy
Tel.: (39) 586 903076
Fax: (39) 586 903076
E-Mail: info@globalparts.it
Web Site: www.globalparts.it
Construction & Excavation Attachment Mfr
S.I.C.: 3531
N.A.I.C.S.: 333120

Doosan Magazine (1)
Doosan Bldg 105-7 Nonhyeon-dong
Gangnam-gu, Seoul, Korea (South)
Tel.: (82) 25104500
Fax: (82) 25104501
E-Mail: jcsinwlk@doosan.com
Emp.: 150
Magazine Advertising Services
S.I.C.: 7313
N.A.I.C.S.: 541840
Jaechur Seung *(VP)*

Doosan Mecatec Co., Ltd. (1)
64 Sinchon-dong
Changwon, Gyeongsangnam-do, Korea (South)
Tel.: (82) 552795555
Fax: (82) 552795777
Web Site: www.doosanmecatec.com
Emp.: 1,000
Industrial Equipment Mfr
S.I.C.: 7699
N.A.I.C.S.: 811310
Young Sik Kim *(CEO)*
Youngho Yoon *(CFO)*

Doosan Motors Corporation (1)
72 Cheongdam-dong
Gangnam-gu, Seoul, Korea (South)
Tel.: (82) 54117962
Fax: (82) 25113632
Web Site: www.doosanhonda.co.kr
Car Sales & Services
S.I.C.: 5511
N.A.I.C.S.: 441110

Doosan Mottrol Co., Ltd. (1)
456-3 Nae-dong
Changwon, Gyeongsangnamdo, 641-050, Korea (South)
Tel.: (82) 552695114
Fax: (82) 552695222
Web Site: www.doosanmottrol.com
Emp.: 500
Hydraulic & Defense Components Mfr
S.I.C.: 3795
N.A.I.C.S.: 336992
Bang Shin Kim *(CEO)*

Doosan Tower Corporation (1)
Doosan Tower 18-12 Euljiro 6-ga
Jung-gu, Seoul, 100-730, Korea (South)
Tel.: (82) 233982386
Fax: (82) 233983028
Web Site: www.doosan.com
Emp.: 1,000
Apparel Designing Services
S.I.C.: 2389
N.A.I.C.S.: 315240
Seong-Beom Lee *(CEO)*

Neoplux Co., Ltd. (1)
Doosan Tower 15th Floor Jangchungdanro 275
Seoul, 100-730, Korea (South)
Tel.: (82) 233981070
Fax: (82) 233981071
Web Site: www.neoplux.co.kr
Investment Management Services
S.I.C.: 6211
N.A.I.C.S.: 523999
Gap Lee Jong *(CEO)*
Ji Pyo Hong *(Mng Dir)*

SRS Korea Co., Ltd. (1)
Yonkang Bldg 270 Yeonji-dong
Jongno-gu, Seoul, 110739, Korea (South)
Tel.: (82) 236708323
Fax: (82) 236708399
E-Mail: eunjung.moon@doosan.com
Web Site: www.srs-korea.com
Restaurant Management Services
S.I.C.: 8748
N.A.I.C.S.: 541618

Plants:

Doosan Corporation - Iksan factory (1)
889 Palbong-dong
Iksan, Jeonbuk, Korea (South)
Tel.: (82) 63 830 8320
Fax: (82) 63 835 5204
Electronic Products Mfr
S.I.C.: 3679
N.A.I.C.S.: 334419

Doosan Corporation - Jeungpyeong Factory (1)
661 Yonggang-ri
Jeungpyeong, Chungbuk, Korea (South)
Tel.: (82) 43 820 8220
Fax: (82) 43 820 8300
Web Site: www.doosan.com
Photovoltaic Device Mfr
S.I.C.: 3674
N.A.I.C.S.: 334413

U.S. Subsidiaries:

Doosan Hydro Technology, Inc. (1)
912 Chad Ln
Tampa, FL 33619
Tel.: (813) 549-0182
Fax: (813) 623-6666
Web Site: www.doosanhydro.com
Waste Water Treatment Services
S.I.C.: 4941
N.A.I.C.S.: 221310
Keun Roh Hyung *(Dir-R&D Center)*

HFC Controls. Corp. (1)
1624 W Crosby Rd Suite 124
Carrollton, TX 75006
Tel.: (469) 568-6500
Fax: (469) 568-6599
Web Site: www.hfcontrols.com
Electronic Component Mfr
S.I.C.: 3679
N.A.I.C.S.: 334419

Non-U.S. Subsidiaries:

Doosan Advertising Company (1)
19th Fl Tower B Gateway No 18 Xiaguangli N Rd E Third Ring
Chaoyang Dist, Beijing, 100027, China
Tel.: (86) 1084547185
Fax: (86) 1084547190
Advertising Services
S.I.C.: 7311
N.A.I.C.S.: 541810

Doosan China Financial Leasing Corp. (1)
20/F Tower B Gateway No 18 Xiaguangli
North Road East Third Ring
Chaoyang District, Beijing, 100027, China
Tel.: (86) 10 8454 7200
Fax: (86) 10 8454 7102
Web Site: www.doosan.com
Financial Leasing Services
S.I.C.: 6141
N.A.I.C.S.: 522220

Doosan Electro-Materials Singapore Pte Co., Ltd. (1)
No 3International 03-14 Nordic European Centre
Singapore, 609927, Singapore
Tel.: (65) 6862 6327
Fax: (65) 6862 6329
Emp.: 8
Electronic Component Whslr
S.I.C.: 5065
N.A.I.C.S.: 423690
Xere Kim *(Mng Dir)*

Doosan Power Systems Co., Ltd. (1)
Doosan House Crawley Business Quarter
Manor Royal
Crawley, West Sussex, RH10 9AD, United Kingdom
Tel.: (44) 1293 612888
Fax: (44) 1293 584321
Web Site: www.doosanpowersystems.com
Power Plant Construction & Maintenance Services
S.I.C.: 1623
N.A.I.C.S.: 237130
Eleftherios Panayiotou *(Mng Dir)*

Subsidiary:

Doosan Lentjes UK Limited (2)
Duke's Court Duke Street
Woking, Surrey, GU21 5BH, United Kingdom UK
Tel.: (44) 14 83 73 00 44
Fax: (44) 14 83 72 95 95
E-Mail: info.luk@aee-lentjes.de

Emp.: 2
Power Generation Plant Construction Engineering Services
S.I.C.: 1629
N.A.I.C.S.: 237990
Michael John Wilkins *(Mng Dir)*

Non-U.S. Subsidiaries:

AE&E Lentjes Praha s.r.o. (2)
Modranska 98
14701 Prague, Czech Republic
Tel.: (420) 2 41 09 51 50
Fax: (420) 2 41 09 51 52
E-Mail: info.praha@aee-lentjes.de
Power Boiler & Heat Exchanger Mfr
S.I.C.: 3559
N.A.I.C.S.: 332410

Doosan Lentjes GmbH (2)
Daniel-Goldbach-Str 19
40880 Ratingen, Germany
Tel.: (49) 2102 166 0
Fax: (49) 2102 166 2500
E-Mail: dl.info@doosan.com
Web Site: www.doosanpowersystems.com
Emp.: 50
Power Generation Plant Construction & Engineering Services
S.I.C.: 1629
N.A.I.C.S.: 237990
Thomas Wehrheim *(COO)*

Hanjung Power Co., Ltd. (1)
PO Box 2803
Boroko, Port Moresby, Papua New Guinea
Tel.: (675) 320 0529
Fax: (675) 321 2984
Electric Power Distribution Services
S.I.C.: 4931
N.A.I.C.S.: 221122

Non-U.S. Plant:

Doosan Engineering & Construction Co., Ltd. - Doosan Vina (CPE Plant) (1)
Dung Quat Econ Zone Binh Thuan
Binh Soon, Quang Ngai, Vietnam
Tel.: (84) 553618900
Fax: (84) 55 3618 954
Chemical Process Equipment Mfr
S.I.C.: 3559
N.A.I.C.S.: 333249
Yang Yong Dai *(Mgr-HR)*

DOOSAN ENGINEERING & CONSTRUCTION CO LTD

105 7 Nonhyeon Dong
Gangnam Gu
135010 Seoul, Korea (South)
Tel.: (82) 25103114
Fax: (82) 8225103724
Web Site: www.doosanenc.com
11160—(KRS)
Sales Range: $1-4.9 Billion
Business Description:
Construction Industry
S.I.C.: 1522
N.A.I.C.S.: 236116
Personnel:
Park Jeongwon *(Chm & Co-CEO)*
Ki-Dong Kim *(Pres & CEO)*

DOOVLE LIMITED

1 Clive Place
Esher, Surrey, KT10 9LH, United Kingdom
Tel.: (44) 1372464753
E-Mail: sales@doovle.com
Web Site: www.doovle.com
Sales Range: $1-9.9 Million
Business Description:
Web Applications
S.I.C.: 7372
N.A.I.C.S.: 511210
Personnel:
Stephen M. Anderson *(CEO)*
Michael Woodley *(CTO)*

DOPLA S.P.A.

via Nuova Trevigiana 126
Casale sul Sile, 31032 Treviso, TV, Italy
Tel.: (39) 0422 3885
Web Site: www.dopla.it
Sales Range: $200-249.9 Million
Emp.: 450
Business Description:
Plastic Cup, Plate & Cutlery Mfr
S.I.C.: 3089
N.A.I.C.S.: 326199

Non-U.S. Joint Venture:

F. Bender Limited (1)
Gresford Industrial Park Chester Road
Wrexham, LL12 8LX, United Kingdom UK
Tel.: (44) 1978 855 661
Fax: (44) 1978 855 101
E-Mail: info@benders.co.uk
Web Site: www.benders.co.uk
Sanitary Food & Beverage Containers & Service Products Mfr
S.I.C.: 2652
N.A.I.C.S.: 322219
Andrew Cunliffe *(Mng Dir)*

DOPPELMAYR GROUP

Rickenbacherstrasse 8 10
PO Box 20
A 6961 Wolfurt, Austria
Tel.: (43) 5574604
Fax: (43) 557475590
E-Mail: dm@doppelmayr.com
Web Site: www.doppelmayr.com
Year Founded: 1892
Sales Range: $550-599.9 Million
Emp.: 2,100
Business Description:
Holding Company
S.I.C.: 6719
N.A.I.C.S.: 551112
Personnel:
Michael Doppelmayr *(CEO)*

Subsidiaries:

Doppelmayr Aufzuge AG (1)
Rickenbacherstrasse 8-10
6961 Wolfurt, Austria
Tel.: (43) 55746040
Fax: (43) 557475590
E-Mail: dm@doppelmayr.com
Web Site: www.doppelmayr-aufzuege.at/
Emp.: 850
Elevator & Moving Stairway Mfr
S.I.C.: 3534
N.A.I.C.S.: 333921
Michael Doppelmayr *(Mng Dir)*

Doppelmayr Holding AG (1)
Rickenbacherstrasse 8-10
Wolfurt, Austria
Tel.: (43) 55746040
Fax: (43) 557475590
E-Mail: dm@doppelmayr.com
Web Site: www.doppelmayr.com
Emp.: 1,000
Holding Company
S.I.C.: 6719
N.A.I.C.S.: 551112
Michael Doppelmayr *(Mng Dir)*

Doppelmayr Seilbahnen GmbH (1)
Rickenbacherstrasse 8-10
PO Box 20
Stetten, 6922 Wolfurt, Austria
Tel.: (43) 226272508
Fax: (43) 557475590
E-Mail: dm@doppelmayr.com
Emp.: 2,400
Conveyor & Conveying Equipment Mfr
S.I.C.: 3535
N.A.I.C.S.: 333922
Michael Doppelmayr *(Mng Dir)*

U.S. Subsidiaries:

Doppelmayr CTEC, Inc. (1)
3160 W 500 S
Salt Lake City, UT 84104
Tel.: (801) 973-7977
Fax: (801) 973-9580
Toll Free: (800) 584-9024
E-Mail: info@doppelmayrctec.com
Web Site: www.doppelmayrctec.com
Emp.: 85
Mfr. of Aerial Tramways, Chair Lifts & Gondola Lifts, Steel Fabrications & Material Handling Equipment
Import Export
S.I.C.: 3559
N.A.I.C.S.: 333249
Mark Bee *(Pres)*

Doppelmayr USA, Inc (1)
12441 W 49th Ave Ste 1
Wheat Ridge, CO 80033
Tel.: (303) 277-9476
Fax: (303) 277-9759
Toll Free: (800) 584-9024
E-Mail: info@doppelmayrusa.com
Web Site: www.doppelmayrusa.com
Emp.: 100
Transportation Equipment Mfr
S.I.C.: 3799
N.A.I.C.S.: 336999
Mark Bee *(Pres)*

Non-U.S. Subsidiaries:

Doppelmayr A/S (1)
Svetsrvaegen 1
PO Box 316
686626 Sunne, Scandinavia, Sweden
Tel.: (46) 65688570
Fax: (46) 65688579
Emp.: 8
Support Activities for Transportation
S.I.C.: 4789
N.A.I.C.S.: 488999
Peter Strandberg *(Mng Dir)*

Doppelmayr Andorra S.A. (1)
Avgda Co-Princep Episcopal n 114 Edifici Prat del Rector
Despatx 2 Encamp, Andorra La Vella, Andorra
Tel.: (376) 732732
Fax: (376) 834593
E-Mail: doppelmayr@andorra.ad
Web Site: www.doppelmayr.com
Emp.: 23
Holding Company
S.I.C.: 6719
N.A.I.C.S.: 551112
Gulien Croses *(Mng Dir)*

Doppelmayr Australia Pty. Ltd. (1)
5 Nettin Circuit
PO Box 515
Jindabyne, 2627 Sydney, NSW, Australia
Tel.: (61) 264562385
Fax: (61) 264562736
E-Mail: info@doppelmayr.com.au
Web Site: www.doppelmayr.com
Emp.: 60
Industrial Machinery & Equipment Whslr
S.I.C.: 5084
N.A.I.C.S.: 423830
Bruce Tyner *(Gen Mgr)*

Doppelmayr Finn Oy (1)
Katajanokankatu 7A
00160 Helsinki, Finland
Tel.: (358) 96844300
Fax: (358) 9624120
Web Site: www.doppelmayr.com
Emp.: 5
Industrial Machinery & Equipment Whslr
S.I.C.: 5084
N.A.I.C.S.: 423830
Reijo Riila *(Mng Dir)*

Doppelmayr France S.A. (1)
837-903 Rue de l Isle - BP 80
Pole industriel de Frejus Moda, 73500 Modane, France
Tel.: (33) 479050371
Fax: (33) 479050018
E-Mail: dmf@doppelmayr.com
Web Site: www.doppelmayr.com
Emp.: 42
Overhead Traveling Crane Hoist & Monorail System Mfr
S.I.C.: 3536
N.A.I.C.S.: 333923
Bernard Teiller *(Chm)*

Doppelmayr Italia Srl (1)
Zona Industriale 14
Lana, 39011 Bolzano, Italy
Tel.: (39) 0473262100
Fax: (39) 0473262201
E-Mail: dmi@doppelmayr.com
Web Site: www.doppelmayr.com
Emp.: 100
Heavy & Civil Engineering Construction
S.I.C.: 1629
N.A.I.C.S.: 237990
Issac Tirion *(Mng Dir)*

Doppelmayr Lanove Drahy, Spol. S r. o. (1)
Drazni 7
62700 Brno, Czech Republic
Tel.: (420) 531022266
Fax: (420) 531022269
E-Mail: office@doppelmayr.cz
Web Site: www.doppelmayr.com
Emp.: 5
Holding Company
S.I.C.: 6719
N.A.I.C.S.: 551112
Lea Klinesou *(Mgr)*

Doppelmayr Lifts (NZ) Ltd. (1)
16 Queen St
PO Box 11
7673 Coalgate, New Zealand
Tel.: (64) 33182725
Fax: (64) 33182605
E-Mail: info@doppelmayr.co.nz
Web Site: www.doppelmayr.co.nz
Emp.: 3
Industrial Machinery & Equipment Whslr
S.I.C.: 5084
N.A.I.C.S.: 423830
Grant Horner *(Mgr)*

Doppelmayr Scandinavia AB (1)
Svetsarevagen 1
68633 Sunne, Sweden
Tel.: (46) 565688570
Fax: (46) 565688579
E-Mail: peter@doppelmayr.com
Web Site: www.doppelmayr.com
Emp.: 7
Fiber Optic Cable Mfr
S.I.C.: 3357
N.A.I.C.S.: 335921
Peter Strandberg *(Mng Dir)*

Doppelmayr Skidalyftur hf. (1)
PO Box 333
Akureyri, Iceland
Tel.: (354) 4621720
Fax: (354) 4611740
Web Site: www.doppelmayr.com
Emp.: 1
Industrial Machinery & Equipment Whslr
S.I.C.: 5084
N.A.I.C.S.: 423830
Ivar Sigmundsson *(Gen Mgr)*

Sanhe Doppelmayr Transport Systems Co., Ltd. (1)
No 13 Yanchang Road Yanjiao Economic & Technological Development Zone, Sanhe, Hebei, 065200, China
Tel.: (86) 3163393030
Fax: (86) 3163393032
E-Mail: info@doppelmayr.cn
Web Site: www.doppelmayr.com
Emp.: 70
Activities for Transportation
S.I.C.: 4789
N.A.I.C.S.: 488999
Yanqiu Li *(Gen Mgr)*

DORA CONSTRUCTION LIMITED

60 Dorey Avenue Suite 200
Dartmouth, NS, B3B 0B1, Canada
Tel.: (902) 468-2941
Fax: (902) 468-2964
E-Mail: info@doraconstruction.com
Web Site: www.doraconstruction.com
Year Founded: 2003
Rev.: $15,642,363
Emp.: 55
Business Description:
Construction Services
S.I.C.: 1542
N.A.I.C.S.: 236220
Personnel:
Donald MacDonald *(Pres)*

DORAL INTERNATIONAL INC.

1991 3e Avenue
Grand-Mere, QC, G9T 2W6, Canada
Tel.: (819) 538-0781

Doral International Inc.—(Continued)

Fax: (819) 538-6330
Web Site: www.doralboat.com
Year Founded: 1972
Rev.: $29,076,000
Emp.: 252
Business Description:
Boat Distr
S.I.C.: 5551
N.A.I.C.S.: 441222
Personnel:
Denis Poliseno *(Pres)*

DORATO RESOURCES INC.

Suite 2300 - 1177 West Hastings Street
Vancouver, BC, V6E 2K3, Canada
Tel.: (604) 638-5817
Fax: (604) 408-7499
E-Mail: info@doratoresources.com
Web Site: www.doratoresources.com
Year Founded: 1981
DRI—(TSXV)
Assets: $748,896
Liabilities: $1,216,442
Net Worth: ($467,546)
Earnings: ($7,087,675)
Fiscal Year-end: 01/31/13
Business Description:
Mineral Exploration Services
S.I.C.: 1081
N.A.I.C.S.: 213114
Personnel:
Rowland Perkins *(Interim Pres & CEO)*
Anton J. Drescher *(CFO)*
Marla K. Ritchie *(Sec)*
Board of Directors:
Carlos Ballon
Anton J. Drescher
Gordon Neal
Rowland Perkins
Legal Counsel:
Blake, Cassels & Graydon LLP
Suite 2600 Three Bentall Centre 595 Burrard Street
PO Box 49314
Vancouver, BC, Canada
Transfer Agent:
Computershare Investor Services Inc.
3rd Floor 510 Burrard St
V6C 3B9 Vancouver, BC, Canada

DORAY MINERALS LIMITED

Level 3 41-43 Ord Street
West Perth, WA, 6005, Australia
Mailing Address:
PO Box 284
West Perth, WA, 6872, Australia
Tel.: (61) 8 9226 0600
Fax: (61) 8 9226 0633
E-Mail: info@dorayminerals.com.au
Web Site: www.dorayminerals.com.au
DRM—(ASX)
Rev.: $639,546
Assets: $153,247,274
Liabilities: $80,365,321
Net Worth: $72,881,953
Earnings: ($8,746,930)
Emp.: 41
Fiscal Year-end: 06/30/13
Business Description:
Gold Mining Services
S.I.C.: 1041
N.A.I.C.S.: 212221
Personnel:
Allan J. Kelly *(Mng Dir)*
Jon Latto *(CFO)*
Iain Garrett *(Sec & Controller-Fin)*
Board of Directors:
Peter Alexander
Heath Hellewell
Leigh Junk
Allan J. Kelly
Jay Stephenson

DORCHESTER GROUP LTD.

3 Tilney St
London, W1K 1BJ, United Kingdom
Tel.: (44) 2076294848
Fax: (44) 2076298080
E-Mail: info@dorchestergrouphotels.com
Web Site: www.dorchester.com
Year Founded: 1996
Emp.: 650
Business Description:
Hotel Holding Company
S.I.C.: 7011
N.A.I.C.S.: 721110
Personnel:
Sean Wheeler *(Dir-HR)*
U.S. Subsidiary:

The Beverly Hills Hotel **(1)**
9641 Sunset Blvd
Beverly Hills, CA 90210-2938
Tel.: (310) 276-2251
Telex: 188586
Fax: (310) 887-2887
Toll Free: (800) 283-8885
E-Mail: concierge@thebeverlyhillshotel.com
Web Site: www.thebeverlyhillshotel.com
Hotels
S.I.C.: 7011
N.A.I.C.S.: 721110
Ed Mady *(Gen Mgr)*

DORE HOLDINGS LIMITED

Unit 3903 39/F Far East Finance Centre 16 Harcourt Road
Admiralty, Hong Kong, China (Hong Kong)
Tel.: (852) 25461223
Fax: (852) 25294720
E-Mail: info@dore-holdings.com.hk
Web Site: www.dore-holdings.com.hk
0628—(HKG)
Sls.: $3,302,925
Assets: $34,233,259
Liabilities: $198,712
Net Worth: $34,034,547
Earnings: $2,124,709
Emp.: 3
Fiscal Year-end: 03/31/13
Business Description:
Entertainment Services
S.I.C.: 7389
N.A.I.C.S.: 561499
Personnel:
Heung Yeung Yeung *(Chm)*
Eric Kwong Leung Chan *(Sec)*
Board of Directors:
Heung Yeung Yeung
Shiow Yue Lee
Percy Wai Hoi Poon
Francis Chi Ho Tang
Butterfield Fulcrum Group (Bermuda) Limited
26 Burnaby Street
Hamilton, HM 11, Bermuda
Transfer Agents:
Union Registrars Limited
18/F Fook Lee Commercial Centre Town Place 33 Lockhart Road
Wanchai, China (Hong Kong)
Butterfield Fulcrum Group (Bermuda) Limited
26 Burnaby Street
Hamilton, HM 11, Bermuda

DOREL INDUSTRIES, INC.

1255 Greene Ave Suite 300
Montreal, QC, H3Z 2A4, Canada
Tel.: (514) 934-3034
Fax: (514) 934-9379
E-Mail: info@dorel.com
Web Site: www.dorel.com
Year Founded: 1962
DIIB—(OTC TSX)
Sls.: $2,490,710,000
Assets: $2,204,086,000
Liabilities: $896,388,000
Net Worth: $1,307,698,000
Earnings: $108,613,000
Emp.: 5,000
Fiscal Year-end: 12/30/12
Business Description:
Mfr of Consumer Products; Ready-to-Assemble Furniture, Juvenile Furniture & Home Furnishings
Import Export
S.I.C.: 3999
N.A.I.C.S.: 339999
Personnel:
Martin Schwartz *(Pres & CEO)*
Jeffrey Schwartz *(CFO, Sec & Exec VP)*
Andrew Coccari *(Global CMO-Recreation & Leisure)*
Norman Braunstein *(Pres/CEO-Home Furnishings Segment)*
Jean-Claude Jacomin *(Pres/CEO-Juvenile Segment)*
Peter Woods *(Interim Pres-Recreational & Leisure Segment)*
Alan Schwartz *(Exec VP-Ops)*
Jeffrey Segel *(Exec VP-Mktg & Sls)*
Board of Directors:
Alain Benedetti
Dian N. Cohen
Rupert J. Duchesne
Harold P. Gordon
Alan Schwartz
Jeffrey Schwartz
Martin Schwartz
Jeffrey Segel
Maurice Tousson
Legal Counsel:
Heenan Blaikie LLP
1250 Rene Levesque Blvd W Ste 2500
Montreal, QC, H3B 4Y1, Canada
Tel.: (514) 846-1212
Transfer Agent:
Computershare Investor Services Inc.
100 University Ave 9th Floor
Toronto, ON, Canada
Subsidiaries:

Dorel Home Products **(1)**
12345 Albert Hudon Suite 100
Montreal, QC, H1G3L1, Canada (100%)
Tel.: (514) 323-1247
Fax: (514) 323-2030
E-Mail: info@dhpfurniture.com
Web Site: www.dorel.com
Emp.: 125
S.I.C.: 5712
N.A.I.C.S.: 442110
Ira Goldstein *(VP)*

Ridgewood **(1)**
3305 Loyalist Street
Cornwall, ON, K6H 6W6, Canada
Web Site: www.mjbridgewood.co.uk/
S.I.C.: 5712
N.A.I.C.S.: 442110

SUGOI Performance Apparel Limited Partnership **(1)**
4084 McConnell Ct
Burnaby, BC, V5A 3N7, Canada
Tel.: (604) 875-0887
Fax: (604) 879-9106
Toll Free: (800) 432-1335
E-Mail: consumer@sugoi.com
Web Site: www.sugoi.com
Emp.: 25
Sportswear & Athletic Clothing Mfr
S.I.C.: 3949
N.A.I.C.S.: 339920
Kyle Weiner *(Pres)*

U.S. Division:

Pacific Cycle Inc. **(1)**
4902 Hammersley Rd
Madison, WI 53711-2614
Tel.: (608) 268-2468
Fax: (608) 268-8955
E-Mail: info@pacific-cycle.com
Web Site: www.pacific-cycle.com
Sales Range: $400-449.9 Million
Emp.: 100
Mfr. & Distr of Bicycles & Accessories
S.I.C.: 5091
N.A.I.C.S.: 423910
Alice Tillett *(Pres)*
Bob Kmoch *(CFO)*

Branch:

Pacific Cycle Inc. **(2)**
4730 E Radio Tower Ln
Olney, IL 62450-4743
Tel.: (618) 393-2991
Fax: (618) 395-1057
Web Site: www.pacific-cycle.com
Emp.: 175
Mfr & Sales of Bicycles & Accessories
Import Export
S.I.C.: 3751
N.A.I.C.S.: 336991
Marty Doan *(Controller)*

U.S. Subsidiaries:

Ameriwood Industries, Inc. **(1)**
305 E S 1st St
Wright City, MO 63390 (100%)
Tel.: (636) 745-3351
Fax: (636) 745-1007
Toll Free: (800) 454-0283
Web Site: www.ameriwood.com
Emp.: 85
Mfr. of Wood Furniture & Plastic Products
S.I.C.: 2511
N.A.I.C.S.: 337122
Jim Elschide *(Gen Mgr)*

Cannondale Bicycle Corporation **(1)**
172 Friendship Rd
Bedford, PA 15522-6600 DE
Tel.: (814) 623-9073
Fax: (814) 623-6173
Toll Free: (800) BIKE-USA
E-Mail: custserv@cannondale.com
Web Site: www.cannondale.com
Sales Range: $200-249.9 Million
Emp.: 75
Aluminum Bicycles, Cycling Accessories & Apparel
Export
S.I.C.: 3751
N.A.I.C.S.: 336991
Bob Burbank *(Gen Mgr)*

Non-U.S. Subsidiary:

Cannondale Japan KK **(2)**
1-4-19 Minamihorie Nishi-Ku Namba
Sumiso Bldg 9f
Osaka, Japan
Tel.: (81) 6 6110 9390
Fax: (81) 6 6110 9361
E-Mail: cjcustserv@cannondale.com
Web Site: www.cannondale.co.jp
Bicycle Mfr
S.I.C.: 3751
N.A.I.C.S.: 336991

Cycling Sports Group Inc. **(1)**
172 Friendship Village Rd
Bedford, PA 15522-6600
Tel.: (814) 623-9073
E-Mail: gtinfo@cyclingsportsgroup.com
Web Site: www.cyclingsportsgroup.com
Bicycle & Sporting Products Mfr
S.I.C.: 3751
N.A.I.C.S.: 336991
Henk-Jan de Vries *(Dir-Matl Mgmt-Oldenzaal)*

Dorel Juvenile Group, Inc. **(1)**
2525 State St
Columbus, IN 47201-7443 IN
Tel.: (812) 372-0141 (100%)
Fax: (812) 372-2154
Toll Free: (800) 544-1108
Web Site: www.djgusa.com
Emp.: 1,100
Step Stools, Bars, Counter Stools, Carts, Baby Products & Baby Furniture Mfr
Import Export
S.I.C.: 3089
N.A.I.C.S.: 326199
Dave Taylor *(Pres & CEO)*
Hani Basile *(Pres-Juvenile Grp)*

Non-U.S. Subsidiary:

Dorel France S.A. (2)
9 Boulevard du Poitou
F-49300 Cholet, France FR
Mailing Address:
PO Box 905
Cholet, 49300, France
Tel.: (33) 241492323
Telex: 270421
Fax: (33) 241656045
Web Site: www.bebeconfort.com
Emp.: 460
Juvenile Products Mfr
S.I.C.: 2511
N.A.I.C.S.: 337122
Dominique Favario *(Chm)*
Jean Louis Lambert *(Mng Dir)*

Non-U.S. Subsidiaries:

AMPA 2P SAS (1)
Zone Industrielle 9 Boulevard Du Poitou
Cholet, Maine Et Loire, 49300, France
Tel.: (33) 241492323
Fax: (33) 241656045
Juvenile Products Distr
S.I.C.: 5137
N.A.I.C.S.: 424330

AMPA Developpement SAS (1)
Zone Industrielle 9 Boulevard Du Poitou
Cholet, France
Tel.: (33) 2 41 49 23 23
Fax: (33) 2 41 65 60 45
Juvenile Products Distr
S.I.C.: 5137
N.A.I.C.S.: 424330

BeBe and Co SAS (1)
Rue De La Vendee
La Seguiniere, Maine Et Loire, 49280, France
Tel.: (33) 241752900
Fax: (33) 241560264
Juvenile Products Distr
S.I.C.: 5137
N.A.I.C.S.: 424330
Laurent Bertin *(Gen Mgr)*

Cycling Sports Group Australia Pty Ltd (1)
Unit 8 31-41 Bridge Road
Stanmore, NSW, 2048, Australia
Tel.: (61) 2 8595 4444
Fax: (61) 2 8595 4499
E-Mail: askus@cyclingsportsgroup.com.au
Emp.: 25
Cycling & Push Bikes Mfr
S.I.C.: 3949
N.A.I.C.S.: 339920

Cycling Sports Group Europe B.V (1)
Hanzepoort 27
Oldenzaal, 7575 DB, Netherlands
Tel.: (31) 541589898
Fax: (31) 541514240
Emp.: 90
Sport & Athletic Goods Mfr
S.I.C.: 3949
N.A.I.C.S.: 339920
Jos Hofste *(Gen Mgr)*

Dorel Belgium SA (1)
Atomiumsquare 1
BP 177
1020 Brussels, Belgium
Tel.: (32) 2 257 44 70
Fax: (32) 2 257 44 71
Child Care Accessories Mfr
S.I.C.: 3942
N.A.I.C.S.: 339930

Dorel Consulting (Shanghai) Co., Ltd. (1)
Rm 205 No 3203 Hongmei Rd
Shanghai, 201103, China
Tel.: (86) 2164468999
Fax: (86) 2164656570
Emp.: 1
Juvenile Products Whslr
S.I.C.: 5137
N.A.I.C.S.: 424330
Wendy Zhang *(Gen Mgr)*

Dorel Germany GmbH (1)
Augustinusstrasse 11 b
50226 Frechen, Germany
Tel.: (49) 2234 96 430
Fax: (49) 2234964333
Emp.: 20
Sport & Athletic Goods Mfr
S.I.C.: 3949
N.A.I.C.S.: 339920
Michael Neumann *(Gen Mgr)*

Dorel Hispania SA (1)
Calle Pare Rodes 26 4 Ed Llac Center
Torre A
Sabadell, Barcelona, 8208, Spain
Tel.: (34) 937247100
Fax: (34) 937243711
Child Care Products Mfr & Sales
S.I.C.: 3942
N.A.I.C.S.: 339930

Dorel Italia SpA (1)
Via Giuseppe Verdi 14
Telgate, Bergamo, 24060, Italy
Tel.: (39) 0354421035
Fax: (39) 0354421048
Children Care Products Mfr & Distr
S.I.C.: 3942
N.A.I.C.S.: 339930

Dorel Netherlands (1)
Korendijkk 5
NL 5704 RD Helmond, Netherlands (100%)
Tel.: (31) 492578111
Fax: (31) 492578166
E-Mail: info@dorelnl.nl
Web Site: www.dorelnl.nl
Emp.: 250
S.I.C.: 5712
N.A.I.C.S.: 442110

Dorel Suisse SARL (1)
Rue de Geneve 77bis
1004 Lausanne, Switzerland
Tel.: (41) 21 622 00 50
Fax: (41) 21 622 00 55
E-Mail: pirchasing@dorel.ch
Emp.: 4
Bicycle Mfr & Whslr
S.I.C.: 3751
N.A.I.C.S.: 336991

Dorel (UK) Ltd. (1)
Hertsmere House
Shenley Road, Borehamwood, Herts, WD6 1TE, United Kingdom (100%)
Tel.: (44) 2082360707
Fax: (44) 2082360770
E-Mail: customercare@uk-dorel.com
Web Site: www.dorel.co.uk
Emp.: 30
Designs, Manufactures & Markets Infant Nursery Products
S.I.C.: 5712
N.A.I.C.S.: 442110
Andrew Radcliffe *(Mng Dir)*

IBD Bikes UK Limited (1)
Vantage Way The Fulcrum
Poole, Dorset, BH12 4NU, United Kingdom
Tel.: (44) 1202 732288
Fax: (44) 1202 723366
E-Mail: sales@cyclingsportsgroup.co.uk
Web Site: www.cyclingsportsgroup.co.uk
Emp.: 42
Sporting Goods Whslr
S.I.C.: 5091
N.A.I.C.S.: 423910
David Lloyd *(Co-Mng Dir)*

IGC Dorel Pty Ltd (1)
655-685 Somerville Rd
Sunshine, VIC, 3020, Australia
Tel.: (61) 3 8311 5300
Fax: (61) 3 8311 5390
E-Mail: sales@igc.com.au
Web Site: www.igc.com.au
Emp.: 100
Baby Care Goods Mfr & Sales
S.I.C.: 3942
N.A.I.C.S.: 339930

Maxi Miliaan B.V (1)
Korendijk 5
Helmond, Noord-Brabant, 5704 RD, Netherlands
Tel.: (31) 492578111
Fax: (31) 492578166
Emp.: 250
Sporting & Athletic Goods Mfr & Distr
S.I.C.: 3949
N.A.I.C.S.: 339920
Jeff Brands *(Mng Dir)*

DOREX MINERALS INC.

505-535 Thurlow Street
Vancouver, BC, V6E 3L2, Canada
Tel.: (604) 688-1160
Fax: (604) 568-4902
E-Mail: dorexinc@gmail.com
Web Site: www.dorexinc.com
DOX—(TSXV)
Assets: $501,276
Liabilities: $833,851
Net Worth: ($332,574)
Earnings: ($269,567)
Fiscal Year-end: 03/31/13

Business Description:
Mineral Exploration Services
S.I.C.: 1081
N.A.I.C.S.: 213114

Personnel:
Julius Galik *(Pres & CEO)*
Peter Walton *(CFO)*

Board of Directors:
Julius Galik
Ron Hughes
Douglas McFaul
Peter Walton

Legal Counsel:
Holmes & King
1300 -1111 West Georgia Street
Vancouver, BC, Canada

Transfer Agent:
Computershare Trust Company of Canada
9th Floor 100 University Avenue
Toronto, ON, Canada

DORFIN INC.

5757 Boul Thimens
Saint Laurent, QC, H4R 2H6, Canada
Tel.: (514) 335-0333
Fax: (514) 335-9341
Toll Free: (888) 936-7346
E-Mail: info@Dorfin.com
Web Site: www.dorfin.com
Year Founded: 1954
Rev.: $23,245,298
Emp.: 90

Business Description:
Consumer Products Supplier
S.I.C.: 7359
N.A.I.C.S.: 532299

Personnel:
Stanley Lesser *(Founder)*
Morris Tryansky *(CEO)*

DORI MEDIA GROUP LTD.

2 Raoul Wallenberg St Ramat Hachayal
69719 Tel Aviv, Israel
Tel.: (972) 3 647 8185
Fax: (972) 3 647 8491
E-Mail: info@dorimedia.com
Web Site: www.dorimedia.com
D7M—(DEU)
Sales Range: $25-49.9 Million

Business Description:
Television Broadcasting Distr & Merchandiser; Owned 38% by Mapal Eden Telenobles Ltd.
S.I.C.: 4833
N.A.I.C.S.: 515120

Personnel:
Tamar Mozes-Borovitz *(Chm)*
Nadav Palti *(Pres & CEO)*
Moshe Pinto *(CFO, Sec & VP-HR & Admin)*

Board of Directors:
Tamar Mozes-Borovitz
Michele Igal Arazi
Yosef Dov Fox
Maya Kogut
Yehuda M. Levy
Nadav Palti
Michael Rosenberg
Hanan Schlesinger
Nathaniel Charles Sebag-Montefiore

Subsidiaries:

Dori Media Ot Ltd. (1)
2 Raoul Wallenberg Street
Tel Aviv, 69719, Israel
Tel.: (972) 37684141
Fax: (972) 36481227
E-Mail: dmo@dorimedia.com
Web Site: www.dorimedia.com
Video Dubbing Services
S.I.C.: 7819
N.A.I.C.S.: 512191
Moshe Sadan *(CEO)*

Dori Media Spike Ltd. (1)
3 Habarzel
Tel Aviv, 69710, Israel
Tel.: (972) 36498282
Fax: (972) 36498288
E-Mail: frontoffice@dorimediaspike.com
Web Site: www.dorimediaspike.com
Emp.: 50
Television Broadcasting Services
S.I.C.: 4833
N.A.I.C.S.: 515120
Claire Elbaz *(CEO)*
Amir Nuriel *(Exec VP)*

Non-U.S. Subsidiaries:

Dori Media Contenidos S.A. (1)
A M de Justo 1960 1 103
Buenos Aires, Argentina (100%)
Tel.: (54) 1151997970
Fax: (54) 1152566434
Web Site: www.dorimedia.com
Motion Picture & Video Production
S.I.C.: 7812
N.A.I.C.S.: 512110
Michal Nashiv *(Pres & CEO)*

Dori Media Distribution Argentina S.A. (1)
Costa Rica 4941
Buenos Aires, C1414BSO, Argentina (100%)
Tel.: (54) 1148333800
Fax: (54) 1148333303
E-Mail: maria@dorimedia.com
Web Site: www.dorimedia.com
Emp.: 12
Motion Picture & Video Production
S.I.C.: 7812
N.A.I.C.S.: 512110
Michal Nashiv *(Pres & CEO)*

Dori Media Distribution GmbH (1)
Forchstrasse
8008 Zurich, Switzerland (100%)
Tel.: (41) 438177050
Fax: (41) 438177055
E-Mail: zurich@dorimedia.com
Web Site: www.dorimedia.com
Management Consulting Services
S.I.C.: 8748
N.A.I.C.S.: 541618
Nadav Palti *(Pres & CEO)*

Dori Media International GmbH (1)
Hochhaus zur Palme
Bleicherweg 33, CH-8002 Zurich, Switzerland (100%)
Tel.: (41) 438177050
Fax: (41) 438177055
E-Mail: info@dorimedia.com
Web Site: www.dorimedia.com
Broadcasting Producer & Distr
S.I.C.: 4833
N.A.I.C.S.: 515120
Nadav Palti *(CEO)*

U.S. Subsidiary:

Dori Media America Inc. (2)
9800 NW 41st St
Miami, FL 33178-2968
Tel.: (786) 662-3051
Music Compact Discs Distr
S.I.C.: 5099
N.A.I.C.S.: 423990
Richard Fernandez *(Pres)*

DORIC NIMROD AIR ONE LIMITED

Anson Place Mill Court La Charroterie
Saint Peter Port, Guernsey GY1 1EJ
Tel.: (44) 1481 722260

Doric Nimrod Air One Limited—(Continued)

Web Site: www.dnairone.com
Year Founded: 2010
DNA—(LSE)

Business Description:
Aircraft Investment Services
S.I.C.: 6211
N.A.I.C.S.: 523999

Personnel:
Charles Wilkinson *(Chm)*

Board of Directors:
Charles Wilkinson
Norbert Bannon
Geoffrey Alan Hall

DORIC NIMROD AIR TWO LIMITED

Anson Place Mill Court La Charroterie
Saint Peter Port, Guernsey GY1 1EJ
Tel.: (44) 1481 722260
Web Site: www.dnairtwo.co.uk
Year Founded: 2011
DNA2—(LSE)
Rev.: $108,074,032
Assets: $1,637,482,040
Liabilities: $1,177,182,167
Net Worth: $460,299,873
Earnings: ($29,099,582)
Fiscal Year-end: 03/31/13

Business Description:
Aircraft Investment Services
S.I.C.: 6211
N.A.I.C.S.: 523999

Personnel:
Norbert Bannon *(Chm)*

Board of Directors:
Norbert Bannon
Geoffrey Alan Hall
Charles Wilkinson

Legal Counsel:
Mourant Ozannes
1 Le Marchant Street
186
Saint Peter Port, Guernsey

Herbert Smith LLP
Exchange House Primrose Street
London, EC2A 2HS, United Kingdom

Transfer Agent:
Anson Registrars (UK) Limited
3500 Parkway Solent Business Park Whiteley
Fareham, Hampshire, PO15 7AL, United Kingdom

DORMA HOLDING GMBH & CO. KGAA

Dorma Platz 1
58256 Ennepetal, Germany
Tel.: (49) 23337930
Fax: (49) 3337934950
Web Site: www.dorma.com
Sales Range: $1-4.9 Billion
Emp.: 6,470

Business Description:
Door Hardware, Door Security Systems, Automatic & Revolving Doors, Glass Fittings, Decorative & Structural Glass Systems, Partitions & Movable Door Mfr
S.I.C.: 3442
N.A.I.C.S.: 332321

Personnel:
Jurgen Rauen *(Chm-Supervisory Bd)*
Otto Koenig *(Vice Chm-Supervisory Bd)*

U.S. Subsidiary:

DORMA Group North America (1)
Dorma Dr Drawer AC
Reamstown, PA 17567-0411
Tel.: (717) 336-3881
Fax: (717) 336-2106
Toll Free: (800) 523-8483
E-Mail: info@dorma-usa.com
Web Site: www.dorma-usa.com
Sales Range: $50-74.9 Million
Emp.: 200
Revolving Doors, Automatic Doors & Door Hardware Mfr
S.I.C.: 3442
N.A.I.C.S.: 332321
Wil Vandewiel *(Pres & CEO)*
Kevin Hollenbach *(CFO & VP-Fin)*

Division:

Modernfold, Inc. (2)
215 W New Rd
Greenfield, IN 46140 IN
Tel.: (317) 468-6700
Fax: (317) 468-6760
Toll Free: (800) 869-9685
E-Mail: info@modernfold.com
Web Site: www.modernfold.com
Emp.: 75
Operable Wall Systems & Space Division Solutions for Interior Environments; Operable Partitions, Moveable Glass Walls & Accordion Doors Designer, Mfr & Servicer Export
S.I.C.: 2522
N.A.I.C.S.: 337214
Dave Smith *(Exec VP)*

DORMAC PTY. LTD.

1 Belfast Road
Bayhead, Durban, South Africa

Mailing Address:
PO Box 12568
Jacobs, Kwa Zulu Natal, 4026, South Africa
Tel.: (27) 312741500
Telex: 6-28100
Fax: (27) 312059041
E-Mail: ship@dormac.net
Web Site: www.dormac.net
Sales Range: $75-99.9 Million
Emp.: 200

Business Description:
Commercial Ship Construction & Repair Services
S.I.C.: 3731
N.A.I.C.S.: 336611

Personnel:
Chris Sparg *(Mng Dir)*

DORNBIRNER SPARKASSE BANK AG

Bahnhofstrasse 2
A 6850 Dornbirn, Austria
Tel.: (43) 5010074000
Fax: (43) 50100974346
E-Mail: patriek.buhnann@dornbirn.sparkasse.at
Web Site: www.sparkasse.at/dornbirn
Year Founded: 1867
Sales Range: $1-4.9 Billion
Emp.: 350

Business Description:
International Banking
S.I.C.: 6029
N.A.I.C.S.: 522110

Personnel:
Hubert Singer *(CEO)*

DORO AB

Magistratsvagen 10
226 43 Lund, Sweden
Tel.: (46) 462805000
Fax: (46) 462805001
E-Mail: info@doro.com
Web Site: www.doro.com
DORO—(OMX)
Rev.: $129,645,000
Assets: $79,938,720
Liabilities: $47,585,520
Net Worth: $32,353,200
Earnings: $8,188,920
Emp.: 81
Fiscal Year-end: 12/31/12

Business Description:
Design-Driven Products Designer, Developer & Seller
S.I.C.: 5064
N.A.I.C.S.: 423620

Personnel:
Bo Kastensson *(Chm)*
Jerome Arnaud *(Pres & CEO)*
Bernt Ingman *(Interim CFO)*

Board of Directors:
Bo Kastensson
Jerome Arnaud
Charlotta Falvin
Jonas Martensson
Karin Moberg

Non-U.S. Subsidiaries:

Doro A/S, Norway (1)
Krakeroyveien 2
Krakeroy, 1671 Fredrikstad, Norway
Tel.: (47) 69358600
Fax: (47) 69358669
Web Site: www.doro.com
Emp.: 5
Telecommunication Equipment Mfr
S.I.C.: 3663
N.A.I.C.S.: 334220
Kjell Reidar Mydske *(Mng Dir)*

Doro Hong Kong Ltd (1)
Unit 222 No 1 Science Park West Avenue
Hong Kong Science Park, Sha Tin, NT, China (Hong Kong)
Tel.: (852) 27302777
Fax: (852) 27302433
Emp.: 6
Mobile Communication Equipment Mfr
S.I.C.: 3663
N.A.I.C.S.: 334220
Calle Krokstade *(Gen Mgr)*

Doro SAS (1)
6 Rue Jean Pierre Timbaud
78180 Montigny-le-Bretonneux, France
Tel.: (33) 130071700
Fax: (33) 130071779
Web Site: www.doro.com
Emp.: 20
Mobile Communication Equipment Mfr
S.I.C.: 3663
N.A.I.C.S.: 334220
Gerome Arnaud *(Mng Dir)*

DORSAVI LTD

Level 1 120 Jolimont Road
Melbourne, VIC, 3002, Australia
Tel.: (61) 3 96522198
Fax: (61) 3 86101024
E-Mail: info@dorsavi.com
Web Site: www.dorsavi.com
DVL—(ASX)

Business Description:
Medical Products Mfr
S.I.C.: 3841
N.A.I.C.S.: 339112

Personnel:
Herbert James Elliott *(Chm)*
Andrew Ronchi *(CEO)*
Daniel Ronchi *(CTO & CIO)*
Brendan Case *(Sec)*

Board of Directors:
Herbert James Elliott
Ashraf Attia
Brendan Case
Michael Panaccio
Andrew Ronchi
Gregory John Tweedly

DORSCH HOLDING GMBH

(d/b/a Dorsch Gruppe)
Berliner Strasse 74-76
63065 Offenbach, Germany
Tel.: (49) 691302570
Fax: (49) 6913025732
E-Mail: mail@dorsch.de
Web Site: www.dorsch.de
Year Founded: 1951
Emp.: 1,500

Business Description:
Engineering Consulting Services
S.I.C.: 8711
N.A.I.C.S.: 541330

Personnel:
Olaf Hoffmann *(CEO)*

Subsidiaries:

BDC Berlin Dorsch Consult Ingenieurgesellschaft mbH (1)
Bernburger Strasse 30 31
D 10963 Berlin, Germany
Tel.: (49) 302639240
Fax: (49) 3026392444
E-Mail: bdc@berlindc.de
Web Site: www.berlindc.de
Emp.: 45
Engineering Services
S.I.C.: 8711
N.A.I.C.S.: 541330

Branch:

BDC Dorsch Consult GmbH - Hamburg (2)
Osterbekstrasse 90c
D 22083 Hamburg, Germany
Tel.: (49) 4022632736
Fax: (49) 4022632739
E-Mail: hamburg@bdc-dorsch.de
Web Site: www.bdc-dorsch.de
Emp.: 40
Engineering Services
S.I.C.: 8711
N.A.I.C.S.: 541330
Martin Steenbuck *(Mgr)*

CDC Chemnitz Dorsch Consult Ingenieurgesellschaft mbH (1)
Weststrasse 49
9112 Chemnitz, Germany
Tel.: (49) 37191360
Fax: (49) 3719136100
E-Mail: cdc@chemnitz-dc.de
Web Site: www.chemnitz-dc.de
Engineering Services
S.I.C.: 8711
N.A.I.C.S.: 541330

DDC Dorsch Consult Ingenieurgesellschaft mbH (1)
Loscherstrasse 16
D 01309 Dresden, Germany
Tel.: (49) 351313060
Fax: (49) 3513130610
E-Mail: ddc@ddc-consult.de
Web Site: www.dresden-dc.de
Emp.: 5
Engineering Services
S.I.C.: 8711
N.A.I.C.S.: 541330
Gerd Toepfer *(Mng Dir)*

Dorsch Consult Airports GmbH (1)
Industriestrasse 5
70565 Stuttgart, Germany
Tel.: (49) 711697890
Fax: (49) 7116978930
E-Mail: info@airplan.de
Web Site: www.airplan.de
Emp.: 22
Engineering Services
S.I.C.: 8711
N.A.I.C.S.: 541330

Dorsch Consult Wiesbaden (1)
Appelallee 29
65203 Wiesbaden, Germany
Tel.: (49) 6112340
Fax: (49) 611234156
E-Mail: wiesbaden@dorsch.de
Web Site: www.dorsch.de
Emp.: 100
Engineering Services
S.I.C.: 8711
N.A.I.C.S.: 541330
Juergen Roeder *(Gen Mgr)*

Non-U.S. Subsidiaries:

Dorsch Consult Abu Dhabi (1)
PO Box 26417
Abu Dhabi, United Arab Emirates
Tel.: (971) 26721923
Fax: (971) 26720809
E-Mail: info@dorsch.ae
Web Site: www.dorsch.de
Emp.: 500
Engineering Services
S.I.C.: 8711
N.A.I.C.S.: 541330
Ayman Heikal *(Gen Mgr)*

Dorsch Consult Asia Jakarta (1)
8th Fl Ste 801 Jl HR Tasuna Said Kav
C 5 Kebayoran Baru, Jakarta, 12940,
Indonesia
Tel.: (62) 215213610
Fax: (62) 215213611
E-Mail: dorshino@indo.net.id
Web Site: dc-asia.dorsch.de/en/index.php?id=1060
Engineering Services
S.I.C.: 8711
N.A.I.C.S.: 541330

Dorsch Consult Asia Ltd. (1)
1016 Str Fueng Fung Bldg Rama 4 Rd
Bangkok, 10500, Thailand
Tel.: (66) 263381047
Fax: (66) 26338109
E-Mail: dct@dorsch.co.th
Web Site: www.dorsch.co.th
Emp.: 10
Engineering Services
S.I.C.: 8711
N.A.I.C.S.: 541330
Juergen Supik *(CEO & Mng Dir)*

Dorsch Consult India Ltd. (1)
236 Oshiwara Industrial Ctr Goegaon W
Mumbai, 400 101, India
Tel.: (91) 2228779012
Fax: (91) 2228778548
E-Mail: dcindia@vsnl.com
Web Site: www.dorsch.de
Sales Range: Less than $1 Million
Emp.: 60
Engineering Services
S.I.C.: 8711
N.A.I.C.S.: 541330
Nirmal G. Humbat *(CFO & Mng Dir)*

Dorsch Consult Wasser und Umwelt Cairo (1)
6 El Sad Ei Ali St
PO Box 31
Cairo, Maadi, 11431, Egypt
Tel.: (20) 2 23 80 25 63
Fax: (20) 2 23 80 23 94
E-Mail: gen@dorscheg.com
Web Site: di.dorsch.de/
Engineering Services & Project Solutions
S.I.C.: 8711
N.A.I.C.S.: 541330

Hydroprojekt CZ a.s. (1)
Taborska 31
14043 Prague, Czech Republic
Tel.: (420) 261102111
Fax: (420) 261215186, ext. 4266793721
E-Mail: praha@hydroprojekt.cz
Web Site: www.hydroprojekt.cz
Emp.: 20
Engineering Services
S.I.C.: 8711
N.A.I.C.S.: 541330
Jan Ctibor *(Dir-Branch Office)*

THE DORSEY GROUP INC.

330 West Street Unit 7
Brantford, ON, N3R 7V5, Canada
Tel.: (519) 759-0033
Fax: (519) 759-3312
Toll Free: (800) 651-5953
E-Mail: info@thedorseygroup.com
Web Site: www.thedorseygroup.com
Year Founded: 1957
Rev.: $10,868,119
Emp.: 45

Business Description:
Insurance Agencies
S.I.C.: 6399
N.A.I.C.S.: 524128
Personnel:
Paula Dorsey *(Pres)*

DORTMUNDER GUSSASPHALT GMBH & CO. KG

Teinenkamp 43
59494 Soest, Germany
Tel.: (49) 2921 8907 0
Fax: (49) 2921 8907 70
E-Mail: info@dga.de
Web Site: www.dga.de
Emp.: 200

Business Description:
Paving Asphalt Mfr
S.I.C.: 2951
N.A.I.C.S.: 324121
Personnel:
K. H. Kolb *(Mng Dir)*

Subsidiary:

Proxan Dichtstoffe GmbH (1)
Liebigstrasse 7
Gera, D-07973, Germany De
Tel.: (49) 3661442980
Fax: (49) 36614429850
E-Mail: info@proxan.de
Web Site: www.proxan.de
Emp.: 10
Polysulphide Sealing Materials Mfr
S.I.C.: 2899
N.A.I.C.S.: 325998
Jurgen Kausch *(Founder & Mng Dir)*

DOSHISHA CO., LTD.

1-5-5 Higashi Shinsaibashi
Chuo-ku, Osaka, 542-8525, Japan
Tel.: (81) 6 6121 5888
Web Site: www.doshisha.co.jp
Year Founded: 1974
7483—(TKS)
Sales Range: $1-4.9 Billion
Emp.: 2,007

Business Description:
Household Product Whslr
S.I.C.: 5064
N.A.I.C.S.: 423620
Personnel:
Masaharu Nomura *(Pres)*
Toshihiro Fujimoto *(Mng Exec Officer)*
Kazuhiro Niki *(Sr Mng Exec Officer)*
Toneri Kimbara *(Exec VP)*
Masayuki Nomura *(Exec VP)*
Board of Directors:
Toshihiro Fujimoto
Toneri Kimbara
Kazuhiro Niki
Masaharu Nomura
Masayuki Nomura

DOST STEELS LIMITED

Plot No 222 Sector 39
Korangi Creek Industrial Area, 74900
Karachi, Pakistan
Tel.: (92) 215110421
Fax: (92) 215110423
E-Mail: ho@doststeels.com
Web Site: www.doststeels.com
DSL—(KAR)
Sales Range: Less than $1 Million

Business Description:
Quenched Steel Bars Mfr
S.I.C.: 3399
N.A.I.C.S.: 331110
Personnel:
Jamal Iftakhar *(Chm & CEO)*
Sajid Ahmed Ashrafi *(CFO)*
Zahid Iftakhar *(Sec)*
Board of Directors:
Jamal Iftakhar
Zahid Iftakhar
Bilal Jamal
Mustafa Jamal
Hamza Raees
Faisal Zahid
Saad Zahid

DOT RESOURCES LTD.

Suite 3 4015 1st Street SE
Calgary, AB, T2G 4X7, Canada
Tel.: (403) 264-2647
Fax: (403) 228-2865
E-Mail: iwasylkiw@dotresourcesltd.com
Web Site: www.dotresourcesltd.com
Year Founded: 2007
DOT—(TSXV)
Assets: $3,505,698
Liabilities: $889,422
Net Worth: $2,616,276
Earnings: ($68,623)
Fiscal Year-end: 12/31/12

Business Description:
Metal Mining Services
S.I.C.: 1099
N.A.I.C.S.: 212299
Personnel:
John J. Komarnicki *(Chm, Pres & CEO)*
Donald D. McKechnie *(CFO & VP-Fin)*
Ihor P. Wasylkiw *(CIO & VP)*
Michael J. Perkins *(Sec)*
Board of Directors:
John J. Komarnicki
James S. Bunyan
Graham A. Karklin
Gordon L. Levang
Frank L. Wells, Jr.

Legal Counsel:
Borden Ladner Gervais LLP
Calgary, AB, Canada

Transfer Agent:
Olympia Trust Company
Calgary, AB, Canada

DOTDIGITALGROUP PLC

No 1 Croydon 12-16 Addiscombe Road
Croydon, CR0 0XT, United Kingdom
Tel.: (44) 845 337 9193
E-Mail: investorrelations@dotdigitalgroup.co.uk
Web Site: www.dotdigitalgroup.com
DOTD—(AIM)
Rev.: $19,262,600
Assets: $19,733,229
Liabilities: $2,934,321
Net Worth: $16,798,908
Earnings: ($4,774,194)
Emp.: 140
Fiscal Year-end: 06/30/13

Business Description:
Web, Online & Email Marketing Services
S.I.C.: 7319
N.A.I.C.S.: 541890
Personnel:
Peter Simmonds *(CEO & Dir-Fin)*
Milan Patel *(CFO)*
Tink Taylor *(COO)*
Simon Bird *(CTO)*
Board of Directors:
Frank Beechinor-Collins
Simone Barratt
Simon Bird
Skip Fidura
Richard Graham Quinton Kellett-Clarke
Peter Simmonds
Tink Taylor

Legal Counsel:
BPE Solicitors LLP
St James House St James Square
Cheltenham, United Kingdom

Subsidiaries:

dotMailer Limited (1)
18th Floor No 1 Croydon 12-16 Addiscombe Road
Croydon, CR0 0XT, United Kingdom
Tel.: (44) 20 8662 2762
Fax: (44) 20 8239 1147
E-Mail: info@dotmailer.co.uk
Web Site: www.dotmailer.co.uk
Emp.: 150
Email Marketing Services
S.I.C.: 7374
N.A.I.C.S.: 518210
Tink Taylor *(Dir-Bus Dev)*

Netcallidus Limited (1)
Hall Farm Wellingborough Road Sywell
Aerodrome Business Park
Sywell, Northampton, NN6 0BN, United Kingdom
Tel.: (44) 1604 781 044
Fax: (44) 1604 212 869
E-Mail: info@netcallidus.com
Web Site: www.netcallidus.com
Emp.: 10
Search Engine Optimization Services
S.I.C.: 2741
N.A.I.C.S.: 519130

DOTTIKON ES HOLDING AG

Dottikon Hemprunnstallsse 17
Dottikon, Aargau, 5605, Switzerland
Tel.: (41) 566168111
Fax: (41) 566168120
E-Mail: info@dottikon.com
Web Site: www.dottikon.com
Year Founded: 1913
DESN—(SWX)
Sls.: $90,729,798
Assets: $366,960,165
Liabilities: $44,650,389
Net Worth: $322,309,776
Earnings: ($5,556,339)
Emp.: 440
Fiscal Year-end: 03/31/13

Business Description:
Fine Chemical Mfr for Pharmaceutical & Chemical Industries
S.I.C.: 2899
N.A.I.C.S.: 325998
Personnel:
Markus Blocher *(Chm & CEO)*
Thomas Fruh *(Deputy Chm)*
Marlene Born *(CFO)*
Board of Directors:
Markus Blocher
Thomas Fruh
Alfred Scheidegger

Subsidiary:

Dottikon Exclusive Synthesis AG (1)
Hembrunnstrasse 17
5605 Dottikon, Switzerland (100%)
Tel.: (41) 566168111
Fax: (41) 566168120
E-Mail: info@dottikon.com
Web Site: www.dottikon.com
Emp.: 500
Research & Development in the Physical Engineering & Life Sciences
S.I.C.: 8731
N.A.I.C.S.: 541712
Markus Blocher *(Mng Dir)*

DOUBLE A (1991) PUBLIC COMPANY LIMITED

187/3 Moo 1 Bangna-Trad km 42 Road
Bangwua District, Bang Pakong, Chacheong-sao, 24180, Thailand
Tel.: (66) 38 538968, ext. 2747
Fax: (66) 38 538968, ext. 2718
E-Mail: webmasteraa@DoubleA1991.com
Web Site: www.doubleapaper.com
Year Founded: 1989
Sales Range: $100-124.9 Million
Emp.: 3,000

Business Description:
Pulp & Paper Mfr
S.I.C.: 2611
N.A.I.C.S.: 322110
Personnel:
Kitti Dumnernchanvanit *(Co-Chm)*
Narong Srisa-an *(Co-Chm)*
Virabongsa Ramangkura *(Chm-Exec Bd)*
Sirin Nimmanhaeminda *(Vice Chm)*
Yothin Dumnernchanvanit *(Pres)*
Thirawit Leetaworn *(Exec VP)*
Board of Directors:
Kitti Dumnernchanvanit
Narong Srisa-an
Anuthra Asawanonda
Poonsombat Dumnernchanvanit
Trirat Dumnernchanvanit
Yothin Dumnernchanvanit

Double A (1991) Public Company Limited—(Continued)

Pracha Jaruthrakulchai
Narong Mahanonda
Sirin Nimmanhaeminda
Virabongsa Ramangkura
Sirichai Sakornrattanakool
Phisamai Supanuntareuk
Panit Tulwatanajit
Watchara Tuntariyanond
Kazuhiko Watanabe

Non-U.S. Subsidiaries:

Double A International Business Korea Ltd **(1)**
6th Fl Kangnam-Building Shisa-Dong Kangnam-Gu
Shinsa-dong Kangnam-gu, 135-722 Seoul, Korea (South)
Tel.: (82) 25155960
Fax: (82) 25155313
E-Mail: information@double-a.co.kr
Web Site: www.double-a.co.kr
Emp.: 35
Paper Mills
S.I.C.: 2621
N.A.I.C.S.: 322121
Ch Lee *(Mgr-Channel Dev)*

Double A International Network B.V. **(1)**
Boompjes 55
3011XB Rotterdam, Netherlands
Tel.: (31) 102229096
Fax: (31) 102229098
E-Mail: info@doubleapaper.nl
Web Site: www.doubleapaper.eu
Emp.: 6
Pulp Mills
S.I.C.: 2611
N.A.I.C.S.: 322110
Ben Veldman *(Mng Dir)*

Double A International Network Co., Ltd **(1)**
51 Lor 17 Geylang Superior Indl Bldg
389838 Singapore, Singapore
Tel.: (65) 67442288
Fax: (65) 67443366
E-Mail: enquiry@doublea.com.sg
Web Site: www.doublea.com.sg
Emp.: 10
Paper Mills
S.I.C.: 2621
N.A.I.C.S.: 322121
Michael Lim *(Gen Mgr)*

Double A International Network (M) Sdn Bhd **(1)**
T1-7-1 7th Fl Tower 1 Jaya 33 Hyperoffice Lot 33
Jalan Semangat Seksyen 14, 46100
Petaling Jaya, Selangor, Malaysia
Tel.: (60) 379609988
Fax: (60) 379606888
E-Mail: kncthuang@doublea.com.my
Web Site: www.doubleapaper.com.my
Emp.: 35
Paper Mills
S.I.C.: 2621
N.A.I.C.S.: 322121
Tan Lin Seng *(Gen Mgr)*

DOUBLE STAR DRILLING (1998) LTD

22833 110 Avenue
Edmonton, AB, T5S 1Y2, Canada
Tel.: (780) 484-4276
Fax: (780) 484-6481
Web Site: www.doublestardrilling.ca
Year Founded: 1986
Rev.: $14,486,726
Emp.: 70
Business Description:
Drilling Contractors
S.I.C.: 1381
N.A.I.C.S.: 213111
Personnel:
Ian Hunt *(Owner & VP)*

DOUBLELINE INCOME SOLUTIONS TRUST

1 First Canadian Place 100 King Street West 3rd Floor Podium
PO Box 150
Toronto, ON, M5X 1H3, Canada
Tel.: (416) 359-4597
Fax: (416) 359-5727
Year Founded: 2013
DSL.UN—(TSX)
Business Description:
Investment Services
S.I.C.: 6211
N.A.I.C.S.: 523999
Personnel:
L. Jacques Menard *(Chm)*
Eric C. Tripp *(Pres)*
Thomas V. Milroy *(CEO)*

DOUBLEVIEW CAPITAL CORP.

310-675 West Hastings St
Vancouver, BC, V6B 1N2, Canada
Tel.: (604) 678-9587
Fax: (604) 683-8260
E-Mail: corporate@doubleview.ca
Web Site: www.doubleview.ca
Year Founded: 2008
DBV.P—(TSXV)
Assets: $908,562
Liabilities: $161,875
Net Worth: $746,687
Earnings: ($279,448)
Fiscal Year-end: 02/28/13
Business Description:
Investment Services
S.I.C.: 6211
N.A.I.C.S.: 523999
Personnel:
Farshad Shirvani *(Pres & CEO)*
Robert Hall *(CFO)*
Board of Directors:
Allan Fabbro
Robert Hall
Andrew Rees
Farshad Shirvani
Bryan Hugh Wilson
Transfer Agent:
Computershare Trust Company of Canada
1003 750 West Pender Street
Vancouver, BC, V6C 2T8, Canada

DOUCETTE REALTY LTD.

1272 5th Avenue
Prince George, BC, V2L 3L2, Canada
Tel.: (250) 562-2121
Fax: (250) 562-0248
Toll Free: (866) 562-2100
E-Mail: info@doucetterealty.com
Web Site: www.doucetterealty.com
Year Founded: 1984
Rev.: $51,668,486
Emp.: 20
Business Description:
Real Estate Brokerage Services
S.I.C.: 6531
N.A.I.C.S.: 531210
Personnel:
Sid Doucette *(Founder & Pres)*

DOUG MARSHALL MOTOR CITY (2000) LTD.

11044 100 Street
Grande Prairie, AB, T8V 2N1, Canada
Tel.: (780) 532-9333
Fax: (780) 539-7310
Toll Free: (800) 263-9722
Web Site: www.dougmarshallgm.com
Year Founded: 2001
Rev.: $23,408,000
Emp.: 50
Business Description:
New & Used Car Dealers
S.I.C.: 5511
N.A.I.C.S.: 441110
Personnel:
Rolly Marie *(Gen Mgr-Sls)*

DOUGHTY HANSON & CO. LTD.

Times Place 45 Pall Mall
London, SW1Y 5JG, United Kingdom
Tel.: (44) 2076639300
Fax: (44) 2076639350
E-Mail: info@doughtyhanson.com
Web Site: www.doughtyhanson.com
Year Founded: 1981
Managed Assets: $3,400,000,000
Emp.: 145
Business Description:
Private Equity Firm
S.I.C.: 6211
N.A.I.C.S.: 523999
Personnel:
Nigel Grierson *(Co-Founder & Mng Dir)*
Richard P. Hanson *(Chm)*
Max Lever *(Co-COO)*
Stephen Marquardt *(Co-COO)*
Julian Gabriel *(Sr Principal-Real Estate)*
Kevin Grundy *(Principal-Real Estate)*

Holdings:

ASCO Group Limited **(1)**
Regent Centre
Regen Rd, Aberdeen, Scotland, AB11 5NS, United Kingdom UK
Tel.: (44) 1224580396
Fax: (44) 1224576172
E-Mail: info@ascoworld.com
Web Site: www.ascoworld.com
Sales Range: $300-349.9 Billion
Emp.: 300
Logistics & Supply Chain Management Services
S.I.C.: 1389
N.A.I.C.S.: 213112
Billy Allan *(Chm)*
Derek Smith *(CEO)*
Mark Walker *(CFO)*
Matt Thomas *(CEO-Australasia)*

Subsidiary:

ASCO Freight Management Ltd. **(2)**
Unit B1/B2 Lombard Centre Kirkhill Industrial Estate
Dyce, Aberdeen, AB21 0GU, United Kingdom
Tel.: (44) 1224 280022
Fax: (44) 1224724477
Web Site: www.ascoworld.com
Emp.: 20
Freight Transportation & Logistics Management
S.I.C.: 4731
N.A.I.C.S.: 488510
Richard Singer *(Mng Dir)*

U.S. Subsidiaries:

ASCO Freight Management **(2)**
1755 Federal Rd
Houston, TX 77015
Tel.: (713) 451-0008
Web Site: www.ascoworld.com
Emp.: 40
Freight Management & Logistics Services
S.I.C.: 4731
N.A.I.C.S.: 488510
John Jordan *(CEO-Americas)*

Harman Technology, Ltd. **(1)**
Town Lane
Mobberley, Knutsford, Cheshire, WA16 7JL, United Kingdom (100%)
Tel.: (44) 156550000
Fax: (44) 1565872734
Web Site: www.ilford.com
Emp.: 380
Mfr. of Copying Machines
S.I.C.: 5044
N.A.I.C.S.: 423420

Joint Venture:

Fourth Dimension Display Ltd. **(1)**
1 St David's Dr
Saint David's Business Park
Dalgety Bay, Dunfermline, Fife, KY11 9PF, United Kingdom
Tel.: (44) 383828800
Fax: (44) 383828801
Emp.: 50
Holding Company
S.I.C.: 6719
N.A.I.C.S.: 551112

U.S. Subsidiary:

Tumi Holdings, Inc. **(1)**
1001 Durham Ave
South Plainfield, NJ 07080 DE
Tel.: (908) 756-4400
Fax: (908) 756-5878
E-Mail: info@tumi.com
Web Site: www.tumi.com
TUMI—(NYSE)
Sls.: $467,438,000
Assets: $506,487,000
Liabilities: $138,489,000
Net Worth: $367,998,000
Earnings: $54,559,000
Emp.: 1,307
Fiscal Year-end: 12/31/13
Holding Company; Luggage, Handbags, Wallets & Accessories Designer & Mfr
S.I.C.: 6719
N.A.I.C.S.: 551112
Jerome Squire Griffith *(Pres & CEO)*
Michael J. Mardy *(CFO & Exec VP)*
Peter L. Gray *(Gen Counsel & Exec VP)*
Thomas H. Nelson *(Sr VP & Mng Dir-Asia Pacific)*
Steven M. Hurwitz *(Sr VP-Product Dev, Mfg & Sourcing)*
Alan M. Krantzler *(Sr VP-Brand Mgmt)*

Subsidiary:

Tumi, Inc. **(2)**
1001 Durham Ave
South Plainfield, NJ 07080 (100%)
Tel.: (908) 756-4400
Fax: (908) 756-5878
Toll Free: (800) 299-TUMI
E-Mail: gopero@tumi.com
Web Site: www.tumi.com
Emp.: 600
Luggage, Handbags, Wallets & Accessories Designer & Mfr
S.I.C.: 3199
N.A.I.C.S.: 316998
Michael J. Mardy *(CFO & Exec VP)*

Non-U.S. Subsidiary:

Tumi (UK) Ltd. **(3)**
Palmerston House
814 Brighton Road, Purley, Surrey, CR8 2BR, United Kingdom
Tel.: (44) 161 332 6451
E-Mail: customerservice@tumi.uk.com
Web Site: uk.tumi.com
Luggage, Handbags, Wallets & Accessories Retailer
S.I.C.: 5948
N.A.I.C.S.: 448320

Non-U.S. Subsidiaries:

TMF Group **(1)**
Parnassustoren Locatellikade 1
1076 AZ Amsterdam, Netherlands
Mailing Address:
PO Box 75215
1070AE Amsterdam, Netherlands
Tel.: (31) 205755600
Fax: (31) 206730016
E-Mail: netherlands@tmf-group.com
Web Site: www.tmf-group.com
Sales Range: $250-299.9 Million
Emp.: 3,020
Global Management & Accounting Outsourcing
S.I.C.: 8742
N.A.I.C.S.: 541611
Hugo van Vredenburch *(CEO)*

TV3 Television Network Limited **(1)**
Westgate Business Pk Ballymount
Dublin, 24, Ireland (100%)
Tel.: (353) 14193333
Fax: (353) 14193300
E-Mail: info@tv3.ie
Web Site: www.tv3.ie
Sales Range: $75-99.9 Million
Emp.: 200
Television Station
S.I.C.: 4833
N.A.I.C.S.: 515120

David McRedmond *(CEO)*

DOUGLAS LAKE CATTLE CO.

(d/b/a Douglas Lake Ranch)
General Delivery
Douglas Lake, BC, V0E 1SO, Canada
Tel.: (250) 350-3344
Fax: (250) 350-3336
E-Mail: info@douglaslake.com
Web Site: www.douglaslake.com
Year Founded: 2004
Sales Range: $10-24.9 Million
Emp.: 110
Business Description:
Beef Cattle
S.I.C.: 0212
N.A.I.C.S.: 112111
Personnel:
E. Stanley Kroenke *(Owner)*

DOURADO RESOURCES LIMITED

Level 2 Spectrum 100 Railway Road
Subiaco, WA, 6008, Australia
Tel.: (61) 89367 8133
Fax: (61) 89367 8812
Web Site: www.dourado.com.au
DUO—(ASX)
Business Description:
Gold, Copper & Uranium Exploration Services
S.I.C.: 1041
N.A.I.C.S.: 212221
Personnel:
Emilio Pietro Del Fante *(Chm)*
Peter Del Fante *(Mng Dir)*
Elizabeth Hunt *(Co-Sec)*
Robert Marusco *(Co-Sec)*
Board of Directors:
Emilio Pietro Del Fante
James Ellingford
Brian Maston
Arlene M. Mendoza
Daryl Smith
Peter Torney

DOUTOR-NICHIRES HOLDINGS CO., LTD.

10-11 Sarugaku-cho 1-chome
Shibuya-ku, Tokyo, 150-8567, Japan
Tel.: (81) 354599178
Fax: (81) 354599179
E-Mail: news-release@doutor.co.jp
Web Site: www.dnh.co.jp
Year Founded: 2007
3087—(OTC TKS)
Sales Range: $100-124.9 Million
Emp.: 2,000
Business Description:
Holding Company; Coffee & Tea Mfr; Restaurant Operator
S.I.C.: 6719
N.A.I.C.S.: 551112
Personnel:
Minoru Yamauchi *(Chm)*
Masanori Hoshino *(Pres)*
Transfer Agent:
Mizuho Trust & Banking Co., Ltd.
2-1 Yaesu 1-Chome Chuo-ku
Tokyo, 103 8670, Japan
Tel.: (81) 332788111
Fax: (81) 332816947

Subsidiaries:

Nippon Restaurant System, Inc. **(1)**
10-11 Sarugaku-cho
Shibuya-ku, Tokyo, 150-8567, Japan JP
Tel.: (81) 354599178
Fax: (81) 0354599179
E-Mail: soumu@n-rs.co.jp
Web Site: www.n-rs.co.jp
Sales Range: $250-299.9 Million
Emp.: 795
Multi-Type Restaurants Operator; Processed Food, Sauces, Confectionaries & Cooking Ingredients Mfr & Whslr
S.I.C.: 5812
N.A.I.C.S.: 722513
Minoru Yamauchi *(Pres & CEO)*

Doutor Coffee Co., Ltd. **(1)**
1-10-1 Jinnan
Tokyo, Shibuya-ku, Japan JP
Tel.: (81) 354599008
Web Site: www.doutor.co.jp
Sales Range: $600-649.9 Million
Emp.: 912
Coffee Distr, Restaurant & Coffee Shop Management, Marketing & Consulting Services
S.I.C.: 2099
N.A.I.C.S.: 311920
Masanori Hoshino *(Chm)*
Yutaka Toriba *(Pres)*
Toshihiko Kurokawa *(Mng Dir)*
Yukitaka Aoki *(Mng Dir)*
Rokurou Inamori *(Mng Dir)*
Masahiro Kanno *(Exec Officer)*
Kiyotaka Ochiai *(Exec Officer)*
Youji Yamashita *(Exec Officer)*

DOUX S.A.

(d/b/a Groupe Doux)
ZI de Lospars
BP 22
29150 Chateaulin, France
Tel.: (33) 298866900
Fax: (33) 298866969
E-Mail: communication@doux.com
Web Site: www.doux.com
Year Founded: 1955
Sales Range: $1-4.9 Billion
Emp.: 10,300
Business Description:
Poultry & Poultry Products Production, Processing & Marketing
S.I.C.: 2015
N.A.I.C.S.: 311615
Personnel:
Charles Doux *(Chm)*
Michel Leonard *(CEO)*

DOVECORP ENTERPRISES INC.

35 Suntract Road
Toronto, ON, M9N 2V8, Canada
Tel.: (416) 782-8788
Sales Range: $10-24.9 Million
Business Description:
Dry Cleaning & Laundry Services
S.I.C.: 7219
N.A.I.C.S.: 812320
Personnel:
Wayne Fraser *(CFO)*

Subsidiaries:

Cadet Cleaners, Inc. **(1)**
5 Dohme Avenue
Toronto, ON, M4B 1Y7, Canada
Tel.: (416) 757-4111
Fax: (416) 757-9322
Web Site: www.cadetdrycleaners.com
Dry Cleaning Services
S.I.C.: 7219
N.A.I.C.S.: 812320

Dove Cleaners, Inc. **(1)**
1560 Yonge St
Delisle Court, Toronto, ON, M4T 2S9, Canada
Tel.: (416) 413-7900
Fax: (416) 413-0619
Toll Free: (866) WWW-DOVE
E-Mail: kelly@dovecleaners.com
Web Site: www.dovecleaners.com
Dry Cleaning Services
S.I.C.: 7219
N.A.I.C.S.: 812320

DOVERIE UNITED HOLDING AD

82 Doundukov Blvd
Sofia, 1000, Bulgaria
Tel.: (359) 2 984 56 11
Fax: (359) 2 984 56 63
E-Mail: doverie@doverie.bg
Web Site: www.doverie.bg
Year Founded: 1996
5DOV—(BUL)
Rev.: $107,242,517
Assets: $174,310,271
Liabilities: $76,137,799
Net Worth: $98,172,472
Earnings: ($11,315,342)
Fiscal Year-end: 12/31/12
Business Description:
Investment Management Services
S.I.C.: 6282
N.A.I.C.S.: 523930
Personnel:
Radosvet Krumov Radev *(Chm-Supervisory Bd)*
Boris Borisov *(Chm-Mgmt Bd)*
Ognyan Ivanov Donev *(Vice Chm-Supervisory Bd)*
Daniela Kolarova *(Member-Mgmt Bd)*
Anna Pavlova *(Member-Mgmt Bd)*
Supervisory Board of Directors:
Radosvet Krumov Hadev
Ognyan Ivanov Donev
Ventsislav Simeonov Stoev

DOVRE GROUP PLC

Unioninkatu 20-22
FIN-00130 Helsinki, Finland
Tel.: (358) 204362000
Fax: (358) 204362500
E-Mail: info@proha.com
Web Site: www.dovregroup.com
DOV1V—(OMX)
Sls.: $126,632,866
Assets: $54,549,501
Liabilities: $23,570,091
Net Worth: $30,979,410
Earnings: $3,862,162
Emp.: 461
Fiscal Year-end: 12/31/12
Business Description:
Project Management & Software Services
S.I.C.: 7371
N.A.I.C.S.: 541511
Personnel:
Hannu Vaajoensuu *(Chm)*
Rainer Haggblom *(Vice Chm)*
Janne Mielck *(CEO)*
Tarja Leikas *(CFO)*
Susanna Karlsson *(Comm Officer)*
Arve Jensen *(Exec VP-Project Personnel)*
Petri Karlsson *(Exec VP-Consulting)*
Board of Directors:
Hannu Vaajoensuu
Rainer Haggblom
Ilari Koskelo
Ossi Pohjola
Anja Silvennoinen

Subsidiaries:

ProCountor International Oy **(1)**
Keilaranta 8
FIN 02150 Espoo, Finland (80%)
Tel.: (358) 20 7879 838
Web Site: www.procountor.com
Sales Range: Less than $1 Million
Emp.: 9
Financial Management Solutions Software
S.I.C.: 7371
N.A.I.C.S.: 541511
Mikko Siivola *(Mng Dir)*

Non-U.S. Subsidiary:

Safran Software Solutions AS **(1)**
Lokkeveien 99
NO-4008 Stavanger, Norway
Mailing Address:
Postbox 77 Sentrum
NO-4001 Stavanger, Norway
Tel.: (47) 5187 4560
Fax: (47) 5187 4561
E-Mail: info@safran.no
Web Site: www.safranna.com
Software Products & Services
S.I.C.: 7372
N.A.I.C.S.: 511210
Juha Pennanen *(Mng Dir)*

DOW MOTORS (OTTAWA) LIMITED

(d/b/a Dow Honda)
845 Carling Avenue
Ottawa, ON, K1S 2E7, Canada
Tel.: (613) 237-2777
Fax: (613) 237-4979
E-Mail: mail@dowhonda.com
Web Site: www.dowhonda.com
Year Founded: 1972
Rev.: $34,281,000
Emp.: 50
Business Description:
New & Used Car Dealers
S.I.C.: 5511
N.A.I.C.S.: 441110
Personnel:
Jeff Mierins *(Pres)*

DOWA HOLDINGS CO., LTD.

22F Akihabara UDX Building 4-14-1 Sotokanda
Chiyoda-ku, Tokyo, 101-0021, Japan
Tel.: (81) 368471106
Fax: (81) 368471272
E-Mail: info@dowa.co.jp
Web Site: www.dowa.co.jp
Year Founded: 1884
5714—(TKS)
Sls.: $4,613,290,000
Assets: $3,847,657,000
Liabilities: $2,281,257,000
Net Worth: $1,566,400,000
Earnings: $167,343,000
Emp.: 5,500
Fiscal Year-end: 03/31/13
Business Description:
Holding Company; Nonferrous Metal Smelting & Refining; Environmental & Recycling Services; Electrical & Electronic Materials Producer; Metal Production & Fabrication Services; Heat Treating
S.I.C.: 6719
N.A.I.C.S.: 551112
Personnel:
Masao Yamada *(Pres)*
Haruo Nishizawa *(Officer)*
Akira Otsuka *(Officer)*
Kenichi Sasaki *(Officer)*
Akira Sekiguchi *(Officer)*
Toshiro Sumida *(Officer)*
Board of Directors:
Eiji Hosoda
Hiroyuki Kai
Katsuji Matsushita
Hiroshi Nakashio
Fumitoshi Sugiyama
Masao Yamada

Divisions:

Dowa Eco-System Co., Ltd. **(1)**
22F Akihabara UDX Building 14-1
Sotokanda 4-chome
Chiyoda-ku, Tokyo, 101-0021, Japan (100%)
Tel.: (81) 368471230
Fax: (81) 368471240
Web Site: www.dowa-eco.co.jp
Sales Range: $350-399.9 Million
Emp.: 100
Environmental & Industrial Waste Management & Recycling
S.I.C.: 4959
N.A.I.C.S.: 562998
Kenichi Sasaki *(Pres)*

Subsidiaries:

Auto Recycle Akita Co., Ltd. **(2)**
96 Sugisawa Kosakakouzan Kosaka-machi
Kazuno-gun, Akita, 017-0202, Japan

Dowa Holdings Co., Ltd.—(Continued)

Tel.: (81) 186 30 7313
Fax: (81) 186 29 5185
Web Site: www.dowa.co.jp/en/about_dowa/group.html
Automobile Mfr
S.I.C.: 3711
N.A.I.C.S.: 336111

Biodiesel Okayama Co,. Ltd. (2)
1-3-1 Kaigan-dori
Minami-ku, Okayama, 702-8506, Japan
Tel.: (81) 86 261 6050
Fax: (81) 86 261 6051
Web Site: www.dowa.co.jp/en/about_dowa/group.html
Biodiesel Fuel Mfr
S.I.C.: 2999
N.A.I.C.S.: 324199

Dowa-Tsuun Co., Ltd. (2)
69-1 Nakada Sakurakawa
Mizusawa-ku, Oshu, Iwate, 023-0003, Japan
Tel.: (81) 197 25 5353
Fax: (81) 197 24 8443
Web Site: www.dowa.co.jp/en/about_dowa/group.html
Transportation & Warehousing Services
S.I.C.: 4789
N.A.I.C.S.: 488999

Eco-System Akita Co., Ltd. (2)
42 Tsutsumisawa Hanaoka-machi
Odate, Akita, 017-0005, Japan
Tel.: (81) 186 46 1436
Fax: (81) 186 46 3628
Industrial Waste Management Services
S.I.C.: 4959
N.A.I.C.S.: 562998

Green Fill Kosaka Co., Ltd. (2)
60-1 Otarube Kosakakouzan Kosaka-machi
Kazuno-gun, Akita, 017-0202, Japan
Tel.: (81) 186 29 2924
Fax: (81) 186 29 2964
Industrial Waste Disposal Services
S.I.C.: 4953
N.A.I.C.S.: 562211
Metoki Shuichi *(Pres)*

Kowa Seiko Co., Ltd. (2)
46-93 Nakabaru
Tobata-ku, Kitakyushu, Fukuoka, 804-0002, Japan
Tel.: (81) 93 872 5155
Fax: (81) 93 873 1030
Web Site: www.kowa-seiko.co.jp
Industrial Waste Recovery Services
S.I.C.: 4959
N.A.I.C.S.: 562998

Meltec Co., Ltd. (2)
2333-29 Atago Yana
Oyama, Tochigi, 323-0158, Japan
Tel.: (81) 285 49 1080
Fax: (81) 285 49 1084
E-Mail: info@meltec-ltd.co.jp
Web Site: www.meltec-ltd.co.jp
Incinerated Ash Recycling Services
S.I.C.: 4212
N.A.I.C.S.: 562111

Okayama Koyu Co., Ltd. (2)
1048-1 Hinotani Kichigahara Misaki-cho
Kume-gun, Okayama, 708-1523, Japan
Tel.: (81) 869 64 2775
Fax: (81) 869 64 2598
Cargo Handling Services
S.I.C.: 4491
N.A.I.C.S.: 488320

Non-U.S. Subsidiaries:

Bangpoo Environmental Complex Ltd. (2)
966 Moo 2 Soi 3 Bangpoo Industrial Estate
Sukhumvit Rd Bangpoo Mai
Mueang Samut Prakan, Samut Prakan, 10280, Thailand
Tel.: (66) 2 709 2546
Fax: (66) 2 709 2547
E-Mail: info@wms-thailand.com
Web Site: www.wtbacc.com
Waste Management Services
S.I.C.: 4959
N.A.I.C.S.: 562998
Yoshihiro Okada *(Pres)*

Dowa Environmental Engineering (Suzhou) Co., Ltd. (2)
No 28 Sanlian Street
Suzhou, Jiangsu, 215129, China
Tel.: (86) 512 8518 7700
Fax: (86) 512 8518 8108
Groundwater Remediation Services
S.I.C.: 1799
N.A.I.C.S.: 562910

Eastern Seaboard Environmental Complex Co., Ltd. (2)
88 Moo 8 Tamborn Bowin Amphur
Sriracha, Chon Buri, 20230, Thailand
Tel.: (66) 38 346 364
Fax: (66) 38 346 368
E-Mail: info@wms-thailand.com
Liquid Waste Treatment Services
S.I.C.: 4953
N.A.I.C.S.: 562212

JIANGXI DOWA ENVIRONMENTAL MANAGEMENT CO., LTD. (2)
10F-2 No 41 Nanking W Rd
Taipei, 10352, Taiwan
Tel.: (886) 2 2558 0577
Fax: (886) 2 2558 2077
Groundwater Recycling Services
S.I.C.: 4953
N.A.I.C.S.: 562920

P.T. Prasadha Pamunah Limbah Industri (2)
Jl Raya Narogong - Desa Nambo
PO Box 18
Cileungsi, Bogor, 16820, Indonesia
Tel.: (62) 21 867 4042
Fax: (62) 21 867 4043
E-Mail: info@ppli-indo.com
Web Site: www.ppli-indo.com
Waste Management Services
S.I.C.: 4959
N.A.I.C.S.: 562998

Waste Management Siam Ltd. (2)
Central City Tower 1 25th Floor 589/142
Bangna-Trad Road Kwang Bangna
Khet Bangna, Bangkok, 10260, Thailand
Tel.: (66) 2745 6926 7
Fax: (66) 2745 6928
E-Mail: info@wms-thailand.com
Web Site: www.wms-thailand.com
Waste Management Services
S.I.C.: 4959
N.A.I.C.S.: 562998

Dowa Electronic Materials Co., Ltd. (1)
22F Akihabara UDX Building 14-1
Sotokanda 4-Chome
Chiyoda-ku, Tokyo, 101-0021, Japan (100%)
Tel.: (81) 368471250
Fax: (81) 368471260
E-Mail: urabes@dowa.co.jp
Sales Range: $450-499.9 Million
Emp.: 4,000
Electronic & Magnetic Materials Supplier
S.I.C.: 3674
N.A.I.C.S.: 334413
Akira Otsuka *(Pres)*

Dowa Metals & Mining Co., Ltd. (1)
22F Akihabara UDX Building 14-1
Sotokanda 4-chome
Tokyo, Chiyoda-ku, 101-0021, Japan (100%)
Tel.: (81) 368471200
Fax: (81) 368471210
E-Mail: metalmine@dowa.co.jp
Web Site: www.dowa.co.jp/en/about_dowa/group.html
Emp.: 30
Non-Ferrous Metal Smelting & Recycling
S.I.C.: 3339
N.A.I.C.S.: 331410
Nobuo Yanazaki *(Pres)*

Subsidiaries:

Acids Co., Ltd. (2)
Daiwai Shimbashi 510 Bldg 5-10-5 Shimbashi
Minato-ku, Tokyo, 105-0004, Japan
Tel.: (81) 3 6402 7531
Fax: (81) 3 3437 0223
Specialty Chemicals Distr
S.I.C.: 5169
N.A.I.C.S.: 424690

Akita Rare Metals Co., Ltd (2)
217-9 Furumichi-Shimokawabata Iijima
Akita, 011-0911, Japan
Tel.: (81) 18 846 1794
Fax: (81) 18 845 9051
Electronic Component Mfr
S.I.C.: 3679
N.A.I.C.S.: 334419

Akita Zinc Recycling Co., Ltd. (2)
1 Sunada Iijima
Akita, 011-0911, Japan
Tel.: (81) 18 846 7918
Fax: (81) 18 845 9051
Web Site: www.dowa.co.jp/en/about_dowa/group.html
Industrial Chemical Mfr
S.I.C.: 2899
N.A.I.C.S.: 325998

Kosaka Smelting & Refining Co., Ltd (2)
60-1 Otarube Kosakakouzan Kosaka-machi
Kazuno-gun, Akita, 017-0202, Japan
Tel.: (81) 186 29 2700
Fax: (81) 186 29 5200
Copper & Lead Smelting Services
S.I.C.: 3339
N.A.I.C.S.: 331410

Dowa Metaltech Co., Ltd. (1)
22F Akihabara UDX Building 14-1
Sotokanda 4-chome
Chiyoda-ku, Tokyo, 101-0021, Japan (100%)
Tel.: (81) 368471252
Fax: (81) 368471272
E-Mail: metalp@dowa.co.jp
Sales Range: $600-649.9 Million
Emp.: 1,000
High-Value-Added Metal Alloy Plating & Processing
S.I.C.: 3351
N.A.I.C.S.: 331420
Hiroyuki Kai *(Pres)*

Subsidiaries:

Dowa Metanix Co., Ltd. (2)
2630 Shingai
Iwata, Shizuoka, 438-0025, Japan JP (90%)
Tel.: (81) 538327138
Fax: (81) 538355574
Web Site: www.metanix.co.jp
Sales Range: $100-124.9 Million
Emp.: 200
Nickel- & Copper-Based Alloys & Electronic Parts Mfr
S.I.C.: 3351
N.A.I.C.S.: 331420
Shigyuki Kihara *(Pres)*

Joint Venture:

Dowa-Olin Metal Corporation (3)
2630 Shingai Iwata-shi
Shizuoka, 438-0025, Japan
Tel.: (81) 538 32 7138
Fax: (81) 538 32 9008
Web Site: www.metanix.co.jp
Sales Range: $50-74.9 Million
Emp.: 16
High-Performance Copper Alloy Marketer & Whslr; Owned 50% by Olin Corporation & 50% by Dowa Metaltech Co., Ltd.
S.I.C.: 5051
N.A.I.C.S.: 423510
Toichi Ishikawa *(Pres)*

New Nippon Brass Co., Ltd. (2)
5844-3 Kamakazu
Asahi, Chiba, 289-2505, Japan
Tel.: (81) 479 62 0444
Fax: (81) 479 62 0404
Web Site: www.dowa.co.jp/en/about_dowa/group.html
Forged Brass Mfr & Distr
S.I.C.: 3351
N.A.I.C.S.: 331420

Non-U.S. Subsidiary:

Dowa Advanced Materials (Shanghai) Co., Ltd. (2)
No 7 Studio 8 Rongxiang Road Shanghai
Songjiang
Shanghai, China
Tel.: (86) 21 5774 8118
Fax: (86) 21 5774 8338
Copper Strip Mfr & Distr
S.I.C.: 3351
N.A.I.C.S.: 331420

Dowa Thermotech Co., Ltd. (1)
22F Akihabara UDX Bldg 4-14-1 Sotokanda
Chiyoda-ku, Tokyo, 101-0021, Japan (100%)
Tel.: (81) 3 6847 1170
Fax: (81) 3 6847 1281
E-Mail: tht@dowa.co.jp
Web Site: www.dowa.co.jp/
Sales Range: $200-249.9 Million
Emp.: 400
Metal Heat Treatment Operations
S.I.C.: 3398
N.A.I.C.S.: 332811
Toshiro Sumida *(Pres)*

Non-U.S. Subsidiary:

Dowa Thermotech (Thailand) Co., Ltd. (2)
300/33 Moo 4 Tambol Tasit
Amphur Pluakdaeng, Rayong, 21140, Thailand
Tel.: (66) 3895 9008
Fax: (66) 3895 9097
Web Site: www.dowa.co.jp/en/about_dowa/group.html
Metal Heat Treatment & Maintenance Services
S.I.C.: 3398
N.A.I.C.S.: 332811

Subsidiaries:

Act-B Recycling Co., Ltd. (1)
278-6 Shiohama-cho
Minamata-shi, 867-0067 Kumamoto, Japan (55%)
Tel.: (81) 966623300
Fax: (81) 966623338
Web Site: www.act-b.co.jp
Consumer Electronics & Appliances Rental
S.I.C.: 7359
N.A.I.C.S.: 532210

Akita Recycle & Finepack Co., Ltd. (1)
76-1 Otarube Kosakakouzan
Kosaka-machi Kazuno-gun, Akita, 017-0202, Japan
Tel.: (81) 186293467
Fax: (81) 186293466
Plastics Material & Resin Mfr
S.I.C.: 2821
N.A.I.C.S.: 325211

Akita Zinc Co., Ltd. (1)
217-2 Furumichi-Shimokawabata
Lijima, Akita, Japan (81%)
Tel.: (81) 188461121
Fax: (81) 188459051
Web Site: www.dowa.co.jp/en/about_dowa/group.html
Emp.: 188
Industrial Process Furnace & Oven Mfr
S.I.C.: 3567
N.A.I.C.S.: 333994
Masamori Shimofufa *(Pres)*

Akita Zinc Solutions Co., Ltd. (1)
1 Sunada
Lijima, Akita, 011-0911, Japan (84%)
Tel.: (81) 188456069
Fax: (81) 188458037
E-Mail: info@dowa.co.jp
Emp.: 70
Primary Smelting & Refining of Nonferrous Metal
S.I.C.: 3339
N.A.I.C.S.: 331410
Takashi Ujihara *(Pres)*

CEMM Co., Ltd. (1)
19-1 Ukishima-cho Mizuho-ku
Miizuho-ku, Nagoya, 467-0854, Japan (100%)
Tel.: (81) 526930181
Fax: (81) 526945337
Web Site: www.cemm.co.jp
Emp.: 80
Power Boiler & Heat Exchanger Mfr
S.I.C.: 3559
N.A.I.C.S.: 332410
Hiroshi Sato *(Pres)*

Dowa Electronics Materials Okayama Co., Ltd. (1)
1-3-1 Kaigan-dori
Okayama-shi, 702-8506 Okayama, Japan (100%)

Tel.: (81) 862621121
Fax: (81) 862629021
Web Site: www.dowa.co.jp/en/about_dowa/group.html
Emp.: 250
Powder Metallurgy Part Mfr
S.I.C.: 3499
N.A.I.C.S.: 332117
Kentaro Yamauchi *(Pres)*

Subsidiary:

Dowa IP Creation Co., Ltd. **(2)**
7 Chikkousakae-machi
Okayama-shi, 702-8053 Okayama, Japan (70%)
Tel.: (81) 862622228
Fax: (81) 862647382
E-Mail: osakat@dowa.co.jp
Web Site: www.dowa.co.jp/en/about_dowa/group.html
Emp.: 120
Powder Metallurgy Part Mfr
S.I.C.: 3499
N.A.I.C.S.: 332117

Dowa F-Tec Co., Ltd. **(1)**
1045 Kichigahara Misaki-cho
Kume-gun, Okayama, 708-1523, Japan
Tel.: (81) 868 62 1144
Fax: (81) 868 62 1146
Web Site: www.dowa.co.jp/en/about_dowa/group.html
Emp.: 30
Ferrite Powder Mfr
S.I.C.: 2899
N.A.I.C.S.: 325998
Masami Mandai *(Gen Mgr)*

Dowa Gallium Wax Sales Co., Ltd. **(1)**
7th Floor Takanoboru 25 Building
1-1-5 Kakyouin, Sendai, Aoba, 980-0013, Japan
Tel.: (81) 222157392
Fax: (81) 222652787
Durable Goods Merchant Whslr
S.I.C.: 5099
N.A.I.C.S.: 423990

Dowa Hightech Co., Ltd. **(1)**
1718 Nitte
Honjou, Saitama, 367- 0002, Japan (100%)
Tel.: (81) 495216111
Fax: (81) 495216116
E-Mail: shimadat@dowa.co.jp
Web Site: www.dowa.co.jp
Emp.: 200
Chemical Product & Preparation Mfr
S.I.C.: 2899
N.A.I.C.S.: 325998
Masami Sakuraba *(Pres)*

Dowa Kohsan Co., Ltd. **(1)**
22F Akihabara UDX Bldg 4-14-1
Sotokanda Chiyoda-ku, 101-0021 Tokyo, Japan
Tel.: (81) 368471272
Fax: (81) 368471281
Web Site: www.dowa.co.jp/en/about_dowa/group.html
Business Support Services
S.I.C.: 7389
N.A.I.C.S.: 561499

Dowa Management Services Co., Ltd. **(1)**
22nd Floor Akihabara Udx Building 4-14-1
Sotokanda Chiyoda-ku, 101-0021 Tokyo, Japan
Tel.: (81) 368471151
Fax: (81) 368471161
Web Site: www.dowa.co.jp/en/about_dowa/group.html
Business Support Services
S.I.C.: 7389
N.A.I.C.S.: 561499
Fumitoshi Sugiyama *(Pres)*

Dowa Metal Co., Ltd. **(1)**
767 Matsunokijima
Iwata-shi, 438-0125 Shizuoka, Japan (100%)
Tel.: (81) 539623131
Fax: (81) 539623996
E-Mail: kiharas@dowa.co.jp
Web Site: www.dowa.co.jp/en/about_dowa/group.html
Emp.: 250
Copper Rolling Drawing & Extruding
S.I.C.: 3351
N.A.I.C.S.: 331420
Shigeyuki Kihara *(Pres)*

Dowa Power Device Co., Ltd. **(1)**
9637-3 Kataoka
Oazakataoka Shiojiri, Nagano, 399-0711, Japan (100%)
Tel.: (81) 263530770
Fax: (81) 263531770
Web Site: www.dowa.co.jp
Emp.: 50
Bare Printed Circuit Board Mfr
S.I.C.: 3672
N.A.I.C.S.: 334412
Iwamoto Kunio *(Pres)*

Dowa Semiconductor Akita Co., Ltd. **(1)**
1 Sunada Iijima
Akita-shi, Akita, 011-0911, Japan (100%)
Tel.: (81) 188468000
Fax: (81) 188469478
E-Mail: info@dowa.co.jp
Emp.: 300
Semiconductor & Related Device Mfr
S.I.C.: 3674
N.A.I.C.S.: 334413

Dowa Techno Engineering Co., Ltd. **(1)**
31-10 Chikkou-Sakaemachi
Okayama, 702-8609, Japan (100%)
Tel.: (81) 862629208
Fax: (81) 862629218
Commercial & Service Industry Machinery Mfr
S.I.C.: 3589
N.A.I.C.S.: 333318

Dowa Techno-Research Co., Ltd. **(1)**
60-1 Otarube Kosakakouzan Kosaka-machi
Kazuno-gun, Akita, 017-0202, Japan
Tel.: (81) 186 29 2781
Fax: (81) 186 29 2792
Environmental Engineering Services
S.I.C.: 8711
N.A.I.C.S.: 541330

Dowa Technology Co., Ltd. **(1)**
22nd Floor Akihabara Udx Building 4-14-1
Sotokanda Chiyoda-ku, 101-0021 Tokyo, Japan (100%)
Tel.: (81) 368471105
Fax: (81) 368471161
Web Site: www.dowa.co.jp/en/about_dowa/group.html
Business Support Services
S.I.C.: 7389
N.A.I.C.S.: 561499
Fumitoshi Sugiyama *(CTO)*

Dowa Tecno-Reseach Co., Ltd. **(1)**
60-1 Otarube Kosakakouzan
Kosaka-machi Kazuno-gun, 017-0202 Akita, Japan
Tel.: (81) 186292781
Fax: (81) 186292792
Web Site: www.dowa.co.jp/en/about_dowa/group.html
Emp.: 100
Environmental Consulting Services
S.I.C.: 8999
N.A.I.C.S.: 541620
Katuo Chonan *(Pres)*

E & E Solutions Inc. **(1)**
Akihabara Udx Bldg 4-14-1
Sotokanda Chiyoda-ku, 101-0021 Tokyo, Japan
Tel.: (81) 363280080
Fax: (81) 352952051
Web Site: www.eesol.co.jp
Emp.: 50
Surveying & Mapping Services
S.I.C.: 8713
N.A.I.C.S.: 541370

Eco-Recycle Co., Ltd. **(1)**
30-2 Douyashiki Hanaoka-machi
Odate-shi, 017-0005 Akita, Japan (59%)
Tel.: (81) 186471001
Fax: (81) 186471002
Web Site: www.dowa.co.jp/en/about_dowa/group.html
Emp.: 100
Consumer Electronics Repair & Maintenance
S.I.C.: 7622
N.A.I.C.S.: 811211
Furusawa Nobuaki *(Mng Dir)*

Eco-System Chiba Co., Ltd. **(1)**
1-1-51 Nagauraтaku
Sodegaura, Chiba, 299-0265, Japan (100%)
Tel.: (81) 438624097
Fax: (81) 438624928
E-Mail: takeda@dowa.co.jp
Emp.: 80
Waste Management Services
S.I.C.: 4959
N.A.I.C.S.: 562998
Kenji Watanabe *(Gen Mgr)*

Eco-System Hanaoka Co., Ltd. **(1)**
42 Tsutsumisawa Hanaoka-machi
Odate, Akita, 017-0005, Japan (100%)
Tel.: (81) 186462311
Fax: (81) 186461651
Emp.: 30
Waste Management Services
S.I.C.: 4959
N.A.I.C.S.: 562998
Masanori Shino Usa *(Mgr)*

Eco-System Japan Co., Ltd. **(1)**
22nd Floor Akihabara Udx Building
4-14-1 Sotokanda Chiyoda-ku, 101-0021 Tokyo, Japan (90%)
Tel.: (81) 368477010
Fax: (81) 368477015
Web Site: www.dowa.co.jp/en/about_dowa/group.html
Emp.: 100
Waste Collection
S.I.C.: 4212
N.A.I.C.S.: 562112

Eco-System Kosaka Co., Ltd. **(1)**
60-1 Otarube Kosakakouzan
Kosaka-machi Kazuno-gun, 017-0202 Akita, Japan (100%)
Tel.: (81) 186292700
Fax: (81) 186295200
Web Site: www.dowa-eco.co.jp
Emp.: 24
Hazardous Waste Collection
S.I.C.: 4212
N.A.I.C.S.: 562112
Shigeru Kawamura *(Mng Dir)*

Eco-System Okayama Co., Ltd. **(1)**
1-3-1 Kaigan-dori
Okayama, 702-8506, Japan (100%)
Tel.: (81) 862629020
Fax: (81) 862640271
Emp.: 30
Nonferrous Metal Rolling Drawing & Extruding
S.I.C.: 3356
N.A.I.C.S.: 331491
Kentaro Yamauchi *(Pres)*

Eco-System Recycling Co., Ltd. **(1)**
1718-3 Nitte Honjou-shi
Saitama, 367-0002, Japan (100%)
Tel.: (81) 495211982
Fax: (81) 495248406
E-Mail: info@dowa-ert.co.jp
Emp.: 200
Recyclable Material Whslr
S.I.C.: 5093
N.A.I.C.S.: 423930
Yoshihiko Maeda *(Pres)*

Eco-System Sanyo Co., Ltd. **(1)**
1125 Kichigahara
Misaki-cho Kume-gun, Okayama, 708-1523, Japan (100%)
Tel.: (81) 868621346
Fax: (81) 868621345
E-Mail: matsunas@dowa.co.jp
Web Site: www.dowa.co.jp
Emp.: 100
Metal Ore Mining
S.I.C.: 1099
N.A.I.C.S.: 212299
Kazuo Yokota *(Pres)*

Geotechnos Co., Ltd. **(1)**
2-22-7 Kameido Koto-ku
136-0071 Tokyo, Japan (100%)
Tel.: (81) 336835141
Fax: (81) 336835142
E-Mail: webmaster@geotechnos.co.jp
Web Site: www.geotechnos.co.jp
Emp.: 50
Water Well Drilling Contractors
S.I.C.: 1623
N.A.I.C.S.: 237110

Hoei Shoji Co., Ltd. **(1)**
1598-1 Kotehashi-cho
Hanamigawa-ku, Chiba, 262-0013, Japan
Tel.: (81) 43 286 2601
Fax: (81) 43 286 2621
Aluminium Products Mfr & Distr
S.I.C.: 3353
N.A.I.C.S.: 331315

Nippon PGM Co., Ltd. **(1)**
76-1 Otarube Kosakakouzan
Kosaka-machi Kazuno-gun, Akita, 017-0202, Japan (60%)
Tel.: (81) 186292744
Fax: (81) 186292722
Emp.: 20
Primary Smelting & Refining Nonferrous Metal
S.I.C.: 3339
N.A.I.C.S.: 331410

Showa Kaihatsu Kogyo Co., Ltd. **(1)**
31-10 Chikkou-Sakaemachi
Okayama, 702-8609, Japan (100%)
Tel.: (81) 862629200
Fax: (81) 862629216
Web Site: www.dowa.co.jp/en/about_dowa/group.html
Crushed & Broken Stone Mining & Quarrying
S.I.C.: 1429
N.A.I.C.S.: 212319
Katsushi Tanaka *(Pres)*

Tonetsu Kosan Co., Ltd. **(1)**
2-6-26 Minowa-cho
Kouhoku-ku, Yokohama, 223-0051, Japan
Tel.: (81) 455652031
Fax: (81) 455652035
Web Site: www.dowa.co.jp/en/about_dowa/group.html
Business Associations
S.I.C.: 8611
N.A.I.C.S.: 813910

Yowa Kouei Co., Ltd. **(1)**
7-2 Chikkou-Sakaemachi
Okayama, 702-8609, Japan (100%)
Tel.: (81) 862649034
Fax: (81) 862648412
Web Site: www.dowa.co.jp/en/about_dowa/group.html
Heavy & Civil Engineering Construction
S.I.C.: 1629
N.A.I.C.S.: 237990

Zinc Excel Co., Ltd. **(1)**
Akihabara Udx Building 4-14-1
Sotokanda Chiyoda-ku, 101-0021 Tokyo, Japan (85%)
Tel.: (81) 368471270
Fax: (81) 368471280
E-Mail: horimott@dowa.co.jp
Web Site: www.dowa.co.jp/en/about_dowa/group.html
Emp.: 40
Metal Service Centers & Offices
S.I.C.: 5051
N.A.I.C.S.: 423510
Kenichi Togashi *(Mgr-Sls)*

U.S. Subsidiaries:

Dowa International Corporation **(1)**
370 Lexington Ave
New York, NY 10017-6503
Tel.: (212) 697-3217
Fax: (212) 697-3902
E-Mail: info@dowa.com
Web Site: www.dowa.com
Emp.: 20
Marketing Consulting Services
S.I.C.: 8742
N.A.I.C.S.: 541613
Junichi Nagao *(Gen Mgr)*

Dowa THT America, Inc. **(1)**
2130 S Woodland Cir
Bowling Green, OH 43402 (100%)
Tel.: (419) 354-4144
Fax: (419) 354-6479
Web Site: www.dowa.co.jp/en/about_dowa/group.html
Emp.: 55
Plumbing Heating & Air-Conditioning Contractors
S.I.C.: 1711
N.A.I.C.S.: 238220

Dowa Holdings Co., Ltd.—(Continued)

Nippon PGM America Inc. (1)
500 Richards Run
Burlington, NJ 08016
Tel.: (609) 747-9994
Fax: (609) 747-8245
E-Mail: jbruno@npgmamerica.com
Web Site: www.dowa.co.jp/en/about_dowa/group.html
Emp.: 10
Crushed & Broken Stone Mining & Quarrying
S.I.C.: 1429
N.A.I.C.S.: 212319
Beth Craig *(Gen Mgr)*

Non-U.S. Subsidiaries:

Dowa Environmental Management Co., Ltd. (1)
28 Sanzhen Rd Suzhou New District
215129 Suzhou, Jiangsu, China
Tel.: (86) 51285188100
Fax: (86) 51285188108
Web Site: www.dowa.co.jp/en/about_dowa/group.html
Emp.: 50
Recyclable Material Merchant Whslr
S.I.C.: 5093
N.A.I.C.S.: 423930
Matuv Moto *(Gen Mgr)*

Dowa F-Tec (Singapore) Pte. Ltd. (1)
No 13 Benoi Crescent
Jurong, 629976 Singapore, Singapore (100%)
Tel.: (65) 62617366
Fax: (65) 62618723
E-Mail: info_eco@dowa.com.sg
Web Site: www.dowa.co.jp/en/about_dowa/group.html
Emp.: 9
Powder Metallurgy Part Mfr
S.I.C.: 3499
N.A.I.C.S.: 332117
Akio Yoshinari *(Mng Dir)*

DOWA HD Europe GmbH (1)
Ostendstrasse 196
90482 Nuremberg, Germany
Tel.: (49) 911 56989 320
Fax: (49) 911 56989 32 50
Emp.: 4
Marketing Consulting Services
S.I.C.: 8742
N.A.I.C.S.: 541613

Dowa Metaltech (Thailand) Co., Ltd. (1)
Gateway City Industrial Estate
Chachoengsao, Thailand
Tel.: (66) 3857 5715
Fax: (66) 3857 5684
Web Site: www.dowa.co.jp/en/about_dowa/group.html
Copper Strip Mfr & Distr
S.I.C.: 3351
N.A.I.C.S.: 331420

Hightemp Furnaces Ltd. (1)
1-C 2nd Phase Peenya Industrial Area
PO Box 5809
560058 Bengaluru, KA, India
Tel.: (91) 8028390490
Fax: (91) 8028390490
E-Mail: hightemp@vsnl.com
Web Site: www.hightemp-furnaces.com
Emp.: 100
Industrial Process Furnace & Oven Mfr
S.I.C.: 3567
N.A.I.C.S.: 333994
M. Gopal *(Mng Dir)*

Minera Tizapa, S.A. de C.V. (1)
Calzada Manuel Gomez Morin # 44
Col Torreon Residencial, 27268 Torreon, Coahulia, Mexico
Tel.: (52) 8717293442
Fax: (52) 8717293375
Copper Ore & Nickel Ore Mining
S.I.C.: 1021
N.A.I.C.S.: 212234

Technochem Environmental Complex Pte. Ltd. (1)
23 Tuas Avenue 11
Singapore, 639086, Singapore
Tel.: (65) 6862 3130
Fax: (65) 6861 1873
E-Mail: info@wms-technochem.com
Web Site: www.wms-technochem.com
Waste Treatment Services
S.I.C.: 4953
N.A.I.C.S.: 562211

Joint Venture:

Nippon PGM Co., Ltd. (1)
Akihabara UDX Building 14-1 Sotokanda 4-chome
Chiyoda-ku, Tokyo, 101 8617, Japan
Tel.: (81) 186292745
Fax: (81) 186292722
Web Site: www.tanaka.co.jp/english/company/group/html/pgm.html
Catalyst Smelting
S.I.C.: 3499
N.A.I.C.S.: 332999

Subsidiary:

Nippon PGM America Inc. (2)
500 Richards Run
Burlington, NJ 08016
Tel.: (609) 747-9994
Fax: (609) 747-8245
Web Site: www.dowa.co.jp/en/about_dowa/group.html
Catalyst Smelting
S.I.C.: 3499
N.A.I.C.S.: 332999

DOWELL PROPERTY HOLDINGS LIMITED

(Formerly Doxen Energy Group Limited)
Suite 1707 to 1709 Harbour Centre
25 Harbour Road, Wanchai, China (Hong Kong)
Tel.: (852) 2596 0668
Fax: (852) 2511 0318
E-Mail: enquiry@dowellproperty.com
Web Site: www.dowellproperty.com
0668—(HKG)
Sales Range: $1-9.9 Million
Emp.: 179

Business Description:
Investment Services
S.I.C.: 6211
N.A.I.C.S.: 523999

Personnel:
Siu Yu Lo *(Chm)*
Shaoying Luo *(Vice Chm)*
Yang Chen *(CEO)*
Lucy Tsui Yue Wong *(Sec)*

Board of Directors:
Siu Yu Lo
Ying Kay Chan
Yang Chen
Shaoying Luo
Hong Qin
Jin Ling Wang
Xiaobo Wang
Yong Xi Yang
Wen Hui Zhu

Legal Counsel:
Mason Ching & Associates
1803 18/F World-Wide House 19 Des Voeux Road
Central, China (Hong Kong)

Transfer Agent:
Computershare Hong Kong Investor Services Limited
Shops 1712-16 17/F Hopewell Centre 183 Queen's Road East
Wanchai, China (Hong Kong)

DOWNER EDI LIMITED

Triniti Business Campus 39 Delhi Road
North Ryde, NSW, 2113, Australia
Tel.: (61) 2 9468 9700
Fax: (61) 2 9813 8915
E-Mail: info@downergroup.com
Web Site: www.downergroup.com
DOW—(ASX)
Rev.: $8,727,602,089
Assets: $4,347,664,126
Liabilities: $2,444,191,361
Net Worth: $1,903,472,765
Earnings: $212,573,811
Emp.: 20,000
Fiscal Year-end: 06/30/13

Business Description:
Infrastructure, Engineering & Mining Services
S.I.C.: 1541
N.A.I.C.S.: 236210

Personnel:
Grant A. Fenn *(CEO & Mng Dir)*
Kevin Fletcher *(CFO)*
Campbell Mason *(Chief Risk Officer)*
Cos Bruyn *(CEO-New Zealand)*
David Cattell *(CEO-Infrastructure)*
David Overall *(CEO-Mining)*
Ross Spicer *(CEO-Rail)*
Peter Tompkins *(Gen Counsel & Co-Sec)*
Peter Lyons *(Co-Sec)*

Board of Directors:
R. Michael Harding
S. Annabelle Chaplain
Grant A. Fenn
Philip Garling
Eve Howell
John S. Humphrey
Kerry Gaye Sanderson
C. Grant Thorne

Subsidiaries:

Advanced Separation Engineering Australia Pty Ltd (1)
3 Alfred Close
East Maitland, Maitland, NSW, 2323, Australia
Tel.: (61) 249379900
Fax: (61) 249379990
Emp.: 130
Engineering Services
S.I.C.: 8711
N.A.I.C.S.: 541330
Bob Drummond *(Mgr)*

Cendrill Supply Pty Limited (1)
51 Fulciun Street
Richlands, QLD, 4077, Australia (100%)
Tel.: (61) 737184444
Fax: (61) 737184422
Industrial Machinery & Equipment Merchant Whslr
S.I.C.: 5084
N.A.I.C.S.: 423830

Clyde Babcock Hitachi (Aust) Pty Ltd. (1)
L 2 Lang Office 19 Lang Parate
Milton, QLD, 4064, Australia (27%)
Tel.: (61) 738780888
Fax: (61) 738700855
E-Mail: cbh@cbh.net.au
Web Site: www.cbh.net.au
Emp.: 60
Fabricated Wire Product Mfr
S.I.C.: 3496
N.A.I.C.S.: 332618

Coomes Consulting Group Pty Limited (1)
L 2 24 Albert Road
Melbourne, Australia (100%)
Tel.: (61) 399937888
Fax: (61) 39997999
E-Mail: consult@au.cpg-gobal.com
Web Site: www.cpg-global.com
Emp.: 200
Engineering Services
S.I.C.: 8711
N.A.I.C.S.: 541330
Mark Brauer *(Gen Mgr)*

Corke Instrument Engineering (Australia) Pty Ltd (1)
15 Export Drive
PO Box 625
Altona North, Brooklyn, VIC, 3025, Australia
Tel.: (61) 3 9362 4100
Fax: (61) 3 9314 7541
E-Mail: corke@corke.com.au
Web Site: www.corke.com.au
Emp.: 50
Instrument & Electrical Engineering Services
S.I.C.: 8711
N.A.I.C.S.: 541330

CPG Australia Pty Ltd (1)
Level 4 469 La Trobe St
Melbourne, VIC, 3000, Australia
Tel.: (61) 399937888
Fax: (61) 399937999
E-Mail: reception.melbourne@spiire.com.au
Web Site: www.spiire.com.au
Emp.: 12
Engineering Consulting Services
S.I.C.: 8711
N.A.I.C.S.: 541330
Stella Gonalaki *(Gen Mgr)*

CPG Resources - Mineral Technologies Pty Ltd (1)
11 Elysium Rd
Carrara, Gold Coast, QLD, 4211, Australia
Tel.: (61) 7 5569 1300
Fax: (61) 7 5525 3810
E-Mail: mineraltechnologies@au.cpg-global.com
Web Site: www.mineraltechnologies.com.au
Emp.: 200
Mineral Processing Services
S.I.C.: 1481
N.A.I.C.S.: 213115
Andrew Foster *(Gen Mgr)*

CPG Resources - MT Holdings Pty Ltd (1)
11 Elysium Rd
Carrara, Gold Coast, QLD, 4211, Australia
Tel.: (61) 755691300
Fax: (61) 755253810
Mineral Mining Services
S.I.C.: 1499
N.A.I.C.S.: 212399

CPG Resources - QCC Pty Ltd (1)
3 Alfred Close
Maitland, NSW, 2323, Australia
Tel.: (61) 249379900
Fax: (61) 249611231
Mineral Mining Services
S.I.C.: 1499
N.A.I.C.S.: 212399

CPG Traffic Pty Ltd (1)
46 Wadhurst Dr
Boronia, VIC, 3155, Australia
Tel.: (61) 388053400
Engineering Services
S.I.C.: 8711
N.A.I.C.S.: 541330

Dean Adams Consulting Pty Ltd. (1)
Lot 1892 Petrick Road
0870 Alice Springs, Australia (100%)
Tel.: (61) 889523358
Highway & Street Construction
S.I.C.: 1622
N.A.I.C.S.: 237310

Downer Australia Pty Ltd (1)
39 Delhi Road
North Ryde, NSW, 2113, Australia
Tel.: (61) 294689700
Fax: (61) 298138915
Civil Engineering Construction Services
S.I.C.: 1629
N.A.I.C.S.: 237990

Downer EDI Engineering Group Pty Limited (1)
Level 7 76 Berry Street
Sydney, NSW, 2060, Australia (100%)
Tel.: (61) 299662400
Fax: (61) 2 9955 9649
E-Mail: info@downerediengineering.com.au
Web Site: www.downerediengineering.com.au
Engineering Services
S.I.C.: 8711
N.A.I.C.S.: 541330
Grant Fenn *(CEO & Mng Dir)*

Division:

Downer EDI Engineering - Contracting / Power Systems (2)
Building B 480 Victoria Road
Gladesville, NSW, 2111, Australia (100%)
Tel.: (61) 298798400
Fax: (61) 298797221

Web Site: www.downeredi.com
Emp.: 100
Telecommunications Contracting Services
S.I.C.: 4899
N.A.I.C.S.: 517919
John Maclellan *(Mgr)*

Downer EDI Engineering Holdings Pty Ltd (1)
39 Delhi Rd
North Ryde, NSW, 2113, Australia
Tel.: (61) 294689700
Fax: (61) 298138919
Emp.: 200
Electronics Engineering Services
S.I.C.: 8711
N.A.I.C.S.: 541330
Grant Fenn *(CEO)*

Downer EDI Engineering - Projects Pty Ltd (1)
39 Delhi Rd
North Ryde, NSW, 2113, Australia
Tel.: (61) 294689700
Fax: (61) 298138915
Engineering Services
S.I.C.: 8711
N.A.I.C.S.: 541330

Downer EDI Engineering Transmission Pty Ltd (1)
Triniti Business Campus 39 Delhi Rd
North Ryde, NSW, 2113, Australia
Tel.: (61) 294689700
Fax: (61) 298138915
Power Plant Construction Engineering Services
S.I.C.: 1629
N.A.I.C.S.: 237130

Downer EDI Mining - Blasting Services Pty Ltd (1)
Sw 1 104 Melbourne St
Brisbane, QLD, 4101, Australia
Tel.: (61) 730266666
Fax: (61) 730266060
E-Mail: info@downeredimining.com
Emp.: 200
Coal Mining Services
S.I.C.: 1241
N.A.I.C.S.: 213113
David Overall *(CEO)*

Downer EDI Mining Holding Pty Ltd. (1)
104 Melbourne St
Brisbane, QLD, 4101, Australia (100%)
Tel.: (61) 755691300
Fax: (61) 730266061
E-Mail: info@downeredimining.com.au
Web Site: www.downergroup.com
Holding Company
S.I.C.: 6719
N.A.I.C.S.: 551112
David Overal *(CEO)*

Subsidiary:

Downer EDI Mining Pty Ltd. (2)
104 Melbourne Street
Brisbane, QLD, 4101, Australia (100%)
Tel.: (61) 730266666
Fax: (61) 730266060
E-Mail: info@downeredimining.com
Web Site: www.downeredimining.com
Emp.: 400
Engineering Services
S.I.C.: 8711
N.A.I.C.S.: 541330
David Overall *(CEO)*

Downer EDI Mining - Minerals Exploration Pty Ltd (1)
L 7 104 Melbourne St
Brisbane, QLD, 4101, Australia
Tel.: (61) 730266666
Fax: (61) 730266060
E-Mail: info@downeredimining.com
Web Site: www.downergroup.com
Emp.: 400
Oil & Gas Well Drilling Services
S.I.C.: 1381
N.A.I.C.S.: 213111
David Overall *(CEO)*

Downer EDI Rail Pty Ltd (1)
2b Factory St
Granville, NSW, 2142, Australia
Tel.: (61) 296378288
Fax: (61) 296377476
Emp.: 300
Rail Rolling Stock Operating Services
S.I.C.: 4789
N.A.I.C.S.: 488210
Peter Borden *(CEO)*

Downer EDI Services Pty Ltd (1)
L 3 190 George St
Sydney, NSW, 2000, Australia
Tel.: (61) 292409000
Engineering Services
S.I.C.: 8711
N.A.I.C.S.: 541330

Downer EDI (USA) Pty Ltd (1)
39 Delhi Rd
North Ryde, NSW, 2113, Australia
Tel.: (61) 294689700
Fax: (61) 298138915
Construction Engineering Services
S.I.C.: 8711
N.A.I.C.S.: 541330

Downer EDI Works Pty Ltd. (1)
37 Syrimi Rd
Burma, 0828 Dalen, NT, Australia (100%)
Tel.: (61) 889722641
Fax: (61) 889443636
E-Mail: nt@downerediworks.com.au
Web Site: www.downer.com.au
Emp.: 40
Highway Street & Bridge Construction
S.I.C.: 1622
N.A.I.C.S.: 237310
John Wade *(Mgr-NT)*

Downer Engineering Power Pty Limited (1)
Triniti Business Campus
39 New Delhi, 2113 North Ryde, NSW, Australia (100%)
Tel.: (61) 94689700
Fax: (61) 98138915
Web Site: www.downergroup.com
Engineering Services
S.I.C.: 8711
N.A.I.C.S.: 541330

Downer Group Finance Pty Limited (1)
L 3 190 George St
Sydney, NSW, Australia (100%)
Tel.: (61) 292519899
Web Site: www.downeredi.com
Holding Company
S.I.C.: 6719
N.A.I.C.S.: 551112

Downer Holdings Pty Ltd (1)
39 Delhi Road
North Ryde, NSW, 2113, Australia
Tel.: (61) 294689700
Fax: (61) 298138915
Investment Management Services
S.I.C.: 6211
N.A.I.C.S.: 523999

Downer MBL Pty Limited (1)
Level 1 650 Lorimer Street
Locked Bag 1200, 3207 Melbourne, VIC, Australia (100%)
Tel.: (61) 395931157
Fax: (61) 395932052
Engineering Services
S.I.C.: 8711
N.A.I.C.S.: 541330
Mark Sullivan *(Mgr)*

Downer Power Transmission Pty Ltd. (1)
480 Victoria Road Building B
Gladesville, NSW, 2111, Australia (100%)
Tel.: (61) 298798400
Fax: (61) 298797221
E-Mail: gladesvile.reception@downerediengineering.com.au
Web Site: www.downerediengineering.com.au
Water & Sewer Line & Related Structures Construction
S.I.C.: 1623
N.A.I.C.S.: 237110

EDI Rail Investments Pty Ltd. (1)
2b Factory St
Granville, NSW, Australia (100%)
Tel.: (61) 296378288
Fax: (61) 96377476
E-Mail: jenni.barren@downeredirail.com.au
Web Site: www.downeredirail.com.au
Emp.: 250
Computer Systems Design Services
S.I.C.: 7373
N.A.I.C.S.: 541512
Peter Bordan *(CEO)*

EDI Rail (Maryborough) Pty Ltd. (1)
23 Bowen St
Maryborough, 4650 Queensland, VIC, Australia (100%)
Tel.: (61) 741208100
Fax: (61) 741224400
Web Site: www.downergroup.com
Emp.: 500
Mining Machinery & Equipment Mfr
S.I.C.: 3532
N.A.I.C.S.: 333131
Quintin Roberts *(Mgr-Facility)*

Emoleum Roads Group Pty Limited (1)
L 11 468 St Kilda Rd
Melbourne, VIC, Australia (100%)
Tel.: (61) 398640868
Financial Investment Activities
S.I.C.: 6211
N.A.I.C.S.: 523999
Robert Stevens *(Gen Mgr-Fin)*

Otraco International Pty Limited (1)
Suite 2-18 Brodie Hall Drive Technology Park
6102 Bentley, WA, Australia (100%)
Tel.: (61) 894737500
Fax: (61) 893616812
Web Site: www.otraco.com
Emp.: 35
Engineering Services
S.I.C.: 8711
N.A.I.C.S.: 541330

Otracom Pty Ltd. (1)
Suite 2/18 Brodie Hall Drive
Bentley, WA, 6102, Australia
Mailing Address:
PO Box 120
Burswood, WA, 6100, Australia
Tel.: (61) 894737500
Fax: (61) 893616812
Web Site: www.otraco.com
Emp.: 25
Custom Computer Programming Services
S.I.C.: 7371
N.A.I.C.S.: 541511
Bernd Thansen *(Mng Dir)*

PT Otraco Indonesia (1)
PO Box 120
6100 Burswood, WA, Australia (100%)
Tel.: (61) 894737500
Fax: (61) 893616812
E-Mail: aust-indo@otraco.com
Web Site: www.otraco.com.au
Emp.: 180
Engineering Services
S.I.C.: 8711
N.A.I.C.S.: 541330
Alistair Swanson *(Gen Mgr)*

Rimtec Pty Ltd (1)
13 Fairbrother St
Belmont, WA, 6104, Australia
Tel.: (61) 894781333
Fax: (61) 894781355
E-Mail: rims@rimtec.com.au
Web Site: www.rimtec.com.au
Emp.: 20
Tire Whslr
S.I.C.: 5014
N.A.I.C.S.: 423130
Allan Campbell *(Gen Mgr)*

Roche Contractors Pty Ltd (1)
L 7 104 Melbourne St
Brisbane, QLD, 4101, Australia
Tel.: (61) 730266666
Fax: (61) 730266060
Construction Engineering Services
S.I.C.: 8711
N.A.I.C.S.: 541330

Singleton Bahen Stansfield Pty Ltd (1)
Level 3 469 Latrobe Street
Melbourne, VIC, 3205, Australia
Tel.: (61) 399937888
Fax: (61) 399937999
Engineering Consulting Services
S.I.C.: 8711
N.A.I.C.S.: 541330

Snowden Mining Industry Consultants Pty Ltd. (1)
87 Colin Street
West Perth, 6005, Australia (100%)
Tel.: (61) 892139213
Fax: (61) 893222576
E-Mail: perth@snowdengroup.com
Web Site: www.snowdengroup.com
Emp.: 120
Management Consulting Services
S.I.C.: 8748
N.A.I.C.S.: 541618
Craig Morley *(CEO)*

Snowden Technologies Pty Ltd. (1)
87 Colin Street
6005 West Perth, WA, Australia (100%)
Tel.: (61) 892139213
Fax: (61) 893222576
E-Mail: cmorley@snowdengroup.com
Web Site: www.snowdengroup.com
Emp.: 110
Business Service Centers561439
S.I.C.: 7389
N.A.I.C.S.: 561439
Craig Morley *(CEO)*

U.S. Subsidiary:

CPG Resources-Mineral Technologies (1)
24 Cathedral Pl Ste 501
Saint Augustine, FL 32084 (100%)
Tel.: (904) 827-1694
Fax: (904) 827-1695
Web Site: www.mineraltechnologies.com.au/
Emp.: 4
Engineering Services
S.I.C.: 8711
N.A.I.C.S.: 541330
William Weldon *(Reg Dir)*

Non-U.S. Subsidiaries:

Chan Lian Construction Pte Ltd (1)
11 Lorong 3 Toa Payoh 03-18 Jackson Square
Singapore, 319579, Singapore
Tel.: (65) 65170757
Fax: (65) 63550626
Civil Engineering Construction Services
S.I.C.: 1629
N.A.I.C.S.: 237990

Construction Professionals Pte Ltd (1)
238b Thomson Road 18-00 Novena Square
Singapore, 307685, Singapore
Tel.: (65) 63574837
Fax: (65) 63574835
Construction Engineering Services
S.I.C.: 8711
N.A.I.C.S.: 541330

CPG Environmental Engineering Co. Ltd (1)
9th Floor Golden Bridge Plaza 585 Xi Zang Zhong Road
Shanghai, 200003, China
Tel.: (86) 21 6351 7888
Fax: (86) 21 6351 9888
Web Site: www.cpgenv.com
Environmental Engineering Services
S.I.C.: 8711
N.A.I.C.S.: 541330
Wen Chai Koa *(Gen Mgr)*

CPG New Zealand (1)
1st Fl John Wickliffe House
265-269 Princess St, Dunedin, 9054, New Zealand (100%)
Tel.: (64) 3 64777133
Fax: (64) 3 4774236
E-Mail: dunedin@nz.cpg-global.com
Web Site: nz.cpg-global.com
Engineering & Consulting Services
S.I.C.: 8711
N.A.I.C.S.: 541330
Wayne Nolan *(CEO)*

CPG Resources - Mineral Technologies (Proprietary) Ltd (1)
14 Dockside Bay
Richards Bay, Kwazulu-Natal, 3900, South Africa
Tel.: (27) 357973230
Fax: (27) 357974629
E-Mail: mt@cpg-global.com

Downer EDI Limited—(Continued)

Emp.: 21
Mineral Mining Services
S.I.C.: 1499
N.A.I.C.S.: 212399
Steven MacDonald *(Gen Mgr)*

DMQA Technical Services (UK) Limited (1)
4100 Park Approach
Leeds, West Yorkshire, LS15 8GB, United Kingdom
Tel.: (44) 1133970890
Civil Engineering Construction Services
S.I.C.: 1629
N.A.I.C.S.: 237990

Downer Construction (Fiji) Limited (1)
Lot 1 Royal Palm Street
Lautoka, Fiji (100%)
Tel.: (679) 6652106
Fax: (679) 6728417
Engineering Services
S.I.C.: 8711
N.A.I.C.S.: 541330
Ken Seward *(Mng Dir)*

Downer EDI Engineering (S) Pte Ltd (1)
11 Lorong 3 Toa Payoh 03-16 Block B Jackson Square
Singapore, 319579, Singapore
Tel.: (65) 65170757
Fax: (65) 63550626
E-Mail: general@downer.com
Emp.: 80
Engineering Services
S.I.C.: 8711
N.A.I.C.S.: 541330

Downer EDI Group Insurance Pte. Ltd. (1)
18 Cross Street 04-00 Marsh & Mclennan Centre
Singapore, 048423, Singapore
Tel.: (65) 62208141
Fax: (65) 62208142
Emp.: 18
Insurance Management Services
S.I.C.: 6411
N.A.I.C.S.: 524298
Serene Cheng *(Gen Mgr)*

Downer EDI Group (NZ) Ltd (1)
Airport Retail Centre Auckland Airport
PO Box 201220
2150 Manukau, New Zealand (100%)
Tel.: (64) 92569810
Fax: (64) 92569811
E-Mail: info@downeredi.co.nz
Web Site: www.downeredi.co.nz
Emp.: 5,000
Engineering Services
S.I.C.: 8711
N.A.I.C.S.: 541330
Paul Honiss *(Mgr-Natl Customer Svc)*

Downer Pte Ltd (1)
11 Lor 3 Toa Payoh 03-16
Singapore, 319579, Singapore
Tel.: (65) 6517 0757
Fax: (65) 6355 0626
Infrastructure Management Services
S.I.C.: 7389
N.A.I.C.S.: 561499

Indeco Consortium Pte Ltd. (1)
238B Thomson Rd
#12-00 Novena Sq Twr B, 307685
Singapore, Singapore (100%)
Tel.: (65) 63574401
Fax: (65) 63574398
Web Site: www.cpgcorp.com.sg
Emp.: 3,000
Professional Organizations
S.I.C.: 8621
N.A.I.C.S.: 813920
Tan Shao Yen *(Gen Mgr)*

Peridian Asia Pte Ltd. (1)
5 Purvis St #02-01
Talib Court, 188584 Singapore,
Singapore (100%)
Tel.: (65) 62277998
Fax: (65) 62270509
E-Mail: peridian@peridianasia.com
Emp.: 50
Geophysical Surveying & Mapping Services
S.I.C.: 8713
N.A.I.C.S.: 541360
Dennis M. Taylor *(Mng Dir)*

PT Century Dinamik Drilling (1)
Chase Plaza 14th Floor
J1 Jend Sudirman Kav 21, 12920 Jakarta, Indonesia (100%)
Tel.: (62) 215201518
Fax: (62) 215201640
Engineering Services
S.I.C.: 8711
N.A.I.C.S.: 541330

Roche Mining (MT) India Pvt Ltd. (1)
406 F Vrindavan Apartments
Vyttila Junction, 682019 Cochin, Vyttila, India (100%)
Tel.: (91) 4842389097
Fax: (91) 4842389506
E-Mail: md_cochin@sify.com
Web Site: www.rochemt.com.br/11288.htm
Emp.: 5
Engineering Services
S.I.C.: 8711
N.A.I.C.S.: 541330
V. L. Kurian *(Mng Dir)*

Sillars (B. & C.E.) Ltd (1)
Sillcon House Graythorp Industrial Estate
Cleveland, Hartlepool, TS25 2DF, United Kingdom
Tel.: (44) 1429268125
Fax: (44) 1429268038
Road Construction Engineering Services
S.I.C.: 1611
N.A.I.C.S.: 237310
John Barr *(Gen Mgr)*

Sillars Holdings Limited (1)
Sillcon House Graythorp Industrial Estate
Cleveland, Hartlepool, TS25 2DF, United Kingdom
Tel.: (44) 1429 268125
Investment Management Services
S.I.C.: 6211
N.A.I.C.S.: 523999

Snowden Mining Industry Consultants Limited (1)
1090 Pender St
W Suite 600, V6E2N7 Vancouver, BC, Canada (100%)
Tel.: (604) 683-7645
Fax: (604) 683-7929
E-Mail: info@snowden.com
Web Site: www.snowdengroup.com
Emp.: 14
Engineering Services
S.I.C.: 8711
N.A.I.C.S.: 541330
Robert McCarthy *(Mng Dir)*

Snowden Training (Pty) Ltd (1)
Corner Victory N Rustenburg Road
Johannesburg, Gauteng, 2121, South Africa
Tel.: (27) 117822379
Fax: (27) 117822396
Web Site: www.snowdengroup.com
Emp.: 20
Professional Development & Training Services
S.I.C.: 8299
N.A.I.C.S.: 611430
Craig Molley *(Gen Mgr)*

TSE Wall Arlidge Limited (1)
Level 1 Manthels Building 19-23 Taranaki Street
PO Box 6643
Wellington, 6141, New Zealand
Tel.: (64) 43850096
Fax: (64) 43845065
Emp.: 37
Property Management Services
S.I.C.: 6531
N.A.I.C.S.: 531312
Tony McCartney *(Mgr)*

Underground Service Locators (1)
Manthel Building 23 Taranaki Street
Wellington, 9016, New Zealand
Tel.: (64) 4 384 2029
Fax: (64) 4 384 5065
E-Mail: enquiries@undergroundlocators.co.nz
Web Site: www.undergroundlocators.co.nz
Emp.: 50
Underground Engineering Services
S.I.C.: 8711
N.A.I.C.S.: 541330
Stephan Nolan *(Gen Mgr)*

Waste Solutions Limited (1)
Unit 4 Westpoint Trade Centre Link Road
Ballincollig, Ireland (100%)
Tel.: (353) 214214901
Fax: (353) 818411091
E-Mail: info@wastesolutions.ie
Web Site: www.wastesolutions.ie/about/contact/
Waste Management Services
S.I.C.: 4959
N.A.I.C.S.: 562998

Works Finance (NZ) Limited (1)
14 Amelia Earhart Avenue Airport Oaks
Mangere
Auckland, New Zealand
Tel.: (64) 9 256 9810
Fax: (64) 9 256 9811
Property Management Services
S.I.C.: 6531
N.A.I.C.S.: 531311

DOWNEY FORD SALES LTD.

35 Consumers Drive
Saint John, NB, E2J3S9, Canada
Tel.: (506) 632-6000
E-Mail: downeyfordsales@gmail.com
Web Site: www.downeyfordsales.dealerconnection.com
Rev.: $29,451,966
Emp.: 100
Business Description:
New & Used Car Dealers
S.I.C.: 5511
N.A.I.C.S.: 441110
Personnel:
Chris Downey *(Pres)*

DOWNS CONSTRUCTION LTD.

870 Devonshire Road
Victoria, BC, V9A 4T6, Canada
Tel.: (250) 384-1390
Fax: (250) 384-1400
Web Site: www.downsconstruction.com
Year Founded: 1981
Rev.: $15,650,091
Emp.: 54
Business Description:
Construction Services
S.I.C.: 1542
N.A.I.C.S.: 236220
Personnel:
Bill Downs *(Pres)*
Denise Downs *(CFO)*

DOWNSVIEW CHRYSLER PLYMOUTH (1964) LTD.

199 Rimrock Road
Toronto, ON, M3J 3C6, Canada
Tel.: (416) 635-1660
Fax: (416) 635-1797
Toll Free: (877) 719-6799
Web Site: www.downsviewchryslerdealer.com
Year Founded: 1964
Sales Range: $25-49.9 Million
Emp.: 100
Business Description:
Car Dealers
S.I.C.: 5511
N.A.I.C.S.: 441110
Personnel:
Peter Kepecs *(Pres)*
Dave McKerracher *(Treas & Sec)*

DOWNSVIEW DRYWALL CONTRACTING

160 Bass Pro Mills Dr
Concord, ON, L4K 0A7, Canada
Tel.: (905) 660-0048
Fax: (905) 738-3864
Web Site: www.downsviewdrywall.com
Year Founded: 1977
Rev.: $10,838,170
Emp.: 100
Business Description:
Drywall & Insulation Contractors
S.I.C.: 1742
N.A.I.C.S.: 238310
Personnel:
Sam Sgotto *(Pres)*

DOWNSVIEW HEATING & AIR CONDITIONING

4299 Queen St E Unit 2
Brampton, ON, L6T 5V4, Canada
Tel.: (905) 794-1489
Fax: (905) 794-1378
Web Site: www.downsview.ca
Rev.: $12,433,128
Emp.: 90
Business Description:
Plumbing Contractors
S.I.C.: 1711
N.A.I.C.S.: 238220
Personnel:
Frank Quattrociocch *(Owner)*

DOWNTOWN MAZDA

259 Lake Shore Blvd East
Toronto, ON, M5A 3T7, Canada
Tel.: (416) 368-0666
Fax: (416) 368-2332
Toll Free: (866) 523-2101
Web Site: downtownhonda.autotrader.ca
Rev.: $13,737,302
Emp.: 30
Business Description:
New & Used Car Dealers
S.I.C.: 5511
N.A.I.C.S.: 441110
Personnel:
Joe Low *(Controller)*

DOWNTOWN PONTIAC BUICK (1983) LIMITED

449 Queen Street West
Saint Marys, ON, N4X1B7, Canada
Tel.: (519) 284-3310
Fax: (519) 284-3160
Web Site: www.downtownpontiac.ca
Year Founded: 1983
Rev.: $11,561,746
Emp.: 26
Business Description:
New & Used Car Dealers
S.I.C.: 5511
N.A.I.C.S.: 441110
Personnel:
Chris West *(Pres)*

DOXA ENERGY LTD.

2060 777 Hornby Street
Vancouver, BC, V6Z 1T7, Canada
Tel.: (604) 662-3692
Fax: (604) 642-2629
Toll Free: (888) 662-3692
E-Mail: info@doxaenergy.com
Web Site: www.doxaenergy.com
Year Founded: 2007
DXA—(DEU OTC TSXV)
Rev.: $2,153,519
Assets: $9,581,190
Liabilities: $6,416,387
Net Worth: $3,164,803
Earnings: $294,832
Fiscal Year-end: 12/31/12
Business Description:
Oil Exploration Services
S.I.C.: 1311
N.A.I.C.S.: 211111
Personnel:
G. Arnold Armstrong *(Chm)*
John D. Harvison *(Pres & CEO)*
Mark Bronson *(CFO)*

Board of Directors:
G. Arnold Armstrong
Mark Bronson
Daniel Frederiksen
Gerald Graham
John D. Harvison
Paul Tavis McKenzie
Jonathon Weiss
Transfer Agent:
Computershare Investor Services Inc.
510 Burrard St 2nd Floor
Vancouver, BC, V6C 3B9, Canada
Tel.: (604) 661-9400

DOXEN ENERGY GROUP LIMITED

(Name Changed to Dowell Property Holdings Limited)

DOYLE HOTELS (HOLDINGS) LIMITED

(d/b/a The Doyle Collection)
156 Pembroke Rd
Ballsbridge, Dublin, 4, Ireland
Tel.: (353) 16070070
Fax: (353) 16781213
E-Mail: marketing@doylecollection.com
Web Site: www.doylecollection.com
Year Founded: 1964
Sales Range: $350-399.9 Million
Emp.: 1,400
Business Description:
Hotel Owner & Operator
S.I.C.: 7011
N.A.I.C.S.: 721110
Personnel:
Bernadette C. Gallagher *(Chm)*
Patrick King *(CEO)*
Seamus Daly *(Sec)*
Board of Directors:
Bernadette C. Gallagher
Walter Beatty
Bryan Evans
John J. Gallagher
Patrick King
Eileen M. Monahan
Conor Roche

DP DATA SYSTEMS LIMITED

15 Carnarvon Street
Manchester, M3 1HJ, United Kingdom
Tel.: (44) 161 832 6969
Fax: (44) 1618326970
E-Mail: info@dpdata.co.uk
Web Site: www.dpdata.co.uk
Sales Range: $100-124.9 Million
Emp.: 100
Business Description:
Computer Products Distr
S.I.C.: 5045
N.A.I.C.S.: 423430
Personnel:
Philip Hodari *(Mng Dir)*

DP POLAND PLC

PO Box 204
Heathfield, East Sussex, TN21 1BQ, United Kingdom
Tel.: (44) 20 3393 6954
Web Site: www.dppoland.com
DPP—(AIM)
Business Description:
Pizza Chain Franchiser
S.I.C.: 5812
N.A.I.C.S.: 722513
Personnel:
Richard Douglas Worthington *(Chm)*
Board of Directors:
Richard Douglas Worthington
Nicholas John Donaldson
Robert Nicholas Lutwyche Morrish
Peter John Edward Shaw

Non-U.S. Subsidiary:

DP Pizza Limited (1)
Unit 1B Toughers Business Park
Co Kildare, Naas, Leinster, Ireland
Tel.: (353) 45437666
Fax: (353) 45437670
Pizza Stores Management Services
S.I.C.: 5812
N.A.I.C.S.: 722511
Colin Halpern *(Mng Dir)*

DPA GROUP N.V.

(d/b/a DPA Group)
Gatwickstraat 11
1043 GL Amsterdam, Netherlands
Mailing Address:
PO Box 9396
1006 AJ Amsterdam, Netherlands
Tel.: (31) 205151555
Fax: (31) 205151551
E-Mail: info@dpagroep.nl
Web Site: www.dpagroep.nl
Year Founded: 1990
DPA—(EUR)
Sales Range: $50-74.9 Million
Emp.: 68
Business Description:
Professional Management, Recruitment & Outsourcing Services
S.I.C.: 7389
N.A.I.C.S.: 541990
Personnel:
Ron Icke *(Chm-Supervisory Bd)*
Eric Winter *(CEO)*
Olav Berten *(COO)*
Supervisory Board of Directors:
Ron Icke
Dirk Lindenbergh

DPS RESOURCES BERHAD

50-1 52-1 & 54-1 Jalan BPM 2
Taman Bukit Piatu Mutiara
75150 Melaka, Malaysia
Tel.: (60) 62832398
Fax: (60) 62830202
E-Mail: info@shantawood.com.my
Web Site: www.dps.com.my
DPS—(KLS)
Rev.: $12,382,329
Assets: $51,630,501
Liabilities: $26,105,315
Net Worth: $25,525,185
Earnings: ($10,170,956)
Fiscal Year-end: 03/31/13
Business Description:
Holding Company
S.I.C.: 6719
N.A.I.C.S.: 551112
Personnel:
Peter Chin Chuan Sow *(Chm & Mng Dir)*
Li Fang Lim *(Sec)*
Board of Directors:
Peter Chin Chuan Sow
Kim Guek Chu
Tahir Hassan
Jaafar Lajis
Emily Mei Chet Sow
Eric Yong Shing Sow
Woon Chin Vong
Yit Yang Yee

Subsidiary:

Shantawood Manufacturing Sdn. Bhd. (1)
Lot 76 77 Kawasan Perindustrian Bukit Rambai
75250 Melaka, Malaysia
Tel.: (60) 63512580
Fax: (60) 63512587
E-Mail: info@shantawood.com.my
Web Site: www.shantawood.com.my
Emp.: 52
Furniture Mfr & Whslr
S.I.C.: 5021
N.A.I.C.S.: 423210
Datuk Chin Chuan Sow *(Gen Mgr)*

DPSC LIMITED

Plot No X1 2 & 3 Block-EP Sector-V
Salt Lake City
Kolkata, 700 091, India
Tel.: (91) 3366094308
Fax: (91) 3323572452
E-Mail: info@dpscl.com
Web Site: www.dpscl.com
DPSCLTD—(NSE)
Rev.: $122,214,160
Assets: $279,152,590
Liabilities: $98,130,236
Net Worth: $181,022,354
Earnings: $5,114,834
Fiscal Year-end: 03/31/13
Business Description:
Coal Producer
S.I.C.: 1221
N.A.I.C.S.: 212111
Personnel:
Siddharth Mehta *(CEO)*
Arun Kedia *(CFO)*
Saikat Bardhan *(Compliance Officer & Sec)*
Somesh Dasgupta *(Pres-Corp Affairs & Admin)*
A. K. Goswami *(Pres-New Initiatives)*
Jyotirmay Bhaumik *(CEO-IPCHL)*
Rakesh Bhatia *(Sr VP & Head-Renewable Bus)*
Gautam Das *(Sr VP-Fin)*
Board of Directors:
Hemant Kanoria
Amit Kiran Deb
Sunil Kanoria
Nand Gopal Khaitan
Debi Prasad Patra
Joyti Kumar Poddar
Sunirmal Talukdar
Tantra Narayan Thakur
Transfer Agent:
C. B. Management Services (P) Ltd
P-22 Bondel Road
700019 Kolkata, India

DPV DRUCK UND PAPIER-VEREDELUNG GMBH

Parkstrasse 14b
86462 Langweid, Germany
Tel.: (49) 821249950
Fax: (49) 8212499570
E-Mail: info@dpv.net
Web Site: www.dpv.net
Rev.: $13,352,415
Emp.: 50
Business Description:
Paper Products Mfr
S.I.C.: 2679
N.A.I.C.S.: 322299
Personnel:
Thomas Mayr *(Mgr-Internal Svcs)*

DQ ENTERTAINMENT PLC

33-37 Athol Street
Douglas, Isle of Man IM1 1LB
Tel.: (44) 1624 638 300
Fax: (44) 1624 638 333
E-Mail: sales@dqentertainment.com
Web Site: www.dqentertainment.com
DQE—(AIM)
Rev.: $42,530,760
Assets: $146,651,400
Liabilities: $48,482,100
Net Worth: $98,169,300
Earnings: $7,063,740
Emp.: 2,128
Fiscal Year-end: 03/31/13
Business Description:
Animation Production Services
S.I.C.: 7819
N.A.I.C.S.: 512199
Personnel:
Tapaas Chakravarti *(Founder, Chm, CEO & Mng Dir)*
Hatim Adenwala *(Sr VP-HR)*
Manoj Mishra *(Sr VP-Licensing & Distr)*
Sumedha Saraogi *(Sr VP-Global Bus Dev & Mgmt Office)*
Board of Directors:
Tapaas Chakravarti
Rashida Adenwala
Kunchitapadam Balasubramanian
Theresa Plummer-Andrews
Santhanaraman Vaidyanathan

Non-U.S. Subsidiary:

DQ Entertainment (International) Limited (1)
644 Aurora Colony Road 3 Banjara Hills
Hyderabad, http://www.dqenterta, 500034, India (75%)
Tel.: (91) 40 23553726
Fax: (91) 40 23552594
Web Site: www.dqentertainment.com
533176—(BOM NSE)
Rev.: $42,532,193
Assets: $139,961,695
Liabilities: $59,847,632
Net Worth: $80,114,064
Earnings: $6,916,628
Fiscal Year-end: 03/31/13
Animation Production
S.I.C.: 7812
N.A.I.C.S.: 512110
Tapaas Chakravarti *(Chm, CEO & Mng Dir)*
Sanjay Choudhary *(CFO)*
Anita Sunil Shankar *(Compliance Officer & Sec)*
Hatim Adenwala *(Sr VP-HR)*
Manoj Mishra *(Sr VP-Licensing & Distr)*
Sumedha Saraogi *(Sr VP-Bus Dev-Global)*

DR. AGARWAL'S EYE HOSPITAL LIMITED

4A Prince Arcade 22-A Cathedral Road
Chennai, 600 086, India
Tel.: (91) 44 39916600
Fax: (91) 44 39916645
E-Mail: dragarwal@vsnl.com
Web Site: www.dragarwal.com
526783—(BOM)
Rev.: $20,343,849
Assets: $11,755,231
Liabilities: $8,856,132
Net Worth: $2,899,100
Earnings: $582,082
Fiscal Year-end: 03/31/13
Business Description:
Eye Care Services
S.I.C.: 8099
N.A.I.C.S.: 621999
Personnel:
Tahira Agarwal *(Co-Founder & Mng Dir)*
Jaiveer Agarwal *(Co-Founder)*
Amar Agarwal *(Chm, Mng Dir & Compliance Officer)*
S. Rajagopalan *(CEO)*
S. Ramanujam *(CFO)*
V. Suresh *(COO)*
Board of Directors:
Amar Agarwal
Adil Agarwal
Anosh Agarwal
Athiya Agarwal
Sanjay Anand
M.R.G. Apparao
Jasvinder Singh Saroya
Prabhat Toshniwal
Transfer Agent:
Integrated Enterprises (India) Ltd
2nd Floor Kences Towers 1 Ramakrishna Street
North Usman Road T Nagar
Chennai, India

DR. AUGUST OETKER KG

Lutterstrasse 14
33617 Bielefeld, Germany

Dr. August Oetker KG—(Continued)

Tel.: (49) 5211550
Fax: (49) 5211552995
E-Mail: presse@oetker.de
Web Site: www.oetkergruppe.de
Year Founded: 1891
Sales Range: $5-14.9 Billion
Emp.: 26,228
Business Description:
Diversified Holding Company
S.I.C.: 6719
N.A.I.C.S.: 551112
Personnel:
Albert Christmann *(Gen Partner & Member-Mgmt Bd-Beer & Non-Alcoholic Beverages)*
Ottmar Gast *(Gen Partner & Member-Mgmt Bd-Shipping)*
Richard Oetker *(Gen Partner & Member-Mgmt Bd-Food)*
Ernst F. Schroder *(Gen Partner & Member-Mgmt Bd-Bank, Other Interest & Corp Fin)*
Hans-Henning Wiegmann *(Gen Partner & Member-Mgmt Bd-Sparkling Wine, Wine & Spirits)*

Subsidiaries:

Hamburg Sudamerikanische Dampfschifffahrts-Gesellschaft KG (1)
Postfach 11 15 33
Hamburg, 20415, Germany
Tel.: (49) 4037050
Fax: (49) 4037052400
E-Mail: central@ham.hamburgsud.com
Web Site: www.hamburgsud.com
Emp.: 4,126
Transportation Services & Travel Agency
S.I.C.: 4412
N.A.I.C.S.: 483111
Ottmar Gast *(Chm)*
Klaus Meves *(Chm)*

Radeberger Gruppe AG (1)
Darmstadter Landstrasse 185
60598 Frankfurt am Main, Germany
Tel.: (49) 6960650
Fax: (49) 696065209
E-Mail: info@radeberger-gruppe.de
Web Site: www.radeberger-gruppe.de
Sales Range: $1-4.9 Billion
Emp.: 700
Brewery
S.I.C.: 2082
N.A.I.C.S.: 312120
Albert Christmann *(CMO)*

DR. BABOR GMBH & CO. KG

Neuenhofstrasse 180
52078 Aachen, Germany
Tel.: (49) 241 5296 0
Fax: (49) 241 5296 175
E-Mail: service@babor.de
Web Site: www.babor.de
Year Founded: 1955
Emp.: 215
Business Description:
Natural Skin Care and Cosmetics
S.I.C.: 2844
N.A.I.C.S.: 325620
Personnel:
Michael Schummert *(CEO & Chm-Mgmt Bd)*
Horst Robertz *(Member-Mgmt Bd)*

U.S. Subsidiary:

Babor Cosmetics America Corp. (1)
580 Village Blvd Ste 140
West Palm Beach, FL 33409 FL
Tel.: (888) 222-6791
Fax: (561) 802-6167
E-Mail: concierge@babor.com
Web Site: www.babor.com
Emp.: 25
Natural Cosmetics and Skin Care Systems
S.I.C.: 2844
N.A.I.C.S.: 325620

DR. FALK PHARMA GMBH

Leinenweberstr 5
79041 Freiburg, Germany
Tel.: (49) 76115140
Fax: (49) 7611514321
E-Mail: zentrale@drfalkpharma.de
Web Site: www.drfalkpharma.de
Year Founded: 1960
Rev.: $216,446,849
Emp.: 89
Business Description:
Drugs Whlsr
S.I.C.: 5122
N.A.I.C.S.: 424210
Personnel:
Ursula Falk *(Mng Dir)*

DR. FODISCH UMWELTMESSTECHNIK AG

Zwenkauer Strasse 159
Markranstadt, D - 04420, Germany
Tel.: (49) 342057550
Fax: (49) 3420575540
E-Mail: info@foedisch.de
Web Site: www.foedisch.de
Year Founded: 1991
Rev.: $13,369,145
Emp.: 49
Business Description:
Environmental Engineering Services
S.I.C.: 8711
N.A.I.C.S.: 541330
Personnel:
Michael Stahl *(Chm)*
Holger Amboldt *(CEO)*
Board of Directors:
Michael Stahl
Klaus Henner Berka
Johann David Herstatt

DR. FRITZ FAULHABER GMBH & CO. KG

(d/b/a Faulhaber Group)
Daimlerstrasse 23 25
71101 Schonaich, Germany
Tel.: (49) 7031 638 0
Fax: (49) 7031 638 100
E-Mail: info@faulhaber.de
Web Site: www.faulhaber.com
Emp.: 1,300
Business Description:
Electric Motor Mfr
S.I.C.: 3679
N.A.I.C.S.: 334419
Personnel:
Fritz Faulhaber *(CEO)*

U.S. Subsidiary:

MicroMo Electronics, Inc. (1)
14881 Evergreen Ave
Clearwater, FL 33762
Tel.: (727) 572-0131
Fax: (727) 572-7763
Toll Free: (800) 807-9166
E-Mail: info@micromo.com
Web Site: www.micromo.com
Sales Range: $50-74.9 Million
Emp.: 65
Motor & Generator Mfr
S.I.C.: 3699
N.A.I.C.S.: 335999
Fritz Faulhaber *(Owner)*

DR. HONLE AG

UV - Technologie Lochhamer Schlag 1
D-82166 Grafelfing, Germany
Tel.: (49) 89856080
Fax: (49) 8985608148
E-Mail: uv@hoenle.de
Web Site: www.hoenle.de
HNL—(DEU)
Rev.: $106,130,602
Assets: $109,172,794
Liabilities: $43,745,756
Net Worth: $65,427,038
Earnings: $9,218,596
Emp.: 526
Fiscal Year-end: 09/30/13
Business Description:
UV Adhesives, Lamps, Measuring Instrumentation, Dryers, Offset Printing Products & Inkjet Printing Products Mfr & Distr
S.I.C.: 3559
N.A.I.C.S.: 333249
Personnel:
Hans-Joachim Vits *(Chm-Supervisory Bd)*
Karl Honle *(Vice Chm-Supervisory Bd)*
Norbert Haimerl *(Mng Dir, CFO & Member-Mgmt Bd)*
Heiko Runge *(Member-Mgmt Bd & Mng Dir-Sls & Tech)*
Supervisory Board of Directors:
Hans-Joachim Vits
Karl Honle
Eckhard Pergande

Subsidiaries:

Aladin GmbH (1)
UV-Strahlerproduktion Am Eckfeld 10
83543 Rott am Inn, Germany
Tel.: (49) 8039 908670
Fax: (49) 8039 90867499
E-Mail: info@aladin-uv.de
Web Site: www.aladin-uv.de
UV Lamp Mfr
S.I.C.: 3648
N.A.I.C.S.: 335129

Eltosch Torsten Schmidt GmbH (1)
Dreyerpfad 1
22415 Hamburg, Germany
Tel.: (49) 4084 00070
Fax: (49) 4084 000720
E-Mail: sales@eltosch.de
Web Site: www.eltosch.de
UV Lamps Designer & Mfr
S.I.C.: 3648
N.A.I.C.S.: 335129
Torsten Schmidt *(Mng Dir)*

GRAFIX GmbH (1)
Kupferstr 40-46
70565 Stuttgart, Germany
Tel.: (49) 711 786900
Fax: (49) 711 7869270
E-Mail: service-helpline@grafix-online.de
Web Site: www.grafix-online.de
Printing Equipment Mfr
S.I.C.: 3555
N.A.I.C.S.: 333244

Mitronic GmbH (1)
Lochhamer Schlag 1
82166 Grafelfing, Germany
Tel.: (49) 89 85608 270
Fax: (49) 89 85608 08271
E-Mail: info@mitronic.com
Web Site: www.mitronic.com
Lighting Products Mfr
S.I.C.: 3648
N.A.I.C.S.: 335129

PrintConcept UV-Systeme GmbH (1)
Philipp Jakob Manz Str 18
72664 Kohlberg, Germany
Tel.: (49) 7025 912770
Fax: (49) 7025 91277660
E-Mail: office@printconcept-uv.com
Web Site: www.printconcept-uv.com
Emp.: 30
UV Lamps Designer & Mfr
S.I.C.: 3648
N.A.I.C.S.: 335129
Juergen Welle *(Mng Dir)*

Raesch Quarz (Germany) GmbH (1)
In den Folgen 3
D-98704 Langewiesen, Germany
Tel.: (49) 3677 469232
Fax: (49) 3677 812805
E-Mail: info@raesch.net
Web Site: www.raesch.net
Lighting Equipment Mfr
S.I.C.: 3648
N.A.I.C.S.: 335129

UV-Technik Speziallampen GmbH (1)
Gewerbegebiet Ost 6
98704 Wolfsburg, Wumbach, Germany
Tel.: (49) 36785 5200
Fax: (49) 36785 52021
E-Mail: info@uvtechnik.com
Web Site: www.uvtechnik.com
UV Lighting Products Mfr
S.I.C.: 3648
N.A.I.C.S.: 335129

Non-U.S. Subsidiaries:

Hoenle UV Technology (Shanghai) Trading Ltd. (1)
Room 821 No 800 Shangcheng Road
Cimic Building Pudong, Shanghai, 200120, China
Tel.: (86) 2164 730200
Fax: (86) 2164 739859
E-Mail: info@hoenle.cn
Web Site: www.hoenle.cn
UV Lamps Sales
S.I.C.: 3648
N.A.I.C.S.: 335129

Honle Spain S.A.U. (1)
Pampeu Fabra 5
Olesa de Bonesvalls, 8795 Barcelona, Spain
Tel.: (34) 93 8984901
Fax: (34) 93 8984900
E-Mail: honlespain@honlespain.com
Web Site: www.honlespain.com
Emp.: 1
UV Lamps Designer & Mfr
S.I.C.: 3648
N.A.I.C.S.: 335129
Genn Mischke *(Mng Dir)*

Honle UV France S.a.r.l. (1)
6 rue Maryse Bastie
69500 Bron, France
Tel.: (33) 472549902
Fax: (33) 472549906
E-Mail: honleuvfrance@orange.fr
Web Site: www.honleuv.fr
Emp.: 7
UV Lamps Designer & Mfr
S.I.C.: 3648
N.A.I.C.S.: 335129
Debose Regis *(Mng Dir)*

Honle UV (UK) Ltd. (1)
Business Centre Kimpton Road
Luton, Beds, LU2 0XS, United Kingdom
Tel.: (44) 1582 522411
Fax: (44) 1582 721341
E-Mail: sales@honleuv.co.uk
Emp.: 5
UV Lamps Designer & Mfr
S.I.C.: 3648
N.A.I.C.S.: 335129
Keith Lane *(Mgr)*

Panacol AG (1)
Althardstr 120
CH-8105 Regensdorf, Switzerland
Tel.: (41) 44 383 22 44
Fax: (41) 44 383 45 24
E-Mail: info@panacol.ch
Web Site: www.panacol.ch
Holding Company; Adhesives Mfr
S.I.C.: 6719
N.A.I.C.S.: 551112
Heiko Runge *(Mng Dir-Sls & Tech)*

Non-U.S. Subsidiaries:

Eleco Produits S.A.S. (2)
125 av Louis Roche
ZA des Basses Noels, 92238 Gennevilliers, Cedex, France
Tel.: (33) 147924180
Fax: (33) 147922272
E-Mail: eleco@eleco-produits.fr
Web Site: www.eleco-produits.fr
Emp.: 30
Glues & Adhesives Mfr
S.I.C.: 5169
N.A.I.C.S.: 424690
Laurent Prevost *(Mng Dir)*

Panacol-Elosol GmbH (2)
Daimler Str 8
61449 Steinbach, Taunus, Germany
Tel.: (49) 6171 62020
Fax: (49) 6171 6202590
E-Mail: info@panacol.de

Web Site: www.panacol.de
Adhesive Products Mfr
S.I.C.: 2891
N.A.I.C.S.: 325520

Raesch Quarz (Malta) Ltd. **(1)**
Oxford Centre F5 Mosta Technopark
Mosta, MST 3000, Malta
Tel.: (356) 21 419615
Fax: (356) 21 437820
E-Mail: info@raesch.net
Web Site: www.raesch.net
UV Lighting Products Mfr
S.I.C.: 3648
N.A.I.C.S.: 335129

DR. ING. GOSSLING MASCHINENFABRIK GMBH

PO Box 1180
46510 Wesel, Germany
Tel.: (49) 285391440
Fax: (49) 2853914499
E-Mail: info@dr-goessling.de
Web Site: www.dr-goessling.de
Rev.: $13,480,350
Emp.: 79
Business Description:
Conveying Equipment Mfr
S.I.C.: 3535
N.A.I.C.S.: 333922
Personnel:
Manfred Gossling *(Gen Mgr)*

DR. ING. K. BUSCH GMBH

Schauinslandstrasse 1
79689 Maulburg, Germany
Tel.: (49) 76226810
Fax: (49) 76225484
E-Mail: info@busch.de
Web Site: www.busch.de
Sales Range: $100-124.9 Million
Emp.: 1,800
Business Description:
Vacuum Pumps, Blowers & Compressor Mfr
S.I.C.: 3563
N.A.I.C.S.: 333912
Personnel:
Karl Busch *(Chm)*

U.S. Subsidiaries:

Busch LLC **(1)**
516 Viking Dr
Virginia Beach, VA 23452
Tel.: (757) 463-7800
Fax: (757) 463-7407
E-Mail: marketing@buschusa.com
Web Site: www.buschusa.com
Emp.: 95
Pumps & Pumping Equipment Mfr
S.I.C.: 5084
N.A.I.C.S.: 423830
Ing K. Busch *(Owner)*
Charles W. Kane *(Pres)*

Busch Manufacturing LLC **(1)**
516-A Viking Drive
Virginia Beach, VA 23452
Tel.: (757) 463-8412
Fax: (757) 463-7407
Vacuum Pumps, Blowers & Compressor Mfr
S.I.C.: 3563
N.A.I.C.S.: 333912
Gary Tedder *(Supvr-Quality Assurance)*

Non-U.S. Subsidiaries:

Ateliers Busch S.A. **(1)**
Zone Industrielle
2906 Chevenez, Switzerland
Tel.: (41) 324760200
Fax: (41) 324760399
E-Mail: info@busch.ch
Web Site: www.busch.ch
Emp.: 200
Vacuum Pumps, Blowers & Compressor Mfr
S.I.C.: 3563
N.A.I.C.S.: 333912
Christian Hoffmann *(Mng Dir)*

BNM Stenstrup A/S **(1)**
Tvaervej 23
5771 Svendborg, Denmark
Tel.: (45) 62261405
Fax: (45) 62263253
E-Mail: info@bnm.dk
Web Site: www.busch.com
Emp.: 20
Vacuum Pumps, Blowers & Compressor Mfr
S.I.C.: 3563
N.A.I.C.S.: 333912
Lars Bo *(Gen Mgr)*

Busch AG **(1)**
Waldweg 22
4312 Rheinfelden, Switzerland
Tel.: (41) 618459090
Fax: (41) 618459099
E-Mail: info@buschag.ch
Web Site: www.buschag.ch
Emp.: 20
Vacuum Pumps, Blowers & Compressor Mfr
S.I.C.: 3563
N.A.I.C.S.: 333912
Christian Muser *(Mng Dir)*

Busch Argentina S.R.L. **(1)**
Amenabar 1444 Piso 10 C
C 1426AJZ Buenos Aires, Argentina
Tel.: (54) 11 4781 4143
Fax: (54) 11 4781 4143
E-Mail: info@busch-vacuum.com.ar
Web Site: www.busch-vacuum.com.ar
Vacuum Pumps, Blowers & Compressor Mfr
S.I.C.: 3563
N.A.I.C.S.: 333912

Busch Australia Pty. Ltd. **(1)**
30 Lakeside Dr
Victoria, Broadmeadows, 3047, Australia
Tel.: (61) 393550600
Fax: (61) 393550699
E-Mail: sales@busch.com.au
Web Site: www.busch.com.au
Emp.: 40
Vacuum Pumps, Blowers & Compressor Mfr
S.I.C.: 3563
N.A.I.C.S.: 333912
K. Porslit *(Mng Dir)*

Busch Austria GmbH **(1)**
Industriepark Nord
2100 Korneuburg, Austria
Tel.: (43) 2262756650
Fax: (43) 22627566520
E-Mail: busch@busch.at
Web Site: www.busch.at
Emp.: 2,600
Vacuum Pumps, Blowers & Compressor Mfr
S.I.C.: 3563
N.A.I.C.S.: 333912
Karl Bluamer *(Gen Mgr)*

Busch B.V. **(1)**
Pompmolenlaan 2
3447 GK Woerden, Netherlands
Tel.: (31) 348462300
Fax: (31) 348422939
E-Mail: info@busch.nl
Web Site: www.busch.nl
Emp.: 80
Vacuum Pumps, Blowers & Compressor Mfr
S.I.C.: 3563
N.A.I.C.S.: 333912

Busch Chile S. A. **(1)**
Calle El Roble N 375-G
Santiago, Chile
Tel.: (56) 23765136
Fax: (56) 27387092
E-Mail: info@busch.cl
Web Site: www.busch.cl
Vacuum Pumps, Blowers & Compressor Mfr
S.I.C.: 3563
N.A.I.C.S.: 333912

Busch do Brasil Ltda. **(1)**
Rod. Edgard Maximo Zambotto Km 64
13240-00 Sao Paulo, Brazil
Tel.: (55) 1140161400
Fax: (55) 1140165399
E-Mail: vendas@buschdobrasil.com.br
Web Site: www.buschdobrasil.com.br
Emp.: 40
Vacuum Pumps, Blowers & Compressor Mfr
S.I.C.: 3563
N.A.I.C.S.: 333912
Hang Lang *(Mng Dir)*

Busch France S.A.S. **(1)**
16 Rue du Bois Chaland
91029 Lisses, France
Tel.: (33) 169898989
Fax: (33) 169898958
E-Mail: busch@busch.fr
Web Site: www.busch.fr
Emp.: 66
Vacuum Pumps, Blowers & Compressor Mfr
S.I.C.: 3563
N.A.I.C.S.: 333912
Eric Lebreton *(Mgr)*

Busch GVT Ltd. **(1)**
Westmere Dr
CW1 6ZT Crewe, Chesire, United Kingdom (100%)
Tel.: (44) 1260274721
Fax: (44) 260276965
E-Mail: sales@busch-gvt.co.uk
Web Site: www.busch-gvt.co.uk
Sls.: $7,432,000
Emp.: 65
Liquid Ring Vacuum Pumps Mfr
S.I.C.: 3561
N.A.I.C.S.: 333911
Ian Graves *(Mng Dir)*

Busch Ireland Ltd. **(1)**
A10-11 Howth Junction Business Centre
Kilbarrack, Dublin, 5, Ireland
Tel.: (353) 18321466
Fax: (353) 18321470
E-Mail: sales@busch.ie
Web Site: www.busch.ie
Emp.: 10
Vacuum Pumps, Blowers & Compressor Mfr
S.I.C.: 3563
N.A.I.C.S.: 333912
Andrew Guard *(Mng Dir)*

Busch Israel Ltd. **(1)**
1 Mevo Sivan Street
8202 Kiryat Gat, Israel
Tel.: (972) 86810485
Fax: (972) 86810486
E-Mail: service_sales@busch.co.il
Web Site: www.busch.co.il
Emp.: 9
Vacuum Pumps, Blowers & Compressor Mfr
S.I.C.: 3563
N.A.I.C.S.: 333912
Daniel Weltman *(Mng Dir)*

Busch Italia S.r.l. **(1)**
Via Ettore Majorana 16
20054 Nova Milanese, Italy
Tel.: (39) 036237091
Fax: (39) 0362370999
E-Mail: info@busch.it
Web Site: www.busch.it
Emp.: 25
Vacuum Pumps, Blowers & Compressor Mfr
S.I.C.: 3563
N.A.I.C.S.: 333912

Busch Korea Ltd. **(1)**
248-2 Ichi-ri Majang-Myun Icheon-si
467-813 Icheon, Kyunggi-Do, Korea (South)
Tel.: (82) 313218114
Fax: (82) 316312838
E-Mail: youngchul.Kin@buschkorea.co.kr
Web Site: www.buschkorea.co.kr
Vacuum Pumps, Blowers & Compressor Mfr
S.I.C.: 3563
N.A.I.C.S.: 333912
Young-Chul Kim *(Mgr)*

Busch Iberica S.A **(1)**
Zona Industrial Raso de Travasso
Fraccao B Armazem 2, 3750 753 Aveiro, Portugal
Tel.: (351) 234648070
Fax: (351) 234648068
E-Mail: geral@buschib.pt
Web Site: www.buschib.pt
Emp.: 3
Vacuum Pumps, Blowers & Compressor Mfr
S.I.C.: 3563
N.A.I.C.S.: 333912
Samuel Patino *(Gen Mgr)*

Busch Malaysia Sdn Bhd **(1)**
4-6 Jalan Taboh 33/22 Seksyen 33 Shah Alam Technology Park
40400 Shah Alam, Malaysia
Tel.: (60) 351222128
Fax: (60) 351222108
E-Mail: busch@busch.com.my
Web Site: www.busch.com.my
Emp.: 10
Vacuum Pumps, Blowers & Compressor Mfr
S.I.C.: 3563
N.A.I.C.S.: 333912
Jimmy Teo *(Mng Dir)*

Busch New Zealand Ltd. **(1)**
Unit D 41 Arrenway Drive Albany
Auckland, 0632, New Zealand
Tel.: (64) 9414 7782
Fax: (64) 9414 7783
E-Mail: sales@busch.co.nz
Web Site: www.busch.co.nz
Emp.: 5
Vacuum Pumps, Blowers & Compressor Mfr
S.I.C.: 3563
N.A.I.C.S.: 333912
Mike Winter *(Mgr)*

Busch N.V. **(1)**
Kruinstraat 7
9160 Lokeren, Belgium
Tel.: (32) 93484722
Fax: (32) 93486535
E-Mail: info@busch.be
Web Site: www.busch.be
Emp.: 22
Vacuum Pumps, Blowers & Compressor Mfr
S.I.C.: 3563
N.A.I.C.S.: 333912
Dirk Strypsteen *(Gen Mgr)*

Busch Polska Sp. z o.o. **(1)**
Ul Chopina 27
87-800 Bydgoszcz, Poland
Tel.: (48) 542315400
Fax: (48) 542327076
E-Mail: busch@busch.com.pl
Web Site: www.busch.com.pl
Vacuum Pumps, Blowers & Compressor Mfr
S.I.C.: 3563
N.A.I.C.S.: 333912

Busch Taiwan Corporation **(1)**
1F No 69 Sec 3 Beishen Road
Taipei, 2244, Taiwan
Tel.: (886) 226620775
Fax: (886) 226620796
E-Mail: info@busch.com.tw
Web Site: www.busch.com.tw
Emp.: 25
Vacuum Pumps, Blowers & Compressor Mfr
S.I.C.: 3563
N.A.I.C.S.: 333912
Plackett Hwang *(Pres)*

Busch (UK) Ltd. **(1)**
Hortonwood 30
Telford, Shrophshire, TF1 7YB, United Kingdom
Tel.: (44) 1952677432
Fax: (44) 1952677423
E-Mail: sales@busch.co.uk
Web Site: www.busch.co.uk
Emp.: 60
Vacuum Pumps, Blowers & Compressor Mfr
S.I.C.: 3563
N.A.I.C.S.: 333912
Ian Graves *(Mng Dir)*

Busch Vacuum India Pvt Ltd. **(1)**
J Block Plot number 5-7 Bhosari Midc
Pune, 411026, India
Tel.: (91) 2064102886
Fax: (91) 2046772905
E-Mail: sales@buschindia.com
Web Site: www.buschindia.com
Vacuum Pumps, Blowers & Compressor Mfr
S.I.C.: 3563
N.A.I.C.S.: 333912

Busch Vacuum Kft. **(1)**
Gare No 3
1225 Szigetszentmiklos, Hungary
Tel.: (36) 24887308
Fax: (36) 2488309
E-Mail: busch@busch-vacuum.hu
Web Site: www.busch-vacuum.hu
Emp.: 6
Vacuum Pumps, Blowers & Compressor Mfr
S.I.C.: 3563
N.A.I.C.S.: 333912
Totok Sandor *(Gen Mgr)*

Busch Vacuum Mexico S de R.L. de C.V **(1)**
Tlaquepaque 4865 Los Altos
Monterrey, 64370, Mexico
Tel.: (52) 8183111385
Fax: (52) 8183111384
E-Mail: info@busch.com.mx
Web Site: www.busch.com.mx
Emp.: 15
Vacuum Pumps, Blowers & Compressor Mfr

Dr. Ing. K. Busch GmbH—(Continued)

S.I.C.: 3563
N.A.I.C.S.: 333912
Louis Gomez *(Mng Dir)*

Busch Vacuum Russia OOO **(1)**
Kotlyakovskaya Str 6/9
115201 Moscow, Russia
Tel.: (7) 4956486726
Fax: (7) 4956486724
E-Mail: info@busch.ru
Web Site: www.busch.de/en/busch/busch-worldwide/europe/russia/
Vacuum Pumps, Blowers & Compressor Mfr
S.I.C.: 3563
N.A.I.C.S.: 333912

Busch Vacuum (Shanghai) Co. Ltd. **(1)**
No 5 Lane 195 Xipu Road
Songjiang Industrial Estate, Shanghai, 201611, China
Tel.: (86) 2167600800
Fax: (86) 2167600700
E-Mail: busch@busch-china.com
Web Site: www.busch-china.com
Emp.: 50
Vacuum Pumps, Blowers & Compressor Mfr
S.I.C.: 3563
N.A.I.C.S.: 333912

Busch Vacuum Singapore Pte. Ltd. **(1)**
20 Shaw Rd Ste 01-03
Singapore, 367956, Singapore
Tel.: (65) 64880866
Fax: (65) 62880877
E-Mail: busch@busch.com.sg
Web Site: www.busch.com.sg
Emp.: 8
Vacuum Pumps, Blowers & Compressor Mfr
S.I.C.: 3563
N.A.I.C.S.: 333912
Sophia Lee *(Mng Dir)*

Busch Vacuum South Africa (Pty) Ltd. **(1)**
87 Mimetes Road
Johannesburg, 2094, South Africa
Tel.: (27) 118560650
Fax: (27) 118560625
E-Mail: joe.jagger@busch.co.za
Web Site: www.busch.co.za
Emp.: 10
Vacuum Pumps, Blowers & Compressor Mfr
S.I.C.: 3563
N.A.I.C.S.: 333912
Joe Jagger *(Mng Dir)*

Busch Vacuum Technics Inc. **(1)**
1740 Lionel Bertrand
Boisbriand, QC, J7H 1N7, Canada
Tel.: (450) 435-6899
Fax: (450) 430-5132
E-Mail: info@busch.ca
Web Site: www.busch.ca
Emp.: 50
Vacuum Pumps, Blowers & Compressor Mfr
S.I.C.: 3563
N.A.I.C.S.: 333912
Paul Wieser *(Founder & Pres)*

Busch Vacuum (Thailand) Co. Ltd. **(1)**
888/30 Moo 19 Soi Yingcharoen
Bangplee-Tamru Road
Bangkok, 10540, Thailand
Tel.: (66) 23825428
Fax: (66) 2 3825429
E-Mail: info@busch.co.th
Web Site: www.busch.co.th
Vacuum Pumps, Blowers & Compressor Mfr
S.I.C.: 3563
N.A.I.C.S.: 333912

Busch Vakuum s.r.o. **(1)**
Prazakova 10
61900 Herspice, Czech Republic
Tel.: (420) 543424855
Fax: (420) 543 424 856
E-Mail: info@buschpumps.cz
Web Site: www.buschpumps.cz
Vacuum Pumps, Blowers & Compressor Mfr
S.I.C.: 3563
N.A.I.C.S.: 333912

Busch Vakuumteknik AB **(1)**
Brata Industriomrade
43533 Molnlycke, Sweden
Tel.: (46) 313380080
Fax: (46) 313380089
E-Mail: info@busch.se
Web Site: www.busch.se
Emp.: 16
Vacuum Pumps, Blowers & Compressor Mfr
S.I.C.: 3563
N.A.I.C.S.: 333912
Patrik Brouzell *(Mng Dir)*

Busch Vakuumteknik Oy **(1)**
Sinikellontie 4
01300 Vantaa, Finland
Tel.: (358) 97746060
Fax: (358) 977460666
E-Mail: info@busch.fi
Web Site: www.busch.fi
Vacuum Pumps, Blowers & Compressor Mfr
S.I.C.: 3563
N.A.I.C.S.: 333912

Busch Vakuumteknik AS **(1)**
Hestehagen 2
1440 Drobak, Norway
Tel.: (47) 64989850
Fax: (47) 64936621
E-Mail: busch@busch.no
Web Site: www.busch.no
Emp.: 20
Vacuum Pumps, Blowers & Compressor Mfr
S.I.C.: 3563
N.A.I.C.S.: 333912
Oyvind Hansen Billing *(Gen Mgr)*

Composites Busch S.A. **(1)**
Chemin des Grandes-Vies 54
2900 Delemont, Switzerland
Tel.: (41) 324657030
Fax: (41) 324657035
E-Mail: composites@busch.ch
Web Site: www.busch.ch
Emp.: 30
Vacuum Pumps, Blowers & Compressor Mfr
S.I.C.: 3563
N.A.I.C.S.: 333912
Mugerris Ahmed *(Mng Dir)*

Nippon Busch K.K. **(1)**
1-23-33 Megumigaoka
Hiratsuka, Kanagawa, 259-1220, Japan
Tel.: (81) 463504000
Fax: (81) 463504004
E-Mail: info@busch.co.jp
Web Site: www.busch.co.jp
Emp.: 70
Vacuum Pumps, Blowers & Compressor Mfr
S.I.C.: 3563
N.A.I.C.S.: 333912
Yoichiro Sasave *(Pres)*

Vakutek **(1)**
Emlak Kredi Ishani No. 179
34672 Uskudar Istanbul, Turkey
Tel.: (90) 2163100573
Fax: (90) 2163435126
E-Mail: vakutek@ttnet.net.tr
Web Site: www.vakutek.com.tr
Vacuum Pumps, Blowers & Compressor Mfr
S.I.C.: 3563
N.A.I.C.S.: 333912

DR. KURT WOLFF GMBH & CO. KG

Johanneswerkstrasse 34-36
33611 Bielefeld, Germany
Tel.: (49) 521880800
Fax: (49) 5218808200
E-Mail: info@alcina.de
Web Site: www.alpecin.de
Rev.: $73,067,500
Emp.: 246

Business Description:
Haircare Product Mfr
S.I.C.: 3999
N.A.I.C.S.: 339999

Personnel:
Eduard R. Dorrenberg *(Mng Dir)*
Christoph Harras-Wolff *(Mng Dir)*
Carsten Heins *(Mng Dir)*

DR. MACH GMBH & CO. KG

Flossmannstrasse 28
85560 Ebersberg, Germany
Tel.: (49) 809220930
Fax: (49) 8092209350
E-Mail: info@dr-mach.de
Web Site: www.dr-mach.de
Year Founded: 1947
Rev.: $16,711,431
Emp.: 60

Business Description:
Medical Applications Lighting Systems Mfr
S.I.C.: 3648
N.A.I.C.S.: 335129

Personnel:
Walter Mach *(Founder)*
Hans-Jorg Kemper *(Mng Dir)*

DR. O.K. WACK CHEMIE GMBH

Bunsenstrasse 6
85053 Ingolstadt, Germany
Tel.: (49) 8416350
Fax: (49) 84163558
Web Site: www.wackchem.com
Rev.: $17,916,883
Emp.: 110

Business Description:
Automobile Care Products Mfr
S.I.C.: 2819
N.A.I.C.S.: 325180

Personnel:
Oskar Kurt Wack *(Pres)*

DR. PAUL LOHMANN GMBH KG

Hasttstrasse 2
31680 Emmerthal, Germany
Tel.: (49) 5155630
Telex: 24555 NAVD
Fax: (49) 515563118
E-Mail: sales@lohmann4minerals.com
Web Site: www.lohmann4minerals.com
Year Founded: 1886
Emp.: 320

Business Description:
Inorganic & Organic Mineral Compounds
S.I.C.: 3299
N.A.I.C.S.: 327999

Personnel:
Juergen Lohmann *(CEO)*

DR. REDDY'S LABORATORIES LIMITED

Door No 8-2-337 Road No 3 Banjara Hills
Hyderabad, Andhra Pradesh, 500 034, India
Tel.: (91) 40 4900 2900
Fax: (91) 40 49002999
E-Mail: umangvohra@drreddys.com
Web Site: www.drreddys.com
Year Founded: 1984
RDY—(BOM NYSE)
Rev.: $2,233,235,700
Assets: $2,500,526,880
Liabilities: $1,319,695,740
Net Worth: $1,180,831,140
Earnings: $283,068,720
Emp.: 16,500
Fiscal Year-end: 03/31/13

Business Description:
Generic & Branded Pharmaceutical Mfr
S.I.C.: 2834
N.A.I.C.S.: 325412

Personnel:
K. Anji Reddy *(Founder & Chm)*
G. V. Prasad *(Chm & CEO)*
Satish Reddy *(Vice Chm & Mng Dir)*
Saumen Chakraborty *(Pres, CFO & Global Head-IT & BPE)*
R. Ananthanarayanan *(Pres-Pharmaceutical Svcs & Active Ingredients)*
Abhijit Mukherjee *(Pres-Generics)*
Sandeep Poddar *(Sec)*
Samiran Das *(Exec VP & Head-FTO & GGPM)*
Vilas Dholye *(Exec VP & Head-Formulations Mfg)*
Amit Biswas *(Exec VP-Integrated Product Dev)*
Raghav Chari *(Exec VP-Proprietary Products)*
K. B. Sankara Rao *(Exec VP-Integrated Product Dev)*
Cartikeya Reddy *(Exec VP-Biologics)*
Amit Patel *(Sr VP & Head-Generics-North America)*
Alok Sonig *(Sr VP & Head-India Bus Generics)*

Board of Directors:
G. V. Prasad
K. Anji Reddy
Ravi Bhoothalingam
Bruce L. A. Carter
Ashok S. Ganguly
Omkar Goswami
Sridar A. Iyengar
J. P. Moreau
Kalpana Morparia
Anupam Pradip Puri
Satish Reddy

Transfer Agent:
Bigshare Services Pvt Ltd
306 Right Wing 3rd Fl Amruta Ville Opp. Yashoda Hospital Raj Bhavan Rd
Somajiguda, Hyderabad, 500 082, India

Subsidiary:

Aurigene Discovery Technologies Limited **(1)**
39-40 KIADB Industrial Area Phase II
Electronic City Hosur Road
Bengaluru, Karnataka, 560100, India
Tel.: (91) 80 6620 4444
Fax: (91) 80 2852 6285
Web Site: www.aurigene.com
Emp.: 400
Drug Discovery Services
S.I.C.: 8731
N.A.I.C.S.: 541711
C. S. N. Murthy *(CEO)*
Murali Ramachandra *(Sr VP-Pre-Clinical Biology)*
Hosahalli Subramanya *(Sr VP-Structural Biology & Lead Generation)*

Non-U.S. Subsidiary:

Aurigene Discovery Technologies (Malaysia) SDN BHD **(2)**
G-I-2 Enterprise 4 Technology Park
Malaysia Lebuh Raya Puchong-Sg Besi
Bukit Jalil, 57000 Kuala Lumpur, Malaysia
Tel.: (60) 3 8996 4577
Fax: (60) 3 8996 4581
E-Mail: partnering@aurigene.com
Web Site: www.aurigene.com
Pharmaceutical Products Mfr
S.I.C.: 2834
N.A.I.C.S.: 325412

U.S. Subsidiaries:

Dr. Reddy's Laboratories-Bristol **(1)**
201 Industrial Dr
Bristol, TN 37620-5413 (100%)
Mailing Address:
PO Box 868
Bristol, TN 37621-0868
Tel.: (423) 652-3100
Fax: (423) 652-3262
E-Mail: info@glaxosmithkline.com
Web Site: www.glaxosmithkline.com
Emp.: 60
Pharmaceuticals Mfr
S.I.C.: 2834
N.A.I.C.S.: 325412

Dr. Reddy's Laboratories, Inc. **(1)**
200 Summerset Corporate Blvd Bldg II
Bridgewater, NJ 08807
Tel.: (908) 203-4900
Fax: (908) 203-4970
E-Mail: info@drreddys.com
Web Site: www.drreddys.com

Emp.: 70
Pharmaceutical Services
S.I.C.: 5122
N.A.I.C.S.: 424210
Umang Vohra *(Exec VP & Head-Generics Bus-North America)*

Subsidiaries:

Dr. Reddy's Laboratories Louisiana LLC (2)
8800 Line Ave
Shreveport, LA 71106
Tel.: (318) 861-8200
Toll Free: (866) 733-3952
Pharmaceutical Product Distr
S.I.C.: 5122
N.A.I.C.S.: 424210

Promius Pharma LLC (2)
200 Somerset Corporate Blvd
Bridgewater, NJ 08807
Tel.: (908) 429-4500
Fax: (908) 429-4579
Toll Free: (888) 384-6929
E-Mail: contactus@promiuspharma.com
Web Site: www.promiuspharma.com
Dermatology Products Research Services
S.I.C.: 8731
N.A.I.C.S.: 541711
Raghav Chari *(Sr VP)*

Dr. Reddy's Laboratories New York, Inc (1)
1974 State Rte 145
Middleburgh, NY 12122-5315
Tel.: (518) 827-7702
Pharmaceutical Products Research Services
S.I.C.: 8731
N.A.I.C.S.: 541711

Non-U.S. Subsidiaries:

Dr. Reddy's Laboratories (Australia) Pty. Limited (1)
Level 1 181 Bay Street
Brighton, VIC, 3186, Australia
Tel.: (61) 3 9595 3828
Fax: (61) 3 9595 3556
Web Site: www.drreddys.com
Pharmaceutical Products Distr
S.I.C.: 5122
N.A.I.C.S.: 424210

Dr. Reddy's Laboratories (EU) Limited (1)
6 Riverview Road
Beverley, North Humberside, HU17 0LD, United Kingdom
Tel.: (44) 1482 860 228
Fax: (44) 1482 872 042
Emp.: 65
Pharmaceutical Products Distr
S.I.C.: 5122
N.A.I.C.S.: 424210

Subsidiary:

Chirotech Technology Limited (2)
410 Milton Road Science Park
Cambridge, Cambridgeshire, CB4 0PE, United Kingdom
Tel.: (44) 1223 728010
Fax: (44) 1223 506701
Emp.: 60
Pharmaceutical Products Mfr
S.I.C.: 2834
N.A.I.C.S.: 325412

Dr. Reddy's Laboratories LLC (1)
5th Floor Street Bazhana 10 A
02140 Kiev, Ukraine
Tel.: (380) 44 207 51 97
Fax: (380) 44 207 51 96
Web Site: www.drreddys.com
Pharmaceutical Product Distr
S.I.C.: 5122
N.A.I.C.S.: 424210
Prashant Khandelwal *(Head-HR)*

Dr. Reddy's Laboratories (Proprietary) Limited (1)
North Wing The Place 1 Sandton Drive
Sandton, 2196, South Africa
Tel.: (27) 11 783 0104
Fax: (27) 11 388 1262
E-Mail: reception@drreddys.co.za
Web Site: www.drreddys.com
Emp.: 65
Pharmaceutical Products Distr
S.I.C.: 5122
N.A.I.C.S.: 424210
Nihar Patnaik *(Country Mgr)*

Dr. Reddy's Laboratories Romania SRL (1)
Str Nicolae Caramfil Nr 71-73 Et 5 Sector 1
Bucharest, Romania
Tel.: (40) 21 224 00 32
Fax: (40) 21 224 02 46
E-Mail: office@drreddys.ro
Web Site: www.drreddys.ro
Emp.: 18
Pharmaceutical Product Distr
S.I.C.: 5122
N.A.I.C.S.: 424210
Cristina Garlasu *(Country Mgr)*

Dr. Reddy's Laboratories (1)
Abbey House 18 / 24 Stoke Rd
SL25AG Slough, United Kingdom (100%)
Tel.: (44) 753495500
Fax: (44) 1753495510
E-Mail: contact@reddy-cheminor.com
Web Site: www.drreddys.com
Emp.: 30
Mfr. of Chemicals
S.I.C.: 2899
N.A.I.C.S.: 325998

Dr. Reddy's New Zealand Ltd. (1)
Level 6 AMI Building 63 Albert St
Auckland, 1142, New Zealand
Tel.: (64) 9 356 7000
Fax: (64) 9 356 7001
E-Mail: admin@drreddysnz.co.nz
Web Site: www.drreddys.com
Pharmaceutical Products Distr
S.I.C.: 5122
N.A.I.C.S.: 424210

Eurobridge Consulting BV (1)
Prins Bernhardplein 200
1097 JB Amsterdam, Netherlands
Tel.: (31) 205214777
Pharmaceutical Products Research Services
S.I.C.: 8731
N.A.I.C.S.: 541711

Industrias Quimicas Falcon de Mexico, S.A. de CV (1)
Carretera Federal Cuernavaca Cuautla Km 4 5 Col Civac
62578 Cuernavaca, Morelos, Mexico
Tel.: (52) 777 329 3450
Fax: (52) 777 329 3465
E-Mail: division.uuimica@drreddys.com
Emp.: 200
Pharmaceutical Product Mfr
S.I.C.: 2834
N.A.I.C.S.: 325412
Alberto Flores *(Gen Mgr)*

Reddy Holding GmbH (1)
Kobelweg 95
86156 Augsburg, Germany
Tel.: (49) 821 748810
Fax: (49) 821 74881420
Pharmaceutical Product Distr
S.I.C.: 5122
N.A.I.C.S.: 424210

Subsidiaries:

beta Healthcare Solutions GmbH (2)
Kobelweg 95
86156 Augsburg, Germany
Tel.: (49) 821 748810
Pharmaceutical Product Mfr
S.I.C.: 2834
N.A.I.C.S.: 325412

beta Institut for Soziaimedizinische Forschung and Entwicklung GmbH (2)
Steinerne Furt 78
86156 Augsburg, Germany
Tel.: (49) 821 450540
Fax: (49) 821 450549166
Laboratory Testing Services
S.I.C.: 8734
N.A.I.C.S.: 541380

betapharm Arzneimittel GmbH (2)
Kobelweg 95
86156 Augsburg, Germany
Tel.: (49) 821 74881 0
Fax: (49) 821 74881 420
E-Mail: info@betapharm.de
Web Site: www.betapharm.de
Pharmaceutical Products Mfr
S.I.C.: 2834
N.A.I.C.S.: 325412
Michael Ewers *(Gen Mgr)*

Reddy Pharma Iberia SA (1)
Chile 10 Las Matas
Madrid, 28290, Spain
Tel.: (34) 91 636 85 48
Fax: (34) 91 630 24 71
E-Mail: info@reddypharma.es
Emp.: 1
Pharmaceutical Products Distr
S.I.C.: 5122
N.A.I.C.S.: 424210
Miguel Angel Dominguez *(Controller-Fin)*

DR. SCHUMACHER GMBH

Am Roggenfeld 3
34323 Melsungen, Germany
Tel.: (49) 566494960
Fax: (49) 56648444
E-Mail: info@schumacher-online.com
Web Site: www.schumacher-online.com
Rev.: $51,036,310
Emp.: 92
Business Description:
Healthcare Product Mfr
S.I.C.: 2834
N.A.I.C.S.: 325412
Personnel:
Dierk Schumacher *(Co-Mng Dir)*
Jens Schumacher *(Co-Mng Dir)*

DR. THEISS NATURWAREN GMBH

Michelinstrasse 10
66424 Homburg, Germany
Tel.: (49) 68417090
Fax: (49) 6841709265
E-Mail: info@naturwaren-theiss.de
Web Site: www.naturwaren-theiss.de
Year Founded: 1978
Sales Range: $10-24.9 Million
Emp.: 1,000
Business Description:
Healthcare & Beauty Products Mfr & Distr
S.I.C.: 2844
N.A.I.C.S.: 325620
Personnel:
Guiseppe Nardi *(Mng Dir)*
Peter Theiss *(Mng Dir)*

Non-U.S. Subsidiaries:

Dr. Theiss Naturwaren Sarl (1)
11 rue du Chene
BP 90114
Nordhouse, 67152 Erstein, France
Tel.: (33) 388598969
Fax: (33) 388598960
E-Mail: stella.melendez@drtheiss.fr
Web Site: www.naturwaren.fr
Emp.: 20
Cosmetics & Healthcare Products Distr
S.I.C.: 5122
N.A.I.C.S.: 446120
Stella Melendez *(Gen Mgr)*

Naturprodukt KFT (1)
Depo Pf 8
2046 Torokbalint, Hungary
Tel.: (36) 23336333
Fax: (36) 23511339
E-Mail: info@naturprodukt.hu
Web Site: www.naturprodukt.hu
Emp.: 20
Natural Skin Care Products & Vitamin Supplements Mfr & Retailer
S.I.C.: 5999
N.A.I.C.S.: 446199

Naturwaren Italia s.r.l. (1)
Centro Il Girasole 207A
20084 Lacchiarella, MI, Italy
Tel.: (39) 02 90090083
Fax: (39) 02 90047070
E-Mail: info@naturwaren.it
Web Site: www.naturwaren.it
Healthcare & Beauty Products Distr
S.I.C.: 5122
N.A.I.C.S.: 424210

DR. THOMAS + PARTNER GMBH & CO. KG

Am Sandfeld 9
76149 Karlsruhe, Germany
Tel.: (49) 72178340
Fax: (49) 7217834119
Web Site: www.tup.com
Rev.: $12,408,238
Emp.: 55
Business Description:
Employee Training Services
S.I.C.: 8299
N.A.I.C.S.: 611430
Personnel:
Frank Thomas *(Founder)*

DR. WILLMAR SCHWABE GMBH & CO. KG

Willmar Schwabe Strasse 4
76227 Karlsruhe, Germany
Tel.: (49) 72140050
Fax: (49) 7214005630
E-Mail: info@schwabe.de
Web Site: www.schwabe.de
Sales Range: $800-899.9 Million
Emp.: 3,200
Business Description:
Phytomedicines Mfr
S.I.C.: 2833
N.A.I.C.S.: 325411
Personnel:
Dirk Reischig *(CEO)*

U.S. Subsidiary:

Nature's Way Holding Co. (1)
825 Challenger Dr
Green Bay, WI 54311
Tel.: (920) 469-1313
Fax: (920) 469-4444
E-Mail: info@naturesway.com
Web Site: www.naturesway.com
Emp.: 200
Holding Company; Nutritional Supplement Mfr
S.I.C.: 6719
N.A.I.C.S.: 551112
Randy Rose *(Pres & CEO)*
Rory Mahony *(COO)*

Subsidiary:

Enzymatic Therapy Inc. (2)
825 Challenger Dr
Green Bay, WI 54311
Tel.: (920) 469-1313
Fax: (920) 570-6460
Web Site: www.enzy.com
Sales Range: $50-74.9 Million
Emp.: 290
Natural & Synthetic Vitamins Mfr
S.I.C.: 2833
N.A.I.C.S.: 325411
Randy Rose *(CEO)*
Cathy Stone *(Sr VP-Ops)*

DRACO PCB PUBLIC COMPANY LIMITED

Bangkadi Industrial Park Mu 5 152 Tiwanon Road
Amphur Muang, Pathumthani, 12000, Thailand
Tel.: (66) 2 5011241
Fax: (66) 2 5011248
E-Mail: webmaster@dracopcb.com
Web Site: www.dracopcb.com
Year Founded: 1989
DRACO—(THA)
Rev.: $19,843,545
Assets: $45,702,172
Liabilities: $7,407,205
Net Worth: $38,294,967
Earnings: ($873,969)
Emp.: 550
Fiscal Year-end: 12/31/12

Draco PCB Public Company Limited—(Continued)

Business Description:
Printed Circuit Board Mfr
S.I.C.: 3679
N.A.I.C.S.: 334418
Personnel:
Viphandh Roengpithya *(Chm)*
Jung Kun Chen *(Mng Dir)*
Laksana Samranthiwawan *(Sec)*
Board of Directors:
Viphandh Roengpithya
Adul Amatavivadhana
Jung Kun Chen
Aung Htun
Vincent Wei-Jin Huang
Pi Chi Lin
Suraphol Pluemarom
Bhilaichit Roengpithya
Fred Shiau

DRAEGERWERK AG & CO. KGAA

Moislinger Allee 53-55
23542 Lubeck, Germany
Tel.: (49) 451 882 0
Fax: (49) 451 882 2080
E-Mail: info@draeger.com
Web Site: www.draeger.com
Year Founded: 1889
DRW3—(DEU EUR)
Rev.: $3,195,127,764
Assets: $2,828,579,135
Liabilities: $1,849,642,965
Net Worth: $978,936,170
Earnings: $181,781,412
Emp.: 12,516
Fiscal Year-end: 12/31/12
Business Description:
Safety & Gas Detection Products Mfr & Sales
S.I.C.: 1389
N.A.I.C.S.: 213112
Personnel:
Nikolaus Schweickart *(Chm-Supervisory Bd)*
Stefan Draeger *(Chm-Exec Bd & CEO)*
Siegfrid Kasang *(Vice Chm-Supervisory Bd)*
Herbert Fehrecke *(Vice Chm-Exec Bd-Pur, Quality & R&D)*
Gert-Hartwig Lescow *(CFO & Member-Exec Bd)*
Anton Schrofner *(Member-Exec Bd-Production, Logistics & IT)*
Supervisory Board of Directors:
Nikolaus Schweickart
Daniel Friedrich
Klaus-Dieter Furstenberg
Thorsten Grenz
Siegfrid Kasang
Stefan Klein
Stefan Lauer
Uwe Luders
Klaus Rauscher
Thomas Rickers
Ulrike Tinnefeld
Reinhard Zinkann

U.S. Subsidiary:

Draeger Safety, Inc. **(1)**
101 Technology Dr
Pittsburgh, PA 15275-1005
Tel.: (412) 787-8383
Telex: 86-6704
Fax: (412) 787-2207
Toll Free: (800) 922-5518
E-Mail: shelly.cosmides@draeger.com
Web Site: www.draeger.com
Emp.: 175
Toxic Gas Monitoring Instrumentation & Respiratory Protection Equipment Mfr Import Export
S.I.C.: 3829
N.A.I.C.S.: 334519
Shelli Cosmides *(Mgr-Mktg Comm)*

Division:

Draeger Safety Diagnostics, Inc. **(2)**
83A Davidson Creek Rd
Durango, CO 81301-7913 (100%)
Tel.: (970) 385-5555
Fax: (970) 385-5522
Web Site: www.draeger-breathalyzer.com
Emp.: 20
Mfr. of Breath-Alcohol Analyzers
S.I.C.: 3829
N.A.I.C.S.: 334519
Hansueli Ryser *(Mng Dir)*

Non-U.S. Subsidiaries:

Beijing Fortune Draeger Safety Equipment Co., Ltd. **(1)**
Beijing Tianzhu Airport Industrial Zone A22 Yu An Rd B Area
Honshayu Shunyi County, Beijing, 100300, China
Tel.: (86) 1080498000
Fax: (86) 1080498005
E-Mail: bfps@draeger.com
Web Site: www.draeger.cn
Emp.: 50
Mfr. of Toxic Gas Monitoring Instrumentation & Respiratory Protection Equipment
S.I.C.: 3823
N.A.I.C.S.: 334513
Joerg Daehn *(Gen Mgr)*

Draeger Safety Pacific Ltd. **(1)**
3 Ferntree Pl Unit 99 45 Gilby Rd
Notting Hill, VIC, 3149, Australia (100%)
Tel.: (61) 392655000
Fax: (61) 392655095
E-Mail: info@draeger.com
Web Site: www.draeger.com
Sales Range: $25-49.9 Million
Emp.: 60
Mfr. of Toxic Gas Monitoring Instrumentation & Respiratory Protection Equipment
S.I.C.: 3823
N.A.I.C.S.: 334513
Andrew Hawk *(Mng Dir)*

Draeger Safety Austria GmbH **(1)**
Wallackgasse 8
A 1230 Vienna, Austria (100%)
Tel.: (43) 1 6093602 0
Fax: (43) 1 6996242
E-Mail: office.safety@draeger.com
Web Site: www.draeger.com
Emp.: 31
Distr of Toxic Gas Monitoring Instrumentation & Respiratory Protection Equipment
S.I.C.: 3823
N.A.I.C.S.: 334513

N.V. Draeger Safety Belgium S.A. **(1)**
Heide 10
1780 Wemmel, Belgium (100%)
Tel.: (32) 24626211
Fax: (32) 24605240
E-Mail: stbe.info@draeger.com
Web Site: www.draeger.com
Rev.: $38,180,672
Emp.: 100
Toxic Gas Monitoring Instrumentation & Respiratory Protection Equipment
S.I.C.: 3823
N.A.I.C.S.: 334513
Peter Stuatuzer *(Gen Mgr)*

Draeger Canada Ltd. **(1)**
7555 Danbro Cres
Mississauga, ON, L5N 6P9, Canada(100%)
Tel.: (905) 821-8988
Fax: (905) 821-2565
E-Mail: info@draeger.com
Web Site: www.draeger.ca
Emp.: 20
Distr of Toxic Gas Monitoring Instrumentation & Respiratory Protection Equipment
S.I.C.: 3823
N.A.I.C.S.: 334513
Joseph Jagdel *(Controller)*

Draeger Croatia d.o.o. **(1)**
Froudeova 13
HR 10020 Zagreb, Croatia (100%)
Tel.: (385) 16599444
Fax: (385) 16599403
E-Mail: hrvoje.krupski@draeger.com
Web Site: www.draeger.com
Sales Range: Less than $1 Million
Emp.: 25
Distr of Toxic Gas Monitoring Instrumentation & Respiratory Protection Equipment
S.I.C.: 3823
N.A.I.C.S.: 334513

Draeger Medical Hispania S.A. **(1)**
C/Xaudaro 5
28034 Madrid, Spain (100%)
Tel.: (34) 917 28 3400
Fax: (34) 91 358 36 19
E-Mail: clientesdraegermedical@draeger.com
Web Site: www.draeger.es
Emp.: 140
Distr of Toxic Gas Monitoring Instrumentation & Respiratory Protection Equipment
S.I.C.: 3823
N.A.I.C.S.: 334513

Draeger Safety S.A. **(1)**
3C Rue De La Federation
PO Box 141
F 67025 Strasbourg, France (100%)
Tel.: (33) 388407676
Fax: (33) 388407667
E-Mail: protection.france@draeger.fr
Web Site: www.draeger.com
Emp.: 70
Distr of Toxic Gas Monitoring Instrumentation & Respiratory Protection Equipment
S.I.C.: 3823
N.A.I.C.S.: 334513
Bernard Hetzel *(Pres)*

Draeger Medical Italiana S.p.A. **(1)**
Via Galvani 7
20094 Corsico, Italy (100%)
Tel.: (39) 02458721
Fax: (39) 02 45 84515
Web Site: www.draeger.com
Distr of Toxic Gas Monitoring Instrumentation & Respiratory Protection Equipment
S.I.C.: 3823
N.A.I.C.S.: 334513

Draeger Safety Ltd. **(1)**
Ullswater Close
Blyth, NE24 4RG, United Kingdom (100%)
Tel.: (44) 1670352891
Fax: (44) 1670356266
E-Mail: marketing@draeger.co.uk
Web Site: www.draeger.com
Emp.: 400
Mfr of Toxic Gas Monitoring Instrumentation & Respiratory Protection Equipment
S.I.C.: 3823
N.A.I.C.S.: 334513
Mike Norris *(Mng Dir)*

Draeger Safety Nederland B V **(1)**
Postbus 310 Edisonstraat 53
NL 2700 AH Zoetermeer, Netherlands (100%)
Tel.: (31) 793444666
Fax: (31) 793444790
E-Mail: daeger@draeger.nl
Web Site: www.draegersafety.com
Sales Range: $25-49.9 Million
Emp.: 150
Mfr. of Toxic Gas Monitoring Instrumentation & Respiratory Protection Equipment
S.I.C.: 3823
N.A.I.C.S.: 334513
Robert Den Brave *(Mng Dir)*

Draeger Safety Norge A/S **(1)**
Nils Hansenvej 2
0667 Oslo, Norway (100%)
Tel.: (47) 23069500
Fax: (47) 23643199
E-Mail: safety.no@draeger.com
Web Site: www.draeger.com
Emp.: 25
Toxic Gas Monitoring Instrumentation & Respiratory Protection Equipment
S.I.C.: 3823
N.A.I.C.S.: 334513

Draeger Safety (Schweiz) AG **(1)**
Rue du Grand Pre 4
1007 Lausanne, Switzerland (100%)
Tel.: (41) 216473700
Fax: (41) 216473800
E-Mail: info@draeger.ch
Web Site: www.draeger.com
Emp.: 35
Distr of Toxic Gas Monitoring Instrumentation & Respiratory Protection Equipment
S.I.C.: 3823
N.A.I.C.S.: 334513
Urs Weder *(Mng Dir)*

Draeger Medical South Africa (Pty) Ltd **(1)**
Drager Medical Little Four Ways Office Park Block A Leslie Road, Johannesburg, 2055, South Africa (100%)
Mailing Address:
PO Box 4656
Rivoni, Bryanston, 2021, South Africa
Tel.: (27) 115572300
Fax: (27) 115572301
E-Mail: info@draeger.com
Web Site: www.draeger.com
Emp.: 52
Distr of Toxic Gas Monitoring Instrumentation & Respiratory Protection Equipment
S.I.C.: 3823
N.A.I.C.S.: 334513
Morus Fourie *(Gen Mgr)*

Draeger Safety Sweden AB **(1)**
Ogardesvagen 19 D
433 30 Partille, Sweden (100%)
Tel.: (46) 313409090
Fax: (46) 313409099
E-Mail: draeger@draegersafety.se
Web Site: www.draegersafety.se
Emp.: 40
Distr of Toxic Gas Monitoring Instrumentation & Respiratory Protection Equipment
S.I.C.: 3823
N.A.I.C.S.: 334513
Marina Wahlen *(Head-Fin)*

Drager Safety Danmark A/S **(1)**
Generatorvej 6B
2730 Herlev, Denmark (100%)
Tel.: (45) 44500000
Fax: (45) 44500001
E-Mail: draeger-safety.dk@draeger.com
Web Site: www.draeger.com
Emp.: 20
Distributor of Toxic Gas Monitoring Instrumentation & Respiratory Protection Equipment
S.I.C.: 3823
N.A.I.C.S.: 334513
Mark Verweij *(Gen Mgr)*

DRAEXLMAIER GRUPPE

Landshuter Strasse 100
D 84137 Vilsbiburg, Germany
Tel.: (49) 8741470
Fax: (49) 8741471940
E-Mail: info@draexlmaier.com
Web Site: www.draexlmaier.com
Sales Range: $1-4.9 Billion
Emp.: 34,000
Business Description:
Electronic Components Mfr & Whslr
S.I.C.: 3679
N.A.I.C.S.: 334419
Personnel:
Fritz Draexlmaier *(Pres)*

Subsidiaries:

DFE Draxlmaier Fahrzeugelektrik GmbH **(1)**
Wankel Strasse 4
26723 Emden, Germany (100%)
Tel.: (49) 4921966200
Fax: (49) 4921966213
E-Mail: info@draexlmaier.de
Web Site: www.draexlmaier.de/lang_en/Standorte/emden.htm
Emp.: 40
Electronic Component Mfr
S.I.C.: 3679
N.A.I.C.S.: 334419
Manfred Pflueger *(Mng Dir)*

DFS Draxlmaier Fahrzeugsysteme GmbH **(1)**
Pascal-Strasse 4
85057 Ingolstadt, Germany

Tel.: (49) 8419515950
Fax: (49) 841951595209
E-Mail: info@draexlmaier.de
Web Site: www.draexlmaier.de/lang_en/Standorte/ingolstadt.htm
Motor Vehicle Parts Mfr
S.I.C.: 3714
N.A.I.C.S.: 336390

DKS Draxlmaier Kunststoffsysteme GmbH (1)
Im Finigen 2
28832 Achim, Germany (100%)
Tel.: (49) 42025190
Fax: (49) 4202519522
E-Mail: info@draexlmaier.de
Web Site: www.draexlmaier.de
Emp.: 260
Rubber & Plastics Hoses & Belting Mfr
S.I.C.: 3052
N.A.I.C.S.: 326220

DSV Draxlmaier Systemverkabelungen GmbH (1)
Dieselstrasse 14
84056 Rottenburg an der Laaber, Germany (100%)
Tel.: (49) 87812080
Fax: (49) 8781208151
E-Mail: info@draexlmaier.de
Web Site: www.draexlmaier.de/lang_en/Standorte/rottenburg.htm
Emp.: 24
Electronic Component Mfr
S.I.C.: 3679
N.A.I.C.S.: 334419
Irngard Daffner *(Office Mgr)*

DVS Draxlmaier Verdrahtungssysteme GmbH (1)
Otto-Lilienthal-Str 26
71034 Boblingen, Germany (100%)
Tel.: (49) 703128600
Fax: (49) 70312860402
E-Mail: info@draexlmaier.de
Web Site: www.draexlmaier.de/lang_en/Standorte/boeblingen.htm
Electronic Component Mfr
S.I.C.: 3679
N.A.I.C.S.: 334419

Eldra Kunststofftechnik GmbH (1)
Wiesenweg 10
Landau, 94405 Hessen, Germany
Tel.: (49) 99516980
Fax: (49) 9951698255
E-Mail: info@draexlmaier.de
Web Site: www.draexlmaier.de
Emp.: 350
Plastics Products Mfr
S.I.C.: 3089
N.A.I.C.S.: 326199
Edmund Eggensberger *(Plant Mgr)*

Holzindustrie Bruchsal GmbH (1)
Ernst Blickle Strasse 21 25
D 76646 Bruchsal, Germany (100%)
Tel.: (49) 72517220
Fax: (49) 7251722190
E-Mail: info-hib@draexlmaier.de
Web Site: www.hibautomotive.de
Emp.: 600
Mfr. & Assembly Company
S.I.C.: 3711
N.A.I.C.S.: 336111
Patrick Oschust *(Mng Dir)*

Lisa Draxlmaier GmbH (1)
Landshuter Strasse 100
84137 Vilsbiburg, Germany (100%)
Tel.: (49) 8741470
Fax: (49) 8741471940
E-Mail: info@draexlmaier.de
Web Site: www.draexlmaier.de/lang_en/impressum.htm
Emp.: 2,400
Electronic Component Mfr
S.I.C.: 3679
N.A.I.C.S.: 334419
Erwin Lechner *(Mgr)*

U.S. Subsidiary:

Draexlmaier Automotive of America, LLC (1)
PO Box 1345
Duncan, SC 29334-1345 SC
Tel.: (864) 433-8910
Fax: (864) 433-8920
E-Mail: info@draexlmaier.de
Web Site: www.draexlmaier-automotive.com
Emp.: 350
Mfr of Motor Vehicle Parts & Accessories Import Export
S.I.C.: 3714
N.A.I.C.S.: 336390
Erik Reiter *(CEO)*

Non-U.S. Subsidiaries:

D&A Electrical Systems Sdn. Bhd. (1)
Lot 2755 Persiaran Kilan Jelapang Light Industrial Estate, 30100 Perak, Ipoh, Malaysia
Tel.: (60) 55280913
Fax: (60) 55280722
E-Mail: info@draexlmaier.de
Electronic Component Mfr
S.I.C.: 3679
N.A.I.C.S.: 334419

D&B Interiors (Pty) Ltd. (1)
30 Helium Street Stand 452
Automotive Supplier Park, 0200 Gauteng, South Africa
Tel.: (27) 125411900
Fax: (27) 125411901
E-Mail: info@draexlmaier.de
Emp.: 51
Specialized Design Services
S.I.C.: 7389
N.A.I.C.S.: 541490
Peter Merrington *(Mng Dir)*

DAU Draxlmaier Automotive UK Ltd. (1)
111 Hollymoor Way Great Park
Birmingham, Rubery, B315HE, United Kingdom (100%)
Tel.: (44) 1212566262
Fax: (44) 121256263
E-Mail: dau@draexlmaier.de
Web Site: www.draexlmaier.de
Emp.: 70
Automotive Transmission Repair
S.I.C.: 7537
N.A.I.C.S.: 811113

DCM Draexlmaier Components Automotive de Mexico S.A. DE C.V. (1)
Avenida Central 180 Park Logistico
78395 San Luis Potosi, Mexico
Tel.: (52) 4441372700
Fax: (52) 4441372848
E-Mail: info@draexlmaier.de
Web Site: www.draexlmaier.de/lang_en/Standorte/san-luis-potosi.htm
Electronic Component Mfr
S.I.C.: 3679
N.A.I.C.S.: 334419
Stesan Dude *(Mng Dir)*

Draexlmaier Automotive Systems (Thailand) Co., Ltd. (1)
7-118 Moo 4 Amata City Industrial Estate
Tambol Mabyangporn Amphur Plua, 21140 Rayong, Thailand
Tel.: (66) 38956340
E-Mail: info@draexlmaier.de
Web Site: www.draexlmaier.com
Emp.: 100
Motor Vehicle Parts Mfr
S.I.C.: 3714
N.A.I.C.S.: 336390

Draexlmaier (Shenyang) Automotive Components Co., Ltd. (1)
Wen Guan Street No 6
Dadong District, 110045 Shenyang, China
Tel.: (86) 2484553888
Fax: (86) 2484553880
E-Mail: info@draexlmaier.de
Emp.: 25
Motor Vehicle Parts Mfr
S.I.C.: 3714
N.A.I.C.S.: 336390

DRE Draexlmaier Elektrotek S.r.o. (1)
Kvasiny 145
51702 Mlada Boleslav, Czech Republic
Tel.: (420) 494539911
Fax: (420) 494539923
E-Mail: info@draexlmaier.de
Engine Equipment Mfr
S.I.C.: 3519
N.A.I.C.S.: 333618

DRM Sisteme Electrice SRL (1)
Strada Vulturului 34
440268 Satu-Mare, Romania (100%)
Tel.: (40) 361403100
Fax: (40) 361403170
E-Mail: info@draexlmaier.de
Web Site: www.draexlmaier.de/lang_en/Standorte/satu-mare.htm
Emp.: 4,000
Electronic Component Mfr
S.I.C.: 3679
N.A.I.C.S.: 334419
Cadar Luliu *(Mng Dir)*

DSE Draxlmaier Systemy Elektryczne Sp. Z o.o. (1)
Ul Spoldzielcza 45
Jelenia Gora, 58500 Legnica, Poland
Tel.: (48) 757538824
Fax: (48) 757538803
E-Mail: info@draexlmaier.de
Web Site: www.draexlmaier.de/lang_en/Standorte/jelenia.htm
Emp.: 600
Electronic Component Mfr
S.I.C.: 3679
N.A.I.C.S.: 334419
Thomas Kruar *(Mng Dir)*

DTR Draxlmaier Sisteme Tehnice Romania S.R.L. (1)
Str Gradinarilor Nr 29
Codlea, 505100 Brasov, Romania
Tel.: (40) 268507200
Fax: (40) 268507298
E-Mail: dtr.general@draexlmaier.com
Web Site: www.draexlmaier.de/lang_en/Standorte/codlea.htm
Emp.: 700
Electronic Component Mfr
S.I.C.: 3679
N.A.I.C.S.: 334419
Suranyi Marius *(Pres)*

EKB Elektro und Kunststofftechnik GmbH (1)
Industriezeile 1-3
5280 Braunau, Austria
Tel.: (43) 77228830
Fax: (43) 7722883202
E-Mail: info@draexlmaier.de
Web Site: www.draexlmaier.de/lang_en/Standorte/braunau.htm
Emp.: 450
Rubber & Plastics Hoses & Belting Mfr
S.I.C.: 3052
N.A.I.C.S.: 326220

Lisa Draxlmaier Autopart Romania SRL (1)
Str N Balcescu Nr 186
Pitesti, 110101 Arges, Romania (100%)
Tel.: (40) 248201342
Fax: (40) 248201446
E-Mail: info@draexlmaier.de
Emp.: 5,000
Automobile Mfr
S.I.C.: 3711
N.A.I.C.S.: 336111

DRAFTTEAM FANTASY SPORTS INC.

(Formerly Intelimax Media Inc.)
Harbour Centre Suite 2320 555 West Hastings Street
Vancouver, BC, V6B 4N4, Canada
Tel.: (604) 742-1111
Fax: (604) 909-5169
Toll Free: (866) 742-1759
E-Mail: ir@draftteam.com
Web Site: www.draftteam.com
DFS—(CNSX DEU OTC)
Rev.: $7,110
Assets: $564,819
Liabilities: $335,625
Net Worth: $229,194
Earnings: ($1,161,550)
Emp.: 1
Fiscal Year-end: 03/31/13

Business Description:
Website & Internet Portal Operator
S.I.C.: 2741
N.A.I.C.S.: 519130

Personnel:
Michael Young *(Co-Founder, Pres & CFO)*
Richard Skujins *(Co-Founder)*
John Buttedahl *(CEO)*

Board of Directors:
John Buttedahl
Paul Anthony Larkin
Richard Skujins
Michael Young

DRAGANFLY INVESTMENTS LIMITED

Pentera Chambers Century Buildings
Patriotic Place
PO Box 79
Saint Helier, Jersey JE4 8PS
Tel.: (44) 1534787878
Fax: (44) 1534787879
Web Site: www.draganflyinvestments.com
DRG—(LSE)
Rev.: $8
Assets: $1,350,313
Liabilities: $51,997
Net Worth: $1,298,317
Earnings: ($27,581)
Fiscal Year-end: 04/30/13

Business Description:
Investment Management Services
S.I.C.: 6211
N.A.I.C.S.: 523999

Personnel:
T. Edward G. Bayman *(Chm)*

Board of Directors:
T. Edward G. Bayman
Lee B. A. De Ste Croix
Dennis Vernon Edmonds
Jamie P. Hamilton

DRAGON BRIGHT MINTAI BOTANICAL TECHNOLOGY (CAYMAN) LIMITED

11/F Shum Tower No 268 Des Voeux Road
Central, China (Hong Kong)
Tel.: (852) 3975 2318
Fax: (852) 3020 6206
E-Mail: anita.ho@dbmintai.com
Web Site: dbmintai.com
DGBMF—(OTC OTCB)
Rev.: $14,928
Assets: $2,654,451
Liabilities: $1,629,764
Net Worth: $1,024,687
Earnings: ($907,884)
Emp.: 35
Fiscal Year-end: 12/31/12

Business Description:
Forest Seedlings Producer
S.I.C.: 0851
N.A.I.C.S.: 115310

Personnel:
Anita Lai Lai Ho *(Chm & CEO)*
Wing Kui Sy *(Interim CFO)*
Cho-Po Chang *(COO)*
Stanley Ang *(Chief Admin Officer)*
Jeffrey Chong Kee Hui *(Gen Counsel)*

Board of Directors:
Anita Lai Lai Ho
Stanley Ang
Jeffrey Chong Kee Hui
Yau Man Hwang

DRAGON CROWN GROUP HOLDINGS LIMITED

Suite 1803 Convention Plaza Office Tower 1 Harbour Road
Wanchai, China (Hong Kong)
Tel.: (852) 25003888
Fax: (852) 25871338
Web Site: www.dragoncrown.com
935—(HKG)

Dragon Crown Group Holdings Limited—(Continued)

Rev.: $33,239,442
Assets: $134,367,705
Liabilities: $10,755,075
Net Worth: $123,612,631
Earnings: $14,692,563
Emp.: 255
Fiscal Year-end: 12/31/12

Business Description:
Terminal Chemical Storage Services
S.I.C.: 5171
N.A.I.C.S.: 424710

Personnel:
Wai Man Ng *(Chm)*
Yian Ann Ting *(CEO)*
Man Kit Chong *(CFO & Sec)*

Board of Directors:
Wai Man Ng
Wan Ming Chan
Yat Chin Chong
Sik Yuen Lau
Shijie Luo
Yian Ann Ting
Wujun Zhu

Codan Trust Company (Cayman) Limited
Cricket Square Hutchins Drive
PO Box 2681
Georgetown, Grand Cayman, Cayman Islands

Transfer Agents:
Tricor Investor Services Limited
26th Floor Tesbury Centre 28 Queens Road East
Wanchai, China (Hong Kong)

Codan Trust Company (Cayman) Limited
Cricket Square Hutchins Drive
PO Box 2681
Georgetown, Grand Cayman, Cayman Islands

DRAGON ENERGY LTD

Suite 8 1297 Hay St
West Perth, WA, 6005, Australia
Mailing Address:
PO Box 1968
West Perth, WA, 6872, Australia
Tel.: (61) 8 9322 6009
Fax: (61) 8 9322 6128
Web Site: www.dragonenergyltd.com
DLE—(ASX)
Rev.: $227,444
Assets: $21,135,522
Liabilities: $394,095
Net Worth: $20,741,427
Earnings: ($1,309,633)
Fiscal Year-end: 06/30/13

Business Description:
Phosphate Mining Services
S.I.C.: 1475
N.A.I.C.S.: 212392

Personnel:
Jie Chen *(Chm)*
Gang Xu *(Mng Dir)*
Leonard Math *(CFO & Co-Sec)*
Ziming Yan *(Co-Sec)*

Board of Directors:
Jie Chen
Rodney Illingworth
Weifeng Li
Gang Xu

Legal Counsel:
Steinepreis Paganin
Level 4 Next Building 16 Milligan St
Perth, Australia

DRAGON HOLDINGS AG

Promenadeplatz 10
80333 Munich, Germany
Tel.: (49) 89 216650 36
Fax: (49) 89 216650 41
E-Mail: michael@dragonholdings.net
Web Site: www.dragonholdings.net
DRGHY—(OTC)
Sales Range: $50-74.9 Million

Business Description:
Holding Company; Investment Services
S.I.C.: 6719
N.A.I.C.S.: 551112

Personnel:
Niraj Goel *(Chm-Supervisory Bd)*
Michael J. Hughes *(CEO & Member-Mgmt Bd)*
Jim Manczak *(COO)*
Pily Wong *(Member-Mgmt Bd)*

Supervisory Board of Directors:
Niraj Goel
Datuk Paul Chong
Paul Kuoch

Non-U.S. Subsidiaries:

Right Deal Ltd. (1)
Flat D 10/F Kai Centre 36 Hung To Road
Kwun Tong, Kwun Tong, China (Hong Kong)
Tel.: (852) 24267428
Fax: (852) 24816848
E-Mail: sales@rightdeal.net
Web Site: www.rightdeal.net
Emp.: 6
Computer Peripheral Equipment Distr
S.I.C.: 5045
N.A.I.C.S.: 423430
Sally Tam *(Mgr)*

Tradeology Ltd. (1)
1 Changi North Street 1
Singapore, 498789, Singapore
Tel.: (65) 6542 6624
Fax: (65) 6542 6674
E-Mail: sales@tradeology.biz
Web Site: www.tradeology.biz
Emp.: 10
Securities Investment Software Retailer
S.I.C.: 5045
N.A.I.C.S.: 423430
Niraj Goel *(Mng Dir)*

DRAGON JADE INTERNATIONAL LIMITED

Unit 2 23/F New World Tower I 18 Queens Road
Hong Kong, China (Hong Kong)
Tel.: (852) 2527 8368
Fax: (852) 2527 0612
DGJI—(OTCB)
Rev.: $124,972
Assets: $506,329
Liabilities: $398,170
Net Worth: $108,159
Earnings: ($181,439)
Emp.: 7
Fiscal Year-end: 03/31/13

Business Description:
Business Consulting Services
S.I.C.: 8742
N.A.I.C.S.: 541611

Personnel:
Lok Bun Law *(Pres)*
Yat Man Lai *(CEO)*
Kwok Wing Fung *(CFO)*
Phoenix Wing Mui Ngai *(Sec)*

Board of Directors:
Kwok Wing Fung
Thomas Fan Wah Lai
Yat Man Lai
Lok Bun Law
Philip Tsz Fung Lo
Daniel Tze Yu Tai

Transfer Agent:
Pacific Stock Transfer Company
4045 S Spencer St Ste 403
Las Vegas, NV 89119
Tel.: (702) 361-3033

DRAGON MINING

Unit B1 431 Roberts Road
Subiaco, WA, 6008, Australia
Tel.: (61) 8 6311 8000
Fax: (61) 8 6311 8004
E-Mail: admin@dragon-mining.com.au
Web Site: www.dragon-mining.com.au
DRA—(ASX)
Rev.: $82,375,921
Assets: $77,279,010
Liabilities: $24,419,529
Net Worth: $52,859,480
Earnings: ($4,442,472)
Emp.: 5
Fiscal Year-end: 12/31/12

Business Description:
Gold Mining
S.I.C.: 1041
N.A.I.C.S.: 212221

Personnel:
Kjell Emil Larsson *(Mng Dir)*
Mark S. C. Cheng *(CFO)*
Shannon Coates *(Sec)*

Board of Directors:
Peter George Cordin
Peter Lynton Gunzburg
Kjell Emil Larsson
Christian Russenberger

Legal Counsel:
Clayton Utz
250 St Georges Terr
Perth, Australia

Non-U.S. Subsidiaries:

Dragon Mining (Sweden) AB (1)
Pautrask 100
923 98 Storuman, Lapland, Sweden
Tel.: (46) 95115451
Fax: (46) 95180022
E-Mail: admin@dragonmining.se
Gold Bullion Mining Services
S.I.C.: 1041
N.A.I.C.S.: 212221

Polar Mining Oy (1)
Kummunkuja 38
Vammala, 38200 Sastamala, Finland
Tel.: (358) 403007800
Fax: (358) 205155490
Web Site: www.dragonmining.fi
Emp.: 20
Gold Mining & Exploration Services
S.I.C.: 1041
N.A.I.C.S.: 212221
Paivi Mikkonen *(Controller-Fin)*

DRAGON MOUNTAIN GOLD LIMITED

Unit 4 62 Ord Street
West Perth, WA, 6005, Australia
Mailing Address:
PO Box 1767
West Perth, WA, 6872, Australia
Tel.: (61) 892156300
Fax: (61) 894816799
E-Mail: info@dragonmountain.com.au
Web Site: www.dragonmountain.com.au
DMG—(ASX)
Rev.: $695,290
Assets: $5,801,756
Liabilities: $121,414
Net Worth: $5,680,342
Earnings: ($508,677)
Fiscal Year-end: 06/30/13

Business Description:
Gold Exploration Services
S.I.C.: 1041
N.A.I.C.S.: 212221

Personnel:
Robert C. Gardner *(Chm & Mng Dir)*
Jay Stephenson *(Sec)*

Board of Directors:
Robert C. Gardner
Duncan Robert MsBain
Paul Piercy

Legal Counsel:
Fairweather & Lemonis
Level 17 Exchange Plz 2 The Esplanade
6000 Perth, WA, Australia

DRAGON PHARMACEUTICAL, INC.

650 W Georgia St Ste 310
PO Box 11638
Vancouver, BC, V6B 4N9, Canada
Tel.: (604) 669-8817
Fax: (604) 669-4243
Toll Free: (877) 388-DRUG
E-Mail: info@dragonpharma.com
Web Site:
Sales Range: $150-199.9 Million
Emp.: 2,406

Business Description:
Biopharmaceutical Mfr
S.I.C.: 2834
N.A.I.C.S.: 325412

Personnel:
Yanlin Han *(Chm & CEO)*
Garry Wong *(CFO)*
Maggie Deng *(COO)*

Board of Directors:
Yanlin Han
Heinz Frey
Jin Li
Xuemei Liu
Peter Mak
Yiu Kwong Sun
Zhanguo Weng
Alexander Wick

DRAGON UKRAINIAN PROPERTIES & DEVELOPMENT PLC

2nd floor Belgravia House 34-44 Circular Road
Douglas, IM1 1AE, Isle of Man
Tel.: (44) 1624643740
Fax: (44) 1624643802
E-Mail: cosecdupd@standardbank.com
Web Site: www.dragon-upd.com
Year Founded: 2007
DUPD—(LSE)
Rev.: $87,000
Assets: $213,378,000
Liabilities: $15,338,000
Net Worth: $198,040,000
Earnings: ($15,273,000)
Fiscal Year-end: 12/31/12

Business Description:
Property Development Services
S.I.C.: 6531
N.A.I.C.S.: 531390

Personnel:
Tracy Duncan *(Sec)*

Board of Directors:
Aloysius Wilhelmus Johannes van der Heijden
Nikolay Artemenko
Tomas Fiala
Rory Macnamara
Fredrik Svinhufvud

Legal Counsel:
Faegre & Benson LLP
7 Pilgrim Street
London, United Kingdom

Cains
15-19 Athol Street
Douglas, Isle of Man

Baker & McKenzie CIS Limited
Renaissance Business Centre 24 Vorovskoho Street
Kiev, Ukraine

U.S. Subsidiary:

Mountcrest LTD (1)
3285 Hillcrest Rd
Medford, OR 97504
Tel.: (541) 608-3898
General Freight Trucking Services
S.I.C.: 4212
N.A.I.C.S.: 484110

Non-U.S. Subsidiaries:

Bi Dolyna Development LLC (1)
Bud 36d Vul Saksaganskogo
1033 Kiev, Ukraine

Tel.: (380) 444907120
Real Estate Property Development Services
S.I.C.: 6531
N.A.I.C.S.: 531390

EF Nova Oselya LLC (1)
Bud 36 D Vul Saksaganskogo
1033 Kiev, Ukraine
Tel.: (380) 444907120
Fax: (380) 4927978
Real Estate Development Services
S.I.C.: 6531
N.A.I.C.S.: 531390

J Komfort Neruhomist LLC (1)
Bud 36-D Vul Saksaganskogo
Kiev, Ukraine
Tel.: (380) 444907120
Fax: (380) 444907121
E-Mail: info@dragon-upd.com
Real Estate Management Services
S.I.C.: 6531
N.A.I.C.S.: 531390

Korona Development LLC (1)
Bud 36-D Vul Saksaganskogo
01033 Kiev, Ukraine
Tel.: (380) 444907120
Real Estate Property Development Services
S.I.C.: 6531
N.A.I.C.S.: 531390

Rivnobud LLC (1)
Bud 36 Lit D Vul Saksaganskogo
Kiev, Ukraine
Tel.: (380) 444907120
Residential Property Management Services
S.I.C.: 6531
N.A.I.C.S.: 531311

DRAGONFLY CAPITAL CORP.

Suite 1518 1030 West Georgia Street
Vancouver, BC, V6E 2Y3, Canada
Tel.: (604) 689-2646
Fax: (604) 689-1289
Year Founded: 2010
DRC.P—(TSXV)
Assets: $170,555
Liabilities: $53,594
Net Worth: $116,961
Earnings: ($202,341)
Fiscal Year-end: 04/30/13
Business Description:
Investment Services
S.I.C.: 6211
N.A.I.C.S.: 523999
Personnel:
Harry Chew *(Pres & CEO)*
Sonny Chew *(CFO)*
Jerry A. Minni *(Sec)*
Board of Directors:
Harry Chew
Sonny Chew
Trent Hunter
Jerry A. Minni
Legal Counsel:
Gowling Lafleur Henderson LLP
Suite 2300-550 Burrard Street
Vancouver, BC, Canada
Transfer Agent:
Equity Transfer & Trust Company
1185 West Georgia Street Suite 1620
Vancouver, BC, V6E 4E6, Canada

DRAGONITE INTERNATIONAL LIMITED

Room 1101 11th Floor China United Centre
28 Marble Road, North Point, China (Hong Kong)
Tel.: (852) 3198 0688
Fax: (852) 2579 0055
E-Mail: general@dragonite329.com.hk
Web Site: www.dragonite.com.hk
0329—(HKG)
Sls.: $2,621,167
Assets: $50,933,961
Liabilities: $10,902,078
Net Worth: $40,031,883
Earnings: ($8,521,016)
Emp.: 105
Fiscal Year-end: 12/31/12
Business Description:
Tobacco & Pharmaceutical Products Mfr & Sales
S.I.C.: 7359
N.A.I.C.S.: 532490
Personnel:
Yin Sen Wong *(Chm)*
Gary Drew Douglas *(Mng Dir)*
Mee Sze Chan *(Sec)*
Board of Directors:
Yin Sen Wong
Mee Sze Chan
Yuk Lun Chung
Gary Drew Douglas
Tak Fun Ho
Lik Hon
Albert Man Sum Lam
Suk Ping Lam
Kwong Sang Liu
Computershare Hong Kong Investor Services Limited
Shops 1712-1716 17th Floor Hopewell Centre
183 Queens Road East
Wanchai, China (Hong Kong)
Transfer Agents:
Royal Bank of Canada Trust Company (Cayman) Limited
4th Floor Royal Bank House 24 Shedden Road
Georgetown, Cayman Islands
Computershare Hong Kong Investor Services Limited
Shops 1712-1716 17th Floor Hopewell Centre
183 Queens Road East
Wanchai, China (Hong Kong)

DRAGONWAVE INC.

411 Legget Drive Suite 600
Ottawa, ON, K2K 3C9, Canada
Tel.: (613) 599-9991
Fax: (613) 599-4265
E-Mail: info@dragonwaveinc.com
Web Site: www.dragonwaveinc.com
Year Founded: 2000
DRWI—(NASDAQ TSX)
Rev.: $123,877,000
Assets: $134,994,000
Liabilities: $79,384,000
Net Worth: $55,610,000
Earnings: ($55,007,000)
Emp.: 278
Fiscal Year-end: 02/28/13
Business Description:
Broadband Wireless Carrier-Grade Microwave Equipment Designer, Developer, Marketer & Sales
S.I.C.: 3663
N.A.I.C.S.: 334220
Personnel:
Erik Boch *(Founder, CTO & VP-Engrg)*
Dave Farrar *(Founder & VP-Ops)*
Claude Carman Haw *(Chm)*
Peter Allen *(Pres & CEO)*
Russell James Frederick *(CFO & Sec)*
Barry Dahan *(Exec VP-Global Sls)*
Board of Directors:
Claude Carman Haw
Peter Allen
Jean-Paul Cossart
Russell James Frederick
Thomas M. Manley
Terence H. Matthews
Tom McLellan
Robert M. Pons
Transfer Agent:
Computershare Investor Services Inc.
100 University Ave 9th Floor
Toronto, ON, Canada
Non-U.S. Branch:

DragonWave Inc. UK (1)
Unit 3 Ground Floor Brooklands
Redditch, Worcs, B98 9DW, United Kingdom
Tel.: (44) 1527583120
Fax: (44) 1527583132
E-Mail: easales@dragonwaveinc.com
Web Site: www.dragonwaveinc.com
Emp.: 10
Wireless Networking Systems Mfr
S.I.C.: 4812
N.A.I.C.S.: 517210
Bill Paulsen *(VP-Sls)*

DRAHTWERK FRIEDR. LOTTERS GMBH & CO. KG

Hellestrasse 40
58675 Hemer, Germany
Tel.: (49) 237286090
Fax: (49) 2372860911
E-Mail: dwl@loetters.de
Web Site: www.loetters.de
Year Founded: 1912
Rev.: $32,415,900
Emp.: 120
Business Description:
Wire Mfr
S.I.C.: 3351
N.A.I.C.S.: 331420
Personnel:
Fritz-Peter Lotters *(Gen Mgr)*

DRAIG RESOURCES LIMITED

Level 28 25 Bligh Street
Sydney, NSW, 2000, Australia
Mailing Address:
PO Box 4309
Sydney, NSW, 2001, Australia
Tel.: (61) 2 9230 0760
Fax: (61) 8 6102 6543
Web Site: www.draigresources.com
DRG—(ASX)
Rev.: $178,128
Assets: $6,664,355
Liabilities: $212,135
Net Worth: $6,452,219
Earnings: ($9,374,497)
Fiscal Year-end: 06/30/13
Business Description:
Coal Exploration Services
S.I.C.: 1222
N.A.I.C.S.: 212112
Personnel:
Peter Doherty *(Chm)*
Jarrod Smith *(Sec)*
Board of Directors:
Peter Doherty
David Meldrum
Jarrod Smith
Legal Counsel:
Steinepreis Paganin
Level 4 The Read Building 16 Milligan Street
Perth, WA, 6000, Australia
Tel.: (61) 8 9321 4000
Fax: (61) 8 9321 4333

DRAKE & MORGAN LIMITED

Suite 199 3rd Floor Temple Chambers Temple Avenue
London, EC4Y 0HP, United Kingdom
Tel.: (44) 207 583 3446
E-Mail: enquiries@drake-morgan.co.uk
Web Site: www.drake-morgan.co.uk
Year Founded: 2008
Sales Range: $25-49.9 Million
Emp.: 267
Business Description:
Bar & Restaurant Operator
S.I.C.: 5813
N.A.I.C.S.: 722410
Personnel:
Jillian MacLean *(Mng Dir)*

DRAKE & SCULL INTERNATIONAL PJSC

PO Box 65794
Dubai, United Arab Emirates
Tel.: (971) 48112300
Fax: (971) 4 8112315
Web Site: www.drakescull.com
DSI—(DFM)
Rev.: $903,982,724
Assets: $1,749,997,641
Liabilities: $996,390,556
Net Worth: $753,607,085
Earnings: $31,312,404
Fiscal Year-end: 12/31/12
Business Description:
Mechanical, Electrical, Plumbing, Infrastructure, Water, Power & Civil Contracting Services
S.I.C.: 1731
N.A.I.C.S.: 238210
Personnel:
Majed Saif Al-Ghurair *(Chm)*
Khaldoun Rashid Tabari *(Vice Chm & CEO)*
Kamil Daniel *(Chief Investment Officer)*
Michael Salmon *(Chief Comml Officer)*
Zeina Tabari *(Chief Corp Affairs Officer)*
Board of Directors:
Majed Saif Al-Ghurair
Talal Jassim Al-Bahar
Khalaf Sultan Al-Daheri
Yusuf Al-Nowais
Jamal Saeed Saleh Al-Nuaimi
Ivor Mark Goldsmith
Saleh Muradweij
Tawfiq Abu Soud
Khaldoun Rashid Tabari
Subsidiaries:

Drake & Scull International L.L.C (1)
Airport Road Opposite Abu Dhabi Chamber of comm
PO Box 44325
Abu Dhabi, 44325, United Arab Emirates
Tel.: (971) 26226005
Fax: (971) 26226008
E-Mail: corporate@drakescull.com
Emp.: 5,000
Electrical & Mechanical Engineering Services
S.I.C.: 3699
N.A.I.C.S.: 335999
Khaldoun R. Tabari *(CEO)*
Khaled Jarrar *(CFO)*
Michael Salmon *(Chief Comml Officer)*

Gulf Technical Construction Company L.L.C (1)
Electra St
PO Box 66123
Abu Dhabi, United Arab Emirates
Tel.: (971) 48112300
Fax: (971) 4 8850967
Web Site: www.gulftcc.com
Emp.: 80
Civil Engineering Services
S.I.C.: 8711
N.A.I.C.S.: 541330
Tariq Annab *(Mgr)*

Non-U.S. Subsidiary:

Passavant-Roediger GmbH (1)
Herriotstrasse 1
60528 Frankfurt, Germany De
Tel.: (49) 69 94 74 15 0 (100%)
Fax: (49) 69 94 74 15 111
E-Mail: info@passavant-roediger.com
Web Site: www.passavant-roediger.de
Sales Range: $75-99.9 Million
Emp.: 125
Water & Sewage Plant Construction & Engineering Services
S.I.C.: 1629
N.A.I.C.S.: 237110
Mazen Bachir *(Mng Dir & CTO)*

DRAKE RESOURCES LIMITED

Level 4 66 Kings Park Road
West Perth, WA, 6005, Australia
Tel.: (61) 8 6141 3585
Fax: (61) 8 6141 3599
E-Mail: info@drakeresources.com.au

Drake Resources Limited—(Continued)

Web Site: www.drakeresources.com.au
DRK—(ASX)
Rev.: $101,014
Assets: $13,432,395
Liabilities: $600,064
Net Worth: $12,832,331
Earnings: ($3,938,392)
Emp.: 6
Fiscal Year-end: 06/30/13
Business Description:
Mining Services
S.I.C.: 1081
N.A.I.C.S.: 213114
Personnel:
Jason Stirbinskis *(CEO)*
Jay Stephenson *(Sec)*
Board of Directors:
Brett Fraser
Robert Beeson
Jay Stephenson
Legal Counsel:
Steinepreis Paganin
Level 4 The Read Building 16 Milligan Street
Perth, WA, 6000, Australia
Tel.: (61) 8 9321 4000
Fax: (61) 8 9321 4333

DRAKKAR & ASSOCIES INC.

780 Brewster Ave Suite 03 200
Montreal, QC, H4C 2K1, Canada
Tel.: (514) 733-6655
Fax: (514) 733-2828
Web Site: www.drakkar.ca
Rev.: $32,500,000
Emp.: 52
Business Description:
Employment & Consulting Agencies
S.I.C.: 7361
N.A.I.C.S.: 561311
Personnel:
Denis Deschamps *(Co-Pres & CEO)*
Michel Blaquiere *(Co-Pres & COO)*

DRAKO CAPITAL CORP.

(Name Changed to Amarok Energy Inc.)

DRAMBUIE LIMITED

Springburn Bond Carlisle Street
Glasgow, G21 1EQ, United Kingdom
Tel.: (44) 1895458680
Fax: (44) 1313161358
E-Mail: marketing@drambuie.com
Web Site: www.drambuie.com
Year Founded: 1990
Emp.: 20
Business Description:
Distilled Spirit Mfr & Distr
S.I.C.: 6719
N.A.I.C.S.: 551112
Personnel:
Richard Stone *(Chm)*
Board of Directors:
Richard Stone

DRANCO CONSTRUCTION LIMITED

1919 Albion Road
Etobicoke, ON, M9W 6J9, Canada
Tel.: (416) 675-2682
Fax: (416) 674-5788
Web Site: www.dranco.com
Year Founded: 1956
Rev.: $24,143,647
Emp.: 200
Business Description:
Sewer & Water Main Construction Services
S.I.C.: 1623
N.A.I.C.S.: 237110

Personnel:
Realdo Di Donato *(Pres)*

DRAX GROUP PLC

Drax Power Station
Selby, N Yorkshire, YO8 8PH, United Kingdom
Tel.: (44) 1757 618381
Fax: (44) 1757612192
Web Site: www.draxgroup.plc.uk
DRX—(LSE OTC)
Rev.: $2,810,820,342
Assets: $3,566,668,536
Liabilities: $1,233,583,419
Net Worth: $2,333,085,117
Earnings: $258,687,702
Emp.: 1,163
Fiscal Year-end: 12/31/12
Business Description:
Power Plant Operator
S.I.C.: 4911
N.A.I.C.S.: 221112
Personnel:
Dorothy Thompson *(CEO)*
Phillip Hudson *(Sec & Dir-Corp Affairs)*
Board of Directors:
Charles A. Berry
Tim Barker
Tim Cobbold
Peter Emery
Melanie Gee
David Lindsell
Tony Quinlan
Paul Taylor
Dorothy Thompson
Tony Thorne
Legal Counsel:
Slaughter & May LLP
One Bunhill Row
London, EC1Y 8YY, United Kingdom
Norton Rose LLP
3 More London Riverside
London, SE1 2AQ, United Kingdom
Tel.: (44) 20 7283 6000
Fax: (44) 20 7283 6500

Subsidiary:

Drax Power Limited **(1)**
Drax Power Station
PO Box 3
Selby, North Yorkshire, YO8 8PH, United Kingdom
Tel.: (44) 1757618381
Fax: (44) 1757618504
Web Site: www.DraxPower.com
Power Plant Operating Services
S.I.C.: 4931
N.A.I.C.S.: 221112
Dorresy Thompson *(Exec Dir)*

DRAYTEK CORPORATION

No 26 Fushing Rd Hukou Hsinchu Industrial Park
303 Hsin-chu, Taiwan
Tel.: (886) 35972727
Fax: (886) 35972121
Web Site: www.draytek.com
6216—(TAI)
Sales Range: $10-24.9 Million
Business Description:
Communications Equipment Mfr
S.I.C.: 3661
N.A.I.C.S.: 334210
Personnel:
Calvin Ma *(Pres & CEO)*

Non-U.S. Subsidiary:

DrayTek GmbH **(1)**
Pirnaer Str 9
68309 Mannheim, Baden-Wurttemberg, Germany
Tel.: (49) 6217176670
Fax: (49) 621 717667 29
E-Mail: info@draytek.de
Web Site: www.draytek.de
Networking Components Distr
S.I.C.: 5065

N.A.I.C.S.: 423690

DRAYTON VALLEY FORD SALES LTD

5214 Power Centre Blvd
PO Box 6389
Drayton Valley, AB, T7A 1R8, Canada
Tel.: (780) 542-4438
Fax: (780) 542-5795
Toll Free: (866) 841-3673
E-Mail: info@draytonvalleyford.com
Web Site: www.draytonvalleyford.com
Rev.: $20,952,086
Emp.: 44
Business Description:
New & Used Car Dealers
S.I.C.: 5511
N.A.I.C.S.: 441110
Personnel:
Darren Gagnon *(CEO)*
Neil Barton *(CFO)*

DRB-HICOM BERHAD

Level 6 Wisma DRB-HICOM 2 Jalan Usahawan
U1/8 Section U1, 40150 Shah Alam, Selangor, Malaysia
Tel.: (60) 320528000
Fax: (60) 320527891
E-Mail: info@drb-hicom.com
Web Site: www.drb-hicom.com
DRBHCOM—(KLS)
Rev.: $4,307,139,678
Assets: $13,815,431,265
Liabilities: $11,075,885,929
Net Worth: $2,739,545,335
Earnings: $229,195,749
Emp.: 52,000
Fiscal Year-end: 03/31/13
Business Description:
Real Estate, Infrastructure & Defense Services & Automotive Mfr & Distr
S.I.C.: 3711
N.A.I.C.S.: 336111
Personnel:
Mohd Khamil Jamil *(Mng Dir)*
Ahmad Fuaad Kenali *(CFO)*
Carol Choy Lin Chan *(Sec & Dir-Corp Affairs)*
Board of Directors:
Mohamad Murtaza
Mohd Khamil Jamil
Marzuki Mohd Noor
Abdul Rahman Mohd Ramli
Ie Cheong Ong
Teik Huat Ooi
Noorrizan Shafie
Ibrahim Taib

Subsidiaries:

HICOM Holdings Bhd **(1)**
2 Jalan Usahawan Wisma DRB-HICOM
40150 Shah Alam, Selangor, Malaysia
Tel.: (60) 320528156
Fax: (60) 320528118
E-Mail: info@drb-hicom.com
Web Site: www.drb-hicom.com
Sales Range: $1-4.9 Billion
Holding Company
S.I.C.: 6719
N.A.I.C.S.: 551112
Mohd Khamil Jamil *(Mng Dir)*

Holdings:

Auto Prominence (M) Sdn Bhd **(2)**
Wisma Keringat 2
Lorong Batu Caves 2, Batu Caves, Selangor, 68100, Malaysia
Tel.: (60) 36189 4414
Fax: (60) 3 6188 4428
Automobile Dealer
S.I.C.: 5012
N.A.I.C.S.: 423110
Mat Termizi Kamarudin *(Gen Mgr)*

Automotive Corporation (Malaysia) Sdn Bhd **(2)**
03 Jalan Perusahaan
Kawasan Perusahaan Batu Caves
Batu Caves, Selangor, 68100, Malaysia
Tel.: (60) 361881133
Fax: (60) 361894337
Web Site: www.acm.com.my
Motor Vehicle Mfr
S.I.C.: 3711
N.A.I.C.S.: 336111
Amr Udin *(Interim CEO)*

Composites Technology Research Malaysia Sdn. Bhd. **(2)**
T02 3rd Floor 2310 Century Square
Jalan Usahawan, 63000 Cyberjaya, Selangor darul Ehsan, Malaysia MY
Tel.: (60) 3 8313 5100
Fax: (60) 3 8313 5111
E-Mail: info@ctrm.com.my
Web Site: www.ctrm.com.my
Aerospace & Commercial Composite Components Mfr
S.I.C.: 3089
N.A.I.C.S.: 326199
Ali Abbas Alhabshee *(Chm)*
Rosdi Mahmud *(CEO)*
Burhanuddin Hilmi Mohamed *(CFO)*
Zulkarnain Mohamed *(COO)*
Abd Halim Abd Majid *(CMO)*

DRB-HICOM Auto Solutions Sdn Bhd **(2)**
No 2 Jalan Usahawan U1/8 Seksyen U1
Shah Alam, Selangor, 40150, Malaysia
Tel.: (60) 320528218
Fax: (60) 320528222
Web Site: www.drb-hicom.com.my
Emp.: 54
Motor Vehicle Business Support Services
S.I.C.: 7389
N.A.I.C.S.: 561499
Dastanam Hanzeh *(COO)*

Edaran Otomobil Nasional Berhad **(2)**
EON Head Office Complex
2 Persiaran Kerjaya Seksy, Shah Alam, Selangor Darul Ehsan, 40150, Malaysia
Tel.: (60) 377112211
Fax: (60) 378063882
E-Mail: customerservice@eon.com.my
Sales Range: $600-649.9 Million
Emp.: 90
Motor Vehicles Distr
S.I.C.: 5571
N.A.I.C.S.: 441228
Marzuki Bin Mohd Noor *(Chm)*

Subsidiaries:

Euromobil Sdn Bhd **(3)**
Audi Centre Glenmarie Lot 27 Jalan Pelukis
U1 46 Seksyen Ultara Satu
Kawasan Perindustrian Temasya, 40150 Shah Alam, Selangor, Darul Ehsan, Malaysia
Tel.: (60) 376887688
Fax: (60) 376280020
E-Mail: customerservice@euromobil.com.my
Web Site: www.euromobil.com.my
Emp.: 52
Used Car Dealers
S.I.C.: 5521
N.A.I.C.S.: 441120
Kulendron Palachandran *(Head-Audi)*

Joint Venture:

Proton Parts Centre Sdn Bhd **(3)**
1 Jalan Arkitek U1-22 Section 11
Hicom Glenmarie Indus Park, Shah Alam, Selangor, Malaysia
Tel.: (60) 378036399
Fax: (60) 378036532
Web Site: www.protonparts.com.my
Motor Vehicle Supplies & New Parts Whslr
S.I.C.: 5013
N.A.I.C.S.: 423120
Encik Rali Mohd Nor *(Mng Dir)*

Euro Truck & Bus (Malaysia) Sdn Bhd **(2)**
KM 6 Jalan Ipoh
Gurun, 08300, Malaysia
Tel.: (60) 44667000
Fax: (60) 4 466 7133

Motor Vehicle Mfr & Distr
S.I.C.: 3711
N.A.I.C.S.: 336111
William Chong Wei Yoon *(CEO)*

HICOM Automotive Manufacturers (Malaysia) Sdn Bhd (2)
Kawasan Perindustrian Peramu Jaya
PO Box 3
Pahang Darul Makmur, Pekan, 26607, Malaysia
Tel.: (60) 94244000
Fax: (60) 94244023
Web Site: www.drb-hicom.com
Emp.: 1,500
Motor Vehicle Assembly Facilities & Testing Equipment Services
S.I.C.: 3711
N.A.I.C.S.: 336111
Shamsuddin Mohammad Yousuf *(CEO)*

Konsortium Logistik Berhad (1)
Lot 22202 Jalan Gambus 33/4 Off Jalan Bukit Kemuning
40350 Shah Alam, Selangor Darul Ehsan, Malaysia (61.6%)
Tel.: (60) 351219988
Fax: (60) 351229898
E-Mail: enquiry@konsortium.net
Web Site: www.klb.my
KONSORT—(KLS)
Rev.: $88,088,166
Assets: $112,858,587
Liabilities: $48,713,828
Net Worth: $64,144,759
Earnings: $5,434,618
Fiscal Year-end: 12/31/12
Logistics Services
S.I.C.: 8742
N.A.I.C.S.: 541611
Eddie W'y-Kit Thoo *(CFO)*
Zarihi Hashim *(COO)*
Oi Wah Leong *(Co-Sec)*
Siau Cheng Lim *(Co-Sec)*
Kamal Said Ali *(Sr VP-Grp HR)*
Pauline Tee *(Sr VP-Value Added Svcs)*

Subsidiaries:

Aman Freight (M) Sdn. Bhd (2)
Lot 6 Jalan Sltn Mhmd 3 Kawasan Perindustrian Selat Klang Utara
Bdr Sltn Sulaiman Darul Ehsan, 42000 Port Klang, Selangor, Malaysia
Tel.: (60) 331769822
Fax: (60) 331769808
E-Mail: aman@pc.jaring.my
Web Site: www.pc.jaring.my
Freight & Forwarding Agency
S.I.C.: 4731
N.A.I.C.S.: 488510

Asia Pacific Freight System Sdn. Bhd. (2)
Lot D 20 Malaysia Airline Freight Forwarders Complex
KLIA Free Comml Zone, 64000 Sepang, Selangor, Malaysia
Tel.: (60) 387873099
Fax: (60) 387873055
E-Mail: mazna.kamaruddin@klb.my
Web Site: www.klb.my
Emp.: 9
Freight Forwarding Agencies
S.I.C.: 4731
N.A.I.C.S.: 488510
Rahman Zamri *(Gen Mgr)*

Cougar Logistics (Malaysia) Sdn. Bhd. (2)
Locked Bag No 246 Lot 16 Lebuh Sultan Muhamed 1
Kaw Perusahaan Bdr, 42000 Port Klang, Selangor, Malaysia
Tel.: (60) 331761995
Fax: (60) 331760469
E-Mail: azmir@cougar.com.my
Web Site: www.cougar.com.my
Emp.: 25
Logistics Services
S.I.C.: 4731
N.A.I.C.S.: 541614

Malaysian Shipping Agencies Sdn. Bhd. (2)
Ground Fl Pelikan Bldg Lot 3410
Batu 12 1 2 Jalan Puchong, Puchong, Selangor, 47100, Malaysia
Tel.: (60) 380605000
Fax: (60) 380605020
Web Site: www.konsortium.com.net
Shipping Agencies
S.I.C.: 4491
N.A.I.C.S.: 488320
Zulkifli Bin Sarkam *(Sr VP)*

Westport Distripark (M) Sdn. Bhd. (2)
Pulau Indah
PO Box 286
42009 Port Klang, Selangor, Malaysia
Tel.: (60) 331011818
Fax: (60) 331011718
Emp.: 31
Private Warehousing Services
S.I.C.: 4226
N.A.I.C.S.: 493190

PROTON Holdings Berhad (1)
HICOM Industrial Estate Batu Tiga
40000 Shah Alam, Selangor Darul Ehsan, Malaysia MY
Tel.: (60) 351911055 (100%)
Fax: (60) 380269744
E-Mail: corporate@proton.com.my
Web Site: www.proton.com
Sales Range: $1-4.9 Billion
Emp.: 12,000
Holding Company; Automotive Engineering, Assembly & Trading
S.I.C.: 6719
N.A.I.C.S.: 551112
Dato Sri Haji Mohd Khamil Bin Jamil *(Chm)*

Subsidiaries:

Lotus Engineering (Malaysia) Sdn. Bhd (2)
G-5 Technology Park Malaysia Lebuhraya Puchong-Sungai Besi
Bukit Jalil, 57000 Kuala Lumpur, Malaysia
Tel.: (60) 389967172
Fax: (60) 389941172
Emp.: 80
Automobile Engineering Services
S.I.C.: 8711
N.A.I.C.S.: 541330
Ian Maxwell *(Gen Mgr)*

Perusahaan Otomobil Nasional Sdn. Bhd. (2)
HICOM Industrial Estate Batu Tiga
40000 Shah Alam, Selangor, Malaysia
Tel.: (60) 351911055
Fax: (60) 351911453
E-Mail:
Web Site: www.proton.com
Emp.: 7,000
Motor Vehicles Mfr
S.I.C.: 3714
N.A.I.C.S.: 336320
Wan Roslan *(Dir-HR)*

PROTON Edar Sdn. Bhd. (2)
Ctr of Excellence Complex KM 33 8
Westbound Shah Alam Expressway
47600 Subang Jaya, Selangor, Malaysia MY
Tel.: (60) 380269999
Fax: (60) 380269399
E-Mail: i.care@proton.com
Web Site: www.proton-edar.com.my
New Car Dealers
S.I.C.: 5511
N.A.I.C.S.: 441110
Ahmad Suhaimi Mohamed Anuar *(CEO)*

Proton Tanjung Malim Sdn. Bhd. (2)
Mukim Hulu Bernam Timur Daerah Batang Padang
Behrang Stesen, 35950 Tanjung Malim, Perak, Malaysia
Tel.: (60) 5 457 8888
New Car Dealers
S.I.C.: 5511
N.A.I.C.S.: 441110
Sukri Hamidi *(Gen Mgr)*

U.S. Subsidiary:

Lotus Cars USA Inc. (2)
2236 Northmont Pkwy
Duluth, GA 30096
Tel.: (770) 476-6577
Fax: (770) 476-6541
Web Site: www.lotuscars.com
Emp.: 9
Sports Car Distr
S.I.C.: 5511
N.A.I.C.S.: 441110
Arnie Johnson *(Dir-Ops)*

Non-U.S. Subsidiaries:

Group Lotus Plc (2)
Potash Ln
Hethel, Norwich, NR14 8EZ, United Kingdom UK
Tel.: (44) 1953608000 (100%)
Fax: (44) 1953608300
E-Mail: group@lotuscars.co.uk
Web Site: www.lotuscars.co.uk
Emp.: 1,400
High Performance Cars Engineering, Consulting & Mfr
S.I.C.: 3711
N.A.I.C.S.: 336111
Aslam Farikullah *(COO)*

Division:

Lotus Cars (3)
Potash Lane Hethel
Norwich, Norfolk, NR14 8EZ, United Kingdom
Tel.: (44) 1953608000
Fax: (44) 1953608300
E-Mail: dbahar@lotuscars.com
Web Site: www.lotuscars.com
Emp.: 1,800
Sports Cars Mfr
S.I.C.: 3799
N.A.I.C.S.: 336999
Dany Bahar *(CEO)*

Subsidiaries:

Lotus Body Engineering Ltd. (3)
Potash Lane
Norwich, Norfolk, NR14 8EZ, United Kingdom
Tel.: (44) 1953608000
Fax: (44) 1953608300
Web Site: www.lotuscars.com
Car Repair & Maintenace Services
S.I.C.: 7538
N.A.I.C.S.: 811111

Lotus Engineering Ltd. (3)
Potash Lane
Hethel, Norwich, Norfolk, NR14 8EZ, United Kingdom (100%)
Tel.: (44) 1953608000
Fax: (44) 1953608300
E-Mail: dbahar@lotus.com
Web Site: www.grouplotus.com
Emp.: 1,500
Design Engineering
S.I.C.: 8711
N.A.I.C.S.: 541330
Aslam Farikullah *(COO)*

U.S. Subsidiary:

Lotus Engineering, Inc. (4)
1254 N Main St
Ann Arbor, MI 48104-1062 MI
Tel.: (734) 995-2544
Fax: (734) 995-9301
Web Site: www.lotuseng.com
Emp.: 75
Automotive Industry Engineering
S.I.C.: 7539
N.A.I.C.S.: 811198
Kai-Uwe Salzmann *(Dir-Vehicle Engrg)*

U.S. Subsidiary:

Lotus Cars USA, Inc. (3)
2236 Northmont Pkwy
Duluth, GA 30096 GA
Tel.: (770) 476-6540
Fax: (770) 476-6541
Toll Free: (800) 24LOTUS
Web Site: www.lotuscars.com
Emp.: 10
Automobile Importer & Distr Import
S.I.C.: 5012
N.A.I.C.S.: 423110
Kevin Smith *(Dir-Sls & Mktg)*

Lotus Finance Ltd. (2)
2 Saint Andrews Place
Lewes, East Sussex, BN7 1UP, United Kingdom
Tel.: (44) 1323492424
Fax: (44) 1273 402708
E-Mail: info@lotus-finance.co.uk
Financial Support Services
S.I.C.: 6141
N.A.I.C.S.: 522291

Proton Cars Australia Pty Limited (2)
Unit 1 25-33 Alfred Road
Chipping Norton, NSW, 2170, Australia
Tel.: (61) 287072707
Fax: (61) 287072700
E-Mail: dealer@proton.com.au
Web Site: www.proton.com.au
Emp.: 18
New Car Dealers
S.I.C.: 5511
N.A.I.C.S.: 441110

Proton Cars (UK) Ltd (2)
1-3 Crowley Wy
Avonmouth, Bristol, BS11 9YR, United Kingdom
Tel.: (44) 1173298230
Fax: (44) 1179380614
E-Mail: sales@proton.co.uk
Web Site: www.proton.co.uk
Emp.: 37
Automobiles Distr
S.I.C.: 5511
N.A.I.C.S.: 441110
John Bulmer *(Mgr-Area)*

Proton Motors (Thailand) Limited (2)
4 Soi 2 Seri 7 Srinakarintara Road
Suan Luang, Bangkok, 10250, Thailand
Tel.: (66) 25611020
Motor Vehicles Distr
S.I.C.: 5012
N.A.I.C.S.: 423110

Proton Singapore Pte Ltd (2)
2 Kung Chong Road
Singapore, Singapore 159140
Tel.: (65) 68970500
Fax: (65) 68960500
E-Mail: sales@proton.com.sg
Web Site: www.proton.com.sg
Emp.: 25
New Car Dealers
S.I.C.: 5511
N.A.I.C.S.: 441110
Gunther Scherz *(Mng Dir)*

PT Proton Edar Indonesia (2)
Jl Sultan Iskandar Muda No 89 Arteri Pondok Indah
Jakarta Selatan, Jakarta, 12240, Indonesia
Tel.: (62) 217392268
Fax: (62) 21 739 2468
E-Mail: customer1st@proton-edar.co.id
Web Site: www.proton-edar.co.id
New Car Dealers
S.I.C.: 5511
N.A.I.C.S.: 441110
Mazlan Zain *(Gen Mgr-Sls & Mktg)*

DRDGOLD LIMITED

50 Constantia Boulevard Constantia Kloof Ext 28
Roodepoort, 1709, South Africa
Tel.: (27) 11 219 8700
Fax: (27) 11 476 2637
E-Mail: ilja.graulich@za.drdgold.com
Web Site: www.drd.co.za
Year Founded: 1895
DRD—(NYSE)
Rev.: $231,944,603
Assets: $298,366,897
Liabilities: $114,255,249
Net Worth: $184,111,647
Earnings: $11,181,170
Emp.: 1,002
Fiscal Year-end: 06/30/13

Business Description:
Gold Mining & Refining
S.I.C.: 1041
N.A.I.C.S.: 212221

Personnel:
Daniel Johannes Pretorius *(CEO)*
Craig Clinton Barnes *(CFO)*
Charles Methley Symons *(COO)*
Themba John Gwebu *(Exec Officer-Legal & Compliance & Sec)*
Wilhelm Jacobus Schoeman *(Exec Officer-Bus Dev)*

Board of Directors:

DRDGOLD Limited—(Continued)

Geoffrey Charles Campbell
Craig Clinton Barnes
Robert Peter Hume
Edmund Jeneker
Daniel Johannes Pretorius
James Turk

Capita IRG plc
Balfour House 390-398 High Rd
Ilford, Essex, 1G1 1NQ, United Kingdom
Tel.: (44) 2086392000
Fax: (44) 2084787717

DREAM DINING CORP.
(Acquired by Toridoll Corporation)

DREAM INCUBATOR INC.
Nakameguro GT Tower 14F 2-1-1 Kamimeguro
Meguro-ku, Tokyo, 153-0051, Japan
Tel.: (81) 357738700
Fax: (81) 357738701
E-Mail: info@dreamincubator.co.jp
Web Site: www.dreamincubator.co.jp
Year Founded: 2000
4310—(TKS)
Sales Range: $25-49.9 Million
Emp.: 181
Business Description:
Investment, Incubation & Consulting Services
S.I.C.: 6211
N.A.I.C.S.: 523999
Personnel:
Koichi Hori *(Chm & CEO)*
Takayoshi Yamakawa *(Pres)*
Board of Directors:
Koichi Hori
Koji Aiba
Soichiro Tahara
Takayoshi Yamakawa

DREAM INTERNATIONAL LTD
6/F China Minmetals Tower 79
Chatham Road South
Tsim Sha Tsui, Kowloon, China (Hong Kong)
Tel.: (852) 23756811
Fax: (852) 23757285
E-Mail: info@dream-i.com.hk
Web Site: www.dream-i.com.hk
1126—(HKG)
Sls.: $174,513,193
Assets: $140,076,838
Liabilities: $31,465,476
Net Worth: $108,611,361
Earnings: $15,725,839
Emp.: 8,578
Fiscal Year-end: 12/31/12
Business Description:
Toy Producer
S.I.C.: 3942
N.A.I.C.S.: 339930
Personnel:
Kyoo Yoon Choi *(Founder, Chm & CEO)*
Young M. Lee *(CFO & VP)*
Shin Hee Cha *(Pres-Dream Inko Co Ltd)*
Sung Sick Kim *(Pres-Dream Vina Co Ltd)*
Tsz Wai Ng *(Sec)*
Board of Directors:
Kyoo Yoon Choi
Byong Hun Ahn
Tae Woong Kang
Hyun Ho Kim
Young M. Lee
James Chuan Yung Wang
Cheong Heon Yi

U.S. Subsidiary:

Dream International USA, Inc (1)
7001 Billage Dr Ste 280
Buena Park, CA 90621
Tel.: (714) 521-6007
Fax: (714) 521-6008
E-Mail: account@dreamiusa.com
Web Site: www.dream-i.com.hk/english/contact.html#los_angeles
Emp.: 7
Doll and Stuffed Toy Mfg
S.I.C.: 3944
N.A.I.C.S.: 339930
James Chuan Yung Wang *(Mng Dir)*

Subsidiary:

J & Y International Company Limited (1)
Room 1604 16th Floor Fortress Twr
North Point, China (Hong Kong)
Tel.: (852) 25129541
Fax: (852) 28062481
E-Mail: jygroup@biesacnetvigagor.com
Emp.: 50
Industrial Machinery & Equipment Merchant Whslr
S.I.C.: 5084
N.A.I.C.S.: 423830

Non-U.S. Subsidiaries:

C&H Toys (Suzhou) Co , Ltd (1)
Cross Liutai Road
Banmao Road Ban Qiao District, Suzhou, Jiangsu, China
Tel.: (86) 51253586555
Fax: (86) 51253568581
E-Mail: account@cnhtc.com
Web Site: www.cnhseoul.com
Doll & Stuffed Toy Mfr
S.I.C.: 3942
N.A.I.C.S.: 339930

Dream VINA Co., Ltd. (1)
Group 3 Ward 5 Uyen Hung Town
Tan Uyen District Ho Chi Minh, Bien Hoa, Binh Duong, Vietnam
Tel.: (84) 650 641 380
Fax: (84) 650 641 389
E-Mail: account@dreamvina.com
Web Site: www.dream-i.com.hk/english/contact.html
Toy & Hobby Goods & Supplies Whslr
S.I.C.: 5092
N.A.I.C.S.: 423920

DREAM UNLIMITED CORP.
30 Adelaide Street East Suite 1600
Toronto, ON, M5C 3H1, Canada
Tel.: (416) 365-3535
Fax: (416) 365-3545
E-Mail: info@dream.ca
Web Site: www.dream.ca
Year Founded: 2013
DRM—(TSX)
Business Description:
Real Estate Investment & Asset Management
S.I.C.: 6211
N.A.I.C.S.: 523999
Personnel:
Michael Cooper *(Pres & CEO)*
Mario Barrafato *(CFO)*
Jason Lester *(COO)*
Jane Gavan *(Exec VP)*
Rene Gulliver *(Sr VP)*
Bruce Traversy *(Sr VP)*
Board of Directors:
Michael Cooper
Bryden Cruise
Richard Gateman
Daniel T. Goodman
Andre Kuzmicki
Vincenza Sera
Sheldon Wiseman

DREAM VISION CO., LTD.
3-2-1 Ishibashi Ikeda-shi
Osaka, 563-0032, Japan
Tel.: (81) 72 7619293
Web Site: www.dreamv.co.jp
3185—(TKS)
Rev.: $68,210,307
Emp.: 120
Fiscal Year-end: 09/30/12
Business Description:
Electronic Shopping
S.I.C.: 5961
N.A.I.C.S.: 454111
Personnel:
Takahiro Oka *(Pres)*

DREAMS LTD.
Knaves Beech
High Wycombe, HP10 9QY, United Kingdom
Tel.: (44) 1628 535 353
Fax: (44) 1628 535 380
Web Site: www.dreams.co.uk
Year Founded: 1985
Sales Range: $400-449.9 Million
Emp.: 2,042
Business Description:
Bed Whslr
S.I.C.: 5712
N.A.I.C.S.: 442110
Personnel:
Mike Clare *(Founder)*
Kim Zaheer *(CFO)*

DREDGING CORPORATION OF INDIA LTD
Core 2 1st Floor SCOPE MINAR Plot No 2A & 2B
Laxminagar District Centre, New Delhi, 110 092, India
Tel.: (91) 1122448528
Fax: (91) 1122448527
E-Mail: rodelhi@dci.gov.in
Web Site: www.dredge-india.com
523618—(BOM)
Rev.: $118,288,871
Assets: $457,091,575
Liabilities: $198,331,205
Net Worth: $258,760,370
Earnings: $3,802,369
Emp.: 620
Fiscal Year-end: 03/31/13
Business Description:
Dredging Services
S.I.C.: 1629
N.A.I.C.S.: 237990
Personnel:
D. K. Mohanty *(Chm & Mng Dir)*
K. Aswini Sreekanth *(Compliance Officer & Sec)*
S. Vasudeva Rao *(Chief Vigilance Officer)*
Board of Directors:
D. K. Mohanty
Vinai Kumar Agarwal
S. Balachandran
M. C. Jauhari
P. Jayapal
P. V. Ramana Murthy
B. Poiyaamozhi
S. Narasimha Rao
Transfer Agent:
Karvy Computershare Private Limited
Plot No 17-24 Vittal Rao Nagar Madhapur
Hyderabad, 500 081, India
Tel.: (91) 40 2342 0818

DREES & SOMMER AG
Obere Waldplatze 11
70569 Stuttgart, Germany
Tel.: (49) 71113170
Fax: (49) 7111317100
E-Mail: info@dreso.com
Web Site: www.dreso.com
Rev.: $232,234,434
Assets: $111,882,059
Liabilities: $83,311,121
Net Worth: $28,570,937
Earnings: $14,937,023
Emp.: 1,350
Fiscal Year-end: 12/31/12
Business Description:
Construction Project Management & Engineering Services
S.I.C.: 1542
N.A.I.C.S.: 236220
Personnel:
Hans Sommer *(Chm-Supervisory Bd)*
Johannes Fritz *(Deputy Chm-Supervisory Bd)*
Peter Tzeschlock *(CEO & Member-Exec Bd)*
Joachim Drees *(CFO & Member-Exec Bd)*
Dierk Mutschler *(COO & Member-Exec Bd)*
Supervisory Board of Directors:
Hans Sommer
Karsten Eisenmann
Johannes Fritz
Bernd Gaiser
Holger Hagge
Volker Mack

DREWEX S.A.
ul Obozowa 42a/2
30-383 Krakow, Poland
Tel.: (48) 338734780
Fax: (48) 338734783
E-Mail: wielkopolska@drewex.com
Web Site: www.drewex.com
DRE—(WAR)
Sales Range: $1-9.9 Million
Business Description:
Furniture & Clothes Mfr
S.I.C.: 5137
N.A.I.C.S.: 424330
Personnel:
Andrzej Krakowka *(Chm-Exec Bd)*
Jacek Szczur *(Vice Chm-Exec Bd)*
Piotr Polak *(CEO)*
Supervisory Board of Directors:
Anna Baranska
Aneta Kazieczko
Katarzyna Polak
Piotr Polak
Wojciech Wesoly

DREXEL CAPITAL CORP.
918 1030 West Georgia Street
Vancouver, BC, V6E 2Y3, Canada
Tel.: (604) 628-5620
Fax: (604) 662-7950
E-Mail: hani@orangecapital.com
Year Founded: 2009
DX.P—(TSXV)
Business Description:
Investment Services
S.I.C.: 6211
N.A.I.C.S.: 523999
Personnel:
Hani Zabaneh *(Pres, CEO & Sec)*
Martin Bajic *(CFO)*
Board of Directors:
Martin Bajic
Hamed Shahbazi
Vince Sorace
Kyle Stevenson
Hani Zabaneh
Transfer Agent:
Olympia Trust Company
1900 925 W Georgia Street
Vancouver, BC, V6C 3L2, Canada

DRILL TORQUE LIMITED
133 Crocodile Crescent Mount St John
Bohle, QLD, 4818, Australia
Mailing Address:
PO Box 1627
Thuringowa, QLD, 4817, Australia
Tel.: (61) 7 4774 5733
Fax: (61) 7 4774 2748
E-Mail: info@drilltorque.com.au
Web Site: www.drilltorque.com.au
DTQ—(ASX)
Rev.: $27,429,993
Assets: $22,524,974
Liabilities: $11,186,999

Net Worth: $11,337,975
Earnings: ($1,992,952)
Emp.: 150
Fiscal Year-end: 06/30/13
Business Description:
Contract Drilling Services
S.I.C.: 1799
N.A.I.C.S.: 238990
Personnel:
Peter Richard Miller *(Mng Dir)*
Robert Ian Witty *(CFO & Sec)*
Board of Directors:
David John Fairfull
Ralph Craven
Guy Hamish Drummond
Peter Richard Miller

Subsidiary:

Notch Holdings Pty Ltd (1)
133 Crocodile Crescent
Bohle, QLD, 4818, Australia
Tel.: (61) 7 47757299
Fax: (61) 7 47742748
E-Mail: info@drilltorque.com.au
Emp.: 175
Oil Well Drilling Services
S.I.C.: 1381
N.A.I.C.S.: 213111
Peter Miller *(Gen Mgr)*

DRILLCO METAL CARBIDES LIMITED

301 Navkar Plaza 3rd Floor Bajaj Road
Vile Parle W, Mumbai, 400056, India
Tel.: (91) 22 26203399
Fax: (91) 22 26240540
E-Mail: secretarial@drillmetal.com
Web Site: www.drillcometal.com
Year Founded: 1975
505693—(BOM)
Assets: $434,188
Liabilities: $885,952
Net Worth: ($451,764)
Earnings: ($104,009)
Fiscal Year-end: 03/31/13
Business Description:
Tungsten Carbide Product Mfr
S.I.C.: 3341
N.A.I.C.S.: 331492
Personnel:
Jugal Mimani *(Compliance Officer)*
Board of Directors:
Ashok Kumar Deorah
Ramesh Nandkishore Khanna
Kartik Maganlal Timbadia
Parth Rahul Timbadia
Rahul Maganlal Timbadia
Praful Vrajlal Vora
Transfer Agent:
Satellite Corporate Services Private Limited
B-302 Sony Apartment Opp St Jude's High School Off Andheri Kurla Road
Jarimari Sakinaka, Mumbai, 400 072, India

DRILLISCH AG

Wilhelm Rontgen Strasse 1 5
63477 Maintal, Germany
Tel.: (49) 61814123
Fax: (49) 6181412183
E-Mail: ir@drillisch.de
Web Site: www.drillisch.de
Year Founded: 1982
DRI—(DEU)
Sls.: $435,744,460
Assets: $703,474,788
Liabilities: $541,325,919
Net Worth: $162,148,869
Earnings: $31,571,725
Emp.: 342
Fiscal Year-end: 12/31/12
Business Description:
Telecommunication Services
S.I.C.: 4899
N.A.I.C.S.: 517919
Personnel:
Marc Brucherseifer *(Chm-Supervisory Bd)*
Susanne Ruckert *(Deputy Chm-Supervisory Bd)*
Johann Weindl *(Deputy Chm-Supervisory Bd)*
Andre Driesen *(CFO)*
Paschalis Choulidis *(Member-Mgmt Bd & Dir-Fin, Fin Comm, Controlling & IT)*
Vlasios Choulidis *(Member-Mgmt Bd & Dir-Sls, Mktg & Customer Care)*
Supervisory Board of Directors:
Marc Brucherseifer
Horst Lennertz
Frank Rothauge
Susanne Ruckert
Bernd H. Schmidt
Johann Weindl

Subsidiaries:

Drillisch Telecom GmbH (1)
Wilhelm Rontgen St 1-5
63477 Maintal, Germany
Tel.: (49) 1805221416
Wireless Telecommunication Service Provider
S.I.C.: 4812
N.A.I.C.S.: 517210

IQ-Optimize Software AG (1)
Wilhelm Rontgen Strasse 10
63477 Maintal, Germany
Tel.: (49) 6181180540
Fax: (49) 61811805499
E-Mail: info@iq-optimize.de
Web Site: www.iq-optimize.de
Emp.: 30
Wireless Telecommunication Software Services
S.I.C.: 7372
N.A.I.C.S.: 511210
Wolgang Egert *(Mng Dir)*

DRILLSEARCH ENERGY LIMITED

Level 16 55 Clarence Street
Sydney, NSW, 2000, Australia
Tel.: (61) 292499600
Fax: (61) 292499630
E-Mail: admin@drillsearch.com.au
Web Site: www.drillsearch.com.au
DLS—(ASX)
Rev.: $106,530,757
Assets: $505,602,952
Liabilities: $206,942,302
Net Worth: $298,660,650
Earnings: $46,953,900
Emp.: 72
Fiscal Year-end: 06/30/13
Business Description:
Petroleum Exploration & Production Services
S.I.C.: 1311
N.A.I.C.S.: 211111
Personnel:
Jim D. McKerlie *(Chm)*
Brad W. Lingo *(Mng Dir)*
Ian W. Bucknell *(CFO & Co-Sec)*
John S. Whaley *(COO)*
David Evans *(CTO)*
Peter Fox *(Chief Comml Officer)*
Jean Moore *(Co-Sec)*
Board of Directors:
Jim D. McKerlie
Philip J. Bainbridge
Teik Seng Cheah
Beng Kai Choo
Brad W. Lingo
Fiona A. Robertson
H. Ross B. Wecker
Legal Counsel:
Ashurst
255 George Street
Sydney, NSW, 2000, Australia

DRIVE MOTOR RETAIL LIMITED

Freemens Commons Rd/Aylestone Rd
Leicester, LE2 7SL, United Kingdom
Tel.: (44) 844 558 3142
Web Site: www.drivevauxhall.co.uk
Sales Range: $350-399.9 Million
Emp.: 700
Business Description:
Car Dealership Owner & Operator
S.I.C.: 5511
N.A.I.C.S.: 441110
Personnel:
Steve Bessex *(Mng Dir & Co-Founder)*
Paul Manning *(Mng Dir & Co-Founder)*

Subsidiaries:

DRIVE Kawasaki Bristol (1)
64-66 Avon Street
Bristol, BS2 0PX, United Kingdom (100%)
Tel.: (44) 1179772272
Fax: (44) 117 9774679
Emp.: 15
Vehicle Motor Retailing
S.I.C.: 5511
N.A.I.C.S.: 441110

DRIVE Vauxhall Aldershot (1)
Bakers Corner
1 Lower Farnham Road, Aldershot, Hants, GU12 4DZ, United Kingdom (100%)
Tel.: (44) 1252369200
Fax: (44) 1252369211
E-Mail: reception@drivevauxhall.co.uk
Emp.: 100
S.I.C.: 4789
N.A.I.C.S.: 488210
Bruce Smith *(Gen Mgr)*

DRIVE Vauxhall Bristol (1)
65-71 Avon St
Bristol, BS2 0PZ, United Kingdom (100%)
Tel.: (44) 8445583189
Fax: (44) 1179775593
Web Site: www.drivevauxhall.co.uk
Vehicle Sales, Servicing, Rentals, Parts, Accessories & Bodyshop
S.I.C.: 5013
N.A.I.C.S.: 423120
Dave Andrews *(Gen Mgr)*

DRIVE Vauxhall Bury St. Edmunds (1)
Cotton Lane
Bury Saint Edmunds, Suffolk, IP33 1XP, United Kingdom (100%)
Tel.: (44) 8445584420
Fax: (44) 1284777223
E-Mail: burystedmunds@drivevauxhall.co.uk
Web Site: www.drivevauxhall.co.uk
Emp.: 100
New Car Dealers
S.I.C.: 5511
N.A.I.C.S.: 441110
Steve Bessex *(Co-Mng Dir)*
Paul Manning *(Co-Mng Dir)*

DRIVE Vauxhall Clevedon (1)
654 Old Church Rd
Clevedon, BS21 6NW, United Kingdom
Tel.: (44) 275872201
Fax: (44) 1275874334
S.I.C.: 4789
N.A.I.C.S.: 488210
Guy W. Adams *(Gen Mgr)*

DRIVE Vauxhall Haverhill (1)
Duddery Hill
Haverhill, Sunnolk, CB9 8DS, United Kingdom (100%)
Tel.: (44) 01440703606
Fax: (44) 1440708447
Web Site: www.drivevauxhall.co.uk/findus/haverhill.shtml
Emp.: 14
S.I.C.: 4789
N.A.I.C.S.: 488210
Marcus Popham *(Gen Mgr)*

DRIVEN CAPITAL CORP.

475 Howe Street Suite 910
Vancouver, BC, V6C 2B3, Canada
Tel.: (604) 638-0979
Fax: (604) 689-3609
E-Mail: info@drivencapital.ca
Web Site: www.drivencapital.ca
Year Founded: 2009
DVV.P—(TSXV)
Int. Income: $2,758
Assets: $741,735
Liabilities: $343,263
Net Worth: $398,472
Earnings: ($1,965,132)
Fiscal Year-end: 03/31/13
Business Description:
Investment Services
S.I.C.: 6211
N.A.I.C.S.: 523999
Personnel:
Toma S. Sojonky *(Pres & CEO)*
Mark S. Achtemichuk *(CFO)*
Margo Peters *(Sec)*
Board of Directors:
Mark S. Achtemichuk
Lindsay R. Bottomer
Toma S. Sojonky
Legal Counsel:
Salley Bowes Harwardt Law Corp
1750 1185 West Georgia Street
Vancouver, BC, Canada
Transfer Agents:
Computershare Investor Services Inc
100 University Avenue 9th Floor North Tower
Toronto, ON, Canada
Computershare Investor Services Inc.
510 Burrard St 2nd Floor
Vancouver, BC, V6C 3B9, Canada
Tel.: (604) 661-9400

DRIVER GROUP PLC

Driver House 4 St Crispin Way
Haslingden, Rossendale, BB4 4PW, United Kingdom
Tel.: (44) 1706223999
Fax: (44) 1706219917
E-Mail: manchester@driver-group.com
Web Site: www.driver-group.com
DRV—(AIM)
Rev.: $61,863,718
Assets: $31,783,347
Liabilities: $15,084,214
Net Worth: $16,699,133
Earnings: $3,663,475
Emp.: 251
Fiscal Year-end: 09/30/13
Business Description:
Construction Consulting Services
S.I.C.: 8999
N.A.I.C.S.: 541690
Personnel:
David Webster *(CEO)*
Thomas Ferns *(Sec)*
Board of Directors:
W. Alan McClue
Colin Davies
Damien McDonald
David Webster
Legal Counsel:
Rosenblatt Solicitors
9-13 St Andrew Street
London, EC4A 3AF, United Kingdom
Cobbetts LLP
Ship Canal House, King Street
Manchester, M2 4WB, United Kingdom

Subsidiaries:

Commercial Management Consultants Ltd. (1)
1-3 Norton Folgate
London, E1 6DB, United Kingdom
Tel.: (44) 20 7377 4949
Fax: (44) 20 7377 4939
E-Mail: london@cmcltd.co.uk
Web Site: www.cmcltd.co.uk
Emp.: 30
Chartered Quantity Surveying Services
S.I.C.: 7389
N.A.I.C.S.: 561499

Driver Group Plc—(Continued)

David Pinnock *(Dir-Comml)*

Driver Consult Limited (1)
Driver House Fourth St Crispin Way
Haslingden, Rossendale, Lancashire, BB4 4PW, United Kingdom
Tel.: (44) 1706223999
Fax: (44) 1706219917
E-Mail: manchester@driverconsult.com
Web Site: www.driverconsult.com
Emp.: 50
Construction Consulting Services
S.I.C.: 8711
N.A.I.C.S.: 541330
John Mullen *(Mng Dir-Middle East)*
Paul Paigge *(Mng Dir-Intl Project Svcs)*
Mark Wheeler *(Mng Dir-UK Consultancy)*

North Gate Executive Search Limited (1)
1 Norton Folgate
London, E1 6DB, United Kingdom
Tel.: (44) 2073929970
Fax: (44) 2070929860
Web Site: www.north-gate.co.uk
Emp.: 6
Construction & Engineering Executives Recruitment Services
S.I.C.: 7361
N.A.I.C.S.: 561311
Barry Haylett *(Mng Dir)*

Non-U.S. Subsidiaries:

Driver Consult (Oman) LLC (1)
PO Box 363
121 Seeb, Oman
Tel.: (968) 24613361
Fax: (968) 24497912
E-Mail: oman@driver-group.com
Web Site: www.driverconsult.com
Emp.: 40
Construction & Engineering Consulting Services
S.I.C.: 8711
N.A.I.C.S.: 541330
Kevin McPhilomy *(Mng Dir)*

Driver Project Services (UAE) LLC (1)
Ofc 105 Al Mansoori Plz Sheikh Hamdan St
Abu Dhabi, United Arab Emirates
Tel.: (971) 26780466
Fax: (971) 26780463
E-Mail: abudhabi@driverconsult.com
Emp.: 30
Construction Engineering Services
S.I.C.: 1629
N.A.I.C.S.: 237990
Andrew Miller *(Gen Mgr)*

THE DRIVING FORCE, INC.

11025 184 Street
Edmonton, AB, T5S 0A6, Canada
Tel.: (780) 483-9559
Fax: (780) 484-7094
Toll Free: (800) 936-9353
E-Mail: info@drivingforce.ca
Web Site: www.drivingforce.ca
Year Founded: 1978
Rev.: $13,911,192
Emp.: 30
Business Description:
New & Used Car Dealers
S.I.C.: 5511
N.A.I.C.S.: 441110
Personnel:
Jeff Polovick *(Pres & CEO)*
Gary Nelner *(CFO)*
Ayman Ammoura *(CIO)*

DRL HOLDINGS LIMITED

Aspinall House Aspinall Close
Horwich, Bolton, PL6 6QQ, United Kingdom
Tel.: (44) 1204672494
Fax: (44) 1204672987
E-Mail: reception@drllimited.co.uk
Web Site: www.appliancesonline.co.uk
Year Founded: 2000
Sales Range: $150-199.9 Million
Emp.: 450
Business Description:
Online Appliance Retailer
S.I.C.: 5722
N.A.I.C.S.: 443141
Personnel:
John Roberts *(CEO)*
Subsidiary:

Expert Logistics Ltd. (1)
Bury Road
Radcliffe, Manchester, M26 2XH, United Kingdom UK
Tel.: (44) 8456037299
Fax: (44) 161 7771193
E-Mail: Enquiries@ExpertLogistics.co.uk
Web Site: www.expertlogistics.co.uk
Emp.: 150
Distribution Company
S.I.C.: 4731
N.A.I.C.S.: 541614
Kieth Earl *(Mng Dir)*

DROEGE INTERNATIONAL GROUP AG

Poststrasse 5 6
40213 Dusseldorf, Germany
Tel.: (49) 211867310
E-Mail: info@droege.groupe.com
Web Site: www.droege-international.com
Business Description:
Management Consulting Services
S.I.C.: 8742
N.A.I.C.S.: 541611
Personnel:
Walter P.J. Droege *(Exec Mng Dir)*
Non-U.S. Holding:

ALSO Holding AG (1)
(Formerly ALSO-Actebis Holding AG)
Meierhofstrasse 5
6032 Emmen, Switzerland
Tel.: (41) 41 266 18 00
Fax: (41) 41 266 18 70
E-Mail:
Web Site: www.also.com
ALSN—(SWX)
Rev.: $6,796,478,040
Assets: $1,442,295,316
Liabilities: $1,017,582,896
Net Worth: $424,712,420
Earnings: $49,972,516
Emp.: 2,990
Fiscal Year-end: 12/31/12
Holding Company; Distribution & Logistics Services
S.I.C.: 6719
N.A.I.C.S.: 551112
Thomas C. Weissmann *(Chm)*
Gustavo Moller-Hergt *(CEO)*
Ralf Retzko *(CFO)*

Non-U.S. Subsidiary:

MEDIUM GmbH (2)
Willstaetterstrasse 7
40549 Dusseldorf, Germany
Tel.: (49) 21152760
Fax: (49) 2115276100
E-Mail: info@medium.de
Web Site: www.medium.de
Sales Range: $50-74.9 Million
Emp.: 50
Presentation Equipments Distr
S.I.C.: 5065
N.A.I.C.S.: 423690
Reinold Imdahl *(Co-Founder & Mng Dir-Mktg & Sls)*
Peter Merczak *(Co-Founder & Mng Dir-Tech & Fin)*
Arno Alberty *(Mng Dir)*
Thomas Vogel *(Mng Dir)*

DROMANA ESTATE LTD

555 Old Moorooduc Rd
Tuerong, Melbourne, VIC, 3933, Australia
Tel.: (61) 359743899
Fax: (61) 359741155
E-Mail: info@dromanaestate.com.au
Web Site: www.dromanaestate.com.au
Year Founded: 1982
DMY—(ASX)
Rev.: $7,634
Assets: $639,515
Liabilities: $649,366
Net Worth: ($9,851)
Earnings: ($412,585)
Fiscal Year-end: 06/30/13
Business Description:
Wine Mfr & Distr
S.I.C.: 2084
N.A.I.C.S.: 312130
Personnel:
Garry W. Bell *(CFO & Sec)*
Board of Directors:
Gabriel Chiappini
Geoffrey J. Bell
Jerko Zuvela
Legal Counsel:
Steinepreis Paganin
Level 4 The Read Building 16 Milligan Street
Perth, WA, 6000, Australia
Tel.: (61) 8 9321 4000
Fax: (61) 8 9321 4333

DROMEAS S.A

Industrial Area Serres Plant
Serres, 62121, Greece
Tel.: (30) 23210 99220
Fax: (30) 23210 99270
E-Mail: dromfin@otenet.gr
Web Site: www.dromeas.gr
Year Founded: 1979
DROME—(ATH)
Emp.: 200
Business Description:
Office Furniture Mfr & Marketing
S.I.C.: 2522
N.A.I.C.S.: 337214
Personnel:
Athanasios K. Papapanagiotou *(Chm, CEO & Dir-Comml)*
Board of Directors:
Athanasios K. Papapanagiotou
Athanasios B. Kalafatis
Dionisios I. Papapanagiotou
Ioannis G. Pelidi
Phedon A. Tsagalidis
Stergios E. Tsintzas
Grigorios B. Zarotiadis

DRON & DICKSON LTD.

18 Whitehouse Road Springkerse Industrial Est
Stirling, FK7 7SS, United Kingdom
Tel.: (44) 1786 449444
Fax: (44) 1786 448118
E-Mail: stirlingsales@drondickson.co.uk
Web Site: www.drondickson.com
Year Founded: 1927
Sales Range: $50-74.9 Million
Emp.: 140
Business Description:
Electrical Equipment Distr
S.I.C.: 5063
N.A.I.C.S.: 423610
Personnel:
Stuart Bell *(Mng Dir)*

DRONCO AG

(Acquired by CMP Capital Management-Partners GmbH)

DRS DATA & RESEARCH SERVICES PLC

1 Danbury Court Linford Wood
Milton Keynes, Bucks, MK14 6LR, United Kingdom
Tel.: (44) 1908666088
Fax: (44) 1908607668
E-Mail: enquiries@drs.co.uk
Web Site: www.drs.co.uk
DRS—(LSE)
Rev.: $31,697,930
Assets: $19,619,520
Liabilities: $7,815,906
Net Worth: $11,803,613
Earnings: $1,754,591
Emp.: 249
Fiscal Year-end: 12/31/12
Business Description:
Optical Mark Reading & Image Scanning Machinery Mfr & Marketer & Data Capture Services
S.I.C.: 3555
N.A.I.C.S.: 333244
Personnel:
Steve Gowers *(CEO)*
Sachel Grant *(HR Officer)*
Sally Hopwood *(Sec)*
Board of Directors:
David Brown
Sandra Dawson
Steve Gowers
John Linwood
Alison Reed
Mark Tebbutt

Subsidiary:

DRS Data Services Limited (1)
1 Danbury Court Linford Wood
Milton Keynes, Bucks, MK14 6LR, United Kingdom
Tel.: (44) 1908666088
Fax: (44) 1908607668
Web Site: www.drs.co.uk
Emp.: 250
Automated Data Capture Services
S.I.C.: 3652
N.A.I.C.S.: 334614
Malcolm Brighton *(Mng Dir)*
Steve Gowers *(Mng Dir)*

DRU VERWARMING B.V.

Ratio 8
6921 RW Duiven, Netherlands
Tel.: (31) 263195319
Fax: (31) 263195348
E-Mail: info@drufire.nl
Web Site: www.drufire.nl
Emp.: 60
Business Description:
Gas and Electrical Fireplace Mfr.
S.I.C.: 3433
N.A.I.C.S.: 333414
Personnel:
Sander Teunissen *(Mgr-Sls)*

Non-U.S. Subsidiary:

Drugasar Ltd. (1)
Deans Rd
Swinton, Manchester, M27 0JH, United Kingdom UK
Tel.: (44) 617938700 (100%)
Fax: (44) 617278057
E-Mail: info@drufire.co.uk
Web Site: www.drufire.co.uk
Emp.: 14
S.I.C.: 3089
N.A.I.C.S.: 326199
Niall Deiraniya *(Controller-Fin & Sec)*

DRUCKFARBEN HELLAS S.A.

Megaridos Ave Kalistiri Area
19300 Aspropyrgos, Greece
Tel.: (30) 2105519300
Fax: (30) 2105519301
E-Mail: contact.us@druckfarben.gr
Web Site: www.druckfarben.gr
DROUK—(ATH)
Sales Range: $100-124.9 Million
Emp.: 325
Business Description:
Printing Ink Producer
S.I.C.: 2893
N.A.I.C.S.: 325910

Personnel:
George Caravasilis *(Chm & Mng Dir)*
Elisabeth Nikolaou *(Vice Chm, VP & Mgr-Pur)*
Board of Directors:
George Caravasilis
Cristos Anastasiadis
Periklis Argyros
Leonidas Maravelis
Elisabeth Nikolaou
Theodoros Papapetropoulos
Dimofon Tsagaris
Non-U.S. Subsidiary:

Druckfarben Romania S.R.L. (1)
St Atomistilor Nr 17 23
Magurele, 077125, Romania
Tel.: (40) 214057100
Fax: (40) 214057101
E-Mail: office@druckfarben.ro
Web Site: www.druckfarben.ro
Emp.: 180
Ink Chemicals Trading Services
S.I.C.: 2899
N.A.I.C.S.: 325998
Valeriu Fagarasan *(Mng Dir)*

DRUMMOND GOLD LIMITED

Suite 8 60 Macgregor Terrace
Bardon, Brisbane, QLD, 4065, Australia
Mailing Address:
PO Box 844
Paddington, Brisbane, QLD, 4064, Australia
Tel.: (61) 733672144
Fax: (61) 733672165
E-Mail: drummond@drummondgold.com.au
Web Site: www.drummondgold.com.au
DGO—(ASX)
Int. Income: $12,236
Assets: $7,533,629
Liabilities: $751,409
Net Worth: $6,782,219
Earnings: ($5,318,769)
Emp.: 3
Fiscal Year-end: 06/30/13
Business Description:
Gold Exploration Services
S.I.C.: 1041
N.A.I.C.S.: 212221
Personnel:
Eduard Eshuys *(Chm)*
Michael J. Ilett *(CFO & Sec)*
Board of Directors:
Eduard Eshuys
Ross C. Hutton
Brice K. Mutton
Legal Counsel:
Hopgood Ganim
Level 8 Waterfront Place 1 Eagle Street
Brisbane, QLD, 4000, Australia

DRUZHBA AD

4 Tutrakan Str
PO Box 63
7200 Razgrad, Bulgaria
Tel.: (359) 84 660 689
Fax: (359) 84 660 424
E-Mail: info@drouzhba.bg
Web Site: www.drouzhba.bg
Year Founded: 1964
4DU—(BUL)
Business Description:
Piston Products Mfr
S.I.C.: 3714
N.A.I.C.S.: 336310
Personnel:
Desislava Gecova Draganova *(Dir-IR)*

DRYERTECH INDUSTRIES LTD.

5614C Burbank Road SE
Calgary, AB, T2H 1Z4, Canada
Tel.: (403) 800-3109
Year Founded: 2010
Business Description:
Compressed Air Dryer Mfr & Distr
S.I.C.: 3563
N.A.I.C.S.: 333912
Personnel:
Walter Romanchuk *(Pres)*
Michel Plante *(CFO & Sec)*
Board of Directors:
Michel Plante
Walter Romanchuk

DRYSHIPS INC.

74-76 V Ipeirou Street
151 25 Athens, Greece
Tel.: (30) 210 809 0570
E-Mail: finance@dryships.com
Web Site: www.dryships.com
Year Founded: 2004
DRYS—(ATH NASDAQ)
Rev.: $1,492,014,000
Assets: $10,123,692,000
Liabilities: $6,291,994,000
Net Worth: $3,831,698,000
Earnings: ($198,028,000)
Emp.: 2,306
Fiscal Year-end: 12/31/13
Business Description:
Holding Company; Deep Sea Freight Transportation Services
S.I.C.: 6719
N.A.I.C.S.: 551112
Personnel:
George Economou *(Chm & CEO)*
Ziad Nakhleh *(CFO)*
Board of Directors:
George Economou
George Demathas
Chryssoula Kandylidis
Vassilis Karamitsanis
Evangelos G. Mytilinaios
George Xiradakis
Legal Counsel:
Seward & Kissel LLP
One Battery Park Plz
New York, NY 10004
Tel.: (212) 574-1200
Fax: (212) 480-8421
Transfer Agent:
American Stock Transfer & Trust Company LLC
59 Maiden Ln
New York, NY 10007
Tel.: (718) 921-8200
Subsidiary:

OceanFreight Inc. (1)
80 Kifissias Ave
15125 Athens, Greece MH
Tel.: (30) 2106140283
Fax: (30) 2106140284
Web Site: www.oceanfreightinc.com
Sales Range: $75-99.9 Million
Holding Company; Deep Sea Freight Transportation Services
S.I.C.: 6719
N.A.I.C.S.: 551112

Subsidiaries:

Oceanship Owners Limited (2)
80 Kifissias Avenue
Athens, 151 25, Greece
Tel.: (30) 2106140283
E-Mail:
Shipping Transportation Services
S.I.C.: 4491
N.A.I.C.S.: 488320

Oceanventure Owners Limited (2)
80 Kifissias Avenue
Athens, 15125, Greece
Tel.: (30) 2106140283
E-Mail: management@oceanfreightinc.com
Shipping Transportation Services
S.I.C.: 4491
N.A.I.C.S.: 488320

Non-U.S. Subsidiaries:

Ocean Rig 1 AS (1)
Svanholmen 6
Stavanger, Norway
Tel.: (47) 51969000
Fax: (47) 51969099
Web Site: www.ocean-rig.com
Emp.: 70
Oil Rig Construction Services
S.I.C.: 1389
N.A.I.C.S.: 213112
Paul Carsten Pedersen *(Mng Dir)*

Ocean Rig AS (1)
Vestre Svanholmen 6
N 4313 Sandnes, Norway
Tel.: (47) 51969000
Fax: (47) 51969000
Web Site: www.ocean-rig.com
Emp.: 45
Oil Rig Construction Services
S.I.C.: 1389
N.A.I.C.S.: 213112
David Mullen *(CEO)*

Ocean Rig ASA (1)
Forus
P O Box 409
Stavanger, Norway
Tel.: (47) 51 96 90 00
Fax: (47) 51 96 90 99
Web Site: www.ocean-rig.com
Offshore Petroleum Extraction Services
S.I.C.: 1311
N.A.I.C.S.: 211111
David Mullen *(CEO)*
Jan Rune Steinsland *(CFO)*
Frank Tollefsen *(COO)*
Ronnie Coull *(Sr VP-HR)*
John Rune Hellevik *(Sr VP-Mktg)*

Ocean Rig UK Ltd. (1)
Johnstone House Rose Street
Aberdeen, AB10 1UD, United Kingdom
Tel.: (44) 1224 367940
Web Site: www.ocean-rig.com
Oil Rig Construction Services
S.I.C.: 1389
N.A.I.C.S.: 213112
David Mullen *(CEO)*

Ocean Rig Norway AS (1)
Vestre Svanholmen 6 Forus
4313 Sandnes, Norway
Tel.: (47) 51969000
Fax: (47) 51969099
Web Site: www.ocean-rig.com
Emp.: 60
Oil Rig Construction Services
S.I.C.: 1389
N.A.I.C.S.: 213112
Jan Rune Steinsland *(CEO & CFO)*

Ocean Rig UDW Inc. (1)
10 Skopa Street Tribune House 2nd Floor Office 202
CY 1075 Nicosia, Cyprus MH
Tel.: (357) 22767517 (73.9%)
Fax: (357) 22761542
Web Site: www.ocean-rig.com
ORIG—(NASDAQ)
Rev.: $1,180,250,000
Assets: $7,620,450,000
Liabilities: $4,640,607,000
Net Worth: $2,979,843,000
Earnings: $63,323,000
Emp.: 1,898
Fiscal Year-end: 12/31/13
Oil Drilling
S.I.C.: 1381
N.A.I.C.S.: 213111
George Economou *(Chm, Pres & CEO)*
Jan Rune Steinsland *(CFO)*
Frank Tollefsen *(COO)*
Ronald Coull *(Sr VP-HR)*

D.S. KULKARNI DEVELOPERS LTD.

1187/60 J M Road Shivajinagar
Pune, 411 005, India
Tel.: (91) 2066047100
Fax: (91) 2025535772
E-Mail: sales@dskdl.com
Web Site: www.dskdl.com
523890—(BOM)
Rev.: $44,913,137
Assets: $244,417,408
Liabilities: $161,858,580
Net Worth: $82,558,829
Earnings: $2,602,632
Emp.: 275
Fiscal Year-end: 03/31/13
Business Description:
Property Development & Construction Services
S.I.C.: 1542
N.A.I.C.S.: 236220
Personnel:
D. S. Kulkarni *(Founder, Chm & Mng Dir)*
Amol Purandare *(Compliance Officer & Sec)*
Board of Directors:
D. S. Kulkarni
V. C. Joshi
R. D. Kharosekar
Shirish Kulkarni
M. K. P. Setty
Kamal Kishor Taparia
Transfer Agent:
Sharepro Services (India) Pvt. Ltd
Samhita Warehousing Complex Gala No-52 to 56 Bldg No.13 A-B Near Sakin
Mumbai, India
Subsidiary:

DSK Global Education and Research P. Ltd. (1)
Survey No 55 54 Tarwadi
Sholapur Rd, Pune, Maharastra, 412308, India
Tel.: (91) 2066784300
Fax: (91) 2066784317
E-Mail: info@dsksic.com
Web Site: www.dsksic.com
Emp.: 100
Industrial Design Services
S.I.C.: 7389
N.A.I.C.S.: 541420

DS SMITH PLC

Beech House Whitebrook Park 68 Lower Cookham Road
Maidenhead, Berkshire, SL6 8XY, United Kingdom
Tel.: (44) 1628 583 400
Fax: (44) 1628583401
E-Mail: ir@dssmith.co.uk
Web Site: www.dssmith.uk.com
SMDS—(LSE)
Rev.: $5,794,888,797
Assets: $5,695,393,527
Liabilities: $3,982,021,806
Net Worth: $1,713,371,721
Earnings: $122,394,975
Emp.: 19,736
Fiscal Year-end: 04/30/13
Business Description:
Producer of Packaging & Paper; Mfr & Distr of Office Products
S.I.C.: 2679
N.A.I.C.S.: 322299
Personnel:
Miles Roberts *(CEO)*
Matthew Jowett *(Grp Gen Counsel & Sec)*
Board of Directors:
Gareth Davis
Chris Britton
Adrian Marsh
Jonathan Nicholls
Kathleen O'Donovan
Miles Roberts
Legal Counsel:
Allen & Overy LLP
One Bishops Square
London, United Kingdom

DS Smith Plc—(Continued)

Subsidiaries:

DS Smith Packaging Ltd. (1)
Beech House Whitebrook Park 68 Lower Cookham Road
Maidenhead, Berkshire, SL6 8XY, United Kingdom
Tel.: (44) 1753754380
Fax: (44) 1628583404
E-Mail: head.office@dssp.com
Web Site: www.dssmith-packaging.com
Emp.: 60
Packaging Mfr
S.I.C.: 2671
N.A.I.C.S.: 322220
Miles Roberts *(CEO)*

Non-U.S. Subsidiaries:

DS Smith Packaging (2)
Culliganlaan 1D
1831 Diegem, Belgium
Tel.: (32) 2 718 37 11
Fax: (32) 2 715 48 15
E-Mail: packaging.marketing@dssmith.eu
Packaging Paper Products Mfr
S.I.C.: 2672
N.A.I.C.S.: 322220
Katia Schotte *(Dir-Comm)*

Non-U.S. Subsidiaries:

DS Smith Corrugated Packaging Ltd (3)
Dodwells Road
Hinckley, Leicestershire, LE10 3BX, United Kingdom
Tel.: (44) 1455 251400
Fax: (44) 1455 251404
E-Mail:
Web Site: www.dssmithpackagingeurope.com
Emp.: 120
Packaging Paper Products Mfr
S.I.C.: 2671
N.A.I.C.S.: 322220
Tom Heys *(Mng Dir)*

DS Smith Packaging Deutschland Stiftung & Co. KG (3)
Rollnerstrasse 14
90408 Nuremberg, Germany
Tel.: (49) 9111801800
Fax: (49) 9111801820
Emp.: 3
Containerboard Distr & Sales
S.I.C.: 5113
N.A.I.C.S.: 424130
Richard Oegl *(Gen Mgr)*

Branches:

DS Smith Packaging Mannheim (4)
Essener Strasse 60
D 68219 Mannheim, Germany (100%)
Tel.: (49) 62189040
Fax: (49) 6218904314
E-Mail:
Web Site: www.dssmithpackagingeurope.com
Emp.: 190
Containerboard Mfr
S.I.C.: 2652
N.A.I.C.S.: 322219
Ivica Serdarevic *(Gen Mgr)*

DS Smith Packaging Witzenhausen (4)
Kasseler Landstrasse 23
D 37213 Witzenhausen, Germany (100%)
Tel.: (49) 55425020
Fax: (49) 5542502116
E-Mail:
Web Site: www.dssmithpackagingeurope.com
Emp.: 200
Packaging Material Mfr
S.I.C.: 2652
N.A.I.C.S.: 322219

DS Smith Packaging France (3)
Avenue Charles de Gaulle 143
92200 Neuilly-sur-Seine, Cedex, France
Tel.: (33) 155 614 411
Fax: (33) 146 248 660
E-Mail:
Web Site: www.dssmithpackagingeurope.com
Emp.: 20
Containerboard Mfr
S.I.C.: 2652
N.A.I.C.S.: 322219
Conaerts Marc *(Gen Mgr)*

DS Smith Packaging Italia SpA (3)
Via Pasubio 6
20154 Milan, Italy (100%)
Tel.: (39) 02239591
Fax: (39) 0223959254
E-Mail:
Web Site: www.dssmithpackagingeurope.com
Corrugated Packaging Box Mfr
S.I.C.: 2653
N.A.I.C.S.: 322211

Branches:

DS Smith Packaging Italia (4)
Via del Frizzone
I 55016 Porcari, Lucca, Italy (100%)
Tel.: (39) 0583 29 66 61
Fax: (39) 0583 29 66 85
E-Mail:
Web Site: www.dssmithpackagingeurope.com
Emp.: 176
Containerboard Mfr
S.I.C.: 2652
N.A.I.C.S.: 322219

DS Smith Packaging Sweden AB (3)
Myntgatan 8D
S 331 30 Varnamo, Sweden (100%)
Tel.: (46) 370 420 00
Fax: (46) 370 193 29
E-Mail: packaging.marketing@dssmith.eu
Web Site: dssmithpackagingeurope.com
Emp.: 170
Containerboard Mfr
S.I.C.: 2652
N.A.I.C.S.: 322219
Peter Thorstensson *(Gen Mgr)*

DS Smith Packaging Switzerland AG (3)
Industriestrasse 11
CH 4665 Oftringen, Switzerland (100%)
Tel.: (41) 627882323
Fax: (41) 627882424
E-Mail:
Web Site: www.dssmithpackagingeurope.com
Emp.: 280
Containerboard Mfr
S.I.C.: 2652
N.A.I.C.S.: 322219
Ivica Serdarevic *(Mng Dir)*

DS Smith Paper Deutschland GmbH (3)
Weichertstrasse 7
D 63741 Aschaffenburg, Germany (100%)
Mailing Address:
Postfach 10 01 01
63741 Aschaffenburg, Germany
Tel.: (49) 60214000
Fax: (49) 6021400270
E-Mail:
Web Site: www.dssmithpackagingeurope.com
Containerboard Mfr
S.I.C.: 2652
N.A.I.C.S.: 322219

DS Smith Recycling Deutschland GmbH (3)
Kufsteiner Strasse 27
83064 Raubling, Germany
Tel.: (49) 8035 87 75 0
Fax: (49) 8035 87 75 99
E-Mail:
Web Site: www.dssmithpackagingeurope.com
Emp.: 21
Paper Materials Recycling Services
S.I.C.: 4953
N.A.I.C.S.: 562920
Herr Achim Wiese *(CEO & Mng Dir)*
Larissa Rutkowski *(Asst Mng Dir-Project Mgmt)*

DS Smith Recycling UK Limited (3)
23 Kings Hill Avenue
West Malling, Kent, ME19 4UA, United Kingdom
Tel.: (44) 622883000
Fax: (44) 622883300
E-Mail:
Web Site: www.dssmithrecycling.com
Emp.: 100
Paper Recycling
S.I.C.: 5093
N.A.I.C.S.: 423930
Peter McGuinness *(CEO)*

DS Smith Verpackung + Display Vertriebsgesellschaft mbH (3)
Bellingerstrasse 5-9
36043 Fulda, Germany
Tel.: (49) 6 61 88 0
Fax: (49) 6 61 88 2 13
E-Mail:
Web Site: www.dssmithpackagingeurope.com
Packaging Paper Products Mfr
S.I.C.: 2672
N.A.I.C.S.: 322220
Richard Oegl *(Mng Dir)*

DS Smith Packaging Nederland BV (3)
Coldenhovenseweg 130
6961 EH Eerbeek, Netherlands
Tel.: (31) 313 67 79 11
Fax: (31) 313 67 79 01
Emp.: 20
Packaging Paper Products Mfr
S.I.C.: 2671
N.A.I.C.S.: 322220
E. Meyer *(Gen Mgr)*

DS Smith Packaging Ceska Republica S.R.O. (3)
Teplicka 109
Jilove u Decina, 407 01 Jilove, Czech Republic
Tel.: (420) 412 595 276
Fax: (420) 412 550 365
E-Mail:
Web Site: www.dssmithpackagingeurope.com
Emp.: 10
Packaging Materials Distr
S.I.C.: 5085
N.A.I.C.S.: 423840

DS Smith Packaging Denmark A/S (3)
Astrupvej 30
8500 Grena, Denmark
Tel.: (45) 72 14 90 00
Fax: (45) 72 14 91 01
E-Mail:
Web Site: www.dssmithpackagingeurope.com
Emp.: 700
Corrugated & Solid Board Mfr
S.I.C.: 2653
N.A.I.C.S.: 322211
Per Frederiksen *(Mng Dir)*

DS Smith Packaging Finland Oy (3)
Lielahdenkatu 10
33400 Tampere, Finland
Tel.: (358) 1024 52 111
Fax: (358) 1024 52 454
Web Site: www.dssmithpackagingeurope.com
Mfr of Corrugated Paper & Paperboard for Containers
S.I.C.: 2652
N.A.I.C.S.: 322219
Sari Ramo *(Mng Dir)*

DS Smith Packaging Poland Sp. z o.o. (3)
ul Pulawska 435A
PL 02-801 Warsaw, Poland (100%)
Tel.: (48) 225468050
Fax: (48) 225468055
E-Mail:
Web Site: www.dssmithpackagingeurope.com
Packaging Mfr & Distr
S.I.C.: 2671
N.A.I.C.S.: 322220
Filip Drofiak *(Gen Mgr)*

Non-U.S. Joint Ventures:

Italmaceri S.r.l. (3)
Strada Lanzo 237
I-101 48 Turin, Italy
Tel.: (39) 011 22 82 911
Fax: (39) 011 22 60 890
E-Mail: info.italmaceri@sca.com
Emp.: 32
Wastepaper Collection & Processing
S.I.C.: 5093
N.A.I.C.S.: 423930

SCA Packaging Turkey (3)
Cavusbasi Cad Ozgur Sk No 26 Fl 1
Kavacik, 81650 Istanbul, Turkey (50%)
Tel.: (90) 2164256666
Fax: (90) 2164256670
E-Mail: info@cukuroya-sca.com
Sales Range: $10-24.9 Million
Emp.: 150
Packaging Products Mfr
S.I.C.: 2672
N.A.I.C.S.: 322220
Zafar Gunany *(Gen Mgr)*

Selkasan Kagit ve Paketleme Malzemeleri Imalati San. ve Tic. A.S. (3)
Organize Sanayi Bolgesi II
Kisim PK 199, 45030 Manisa, Turkey
Tel.: (90) 236 213 02 73
Fax: (90) 236 213 02 78
E-Mail: info@selkasan.com
Web Site: www.selkasan.com
Emp.: 100
Paperboard Mfr
S.I.C.: 2679
N.A.I.C.S.: 322299

DS Smith Paper Limited (1)
Kemsley Paper Mill
Sittingbourne, Kent, ME10 2TD, United Kingdom
Tel.: (44) 1795518900
Fax: (44) 1795 514305
Web Site: www.dssmithpaper.com
Emp.: 400
Recycling Paper Mfr
S.I.C.: 2679
N.A.I.C.S.: 322299
Chris Rosser *(Mng Dir)*

Plants:

DS Smith Paper Ltd - Higher Kings Paper Mill (2)
Higher Kings Paper Mill
Cullompton, Devon, EX15 1QJ, United Kingdom
Tel.: (44) 1884 836300
Fax: (44) 1884 836330
Web Site: www.dssmithpaper.com
Emp.: 110
Paper Mfr
S.I.C.: 2679
N.A.I.C.S.: 322299

DS Smith Paper Ltd - Hollins Paper Mill (2)
Hollins Road
Darwen, Lancashire, BB3 0BE, United Kingdom
Tel.: (44) 1254702728
Fax: (44) 1254873558
Emp.: 120
Paper Mfr
S.I.C.: 2679
N.A.I.C.S.: 322299
Graham Plummer *(Gen Mgr)*

DS Smith Paper Ltd - Wansbrough Paper Mill (2)
Wansbrough Paper Mill
Watchet, Somerset, TA23 0AY, United Kingdom
Tel.: (44) 1984631456
Fax: (44) 1984634123
Web Site: www.dssmithpaper.com
Emp.: 150
Paper Mfr
S.I.C.: 2679
N.A.I.C.S.: 322299
Craig Nicol *(Gen Mgr)*

DS Smith Plastics Ltd. (1)
Butlers Leap Clifton Road
Rugby, Warks, CV21 3RQ, United Kingdom (100%)
Tel.: (44) 1788532861
Fax: (44) 1788569248
E-Mail: marketing@dssplastics.com
Web Site: www.dssmith-plastics.com
Emp.: 40
Plastic Container Mfr
S.I.C.: 3089

N.A.I.C.S.: 326199
Keith Eagle *(Gen Mgr)*

Subsidiaries:

DS Smith Replen (2)
Madleaze Industrial Estate Bristol Rd
Gloucester, GL1 5SG, United Kingdom
Tel.: (44) 1452 316565
Fax: (44) 1452 502828
E-Mail: sales@dssmithreplen.com
Web Site: www.dssmithreplen.com
Emp.: 7
Injection Molded Plastic Products Mfr
S.I.C.: 3089
N.A.I.C.S.: 326199
Peter Maple *(Mng Dir)*

DS Smith Worldwide Dispensers (2)
Lee Road Merton Park Estate
Merton, London, SW19 3WD, United Kingdom (100%)
Tel.: (44) 2085457500
Telex: 928616 WADVAL G
Fax: (44) 2085457502
E-Mail: marketing@dsswd.com
Web Site: www.worldwide-dispensers.com
Emp.: 100
Plastic Container Mfr
S.I.C.: 3085
N.A.I.C.S.: 326160
Olivier Martin *(Mgr-Sls)*

U.S. Subsidiary:

David S. Smith America Inc (2)
78 Second Ave S
Lester Prairie, MN 55354
Tel.: (320) 395-2553
Fax: (320) 395-2656
E-Mail: wdsales@dsswdus.com
Web Site: www.worldwidedispensers.com
Injection Molded Plastic Products Mfr
S.I.C.: 3089
N.A.I.C.S.: 326199

DS Smith Recycling (1)
Ty Gwyrdd 11 Beddau Way
Caerphilly, CF83 2AX, United Kingdom
Tel.: (44) 2920718400
Fax: (44) 2920718480
E-Mail: enquire@dssmithrecycling.com
Web Site: www.dssmithrecycling.com
Emp.: 700
Waste Paper Collection & Processing Services
S.I.C.: 2679
N.A.I.C.S.: 322299
Mathew Prosser *(Dir-Comml)*

St. Regis Paper Company Limited (1)
Kemsley Mill
Sittingbourne, Kent, ME10 2TD, United Kingdom
Tel.: (44) 1795518900
Fax: (44) 179514305
Web Site: www.stregis.co.uk
Emp.: 500
Waste Paper Processing Services
S.I.C.: 2679
N.A.I.C.S.: 322299
Chris Rosser *(Mng Dir)*

U.S. Subsidiary:

DSS Rapak Inc (1)
2995 Ahern Ave
Union City, CA 94587
Tel.: (510) 324-0170
Corrugated & Solid Fiber Box Mfr
S.I.C.: 2653
N.A.I.C.S.: 322211

Non-U.S. Subsidiaries:

Carton Plastico s.a. (1)
C/ Portugal 6-7 Pol Ind Fagober
28802 Alcala de Henares, Madrid, Spain
Tel.: (34) 918821014
Fax: (34) 918 82 10 13
Emp.: 4
Plastics Product Mfr
S.I.C.: 3089
N.A.I.C.S.: 326199

DS Smith Kaysersberg S.A.S. (1)
BP 1
68120 Kunheim, France
Tel.: (33) 389722454
Fax: (33) 389726154
E-Mail: direction@dssp.fr
Web Site: www.dssmith-kaysersberg.com
Sales Range: $300-349.9 Million
Emp.: 380
Corrugated Packaging, Paper & Plastic Products Mfr
S.I.C.: 2653
N.A.I.C.S.: 322211
Mark Shaw *(Pres)*

Subsidiaries:

DS SMITH DUCAPLAST (2)
Zone d'Entreprises de la Kruysstraete
59470 Wormhout, France
Tel.: (33) 3 28 65 98 90
Fax: (33) 3 28 65 98
Emp.: 40
Injection Molded Plastic Products Mfr
S.I.C.: 3089
N.A.I.C.S.: 326199

DS SMITH RIVATEX (2)
P A E de Tournebride
44118 La Chevroliere, France
Tel.: (33) 2 51 70 91 12
Fax: (33) 2 51 70 91 13
Web Site: www.kaysersberg-plastics.com
Injection Molded Plastic Products Mfr
S.I.C.: 3089
N.A.I.C.S.: 326199

Non-U.S. Subsidiaries:

DS SMITH CORREX (2)
Madleaze Industrial Estate Bristol Road
Gloucester, GL1 5SG, United Kingdom
Tel.: (44) 1452316510
Fax: (44) 1452316529
E-Mail: sales@correx.com
Web Site: www.dssmithcorrex.com
Emp.: 70
Plastic Sheets Mfr
S.I.C.: 3089
N.A.I.C.S.: 326199
Iain Hannan *(Dir-Site)*

DS Smith Polska S.A. (2)
150 Malikow Str
25 639 Kielce, Poland
Tel.: (48) 413673900
Fax: (48) 413456440
E-Mail: dss@dss.com.pl
Web Site: www.dss.com.pl
Emp.: 550
Mfr of Corrugated Board & Packaging
S.I.C.: 2653
N.A.I.C.S.: 322211
Krzysztof Sadowski *(Gen Mgr)*

DS Smith Slovakia s.r.o. (2)
Novozamocka Cesta 3397
947 03 Hurbanovo, Slovakia
Tel.: (421) 35 77 10 894
Fax: (421) 32 28 12 009
Injection Molded Plastic Products Mfr
S.I.C.: 3089
N.A.I.C.S.: 326199

Ducaplast S.A.S (1)
La Kruys Straete Zone D Entreprises
59470 Wormhout, France
Tel.: (33) 328659890
Fax: (33) 328659899
Plastics Foam Packaging Whslr
S.I.C.: 5085
N.A.I.C.S.: 423840

DW Plastics NV (1)
Nijverheidsstraat 26
3740 Bilzen, Belgium
Tel.: (32) 89412291
Fax: (32) 89417173
E-Mail: info@dwplastics.be
Web Site: www.dwplastics.com
Emp.: 75
Plastic Pallets Mfr
S.I.C.: 3089
N.A.I.C.S.: 326199
Paul Baeyens *(Gen Mgr)*

Rapak Asia Pacific Limited (1)
Building C1 The Gate 373 Neilson Street
Onehunga, Auckland, 1061, New Zealand
Tel.: (64) 96362660
Fax: (64) 96360572
E-Mail: jennifer_barton@copal.com
Emp.: 100
Corrugated Board & Boxes Mfr
S.I.C.: 2653
N.A.I.C.S.: 322211
Simon Mander *(Gen Mgr)*

U.S. Subsidiary:

Rapak USA (2)
1201 Windham Pkwy Ste D
Romeoville, IL 60446
Tel.: (630) 296-2000
Fax: (630) 296-2195
Corrugated Board & Boxes Mfr
S.I.C.: 2653
N.A.I.C.S.: 322211
Kevin Grogan *(Gen Mgr)*

Non-U.S. Subsidiaries:

Rapak AD (2)
Industrialna Str 45
Shumen, 9704, Bulgaria
Tel.: (359) 54 851045
Fax: (359) 54 860424
Corrugated Board & Box Mfr
S.I.C.: 2653
N.A.I.C.S.: 322211

Rapak AUSTRALIA (2)
6 Enterprise Court
Mulgrave, VIC, 3170, Australia
Tel.: (61) 395353900
Fax: (61) 3 9535 3911
Corrugated Board & Boxes Mfr
S.I.C.: 2653
N.A.I.C.S.: 322211

Rapak FRANCE (2)
28 Avenue de Fontcouverte
BP 681
84033 Avignon, France
Tel.: (33) 490898571
Fax: (33) 490899245
Web Site: www.rapak.com
Emp.: 10
Plastics Foam Packaging Materials Whslr
S.I.C.: 5085
N.A.I.C.S.: 423840

Rapak GERMANY (2)
Dortmunder Strasse 6
68723 Schwetzingen, Germany
Tel.: (49) 620220970
Corrugated Board & Boxes Mfr
S.I.C.: 2653
N.A.I.C.S.: 322211

Rapak THAILAND (2)
1st Floor ABICO Building 401/1
Phaholyothin Road Khukot
Lam Luk Ka, Pathumthani, 12130, Thailand
Tel.: (66) 29925870
Fax: (66) 2 992 5869
Emp.: 1
Corrugated Board & Boxes Mfr
S.I.C.: 2653
N.A.I.C.S.: 322211
Chris Wevers *(Mng Dir)*

RAPAK - UK (2)
Butlers Leap Clifton Road
Rugby, CV21 3RQ, United Kingdom
Tel.: (44) 1788 570612
Fax: (44) 1788 569248
Web Site: www.rapak.co.uk
Corrugated Board & Boxes Mfr
S.I.C.: 2653
N.A.I.C.S.: 322211

Rapak Vostok (2)
Bld 4 4th Lesnoy Pereulok
125047 Moscow, Russia
Tel.: (7) 495 641 37 65
Fax: (7) 495 225 85 00
Corrugated Board & Box Mfr
S.I.C.: 2653
N.A.I.C.S.: 322211

Rapak GmbH & Co KG Systemverpackungen (1)
Dortmunder Strasse 6
68723 Schwetzingen, Germany
Tel.: (49) 620220970
Fax: (49) 6202209754
Web Site: www.rapak.com
Emp.: 250
Corrugated Board & Boxes Mfr
S.I.C.: 2653
N.A.I.C.S.: 322211
Bridget Rothwell *(Mng Dir)*

StePac L.A. Limited (1)
Tefen Industrial Park Building 12
PO Box 73
Migdal Tefen, Israel
Tel.: (972) 49872131
Fax: (972) 49872946
E-Mail: info@stepac.com
Web Site: www.stepac.com
Fresh Fruits & Vegetables Packaging Services
S.I.C.: 0723
N.A.I.C.S.: 115114
Israel Ben Tzur *(CEO)*
Varda Talisman *(CFO)*

U.S. Subsidiary:

StePac USA Corporation (2)
619 Vulcan Ave Ste 210
Encinitas, CA 92024
Tel.: (760) 479-2548
Fax: (630) 296-2186
Web Site: www.stepac.com
Plastic Products Mfr
S.I.C.: 3089
N.A.I.C.S.: 326199
Don Stidham *(Pres)*

Non-U.S. Subsidiary:

StePac Brasil Ltda (2)
Rua Itapolis 1921 Pacaembu
Sao Paulo, 01245-000, Brazil
Tel.: (55) 11 3596 7450
Fax: (55) 11 3596 7453
E-Mail: stepac@stepac.com.br
Web Site: www.stepac.com.br
Corrugated Board & Boxes Mfr
S.I.C.: 2653
N.A.I.C.S.: 322211
Ivo Tunchel *(Reg Mgr)*

Toscana Ondulati SpA (1)
Via del Fanuccio 126
55014 Marlia, Italy
Tel.: (39) 583440911
Fax: (39) 0583407592
E-Mail: info@toscanaondulati.it
Web Site: www.toscanaondulati.it
Corrugated Board & Boxes Mfr
S.I.C.: 2653
N.A.I.C.S.: 322211
Michael Phelan *(Bus Mgr)*

Non-U.S. Plant:

DS Smith Plc - KARTOTEX Plant (1)
Via Sicilia 111
Perignano, Lari, 56030, Italy
Tel.: (39) 58761921
Fax: (39) 0587619292
E-Mail: kartotex@toscanaondulati.it
Corrugated Board & Boxes Mfr
S.I.C.: 2653
N.A.I.C.S.: 322211

DS SPEDITION GMBH

Leopoldstr 230
80807 Munich, Germany
Tel.: (49) 89350350
Fax: (49) 8935035129
E-Mail: info@dsspedition.de
Web Site: www.ds-spedition.de
Year Founded: 1983
Rev.: $27,340,620
Emp.: 42
Business Description:
Freight Transport Logistics Services
S.I.C.: 4731
N.A.I.C.S.: 541614
Personnel:
Janusch Swoboda *(Co-CEO)*
Anton Zacherl *(Co-CEO)*

DS STEEL CO. LTD.

1116 Yeok Ri Haengahn Myeon
579833 Buan, Korea (South)
Tel.: (82) 25985133
Fax: (82) 226046698
E-Mail: kimhc@ds-steel.co.kr
Web Site: www.ds-steel.co.kr
9730—(KRS)
Sales Range: $50-74.9 Million

DS Steel Co. Ltd.—(Continued)

Emp.: 100
Business Description:
Stainless Steel Pipes
S.I.C.: 3498
N.A.I.C.S.: 332996
Personnel:
Jung Sun Yim *(CEO)*

DSG INTERNATIONAL LIMITED

Room 1505 Millennium Trade Centre
56 Kwai Cheong Road, Kwai Chung, NT, China (Hong Kong)
Tel.: (852) 3527 6820
Fax: (852) 24804491
Web Site: www.dsgil.com
Year Founded: 1973
Sales Range: $900-999.9 Million
Emp.: 40,012
Business Description:
Baby Diapers, Adult Incontinence, Feminine Napkins & Training Pants Products Mfr & Distr
S.I.C.: 2676
N.A.I.C.S.: 322291
Personnel:
Brandon S.L. Wang *(Chm & CEO)*
Johnny S.L. Tsui *(Sec)*
Steven Pankow *(Exec VP)*

Subsidiary:

Disposable Soft Goods Limited (1)
Room 1503 Millennium Trade Centre
56 Kwai Cheong Road, Kwai Chung, NT, China (Hong Kong) (100%)
Tel.: (852) 24276951
Fax: (852) 24804491
Web Site: www.dsgil.com
Emp.: 30
S.I.C.: 2676
N.A.I.C.S.: 322291
Christophe Ho *(CFO)*

Non-U.S. Subsidiaries:

Disposable Soft Goods (Malaysia) Sdn. Bhd. (1)
542 Jalan Subeng 2 Penaga Indus Pk
47500 Subang Jaya, Selangor, Malaysia
Tel.: (60) 380231833
Fax: (60) 380249033
E-Mail: info@dsg.com.my
Web Site: www.dsg.com.my
Emp.: 200
S.I.C.: 2676
N.A.I.C.S.: 322291
Eng Chuen Foo *(COO)*

Disposable Soft Goods (S) Pte. Ltd. (1)
3 Bukit Batok St 22
Singapore, 659582, Singapore (100%)
Tel.: (65) 68619155
Fax: (65) 68619313
E-Mail: enquiry@dsg.com.my
Web Site: www.fitti.com
Emp.: 20
S.I.C.: 2676
N.A.I.C.S.: 322291

Disposable Soft Goods (Zhongshan) Limited (1)
Jinchang Industrial Road
Shalang, Zhongshan, Guangdong, 528411, China (100%)
Tel.: (86) 76088550004
Fax: (86) 76088558794
E-Mail: fitticn@dsgil.com
Web Site: www.fittl.com
Emp.: 200
S.I.C.: 2676
N.A.I.C.S.: 322291
Ambrose Chan *(Gen Mgr)*

DSG International (Thailand) Limited (1)
448 11 Latphrao 53 Choke Chai Latphrao Rd
Bangkapi, Bangkok, 10230, Thailand (100%)
Tel.: (66) 29332922
Fax: (66) 29332888
E-Mail: info@dsgt.co.th
Web Site: www.dsgt.co.th
Sales Range: $10-24.9 Million
Emp.: 450
S.I.C.: 2676
N.A.I.C.S.: 322291
Chan Ambrose *(Mng Dir)*

DSG (Malaysia) Sdn. Bhd. (1)
542 Jalan Subeng 2 Penaga Industrial Park
47500 Subang Jaya, Selangor, Malaysia (100%)
Tel.: (60) 380231833
Fax: (60) 380249633
E-Mail: enquiry@dsg.com.my
Web Site: www.dsg.com.my
Emp.: 200
S.I.C.: 2676
N.A.I.C.S.: 322291
Ambrose K. S. Chan *(CEO)*

DSM DEMOLITION GROUP

Arden House Arden Road Heartlands
Birmingham, B8 1DE, United Kingdom
Tel.: (44) 1213222225
Fax: (44) 1213222227
E-Mail: info@dsmgroup.info
Web Site: www.dsmdemolition.co.uk
Year Founded: 1988
Rev.: $52,929,718
Emp.: 146
Business Description:
Building Demolition Services
S.I.C.: 1799
N.A.I.C.S.: 238910
Personnel:
Robin Powell *(Mng Dir)*

DSME

85 Da-dong Jung-gu
Seoul, 100-180, Korea (South)
Tel.: (82) 221290114
Fax: (82) 27564390
E-Mail: swirisish@dsme.co.kr
Web Site: www.dsme.co.kr
042660—(KRS)
Sls.: $13,073,771,670
Assets: $14,993,672,970
Liabilities: $10,758,213,030
Net Worth: $4,235,459,940
Earnings: $163,543,290
Emp.: 30,000
Fiscal Year-end: 12/31/12
Business Description:
Shipbuilding, Repair & Heavy Construction Services
S.I.C.: 3731
N.A.I.C.S.: 336611
Personnel:
Jaeho Ko *(Pres & CEO)*
Gap-Jung Kim *(CFO & Sr Exec VP)*
Dong-Hyeok Park *(Chief Production Officer & Sr Exec VP)*
Board of Directors:
Gyeong-Taek Han
Jeon-Hyeok Jo
Gap-Jung Kim
Jaeho Ko
Sang-Gon Ko
Yeong-Min Kwon
Sang-Geun Lee
Dong-Hyeok Park
Gwang-Sik Shin

Subsidiaries:

DSEC Co., Ltd. (1)
74-1 438 Jungangdong Jung-gu
Busan, 600816, Korea (South)
Tel.: (82) 516602114
Fax: (82) 516602119
E-Mail: Coopa1@dsme.co.kr
Web Site: www.idsec.co.kr
Emp.: 500
Ship Building Services
S.I.C.: 3731
N.A.I.C.S.: 336611
Song Tinyong *(Gen Mgr)*

DSME E&R Ltd. (1)
201 Panam-Techno Twn
239-2 Panam-dong Dong-gu, Daejeon, 300-832, Korea (South)
Tel.: (82) 422730021
Fax: (82) 422720031
Web Site: www.dsme.enr.co.kr
Sonar Systems & Underwater Cameras Mfr
S.I.C.: 3812
N.A.I.C.S.: 334511

Shinhan Machinery Co., Ltd. (1)
117 Woobong-Ri
Onsan-Eup Ulju-Gun, Ulsan, 689 890, Korea (South)
Tel.: (82) 522405101
Fax: (82) 522405041
E-Mail: penus2001s@psme.co.kr
Web Site: www.shinerpia.com
Emp.: 1,000
Ship Building Services
S.I.C.: 3731
N.A.I.C.S.: 336611
Young Man Kim *(Pres)*

DSNR MEDIA GROUP

8 Hapnina Street
43215 Ra'anana, Israel
Tel.: (972) 9 7626161
Fax: (972) 9 7626110
E-Mail: sales@dsnrmg.com
Web Site: www.dsnrmg.com
Year Founded: 2001
Sales Range: $10-24.9 Million
Emp.: 25
Business Description:
Online & Mobile Advertising Solutions
S.I.C.: 7319
N.A.I.C.S.: 541890
Personnel:
Nino Ransenberg *(Pres)*
Inbar Chap *(CEO)*

DSPACE GMBH

Rathenaustrasse 26
33102 Paderborn, Germany
Tel.: (49) 525116380
Fax: (49) 525161980
E-Mail: info@dspace.de
Web Site: www.dspace.com
Year Founded: 1988
Rev.: $124,146,000
Emp.: 800
Business Description:
Digital Signal Processing & Control Engineering Services
S.I.C.: 8711
N.A.I.C.S.: 541330
Personnel:
Herbert Hanselmann *(Pres & CEO)*

DSR CORP.

1551-1 Songjung-dong Gangseo-gu
Busan, 618-270, Korea (South)
Tel.: (82) 51 979 0500
Fax: (82) 51 979 0600
Web Site: www.dsrcorp.com
155660—(KRS)
Sales Range: $150-199.9 Million
Emp.: 30
Business Description:
Fishing Nets & Ropes Mfr
S.I.C.: 2296
N.A.I.C.S.: 314994
Personnel:
Seok-Bin Hong *(CEO)*

DSR WIRE CORPORATION

Noksansanupjoonro 192-Gil 7
Songjeong-dong
Gangseo-gu, Busan, 618-818, Korea (South)
Tel.: (82) 51 979 0500
Fax: (82) 51 979 0600
E-Mail: sales@dsrcorp.com
Web Site: www.dsrcorp.com
Year Founded: 1965
069730—(KRS)
Business Description:
Wire Rope Mfr
S.I.C.: 3496
N.A.I.C.S.: 332618
Personnel:
Ha Jong Hong *(CEO)*

DSV A/S

Banemarksvej 58
PO Box 318
2605 Brondby, Denmark
Tel.: (45) 43203040
Fax: (45) 43203041
E-Mail: investor@dsv.dk
Web Site: www.dsv.dk
Year Founded: 1976
DSV—(CSE OTC)
Rev.: $8,100,328,320
Assets: $4,111,125,840
Liabilities: $3,139,887,240
Net Worth: $971,238,600
Earnings: $257,914,800
Emp.: 21,932
Fiscal Year-end: 12/31/12
Business Description:
Freight Transportation & Logistic Services
S.I.C.: 4731
N.A.I.C.S.: 541614
Personnel:
Kurt K. Larsen *(Chm)*
Erik B. Pedersen *(Deputy Chm)*
Jens Bjorn Andersen *(CEO & Member-Exec Bd)*
Jens H. Lund *(CFO & Member-Exec Bd)*
Jesper Erichsen *(CIO)*
Rene Falch Olesen *(Chief Comml Officer)*
Brian Ejsing *(CEO-DSV Solutions Holding A/S)*
Jorgen Moller *(CEO-DSV Air & Sea Holding A/S)*
Soren Schmidt *(CEO-DSV Road Holding A/S)*
Board of Directors:
Kurt K. Larsen
Kaj Christiansen
Birgit W. Norgaard
Erik B. Pedersen
Thomas Stig Plenborg
Annette Sadolin

Subsidiaries:

DSV Air & Sea A/S (1)
Kornmarksvej 1
Postboks 318
2605 Brondby, Denmark
Tel.: (45) 43 20 30 40
Fax: (45) 43 20 30 41
E-Mail: info@dk.dsv.com
Air & Sea Freight Transportation Services
S.I.C.: 4512
N.A.I.C.S.: 481112

DSV Insurance A/S (1)
Banemarksvej 58
2605 Brondby, Denmark
Tel.: (45) 43203040
E-Mail: Insurance@dsv.com
Cargo Insurance Services
S.I.C.: 6411
N.A.I.C.S.: 524298

DSV Road A/S (1)
Kornmarksvej 1
Postboks 318
2605 Brondby, Denmark
Tel.: (45) 43203040
Fax: (45) 43 20 30 41
E-Mail: info@dk.dsv.com
Road Transport & Logistics Services
S.I.C.: 4212
N.A.I.C.S.: 484110

DSV Road Holding A/S (1)
Banemarksvej 58
2605 Brondby, Denmark
Tel.: (45) 43203040

Fax: (45) 43253460
E-Mail: info@dsv.com
Web Site: www.dsv.com
Emp.: 25
Road Transport Services
S.I.C.: 4212
N.A.I.C.S.: 484110
Soren Schmidt *(COO)*

DSV Solutions A/S (1)
Nokiavej 30 Lund
8700 Horsens, Denmark
Tel.: (45) 72162900
Fax: (45) 72162901
E-Mail: solutions@dk.dsv.com
Emp.: 1,000
Road Transport & Logistics Services
S.I.C.: 4212
N.A.I.C.S.: 484110
Jens Bjorn *(Gen Mgr)*

U.S. Subsidiaries:

DSV Air & Sea Inc. (1)
100 Walnut Ave Ste 405
Clark, NJ 07066
Tel.: (732) 850-8000
Fax: (732) 850-8010
E-Mail: info@us.dsv.com
Web Site: www.dsv.com
Emp.: 440
Air & Sea Freight Services
S.I.C.: 4522
N.A.I.C.S.: 481212
Carsten Trolle *(Pres)*

DSV Transport (US), Inc. (1)
100 Walnut Ave Ste 405
Clark, NJ 07066 DE
Tel.: (732) 850-8000
Fax: (732) 850-8010
Web Site: www.dsv.com
Emp.: 80
Provider of Freight Transportation Arrangement Services
S.I.C.: 4731
N.A.I.C.S.: 488510
Joergen Moeller *(Pres)*
Soren Pedersen *(CFO)*
Walter Klincewicz *(CIO)*

Non-U.S. Subsidiaries:

Campbell Freight Agencies Limited (1)
World Cargo Centre 605 Antrim Road
Newtown Abbey, Belfast, BT36 4RF, United Kingdom
Tel.: (44) 2890849000
Fax: (44) 1255252548
E-Mail: sales@uk.dsv.com
Web Site: www.dsv.com
Emp.: 50
Air & Sea Freight Transportation Services
S.I.C.: 4512
N.A.I.C.S.: 481112
Marshall Boyd *(Mng Dir)*

Collico Verpackungslogistik und Service GmbH (1)
Schifferstrasse 94
47059 Duisburg, Nordrhein-Westfalen, Germany
Tel.: (49) 91818994435
Fax: (49) 2039306505
E-Mail: info@collico.de
Web Site: www.collico.de
Emp.: 35
Packaging & Logistics Services
S.I.C.: 7389
N.A.I.C.S.: 561910
Peter Koehler *(Mng Dir)*

DSV Air & Sea AB (1)
Fraktvagen 44
190 46 Stockholm, Sweden
Tel.: (46) 8 594 920 30
E-Mail: info.airsea@se.dsv.com
Air & Sea Freight Transportation Services
S.I.C.: 4512
N.A.I.C.S.: 481112

DSV Air & Sea AS (1)
Ruzgarli Bahce Mah Kavak Sok Imga Plaza No 12 and 12A
Beykoz, 34805 Istanbul, Turkey
Tel.: (90) 216 444 43 78
Fax: (90) 216 537 72 22
E-Mail: info@tr.dsv.com
Web Site: www.dsv.com
Emp.: 35
Air & Sea Freight Transportation Services
S.I.C.: 4512
N.A.I.C.S.: 481112
Ozan Onder *(Country Mgr)*

DSV Air & Sea AS (1)
Gneisveien 16
2020 Skedsmokorset, Norway
Tel.: (47) 09870
E-Mail: infoairsea@no.dsv.com
Web Site: www.dsv.com
Air & Sea Freight Transportation Services
S.I.C.: 4512
N.A.I.C.S.: 481112

DSV Air & Sea Co. Ltd. (1)
Osaka Sangyo Bldg 2F 1-10-2 Shinmachi
Nishi-ku, Osaka, 550-0013, Japan
Tel.: (81) 643904321
Fax: (81) 0643904333
E-Mail: osakahq@jp.dsv.com
Web Site: www.dsv.com
Emp.: 20
Air & Sea Freight Transportation Services
S.I.C.: 4512
N.A.I.C.S.: 481112

DSV Air & Sea Co., Ltd (1)
12 F 275 Nanking East Road Section 3
10550 Taipei, Taiwan
Tel.: (886) 227191215
Fax: (886) 2 2719 6829
Web Site: www.dsv.com
Freight Forwarding Services
S.I.C.: 4731
N.A.I.C.S.: 488510
Tim Han *(Gen Mgr)*

DSV Air & Sea Co. Ltd. (1)
38F 1 Grand Gateway No 1 Hongqiao Road
Shanghai, China
Tel.: (86) 2154069800
E-Mail: sales@cn.dsv.com
Web Site: www.dsv.com
Emp.: 635
Air & Sea Freight Transportation Services
S.I.C.: 4512
N.A.I.C.S.: 481112
Claus M. Thomsen *(Mng Dir)*

DSV Air & Sea Co. Ltd. (1)
5th Floor Saigon Riverside Office Center
2A-4A Ton Duc Thang Street
Room 505-506, Ho Chi Minh City, Vietnam
Tel.: (84) 8 3823 3799
Fax: (84) 8 3827 2684
E-Mail: info@vn.dsv.com
Web Site: www.dsv.com
Emp.: 20
Air & Sea Freight Transportation Services
S.I.C.: 4512
N.A.I.C.S.: 481112
Erik Koergnsen *(Mng Dir)*

DSV Air & Sea GmbH (1)
Langer Kornweg 36
65451 Kelsterbach, Germany
Tel.: (49) 61077070
Fax: (49) 6107707149
Web Site: www.dsv.com
Sales Range: $50-74.9 Million
Emp.: 120
Freight Forwarding
S.I.C.: 4731
N.A.I.C.S.: 488510
Max Obermeier *(Gen Mgr-Europe)*

DSV Air & Sea (Hungary) Ltd. (1)
42-44 5th Floor Raday Street
1092 Budapest, Hungary
Tel.: (36) 14564571
Fax: (36) 14564575
E-Mail: airandsea@hu.dsv.com
Web Site: www.dsv.com
Emp.: 100
Air & Sea Freight Transportation Services
S.I.C.: 4512
N.A.I.C.S.: 481112
Martin Hvilsom *(Mgr)*

DSV Air & Sea Inc. (1)
2A Johanne Street Bo Ibayo Baragay Sto Nino
1704 Paranaque, Philippines
Tel.: (63) 2 8529250
Fax: (63) 2 8523306
E-Mail: inquiries@ph.dsv.com
Web Site: www.dsv.com
Air & Sea Freight Services
S.I.C.: 4522
N.A.I.C.S.: 481212

DSV Air & Sea LLC (1)
Mega Terminal - Office 4048 Dubai Cargo Village
PO Box 126110
Dubai, United Arab Emirates
Tel.: (971) 42900700
Fax: (971) 42900710
E-Mail: info.ae@ae.dsv.com
Web Site: www.dsv.com
Emp.: 80
Air & Sea Freight Transportation Services
S.I.C.: 4512
N.A.I.C.S.: 481112
Sheena Jiju *(Mgr-HR)*

DSV Air & Sea Limited (1)
Unit 2 Euro House Little Island
Cork, Ireland
Tel.: (353) 214520951
Fax: (353) 214354648
E-Mail: info@ie.dsv.com
Web Site: www.dsv.com
Emp.: 10
Air & Sea Freight Transportation Services
S.I.C.: 4512
N.A.I.C.S.: 481112
Martin Slott *(Mgr)*

DSV Air & Sea Ltd (1)
50 Mohakali 15th Floor Bay
Mohakali, Dhaka, Bangladesh
Tel.: (880) 28816321
Fax: (880) 2 881 8300
E-Mail: info@bd.dsv.com
Web Site: www.dsv.com
Freight Forwarding Services
S.I.C.: 4731
N.A.I.C.S.: 488510

DSV Air & Sea Ltd. (1)
6th Floor Sing Song Building 25 Year Ito Tung Yeung Gteo Ngupo
Mapo-ku, Seoul, 150-879, Korea (South)
Tel.: (82) 2 323 1313
Fax: (82) 2 323 1212
E-Mail: korea@kr.dsv.com
Web Site: www.dsv.com
Emp.: 60
Air & Sea Freight Transportation Services
S.I.C.: 4512
N.A.I.C.S.: 481112
Moonho Choi *(Gen Mgr)*

DSV Air & Sea Ltd. (1)
7th Floor Vibulthani Tower 1 3195/12 Rama IV Rd Klongton
Klongtoey, 10110 Bangkok, Thailand
Tel.: (66) 26848100
Fax: (66) 2 684 8199
E-Mail: info@th.dsv.com
Web Site: www.dsv.com
Emp.: 180
Air & Sea Freight Transportation Services
S.I.C.: 4512
N.A.I.C.S.: 481112
Steve Henry *(Mng Dir)*

DSV Air & Sea Limited (1)
7 Landing Dr Airport Oaks
Auckland, New Zealand
Tel.: (64) 92560011
Fax: (64) 92759692
E-Mail: aklcustomerservices@nz.dsv.com
Web Site: www.dsv.com
Emp.: 22
Freight Forwarding Services
S.I.C.: 4731
N.A.I.C.S.: 488510
Paul Thomson *(Mng Dir)*

DSV Air & Sea Limited (1)
Stonehouse Lane
Purfleet, Essex, RM19 1NX, United Kingdom
Tel.: (44) 1708892000
Fax: (44) 125524460
E-Mail: info@uk.dsv.com
Web Site: www.dsv.com
Emp.: 35
Air & Sea Freight Transportation Services
S.I.C.: 4512
N.A.I.C.S.: 481112
Graham Riches *(Mng Dir)*

DSV Air & Sea Ltd. (1)
11F Tower 1 Kowloon Commerce Centre
No 51 Kwai Cheong Road
Kwai Chung, NT, China (Hong Kong)
Tel.: (852) 22325300
Fax: (852) 23676896
E-Mail: info@hk.dsv.com
Web Site: www.dsv.com
Emp.: 200
Air & Sea Freight Transportation Services
S.I.C.: 4512
N.A.I.C.S.: 481112
Peter Minor *(Mng Dir)*

DSV Air & Sea NV (1)
Spitsenstraat 36B Haven 27
2030 Antwerp, Belgium
Tel.: (32) 35 43 68 00
Fax: (32) 35 43 68 09
E-Mail: info.sea@be.dsv.com
Emp.: 40
Air & Sea Freight Transportation Services
S.I.C.: 4512
N.A.I.C.S.: 481112
Gernbaptista Vanelslander *(Mgr-Sls)*

DSV Air & Sea OOD (1)
Gara Iskar Industrial District
1592 Sofia, Bulgaria
Tel.: (359) 29267891
Fax: (359) 29267890
E-Mail: salesairsea@bg.dsv.com
Web Site: www.dsv.com
Emp.: 11
Road Transport & Logistics Services
S.I.C.: 4212
N.A.I.C.S.: 484110
Boriana Ilieva *(Mgr)*

DSV Air & Sea Oy (1)
Ansatie 4
01740 Vantaa, Finland
Tel.: (358) 207388344
Fax: (358) 207388810
E-Mail: airseasales@fi.dsv.com
Air & Sea Freight Transportation Services
S.I.C.: 4512
N.A.I.C.S.: 481112
Daniel Wikman *(Mng Dir)*

DSV Air & Sea Pvt. Ltd. (1)
The Qube 2nd Fl B-201 B-204 MV Rd
Marol Andheri E, Mumbai, Maharashtra, 400059, India
Tel.: (91) 2271999000
Fax: (91) 2271999001
E-Mail: info@in.dsv.com
Web Site: www.dsv.com
Emp.: 80
Air & Sea Freight Transportation Services
S.I.C.: 4512
N.A.I.C.S.: 481112
Martin Roos *(Mgr-Sls)*

DSV Air & Sea Pte. Ltd (1)
300 Tampines Avenue 5 Unit 07-07 NTUC Income Tampines Junction
Singapore, 529653, Singapore
Tel.: (65) 62278191
Fax: (65) 64 77 85 16
E-Mail: sin@sg.dsv.com
Web Site: www.dsv.com
Emp.: 70
Logistics & Freight Services
S.I.C.: 4522
N.A.I.C.S.: 481212
Nick Wong *(Mng Dir)*

DSV Air & Sea Pty. Ltd. (1)
Unit A2 Portside Distribution Centre 2-8 McPherson Street
Banksmeadow, NSW, 2019, Australia
Tel.: (61) 283359888
Fax: (61) 283359899
E-Mail: info@au.dsv.com
Web Site: www.dsv.com
Emp.: 135
Air & Sea Freight Transportation Services
S.I.C.: 4512
N.A.I.C.S.: 481112
Danny Ayoub *(Mng Dir)*

DSV Air & Sea S.A. De C.V. (1)
Insurgentes Sur No 1032 Primer piso Col Insurgentes San Borja
Mexico, 03100, Mexico
Tel.: (52) 5556156525
Fax: (52) 5556156526
E-Mail: info@mx.dsv.com
Web Site: www.dsv.com
Emp.: 30
Air & Sea Freight Transportation Services
S.I.C.: 4522
N.A.I.C.S.: 481212

DSV A/S—(Continued)

Erik Magnusson *(Mgr-Route Dev)*

DSV Air & Sea SAS (1)
8 rue des Deux Cedres Zone de Fret 3
BP 12439
95707 Roissy-en-France, Val-d'Oise, France
Tel.: (33) 800 00 51 93
Fax: (33) 1 48 62 60 53
E-Mail: sales@sr.dsv.com
Emp.: 100
Air & Sea Freight Transportation Services
S.I.C.: 4512
N.A.I.C.S.: 481112
Stephane Gautrais *(Gen Mgr)*

DSV Air & Sea S.A.U. (1)
c/Pagesia s/n Poligono Industrial Moli de la Bastida
08191 Rubi, Barcelona, Spain
Tel.: (34) 931807400
Fax: (34) 93 180 74 01
E-Mail: info@es.dsv.com
Air & Sea Freight Transportation Services
S.I.C.: 4512
N.A.I.C.S.: 481112
Evan Mas *(Gen Mgr)*

DSV Air & Sea Sdn. Bhd. (1)
B 7-2 BBT One The Towers Lebuh Batu Nilam 2 Bandar Bukit Tinggi
41200 Kelang, Selangor, Malaysia
Tel.: (60) 333251100
Fax: (60) 333251199
E-Mail: pkg@my.dsv.com
Web Site: www.dsc.com
Emp.: 50
Air & Sea Freight Services
S.I.C.: 4512
N.A.I.C.S.: 481112
Bruhn Christensen Kenneth *(Mng Dir)*

DSV Air & Sea Sp. z.o.o (1)
ul Poludniowa 2 Oltarzew
05-850 Ozarow Mazowiecki, Masovian, Poland
Tel.: (48) 222447600
Fax: (48) 22036561
E-Mail: centrala.dsvairsea@pl.dsv.com
Freight Forwarding Services
S.I.C.: 4731
N.A.I.C.S.: 488510

DSV Air & Sea s.r.o (1)
Budova Paramount Na Maninach 876/7
Holesovice, Prague, Czech Republic
Tel.: (420) 234091268
Fax: (420) 234091250
E-Mail: sea@cz.dsv.com
Web Site: www.dsv.com
Emp.: 19
Air & Sea Freight Transportation Services
S.I.C.: 4512
N.A.I.C.S.: 481112

DSV Commercials Ltd. (1)
Eastfield Road South
Killingholme, Lincs, DN40 3DR, United Kingdom
Tel.: (44) 1469553672
Fax: (44) 1469553631
E-Mail: info@uk.dsv.com
General Freight Trucking Services
S.I.C.: 4214
N.A.I.C.S.: 484110
Chris Marshal *(Gen Mgr)*

DSV Hellas S.A. (1)
69 Possidonos Ave & Alimou Ave
Alimos, 174 55 Athens, Greece
Tel.: (30) 2109883049
Fax: (30) 2109841636
E-Mail: info@gr.dsv.com
Web Site: www.dsv.com
Emp.: 50
Freight Trucking & Logistics Management Services
S.I.C.: 4512
N.A.I.C.S.: 481112
Markos Goutis *(Mgr)*

DSV Hrvatska d.o.o. (1)
Industrijska 20
10431 Sveta Nedelja, Zagreb, Croatia
Tel.: (385) 1 6400891
Fax: (385) 1 6400898
Web Site: www.dsv.com
Freight Trucking & Logistics Management Services
S.I.C.: 4214
N.A.I.C.S.: 484110

DSV Hungaria Kft (1)
11 Vasut Street
2040 Budaors, Hungary
Tel.: (36) 23802100
Fax: (36) 23802190
E-Mail: dsv@hu.dsv.com
Web Site: www.dsv.com
Logistics & Freight Forwarding Services
S.I.C.: 4731
N.A.I.C.S.: 541614

DSV Logistics Co., Ltd. (1)
Building 69 No 36 Yiwei Road Waigaoqiao Free Trade Zone
Shanghai, 201131, China
Tel.: (86) 2150460662
Fax: (86) 2150462632
E-Mail: sales@cn.dsv.com
Web Site: www.dsv.com
Emp.: 100
Freight Trucking & Logistics Management Services
S.I.C.: 4214
N.A.I.C.S.: 484110

DSV Logistics SA (1)
Via Passeggiata 24
6828 Balerna, Ticino, Switzerland
Tel.: (41) 916950606
Fax: (41) 91 68 30 464
E-Mail: info.balerna@ch.dsv.com
Web Site: www.dsv.com
Freight Trucking & Logistics Management Services
S.I.C.: 4214
N.A.I.C.S.: 484110

DSV Osterreich Spedition GmbH (1)
Flughafenstrasse 1
4063 Horsching, Austria
Tel.: (43) 7221 602 0
Fax: (43) 503781599
E-Mail: pascal.ringhofer@at.dsv.com
Web Site: www.dsv.com
Emp.: 15
Road Transport & Logistics Services
S.I.C.: 4214
N.A.I.C.S.: 484110
Roman Fuchsberger *(Mgr-Security)*

DSV Road AB (1)
Bjurogatan 15
PO Box 50122
SE 211 24 Malmo, Sweden
Tel.: (46) 406801000
Fax: (46) 406801029
E-Mail: jonas.fredrickson@se.dsv.com
Web Site: www.dsv.com
Emp.: 230
Transportation Services
S.I.C.: 4789
N.A.I.C.S.: 488999
Magnus Malmqvist *(Gen Mgr-Sls & Mktg)*

Branch:

DSV Road AB (2)
Stenbrovagen 15
PO Box 611
SE 251 06 Helsingborg, Sweden
Tel.: (46) 42179000
Fax: (46) 42299600
Web Site: www.dsv.se
Emp.: 400
S.I.C.: 3531
N.A.I.C.S.: 333120

DSV Road & Solutions A.S. (1)
No 2/A 10 Kat No 154
Buyukcekmece, 34528 Istanbul, Turkey
Tel.: (90) 2128861030
Fax: (90) 2128862677
E-Mail: info@tr.dsv.com
Web Site: www.dsv.com
Emp.: 50
Freight Trucking & Logistics Services
S.I.C.: 4214
N.A.I.C.S.: 484110
Morten Joergensen *(Gen Mgr)*

DSV Road a.s. (1)
Uprapi 224 Dobroviz
25261 Prague, Czech Republic
Tel.: (420) 311332444
Fax: (420) 311332440
E-Mail: info@cz.dsv.com
Web Site: www.dsv.com
Emp.: 100
Road Transport & Logistics Services
S.I.C.: 4212
N.A.I.C.S.: 484110

DSV Road AS (1)
Asbieveien 15
4848 Arendal, Norway
Tel.: (47) 37004500
Fax: (47) 37004509
E-Mail: info@no.dsv.com
Web Site: www.dsv.com
General Freight Trucking Services
S.I.C.: 4212
N.A.I.C.S.: 484110
Dag Jonassen *(Mng Dir)*

DSV Road EOOD (1)
Gara Iskar Industrial District 16 Nedelcho Bonchev Str
1592 Sofia, Bulgaria
Tel.: (359) 29267800
Fax: (359) 29267850
E-Mail: sales@bg.dsv.com
Web Site: www.dsv.com
Emp.: 95
Road Transport & Logistics Services
S.I.C.: 4212
N.A.I.C.S.: 484110

DSV Road GmbH (1)
Hanns-Martin-Schleyer-Strasse 18 A Haus 5
47877 Willich, Nordrhein-Westfalen, Germany
Tel.: (49) 2154 9544 0
Fax: (49) 2154 9544 132
E-Mail: info.road@de.dsv.com
General Freight Trucking Services
S.I.C.: 4214
N.A.I.C.S.: 484110
Nicolai Knudsen *(Mng Dir)*

DSV Road Holding NV (1)
Tasmanweg 2 Venlo
5298 LH Venlo, Limburg, Netherlands
Tel.: (31) 773892222
Fax: (31) 773892200
E-Mail: info.vem@nl.dsv.com
Web Site: www.dsv.com
Emp.: 200
Management Services
S.I.C.: 8741
N.A.I.C.S.: 551114
Rob Hermans *(Mng Dir)*

DSV Road Limited (1)
Tougher Business Park Ladytown
Naas, Kildare, Ireland
Tel.: (353) 45444777
Fax: (353) 45444799
E-Mail: info@ie.dsv.com
Web Site: www.dsv.com
Emp.: 400
Freight Trucking & Logistics Management Services
S.I.C.: 4214
N.A.I.C.S.: 484110
Sean Darcy *(Mng Dir)*
Brendon Murphy *(Mng Dir)*

DSV Road Ltd. (1)
Stonehouse Lane
Purfleet, Essex, RM19 1NX, United Kingdom
Tel.: (44) 1708892000
Fax: (44) 1708 892 001
E-Mail: info@uk.dsv.com
Web Site: www.dsv.com
Emp.: 250
Freight Trucking & Logistics Management Services
S.I.C.: 4212
N.A.I.C.S.: 484110
Jesper Hansen *(Mng Dir)*

DSV Road NV (1)
Industriezone Puurs 533 Schoonmansveld 40
2870 Puurs, Antwerp, Belgium
Tel.: (32) 38972500
Fax: (32) 38972509
E-Mail: info.road@be.dsv.com
Web Site: www.dsv.com
Road Transport & Logistics Services
S.I.C.: 4212
N.A.I.C.S.: 484110
Jan Casier *(Branch Mgr)*

DSV Road Oy (1)
Tulkintie 29
01740 Vantaa, Finland
Tel.: (358) 207388388
Fax: (358) 207388800
E-Mail: info@fi.dsv.com
Web Site: www.dsv.fi
Emp.: 300
Freight Trucking & Customs Clearance Services
S.I.C.: 4214
N.A.I.C.S.: 484110
Juha-Pekka Nurmela *(Mgr-Fin)*

Subsidiary:

Uudenmaan Pikakuljetus Oy (2)
Tulkintie 29
01740 Vantaa, Finland
Tel.: (358) 207388222
Fax: (358) 207388851
E-Mail: toimisto@upk.fi
Web Site: www.upk.fi
Sls.: $24,236,820
Emp.: 80
Freight Forwarding Services
S.I.C.: 4731
N.A.I.C.S.: 488510
Dick Backstrom *(Gen Mgr)*

DSV Road S.A. (1)
39 Zone Industrielle
L-8287 Kehlen, Capellen, Luxembourg
Tel.: (352) 312828
Fax: (352) 312829
Web Site: www.dsv.com
Emp.: 45
Road Transportation Services
S.I.C.: 4214
N.A.I.C.S.: 484110
Finn Schimdt *(Mgr)*

DSV Road S.A.U. (1)
Calle 7 Parcela 7 Pol Ind Pla de la Vallonga
03006 Alicante, Spain
Tel.: (34) 965 99 39 50
Fax: (34) 965 99 39 51
E-Mail: info@es.dsv.com
Emp.: 12
Freight Trucking & Logistics Management Services
S.I.C.: 4214
N.A.I.C.S.: 484110
Soren Schmidt *(Pres)*

DSV Road Sp. z.o.o (1)
ul Poludniowa 2 Oltarzew
05-850 Ozarow Mazowiecki, Mazowsze, Poland
Tel.: (48) 227392300
Fax: (48) 227392301
E-Mail: centrala.dsvroad@pl.dsv.com
Emp.: 70
General Freight Trucking Services
S.I.C.: 4212
N.A.I.C.S.: 484110
Piotr Wojciech Krawiecki *(Chm)*

DSV S.A. (1)
Parc d'activites du Melantois Rue des Sequoias
BP 207
59812 Lesquin, Nord, France
Tel.: (33) 3 20 60 72 81
Fax: (33) 3 20609090
Web Site: www.dsv.com
Emp.: 93
Freight Trucking & Logistics Management Services
S.I.C.: 4214
N.A.I.C.S.: 484110
Vincent Merletti *(CEO)*

DSV SGPS, Lda. (1)
Rua Campo do Martelo 319
4485-959 Vilar do Pinheiro, Portugal
Tel.: (351) 229479200
Fax: (351) 229418574
E-Mail: info.zeral@pt.dsv.com
Web Site: www.dsv.com
Emp.: 110
Freight Trucking & Logistics Management Services
S.I.C.: 4212
N.A.I.C.S.: 484110
Jose Alberto Alves de Oliveira *(Mgr)*

DSV Solutions 2 BV (1)
Cacaoweg 20-86L
1047 BM Amsterdam, Noord-Holland, Netherlands
Tel.: (31) 20 407 0600
Logistics & Warehousing Services

S.I.C.: 4225
N.A.I.C.S.: 493110

DSV Solutions AB (1)
Nettovagen 4
175 89 Jarfalla, Stockholm, Sweden
Tel.: (46) 8 580 883 00
Fax: (46) 8 580 883 02
E-Mail: solutions@se.dsv.com
Freight Trucking & Logistics Management Services
S.I.C.: 4212
N.A.I.C.S.: 484110
Lars Andreasson *(Mgr-Sls)*

DSV Solutions AS (1)
Gneisveien 16
2020 Skedsmokorset, Norway
Tel.: (47) 40403600
Fax: (47) 22642995
E-Mail: info-solutions@no.dsv.com
Web Site: www.dsv.com
Emp.: 100
Logistics & Warehousing Services
S.I.C.: 4731
N.A.I.C.S.: 541614
Jens Hesselberg Lund *(Vice Chm)*

DSV Solutions (Automotive) NV (1)
Langerbruggestraat 101 Havennr
9000 Gent, Oost-Vlaanderen, Belgium
Tel.: (32) 92180000
Fax: (32) 92180014
E-Mail: admin.automotive@be.dsv.com
Web Site: www.dsv.com
Emp.: 600
Road Transport & Logistics Services
S.I.C.: 4214
N.A.I.C.S.: 484110

DSV Solutions B.V. (1)
Tradeboulevard 4
4761 RL Moerdijk, North Brabant, Netherlands
Tel.: (31) 168 41 30 00
Fax: (31) 168 41 40 00
E-Mail: info.moerdijk@nl.dsv.com
Web Site: www.dsv.com
Emp.: 60
Logistics & Warehousing Services
S.I.C.: 4731
N.A.I.C.S.: 541614
Harco Eising *(Mgr-Site)*

DSV Solutions Group GmbH (1)
Schlachte 15-18
28195 Bremen, Germany
Tel.: (49) 42117680
Fax: (49) 4211 768 420
E-Mail: info@dsv.de.com
Web Site: www.de.dsv.com
Emp.: 180
Freight Trucking & Logistics Management Services
S.I.C.: 4212
N.A.I.C.S.: 484110
Tobias Schmidt *(Mng Dir)*

DSV Solutions Lda. (1)
Quinta da Torre 9001A Quinta do Anjo Parque Industrial
2950-635 Palmela, Portugal
Tel.: (351) 212110300
Fax: (351) 212110340
E-Mail: info.geral@pt.dsv.com
Web Site: www.dsv.com
Emp.: 26
Logistics & Freight Forwarding Services
S.I.C.: 4731
N.A.I.C.S.: 488510
Carlos Aires *(Mng Dir)*

DSV Solutions Ltd. (1)
Maidstone Road Kingston
Milton Keynes, Bucks, MK10 0AJ, United Kingdom
Tel.: (44) 1908512215
Fax: (44) 1255252405
E-Mail: solutions@uk.dsv.com
Emp.: 100
Logistics & Warehousing Services
S.I.C.: 4225
N.A.I.C.S.: 493110

DSV Solutions NV (1)
Eddastraat 21 Kennedy Industriepark
9042 Gent, Oost-Vlaanderen, Belgium
Tel.: (32) 92500811
Fax: (32) 92517133
E-Mail: dbe.sahahhotel@infosolutions.com
Emp.: 300
Road Transport & Logistics Services
S.I.C.: 4214
N.A.I.C.S.: 484110
Samdsra Nyeuwenhove *(Mgr)*

DSV Solutions OOO (1)
Moskovskaya obl Istrinsky r-n
143550 Luchinskoye, Russia
Tel.: (7) 495 514 1115
Fax: (7) 495 514 1116
General Freight Trucking Services
S.I.C.: 4214
N.A.I.C.S.: 484110

DSV Solutions Oy (1)
Honkanummentie 3
01260 Vantaa, Finland
Tel.: (358) 207388322
Fax: (358) 207388800
E-Mail: info@fi.dsv.com
Web Site: www.dsv.fi
Emp.: 150
Logistics & Warehousing Services
S.I.C.: 4731
N.A.I.C.S.: 541614
Dick Backstrom *(Gen Mgr)*

DSV Solutions Puurs NV (1)
Schoonmansveld 34
2870 Puurs, Antwerp, Belgium
Tel.: (32) 38603500
Fax: (32) 38603599
E-Mail: puurs.solutions@be.dsv.com
Web Site: www.dsv.com
Road Transport & Logistics Services
S.I.C.: 4214
N.A.I.C.S.: 484110
Jorrit Nieuwenhuis *(Mng Dir)*

DSV Solutions S.A. (1)
ZI de la Martinoire 30 rue de Chardonnet
BP 147
59391 Wattrelos, Nord, France
Tel.: (33) 3 88 65 81 65
Fax: (33) 3 88 68 61 21
Web Site: www.fr.dsv.com
Emp.: 130
Logistics & Warehousing Services
S.I.C.: 4225
N.A.I.C.S.: 493110
Alain Leblond *(Mgr)*

DSV Solutions S.A.U. (1)
Avda de la Industria 3 Puerto Seco
19200 Azuqueca de Henares, Guadalajara, Spain
Tel.: (34) 949871800
Fax: (34) 949871801
E-Mail: info@es.dsv.com
Web Site: www.dsv.com
Logistics & Warehousing Services
S.I.C.: 4731
N.A.I.C.S.: 541614

DSV Solutions Sp. z.o.o. (1)
ul Minska 63
03-828 Warsaw, Poland
Tel.: (48) 22 244 76 36
Fax: (48) 22 670 68 07
E-Mail: centrala.dsvsolutions@pl.dsv.com
Logistics & Warehousing Services
S.I.C.: 4225
N.A.I.C.S.: 493110

DSV Solutions SRL (1)
Bucharest West Park for Logistics 287/1 DE Street
077096 Bucharest, Romania
Tel.: (40) 21 431 31 00
Fax: (40) 21 431 31 03
E-Mail: marketing@ro.dsv.com
Web Site: www.dsv.com
Emp.: 300
Logistics & Warehousing Services
S.I.C.: 4731
N.A.I.C.S.: 541614
Sergiu Iordache *(Mng Dir)*

DSV Stuttgart GmbH & Co. KG (1)
Markgroninger Strasse 50
71701 Schwieberdingen, Baden-Wurttemberg, Germany
Tel.: (49) 71503900
Fax: (49) 7150390201
E-Mail: info.schwieberdingen@de.dsv.com
Web Site: www.dsv.com
Freight Trucking & Logistics Management Services
S.I.C.: 4212
N.A.I.C.S.: 484110

DSV Transitarios Lda. (1)
Rua Campo do Martelo 319
4485-000 Vilar do Pinheiro, Portugal
Tel.: (351) 22 94 79 200
Fax: (351) 229479868
E-Mail: info.geral@pt.dsv.com
Web Site: www.dsv.com
Emp.: 57
Freight Trucking & Logistics Management Services
S.I.C.: 4212
N.A.I.C.S.: 484110
Jose Alves *(Gen Mgr)*

DSV Transport AS (1)
Parnu Mnt 535
76401 Saku, Harju, Estonia
Tel.: (372) 6599999
Fax: (372) 6599990
E-Mail: info@ee.dsv.com
Web Site: www.dsv.com
Emp.: 150
Freight Trucking & Logistics Management Services
S.I.C.: 4212
N.A.I.C.S.: 484110
Jaan Lepp *(Exec Dir-Mgmt Bd)*
Aivo Kurik *(Dir-Fin-Mgmt Bd)*
Jaanika Roosmann *(Dir-Production Svcs-Mgmt Bd)*
Alvar Toruke *(Dir-Logistics-Mgmt Bd)*

DSV Transport d.o.o. (1)
Struzevo 90
4000 Kranj, Slovenia
Tel.: (386) 45021100
Fax: (386) 45021144
E-Mail: info@si.dsv.com
Web Site: www.dsv.com
Emp.: 90
Freight Trucking & Logistics Management Services
S.I.C.: 4214
N.A.I.C.S.: 484110
Robert Gortnar *(Mng Dir)*

DSV Transport International S.A. (1)
355 Boulevard Mohamed V Espace Yousra
Casablanca, Morocco
Tel.: (212) 522401666
Fax: (212) 522401690
E-Mail: info@ma.dsv.com
Web Site: www.dsv.com
Emp.: 30
Freight Transport & Logistics Services
S.I.C.: 4731
N.A.I.C.S.: 488510
Alain de Mirbeck *(Mgr)*

DSV Transport Ltd. (1)
Olesheva St Bldg 9 Office 15
220125 Minsk, Belarus
Tel.: (375) 172684220
Fax: (375) 172684221
E-Mail: info@by.dsv.com
Web Site: www.dsv.com
Emp.: 30
Freight Trucking & Logistics Management Services
S.I.C.: 4212
N.A.I.C.S.: 484110
Shepochkim Zaleriy *(Mgr)*

DSV Transport SIA (1)
Krustpils iela 31
1073 Riga, Latvia
Tel.: (371) 67100701
Fax: (371) 37167100703
E-Mail: sales@lv.dsv.com
Web Site: www.dsv.com
Emp.: 130
Freight Trucking & Logistics Management Services
S.I.C.: 4214
N.A.I.C.S.: 484110
Jens Bjorn Andersen *(Chm)*
Janis Meikulans *(Mng Dir)*

DSV Transport UAB (1)
Stasylu 21
02241 Vilnius, Lithuania
Tel.: (370) 52686200
Fax: (370) 52686201
E-Mail: vilnius@lt.dsv.com
Web Site: www.dsv.com
Emp.: 80
Freight Trucking & Logistics Management Services
S.I.C.: 4212
N.A.I.C.S.: 484110
Kim Bartoldy *(Mng Dir)*

DSV Ukraine (1)
1 Dachna Str Chayki Vlg
Kievo-Svyatoshinskiy, 08130 Kiev, Ukraine
Tel.: (380) 443905121
Fax: (380) 443905120
E-Mail: info@ua.dsv.com
Web Site: www.dsv.ua
Emp.: 120
Freight Trucking & Logistics Services
S.I.C.: 4212
N.A.I.C.S.: 484110
Andrey Potseluenko *(Gen Mgr)*

Logimar SRL (1)
Via Bolgare 1/A
Carobbio degli Angeli, Bergamo, Italy
Tel.: (39) 035951468
Fax: (39) 035951665
E-Mail: info@logimar.it
Web Site: www.logimar.it
Emp.: 12
Logistics & Freight Forwarding Services
S.I.C.: 4731
N.A.I.C.S.: 488510
Marcello Saponaro *(Mgr)*

NTS European Distribution AB (1)
Stenbrovagen 15
25107 Helsingborg, Skane, Sweden
Tel.: (46) 42179000
Web Site: www.dsv.com
Logistics & Warehousing Services
S.I.C.: 4225
N.A.I.C.S.: 493110

OOO DSV Transport (1)
Datsky Proezd 3 Dorozhnoie
Gurievsky, Kaliningrad, 236028, Russia
Tel.: (7) 40 12 306215
Fax: (7) 40 12 306245
E-Mail: kaliningrad@ru.dsv.com
Emp.: 150
General Freight Trucking Services
S.I.C.: 4214
N.A.I.C.S.: 484110
Oleg Vadimovich Kalashnik *(Dir-Mktg)*

POP Gesellschaft fur Prozesslogistik mbH (1)
Am Mittelkai 9
70327 Stuttgart, Baden-Wurttemberg, Germany
Tel.: (49) 7119189360
Fax: (49) 711 918936 44
Freight Trucking & Logistics Management Services
S.I.C.: 4212
N.A.I.C.S.: 484110

Saima Avandero SpA (1)
Via Dante Alighieri 134
20096 Pioltello, Milan, Italy
Tel.: (39) 02921341
Fax: (39) 029267304
E-Mail: sainfo@saima.it
Web Site: www.dsv.com
Air & Sea Freight Transportation Services
S.I.C.: 4512
N.A.I.C.S.: 481112

Sandtorp Thermotransport AS (1)
Ramstadlokka 6
1850 Mysen, Norway
Tel.: (47) 69 89 15 69
Fax: (47) 69 89 21 01
E-Mail: post@sandtorp.no
Web Site: www.sandtorp.no
Emp.: 30
General Freight Trucking Services
S.I.C.: 4214
N.A.I.C.S.: 484110
Heyerdahl Jarle *(Mng Dir)*

Waagan Bil AS (1)
Blindheim Industrivei 4
6020 Alesund, Norway
Tel.: (47) 70 19 70 09
Fax: (47) 70 19 70 01
E-Mail: asle@waagan.no
Web Site: www.waagan.no/default.asp?menu=4
Emp.: 100
Freight Trucking & Logistics Management Services
S.I.C.: 4214
N.A.I.C.S.: 484110

DSV A/S—(Continued)

Sten Arva Waagan *(Mng Dir)*

DTB-DEUTSCHE BIOGAS AG

Barsseler Str 65
26169 Friesoythe, Germany
Tel.: (49) 44919395930
Fax: (49) 44919395939
E-Mail: energie@deutsche-biogas.de
Web Site: www.deutsche-biogas.de
DB9—(DEU)
Business Description:
Biogas Plants Construction Services
S.I.C.: 1629
N.A.I.C.S.: 236210
Personnel:
Joachim Meier zu Uphausen *(Chm-Supervisory Bd)*
Horst Lammers *(CEO)*
Claudia Lammers *(CFO)*
Supervisory Board of Directors:
Joachim Meier zu Uphausen
Helga Klaren
Enno Schweers

DTCOM - DIRECT TO COMPANY S/A

AV Dom Pedro II 1720 Itapira
83420-000 Brasilia, PR, Brazil
Tel.: (55) 41 3671 9000
Fax: (55) 41 3671 9000
Web Site: www.dtcom.com.br
Year Founded: 2000
DTCY3—(BRAZ)
Sales Range: $1-9.9 Million
Emp.: 54
Business Description:
Distance Education Services
S.I.C.: 8299
N.A.I.C.S.: 611710
Personnel:
Marcelo Renato Nascimento Cerqueira *(Dir-IR)*

DTI SOFTWARE

388 Rue St Jacques Ouest 1st Fl
Montreal, QC, H2Y 1S1, Canada
Tel.: (514) 499-0910
Fax: (514) 499-0715
Web Site: www.dtisoft.com
Rev.: $9,621,000
Business Description:
Online Game Developer
S.I.C.: 3944
N.A.I.C.S.: 339930
Personnel:
Louis Belanger-Martin *(Founder)*
Nicolas Belanger *(Pres & CEO)*

DTM SYSTEMS INC.

Unit 130 2323 Boundary Road
Vancouver, BC, Canada V5M 4V8
Tel.: (604) 257-6700
Fax: (604) 257-6749
Toll Free: (888) 655-3282
E-Mail: info@dtm.ca
Web Site: www.dtm.ca
Year Founded: 1986
Rev.: $22,442,341
Emp.: 38
Business Description:
Computer & Software Stores
S.I.C.: 5946
N.A.I.C.S.: 443142
Personnel:
Paul J. Martin *(CEO)*

DTS CORPORATION

6-19-13 Shimbashi
Minato-ku, Tokyo, 105-0004, Japan
Tel.: (81) 334375488
Fax: (81) 334375330
Web Site: www.dts.co.jp
9682—(TKS)
Sls.: $671,437,547
Assets: $484,178,893
Liabilities: $116,000,247
Net Worth: $368,178,646
Earnings: $23,948,694
Emp.: 4,469
Fiscal Year-end: 03/31/13
Business Description:
Computer Services
S.I.C.: 7373
N.A.I.C.S.: 541512
Personnel:
Kouichi Nishida *(Pres)*

Subsidiaries:

ASTERIKS Inc. (1)
5-32-8 Shimbashi
Minato-ku, Tokyo, 105-0004, Japan
Tel.: (81) 334375151
Fax: (81) 3 3437 5195
Web Site: www.asteriks.co.jp
Software Business Consulting Services
S.I.C.: 8742
N.A.I.C.S.: 541611

FAITEC CORPORATION (1)
Shirokane 1-27-6 Shirokanetakanawa Station Bldg 9th Fl
Minato-ku, Tokyo, Japan
Tel.: (81) 354201213
Fax: (81) 3 5420 2060
Web Site: www.faitec.co.jp
Insurance & Pension Property Management Services
S.I.C.: 6351
N.A.I.C.S.: 524126

JAPAN SYSTEMS ENGINEERING CORPORATION (1)
4th Fl Helios II Bldg 1-12-11 Funado
Itabashi-ku, Tokyo, Japan
Tel.: (81) 359706565
Fax: (81) 3 5970 6575
Web Site: www.jse.co.jp
Software Development Services
S.I.C.: 7371
N.A.I.C.S.: 541511
Sato Kouiti *(Pres)*

KYUSYU DTS CORPORATION (1)
7th Fl Taihaku-Ctr Bldg 2-19-24 Hakata-Ekimae
Hakata-ku, Fukuoka, 812-0011, Japan
Tel.: (81) 924017575
Fax: (81) 924016665
Web Site: www.qdts.co.jp
System Integration Services
S.I.C.: 7373
N.A.I.C.S.: 541512

MIRUCA CORPORATION (1)
4th Fl NOF Techno-Port Kamata Ctr Bldg 2-16-1 Minami-Kamata
Ota-ku, Tokyo, 144-0035, Japan
Tel.: (81) 357137677
Fax: (81) 357137678
E-Mail: kiite@miruca.jp
Web Site: www.miruca.jp
Emp.: 20
Education Consulting & Professional Training Services
S.I.C.: 8299
N.A.I.C.S.: 611430
Shinichi Ito *(Pres)*

SOUGOU SYSTEM SERVICE CORPORATION (1)
Sumitomo-Seimei Karasuma-Dori Bldg 680 Omandokoro-Cho BukkojiShita-Ru
Karasuma-Dori Shimogyo-ku, Kyoto, 600-8413, Japan
Tel.: (81) 753441122
Fax: (81) 753440774
Web Site: www.sgs.co.jp
Emp.: 140
Computer Sales & Data Processing Services
S.I.C.: 7374
N.A.I.C.S.: 518210

Non-U.S. Subsidiary:

DTS (Shanghai) CORPORATION (1)
Rm 705 Jiaxing Bldg No 877 Dongfang Rd
Pudong New Area, Shanghai, China
Tel.: (86) 2150813773
Fax: (86) 2150819770
E-Mail: info@dts-cn.com
Web Site: www.dts-cn.com
System Integration Services
S.I.C.: 7373
N.A.I.C.S.: 541512

DTS8 COFFEE COMPANY, LTD.

(Formerly Berkeley Coffee & Tea, Inc.)
Building B #439 Jinyuan Ba Lu
Jiangqiao Town Jiading District,
Shanghai, 201812, China
Tel.: (86) 181 0181 9011
Web Site: dts8coffee.com
Year Founded: 2009
BKCT—(OTC OTCB)
Sls.: $253,790
Assets: $4,601,474
Liabilities: $755,882
Net Worth: $3,845,592
Earnings: ($1,115,911)
Emp.: 5
Fiscal Year-end: 04/30/13
Business Description:
Coffee Distr
S.I.C.: 5149
N.A.I.C.S.: 424490
Personnel:
Sean Tan *(Pres, CEO, CFO & Sec)*
Board of Directors:
Alexander Liang
Sean Tan

DU PAREIL AU MEME SA

3 rue Christophe Colomb
91300 Massy, France
Tel.: (33) 2 54 29 17 49
Web Site: www.dpam.com
Emp.: 1,400
Business Description:
Children's Clothing & Shoes Retailer
S.I.C.: 5641
N.A.I.C.S.: 448130

DUALEX ENERGY INTERNATIONAL INC.

Suite 200 521 - 3rd Avenue SW
Calgary, AB, T2P 3T3, Canada
Tel.: (403) 265-8011
Fax: (403) 265-8022
E-Mail: info@dualexen.com
Web Site: www.dualexen.com
DXE—(TSXV)
Sls.: $2,410,950
Assets: $4,186,595
Liabilities: $533,076
Net Worth: $3,653,519
Earnings: ($445,921)
Emp.: 5
Fiscal Year-end: 12/31/12
Business Description:
Oil & Natural Gas Exploration
S.I.C.: 1311
N.A.I.C.S.: 211111
Personnel:
Garry T. Hides *(Pres & CEO)*
Lorne A. Morozoff *(CFO, Sec & VP-Fin)*
Kenneth M. Tompson *(COO & Exec VP)*
Board of Directors:
Garry T. Hides
Roy H. Hudson
John Nelson
Bradley B. Porter
David J. Rain
Kenneth M. Tompson
Legal Counsel:
Davis LLP
1000 250 2nd St SW
Calgary, AB, Canada
Transfer Agent:
Olympia Trust Company
125 9th Avenue SE Suite 2300
Calgary, AB, T2G 0P6, Canada
Tel.: (403) 261-0900

DUBAI AEROSPACE ENTERPRISE LTD

DIFC The Gate District Building 4
Level 3
Dubai, United Arab Emirates
Tel.: (971) 44289600
Fax: (971) 44250382
E-Mail: info@dubaiaerospace.com
Web Site: www.dubaiaerospace.com
Year Founded: 2006
Emp.: 30
Business Description:
Aviation Manufacturing, Services & Education
S.I.C.: 4581
N.A.I.C.S.: 488119
Personnel:
Ahmed Bin Saeed Al-Maktoum *(Chm)*

Subsidiaries:

DAE Airports (1)
DIFC The Gate District Building 4 Level 3
Dubai, United Arab Emirates
Tel.: (971) 4 329 2420
Airport Operations
S.I.C.: 4581
N.A.I.C.S.: 488119

U.S. Subsidiary:

Standard Aerospace (2)
1524 W 14th St Ste 110
Tempe, AZ 85281
Tel.: (480) 377-3100
Fax: (480) 377-3105
Toll Free: (800) 492-9977
Web Site: www.standardaero.com
Emp.: 70
Fixed Aviation Base Operator
S.I.C.: 4581
N.A.I.C.S.: 488119
David Smoot *(Vice Chm)*
Firoz Tarapore *(Interim Pres)*
Russell Ford *(CEO)*
Rob Cords *(Sr VP-Airlines & Fleets)*

Non-U.S. Subsidiary:

StandardAero (3)
33 Allen Dyne Rd
Winnipeg, MB, R3H 1A1, Canada
Tel.: (204) 775-9711
Web Site: www.standardaero.com
Emp.: 1,350
Aircraft Engine Repair & Overhaul Services
S.I.C.: 3724
N.A.I.C.S.: 336412
Kyle Hultquist *(VP-Mktg & Comm)*

DUBAI FINANCIAL SERVICES AUTHORITY

DIFSA Level 13 The Gate Bldg
PO Box 75850
Dubai, United Arab Emirates
Tel.: (971) 43621500
Fax: (971) 43620801
E-Mail: info@dfsa.ae
Web Site: www.dfsa.ae
Emp.: 99
Business Description:
Financial Services
S.I.C.: 6011
N.A.I.C.S.: 521110
Personnel:
Saeb Eigner *(Chm)*
Ian Johnston *(CEO)*
Board of Directors:
Saeb Eigner
Apurv Bagri
Robert L. Clarke
David Currie
Charles Flint
The Earl of Home
Robert Owen

Abdullah M. Saleh
J. Andrew Spindler
George Wittich

DUBAI HOLDING LLC

Emirates Towers Sheikh Zayed Road
PO Box 66000
Dubai, United Arab Emirates
Tel.: (971) 43622000
Fax: (971) 43622091
E-Mail: info@dubaiholding.com
Web Site: www.dubaiholding.com
Emp.: 15,000
Business Description:
Holding Company
S.I.C.: 6719
N.A.I.C.S.: 551112
Personnel:
Mohammed Al Gergawi *(Chm)*
Ibrahim Al Ansari *(CEO-Dubai First)*

Subsidiaries:

Dubai Group (1)
Emirates Towers Level 15
PO Box 213311
Sheikh Zayed Rd, Dubai, United Arab Emirates
Tel.: (971) 43300707
Fax: (971) 43303260
E-Mail: info@dubaigroup.com
Web Site: www.dubaigroup.com
Holding Company: Investment Banking & Insurance
S.I.C.: 6719
N.A.I.C.S.: 551112
Soud Ba'alawy *(Chm)*
Ahmed al-Qassim *(CEO)*
Jacqueline Asher *(Mng Dir)*
Abdulrazak M. Aljassim *(COO)*

Subsidiaries:

Dubai Financial Group (2)
Emirates Tower Level 30 Sheikh Zayed Road
PO Box 213311
Dubai, United Arab Emirates
Tel.: (971) 4 3300707
Fax: (971) 4 3303260
E-Mail: info@dubaigroup.com
Web Site: dubaigroup.com
Banking, Brokerage & Asset Management Services
S.I.C.: 6029
N.A.I.C.S.: 522110
Trevor Regan *(Chief Investment Officer)*

Non-U.S. Subsidiary:

TAIB Bank B.S.C. (c) (3)
TAIB Tower Diplomatic Area
PO Box 20485
Manama, Bahrain (60%)
Tel.: (973) 17549494
Fax: (973) 17533174
E-Mail: taibprivatebank@taib.com
Web Site: www.taib.com
TAIB—(BAH)
Sales Range: $1-9.9 Million
Emp.: 124
Banking & Investment Services
S.I.C.: 6029
N.A.I.C.S.: 522110
Abdulrahman Hareb Rashed Al Hareb *(Chm)*
Ramzi K. Y. Abukhadra *(Vice Chm)*
Dayanand Shetty *(Sr VP-Corp Svcs)*

Subsidiary:

TAIB Securities WLL (4)
TAIB Tower Diplomatic Area
PO Box 20485
Manama, Bahrain
Tel.: (973) 17549499
Fax: (973) 17531213
E-Mail: tswll@taib.com
Web Site: www.taib.com
Emp.: 12
Securities Brokerage Services
S.I.C.: 6211
N.A.I.C.S.: 523120
Khaldoon Bin Latif *(Mgr)*

Non-U.S. Subsidiaries:

TAIB Capital Corporation Ltd. (4)
1st Fl Esteem Regency
No 6 Richmond Road, Bengaluru, 560025, India
Tel.: (91) 80 40458999
Fax: (91) 80 40458900
E-Mail: tccl@taib.com
Web Site: www.taib.com
Asset Management Services
S.I.C.: 6282
N.A.I.C.S.: 523930

TAIB Kazak Bank (4)
103 Furmanova St
Almaty, 050000, Kazakhstan
Tel.: (7) 272587030
Fax: (7) 272587009
E-Mail: tkb@taib.com
Web Site: www.taib.com
Emp.: 40
Commercial Banking Services
S.I.C.: 6029
N.A.I.C.S.: 522110
Zain Mazhidulla *(Chm & CEO)*

TAIB Securities (India) Ltd. (4)
Sadhana House 1st Fl 570 PB Marg
Behind Mahindra Tower Worli, Mumbai, 400 018, India
Tel.: (91) 2256626000
Fax: (91) 2256626100
Emp.: 10
Securities Brokerage & Asset Management Services
S.I.C.: 6282
N.A.I.C.S.: 523930

TAIB Securities Ltd (4)
11 Carlos Pl
Mayfair, London, W1K 3AX, United Kingdom
Tel.: (44) 845 868 0529
Fax: (44) 207 533 1600
E-Mail: tsl@taib.com
Web Site: www.taib.com
Emp.: 4
Real Estate Investment Services
S.I.C.: 6531
N.A.I.C.S.: 531390

TAIB Yatirim A.S. (4)
Buyukdere Cad Ozsezen Is Merkezi No 122 A Blok Kat 6
Zincirlikuku, 34394 Istanbul, Turkey
Tel.: (90) 212 347 54 54
Fax: (90) 212 347 01 11
E-Mail: ty@yatirimbank.com.tr
Asset Management & Investment Services
S.I.C.: 6282
N.A.I.C.S.: 523930

TAIB YatirimBank A.S. (4)
Buyukdere Cd # 22 Park Plaza
No 22 A Blok Kat 6
Maslak, 34398 Istanbul, Turkey
Tel.: (90) 2123450711
Fax: (90) 2123450712
E-Mail: info@yatrimbank.com.tr
Web Site: www.taib.com
Commercial Banking Services
S.I.C.: 6029
N.A.I.C.S.: 522110
Shezad Abedi *(Gen Mgr)*

Dubai Insurance Group (2)
Emirates Towers Level 30
PO Box 213311
Sheikh Zayed Road, Dubai, United Arab Emirates
Tel.: (971) 43300707
Fax: (971) 43303260
E-Mail: reception.dg@dubaigroup.com
Web Site: www.dubaigroup.com
Emp.: 21
Holding Company; Insurance
S.I.C.: 6719
N.A.I.C.S.: 551112
Jon Cimino *(Dir-Fin)*

Dubai Investment Group (2)
Emirates Towers Level 38
Sheikh Zayed Road, Dubai, United Arab Emirates
Mailing Address:
PO Box 73311
Dubai, United Arab Emirates
Tel.: (971) 9143189727
Fax: (971) 43303260
E-Mail: info@dubaigroup.com
Web Site: www.dubaigroup.org
Global Financial Investor
S.I.C.: 6211
N.A.I.C.S.: 523999
Soud Ba'alawy *(Chm)*

Dubai International Capital, LLC (1)
Gate Building Level 13 Dubai International Financial Centre
PO Box 72888
Dubai, United Arab Emirates (100%)
Tel.: (971) 43621888
Fax: (971) 43620888
E-Mail: info@dubaiic.com
Web Site: www.dubaiic.com
Private Equity Firm
S.I.C.: 6211
N.A.I.C.S.: 523999
Andrew Wright *(Mng Dir-Legal)*
Anand S. Krishnan *(COO)*
Samer Al Saifi *(CEO-Asset Mgmt)*
David Smoot *(CEO-Private Equity)*

Non-U.S. Holdings:

Almatis GmbH (2)
Lioner St 9
60528 Frankfurt, Germany
Tel.: (49) 699573410
Fax: (49) 6995734113
E-Mail: info@almatis.com
Web Site: www.almatis.com
Emp.: 40
Alumina-Based Material Mfr
S.I.C.: 3334
N.A.I.C.S.: 331313
Taco Jerpranta *(CEO)*

Plant:

Almatis GmbH (3)
Giulini Strasse 2
67065 Ludwigshafen, Germany
Tel.: (49) 6215707118
Telex: 4 64 799 aclu g
Fax: (49) 6215707230
E-Mail: info@almatis.com
Web Site: www.almatis.com
Emp.: 180
Alumina Based Chemicals Mfr
S.I.C.: 3334
N.A.I.C.S.: 331313
Remco Dejong *(CEO)*

U.S. Subsidiary:

Almatis Inc. (3)
501 W Park Rd
Leetsdale, PA 15056
Tel.: (412) 630-2800
Web Site: www.almatis.com
Emp.: 800
Alumina Base Chemicals Mfr & Distr
S.I.C.: 3334
N.A.I.C.S.: 331313
William Smith *(Mgr-Ops)*

Non-U.S. Subsidiaries:

Almatis B.V. (3)
Theemsweg 30
3197 KM Rotterdam, Netherlands
Tel.: (31) 181270100
Fax: (31) 181217853
Web Site: www.almatis.com
Emp.: 110
Tabular Alumina & Alumina Chemicals Mfr
S.I.C.: 3334
N.A.I.C.S.: 331313
Peter Post *(Mng Dir)*

Qingdao Almatis Co. Ltd. (3)
Room 1501 Sunshine 15th Fl
Hong Kong Road, Qingdao, 266555, China
Tel.: (86) 53285728035
Fax: (86) 5325728551
Web Site: www.almatis.com
Emp.: 200
Alumina Based Products Mfr
S.I.C.: 3334
N.A.I.C.S.: 331313
Remco De Jong *(Pres)*

Non-U.S. Joint Venture:

Almatis Limited (3)
1815 2 Nagano
Iwanuki, Iwakuni, Yamaguchi, 740 0045, Japan
Tel.: (81) 827381271
Fax: (81) 827382828
Web Site: www.almatis.com
Emp.: 50
Alumina Based Chemical Mfr & Distr; Owned 80% by Almatis GmbH & 20% by Morimura Bros., Inc.
S.I.C.: 3334
N.A.I.C.S.: 331313
Hayashi Shibuya *(Pres)*

Doncasters Group Ltd. (2)
Milleniem Court 1st Avenue Centrum 100
Burton-on-Trent, Staffs, DE14 2WH, United Kingdom NY
Tel.: (44) 1332864900
Fax: (44) 1332864888
E-Mail: info@doncasters.com
Web Site: www.doncasters.com
Emp.: 30
Holding Company; Aerospace, Automotive & Industrial Turbine Precision Components & Assemblies Mfr
Import Export
S.I.C.: 6719
N.A.I.C.S.: 551112
William M. Ellis *(CEO)*
Michael J. Schurch *(CFO)*
Howard W. Jackson *(Sec)*

Subsidiaries:

Doncasters Aerospace Components (3)
Whitchurch Road
Shrewsbury, Shropshire, SY1 4DP, United Kingdom (100%)
Tel.: (44) 1743454300
Telex: 35623
Fax: (44) 1743454396
Web Site: www.doncasters.com
Sls.: $53,503,496
Emp.: 400
Aerospace Gas Turbine Components Mfr
S.I.C.: 3724
N.A.I.C.S.: 336412
John Patterson *(Mng Dir)*

Doncasters Trucast Ltd. (3)
Marlborough Road
Ryde, Isle of Wight, PO33 1AD, United Kingdom UK
Tel.: (44) 1983 567611
Telex: 86180
Fax: (44) 1983 567618
Web Site: www.doncasters.com
Automotive & Power Generation Hot-End Turbocharger Wheels Mfr
S.I.C.: 3559
N.A.I.C.S.: 333249

Ross & Catherall Limited (3)
Forge Lane Killamarsh
Sheffield, Derbyshire, S21 1BA, United Kingdom UK
Tel.: (44) 1142486404 (100%)
Telex: 54463 ROSCAT G
Fax: (44) 1142475999
E-Mail: russcatherall@doncasters.com
Web Site: www.doncasters.com
Emp.: 100
High-Performance Vacuum-Refined Alloys Mfr
S.I.C.: 3341
N.A.I.C.S.: 331492
Nick Davis *(Gen Mgr)*

Subsidiary:

Ross Ceramics Limited (4)
Derby Road
Derby, DE5 8NX, United Kingdom
Tel.: (44) 1773570800
Fax: (44) 1773570152
E-Mail: info@rossceramics.com
Web Site: www.rossceramics.com
Ceramic Casting Cores Mfr
S.I.C.: 3369
N.A.I.C.S.: 331529
William Hodges *(Mng Dir)*

U.S. Division:

Integrated Energy Technologies, Inc. (3)
225 W Morgan Ave
Evansville, IN 47710-2515 DE
Tel.: (812) 421-7810
Fax: (812) 421-7812
Web Site: ietglobal.com

Dubai Holding LLC—(Continued)

Emp.: 45
Aerospace Engine & Turbine Component Mfr
S.I.C.: 3724
N.A.I.C.S.: 336412
Marvin Miller *(Gen Mgr)*

Subsidiaries:

GCE Industries, Inc. (4)
1891 Nirvana Ave
Chula Vista, CA 91911 DE
Tel.: (619) 421-1151
Fax: (619) 421-1506
Web Site: ietglobal.com
Sls.: $45,000,000
Emp.: 230
Aerospace Engine Turbine Component Mfr
S.I.C.: 3724
N.A.I.C.S.: 336412

MECO, Inc. (4)
2121 S Main St
Paris, IL 61944 DE
Tel.: (217) 465-6500
Fax: (217) 465-5230
Web Site: ietglobal.com
Emp.: 100
Aerospace Turbine Cooling Component Mfr
S.I.C.: 3724
N.A.I.C.S.: 336412
Martin Miller *(Gen Mgr)*

Spun Metals, Inc. (4)
2121 S Main St
Paris, IL 61944-2965 DE
Tel.: (812) 448-2651
Fax: (812) 446-2277
Toll Free: (800) 526-3674
Web Site: ietglobal.com
Specialty Spun Metal Component Mfr
S.I.C.: 3499
N.A.I.C.S.: 332999
Wayne Green *(Gen Mgr)*

U.S. Subsidiaries:

Certified Alloy Products, Inc. (3)
3245 Cherry Ave
Long Beach, CA 90807-5213
Tel.: (562) 595-6621
Fax: (562) 427-8667
Web Site: www.doncasters.com
Sls.: $25,000,000
Emp.: 135
High-Performance Vacuum-Refined Alloys Mfr
S.I.C.: 3341
N.A.I.C.S.: 331492
Richard N. Greenwood *(Pres)*

The Ferry Cap & Set Screw Company (3)
13300 Bramley Ave
Lakewood, OH 44107 OH
Tel.: (216) 771-2533
Fax: (216) 861-6747
Web Site: www.ferrycap.com
Cold-Headed Industrial Fasteners Mfr
S.I.C.: 3452
N.A.I.C.S.: 332722
Joe McAuliffe *(Pres)*

General Products, Aerospace & Defense LLC (3)
739 Wall Rd
Brownsboro, AL 35741 DE
Mailing Address:
PO Box 3248
Huntsville, AL 35810
Tel.: (256) 859-5114
Fax: (256) 859-5390
Web Site: www.gp-llc.com
Emp.: 40
Aerospace & Defense Industry Components Precision Machining, Fabrication & Assembly Services
S.I.C.: 3499
N.A.I.C.S.: 332999
Jeff Hunter *(VP-Sls & Mktg)*

Nelson Stud Welding, Inc. (3)
7900 W Rdg Rd PO Box 4019
Elyria, OH 44036-2019 DE
Tel.: (440) 329-0400
Fax: (440) 329-0521
Toll Free: (800) 635-9353
E-Mail: nelson.sales@nelsonstud.com
Web Site: www.nelsonstud.com
Emp.: 500
Industrial, Construction & Automotive Fastener Systems Mfr
S.I.C.: 3965
N.A.I.C.S.: 339993
Ken Caratelli *(Pres)*

Subsidiary:

Automatic Screw Machine Products Company, Inc. (4)
709 2nd Ave SE
Decatur, AL 35601-2517 AL
Tel.: (256) 353-1931 (100%)
Fax: (256) 355-3612
Toll Free: (800) 237-1097
Sales Range: $50-74.9 Million
Emp.: 115
Specialized Machine Parts Mfr
S.I.C.: 3451
N.A.I.C.S.: 332721
Mike Selby *(Pres)*

Specialty Bar Products Company (3)
200 Martha St PO Box 127
Blairsville, PA 15717 PA
Tel.: (724) 459-7500
Fax: (724) 459-0944
E-Mail: sales@specialty-bar.com
Web Site: www.specialty-bar.com
Emp.: 50
Specialty Steel Bar Machining Services & Mfr
S.I.C.: 3317
N.A.I.C.S.: 331210

MAUSER AG (2)
Schildgesstrasse 71 163
50321 Bruhl, Germany
Tel.: (49) 2232781000
Fax: (49) 2232781208
E-Mail: info@mausergroup.com
Web Site: www.mausergroup.com
Sales Range: $1-4.9 Billion
Emp.: 3,675
Industrial Packaging Material Mfr
S.I.C.: 3565
N.A.I.C.S.: 333993
Sameer Al-Ansari *(Chm-Supervisory Bd)*
Clemens Vellee *(CEO)*
Winfried Klar *(CFO)*

U.S. Subsidiary:

MAUSER Corp. (3)
685 Rte 202 206
Bridgewater, NJ 08807
Tel.: (908) 203-9500
Fax: (908) 203-1940
Web Site: www.mauser.com
Emp.: 100
Industrial Packaging Material Distr
S.I.C.: 2671
N.A.I.C.S.: 322220
Ronald M. Litchkowski *(Pres)*

Tatweer Dubai LLC (1)
31st/24th Floor Emirates Towers Sheikh Zayed Road
PO Box 65999
Dubai, United Arab Emirates (100%)
Tel.: (971) 43302222
Fax: (971) 43302233
Real Estate Development/Leisure & Entertainment
S.I.C.: 6531
N.A.I.C.S.: 531390
Stephanie Goodell *(Sr Mgr-PR & Comm)*

Joint Venture:

Dubai Mercantile Exchange Limited (2)
Bldg 2 Dubai International Financial Centre
PO Box 66500
Dubai, United Arab Emirates
Tel.: (971) 43655500
Fax: (971) 43655599
E-Mail: info@dubaimerc.com
Web Site: www.dubaimerc.com
Sales Range: $650-699.9 Million
Emp.: 45
Commodities Exchange; Owned by New York Mercantile Exchange, Inc., by Dubai Holding LLC & by Oman Investment Fund
S.I.C.: 6231
N.A.I.C.S.: 523210
Ahmad Sharaf *(Chm)*
Thomas Leaver *(CEO)*
Matthew Thompson *(Chief Strategy & Bus Dev Officer)*
Shahnaz Qaedi *(Gen Counsel, Sec & Head-Membership)*

TECOM Investments LLC (1)
PO Box 66000
Dubai, United Arab Emirates (100%)
Tel.: (971) 43189292
Web Site: dubaiholding.com
Real Estate & Licensing Services
S.I.C.: 6531
N.A.I.C.S.: 531390

DUBAI INSURANCE

Al Riqqa Road Deira
PO Box 3027
Dubai, United Arab Emirates
Tel.: (971) 42693030
Fax: (971) 42693727
E-Mail: info@dubins.ae
Web Site: www.dubins.ae
DIN—(DFM)
Rev.: $91,210,512
Assets: $151,071,332
Liabilities: $74,733,824
Net Worth: $76,337,508
Earnings: $7,922,071
Fiscal Year-end: 12/31/12

Business Description:
Insurance Services
S.I.C.: 6311
N.A.I.C.S.: 524113

Personnel:
Buti Obaid Al Mulla *(Chm)*
Marwan Abdullah Al Rostamani *(Vice Chm)*
Ramanathan Narayana *(CFO)*
Mohammed Tahsin *(COO)*

Board of Directors:
Buti Obaid Al Mulla
Abu Bakr Abdulla Al Futtaim
Abdulla Mohammed Rashid Al Huraiz
Mohammed Ahmad Abdulla Al Moosa
Marwan Abdullah Al Rostamani
Khaled Adbul Wahed Al Rustamani
Ahmed Eissa Al Serkal

DUBAI INVESTMENTS PJSC

PO Box 28171
Dubai, United Arab Emirates
Tel.: (971) 48122400
Fax: (971) 48122344
E-Mail: info@dubaiinvestments.com
Web Site: www.dubaiinvestments.com
Year Founded: 1995
Rev.: $719,005,658
Assets: $3,547,690,744
Liabilities: $1,109,675,410
Net Worth: $2,438,015,334
Earnings: $70,364,790
Emp.: 50
Fiscal Year-end: 12/31/12

Business Description:
Investment Services
S.I.C.: 6211
N.A.I.C.S.: 523110

Personnel:
Khalid Jassim Kalban *(CEO & Mng Dir)*

Board of Directors:
Suhail Fares Ghanim Al Mazrui
Hussain Mahyoob Sultan Al Junaidy
Mohamed Saif Darwish Ahmed Al Ketbi
Ali Fardan Ali Al Fardan
Khalid Jassim Kalban

Subsidiaries:

Dubai Cranes & Technical Services Ltd. (1)
PO Box 113744
Dubai, United Arab Emirates (70%)
Tel.: (971) 43452940
Fax: (971) 3452950
Web Site: www.dubaiinvestments.com
Specialist in Advanced Overhead Lifting Solutions & Maintenance Services
S.I.C.: 3536
N.A.I.C.S.: 333923
Andrew Kay *(Gen Mgr)*

Dubai International Driving Center (DIDC) (1)
PO Box 28171
Dubai, United Arab Emirates
Tel.: (971) 48122400
Fax: (971) 48122424
Web Site: www.dubaiinvestments.com
Driver Training Centers
S.I.C.: 8299
N.A.I.C.S.: 611692
Jaffar Al Ansari *(Gen Mgr)*

Dubai Investments Park Development Company LLC (1)
Emirates Road
28171
Dubai, United Arab Emirates (100%)
Tel.: (971) 43379333
Fax: (971) 48851007
E-Mail: infodip@dipark.com
Web Site: www.dipark.com
Miscellaneous Financial Investment Activities
S.I.C.: 6211
N.A.I.C.S.: 523999

Dubai Investments Real Estate Company (1)
PO Box 22727
Dubai, United Arab Emirates (100%)
Tel.: (971) 2328888
Fax: (971) 2328822
E-Mail: info@di-realestate.com
Web Site: www.di-realestate.com
Real Estate Investment Trusts
S.I.C.: 6726
N.A.I.C.S.: 525990
Obobaid Alsalami *(Gen Mgr)*

Edible Oil Company (D) LLC (1)
PO Box 17799
Dubai, United Arab Emirates (70%)
Tel.: (971) 48811160
Fax: (971) 48811125
E-Mail: info@edibleoil.dubai.com
Other Oilseed Processing
S.I.C.: 2079
N.A.I.C.S.: 311224
Alexander Ramos *(Gen Mgr)*

Emirates Building Systems Company LLC (1)
31396
Dubai, United Arab Emirates (51%)
Tel.: (971) 48851122
Fax: (971) 48851211
E-Mail: bsdxb@emirates.net.ae
Web Site: www.ebsl.com
Emp.: 200
Other Building Material Dealers
S.I.C.: 5211
N.A.I.C.S.: 444190
Samir Akra *(Gen Mgr)*

Emirates District Cooling Company LLC (1)
PO Box 9152
Dubai, United Arab Emirates (50%)
Tel.: (971) 48852452
Fax: (971) 48852453
E-Mail: info@emicool.net
Web Site: www.emicool.net
Emp.: 57
Engineering Services
S.I.C.: 8711
N.A.I.C.S.: 541330
Abib Moubadder *(Mng Dir)*

Emirates Extruded Polystyrene LLC (1)
PO Box 28807
Dubai, United Arab Emirates (51%)
Tel.: (971) 48850471
Fax: (971) 48853920
E-Mail: info@eepdubai.com
Web Site: www.dubaiinvestments.com
Emp.: 40
Other Building Material Dealers
S.I.C.: 5211
N.A.I.C.S.: 444190
Malik Arjuna *(Gen Mgr)*

Emirates Extrusions Factory LLC (1)
PO Box 3501
Ajman, United Arab Emirates (100%)

Tel.: (971) 67434163
Fax: (971) 67434625
E-Mail: eef@emirates.net.ae
Web Site: www.emiratesextrusions.com
Emp.: 200
Aluminum Extruded Product Mfr
S.I.C.: 3354
N.A.I.C.S.: 331318
Khalfan Alsueeidi *(Mng Dir)*

Emirates Float Glass LLC (1)
PO Box 8869
Abu Dhabi, United Arab Emirates
Tel.: (971) 25994000
Fax: (971) 25501701
Web Site: www.dubaiinvestments.com
Emp.: 400
Clear Molten Glass Mfr
S.I.C.: 3231
N.A.I.C.S.: 327215
Ghassan Mashal *(Gen Mgr)*

Emirates Glass LLC (1)
PO Box 29769
Dubai, United Arab Emirates (100%)
Tel.: (971) 43471515
Fax: (971) 43471440
E-Mail: emiglass@emirates.net.ae
Web Site: www.emiratesglass.com
Emp.: 300
Glass Product Mfr Made Purchased Glass
S.I.C.: 3231
N.A.I.C.S.: 327215
A. Hiziat *(Gen Mgr)*

Folcra Beach Industrial Company LLC (1)
PO Box 46536
Abu Dhabi, United Arab Emirates (80%)
Tel.: (971) 25510888
Fax: (971) 25511512
E-Mail: info@folcrabeach.com
Web Site: www.dubaiinvestments.com
Emp.: 100
Mfr & Industrial Building Construction
S.I.C.: 1629
N.A.I.C.S.: 236210
Marwan Naman *(Gen Mgr)*

Gulf Dynamic Services LLC (GDS) (1)
Industrial area 17 Al malaiah street no 19 bldg 99
PO Box 1298
Sharjah, United Arab Emirates (70%)
Tel.: (971) 65344424
Fax: (971) 65344481
E-Mail: gds@gdsuae.com
Web Site: www.gdsuae.com
Sales Range: $50-74.9 Million
Emp.: 300
Interior Design Services
S.I.C.: 7389
N.A.I.C.S.: 541410
Norbert Brauneise *(Mgr)*

Gulf Metal Craft (GMC) (1)
PO Box 16893
Jebel Ali, Dubai, United Arab Emirates (10%)
Tel.: (971) 48815151
Fax: (971) 48815163
E-Mail: info@gulfmetalcraft.com
Web Site: www.gulfmetalcraft.com
Sales Range: $10-24.9 Million
Emp.: 125
Architectural Stainless Steel Products Mfr
S.I.C.: 8712
N.A.I.C.S.: 541310
Vasen Abushamleh *(Gen Mgr)*

International Rubber Co. LLC (1)
PO Box 27140
Dubai, United Arab Emirates (51%)
Tel.: (971) 48859880
Fax: (971) 48859890
E-Mail: ircruber@emirates.net.ae
Web Site: www.intrubber.com
Emp.: 100
Synthetic Rubber Mfr
S.I.C.: 2822
N.A.I.C.S.: 325212
Urfi Kidwai *(Gen Mgr)*

Lite Tech Industries LLC (1)
PO Box 60305
Dubai, United Arab Emirates
Tel.: (971) 43331387
Fax: (971) 43331212
E-Mail: litetech@emirates.net.ae
Web Site: www.litetechind.com
Emp.: 100
Commercial Industrial & Institutional Electric Lighting Fixture Mfr
S.I.C.: 3646
N.A.I.C.S.: 335122
Bonniah Pillei *(Gen Mgr)*

Lumi Glass Industries LLC (1)
PO Box 113744
Dubai, United Arab Emirates (67%)
Tel.: (971) 43403919
Fax: (971) 43404515
E-Mail: info@lumiglassindustries.com
Web Site: www.lumiglassindustries.com
Emp.: 150
Glass & Glazing Contractors
S.I.C.: 1793
N.A.I.C.S.: 238150
Ziad Yzaback *(Gen Mgr)*

M/S Gulf Dynamic Switchgear Co. Ltd (1)
BMW Rd
PO Box 6155
Sharjah, United Arab Emirates (100%)
Tel.: (971) 65338568
Fax: (971) 65336383
E-Mail: info@gulfdynamic.com
Web Site: www.gulfdynamic.com
Emp.: 100
Other Lighting Equipment Mfr
S.I.C.: 3648
N.A.I.C.S.: 335129

Marmum Dairy Farm LLC (1)
PO Box 31671
Dubai, United Arab Emirates (100%)
Tel.: (971) 48326440
Fax: (971) 48326432
E-Mail: marmum@emiretes.net.ae
Web Site: www.marmum.ae
Dairy Product (except Dried or Canned) Whslr
S.I.C.: 5143
N.A.I.C.S.: 424430
Waeel Barhaji *(Gen Mgr)*

MSharie LLC (1)
Enoc No1 Building 3rd Floor Oud Mehtha Road
28171
Dubai, United Arab Emirates (100%)
Tel.: (971) 43379333
Fax: (971) 43346547
E-Mail: info@msharie.com
Web Site: www.msharie.com
Miscellaneous Financial Investment Activities
S.I.C.: 6211
N.A.I.C.S.: 523999

National Insulated Blocks Industries (1)
PO Box 62869
Dubai, United Arab Emirates
Tel.: (971) 48851112
Fax: (971) 48851017
E-Mail: admin@insulite.ae
Emp.: 37
Commercial & Institutional Building Construction
S.I.C.: 1542
N.A.I.C.S.: 236220
Deepak Menon *(Gen Mgr)*

Stromek Emirates Foundations LLC (1)
PO Box 62124
Dubai, United Arab Emirates (51%)
Tel.: (971) 43979505
Fax: (971) 43979506
E-Mail: stromek@emirates.net.ae
Web Site: www.stromek.ae
Emp.: 500
Building Equipment & Other Machinery Installation Contractors
S.I.C.: 1711
N.A.I.C.S.: 238220
Aadil Ahmed *(Mng Dir)*

Syscom Emirates LLC (1)
PO Box 49700
Dubai, United Arab Emirates (100%)
Tel.: (971) 43934788
Fax: (971) 43936988
E-Mail: info@syscom.ae
Web Site: www.syscom.ae
Sales Range: $25-49.9 Million
Internal Communications Network Installations & Maintenance Services
S.I.C.: 4899
N.A.I.C.S.: 517919

Technological Laboratory Furniture Manufacturer (LABTEC) (1)
PO Box 4275
Sharjah, United Arab Emirates (70%)
Tel.: (971) 65344480
Fax: (971) 65344481
E-Mail: labtec@labtecllc.com
Web Site: www.labtecllc.com
Emp.: 70
Laboratory Apparatus & Furniture Mfr
S.I.C.: 2599
N.A.I.C.S.: 337127

Thermoset Technologies (Middle East) LLC (1)
PO Box 118157
Dubai, United Arab Emirates (51%)
Tel.: (971) 48852228
Fax: (971) 48852226
E-Mail: info@thermosetme.ae
Web Site: www.thermosetme.ae
Emp.: 35
All Other Professional Scientific & Technical Services
S.I.C.: 7389
N.A.I.C.S.: 541990
N. C. Babu *(Gen Mgr)*

Non-U.S. Subsidiary:

Saudi American Glass Company (1)
PO Box 8418
11482 Riyadh, Saudi Arabia (100%)
Tel.: (966) 12651212
Fax: (966) 12651738
E-Mail: saglass@saglass.com
Web Site: www.saglass.com
Emp.: 250
Architectural Services
S.I.C.: 8712
N.A.I.C.S.: 541310
Chafic Khoury *(Mgr-Ops)*

DUBAI ISLAMIC BANK PSJ

9th Floor DIB Head Office
PO Box 1080
Dubai, United Arab Emirates
Tel.: (971) 46092222
Fax: (971) 42954111
Web Site: www.dib.ae
Year Founded: 1975
DIB—(DFM)
Rev.: $1,368,064,866
Assets: $25,956,363,774
Liabilities: $23,082,182,440
Net Worth: $2,874,181,334
Earnings: $324,480,476
Fiscal Year-end: 12/31/12

Business Description:
Banking Services
S.I.C.: 6029
N.A.I.C.S.: 522110

Personnel:
Mohammad Ibrahim Abdulrahman Alshaibani *(Chm)*
Tariq Humaid Matar Mohd. Altayer *(Vice Chm)*
Abdulla Ali Obaid Alhamli *(CEO)*
Ahmed Fathy Al-Gebali *(CFO)*
Ahmed Ramez *(Sr Officer-Shareholders Rels)*
Kashif Moosa *(Sr VP & Head-Strategy, IR & PMO)*

Board of Directors:
Abdulla Ali Obaid Alhamli
Ahmad Mohammad Saeed Humaidan
Yahya Saeed Ahmad Nasser Lootah
Tariq Humaid Matar Mohd. Altayer

Subsidiaries:

DIB Capital Limited (1)
DIFC Gate East Wing 3rd Floor
Dubai, United Arab Emirates
Tel.: (971) 43634100
Fax: (971) 43620548
E-Mail: Private.Equity@dibcapital.com
Web Site: www.dibcapital.com
Investment Banking Services
S.I.C.: 6211
N.A.I.C.S.: 523110
Abdulla Al Hamli *(Chm)*
Mohamed Saeed Al Sharif *(CEO)*
Syed Zamir Bukhari *(CFO)*

Naseej Fabric Manufacturing L.L.C. (1)
Al Bashar Area
PO Box 52881
Dubai, United Arab Emirates (99%)
Tel.: (971) 43470808
Fax: (971) 43470201
E-Mail: naseej@uitedarabemirares.ae
Emp.: 190
Fabricated Metal Product Mfr
S.I.C.: 3499
N.A.I.C.S.: 332999
Fabri Luthvi *(Gen Mgr)*

Tamweel PJSC (1)
Business Avenue Building Port Saeed
PO Box 111555
Deira, United Arab Emirates (58.3%)
Tel.: (971) 42944400
Fax: (971) 42944331
E-Mail: tamweel@tamweel.ae
Web Site: www.tamweel.ae
TAMWEEL—(DFM)
Rev.: $164,204,289
Assets: $2,979,517,988
Liabilities: $2,353,781,339
Net Worth: $625,736,649
Earnings: $19,727,062
Emp.: 200
Fiscal Year-end: 12/31/12
Real Estate Financial & Investment Services
S.I.C.: 6159
N.A.I.C.S.: 522292
Abdulla Ali AlHamli *(Chm)*
Mohamed Abdulla Al Nahdi *(Vice Chm)*
Varun Sood *(Acting CEO)*
Guarav Agarwal *(CFO)*
Hamid Chinoy *(COO)*
Sohail Akbar *(Chief Risk Officer)*
Nasser Abdullah Alawadi *(Chief Bus Dev Officer)*

Non-U.S. Subsidiaries:

Jordan Dubai Islamic Bank (1)
Jabal Amman 2nd Circle Al Koliyah Al Elmiyah Al Islamiyah Street
PO Box 1982
Amman, 11118, Jordan
Tel.: (962) 64602200
Fax: (962) 64647821
E-Mail: info@jdib.com
Web Site: www.jdib.jo
JDIB—(AMM)
Sales Range: $10-24.9 Million
Emp.: 106
Banking Services
S.I.C.: 6029
N.A.I.C.S.: 522110
Ismail Tahboub *(Chm)*
Mohammed Sa'aid Al Sharif *(Deputy Chm)*
Sami Husam Eddin Sabri Al Afghani *(CEO)*
Ahmed Abdullah Ahmed Abdullah *(Deputy CEO & Chief Risk Officer)*
Rami Z. Al Khayyat *(Deputy CEO & Chief-Corp Banking)*
Hani Al-Zrari *(Deputy CEO & Chief-Ops & IT)*
Mohammad Mohammad Fayyad *(Deputy CEO & Chief-Treasury & Investment)*
Haitham Marouf Hamad Jouher *(Deputy CEO & Chief-HR)*
Taj Omran Khomosh *(Deputy CEO & Chief-Retail Banking)*

DUBAI ISLAMIC INSURANCE & REINSURANCE COMPANY P.S.C

Gulf Tower - B1 Mezzanine Floor
Oud Metha Road
PO Box 157
Dubai, United Arab Emirates
Tel.: (971) 4 3193111
Fax: (971) 4 3193112
Web Site: www.aman-diir.ae
Year Founded: 2002
AMAN—(EMI)

Dubai Islamic Insurance & Reinsurance Company P.S.C—(Continued)

Rev.: $134,417,824
Assets: $137,083,559
Liabilities: $98,319,206
Net Worth: $38,764,354
Earnings: ($1,240,525)
Fiscal Year-end: 12/31/12

Business Description:
Insurance Services
S.I.C.: 6411
N.A.I.C.S.: 524298

Personnel:
Mohammed Omair Yosef Al Muhairi *(Chm)*
Husein Mohammed Salem
Mohammed Al Meeza *(CEO & Mng Dir)*
Rashid Hussain Al Meeza *(Deputy COO)*
Rached Diab *(COO)*
Mohammed Iqbal Mankani *(COO)*
Ahmad Hamad Al Suwaidi *(Chief Comml Officer & Chief Dev Officer)*

Board of Directors:
Mohammed Omair Yosef Al Muhairi
Khalifa Hassan Al Hammadi
Mohamed Omair Yousef Al Mheiri
Naser Al-Falah Al Qahtani
Khalifa Hassan Ali Saleh Alhammadi
Abdullah Saad Alkhnbashi
Mohammed Ali Hosne

DUBAI NATIONAL INSURANCE & REINSURANCE PSC

Dubai National Insurance Bldg Fl 7 & 9 Opp to Deira City Ctr
Next to Flora Creek Hotel, Dubai, United Arab Emirates
Tel.: (971) 42956700
Fax: (971) 42956711
Web Site: www.dnirc.com
DNIR—(DFM)
Sales Range: $50-74.9 Million
Emp.: 70

Business Description:
Insurance & Reinsurance Services
S.I.C.: 6311
N.A.I.C.S.: 524113

Personnel:
Khalaf Ahmad Al Habtoor *(Chm)*
Sultan Ahmad Al Habtoor *(Deputy Chm)*

Board of Directors:
Khalaf Ahmad Al Habtoor
Mohamed Al Falasy
Mohammed Khalaf Al Habtoor
Sultan Ahmad Al Habtoor
Ahmed Ateeq Al Qemzi

DUBAI REFRESHMENTS (P.S.C.)

PO Box 420
Dubai, United Arab Emirates
Tel.: (971) 43393000
Fax: (971) 43381684
E-Mail: info@pepsidrc.ae
Web Site: www.pepsidrc.com
Year Founded: 1959
DRC—(DFM)
Sls.: $273,301,926
Assets: $258,179,061
Liabilities: $76,985,841
Net Worth: $181,193,220
Earnings: $44,246,125
Fiscal Year-end: 12/31/12

Business Description:
Soft Drinks Mfr & Distr
S.I.C.: 2086
N.A.I.C.S.: 312111

Personnel:
Ahmad Eisa Al Serkal *(Chm)*
Ali Humaid Al Owais *(Vice Chm)*
Mana Mohammed Saeed Al Mulla *(Mng Dir)*
Neeraj Vohra *(CFO)*

Board of Directors:
Ahmad Eisa Al Serkal
Muhannad Saif Abdul Rahman Al Ashram
Mohamed Hadi Ahmed Al Hussaini
Mana Mohammed Saeed Al Mulla
Ali Humaid Al Owais
Mohamed AbdulAziz Al Owais
Ibrahim AbdulRazaq Mohd Ustadi

Plant:

Dubai Refreshments (P.S.C.) - Dubai Main Production Facility **(1)**
Sheikh Zayed Rd 2nd Interchange beside Al Yousuf Motors
Dubai, United Arab Emirates
Tel.: (971) 4 3393000
Fax: (971) 4 3381684
E-Mail: pepsidrc@pepsidrc.ae
Web Site: www.pepsidrc.com
Soft Drink Mfr
S.I.C.: 2086
N.A.I.C.S.: 312111

DUBAI TOURISM & COMMERCE MARKETING

PO Box 594
Dubai, United Arab Emirates
Tel.: (971) 42230000
Fax: (971) 42821131
E-Mail: info@dubaitourism.ae
Web Site: www.dubaitourism.ae
Emp.: 250

Business Description:
Tourism & Commerce Promotor
S.I.C.: 8621
N.A.I.C.S.: 813920

Personnel:
Mohammed bin Rashid Al Maktoum *(Chm)*
Khalid A. Sulayem *(Dir Gen)*

DUBAI WORLD CORPORATION

PO Box 17000
Dubai, United Arab Emirates
Tel.: (971) 43903800
Fax: (971) 43903806
E-Mail: info@dubaiworld.ae
Web Site: www.dubaiworld.ae
Emp.: 50,000

Business Description:
Investment Holding Company
S.I.C.: 6719
N.A.I.C.S.: 551112

Personnel:
Ahmed Saeed Al Maktoum *(Chm)*

Board of Directors:
Ahmed Saeed Al Maktoum
Mohammad Ibrahim Al Shaibani
Soon Young Chang
Abdul Rahim Hassan Al Rais
Hamad Mubarak Bu Amim
Abdul Rahman Saleh Al Saleh

Holdings:

DP World Limited **(1)**
5th Floor JAFZA 17 Jebel Ali Free Zone
PO Box 17000
Dubai, United Arab Emirates
Tel.: (971) 4 881 1110
Fax: (971) 4 881 1331
E-Mail: info@dpworld.com
Web Site: www.dpworld.ae
DPW—(NASDAQDBAI)
Sales Range: $1-4.9 Billion
Emp.: 30,000
Marine Terminal Operations & Logistics Services
S.I.C.: 4491
N.A.I.C.S.: 488310
Ahmed Sulayem *(Chm)*
John L. Parker *(Vice Chm)*
Mohammed Sharaf *(CEO)*
Mohammed Al Muallem *(Mng Dir & Sr VP-UAE Reg)*
Yuvraj Narayan *(CFO)*
Anil Wats *(COO & Exec VP)*
Yousif Almutawa *(CIO)*
Olivier Schwartz *(Gen Counsel & Sr VP)*
Adnan Al Abbar *(Sr VP-Plng & Dev)*
Suhail Al Banna *(Sr VP-Govt Rels)*
Hassan Hadi *(Sr VP-R&D)*
Sarah Lockie *(Sr VP-Corp Comm)*
Paul Hayward Smith *(Sr VP-HR)*
Anwar Wajdi *(Sr VP-Comml & Corp Strategy)*
Robin Windley *(Sr VP-Human Capital)*
John Woollacott *(Sr VP-Bus Dev)*

U.S. Subsidiaries:

DP World Americas Ro, Inc. **(2)**
5605 Carnegie Blvd Ste 420
Charlotte, NC 28209 NC
Tel.: (704) 246-0343
Fax: (704) 246-0344
E-Mail: info.americas@dpworld.com
Web Site: www.dpworld.com
Emp.: 10
Marine Terminal Development & Operation
S.I.C.: 4491
N.A.I.C.S.: 488310
Matthew Leech *(Sr VP & Mng Dir-Americas)*

Non-U.S. Subsidiaries:

DP World Limited **(2)**
16 Palace Sreet
London, SW1E 5JQ, United Kingdom UK
Tel.: (44) 2079014000
Telex: 885551
Fax: (44) 02079014015
E-Mail: simion.haoo@dpworld.com
Web Site: www.dpworld.com
Marine Terminal Operations & Logistics Services
S.I.C.: 4491
N.A.I.C.S.: 488310
Flemming Dalgaard *(Sr VP & Mng Dir)*

Subsidiaries:

P&O Ferries Holdings Limited **(3)**
Channel House Channel View Road
Dover, CT17 9TJ, United Kingdom UK
Tel.: (44) 1304863000
Telex: 739156
Fax: (44) 1304863223
E-Mail: communications@poferries.com
Web Site: www.poferries.com
Ferry Operator
S.I.C.: 4481
N.A.I.C.S.: 483114
Brian Rees *(Head-Press & PR)*
Helen Deeble *(CEO)*
Karl Howarth *(CFO)*
Andrew Reeves *(CIO)*
Susan Kitchin *(Sec)*

Subsidiaries:

P&O Ferries Ltd. **(4)**
Channel House Channel View Rd
Dover, Kent, CT17 9TJ, United Kingdom UK
Tel.: (44) 1304863875
Telex: 965104 TTDFLE G
Fax: (44) 1304863439
E-Mail: freightsales.dover@poferries.com
Web Site: www.poferriesfreight.com
Ferry Operator
S.I.C.: 4731
N.A.I.C.S.: 488510
Helen Deeble *(CEO)*

P&O Ferrymasters Limited **(4)**
Wherstaid Park
Whestaird, Ipswich, IP9 2WJ, United Kingdom UK
Tel.: (44) 473585200
Fax: (44) 473786390
E-Mail: enquiries@pofm.com
Web Site: www.poferrymasters.com
Emp.: 85
Cargo Handling
S.I.C.: 4491
N.A.I.C.S.: 488320
Bis Belder *(Mng Dir)*

Affiliate:

Wysepower Limited **(3)**
Lincoln Road
High Wycombe, Bucks, HP12 3RH, United Kingdom
Tel.: (44) 1494560900
Fax: (44) 1494 560889
E-Mail: webmaster@wysepower.com
Web Site: www.wysepower.com
Emp.: 100
Contractors Hire & Support Services
S.I.C.: 1799
N.A.I.C.S.: 238990
Mell Curran *(Mng Dir)*

U.S. Subsidiaries:

Boston Wharf Company **(3)**
253 Summer St
Boston, MA 02210-1114
Tel.: (617) 426-6034
Fax: (617) 330-5113
Web Site: www.bostonwharf.com
Emp.: 22
Lessors of Office Space
S.I.C.: 6512
N.A.I.C.S.: 531120

Denver Technological Center **(3)**
5750 DTC Pkwy Ste 200
Greenwood Village, CO 80111-3226
Tel.: (303) 773-1700
Fax: (303) 740-6954
Web Site: www.dtcmeridian.com
Emp.: 40
Real Estate Operators
S.I.C.: 6552
N.A.I.C.S.: 237210

DP World Logistics (Hong Kong) Ltd. **(2)**
13th Floor ATL Logistics Centre B Berth 3
Kwai Chung, China (Hong Kong) HK
Tel.: (852) 2489 5096
Fax: (852) 2418 9376
E-Mail: dpwasia@dpworld.com
Logistics, Distribution & Transportation Services
S.I.C.: 4731
N.A.I.C.S.: 541614

DP World Private Limited **(2)**
Darabshaw House Level 1 Narottam Morarji Road
Ballard Estate, Mumbai, 400 001, India In
Tel.: (91) 2222610570
Web Site: www.dpworld.com
Emp.: 21
Marine Terminal Operations & Logistics Services
S.I.C.: 4491
N.A.I.C.S.: 488310
Anil Singh *(Mng Dir-Indian Subcontinent & Sr VP)*

Non-U.S. Subsidiary:

MacKinnon MacKenzie & Co. of Pakistan (Pvt.) Ltd. **(3)**
MacKinnons Bldg II Chundrigar Rd
PO Box 4679
Karachi, 74000, Pakistan
Tel.: (92) 2124130417
Fax: (92) 212424115
E-Mail: karachi@mackpak.com
Web Site: www.mackpak.com
Shipping Agents
S.I.C.: 4731
N.A.I.C.S.: 488510

DP World **(2)**
Al Slaimanyah Prince Abdulazzia Bin M. Jawly Street
PO Box 57207
Riyadh, 11574, Saudi Arabia
Tel.: (966) 14623550
Fax: (966) 14710052
E-Mail: admincom.jcst@dpworld.com
Web Site: webapps.dpworld.com
Emp.: 2,000
Logistics, Distribution & Transportation Services
S.I.C.: 4731
N.A.I.C.S.: 541614
Ahmed Al Amoudi *(Gen Mgr)*

Drydocks World LLC **(1)**
PO Box 8988
Dubai, United Arab Emirates AE
Tel.: (971) 43450626
Fax: (971) 43450116
E-Mail: drydocks@drydocks.gov.ae
Web Site: www.drydocks.gov.ae

Ship Building, Repairing & Offshore Engineering Services
S.I.C.: 3731
N.A.I.C.S.: 336611
Khamis Juma Buamim *(Chm)*
Stella Toresse *(Sec & Head-Legal)*

Istithmar PJSC (1)
6th Floor Bldg 4 The Galleries
Downtown Jebel Ali
PO Box 17000, Dubai, United Arab Emirates AE
Tel.: (971) 4 364 4239
Fax: (971) 4 364 4292
E-Mail: info@istithmarworld.com
Web Site: www.istithmarworld.com
Emp.: 50
Equity Investment Firm
S.I.C.: 6211
N.A.I.C.S.: 523999
Ahmed Sulayem *(Chm)*
Hamza Mustafa *(CEO)*
Sandesh Panhare *(Mng Dir & Head-Private Equity)*
Shuja Ali *(Mng Dir)*
Binod Narsimhan *(CFO)*
Andy Watson *(Chief Investment Officer)*
Nick Hornung *(Gen Counsel)*

U.S. Holdings:

Hotel Washington, Inc. (2)
515 15th St NW
Washington, DC 20004-1099
Tel.: (202) 638-5900
Fax: (202) 638-4275
E-Mail: sales@hotelwashington.com
Web Site: www.hotelwashington.com
Luxury Hotel
S.I.C.: 7011
N.A.I.C.S.: 721110

Loehmann's Holdings Inc. (2)
2500 Halsey St
Bronx, NY 10461 DE
Tel.: (718) 409-2000
E-Mail: insider@loehmanns.com
Web Site: www.loehmanns.com
Sales Range: $350-399.9 Million
Emp.: 1,900
Holding Company; Women's & Men's Discount Branded Apparel & Accessories Stores Owner & Operator
S.I.C.: 6719
N.A.I.C.S.: 551112
Arthur E. Reiner *(Chm)*
Gerald Politz *(Pres)*
Steven M. Newman *(CEO)*
Joan Durkin *(CFO & Sr VP-Fin)*
Joe Melvin *(COO)*
Frank Lamolino *(CIO & Sr VP)*
Nancy Straface *(Sr VP-HR)*

Subsidiary:

Loehmann's, Inc. (3)
2500 Halsey St
Bronx, NY 10461 DE
Tel.: (718) 409-2000
E-Mail: insider@loehmanns.com
Web Site: www.loehmanns.com
Women's & Men's Discount Branded Apparel & Accessories Stores Operator
S.I.C.: 5621
N.A.I.C.S.: 448120
Jerald S. Politzer *(CEO)*
Frank Lamolino *(CIO & Sr VP)*
Nancy Straface *(Sr VP-HR)*

Non-U.S. Subsidiary:

P&O Estates Ltd. (2)
16 Palace St
London, SW1Y 5EJ, United Kingdom
Tel.: (44) 2079014200
Fax: (44) 2079014027
E-Mail: info@poestates.com
Web Site: www.poestates.com
Emp.: 50
International Property Management
S.I.C.: 6531
N.A.I.C.S.: 531390
Ian Pirnett *(Mng Dir)*

Subsidiary:

P&O Developments Ltd. (3)
4 Carlton Gardens
Pall Mall, London, SW1Y 5AB, United Kingdom UK
Tel.: (44) 2078395611
Fax: (44) 2079302098
E-Mail: info@podevelopments.com
Web Site: www.podevelopments.com
Emp.: 20
Commercial Property Development
S.I.C.: 6531
N.A.I.C.S.: 531312

Limitless PJSC (1)
Al Khail Road
PO Box 261919
Dubai, United Arab Emirates AE
Tel.: (971) 4 435 8888
Fax: (971) 4 435 8889
E-Mail: info@limitless.com
Web Site: www.limitless.com
Residential & Commercial Real Estate Developer
S.I.C.: 6552
N.A.I.C.S.: 237210
Ali Rashid Ahmed Lootah *(Chm)*
Mohammed Rashed Dhabeah *(CEO)*

Nakheel PVT JSC (1)
PO Box 17777
Dubai, United Arab Emirates
Tel.: (971) 4 390 3333
Fax: (971) 4 390 3314
E-Mail: info@nakheel.com
Web Site: www.nakheel.com
Emp.: 1,500
Property Development Services
S.I.C.: 1629
N.A.I.C.S.: 237990
Ali Rashid Ahmed Lootah *(Chm)*
Chris O'Donnell *(CEO)*
Saeed Ahmed Saeed *(Mng Dir)*

DUBEK LTD.

9 Martin Gehl Street
49512 Petah Tiqwa, Israel
Tel.: (972) 39265050
Fax: (972) 39265183
E-Mail: marketing@dubek.co.il
Web Site: www.dubek.co.il
Year Founded: 1935
Sales Range: $25-49.9 Million
Emp.: 265
Business Description:
Tobacco Products Mfr & Marketer Import Export
S.I.C.: 2131
N.A.I.C.S.: 312230
Personnel:
Roy Gehm *(Chm & CEO)*
Shmuel Kalush *(CFO)*
Subsidiaries:

Israel Tobacco Co. (M.T.) Ltd. (1)
9 Martin Gehl Street Fl 1
Petah Tiqwa, 49512, Israel
Tel.: (972) 39265050
Fax: (972) 39265142
E-Mail: korint@dubeknocoil.com
Web Site: www.dubek.com
Emp.: 300
Cigarette Mfr
S.I.C.: 2131
N.A.I.C.S.: 312230
Gehl Roy *(Mgr)*

Jerusalem Cigarette Co. Ltd. (1)
Old Jericho Rd
Jerusalem, 97913, Israel
Tel.: (972) 22799777
Fax: (972) 9702799770
E-Mail: iform@jerucig.com
Web Site: www.JeruCig.com
Emp.: 120
Cigarette Mfr
S.I.C.: 2131
N.A.I.C.S.: 312230
Mohammad Alami *(Chm & Gen Mgr)*

DUBRAC TP

36 rue du Marechal Lyantey
93200 Saint Denis, France
Tel.: (33) 149711090
Fax: (33) 148268353
Web Site: www.dubrac.com
Rev.: $23,800,000
Emp.: 200
Business Description:
Highway & Street Construction
S.I.C.: 1611
N.A.I.C.S.: 237310
Personnel:
Francis Dubrac *(Chm)*

DUBREUIL AUTOMOBILES

4 Place Jean Jaures
27400 Louviers, France
Tel.: (33) 232400228
Web Site: concessions.peugeot.fr/louviers/accueil/bienvenue-chez-peugeot/site-Louviers
Sales Range: $25-49.9 Million
Emp.: 84
Business Description:
Automobile Sales
S.I.C.: 5511
N.A.I.C.S.: 441110
Personnel:
Sylvain Dubreuil *(Dir-Pur)*

DUBUS INDUSTRIES

68 rue du General Patton
Malesherbes, 45330 Fontainebleau, France
Tel.: (33) 238327575
Fax: (33) 238327580
Web Site: www.dubus-fr.com
Sls.: $20,200,000
Emp.: 105
Business Description:
Woodworking Machinery
S.I.C.: 3554
N.A.I.C.S.: 333243
Personnel:
Thierry Nouchet *(Pres)*

DUC LONG GIA LAI GROUP JSC

02 Dang Tran Con St Tra Ba Ward
Pleiku, Gia Lai, Vietnam
Tel.: (84) 59 3 748 367
Fax: (84) 59 3 747 366
E-Mail: duclong@duclonggroup.com
Web Site: www.duclonggroup.com
Year Founded: 1995
DLG—(HOSE)
Business Description:
Hotel Management Services
S.I.C.: 7011
N.A.I.C.S.: 721110
Personnel:
Phap Bui *(Chm)*
Dinh Trac Nguyen *(Vice Chm, CEO & Gen Dir)*
Board of Directors:
Phap Bui
Thanh Do
Dinh Trac Nguyen
Hoang Chau Vo
Thi Hai Vu

DUC S.A.

Grande Rue
89771 Chailley, Cedex, France
Tel.: (33) 386435443
Fax: (33) 386435454
E-Mail: contact@duc.fr
Web Site: www.duc.fr
DUC—(EUR)
Sales Range: $200-249.9 Million
Emp.: 949
Business Description:
Chicken & Poultry Products Production, Packaging, Slaughtering & Sales
S.I.C.: 2015
N.A.I.C.S.: 311615
Personnel:
Francois Gontier *(Chm)*
Joel Marchand *(CEO & Dir Gen)*
Board of Directors:
Francois Gontier
Guenole Alix
Pascal Breton
Jean-Pierre Chareyron
Frederic Doulcet
Jean-Michel Jannez
Joel Marchand
Andre Msika

DUCATEX S.A.

Ana Ipatescu Street No 44
077120 Jilava, Ilfov, Romania
Tel.: (40) 21 457 00 16
Fax: (40) 21 457 00 18
E-Mail: office@ducatex.ro
Web Site: www.ducatex.ro
GUFX—(BUC)
Rev.: $4,672,660
Assets: $4,109,728
Liabilities: $2,731,261
Net Worth: $1,378,468
Earnings: $15,905
Emp.: 105
Fiscal Year-end: 12/31/12
Business Description:
Rubber Products Mfr
S.I.C.: 3069
N.A.I.C.S.: 326299
Personnel:
Catalin Georgian Militaru *(Pres)*
Board of Directors:
Catalin Georgian Militaru
Cornelia Rebosapca

DUCATT NV

Balendijk 161
Lommel, 3920, Belgium
Tel.: (32) 11 559 300
Fax: (32) 11 559 310
E-Mail: mail@ducatt.com
Web Site: www.ducatt.com
Business Description:
Glass Mfr
S.I.C.: 3229
N.A.I.C.S.: 327212
Personnel:
Danny Berrens *(CFO)*
Non-U.S. Subsidiary:

Centrosolar Glas GmbH & Co. KG (1)
Siemensstrasse 3
90766 Furth, Germany
Tel.: (49) 911950980
Fax: (49) 91195098519
E-Mail: info@centrosolarglas.com
Web Site: www.centrosolarglas.com
Emp.: 320
Solar Components Mfr
S.I.C.: 3674
N.A.I.C.S.: 334413
Ralf Ballasch *(Mng Dir)*

DUCKYANG INDUSTRY CO., LTD.

945 Yeonam Dong Buk Gu
683370 Ulsan, Korea (South)
Tel.: (82) 522191114
Fax: (82) 522873130
Web Site: www.duckyang.co.kr
024900—(KRS)
Sales Range: $350-399.9 Million
Business Description:
Automotive Interior Products Mfr
S.I.C.: 3714
N.A.I.C.S.: 336390
Personnel:
Yonseong Park *(Pres)*

DUDLEY BUILDING SOCIETY

Dudley House Stone Street
Dudley, W Midlands, DY1 1NP, United Kingdom
Tel.: (44) 1384231414
Fax: (44) 1384233250

Dudley Building Society—(Continued)

E-Mail: enquiries@dudleybuildingsociety.co.uk
Web Site: www.dudleybuildingsociety.co.uk
Rev.: $16,754,688
Assets: $504,313,096
Liabilities: $7,981,732
Net Worth: $496,331,365
Earnings: $186,356
Emp.: 60
Fiscal Year-end: 03/31/13
Business Description:
Mortgage Lending Services
S.I.C.: 6163
N.A.I.C.S.: 522310
Personnel:
J. R. Wood *(CEO)*
S. Fennell *(Sec)*
Board of Directors:
A. East
J. R. D. Anton
J. N. Bland
P. E. Doona
D. A. Gamble
K. A. Langley
D. J. Milner
J. R. Wood

DUET GROUP

Level 15 55 Hunter Street
Sydney, NSW, 2000, Australia
Mailing Address:
GPO Box 5282
Sydney, NSW, 2001, Australia
Tel.: (61) 282242701
Fax: (61) 282242799
E-Mail: duet@duet.net.au
Web Site: www.duet.net.au
DUE—(ASX OTC)
Rev.: $1,368,679,551
Assets: $8,863,523,192
Liabilities: $7,277,395,930
Net Worth: $1,586,127,263
Earnings: $20,417,865
Emp.: 6
Fiscal Year-end: 06/30/13
Business Description:
Investors Services
S.I.C.: 6211
N.A.I.C.S.: 523110
Personnel:
John Stuart Hugh Roberts *(Chm)*
David James Bartholomew *(CEO)*
Jason Conroy *(CFO)*
Tayfun Ozturk *(COO)*
Pierre Bruyant *(Chief Risk Officer)*
Tue Sando *(Gen Counsel)*
Leanne Pickering *(Sec & Gen Mgr-Legal & Compliance)*
Board of Directors:
Douglas James Halley
John Stuart Hugh Roberts
Ron Finlay
Shirley In't Veld
Emma Stein
Duncan Sutherland
Subsidiaries:

DBNGP Holdings Pty Ltd (1)
Level 6 12-14 The Esplanade
Perth, WA, 6000, Australia
Tel.: (61) 892234300
Fax: (61) 892234301
Emp.: 230
Oil & Gas Exploration Services
S.I.C.: 1389
N.A.I.C.S.: 213112
Stuart Johnston *(CEO)*

DBNGP (WA) Nominees Pty Ltd (1)
Level 6 12-14 The Esp
Perth, WA, 6000, Australia
Tel.: (61) 892234300
Fax: (61) 892234301
E-Mail: s.heasman@guet.net.au
Natural Gas Transmission Services
S.I.C.: 4922
N.A.I.C.S.: 486210

DBNGP (WA) Transmission Pty Ltd (1)
Level 6 12-14 The Esplanade
Perth, WA, 6000, Australia
Tel.: (61) 892234300
Fax: (61) 892234301
Natural Gas Pipeline Construction Services
S.I.C.: 1623
N.A.I.C.S.: 237120
Anthony Cribb *(Gen Mgr)*

DUET Investment Holdings Limited (1)
Level 11 1 Martin Pl
Sydney, NSW, 2000, Australia
Tel.: (61) 282324491
Fax: (61) 282324713
Web Site: www.duet.com
Emp.: 12
Investment Management Services
S.I.C.: 6282
N.A.I.C.S.: 523920
David Bartholomew *(Gen Mgr)*

Energy Partnership (Gas) Pty Ltd (1)
43-45 The Centreway
PO Box 449
Mount Waverley, VIC, 3149, Australia
Tel.: (61) 385407889
Fax: (61) 388469999
Web Site: www.multinetgas.com.su
Emp.: 1
Natural Gas Distribution Services
S.I.C.: 4924
N.A.I.C.S.: 221210
David Bartholomew *(CEO)*

United Energy Distribution Holdings Pty Ltd (1)
1 3 501 Blackburn Rd
Locked Bag 7000
Mount Waverley, VIC, 3149, Australia
Tel.: (61) 385449000
Fax: (61) 385407889
Emp.: 3,000
Electricity Distribution Services
S.I.C.: 4911
N.A.I.C.S.: 221122
Hugh Gleason *(Mng Dir)*

United Energy Distribution Pty Ltd (1)
C/O Jemena
Locked Bag 7000
Mount Waverley, VIC, 3149, Australia
Tel.: (61) 385449000
Fax: (61) 385407889
Web Site: www.unitedenergy.com.au
Electricity Distribution Services
S.I.C.: 4911
N.A.I.C.S.: 221122

DUFAYLITE DEVELOPMENTS LIMITED

Cromwell Rd
Saint Neots, Cambs, PE19 1QW, United Kingdom
Tel.: (44) 1480215000
Fax: (44) 1480405526
E-Mail: enquiries@dufaylite.com
Web Site: www.dufaylite.com
Year Founded: 1955
Emp.: 75
Business Description:
Paper Honeycomb Materials for Doors & Panels, Packaging & Fire Protection Products
S.I.C.: 2493
N.A.I.C.S.: 321219
Personnel:
Tony Moscrop *(Chm)*
Mike Burnell *(Mng Dir)*

DUFERCO S.A.

Via Bagutti 9
CH 6900 Lugano, Switzerland
Tel.: (41) 918225600
Fax: (41) 918225700
E-Mail: info@duferco.com
Web Site: www.duferco.com
Year Founded: 1979
Emp.: 360
Business Description:
Trader of Steel Products, Tin Plate & Special Steels; Producer, Transformer & Distr of Steel Products
S.I.C.: 3312
N.A.I.C.S.: 331110
Personnel:
Bruno Bolfo *(Chm)*
Bob Brannan *(Mng Dir)*
Benedict J. Sciortino *(Mng Dir)*
Board of Directors:
Bruno Bolfo
Massimo Bolfo
Libert Froidmont
Antonio Gozzi
Olivier Gutt
Benedict J. Sciortino
Robert Stein
Pascal Verpoorten
U.S. Subsidiary:

Duferco Steel Inc. (1)
Metro Park S 100 Matawan Rd Ste 400
Matawan, NJ 07747-3916
Tel.: (732) 566-3130
Fax: (732) 583-9406
Toll Free: (888) 783-3588
E-Mail: duferco@duferconj.com
Web Site: www.duferco.com
Sales Range: $400-449.9 Million
Emp.: 40
Steel Roll Products Whslr
S.I.C.: 5051
N.A.I.C.S.: 423510
Joseph Deverter *(Pres)*
Mike Vignale *(Sr VP)*

U.S. Joint Venture:

Kreher Steel Company, LLC (1)
1550 25th Ave
Melrose Park, IL 60160-1801 NY
Tel.: (708) 345-8180
Fax: (708) 345-8293
Toll Free: (800) 323-0745
E-Mail: chicago@kreher.com
Web Site: www.kreher.com
Sales Range: $50-74.9 Million
Emp.: 110
Distr & Marketing of Steel Import Export
S.I.C.: 5051
N.A.I.C.S.: 423510
Joseph L. Druzak *(Pres & CEO)*

Subsidiary:

Kreher Wire Processing, Inc. (2)
34822 Goddard Rd
Romulus, MI 48174-3406
Tel.: (734) 941-9500
Fax: (763) 941-5100
E-Mail: info@krehersteel.com
Web Site: www.krehersteel.com
Emp.: 20
Mfr. Of Metal Products
S.I.C.: 5051
N.A.I.C.S.: 423510
Fred Smith *(Gen Mgr)*

DUFRY AG

Brunngasslein 12
CH - 4010 Basel, Switzerland
Tel.: (41) 61 266 44 44
Fax: (41) 61 261 77 71
E-Mail: headoffice@dufry.ch
Web Site: www.dufry.com
Year Founded: 1865
DUFN—(BRAZ OTC SWX)
Sls.: $3,304,985,772
Assets: $3,805,250,592
Liabilities: $2,329,604,288
Net Worth: $1,475,646,304
Earnings: $170,748,424
Emp.: 14,361
Fiscal Year-end: 12/31/12
Business Description:
International Travel Retailer
S.I.C.: 4724
N.A.I.C.S.: 561510
Personnel:
Juan Carlos Torres Carretero *(Chm)*
Julian Diaz Gonzalez *(CEO)*
Andreas Schneiter *(CFO)*
Jose Antonio Gea *(COO)*
Dante Marro *(Pres-Europe, Africa & Asia)*
Pascal C. Duclos *(Gen Counsel)*
Board of Directors:
Juan Carlos Torres Carretero
Jorge Born
Xavier Bouton
Joaquin Moya-Angeler Cabrera
James Cohen
Jose Lucas Ferreira de Melo
Julian Diaz Gonzalez
Luis Andres Holzer Neumann
Subsidiaries:

Dufry BaBasel Mulhouse Ltd. (1)
Basel Lulhouse 80
Euro Airport, 4030 Basel, Switzerland
Tel.: (41) 613252880
Fax: (41) 613253945
Emp.: 60
Commercial Products Retailer
S.I.C.: 5099
N.A.I.C.S.: 423990
Christian Rahn *(Mgr-Retail)*

Dufry Holdings & Investments AG (1)
Hardstrasse 95
Basel, 4052, Switzerland
Tel.: (41) 612664444
Fax: (41) 612664573
Emp.: 130
Investment Management Services
S.I.C.: 6211
N.A.I.C.S.: 523999
Julian Diaz Gonzalez *(CEO)*

Dufry Management Ltd. (1)
Brunngasslein 12
Basel, CH 4020, Switzerland
Tel.: (41) 61 266 4444
Fax: (41) 61 266 44 83
E-Mail: headoffice@dufry.ch
Web Site: www.dufry.ch
Emp.: 140
Business Management Services
S.I.C.: 7389
N.A.I.C.S.: 561499
Xavier Rossinyol *(COO-Europe, Asia & Africa)*

Dufry Samnaun Ltd. (1)
Plan Bell
Samnaun, Graubunden, 7563, Switzerland
Tel.: (41) 818618020
Fax: (41) 818618021
Emp.: 5
Commercial Products Retailer
S.I.C.: 5311
N.A.I.C.S.: 452111

Dufry Travel Retail Ltd. (1)
Hardstrasse 95
4052 Basel, Switzerland
Tel.: (41) 612664444
Fax: (41) 612617771
Emp.: 30
Travel Magazines & Books Retailer
S.I.C.: 5192
N.A.I.C.S.: 424920
Gulian Biaz *(CEO)*

U.S. Subsidiary:

Hudson News Company (1)
1 Meadowlands Plz
East Rutherford, NJ 07073 NJ
Tel.: (201) 867-3600
Fax: (201) 867-0067
E-Mail: info@hudsongroup.com
Web Site: www.hudsongroup.com
Emp.: 1,600
Distributor of Magazines & Books
S.I.C.: 5192
N.A.I.C.S.: 424920
Joseph DiDomizio *(Pres & CEO)*
Adrian Bartella *(CFO)*
Gary MacRae *(Sr VP & CIO)*
Roger Fordyce *(Exec VP & COO-Ops)*
Brian Quinn *(Exec VP & COO-Ops)*

Jay Marshall *(Gen Counsel)*
Michael Mullaney *(Exec VP-Bus Strategy & Dev)*
Hope Remoundos *(Exec VP-Sls & Mktg)*
Tom Kornacki *(Sr VP-Food & Beverage)*
Michael Levy *(Sr VP & Chief Mdsg Officer)*
Steven L. Silver *(Sr VP-Design, Facilities & Store Dev)*
Bill Wolf *(Sr VP-Fin)*
Rick Yockelson *(Sr VP-People & Admin)*

Non-U.S. Subsidiaries:

Dufry France (1)
Nice Cote d'Azur Airport
Nice, France
Toll Free: 8666697978
Web Site: www.dufry.com
Sales Range: $10-24.9 Million
Emp.: 70
Travel Retailer
S.I.C.: 4729
N.A.I.C.S.: 561599
Xavier Rossinyol *(COO-Europe, Africa & Asia)*

Dufry Shop Finance Limited Srl. (1)
Viale Vincenzo Lancetti 43
Milan, 20158, Italy
Tel.: (39) 2698151
Fax: (39) 0269815241
E-Mail: info@dufry.it
Web Site: www.dufry.com
Fur & Leather Apparels Retailer
S.I.C.: 5699
N.A.I.C.S.: 448190
Marro Arnosto *(Gen Dir)*

Duty Free Caribbean Holdings Ltd. (1)
24 Broad St
Bridgetown, Barbados
Tel.: (246) 227 1325
Web Site: www.dutyfreecaribbean.com
Holding Company; Duty Free Retail Stores Owner & Operator
S.I.C.: 6719
N.A.I.C.S.: 551112
Geoffrey Cave *(Chm)*
Peter Allan *(CEO)*
Ian Gibson *(CFO)*
Alan Huxtable *(COO)*
Maureen Davis *(Chief Dev Officer)*

DUFU TECHNOLOGY CORP. BERHAD

19 Hilir Sungai Keluang 2 Fasa IV
Taman Perindustrian Bayan Lepas
Bayan Lepas, Penang, 11900, Malaysia
Tel.: (60) 46161300
Fax: (60) 46161302
E-Mail: johnloh@dufu.com.my
Web Site: www.dufutechnology.com
Year Founded: 1987
DUFU—(KLS)
Rev.: $37,554,288
Assets: $52,801,897
Liabilities: $25,430,348
Net Worth: $27,371,548
Earnings: ($719,628)
Emp.: 1,000
Fiscal Year-end: 12/31/12

Business Description:
Holding Company; Industrial Machine & Computer Peripherals Mfr
S.I.C.: 6719
N.A.I.C.S.: 551112

Personnel:
Chin-Shui Hsu *(Chm)*
Poh Yow Yong *(CEO)*
Hui-Ta Lee *(CFO)*
Wee Ling How *(Co-Sec)*
Ean Hoon Ooi *(Co-Sec)*

Board of Directors:
Chin-Shui Hsu
Siak Keng Ang
Baqir Hussain Hatim Ali
Lay Tatt Khoo
Hui-Ta Lee
Mao-Yuan Wu
Poh Yow Yong

Non-U.S. Subsidiary:

Dufu Industries Services Pte Ltd (1)
623 Aljunied Rd 05-01
Aljunied Industrial Complex, 389835
Singapore, Singapore
Tel.: (65) 68460919
Fax: (65) 68460915
E-Mail: bellyna@dufu.com.sg
Web Site: www.dufu.com.my
Emp.: 10
Screw Machine Products Mfr
S.I.C.: 3541
N.A.I.C.S.: 333517
Roger Wong *(Mgr)*

DUGA HOLDING AD

Viline Vode 6
11000 Belgrade, Serbia
Tel.: (381) 113392359
Fax: (381) 113392472
E-Mail: info@duga-ibl.com
Web Site: www.duga-ibl.com
Emp.: 370

Business Description:
Paints, Varnishes, Resins, Corrosion Inhibitors & PET
S.I.C.: 2851
N.A.I.C.S.: 325510

Personnel:
Branko Dunjic *(Chm)*
Bojan Mikec *(Gen Dir)*

DUISBURGER VERSORGUNGS- UND VERKEHRSGESELLSCHAFT MBH

Bungertstrasse 27
47053 Duisburg, Germany
Tel.: (49) 2036040
Fax: (49) 203 604 2900
E-Mail: info@dvv.de
Web Site: www.dvv.dvv.de
Year Founded: 1971
Sales Range: $1-4.9 Billion
Emp.: 116

Business Description:
Electric Power Generation & Distr
S.I.C.: 4911
N.A.I.C.S.: 221122

Personnel:
Hermann Janning *(Chm)*

DUJODWALA PAPER CHEMICALS LIMITED

907 Raheja Centre 214
Nariman Point, Mumbai, India 400 021
Tel.: (91) 22 675 22 780
Fax: (91) 22 675 22 784
E-Mail: resins@dpcl.net
Web Site: www.dpcl.net
Year Founded: 1993
524276—(BOM)
Rev.: $35,741,820
Assets: $40,554,470
Liabilities: $34,616,534
Net Worth: $5,937,936
Earnings: $375,546
Fiscal Year-end: 03/31/13

Business Description:
Resin & Paper Chemical Mfr & Whslr
S.I.C.: 2821
N.A.I.C.S.: 325211

Personnel:
Atanu Banerjee *(Head-North)*

DUJODWALA PRODUCTS LIMITED

812 Tulsianil Chamber 212 Nariman Point
Mumbai, 400021, India
Tel.: (91) 22 22824089
Fax: (91) 22 22841284
E-Mail: admin@dujodwala.com
Web Site: www.dujodwala.com
514418—(BOM)
Sales Range: $10-24.9 Million

Business Description:
Chemical Products Mfr & Distr
S.I.C.: 2869
N.A.I.C.S.: 325199

Personnel:
Kamal Dujodwala *(Chm)*
Pannkaj Dujodwala *(Mng Dir)*

Board of Directors:
Kamal Dujodwala
Pannkaj Dujodwala
Narendra Goenka
Rajkumar Jatia
Rajkumar Saraf
S. C. Sen
R. K. Shriya

DUKANG DISTILLERS HOLDINGS LIMITED

14/F Landmark Plaza 1 Shangwu
Waihuan Road
CBD Zhengdong New District,
Zhengzhou, Henan, China
Tel.: (86) 37188880988
Fax: (86) 37187518096
E-Mail: trumpdragon@china45wine.com
Web Site: www.dukang.com
911616—(SES TAI)
Emp.: 980

Business Description:
Distilled Wine Producer & Marketer
S.I.C.: 2084
N.A.I.C.S.: 312130

Personnel:
Gao Feng *(Chm)*
Zhou Tao *(Deputy Chm, CEO & Gen Mgr)*

DUKE OFFSHORE LIMITED

403 Urvashi Off Sayani Road
Prabhadevi
Mumbai, 400 025, India
Tel.: (91) 22 24221225
Fax: (91) 22 24227606
E-Mail: info@dukeoffshore.com
Web Site: www.dukeoffshore.com
Year Founded: 1985
531471—(BOM)
Rev.: $1,066,674
Assets: $1,544,948
Liabilities: $221,186
Net Worth: $1,323,762
Earnings: $243,434
Fiscal Year-end: 03/31/13

Business Description:
Offshore Engineering Services
S.I.C.: 1389
N.A.I.C.S.: 213112

Personnel:
Avik G. Duke *(Chm & Mng Dir)*
Suresh S. Pawar *(Compliance Officer & Dir-Admin)*

Board of Directors:
Avik G. Duke
Pramod D. Patekar
Suresh S. Pawar
Alan Quadros

Transfer Agent:
Purva Sharegistry India (P) Ltd.
9 Shiv Shakti Industrial Estate Ground Floor J R Boricha Road
Mumbai, 400011, India

DUKE STREET CAPITAL LIMITED

Nations House 103 Wigmore Street
London, W1U 1QS, United Kingdom
Tel.: (44) 2076638500
Fax: (44) 2076638501
E-Mail: mail@dukestreet.com
Web Site: www.dukestreet.com
Year Founded: 1988
Managed Assets: $2,547,800,000
Emp.: 35

Business Description:
Private Equity Firm
S.I.C.: 6211
N.A.I.C.S.: 523999

Personnel:
Peter Taylor *(Mng Partner)*
Didier Bismuth *(Partner)*
Miles Cresswell-Turner *(Partner)*
Jean-Marc Dayan *(Partner)*
Iain Kennedy *(Partner)*
Buchan Scott *(Partner-IR)*
Charlie Troup *(Partner)*
Lilimarlen Hoff *(Gen Counsel & Compliance Officer)*

Holdings:

Burton's Foods Ltd. (1)
St Albans Charter Court
74-78 Victoria Street, Saint Albans, AL1 3XH, United Kingdom
Tel.: (44) 1727899700
Fax: (44) 1727899701
Web Site: www.burtonsfoods.com
Emp.: 3,000
Cookies & Crackers Mfr
S.I.C.: 2052
N.A.I.C.S.: 311821
Ben Clark *(CEO)*
Stuart Wilson *(CMO)*

Oasis Healthcare Limited (1)
Oasis Support Centre Vantage Park Old Gloucester Road
Hambrook, Bristol, BS16 1GW, United Kingdom UK
Tel.: (44) 8456029335
Fax: (44) 8456029328
E-Mail: marketing@Oasisdentalhealthcare.com
Web Site: www.oasis-healthcare.co.uk
Sales Range: $150-199.9 Million
Emp.: 80
Holding Company; Dental Offices Owner & Operator
S.I.C.: 6719
N.A.I.C.S.: 551112
Stuart Rose *(Chm)*
Justin Ash *(CEO)*

Holding:

Oasis Dental Care Limited (2)
Oasis Support Centre Bldg E Vantage Pk Old Gloucester Rd
Hambrook, Bristol, BS16 1GW, United Kingdom
Tel.: (44) 8456029335
Fax: (44) 8456029328
E-Mail: info@oasisdentalcare.co.uk
Web Site: www.oasisdentalcare.co.uk
Emp.: 50
Dental Office Operator
S.I.C.: 8021
N.A.I.C.S.: 621210
Justin Ash *(CEO)*

Non-U.S. Holding:

Payzone Ireland Limited (1)
Payzone House 4 Heather Rd
Sandyford Indus Estate, Dublin, 18, Ireland
Tel.: (353) 12076000
Fax: (353) 12076039
E-Mail: info@payzone.ie
Web Site: www.payzone.ie
Sales Range: $1-4.9 Billion
Emp.: 821
Automatic Teller Machine & Payment Networks
S.I.C.: 6099
N.A.I.C.S.: 522320
Jim Deignan *(Mng Dir)*

Non-U.S. Subsidiaries:

Payzone UK Limited (2)
Davidson House
Gadbrook Pk, Northwich, Cheshire, CW9 7TW, United Kingdom
Tel.: (44) 1606338200
Fax: (44) 1606338290
Web Site: www.payzone.co.uk

Duke Street Capital Limited—(Continued)

Sales Range: $900-999.9 Million
Emp.: 103
Retail Payment Outlet
S.I.C.: 6099
N.A.I.C.S.: 522320
Bill Thomson *(Mng Dir)*

Non-U.S. Joint Venture:

Sandpiper CI Limited **(1)**
1-3 L'Avenue Le Bas
Longueville, Saint Saviour, JE4 8NB, Jersey JE
Tel.: (44) 1534508200
Fax: (44) 1534768858
Web Site: www.sandpiperci.com
Emp.: 500
Holding Company; General Retail, Liquor & Convenience Stores & Supermarket Franchises Operator; Owned by Duke Street Capital Limited & by Europa Capital Partners Limited
S.I.C.: 6719
N.A.I.C.S.: 551112
Tony O'Neill *(CEO)*

Subsidiary:

Sandpiper CI Retail Limited **(2)**
1-3 L'Avenue Le Bas
Longueville, Saint Saviour, JE4 8NB, Jersey JE
Tel.: (44) 1534508200
Fax: (44) 1534768858
Web Site: www.sandpiperci.com
Sales Range: $600-649.9 Million
Emp.: 533
Holding Company; General Retail, Liquor & Convenience Stores & Supermarket Franchises Operator
S.I.C.: 6719
N.A.I.C.S.: 551112
Tony O'Neill *(CEO)*

DUKSUNG CO., LTD.

557-1 Sin-Dong
Yeongtong-Gu, Suwon, GyeongGi-Do, Korea (South)
Tel.: (82) 31 204 0781
Fax: (82) 31 204 0787
Web Site: www.duksung21.com
Year Founded: 1966
004830—(KRS)
Business Description:
Artificial Leather Mfr
S.I.C.: 2295
N.A.I.C.S.: 313320
Personnel:
Bong Geun Lee *(Pres & CEO)*

DULUTH METALS LIMITED

80 Richmond St West Suite 1500
Toronto, ON, M5H 2A4, Canada
Tel.: (416) 369-1500
Fax: (416) 369-1501
E-Mail: IR@duluthmetals.com
Web Site: www.duluthmetals.com
DM—(TSX)
Rev.: $306,398
Assets: $169,959,853
Liabilities: $31,449,952
Net Worth: $138,509,901
Earnings: ($40,039,229)
Emp.: 64
Fiscal Year-end: 12/31/12
Business Description:
Mineral Exploration Services
S.I.C.: 1481
N.A.I.C.S.: 213115
Personnel:
Christopher C. Dundas *(Chm & CEO)*
Vern Baker *(Pres)*
Marvin E. Dee *(CFO)*
Kelly J. Osborne *(COO)*
H. James Blake *(Sec)*
Dean M. Peterson *(Sr VP-Exploration)*
Board of Directors:
Christopher C. Dundas
Mark D. Cowan
James Joseph Jackson
Thomas F. Pugsley
John F. Sattler
Barry D. Simmons
Alar Soever
Transfer Agent:
Equity Financial Trust Company
Toronto, ON, Canada

U.S. Subsidiary:

Duluth Metals Corp. **(1)**
7300 Hudson Blvd Ste 290
Oakdale, MN 55128-7141
Tel.: (651) 389-9990
Fax: (651) 389-9991
Emp.: 4
Metal Exploration Services
S.I.C.: 1081
N.A.I.C.S.: 213114
David Spaulding *(Bus Mgr)*

DULUXGROUP LIMITED

1956 Dandenong Rd
Clayton, VIC, 3168, Australia
Tel.: (61) 3 9263 5678
Fax: (61) 3 9263 5030
E-Mail: company.info@duluxgroup.com.au
Web Site: www.duluxgroup.com.au
DLX—(ASX)
Rev.: $1,558,039,542
Assets: $1,076,287,133
Liabilities: $835,595,380
Net Worth: $240,691,753
Earnings: $68,300,276
Emp.: 4,000
Fiscal Year-end: 09/30/13
Business Description:
Holding Company; Paints, Coatings & Other Building Materials & Products Mfr
S.I.C.: 6719
N.A.I.C.S.: 551112
Personnel:
Patrick Houlihan *(CEO & Mng Dir)*
Stuart Boxer *(CFO)*
Simon Black *(Gen Counsel & Sec)*
Board of Directors:
Peter Kirby
Stuart Boxer
Gaik Hean Chew
Patrick Houlihan
Garry Arthur Hounsell
Andrew Larke
Judith Swales

Subsidiary:

Alesco Corporation Limited **(1)**
Level 24 207 Kent Street
Sydney, NSW, 2000, Australia AU
Tel.: (61) 292482000
Fax: (61) 292482099
E-Mail:
Web Site: www.alesco.com.au
Emp.: 1,380
Holding Company; Residential, Commercial & Industrial Building Materials & Products Mfr
S.I.C.: 6719
N.A.I.C.S.: 551112

Subsidiaries:

Lincoln Sentry Group Pty Limited **(2)**
48 Weaver St Archerfield
PO Box 276
Coopers Plains, QLD, 4108, Australia
Tel.: (61) 7 3244 3200
Fax: (61) 732443255
E-Mail: info@lincolnsentry.com.au
Web Site: www.lincolnsentry.com.au
Emp.: 500
Hardware & Components Distr
S.I.C.: 5072
N.A.I.C.S.: 423710

Parchem Construction Supplies Pty Limited **(2)**
7 Lucca Road
Wyong, NSW, 2259, Australia
Tel.: (61) 243505000
Fax: (61) 46505070
E-Mail: info@parchem.com.au
Web Site: www.parchem.com.au
Emp.: 100
Construction Products & Equipment Mfr & Distr
S.I.C.: 3531
N.A.I.C.S.: 333120
Paolo Boni *(Branch Mgr-Queenslandd)*

Non-U.S. Subsidiaries:

B&D Doors (NZ) Limited **(2)**
30 C Allens Road E Tamaki
Manukau, Auckland, 2013, New Zealand
Mailing Address:
PO Box 58 019
Botany, Auckland, 2163, New Zealand
Tel.: (64) 92738600
Fax: (64) 92738601
E-Mail: lalit.chand@bnd.co.nz
Web Site: www.bnd.co.nz
Emp.: 30
Garage Doors & Automatic Door Openers Mfr
S.I.C.: 3999
N.A.I.C.S.: 339999
Lalit Chand *(Mgr)*

Concrete Plus Limited **(2)**
23 Watts Rd
Sockburn, Christchurch, 8042, New Zealand
Tel.: (64) 33430090
Fax: (64) 33430202
E-Mail: frank@concreteplus.co.nz
Web Site: www.concreteplus.co.nz
Emp.: 7
Construction Products & Equipment Distr
S.I.C.: 5039
N.A.I.C.S.: 423390
Ron Johnston *(Gen Mgr)*

Countermast Limited **(2)**
Unit 29-24 Polka Hoi Luen Industrial Center
Hoi Yuen Rd
Kwun Tong, Kowloon, China (Hong Kong)
Tel.: (852) 23954257
Fax: (852) 27893960
E-Mail: cyrus@countermast.com.hk
Emp.: 50
Engineering Services
S.I.C.: 8711
N.A.I.C.S.: 541330
Cyrus Wong *(Gen Mgr)*

DUMAS AUTOMOBILES

Route De Montelimar
07200 Bourg-les-Valence, Aubenas, France
Tel.: (33) 475898295
Fax: (33) 475878277
E-Mail: dumas.automobiles@wanagoo.fr
Sls.: $20,200,000
Emp.: 44
Business Description:
New & Used Car Dealers
S.I.C.: 5511
N.A.I.C.S.: 441110
Personnel:
Francois Dumas *(Pres)*

DUNAV A.D. GROCKA

Bulevar Revolucije 15
Grocka, 11306 Belgrade, Serbia
Tel.: (381) 11 850 10 52
Fax: (381) 11 850 09 88
E-Mail: office@dunavgrocka.rs
Web Site: www.dunavgrocka.rs
DNVG—(BEL)
Business Description:
Texturised Yarn Mfr
S.I.C.: 2299
N.A.I.C.S.: 313110
Personnel:
Petar Stojanovic *(Pres & CEO)*
Manuela Milev *(Sec)*

DUNAV OSIGURANJE AD BANJA LUKA

Veselina Maslese 28
78000 Banja Luka, Bosnia & Herzegovina
Tel.: (387) 51246100
Fax: (387) 51246110
E-Mail: kosigdunav@inecco.net
Web Site: www.kosigdunav.com
Year Founded: 1991
KDVO-R-A—(BANJ)
Sales Range: $10-24.9 Million
Emp.: 200
Business Description:
Insurance Services
S.I.C.: 6331
N.A.I.C.S.: 524126
Personnel:
Sasa Cudic *(Mng Dir)*

DUNAV RE A.D.

Knez Mihailova 6/II
11000 Belgrade, Serbia
Tel.: (381) 11 263 47 55
Fax: (381) 11 263 38 45
Web Site: www.dunavre.rs
DNREM—(BEL)
Business Description:
Reinsurance Services
S.I.C.: 6399
N.A.I.C.S.: 524130
Personnel:
Ljubodrag Markovic *(Pres)*
Branislav Savic *(Gen Dir)*
Board of Directors:
Ljubodrag Markovic
Verica Matkovic
Evica Milenkovic

DUNAV RESOURCES LTD.

1111 St-Charles Street West West Tower Suite 101
Longueuil, QC, J4K 5G4, Canada
Tel.: (450) 677-3868
Fax: (450) 677-2601
E-Mail: info@dunavresources.com
Web Site: www.dunavresources.com
Year Founded: 1996
DNV—(TSXV)
Rev.: $76,528
Assets: $2,793,225
Liabilities: $636,067
Net Worth: $2,157,158
Earnings: ($15,220,310)
Fiscal Year-end: 12/31/12
Business Description:
Mineral Exploration Services
S.I.C.: 1081
N.A.I.C.S.: 213114
Personnel:
David A. Fennell *(Chm)*
James Arnott Crombie *(Pres & CEO)*
Alan Krushnisky *(CFO)*
Carole Plante *(Gen Counsel & Sec)*
Sean Hasson *(Exec VP-Exploration)*
Board of Directors:
David A. Fennell
Elaine Bennett
James Arnott Crombie
Louis-Pierre Gignac
Adrian Goldstone
Jonathan C. Goodman
Sean Hasson
Robert Minto
John Wakeford
Transfer Agent:
Olympia Transfer Services Inc.
Suite 920 120 Adelaide Street West
Toronto, ON, Canada

DUNBIA GROUP

Granville Industrial Estate
Dungannon, Co Tyrone, BT70 1NJ, United Kingdom
Tel.: (44) 2887 723350
Fax: (44) 2887 721810
E-Mail: info@dunbia.com
Web Site: www.dunbia.com
Year Founded: 1976
Sales Range: $1-4.9 Billion

Emp.: 3,156
Business Description:
Meat Product Whslr
S.I.C.: 5147
N.A.I.C.S.: 424470
Personnel:
Jim Dobson *(Group Mng Dir)*

DUNCAN HAMILTON & CO LIMITED

PO Box 222
Hook, England, RG27 9YZ, United Kingdom
Tel.: (44) 1256765000
Fax: (44) 1256766000
E-Mail: sales@duncanhamilton.com
Web Site: www.duncanhamilton.com
Rev.: $22,518,711
Emp.: 6
Business Description:
Used Car Dealers
S.I.C.: 5521
N.A.I.C.S.: 441120
Personnel:
Adrian Hamilton *(Mng Dir)*

DUNCAN PARK HOLDINGS CORPORATION

Suite 406 372 Bay Street
Toronto, ON, M5H 2W9, Canada
Tel.: (416) 203-0860
Fax: (416) 364-7256
E-Mail: info@duncanpark.com
Web Site: www.duncanpark.com
DPH—(OTC TSXV)
Assets: $2,697,265
Liabilities: $138,357
Net Worth: $2,558,908
Earnings: ($264,552)
Fiscal Year-end: 11/30/12
Business Description:
Metal Exploration Services
S.I.C.: 1081
N.A.I.C.S.: 213114
Personnel:
Ian M. T. McAvity *(Pres & CEO)*
Harold J. Doran *(CFO & Sec)*
Board of Directors:
Larry D. Kornze
Ian M. T. McAvity
Eric P. Salsberg
David Roy Shaddrick
Legal Counsel:
Baker & McKenzie LLP
Toronto
Toronto, ON, Canada

DUNCANS INDUSTRIES LIMITED

97 Park Street Block-C 3rd Floor
Kolkata, 700016, India
Tel.: (91) 33 226 4878
Fax: (91) 33 245 7337
Web Site: www.duncans-tea.com
590063—(BOM)
Business Description:
Tea Mfr
S.I.C.: 2099
N.A.I.C.S.: 311920
Personnel:
G. P. Goenka *(Chm)*
K. Mukhopadhyay *(Sec)*
Board of Directors:
G. P. Goenka
A. L. Ananthanarayanan
R. K. Bhargava
T. S. Broca
M. H. Chinoy
A. K. Goel
Shrivardhan Goenka
D. Sengupta

DUNCASTLE GOLD CORP.

Suite 1100 1199 West Hastings Street
Vancouver, BC, V6E 3T5, Canada
Tel.: (604) 684-9384
Fax: (604) 688-4670
Toll Free: (888) 456-1112
E-Mail: info@mnxltd.com
Web Site: www.duncastlegoldcorp.com
Year Founded: 2006
DUN—(TSXV)
Int. Income: $111
Assets: $593,869
Liabilities: $850,734
Net Worth: ($256,865)
Earnings: ($490,748)
Fiscal Year-end: 03/31/13
Business Description:
Mineral Exploration Services
S.I.C.: 1081
N.A.I.C.S.: 213114
Personnel:
Lawrence Page *(Chm)*
Michael Rowley *(Pres & CEO)*
Graham Thatcher *(CFO)*
Arie Page *(Sec)*
Board of Directors:
Lawrence Page
Victor Jones
Michael Rowley
Douglas Warkentin
Legal Counsel:
Jeffrey T.K. Fraser Law Corporation
Suite 950 1199 West Hastings Street
Vancouver, BC, Canada
Transfer Agent:
Computershare
100 University Avenue 9 Floor
Toronto, ON, Canada

DUNDARAVE RESOURCES INC.

1502 - 543 Granville Street
Vancouver, BC, V6C 1X8, Canada
Tel.: (604) 648-6240
Fax: (604) 688-8001
Web Site: www.dundaraveresources.com
DDX—(TSXV)
Int. Income: $6,365
Assets: $921,385
Liabilities: $14,837
Net Worth: $906,548
Earnings: ($167,179)
Fiscal Year-end: 12/31/12
Business Description:
Mineral Exploration Services
S.I.C.: 1081
N.A.I.C.S.: 213114
Personnel:
Paul Matysek *(Pres & CEO)*
George Lim *(CFO)*
Christine Thomson *(Sec)*
Board of Directors:
Paul Matysek
Andre M. Pauwels
Brent Peters
Transfer Agent:
Computershare Investor Services Inc.
100 University Ave 9th Floor
Toronto, ON, Canada

DUNDAS DATA VISUALIZATION, INC.

500 250 Ferrand Drive
Toronto, ON, M3C 3G8, Canada
Tel.: (416) 467-5100
Fax: (416) 422-4801
Toll Free: (800) 463-1492
E-Mail: info@dundas.com
Web Site: www.dundas.com
Sales Range: $10-24.9 Million
Emp.: 70
Business Description:
Data Visualization & Dashboarding Solutions
S.I.C.: 7372
N.A.I.C.S.: 511210
Personnel:
David Cunningham *(Founder & Chm)*
Troy Marchand *(Pres & CEO)*

DUNDEE CORPORATION

1 Adelaide Street East 21st Floor
Toronto, ON, M5C 2V9, Canada
Tel.: (416) 863-6990
Fax: (416) 363-4536
E-Mail: investor@dundeebancorp.com
Web Site: www.dundeecorporation.com
DC.A—(OTC TSX)
Sales Range: $50-74.9 Million
Emp.: 352
Business Description:
Holding Company; Wealth Management & Real Estate Investment Services
S.I.C.: 6719
N.A.I.C.S.: 551112
Personnel:
Harold P. Gordon *(Chm)*
Nathan Goodman *(Pres & CEO)*
Lucie Presot *(CFO & VP)*
Lili Mance *(Sec)*
Mark E. Goodman *(Exec VP)*
Board of Directors:
Harold P. Gordon
Normand Beauchamp
Michael J. Cooper
Daniel T. Goodman
David J. Goodman
Jonathan C. Goodman
Mark E. Goodman
Nathan Goodman
Ellis Jacob
Frederick H. Lowy
Garth A. C. MacRea
Robert L. McLeish
K. Barry Sparks
Harry R. Steele
Transfer Agent:
Computershare Investor Services Inc
100 University Avenue
Toronto, ON, Canada

Subsidiaries:

Dundee Capital Markets Inc. **(1)**
21st Fl Adelaide Street East Ste 2000
Toronto, ON, M5C 2V9, Canada ON
Tel.: (416) 350-3388 (100%)
Fax: (416) 865-3463
Toll Free: (888) 332-2661
Web Site: www.dundeecapitalmarkets.com
Investment Banking Services
S.I.C.: 6211
N.A.I.C.S.: 523110
Daniel T. Goodman *(Chm)*
Jonathan C. Goodman *(Pres & CEO)*
Robert Sellars *(CFO & Exec VP)*
Lillian Mance *(Sec)*

Dundee Energy Limited **(1)**
1 Adelaide St E Dundee Place Suite 2100
Toronto, ON, M5C 2V9, Canada (57%)
Tel.: (416) 863-6990
Fax: (416) 363-4536
E-Mail: dundee-energy@dundee-energy.com
Web Site: www.dundee-energy.com
DEN—(TSX)
Rev.: $35,659,473
Assets: $168,616,607
Liabilities: $112,029,036
Net Worth: $56,587,571
Earnings: ($16,580,254)
Emp.: 35
Fiscal Year-end: 12/31/12
Crude Petroleum & Natural Gas Extraction
S.I.C.: 1311
N.A.I.C.S.: 211111
Daniel T. Goodman *(Chm)*
M. Jaffar Khan *(Pres & CEO)*
David Bhumgara *(CFO)*
Bruce Sherley *(Pres-Dundee Oil & Gas Limited)*

Dundee Realty Corporation **(1)**
30 Adelaide Street East Suite 1600
Toronto, ON, M5C 3H1, Canada BC
Tel.: (416) 365-3535 (70%)
Fax: (416) 365-6565
E-Mail: info@dundeerealty.com
Web Site: www.dundeerealty.com
Emp.: 100
Holding Company; Real Estate Investment, Asset Management & Brokerage Services
S.I.C.: 6719
N.A.I.C.S.: 551112
Carol Webb *(VP-Comm)*

Subsidiary:

Dundee Realty Management Corporation **(2)**
30 Adelaide St E Ste 1600
Toronto, ON, M5C 3H1, Canada
Tel.: (416) 365-3535
Fax: (416) 365-6565
E-Mail: info@dundeerealty.com
Web Site: www.dundeerealty.com
Emp.: 500
Real Estate Services
S.I.C.: 6531
N.A.I.C.S.: 531390
Daniel T. Goodman *(Chm)*
Michael J. Cooper *(CEO)*
Mario Barrafato *(CFO & Sr VP)*

Subsidiaries:

Bellanca Developments Ltd. **(3)**
5201 - 50th Ave Ste 804
Yellowknife, NT, X1A 3S9, Canada
Tel.: (867) 920-2324
Fax: (867) 873-8710
E-Mail: cavalli@dundeerealty.com
Emp.: 30
Real Estate Property Management Services
S.I.C.: 6531
N.A.I.C.S.: 531312
Darin Benoit *(Gen Mgr)*

Dundee Realty Management (B.C.) Corp. **(3)**
Station Tower Ste 1620 13401-108th Ave
Surrey, BC, V3T 5T3, Canada
Tel.: (604) 586-5117
Fax: (604) 586-5100
Web Site: www.dundeerealty.com
Emp.: 9
Property Management Services
S.I.C.: 6531
N.A.I.C.S.: 531312
Dawn Surette *(Sr Mgr-Property)*

Dundee Realty Management (Sask) Corp. **(3)**
Princeton Tower 123 2nd Ave Ste 602
Saskatoon, SK, S7K 7E6, Canada
Tel.: (306) 665-6120
Fax: (306) 664-6502
Emp.: 9
Property Management & Leasing Services
S.I.C.: 6513
N.A.I.C.S.: 531110

U.S. Subsidiary:

Dundee Realty USA Inc. **(3)**
225 Main St G 3003
Edwards, CO 81632
Tel.: (970) 845-7838
Fax: (970) 845-7237
E-Mail: dundeerealty@comcast.net
Web Site: www.dundeerealty.com
Emp.: 3
Real Estate Services
S.I.C.: 6552
N.A.I.C.S.: 237210
Michael Cooper *(Pres)*

Affiliates:

Dundee Industrial Real Estate Investment Trust **(2)**
30 Adelaide Street East Suite 1600
Toronto, ON, M5C 3H1, Canada ON
Tel.: (416) 365-3535
Fax: (416) 365-3545
E-Mail:
Web Site: www.dundeeindustrial.com
DIR—(TSX)
Real Estate Investment Trust
S.I.C.: 6726
N.A.I.C.S.: 525990

Dundee Corporation—(Continued)

Randy Cameron *(Interim Pres & CEO)*
Mario Barrafato *(CFO)*

Holding:

DIR Industrial Properties Inc. **(3)**
(Formerly C2C Industrial Properties Inc.)
30 Adelaide Street East Suite 1600
Toronto, ON, M5C 3H1, Canada ON
Tel.: (416) 365-3535
Fax: (416) 365-3545
E-Mail:
DIN.DB—(TSX)
Rev.: $15,650,845
Assets: $211,401,215
Liabilities: $130,984,997
Net Worth: $80,416,218
Earnings: $9,736,426
Fiscal Year-end: 12/31/12
Industrial Property Real Estate Investment Trust
S.I.C.: 6726
N.A.I.C.S.: 525990
Randall Cameron *(Interim Pres & CEO)*
Mario Barrafato *(CFO)*

Dundee International Real Estate Investment Trust **(2)**
State Street Financial Centre Suite 1600 30 Adelaide St E
Toronto, ON, M5C 3H1, Canada ON
Tel.: (416) 365-3535
Fax: (416) 365-6565
Toll Free: (877) 365-3535
E-Mail: info@dundeeinternational.com
Web Site: www.dundeeinternational.com
DI.DB—(TSX)
Rev.: $137,831,807
Assets: $1,391,895,391
Liabilities: $799,381,938
Net Worth: $592,513,454
Earnings: $10,850,722
Emp.: 27
Fiscal Year-end: 12/31/12
Real Estate Investment Trust
S.I.C.: 6726
N.A.I.C.S.: 525990
Detlef Bierbaum *(Chm)*
Michael J. Cooper *(Vice Chm)*
Jane Gavan *(Pres & CEO)*
Rene Gulliver *(CFO)*
Doug Quesnel *(Chief Acctg Officer)*

Dundee Real Estate Investment Trust **(2)**
State Street Financial Centre Suite 1600 30 Adelaide Street East
Toronto, ON, M5C 3H1, Canada ON
Tel.: (416) 365-3535
Fax: (416) 365-6565
E-Mail: info@dundeereit.com
Web Site: www.dundeereit.com
D.UN—(TSX)
Rev.: $604,161,380
Assets: $6,314,997,132
Liabilities: $3,038,310,598
Net Worth: $3,276,686,534
Earnings: $289,332,383
Emp.: 571
Fiscal Year-end: 12/31/12
Real Estate Investment Trust
S.I.C.: 6726
N.A.I.C.S.: 525990
Daniel T. Goodman *(Chm)*
Michael J. Cooper *(Vice Chm & CEO)*
Mario Barrafato *(CFO & Sr VP)*
Ana Radic *(COO)*
Jane Gavan *(Sec)*

Holding:

World Wide Minerals Ltd. **(1)**
211 Queen's Quay Blvd West Suite 917
Toronto, ON, M5J 2M6, Canada
Tel.: (416) 369-7217
Fax: (416) 369-6088
E-Mail: info@worldwideminerals.com
Web Site: www.worldwideminerals.com
Emp.: 6
Producer of Mineral Resources
S.I.C.: 1481
N.A.I.C.S.: 213115
Paul A. Carroll *(Pres & CEO)*

DUNDEE INDUSTRIAL REAL ESTATE INVESTMENT TRUST

(See Under Dundee Corporation)

DUNDEE INTERNATIONAL REAL ESTATE INVESTMENT TRUST

(See Under Dundee Corporation)

DUNDEE PRECIOUS METALS INC.

1 Adelaide Street East Suite 500
PO Box 195
Toronto, ON, M5C 2V9, Canada
Tel.: (416) 365-5191
Fax: (416) 365-9080
E-Mail: info@dundeeprecious.com
Web Site: www.dundeeprecious.com
DPM—(TSX)
Rev.: $384,685,000
Assets: $972,185,000
Liabilities: $217,844,000
Net Worth: $754,341,000
Earnings: $29,831,000
Emp.: 2,800
Fiscal Year-end: 12/31/12

Business Description:
Gold Mining Services
S.I.C.: 1041
N.A.I.C.S.: 212221

Personnel:
Rick Howes *(Pres & CEO)*
Hume D. Kyle *(CFO & Exec VP)*
Michael Frilegh *(Treas & VP)*
Lori E. Beak *(Sec & Sr VP-Investor & Regulatory Affairs)*
Adrian Goldstone *(Exec VP-Sustainable Bus Dev)*
Michael Dorfman *(Sr VP-Corp Dev)*
Richard Gosse *(Sr VP-Exploration)*
Paul Proulx *(Sr VP-Corp Svcs)*
David Rae *(Sr VP-Ops)*

Board of Directors:
Derek H. L. Buntain
Peter Gillin
Rick Howes
W. Murray John
Jeremy Kinsman
Garth A. C. MacRae
Peter B. Nixon
Ronald Singer
Eira Thomas
Anthony Walsh
William G. Wilson
Donald Young

Transfer Agent:
Computershare Investor Services Inc
100 University Avenue 9th Floor
Toronto, ON, Canada

Non-U.S. Subsidiaries:

Balkan Mineral and Mining EAD **(1)**
26 Bacho Kiro Street Floor 3
1000 Sofia, Bulgaria
Tel.: (359) 2 930 1500
Fax: (359) 2 930 1595
E-Mail: office_sofia@dundeeprecious.com
Web Site: www.dundeeprecious.com
Mineral Mining Services
S.I.C.: 1479
N.A.I.C.S.: 212393
Adrian Goldstone *(Exec Dir)*

Chelopech Mining EAD **(1)**
26 Bacho Kiro Street Floor 3
1000 Sofia, Bulgaria
Tel.: (359) 2 930 1500
Fax: (359) 2 930 1595
E-Mail: info@dpm-group.com
Web Site: www.dpm-group.com
Copper & Gold Mining Services
S.I.C.: 1041
N.A.I.C.S.: 212221
Robert B. Howie *(Gen Mgr)*

Namibia Custom Smelters (Pty) Limited **(1)**
Smelter Road
PO Box 936
Tsumeb, Namibia
Tel.: (264) 672234000
Fax: (264) 67 223 4330
Web Site: www.dundeeprecious.com
Metal Ore Exploration Services
S.I.C.: 1099
N.A.I.C.S.: 212299
William Skinner *(Gen Mgr)*

DUNDEE REAL ESTATE INVESTMENT TRUST

(See Under Dundee Corporation)

DUNEDIN ENTERPRISE INVESTMENT TRUST PLC

Saltire Court 20 Castle Terrace
Edinburgh, EH1 2EN, United Kingdom
Tel.: (44) 1312256699
Fax: (44) 1317182300
E-Mail: info@dunedinenterprise.co.uk
Web Site: www.dunedinenterprise.com
Year Founded: 1974
DNE—(LSE)
Rev.: $11,626,733
Assets: $217,127,106
Liabilities: $451,677
Net Worth: $216,675,429
Earnings: $2,154,152
Fiscal Year-end: 12/31/12

Business Description:
Investment Services
S.I.C.: 6211
N.A.I.C.S.: 523999

Board of Directors:
David Gamble
Liz Airey
Duncan Budge
Brian Finlayson
Federico Marescotti

Subsidiary:

Dunedin Capital Partners Limited **(1)**
Saltire Ct 20 Castle Ter
Edinburgh, EH1 2EN, United Kingdom (100%)
Tel.: (44) 131 225 6699
Fax: (44) 131 718 2300
E-Mail: info@dunedin.com
Web Site: www.dunedin.com
Emp.: 18
Private Equity Firm
S.I.C.: 6211
N.A.I.C.S.: 523999
Simon Miller *(Chm)*
Ross Marshall *(CEO & Sr Partner)*
Dougal Bennett *(Partner)*
Giles Derry *(Partner)*
Nicol Fraser *(Partner)*
Mark Ligertwood *(Partner)*
David Williams *(Partner)*
Nicholas Hoare *(COO)*

DUNELM GROUP PLC

Watermead Business Park
Syston, Leicester, LE7 1AD, United Kingdom
Tel.: (44) 1162644400
Fax: (44) 1162644490
E-Mail: enquiries@dunelm.com
Web Site: www.dunelm-mill.com
Year Founded: 1979
DNLM—(LSE)
Rev.: $1,069,482,554
Assets: $494,622,573
Liabilities: $182,406,416
Net Worth: $312,216,157
Earnings: $128,639,488
Emp.: 4,774
Fiscal Year-end: 06/29/13

Business Description:
Homewares Retailer
S.I.C.: 5719
N.A.I.C.S.: 442299

Personnel:
Bill Adderley *(Founder)*
Will Adderley *(Deputy Chm)*
Nick Wharton *(CEO)*
Dawn Durrant *(Sec)*

Board of Directors:
Geoffrey I. Cooper
Will Adderley
Matt S. Davies
Liz Doherty
Simon Emeny
Marion J. Sears
David Stead
Nick Wharton

Legal Counsel:
Allen & Overy LLP
One Bishops Square
London, United Kingdom

DUNI AB

Ubatshallen Submarine Hall Ostra Varvsgatan 9 A
PO Box 237
SE-201 22 Malmo, Sweden
Tel.: (46) 40106200
Fax: (46) 40396630
E-Mail: info@duni.com
Web Site: www.duni.com
Year Founded: 1970
DUNI—(OMX OTC)
Sls.: $567,961,200
Assets: $543,967,200
Liabilities: $317,494,800
Net Worth: $226,472,400
Earnings: $19,195,200
Emp.: 1,875
Fiscal Year-end: 12/31/12

Business Description:
Napkins, Table Covers, Paper Plates, Cups & Other Food Service Disposable Items
Export
S.I.C.: 2676
N.A.I.C.S.: 322291

Personnel:
Anders Bulow *(Chm)*
Thomas Gustafsson *(Pres & CEO)*
Mats Lindroth *(CFO)*

Board of Directors:
Anders Bulow
Tina Andersson
Thomas Gustafsson
Per-Ake Halvordsson
Henry Olsen
Pia Rudengren
Magnus Yngen

Divisions:

Rexcell Tissue & Airlaid AB **(1)**
Bruksvaegen 6
Skapafors, Se 666 40 Bengtsfors, Sweden
Tel.: (46) 53172800
Fax: (46) 4653112283
E-Mail: info@rexcell.se
Web Site: www.rexcell.se
Emp.: 200
Disposable Sanitary Paper Mfr
S.I.C.: 2676
N.A.I.C.S.: 322291
Patrik Soederstjerna *(CEO)*

Non-U.S. Subsidiaries:

Duni AG **(1)**
Lettenstrasse 11
PO Box 241
Rotkreuz, Zug, 6343, Switzerland (100%)
Tel.: (41) 417980171
Fax: (41) 417980172
E-Mail: info-switzerland@duni.com
Web Site: www.duni.com
Emp.: 21
Mfr. of Disposable Paper Items
S.I.C.: 2676
N.A.I.C.S.: 322291
Peter Nobs *(CEO)*

Duni & Co. KG **(1)**
Robert Bosch St 4
Bramsche, Niedersachsen, 49565, Germany (100%)
Tel.: (49) 5461820
Fax: (49) 546182201
E-Mail: info@duni.com
Emp.: 1,000

Mfr. of Paper Napkins, Tablecloths, Plates, Plastic Cups
S.I.C.: 2676
N.A.I.C.S.: 322291

Duni Benelux B.V. (1)
Tinstraat 15
4823 AA Breda, Netherlands
Tel.: (31) 765432300
Fax: (31) 76 543 2333
E-Mail: info.duninl@duni.com
Web Site: www.duni.com
Table Setting Products Distr
S.I.C.: 5099
N.A.I.C.S.: 423990

Duni Beteiligungsgesellschaft mbH (1)
Robert-Bosch-Str 4
49565 Bramsche, Germany
Tel.: (49) 5461 820
Fax: (49) 5461 82201
E-Mail: dfs@duni.com
Table Top & Servings Distr
S.I.C.: 5023
N.A.I.C.S.: 423220

Duni (CZ) s.r.o. (1)
Milady Horakovre 2725
272 01 Kladno, Czech Republic
Tel.: (420) 312818337
Fax: (420) 312818339
E-Mail: duni@duni.cz
Web Site: www.duni.cz
Emp.: 10
Paper Cups Mfr
S.I.C.: 2679
N.A.I.C.S.: 322299
Peter Holub *(Gen Mgr)*

Duni EFF Sp. z o.o. (1)
Solidarnosci 46
Poznan, 61-696, Poland
Tel.: (48) 616560700
Fax: (48) 616560701
E-Mail: reception.eff@duni.com
Emp.: 4
Table Top & Servings Distr
S.I.C.: 5023
N.A.I.C.S.: 423220
Krister Gullstroem *(Gen Mgr)*

Duni GmbH (1)
Moosstrasse 41
Salzburg, 5020, Austria (100%)
Tel.: (43) 6628354960
Fax: (43) 6628354964
E-Mail: office@duni.com
Rev.: $6,290,465
Emp.: 11
Mfr. of Disposable Paper Items
S.I.C.: 2676
N.A.I.C.S.: 322291
Heinz Purtaller *(Mng Dir)*

Duni Holding BV (1)
Tinstraat 15
Breda, 4823 AA, Netherlands
Tel.: (31) 765432300
Fax: (31) 765432333
Table Setting Products Distr
S.I.C.: 5099
N.A.I.C.S.: 423990

Non-U.S. Subsidiaries:

Duni A/S (2)
AP Mollers Alle 13
2791 Dragor, Denmark
Tel.: (45) 44848422
Fax: (45) 44847756
Table Setting Products Distr
S.I.C.: 5099
N.A.I.C.S.: 423990

Duni AS (2)
Tvetenveien 32a
Oslo, 0666, Norway
Tel.: (47) 23304500
Fax: (47) 22688796
Table Setting Products Distr
S.I.C.: 5099
N.A.I.C.S.: 423990

Duni OY (2)
Elimaenk 29
510 Helsinki, Finland
Tel.: (358) 98 68 98 10
Fax: (358) 91 46 2133
E-Mail: duni@duni.com
Web Site: www.duni.com
Emp.: 19
Candles Mfr
S.I.C.: 3999
N.A.I.C.S.: 339999
Miisa Jallow *(Country Mgr)*

Duni Verwaltungs GmbH (2)
Robert Bosch Str 4
Bramsche, 49565, Germany
Tel.: (49) 5461820
Fax: (49) 546182201
Web Site: www.duni.com
Table Setting Products Distr
S.I.C.: 5099
N.A.I.C.S.: 423990
Ulfert Rott *(Gen Mgr)*

Duni Iberica S.L. (1)
Puerto Tarraco Moll Lleida Edificio 1 Planta 2 Oficina C
ES 43004 Tarragona, Spain (100%)
Tel.: (34) 900983314
Fax: (34) 977206470
E-Mail: info@duni.com
Emp.: 31
Disposable Paper Items Mfr & Distr
S.I.C.: 2676
N.A.I.C.S.: 322291

Duni Ltd. (1)
Chester Road
Preston Brook, WA73FR Runcorn, Cheshire, United Kingdom (100%)
Tel.: (44) 928712377
Telex: 628132 DUNIB G
Fax: (44) 928754580
E-Mail: duncan.reception@duni.com
Web Site: www.duni.com
Emp.: 20
Mfr. of Paper Tablecloths, Dining Items & Handkerchiefs
S.I.C.: 2676
N.A.I.C.S.: 322291
Paul Sabian *(Mng Dir)*

Duni Sales Poland Sp. z o.o. (1)
Ul Syrenia 4
61-017 Poznan, Poland
Tel.: (48) 618735000
Fax: (48) 618735002
Emp.: 25
Table Setting Products Distr
S.I.C.: 5099
N.A.I.C.S.: 423990
Robert Wolniakowski *(Mng Dir)*

Duni ZAO (1)
Pr Mira h 6
129 090 Moscow, Russia
Tel.: (7) 4956462971
Fax: (7) 495 646 29 72
E-Mail: moscow@duni.com
Web Site: www.duni.com
Emp.: 20
Table Setting Products Dist
S.I.C.: 5099
N.A.I.C.S.: 423990
Antoine Khytrov *(Gen Mgr)*

DUNLOP INDIA LTD
Ruia Centre 46 Syed Amir Ali Avenue
Kolkata, 700017, India
Tel.: (91) 33 2289 4747
Fax: (91) 33 2289 3433
E-Mail: feedback@dunlop.co.in
Web Site: www.dunlop.co.in
509130—(BOM)
Sales Range: $25-49.9 Million
Business Description:
Tire Mfr
S.I.C.: 3011
N.A.I.C.S.: 326211
Personnel:
Kanhaiya Lal Sharma *(Sec)*
Board of Directors:
Mohan Lall Chauhan
Samir Paul
S. Ravi
Ram Krishnen Sadhu
Transfer Agent:
CB Management Services (P) Limited
P22 Bondel Road
Kolkata, India

DUNLOP SLAZENGER GROUP LTD.
Dunlop House Riverside Way
Camberley, Surrey, GU15 3YL, United Kingdom
Tel.: (44) 1276 803399
Fax: (44) 1276 679680
Web Site: www.slazenger.com
Business Description:
Sports Equipment
S.I.C.: 3949
N.A.I.C.S.: 339920

DUNNS (LONG SUTTON) LTD
Phoenix Lodge Winters Lane
Long Sutton, Spalding, Lincolnshire, PE12 9BE, United Kingdom
Tel.: (44) 1406 362141
Fax: (44) 1406 364444
E-Mail: info@dunns-ls.co.uk
Web Site: www.dunns-ls.co.uk
Year Founded: 1834
Sales Range: $10-24.9 Million
Emp.: 30
Fiscal Year-end: 12/31/12
Business Description:
Seed Processor & Distr
S.I.C.: 2079
N.A.I.C.S.: 311224
Personnel:
David Shepherd *(Mng Dir)*

DUOBACK KOREA CO., LTD.
543-2 Gajwa-Dong
Seo-Ku, Incheon, 404-250, Korea (South)
Tel.: (82) 32 584 3713
Fax: (82) 32 816 4817
E-Mail: export@duorest.co.kr
Web Site: www.duorest.com
Year Founded: 1987
073190—(KRS)
Business Description:
Office Furniture Mfr
S.I.C.: 2522
N.A.I.C.S.: 337214
Personnel:
Kwan-Young Jung *(CEO)*

DUOYUAN INVESTMENTS LIMITED
5/F Duoyuan Building 3 Jinyuan Road Daxing District
Industrial Development Zone, Beijing, 102600, China
Tel.: (86) 10 60212222
Fax: (86) 10 60212164
Web Site: www.duoyuan.com
Business Description:
Investment Holding Company
S.I.C.: 6719
N.A.I.C.S.: 551112
Personnel:
Wenhua Guo *(Chm & CEO)*
Holdings:

Duoyuan Global Water Inc. (1)
3 Jinyuan Road Daxing Industrial Development Zone
Beijing, 102600, China VG
Tel.: (86) 10 60212222
Fax: (86) 10 60212164
E-Mail: dyshui@duoyuan.com
Web Site: www.duoyuan-we.com
Sales Range: $100-124.9 Million
Emp.: 1,166
Water Treatment Equipment Supplier
S.I.C.: 4971
N.A.I.C.S.: 221310
Wenhua Guo *(Chm & CEO)*
Ronglin Qiao *(COO)*
Lixin Wang *(CTO)*

DUOYUAN PRINTING, INC. (1)
3 Jinyuan Road Daxing Industrial Development Zone
Beijing, 102600, China WY
Tel.: (86) 10 6021 2222 (70.25%)
Fax: (86) 10 6021 2164
E-Mail: ir@duoyuan.com
Web Site: www.duoyuan.com
Sales Range: $100-124.9 Million
Emp.: 1,339
Offset Printing Equipment Mfr & Supplier
S.I.C.: 3555
N.A.I.C.S.: 333244
Wenhua Guo *(Chm)*
Xiqing Diao *(CEO)*
Baiyun Sun *(CFO)*
Wenzhong Liu *(COO)*
Yubao Wei *(CTO)*

DUQUETTE CONSTRUCTION
2336 Chemin de la Petite Cote
Laval, QC, H7L 5N1, Canada
Tel.: (450) 622-8111
Fax: (450) 682-6414
E-Mail: info@duquetteconstruction.com
Web Site: www.duquetteconstruction.com
Year Founded: 1964
Rev.: $12,115,163
Emp.: 1
Business Description:
Building Construction Services
S.I.C.: 1542
N.A.I.C.S.: 236220
Personnel:
Donat Duquette *(Founder)*

DURA UNDERCUSHIONS LTD.
8525 Delmeade Rd
Montreal, QC, H4T 1M1, Canada
Tel.: (514) 737-6561
Fax: (514) 342-7940
Toll Free: (800) 295-4126
E-Mail: info@dura-undercushions.com
Web Site: www.duracushion.com
Year Founded: 1957
Sales Range: $10-24.9 Million
Emp.: 30
Business Description:
Carpet Cushion Underpadding Mfr Import Export
S.I.C.: 2299
N.A.I.C.S.: 313210
Personnel:
Michael N. Wilson *(Pres)*

DURABUILT WINDOWS & DOORS
10920 178 Street
Edmonton, AB, T5S 1R7, Canada
Tel.: (780) 455-0440
Fax: (780) 455-5775
Toll Free: (800) 544-3815
E-Mail: information@durabuiltwindows.com
Web Site: www.durabuiltwindows.com
Year Founded: 1989
Rev.: $89,500,000
Emp.: 450
Business Description:
Windows & Doors Mfr
S.I.C.: 2431
N.A.I.C.S.: 321911
Personnel:
Harry Sunner *(VP)*

DURAN VENTURES INC.
40 University Avenue Suite 710
Toronto, ON, M5J 1T1, Canada
Tel.: (416) 867-1591
Fax: (416) 479-4371
E-Mail: info@duranventuresinc.com
Web Site: www.duranventuresinc.com
Year Founded: 1997
DRV—(TSXV)

Duran Ventures Inc.—(Continued)

Assets: $3,580,430
Liabilities: $451,854
Net Worth: $3,128,577
Earnings: ($4,703,780)
Fiscal Year-end: 12/31/12

Business Description:
Mineral Exploration Services
S.I.C.: 1081
N.A.I.C.S.: 213114

Personnel:
Joseph Del Campo *(Chm)*
Jeffrey J. Reeder *(Pres & CEO)*
Daniel Hamilton *(CFO & Sec)*
Carmen Yuen *(Treas)*

Board of Directors:
Joseph Del Campo
Alex Black
Steve Brunelle
Oscar Francisco Pezo Camacho
David Prins
Jeffrey J. Reeder
John P. Thompson

Transfer Agent:
Equity Financial Trust Company
200 University Avenue Suite 400
Toronto, ON, Canada

Non-U.S. Subsidiary:

Minera Aguila de Oro SAC **(1)**
Calle Juan De Arona No 670 Dpto 401
Miraflores
San Isidro, Lima, Peru
Tel.: (51) 1 4221467
Mineral Mining Services
S.I.C.: 1499
N.A.I.C.S.: 212399

DURANCE GRANULATS

Route De La Durance
13860 Peyrolles-en-Provence, ne, France
Tel.: (33) 442670930
Fax: (33) 442670931
E-Mail: informations@durance-granulats.fr
Web Site: www.durance-granulats.fr
Sales Range: $25-49.9 Million
Emp.: 65

Business Description:
Construction Sand & Gravel Mining
S.I.C.: 1442
N.A.I.C.S.: 212321

Personnel:
Henri Albert *(Pres)*
Bernard Soulas *(CEO)*

DURAND SA

16 Rue De La Tour De Varan
42700 Firminy, Loire, France
Tel.: (33) 477563566
Sales Range: $10-24.9 Million
Emp.: 70

Business Description:
New & Used Car Dealers
S.I.C.: 5511
N.A.I.C.S.: 441110

Personnel:
Bernard Durand *(Pres)*

DURAND SERVICES

301 Rue Louis Neel ZI du Levatel
38 140 Saint Etienne, Rives sur Fure, France
Tel.: (33) 476914602
Fax: (33) 476911052
Web Site: www.durandservices.fr
Rev.: $23,700,000
Emp.: 120

Business Description:
Automotive Repair Shops
S.I.C.: 7539
N.A.I.C.S.: 811118

Personnel:
Chantal Durand *(Gen Mgr)*

DURANGO RESOURCES INC.

(Formerly Atocha Resources Inc.)
248 515 West Pender Street
Vancouver, BC, V6B 6H5, Canada
Tel.: (604) 428-2900
Fax: (888) 266-3983
Web Site: www.durangoresourcesinc.com
Year Founded: 2006
DGO—(TSXV)
Assets: $670,195
Liabilities: $72,815
Net Worth: $597,380
Earnings: ($1,473,719)
Fiscal Year-end: 07/31/13

Business Description:
Metal Mining Services
S.I.C.: 1099
N.A.I.C.S.: 212299

Personnel:
Marcy Kiesman *(Pres & CEO)*
Veronica Liu *(CFO)*

Board of Directors:
Peter M. Dimmell
Marcy Kiesman
Veronica Liu

Transfer Agent:
Computershare Investor Services Inc.
100 University Ave 9th Floor
Toronto, ON, Canada

DURISOL RAALTE B.V.

Almelosestraat 83
8102 HC Raalte, Netherlands

Mailing Address:
PO Box 40
8100 AA Raalte, Netherlands
Tel.: (31) 572346400
Fax: (31) 572346499
E-Mail: info@durisol.nl
Web Site: www.durisol.nl
Year Founded: 1904
Emp.: 40

Business Description:
Sound Insulation Technology & Wood Fibre Concrete Mfr
S.I.C.: 3272
N.A.I.C.S.: 327390

Personnel:
John Dogger *(Fin Dir)*

DURO DAKOVIC HOLDING D.D.

Dr Mile Budaka 1
35000 Slavonski Brod, Croatia
Tel.: (385) 35446256
Fax: (385) 354441018
E-Mail: uprava@duro-dakovic.com
Web Site: www.duro-dakovic.com
Year Founded: 1921
Emp.: 4,200

Business Description:
Holding Company
S.I.C.: 6719
N.A.I.C.S.: 551112

Personnel:
Leo Begovic *(Chm-Supervisory Bd)*
Marko Milic *(Vice Chm-Supervisory Bd)*
Marija Tolic *(Member-Mgmt Bd)*

Supervisory Board of Directors:
Leo Begovic
Pavo Durdevic
Leopoldina Duvnjak
Marko Milic
Mato Oroz
Zoran Posinovec

Subsidiaries:

Duro Dakovic Elektromont d.d. **(1)**
Dr Mile Budaka 1
35 000 Slavonski Brod, Croatia
Tel.: (385) 35 446 089
Fax: (385) 35 448 329
E-Mail: dd-elektromont@sb.htnet.hr
Web Site: www.dd-elektromont.com
Electricity Generation Services
S.I.C.: 4911
N.A.I.C.S.: 221122

Duro Dakovic Energetika i infrastruktura d.o.o. **(1)**
Dr Mile Budaka 1
35 000 Slavonski Brod, Croatia
Tel.: (385) 35 218 010
Fax: (385) 35 218 818
E-Mail: dd-energetika-infrastruktura@sb.htnet.hr
Energy & Infrastructure Services
S.I.C.: 4911
N.A.I.C.S.: 221122

Duro Dakovic Inzenjering d.d. **(1)**
Dr Mile Budaka 1
35 000 Slavonski Brod, Croatia
Tel.: (385) 35 448 324
Fax: (385) 35 441 113
E-Mail: dd-inzenjering@sb-t-com.hr
Web Site: www.dd-inzenjering.com
Emp.: 15
Engineering Services
S.I.C.: 8711
N.A.I.C.S.: 541330
Hrvoje Kekez *(Exec Dir)*

Duro Dakovic Proizvodnja opreme d.o.o. **(1)**
Dr Mile Budaka 1
35 000 Slavonski Brod, Croatia
Tel.: (385) 35 218 409
Fax: (385) 35 218 422
E-Mail: pavao.ancic@dd-po.hr
Web Site: www.duro-dakovic.com
Engineering Services
S.I.C.: 8711
N.A.I.C.S.: 541330

Duro Dakovic Slobodna zona d.o.o. **(1)**
Dr Mile Budaka 1
35 000 Slavonski Brod, Croatia
Tel.: (385) 35 218 621
Fax: (385) 35 218 807
E-Mail: josip.salantic@freezone-dd.sb.t-com.hr
Web Site: www.freezone-brod.hr
Engineering Services
S.I.C.: 8711
N.A.I.C.S.: 541330

Duro Dakovic Specijalna vozila d.d. **(1)**
Dr Mile Budaka 1
35 000 Slavonski Brod, Croatia
Tel.: (385) 35 446 045
Fax: (385) 35 446 181
E-Mail: marketing@ddsv.hr
Web Site: www.ddsv.hr
Engineering Services
S.I.C.: 8711
N.A.I.C.S.: 541330

Duro Dakovic Strojna obrada d.o.o. **(1)**
Dr Mile Budaka 1
35 000 Slavonski Brod, Croatia
Tel.: (385) 35 446 469
Fax: (385) 35 444 702
E-Mail: hrvoje.kekez@strojan-obrada.hr
Web Site: www.strojna-obrada.hr
Emp.: 136
Engineering Services
S.I.C.: 8711
N.A.I.C.S.: 541330
Christian Kochmann *(Gen Mgr)*

DURO DE MEXICO, S.A. DE C.V.

Ave 498 Parqe Industrial Cartadema 10 Piso
Col Cuauhtemoc CP, 31110 Mexico, DF, Mexico
Tel.: (52) 5558992740
Fax: (52) 5558881466
E-Mail: sales@duromex.com.mx
Web Site: www.duromex.com.mx
Year Founded: 1968
Sales Range: $10-24.9 Million
Emp.: 300

Business Description:
Mfr. of Lamps & Lighting Products
S.I.C.: 3648
N.A.I.C.S.: 335129

Personnel:
Andres Wilson *(Mgr-Export Sls)*

DURO FELGUERA, S.A.

Parque Cientifico Tecnologico C/ Ada Byron 90
33203 Gijon, Spain
Tel.: (34) 985199132
Fax: (34) 985109050
E-Mail: direccion.desarrollo@durofelguera.com
Web Site: www.durofelguera.com
Year Founded: 1858
MDF—(MAD)
Rev.: $1,233,484,802
Assets: $1,552,256,511
Liabilities: $1,133,516,871
Net Worth: $418,739,640
Earnings: $158,973,254
Emp.: 1,807
Fiscal Year-end: 12/31/12

Business Description:
Construction Engineering Services
S.I.C.: 8711
N.A.I.C.S.: 541330

Personnel:
Angel Antonio del Valle Suarez *(Chm & CEO)*
Juan Gonzalo Alvarez Arrojo *(Vice Chm)*
Pedro Peon Tamargo *(CFO)*
Francisco J. Alaez Diez *(CIO & Sr VP-Engrg)*
Jesus Salmeron Unturbe *(Gen Counsel)*
Secundino Felgueroso Fuentes *(Sec)*
Angel Guijarro Castro *(Exec VP-Oil & Gas)*
Fernando Lopez Gonzalez *(Exec VP-Mfg)*
Roberto Perez Lopez *(Exec VP-Mining & Handling)*
Rafael Murillo Quiros *(Exec VP-Energy)*
Juan Jose Herrero Rodriguez *(Exec VP-Svcs)*
Emilio Seoane Fidalgo *(Sr VP-Procurement)*
Jose Luis Fernaandez Getino *(Sr VP-Sls)*
Juan Outeiral Viana *(Sr VP-HR)*

Board of Directors:
Angel Antonio del Valle Suarez
Jose Antonio Aguilera Izquierdo
Marta Aguilera Martinez
Juan Gonzalo Alvarez Arrojo
Ramiro Arias Lopez
Acacio Faustino Rodriguez Garcia
Javier Sierra Villa
Carlos Solchage Catalan
Francisco Javier Valero Artola

Subsidiaries:

DF Mompresa, S.A.U. **(1)**
Calle Ada Byron Pq Cientifico Y Tecnologico 90
Gijon, Asturias, 33203, Spain
Tel.: (34) 985 35 53 77
Turbine Fitting & Maintenance Services
S.I.C.: 7699
N.A.I.C.S.: 811310

Duro Felguera Oil & Gas S.A. **(1)**
Parque Empresarial Las Rozas C/ Jacinto Benavente 4
28230 Las Rozas, Spain
Tel.: (34) 91 640 20 51
Fax: (34) 91 640 21 00
E-Mail: oilgas@durofelguera.com
Industrial Pressure Vessel Mfr
S.I.C.: 3443
N.A.I.C.S.: 332420

Duro Felguera Plantas Industriales, S.A.U. (1)
Edif Centro de Protectros e Ingenieria
C/Hornos Altos S/N Le Felguera
Asturias, 33203, Spain
Tel.: (34) 98 567 98 25
Fax: (34) 98 567 65 45
Waste Management Services
S.I.C.: 4953
N.A.I.C.S.: 562920

Non-U.S. Subsidiary:

Felguera Gruas India Private Limited (2)
3rd Floor 10-50-24/A Sravya Manor
Siripuram, Visakhapatnam, Andhra Pradesh, 530003, India
Tel.: (91) 891 255 8343
Fax: (91) 891 255 8345
E-Mail: fgi@durofelguera.com
Web Site: www.fgindia.com
Construction Engineering Services
S.I.C.: 8711
N.A.I.C.S.: 541330
T. P. Chakrapani *(Head-Fin & Acct)*

Felguera Caldereria Pesada, S.A.U. (1)
Travesia del Mar s/n
33212 Gijon, Spain
Tel.: (34) 98 532 26 00
Fax: (34) 98 532 56 50
E-Mail: fcpsales@fcp.durofelguera.com
Industrial Pressure Vessel Mfr
S.I.C.: 3443
N.A.I.C.S.: 332420
Ana Bernardo *(Gen Mgr)*

Felguera Construcciones Mecanicas, S.A.U. (1)
Crta de Langreo-Oviedo s/n
Barros, 33930 Langreo, Spain
Tel.: (34) 98 567 97 00
Fax: (34) 98 567 97 02
E-Mail: fcm@durofelguera.com
Mechanical Equipment Mfr
S.I.C.: 3589
N.A.I.C.S.: 333318

Felguera Melt, S.A.U. (1)
Prolg Ing Fernando Casariego s/n
La Felguera, 33930 Langreo, Spain
Tel.: (34) 98 569 56 11
Fax: (34) 98 569 64 65
E-Mail: fmelt@durofelguera.com
Construction Engineering Services
S.I.C.: 8711
N.A.I.C.S.: 541330

Felguera Rail, S.A.U. (1)
Ablana s/nn
33600 Mieres, Spain
Tel.: (34) 98 545 41 47
Fax: (34) 98 545 39 03
E-Mail: frail@durofelguera.com
Railway Equipment Mfr
S.I.C.: 3559
N.A.I.C.S.: 333249

Nucleo de Comunicaciones y Control, S.L. (1)
Av de la Industria 24
28760 Tres Cantos, Spain
Tel.; (34) 91 807 39 99
Fax: (34) 91 803 18 04
E-Mail: nucleo@nucleocc.com
Construction Engineering Services
S.I.C.: 8711
N.A.I.C.S.: 541330

Tecnicas de Entibacion, S.A.U. (1)
Poligono de Silvota parcela 10
33192 Llanera, Spain
Tel.: (34) 98 526 04 64
Fax: (34) 98 526 14 16
E-Mail: tedesa@durofelguera.com
Industrial Equipment Mfr
S.I.C.: 3589
N.A.I.C.S.: 333318

Non-U.S. Subsidiaries:

DF DO BRASIL DESENVOLVIMIENTO DE PROJETOS LTDA (1)
Rua da Quitanda n 52 11 andar
Rio de Janeiro, 20011-030, Brazil
Tel.: (55) 21 2505 2600
E-Mail: danielle.martins@durofelguera.com
Construction Engineering Services
S.I.C.: 8711
N.A.I.C.S.: 541330

Duro Felguera Industrial Projects Consulting Co., Ltd. (1)
Suite 2001 West Gate Mall 1038 Nanjing Xi Lu
200041 Shanghai, China
Tel.: (86) 21 621 80301
Fax: (86) 159 211 95952
E-Mail: eduardo.garciajul@durofelguera.com
Construction Engineering Services
S.I.C.: 8711
N.A.I.C.S.: 541330

PT Duro Felguera Indonesia (1)
Ariobimo Sentral Building 4th fl Jl HR Rasuna Said Kav X-2/5
Jakarta, 12950, Indonesia
Tel.: (62) 21 5270737
Fax: (62) 21 2525760
Construction Engineering Services
S.I.C.: 8711
N.A.I.C.S.: 541330
Sad Adi Nugroho *(Project Mgr)*

Turbogeneradores del Peru, S.A.C. (1)
C/ Pablo Carriquiry Maure 222
San Isidro, Lima, Peru
Tel.: (51) 1 2421672
Fax: (51) 1 5776924
Industrial Equipment Maintenance Services
S.I.C.: 7699
N.A.I.C.S.: 811310

DUROC AB

Reprovaegen 15
SE-183 77 Taby, Sweden
Mailing Address:
PO Box 340
SE-183 13 Taby, Sweden
Tel.: (46) 87891130
Fax: (46) 87891131
E-Mail: info@duroc.com
Web Site: www.duroc.com
DURC-B—(OMX)
Sales Range: $75-99.9 Million
Emp.: 300

Business Description:
Metallic Materials & Components Surface Refinement Using Laser Technology
S.I.C.: 3341
N.A.I.C.S.: 331492

Personnel:
Erik Albinsson *(CEO & Mng Dir)*
Hakan Cranneng *(CFO)*

Board of Directors:
Sten-Ake Aronsson
Klas Astrom
Lennart Pihl
Bo Richter
Petter Stillstrom

Subsidiaries:

Duroc Engineering i Goteborg AB (1)
Importgatan 19-21
SE-422 46 Hisings Backa, Sweden
Tel.: (46) 31525265
Fax: (46) 31529187
E-Mail: magmmuqs.edem@duroc.com
Web Site: www.duroc.se
Emp.: 10
Laser Refined Surface Products for Industry
S.I.C.: 3589
N.A.I.C.S.: 333318
Magmmuqs Edem *(Mng Dir)*

Duroc Engineering i Helsingborg AB (1)
Lagerhaggsgatan 7
SE-256 68 Helsingborg, Sweden
Tel.: (46) 42240420
Fax: (46) 4224 0820
Laser Refined Surface Products for Industry
S.I.C.: 3541
N.A.I.C.S.: 333517

Duroc Engineering i Umea AB (1)
Industrivagen 8
SE-90130 Umea, Sweden
Tel.: (46) 90711700
Fax: (46) 90711719
E-Mail: engineering@duroc.se
Web Site: www.duroc.se
Emp.: 12
Laser Refined Surface Products for Industry
S.I.C.: 3589
N.A.I.C.S.: 333318
Daniel Eriksson *(Mgr-Sls)*

Duroc Machine Tool AB (1)
Reprovagen 15
183 77 Taby, Sweden
Mailing Address:
PO Box 340
183 13 Taby, Sweden
Tel.: (46) 8630 2300
Fax: (46) 8630 2301
E-Mail: info.machinetool.se@duroc.com
Web Site: www.durocmachinetool.com
Emp.: 45
Machine Tool Mfr
S.I.C.: 3542
N.A.I.C.S.: 333517
Juergen Engelbrecht *(Mng Dir)*

Duroc Rail AB (1)
Kontorsgatan 37
Lulea, Sweden
Tel.: (46) 92035404
Fax: (46) 92035405
E-Mail: info@duroc.se
Web Site: www.duroc.se
Emp.: 30
Railway Wheels Maintenance Services
S.I.C.: 4789
N.A.I.C.S.: 488210
Ban Bergman *(Mng Dir)*

Non-U.S. Subsidiaries:

SFW Schienenfahrzeugwerk Delitzsch GmbH (2)
Karl-Marx-Strsse 39
D-04509 Delitzsch, Germany
Tel.: (49) 3420253026
Fax: (49) 3420256045
E-Mail: info@sfw-delitzsch.de
Web Site: www.sfw-delitzsch.de
Emp.: 226
Rail Services
S.I.C.: 4789
N.A.I.C.S.: 488210
Hermann Weise *(Mng Dir)*

Duroc Special Steel AB (1)
Svartons Industriomrade
SE-971 88 Lulea, Sweden
Tel.: (46) 920 43 22 00
Fax: (46) 920 25 58 56
E-Mail: info.specialsteel@duroc.com
Web Site: www.duroc.com
Emp.: 36
Carbon Steel Mfr & Distr
S.I.C.: 3312
N.A.I.C.S.: 331110
Niclas Lidstrom *(Gen Mgr)*

Duroc Tooling i Olofstrom AB (1)
Ingenjorsgatan 26
SE-293 24 Olofstrom, Sweden
Tel.: (46) 45448930
Fax: (46) 45448933
E-Mail: olofstrom@duroc.se
Web Site: www.duroc.se
Emp.: 7
Metalworking Machines Mfr
S.I.C.: 3542
N.A.I.C.S.: 333517
Jan Kvist *(Plant Mgr)*

Micor AB (1)
Industrigatan 10
SE-312 34 Laholm, Sweden SE
Tel.: (46) 4304 9200
Fax: (46) 4304 9201
E-Mail: info@micor.se
Web Site: www.micor.se
Emp.: 35
Saw Blade Mfr
S.I.C.: 3553
N.A.I.C.S.: 333243
Bjoern Bernsfelt *(Mng Dir & Mgr-Market)*
Yvonn Lunderot *(CFO)*

Swedish Saw Blades AB (1)
Industrigatan 10
SE-312 34 Laholm, Sweden
Tel.: (46) 43049205
Fax: (46) 43049201
Web Site: www.swesaw.se
Industrial Saw Blades Mfr
S.I.C.: 3423
N.A.I.C.S.: 332216
Patrik Jenemark *(Mng Dir)*

Affiliate:

Impact Coatings AB (1)
Westmansgatan 29
SE-582 16 Linkoping, Sweden
Tel.: (46) 013103780
Fax: (46) 13103790
E-Mail: info@impactcoatings.se
Web Site: www.impactcoatings.se
Thin Film Coating Development & Services
S.I.C.: 3479
N.A.I.C.S.: 332812
Torsten Rosell *(Chm)*
Henrik Ljungcrantz *(CEO)*

Non-U.S. Subsidiaries:

Duroc Machine Tool AS (1)
Besoek Anolitveien 7
1401 Ski, Norway
Tel.: (47) 64 91 48 80
Fax: (47) 64 91 48 90
E-Mail: info.machinetool.no@duroc.com
Emp.: 5
Machine Tools Distr
S.I.C.: 5084
N.A.I.C.S.: 423830
Jan-Erik Stokkebek *(Gen Mgr)*

Duroc Machine Tool OU (1)
Voru 47e
50111 Tartu, Estonia
Tel.: (372) 736 6648
Fax: (372) 736 2264
E-Mail: info@duroc.ee
Emp.: 5
Machine Tools Distr
S.I.C.: 5084
N.A.I.C.S.: 423830
Peeter Sekavin *(Country Mgr)*

Duroc Machine Tool SIA (1)
Tilta 12/2
Riga, 1005, Latvia
Tel.: (371) 67355175
Fax: (371) 67355176
Machine Tools Mfr
S.I.C.: 3542
N.A.I.C.S.: 333517

Gomex Tools Ltd (1)
Unit 1 Phoenix Court Denington I/E
Wellingborough, Northamptonshire, NN8 2QE, United Kingdom
Tel.: (44) 19 33 22 81 85
Fax: (44) 19 33 22 92 24
E-Mail: info@gomex.co.uk
Web Site: www.micor.se/default.asp?ML=97
Emp.: 3
Saw Blades Mfr
S.I.C.: 3554
N.A.I.C.S.: 333243
Peter Newiadomy *(Mgr)*

DURON ONTARIO LTD.

1860 Shawson Drive
Mississauga, ON, L4W 1R7, Canada
Tel.: (905) 670-1998
Fax: (905) 670-4662
E-Mail: info@duron.ca
Web Site: www.duron.ca
Rev.: $43,472,475
Emp.: 70

Business Description:
Flooring, Roofing & Restoration Services
S.I.C.: 1752
N.A.I.C.S.: 238330

Personnel:
John Schenk *(Sr Partner)*

DUROPACK LTD

B-4/160 Safdarjung Enclave
New Delhi, 110029, India
Tel.: (91) 11 26183275
Fax: (91) 11 26177280
E-Mail: duropack@vsnl.com

DUROPACK LTD—(Continued)

Web Site: www.duropackindia.com
Year Founded: 1988
526355—(BOM)
Rev.: $1,636,347
Assets: $1,043,783
Liabilities: $145,316
Net Worth: $898,467
Earnings: $86,461
Fiscal Year-end: 03/31/13

Business Description:
Holographic Product Mfr & Distr
S.I.C.: 2678
N.A.I.C.S.: 322230

Personnel:
Vivek Jain *(Mng Dir & Compliance Officer)*

Board of Directors:
Sharad Aggarwal
Sachi Chaudhuri
Krishan Kumar Gupta
Vineet Jain
Vivek Jain
Vikram Vijh

Transfer Agent:
Abhipra Capital Limited
Abhipra Complex A-307 Dilkush Industrial Area
GT Road Azadpur
Delhi, India

DURR AG

Carl Benz Strasse 34
74321 Bietigheim-Bissingen, Germany
Tel.: (49) 7142780
Telex: 7252194
Fax: (49) 7142781716
E-Mail: corpcom@durr.com
Web Site: www.durr.com
Year Founded: 1895
DUE—(DEU)
Rev.: $3,230,579,151
Assets: $2,433,478,240
Liabilities: $1,851,822,414
Net Worth: $581,655,826
Earnings: $149,943,145
Emp.: 7,652
Fiscal Year-end: 12/31/12

Business Description:
Automotive Products Whslr
Export
S.I.C.: 5012
N.A.I.C.S.: 423110

Personnel:
Ralf W. Dieter *(Chm-Mgmt Bd & CEO)*
Hayo Raich *(Deputy Chm-Supervisory Bd)*
Norbert Loos *(Deputy Chm-Supervisory Bd)*
Ralph Heuwing *(CFO)*
Sandra Bieberstein *(Corp Comm & IR Officer)*
Martina Rusing *(Corp Comm & IR Officer)*
Katja Stiber *(Corp Comm & IR Officer)*
Astrid Weisseise *(Corp Comm & IR Officer)*

Supervisory Board of Directors:
Stefan Albert
Mirko Becker
Alexandra Durr
Klaus Eberhardt
Thomas Hohmann
Guido Lesch
Norbert Loos
Herbert Muller
Hayo Raich
Martin Schwarz-Kocher
Karl-Heinz Streibich
Klaus Wucherer

Subsidiaries:

Durr Assembly Products GmbH **(1)**
Kollner Strasse 122 - 128
66346 Puttlingen, Germany
Tel.: (49) 6898 692 0
Fax: (49) 6898 692 5400
E-Mail: durr-ap@durr.com
Web Site: www.durr-ap.de
Emp.: 300
Vehicle Assembly Testing & Repair Services
S.I.C.: 7539
N.A.I.C.S.: 811198
Horst Hartmann *(Mng Dir)*

Durr Automotion GmbH **(1)**
Gewerbestrasse 1
Industriegebiet Ost, D 79639 Grenzach-Wyhlen, Germany (100%)
Tel.: (49) 7624310
Fax: (49) 76244045
E-Mail: dsmh@durr.com
Web Site: www.durr.com
Emp.: 14
Provider of Turnkey Paint Shops to the Automotive Industry
S.I.C.: 7532
N.A.I.C.S.: 811121
Ralf Dieter *(CEO)*

Durr Automotion GmbH **(1)**
Carl-Benz-Strasse 34
74321 Bietigheim-Bissingen, Germany
Tel.: (49) 71113600
Fax: (49) 7142782107
E-Mail: corpcom@durr.com
Web Site: www.durr.com
Emp.: 1,500
Turnkey Paint Shops to the Automotive Industry
S.I.C.: 7532
N.A.I.C.S.: 811121
Ralph Dieter *(CEO)*

Durr Ecoclean GmbH **(1)**
Hans-Georg-Weiss-Str 10
Monschau, 52156 Berlin, Germany (100%)
Tel.: (49) 2472830
Fax: (49) 247283165
E-Mail: info@durr.com
Web Site: www.durr-ecoclean.com
Emp.: 200
Industry Machinery Manufacturing
S.I.C.: 7532
N.A.I.C.S.: 811121
William Bell *(Mng Dir)*

Durr Ecoclean GmbH **(1)**
Muhlenstrasse 12
D 70794 Filderstadt, Germany (100%)
Tel.: (49) 71170060
Fax: (49) 711703674
E-Mail: info@ecocleandurr.com
Web Site: www.durr-ecoclean.com
Sls.: $257,977,504
Emp.: 200
Industrial Machinery
S.I.C.: 3569
N.A.I.C.S.: 333999
Fritz Dorner *(Chm)*

Durr IT Service GmbH **(1)**
Carl-Benz-Str 34
74321 Bietigheim-Bissingen, Baden-Wurttemberg, Germany
Tel.: (49) 711 1360
Fax: (49) 714 2782107
Web Site: www.durr-it-service.com
Information Technology Consulting Services
S.I.C.: 7373
N.A.I.C.S.: 541512
Ursula Ziwey *(Gen Mgr)*

Durr Somac GmbH **(1)**
Zwickauer Strasse 30
9366 Stollberg, Germany
Tel.: (49) 37296 547 0
Fax: (49) 37296 547 300
E-Mail: office@somac-filling.com
Web Site: www.somac-filling.com
Emp.: 15
Filling Equipment Mfr
S.I.C.: 3559
N.A.I.C.S.: 333249
Bernd Preissler *(Mng Dir)*

Durr Systems GmbH **(1)**
Schutzenstrasse 142
Ochtrup, 48607 Berlin, Germany (100%)
Tel.: (49) 25539270
Fax: (49) 25538100
E-Mail: peter.naepfel@durr.com
Web Site: www.durr.com
Emp.: 40
Environmental Systems & Automation & Conveyor Systems
S.I.C.: 3535
N.A.I.C.S.: 333922
Peter Naepfel *(Chm)*

Durr Systems GmbH **(1)**
Carl-Benz-Strasse 34
74321 Bietigheim-Bissingen, Germany (100%)
Tel.: (49) 7111360
Fax: (49) 7142782107
E-Mail: corpcom@durr.com
Emp.: 1,500
Environmental Systems & Automation & Conveyor Systems
S.I.C.: 1731
N.A.I.C.S.: 238210
Ralph Dieter *(Chm-Mgmt Bd)*

Durr Systems GmbH **(1)**
Rosenstrasse 39
D74321 Bietigheim-Bissingen, Bietigheim Bissingen, Germany (100%)
Tel.: (49) 497142780
Fax: (49) 7142782107
E-Mail: durr.systems.bietigheim@durr.com
Web Site: www.durr.com
Environmental Systems & Automation & Conveyor Systems
S.I.C.: 3535
N.A.I.C.S.: 333922

Durr Systems Wolfsburg GmbH **(1)**
Westrampe 8
38442 Wolfsburg, Germany
Tel.: (49) 5362 9637 0
Fax: (49) 5362 963750
E-Mail: info@intgmbh.com
Paint & Coating Mfr
S.I.C.: 2851
N.A.I.C.S.: 325510

Schenck RoTec GmbH **(1)**
Landwehrstrasse 55
64293 Darmstadt, Germany
Tel.: (49) 61 51 32 23 11
Fax: (49) 61 51 32 23 15
E-Mail: rotec@schenck.net
Web Site: www.schenck-rotec.de
Sls.: $283,160,000
Emp.: 110
Diagnostic System Mfr
S.I.C.: 3845
N.A.I.C.S.: 334510
Ralf-Michael Fuchs *(Co-Mng Dir)*
Franz Peter Matheis *(Co-Mng Dir)*

Non-U.S. Subsidiary:

Datatechnic S.A.S. **(2)**
5 Impasse Du Stade
88390 Uxegney, France
Tel.: (33) 3 29 81 26 80
Web Site: www.datatechnic.net
Sls.: $84,568,960
Emp.: 34
Balancing Machinery Mfr
S.I.C.: 3559
N.A.I.C.S.: 333249
Rene Baer *(Pres)*
Regis Fond *(CFO)*
William Bocquenet *(COO)*

Schenck Technologie und Industriepark GmbH **(1)**
Landwehrstrasse 55
64293 Darmstadt, Germany
Tel.: (49) 6151 32 1200
Fax: (49) 6151 32 3800
E-Mail: schenck-technologiepark@schenck.net
Web Site: www.schenck-technologiepark.de
Infrastructure Management Services
S.I.C.: 7389
N.A.I.C.S.: 561499

U.S. Subsidiaries:

Durr Automation, Inc. **(1)**
40600 Plymouth Rd
Plymouth, MI 48170-4247 (100%)
Tel.: (248) 960-4630
Fax: (248) 960-4633
Toll Free: (866) 387-7178
Web Site: www.durrautomation.com
Sales Range: $10-24.9 Million
Emp.: 85
Industrial Automation
S.I.C.: 3535
N.A.I.C.S.: 333922

Durr Ecoclean Inc **(1)**
31077 Durr Dr
Wixom, MI 48393
Tel.: (248) 560-2100
Fax: (248) 560-2120
E-Mail: info.usa@ecoclean.durr.com
Web Site: www.durr-ecoclean.com
Industrial Cleaning Machinery Whslr
S.I.C.: 5084
N.A.I.C.S.: 423830

Durr Environmental Inc. **(1)**
40600 Plymouth Rd
Plymouth, MI 48170
Tel.: (734) 459-6800
Fax: (734) 459-5837
E-Mail: sales@durrenvironmental.com
Web Site: www.durr.com
Emp.: 250
Paint Finishing Systems
S.I.C.: 3567
N.A.I.C.S.: 333994
Dave Maynell *(Pres)*

Durr Inc. **(1)**
40600 Plymouth Rd
Plymouth, MI 48170-4297
Tel.: (734) 459-6800
Fax: (734) 459-5837
Web Site: www.durr.com
Emp.: 300
Automobile Component Mfr
S.I.C.: 3714
N.A.I.C.S.: 336390

Durr Industries, Inc. **(1)**
40600 Plymouth Rd
Plymouth, MI 48170-4247 (100%)
Tel.: (734) 459-6800
Fax: (734) 459-5837
Web Site: www.durr.com
Sales Range: $75-99.9 Million
Emp.: 210
Paint Finishing Systems, Industrial Cleaning Systems, Automation & Conveyor Systems, Environmental Systems & Paint Application Systems
S.I.C.: 3559
N.A.I.C.S.: 333249
Bruno Welsh *(Pres & CEO)*

Durr Systems, Inc. **(1)**
2469 Executive Hills Dr
Auburn Hills, MI 48326-2981 (100%)
Tel.: (248) 745-8500
Fax: (248) 745-8586
E-Mail: behr@behr.durr-usa.com
Web Site: www.durr.com
Sales Range: $25-49.9 Million
Emp.: 105
Paint Finishing Systems
S.I.C.: 3559
N.A.I.C.S.: 333249

Henry Filters, Inc. **(1)**
1350 Van Camp Rd
Bowling Green, OH 43402
Tel.: (419) 352-7501
Fax: (419) 352-0224
Web Site: www.durr-ecoclean.com
Emp.: 150
Environmental Systems & Automation & Conveyor Systems
S.I.C.: 3569
N.A.I.C.S.: 333999
Roy Martinez *(VP-Ops)*

H.R. Black Co. Inc. **(1)**
1350 Van Camp Rd
Bowling Green, OH 43402
Tel.: (419) 352-7501
Fax: (419) 352-0224
E-Mail: info@durr-ecoclean.com
Web Site: www.durr-ecoclean.com
Environmental Systems & Automation & Conveyor Systems
S.I.C.: 3569
N.A.I.C.S.: 333999
Roy Martinez *(VP)*

Schenck RoTec Corporation **(1)**
2469 Executive Hills Blvd
Auburn Hills, MI 48326-2981
Tel.: (248) 377-2100

Fax: (248) 783-1362
E-Mail: sales@schenck-usa.com
Web Site: www.schenck-usa.com
Automotive Balancing & Diagnostic System Mfr
S.I.C.: 3714
N.A.I.C.S.: 336390
Bertram Dittmar *(Pres)*

Schenck Trebel Corporation (1)
535 Acorn St
Deer Park, NY 11729
Tel.: (631) 242-4010
Fax: (631) 242-4147
Toll Free: (800) 873-2352
E-Mail: sales@schenck-usa.com
Web Site: www.schenck-usa.com
Industrial Balancing System Mfr
S.I.C.: 3559
N.A.I.C.S.: 333249
Bertram Dittmar *(Pres)*

Non-U.S. Subsidiaries:

Carl Schenck Machines en Installaties B.V (1)
Schiedamsedijk 65a-66a
3011 EJ Rotterdam, Netherlands
Tel.: (31) 10 4117540
Fax: (31) 10 4115687
Web Site: www.schenck-rotec.nl
Industrial Machinery Mfr
S.I.C.: 3559
N.A.I.C.S.: 333249

CPM S.p.A. (1)
Via San Luigi 4
I 10092 Beinasco, TO, Italy
Tel.: (39) 0113988424
Fax: (39) 0113988470
E-Mail: cpm@cpm-spa.com
Web Site: www.cpm-spa.com
Emp.: 50
Paint Finishing Systems
S.I.C.: 2851
N.A.I.C.S.: 325510
Mariza Batteano *(Mgr-Acctg)*

Durr AIS S.A. de C.V. (1)
Calle Urbina No 6
Parque Industrial
Naucalpan de Juarez, 53370 Naucalpan, Mexico
Tel.: (52) 5553291188
Fax: (52) 55 53 29 39 23
E-Mail: durr.mexico@durrmex.com.mx
Environmental Systems & Automation & Conveyor Systems
S.I.C.: 3822
N.A.I.C.S.: 334512

Durr Anlagenbau GmbH (1)
Durrweg 2
2225 Zistersdorf, Austria (100%)
Tel.: (43) 25322546
Fax: (43) 25322545
E-Mail: durr.zistersdorf@durr.com
Web Site: www.durr.com
Sales Range: $1-9.9 Million
Emp.: 80
Environmental Systems & Automation & Conveyor Systems
S.I.C.: 3822
N.A.I.C.S.: 334512
Rubert Fischhuber *(Mgr-Logistics)*

Durr Brasil Ltda. (1)
Rua Arnaldo Magniccaro 500
CEP 04691 903 Sao Paulo, SP, Brazil (100%)
Tel.: (55) 156333500
Fax: (55) 156313884
E-Mail: durrbr@durr.com.br
Web Site: www.durr.com.br
Emp.: 200
Environmental Systems & Automation & Conveyor Systems
S.I.C.: 3822
N.A.I.C.S.: 334512

Durr de Mexico S.A. de C.V. (1)
Calle Urbina No 6
Parque Industrial
Naucalpan De Juarez, 53370 Mexico, Mexico (100%)
Tel.: (52) 53293900
Fax: (52) 53293923
E-Mail: Durr.mexico@durrmex.com.mx
Web Site: www.durr.com
Sales Range: $10-24.9 Million
Emp.: 90
Environmental Systems & Automation & Conveyor Systems
S.I.C.: 3822
N.A.I.C.S.: 334512

Durr Ecoclean S.A.S. (1)
Rue des Etats Unis B P No 1
72540 Loue, France FR
Tel.: (33) 243397800
Fax: (33) 2 43 39 78 01
E-Mail: info.france@ecoclean.durr.com
Industrial Cleaning Technology Mfr
S.I.C.: 3559
N.A.I.C.S.: 333249

Durr Japan K.K. (1)
Nisso Building 6th Floor 3-8-8 Shin-yokohama
Kohoku-ku, Yokohama, 222-0033, Japan
Tel.: (81) 45 47 53 67 1
Fax: (81) 45 47 53 67 2
Emp.: 4
Industrial Machinery & Equipment Whslr
S.I.C.: 5084
N.A.I.C.S.: 423830
Norio Ochiai *(Pres)*

Durr Ltd. (1)
Broxell Close
Warwick, CV 34 5QF, United Kingdom (100%)
Tel.: (44) 1926418800
Fax: (44) 1926400679
E-Mail: scurzonf@durr.co.uk
Web Site: www.durr.com
Emp.: 80
Environmental Systems & Automation & Conveyor Systems
S.I.C.: 3822
N.A.I.C.S.: 334512
Frank Coancey *(Mng Dir)*

Durr Paintshop Systems Engineering (Shanghai) Co. Ltd. (1)
28 Fl Super Ocean Finance Ctr Bldg
GUIPING, Shanghai, 200336, China CN
Tel.: (86) 2162193719 (100%)
Fax: (86) 2162194519
E-Mail: general@durr.com.cn
Web Site: www.durr.com
Emp.: 300
Mfr. of Paints
S.I.C.: 2851
N.A.I.C.S.: 325510
Reiner Schmid *(Gen Mgr)*

Durr Poland Sp. z o.o. (1)
Ul Zolkiewskiego 125
26-600 Radom, Poland
Tel.: (48) 48 36 10 100
Fax: (48) 48 36 10 101
E-Mail: durr@durr.pl
Web Site: www.durr.pl
Emp.: 15
Conveyor System Mfr & Whslr
S.I.C.: 3535
N.A.I.C.S.: 333922
Dirk Bethmann *(Pres)*
Maria Wcislik *(CFO)*

Durr South Africa (Pty.) Ltd (1)
Roshan Road Framesby
PO Box 1017
Port Elizabeth, 6070, South Africa
Tel.: (27) 41 393 54 00
Fax: (27) 41 363 58 99
E-Mail: durr@durrsa.co.za
Emp.: 4
Automotive Paint & Assembly System Mfr
S.I.C.: 2851
N.A.I.C.S.: 325510
Michael Broek *(Gen Mgr)*

Durr System Spain SA (1)
Calle Doctor Esquerdo No 136 7 Planta
E 28007 Madrid, Spain (100%)
Tel.: (34) 915517663
Fax: (34) 915011416
E-Mail: durr@durr-spain.com
Web Site: www.durr.com
Emp.: 16
Environmental Systems & Automation & Conveyor Systems
S.I.C.: 3535
N.A.I.C.S.: 333922
Carlos Ibanez *(Mgr-Sls)*

Durr Systems Makine Muhendislik Proje Ithalat ve Ihracat Ltd (1)
Kucukbakkalkoy Kayisdagi Cad 111
Atasehir, Istanbul, Turkey
Tel.: (90) 216 569 83 05
Fax: (90) 216 569 83 10
Industrial Machinery Distr
S.I.C.: 5084
N.A.I.C.S.: 423830

Durr Systems S.A.S. (1)
Immeuble Gaia - 9 Parc Ariane Boulevard Des Chenes
78280 Guyancourt, France
Tel.: (33) 1 81 88 01 40
Fax: (33) 1 81 88 02 77
E-Mail: durr.france@durr.com
Web Site: www.durr.com
Automotive Paint Assembly & Maintenance Services
S.I.C.: 7532
N.A.I.C.S.: 811121

Durr Systems Slovakia spol. s r.o. (1)
Tomasikova 50/B
83104 Bratislava, Slovakia
Tel.: (421) 41 507 84 03
Fax: (421) 41 507 84 62
E-Mail: info.slovakia@durr.com
Automotive Paint Mfr
S.I.C.: 2851
N.A.I.C.S.: 325510
Meinols Ostremwinter *(Gen Mgr)*

Durr Systems Spain (1)
Avda De Zarauz 82
Edificio Lorea, E 20009 San Sebastian, Spain (100%)
Tel.: (34) 943317000
Fax: (34) 943317200
E-Mail: durr@durr-spain.com
Web Site: www.durr-spain.com
S.I.C.: 3589
N.A.I.C.S.: 333318

Durr Systems (1)
Oruzheyny Lane 15A
125047 Moscow, Russia
Tel.: (7) 4957410051
Fax: (7) 4957410051
E-Mail: durr@durr.msk.ru
Web Site: www.durr.com
Emp.: 20
Environmental Systems & Automation & Conveyor Systems
S.I.C.: 3535
N.A.I.C.S.: 333922
Mike Droese *(Gen Mgr)*

Durrpol Sp.z.o.o. (1)
Ul Zolkiewskiego 125
PL 26600 Radom, Poland (87.5%)
Tel.: (48) 483610100
Fax: (48) 483610101
E-Mail: dur@dur.pl
Web Site: www.durrpol.com.pl
Emp.: 120
Environmental Systems & Automation & Conveyor Systems
S.I.C.: 3822
N.A.I.C.S.: 334512
Dirk Bethmann *(Pres)*

Henry Filters (Europe) Ltd. (1)
Broxell Close
Warwick, CV34 5QF, United Kingdom (100%)
Tel.: (44) 1926 418800
Fax: (44) 1926474031
E-Mail: saleshf@henryfilters.co.uk
Web Site: www.durr.com
Emp.: 20
Environmental Systems & Automation & Conveyor Systems
S.I.C.: 3535
N.A.I.C.S.: 333922

Olpidurr S.T.A (1)
Via G Pascoli 14
I 20090 Milan, Italy
Tel.: (39) 02702121
Fax: (39) 0270200353
E-Mail: sales@olpidurr.it
Web Site: www.olpidurr.it
Emp.: 60
Environmental Systems & Automation & Conveyor Systems
S.I.C.: 3535
N.A.I.C.S.: 333922
Marco Pizzamiglio *(Mng Dir)*

Schenck Italia S.r.l. (1)
Via Varese 6/ B
20037 Paderno Dugnano, Milan, Italy
Tel.: (39) 02 91002431
Fax: (39) 02 91002439
Web Site: www.schenck-rotec.it
Aircraft Equipment Mfr
S.I.C.: 3728
N.A.I.C.S.: 336413
Remo Moreo *(Mgr-Rotec Div)*

Schenck Ltd (1)
Broxell Close
Warwick, CV34 5QF, United Kingdom
Tel.: (44) 1926 474 090
Fax: (44) 1926 474 033
E-Mail: sales@schenck.co.uk
Web Site: www.schenck.co.uk
Emp.: 2
Rotating & Oscillating Machinery Mfr
S.I.C.: 3559
N.A.I.C.S.: 333249
Roy Fulton *(Mng Dir)*

Schenck Shanghai Machinery Corporation Ltd (1)
No 36 Lane 239 Nujiang Road N
200333 Shanghai, China
Tel.: (86) 21 6265 9663
Fax: (86) 21 6265 5326
E-Mail: sales.rotec@schenck.cn
Web Site: www.schenck.cn
Industrial Machinery Mfr
S.I.C.: 3559
N.A.I.C.S.: 333249
Lenny Fan *(Mgr)*

Schenck Test Automation Ltd (1)
Broxell Close
Warwick, CV34 5QF, United Kingdom
Tel.: (44) 1926 474 090
Fax: (44) 1926 474 026
Oscillating Component Research & Development Services
S.I.C.: 8731
N.A.I.C.S.: 541712

Shinhang Durr Inc. (1)
604 1 Yoksam Dong
Kangnam Ku, Seoul, 135-080, Korea (South)
Tel.: (82) 25692244
Fax: (82) 25581881
E-Mail: koch@durr.co.kr
Web Site: www.durr.co.kr
Emp.: 54
Turnkey Paint Shops to the Automotive Industry
S.I.C.: 7532
N.A.I.C.S.: 811121

UCM AG (1)
Langenhagstr 25
9424 Rheineck, Switzerland
Tel.: (41) 71 886 67 60
Fax: (41) 71 886 67 61
E-Mail: info@ucm-ag.com
Web Site: www.ucm-ag.com
Precision Cleaning Machinery Mfr
S.I.C.: 3589
N.A.I.C.S.: 333318
Volker Lehmann *(Mgr)*

Non-U.S. Affiliates:

Olpidurr S.p.A. (1)
Via G Pascoli 14
I 20090 Novegro di Segrate, MI, Italy (49%)
Tel.: (39) 02702121
Fax: (39) 0270200353
E-Mail: service@olpidurr.it
Web Site: www.olpidurr.it
Emp.: 60
Paint Finishing Systems
S.I.C.: 2851
N.A.I.C.S.: 325510
Marco Pizzamiglio *(Mng Dir)*

Verind S.p.A. (1)
Via Papa Giovanni 25 29
20090 Rodano, MI, Italy (25%)
Tel.: (39) 0295320974
Fax: (39) 0295320914
E-Mail: direzione@verind.it
Web Site: www.verind.it
Emp.: 70

Durr AG—(Continued)

Provider of Turnkey Paint Shops to the Automotive Industry
S.I.C.: 7532
N.A.I.C.S.: 811121
Claudio Minelli *(Dir)*

DURWEST CONSTRUCTION MANAGEMENT
301 4400 Chatterton Way
Victoria, BC, V8X 5J2, Canada
Tel.: (250) 881-7878
Fax: (250) 881-7333
E-Mail: durwest@durwest.com
Web Site: www.durwest.com
Year Founded: 1983
Rev.: $12,100,000
Emp.: 70
Business Description:
Project & Construction Management Services
S.I.C.: 1542
N.A.I.C.S.: 236220
Personnel:
Darcy Kray *(Co-Owner & Pres)*
Carl Novak *(Co-Owner & VP)*

DUSIT THANI PUBLIC COMPANY LIMITED
The Dusit Thani Building 946 Rama IV Road
Bangkok, 10500, Thailand
Tel.: (66) 22009000
Fax: (66) 26363630
E-Mail: somnuek.ng@dusit.com
Web Site: www.dusit.com
Year Founded: 1949
DTC—(THA)
Rev.: $141,049,062
Assets: $278,360,638
Liabilities: $127,515,192
Net Worth: $150,845,445
Earnings: $1,219,881
Fiscal Year-end: 12/31/12
Business Description:
Hotels & Resorts Owner & Operator
S.I.C.: 7011
N.A.I.C.S.: 721110
Personnel:
Chatri Sophonpanich *(Chm)*
Giovanni Angelini *(Vice Chm-Dusit International)*
Chanin Donavanik *(CEO & Mng Dir)*
David Ian Shackleton *(COO)*
Sinee Thienprasiddhi *(Sec)*
Chamnarnsil Chamnarnkit *(Sr VP-Fin)*
Board of Directors:
Chatri Sophonpanich
Chatrachai Bunya-Ananta
Varang Chaiyawan
Chanin Donavanik
Sakdi Kiewkarnkha
Kenneth Gaw Korsirisophon
Sansern Kraichitti
Pranee Phasipol
Hiran Radeesri
Sinee Thienprasiddhi
Soradis Vinyaratn
Legal Counsel:
Dherakupt Law Office Co. Ltd
546 Univest Complex Building 15th Fl
Ratchadaphisek Rd Ladyao Jatujak
Bangkok, Thailand

DUSKIN CO., LTD.
1-33 Toyotsu-Cho Suita-shi
Osaka, 564-0051, Japan
Tel.: (81) 6 6821 5801
Fax: (81) 6 6821 5703
E-Mail: ikuo_miyagawa@hmail.duskinn.co.jp
Web Site: www.duskin.co.jp
Year Founded: 1963
4665—(TKS)
Sls.: $1,849,793,000
Assets: $2,226,125,000
Liabilities: $545,204,000
Net Worth: $1,680,921,000
Earnings: $67,012,000
Emp.: 3,512
Fiscal Year-end: 03/31/13
Business Description:
Dust Control Product Rental, Cleaning/Maintenance Service & Cleaning Products
Import Export
S.I.C.: 5169
N.A.I.C.S.: 424690
Personnel:
Teruji Yamamura *(Pres & CEO)*
Board of Directors:
Osaharu Fujii
Osamu Ihara
Kenichi Miyajima
Yoichi Naganuma
Junichi Narahara
Kazuo Okai
Hiroshi Takeda
Akihisa Tsurumi
Fukiko Uchiya
Teruji Yamamura

DUSSMANN AG & CO. KGAA
Friedrichstrasse 90
D 10117 Berlin, Germany
Tel.: (49) 3020250
Fax: (49) 3020251169
E-Mail: info@dussmann.de
Web Site: www.dussmann.com
Year Founded: 1976
Sales Range: $1-4.9 Billion
Emp.: 54,000
Business Description:
Facility Management, Food Service, Cleaning, Security & Safety Services
S.I.C.: 7382
N.A.I.C.S.: 561621
Personnel:
Catherine von Furstenberg-Dussmann *(Chm-Supervisory Bd)*
Thomas Greiner *(CEO & Chm-Exec Bd)*
Jorg Braesecke *(Member-Exec Bd)*
Dirk Brouwers *(Member-Exec Bd)*
Axel Granitz *(Member-Exec Bd)*
Christiane Jaap *(Member-Exec Bd)*
Supervisory Board of Directors:
Catherine von Furstenberg-Dussmann
Wolfgang Clement
Giuseppe Di Vita
Tessen von Heydebreck

U.S. Subsidiaries:

Pedus Building Services Inc. **(1)**
PO Box 513617
Los Angeles, CA 90051-3617 (100%)
Tel.: (323) 720-1020
Fax: (323) 724-4661
Emp.: 321
Security & Safety Services
S.I.C.: 7349
N.A.I.C.S.: 561720

Pedus Food Services Inc. **(1)**
PO Box 513617
Los Angeles, CA 90051-3617
Tel.: (323) 720-1020
Fax: (323) 724-4661
Emp.: 174
Food Preparation, Service & Management
S.I.C.: 5812
N.A.I.C.S.: 722310

Non-U.S. Subsidiaries:

Dussmann Property Management (Shanghai) Co. Ltd. **(1)**
Unit 901Tower B Sunyung Building
28 Xuanhua Rd, Shanghai, 200050, China CN
Tel.: (86) 2152551535 (100%)
Fax: (86) 2132505738
E-Mail: info@dussmann.com.cn
Web Site: www.dussmann.com.cn
Emp.: 52
Property Management Services
S.I.C.: 6519
N.A.I.C.S.: 531190

Kursana AG **(1)**
Am Spiser Tor
Moosbrugg Strasse 1, CH 9000 Saint Gallen, Switzerland (100%)
Tel.: (41) 712288282
Fax: (41) 712288284
E-Mail: info@kursana.gh
Web Site: www.kursana.gh
Sls.: $4,141,291
Emp.: 49
S.I.C.: 7382
N.A.I.C.S.: 561621
Cornales Vanderluyt *(Mng Dir)*

P. Dussmann Eesti OU **(1)**
Pirni Tn 12
10617 Tallinn, Estonia EE
Tel.: (372) 6990140 (100%)
Fax: (372) 6990150
E-Mail: dussmann@dussmann.ee
Web Site: www.dussmann.ee
Sales Range: $10-24.9 Million
Emp.: 150
Security & Safety Services
S.I.C.: 7382
N.A.I.C.S.: 561621
Thomas Greiner *(Chm)*

P. Dussmann EOOD **(1)**
Hristo Georgiew Str 4 2nd Fl
15504 Sofia, Bulgaria BG
Tel.: (359) 29438398 (100%)
Fax: (359) 29438410
E-Mail: office@dussmannbg.com
Web Site: www.dussmannbg.com
Emp.: 16
Provider of Networking Services
S.I.C.: 7373
N.A.I.C.S.: 541512
Vassil Popov *(Mgr)*

P. Dussmann Ges.m.b.H. **(1)**
Gruberstrasse 2
A-4020 Linz, Austria AT
Tel.: (43) 7327819510
Fax: (43) 732781951111
E-Mail: sekretariat@dussmann.at
Web Site: www.dussmann.at
Emp.: 13
Security & Safety Services
S.I.C.: 7382
N.A.I.C.S.: 561621
Kunter Operrausl *(Mgr)*

P. Dussmann Guvenlik, Temizlik, Bakim, Onarim, Hizmet Limited Sirketi **(1)**
Sirket 1 Yildez Caddesi Emek Is Merkezi 37 5 Yildiz
80690 Istanbul, Turkey TR
Tel.: (90) 2123479380
Fax: (90) 2123479385
E-Mail: pedus@superonline.com
Emp.: 26
Security & Safety Services
S.I.C.: 7382
N.A.I.C.S.: 561621

P. Dussmann Hong Kong Ltd. **(1)**
8/F Edward Wong Tower 910 Cheung Sha Wan Road
910 Cheung Sha Wan Road, Kowloon, China (Hong Kong) HK
Tel.: (852) 25040777 (100%)
Fax: (852) 28811446
E-Mail: info@dussmann.com.hk
Web Site: www.dussmann.com.hk
Emp.: 1,200
Security & Safety Services
S.I.C.: 7382
N.A.I.C.S.: 561621
Gordon Lau *(Gen Mgr)*

P. Dussmann Kft. **(1)**
East West Business Center Rakoczi 1-3
H-1088 Budapest, Hungary HU
Tel.: (36) 12661066
Fax: (36) 12666360
E-Mail: dussmann@dussmann.hu
Web Site: www.dussmann.com
Networking Services
S.I.C.: 7373
N.A.I.C.S.: 541512

P. Dussmann Romania S.R.L. **(1)**
Chiscani 25 27 Sekto 1
Bucharest, Romania RO
Tel.: (40) 212017983
Fax: (40) 212221658
E-Mail: office@dussman.ro
Web Site: www.dussmann.ro
Emp.: 12
Networking Services
S.I.C.: 7373
N.A.I.C.S.: 541512
Mona Constinescu *(Mgr)*

P. Dussmann spol. s.r.o. **(1)**
Zitna 1578/52
CZ 12000 Prague, 2, Czech Republic (100%)
Tel.: (420) 222874479
Fax: (420) 222874130
E-Mail: pedus-service.praha@dussmann.cz
Web Site: www.dussmann.cz/en/
Emp.: 300
Security & Safety Services
S.I.C.: 7382
N.A.I.C.S.: 561621

P. Dussmann spol. s.r.o. **(1)**
Pri Starej Pracharni 14
83104 Bratislava, Slovakia Sk
Tel.: (421) 255576363 (100%)
E-Mail: pedus-service.bratislava@dussmann.sk
Web Site: www.dussmann.sk
Emp.: 300
Networking Services
S.I.C.: 7373
N.A.I.C.S.: 541512
Monika Mattova *(Mng Dir)*

P. Dussmann Sp.zo.o. **(1)**
Ul Kurpinskiego 55A
02733 Warsaw, Poland PL
Tel.: (48) 228272290 (99%)
Fax: (48) 228272298
E-Mail: dussmann@dussmann.pl
Web Site: www.dussmann.pl
Rev.: $33,643,352
Emp.: 15
Security & Safety Services
S.I.C.: 7382
N.A.I.C.S.: 561621

P. Dussmann TNHH **(1)**
384 Kha Van Can St
Hiep Binh Chanh Ward
Thu Duc District, Ho Chi Minh City, Vietnam VN
Tel.: (84) 838275600
Fax: (84) 838233453
E-Mail: bina.pham@dussmann.vn
Web Site: www.dussmann.com
Emp.: 37
Security & Safety Services
S.I.C.: 7382
N.A.I.C.S.: 561621
Bengamin Gonis Yefendorf *(Pres)*

P. Dussmann UAB **(1)**
Ukmerges 223
LT-2600 Vilnius, Lithuania
Tel.: (370) 52127936
Fax: (370) 52339402
E-Mail: info@dussmann.lt
Web Site: www.dussmann.lt
Emp.: 700
Security & Safety Services
S.I.C.: 7382
N.A.I.C.S.: 561621
Aurelija Maldutyte *(Gen Dir)*

Pedus Service S.a.r.l. **(1)**
Zl Bombicht
L 6947 Niederanven, NIL, Luxembourg (100%)
Tel.: (352) 3420501
Fax: (352) 349949
E-Mail: reception.niederanven@dussmann.lu
Web Site: www.pedus.lu
Emp.: 42
Security & Safety Services
S.I.C.: 7382
N.A.I.C.S.: 561621

Peter Dussmann - Vostok **(1)**
Ul Tschetinkina 49
Buro 402, 630099 Novosibirsk, Russia RU
Tel.: (7) 3832036071 (100%)
Fax: (7) 3832036071
E-Mail: east@dussmann.ru

Security & Safety Services
S.I.C.: 7382
N.A.I.C.S.: 561621

SIA P. Dussmann (1)
Perses Iela 9 11
LV 1011 Riga, Latvia LV
Tel.: (371) 7289515 (100%)
Fax: (371) 7285979
E-Mail: latvia@dussmann.lv
Web Site: www.dussman.lv
Emp.: 300
Security & Safety Services
S.I.C.: 7382
N.A.I.C.S.: 561621

DUTALAND BERHAD

Level 23 Menara Olympia No 8 Jalan Raja Chulan
50200 Kuala Lumpur, Malaysia
Tel.: (60) 20723993
Fax: (60) 20723996
E-Mail: dutaland@dutaland.com.my
Web Site: www.dutaland.com.my
DUTALND—(KLS)
Rev.: $19,107,243
Assets: $344,178,602
Liabilities: $68,239,824
Net Worth: $275,938,777
Earnings: ($6,735,149)
Fiscal Year-end: 06/30/13
Business Description:
Oil Palm Plantations & Property Development Services
S.I.C.: 6531
N.A.I.C.S.: 531312
Personnel:
Yong Seong Yap *(Mng Dir)*
Yoke Si Lim *(Co-Sec)*
Siok Teng Pang *(Co-Sec)*
Board of Directors:
Ahmad Shah Sultan Salahuddin Abdul Aziz Shah
Wong Sang Cheong
Hazli Ibrahim
Lamin Mohd Yunus
Wee Chun Yap
Wee Keat Yap
Yong Seong Yap

Subsidiaries:

Duta Plantations Sdn. Bhd. (1)
Level 23 Menara Olympia No 8 Jalan Raja Chulan
Kuala Lumpur, 50200, Malaysia
Tel.: (60) 320723993
Fax: (60) 320723996
Emp.: 100
Investment Holding Services
S.I.C.: 6282
N.A.I.C.S.: 523920
Yap Yong Seong *(Grp Mng Dir)*

Jiwa Realty Sdn. Bhd. (1)
Level 12 Menara Olympia 8 Jalan Raja Chulan B4-1
50200 Kuala Lumpur, Wilayah Persekutuan, Malaysia
Tel.: (60) 320706688
Fax: (60) 320708866
E-Mail: kcng@dutaland.com.my
Emp.: 1
Residential Property Development Services
S.I.C.: 1522
N.A.I.C.S.: 236116
Yap Yong Seong *(Mng Dir)*

KH Land Sdn. Bhd. (1)
Ground Floor Block P 1-13 & 1-15 Plaza Damas Jln Sri Hartamas 1
Sri Hartamas, 50480 Kuala Lumpur, Malaysia
Tel.: (60) 362018388
Fax: (60) 362012898
E-Mail: enquiry@kennyheights.com.my
Web Site: www.kennyheights.com.my
Emp.: 15
Residential Property Development Services
S.I.C.: 1522
N.A.I.C.S.: 236116
Cheah Chee Yuan *(Mgr)*

Oakland Holdings Sdn. Bhd. (1)
Level 24 Menara Olympia No 8 Jalan Raja Chulan
50200 Kuala Lumpur, Malaysia
Tel.: (60) 320723993
Fax: (60) 320700011
E-Mail: kcng@dutaland.com.my
Web Site: www.olympia.com.my
Emp.: 5
Property Development Services
S.I.C.: 6531
N.A.I.C.S.: 531390
Cho Kah Hing *(Gen Mgr-Mktg & Project)*

Olympia Land Berhad (1)
Level 23 Menara Olympia No 8 Jalan Raja Chulan
Kuala Lumpur, 50200, Malaysia
Tel.: (60) 320706688
Fax: (60) 320723996
Emp.: 12
Residential Property Management Services
S.I.C.: 6531
N.A.I.C.S.: 531311
Yong Seong Yap *(Mng Dir)*

Pertama Land & Development Sdn. Bhd. (1)
Level 23 Menara Olympia No 8 Jalan Raja Chulan
50200 Kuala Lumpur, Malaysia (100%)
Tel.: (60) 3 2072 3993
Fax: (60) 3 2072 3996
Web Site: www.dutaland.com.my
Land & Property Development
S.I.C.: 6552
N.A.I.C.S.: 237210

DUTCH-BANGLA BANK LIMITED

Sena Kalyan Bhaban 3rd Floor 195 Motijheel Commercial Area
Dhaka, 1000, Bangladesh
Tel.: (880) 27176390
Fax: (880) 29561889
E-Mail: contact@dutchbanglabank.com
Web Site: www.dutchbanglabank.com
DUTCHBANGL—(DHA)
Int. Income: $172,386,829
Assets: $1,930,271,766
Liabilities: $1,795,893,063
Net Worth: $134,378,703
Earnings: $28,648,601
Emp.: 5,268
Fiscal Year-end: 12/31/12
Business Description:
Commercial Banking Services
S.I.C.: 6029
N.A.I.C.S.: 522110
Personnel:
Abedur Rashid Khan *(Chm)*
K. Shamshi Tabrez *(Mng Dir)*
Khan Tariqul Islam *(CFO & Deputy Mng Dir)*
Md. Sayedul Hasan *(Deputy Mng Dir)*
Abul Kashem Md. Shirin *(Deputy Mng Dir)*
Md. Mosaddiqur Rahman *(Deputy Mng Dir)*
Md. Monirul Alam *(Sec & VP)*
Moyen Uddin Ahmed *(Exec VP-Mktg & Dev)*
Iqbal Amin *(Exec VP-HR)*
Md. Abul Kashem Khan *(Exec VP-IT Ops Div)*
A.K.M. Shah Alam *(Exec VP-CAMLCO)*
Mohd. Rafat Ullah Khan *(Exec VP-Credit Div)*
Jalal Uddin Ahmed *(Sr VP-Treasury Div)*
Syed Mahmud Akhter *(Sr VP-Agrabad)*
Mohammad Harun Azad *(Sr VP-Vigilance Cell)*
Masud Hossain *(Sr VP-Intl Div-Treasury Back Office)*
Patrick A. Rodrigues *(Sr VP-Gen Svc Div)*
Md. Shamsuddin Yousuf Khaled *(Sr VP-Internal Control & Compliance Div)*
Board of Directors:
Abedur Rashid Khan
Sayem Ahmed
Md. Yeasin Ali
Syed Fakhrul Ameen
Chowdhury M. Ashraf Hossain
Barbara Yuen Mei Frey-Tang
Md. Fakhrul Islam
Irshad Kamal Khan
K. Shamshi Tabrez

DUTCHMASTER NURSERIES LTD.

3735 Sideline 16 North
Brougham, ON, L0H 1A0, Canada
Tel.: (905) 683-8211
Fax: (905) 683-3734
E-Mail: sales@dutchmasternurseries.com
Web Site: www.dutchmasternurseriesltd.com
Year Founded: 1971
Rev.: $19,800,000
Emp.: 100
Business Description:
Nursery Product & Plant Producer
S.I.C.: 0181
N.A.I.C.S.: 111421
Personnel:
Henry Tillaart *(Founder)*

DUTEXDOR

15 avenue du Parc de l'Horloge
59840 Perenchies, France
Tel.: (33) 320009999
E-Mail: contact@dutexdor.fr
Web Site: www.imp-exp.cc/fr/company/index.asp?id=8
Sls.: $24,100,000
Emp.: 40
Business Description:
Clothing: Womens, Childrens & Infants
S.I.C.: 5137
N.A.I.C.S.: 424330
Personnel:
Jean-Marc Terrier *(Pres)*

DUTRON POLYMERS LIMITED

Dutron House Nr Mithakhali Underbridge
Navrangpura, Ahmedabad, 380 009, India
Tel.: (91) 7926561849
Fax: (91) 7926420894
E-Mail: info@dutronindia.com
Web Site: www.dutronindia.com
Year Founded: 1962
517437—(BOM)
Rev.: $15,517,376
Assets: $5,619,385
Liabilities: $3,014,128
Net Worth: $2,605,257
Earnings: $213,413
Fiscal Year-end: 03/31/13
Business Description:
Plastic Pipe Mfr
S.I.C.: 3089
N.A.I.C.S.: 326122
Personnel:
Sudipbhai B. Patel *(Chm)*
Rasesh H. Patel *(Mng Dir)*
Board of Directors:
Sudipbhai B. Patel
Alpesh B. Patel
Rasesh H. Patel
Mitesh C. Shah
Praful G. Shah
Transfer Agent:
Sharepro Services (India) Pvt. Ltd.
416-420 4th Floor Devnandan Mall Opp. Sanyash Ashram Ellisbridge
Ahmedabad, India

DUTY FREE SHOPS S.A.

(See Under Folli Follie S.A.)

DUYEN HAI MULTI MODAL TRANSPORT JOINT STOCK COMPANY

189 Road Dinh Vu Dong Hai 2
Hai An, Haiphong, Vietnam
Tel.: (84) 313614018
Fax: (84) 313614016
E-Mail: tasaduyenhai@vnn.vn
Web Site: www.tasaduyenhai.com
Emp.: 290
Business Description:
Container Transportation & Warehousing Services
S.I.C.: 4731
N.A.I.C.S.: 488510
Personnel:
Chung Dinh Nguyen *(Chm & Gen Mgr)*
Board of Directors:
Chung Dinh Nguyen
Lan Thi Ngoc Hoang
Cuong Thai Le
Do Van Le
Phu Thi Vu

DV RESOURCES LTD.

Suite 1710 1177 West Hastings Street
Vancouver, BC, V6E 2L3, Canada
Mailing Address:
67 Yonge Street Suite 1201
Toronto, ON, M5E 1J8, Canada
Tel.: (604) 640-6357
Fax: (604) 681-0139
Year Founded: 1979
DLV—(TSXV)
Rev.: $15,253
Assets: $1,463,185
Liabilities: $27,852
Net Worth: $1,435,333
Earnings: ($104,869)
Fiscal Year-end: 11/30/12
Business Description:
Mineral Exploration Services
S.I.C.: 1099
N.A.I.C.S.: 212299
Personnel:
Clinton Smyth *(Pres & CEO)*
Peter Hogg *(CFO)*
Carl R. Jonsson *(Sec)*
Board of Directors:
Raymond Davies
Carl R. Jonsson
Douglas Proctor
Clinton Smyth

DVB BANK SE

Platz der Republik 6
60325 Frankfurt am Main, Germany
Tel.: (49) 69975040
Fax: (49) 6997504444
E-Mail: info@dvbbank.com
Web Site: www.dvbbank.com
DVB—(DEU)
Int. Income: $1,329,746,726
Assets: $32,045,307,616
Liabilities: $30,145,457,895
Net Worth: $1,899,849,721
Earnings: $168,136,633
Emp.: 558
Fiscal Year-end: 12/31/12
Business Description:
Transport Finance Services
S.I.C.: 6211
N.A.I.C.S.: 523999
Personnel:
Frank Westhoff *(Chm-Supervisory Bd)*
Wolfgang F. Driese *(Chm-Mgmt Bd & CEO)*

DVB Bank SE—(Continued)

Peter Klaus *(Deputy Chm-Supervisory Bd)*
Bertrand Grabowski *(Member-Mgmt Bd)*
Dagfinn Lunde *(Member-Mgmt Bd)*
Supervisory Board of Directors:
Frank Westhoff
Stephan Gotzl
Peter Klaus
Wolfgang Kohler
Dorinus Legters
Adnan Mohammed
Klaus Nittinger
Carl Erik Steen
Martin Wolfert

Subsidiaries:

DVB LogPay GmbH (1)
Schwalbacher Str72
D-65760 Eschborn, Germany
Tel.: (49) 6196774500
Fax: (49) 6197745040
E-Mail: info@logpay.de
Web Site: www.logpay.de
Emp.: 50
Other Activities Related to Credit Intermediation
S.I.C.: 6099
N.A.I.C.S.: 522390
Horst Winzer *(Mng Dir)*

U.S. Subsidiaries:

DVB Capital Markets LLC (1)
609 5th Ave
New York, NY 10017
Tel.: (212) 858-2623
Fax: (212) 858-2662
Web Site: www.dvbbank.com
Emp.: 6
Investment Banking & Securities Dealing
S.I.C.: 6211
N.A.I.C.S.: 523110
William Abraham *(Mng Dir)*

Non-U.S. Subsidiaries:

DVB Bank N.V. (1)
Parklaan 2
3016BB Rotterdam, Netherlands
Tel.: (31) 102067900
Fax: (31) 104362957
E-Mail: reception.rotterdam@dvbbank.com
Web Site: www.dvbbank.com
Emp.: 60
Commercial Banking
S.I.C.: 6029
N.A.I.C.S.: 522110
Dagsinn Lunde *(Gen Mgr)*

DVB Group Merchant Bank (Asia) Ltd (1)
77 Robinson Road #30-02
068896 Singapore, Singapore
Tel.: (65) 65113433
Fax: (65) 65110700
Web Site: www.dav.com
Emp.: 55
Commercial Banking
S.I.C.: 6029
N.A.I.C.S.: 522110
Evan Cohen *(Mng Dir)*

DVB Transport Finance Ltd (1)
The Imperial Hotel Tower 14th Floor A-2
Uchisaiwaicho 1-1-1
Chiyoda-ku, Tokyo, 100-0011, Japan (100%)
Tel.: (81) 335937700
Fax: (81) 335937860
E-Mail:
Web Site: www.dvb-bank.com
Emp.: 4
All Other Support Activities for Transportation
S.I.C.: 4789
N.A.I.C.S.: 488999
Kinichi Yuki *(Mng Dir)*

DVX, INC.

Mejiro Nakano Building 5th Floor
2-17-22 Takada
Toshima-ku, Tokyo, 171-0033, Japan
Tel.: (81) 359856110
Fax: (81) 359856106
E-Mail: dvx@dvx.jp
Web Site: www.dvx.jp
Year Founded: 1986
3079—(TKS)
Sales Range: $125-149.9 Million
Emp.: 100
Business Description:
Medical Devices Mfr & Sls; Software & Book Publisher
S.I.C.: 3841
N.A.I.C.S.: 339112
Personnel:
Makoto Wakabayashi *(Pres & CEO)*
Hiroshi Shibasaki *(Chief Sls Officer & VP)*
Board of Directors:
Mitsuharu Muramatsu
Hiroshi Shibasaki
Sachiko Toda
Makoto Wakabayashi

DWARF TECHNOLOGY HOLDINGS, INC.

10/Floor Weixing Building 252 Wensan Road
Hangzhou, Zhejiang, 310012, China
Tel.: (86) 571 28188199
Fax: (86) 571 89988474
Web Site: www.4006009090.cn
Year Founded: 2007
Sales Range: $1-9.9 Million
Emp.: 53
Business Description:
E-Commerce & IT Solutions
S.I.C.: 7379
N.A.I.C.S.: 541519
Personnel:
Mianfu Zhang *(Chm, Pres & CEO)*
Jiangling Wang *(CFO)*
Jian Xu *(COO)*
Xizhen Ye *(Sec)*
Board of Directors:
Mianfu Zhang
Xizhen Ye

DWARIKESH SUGAR INDUSTRIES LTD

511 Maker Chambers V 221 Nariman Point
Mumbai, 400 021, India
Tel.: (91) 22025810
Fax: (91) 22808650
E-Mail: corporate@dwarikesh.com
Web Site: www.dwarikesh.com
DWARKESH—(NSE)
Rev.: $134,590,431
Assets: $139,450,101
Liabilities: $114,426,965
Net Worth: $25,023,137
Earnings: ($2,096,025)
Emp.: 948
Fiscal Year-end: 09/30/12
Business Description:
Sugar Mfr & Distr
S.I.C.: 2061
N.A.I.C.S.: 311314
Personnel:
G. R. Morarka *(Chm & Mng Dir)*
Vijay S. Banka *(CFO)*
B. J. Maheshwari *(Chief Compliance Officer & Sec)*
Board of Directors:
G. R. Morarka
Balkumar K. Agarwal
Vijay S. Banka
K. L. Garg
B. J. Maheshwari
Aggarwal L. P.
K. N. Prithviraj
Transfer Agent:
Universal Capital Securities Pvt. Ltd
21 Shakil Niwas Mahakali Caves Road Andheri East
Mumbai, India

DWF LLP

Bridgewater Place Water Lane
Water Lane, Leeds, LS11 5DY, United Kingdom
Tel.: (44) 113 261 6000
Fax: (44) 870 094 0939
E-Mail: enquiries@dwf.co.uk
Web Site: www.dwf.co.uk
Sales Range: $150-199.9 Million
Business Description:
Law Firm
S.I.C.: 8111
N.A.I.C.S.: 541110
Personnel:
Andrew Leaitherland *(Mng Partner)*
Andrew Breckenridge *(Partner)*
Graham Dickinson *(Partner)*
Jonathan Edwards *(Partner)*
Leslie Smythe *(Partner)*

DWS LIMITED

Level 4 500 Collins St
Melbourne, VIC, 3000, Australia
Tel.: (61) 3 9650 9777
Fax: (61) 3 9650 9444
E-Mail: dws@dws.com.au
Web Site: www.dws.com.au
DWS—(ASX)
Rev.: $113,644,131
Assets: $77,673,966
Liabilities: $14,419,538
Net Worth: $63,254,428
Earnings: $17,567,722
Emp.: 580
Fiscal Year-end: 06/30/13
Business Description:
Information Technology Services
S.I.C.: 7373
N.A.I.C.S.: 541512
Personnel:
Danny Wallis *(CEO & Mng Dir)*
Lachlan Armstrong *(CFO & Sec)*
Board of Directors:
Harvey Parker
Ken Barry
Gary Ebeyan
Martin Ralston
Danny Wallis
Legal Counsel:
Gadens Lawyers
Level 25 Bourke Place 600 Bourke Street
Melbourne, Australia

Subsidiary:

Wallis Nominees (Computing) Pty. Ltd. (1)
Level 22 15 Collins St
Melbourne, Victoria, 3000, Australia
Tel.: (61) 396509777
Fax: (61) 396509444
Web Site: www.dws.com.au
Computer Repair & Maintenance Services
S.I.C.: 7629
N.A.I.C.S.: 811212
Danny Wallis *(Mng Dir)*

DX (GROUP) PLC

DX House Ridgeway
Iver, Bucks, SL0 9JQ, United Kingdom
Tel.: (44) 1753630630
Fax: (44) 1753631631
Web Site: www.thedx.co.uk
Year Founded: 1975
DX—(AIM)
Sales Range: $500-549.9 Million
Emp.: 5,500
Business Description:
Logistics & Parcel Distr
S.I.C.: 4731
N.A.I.C.S.: 541614
Personnel:
David Alexander Hoare *(Chm)*
Petar Cvetkovic *(CEO)*
Ian Richard Pain *(CFO)*
Stuart Godman *(COO)*
Mike Sturrock *(CIO)*
Board of Directors:
David Alexander Hoare
Petar Cvetkovic
Robert Holt
Ian Richard Pain

DXN HOLDINGS BHD.

Wisma DXN No 213 Lebuhraya Sultan Abdul Halim
05400 Alor Setar, Kedah Darul Aman, Malaysia
Tel.: (60) 4 772 3388
Fax: (60) 4 772 1188
E-Mail: csu_pj1@dxn2u.com
Web Site: www.dxnmalaysia.com
Sales Range: $75-99.9 Million
Business Description:
Dietary Supplements, Food & Beverages Mfr
S.I.C.: 2023
N.A.I.C.S.: 311514
Personnel:
Siow Jin Lim *(Founder, Chm & CEO)*
Boon Yee Lim *(Mng Dir)*

Subsidiaries:

DXN Comfort Tours Sdn. Bhd. (1)
No 99 Lebuhraya Sultan Abdul Halim
Alor Setar, Kedah, Malaysia
Tel.: (60) 47721199
Fax: (60) 47711199
E-Mail: comfortas@dxn2u.com
Web Site: www.comfort.dxn2u.com
Emp.: 1
Touring & Travel Services
S.I.C.: 4725
N.A.I.C.S.: 561520
Lim Yew Lin *(Exec Dir)*

DXN Industries (M) Sdn. Bhd. (1)
213 Lebuhraya Sultan Abdul
05400 Alor Setar, Kedah, Malaysia
Tel.: (60) 47723388
Fax: (60) 47721188
E-Mail: csu_pj1@dxn2u.com
Web Site: www.dxn2u.com
Health Food Supplements Mfr
S.I.C.: 2099
N.A.I.C.S.: 311999
Lim Boon Yee *(Mng Dir)*

DXN Marketing Sdn. Bhd. (1)
43 Jalan SS 22/23 Damansara Jaya
47000 Petaling Jaya, Selangor, Malaysia
Tel.: (60) 377253388
Fax: (60) 377251188
E-Mail: csu_pj1@dxn2u.com
Web Site: www.dxn2u.com
Emp.: 30
Health Food Supplements Whslr
S.I.C.: 5149
N.A.I.C.S.: 424490
Lim Siow Jin *(Founder)*
Suhail Lambay *(Partner)*

DXN Pharmaceutical Sdn. Bhd. (1)
Kg Padang Panjang Jalan Bukit Wang
06000 Jitra, Kedah, Malaysia
Tel.: (60) 49161288
Fax: (60) 49173610
Emp.: 600
Health Food Supplements Mfr
S.I.C.: 2099
N.A.I.C.S.: 311999

Yiked-DXN Stargate Sdn. Bhd. (1)
99 Lebuhraya Sultan Abdul Halim
05400 Alor Setar, Kedah, Malaysia
Tel.: (60) 47723399
Fax: (60) 47711199
E-Mail: dxndev@dxn2u.com
Web Site: www.stargate.net.my
Emp.: 22
Housing Development Services
S.I.C.: 1531
N.A.I.C.S.: 236117

Lim Boon Yee *(Mgr)*

U.S. Subsidiary:

Daxen, Inc. **(1)**
565 Brea Canyon Rd Ste B
Walnut, CA 91789
Tel.: (909) 348-0188
Fax: (909) 348-0189
E-Mail: sales@dxnusa.com
Web Site: www.international.dxn2u.com
Health Care Products Distr
S.I.C.: 5122
N.A.I.C.S.: 424210

Non-U.S. Subsidiaries:

DXN Herbal Manufacturing (India) Private Limited **(1)**
141/4 & 142/5 Whirlpool Road Thiruvandar Koil
Mannadipet, Pondicherry, 605102, India
Tel.: (91) 4132640618
Web Site: www.dxn2u.com
Medicine & Health Food Products Mfr
S.I.C.: 2834
N.A.I.C.S.: 325412
Ramesh Subramaniam *(Mng Dir)*

DXN International (Australia) Pty. Ltd. **(1)**
Suite 504 Level 5 Office Tower Westfield Shoppingtown
159-175 Church Street, Parramatta, NSW, 2150, Australia
Tel.: (61) 296892755
Fax: (61) 296891755
E-Mail: dxnmail@dxnaus.com.au
Web Site: www.dxnaus.com.au
Emp.: 7
Health Food Supplements Distr
S.I.C.: 5122
N.A.I.C.S.: 446191
Frank Li *(Mgr)*

DXN International (Hong Kong) Limited **(1)**
Room 921-923 9/F Hollywood Plaza 610 Nathan Road
Mongkok, Kowloon, China (Hong Kong)
Tel.: (852) 23886583
Fax: (852) 23886298
E-Mail: info_hk@dxn2u.com
Web Site: www.hk.dxn2u.com
Emp.: 5
Health Food Supplements Whslr
S.I.C.: 5149
N.A.I.C.S.: 424490
Peggy Lam *(Mgr)*

DXN International Pakistan (Private) Limited **(1)**
2nd Floor OPF Building Plot No 20-A/II Block-06
PECHS Shahar-e-Faisal, Karachi, Sindh, Pakistan
Tel.: (92) 21 4324475
Fax: (92) 21 4324479
E-Mail: dxnpakistan@dxn2u.com
Web Site: www.pakistan.dxn2u.com
Herbal Products & Food Supplements Distr
S.I.C.: 5149
N.A.I.C.S.: 424490
Bruce Gorrie *(Mgr)*

DXN International Peru S.A.C. **(1)**
Av Angamos Oeste 547
Miraflores, Lima, Peru
Tel.: (51) 1 241 7148
Fax: (51) 1 447 8813
Web Site: www.peru.dxn2u.com
Beverage Mixes Distr
S.I.C.: 5149
N.A.I.C.S.: 424490
Evlyne Ng *(Mgr)*

DXN (Singapore) Pte Ltd **(1)**
520 North Bridge Road 02-01 Wisma Alsagoff
188742 Singapore, Singapore
Tel.: (65) 62732668
Fax: (65) 62732667
E-Mail: gm_sg@dxn2u.com
Web Site: www.singapore.dxn2u.com
Emp.: 5
Health Foods Mfr & Distr
S.I.C.: 2099
N.A.I.C.S.: 311999
Elaine Leong *(Mng Dir)*

DXSTORM.COM INC.

824 Winston Churchill Blvd
Oakville, ON, L6J 7X2, Canada
Tel.: (905) 842-8262
Fax: (905) 842-3255
Toll Free: (877) 397-8676
E-Mail: info@dxstorm.com
Web Site: www.dxstorm.com
Year Founded: 1993
DXX—(TSXV)
Rev.: $952,822
Assets: $732,647
Liabilities: $836,307
Net Worth: ($103,659)
Earnings: ($330,498)
Fiscal Year-end: 06/30/13

Business Description:
E-Commerce Solutions
S.I.C.: 4899
N.A.I.C.S.: 517919

Personnel:
Zoran Popovic *(Pres, CEO & CFO)*
Steve Smashnuk *(CTO)*

Board of Directors:
Hugh T. Cameron
Joseph Cordiano
Daniel McKenzie
Zoran Popovic
John W. Ryan

Legal Counsel:
Heenan Blaikie LLP
S Tower Royal Bank Plaza Ste 2600
Toronto, ON, Canada

Transfer Agent:
Computershare Investor Services inc
3rd Fl 510 Burrard Street
Vancouver, BC, Canada

Subsidiary:

Medical Diagnostic Exchange Corp **(1)**
824 Winston Churchill Blvd
Oakville, ON, L6J 7X2, Canada
Tel.: (905) 707-5040
Fax: (905) 707-2657
Toll Free: (888) 698-1002
Web Site: www.mdxcorp.com
Medical Image Analysis Software Development Services
S.I.C.: 7372
N.A.I.C.S.: 511210
Zoran Popovic *(Pres & CEO)*

DYDO DRINCO INC.

2-2-7 Nakanoshima Kita-ku
Osaka, Japan
Tel.: (81) 662222621
Fax: (81) 662222623
Web Site: www.dydo.co.jp
2590—(TKS)
Sls.: $1,637,922,000
Assets: $1,545,357,000
Liabilities: $870,067,000
Net Worth: $675,290,000
Earnings: $48,510,000
Emp.: 2,916
Fiscal Year-end: 01/20/13

Business Description:
Alcoholic Beverage Mfr
S.I.C.: 5182
N.A.I.C.S.: 424820

Personnel:
Tomihiro Takamatsu *(Pres)*

Subsidiaries:

Daido Pharmaceutical Corporation **(1)**
214-1 Shimura
Katsuragi, Nara, Japan
Tel.: (81) 745625031
Coffee Beverages Mfr
S.I.C.: 2099
N.A.I.C.S.: 311920

DyDo Beverage Shizuoka Inc. **(1)**
2276 Yamashina Fukuroi-shi
Shizuoka, 437-0066, Japan
Tel.: (81) 538431066
Fax: (81) 538431066
Web Site: www.dydo.co.jp/corporate/ir_eng/data/
Emp.: 128
Coffee Beverages Mfr
S.I.C.: 2095
N.A.I.C.S.: 311920
Aoki Dydo *(Pres)*

DYER HOLDINGS PTY. LTD.

1299 Boundary Rd
Wacol, QLD, 4076, Australia
Tel.: (61) 7 3331 5200
Fax: (61) 7 3331 5350
Year Founded: 1959
Sales Range: $75-99.9 Million
Emp.: 500

Business Description:
Holding Company
S.I.C.: 6719
N.A.I.C.S.: 551112

Personnel:
Simon John Dyer *(CEO)*

Subsidiary:

Madad Pty. Ltd. **(1)**
1299 Boundary Road
Wacol, QLD, 4076, Australia
Tel.: (61) 7 3331 5200
Fax: (61) 7 3331 5350
Web Site: www.sealy.com.au
Mattress Mfr & Distr
S.I.C.: 2515
N.A.I.C.S.: 337910
Simon John Dyer *(CEO)*
David Noel Wood *(CFO)*

DYESOL LTD.

3 Dominion Place
Queanbeyan, NSW, 2620, Australia
Tel.: (61) 262991592
Fax: (61) 262991698
Web Site: www.dyesol.com
DYE—(ASX OTC)
Rev.: $997,388
Assets: $19,894,043
Liabilities: $8,718,763
Net Worth: $11,175,280
Earnings: ($9,791,776)
Emp.: 60
Fiscal Year-end: 06/30/13

Business Description:
Dye Solar Cell (DSC) Technology
S.I.C.: 3674
N.A.I.C.S.: 334413

Personnel:
Richard Caldwell *(Chm & CEO)*
Kian Lin Niu *(CFO)*
Damion Milliken *(CTO)*
Andrew King *(Pres-Europe)*
Marc Thomas *(CEO-Dyesol Inc & Gen Mgr-Global Glass Bus Grp)*
Kimberley Hogg *(Sec)*

Board of Directors:
Richard Caldwell
Gerry Grove-White
Ian Neal
Nicola Jane Swift
Gordon Thompson

Subsidiary:

Dyesol Industries Pty. Ltd. **(1)**
3 Dominion Place
Queanbeyan, NSW, 2620, Australia
Tel.: (61) 262991592
Fax: (61) 262991698
E-Mail: information@dyesol.com
Web Site: www.dyesol.com
Emp.: 30
Solar Cells Mfr
S.I.C.: 3674
N.A.I.C.S.: 334413
Richard Caldwell *(Mng Dir)*

Subsidiary:

Dyesol Australia Pty. Ltd. **(2)**
3 Dominion Pl
Queanbeyan, NSW, 2620, Australia
Tel.: (61) 262991592
Fax: (61) 262991698
E-Mail: info@dyesol.com
Web Site: www.dyesol.com
Emp.: 30
Solar Cells Mfr
S.I.C.: 3674
N.A.I.C.S.: 334413
Richard Caldwell *(Mng Dir)*

Non-U.S. Subsidiaries:

Dyesol East Asia Pte. Ltd. **(2)**
12 Lorong Limau No 06-07
Singapore, 328741, Singapore
Tel.: (65) 9823 8955
Fax: (65) 6259 1578
Web Site: www.dyesol.com
Emp.: 50
Solar Cells Mfr
S.I.C.: 3674
N.A.I.C.S.: 334413
Gavin E. Tulloch *(CTO)*

Dyesol UK Ltd. **(2)**
OpTIC Technium Ford William Morgan
St Asaph Bus Park, Saint Asaph, Denbighshire, LL17 0JD, United Kingdom
Tel.: (44) 1745535175
Fax: (44) 1745535176
E-Mail: information@dyesol.com
Web Site: www.dyesol.com
Emp.: 10
Solar Cells Mfr
S.I.C.: 3674
N.A.I.C.S.: 334413

Greatcell Solar SA **(2)**
Chemin de la Plantaz 59
1095 Lutry, Vaud, Switzerland
Tel.: (41) 21 791 6340
Fax: (41) 21 791 6342
Web Site: www.greatcell.com
Emp.: 1
Solar Cells Mfr
S.I.C.: 3674
N.A.I.C.S.: 334413
Andreas Luzzi *(Pres)*
Keith Brooks *(Mng Dir)*
Gavin Tulloch *(Dir Gen)*

DYFED STEELS LIMITED

Maescanner Road Dafen
Llanelli, Dyfed, SA14 8NS, United Kingdom
Tel.: (44) 1554772255
Fax: (44) 1554777701
E-Mail: info@dyfedsteel.co.uk
Web Site: www.dyfedsteel.co.uk
Rev.: $80,642,683
Emp.: 250

Business Description:
Steel Products Mfr
S.I.C.: 3317
N.A.I.C.S.: 331210

Personnel:
David Thomas *(Owner & Mng Dir)*

DYMIN STEEL INC.

133 Van Kirk Dr
Brampton, ON, L7A 1A4, Canada
Tel.: (905) 840-0808
Fax: (905) 840-5333
Toll Free: (800) 461-4675
E-Mail: info@dymin-steel.com
Web Site: www.dymin-steel.com
Year Founded: 1992
Rev.: $15,300,000
Emp.: 240

Business Description:
Structure Shaped Steel Distr
S.I.C.: 1791
N.A.I.C.S.: 238120

Personnel:
Jack Dym *(Pres)*
Garry Minielly *(Exec VP & Sec)*

DYNA-MAC HOLDINGS LTD.

45 Gul Road
Singapore, 629350, Singapore
Tel.: (65) 6762 5816
Fax: (65) 6762 3465

Dyna-Mac Holdings Ltd.—(Continued)

E-Mail: enq@dyna-mac.com
Web Site: www.dyna-mac.com
NO4—(SES)
Rev.: $174,312,768
Assets: $214,587,871
Liabilities: $65,210,008
Net Worth: $149,377,863
Earnings: $22,978,718
Fiscal Year-end: 12/31/12

Business Description:
Offshore Oil & Gas Engineering & Construction Services
S.I.C.: 1629
N.A.I.C.S.: 237990

Personnel:
Desmond Tze Jong Lim *(Chm & CEO)*
Joyce Sai Lan Tiong *(CFO)*
Tjew Yok Lim *(COO)*
Simon Boon Hwee Teo *(CMO)*
John Varghese *(CTO & Chief Corp Officer)*
Juliana Kim Lian Lee *(Co-Sec)*
Meng Ling Liew *(Co-Sec)*

Board of Directors:
Desmond Tze Jong Lim
Michael Hock Chye Chia
Tjew Yok Lim
Seh Hong Ong
Soo Kiat Tan
John Varghese

Legal Counsel:
RHT Law LLP
6 Battery Road 10 01
Singapore, 049909, Singapore

Subsidiaries:

Dyna-Mac Engineering Services Pte Ltd **(1)**
45 Gul Road
Singapore, 629350, Singapore
Tel.: (65) 6762 5816
Fax: (65) 6762 3465
E-Mail: enq@dyna-mac.com
Emp.: 700
Oil & Gas Line Construction Engineering Services
S.I.C.: 1623
N.A.I.C.S.: 237120
Desmond Lim *(CEO)*

Dyna-Mac Offshore Services Pte. Ltd. **(1)**
45 Gul Road
Singapore, 629350, Singapore
Tel.: (65) 67625816
Fax: (65) 67623465
Marine Engineering Services
S.I.C.: 8711
N.A.I.C.S.: 541330

Haven Automation Industries (S) Pte. Ltd. **(1)**
84 Tuas Avenue 11
Singapore, 639098, Singapore
Tel.: (65) 68610880
Fax: (65) 68616628
E-Mail:
Emp.: 150
Ship Building & Repair Services
S.I.C.: 3731
N.A.I.C.S.: 336611
Eric Chong *(VP)*

DYNAC SDN. BHD.

(d/b/a Dynac Group)
PLO 110 Jalan Nibong 3
Tanjung Langsat Industrial Estate, Pasir Gudang, Johor Darul Takzim, 81707, Malaysia
Tel.: (60) 7 259 9888
Fax: (60) 7 259 9988
Web Site: www.dynac.com.my
Year Founded: 1982

Business Description:
Oil, Gas & Chemical Industry Heating, Ventilation & Air Conditioning Equipment Designer, Mfr, Whslr & Installation Services
S.I.C.: 3585
N.A.I.C.S.: 333415

Personnel:
Paul Hart *(Dir-UK)*

Non-U.S. Subsidiary:

Dynac UK Ltd. **(1)**
Charrington Park West Carr Lane
Kingston upon Hull, HU7 0BW, United Kingdom UK
Tel.: (44) 1482 225 122
Web Site: www.dynac.co.uk
Oil, Gas & Chemical Industry Heating, Ventilation & Air Conditioning Equipment Whslr & Installation Services
S.I.C.: 5075
N.A.I.C.S.: 423730
Paul Hart *(Mng Dir)*

Subsidiary:

North Sea Ventilation Limited **(2)**
Charrington Park West Carr Lane
Kingston upon Hull, HU7 0BW, United Kingdom UK
Tel.: (44) 1482 834 050 (100%)
Fax: (44) 1482 834 060
E-Mail: enquiries@nsv.co.uk
Web Site: www.nsv.co.uk
Emp.: 150
Oil, Gas & Chemical Industry Heating, Ventilation & Air Conditioning Equipment Designer, Mfr, Whslr & Installation Services
S.I.C.: 3585
N.A.I.C.S.: 333415
Paul Hart *(Mng Dir)*

DYNACERT INC.

(Formerly Dynamic Fuel Systems Inc.)
101-501 Alliance Avenue
Toronto, ON, M6N 2J1, Canada
Tel.: (905) 831-2440
Fax: (905) 831-3282
E-Mail: info@dynacert.com
Web Site: www.dynacert.com
DYA—(TSXV)
Rev.: $32,306
Assets: $177,396
Liabilities: $5,708,726
Net Worth: ($5,531,331)
Earnings: ($1,692,700)
Fiscal Year-end: 12/31/12

Business Description:
Generator Mfr & Sales
S.I.C.: 3621
N.A.I.C.S.: 335312

Personnel:
James Payne *(CEO)*
Rakesh Malhotra *(CFO)*

Board of Directors:
Jay Freeman
James Payne
Ronald Perry
David Sikkema
Wilf Wikkerink

DYNACONS SYSTEMS & SOLUTIONS LTD.

78 Ratnajyot Industrial Estate Irla Lane Vile Parle W
Mumbai, 400056, India
Tel.: (91) 2266889900
Fax: (91) 2226716641
E-Mail: sales@dynacons.com
Web Site: www.dynacons.com
532365—(BOM NSE)
Rev.: $10,882,906
Assets: $5,554,769
Liabilities: $2,654,168
Net Worth: $2,900,602
Earnings: $95,796
Fiscal Year-end: 03/31/13

Business Description:
Information Technology Consulting Services
S.I.C.: 7373
N.A.I.C.S.: 541512

Personnel:
Shirish M. Anjaria *(Chm & Mng Dir)*
Dharmesh S. Anjaria *(CFO)*
Ravishankar Singh *(Compliance Officer & Sec)*

Board of Directors:
Shirish M. Anjaria
Dharmesh S. Anjaria
Vishal G. Chappar
Parag J. Dalal
Mukesh P. Shah
Viren Shah

Transfer Agent:
Bigshare Services Pvt. Ltd.
E-2 Ansa Industrial Estate Saki Vihar Road
Andheri East
Mumbai, India

DYNACOR GOLD MINES INC.

2000 McGill College Avenue Suite 510
Montreal, QC, H3A 3H3, Canada
Tel.: (514) 288-3224
Fax: (514) 288-8179
Toll Free: (877) 664-3224
E-Mail: investors@dynacorgold.com
Web Site: www.dynacorgold.com
DNG—(TSX)
Sls.: $104,994,162
Assets: $30,122,785
Liabilities: $7,858,495
Net Worth: $22,264,290
Earnings: $7,715,957
Emp.: 273
Fiscal Year-end: 12/31/12

Business Description:
Gold Mining Services
S.I.C.: 1041
N.A.I.C.S.: 212221

Personnel:
Rene Branchaud *(Chm)*
Jean Martineau *(Pres & CEO)*
Leonard Teoli *(CFO & VP)*

Board of Directors:
Rene Branchaud
Eddy Canova
Roger Demers
Richard DeVitre
Johanne Duchesne
Denis V. Lachance
Robert Lapalme
Jean Martineau

Legal Counsel:
Lavery, de Billy
1 Place Ville-Marie, Ste. 4000
Montreal, QC, H3B 4M4, Canada

Transfer Agent:
Canadian Stock Transfer Company Inc
Montreal, QC, Canada

Non-U.S. Subsidiary:

Minera Dynacor del Peru, S.A.C. **(1)**
Cal Luis Pasteur Nro 1297
Lynx, Lima, Peru
Tel.: (51) 12027630
Gold Mining Services
S.I.C.: 1041
N.A.I.C.S.: 212221

DYNACTION SA

23 Rue Bossuet Zi De La Vigne Aux Loups
PO Box 181
91161 Longjumeau, Cedex, France
Tel.: (33) 169796062
Fax: (33) 164483359
Web Site: www.dynaction.fr
DYT—(EUR)
Sales Range: $200-249.9 Million
Emp.: 930

Business Description:
Holding Company; Fine & Specialty Chemicals Mfr
S.I.C.: 2899
N.A.I.C.S.: 325998

Personnel:
Christian Moretti *(Chm)*
Philippe Delwasse *(CEO & Dir Gen)*

Board of Directors:
Christian Moretti
Alain Ferri
Michel Fleuriet
Jean-Robert Kervarec
Jean-Louis Milin
Caroline Millot
Jean-Pierre Richard

Subsidiary:

Produits Chimiques Auxiliaires et de Synthese SA **(1)**
BP 181-23 Rue Bossuet ZI La Vigne aux Loups
91160 Longjumeau, France FR
Tel.: (33) 169097785 (67.8%)
Fax: (33) 164482319
E-Mail: info@pcas.fr
Web Site: www.pcas.com
PCA—(EUR)
Sls.: $230,329,687
Assets: $239,752,877
Liabilities: $142,424,786
Net Worth: $97,328,091
Earnings: $4,038,510
Emp.: 909
Fiscal Year-end: 12/31/12
Fine & Specialty Chemicals Mfr
S.I.C.: 2899
N.A.I.C.S.: 325998
Christian Moretti *(Chm)*
Philippe Delwasse *(Vice Chm & Vice CEO)*
Vincent Touraille *(CEO)*
Henri Viguier *(COO)*
Eric Moissenot *(Sr VP-Fin & Admin)*

Subsidiaries:

Expansia S.A.S. **(2)**
23 rue Bossuet
BP 181
ZI de la Vigne-aux-Loups, 91160
Longjumeau, Essonne, France
Tel.: (33) 466570101
Fax: (33) 4 66 57 01 48
Web Site: www.pcas.com
Pharmaceutical Chemicals Mfr
S.I.C.: 2899
N.A.I.C.S.: 325998

VLG Chem S.A.S. **(2)**
25 Avenue Jean-Jaures
92390 Villeneuve-la-Garenne, Hauts-de-Seine, France
Tel.: (33) 146859191
Fax: (33) 146859161
Web Site: www.pcas.com
Pharmaceutical Chemicals Mfr
S.I.C.: 2899
N.A.I.C.S.: 325998

Plants:

Produits Chimiques Auxiliaires et de Synthese SA - Usine de Bourgoin Plant **(2)**
15 avenue des Freres-Lumiere
38300 Bourgoin-Jallieu, Isere, France
Tel.: (33) 4 74 93 63 33
Fax: (33) 4 74 28 29 98
Web Site: www.pcas.com
Emp.: 70
Pharmaceutical Chemicals Mfr
S.I.C.: 2899
N.A.I.C.S.: 325998
Pascal Guerrini *(Mgr)*

Produits Chimiques Auxiliaires et de Synthese SA - Usine de Couterne Plant **(2)**
Route de Lassay
61410 Couterne, Orne, France
Tel.: (33) 2 33 37 50 20
Fax: (33) 2 33 37 50 21
Web Site: www.pcas.com
Emp.: 245
Pharmaceutical Chemicals Mfr
S.I.C.: 2899
N.A.I.C.S.: 325998

Produits Chimiques Auxiliaires et de Synthese SA - Usine de Limay Plant **(2)**
19 route de Meulan
78520 Limay, Yvelines, France

Tel.: (33) 1 34 78 87 87
Fax: (33) 1 30 92 03 46
E-Mail: accueil.limay@pcas.com
Web Site: www.pcas.com
Pharmaceutical Chemicals Mfr
S.I.C.: 2869
N.A.I.C.S.: 325199

U.S. Subsidiary:

PCAS America Inc. (2)
208 3rd St
Hoboken, NJ 07030-3838
Tel.: (201) 633-0290
Fax: (201) 377-0383
Web Site: www.pcas.com
Emp.: 1
Pharmaceutical Preparations Mfr
S.I.C.: 2834
N.A.I.C.S.: 325412
Joe Tessier *(VP)*

Non-U.S. Subsidiaries:

PCAS China (2)
Qi Hua Building 6F 1375 Huai Hai Zhong Lu
Shanghai, China
Tel.: (86) 2164331616
Fax: (86) 2164335061
Web Site: www.pcaschina.com
Fine Chemicals Mfr
S.I.C.: 2899
N.A.I.C.S.: 325199

PCAS Finland Oy (2)
Messukentankatu 8
PO Box 979
20101 Turku, Finland
Tel.: (358) 23305542
Fax: (358) 23305500
E-Mail: info@pcasfinland.com
Web Site: www.pcasfinland.com
Emp.: 120
Pharmaceutical Chemicals Mfr
S.I.C.: 2899
N.A.I.C.S.: 325998
Elina Perez *(CFO)*

PCAS GmbH (2)
Wiesenstrasse
63128 Dietzenbach, Hessen, Germany
Tel.: (49) 6074 2115466
Fax: (49) 6074 2117652
Web Site: www.pcas.com
Pharmaceutical Chemicals Mfr
S.I.C.: 2899
N.A.I.C.S.: 325998

St. Jean Photochemicals Inc. (2)
725 Trotter St
Saint-Jean, QC, J3B 8J8, Canada FR
Tel.: (450) 348-0901 (100%)
Fax: (450) 349-1528
E-Mail: info@sjpc.com
Web Site: www.sjpc.com
Emp.: 50
Sales & Marketing of Chemicals
S.I.C.: 5169
N.A.I.C.S.: 424690
Philippe Hugele *(Pres)*

DYNAGAS LNG PARTNERS LP

97 Poseidonos Avenue & 2 Foivis Street
16674 Glyfada, Greece
Tel.: (30) 210 8917 260
DLNG—(NASDAQ)
Rev.: $77,498,000
Assets: $476,275,000
Liabilities: $401,100,000
Net Worth: $75,175,000
Earnings: $29,836,000
Fiscal Year-end: 12/31/12
Business Description:
LNG Carrier Owner & Operator
S.I.C.: 4499
N.A.I.C.S.: 488390
Personnel:
George Prokopiou *(Chm)*
Tony Lauritzen *(CEO)*
Michael Gregos *(CFO)*
Board of Directors:
George Prokopiou
Levon A. Dedegian
Tony Lauritzen
Alexios Rodopoulos
Evangelos Vlahoulis

DYNAM JAPAN HOLDINGS, CO., LTD.

2-25-1-702 Nishinippori
Arakawa-ku, Tokyo, 116-0013, Japan
Tel.: (81) 3 5615 1222
Fax: (81) 3 5615 1776
Web Site: www.dyjh.co.jp
6889—(HKG)
Emp.: 31
Business Description:
Game Hall Management Consulting Services
S.I.C.: 8742
N.A.I.C.S.: 541611
Personnel:
Yoji Sato *(Pres)*
Hirobumi Yonehata *(Exec Officer & Co-Sec)*
Shizuo Okayasu *(Exec Officer)*
Yukiharu Uno *(Exec Officer)*
Ming Wai Mok *(Co-Sec)*
Board of Directors:
Katsuhide Horiba
Mitsutoshi Kato
Yoji Sato
Ichiro Takano
Noriaki Ushijima
Thomas Yip
Yukio Yoshida

DYNAMATIC TECHNOLOGIES LIMITED

Dynamatic Park Peenya Industrial Area
Bengaluru, 560 058, India
Tel.: (91) 8028394933
Fax: (91) 8028395823
E-Mail: hrd@dynamatics.net
Web Site: www.dynamatics.com
Emp.: 900
Business Description:
Hydraulic Gear Pump, Non-Ferrous Alloy Casting, Automotive Engine Parts & Aircraft Structural Components Mfr
S.I.C.: 3561
N.A.I.C.S.: 333911
Personnel:
Vijay Kapur *(Chm)*
V. Sunder *(Pres & CFO)*
Udhyant Malhotra *(Mng Dir)*
Board of Directors:
Vijay Kapur
Ramesh Venkataraman

Non-U.S. Subsidiary:

Dynamatic Limited UK (1)
Cheney Manor Industrial Estates
Swindon, Wilts, SN2 2PZ, United Kingdom
Tel.: (44) 1793530101
Fax: (44) 1793528301
Web Site: www.dynamatics.net
Sales Range: $10-24.9 Million
Emp.: 250
Open Circuit Gear Pump Mfr
S.I.C.: 3561
N.A.I.C.S.: 333911
Udayant Malhoutra *(Chm, CEO & Mng Dir)*
Ray Lawton *(COO & Exec Dir)*

DYNAMIC & PROTO CIRCUITS INC.

869 Barton St
Stoney Creek, ON, L8E 5G6, Canada
Tel.: (905) 643-9900
Fax: (905) 643-9911
Toll Free: (866) 643-9900
E-Mail: dynamic@dapc.com
Web Site: www.dapc.com
Year Founded: 1974
Rev.: $12,000,000
Emp.: 120
Business Description:
Electric Circuit Boards Mfr
S.I.C.: 3672
N.A.I.C.S.: 334412
Personnel:
Carl Hewitt *(Gen Mgr)*

DYNAMIC ARCHITECTURAL WINDOWS & DOORS INC.

30440 Progressive Way
Abbotsford, BC, V2T 6W3, Canada
Tel.: (604) 864-8200
Fax: (604) 864-6072
Toll Free: (800) 661-8111
E-Mail: sales@dynamicwindows.com
Web Site: www.dynamicwindows.com
Rev.: $10,924,369
Emp.: 20
Business Description:
Windows & Doors Distr
S.I.C.: 5211
N.A.I.C.S.: 444190
Personnel:
John Mathews *(Pres)*

DYNAMIC COLOURS LIMITED

55A Yishun Industrial Park SL Building
Singapore, 768729, Singapore
Tel.: (65) 67523988
Fax: (65) 67523788
E-Mail: enquiry@dynamiccolours.com
Web Site: www.dynamiccolours.com
D6U—(SES)
Rev.: $76,924,142
Assets: $48,799,491
Liabilities: $16,606,385
Net Worth: $32,193,106
Earnings: $2,262,778
Fiscal Year-end: 12/31/12
Business Description:
Color Pigments Mfr
S.I.C.: 2816
N.A.I.C.S.: 325130
Personnel:
Hock Leng Yeo *(Chm & Mng Dir)*
Seok Eng Goh *(Deputy Mng Dir & Dir-Technical)*
Lai Yin Chan *(Co-Sec)*
Ping Ping Tan *(Co-Sec)*
Board of Directors:
Hock Leng Yeo
Sebastian Yee Siew Chong
Seok Eng Goh
Kim Liang Lim
Boon Siong Soon
Lye Huat Tan

Subsidiary:

S.L. Packaging Industries Pte Ltd (1)
SL Building 55A Yishun Industrial Park A
Singapore, Singapore
Tel.: (65) 67523988
Fax: (65) 67523788
E-Mail: sales@slpack.com
Web Site: www.slpack.com
Emp.: 15
Polyethylene Bags Mfr
S.I.C.: 2673
N.A.I.C.S.: 326111
Audrick Keek *(Deputy Gen Mgr)*

Non-U.S. Subsidiaries:

Huiye (Vietnam) Plastic Co., Ltd. (1)
Vietnam-Singapore Industrial Park 25-27 Dan Chu Street
Hoa Phu Ward, Thu Dau Mot, Binh Duong, Vietnam
Tel.: (84) 650 363 5388
Fax: (84) 650 363 5366
E-Mail: sales@huiyevp.com
Injection Molded Plastic Products Mfr
S.I.C.: 3082
N.A.I.C.S.: 326121

Suzhou Huiye Chemical & Light Industry Co., Ltd. (1)
No 96 Yingchun South Road
Wuzhong District, Suzhou, Jiangsu, 311500, China
Tel.: (86) 51265625900
Fax: (86) 51265272366
Food Coloring Mfr
S.I.C.: 2099
N.A.I.C.S.: 311942

Suzhou Huiye Plastic Industry Co., Ltd. (1)
No 96 Yingchun Road
Wuzhong District, Suzhou, Jiangsu, 215128, China
Tel.: (86) 51265285023
Fax: (86) 51265658530
Resin Compounding Services
S.I.C.: 3087
N.A.I.C.S.: 325991

DYNAMIC ELECTRONICS CO., LTD.

356 Shan Ing Road Guei Shan
Taoyuan, 333, Taiwan
Tel.: (886) 33493300
Fax: (886) 33595131
E-Mail: inquiry@dynamicpcb.com.tw
Web Site: www.dynamicpcb.com.tw
Year Founded: 1988
6251—(TAI)
Sales Range: $350-399.9 Million
Emp.: 6,580
Business Description:
Printed Circuit Boards & Other Electronic Components Mfr
S.I.C.: 3672
N.A.I.C.S.: 334412
Personnel:
Maochang Tseng *(Chm)*
Muchuan Lin *(Pres)*

DYNAMIC FUEL SYSTEMS INC.

(Name Changed to dynaCERT Inc.)

DYNAMIC GOLD CORP.

501-675 West Hastings Street
Vancouver, BC, V6B 1N2, Canada
Tel.: (604) 681-3131
Year Founded: 2004
DYGO—(OTCB)
Assets: $1,369
Liabilities: $26,462
Net Worth: ($25,093)
Earnings: ($120,932)
Fiscal Year-end: 06/30/13
Business Description:
Gold Mining Services
S.I.C.: 1041
N.A.I.C.S.: 212221
Personnel:
Tim Coupland *(Pres & CEO)*
Robert T. Hall *(CFO)*
Tamiko Coupland *(Sec)*
Board of Directors:
Tim Coupland
Brian David Game
Robert T. Hall

DYNAMIC HOLDINGS LIMITED

17th Floor Eton Tower 8 Hysan Avenue
Causeway Bay, China (Hong Kong)
Tel.: (852) 28815221
Fax: (852) 28815224
Web Site: www.dynamic-hk.com
0029—(HKG)
Sls.: $19,415,873
Assets: $316,177,147
Liabilities: $82,279,255
Net Worth: $233,897,892
Earnings: $16,197,667
Emp.: 80
Fiscal Year-end: 06/30/13

Dynamic Holdings Limited—(Continued)

Business Description:
Construction Industry
S.I.C.: 6719
N.A.I.C.S.: 551112
Personnel:
Harry Chua Tan *(Chm)*
Frank Wing Kit Chan *(CEO)*
Polly Oi Yee Wong *(Sec)*
Board of Directors:
Harry Chua Tan
Frank Wing Kit Chan
Chi Ming Cheung
Allan Siu Hung Chiu
Kenneth Kim Chan Chong
John Kam Chu Fok
Patrick Lim Go
Ramon Sy Pascual
Robin Sy
Lucio Khao Tan, Jr.
Michael Gonzales Tan
Patrick Sai Tat Wong
MUFG Fund Services (Bermuda) Limited
26 Burnaby Street
Hamilton, Bermuda
Subsidiaries:

Strong Way Investment Limited **(1)**
1702 Eton Tower 8 Hysan Ave
Causeway Bay, China (Hong Kong)
Tel.: (852) 28815221
Fax: (852) 28815224
Emp.: 10
Investment Management Services
S.I.C.: 6282
N.A.I.C.S.: 523920
Sai Tat Wong *(Mgr)*

DYNAMIC PAINT PRODUCTS
7040 Financial Dr
Mississauga, ON, L5N 7H5, Canada
Tel.: (905) 812-9319
Fax: (905) 812-9322
Toll Free: (800) 668-1124
E-Mail: info@dynamicsundries.com
Web Site: www.getpainting.com
Rev.: $21,400,000
Emp.: 100
Business Description:
Paint & Related Products Mfr
S.I.C.: 2851
N.A.I.C.S.: 325510
Personnel:
James Mumby *(Pres)*

DYNAMIC SOURCE MANUFACTURING INC.
Unit 117 2765 48th Avenue NE
Calgary, AB, T3J 5M9, Canada
Tel.: (403) 516-1888
Fax: (403) 532-0412
E-Mail: dsmsales@dynamicsourcemfg.com
Web Site: www.dynamicsourcemfg.com
Year Founded: 2000
Rev.: $23,660,619
Emp.: 125
Business Description:
Electronic Products Mfr
S.I.C.: 3679
N.A.I.C.S.: 334419
Personnel:
Duane Macauley *(Pres & CEO)*

DYNAMIC SPECIALTY VEHICLES LTD.
(d/b/a Dynamic Bus Sales & Service)
18550 96th Avenue
Surrey, BC, V4N 3P9, Canada
Tel.: (604) 882-9333
Fax: (604) 882-3555
Toll Free: (888) 416-9333
Web Site: www.dynamicspecialty.com
Year Founded: 1987
Rev.: $10,012,849
Emp.: 20
Business Description:
Automobile Mfrs & Distr
S.I.C.: 3711
N.A.I.C.S.: 336111
Personnel:
D. Shawn Francis *(Pres)*

DYNAMIC SYSTEMS HOLDINGS, INC.
780 Broadway
Orangeville, ON, L9W 2Y9, Canada
E-Mail: info@dynamicmsrm.com
Web Site: www.dynamicmsrm.com
DYOA—(DEU)
Business Description:
Fuel Efficiency Motor Mfr
S.I.C.: 3621
N.A.I.C.S.: 335312
Personnel:
Allen Scott *(Pres)*

DYNAMIC TIRE CORP.
155 Delta Park Boulevard
Brampton, ON, L6T 5M8, Canada
Tel.: (905) 595-5558
Fax: (905) 595-0469
Toll Free: (800) 668-8473
E-Mail: info@dynamictire.com
Web Site: www.dynamictire.com
Sales Range: $50-74.9 Million
Emp.: 50
Business Description:
Tire Mfr & Distr
S.I.C.: 3011
N.A.I.C.S.: 326211
Personnel:
Robert Sherkin *(CEO)*
John Overing *(Pres-Wholesale & Distr Bus)*

DYNAMIX BALWAS GROUP OF COMPANIES
Dynamix House Yashodham General AK Vaidya Marg
Goregaon (E), Mumbai, 400 063, India
Tel.: (91) 2240778600
Fax: (91) 2228415550
E-Mail: info@dbg.co.in
Web Site: www.dbg.co.in
Emp.: 250
Business Description:
Holding Company
S.I.C.: 6719
N.A.I.C.S.: 551112
Personnel:
Vinod K. Goenka *(Chm)*
Subsidiary:

DB Realty Limited **(1)**
DB House General A K Vaidya Marg
Goregaon E
Mumbai, 400 063, India
Tel.: (91) 2240778600
Fax: (91) 2228415550
E-Mail: info@dbg.co.in
Web Site: www.dbrealty.in
DBREALTY—(BOM NSE)
Rev.: $68,124,393
Assets: $976,839,366
Liabilities: $337,952,433
Net Worth: $638,886,933
Earnings: $620,523
Emp.: 200
Fiscal Year-end: 03/31/13
Real Esate Services
S.I.C.: 6531
N.A.I.C.S.: 531390
Vinod K. Goenka *(Co-Founder, Chm & Co-Mng Dir)*
Shahid U. Balwa *(Co-Founder, Vice Chm & Co-Mng Dir)*
Vipul Bansal *(CEO)*
N. M. Gattu *(CFO)*
S. A. K. Narayanan *(Compliance Officer & Sec)*

DYNAPAC CO., LTD.
3-14-15 Nishiki
Naka-Ku, Nagoya, Aichi, 460-0003, Japan
Tel.: (81) 52 971 2651
Fax: (81) 52 968 2395
Web Site: www.dynapac-gr.co.jp
Year Founded: 2005
3947—(TKS)
Sales Range: Less than $1 Million
Emp.: 1,648
Business Description:
Packaging Material Mfr & Whslr
S.I.C.: 2672
N.A.I.C.S.: 322220
Personnel:
Atsushi Kojima *(Pres)*

DYNAPLAST-EXTRUCO INC.
10 500 rue Colbert
Montreal, QC, H1J 2H8, Canada
Tel.: (514) 355-6868
Fax: (514) 355-0352
Toll Free: (800) 263-5546
E-Mail: info@dynaplastinc.com
Web Site: www.dynaplastextruco.com
Emp.: 80
Business Description:
Plastic Profiles Mfr
S.I.C.: 3089
N.A.I.C.S.: 326199
Personnel:
Gerald Gravel *(Pres)*

DYNASTY CERAMIC PUBLIC COMPANY LIMITED
37/7 Suttisarn-Vinichai Road
Samsen-Nok Sub-district
HuayKwang District, Bangkok, 10310, Thailand
Tel.: (66) 22769275
Fax: (66) 22760313
E-Mail: maruth@dynastyceramic.com
Web Site: www.dynastyceramic.com
Year Founded: 1989
DCC—(THA)
Rev.: $251,879,002
Assets: $157,662,979
Liabilities: $68,148,365
Net Worth: $89,514,614
Earnings: $41,734,995
Emp.: 2,471
Fiscal Year-end: 12/31/12
Business Description:
Ceramic Tiles Mfr & Distr
S.I.C.: 3297
N.A.I.C.S.: 327120
Personnel:
Roongroj Saengsastra *(Chm)*
Sanchai Janejarat *(Pres)*
Cattleya Saengsastra *(Sec)*
Chana Suthiwangcharoen *(Sr Exec VP-Mktg)*
Monrak Saengsastra *(Exec VP-Admin)*
Sontaya Yaowalee *(Exec VP-Outlets & Support)*
Suthee Boonnak *(Sr VP-Technical)*
Jaruwat Traithavil *(Sr VP-Production)*
Board of Directors:
Roongroj Saengsastra
Sanchai Janejarat
Yothin Juangbhanich
Phachon Khachitsarn
Surasak Kosiyajinda
Cattleya Saengsastra
Monrak Saengsastra
Suvit Smarnpanchai
Chaiyasith Viriyamettakul
Subsidiaries:

Muangthong Ceramic Co., Ltd. **(1)**
37 7 Sutthisan Vinitchai Rd Samsennok
Huaykwanq, Bangkok, 10310, Thailand
Tel.: (66) 22769275
Fax: (66) 22760313
E-Mail: karya@dynastyceramic.com
Emp.: 100
Tiles & Ceramics Mfr
S.I.C.: 3255
N.A.I.C.S.: 327120
Rungrot Saengsattra Saengsattra *(Mng Dir)*

Tile Top Industry Co., Ltd. **(1)**
48 5 Ratchada Rd
Samsennk Huaikhwang, Bangkok, 10310, Thailand
Tel.: (66) 22769276
Fax: (66) 22769269
E-Mail: jariya@dynastyceramic.com
Web Site: www.dynastyceramic.com
Emp.: 100
Tiles & Ceramics Mfr
S.I.C.: 3255
N.A.I.C.S.: 327120
Chana Suthiwang Charoen *(Mgr-Mktg & Export)*

DYNASTY FINE WINES GROUP LIMITED
Suite 5506 55/F Central Plaza
18 Harbour Road, Wanchai, China (Hong Kong)
Tel.: (852) 2918 8000
Fax: (852) 2918 8099
E-Mail: info@dynasty-wines.com
Web Site: www.dynasty-wines.com
Year Founded: 1980
Sales Range: $150-199.9 Million
Emp.: 650
Business Description:
Wine Producer
S.I.C.: 2084
N.A.I.C.S.: 312130
Personnel:
Zhisheng Bai *(Chm)*
Chi Tat Yeung *(Sec & Controller-Fin)*
Board of Directors:
Zhisheng Bai
Jingrui Dong
Feifei Hao
Francois Heriard-Dubreuil
Yaqiang Huang
Herbert Ho Ming Hui
Jean-Marie Laborde
Luc Robert
David Lee Sun
Weidong Wang
Ching Chung Wong
Emory Ting Lap Derek Yeung
HSBC Trustee (Cayman) Limited
HSBC House 68 West Bay Road
PO Box 484
Georgetown, Cayman Islands
Transfer Agents:
Tricor Investor Services Limited
26/F Tesbury Centre 28 Queen's Road East
Hong Kong, China (Hong Kong)
HSBC Trustee (Cayman) Limited
HSBC House 68 West Bay Road
PO Box 484
Georgetown, Cayman Islands

DYNASTY GOLD CORP.
1180 - 625 Howe Street
Vancouver, BC, V6C 2T6, Canada
Tel.: (604) 633-2100
Fax: (604) 484-3559
E-Mail: info@dynastygoldcorp.com
Web Site: www.dynastygoldcorp.com
Year Founded: 1985
DYG—(TSXV)
Int. Income: $15,932
Assets: $1,767,727
Liabilities: $112,723
Net Worth: $1,655,005

Earnings: ($518,428)
Fiscal Year-end: 12/31/12
Business Description:
Mineral Exploration Services
S.I.C.: 1081
N.A.I.C.S.: 213114
Personnel:
Robert Stuart Angus *(Chm)*
Ivy Chong *(Pres & CEO)*
Board of Directors:
Robert Stuart Angus
Ivy Chong
Robert Gallagher
Larry D. Kornze
Maurice A. Tagami

DYNASTY METALS & MINING INC.

666 Burrard Street Suite 270
Vancouver, BC, V6C 2X8, Canada
Tel.: (604) 687-7810
Fax: (604) 687-0885
Toll Free: (888) 735-3881
E-Mail: info@dynastymining.com
Web Site: www.dynastymining.com
Year Founded: 2000
DMM—(TSX)
Assets: $72,845,130
Liabilities: $8,730,094
Net Worth: $64,115,036
Earnings: ($5,820,493)
Emp.: 447
Fiscal Year-end: 12/31/12
Business Description:
Metals Mining Services
S.I.C.: 1099
N.A.I.C.S.: 212299
Personnel:
Robert Washer *(Pres & CEO)*
Nicholas Furber *(CFO & Sec)*
Board of Directors:
Mark H. Bailey
Leonard Michael Clough
Segundo Jesus Ernesto Andrade
Gordon Brian Speechly
Robert Washer
Legal Counsel:
Fasken Martineau
Vancouver, BC, Canada
Transfer Agent:
Computershare Investor Services Inc.
3rd Floor 510 Burrard St
V6C 3B9 Vancouver, BC, Canada

DYNASTY METALS AUSTRALIA LTD

Level 4 35 Havelock Street
West Perth, WA, 6005, Australia
Tel.: (61) 86316 4414
Fax: (61) 86316 4404
Web Site: www.dynastymetals.com.au
DMA—(ASX)
Int. Income: $74,567
Assets: $1,997,865
Liabilities: $176,560
Net Worth: $1,821,305
Earnings: ($1,541,399)
Fiscal Year-end: 06/30/13
Business Description:
Mineral Resources
S.I.C.: 1481
N.A.I.C.S.: 213115
Personnel:
Lewis Tay *(Mng Dir)*
Louise Edwards *(Sec)*
Board of Directors:
Thomas Pickett
Lewis Tay
Bin Wang
Legal Counsel:
Gadens Lawyers
Level 1 16 St Georges Tce
West Perth, Australia

DYNAVEST PTE. LTD.

23 Gul Ave
Singapore, 629663, Singapore
Tel.: (65) 68611881
Fax: (65) 68617070
E-Mail: info@dynavest.com.sg
Web Site: www.dynavest.com.sg
Year Founded: 1980
Emp.: 18
Business Description:
Electronics Equipment & Components; Chemicals & Raw Materials
S.I.C.: 3679
N.A.I.C.S.: 334419
Personnel:
Lawrence Kar Wah Yu *(Pres)*
Subsidiaries:

Comacraft Sdn Bhd **(1)**
2033 Jalan Bukit Minyak Kawasan Industrial Ringan Asas Jaya, Bukit Minyak, 14000, Malaysia
Tel.: (60) 45889933
Fax: (60) 45889953
E-Mail: info@dynavest.com.sg
Web Site: www.dynavest.com.sg/
Electronic Components
S.I.C.: 3679
N.A.I.C.S.: 334419

Dynavest Technologies (Suzhou) Co, Ltd **(1)**
445# Su Hong Middle Road
Suzhou Ind Park, Suzhou, China
Tel.: (86) 512625588516
E-Mail: info@dynavest.com.sg
Web Site: www.dynavest.com.sg/rs_main.htm
Electronics Equipment & Components
S.I.C.: 3679
N.A.I.C.S.: 334419

Dynavest (Thailand) Co, Ltd **(1)**
109/75 Sukaphiban 2 Road Soi Suansiam Kannayao Buangkum, Bangkok, Thailand
Tel.: (66) 29196945
Web Site: www.dynavest.com.sg/rs_main.htm
Electronic Components
S.I.C.: 3679
N.A.I.C.S.: 334419

DYNELYTICS AG

Schneckenmannstrasse 25
CH-8044 Zurich, Switzerland
Tel.: (41) 44 266 9030
Fax: (41) 44 266 9039
E-Mail: info@dynelytics.com
Web Site: www.dynelytics.com
Sales Range: $1-9.9 Million
Business Description:
Predictive Analytics & Data Mining Software Distr & Technical Consulting Services
S.I.C.: 5045
N.A.I.C.S.: 423430
Personnel:
Gisela Boddenberg *(Mng Partner)*
Josef Schmid *(Mng Partner)*

DYNEMIC PRODUCTS LTD.

B-301 Satyamev Complex-1 Opp New Gujarat High Court Sarkhej-Gandhinaga
Sola, Ahmedabad, 380 060, India
Tel.: (91) 79 27663071
Fax: (91) 79 27662176
E-Mail: info@dynemic.com
Web Site: www.dynemic.com
Year Founded: 1990
532707—(BOM)
Rev.: $16,096,445
Assets: $14,340,281
Liabilities: $6,726,642
Net Worth: $7,613,639
Earnings: $816,062
Emp.: 130
Fiscal Year-end: 03/31/13
Business Description:
Organic Dye & Food Color Mfr
S.I.C.: 2816
N.A.I.C.S.: 325130
Personnel:
Bhagwandas K. Patel *(Chm & Mng Dir)*
Varsha Mehta *(Compliance Officer & Sec)*
Board of Directors:
Bhagwandas K. Patel
Ashishbhai R. Joshi
Shankarlal B. Mundra
Dashrathbhai P. Patel
Dixit B. Patel
Rameshbhai B. Patel
Vishnubhai G. Patel
Jagdishbhai S. Shah
Transfer Agent:
Bigshare Services Private Limited
E-2 Ansa Industrial Estate Sakivihar Road Saki Naka Andheri (E)
Mumbai, India

DYSON GROUP PLC

Totley Works Baslow Road
Sheffield, S17 3BL, United Kingdom
Tel.: (44) 1142355300
Fax: (44) 011423556010
E-Mail: en2@dyson-group.com
Web Site: www.dyson-group.com
Year Founded: 1810
Sales Range: $50-74.9 Million
Emp.: 83
Business Description:
Develops & Researches Performance Materials (Metal Composites, Fibers) & Thermal Products (Ceramics, Refractories)
S.I.C.: 3499
N.A.I.C.S.: 332999
Personnel:
Julian Cooper *(Chm)*
Richard P. McQuinn *(Sec)*
Board of Directors:
Julian Cooper
Gavin Rosson
Magnus Sternbrink
Legal Counsel:
Irwin Mitchell
Riverside East 2 Millsands
Sheffield, United Kingdom
DLA Piper UK LLP
1 Saint Paul's Place
Sheffield, S1 2JX, United Kingdom
Non-U.S. Subsidiary:

P.T. Dyson Zedmark Indonesia Limited **(1)**
Jl Sulawesi II Kawasan Industri MM 2100 Bl F-2-1
17520 Bekasi, Indonesia
Tel.: (62) 218981269
Fax: (62) 218981271
E-Mail: dzindo@indo.net.id
Emp.: 101
Ceramic Wall & Floor Tile Mfr
S.I.C.: 3255
N.A.I.C.S.: 327120
Michael Charles *(Mng Dir)*

DYSON LTD.

Tetbury Hill
Malmesbury, SN16 0RP, United Kingdom
Tel.: (44) 1666827200
Fax: (44) 166682799
E-Mail: press.office@dyson.com
Web Site: www.dyson.co.uk
Sales Range: $1-4.9 Billion
Emp.: 2,700
Business Description:
Vacuum Cleaner & Washing Machine Mfr
S.I.C.: 3639
N.A.I.C.S.: 335210
Personnel:
James Dyson *(Founder)*
Robert Ayling *(Chm)*
U.S. Subsidiary:

Dyson Inc. **(1)**
600 W Chicago Ave Ste 275
Chicago, IL 60654
Tel.: (866) 693-9766
E-Mail: questions@dyson.com
Web Site: www.dyson.com
Vacuum Cleaner & Washing Machine Mfr
S.I.C.: 3639
N.A.I.C.S.: 335210

DYTECNA LIMITED

Unit 2 Kites Croft
Fareham, PO14 0LW, United Kingdom
Tel.: (44) 1684 579000
Fax: (44) 1684575306
E-Mail: info@dytecna.com
Web Site: www.dytecna.co.uk
Year Founded: 1965
Sales Range: $50-74.9 Million
Business Description:
Engineering Services
S.I.C.: 8711
N.A.I.C.S.: 541330
Personnel:
John Fulford *(Pres & Mng Dir)*
Simon Finch *(Exec VP-Fin)*
Allen Merrick *(Exec VP-Programs & Ops)*
Subsidiary:

Dytecna Engineering Ltd **(1)**
Unit 2 Kite's Croft
Fareham, Hampshire, PO14 4LW, United Kingdom
Tel.: (44) 1329 840 683
Fax: (44) 1329 842 944
Engineering Services
S.I.C.: 8711
N.A.I.C.S.: 541330

DZ BANK DEUTSCHE ZENTRAL-GENOSSENSCHAFTSBANK AG

Platz der Republik
60265 Frankfurt am Main, Germany
Tel.: (49) 69744701
Telex: 412291 dg d
Fax: (49) 6974471685
E-Mail: mail@dzbank.de
Web Site: www.dzbank.de
Year Founded: 1895
Rev.: $11,501,676,480
Assets: $548,208,886,120
Liabilities: $531,191,951,150
Net Worth: $17,016,934,970
Earnings: $1,304,438,730
Emp.: 23,420
Fiscal Year-end: 12/31/12
Business Description:
International Banking
S.I.C.: 6159
N.A.I.C.S.: 522293
Personnel:
Helmut Gottschalk *(Chm-Supervisory Bd)*
Wolfgang Apitzsch *(Deputy Chm-Supervisory Bd)*
Henning Deneke-Johrens *(Deputy Chm-Supervisory Bd)*
Wolfgang Kirsch *(CEO & Member-Mgmt Bd)*
Lars Hille *(Member-Mgmt Bd)*
Wolfgang Kohler *(Member-Mgmt Bd)*
Hans-Theo Macke *(Member-Mgmt Bd)*
Albrecht Merz *(Member-Mgmt Bd)*
Cornelius Riese *(Member-Mgmt Bd)*
Thomas Ullrich *(Member-Mgmt Bd)*
Frank Westhoff *(Member-Mgmt Bd)*

DZ BANK Deutsche Zentral-Genossenschaftsbank AG—(Continued)

Supervisory Board of Directors:
Helmut Gottschalk
Wolfgang Apitzsch
Heiner Beckmann
Rudiger Beins
Ulrich Birkenstock
Werner Bohnke
Hermann Buerstedde
Henning Deneke-Johrens
Karl Eichele
Uwe Frohlich
Roman Glaser
Bernd Huhn
Sigmar Kleinert
Rainer Mangels
Walter Muller
Gerhard J. Rastetter
Dieter Rembde
Stephen Schack
Gudrun Schmidt
Uwe Spitzbarth

U.S. Branch:

DZ Bank New York Branch (1)
609 5th Ave
New York, NY 10017-1021 (100%)
Tel.: (212) 745-1400
Telex: WUI 6 66755
Fax: (212) 745-1550
E-Mail: new.york@dzbank.de
Web Site: www.dzbank.de.com
Emp.: 100
Providers of International Banking Services
S.I.C.: 6211
N.A.I.C.S.: 523120
Florian Strassberger *(Gen Mgr)*

U.S. Subsidiary:

DZ Financial Markets LLC (1)
609 5th Ave
New York, NY 10017-1021
Tel.: (212) 745-1600
Fax: (212) 745-1616
E-Mail:
Web Site: www.dzbank.de
Emp.: 50
International Banking
S.I.C.: 6211
N.A.I.C.S.: 523120
Gerhard Summerer *(Pres)*

Subsidiaries:

DZ BANK International S.A (1)
Rue Thomas Edison 4
1445 Strassen, Luxembourg (89%)
Tel.: (352) 449031
Fax: (352) 49932110
E-Mail: info@dzi.lu
Web Site: www.dzi.lu
Rev.: $17,961,970
Emp.: 800
International Banking
S.I.C.: 6159
N.A.I.C.S.: 522293
Frankz Bruner *(Mng Dir)*

DZ BANK Ireland plc (1)
International House 3 Harbourmaster Pl IFSC
Dublin, 1, Ireland (100%)
Tel.: (353) 16700715
Fax: (353) 18290298
E-Mail: info@dzbank.ie
Web Site: www.dzbank.ie
Emp.: 25
International Banking
S.I.C.: 6159
N.A.I.C.S.: 522293
Mark Jacob *(Mng Dir)*

DZ BANK Polska (1)
Plac Pilsudskiego 3
PL 00078 Warsaw, Poland
Tel.: (48) 225057000
Fax: (48) 225057442
E-Mail: info@dzbank.pl
Web Site: www.dzbank.pl
Emp.: 200
International Banking
S.I.C.: 6159
N.A.I.C.S.: 522293

Rainer Fuhrmann *(Pres)*

DZ Private Bank Switzerland (1)
Muensterhof 12
8022 Zurich, Switzerland
Tel.: (41) 442149111
Fax: (41) 442149582
E-Mail: info.ch@dz-privatbank.com
Web Site: www.dz-privatbank.com
Emp.: 200
International Banking
S.I.C.: 6159
N.A.I.C.S.: 522293
Marion Pester *(Gen Mgr)*

TeamBank AG (1)
Rathenauplatz 12-18
90489 Berlin, Germany (100%)
Tel.: (49) 91153900
Fax: (49) 9 11 53 90 22 22
E-Mail: service@teambank.de
Web Site: www.teambank.de
Commercial Banking
S.I.C.: 6029
N.A.I.C.S.: 522110
Theophil Graband *(Chm & CEO)*
Albrecht Merz *(Chm-Supervisory Bd)*

E&A LIMITED

Level 27 91 King William Street
Adelaide, SA, 5000, Australia
Tel.: (61) 8 8212 2929
Fax: (61) 8 8231 1647
Web Site: www.ealimited.com.au
EAL—(ASX)
Rev.: $208,462,726
Assets: $152,693,703
Liabilities: $88,258,575
Net Worth: $64,435,127
Earnings: $8,030,423
Emp.: 700
Fiscal Year-end: 06/30/13
Business Description:
Holding Company
S.I.C.: 6719
N.A.I.C.S.: 551112
Personnel:
Stephen Young *(Chm)*
Matt Proctor *(Sec)*
Board of Directors:
Stephen Young
Michael Abbott
David Klingberg
Michael J. Terlet
Mark Vartuli
Legal Counsel:
Thomsons Lawyers
101 Pirie Street
Adelaide, SA, 5000, Australia
Subsidiaries:

Blucher (Australia) Pty. Ltd. (1)
Corunna Avenue Melrose Park
Mitcham, SA, 5039, Australia
Tel.: (61) 883743426
Fax: (61) 883743428
E-Mail: blucher@blucher.com.au
Web Site: www.blucher.com.au
Emp.: 13
Stainless Steel Plumbing Equipment Mfr
S.I.C.: 7359
N.A.I.C.S.: 532490
Adam Howkins *(Mgr-Mktg)*

E&A Contractors Pty. Ltd. (1)
39 Plymouth Road Wingfield
Adelaide, SA, 5013, Australia
Tel.: (61) 882448605
Fax: (61) 881599599
Web Site: www.eacontractors.com.au
Emp.: 460
Mining Engineering Services
S.I.C.: 8711
N.A.I.C.S.: 541330

Equity & Advisory Ltd. (1)
Level 27 91 King William St
Adelaide, SA, 5000, Australia
Tel.: (61) 882122929
Fax: (61) 882311647
Web Site: www.ealtd.com.au
Emp.: 12
Corporate Advisory Services
S.I.C.: 6282
N.A.I.C.S.: 523930
Mark Vartuli *(Mng Dir)*

Fabtech S.A. Pty. Ltd. (1)
53 S Terrace Wingfield
Adelaide, SA, 5013, Australia
Tel.: (61) 883473111
Fax: (61) 883473729
E-Mail: admin@fabtech.com.au
Web Site: www.fabtech.com.au
Emp.: 70
Waste Water Management Services
S.I.C.: 4959
N.A.I.C.S.: 562998
Graham Fairhead *(Mng Dir)*

Heavymech Pty. Ltd. (1)
717 Grand Junction Road Northfield
5085 Adelaide, SA, Australia
Tel.: (61) 882621420
Fax: (61) 883494680
E-Mail: enquiries@heavymech.com.au
Web Site: www.heavymech.com.au
Emp.: 25
Mining Equipment Services
S.I.C.: 7699
N.A.I.C.S.: 811310
Stephen Young *(CEO)*

ICE Engineering & Construction Pty. Ltd. (1)
14 Beerwoth Av
Whyalla Playford, Whyalla, SA, 4601, Australia
Tel.: (61) 886442333
Fax: (61) 8 8644 2444
Emp.: 75
Construction Engineering Services
S.I.C.: 1629
N.A.I.C.S.: 237990

Ottoway Engineering Pty. Ltd. (1)
22 Duncan Court Ottoway
Adelaide, SA, 5013, Australia
Tel.: (61) 883410045
Fax: (61) 883410876
E-Mail: enquiries@ottowayengineering.com.au
Web Site: www.ottowayengineering.com.au
Emp.: 300
Steel Fabrication Services
S.I.C.: 3324
N.A.I.C.S.: 331512
Brian Tidswell *(CEO)*

Quarry & Mining Manufacture Pty. Ltd. (1)
11-15 Maxwell Rd
Pooraka, SA, 5095, Australia
Tel.: (61) 882684085
Fax: (61) 0883490999
E-Mail: sales@qmm-sa.com.au
Web Site: www.quarrymining.com.au
Emp.: 25
Quarry & Mining Equipments Mfr
S.I.C.: 3532
N.A.I.C.S.: 333131
Darryl Constable *(Mng Dir)*

Quarry & Mining Manufacture (QLD) Pty. Ltd. (1)
46 Kremzow Road Brendale
Brisbane, QLD, 4500, Australia
Tel.: (61) 732056699
Fax: (61) 732052739
E-Mail: sales@qmm.net.au
Web Site: www.quarrymining.com.au
Emp.: 20
Quarry & Mining Equipments Mfr
S.I.C.: 3532
N.A.I.C.S.: 333131
David O'Sullivan *(Mng Dir)*

E & E SEEGMILLER LTD

(d/b/a Hogg Fuel & Supply)
5 Hill St
Kitchener, ON, N2G 3X4, Canada
Tel.: (519) 579-5330
Fax: (519) 579-2531
Year Founded: 1900
Rev.: $11,561,746
Emp.: 75
Business Description:
Fuel Supplier
S.I.C.: 5989
N.A.I.C.S.: 454310
Personnel:
Bill Seegmiller *(Pres)*

E&M BRUNNENBAU UND BOHRTECHNIK GMBH

Hofer Strasse 19
Hof, D 95030, Germany
Mailing Address:
PO Box 3255
Hof, D95004, Germany
Tel.: (49) 92 81 14450
Fax: (49) 92 81 91688
E-Mail: info@em-bohr.de
Web Site: www.em-bohr.de
Year Founded: 1919
Emp.: 140
Business Description:
Drilling & Water Well Products & Services
S.I.C.: 1623
N.A.I.C.S.: 237110
Personnel:
Hermann Etschel *(Owner)*

E & S HOME OF COLOR, INC

ELC Schiffstraat 246
7547 RD Enschede, Netherlands
Mailing Address:
Postbus 261
7500 AG Enschede, Netherlands
Tel.: (31) 534601010
Fax: (31) 534601009
Sales Range: $10-24.9 Million
Emp.: 70
Business Description:
Wallpaper & Fabrics
S.I.C.: 5231
N.A.I.C.S.: 444120

E. BON HOLDINGS LTD

16-18F First Commercial Building 33 Leighton Road
Causeway Bay, China (Hong Kong)
Tel.: (852) 31050599
Fax: (852) 28345582
E-Mail: ebon@ebon.com.hk
Web Site: www.ebon.com.hk
599—(HKG)
Rev.: $61,556,990
Assets: $64,341,279
Liabilities: $22,181,592
Net Worth: $42,159,687
Earnings: $3,160,822
Emp.: 191
Fiscal Year-end: 03/31/13
Business Description:
Hardware Whslr
S.I.C.: 5072
N.A.I.C.S.: 423710
Personnel:
Henry Sun Fat Tse *(Co-Founder & Chm)*
Albert Sun Wai Tse *(Co-Founder & Vice Chm)*
Tony Sun Po Tse *(Mng Dir)*
Kevin Hon Kit Tse *(Deputy Mng Dir)*
Benthony Fu Wa Ip *(Sec)*
Board of Directors:
Henry Sun Fat Tse
Terence Shiu Sun Lau
Kwong Kin Leung
Albert Sun Wai Tse
Kevin Hon Kit Tse
Tony Sun Po Tse
Wilson Sze Chung Wan
Dominic Wah Wong

Legal Counsel:
Pang, Wan & Choi
7th Floor, Chinachem Tower 34-37 Connaught Central, China (Hong Kong)
Conyers Dill & Pearman
Cricket Square, Hutchins Drive P.O. Box 2681 KY1-1111 Georgetown, Cayman Islands
Royal Bank of Canada Trust Company (Cayman) Limited
4th Floor Royal Bank House 24 Shedden Road Georgetown, Cayman Islands
Transfer Agents:
Tricor Abacus Limited
26th Floor Tesbury Centre 28 Queen's Road East
Wanchai, China (Hong Kong)
Royal Bank of Canada Trust Company (Cayman) Limited
4th Floor Royal Bank House 24 Shedden Road Georgetown, Cayman Islands

Subsidiaries:

Bonco Ironmongery Limited (1)
17 Fl First Comml Bldg 33-35 Leighton Rd
Causeway Bay, China (Hong Kong)
Tel.: (852) 28919984
Fax: (852) 28345582
E-Mail: info@massford.com
Web Site: www.ebon.com.hk
Hardware Sales
S.I.C.: 5072
N.A.I.C.S.: 423710
Kevin Tse *(Gen Mgr)*

E. Bon Building Materials Company Limited (1)
Rm A1 18 Fl First Comml Bldg 33 Leighton Rd
Causeway Bay, China (Hong Kong)
Tel.: (852) 28913389
Fax: (852) 28345582
E-Mail: info@massford.com
Web Site: www.ebon.com.hk
Emp.: 300
Hardware Whslr
S.I.C.: 5072
N.A.I.C.S.: 423710
Tony Tse *(CEO)*

H2O (Pro) Limited (1)
16 F First Comml Bldg 33 Leighton Rd
Causeway Bay, China (Hong Kong)
Tel.: (852) 28919772
Fax: (852) 28345582
E-Mail: info@h2opro.com.hk
Web Site: www.h2opro.com.hk
Emp.: 50
Bathroom Hardware Fixtures Sales
S.I.C.: 5023
N.A.I.C.S.: 423220
Tony Tse *(Mgr)*

Kitchen (Pro) Limited (1)
16 F First Comml Bldg 33 Leighton Rd
Causeway Bay, China (Hong Kong)
Tel.: (852) 28913389
Fax: (852) 28342086
E-Mail: info@kitchenpro.biz
Web Site: www.kitchenpro.biz
Kitchen Fittings Whslr
S.I.C.: 5031
N.A.I.C.S.: 423310

Massford (Hong Kong) Limited (1)
17 Fl First Comml Bldg 33 Leighton Rd
Causeway Bay, China (Hong Kong)
Tel.: (852) 28916860
Fax: (852) 28343029
E-Mail: info@massford.com
Web Site: www.ebon.com
Emp.: 100
Hardware Whslr
S.I.C.: 5072
N.A.I.C.S.: 423710

Right Century Limited (1)
Ground Fl Kai Kwong Comml Bldg 332-334 Lockhart Rd
Wanchai, China (Hong Kong)
Tel.: (852) 28341661
Fax: (852) 28341665
E-Mail: h2o1@h2opro.com.hk
Emp.: 4
Bathroom Hardwares Sales
S.I.C.: 5023
N.A.I.C.S.: 423220

Sunny Building And Decoration Materials Company Limited (1)
Ground Fl 345 Lockhart Rd
Wanchai, China (Hong Kong)
Tel.: (852) 28939118
Fax: (852) 28380370
E-Mail: sunnyhk@h2opro.com.hk
Web Site: www.ebon.com
Emp.: 5
Hardware Retailer
S.I.C.: 5251
N.A.I.C.S.: 444130
Eddie Lung *(Mgr)*

Techpro Trading Limited (1)
16 F First Comml Bldg 33 Leighton Rd
Causeway Bay, China (Hong Kong)
Tel.: (852) 28919984
Fax: (852) 28342080
E-Mail: info@techprohk.com
Web Site: www.techprohk.com
Emp.: 30
Architectural Builders Hardware Whslr
S.I.C.: 5072
N.A.I.C.S.: 423710

E-BOOK SYSTEMS PTE. LTD.

Blk 13 Lorong 8 Toa Payoh
#06-02 Braddell Tech Park,
Singapore, 319261, Singapore
Tel.: (65) 6258 6100
Fax: (65) 6258 7300
E-Mail: sales@ebooksys.com
Web Site: www.flipviewer.com
Sales Range: $1-9.9 Million
Business Description:
Digital Publishing
S.I.C.: 2741
N.A.I.C.S.: 511199
Personnel:
Khoon Wan Hong *(CEO)*

U.S. Subsidiary:

E-Book Systems Inc. (1)
5201 Great America Pkwy Ste 320
Santa Clara, CA 95054
Tel.: (919) 656-8898
Fax: (405) 562-5745
Digital Publishing
S.I.C.: 2741
N.A.I.C.S.: 511199
Seng-Beng Ho *(Pres)*

Non-U.S. Subsidiary:

E-Book Systems Europe (1)
Oppelner Str 30
10997 Berlin, Germany
Tel.: (49) 30 44 033 223
Fax: (49) 30 440 575 28
Digital Publishing
S.I.C.: 2741
N.A.I.C.S.: 511199

E. BOWMAN & SONS LTD

First Floor Cherryholt House
Cherryholt Road
Stamford, Lincolnshire, PE9 2EP, United Kingdom
Tel.: (44) 1780751015
Fax: (44) 1780759051
E-Mail: mail@bowmanstamford.com
Web Site: www.bowmanstamford.com
Year Founded: 1886
Rev.: $15,559,838
Emp.: 78
Business Description:
Modern & Historical Building Services
S.I.C.: 1542
N.A.I.C.S.: 236220
Personnel:
James Deacon *(Mng Dir)*

E C CONSULTING INTERNATIONAL, INC.

Im Aeschfeld 12
4147 Aesch, Switzerland
Tel.: (41) 61 703 8676
E-Mail: info@ecconsultintl.com
Web Site: www.ecconsultintl.com
Year Founded: 2000
ECCO—(OTC OTCB)
Assets: $4,124
Liabilities: $16,954
Net Worth: ($12,830)
Earnings: ($25,518)
Emp.: 1
Fiscal Year-end: 03/31/13
Business Description:
Consulting Services
S.I.C.: 8742
N.A.I.C.S.: 541611
Personnel:
Jean-Claude E. Gehret *(Chm, Pres, CEO, CFO, Principal Fin Officer & Treas)*
Danielle J. Gehret *(Sec)*
Board of Directors:
Jean-Claude E. Gehret
Danielle J. Gehret

E-COMMERCE CHINA DANGDANG INC.

21/F Jing An Center No 8 North Third Ring Road East Chaoyang District
Beijing, 100028, China
Tel.: (86) 10 5799 2306 (Investor Relations)
Web Site: www.dangdang.com
Year Founded: 1999
DANG—(NYSE)
Rev.: $825,036,560
Assets: $569,179,565
Liabilities: $451,710,149
Net Worth: $117,469,416
Earnings: ($70,505,731)
Emp.: 2,907
Fiscal Year-end: 12/31/12
Business Description:
Business-to-Consumer Electronic Shopping Services
S.I.C.: 5961
N.A.I.C.S.: 454111
Personnel:
Peggy Yu Yu *(Chm)*
Guoqing Li *(CEO)*
Jun Zou *(CFO)*
Danqian Yao *(Sr VP)*
Board of Directors:
Peggy Yu Yu
Guoqing Li
Xiaolong Li
Ruby Rong Lu
Ke Zhang

E-DEBIT GLOBAL CORPORATION

12 3620 - 29th Street NE
Calgary, AB, T1Y 5Z8, Canada
Tel.: (403) 290-0264
Web Site: www.edebitglobal.com
Year Founded: 1998
WSHE—(OTC)
Rev.: $2,335,553
Assets: $636,246
Liabilities: $2,592,403
Net Worth: ($1,956,157)
Earnings: ($831,276)
Emp.: 12
Fiscal Year-end: 12/31/12
Business Description:
Non-Conventional Banking Services
S.I.C.: 6211
N.A.I.C.S.: 523110
Personnel:
Douglas N. Mac Donald *(Pres & CEO)*
Kim S. Law *(CFO & VP-Fin)*
Robert L. Robins *(Treas, Sec & VP)*
Board of Directors:
Kim S. Law
Douglas N. Mac Donald
Roy L. Queen
Bernd Reuscher
Robert L. Robins
Jack Thomson

E-ENERGY VENTURES INC.

3467 Commercial Street
Vancouver, BC, V5N 4E8, Canada
Tel.: (604) 687-4191
Fax: (604) 871-9926
E-Mail: info@eev.ca
Web Site: www.eev.ca
EEV—(TSXV)
Int. Income: $4,228
Assets: $2,090,839
Liabilities: $3,411
Net Worth: $2,087,427
Earnings: ($3,351,196)
Fiscal Year-end: 03/31/13
Business Description:
Mineral Exploration Services
S.I.C.: 1081
N.A.I.C.S.: 213114
Personnel:
Simon Tam *(Pres & CEO)*
Simon Ma *(CFO)*
Board of Directors:
David Hugh Rankin
Simon Tam
Craig Walker
Legal Counsel:
Fang & Associates
576 Seymour St Suite 300
Vancouver, BC, Canada
Transfer Agent:
CIBC Mellon Trust Company
1600 - 1066 W Hastings Street
Vancouver, BC, Canada

E-GUARDIAN, INC.

Place Astre Bldg 4F 1-2-3 Azabu-Juban
Minato-ku, Tokyo, 106-0045, Japan
Tel.: (81) 3 5575 2561
Fax: (81) 3 5575 0621
Web Site: www.e-guardian.co.jp
Year Founded: 1998
6050—(TKS)
Sls.: $29,082,960
Assets: $15,245,100
Liabilities: $3,505,070
Net Worth: $11,740,030
Earnings: $664,530
Emp.: 101
Fiscal Year-end: 09/30/12
Business Description:
Online Monitoring Services
S.I.C.: 2741
N.A.I.C.S.: 519130
Personnel:
Yasuhisa Takatani *(Pres)*

E. HAWLE ARMATURENWERKE GMBH

Wagrainer Strasse 13
4840 Vocklabruck, Austria
Tel.: (43) 767272576
Fax: (43) 767278464
E-Mail: hawle@hawle.at
Web Site: www.hawle.at
Year Founded: 1948
Rev.: $119,500,000
Emp.: 335
Business Description:
Valve Mfr
S.I.C.: 3491
N.A.I.C.S.: 332911
Personnel:
Alexander Lukas *(Head-Intl Sls & Area Mgr-Bus)*

E-HOUSE (CHINA) HOLDINGS LIMITED

17/F East Tower No 333 North Chengdu Road
Shanghai, 200041, China

E-House (China) Holdings Limited—(Continued)

Tel.: (86) 21 5298 0808
Fax: (86) 21 5298 0009
Web Site: www.ehousechina.com
EJ—(NYSE)
Rev.: $462,439,368
Assets: $1,011,961,518
Liabilities: $266,847,569
Net Worth: $745,113,949
Earnings: ($71,049,371)
Emp.: 15,088
Fiscal Year-end: 12/31/12
Business Description:
Holding Company; Real Estate Brokerage, Consulting & Investment Management Services
S.I.C.: 6719
N.A.I.C.S.: 551112
Personnel:
Xin Zhou *(Co-Founder, Co-Chm & CEO)*
Charles Guowei Chao *(Co-Chm)*
Zuyu Ding *(Co-Pres)*
Jianjun Zang *(Co-Pres)*
Bin Laurence *(CFO)*
Li-Lan Cheng *(COO)*
Yan Zhang *(Sr VP)*
Board of Directors:
Charles Guowei Chao
Xin Zhou
Fan Bao
Yunchang Gu
Canhao Huang
Neil Nanpeng Shen
Bing Xiang
Jeffrey Zhijie Zeng
Hongchao Zhu
Subsidiaries:

China Real Estate Information Corporation (1)
383 Guangyan Road Zhabei District
Shanghai, 200072, China Ky
Tel.: (86) 2160868888 (100%)
Fax: (86) 2160867663
Web Site: www.cric.com
Emp.: 3,712
Real Estate Information & Consulting Services
S.I.C.: 6531
N.A.I.C.S.: 531390
Xin Zhou *(Chm & CEO)*

Leju Holdings Limited (1)
15/F Shoudong International Plaza No 5 Building Guangqu Home
Dongcheng District, Beijing, 100022, China Ky
Tel.: (86) 10 5895 1000
Web Site: www.leju.com
Rev.: $335,421,516
Assets: $402,938,245
Liabilities: $151,148,210
Net Worth: $251,790,035
Earnings: $42,650,028
Emp.: 4,204
Fiscal Year-end: 12/31/13
Online Real Estate Services
S.I.C.: 6531
N.A.I.C.S.: 531390
Xin Zhou *(Chm)*
Keyi Chen *(Co-Pres)*
Weijie Ma *(Co-Pres)*
Yinyu He *(CEO)*
Min Chen *(CFO)*

E INK HOLDINGS, INC,

No 3 Lising 1st Rd East District
Hsin-chu, 300, Taiwan
Tel.: (886) 35798599
Fax: (886) 35798699
Web Site: www.eink.com
Year Founded: 1992
8069—(TAI)
Emp.: 6,000
Business Description:
LCD Screen Mfr; Electronic Paper Display Technology Developer & Mfr
S.I.C.: 3679
N.A.I.C.S.: 334419
Personnel:
Sicheng Liu *(Chm & CEO)*
U.S. Subsidiary:

E Ink Corporation (1)
733 Concord Ave
Cambridge, MA 02138
Tel.: (617) 499-6000
Fax: (617) 499-6200
Web Site: www.eink.com
Sales Range: $75-99.9 Million
Emp.: 127
Electronic Paper Display Technology Developer
S.I.C.: 3679
N.A.I.C.S.: 334419
Felix Ho *(Chm & Pres)*
Tien-Haw Peng *(Exec VP)*

E-KANCELARIA GRUPA PRAWNO-FINANSOWA S.A.

Bema Plaza Building ul Gen Jozefa Bema 2
50-265 Wroclaw, Poland
Tel.: (48) 71 327 28 00
Fax: (48) 71 327 29 04
E-Mail: kontakt@e-kancelaria.com
Web Site: www.e-kancelaria.com
Year Founded: 2003
EKA—(WAR)
Emp.: 230
Business Description:
Debt Collection & Legal Services
S.I.C.: 7322
N.A.I.C.S.: 561440
Personnel:
Jan Misko *(Chm-Supervisory Bd)*
Mariusz Pawlowski *(Chm-Mgmt Bd)*
Alicja Pawlowska *(Vice Chm-Supervisory Bd)*
Supervisory Board of Directors:
Jan Misko
Mariusz Muszynski
Alicja Pawlowska
Zdzislaw Simon
Grzegorz Wojtylak

E-KONG GROUP LIMITED

3705 Gloucester Tower The Landmark 15 Queen's Road
Central, China (Hong Kong)
Tel.: (852) 2801 7188
Fax: (852) 2801 7238
Web Site: www.e-kong.com
524—(HKG)
Sls.: $71,527,147
Assets: $49,355,097
Liabilities: $21,821,435
Net Worth: $27,533,662
Earnings: $1,773,707
Emp.: 141
Fiscal Year-end: 12/31/12
Business Description:
Information Technology Services
S.I.C.: 7373
N.A.I.C.S.: 541512
Personnel:
Richard John Siemens *(Chm)*
Anthony Wei Kit Wong *(CFO)*
Raymond Wai Ming Lau *(Sec)*
Board of Directors:
Richard John Siemens
Thaddeus Thomas Beczak
John William Crawford
Gerald Clive Dobby
William Bruce Hicks
Shyang Guey Lim
Jennifer Wes Saran

Butterfield Fulcrum Group (Bermuda) Limited
26 Burnaby Street
Hamilton, HM 11, Bermuda

E-L FINANCIAL CORPORATION LIMITED

165 University Avenue 10th Floor
Toronto, ON, M5H 3B8, Canada
Tel.: (416) 947-2578
Fax: (416) 362-2592
E-Mail: info@empirelife.com
Web Site: www.empirelife.com
Year Founded: 1968
ELF—(OTC TSX)
Premiums: $2,165,609,745
Assets: $16,562,698,213
Liabilities: $12,618,792,652
Net Worth: $3,943,905,561
Earnings: $479,629,560
Emp.: 2,192
Fiscal Year-end: 12/31/12
Business Description:
Holding Company
S.I.C.: 6719
N.A.I.C.S.: 551112
Personnel:
Duncan N. R. Jackman *(Chm, Pres & CEO)*
Mark M. Taylor *(CFO & Exec VP)*
Richard Cleaver *(CTO-The Empire Life Insurance Company & Sr VP)*
Gaelen Morphet *(Chief Investment Officer-The Empire Life Insurance Co & Sr VP)*
J. Edward Gibson *(Chief Actuary & Sr VP-Strategy-The Empire Life Insurance Company)*
Gary J. McCabe *(CFO-The Empire Life Insurance Company & Sr VP)*
Anne E. Butler *(Gen Counsel, Sec & Sr VP-The Empire Life Insurance Company)*
Richard B. Carty *(Gen Counsel, Sec & VP)*
Susan C. Clifford *(Treas)*
George L. Cooke *(Exec VP)*
Leslie C. Herr *(Exec VP)*
Drew E. Wallace *(Exec VP-Retail-The Empire Life Insurance Company)*
Timo J. Hytonen *(Sr VP-HR & Corp Initiatives-The Empire Life Insurance Company)*
Steve S. Pong *(Sr VP-Grp Products-The Empire Life Insurance Company)*
Board of Directors:
Duncan N. R. Jackman
J. Christopher Barron
James F. Billett
William J. Corcoran
Henry N. R. Jackman
R. B. Matthews
Mark M. Taylor
Douglas C. Townsend
Transfer Agent:
Computershare Investor Services Inc.
100 University Ave 9th Floor
Toronto, ON, Canada
Subsidiaries:

E-L Financial Services Limited (1)
259 King St E
Kingston, ON, K7L 3A8, Canada
Tel.: (613) 548-1890
Fax: (800) 920-5868
General Insurance Services
S.I.C.: 6311
N.A.I.C.S.: 524113

The Empire Life Insurance Company (1)
259 King St E
Kingston, ON, K7L 3A8, Canada Ca
Tel.: (613) 548-1881 (100%)
Fax: (613) 548-3854
E-Mail: customerservice@empire.ca
Web Site: www.empire.ca
Sales Range: $550-599.9 Million
Emp.: 625
Life Insurance & Financial Products
S.I.C.: 6311
N.A.I.C.S.: 524113
Leslie C. Herr *(Pres & CEO)*
Gary J. McCabe *(CFO & Sr VP)*
J. Edward Gibson *(Chief Actuary & Sr VP)*
Anne E. Butler *(Gen Counsel, Sec & Sr VP)*
Richard Cleaver *(Tech & Svcs)*
Timo Hygmon *(Sr VP-HR)*
Steve S. Pong *(Sr VP-Grp Products)*

E-LAND FASHION CHINA HOLDINGS, LIMITED

Room 1101 Parker House
72 Queen's Road, Central, China (Hong Kong)
Tel.: (852) 25265024
Fax: (852) 25265025
E-Mail: enquiry@elandfashion.cn
Web Site: www.elandfashionchina.com
Sales Range: $200-249.9 Million
Emp.: 600
Business Description:
Women's Apparel & Accessories Retailer
S.I.C.: 5621
N.A.I.C.S.: 448120
Personnel:
Koan Ju Ko *(CFO)*
Kam Lung Liu *(Sec)*
Board of Directors:
Hyun Jun Kim

E-LAND WORLD LTD.

(d/b/a The E-Land Group)
19-8 Chanjeon-dong
Mapo-gu, Seoul, 121-190, Korea (South)
Tel.: (82) 2 323 0456
Fax: (82) 2 323 5582
Web Site: www.eland.co.kr
Sales Range: $5-14.9 Billion
Business Description:
Holding Company
S.I.C.: 6719
N.A.I.C.S.: 551112
Personnel:
SungKyung Park *(Pres)*
U.S. Subsidiary:

K-Swiss Inc. (1)
31248 Oak Crest Dr
Westlake Village, CA 91361 DE
Tel.: (818) 706-5100
Fax: (818) 706-5390
Toll Free: (800) 938-8000
E-Mail: kscs@k-swiss.com
Web Site: www.kswiss.com
Rev.: $222,851,000
Assets: $176,723,000
Liabilities: $45,109,000
Net Worth: $131,614,000
Earnings: ($34,779,000)
Emp.: 542
Fiscal Year-end: 12/31/12
Athletic Footwear Designer, Developer & Marketer
Import Export
S.I.C.: 2389
N.A.I.C.S.: 316210
Byeng Gweon Kim *(Chm)*
Larry Remington *(Pres & CEO)*
Edward Flora *(COO)*
Barney Waters *(CMO)*

Subsidiaries:

K-Swiss Direct, Inc (2)
31248 Oak Crest Dr
Westlake Village, CA 91361
Tel.: (818) 706-5100
Fax: (818) 706-5390
E-Mail: Kscs@k-swiss.com
Sales Range: $150-199.9 Million
Athletic Footwear Designer, Developer & Marketer
S.I.C.: 3291
N.A.I.C.S.: 327910
Steven B. Nichols *(Pres)*

K-Swiss Pacific Inc. (2)
31248 Oak Crest Dr
Westlake Village, CA 91361-4692
Tel.: (818) 706-5100
Fax: (818) 706-5390
Athletic Footwear Designer & Marketer
S.I.C.: 2389
N.A.I.C.S.: 316210
David Mikel *(Pres)*

K-Swiss Sales Corp. (2)
31248 Oak Crest Dr
Westlake Village, CA 91361

Tel.: (818) 706-5100
Fax: (818) 706-5390
E-Mail: info@kswiss.com
Web Site: www.kswiss.com
Sales Range: $25-49.9 Million
Emp.: 50
Athletic Footwear Designer, Developer & Marketer
S.I.C.: 2389
N.A.I.C.S.: 316210
Steven B. Nichols *(Pres)*

Non-U.S. Subsidiaries:

K S UK Limited (2)
Tannery House
4 Middle Leigh St, Somerset, BA16 0LA, United Kingdom
Tel.: (44) 1458449301
Fax: (44) 1458446536
E-Mail: srobins@k-swiss.co.uk
Web Site: www.k-swiss.co.uk
Sales Range: $75-99.9 Million
Emp.: 10
Athletic Footwear Designer, Developer & Marketer
S.I.C.: 2389
N.A.I.C.S.: 316210
Sarah Robins *(Mgr-Mktg)*

K-Swiss Australia (2)
43-53 Bridge Road
Stanmore, NSW, 2048, Australia
Tel.: (61) 295501187
Fax: (61) 2 9550 1189
Web Site: www.k-swiss.com.au
Sales Range: $75-99.9 Million
Athletic Footwear Designer, Developer & Marketer
S.I.C.: 2389
N.A.I.C.S.: 316210

K-Swiss Canada (2)
4800 East Gate Parkway Ste 6
Mississauga, ON, L4W 3W6, Canada
Tel.: (905) 625-4940
Fax: (905) 625-7876
Sales Range: $50-74.9 Million
Emp.: 100
Athletic Footwear Designer, Developer & Marketer
S.I.C.: 2389
N.A.I.C.S.: 316210
Tina Rizzo *(Country Mgr)*

K-Swiss Europe B.V. (2)
Diakenhuisweg 45
2033 AP Haarlem, Netherlands
Tel.: (31) 235430543
Fax: (31) 235430555
E-Mail: info@kswiss.nl
Web Site: www.kswiss.nl
Sales Range: $25-49.9 Million
Emp.: 35
Athletic Footwear Designer, Developer & Marketer
S.I.C.: 2389
N.A.I.C.S.: 316210

K-Swiss Germany GmbH (2)
Oelser Strasse 9
40231 Dusseldorf, Germany
Tel.: (49) 2114371580
Fax: (49) 21143715899
E-Mail: info@kswiss.de
Web Site: www.kswiss.de
Sales Range: $75-99.9 Million
Emp.: 25
Athletic Footwear Designer, Developer & Marketer
S.I.C.: 2389
N.A.I.C.S.: 316210
Monica Roberts *(Office Mgr)*

K-Swiss (Hong Kong) Ltd. (2)
Unis 2001 Exchange Tower 33 Wang Chiu Road
Kowloon Bay, Hong Kong, China (Hong Kong)
Tel.: (852) 24852288
Fax: (852) 24852299
E-Mail: hkmarketing@k-swiss.com
Web Site: www.k-swiss.com.hk
Athletic Footwear Designer & Marketer
S.I.C.: 2389
N.A.I.C.S.: 316210

K-Swiss Retail Ltd. (2)
4 Middle Leigh
Street, Somerset, BA16 0LA, United Kingdom
Tel.: (44) 1458445502
E-Mail: mail@k-swiss.co.uk
Emp.: 10
Athletic Footwear Designer & Marketer
S.I.C.: 2389
N.A.I.C.S.: 316210

E-LEAD ELECTRONIC CO., LTD.

NO 37 Gungdung 1st Rd
Shengang, Changhua, Taiwan
Tel.: (886) 47977277
Fax: (886) 47977172
E-Mail: e_lead@elead.com.tw
Web Site: www.e-lead.com.tw
2497—(TAI)
Sales Range: $10-24.9 Million
Business Description:
Car Electronics Mfr
S.I.C.: 5013
N.A.I.C.S.: 441310
Personnel:
Tonny Chen *(Chm)*

Non-U.S. Subsidiaries:

E-LEAD Electronic Technology (Jiangsu) Co., Ltd. (1)
No 167 Jin Hu West Road
Wujiang, Jiangsu, China
Tel.: (86) 512 63404789
Fax: (86) 512 63404533
Web Site: www.e-lead.com.tw/elead/index.php?option=com_content&view=article&id=85&Itemid=103=en
Electronic Components Mfr
S.I.C.: 3651
N.A.I.C.S.: 334310

E-Lead Electronic (Thailand) Co., Ltd. (1)
888/4 Moo 7 Sukhumvit Road Tambon Bangpoomai
Amphur Muang, Samut Prakan, Thailand
Tel.: (66) 2 3230558
Fax: (66) 2 3230559
Web Site: www.e-lead.com.tw/elead/index.php?option=com_content&view=article&id=85&Itemid=103&lang=en
Automobile Electronic Products Mfr
S.I.C.: 3714
N.A.I.C.S.: 336320

E-LEATHER LTD.

Kingsbridge Centre Sturrock Way
Peterborough, PE3 8TZ, United Kingdom
Tel.: (44) 1733 843939
Fax: (44) 1733 843940
E-Mail: info@eleathergroup.com
Web Site: www.eleathergroup.com
Year Founded: 2006
Sales Range: $10-24.9 Million
Emp.: 102
Business Description:
Leather Products Mfr
S.I.C.: 3199
N.A.I.C.S.: 316998
Personnel:
Chris McBean *(CEO)*

E-LITECOM CO., LTD.

520-1 Metan-dong
Yeongtong-Ku, Suwon, Korea (South)
Tel.: (82) 31 213 3881
Fax: (82) 31 211 2667
E-Mail: ir@e-litecom.com
Web Site: www.e-litecom.com
Year Founded: 1984
041520—(KRS)
Sales Range: $100-124.9 Million
Business Description:
Electronic Component Mfr
S.I.C.: 3679
N.A.I.C.S.: 334419
Personnel:
Joong-Heon kim *(CEO)*

E-NET JAPAN CORP.

1-1-1, Manfukuji, Aso-ku
Kawasaki, 215-0004, Japan
Tel.: (81) 449695223
Web Site: www.enet-japan.com
Sls.: $71,506,000
Earnings: $1,113,000
Business Description:
Electric Appliances & Computer Sales
S.I.C.: 5722
N.A.I.C.S.: 443141

E. PAIRIS S.A.

Thesi Goritsa
19300 Aspropyrgos, Greece
Tel.: (30) 210 5515555
Fax: (30) 210 5576192
Web Site: www.pairis.gr
Year Founded: 1974
PAIR—(ATH)
Emp.: 130
Business Description:
Plastics Bottle Mfr
S.I.C.: 3085
N.A.I.C.S.: 326160
Personnel:
Ioannis Emmanuel Pairis *(Chm & Mng Dir)*
Ioannis Petros Velentzas *(Vice Chm)*
Board of Directors:
Ioannis Emmanuel Pairis
Theodosios Nikolaos Apostolides
Panayiota Balta-Pair
Doris Demetrios Pairi
Ioannis Petros Velentzas

E-PAY ASIA LIMITED

(Acquired by GHL Systems Berhad)

E-PLEX LTD.

George Summers Close
Medway City Est, Rochester, Kent, ME2 4EL, United Kingdom
Tel.: (44) 1634778704
Fax: (44) 1634290773
E-Mail: sales@e-plex.co
Web Site: www.e-plex.co
Emp.: 10
Business Description:
Data Transfer Modules & Logging Systems Mfr
S.I.C.: 3829
N.A.I.C.S.: 334519
Personnel:
Paul Holland *(Mng Dir)*

E-P:N MINKINREHU OY

Luhtalantie 160
62420 Kortesjarvi, Finland
Tel.: (358) 64880500
Fax: (358) 64885563
E-Mail: e-p.minkinrehu@netikka.fi
Web Site: www.ep-minkinrehu.fi
Sales Range: $10-24.9 Million
Emp.: 18
Business Description:
Fur-Bearing Animal Feed Mfr
S.I.C.: 2048
N.A.I.C.S.: 311119
Personnel:
Jouko Huhtala *(CEO)*

Subsidiary:

Monas Feed Oy AB (1)
Monasvagen 442
Hirvlax, FIN 66970 Uusikaarlepyy, Finland
Tel.: (358) 67688100
Fax: (358) 67646121
Web Site: www.monasfeed.fi
Emp.: 15
Fur-Bearing Animal Feed Mfr
S.I.C.: 2048
N.A.I.C.S.: 311119
Ralf Haggblom *(Mng Dir)*

E-SEIKATSU CO., LTD.

2-32 Minamiazabu 5-chome Minato-ku
Tokyo, 106-0047, Japan
Tel.: (81) 354237820
Fax: (81) 354237840
Web Site: www.e-seikatsu.info
3796—(TKS)
Sls.: $20,141,000
Assets: $22,176,000
Liabilities: $4,202,000
Net Worth: $17,974,000
Earnings: $638,000
Emp.: 137
Fiscal Year-end: 03/31/13
Business Description:
Internet Services
S.I.C.: 7379
N.A.I.C.S.: 518210
Personnel:
Kiyotaka Nakamura *(Pres & Co-CEO)*
Zenichi Maeno *(Co-CEO & Exec VP)*
Hiroyuki Shiokawa *(CFO & Exec VP)*
Hiroyoshi Kitazawa *(COO & Exec VP)*
Akira Matsuzaki *(CTO)*
Board of Directors:
Hiroyoshi Kitazawa
Zenichi Maeno
Akira Matsuzaki
Kiyotaka Nakamura
Hiroyuki Shiokawa

E-STAR ALTERNATIVE PLC.

Szekacs Utca 29
1122 Budapest, Hungary
Tel.: (36) 1 279 3550
Fax: (36) 1 279 3551
E-Mail: info@e-star.hu
Web Site: www.e-star.hu
Year Founded: 2000
E-STAR—(BUD)
Sales Range: $1-9.9 Million
Business Description:
Energy Consulting Services
S.I.C.: 8999
N.A.I.C.S.: 541690
Personnel:
Csaba Soos *(Chm & CEO)*
Jozsef Veress *(Chm-Supervisory Bd)*
Akos Benke *(CFO)*
Board of Directors:
Csaba Soos
Daniel Molnos
George Elemer Pataki
Maximilian N. Teleki
Supervisory Board of Directors:
Jozsef Veress
Gyula Bakacsi

E. SUN FINANCIAL HOLDING CO., LTD.

14F No 117 & 1F No 115 Sec 3
Minsheng E Rd
Taipei, Taiwan
Tel.: (886) 21751313
Fax: (886) 25475613
Web Site: www.esunfhc.com.tw/en/
2884—(TAI)
Rev.: $803,255,738
Assets: $42,137,551,266
Liabilities: $39,591,407,581
Net Worth: $2,546,143,685
Earnings: $239,062,453
Emp.: 6,338
Fiscal Year-end: 12/31/12
Business Description:
Bank Holding Company
S.I.C.: 6712
N.A.I.C.S.: 551111
Personnel:
Yung-Jen Huang *(Chm)*
Joseph N. C. Huang *(Pres)*
Suka Chen *(Deputy Pres)*

E. Sun Financial Holding Co., Ltd.—(Continued)

Magi Chen *(CFO)*
Joseph Shue *(Vice CFO)*
Wan-Li Hsieh *(CIO)*
Bright Wen *(CMO)*
Jhong-Cheng Shun *(Vice Chief Risk Officer)*
Kuan-Her Wu *(Chief Acctg Officer)*
Oliver Shieh *(Chief Risk Officer)*
J. C. Wang *(Chief HR Officer)*
Wu-Lin Duh *(Chief Brand Officer)*
Ben Chen *(Sr Exec VP)*
Mao-Cin Chen *(Sr Exec VP)*
L. C. Lin *(Sr Exec VP)*
Shui-Chin Shen *(Sr Exec VP)*
Scott Chou *(Exec VP)*

Board of Directors:
Yung-Jen Huang
Chai-Kuo Chen
Suka Chen
Wu-Lin Duh
Chiu-Hsiong Huang
Joseph N. C. Huang
Chen-En Ko
Chi-Jen Lee
Chen-Chen Chang Lin
Hsin-I Lin
Jackson Mai
Kuo-Lieh Tseng
Chen-Li Wu

Subsidiaries:

E.Sun Commercial Bank, Ltd. **(1)**
12th Floor 115 Min Sheng E Rd Sec 3
Taipei, Taiwan (100%)
Tel.: (886) 221751313
Fax: (886) 225475613
E-Mail: steven-08005@inmail.esunbank.com.tw
Web Site: www.esunbank.com.tw
Commercial Banks
S.I.C.: 6029
N.A.I.C.S.: 522110
Yung-Jen Huang *(Chm)*

E.Sun Insurance Broker Co., Ltd. **(1)**
12th Floor 115 Min Sheng E Rd Sec 3
Taipei, Taiwan (100%)
Tel.: (886) 221751313
Fax: (886) 225475613
Web Site: www.esun.com
Emp.: 4,000
Insurance Agencies & Brokerages
S.I.C.: 6411
N.A.I.C.S.: 524210

E.Sun Securities Investment Trust Co., Ltd. **(1)**
8F No 117 Sec 3
Minsheng E Rd, Taipei, Taiwan (100%)
Tel.: (886) 55561313
Web Site: www.esunfhc.com.tw/en/service/
Investment Banking & Securities Dealing
S.I.C.: 6211
N.A.I.C.S.: 523110
Chi-Chang Huang *(Pres)*

E.Sun Venture Capital Corp. **(1)**
4th Floor No117 Sec 3
Taipei, Taiwan (100%)
Tel.: (886) 227196613
Fax: (886) 0287122616
Web Site: www.esunfhc.com.tw
Emp.: 10
Bank Holding Company
S.I.C.: 6712
N.A.I.C.S.: 551111
Lanzo Huang *(Pres)*

E-THERAPEUTICS PLC
Clavering House Clavering Place
Newcastle upon Tyne, NE1 3NG, United Kingdom
Tel.: (44) 1912331317
Fax: (44) 1912331303
E-Mail: contact@etherapeutics.co.uk
Web Site: www.etherapeutics.co.uk
ETX—(LSE)
Rev.: $352,182
Assets: $18,111,298
Liabilities: $1,402,410
Net Worth: $16,708,888
Earnings: ($6,598,274)
Emp.: 18
Fiscal Year-end: 01/31/13

Business Description:
Drug Research & Development
S.I.C.: 2834
N.A.I.C.S.: 325412

Personnel:
Malcolm Young *(CEO)*
Daniel Elger *(CFO)*
Sean Nicolson *(Sec)*

Board of Directors:
Oliver Francis Wintour James
Rajesh Chopra
Daniel Elger
Brad Hoy
Steve Raymond Self
Malcolm Young

Legal Counsel:
Dickinson Dees LLP
St Ann's Warf 112 Quayside
Newcastle upon Tyne, United Kingdom

Subsidiary:

InRotis Technologies Limited **(1)**
Block B Holland Park Holland Dr
Newcastle upon Tyne, Tyne and Wear, NE2 4LZ, United Kingdom
Tel.: (44) 1912331317
Fax: (44) 1912331303
Emp.: 20
Drug Development Services
S.I.C.: 8731
N.A.I.C.S.: 541712
Malcolm Young *(CEO)*

E-TIVITY CORP. (APAC) PTY LTD.
Suite G3 18-20 Ross Street
North Parramatta, Sydney, NSW, 2151, Australia
Tel.: (61) 2 8838 2200
Fax: (61) 2 8838 2211
E-Mail: info@etivitycorp.com
Web Site: www.etivitycorp.com
Emp.: 4

Business Description:
Software Development Services
S.I.C.: 7371
N.A.I.C.S.: 541511

Personnel:
Craig Dwyer *(Gen Mgr)*

E1 CORPORATION
ASEM Tower 13th FL 159-1
Samsung-dong
Gangnam-gu, Seoul, Korea (South) 135-798
Tel.: (82) 2 3441 4270
Fax: (82) 2 6008 2418
Web Site: www.e1.co.kr
Year Founded: 1984
017940—(KRS)
Sls.: $6,894,389,460
Assets: $3,266,550,600
Liabilities: $2,150,408,310
Net Worth: $1,116,142,290
Earnings: $84,128,730
Fiscal Year-end: 12/31/12

Business Description:
Petroleum Whslr
S.I.C.: 5172
N.A.I.C.S.: 424720

Personnel:
J. Y. Koo *(Chm & CEO)*
Y. C. Choi *(Exec VP & Head-Supply Div)*
S. R. Yoon *(Exec VP & Head-Fiscal Div)*
J. S. Kang *(Sr VP & Head-Mgmt Support Div)*
Y. M. Park *(Sr VP & Head-Mktg Div)*

E2V TECHNOLOGIES PLC
106 Waterhouse Lane
Chelmsford, Essex, CM1 2QU, United Kingdom
Tel.: (44) 1245 493493
Fax: (44) 1245 492492
E-Mail: enquiries@e2vtechnologies.com
Web Site: www.e2v.com
Year Founded: 1947
E2V—(LSE)
Rev.: $316,431,282
Assets: $362,175,417
Liabilities: $122,202,302
Net Worth: $239,973,116
Earnings: $42,212,842
Emp.: 1,525
Fiscal Year-end: 03/31/13

Business Description:
RF, Microwave & Sensing Component & Sub-Systems Mfr
S.I.C.: 3669
N.A.I.C.S.: 334290

Personnel:
Steve Blair *(CEO)*
Charlotte Parmenter *(Sec)*

Board of Directors:
Neil Johnson
Kevin Dangerfield
Charles Hindson
Krishnamurthy Rajagopal
Alison Wood

Legal Counsel:
Macfarlanes LLP
20 Cursitor Street
London, EC4A 1LT, United Kingdom
Tel.: (44) 20 7831 9222

Birkett Long
Number One Legg Street
Chelmsford, Essex, CM1 1JS, United Kingdom

Subsidiaries:

e2v Limited **(1)**
106 Waterhouse La
Chelmsford, CM1 2QU, United Kingdom
Tel.: (44) 1245 493493
Electronic Component Mfr
S.I.C.: 3679
N.A.I.C.S.: 334419

e2v Technologies (UK) Ltd **(1)**
106 Waterhouse Lane
CM12QU Chelmsford, Essex, United Kingdom (100%)
Tel.: (44) 1245493493
Fax: (44) 1245492492
E-Mail: enquiries@e2v.com
Web Site: www.e2v.com
Emp.: 800
Electronic Capacitor Mfr
S.I.C.: 3677
N.A.I.C.S.: 334416
Keith Attwood *(Mng Dir)*

U.S. Subsidiary:

e2v Holdings, Inc. **(1)**
520 White Plains Rd Ste 450
Tarrytown, NY 10591 (100%)
Tel.: (914) 592-6050
Fax: (914) 529-5148
Web Site: www.e2v.com
Emp.: 47
Electron Tube Mfr
S.I.C.: 3679
N.A.I.C.S.: 334419
Edward Galati *(CEO)*

Subsidiaries:

E2v aerospace and defense inc **(2)**
765 Sycamore Dr
Milpitas, CA 95035
Tel.: (408) 737-0992
Fax: (408) 736-8708
Web Site: www.e2v.com
Emp.: 100
Electronic Component Mfr
S.I.C.: 3679
N.A.I.C.S.: 334419
Robert Brevelle *(Pres)*

e2v Inc **(2)**
520 White Plains Rd Ste 450
Tarrytown, NY 10510
Tel.: (914) 592-6050
Fax: (914) 592-5148
Electronic Component Mfr
S.I.C.: 3679
N.A.I.C.S.: 334419

Non-U.S. Subsidiaries:

e2v Semiconductors SAS **(1)**
Avenue De Rochepleine
38521 Saint Egreve, France
Tel.: (33) 476583000
Fax: (33) 476583480
E-Mail: info@e2v.com
Web Site: www.e2v.com
Emp.: 500
Electrical Equipment & Component Mfr
S.I.C.: 3699
N.A.I.C.S.: 335999
Bruno Wirth *(Gen Mgr)*

e2v Technologies GmbH **(1)**
Industriestrabe 29
Grobenzell, 82194 Munich, Germany
Tel.: (49) 8142410570
Fax: (49) 8142284547
E-Mail: enquiries-de@e2vtechnologies.com
Web Site: www.e2vtechnologies.com
Emp.: 10
Electron Tube Mfr
S.I.C.: 3679
N.A.I.C.S.: 334419
Koeps Birgit *(Office Mgr)*

e2v Technologies SAS **(1)**
16 Burospace
91572 Bievres, France
Tel.: (33) 160195500
Fax: (33) 160195529
E-Mail: enquiries-fr@e2v.com
Web Site: www.e2vtechnologies.com
Emp.: 16
Specialized Design Services
S.I.C.: 7389
N.A.I.C.S.: 541490

Subsidiary:

e2v SAS **(2)**
Parc Burospace Batiment 16
91572 Bievres, France
Tel.: (33) 160195500
Fax: (33) 160195529
E-Mail: enquiries-fr@e2vtechnologies.com
Web Site: www.e2v.com
Emp.: 13
Specialized Design Services
S.I.C.: 7389
N.A.I.C.S.: 541490
Francis Ruffin *(Pres)*

EA HOLDINGS BERHAD
Units J-3A-7 & J-3A-8 Level 3A
Block J Solaris Mont Kiara
2 Jalan Solaris, 50480 Kuala Lumpur, Malaysia
Tel.: (60) 3 6204 0050
Fax: (60) 3 6204 0051
E-Mail: corporate@eah.com.my
Web Site: www.eah.com.my
EAH—(KLS)
Sales Range: $1-9.9 Million
Emp.: 32

Business Description:
Investment Holding, Management & Consulting Services; Software & Computer Related Solutions
S.I.C.: 6719
N.A.I.C.S.: 551112

Personnel:
Mohammad Sobri Bin Saad *(Chm & CEO)*
Tay Mun Kit *(CFO)*
Eugene Surendran *(CTO-RFID)*
Eddy Lee Sin Ti *(CTO-Bus Intelligence & Banking Solutions)*

Board of Directors:
Mohammad Sobri Bin Saad
Basir Bin Bachik
Abdul Fattah Bin Mohamed Yatim
Azahar Bin Rasul
Choo Seng Choon
Ow Pung Hock
Tan Siow Hui

E.A. JUFFALI & BROTHERS COMPANY
Juffali Building Medina Road
PO Box 1049
Jeddah, 21431, Saudi Arabia
Tel.: (966) 26672222
Fax: (966) 26694010
E-Mail: juffali@eajb.com.sa
Web Site: www.eajb.com
Emp.: 6,500
Business Description:
Trading Company; Automobiles; Chemicals
S.I.C.: 6719
N.A.I.C.S.: 551112
Personnel:
Ali Al Juffali *(Owner)*
Amin Afifi *(CEO)*

Subsidiary:

Juffali Chemical Company (1)
Medinah Road
PO Box 5728
Jeddah, 21432, Saudi Arabia
Tel.: (966) 26633516
Fax: (966) 26606508
E-Mail: chemical.div@eajb.com.sa
Web Site: www.jufallimall.com
Chemicals Distr
S.I.C.: 5169
N.A.I.C.S.: 424690
Souhail Farouki *(Gen Mgr)*

Joint Ventures:

Arabian Chemical Company (Latex) Ltd. (2)
Madinah Rd
PO Box 5728
Jeddah, 21432, Saudi Arabia
Tel.: (966) 26633516
Fax: (966) 26609028
Sales Range: $150-199.9 Million
Chemicals Distr; 50% Owned by Juffali Chemical Company & 50% by The Dow Chemical Company
S.I.C.: 5169
N.A.I.C.S.: 424690

Arabian Chemical Company (Polystyrene) Limited (2)
Madinah Road
PO Box 5728
Jeddah, 21432, Saudi Arabia
Tel.: (966) 26633516
Fax: (966) 26609028
E-Mail: dow.juffali@eajb.com.sa
Web Site: www.eajb.com.sa
Sales Range: $75-99.9 Million
Emp.: 100
Chemcials Distr; 50% Owned by Juffali Chemical Company & 50% by The Dow Chemical Company
S.I.C.: 5169
N.A.I.C.S.: 424690
Souhain Enfarouki *(Gen Mgr)*

EACCESS LTD.
Toranomon Twin Building 10-1
Toranomon 2-chome
Minato-ku, Tokyo, 105 0001, Japan
Tel.: (81) 3 5425 2700
Web Site: www.eaccess.net
Year Founded: 1999
9427—(TKS)
Rev.: $2,427,810,000
Assets: $3,869,107,000
Liabilities: $3,025,242,000
Net Worth: $843,865,000
Earnings: ($26,521,000)
Emp.: 1,250
Fiscal Year-end: 03/31/13
Business Description:
Internet Access Services
S.I.C.: 4899
N.A.I.C.S.: 517919
Personnel:
Sachio Semmoto *(Founder)*
Eric Fook-kin Gan *(Pres)*
Board of Directors:
Shuji Ayabe
Kazuhiko Fujihara
Eric Fook-kin Gan
Masashi Ishida
Junichi Miyakawa
Ken Miyauchi
Sachio Semmoto

EAF SUPPLY CHAIN LIMITED
(Formerly Acal Supply Chain Limited)
12 Ashville Way
Wokingham, Berkshire, RG41 2PL, United Kingdom
Tel.: (44) 1189120000
Fax: (44) 1189120001
E-Mail: info@eafsupplychain.com
Web Site: www.eafsupplychain.com
Sales Range: $25-49.9 Million
Emp.: 100
Business Description:
Logistics Equipment Mfr
S.I.C.: 5065
N.A.I.C.S.: 423690
Personnel:
Robert Hall *(Mng Dir)*

EAG-BETEILIGUNGS AG
Fischhof 3/6
A-1010 Vienna, Austria
Tel.: (43) 1230603834
Fax: (43) 1 230 60 3835
E-Mail: ir@eag-bag.com
Web Site: www.eag-bag.com
EYBL—(VIE)
Sales Range: $1-9.9 Million
Business Description:
Investment Holding Company
S.I.C.: 6719
N.A.I.C.S.: 551112
Personnel:
Rudolf Fries *(Chm-Supervisory Bd)*
Markus Gahleitner *(CFO)*
Supervisory Board of Directors:
Rudolf Fries
Elisabeth Bukowiecki-Fries
Knut Consemuller

EAGLE BRAND HOLDINGS LTD.
Dajiang Road
Chancheng District, Foshan, Guangdong, 528031, China
Tel.: (86) 75783962288
Fax: (86) 757 8227 1664
E-Mail: international@eagleceramics.com
Web Site: en.eaglebrandgroup.com
Year Founded: 1995
E04—(SES)
Sales Range: $50-74.9 Million
Emp.: 2,920
Business Description:
Ceramic Sanitary Wares & Tiles Mfr
S.I.C.: 3297
N.A.I.C.S.: 327120
Personnel:
Wei Zhang *(Chm)*
James Mengyou Zhang *(CEO)*
Feng Xiang Dai *(CFO & Sec)*
Board of Directors:
Wei Zhang
Pheng Mun
See Yen Tarn
Shi Wei
Raymond Chuen Ming Wong
James Mengyou Zhang

EAGLE COPTERS LTD.
823 McTavish Road NE
Calgary, AB, T2E 7G9, Canada
Tel.: (403) 250-7370
Fax: (403) 250-7110
E-Mail: admin@eaglecopters.com
Web Site: www.eaglecopters.com
Year Founded: 1975
Sales Range: $10-24.9 Million
Emp.: 175
Business Description:
Helicopters Leasing, Sales & Maintenance
S.I.C.: 4581
N.A.I.C.S.: 488190
Personnel:
Mike O'Reilly *(Pres)*

Joint Venture:

Dart Holding Company Ltd. (1)
1270 Aberdeen Street
Hawkesbury, ON, K6A 1K7, Canada
Tel.: (613) 632-3336
Fax: (613) 632-4443
Holding Company
S.I.C.: 6719
N.A.I.C.S.: 551112
Mike O'Reilly, *(Pres)*

Holding:

Dart Helicopter Services Canada, Inc. (2)
1270 Aberdeen Street
Hawkesbury, ON, K6A 1K7, Canada
Tel.: (613) 632-3336
Fax: (613) 632-4443
Markets & Sells Helicopters & Aftermarket Helicopter Accessories
S.I.C.: 4581
N.A.I.C.S.: 488190
Mike O'Reilly *(CEO)*

Non-U.S. Subsidiary:

Eagle Copters South America S.A. (1)
Aerodromo de Chicureo
Camino Guay Guay s/n, Colina, CP 9340000, Chile
Tel.: (56) 2 948 3200
Fax: (56) 2 247 8290
Web Site: www.eaglecopters.cl
Helicopters Maintenance & Parts
S.I.C.: 4581
N.A.I.C.S.: 488190

EAGLE ENERGY TRUST
Suite 900 639 5th Avenue SW
Calgary, AB, T2P 0M9, Canada
Tel.: (403) 531-1575
Fax: (403) 266-4124
E-Mail: info@eagleenergytrust.com
Web Site: www.eagleenergytrust.com
Year Founded: 2010
EGL.UN—(OTC TSX)
Rev.: $58,372,830
Assets: $283,098,884
Liabilities: $59,266,454
Net Worth: $223,832,430
Earnings: $6,080,420
Emp.: 33
Fiscal Year-end: 12/31/12
Business Description:
Oil & Gas Exploration Services
S.I.C.: 1311
N.A.I.C.S.: 211111
Personnel:
David M. Fitzpatrick *(Chm)*
Richard W. Clark *(Pres & CEO)*
Kelly A. Tomyn *(CFO)*
Jo-Anne M. Bund *(Gen Counsel & Sec)*
Board of Directors:
David M. Fitzpatrick
Joseph Blandford
Richard W. Clark
Bruce K. Gibson
Warren Steckley
Transfer Agent:
Computershare Trust Company of Canada
Calgary, AB, Canada

Subsidiary:

Eagle Energy Inc. (1)
Ste 900 639-5th Ave SW
Calgary, AB, T2P 0M9, Canada
Tel.: (403) 531-1575
Fax: (403) 266-4124
Web Site: www.eagleenergytrust.com
Oil & Gas Exploration Services
S.I.C.: 1311
N.A.I.C.S.: 211111

U.S. Subsidiary:

EEI Holdings Inc. (1)
700 N MacArthur Blvd
Springfield, IL 62702
Tel.: (217) 528-4001
Fax: (217) 528-1677
Oil & Gas Exploration Services
S.I.C.: 1311
N.A.I.C.S.: 211111

EAGLE HILL EXPLORATION CORPORATION
Suite 601 999 Canada Place
Vancouver, BC, V6C 3E1, Canada
Tel.: (604) 697-5791
Fax: (604) 697-0790
E-Mail: info@eaglehillexploration.com
Web Site: www.eaglehillexploration.com
EAG—(OTC TSXV)
Int. Income: $23,951
Assets: $18,786,173
Liabilities: $3,404,453
Net Worth: $15,381,720
Earnings: ($3,192,071)
Emp.: 6
Fiscal Year-end: 10/31/12
Business Description:
Mineral Exploration Services
S.I.C.: 1081
N.A.I.C.S.: 213114
Personnel:
P. Bradley Kitchen *(Pres & CEO)*
Danny Lee *(CFO)*
Amandeep Rai *(Sec & VP-Compliance)*
Board of Directors:
P. Bradley Kitchen
Andre C. Tessier
Transfer Agent:
Computershare Investor Services
510 Burrard St
Vancouver, BC, Canada

EAGLE I CAPITAL CORPORATION
1311 Howe Street Suite 405
Vancouver, BC, V6Z 2P3, Canada
Tel.: (561) 352-8847
Year Founded: 2007
EIC.P—(TSXV)
Business Description:
Investment Services
S.I.C.: 6211
N.A.I.C.S.: 523999
Personnel:
Barry Atkins *(Pres & CEO)*
Board of Directors:
Barry Atkins
David J. Horton
Donald Padgett

EAGLE-I HOLDINGS PLC
Apollo House 41 Halton Station Road
Runcorn, Cheshire, WA7 3DN, United Kingdom
Tel.: (44) 1928795400
Fax: (44) 1928795401
Web Site: www.eagle-i-telematics.com
Sales Range: $1-9.9 Million
Emp.: 5
Business Description:
Vehicle Tracking & Communication System Sales
S.I.C.: 5013
N.A.I.C.S.: 423120
Board of Directors:
Rodney Graves

Eagle-i Holdings Plc—(Continued)

Terry Krell
Ralph Stross

EAGLE INDUSTRY CO., LTD.

7F Seiwa Bldg 1-12-15 Shiba Daimon
Minato-ku, Tokyo, 105-8587, Japan
Tel.: (81) 334382291
Fax: (81) 334325448
E-Mail: info@ekk.co.jp
Web Site: www.ekk.co.jp
Year Founded: 1964
6486—(TKS)
Sls.: $1,130,987,000
Assets: $1,349,238,000
Liabilities: $771,287,000
Net Worth: $577,951,000
Earnings: $49,511,000
Emp.: 4,972
Fiscal Year-end: 03/31/13

Business Description:
Holding Company; Mechanical Seals, Valves, Marine Equipment, Bellows & Plant Devices Mfr
S.I.C.: 6719
N.A.I.C.S.: 551112

Personnel:
Masato Tsuru *(Chm)*
Tetsuji Tsuru *(Pres)*
Shinji Abe *(Sr Mng Dir)*
Fumiaki Aono *(Sr Mng Dir)*
Yasunari Unemura *(Sr Mng Dir)*
Hidenori Goto *(Operating Officer)*
Sumio Ikeda *(Operating Officer)*
Masanobu Ito *(Operating Officer)*
Yukinori Kakeda *(Sr Operating Officer)*
Masaki Nakao *(Sr Operating Officer)*
Takao Shimomura *(Sr Operating Officer)*
Shozo Takahashi *(Sr Operating Officer)*
Shuzo Takami *(Operating Officer)*
Takanori Todoroki *(Operating Officer)*
Takafumi Tsuchiya *(Sr Operating Officer)*
Eiichi Tsuruta *(Sr Operating Officer)*
Norio Uemura *(Operating Officer)*
Toshiyuki Yamaguchi *(Sr Operating Officer)*
Sumio Yamamoto *(Operating Officer)*

Board of Directors:
Masato Tsuru
Shinji Abe
Fumiaki Aono
Tetsuji Tsuru
Yasunari Unemura

Transfer Agent:
Mitsubishi UFJ Trust & Banking Corporation
7-10-11 Higashisuna Koto-ku
Tokyo, Japan

Subsidiaries:

Eagle Engineering Aerospace Co., Ltd. **(1)**
13th Floor Shiba NBF Tower
1-1-30 Shiba-Daimon, 105-0012 Tokyo, Minatoku, Japan JP
Tel.: (81) 334320506
Fax: (81) 334382336
Web Site: www.eea.co.jp
Aerospace Equipment & Components Mfr & Whslr
S.I.C.: 3728
N.A.I.C.S.: 336413

U.S. Subsidiary:

Aerospace Reserch & Trading, Inc. **(2)**
1731 Technology Dr Ste 840
San Jose, CA 95110-1370
Tel.: (408) 392-4047
Fax: (408) 392-4048
Web Site: www.eea.com.sg/contact.html
Aerospace Research & Development Services
S.I.C.: 8731
N.A.I.C.S.: 541712

Non-U.S. Subsidiaries:

Eagle Engineering Aerospace Korea Co., Ltd. **(2)**
503 Young-Ma Building 5F 173 Happo-ro
Masanhappo-gu, Changwon, Gyeongsannam, 631-856, Korea (South) Ks
Tel.: (82) 55 2217 284
Fax: (82) 55 2217 283
E-Mail: eeakoyjk@elim.net
Emp.: 4
Aerospace Equipment & Components Whslr
S.I.C.: 5088
N.A.I.C.S.: 423860
Jang Geun Suk *(Pres)*

Eagle Engineering Aerospace Singapore Pte. Ltd. **(2)**
10 Ubi Crescent Unit 07-78
Ubi Techpark Lobby D, Singapore, 408564, Singapore SG
Tel.: (65) 64836162
Fax: (65) 64836163
E-Mail: info@eea.com.sg
Web Site: www.eea.com.sg
Emp.: 7
Aerospace Equipment & Components Whslr
S.I.C.: 5088
N.A.I.C.S.: 423860
David Lim *(Deputy Gen Mgr)*

Eagle Engineering Aerospace Taiwan Co., Ltd. **(2)**
No 7 Lane 144
Chi Lin Rd, Taipei, Taiwan
Tel.: (886) 225629980
Fax: (886) 225626291
E-Mail: yh.furngrong@msa.hinet.net
Web Site: www.eea.co.jp
Emp.: 1
Aerospace Equipment & Components Whslr
S.I.C.: 5088
N.A.I.C.S.: 423860

Eagle Highcast Co., Ltd. **(1)**
36 Asari-cho
Gotsu, Shimane, 695-0002, Japan
Tel.: (81) 855 55 1076
Fax: (81) 855 55 1078
Industrial Machinery Mfr
S.I.C.: 3559
N.A.I.C.S.: 333249

EagleBurgmann Japan Co., Ltd. **(1)**
5-1-4 Nakagawashin Gosen-shi
959-1693 Niigata, Japan JP
Tel.: (81) 250471111
Fax: (81) 250483070
E-Mail: takafumi.tsuchiya@jp.eagleburgmann.com
Web Site: www.eagleburgmann.com
Emp.: 700
Metal Valve & Pipe Fitting Mfr
S.I.C.: 3494
N.A.I.C.S.: 332919
Takafumi Tsuchiya *(Pres)*

Hiroshima Eagle Co., Ltd. **(1)**
6 Shin-Ujigami Kitahiroshima-cho
Yamagata-gun, Hokkaido, Hiroshima, 731-1514, Japan
Tel.: (81) 826 72 5900
Fax: (81) 826 72 5911
Web Site: www.ekk.co.jp/eng/profile/office/japan/index.html
Construction Machinery Mfr
S.I.C.: 3531
N.A.I.C.S.: 333120

Kemel Co., Ltd. **(1)**
NBF Tower 13F 1-1-30 Shiba-Daimon
Tokyo, Minato-ku, 105 0012, Japan
Tel.: (81) 334364840
Fax: (81) 334364890
Web Site: www.kemel.com
Emp.: 144
SternTube Seal, SternTube Bearing & Intermediate Bearing Mfr
S.I.C.: 3562
N.A.I.C.S.: 332991
Todoroki Takanori *(Pres)*

Okayama Eagle Co., Ltd. **(1)**
4003-1 Ukan Ukan-cho
Takahashi, Okayama, 716-1321, Japan
Tel.: (81) 866 57 3150
Fax: (81) 866 57 3180
Web Site: www.ekk.co.jp/eng/profile/office/japan/index.html
Automotive Parts Mfr
S.I.C.: 3714
N.A.I.C.S.: 336390

Shimane Eagle Co., Ltd. **(1)**
212-3 Tane Kakeya-cho
Unnan, Shimane, 690-2706, Japan
Tel.: (81) 854 62 1581
Fax: (81) 854 62 1583
Web Site: www.ekk.co.jp/eng/profile/office/japan/index.html
Automotive Parts Mfr
S.I.C.: 3714
N.A.I.C.S.: 336390

Valcom Co., Ltd. **(1)**
3-7-25 Minowa
Toyonaka, Osaka, 560-0035, Japan
Tel.: (81) 6 6857 1811
Fax: (81) 6 6857 1003
E-Mail: info@valcom.co.jp
Web Site: www.ekk.co.jp/eng/profile/office/japan/index_042.html
Pressure Sensor Mfr & Distr
S.I.C.: 3823
N.A.I.C.S.: 334513
Eiichi Tsuruta *(Pres)*

Plants:

Eagle Industry Co., Ltd. - Okayama Factory **(1)**
1212 Abe Ochiaicho
Takahashi, Okayama, 716-8511, Japan
Tel.: (81) 866 22 4061
Fax: (81) 866 22 5352
Mechanical Seals Mfr
S.I.C.: 3053
N.A.I.C.S.: 339991

Eagle Industry Co., Ltd. - Saitama Factory **(1)**
1500 Katayanagi
Sakado, Saitama, 350-0285, Japan
Tel.: (81) 49 281 1111
Fax: (81) 49 283 4843
Industrial Machinery Mfr
S.I.C.: 3559
N.A.I.C.S.: 333249

KEMEL Co., Ltd. - Kure Factory **(1)**
8-1 Showa-cho
Kure, Hiroshima, 737-0027, Japan
Tel.: (81) 823 25 7121
Fax: (81) 823 25 7120
Industrial Machinery Mfr
S.I.C.: 3559
N.A.I.C.S.: 333249

KEMEL Co., Ltd. - Takasago Factory **(1)**
2-3-1 Shinhama Arai-cho
Takasago, Hyogo, 676-8670, Japan
Tel.: (81) 794 45 7109
Fax: (81) 794 45 7246
Web Site: www.ekk.co.jp/eng/profile/office/japan/index.html
Industrial Machinery Mfr
S.I.C.: 3559
N.A.I.C.S.: 333249

Non-U.S. Subsidiaries:

Actuator Components GmbH & Co. KG **(1)**
Hohnerweg 2-4
69465 Weinheim, Germany
Tel.: (49) 620180 6694
Fax: (49) 620188 6694
Web Site: www.ekk.co.jp/eng/profile/office/europe/index.html
Automotive Actuator Component Mfr & Distr
S.I.C.: 3714
N.A.I.C.S.: 336390

Eagle Holding Europe B.V. **(1)**
Hopelerweg 250
6468 XX Kerkrade, Netherlands
Tel.: (31) 45 546 9201
Fax: (31) 45 546 4730
Web Site: www.ekk.co.jp/eng/profile/office/europe/index.html
Emp.: 60
Investment Management Services
S.I.C.: 6211
N.A.I.C.S.: 523999
Dennis van Well *(Gen Mgr)*

Eagle Industry France S.A.S. **(1)**
5 Avenue de Lorraine
57380 Faulquemont, France
Tel.: (33) 3 8729 7980
Fax: (33) 3 8729 7990
Web Site: www.ekk.co.jp/eng/profile/office/europe/index_004.html
Industrial Machinery Mfr
S.I.C.: 3559
N.A.I.C.S.: 333249

Eagle Industry Taiwan Corporation **(1)**
No 134 Hsi Lin Road Yenchao
Kaohsiung, Taiwan
Tel.: (886) 76164401
Fax: (886) 6167541
E-Mail: chuky.wang@ekk.tw
Web Site: www.ekk.co.jp/eng/company/company06.html
Emp.: 200
Adhesive Mfr
S.I.C.: 2891
N.A.I.C.S.: 325520
Kaneko Toshiei *(Gen Mgr)*

Eagle New Zealand Limited **(1)**
47 William Pickering Dr
PO Box 34285
Rosedale, Auckland, New Zealand
Tel.: (64) 94435772
Fax: (64) 94150599
Web Site: www.eagleseal.co.nz/contactus.htm
Emp.: 40
Gasket Packing & Sealing Device Mfr
S.I.C.: 3053
N.A.I.C.S.: 339991
John Hill *(Mng Dir)*

EagleBurgmann Australasia Pty. Ltd. **(1)**
(Formerly EagleBurgmann Australia Pty. Ltd.)
16 Stennett Road
Sydney, NSW, 2565, Australia AU
Tel.: (61) 296056444
Fax: (61) 298296958
E-Mail: sales@au.eagleburgmann.com
Web Site: www.eagleburgmann.com.au
Rev.: $3,190,000
Emp.: 38
Mechanical Seals & Packing Mfr & Sls
S.I.C.: 3053
N.A.I.C.S.: 339991
Wolfgang Kindinger *(Mng Dir)*
Ian Nipper *(Mgr-Sls-Victoria)*

Branch:

EagleBurgmann Australasia Pty. Ltd. - Melbourne **(2)**
19 Inglewood Drive
Thomastown, Melbourne, VIC, 3074, Australia
Tel.: (61) 394646344
Fax: (61) 394646511
E-Mail: vic@au.eagleburgmann.com
Web Site: www.eagleburgmann.com
Mechanical Seals Mfr
S.I.C.: 3546
N.A.I.C.S.: 333991
Mike Newman *(Area Mgr)*

EagleBurgmann India Pvt. Ltd. **(1)**
Gazebo House 52 Gulmohar Road Opp Cross Road #7
JVPD Scheme Vile Parle West, Mumbai, 400049, India In
Tel.: (91) 22 6702 1489
Fax: (91) 22 6702 1487
E-Mail: ebipl.mumbai@in.eagleburgmann.com
Web Site: www.eagleburgmann.com
Emp.: 180
Mechanical Seals & Packings Mfr & Sls
S.I.C.: 3053
N.A.I.C.S.: 339991

Branch:

EagleBurgmann India Pvt. Ltd. **(2)**
Door No 10-50-18/17 Flat No 1/7 First Floor
Siripuram Towers
Siripuram VIP Road, 530 003
Visakhapatnam, India
Tel.: (91) 8912755703
Fax: (91) 8912550306
Mechanical Sealing Device Mfr

S.I.C.: 3053
N.A.I.C.S.: 339991

EagleBurgmann New Zealand, Ltd. (1)
47 William Pickering Drive
PO Box 300-858
North Shore City Albany, Auckland, 752, New Zealand
Tel.: (64) 94485001
Fax: (64) 94150599
E-Mail: sales@nz.eagleburgmann.com
Emp.: 45
Mechanical Seal Mfr
S.I.C.: 3053
N.A.I.C.S.: 339991
John Hill *(Gen Mgr)*

EBI Asia Pacific Pte Ltd (1)
1 International Business Pk #03-01A The Synergy
609917 Singapore, Singapore
Tel.: (65) 65656623
Fax: (65) 5659663
Web Site: www.eagleburgmann.com
Emp.: 20
Holding Company
S.I.C.: 6719
N.A.I.C.S.: 551112
Yinyee Foo *(COO)*

EKK Eagle Industry Asia-Pacific Pte. Ltd. (1)
52 Serangoon North Avenue 4
#03-02 Ever Tech Building, Singapore, 555853, Singapore SG
Tel.: (65) 64836005
Fax: (65) 64836007
E-Mail: info@ekk.com.sg
Web Site: www.ekk.co.jp/eng/company/company06.html
Emp.: 2
Industrial Supplies Whslr
S.I.C.: 5085
N.A.I.C.S.: 423840
K. Suzuki San *(Gen Mgr)*

EKK Eagle (Thailand) Co. Ltd. (1)
700/852 Moo 1 Panthong Subdistrict
Panthong District, Chon Buri, 20160, Thailand
Tel.: (66) 3818516074
Fax: (66) 3818517576
Web Site: www.ekk.co.jp/eng/company/company06.html
Emp.: 100
Metal Valve & Pipe Fitting Mfr
S.I.C.: 3494
N.A.I.C.S.: 332919

Kemel Asia Pacific Pte. Ltd. (1)
26 Pandan Loop
128244 Singapore, Singapore
Tel.: (65) 67791300
Fax: (65) 67779224
Web Site: www.kemel.com
Emp.: 20
SternTube Seal, SternTube Bearing & Intermediate Bearing Mfr
S.I.C.: 3562
N.A.I.C.S.: 332991

Kemel Europe Limited (1)
Unit 9 Tower Road Glover Industrial Estate
Washington, Tyne and Wear, NE37 2SH, United Kingdom
Tel.: (44) 1914160232
Fax: (44) 1914155016
Web Site: www.kemel.com
Emp.: 6
SternTube Seal, SternTube Bearing & Intermediate Bearing Mfr
S.I.C.: 3562
N.A.I.C.S.: 332991
Kazuma Tsukada *(Gen Mgr)*

NEK Co., Ltd. (1)
284-1 Daechi-Ri
Chilseo, Gyeongsangnam-do, Korea (South)
Tel.: (82) 55 5871212
Fax: (82) 55 5871127
E-Mail: account@nekkorea.com
Web Site: www.nekkorea.com
Industrial Machinery Mfr
S.I.C.: 3559
N.A.I.C.S.: 333249

P.T. Eagle Industry Indonesia (1)
EJIP Industrial Park Plot 7G-4
Lemah Abang, Bekasi, Cikarang, 12770, Indonesia
Tel.: (62) 218970178
Fax: (62) 218970179
Web Site: www.ekk.co.jp/eng/company/company06.html
Emp.: 60
Gasket Packing & Sealing Device Mfr
S.I.C.: 3053
N.A.I.C.S.: 339991

P.T. EagleBurgmann Indonesia (1)
Jl Jababeka Blok J6 E
Kawasan Industri Cikarang, Bekasi, Jawa Barat, 17550, Indonesia ID
Tel.: (62) 218935313
Fax: (62) 218935315
E-Mail: bri@burgmann.co.id
Web Site: www.eagleburgmann.com
Emp.: 109
Mechanical Seals & Packings Mfr & Sls
S.I.C.: 3053
N.A.I.C.S.: 339991

EAGLE LEGEND ASIA LIMITED

(Formerly Manta Holdings Company Limited)
Unit 6A Winbase Centre
208-220 Queen's Road, Central, China (Hong Kong)
Tel.: (852) 2922 9722
Fax: (852) 2851 3788
E-Mail: infoela@elasialtd.com
Web Site: www.elasialtd.com
Year Founded: 1975
0936—(HKG)
Rev.: $25,932,361
Assets: $75,360,701
Liabilities: $19,069,126
Net Worth: $56,291,575
Earnings: ($252,355)
Emp.: 99
Fiscal Year-end: 12/31/12

Business Description:
Engineering & Construction Equipment Rental & Maintenance Services
S.I.C.: 7359
N.A.I.C.S.: 532412

Personnel:
Chung So *(Chm)*
Chang Yeow Quek *(CEO)*
Ka Bong Wong *(Sec)*

Board of Directors:
Chung So
Mo Chan
Gar Lok Ho
Woon Kun Lam
Betty Miu Sheung Lo
Man So

Legal Counsel:
P. C. Woo & Co
12th Floor, Princes Building 10 Chater Road, Central
Hong Kong, China (Hong Kong)

Appleby Trust (Cayman) Ltd.
Clifton House 75 Fort Street
PO Box 1350
Grand Cayman, Cayman Islands

Transfer Agents:
Tricor Investor Services Limited
26th Floor Tesbury Centre 28 Queens Road East
Wanchai, China (Hong Kong)

Appleby Trust (Cayman) Ltd.
Clifton House 75 Fort Street
PO Box 1350
Grand Cayman, Cayman Islands

Subsidiary:

Manta Engineering & Equipment Co. Ltd. (1)
Unit H 9F Valiant Industrial Centre
2-12 Au Pui Wan Street Fo Tan, Sha Tin, New Territories, China (Hong Kong)
Tel.: (852) 2369 6411
Fax: (852) 2723 4985
E-Mail: general@mantagroup.com.hk
Web Site: www.mantagroup.com.hk
Equipment Rental & Maintenance Services
S.I.C.: 7699
N.A.I.C.S.: 811310

EAGLE MOUNTAIN GOLD CORP.

(Acquired & Absorbed by Goldsource Mines Inc.)

EAGLE NICE (INTERNATIONAL) HOLDINGS LTD.

9th Floor Tower B Regent Centre 70 Ta Chuen Ping Street
Kwai Chung, New Territories, China (Hong Kong)
Tel.: (852) 26101338
Fax: (852) 26100938
E-Mail: info@eaglenice.com.hk
Web Site: www.eaglenice.com.hk
2368—(HKG)
Rev.: $186,203,026
Assets: $232,469,513
Liabilities: $85,146,846
Net Worth: $147,322,667
Earnings: $9,408,708
Emp.: 10,000
Fiscal Year-end: 03/31/13

Business Description:
Apparel & Accessories
S.I.C.: 2399
N.A.I.C.S.: 315990

Personnel:
Yuk Sing Chung *(Chm)*
Hsiao Ying Chen *(CEO)*
Wen Hsiang Chang *(CFO)*
Man Chi Woo *(Sec & Controller-Fin)*

Board of Directors:
Yuk Sing Chung
Cheuk Ho Chan
Christina Fang Mei Chen
Hsiao Ying Chen
Tony Yung Hui Cheng
Tai Yu Kuo
Chi Chant Lu

Legal Counsel:
Vincent T. K. Cheung, Yap & Co.
11th Floor Central Building 1-3 Pedder Street
Central, China (Hong Kong)

HSBC Trustee (Cayman) Limited
HSBC House 68 West Bay Road
PO Box 484
Georgetown, Grand Cayman, Cayman Islands

Transfer Agents:
Tricor Tengis Limited
26th Floor Tesbury Centre 28 Queen's Road East
Wanchai, China (Hong Kong)
Tel.: (852) 29801333
Fax: (852) 28108185

HSBC Trustee (Cayman) Limited
HSBC House 68 West Bay Road
PO Box 484
Georgetown, Grand Cayman, Cayman Islands

Subsidiaries:

Eagle Nice Development Limited (1)
Well Fung Industrial Center
Kwai Chung, NT, China (Hong Kong)
Tel.: (852) 26101338
Fax: (852) 26100938
Sportswear Mfr & Sales
S.I.C.: 2389
N.A.I.C.S.: 315210

Far East (EAG) Limited (1)
Rm 7-9 9 F Regent Ctr Block B 63 Wo Yi Hop Rd
Kwai Chung, New Territories, China (Hong Kong)
Tel.: (852) 26100378
Fax: (852) 26100833
Sportswear Mfr & Sales
S.I.C.: 2399
N.A.I.C.S.: 315210

EAGLE NICKEL LIMITED

Level 7 231 Adelaide Terrace
Perth, WA, 6000, Australia
Tel.: (61) 8 9225 4718
Fax: (61) 8 9225 6474
E-Mail: info@eaglenickel.com.au
Web Site: www.eaglenickel.com.au
ENL—(ASX)
Rev.: $37,085
Assets: $1,057,475
Liabilities: $54,623
Net Worth: $1,002,852
Earnings: ($373,243)
Emp.: 20
Fiscal Year-end: 06/30/13

Business Description:
Nickel Uranium & Molybdenum Exploration
S.I.C.: 2819
N.A.I.C.S.: 325180

Personnel:
Andrew William Bursill *(Sec)*

Board of Directors:
Xuefeng Mei
Hui Guo
Robert Sebek

Legal Counsel:
Lawton Gillon
Level 11 16 St Georges Terrace
Perth, Australia

EAGLE NORTH HOLDINGS INC

(d/b/a Cambridge Toyota)
2400 Eagle Street North
Cambridge, ON, N3H 4R7, Canada
Tel.: (519) 653-7030
Fax: (519) 653-6948
E-Mail: info@cambridge.toyota.ca
Web Site: www.cambridgetoyota.com
Year Founded: 1979
Rev.: $24,100,000
Emp.: 45

Business Description:
New & Used Car Dealers
S.I.C.: 5511
N.A.I.C.S.: 441110

Personnel:
Cam Beaton *(Pres)*

EAGLE PLAINS RESOURCES LTD.

Suite 200 44 - 12th Ave S
Cranbrook, BC, V1C 2R7, Canada
Tel.: (250) 426-0749
Fax: (250) 426-6899
Toll Free: (866) 486-8673
E-Mail: info@eagleplains.com
Web Site: www.eagleplains.com
Year Founded: 1992
EPL—(TSXV)
Sls.: $5,265,176
Assets: $12,782,359
Liabilities: $407,287
Net Worth: $12,375,072
Earnings: $176,182
Fiscal Year-end: 12/31/12

Business Description:
Mineral Exploration Services
S.I.C.: 1081
N.A.I.C.S.: 213114

Personnel:
Timothy Jay Termuende *(Pres & CEO)*
Glen J. Diduck *(CFO)*
Jesse Campbell *(Pres/Gen Mgr-Terralogic Exploration Sevices)*
Darren Fach *(Sec)*

Board of Directors:
Glen J. Diduck
Charles C. Downie
Darren Fach
Ron Netolitzky
Timothy Jay Termuende

Legal Counsel:
McLeod & Company
Calgary, AB, Canada

EAGLE PROFESSIONAL RESOURCES INC
170 Laurier Avenue W Suite 902
Ottawa, ON, K1P 5V5, Canada
Tel.: (613) 234-1810
Fax: (613) 234-0797
Toll Free: (888) 798-8181
Web Site: www.eagleonline.com
Year Founded: 1996
Rev.: $67,462,000
Emp.: 88
Business Description:
Employment & Consulting Agencies
S.I.C.: 7361
N.A.I.C.S.: 561311
Personnel:
Terry Power *(Pres)*
Kevin Dee *(CEO)*
Jonah Laist *(CFO)*
Janis Grantham *(COO)*
Bill Hanniman *(Exec VP)*

EAGLE RIVER CHRYSLER LTD.
3315 Caxton Street
PO Box 1558
Whitecourt, AB, T7S 1P4, Canada
Tel.: (780) 778-2844
Fax: (780) 778-8950
Toll Free: (888) 778-6668
E-Mail: info@eagleriver.ab.ca
Web Site: www.eagleriver.ca
Year Founded: 1994
Rev.: $10,085,614
Emp.: 22
Business Description:
New & Used Car Dealers
S.I.C.: 5511
N.A.I.C.S.: 441110
Personnel:
Mike Stuckless *(Co-Owner & Gen Mgr)*

EAGLE STAR MINERALS CORP.
Suite 1170 666 Burrard Street
Vancouver, BC, V6C 2X8, Canada
Tel.: (604) 282-7222
Fax: (604) 669-2322
E-Mail: ir@eaglestarminerals.com
Web Site: www.eaglestaroil.com
Year Founded: 2004
EGE.V—(DEU TSXV)
Assets: $2,002,943
Liabilities: $681,726
Net Worth: $1,321,217
Earnings: ($3,003,218)
Fiscal Year-end: 09/30/12
Business Description:
Minerals Exploration Services
S.I.C.: 1499
N.A.I.C.S.: 212399
Personnel:
Eran Friedlander *(Pres & CEO)*
Leslie Shen *(CFO)*
Jose Eloi Guimaraes Campos *(COO)*
Board of Directors:
Gustavo Dalla Valle Baptista de Silva
Eran Friedlander
Jose Eloi Guimaraes Campos
Jill Leversage
Carlos Perucca

EAGLE VET. TECH CO., LTD.
278-20 Sungsu-2Ga
Sungdong-Gu, Seoul, Korea (South)
Tel.: (82) 80 022 6644
Fax: (82) 2 469 0309
E-Mail: an@eaglevet.com
Web Site: www.eaglevet.com
Year Founded: 1970
044960—(KRS)
Sls.: $13,963,020
Assets: $19,890,840
Liabilities: $4,837,860
Net Worth: $15,052,980
Earnings: $640,770
Fiscal Year-end: 12/31/12
Business Description:
Pharmaceutical Product Mfr
S.I.C.: 2834
N.A.I.C.S.: 325412
Personnel:
Seung Jo Kang *(Pres)*

EAGLEFORD ENERGY INC.
1 King Street West Suite 1505
Toronto, ON, M5H 1A1, Canada
Tel.: (416) 364-4039
Fax: (416) 364-8244
Toll Free: (877) 723-5542
Web Site: www.eagleford.com
EFRDF—(OTC OTCB)
Rev.: $29,882
Assets: $6,876,825
Liabilities: $6,735,531
Net Worth: $141,294
Earnings: ($4,240,535)
Emp.: 1
Fiscal Year-end: 08/31/13
Business Description:
Oil & Gas Exploration Services
S.I.C.: 1311
N.A.I.C.S.: 211111
Personnel:
James C. Cassina *(Pres, CEO & CFO)*
Board of Directors:
James C. Cassina
Alan D. Gaines
Milton Klyman
Colin McNeil
Legal Counsel:
Gottbetter & Partners LLP
488 Madison Ave 12th Fl
New York, NY 10022
Transfer Agent:
Equity Financial Trust Company
200 University Avenue Suite 400
Toronto, ON, Canada

EAGLEMOSS PUBLICATIONS LTD
1st Floor Beaumont House
Kensington Village
Avonmore Road, London, W14 8TS, United Kingdom
Tel.: (44) 20 7605 1200
Fax: (44) 20 7605 1201
E-Mail: info@eaglemoss.co.uk
Web Site: www.eaglemoss.com
Emp.: 85
Business Description:
Literature Publisher & Figurine Mfr
S.I.C.: 2731
N.A.I.C.S.: 511130

Non-U.S. Subsidiary:

GE Fabbri Phoenix Sp. Z .o.o. Ltd. **(1)**
Swojczycka 38
Wroclaw, Poland (67%)
Tel.: (48) 713447775
Fax: (48) 713460174
Emp.: 100
Newspaper Publishers
S.I.C.: 2711
N.A.I.C.S.: 511110

EAGLEWOOD ENERGY INC.
602 304 - 8 Avenue SW
Calgary, AB, T2P 1C2, Canada
Tel.: (403) 264-6944
Fax: (403) 266-6441
E-Mail: info@eaglewoodenergy.ca
Web Site: www.eaglewoodenergy.ca
EWD—(OTC TSXV)
Sales Range: Less than $1 Million
Business Description:
Oil & Gas Exploration Services
S.I.C.: 1389
N.A.I.C.S.: 213112
Personnel:
Raymond Peter Antony *(Chm)*
Michael McGowan *(Pres & COO)*
Brad Hurtubise *(CEO)*
Ross Jones *(Interim CFO & Controller)*
Board of Directors:
Raymond Peter Antony
Stan Grad
Brad Hurtubise
Mark Sarssam
Legal Counsel:
Davis LLP
Calgary, AB, Canada

EAM SOLAR ASA
Dronningen 1
0287 Oslo, Norway
Tel.: (47) 241 15 796
Web Site: www.eamsolar.no
Year Founded: 2011
EAM—(OSL)
Business Description:
Solar Power Plants Owner & Operator
S.I.C.: 4931
N.A.I.C.S.: 221118
Personnel:
Viktor Jakobsen *(Chm)*
Audun W. Iversen *(CEO)*
Roar Alme *(CFO)*
Rolfe Jarle Aaberg *(COO)*
Board of Directors:
Viktor Jakobsen
Ingelise Arntsen
Paal E. Johnsen

EAO AG
Tannwaldstrasse 88
4600 Olten, Switzerland
Tel.: (41) 622869111
Fax: (41) 622962162
E-Mail: info@eao.com
Web Site: www.eao.com
Year Founded: 1947
Emp.: 600
Business Description:
Industrial Electrical Equipment Mfr
Export
S.I.C.: 3699
N.A.I.C.S.: 335999
Personnel:
Kurt Loosli *(CEO)*

Subsidiary:

EAO Verkauf (Schweiz) AG **(1)**
Altgraben 441
Haerkingen, 4624, Switzerland (100%)
Tel.: (41) 623889500
Fax: (41) 622962162
Web Site: www.eao.ch/com
Sls.: $5,933,258
Emp.: 10
Mfr. of Electronic Controls & Regulators
S.I.C.: 3714
N.A.I.C.S.: 336320
Stefhen Rueegg *(Dir-Mktg)*

U.S. Subsidiaries:

EAO Switch Corporation **(1)**
98 Washington St
Milford, CT 06460-3670 (100%)
Tel.: (203) 877-4577
Fax: (203) 877-3694
E-Mail: info@eaoswitch.com
Web Site: www.eaoswitch.com
Emp.: 27
General Purpose Pushbutton Switches, Keypads, Indicators, Membranes & Custom Front Panels Mfr
Import
S.I.C.: 5063
N.A.I.C.S.: 423610
Joseph Torzillo *(VP-Sls)*

Switches Plus, Inc. **(1)**
98 Washington St
Milford, CT 06460-3670
Tel.: (203) 876-2697
Fax: (203) 877-3694
E-Mail: info@eaoswitch.com
Web Site: www.eaoswitch.com
Emp.: 40
Distr of Switches
S.I.C.: 5063
N.A.I.C.S.: 423610
Lance A. Scott *(Pres)*

Non-U.S. Subsidiaries:

EAO Far East Ltd. **(1)**
Unit A1 1 F Block A Tin On Industrial Bldg
777 Cheung Sha Wan Rd Lai Chi, Kowloon, China (Hong Kong) (100%)
Tel.: (852) 27869141
Fax: (852) 27869561
E-Mail: eao@eaofareast.com.hk
Web Site: www.eao.com
Emp.: 70
Mfr. of Electronic Controls & Regulators
S.I.C.: 3625
N.A.I.C.S.: 335314
Joseph Chung *(Gen Mgr)*

EAO Benelux B.V. **(1)**
Kamerlingh Onnesweg 46
NL 3316 GL Dordrecht, Netherlands (100%)
Tel.: (31) 786531700
Fax: (31) 786531799
E-Mail: sales.enl@eao.nl
Web Site: www.eao.nl
Emp.: 16
Mfr. of Electronic Controls & Regulators
S.I.C.: 3714
N.A.I.C.S.: 336320
Dave Polman *(Mng Dir)*

EAO Limited **(1)**
Highland House Albert Drive
RH15 9TN Burgess Hill, Sussex, United Kingdom (100%)
Tel.: (44) 01444245021
Fax: (44) 1444236641
E-Mail: info@eao.com
Web Site: www.eao.com
Emp.: 30
Mfr. of Electronic Controls & Regulators
S.I.C.: 3625
N.A.I.C.S.: 335314
Robert Davies *(Mgr-Mktg)*

EAO Lumitas GmbH **(1)**
Langenberger Strasse 570
45277 Essen, Germany (100%)
Tel.: (49) 20185870
Fax: (49) 2018587255
E-Mail: eao.lumitas@t-online.de
Web Site: www.eao.com
Emp.: 60
Mfr. of Electronic Controls & Regulators
S.I.C.: 3714
N.A.I.C.S.: 336320
Manfred Shveehorst *(Mng Dir)*

EAO Svenska AB **(1)**
Grahundsvagen 80
Skarpnaeck, Stockholm, 12822, Sweden (100%)
Tel.: (46) 86838660
Fax: (46) 87242912
E-Mail: gunnar.aspero@eao.se
Web Site: www.eao.se
Sls.: $3,299,151
Emp.: 8
Mfr. of Electronic Controls & Regulators
S.I.C.: 3714
N.A.I.C.S.: 336320
Robert Gurnatton *(Mng Dir)*

EAO Secme SAS **(1)**
5 Rue Henri Francois
BP 3
Ozoir-la-Ferriere, France (100%)
Tel.: (33) 164433737
Fax: (33) 164433748
E-Mail: sales.ese@eao.com
Web Site: www.eao.fr
Emp.: 9
Mfr of Electronic Controls & Regulators
S.I.C.: 3677
N.A.I.C.S.: 334416
David Lemadre *(Mng Dir)*

EARL SHILTON BUILDING SOCIETY
22 The Hollow Earl Shilton
Leicester, LE9 7NB, United Kingdom

Tel.: (44) 1455 844422
Fax: (44) 1455 845857
E-Mail: enquire@esbs.co.uk
Web Site: www.esbs.co.uk
Rev.: $5,425,338
Assets: $171,598,974
Liabilities: $11,002,650
Net Worth: $160,596,324
Earnings: $633,734
Emp.: 30
Fiscal Year-end: 03/31/13
Business Description:
Mortgage Lending & Other Financial Services
S.I.C.: 6163
N.A.I.C.S.: 522310
Personnel:
Paul Tilley *(CEO & Sec)*
Neil D. Adams *(Deputy CEO & Dir-Fin)*
Board of Directors:
Rupert A. Clarke
Neil D. Adams
David R. Crooks
Audrey L. Green
Richard Krasucki
Christopher J. Newton
Christopher G. Packham
William H. Summ
Paul Tilley

EARLY AGE CO., LTD.
Akasaka Twin Tower Shinkan 5F 11-7
Akasaka 2-chome Minato-ku
Tokyo, 107-0052, Japan
Tel.: (81) 355755590
Fax: (81) 355755591
E-Mail: info@early-age.co.jp
Web Site: www.early-age.co.jp
Year Founded: 1986
3248—(TKS)
Sales Range: $25-49.9 Million
Emp.: 35
Business Description:
Real Estate Leasing Services
S.I.C.: 6519
N.A.I.C.S.: 531190
Personnel:
Tatsuya Mukaiyama *(Pres)*

EARLY EQUITY PLC
Edgbaston House 3 Duchess Place
Birmingham, B16 8NH, United Kingdom
Tel.: (44) 121 456 7948
E-Mail: info@earlyequity.co.uk
Web Site: www.earlyequity.co.uk
EEQP—(ISDX)
Sales Range: Less than $1 Million
Business Description:
Investment Services
S.I.C.: 6211
N.A.I.C.S.: 523999
Personnel:
Robert Painting *(CEO & Sec)*
Board of Directors:
Gregory Collier
Jonathan Hall
Chua Siew Lian
Robert Painting
Legal Counsel:
Wilkes & Co.
Birmingham, United Kingdom

EARN-A-CAR, INC.
Office 1 The Falls Centre Corner
Great North & Webb
Northmead, Benoni, 1522, South Africa
Tel.: (27) 11 425 1666
Web Site: www.earnacar.co.za
Year Founded: 2009
EACR—(OTC OTCB)
Rev.: $3,498,352
Assets: $6,058,626
Liabilities: $5,244,769
Net Worth: $813,857
Earnings: $524,559
Emp.: 38
Fiscal Year-end: 02/28/13
Business Description:
Car Rental Services
S.I.C.: 7514
N.A.I.C.S.: 532111
Personnel:
Graeme Thomas Hardie *(Chm)*
John Clifford Storey *(Pres & CEO)*
Bruce Dunnington *(CFO)*
Board of Directors:
Graeme Thomas Hardie
John Clifford Storey

EARNEST INVESTMENTS HOLDINGS LTD
Room A 5/F Xiu Hua Commerical
Building No 211-213 Jaffe Road
Wanchai, China (Hong Kong)
Tel.: (852) 28517622
Fax: (852) 28153922
E-Mail: enquiry@earnest-inv.com
Web Site: www.earnest-inv.com
0339—(HKG)
Sls.: $1,041,679
Assets: $5,396,303
Liabilities: $27,698
Net Worth: $5,368,604
Earnings: ($936,260)
Emp.: 7
Fiscal Year-end: 12/31/12
Business Description:
Securities
S.I.C.: 6726
N.A.I.C.S.: 525990
Personnel:
Chak Paul Chan *(Chm)*
Wah Sang Ngai *(Deputy Chm & CEO)*
Yee Man Chui *(Sec)*
Board of Directors:
Chak Paul Chan
Francis Ping Kuen Chan
Wah Sang Ngai
Yee Boon Tan
Daming Wang
Jia Hua Wang
Appleby Management (Bermuda) Ltd.
Canon's Court 22 Victoria Street
HM 12 Hamilton, Bermuda

EARNY RESOURCES LIMITED
1575 Kamloops Street
Vancouver, BC, V5K 3W1, Canada
Tel.: (604) 251-6320
E-Mail: naveenv@shaw.ca
Year Founded: 2011
ERN.P—(TSXV)
Business Description:
Investment Services
S.I.C.: 6211
N.A.I.C.S.: 523999
Personnel:
Navin Varshney *(Pres, CEO, CFO & Sec)*
Board of Directors:
Wally E. Boguski
Ernest J. Crepnjak
Leif Smither
Navin Varshney
Transfer Agent:
Computershare Investor Services Inc.
3rd Floor 510 Burrard St
V6C 3B9 Vancouver, BC, Canada

EARTH HEAT RESOURCES LIMITED
Level 7 Ferrari House 28-30 Grenfell Street
Adelaide, SA, 5000, Australia
Tel.: (61) 882120579
Fax: (61) 882122230
E-Mail: info@earthheat.com.au
Web Site: www.earthheat.com.au
EHR—(ASX)
Business Description:
Geothermal Exploration Services
S.I.C.: 1481
N.A.I.C.S.: 213115
Personnel:
Raymond Shaw *(Chm)*
Torey Marshall *(Mng Dir)*
Mal Lucas-Smith *(Sec)*
Board of Directors:
Raymond Shaw
Torey Marshall
Norman J. Zillman
Legal Counsel:
Hopgood Ganim
Level 8 Waterfront Place 1 Eagle Street
Brisbane, QLD, 4000, Australia

EARTH SIGNAL PROCESSING LTD.
Suite 1600 715 - 5th Avenue SW
Calgary, AB, Canada
Tel.: (403) 264-8722
Fax: (403) 264-8725
Toll Free: (866) 750-3775
E-Mail: info@earthsignal.com
Web Site: www.earthsignal.com
Year Founded: 1993
Rev.: $10,000,000
Emp.: 200
Business Description:
Seismic Data Processing Services
S.I.C.: 7379
N.A.I.C.S.: 518210
Personnel:
Steve P. Fuller Geoph *(Pres)*

EARTHPORT PLC
21 New Street
London, EC2M 4TP, United Kingdom
Tel.: (44) 2072209700
Fax: (44) 2072209701
E-Mail: info@earthport.com
Web Site: www.earthport.com
EPO—(LSE)
Rev.: $6,542,998
Assets: $25,687,152
Liabilities: $909,671
Net Worth: $24,777,481
Earnings: ($12,834,890)
Emp.: 75
Fiscal Year-end: 06/30/13
Business Description:
Electronic Payment Services
S.I.C.: 6726
N.A.I.C.S.: 525990
Personnel:
Christopher Cowlard *(COO)*
Paul Thomas *(Chief Comml Officer)*
A. Ali *(Sec)*
Board of Directors:
Philip George Hickman
Christopher Cowlard
Mohit Davar
Vinode Bhesham Ramgopal
Paul Thomas
Hank Uberoi
Terence John Williams
Legal Counsel:
Bird & Bird LLP
15 Fetter Lane
EC4A 1JP London, United Kingdom
Non-U.S. Subsidiary:

Earthport Middle East Ltd. **(1)**
Dubai Internet City Building 17 Office 167
PO Box 500675
Dubai, United Arab Emirates
Tel.: (971) 4 434 7181
Fax: (971) 4 437 6451
E-Mail: earthportuae@earthport.com
International Payment Solutions
S.I.C.: 7389
N.A.I.C.S.: 561499

EARTHWORKS INDUSTRIES INC.
Suite 1608 - 675 West Hastings Street
Vancouver, BC, V6B 1N2, Canada
Tel.: (604) 669-3143
Fax: (604) 669-3107
Toll Free: (800) 422-5141
E-Mail: info@earthworksinc.com
Web Site: www.earthworksinc.com
Year Founded: 1993
EWK—(TSXV)
Assets: $8,094,475
Liabilities: $6,972,191
Net Worth: $1,122,283
Earnings: ($2,655,855)
Fiscal Year-end: 11/30/12
Business Description:
Waste Management Services
S.I.C.: 4959
N.A.I.C.S.: 562998
Personnel:
David B. Atkinson *(Pres & CEO)*
Barbara Russell *(CFO)*
Carl Roland Jonsson *(Sec)*
Board of Directors:
David F. Andrews
David B. Atkinson
Giulio T. Bonifacio
Carl Roland Jonsson
David Scott
Transfer Agents:
Computershare Trust Company of Canada
100 University Avenue 9th Floor North Tower
Toronto, ON, Canada
Computershare Trust Company of Canada
510 Burrard St 2nd Fl
Vancouver, BC, Canada

EASON PAINT PUBLIC COMPANY LIMITED
7/1-2 Moo 1 Panthong Pantong
Chon Buri, 20160, Thailand
Tel.: (66) 3 845 1833
Fax: (66) 3 845 1825
E-Mail: info@easonpaint.co.th
Web Site: www.easonpaint.co.th
Year Founded: 1965
EASON—(THA)
Rev.: $21,996,315
Assets: $24,864,156
Liabilities: $4,099,374
Net Worth: $20,764,783
Earnings: $3,621,063
Fiscal Year-end: 12/31/12
Business Description:
Paint Mfr & Distr
S.I.C.: 2851
N.A.I.C.S.: 325510
Personnel:
Sanan Eksangkul *(Chm & CEO)*
Petcharat Eksangkul *(Mng Dir)*
Mum Annoppong *(Deputy Mng Dir)*
Nathapol Eksangkul *(Asst Mng Dir & Acting Mgr-HR)*
Sanit Eksangkul *(Deputy Mng Dir)*
Sirinun Eksangkul *(Asst Mng Dir)*
Wichai Eksangkul *(Deputy Mng Dir)*
Board of Directors:
Sanan Eksangkul
Pismai Boonyakiat
Petcharat Eksangkul
Sanit Eksangkul
Sirinun Eksangkul
Wichai Eksangkul
Vitien Nildum
Thipawan Uthaisang
Jane Wongisariyakul

EASSON TELECOM LIMITED

Room 1107 New Victory House
93-103 Wing Lok Street
Sheung Wan, China (Hong Kong)
Tel.: (852) 2851 8000
Fax: (852) 2892 1177
E-Mail: info@eassontelecom.com
Web Site: www.eassontelecom.com
Year Founded: 2003
MLEAS—(EUR)
Sales Range: Less than $1 Million

Business Description:
Mobile Value Added Services
S.I.C.: 4812
N.A.I.C.S.: 517210

Personnel:
Sylvester Sit *(Chm & CEO)*
Francis Yeung *(CFO)*
Patrick Leung *(COO)*
Rita Wu *(CTO)*

Board of Directors:
Sylvester Sit
Rey Chiu
Kersten Hui
Joseph Ma
Rita Wu

EASSONS TRANSPORT LIMITED

151 Foster St
PO Box 159
Berwick, NS, B0P 1E0, Canada
Tel.: (902) 538-8045
Fax: (902) 538-9677
Toll Free: (888) 276-2211
Web Site: www.eassons.com
Year Founded: 1945
Rev.: $21,013,557
Emp.: 146

Business Description:
Transportation Services
S.I.C.: 4789
N.A.I.C.S.: 488999

Personnel:
Paul Easson *(Pres)*

EAST AFRICA METALS INC.

3114 1055 Dunsmuir Street
Vancouver, BC, V7X 1G4, Canada
Tel.: (604) 488-0822
Fax: (604) 899-1240
Toll Free: (866) 488-0822
E-Mail: investors@eastafricametals.com
Web Site: www.eastafricametals.com
Year Founded: 2012
EAM—(TSXV)

Business Description:
Metal Mining
S.I.C.: 1099
N.A.I.C.S.: 212299

Personnel:
Jingbin Wang *(Chm)*
Andrew Lee Smith *(CEO)*
Peter Granata *(CFO)*

Board of Directors:
Jingbin Wang
Shuixing Fu
Antony Harwood
Andrew Lee Smith

Legal Counsel:
Cassels Brock & Blackwell LLP
2200 885 West Georgia Street
Vancouver, BC, Canada

EAST AFRICA RESOURCES LIMITED

288 Stirling Street
Perth, WA, 6000, Australia
Tel.: (61) 8 9227 3270
Fax: (61) 8 9227 3211
E-Mail: info@eastafricaresources.com.au
Web Site: www.eastafricaresources.com.au
EAF—(ASX)
Rev.: $173,206
Assets: $3,908,045
Liabilities: $467,439
Net Worth: $3,440,606
Earnings: ($4,061,946)
Fiscal Year-end: 06/30/13

Business Description:
Uranium & Other Metal Mining Services
S.I.C.: 1094
N.A.I.C.S.: 212291

Personnel:
Katina Law *(CEO)*
Peter Munachen *(CFO & Dir-Fin)*
Ernie Myers *(Co-Sec)*
Eva Witheridge *(Co-Sec)*

Board of Directors:
Lindsay Arthur Colless
David Kennedy
Katina Law
Peter Munachen
Gerard Zytkow

EAST AFRICAN CABLES LIMITED

(d/b/a E.A. Cables Limited/EAC)
Addis Ababa Road Industrial Area
PO Box 18243
Nairobi, 00500, Kenya
Tel.: (254) 206607000
Fax: (254) 20559310
E-Mail: info@eacables.com
Web Site: www.eacables.com
Year Founded: 1965
CABL—(NAI)
Rev.: $48,295,828
Assets: $70,172,250
Liabilities: $37,324,174
Net Worth: $32,848,076
Earnings: $5,862,734
Emp.: 100
Fiscal Year-end: 12/31/12

Business Description:
Copper & Aluminum Electrical Cables & Conductors Mfr
S.I.C.: 3357
N.A.I.C.S.: 335929

Personnel:
Zephaniah Gitau Mbugua *(Chm)*
George Mwangi *(CEO)*
Virginia Ndunge *(Sec)*

Board of Directors:
Zephaniah Gitau Mbugua
Peter Kanyago
Gachao Kiuna
George Mwangi
Bruno Thomas
Michael G. Waweru

Legal Counsel:
Muthaura Mugambi Ayugi & Njonjo Advocates
4th Floor, Capitol Hill Square Upper Hill
Nairobi, Kenya

Kaplan & Stratton Advocates
9th Floor, Williamson House 4th Ngong Avenue
Upper Hill
PO Box 40111
00100 Nairobi, Kenya

Non-U.S. Subsidiary:

Tanzania Daesung Cable Company (1)
Plot 31 Pugu Rd
PO Box 508
Dar es Salaam, Tanzania (51%)
Tel.: (255) 222862834
Fax: (255) 222862907
E-Mail: infotz@eacable.com
Web Site: www.eacable.com
Sls.: $2,500,000
Emp.: 43
Mfr of Copper & Aluminum Cables & Connectors
S.I.C.: 3357
N.A.I.C.S.: 335929
Joseph Hunja *(Mgr-Fin)*

EAST AFRICAN PORTLAND CEMENT COMPANY LIMITED

LR 337/113/1 Namanga Rd off Mombasa Rd
PO Box 20
00204 Athi River, Kenya
Tel.: (254) 456620627
Fax: (254) 456620406
E-Mail: info@eapcc.co.ke
Web Site: www.eastafricanportland.com
EAPC—(NAI)
Sales Range: $100-124.9 Million

Business Description:
Cement Mfr
S.I.C.: 2891
N.A.I.C.S.: 325520

Personnel:
Mark K. Ole Karbolo *(Chm)*
Kephar L. Tande *(Mng Dir)*
J. L. G. Maonga *(Sec)*

Board of Directors:
Mark K. Ole Karbolo
Alex Kazongo
K. H. W. Keith
Karanja Kibicho
J. L. G. Maonga
Titus T. Naikuni
Kephar L. Tande

Transfer Agent:
Haki Registrars
PO Box 40868-00100
Nairobi, Kenya

EAST & WEST ALUM CRAFT LTD.

7465 Conway Avenue
Burnaby, BC, Canada
Tel.: (604) 438-6261
Fax: (604) 438-4021
Toll Free: (800) 661-2773
E-Mail: info@ewalumcraft.com
Web Site: www.ewalumcraft.com
Year Founded: 1973
Rev.: $12,208,424
Emp.: 10

Business Description:
Architectural Metal Work Mfr
S.I.C.: 3449
N.A.I.C.S.: 332323

Personnel:
G. Zen *(Pres)*

EAST ASIA MINERALS CORP.

Suite 1588-609 Granville Street
Vancouver, BC, V7Y 1G5, Canada
Tel.: (604) 684-2183
Fax: (604) 357-1987
Toll Free: (888) 371-5832
E-Mail: info@eaminerals.com
Web Site: www.eaminerals.com
EAS—(OTC TSXV)
Int. Income: $66,026
Assets: $36,004,080
Liabilities: $931,477
Net Worth: $35,072,603
Earnings: ($9,286,505)
Fiscal Year-end: 08/31/13

Business Description:
Gold & Copper Mining
S.I.C.: 1041
N.A.I.C.S.: 212221

Personnel:
Peter U. Sederowsky *(Chm)*
Edward C. Rochette *(CEO)*
Michael Nayyar *(CFO)*

Board of Directors:
Peter U. Sederowsky
David H. Anthony
Ed R. Flood
Edward C. Rochette
David M. Stein
Thomas S. Weng

Legal Counsel:
Fang & Associates
Suite 300 - 576 Seymour Street
Vancouver, BC, Canada

Transfer Agent:
Computershare
510 Burrard St 2nd Floor
Vancouver, BC, Canada

THE EAST ASIATIC COMPANY LTD. A/S

(d/b/a EAC)
East Asiatic House 20 Indiakaj
DK 2100 Copenhagen, Denmark
Tel.: (45) 35254300
Fax: (45) 35254313
E-Mail: eac@eac.dk
Web Site: www.eac.dk
Year Founded: 1897
EAC—(CSE)
Rev.: $1,469,032,200
Assets: $1,258,732,440
Liabilities: $692,943,120
Net Worth: $565,789,320
Earnings: $33,005,880
Emp.: 6,620
Fiscal Year-end: 12/31/12

Business Description:
Holding Company; Food Products Distr; Specialty Chemicals Marketer; Moving & Storage Services Export
S.I.C.: 6719
N.A.I.C.S.: 551112

Personnel:
Henning Kruse Petersen *(Chm)*
Preben Sunke *(Deputy Chm)*
Niels Henrik Jensen *(Pres & CEO)*
Michael Osterlund Madsen *(CFO)*
Bent Ulrik Porsborg *(Pres-Plumrose Latinoamericana & Sr VP-EAC)*

Board of Directors:
Henning Kruse Petersen
Connie Astrup-Larsen
Mats Lonnqvist
Preben Sunke

Subsidiaries:

EAC Consumer Products Ltd. APS (1)
Indiakaj 20
Copenhagen, 2100, Denmark (100%)
Tel.: (45) 35254300
Fax: (45) 35254313
Web Site: www.eastasiatic.com —(CSE)
Emp.: 10
S.I.C.: 5084
N.A.I.C.S.: 425120
Niels Hendrick Jinsin *(CEO)*

Santa Fe Group Holding Ltd. A/S (1)
Indiakaj 20
2100 Copenhagen, Denmark
Tel.: (45) 35254300
Fax: (45) 35254313
Emp.: 1
Investment Management Services
S.I.C.: 6211
N.A.I.C.S.: 523999
Niels Henrik Jensen *(Gen Mgr)*

Non-U.S. Subsidiaries:

Briscoe Timber Limited (1)
16 18 Fatai Atere Way
PO Box 2104
Matori Industrial Scheme Lagos, Oshodi, Nigeria (80.5%)
Tel.: (234) 14520564
Fax: (234) 4524519
S.I.C.: 5084
N.A.I.C.S.: 425120

Domino Coding Ltd. (1)
Beijing Tianzhu Airport Industrial Zone
12 Tianzhu West Street, 101312 Beijing, China (50%)
Tel.: (86) 21 5050 9999
Fax: (86) 21 5032 9901

E-Mail: marketing@domino.com.cn
Web Site: www.domino.com.cn
Mfr & Supplier of Industrial Inks & Laser Printing Equipment
S.I.C.: 2893
N.A.I.C.S.: 325910
Kevin An *(Reg Mgr-Sls)*

EAC Chemicals Singapore Pte. Ltd. (1)
47 Scotts Rd 06 00
Goldbell Towers, Singapore, 228233, Singapore (100%)
Tel.: (65) 62139095
Fax: (65) 62139090
Emp.: 50
S.I.C.: 7389
N.A.I.C.S.: 425120

EAC (Philippines) Inc. (1)
3rd Fl IDC Bldg E Rodrigues Jr Ave
Bo Ugong Norte Libis
Quezon City, Philippines (92.6%)
Tel.: (63) 26381818
Fax: (63) 26387811
E-Mail: nutrition@dumex.com.ph
Develop & Market Nutritional Food Products
S.I.C.: 7389
N.A.I.C.S.: 425120

The East Asiatic 2010 (Thailand) Company Ltd. (1)
1168/98-100 Lumpini Tower 33rd Floor
Rama IV Road Thungmahamek Sathorn
Bangkok, 10120, Thailand
Tel.: (66) 2 689 5999
Industrial Machinery Mfr
S.I.C.: 3559
N.A.I.C.S.: 333249

Empacadora Ecuatoriano Danesa (ECUADASA) S.A. (1)
Avenida Pedro J Menendez Gilbert
Apartado 09-01-6368, Guayaquil, Ecuador (53.5%)
Tel.: (593) 42288500
Fax: (593) 42280951
E-Mail: ecuadasa@plumrose.com.ec
Web Site: www.eac.com
S.I.C.: 5084
N.A.I.C.S.: 425120

Griffin Travel (HK) Ltd. (1)
1701 7 Fl CC Wu Bldg 302 306
Wanchai, China (Hong Kong) (25%)
Tel.: (852) 28335083
Fax: (852) 25748563
E-Mail: info@griffintravel.com
Web Site: www.griffintravel.com
Emp.: 20
S.I.C.: 5084
N.A.I.C.S.: 425120
Elveit Jfeung *(Gen Mgr)*

Heidelberg Hong Kong (1)
Unit 1605-1616 Metropolis Tower 10
Metropolis Drive
Hunghom, Kowloon, China (Hong Kong) (100%)
Tel.: (852) 28142300
Fax: (852) 28736106
E-Mail: online.hcn@heidelberg.com
Web Site: www.heidelberg.com
Importer, Marketer & Distributor of Machinery, Equipment & Consumer Products
S.I.C.: 5084
N.A.I.C.S.: 423830

Interdean Auguste Daleiden Sarl (1)
Allee de la Poudrerie
1899 Kockelscheuer, Luxembourg
Tel.: (352) 48 44 22
Fax: (352) 40 29 79
Emp.: 6
Relocation Service
S.I.C.: 9721
N.A.I.C.S.: 928120
Nicholas Sepulchre *(Gen Mgr)*

Interdean Bulgaria EOOD (1)
Kv Orlandovtzi Blvd First Bulgarian Army
Sofia, 1225, Bulgaria
Tel.: (359) 2 9366203
Fax: (359) 2 9367214
E-Mail: sofia@interdean.com
Emp.: 5
Relocation Service
S.I.C.: 9721
N.A.I.C.S.: 928120
Anton Vangelov *(Gen Mgr)*

Interdean B.V. (1)
Albert Einsteinweg 12
2408 AR Alphen aan den Rijn, Netherlands
Tel.: (31) 172 447979
Fax: (31) 172 447974
E-Mail: main@interdean.com
Web Site: www.interdean.nl
Relocation Service
S.I.C.: 9721
N.A.I.C.S.: 928120

Interdean Central Asia LLC (1)
103 Furmanova 8th Fl Office 836
50000 Almaty, Kazakhstan
Tel.: (7) 727 272 52 51
Fax: (7) 727 333 44 29
Emp.: 25
Relocation Service
S.I.C.: 9721
N.A.I.C.S.: 928120
Stanislav Zyukov *(Mng Dir)*

Interdean D.O.O (1)
III Nova 28
Dobanovci, 11272 Belgrade, Serbia
Tel.: (381) 11 35 36 350
Fax: (381) 11 35 36 352
E-Mail: belgrade@interdean.com
Emp.: 6
Relocation Service
S.I.C.: 9721
N.A.I.C.S.: 928120
Vesna Dragic *(Mgr)*

Interdean Eastern Europe Ges.m.b.H (1)
Eitnergasse 5
1230 Vienna, Austria
Tel.: (43) 1 865 4706
Fax: (43) 1907616820
Web Site: www.Interdean.com
Emp.: 4
Relocation Services
S.I.C.: 9721
N.A.I.C.S.: 928120
Dale Collins *(Gen Mgr)*

Interdean Holdings Limited (1)
Central Way Park Royal Brent
London, NW10 7XW, United Kingdom
Tel.: (44) 2089632500
Investment Management Services
S.I.C.: 6211
N.A.I.C.S.: 523999

Interdean Hungaria Nemzetkozi Koltozteto Kft (1)
Szallito UTCA 6
1211 Budapest, Hungary
Tel.: (36) 1888 6750
Fax: (36) 1277 2877
E-Mail: budapest@interdean.com
Emp.: 1
Relocation Services
S.I.C.: 9721
N.A.I.C.S.: 928120
Anthony Heszberger *(Mgr)*

Interdean Int' Movers s.r.l. (1)
Via Zenale 82
20024 Garbagnate Milanese, Italy
Tel.: (39) 02 9955649
Fax: (39) 02 9953055
E-Mail: milan@interdean.com
Web Site: www.interdean.com
Relocation Services
S.I.C.: 9721
N.A.I.C.S.: 928120

Interdean International Relocation SA (1)
Centro Empresarial Sintra Estoril I
Armazem Q Estrada de Albarraque
Linho, 2710-297 Sintra, Portugal
Tel.: (351) 219 245 050
Fax: (351) 219 240 170
E-Mail: lisbon@interdean.com
Emp.: 15
Relocation Service
S.I.C.: 9721
N.A.I.C.S.: 928120
Isabel Delgado *(Area Mgr)*

Interdean International Relocation Ukraine LLC (1)
34 Chervonohvardiiska Street
Kiev, 2094, Ukraine
Tel.: (380) 44 576 73 70
Fax: (380) 44 559 13 22
E-Mail: kiev@interdean.com
Web Site: www.interdean.com
Emp.: 15
Relocation Services
S.I.C.: 9721
N.A.I.C.S.: 928120
Marina Chornokozha *(Gen Mgr)*

Interdean Internationale Spedition Ges.m.b.H (1)
Eitnerg 5
1230 Vienna, Austria
Tel.: (43) 1 8654706 0
Fax: (43) 1 8654708
E-Mail: vienna@interdean.com
Web Site: www.interdean.com
Emp.: 6
Relocation Service
S.I.C.: 9721
N.A.I.C.S.: 928120
Axel Miller *(Mgr)*

Interdean Limited (1)
Ismail Qutkashenli Str 99/16
AZ1073 Baku, Azerbaijan
Tel.: (994) 12 447 4346
Fax: (994) 12 510 4931
E-Mail: baku@interdean.com
Web Site: www.interdean.com
Emp.: 10
Relocation Services
S.I.C.: 9721
N.A.I.C.S.: 928120
Vagiv Samosud *(Mgr)*

Interdean Relocation Services GmbH (1)
Haupstr 7
14979 Grossbeeren, Germany
Tel.: (49) 33701 213
Fax: (49) 33701 21555
E-Mail: berlin@interdean.com
Web Site: www.interdean.com
Emp.: 15
Relocation Services
S.I.C.: 4731
N.A.I.C.S.: 541614
Ralf Kessel *(Mgr)*

Interdean Relocation Services NV (1)
Jan-Baptist Vinkstraat 9
3070 Kortenberg, Belgium
Tel.: (32) 2 757 9285
Fax: (32) 2 757 93 79
E-Mail: brussels@interdean.com
Emp.: 3
Relocation Services
S.I.C.: 9721
N.A.I.C.S.: 928120
Jesse van Sas *(Mng Dir)*

Interdean SA (1)
Im Langhag 9
Effretikon, 8307 Zurich, Switzerland
Tel.: (41) 52 355 36 36
Fax: (41) 52 355 3637
E-Mail: zurich@interdean.com
Web Site: www.interdean.com
Relocation Service
S.I.C.: 9721
N.A.I.C.S.: 928120
Roger Graf *(Mgr)*

Interdean Sp. Z.o.o (1)
Ul Geodetow 172
05500 Piaseczno, Poland
Tel.: (48) 227017171
Fax: (48) 227017177
E-Mail: warsaw@interdean.com
Relocation Service
S.I.C.: 9721
N.A.I.C.S.: 928120

Interdean, spol s.r.o (1)
6 Ruzyne U Silnice 949
161 00 Prague, Czech Republic
Tel.: (420) 2 3331 3157
Fax: (420) 2 3331 3156
E-Mail: prague@interdean.com
Emp.: 2
Relocation Services
S.I.C.: 9721
N.A.I.C.S.: 928120
Michael Vincenec *(Mgr)*

Interdean Srl (1)
Str Migdalului No 38 Sector 6
60592 Bucharest, Romania
Tel.: (40) 21 220 11 68
Fax: (40) 21 220 70 43
E-Mail: bucharest@interdean.com
Emp.: 5
Relocation Service
S.I.C.: 9721
N.A.I.C.S.: 928120
Cristian Borcos *(Gen Mgr)*

Interdean SRO (1)
Agatova 22
84103 Bratislava, Slovakia
Tel.: (421) 252632447 9
E-Mail: bratislava@interdean.com
Emp.: 7
Relocation Services
S.I.C.: 9721
N.A.I.C.S.: 928120
Anthony Heszberger *(Mng Dir)*

MY Associates Ltd (1)
216 Bogyoke Aung San Rd
PO Box 11161
Botahtaung Township, Yangon, Myanmar (100%)
Tel.: (95) 1392502
Fax: (95) 1392571
E-Mail: myassoco@mptmail.net.mn
Web Site: www.myassoco.asia
Equipment Distr
S.I.C.: 7389
N.A.I.C.S.: 425120

Plumrose Caracas C.A. (1)
Prolongacion Av Trieste Con Calle Miranda
Edf Plumrose Urb
Los Ruices Sur, Caracas, 1060, Venezuela
Tel.: (58) 212 2738711
Fax: (58) 212 2738820
E-Mail:
Meat Products Distr
S.I.C.: 5147
N.A.I.C.S.: 424470

Plumrose Latinoamericana C.A. (1)
Edificio Plumrose Urbanizacion Los Ruices
Sur Ave Trieste Con
Calle Miranda Piso 2, Caracas, 1060, Venezuela (100%)
Tel.: (58) 2122738711
Fax: (58) 2122560025
E-Mail: info@eac.com
Web Site: www.eac.com
Emp.: 100
S.I.C.: 7389
N.A.I.C.S.: 425120
Bent Porsborg *(Pres)*

PT Santa Fe Indonusa (1)
Building 208 Cilandak Commercial Estate Jl
Raya Cilandak KKO
Jakarta, 12560, Indonesia
Tel.: (62) 21 789 2033
Fax: (62) 21 789 2034
E-Mail: sales@santaferelo.co.id
Relocation Services
S.I.C.: 4731
N.A.I.C.S.: 541614
Jason Will *(Mng Dir)*

Santa Fe Holdings Ltd. (1)
18/F C C Wu Bldg 302 - 308 Hennessy Rd
Wanchai, China (Hong Kong)
Tel.: (852) 25746204
Fax: (852) 25740454
Investment Management Services
S.I.C.: 6799
N.A.I.C.S.: 523920

Santa Fe India Private Limited (1)
1189/C 13th Main HAL II Stage
Indiranagar, Bengaluru, 560 008, India
Tel.: (91) 80 40522222
Fax: (91) 80 41269269
E-Mail: immigration@santafe.in
Web Site: www.santafe.in
Emp.: 45
Relocation Services
S.I.C.: 9721
N.A.I.C.S.: 928120
Kim Becker *(Mng Dir)*

Santa Fe Moving and Relocation Services Phils., Inc. (1)
Unit 2 & 3 1st Avenue
Manalac, Taguig, Metro Manila, 1604, Philippines
Tel.: (63) 2 838 1761
Fax: (63) 2 838 8190
E-Mail: santafe.manila@santafe.com.ph

The East Asiatic Company Ltd. A/S—(Continued)

Web Site: www.santaferelo.com
Emp.: 10
Relocation & Immigration Services
S.I.C.: 9721
N.A.I.C.S.: 928120
Vedit Kurangil *(Mng Dir)*

Santa Fe Relocation Services Japan K.K. **(1)**
AB Bldg 6th Floor 3-1-17 Roppongi
Minato-ku, Tokyo, 106-0032, Japan
Tel.: (81) 3 3589 6666
Fax: (81) 3 3589 0420
E-Mail: santafe@santafejapan.co.jp
Web Site: www.santafejapan.co.jp
Relocation Service
S.I.C.: 9721
N.A.I.C.S.: 928120
Scott Erickson *(Gen Mgr)*

Santa Fe Relocation Services Korea Co. Ltd. **(1)**
5/F J-Tower 373-35 Sindang-dong
Jung-gu, Seoul, Korea (South)
Tel.: (82) 2 2234 3383
Fax: (82) 2 797 3386
E-Mail: korea@santaferelo.co.kr
Relocation & Immigration Services
S.I.C.: 9721
N.A.I.C.S.: 928120
Jamie Wong *(Gen Mgr)*

Santa Fe Relocation Services LLC **(1)**
Warsan Building 501 Tecom
PO Box 125478
Dubai, United Arab Emirates
Tel.: (971) 4454 2724
Fax: (971) 4454 2726
Web Site: www.santaferelo.com
Emp.: 3
Relocation & Immigration Services
S.I.C.: 9721
N.A.I.C.S.: 928120
Kim Creutzburg *(Mng Dir)*

Santa Fe Relocation Services Sdn. Bhd. **(1)**
No 4 Jalan Pengarah U1/29 Hicom-Glenmarie Industrial Park
40150 Shah Alam, Selangor, Malaysia
Tel.: (60) 3 7805 4322
Fax: (60) 3 7805 3766
E-Mail: info@santafe.com.my
Web Site: www.santaferelo.com
Relocation & Immigration Services
S.I.C.: 9721
N.A.I.C.S.: 928120
Robert Cormier *(Mng Dir)*

Santa Fe Relocation Services Taiwan Co., Ltd **(1)**
13F-4 No 141 Sec 1 Keelung Road
Xinyi District, Taipei, 11070, Taiwan
Tel.: (886) 2 2749 4420
Fax: (886) 2 2749 4039
E-Mail: sales@santaferelo.com.tw
Web Site: www.santaferelo.com
Relocation Services
S.I.C.: 9721
N.A.I.C.S.: 928120
Jim Hill *(Gen Mgr)*

Santa Fe Relocation Services **(1)**
8th Fl Thien Son Bldg 5 Nguyen Gia Thieu St
Dist 3, Ho Chi Minh City, Vietnam
Tel.: (84) 8 3933 0065
Fax: (84) 8 3930 5889
E-Mail: info@santaferelo.com.vn
Web Site: www.santaferelo.com
Emp.: 40
Relocation Services
S.I.C.: 9721
N.A.I.C.S.: 928120
Binh Vo *(Gen Dir)*

Santa Fe Transport International Limited **(1)**
18 Fl C C Wu Bldg
302 308 Hennessy Rd, Wanchai, China (Hong Kong) (100%)
Tel.: (852) 25746204
Fax: (852) 28345380
Web Site: www.santaferelo.com
Emp.: 250
S.I.C.: 7389
N.A.I.C.S.: 425120
Lars Lykke Iversen *(CEO)*

Subsidiary:

Santa Fe International Projects Limited **(2)**
18 F C C Wu Bldg
302 308 Hennessy Rd, Hong Kong, China (Hong Kong) (100%)
Tel.: (852) 25746204
Fax: (852) 25751907
Web Site: www.santaferelo.com
Emp.: 250
S.I.C.: 7389
N.A.I.C.S.: 425120
Lance Allen *(Mng Dir)*

Non-U.S. Subsidiaries:

Interdean International Ltd. **(2)**
Central Way Park Royal
NW10 7XW London, United Kingdom
Tel.: (44) 2089614141
Fax: (44) 2089654484
E-Mail: london@interdean.com
Web Site: www.interdean.com
Sales Range: $200-249.9 Million
Emp.: 160
Freight Forwarding Services
S.I.C.: 4731
N.A.I.C.S.: 488510
Dale Collins *(CEO)*

Santa Fe Relocation Services Singapore Pvt. Ltd. **(2)**
54 Pandan Rd
Singapore, 609292, Singapore (100%)
Tel.: (65) 63988588
Fax: (65) 62650245
E-Mail: sales@santafe.com.sg
Web Site: www.santaferelo.com
Sales Range: $10-24.9 Million
Emp.: 159
S.I.C.: 7389
N.A.I.C.S.: 425120
Bill Cain *(Mng Dir)*

Santa Fe (Thailand) ltd. **(2)**
207 Soi Saeng Uthai 50 Sukhumvit Rd
Kwang Prakanong Khet Klongtoey, 10110
Bangkok, Thailand (100%)
Tel.: (66) 27429890
Fax: (66) 27414089
E-Mail: santafe@santafe.co.th
Web Site: www.santaferelo.com
Emp.: 97
Relocation Service
S.I.C.: 4225
N.A.I.C.S.: 493110

Santa Fe Van Lines Co. Ltd. **(2)**
Beijing, China (95%)
Industrial Machinery & Equipment
S.I.C.: 5084
N.A.I.C.S.: 423830

Sino Santa Fe International Services Corporation **(2)**
2F Block J Eask Lk Villas
35 Dongzhimenwai Main St, Beijing, 100027, China (50%)
Tel.: (86) 1084516666
Fax: (86) 1084518118
Web Site: www.santaferelo.com
Emp.: 350
S.I.C.: 7389
N.A.I.C.S.: 425120
Chad Forrest *(Gen Mgr)*

Wridgways Australia Limited **(2)**
26-40 Nina Link
Dandenong, VIC, 3175, Australia
Mailing Address:
PO Box 4055
Dandenong, VIC, 3164, Australia
Tel.: (61) 395547300
Fax: (61) 387687911
E-Mail: Melbourne@wridgways.com.au
Web Site: www.wridgways.com.au
Sales Range: $100-124.9 Million
Removal & Storage Services
S.I.C.: 5085
N.A.I.C.S.: 423840
Desmond F. Stickland *(CEO & Mng Dir)*
Brian C. Clarke *(Sec & Dir-Fin)*

Division:

Wridgways Australia Limited - Wridgways Move Solutions **(3)**
Ste 302 Level 3 697 Burke Rd
Camberwell, VIC, 3124, Australia
Tel.: (61) 398823400
Fax: (61) 398823411
E-Mail: enquiry@wridgways.com.au
Web Site: www.wridgwaysmovesolutions.com.au
Emp.: 10
Relocation Services
S.I.C.: 7389
N.A.I.C.S.: 561499
Steven Crowle *(Gen Mgr)*

Subsidiaries:

Wridgways Business Relocations Pty Limited **(3)**
2 2nd Avenue Moorabbin Airport
Mentone, VIC, 3194, Australia
Tel.: (61) 395837000
Fax: (61) 395839000
Emp.: 15
Business Relocation Services
S.I.C.: 8999
N.A.I.C.S.: 541612
Steve McIlroy *(Gen Mgr)*

Wridgways Limited **(3)**
5-21 Oxenham St
Dudley Park, Adelaide, SA, 5008, Australia
Tel.: (61) 882695566
Fax: (61) 882697566
E-Mail: adelaide@wridgways.com.au
Emp.: 50
Packing & Moving Services
S.I.C.: 4212
N.A.I.C.S.: 484210
Uwe Sauer *(Gen Mgr)*

Subsidiary:

Movedynamics **(4)**
14 Epic Pl
Villawood, NSW, 2163, Australia
Tel.: (61) 296457744
Fax: (61) 296457755
E-Mail: contactus@movedynamics.com.au
Web Site: www.movedynamics.com.au
Emp.: 2
Removal Brokerage Services
S.I.C.: 4214
N.A.I.C.S.: 484210
Oliver Kuck *(Mgr)*

Sino Santa Fe Real Estate (Beijing) Co. Ltd. **(1)**
Rm 1307 West Tower Guangzhou International Commercial Center No122
Tiyu Dong Rd, Guangzhou, 510620, China
Tel.: (86) 2038870630
Fax: (86) 2038870629
Emp.: 4
Real Estate Management Services
S.I.C.: 6531
N.A.I.C.S.: 531390
Eva Huang *(Branch Mgr)*

Southland Veneers Ltd. **(1)**
9 Matheson Rd Kennington
Invercargill, Southland, New Zealand (66.7%)
Tel.: (64) 32304820
Fax: (64) 32304410
E-Mail: info@southlandveneers.co.nz
Emp.: 25
S.I.C.: 7389
N.A.I.C.S.: 425120
Hans Jensen *(Mng Dir)*

Thai Poly Acrylic Public Company Ltd. **(1)**
Sathon Highlight 134 5 Krung Thonburi Rd
Bangkok, Klongtonsai, 10600, Thailand (16.67%)
Tel.: (66) 28608765
Fax: (66) 28609106
Web Site: www.thaipolyacrylic.com
Emp.: 300
S.I.C.: 7389
N.A.I.C.S.: 425120
Suchirt Srivetbodee *(Mng Dir)*

EAST BALKAN PROPERTIES PLC

Dixcart House Sir William Place
Saint Peter Port, GY1 4EZ, Guernsey
Tel.: (44) 1481 738723
E-Mail: info@ebp-plc.com
Web Site: www.ebp-plc.com
Sales Range: $1-9.9 Million
Business Description:
Investment Services
S.I.C.: 6211
N.A.I.C.S.: 523999
Personnel:
Philip Scales *(Sec)*
Board of Directors:
James Ede-Golightly
Mark Butcher
Graham Smith
Pradeep Verma
Legal Counsel:
Gibson, Dunn & Crutcher LLP
2 4 Temple Ave
London, United Kingdom

EAST BUILDTECH LTD

D-3/2 Okhla Industrial Area Phase-II
New Delhi, 110 020, India
Tel.: (91) 11 47105100
Fax: (91) 11 41615273
E-Mail: secretarial@ebl.co.in
Web Site: www.ebl.co.in
Year Founded: 1984
507917—(BOM)
Rev.: $230,916
Assets: $1,431,084
Liabilities: $302,462
Net Worth: $1,128,623
Earnings: $36,079
Fiscal Year-end: 03/31/13
Business Description:
Real Estate Development Services
S.I.C.: 6531
N.A.I.C.S.: 531390
Personnel:
Madhusudan Chokhani *(Chm, Mng Dir & Compliance Officer)*
Board of Directors:
Madhusudan Chokhani
Vivek Garg
Suresh Kumar Goenka
Transfer Agent:
Beetal Financial & Computer Services Pvt Ltd
Beetal House 3rd Floor 99 Madangir Near Dada Harsukh Das Mandir
New Delhi, 110062, India

EAST CAPITAL EXPLORER AB

Kungsgatan 33
PO Box 7214
Sverige, 10388 Stockholm, Sweden
Tel.: (46) 850597700
Fax: (46) 850597706
E-Mail: info@eastcapitalexplorer.com
Web Site: www.eastcapitalexplorer.com
Year Founded: 2007
ECEX—(OMX)
Rev.: $41,394,728
Assets: $475,739,170
Liabilities: $11,803,219
Net Worth: $463,935,952
Earnings: $26,317,624
Emp.: 5
Fiscal Year-end: 12/31/12
Business Description:
Equity Funds Investment Services
S.I.C.: 6722
N.A.I.C.S.: 525910
Personnel:
Paul Bergqvist *(Chm)*
Mia Jurke *(CEO)*
Mathias Pedersen *(CFO)*
Stefano Grace *(Gen Counsel)*
Board of Directors:
Paul Bergqvist
Lars O. Gronstedt
Louise Hedberg
Karine Hirn
Alexander V. Ilkonnikov

EAST COAST FURNITECH PUBLIC COMPANY LIMITED

37/9 Moo 3 Banbung-Klaeng Rd
Klaeng, Rayong, 21110, Thailand
Tel.: (66) 38671361
Fax: (66) 38886375
Web Site: www.eastcoast.co.th
ECF—(THA)
Business Description:
Wood Furniture Mfr & Distr
S.I.C.: 2511
N.A.I.C.S.: 337122
Personnel:
Thoedsak Marom *(Chm)*

EAST COAST INVESTMENT GRADE INCOME FUND

c/o Arrow Capital Management Inc.
36 Toronto Street Suite 750
Toronto, ON, M5C 2C5, Canada
Tel.: (416) 323-0477
Fax: (416) 323-3199
E-Mail: rparsons@arrow-capital.com
Year Founded: 2012
ECF.UN—(TSX)
Business Description:
Investment Services
S.I.C.: 6211
N.A.I.C.S.: 523999
Personnel:
James McGovern *(Chm & CEO)*
Robert Maxwell *(CFO & Sec)*
Robert Parsons *(COO)*
Board of Directors:
James McGovern
Frederick Dalley
Robert Maxwell
Mark Purdy
Transfer Agent:
Equity Financial Trust Company
Toronto, ON, Canada

EAST-COURT FORD LINCOLN SALES

4700 Sheppard Avenue East
Toronto, ON, M1S3V6, Canada
Tel.: (416) 292-1171
Fax: (416) 292-3342
Web Site: www.east-court.dealerconnection.com
Sales Range: $25-49.9 Million
Emp.: 62
Business Description:
New & Used Car Dealers
S.I.C.: 5511
N.A.I.C.S.: 441110
Personnel:
Prince Sibal *(Gen Mgr)*

EAST ENERGY RESOURCES LIMITED

Level 1 12 Kings Park Road
West Perth, WA, 6005, Australia
Mailing Address:
PO Box 44
West Perth, WA, 6872, Australia
Tel.: (61) 8 9225 5833
Fax: (61) 8 9225 7311
E-Mail: info@eastenergy.com.au
Web Site: www.eastenergy.com.au
EER—(ASX)
Rev.: $884,598
Assets: $77,267,667
Liabilities: $20,399,090
Net Worth: $56,868,578
Earnings: ($3,213,491)
Emp.: 3
Fiscal Year-end: 06/30/13
Business Description:
Coal Exploration & Development
S.I.C.: 1222
N.A.I.C.S.: 212112
Personnel:
Mark Basso-Brusa *(Chm & Mng Dir)*
Andrea Betti *(CFO)*
Ranko Matic *(Sec)*
Board of Directors:
Mark Basso-Brusa
Rex Littlewood
Ranko Matic
Legal Counsel:
Nova Legal
Ground Floor 10 Ord Street
West Perth, WA, Australia
Jackson McDonald Lawyers
140 St Georges Terrace
Perth, Australia

EAST JAPAN MARKETING & COMMUNICATIONS, INC.

JR Ebisu Building 1-5-5 Ebisu-Minami
Shibuya-ku, Tokyo, 150-8508, Japan
Tel.: (81) 3 5447 7800
Fax: (81) 3 5447 7810
E-Mail: info@jeki.co.jp
Web Site: www.jeki.co.jp
Year Founded: 1988
Sales Range: $900-999.9 Million
Emp.: 637
Business Description:
Advertising Services
S.I.C.: 7311
N.A.I.C.S.: 541810
Personnel:
Nobuyuki Sasaki *(Pres)*
Akira Misawa *(Sr Mng Dir)*
Syunichi Rouyama *(Mng Dir)*
Hiroyuki Iwabuchi *(Mng Dir)*
Shuji Kurimoto *(Mng Dir & Deputy Chief-Acct Svcs-Headquarters & JR Div)*
Board of Directors:
Masato Endo
Hiroyuki Iwabuchi
Yuji Kondo
Shuji Kurimoto
Tetsushiro Matsuzaki
Seishirou Morikawa
Jun Sakurai
Nobuyuki Sasaki
Syunichiro Satou
Yoshinobu Suzuki
Tetsu Takeda
Toshihiko Yamaguchi

EAST JAPAN RAILWAY COMPANY

(d/b/a JR East Group)
2-2 Yoyogi 2-chome
Shibuya-ku, Tokyo, 151-8578, Japan
Tel.: (81) 3 5334 1310
Fax: (81) 3 5334 1297
E-Mail: ir@jreast.co.jp
Web Site: www.jreast.co.jp
Year Founded: 1987
9020—(TKS)
Rev.: $29,390,053,000
Assets: $79,455,255,000
Liabilities: $56,925,132,000
Net Worth: $22,530,123,000
Earnings: $1,929,235,000
Emp.: 73,017
Fiscal Year-end: 03/31/13
Business Description:
Holding Company; Passenger & Freight Railway, Shopping Centers & Hotels Operator
S.I.C.: 6719
N.A.I.C.S.: 551112
Personnel:
Satoshi Seino *(Chm)*
Masaki Ogata *(Vice Chm-Tech & Overseas Related Affairs)*
Tetsuro Tomita *(Pres & CEO)*
Toshiro Ichinose *(Dir Gen-Corp Plng-Inquiry, Audit Dept & Fin Dept)*
Yuji Morimoto *(Dir Gen-Life-Style Bus Dev-Personnel, Health & Welfare Dept)*
Masahiko Nakai *(Mng Dir)*
Yoshitaka Taura *(Dir Gen-IT & Suica Bus Dev-PR, Legal & Gen Affairs Dept)*
Naomichi Yagishita *(Dir Gen-Railway Ops)*
Tsukasa Haraguchi *(Deputy Dir Gen-Railway Ops)*
Osamu Kawanobe *(Deputy Dir Gen-Railway Ops-Transport Safety Dept)*
Takashi Sawamoto *(Deputy Dir Gen-Railway Ops-Info Sys Plng Dept)*
Yuji Fukasawa *(Exec VP)*
Tsugio Sekiji *(Exec VP)*
Board of Directors:
Satoshi Seino
Hidemi Deguchi
Yuji Fukasawa
Tomokazu Hamaguchi
Tsukasa Haraguchi
Toshiro Ichinose
Osamu Kawanobe
Yuji Morimoto
Masahiko Nakai
Masaki Ogata
Takeshi Sasaki
Takashi Sawamoto
Tsugio Sekiji
Makoto Takahashi
Yoshitaka Taura
Tetsuro Tomita
Yasuyoshi Umehara
Naomichi Yagishita
Transfer Agent:
Mitsubishi UFJ Trust & Banking Corporation
4-5 Marunouchi 1-Chome Chiyoda-ku
Tokyo, 100-8212, Japan
Tel.: (81) 3 3212 1211

Subsidiaries:

JR East Japan Information Systems Company **(1)**
JR East Head Office Building 9th Floor
2-2-2 Yoyogi
Shibuya-ku, Tokyo, 151 0053, Japan JP
Tel.: (81) 332991258 (100%)
Fax: (81) 333788317
Web Site: www.jeis.co.jp/e/index.html
Emp.: 1,378
Development & Operation of Information Processing Systems; Information Services; Consulting Services
S.I.C.: 7389
N.A.I.C.S.: 519190
Teruo Kobayashi *(Pres)*

JR East Net Station Co., Ltd. **(1)**
JR East Japan Head Office Bldg 10th Floor
2-2-2 Yoyogi Shibuya-ku, Tokyo,
Japan JP
Tel.: (81) 353331576 (100%)
Fax: (81) 353331578
E-Mail: info@jrnets.com
Web Site: www.jrnets.com
Information Processing
S.I.C.: 7389
N.A.I.C.S.: 519190

JR East Retail Net Co., Ltd. **(1)**
Tetsudo Kosei Kaikan 5-1 Kojimachi
Chiyoda-ku, Tokyo, Japan (100%)
Tel.: (81) 352756713
Emp.: 2,000
Convenience Store & News Stand Operator
S.I.C.: 5411
N.A.I.C.S.: 445120

Nippon Hotel Co. Ltd. **(1)**
2-2 Yoyogi 2-chome
Shibuya-ku, Tokyo, 151-8578, Japan JP
Tel.: (81) 3 3239 8522 (100%)
Web Site: www.jrhotelgroup.com
Holding Company; Hotel Network Operator
S.I.C.: 6719
N.A.I.C.S.: 551112
Tetsuro Tomita, *(Pres & CEO)*

Subsidiary:

Hotel Metropolitan Nagano Co., Ltd. **(2)**
1346 Minami-ishido-cho
Nagano, 380-0824, Japan JP
Tel.: (81) 26 291 7000
Fax: (81) 26 291 7007
Web Site: www.metro-n.co.jp
Hotel Operator
S.I.C.: 7011
N.A.I.C.S.: 721110

Unit:

Hotel Metropolitan Tokyo **(2)**
1-6-1 Nishi Ikebukuro
Toshima-ku, Tokyo, 171-8505, Japan
Tel.: (81) 3 3980 1111
Fax: (81) 3 3980 5600
E-Mail: info@metropolitan.jp
Web Site: www.metropolitan.jp
Hotel Operator
S.I.C.: 7011
N.A.I.C.S.: 721110

U.S. Representative Office:

East Japan Railway Company - New York Office **(1)**
1 Rockefeller Plz Ste 1410
New York, NY 10020
Tel.: (212) 332-8686
Fax: (212) 332-8690
E-Mail:
Representative Office
S.I.C.: 8741
N.A.I.C.S.: 551114

EAST MONEY INFORMATION CO., LTD.

1 2999 Baoan Road
Jiading District, Shanghai, 201800, China
Tel.: (86) 2164382978
Fax: (86) 2164389508
Web Site: www.eastmoney.com
300059—(CHIN)
Sales Range: $25-49.9 Million
Business Description:
Financial Network Platform
S.I.C.: 7374
N.A.I.C.S.: 518210
Personnel:
Jun Chen *(Chm)*

EAST OCEAN OILS & GRAINS INDUSTRIES

Jingang
215634 Zhangjiagang, China
Tel.: (86) 51258381018
Fax: (86) 51258388520
Web Site: www.eogi.com.cn
Sales Range: $1-4.9 Billion
Emp.: 2,000
Business Description:
Oil & Grain Processing Services
S.I.C.: 2079
N.A.I.C.S.: 311225
Personnel:
Xu Xingping *(Gen Mgr)*

EAST WEST INSURANCE CO., LTD.

410-414 EFU House M A Jinnah Road
Karachi, Pakistan
Tel.: (92) 2132313304
Fax: (92) 2132310851
E-Mail: info@eastwestinsurance.com.pk
Web Site: www.eastwestinsurance.com.pk
Premiums: $4,738,044
Assets: $8,462,116
Liabilities: $3,740,523
Net Worth: $4,721,593
Earnings: $689,417
Fiscal Year-end: 12/31/12

East West Insurance Co., Ltd.—(Continued)

Business Description:
Property & Casualty Insurance Services
S.I.C.: 6331
N.A.I.C.S.: 524126
Personnel:
Mian Mahboob Ahmad *(Chm)*
Naved Yunus *(CFO, Mng Dir, Member-Mgmt Bd & Sec)*
Shabbir Ali Kanchwala *(CFO, Member-Mgmt Bd & Dir-Fin)*
Mohammad Fayyaz Khokhar *(Member-Mgmt Bd & Gen Mgr-Mktg)*
Umeed Ansari *(Member-Mgmt Bd & Dir-Dev)*
Kazim Raza *(Member-Mgmt Bd & Dir-Ops)*
Javed Yunus *(Member-Mgmt Bd & Dir-Mktg)*
Pervez Yunus *(Member-Mgmt Bd & Dir-Ops)*
Sajjad Zafar *(Member-Mgmt Bd & Dir-Central)*
Board of Directors:
Mian Mahboob Ahmad
A. K. M. Sayeed
Javed Yunus
Maheen Yunus
Naved Yunus
Pervez Yunus
Tulu Javed Yunus

EAST WEST LIFE ASSURANCE COMPANY LIMITED

310 EFU House M A Jinnah Road
Karachi, Pakistan
Tel.: (92) 21 32311662
Fax: (92) 21 32311667
E-Mail: info@eastwestlifeco.com
Web Site: www.eastwestlifeco.com
EWLA—(KAR)
Rev.: $123,231
Assets: $4,192,502
Liabilities: $3,052,316
Net Worth: $1,140,187
Earnings: ($75,113)
Fiscal Year-end: 12/31/12
Business Description:
Life & Health Insurance Services
S.I.C.: 6311
N.A.I.C.S.: 524113
Personnel:
Mahboob Ahmad *(Chm)*
Maheen Yunus *(CEO & Mng Dir)*
Sohail Nazeer *(CFO & Sec)*
Imran Ali Dodani *(COO)*
Muhammad Aslam *(Chief Medical Officer)*
Muhammad Gulfam Ahmed *(Medical Officer)*
Syed Kashif Hamid *(Medical Officer)*
Muhammad Abu Bakar Rashid *(Medical Officer)*
Board of Directors:
Mahboob Ahmad
A. K. M. Sayeed
Javed Yunus
Maheen Yunus
Naved Yunus
Omar P. Yunus
Pervez Yunus

EAST WEST PETROLEUM CORP.

1210-1095 West Pender Street
Vancouver, BC, V6E 2M6, Canada
Tel.: (604) 682-1558
Fax: (604) 682-1568
E-Mail: info@eastwestpetroleum.ca
Web Site: www.eastwestpetroleum.ca
Year Founded: 1987
EW—(OTC TSXV)
Sls.: $159,908
Assets: $31,267,874
Liabilities: $217,908
Net Worth: $31,049,966
Earnings: ($2,222,376)
Fiscal Year-end: 12/31/12
Business Description:
Oil & Gas Exploration Services
S.I.C.: 1389
N.A.I.C.S.: 213112
Personnel:
David Sidoo *(Founder, Pres & CEO)*
Nick DeMare *(CFO)*
James L. Harris *(Sec)*
Board of Directors:
R. Marc Bustin
Nick DeMare
Herb Dhaliwal

EASTCOAL INC.

130-889 Harbourside Drive
North Vancouver, BC, V7P 3S1, Canada
Tel.: (604) 973-0079
Fax: (604) 770-1300
E-Mail: info@eastcoal.ca
Web Site: www.eastcoal.ca
Year Founded: 1986
ECX—(AIM TSXV)
Rev.: $3,964,152
Assets: $92,763,934
Liabilities: $26,443,914
Net Worth: $66,320,020
Earnings: ($5,319,995)
Fiscal Year-end: 12/31/12
Business Description:
Mineral Exploration Services
S.I.C.: 1081
N.A.I.C.S.: 213114
Personnel:
John Joseph Byrne *(Chm & CEO)*
Abraham Jonker *(Pres & Interim CFO)*
Vernon King *(COO)*
Hendrik Dietrichsen *(Gen Counsel & Sec)*
Board of Directors:
John Joseph Byrne
Gregory M. Cameron
John Conlon
Abraham Jonker
Frank Moxon
Legal Counsel:
FMC Law LLP
20th Floor 250 Howe Street
Vancouver, BC, Canada V6C 3R8
Transfer Agent:
Computershare Trust Company of Canada
510 Burrard St
Vancouver, BC, Canada

EASTCOMPEACE SMART CARD CO., LTD.

(Name Changed to Eastcompeace Technology Co., Ltd.)

EASTCOMPEACE TECHNOLOGY CO., LTD.

(Formerly Eastcompeace Smart Card Co., Ltd.)
No 8 Gongzhong Road Nanping Technology Industrial Park
Zhuhai, Guangdong, 519060, China
Tel.: (86) 7568682892
Fax: (86) 7568695237
Web Site: www.eastcompeace.com
002017—(SSE)
Sales Range: $125-149.9 Million
Emp.: 2,115
Business Description:
Smart Card Mfr
S.I.C.: 7379
N.A.I.C.S.: 541519
Personnel:
Zhongguo Zhou *(Chm & Pres)*

EASTERN & ORIENTAL BERHAD

Level 3A Annexe Menara Milenium No 8 Jalan Damanlela
Damansara Heights, 50490 Kuala Lumpur, Malaysia
Tel.: (60) 320956868
Fax: (60) 320959898
E-Mail: corp.comm@easternandoriental.com
Web Site: www.easternandoriental.com
E&O—(KLS)
Rev.: $198,567,365
Assets: $812,543,458
Liabilities: $344,976,103
Net Worth: $467,567,355
Earnings: $44,848,307
Fiscal Year-end: 03/31/13
Business Description:
Hotel & Property Management Services
S.I.C.: 6531
N.A.I.C.S.: 531311
Personnel:
Ka Hon Tham *(Mng Dir)*
Kok Leong Chan *(Deputy Mng Dir)*
Hong Mai Ang *(Sec)*
Board of Directors:
Azizan Abd Rahman
Kamil Ahmad Merican
Christopher Martin Boyd
Kok Leong Chan
Meng Chow Kok
Abd Wahab Maskan
Mohd Bakke Salleh
Kar Leng Tan
Ka Hon Tham
V. Thamotharam Pillay

Subsidiaries:

Ambangan Puri Sdn. Bhd **(1)**
Level 3A X Menara Milenium 8 Jalan Damanlela Damansara
50490 Kuala Lumpur, Malaysia
Tel.: (60) 320956868
Fax: (60) 320939060
Residential Real Estate Property Development Services
S.I.C.: 6531
N.A.I.C.S.: 531311

Subsidiary:

Seventy Damansara Sdn. Bhd. **(2)**
Seventy Guard House Jalan Damansara
50480 Kuala Lumpur, Malaysia
Tel.: (60) 320953062
Fax: (60) 320932876
Residential Property Development Services
S.I.C.: 6531
N.A.I.C.S.: 531311
Mike Low *(Mgr)*

The Delicious Group Sdn. Bhd. **(1)**
72A Jalan Sungai Besi
57100 Kuala Lumpur, Malaysia
Tel.: (60) 392219255
Fax: (60) 392217266
Emp.: 100
Restaurant Management Services
S.I.C.: 7011
N.A.I.C.S.: 721110
Steve Allen *(Gen Mgr)*

E&O Customer Services Sdn. Bhd. **(1)**
Pondok Jaga Idamansara Jalan Rosa 5 Bukit Damansara
50490 Kuala Lumpur, Malaysia
Tel.: (60) 320952662
Fax: (60) 20959898
Web Site: www.eopro.com
Emp.: 150
Property Management Services
S.I.C.: 6531
N.A.I.C.S.: 531311
Wong Laiyee *(Mgr-HR)*

E&O Property Development Berhad **(1)**
Level 3A Annexe Menara Milenium No 8 Jalan Damanlela
Damansara Heights, 50490 Kuala Lumpur, Malaysia
Tel.: (60) 320956868
Fax: (60) 320959898
E-Mail: corp.comm@easternandoriental.com
Web Site: www.eoprop.com
Emp.: 150
Property Development Services
S.I.C.: 6531
N.A.I.C.S.: 531390
Eric Chan *(CEO)*

Non-U.S. Subsidiary:

E&O Property (Singapore) Pte. Ltd. **(2)**
The Sales Gallery 11 Beach Rd 01-02
Singapore, 189675, Singapore
Tel.: (65) 63371680
Fax: (65) 63379848
E-Mail: eospore@easternandoriental.com
Web Site: www.easternandoriental.com.sg
Emp.: 4
Real Estate Property Development Services
S.I.C.: 6531
N.A.I.C.S.: 531390
Aileen Han *(Country Mgr)*

E&O Property (Penang) Sdn. Bhd. **(1)**
The Sales Gallery Seri Tanjung Pinang Tanjung Tokong
10470 George Town, Pulau Penang, Malaysia
Tel.: (60) 48918000
Fax: (60) 48912525
Web Site: www.seritanjungpinang.com
Emp.: 8
Residential Property Development Services
S.I.C.: 6531
N.A.I.C.S.: 531311
Jeremy Chee *(Sr Mgr-Sls & Mktg)*

Eastern & Oriental Hotel Sdn. Bhd. **(1)**
10 Lebuh Farquhar
10200 George Town, Penang, Malaysia
Tel.: (60) 42222000
Fax: (60) 42616333
E-Mail: luxury@e-o-hotel.com
Web Site: www.e-o-hotel.com
Hotel Management Services
S.I.C.: 7011
N.A.I.C.S.: 721110

Edisi Utama Sdn. Bhd. **(1)**
Level 15A Dua Residency Tower A Jalan Tun Razak
50400 Kuala Lumpur, Malaysia
Tel.: (60) 321629660
Fax: (60) 321626113
Web Site: www.eoprop.com
Emp.: 10
Residential Property Development Services
S.I.C.: 6531
N.A.I.C.S.: 531311
Annie Lim *(Mgr)*

Eminent Pedestal Sdn. Bhd **(1)**
B-M-2 M Northpoint Offices Mdn Syed Putra Mid Valley City
59200 Kuala Lumpur, Federal Territory, Malaysia
Tel.: (60) 322879220
Fax: (60) 22878720
Emp.: 6
Restaurant Operation Services
S.I.C.: 5812
N.A.I.C.S.: 722511
Serina Cheh *(Mgr-Restaurant)*

Lone Pine Hotel (c) Sdn. Bhd. **(1)**
97 Batu Ferringhi
11200 Penang, Malaysia
Tel.: (60) 48868686
Fax: (60) 48811282
E-Mail: info@lonepinehotel.com
Web Site: www.lonepinehotel.com
Emp.: 190
Hotel Management Services
S.I.C.: 7011
N.A.I.C.S.: 721110

Khoo Boon Lim *(Asst Mgr)*

Regal Alliance Sdn. Bhd. (1)
No 8 Jln Daman Lela Damansara Heights
50490 Kuala Lumpur, Malaysia
Tel.: (60) 320938888
Fax: (60) 320950293
Web Site: www.easternoriental.com
Residential Property Development Services
S.I.C.: 6531
N.A.I.C.S.: 531311

EASTERN ASIA TECHNOLOGY LTD.

6 Shenton Way Suite 28-09 DBS Building Tower Two
Singapore, 06809, Singapore
Tel.: (65) 6250 0718
Fax: (65) 6250 0728
E-Mail: kh.wong@eastech.com
Web Site: www.eastech.com
Sales Range: $250-299.9 Million
Business Description:
Contract Mfr of Electronic Components & Equipment
S.I.C.: 3679
N.A.I.C.S.: 334419
Personnel:
Jenq-Lin Liou *(Chm & CEO)*
Non-U.S. Subsidiaries:

East Synergy Limited (1)
Unit 1703-7 10 16 17F Hewlett Centre 54 Hoi Yuen Road
Kwun Tong, China (Hong Kong)
Tel.: (852) 23434225
Fax: (852) 2372 8399
Emp.: 20
Electronic Equipments Distr
S.I.C.: 5064
N.A.I.C.S.: 423620
William Ho Hai Wai *(Mgr)*

Eastech Electronics (HK) Limited (1)
Rm 1703-1707 17F Hewlett Center
54 Hoi Yuen Road Kwun Tong, Kowloon, China (Hong Kong) (94.23%)
Tel.: (852) 23431711
Fax: (852) 29510922
E-Mail:
Web Site: www.eastech.com
Durable Goods Whslr
S.I.C.: 5099
N.A.I.C.S.: 423990

Eastech Electronics (Taiwan) Inc. (1)
8F-1 No 188 Baoqiao Road
Xindian District, New Taipei City, 23145, Taiwan
Tel.: (886) 2 2910 2626
Fax: (886) 2 2910 9292
Electronic Components Mfr
S.I.C.: 3679
N.A.I.C.S.: 334419
Nancy Teng *(Asst VP)*

Eastern Asia Industries Sdn. Bhd (1)
Plot 326 Jalan Pknk 3-3
Sungai Petani, Malaysia (100%)
Tel.: (60) 44417789
Emp.: 200
Audio & Video Equipment Mfr
S.I.C.: 3651
N.A.I.C.S.: 334310
Kim Yu *(Mng Dir)*

Eastern Asia Technology (HK) Limited (1)
Units 1703-1707 17th Floor Hewlett Centre
54 Hoi Yuen Road Kwun Tong, Kowloon, China (Hong Kong) (100%)
Tel.: (852) 27970268
Fax: (852) 23436099
E-Mail: mandy.hau@eastech.com
Durable Goods Whslr
S.I.C.: 5099
N.A.I.C.S.: 423990

Hifi Orient (Thai) Co., Ltd (1)
83/161-162 Moo 6 Soi Chinaket 2
Ngamwongwan Rd, 10210 Bangkok, Thailand (56.91%)
Tel.: (66) 29545281
Fax: (66) 25807443
E-Mail: anyaiath@hifithai.co.th
Web Site: www.hifithai.co.th
Emp.: 300
Electronic Parts & Equipment Whslr
S.I.C.: 5065
N.A.I.C.S.: 423690
Michael Lin *(Mng Dir)*

EASTERN BANK LIMITED

10 Dilkusha C/A Jiban Bima Bhaban
Dhaka, Bangladesh
Tel.: (880) 29556360
Fax: (880) 29558392
E-Mail: info@ebl.bd.com
Web Site: www.ebl-bd.com
EBL—(DHA)
Int. Income: $170,158,227
Assets: $1,820,410,149
Liabilities: $1,606,860,767
Net Worth: $213,549,382
Earnings: $29,621,998
Emp.: 1,343
Fiscal Year-end: 12/31/12
Business Description:
Commercial Banking Services
S.I.C.: 6029
N.A.I.C.S.: 522110
Personnel:
Ghaziul G. Haque *(Chm)*
Md. Fakhrul Alam *(Deputy Mng Dir-Corp Banking & Treasury)*
Muklesur Rahman *(Deputy Mng Dir-Consumer Banking)*
Hassan O. Rashid *(Deputy Mng Dir)*
Md. Safiar Rahman *(Sec & Sr Exec VP)*
S. M. Akhtaruzzaman Akhtaruzzaman *(Sr Exec VP & Head-Ops)*
Sami Karim *(Sr Exec VP & Head-SAMD)*
Mahbubul Alam Tayiab *(Sr Exec VP & Head-Ops)*
Board of Directors:
Ghaziul G. Haque
A. M. Shaukat Ali
Salina Ali
A. Q. I. Chowdhury
Md. Showkat Ali Chowdhury
Gazi Md. Shakhawat Hossain
Nasir Hossain
Asif Mahmood
Ormaan Rafay Nizam
Meah Mohammed Abdur Rahim
Md. Safiar Rahman

EASTERN CARIBBEAN AMALGAMATED BANK

1000 Airport Boulevard at Pavilion Drive
PO Box 315
Coolidge, Antigua & Barbuda
Tel.: (268) 2684805300
Fax: (268) 2684805433
E-Mail: csedwards@ecabank.com
Web Site: www.ecabank.com
Business Description:
Banking Services
S.I.C.: 6029
N.A.I.C.S.: 522110
Personnel:
Edmund W. Lawrence *(Chm)*
Robert W. Norstrom *(Deputy Chm)*
Gail Pero *(Gen Counsel & Corp Sec)*
Megan Samuel-Fields *(Sec)*
Board of Directors:
Edmund W. Lawrence
Whitfield Harris, Jr.
Gladstron S. Joseph
Robert W. Norstrom
Megan Samuel-Fields
Bernard Thomas
Craig J. Walter
Derry T. Williams

EASTERN CARIBBEAN CENTRAL BANK

PO Box 89
Basseterre, Saint Kitts & Nevis
Tel.: (869) 4652537
Fax: (869) 4659562
E-Mail: info@eccb-centralbank.org
Web Site: www.eccb-centralbank.org
Sales Range: $25-49.9 Million
Emp.: 228
Fiscal Year-end: 03/31/13
Business Description:
Banking Services
S.I.C.: 6029
N.A.I.C.S.: 522110
Personnel:
Dwight Venner *(Chm)*
Jennifer Nero *(Mng Dir)*
Board of Directors:
Dwight Venner
Timothy Antoine
Lindorna Brade
Reginald Darius
Maurice Edwards
Rosamund Edwards
Whitfield Harris, Jr.
Wendell Lawrence
Kathleen Rogers

EASTERN CARIBBEAN SECURITIES EXCHANGE

Bird Rock
PO Box 94
Basseterre, Saint Kitts & Nevis
Tel.: (869) 4667192
Fax: (869) 4653798
E-Mail: info@ecseonline.com
Web Site: www.ecseonline.com
Rev.: $1,083,691
Assets: $8,246,604
Liabilities: $6,820,947
Net Worth: $1,425,656
Earnings: $262,462
Emp.: 8
Fiscal Year-end: 03/31/13
Business Description:
Stock Exchange Services
S.I.C.: 6231
N.A.I.C.S.: 523210
Personnel:
K. Dwight Venner *(Chm)*
Michael Morton *(Deputy Chm)*
Trevor E. Blake *(CEO & Gen Mgr)*
Maria Barthelmy *(Sec)*
Board of Directors:
K. Dwight Venner
Peter Blanchard
George S. Goodluck
Sephlin Lawrence
Michael Morton
Jennifer Nero
Reginald Thomas
Legal Counsel:
Kelsick Wilkin & Ferdinand
South Independence Square Street
Basseterre, Saint Kitts & Nevis

EASTERN CONSTRUCTION COMPANY LIMITED

505 Consumers Rd Ste 1100
Toronto, ON, M2J 5G2, Canada
Tel.: (416) 497-7110
Fax: (416) 497-7241
E-Mail: info@easternconstruction.com
Web Site: www.easternconstruction.com
Year Founded: 1951
Emp.: 140
Business Description:
General Contracting Services
S.I.C.: 1542
N.A.I.C.S.: 236220
Personnel:
Frank DeCaria *(Pres & CEO)*
Ron Littlejohns *(Sr VP-Fin)*

EASTERN ENVIRONMENT SOLUTIONS, CORP.

Harbin Dongdazhi Street 165
Harbin, 150001, China
Tel.: (86) 451 53948666
Fax: (86) 451 53990366
E-Mail: eesc@vip.163.com
Web Site: www.useesc.com
EESC—(OTC)
Sales Range: $10-24.9 Million
Emp.: 56
Business Description:
Solid Waste Disposal
S.I.C.: 4953
N.A.I.C.S.: 562212
Personnel:
Feng Yan *(Chm & CEO)*
Guofeng Song *(CFO & Exec VP-Fin)*
Shibin Jiang *(COO)*
Board of Directors:
Feng Yan
Gene Hsiao
Shibin Jiang
Kenneth Leung
Shiping Wang
Subsidiary:

Harbin Yifeng Eco-environment Co., Ltd. (1)
No 165 Dongdazhi Street
Nangang Dist, Harbin, 150001, China
Tel.: (86) 45153948666
Fax: (86) 45153990366
E-Mail: eesc@vip.163.com
Emp.: 55
Solid Waste Processing Services
S.I.C.: 4953
N.A.I.C.S.: 562213
Feng Yan *(Gen Mgr)*

THE EASTERN EUROPEAN TRUST PLC

(Name Changed to BlackRock Emerging Europe plc)

EASTERN GASES LIMITED

43 Palace Court 1 Kyd Street
Kolkata, 700016, India
Tel.: (91) 33 22299897
Fax: (91) 33 22496826
E-Mail: info@eastgas.co.in
Web Site: www.eastgas.co.in
Year Founded: 1995
590080—(BOM)
Rev.: $38,875,432
Assets: $12,055,005
Liabilities: $7,331,124
Net Worth: $4,723,881
Earnings: $404,135
Fiscal Year-end: 03/31/13
Business Description:
Gas Distr
S.I.C.: 4924
N.A.I.C.S.: 221210
Personnel:
Sushil Kumar Bhansali *(Chm & Mng Dir)*
Swati Basu *(Compliance Officer)*
Board of Directors:
Sushil Kumar Bhansali
Debabrata Choudhury
Anil Choudhary Legha
Tejvir Singh
Transfer Agent:
S. K. Infosolutions Pvt. Ltd.
34/1A Sudhir Chatterjee Street
Kolkata, India

EASTERN HOLDINGS LTD.

1100 Lower Delta Road 02-01 EPL Building
Singapore, 169206, Singapore
Tel.: (65) 6379 2888
Fax: (65) 6379 2803
E-Mail: corporate@epl.com.sg

Eastern Holdings Ltd.—(Continued)

Web Site: www.epl.com.sg
Year Founded: 1981
5KU—(SES)
Rev.: $8,530,529
Assets: $81,263,759
Liabilities: $21,798,301
Net Worth: $59,465,459
Earnings: $1,635,630
Emp.: 70
Fiscal Year-end: 03/31/13
Business Description:
Holding Company; Property Development; Publishing
S.I.C.: 6719
N.A.I.C.S.: 551112
Personnel:
Stephen Thian Boon Tay *(Chm & Mng Dir)*
Gwendolyn Jong Yuh Gn *(Sec)*
Board of Directors:
Stephen Thian Boon Tay
Tai Pew Diong
Nicholas Jeyaraj
Kenneth Kay Soon Tan
Transfer Agent:
Boardroom Corporate & Advisory Services Pte. Ltd.
50 Raffles Place 32-01 Singapore Land Tower
Singapore, Singapore
Subsidiaries:

Eastern Publishing Pte Ltd **(1)**
1100 Lower Delta Rd 04-01 EPL Bldg
Singapore, 169206, Singapore
Tel.: (65) 63792888
Fax: (65) 63792803
Magazines & Periodicals Publishing Services
S.I.C.: 2721
N.A.I.C.S.: 511120

Eastern Trade Media Pte Ltd **(1)**
EPL Building 1100 Lower Delta Road 04-02
Singapore, 169206, Singapore
Tel.: (65) 6379 2888
Fax: (65) 6379 2805
Emp.: 80
Magazines Publishing Services
S.I.C.: 2721
N.A.I.C.S.: 511120
Lum Kum Kuen *(Gen Mgr)*

Motherhood Pte Ltd **(1)**
1100 Lower Delta Road 04-01 EPL Building
Singapore, 169206, Singapore
Tel.: (65) 6379 2888
Fax: (65) 6379 2806
E-Mail: mhex@epl.com.sg
Web Site: www.motherhood.com.sg
Child Care Magazine Publishing Services
S.I.C.: 2721
N.A.I.C.S.: 511120
Shenielle Aloysis *(Editor)*

EASTERN IRON LIMITED

Level 1 80 Chandos Street
Saint Leonards, NSW, 2065, Australia
Mailing Address:
PO Box 956
Crows Nest, NSW, 1585, Australia
Tel.: (61) 299067551
Fax: (61) 299065233
E-Mail: info@easterniron.com.au
Web Site: www.easterniron.com.au
EFE—(ASX)
Rev.: $1,325,593
Assets: $7,790,218
Liabilities: $529,578
Net Worth: $7,260,640
Earnings: ($1,206,290)
Emp.: 2
Fiscal Year-end: 06/30/13
Business Description:
Iron Ore Exploration
S.I.C.: 1011
N.A.I.C.S.: 212210
Personnel:
Greg De Ross *(Mng Dir)*
Ian K. White *(Sec)*
Board of Directors:
Stephen Geoffrey Gemell
Wendy L. Corbett
Adrian Critchlow
Greg De Ross
Gregory F. P. Jones
Ivo Polovineo
Legal Counsel:
Dibbs Barker
Level 8 123 Pitt Street
GPO Box 983
Sydney, Australia

EASTERN LUBRICANTS BLENDERS LIMITED

198 Sadarghat Road Post Box 04
Chittagong, 4000, Bangladesh
Tel.: (880) 31 614235 37
Fax: (880) 31 618312
Web Site: www.bpc.gov.bd
Year Founded: 1963
EASTRNLUB—(DHA)
Business Description:
Lubricant Blending Services
S.I.C.: 2079
N.A.I.C.S.: 311225
Personnel:
A. R. Khan *(Chm)*
Board of Directors:
A. R. Khan
Amzad Hossain
Mohammad Nazrul Islam
A. H. Khan
M. A. Malek

EASTERN MEDIA INTERNATIONAL CORPORATION

8F No 368 Sec 1 Fuxing S Road
Da-an District, Taipei, 10656, Taiwan
Tel.: (886) 227557565
Fax: (886) 227028079
E-Mail: spokesman@emic.com.tw
Web Site: www.emic.com.tw
2614—(TAI)
Sales Range: $50-74.9 Million
Business Description:
Warehousing Services
S.I.C.: 4225
N.A.I.C.S.: 531130
Personnel:
Shang Wen Liao *(Chm & Pres)*
Yen Hsu *(CEO-Strategy Dev Center)*
Michael L.Y. Pan *(Exec VP)*
Subsidiary:

Eastern Home Shopping & Leisure Co., Ltd. **(1)**
258 Ching Ping Rd
Zhonghe District, Taipei, 23581, Taiwan
Tel.: (886) 229437888
Fax: (886) 229430091
Web Site: www.etmall.com.tw
Emp.: 100
Virtual Shopping Services
S.I.C.: 5961
N.A.I.C.S.: 454111

EASTERN MOTION (CHINA) CO., LTD.

Rm 403 Bldg 7 No 108 Qinzhou Rd
Shanghai, 200235, China
Tel.: (86) 2164837614
Fax: (86) 21 64837617
E-Mail: sales@eastern-motion.com.cn
Web Site: www.eastern-motion.com.cn
Business Description:
Automated Electric & Industrial Controls Mfr
S.I.C.: 3823
N.A.I.C.S.: 334513

EASTERN PLATINUM LIMITED

Suite 501 837 West Hastings Street
Vancouver, BC, V6C 3N6, Canada
Tel.: (604) 685-6851
Fax: (604) 685-6493
E-Mail: info@eastplats.com
Web Site: www.eastplats.com
ELR—(TSX)
Rev.: $83,095,000
Assets: $744,590,000
Liabilities: $49,922,000
Net Worth: $694,668,000
Earnings: ($113,942,000)
Fiscal Year-end: 12/31/12
Business Description:
Platinum Exploration Services
S.I.C.: 1099
N.A.I.C.S.: 212299
Personnel:
David W. Cohen *(Chm)*
Ian Rozier *(Pres & CEO)*
Horng Dih Lee *(CFO, Sec & VP-Fin)*
Board of Directors:
David W. Cohen
John Andrews
Robert J. Gayton
Gordon Bruce Keep
Merfyn Roberts
Ian Rozier
Legal Counsel:
Norton Rose
3 More London Riverside
London, United Kingdom SE1 2AQ

McMillan LLP
1500 1055 West Georgia Street
V6E4N7 Vancouver, BC, Canada
Transfer Agent:
Computershare
3rd Floor 510 Burrard Street
Vancouver, BC, Canada
Non-U.S. Subsidiary:

Barplats Investments Limited **(1)**
Platinum Pl Turnberry Ofc Park 48
Grosvenor Rd Bryanston
Sandton, Johannesburg, Gauteng, 2196, South Africa
Tel.: (27) 114630050
Fax: (27) 114840254
E-Mail: info@barplats.net
Web Site: www.barplatsinvestments.co.za
Emp.: 1,990
Platinum Group Metals Mining Services
S.I.C.: 1099
N.A.I.C.S.: 212299
Ian Rozier *(Chm)*
Trevor Savage *(Grp Sec)*

EASTERN PROPERTY HOLDINGS LIMITED

RG Hodge Plaza Wickhams Cay 1
PO Box 3483
Road Town, Tortola, Virgin Islands (British)
Tel.: (284) 4944692
Fax: (284) 4944695
E-Mail: contact@easternpropertyholdings.com
Web Site: www.easternpropertyholdings.com
EPH—(SWX)
Rev.: $15,668,441
Assets: $349,590,884
Liabilities: $60,724,604
Net Worth: $288,866,280
Earnings: $11,926,954
Fiscal Year-end: 12/31/12
Business Description:
Real Estate Services & Developer
S.I.C.: 6519
N.A.I.C.S.: 531210
Personnel:
Gustav Stenbolt *(Chm)*
Board of Directors:
Gustav Stenbolt
Michael Cuthbert
Tomasz Dukala
Olga Melnikova
Hans Messmer
Christodoulos G. Vassiliades

EASTERN REFRIGERATION SUPPLY CO.

49 Riviera Drive
Markham, ON, L3R 5J6, Canada
Tel.: (905) 475-0075
Fax: (905) 475-0388
E-Mail: eastern@easternref.ca
Web Site: www.easternref.ca
Year Founded: 1963
Rev.: $22,744,800
Emp.: 42
Business Description:
Refrigeration Equipment & Supplies Merchant Whslr
S.I.C.: 5078
N.A.I.C.S.: 423740
Personnel:
George Merkel *(Founder, Co-Owner & Pres)*
David Merkel *(Co-Owner)*
Doug Merkel *(Co-Owner)*

EASTERN SECURITY & PROTECTION SERVICES, INC.

68 Harbin Road
Shenyang, Liaoning, 110002, China
Tel.: (86) 24 2250 1035
Year Founded: 2005
EAST—(OTC)
Sales Range: $10-24.9 Million
Emp.: 148
Business Description:
Security & Safety Systems Mfr
S.I.C.: 7382
N.A.I.C.S.: 561621
Personnel:
Rui Tan *(Pres, CEO & Sec)*
Jing Wang *(CFO)*
Xin Tian *(COO)*
Board of Directors:
Chen Fang
Chuang Gao
Rui Tan
Jing Wang
Transfer Agent:
TranShare Corporation
5105 DTC Pkwy Ste 325
Greenwood Village, CO 81069

EASTERN SILK INDUSTRIES LIMITED

19 R N Mukherjee Road
Kolkata, West Bengal, 700 001, India
Tel.: (91) 3322430817
Fax: (91) 3322482486
E-Mail: sales@easternsilk.com
Web Site: www.easternsilk.com
EASTSILK—(NSE)
Rev.: $17,770,887
Assets: $114,852,723
Liabilities: $90,939,868
Net Worth: $23,912,855
Earnings: ($17,679,577)
Emp.: 20,000
Fiscal Year-end: 03/31/13
Business Description:
Silk Yarn Mfr
S.I.C.: 2299
N.A.I.C.S.: 313110
Personnel:
S. S. Shah *(Chm & Mng Dir)*
Varun Shah *(Pres-Bangalore Unit)*
Deepak Agarwal *(Sec)*
Board of Directors:
S. S. Shah
H. S. Gopalka
G. D. Harnathka
R. S. Rungta
Sundeep Shah

Transfer Agent:
ABS Consultant Pvt. Ltd
99 Stephen House 6th Floor 4 BBD Bag East
Kolkata, India

EASTERN TECHNOLOGIES HOLDING LIMITED

8F-1 No 188 Baoqiao Road
Xindian District, New Taipei City, 23145, Taiwan
Tel.: (886) 2 89113535
Fax: (886) 2 29147070
E-Mail: ir@kyetek.com
Web Site: www.kyetek.com
Year Founded: 1971
5225—(TAI)
Sls.: $149,542,519
Assets: $98,425,746
Liabilities: $35,835,002
Net Worth: $62,590,744
Earnings: $10,017,764
Emp.: 3,225
Fiscal Year-end: 12/31/12
Business Description:
Audio & Video Products Mfr
S.I.C.: 3651
N.A.I.C.S.: 334310
Personnel:
Jenq Lin Liou *(Chm)*
Pai Chin Chang *(Pres)*
Polline Pui Man Lam *(CFO)*
Board of Directors:
Jenq Lin Liou
Pai Chin Chang
Shan-Juh Chang
Tung-I Chang
Ko-Hung Chen
Keenan Ken Kwok-King Lam
Fung-Shyung Shiau
Transfer Agent:
Sinopac Securities Corporation
3rd Fl 17 Boai Rd
Taipei, Taiwan

EASTERN TREADS LIMITED

3A 3rd Floor Eastern Corporate Office NH Bypass Edappally
Ernakulam, Kochi, Kerala, 682024, India
Tel.: (91) 484 239 35 50
Fax: (91) 484 239 55 10
E-Mail: treads@eastern.in
Web Site: www.easterntreads.com
Year Founded: 1993
531346—(BOM)
Rev.: $12,057,689
Assets: $4,284,305
Liabilities: $1,811,440
Net Worth: $2,472,865
Earnings: $197,485
Emp.: 300
Fiscal Year-end: 03/31/13
Business Description:
Tread Mfr
S.I.C.: 3011
N.A.I.C.S.: 326211
Personnel:
M. E. Mohamed *(Mng Dir)*
T. Baiju *(Sec)*
Board of Directors:
Navas M. Meeran
K. S. Neelacanta Iyer
Naiju Joseph
M. E. Mohamed
K. V. Rajagopalan Nair
M. S. Ranganathan
M. S. Sebastian
Transfer Agent:
Integrated Enterprises (India) Limited
2nd Floor Kences Towers No 1 Ramakrishna Street North Usman Road
T Nagar, Chennai, India

EASTERN WATER RESOURCES DEVELOPMENT & MANAGEMENT PUBLIC COMPANY LIMITED

Fl 23-26 Eastwater Building 1
Vibhavadi Rangsit Rd
Jomphol Chatuchak, Bangkok, 10900, Thailand
Tel.: (66) 2 2721600
Fax: (66) 2 2721601
E-Mail: ir@eastwater.com
Web Site: www.eastwater.com
Year Founded: 1992
EASTW—(THA)
Rev.: $123,440,694
Assets: $412,140,017
Liabilities: $169,613,171
Net Worth: $242,526,846
Earnings: $41,086,883
Emp.: 151
Fiscal Year-end: 12/31/12
Business Description:
Integrated Water Resources Management Services
S.I.C.: 4941
N.A.I.C.S.: 221310
Personnel:
Chanin Yensudchai *(Chm)*
Praphant Asava-Aree *(Pres & CEO)*
Namphon Rassadanukul *(Sec & Sr VP)*
Namsak Wannavisute *(Exec VP-Fin & Acctg)*
Jaroensuk Worapansopak *(Exec VP-Ops)*
Thidarut Kraiprasit *(Sr VP-Internal Audit)*
Board of Directors:
Chanin Yensudchai
Praphant Asava-Aree
Chinawat Assavapokee
Chuchai Boonyoi
Verapong Chaiperm
Thairatana Jotikabhukkana
Rattana Kitchawan
Prinya Nakchudtree
Jiratt Nithianantpom
Sahust Pratuknukul
Kallayana Vipattipumiprates

Subsidiary:

Nakornsawan Water Supply Company Limited **(1)**
1 Soi Vibhavadi Rangsit 5 Vibhavadi Rangsit Road Floor 23-25
Chatuchak, Bangkok, 10900, Thailand
Tel.: (66) 56256690
Fax: (66) 22721690
Drinking Water Distr
S.I.C.: 4971
N.A.I.C.S.: 221310

U.S. Subsidiary:

Global Water Group, Inc. **(1)**
8601 Sovereign Row
Dallas, TX 75247
Tel.: (214) 678-9866
Fax: (214) 678-9811
E-Mail: info@globalwater.com
Web Site: www.globalwater.com
Water Purification, Wastewater Processing & Wastewater Effluent Recycling Equipment Mfr
S.I.C.: 3559
N.A.I.C.S.: 333249
Alan M. Weiss *(Chm, Pres & CEO)*
Ricky D. Stafford *(COO)*
Volker Hohmann *(Sr VP-Mktg & Corp Dev)*

EASTFIELD RESOURCES LTD.

325 Howe St Ste 110
Vancouver, BC, V6C 1Z7, Canada
Tel.: (604) 681-7913
Fax: (604) 681-9855
E-Mail: info@eastfieldgroup.com
Web Site: www.eastfieldresources.com
ETF—(TSXV)
Sales Range: Less than $1 Million
Emp.: 3
Business Description:
Mineral Exploration Processes; Base & Precious Metal Exploration
S.I.C.: 1081
N.A.I.C.S.: 213114
Personnel:
William Morton *(Pres & CEO)*
Don Sharp *(CFO)*
Glen Garratt *(Sec & VP)*
Board of Directors:
Glen Garratt
Ed Kimura
William Morton
Alan Scott
Don Sharp
Paul Way
Legal Counsel:
Miller Thompson
1000-840 Howe Street
Vancouver, BC, Canada
Transfer Agent:
Olympia Trust Company
1900 925 W Georgia Street
Vancouver, BC, V6C 3L2, Canada

EASTGATE TECHNOLOGY LIMITED

20 Tampiness Street 92
528875 Singapore, Singapore
Tel.: (65) 67863100
Fax: (65) 67881478
E-Mail: info@eastgate.com.sg
Web Site: www.eastgate.com.sg
Year Founded: 1989
EAST—(SES)
Sales Range: $25-49.9 Million
Emp.: 3
Business Description:
Fasteners & Precision Components Mfr
S.I.C.: 3679
N.A.I.C.S.: 334419
Personnel:
Teck Leong Teo *(Mng Dir)*
Eng Thian Teo *(COO & Exec Dir)*
Lo Wingco *(CIO)*
Siew Chuan Wong *(Sec)*
Board of Directors:
Sik Ting Chau
Dah Khang Lee
Meng Tee Saw
Teck Leong Teo

Subsidiaries:

MediaGate Pte Ltd. **(1)**
20 Tampines Street 92
Singapore, 528875, Singapore
Tel.: (65) 67863100
Web Site: www.eastgate.com.sg/enquiries.htm
CD Disc Mfr
S.I.C.: 3089
N.A.I.C.S.: 326199

Non-U.S. Subsidiaries:

PrimeDisc International Limited **(1)**
12th Floor Unison Industrial Centre 27-31 Au Pui Wan Street
Fo Tan Shatin, Hong Kong, NT, China (Hong Kong)
Tel.: (852) 26903656
Fax: (852) 26903659
E-Mail: sales@primedisc.com.hk
Web Site: www.primedisc.com.hk
Emp.: 140
Blank CD & DVD Discs Mfr
S.I.C.: 3089
N.A.I.C.S.: 326199
Joshua Ying Ming Chan *(Mng Dir)*

StoreWell Media Manufacturing Ltd. **(1)**
No 11 Singhua Road
Taoyuan City, Taoyuan, 330, Taiwan
Tel.: (886) 33639288
Fax: (886) 33620760
E-Mail: casey@storewell.com.tw
Web Site: www.storewell.com.tw
CD & DVD Discs Mfr
S.I.C.: 3695
N.A.I.C.S.: 334613

EASTLAND EQUITY BERHAD

No 24, Jalan 8/23E, Taman Danau Kota Setapak
53300 Kuala Lumpur, Malaysia
Tel.: (60) 3441498200
Fax: (60) 341498120
E-Mail: contact@fbo.com.my
Web Site: www.fbo.com.my
FBO—(KLS)
Rev.: $11,837,912
Assets: $98,802,296
Liabilities: $45,154,584
Net Worth: $53,647,712
Earnings: $426,296
Fiscal Year-end: 12/31/12
Business Description:
Investment Services
S.I.C.: 6211
N.A.I.C.S.: 523999
Personnel:
Sydney Tau Chin Lim *(Mng Dir & CFO)*

Subsidiaries:

Discover Orient Holidays Sdn. Bhd. **(1)**
B-9-5 9th Floor Megan Avenue 1 Block B
189 Jalan Tun Razak
50400 Kuala Lumpur, Malaysia
Tel.: (60) 321662666
Fax: (60) 321662663
E-Mail: doh2@streamyx.com
Web Site: www.discover-orient.com.my
Emp.: 30
Touring Support Services
S.I.C.: 4725
N.A.I.C.S.: 561520
Sophie Wong *(Mng Dir)*

FBO Land (Setapak) Sdn. Bhd. **(1)**
No 24 Jalan 8/23e Danau Kota
53300 Kuala Lumpur, Malaysia
Tel.: (60) 341498200
Fax: (60) 341429788
Property Management & Development Services
S.I.C.: 6531
N.A.I.C.S.: 531311

EASTMAIN RESOURCES INC.

36 Toronto Street Suite 1000
Toronto, ON, M5C 2C5, Canada
Tel.: (519) 940-4870
Fax: (519) 940-4871
E-Mail: info@eastmain.com
Web Site: www.eastmain.com
ER—(TSX)
Rev.: $2,960,361
Assets: $59,483,659
Liabilities: $4,172,016
Net Worth: $55,311,643
Earnings: $904,236
Emp.: 20
Fiscal Year-end: 10/31/12
Business Description:
Gold Mining Services
S.I.C.: 1041
N.A.I.C.S.: 212221
Personnel:
Donald J. Robinson *(Pres & CEO)*
James L. Bezeau *(CFO)*
Jay Goldman *(Sec)*
Board of Directors:
Ian J. Bryans
John A. Hansuld
David K. Joyce
Donald J. Robinson
Murray Short
Legal Counsel:
Cassels, Brock & Blackwell LLP
2100 Scotia Plaza 40 King St W
Toronto, ON, M5H 3C2, Canada

Eastmain Resources Inc.—(Continued)

Tel.: (416) 869-5300
Telex: 6-23415
Fax: (416) 360-8877
Transfer Agent:
Equity Financial Trust Corporation
200 University Avenue Suite 400
Toronto, ON, Canada

EASTON INVESTMENTS LIMITED

Level 16 90 Collins Street
Melbourne, VIC, 3000, Australia
Tel.: (61) 3 9661 0444
Fax: (61) 3 9639 0311
E-Mail: info@eastoninvest.com
Web Site: www.eastoninvest.com
EAS—(ASX)
Rev.: $3,653,540
Assets: $14,120,560
Liabilities: $4,228,772
Net Worth: $9,891,788
Earnings: ($3,550,514)
Emp.: 14
Fiscal Year-end: 06/30/13
Business Description:
Investment Services
S.I.C.: 6211
N.A.I.C.S.: 523999
Personnel:
Kevin White *(CEO & Mng Dir)*
Geoffrey J. Robinson *(CFO)*
Campbell Gordon McComb *(COO)*
Mark Licciardo *(Sec)*
Board of Directors:
Rodney Green
Jonathan W. Sweeney
Kevin White
Legal Counsel:
Norton Gledhill
Level 23 459 Collins St
Melbourne, Australia
Corrs Chambers Westgarth
Level 36 600 Bourke Street
Melbourne, Australia

EASTPACK LIMITED

678 Eastbank Road
Edgecumbe, Auckland, Bay of Plenty, 3193, New Zealand
Tel.: (64) 7 304 8226
Fax: (64) 7 304 8262
E-Mail: info@eastpack.co.nz
Web Site: www.eastpack.co.nz
Year Founded: 1983
Business Description:
Fresh Fruit Packer & Distr
S.I.C.: 5148
N.A.I.C.S.: 424480
Personnel:
Ray Sharp *(Chm)*
Grant Eynon *(Deputy Chm)*
Tony Hawken *(CEO)*
Jason Gibbs *(CFO)*
Board of Directors:
Ray Sharp
Mike Ashby
Grant Eynon
Adrian Gault
Mark Hudson
Maurice Kidd
Michael Maltby
Murray McBride
Michael Montgomery
Hendrik Pieters
Subsidiaries:

EastPack Avocado Company Limited (1)
(Formerly Bravo Avocado Company Limited)
Washer Road
Te Puke, Bay of Plenty, 3119, New Zealand NZ
Tel.: (64) 75733400
Fax: (64) 75738604
E-Mail:
Avocado Farming Services
S.I.C.: 0179
N.A.I.C.S.: 111339

EASTPHARMA LTD.

Halkali Merkez Mah Basin Ekspres Caddesi No 1 Kucukcekmece
Istanbul, 34303, Turkey
Tel.: (90) 2126929326
Fax: (90) 2126970614
E-Mail: info@eastpharmaltd.com
Web Site: www.eastpharmaltd.com
Year Founded: 2006
EAST—(LSE)
Rev.: $231,983,492
Assets: $561,172,824
Liabilities: $200,656,506
Net Worth: $360,516,318
Earnings: $11,599,029
Fiscal Year-end: 12/31/12
Business Description:
Pharmaceutical Products Mfr & Distr
S.I.C.: 2834
N.A.I.C.S.: 325412
Personnel:
Philipp Daniel Haas *(Chm & CEO)*
Board of Directors:
Philipp Daniel Haas
Mesut Cetin
John Coombe-Tennant
Christoph Sven Hoffmann
Beat Schlagenhauf
Subsidiary:

Deva Holding A.S. (1)
Halkali Merkez Mah Basin Ekspres Caddesi No 1 Kucukcekmece
Istanbul, Turkey
Tel.: (90) 2126929292
Fax: (90) 2126970024
E-Mail: deva@deva.com.tr
Web Site: www.devaholding.com.tr
DEVA—(IST)
Rev.: $237,077,923
Assets: $408,733,820
Liabilities: $194,758,805
Net Worth: $213,975,015
Earnings: $19,351,475
Emp.: 1,655
Fiscal Year-end: 12/31/12
Holding Company; Pharmaceuticals
S.I.C.: 6719
N.A.I.C.S.: 551112
Philipp Daniel Haas *(Chm & CEO)*
Mesut Cetin *(Vice Chm & CFO)*

Non-U.S. Subsidiary:

Deva Holdings (NZ) Ltd. (2)
Level 1 92 Spey Street
PO Box 1705
Invercargill, 9840, New Zealand
Tel.: (64) 3 2189933
Fax: (64) 3 2189933
E-Mail: office@deva.co.nz
Pharmaceutical Products Mfr
S.I.C.: 2834
N.A.I.C.S.: 325412

EASTSIBERIAN PLC

1000-505 3rd Street Southwest
Calgary, AB, T2P 3E6, Canada
Tel.: (403) 247-0005
Fax: (403) 247-0041
E-Mail: cbrackman@petrokamchatka.com
Web Site: www.petrokamchatka.com
Year Founded: 1998
PKP—(TSXV)
Assets: $545,231
Liabilities: $1,471,273
Net Worth: ($926,042)
Earnings: ($1,615,879)
Fiscal Year-end: 05/31/13
Business Description:
Petroleum & Natural Gas Exploration Services
S.I.C.: 1389
N.A.I.C.S.: 213112
Personnel:
Greame Phipps *(Chm & Pres)*
Maxim Sidorin *(CEO)*
Richard Jaggard *(CFO)*
Board of Directors:
Greame Phipps
Jonathan Morley-Kirk
Maxim Sidorin
Transfer Agent:
Computershare Trust Company of Canada
100 University Avenue 9th Floor
Toronto, ON, M5J 2Y1, Canada
Tel.: (416) 663-9097
Fax: (416) 263-9694

EASTSIDE DODGE CHRYSLER JEEP LTD.

815-36th Street North-East
Calgary, AB, T2A4W3, Canada
Tel.: (403) 273-4313
Fax: (403) 273-2287
Toll Free: (866) 980-1549
Web Site: www.eastsidedodge.com
Year Founded: 1976
Rev.: $55,370,821
Emp.: 134
Business Description:
New & Used Car Dealers
S.I.C.: 5511
N.A.I.C.S.: 441110
Personnel:
Jim McManes *(Pres)*

EASTWAY PLYMOUTH CHRYSLER LTD

(d/b/a Eastway Chrysler Dodge Jeep Ltd.)
2851 Eglinton Avenue East
Toronto, ON, M1J2E2, Canada
Tel.: (416) 264-2501
Fax: (416) 264-2410
Toll Free: (877) 764-9455
Web Site: www.eastwaychrysler.com
Rev.: $15,328,800
Emp.: 40
Business Description:
New & Used Car Dealers
S.I.C.: 5511
N.A.I.C.S.: 441110
Personnel:
Craig Hind *(Owner)*

EASUN REYROLLE LTD

6th Floor Temple Tower 672 Anna Salai
Nandanam, Chennai, 600 035, India
Tel.: (91) 4424346425
Fax: (91) 4424346435
E-Mail: chennai@easunreyrolle.com
Web Site: www.easunreyrolle.com
EASUNREYRL—(NSE)
Rev.: $58,209,927
Assets: $120,991,539
Liabilities: $83,767,372
Net Worth: $37,224,167
Earnings: ($662,508)
Emp.: 385
Fiscal Year-end: 03/31/13
Business Description:
Electric Power Generation & Distribution Services
S.I.C.: 4911
N.A.I.C.S.: 221118
Personnel:
Raj H. Eswaran *(Mng Dir)*
K. N. Nagesha Rao *(Compliance Officer, Sec & VP-Corp Fin)*
Board of Directors:
Hari Eswaran
Raj H. Eswaran
Rakesh Garg
W. S. Jones
M. Raman
J. D. N. Sharma
Brahmayya & Co.
48 Masilamani Road Balaji Nagar Royapettah
Chennai, India
Transfer Agent:
Integrated Enterprises (India) Ltd
2nd Floor Kences Towers 1 Ramakrishna Street North Usman Road T Nagur, Chennai, 600017, India

EASY DATE HOLDINGS LTD

23 Manor Place
Edinburgh, EH3 7DX, United Kingdom
Tel.: (44) 1312264890
Fax: (44) 131 220 4884
E-Mail: info@easydategroup.com
Web Site: www.easydategroup.com
Year Founded: 2002
Rev.: $15,467,131
Emp.: 140
Business Description:
Online Dating Services
S.I.C.: 2741
N.A.I.C.S.: 519130
Personnel:
Bill Dobbie *(CEO)*
Max Polyakov *(COO)*
Board of Directors:
Bill Dobbie
Mark Doughty
Martin Higginson
Max Polyakov

EASY SOFTWARE AG

Am Hauptbahnhof 4
45468 Mulheim an der Ruhr, Germany
Tel.: (49) 208450160
Fax: (49) 2084501690
E-Mail: info@easy.de
Web Site: www.easy.de
ESY—(DEU)
Sales Range: $25-49.9 Million
Business Description:
Hardware & Software Development & Distr
S.I.C.: 7372
N.A.I.C.S.: 511210
Personnel:
Gereon Neuhaus *(CEO)*
Subsidiary:

EASY INTERNATIONAL CONSULTING GmbH. (1)
Essener Str 2-24
46047 Oberhausen, Nordrhein-Westfalen, Germany
Tel.: (49) 208450160
E-Mail: info@easy.de
Web Site: www.easy-international-consulting.de
Software Consulting Services
S.I.C.: 7373
N.A.I.C.S.: 541512

Non-U.S. Subsidiaries:

EASY SOFTWARE (UK) PLC. (1)
Reflection House The Anderson Ctr Olding Rd Bury St
Bury Saint Edmunds, Suffolk, IP33 3TA, United Kingdom
Tel.: (44) 1284727870
Fax: (44) 1284727871
E-Mail: info@easysoftware.co.uk
Web Site: www.easysoftware.co.uk
Emp.: 10
Software Development Services
S.I.C.: 7371
N.A.I.C.S.: 541511
Tony Cheung *(Dir-Ops)*

EASY SOLUTIONS Austria GmbH. (1)
Sebastian-Kneipp-Strasse 12
5020 Salzburg, Austria
Tel.: (43) 662461546
Fax: (43) 66246154655

E-Mail: office@easy-austria.at
Web Site: www.easy-austria.at
Emp.: 5
Documentation Software Development Services
S.I.C.: 7371
N.A.I.C.S.: 541511
Christian Maerzendorfer *(Mng Dir)*

EASYACCESS FINANCIAL SERVICES LIMITED

21 Venkatakrishna Road
Mandaveli, Chennai, Tamil Nadu, 600 028, India
Tel.: (91) 44 39169800
Fax: (91) 44 39169812
E-Mail: itadmin@easyaccess.co.in
Web Site: www.easyaccess.co.in
Emp.: 15

Business Description:
Financial Management Consulting Services
S.I.C.: 8742
N.A.I.C.S.: 541611

Personnel:
K. C. Suresh *(Head-Channel Fin)*

EASYCALL COMMUNICATIONS PHILIPPINES, INC.

2/F Mary Bachrach Building 25th cor AC Delgado Sts Port Area
Manila, Philippines
Tel.: (63) 5281263
Fax: (63) 5288918
E-Mail: marketing2@easycall.com.ph
Web Site: www.easycall.com.ph
ECP—(PHI)
Rev.: $490,852
Assets: $2,835,276
Liabilities: $546,246
Net Worth: $2,289,031
Earnings: $99,376
Emp.: 14
Fiscal Year-end: 12/31/12

Business Description:
Internet Services
S.I.C.: 2741
N.A.I.C.S.: 511140

Personnel:
J. Roberto C. Delgado *(Chm & CEO)*
Modesto N. Cervantes *(Vice Chm)*
Socorro Z. Niro *(Pres)*
Jose Enrique C. Santiago *(Acting Treas)*
Millicent Rose L. Sim-Asuncion *(Sec)*

Board of Directors:
J. Roberto C. Delgado
Felipe P. Araullo
Clifford W. Beek
Jonathan M. Cervantes
Modesto N. Cervantes
Rafael M. Garcia, III
Socorro Z. Niro

EASYHOME LTD.

33 City Centre Drive Suite 510
Mississauga, ON, L5B 2N5, Canada
Tel.: (905) 272-2788
Fax: (905) 272-9886
Web Site: www.easyhome.ca
Year Founded: 1990
EH—(TSX)
Rev.: $198,478,955
Assets: $188,791,237
Liabilities: $84,406,214
Net Worth: $104,385,022
Earnings: $10,990,879
Emp.: 1,241
Fiscal Year-end: 12/31/12

Business Description:
Mechandise Leasing & Retail Services
S.I.C.: 7359
N.A.I.C.S.: 532210

Personnel:
Donald K. Johnson *(Chm)*
David B. Ingram *(Pres & CEO)*
Steve Goertz *(CFO & Sr VP)*
Rick Atkinson *(Sr VP-Dev)*
Charlie Hamill *(Sr VP-Ops-Leasing)*
David Maries *(Sr VP-Mktg & Mdsg)*
Jason Mullins *(Sr VP-Ops-easyfinancial)*

Board of Directors:
Donald K. Johnson
David Appel
David B. Ingram
David A. Lewis
Sean Morrison
David J. Thomson

Legal Counsel:
Blake, Cassels & Graydon LLP
Toronto, ON, Canada

Transfer Agent:
Equity Financial Trust Company
Toronto, ON, Canada

Subsidiaries:

easyfinancial Services Inc. (1)
930 18th St
Brandon, MB, Canada
Tel.: (204) 725-2855
Fax: (204) 725-2994
Toll Free: (877) 554-4559
E-Mail: loans@easyhome.ca
Web Site: www.easyfinancialservices.ca
Consumer Lending Services
S.I.C.: 6141
N.A.I.C.S.: 522291

easyhome U.S. Ltd. (1)
33 City Centre Dr Ste 510
Mississauga, ON, L5B 2N5, Canada
Tel.: (905) 272-2788
Fax: (905) 272-9886
Web Site: easyhome.ca
Emp.: 320
Household Merchandise Leasing Services
S.I.C.: 6141
N.A.I.C.S.: 522220
Jackie Forester *(Office Mgr)*

RTO Asset Management Inc. (1)
33 City Centre Dr Ste 510
Mississauga, ON, L5B 2N5, Canada
Tel.: (905) 272-2788
Fax: (905) 272-9886
Web Site: www.easyhome.ca
Emp.: 100
Furniture Leasing Services
S.I.C.: 7359
N.A.I.C.S.: 532299
David Ingram *(CEO)*

RTO Distribution Inc (1)
10239 178 Street Northwest
Edmonton, AB, T5S 1M3, Canada
Tel.: (780) 444-2575
Fax: (780) 481-7426
Emp.: 1,126
Electrical Appliance Television & Radio Set Whslr
S.I.C.: 5064
N.A.I.C.S.: 423620
David Ingram *(CEO)*

EASYJET PLC

Hangar 89 London Luton Airport
Luton, Beds, LU2 9PF, United Kingdom
Tel.: (44) 871 244 2366
Fax: (44) 1582 443 355
E-Mail: investor.relations@easyjet.com
Web Site: www.easyjet.com
Year Founded: 1995
EZJ—(LSE)
Rev.: $7,074,411,520
Assets: $7,330,273,280
Liabilities: $3,979,148,800
Net Worth: $3,351,124,480
Earnings: $661,253,120
Emp.: 8,945
Fiscal Year-end: 09/30/13

Business Description:
Airline Services
S.I.C.: 4512
N.A.I.C.S.: 481111

Personnel:
Stelios Haji-Ioannou *(Founder)*
Carolyn McCall *(CEO)*
Chris Kennedy *(CFO)*
Warwick Brady *(COO)*
Trevor Didcock *(CIO)*
Giles Pemberton *(Gen Counsel & Dir-Corp Governance)*

Board of Directors:
John Barton
Adele Anderson
David Bennett
John Browett
Rigas Doganis
Charles Gurassa
Keith Hamill
Chris Kennedy
Andy Martin
Carolyn McCall

EASYKNIT INTERNATIONAL HOLDINGS LTD.

Block A 7th Floor Hong Kong Spinners Building Phase 6
481-483 Castle Peak Road, Kowloon, China (Hong Kong)
Tel.: (852) 27456338
Fax: (852) 21711503
Web Site: www.easyknit.com
1218—(HKG)
Sales Range: $50-74.9 Million
Emp.: 57

Business Description:
Cotton-Based Knit Garments Mfr
S.I.C.: 2389
N.A.I.C.S.: 315240

Personnel:
Yuk Chu Lui *(Co-Founder & VP)*
Wing Yee Koon *(Co-Founder)*
Jimmy Cheung Tim Kwong *(Pres & CEO)*
Simon Po Wing Lee *(Sec)*

Board of Directors:
Tam Chun Hon
Koon Sang Jong
Candy Ho Yan Koon
Jimmy Cheung Tim Kwong
Yuk Chu Lui
Ricky Wing Chiu Tse
Chun Kong Tsui

Legal Counsel:
Appleby
8th Floor, Bank of America Tower, 12 Harcourt Road
Central, China (Hong Kong)

Butterfield Fulcrum Group (Bermuda) Limited
26 Burnaby Street
Hamilton, HM 11, Bermuda

Transfer Agents:
Tricor Secretaries Limited
26th Floor Tesbury Centre 28 Queen's Road East
Wanchai, China (Hong Kong)

Butterfield Fulcrum Group (Bermuda) Limited
26 Burnaby Street
Hamilton, HM 11, Bermuda

Subsidiaries:

Easyknit Enterprises Holdings Limited (1)
Block A 7th Floor Hong Kong Spinners Building Phase 6 Cheung Sha Wan
481-483 Castle Peak Road, Cheung Sha Wan, Kowloon, China (Hong Kong) BM
Tel.: (852) 2745 6338
Fax: (852) 2171 1503
E-Mail: 616share@easyknit.com
Web Site: www.easyknitenterp.com
0616—(HKG)
Sls.: $28,853,336
Assets: $129,463,092
Liabilities: $26,576,595
Net Worth: $102,886,497
Earnings: $605,420
Emp.: 39
Fiscal Year-end: 03/31/13
Holding Company; Garment Sourcing & Exporting
S.I.C.: 6719
N.A.I.C.S.: 551112
Jimmy Cheung Tim Kwong *(Chm & CEO)*
Yuk Chu Lui *(Deputy Chm)*
Simon Po Wing Lee *(Sec)*

Easyknit Global Company Limited (1)
Block A 7 F Phase 6 Hong Kong Spinners Bldg
481-483 Castle Peak Rd, Cheung Sha Wan, Kowloon, China (Hong Kong)
Tel.: (852) 29906822
Fax: (852) 21711566
Clothing Merchant Whslr
S.I.C.: 5136
N.A.I.C.S.: 424320

Easyknit Properties Management Limited (1)
Block A 7 F Phase 6 Hong Kong Spinners Bldg
481-483 Castle Peak Rd, Cheung Sha Wan, Kowloon, China (Hong Kong)
Tel.: (852) 27456338
Fax: (852) 27457131
Property Management Services
S.I.C.: 6531
N.A.I.C.S.: 531311

U.S. Subsidiary:

Mary Mac Apparel Inc. (1)
1412 Broadway Ste 1705
New York, NY 10018
Tel.: (212) 840-9191
Fax: (212) 840-0500
Apparel Retailers
S.I.C.: 5651
N.A.I.C.S.: 448140

EASYMED SERVICES INC.

1250 West Hastings Street Suite 1100
Vancouver, BC, V6E 2M4, Canada
Tel.: (416) 662-3971
Fax: (604) 749-1509
Web Site: www.easymedmobile.com
Year Founded: 2009
EZM—(CNSX)
Rev.: $1,593
Assets: $24,701
Liabilities: $1,821,907
Net Worth: ($1,797,206)
Earnings: ($1,379,151)
Fiscal Year-end: 10/31/12

Business Description:
Health Management Services
S.I.C.: 8748
N.A.I.C.S.: 541618

Personnel:
Tejinder Sahota *(CEO)*
Jared W. Scharf *(CFO)*
Carmelo Bisognano *(COO)*
Thomas Wacinski *(CTO)*

Board of Directors:
Thomas Aretz
Carmelo Bisognano
Frank Christ
Christian Lovis
Andrew Ritchie
Jared W. Scharf
Thomas Wacinski

Transfer Agent:
Computershare Investor Services Inc.
3rd Floor 510 Burrard Street
Vancouver, BC, Canada

EASYVISTA S.A.

Immeuble Horizon 10 Allee Bienvenue
93885 Noisy-le-Grand, Cedex, France
Tel.: (33) 1 55 85 91 00
Fax: (33) 1 55 85 91 11
Web Site: www.easyvista.com
Year Founded: 1988

EasyVista S.A.—(Continued)

ALEZV—(EUR)
Business Description:
Information Technology Services
S.I.C.: 7373
N.A.I.C.S.: 541512
Personnel:
Sylvain Gauthier *(CEO)*
Remy Dessagnat *(CFO)*
Jamal Labed *(COO)*
Andrew White *(CMO, Exec VP & Gen Mgr-Americas)*
Jean-Daniel Touly *(CTO)*

EAT & CO.

2-1-5 Minamikyuhojimachi Chuo-ku
Osaka-shi, Osaka, 541-0058, Japan
Tel.: (81) 6 6271 1110
Web Site: www.eat-and.jp
Year Founded: 1977
2882—(TKS)
Sales Range: $200-249.9 Million
Emp.: 250
Business Description:
Restaurant Owner & Operator; Frozen Food Mfr & Marketer
S.I.C.: 5812
N.A.I.C.S.: 722511
Personnel:
Naoki Fumino *(Pres)*

EATMORE SPROUTS AND GREENS LTD.

2604 Grieve Rd
Courtenay, BC, V9J 1S7, Canada
Tel.: (250) 338-4860
Fax: (250) 334-0216
E-Mail: eatmore@shawpiz.ca
Web Site: www.eatmoresprouts.com
Rev.: $21,368,354
Emp.: 35
Business Description:
Organic Farm Products Mfr
S.I.C.: 0119
N.A.I.C.S.: 111199
Personnel:
Carmen Wakeling *(Co-Owner)*
Glenn Wakeling *(Co-Owner)*

EATON CORPORATION PLC

Fitzwilliam Hall Fitzwilliam Place
Dublin, 2, Ireland
Tel.: (353) 1 523 5000
Web Site: www.eaton.com
Year Founded: 2012
ETN—(NYSE)
Sls.: $22,046,000,000
Assets: $35,491,000,000
Liabilities: $18,628,000,000
Net Worth: $16,863,000,000
Earnings: $1,873,000,000
Emp.: 102,000
Fiscal Year-end: 12/31/13
Business Description:
Holding Company; Electrical & Industrial Equipment Mfr & Distr
S.I.C.: 6719
N.A.I.C.S.: 551112
Personnel:
Alexander M. Cutler *(Chm, Pres & CEO)*
Richard H. Fearon *(Vice Chm, CFO & Chief Plng Officer)*
Craig Arnold *(Vice Chm & COO-Indus Sector)*
Thomas S. Gross *(Vice Chm & COO-Electrical Sector)*
Cynthia K. Brabander *(Chief HR Officer & Exec VP)*
Mark M. McGuire *(Gen Counsel & Exec VP)*
Thomas E. Moran *(Sec & Sr VP)*
Ken D. Semelsberger *(Sr VP & Controller)*

Board of Directors:
Alexander M. Cutler
George S. Barrett
Todd M. Bluedorn
Christopher M. Connor
Michael J. Critelli
Charles E. Golden
Linda A. Hill
Arthur E. Johnson
Ned C. Lautenbach
Deborah L. McCoy
Gregory R. Page
Gerald B. Smith

Legal Counsel:
Jones Day
North Point 901 Lakeside Ave
Cleveland, OH 44114
Tel.: (216) 586-3939
Fax: (216) 579-0212

Transfer Agent:
BNY Mellon Shareowner Services
480 Washington Blvd
Jersey City, NJ 07310-1900
Tel.: (201) 680-4000

Corporate Headquarters:

Eaton Corporation **(1)**
Eaton Ctr 1111 Superior Ave
Cleveland, OH 44114-2584 OH
Tel.: (216) 523-5000
Fax: (216) 523-4787
Toll Free: (800) 386-1911
E-Mail: customer@eaton.com
Web Site: www.eaton.com
Emp.: 73,000
Holding Company; Electrical Power, Aerospace, Hydraulic & Motor Vehicle Systems Mfr
Import Export
S.I.C.: 6719
N.A.I.C.S.: 551112
Alexander M. Cutler *(Chm, Pres & CEO)*
Richard H. Fearon *(Vice Chm, CFO & Chief Plng Officer)*
Craig Arnold *(Vice Chm & COO-Indus Sector)*
Thomas S. Gross *(Vice Chm & COO-Electrical Sector)*
William W. Blausey, Jr. *(CIO & Sr VP)*
Ramanath Ramakrishnan *(CTO & Exec VP)*
Jeff Lowinger *(CTO-Indus Sector & Sr VP)*
Cynthia K. Brabander *(Chief HR Officer & Exec VP)*
Kenneth F. Davis *(Pres-Vehicle Grp)*
William R. VanArsdale *(Pres-Hydraulics Grp)*
Mark M. McGuire *(Gen Counsel & Exec VP)*
Thomas E. Moran *(Sec & Sr VP)*
Nanda Kumar *(Exec VP-Eaton Bus Sys)*
Steven M. Boccadoro *(Sr VP-Sls & Mktg)*
Donald H. Bullock, Jr. *(Sr VP-IR)*
William B. Doggett *(Sr VP-Pub & Community Affairs)*
David B. Foster *(Sr VP-Corp Dev & Treasury)*
Harold V. Jones *(Sr VP-Environment, Health & Safety)*
John J. Matejka *(Sr VP-Internal Audit)*
Donald J. McGrath *(Sr VP-Comm)*
Trent Meyerhoefer *(Sr VP-Treasury)*
John S. Mitchell *(Sr VP-Taxes)*
Barbara O'Dell *(Sr VP-Quality)*
Pavan Pattada *(Sr VP-Supply Chain Mgmt)*
Lou Rosen *(Sr VP-Asia Pacific)*
Deborah Severs *(Sr VP-Global Ethics & Compliance)*

Groups:

Eaton Aerospace LLC **(2)**
9650 Jeronimo Rd
Irvine, CA 92618 DE
Tel.: (949) 452-9500
Fax: (949) 452-9555
Web Site: www.eaton.com
Aerospace Conveyance Systems, Fuel Systems, Hydraulic Systems, Electrical Sensor & Controls Mfr
S.I.C.: 3728
N.A.I.C.S.: 336413
Uday Yadav *(Pres)*

Units:

Eaton Aerospace LLC - Conveyance Systems Division, Jackson **(3)**
300 SE Ave
Jackson, MI 49203-1972
Tel.: (517) 787-8121
Fax: (517) 789-2947
Web Site: www.eaton.com
Sales Range: $50-74.9 Million
Emp.: 350
Aircraft Fuel Conveyance Hoses, Couplings, Ducting & Seals Mfr
S.I.C.: 3492
N.A.I.C.S.: 332912
Andy Weeks *(Gen Mgr)*

Eaton Aerospace LLC - Electrical Sensing & Controls Division, Costa Mesa **(3)**
3184 Pullman St
Costa Mesa, CA 92626-3319
Tel.: (949) 642-2427
Fax: (714) 957-6143
Web Site: www.eaton.com
Sales Range: $50-74.9 Million
Emp.: 175
Aircraft Electrical Sensors & Controls Mfr
S.I.C.: 3812
N.A.I.C.S.: 334511
Mike Smith *(Plant Mgr)*

Eaton Aerospace LLC - Electrical Sensing & Controls Division, Glenolden **(3)**
24 E Glenolden Ave
Glenolden, PA 19036-2107
Tel.: (610) 522-4000
Fax: (610) 522-4902
Web Site: www.eaton.com
Sales Range: $125-149.9 Million
Emp.: 190
Aircraft Electrical Sensors & Controls Mfr & Distr
S.I.C.: 3812
N.A.I.C.S.: 334511
John Kampanis *(Gen Mgr)*

Eaton Aerospace LLC - Electrical Sensing & Controls Division, Grand Rapids **(3)**
3675 Patterson Ave SE
Grand Rapids, MI 49512-4022
Tel.: (616) 949-1090
Fax: (616) 949-2861
Web Site: www.eaton.com
Aircraft Electrical Sensors & Controls Mfr
S.I.C.: 3812
N.A.I.C.S.: 334511
Paul Davis *(Principal)*

Eaton Aerospace LLC - Electrical Sensing & Controls Division, Sarasota **(3)**
2250 Whitfield Ave
Sarasota, FL 34243-3926
Tel.: (941) 758-7726
Fax: (941) 751-7158
E-Mail: enginetransmissioncontrolssales@eaton.com
Web Site: www.aerospace.eaton.com
Sales Range: $100-124.9 Million
Emp.: 340
Aircraft Electrical Sensors & Controls Mfr
S.I.C.: 3812
N.A.I.C.S.: 334511

Eaton Aerospace LLC - Fuel Systems Division, Cleveland **(3)**
23555 Euclid Ave
Cleveland, OH 44117-1703
Tel.: (216) 692-6000
Fax: (216) 692-6331
Web Site: www.eaton.com
Sales Range: $200-249.9 Million
Emp.: 736
Aerospace Fuel Systems Equipment Mfr
Export
S.I.C.: 3728
N.A.I.C.S.: 336413
Frank Dubey *(VP & Gen Mgr-Fuel Sys Div)*

Eaton Aerospace LLC - Hydraulic Systems Division, Jackson **(3)**
5353 Highland Dr
Jackson, MS 39206
Tel.: (601) 981-2811
Fax: (601) 987-3429
Web Site: www.eaton.com
Sales Range: $25-49.9 Million
Emp.: 550
Aerospace Hydraulic Systems Mfr
S.I.C.: 3569
N.A.I.C.S.: 333999
Cathy Randall *(Mgr-HR)*

Eaton Aerospace LLC - Hydraulic Systems Division, Los Angeles **(3)**
4690 Colorado Blvd
Los Angeles, CA 90039-1106
Tel.: (818) 409-0200
Fax: (818) 409-1565
Web Site: www.eaton.com
Sales Range: $50-74.9 Million
Emp.: 340
Aerospace Hydraulic Systems Mfr
S.I.C.: 3728
N.A.I.C.S.: 336413
Pedro Mendieta *(Plant Mgr)*

Non-U.S. Subsidiaries:

Eaton Aerospace Limited **(3)**
Abbey Park Southampton Road
Titchfield, Fareham, Hants, PO14 4QA, United Kingdom UK
Tel.: (44) 1329853000
Fax: (44) 1329853797
Web Site: www.eaton.com
Emp.: 1,000
Aircraft Fuel Systems Equipment, Fuel Conveyance Components & Hydraulic Equipment Mfr
S.I.C.: 3728
N.A.I.C.S.: 336413

Eaton Aviation S.A.S. **(3)**
2 Rue Lavoisier
BP 45
F-78310 Coignieres, France FR
Tel.: (33) 130693000
Fax: (33) 130693056
Aircraft Fuel Conveyance Components Mfr & Distr
S.I.C.: 3492
N.A.I.C.S.: 332912

Unit:

Eaton Aviation S.A.S. - Conveyance Systems Division, Serres-Castet **(4)**
62 Chemin du Pau
F-64121 Serres-Castet, France
Tel.: (33) 559333864
Telex: 83152214
Fax: (33) 559333865
E-Mail: annieablanc@eaton.com
Sales Range: $25-49.9 Million
Emp.: 50
Aircraft Fuel Conveyance Components Mfr & Distr
S.I.C.: 3492
N.A.I.C.S.: 332912
Denis Raveau *(Plant Mgr)*

Non-U.S. Unit:

Eaton Germany GmbH - Aerospace Group, Conveyance Systems **(3)**
Rudolf-Diesel-Strasse 8
D-82205 Gilching, Germany
Tel.: (49) 81057530
Fax: (49) 81057555
Web Site: www.eaton.com
Sales Range: $25-49.9 Million
Emp.: 50
Aircraft Fuel Conveyance Systems Mfr
S.I.C.: 3492
N.A.I.C.S.: 332912
Franziska Hegewald *(Sec)*

Eaton Corp. - Electrical Sector, Americas **(2)**
1000 Cherrington Pkwy
Moon Township, PA 15108-4312
Tel.: (412) 893-3300
Fax: (412) 893-2113
Web Site: www.eaton.com
Sales Range: $200-249.9 Million
Emp.: 500
Electrical Power Distribution, Control & Management Products Mfr & Distr
Export
S.I.C.: 3699
N.A.I.C.S.: 335999
Revathi Advaithi *(Pres)*

Subsidiaries:

E. A. Pedersen Company (3)
3900 Dahlman Ave
Omaha, NE 68107 NE
Tel.: (402) 734-3900
Fax: (402) 734-0622
Web Site: www.eapedersen.com
Sales Range: $25-49.9 Million
Emp.: 150
Medium Voltage Switchgear Apparatus Mfr
S.I.C.: 3613
N.A.I.C.S.: 335313
Frank C. Sommer, III *(Bus Mgr)*

Intelligent Switchgear Organization LLC (3)
4955 Marconi Dr
Alpharetta, GA 30004 DE
Tel.: (770) 442-9442
Web Site: www.industrynet.com
Sales Range: $25-49.9 Million
Emp.: 140
Switchgear Mfr & Tester
S.I.C.: 3613
N.A.I.C.S.: 335313
Jim Cunningham *(Gen Mgr)*

Unit:

Eaton Corp. - Electrical Sector, Power Quality USA (3)
8609 Six Forks Rd
Raleigh, NC 27615-5276
Tel.: (919) 872-3020
Fax: (800) 753-9433
Toll Free: (800) 356-5794
E-Mail: powerquality@eaton.com
Web Site: powerquality.eaton.com
Sales Range: $100-124.9 Million
Emp.: 300
Electrical Monitoring & Power Management Systems Mfr, Distr & Support Services
Import Export
S.I.C.: 3825
N.A.I.C.S.: 334515

Plants:

Eaton Corp. - Electrical Sector, Columbus (3)
811 Greencrest Dr
Columbus, OH 43031
Tel.: (614) 882-3282
Telex: 756257
Fax: (614) 895-7111
Web Site: www.eaton.com
Sales Range: $25-49.9 Million
Emp.: 50
Mfr. of Color Graphics, Software, Terminals & Industrial Workstations
S.I.C.: 3575
N.A.I.C.S.: 334118
Clyde Thomas *(Mgr-Mktg)*

Eaton Corp. - Electrical Sector, Watertown (3)
901 S 12th St
Watertown, WI 53094-7101
Tel.: (920) 261-4070
Telex: 910-260-3713
Fax: (920) 261-9097
Sales Range: $50-74.9 Million
Emp.: 200
Counting Devices & Control Instruments Mfr
Export
S.I.C.: 3823
N.A.I.C.S.: 334513
Joe Massey *(Dir-Organizational Dev)*

Non-U.S. Subsidiaries:

Eaton Electrical Canada (3)
5050 Mainway
Burlington, ON, L7L 5Z1, Canada
Tel.: (905) 333-6442
Telex: 65-25249
Fax: (905) 631-4248
Web Site: www.eatoncanada.ca
Sales Range: $25-49.9 Million
Emp.: 112
Starters, Contactors, Overload Relays, Resistors & Brake Rectifier Panels Mfr
S.I.C.: 3613
N.A.I.C.S.: 335313
Jeffery M. Krakowiak *(VP & Gen Mgr-Americas Reg)*

Subsidiaries:

Eaton Power Quality Company (4)
380 Carlingview Dr
Toronto, ON, M9W 5X9, Canada ON
Tel.: (416) 798-0112
Fax: (416) 798-3532
Toll Free: (800) 461-9166
Web Site: www.eaton.com
Emp.: 50
Electrical Monitoring & Power Management Systems Mfr, Distr & Support Services
S.I.C.: 3825
N.A.I.C.S.: 334515

Moeller Canada Ltd. (4)
6175 Kenway Drive
Mississauga, ON, L5T 2L3, Canada Ca
Tel.: (905) 542-2323
Fax: (905) 542-2321
Toll Free: (800) 663-5537
E-Mail: info@moeller.ca
Web Site: www.moeller.ca
Sales Range: $10-24.9 Million
Emp.: 35
Electrical Circuit Breaker, Relay & Control Device Mfr
S.I.C.: 3699
N.A.I.C.S.: 335999

Eaton Electrical S.A. (3)
300 metros Oeste de la Universidad Catolica
Moravia, 10156-1000 San Jose, Costa Rica CR
Tel.: (506) 22477600 (97.53%)
Telex: 2170 CUTLER CR
Fax: (506) 22477680
E-Mail: jorgeeurena@eaton.com
Web Site: www.eaton.cr/Caribbean
Emp.: 200
Starters, Contactors & Overload Relays
S.I.C.: 3625
N.A.I.C.S.: 335314
Walter S. Angulo *(Gen Mgr)*

Eaton Power Quality S.A. (3)
Lima 355 Planta Baja
C1073AAF Buenos Aires, Argentina Ar
Tel.: (54) 11 4124 4000
Fax: (54) 11 4124 4080
Web Site: powerquality.eaton.com
Sales Range: $100-124.9 Million
Electrical Monitoring & Power Management Systems Distr & Support Services
S.I.C.: 5063
N.A.I.C.S.: 423610
Gustavo Gallupo *(Dir-Comm)*

Eaton Power Solutions Ltda. (3)
Av Ermano Marchetti 1435 Agua Branca
05038-001 Sao Paulo, SP, Brazil BR
Tel.: (55) 11 3616 8500
Web Site: powerquality.eaton.com
Sales Range: $100-124.9 Million
Electrical Monitoring & Power Management Systems Distr & Support Services
S.I.C.: 5063
N.A.I.C.S.: 423610
Georgia Thome *(Supvr-Mktg-Brazil)*

Eaton Technologies, S. de R.L. de C.V. (3)
Montecito No 38 piso 26
Col Napoles, CP 03810 Mexico, DF, Mexico MX
Tel.: (52) 55 8503 5450 (Switchboard)
Telex: 1771013 CHMXME
Fax: (52) 55 8503 5499
E-Mail: chmexicocsc@eaton.com
Web Site: www.eaton.mx
Sales Range: $50-74.9 Million
Emp.: 200
Electrical Distribution & Power Control Products Mfr & Distr
S.I.C.: 3613
N.A.I.C.S.: 335313

Branches:

Eaton Electrical Mexico - Guadalajara Sales Office (4)
Calle Lerdo de Tejada No 2105 Esq Marsella
Col Americana, 44160 Guadalajara, Jal, Mexico
Tel.: (52) 33 3630 3185
Web Site: www.eaton.mx/Mexico/Contacto
Sales Range: $1-9.9 Million
Emp.: 5
Electrical Power Distribution & Control Products Distr
S.I.C.: 5063
N.A.I.C.S.: 423610
Luis Driy *(Gen Mgr)*

Eaton Electrical Mexico - Monterrey Sales Office (4)
Calle Loma Redona 2712
Col Lomas de San Francisco, CP 64710 Monterrey, Mexico
Tel.: (52) 8181239154
Fax: (52) 8181239160
Web Site: www.eaton.mx/Mexico/Contacto
Sales Range: $1-9.9 Million
Emp.: 10
Electrical Power Distribution & Control Products Distr
S.I.C.: 5063
N.A.I.C.S.: 423610
Javier H. Rosas *(Reg Mgr-Sls)*

Unit:

Eaton Power Solutions - Mexico & Central America (4)
Montecito No 38 Piso 7 Oficinas 29 a 32
Col Napoles, CP 03810 Mexico, DF, Mexico
Tel.: (52) 55 9000 5252
Fax: (52) 55 1084 7454
Sales Range: $100-124.9 Million
Electrical Monitoring & Power Management Systems Distr & Support Services
S.I.C.: 5063
N.A.I.C.S.: 423610
Andrea Perez de Ramer *(Mktg Mgr-Strategic-Latin America & Caribbean)*

Eaton Corp. - Vehicle Group (2)
13100 E Michigan Ave
Galesburg, MI 49053
Tel.: (269) 342-3163
Web Site: www.eten.com
Emp.: 500
Motor Vehicle Components Mfr
S.I.C.: 3714
N.A.I.C.S.: 336390
Kenneth F. Davis *(Pres)*
Patrick Randrianarison *(Pres-EMEA)*

Divisions:

Eaton Corp. - Vehicle Group, Automotive Division (3)
1101 W Hanover St
Marshall, MI 49068-1756
Tel.: (269) 781-2811
Fax: (269) 781-2811
E-Mail: automotivewebmaster@eaton.com
Sales Range: $250-299.9 Million
Motor Vehicle Components Mfr & Distr
S.I.C.: 3714
N.A.I.C.S.: 336390
Jake Hooks *(Pres-Engine Air Mgmt Bus)*

Eaton Corp. - Vehicle Group, Truck Division (3)
13100 E Michigan Ave
Galesburg, MI 49053
Tel.: (269) 342-3000
Fax: (269) 342-3831
Toll Free: (800) 826-HELP
Web Site: www.eaton.com
Sales Range: $100-124.9 Million
Emp.: 500
Commercial Vehicle Drive Train & Safety Systems Mfr
Import Export
S.I.C.: 3714
N.A.I.C.S.: 336390
Tim Sinden *(Pres-North America)*

Joint Venture:

U.S. Engine Valve Corporation (3)
7039 S Hwy 11
Westminster, SC 29693
Tel.: (864) 647-2061
Fax: (864) 647-2649
Web Site: www.usenginevalve.com
Sales Range: $75-99.9 Million
Emp.: 325
Engine Valve Mfr
S.I.C.: 3714
N.A.I.C.S.: 336310

Units:

Eaton Corp. - Engine Air Management (3)
19218 B Dr S
Marshall, MI 49068-9790
Tel.: (269) 781-0200
Fax: (269) 781-0296
Web Site: www.eaton.com
Sales Range: $100-124.9 Million
Emp.: 260
Internal Combustion Engine Components, Precision Forged Gears
S.I.C.: 3714
N.A.I.C.S.: 336390

Eaton Corp. - Fluid Connectors (3)
19700 Hall Rd
Clinton Township, MI 48038-4451
Tel.: (586) 228-5000
Fax: (586) 286-1670
Web Site: www.eaton.com
Sales Range: $75-99.9 Million
Emp.: 200
Mfr. of Air Conditioning, Power Steering & Transmission Cooling Hose & Tube Assemblies
S.I.C.: 3052
N.A.I.C.S.: 326220

Eaton Corp. - Superchargers (3)
19218 B Dr S
Marshall, MI 49068-8600
Tel.: (706) 543-5250
Fax: (706) 583-4700
E-Mail: superchargerinfo@eaton.com
Web Site: www.eaton.com
Sales Range: $100-124.9 Million
Emp.: 250
Supercharger Mfr
S.I.C.: 3714
N.A.I.C.S.: 336340

Eaton Corp. - Transmissions (3)
744 S Battleground Ave
Kings Mountain, NC 28086-1728
Mailing Address:
PO Box 1728
Kings Mountain, NC 28086-1728
Tel.: (704) 937-7411
Fax: (704) 937-4354
Web Site: www.eaton.com
Sales Range: $125-149.9 Million
Emp.: 300
Heavy Duty Transmission Mfr
S.I.C.: 3714
N.A.I.C.S.: 336350
Rita Ramos *(Gen Mgr)*

Plants:

Eaton Corp. - Vehicle Group, Belmond Plant (3)
700 Lucks Ln
Belmond, IA 50421-0303
Mailing Address:
PO Box 303
Belmond, IA 50421-0303
Tel.: (641) 444-3535
Fax: (641) 444-5340
Web Site: www.EatonCorporation.com
Sales Range: $100-124.9 Million
Emp.: 450
Eaton Automotive Engine Valves
S.I.C.: 3714
N.A.I.C.S.: 336310
Scott Davies *(Plant Mgr)*

Eaton Corp. - Vehicle Group, Kearney Plant (3)
4200 Hwy 30 E
Kearney, NE 68848-9795
Tel.: (308) 234-1841
Fax: (308) 233-5446
Web Site: www.eaton.com
Sales Range: $125-149.9 Million
Emp.: 400
Precision Forged Gears
S.I.C.: 3714
N.A.I.C.S.: 336310
Kris Baldwin *(Mgr-Automotive Valvetrain Facility)*

Non-U.S. Subsidiaries:

Eaton Truck Components (Pty.) Limited (3)
3 Eaton Africa Place Aeroport Spartan Extension 2
PO Box 17122
1619 Johannesburg, Norkem Park, South Africa
Tel.: (27) 0113927770
Fax: (27) 3927001
E-Mail: kellettom@eaton.com
Web Site: www.roadranger.com
Sales Range: $25-49.9 Million
Emp.: 20
Truck Components Mgr & Distr

EATON CORPORATION plc—(Continued)

S.I.C.: 3714
N.A.I.C.S.: 336340
Tom Kellett *(Mgr-Sls)*

Eaton Hydraulics LLC (2)
14615 Lone Oak Rd
Eden Prairie, MN 55344-2079 DE
Tel.: (952) 937-9800
Fax: (952) 937-7394
Toll Free: (888) 258-0222
Web Site: www.eaton.com
Sales Range: $75-99.9 Million
Emp.: 250
Hydraulic Motors, Pumps & Hydrostatic Transmissions Mfr
Export
S.I.C.: 3625
N.A.I.C.S.: 335314
Bill VanArsdale *(Pres)*
Shyam Kambeyanda *(Pres-Americas)*

Divisions:

Eaton Cylinder (3)
2425 W Michigan Ave
Jackson, MI 49202-3964 (100%)
Tel.: (517) 787-7220
Fax: (517) 787-3450
Sales Range: $75-99.9 Million
Emp.: 200
Hydraulic & Pneumatic Cylinder Mfr
Import Export
S.I.C.: 3593
N.A.I.C.S.: 333995

Eaton Filtration LLC (3)
70 Wood Ave S
Iselin, NJ 08830 DE
Tel.: (732) 767-4200
Fax: (732) 494-0793
E-Mail: filtrationinfo@eaton.com
Web Site: www.eaton.com
Sales Range: $100-124.9 Million
Emp.: 600
Industrial Filtration Systems & Separators Mfr
S.I.C.: 3569
N.A.I.C.S.: 333999
Richard B. Jacobs *(Gen Mgr-Filtration Div)*

Unit:

Eaton Filtration LLC - Ronningen-Petter (4)
9151 Shaver Rd
Portage, MI 49024
Tel.: (269) 323-1313
Fax: (269) 323-2403
E-Mail: filtration@eaton.com
Web Site: www.ronningen-petter.com
Sales Range: $25-49.9 Million
Emp.: 42
Filtration Equipment Mfr
S.I.C.: 3569
N.A.I.C.S.: 333999

Plants:

Eaton Hydraulics LLC - Berea (3)
1000 W Bagley Rd
Berea, OH 44017-2906
Tel.: (440) 826-1115
Sales Range: $25-49.9 Million
Emp.: 200
Quick Connective Fluid Line Coupling Mfr
S.I.C.: 3492
N.A.I.C.S.: 332912

Eaton Hydraulics LLC - Spencer (3)
32 Ave W
Spencer, IA 51301
Tel.: (712) 264-3300
Fax: (712) 264-3382
E-Mail: info@eatonhydraulics.com
Web Site: www.eatonhydraulics.com
Sales Range: $100-124.9 Million
Emp.: 400
Hydraulic Solutions
S.I.C.: 3594
N.A.I.C.S.: 333996
Tom Schneider *(VP-Sls & Mktg)*

Non-U.S. Subsidiaries:

Eaton Fluid Power Ltd. (3)
Uruma kowa Building 11-37 8 chome
Tokyo, 107-0052, Japan
Tel.: (81) 357862560
Telex: 223382
Fax: (81) 0357862561
Web Site: www.hydraulics.eaton.com
Sales Range: $25-49.9 Million
Emp.: 30
Hydraulic Motors, Hoses & Fittings Mfr
S.I.C.: 3594
N.A.I.C.S.: 333996

Vickers Systems Ltd. (3)
Unit 18 30 19th Fl Call Ops Park
11 Onlai St, Sha Tin, China (Hong Kong) (100%)
Tel.: (852) 26377803
Telex: 78052002
Fax: (852) 26377212
E-Mail: info@eaton.com
Sls.: $7,400,000
Emp.: 30
Marketing & Sales of Hydraulic Systems
S.I.C.: 3714
N.A.I.C.S.: 336340

Vickers Systems SBPD (3)
Lot 5 Lorang 51A 227B
PO Box 418
46750 Petaling Jaya, Selangor, Malaysia (100%)
Tel.: (60) 377853809
Telex: 78437130
Fax: (60) 378737153
E-Mail: sghyd_si@eaton.com
Sales Range: $10-24.9 Million
Emp.: 10
Distr of Hydraulic Systems
S.I.C.: 3714
N.A.I.C.S.: 336340
George Hendro *(Gen Mgr)*

Non-U.S. Units:

Eaton Ltd. - Hydraulic Systems (3)
Larchwood Avenue
Bedhampton, Havant, Hants, PO9 3QL, United Kingdom (100%)
Tel.: (44) 2392487260
Telex: 851 86749
Fax: (44) 2392492400
E-Mail: help@eaton.com
Web Site: www.aerospace.eaton.com
Sales Range: $50-74.9 Million
Emp.: 135
Mfr. of Valves
S.I.C.: 3492
N.A.I.C.S.: 332912
Collin Hunt *(Plant Mgr)*

Non-U.S. Plant:

Eaton Ltda. - Fluid Power Division, Guaratingueta Plant (3)
Rodovia Washington Luiz 2755 Km 181
Bairro Rio Comprido, CEP 12522-010
Guaratingueta, SP, Brazil
Tel.: (55) 12 3128 6000 (Factory)
Web Site: www.eaton.com.br/fluidpower/fluidpower.asp
Fluid Power Hose, Hose Fittings & Adaptors Mfr
S.I.C.: 3492
N.A.I.C.S.: 332912
Joao Sella *(Dir-Ops)*

Subsidiaries:

Cooper US, Inc. (2)
600 Travis St Ste 5600
Houston, TX 77002-1001 DE
Tel.: (713) 209-8400
Fax: (713) 209-8995
E-Mail: info@cooperindustries.com
Web Site: www.cooperindustries.com
Holding Company; Regional Managing Office
S.I.C.: 6719
N.A.I.C.S.: 551112
Heath B. Monesmith *(VP-HR)*

Subsidiaries:

Cooper B-Line, Inc. (3)
509 W Monroe St
Highland, IL 62249 DE (100%)
Tel.: (618) 654-2184
Fax: (800) 356-1438
Toll Free: (800) 851-7415
E-Mail: blineus@cooperindustries.com
Web Site: www.cooperbline.com
Sales Range: $75-99.9 Million
Emp.: 427
Electronic Products Mfr
S.I.C.: 3441
N.A.I.C.S.: 332312
Joe Klein *(VP-Mktg)*

Subsidiary:

Tolco Incorporated (4)
1375 Sampson Ave
Corona, CA 92879
Tel.: (951) 737-5599
Fax: (951) 737-0330
Toll Free: (800) 786-5266
Web Site: www.tolco.com
Sales Range: $10-24.9 Million
Emp.: 175
Strapping Metal Services
S.I.C.: 3499
N.A.I.C.S.: 332999
Rex R. Martin *(Chm & CEO)*

Plant:

Cooper B-Line, Inc. - Pinckneyville (4)
3764 Longspur Rd
Pinckneyville, IL 62274
Tel.: (618) 357-5353
Fax: (618) 357-3605
Toll Free: (800) 851-9341
E-Mail: blineus@cooperindustries.com
Web Site: www.cooperbline.com
Sales Range: $10-24.9 Million
Emp.: 220
Commercial & Industrial Metal Products
S.I.C.: 3499
N.A.I.C.S.: 332999

Non-U.S. Subsidiary:

Cooper B-Line Limited (4)
Walrow Industrial Estate Highbridge
Somerset, TA9 4AQ, United Kingdom UK (100%)
Tel.: (44) 1278783371
Fax: (44) 1278789037
E-Mail: sales@cooperbline.co.uk
Web Site: www.cooperbline.co.uk
Sales Range: $75-99.9 Million
Emp.: 140
Enclosures for Electronic Products Mfr
S.I.C.: 3663
N.A.I.C.S.: 334220
Nigel Power *(Mng Dir)*

Cooper Bussmann, Inc. (3)
114 Old State Rd
Ellisville, MO 63021-5942 DE
Mailing Address:
PO Box 14460
Saint Louis, MO 63178-4460
Tel.: (636) 394-2877
Fax: (636) 527-1405
E-Mail: fusebox@cooperindustries.com
Web Site: www.cooperbussmann.com
Sales Range: $150-199.9 Million
Emp.: 300
Circuit Protection Management Products Mfr
Export
S.I.C.: 3613
N.A.I.C.S.: 335313
Ivo Jurek *(Pres)*

Non-U.S. Branch:

Cooper (UK) Ltd. Bussman Division (4)
Burton-on-the-Wolds
Loughborough, Leics, LE12 5TH, United Kingdom UK (100%)
Tel.: (44) 1509882737
Fax: (44) 1509882786
E-Mail: exportsales@bussmann.co.uk
Web Site: www.cooperbussmann.com
Sales Range: $50-74.9 Million
Emp.: 220
Electrical Switching & Lighting Equipment Mfr
S.I.C.: 3613
N.A.I.C.S.: 335313
Enzo Strappazzon *(Mng Dir)*

Non-U.S. Subsidiaries:

Arrow-Hart, S.A. de C.V. (4)
Poniente 148 No 933
02300 Mexico, DF, Mexico MX (100%)
Tel.: (52) 5555870211
Fax: (52) 5555674893
Sales Range: $100-124.9 Million
Circuit Protection Products Mfr
S.I.C.: 3613
N.A.I.C.S.: 335313

Martek Power S.A. (4)
15 Rue Bicentenaire de la Revolution ZA Du Parc
Le Plessis-Pate, 91731 Bretigny-sur-Orge, France
Tel.: (33) 69888397
Fax: (33) 69888037
E-Mail: sales@martekpower.fr
Web Site: www.martekpower.com
Sales Range: $200-249.9 Million
Designer & Mfr of Custom Power Systems
S.I.C.: 3612
N.A.I.C.S.: 335311

U.S. Subsidiaries:

Martek Power Abbott, Inc. (5)
1111 Knox St
Torrance, CA 90502
Tel.: (310) 202-8820
Fax: (310) 836-4926
E-Mail: sales.mpa@martekpower.com
Web Site: www.martekpowerabbott.com
Sales Range: $10-24.9 Million
Emp.: 200
Military & Aerospace Power & Electronic Systems
Export
S.I.C.: 3679
N.A.I.C.S.: 334419
Ahmad Innab *(Pres)*

Martek Power Laser Drive LLC (5)
5318 Ranalli Dr
Gibsonia, PA 15044
Tel.: (724) 443-7688
Fax: (724) 444-6430
E-Mail: lasersales@martekpower.com
Web Site: www.laserdrive.com
Emp.: 67
Power Supply Equipment Mfr
S.I.C.: 3699
N.A.I.C.S.: 335999
Richard Matta *(Pres)*

Cooper Crouse-Hinds, LLC (3)
Wolf 7th N St
Syracuse, NY 13221
Mailing Address:
PO Box 4999
Syracuse, NY 13221-4999
Tel.: (315) 477-5531
Fax: (315) 477-5179
Toll Free: (866) 764-5454
E-Mail: crouse.customerctr@cooperindustries.com
Web Site: www.crouse-hinds.com
Sales Range: $250-299.9 Million
Emp.: 600
Explosion-Proof & Non-Explosion-Proof Fittings, Enclosures, Industrial Lighting Plugs & Receptacles, Molded Electrical Products & Conduit & Cable Fittings Mfr
Export
S.I.C.: 5084
N.A.I.C.S.: 423830
Mark Doheny *(VP-Bus Dev)*

Unit:

Cooper Interconnect (4)
23 Front St
Salem, NJ 08079 PA
Tel.: (856) 935-7560
Fax: (856) 935-0102
Toll Free: (800) 840-0502
E-Mail: info@cooperinterconnect.com
Web Site: www.cooperinterconnect.com
Sales Range: $250-299.9 Million
Emp.: 450
Military & Industrial Cable & Connector Mfr
Import Export
S.I.C.: 3357
N.A.I.C.S.: 335929
John Scott Blaine *(Reg Mgr-Sls-West)*

Branches:

Cooper Interconnect (5)
5455 Endeavour Ct
Moorpark, CA 93021-1712
Tel.: (805) 553-9633
Fax: (805) 553-9655
E-Mail: info@cooperinterconnect.com
Web Site: www.cooperinterconnect.com

Sls.: $15,000,000
Emp.: 100
Military & Industrial Wire & Connector Mfr
Import Export
S.I.C.: 3678
N.A.I.C.S.: 334417
Barton Baisley *(Mgr-Reg Sls-Maryland & Virginia)*

Cooper Interconnect (5)
750 W Ventura Blvd
Camarillo, CA 93010-8382 DE
Tel.: (805) 484-0543
Fax: (805) 987-5062
Web Site: www.cooperinterconnect.com
Sales Range: $25-49.9 Million
Emp.: 125
Military & Industrial Cable & Connector Mfr
S.I.C.: 3643
N.A.I.C.S.: 335931
Josh Courval *(Dir-HR)*

Cooper Interconnect (5)
4758 Washington St
La Grange, NC 28551-8150
Tel.: (252) 566-3014
Telex: 579332
Fax: (252) 566-9337
Web Site: www.cooperinterconnect.com
Sales Range: $75-99.9 Million
Emp.: 100
Military & Commercial Cable & Connector Mfr
S.I.C.: 3357
N.A.I.C.S.: 335929
Tom Gray *(Mgr-Matls)*

Non-U.S. Subsidiaries:

CEAG Apparatebau Hundsbach Verwaltungsgesellschaft mbH (4)
Bussmatten 10-12
77815 Buhl, Germany De
Tel.: (49) 72239909117 (100%)
Fax: (49) 7229 9909140
Sales Range: $100-124.9 Million
Electric Protection Products Mfr
S.I.C.: 3669
N.A.I.C.S.: 334290

Subsidiary:

CEAG Notlichtsysteme GmbH (5)
Senator-Schwartz-Ring 26
D-59494 Soest, Germany De
Tel.: (49) 72239909117 (100%)
Fax: (49) 29216909
Web Site: www.ceag.de
Sales Range: $900-999.9 Million
Electronic Protection Products Mfr
S.I.C.: 3548
N.A.I.C.S.: 333992

Cooper Crouse-Hinds GmbH (4)
Senator-Schwartz-Ring
59494 Soest, Germany De
Tel.: (49) 2921690 (100%)
Fax: (49) 292169625
E-Mail: info-ex@cooperindustries.com
Web Site: www.ceag.de
Sales Range: $75-99.9 Million
Emp.: 380
Security Lighting Mfr
S.I.C.: 3646
N.A.I.C.S.: 335122
Guerjen Kuehl *(Mgr-HR)*

Cooper Crouse-Hinds Pte. Ltd. (4)
2 Serangoon N Ave 5 Unit 06-01
554911 Singapore, Singapore SG
Tel.: (65) 62974849 (100%)
Fax: (65) 62974819
Web Site: www.cchspore.com.sg
Sales Range: $900-999.9 Million
Emp.: 40
Electronic Fittings & Enclosures Mfr
S.I.C.: 3548
N.A.I.C.S.: 333992
Derick Teng *(Mgr)*

Cooper Crouse-Hinds S.A. de C.V. (4)
Av Javierr Rojo Gomez No 1170
9300 Mexico, Mexico MX
Tel.: (52) 5558044040 (100%)
Fax: (52) 55580488
E-Mail: invoices.cchm@cooperindustries.com
Web Site: www.crouse-hind.com.mx
Sales Range: $300-349.9 Million
Emp.: 600
Electronic Fittings & Enclosures Mfr
S.I.C.: 3548
N.A.I.C.S.: 333992
Fernando Villanueva *(Dir-Ops)*

Cooper Industries GmbH (4)
Senator-Schwartz-Ring
59494 Soest, Germany De
Tel.: (49) 2921690 (100%)
Fax: (49) 292169625
E-Mail: info@ceag.de
Web Site: www.ceag.de
Sales Range: $100-124.9 Million
Lighting Products Mfr
S.I.C.: 3648
N.A.I.C.S.: 335129

Subsidiary:

Cooper Industries Holdings GmbH (5)
Senator-Schwartz-Ring 26
59494 Soest, Germany De
Tel.: (49) 292169780 (100%)
Fax: (49) 292169618
Web Site: www.stiag.com
Sales Range: $250-299.9 Million
Holding Company
S.I.C.: 6719
N.A.I.C.S.: 551112

Crouse-Hinds (Australia) Pty. Ltd. (4)
391 Park Road
Regents Park, Sydney, NSW, 2143, Australia
Tel.: (61) 2 9743 7000
Fax: (61) 2 9743 7069
Sales Range: $25-49.9 Million
Emp.: 88
Electrical Switching & Lighting Equipment Mfr
S.I.C.: 3613
N.A.I.C.S.: 335313

MTL Instruments Group Ltd. (4)
Great Malin
Butterfield, Luton, LU2 8TL, United Kingdom
Tel.: (44) 1582723633
Fax: (44) 1582422283
E-Mail: enquiry@mtl-inst.com
Web Site: www.mtl-inst.com
Sales Range: $10-24.9 Million
Emp.: 800
Process Control, Safety & Surge Protection Products Mfr
S.I.C.: 5085
N.A.I.C.S.: 423840
David Denton *(Pres-Hazardous Area Bus Unit)*
Dennis Gillespie *(Pres-Open Sys Tech)*
Joreg Shiffer *(Pres-Visualisation Bus Unit)*

Subsidiaries:

Hitech Instruments Limited (5)
20 Titan Court
Laporte Way, Luton, Beds, LU4 8EF, United Kingdom
Tel.: (44) 1582456900
Fax: (44) 1582435600
Web Site: www.hitech-inst.co.uk
Sales Range: $100-124.9 Million
Gas Flow Measurement & Analysis Equipment Mfr
S.I.C.: 3823
N.A.I.C.S.: 334513
John Gass *(Mng Dir)*

Measurement Technology Limited (5)
Great Marlings Butterfield
Luton, Bedfordshire, LU2 8DL, United Kingdom
Tel.: (44) 1582723633
Fax: (44) 158242283
E-Mail: enquiry@mtl-inst.com
Web Site: www.mtl-inst.com
Sales Range: $50-74.9 Million
Emp.: 320
Process Control, Safety & Surge Protection Products Mfr
S.I.C.: 3823
N.A.I.C.S.: 334513
David Frost *(Dir-Sls)*

U.S. Subsidiary:

Atlantic Scientific Corporation (5)
4300 Fortune Pl Ste A
Melbourne, FL 32904-1527
Tel.: (321) 725-8000
Fax: (321) 727-0736
E-Mail: info@atlanticscientific.com
Web Site: www.atlanticscientific.com
Sales Range: $10-24.9 Million
Emp.: 40
Voltage Surge Suppression Equipment Mfr
S.I.C.: 3643
N.A.I.C.S.: 335931
Kimberly Doran *(Dir-Mktg-Sls)*

Non-U.S. Subsidiaries:

GECMA Components Electronic GmbH (5)
Heisenbergstrasse 26 40
50169 Kerpen, Germany
Tel.: (49) 223769960
Fax: (49) 2237699699
E-Mail: joerg.schiffer@cooperindustries.com
Web Site: www.gecma.com
Sales Range: $900-999.9 Million
Emp.: 30
Remote Computer Terminal Developer & Mfr
S.I.C.: 3571
N.A.I.C.S.: 334111
Jorg Schiffer *(Mng Dir)*

MTL Instruments BV (5)
de Houtakker 33
6681 CW Bemmel, Netherlands
Tel.: (31) 767505360
Fax: (31) 481450260
E-Mail: info@mtlbenelux.com
Web Site: www.mpoenfp.com
Sales Range: $100-124.9 Million
Process Control, Safety & Surge Protection Products Mfr
S.I.C.: 3823
N.A.I.C.S.: 334513
C. J. Pont *(Mng Dir)*

MTL Instruments GmbH (5)
An der Gumpgesbrucke 17
41564 Kaarst, Germany
Tel.: (49) 2131718930
Fax: (49) 21317189333
E-Mail: info@mtl.de
Web Site: www.mtl.de
Sales Range: $100-124.9 Million
Emp.: 6
Process Control, Safety & Surge Protection Products Mfr
S.I.C.: 3823
N.A.I.C.S.: 334513
Peter Maxwell *(Gen Mgr-MTL Europe)*

MTL Instruments KK (5)
2-7-5 Shiba Daimon
Minato-ku, Tokyo, 105-0012, Japan
Tel.: (81) 364303128
Fax: (81) 364303129
E-Mail: sales@mtlkk.co.jp
Web Site: www.cooperindustries.jp
Sales Range: $100-124.9 Million
Emp.: 20
Process Control, Safety & Surge Protection Products Mfr
S.I.C.: 3823
N.A.I.C.S.: 334513

MTL Instruments Pvt Limited (5)
No 36 Nehru St Off Old Mahabalipuram Rd
Sholinganallur, Chennai, 600 119, India
Tel.: (91) 4424501660
Fax: (91) 4424501463
E-Mail: sales@mtlindia.com
Web Site: www.mtl-inst.com
Sales Range: $25-49.9 Million
Emp.: 230
Process Control, Safety & Surge Protection Products Mfr
S.I.C.: 3823
N.A.I.C.S.: 334513
R. Srinivasan *(Mgr-Quality & Trng)*

MTL Instruments Pte Limited (5)
31 UBI Road 1
04 01 Aztech Building, Singapore, 408694, Singapore
Tel.: (65) 64877887
Fax: (65) 64877997
Web Site: www.mtl-inst.com
Sales Range: $10-24.9 Million
Emp.: 20
Process Control, Safety & Surge Protection Products Mfr
S.I.C.: 3823
N.A.I.C.S.: 334513
P. T. Lim *(Mng Dir)*

MTL Instruments Pty Limited (5)
Suite 9 12 Billabong Street
Stafford, QLD, 4053, Australia
Tel.: (61) 894552994
Fax: (61) 1300308463
E-Mail: enquiries@mtlaus.com.au
Web Site: www.mtl-inst.com
Sales Range: $100-124.9 Million
Emp.: 2
Process Control, Safety & Surge Protection Products Mfr
S.I.C.: 3823
N.A.I.C.S.: 334513
Michiel Giucy *(Mng Dir)*

MTL Instruments Sarl (5)
7 Rue Des Rosieristes
10 rue des Roiseristes, 69410 Champagne-au-Mont-d'Or, France
Tel.: (33) 478649832
Fax. (33) 478357941
E-Mail: info.chcm@cooperindustries.com
Web Site: www.mtl-inst.com
Sales Range: $1-9.9 Million
Emp.: 8
Process Control, Safety & Surge Protection Products Mfr
S.I.C.: 3823
N.A.I.C.S.: 334513
Samuel Samouelian *(Gen Mgr)*

Cooper Lighting, Inc. (3)
1121 Hwy 74 S
Peachtree City, GA 30269 DE
Tel.: (770) 486-4800 (100%)
Fax: (770) 486-4677
Web Site: www.cooperlighting.com
Sales Range: $150-199.9 Million
Emp.: 600
Lighting Fixtures Mfr
S.I.C.: 3648
N.A.I.C.S.: 335129
Mark Eubanks *(VP & Gen Mgr)*

Plants:

Cooper Lighting (4)
4 Hummingbird Ln
Eufaula, AL 36027-3336
Tel.: (334) 687-5781
Fax: (334) 688-1157
E-Mail: info@cooperlighting.com
Web Site: www.cooperlighting.com
Sales Range: $300-349.9 Million
Emp.: 400
Light Fixtures Mfr
S.I.C.: 2652
N.A.I.C.S.: 322219
Kerk Hetchigian *(Pres)*

Cooper Lighting (4)
1101 Southerfield Rd
Americus, GA 31719
Tel.: (229) 924-8000
Fax: (223) 931-4581
Web Site: www.coopertools.com
Sales Range: $200-249.9 Million
Emp.: 320
Fluorescent Lighting Products Mfr
S.I.C.: 3645
N.A.I.C.S.: 335121

Cooper Lighting (4)
PO Box 820824
Vicksburg, MS 39182-0824
Tel.: (601) 638-1522
Fax: (601) 634-9669
Web Site: www.cooperlighting.com
Sales Range: $150-199.9 Million
Emp.: 500
Lighting Fixtures Mfr
S.I.C.: 3645
N.A.I.C.S.: 335121
Joel Osborne *(Controller)*

Non-U.S. Subsidiary:

Iluminacion Cooper de las Californias S. de R.L. de C.V. (4)
Calle Orbita 3
Col Parque Industrial Mexicali
II, Mexicali, Baja California, 21600,

EATON CORPORATION plc—(Continued)

Mexico MX
Tel.: (52) 6865611916 (100%)
Fax: (52) 6865611832
Web Site: www.grupoalianzaempresarial.com
Sales Range: $200-249.9 Million
Emp.: 750
Lighting Products Mfr
S.I.C.: 3648
N.A.I.C.S.: 335129
Alahnero Jarza *(Mgr)*

Cooper Power Systems, Inc. **(3)**
2300 Badger Dr
Waukesha, WI 53188-5931 DE
Mailing Address: (100%)
PO Box 1640
Waukesha, WI 53187-1640
Tel.: (262) 896-2400
Fax: (262) 896-2313
E-Mail: info@cooperpower.com
Web Site: www.cooperpower.com
Sales Range: $150-199.9 Million
Emp.: 500
Electricity Generators, Regulators & Distributors Mfr
S.I.C.: 3612
N.A.I.C.S.: 335311
Michael A. Stoessl *(Pres)*

Subsidiaries:

Cooper Power Systems Transportation Co. **(4)**
2300 Badger Dr
Waukesha, WI 53188-5931 WI
Tel.: (262) 896-2373
Fax: (262) 896-2355
Web Site: cooperindustries.com
Sales Range: $1-9.9 Million
Emp.: 1,800
Trucking Services
S.I.C.: 4213
N.A.I.C.S.: 484122
Mike Stoessel *(Pres)*

Cooper Power Systems **(4)**
505 Hwy 169 N Ste 1200
Minneapolis, MN 55441
Tel.: (763) 595-7777
Fax: (763) 543-7777
Toll Free: (800) 827-7966
E-Mail: info@cannontech.com
Web Site: www.cooperindustries.com
Sls.: $15,182,117
Emp.: 45
Smart Grid Training & Electrical Power Systems Solutions
S.I.C.: 4931
N.A.I.C.S.: 221122
Jim Losleben *(VP-Bus Dev)*

Plants:

Cooper Power Components & Protective Equipment **(4)**
1045 Hickory St
Pewaukee, WI 53072-3712 (100%)
Tel.: (262) 691-0070
Fax: (262) 691-1148
Web Site: www.cooperpower.com
Sales Range: $400-449.9 Million
Emp.: 410
Molded Rubber & Transformer Components Mfr
S.I.C.: 4971
N.A.I.C.S.: 221310

Cooper Power Systems Kearney Operation **(4)**
3660 S School St
Fayetteville, AR 72701-8026 DE
Tel.: (479) 521-3700 (100%)
Fax: (479) 521-0816
Web Site: www.cooperpower.com
Sales Range: $50-74.9 Million
Emp.: 200
Electrical Components Mfr
S.I.C.: 3612
N.A.I.C.S.: 335311

Cooper Power Systems-Olean Plant **(4)**
1648 Dugan Rd
Olean, NY 14760-9527
Tel.: (716) 375-7100
Fax: (716) 375-7202
E-Mail: oleancommunications@cooperpower.com
Web Site: www.cooperpowersystems.com
Sales Range: $75-99.9 Million
Emp.: 229
Surge Arresters & Current-Limiting Fuse Mfr
S.I.C.: 3612
N.A.I.C.S.: 335311
Michael Salentine *(Gen Mgr)*

Cooper Power Systems **(4)**
2315 SE Stallings Dr Loop 224
Nacogdoches, TX 75961 (100%)
Tel.: (936) 569-9422
Fax: (936) 569-7834
Web Site: www.cooperpower.com
Sales Range: $25-49.9 Million
Emp.: 120
Transformer Mfr
S.I.C.: 3675
N.A.I.C.S.: 334416

Cooper Power Systems **(4)**
1900 E N St
Waukesha, WI 53188-3844
Tel.: (262) 547-1251
Fax: (770) 268-7066
E-Mail: info@cooperpowercentral.com
Web Site: www.cooperpower.com
Sales Range: $50-74.9 Million
Emp.: 300
Transformers & Switches Mfr & Distr
S.I.C.: 3612
N.A.I.C.S.: 335311
Michael Stoessl *(Pres)*

Kyle Distribution Switchgear **(4)**
2800 9th Ave
South Milwaukee, WI 53172-3219 (100%)
Tel.: (414) 762-1200
Fax: (414) 768-8401
Web Site: www.cooperpower.com
Sales Range: $150-199.9 Million
Emp.: 500
Switchgear Mfr
S.I.C.: 3699
N.A.I.C.S.: 335999

Non-U.S. Subsidiaries:

Cooper Electrical Australia Pty. Limited **(4)**
205-209 Woodpark Rd
Smithfield, NSW, 2164, Australia AU
Tel.: (61) 287872778 (100%)
Fax: (61) 296092746
Web Site: www.cooperelectrical.com.au
Sales Range: $10-24.9 Million
Emp.: 65
Electricity Generators, Regulators & Distributors Mfr
S.I.C.: 3677
N.A.I.C.S.: 334416
Peter Raynoodson *(Mgr)*

Cooper Power Systems do Brasil Ltda. **(4)**
R Placido Vieira 79
Sao Paulo, 04754-080, Brazil BR
Tel.: (55) 1156413451 (100%)
Fax: (55) 1165430728
E-Mail: zendas@cooperpower.com.br
Web Site: www.cooperpower.com
Sales Range: $1-9.9 Million
Emp.: 60
Electricity Generators, Regulators & Distributors Mfr
S.I.C.: 3677
N.A.I.C.S.: 334416

Electromanufacturas S.A. de C.V. **(4)**
Antiguo Camino A Tlajomulco No 60
45640 Jalisco, Mexico MX
Tel.: (52) 3337703682 (100%)
Fax: (52) 3337703670249
E-Mail: cooperpowersystems@cooperpower.com.mx
Web Site: www.cooperpower.com
Sales Range: $100-124.9 Million
Emp.: 200
Transformer Mfr
S.I.C.: 3677
N.A.I.C.S.: 334416

Non-U.S. Plant:

Cooper Power Systems Inc. **(4)**
2-7 Nan-Yuan
Chung Li Industrial Zone, Taoyuan, Hsien, 32041, Taiwan TW
Tel.: (886) 34529101 (100%)
Fax: (886) 34529102
Web Site: www.cooperpower.com
Sales Range: $25-49.9 Million
Emp.: 100
Fuses & Molded Rubber Products Mfr
S.I.C.: 3069
N.A.I.C.S.: 326299

Cooper Wiring Devices **(3)**
203 Cooper Cir
Peachtree City, GA 30269 NY
Tel.: (770) 631-2100 (100%)
Fax: (770) 631-2106
Toll Free: (866) 853-4293
E-Mail: custserv@cooperwiringdevices.com
Web Site: www.cooperwiringdevices.com
Sales Range: $100-124.9 Million
Wiring Device Mfr
Import Export
S.I.C.: 3643
N.A.I.C.S.: 335931
Tom Benton *(VP-Mktg)*

Innovative Technology, Inc. **(2)**
1000 Cherrington Pkwy
Pittsburgh, PA 15108
Tel.: (352) 799-0713
Fax: (352) 796-0316
Toll Free: (800) 647-8877
Web Site: www.innovativetechnology.com
Sales Range: $1-9.9 Million
Emp.: 6
Voltage Surge Supressors
S.I.C.: 3643
N.A.I.C.S.: 335931

Wright Line LLC **(2)**
160 Gold Star Blvd
Worcester, MA 01606-2791
Tel.: (508) 852-4300
Fax: (508) 365-6178
Electrical Equipment Mfr
S.I.C.: 3699
N.A.I.C.S.: 335999
Daniel Herrick *(VP-Global Supply Chain)*

Joint Venture:

Engineered Sintered Components Co. **(2)**
250 Old Murdock Rd
Troutman, NC 28166-9655
Tel.: (704) 528-7500
Fax: (704) 528-7529
E-Mail: webmaster@engsin.com
Web Site: www.engsin.com
Sales Range: $100-124.9 Million
Powered Metal Structural Parts for Drivetrain & Engine Accessory Applications in Cars, Light Trucks & Off-Highway Vehicles; Joint Venture between Sumitomo Electric Industries Ltd. (96.5%) & Eaton Corporation (3.5%)
S.I.C.: 3462
N.A.I.C.S.: 332111
Ryu Goto *(Pres)*

Units:

Eaton Corp. - Airflex **(2)**
9919 Clinton Rd
Cleveland, OH 44144-1035
Tel.: (216) 281-2211
Telex: 212-559 aflx ur
Fax: (216) 281-3890
Toll Free: (800) AIRFLEX
E-Mail: airflexcustomerservice@eaton.com
Web Site: www.airflex.com
Sales Range: $75-99.9 Million
Emp.: 200
Industrial Clutches, Brakes & Assemblies Mfr
Import Export
S.I.C.: 3714
N.A.I.C.S.: 336340

Eaton Corp. - Golf Grip **(2)**
16900 Aberdeen Rd
Laurinburg, NC 28352
Mailing Address:
PO Box 1848
Laurinburg, NC 28353-1848
Tel.: (910) 277-3770
Telex: 70-5152 eaton ud
Fax: (910) 277-3700
Web Site: www.golfpride.com
Sales Range: $50-74.9 Million
Emp.: 100
Golf Club Grip Mfr
S.I.C.: 3069
N.A.I.C.S.: 326299
Jeff Fiorini *(Gen Mgr)*

Eaton Corp. - Industrial Controls **(2)**
4201 N 27th St
Milwaukee, WI 53216-1807
Tel.: (414) 449-6207
Telex: 26-716 EATON CH MIL
Fax: (414) 449-7368
Toll Free: (800) 962-0820
Web Site: www.eaton.com
Sales Range: $25-49.9 Million
Emp.: 50
Switches Mfr
Export
S.I.C.: 3621
N.A.I.C.S.: 335312

Non-U.S. Subsidiaries:

Aeroquip Iberica S.L. **(2)**
Avda Complutense 109
Alcala de Henares, 28805, Spain
Tel.: (34) 918770555
Fax: (34) 918882313
Electrical Equipment Mfr
S.I.C.: 3699
N.A.I.C.S.: 335999

Centralion Industrial Inc. **(2)**
No 93 Shin Hu 3rd Rd
Neihu, Taipei, 114, Taiwan
Tel.: (886) 227946363
Fax: (886) 266068704
Web Site: www.centralion.com.tw
Electrical Equipment Manufacturers
S.I.C.: 3699
N.A.I.C.S.: 335999
Hsui-Chu Cheng *(Pres)*
Alex Wei *(Mng Dir)*

Cooper Controls Ltd. **(2)**
Usk House Lakeside
Llantarnam Park, Cwmbran, NP44 3HD, United Kingdom
Tel.: (44) 1633833120
Fax: (44) 1633867880
E-Mail: enquiries@coopercontrols.co.uk
Web Site: www.coopercontrol.com
Emp.: 80
Lighting Controls
S.I.C.: 3646
N.A.I.C.S.: 335122
Chris Claton *(Gen Mgr)*

U.S. Division:

Cooper Controls Ltd. **(3)**
203 Cooper Cir
Peachtree City, GA 30269
Tel.: (770) 486-4782
Fax: (800) 954-7016
Toll Free: (800) 553-3879
E-Mail: controls@cooperindustries.com
Web Site: www.coopercontrol.com
Emp.: 75
Energy Management, Architectural, Entertainment & Lighting Controls
S.I.C.: 3648
N.A.I.C.S.: 335129
Kenneth Walma *(Gen Mgr)*

Unit:

Cooper Controls **(4)**
6 Green Tree Dr
South Burlington, VT 05403-6025
Tel.: (802) 658-6445
Fax: (802) 658-6934
E-Mail: info@pcilightingcontrols.com
Web Site: www.pcilightingcontrols.com
Sales Range: $1-9.9 Million
Emp.: 25
Digital Lighting Control Panels Mfr
S.I.C.: 3648
N.A.I.C.S.: 335129
Michael Lunn *(Mgr-IT & Quotations & Applications)*

Cooper Industries (Canada), Inc. **(2)**
5925 McLaughlin Road
Mississauga, ON, L5R 1B8, Canada ON
Tel.: (905) 501-3000 (100%)
Web Site: www.cooperindustries.com
Sales Range: $25-49.9 Million
Emp.: 30
Hand Tools Distr
S.I.C.: 3423
N.A.I.C.S.: 332216

Paul Whalen *(Mgr-Sls)*

Cooper Safety (2)
Jephson Court
Tancred Close, Leamington Spa, Warks, CV31 3RZ, United Kingdom (100%)
Tel.: (44) 1926439200
Fax: (44) 1926 439240
E-Mail: enquiries@cooper-safety.com
Web Site: www.cooper-safety.com
Emp.: 2,000
Emergency Lighting, Security Systems, Fire Detection Systems, Lighting Fixtures & Lamps & Electrical Installation Materials Mfr
S.I.C.: 3646
N.A.I.C.S.: 335122

Subsidiaries:

Mount Engineering Plc (3)
Chocolate Works
Bishopthorpe Rd
York, York, YO23 1DE, United Kingdom
Tel.: (44) 7778160365
Fax: (44) 7834046121
Sales Range: $10-24.9 Million
Emp.: 84
Engineering Manufacturing & Distribution Providers
S.I.C.: 8711
N.A.I.C.S.: 541330
Colin Davies *(Dir-Fin)*

Subsidiaries:

Raxton Limited (4)
Kingsway S
Westgate, Aldridge, West Midlands, United Kingdom
Tel.: (44) 1922450400
Fax: (44) 1922450401
E-Mail: enquiries@raxton.co.uk
Web Site: www.raxton.co.uk
Emp.: 30
Electrical Thread Adaptors & Reducers & Stopping Plugs Mfr
S.I.C.: 3612
N.A.I.C.S.: 335311

Redapt Engineering Company Limited (4)
Units 46 & 47 Darlaston Cent Trading Estate Salisbury St
Darlaston, West Midlands, WS10 8XB, United Kingdom
Tel.: (44) 1215267058
Fax: (44) 1215265076
E-Mail: redapt@redapt.co.uk
Web Site: www.redapt.co.uk
Emp.: 29
Plugs & Adaptors Mfr
S.I.C.: 3676
N.A.I.C.S.: 334416

Subsidiary:

Fulleon Limited (3)
Llantarnam Pk
Cwmbran, Gwent, NP44 3AW, United Kingdom UK
Tel.: (44) 1633628500 (100%)
Fax: (44) 1633866346
E-Mail: information@fulleon.co.uk
Web Site: www.fulleon.co.uk
Sales Range: $25-49.9 Million
Emp.: 100
Emergency Lighting & Security Systems Mfr
S.I.C.: 3648
N.A.I.C.S.: 335129
Robert Campbell *(Mng Dir)*

Unit:

Cooper Lighting & Safety Ltd. (3)
Wheatley Hall Rd
Doncaster, S Yorkshire, DN2 4NB, United Kingdom UK
Tel.: (44) 01302321541 (100%)
Fax: (44) 01302303213
E-Mail: user@cooperindustries.com
Web Site: www.cooper-ls.com
Sales Range: $250-299.9 Million
Emp.: 800
Mains Lighting, Emergency Lighting & Fire Detection Equipment Mfr
Import Export
S.I.C.: 3648
N.A.I.C.S.: 335129
Gavin Smith *(Mng Dir)*

U.S. Division:

Cooper Wheelock (3)
273 Branchport Ave
Long Branch, NJ 07740-6830
Tel.: (732) 222-6880
Fax: (732) 222-8707
Toll Free: (800) 631-2148
Web Site: www.cooperwheelock.com
Sls.: $30,000,000
Emp.: 350
Fire Safety & Emergency Incident Communications Systems & Devices Designer & Mfr
S.I.C.: 3669
N.A.I.C.S.: 334290
Scott Hearn *(Pres)*

Non-U.S. Subsidiaries:

CEAG Notlichtsysteme GmbH (3)
Senator-Schwartz-Ring 26
59494 Soest, Germany
Tel.: (49) 2921690
Fax: (49) 292169617
E-Mail: info-n@ceag.de
Web Site: www.ceag.de
Sales Range: $50-74.9 Million
Emp.: 200
Emergency Lighting & Battery Systems Mfr
S.I.C.: 3646
N.A.I.C.S.: 335122
Marcus Eisenhuth *(Mng Dir)*
Klaus Vatter *(Mng Dir)*

Cooper Menvier B.V. (3)
PO Box 3397
4800 DJ Breda, Netherlands NL
Tel.: (31) 765715160 (100%)
Fax: (31) 765871422
E-Mail: info@coopersafety.nl
Web Site: www.coopersafety.nl
Sales Range: $10-24.9 Million
Emp.: 50
Emergency Lighting, Fire Detection & Security Systems Mfr
S.I.C.: 3648
N.A.I.C.S.: 335129
E. DeGrande *(Mng Dir)*

HERNIS Scan Systems AS (3)
Tangen Alle 41
PO Box 791
4809 Arendal, Norway (100%)
Tel.: (47) 37063700
Fax: (47) 37063706
E-Mail: cctv@hernis.no
Web Site: www.hernis.com
Emp.: 120
CCTV Systems Mfr
S.I.C.: 4813
N.A.I.C.S.: 517110
Egil Norman OLsen *(Mng Dir)*

Subsidiaries:

HERNIS Scan Systems Asia Pte Ltd (4)
2 Serangoon North Avenue 5
06-01 Fu Yu Building, Singapore, 554911, Singapore
Tel.: (65) 65459068
Fax: (65) 65429068
E-Mail: cctv.singapore@hernis.com
Web Site: www.hernis.com
Emp.: 12
CCTV Systems Mfr
S.I.C.: 3663
N.A.I.C.S.: 334220
Olav Eikrem *(Mng Dir)*

HERNIS Scan Systems do Brasil (4)
Av. Francisco Alexandre Vieira
1660-LT01-QD03 Rio de Janeiro, Riovonico, 2880-000, Brazil
Tel.: (55) 2127340275
Fax: (55) 2136344653
Emp.: 15
CCV Systems Mfr
S.I.C.: 4813
N.A.I.C.S.: 517110
Gare Logfdom *(Office Mgr)*

HERNIS Scan Systems - US Inc. (4)
2000 Dairy Ashford
Houston, TX 77077
Tel.: (281) 560-8050
Fax: (281) 560-8054
CCTV Systems Mfr
S.I.C.: 4813
N.A.I.C.S.: 517110

Petronica-Precisao Electronica, Lda. (3)
Parque Industrial Serra Das Minas
Armazem C Piso 2
2635-001 Rio de Mouro, Portugal PT
Tel.: (351) 219198500 (100%)
Fax: (351) 219198501
E-Mail: geral@cooperpetronica.com
Web Site: www.cooperpetronica.pt
Sales Range: $10-24.9 Million
Emp.: 15
Emergency Lighting & Security Systems Mfr
S.I.C.: 3648
N.A.I.C.S.: 335129
Paolo Almeida *(Dir-Fin & Admin)*

CopperLogic, Ltd. (2)
505 Rue Edouard
Granby, QC, J2G 3Z5, Canada
Tel.: (450) 378-2244
Electronic Control Mfr
S.I.C.: 3625
N.A.I.C.S.: 335314

Eaton Automotive G.m.b.H. (2)
Bleicheroder Strasse 2
Nordhausen, 99734, Germany
Tel.: (49) 36319290
Fax: (49) 3631929113
Automotive Component Mfr
S.I.C.: 3714
N.A.I.C.S.: 336390

Eaton Controls, S. de R.L. de C.V. (2)
Av Chapultepec S/N
Reynosa, Tamaulipas, 88500, Mexico
Tel.: (52) 8999211510
Electrical Equipment Mfr
S.I.C.: 3699
N.A.I.C.S.: 335999

Eaton Electrical, S.A. (2)
Avenida Libertador El Rosal Ed Lex Piso 1
Caracas, 1060, Venezuela
Tel.: (58) 2129531697
Fax: (58) 2129532585
Web Site: www.Eaton.com
Emp.: 20
Electrical Equipment Mfr
S.I.C.: 3699
N.A.I.C.S.: 335999
Norberto Irausquin *(Gen Mgr)*

Eaton Filtration (Shanghai) Co. Ltd. (2)
No 3 Lane 280 Linhong Road
Changning District, Shanghai, 200335, China
Tel.: (86) 21 5200 0422
Fax: (86) 21 5200 0400
Web Site: www.eaton.com
Electrical Equipment Mfr
S.I.C.: 3699
N.A.I.C.S.: 335999

Eaton Holec AB (2)
PO Box 50105
202 11 Malmo, Sweden SE
Tel.: (46) 40438840
Fax: (46) 40438859
E-Mail: infose@eaton.com
Electrical Equipment Mfr
S.I.C.: 3699
N.A.I.C.S.: 335999

Eaton Industrial Systems Private Limited (2)
Plot No B-33 Ranjangaon Industrial Area
Ranjangaon Taluka
Shirur, Pune, Maharashtra, 412 210, India
Tel.: (91) 2138 674500
Electrical Equipment Mfr
S.I.C.: 3699
N.A.I.C.S.: 335999
Nitin Chalke *(Mng Dir)*

Eaton Industries Manufacturing GmbH (2)
Route de la Longeraie 7
CH-1110 Morges, Switzerland CH
Tel.: (41) 218114600
Fax: (41) 218114601
Web Site: www.eaton.com
Emp.: 150
Holding Company; Regional Managing Office
S.I.C.: 6719
N.A.I.C.S.: 551112
Yannis P. Tsavalas *(Reg Pres-Europe, Middle East & Africa)*
Frank C. Campbell *(Pres-Electrical Sector-EMEA)*

Subsidiary:

Eaton Manufacturing GmbH (3)
Route de la Longeraie 7
CH-1110 Morges, Switzerland CH
Tel.: (41) 218114600
Fax: (41) 218114601
E-Mail: ehq-reception@eaton.com
Emp.: 150
Electrical, Hydraulic, Aerospace & Motor Vehicle Products Mfr, Distr & Support Services
S.I.C.: 5063
N.A.I.C.S.: 423610
Cyrille Brisson *(VP & Gen Mgr-Distributed Power Quality Div)*

Affiliate:

Micro Innovation Holding AG (3)
Spinnereistrasse 8 14
9008 Saint Gallen, Switzerland
Tel.: (41) 712432400
Fax: (41) 712432490
E-Mail: info@eaton.com
Web Site: www.eaton-ultimation.com
Sales Range: $50-74.9 Million
Emp.: 100
Holding Company
S.I.C.: 6719
N.A.I.C.S.: 551112
Craig McDonald *(VP)*

Subsidiary:

Micro Innovation AG (4)
Spinnereistrasse 8 14
9008 Saint Gallen, Switzerland
Tel.: (41) 712432424
Fax: (41) 712432490
E-Mail: info@eaton.com
Web Site: www.eaton-automation.com
Sales Range: $100-124.9 Million
Emp.: 40
Process Automation Electronic Sensor, Software & Component Developer & Mfr
S.I.C.: 3823
N.A.I.C.S.: 334513
M. Allenspach *(Head-Tech)*

Non-U.S. Subsidiaries:

Eaton Electric ApS (3)
Niels Bohrs Vej 2
7100 Vejle, Denmark DK
Tel.: (45) 76405400 (100%)
Fax: (45) 76405401
E-Mail: infodk@eaton.com
Web Site: www.eatonelectric.dk
Sales Range: $25-49.9 Million
Emp.: 120
Mfr of Switchgears
S.I.C.: 3613
N.A.I.C.S.: 335313

Eaton Electric Limited (3)
Reddings Lane
Tyseley, Birmingham, B11 3EZ, United Kingdom UK
Tel.: (44) 1216852100
Fax: (44) 12 706 2012
E-Mail: ukcommorders@eaton.com
Electrical Distribution & Power Control Equipment Mfr & Distr
S.I.C.: 3699
N.A.I.C.S.: 335999

Eaton Electric Sales S.A.S. (3)
346 Rue de la Belle Etoile
PO Box 51060
Charles De Gaulle, F-95947 Roissy-en-France, France FR
Tel.: (33) 141845050
Fax: (33) 141845040
E-Mail: eatonelctricfrance@eaton.com
Web Site: www.eaton.fr
Sales Range: $50-74.9 Million
Emp.: 75
Electrical Circuit Breaker, Relay & Control Device Mfr
S.I.C.: 3699
N.A.I.C.S.: 335999
Anne Varon *(Mng Dir)*

EATON CORPORATION plc—(Continued)

Eaton Germany GmbH (3)
Dr Reckeweg Strasse 1
D-76532 Baden-Baden, Germany De
Tel.: (49) 72216820 (100%)
Fax: (49) 7221682277
Web Site: www.eaton.de
Sales Range: $400-449.9 Million
Emp.: 650
Electrical & Filtration Products Mfr & Distr
S.I.C.: 8741
N.A.I.C.S.: 561110
Carsten Krenz *(Mng Dir)*
Gunter Lungershausen *(Mng Dir)*
Jorg Quittkat *(Mng Dir)*

Subsidiaries:

Eaton Holding Investments GmbH & Co. KG (4)
Hammfelddamm 6
Allerheiligen, D-41460 Neuss, Germany De
Mailing Address: (100%)
Postfach 21 03 62
D-41429 Neuss, Germany
Tel.: (49) 213140630
Fax: (49) 21314063188
E-Mail: elekinfo@eaton.com
Web Site: www.elek.de
Sales Range: $10-24.9 Million
Emp.: 10
Switchgear Mfr
S.I.C.: 3613
N.A.I.C.S.: 335313
Andrea Pestheges *(Controller)*

Eaton Industries GmbH (4)
Hein Moeller Str 7 11
53115 Bonn, Germany De
Tel.: (49) 2286020
Fax: (49) 2286022433
E-Mail: info@eaton.com
Web Site: www.moeller.net
Sales Range: $1-4.9 Billion
Emp.: 9,550
Power Distribution & Control System Electrical Components Mfr
S.I.C.: 3823
N.A.I.C.S.: 334513

Non-U.S. Subsidiaries:

Eaton GmbH (5)
Scheydgasse 42
1215 Vienna, Austria
Tel.: (43) 1 277 45 0
Fax: (43) 50868 3500
E-Mail: infoAustria@eaton.com
Web Site: wwweaton.com
Sales Range: $450-499.9 Million
Emp.: 1,250
Commercial & Residential Lighting, Heating & Air Conditioning Control Systems Mfr
S.I.C.: 3822
N.A.I.C.S.: 334512
Erich Weber *(Mng Dir)*

Moeller Electric NV/SA (5)
Leuvensesteenweg 555 ingang 4
1930 Zaventem, Belgium
Tel.: (32) 27198811
Fax: (32) 27250072
E-Mail: receptionzaventem@eaton.com
Web Site: www.moeller.be
Sales Range: $10-24.9 Million
Emp.: 19
Electrical Circuit Breaker, Relay & Control Device Mfr
S.I.C.: 3548
N.A.I.C.S.: 333992

Eaton Industries (Netherlands) B.V. (3)
Europlaan 202
7559 SC Hengelo, Netherlands NL
Mailing Address:
Postbus 23
7550 AA Hengelo, Netherlands
Tel.: (31) 1742469111
Fax: (31) 174246444
E-Mail: holec-info@eaton.com
Web Site: www.eaton.com
Sales Range: $450-499.9 Million
Emp.: 1,000
Electrical Components Mfr
S.I.C.: 3548
N.A.I.C.S.: 333992
John Stampsal *(Gen Mgr)*

Division:

Eaton Industries (Netherlands) B.V. - Hydraulics Division (4)
Hoppenkuil 6
NL-5626 DD Eindhoven, Netherlands
Mailing Address:
Postbus 9707
5602 LS Eindhoven, Netherlands
Tel.: (31) 402629900
Fax: (31) 40 262 3325
E-Mail: info.hydrowa@eaton.com
Web Site: www.eatonindustries.nl/cms
Sales Range: $50-74.9 Million
Emp.: 100
Hydraulic Cylinder Mfr
S.I.C.: 3593
N.A.I.C.S.: 333995
Peter Claessens *(Reg Mgr)*

Eaton Power Quality Limited (3)
221 Dover Road
Slough, Berks, SL1 4RF, United Kingdom UK
Tel.: (44) 1753608700
Fax: (44) 1753608995
E-Mail: powerqualityuk-info@eaton.com
Web Site: www.powerquality.eaton.com
Emp.: 70
Electrical Monitoring & Power Management Systems Distr & Support Services
S.I.C.: 5063
N.A.I.C.S.: 423610
Mark Derbyshire *(Mng Dir)*

Subsidiary:

Eaton Power Solutions Limited (4)
Heath Place
Ash Grove, Bognor Regis, W Sussex, PO22 9SJ, United Kingdom UK
Tel.: (44) 1243810500
Telex: 86543 WEIR G
Fax: (44) 1243868613
Web Site: www.powerware.com
Sales Range: $25-49.9 Million
Emp.: 100
Electrical Monitoring & Power Management Systems Distr & Support Services
S.I.C.: 5063
N.A.I.C.S.: 423610
Iaim Coopet *(Mng Dir)*

Eaton Industries Private Limited (2)
Interim Building 145 Masulkar Colony
Off Mumbai Pune Road, Pimpri, Pune, 411 018, India
Tel.: (91) 2066338610
Fax: (91) 2066338585
Electrical Equipment Mfr
S.I.C.: 3699
N.A.I.C.S.: 335999

Eaton Industries, S. de R.L. de C.V. (2)
Brecha E Ste 99 S/N Carr Reynosa Rio Bravo
Reynosa, TAM, 88780, Mexico
Tel.: (52) 8999540200
Fax: (52) 8999540220
Electrical Equipment Mfr
S.I.C.: 3699
N.A.I.C.S.: 335999

Eaton Industries (Shanghai) Co., Ltd. (2)
No 3 Lane 280 Linhong Road
Changning District, Shanghai, 200335, China CN
Tel.: (86) 2152000099
Fax: (86) 2152000400
E-Mail: ChinaWeb@eaton.com
Web Site: www.eaton.com.cn
Holding Company; Regional Managing Office
S.I.C.: 6719
N.A.I.C.S.: 551112
Curtis J. Hutchins *(Reg Pres-Asia Pacific)*
Howard Liu *(Pres-Vehicle Grp-Asia Pacific)*
Erbing Shang *(Pres-China)*
Joe-Tao Zhou *(Pres-Aerospace Grp-Asia Pacific)*

Subsidiary:

Eaton Electrical Ltd. (3)
No 3 Lane 280 Linhong Road
Changning District, Shanghai, 200335, China CN
Tel.: (86) 21 5200 0099
Fax: (86) 21 5200 0500
Web Site: www.eatonelectrical.com.cn
Emp.: 300
Electrical Power Distribution, Control & Management Products Mfr & Distr
S.I.C.: 3699
N.A.I.C.S.: 335999
Curt Hutchins *(Pres-Asia Pacific)*

Subsidiary:

Zhenjiang Daqo Eaton Electrical Systems Company Limited (4)
No 66 Xin Zhong South Road Xinba Town
Yangzhong, Jiangsu, 212211, China CN
Tel.: (86) 511 88411360
Fax: (86) 511 822 1717
Web Site: en.daqo.com
Sales Range: $100-124.9 Million
Switchgear Mfr
S.I.C.: 3613
N.A.I.C.S.: 335313

Non-U.S. Subsidiaries:

Eaton Industries Pty. Ltd. (3)
10 Kent Road
Mascot, NSW, 2020, Australia AU
Tel.: (61) 296939333 (100%)
Telex: AA 24570 CUTHAM
Fax: (61) 296673820
E-Mail: australiasupport@eaton.com
Web Site: www.eatonelectric.com.au
Sales Range: $50-74.9 Million
Emp.: 120
Mfr of Power Distribution Equipment, Electrical Control Products, & Advanced Industrial Automation Solutions
S.I.C.: 3612
N.A.I.C.S.: 541420

Eaton Technologies Limited (3)
No 3 Lane 280 LinHong Road
Shanghai, 200335, China (100%)
Tel.: (86) 21 5200 0099
Telex: 780-49217
Web Site: www.eaton.com.cn
Sales Range: $75-99.9 Million
Technological Services
S.I.C.: 7389
N.A.I.C.S.: 541990

Non-U.S. Unit:

Bill Switchgear (3)
2413 Lorong Perusahaan 10
13600 Penang, Malaysia
Tel.: (60) 43897566
Fax: (60) 43907643
E-Mail: cheekheongong@eaton.com
Web Site: www.etn.com
Sales Range: $75-99.9 Million
Emp.: 55
Switchgear Mfr
S.I.C.: 3613
N.A.I.C.S.: 335313
Chee Kheong Ong *(Mng Dir)*

Eaton Phoenixtec MMPL Co.,Ltd. (2)
No 114 Shi Wan Road Kuijen Hsiang
Taipei, 71152, Taiwan
Tel.: (886) 65950100
Fax: (886) 65952612
Electrical Equipment Mfr
S.I.C.: 3699
N.A.I.C.S.: 335999

Eaton Power Quality AB (2)
Leverantorsreskontra
Box 1085
164 25 Kista, Sweden
Tel.: (46) 859894000
Fax: (46) 859894040
E-Mail: infosweden@eaton.com
Web Site: www.powerquality.eaton.com
Electrical Equipment Mfr
S.I.C.: 3699
N.A.I.C.S.: 335999

Eaton Power Quality Oy (2)
Koskelontie 14
PL 54
2920 Espoo, Finland
Tel.: (358) 9452661
Fax: (358) 945266568
Web Site: www.eaton.com
Electrical Equipment Mfr
S.I.C.: 3699
N.A.I.C.S.: 335999
Petri Koskinen *(Gen Mgr)*

Institute for International Product Safety GmbH (2)
Hein-Moeller-Str 7-11
Bonn, 53115, Germany
Tel.: (49) 2286022538
Fax: (49) 2286021149
Electrical Equipment Mfr
S.I.C.: 3699
N.A.I.C.S.: 335999

Moeller Electric SIA (2)
Zemitana iela 2b
Riga, 1012, Latvia
Tel.: (371) 67844435
Fax: (371) 67844436
E-Mail: office.lv@eaton.com
Emp.: 11
Electrical Equipment Mfr
S.I.C.: 3699
N.A.I.C.S.: 335999
Ragnar Roos *(Mgr-Sls)*

EATONFIELD GROUP PLC

Haycroft Farm Peckforton Hall Lane
Spurstow, Tarporley, Cheshire, CW6 9TF, United Kingdom
Tel.: (44) 1829 261910
Fax: (44) 1819 261911
E-Mail: enquiries@eatonfield.co.uk
Web Site: www.eatonfield.co.uk
EFD—(AIM)
Emp.: 14

Business Description:
Commercial Property & Real Estate Development & Sales
S.I.C.: 6531
N.A.I.C.S.: 531390

Personnel:
Brian Corfe *(Chm)*
Rob J. W. Lloyd *(CEO)*
Keith Mather *(Sec)*

Board of Directors:
Brian Corfe
Rob J. W. Lloyd

Legal Counsel:
Davenport Lyons
30 Old Burlington Street
London, W1S 3NL, United Kingdom

Subsidiary:

Eatonfield Developments Limited (1)
Haycroft Farm Peckforton Hall Ln
Spurstow, Tarporley, Cheshire, CW6 9TF, United Kingdom
Tel.: (44) 1829261910
Fax: (44) 1829261911
E-Mail: enquiries@eatonfield.co.uk
Web Site: www.eatonfield.co.uk
Emp.: 9
Commercial Property Development Services
S.I.C.: 6531
N.A.I.C.S.: 531312
Ian Arnott *(Dir-Dev)*

EATWARE INC.

23rd Floor Westin Center 26 Hung To Road
Kwun Tong, Kowloon, China (Hong Kong)
Tel.: (852) 2295 1818
CHSH—(OTC)
Sales Range: $1-9.9 Million

Business Description:
Flatware Mfr
S.I.C.: 3421
N.A.I.C.S.: 332215

Personnel:
Man-Shing Wu *(Chm & CEO)*

EAVS SA

12 avenue des Coquelicots ZA des Petits Carreaux
94138 Bonneuil-sur-Marne, France
Tel.: (33) 145132860
Fax: (33) 143779447
E-Mail: foemso@eavs.fr

Web Site: www.eavs.fr
MLEAV—(EUR)
Sales Range: $1-9.9 Million
Emp.: 40

Business Description:
Audiovisual & Surveillance Products
S.I.C.: 3651
N.A.I.C.S.: 334310

Personnel:
Christophe Botteri *(Pres)*

E.B. CREASY & COMPANY PLC

No 98 Sri Sangaraja Mawatha
Colombo, 10, Sri Lanka
Tel.: (94) 114766000
Fax: (94) 112478775
E-Mail: hardware@creasy.lk
Web Site: www.ebcreasy.com
EBCR—(COL)
Rev.: $228,386,393
Assets: $232,656,942
Liabilities: $162,723,914
Net Worth: $69,933,028
Earnings: $5,845,212
Emp.: 26,000
Fiscal Year-end: 03/31/13

Business Description:
Batteries & Spray Paint Mfr
S.I.C.: 1761
N.A.I.C.S.: 238160

Personnel:
Alagarajah Rajaratnam *(Chm)*
S. Dhaman Rajendram Arudpragasam *(Mng Dir)*
Parakrama Maithri Asoka Sirimane *(CFO)*
Sanjeev Rajaratnam *(Deputy Mng Dir)*

Board of Directors:
Alagarajah Rajaratnam
S. Dhaman Rajendram Arudpragasam
Ranjit Noel Bopearatchy
Shanthikumar Nimal Placidus Palihena
Sanjeev Rajaratnam
Albert Rasakantha Rasiah
Parakrama Maithri Asoka Sirimane
Rohan Chrisantha Anil Welikala

Legal Counsel:
Julius & Creasy
PO Box 154
Colombo, Sri Lanka

EB MAWSON & SONS PTY LTD.

141 King George St
Cohuna, VIC, 3568, Australia
Tel.: (61) 0354562409
Fax: (61) 0354562428
E-Mail: enquiries@mawsons.com.au
Web Site: www.mawsons.com.au
Sales Range: $25-49.9 Million
Emp.: 200

Business Description:
Concrete Products & Equipment
S.I.C.: 3272
N.A.I.C.S.: 327390

Personnel:
John Mawson *(Mng Dir)*

EBARA CORPORATION

11-1 Haneda Asahi-cho
Ohta-ku, Tokyo, 144-8510, Japan
Tel.: (81) 337436111
Telex: J22988 EBARA TYO
Fax: (81) 357363100
E-Mail: webmaster@ebara.com
Web Site: www.ebara.co.jp
Year Founded: 1912
6361—(TKS)
Sls.: $4,689,322,000
Assets: $5,550,336,000
Liabilities: $3,440,690,000
Net Worth: $2,109,646,000
Earnings: $168,333,000
Emp.: 15,170
Fiscal Year-end: 03/31/13

Business Description:
Mfr of Fluid Machinery; Construction of Environment Protection Facilities; Manufacturing of Precision Machinery for Semiconductor Industry
Import Export
S.I.C.: 3589
N.A.I.C.S.: 333318

Personnel:
Natsunosuke Yago *(Chm)*
Toichi Maeda *(Pres)*
Masao Asami *(Exec Officer)*
Kengo Choki *(Exec Officer)*
Tetsuji Fujimoto *(Sr Mng Exec Officer)*
Kiyoshi Hirono *(Exec Officer)*
Takao Inoue *(Exec Officer)*
Akira Itoh *(Mng Exec Officer)*
Hidenori Iwanaga *(Exec Officer)*
Seiji Katsuoka *(Exec Officer)*
Akihiro Kida *(Exec Officer)*
Norio Kimura *(Exec Officer)*
Shotaro Kuryu *(Mng Exec Officer)*
Takafumi Maehara *(Exec Officer)*
Hisao Matsumoto *(Exec Officer)*
Nobuharu Noji *(Mng Exec Officer)*
Akira Ogata *(Mng Exec Officer)*
Kazuhiro Ogawara *(Exec Officer)*
Atsuo Ohi *(Mng Exec Officer)*
Yoshiaki Okiyama *(Exec Officer)*
Koji Ota *(Exec Officer)*
Masaru Shibuya *(Mng Exec Officer)*
Susumu Shiga *(Exec Officer)*
Mitsuhiko Shirakashi *(Exec Officer)*
Minoru Takano *(Exec Officer)*
Akio Teragaki *(Mng Exec Officer)*
Kazuo Toriumi *(Exec Officer)*
Manabu Tsujimura *(Sr Mng Exec Officer)*
Hideki Yamada *(Exec Officer)*

Board of Directors:
Natsunosuke Yago
Tetsuji Fujimoto
Shiro Kuniya
Toichi Maeda
Akio Mikuni
Masao Namiki
Nobuharu Noji
Akira Ogata
Atsuo Ohi
Masaru Shibuya
Manabu Tsujimura
Sakon Uda

Transfer Agent:
Sumitomo Mitsui Trust Bank, Limited
4-1 Marunouchi 1-chome Chiyoda-ku
Tokyo, Japan

Subsidiaries:

E-Square Co., Ltd. **(1)**
22-2 Nakasode
Sodegaura, Chiba, Japan 299-0267
Tel.: (81) 438 64 3101
Fax: (81) 438 64 3104
Web Site: www.ebara.co.jp/en/company/concern/machin.html
Electric Power Distribution Services
S.I.C.: 4911
N.A.I.C.S.: 221122

Ebara Agency Co., Ltd. **(1)**
11-1 Hanedaasahicho
Ota-Ku, Tokyo, 144-0042, Japan
Tel.: (81) 362758100
Fax: (81) 357363123
Web Site: www.ea.ebara.com
Emp.: 100
Real Estate Management Services
S.I.C.: 6531
N.A.I.C.S.: 531390
Akira Ito *(Pres)*

Ebara-Byron Jackson, Ltd. **(1)**
4F Asahiseimei Bldg 5-25-16 Higashi-gotanda
Shinagawa-ku, Tokyo, 141-0022, Japan
Tel.: (81) 3 3442 1711
Fax: (81) 3 3442 1723
Web Site: www.ebara.co.jp/en/company/concern/machin.html
Industrial Pump Sales & Maintenance Services
S.I.C.: 5084
N.A.I.C.S.: 423830

EBARA DENSAN LTD. **(1)**
Ebara-Ohmori Bldg 3-2-16 Ohmori-kita
Ohta-ku, Tokyo, 143-0016, Japan
Tel.: (81) 363848511
Fax: (81) 354930801
Web Site: www.ebd.co.jp
Electronic Equipment Mfr & Distr
S.I.C.: 3679
N.A.I.C.S.: 334419

Ebara Environmental Plant Co., Ltd. **(1)**
11-1 Haneda Asahi-cho
ohta-ku, Tokyo, 144-0042, Japan
Tel.: (81) 3 6275 8600
Fax: (81) 3 5736 3162
Web Site: www.eep.ebara.com
Waste Treatment Services
S.I.C.: 4953
N.A.I.C.S.: 562219

Ebara Environmental Technologies Hokkaido Co., Ltd. **(1)**
2-4-15 Jinyamachi
Muroran, Hokkaido, 050-0067, Japan
Tel.: (81) 143 50 2211
Fax: (81) 143 50 2201
Web Site: www.ebara.co.jp/en/company/concern/machin.html
Industrial Machinery Mfr
S.I.C.: 3559
N.A.I.C.S.: 333249

Ebara Field Tech. Corporation **(1)**
4-2-1 Honfujisawa
Fujisawa, Kanagawa, 251-0875, Japan
Tel.: (81) 466 83 9171
Fax: (81) 466 83 1100
Web Site: www.eft.ebara.com
Emp.: 10
Semiconductor Device Repair Services & Distr
S.I.C.: 7699
N.A.I.C.S.: 811219
Sadao Suruya *(Gen Mgr)*

EBARA HAMADA BLOWER CO., LTD. **(1)**
2470 Takaoka-cho
Suzuka, Mie-ken, 513-0014, Japan
Tel.: (81) 593838700
Fax: (81) 593812021
Web Site: www.ehb.ebara.com
Emp.: 150
Industrial Fan & Blower Mfr
S.I.C.: 3564
N.A.I.C.S.: 333413

Ebara Material Co., Ltd. **(1)**
30-1 Nakasode
Sodegaura, Chiba, 299-0267, Japan
Tel.: (81) 438 60 1551
Fax: (81) 438 60 1561
Web Site: www.ebara.co.jp/en/company/concern/machin.html
Cast Products Mfr
S.I.C.: 3353
N.A.I.C.S.: 331315

Ebara Meister Co., Ltd. **(1)**
11-1 Haneda Asahi-cho
Ohta-ku, Tokyo, 144-0042, Japan
Tel.: (81) 3 6275 9510
Temporary Staffing Services
S.I.C.: 7363
N.A.I.C.S.: 561320

Ebara Refrigeration Equipment & Systems Co., Ltd. **(1)**
Ebara-Ohmori Bldg 3-2-16 Ohmori-kita
Ohta-ku, Tokyo, 143-0016, Japan
Tel.: (81) 3 6384 8080
Fax: (81) 3 5493 0702
Web Site: www.ers.ebara.com
Emp.: 765
Heating Equipment Mfr & Distr
S.I.C.: 3433
N.A.I.C.S.: 333414
Hiroshi Otani *(Pres)*

EBARA SHOHNAN SPORTS CENTER INC. **(1)**
1-9-1 Inari
Fujisawa, Kanagawa, 251-0862, Japan
Tel.: (81) 466 81 3411
Fax: (81) 466 83 0012
E-Mail: contactus@ebarassc.co.jp
Web Site: www.ebarassc.co.jp
Emp.: 6
Sports Club Operating Services
S.I.C.: 7941
N.A.I.C.S.: 711211
Masaru Uchiyama *(Pres)*

Ebara Yoshikura Hydro-Tech Co., Ltd. **(1)**
1-5-3 Nihonbashi-muromachi
Chuo-ku, Tokyo, 103-0022, Japan
Tel.: (81) 3 3510 7400
Fax: (81) 3 3510 7839
Web Site: www.eyh.ebara.com
Industrial Pump Mfr & Distr
S.I.C.: 3561
N.A.I.C.S.: 333911

Elliott Ebara Turbomachinery Corporation **(1)**
20-1 Nakasode
Sodegaura, Chiba, 299-0296, Japan
Tel.: (81) 438 60 6111
Fax: (81) 438 60 6070
Web Site: www.eetc.ebara.com
Industrial Machinery Mfr & Distr
S.I.C.: 3559
N.A.I.C.S.: 333249

U.S. Subsidiaries:

Airvac, Inc. **(1)**
4217 N OUS 31
Rochester, IN 46975-0528
Tel.: (574) 223-3980
Fax: (574) 223-5566
E-Mail: info@airvac.com
Web Site: www.airvac.com
Emp.: 70
Mfr. & Sales of Valves for Vacuum Sewage Collection Systems
S.I.C.: 3492
N.A.I.C.S.: 332912
Mark Jones *(Pres)*

Ebara International Corp. **(1)**
350 Salomon Cir
Sparks, NV 89434-6635
Tel.: (775) 356-2796
Fax: (775) 356-2884
Web Site: www.ebaracryo.com
Emp.: 140
Mfr. & Marketing of Pumps
S.I.C.: 3561
N.A.I.C.S.: 333911
Lou Baldoni *(Mgr-Contracts & After Market Svcs)*

Ebara Technologies Inc. **(1)**
51 Main Ave
Sacramento, CA 95838-2014
Tel.: (916) 920-5451
Fax: (916) 925-6654
Web Site: www.ebaratech.com
Emp.: 90
Sale & Manufacture of Precision Machines
S.I.C.: 3563
N.A.I.C.S.: 333912
Ray Campbell *(Gen Mgr)*

Elliott Company **(1)**
901 N 4th St
Jeannette, PA 15644-1473
Tel.: (724) 527-2811
Fax: (724) 600-8442
E-Mail: info@elliott-turbo.com
Web Site: www.elliott-turbo.com
Sales Range: $125-149.9 Million
Emp.: 800
Plant Air & Gas Compressors, Steam Turbines & Other Related Power Generating Equipment Mfr
S.I.C.: 3511
N.A.I.C.S.: 333611
Antonio Casillo *(Pres)*
Yasuyuki Uruma *(CEO)*

Non-U.S. Holdings:

Elliott Turbomachinery Canada, Inc. **(2)**
955 Maple Ave
Burlington, ON, L7S 2J4, Canada (100%)

Ebara Corporation—(Continued)

Tel.: (905) 333-4101
Fax: (905) 333-3863
Web Site: www.elliott-turbo.com
Emp.: 35
Mfr. of Industrial Machinery
S.I.C.: 3559
N.A.I.C.S.: 333249

Elliott Turbomachinery Ltd. (2)
Unit 11 Easter Park Benyon Road
Silchester, Reading, RG7 2PQ, United Kingdom (100%)
Tel.: (44) 1256354334
Telex: 739717 ELLIOT G
Fax: (44) 1189701333
Web Site: www.elliott-turbo.com
Emp.: 50
Compressor & Turbine Services
S.I.C.: 3563
N.A.I.C.S.: 333912
Graham Pungis *(Dir-Ops)*

Elliott Turbomachinery S.A. (2)
Seldstrasse 2
Lachen, 8853, Switzerland (100%)
Tel.: (41) 554518000
Telex: 817 275
Fax: (41) 554518099
E-Mail: info@elliott-turbo.co.uk
Web Site: www.elliott-turbo.co.uk
Emp.: 50
Machinery Products Sales
S.I.C.: 5088
N.A.I.C.S.: 423860
Guito Vesti *(Gen Mgr)*

Non-U.S. Subsidiaries:

Advanced Design Technology Limited (1)
Dilke House 1 Malet St
London, WC1E 7JN, United Kingdom (50%)
Tel.: (44) 20 7299 1170
Fax: (44) 20 7636 8028
E-Mail: info@adtechnology.co.uk
Web Site: www.adtechnology.co.uk
Sales Range: $1-9.9 Million
Emp.: 10
Sale of Inverse Design Technology Program & Related Consulting Services
S.I.C.: 8999
N.A.I.C.S.: 541690

Asia Shinwa Engineering Co., Ltd. (1)
ACME Bldg 125 Phetchburi Rd
Rajthevee, Bangkok, 10400, Thailand
Tel.: (66) 26120314
Fax: (66) 6120309
E-Mail: suzuki@asec.co.th
Emp.: 25
S.I.C.: 3589
N.A.I.C.S.: 333318
Setsuo Suzuki *(Gen Mgr)*

Ebara Densan (Kunshan) Mfg. Co., Ltd. (1)
No 521 Qingyang N Road
Zhoushi Town, Kunshan, Jiangsu, 215314, China
Tel.: (86) 512 5762 6121
Fax: (86) 512 5762 6125
Web Site: www.ebara.co.jp/en/company/concern/machin.html
Industrial Pump Mfr & Distr
S.I.C.: 5084
N.A.I.C.S.: 423830

Ebara-Densan Taiwan Manufacturing Co., Ltd. (1)
7 Nan-Yuen 2nd Road
Chung-li, Tao Yuen Hsien, Taiwan (100%)
Tel.: (886) 34515881
Fax: (886) 34527904
Web Site: www.ebara.co.jp/en/profile/machinery.html
Emp.: 70
Pumps & Submersible Motors Mfr, Sales & Services
S.I.C.: 3561
N.A.I.C.S.: 333911

Ebara-Elliott Service (Taiwan) Co., Ltd. (1)
1 Rd 42 Industrial Zone
Taichung, 00407, Taiwan (51%)
Tel.: (886) 423594202
Fax: (886) 423595510
Web Site: www.elliott-turbo.com
Emp.: 35
Maintenance & Repair of Turbomachinery & Compressors
S.I.C.: 3589
N.A.I.C.S.: 333318

Ebara Engineering Singapore Pte. Ltd. (1)
No 1 Tuas Link 2
Singapore, 638550, Singapore (100%)
Tel.: (65) 68623536
Telex: RS 37018 EBRSIN
Fax: (65) 68610589
E-Mail: ebaranet@singnet.com.sg
Web Site: www.ebara.com
Emp.: 98
Engineering & Construction; Maintenance Services for Precision Machines
S.I.C.: 3589
N.A.I.C.S.: 333318
Kuzo Tsuchiya *(Mng Dir)*

Ebara Espana Bombas S.A. (1)
Poligono la Estacion Calle Cormoranes no 6 & 8
28320 Pinto, Madrid, Spain (98%)
Tel.: (34) 916923630
Fax: (34) 916910818
E-Mail: conpras@ebara.es
Web Site: www.ebara.es
Emp.: 15
Mfr. & Sales of Industrial & Standard Pumps
S.I.C.: 3561
N.A.I.C.S.: 333911
Angel Diaz *(Dir Gen)*

Ebara Hai Duong Company Ltd. (1)
Nguyen Trai Road
Hai Duong, Vietnam (70%)
Tel.: (84) 3203850182
Fax: (84) 3203850180
Emp.: 105
Mfr. & Sales of Pumps
S.I.C.: 3561
N.A.I.C.S.: 333911

Ebara Industrias Mecanicas e Comercio Ltda. (1)
Rua Joaquim Marques De Figueiredo 2 31
Bauru, SP, Brazil (100%)
Tel.: (55) 14 3103 0000
Fax: (55) 14 3103 0044
E-Mail: bauru@ebara.com.br
Web Site: www.ebara.com.br
Emp.: 152
Mfr. & Sales of Pumps
S.I.C.: 3561
N.A.I.C.S.: 333911

Ebara Kailay Environmental Engineering Co., Ltd. (1)
Rm N 818 8F Chia Hsin Rear Bldg No 9 Ln 3
Min Sheng West Rd, Taipei, 104, Taiwan (95%)
Tel.: (886) 225432727
Fax: (886) 225374590
E-Mail: ek303@ekeec.com.tw
Web Site: www.pumpsebara.com
Emp.: 23
Engineering & Construction of Environmental Facilities
S.I.C.: 8711
N.A.I.C.S.: 541330

Ebara Machinery China Co., Ltd. (1)
Beizang Cun Countryside Tiangon Industry Area
Daxing Xian, Beijing, 102609, China (100%)
Tel.: (86) 1060275167
Fax: (86) 10 6027 5163
Web Site: www.ebara.co.jp/en/company/concern/machin.html
Standard Pumps & Related Equipment Mfr, Sales & Service
S.I.C.: 3559
N.A.I.C.S.: 333249

Ebara Precision Machinery Europe GmbH (1)
Roden Bacher Chaussee 6
Hanau, Hessen, 63457, Germany (100%)
Tel.: (49) 618118760
Fax: (49) 6181187640
E-Mail: info-pm@ebara-europe.com
Web Site: www.ebara-europe.com
Emp.: 130
Maintenance Services for Pumps & Precision Machines
S.I.C.: 7699
N.A.I.C.S.: 811219
K. Nakao *(Chm)*
Mansred Schroeder *(Pres)*

Ebara Precision Machinery Korea Incorporated (1)
15th Floor Kangnam Building 1321 Seocho Dong
Seocho Ku, 1370070 Seoul, Korea (South) (100%)
Tel.: (82) 25816901
Fax: (82) 25814211
Web Site: www.ebara.co.kr
Emp.: 25
Maintenance Services for Precision Machines
S.I.C.: 3589
N.A.I.C.S.: 333318
Kyung Suk Lee *(Gen Mgr)*

Ebara Precision Machinery Taiwan Incorporated (1)
Rm No 1402 No 96 Chung Shan
North Rd Sec 2, Taipei, 104, Taiwan (100%)
Tel.: (886) 225601166
Fax: (886) 225601177
Emp.: 183
Maintenace Services for Precision Machines
S.I.C.: 5084
N.A.I.C.S.: 423830

Ebara Pump Industries P.J.S. (1)
No 1 4th Alley Eshghyar Niloofar St
Khorramshahr Ave, Tehran, Iran (44%)
Tel.: (98) 2188514828
Fax: (98) 2188514834
E-Mail: info@ebarairan.com
Web Site: www.ebara.ir
Emp.: 35
Standard Pump Sales
S.I.C.: 5084
N.A.I.C.S.: 423830
Tarviz Pirouz *(Mgr)*

Ebara Pumps Australia Pty. Ltd. (1)
7 Holloway Dr
Bayswater, VIC, 3153, Australia (80%)
Tel.: (61) 397613033
Fax: (61) 397613044
Web Site: www.ebara.com.au
Sales Range: $10-24.9 Million
Emp.: 7
Sale of Standard Pumps
S.I.C.: 3561
N.A.I.C.S.: 333911
Mark Barrett *(Gen Mgr)*

Ebara Pumps Europe S.p.A. (1)
Via Pacinotti 32
Brendola, 36040 Vicenza, Italy IT (100%)
Tel.: (39) 0444706811
Fax: (39) 0444706950
E-Mail: marketing@ebaraeurope.com
Web Site: www.ebara.it
Emp.: 140
Pump Mfr & Sales
S.I.C.: 3561
N.A.I.C.S.: 333911

Ebara Qingdao Co. Ltd. (1)
412 Beijing Fortune Bldg
5 Dong Sanhuan Bei Lu, 100004 Beijing, China (100%)
Tel.: (86) 65908150
Fax: (86) 1065908158
Emp.: 15
Mfr. of Boilers
S.I.C.: 3589
N.A.I.C.S.: 333318

Elliott Ebara Singapore Pte. Ltd. (1)
1A International Business Park 07-01
Singapore, 609933, Singapore
Tel.: (65) 6563 6776
Fax: (65) 6563 1387
Emp.: 35
Fluid Machinery Sales & Maintenance Services
S.I.C.: 5084
N.A.I.C.S.: 423830
John Baron *(Mng Dir)*

P.T. Ebara Indonesia (1)
JL Raya Jakarta Bogor Km 32
Desa Curug Cimanggis Depok, Bogor, Jawa Barat, 16953, Indonesia (55%)
Tel.: (62) 218740852
Fax: (62) 218740033
E-Mail: marketing@ebaraindonesia.com
Web Site: www.ebaraindonesia.com
Emp.: 400
Mfr. & Sales of Pumps
S.I.C.: 3561
N.A.I.C.S.: 333911

P.T. Ebara Prima Indonesia (1)
Jl Raya Jakarta Bogor KM 32
Desa Curug Cimanggis, Bogor, Jawa Barat, Indonesia (92%)
Tel.: (62) 218740853
Fax: (62) 218740033
Web Site: www.ebara.co.jp/company/concern/oversea.html
Emp.: 384
Mfr. & Sales of Activated Carbon
S.I.C.: 2899
N.A.I.C.S.: 325998

Qingdao Jiaonan Ebara Electric Power Co., Ltd. (1)
183 Changcheng Road
Jiaonan, Shandong, China (57.6%)
Tel.: (86) 532 6181937
Fax: (86) 532 6181251
Web Site: www.ebara.co.jp/company/concern/oversea.html
Special Industry Services
S.I.C.: 3589
N.A.I.C.S.: 333318

Shanghai Ebara Engineering and Services Co., Ltd. (1)
20th Floor N Gate Plaza 99 Tian Mu West Road
Shanghai, 200070, China (90%)
Tel.: (86) 2151017677
Fax: (86) 2151017675
Web Site: www.ebara.biz.sh.cn
Emp.: 50
Engineering & Construction of Environmental Facilities
S.I.C.: 8711
N.A.I.C.S.: 541330

Shanghai Ebara Precision Machinery Co., Ltd. (1)
Tech Park No 76 Lane 887
Zuchongzhi Road, Shanghai, 200122, China
Tel.: (86) 151317008
Fax: (86) 21 5131 7048
Maintenances Services for Precision Machines
S.I.C.: 7699
N.A.I.C.S.: 811219

Sumoto S.r.l. (1)
Via Peripoli R E G 1 3
36075 Montecchio Maggiore, Vicenza, Italy (100%)
Tel.: (39) 0444490515
Fax: (39) 0444490518
E-Mail: info@sumoto.com
Web Site: www.sumoto.com
Emp.: 50
Mfr., Producer & Marketer of Submersible Motors for Deep Well Pumps
S.I.C.: 3589
N.A.I.C.S.: 333318

Yantai Ebara Air Conditioning Equipment Co., Ltd. (1)
720 Yongda Rd New And Hi Tech Industrial Zone
Fushan, Yantai, Shandong, China (60%)
Tel.: (86) 356321588
Fax: (86) 535 6322328
Web Site: www.ytebara.com.cn
Emp.: 264
Mfr. & Sales of Refrigerating Machineries
S.I.C.: 3822
N.A.I.C.S.: 334512

Yingkou Ebara Co., Ltd. (1)
Economic And Technique Development Zone
Yingkou, Liaoning, 115007, China (60%)
Tel.: (86) 4176252125
Fax: (86) 4176253731
Web Site: www.pumpsebara.com
Mfr. of Wooden Patterns & Procurement of Pump Darts
S.I.C.: 2519
N.A.I.C.S.: 337125

Non-U.S. Affiliate:

Ebara (Thailand) Limited (1)
ACME Bldg 125 Petchburi Rd
Bangkok, 10400, Thailand (33%)
Tel.: (66) 22164935
Fax: (66) 22164937
E-Mail: info@ebara.co.th
Web Site: www.ebara.co.th
Sales Range: $1-9.9 Million
Emp.: 40
Marketing, Engineering & Construction of Ebara Products
S.I.C.: 3589
N.A.I.C.S.: 333318
Hisa Gakao *(Mgr)*

Non-U.S. Joint Ventures:

Benguet Ebara Real Estate Corp. (1)
Canlubang Industrial Estate Diezmo Cabuyao
Cebuyao, Laguna, 4025, Philippines
Tel.: (63) 495491914
Fax: (63) 495491915
Web Site: www.ebaraphilippines.com
Sales Range: Less than $1 Million
Emp.: 1
Real Estate; Joint Venture of Benguet Corporation (60%) & Ebara Corporation (40%)
S.I.C.: 6531
N.A.I.C.S.: 531210
Valentino Niocena *(Pres)*

Ebara-Benguet, Inc. (1)
Terelay Phase Canlubang Industrial Est
4025 Cabugao, Laguna, Philippines
Tel.: (63) 495491806
Fax: (63) 495491915
E-Mail: ebisales@ebaraphilippines.com
Web Site: www.ebaraphilippines.com
Sales Range: $1-9.9 Million
Emp.: 100
Castings Mfr
S.I.C.: 3364
N.A.I.C.S.: 331523
Valentino Niocena *(Pres)*

Hyosung Ebara Co., Ltd. (1)
450 Kongduk Dong
Mapo Ku, Seoul, 121 020, Korea (South) (28%)
Tel.: (82) 27076114
Web Site: www.hyosungebara.com
Emp.: 40
Mfr. & Sales of Pumps; Joint Venture of Ebara Corporation & Hyosung Corporation
S.I.C.: 3561
N.A.I.C.S.: 333911

EBC INC.

1095 Valet Street
CP 158
L'Ancienne-Lorett, QC, G2E 4M7, Canada
Tel.: (418) 872-0600
Fax: (418) 872-8177
E-Mail: ebc@ebcinc.qc.ca
Web Site: www.ebcinc.qc.ca
Year Founded: 1968
Sales Range: $250-299.9 Million
Emp.: 1,000

Business Description:
General Construction Contractor
S.I.C.: 1542
N.A.I.C.S.: 236220

Personnel:
Fernand Houle *(Chm)*
Marie-Claude Houle *(Pres & VP-Dev)*

EBCO INDUSTRIES LTD.

7851 Alderbridge Way
Richmond, BC, V6X 2A4, Canada
Tel.: (604) 278-5578
Fax: (604) 278-7230
E-Mail: info@ebco.com
Web Site: www.ebco.com
Year Founded: 1956
Rev.: $17,934,574
Emp.: 200

Business Description:
Heavy Industrial Machinery Mfr
S.I.C.: 3559
N.A.I.C.S.: 333249

Personnel:
Bill Merritt *(Owner)*
Helmut Eppich *(Pres)*

EBERTLANG DISTRIBUTION GMBH

Garbenheimer Strasse 36
D-35578 Wetzlar, Germany
Tel.: (49) 6441 67118 0
Fax: (49) 6441 67118 222
Web Site: www.ebertlang.com
Sales Range: $1-9.9 Million

Business Description:
Computer Products & Software Distr
S.I.C.: 5045
N.A.I.C.S.: 423430

Personnel:
Steffen Ebert *(Member-Mgmt Bd)*
Volker Lang *(Member-Mgmt Bd)*

EBET LIMITED

Unit 13 112-118 Talavera Road
North Ryde, NSW, 2113, Australia
Tel.: (61) 288174700
Fax: (61) 288174770
E-Mail: investorrelations@ebetgroup.com
Web Site: www.ebetgroup.com
EBT—(ASX)
Rev.: $47,455,150
Assets: $47,700,043
Liabilities: $25,131,284
Net Worth: $22,568,760
Earnings: $5,012,501
Fiscal Year-end: 06/30/13

Business Description:
Electronic Gaming Machines
S.I.C.: 7999
N.A.I.C.S.: 713290

Personnel:
Anthony P. Toohey *(CEO & Mng Dir)*
Robert Fredericks *(CFO)*
Jenny Fletcher *(Sec)*

Board of Directors:
Paul N. Oneile
Michael B. Hale
Ian R. James
Allan C. Sullivan
Anthony P. Toohey

Subsidiaries:

eBet Gaming Systems Pty Limited (1)
112-118 Talavera Rd Unit 13118
North Ryde, NSW, 2113, Australia
Tel.: (61) 288174700
Fax: (61) 288174770
E-Mail: sales@ebetgamingsystems.com
Web Site: www.ebetgamingsystems.com
Emp.: 50
Online Gaming Services
S.I.C.: 2741
N.A.I.C.S.: 519130
Tony Toohey *(CEO & Mng Dir)*

eBet Systems Pty Limited (1)
Unit 13 112-118 Talavera Rd
North Ryde, NSW, 2113, Australia
Tel.: (61) 288174700
Emp.: 80
Online Gaming Services
S.I.C.: 2741
N.A.I.C.S.: 519130
John Toohey *(CEO)*

U.S. Subsidiary:

eBet Inc. (1)
2440 Grand Ave Ste B
Vista, CA 92081-7829
Tel.: (760) 599-6533
Fax: (760) 599-6553
Gaming Platform & Software Development Services
S.I.C.: 7372
N.A.I.C.S.: 511210

EBEWE PHARMA GES.MBH NFG. KG

Mondseestrasse 11
Unterach, 4866, Austria
Tel.: (43) 766581230
Fax: (43) 7665812311
E-Mail: office.ebewe@sandoz.com
Web Site: www.ebewe.com
Year Founded: 1934
Sales Range: $250-299.9 Million
Emp.: 830

Business Description:
Pharmaceuticals Mfr
S.I.C.: 2834
N.A.I.C.S.: 325412

Personnel:
Friedrich Hillebrand *(Head-Global Oncology Injectables Bus Unit)*

Non-U.S. Subsidiaries:

Ebewe Italia S.r.l. (1)
Via Viggiano 90
00144 Rome, Italy
Tel.: (39) 06 515934 1
Fax: (39) 06 515934 20
Web Site: www.ebewe.it/index.php?id=391&L=1
Drugs & Druggists Sundries Whslr
S.I.C.: 5122
N.A.I.C.S.: 424210

Ebewe Pharma (1)
Bldg 68/70 Contruction 1 Butyrski Val
127055 Moscow, Russia
Tel.: (7) 4959338702
Fax: (7) 9338715
E-Mail: info.ru@ebewepharma.com
Web Site: www.ebewe.ru
Emp.: 100
Pharmaceutical Mfr & Distr
S.I.C.: 2834
N.A.I.C.S.: 325412
SerGey Gerevyannyth *(Mgr)*

Ebewe Pharma (Asia) Limited (1)
8th Fl Eastwood Centre
5 A Kung Ngam Village Road, Shau Kei Wan, China (Hong Kong) (100%)
Tel.: (852) 25656309
Fax: (852) 25645374
Web Site: www.everpharma.com
Emp.: 22
Drugs & Druggists Sundries Whslr
S.I.C.: 5122
N.A.I.C.S.: 424210
Leo Law *(Mng Dir)*

Ebewe Pharma France SAS (1)
49 Avenue Chateau Ponpigou
92593 Levallois-Perret, France (100%)
Tel.: (33) 472520930
Fax: (33) 149645833
Web Site: www.ebewe.it
Emp.: 200
Drugs & Druggists Sundries Whslr
S.I.C.: 5122
N.A.I.C.S.: 424210
Patrick van den Berg *(Mng Dir)*

U.S. Subsidiary:

Ebewe Parenta Pharmaceuticals Inc. (1)
506 Carnegie Ctr Ste 400
Princeton, NJ 08540-6243
Tel.: (803) 461-5500
Fax: (803) 461-5501
Web Site: www.parentarx.com
Emp.: 10
Pharmaceutical Preparation Mfr
S.I.C.: 2834
N.A.I.C.S.: 325412
Mark Sedele *(CEO)*

EBIOSS ENERGY AD

49 Bulgaria Boulevard 11-12 Floors
1404 Sofia, Bulgaria
Tel.: (359) 2 8587723
Fax: (359) 2 9586361
E-Mail: info@ebioss.com
Web Site: www.ebioss.com
EBI—(MAD)

Business Description:
Waste Gasification Power Plants Mfr
S.I.C.: 1629
N.A.I.C.S.: 237130

Personnel:
Jose Oscar Leiva Mendez *(Chm & Co-CEO)*
Luis Sanchez Angrill *(Co-CEO)*

EBIQUITY PLC

The Registry Royal Mint Court
London, EC3N 4QN, United Kingdom
Tel.: (44) 2076509600
Fax: (44) 2076509650
E-Mail: towerhill.reception@ebiquity.com
Web Site: www.ebiquity.com
EBQ—(LSE)
Rev.: $101,147,207
Assets: $149,015,487
Liabilities: $82,502,110
Net Worth: $66,513,378
Earnings: $8,153,874
Emp.: 752
Fiscal Year-end: 04/30/13

Business Description:
Analysis & Consultancy Services For Advertisers
S.I.C.: 8732
N.A.I.C.S.: 541910

Personnel:
Michael E. Greenlees *(CEO)*
Andrew Beach *(CFO)*
Nick Manning *(Pres-Intl)*
Morag Blazey *(CEO-UK)*
Andrew Watkins *(Gen Counsel & Sec)*

Board of Directors:
Michael Higgins
Andrew Beach
Michael E. Greenlees
Nick Manning
Richard Nichols
Christopher Russell
Jeffrey Taylor Stevenson
Sarah Jane Thomson
Stephen Thomson

Legal Counsel:
Lewis Silkin LLP
5 Chancery Lane Cliffords Inn
London, United Kingdom

Subsidiaries:

Billetts International Limited (1)
2nd Fl The Registry Royal Mint Ct
London, EC3N 4QN, United Kingdom
Tel.: (44) 2076509600
Fax: (44) 2076509650
E-Mail: info@ebiquity.com
Web Site: www.ebiquity.com
Emp.: 100
Media Consulting Services
S.I.C.: 7311
N.A.I.C.S.: 541810
Martin Sambrook *(Mng Dir & Head-Intl Ops)*

Billetts Marketing Sciences Limited (1)
2nd Fl The Registry Royal Mint Ct
London, EC3N 4QN, United Kingdom
Tel.: (44) 2076509600
Fax: (44) 2076509650
E-Mail: info@billetts.com
Web Site: www.billetts.com
Emp.: 100
Marketing Consulting Services
S.I.C.: 8742
N.A.I.C.S.: 541613
Andrew Challier *(Mng Partner)*

Billetts Media Consulting Limited (1)
2nd Fl The Registry Royal Mint Ct
London, EC3N 4QN, United Kingdom
Tel.: (44) 2076509600
Fax: (44) 2076509650
E-Mail: info@billetts.com
Web Site: www.billetts.com
Emp.: 100
Media Consulting Services
S.I.C.: 7311

Ebiquity plc—(Continued)

N.A.I.C.S.: 541810
Simon Cross *(Head-Media)*

Ebiquity Associates Limited (1)
2nd Fl The Registry Royal Mint Ct
London, EC3N 4QN, United Kingdom
Tel.: (44) 2076509600
Fax: (44) 2076509650
E-Mail: towerhill.reception@ebiquity.com
Web Site: www.ebiquity.com
Emp.: 120
Technology & Media Monitoring Services
S.I.C.: 8732
N.A.I.C.S.: 541910
Johnson Chapman *(Head-IT)*

EBN B.V.

Office Building Hoog Overborch 4th Floor Moreelsepark 48
3511 EP Utrecht, Netherlands
Mailing Address:
Postbus 19063
3501 DB Utrecht, Netherlands
Tel.: (31) 30 23339001
Telex: 56018 arc
E-Mail: ebn.mail@ebn.nl
Web Site: www.ebn.nl
Year Founded: 1973
Sls.: $11,480,137,760
Assets: $7,760,670,050
Liabilities: $7,491,436,050
Net Worth: $269,234,000
Earnings: $3,176,961,200
Emp.: 70
Fiscal Year-end: 12/31/12
Business Description:
Petroleum & Natural Gas Producer
S.I.C.: 1311
N.A.I.C.S.: 211111
Personnel:
Hein van Oorschot *(Chm-Supervisory Bd)*
Jan Dirk Bokhoven *(CEO)*
Sander van Rootselaar *(Press Officer)*
Supervisory Board of Directors:
Hein van Oorschot
Gert-Jan Kramer
Arnold Gratama van Andel
Rien Zwitserloot

Subsidiary:

K13 Extensie Beheer B.V. (1)
Moreelsepark 48
3511EP Utrecht, Netherlands
Mailing Address:
Postbus 19063
3501DB Utrecht, Netherlands
Tel.: (31) 30 2339001
Oil & Natural Gas Exploration Services
S.I.C.: 1389
N.A.I.C.S.: 213112

EBNER GMBH & CO. KG

Karl-Ebner-Str 8
D-36132 Fulda, Germany
Tel.: (49) 66728900
Fax: (49) 6672890133
E-Mail: info@ebner-co.de
Web Site: www.ebnerco.de
Year Founded: 1965
Rev.: $31,753,788
Emp.: 120
Business Description:
Plant & Apparatus Construction Services
S.I.C.: 3559
N.A.I.C.S.: 333249
Personnel:
Stefan Ebner *(Mng Partner)*
Dieter Kremer *(Mng Dir)*

EBOOK INITIATIVE JAPAN CO., LTD.

2-5-2 Nishikanda Chiyoda-ku
Tokyo, 101-0065, Japan
Tel.: (81) 3 62729244
Web Site: www.ebookjapan.jp
3658—(TKS)
Sales Range: $10-24.9 Million
Emp.: 30
Business Description:
E-Book Retailer
S.I.C.: 5045
N.A.I.C.S.: 423430
Personnel:
Hitoshi Koide *(Pres)*

EBOS GROUP LIMITED

108 Wrights Road
PO Box 411
Christchurch, 8024, New Zealand
Tel.: (64) 33380999
Fax: (64) 33395111
E-Mail: ebos@ebos.co.nz
Web Site: www.ebos.co.nz
EBO—(ASX NZE)
Rev.: $1,525,992,453
Assets: $2,119,065,543
Liabilities: $1,863,883,494
Net Worth: $255,182,049
Earnings: $23,609,259
Emp.: 2,000
Fiscal Year-end: 06/30/13
Business Description:
Surgical & Medical Equipment Retailers
S.I.C.: 5047
N.A.I.C.S.: 423450
Personnel:
Rick Christie *(Chm)*
Mark Waller *(CEO & Mng Dir)*
Dennis Doherty *(CFO & Sec)*
Patrick Davies *(CEO-Symbion Grp)*
Sean Duggan *(CEO-Masterpet Grp)*
Board of Directors:
Rick Christie
Elizabeth Coutts
Peter Kraus
Stuart McGregor
Sarah Ottrey
Barry Wallace
Mark Waller
Peter Williams
Legal Counsel:
Chapman Tripp
Christchurch, New Zealand

Subsidiary:

Health Support Limited (1)
56 Carrington Road
Point Chevalier, Auckland, 1025, New Zealand
Tel.: (64) 98152600
Fax: (64) 9 849 6505
E-Mail: customerservices@healthsupport.co.nz
Web Site: www.healthsupport.co.nz
Rev.: $71,058,000
Emp.: 110
Surgical & Medical Products Distr
S.I.C.: 5047
N.A.I.C.S.: 423450
Greg Managh *(Gen Mgr)*

Non-U.S. Subsidiaries:

Ebos Group Pty Limited (1)
Unit 2 109 Vanessa St
Kingsgrove, NSW, 2208, Australia
Tel.: (61) 295028410
Fax: (61) 295028411
E-Mail: ebos@ebosgroup.com.au
Web Site: www.ebosonline.com.au
Emp.: 100
Healthcare Services
S.I.C.: 8011
N.A.I.C.S.: 621491
David Lewis *(Gen Mgr)*

Ebos Health & Science Pty Limited (1)
Ste 2 109 Vanessa St
Kingsgrove, NSW, 2208, Australia
Tel.: (61) 295028410
Fax: (61) 295028473
Healthcare Services
S.I.C.: 8011
N.A.I.C.S.: 621491

EBRAHIM K. KANOO COMPANY B.S.C.

Bldg 510 Qassim Al-Mehzaa Rd 225 Block 302
PO Box 119
Manama, Bahrain
Tel.: (973) 17262262
Fax: (973) 17258865
E-Mail: skalibhat@ekkanoo.com.bh
Web Site: www.ekkanoo.com.bh
Emp.: 200
Business Description:
Holding Company; Motor Vehicle Leasing & Distr; Automotive Equipment & Tool Distr; IT Services; Industrial Power Solutions; Security & Automation System Services
S.I.C.: 6719
N.A.I.C.S.: 551112
Personnel:
Mohamed Ebrahim Kanoo *(Pres)*

Divisions:

Ebrahim K. Kanoo Company B.S.C - Auto Paint Division (1)
44 Sh Mhd Ave Rd 331 Blk 302
Manama, Bahrain
Tel.: (973) 17252689, ext. 17786877
Fax: (973) 17272387
Automotive Painting Services
S.I.C.: 7532
N.A.I.C.S.: 811121

Ebrahim K. Kanoo Company B.S.C - Kanoo IT Division (1)
Villa 280 Rd 2510 Gudaibiya 325
PO Box 119
Manama, Bahrain
Tel.: (973) 17711722
Fax: (973) 17746484
E-Mail: admin@kit.com.bh
Web Site: www.kanooit.com
Emp.: 38
Information Technology Services
S.I.C.: 7371
N.A.I.C.S.: 541511
Waleed Kanoo *(Gen Mgr)*

Ebrahim K. Kanoo Company B.S.C - Kanoo Vehicle Leasing Division (1)
800 Rd 123 Blk 701
Tubli, Isatown, Bahrain
Tel.: (973) 17784042
Fax: (973) 17789264
E-Mail: kbghelpdesk@ekkanoo.com.bh
Web Site: www.kbl.com.de
Emp.: 5
Cars & Commercial Vehicles Leasing Services
S.I.C.: 7515
N.A.I.C.S.: 532112
Fawaz Kanoo *(Mng Dir)*

Ebrahim K. Kanoo Company B.S.C - Oils & Lubricants Division (1)
Bldg 510 Qassim Al-Mehzaa Rd 225 Block 302
PO Box 119
Manama, Bahrain
Tel.: (973) 17241001
Fax: (973) 17258865
Oils & Lubricants Distr
S.I.C.: 7549
N.A.I.C.S.: 811191

Ebrahim K. Kanoo Company B.S.C - Security 1 Division (1)
Bldg 1489 Rd 2630 Block 626 W Eker
PO Box 119
Manama, Bahrain
Tel.: (973) 17738738
Fax: (973) 17738739
E-Mail: info@security1.com.bh
Web Site: www.security1.com.bh
Emp.: 25
Security Systems Mfr & Monitoring Services
S.I.C.: 3669
N.A.I.C.S.: 334290
Waleed Kanoo *(Gen Mgr)*

EBRO FOODS S.A.

Paseo de la Castellana 20
28046 Madrid, Spain
Tel.: (34) 91 724 5250
Fax: (34) 91 724 5341
E-Mail: oficinadelaccionista@ebrofoods.es
Web Site: www.ebrofoods.es
EBRO—(MAD OTC)
Rev.: $2,747,891,051
Assets: $3,677,483,360
Liabilities: $1,398,098,508
Net Worth: $2,279,384,852
Earnings: $213,301,983
Emp.: 4,984
Fiscal Year-end: 12/31/12
Business Description:
Food Production Services
S.I.C.: 2034
N.A.I.C.S.: 311423
Personnel:
Antonio Hernandez Callejas *(Chm)*
Demetrio Carceller Arce *(Vice Chm)*
Miguel Angel Perez Alvarez *(Sec)*
Board of Directors:
Antonio Hernandez Callejas
Demetrio Carceller Arce
Fernando Castello Clemente
Sol Daurella Comadran
Carlos Gasco Travesedo
Felix Hernandez Callejas
Blanca Hernandez Rodriguez
Jose Nieto de la Cierva
Rudolf-August Oetker
Eugenio Ruiz-Galvez Priego
Jose Ignacio Comenge Sanchez Real
Jose Antonio Segurado Garcia

Division:

Biosearch Life (1)
Camino de Purchil 66
18004 Granada, Spain
Tel.: (34) 958240152
Fax: (34) 958240160
E-Mail: info@biosearchlife.es
Web Site: www.biosearchlife.com
Sales Range: $10-24.9 Million
Emp.: 150
Health Food Products Based On Natural Compounds Mfr, Researcher & Developer
S.I.C.: 2836
N.A.I.C.S.: 325414
Gregorio Vicente Jimenez Lopez *(Chm)*
Miguel Angel Perez Alvarez *(Sec)*

Subsidiaries:

Herba Nutricion, S.L.U. (1)
Calle Real 43
San Juan de Aznalfarache, 41920 Seville, Spain
Tel.: (34) 954 589200
Fax: (34) 954 160260
Web Site: www.herba.es
Food Processing Services
S.I.C.: 2099
N.A.I.C.S.: 311999

Herba Ricemills, S.L.U. (1)
Calle Real 43
San Juan de Aznalfarache, 41920 Seville, Spain
Tel.: (34) 954 589200
Fax: (34) 954 160260
Web Site: www.herba.es
Rice Production Services
S.I.C.: 2044
N.A.I.C.S.: 311212

U.S. Subsidiaries:

New World Pasta Company (1)
85 Shannon Rd
Harrisburg, PA 17112-2799
Tel.: (717) 526-2200
Fax: (717) 526-2468
Toll Free: (800) 730-5957
E-Mail:
Web Site: www.newworldpasta.com
Emp.: 800
Pasta Products Mfr
S.I.C.: 2045
N.A.I.C.S.: 311824

Bastiaan de Zeeuw *(Pres & CEO)*
Gregory Richardson *(CFO & Sr VP)*
Leonardo Alvarez Arias *(CIO)*
Susie Woodard *(Gen Counsel & Sr VP)*
Brett Beckfield *(Sr VP-Ops)*
Shane Faucett *(Sr VP-Sls & Customer Dev)*
Gerard Ferguson *(Sr VP-HR)*

Plant:

New World Pasta Company **(2)**
2704 S Maple Ave
Fresno, CA 93725
Tel.: (559) 485-8110
Fax: (559) 485-5134
E-Mail: info@newworldpasta.com
Web Site: www.newworldpasta.com
Sales Range: $1-9.9 Million
Emp.: 100
Mfr of Macaroni & Egg Noodle Products
S.I.C.: 2098
N.A.I.C.S.: 311824
Don Capshew *(Mgr)*

Riviana Foods Inc. **(1)**
2777 Allen Pkwy
Houston, TX 77019-2141 DE
Mailing Address:
PO Box 2636
Houston, TX 77252-2636
Tel.: (713) 529-3251
Fax: (713) 529-1661
Web Site: www.riviana.com
Sales Range: $350-399.9 Million
Emp.: 2,752
Branded & Private-Label Rice & Other Food Products Mfr, Marketer & Distr
Export
S.I.C.: 2044
N.A.I.C.S.: 311212
Antonio Hernandez Callejas *(Chm)*
Gregory S. Richardson *(VP & CFO)*
Elizabeth B. Woodard *(VP & Gen Counsel)*

Unit:

Riviana International Inc. **(2)**
2777 Allen Pkwy
Houston, TX 77019-2141 DE
Tel.: (713) 529-3251
Fax: (713) 529-1866
Web Site: www.riviana.com
Emp.: 600
Holding Company
S.I.C.: 2044
N.A.I.C.S.: 311212

Non-U.S. Subsidiaries:

Boost Nutrition C.V. **(2)**
Oostkaai 16
PO Box 30
B 2170 Merksem, Belgium
Tel.: (32) 36419200
Fax: (32) 36464528
E-Mail: info@boost.be
Web Site: www.herba.es
Emp.: 120
Mfr. of Rice Products
S.I.C.: 2044
N.A.I.C.S.: 311212
Zes Huenaerts *(Dir-Fin)*

Pozuelo, S.A. **(2)**
La Uruca Diagonal A Grupo Taca Apto 1750
1000 San Jose, Costa Rica CR
Tel.: (506) 22991234
E-Mail: riviana@pozuelo.co.cr
Web Site: www.pozuelo.com
Emp.: 900
Mfr. of Cookies & Crackers
S.I.C.: 2052
N.A.I.C.S.: 311821

S&B Herba Foods, Ltd. **(2)**
Berwick House 8-10 Knoll Rise
Orpington, Kent, BR6 0EL, United Kingdom UK
Tel.: (44) 1689877799 (100%)
Fax: (44) 1689875887
Web Site: www.sbhf.com
Sales Range: $75-99.9 Million
Emp.: 36
Food Services
S.I.C.: 2044
N.A.I.C.S.: 311212
Peter Cattaneo *(Mng Dir)*

Non-U.S. Subsidiaries:

Danrice A/S **(1)**
Odensevej 16 Orbaek
5853 Nyborg, Denmark
Tel.: (45) 6533 1770
E-Mail: mail@danrice.dk
Web Site: www.danrice.dk
Rice & Pasta Producer
S.I.C.: 2044
N.A.I.C.S.: 311212

Euryza Reis GmbH **(1)**
Oberwerder Damm 11-21
20539 Hamburg, Germany
Tel.: (49) 4078 1060
Fax: (49) 4078 7245
Web Site: www.euryza.de
Rice Producer
S.I.C.: 2044
N.A.I.C.S.: 311212

Herba Ricemills Rom S.r.l. **(1)**
18 Mircea Eliade Blv 2nd floor Entry A room A4
District 1, 012015 Bucharest, Romania
Tel.: (40) 213 193123
Rice Producer
S.I.C.: 2044
N.A.I.C.S.: 311212

Lassie B.V. **(1)**
Lassiestraat 1
1531 MG Wormer, Netherlands
Tel.: (31) 75 6471200
Web Site: www.lassie.nl
Rice Producer
S.I.C.: 2044
N.A.I.C.S.: 311212

Mundi Riso S.r.l. **(1)**
Via C DeRossi 14
13100 Vercelli, Italy
Tel.: (39) 0 161 282828
Fax: (39) 0 161 213365
E-Mail: info@mundiriso.com
Web Site: www.mundiriso.com
Rice Producer
S.I.C.: 2044
N.A.I.C.S.: 311212

Mundiriz, S.A. **(1)**
148 Rue Allal Ben Abdellah
Larache, Morocco
Tel.: (212) 395 10 416
Fax: (212) 395 10 418
Rice Producer
S.I.C.: 2044
N.A.I.C.S.: 311212

Olivieri Foods Limited **(1)**
1631 Derwent Way
Apartado Aero No 4028, Delta, BC, V3M 6K8, Canada (100%)
Tel.: (604) 525-2278
Fax: (604) 525-1302
E-Mail: info@olivierifoods.ca
Web Site: www.olivierifoods.ca
Sales Range: $100-124.9 Million
Emp.: 375
Fresh & Frozen Pasta & Sauce Products Mfr
S.I.C.: 2099
N.A.I.C.S.: 311999

Riceland Magyarorszag Kft **(1)**
Vaci utca 18
1132 Budapest, Hungary
Tel.: (36) 1 302 9292
Fax: (36) 1 302 9291
Web Site: www.riceland.hu
Rice Producer
S.I.C.: 2044
N.A.I.C.S.: 311212

EBX GROUP LTD.

Praia do Flamengo 154 10 Andar Flamengo
Rio de Janeiro, Brazil
Tel.: (55) 21 2555 550
Fax: (55) 21 2555 5550
Web Site: www.ebx.com.br
Emp.: 3,500

Business Description:
Investment Holding Company
S.I.C.: 6719
N.A.I.C.S.: 551112

Personnel:
Eike Fuhrken Batista *(Chm & Founder)*
Armando Mariante *(CFO)*

Subsidiaries:

AUX Mineracao de Ouro **(1)**
Praia do Flamengo 154 10 Andar Flamengo
Rio de Janeiro, Brazil
Tel.: (55) 21 2555 5550
Gold Mining
S.I.C.: 1041
N.A.I.C.S.: 212221
Eike Batista *(CEO)*

LLX Logistica S.A. **(1)**
Praca Mahatma Gandhi 14 5th Floor
Rio de Janeiro, 20031-100, Brazil (54%)
Tel.: (55) 21 25555661
Fax: (55) 21 25555670
E-Mail: ri.llx@llx.com.br
Web Site: www.llx.com.br
LLXL3—(BRAZ)
Rev.: $33,806,124
Assets: $1,799,696,635
Liabilities: $1,333,795,151
Net Worth: $465,901,484
Earnings: ($17,993,336)
Fiscal Year-end: 12/31/12
Port Operator
S.I.C.: 4491
N.A.I.C.S.: 488310
Roberto D'Araujo Senna *(Chm)*
Marcus Vinicius Botrel Berto *(CEO & IR Officer)*
Leonardo Pimenta Gadelha *(CFO)*
Luis Eduardo Simonetti Baroni *(Implementations Officer)*
Luis Alfredo Osorio de Castro *(Engrg Officer)*
Eugenio Leite de Figueiredo *(Economic & Fin Officer)*
Alberto F. Guimaraes *(Exec Officer)*
Flavio Valle *(Legal Officer)*

MMX Mineracao e Metalicos S.A. **(1)**
Praia do Flamengo 66 10th Fl
22 210-903 Rio de Janeiro, Brazil
Tel.: (55) 2125555557
Fax: (55) 2125554011
E-Mail: ri@mmx.com.br
Web Site: www.mmx.com.br
MMXM3—(BRAZ)
Sales Range: $400-449.9 Million
Emp.: 178
Iron Ore Mineral Mining Services
S.I.C.: 1011
N.A.I.C.S.: 212210
Eike Fuhrken Batista *(Founder & Chm)*
Carlos Gonzalez *(CEO)*
Ricardo de Souza Assef *(CFO)*
Alexandro Avila de Moura *(Officer)*
Luciano Costa Ferreira *(Chief Officer-Port Ops)*
Chequer Hanna Bou Habib *(Exec Officer-Sls)*
Antonio Alberto Schettino Froes *(Exec Officer-Mining Ops)*

Eneva S.A. **(1)**
(Formerly MPX Energia S.A.)
Praca Mahatma Gandhi no 14 9th floor Centro
Rio de Janeiro, 20031-100, Brazil BR
Tel.: (55) 21 2555 4061 (54%)
Fax: (55) 21 2555 5630
E-Mail:
Web Site: www.eneva.com.br
MPXE3—(BRAZ)
Rev.: $241,468,801
Assets: $4,648,950,768
Liabilities: $3,394,828,024
Net Worth: $1,254,122,744
Earnings: ($214,070,528)
Fiscal Year-end: 12/31/12
Power Generation Services
S.I.C.: 4931
N.A.I.C.S.: 221112
Jorgen Kildahl *(Chm)*
Fabio Bicudo *(CEO)*
Frank Possmeier *(Deputy CEO)*

OGX Petroleo e Gas Participacoes S.A. **(1)**
Praia do Flamengo N 154 5 Andar Flamengo
Rio de Janeiro, 22210 030, Brazil (62%)
Tel.: (55) 21 2555 6237
Fax: (55) 21 2555 5202
E-Mail: ri@ogx.com.br
Web Site: www.ogx.com.br
OGXP3—(BRAZ)
Sales Range: $400-449.9 Million
Emp.: 213
Oil & Natural Gas Exploration & Production Services
S.I.C.: 1311
N.A.I.C.S.: 211111
Eike Fuhrken Batista *(Chm)*
Paulo Narcelio Simoes Amaral *(CEO & CFO)*
Reinaldo Jose Belotti *(Officer-Production & Dev)*
Marcelo Faber Torres *(Chief IR Officer)*

OSX Brasil SA **(1)**
Praca Mahatma Gandhi 14 13th Floor Centro
Rio de Janeiro, Brazil 20031-100 (78.93%)
Tel.: (55) 2121639239
Fax: (55) 21 2555 5550
E-Mail: ri.osx@osx.com.br
Web Site: www.osx.com.br
OSXB3—(BRAZ)
Rev.: $213,368,601
Assets: $4,820,383,287
Liabilities: $3,181,023,117
Net Worth: $1,639,360,170
Earnings: ($16,096,608)
Fiscal Year-end: 12/31/12
Offshore Oil & Gas Industry Equipment & Support Services
S.I.C.: 1389
N.A.I.C.S.: 213112
Eike Fuhrken Batista *(Chm)*
Eliezer Batista da Silva *(Vice Chm)*
Marcelo Luiz Maia Gomes *(CEO)*
Luiz Guilherme Esteves Marques *(CFO & IR Officer)*
Ivo Dworschak Filho *(Shipbuilding Officer)*

EC-FOUNDER (HOLDINGS) COMPANY LIMITED

Unit 1408 14th Floor Cable TV Tower
9 Hoi Shing Road
Tsuen Wan, New Territories, China (Hong Kong)
Tel.: (852) 2989 1200
Fax: (852) 2989 1204
E-Mail: ir@founder.com.hk
Web Site: www.ecfounder.com.hk
618—(HKG)
Rev.: $351,289,330
Assets: $173,401,257
Liabilities: $132,140,481
Net Worth: $41,260,776
Earnings: ($3,191,899)
Emp.: 523
Fiscal Year-end: 12/31/12

Business Description:
Computer Product Whslr
S.I.C.: 5045
N.A.I.C.S.: 423430

Personnel:
Zhao Dong Zhang *(Chm)*
Geng Chen *(Pres)*
Yvonne Yuk Bo Tang *(Sec)*

Board of Directors:
Zhao Dong Zhang
Qian Cao
Geng Chen
Fat Chung Li
Lam Kit Yee Wong
Yang Jun Xia
Ke Hai Xie
Fu Shuang Zheng

Butterfield Fulcrum Group (Bermuda) Limited
26 Burnaby Street
Hamilton, HM 11, Bermuda

Transfer Agent:
Tricor Tengis Limited
26/F Tesbury Centre, 28 Queens Road East
Hong Kong, China (Hong Kong)

ECCLESIASTICAL INSURANCE OFFICE PLC

Beaufort House Brunswick Road
Gloucester, GL1 1JZ, United Kingdom
Tel.: (44) 1452528533

Ecclesiastical Insurance Office plc—(Continued)

Fax: (44) 1452423557
E-Mail: information@ecclesiastical.com
Web Site: www.ecclesiastical.com
ELLA—(LSE)
Premiums: $760,165,973
Assets: $2,299,700,506
Liabilities: $1,580,085,962
Net Worth: $719,614,544
Earnings: $43,616,831
Emp.: 1,108
Fiscal Year-end: 12/31/12

Business Description:
Insurance & Financial Advisory Services
S.I.C.: 6411
N.A.I.C.S.: 524298

Personnel:
Mark C. J. Hews *(CEO)*
A. Smith *(Chief Risk Officer)*
R. J. Hall *(Sec)*

Board of Directors:
Will M. Samuel
T. J. Carroll
David Christie
Mark C. J. Hews
John F. Hylands
A. P. Latham
C. L. Wilson
Denise P. Wilson
S. A. Wood

Legal Counsel:
Speechly Bircham LLP
London, United Kingdom

Rickerbys LLP
Cheltenham, United Kingdom

McDowell Purcell Solicitors
Dublin, Ireland

Matheson
Dublin, Ireland

Addleshaw Goddard LLP
Leeds, United Kingdom

ECCO SKO A/S

Industrivej 5
6261 Bredebro, Denmark
Tel.: (45) 74911625
Fax: (45) 74710360
E-Mail: mail@ecco.com
Web Site: www.ecco.com
Year Founded: 1963
Rev.: $1,453,924,525
Assets: $1,022,953,944
Liabilities: $423,741,752
Net Worth: $599,212,192
Earnings: $123,307,082
Emp.: 19,426
Fiscal Year-end: 12/31/12

Business Description:
Shoe Retailer, Distr & Mfr
S.I.C.: 2389
N.A.I.C.S.: 316210

Personnel:
Karsten Borch *(Vice Chm-Supervisory Bd)*
Dieter Kasprzak *(Pres, CEO & Member-Mgmt Bd)*
Steen Borgholm *(CFO, Member-Mgmt Bd & Exec VP-Fin)*
Michael Hauge Soerensen *(COO & Member-Mgmt Bd)*
Michel Krol *(Member-Mgmt Bd & Exec VP-Global Sls)*
Panagiotis Mytaros *(Member-Mgmt Bd & Exec VP-Production Grp)*
Andreas Wortmann *(Member-Mgmt Bd & Exec VP-Brand & Products)*

Supervisory Board of Directors:
Karsten Borch
Erik G. Hansen
Gitte Jochimsen
Dieter Kasprzak
Kjeld Mortensen
Gerd Vibeke Rahbek-Clemmensen

Subsidiary:

Ecco USA Inc. **(1)**
16 Delta Dr
Londonderry, NH 03053-2328 NH
Tel.: (603) 537-7300
Fax: (603) 537-9321
Web Site: www.eccousa.com
Emp.: 200
Footwear Sales
Import Export
S.I.C.: 5139
N.A.I.C.S.: 424340
Deborah Eppler *(Mgr-Visual Mdsg)*

ECCOR SOLAR INC.

Fortis House 160 London Road
Barking, Essex, IG11 8BB, United Kingdom
Tel.: (44) 208 214 1137
Fax: (44) 203 014 9455
E-Mail: info@eccorsolar.com
Web Site: www.eccorsolar.com
2EC—(DEU)

Business Description:
Solar Cell Mfr
S.I.C.: 3674
N.A.I.C.S.: 334413

Personnel:
John Darrow *(Mng Dir)*
Larry Wolf *(Mng Dir)*

ECE INDUSTRIES LIMITED

ECE House 28-A Kasturba Gandhi Marg
New Delhi, 110 001, India
Tel.: (91) 1123314237
Fax: (91) 1123310410
E-Mail: eceho@satyam.net.in
Web Site: www.eceindustriesltd.com
ECEIND—(NSE)
Rev.: $27,498,639
Assets: $38,124,006
Liabilities: $11,991,097
Net Worth: $26,132,909
Earnings: $174,369
Fiscal Year-end: 03/31/13

Business Description:
Power Transmission Equipment Mfr & Distr
S.I.C.: 3568
N.A.I.C.S.: 333613

Personnel:
Prakash Kumar Mohta *(Chm & Mng Dir)*
R. Prasad *(Pres-Corp Affairs, Fin & Legal)*
A. V. Ramachandran *(Pres-Transformer Div)*
Piyush Agarwal *(Sec)*

Board of Directors:
Prakash Kumar Mohta
Mahendra Kukmar Jajoo
Om Prakash Khaitan
Sakate Khaitan
Vikram Prakash

Transfer Agent:
MAS Services Limited
T-34 2nd Floor Okhla Industrial Area Phase - II
New Delhi, India

Divisions:

ECE Industries Limited - Elevator Division **(1)**
A-20 Industrial Area Meerut Road
Ghaziabad, Uttar Pradesh, 201 001, India
Tel.: (91) 120 2712065
Fax: (91) 120 2723950
E-Mail: ecegzb@satyam.net.in
Emp.: 50
Elevator Mfr
S.I.C.: 3534
N.A.I.C.S.: 333921
S. B. Khandelwal *(Sr Mgr)*

ECE Industries Limited - Meter Division **(1)**
Ashok Marg
Sanathnagar, Hyderabad, Andhra Pradesh, 500 018, India
Tel.: (91) 40 23814433
Fax: (91) 40 23817702
E-Mail: ecehyd@eceindustries.com
Emp.: 7
Electric Meter Mfr
S.I.C.: 3825
N.A.I.C.S.: 334515
H. M. Mot *(Gen Mgr)*

ECE PROJEKTMANAGEMENT GMBH & CO KG

Heegbarg 30
22391 Hamburg, Germany
Tel.: (49) 40 60 60 60
Web Site: www.ece.de
Year Founded: 1965

Business Description:
Developer & Builder of Transport Complexes, Logistics & Shopping Centers & Other Real Estate Investment Properties
S.I.C.: 6531
N.A.I.C.S.: 531390

Personnel:
Alexander Otto *(CEO & Member-Mgmt Bd)*
Gerhard L. Dunstheimer *(Mng Dir-Dev, Deputy CEO & Member-Mgmt Bd)*
Karsten Hinrichs *(Mng Dir-Fin, CFO & Member-Mgmt Bd)*
Henrie W. Kotter *(Mng Dir-Center Mgmt & Member-Mgmt Bd)*
Lothar Kappich *(Mng Dir-HR & Corp Svcs & Member-Mgmt Bd)*
Markus Lentzler *(Mng Dir-Architecture & Member-Mgmt Bd)*
Jens-Ulrich Maier *(Mng Dir-Construction & Member-Mgmt Bd)*
Andreas Mattner *(Mng Dir-Office, Traffic, Industries/Corp Comm & Member-Mgmt Bd)*
Klaus Striebich *(Mng Dir-Leasing & Member-Mgmt Bd)*

ECHELON PETROLEUM CORP.

(Formerly Rara Terra Minerals Corp.)
Suite 830 1100 Melville Street
PO Box 43
Vancouver, BC, V6E 4A6, Canada
Tel.: (604) 681-7822
Fax: (604) 628-9875
Web Site: www.echelonpetroleum.com
Year Founded: 2009
ECH—(TSXV)
Assets: $1,863,506
Liabilities: $48,824
Net Worth: $1,814,682
Earnings: ($887,844)
Fiscal Year-end: 03/31/13

Business Description:
Petroleum Exploration Services
S.I.C.: 1311
N.A.I.C.S.: 211111

Personnel:
Alexander Helmel *(Pres & CEO)*
Roger Flowerdew *(CFO & Sec)*

Board of Directors:
Roger Flowerdew
Alexander Helmel
John E. Veltheer

Legal Counsel:
Clark Wilson LLP
800-885 West Georgia Street
Vancouver, BC, Canada V6C 3H1

Transfer Agent:
Computershare Investor Services Inc
100 University Avenue 9th Floor North Tower
Toronto, ON, Canada

ECHO ENTERTAINMENT GROUP LIMITED

Level 3 159 William Street
Brisbane, QLD, 4000, Australia
Mailing Address:
PO Box 13348
George Street Post Shop, Brisbane, QLD, 4003, Australia
Tel.: (61) 7 3228 0000
Fax: (61) 7 3228 0099
E-Mail: investor@echoent.com.au
Web Site: www.echoentertainment.com.au
EGP—(ASX)
Rev.: $1,811,065,590
Assets: $4,528,549,760
Liabilities: $1,545,434,300
Net Worth: $2,983,115,460
Earnings: $87,015,350
Emp.: 8,000
Fiscal Year-end: 06/30/13

Business Description:
Casino Operator
S.I.C.: 7011
N.A.I.C.S.: 721120

Personnel:
Matt Bekier *(CFO)*
Paula Martin *(Gen Counsel & Sec)*

Board of Directors:
John O'Neill
Matt Bekier
Gerard Bradley
Anne Brennan
Katie Lahey
Richard Sheppard

Subsidiaries:

Jupiters Hotel & Casino **(1)**
Broadbeach Island
PO Box 1515
Broadbeach, Gold Coast, QLD, 4218, Australia AU
Tel.: (61) 7 5592 8100
E-Mail: jupitersgc@echoent.com.au
Web Site: www.jupitersgoldcoast.com.au
Casino Hotel Operator
S.I.C.: 7011
N.A.I.C.S.: 721120

Star City Holdings Limited **(1)**
80 Pyrmont St
PO Box Q192
Pyrmont, NSW, 2009, Australia (100%)
Tel.: (61) 297779000
Fax: (61) 296577570
E-Mail: reservations@starcity.com.au
Web Site: www.star.com.au
Emp.: 4,200
Holding Company; Casino Owner & Operator
S.I.C.: 6719
N.A.I.C.S.: 551112
Brad Schmitt *(Dir-Media)*

Star City Pty. Ltd. **(1)**
80 Pyrmont Street
Pyrmont, NSW, 2009, Australia
Tel.: (61) 297779000
Fax: (61) 296578344
E-Mail: starreservations@tabcorp.com.au
Web Site: www.starcity.com.au
Emp.: 3,000
Hotel & Casino Operation Services
S.I.C.: 7011
N.A.I.C.S.: 721120
Peter Grimshaw *(Gen Mgr-Govt Rels)*

ECHO INTERNATIONAL HOLDINGS GROUP LIMITED

Room 05 22/F Cable TV Tower 9 Hoi Shing Road
Tsuen Wan, China (Hong Kong)
Tel.: (852) 2412 0878
Fax: (852) 2415 4249
E-Mail: info@echogroup.com.hk
Web Site: www.echogroup.com.hk
Year Founded: 1989
8218—(HKG)
Sales Range: $1-9.9 Million
Emp.: 270

Business Description:
Electrical Equipment Mfr
S.I.C.: 3699
N.A.I.C.S.: 335999
Personnel:
Yan Yee Lo *(Chm)*
Raymond Kwing Sang Cheng *(Pres)*

ECHO INVESTMENT S.A.

Aleja Solidarnosci 36
25-323 Kielce, Poland
Tel.: (48) 413333333
Fax: (48) 413332333
E-Mail: office@echo.com.pl
Web Site: www.echo.com.pl
ECH—(WAR)
Rev.: $184,812,264
Assets: $1,729,364,753
Liabilities: $958,217,809
Net Worth: $771,146,945
Earnings: $118,646,261
Emp.: 304
Fiscal Year-end: 12/31/12
Business Description:
Real Estate & Property Development Services
S.I.C.: 6531
N.A.I.C.S.: 531311
Personnel:
Wojciech Ciesielski *(Chm-Supervisory Bd)*
Piotr Gromniak *(Chm-Mgmt Bd)*
Andrzej Majcher *(Vice Chm-Supervisory Bd)*
Artur Langner *(Vice Chm-Mgmt Bd)*
Waldemar Lesiak *(Vice Chm-Mgmt Bd)*
Supervisory Board of Directors:
Wojciech Ciesielski
Andrzej Majcher
Robert Oskard
Mariusz Waniolka
Karol Zbikowski

ECHO RESOURCES LIMITED

992 Albany Highway
Victoria Park, WA, 6101, Australia
Tel.: (61) 8 9362 4806
Fax: (61) 8 9355 3164
E-Mail: admin@echoresources.com.au
Web Site: www.echoresources.com.au
EAR—(ASX)
Sales Range: Less than $1 Million
Business Description:
Mineral Exploration
S.I.C.: 1481
N.A.I.C.S.: 213115
Personnel:
Ernst Kohler *(Mng Dir)*
Graham Douglas Anderson *(Sec)*
Board of Directors:
Graham Douglas Anderson
Peter Andrews
Ernst Kohler
Peter Stedwell

ECI PARTNERS LLP

Brettenham House Lancaster Place
London, WC2E 7EN, United Kingdom
Tel.: (44) 2076061000
Fax: (44) 2072405050
E-Mail: enquiries@eci.partners.com
Web Site: www.eciv.co.uk
Emp.: 35
Business Description:
Private Equity Firm
S.I.C.: 6211
N.A.I.C.S.: 523999
Personnel:
Lewis Bantin *(Partner)*
Sean Whelan *(Mng Dir)*

Holdings:

Citation Ltd. (1)
Citation House
1 Macclesfield Road, Wilmslow, Chesire, SK9 1BZ, United Kingdom
Tel.: (44) 845 234 0404
Fax: (44) 1625 415501
E-Mail: enquiries@citation.co.uk
Web Site: www.citation.co.uk
Professional Advice & Compliance Services
S.I.C.: 7389
N.A.I.C.S.: 561499
Dave Lambert *(Dir-Sls)*

Subsidiary:

Bibby Consulting & Support Limited (2)
Brunswick Court Brunswick Street
Newcastle-under-Lyme, Staffordshire, ST5 1HH, United Kingdom
Tel.: (44) 8453 100 600
Fax: (44) 8453 100 650
E-Mail: enquiries@bibbycas.com
Web Site: www.bibbycas.com
Business Consulting & Support Services
S.I.C.: 8742
N.A.I.C.S.: 541611
Michael Slade *(Mng Dir)*

Kelvin Hughes Limited (1)
Voltage Mollison Avenue
Hainault, Enfield, EN3 7XQ, United Kingdom
Tel.: (44) 2085026887
Telex: 896401
Fax: (44) 2085000837
E-Mail: marketing@kelvinhughes.co.uk
Web Site: www.kelvinhughes.com
Emp.: 250
Naval & Maritime Navigational Radar & Systems
S.I.C.: 3812
N.A.I.C.S.: 334511
Russell Gould *(CEO)*

Division:

ChartCo Ltd. (2)
Unit 4 Voltage Mollison Av
Hainault, Enfield, EN3 7XQ, United Kingdom
Tel.: (44) 2082670003
Fax: (44) 2082670004
E-Mail: commercial@chartco.com
Web Site: www.chartco.com
Emp.: 50
Maritime Charts
S.I.C.: 3812
N.A.I.C.S.: 334511
Stephen Mariner *(Dir-Bus Dev)*

Non-U.S. Subsidiaries:

A/S Kelvin Hughes (2)
Rudolfgardsvej 9
Viby, J, Denmark DK
Tel.: (45) 86112888
Fax: (45) 86112260
E-Mail: service@kelvinhughes.dk
Web Site: www.kelvinhughes.com
Emp.: 12
Marine Navigation Equipment Mfr
S.I.C.: 3812
N.A.I.C.S.: 334511

Kelvin Hughes (Nederland) B.V. (2)
Klompenmakrstraat 64
3194 Rotterdam, Netherlands
Tel.: (31) 104167622
Fax: (31) 104167218
E-Mail: nlsales@kelvinhughes.nl
Web Site: www.kelvinhughes.nl
Emp.: 20
Navigation Equipment
S.I.C.: 3812
N.A.I.C.S.: 334511
Bruce N. de Bies *(Mgr-Sls)*

Kelvin Hughes (Singapore) Pte. Ltd. (2)
896 Dunearn Rd Ste 03-05 Sime Darby Ctr
Singapore, 589472, Singapore SG
Tel.: (65) 65459880
Telex: 23482
Fax: (65) 65458892
E-Mail: cams@khsing.com
Web Site: www.kelvinhughes.com
Emp.: 30
Marine Navigation Equipment
S.I.C.: 3812
N.A.I.C.S.: 334511
Clarence Khoh *(Gen Mgr)*

Premier Research Group plc (1)
1st Floor Rubra 2 Mulberry Business Park
Fishponds Road, Wokingham, RG45 6LS, United Kingdom
Tel.: (44) 1189364000
Fax: (44) 1189364001
Sales Range: $50-74.9 Million
Emp.: 557
Pharmaceutical & Medical Device Clinical Research Services
S.I.C.: 8734
N.A.I.C.S.: 541380
Troy McCall *(COO)*
Bernard Gallagher *(Chief Dev Officer)*
Philip Butler *(Exec VP-Strategic Dev)*

U.S. Subsidiary:

Pivotal Research Centers LLC (2)
13128 N 94th Dr Ste 200
Peoria, AZ 85381
Tel.: (623) 815-9714
Fax: (623) 815-9759
Web Site: www.pivotalresearch.com
Sales Range: $1-9.9 Million
Clinical Research Services
S.I.C.: 8731
N.A.I.C.S.: 541712
Joanne Mashburn *(COO)*

U.S. Headquarters

Premier Research Group International Ltd. (2)
1500 Market St Ste 3500
Philadelphia, PA 19102
Tel.: (215) 282-5500
Fax: (215) 282-5528
Web Site: www.premier-research.com
Emp.: 100
Pharmaceutical & Medical Device Clinical Testing Services
S.I.C.: 8734
N.A.I.C.S.: 541380
Ludo Reynders *(CEO)*

Wireless Logic Ltd. (1)
Grosvenor House Horseshoe Crescent
Beaconsfield, HP9 1LJ, United Kingdom
Tel.: (44) 8448 044111
E-Mail: info@wirelesslogic.com
Web Site: www.wirelesslogic.com
Sales Range: $10-24.9 Million
Emp.: 20
Wireless Data Solutions
S.I.C.: 7373
N.A.I.C.S.: 541512
Oliver Tucker *(Mng Dir)*

ECKELMANN AG

Berliner Strasse 161
65205 Wiesbaden, Germany
Tel.: (49) 61171030
Fax: (49) 6117103133
E-Mail: info@eckelmann.de
Web Site: www.eckelmann.de
Sales Range: $50-74.9 Million
Emp.: 365
Business Description:
Electronic Control System Mfr
S.I.C.: 3823
N.A.I.C.S.: 334513
Personnel:
Hubertus Krossa *(Chm-Supervisory Bd)*
Gerd Eckelmann *(Chm-Mgmt Bd)*
Peter Cordes *(Member-Mgmt Bd)*
Frank-Thomas Mellert *(Member-Mgmt Bd)*

ECKERT & ZIEGLER STRAHLEN- UND MEDIZINTECHNIK AG

(d/b/a Eckert & Ziegler AG)
Robert-Rossle-Strasse 10
13125 Berlin, Germany
Tel.: (49) 309410840
Fax: (49) 30941084112
E-Mail: info@ezag.de
Web Site: www.ezag.com
Year Founded: 1997
EUZ—(DEU EUR)
Rev.: $161,536,361
Assets: $221,369,579
Liabilities: $104,293,175
Net Worth: $117,076,405
Earnings: $15,837,690
Emp.: 611
Fiscal Year-end: 12/31/12
Business Description:
Holding Company; Radioisotopes Processor & Isotope Technologies Developer, Mfr & Distr
S.I.C.: 6719
N.A.I.C.S.: 551112
Personnel:
Wolfgang Maennig *(Chm-Supervisory Bd)*
Andreas Eckert *(Chm-Exec Bd)*
Andre Hess *(Member-Exec Bd)*
Edgar Loffler *(Member-Exec Bd)*
Supervisory Board of Directors:
Wolfgang Maennig
Gudrun Erzgraber
Nikolaus Fuchs
Detlev Ganten
Hans-Jorg Hinke
Fritz Oesterle

Subsidiaries:

Eckert & Ziegler EURO-PET Berlin GmbH (1)
Max-Planck-Street 4
12489 Berlin, Germany
Tel.: (49) 3063922491
Fax: (49) 30 6392 2499
E-Mail: info@ezag.de
Web Site: www.ezag.de
Emp.: 11
Radioactive Isotopes Mfr
S.I.C.: 2819
N.A.I.C.S.: 325180
Axel Schmidt *(Gen Mgr)*

Eckert & Ziegler Eurotope GmbH (1)
Robert Rossle Street 10
13125 Berlin, Germany
Tel.: (49) 30 941084 197
Fax: (49) 30 941084 470
E-Mail: eurotope@ezag.de
Web Site: www.ezag.com
Pharmaceuticals Mfr
S.I.C.: 2819
N.A.I.C.S.: 325180

Eckert & Ziegler f-con Europe GmbH (1)
Nicolaus August Otto Street 7a D
56357 Holzhausen an der Haide, Germany
Tel.: (49) 6772 96 81 0
Fax: (49) 6772 96 81 29
E-Mail: fcon@ezag.de
Web Site: www.ezag.com
Emp.: 5
Medical Instruments Mfr
S.I.C.: 3841
N.A.I.C.S.: 339112
Axel Schmidt *(Gen Mgr)*

Subsidiary:

Eckert & Ziegler f-con Deutschland GmbH (2)
Nicolaus August Otto St 7a D
56357 Holzhausen an der Haide, Rhineland-Palatinate, Germany
Tel.: (49) 6772 96 81 0
Fax: (49) 6772 96 81 29
E-Mail: fcon@ezag.de
Web Site: www.ezag.com
Emp.: 6
Medical Instruments Mfr
S.I.C.: 3841
N.A.I.C.S.: 339112
Axel Schmidt *(Mng Dir)*

Eckert & Ziegler Nuclitec GmbH (1)
Gieselweg 1
38110 Braunschweig, Germany De
Tel.: (49) 53079320
Fax: (49) 5307932293
E-Mail: infonuclitec@ezag.com
Web Site: www.nuclitec.com

Eckert & Ziegler Strahlen- und Medizintechnik AG—(Continued)

Sales Range: $25-49.9 Million
Emp.: 125
Radiation Detection Equipment, Medical Product & Radioactive Reference Device Distr
S.I.C.: 3829
N.A.I.C.S.: 334519

Eckert & Ziegler Radiopharma GmbH **(1)**
Robert Rossle Strasse 10
13125 Berlin, Germany
Tel.: (49) 30 94 10 84 280
Fax: (49) 30 94 10 84 470
E-Mail: radiopharma@ezag.de
Web Site: www.ezag.com
Radiopharmaceutical Products Mfr
S.I.C.: 2834
N.A.I.C.S.: 325412

Kompetenzzentrum fur sichere Entsorgung GmbH **(1)**
Gieselweg 1 D
38110 Braunschweig, Germany
Tel.: (49) 5307932481
Fax: (49) 5307 932 272
Radioactive Isotope Mfr
S.I.C.: 2834
N.A.I.C.S.: 325412

U.S. Subsidiaries:

Eckert & Ziegler Analytics,Inc. **(1)**
1380 Seaboard Industrial Blvd
Atlanta, GA 30318
Tel.: (404) 352-8677
Fax: (404) 352-2837
E-Mail: analytics@ezag.com
Web Site: www.analyticsinc.com
Radioactive Isotopes Mfr
S.I.C.: 2819
N.A.I.C.S.: 325180

Eckert & Ziegler Isotope Products, Inc. **(1)**
24937 Ave Tibbitts
Valencia, CA 91355 CA
Tel.: (661) 309-1010 (100%)
Fax: (661) 257-8303
Web Site: www.isotopeproducts.com
Sls.: $15,502,450
Emp.: 84
Radioactive Components, Nuclear Imaging Reference & Testing Apparatus Mfr
S.I.C.: 3826
N.A.I.C.S.: 334516
Frank Yeager *(Pres & CEO)*

Non-U.S. Subsidiary:

Eckert & Ziegler Isotope Products, GmbH **(2)**
Harxbutteler Str 3
13125 Braunschweig, Germany
Tel.: (49) 30941084300
Fax: (49) 5307201656
E-Mail: ipe@ezag.de
Web Site: www.ezag.de
Emp.: 7
Radioactive Isotopes Mfr
S.I.C.: 2834
N.A.I.C.S.: 325412
Andreas Eckert *(Mng Dir)*

Non-U.S. Subsidiaries:

Eckert & Ziegler BEBIG S.A. **(1)**
Zone Industrielle C
7180 Seneffe, Belgium BE
Tel.: (32) 64520808 (78.68%)
Fax: (32) 64520801
E-Mail: info@bebig.eu
Web Site: www.bebig.eu
EZBG—(EUR)
Sls.: $42,779,936
Assets: $82,195,794
Liabilities: $24,408,754
Net Worth: $57,787,040
Earnings: $5,208,332
Emp.: 148
Fiscal Year-end: 12/31/12
Cancer Treatment Radiation Therapy Technologies Developer, Mfr & Marketer
S.I.C.: 3841
N.A.I.C.S.: 339112
Andreas Eckert *(Chm)*
Edgar Loffler *(Mng Dir)*
Abel Luzuriaga *(Mng Dir)*

Non-U.S. Subsidiaries:

Eckert & Ziegler BEBIG do Brasil Ltda. **(2)**
Avenida Dom Luis 500 Sala 1925
60160 230 Fortaleza, Brazil
Tel.: (55) 85 3241 0899
Fax: (55) 8532411164
E-Mail: kentaro.mazur@bebig.eu
Web Site: www.bebig.eu
Emp.: 1
Cancer Treatment Radiation Therapy Technologies Developer & Mfr
S.I.C.: 3841
N.A.I.C.S.: 339112
John T. Spitznagel *(Gen Mgr-Latin America)*

Eckert & Ziegler BEBIG GmbH **(2)**
Robert-Rossle-Strasse 10
D-13125 Berlin, Germany De
Tel.: (49) 30941084130 (100%)
Fax: (49) 30941084112
E-Mail: info@evag.de
Web Site: www.ibt-bebig.eu
Emp.: 400
Cancer Treatment Radiation Therapy Technologies Developer & Mfr
S.I.C.: 3845
N.A.I.C.S.: 334510
Edgar Loffler *(Member-Mgmt Bd-Sls/Mktg/New Bus Dev)*

Eckert & Ziegler BEBIG Ltd. **(2)**
Imperial House 4th Floor 15 Kingsway
London, WC2B 6UN, United Kingdom
Tel.: (44) 1446 773 433
Fax: (44) 7900 141 017
Cancer Treatment Radiation Therapy Technologies Developer & Mfr
S.I.C.: 3841
N.A.I.C.S.: 339112

Eckert & Ziegler BEBIG SARL **(2)**
67 rue de Dunkerque
75009 Paris, France
Tel.: (33) 1 55 28 00 30
Fax: (33) 1 40 21 06 09
Web Site: www.bebig.eu
Emp.: 4
Cancer Treatment Radiation Therapy Technologies Developer & Mfr
S.I.C.: 3841
N.A.I.C.S.: 339112
Kentaro Mazur *(Gen Mgr)*

Eckert & Ziegler Iberia S.L. **(2)**
c/ Lanzarote 15
San Sebastian de los Reyes, 28703, Spain
Tel.: (34) 91 6526248
Fax: (34) 91 6535352
Emp.: 5
Cancer Treatment Radiation Therapy Technologies Developer & Mfr
S.I.C.: 3841
N.A.I.C.S.: 339112
Aurora Gutierrez *(Dir-Sls)*

Eckert & Ziegler Italia s.r.l. **(2)**
Via Fiuggi 2
20159 Milan, Italy
Tel.: (39) 02 69900435
Fax: (39) 02 69010218
Cancer Treatment Radiation Therapy Technologies Developer & Mfr
S.I.C.: 3841
N.A.I.C.S.: 339112

Eckert & Ziegler Cesio s.r.o. **(1)**
Radiova 1
102 27 Prague, Czech Republic
Tel.: (420) 267008235
Fax: (420) 267008424
E-Mail: cesio@ezag.com
Web Site: www.ip-cesio.com
Emp.: 25
Radioactive Isotopes Mfr
S.I.C.: 2834
N.A.I.C.S.: 325412
Ivan Simmer *(Mng Dir)*

ECKES AG

Ludwig-Eckes-Platz 1
55268 Nieder-Olm, Germany
Tel.: (49) 6136 35 0
Fax: (49) 6136 35 1081
Web Site: www.eckes-granini.com
Year Founded: 1857
Sales Range: $1-4.9 Billion
Emp.: 1,640

Business Description:
Holding Company
Import Export
S.I.C.: 6719
N.A.I.C.S.: 551112

Personnel:
Axel Hamm *(Chm-Supervisory Bd)*
Thomas Hinderer *(Chm-Exec Bd)*
Karl Brings *(Deputy Chm-Supervisory Bd)*
Sidney Coffeng *(Member-Exec Bd)*
Albert Gratz *(Member-Exec Bd)*

Supervisory Board of Directors:
Axel Hamm
Karl Brings
Christian Kohler
Christina Oelbermann
Thierry Paternot
Willi Schwerdtle

Subsidiaries:

Eckes-Granini Group GmbH **(1)**
Ludwig-Eckes-Platz 1
55268 Nieder-Olm, Germany De
Tel.: (49) 6136 35 0
Fax: (49) 6136 35 1400
E-Mail: info@eckes-granini.com
Web Site: www.eckes-granini.com
Sales Range: $1-4.9 Billion
Holding Company; Branded Fruit Juice & Fruit Beverage Mfr & Distr
S.I.C.: 6719
N.A.I.C.S.: 551112
Thomas Hinderer *(Chm-Exec Bd)*
Ulrich Bunk *(Member-Exec Bd & Sr VP-Supply Chain)*
Sidney Coffeng *(Member-Exec Bd & Sr VP-IT, Controlling & Fin)*
Jose Marti Cos *(Member-Exec Bd & Sr VP-Mktg & R&D)*
Sabine Holtkamp *(Member-Exec Bd & Sr VP-HR & Org Dev)*
Albert Gratz *(Member-Exec Bd & Gen Mgr-Bus Dev-Intl)*

Subsidiary:

Eckes-Granini Deutschland GmbH **(2)**
Ludwig-Eckes-Platz 1
55268 Nieder-Olm, Germany De
Tel.: (49) 6136 35 04 (100%)
Fax: (49) 6136 35 1400
E-Mail: info@eckes-granini.de
Web Site: www.eckes-granini.de
Emp.: 400
Fruit Juice & Fruit Beverage Mfr & Distr
Import Export
S.I.C.: 2037
N.A.I.C.S.: 311411
Heribert Gathof *(Mng Dir)*

Non-U.S. Subsidiaries:

Bramhults Juice AB **(2)**
Box 71
Bramhult, 507 20 Boras, Sweden NO
Tel.: (46) 33 20 4500 (100%)
Fax: (46) 33 20 4501
Web Site: www.bramhults.se
Fruit Juice & Fruit Beverage Mfr & Distr
Import Export
S.I.C.: 2037
N.A.I.C.S.: 311411
Stefan Bostrom *(Mng Dir)*

Eckes-Granini Austria GmbH **(2)**
Pummerinfeld 1b
Saint Florian, 4490 Asten, Austria AT
Tel.: (43) 72 24 418 880
Fax: (43) 72 24 418 88180
Web Site: www.eckes-granini.at
Fruit Juice & Fruit Beverage Mfr & Distr
Import Export
S.I.C.: 2037
N.A.I.C.S.: 311411
Silke Goos-Perneker *(Mng Dir)*
Jarek Kluszczynski *(CFO)*

Subsidiary:

PAGO International GmbH **(3)**
Schroedingerstrasse 61
9021 Klagenfurt, Austria AT
Tel.: (43) 463 33 444-0
Fax: (43) 463 38 1988
E-Mail: office@pago.cc
Web Site: www.pago.cc
Sales Range: $100-124.9 Million
Emp.: 100
Fruit Juice Mfr & Distr
S.I.C.: 2037
N.A.I.C.S.: 311411
Alle Ypma *(Mng Dir)*

Eckes-Granini Finland Oy Ab **(2)**
PO Box 411
20101 Turku, Finland (100%)
Tel.: (358) 207 207 300
Fax: (358) 207 207 301
Web Site: www.eckes-granini.fi
Fruit Juice & Fruit Beverage Mfr & Distr
Import Export
S.I.C.: 2037
N.A.I.C.S.: 311411
Timo Laukkanen *(Mng Dir)*

Eckes-Granini Iberica S.A.U. **(2)**
Travessera de Gracia No 73-79 3rd andar
08006 Barcelona, Spain ES
Tel.: (34) 93 238 4384 (100%)
Web Site: www.granini.es
Emp.: 60
Fruit Juices Distr
Import
S.I.C.: 5149
N.A.I.C.S.: 424490
Javier Lorenzo Benavides *(Mng Dir)*

Eckes-Granini (Suisse) S.A. **(2)**
Route de la Gare 1
1525 Henniez, Switzerland CH
Tel.: (41) 26 66 86 868 (51%)
Fax: (41) 26 66 86 820
Web Site: www.eckes-granini.ch
Fruit Juice & Fruit Beverage Mfr & Distr
Import Export
S.I.C.: 2037
N.A.I.C.S.: 311411
Marc Bandelier *(Mng Dir)*

Sio-Eckes Kft. **(2)**
Majus 1 Utca 61
8600 Siofok, Hungary HU
Tel.: (36) 84 501 501 (100%)
Fax: (36) 84 501 500
Web Site: www.sioeckes.hu
Fruit Juice & Fruit Beverage Mfr & Distr
Import Export
S.I.C.: 2037
N.A.I.C.S.: 311411
Endre Fazekas *(Mng Dir)*

UAB Eckes-Granini Lietuva **(2)**
Laisves Av 125
06118 Vilnius, Lithuania LT
Tel.: (370) 5 279 4408 (100%)
Fax: (370) 5 248 1646
Web Site: www.eckes-granini.lt
Fruit Juice & Fruit Beverage Mfr & Distr
Import Export
S.I.C.: 2037
N.A.I.C.S.: 311411
Marius Gudauskas *(Mng Dir)*

Non-U.S. Affiliate:

Yildiz Granini Meyve Suyu Sanayi Ve Ticaret A.S. **(2)**
Kisikli Mah Ferah Cad No 1
Camlica Uskudar, 34692 Istanbul, Turkey TR
Tel.: (90) 216 524 1525 (50%)
Fax: (90) 216 481 3462
Web Site: www.ulker.com.tr
Fruit Juice & Fruit Beverage Distr
Import
S.I.C.: 5149
N.A.I.C.S.: 424490
Mehmet Yilmaz *(Mng Dir)*

ECKOH PLC

Telford House Corner Hall
Hemel Hempstead, HP3 9HN, United Kingdom
Tel.: (44) 1442458300
Fax: (44) 8701107107
E-Mail: reception@eckoh.com
Web Site: www.eckoh.com
ECK—(LSE)
Rev.: $17,348,501
Assets: $24,262,632
Liabilities: $3,548,665

Net Worth: $20,713,968
Earnings: $3,013,285
Emp.: 74
Fiscal Year-end: 03/31/13
Business Description:
Hosted Speech Recognition Products & Services
S.I.C.: 7389
N.A.I.C.S.: 561499
Personnel:
Nik B. Philpot *(CEO)*
Adam P. Moloney *(Sec & Dir-Fin)*
Board of Directors:
Chris M. Batterham
Clive Ansell
Adam P. Moloney
Nik B. Philpot
Legal Counsel:
Travers Smith
10 Snow Hill
London, EC1A 2AL, United Kingdom
Tel.: (44) 171 248 9133
Telex: 887117 Traver G
Fax: (44) 171 236 3728
Subsidiary:

Eckoh UK Limited (1)
Telford House Corner Hall
Hemel Hempstead, Hertfordshire, HP3 9HN, United Kingdom
Tel.: (44) 1442 458300
Fax: (44) 1442283328
E-Mail: reception@eckoh.com
Web Site: www.eckoh.com
Emp.: 75
Telecommunication Services
S.I.C.: 4899
N.A.I.C.S.: 517919
Nik Philpot *(Gen Mgr)*

ECL ENVIROCLEAN VENTURES LTD.
5730 Production Way
Langley, BC, V3A 4N4, Canada
Tel.: (604) 532-5311
Fax: (604) 532-5377
Toll Free: (888) 792-4411
E-Mail: info@envirocoatings.com
Web Site: www.envirocoatings.com
ECL—(DEU TSXV)
Sales Range: Less than $1 Million
Business Description:
Ceramic Coating Mfr
S.I.C.: 2851
N.A.I.C.S.: 325510
Personnel:
Roland Langset *(Chm, Pres & CEO)*
Ken Sahli *(COO & Sr VP)*
Board of Directors:
Roland Langset
Aaron Langset
Ken Sahli
Legal Counsel:
InterMark Law Corp
Suite 105 - 900 West Georgia Street
Vancouver, BC, Canada
Transfer Agent:
Computershare Trust Company of Canada
Suite 401-501 Burrard Street
Vancouver, BC, Canada
Subsidiaries:

ECI Envirocoatings (Canada) Inc. (1)
5730 Production Way
Langley, BC, V3A 4N4, Canada
Tel.: (604) 532-5311
Fax: (604) 532-6099
Toll Free: (888) 792-4411
E-Mail: info@envirocoatings.com
Web Site: www.envirocoatings.com
Waterproof Protective Coating Distr
S.I.C.: 5198
N.A.I.C.S.: 424950

Envirocoat Technologies Inc. (1)
5730 Production Way
Langley, BC, V3A 4N4, Canada
Tel.: (604) 532-5311
Fax: (604) 532-5377
Paint & Coating Mfr
S.I.C.: 2851
N.A.I.C.S.: 325510

ECLAT TEXTILE CO., LTD.
No 28 Wuchuan Rd Wugu Industrial Park
Taipei, Taiwan
Tel.: (886) 222996000
Fax: (886) 222995483
E-Mail: service@eclat.com.tw
Web Site: www.eclat.com.tw
1476—(TAI)
Sales Range: $100-124.9 Million
Emp.: 2,550
Business Description:
Yarn Dyeing Mills
S.I.C.: 2269
N.A.I.C.S.: 313310
Personnel:
Cheng-Hai Hung *(Chm & Gen Mgr)*
U.S. Subsidiary:

Antaeus Fashions Inc. (1)
2411 N Loma Ave
South El Monte, CA 91733-1617 CA
Tel.: (626) 452-0797
Fax: (626) 452-0984
Web Site: www.antaeusfashion.com
Zipper Jackets Mfr
S.I.C.: 2399
N.A.I.C.S.: 315210
Michael Lin *(Gen Mgr)*

ECLECTIC BAR GROUP PLC
533 Kings Road
London, SW10 0TZ, United Kingdom
Tel.: (44) 20 7376 6300
Fax: (44) 20 7823 3756
E-Mail: info@eclecticbars.co.uk
Web Site: www.eclecticbars.co.uk
Year Founded: 2006
BAR—(AIM)
Sales Range: $25-49.9 Million
Emp.: 210
Business Description:
Bar Owner & Operator
S.I.C.: 5813
N.A.I.C.S.: 722410
Personnel:
Jim Fallon *(Chm)*
Reuben Harley *(CEO)*
John Smith *(CFO)*
Board of Directors:
Jim Fallon
Reuben Harley
Richard Howard Kleiner
John Smith
Clive Watson

ECLECTIC INVESTMENT COMPANY PLC
Northern House Woodsome Park
Fenay Bridge, Huddersfield, W Yorkshire, HD8 0LA, United Kingdom
Tel.: (44) 2086392157
Web Site: www.eclecticinvest.com
ECIT—(LSE)
Sales Range: $1-9.9 Million
Emp.: 1
Business Description:
Investment Services
S.I.C.: 6211
N.A.I.C.S.: 523999
Personnel:
Anthony Bushell *(Chm)*
Board of Directors:
Anthony Bushell
Peter I. Burrows
Bruce C. Hervey
Warren J. McLeland

ECLERX SERVICES LTD
Sonawala Building 1st Floor 29 Bank Street Fort
Mumbai, Maharashtra, 400 023, India
Tel.: (91) 2266148300
Fax: (91) 2266148655
Web Site: www.eclerx.com
ECLERX—(BOM NSE)
Rev.: $122,463,004
Assets: $111,636,200
Liabilities: $30,370,189
Net Worth: $81,266,011
Earnings: $31,815,011
Emp.: 5,954
Fiscal Year-end: 03/31/13
Business Description:
Data Solutions Technical Services
S.I.C.: 7374
N.A.I.C.S.: 518210
Personnel:
Anjan Malik *(Co-Founder)*
P. D. Mundhra *(Co-Founder)*
Rohitash Gupta *(CFO)*
Gaurav Tongia *(Compliance Officer & Sec)*
Scott Houchin *(Mng Principal)*
Amit Bakshi *(Principal-Ops)*
Sandeep Dembi *(Principal-Fin Svcs)*
Charles J. Haven *(Principal)*
Bob Horan *(Principal-Cable & Telco Svcs)*
Sanjay Kukreja *(Principal-Tech Svcs)*
Hoshi Mistry *(Principal-Sls & Mktg Svcs)*
Chitra Padmanabhan *(Principal-Resource Mgmt Grp)*
Alan Paris *(Principal-Fin Svcs)*
Board of Directors:
V. K. Mundhra
Biren Gabhawala
Nityanath Ghanekar
Anish Ghoshal
Alok Goyal
Deepa Kapoor
Pradeep Kapoor
Vikram Limaye
Anjan Malik
P. D. Mundhra
Transfer Agent:
Karvy Computershare Private Limited
17-24 Vittal Rao Nagar Madhapur
Hyderabad, India
Non-U.S. Subsidiary:

eClerx Limited (1)
19 Berkeley St
London, W1J 8ED, United Kingdom
Tel.: (44) 2075296000
Web Site: www.eclerx.com
Business Process Outsourcing Services
S.I.C.: 7389
N.A.I.C.S.: 561499

ECLIPSE METALS LTD.
Suite 1/56 Kings Park Road
West Perth, WA, 6005, Australia
Mailing Address:
PO Box 1395
West Perth, WA, 6872, Australia
Tel.: (61) 8 9481 0544
Fax: (61) 8 9481 0655
E-Mail: info@eclipsemetals.com.au
Web Site: www.eclipsemetals.com.au
EPM—(ASX)
Rev.: $232,456
Assets: $5,371,678
Liabilities: $496,174
Net Worth: $4,875,504
Earnings: ($16,335,798)
Fiscal Year-end: 06/30/13
Business Description:
Mineral Exploration Services
S.I.C.: 1094
N.A.I.C.S.: 212291
Personnel:
Carl Popal *(Mng Dir)*
Keith Bowker *(Sec)*
Board of Directors:
Justin Barton
Rodney Dale
Carl Popal
Legal Counsel:
Bennett & Co
Level 10 BGC Centre 28 The Esplanade
Perth, Australia

ECLIPSE RESIDENTIAL MORTGAGE INVESTMENT CORPORATION
181 Bay Street Suite 2930
Toronto, ON, M5J 2T3, Canada
Tel.: (614) 642-9050
Fax: (416) 642-6001
E-Mail: kikuchi@bromptongroup.com
Year Founded: 2013
ERM—(TSX)
Business Description:
Real Estate Investment Services
S.I.C.: 6211
N.A.I.C.S.: 523999
Personnel:
Mark A. Caranci *(Pres & CEO)*
Craig T. Kikuchi *(CFO)*
Moyra E. MacKay *(Sec & VP)*
Christopher Cullen *(Sr VP)*
Board of Directors:
Peter A. Braaten
Mark A. Caranci
James W. Davie
Raymond R. Pether
Arthur R.A. Scace
Ken S. Woolner
Transfer Agent:
Equity Financial Trust Company
Toronto, ON, Canada

ECM EQUITY CAPITAL MANAGEMENT GMBH
Taunusanlage 18
D-60325 Frankfurt, Germany
Tel.: (49) 69971020
Fax: (49) 6997 102 24
E-Mail: info@ecm-pe.de
Web Site: www.ecm-pe.de
Business Description:
Private Equity & Investment Management Services
S.I.C.: 6211
N.A.I.C.S.: 523999
Personnel:
Axel Eichmeyer *(Mng Partner)*
Richard E. Gritsch *(Partner)*
Christopher L. Peisch *(Sr Partner)*
Harald Sipple *(Partner)*

ECM LIBRA FINANCIAL GROUP BERHAD
2nd Floor West Wing Bangunan ECM Libra 8 Jalan Damansara Endah
Damansara Heights, 50490 Kuala Lumpur, Malaysia
Tel.: (60) 321781888
Fax: (60) 320961188
E-Mail: groupcomm@ecmlibra.com
Web Site: www.ecmlibra.com
ECM—(KLS)
Rev.: $5,970,439
Assets: $302,821,331
Liabilities: $4,433,806
Net Worth: $298,387,525
Earnings: ($13,815,598)
Fiscal Year-end: 01/31/13
Business Description:
Investment Banking Services
S.I.C.: 6211
N.A.I.C.S.: 523110
Personnel:
Azlin Arshad *(CEO)*
Soon Lee Chan *(CFO & Co-Sec)*
Raymond Wai Mun Kong *(Co-CIO-Libra Invest Berhad)*
Jason Wei Chung Lee *(Co-CIO-Libra Invest Berhad)*
Thim Loong Lye *(Deputy CIO-Libra Invest Berhad)*

ECM Libra Financial Group Berhad—(Continued)

Tony Chee Hoong Lai *(CMO)*
Mohd Fadzil Mohamed *(CEO-Libra Invest Berhad)*
Irene Yuet Chun Low *(Co-Sec)*
Board of Directors:
Kalimullah Masheerul Hassan
Othman Abdullah
Mahadzir Azizan
Kian Onn Lim
Sing Fai Lum
Kamarudin Md Ali
Ab. Halim Mohyiddin

Subsidiary:

Avenue Invest Berhad (1)
Level Bangunan ECM Libra 8 Jalan Damansara Endah
Damansara Heights, 50490 Kuala Lumpur, Federal Territory, Malaysia
Tel.: (60) 320892800
Fax: (60) 320961020
E-Mail: invest@ecmlibra.com
Web Site: www.oneinvest.com.my
Emp.: 200
Fund Management Services
S.I.C.: 6371
N.A.I.C.S.: 524292
Hoo See Kheng *(CEO)*
Tan Jin Teik *(Mng Dir)*

ECM REAL ESTATE INVESTMENTS A.G.

2 Charles de Gaulle
1653 Luxembourg, Luxembourg
Tel.: (352) 26976165
Fax: (352) 26897404
E-Mail: info@ecm.cz
Web Site: www.ecm.cz
Year Founded: 1991
ECM—(PRA)
Sales Range: $10-24.9 Million
Business Description:
Real Estate Development Services
S.I.C.: 6531
N.A.I.C.S.: 531390
Personnel:
Milan Janku *(Founder, Chm & Pres)*
Alexandria Ludowicy Anderson *(Sec)*
Board of Directors:
Milan Janku
Antonin Jakubse

ECO ANIMAL HEALTH GROUP PLC

78 Coombe Road
New Malden, Surrey, KT3 4QS, United Kingdom
Tel.: (44) 2083362900
Fax: (44) 2083360909
E-Mail: enquiries@shareregistrars.uk.com
Web Site: www.ecoanimalhealthgroupplc.com
EAH—(LSE)
Rev.: $45,777,227
Assets: $110,611,665
Liabilities: $15,393,529
Net Worth: $95,218,136
Earnings: $4,822,525
Emp.: 154
Fiscal Year-end: 03/31/13
Business Description:
Developer, Mfr & Distr of Animal Health Products
S.I.C.: 2834
N.A.I.C.S.: 115210
Personnel:
Peter A. Lawrence *(Founder & Chm)*
Marc D. Loomes *(CEO)*
Julia Trouse *(Sec)*
Board of Directors:
Peter A. Lawrence
Brett Clemo
David Danson
Julia Henderson
Marc D. Loomes
Kevin Stockdale
Julia Trouse

Subsidiary:

Eco Animal Health Limited (1)
PO Box 47542
London, N14 6WS, United Kingdom
Tel.: (44) 2084478899
Fax: (44) 20 8 447 9292
E-Mail: enquiries@ecoanimalhealth.com
Web Site: www.ecoanimalhealth.com
Emp.: 50
Animal Drugs Mfr
S.I.C.: 5122
N.A.I.C.S.: 424210

Non-U.S. Subsidiary:

Zhejiang Eco Biok Animal Health Products Limited (1)
A-21b Yueda International Bldg 1118 Changshou Rd, Shanghai, Shandong, China
Tel.: (86) 2152376380
Fax: (86) 2152376385
Pharmaceutical Products Mfr
S.I.C.: 2834
N.A.I.C.S.: 325412

ECO (ATLANTIC) OIL & GAS LTD.

120 Adelaide St W Suite 1204
Toronto, ON, M5H 1T1, Canada
Tel.: (416) 361-2211
Fax: (416) 361-6455
E-Mail: info@ecooilandgas.com
Web Site: www.ecooilandgas.com
Year Founded: 2007
EOG—(TSXV)
Int. Income: $63,476
Assets: $9,849,111
Liabilities: $230,840
Net Worth: $9,618,271
Earnings: ($3,960,376)
Fiscal Year-end: 03/31/13
Business Description:
Oil & Gas Exploration Services
S.I.C.: 1311
N.A.I.C.S.: 211111
Personnel:
Gil Holzman *(Co-Founder, Pres & CEO)*
Colin B. Kinley *(Co-Founder & COO)*
Alan Friedman *(Co-Founder & Exec VP)*
Moshe Peterburg *(Chm)*
Alan Rootenberg *(CFO)*
Board of Directors:
Moshe Peterburg
Helmut Angula
Alan Friedman
Gil Holzman
Colin B. Kinley
Peter Nicol
Legal Counsel:
Stikeman Elliott LLP
5300 Commerce Court West 199 Bay Street
Toronto, ON, Canada

ECO CITY VEHICLES PLC

Hemming House Hemming Street
London, E1 5BL, United Kingdom
Tel.: (44) 2073772182
Fax: (44) 2072471481
E-Mail: info@ecvplc.com
Web Site: www.ecocityvehicles.com
ECV—(LSE)
Rev.: $48,108,332
Assets: $15,148,550
Liabilities: $14,404,704
Net Worth: $743,846
Earnings: ($1,522,436)
Emp.: 73
Fiscal Year-end: 12/31/12
Business Description:
Sales & Service of New & Used Taxicabs
S.I.C.: 5571
N.A.I.C.S.: 441228
Personnel:
Trevor Parker *(CEO)*
Steven McCarthy *(COO)*
Rob Bowers *(Sec)*
Board of Directors:
John Swingewood
Peter DaCosta
Jonathan Moritz
Trevor Parker
Legal Counsel:
Olswang LLP
90 High Holborn
London, United Kingdom

Subsidiary:

KPM-UK Taxis Plc (1)
Hemming St
London, E1 5BL, United Kingdom
Tel.: (44) 2073772182
Fax: (44) 2072477952
E-Mail: post@kpmuktaxis.com
Web Site: www.kpmuktaxis.com
Emp.: 100
New & Used Taxi & Cab Dealers
S.I.C.: 5511
N.A.I.C.S.: 441110
Peter DaCosta *(Co-Mng Dir)*
Michael Troullis *(Co-Mng Dir)*

ECO ENERGY HOLDINGS CO., LTD.

1302-7 Totaleco Bdg Seocho-Dong
Seocho-Gu, Seoul, Korea (South)
Tel.: (82) 2 3483 2900
Fax: (82) 2 3493 2929
E-Mail: ecoholdings@ecoholdings.co.kr
Web Site: www.ecoenergyholdings.com
Year Founded: 1989
038870—(KRS)
Business Description:
Renewable Energy Development Services
S.I.C.: 4939
N.A.I.C.S.: 221118
Personnel:
Hyo-Soon Song *(CEO)*

ECO FRIENDLY FOOD PROCESSING PARK LTD.

S-520 Greater Kailash Part I
New Delhi, 110 048, India
Tel.: (91) 11 32971926
E-Mail: info@ecofriendly.in
Web Site: www.ecofriendlyfood.in
534839—(BOM)
Business Description:
Wheat, Rice & Vegetables Mfr
S.I.C.: 0111
N.A.I.C.S.: 111140
Personnel:
Amar S. Bisht *(Exec Dir)*

ECO ORO MINERALS CORP.

Suite 1430 - 333 Seymour Street
Vancouver, BC, V6B 5A6, Canada
Tel.: (604) 682-8212
Fax: (604) 682-3708
E-Mail: contact@eco-oro.com
Web Site: www.eco-oro.com
EOM—(TSX)
Int. Income: $264,000
Assets: $47,591,000
Liabilities: $12,007,000
Net Worth: $35,584,000
Earnings: ($35,171,000)
Emp.: 101
Fiscal Year-end: 12/31/12
Business Description:
Metal Exploration Services
S.I.C.: 1081
N.A.I.C.S.: 213114
Personnel:
Juan Esteban Orduz *(Co-Chm)*
Anna Eleni Stylianides *(Co-Chm)*
Joao Carrela *(Pres & CEO)*
Mary Ellen Thorburn *(CFO)*
James Atherton *(Sec & VP-Legal)*
Board of Directors:
Juan Esteban Orduz
Anna Eleni Stylianides
Jean-Sebastien Blanchette
Joao Carrela
Eduardo Jaramillo
Hubert R. Marleau
Samuel Jed Rubin
Legal Counsel:
Bull, Housser & Tupper LLP
3000 - 1055 West Georgia Street
Vancouver, BC, Canada
Transfer Agent:
Computershare Canada
3rd Floor 510 Burrard Street
Vancouver, BC, V6C 3B9, Canada

ECO QUEST LIMITED

Suite 1 1233 High Street
Armadale, VIC, 3143, Australia
Mailing Address:
PO Box 7165
Hawthorn, VIC, 3122, Australia
Tel.: (61) 3 98245254
Fax: (61) 3 98227735
E-Mail: admin@ecoquest.com.au
Web Site: www.ecoquest.com.au
ECQ—(ASX)
Rev.: $35,394
Assets: $1,868,009
Liabilities: $156,002
Net Worth: $1,712,007
Earnings: ($954,252)
Fiscal Year-end: 06/30/13
Business Description:
Biodegradable Non Woven Product Mfr
S.I.C.: 2297
N.A.I.C.S.: 313230
Personnel:
Stewart Washer *(Chm)*
Ross Macdonald *(CEO & Mng Dir)*
Peter Webse *(Sec)*
Board of Directors:
Stewart Washer
Howard Digby
Ross Macdonald
Peter Webse
Legal Counsel:
GTP Legal
Level 1 28 Ord Street
West Perth, Australia

ECO RECOVERY CORPORATION

Six Nations of the Grand River
Hagersville, ON, Canada
Tel.: (519) 445-1677
Web Site: www.ecorecoverycorp.com
SKP—(DEU)
Business Description:
Waste Management Services
S.I.C.: 4959
N.A.I.C.S.: 562998
Personnel:
H. Sam Hyams *(Pres & CEO)*
Philip Kung *(Exec VP)*
Board of Directors:
Chaim Flatt
H. Sam Hyams
Philip Kung
Randy Dae-Won Su

ECO RECYCLING LIMITED.

205 2nd Floor Center Point Adjacent to Hotel Kohinoor
Andheri Kurla Road Andheri E, Mumbai, 400059, India
Tel.: (91) 22 40052951

Fax: (91) 22 40052954
E-Mail: info@ecoreco.com
Web Site: ecoreco.com
530643—(BOM)
Rev.: $4,176,754
Assets: $10,904,551
Liabilities: $4,895,471
Net Worth: $6,009,079
Earnings: $118,768
Fiscal Year-end: 03/31/13
Business Description:
Electronic Waste Recycling Services
S.I.C.: 4959
N.A.I.C.S.: 562998
Personnel:
B. K. Soni *(Chm & Mng Dir)*
Anita Choudhari *(Compliance Officer)*
Board of Directors:
B. K. Soni
Srikrishna Bhamidipati
T. R. Rao
Aruna Soni
Transfer Agent:
Bigshare Services Private Limited
E-2 Ansa Industrial Estate Sakivihar Road Saki Naka Andheri (E)
Mumbai, India

ECO SUPPLIES EUROPE AB

Stora Avagen 21
Askim, 436 34 Gothenburg, Sweden
Tel.: (46) 317232122
Fax: (46) 317232129
E-Mail: info@ecosupplies.eu
Web Site: www.ecosupplieseuropea b.com
7C0 —(DEU)
Sales Range: $1-9.9 Million
Emp.: 100
Business Description:
Office Systems & Printers Distr
S.I.C.: 5044
N.A.I.C.S.: 423420
Personnel:
Svante Kumlin *(Founder, Chm & CEO)*
Mikael Yngman *(CEO-Solar)*
Non-U.S. Subsidiaries:

Direct Printer Service GmbH (1)
Bockgasse 2b
4020 Linz, Upper Austria, Austria
Tel.: (43) 732749290
Fax: (43) 732 74929 15
E-Mail: office@directprinterservice.com
Web Site: www.directprinterservice.com
Recycled Toner & Ink Cartridges Mfr
S.I.C.: 3861
N.A.I.C.S.: 325992
Rene Hochholdinger *(Mng Dir)*

European Office Systems B.V. (1)
Vasteland 12A
3011 BL Rotterdam, Zuid-Holland, Netherlands
Tel.: (31) 107988000
Fax: (31) 107988001
E-Mail: nl@eosprint.com
Web Site: www.eosprint.com
Laser & Ink Cartridges Sales
S.I.C.: 5112
N.A.I.C.S.: 424120

European Office Systems GmbH (1)
Virchowstr 17-19
22767 Hamburg, Germany
Tel.: (49) 4032024500
Fax: (49) 4032024501
E-Mail: de@eosprint.com
Web Site: www.eosprint.com
Laser & Ink Cartridges Sales
S.I.C.: 5112
N.A.I.C.S.: 424120

European Office Systems S.A.R.L (1)
31 rue de Paris
06000 Nice, Alpes-Maritimes, France
Tel.: (33) 4 97 19 00 29
Fax: (33) 4 97 19 00 24
E-Mail: FR@eosprint.com
Web Site: www.eosprint.com
Laser & Ink Cartridges Sales
S.I.C.: 5112
N.A.I.C.S.: 424120

ECO-TEK GROUP INC.

15-65 Woodstream Boulevard
Woodbridge, ON, L4L 7X6, Canada
Toll Free: (877) 275-2545
E-Mail: sales@eco-tekgroup.com
Web Site: www.eco-tekgroup.net
Year Founded: 2007
ETEK—(OTC)
Sls.: $282,175
Assets: $86,143
Liabilities: $1,006,313
Net Worth: ($920,170)
Earnings: ($868,195)
Emp.: 2
Fiscal Year-end: 12/31/12
Business Description:
Eco-Friendly Products for Automotive & Industrial Sectors
S.I.C.: 2992
N.A.I.C.S.: 324191
Personnel:
Stephen W. Tunks *(Pres, CEO & CFO)*
Maurizio Cochi *(Treas & Sec)*
Board of Directors:
Maurizio Cochi
Joseph Farella
Stephen W. Tunks

ECO WORLD DEVELOPMENT SDN BHD

No 60 Setia Avenue No 2 Jalan Setia Prima S U13/S
Setia Alam Seksyen U1, 40170 Shah Alam, Malaysia
Tel.: (60) 3 3344 2552
Fax: (60) 3 3345 2552
E-Mail: corp@ecoworld.my
Web Site: www.ecoworld.my
Business Description:
Real Estate Development Services
S.I.C.: 6519
N.A.I.C.S.: 531190
Personnel:
Khim Wah Chang *(CEO)*

ECOBANK TRANSNATIONAL INCORPORATED

(d/b/a Ecobank Group)
2365 Boulevard du Mono
BP 3261 Lome, Togo
Tel.: (228) 221 0303
Fax: (228) 221 5119
E-Mail: info@ecobank.com
Web Site: www.ecobank.com
Year Founded: 1985
ETI—(GHA NIGE)
Int. Income: $1,356,967,000
Assets: $19,950,335,000
Liabilities: $17,773,863,000
Net Worth: $2,176,472,000
Earnings: $286,732,000
Emp.: 18,564
Fiscal Year-end: 12/31/12
Business Description:
Bank Holding Company
S.I.C.: 6712
N.A.I.C.S.: 551111
Personnel:
Kolapo Lawson *(Chm)*
Albert Kobina Essien *(CEO)*
Evelyne Tall *(Deputy CEO & COO)*
Samuel K. Ayim *(Sec)*
Board of Directors:
Kolapo Lawson
Sena Agbayissah
Babatunde Ademola M. Ajibade
Patrick Akinwuntan
Kwasi A. Boatin
Albert Kobina Essien
Paulo Gomes
Bashir Mamman Ifo
Assaad J. Jabre
Daniel Matjila
Sipho G. Mseleku
Eddy Ogbogu
Andre Siaka
Evelyne Tall
Isyaku Umar

PricewaterhouseCoopers
Plot 252E Muri Okunola Street
Lagos, Victoria Island, Nigeria

EDC Securities Limited
139 Broad Street
Lagos, Nigeria

EDC Investment Corporation
Immeuble Alliance 4eme etage
Avenue Terrasson de Fougeres
01 BP 4107, Abidjan, 01, Cote d'Ivoire
Tel.: (225) 20 211 044
Fax: (225) 20 211 046

Subsidiaries:

Ecobank Development Corporation (1)
2 Avenue Sylvanus Olympio
PO Box 3261
Lome, Togo (100%)
Tel.: (228) 2213168
Fax: (228) 2215119
E-Mail: edc@ecobank.com
Web Site: www.ecobank.com
Investment Banking Services
S.I.C.: 6211
N.A.I.C.S.: 523110

Non-U.S. Subsidiaries:

EDC Investment Corporation (2)
Immeuble Alliance 4eme Etage
Avenue Terrasson de Fougeres
01 BP 4107 Abidjan, 01, Cote d'Ivoire
Tel.: (225) 20211044
Fax: (225) 20211046
E-Mail: eie@ecobank.com
Web Site: www.ecobank.com
Emp.: 15
Investment Banking Services
S.I.C.: 6211
N.A.I.C.S.: 523110
Seka Agonis *(Mng Dir)*

EDC Stockbrokers Limited (2)
Second Ridge Link North Ridge
Accra, Ghana
Tel.: (233) 21251723
Fax: (233) 21251734
E-Mail: cbrindt@ecobank.com
Web Site: www.ecobank.com
Investment Banking Services
S.I.C.: 6211
N.A.I.C.S.: 523110
Michael Ashong *(Mng Dir)*

Ecobank Togo S.A. (1)
20 Avenue Sylvanus Olympio
BP 3 302
Lome, Togo TG
Tel.: (228) 2217214
Fax: (228) 2214237
E-Mail: ecobanktg@ecobank.com
Web Site: www.ecobank.com
Emp.: 238
Commercial Banking Services
S.I.C.: 6029
N.A.I.C.S.: 522110
Michel Klousseh *(Chm)*
Didier Alexandre Correa *(Dir Gen)*
Eusebe Homefa Afoutou *(Sec & Head-Legal)*

eProcess International S.A. (1)
20 Avenue Sylvanus Olympio
BP 4385
Lome, Togo (100%)
Tel.: (228) 2222370
Fax: (228) 2222434
Web Site: www.ecobank.com
Technology Support & Shared Services
S.I.C.: 7389
N.A.I.C.S.: 541990
Patrick Akinwuntan *(Mng Dir)*
Edward Ogbogu *(Mng Dir)*

Non-U.S. Subsidiaries:

EBI SA (1)
Les Collines de l'Arche 76 route de la Demi Lune
Immeuble Concorde F, 92057 Paris, La Defense, Cedex, France FR
Tel.: (33) 155232340
Fax: (33) 147764241
E-Mail: ebifr@ecobank.com
Web Site: www.ecobank.com
Emp.: 40
Commercial Banking Services
S.I.C.: 6029
N.A.I.C.S.: 522110
Christoph Boulland *(Mng Dir)*

Ecobank Centrafrique (1)
Place de la Republique
BP 910
Bangui, Central African Republic (72%)
Tel.: (236) 21610042
Fax: (236) 21616136
E-Mail: ecobankcf@ecobank.com
Web Site: www.ecobank.com
Emp.: 171
Commercial Banking Services
S.I.C.: 6029
N.A.I.C.S.: 522110
Christian Assossou *(Dir Gen)*
Celestin Yanindji *(Deputy Dir Gen)*
Irene Bella *(Sec & Head-Legal)*

Ecobank Cote d'Ivoire S.A. (1)
Immeuble Alliance Avenue Terrasson de Fougeres Plateau 01
BP 4107
Abidjan, 01, Cote d'Ivoire
Tel.: (225) 2031 9200
Fax: (225) 2021 1652
E-Mail: ecobankci@ecobank.com
Web Site: www.ecobank.com
Sales Range: $75-99.9 Million
Emp.: 429
Commercial Banking Services
S.I.C.: 6029
N.A.I.C.S.: 522110
Pierre Rene Magne *(Chm)*
Charles Daboiko *(Dir Gen)*

Ecobank Ghana Limited (1)
19 Seventh Avenue Ridge West
PO Box 16746
Accra, Ghana GH
Tel.: (233) 0302 68 0437 (60.41%)
Fax: (233) 0302 68 0428
E-Mail: ecobankgh@ecobank.com
Web Site: www.ecobank.com
EBG—(GHA)
Sales Range: $125-149.9 Million
Emp.: 890
Commercial Banking Services
S.I.C.: 6029
N.A.I.C.S.: 522110
Lionel Van Lare Dosoo *(Chm)*
Samuel Ashitey Adjei *(Mng Dir)*
Awuraa Abena Asafo-Boakye *(Sec)*

Ecobank Kenya Limited (1)
Ecobank Towers Muindi Mbingu Street
PO Box 49584
00100 Nairobi, Kenya KE
Tel.: (254) 20 288 3000
Fax: (254) 20 288 3304
E-Mail: eke-fedhamgr@ecobank.com
Web Site: www.ecobank.com
Commercial Banking Services
S.I.C.: 6029
N.A.I.C.S.: 522110
Nok Bwonditi *(Exec Dir)*

Ecobank Malawi Limited (1)
Corner Victoria Avenue & Henderson Street
Chichiri, Blantyre, Malawi MW
Mailing Address:
Private Bag 389
Chichiri, Blantyre, 3, Malawi
Tel.: (265) 1 820 437
Fax: (265) 1 822 683
E-Mail: emwho@ecobank.com
Web Site: www.ecobank.com
Sales Range: $1-9.9 Million
Emp.: 49
Commercial Banking Services
S.I.C.: 6029
N.A.I.C.S.: 522110
Olufemi Salu *(Mng Dir)*

Ecobank Nigeria Plc (1)
Plot 21 Ahmadu Bello Way
PO Box 72688
Victoria Island, Lagos, Nigeria NG
Tel.: (234) 1 271 0391
Fax: (234) 1 221 5119

Ecobank Transnational Incorporated—(Continued)

E-Mail: ecobank@ecobank.com
Web Site: www.ecobank.com
Emp.: 7,759
Commercial Banking Services
S.I.C.: 6029
N.A.I.C.S.: 522110
Arnold Ekpe *(CEO)*
Jibril Aku *(Mng Dir)*
Anthony Okpanachi *(Deputy Mng Dir)*
Adenike Laoye *(Sec)*

Ecobank Tchad S.A. **(1)**
Avenue de Charles De Gaulle
BP 87
N'djamena, Chad TD
Tel.: (235) 2252 43 14 (-21)
Fax: (235) 2252 23 45
E-Mail: ecobanktd@ecobank.com
Web Site: www.ecobank.com
Sales Range: $10-24.9 Million
Commercial Banking Services
S.I.C.: 6029
N.A.I.C.S.: 522110
Mamby Koulibaly *(Acting Chm)*
Mahamat Ali Kerim *(Dir Gen)*
Kossi Jean Clement Dabire *(Deputy Dir Gen)*

Ecobank Zambia Limited **(1)**
Plot No 22768 Thabo Mbeki Road
PO Box 30705
Lusaka, Zambia ZM
Tel.: (260) 211 250 056 (-057)
Fax: (260) 211 250 171
E-Mail: ecobankzm@ecobank.com
Web Site: www.ecobank.com
Sales Range: $1-9.9 Million
Commercial Banking Services
S.I.C.: 6029
N.A.I.C.S.: 522110
Charity Chanda Lumpa *(Mng Dir)*

ECOBOARD INDUSTRIES LTD

Ecohouse 65/1-A Akarshak Building
Opp Nal Stop Karve Road
Pune, Maharashtra, 411 004, India
Tel.: (91) 20 41080808
Fax: (91) 20 25465328
E-Mail: info@ecoboard.in
Web Site: www.ecoboard.in
Year Founded: 1986
523732—(BOM)
Rev.: $7,031,425
Assets: $14,152,157
Liabilities: $7,730,513
Net Worth: $6,421,644
Earnings: ($1,280,910)
Fiscal Year-end: 03/31/13

Business Description:
Wood Board Mfr
S.I.C.: 2493
N.A.I.C.S.: 321219

Personnel:
V. S. Raju *(Chm)*
G. R. K. Raju *(Mng Dir)*

Board of Directors:
V. S. Raju
Praveen Kumar Raju Gottumukkala
U. S. Kadam
Narasimhan Krishnan
Srinivas Raju P.
G. R. K. Raju
P. Satyanarayana Raju
N. A. Ramaiah
V. P. Rane
Ramchandra Raju P. S.

Transfer Agent:
Link Intime India Private Ltd
202-A 2nd Fl Akshay Complex Off Dhole Patil Rd
Pune, India

ECOFIRST CONSOLIDATED BHD

1 61 First Floor South City Plaza
Persiaran Serdang Perdana
Seksyen 1, 43300 Seri Kembangan,
Selangor Darul Ehsan, Malaysia
Tel.: (60) 3 89381188
Fax: (60) 3 89381133
Web Site: www.ecofirst.com.my
ECOFIRS—(KLS)
Rev.: $25,041,611
Assets: $132,171,763
Liabilities: $78,460,107
Net Worth: $53,711,656
Earnings: $7,794,003
Fiscal Year-end: 05/31/13

Business Description:
Construction Services
S.I.C.: 1521
N.A.I.C.S.: 236115

Personnel:
Seng Foo Teoh *(Pres)*
Kwing Hee Tiong *(CEO)*
Choon Yin Cheong *(Co-Sec)*
Siew Yeen Wong *(Co-Sec)*

Board of Directors:
Ariff Fadzillah Awalluddin
Chin Gan Boey
Een Hong Lim
Amos Boon Yeong Siew
Seng Foo Teoh
Kwing Hee Tiong

Subsidiaries:

EcoFirst Products Sdn Bhd **(1)**
Lot 63A Lower Ground Level South City Plaza Persiaran Serdang Perdana
43300 Seri Kembangan, Selangor, Malaysia
Tel.: (60) 389452185
Fax: (60) 389450985
E-Mail: contact@ecofirstproducts.com
Web Site: www.ecofirstproducts.com
Emp.: 14
Personal Care Products Mfr
S.I.C.: 2844
N.A.I.C.S.: 325620
Norlamah Mohammad Khalid *(Gen Mgr)*

Tashima Development Sdn Bhd **(1)**
No 6 Jalan Nagasari 20 Bandar Segamat Baru
85000 Segamat, Johor, Malaysia
Tel.: (60) 79436222
Fax: (60) 79436888
Property Development Services
S.I.C.: 6531
N.A.I.C.S.: 531390
Danny Yap *(Mgr)*

ECOGREEN FINE CHEMICALS GROUP LIMITED

Suite 3706 37/F Central Plaza 18
Harbour Road
Wanchai, China (Hong Kong)
Tel.: (852) 25300609
Fax: (852) 25300619
E-Mail: ecogreen@ecogreen.com
Web Site: www.ecogreen.com
Year Founded: 1994
2341—(HKG)
Rev.: $167,963,383
Assets: $319,452,116
Liabilities: $130,552,938
Net Worth: $188,899,178
Earnings: $20,304,525
Emp.: 446
Fiscal Year-end: 12/31/12

Business Description:
Fine Chemicals Mfr
S.I.C.: 2899
N.A.I.C.S.: 325998

Personnel:
Yirong Yang *(Chm & Pres)*
Kwok Kin Lam *(Sec & Controller-Fin)*
Xionghui Gong *(Sr VP-Engrg Project Mgmt)*
Huan Guang Han *(Sr VP-Grp Strategic Investments & Capital Markets)*
Jiahua Lu *(Sr VP-Grp Fin Control)*

Board of Directors:
Yirong Yang
Tao Feng
Xionghui Gong
Huan Guang Han
Derrick Wang Yip Lau
Zhigang Lin
Jiahua Lu
John Yik Chung Wong
Fook Chuen Yau

Bank of Bermuda (Cayman) Limited
2nd Fl Strathvale House North Church St
PO Box 513 GT
Georgetown, Cayman Islands

Transfer Agents:
Tricor Tengis Limited
26th Floor Tesbury Centre 28 Queen's Road East
Wanchai, China (Hong Kong)
Tel.: (852) 29801333
Fax: (852) 28108185

Bank of Bermuda (Cayman) Limited
2nd Fl Strathvale House North Church St
PO Box 513 GT
Georgetown, Cayman Islands

Subsidiaries:

EcoGreen Fine Chemicals Limited **(1)**
3706 37/F Central Plz
Wanchai, China (Hong Kong)
Tel.: (852) 25300609
Fax: (852) 25300619
E-Mail: ecogreen@ecogreen.com
Web Site: www.ecogreen.com
Emp.: 5
Natural Fine Chemical Products Research, Development, Production & Distribution
S.I.C.: 2899
N.A.I.C.S.: 325998
Yirong Yang *(Chm)*

EcoGreen Manufacturing **(1)**
Rm 3706 37th Fl Ctr PLz
Wanchai, China (Hong Kong)
Tel.: (852) 25300609
Fax: (852) 25300619
E-Mail: ecogreen@ecogreen.com
Web Site: www.ecogreen.com
Emp.: 5
Holding Company
S.I.C.: 6719
N.A.I.C.S.: 551112
Yirong Yung *(Mng Dir)*

Non-U.S. Subsidiaries:

Shanghai Fine Chemicals Co., Ltd. **(2)**
Rms 716/719 No 8-9 Max Mall Lane
1500 South Lianhua Rd, Shanghai, PC, 201108, China
Tel.: (86) 2133581117
Fax: (86) 2133581128
E-Mail: sfcc@sfcc-chem.com
Web Site: www.sfcc-chem.com
Emp.: 15
Fine Chemical Products Research, Development & Marketing of Other Technological Services
S.I.C.: 2899
N.A.I.C.S.: 325998
Wendy Wu *(Mgr)*

Xiamen Doingcom Chemical Co., Ltd. **(2)**
No 30 Xinchang Road
Xinyang Industrial Zone, Xiamen, 361026, China
Tel.: (86) 5926515068
Fax: (86) 592 6515489
Web Site: www.doingcom.com
Fine Chemical Products Research, Development, Production & Marketing
S.I.C.: 2899
N.A.I.C.S.: 325998

Non-U.S. Subsidiary:

Sino Bright International Trading Limited **(1)**
8F East Block 2 Seg Scientific Industrial Zone
North Huaqiang Road, Shenzhen, China HK
Tel.: (86) 7553767533
Fax: (86) 755 376 3600
Trading of Fine Chemicals
S.I.C.: 5169
N.A.I.C.S.: 424690

ECOLOGY BUILDING SOCIETY

7 Belton Road
Silsden, Keighley, W Yorkshire, BD20 0EE, United Kingdom
Tel.: (44) 845 674 5566
Fax: (44) 1535 650780
E-Mail: info@ecology.co.uk
Web Site: www.ecology.co.uk
Year Founded: 1981
Rev.: $6,029,729
Assets: $173,297,071
Liabilities: $163,863,972
Net Worth: $9,433,099
Earnings: $724,894
Emp.: 16
Fiscal Year-end: 12/31/12

Business Description:
Mortgage Lending & Other Financial Services
S.I.C.: 6163
N.A.I.C.S.: 522310

Personnel:
Paul Ellis *(CEO)*
George Haslem *(COO)*
Pam Waring *(Sec & Dir-Fin)*

Board of Directors:
Malcolm Lynch
Paul Ellis
Steven Round
Helen Ashley Taylor
Tony Taylor
Pam Waring

Legal Counsel:
Addleshaw Goddard
Sovereign House Sovereign Street
Leeds, LS1 1HQ, United Kingdom

ECOLUTIONS GMBH & CO. KGAA

Grueneburgweg 18
D-60322 Frankfurt am Main, Germany
Tel.: (49) 6991501080
Fax: (49) 69915010811
E-Mail: info@ecolutions.de
Web Site: www.ecolutions.de
EO2—(DEU EUR)
Emp.: 8

Business Description:
Climate Protection Investment & Management Services
S.I.C.: 8999
N.A.I.C.S.: 541620

Personnel:
Emmanuel Guyot *(Dir-Intl Ops)*

Non-U.S. Subsidiaries:

Ecolutions Carbon India Pvt. Ltd. **(1)**
Mahendra Chambers 15 Opp Dukes Factory
619/28 WT Patil Marg, 400 071 Mumbai, India
Tel.: (91) 2225201742
Fax: (91) 2225201744.
E-Mail: info@ecolutions.de
Web Site: www.ecolutions.in
Emp.: 30
Investment Management & Consulting Services
S.I.C.: 8748
N.A.I.C.S.: 541618
Kiran Patil *(Mng Dir)*

Ecolutions New Energy Investment Co., Ltd. **(1)**
1505 Block 15 China Cent Pl 89 Jianguo Rd
Beijing, Choayang, 100025, China
Tel.: (86) 1052036828
Fax: (86) 1052036827
Web Site: www.ecolutions.de/100-1-Contact.html
Emp.: 9
Investment Management Services
S.I.C.: 8748
N.A.I.C.S.: 541618
Lex Liu *(Project Mgr)*

E.COM INFOTECH (INDIA) LIMITED

Level 3 Neo Vikram New Link Road
Andheri West
Mumbai, Maharashtra, 400 058, India
Tel.: (91) 22 32944663
Fax: (91) 22 28877077
E-Mail: info@ecominfotech.biz
Web Site: www.ecominfotech.biz
Year Founded: 1983
531533—(BOM)
Rev.: $30,091
Assets: $868,554
Liabilities: $17,335
Net Worth: $851,218
Earnings: $134
Fiscal Year-end: 03/31/13

Business Description:
Information Technology Consulting Services
S.I.C.: 7373
N.A.I.C.S.: 541512

Personnel:
Ashwin K. Chaudhary *(Chm, Mng Dir & Compliance Officer)*

Board of Directors:
Ashwin K. Chaudhary
Dalpat Anjaria
Priya A. Chaudary
J. K. Subramanian

Transfer Agent:
Sharex Dynamic (India) Pvt. Ltd.
Unit-1 Luthra Ind Premises Safed Pool Andheri Kurla Rd Andheri (E)
Mumbai, India

ECOMETALS LIMITED

1090 West Georgia Street Suite 1305
Vancouver, BC, V6E 3V7, Canada
Tel.: (604) 685-9316
Fax: (604) 683-1585
Web Site:
Year Founded: 1987
EC—(TSXV)
Sales Range: Less than $1 Million

Business Description:
Mineral Exploration Services
S.I.C.: 1081
N.A.I.C.S.: 213114

Personnel:
Russell Fryer *(Chm)*
William G. Lamarque *(CEO)*
Andrew Robertson *(CFO & Sec)*

Legal Counsel:
Norton Rose LLP
79 Wellington Street West Suite 2300
Toronto, ON, Canada

Transfer Agent:
Computershare Trust Company of Canada
510 Burrard St 2nd Fl
Vancouver, BC, Canada

ECOMMERCE ALLIANCE AG

Neuhauserstrasse 15a
80331 Munich, Germany
Tel.: (49) 8924209555
Fax: (49) 8924209670
Web Site: www.ecommerce-alliance.com
ECF—(DEU)
Sales Range: $1-9.9 Million

Business Description:
E-Commerce Business
S.I.C.: 7389
N.A.I.C.S.: 425110

Personnel:
Michael Birkel *(Vice Chm-Supervisory Bd)*
Daniel Wild *(CEO)*

Supervisory Board of Directors:
Maximilian Ardelt
Michael Birkel
Tim Schwenke
Daniel Wild

Non-U.S. Subsidiaries:

Premingo GmbH (1)
Neuhauser Strasse 15a
Munich, Bavaria, 80331, Germany
Tel.: (49) 8918916680
Fax: (49) 89 189 166 870
E-Mail: info@premingo.de
Web Site: www.premingo.de
Emp.: 1
Internet Payment Services
S.I.C.: 6099
N.A.I.C.S.: 522320
Sinisa Preradovic *(Mng Dir)*

ECONET WIRELESS ZIMBABWE LIMITED

Econet Park No 2 Old Mutare Road
Msasa
PO Box BE 1298
Belvedere, Harare, Zimbabwe
Tel.: (263) 4486121
Fax: (263) 4486120
E-Mail: info@econet.co.zw
Web Site: www.econet.co.zw
ECO—(ZIM)
Rev.: $694,843,608
Assets: $1,015,109,955
Liabilities: $522,226,718
Net Worth: $492,883,237
Earnings: $139,938,220
Emp.: 15,000
Fiscal Year-end: 02/28/13

Business Description:
Cellular Network Operator
S.I.C.: 4812
N.A.I.C.S.: 517210

Personnel:
Strive T. Masiyiwa *(Founder & Grp Chm)*
Douglas Mboweni *(CEO)*
James Museba *(CIO)*
Isaiah Nyangari *(CMO)*
Stanley Henning *(Chief Comml Officer & Chief Customer Svcs Officer)*
Innocent Magaya *(Chief HR Officer)*
Sheilla Mugugu *(Gen Counsel)*
Charles Alfred Banda *(Sec)*

Board of Directors:
Strive T. Masiyiwa
James Myers
Krison V. Chirairo
Martin Edge
Craig Fitzgerald
Godfrey Gomwe
Douglas Mboweni
Tracy P. Mpofu
Beatrice Mtetwa
Sherree Gladys Shereni

Legal Counsel:
Mtetwa and Nyambirai
2 Meredith Drive Eastlea
Harare, Zimbabwe

Transfer Agent:
First Transfer Secretaries (Private) Limited
No 1 Armagh Avenue Eastlea
Harare, Zimbabwe

Subsidiary:

Econet Wireless (Pvt) Ltd (1)
Econet Park 2 Old Mutare Road
PO Box BE 1298
Harare, Zimbabwe
Tel.: (263) 4486121
Fax: (263) 4486120
E-Mail: enquiry@econet.co.zw
Telecommunication Services
S.I.C.: 4812
N.A.I.C.S.: 517210
Tawanda Nyambirai *(Chm)*
Strive Taputaira Masiywa *(CEO)*
Douglas Mboweni *(Mng Dir)*

ECONOCARIBE CONSOLIDATORS INC.

(Acquired by Allcargo Logistics Limited)

ECONOCOM GROUP SA

Chaussee de Louvain 510/80
1930 Zaventem, Belgium
Tel.: (32) 27908111
Fax: (32) 27908120
E-Mail: info.be@econocom.com
Web Site: www.econocom.com
ECONB—(EUR)
Rev.: $2,070,867,158
Assets: $1,478,517,357
Liabilities: $1,266,937,126
Net Worth: $211,580,231
Earnings: $63,999,614
Emp.: 3,700
Fiscal Year-end: 12/31/12

Business Description:
Network Services
S.I.C.: 7373
N.A.I.C.S.: 541512

Personnel:
Jean Louis Bouchard *(Chm)*
Bruno Lemaistre *(Co-CEO & Mng Dir)*
Jean-Philippe Roesch *(Co-CEO & Mng Dir)*
Veronique di Benedetto *(Deputy Mng Dir)*

Board of Directors:
Jean Louis Bouchard
Robert Bouchard
Christian Bret
Charles de Water
Gaspard Durrleman
Bruno Lemaistre
Jean-Philippe Roesch

Subsidiaries:

Econocom Lease SA/NV (1)
Leuvensesteenweg 510-80
1930 Zaventem, Belgium
Tel.: (32) 2 790 81 11
Fax: (32) 2 790 81 20
Information Technology Consulting Services
S.I.C.: 7373
N.A.I.C.S.: 541512

Non-U.S. Subsidiary:

Econocom Luxembourg SA (2)
4 Rue D'Arlon
8399 Windhof, Luxembourg
Tel.: (352) 39 55 50
Fax: (352) 39 55 88
E-Mail: ecenocompss@econocom.com
Emp.: 15
Information Technology Consulting Services
S.I.C.: 7373
N.A.I.C.S.: 541512
Johan Runesson *(Mgr-Bus Dev)*

Econocom Products & Solutions Belux SA/NV (1)
Leuvensesteenweg 510-80
Zaventem, 1930, Belgium
Tel.: (32) 27908111
Fax: (32) 27908120
E-Mail: info.be@econocom.com
Web Site: www.econocom.com
Emp.: 800
Information Technology Consulting Services
S.I.C.: 7373
N.A.I.C.S.: 541512
Chantal de Vrieze *(Gen Mgr)*

Non-U.S. Subsidiaries:

Aperleasing Srl (1)
Via Santa Radegonda 11
Milan, Italy (95%)
Tel.: (39) 026596056
Machinery & Equipment Rental & Leasing
S.I.C.: 7359
N.A.I.C.S.: 532420

Atlance France SAS (1)
42-46 rue Mederic
92582 Clichy, France (100%)
Tel.: (33) 147563700
Fax: (33) 0147563705
E-Mail: yzes.larsouelloux@atlance.com
Web Site: www.atlance.com
Emp.: 150
Management Consulting Services
S.I.C.: 8748
N.A.I.C.S.: 541618
Yzes Larsoualloux *(Dir)*

Data Networks France SARL (1)
106 rue des Trois Fontaines
92751 Nanterre, Cedex, France (100%)
Tel.: (33) 1 41 67 3000
Fax: (33) 1 41 67 3100
Web Site: www.econocom.com
Emp.: 100
Store Retailers
S.I.C.: 5999
N.A.I.C.S.: 453998
Bouchahda Joelouise *(Gen Mgr)*

Econocom Expert International Holding BV (1)
Rome C fort 38
3439 Nieuwegein, Netherlands (50.1%)
Tel.: (31) 306358333
Fax: (31) 306358300
E-Mail: infol@econocom.nl
Web Site: www.econocom.nl
Emp.: 35
Trusts Estates & Agency Accounts
S.I.C.: 6733
N.A.I.C.S.: 525920
Frans van Gils *(Mng Dir)*

Econocom Financial Services International BV (1)
Rond Het Fort 36-40
Nieuwegein, 3439 MK, Netherlands
Tel.: (31) 306358333
Financial Management Services
S.I.C.: 6211
N.A.I.C.S.: 523999

Econocom France SAS (1)
42-46 Rue Mederic
92582 Clichy, France (100%)
Tel.: (33) 147563700
Fax: (33) 147310300
E-Mail: info@econocom.fr
Web Site: www.econocom.fr
Emp.: 150
Computer & Computer Peripheral Equipment & Software Merchant Whslr
S.I.C.: 5045
N.A.I.C.S.: 423430
Gean Loius Bocheard *(Gen Mgr)*

Econocom Location SAS (1)
42-46 Rue Mederic
92582 Clichy, France (100%)
Tel.: (33) 147563700
Fax: (33) 147310300
E-Mail: info@econocom.fr
Web Site: www.econocom.fr
Emp.: 150
Machinery & Equipment Rental & Leasing
S.I.C.: 7377
N.A.I.C.S.: 532420
Sebouchare Geanoouas *(Mng Dir)*

Econocom Managed Services SAS (1)
106 rue des Trois Fontanot
92751 Nanterre, Cedex, France (100%)
Tel.: (33) 169182000
Fax: (33) 169182020
E-Mail: info@econocom.fr
Web Site: www.econocom.fr
Emp.: 150
Computer & Machine Repair & Maintenance
S.I.C.: 7378
N.A.I.C.S.: 811212
Jean-Philippe Roesch *(CEO)*

Non-U.S. Subsidiary:

Econocom Maroc Sarl (2)
Immeuble Casablanca Business Center
6eme Etage Lot 2 Lotissement
Mandarina Sidi Maarouf, 20000
Casablanca, Morocco
Tel.: (212) 522 78 90 30
Fax: (212) 522 78 60 33
Emp.: 4
Information Technology Consulting Services
S.I.C.: 7373
N.A.I.C.S.: 541512
Angel Benguigui *(Pres)*

Econocom Nederland BV (1)
Rond D Fort 38
3439 MK Nieuwegein, Netherlands (100%)
Tel.: (31) 306358333
Fax: (31) 306358300

Econocom Group SA—(Continued)

Web Site: www.econocom.nl
Emp.: 35
Machinery & Equipment Rental & Leasing
S.I.C.: 7359
N.A.I.C.S.: 532420
Frans van Gils *(Mng Dir)*

Econocom Products and Solutions SAS (1)
1 rue Terre Neuve
BP 62
91942 Les Ulis, France (100%)
Tel.: (33) 169182000
Fax: (33) 169182020
E-Mail: info@econocom.fr
Web Site: www.econocom.fr
Emp.: 150
Electronic Parts & Equipment Merchant Whslr
S.I.C.: 5065
N.A.I.C.S.: 423690

Subsidiary:

Econocom Telecom Services SAS (2)
42 Rue Mederic
Clichy, 92110, France
Tel.: (33) 147563700
Fax: (33) 147310300
Emp.: 250
Telecommunication Services
S.I.C.: 4899
N.A.I.C.S.: 517919
Jean-Louis Bouchard *(Mng Dir)*

Econocom PSF SA (1)
4 Rue d Arlon
8399 Windhof, Luxembourg
Tel.: (352) 39 55 50
Fax: (352) 39 55 57
Information Technology Consulting Services
S.I.C.: 7373
N.A.I.C.S.: 541512

Econocom SA (1)
C-o Josefa Valcarcel N 42 5 Planta
28027 Madrid, Spain (100%)
Tel.: (34) 914119120
Fax: (34) 915639233
Holding Company
S.I.C.: 6719
N.A.I.C.S.: 551112

Econocom SAS (1)
42-46 Rue Mederic
92582 Clichy, France (100%)
Tel.: (33) 147563700
Fax: (33) 147310300
E-Mail: info@econocom.fr
Web Site: www.econocom.fr
Emp.: 800
Computer & Computer Peripheral Equipment & Software Merchant Whslr
S.I.C.: 5045
N.A.I.C.S.: 423430
Jean-Louis Bouchard *(CEO)*

Subsidiary:

Econocom Managed Services SA/NV (2)
1 Rue de la Terre Neuve
Les Ulis, 91940, France
Tel.: (33) 1 69 18 35 00
Information Technology Consulting Services
S.I.C.: 7373
N.A.I.C.S.: 541512

Econocom Telecom BV (1)
Rond T Fort 38
3439 MK Nieuwegein, Netherlands
Tel.: (31) 306358333
Fax: (31) 306358300
E-Mail: info.nl@econocom.nl
Web Site: www.econocom-nederland.nl
Emp.: 45
Computer & Software Stores
S.I.C.: 5731
N.A.I.C.S.: 443142
Frans van Gils *(Mng Dir)*

EFS International BV (1)
42-46 rue Mederic
92582 Clichy, France (100%)
Tel.: (33) 147563700
Fax: (33) 147310300
E-Mail: jeanl.bouchard@econocom.fr
Web Site: www.econocom.com
Emp.: 150
Store Retailers
S.I.C.: 5999
N.A.I.C.S.: 453998

Osiatis SA (1)
1 rue du Petit Clamart
78142 Velizy-Villacoublay, France (51.9%)
Tel.: (33) 1 41 28 30 00
Fax: (33) 141283020
E-Mail: communication@osiatis.com
Web Site: www.osiatis.com
Sales Range: $350-399.9 Million
Emp.: 3,630
Computer Applications for Infrastructure & Facilities Management
S.I.C.: 7373
N.A.I.C.S.: 541512
Jean-Maurice Fritsch *(Co-Chm-Mgmt Bd)*
Bruno Grossi *(Co-Chm-Mgmt Bd)*
Walter Butler *(Chm-Supervisory Bd)*
Laurent Parquet *(Vice Chm-Supervisory Bd)*
Arnaud Beraud-Sudreau *(CFO)*

Subsidiary:

Osiatis Ingenierie S.A.S (2)
75 Cours Albert Thomas
69003 Lyon, France
Tel.: (33) 4 72 13 16 16
Fax: (33) 4 72 34 55 38
E-Mail: Communication@osiatis.com
Web Site: www.osiatis.fr
Construction Engineering Services
S.I.C.: 8711
N.A.I.C.S.: 541330

Non-U.S. Subsidiaries:

Osiatis Belgium NV (2)
Leuvensesteenweg 573/2
1930 Zaventem, Belgium
Tel.: (32) 2 718 26 11
Fax: (32) 2 718 26 14
E-Mail: info@osiatis.be
Web Site: www.osiatis.be
Emp.: 80
Information Technology Consulting Services
S.I.C.: 7373
N.A.I.C.S.: 541512
Jan Van Dee Broek *(Gen Mgr)*

Osiatis Computer Services GmbH (2)
Franzosengraben 12
1030 Vienna, Austria
Tel.: (43) 1 795 20 0
Fax: (43) 1 795 20 550
E-Mail: office@osiatis.at
Web Site: www.osiatis.at
Sls.: $14,158,000
Emp.: 90
Information Technology Consulting Services
S.I.C.: 7373
N.A.I.C.S.: 541512
Robert Musil *(Mng Dir)*

Synopse SAS (1)
BP 95 1 rue de Terre Neuve
91943 Les Ulis, France (100%)
Tel.: (33) 169353070
Fax: (33) 169353069
E-Mail: synopse@synopse.fr
Web Site: www.synopse.fr
Emp.: 50
Computer Systems Design Services
S.I.C.: 7373
N.A.I.C.S.: 541512
Maraa Pieraar *(Dir)*

ECONOMIC INSTITUTE AD BANJA LUKA

Ulica Kralja Alfonsa XIII br 18
78000 Banja Luka, Bosnia & Herzegovina
Tel.: (387) 51 211 501
Fax: (387) 51 211 509
E-Mail: office@ekinst.org
Web Site: www.ekinst.org
Year Founded: 1960
EKIN—(BANJ)
Emp.: 15
Business Description:
Consulting Services
S.I.C.: 8999
N.A.I.C.S.: 541690
Personnel:
Milorad Dekanovic *(Project Mgr)*

THE ECONOMICAL INSURANCE GROUP

111 Westmount Rd S
Box 2000
Waterloo, ON, N2J 4S4, Canada
Tel.: (519) 570-8200
Fax: (519) 570-8389
Toll Free: (800) 265-2180
E-Mail: corporate.communications@economical.com
Web Site: www.economicalinsurance.com
Year Founded: 1871
Premiums: $1,808,821,176
Assets: $4,797,306,521
Liabilities: $3,341,849,515
Net Worth: $1,455,457,006
Earnings: $151,806,734
Emp.: 2,600
Fiscal Year-end: 12/31/12
Business Description:
Holding Company; Property & Casualty Insurance
S.I.C.: 6351
N.A.I.C.S.: 524126
Personnel:
Gerald A. Hooper *(Chm)*
John H. Bowey *(Vice Chm)*
Karen L. Gavan *(Pres & CEO)*
Philip Mather *(CFO)*
Toomas Reikman *(COO & Sr VP)*
Michael Gagnier *(CIO & Sr VP)*
Innes Dey *(Chief Legal Officer, Sec & Sr VP)*
Dean Bulloch *(Chief HR Officer & Sr VP)*
Linda Goss *(Sr VP & Chief Actuary)*
Edward M. Berko *(Chief Risk Officer)*
Jorge Arruda *(Sr VP-Sls, Distribution & Underwriting Ops)*
Board of Directors:
Gerald A. Hooper
John H. Bowey
A. Scott Carson
Elizabeth L. DelBianco
Barbara Fraser
Richard M. Freeborough
Karen L. Gavan
Charles M.W. Ormston
Michael P. Stramaglia
David Wilson

Subsidiaries:

Federation Insurance Company of Canada (1)
1 plc Ville Marie Suiet 1400
Montreal, QC, H3B0A8, Canada (100%)
Tel.: (514) 875-5790
Fax: (514) 875-9769
E-Mail: info@federation.ca
Web Site: www.federation.ca
Emp.: 200
Provider of Property & Casualty Insurance
S.I.C.: 6399
N.A.I.C.S.: 524128
Mayssa Rifai *(VP)*

Economical Insurance (1)
20 York Mills Rd
Willowdale, ON, M2P 2C2, Canada
Tel.: (416) 733-1777
Fax: (416) 733-1463
E-Mail: susan.micalles@teig.com
Web Site: www.teig.com
Emp.: 97
Insurance For Commercial Lines
S.I.C.: 6399
N.A.I.C.S.: 524128
Noel Walpole *(CFO)*

Subsidiary:

The Economical Insurance Group (2)
111 Westmount S Rd
PO Box 2000
Waterloo, ON, N2J 4S4, Canada (100%)
Tel.: (519) 570-8500
Fax: (519) 570-8389
E-Mail: zm@teig.com
Web Site: www.economical.com
Emp.: 500
Life Insurance
S.I.C.: 6311
N.A.I.C.S.: 524113
Linda Goss *(Chief Actuary & Sr VP)*

THE ECONOMIST GROUP LIMITED

20 Cabot Square
London, A14 4QW, United Kingdom
Tel.: (44) 2078307000
Fax: (44) 2078392968
Web Site: www.economistgroup.com
Year Founded: 1843
Sales Range: $450-499.9 Million
Emp.: 900
Business Description:
Periodical Publishers
S.I.C.: 2721
N.A.I.C.S.: 511120
Personnel:
Rupert L. Pennant-Rea *(Chm)*
Chris Stibbs *(CEO)*
Oscar Grut *(Mng Dir, Grp Gen Counsel & Sec)*
Laurie Battaglia *(Mng Dir & Exec VP-CQ Roll Call)*
Nigel Ludlow *(Mng Dir)*
Shane Naughton *(CFO)*
Board of Directors:
Rupert L. Pennant-Rea
David Bell
Lynn Forester De Rothschild
John Philip Elkann
Rona Alison Fairhead
John Gardiner
Philip R. Mengel
John Micklethwait
Nigel W. Morris
Lord Stevenson of Coddenham
Simon Robertson
Eric Schmidt
Luke Swanson

U.S. Subsidiaries:

CQ Roll Call (1)
77 K St NE
Washington, DC 20002
Tel.: (202) 650-6500
Fax: (202) 419-8760
Toll Free: (800) 432-2250
E-Mail: customerservice@cqrollcall.com
Web Site: corporate.cqrollcall.com
Emp.: 300
Books, Magazines, Daily Newspapers & E-Newsletters with Information Relating to Events on Capitol Hill, Congressional Activity & Background Information on Political Figures
S.I.C.: 2721
N.A.I.C.S.: 511120
Keith A. White *(Mng Dir & Sr Exec VP)*
Dennis Arndt *(CTO & Sr VP)*
Mike Mills *(Sr VP)*

Roll Call Inc. (1)
77 K St NE
Washington, DC 20002 DE
Tel.: (202) 650-6500 (100%)
E-Mail: advertise@cqrollcall.com
Web Site: www.rollcall.com
Sales Range: $10-24.9 Million
Emp.: 370
Periodical Publisher
S.I.C.: 2721
N.A.I.C.S.: 511120
Keith White *(Mng Dir)*
Dennis Arndt *(CTO & Sr VP)*

ECONOMY WHEELS LTD

129 Angeline Street North
Lindsay, ON, K9V 4M9, Canada
Tel.: (705) 324-5566
Fax: (705) 324-0332
E-Mail: nissan@economywheels.com
Web Site: www.economywheels.com

Rev.: $13,650,357
Emp.: 18
Business Description:
New & Used Car Dealers
S.I.C.: 5511
N.A.I.C.S.: 441110
Personnel:
Chris Pretty *(Mgr-Sls)*

ECOPACK LTD
112-113 Phase V Hattar Industrial Estate Hattar
Haripur, Pakistan
Tel.: (92) 995617682
Fax: (92) 995617074
E-Mail: headoffice@ecopack.com.pk
Web Site: www.ecopack.com.pk
ECOP—(KAR)
Sls.: $17,930,080
Assets: $16,414,196
Liabilities: $13,150,736
Net Worth: $3,263,461
Earnings: $24,950
Fiscal Year-end: 06/30/13
Business Description:
Pet Bottles & Preforms Mfr
S.I.C.: 2086
N.A.I.C.S.: 312112
Personnel:
Hussian Jamil *(Chm & CEO)*
Muhammad Ali Adil *(CFO & Sec)*
Mohammad Raza Chinoy *(COO)*
Board of Directors:
Hussian Jamil
Asad Ali
Mohammad Raza Chinoy
Deborah Jamil
Laila Jamil
Shahid Jamil
Ayesha Khan

ECOPACK SA GHIMBAV
46 Fagarasului St
Ghimbav, Brasov, 2251, Romania
Tel.: (40) 268 258555
Fax: (40) 268 258777
E-Mail: office@ecopack.ro
Web Site: www.ecopack.ro
AMCP—(BUC)
Business Description:
Paperboard Container Mfr
S.I.C.: 2652
N.A.I.C.S.: 322219
Personnel:
Vili Dorin *(Pres)*
Board of Directors:
Vili Dorin
Craciun Octavian Remus

ECOPETROL S.A.
(d/b/a Empresa Colombiana de Petroleos)
Carrera 13 No 36-24
Bogota, Colombia
Tel.: (57) 12345190
Fax: (57) 12345628
Web Site: www.ecopetrol.com.co/english/
EC—(COLO LIM NYSE)
Rev.: $38,557,121,120
Assets: $63,772,563,680
Liabilities: $26,060,456,800
Net Worth: $37,712,106,880
Earnings: $8,276,210,320
Emp.: 9,701
Fiscal Year-end: 12/31/12
Business Description:
Petroleum & Natural Gas Distr
S.I.C.: 1311
N.A.I.C.S.: 211111
Personnel:
Roberto Ricardo Steiner Sampedro *(Vice Chm)*
Javier Genaro Gutierrez Pemberthy *(Pres)*
Gonzalo Restrepo Lopez *(Pres)*
Magda Manosalva *(CFO)*
Rodolfo Garcia *(Gen Counsel)*
Margarita Obregon *(Sec)*
Hector Manosalva Rojas *(Exec VP-Exploration & Production)*
Board of Directors:
Gonzalo Restrepo Lopez
Joaquin Moreno Uribe
Margarita Obregon
Luis Fernando Ramirez
Horacio Ferreira Rueda
Roberto Ricardo Steiner Sampedro
Jorge Gabino Pinzon Sanchez

Subsidiary:

Propilco S A (1)
Zona Industrial Mamonal KM 8
Cartagena, Colombia
Tel.: (57) 56688700
Fax: (57) 5 668 57 57
E-Mail: mario.contreras@propilco.com
Web Site: www.propilco.com
Emp.: 182
Polypropylene Resins Mfr
S.I.C.: 2821
N.A.I.C.S.: 325211
Juan Mejia *(Gen Mgr)*

Joint Venture:

Equion Energia Ltd. (1)
Carrera 9A No 99-02 9th Floor
Bogota, Colombia
Tel.: (57) 16284000
Fax: (57) 1 6115477
Web Site: www.equion-energia.com
Emp.: 500
Petroleum Exploration & Production; Joint Venture of Ecopetrol S.A. (51%) & Talisman Energy Inc. (49%)
S.I.C.: 1311
N.A.I.C.S.: 211111
Maria Victoria Riano Salgar *(Pres)*

ECOPLASTIC CORPORATION
48 Hwangseong Dong
780130 Gyeongju, Gyeongsangbuk Do, Korea (South)
Tel.: (82) 82547703255
Fax: (82) 82547713101
Web Site: www.eco-plastic.com
38110—(KRS)
Sales Range: $300-349.9 Million
Business Description:
Automobile Components Mfr
S.I.C.: 3429
N.A.I.C.S.: 332510
Personnel:
Yil Gyu Shin *(CEO)*
Board of Directors:
Yong Guk Kim
Byeong Hui Park

ECORODOVIAS INFRAESTRUCTURA E LOGISTICA S.A.
(d/b/a Grupo EcoRodovias)
Rua Gomes de Carvalho 1510 3rd Floor
Vila Olimpia, CEP 04547-005 Sao Paulo, SP, Brazil
Tel.: (55) 11 3787 2667
Fax: (55) 11 3787 2668
E-Mail: invest@ecorodovias.com.br
Web Site: www.ecorodovias.com.br
ECOR3—(BRAZ)
Sales Range: $800-899.9 Million
Emp.: 3,000
Business Description:
Intermodal Logistics & Infrastructure Construction Services
S.I.C.: 4731
N.A.I.C.S.: 541614
Personnel:
Marco Antonio Cassou *(Chm)*
Marcelino Rafart de Seras *(CEO)*
Federico Botto *(Exec VP)*
Board of Directors:
Marco Antonio Cassou
Cesar Beltrao de Almeida
Geraldo Jose Carbone
Carlos Cesar da Silva Souza
Guillermo Osvaldo Diaz
Joao Alberto Gomes Bernacchio
Alessandro Rivano
Massimo Villa

ECOSAVE HOLDINGS LIMITED
Unit 4 42 Carrington Road
Castle Hill, NSW, 2154, Australia
Tel.: (61) 1300 557 764
Fax: (61) 1300 557 768
Web Site: www.ecosave.com.au
ECV—(ASX)
Business Description:
Energy Efficiency Services
S.I.C.: 8999
N.A.I.C.S.: 541620
Personnel:
Marcelo Javier Rouco *(Chm & CEO)*
Robin Dale Archibald *(COO)*
Board of Directors:
Marcelo Javier Rouco
Robin Dale Archibald
Glenda Ann Nixon

ECOSSE ENERGY CORP.
8 King Street East Suite 300
Toronto, ON, M4C 1S9, Canada
Tel.: (416) 899-3304
Fax: (416) 352-2862
E-Mail: ca@ecosseenergy.com
Web Site: www.ecosseenergy.com
ECS—(CNSX)
Business Description:
Investment Services; Oil & Gas Exploration Services
S.I.C.: 6211
N.A.I.C.S.: 523999
Personnel:
Alan W. Morrison *(Pres & CEO)*
Iain Steele *(CFO)*
Board of Directors:
Paul Griggs
Brian Henry
Alan W. Morrison
Iain Steele

ECOSYNTHETIX, INC.
3365 Mainway
Burlington, ON, L7M 1A6, Canada
Tel.: (289) 878-0286
Fax: (905) 335-5669
E-Mail: info@EcoSynthetix.com
Web Site: www.ecosynthetix.com
Year Founded: 1996
ECO—(TSX)
Sls.: $19,552,345
Assets: $118,068,797
Liabilities: $4,509,216
Net Worth: $113,559,581
Earnings: ($11,430,735)
Emp.: 45
Fiscal Year-end: 12/31/12
Business Description:
Chemical Mfr
S.I.C.: 2899
N.A.I.C.S.: 325998
Personnel:
John van Leeuwen *(Co-Founder & CEO)*
Steven Bloembergen *(Co-Founder & Exec VP-Tech)*
David W. Colcleugh *(Chm)*
Robert Haire *(CFO & Sec)*
Diane Richard *(Sr VP-Product Innovation & Market Dev)*
Edward van Egdom *(Sr VP-Market Realization & Product Mfg)*
Board of Directors:
David W. Colcleugh
John E. Barker
Arthur Carty
John van Leeuwen
John Varghese
Legal Counsel:
Cassels, Brock & Blackwell LLP
2100 Scotia Plaza 40 King St W
Toronto, ON, M5H 3C2, Canada
Tel.: (416) 869-5300
Telex: 6-23415
Fax: (416) 360-8877
Transfer Agent:
CIBC Mellon Trust Company
PO Box 7010
Adelaide Street Postal Station, Toronto, ON, M5C 2W9, Canada
Tel.: (416) 643-5500
Fax: (416) 643-5501
Toll Free: (800) 387-0825

ECOTEC S.R.L.
Zona Industriale Ex Area SIR
Lotto 50/E Comparto 5, 88048
Lamezia, Catanzaro, Italy
Tel.: (39) 0968 209863
Fax: (39) 0968 209260
Web Site: www.ecotecweb.net
Personnel:
Rita Chaco *(Head-Pur)*

Subsidiary:

Duratel S.p.A. (1)
Via Antonio Meucci 32
50041 Calenzano, Italy (50.66%)
Tel.: (39) 055883201
Fax: (39) 0558826525
E-Mail: duratel@duratel.it
Web Site: www.duratel.it
Telephone Apparatus Mfr
S.I.C.: 3661
N.A.I.C.S.: 334210

ECOTEL COMMUNICATION AG
Prinzenallee 11
40549 Dusseldorf, Germany
Tel.: (49) 211550070
Fax: (49) 21155007977
E-Mail: info@ecotel.de
Web Site: www.ecotel.de
Year Founded: 1998
E4C—(EUR)
Rev.: $128,430,493
Assets: $57,465,067
Liabilities: $31,453,402
Net Worth: $26,011,665
Earnings: ($2,219,327)
Emp.: 189
Fiscal Year-end: 12/31/12
Business Description:
Holding Company; Voice, Data & Mobile Telecommunications Services
S.I.C.: 6719
N.A.I.C.S.: 551112
Personnel:
Johannes Borgmann *(Chm-Supervisory Bd)*
Peter Zils *(Chm-Mgmt Bd & CEO)*
Mirko Mach *(Deputy Chm-Supervisory Bd)*
Bernhard Seidl *(CFO & Member-Mgmt Bd)*
Achim Theis *(Chief Sls Officer & Member-Mgmt Bd)*
Supervisory Board of Directors:
Johannes Borgmann
Norbert Bensel
Brigitte Holzer
Mirko Mach
Sascha Magsamen
Thorsten Reinhard

Subsidiaries:

easybell GmbH (1)
Forsterweg 1
14482 Potsdam, Brandenburg, Germany
Tel.: (49) 33158815230
Fax: (49) 180 32792359
Web Site: www.easybell.de

ecotel communication ag—(Continued)

Telecommunication Services
S.I.C.: 4899
N.A.I.C.S.: 517919

ecotel private GmbH (1)
Prinzenallee 9-11
Dusseldorf, Nordrhein-Westfalen, 40549, Germany
Tel.: (49) 211550070
Fax: (49) 21155007222
E-Mail: info@ecotel.de
Emp.: 200
Telecommunication Services
S.I.C.: 4899
N.A.I.C.S.: 517919

i-cube GmbH (1)
Prinzenallee 11
40549 Dusseldorf, Nordrhein-Westfalen, Germany
Tel.: (49) 211 547 618 0
Fax: (49) 21155007222
E-Mail: info@i-cube.de
Web Site: www.i-cube.de
Telecommunications Services
S.I.C.: 4899
N.A.I.C.S.: 517919

nacamar GmbH (1)
Robert-Bosch-Strasse 32
D-63303 Dreieich, Germany De
Tel.: (49) 61039160 (100%)
Web Site: www.tiscali-business.de
Business-to-Business Telecommunications Services
S.I.C.: 4813
N.A.I.C.S.: 517911
Peter Zils *(CEO)*

Sparcall GmbH (1)
Presseabteilung Fr Engels Strasse 7
14806 Belzig, Brandenburg, Germany
Tel.: (49) 3384 18 96 888
Fax: (49) 18 96 8890
E-Mail: kontakt@sparcall.com
Web Site: www.sparcall.com
Telecommunication Services
S.I.C.: 4899
N.A.I.C.S.: 517919
Andreas Bahr *(Pres)*

synergyPLUS GmbH (1)
Grunauer Fenn 42
14712 Rathenow, Brandenburg, Germany
Tel.: (49) 1805682682
Fax: (49) 1805682329
E-Mail: info@synergyplus.de
Web Site: www.synergyplus.de
Telecommunications Consulting Services
S.I.C.: 4899
N.A.I.C.S.: 517919

ECOURIER UK LTD.

Cityside House 40 Adler St
London, E1 1EE, United Kingdom
Tel.: (44) 8451451000
Fax: (44) 2078776501
E-Mail: info@ecourier.co.uk
Web Site: www.ecourier.co.uk
Year Founded: 2004
Sales Range: $10-24.9 Million
Emp.: 58

Business Description:
Courier Services
S.I.C.: 4513
N.A.I.C.S.: 492110

Personnel:
Peter Davies *(Chm)*

Board of Directors:
Peter Davies
Reinout Croon
John Stevens

ECOVER BELGIUM NV

Industrieweg 3
Malle, 2390, Belgium
Tel.: (32) 3309 2500
Web Site: www.ecover.com
Year Founded: 1980
Sales Range: $200-249.9 Million
Emp.: 300

Business Description:
Dish & Laundry Detergent Mfr
S.I.C.: 2844
N.A.I.C.S.: 325611

Personnel:
Philip Malmberg *(CEO)*

U.S. Subsidiary:

Method Products, Inc. (1)
637 Commercial St Ste 300
San Francisco, CA 94111 DE
Tel.: (415) 931-3947
Fax: (415) 568-4693
Toll Free: (866) 9METHOD
E-Mail: info@methodhome.com
Web Site: www.methodhome.com
Sales Range: $25-49.9 Million
Emp.: 57
Biodegradable Laundry Detergent, Dish Soap, Spray Cleaners & Scented Plug-Ins Mfr
S.I.C.: 2841
N.A.I.C.S.: 325611
Adam Lowry *(Co-Founder)*
Eric Ryan *(Co-Founder)*
Andrew Fraser *(Pres & CEO)*

ECOWISE HOLDINGS LIMITED

17 Kallang Junction No 04 03
Singapore, 339274, Singapore
Tel.: (65) 65362489
Fax: (65) 65367672
E-Mail: enquiries@ecowise.com.sg
Web Site: www.ecowise.com.sg
Year Founded: 1979
5CT—(SES)
Rev.: $73,293,043
Assets: $83,369,511
Liabilities: $34,398,445
Net Worth: $48,971,066
Earnings: $1,391,030
Fiscal Year-end: 10/31/12

Business Description:
Holding Company; Waste Collection & Recycling Services
S.I.C.: 6719
N.A.I.C.S.: 551112

Personnel:
Thaim Seng Lee *(Chm & CEO)*
Kian Beng Low *(Deputy CEO)*
Lilian Yin Yen Tan *(CFO)*
Xiaowen Zhong *(Sec)*

Board of Directors:
Thaim Seng Lee
Mong Seng Ang
Kian Beng Low
Cher Yan Ng
Teck Ghee Ong

Subsidiaries:

Bee Joo Environmental Pte. Ltd. (1)
5 Sungei Kadut Street 6
728853 Singapore, Singapore
Tel.: (65) 63653288
Fax: (65) 63653088
Waste Management Services
S.I.C.: 4953
N.A.I.C.S.: 562211

Bee Joo Industries Pte. Ltd. (1)
5 Sungei Kadut St 6
728853 Singapore, Singapore
Tel.: (65) 91061877
Fax: (65) 63653088
E-Mail: enquiries@ecowise.com.sg
Web Site: www.ecowise.com.sg
Emp.: 300
Waste Treatment Services
S.I.C.: 4212
N.A.I.C.S.: 562112
Lee Thiam Seng *(CEO)*

ecoWise Solutions Pte. Ltd. (1)
No 5 Sungei Kadut St 6
Singapore, 728853, Singapore SG
Tel.: (65) 63653288
Fax: (65) 63653088
Web Site: www.ecoWise.com
Recycling & Environmental Management Services
S.I.C.: 4959
N.A.I.C.S.: 562998

Non-U.S. Subsidiaries:

Sun Rubber Industry Sdn. Bhd (1)
Lot 53 Senawang Industrial Estate
70450 Seremban, Malaysia
Tel.: (60) 66771711
Fax: (60) 66774945
Web Site: www.suntex.com
Emp.: 500
Rubber Products Mfr
S.I.C.: 3011
N.A.I.C.S.: 326211
Chin Hon Meng *(Gen Mgr-Mfg)*

Sun Tyre Industries Sdn. Bhd (1)
53 & 54 Senawang Industrial Estate
Senawang, 70450 Seremban, Negeri Sembilan, Malaysia
Tel.: (60) 66771711
Fax: (60) 6 678 5359
Web Site: www.suntex.com
Emp.: 500
Tire Retreading Services
S.I.C.: 7534
N.A.I.C.S.: 326212
Low Kian Beng *(Mng Dir)*

Sunrich Integrated Sdn. Bhd (1)
53 Senawang Industrial Estate
70450 Seremban, Negeri Sembilan, Malaysia
Tel.: (60) 66771711
Fax: (60) 6 6793561
E-Mail: sresport@sunrich.com
Emp.: 400
Rubber Products Mfr & Distr
S.I.C.: 3011
N.A.I.C.S.: 326211
Hon Meng Chin *(Head-Mfr)*

Sunrich Marketing Sdn. Bhd (1)
53 Senawang Industrial Estate
70450 Seremban, Negeri Sembilan, Malaysia
Tel.: (60) 66771711
Fax: (60) 67777872
Web Site: www.suntex.com
Emp.: 500
Tire Retreading Services
S.I.C.: 7534
N.A.I.C.S.: 326212
Chin Hon Meng *(Gen Mgr-Mfg)*

ECOYA LIMITED

(Name Changed to Trilogy International Limited)

ECR MINERALS PLC

Peek House 20 Eastcheap
London, EC3M 1EB, United Kingdom
Tel.: (44) 2079291010
Fax: (44) 2079291015
E-Mail: info@mercatorgold.com
Web Site: www.mercatorgold.com
ECR—(AIM)
Rev.: $4,765
Assets: $22,332,487
Liabilities: $6,185,626
Net Worth: $16,146,862
Earnings: ($6,726,376)
Emp.: 123
Fiscal Year-end: 09/30/12

Business Description:
Mineral Mining Services
S.I.C.: 1499
N.A.I.C.S.: 212399

Personnel:
Stephen Clayson *(CEO)*

Board of Directors:
Paul Johnson
Stephen Clayson
Richard Watts

Legal Counsel:
Gowlings (UK) LLP
15th Floor 125 Old Broad Street
London, EC2N 1AR, United Kingdom

Edwin Coe LLP
2 Stone Buildings Lincolns Inn
London, WC2A 4AR, United Kingdom

ECRC

1201 275 Slater St
Ottawa, ON, K1P 5H9, Canada
Tel.: (613) 230-7369
Fax: (613) 230-7344
E-Mail: general_info@ecrc.ca
Web Site: www.ecrc.ca
Year Founded: 1995
Rev.: $10,116,528
Emp.: 170

Business Description:
Ship & Oil Handling Services
S.I.C.: 3731
N.A.I.C.S.: 336611

Personnel:
Paul Pouliotte *(CFO)*

ECS ELECTRICAL CABLE SUPPLY LTD.

3135 - 6900 Graybar Road
Richmond, BC, V6W 0A5, Canada
Tel.: (604) 276-9913
Fax: (604) 276-9915
Toll Free: (800) 661-4165
E-Mail: info@ecswire.com
Web Site: www.ecswire.com
Year Founded: 1984
Rev.: $19,480,245
Emp.: 90

Business Description:
Electrical & Electronic Wire & Cable Distr
S.I.C.: 5064
N.A.I.C.S.: 423620

Personnel:
Mohammad H. Mohseni *(Founder & Chm)*
Gordon Thursfield *(Pres)*

ECS ENGINEERING & CONSTRUCTION LIMITED

51 Ritin Lane Unit 1
Concord, ON, L4K 4E1, Canada
Tel.: (905) 761-7009
Fax: (905) 761-7082
Web Site: www.ecsengineering.com
Year Founded: 1992
Rev.: $26,076,800
Emp.: 50

Business Description:
Engineering & Construction Services
S.I.C.: 1542
N.A.I.C.S.: 236220

Personnel:
Jason Chidiac *(Pres)*

ECS IT BERHAD

Lot 3 Jalan Teknologi 3/5 Taman Sains
Selangor Kota Damansara, Petaling Jaya, 48710, Malaysia
Tel.: (60) 362868222
Fax: (60) 361400030
E-Mail: ecsastar@ecsm.com.my
Web Site: www.ecsm.com.my
Year Founded: 1985
Emp.: 281

Business Description:
Holding Company; Information & Communications Technology Products
S.I.C.: 6719
N.A.I.C.S.: 551112

Personnel:
Teo Chiang Quan *(Chm)*
Foo Sen Chin *(Mng Dir)*

Board of Directors:
Teo Chiang Quan
Ahmad Subri Bin Abdullah
Foo Sen Chin
Wong Heng Chong
Foo Toon Ee
Tae Eng Hoe
Soong Jan Hsung
Ho Chee Kit
Quah Chek Tin

ECS LIMITED
M11 Business Avenue
Sheikh Rashid Road Deira, Dubai, United Arab Emirates
Tel.: (971) 50 3414048
Web Site: www.ecs-limited.com
Business Description:
Information Technology & Management Consulting Services
S.I.C.: 8748
N.A.I.C.S.: 541618
Personnel:
Arvind R. Arora *(CEO)*
Non-U.S. Subsidiary:

Parity Training Limited (1)
3rd Floor
120 Moorgate, London, EC2M 6SS, United Kingdom
Tel.: (44) 2085409393
Fax: (44) 2085409393
E-Mail: t.marketing@parity.net
Web Site: www.paritytraining.com
Sales Range: $25-49.9 Million
Emp.: 250
Computer Training
S.I.C.: 8243
N.A.I.C.S.: 611420
Paul Stephanson *(Mgr-Bus Dev)*

ECSI LIMITED
Level 11 499 St Kilda Road
Melbourne, VIC, 3000, Australia
Web Site: www.ecsilimited.com
ECS—(ASX)
Assets: $8,229
Liabilities: $768,936
Net Worth: ($760,707)
Earnings: ($624,959)
Fiscal Year-end: 06/30/13
Business Description:
Security Services
S.I.C.: 1731
N.A.I.C.S.: 238210
Personnel:
George Karafotias *(Chm, CEO & Interim Sec)*
Board of Directors:
George Karafotias
Eric Jiang
Ashley Kelly
Jeffrey Hua Yuen Tan
Wilton Yao

ECUADOR GOLD AND COPPER CORP.
5000 Yonge Street Suite 1901
Toronto, ON, M2N 7E9, Canada
Tel.: (416) 227-3402
Fax: (416) 628-3801
E-Mail: cphillips@ecuadorgoldandcopper.com
Web Site: www.ecuadorgoldandcopper.com
Year Founded: 2008
EGX—(TSXV)
Assets: $17,426,853
Liabilities: $3,902,820
Net Worth: $13,524,034
Earnings: ($3,434,685)
Fiscal Year-end: 10/31/12
Business Description:
Gold & Copper Exploration Services
S.I.C.: 1041
N.A.I.C.S.: 212221
Personnel:
Glenn Laing *(Pres & CEO)*
Board of Directors:
Mario I. Blejer
Guoqing Hunag
Paul C. Jones
Glenn Laing
Carson Phillips
Branislav Trajkovski
James Xiang

ECUPHAR NV/SA
Legeweg 157 i
8020 Oostkamp, Belgium
Tel.: (32) 50 31 45 10
Fax: (32) 50 54 50 67
E-Mail: info@ecuphar.com
Web Site: www.ecuphar.com
Business Description:
Veterinary Healthcare Product Mfr
S.I.C.: 2834
N.A.I.C.S.: 325412
Personnel:
Chris Cardon *(Chm & CEO)*
Tom Almey *(COO)*
Jeroen Bastijns *(Chief Sls Officer)*

ECUSTA FIBRES LTD.
346 Kimberly Road
PO Box 958
Winkler, MB, R6W 4V1, Canada
Tel.: (204) 325-4782
Fax: (204) 325-8051
Year Founded: 1994
Sales Range: $10-24.9 Million
Emp.: 40
Business Description:
Flax Straw Processing Services
S.I.C.: 2611
N.A.I.C.S.: 322110

ECZACIBASI HOLDING A.S.
(d/b/a Eczacibasi Group)
Kanyon Office Buyukdere Caddesi 185
Levent, 34394 Istanbul, Turkey
Tel.: (90) 212 371 7000
Fax: (90) 212 371 7110
Web Site: www.eczacibasi.com
Sales Range: $1-4.9 Billion
Emp.: 10,950
Business Description:
Holding Company
S.I.C.: 6719
N.A.I.C.S.: 551112
Personnel:
Bulent Eczacibasi *(Chm)*
Sezgin Bayraktar *(Vice Chm)*
Faruk Eczacibasi *(Vice Chm)*
Erdal Karamercan *(Pres & CEO)*
Sacit Basmaci *(Exec VP, Comptroller & Head-Legal Affairs)*
Sedat Birol *(Exec VP-Healthcare Div)*
Levent Ersalman *(Exec VP-Strategic Plng & Fin)*
Husamettin Onanc *(Exec VP-Building Products Div)*
Hakan Uyanik *(Exec VP-Consumer Products Div)*
Board of Directors:
Bulent Eczacibasi
Asaf Savas Akat
Oztin Akguc
Sezgin Bayraktar
Ant Bozkaya
Mustafa Fadlullah Cerrahoglu
Faruk Eczacibasi
Oktay Tulpar
Subsidiary:

Ipek Kagit San. ve Tic. A.S. (1)
Kavacik Ofis Ruzgarli Bahce Mahallesi
Kavak Sokak No 20, 34805 Istanbul, Beykoz, Turkey TR
Tel.: (90) 216 333 7700 (100%)
Fax: (90) 216 333 7083
E-Mail: info@ipekkagit.com.tr
Web Site: www.eczacibasi.com
Tissue Paper Products Mfr & Marketer
S.I.C.: 2621
N.A.I.C.S.: 322121
Sertac Nisli *(Gen Mgr)*
Holding:

Eczacibasi Pharmaceutical & Industrial Investment Co. (1)
Buyukdere Cad Ali Kaya Sok No 7
Levent, 34394 Istanbul, Turkey (50.62%)
Tel.: (90) 212 350 80 00
Fax: (90) 212 350 85 33
Web Site: www.eis.com.tr
Financial Investments
S.I.C.: 6211
N.A.I.C.S.: 523999
Bulent Eczacibasi *(Chm)*
Faruk Eczacibasi *(Vice Chm)*

Holding:

Eczacibasi Monrol Nukleer Urunler San. ve Tic. A.S. (2)
Tubitak Mam Teknoparki Gebze
41470 Kocaeli, Turkey
Tel.: (90) 262 648 02 00
Fax: (90) 262 646 40 39
Web Site: www.monrol.com.tr
Emp.: 200
Nuclear Medicine Development
S.I.C.: 8731
N.A.I.C.S.: 541712
Erdal Karamercan *(Chm)*

U.S. Subsidiary:

Capintec Inc. (3)
6 Arrow Rd
Ramsey, NJ 07446-1236 DE
Tel.: (201) 825-9500
Fax: (201) 825-1336
Toll Free: (800) 631-3826
E-Mail: getinfo@capintec.com
Web Site: www.capintec.com
Sales Range: $10-24.9 Million
Emp.: 70
Mfr, Developer & Marketer of Radiation Measuring & Monitoring Instrumentation Import Export
S.I.C.: 3829
N.A.I.C.S.: 334519
Arthur M. Weis *(Chm)*
Jessica Bede *(Pres & CEO)*

Plant:

Capintec Inc. (4)
620 Alpha Dr
Pittsburgh, PA 15238-2912 DE
Tel.: (412) 963-1988 (100%)
Fax: (412) 963-0610
Toll Free: (800) 227-6832
E-Mail: getinfo@capintec.com
Web Site: www.capintec.com
Emp.: 60
Mfr of Radiation Measuring & Monitoring Instrumentation
S.I.C.: 3829
N.A.I.C.S.: 334519
Mary Ann Dell *(Gen Mgr)*

ED&F MAN HOLDINGS LIMITED
Cottons Centre Hay's Lane
London, SE1 2QE, United Kingdom
Tel.: (44) 2070898000
Fax: (44) 2070898070
E-Mail: corporateinfo@edfman.com
Web Site: www.edfman.com
Year Founded: 1860
Sales Range: $10-24.9 Million
Emp.: 200
Fiscal Year-end: 12/31/12
Business Description:
Sugar, Molasses & Coffee Trader & Distr
S.I.C.: 5149
N.A.I.C.S.: 424490
Board of Directors:
Eduardo F.C. Alba
Fred W. Ganning
Peter J.M. Harding
Philip A. Howell
Subsidiary:

ED&F Man Terminals UK Limited (1)
19 Sandhills Lane
Liverpool, Merseyside, L5 9XE, United Kingdom UK
Tel.: (44) 151 922 2848
Fax: (44) 151 933 9144
Bulk Liquid Storage & Other Related Services
S.I.C.: 4226
N.A.I.C.S.: 493190
Stuart Ross *(Reg Mgr-HSEQ-Europe)*
U.S. Subsidiaries:

Agman Louisiana, Inc. (1)
365 Canal St Ste 2900
New Orleans, LA 70130 DE
Tel.: (504) 525-9741
Fax: (504) 522-1638
E-Mail:
Holding Company
S.I.C.: 6719
N.A.I.C.S.: 551112
James B. Jenkins *(CEO-Westway Grp)*

Westway Feed Products LLC (1)
14015 Park Dr Ste 217
Tomball, TX 77377 DE
Tel.: (281) 351-4420
Fax: (281) 290-3000
Web Site: www.westwayfeed.com
Liquid Animal Feed Products Mfr & Distr
S.I.C.: 2048
N.A.I.C.S.: 311119
Steven Boehmer *(Pres)*
Joe Harris *(Exec VP)*

Plant:

Westway Feed Products LLC - Western Regional Office (2)
2030 W Washington St
Stockton, CA 95203-2932
Mailing Address:
PO Box 369
Stockton, CA 95201-3069
Tel.: (209) 946-0914
Fax: (209) 487-2112
Web Site: www.westwayfeed.com
Liquid Animal Feed Products Mfr & Distr
S.I.C.: 2048
N.A.I.C.S.: 311119
Rick Watson *(Mgr-Ops-Western Reg)*

Non-U.S. Subsidiary:

ED&F Man Liquid Products Nederland B.V. (1)
De Ruijterkade 6 6e etage
1013 AA Amsterdam, Netherlands NL
Tel.: (31) 20 754 0111
Fax: (31) 20 754 0122
Web Site: www.manliquidproducts.com
Sugar & Molasses Wholesale Trading Services
S.I.C.: 7389
N.A.I.C.S.: 425120
Otto Langelaar *(Head-Trading)*

U.S. Subsidiary:

ED&F Man Liquid Products LLC (2)
365 Canal St Ste 2900
New Orleans, LA 70130 DE
Tel.: (504) 525-9741
Fax: (504) 522-1638
Web Site: www.manliquidproducts.com
Emp.: 100
Trader & Distributor of Molasses
S.I.C.: 4226
N.A.I.C.S.: 493190
Georgette O'Connor *(Asst Mgr-Marine Div)*

ED CO., LTD.
517-15 Sangdaewon-Dong
Jungwon-Gu, Seongnam, Gyeonggido, Korea (South) 462-806
Tel.: (82) 31 730 7525
Fax: (82) 31 730 7313
E-Mail: trade@ed.co.kr
Web Site: www.ed.co.kr
Year Founded: 1986
033110—(KRS)
Business Description:
Electronic Equipment Mfr
S.I.C.: 3679
N.A.I.C.S.: 334419
Personnel:
Yong-hoo Park *(Pres & CEO)*

ED INVEST S.A.
ul Bor-Komorowski 35 lok 218
03-982 Warsaw, Poland
Tel.: (48) 22 671 69 38

ED Invest S.A.—(Continued)

E-Mail: biuro@edinvest.pl
Web Site: www.edinvest.pl
EDI—(WAR)
Sales Range: $10-24.9 Million
Emp.: 11
Business Description:
Residential Housing & Commercial Buildings Construction & Investment Services
S.I.C.: 6531
N.A.I.C.S.: 531390
Personnel:
Bohdan Brym *(Chm-Supervisory Bd)*
Zofia Egierska *(Chm-Mgmt Bd)*
Henryk Kacprzak *(Vice Chm-Supervisory Bd)*
Jerzy Dyrcz *(Vice Chm-Mgmt Bd)*
Marek Uzdowski *(Vice Chm-Mgmt Bd)*
Zbigniew Wasilewski *(Vice Chm-Mgmt Bd)*
Supervisory Board of Directors:
Bohdan Brym
Bartlomiej Bieleninnik
Henryk Kacprzak
Krzysztof Mikolajczyk
Edyta Rytel

ED LEARN FORD SALES LTD.
375 Ontario Street
PO Box 24040
Saint Catharines, ON, Canada L2R 7P7
Tel.: (905) 684-8791
Fax: (905) 684-3717
Toll Free: (877) 218-4048
Web Site: www.edlearnford.com
Year Founded: 1978
Rev.: $17,800,000
Emp.: 83
Business Description:
New & Used Car Dealers
S.I.C.: 5511
N.A.I.C.S.: 441110
Personnel:
Drew Donoghue *(Gen Mgr)*

EDAN INSTRUMENTS, INC.
3/F B Nanshan Medical Equipment Park
1019 Nanhai Road Shekou
Nanshan, Shenzhen, 518067, China
Tel.: (86) 755 26882220
Fax: (86) 755 26882223
E-Mail: info@edan.com.cn
Web Site: www.edan.com.cn
Year Founded: 1995
300206—(CHIN)
Sales Range: $300-349.9 Million
Emp.: 800
Business Description:
Electronic Medical Device Mfr
S.I.C.: 3845
N.A.I.C.S.: 334510
Personnel:
Hao Zhang *(Chm)*

EDAP TMS S.A.
Parc d'Activites la Poudrette-Lamartine 4/6 Rue du Dauphine
69120 Vaulx-en-Velin, France
Tel.: (33) 472153150
Fax: (33) 472153151
E-Mail: bconfort@edap-tms.com
Web Site: www.edap-tms.com
Year Founded: 1979
EDAP—(NASDAQ)
Rev.: $35,087,921
Assets: $40,982,799
Liabilities: $29,996,706
Net Worth: $10,986,093
Earnings: ($10,062,621)
Emp.: 143
Fiscal Year-end: 12/31/12
Business Description:
Mfr of Urological Medical Devices
S.I.C.: 3845
N.A.I.C.S.: 334510
Personnel:
Philippe Chauveau *(Chm)*
Marc Oczachowski *(Pres)*
Eric Soyer *(CFO)*
Emmanuel Blanc *(CTO)*
Board of Directors:
Philippe Chauveau
Pierre Beysson
Karim Fizazi

Non-U.S. Subsidiaries:

EDAP Technomed Co. Ltd. (1)
Round Cross Akasakamitsuke F9
3-9-18 Aksaka, Tokyo, Minato-ku, 107 0052, Japan JP
Tel.: (81) 355750981 (100%)
Fax: (81) 355756723
E-Mail: marketing@edaptechnomed.co.jp
Web Site: www.edaptechnomed.co.jp
Emp.: 32
Sales & Regulator of Urological Medical Devices
S.I.C.: 3841
N.A.I.C.S.: 339112
Jean Francois Pahelard *(Gen Mgr)*

EDAP Technomed Italia Srl (1)
Via Leonida Rech 44th Fl
00156 Rome, Italy IT
Tel.: (39) 0686897190 (100%)
Fax: (39) 0686897188
E-Mail: info.edap@edap-tms.it
Web Site: www.edap-tms.com
Marketer of Urological Medical Devices
S.I.C.: 3841
N.A.I.C.S.: 339112
Sergio Pontecorvi *(Gen Mgr)*

EDAP Technomed (M) Sdn Bhd (1)
16 1st Fl Jalan USJ 10/1B Taipan Triangle
UEP Suban Jaya, 47620 Petaling Jaya, Malaysia MY
Tel.: (60) 356349335 (100%)
Fax: (60) 356349733
E-Mail: leong@edaptms.po.my
Web Site: www.edap-tms.com
Emp.: 7
Marketer of Urological Medical Devices
S.I.C.: 3841
N.A.I.C.S.: 339112
Herve de Soultrait *(Gen Mgr)*

EDAP TMS Korea (1)
Gangnam Landmark Tower Suite 1809
837-36 Yeoksam-Dong
Gangnam-Gu, 135937 Seoul, Korea (South) Ks
Tel.: (82) 221128151 (100%)
Fax: (82) 221128153
E-Mail: yht@edap-tms.co.kr
Web Site: www.edap-tms.com
Emp.: 2
Mfr of Therapeutic Ultrasound Devices
S.I.C.: 3845
N.A.I.C.S.: 334510
Young Hwan Park *(Gen Mgr)*

EDAP GmbH (1)
Hulm 42
24937 Flensburg, Germany De
Tel.: (49) 4618072590 (100%)
Fax: (49) 46180725920
E-Mail: info@edap-tms.de
Web Site: www.edap-tms.de
Emp.: 9
Ultrasound Therapeutic Device Mfr
S.I.C.: 3829
N.A.I.C.S.: 334519
Judith Johannsen *(Gen Mgr)*

EDAP Russia (1)
Quai Bersenevskaja Imm 20/2 Office 601
119072 Moscow, Russia RU
Tel.: (7) 79165224104 (100%)
Fax: (7) 4955892729
Web Site: www.edap-tms.com
Therapeutic Ultrasound Device Mfr
S.I.C.: 3845
N.A.I.C.S.: 334510
Jean-Francois Bachelard *(Bus Dir)*

Subsidiary:

EDAP TMS France S.A. (1)
Parc d/Activites la Poudrette Lamartine
4 rue du Dauphine, 69120 Vaulx-en-Velin, France FR
Tel.: (33) 472153150
Fax: (33) 472153151
E-Mail: info@edap-tms.com
Web Site: www.edap-tms.com
Emp.: 90
Developer & Marketer of Therapeutic Ultrasound Devices
S.I.C.: 3845
N.A.I.C.S.: 334510
Marc Ocazachowski *(CEO)*
Eric Soyer *(CFO)*

EDB INVESTMENTS PTE. LTD.
250 N Bridge Rd
20 00 Raffles City Tower, Singapore, 179101, Singapore
Tel.: (65) 68326832
Fax: (65) 63366325
E-Mail: infohq@edbi.com
Web Site: www.edbi.com
Emp.: 500
Business Description:
Investment Holding Company
S.I.C.: 6211
N.A.I.C.S.: 523999
Personnel:
Leo Seng-Cheong Yip *(Chm)*
Swee-Yeok Chu *(CEO)*

Subsidiary:

S*BIO Pte. Ltd. (1)
1 Science Park Road 05 09 The Capricorn
Singapore Science Park II, Singapore, 117 528, Singapore
Tel.: (65) 68275000
Fax: (65) 68275005
Web Site: www.sbio.com
Biotechnology Research & Development Services
S.I.C.: 8731
N.A.I.C.S.: 541711
Jan-Anders Karlsson *(CEO)*
Stephen Keith Rhind *(Sr VP-Corp Dev)*
Joy Zhu *(Sr VP-Global Clinical Dev)*

EDDY GROUP LIMITED
660 St Anne St
PO Box 146
Bathurst, NB, E2A 3Z1, Canada
Tel.: (506) 546-6631
Fax: (506) 548-3575
E-Mail: bathurst@eddygroup.com
Web Site: www.eddygroup.com
Year Founded: 1800
Rev.: $29,572,830
Emp.: 112
Business Description:
Residential & Commercial Products Distr
S.I.C.: 5211
N.A.I.C.S.: 444190
Personnel:
Robyn L. Eddy *(Pres)*
Keith M. Assaff *(CFO)*
Krystyna Fecteau *(CIO)*

EDEKA ZENTRALE AG & CO. KG
New York Ring 6
22297 Hamburg, Germany
Tel.: (49) 4063770
Fax: (49) 4063772231
E-Mail: info@edeka.de
Web Site: www.edeka.de
Year Founded: 1907
Sales Range: $25-49.9 Billion
Emp.: 200,000
Business Description:
Groceries Whslr & Retailer
S.I.C.: 5411
N.A.I.C.S.: 445110
Personnel:
Markus Mosa *(CFO & CIO)*
Subsidiaries:

Marktkauf Holding GmbH (1)
Fuggerstrasse 11
D-33689 Bielefeld, Germany De
Tel.: (49) 52059401
Fax: (49) 52 05 94 10 29
E-Mail: info@marktkauf.de
Web Site: www.marktkauf.de
Sales Range: $5-14.9 Billion
Emp.: 14,150
Infrastructure Inspection Camera & Remote Control System Design & Mfr
S.I.C.: 6719
N.A.I.C.S.: 551112

Netto Marken-Discount AG & Co. KG (1)
Industriepark Ponholz 1
93142 Maxhutte-Haidhof, Germany De
Tel.: (49) 94713200 (100%)
Fax: (49) 9471320149
E-Mail: netto@netto-online.de
Web Site: www.netto-online.de
Emp.: 600
Grocery & Convenience Store Operator
S.I.C.: 5411
N.A.I.C.S.: 445110
Manfred Karl *(Mng Dir)*

EDEL AG
Neumuhlen 17
D 22763 Hamburg, Germany
Tel.: (49) 40890850
Fax: (49) 40896521
E-Mail: info@edel.com
Web Site: www.edel.com
EDL—(DEU)
Sales Range: $150-199.9 Million
Emp.: 905
Business Description:
Music & Entertainment Product Production & Distribution
S.I.C.: 2741
N.A.I.C.S.: 512230
Personnel:
Walter Lichte *(Chm-Supervisory Bd)*
Joel H. Weinstein *(Deputy Chm-Supervisory Bd)*
Michael Haentjes *(CEO)*
Timo Steinberg *(CFO & COO)*
Supervisory Board of Directors:
Walter Lichte
Joel H. Weinstein
Egbert Diehl

Subsidiaries:

Edel Germany GmbH (1)
Neumuhlen 17
22763 Hamburg, Germany
Tel.: (49) 40 89 08 50
Fax: (49) 89085320
Web Site: www.edel.com
Emp.: 16
Commercial Books Mfr & Distr
S.I.C.: 2759
N.A.I.C.S.: 323111
Michael Haentjes *(Gen Mgr)*

Subsidiaries:

Edel Classics GmbH (2)
Neumuehlen 17
22763 Hamburg, Germany (100%)
Tel.: (49) 4089085339
Fax: (49) 4089085320
E-Mail: classics.de@edel.com
Web Site: www.edelclassics.com
Emp.: 150
Music Distributor
S.I.C.: 7389
N.A.I.C.S.: 512290
Michael Haentjes *(Founder, CEO, Principal & Gen Mgr)*

Edel Media & Entertainment GmbH (2)
Neumuehlen 17
22763 Hamburg, Germany (100%)
Tel.: (49) 40890850
Fax: (49) 4089085361

E-Mail: info@edel.com
Emp.: 150
Music Producer
S.I.C.: 7929
N.A.I.C.S.: 711130
Michael Haentjes *(Gen Mgr)*

Edel Records GmbH **(2)**
Neumuehlen 17
22763 Hamburg, Germany (100%)
Tel.: (49) 40890850
Fax: (49) 4089085320
E-Mail: info.de@edel.com
Web Site: www.edel.com
Emp.: 50
Music Distributor
S.I.C.: 7389
N.A.I.C.S.: 512290
Michel Michaes *(Mng Dir)*

Non-U.S. Divisions:

Edel Musica Vertriebs GmbH **(3)**
Lustenauerstrasse 27
6850 Dornbirn, Austria (100%)
Tel.: (43) 557223494
Fax: (43) 557223498
E-Mail: info.at@edel.com
Web Site: www.edel.at
Emp.: 50
Music Distributor
S.I.C.: 7389
N.A.I.C.S.: 512290

Edel Records Finland Oy **(3)**
Saynaslahdent 12
00560 Helsinki, Finland (100%)
Tel.: (358) 97288320
Fax: (358) 972883220
E-Mail: info.fl@edel.com
Web Site: www.edel.fi
Sls.: $9,692,800
Emp.: 14
Music Distributor
S.I.C.: 7389
N.A.I.C.S.: 512290
Jorma Kosonen *(Mng Dir)*

Edel Records (Switzerland) AG **(3)**
Zuercher Strasse 77
Postfach 322
8401 Winterthur, Switzerland
Tel.: (41) 522020222
Fax: (41) 522020337
E-Mail: info.ch@edel.com
Music Distributor
S.I.C.: 7389
N.A.I.C.S.: 512290

Edel UK Records Ltd. **(3)**
12 Oval Rd
London, NW1 7DH, United Kingdom(100%)
Tel.: (44) 2074824848
Fax: (44) 2074824846
E-Mail: contactuk@edel.com
Web Site: www.edel.com
Emp.: 100
Music Distributor
S.I.C.: 7389
N.A.I.C.S.: 512290

EdelNET GmbH **(2)**
Neumuhlen 17
22763 Hamburg, Germany (100%)
Tel.: (49) 40890850
Fax: (49) 4089085310
E-Mail: info@edel.com
Web Site: edel.com
Emp.: 150
Music Distributor
S.I.C.: 7389
N.A.I.C.S.: 512290
Michael Haentjes *(Gen Mgr)*

Kontor New Media GmbH **(1)**
Neumuhlen 17
22763 Hamburg, Germany
Tel.: (49) 40 646 905 10
Fax: (49) 40 646 905 186
E-Mail: contact@kontornewmedia.com
Web Site: www.kontornewmedia.com
Emp.: 19
Marketing Consulting Services
S.I.C.: 8742
N.A.I.C.S.: 541613
Michael Pohl *(Mng Dir)*

Kontor Records GmbH **(1)**
Neumuhlen 17
22763 Hamburg, Germany
Tel.: (49) 406469050
Fax: (49) 4064690525
E-Mail: info@kontorl.de
Web Site: www.kontorrecords.de
Emp.: 30
Music Publishers
S.I.C.: 2741
N.A.I.C.S.: 512230
Jen Thele *(Mng Dir)*

Optimal Media Production GmbH **(1)**
Glienholzweg 7
Roebel, 17207 Berlin, Germany (100%)
Tel.: (49) 3993156500
Fax: (49) 3993156555
E-Mail: info@optimal-online.de
Web Site: www.optimal-online.de
Emp.: 35
Mfr. & Distribution of CDs, DVDs, Cassettes & Vinyl Records
S.I.C.: 3651
N.A.I.C.S.: 334310
Jorg Hahn *(CEO)*

Joint Venture:

Connected Music **(1)**
Zippelhaus 5 A
20457 Hamburg, Germany (100%)
Tel.: (49) 4031803100
Fax: (49) 4031803130
E-Mail: info@connected-music.de
Web Site: www.connectedmusic.co.uk
Emp.: 65
Distributor of Music
S.I.C.: 7389
N.A.I.C.S.: 512290

Non-U.S. Subsidiaries:

Eddy Ouwens Productions B.V. **(1)**
Laapersveld 53 A
1213 Hilversum, Netherlands (100%)
Tel.: (31) 356247878
Fax: (31) 356244043
E-Mail: info@abcd.nl
Music Production
S.I.C.: 7929
N.A.I.C.S.: 711130

Edel Music France S.a.r.l. **(1)**
48 Rue Laborde
75008 Paris, France (100%)
Tel.: (33) 153431353
Fax: (33) 153431364
E-Mail: info.fr@edel.com
Web Site: www.edel.com
Music Distributor
S.I.C.: 7389
N.A.I.C.S.: 512290

Edel Music S.A. **(1)**
Gran via 39 7a
28013 Madrid, Spain
Tel.: (34) 917013990
Fax: (34) 915324060
E-Mail: info.es@edel.com
Web Site: www.edel.com
Music Distributor
S.I.C.: 7389
N.A.I.C.S.: 512290

Edel Publishing Ltd. **(1)**
12 Oval Rd
London, NW1 7DH, United Kingdom(100%)
Tel.: (44) 2074829700
Fax: (44) 2074824840
E-Mail: info.uk@edel.com
Web Site: www.edel.com
Music Publishing
S.I.C.: 7389
N.A.I.C.S.: 512290

Edlp Marketing, Lda. **(1)**
Rua Quirino Da Fonseca 6 3 Dto
1000 252 Lisbon, Portugal (100%)
Tel.: (351) 218438580
E-Mail: lisboa@edel.com
Sales Range: Less than $1 Million
Emp.: 2
Music Producer Advertiser
S.I.C.: 8732
N.A.I.C.S.: 541910
Peter Cooper *(Mng Dir)*

Phonag Records AG **(1)**
Zuercherstrasse 77
8401 Winterthur, Switzerland
Tel.: (41) 522020151
Fax: (41) 522020337
Web Site: www.edel.com
Music Distributor
S.I.C.: 7389
N.A.I.C.S.: 512290

Playground Music Scandinavia AB **(1)**
Jorgen Ankersgatan 13B
211 45 Malmo, Sweden SE
Mailing Address:
PO Box 3171
200 22 Malmo, Sweden
Tel.: (46) 4028 8180
Fax: (46) 4028 8190
E-Mail: info@playgroundmusic.com
Web Site: www.playgroundmusic.com
Emp.: 30
Physical & Digital Music Media Production, Marketing & Distribution
S.I.C.: 3652
N.A.I.C.S.: 512220
Torgny Sjoeoe *(Mng Dir)*

Non-U.S. Branches:

Playground Music Scandinavia AB - Oslo Branch **(2)**
Ulvenveien 90B
581 Oslo, Norway
Tel.: (47) 22666560
Fax: (47) 22666561
E-Mail: info.norge@playgroundmusic.com
Web Site: www.playgroundmusic.com
Emp.: 6
Physical & Digital Music Media Production, Marketing & Distribution
S.I.C.: 3652
N.A.I.C.S.: 512220
Tom Pannula *(Gen Mgr)*

Playground Music Scandinavia AB - Copenhagen Branch **(2)**
Gronnegade 3
DK-1107 Copenhagen, Denmark
Tel.: (45) 33186572
Fax: (45) 33323341
E-Mail: info.dk@edel.com
Web Site: www.playgroundmusic.com
Emp.: 7
Physical & Digital Music Media Production, Marketing & Distribution
S.I.C.: 3652
N.A.I.C.S.: 512220
Soren Krogh Thompson *(Gen Mgr)*

EDELWEISS FINANCIAL SERVICES LTD.

Edelweiss House Off CST Road Kalina
Mumbai, 400 098, India
Tel.: (91) 2222864400
Fax: (91) 2222864278
E-Mail: ir@edelweissfin.com
Web Site: www.edelweissfin.com
532922—(BOM NSE)
Rev.: $404,918,050
Assets: $3,065,274,191
Liabilities: $2,509,994,887
Net Worth: $555,279,304
Earnings: $31,735,660
Emp.: 4,000
Fiscal Year-end: 03/31/13

Business Description:
Financial Services
S.I.C.: 6799
N.A.I.C.S.: 523920

Personnel:
Rashesh Shah *(Chm & CEO)*
S. Ranganathan *(CFO)*
Himanshu Kaji *(COO)*
B. Renganathan *(Compliance Officer, Sec & Sr VP)*

Board of Directors:
Rashesh Shah
Kunnasagarah Chinniah
Berjis Desai
Narendra Jhaveri
Himanshu Kaji
Sanjiv Misra
Sunil Mitra
Navtej S. Nandra
Rujan Panjwani
Venkat Ramaswamy
P.N. Venkatachalam

Transfer Agent:
Link Intime India Pvt. Ltd
C-13 Pannalal Silk Mills Compound LBS Marg
Bhandup (West)
Mumbai, India

Subsidiaries:

ECL Finance Limited **(1)**
Nariman Point 14th Fl Express Towers
Mumbai, Maharastra, 400021, India
Tel.: (91) 2222864400
Fax: (91) 2222864253
Web Site: www.edelcap.com
Emp.: 45
Non Banking Financial Services
S.I.C.: 6211
N.A.I.C.S.: 523999
Ravi R. Bubna *(VP)*

Edelweiss Broking Limited **(1)**
Edelweiss House off CST Road Kalina
Mumbai, 400 098, India
Tel.: (91) 22 2286 4400
Web Site: www.edelweissfin.com
Emp.: 6
Securities Broking Services
S.I.C.: 6211
N.A.I.C.S.: 523120
Jinesh Shah *(Compliance Officer)*

Edelweiss Financial Products and Solutions Limited **(1)**
New India Ctr Ground Fl 17 A Cooperage Rd Colaba
Mumbai, Maharastra, 400 039, India
Tel.: (91) 2240885757
Fax: (91) 2266242634
Web Site: www.edelweiss.in
Emp.: 3,000
Investment Management Services
S.I.C.: 8748
N.A.I.C.S.: 541618
Ravi Bubna *(VP)*

Edelweiss Insurance Brokers Limited **(1)**
312 D M Tower Race Course Rd
Indore, Madhya Pradesh, 452001, India
Tel.: (91) 7314266631
Fax: (91) 7314266635
E-Mail: indore@edelcap.com
Web Site: www.edelcap.com
Emp.: 20
Insurance Broking Services
S.I.C.: 6411
N.A.I.C.S.: 524210
Bimbsar Singh *(Mgr)*

Edelweiss Securities Limited **(1)**
Nariman Point 14th Fl Express Towers
Mumbai, Maharastra, 400021, India
Tel.: (91) 2222864400
Fax: (91) 2243428029
E-Mail: edelweissficsales@edelcap.com
Web Site: www.edelcap.com
Emp.: 80
Stock Brokerage Services
S.I.C.: 6211
N.A.I.C.S.: 523120
Pankaj Jain *(Mgr)*

EDEN BRACKNELL

Bilton Industrial Estate
Bracknell, Berkshire, RG12 8YT, United Kingdom
Tel.: (44) 8451254574
Fax: (44) 1344483774
Web Site: www.edenvauxhall.co.uk
Sales Range: $50-74.9 Million
Emp.: 150

Business Description:
Car Dealership
S.I.C.: 5511
N.A.I.C.S.: 441110

Personnel:
Graeme J. Potts *(Mng Dir)*

EDEN ENERGY LTD

Level 15 197 St Georges Terrace
Perth, WA, 6000, Australia
Tel.: (61) 892825889

Eden Energy Ltd—(Continued)

Fax: (61) 892825866
E-Mail: mailroom@edenenergy.com.au
Web Site: www.edenenergy.com.au
EDE—(ASX)
Rev.: $1,199,854
Assets: $6,771,166
Liabilities: $1,353,178
Net Worth: $5,417,987
Earnings: ($1,611,166)
Fiscal Year-end: 06/30/13

Business Description:
Oil & Gas Industry
S.I.C.: 1311
N.A.I.C.S.: 211111

Personnel:
Gregory Howard Solomon *(Chm)*
Aaron P. Gates *(CFO & Sec)*
Roger W. Marmaro *(Pres/CEO-Hythane Company LLC)*
Manish H. Dixit *(Pres-Mktg-Eden Energy India Pvt Ltd)*

Board of Directors:
Gregory Howard Solomon
Richard Beresford
Guy Touzeau Le Page
Douglas Howard Solomon

Legal Counsel:
Solomon Brothers
Level 15 197 St Georges Terrace
Perth, Australia

U.S. Subsidiary:

Hythane Company LLC. (1)
12420 N Dumont Way
Littleton, CO 80125-9755
Tel.: (303) 468-1705
Fax: (303) 791-7975
E-Mail: info@hythane.com
Web Site: www.hythane.com
Hythane Fuels Mfr
S.I.C.: 2911
N.A.I.C.S.: 324110
Gregory Solomon *(Exec Chm)*
Roger Marmaro *(Pres & CEO)*

EDEN HOTEL LANKA PLC

33 St Michaels Rd
3 Colombo, Sri Lanka
Tel.: (94) 112333320
Fax: (94) 112333324
E-Mail: confifi@confifi.net
Web Site: www.confifihotels.com
EDEN—(COL)
Sales Range: $1-9.9 Million

Business Description:
Hotel Management Services
S.I.C.: 7011
N.A.I.C.S.: 721110

Personnel:
M.T. A. Furkhan *(Chm)*

Board of Directors:
M.T. A. Furkhan
Fazal Hassen Ansar
Dayantha Eraj de Mel
Stefan Furkhan
R.A. C. Jayemanne
M. Ifham Raji
W.C. Ananda Wimaladharma

EDEN INTERNATIONAL SA

Chemin du Tresi 9A
1028 Preverenges, Switzerland
Tel.: (41) 58 404 20 00
Web Site: www.edensprings.com
Emp.: 2,000

Business Description:
Office Water & Coffee Machine Services
S.I.C.: 8744
N.A.I.C.S.: 561210

Personnel:
Raanan Zilberman *(CEO)*

Non-U.S. Subsidiary:

Kafevend Group Limited (1)
Unit D The Fleming Centre Fleming Way
Crawley, West Sussex, RH10 9NN, United Kingdom UK
Tel.: (44) 1293 523 222
Web Site: www.kafevendingmachines.co.uk
Sales Range: $25-49.9 Million
Emp.: 100
Vending Machines Distribution & Management Services
S.I.C.: 5962
N.A.I.C.S.: 454210
John Collins *(Mng Dir)*

EDEN RESEARCH PLC

Keble House Church End South Leigh
Witney, Oxon, OX29 6UR, United Kingdom
Tel.: (44) 1993 862761
Fax: (44) 1993 776480
E-Mail: info@edenresearch.com
Web Site: www.edenresearch.com
EDEN—(AIM)
Sales Range: Less than $1 Million
Emp.: 5

Business Description:
Pesticide Mfr
S.I.C.: 2879
N.A.I.C.S.: 325320

Personnel:
Ben Gill *(Chm)*
Ken Brooks *(Deputy Chm)*
Clive Newitt *(Mng Dir)*
Alex Abrey *(CFO)*
Robin Sims *(Sec)*

Board of Directors:
Ben Gill
Alex Abrey
Ken Brooks
Clive Newitt

Legal Counsel:
BrookStreet Des Roches
1 Des Roches Square
Witan Way, Witney, Oxfordshire, OX8 6BE, United Kingdom

EDENRED S.A.

166-180 Boulevard Gabriel Peri
92245 Malakoff, Cedex, France
Tel.: (33) 1 74 31 75 00
Fax: (33) 1 74 31 98 03
Web Site: www.edenred.com
EDEN—(EUR)
Rev.: $1,436,363,390
Assets: $5,874,685,880
Liabilities: $7,265,279,490
Net Worth: ($1,390,593,610)
Earnings: $273,272,510
Emp.: 5,915
Fiscal Year-end: 12/31/12

Business Description:
Voucher Management Services
S.I.C.: 7389
N.A.I.C.S.: 561499

Personnel:
Jacques Stern *(Chm & CEO)*
Gilles Bonnin *(Exec VP-Tech & Strategic Info Sys)*
Gilles Coccoli *(Exec VP-Strategy & Dev)*
Philippe Dufour *(Exec VP-Alternative Investments)*
Jeanne Renard *(Exec VP-HR)*

Board of Directors:
Jacques Stern
Jean-Paul Bailly
Sebastien Bazin
Anne Bouverot
Philippe Citerne
Roberto Oliveira de Lima
Gabriele Galateri di Genola
Francoise Gri
Bertrand Meheut
Nadra Moussalem

Deloitte & Associes
185 avenue Charles-de-Gaulle
Neuilly-sur-Seine, France

Subsidiary:

Accentiv' Kadeos S.A.S. (1)
166-180 Blvd Gabriel Peri
92240 Malakoff, France
Tel.: (33) 174317500
Fax: (33) 174317501
Web Site: www.ticket-kadeos.fr
Gift Card Retailer
S.I.C.: 5947
N.A.I.C.S.: 453220

U.S. Subsidiary:

Wiredcommute, LLC. (1)
320 Nevada St 4th Fl
Newton, MA 02460
Tel.: (800) 531-2828
E-Mail: info@wiredcommute.com
Web Site: www.wiredcommute.com
Emp.: 50
Software Consulting Services
S.I.C.: 7373
N.A.I.C.S.: 541512
Gerard Bridi *(Gen Mgr)*

Non-U.S. Subsidiaries:

Accentiv Bresil Mimetica (1)
Sergio Marcondes Cesar Rua Jesuino 49
Vila Olimpia, 04544 050 Sao Paulo, Brazil
Tel.: (55) 11 30532222
Fax: (55) 11 30471443
E-Mail: smarcondes@accmm.com.br
Emp.: 30
Marketing Consulting Services
S.I.C.: 8742
N.A.I.C.S.: 541613
Sergio Marcondes *(Gen Mgr)*

Accentiv Shanghai Company (1)
6F Cross Tower 318 Fuzhou Road
Shanghai, 200001, China
Tel.: (86) 21 2306 6000
Fax: (86) 21 2306 6001
E-Mail: loyalty-cn@edenred.com
Web Site: www.accentiv.cn
Marketing Consulting Services
S.I.C.: 8742
N.A.I.C.S.: 541613

AS CHILE ENERGY GROUP S.A. (1)
Avda Tobalaba 4033 D Metro Bilbao
Santiago, 7540569, Chile
Tel.: (56) 22777480
Fax: (56) 22777476
Mineral Products Mfr
S.I.C.: 3299
N.A.I.C.S.: 327999

Delicard AB (1)
Liljeholmsstranden 3
105 40 Stockholm, Sweden
Tel.: (46) 855611600
E-Mail: kundservice@delicard.se
Web Site: www.delicard.se
Emp.: 6
Employee Benefit Services
S.I.C.: 7389
N.A.I.C.S.: 561499
Tatsuto Soichi *(Gen Mgr)*

Delicard Group AB (1)
Augustendalsvagen 19
Nacka Strand, Stockholm, Sweden
Tel.: (46) 855611600
Employee Benefit Services
S.I.C.: 7389
N.A.I.C.S.: 561499

Delicard Oy (1)
Elimaenkatu 9 A
510 Helsinki, Finland
Tel.: (358) 975942847
E-Mail: info@delicard.com
Web Site: www.delicard.fi
Emp.: 16
Gift Store Operating Services
S.I.C.: 5947
N.A.I.C.S.: 453220
Markus Mustelin *(Gen Mgr)*

E-Lunch srl (1)
Via Giovanni Battista Trener 8
Trento, 38121, Italy
Tel.: (39) 0461421418
Fax: (39) 0461422308
E-Mail: info@e-lunch.it
Web Site: www.e-lunch.it
Catering Management Services
S.I.C.: 5812
N.A.I.C.S.: 722320

Edenred Argentina (1)
Av Corrientes 316 6to Piso
C1043AAQ Buenos Aires, Argentina (83.99%)
Tel.: (54) 11 4909 1400
Fax: (54) 11 4909 1234
Web Site: www.edenred.com.ar
Employer Subsidized Voucher Schemes
S.I.C.: 7389
N.A.I.C.S.: 561499

Edenred Austria GmbH (1)
Wagenseilgasse 14
1120 Vienna, Austria
Tel.: (43) 18150800
Fax: (43) 18150820
E-Mail: info-at@edenred.com
Web Site: www.edenred.at
Emp.: 15
Tax Free Consulting Services
S.I.C.: 8742
N.A.I.C.S.: 541611
Ursula Wurzl *(Gen Mgr)*

Edenred Belgium sa (1)
Avenue Herrmann-Debroux 54
1160 Brussels, Belgium
Tel.: (32) 26782811
Fax: (32) 26782828
E-Mail: customer-be@edenred.com
Web Site: www.edenred.be
Emp.: 20
Employees Meal Voucher Organizing Services
S.I.C.: 7389
N.A.I.C.S.: 561499
Michael Verhulsdonk *(Gen Mgr)*

Edenred Bulgaria ad (1)
137 Tsarigradsko Shousse Bould
1784 Sofia, Bulgaria
Tel.: (359) 29740220
Fax: (359) 29740550
E-Mail: bulgaria@edenred.com
Web Site: www.edenred.bg
Emp.: 2
Social Security Services
S.I.C.: 9441
N.A.I.C.S.: 923130
Herve Combal *(Gen Mgr)*

Edenred CZ s.r.o (1)
Na Porici 1076/5
110 00 Prague, Czech Republic
Tel.: (420) 234662300
Fax: (420) 234662309
E-Mail: informace-cz@edenred.com
Web Site: www.edenred.cz
Emp.: 14
Social Security Services
S.I.C.: 9441
N.A.I.C.S.: 923130
Fernando Alvarez *(Gen Mgr)*

Edenred Deutschland GmbH (1)
Claudius-Keller-Strasse 3C
81669 Munich, Germany
Tel.: (49) 89 558 915 0
Fax: (49) 89 558 915 310
E-Mail: info-de@edenred.com
Web Site: www.edenred.de
Employee Motivation Services
S.I.C.: 7389
N.A.I.C.S.: 561499
Christian Aubry *(Gen Mgr)*

Edenred Employee Benefits UK Ltd (1)
Crown House 72 Hammersmith Rd
London, W14 8TH, United Kingdom
Tel.: (44) 2073485500
Employee Benefit Plan Services
S.I.C.: 6371
N.A.I.C.S.: 525120

Edenred Espana S.A. (1)
Ribera Del Loira 56-58
Campo De Las Naciones, 28042 Madrid, Spain (100%)
Tel.: (34) 911254500
Fax: (34) 915566977
E-Mail: info-es@edenred.com
Web Site: www.edenred.es

Emp.: 105
Voucher Management Services
S.I.C.: 7389
N.A.I.C.S.: 561499

Edenred Hong-Kong Limited (1)
Rm 1025 10/F Hitec 1 Trademart Dr
Kowloon, China (Hong Kong)
Tel.: (852) 21318998
Fax: (852) 21318999
Restaurant Management Services
S.I.C.: 5812
N.A.I.C.S.: 722511

Edenred Incentives & Motivation Ltd (1)
Carlton House Sandpiper Way
Chester, CH4 9QE, United Kingdom
Tel.: (44) 1244625400
Fax: (44) 1244318260
Management Consulting Services
S.I.C.: 8742
N.A.I.C.S.: 541611

Edenred Incentives & Rewards Deutschland (1)
Friedrich-Bergius-Strasse 15-17
65203 Wiesbaden, Germany
Tel.: (49) 611188870
Fax: (49) 61118887102
E-Mail: info-de@edenred.com
Employee Motivation Services
S.I.C.: 7389
N.A.I.C.S.: 561499

Edenred (India) PVT Ltd (1)
2nd Floor Camera House Majiwade Village Road
Majiwade, Thane, 400 601, India
Tel.: (91) 22 2545 5500
Fax: (91) 22 2543 6411
E-Mail: assist-IN@edenred.com
Web Site: www.edenred.co.in
Emp.: 50
Employee Benefit Services
S.I.C.: 8631
N.A.I.C.S.: 813930
Johann Vaucanson *(CEO & Mng Dir)*

Edenred Italia Srl (1)
Via Giovanni Battista Pirelli 18
Milan, 20124, Italy
Tel.: (39) 02269041
Fax: (39) 0226904501
Emp.: 300
Employee Benefit Services
S.I.C.: 8999
N.A.I.C.S.: 541612
Maria Grazia Filippini *(CEO)*

Edenred Liban (1)
Electricity St
Bauchrieh, Beirut, Lebanon
Tel.: (961) 1900333
Fax: (961) 1900555
E-Mail: info-lb@edenred.com
Web Site: www.edenred.com.lb
Emp.: 15
Restaurant Management Services
S.I.C.: 5812
N.A.I.C.S.: 722511
Gildas Rault *(Chm & CEO)*

Edenred Maroc SAS (1)
110 Bd Mohamed Zerktouni 4 Et 5 Et
20140 Casablanca, Morocco
Tel.: (212) 522222872
Fax: (212) 522466700
Web Site: www.edenred.ma
Emp.: 22
Restaurant Management Services
S.I.C.: 5812
N.A.I.C.S.: 722511
Badre Ouaicha *(Mng Dir)*

Edenred Mexico (1)
Lago Rodollo 29 Colonia Grana
11520 Mexico, DF, Mexico (49%)
Tel.: (52) 5552628888
Fax: (52) 55 52 62 8835
E-Mail: telemarketing@accor.com.mx
Web Site: www.accor.com.mx
Voucher Management Services
S.I.C.: 7389
N.A.I.C.S.: 561499

Edenred Peru SA (1)
777 Antequera St Fl 2
San Isidro, Lima, Peru
Tel.: (51) 14425555
E-Mail: info-pe@edenred.com
Employee Benefit Services
S.I.C.: 7389
N.A.I.C.S.: 561990

Edenred Polska Sp. z o.o (1)
ul Przemyslowa 30
00-450 Warsaw, Poland
Tel.: (48) 226272126
Fax: (48) 226272127
E-Mail: info-pl@edenred.com
Web Site: www.edenred.pl
Restaurant Management Services
S.I.C.: 5812
N.A.I.C.S.: 722511
Vianney Duparc *(Gen Mgr)*

Edenred Portugal Lda (1)
Northwind Building Tower B Av D Joao II Lt 1 12 02 5th Fl A/B
1990-077 Lisbon, Portugal
Tel.: (351) 218917700
Fax: (351) 218917717
E-Mail: geral.pt@edenred.com
Web Site: www.edenred.pt
Employees Benefit Services
S.I.C.: 8631
N.A.I.C.S.: 813930

Edenred Shanghai (China) (1)
6F Cross Tower 318 Fuzhou Road
Shanghai, 200001, China
Tel.: (86) 2123066000
Fax: (86) 2123066001
E-Mail: info-shanghai-cn@edenred.com
Restaurant Management Services
S.I.C.: 5812
N.A.I.C.S.: 722511

Edenred Slovakia, s.r.o (1)
Karadzicova 8
Bratislava, 820 15, Slovakia
Tel.: (421) 250707222
Fax: (421) 250707221
E-Mail: informacie-sk@edenred.com
Web Site: www.edenred.sk
Restaurant Management Services
S.I.C.: 5812
N.A.I.C.S.: 722511
Natalia Hercegova *(Dir-Bus Dev & Mktg)*

Edenred Suisse SA (1)
4 Chemin de l'Esparcette
1023 Crissier, Switzerland
Tel.: (41) 219668090
Fax: (41) 219668092
E-Mail: info-ch@edenred.com
Web Site: www.edenred.ch
Restaurant Operating Services
S.I.C.: 5812
N.A.I.C.S.: 722511

Edenred Travel Limited (1)
Sandpiper Way Chester Business Park
Chester, CH4 9QE, United Kingdom
Tel.: (44) 1244625400
Fax: (44) 1244625401
E-Mail: admin@your-travel-club.co.uk
Web Site: www.edenredtravel.co.uk
Travel Agency Services
S.I.C.: 4724
N.A.I.C.S.: 561510

Edenred UK (1)
50 Vauxhall Bridge Rd
London, SW1V 2RS, United Kingdom (100%)
Tel.: (44) 8453304411
Fax: (44) 8453304410
Web Site: www.edenred.co.uk
Sls.: $17,841,600
Emp.: 140
Voucher Management Services
S.I.C.: 7389
N.A.I.C.S.: 561499
Derrick Hardman *(Mng Dir)*

Edenred Vouchers Deutschland (1)
Claudius-Keller-Strasse 3C
81669 Munich, Germany
Tel.: (49) 895589150
Fax: (49) 89558915310
E-Mail: info-de@edenred.com
Employee Motivation Services
S.I.C.: 7389
N.A.I.C.S.: 561499

Ticket Rikskuponger AB (1)
Liljeholmsstranden 3
SE 105 40 Stockholm, Sweden (100%)
Tel.: (46) 86818100
Fax: (46) 6818187
E-Mail: kundservice@ticketrikskuponger.se
Web Site: www.ticketrikskuponger.se
Emp.: 80
Voucher Management Services
S.I.C.: 7389
N.A.I.C.S.: 561499
Rowland Morizet *(Gen Mgr)*

Ticket Servicos S.A. (1)
Av. Paulista 2313
2 3 Andares, Sao Paulo, 01311-934, Brazil
Tel.: (55) 1138898754
Web Site: www.ticket.com.br
Emp.: 1,200
Voucher Services
S.I.C.: 7389
N.A.I.C.S.: 561499
Daniela Regina Silva *(Mgr-HR)*

Tintelingen B.V (1)
Oranje Nassaulaan 27
's-Hertogenbosch, 5211 AT, Netherlands
Tel.: (31) 736904050
Fax: (31) 736904067
E-Mail: info@tintelingen.nl
Web Site: www.tintelingen.nl
Emp.: 17
Gift Shop Operating Services
S.I.C.: 5947
N.A.I.C.S.: 453220
Carl Winters *(Gen Mgr)*

EDENVILLE ENERGY PLC

Aston House Cornwall Avenue
London, N3 1LF, United Kingdom
Tel.: (44) 2070991940
E-Mail: info@edenville-energy.com
Web Site: www.edenville-energy.com
EDL—(LSE)
Rev.: $16
Assets: $18,146,941
Liabilities: $2,204,637
Net Worth: $15,942,304
Earnings: ($1,016,813)
Emp.: 11
Fiscal Year-end: 12/31/12

Business Description:
Coal & Uranium Mining
S.I.C.: 1241
N.A.I.C.S.: 213113

Personnel:
Sally Joy Schofield *(Chm)*
Mark Jonathan Pryor *(CEO)*

Board of Directors:
Sally Joy Schofield
Rakesh Ramesh Patel
Mark Jonathan Pryor
Simon Rollason
Rufus Victor Short

Legal Counsel:
Harbottle & Lewis LLP
Hanover House 14 Hanover Square
London, W1S 1HP, United Kingdom

EDGE GROUP LIMITED

1 Marylebone High Street
London, W1U 4LZ, United Kingdom
Tel.: (44) 2073171300
Fax: (44) 2073171313
E-Mail: info@edge.uk.com
Web Site: www.edge.uk.com
Emp.: 10

Business Description:
Holding Company; Asset Management, Corporate Finance, Investment Advisory & Consulting Services
S.I.C.: 6719
N.A.I.C.S.: 551112

Personnel:
David Glick *(Founder)*
Kate Glick *(Sec)*

Subsidiaries:

Edge Investment Management Limited (1)
1 Marylebone High Street
London, W1U 4LZ, United Kingdom UK
Tel.: (44) 20 7317 1300
E-Mail: info@edge.uk.com
Web Site: www.edge.uk.com
Investment Management Services
S.I.C.: 6799
N.A.I.C.S.: 523920
David Glick *(Founder & CEO)*
Gordon Power *(Chm)*

Edge Performance VCT plc (1)
1 Marylebone High Street
London, W1U 4LZ, United Kingdom UK
Tel.: (44) 2073171300
Web Site: www.edge.co.uk/edgeperformancevct
Equity Investment Firm
S.I.C.: 6211
N.A.I.C.S.: 523999
Robin Miller *(Chm)*
Robin Smeaton *(Sec)*

Holding:

Coolabi Limited (2)
First Floor Watergate House 13-15 York Buildings
London, WC2N 6JU, United Kingdom
Tel.: (44) 2070040980
Fax: (44) 2070040981
E-Mail: info@coolabi.com
Web Site: www.coolabi.com
Sales Range: $1-9.9 Million
Emp.: 12
Family Entertainment Production & Rights Management Services
S.I.C.: 7812
N.A.I.C.S.: 512110
Jeremy Banks *(CEO)*

EDGE RESOURCES INC.

Elveden House Suite 1400 717-7th Avenue SW
Calgary, AB, T2P 0Z3, Canada
Tel.: (403) 767-9905
E-Mail: info@edgeres.com
Web Site: www.edgeres.com
EDE—(AIM TSXV)
Sls.: $8,365,683
Assets: $37,031,329
Liabilities: $24,708,964
Net Worth: $12,322,365
Earnings: ($6,661,749)
Fiscal Year-end: 03/31/13

Business Description:
Oil & Natural Gas Exploration Services
S.I.C.: 1311
N.A.I.C.S.: 211111

Personnel:
Brad Nichol *(Pres & CEO)*
Nathan Steinke *(CFO)*

Board of Directors:
Christopher R. Cooper
Brad Nichol
Vishnu Reddy
Scott Reeves

Legal Counsel:
Tingle Merrett LLP
1250 Standard Life Building 639-5th Ave SW
Calgary, AB, Canada

Fox Williams LLP
10 Dominion St
London, United Kingdom

Transfer Agent:
Computershare Trust Company of Canada
510 Burrard St 2nd Fl
Vancouver, BC, Canada

EDGEFRONT REALTY CORP.

1 Toronto Street Suite 201
Toronto, ON, M5C 2V6, Canada
Tel.: (416) 906-2379
E-Mail: kellyhanczyk@yahoo.ca
Year Founded: 2012
ED.P—(TSXV)

Business Description:
Investment Services
S.I.C.: 6211
N.A.I.C.S.: 523999

Edgefront Realty Corp.—(Continued)

Personnel:
Mario Forgione *(Chm)*
Kelly C. Hanczyk *(Pres & CEO)*
Robert P. Chiasson *(CFO & Sec)*
Board of Directors:
Mario Forgione
Kelly C. Hanczyk
Ted Manziaris
Peter M. Vukanovich

EDGESTONE CAPITAL PARTNERS INC.

141 Adellage St W Ste 1002
Toronto, ON, M5H 3L5, Canada
Tel.: (416) 860-3740
Fax: (416) 860-9838
E-Mail: info@edgestone.com
Web Site: www.edgestone.com
Emp.: 20
Business Description:
Private Equity Firm
S.I.C.: 6211
N.A.I.C.S.: 523999
Personnel:
Samuel L. DuBoc *(Founder)*
Gilbert S. Palter *(Chief Investment Officer & Mng Partner)*
Stephen O. Marshall *(Partner-Equity Fund)*
Sarah Goel *(Principal)*
Legal Counsel:
Goodmans LLP
250 Yonge Street, #2400
Toronto, ON, M5B 2M6, Canada
Tel.: (413) 979-2211
Fax: (416) 979-1234
Transfer Agent:
CIBC Mellon Trust Company
PO Box 7010
Adelaide Street Postal Station, Toronto, ON, M5C 2W9, Canada
Tel.: (416) 643-5500
Fax: (416) 643-5501
Toll Free: (800) 387-0825
U.S. Subsidiary:

Specialty Commerce Corporation **(1)**
400 Manley St
West Bridgewater, MA 02379
Tel.: (508) 638-7000
E-Mail: custserv@scdirect.com
Web Site: www.scdirect.com
Sales Range: $10-24.9 Million
Emp.: 450
Wigs, Hairpieces, Extensions & Specialty Apparel Direct Marketer
Import Export
S.I.C.: 5963
N.A.I.C.S.: 454390
Michael Ippolito *(CEO)*
Peter Tulp *(CFO & COO)*

Subsidiaries:

Paula Young Catalog **(2)**
400 Manley St W
West Bridgewater, MA 02379-1100
Tel.: (508) 238-0199
Fax: (508) 238-1965
Toll Free: (800) 364-9060
E-Mail: customerservice@paulayoung.com
Web Site: www.paulayoung.com
Emp.: 250
Hair & Wig Catalog & Mail Order
Import Export
S.I.C.: 5961
N.A.I.C.S.: 454113
Peter Tulp *(CFO)*

Western Schools, Inc. **(2)**
Western Schools
Brockton, MA 02303
Tel.: (508) 638-7000
Toll Free: (800) 953-8731
E-Mail: customerservice@westernschools.com
Web Site: www.westernschools.com
Emp.: 400
Home Study Continuing Education for Nurses
S.I.C.: 8299
N.A.I.C.S.: 611710
John Bernstein *(Pres & CEO)*

EDGEWATER EXPLORATION LTD.

Suite 1820 999 West Hastings Street
Vancouver, BC, V6C 2W2, Canada
Tel.: (604) 628-1010
Fax: (604) 628-1011
Toll Free: (888) 550-5441
Web Site: www.edgewaterx.com
Year Founded: 2007
EDW—(OTC TSXV)
Rev.: $46,221
Assets: $36,800,515
Liabilities: $6,456,037
Net Worth: $30,344,478
Earnings: ($2,192,382)
Fiscal Year-end: 12/31/12
Business Description:
Gold Mining Services
S.I.C.: 1041
N.A.I.C.S.: 212221
Personnel:
George Gregory Salamis *(Pres & CEO)*
Edward C. Farrauto *(CFO)*
John Alan Thomas *(COO)*
Board of Directors:
Douglas B. Forster
Blayne Johnson
Ryan C. King
Danny W. K. Lee
George Gregory Salamis
Michael Vint
Legal Counsel:
McCullough O'Connor Irwin, LLP
Ste 2610 Oceanic Plz 1066 W Hastings St
Vancouver, BC, V6E 3X1, Canada
Transfer Agent:
Computershare
510 Burrard St 2nd Floor
Vancouver, BC, Canada
Non-U.S. Subsidiary:

Rio Narcea Gold Mines S.L **(1)**
Calle Serrano 85 Piso 6 Iz
Madrid, 28006, Spain
Tel.: (34) 924518173
Fax: (34) 924516607
Precious Metal Mining Services
S.I.C.: 1041
N.A.I.C.S.: 212221

EDGEWATER WIRELESS SYSTEMS INCORPORATED

1125 Innovation Drive
Ottawa, ON, K2K 3G6, Canada
Tel.: (613) 271-3710
Fax: (613) 271-1152
E-Mail: info@edgewaterwireless.com
Web Site: www.edgewaterwireless.com
Year Founded: 1980
YFI—(TSXV)
Sales Range: Less than $1 Million
Business Description:
Communication Equipment Mfr
S.I.C.: 3669
N.A.I.C.S.: 334290
Personnel:
Andrew Skafel *(Pres)*
Duane Anderson *(Interim CEO)*
Sam Sgabellone *(CFO)*
Board of Directors:
Duane Anderson
Lew Dillman
Claude Haw
Bert Whyte

EDIFIER TECHNOLOGY CO., LTD.

Room 2207-9 22nd Floor Lippo Centre Tower II
89 Queensway, Hong Kong, China (Hong Kong)
Tel.: (852) 8200 1383
Fax: (852) 8200 1893
E-Mail: inquiry_os@edifier.com
Web Site: www.edifier.com
002351—(SSE)
Sales Range: $75-99.9 Million
Emp.: 2,780
Business Description:
Multimedia Sound Boxes, Headphones & Automobile Audio Products Mfr
S.I.C.: 3651
N.A.I.C.S.: 334310
Personnel:
Wendong Zhang *(Chm)*

EDIMAX TECHNOLOGY CO., LTD.

No 3 Wu Chuan 3rd Rd Wu-Ku Industrial Park
Taipei, Taiwan
Tel.: (886) 277396888
Fax: (886) 277396887
Web Site: www.edimax.com
3047—(TAI)
Sales Range: $50-74.9 Million
Business Description:
Routers & Switches Mfr
S.I.C.: 3661
N.A.I.C.S.: 334210
Personnel:
Genne Renn *(Chm & Gen Mgr)*
U.S. Subsidiary:

Edimax Computer Company **(1)**
3350 Scott Blvd Bldg 15
Santa Clara, CA 95054
Tel.: (408) 496-1105
Fax: (408) 980-1530
E-Mail: sales@edimax.com
Web Site: www.edimax.com
Networking Components Distr
S.I.C.: 5065
N.A.I.C.S.: 423690

Non-U.S. Subsidiaries:

Beijing Edimax Science & Technology Co., Ltd. **(1)**
17 1708 Ideal Plaza No 111 ZhiChun Road
HaiDian District, Beijing, 100085, China
Tel.: (86) 1082665815
Fax: (86) 1082665795
E-Mail: sales@edimax.com.cn
Networking Components Mfr
S.I.C.: 3661
N.A.I.C.S.: 334210
Joseph Zheng *(Gen Mgr)*

Edimax Technology Australia Pty. Ltd. **(1)**
Unit 9 19-23 Clarinda Road
Oakleigh South, Melbourne, VIC, 3168, Australia
Tel.: (61) 3 9543 1888
Fax: (61) 3 9543 1900
E-Mail: sales@edimax.com.au
Web Site: www.edimax.com
Networking Components Distr
S.I.C.: 5065
N.A.I.C.S.: 423690

Edimax Technology Europe B.V. **(1)**
Nijverheidsweg 25
5683 CJ Best, North Brabant, Netherlands
Tel.: (31) 499 377344
Fax: (31) 499 372647
E-Mail: sales@edimax.nl
Web Site: www.edimax.com
Emp.: 13
Networking Components Distr
S.I.C.: 5045
N.A.I.C.S.: 423430
Gene Renn *(Pres)*

Edimax Technology MEA FZE **(1)**
Jebel Ali Free Zone
PO Box 262548
Dubai, United Arab Emirates
Tel.: (971) 48041888
Fax: (971) 48834079
E-Mail: murtuza@edimax-me.com
Web Site: www.edimax-de.eu
Emp.: 70
Networking Components Distr
S.I.C.: 5045
N.A.I.C.S.: 423430
Jihad Youssef *(Gen Mgr-HR)*

Edimax Technology Poland Sp. Z o.o. **(1)**
Ul Postepu 14
02-676 Warsaw, Poland
Tel.: (48) 226079480
Fax: (48) 22 6079481
E-Mail: sales@edimax.pl
Web Site: www.edimax.pl
Emp.: 10
Networking Components Distr
S.I.C.: 5045
N.A.I.C.S.: 423430
Renn Guansheng *(Chm)*

Edimax Technology (SE Asia) Pte. Ltd. **(1)**
21 Bukit Batok Crescent Wcega Tower 12-79
Singapore, Singapore
Tel.: (65) 66314857
E-Mail: sales@edimax.com.sg
Web Site: www.edimax.com
Emp.: 8
Networking Components Distr
S.I.C.: 5065
N.A.I.C.S.: 423690
Kenneth Teh *(Gen Mgr)*

Edimax Technology (UK) Ltd. **(1)**
Suite 378 Silbury Court Silbury Boulevard
Milton Keynes, Bucks, MK9 2AF, United Kingdom
Tel.: (44) 8451238307
Fax: (44) 8451238306
E-Mail: info@edimax.co.uk
Web Site: www.edimax.co.uk
Emp.: 10
Networking Components Distr
S.I.C.: 5045
N.A.I.C.S.: 423430
Wilson Chu *(Mng Dir)*

THE EDINBURGH WOOLLEN MILL LTD.

Waverley Mills
Langholm, Dumfriesshire, DG13 0EB, United Kingdom
Tel.: (44) 13873 80611
Web Site: www.ewm.co.uk
Year Founded: 1946
Sales Range: $350-399.9 Million
Emp.: 4,955
Business Description:
Clothing Store Operator
S.I.C.: 5651
N.A.I.C.S.: 448140
Personnel:
Philip Day *(Chm & CEO)*

EDION CORPORATION

Dojima Grand Bldg 1-5-17 Dojima
Kita-ku
Osaka, Japan
Tel.: (81) 6 6640 8711
Fax: (81) 6 6640 8740
Web Site: www.edion.co.jp
Year Founded: 2002
2730—(TKS)
Sls.: $7,536,595,000
Assets: $4,158,957,000
Liabilities: $2,635,578,000
Net Worth: $1,523,379,000
Earnings: ($29,051,000)
Emp.: 9,602
Fiscal Year-end: 03/31/13
Business Description:
Electronics Retailer
S.I.C.: 5946
N.A.I.C.S.: 443142
Personnel:
Masataka Kubo *(Chm & Pres)*
Shoichi Okajima *(Deputy Chm)*
Kazutoshi Tomonori *(Deputy Chm)*
Hirohisa Kato *(CMO & Exec VP)*

Masayuki Umehara *(Chief Admin Officer & Exec VP)*
Seiichi Funamori *(Chief Bus Dev Officer & Exec VP)*
Yuji Asada *(Chief Logistics Svcs Officer & Exec VP)*
Norio Yamasaki *(Chief Corp Plng Officer & Exec VP)*
Ryuji Yuyama *(Sr VP & Gen Mgr-Gen Affairs Div)*
Board of Directors:
Masataka Kubo
Yuji Asada
Seiichi Funamori
Hirohisa Kato
Shoichi Okajima
Kazutoshi Tomonori
Masayuki Umehara
Norio Yamasaki
Ryuji Yuyama
Transfer Agent:
Mitsubishi UFJ Trust & Banking Corporation
1-4-5 Marunouchi Chiyoda-ku
Tokyo, Japan

Subsidiaries:

3Q Co., Ltd. (1)
2-3 Shinbo-cho
Fukui, 910-0832, Japan
Tel.: (81) 776571870
Fax: (81) 776571873
Consumer Electronics Retailer
S.I.C.: 5064
N.A.I.C.S.: 423620
Seiichiro Shibata *(Pres)*

COMNET Co., Ltd. (1)
7-2600-6 Shinogicho
Kasugai, Aichi, 486-0851, Japan
Tel.: (81) 568849150
Fax: (81) 568847787
Web Site: www.comnet21.co.jp
Consumer Electronics Retailer
S.I.C.: 5064
N.A.I.C.S.: 423620
Takuo Shibata *(Mgr)*

DEODEO Corporation (1)
8 22 Mokuzaiko Minami
Hatsukaichi City, Hiroshima, 738 0022, Japan JP (100%)
Tel.: (81) 3 5297 2311
Fax: (81) 3 5297 2312
Web Site: my.edion.jp/pc/
Sales Range: $1-4.9 Billion
Emp.: 3,326
Consumer Electronics Retailer
S.I.C.: 5946
N.A.I.C.S.: 443142
Kazutoshi Tomonori *(Pres)*

EDION EAST Corporation (1)
2-80-1 Enjaku-cho
Minato-ku, Nagoya, Aichi, 455-0054, Japan
Tel.: (81) 526596611
Fax: (81) 527592638
Consumer Electronics Retailer
S.I.C.: 5064
N.A.I.C.S.: 423620

EIDEN COMMUNICATIONS Co., Ltd. (1)
4-22-25 Meieki
Nakamura-ku, Nagoya, Aichi, 450-0002, Japan
Tel.: (81) 524860840
Fax: (81) 52 589 9815
Web Site: www.e-coms.ne.jp
Mobile Communication Carriers
S.I.C.: 4812
N.A.I.C.S.: 517210

NWORK Co., Ltd. (1)
Ikeshita ES Building 5F 8-70-1 Kakuozan-dori
Chikusa-ku, Nagoya, Aichi, 464-0841, Japan
Tel.: (81) 527592611
Fax: (81) 527592615
Web Site: www.nwork.co.jp
Enterprise Resource Planning Software Development Services
S.I.C.: 7371
N.A.I.C.S.: 541511

EDIPRESSE SA
33 Ave De La Gare
1001 Lausanne, Switzerland
Tel.: (41) 213494545
E-Mail: communication@tamadia.ch
Web Site: www.tamadia.ch
Sales Range: $150-199.9 Million
Emp.: 3,500
Business Description:
Newspaper & Magazine Publisher & Printer
S.I.C.: 2711
N.A.I.C.S.: 511110
Personnel:
Pierre Lamuniere *(Chm)*
Board of Directors:
Pierre Lamuniere
Andre Kudelski
Claude Smadja
Subsidiaries:

Edipresse Publications SA (1)
Avenue de la Gare 33
1001 Lausanne, Switzerland (100%)
Tel.: (41) 213494545
Fax: (41) 213494110
E-Mail: tamedia.publication.romandes@r.tamedia.ph
Web Site: www.edipresse.ch
Emp.: 1,300
Holding company
S.I.C.: 6719
N.A.I.C.S.: 551112
Patrick Lamuniere *(Mng Dir)*
Adler Tibere *(Mng Dir)*

Edipub SA (1)
C-o Edipresse SA
8043 Lausanne, Switzerland (100%)
Tel.: (41) 442513575
Fax: (41) 213495022
E-Mail: edipub@edipresse.ch
Web Site: www.edipub.ch
Emp.: 100
Publishers
S.I.C.: 2741
N.A.I.C.S.: 511199
Pierre Lamuneiri *(Mng Dir)*

Le Temps SA (1)
Cormavim No 3
PO Box 3570
1211 Geneva, Switzerland (82.7%)
Tel.: (41) 227995858
Fax: (41) 227995859
E-Mail: info@letemps.ch
Web Site: www.letemps.ch
Emp.: 120
Newspaper Publishers
S.I.C.: 2711
N.A.I.C.S.: 511110
Jean jacques Roth *(CFO)*

Presse Publications SR SA (1)
Avenue De La Gare 33
Lausanne, 1100, Switzerland (100%)
Tel.: (41) 213494545
Fax: (41) 213414540
E-Mail: info@tamedia.ca
Web Site: www.tamedia.ca
Emp.: 1,600
Holding Company
S.I.C.: 6719
N.A.I.C.S.: 551112
Adler Tibere *(CEO)*

Societe Anonyme de la Tribune de Geneve (1)
Rue Des Rois 11
Geneva, Switzerland (100%)
Tel.: (41) 223224000
Fax: (41) 227810107
E-Mail: reduction@tdg.ch
Web Site: www.tdgh.ch
Emp.: 1,000
Newspaper Publishers
S.I.C.: 2711
N.A.I.C.S.: 511110
Peuuaffa Lamneufu *(Mng Dir)*

Joint Ventures:

LC Lausanne-cites S.A. (1)
Avenue d'Echallens 17
1004 Lausanne, Switzerland CH (50%)
Tel.: (41) 215550501
Fax: (41) 0215550502
E-Mail: info@lausannecites.ch
Web Site: www.lausannecites.ch
Emp.: 50
Newspaper Publishers
S.I.C.: 2711
N.A.I.C.S.: 511110
Fleure Pascal *(Mng Dir)*

Non-U.S. Subsidiaries:

Edipresse AS Romania SRL (1)
Strada Buzesti 50-52 Floor 1 Sect 1
011015 Bucharest, Romania (100%)
Tel.: (40) 213193559
Fax: (40) 213193568
E-Mail: office@edipresse.ro
Web Site: www.edipresse.ro
Emp.: 100
Periodical Publishers
S.I.C.: 2721
N.A.I.C.S.: 511120
Cristiana Simion *(Mng Dir)*

Edipresse Asia Ltd (1)
6th Fl Guardian House
32 Oi Kwan Rd, Wanchai, China (Hong Kong) (100%)
Tel.: (852) 25477117
Fax: (852) 28582671
E-Mail: enquiry@edipress.com.hk
Web Site: www.edipresseasia.com
Emp.: 90
Publishers
S.I.C.: 2741
N.A.I.C.S.: 511199
Marc Lamuniere *(Vice Chm)*

Edipresse-Konliga ZAO (1)
Ul Bakuninskaya 71 Bldg 10 6th Floor
105082 Moscow, Russia (69.9%)
Tel.: (7) 04957751435
Fax: (7) 4957751434
E-Mail: konliga@konliga.ru
Web Site: www.konliga.ru
Emp.: 200
Publishers
S.I.C.: 2741
N.A.I.C.S.: 511199
Maxim Zimin *(Gen Dir)*

Edipresse Polska SA (1)
Ul Wiejska 19
00-480 Warsaw, Poland
Tel.: (48) 225842200
Fax: (48) 225842413
E-Mail: office@edipresse.pl
Web Site: www.edipresse.pl
Emp.: 320
Periodical Publishers
S.I.C.: 2721
N.A.I.C.S.: 511120
Alicja Modzelewska *(Mng Dir)*

Focus Ediciones SL (1)
Paseo de la Castellana 129 1st Floor
28046 Madrid, Spain (60%)
Tel.: (34) 915973090
Fax: (34) 915972326
E-Mail: camado@focusediciones.com
Web Site: www.edipresse.com
Emp.: 160
Commercial Printing
S.I.C.: 2759
N.A.I.C.S.: 323111
Daniel Medvene *(Mng Dir)*

Kilokalories SA (1)
18 rue Seguier
Paris, France (55%)
Tel.: (33) 155422026
Fax: (33) 155422021
E-Mail: contact@citizen-k.com
Emp.: 120
Management Consulting Services
S.I.C.: 8748
N.A.I.C.S.: 541618

Servicios de EdiciOn Mexico SA de CV (1)
Av Insurgentes Sur 1971 Local 30
Nivel Terraza Col Guadalupe In, 01020
Mexico, Mexico (100%)
Tel.: (52) 5556627800
Fax: (52) 5556627800
Web Site: www.semexico.com
Publishers
S.I.C.: 2741
N.A.I.C.S.: 511199

Non-U.S. Joint Ventures:

Semana SL (1)
Cuesta de San Vicente 28
28008 Madrid, Spain (50%)
Tel.: (34) 915472300
Fax: (34) 915414609
E-Mail: cmontiel@semana.es
Web Site: www.semana.es
Emp.: 50
Newspaper Publishers
S.I.C.: 2711
N.A.I.C.S.: 511110
Charo Montiel *(Mng Dir)*

Sucesores de Rivadeneyra SA (1)
P Ind Los Angeles
Torneros 16, Getafe, Spain (50%)
Tel.: (34) 912089150
Fax: (34) 916839687
Web Site: www.rivandeneyra.com
Graphic Design Services
S.I.C.: 7336
N.A.I.C.S.: 541430
Arakil Gosamaria *(Mng Dir)*

EDISUN POWER EUROPE AG
Universitaetstr 51
8006 Zurich, Switzerland
Tel.: (41) 442666120
Fax: (41) 442666122
E-Mail: info@edisunpower.com
Web Site: www.edisunpower.com
ESUN—(SWX)
Sls.: $8,418,696
Assets: $82,439,541
Liabilities: $65,553,580
Net Worth: $16,885,961
Earnings: ($2,831,056)
Emp.: 13
Fiscal Year-end: 12/31/12
Business Description:
Solar Power Generation
S.I.C.: 4939
N.A.I.C.S.: 221118
Personnel:
Giatgen Peder Fontana *(Chm)*
Martin Eberhard *(Vice Chm)*
Rainer Isenrich *(CEO & CFO)*
Markus Kohler *(CTO)*
Board of Directors:
Giatgen Peder Fontana
Martin Eberhard
Theodor Scheidegger

EDITA PLC
(Name Changed to Nordic Morning Plc)

EDITION MULTI MEDIA ELECTRONIQUES
52 Rue Marcel Dassault
92100 Boulogne-Billancourt, Hauts De Seine, France
Tel.: (33) 146081559
Sls.: $20,300,000
Emp.: 44
Business Description:
Book Publishing
S.I.C.: 2731
N.A.I.C.S.: 511130
Personnel:
Eric Kalasz *(Dir-Mktg)*

EDITIONS GRANADA SA
23 Rue Balzac
75008 Paris, France
Tel.: (33) 1 41 22 38 00
Fax: (33) 1 41 22 38 30
E-Mail: tarak.makhlouf@granadaeditions.com
Web Site: www.granadaeditions.com
MLGRA—(EUR)
Sales Range: $1-9.9 Million
Business Description:
Arabic Language Textbooks, CD-ROMs & Other Educational Products

Editions Granada SA—(Continued)

S.I.C.: 2731
N.A.I.C.S.: 511130
Personnel:
Tarak Maklouf *(Pres)*

EDIZIONE S.R.L.

Via Calmaggiore 23
31100 Treviso, Italy
Tel.: (39) 0422 5995
Fax: (39) 0422 412176
E-Mail: mailbox@edizione.it
Web Site: www.edizione.it
Rev.: $16,632,569,781
Assets: $53,911,708,279
Liabilities: $41,416,536,800
Net Worth: $12,495,171,479
Earnings: $1,122,070,388
Emp.: 68,382
Fiscal Year-end: 12/31/12
Business Description:
Investment Holding Company
S.I.C.: 6719
N.A.I.C.S.: 551112
Personnel:
Gilberto Benetton *(Chm)*
Carlo Benetton *(Deputy Chm)*
Gianni Mion *(Deputy Chm)*
Carlo Bertazzo *(CEO)*
Board of Directors:
Gilberto Benetton
Alessandro Benetton
Carlo Benetton
Christian Benetton
Franca Bertagnin Benetton
Giuliana Benetton
Luciano Benetton
Sabrina Benetton
Fabio Cerchiai
Giovanni Costa
Gianni Mion
Subsidiaries:

Autogrill S.p.A. (1)
Centro Direzionale Milano Fiori Strada 5
Palazzo Z
20089 Rozzano, Milano, Italy IT
Tel.: (39) 0248261 (59.28%)
Fax: (39) 0248263443
Web Site: www.autogrill.com
AGL—(ITA OTC)
Rev.: $9,176,585,118
Assets: $5,270,333,628
Liabilities: $4,127,867,418
Net Worth: $1,142,466,209
Earnings: $148,434,089
Emp.: 47,762
Fiscal Year-end: 12/31/12
Holding Company; Restaurant Food & Beverage Services & In-Flight Catering Services Contractor
S.I.C.: 6719
N.A.I.C.S.: 551112
Gilberto Benetton *(Chm)*
Gianmario Tondato da Ruos *(CEO)*
Giuseppe Cerroni *(Mng Dir)*
Paola Bottero *(Gen Counsel & Sec)*

U.S. Subsidiary:

HMSHost Corporation (2)
6905 Rockledge Dr
Bethesda, MD 20817 DE
Tel.: (240) 694-4100
E-Mail: comments@hmshost.com
Web Site: www.hmshost.com
Sales Range: $1-4.9 Billion
Emp.: 26,000
Food & Beverage Services Contractor
S.I.C.: 5812
N.A.I.C.S.: 722310
Tom Fricke *(Pres & CEO)*
Sarah Naqvi *(CIO)*

Non-U.S. Subsidiaries:

Autogrill Catering UK Limited (2)
5 Pond Street
London, NW3 2PN, United Kingdom UK
Tel.: (44) 845 0949 094
Web Site: www.autogrillcateringuk.com
Food & Beverage Services Contractor
S.I.C.: 5812
N.A.I.C.S.: 722310
Dawn Wilding *(Mng Dir)*

Autogrill Iberia S.L.U (2)
Mendez Alvaro 1 Estatcion Puerta de Atocha AVE
28045 Madrid, Spain ES
Tel.: (34) 91 423 0200
Fax: (34) 91 468 7001
Web Site: www.autogrill.es
Food & Beverage Services Contractor
S.I.C.: 5812
N.A.I.C.S.: 722310

Benetton Group S.p.A. (1)
Villa Minelli
31050 Ponzano Veneto, Treviso, Italy IT
Tel.: (39) 0422519111 (100%)
Fax: (39) 0422969501
E-Mail: info@benetton.it
Web Site: www.benetton.com
Emp.: 9,557
Casual Knitwear & Sportswear Mfr
S.I.C.: 2259
N.A.I.C.S.: 315190
Alessandro Benetton *(Chm)*
Carlo Benetton *(Deputy Chm)*
Biagio Chiarolanza *(Co-CEO)*
Franco Furno *(Co-CEO)*
Alberto Nathansohn *(CFO)*
Fabio Sartori *(COO)*
You Nguyen *(Chief Mdsg Officer & Dir-Creative)*
Aldo Chiaradia *(Chief IT Officer)*
Andrea Pezzangora *(Gen Counsel & Head-Legal & Corp Affairs)*

U.S. Subsidiary:

Benetton U.S.A. Corporation (2)
601 Fifth Ave
New York, NY 10017-8260 DE
Tel.: (212) 593-0290
Toll Free: (800) 535-4491
Emp.: 60
Retail Sportswear Stores
S.I.C.: 5699
N.A.I.C.S.: 315220
Carlo Tunioli *(Pres)*

World Duty Free S.p.A. (1)
Via Greppi 2
28100 Novara, NO, Italy IT
Tel.: (39) 06 3996 7700 (59.28%)
Web Site: www.worlddutyfreegroup.com
WDF—(ITA)
Holding Company; Airport Retail Stores Operator
S.I.C.: 6719
N.A.I.C.S.: 551112
Gianmario Tondato da Ruos *(Chm)*
Jose Maria Palencia Saucedo *(CEO)*
David Jimenez-Blanco *(CFO)*

Corporate Headquarters:

World Duty Free Group S.A.U. (2)
Edificio Merrimack IV Calle Josefa Vacarcel 30
28027 Madrid, Spain ES
Tel.: (34) 91 274 2200
Web Site: www.worlddutyfreegroup.com
Sales Range: $1-4.9 Billion
Holding Company; Airport Retail Stores Operator
S.I.C.: 6719
N.A.I.C.S.: 551112
Jose Maria Palencia Saucedo *(CEO)*
David Jimenez-Blanco *(CFO)*
Eugenio M. Andrades Yunta *(Chief Comml Officer)*
Pablo Olivera Masso *(Gen Counsel & Sec)*

Subsidiary:

World Duty Free Group Espana S.A. (3)
Edificio Merrimack IV Calle Josefa Valcarcel 30
28027 Madrid, Spain ES
Tel.: (34) 912 742 200
Web Site: www.worlddutyfreegroup.com
Airport Retail Stores Operator
S.I.C.: 5999
N.A.I.C.S.: 453998
Eugenio M. Andrades Yunta *(Chief Comml Officer)*

U.S. Subsidiary:

WDFG North America LLC (3)
(Formerly World Duty Free Group US Inc.)
6905 Rockledge Dr
Bethesda, MD 20817 DE
Tel.: (240) 694-4100
Web Site: www.worlddutyfreegroup.com
Holding Company; Regional Managing Office; Airport Retail Stores Operator
S.I.C.: 6719
N.A.I.C.S.: 551112
Padraig Damian Drennan *(Chm & CEO)*

Subsidiary:

World Duty Free US, Inc. (4)
8500 Parkline Blvd Ste 100
Orlando, FL 32809 FL
Tel.: (407) 888-9902
Web Site: www.worlddutyfreegroup.com
Airport Retail Stores Operator
S.I.C.: 5999
N.A.I.C.S.: 453998
Padraig Damian Drennan *(Chm & CEO)*
Antoni Felany Bender *(Pres)*

Non-U.S. Subsidiary:

WDFG UK Limited (3)
4 New Square Bedfont Lakes
Feltham, Mddx, TW14 8HA, United Kingdom UK
Tel.: (44) 20 8624 4300
Web Site: www.worlddutyfreegroup.com
Airport Retail Stores Operator
S.I.C.: 5999
N.A.I.C.S.: 453998
Sarah Branquinho *(Dir-Bus Rels & External Affairs)*

EDLEUN GROUP, INC.

Suite 200 30 Glendeer Circle SE
Calgary, AB, T2H 2Z7, Canada
Tel.: (403) 705-0362
Fax: (403) 705-0366
Toll Free: (888) 808-2252
E-Mail: info@edleungroup.com
Web Site: www.edleungroup.com
Year Founded: 2005
EDU—(TSXV)
Rev.: $36,208,173
Assets: $83,472,830
Liabilities: $26,302,763
Net Worth: $57,170,066
Earnings: ($4,435,317)
Emp.: 648
Fiscal Year-end: 12/31/12
Business Description:
Educational Learning & Child Care Centre Services
S.I.C.: 8351
N.A.I.C.S.: 624410
Personnel:
Jeffrey Olin *(Chm)*
Dale Kearns *(Pres & CFO)*
Mary Ann Curran *(CEO)*
Dean Michaels *(Sr VP-Acq & Dev)*
Board of Directors:
Jeffrey Olin
Adam Berkowitz
Colley Clarke
Daniel F. Gallivan
Gary Goodman
Mitchell Rosen
John Snobelen
Transfer Agent:
Computershare Trust Company of Canada
1500 University Street Suite 700
Montreal, QC, Canada
Subsidiaries:

Appleby Learning and Child Care Centre Inc. (1)
676 Appleby Line Fairview St
Burlington, ON, L7L 5Y1, Canada
Tel.: (905) 637-5437
Fax: (905) 637-0976
E-Mail: info@applebychildcare.ca
Web Site: www.applebychildcare.ca
Child Care Services
S.I.C.: 8351
N.A.I.C.S.: 624410

Edleun, Inc. (1)
30 Glendeer Circle SE
Calgary, AB, T2H 2Z7, Canada
Tel.: (403) 705-0362
Child Care Services
S.I.C.: 8351
N.A.I.C.S.: 624410

Kinder Meals Inc (1)
3780 Fallowfield Rd
Nepean, ON, K2J 1A1, Canada
Tel.: (613) 825-4441
Restaurant Operator
S.I.C.: 5812
N.A.I.C.S.: 722511

Strandherd Montessori Daycare Inc. (1)
4100 Strandherd Drive
Nepean, ON, K2J 0V2, Canada
Tel.: (613) 843-4100
Child Care Services
S.I.C.: 8351
N.A.I.C.S.: 624410

U.S. Subsidiaries:

Little Scholars Montessori Learning Centre Inc (1)
1014 Highland Ave
Duarte, CA 91010
Tel.: (626) 359-6011
Child Care Services
S.I.C.: 8351
N.A.I.C.S.: 624410

Skills Development Inc. (1)
2923 Saint Marys Ave
Hannibal, MO 63401
Tel.: (573) 221-3282
Child Care Services
S.I.C.: 8351
N.A.I.C.S.: 624410

Non-U.S. Subsidiary:

Marlborough Day Nursery Ltd. (1)
Marlborough Square
Coalville, Leicestershire, LE67 3LT, United Kingdom
Tel.: (44) 1530 814 051
E-Mail: marlborough@sclnurseries.co.uk
Web Site: www.marlboroughnursery.co.uk
Child Care Services
S.I.C.: 8322
N.A.I.C.S.: 624110

EDMOND DE ROTHSCHILD HOLDING S.A.

Rte de Pregny 21
Geneva, 1292, Switzerland
Tel.: (41) 227589544
Fax: (41) 0041588180609
Web Site: www.edmond-de-rothschild.com
Year Founded: 1953
Emp.: 10
Business Description:
Holding Company
S.I.C.: 6712
N.A.I.C.S.: 551111
Personnel:
Benjamin de Rothschild *(Chm)*
Subsidiaries:

Banque Privee Edmond de Rothschild S.A. (1)
18 rue de Hesse
1204 Geneva, Switzerland
Tel.: (41) 588189111
Fax: (41) 588189121
E-Mail: contact@bper.ch
Web Site: www.groupedr.eu
Sales Range: $25-49.9 Million
Emp.: 1,614
Asset & Wealth Management Services for Private Clients
S.I.C.: 6211
N.A.I.C.S.: 523999
Claude Messulam *(Chm & CEO-Fin Mkts, Ops & Admin)*
E. Trevor Salathe *(Vice Chm)*

Jean-Pierre Pieren *(Deputy CEO-HR, Risks & Banking)*
Sylvain Roditi *(Deputy CEO-Banking)*
Manuel Dami *(Sec)*
Philippe Currat *(Sr VP)*
Bernard Schaub *(Sr VP)*
Patrick Segal *(Sr VP-Capital Mkts)*

Non-U.S. Subsidiary:

Banque Privee Edmond de Rothschild Europe (2)
20 Boulevard Emmanuel Servais
2535 Luxembourg, Luxembourg
Mailing Address:
BP 474
2014 Luxembourg, Luxembourg
Tel.: (352) 24881
Fax: (352) 24888222
E-Mail: info@bpere.eu
Web Site: www.edmond-de-rothschild.eu
Sales Range: $25-49.9 Million
Emp.: 716
Investment Fund Administration, Wealth Management, Global Asset Management, Custody & Banking Services
S.I.C.: 6211
N.A.I.C.S.: 523999
Marc Ambroisien *(CEO & Chm)*
Geoffroy Linard *(Vice Chm & Sr VP)*
Rudy Paulet *(Vice Chm & Sr VP)*
Franck Sarrazin *(Vice Chm & Sr VP)*
Claude Pech *(First VP & Vice Chm)*
Pierre-Marie Valenne *(Vice Chm & Deputy Gen Mgr)*
Jean-Francois Lafond *(Vice Chm & Central Dir)*
Luc Gregoire *(Gen Sec)*
Philippe Anstett *(Sr VP-Investment Funds)*
Didier Bensadoun *(Sr VP-Banking, Asset Mgmt & Bus Dev)*
Raphael Delplanque *(Sr VP-Banking, Asset Mgmt & Bus Dev)*
Raymond Glode *(Sr VP-Banking, Asset Mgmt & Bus Dev)*
Franck Payrar *(Sr VP-Banking, Asset Mgmt & Family Office)*
Philippe Postal *(Sr VP-Family Office & Bus Dev)*
Jean-Marc Robinet *(Sr VP-Banking & Asset Mgmt)*
Jean-Charles Schlitz *(Sr VP-Banking, Asset Mgmt & Family Office)*
Guy Verhoustraeten *(Sr VP-Banking, Asset Mgmt & Bus Dev)*

Subsidiary:

Adjutoris Conseil S.A. (3)
18 Blvd Emmanuel Servais
L-2535 Luxembourg, Luxembourg
Tel.: (352) 26262392
Fax: (352) 26262394
E-Mail: contact@adjutoris.lu
Web Site: www.adjutoris.lu
Brokerage Services
S.I.C.: 6211
N.A.I.C.S.: 523120
Anne-Sophie Kaiser *(Mgr-Broker Svcs)*

Non-U.S. Subsidiaries:

BPER Europe Israel (3)
46 Rothschild Boulevard
68883 Tel Aviv, Israel (100%)
Tel.: (972) 35669818
Fax: (972) 35669821
Web Site: www.edmond-de-rothschild.eu
Emp.: 3
Wealth Management, Family Advisory Services & Wealth Engineering
S.I.C.: 6211
N.A.I.C.S.: 523999
Ariel Seidman *(Mng Dir)*

Divisions:

Edmond de Rothschild Investment Services Limited (4)
ALrov Tower 46 Rothschild Blvd
66883 Tel Aviv, Israel
Tel.: (972) 37130300
Fax: (972) 35666689
E-Mail: bank@edris.co.il
Web Site: www.edris.co.il/
Emp.: 60
Wealth Management, Corporate Advisory Services & Asset Management
S.I.C.: 6211
N.A.I.C.S.: 523999
Jimmy Pinto *(Chm)*

Edmond de Rothschild Private Equity Management Ltd. (4)
23 Menachem Begin Road Levenstein Tower, 19th floo
66183 Tel Aviv, Israel
Tel.: (972) 37979100
Fax: (972) 35107226
E-Mail: mail@edrpe.com
Web Site: www.edrpe.com
Emp.: 3
Private Equity Management Services
S.I.C.: 6211
N.A.I.C.S.: 523999
James Pinto *(Chm)*
Joel Warschawski *(Pres & CEO)*

La Compagnie Benjamin de Rothschild S.A. (1)
29 Route de Pre-Bois
Case Postale 490
1215 Geneva, Switzerland
Tel.: (41) 223197500
Fax: (41) 223197560
E-Mail: contact@ctbr.ch
Web Site: www.cbr.groupedr.ch
Emp.: 60
Financial Risk Management Services
S.I.C.: 6211
N.A.I.C.S.: 523999
Benjamin de Rothschild *(Chm)*

U.S. Joint Venture:

Duff & Phelps Corporation (1)
55 E 52nd St 31 Fl
New York, NY 10055 DE
Tel.: (212) 871-2000
Toll Free: (866) 282-8258
E-Mail:
Web Site: www.duffandphelps.com
Rev.: $484,701,000
Assets: $715,913,000
Liabilities: $325,732,000
Net Worth: $390,181,000
Earnings: $26,301,000
Emp.: 1,438
Fiscal Year-end: 12/31/12
Financial Advisory & Investment Banking Services
S.I.C.: 6726
N.A.I.C.S.: 525990
Noah Gottdiener *(Chm & CEO)*
Jacob L. Silverman *(Pres)*
David Lu *(Mng Dir & Head-Investment Banking Practice-China)*
Michael Braverman *(Mng Dir)*
Stephen M. Burt *(Mng Dir)*
Andrew Capitman *(Mng Dir)*
Michael H. Dolan *(Mng Dir)*
Frank La Greca *(Mng Dir)*
Patrick M. Puzzuoli *(CFO & Exec VP)*
Brett Marschke *(COO & Exec VP)*
Edward S. Forman *(Gen Counsel, Sec & Exec VP)*

Subsidiaries:

Ceteris US, LLC (2)
Monadnock Bldg 53 W Jackson Ste 1651
Chicago, IL 60604 IL
Tel.: (312) 253-0910
Emp.: 50
Scientific & Technical Consulting Services
S.I.C.: 8999
N.A.I.C.S.: 541690
Theresa Poppe *(Mng Dir)*

Chanin Capital Partners LLC (2)
11150 Santa Monica Blvd 6th Fl
Santa Monica, CA 90025
Tel.: (310) 445-4010
Fax: (310) 445-4028
Web Site: www.chanin.com
Sales Range: $650-699.9 Million
Emp.: 20
Financial Advisory Services
S.I.C.: 6282
N.A.I.C.S.: 523930
Russell Belinsky *(Sr Mng Dir)*
Skip Victor *(Sr Mng Dir)*

Duff & Phelps Securities, LLC (2)
311 S Wacker Dr Ste 4200
Chicago, IL 60606
Tel.: (312) 697-4600
Emp.: 200
Financial Advisory & Investment Banking Services
S.I.C.: 6282
N.A.I.C.S.: 523930
Robert A. Bartell *(Mng Dir)*
Mike Heimert *(Mng Dir)*

Non-U.S. Subsidiaries:

Duff & Phelps B.V. (2)
Amstelplein 1 Rembrandt Tower
1096 HA Amsterdam, Netherlands NL
Tel.: (31) 208515151
Fax: (31) 208515152
Web Site: www.duffphelps.com
Sales Range: $100-124.9 Million
Emp.: 30
Financial Advisory & Investment Banking Services
S.I.C.: 6211
N.A.I.C.S.: 523110
Henk Oosterhout *(Mng Dir)*

Duff & Phelps Canada Limited (2)
80 Richmond Street West Suite 2000
Toronto, ON, M5H 2A4, Canada
Tel.: (416) 364-9700
Fax: (416) 364-9707
Financial Advisory & Investment Banking Services
S.I.C.: 6726
N.A.I.C.S.: 525990
Stephen R. Cole *(Pres)*
Joseph Coltson *(Mng Dir)*
A. Scott Davidson *(Mng Dir)*
Tony Davies *(Mng Dir)*
William Dovey *(Mng Dir)*
Peter Farkas *(Mng Dir)*
Andrew Freedman *(Mng Dir)*
Andrew Harington *(Mng Dir)*
Robert Harlang *(Mng Dir)*
Robert Kofman *(Mng Dir)*

Duff & Phelps GmbH (2)
Leopoldstrasse 8
80802 Munich, Germany De
Tel.: (49) 89388884100
Fax: (49) 89388884444
Web Site: www.duffandphelps.com
Sales Range: $1-4.9 Billion
Emp.: 20
Financial Advisory & Investment Banking Services
S.I.C.: 6211
N.A.I.C.S.: 523110
Christian Aders *(Mng Dir)*

Duff & Phelps K.K. (2)
Fukoku Seimei Building 21F
2 2 2 Uchisaiwaicho Chiyoda ku, Tokyo, 100 0011, Japan JP
Tel.: (81) 335930101
Fax: (81) 335930102
Web Site: www.duffandphelps.com
Sales Range: $150-199.9 Million
Emp.: 15
Financial Advisory & Investment Banking Services
S.I.C.: 6211
N.A.I.C.S.: 523110

Duff & Phelps, Ltd. (2)
40 Bank St Canary Wharf
London, E14 5NR, United Kingdom
Tel.: (44) 2077156711
Fax: (44) 02077156710
Web Site: www.duffandphelps.com
Sales Range: $100-124.9 Million
Emp.: 30
Financial Advisory & Investment Banking Services
S.I.C.: 6211
N.A.I.C.S.: 523110
Mathias Schumacher *(Mng Dir)*

Duff & Phelps SAS (2)
8 Boulevard des Capucines
75009 Paris, France FR
Tel.: (33) 140064101
Web Site: www.duffandphelps.com
Sales Range: $1-4.9 Billion
Financial Advisory & Investment Banking Services
S.I.C.: 6211
N.A.I.C.S.: 523110
Yann Magnan *(Mng Dir)*

Duff & Phelps Switzerland GmbH (2)
Stockerhof Dreikonigstrasse 31a
Zurich, 8002, Switzerland CH
Tel.: (41) 442083178
Fax: (41) 442083500
Web Site: www.DuffPhelps.com
Sales Range: $75-99.9 Million
Emp.: 4
Financial Advisory & Investment Banking Services
S.I.C.: 6211
N.A.I.C.S.: 523110
Theodor van Stephoudt *(Mng Dir)*

Non-U.S. Subsidiary:

La Compagnie Financiere Edmond de Rothschild (1)
47 rue du Faubourg Saint-Honore
75401 Paris, Cedex, France
Tel.: (33) 1 40 17 25 25
Fax: (33) 1 40 17 24 02
Financial Holding Company
S.I.C.: 6712
N.A.I.C.S.: 551111
Marc Samuel *(Deputy Gen Mgr)*

Subsidiary:

La Compagnie Financiere Edmond De Rothschild Banque (2)
47 rue du Faubourg
Saint Honore, Paris, Cedex, 75401, France (91%)
Tel.: (33) 140172525
Fax: (33) 140172402
Web Site: www.groupedr.fr
Private Banking & Asset Management Services
S.I.C.: 6211
N.A.I.C.S.: 523999
Michel Cicurel *(Chm)*
Benjamin de Rothschild *(Chm-Supervisory Bd)*

Subsidiaries:

Edmond de Rothschild Asset Management (3)
47 rue du Faubourg Saint-Honore
75401 Paris, France
Tel.: (33) 140172525
Fax: (33) 140172442
Web Site: www.groupedr.fr
Asset Management Services
S.I.C.: 6211
N.A.I.C.S.: 523999

Edmond de Rothschild Corporate Finance (3)
47 rue du Faubourg Saint-Honore
75401 Paris, France (100%)
Tel.: (33) 140172111
Fax: (33) 140172501
Web Site: www.edrcf.com
Emp.: 25
Financial Services
S.I.C.: 6211
N.A.I.C.S.: 523999

Edmond de Rothschild Enterprises Patrimoniales Croissance (3)
47 rue du Faubourg Saint Honore
75401 Paris, Cedex, 08, France
Tel.: (33) 1 40 17 3163
Web Site: www.groupedr.fr
Investments
S.I.C.: 6211
N.A.I.C.S.: 523999

Edmond de Rothschild Enterprises Patrimoniales (3)
47 rue du Faubourg Saint-Honore
75401 Paris, France
Tel.: (33) 140173163
Fax: (33) 140172501
Web Site: www.edrep.fr
Emp.: 35
Investment Management Services
S.I.C.: 6211
N.A.I.C.S.: 523999
Francois Pailler *(Mgr)*

Edmond de Rothschild Investment Partners (3)
47 rue du Faubourg Saint-Honore
75401 Paris, Cedex 08, France
Tel.: (33) 1 40 17 23 74
Fax: (33) 1 40 17 31 43
E-Mail: edrip@lcfr.fr
Web Site: www.edmond-de-rothschild.fr
Asset Management Structured Products

Edmond de Rothschild Holding S.A.—(Continued)

S.I.C.: 6211
N.A.I.C.S.: 523999
Pierre-Michel Passy *(Pres)*
Jerome Bevierre *(CFO)*
Andrei Buzdugan *(Deputy CFO)*

EDMONDS CHEVROLET BUICK GMC

138 Hanes Road
Huntsville, ON, P1H 1M4, Canada
Tel.: (705) 789-7500
Fax: (705) 789-2465
Toll Free: (877) 661-7848
E-Mail: info@edmondsgm.com
Web Site: www.edmondsgm.ca
Rev.: $18,742,700
Emp.: 115
Business Description:
New & Used Vehicles
S.I.C.: 5571
N.A.I.C.S.: 441228
Personnel:
Beatrice Edmonds *(Treas & Corp Sec)*

EDMONTON KENWORTH LTD.

17335 - 118 Ave
Edmonton, AB, T5S 2P5, Canada
Tel.: (780) 453-3431
Fax: (780) 454-6124
Web Site: www.edmkw.com
Year Founded: 1954
Rev.: $258,212,875
Emp.: 288
Business Description:
New & Used Truck Leasing, Sales & Service
S.I.C.: 7513
N.A.I.C.S.: 532120
Personnel:
Gary King *(Pres)*

EDOKO FOOD IMPORTERS LTD.

1335 Kebet Way
Port Coquitlam, BC, V3C 6G1, Canada
Tel.: (604) 944-7332
Fax: (604) 944-8557
E-Mail: info@edokofood.com
Web Site: www.edokofood.ca
Year Founded: 1957
Rev.: $10,172,559
Emp.: 35
Business Description:
General Food Products Whslr
S.I.C.: 5499
N.A.I.C.S.: 446191
Personnel:
Neal Letourneau *(Pres)*

EDOM TECHNOLOGY CO., LTD.

8F No 50 Lane 10 Kee Hu Road Nei Hu
Taipei, 114, Taiwan
Tel.: (886) 226578811
Fax: (886) 226579090
E-Mail: ir@edom.com.tw
Web Site: www.edom.com.tw
3048—(TAI)
Sls.: $897,917,443
Assets: $218,609,715
Liabilities: $148,283,029
Net Worth: $70,326,686
Earnings: $5,329,919
Emp.: 379
Fiscal Year-end: 12/31/12
Business Description:
Electronic Components Mfr
S.I.C.: 3677
N.A.I.C.S.: 334416
Personnel:
Wayne Tseng *(Chm & CEO)*

Non-U.S. Subsidiaries:

EDOM TECHNOLOGY (SHANGHAI) LTD. **(1)**
Floor 16 No 20 Building No 487 Tianlin Road Caohejing Hi Tech Park
Xuhui District, Shanghai, Guangdong, 200233, China
Tel.: (86) 21 3367 5222
Fax: (86) 21 5445 2834
E-Mail: sales@edom-tech.com
Web Site: www.edom.com.tw/tw/index.jsp?m=intro&id=location
Integrated Circuits Distr
S.I.C.: 5065
N.A.I.C.S.: 423690

EDOM TRADING (SHENZHEN) LTD. **(1)**
Room 2703 Hua Rong Building No 178 Mintian Road
Futian District, Shenzhen, Guangdong, 518048, China
Tel.: (86) 75583588188
Fax: (86) 755 8386 7117
E-Mail: sales@edom-tech.com
Web Site: www.edomtechnology.com
Emp.: 100
Computer Peripherals Distr
S.I.C.: 5045
N.A.I.C.S.: 423430
Paul Chung *(Mgr)*

EDP - ENERGIAS DE PORTUGAL, S.A.

Praca Marques de Pombal 12
1250-162 Lisbon, Portugal
Tel.: (351) 210012680
Fax: (351) 210012910
E-Mail: ir@edp.pt
Web Site: www.edp.pt
EDP—(EUR)
Sls.: $21,996,221,259
Assets: $57,384,324,757
Liabilities: $41,995,356,245
Net Worth: $15,388,968,512
Earnings: $1,591,381,596
Emp.: 12,275
Fiscal Year-end: 12/31/12
Business Description:
Electric Power Generation, Supply & Distribution
S.I.C.: 4931
N.A.I.C.S.: 221122
Personnel:
Eduardo de Almeida Catroga *(Chm-Supervisory Bd)*
Antonio Luis Guerra Nunes Mexia *(Chm-Exec Bd & CEO)*
Dingming Zhang *(Vice Chm-Supervisory Bd)*
Nuno Maria Pestana de Almeida Alves *(CFO & Member-Exec Bd)*
Antonio Fernando Melo Martins da Costa *(Member-Exec Bd)*
Joao Marques da Cruz *(Member-Exec Bd)*
Antonio Manuel Barreto Pita de Abreu *(Member-Exec Bd)*
Miguel Stilwell de Andrade *(Member-Exec Bd)*
Joao Manuel Manso Neto *(Member-Exec Bd)*
Maria Teresa Isabel Pereira *(Sec)*
Supervisory Board of Directors:
Eduardo de Almeida Catroga
Harkat Abderezak
Mohamed Ali Al Fahim
Maria Celeste Ferreira Lopes Cardona
Vitor Fernando da Conceicao Goncalves
Luis Filipe da Conceicao Pereira
Ilidio da Costa Leite de Pinho
Nuno Manuel da Silva Amado
Paulo Jorge de Assuncao Rodrigues Teixeira Pinto
Alberto Joao Coraceiro de Castro
Manuel Fernando de Macedo Alves Monteiro
Jorge Braga de Macedo
Felipe Fernandez Fernandez
Fernando Masaveu Herrero
Guojun Lu
Augusto Carlos Serra Ventura Mateus
Antonio Sarmeto Gomes Mota
Rui Eduardo Ferreira Rodrigues Pena
Jose Maria Espirito Santo Silva Ricciardi
Vasco Joaquim Rocha Vieira
Shengliang Wu
Ya Yang
Dingming Zhang

Subsidiaries:

Balwerk - Consultadoria Economica e Participacoes, Sociedade Unipessoal, Lda. **(1)**
Avenida Jose Malhoa Lote a -13
Lisbon, Portugal
Tel.: (351) 217817700
Business Management Consulting Services
S.I.C.: 8742
N.A.I.C.S.: 541611

EDP Distribuicao de Energia, S.A. **(1)**
R Camilo Castelo Branco 43
Lisbon, 1250-162, Portugal
Tel.: (351) 213172300
Fax: (351) 213171610
Web Site: www.edp.pt
Electric Power Distribution Services
S.I.C.: 4931
N.A.I.C.S.: 221122
Antonio Mexia *(VP)*

EDP Distribuicao **(1)**
Praca Marques de Pombal 12
1250-162 Lisbon, Portugal PT
Tel.: (351) 210012500 (100%)
Fax: (351) 210021403
E-Mail: rh_edp@edp.pt
Web Site: www.edp.pt/EDPI/Internet/PT/Group/EDPDistribuicao/default.htm
Sales Range: $5-14.9 Billion
Emp.: 4,980
Distribution & Sale of Electric Power
S.I.C.: 4911
N.A.I.C.S.: 221122
Manuel Brandao *(Pres)*

EDP Gas Servico Universal, S.A. **(1)**
Rua Linhas de Torres 41
Porto, Portugal
Tel.: (351) 225071400
Fax: (351) 225402426
Natural Gas Distribution Services
S.I.C.: 4924
N.A.I.C.S.: 221210

EDP Gas - S.G.P.S., S.A. **(1)**
Praca Marques Pombal 12
1250-162 Lisbon, Portugal
Tel.: (351) 210 012 500
Fax: (351) 210 017290
Web Site: www.edp.pt
Emp.: 2
Oil & Gas Exploration Services
S.I.C.: 1389
N.A.I.C.S.: 213112
Alexander Potapenko *(Chm)*

EDP - Gestao da Producao de Energia, S.A. **(1)**
Avenida Jose Malhoa Lote A 13
Lisbon, 1070 157, Portugal
Tel.: (351) 21 001 2000
Fax: (351) 21 001 2300
Electric Power Generation Services
S.I.C.: 4911
N.A.I.C.S.: 221118

EDP Inovacao, S.A. **(1)**
Avenida Sidonio Pais 24 R/C Esq
1050-215 Lisbon, Portugal
Tel.: (351) 210012500
Emp.: 21
Power Project Engineering Services
S.I.C.: 8711
N.A.I.C.S.: 541330
Antonio Vidigal *(Gen Dir)*

EDP - Projectos S.G.P.S., S.A. **(1)**
Praca Marques De Pombal 12
Lisbon, Portugal
Tel.: (351) 210015300
Electric Power Generation Services
S.I.C.: 4939
N.A.I.C.S.: 221118

Subsidiary:

EDP GAS.Com - Comercio de Gas Natural, S.A. **(2)**
Praca Marques De Pombal 12
1250-162 Lisbon, Portugal
Tel.: (351) 225071400
Fax: (351) 225402426
Natural Gas Distr
S.I.C.: 4924
N.A.I.C.S.: 221210

EDP Renovaveis S.A. **(1)**
Praca Marques de Pombal 12
1250-162 Lisbon, Portugal (51%)
Tel.: (351) 21 001 2680
Fax: (351) 21 001 2910
Web Site: www.edprenovaveis.com
EDPR—(EUR)
Rev.: $1,558,590,241
Assets: $17,906,716,993
Liabilities: $10,167,818,551
Net Worth: $7,738,898,443
Earnings: $183,146,429
Emp.: 861
Fiscal Year-end: 12/31/12
Power Distr
S.I.C.: 4911
N.A.I.C.S.: 221118
Antonio Luis Guerra Nunes Mexia *(Chm)*
Joao Manuel Manso Neto *(Vice Chm & CEO)*
Rui Teixeira *(CFO)*
Luis Adao da Fonseca *(Chief Bus Dev Officer)*

EDP Servicos - Sistemas para a Qualidade e Eficiencia Energetica, S.A. **(1)**
Praca Marques De Pombal 13
1250-162 Lisbon, Portugal
Tel.: (351) 210012500
Fax: (351) 210021403
Business Management Consulting Services
S.I.C.: 8742
N.A.I.C.S.: 541611
Juan Tosh *(Gen Mgr)*

EDP Serviner - Servicos de Energia, S.A. **(1)**
Pc Marques Pombal Nr 13
Lisbon, 1250-162, Portugal
Tel.: (351) 210012500
Fax: (351) 210012910
Business Management & Consulting Services
S.I.C.: 8742
N.A.I.C.S.: 541611

Empresa Hidroelectrica do Guadiana, S.A. **(1)**
Rua Vale C Hidroelectrica
7960-049 Vidigueira, Portugal
Tel.: (351) 284450010
Electric Power Generation Services
S.I.C.: 4911
N.A.I.C.S.: 221111

FISIGEN - Empresa de Cogeracao, S.A. **(1)**
Avenida Jose Malhoa Lote a 13
1070-157 Lisbon, Portugal
Tel.: (351) 212066810
Fax: (351) 212066018
Emp.: 12
Electric Power Generation Services
S.I.C.: 4911
N.A.I.C.S.: 221118
Rodrigues Alves *(Mgr)*

O&M Servicos - Operacao e Manutencao Industrial, S.A. **(1)**
Lugar Do Freixo Nr 45
Mortagua, Viseu, 3450-116, Portugal
Tel.: (351) 231927530
Electric Power Generation Services
S.I.C.: 4939
N.A.I.C.S.: 221118

Portgas-Sociedade de Producao e Distribuicao de Gas SA **(1)**
Rua Linhas de Torres 41
4350 214 Porto, Portugal (72%)
Tel.: (351) 225071400

Fax: (351) 225402426
E-Mail: mail@portgas.pt
Web Site: www.portgas.pt
Sales Range: $125-149.9 Million
Emp.: 100
Natural Gas Distribution
S.I.C.: 4924
N.A.I.C.S.: 221210
Antonio Jose Tomas Gomes de Pinho *(Chm)*

U.S. Subsidiaries:

EDP Renewables North America, L.L.C. (1)
808 Travis St Ste 700
Houston, TX 77002
Tel.: (713) 265-0350
Fax: (713) 265-0365
Web Site: www.edprenovaveis.com
Wind Power Plant Construction Engineering Services
S.I.C.: 1629
N.A.I.C.S.: 237130
John Taylor *(Mgr-Property Tax)*

Subsidiaries:

Marble River, L.L.C. (2)
5591 State Rte 11
Ellenburg Center, NY 12934
Tel.: (518) 497-0033
Wind Electric Power Generation Services
S.I.C.: 4939
N.A.I.C.S.: 221118

Meadow Lake Wind Farm IV, L.L.C. (2)
808 Travis St Ste 700
Houston, TX 77002-5774
Tel.: (713) 265-0350
Emp.: 300
Wind Power Plant Operating Services
S.I.C.: 4911
N.A.I.C.S.: 221118
Gabriel Alonso *(Gen Mgr)*

Meadow Lake Wind Farm, L.L.C. (2)
808 Travis St Ste 700
Houston, TX 77002-5774
Tel.: (713) 265-0350
Wind Power Plant Operating Services
S.I.C.: 4939
N.A.I.C.S.: 221118

Paulding Wind Farm II, L.L.C. (2)
808 Travis St Ste 700
Houston, TX 77002-5774
Tel.: (713) 265-0350
Electric Power Generation Services
S.I.C.: 4931
N.A.I.C.S.: 221118

Horizon Wind Energy LLC (1)
808 Travis Ste 700
Houston, TX 77002 (100%)
Tel.: (713) 265-0350
Fax: (713) 265-0365
E-Mail: mail@edpr.com
Web Site: www.edpr.com
Emp.: 150
Wind Power Generation & Bulk Transmission
S.I.C.: 4939
N.A.I.C.S.: 221118
Gabriel Alonso *(CEO)*
Jayshree Desai *(CFO)*
Andre Young *(Chief Comml Officer & Chief Dev Officer)*
Leslie Freiman *(Gen Counsel)*

Non-U.S. Subsidiaries:

Agrupacion Eolica, S.L.U. (1)
Plaza Antonio Beltran Martinez 1-Piso 4 F Ct Emp
Zaragoza, 50002, Spain
Tel.: (34) 976210664
Electric Power Generation Services
S.I.C.: 4931
N.A.I.C.S.: 221118

Bon Vent de L Ebre, S.L. (1)
Calle Navas De Tolosa 161
Terrassa, Barcelona, 08224, Spain
Tel.: (34) 937454400
Electric Power Generation Services
S.I.C.: 4939
N.A.I.C.S.: 221118

Ceasa Promociones Eolicas, S.L.U. (1)
Plaza Antonio Beltran Martinez Ct Emp El Trovador 1-4 f
Zaragoza, 50002, Spain
Tel.: (34) 976216735
Fax: (34) 985256889
Electric Power Generation Services
S.I.C.: 4931
N.A.I.C.S.: 221118

Corporacion Empresarial de Renovables Alternativas, S.L.U. (1)
Paseo Pamplona 5 5
Zaragoza, Spain
Tel.: (34) 976216735
Electric Power Generation Services
S.I.C.: 4931
N.A.I.C.S.: 221118

Desarrollos Eolicos Promocion, S.A. (1)
Avenida Montes Sierra 36-2 Planta
Seville, 41007, Spain
Tel.: (34) 954269240
Fax: (34) 954269250
Emp.: 55
Engineering Services
S.I.C.: 8711
N.A.I.C.S.: 541330
Francisco Galvan *(Dir-Civil)*

Desarrollos Eolicos, S.A. (1)
Avenida Montes Sierra 36
Seville, 41007, Spain
Tel.: (34) 954269240
Fax: (34) 954269250
Emp.: 60
Wind Turbine Mfr
S.I.C.: 3511
N.A.I.C.S.: 333611
Francisco Galvan *(Mng Dir)*

EDP - Energias do Brasil S.A. (1)
Rua Bandeira Paulista 530 14 andar
04532-001 Sao Paulo, SP, Brazil (62.4%)
Tel.: (55) 11 2185 5900
Fax: (55) 11 2185 5975
E-Mail: ri@enbr.com.br
Web Site: www.energiasdobrasil.com.br
ENBR3—(BRAZ)
Sales Range: $1-4.9 Billion
Emp.: 3,254
Holding Company; Electric Power Generation, Supply & Distribution
S.I.C.: 4931
N.A.I.C.S.: 221122
Antonio Luis Guerra Nunes Mexia *(Chm)*
Antonio Manuel Barreto Pita de Abreu *(CEO)*

Subsidiaries:

Bandeirante Energia SA (2)
Rua Bandeira Pualista 530 3 andar
Chacara Itaim, Sao Paulo, 04532 001, Brazil (100%)
Tel.: (55) 11 2185 5801
Web Site: www.bandeirante.com.br
EBEN3—(BRAZ)
Emp.: 1,080
Electricity Generation, Transmission, Distribution & Sale
S.I.C.: 4931
N.A.I.C.S.: 221122
Antonio Mexia *(Chm)*
Antonio Manuel Barreto Pita de Abreu *(CEO)*

EDP Escelsa - Espirito Santo Centrais Eletricas S.A. (2)
R Bandeira Paulista 530 3 andar
Chacara Itaim, Sao Paulo, SP, CEP 04532-001, Brazil BR
Tel.: (55) 11 2185 5985 (100%)
Web Site: www.edpescelsa.com.br
Electricity Distr
S.I.C.: 4931
N.A.I.C.S.: 221122
Antonio Eduardo da Silva Oliva *(CEO)*

Empresa Energetica do Mato Grosso do Sul S.A. (2)
Av Gury Marques no 8000
CEP 79072 900 Campo Grande, MS, Brazil
Tel.: (55) 6733984000
E-Mail: comunicacaosocialenersul@enersul.com.br
Web Site: www.enersul.com.br
ENER3—(BRAZ)
Emp.: 898
Electricity Generation, Transmission & Distribution
S.I.C.: 4939
N.A.I.C.S.: 221122
Antonio Eduardo da Silva Oliva *(CEO)*
Jorge Manuel Moreira Martins *(Mng Dir)*
Thomas Daniel Brull *(CFO, Chief Admin Officer & Dir-IR)*

Enertrade (2)
rua gomes de carvalho 1996 7F
Chacara Itaim, Sao Paulo, 04547006, Brazil
Tel.: (55) 1121855801
Fax: (55) 55112185802
E-Mail: mesa@edpbr.com.br
Web Site: www.edpcomercialieadao.com.br
Emp.: 25
Electricity Trading & Supply Services
S.I.C.: 4939
N.A.I.C.S.: 221122
Esoani Portes *(Mgr-Comml)*

EDP Renewables Canada, Ltd (1)
449 Winchester Main
Winchester, ON, K0C 2K0, Canada
Tel.: (613) 774-4068
Electric Power Generation Services
S.I.C.: 4939
N.A.I.C.S.: 221118

EDP Renewables Polska, SP. Z.O.O (1)
ul Posteepu 17B
02-676 Warsaw, Poland
Tel.: (48) 22 331 01 88
Fax: (48) 22 310 97 32
E-Mail: office@edpr.com
Web Site: www.edprenovaveis.com
Emp.: 40
Electric Power Generation Services
S.I.C.: 4931
N.A.I.C.S.: 221118
Grzegorz Szymczak *(Gen Mgr)*

Electrica de la Ribera del Ebro, S.A. (1)
Poligono Industrial Castejon Par M 04
Castejon, 31590, Spain
Tel.: (34) 948814400
Fax: (34) 948814262
Electric Power Generation Services
S.I.C.: 4911
N.A.I.C.S.: 221118

Energia e Industria de Toledo, S.A. (1)
Plaza De La Gesta 2
Oviedo, 33007, Spain
Tel.: (34) 98 523 03 00
Fax: (34) 98 525 37 87
Electric Power Generation Services
S.I.C.: 4911
N.A.I.C.S.: 221118

Eolica Arlanzon, S.A. (1)
Calle Serrano Galvache 56-Ed Encina
Madrid, 28033, Spain
Tel.: (34) 917819353
Fax: (34) 913997902
Wind Electric Power Generation Services
S.I.C.: 4931
N.A.I.C.S.: 221118

Eolica Campollano S.A. (1)
Calle Serrano Galvache 56-Edif Encina 1 Planta
Madrid, 28033, Spain
Tel.: (34) 917819353
Fax: (34) 913997902
Electric Power Generation Services
S.I.C.: 4931
N.A.I.C.S.: 221118

Eolica Guadalteba, S.L. (1)
Avenida Montes Sierra 36-Plt 2
Seville, 41007, Spain
Tel.: (34) 954269240
Electric Power Generation Services
S.I.C.: 4931
N.A.I.C.S.: 221118

Greenwind, S.A. (1)
Avenue Pasteur 6 Building H
Wavre, Louvain-la-Neuve, 1300, Belgium
Tel.: (32) 1 068 64 85
Fax: (32) 143422453
Web Site: www.edprenovapeis.com
Emp.: 1
Wind Electric Power Generation Services
S.I.C.: 4911
N.A.I.C.S.: 221118
Frederic Lanoe *(Gen Mgr)*

HC Naturgas Comercializadora de Ultimo Recurso, S.A. (1)
Plaza De La Gesta 2
Oviedo, 33007, Spain
Tel.: (34) 985230300
Fax: (34) 985253787
Natural Gas Distribution Services
S.I.C.: 4924
N.A.I.C.S.: 221210

Hidrocantabrico Cogeneracion, S.L. (1)
Plaza Gesta 2
33007 Oviedo, Spain
Tel.: (34) 985230300
Fax: (34) 985242266
Electric Power Generation Services
S.I.C.: 4911
N.A.I.C.S.: 221118

HidroElectrica del Cantabrico, S.A. (1)
Plaza de la Gesta 2
33007 Oviedo, Spain (96%)
Tel.: (34) 985230300
Fax: (34) 985256889
E-Mail: fundacionhc@hcenergia.com
Web Site: www.h-c.com
Emp.: 200
Electricity Output, Transportation, Conversion & Distribution Services
S.I.C.: 4911
N.A.I.C.S.: 221122
Manuel Menendez Menendez *(Chm)*
Joao Manuel Manso Neto *(CEO)*
Jorge Pragana de Cruz Morais *(CFO)*
Emilio Garcia-Conde Noriega *(Gen Counsel)*
Jose Luis Martinez Mohedano *(Sec)*

Subsidiaries:

HC Energia (2)
Plaza de la Gesta 2
33007 Oviedo, Spain (80%)
Tel.: (34) 902830100
Fax: (34) 985213969
Engineering & Construction of Renewable Energy Plants
S.I.C.: 8711
N.A.I.C.S.: 541330
Marcos Enrique Antuna Egocheaga *(CEO)*

HidroCantabrico Energia, S.A.U. (2)
Plaza de la Gesta 2
33007 Oviedo, Spain (100%)
Tel.: (34) 902830100
Fax: (34) 985253787
Web Site: www.hcenergia.com
Retail & Supply of Electricity
S.I.C.: 4911
N.A.I.C.S.: 221121
Joao Manuel Manso Neto *(CEO)*

Le Mee, S.A. R.L. (1)
Bel Air 22100
Aucaleuc, France
Tel.: (33) 296394564
Fax: (33) 296394158
Grain & Animal Feed Whslr
S.I.C.: 5159
N.A.I.C.S.: 424590

Parques Eolicos del Cantabrico S.A. (1)
Plaza De La Gesta 2-Planta 4
Oviedo, 33007, Spain
Tel.: (34) 917819353
Fax: (34) 913997902
E-Mail: contactus@edpr.com
Web Site: www.edpr.com
Electric Power Generation Services
S.I.C.: 4939
N.A.I.C.S.: 221118

Santa Quiteria Energia, S.L.U. (1)
Pz Antonio Beltran Martinez 1
Zaragoza, 50002, Spain
Tel.: (34) 976216735
Wind Power Plant Construction Services
S.I.C.: 1623
N.A.I.C.S.: 237130

Sinae Inversiones Eolicas S.A. (1)
C/ Serrano Galvache 56
28033 Madrid, Spain

EDP - Energias de Portugal, S.A.—(Continued)

Tel.: (34) 917819353
Fax: (34) 913997902
Investment Management Services
S.I.C.: 6211
N.A.I.C.S.: 523999

EDRAN BERHAD

No 33-1 Jalan 2/7 6C Desa Pandan
55100 Kuala Lumpur, Malaysia
Tel.: (60) 3 92067381
Fax: (60) 39283 0192
E-Mail: support@edaran.com
Web Site: www.edaran.com
EDARAN—(KLS)
Rev.: $14,336,446
Assets: $17,868,441
Liabilities: $6,404,587
Net Worth: $11,463,855
Earnings: ($374,095)
Fiscal Year-end: 06/30/13
Business Description:
Information Technology Services
S.I.C.: 7372
N.A.I.C.S.: 511210
Personnel:
Bistamam Ramli *(Mng Dir)*
Rizana Mohamad Daud *(Sec)*
Md Arif Hasan *(Exec VP-Edaran IT Services Sdn Bhd)*
Board of Directors:
Tajudin Ramli
Azlan Mohd Agel
Abdul Malek Ahmad Shazili
Abdul Halim Abdullah
Abdul Hamid Mustapha
Mohd Shu'aib Ishak
Kheng Yew Lim
Kamal Mohd Ali
Mohd Haniff Mohd Hussain
Bistamam Ramli
Fazlan Azri Tajudin
Subsidiaries:

Edaran IT Services Sdn. Bhd. (1)
32 Jalan 1/76C Desa Pandan
55100 Kuala Lumpur, Malaysia
Tel.: (60) 392067200
Fax: (60) 392838515
E-Mail: support@edaran.com
Emp.: 30
Software Development Services
S.I.C.: 7371
N.A.I.C.S.: 541511
Bistamam Ramli *(Pres & CEO)*
Mustafa Rawther Mohamed Rawther *(Exec VP)*
Hatta Amirrul Amran *(Sr VP-Sls & Mktg)*
Razak Md Nor *(Sr VP-Solutions Integration)*
Abdul Aziz Shik Razak *(Sr VP-Infrastructure Svcs)*

SIDIC Technology Sdn. Bhd. (1)
32 Jalan 1/76C Desa Pandan
55100 Kuala Lumpur, Malaysia
Tel.: (60) 392067200
Fax: (60) 392838515
Web Site: www.edaran.com
Surveillance System Installation Services
S.I.C.: 7389
N.A.I.C.S.: 561990
Mustafa Mohamed *(Exec VP)*

Non-U.S. Subsidiary:

Shinba-Edaran Sdn. Bhd. (1)
Unit 1 Level 3 Bangunan Dar Takaful IBB Utama Jalan Pemancha
Bandar Seri Begawan, Brunei Darussalam
Tel.: (673) 2236777
Fax: (673) 2232320
E-Mail: edward@edaran.com
Emp.: 5
Software Development Services
S.I.C.: 7371
N.A.I.C.S.: 541511
Awangku Shariffull Bahri Ismail *(Mng Dir)*

EDRASIS - C. PSALLIDAS S.A.

47th Km of Attiki Odos
19400 Koropi, Greece
Tel.: (30) 2106680600
Fax: (30) 2106680610
E-Mail: edrasis@edrasis.gr
Web Site: www.edrasis.gr
EDRA—(ATH)
Sales Range: $10-24.9 Million
Emp.: 504
Business Description:
Geo Technical Engineering Contract Services
S.I.C.: 8711
N.A.I.C.S.: 541330
Personnel:
Constantinos Psallidas *(Chm & Mng Dir)*
Christodoulos Psallidas *(Vice Chm)*
Ioannis Tountas *(CFO)*
Board of Directors:
Constantinos Psallidas
Mihalis Alepis
Christodoulos Psallidas
Antonios Samaras
Evangelos Valmas
Subsidiaries:

Edraco S.A. (1)
47th Km Attiki Odos
19400 Koropi, Greece
Tel.: (30) 210668 06 00
Fax: (30) 210668 09 40
Commercial Building Construction Services
S.I.C.: 1542
N.A.I.C.S.: 236220

Enviprosystems S.A. (1)
47 Km Attiki Odos
19 400 Koropi, Greece
Tel.: (30) 2106680600
Fax: (30) 2106680610
E-Mail: envipro@edrasis.gr
Environmental Protection Systems Design & Construction Services
S.I.C.: 1731
N.A.I.C.S.: 238210
Costas Psallidas *(Gen Mgr)*

Non-U.S. Subsidiary:

Redra Construct Group S.A (1)
Bd Libertatii nr 8 bl 115 sc 1 ap 15
Sector 4, Bucharest, 062203, Romania
Tel.: (40) 213118365
Fax: (40) 21 311 83 63
Commercial Building Construction Services
S.I.C.: 1542
N.A.I.C.S.: 236220

THE EDRINGTON GROUP

2500 Great Western Road
Glasgow, G15 6RW, United Kingdom
Tel.: (44) 1419404000
Fax: (44) 1419404040
E-Mail: group@edrington.co.uk
Web Site: www.edringtongroup.com
Year Founded: 1887
Sls.: $1,103,134,065
Assets: $2,448,669,145
Liabilities: $1,230,424,839
Net Worth: $1,218,264,306
Earnings: ($230,576,340)
Emp.: 2,250
Fiscal Year-end: 03/31/13
Business Description:
Scotch & Whiskey Mfr
S.I.C.: 2085
N.A.I.C.S.: 312140
Personnel:
Ian B. Curle *(CEO)*
Martin A. Cooke *(Sec)*
Board of Directors:
K. Callum O. Barton
Ronnie J. S. Bell
Ian B. Curle
W. R. Farrar
Richard J. A. Hunter
Graham R. Hutcheon
Scott J. McCroskie
Norman L. Murray

Subsidiary:

Highland Park Distillery (1)
Holm Road
Kirkwall, Orkney, KW15 1SU, United Kingdom UK (100%)
Tel.: (44) 01856873107
Fax: (44) 1856876091
Web Site: www.highlandpark.co.uk
Emp.: 30
Distilled & Blended Liquors
Import Export
S.I.C.: 2084
N.A.I.C.S.: 312130
Gerry Tosh *(Controller-Global Brands)*

Subsidiaries:

Alfred Dunhill Scotch Whisky Ltd. (2)
W Kinfauns
Perth, PH2 7XZ, United Kingdom UK (100%)
Tel.: (44) 738440000
Fax: (44) 1738628167
E-Mail: group@edrington.co.uk
Emp.: 2
Scotch & Whiskey Mfr
S.I.C.: 2082
N.A.I.C.S.: 312120

Macallan Distillery Ltd (2)
Macallan Distillery
Craigellachie, Banffshire, AB38 9RX, United Kingdom UK (75%)
Tel.: (44) 1340871471
Fax: (44) 1340871212
E-Mail: webmaster@themacallan.com
Web Site: www.themacallan.com
Emp.: 50
S.I.C.: 5921
N.A.I.C.S.: 445310

Plants:

Glenrothes Distillery Co Ltd (2)
Rothes
Rothes, Morayshire, AB38 7AA, United Kingdom UK (100%)
Tel.: (44) 1340872300
Fax: (44) 1340872172
Web Site: www.glenrothes.com
Emp.: 40
Distilled & Blended Liquors
S.I.C.: 2084
N.A.I.C.S.: 312130
Alistair Anderson *(Gen Mgr)*

Glenturret Distillery Limited (2)
The Hosh
Crieff, Perthshire, PH7 4HA, United Kingdom UK (100%)
Tel.: (44) 1764656565
Fax: (44) 1764564366
E-Mail: enquiries@thefamousgrouseexperience.com
Web Site: www.thefamousgrouse.com
Emp.: 40
Distilled & Blended Liquors
S.I.C.: 2084
N.A.I.C.S.: 312130
Trecy McCefferty *(Gen Mgr)*

Non-U.S. Subsidiary:

Maxxium Taiwan Ltd. (2)
5th Fl 310 Chung Hsiao East Rd Sec 4
Taipei, 106, Taiwan (100%)
Tel.: (886) 287739099
Fax: (886) 287739380
E-Mail: amy.lru@maxxium.tw
Web Site: www.maxxium.com
Emp.: 100
Wines Distr
S.I.C.: 5182
N.A.I.C.S.: 424820
Gerund Fund *(Mng Dir)*

ED'S EASY DINER GROUP LIMITED

Avenfield House 118-127 Park Lane
London, W1K 7AG, United Kingdom
Tel.: (44) 20 7629 6151 (Intl)
Fax: (44) 2074999010
E-Mail: samancha@edseasydiner.com
Web Site: www.edseasydiner.com
Year Founded: 1987
Sales Range: $10-24.9 Million
Emp.: 20
Business Description:
Retro-American Diner-Style Restaurants Operator
S.I.C.: 5812
N.A.I.C.S.: 722511
Personnel:
Andrew Guy *(CEO)*

EDSERV SOFTSYSTEMS LIMITED

New No 50 Old No 72 Arya Gowder Road West Mambalam
Chennai, 600 033, India
Tel.: (91) 44 3988 5533
Fax: (91) 4423723908
E-Mail: info@edserv.in
Web Site: www.edserv.in
EDSERV—(BOM NSE)
Rev.: $3,682,266
Assets: $55,746,128
Liabilities: $6,261,088
Net Worth: $49,485,040
Earnings: ($1,225,550)
Fiscal Year-end: 03/31/13
Business Description:
IT Products & Services
S.I.C.: 7373
N.A.I.C.S.: 541512
Personnel:
S. Giridharan *(Chm, CEO & Mng Dir)*
K. T. Srinivasan *(Compliance Officer)*
Board of Directors:
S. Giridharan
Ilango Balakrishna
Transfer Agent:
Karvy Computershare Private Limited
Karvy House 17-24 Near Image Hospital
Reliance Cybervilae Madhapur
Hyderabad, India

EDSR GMBH

Gemeindewald 19
86672 Thierhaupten, Germany
Tel.: (49) 8271818315
Fax: (49) 8271818378
E-Mail: info@eds-r.com
Web Site: www.eds-r.com
Emp.: 100
Business Description:
Environmental Consulting Services
S.I.C.: 8999
N.A.I.C.S.: 541620
Personnel:
Johann Schmidt *(Gen Mgr)*

EDUARD KETTNER

Z I Metz Nord 57 B Avenue Des 2 Fontaines
57050 Metz, Moselle, France
Tel.: (33) 387347373
Fax: (33) 145746959
Sls.: $36,700,000
Emp.: 80
S.I.C.: 5941
N.A.I.C.S.: 451110
Personnel:
Francis Gerard *(Dir-Admin)*

EDUCATION MEDIA & PUBLISHING GROUP (CHINA) LIMITED

(d/b/a Education Media & Publishing Group International)
75 Saint Stephens Green
Dublin, 2, Ireland
Tel.: (353) 1 511 0100
E-Mail: information@empgi.com
Web Site: www.empgi.com
Business Description:
Media & Publishing Investment Holding Company
S.I.C.: 6719

N.A.I.C.S.: 551112
Personnel:
Barry O'Callaghan *(Chm)*
Tim Griffiths *(CEO)*
David Clayton *(CFO)*
Justin Cahill *(Pres/CEO-RISE Global)*
Paul Wang *(CEO-RISE China)*
Board of Directors:
Barry O'Callaghan
William J. Bennett
Tony Lucki
David Puttnam
Paul Wang

EDUCATIONAL HOLDING GROUP COMPANY KSC

Chamber of Commerce & Industry Building
2nd Floor Al-Shouhada Str
PO Box 27215 Safat, Kuwait, 13133, Kuwait
Tel.: (965) 22407307
Fax: (965) 22407048
E-Mail: info@edu.com.kw
Web Site: www.edu.com.kw
EDU—(KUW)
Sales Range: $1-9.9 Million
Emp.: 36
Business Description:
Educational & Training Services
S.I.C.: 8299
N.A.I.C.S.: 611710
Personnel:
Abdul-Rahman Saleh Al-Muhailan *(Chm & Mng Dir)*
Muna Bu Rahma *(Deputy Chm)*
Bader Alzaid Al-Traiji *(CEO)*
Firas Mohammed Al-Oda *(Deputy Mng Dir)*
Board of Directors:
Abdul-Rahman Saleh Al-Muhailan
Salman Marzouq Mohammad Al-Alwan
Bader Naser Mansour Al-Mutairi
Bader Alzaid Al-Traiji
Amer Mahmoud Khawar Mahmoud
Muna Bu Rahma
Subsidiaries:

Human Dimensions Company (W.L.L) **(1)**
Al Shamiya Tower 6th Fl
PO Box 28326
Al Sour St Al Qibla Area Safat, Kuwait, 13144, Kuwait
Tel.: (965) 22331600
Fax: (965) 22331601
E-Mail: enquiry@hdmena.com
Web Site: www.hdmena.com
Recruitment Services
S.I.C.: 7361
N.A.I.C.S.: 561311
Tariq Ali *(Gen Mgr)*

SOS Consulting and Recruitment **(1)**
Al Khaleej Towers
PO Box 29273
Kuwait, Kuwait
Tel.: (965) 22243900
Fax: (965) 22243901
E-Mail: soskwt@soshr.net
Web Site: www.soshr.net
Emp.: 13
Recruitment Services
S.I.C.: 7361
N.A.I.C.S.: 561311
V. Jumana *(Deputy Gen Mgr)*

Synergy Corporation **(1)**
Marzouq Tower 16th Fl Al-Qibla Area
PO Box 34575
Block 14 St 3 A, Kuwait, Kuwait
Tel.: (965) 22477109
Fax: (965) 22477094
E-Mail: info@synergycorp.com.kw
Web Site: www.synergycorp.com.kw
Emp.: 15
Management Consulting Services
S.I.C.: 8742
N.A.I.C.S.: 541611
Jassem M. Al-Safran *(CEO)*

EDUCOMP SOLUTIONS, LTD.

1211 Padma Tower 1 5 Rajendra Place
New Delhi, 110008, India
Tel.: (91) 25753258
Fax: (91) 25766775
E-Mail: info@educomp.com
Web Site: www.educomp.com
EDUCOMP—(NSE)
Rev.: $245,919,937
Assets: $1,036,727,692
Liabilities: $495,573,273
Net Worth: $541,154,419
Earnings: ($26,489,396)
Emp.: 16,919
Fiscal Year-end: 03/31/13
Business Description:
Educational Technology Products & Services
S.I.C.: 8299
N.A.I.C.S.: 611710
Personnel:
Shantanu Prakash *(Chm & Mng Dir)*
Sanjay Jain *(CEO)*
Harish Popli *(Sec)*
Board of Directors:
Shantanu Prakash
Roy Campbell, II
Shonu Chandra
Rajiv Krishan Luthra
Jagdish Prakash
Sankalp Srivastava
Subbarao Valluri Venkata
Transfer Agent:
Link Intime India Private Limited
44 Community Centre Naraina Industrial Area Phase-I
New Delhi, 110028, India
Non-U.S. Subsidiary:

ASKnLearn Pte Ltd. **(1)**
10 Science Park Road 03 13 The Alpha
Singapore Science Park II, Singapore, 117684, Singapore
Tel.: (65) 67762013
Fax: (65) 67731610
E-Mail: admin1@asknlearn.com
Web Site: www.asknlearn.com
Emp.: 100
Internet-Based E-Learning Solutions, Content & Services for Schools
S.I.C.: 8299
N.A.I.C.S.: 611710

EDUN APPAREL LTD.

30 32 Sir John Rogersons Quay
Dublin, 2, Ireland
Tel.: (353) 12561289
Fax: (353) 12561299
E-Mail: info@edun.ie
Web Site: www.edun.com
Year Founded: 2005
Emp.: 20
Business Description:
Clothing Mfr & Retailer
S.I.C.: 2389
N.A.I.C.S.: 315240
Personnel:
Ali Hewson *(Founder)*

EDWARD B. BEHARRY & CO. LTD.

191 Charlotte St
Georgetown, Guyana
Tel.: (592) 2270632
Fax: (592) 2256062
E-Mail: ebbsec2@beharrygroup.com
Web Site: www.beharrygroup.com
Year Founded: 1935
Emp.: 1,500
Business Description:
Holding Company
S.I.C.: 6719
N.A.I.C.S.: 551112
Personnel:
Suresh Beharry *(Chm)*
Board of Directors:
Suresh Beharry
Rabindranauth Beharry
Subsidiary:

Secure International Finance Co. Inc. **(1)**
191 Charlotte St
Lacytown, Georgetown, Guyana
Tel.: (592) 22706325
Fax: (592) 2256062
E-Mail: sbeharry@beharrygroup.com
Web Site: www.beharrygroup.com
Emp.: 9
Financial Management Services
S.I.C.: 6211
N.A.I.C.S.: 523999
Suresh Beharry *(Chm)*

Subsidiary:

Guyana Bank for Trade & Industry Ltd. **(2)**
47-48 Water St
PO Box 10280
Georgetown, Guyana (61%)
Tel.: (592) 2268430
Fax: (592) 2271612
Web Site: www.gbtibank.com
Sales Range: $1-9.9 Million
Emp.: 250
Banking Services
S.I.C.: 6029
N.A.I.C.S.: 522110
Radhakrishna Sharma *(CEO)*
John Tracey *(Sec & Dir-Credit)*

EDWARD BILLINGTON & SON LTD.

Cunard Building
Liverpool, L3 1EL, United Kingdom
Tel.: (44) 151 243 9000
Fax: (44) 151 243 9015
E-Mail: ebs@ebsgroup.co.uk
Web Site: www.ebsgroup.co.uk
Year Founded: 1898
Sales Range: $350-399.9 Million
Emp.: 638
Business Description:
Investment Management Services
S.I.C.: 6799
N.A.I.C.S.: 523920
Personnel:
Lloyd Whiteley *(Chm)*
Gary Blake *(CEO)*
Board of Directors:
Lloyd Whiteley
Edward Billington
Gary Blake
Dave Brooks
Andrew King
David Marshall

EDWARD DILLON & CO. LTD.

Estuary House Block P7 East Point Business Park
Fairview, Dublin, 3, Ireland
Tel.: (353) 18193300
Fax: (353) 18555852
Web Site: www.edwarddillon.com
Business Description:
Wines & Spirit Distr
S.I.C.: 5182
N.A.I.C.S.: 424820
Personnel:
Andy O'Hara *(CEO)*

EDWARDS DOORS SYSTEMS LIMITED

PO Box 607
Sarnia, ON, N7T 7J4, Canada
Tel.: (519) 336-4991
Fax: (519) 336-6063
E-Mail: eds@edwardsdoors.com
Web Site: www.edwardsdoors.com
Year Founded: 1972
Rev.: $10,617,200
Emp.: 30
Business Description:
Electronic High Security Locks
Industrial Doors Mfr
S.I.C.: 5031
N.A.I.C.S.: 423310
Personnel:
Eleanor Cassidy *(Pres)*
G. W. Cassidy *(CEO)*

EDWARDS GARAGE LTD.

4403 42nd Avenue
PO Box 880
Red Deer, AB, T4T 1A6, Canada
Tel.: (403) 845-3328
Fax: (403) 845-4661
Toll Free: (800) 668-2438
E-Mail: main@edwardsgarage.com
Web Site: www.edwardsgarage.com
Rev.: $17,883,600
Emp.: 50
Business Description:
New & Used Car Dealers
S.I.C.: 5511
N.A.I.C.S.: 441110
Personnel:
Kathy De Wolfe *(Controller)*

EDYNAMICS SOLUTIONS LTD

Shop No 6 West Guru Angad Nagar
Opp DDA Building
Laxmi Nagar, Delhi, 110092, India
Tel.: (91) 1132971727
E-Mail: edynamicssolutions@yahoo.com
Web Site: www.edynamicssolutions.com
535694—(BOM)
Business Description:
Internet Retailer
S.I.C.: 5961
N.A.I.C.S.: 454111
Personnel:
Eti Vashist *(Compliance Officer & Sec)*
Board of Directors:
Anita Gupta
Bharat Gupta
Manish Kumar Gupta
Vikas Saini

EEELPA S.A.

Centre Commercial La Ponet
120 avenue du General Leclerc,
15000 Aurillac, France
Tel.: (33) 471646363
Fax: (33) 471649882
Sales Range: $10-24.9 Million
Emp.: 51
Business Description:
Grocery Store Operator
S.I.C.: 5411
N.A.I.C.S.: 445110
Personnel:
Pierre Fournier *(Pres)*

EEII AG

Alpenstrasse 15
PO Box 4853
6304 Zug, Switzerland
Tel.: (41) 417294280
Fax: (41) 417294229
E-Mail: info@eeii.ch
Web Site: www.eeii.ch
EEII—(SWX)
Int. Income: $16,137
Assets: $16,397,593
Liabilities: $295,444
Net Worth: $16,102,148
Earnings: ($15,126,347)
Fiscal Year-end: 12/31/12

EEII AG—(Continued)

Business Description:
Energy & Commodity Service Sectors
S.I.C.: 7389
N.A.I.C.S.: 541990
Personnel:
Beat Imwinkelried *(Sec)*
Board of Directors:
Heinz-Dieter Waffel
Victor Lorenz Gnehm
Beat Imwinkelried

EEMS ITALIA S.P.A

Viale delle Scienze 5
02015 Cittaducale, Italy
Tel.: (39) 07466041
Fax: (39) 0746604262
E-Mail: contact@eems.com
Web Site: www.eems.com
Year Founded: 1994
EEMS—(ITA)
Sales Range: $200-249.9 Million
Emp.: 1,431
Business Description:
Semiconductor Assembly & Test Solutions
S.I.C.: 3559
N.A.I.C.S.: 333242
Personnel:
Carlo Bernardocchi *(Chm)*
Paolo Andrea Mutti *(CEO)*
Board of Directors:
Carlo Bernardocchi
Simone Castronovo
Adriano De Maio
Stefano Lunardi
Giancarlo Malerba
Marco Stefano Mutti
Paolo Andrea Mutti

Subsidiary:

Solsonica (1)
Viale delle Scienze 5
Cittaducale, 02015, Italy
Tel.: (39) 0746604500
Fax: (39) 0746604309
E-Mail: info@solsonica.com
Web Site: www.solsonica.com
Emp.: 236
Photovoltaic & Solar Energy Management
S.I.C.: 9631
N.A.I.C.S.: 926130
Paolo Mutgi *(Gen Mgr)*

EESTI ENERGIA AS

Laki tn 2
12915 Tallinn, Estonia
Tel.: (372) 715 2222
Fax: (372) 715 2200
E-Mail: info@energia.ee
Web Site: www.energia.ee
Year Founded: 1939
Rev.: $1,106,686,357
Assets: $3,361,924,958
Liabilities: $1,465,036,811
Net Worth: $1,896,888,147
Earnings: $103,520,473
Emp.: 7,560
Fiscal Year-end: 12/31/12
Business Description:
Power & Electricity Producer, Distributor, Transmitter & Sales
S.I.C.: 3612
N.A.I.C.S.: 335311
Personnel:
Juri Kao *(Chm-Supervisory Bd)*
Sandor Liive *(Chm-Mgmt Bd & CEO)*
Margus Kaasik *(CFO & Member-Mgmt Bd)*
Margus Rink *(Member-Mgmt Bd & Mgr-Energy Sls)*
Raine Pajo *(Member-Mgmt Bd-Electricity & Heat Production)*
Supervisory Board of Directors:
Juri Kao
Meelis Atonen
Toomas Luman
Kalle Palling
Andres Saame
Olari Taal
Toomas Tauts
Mart Vooglaid

Subsidiaries:

Eesti Polevkivi AS (1)
Jaama tn 10
41533 Johvi, Estonia (100%)
Tel.: (372) 3364801
Fax: (372) 3364803
E-Mail: kaevandused@energia.ee
Web Site: www.ep.ee
Emp.: 3,000
Crude Petroleum & Natural Gas Extraction
S.I.C.: 1311
N.A.I.C.S.: 211111
Veljo Aleksandrov *(Chm)*

Elpec AS (1)
Kadaka 63
12915 Tallinn, Estonia (100%)
Tel.: (372) 7154100
Fax: (372) 7154101
Web Site: www.elpec.ee
Emp.: 80
Architectural Services
S.I.C.: 8712
N.A.I.C.S.: 541310
Mike Teske *(Mng Dir)*

Energoremont AS (1)
Tiigi 6
Narva, 20104, Estonia (100%)
Tel.: (372) 7166702
Fax: (372) 7166790
E-Mail: tehnoloogiatoostus@energia.ee
Emp.: 2
Plate Work Mfr
S.I.C.: 3443
N.A.I.C.S.: 332313
Martti Kork *(CEO)*

Iru Elektrijaam OU (1)
Peterburi tee 105
74114 Maardu, Estonia (100%)
Tel.: (372) 7153222
Fax: (372) 7153200
E-Mail: iru@energia.ee
Web Site: www.iruenergia.ee
Emp.: 51
Other Electric Power Generation
S.I.C.: 4939
N.A.I.C.S.: 221118
Anatoli Petrov *(Product Mgr)*

Jaotusvork OU (1)
Kadaka tee 63
Tallinn, Estonia (100%)
Tel.: (372) 7154230
Fax: (372) 7151200
E-Mail: jb@anargia.ee
Web Site: www.anargia.ee
Emp.: 800
Instrument Mfr for Measuring & Testing Electricity & Electrical Signals
S.I.C.: 3825
N.A.I.C.S.: 334515
Dar Mera *(Gen Mgr)*

Maetehnika AS (1)
8 Malmi
Johvi, 41537, Estonia (100%)
Tel.: (372) 3364301
Fax: (372) 3364302
Web Site: www.tehmoloogiatoost.ee
Emp.: 360
Mining Machinery & Equipment Mfr
S.I.C.: 3532
N.A.I.C.S.: 333131
Martti Kork *(Mng Dir)*

Narva Elektrijaamad As (1)
Elektrijaama Tee 59
Narva, Tallinn, Estonia (100%)
Tel.: (372) 7166100
Fax: (372) 7166200
E-Mail: nag@energia.ee
Emp.: 1,300
Instrument Mfr for Measuring & Testing Electricity & Electrical Signals
S.I.C.: 3825
N.A.I.C.S.: 334515
Tonu Aas *(Mng Dir)*

Narva Soojusvork AS (1)
Oru 2
Narva, 20203 Tallinn, Estonia (66%)
Tel.: (372) 3591250
Fax: (372) 3560672
Business Service Centers
S.I.C.: 7334
N.A.I.C.S.: 561439

Nordic Energy Link AS (1)
Laki 24
Tallinn, 12915, Estonia (100%)
Tel.: (372) 7152307
E-Mail: gunnar.virk@energia.ee
Electrical Apparatus & Equipment Wiring Supplies & Construction Material Whslr
S.I.C.: 5063
N.A.I.C.S.: 423610

Pohivork OU (1)
Kadaka tee 42
12915 Tallinn, Estonia (100%)
Tel.: (372) 7151209
Fax: (372) 7151200
E-Mail: info@elering.ee
Web Site: www.elering.ee
Emp.: 150
Instrument Mfr for Measuring & Testing Electricity & Electrical Signals
S.I.C.: 3825
N.A.I.C.S.: 334515
Taavi Veskimagi *(Chm)*

Polevkivi Kaevandamise AS (1)
10 Jaama
41533 Johvi, Estonia (100%)
Tel.: (372) 3364801
Fax: (372) 3364803
Web Site: www.ep.ee/?lang=en
Emp.: 8
Crude Petroleum & Natural Gas Extraction
S.I.C.: 1311
N.A.I.C.S.: 211111

Non-U.S. Subsidiaries:

Jordan Oil Shale Energy Company (1)
PO Box 962497
Amman, 11196, Jordan
Tel.: (962) 65157064
Fax: (962) 65157046
E-Mail: info@joseco.com.jo
Web Site: www.joseco.com.jo
JOSE—(AMM)
Sales Range: Less than $1 Million
Emp.: 10
Oil Shale & Oil Sand Exploration & Production Services
S.I.C.: 1311
N.A.I.C.S.: 211111
Abdul Rahim Ali Al-Zoubi *(Dir Gen)*

EFACEC CAPITAL, SGPS, S.A.

Arroteia Leca do Balio Apartado 1018
4466-952 Porto, Portugal
Tel.: (351) 229562300
Fax: (351) 229518933
E-Mail: sgps@efacec.pt
Web Site: www.efacec.pt
Year Founded: 1948
Sls.: $1,050,143,356
Assets: $1,349,934,163
Liabilities: $1,252,849,375
Net Worth: $97,084,788
Earnings: $11,104,383
Emp.: 4,388
Fiscal Year-end: 12/31/12
Business Description:
Power Generation, Transmission & Distribution Equipment Mfr
S.I.C.: 3568
N.A.I.C.S.: 333613
Personnel:
Pedro Maria Guimaraes Jose de Mello *(Chm)*
Luis Francisco Valente de Oliveira *(Chm-Supervisory Bd)*
Joao Afonso Ramalho Sopas Pereira Bento *(Vice Chm & CEO)*
Manuel Antonio Carvalho Goncalves *(Vice Chm)*
Francisco de La Fuente Sanchez *(Vice Chm)*
Rui Alexandre Pires Diniz *(CFO)*
Joana Martins Mendes *(Sec)*
Board of Directors:
Pedro Maria Guimaraes Jose de Mello
Daniel Bessa Fernandes Coelho
Luis Eduardo Brito Freixial de Goes
Rui Manuel Campos Guimaraes
Manuel Antonio Carvalho Goncalves
Alberto de Freitas Martins
Francisco de La Fuente Sanchez
Alberto Joaquim Milheiro Barbosa
Luis Augusto Nesbitt Rebelo da Silva
Luis Miguel Nogueira Freire Cortes Martins
Rui Alexandre Pires Diniz
Joao Afonso Ramalho Sopas Pereira Bento
Francisco Bernardo Sampaio de Almada-Lobo
Supervisory Board of Directors:
Luis Francisco Valente de Oliveira
Luis Black Freire d'Andrade
Maria Leonor Aires

U.S. Subsidiary:

Advanced Control Systems, Inc. (1)
2755 Northwoods Pkwy
Norcross, GA 30071
Tel.: (770) 446-8854
Fax: (770) 448-0957
Toll Free: (800) 831-7223
E-Mail: sales@acsatlanta.com
Web Site: www.acsatlanta.com
Sales Range: $50-74.9 Million
Emp.: 108
Electricty Transmission & Generation Control Systems
S.I.C.: 3825
N.A.I.C.S.: 334515
Jose Barbosa *(CEO)*

EFAD REAL ESTATE COMPANY

PO Box 21876
Kuwait, 13079, Kuwait
Tel.: (965) 22427060
Fax: (965) 2414535
E-Mail: info@efadholding.com
Web Site: www.efadre.com
Business Description:
Holding Company
S.I.C.: 6719
N.A.I.C.S.: 551112
Personnel:
Rezam Mohamed Al Roumi *(CEO)*
Antar Gad *(Exec VP-Fin & Investment Affairs)*
Mahmoud Samy *(Exec VP-Strategic Investment & Risk Mgmt)*

Subsidiary:

Adeem Investment & Wealth Management Co., K.S.C.C. (1)
PO Box 29092
13151 Kuwait, Safat, Kuwait
Tel.: (965) 222 33 000
Fax: (965) 222 33 003
E-Mail: info@adeeminv.com
Web Site: www.adeeminv.com
Investment & Wealth Management Services
S.I.C.: 6211
N.A.I.C.S.: 523999
Najeeb Abdelaziz Al-Humaidhi *(Chm)*
Mahmoud Sami Mohammad Ali *(Vice Chm & Mng Dir)*

Affiliate:

Investment Dar Company K.S.C.C. (2)
Sharq Al Shuhada Street Arraya Center
31st Floor
PO Box 5963
Safat, Kuwait, 13060, Kuwait
Tel.: (965) 22324000
Fax: (965) 22324001
E-Mail: info@inv-dar.com
Web Site: www.inv-dar.com
Sales Range: $650-699.9 Million
Emp.: 211

Financial, Real Estate & Investment Services
S.I.C.: 6211
N.A.I.C.S.: 523999
Adnan A. Al-Musallam *(Chm & Mng Dir)*
Ghanim Al-Shaheen Al-Ghanim *(Vice Chm)*
Abdullah Al-Humaidhi *(CEO)*
Fawzi Al-Najdi *(Exec VP-Real Estate)*

Non-U.S. Holding:

Aston Martin Lagonda Limited (3)
Banbury Rd
Gaydon, Warwickshire, CV35 0DB, United Kingdom UK
Tel.: (44) 1926644644
Fax: (44) 1926644733
E-Mail: enquiries@astonmartin.com
Web Site: www.astonmartin.com
Emp.: 1,200
Luxury Sportscar Mfr
S.I.C.: 3711
N.A.I.C.S.: 336111
David Richards *(Chm)*
Ulrich Bez *(CEO)*
Hanno Kirner *(CFO)*
Adham Charanoglu *(CEO-Middle East, North Africa & India)*

Branch:

Aston Martin Lagonda (4)
Tickford Street
Newport Pagnell, MK16 9AN, United Kingdom
Tel.: (44) 1908610620
Fax: (44) 1908210481
E-Mail: enquiries@astonmartin.com
Web Site: www.astonmartin.com
Emp.: 250
Automotive Design Services
S.I.C.: 8711
N.A.I.C.S.: 541330
Ulrich Bez *(CEO)*

U.S. Subsidiaries:

Aston Martin Lagonda of North America, Inc. (4)
9920 Ervine Center Dr
Irvine, CA 92618 CT
Tel.: (949) 379-3100
Fax: (949) 379-3140
E-Mail: amparts@astonmartin.com
Web Site: www.astonmartin.com
Automobiles & Parts Importer & Distr Import
S.I.C.: 5012
N.A.I.C.S.: 423110
Julian Jenkins *(VP & Gen Mgr)*

EFANOR INVESTIMENTOS, SGPS, SA

Avenida da Boavista
1277/81 4, Porto, Portugal
Tel.: (351) 229487522
Fax: (351) 226077750
Business Description:
Investment Holding Company
S.I.C.: 6211
N.A.I.C.S.: 523999
Personnel:
Belmiro Mendes de Azevedo *(Owner & Chm)*

Holdings:

Sonae Industria, SGPS, S.A. (1)
Lugar do Espido - Via Norte Apartado 1096
4470-177 Maia, Portugal
Tel.: (351) 220 100 400
Fax: (351) 220 100 436
E-Mail: sonaeindustria@sonaeindustria.com
Web Site: www.sonaeindustria.com
SONI—(EUR)
Sls.: $1,772,489,148
Assets: $1,708,313,324
Liabilities: $1,526,368,936
Net Worth: $181,944,388
Earnings: ($134,686,865)
Emp.: 4,408
Fiscal Year-end: 12/31/12
Wood Panel Mfr
S.I.C.: 2436
N.A.I.C.S.: 321212
Belmiro Mendes de Azevedo *(Chm)*
Duarte Paulo Teixeira de Azevedo *(Deputy Chm)*
Julia Maria Moreira da Silva Santos *(Sec)*

Sonae SGPS, SA (1)
Lugar Do Espido Via Norte Apartado 1011
4471 909 Maia, Portugal (52.99%)
Tel.: (351) 229487522
Fax: (351) 229487722
E-Mail: comucacao@sonae.pt
Web Site: www.sonae.pt
SON—(EUR)
Sls.: $6,128,503,374
Assets: $8,124,614,457
Liabilities: $5,878,450,494
Net Worth: $2,246,163,963
Earnings: $96,507,443
Emp.: 40,000
Fiscal Year-end: 12/31/12
Shopping Center Retail Operations, Supermarket Chain Supplier, Real Estate Services & Telecommunications
S.I.C.: 5999
N.A.I.C.S.: 453998
Belmiro Mendes de Azevedo *(Chm)*
Duarte Paulo Teixeira de Azevedo *(CEO)*
Luzia Leonor Borges e Gomes Ferreira *(Sec)*

Subsidiaries:

Modelo Continente, SGPA, SA (2)
Rua Joao Mondoca 529-6
Serzedo, Portugal
Tel.: (351) 229561958
Fax: (351) 22 956 1318
Operates Supermarkets
S.I.C.: 5411
N.A.I.C.S.: 445110

Sonae Capital, SGPS, SA (2)
Lugar do Espido Via Norte
4471 909 Maia, Portugal
Tel.: (351) 22 012 95 00
Fax: (351) 22 012 95 21
E-Mail: ir@sonaecapital.pt
Web Site: www.sonaecapital.pt
SONC—(EUR)
Sls.: $69,887,844
Assets: $884,991,407
Liabilities: $448,890,078
Net Worth: $436,101,329
Earnings: ($15,786,292)
Emp.: 1,502
Fiscal Year-end: 12/31/12
Investment Banking Services
S.I.C.: 6211
N.A.I.C.S.: 523110
Belmiro Mendes de Azevedo *(Chm)*
Maria Claudia Teixeira de Azevedo *(CEO)*
Ivone Maria Pinho Teixeira *(CFO)*
Barbara Almeida *(IR Officer)*
Anabela Nogueira de Matos *(Sec)*

Sonae.com (2)
Rua Henrique Pousao 432 - 7
Senhora da Hora, 4460-841 Lisbon, Portugal
Tel.: (351) 229572000
Fax: (351) 931002204
E-Mail: paulo.azevedo@sonae.com
Web Site: www.sonae.com
Wireless Communications Website
S.I.C.: 4899
N.A.I.C.S.: 517919

Holding:

Sonae Sierra SGPS, SA (2)
Rua Amilcar Cabral 23
1750-018 Lisbon, Portugal (50%)
Tel.: (351) 217515000
Fax: (351) 217582688
Web Site: www.sonaesierra.com
Emp.: 800
Shopping Center Owner, Manager & Developer
S.I.C.: 6531
N.A.I.C.S.: 531312
Paulo Azevedo *(Chm)*
Fernando Guedes de Oliveira *(Deputy CEO)*

EFESAN GROUP

Barbaros Bulvari Dr Orhan Birman is Merkezi 149 Kat 3-4
Besiktas, 34349 Istanbul, Turkey
Tel.: (90) 2122887070
Fax: (90) 2122887078
E-Mail: info@efesan.com.tr
Web Site: www.efesan.com.tr
Emp.: 1,000
Business Description:
Steel Mfr
S.I.C.: 3399
N.A.I.C.S.: 331110
Personnel:
Kadir Efe *(Chm & Owner)*

EFFICIENT E-SOLUTIONS BHD.

No 3 Jalan Astaka U8/82 Taman Perindustrian
Bukit Jelutong Seksyen U8 Bukit Jelutong, 40150 Shah Alam, Selangor Darul Ehsan, Malaysia
Tel.: (60) 378452555
Fax: (60) 378423155
E-Mail: contactus@efficient.com.my
Web Site: www.efficient.com.my
EFFICEN—(KLS)
Rev.: $13,753,843
Assets: $41,763,623
Liabilities: $3,638,261
Net Worth: $38,125,363
Earnings: $1,321,213
Emp.: 360
Fiscal Year-end: 12/31/12
Business Description:
Business Process Outsourcing Services
S.I.C.: 7389
N.A.I.C.S.: 561439
Personnel:
Vincent Chee Kong Cheah *(Mng Dir)*
Chen Tong Chong *(Sec)*
Esther Yoke Leng Soon *(Sec)*
Kean Wai Tan *(Sec)*
Board of Directors:
Abdul Latif Abdullah
Victor Chee Wai Cheah
Vincent Chee Kong Cheah
Hin Choy Ho
Hin Lee Ng
Esther Yoke Leng Soon
Kian Yee Voong

Subsidiaries:

Efficient Mailcom Sdn. Bhd. (1)
No 49 Jln Petaling Utama 3 Taman Petaling Utama
46000 Petaling Jaya, Selangor, Malaysia
Tel.: (60) 377812555
Fax: (60) 3 7781 6846
Business Process Outsourcing Services
S.I.C.: 8641
N.A.I.C.S.: 813990

Efficient Softech Sdn. Bhd. (1)
45-49 Jalan Petaling Utama 3 Taman Petaling Utama
46000 Petaling Jaya, Selangor, Malaysia
Tel.: (60) 377812555
Fax: (60) 377816846
Emp.: 30
Information Tecnology Services
S.I.C.: 7371
N.A.I.C.S.: 541511

EFFICIENT GROUP LIMITED

81 Dely Road
Hazelwood, Pretoria, 0081, South Africa
Tel.: (27) 12 460 9580
Fax: (27) 12 346 6135
E-Mail: info@efgroup.co.za
Web Site: www.efgroup.co.za
EFG—(JSE)
Rev.: $8,825,640
Assets: $10,014,017
Liabilities: $2,081,865
Net Worth: $7,932,152
Earnings: $279,362
Emp.: 154
Fiscal Year-end: 08/31/13
Business Description:
Financial & Asset Management Services
S.I.C.: 6211
N.A.I.C.S.: 523999
Personnel:
Heiko Weidhase *(CEO)*
Anton de Klerk *(CFO)*
Robert Walton *(CEO-Efficient Invest)*
Rudi Barnard *(Sec & Head-Legal & Compliance)*
Board of Directors:
Steve Booysen
Mariam Cassim
Zee Cele
Anton de Klerk
Abrie du Preez
Jerry Mabena
Dawie Roodt
Joe Rosen
Lyn Taylor
Robert Walton
Heiko Weidhase
Legal Counsel:
Java Capital (Pty) Ltd
2nd Floor 2 Arnold Road
2196 Rosebank, South Africa
Transfer Agent:
Link Market Services South Africa (Pty) Limited
13th Floor Rennie House 19 Ameshoff Street
Braamfontein, South Africa

EFFINGO TEXTILE & TRADING LIMITED

102 Akashdeep Building 26A
Barakhamba Road
New Delhi, 110 001, India
Tel.: (91) 11 23752970
E-Mail: maltitextile@yahoo.com
Web Site: www.maltitextiles.com
Year Founded: 1985
512207—(BOM)
Rev.: $874,094
Assets: $2,742,736
Liabilities: $436,219
Net Worth: $2,306,517
Earnings: $6,183
Fiscal Year-end: 03/31/13
Business Description:
Textile Product Mfr
S.I.C.: 2399
N.A.I.C.S.: 314999
Personnel:
Priya Rawal *(CEO & Mng Dir)*
Manish Jain *(Compliance Officer)*
Board of Directors:
Rajendra Prasad Gogawat
Manish Jain
Priya Rawal
Anil Tandon
Transfer Agent:
ABHIPRA CAPITAL LTD
BM-1 A-387 Abhipra Complex Dilkhush
Industrial Area G T Karnal Road
Azadpur, New Delhi, 110 033, India

EFG-HERMES HOLDING COMPANY

Building No B129 Phase 3 Smart Village Km 28
Cairo Alexandria Desert Road, Cairo, 12577, Egypt
Tel.: (20) 2 3535 6499
Fax: (20) 2 3537 0942
E-Mail: corporate@efg-hermes.com
Web Site: www.efg-hermes.com
Year Founded: 1980
HRHO—(EGX LSE)
Rev.: $67,806,280
Assets: $8,837,540,479
Liabilities: $7,142,514,667
Net Worth: $1,695,025,812
Earnings: $31,362,402

EFG-Hermes Holding Company—(Continued)

Emp.: 1,055
Fiscal Year-end: 12/31/12
Business Description:
Investment Banking & Financial Services
S.I.C.: 6211
N.A.I.C.S.: 523110
Personnel:
Karim Awad *(Co-CEO)*
Yasser El Mallawany *(Co-CEO)*
Khalid Ellaicy *(CFO)*
Takis Arapoglou *(CEO-Comml Banking)*
Board of Directors:
Mona Zulficar
Takis Arapoglou
Karim Awad
Robert Eichfeld
Yasser El Mallawany
D. William J. Garrett
Joseph Iskander
Marwan Ahmead Lutfi
Charles McVeigh, III
Thomas S. Volpe

Subsidiaries:

EFG-Hermes Investment Banking (1)
58 El Tahrir St
Gokki, Giza, Egypt (100%)
Web Site: www.efg-hermes.com
Emp.: 18
Provider of Investment Banking Services
S.I.C.: 6282
N.A.I.C.S.: 523930

Financial Brokerage Group (1)
58 El Tahrir St
Giza, Egypt (100%)
Tel.: (20) 23374713
Fax: (20) 23385400
Provider of Financial Services
S.I.C.: 6282
N.A.I.C.S.: 523930

Hermes Financial Management Egypt, Ltd. (1)
58 El Tahrir St
Giza, Egypt
Tel.: (20) 23365960
Fax: (20) 23365589
Web Site: www.efg-hermes.com
Emp.: 15
Provider of Financial Management Services
S.I.C.: 6282
N.A.I.C.S.: 523930

Hermes Securities Brokerage (1)
Building No B 129 Phase 3 Smart Village
Km 28 Cairo-Alexandria Desert
Road 6 October, 12577 Cairo, Egypt (100%)
Tel.: (20) 235356499
Web Site: www.efg-hermes.com
Online Securities Brokerage Services
S.I.C.: 6211
N.A.I.C.S.: 523120

Non-U.S. Subsidiaries:

EFG Hermes Financial Management (Egypt) Ltd (1)
C/o International Corporate Management Of Bermuda 19 Par-La-Ville Road
Hamilton, Bermuda
Tel.: (441) 292 3580
Fax: (441) 292 5898
Investment Management Services
S.I.C.: 6211
N.A.I.C.S.: 523999

EFG Hermes UAE Ltd (1)
The Gate Building Dubai International Financial Centre
Dubai, United Arab Emirates
Tel.: (971) 43634000
Fax: (971) 43621170
Investment Banking & Securities Brokerage Services
S.I.C.: 6211
N.A.I.C.S.: 523110
Seif Fikry *(CEO)*

Vision Securities Company LLC (1)
PO Box 712
Muscat, 131, Oman
Tel.: (968) 24726000
Fax: (968) 2409902
Web Site: www.investvis.com
Securities Brokerage Services
S.I.C.: 6211
N.A.I.C.S.: 523120

EFG INTERNATIONAL AG

Bahnhofstrasse 12
8001 Zurich, Switzerland
Tel.: (41) 442261850
Fax: (41) 442261855
E-Mail: investorrelations@efginternational.com
Web Site: www.efginternational.com
EFGN—(SWX)
Rev.: $472,634,228
Assets: $25,499,906,388
Liabilities: $24,079,089,540
Net Worth: $1,420,816,848
Earnings: $133,511,884
Emp.: 2,260
Fiscal Year-end: 12/31/12
Business Description:
Asset Management & Private Banking Services
S.I.C.: 6211
N.A.I.C.S.: 523110
Personnel:
Jean Pierre Cuoni *(Chm)*
Hugh Napier Matthews *(Vice Chm)*
John Williamson *(CEO)*
Patrick Zbinden *(COO-Asset Mgmt)*
Giorgio Pradelli *(CFO)*
Mark Bagnall *(COO)*
Fredrick Link *(Chief Risk Officer)*
Henric Immink *(Gen Counsel)*
Board of Directors:
Jean Pierre Cuoni
Nico H. Burki
Emmanuel L. Bussetil
Erwin Richard Caduff
Michael Higgin
Spiro J. Latsis
Hugh Napier Matthews
Hans Niederer
Pericles Petalas
Bernd-A. von Maltzan

Subsidiaries:

EFG Asset Management Holding AG (1)
Bahnhofstrasse 12
Zurich, 8001, Switzerland
Tel.: (41) 442261850
Investment Management Services
S.I.C.: 6211
N.A.I.C.S.: 523999

EFG Bank AG (1)
Bahnhofstrasse 16
PO Box 2255
8022 Zurich, Switzerland (100%)
Tel.: (41) 442261717
Fax: (41) 442261726
E-Mail: enquiries_ch@efgbank.com
Web Site: www.efgbank.com
Commercial Banking
S.I.C.: 6029
N.A.I.C.S.: 522110
Albert Chiu *(CEO)*
Kong Eng Huat *(CEO-Singapore & South East Asia)*

On Finance SA (1)
Via Peri 9d
6900 Lugano, Switzerland
Tel.: (41) 91 910 20 60
Fax: (41) 91 910 20 61
E-Mail: ask@onfinance.ch
Web Site: www.onfinance.ch
Financial Management Services
S.I.C.: 6211
N.A.I.C.S.: 523999
Stefano Pezzoli *(Founder & Partner)*

SIF Swiss Investment Funds S.A. (1)
Quai du Seujet 26
CH 1211 Geneva, 2, Switzerland
Tel.: (41) 229187388
Fax: (41) 229187389
E-Mail: info@swiss-if.ch
Web Site: www.swiss-if.ch
Emp.: 6
Investment Services
S.I.C.: 6211
N.A.I.C.S.: 523110
Rebos Zumac *(Gen Mgr)*

U.S. Subsidiaries:

EFG Capital International Corp. (1)
701 Brickell Ave 9th Fl
Miami, FL 33131
Tel.: (305) 482-8000
Fax: (305) 482-8200
Web Site: www.efgcapital.com
Emp.: 130
Investment Banking Services
S.I.C.: 6211
N.A.I.C.S.: 523110
Victor Echevarria *(CEO)*

PRS International Consulting Inc (1)
801 Brickell Ave Ste 1600
Miami, FL 33131
Tel.: (305) 381-8340
Fax: (305) 381-8334
E-Mail: marketing@prsint.com
Asset Management & Financial Consulting Services
S.I.C.: 8742
N.A.I.C.S.: 541611
Benjamin Hein *(Co-Pres)*
Gonzalo Rodriguez-Frail *(Co-Pres)*

Non-U.S. Subsidiaries:

Bank von Ernst (Liechtenstein) AG (1)
Egertastrasse 10
FL-9490 Vaduz, Liechtenstein
Tel.: (423) 2655353
Fax: (423) 2655363
E-Mail: info@bve.li
Web Site: www.efgbankvonernst.com
Emp.: 20
Banking Services
S.I.C.: 6029
N.A.I.C.S.: 522110
Ernst Weder *(CEO)*

Bull Wealth Management Group Inc. (1)
4100 Yonge Street Suite 612
Toronto, ON, M2P 2B5, Canada
Tel.: (416) 223-2053
Fax: (416) 223-7940
E-Mail: bwmg@bullwealth.com
Web Site: www.bullwealth.com
Emp.: 30
Investment Services
S.I.C.: 6211
N.A.I.C.S.: 523999
James A. Bull *(Founder, Pres & CEO)*

EFG Bank AB (1)
Jakobsbergsgatan 16
Box 55963
102 16 Stockholm, Sweden
Tel.: (46) 8 555 09 400
Fax: (46) 8 662 21 50
E-Mail: info@efgbank.se
Web Site: www.efgbank.se
Commercial Banking Services
S.I.C.: 6029
N.A.I.C.S.: 522110
Lars Thoren *(CEO & Gen Mgr)*

EFG Bank (Gibraltar) Ltd (1)
Corral Road 1
PO Box 561
Gibraltar, Gibraltar
Tel.: (350) 200 40 117
Fax: (350) 200 40 110
E-Mail: enquiries_gi@efgbank.com
Commercial Banking Services
S.I.C.: 6029
N.A.I.C.S.: 522110

EFG Bank (Luxembourg) SA (1)
14 Allae Marconi
2120 Luxembourg, Luxembourg
Tel.: (352) 26 454 1
Fax: (352) 26 454 500
E-Mail: infolux@efgbank.com
Web Site: www.efgbank.lu
Commercial Banking Services
S.I.C.: 6029
N.A.I.C.S.: 522110
Ian Cookson *(Chm)*
Ludovic Chechin-Laurans *(Co-Mng Dir)*
Francois-Regis Montazel *(Co-Mng Dir)*
Huguette Espen *(Sr VP)*

EFG Bank (Monaco) (1)
Villa Les Aigles 15 Avenue d'Ostende
BP 37
Monaco, 98001, Monaco
Tel.: (377) 93 15 11 11
Fax: (377) 93 15 11 12
E-Mail: enquiries_mco@efgbank.com
Commercial Banking Services
S.I.C.: 6029
N.A.I.C.S.: 522110

EFG Bank von Ernst AG (1)
Egertastrasse 10
9490 Vaduz, Liechtenstein
Tel.: (423) 265 53 53
Fax: (423) 265 53 63
E-Mail: info@efgbankvonernst.com
Web Site: www.efgbankvonernst.com
Emp.: 25
Investment Banking Services
S.I.C.: 6211
N.A.I.C.S.: 523110
Rudy van den Steen *(Chm)*
Gerhard H. Muller *(Vice Chm)*
Daniel Taverna *(Exec VP)*
Ernst Weder *(Exec VP)*
Karl Drawitsch *(Sr VP)*

EFG Banque Privee SA (1)
5 Boulevard de la Tour Maubourg
75007 Paris, France
Tel.: (33) 1 44 11 13 00
Fax: (33) 1 44 11 13 01
E-Mail: information@efggroup.com
Web Site: www.efgfrance.com
Investment Management Services
S.I.C.: 6211
N.A.I.C.S.: 523999

EFG Investment Bank (1)
Engelbrektsgatan 9-11
114 32 Stockholm, Sweden
Tel.: (46) 84596400
Fax: (46) 8 662 2150
E-Mail: info@efgib.com
Web Site: www.efgib.com
Investment Services
S.I.C.: 6211
N.A.I.C.S.: 523110
Martin Nilsson *(CEO)*

EFG Platts Flello Ltd (1)
33 Great Charles Street
Birmingham, West Midlands, B3 3JN, United Kingdom
Tel.: (44) 121 200 2255
Fax: (44) 121 200 0950
Emp.: 15
Financial Management Services
S.I.C.: 6211
N.A.I.C.S.: 523999
John Male *(Gen Mgr)*

EFG Private Bank Limited (1)
Leconfield House
Curzon Street, London, W1J 5JB, United Kingdom
Tel.: (44) 2074919111
Fax: (44) 2078723706
E-Mail: info@efgl.com
Web Site: www.efgl.com
Emp.: 250
Banking Services
S.I.C.: 6029
N.A.I.C.S.: 522110

Subsidiaries:

EFG Ashby London Financial Services Limited (2)
Waterloo Ct 31 Waterloo Rd
Wolverhampton, WV1 4DJ, United Kingdom
Tel.: (44) 1902710402
Fax: (44) 1902422975
E-Mail: enquiries@efgashbylondon.com
Web Site: www.efgashbylondon.com
Emp.: 25
Investment Banking Services
S.I.C.: 6211
N.A.I.C.S.: 523110
Phil Oaten *(Mng Dir)*

EFG Asset Management (UK) Ltd. (2)
Leconfield House
Curzon St, London, W1J 5JB, United Kingdom UK
Tel.: (44) 2074919111
Fax: (44) 2078723706
Web Site: www.efgl.com
Asset Management Services
S.I.C.: 6211
N.A.I.C.S.: 523110
Mozamil Afzal *(Chief Investment Officer)*

EFG Harris Allday (2)
33 Great Charles Street
Birmingham, B3 3JN, United Kingdom
Tel.: (44) 121 333 1222
Fax: (44) 121 236 2587
E-Mail: info@efgha.com
Web Site: www.efgoffshore.com
Investment Banking Services
S.I.C.: 6211
N.A.I.C.S.: 523110
Ronald Treverton-Jones *(Mng Dir)*

EFG Independent Financial Advisors Ltd (2)
33 Great Charles Street
Birmingham, B3 3JN, United Kingdom
Tel.: (44) 121 200 2255
Fax: (44) 121 200 0950
E-Mail: enquiries@efg-ifa.com
Web Site: www.efg-ifa.com
Financial Advisory Services
S.I.C.: 6282
N.A.I.C.S.: 523930
Peter London *(Chm)*
John Male *(Mng Dir)*

EFG Platts Fiello Limited (2)
33 Great Charls St
Birmingham, B3 3JN, United Kingdom
Tel.: (44) 1212002255
Fax: (44) 1212000950
E-Mail: enquiries@efgl.com
Web Site: www.efgl.com
Emp.: 50
Investment Banking Services
S.I.C.: 6211
N.A.I.C.S.: 523110
Mike Knott *(Mng Dir)*

Non-U.S. Subsidiaries:

EFG Offshore Limited (2)
Seaton Place
PO Box 641 1
Saint Helier, JE4 8YJ, Jersey
Tel.: (44) 1534605600
Fax: (44) 1534605605
E-Mail: office@efgoffshore.com
Web Site: www.efgoffshore.com
Emp.: 90
Investment Banking Services
S.I.C.: 6211
N.A.I.C.S.: 523110
Gerard Gardner *(Mng Dir)*

EFG Private Bank (Channel Islands) Limited (2)
PO Box 603 EFG House Saint Julian's Avenue
Saint Peter Port, GY1 4NN, Guernsey
Tel.: (44) 1481723432
Fax: (44) 1481 723488
Web Site: www.efgoffshore.com
Banking Services
S.I.C.: 6029
N.A.I.C.S.: 522110
Gerard Gardner *(Mng Dir)*

EFG Wealth Management (Canada) Limited (1)
350 Sparks Street Suite 909
Ottawa, ON, K1R 7S8, Canada
Tel.: (613) 565-4334
Fax: (613) 565-4333
E-Mail: efgcanada@efgcanada.com
Web Site: www.efgcanada.com
Investment Advisory Services
S.I.C.: 6282
N.A.I.C.S.: 523930

EFG Wealth Management (India) Private Limited (1)
Marshall Building 1st Floor Shoorji Vallabhdas Marg Ballard Estate
400 038 Mumbai, India
Tel.: (91) 22 6634 9946
Fax: (91) 22 6634 9926
Financial Management Services
S.I.C.: 6211
N.A.I.C.S.: 523999
Pradeep Nair *(CEO)*

Quesada Kapitalforvaltning AB (1)
Jakobsbergsgatan 16
111 44 Stockholm, Sweden
Tel.: (46) 8 555 096 50
Fax: (46) 8 555 096 51
E-Mail: info@quesada.se
Emp.: 4
Investment Management Services
S.I.C.: 6211
N.A.I.C.S.: 523999
Lars Thoren *(Gen Mgr)*

EFORCE HOLDINGS LIMITED

Suite 3008 Man Yee Building 68 Des Voeux Road Central
Central, China (Hong Kong)
Tel.: (852) 2165 8000
Fax: (852) 2165 8008
Web Site: www.eforce.com.hk
943—(HKG)
Sls.: $19,282,409
Assets: $63,644,820
Liabilities: $68,262,519
Net Worth: ($4,617,699)
Earnings: ($26,097,030)
Fiscal Year-end: 12/31/12

Business Description:
Healthcare Product Mfr
S.I.C.: 2834
N.A.I.C.S.: 325412

Personnel:
Franky Lup Wai Tam *(Chm)*
Liyang Liu *(Deputy Chm & CEO)*
Tsz Leung Chan *(Sec)*

Board of Directors:
Franky Lup Wai Tam
Chunming Jiang
Bing Kwan Lam
Ming On Lam
Liyang Liu
Mujuan Lu
Xiaohong Luo
Shouquan Wan

Butterfield Fulcrum Group (Bermuda) Limited
26 Burnaby Street
Hamilton, HM 11, Bermuda

EFORE PLC

Quartetto Business Park Linnoitustie 4B
PO Box 260
02600 Espoo, Finland
Tel.: (358) 9478466
Fax: (358) 947846500
E-Mail: webmaster@efore.fi
Web Site: www.efore.com
Year Founded: 1975
EFO1V—(HEL)
Sls.: $103,229,630
Assets: $57,230,722
Liabilities: $29,910,984
Net Worth: $27,319,738
Earnings: ($3,094,695)
Emp.: 804
Fiscal Year-end: 10/31/12

Business Description:
Electronic Component Mfr
S.I.C.: 3679
N.A.I.C.S.: 334419

Personnel:
Matti Vikkula *(Chm)*
Vesa Vahamottonen *(Pres & CEO)*
Olli Nermes *(CFO & Exec VP)*
Panu Kaila *(Exec VP-Ops & Programs)*
Markku Kukkonen *(Exec VP-Product Dev & Tech)*
Alexander Luiga *(Exec VP-Sls & Mktg)*
Jukka Pietarinen *(Exec VP-Indus Bus Area)*

Board of Directors:
Matti Vikkula
Olli Heikkila
Tei-Hu Liu
Marko Luoma
Ari Siponmaa

Non-U.S. Subsidiaries:

Efore AB (1)
Manskarsvagen 10B
141 75 Kungens Kurva, Sweden
Tel.: (46) 768 714 600
E-Mail: sales.scandinavia@efore.fi
Electronic Component Mfr
S.I.C.: 3679
N.A.I.C.S.: 334419

Efore (Suzhou) Automotive Technology Co., Ltd. (1)
Building 21 A And B No 428 Xinglong Street
Suzhou Industrial Park
Suzhou, China 215126
Tel.: (86) 512 6767 1500
Fax: (86) 512 6283 3080
E-Mail: sales@efore.com.cn
Electronic Component Mfr
S.I.C.: 3679
N.A.I.C.S.: 334419

Efore (Suzhou) Electronics Co., Ltd. (1)
Building 21 A & B No 428 Xinglong Street
Suzhou Industrial Park
Suzhou, China 215126
Tel.: (86) 512 6767 1500
Fax: (86) 512 6283 3080
E-Mail: sales@efore.com.cn
Electronic Component Mfr
S.I.C.: 3679
N.A.I.C.S.: 334419

EFT CANADA INC.

801 Eglinton West Suite 400
Toronto, ON, M5N 1E3, Canada
Tel.: (416) 781-0666
Fax: (416) 781-3318
E-Mail: info@eftcanada.com
Web Site: www.eftcanada.com
EFT—(TSXV)
Rev.: $2,403,030
Assets: $7,590,333
Liabilities: $5,955,576
Net Worth: $1,634,756
Earnings: $238,025
Fiscal Year-end: 06/30/13

Business Description:
Electronic Payment Services
S.I.C.: 6099
N.A.I.C.S.: 522320

Personnel:
Jonathan R. Pasternak *(Pres & CEO)*
Randy Waxman *(COO & Exec VP)*

Board of Directors:
John Cerenzia
Brian Courtney
Ray Martins
Jonathan R. Pasternak
Randy Waxman

Transfer Agent:
Equity Financial Trust Company
200 University Avenue Suite 400
Toronto, ON, Canada

EFTEL LTD.

(Acquired by M2 Telecommunications Group Limited)

EFU GENERAL INSURANCE LTD.

EFU House M A Jinnah Road
PO Box 5005
Karachi, 74000, Pakistan
Tel.: (92) 21 2313471
Fax: (92) 21 2310450
E-Mail: info@efuinsurance.com
Web Site: www.efuinsurance.com
Year Founded: 1932
EFUG—(KAR LAH)
Rev.: $60,870,724
Assets: $294,135,754
Liabilities: $181,377,062
Net Worth: $112,758,691
Earnings: $16,248,976
Emp.: 1,252
Fiscal Year-end: 12/31/12

Business Description:
Insurance Services
S.I.C.: 6733
N.A.I.C.S.: 525190

Personnel:
Saifuddin N. Zoomkawala *(Chm)*
Hasanali Abdullah *(CEO & Mng Dir)*
Altaf Qamruddin Gokal *(CFO, Sec & Exec Dir)*
Nudrat Ali *(Deputy Mng Dir)*
Malik Akbar Awan *(Deputy Mng Dir)*
Jaffer Dossa *(Deputy Mng Dir)*
Qamber Hamid *(Sr Deputy Mng Dir)*
Abdur Rehman Khandia *(Deputy Mng Dir)*
Mahmood Lotia *(Sr Deputy Mng Dir)*
S. Salman Rashid *(Deputy Mng Dir)*
Pervez Ahmad *(Sr Exec VP)*
Khalid Ashfaq Ahmed *(Sr Exec VP)*
Muhammad Rashid Akmal *(Sr Exec VP)*
Muhammad Naeem M. Hanif *(Sr Exec VP)*
Ross Masood *(Sr Exec VP)*
Mazhar H. Qureshi *(Sr Exec VP)*
Babar A. Sheikh *(Sr Exec VP)*
Badar Amin Sissodia *(Sr Exec VP)*
Abdul Wahid *(Sr Exec VP)*
Zarar Zahoor Bandey *(Sr Exec VP)*
Mansoor Abbas Abbasi *(Exec VP)*
Aamir Ahmad *(Exec VP)*
Riaz Ahmad *(Exec VP)*
Muhammad Tawheed Alam *(Exec VP)*
Muhammad Azhar Ali *(Exec VP)*
Adam Dur Mohammad Baloch *(Exec VP)*
Muhammad Razzaq Chaudhry *(Exec VP)*
Aslam A. Ghole *(Exec VP)*
Mohammad Rizwanul Haq *(Exec VP)*
Mohammad Haji Hashim *(Exec VP)*
Ahmad Hassan *(Exec VP)*
Masroor Hussain *(Exec VP)*
A. Ghaffar A. Kareem *(Exec VP)*
Liaquat Ali Khan *(Exec VP)*
Mohammad Afzal Khan *(Exec VP)*
Zafar Ali Khokhar *(Exec VP)*
Shazim Altaf Kothawala *(Exec VP)*
Zia Mahmood *(Exec VP)*
Abdul Majeed *(Exec VP)*
Abdul Qadir Memon *(Exec VP)*
Mohammad Nasir *(Exec VP)*
Mohammad Pervaiz *(Exec VP)*
Abdul Razzak A. Sattar *(Exec VP)*
Mohammad Naeem Shaikh *(Exec VP)*
Mohammad Shoaib *(Exec VP)*
Wasim Tasawar *(Exec VP)*
Shahzad Zakaria *(Exec VP)*
Shah Asghar Abbas *(Sr VP)*
Farman Ali Afridi *(Sr VP)*
Rizwan Ahmed *(Sr VP)*
Malik Firdaus Alam *(Sr VP)*
Sohail Shaukat Ali *(Sr VP)*
Usman Ali *(Sr VP)*
Atif Anwar *(Sr VP)*
Fatima Bano *(Sr VP)*
Abdul Mateen Farooqui *(Sr VP)*
S. Tayyab Hussain Gardezi *(Sr VP)*
Shahid Abdullah Godil *(Sr VP)*
Faisal Gulzar *(Sr VP)*
Ghulam Haider *(Sr VP)*
Abdul Hameed *(Sr VP)*
S. Anwar Hasnain *(Sr VP)*
Zahid Hussain *(Sr VP)*
Liaquat Imran *(Sr VP)*
Farhat Iqbal *(Sr VP)*

EFU General Insurance Ltd.—(Continued)

Rashid Mohammad Iqbal *(Sr VP)*
Quaid Johar *(Sr VP)*
S. M. Aamir Kazmi *(Sr VP)*
Arshad Ali Khan *(Sr VP)*
Javed Iqbal Khan *(Sr VP)*
Rao Abdul Hafeez Khan *(Sr VP)*
Murtaza Noorani *(Sr VP)*
M. A. Qayum *(Sr VP)*
Abdul Quddus *(Sr VP)*
Ali Raza *(Sr VP)*
Zia Ur Rehman *(Sr VP)*
Fakhruddin Saifee *(Sr VP)*
Muhammad Salahuddin *(Sr VP)*
Imran Saleem *(Sr VP)*
Mohammad Amin Sattar *(Sr VP)*
S. M. Shamim *(Sr VP)*
Board of Directors:
Saifuddin N. Zoomkawala
Hasanali Abdullah
Muneer R. Bhimjee
Rafique R. Bhimjee
Abdul Rehman Habib
Taher G. Sachak
Ali Raza Siddiqui
Jahangir Siddiqui

Division:

EFU General Insurance Ltd - Central Division **(1)**
1st Floor Kashif Centre Shahrah E F
Karachi, Pakistan
Tel.: (92) 21 35653907
Fax: (92) 21 35640512
Web Site: www.efuinsurance.com
General Insurance Services
S.I.C.: 6411
N.A.I.C.S.: 524210
Sattar Baloch *(Gen Mgr)*

EFUTURE INFORMATION TECHNOLOGY INC.

8F Topnew Tower 15 Guanghua Road
Chaoyang District, Beijing, 100026, China
Tel.: (86) 10 5293 7699
Fax: (86) 10 5165 0988
E-Mail: info@e-future.com.cn
Web Site: www.e-future.com.cn
EFUT—(NASDAQ)
Rev.: $31,508,671
Assets: $39,559,275
Liabilities: $19,595,253
Net Worth: $19,964,022
Earnings: ($716,353)
Emp.: 822
Fiscal Year-end: 12/31/12
Business Description:
Holding Company
S.I.C.: 6719
N.A.I.C.S.: 551112
Personnel:
Adam Yan *(Founder, Chm, CEO & Interim CFO)*
Qicheng Yang *(Founder & CTO)*
Hongjun Zou *(Founder, Chief Innovation Officer & Sr VP)*
James Mu *(CMO & VP)*
Zhou Kefu *(Chief Architecture Officer)*
Troe Wen *(Sec)*
Tony Zhao *(Sr VP)*
Board of Directors:
Adam Yan
Dong Cheng
John Dai
Dennis O. Laing
Brian Lin
Deliang Tong
Ping Yu
Ming Zhu

EG CORPORATION

459 Seodaesanro
Geumsangun, Chubu-myeon, Chungcheongnam-do, Korea (South) 312-943
Tel.: (82) 41 750 7724
Fax: (82) 41 750 7745
Web Site: www.egcorp.co.kr
Year Founded: 1987
037370—(KRS)
Sls.: $94,590,300
Assets: $79,081,620
Liabilities: $31,806,000
Net Worth: $47,275,620
Earnings: ($1,198,770)
Fiscal Year-end: 12/31/12
Business Description:
Chemical Mfr
S.I.C.: 2819
N.A.I.C.S.: 325180
Personnel:
Kwang-Hyung Lee *(Vice Chm)*

EG INDUSTRIES BERHAD

Ste 18 01 18th Floor MWE Plaza No 8 Lebuh Farquhar
10200 Penang, Malaysia
Tel.: (60) 42637762
Fax: (60) 42635901
Web Site: www.eg.com.my
EG—(KLS)
Rev.: $262,417,381
Assets: $124,102,467
Liabilities: $86,405,875
Net Worth: $37,696,592
Earnings: $465,593
Fiscal Year-end: 06/30/13
Business Description:
Printed Circuit Boards Mfr
S.I.C.: 3672
N.A.I.C.S.: 334412
Personnel:
Keik Hock Tai *(Chm)*
Yeong Sheng Tai *(Mng Dir)*
Churn Hwa Chai *(Sec)*
Board of Directors:
Keik Hock Tai
Seng Wong Ang
Pang Kiang Kang
Damien Yat Seng Lim
Sze Yan Lim
Lee Keow Tai
Yeong Sheng Tai
Subsidiaries:

Mastimber Industries Sdn. Bhd. **(1)**
Lot 25 Kuala Ketil Industrial Estate
Kuala Ketil, Kedah, Malaysia
Tel.: (60) 44162828
Fax: (60) 44162020
E-Mail: mtisb@tm.net.my
Emp.: 45
Hardwood Parquetry Mfr
S.I.C.: 2499
N.A.I.C.S.: 321999
Tai Keik Hock *(Mng Dir)*

SMT Technologies Sdn. Bhd. **(1)**
Plot 102 Bakar Arang Industrial Estate
08000 Sungai Petani, Kedah, Malaysia
Tel.: (60) 44229881
Fax: (60) 44229885
Telecommunication Products Mfr
S.I.C.: 3661
N.A.I.C.S.: 334210
Cheah Saw Ann *(Bus Dir)*

Non-U.S. Subsidiary:

SMT Industries Co. Ltd. **(1)**
196 Moo 10 304 Industrial Park Thatoom Sub district
Srimahaphote District, Prachin Buri, 25140, Thailand
Tel.: (66) 37274423
Fax: (66) 37 274425
Electronic Products Mfr
S.I.C.: 3812
N.A.I.C.S.: 334511
Robert Teoh *(Mgr-Production)*

EG PENNER BUILDING CENTRES

200 Park Road West
Steinbach, MB, R5G 1A1, Canada
Tel.: (204) 326-1325
Fax: (204) 326-5590
Toll Free: (800) 353-8733
E-Mail: info@egpenner.com
Web Site: www.egpenner.com
Year Founded: 1960
Rev.: $11,850,007
Emp.: 175
Business Description:
Building Construction Service
S.I.C.: 1542
N.A.I.C.S.: 236220
Personnel:
Ernest Penner *(Pres)*

EG SOLUTIONS PLC

Barn 1 Dunston Business Village
Stafford Road Dunston
Stafford, ST18 9AB, United Kingdom
Tel.: (44) 1785715772
Fax: (44) 1785712541
E-Mail: ask@eguk.co.uk
Web Site: www.eguk.co.uk
EGS—(LSE)
Rev.: $7,819,065
Assets: $5,789,677
Liabilities: $3,548,665
Net Worth: $2,241,013
Earnings: ($476,946)
Emp.: 36
Fiscal Year-end: 01/31/13
Business Description:
IT & Software Support Services
S.I.C.: 7371
N.A.I.C.S.: 541511
Personnel:
Elizabeth Gooch *(Acting CEO)*
Board of Directors:
Duncan McIntyre
Rodney Baker-Bates
Elizabeth Gooch
Paul Michael Hoban
Phil Lee
Spencer Mallder
Legal Counsel:
TLT Solicitors
20 Gresham Street
London, EC2V 7JE, United Kingdom
Non-U.S. Subsidiary:

eg operations management solutions (pty) limited **(1)**
Ground Fl Spire House,Fountain Grove Ofc Park,% 2nd Ave,Hyde park
Sandton, Johannesburg, Gauteng, 2024, South Africa
Tel.: (27) 0114476218
Fax: (27) 0114470303
E-Mail: ask@egsa.co.za
Web Site: www.egsa.co.za
Emp.: 15
Software Services
S.I.C.: 7371
N.A.I.C.S.: 541511
Wendy Jeavons *(Mng Dir)*

EGAN VISUAL INC.

300 Hanlan Road
Woodbridge, ON, L4L 3P6, Canada
Tel.: (905) 851-2826
Fax: (905) 851-3426
Toll Free: (800) 263-2387
E-Mail: evi@egan.com
Web Site: www.egan.com
Year Founded: 1967
Rev.: $26,083,485
Emp.: 130
Business Description:
Visual Communication Systems & Furniture Mfr
S.I.C.: 3669
N.A.I.C.S.: 334290
Personnel:
James Egan *(Pres)*

EGAT PUBLIC COMPANY LIMITED

EGCO Tower 222 Moo 5 Vibhavadi Rangsit Road
Tungsonghong Laksi, Bangkok, 10210, Thailand
Tel.: (66) 29985000
Fax: (66) 29550956
Web Site: www.egco.com
Year Founded: 1992
Sales Range: $350-399.9 Million
Emp.: 650
Business Description:
Electric Power Distr
S.I.C.: 3612
N.A.I.C.S.: 335311
Personnel:
Sunanta Kietsirikul *(CFO)*
Sutat Patmasiriwat *(Sec)*
Somboon Arayaskul *(Exec VP)*
Subsidiaries:

EGCO Engineering and Service Co. Ltd **(1)**
EGCO Tower 222 Moo 5 Vibhavadi Rangsit Road
Tungsonghong Laksi, 10210 Bangkok, Thailand (99.99%)
Tel.: (66) 29985999
Fax: (66) 295509568
Web Site: www.egco.co.th/en/contact_us.asp
Electrical Contractors
S.I.C.: 1731
N.A.I.C.S.: 238210
Pinijyos Saaudaium *(Mng Dir)*

Egcom Tara Co. Ltd. **(1)**
EGCO Tower 222 Moo 5 Vibhavadi Rangsit Road
Tungsonghong Laksi, 10210 Bangkok, Thailand (70%)
Tel.: (66) 29985710
Fax: (66) 29550945
Web Site: www.egcom.com
Emp.: 200
Nuclear Electric Power Generation
S.I.C.: 4911
N.A.I.C.S.: 221113
Thongzhai Chotkajoinde *(Mng Dir)*

Gulf Electric Public Co. Ltd **(1)**
11th Floor M Thai I All Seasons Place
Wireless Road Phathumwan, 10330
Bangkok, Thailand (50%)
Tel.: (66) 26540155
Fax: (66) 26540156
E-Mail: thamyathorn@gulf.co.th
Web Site: www.gulf.co.th
Emp.: 100
Electric Power Generation
S.I.C.: 4931
N.A.I.C.S.: 221118
Sarath Ratanadadi *(Pres)*

Khanom Electricity Generating Co. Ltd. **(1)**
EGCO Tower 222 Moo 5 Vibhavadi Rangsit Road
Tungsonghong Laksi, 10210 Bangkok, Thailand (99.99%)
Tel.: (66) 29985997
Fax: (66) 29550932
E-Mail: chankij.jearapsunt@egco.com
Web Site: www.egco.co.th
Emp.: 150
Electric Power Generation
S.I.C.: 4911
N.A.I.C.S.: 221118
Chankij Jearapsunt *(Mng Dir)*

Rayong Electricity Generating Co. Ltd. **(1)**
EGCO Tower 222 Moo 5 Vibhavadi Rangsit Road
Tungsonghong Laksi, 10210 Bangkok, Thailand (99.99%)
Tel.: (66) 29985999
Fax: (66) 295509568
Web Site: www.egco.com
Electrical Contractors
S.I.C.: 1731
N.A.I.C.S.: 238210
Pinijyos Saaudaium *(Mng Dir)*

Roi-Et Green Co. Ltd (1)
EGCO Tower 222 Moo 5 Vibhavadi Rangsit Road
Tungsonghong Laksi, 10210 Bangkok, Thailand (95%)
Tel.: (66) 29985881
Fax: (66) 29985885
E-Mail: siriluk.soo@egco.com
Web Site: www.egco.co.th
Emp.: 5
Measuring & Testing Electricity & Electrical Signals Instrument Mfr
S.I.C.: 3825
N.A.I.C.S.: 334515

Joint Venture:

Amata B. Grimm Power 1 Limited (1)
Amata Nakorn Industrial Estate
700-371 Moo 6 Nongmaidaeng
Ampur Muang, 20000 Chon Buri, Thailand (50%)
Tel.: (66) 3821 3317
Fax: (66) 3821 4363
Web Site: www.amatapower.com
Emp.: 35
Electric Power Generation
S.I.C.: 4931
N.A.I.C.S.: 221118

EGDON RESOURCES PLC

The Wheat House 98 High Street
Odiham, Hampshire, RG29 1LP, United Kingdom
Tel.: (44) 1256702292
Fax: (44) 1256702293
E-Mail: info@egdon-resources.com
Web Site: www.egdon-resources.com
EDR—(AIM)
Rev.: $5,277,070
Assets: $32,343,046
Liabilities: $5,811,400
Net Worth: $26,531,646
Earnings: ($1,133,286)
Emp.: 13
Fiscal Year-end: 07/31/13

Business Description:
Petroleum Exploration & Production Services
S.I.C.: 1311
N.A.I.C.S.: 211111

Personnel:
Mark Abbott *(Mng Dir)*
Walter Roberts *(Sec)*

Board of Directors:
Philip Stephens
Mark Abbott
Jerry James Field
Andrew Lodge
Ken Ratcliff
Walter Roberts

Legal Counsel:
Norton Rose LLP
3 More London Riverside
London, United Kingdom

Subsidiaries:

Egdon Resources (New Ventures) Ltd (1)
The Wheat House 98 High Street
Oldham, Hants, RG29 1LP, United Kingdom
Tel.: (44) 1256702292
Fax: (44) 1256702293
E-Mail: info@egdon-resources.com
Web Site: www.egdon-resources.com
Emp.: 5
Oil & Gas Exploration Services
S.I.C.: 1389
N.A.I.C.S.: 213112
Mark Abbott *(Mng Dir)*

Egdon Resources U.K. Limited (1)
The Wheat House 98 High Street
Odiham, Hants, RG29 1LP, United Kingdom
Tel.: (44) 1256702292
Fax: (44) 1256702293
E-Mail: info@egdon-resources.com
Web Site: www.egdon-resources.com
Emp.: 8
Oil & Gas Exploration Services
S.I.C.: 1389
N.A.I.C.S.: 213112
Mark Abbott *(Mng Dir)*

EGERIA CAPITAL MANAGEMENT B.V.

Sarphatikade 12
1017 WV Amsterdam, Netherlands
Tel.: (31) 205306868
Fax: (31) 205306869
E-Mail: egeria@egeria.nl
Web Site: www.egeria.nl
Sales Range: $50-74.9 Million
Emp.: 20

Business Description:
Private Equity Firm
S.I.C.: 6211
N.A.I.C.S.: 523999

Personnel:
Peter Visser *(Mng Partner)*
Caroline Huyskes-van Doorne *(Partner)*
Floris Muijser *(Partner)*
Mark Wetzels *(Partner)*

Holdings:

Axent Nabestaandenzorg N.V. (1)
Leonard Springerlaan 31
9727 KB Groningen, Netherlands
Tel.: (31) 58 2446416
Web Site: www.vz-verzekeringen.nl
Sales Range: $75-99.9 Million
Funeral Insurance Services
S.I.C.: 6411
N.A.I.C.S.: 524298
Hans Croes *(Gen Mgr)*

Muelink & Grol B.V. (1)
Duinkerkenstraat 27
9723 BP Groningen, Netherlands
Tel.: (31) 503139944
Fax: (31) 503185423
E-Mail: info-nl@mg-flues.com
Web Site: www.muelink-grol.nl
Sales Range: $125-149.9 Million
Emp.: 180
Venting Product Mfr
S.I.C.: 3585
N.A.I.C.S.: 333415
Wim Straver *(Mng Dir)*

U.S. Subsidiary:

M&G Dura-Vent, Inc. (2)
877 Cotting Ct
Vacaville, CA 95688-9354 CA
Mailing Address:
PO Box 1510
Vacaville, CA 95696-1510
Tel.: (707) 446-1786
Fax: (707) 446-4740
Toll Free: (800) 835-4429
E-Mail: customerservice@duravent.com
Web Site: www.duravent.com
Sales Range: $100-124.9 Million
Emp.: 450
Gas Vents, All-Fuel Chimneys, Stovepipes, Chimney Liners & Pellet Vents Mfr
Import Export
S.I.C.: 3444
N.A.I.C.S.: 332322
Stephen P. Eberhard *(Pres & CEO)*

Joint Venture:

N.V. Nationale Borg-Maatschappij (1)
Keizersgracht 165
1016 DP Amsterdam, Netherlands
Mailing Address:
PO Box 955
1000AZ Amsterdam, Netherlands
Tel.: (31) 205533900
Fax: (31) 205533999
E-Mail: nationaleborg@nationaleborg.nl
Web Site: www.nationaleborg.nl
Rev.: $123,542,059
Assets: $275,672,731
Liabilities: $163,388,691
Net Worth: $112,284,040
Earnings: $13,386,314
Emp.: 50
Fiscal Year-end: 12/31/12
Non-Life Insurance & Reinsurance
S.I.C.: 6399
N.A.I.C.S.: 524128
A. P. Jos C. Kroon *(CEO & Member-Mgmt Bd)*
Laura Pool *(CFO, Chief Risk Officer & Member-Mgmt Bd)*
Tom Nederlof *(Member-Mgmt Bd & Dir-Guarantees)*

EGERSUND GROUP AS

Svanavagen 30
N-4374 Egersund, Norway
Tel.: (47) 51 46 29 00
Fax: (47) 51 46 29 01
E-Mail: post@egersundgroup.no
Web Site: www.egersundgroup.no

Business Description:
Fishing, Aquaculture & Trade Services
S.I.C.: 0921
N.A.I.C.S.: 112511

Personnel:
Hans Kristian Mong *(Mng Dir)*

Subsidiary:

AKVA Group ASA (1)
Nordlysveien 4
PO Box 271
4349 Bryne, Norway
Tel.: (47) 51 77 85 00
Fax: (47) 51 77 85 01
E-Mail: info@akvagroup.com
Web Site: www.akvagroup.com
AKVA—(OSL)
Rev.: $145,014,256
Assets: $121,729,530
Liabilities: $62,858,189
Net Worth: $58,871,341
Earnings: $1,859,491
Emp.: 653
Fiscal Year-end: 12/31/12
Steel & Plastic Cages Mfr
S.I.C.: 3315
N.A.I.C.S.: 331222
Amund Skarholt *(Chm)*
Trond Williksen *(CEO)*
Eirik Borve Monsen *(CFO)*
Trond Severinsen *(CMO & COO-Exports)*

Subsidiaries:

AKVA group Software AS (2)
Karvag
6530 Averoy, More og Romsdal, Norway (50.01%)
Tel.: (47) 71517300
Fax: (47) 73517399
E-Mail: office@maritech.no
Web Site: www.maritech.no
Emp.: 50
Software Development Services
S.I.C.: 7371
N.A.I.C.S.: 541511
Steinar Mykloy *(Mgr-Sls)*

Helgeland Plast AS (2)
Basmosjyen 4
8616 Mo i Rana, Nordland, Norway
Tel.: (47) 75143750
Fax: (47) 75143751
E-Mail: info@akvagroup.com
Emp.: 200
Plastic Cages & Fishing Boats Distr
S.I.C.: 5084
N.A.I.C.S.: 423830
Trond Severinsen *(Dir-Mktg)*

Non-U.S. Subsidiaries:

AKVA group Chile S.A. (2)
Ruta 5 Sur Km 1030
Puerto Montt, Llanquihue, 5480000, Chile
Tel.: (56) 65250250
Fax: (56) 65257119
E-Mail: info@akvagroup.com
Emp.: 310
Fishing Equipment & Supplies Distr
S.I.C.: 5091
N.A.I.C.S.: 423910
Andrew Campbell *(Mng Dir-Americas & Oceania)*

AKVA group Denmark A/S (2)
Navervej 10
7000 Fredericia, Denmark
Tel.: (45) 75513211
Fax: (45) 75514211
E-Mail: info@akvagroup.com
Web Site: www.akvasmart.com
Emp.: 25
Fish Farming Products Distr
S.I.C.: 5146
N.A.I.C.S.: 424460
Jacob Bregnballe *(Dir-Sls-Land Based Sys)*

AKVA group North America Inc. (2)
1495 Baikie Rd
PO Box 397
Campbell River, BC, V9W0C2, Canada
Tel.: (250) 286-8802
Fax: (250) 286-8805
E-Mail: info@akvagroup.com
Emp.: 7
Fishing Equipment & Supplies Distr
S.I.C.: 5091
N.A.I.C.S.: 423910
Wade Kaskiw *(Mng Dir)*

AKVA group Scotland Ltd. (2)
36F Shore St
Inverness, Scotland, IV1 1NF, United Kingdom
Tel.: (44) 1463221444
Fax: (44) 1463223535
E-Mail: info@akvagroup.com
Web Site: www.akvasmart.com
Emp.: 30
Commercial Fish Farming Products Distr
S.I.C.: 5091
N.A.I.C.S.: 423910
David Thorburn *(Gen Mgr)*

Maritech ehf (2)
Borgartun 26
105 Reykjavik, Iceland
Tel.: (354) 545 3200
Fax: (354) 545 3232
E-Mail: info@maritech.is
Web Site: www.maritech.is
Emp.: 70
Business Management Software Development Services
S.I.C.: 7371
N.A.I.C.S.: 541511
Jon Heioar Palsson *(VP-Sls)*

EGGED ISRAEL TRANSPORT COOPERATIVE SOCIETY LTD.

Airport Complex Hayarden St
PO Box 43
Ben Gurion Intl Airport, Tel Aviv, 70150, Israel
Tel.: (972) 36948888
Web Site: www.egged.co.il
Year Founded: 1933
Sales Range: $300-349.9 Million
Emp.: 6,200

Business Description:
Public Transportation Services
Import
S.I.C.: 4119
N.A.I.C.S.: 485999

Subsidiary:

Egged Holding (1)
11 Hamelacha North Ind Z
Lod, Israel
Tel.: (972) 8 6220444
Transportation Route & Railway Line Operator
S.I.C.: 4111
N.A.I.C.S.: 485111

Non-U.S. Subsidiary:

Egged Bulgaria (2)
74 Treti Mart Bul
Ruse, 7000, Bulgaria
Tel.: (359) 82 82 00 12
Fax: (359) 82 82 00 05
Transportation Route & Railway Line Operator
S.I.C.: 4111
N.A.I.C.S.: 485111

Non-U.S. Subsidiaries:

PKS Ostroleka S.A. (1)
ul T Zawadzkiego Zoski 1
07-412 Ostroleka, Poland
Tel.: (48) 29 760 26 71 3
E-Mail: pks@pks-ostroleka.pl
Public Transport Bus Services
S.I.C.: 4111

Egged Israel Transport Cooperative Society Ltd.—(Continued)

N.A.I.C.S.: 485113

PKS Plock S.A. (1)
ul Bielska 53
09-400 Plock, Poland
Tel.: (48) 24 267 65 00
Public Transport Bus Services
S.I.C.: 4111
N.A.I.C.S.: 485113

EGHTESAD NOVIN BANK

No 24 Esfandiyar Blvd Valiasr Ave
PO Box 19395-3796
1968655944 Tehran, Iran
Tel.: (98) 21 8233 0000
E-Mail: info@enbank.ir
Web Site: www.enbank.ir
Year Founded: 2001
NOVN—(THE)

Business Description:
Banking Services
S.I.C.: 6029
N.A.I.C.S.: 522110

Personnel:
Seyed Mohammad Sadr Hasheminejad *(Chm)*
Seyed Abdolhossein Sabet *(Vice Chm)*
Mohammad Hashem Botshekan *(CEO & Exec VP)*

Board of Directors:
Seyed Mohammad Sadr Hasheminejad
Morteza Azizi
Mohammad Hashem Botshekan
Ali Manavi Rad
Seyed Abdolhossein Sabet

EGI FINANCIAL HOLDINGS INC.

2680 Matheson Blvd E Suite 300
Mississauga, ON, L4W 0A5, Canada
Tel.: (905) 214-7880
Fax: (905) 214-8028
E-Mail: ir@egi.ca
Web Site: www.egi.ca
EFH—(TSX)
Rev.: $211,347,538
Assets: $543,756,773
Liabilities: $379,342,883
Net Worth: $164,413,890
Earnings: $19,250,191
Emp.: 177
Fiscal Year-end: 12/31/12

Business Description:
Insurance
S.I.C.: 6351
N.A.I.C.S.: 524126

Personnel:
Robert Purves *(Chm)*
Douglas E. McIntyre *(Vice Chm)*
Steve Dobronyi *(CEO)*
Alvin Sharma *(CFO)*
Sylvain Guilbert *(CIO & VP)*
Michel Trudeau *(Chief Actuary)*
James Cizek *(Pres-American Colonial)*
George Kalopsis *(Pres-Echelon)*
Brian Clausen *(CEO-Qudos Insurance)*
Ken Coulson *(VP-Legal Counsel)*
John A. Czerwinski *(Exec VP-Strategic Market Dev & Branch Mgmt)*
Mark Sylvia *(Sr VP-Ops-Canada)*

Board of Directors:
Robert Purves
Mary G. Connolly
Peter Crawford
G. Mark Curry
Patrick W. E. Hodgson
Paul F. Little
Douglas E. McIntyre
Angus Ross
Bruce West

Transfer Agent:
Computershare Trust Company of Canada
100 University Avenue 9th Floor
Toronto, ON, M5J 2Y1, Canada
Tel.: (416) 663-9097
Fax: (416) 263-9694

Subsidiaries:

Echelon General Insurance Company (1)
2680 Matheson Blvd E Ste 300
Mississauga, ON, L4W 0A5, Canada
Tel.: (905) 214-7880
Fax: (905) 214-7881
Toll Free: (800) 324-3566
Web Site: www.echelon-insurance.ca
Emp.: 60
Insurance Services
S.I.C.: 6311
N.A.I.C.S.: 524113
Mark Sylvia *(CEO)*
Hemraj Singh *(CFO)*
George Kalopsis *(COO)*

Divisions:

Echelon General Insurance Company Automobile Division (2)
2680 Matheson Blvd E Ste 300
Mississauga, ON, L4W 0A5, Canada
Tel.: (905) 214-7880
Fax: (905) 214-7893
Toll Free: (800) 324-3566
Web Site: www.echelon-insurance.ca
Emp.: 115
Insurance Services
S.I.C.: 6311
N.A.I.C.S.: 524113
Engrid Wilson *(VP-HR)*

Echelon General Insurance Company Niche Products Division (2)
2680 Matheson Blvd
E Ste 300, Mississauga, ON, L4W 0A5, Canada
Tel.: (905) 214-7880
Fax: (905) 214-7882
Toll Free: (800) 324-3566
E-Mail: offciesevices@egi.ca
Emp.: 140
Insurance Services
S.I.C.: 6311
N.A.I.C.S.: 524113

EGI Insurance Managers Inc. (1)
2680 Matheson Blvd E Ste 300
Mississauga, ON, L4W 0A5, Canada
Tel.: (905) 214-7880
Fax: (905) 214-7881
Toll Free: (800) 324-3566
Web Site: www.echelon-insurance.ca
Emp.: 18
Insurance Agencies
S.I.C.: 6411
N.A.I.C.S.: 524210
Zahir Moosa *(Bus Mgr-Comm)*

EGIDE SA

Parc d'Activites de Pissaloup
78190 Trappes, France
Tel.: (33) 130688100
Fax: (33) 130660651
E-Mail: egide@egide.fr
Web Site: www.egide.fr
Year Founded: 1986
GID—(EUR)
Sls.: $34,455,221
Assets: $19,002,536
Liabilities: $12,660,729
Net Worth: $6,341,807
Earnings: ($1,165,783)
Emp.: 288
Fiscal Year-end: 12/31/12

Business Description:
Aluminum Hermetic Packages, Modulators, Multi-Chip Modules, Relay Headers & Infra-Red Detector Packages Designer, Mfr & Distr
S.I.C.: 3679
N.A.I.C.S.: 334419

Personnel:
Philippe Bregi *(Chm & CEO)*

Board of Directors:
Philippe Bregi
Catherine Gerst
Eric Michel
Albert Schune

PricewaterhouseCoopers Audit
63 rue de Villiers
92208 Neuilly-sur-Seine, Cedex, France

U.S. Subsidiary:

Egide USA, LLC (1)
4 Washington St
Cambridge, MD 21613 DE
Tel.: (410) 901-6100 (100%)
Fax: (410) 901-6250
Web Site: www.egide.fr/index_english.html
Holding Company; Aluminum Hermetic Packages, Modulators, Multi-Chip Modules, Relay Headers & Infra-Red Detector Packages Mfr & Distr
S.I.C.: 6719
N.A.I.C.S.: 551112
Philippe Bregi *(Chm & CEO)*

Subsidiary:

Egide USA, Inc. (2)
4 Washington St
Cambridge, MD 21613 DE
Tel.: (410) 901-6100 (100%)
Fax: (410) 901-6250
Web Site: www.egide.fr/index_english.html
Aluminum Hermetic Packages, Modulators, Multi-Chip Modules, Relay Headers & Infra-Red Detector Packages Mfr & Distr
S.I.C.: 3679
N.A.I.C.S.: 334419
James Collins *(VP & Gen Mgr)*

EGING PHOTOVOLTAIC TECHNOLOGY CO., LTD.

No 18 Jinwu Road
Jintan, Changzhou, Jiangsu, China
Tel.: (86) 519 82585880
Fax: (86) 519 82581868
E-Mail: EGing@EGingpv.com
Web Site: www.egingpv.com
Year Founded: 2003
600537—(SHG)

Business Description:
Solar Module Mfr
S.I.C.: 3699
N.A.I.C.S.: 335999

Personnel:
Jianhua Xun *(Chm & Gen Mgr)*

EGMONT INTERNATIONAL HOLDING A/S

Vognmagergade 11
1148 Copenhagen, Denmark
Tel.: (45) 33305550
Fax: (45) 33321902
E-Mail: egmont@egmont.com
Web Site: www.egmont.com
Year Founded: 1878
Emp.: 3,533

Business Description:
Weekly Newspapers, Magazines, Comics, Books, Film, TV Programs, Textbooks & Games
S.I.C.: 2711
N.A.I.C.S.: 511110

Personnel:
Mikael O. Olufsen *(Chm)*
Steffen Kragh *(Pres & CEO)*
Hans J. Carstensen *(CFO & Exec VP)*

Subsidiaries:

Alinea (1)
Vognmagergade 5
1148 Copenhagen, Denmark
Tel.: (45) 33694666
E-Mail: skoleservice@alinea.dk
Web Site: www.alinea.dk
Emp.: 80
Book Publishers
S.I.C.: 2731
N.A.I.C.S.: 511130
Ebbe Dam Nielsen *(Mng Dir)*

Egmont Administration A/S (1)
Vognmagergade 11
K 1148 Copenhagen, Denmark (100%)
Tel.: (45) 33305550
Fax: (45) 33321902
E-Mail: egmont@egmont.com
Web Site: www.egmont.com
Emp.: 700
Periodical Publishers
S.I.C.: 2721
N.A.I.C.S.: 511120
Steffen Kragh *(Pres & CEO)*

Egmont Creative A/S (1)
Vognmagergade 9 4th & 5th Fl
DK 1148 Copenhagen, Denmark (100%)
Tel.: (45) 33305550
Fax: (45) 33305502
Web Site: www.egmont.com
Emp.: 400
Periodical Publishers
S.I.C.: 2721
N.A.I.C.S.: 511120
Steffen Kragh *(Mng Dir)*

Egmont Holding A/S (1)
Vognmagergade 11 6
K 1148 Copenhagen, Denmark (100%)
Tel.: (45) 33305550
Fax: (45) 33916058
Web Site: www.egmont.com
Emp.: 700
Periodical Publishers
S.I.C.: 2721
N.A.I.C.S.: 511120
Steffen Kragh *(Pres & CEO)*

Egmont Imagination A/S (1)
Mosedalvej 14
2500 Valby, Denmark
Tel.: (45) 36188200
Fax: (45) 36189300
Web Site: www.egmont.com
Emp.: 2
Motion Picture & Video Production
S.I.C.: 7812
N.A.I.C.S.: 512110
Allan Hansen *(Mng Dir)*

Egmont Magasiner A/S (1)
Hellerupvej 51
2900 Hellerup, Denmark
Tel.: (45) 39457500
Fax: (45) 39457480
Web Site: www.egmontmagasiner.dk
Emp.: 250
Periodical Publishers
S.I.C.: 2721
N.A.I.C.S.: 511120
Torsten Bjerre Rasmussen *(Dir-Egmont Magasiner)*

Egmont Serieforlaget A/S (1)
Vognmagergade 11
1148 Copenhagen, Denmark (100%)
Tel.: (45) 70205035
Fax: (45) 33305760
Web Site: www.egmont.com
Emp.: 50
Periodical Publishers
S.I.C.: 2721
N.A.I.C.S.: 511120
Steffen Kragh *(Pres & CEO)*

Egmont Specialblade A/S (1)
Hellerupvej 51
2900 Hellerup, Denmark
Tel.: (45) 39457770
Fax: (45) 39457404
E-Mail: lucas@egmontmagasiner.dk
Web Site: www.egmontmagasiner.dk
Emp.: 200
Periodical Publishers
S.I.C.: 2721
N.A.I.C.S.: 511120
Torsten Erik Rasmussen *(Mng Dir)*

Egmont (1)
Vognmagergade 11
1148 Copenhagen, K, Denmark (100%)
Tel.: (45) 33305550
Fax: (45) 33305760
E-Mail: info@egmont.com
Web Site: www.egmont.com
Emp.: 700
Periodical Publishers

S.I.C.: 2721
N.A.I.C.S.: 511120
Steffen Kragh *(Pres & CEO)*

Euro Broadcast Hire A/S (1)
Titangade 1
2200 Copenhagen, Denmark (100%)
Tel.: (45) 35828220
Fax: (45) 35828219
E-Mail: ebh@ebh.dk
Web Site: www.ebh.cc
Emp.: 10
Motion Picture & Video Production
S.I.C.: 7812
N.A.I.C.S.: 512110
Soren Damgaard *(Gen Mgr)*

Lindhardt og Ringhof Forlag A/S (1)
Vognmagergade 11
1148 Copenhagen, Denmark (100%)
Tel.: (45) 33305550
Fax: (45) 33305760
Web Site: www.lindhardtogringhof.dk
Emp.: 600
Periodical Publishers
S.I.C.: 2721
N.A.I.C.S.: 511120
Steffen Kragh *(Mng Dir)*

Nordisk Film A/S (1)
Mosedalvej 14
2500 Valby, Denmark
Tel.: (45) 36188200
Fax: (45) 36189300
Web Site: www.nordiskfilm.com
Emp.: 350
Motion Picture & Video Production
S.I.C.: 7812
N.A.I.C.S.: 512110
Allan Hansen *(CEO)*

Nordisk Film Biografer A/S (1)
Axeltorv 9
1609 Copenhagen, Denmark
Tel.: (45) 33147606
Fax: (45) 36189300
E-Mail: info@nordiskfilm.com
Web Site: www.nordiskfilm.com
Emp.: 300
Motion Picture Theaters
S.I.C.: 7832
N.A.I.C.S.: 512131
John Tonnes *(Mng Dir)*

Nordisk Film Post Production A/S (1)
Tagensvej 85 D
Copenhagen, 2200, Denmark
Tel.: (45) 35877777
Fax: (45) 35877778
E-Mail: info@shortcut.com
Web Site: www.shorcut.com
Emp.: 50
Motion Picture & Video Production
S.I.C.: 7812
N.A.I.C.S.: 512110
Pia Tellefsen *(Gen Mgr)*

Non-U.S. Subsidiaries:

Cappelen Damm AS (1)
Akersgata 47/49
0055 Oslo, Norway
Tel.: (47) 21616500
Fax: (47) 21616501
E-Mail: webmail@cappelendamm.no
Web Site: www.cappelendamm.no
Emp.: 400
Book Publishers
S.I.C.: 2731
N.A.I.C.S.: 511130
Tom Harald Jenssen *(Mng Dir)*

Egmont AS (1)
Fridtjof Nansens vei 14
0055 Oslo, Norway
Tel.: (47) 24051300
Fax: (47) 24051599
E-Mail: v.r.petersen@egmont.no
Web Site: www.egmont.no
Emp.: 150
Book Publishers
S.I.C.: 2731
N.A.I.C.S.: 511130

Egmont Holding AB (1)
Skeppsgatan 9
20507 Malmo, Sweden (100%)
Tel.: (46) 40385200
Fax: (46) 40385398
E-Mail: info@egmont.se
Web Site: www.egmont.se
Emp.: 100
Holding Company
S.I.C.: 6719
N.A.I.C.S.: 551112
Per Kjellander *(Mng Dir)*

Egmont Karnan AB (1)
Drottningtorget 14
20508 Malmo, Sweden
Tel.: (46) 406939400
Fax: (46) 406939498
E-Mail: info@egmontkarnan.se
Web Site: www.egmontkarnan.se
Emp.: 160
Periodical Publishers
S.I.C.: 2721
N.A.I.C.S.: 511120
Jannicke Apelgren *(Mng Dir)*

Egmont Serieforlaget AS (1)
Fridtjof Nansens vei 14
0055 Oslo, Norway
Tel.: (47) 24051300
Fax: (47) 24051597
Web Site: www.egmont.com
Emp.: 150
Book Publishers
S.I.C.: 2731
N.A.I.C.S.: 511130
Dannecke Apel Grem *(Gen Mgr)*

Egmont Tidskrifter AB (1)
Skeppsgatan 9
205 07 Malmo, Sweden (100%)
Tel.: (46) 40385200
Fax: (46) 40385396
E-Mail: info@egmont.se
Web Site: www.egmont.se
Emp.: 100
Periodical Publishers
S.I.C.: 2721
N.A.I.C.S.: 511120
Ter Kjaander *(Mng Dir)*
Per Kjellander *(Mng Dir)*

Mailbox Media MBM AB (1)
Enhagfflimgham 4
18740 Taby, Sweden
Tel.: (46) 854496350
Fax: (46) 854493669
E-Mail: info@mailboxmedia.se
Web Site: www.mailboxmedia.se
Emp.: 6
Commercial Printing
S.I.C.: 2759
N.A.I.C.S.: 323111
Oddvv Estmam *(Mgr)*

Matila Rohr Productions (MRP) (1)
Tallberginkatu 1A 141
Helsinki, 00180, Finland (100%)
Tel.: (358) 96689990
Fax: (358) 966899966
E-Mail: info@nordiskfilmtv.fi
Web Site: www.nordiskfilmtv.fi
Emp.: 25
Motion Picture & Video Production
S.I.C.: 7812
N.A.I.C.S.: 512110
Antti Vaisanen *(Mng Dir)*

Nordisk Film AB (1)
Karlsrovagen 2 D
Danderyd, Sweden
Tel.: (46) 86013200
Fax: (46) 8 601 3210
Web Site: www.nordiskfilm.com
Emp.: 50
Motion Picture & Video Production
S.I.C.: 7812
N.A.I.C.S.: 512110
Jens Alex *(Mng Dir)*

Nordisk Film & TV AS (1)
Distribution Nydalen
0421 Oslo, Norway
Tel.: (47) 21544800
Fax: (47) 21544810
E-Mail: allen.hansen@nordiskfilm.com
Web Site: www.nordiskfilm.com
Motion Picture & Video Production
S.I.C.: 7812
N.A.I.C.S.: 512110
Allan Hansen *(Mng Dir)*

Nordisk Film Post Production Stockholm AB (1)
Tullvaktsvagen 2
Stockholm, Sweden
Tel.: (46) 84504500
Fax: (46) 84504504
E-Mail: nfpp.reception@nordiskfilm.com
Web Site: www.nordiskfilm-postproduction.com
Emp.: 60
Motion Picture & Video Production
S.I.C.: 7812
N.A.I.C.S.: 512110
Anétte Mattfsson *(CEO)*

Nordisk Film Production Sverige AB (1)
Tegeluddsvagen 80
10252 Stockholm, Sweden
Tel.: (46) 86013200
Fax: (46) 86013210
Web Site: www.nordiskfilm-postproduction.com
Emp.: 100
Motion Picture & Video Production
S.I.C.: 7812
N.A.I.C.S.: 512110

Nordisk Film TV Produktion AB (1)
Tegeluddsvagen 80 6 tr
PO Box 271 84
Stockholm, 102 52, Sweden
Tel.: (46) 86013200
Fax: (46) 86013210
Web Site: www.nordiskfilmtv.com
Emp.: 50
Motion Picture & Video Production
S.I.C.: 7812
N.A.I.C.S.: 512110
Karin Stjarne *(Mgr-Television)*

Oy Nordisk Film AB (1)
Mechelininkatu 1a
Helsinki, 00180, Finland
Tel.: (358) 94764460
Fax: (358) 947644640
E-Mail: morich.nyman@nordiskfilm.com
Web Site: www.nordiskfilm.fi
Emp.: 30
Motion Picture & Video Production
S.I.C.: 7812
N.A.I.C.S.: 512110
Morich Nyman *(Mng Dir)*

TV 2 AS (1)
Nostegaten 72
PO Box 7222
N 5020 Bergen, Norway (100%)
Tel.: (47) 55908070
Fax: (47) 55908090
E-Mail: administrasjon@tv2.no
Web Site: www.tv2.no
Emp.: 800
Television Broadcasting
S.I.C.: 2711
N.A.I.C.S.: 515120
Alf Hildrum *(Mng Dir)*

Vagabond Media AB (1)
Gotgatan 95
PO Box 20 123
10460 Stockholm, Sweden
Tel.: (46) 80 555 240 00
Fax: (46) 80 555 240 01
Web Site: www.vagabond.se/
Periodical Publishers
S.I.C.: 2721
N.A.I.C.S.: 511120
Alexandra Kindblom *(Mng Dir)*

Non-U.S. Joint Ventures:

Bladcentralen ANS (1)
Haraldrudveien 20
PO Box 53
0581 Oslo, Norway (43%)
Tel.: (47) 22726200
Fax: (47) 22726217
E-Mail: post@bladcentralen.no
Web Site: www.bladcentralen.no
Emp.: 50
Freight Transportation Arrangement
S.I.C.: 4731
N.A.I.C.S.: 488510
Paul Berddahl *(Mgr)*

Bladcentralens Eiendomsselskap AS (1)
Haraldrudveien 20
PO Box 53
0581 Oslo, Norway (43%)
Tel.: (47) 22726200
Fax: (47) 22726266
E-Mail: firmapost@bladcentralens.no
Web Site: www.bladcentralens.no
Emp.: 80
Real Estate Agents & Brokers
S.I.C.: 6531
N.A.I.C.S.: 531210
Paul Bergdahl *(Pres)*

Bokklubben Villmarksliv ANS (1)
Gullhaugtorg 1
0043 Oslo, Norway (50%)
Tel.: (47) 22022177
Fax: (47) 22022210
Web Site: www.bokklubbenvillmarksliv.no
Emp.: 55
Book Publishers
S.I.C.: 2731
N.A.I.C.S.: 511130
Bente Eriksen *(Mng Dir)*

E'GRAND CO., LTD.

1-2-1 Kandanishiki-cho Chiyoda-ku
Tokyo, 101-0054, Japan
Tel.: (81) 3 3219 5050
Web Site: www.e-grand.co.jp
3294—(JAS)
Rev.: $101,813,635
Emp.: 60
Fiscal Year-end: 03/31/13

Business Description:
Housing Restoration & Sales
S.I.C.: 1522
N.A.I.C.S.: 236118

Personnel:
Hisashi Eguchi *(Pres)*

EGREEN CO., LTD.

Icheon-si
Icheon, Gyeonggi, Korea (South)
Tel.: (82) 31 7836733
Fax: (82) 31 7836734
Web Site: www.e-greenglobal.com
185280—(KRS)

Business Description:
Animal Corn Feed Mfr
S.I.C.: 0115
N.A.I.C.S.: 111150

Personnel:
Jong-Moon Park *(CEO)*

EGUARANTEE, INC.

4-20-3 Ebisu
Ebisu Garden Place Tower 2/F
Shibuya-ku, Tokyo, 150-0013, Japan
Tel.: (81) 3 54473577
Fax: (81) 3 54473580
Web Site: www.eguarantee.co.jp
Year Founded: 2000
8771—(JAS TKS)
Sales Range: $25-49.9 Million

Business Description:
Credit Intermediation
S.I.C.: 6099
N.A.I.C.S.: 522390

Personnel:
Masanori Eto *(Pres & CEO)*

Board of Directors:
Masanori Eto
H. Karatsu
Kazuhiko Kato
Joji Nagai
Ryoichi Nagasawa
Kazuhiro Yamamoto

EGYPT KUWAIT HOLDING CO. S.A.E

14 Hassan Mohamed El Razzaz Street
Agouza, Giza, Egypt
Tel.: (20) 233363300
Fax: (20) 233358989
E-Mail: info@ekholding.com
Web Site: www.ekholding.com
Year Founded: 1997
EKHO—(EGX)
Rev.: $844,990,000
Assets: $2,280,182,000
Liabilities: $997,452,000

Egypt Kuwait Holding Co. S.A.E—(Continued)

Net Worth: $1,282,730,000
Earnings: $134,963,000
Emp.: 5,000
Fiscal Year-end: 12/31/12
Business Description:
Private Equity Holdings
S.I.C.: 6719
N.A.I.C.S.: 551112
Personnel:
Moataz Al-Alfi *(Chm & CEO)*
Loay Jassim Al-Kharafi *(Vice Chm)*
Sahar Farahat *(CFO & Exec VP)*
Ahmed El Mofty *(COO)*
Khaled El Demerdash *(Legal Counsel)*
Ahmed ElBassiouny *(Sr VP-Investments)*
Board of Directors:
Moataz Al-Alfi
Assad Al-Banwan
Abdel Mohsen Al-Fares
Bassam Yusuf Al-Ghanim
Marzouk Al-Ghanim
Hussein Al-Kharafi
Loay Jassim Al-Kharafi
Mubarak Abdulla Al-Mubarak Al-Sabah
Saad Al-Saad
Galal Al-Zorba
Mohamed El Ansary
Sanaa El Banna
Ali Mohamed Faramawy
Ayman Laz
Ismail Osman

EGYPTAIR HOLDING COMPANY

6 Adly Street
Cairo, Egypt
Tel.: (20) 23900999
Web Site: www.egyptair.com.eg
Year Founded: 1932
Business Description:
Holding Company; Air Transportation Services
S.I.C.: 6719
N.A.I.C.S.: 551112
Personnel:
Hossam Kamal *(Chm & CEO)*
Subsidiaries:

EGYPTAIR CARGO **(1)**
3rd Floor Middle Building Airport Road
Cairo, Egypt
Tel.: (20) 222674500
E-Mail: cargo-salesprom@egyptair.com
Web Site: www.egyptair-cargo.com
Airport Cargo Handling Services
S.I.C.: 4581
N.A.I.C.S.: 488119
Baseam Gohar *(Chm & CEO)*
Walid Mourad *(Vice Chm)*

EGYPTAIR MAINTENANCE & ENGINEERING **(1)**
Cairo International Airport
Post Office 02
Airport 1, Cairo, Egypt 11776
Tel.: (20) 2 2267 4512
Fax: (20) 2 2267 6050
E-Mail: contactus_me@egyptair.com
Web Site: www.egyptair-me.com
Aircraft Maintenance Services
S.I.C.: 4581
N.A.I.C.S.: 488190
Abou Taleb Tawfik *(Chm-Exec Bd & CEO)*
Hisham Nasser *(Vice Chm-Exec Bd & Mgr-Accountable)*
Khaled Ashmawy *(Sr Dir-A/C Maintenance)*
Ahmed El Baz *(Sr Dir-Continuous Airworthiness Mgmt)*
Magdy Hassanin *(Sr Dir-Overhaul Workshops)*

EGYPTIAN MEDIA PRODUCTION CITY SAE

6th Of October City
PO Box 31
Cairo, 12568, Egypt
Tel.: (20) 238555262
Fax: (20) 238555261
E-Mail: chairman@empc.com.eg
Web Site: www.empc.com.eg
MPRC—(EGX)
Sales Range: $25-49.9 Million
Emp.: 650
Business Description:
Film & Television Producer & Distr
S.I.C.: 7812
N.A.I.C.S.: 512110
Personnel:
Sayed Al Sayed *(Chm)*
Sami Badawy *(Mng Dir)*

EHC GLOBAL

1287 Boundary Rd
Oshawa, ON, L1J 6Z7, Canada
Tel.: (905) 432-3200
Fax: (905) 432-2906
Toll Free: (800) 490-7915
E-Mail: info@ehc-global.com
Web Site: www.ehc-global.com
Year Founded: 1977
Business Description:
Mfr & Distr of Escalator & Elevator Components, Escalator Handrail Advertising, Escalator Handrail Field Services & Custom Engineered Polyurethane Products
S.I.C.: 3534
N.A.I.C.S.: 333921
Personnel:
Jeno Eppel *(Pres)*

EHG CORPORATION LIMITED

Level 2 350 Kent Street
Sydney, NSW, 2000, Australia
Tel.: (61) 2 9299 2289
Fax: (61) 2 9299 2239
Web Site: www.ehgcorp.com.au
EHG—(ASX)
Sales Range: Less than $1 Million
Business Description:
Electronic Product Mfr & Whslr
S.I.C.: 3679
N.A.I.C.S.: 334419
Personnel:
Steve Nicols *(Chm)*
Board of Directors:
Steve Nicols
Adam Blumenthal
Greg Cornelsen

THE EHIME BANK, LTD.

1 Katsuyama-cho 2-chome
Matsuyama, Ehime, 790-8580, Japan
Tel.: (81) 899331111
Fax: (81) 89 933 1027
Web Site: www.himegin.co.jp
Year Founded: 1943
8541—(TKS)
Rev.: $457,556,000
Assets: $25,639,548,000
Liabilities: $24,642,299,000
Net Worth: $997,249,000
Earnings: $41,888,000
Emp.: 1,405
Fiscal Year-end: 03/31/13
Business Description:
Banking Services
S.I.C.: 6029
N.A.I.C.S.: 522110
Personnel:
Kojiro Nakayama *(Chm)*
Motohiro Honda *(Pres)*
Mitsuo Harada *(Sr Mng Dir)*
Eiki Shimizu *(Sr Mng Dir)*
Akihiro Endo *(Mng Dir)*
Osamu Fukutomi *(Mng Dir)*
Yujiro Shimada *(Mng Dir)*
Board of Directors:
Kojiro Nakayama
Akihiro Endo
Osamu Fukutomi
Mitsuo Harada
Mitsuru Hino
Motohiro Honda
Tamaki Kidou
Morinobu Kihara
Akira Morimoto
Yoshinori Nishikawa
Yuzou Ojuku
Yujiro Shimada
Eiki Shimizu
Masahiko Wakimizu
Keizou Yamamoto
Takeshi Yamashita
Subsidiaries:

Ehime-JCB Co., Ltd. **(1)**
2 4 7 Katsuyama cho
Matsuyama, Ehime, 790 0878, Japan
Tel.: (81) 899212303
Fax: (81) 899339526
Credit Card Services
S.I.C.: 6099
N.A.I.C.S.: 522320
Moriyama Masaki *(Gen Mgr)*

Himegin Business Service Co., Ltd. **(1)**
5 6 1 Chifunemachi Matsuyama Shi
Matsuyama, Ehime, 790 0011, Japan
Tel.: (81) 899323486
ATM Facilities Maintenance & Management
S.I.C.: 1799
N.A.I.C.S.: 238290

HIMEGIN Lease Co., Ltd. **(1)**
2 1 Katsuyama cho
Matsuyama, Ehime, 790 0878, Japan
Tel.: (81) 899338383
Fax: (81) 9333354
Leasing & Investment Services
S.I.C.: 6282
N.A.I.C.S.: 523920

Himegin Soft Co., Ltd. **(1)**
27 1 Minami mochidamachi
Matsuyama, 790 0874, Japan
Tel.: (81) 899437767
Computer Software Development Services
S.I.C.: 7371
N.A.I.C.S.: 541511

EHINGER-SCHWARZ GMBH & CO. KG

Am Hochstrass 8
89081 Ulm, Germany
Tel.: (49) 731509750
Fax: (49) 73150975299
E-Mail: info@Charlotte.de
Web Site: www.Charlotte.de
Year Founded: 1876
Rev.: $24,829,200
Emp.: 120
Business Description:
Jewelry Mfr
S.I.C.: 5094
N.A.I.C.S.: 423940
Personnel:
Wolf-Peter Schwarz *(Chm-Mgmt Bd)*
Hans Layer *(Member-Mgmt Bd)*
Caroline Schwarz *(Member-Mgmt Bd)*
Olaf Zimmermann *(Member-Mgmt Bd)*

EHOTEL AG

Greifswalder Strasse 208
10405 Berlin, Germany
Tel.: (49) 30473730
Fax: (49) 30473731000
E-Mail: info@ehotel.de
Web Site: www.ehotel.de
Rev.: $17,518,380
Emp.: 25
Business Description:
Hotel Reservation Services
S.I.C.: 4729
N.A.I.C.S.: 561599
Personnel:
Fritz Zerweck *(CEO)*

EHWA TECHNOLOGIES INFORMATION CO. LTD.

7F Sukho B/d 66-11 Nonhyeon2-dong
Gangnam-gu, Seoul, 135-816, Korea (South)
Tel.: (82) 2 414 8111
Fax: (82) 2 414 1473
E-Mail: sales@eti21.com
Web Site: www.eti21.com
Year Founded: 1956
024810—(KRS)
Business Description:
Electric Equipment Mfr & Whslr
S.I.C.: 3699
N.A.I.C.S.: 335999
Personnel:
Jung Hwan Kim *(CEO)*

EICHER MOTORS LIMITED

3rd Floor-Select Citywalk A-3 District Centre Saket
New Delhi, 110 017, India
Tel.: (91) 1129563722
Fax: (91) 1129225521
E-Mail: investors@eicher.in
Web Site: www.eicher.in
EICHERMOT—(NSE)
Rev.: $1,296,880,416
Assets: $829,012,392
Liabilities: $327,811,302
Net Worth: $501,201,090
Earnings: $88,037,190
Emp.: 927
Fiscal Year-end: 12/31/12
Business Description:
Automotive Component Mfr
S.I.C.: 3711
N.A.I.C.S.: 336111
Personnel:
Siddhartha Lal *(CEO & Mng Dir)*
Board of Directors:
S. Sandilya
Priya Brat
Prateek Jalan
Siddhartha Lal
R. L. Ravichandran
M. J. Subbaiah
Transfer Agent:
MCS Limited
F-65 Okhla Industrial Area Phase-I
New Delhi, India

EICKHOFF MASCHINENFABRIK GMBH

Hunscheidstrasse 176
PO Box 100629
44789 Bochum, Germany
Tel.: (49) 2349750
Fax: (49) 2349752579
E-Mail: kontakt@eickhoff-bochum.de
Web Site: www.eickhoff-bochum.de
Emp.: 900
Business Description:
Mfr. of Drum Loaders for Stable & Rise Driving Machines
S.I.C.: 3535
N.A.I.C.S.: 333922
Personnel:
Paul Rheinlander *(CEO)*
Karl Nienhaus *(Mng Dir-Tech)*
U.S. Subsidiary:

Eickhoff Corporation **(1)**
200 Parkwest Dr
Pittsburgh, PA 15275-1002 (100%)
Tel.: (412) 788-1400
Fax: (412) 788-4100
E-Mail: info@eickhoffcorp.com
Web Site: www.eickhoffcorp.com
Emp.: 12
Mfr. & Wholesaler of Longwall Mining Machinery
Import
S.I.C.: 5082
N.A.I.C.S.: 423810
Richard Liconti *(VP)*

Subsidiaries:

Eickhoff Australia Pty. Ltd (1)
Prince William Dr 41
Seven Hills, NSW, 2147, Australia (100%)
Tel.: (61) 296746733
Fax: (61) 296746581
E-Mail: john.smallwood@eickhoff.com
Web Site: www.eickhoffcorp.com
Emp.: 30
Industrial Machinery Producer
S.I.C.: 3559
N.A.I.C.S.: 333249
John Smallwood *(Mng Dir)*

Eickhoff Bergbautechnik GmbH (1)
Hunscheidtstrasse 176
44789 Bochum, Germany
Tel.: (49) 2349750
Fax: (49) 2349752445
E-Mail: kontakt@eickhoff-bochum.de
Web Site: www.eickhoff-bochum.de
Mining & Tunneling Shearer Loader Equipment Mfr
S.I.C.: 3559
N.A.I.C.S.: 333249

Eickhoff (G.B.) Ltd. (1)
Darnall Works
Prince of Wales Road, Sheffield, S9 4EX, United Kingdom
Tel.: (44) 87 122 1164
Fax: (44) 87 122 1165
E-Mail: contact@eickhoffgb.idps.co.uk
Web Site: www.eickhoffcorp.com
Industrial Machinery Producer
S.I.C.: 3559
N.A.I.C.S.: 333249

Eickhoff Giesserei GmbH (1)
Hunscheidtstrasse 176
44789 Bochum, Germany (100%)
Tel.: (49) 2349752760
Fax: (49) 2349752411
E-Mail: contact@eickhoff-bochum.de
Web Site: www.eickhoff-bochum.de
Emp.: 200
Industrial Machines Producer
S.I.C.: 3559
N.A.I.C.S.: 333249
Ralf Funke *(CEO)*

Eickhoff Polonia Ltd. (1)
Ul Podleska 72
Mikolow, PL 43190 Mirkow, Poland (100%)
Tel.: (48) 322066010
Fax: (48) 322028744
Web Site: www.eickhoffcorp.com
Industrial Machinery Producer
S.I.C.: 3559
N.A.I.C.S.: 333249

Eickhoff Pty Ltd (1)
12 Strauss Crescent Wadeville Ext 6
PO Box 74
Germiston, 4322, South Africa (100%)
Tel.: (27) 1190256301
Fax: (27) 119025830
E-Mail:
Web Site: www.eickhoffcorp.com
Emp.: 100
Industrial Machinery Producer
S.I.C.: 3559
N.A.I.C.S.: 333249
Werner Mars *(Mgr-Fin)*

Schalker Eisenhuette Maschinenfabrik GmbH (1)
Magdeburger Strasse 37
D 45881 Gelsenkirchen, Germany (100%)
Tel.: (49) 20998050
Fax: (49) 2099805155
E-Mail: info@schalke.de
Web Site: www.schalke.de
Emp.: 95
Industrial Machinery Producer
S.I.C.: 3559
N.A.I.C.S.: 333249

EICL LIMITED

TC-79 4 Veli
Thiruvananthapuram, Kerala, 695 021, India
Tel.: (91) 4712741133
Fax: (91) 4712742233
E-Mail: claysales.trv@eicl.in
Web Site: www.eicl.in
526560—(BOM)
Rev.: $81,007,271
Assets: $68,446,891
Liabilities: $38,562,505
Net Worth: $29,884,386
Earnings: $2,200,259
Fiscal Year-end: 03/31/13

Business Description:
Kaolin Clay Mining & Manufacturing
S.I.C.: 1455
N.A.I.C.S.: 212324

Personnel:
Karan Thapar *(Chm)*
Venkatesh Padmanabhan *(CEO & Mng Dir)*
P. S. Saini *(Compliance Officer, Sec & Head-Corp Legal)*
S. K. Jain *(Sr VP-Corp Fin Accts & Admin)*

Board of Directors:
Karan Thapar
T. Balakrishnan
Jainender Kumar Jain
Venkatesh Padmanabhan
Vijay Rai
Praveen Sachdev

Transfer Agent:
RCMC Share Registry Pvt. Ltd.
B-106 Sector-2
Noida, India

EIDAI CO., LTD.

10-60 Hirabayashi Minami 2-chome
Suminoe-ku
Osaka, 559-8658, Japan
Tel.: (81) 666843000
Fax: (81) 666811150
E-Mail: cs@eidai-sangyo.co.jp
Web Site: www.eidai.com
Year Founded: 1946
7822—(TKS)
Sales Range: $700-749.9 Million
Emp.: 1,317

Business Description:
Household & Interior Wooden Building Materials Mfr & Sales
S.I.C.: 2435
N.A.I.C.S.: 321211

Personnel:
Yasunaga Yoshikawa *(CEO)*

EIDESVIK HOLDING A/S

Langevaag
N 5443 Bomlo, Norway
Tel.: (47) 53448000
Fax: (47) 53448001
E-Mail: office@eidesvik.no
Web Site: www.eidesvik.no
Sales Range: $75-99.9 Million
Emp.: 400

Business Description:
Holding Company
S.I.C.: 6719
N.A.I.C.S.: 551112

Personnel:
Svein Ovenerstvdt *(CFO & VP-Fin)*

Subsidiaries:

Eidesvik AS (1)
Langevaag
5443 Bomlo, Norway (100%)
Tel.: (47) 53448000
E-Mail: office@eidesvik.no
Web Site: www.eidesvik.no
Emp.: 470
Vessels Fleet Operating Manager
S.I.C.: 4499
N.A.I.C.S.: 488390
Jinsredrik Meilng *(CEO)*

Joint Venture:

NorSea Group AS (1)
Risavika Havnering 14
PO Box 70
Tananger, Norway
Tel.: (47) 51 85 30 00
Fax: (47) 51 85 30 01
E-Mail: norseagroup@norseagroup.com
Web Site: www.norseagroup.com
Support Activities for Oil & Gas Operations
S.I.C.: 1389
N.A.I.C.S.: 213112
John E. Stangeland *(Pres & CEO)*
Steinar Modalslid-Meling *(Exec VP & CFO)*
Lars Haug *(Exec VP & COO)*
Leif Emil Brekke *(Exec VP)*

Subsidiaries:

NorSea AS (2)
Risavika Havnering 14
N 4056 Tananger, Norway
Mailing Address:
PO Box 70
4098 Tananger, Norway
Tel.: (47) 51853000
Fax: (47) 51853001
E-Mail: info@norseagroup.com
Web Site: www.norseagroup.com
Emp.: 200
Supply Bases, Logistics & Support Services Supplier to the Onshore & Offshore Industries
S.I.C.: 1389
N.A.I.C.S.: 213112
Rune Veenstra *(Mng Dir)*

Vestbase AS (2)
Omagaten 110 C
N 6500 Kristiansund, Norway
Tel.: (47) 71572200
Fax: (47) 71572210
E-Mail: vestbase@norseagroup.com
Web Site: www.vestbase.com
Emp.: 70
Logistics Supplier for Offshore Related Activities
S.I.C.: 1311
N.A.I.C.S.: 211111
Alf Dahl *(Mng Dir)*

EIENDOMSSPAR ASA

Ovre Slottsgate 12B
0113 Oslo, Norway
Tel.: (47) 22330550
Fax: (47) 22330551
E-Mail: post@eiendomsspar.no
Web Site: www.eiendomsspar.no
Emp.: 35

Business Description:
Real Estate Holding Company
S.I.C.: 6531
N.A.I.C.S.: 531390

Personnel:
Christian Ringnes *(CEO)*

Non-U.S. Joint Venture:

Pandox AB (1)
Grev Turegatan 44
SE 114 38 Stockholm, Sweden
Tel.: (46) 850620550
Fax: (46) 850620570
E-Mail: pandox@pandox.com
Web Site: www.pandox.se
Emp.: 26
Hotel Property Management Services; Joint Venture of Eiendomsspar ASA & Sundt AS
S.I.C.: 6519
N.A.I.C.S.: 531190
Anders Nissen *(CEO)*
Liia Nou *(Sr VP & CFO)*
Lars Haggstrom *(Sr VP-Asset Mgmt)*

Non-U.S. Subsidiaries:

Norgani Finland Holding OY (2)
Etelaesplanadi 22B 3rd Floor
00130 Helsinki, Finland
Tel.: (358) 9 67 77 24
Hotel Management & Services
S.I.C.: 7011
N.A.I.C.S.: 721110

Norgani Hotels ASA (2)
Stramdem 3 A 6th Fl
0250 Oslo, Norway
Tel.: (47) 40004303
Fax: (47) 22831850
E-Mail: norgani@norgani.no
Web Site: www.norgani.no
Sales Range: $75-99.9 Million
Emp.: 19
Hotel Management & Services
S.I.C.: 7011
N.A.I.C.S.: 721110
Anders Vatne *(CEO)*
Eva Salvesen *(CFO)*

EIFFAGE S.A.

163 quai du Docteur Dervaux
92600 Asnieres, France
Tel.: (33) 141328000
Fax: (33) 1 41 32 81 10
E-Mail: dircom@eiffage.fr
Web Site: www.eiffage.com
Year Founded: 1844
FGR—(EUR)
Rev.: $18,884,072,760
Assets: $36,326,397,450
Liabilities: $33,310,976,650
Net Worth: $3,015,420,800
Earnings: $345,965,690
Emp.: 68,591
Fiscal Year-end: 12/31/12

Business Description:
Construction & Public Works Services
S.I.C.: 1542
N.A.I.C.S.: 236220

Personnel:
Pierre Berger *(Chm & CEO)*
Jean-Francois Roverato *(Vice Chm)*
Christian Cassayre *(CFO)*

Board of Directors:
Pierre Berger
Beatrice Breneol
Therese Cornil
Laurent Dupont
Bruno Flichy
Jean-Yves Andre Aime Gilet
Jean Guenard
Marie Lemarie
Dominique Marcel
Jean-Francois Roverato
Demetrio Ullastres

KPMG SA
1 cours Valmy
Paris, France

Subsidiaries:

A lienor S.A., (1)
40 rue de Liege
64000 Pau, France
Tel.: (33) 5 59 81 47 47
Web Site: www.a65-alienor.com
Road & Bridge Construction Services
S.I.C.: 1622
N.A.I.C.S.: 237310

Alsatel (1)
Zone Aeroparc II 8 rue des Herons
67960 Entzheim, France
Tel.: (33) 3 88 76 22 22
Fax: (33) 3 88 78 59 82
E-Mail: marketing@alsatel.fr
Web Site: www.alsatel.fr
Telecommunication Engineering Services
S.I.C.: 4899
N.A.I.C.S.: 517919
Michelle Paolillo *(Gen Mgr)*

Armor Connectic SAS (1)
163 Quai du Docteur Dervaux
92601 Asnieres-sur-Seine, France
Tel.: (33) 141328264
Fax: (33) 141328185
E-Mail: contact@armorconnectic.com
Web Site: www.armorconnectic.com
Broadband Internet Service Provider
S.I.C.: 4899
N.A.I.C.S.: 517919

Clemessy Emcs (1)
172 Av Aristide Briand
68200 Mulhouse, France
Tel.: (33) 389 323 720
Fax: (33) 389 323 201
Industrial Engineering Services
S.I.C.: 8711
N.A.I.C.S.: 541330

Compagnie Eiffage du Viaduc de Millau (1)
Peage de Saint Germain
BP 60457
12104 Millau, France

Eiffage S.A.—(Continued)

Tel.: (33) 5 65 61 61 61
Fax: (33) 5 65 61 61 60
Web Site: www.leviaducdemillau.com
Bridge Construction Services
S.I.C.: 1622
N.A.I.C.S.: 237310
Immanuel Cachot *(Mng Dir)*

Eiffage Construction (1)
3 Ave Morane Saulnier
78141 Velizy-Villacoublay, France (100%)
Tel.: (33) 134658989
Fax: (33) 0134658590
Web Site: www.eiffageconstruction.com
Sales Range: $1-4.9 Billion
Emp.: 100
Commercial & Institutional Construction Services
S.I.C.: 1542
N.A.I.C.S.: 236220
Fracois Masse *(Pres)*
Michel Gostoli *(Dir Gen)*

Subsidiaries:

Eiffage Construction Alsace Franche Comte S.N.C (2)
10 Rue Du Vallon
Ecole-Valentin, Doubs, 25480, France
Tel.: (33) 381483434
Fax: (33) 381530300
Construction Engineering Services
S.I.C.: 8711
N.A.I.C.S.: 541330

Eiffage Construction Artois Hainaut S.N.C. (2)
Zone Industrielle Douai Dorignies 350 R F Pilatre De Rozier
59500 Douai, Nord, France
Tel.: (33) 327991499
Fax: (33) 327969474
Construction Engineering Services
S.I.C.: 8711
N.A.I.C.S.: 541330

Eiffage Construction Auvergne SNC (2)
49 Rue Georges Besse
Clermont-Ferrand, Puy-de-Dome, 63100, France
Tel.: (33) 473980650
Fax: (33) 473928798
Construction Engineering Services
S.I.C.: 8711
N.A.I.C.S.: 541330

Eiffage Construction Basse Normandie (2)
Rue Roger Anne
Cherbourg-Octeville, Manche, 50100, France
Tel.: (33) 233876420
Fax: (33) 233040807
Construction Engineering Services
S.I.C.: 1629
N.A.I.C.S.: 237990

Eiffage Construction Bourgogne (2)
4 Rue Lavoisier
21600 Longvic, Cote-d Or, France
Tel.: (33) 380692929
Construction Engineering Services
S.I.C.: 1629
N.A.I.C.S.: 237990

Eiffage Construction Bretagne S.N.C (2)
40 bd de La Tour d'Auvergne
Rennes, 35000, France
Tel.: (33) 299653131
Fax: (33) 299653110
Construction Engineering Services
S.I.C.: 1629
N.A.I.C.S.: 237990

Eiffage Construction Centre (2)
5 Rue Claude Lewy
Orleans, Loiret, 45100, France
Tel.: (33) 238226666
Fax: (33) 238565758
Construction Engineering Services
S.I.C.: 1629
N.A.I.C.S.: 237990

Eiffage Construction Champagne (2)
19 rue Maurice Prevoteau
Reims, 51100, France
Tel.: (33) 3 26 82 82 35
Fax: (33) 3 26 82 82 36
Construction Engineering Services
S.I.C.: 1629
N.A.I.C.S.: 237990

Eiffage Construction Cote d Azur S.N.C. (2)
Les Vaisseaux de Sophia Ba 300 Rue Du Vallon
6560 Valbonne, Alpes-Maritimes, France
Tel.: (33) 492384600
Construction Engineering Services
S.I.C.: 1629
N.A.I.C.S.: 237990

Eiffage Construction Limousin (2)
Les Hauts De Bel Air 50 Rue Pierre Et Marie Curie
Limoges, Haute-Vienne, 87000, France
Tel.: (33) 555064949
Fax: (33) 555015603
Construction Engineering Services
S.I.C.: 8711
N.A.I.C.S.: 541330
Michel Berthou *(Gen Mgr)*

Eiffage Construction Lorraine S.N.C (2)
9 Rue Paul Langevin
Maxeville, Meurthe-et-Moselle, 54320, France
Tel.: (33) 383574831
Fax: (33) 383543211
Construction Engineering Services
S.I.C.: 8711
N.A.I.C.S.: 541330

Eiffage Construction Materiel (2)
11 Place de L Europe
Velizy-Villacoublay, Yvelines, 78140, France
Tel.: (33) 134658989
Construction Material Distr
S.I.C.: 5032
N.A.I.C.S.: 423320

Eiffage Construction Metallique S.A. (2)
48/50 rue de Seine
92707 Colombes, France
Tel.: (33) 1 47 60 47 00
Fax: (33) 1 47 60 47 01
Web Site: www.eiffageconstructionmetallique.com
Emp.: 4,800
Civil Engineering Construction Services
S.I.C.: 1629
N.A.I.C.S.: 237990

Eiffage Construction Midi Pyrenees S.N.C (2)
Batiment C 109 Avenue De Lespinet
Toulouse, Haute-Garonne, 31400, France
Tel.: (33) 534312000
Construction Engineering Services
S.I.C.: 8711
N.A.I.C.S.: 541330

Eiffage Construction Nord (2)
10 Allee Lavoisier
Villeneuve d'Ascq, Nord, 59650, France
Tel.: (33) 328389666
Fax: (33) 0328389660
Construction Engineering Services
S.I.C.: 8711
N.A.I.C.S.: 541330

Eiffage Construction Paris Patrimoine (2)
423 Les Bureaux De La Colline
92210 Saint-Cloud, France
Tel.: (33) 147755873
Construction Engineering Services
S.I.C.: 8711
N.A.I.C.S.: 541330

Eiffage Construction Poitou Charentes (2)
14 rue de Pied de Fond
79004 Niort, France
Tel.: (33) 5 49 34 07 07
Fax: (33) 5 49 09 05 62
Construction Engineering Services
S.I.C.: 8711
N.A.I.C.S.: 541330

Eiffage Construction Provence S.N.C (2)
Parc du Roy D Espagne 8 A 14 8 Allee Cervantes
Marseille, Bouches-du-Rhone, 13009, France
Tel.: (33) 491166900
Construction Engineering Services
S.I.C.: 8711
N.A.I.C.S.: 541330

Eiffage Construction Rhone-Alpes S.N.C. (2)
3 rue Hrant Dink
Lyon, Rhone, 69002, France
Tel.: (33) 478601515
Fax: (33) 0478600207
Emp.: 400
Construction Engineering Services
S.I.C.: 8711
N.A.I.C.S.: 541330
Gauden Domecho *(Gen Mgr)*

Eiffage Construction Services (2)
361 Avenue du General de Gaulle
92140 Clamart, France
Tel.: (33) 1 40 83 17 50
Construction Engineering Services
S.I.C.: 1629
N.A.I.C.S.: 237990

Eiffage Construction Val de Seine S.N.C (2)
Zone Industrielle 3 Rue Ampere
91430 Igny, Essonne, France
Tel.: (33) 169337100
Fax: (33) 169412249
Construction Engineering Services
S.I.C.: 8711
N.A.I.C.S.: 541330

Fougerolle S.A. (2)
Rue de la longueraie Z A des Landelles
35520 Melesse, France
Tel.: (33) 2 99 66 08 17
Fax: (33) 2 99 66 08 24
E-Mail: sales@fougerolle-fr.com
Web Site: www.fougerolle-fr.com
Audio & Video Equipment Mfr
S.I.C.: 3651
N.A.I.C.S.: 334310
Christian Lanoiselee *(Mng Dir)*

Genie Civil Industriel (2)
Zi Molina la Chazote Cplt Lieu Dit le Montcel
42650 Saint-Jean-Bonnefonds, Loire, France
Tel.: (33) 477476080
Civil Engineering Services
S.I.C.: 1629
N.A.I.C.S.: 237990

Socamip (2)
Residence Le Bastion 49 rue du Rempart Saint Claude
La Rochelle, Charente-Maritime, 17000, France
Tel.: (33) 546341202
Fax: (33) 546341018
Web Site: www.socamip.fr
Construction Engineering Services
S.I.C.: 8711
N.A.I.C.S.: 541330

Non-U.S. Subsidiaries:

Antwerpse Bouwwerken NV (2)
Bouwensstraat 35
2140 Antwerp, Belgium
Tel.: (32) 3 205 28 00
Fax: (32) 3 232 53 49
E-Mail: ab@antwerpsebouwwerken.eiffage.be
Web Site: www.antwerpsebouwwerken.be
Civil Engineering Construction Services
S.I.C.: 1629
N.A.I.C.S.: 237990

Auto Park Poznan Sp. z o.o. (2)
ul Sw Michala 43
Poznan, 61-119, Poland
Tel.: (48) 618 50 18 40
Fax: (48) 618 50 14 68
Construction Engineering Services
S.I.C.: 1629
N.A.I.C.S.: 237990

Collignon Eng SA (2)
Briscol 4
6779 Erezee, Belgium
Tel.: (32) 86 47 77 00
Fax: (32) 86 47 77 11
E-Mail: collignon.eng@collignon.net
Web Site: www.collignon.net
Emp.: 10
Electrical Lightning Installation Services
S.I.C.: 1731
N.A.I.C.S.: 238210

De Graeve Entreprises Generales SA (2)
Avenue Reine Elisabeth 16
Namur, 5000, Belgium
Tel.: (32) 8 122 77 81
Fax: (32) 8 123 11 77
Construction Engineering Services
S.I.C.: 1629
N.A.I.C.S.: 237990

Eiffage Budownictwo Mitex S.A (2)
ul Postepu 5a
02-676 Warsaw, Poland
Tel.: (48) 22 5664900
Fax: (48) 22 5664950
E-Mail: biuro@budownictwo.eiffage.pl
Web Site: www.budownictwo.eiffage.pl
Rev.: $280,608,000
Emp.: 50
Construction Engineering Services
S.I.C.: 1629
N.A.I.C.S.: 237990
Zbigniew Zajaczkowski *(Chm-Mgmt Bd)*
Eric Roux *(Vice Chm-Mgmt Bd)*
Ewa Katarzyna Wolska *(Vice Chm-Mgmt Bd)*

Eiffage Polska Koleje Sp. z o.o. (2)
ul Marynarska 19A
Warsaw, 02-674, Poland
Tel.: (48) 223 51 06 02
Fax: (48) 223 51 06 03
E-Mail: warszawa@tchaspolska.pl
Web Site: www.tchaspolska.pl
Emp.: 15
Construction Engineering Services
S.I.C.: 1629
N.A.I.C.S.: 237990
Leszek Kaczorek *(Gen Mgr)*

Eiffage Polska Nieruchomosci Sp. z o.o. (2)
Postepu 5 A
02-676 Warsaw, Poland
Tel.: (48) 22 566 48 33
Fax: (48) 22 566 49 55
Web Site: www.eiffage.pl
Real Estate Management Services
S.I.C.: 6531
N.A.I.C.S.: 531390
Zbigniew Zajaczkowski *(Pres)*

Limpens SA (2)
Rue Bara 71
Brussels, 1070, Belgium
Tel.: (32) 2 523 81 96
Fax: (32) 2 520 16 75
E-Mail: info@limpens.eiffage.be
Web Site: www.limpens.be
Heating & Plumbing Services
S.I.C.: 1711
N.A.I.C.S.: 238220

Perrard S.A. (2)
94 rue du Grunewald
1912 Luxembourg, Luxembourg
Tel.: (352) 4253531
Fax: (352) 425349
E-Mail: perrard@perrard.lu
Web Site: www.perrard.lu
Civil Engineering & Construction Services
S.I.C.: 1629
N.A.I.C.S.: 237990

PIT Antwerpen NV (2)
Starrenhoflaan 27
2950 Kapellen, Belgium
Tel.: (32) 3 605 14 33
Fax: (32) 3 605 14 76
E-Mail: info@pitantwerpen.be
Web Site: www.pitantwerpen.be
Emp.: 27
Apartment Building Construction Services
S.I.C.: 1531
N.A.I.C.S.: 236117
Kristof Joosen *(Gen Mgr)*

SA Eiffage Benelux (2)
Avenue Brugmann 27A
1060 Brussels, Belgium
Tel.: (32) 2 543 45 00
Fax: (32) 2 534 57 48
E-Mail: info@benelux.eiffage.be
Web Site: www.eiffagebenelux.be
Civil Engineering Construction Services
S.I.C.: 1629

N.A.I.C.S.: 237990
Paul Danaux *(Chm & Mng Dir)*

Yvan Paque S.A. **(2)**
Rue de l'Arbre Courte Joie 48
Rocourt, 4000 Liege, Belgium
Tel.: (32) 4 224 77 24
Fax: (32) 4 225 07 06
E-Mail: info@paque.eiffage.be
Web Site: www.paque.be
Emp.: 400
Electronic Lightning Installation Services
S.I.C.: 1731
N.A.I.C.S.: 238210
Dominique Scherpenbergs *(Gen Mgr)*

Plant:

Yvan Paque S.A. - Villeroux Plant **(3)**
Parc Artisanal de Villeroux 3
6640 Vaux-sur-Sure, Belgium
Tel.: (32) 61 28 85 07
Fax: (32) 61 28 95 53
Street & Traffic Light Construction Services
S.I.C.: 1622
N.A.I.C.S.: 237310

Eiffage Energie S.A.S. **(1)**
117 rue du Landy
BP 80008
F-93213 La Plaine Saint-Denis, Cedex, France FR
Tel.: (33) 1 5587 5100 (100%)
Fax: (33) 1 5587 5101
Web Site: www.eiffageenergie.com
Sales Range: $1-4.9 Billion
Power Plant Design, Construction & Operation Services
S.I.C.: 1541
N.A.I.C.S.: 236210
Pierre Berger *(CEO)*

Subsidiaries:

Eiffage Energie Electronique S.A.S. **(2)**
Route Nationale 37
F-62131 Verquin, France FR
Tel.: (33) 3 2164 6812
Fax: (33) 3 2164 5397
Web Site: www.eiffageenergie.com
Electrical System Installation Services
S.I.C.: 1731
N.A.I.C.S.: 238210

Eiffage Energie Poitou-Charentes S.A.S. **(2)**
Zone Republique 1 3 Rue Des Entrepreneurs
F-86000 Poitiers, Vienne, France FR
Tel.: (33) 549384200
Fax: (33) 549478520
Web Site: www.eiffageenergie.com
Construction Engineering Services
S.I.C.: 8711
N.A.I.C.S.: 541330

Eiffage Energie Thermie S.A.S. **(2)**
Rue Michel Manoll Zac Chantrerie Ilot Perverie Erdrerie II, F-44300 Nantes, France FR
Tel.: (33) 2 40 25 49 49
Fax: (33) 2 40 25 11 96
Web Site: www.eiffageenergie.com
Electrical System Installation Services
S.I.C.: 1731
N.A.I.C.S.: 238210

Eiffage Energie Transport & Distribution S.A.S. **(2)**
Route 937
F-62131 Verquin, France FR
Tel.: (33) 3 2164 6808
Web Site: www.eiffageenergie.com
Transportation Facilities Construction & Installation Services
S.I.C.: 1611
N.A.I.C.S.: 237310

Eiffage Energie Val de Loire S.A.S. **(2)**
6 8 rue Denis Papin
37300 Joue-les-Tours, France FR
Tel.: (33) 2 47 68 44 44
Fax: (33) 2 47 68 44 97
E-Mail: forclumvaldeloire@eiffage.com
Electrical Engineering Services
S.I.C.: 8711
N.A.I.C.S.: 541330

Forclum Alsace Franche Comte SAS **(2)**
1 rue Pierre et Marie Curie
67540 Ostwald, Bas-Rhin, France
Tel.: (33) 388555455
Fax: (33) 388555008
Institutional Building Construction Services
S.I.C.: 1542
N.A.I.C.S.: 236220

Forclum Reseaux Nord S.A.S **(2)**
3 Route D'Estaires Zone Porte
BP 23
La Bassee, 59480, France
Tel.: (33) 3 20 29 99 29
Fax: (33) 3 20 29 99 39
Electrical System Installation Services
S.I.C.: 1731
N.A.I.C.S.: 238210

Forclum Rhone Alpes S.A.S **(2)**
170 Allee Des Marais
74130 Bonneville, Haute-Savoie, France
Tel.: (33) 450257260
Fax: (33) 450256185
Construction Engineering Services
S.I.C.: 1629
N.A.I.C.S.: 237990

Units:

Eiffage Energie Centre-est **(2)**
3 rue Hrant Dink
F-69285 Lyon, Cedex 02, France
Tel.: (33) 4 3724 2750
Fax: (33) 4 3724 2751
Web Site: www.eiffageenergie.com
Electrical Installation Services
S.I.C.: 1731
N.A.I.C.S.: 238210

Eiffage Energie Ile-de-France **(2)**
2 rue Flora Tristan
BP 30012
93213 La Plaine Saint-Denis, Cedex, France
Tel.: (33) 1 5869 2030
Fax: (33) 1 5869 2049
Web Site: www.eiffageenergie.com
Electrical System Installation Services
S.I.C.: 1731
N.A.I.C.S.: 238210

Eiffage Energie Nord **(2)**
36 Place Cormontaigne
F-59000 Lille, Nord, France
Tel.: (33) 320223377
Fax: (33) 320223967
Web Site: www.eiffageenergie.com
Construction Engineering Services
S.I.C.: 8711
N.A.I.C.S.: 541330

Eiffage Immobilier **(1)**
3 Avenue Morane Saulnier
BP 46
78141 Velizy-Villacoublay, Yvelines, France
Tel.: (33) 1 34 65 89 89
Fax: (33) 1 34 65 85 64
Web Site: www.eiffageimmobilier.fr
Real Estate Management Services
S.I.C.: 6531
N.A.I.C.S.: 531390

Eiffage Travaux Publics SAS **(1)**
2 rue Helene Boucher
BP 92
92337 Neuilly-sur-Marne, France
Tel.: (33) 1 49 44 90 00
Fax: (33) 1 49 44 90 09
Web Site: www.eiffagetravauxpublics.com
Highway Construction Services
S.I.C.: 1622
N.A.I.C.S.: 237310
Jean-Louis Servranckx *(Gen Mgr)*

Subsidiaries:

Antrope SNC **(2)**
Hameau de Samson
60150 Chevincourt, France
Tel.: (33) 3 44 96 31 90
Fax: (33) 3 44 76 37 26
Civil Engineering Services
S.I.C.: 1629
N.A.I.C.S.: 237990

Appia Grands Travaux SNC **(2)**
3 Rue Hrant Dink
Lyon, Rhone, 69002, France
Tel.: (33) 478036401
Fax: (33) 437233429
Civil Engineering Services
S.I.C.: 1629
N.A.I.C.S.: 237990
Xavier Monni *(Gen Mgr)*

Appia Liants Emulsion Rhone Alpes **(2)**
3 Rue Hrant Dink
Lyon, 69002, France
Tel.: (33) 4 78 03 64 01
Fax: (33) 4 78 03 64 09
Highway Construction Services
S.I.C.: 1611
N.A.I.C.S.: 237310

Carriere de la Roche Blain **(2)**
La Roche Blain
BP 4
14680 Fresney-le-Puceux, Calvados, France
Tel.: (33) 2 31 15 36 00
Fax: (33) 2 31 15 36 09
Emp.: 50
Civil Engineering Services
S.I.C.: 1629
N.A.I.C.S.: 237990
Philippe Boutteau *(Gen Mgr)*

Carriere des Chenes S.A. **(2)**
Route N 7 Rn 7
Andancette, France
Tel.: (33) 4 75 23 11 55
Fax: (33) 4 75 03 10 21
Construction Engineering Services
S.I.C.: 1629
N.A.I.C.S.: 237990

Desquesnes SNC **(2)**
198 Au 212 198 Rue Casimir Beugnet
Auchel, Pas-de-Calais, 62260, France
Tel.: (33) 321613600
Fax: (33) 321267367
Construction Engineering Services
S.I.C.: 1629
N.A.I.C.S.: 237990

Dle Ouest **(2)**
5 Rue de la Catalogne
44240 La Chapelle-sur-Erdre, France
Tel.: (33) 2 40 77 89 89
Fax: (33) 2 40 77 80 48
Civil Engineering Services
S.I.C.: 1629
N.A.I.C.S.: 237990

Dle Specialites **(2)**
78 A Rue de la Garde
Nantes, 44300, France
Tel.: (33) 2 51 89 59 59
Fax: (33) 2 51 89 59 50
Civil Engineering Construction Services
S.I.C.: 1622
N.A.I.C.S.: 237310

Eiffage International S.A. **(2)**
2 rue Helene Boucher
93330 Neuilly-sur-Seine, France
Tel.: (33) 149449000
Fax: (33) 149449009
Civil Construction & Engineering Services
S.I.C.: 1629
N.A.I.C.S.: 237990

Eiffage TP **(2)**
2 Rue Helene Boucher
Neuilly-sur-Marne, Seine-Saint-Denis, 93330, France
Tel.: (33) 149449200
Fax: (33) 149449009
Civil Engineering Services
S.I.C.: 1629
N.A.I.C.S.: 237990

Eiffage Travaux Publics Est **(2)**
1 R W Et Catherine Booth
10000 Troyes, France
Tel.: (33) 3 25 76 24 24
Fax: (33) 3 25 76 24 24
Road Construction Services
S.I.C.: 1611
N.A.I.C.S.: 237310

Eiffage Travaux Publics Mediterranee **(2)**
Zone Industrielle Les Estroublans 4 rue de Copenhague
Vitrolles, Bouches-du-Rhone, 13127, France
Tel.: (33) 442023400
Fax: (33) 442023418
Construction Engineering Services
S.I.C.: 8711
N.A.I.C.S.: 541330

Eiffage Travaux Publics Nord S.N.C **(2)**
53 Boulevard Faidherbe
62033 Arras, France
Tel.: (33) 3 21 22 76 76
Fax: (33) 3 27 78 17 83
Road Construction Services
S.I.C.: 1622
N.A.I.C.S.: 237310

Eiffage Travaux Publics Ouest S.N.C **(2)**
6 Place de Boston
14200 Herouville-Saint-Clair, France
Tel.: (33) 2 35 66 43 43
Fax: (33) 2 31 53 13 14
Construction Engineering Services
S.I.C.: 1629
N.A.I.C.S.: 237990

Eiffage Travaux Publics Reseaux **(2)**
Zi de la Petite Montagne Sud 1 3 rue du Bourbonnais
Lisses, Essonne, 91090, France
Tel.: (33) 169115020
Construction Engineering Services
S.I.C.: 1629
N.A.I.C.S.: 237990

Eiffage Travaux Publics Sud Ouest S.N.C **(2)**
Parc de Canteranne 21 Avenue de Canteranne
Pessac, Gironde, 33600, France
Tel.: (33) 251273610
Construction Engineering Services
S.I.C.: 8711
N.A.I.C.S.: 541330

SNC Travaux Publics de Provence **(2)**
30 Quartier Prignan
Istres, Bouches-du-Rhone, 13800, France
Tel.: (33) 442569121
Construction Engineering Services
S.I.C.: 1629
N.A.I.C.S.: 237990

Societe des Carrieres de la 113 **(2)**
Domaine De La Plaine
11200 Raissac-d'Aude, Aude, France
Tel.: (33) 468901414
Fax: (33) 468901421
Construction Engineering Services
S.I.C.: 1629
N.A.I.C.S.: 237990

Sopal **(2)**
15 rue Gen de Lattre de Tassigny
Eschau, 67114, France
Tel.: (33) 388640369
Fax: (33) 388642997
Painting Supplies Distr
S.I.C.: 5198
N.A.I.C.S.: 424950

Stinkal **(2)**
Ham Beaulieu
62250 Ferques, Pas-de-Calais, France
Tel.: (33) 321323945
Construction Engineering Services
S.I.C.: 8711
N.A.I.C.S.: 541330

Tinel SA **(2)**
Zone Industrielle Chemin de Chomaget 10 Rue de Chomaget
43100 Brioude, Haute-Loire, France
Tel.: (33) 471502705
Construction Engineering Services
S.I.C.: 1629
N.A.I.C.S.: 237990

Transroute SA **(2)**
12 Rue De Molsheim
Wolxheim, 67120, France
Tel.: (33) 388479494
Fax: (33) 388479495
Highway Construction Services
S.I.C.: 1622
N.A.I.C.S.: 237310
Gael Leparoux *(Gen Mgr)*

Travaux Publics et Assainissement **(2)**
22 Route de Chambry
02840 Athies-sous-Laon, Aisne, France

Eiffage S.A.—(Continued)

Tel.: (33) 3 23 24 66 00
Fax: (33) 3 23 24 66 01
Highway & Bridge Construction Services
S.I.C.: 1622
N.A.I.C.S.: 237310

Non-U.S. Subsidiaries:

Aglomerados Albacete SA (2)
Calle Madrid Km 594
Almansa, Albacete, 2640, Spain
Tel.: (34) 967345727
Fax: (34) 967310531
Construction Engineering Services
S.I.C.: 1629
N.A.I.C.S.: 237990

Aglomerados Los Serranos SA (2)
Calle Manuel Macia Juan 4
Elche, Alicante, 03203, Spain
Tel.: (34) 966615242
Fax: (34) 966612496
E-Mail: administracion@los-serranos.com
Web Site: www.infraestructuras.eiffage.es
Emp.: 300
Construction Engineering Services
S.I.C.: 1629
N.A.I.C.S.: 237990
Cesar Nohales *(Gen Mgr)*

Dle Outre-Mer (2)
Lieu Dit Sicama Chemin Gibelin
Matoury, Guyane, 97351, French Guiana
Tel.: (594) 594357090
Civil Engineering Construction Services
S.I.C.: 1629
N.A.I.C.S.: 237990

Eiffage Deutschland Bauholding Gmbh (2)
Neumuhlenallee 32
Borken, 46325, Germany
Tel.: (49) 2861 800 821
Fax: (49) 2861 800 822
Civil Engineering Construction Services
S.I.C.: 1629
N.A.I.C.S.: 237990

Eiffage Infraestructuras (2)
Pol Industrial Vicalvaro C/ Mir s/n
28052 Madrid, Spain
Tel.: (34) 917 765 521
Fax: (34) 917 765 178
E-Mail: info@infraestructuras.eiffage.es
Web Site: www.infraestructuras.eiffage.es
Civil Engineering Construction Services
S.I.C.: 1629
N.A.I.C.S.: 237990

Heinrich Walter Bau Gmbh (2)
Neumuhlenallee 32
46325 Borken, Germany
Tel.: (49) 28 61 80 08 0
Fax: (49) 28 61 80 08 22
E-Mail: hw@heinrich-walter.eiffage.de
Web Site: www.heinrich-walter.de
Rev.: $89,336,980
Emp.: 236
Construction Engineering Services
S.I.C.: 1629
N.A.I.C.S.: 237990
Dany Brodhag *(Co-Mng Dir)*
Emeric de Foucauld *(Co-Mng Dir)*

Hormigones Los Serranos S.L (2)
Calle Raco S/N-Part
Gandia, 46702, Spain
Tel.: (34) 966 61 54 44
Fax: (34) 965 42 38 60
Civil Engineering Construction Services
S.I.C.: 1629
N.A.I.C.S.: 237990

Hormigones y Morteros Serrano SL (2)
Calle Clemente Gonzalvez Valls 38
Elche, Alicante, 03202, Spain
Tel.: (34) 966615444
Fax: (34) 966613989
Construction Engineering Services
S.I.C.: 1629
N.A.I.C.S.: 237990

Lanwehr Asphalt Gmbh (2)
Sudstrasse 16
48231 Warendorf, Germany
Tel.: (49) 2581 937 345
Fax: (49) 2581 937 344
E-Mail: info@lanwehr.eiffage.de
Web Site: www.lanwehr.de/index.php?option=com_content&view=article&id=101&Itemid=211
Construction Engineering Services
S.I.C.: 1629
N.A.I.C.S.: 237990

Lanwehr Bau Gmbh (2)
Sudstrasse 16
48231 Warendorf, Germany
Tel.: (49) 2581 937 30
Fax: (49) 2581 937 355
E-Mail: info@lanwehr.eiffage.de
Web Site: www.lanwehr.de
Emp.: 250
Civil Engineering Construction Services
S.I.C.: 1611
N.A.I.C.S.: 237310
Wilfried Termath *(Mng Dir)*

Masfalt S.A (2)
Parque Comercial Malaga Nostrum C Jaen n 9 Edif Galia Ofic 105
29004 Malaga, Spain
Tel.: (34) 952 122 633
Fax: (34) 952 602 977
E-Mail: info@masfalt.com
Web Site: www.masfalt.com
Civil Engineering Construction Services
S.I.C.: 1629
N.A.I.C.S.: 237990

Serrano Aznar Obras Publicas S.L (2)
Lugar Paraje Tres Santos
Abanilla, Murcia, 30640, Spain
Tel.: (34) 965492799
Fax: (34) 966612496
Construction Engineering Services
S.I.C.: 8711
N.A.I.C.S.: 541330

Wittfeld Gmbh (2)
Hansastrasse 83
49134 Wallenhorst, Germany
Tel.: (49) 54075010
Fax: (49) 5407501239
E-Mail: info@wittfeld.eiffage.de
Web Site: www.wittfeld.de
Rev.: $169,896,000
Emp.: 500
Civil Engineering Construction Services
S.I.C.: 1629
N.A.I.C.S.: 237990
Emeric de Foucauld *(Co-Mng Dir)*
Joerg Hermsen *(Co-Mng Dir)*

Eiffel Industrie S.A.S (1)
48/50 rue de Seine
92707 Colombes, France
Tel.: (33) 1 47 60 47 00
Fax: (33) 1 47 60 47 01
Web Site: www.eiffel-industrie.com
Industrial Maintenance & Engineering Services
S.I.C.: 8711
N.A.I.C.S.: 541330

Etcm SA (1)
Parc D Activites De La Brayell 481 R Du Faubourg D Esquerchin
59553 Cuincy, Nord, France
Tel.: (33) 327957500
Fax: (33) 327957501
Construction Engineering Services
S.I.C.: 8711
N.A.I.C.S.: 541330

Fontanie (1)
Zone Industrielle de Thibaud 4 rue Colomies
31100 Toulouse, Haute-Garonne, France
Tel.: (33) 561190331
Fax: (33) 561190551
Industrial Engineering Services
S.I.C.: 8711
N.A.I.C.S.: 541330

Game Ingenierie S.A.S (1)
17 rue de la Belle Etoile
Ormoy, Essonne, 91540, France
Tel.: (33) 160905858
Construction Engineering Services
S.I.C.: 8711
N.A.I.C.S.: 541330

Ger2i (1)
Zae Rue De Seine
78260 Acheres, Yvelines, France
Tel.: (33) 139114530
Fax: (33) 139117191
Industrial Maintenance & Engineering Services
S.I.C.: 8711
N.A.I.C.S.: 541330

Secauto S.A (1)
15 a 17 rue A Nobel chateau de l
69552 Feyzin, France
Tel.: (33) 4 72 89 04 40
Fax: (33) 4 78 70 50 68
E-Mail: info@secauto.com
Web Site: www.secauto.fr
Emp.: 280
Engineering Project Consulting Services
S.I.C.: 8711
N.A.I.C.S.: 541330
Jean-Marc Borrel *(Mgr)*

Tpam SAS (1)
Impasse Edouard Branly ZI de la Peyenniere
Mayenne, 53100, France
Tel.: (33) 2 43 04 04 04
Fax: (33) 2 43 32 12 12
Road & Bridge Construction Services
S.I.C.: 1611
N.A.I.C.S.: 237310

Joint Venture:

Financiere Eiffarie (1)
163 quai du Docter Dervaux
Asnieres-sur-Seine, 92600, France
Tel.: (33) 141328000
Holding Company; Owned by Eiffage S.A. & Macquarie Bank Limited
S.I.C.: 6719
N.A.I.C.S.: 551112
Jean-Francois Roverato *(Pres)*

Holding:

Autoroutes Paris-Rhin-Rhone (2)
36 rue du Docteur-Schmitt
21850 Saint Apollinaire, France
Tel.: (33) 380776700
Web Site: www.parisrhinrhone.com
Sales Range: $1-4.9 Billion
Emp.: 4,391
Motorways, Services, Telecoms, Secure Car Parks & Railroad Transportation
S.I.C.: 4789
N.A.I.C.S.: 488999
Jean-Claude Roussel *(Deputy Mng Dir)*
Phillipe Serain *(CFO)*

Subsidiary:

AREA Societe des Autoroutes Rhones-Alpes SA (3)
260 avenue Jean Monnet
Cedex, BP48 - 69671 Bron, France
Tel.: (33) 472353200
Fax: (33) 472353201
E-Mail: dircom@area.aprr.fr
Web Site: www.area-enlijne.com
Sales Range: $450-499.9 Million
Emp.: 150
Bus Terminal & Service Facilities
S.I.C.: 1622
N.A.I.C.S.: 237310
Philippe Nourry *(Pres)*

U.S. Subsidiary:

Eis Inc. (1)
9210 Wyoming Ave. N, Ste. 215
Brooklyn Park, MN 55445
Tel.: (678) 255-3600
Fax: (678) 255-3753
Toll Free: (800) 949-9992
Construction Engineering Services
S.I.C.: 8711
N.A.I.C.S.: 541330
Robert Thomas *(Pres & CEO)*
Matthew Tyser *(CFO & Sr VP)*
Peter Sheehan *(Pres-Cobra Wire & Cable Div & Sr VP-Specialty Wire & Cable)*
Alex Gonzalez *(Sr VP-Electrical & Electronic)*
Larry Griffin *(Sr VP-Mktg)*
Tom Jones *(Sr VP-Mfg)*
Bill Knight *(Sr VP-Ops & Logistics)*
William Knight *(Sr VP-Ops & Logistics)*
David Quinn *(Sr VP-Seacoast Electric Div)*

Non-U.S. Divisions:

Collignon Eng SA - Bruxelles Division (1)
Parc Industriel 11
1440 Wauthier Brain, Belgium
Tel.: (32) 2 385 14 32
Fax: (32) 2 387 32 98
Electrical Equipment Distr
S.I.C.: 5063
N.A.I.C.S.: 423610
Serge de Moffarts *(Mng Dir)*

Collignon Eng SA - Liege Division (1)
Z I de Grace-Hollogne Rue de l'Expansion 45
4460 Grace-Hollogne, Belgium
Tel.: (32) 4 388 15 15
Fax: (32) 4 388 30 61
Electrical Installation Services
S.I.C.: 1731
N.A.I.C.S.: 238210

Non-U.S. Subsidiaries:

COLLIGNON Luxembourg SARL (1)
Z I de Kehlen
8287 Kehlen, Luxembourg
Tel.: (352) 26 10 30 20
Fax: (352) 26 10 30 20 09
Web Site: www.collignon.net
Emp.: 25
Electrical Equipment Distr
S.I.C.: 5063
N.A.I.C.S.: 423610
Bastin Jacques *(Gen Mgr)*

ECV (1)
Rue du Travail 5
4460 Grace-Hollogne, Belgium
Tel.: (32) 4 247 22 05
Fax: (32) 4 247 20 05
E-Mail: info@ecv.eiffage.be
Web Site: www.ecv-sa.be
Street & Highway Lightning Construction Services
S.I.C.: 1623
N.A.I.C.S.: 237130

Eiffage Energia S.L (1)
Avda de la Mancha 280 Esquina C Trovadores
02006 Albacete, Spain
Tel.: (34) 967 190 116
Fax: (34) 967 241 100
Web Site: www.energia.eiffage.es
Electrical System Installation Services
S.I.C.: 1731
N.A.I.C.S.: 238210

Elomech Elektroanlagen GmbH (1)
Mainstrasse 21
45478 Mulheim an der Ruhr, Germany
Tel.: (49) 208 58 87 0
Fax: (49) 208 58 87 299
E-Mail: info@elomech.de
Web Site: www.elomech.de
Electrical Installation Services
S.I.C.: 1731
N.A.I.C.S.: 238210
Christoph Bleckmann *(Mgr)*

Feyens SA (1)
Parc Industriel 11
1440 Wauthier Brain, Belgium
Tel.: (32) 23851432
Fax: (32) 23873298
Web Site: www.collignon.net
Electrical Installation Services
S.I.C.: 1731
N.A.I.C.S.: 238210

Forclumeca Antilles Guyane (1)
10 Zac La Marie 10 Rue Raymond Berger
Ducos, 97224, Martinique
Tel.: (596) 596561552
Fax: (596) 596664020
Construction Engineering Services
S.I.C.: 8711
N.A.I.C.S.: 541330

JOAO JACINTO TOME, S.A. (1)
Rua Possidonio da Silva n 158 A
1399-008 Lisbon, Portugal
Tel.: (351) 213 920 910
Fax: (351) 213 975 167
E-Mail: geral@jjtome-sa.com
Web Site: www.jjtome-sa.com
Emp.: 6
Electrical Installation Services
S.I.C.: 1731
N.A.I.C.S.: 238210
Patrick Steinfort *(Gen Mgr)*

Oostvlaams Milieubeheer (1)
Havennummer 4410B J Kennedylaan 50
9042 Gent, Belgium

Tel.: (32) 93429567
Fax: (32) 93429577
E-Mail: info@ovmb.eiffage.be
Web Site: www.ovmb.be
Emp.: 14
Industrial Waste Management Services
S.I.C.: 4959
N.A.I.C.S.: 562998

Romarco NV (1)
Baaikensstraat 17 B
9240 Zele, Belgium
Tel.: (32) 52 44 86 94
Fax: (32) 52 44 87 45
E-Mail: info@romarco.be
Web Site: www.romarco.be
Industrial Cleaning Services
S.I.C.: 7349
N.A.I.C.S.: 561720
Peter Rooms *(Gen Mgr)*

SATRA SA (1)
Berismenil 93C
6980 Berismenil, Belgium
Tel.: (32) 84 44 41 70
Fax: (32) 84 44 45 70
Web Site: www.collignon.net
Underground Cable Laying Construction Services
S.I.C.: 1623
N.A.I.C.S.: 237130

Soprano Oyj (1)
Ludviginkatu 1
00130 Helsinki, Finland
Tel.: (358) 10 34 66 440
Fax: (358) 10 34 66 448
E-Mail: info@soprano.fi
Web Site: www.soprano.fi
SOPRA—(HEL)
Emp.: 110
Communications & Information Technology Marketing, Advertising & Consulting Services
S.I.C.: 8742
N.A.I.C.S.: 541613
Pekka Vennamo *(Chm)*
Arto Tenhunen *(CEO)*
Panu Kauppinen *(CFO)*
Mika Taberman *(Sec)*

THE EIGHTEENTH BANK, LIMITED

1-11 Doza-machi
Nagasaki, NGS 850-0841, Japan
Tel.: (81) 958288073
Fax: (81) 958236262
Web Site: www.18bank.co.jp
Year Founded: 1877
8396—(FKA TKS)
Rev.: $552,354,000
Assets: $28,735,069,000
Liabilities: $27,242,270,000
Net Worth: $1,492,799,000
Earnings: $39,765,000
Emp.: 1,601
Fiscal Year-end: 03/31/13

Business Description:
Banking Services
S.I.C.: 6029
N.A.I.C.S.: 522110

Personnel:
Masatoshi Miyawaki *(Pres & Exec Officer)*
Yasujiro Miyahara *(Sr Mng Exec Officer)*

Board of Directors:
Yasujiro Miyahara
Masatoshi Miyawaki
Katsunari Mori
Takujiro Mori
Hiroshi Nanjo
Hiroshi Ogawa
Hiroshi Saito

Subsidiaries:

Juhachi Capital Co., Ltd. (1)
1-11 Dozamachi
Nagasaki, 850-0841, Japan
Tel.: (81) 958203818
Fax: (81) 958228432
Venture Capital Investment Services
S.I.C.: 6211
N.A.I.C.S.: 523999

Juhachi Software Co. Ltd (1)
Edomachi Center Bldg
Nagasaki, Japan
Tel.: (81) 958240018
Fax: (81) 958240754
Custom Computer Programming Services
S.I.C.: 7371
N.A.I.C.S.: 541511

Nagasaki Hosho Service Co., Ltd. (1)
10-10 Dejimamachi
Nagasaki, 850-0862, Japan
Tel.: (81) 958243098
Fax: (81) 958259935
Investment Banking Services
S.I.C.: 6211
N.A.I.C.S.: 523110

Nagasaki Research Institute Limited (1)
The Eighteen Bank 1-11 Doza-machi
Nagasaki, 850-0841, Japan
Tel.: (81) 958288859
Fax: (81) 958210214
Web Site: www.nagasaki-keizai.co.jp
Emp.: 30
Economic Research & Development Services
S.I.C.: 8732
N.A.I.C.S.: 541720
Takamitsu Sato *(Pres)*

EIH ASSOCIATED HOTELS LIMITED

1/24 GST Road Meenambakkam
Chennai, 6000027, India
Tel.: (91) 4422344747
Fax: (91) 4422344985
Web Site: www.eihassociatedhotels.in
EIHAHOTELS—(NSE)
Rev.: $39,481,486
Assets: $64,708,493
Liabilities: $27,916,790
Net Worth: $36,791,703
Earnings: $3,801,071
Emp.: 1,353
Fiscal Year-end: 03/31/13

Business Description:
Hotel Management Services
S.I.C.: 7011
N.A.I.C.S.: 721110

Personnel:
Prithviraj Singh Oberoi *(Chm & CEO)*
Vikramjit Singh Oberoi *(Mng Dir)*
Indrani Ray *(Compliance Officer & Sec)*

Board of Directors:
Prithviraj Singh Oberoi
Lakshminarayan Ganesh
Rajesh Gordhandas Kapadia
Shib Sanker Mukherji
Anil Kumar Nehru
Vikramjit Singh Oberoi
Rajan Biharilal Raheja
Sudipto Sarkar

Transfer Agent:
EIH Limited
4 Mangoe Lane
Kolkata, India

EIK BANK P/F

Yvirivid Strond 2
PO Box 34
FO-110 Torshavn, Faroe Islands
Tel.: (298) 348000
Fax: (298) 348800
E-Mail: eik@eik.fo
Web Site: www.eik.fo
FO-EIK—(CSE ICE)
Sales Range: $200-249.9 Million
Emp.: 330

Business Description:
Banking Services
S.I.C.: 6029
N.A.I.C.S.: 522110

Personnel:
Frithleif Olsen *(Chm)*
Odd Arild Bjellvag *(Deputy Chm)*
Bjarni Olsen *(Mng Dir)*

Board of Directors:
Frithleif Olsen
Odd Arild Bjellvag
Rakul Dam
Petur D.W. Hammer
Jakup Egil Jensen
Tormund A. Joensen
Gert Langgaard
Jacob Leth
Hanna Thorleifsson
Rolant Vidfeldt

Subsidiary:

P F Inni (1)
Niels Finsensgota 37
PO Box 364
FO 110 Torshavn, Faroe Islands
Tel.: (298) 354200
Fax: (298) 354201
E-Mail: inni@inni.fo
Web Site: www.inni.fo
Emp.: 6
Real Estate Services
S.I.C.: 6531
N.A.I.C.S.: 531390
Kara Dunga *(Mgr)*

EIKEN CHEMICAL CO. LTD.

4-19-9 Taito Taito-ku
Tokyo, 110-8408, Japan
Tel.: (81) 338135401
Web Site: www.eiken.co.jp
4549—(TKS)
Sls.: $315,095,000
Assets: $386,518,000
Liabilities: $126,049,000
Net Worth: $260,469,000
Earnings: $26,983,000
Emp.: 614
Fiscal Year-end: 03/31/13

Business Description:
Clinical Diagnostics & Equipments Mfr & Sales
S.I.C.: 3845
N.A.I.C.S.: 334510

Personnel:
Tadao Kurozumi *(Chm)*
Tetsuya Teramoto *(Pres & CEO)*
Masaaki Arakawa *(Exec Officer)*
Tsutomu Naito *(Exec Officer)*
Norihisa Noguchi *(Exec Officer)*
Tsugunori Noutomi *(Exec Officer)*
Shinya Sadamoto *(Exec Officer)*
Takahiko Sekine *(Exec Officer)*
Masaru Shioda *(Exec Officer)*
Kazuhisa Ueda *(Exec Officer)*
Yoshiharu Ichikawa *(Sr VP)*

Board of Directors:
Tadao Kurozumi
Takehisa Irisawa
Yukihiro Kimura
Yasuhiro Nakano
Tetsuya Teramoto
Morifumi Wada
Syoichi Yamada

Transfer Agent:
Mitsubishi UFJ Trust & Banking Corporation
1-4-5 Marunouchi Chiyoda-ku
Tokyo, Japan

EIKEN INDUSTRIES CO., LTD

1370 Kadoya Omaezaki-shi
Shizuoka, 437-1698, Japan
Tel.: (81) 537 85 4132
Fax: (81) 537 85 2033
E-Mail: boeki@eiken-kk.co.jp
Web Site: www.eiken-kk.co.jp
Year Founded: 1967
7265—(JAS)

Business Description:
Oil Filter Mfr
S.I.C.: 1389
N.A.I.C.S.: 213112

Personnel:
Y. Hayama *(Pres)*

EIKOH HOLDINGS INC.

11-11-chome Chiyoda-ku
Fujimi, Tokyo, 102-0071, Japan
Tel.: (81) 3 52751681
Fax: (81) 3 52751671
Web Site: www.eikoh.co.jp
6053—(TKS)
Emp.: 406

Business Description:
Holding Company; Exam Preparation & Tutoring
S.I.C.: 6719
N.A.I.C.S.: 551112

Personnel:
Yoshinori Kondo *(Pres)*

EIMCO ELECON INDIA LTD

Anand Sojitra Road Vallabh Vidyanagar
Anand, 388120, India
Tel.: (91) 2692230902
Fax: (91) 2692236506
Web Site: www.eimcoelecon.in
523708—(BOM)
Sls.: $33,634,675
Assets: $36,176,342
Liabilities: $4,660,956
Net Worth: $31,515,386
Earnings: $2,806,085
Fiscal Year-end: 03/31/13

Business Description:
Underground & Opencast Mines Equipment Marketing & Mfr
S.I.C.: 3532
N.A.I.C.S.: 333131

Personnel:
P. B. Patel *(Mng Dir)*
Nilesh D. Shelat *(Compliance Officer, Sec & VP-Accts)*
R. L. Luthra *(Exec VP-Engrg Dept)*

Board of Directors:
P. M. Patel
P. C. Amin
Nirmal Bhogilal
H. S. Parikh
P. B. Patel
M. G. Rao
Nalin M. Shah
Vihang Virkar

Transfer Agent:
Link Intime India Pvt. Ltd
C-13 Pannalal Silk Mills Compound LBS Marg
Bhandup (West)
Mumbai, India

EIMSKIPAFELAG ISLANDS HF.

Korngardar 2
104 Reykjavik, Iceland
Tel.: (354) 5257000
Fax: (354) 5157701
E-Mail: investors@eimskip.is
Web Site: www.eimskip.is
EIM—(ICE OMX)
Rev.: $557,758,616
Assets: $421,729,484
Liabilities: $153,035,298
Net Worth: $268,694,186
Earnings: $17,138,090
Emp.: 1,272
Fiscal Year-end: 12/31/12

Business Description:
Air, Land & Sea Transportation & Logistics Services
S.I.C.: 4512
N.A.I.C.S.: 481112

Personnel:
Richard Winston Mark d'Abo *(Chm)*
Gunnar Karl Gudmundsson *(Vice Chm)*
Gylfi Sigfusson *(CEO)*
Hilmar P. Valgardsson *(CFO)*

Eimskipafelag Islands Hf.—(Continued)

David Ingi Jonsson *(Compliance Officer)*
Bragi Thor Marinosson *(Exec VP-Intl)*
Board of Directors:
Richard Winston Mark d'Abo
Gunnar Karl Gudmundsson
Helga Melkorka Ottarsdottir
Hrund Rudolfsdottir
Viglundur Thorsteinsson

Subsidiaries:

Air Atlanta Icelandic (1)
Hlidasmari 3, 201 Kopavogur, Iceland
Tel.: (354) 4584000
Fax: (354) 4584001
E-Mail: info@airatlanta.com
Web Site: www.airatlanta.com
Emp.: 1,500
Airline Services
S.I.C.: 4512
N.A.I.C.S.: 481111
Hannes Hilmarsson *(CEO)*

Eimskip (1)
Korngordum 2
104 Reykjavik, Iceland
Tel.: (354) 5257000
Fax: (354) 5257009
E-Mail: gnv@eimskip.is
Web Site: www.eimskip.is
Emp.: 1,000
Marine Shipping & Logistics Services
S.I.C.: 4491
N.A.I.C.S.: 488320
Gylfi Sigsusson *(CEO)*

Non-U.S. Subsidiaries:

VersaCold International Corporation (2)
2115 Commissioner St
Vancouver, BC, V5L 1A6, Canada BC
Tel.: (604) 255-4656
Fax: (604) 255-4330
Toll Free: (800) 563-2653
E-Mail: info@versacold.com
Web Site: www.versacold.com
Sales Range: $650-699.9 Million
Emp.: 1,000
Refrigerated Warehousing & Logistics Services
S.I.C.: 4222
N.A.I.C.S.: 493120
Joel M. Smith *(CEO)*

U.S. Subsidiary:

Eimskip USA Inc. (1)
1 Columbus Ctr Ste 500
Virginia Beach, VA 23462
Tel.: (757) 627-4444
Fax: (757) 627-9367
E-Mail: cah@eimskipusa.com
Web Site: www.eimskipusa.com
Emp.: 15
Freight & Transportation Services
S.I.C.: 4412
N.A.I.C.S.: 483111
Brent Sudgen *(CEO)*

Non-U.S. Subsidiaries:

Excel Airways Group plc (1)
Explorer House
Fleming Way, Crawley, West Sussex, RH10 9EA, United Kingdom
Tel.: (44) 1293439100
Fax: (44) 1293439150
E-Mail: media@excelairways.com
Web Site: www.excelairwaysgroup.com
Emp.: 1,700
Airline Services
S.I.C.: 4512
N.A.I.C.S.: 481111
Phil Wyatt *(CEO)*
Halldor Sigurdarson *(CFO)*

Non-U.S. Subsidiary:

Star Airlines (2)
10 allee Bienvenue
93885 Noisy-le-Grand, France
Tel.: (33) 148159000
Fax: (33) 148159050
E-Mail: webmaster@star-airlines.fr
Web Site: www.star-airlines.fr
Airline Services
S.I.C.: 4512
N.A.I.C.S.: 481111

EINBECKER BRAUHAUS AG

Papenstrasse 4-7
37574 Einbeck, Germany
Tel.: (49) 5561 797 0
Fax: (49) 5561 797 119
Web Site: www.einbeckerbrauhaus.de
HAK—(DEU)
Sales Range: $50-74.9 Million
Emp.: 173
Business Description:
Beer Mfr
S.I.C.: 2082
N.A.I.C.S.: 312120
Personnel:
Robert A. Depner *(Chm-Supervisory Bd)*
Lothar Gauss *(Member-Mgmt Bd-Logistic, Technics & Admin)*
Walter Schmidt *(Member-Mgmt Bd-Mktg & Sls)*

EINFOCHIPS LIMITED

11 A-B Chandra Colony Off C G Road
Ahmedabad, 380 006, India
Tel.: (91) 7926563705
Fax: (91) 7926560722
E-Mail: info@einfochips.com
Web Site: www.einfochips.com
Year Founded: 1994
Emp.: 750
Business Description:
Chip & Product Design Services
S.I.C.: 3674
N.A.I.C.S.: 334413
Personnel:
Pratul Shroff *(Pres & CEO)*
Upendra Patel *(CTO)*

U.S. Subsidiary:

eInfochips, Inc. (1)
1230 Midas Way Ste 200
Sunnyvale, CA 94085
Tel.: (408) 496-1882
Fax: (801) 650-1480
E-Mail: sales@einfochips.com
Web Site: www.einfochips.com
ASIC Design, Embedded Systems, Application Software
S.I.C.: 3674
N.A.I.C.S.: 334413

EINHELL GERMANY AG

Wiesenweg 22
94405 Landau, Germany
Tel.: (49) 99519420
Fax: (49) 99511702
E-Mail: info@einhell.de
Web Site: www.einhell.com
EIN3—(DEU)
Rev.: $511,358,829
Assets: $349,141,305
Liabilities: $133,381,216
Net Worth: $215,760,089
Earnings: $7,511,629
Emp.: 1,301
Fiscal Year-end: 12/31/12
Business Description:
Power Tool, Garden Equipment & Heating & Air Conditioning Equipment Mfr
S.I.C.: 3546
N.A.I.C.S.: 333991
Personnel:
Josef Thannhuber *(Chm-Supervisory Bd)*
Andreas Kroiss *(Chm-Mgmt Bd)*
Jan Teichert *(CFO & Member-Mgmt Bd)*
Markus Thannhuber *(CTO & Member-Mgmt Bd)*
Supervisory Board of Directors:
Josef Thannhuber
Maximilian Fritz
Dieter Spath

Subsidiary:

iSC GmbH (1)
Eschenstrasse 6
94405 Landau, Germany (100%)
Tel.: (49) 1805120509
Fax: (49) 180 5 835830
Web Site: www.isc-gmbh.info
Power Tool Distr
S.I.C.: 5072
N.A.I.C.S.: 423710
Markus Thannhuber *(Mng Dir)*

Non-U.S. Subsidiary:

iSC Italia s.r.l. (2)
Corso Roma 7
Beregazzo con Figliaro, 22070, Italy
Tel.: (39) 031 800863
Fax: (39) 031 941618
E-Mail: info@isc-italy.it
Industrial Machinery Distr
S.I.C.: 5084
N.A.I.C.S.: 423830

Non-U.S. Subsidiaries:

Einhell Espana (1)
Pol Industrial El Nogal Travesia de Villa Esther 15
28119 Algete, Madrid, Spain (100%)
Tel.: (34) 91 7294888
Fax: (34) 91 3581500
E-Mail: einhell.spain@einhell.com
Web Site: www.einhell.es
Mfr, Sales & Training of Various Tools & Equipment for DIY Enthusiasts & Semi-Professionals
S.I.C.: 3546
N.A.I.C.S.: 333991
Miguel Lorente *(Mng Dir)*

Einhell Argentina S. A (1)
Av 12 de Octubre 1824
1629 Pilar, Argentina
Tel.: (54) 2320 301800
Fax: (54) 2320 301800
Web Site: www.einhell.com
Emp.: 15
Business Services
S.I.C.: 7389
N.A.I.C.S.: 561499
Eric Castanier *(Mng Dir)*

Einhell Australia Pty. Ltd. (1)
6 166 Wellington Street
Collingwood, VIC, 3066, Australia (100%)
Tel.: (61) 384134300
Fax: (61) 394172715
Web Site: www.einhell.com.au
Emp.: 10
Power Tool, Garden Equipment & Heating & Air Conditioning Equipment Mfr
S.I.C.: 3546
N.A.I.C.S.: 333991
Christopher O'Neill *(Mng Dir)*

Einhell Benelux B.V. (1)
Mijkenbroek 16
4824 AB Breda, Netherlands (100%)
Tel.: (31) 765986470
Fax: (31) 885986478
E-Mail: info@einhell.nl
Web Site: www.einhell.nl
Emp.: 12
Power Tool, Garden Equipment & Heating & Air Conditioning Equipment Mfr
S.I.C.: 3546
N.A.I.C.S.: 333991
Gerard Breukelman *(Mng Dir)*

Einhell BiH d.o.o (1)
Poslovni Centar 96
72250 Vitez, Bosnia & Herzegovina (66.7%)
Tel.: (387) 30717250
Fax: (387) 30717255
E-Mail: info@einhell.ba
Web Site: www.einhell.ba
Emp.: 15
Power Tool, Garden Equipment & Heating & Air Conditioning Equipment Mfr
S.I.C.: 3546
N.A.I.C.S.: 333991
Silvio Jurkovic *(Mng Dir)*

Einhell Brasil Com. Distr. Ferr. E Equip. Ltda (1)
Av Dr Betim 619 Vila Marieta
13042-020 Campinas, SP, Brazil (90%)
Tel.: (55) 193 3682 809
Fax: (55) 1925128450
E-Mail: contato.brasil@einhell.com
Web Site: www.einhell.com.br
Emp.: 40
Power Tool, Garden Equipment & Heating & Air Conditioning Equipment Mfr
S.I.C.: 3546
N.A.I.C.S.: 333991
Pedro Braga *(Mng Dir)*

Einhell Bulgaria Ltd. (1)
Blvd Tzar Osvoboditel N 331
9000 Varna, Bulgaria (67%)
Tel.: (359) 52739038
Fax: (359) 52739098
E-Mail: office@einhell.bg
Web Site: www.einhell.bg
Power Tool, Garden Equipment & Heating & Air Conditioning Equipment Mfr
S.I.C.: 3546
N.A.I.C.S.: 333991
Rumen Radev *(Mng Dir)*

Einhell Chile S.A. (1)
Av Recoleta 1223
Santiago, Chile (90%)
Tel.: (56) 27379312
Fax: (56) 2 7376799
Power Tool, Garden Equipment & Heating & Air Conditioning Equipment Mfr
S.I.C.: 3546
N.A.I.C.S.: 333991
Claudio Rosenstock *(Mng Dir)*

Einhell Croatia d.o.o (1)
Velika Ves 2
49224 Lepajci, Croatia (100%)
Tel.: (385) 49 342444
Fax: (385) 49 342392
E-Mail: einhell.info@einhell.com
Web Site: www.einhell.com
Emp.: 14
Power Tool, Garden Equipment & Heating & Air Conditioning Equipment Mfr
S.I.C.: 3546
N.A.I.C.S.: 333991
Zdravko Lesko *(Mng Dir)*

EINHELL d. o. o. (1)
Vojvodjanska 386
11 271 Belgrade, Serbia (100%)
Tel.: (381) 11 2269161
Fax: (381) 11 2269 163
E-Mail: info.serbia@einhell.com
Power Tool, Garden Equipment & Heating & Air Conditioning Equipment Mfr
S.I.C.: 3546
N.A.I.C.S.: 333991
Ivan Kuzmanoski *(Mng Dir)*

Einhell Denmark ApS (1)
A C Illumsvej 21 A-B
8600 Silkeborg, Denmark
Tel.: (45) 87 201200
Fax: (45) 87 201203
E-Mail: info@einhell.dk
Web Site: www.einhell.com
Automotive Parts Mfr
S.I.C.: 3714
N.A.I.C.S.: 336390
Christian Dybro *(Mng Dir)*

Einhell France S.A.S. (1)
Paris Nord 2 33 rue des Vanesses
95945 Roissy-en-France, France (70%)
Tel.: (33) 148170053
Fax: (33) 148632772
E-Mail: info.france@einhell.fr
Web Site: www.einhell.fr
Emp.: 12
Power Tool, Garden Equipment & Heating & Air Conditioning Equipment Mfr
S.I.C.: 3546
N.A.I.C.S.: 333991
Vincent Rinie *(Mng Dir)*

Einhell Hellas S.A. (1)
4th floor Ifigenias 81
14231 Nea Ionia, Greece
Tel.: (30) 2102790930
Fax: (30) 2102790968
E-Mail: info@einhell.com
Emp.: 13
Power Tool, Garden Equipment & Heating & Air Conditioning Equipment Mfr

S.I.C.: 3546
N.A.I.C.S.: 333991
Evangelos Nikolaidis *(Mng Dir)*

Einhell Holding Gesellschaft m.b.H. (1)
Brunnerstrasse 81a
Vienna, 1230, Austria
Tel.: (43) 18691480
Fax: (43) 1869148080
Emp.: 30
Financial Investment Services
S.I.C.: 6211
N.A.I.C.S.: 523999
Christoph Hinterecker *(Gen Mgr)*

Einhell Hungaria Ltd. (1)
Mazsa Platz 5 7
H 1107 Budapest, Hungary (100%)
Tel.: (36) 13039401
Fax: (36) 12101179
E-Mail: einhell@einhell.hu
Web Site: www.einhell.hu
Emp.: 15
Power Tool, Garden Equipment & Heating & Air Conditioning Equipment Mfr
S.I.C.: 3546
N.A.I.C.S.: 333991

Einhell Intratek Muhendislik ve Dis Ticaret A.S. (1)
Ataturk Mah Girne Cad No 45
Atasehir, 34750 Istanbul, Turkey
Tel.: (90) 216 456 60 60
Fax: (90) 216 456 60 84
E-Mail: info@intratek.com.tr
Web Site: www.intratek.com.tr
Industrial Supplies Distr
S.I.C.: 5085
N.A.I.C.S.: 423840

Einhell Italia s.r.l. (1)
Via Marconi 16
22070 Beregazzo con Figliaro, Italy (100%)
Tel.: (39) 31992080
Fax: (39) 031 992084
E-Mail: info@einhell.it
Power Tool, Garden Equipment & Heating & Air Conditioning Equipment Mfr
S.I.C.: 3546
N.A.I.C.S.: 333991
Beniamino Gelmi *(Mng Dir)*

Einhell Middle East Trading FZC (1)
Rak Free Trade Zone Shed No 26
Technology Park
Ras al Khaimah, United Arab Emirates
Tel.: (971) 72447449
Fax: (971) 72447443
E-Mail: info.me@einhell.com
Web Site: www.einhell.com
Emp.: 12
Electronic Component Mfr
S.I.C.: 3679
N.A.I.C.S.: 334419
Nasir Khatib *(Gen Mgr)*

Einhell Norway AS (1)
Elveveien 26
3255 Larvik, Norway
Tel.: (47) 33 11 35 40
Fax: (47) 33 11 35 41
E-Mail: post@einhell.no
Web Site: www.einhell.com
Automotive Component Mfr
S.I.C.: 3714
N.A.I.C.S.: 336390
Herbert Lerner *(Mng Dir)*

Einhell Polska sp. Z.o.o. (1)
Ul Wymyslowskiego 1
55 080 Nowa Wies Wroclawska, Poland (90%)
Tel.: (48) 713346508
Fax: (48) 3871360306
E-Mail: einhell@einhell.pl
Web Site: www.einhell.pl
Emp.: 40
Power Tool, Garden Equipment & Heating & Air Conditioning Equipment Mfr
S.I.C.: 3546
N.A.I.C.S.: 333991
Ryszard Turkiewicz *(Pres)*

Einhell Portugal Lda. (1)
Rua da Aldeia 225 Apartado 2100
P 4410 459 Arcozelo, Portugal (100%)
Tel.: (351) 220917500
Fax: (351) 227536109
E-Mail: einhell@einhell.pt
Web Site: www.einhell.pt
Emp.: 13
Power Tool, Garden Equipment & Heating & Air Conditioning Equipment Mfr
S.I.C.: 3546
N.A.I.C.S.: 333991
Ricardo Fernandes *(Mng Dir)*

Einhell Romania S.R.L. (1)
Sat Dragomiresti Deal Comuna Dragomiresti Vale Parc Industrial
Hala B1 Judet Ilfov, 077096 Bucharest, Romania
Tel.: (40) 213185544
Fax: (40) 213185547
E-Mail: officeeinhellromania@einhell.com
Web Site: www.einhell.ro
Emp.: 25
Power Tool, Garden Equipment & Heating & Air Conditioning Equipment Mfr
S.I.C.: 3546
N.A.I.C.S.: 333991
Cornel Tutuianu *(Mng Dir)*

Einhell Schweiz AG (1)
St Gallerstrasse 182
8404 Winterthur, Switzerland (100%)
Tel.: (41) 522358787
Fax: (41) 522358700
E-Mail: info@einhell.ch
Power Tool, Garden Equipment & Heating & Air Conditioning Equipment Mfr
S.I.C.: 3546
N.A.I.C.S.: 333991
Rainer Koch *(Mng Dir)*

Einhell Skandinavia Aps (1)
Bergsoesvej 36
8600 Silkeborg, Denmark (100%)
Tel.: (45) 87201200
Fax: (45) 87201203
E-Mail: info@einhell.dk
Power Tool, Garden Equipment & Heating & Air Conditioning Equipment Mfr
S.I.C.: 3546
N.A.I.C.S.: 333991
Christian Dybro *(Mng Dir)*

Einhell Slovakia s.r.o. (1)
Dianicna Cesta 18
903 01 Senec, Slovakia (100%)
Tel.: (421) 220903780
Fax: (421) 245241579
E-Mail: einhell@einhell.sk
Web Site: www.einhell.sk
Emp.: 6
Power Tool, Garden Equipment & Heating & Air Conditioning Equipment Mfr
S.I.C.: 3546
N.A.I.C.S.: 333991
Petr Haak *(Mng Dir)*

Einhell Ukraine TOV (1)
134 Kutuzov Str
07400 Brovary, Ukraine (100%)
Tel.: (380) 44 332 6114
Fax: (380) 44 353 5435
E-Mail: ukraine@einhell.pl
Web Site: www.einhell.ua
Power Tool, Garden Equipment & Heating & Air Conditioning Equipment Mfr
S.I.C.: 3546
N.A.I.C.S.: 333991
Tomasz Jacyna *(Mng Dir)*

Einhell Unicore s.r.o. (1)
Holeckova 4
360 17 Karlovy Vary, Czech Republic (100%)
Tel.: (420) 353440218
Fax: (420) 359607229
E-Mail: info@einhell.cz
Web Site: www.einhell.cz
Emp.: 25
Power Tool, Garden Equipment & Heating & Air Conditioning Equipment Mfr
S.I.C.: 3546
N.A.I.C.S.: 333991
Petr Haak *(Mng Dir)*

Einhell UK Ltd. (1)
Morpeth Wharf Twelve Quays
Birkenhead, CH41 1LF, United Kingdom (100%)
Tel.: (44) 1516491500
Fax: (44) 151 6491501
E-Mail: sales@einhell.co.uk
Web Site: www.einhell-uk.co.uk
Power Tool, Garden Equipment & Heating & Air Conditioning Equipment Mfr
S.I.C.: 3546
N.A.I.C.S.: 333991
David Hall *(Mng Dir)*

Hans Einhell (China) Chongqing Co., Ltd. (1)
Caohejing High Tech Park Qinzhou North Street No 1122
Building 92 Fl 1 3, Shanghai, 200233, China (100%)
Tel.: (86) 2124122888
Fax: (86) 54265676
Emp.: 200
Power Tool, Garden Equipment & Heating & Air Conditioning Equipment Mfr
S.I.C.: 3546
N.A.I.C.S.: 333991
Andreas Weichselgartner *(Mng Dir)*

Hans Einhell Osterreich GmbH (1)
Brunner Strasse 81 A
A 1230 Vienna, Austria (100%)
Tel.: (43) 18691480
Fax: (43) 1869148080
E-Mail: info@einhell.at
Emp.: 25
Power Tool, Garden Equipment & Heating & Air Conditioning Equipment Mfr
S.I.C.: 3546
N.A.I.C.S.: 333991
Christoph Hinterecker *(Mng Dir)*

Hansi Anhai Far East Ltd. (1)
15 F OTB Building 160 Gloucester Rd
Wanchai, China (Hong Kong) (100%)
Tel.: (852) 25015556
Fax: (852) 28104494
Power Tool, Garden Equipment & Heating & Air Conditioning Equipment Mfr
S.I.C.: 3546
N.A.I.C.S.: 333991
Juergen Kracht *(Mng Dir)*

Svenska Einhell AB (1)
Ostergarde Industriomrade 415
41729 Gothenburg, Sweden (100%)
Tel.: (46) 31 550999
Fax: (46) 31 550998
E-Mail: info@einhell.se
Web Site: www.einhell.se
Power Tool, Garden Equipment & Heating & Air Conditioning Equipment Mfr
S.I.C.: 3546
N.A.I.C.S.: 333991
Thomas Seleskog *(Mng Dir)*

EINS EDUTEEH LIMITED

Office No 212 C Wing Crystal Plaza
New Link Road Oshiwara
Andheri W, Mumbai, 400 053, India
Tel.: (91) 22 40045341
E-Mail: einsedutech@gmail.com
Web Site: www.einsedutechltd.com
511064—(BOM)
Rev.: $25,124
Assets: $1,198,128
Liabilities: $31,625
Net Worth: $1,166,503
Earnings: $7,047
Fiscal Year-end: 03/31/13

Business Description:
Online Training Services
S.I.C.: 8299
N.A.I.C.S.: 611710

Personnel:
Shweta Agrawal *(Compliance Officer & Sec)*

Board of Directors:
Bhagwan Das Agarwal
Akhil Agarwal
Priti Agarwal
Pramod Kumar Gupta
Ramawtar Gupta
Sachin Somaiya

Transfer Agent:
Sharepro Services (India) Pvt Ltd
13AB Samhita Warehousing Complex 2nd Fl
Sakinaka Telephone Exchange Ln
Off Andheri-Kurla Road Sakinaka Andheri East, Mumbai, 400 072, India

EION INC.

320 March Rd Ste 500
Ottawa, ON, K2K 2E3, Canada
Tel.: (613) 271-4400
Fax: (613) 271-7040
Web Site: www.eionwireless.com
Year Founded: 2001
Sales Range: $1-9.9 Million

Business Description:
IP Solutions for Data & Voice Over Satellite, Wired & Wireless Networks
Export
S.I.C.: 4899
N.A.I.C.S.: 517410

Personnel:
Kalai Kalaichelvan *(Founder, Chm & CEO)*

EISAI CO., LTD.

4-6-10 Koishikawa
Bunkyo-ku, Tokyo, 112-8088, Japan
Tel.: (81) 338173700
Fax: (81) 338113077
Web Site: www.eisai.com
Year Founded: 1941
4523—(TKS)
Sls.: $6,310,238,000
Assets: $10,892,739,000
Liabilities: $5,675,406,000
Net Worth: $5,217,333,000
Earnings: $531,025,000
Emp.: 10,495
Fiscal Year-end: 03/31/13

Business Description:
Pharmaceutical Products & Equipment Mfr
Export
S.I.C.: 2834
N.A.I.C.S.: 325412

Personnel:
Tokuji Izumi *(Chm)*
Haruo Naito *(Pres & CEO)*
Hideki Hayashi *(Chief Product Creation Officer & Deputy Pres)*
Hajime Shimizu *(Deputy Pres & CFO-Japan Subsidiaries)*
Yutaka Tsuchiya *(Deputy Pres)*
Kazuo Hirai *(CIO & VP-Gen Affairs, Environmental & Safety Affairs)*
Hideto Ueda *(Chief Compliance Officer & VP-Internal Control & Audit)*
Edward Stewart Geary *(Chief Medical Officer, Sr VP & Gen Mgr-Corp Medical Affairs)*
Ryohei Yanagi *(Chief IR Officer, Deputy CFO & Dir-IR)*
Lynn Kramer *(Pres-Neuroscience & General Medicine PCU & Chief Clinical Officer)*
Yasushi Okada *(Chief Talent Officer, Exec VP & Gen Mgr-Talent Innovation)*
Lonnel Coats *(Pres-Americas & Exec VP)*
Hideshi Honda *(Pres-Asia & Exec VP)*
Yasunobu Kai *(Pres-Oncology hhc Unit, VP & Dir-Oncology Medical Dept)*
Gary Hendler *(Pres-EMEA & VP)*
Kenji Matsumae *(Pres-Integrated Community hhc Unit-Eisai Japan)*
Kenta Takahashi *(Gen Counsel, Sr VP-Intellectual Property & Dir-Legal Dept)*
Takafumi Asano *(Exec VP)*

Board of Directors:
Tokuji Izumi
Michikazu Aoi
Nobuo Deguchi
Graham Fry
Akira Fujiyoshi
Koichi Masuda
Hideaki Matsui
Haruo Naito
Kiyochika Ota
Patricia Robinson
Osamu Suzuki

Eisai Co., Ltd.—(Continued)

Transfer Agent:

Mitsubishi UFJ Trust & Banking Corporation
4-5 Marunouchi 1-Chome Chiyoda-ku
Tokyo, 100-8212, Japan
Tel.: (81) 3 3212 1211

Subsidiaries:

EIDIA Co., Ltd. (1)
1-10-6 Iwamoto-cho
Chiyoda-ku, Tokyo, 101-0032, Japan (100%)
Tel.: (81) 338654311
Fax: (81) 338645644
Web Site: www.sanko-junyaku.co.jp
Emp.: 172
In-Vitro Diagnostics, Laboratory Reagents & Laboratory Instruments Mfr & Sales
S.I.C.: 2835
N.A.I.C.S.: 325413
Keisuke Watanabe *(Gen Mgr)*

Eisai Distribution Co., Ltd. (1)
Iiyama Daichido 3039 1
Atsugi, Kanagawa, 243 0213 2655, Japan (100%)
Tel.: (81) 462482655
Fax: (81) 462485909
Web Site: www.edc.eisai.co.jp
Emp.: 95
Distributor of Pharmaceuticals
S.I.C.: 5122
N.A.I.C.S.: 424210

Eisai Food & Chemicals Co., Ltd. (1)
13-10 Nihonbashi 2 chome
Chuo-ku, Tokyo, 103 0027, Japan
Tel.: (81) 335483560
Fax: (81) 332732084
E-Mail: ml_info@eisai-fc.co.jp
Web Site: www.eisai-fc.co.jp
Emp.: 50
Development & Marketing of Pharmaceutical & Cosmetic Raw Materials, Food Ingredients & Food Additives, Supplements & Nutrition & Vitamins
S.I.C.: 2834
N.A.I.C.S.: 325412
Minoru Tanaka *(Pres)*

Eisai R&D Management Co., Ltd. (1)
4-6-10 Koishikawa
Tokyo, 112-8088, Japan
Tel.: (81) 338173658
Fax: (81) 338155748
Emp.: 2
Clinical Research
S.I.C.: 8731
N.A.I.C.S.: 541712
Nobuo Deguchi *(Sr VP-R&D)*

Eisai Seikaken Co., Ltd. (1)
312-4 Toriko Nishiharamura
Aso Gun, Kumamoto, 861 2401, Japan (70%)
Tel.: (81) 962793133
Fax: (81) 962792897
Web Site: www.eisaiseikaken.co.jp
Sales Range: $10-24.9 Million
Emp.: 25
Mfr. & Sales of Agro Chemicals
S.I.C.: 2879
N.A.I.C.S.: 325320

Elmed Eisai Co., Ltd. (1)
Toshima Ku
Tokyo, 10070, Japan (100%)
Tel.: (81) 339806633
Fax: (81) 339806634
E-Mail: web-admin@emec.co.jp
Web Site: www.emec.co.jp
Emp.: 15
Marketer of Generic Pharmaceuticals
S.I.C.: 5122
N.A.I.C.S.: 424210
Masaki Nemoto *(Pres)*

Gakuen Shoji Co., Ltd. (1)
Tokodai
Tsukuba, Ibaraki, Japan (95%)
Tel.: (81) 298478422
Fax: (81) 298475039
Emp.: 80
Provider of Catering & Horticultural Services
S.I.C.: 5812
N.A.I.C.S.: 722320

Herusu Co., Ltd. (1)
Nakami Bldg 1 13 Nishi Ikeburo 3 Chome
Toshima Ku, Tokyo, 171 0021, Japan (75%)
Tel.: (81) 339714919
Fax: (81) 339715346
Emp.: 30
Mfr. of Pharmaceutical Machinery
S.I.C.: 3589
N.A.I.C.S.: 333318

KAN Research Institute, Inc. (1)
3F Kobe MI R&D Center 6-7-3 Minatojima-minamimachi
Chuo-ku, Kobe, 650 0047, Japan (100%)
Tel.: (81) 783065910
Fax: (81) 783065920
Web Site: www.kan-research.co.jp
Emp.: 39
Research of Pharmaceuticals & Research Related to Life Sciences
S.I.C.: 8731
N.A.I.C.S.: 541712

Kawashima Co., Ltd. (1)
Hashima
Gifu, Japan (85%)
Tel.: (81) 582626438
Fax: (81) 58 6893691
Emp.: 40
Provider of Catering & Administrative Services
S.I.C.: 5812
N.A.I.C.S.: 722320

Palma Bee'Z Research Institute Co., Ltd. (1)
3262-12 Yoshiwara Ami-machi
Inashiki-gun, Ibaraki, 300-1155, Japan
Tel.: (81) 29 833 6033
Fax: (81) 29 889 1137
Web Site: www.eisai.com
Diagnostic Products Research & Development Services
S.I.C.: 8731
N.A.I.C.S.: 541711

Sannova Co., Ltd. (1)
3038 2 Serada Ojimachi
3700426 Gunma, Japan (80%)
Tel.: (81) 276523611
Fax: (81) 276521341
E-Mail: information@sannova.co.jp
Web Site: www.sannova.com
Emp.: 400
Sales of Pharmaceuticals
S.I.C.: 5122
N.A.I.C.S.: 424210
Toshio Kaneko *(Pres)*

Seiansha Co., Ltd. (1)
Toshima-ku, Tokyo, Japan (84.56%)
Tel.: (81) 3 3980 1021
Fax: (81) 3 3980 7302
Provider of Sales Promotion Services
S.I.C.: 5122
N.A.I.C.S.: 446191

Sunplanet Co., Ltd. (1)
3-5-10 Otsuka
Bunkyo-Ku, Tokyo, 112 0012, Japan (85%)
Tel.: (81) 359781941
Fax: (81) 359781965
Web Site: www.sunplanet.co.jp
Sls.: $123,585,000
Emp.: 550
Administrative, Catering, Printing, & Real Estate Management Services
S.I.C.: 6719
N.A.I.C.S.: 551112
Hidenobu Ando *(CEO)*

Joint Venture:

Bracco-Eisai Co., Ltd. (1)
3-11-6 Ohtsuka
Bunkyo-ku, Tokyo, 112-0012, Japan JP (49%)
Tel.: (81) 3 5319 3381
Fax: (81) 3 5319 3387
E-Mail: murao@bracco-eisai.co.jp
Sales Range: $1-9.9 Million
Emp.: 50
Medical Contrast Imaging Products Mfr & Distr
Import
S.I.C.: 2834
N.A.I.C.S.: 325412
Neil Foust *(Gen Mgr)*

Plants:

Eisai Co., Ltd. - Kashima Plant (1)
22 Sunayama
Kamisu, Ibaraki, 314-0255, Japan
Tel.: (81) 479 46 1155
Fax: (81) 479 46 1095
Pharmaceutical Products Mfr
S.I.C.: 2834
N.A.I.C.S.: 325412

Eisai Co., Ltd. - Misato Plant (1)
950 Oaza-Hiroki Misato-machi
Kodama-gun, Misato, Saitama, 367-0198, Japan
Tel.: (81) 495 76 3111
Fax: (81) 495 76 1841
Emp.: 210
Pharmaceutical Products Mfr
S.I.C.: 2834
N.A.I.C.S.: 325412

U.S. Subsidiary:

Eisai Corporation of North America (1)
100 Tice Blvd
Woodcliff Lake, NJ 07677
Tel.: (201) 692-1100
Fax: (201) 746-2940
Web Site: www.eisai.com
Holding Company
S.I.C.: 6719
N.A.I.C.S.: 551112
Lonnel Coats *(Pres & CEO)*

Subsidiaries:

Eisai Inc. (2)
100 Tice Blvd
Woodcliff Lake, NJ 07677
Tel.: (201) 692-1100
Fax: (201) 692-1804
Web Site: www.eisai.com
Sales Range: $1-4.9 Billion
Emp.: 900
Pharmaceutical Prescriptions & Ethical Health Care Products Mfr & Sales
S.I.C.: 2834
N.A.I.C.S.: 325412
Yuji Matsue *(Chm & CEO)*
Shaji Procida *(Pres & COO)*
Steven Sembler *(Chief Comml Officer & Sr VP)*
Allen Waxman *(Gen Counsel & Sr VP)*

Units:

Eisai Inc. - Andover Research Laboratory (3)
4 Corporate Dr
Andover, MA 01810-2447
Tel.: (978) 794-1117
Fax: (978) 794-4910
E-Mail: info@eisai.com
Web Site: www.eisai.com
Mfr. & Sale of Pharmaceuticals Prescriptions & Ethical Health Care Products
S.I.C.: 8732
N.A.I.C.S.: 541720

Eisai Inc. - Research Triangle Park (3)
900 Davis Dr
Durham, NC 27709
Tel.: (919) 941-6920
Fax: (919) 941-6931
Web Site: www.eisai.com
Emp.: 300
Pharmaceuticals Prescriptions & Ethical Health Care Products
S.I.C.: 8732
N.A.I.C.S.: 541720

H3 Biomedicine Inc. (2)
300 Technology Sq 5th Fl
Cambridge, MA 02139
Tel.: (617) 252-5000
Fax: (617) 252-5098
Web Site: www.h3biomedicine.com
Emp.: 40
Biotechnology Research & Development Services
S.I.C.: 8731
N.A.I.C.S.: 541711
Markus Warmuth *(Pres & CEO)*
Yutaka Ishizaka *(Sr VP-Plng & Ops)*

Morphotek, Inc. (2)
210 Welsh Pool Rd
Exton, PA 19341
Tel.: (610) 423-6100
Fax: (610) 423-6199
E-Mail: info@morphotek.com
Web Site: www.morphotek.com
Emp.: 100
Clinical Research
S.I.C.: 8731
N.A.I.C.S.: 541712
Nicholas Nicolaides *(Pres & CEO)*
Rodney Dausch *(CFO & VP-Project Mgmt)*
Philip Sass *(COO & Exec VP)*
Martin Phillips *(Sr VP-Clinical Dev & Chief Medical Officer)*
Luigi Grasso *(Sr VP-R&D)*

Non-U.S. Subsidiaries:

Eisai China Inc. (1)
39th-40th Floors Park Place 1601 Nanjjing Xi Road
Shanghai, 200040, China (100%)
Tel.: (86) 2124192888
Fax: (86) 2124192881
Emp.: 200
Pharmaceuticals Mfr & Sales
S.I.C.: 2834
N.A.I.C.S.: 325412
Victor Liu *(Gen Mgr)*

Plant:

Eisai China Inc. - Suzhou Factory (2)
Bai Yu Road 32 Suzhou Industrial Park
Suzhou, Jiangsu, 215021, China
Tel.: (86) 512 6761 3211
Fax: (86) 512 6761 8640
Pharmaceutical Products Mfr
S.I.C.: 2834
N.A.I.C.S.: 325412

Eisai Clinical Research Singapore Pte Ltd. (1)
#15-05/07 152 Beach Rd Gateway E
Singapore, 189721, Singapore
Tel.: (65) 62976624
Fax: (65) 62976328
Web Site: www.eisai.co.jp/ecompany/eprofile/egroup.html
Emp.: 8
Clinical Research
S.I.C.: 8731
N.A.I.C.S.: 541712
Masashi Yoshikawa *(Mng Dir)*

Eisai Europe Ltd. (1)
European Knowledge Centre
Mosquito Way, Hatfield, AL10 9SN, United Kingdom
Tel.: (44) 8456761400
Web Site: www.eisai.co.uk
Holding Company
S.I.C.: 6719
N.A.I.C.S.: 551112
Yutaka Tsuchiya *(VP)*

Subsidiaries:

Eisai Ltd. (2)
Mosquito Way
Hatfield, Herts, AL10 9SN, United Kingdom (100%)
Tel.: (44) 2086001400
Fax: (44) 2086001401
E-Mail: recruitment@eisai.net
Web Site: www.eisai.co.uk
Emp.: 450
Pharmaceutical Sls & Clinical Research
S.I.C.: 8731
N.A.I.C.S.: 541712
Yuji Naito *(Chm)*

Eisai Manufacturing Ltd. (2)
3 Shortlands
London, W6 8EE, United Kingdom
Tel.: (44) 845 676 1200
Pharmaceuticals
S.I.C.: 2834
N.A.I.C.S.: 325412
Yutaka Tsuchiya *(VP)*

Non-U.S. Subsidiaries:

Eisai AB (2)
Svardvagen 3A
PO Box 23060
18233 Danderyd, 10435, Sweden

Tel.: (46) 850101600
Fax: (46) 850101699
E-Mail: nordic_medinfo@eisai.net
Web Site: www.eisai.se
Emp.: 25
Pharmaceutical Sales
S.I.C.: 5122
N.A.I.C.S.: 424210
Clas Lindbergson *(Mng Dir)*

Eisai B.V. (2)
Strawinskylaan 1141
NL 1077 XX Amsterdam, Netherlands (100%)
Tel.: (31) 205753340
Fax: (31) 205753341
Web Site: www.eisai.com
Emp.: 3
Mfr. & Sales of Pharmaceuticals
S.I.C.: 2834
N.A.I.C.S.: 325412

Eisai Farmaceutica S.A. (2)
Arturo Soria 336 3 Fl
28053 Madrid, Spain
Tel.: (34) 914559455
Fax: (34) 917210506
E-Mail: info@eisai.com
Web Site: www.eisai.net
Sales Range: $10-24.9 Million
Emp.: 33
Pharmaceutical Sales Promotion
S.I.C.: 5122
N.A.I.C.S.: 424210

Non-U.S. Subsidiary:

Eisai Farmaceutica, Unipessoal Lda. (3)
Lagoas Park Edificio 5A Piso 6
2740-298 Porto Salvo, Portugal
Tel.: (351) 21 487 55 40
Fax: (351) 21 487 55 48
Web Site: www.eisai.com
Emp.: 14
Pharmaceutical Products Distr
S.I.C.: 5122
N.A.I.C.S.: 424210

Eisai GesmbH (2)
Saturn Tower Leonard-Bernstein-Strasse 10
1220 Vienna, Austria
Tel.: (43) 1 5351980 0
Fax: (43) 1 5351980 80
E-Mail: contact_vien@eisai.com
Emp.: 1
Pharmaceutical Products Distr
S.I.C.: 5122
N.A.I.C.S.: 424210

Eisai GmbH (2)
Lyoner Strasse 36
Frankfurt, Hessen, 60528, Germany (100%)
Tel.: (49) 69665850
Fax: (49) 696658525
E-Mail: info@eisai.net
Web Site: www.eisai.de
Emp.: 50
Sales of Pharmaceuticals
S.I.C.: 5122
N.A.I.C.S.: 424210

Eisai Pharma AG (2)
Schaffhauserstrasse 611
8052 Zurich, Switzerland
Tel.: (41) 443061212
Fax: (41) 443061280
Web Site: www.eisai.com
Pharmaceutical Sales
S.I.C.: 5122
N.A.I.C.S.: 424210

Eisai S.A.S. (2)
Tour Manhattan 5- 6 place de l'Iris
92095 Paris, La Defense, France (100%)
Tel.: (33) 147670005
Fax: (33) 147670015
Web Site: www.eisai.com
Sales Range: $150-199.9 Million
Emp.: 70
Sales of Pharmaceuticals
S.I.C.: 5122
N.A.I.C.S.: 424210
Satoshi Suzuki *(Pres)*

Eisai S.r.l. (2)
Via dell'Unione Europea 6
20097 San Donato Milanese, Italy
Tel.: (39) 025181401
Fax: (39) 0251814020
E-Mail: info@eisai.it
Web Site: www.eisai.it
Emp.: 80
Pharmaceutical Sales
S.I.C.: 5122
N.A.I.C.S.: 424210
Franco Merckling *(Mng Dir)*

Eisai Hong Kong Co., Ltd. (1)
Rm 2007 Fortress Tower
250 Kings Rd, North Point, China (Hong Kong) (100%)
Tel.: (852) 25166128
Fax: (852) 25615042
E-Mail: ehk6128@eisaihk.com
Web Site: www.eisai.com
Emp.: 13
Mfr. & Sales of Pharmaceuticals
S.I.C.: 2834
N.A.I.C.S.: 325412
Wyeman Tan *(Gen Mgr)*

Eisai Korea, Inc. (1)
10th Fl Revessant Bldg 147-17 Sanseong-Tong Kangnam Ku
Seoul, 135878, Korea (South) (100%)
Tel.: (82) 234515500
Fax: (82) 234515599
Web Site: www.eisaikorea.com
Sales Range: $25-49.9 Million
Emp.: 80
Sales of Pharmaceuticals
S.I.C.: 5122
N.A.I.C.S.: 424210
Pyuong Chic Cho *(Pres)*

Eisai (Malaysia) Sdn. Bhd. (1)
Lot 6/1 6th FL Menara Lien Hoe No 8
Persiaran Tropicana, 47410 Petaling Jaya, Selangor Darul Ehsan, Malaysia (98.09%)
Tel.: (60) 378039096
Fax: (60) 378030060
E-Mail: eisaihhc@tm.net.my
Web Site: www.eisai.com
Emp.: 36
Sales of Pharmaceuticals
S.I.C.: 5122
N.A.I.C.S.: 424210

Eisai Pharmaceuticals India Private Ltd. (1)
1st Floor B Wing Marwah Centre Krishanlal Marwah Marg Andheri E
Mumbai, 400 072, India
Tel.: (91) 2228579740
Fax: (91) 2228579720
E-Mail: info@eisai.co
Web Site: www.eisai.co.jp/ecompany/eprofile/egroup.html
Emp.: 60
Pharmaceutical Production & Sales
S.I.C.: 2834
N.A.I.C.S.: 325412
Deepak Naik *(Mng Dir)*

Eisai Pharmatechnology & Manufacturing Pvt. Ltd. (1)
Ramky Pharma City SEZ Plot Nos 96 97 98 124 & 126 Parawada
531 019 Visakhapatnam, Andhra Pradesh, India
Tel.: (91) 892 428 2500
Fax: (91) 892 428 2528
Web Site: www.eisai.com
Emp.: 300
Pharmaceutical Products Mfr
S.I.C.: 2834
N.A.I.C.S.: 325412
Sanjit Singh Lamba *(Mng Dir)*

Eisai (Singapore) Pte. Ltd. (1)
152 Beach Road 15-05/08 Gateway East
Singapore, 189721, Singapore
Tel.: (65) 6296 6977
Fax: (65) 6296 6577
Web Site: www.eisai.com
Pharmaceutical Products Distr
S.I.C.: 5122
N.A.I.C.S.: 424210

Eisai Taiwan, Inc. (1)
9th Fl No 18 Chang An East Rd Sec 1
Taipei, 104, Taiwan (100%)
Tel.: (886) 225314175
Fax: (886) 225310063
Web Site: www.eisai.com.tw
Emp.: 40
Mfr. & Sales of Pharmaceuticals
S.I.C.: 2834
N.A.I.C.S.: 325412

Eisai (Thailand) Marketing Co., Ltd. (1)
6th Fl GPF Witthayu Tower A 93/1 Wireless Rd
Lumpini Patumwan, Bangkok, 10330, Thailand (50%)
Tel.: (66) 22566296
Fax: (66) 22566299
Web Site: www.eisai.com
Emp.: 20
Mfr. & Sales of Pharmaceuticals
S.I.C.: 2834
N.A.I.C.S.: 325412

Hi-Eisai Pharmaceuticals, Inc. (1)
Fl 20 6805 Ayala Ave
Makati, Metro Manila, 1226, Philippines (49.9%)
Tel.: (63) 28871047
Fax: (63) 28875172
E-Mail: gcpangen@eisai.com.ph
Web Site: www.eisai.co.ph
Emp.: 109
Marketer & Sales of Pharmaceuticals
S.I.C.: 2834
N.A.I.C.S.: 325412
Lourdes Magno *(Pres)*

PT. Eisai Indonesia (1)
Sentral Senayan II, 12 Floor Jl. Asia Afrika No. 8,Senayan
Jakarta, Pusat, 12070, Indonesia Id
Tel.: (62) 2157951994 (80%)
Fax: (62) 21579581995
E-Mail: info@eisai.co.id
Web Site: www.eisai.co.id
Emp.: 80
Pharmaceuticals & Cosmetics Mfr & Sales
S.I.C.: 2834
N.A.I.C.S.: 325412
Lia Muslimah *(Sec)*

Plant:

PT. Eisai Indonesia - Bogor Factory (2)
Ji Lanbau Desa Karang Asem Barat Kecamatan Citeureup
Bogor, Jawa-Barat, 16810, Indonesia
Tel.: (62) 21 875 3202
Fax: (62) 21 876 4886
Pharmaceutical Products Mfr
S.I.C.: 2834
N.A.I.C.S.: 325412

EISENBAU KRAMER GMBH

Karl-Kramer-Strasse 12
D-57223 Kreuztal, Germany
Mailing Address:
Postfach 4020
D-57263 Hilchenbach, Germany
Tel.: (49) 27325880
Fax: (49) 2732588102
E-Mail: info@eisenbau-kraemer.de
Web Site: www.eisenbau-kraemer.de
Year Founded: 1921
Sales Range: $10-24.9 Million
Emp.: 280
Business Description:
Rolled & Welded Steel Pipes & Shells Mfr
S.I.C.: 3399
N.A.I.C.S.: 331221
Personnel:
Rainer Seelbach *(Mng Partner)*

EISENMANN AG

Tubinger Strasse 81
71032 Boblingen, Germany
Tel.: (49) 7031780
Fax: (49) 7031781000
E-Mail: info@eisenmann.com
Web Site: www.eisenmann.com
Year Founded: 1951
Rev.: $212,012,500
Emp.: 2,160
Business Description:
Industrial Equipments Distr
S.I.C.: 5085
N.A.I.C.S.: 423840
Personnel:
Peter Eisenmann *(Chm-Supervisory Bd)*
Matthias von Krauland *(Chm-Mgmt Bd)*
Thomas Beck *(Member-Mgmt Bd)*
Kersten Christoph Link *(Member-Mgmt Bd)*

EISSMANN AUTOMOTIVE DEUTSCHLAND GMBH

Munsinger Str 150
72574 Bad Urach, Germany
Tel.: (49) 712593730
Fax: (49) 7125937319
E-Mail: info@eissmann.de
Web Site: www.eissmann.de
Year Founded: 1964
Rev.: $122,346,159
Emp.: 2,100
Business Description:
Automotive Interiors Mfr
S.I.C.: 3714
N.A.I.C.S.: 336390
Personnel:
Jurgen Eissmann *(Co-CEO)*
Klaus Elmer *(Co-CEO)*
Norman Willich *(Co-CEO)*

EITA RESOURCES BERHAD

Lot 4 Block A Jalan SS13/7 Subang Jaya Industrial Estate
Subang Jaya, Selangor, 47500, Malaysia
Tel.: (60) 3 5637 8099
Fax: (60) 3 5637 8128
E-Mail: enquiry@eita.com.my
Web Site: www.eita.com.my
EITA—(KLS)
Rev.: $63,633,515
Assets: $51,635,266
Liabilities: $17,689,949
Net Worth: $33,945,317
Earnings: $4,522,879
Fiscal Year-end: 12/31/12
Business Description:
Elevator Systems & Busduct Systems
S.I.C.: 3534
N.A.I.C.S.: 333921
Personnel:
Wing Hoong Fu *(Mng Dir)*
Poh Gek Kow *(CFO)*
Sor Hua Tea *(Co-Sec)*
Yen Ling Yong *(Co-Sec)*
Board of Directors:
Kim Lun Siow
Lik Khai Chia
Mak Hooi Chia
Lee Chang Chong
Yoke Peng Chong
Wing Hoong Fu
Peng Sian Lee
Joo Swee Lim
Chuan Hock Tan
Subsidiaries:

Eita Electric Sdn. Bhd. (1)
Lot 4 Block A Jalan Ss 13/7 Subang Jaya Industrial Estate
47500 Subang Jaya, Selangor, Malaysia
Tel.: (60) 3 56378088
Fax: (60) 3 56354719
Electrical Equipment Distr
S.I.C.: 5063
N.A.I.C.S.: 423610

EITA Elevator (Malaysia) Sdn. Bhd. (1)
60-G Pesiaran Mahsuri 1/2
Sunway Tunas, 11900 Bayan Baru, Penang, Malaysia
Tel.: (60) 4 6449472
Fax: (60) 4 6449473
Elevator Mfr
S.I.C.: 3534
N.A.I.C.S.: 333921

Eita Resources Berhad—(Continued)

Non-U.S. Subsidiary:

EITA Technologies Pte. Ltd. (1)
49 Jalan Pemimpin 04-12 APS Industrial Building
Singapore, 577203, Singapore
Tel.: (65) 62563080
Fax: (65) 62563811
Electrical Equipment Whslr
S.I.C.: 5063
N.A.I.C.S.: 423610

EITZEN CHEMICAL ASA

Ruselokkveien 6
0251 Oslo, Norway
Tel.: (47) 23114320
Fax: (47) 24006101
E-Mail: chemosl@eitzen-chemical.com
Web Site: www.eitzen-chemical.com
ECHEM—(OSL)
Rev.: $401,248,000
Assets: $962,622,000
Liabilities: $994,766,000
Net Worth: ($32,144,000)
Earnings: ($136,316,000)
Emp.: 1,329
Fiscal Year-end: 12/31/12

Business Description:
Marine Chemical Transportation Services
S.I.C.: 5091
N.A.I.C.S.: 423910

Personnel:
Aage Figenschou *(Chm)*
Per Sylvester Jensen *(Pres & CEO)*
Andreas Reklev *(CFO)*
Geir Frode Abelsen *(CTO)*
Aage Rasmussen *(Sr VP-Chartering)*
Martin D. Solberg *(Sr VP-Fin & Acctg)*

Board of Directors:
Aage Figenschou
Helene Jebsen Anker
Erik Bartnes
Thor J. Guttormsen
Heidi M. Petersen

U.S. Subsidiaries:

Eitzen Chemical (USA) LLC (1)
1 Gorham Is
Westport, CT 06880
Tel.: (203) 341-3600
Fax: (203) 341-3610
E-Mail: charteringusa@eitzen-chemical.com
Web Site: www.eitzen-chemical.com
Emp.: 15
Marine Chemical Transportation Services
S.I.C.: 4412
N.A.I.C.S.: 483111
Jan Hansen *(Gen Mgr)*

Team Tankers (USA) LLC (1)
One Gorham Island
Westport, CT 06880
Tel.: (203) 341-3620
Fax: (203) 341-3630
Emp.: 13
Marine Chemical Transportation Services
S.I.C.: 4412
N.A.I.C.S.: 483111
Terje Askvig *(Mng Dir)*

Non-U.S. Subsidiaries:

Eitzen Chemical A/S (1)
Camillo Eitzen House Amerika Plads 38
2100 Copenhagen, Denmark
Tel.: (45) 39970300
Fax: (45) 39970301
E-Mail: seccph@eitzen-chemical.com
Emp.: 65
Chemical Transportation Services
S.I.C.: 4111
N.A.I.C.S.: 485999

Eitzen Chemical (France) S.A.S. (1)
130 rue Victor Hugo
92300 Levallois-Perret, Hauts-de-Seine, France
Tel.: (33) 147155581
Fax: (33) 147155589
E-Mail: charteringeur@eitzen-chemical.com
Web Site: www.eitzen-chemical.com
Chemical Transportation Services
S.I.C.: 4119
N.A.I.C.S.: 485999
Terje Askvig *(Pres)*
Raymond Jean Roussel *(Dir Gen)*

Eitzen Chemical (Singapore) Pte. Ltd. (1)
One Temasek Avenue 35-05 Millenia TowerSingapore
Singapore, Singapore
Tel.: (65) 65577600
Fax: (65) 63372526
E-Mail: charteringasia@eitzen-chemical.com
Web Site: www.eitzen-chemical.com
Emp.: 15
Chemical Transportation Services
S.I.C.: 4214
N.A.I.C.S.: 484220

Eitzen Chemical (Spain) S.A. (1)
Avda Severo Ochoa 28-5 A/D
29603 Marbella, Malaga, Spain
Tel.: (34) 952765177
Fax: (34) 952765885
E-Mail: chammar@eitzen-chemical.com
Web Site: www.eitzen-chemical.com
Emp.: 8
Chemical Trucking Services
S.I.C.: 4214
N.A.I.C.S.: 484110
Lucas Fernandez *(Mng Dir)*

EIZO CORPORATION

(Formerly Eizo Nanao Corporation)
153 Shimokashiwano
Hakusan, Ishikawa, 924-8566, Japan
Tel.: (81) 76 275 4121
Fax: (81) 76 275 4125
E-Mail: global_eizo@eizo.co.jp
Web Site: www.eizo.com
Year Founded: 1968
6737—(TKS)
Sls.: $640,970,000
Assets: $873,048,000
Liabilities: $197,296,000
Net Worth: $675,752,000
Earnings: $17,578,000
Emp.: 1,637
Fiscal Year-end: 03/31/13

Business Description:
Computer Monitors & Peripherals Mfr
S.I.C.: 3575
N.A.I.C.S.: 334118

Personnel:
Yoshitaka Jitsumori *(Pres & CEO)*
Tsutomo Tanabe *(CFO & Exec VP)*
Masayuki Hashimoto *(Exec Mng Officer)*
Yuichi Murai *(Exec Mng Officer)*
Masaki Ono *(Exec Mng Officer)*
Kazuhiko Deminami *(Mng Officer)*
Toshimine Hiraki *(Mng Officer)*
Hidenori Kojima *(Mng Officer)*
Kazuya Maeda *(Mng Officer)*
Kazuhide Shimura *(Mng Officer)*
Eiji Tsurumi *(Mng Officer)*

Board of Directors:
Yoshitaka Jitsumori
Yuichi Murai
Masaki Ono
Kazuhide Shimura
Masaaki Suzuki
Tsutomo Tanabe

Subsidiaries:

Eizo Engineering Corporation (1)
153 Shimokashiwano
Hakusan, Ishikawa, 924-8566, Japan
Tel.: (81) 762742448
Fax: (81) 76 274 0041
Web Site: www.eizoeg.com
Liquid Crystal Displays Mfr
S.I.C.: 3679
N.A.I.C.S.: 334419

Eizo Nanao MS Corporation (1)
37-9-Re Jike
Hakui, Ishikawa, 925-8566, Japan
Tel.: (81) 767227121
Fax: (81) 767226601
Emp.: 200
Liquid Crystal Displays Mfr
S.I.C.: 3679
N.A.I.C.S.: 334419

Eizo Support Network Corporation (1)
153 Shimokashiwano
Hakusan, Ishikawa, 924-8566, Japan
Tel.: (81) 762742424
Fax: (81) 762742416
Web Site: www.eizo-support.co.jp
Emp.: 86
Monitors Sales & Maintenance Services
S.I.C.: 7629
N.A.I.C.S.: 811212
Yoshitaka Jitsumori *(Pres)*

Irem Software Engineering Inc. (1)
655 Fukudome
Hakusan, Ishikawa, 924-8533, Japan
Tel.: (81) 762773800
Fax: (81) 762773622
Web Site: www.irem.co.jp
Emp.: 190
Video Game Software Development Services
S.I.C.: 3652
N.A.I.C.S.: 334614

Nanao Agency Corporation (1)
153 Shimokashiwano
Hakusan, Ishikawa, 924-8566, Japan
Tel.: (81) 76 275 4121
Fax: (81) 76 275 4125
Web Site: www.eizo.com
Medical Imaging Monitors Distr
S.I.C.: 5047
N.A.I.C.S.: 423450

U.S. Subsidiaries:

Eizo Nanao Technologies Inc. (1)
5710 Warland Dr
Cypress, CA 90630
Tel.: (562) 431-5011
Fax: (562) 431-4811
Toll Free: (800) 800-5202
E-Mail: orders@eizo.com
Web Site: www.eizo.com
Sls.: $60,000,000
Emp.: 19
Sales of Computer Monitors & Peripherals
S.I.C.: 5045
N.A.I.C.S.: 423430
Akihito Matsudara *(Mgr-HR)*

Tech Source, Inc. (1)
442 Northlake Blvd
Altamonte Springs, FL 32701
Tel.: (407) 262-7100
Fax: (407) 339-2554
E-Mail: info@techsource.com
Web Site: www.techsource.com
Emp.: 20
Air Traffic Control Components Mfr
S.I.C.: 3812
N.A.I.C.S.: 334511
Selwyn L. Henriques *(Pres)*

Non-U.S. Subsidiaries:

EIZO Display Technologies (Suzhou) Co., Ltd. (1)
5B Zhongxin Science & Tech Industrial Zone 8 Zhanye Road
Suzhou Industrial Park, Suzhou, 215122, China
Tel.: (86) 512 6252 0100
Fax: (86) 512 6252 1508
Computer Monitors & Peripherals Mfr
S.I.C.: 3575
N.A.I.C.S.: 334118

EIZO GmbH (1)
Siemensallee 84
76187 Karlsruhe, Baden-Wurttemberg, Germany
Tel.: (49) 721203210
Fax: (49) 72120321471
E-Mail: dt-contact@eizo.com
Web Site: www.eizo.eu
Emp.: 300
Medical Monitors Distr
S.I.C.: 5045
N.A.I.C.S.: 423430
Peter Ziegler *(CEO)*

Eizo Nanao AG (1)
Moosacherstrasse 6 Au
8820 Wadenswil, Zurich, Switzerland
Tel.: (41) 447822440
Fax: (41) 447822450
E-Mail: info@eizo.ch
Web Site: www.eizo.ch
Emp.: 15
Monitors Distr
S.I.C.: 5045
N.A.I.C.S.: 423430
Kunihiro Arata *(Mng Dir)*

EIZO Nordic AB (1)
Lovangsvagen 14
194 61 Upplands Vasby, Sweden
Tel.: (46) 8 594 10500
Fax: (46) 8 590 91575
Computer Monitors & Peripherals Mfr
S.I.C.: 3575
N.A.I.C.S.: 334118

EIZO Technologies GmbH (1)
Buergermeister-Seidl-Strasse 8
82515 Wolfratshausen, Bavaria, Germany
Tel.: (49) 817134920
Fax: (49) 8171349216
E-Mail: info@eizo-tech.com
Web Site: www.eizo-tech.com
Emp.: 65
Monitors & Converter Cards Mfr
S.I.C.: 3577
N.A.I.C.S.: 334118
Andy Kuerz *(Pres)*

EIZO NANAO CORPORATION

(Name Changed to EIZO Corporation)

EJADA FOR FINANCIAL INVESTMENTS PLC

Darkom Investment Complex-Shemesani
PO Box 962365
Amman, 11196, Jordan
Tel.: (962) 65623116
Fax: (962) 65623118
E-Mail: info@cjadainv.com
Year Founded: 1995
EJAD—(AMM)
Rev.: $56,852
Assets: $6,608,810
Liabilities: $3,922,523
Net Worth: $2,686,287
Earnings: ($2,033,913)
Emp.: 8
Fiscal Year-end: 12/31/12

Business Description:
Investment Management Services
S.I.C.: 6211
N.A.I.C.S.: 523999

Personnel:
Mohamad Mahmoud Issa Diab *(Gen Mgr)*

EKAM LEASING & FINANCE CO. LTD.

3rd Floor 14 Rani Jhansi Road
New Delhi, 110055, India
Tel.: (91) 11 32033277
Fax: (91) 11 23528015
E-Mail: info@ekamleasing.com
Web Site: www.ekamleasing.com
Year Founded: 1993
530581—(BOM)
Rev.: $81,297
Assets: $977,290
Liabilities: $597,615
Net Worth: $379,675
Earnings: $6,111
Fiscal Year-end: 03/31/13

Business Description:
Financial Leasing Services
S.I.C.: 6159
N.A.I.C.S.: 522220

Personnel:
Rakesh Jain *(Chm & Mng Dir)*

Board of Directors:
Rakesh Jain
Narendra Kumar Jain
Vishal Jain
Vikas Kucheria
Transfer Agent:
Alankit Assignments Limited
Alankit House 2E/21 Jhandewalan Extension
New Delhi, India

EKARAT ENGINEERING PUBLIC COMPANY LIMITED

9/291 UM Tower 28th Floor
Ramkamhaeng Rd Suanluang District
Bangkok, 10250, Thailand
Tel.: (66) 2 719 8777
Fax: (66) 2 719 8760
E-Mail: service@ekarat-transformer.com
Web Site: www.ekarat-transformer.com
Year Founded: 1981
AKR—(THA)
Rev.: $76,635,860
Assets: $71,173,504
Liabilities: $58,236,626
Net Worth: $12,936,878
Earnings: $3,680,571
Fiscal Year-end: 12/31/12
Business Description:
Transformer Mfr
S.I.C.: 3677
N.A.I.C.S.: 334416
Personnel:
Vichit Yamboonruang *(Chm)*
Danucha Noichaiboon *(Mng Dir)*
Anan Santichewasarian *(CFO)*
Ekasak Chiamcharoen *(Deputy Mng Dir-Factory)*
Daranee Kantamara *(Deputy Mng Dir-Gen Admin Div)*
Daroonwat Noichaiboon *(Deputy Mng Dir-Svc Div)*
Vithep Vachirabhahu *(Deputy Mng Dir-Sls & Mktg Div)*
Board of Directors:
Vichit Yamboonruang
Pitak Chaicharoen
Urawee Kanokpruk
Daranee Kantamara
Prinya Nakchatree
Danucha Noichaiboon
Anan Santichewasarian
Chalit Satidthong
Wara Tongprasin
Vinai Vittavasgarnvej

EKATO RUHR- UND MISCHTECHNIK GMBH

Kappelemattweg 2
79650 Schopfheim, Germany
Tel.: (49) 7622290
Fax: (49) 762229213
E-Mail: info@ekato.com
Web Site: www.ekato.com
Sales Range: $200-249.9 Million
Emp.: 600
Business Description:
Industrial Process Equipment Mfr
S.I.C.: 3559
N.A.I.C.S.: 333249
Personnel:
Helmut Ganser *(Co-Pres)*
Christian Watzelt *(Co-Pres)*

EKB CONTAINER LOGISTIK GMBH & CO. KG

(Acquired by CTS Spedition GmbH)

EKF DIAGNOSTICS HOLDINGS PLC

14 Kinnerton Place South
London, SW1X 8EH, United Kingdom
Tel.: (44) 2920710570
Fax: (44) 2920705715
E-Mail: info@ekfdiagnostics.com
Web Site: www.ekfdiagnostics.com
EKF—(AIM)
Rev.: $41,156,297
Assets: $87,993,301
Liabilities: $25,726,634
Net Worth: $62,266,667
Earnings: $3,164,897
Emp.: 302
Fiscal Year-end: 12/31/12
Business Description:
Laboratory Instrument Mfr
S.I.C.: 3826
N.A.I.C.S.: 334516
Personnel:
David Evans *(Chm)*
Julian Baines *(CEO)*
Paul Foulger *(Sec)*
Board of Directors:
David Evans
Julian Baines
Richard Anthony Evans
Paul Foulger
Gordon James Hall
Adam Reynolds
Kevin William Wilson
Legal Counsel:
Berry Smith LLP
Haywood House Dumfries Place
Cardiff, CF10 3GA, United Kingdom
U.S. Subsidiaries:

Separation Technology, Inc. **(1)**
582 Monroe Rd Ste 1424
Sanford, FL 32771
Tel.: (407) 788-8791
Fax: (407) 788-3677
Toll Free: (800) 777-6668
E-Mail: custserv@separationtechnology.com
Web Site: www.separationtechnology.com
Sales Range: $1-9.9 Million
Emp.: 15
Centrifugation Products Mfr
S.I.C.: 3826
N.A.I.C.S.: 334516
Jami Meeks *(Pres)*

Stanbio Laboratory LP **(1)**
1261 N Main St
Boerne, TX 78006 TX
Tel.: (830) 249-0772
Fax: (830) 249-0851
Toll Free: (800) 531-5535
Web Site: www.stanbio.com
Emp.: 75
Pharmaceutical Preparations
S.I.C.: 2834
N.A.I.C.S.: 325412
William R. Pippin *(Pres)*

EKINOPS SA

3 rue Blaise Pascal
22300 Lannion, France
Tel.: (33) 1 49 97 04 04
Web Site: www.ekinops.net
Year Founded: 2003
EKI—(EUR)
Business Description:
Telecommunications Equipment
S.I.C.: 3663
N.A.I.C.S.: 334220
Personnel:
Didier Bredy *(Chm & CEO)*
Dmitri Pigoulevski *(CFO)*
Francois Xavier Ollivier *(COO)*
Board of Directors:
Didier Bredy
Julien Andrieux
Jean Bourcereau
Stanislas Cuny
Sebastien Descarpentries
Jean-Pierre Dumolard
Francois Xavier Ollivier

EKITAN & CO., LTD.

6-2-1 Ginza Chuo-ku
Tokyo, 104-0061, Japan
Tel.: (81) 362523670
E-Mail: ir@ekitan.co.jp
Web Site: www.ekitan.co.jp
3646—(TKS)
Sales Range: $25-49.9 Million
Emp.: 70
Business Description:
Network Communications
S.I.C.: 4899
N.A.I.C.S.: 517919
Personnel:
Taro Nakamura *(Pres)*

EKIZ YAG VE SABUN SANAYI A.S.

(d/b/a Ekiz Olive Oil)
Sehitler Caddesi 1508 Sokak 4
Alsancak
35230 Izmir, Turkey
Tel.: (90) 2324885700
Fax: (90) 2324630918
E-Mail: ekiz@ekizyag.com
Web Site: www.ekizyag.com
Year Founded: 1946
Sales Range: $10-24.9 Million
Emp.: 90
Business Description:
Olive & Vegetable Oil Refiner, Producer & Marketer
S.I.C.: 2079
N.A.I.C.S.: 311225
Personnel:
Husnu Ekiz *(Chm & Gen Mgr)*

EKO EXPORT S.A.

ul Strazacka 81
43-382 Bielsko-Biala, Poland
Tel.: (48) 33 81 96 292
Fax: (48) 33 81 96 287
E-Mail: info@ekoexport.pl
Web Site: www.ekoexport.pl
EEX—(WAR)
Sales Range: $1-9.9 Million
Business Description:
Microspheres Distr & Exporter
S.I.C.: 5169
N.A.I.C.S.: 424690
Personnel:
Igor Bokun *(Chm-Supervisory Bd)*
Jacek Dziedzic *(Chm-Mgmt Bd)*
Jolanta Sidzina-Bokun *(Deputy Chm-Supervisory Bd)*
Supervisory Board of Directors:
Igor Bokun
Marzena Bednarczyk
Agnieszka Bokun
Marcel Dziedzic
Jolanta Sidzina-Bokun

EKORNES ASA

Industrivegen 1
6222 Ikornnes, Norway
Tel.: (47) 70255200
Fax: (47) 70255300
E-Mail: office@ekornes.no
Web Site: www.ekornes.com
EKO—(OSL)
Rev.: $490,913,294
Assets: $395,823,863
Liabilities: $87,289,486
Net Worth: $308,534,377
Earnings: $60,645,224
Emp.: 1,626
Fiscal Year-end: 12/31/12
Business Description:
Furniture Mfr
S.I.C.: 2519
N.A.I.C.S.: 337125
Personnel:
Olav Kjell Holtan *(Chm)*
Kjersti Kleven *(Vice Chm)*
Nils-Fredrik Drablos *(CEO)*
Robert Svendsen *(CFO)*
Jon-Erlend Alstad *(CEO-Ekornes Fetsund AS)*
Board of Directors:
Olav Kjell Holtan
Atle Berntzen
Stian Ekornes
Bjorn Gulden
Tone Helen Hanken
Arnstein Johannessen
Kjersti Kleven
Nora Forisdal Larssen
Subsidiaries:

Ekornes Fetsund AS **(1)**
J A Ekornes 22
Fetsund, N 1900 Oslo, Norway (100%)
Tel.: (47) 63883300
Fax: (47) 63880273
E-Mail: svane@ekornes.no
Web Site: www.ekornes.no
Emp.: 130
Other Knit Fabric & Lace Mills
S.I.C.: 2259
N.A.I.C.S.: 313240
Jon Erlend Alstad *(Mng Dir)*

Ekornes Skandinavia AS **(1)**
Industrivegen 1
6222 Ikornnes, Norway
Tel.: (47) 70 25 52 00
Fax: (47) 70 25 53 00
E-Mail: office@ekornes.no
Household Furniture Mfr
S.I.C.: 2512
N.A.I.C.S.: 337121

J.E. Ekornes AS **(1)**
Industrivegen 1
Ikornnes, 6222, Norway
Tel.: (47) 70255200
Fax: (47) 70255300
E-Mail: office@Ekornes.no
Web Site: www.ekornes.no
Emp.: 800
Household Furniture Mfr
S.I.C.: 2512
N.A.I.C.S.: 337121
Ola Arne Ramstad *(Mgr-Production)*

Stay AS **(1)**
Tveten vn 44
PO Box 193
0666 Oslo, Norway
Tel.: (47) 23194600
Fax: (47) 23194601
E-Mail: post@stay.no
Web Site: www.stay.no
Emp.: 7
Hotel Interior Design Services
S.I.C.: 7389
N.A.I.C.S.: 541410
Morten-Henrik Greidung *(Mng Dir)*

U.S. Subsidiary:

Ekornes Inc. **(1)**
615 Pierce St
Somerset, NJ 08873 (100%)
Tel.: (732) 302-0097
Fax: (732) 868-5412
Web Site: www.ekornes.com
Emp.: 44
Nonupholstered Wood Household Furniture Mfr
S.I.C.: 2511
N.A.I.C.S.: 337122
Peter Bjerregaard *(Pres)*

Non-U.S. Subsidiaries:

Ekornes Asia Pte Ltd **(1)**
10 Eunos Road 8
Singapore, Singapore (100%)
Tel.: (65) 68424000
Fax: (65) 68424300
E-Mail: info@ekornes.com
Web Site: www.ekornes.com
Emp.: 1,500
All Other Business Support Services
S.I.C.: 7389
N.A.I.C.S.: 561499
Mark Kelsey *(Mng Dir)*

Ekornes Iberica SL **(1)**
Calle Roger De Lluria
Barcelona, Spain (100%)
Tel.: (34) 559802510
Other Miscellaneous Durable Goods Merchant Whslr
S.I.C.: 5099

Ekornes ASA—(Continued)

N.A.I.C.S.: 423990
Mikael Gaultier *(Mng Dir)*

Ekornes KK (1)
Daiki Bldg 3rd Floor
3-11-1 Hatchobori, 104-003 Tokyo, Japan (100%)
Tel.: (81) 362223511
Fax: (81) 362223520
Web Site: www.ekornes.jp
Theater Companies & Dinner Theaters
S.I.C.: 7922
N.A.I.C.S.: 711110
Hajime Osawa *(Mng Dir)*

Ekornes Latin America Ltda (1)
Rue General Almerio de Moura 780
Morumbi, 05690-080 Sao Paulo, Brazil
Tel.: (55) 11 3755 1075
E-Mail: contaco@ekornes.com
Emp.: 5
Office Furniture Mfr
S.I.C.: 2522
N.A.I.C.S.: 337214

Ekornes Ltd (1)
Kings Court No 2-16 Goodge St
W1T2QA London, United Kingdom (100%)
Tel.: (44) 2074620440
Fax: (44) 2074361049
E-Mail: office@ekornes.co.uk
Web Site: www.ekornes.co.uk
Emp.: 17
Household Furniture (except Wood and Metal) Mfr
S.I.C.: 2519
N.A.I.C.S.: 337125

Ekornes Moebelvertriebs GmbH (1)
Am Stadtrand 56
Hamburg, Germany (100%)
Tel.: (49) 406969800
Fax: (49) 406931205
E-Mail: office@ekornes.de
Web Site: www.ekornes.de
Emp.: 30
Institutional Furniture Mfr
S.I.C.: 2599
N.A.I.C.S.: 337127

Ekornes S.A.R.L. (1)
Centre dAffaires Activa
Allees Condorcet, 64011 Pau, France (100%)
Tel.: (33) 559842510
Fax: (33) 559801878
E-Mail: office@ekornes.fr
Web Site: www.ekornes.fr
Emp.: 40
Other Miscellaneous Durable Goods Whslr
S.I.C.: 5099
N.A.I.C.S.: 423990
Lafond Berand *(Mng Dir)*

Ekornes Sp. z.o.o. (1)
AL Jana Pawla II 80
00-175 Warsaw, Poland (100%)
Tel.: (48) 224354756
Other Miscellaneous Nondurable Goods Whslr
S.I.C.: 5199
N.A.I.C.S.: 424990

J.E. Ekornes Aps (1)
Svendborgvej 83
5000 Odense, Denmark
Tel.: (45) 40754272
Fax: (45) 55779834
E-Mail: office@ekornes.dk
Web Site: www.ekornes.dk
Emp.: 4
Other Knit Fabric & Lace Mills
S.I.C.: 2259
N.A.I.C.S.: 313240
Peter Hjelmholm *(Mng Dir)*

Oy Ekornes AB (1)
Asemantie 10 PL 109
03100 Nummela, Finland (100%)
Tel.: (358) 92242800
Fax: (358) 92248484
Web Site: www.ekornes.no
Sales Financing
S.I.C.: 6153
N.A.I.C.S.: 522220
Kaj Juutilainen *(Mng Dir)*

EKOVEST BERHAD

3rd Floor Wisma Ekovest No 118
Jalan Gombak
53000 Kuala Lumpur, Malaysia
Tel.: (60) 340215948
Fax: (60) 340215943
Web Site: www.ekovest.com.my
EKOVEST—(KLS)
Rev.: $46,225,571
Assets: $664,171,791
Liabilities: $362,001,054
Net Worth: $302,170,738
Earnings: $16,407,477
Fiscal Year-end: 06/30/13

Business Description:
Civil Engineering Services
S.I.C.: 8711
N.A.I.C.S.: 541330

Personnel:
Kang Hoo Lim *(Co-Founder & Chm)*
Nang Seng Khoo *(Co-Founder)*
Keng Cheng Lim *(Mng Dir)*
Thiam Wah Lim *(Sec)*

Board of Directors:
Kang Hoo Lim
Yoon Sam Chow
Hui Ling Kang
Nang Seng Khoo
Wai Kuen Lee
Hoe Lim
Keng Cheng Lim
Ts-Fei Lim
Kai Fatt Wong

Subsidiaries:

Binawani Sdn Bhd (1)
No 33-35 2nd Floor Wisma Ekovest Jalan Desa Gombak 6 Taman Sri Setapak
Off Jalan Gombak, 53000 Kuala Lumpur, Wilayah Persekutuan, Malaysia
Tel.: (60) 340215948
Fax: (60) 340215798
Civil Engineering Services
S.I.C.: 8711
N.A.I.C.S.: 541330
Lim Keng Cheng *(Gen Mgr)*

Milan Resources Sdn. Bhd. (1)
Ground Floor Wisma Ecovest No 33-35
Jalan 6/50A Taman Sri Setapak
53000 Kuala Lumpur, Malaysia
Tel.: (60) 340246115
Fax: (60) 340246117
Emp.: 100
Civil Engineering Services
S.I.C.: 8711
N.A.I.C.S.: 541330

EKS FRANCE

12 Rue De Baldenheim
Wittisheim, 67820 Strasbourg, France
Tel.: (33) 388858400
Fax: (33) 388858333
E-Mail: info@eks-france.fr
Web Site: www.eks-france.fr
Emp.: 193

Business Description:
Controlling Device Mfr
S.I.C.: 3829
N.A.I.C.S.: 334519

Personnel:
Susan Lau *(Gen Mgr)*

EKSONS CORPORATION BERHAD

TB 4327 Block 31 2nd Fl Fajar
Complex Jalan Haji Karim
91000 Tawau, Sabah, Malaysia
Tel.: (60) 89757911
Fax: (60) 89757008
E-Mail: enquiry@eksons.com.my
Web Site: www.eksons.com.my
EKSONS—(KLS)
Rev.: $111,067,151
Assets: $172,810,964
Liabilities: $30,230,275
Net Worth: $142,580,689
Earnings: $7,697,195
Fiscal Year-end: 03/31/13

Business Description:
Plywood Mfr
S.I.C.: 2436
N.A.I.C.S.: 321212

Personnel:
Hua Sin Tay *(Mng Dir)*
Emily Swee Ming Yeo *(Sec)*

Board of Directors:
Abdul Aziz Hussain
Philip Hon Keong Chan
Mei Ling Lai
Uh Hing Sui
Seng Fatt Tang
Hua Sin Tay

Subsidiaries:

Rajang Plywood (Sabah) Sdn. Bhd. (1)
TB4327 2nd Floor Fajar Complex Jalan Haji Karim
PO Box 62105
91031 Tawau, Sabah, Malaysia
Tel.: (60) 89757913
Fax: (60) 89761022
E-Mail: rpsabah@streamyx.com
Plywood & Veneer Mfr
S.I.C.: 2435
N.A.I.C.S.: 321211

Rajang Plywood Sawmill Sdn. Bhd. (1)
No 69 2nd Floor Jalan Tuanku Osman
96000 Sibu, Sarawak, Malaysia
Tel.: (60) 84320909
Fax: (60) 84331244
Plywood Mfr
S.I.C.: 2435
N.A.I.C.S.: 321211

EKSPORTFINANS ASA

Dronning Mauds Gate 15
119 Oslo, Norway
Tel.: (47) 22012201
Fax: (47) 22012202
E-Mail: mail@eksportfinans.no
Web Site: www.eksportfinans.no
Year Founded: 1962
Rev.: $854,338,318
Assets: $28,488,997,186
Liabilities: $25,423,351,825
Net Worth: $3,065,645,361
Earnings: ($3,213,637,988)
Emp.: 98
Fiscal Year-end: 12/31/12

Business Description:
Financial Services for Export Industries
S.I.C.: 6159
N.A.I.C.S.: 522220

Personnel:
Geir Bergvoll *(Chm)*
Sigurd Carlsen *(Deputy Chm)*
Gisele Marchand *(Pres & CEO)*
Geir Ove Olsen *(Exec VP & CFO)*
Jens Olav Feiring *(Gen Counsel & Exec VP)*
Christian Grom *(Exec VP-Risk Mgmt)*
Martine Mills Hagen *(Exec VP-Funding & Lending)*

Board of Directors:
Geir Bergvoll
Live Haukvik Aker
Tone Lunde Bakker
Christian Berg
Marianne Heien Blystad
Sigurd Carlsen
Rune Helgeland
Bodil P. Hollingsaeter

EKTER S.A.

15 Nikis St
10557 Athens, Greece
Tel.: (30) 2103259700
Fax: (30) 2103259710
E-Mail: ekter@ekter.gr
Web Site: www.ekter.gr
Year Founded: 1959
EKTER—(ATH)
Sales Range: $1-4.9 Billion
Emp.: 26

Business Description:
Civil Engineering Contract Services
S.I.C.: 1629
N.A.I.C.S.: 237990

Personnel:
Athanasios Sipsas *(Chm)*
Ioannis Kavetsos *(CEO)*

Board of Directors:
Athanasios Sipsas
Ioannis Alexandris
Androniki Ioannidou
Annoula Kaminioti
Ioannis Kavetsos
Konstantinos Stoumpos

Subsidiary:

IFIKLIS S.A. (1)
21 Karneadou
10675 Athens, Greece
Tel.: (30) 2107294288
Fax: (30) 2107292597
Highway Construction Management Services
S.I.C.: 1611
N.A.I.C.S.: 237310

EKTTITAB HOLDING COMPANY S.A.K.C.

Mirgab-Al-Sour Street Jasem Al-Asfour Tower
PO Box 2799
Safat, 13028 Kuwait, Kuwait
Tel.: (965) 2960 777
Fax: (965) 2476 857
E-Mail: info@ekttetab.com
Web Site: www.ektettab.com
EKTTITAB—(KUW)
Rev.: $6,155,113
Assets: $109,285,411
Liabilities: $26,600,951
Net Worth: $82,684,460
Earnings: $3,619,933
Fiscal Year-end: 12/31/12

Business Description:
Investment Services; Owned 26.8% by Al-Madina For Finance & Investment Co. S.A.K.C.
S.I.C.: 6211
N.A.I.C.S.: 523999

Personnel:
Emad Hussen Nameh *(Chm)*
Abdulmohsen Shahrayan Hassan Ali *(Vice Chm)*

Board of Directors:
Emad Hussen Nameh
Ahmed Assel Taqi Aldeen
Abdulmohsen Shahrayan Hassan Ali
Omar Masowd
Abdulraoof Tawffiq

Baker Tilly International
PO Box 1486
Safat, Kuwait, Kuwait

EKWIENOX LIMITED

160 Brompton Road
Knightsbridge, London, SW3 1HW, United Kingdom
Tel.: (44) 20 7594 0660
Fax: (44) 20 7594 0666
E-Mail: info@aspone.co.uk
Web Site: www.ekwienox.com

Business Description:
Holding Company
S.I.C.: 6719
N.A.I.C.S.: 551112

Personnel:
Arthur Hughes *(CEO)*
Geoffrey Ronald Mayhill *(Gen Counsel)*
Romina Vucic *(Sec)*

Holding:

Baydonhill Plc (1)
1st Floor 21 New Street
London, EC2M 4TP, United Kingdom (51%)
Tel.: (44) 2075940584
Fax: (44) 8703305950
E-Mail: enquiries@baydonhill.com
Web Site: www.baydonhillfx.com
Sales Range: $1-4.9 Billion
Emp.: 59
Financial Services
S.I.C.: 6726
N.A.I.C.S.: 525990
Eric Peacock *(Chm)*
Wayne Mitchell *(CEO)*

EL AL AIRLINES LTD.

Ben Gurion International Airport
PO Box 41
Lod, 70100, Israel
Tel.: (972) 39716111
Telex: 381007
Fax: (972) 39717334
E-Mail: corporate@elal.co.il
Web Site: www.elal.co.il
Year Founded: 1948
ELAL—(TAE)
Sales Range: $1-4.9 Billion
Emp.: 3,718

Business Description:
Air Transportation Services
S.I.C.: 4512
N.A.I.C.S.: 481111

Personnel:
Amikam Cohen *(Chm)*
Tamar Mozes Borovitz *(Vice Chm)*
Nisin Malki *(CFO)*

Board of Directors:
Amikam Cohen
Tamar Mozes Borovitz
Pinchas Ginsburg
Shlomo Hanael
Eran Ilan
Shopia Kimerling
Yehuda Levy
Amnon Lipkin-Shahak
Nadav Palti
Yair Rabinowitch
Amiaz Sagis
Joshua Shemer

U.S. Subsidiaries:

Borenstein Caterers, Inc. (1)
179-29 150th Rd
Jamaica, NY 11434 (100%)
Tel.: (718) 656-3600
Fax: (718) 656-7632
E-Mail: customerservice@bcelal.com
Web Site: www.bcelal.com
Emp.: 110
Airlines Prepared Kosher Meals Producer & Supplier
S.I.C.: 5812
N.A.I.C.S.: 722320

El Al Israel Airlines, Ltd. (1)
15 E 26th St 6th Fl
New York, NY 10010 (100%)
Tel.: (212) 852-0600
Fax: (212) 852-0641
Toll Free: (800) 223-6700
Web Site: www.elal.com
Emp.: 160
International Airline Services
S.I.C.: 4512
N.A.I.C.S.: 481111
Amikam Cohen *(Chm)*
David Maimon *(Pres & CEO)*

Non-U.S. Subsidiary:

Superstar Holidays Ltd (1)
UK House 180 Oxford Street
London, W1D 1EL, United Kingdom (100%)
Tel.: (44) 20 7957 4300
Web Site: www.superstar.co.uk
Emp.: 10
Travel Agency
S.I.C.: 4724
N.A.I.C.S.: 561510

EL CONDOR MINERALS INC.

Suite 1200 570 Granville Street
Vancouver, BC, V6C 3P1, Canada
Tel.: (604) 689-8336
Toll Free: (888) 691-0529
E-Mail: info@elcondorminerals.com
Web Site: www.elcondorminerals.com
LCO—(TSXV)
Int. Income: $5,693
Assets: $5,801,765
Liabilities: $2,771,261
Net Worth: $3,030,504
Earnings: ($943,702)
Fiscal Year-end: 12/31/12

Business Description:
Metal Exploration Services
S.I.C.: 1081
N.A.I.C.S.: 213114

Personnel:
Leigh W. Freeman *(Pres & CEO)*
D. Barry Lee *(CFO)*
Jose Pinedo *(Gen Counsel & VP-Admin)*

Board of Directors:
Michael S. Bader
Robert S. Chenery
Leigh W. Freeman
R. Patrick Highsmith
D. Barry Lee

EL CORPORATION LIMITED

99 Mount Street
Sydney, NSW, 2060, Australia
Tel.: (61) 2 9922 4278
Fax: (61) 2 9922 7862
Web Site: www.elcorporation.com
EIM—(ASX)
Rev.: $13
Assets: $790,572
Liabilities: $601,282
Net Worth: $189,290
Earnings: ($440,967)
Fiscal Year-end: 12/31/12

Business Description:
Metal Exploration Services
S.I.C.: 1081
N.A.I.C.S.: 213114

Personnel:
Sim Pin Quek *(Chm)*
Poh Seng Isaac Ng *(CEO)*
Tom Bloomfield *(Sec)*

Board of Directors:
Sim Pin Quek
Hee Kok Chng
Mark Roy Howard-Browne
Poh Seng Isaac Ng
Rajen Rai

EL CORTE INGLES, S.A.

Calle Hermosilla 112 Planta 3
E 28009 Madrid, Spain
Tel.: (34) 914028112
Fax: (34) 914025821
Web Site: www.elcorteingles.es
Year Founded: 1940
Sales Range: $10-24.9 Million
Emp.: 72,000

Business Description:
Department Store, Supermarket & Travel Agency Operator
S.I.C.: 5311
N.A.I.C.S.: 452111

Personnel:
Isidoro Alvarrez *(Chm)*

Subsidiaries:

Convenience Shops, S.A. (1)
Hermosilla 112
Madrid, Spain
Tel.: (34) 901122122
E-Mail: servicio_clientes@elcorteingles.es
Web Site: www.elcorteinglescorporativo.es/elcorteinglescorporativo/elcorteinglescorporativo/portal.do?IDM=5&NM=2
Extended Hour Department Stores
S.I.C.: 5311
N.A.I.C.S.: 452111

Correduria de Seguros, S.A. (1)
Hermosilla, 112
Madrid, 28009, Spain
Tel.: (34) 901 116 146
Web Site: www.elcorteingles.es/centrodeseguros/centroseguros4/index.html
Insurance Broker
S.I.C.: 6411
N.A.I.C.S.: 524298

El Corte Ingles Life, Pensions and Insurance, S.A. (1)
Hermosilla, 112
28009 Madrid, Spain
Tel.: (34) 901 116 821
E-Mail: atencionalcliente@seguroseci.es
Life Insurance & Pension Plans
S.I.C.: 6311
N.A.I.C.S.: 524113

El Corte Ingles, S.A. Computers (1)
Hermosilla 112
28009 Madrid, Spain
Tel.: (34) 901122122
E-Mail: mkt@lecl.es
Web Site: www.elcorteingles.es/comun/eci/informacion/EN/devolver.asp
Computer Solutions, Products & Services
S.I.C.: 7379
N.A.I.C.S.: 541519

El Corte Ingles, S.A. Travel (1)
Avda. Cantabria, 51
28042 Madrid, Spain
Tel.: (34) 901122122
E-Mail: viajeseci@elcorteingles.es
Web Site: www.nato.int/docu/pr/2003/p03-023e.htm
Travel Agency
S.I.C.: 4724
N.A.I.C.S.: 561510

Financiera El Corte Ingles E.F.C., S.A. (1)
Hermosilla 112
Madrid, Spain
Tel.: (34) 901122122
Fax: (34) 913093225
E-Mail: financiera@elcorteingles.es
Web Site: www.elcorteingles.es/informacion/financiera/financiera.htm
Financial Management
S.I.C.: 8742
N.A.I.C.S.: 541611

Gespevesa, S.A. (1)
Paseo de la Castellana, 257
Madrid, Spain
Tel.: (34) 901122122
Gasoline Stations with Convenience Stores
S.I.C.: 5541
N.A.I.C.S.: 447110

Hipercor, S.A. (1)
Hermosilla 112
28009 Madrid, Spain
Tel.: (34) 901122122
E-Mail: servicio_clientes@hipercor.es
Web Site: www.hipercor.es
Sells Textiles, Household Goods, Groceries & Other Perishable Goods
S.I.C.: 5411
N.A.I.C.S.: 445110

Investronica, S.A. (1)
Ronda de Valdecarrizo, 7
28760 Madrid, Spain
Tel.: (34) 902354435
Computer Products & Service Whslr
S.I.C.: 5045
N.A.I.C.S.: 423430

Sfera Joven, S.A. (1)
Hermosilla, 112
Madrid, Spain
Tel.: (34) 901 122 122
E-Mail: servicio_clientes@elcorteingles.es
Web Site: www.elcorteingles.es/informacion/financiera/financiera.htm
Women's, Men's & Childrens' Apparel Stores
S.I.C.: 5621
N.A.I.C.S.: 448120

Supercor, S.A. (1)
Hermosilla 112
Madrid, 28009, Spain
Tel.: (34) 901122
E-Mail: servicio_clientes@elcorteingles.es
Web Site: www.elcorteinglescorporativo.es
Supermarket Management
S.I.C.: 5411
N.A.I.C.S.: 445110

Telecor, S.A. (1)
Hermosilla, 112
28009 Madrid, Spain
Tel.: (34) 902141500
E-Mail: atencionalcliente@telecor.es
Web Site: www.telecor.es
Telecommunications Services Marketing
S.I.C.: 4899
N.A.I.C.S.: 517919

EL. D. MOUZAKIS S.A.

Kifisou 41
122 42 Aegaleo, Attiki, Greece
Tel.: (30) 210 3490500
Fax: (30) 210 3490598
E-Mail: exports@mouzakis.gr
Web Site: www.mouzakis.gr
Year Founded: 1968
MOYZK—(ATH)
Emp.: 249

Business Description:
Cotton Yarn Mfr
S.I.C.: 2299
N.A.I.C.S.: 313110

Personnel:
Christos K. Tzanneteas *(Chm)*
Nikolaos T. Sarafis *(Vice Chm & Grp Production Officer)*
Stefanos K. Kouris *(Mng Dir & Mgr-Fin)*

Board of Directors:
Christos K. Tzanneteas
Vasilios H. Kolovos
Stefanos K. Kouris
Spyridon P. Ladas
Eleftheria E. Mouzaki
Nikitas Niarchos
Dionyssios T. Sarafis
Eleftherios N. Sarafis
Nikolaos T. Sarafis

Subsidiary:

Serres Ginning S.A. (1)
Gazoros
62050 Serres, Greece
Tel.: (30) 240 42430 3
Fax: (30) 240 42435
E-Mail: serregin@ser.forthnet.gr
Yarn & Thread Mfr
S.I.C.: 2299
N.A.I.C.S.: 313110

Non-U.S. Subsidiary:

ELVIP s.r.o. (1)
Tovarni 302
26712 Lodenice u Berouna, Czech Republic
Tel.: (420) 311 671799
Fax: (420) 311 671805
E-Mail: elvip@pha.pvtnet.cz
Yarn & Thread Mfr
S.I.C.: 2299
N.A.I.C.S.: 313110

EL FORGE LTD

338 Ambujammal St
Alwarpet
600018 Chennai, Tamil Nadu, India
Tel.: (91) 4442207800
Fax: (91) 4442014708
Web Site: www.elforge.com
ELFORGE—(BOM NSE)
Sales Range: $10-24.9 Million

Business Description:
Automotive Parts Mfr
S.I.C.: 5531
N.A.I.C.S.: 441310

Personnel:
V. Srikanth *(Chm)*

Board of Directors:
V. Srikanth

El Forge Ltd—(Continued)

V. Ramachandran
P. L. Reddy

Divisions:

El Forge Ltd - Appur Division (1)
1A Sriperumbudur High Rd Appur village
Singaperumal Kovil
Kancheepuram, Chennai, Tamil Nadu, 603 204, India
Tel.: (91) 4447112500
Fax: (91) 4447112523
E-Mail: elforge2@elforge.com
Web Site: www.elforge.com
Emp.: 400
Machine Parts Mfr
S.I.C.: 3714
N.A.I.C.S.: 336330
Meena Goel *(VP-Mktg)*

El Forge Ltd - Hosur Division (1)
Denkanikottai Rd
PO Box 11
Hosur, Tamil Nadu, 635 109, India
Tel.: (91) 4344222486
Fax: (91) 4344222841
E-Mail: elforgehosur@elforge.com
Web Site: www.elforge.com
Emp.: 300
Machine Parts Mfr
S.I.C.: 3714
N.A.I.C.S.: 336330

EL NINO VENTURES INC.

650 - 555 West 12th Avenue City Square West Tower
Vancouver, BC, V5Z 3X7, Canada
Tel.: (604) 685-1870
Fax: (604) 685-8045
Toll Free: (800) 667-1870
E-Mail: info@elninoventures.com
Web Site: www.elninoventures.com
Year Founded: 1989
ELN—(DEU OTC TSXV)
Rev.: $152,828
Assets: $8,846,605
Liabilities: $642,775
Net Worth: $8,203,830
Earnings: ($1,696,598)
Fiscal Year-end: 01/31/13

Business Description:
Copper Mining Exploration & Development Services
S.I.C.: 1021
N.A.I.C.S.: 212234

Personnel:
Harry Barr *(Chm & CEO)*
Robert Guanzon *(CFO)*
John G. Oness *(COO)*
Coreena Hansen *(Sec)*
William Stone *(Exec VP-Exploration)*

Board of Directors:
Harry Barr
Linda Holmes
Gary Moore
Michael Francis Neumann
John G. Oness

Legal Counsel:
K MacInnes Law Group
Suite 1100 -736 Granville Street
Vancouver, BC, Canada

Transfer Agent:
Computershare Trust Company of Canada
510 Burrard St 3rd Fl
Vancouver, BC, V6C 3B9, Canada

EL PUERTO DE LIVERPOOL S.A.B. DE C.V.

Avenida Mariano Escobedo No 425
Col Polanco Reforma, 11570 Mexico, DF, Mexico
Tel.: (52) 5553286400
Fax: (52) 55 5203 8855
E-Mail: liverpool@liverpool.com.mx
Web Site: www.liverpool.com.mx
Year Founded: 1847
LIVEPOL—(MEX)
Sales Range: $1-4.9 Billion
Emp.: 25,887

Business Description:
Retail & Department Stores; Shopping Outlets & Real Estate Seller & Leaser
S.I.C.: 5311
N.A.I.C.S.: 452112

Personnel:
Max David *(Chm)*
S. Madeleine Bremond *(Vice Chm)*
Miguel Guichard *(Vice Chm)*
Jose Calderon Munoz de Cote *(CEO)*
Ignacio Pesquiera *(Sec)*

Board of Directors:
Max David
S. Enrique Bremond
S. Madeleine Bremond
Juan David
Jose Calderon Munoz de Cote
Juan Miguel Gandoulf
Ricardo Guajardo
Graciano Guichard
Miguel Guichard
Esteban Malpica
G. Maximino Michel
Ignacio Pesquiera
Armando Garza Sada
Guillermo Siman
Luis Tames
Pedro Velasco

EL RAN FURNITURE

2751 Transcanada Highway
Pointe-Claire, QC, H9R 1B4, Canada
Tel.: (514) 630-5656
Fax: (514) 630-9150
Toll Free: (800) 361-6546
E-Mail: info@elran.com
Web Site: www.elran.com
Year Founded: 1967
Rev.: $65,905,893
Emp.: 625

Business Description:
Furniture Mfr & Distr
S.I.C.: 2519
N.A.I.C.S.: 337125

Personnel:
Irving Lubin *(Founder)*
Sheldon Lubin *(Pres)*
Eric Abecassis *(Exec VP)*

EL SEWEDY ELECTRIC COMPANY

Plot 27 1st District 5th Settlement
New Cairo
Cairo, Egypt
Tel.: (20) 2 27599700
Fax: (20) 2 27599731
E-Mail: info@elsewedy.com
Web Site: www.elsewedyelectric.com
Year Founded: 1984
SWDY—(EGX)
Rev.: $2,155,658,104
Assets: $2,015,788,742
Liabilities: $1,236,577,746
Net Worth: $779,210,996
Earnings: $21,677,291
Emp.: 10,000
Fiscal Year-end: 12/31/12

Business Description:
Integrated Cables & Electrical Products Mfr
Export
S.I.C.: 1629
N.A.I.C.S.: 335929

Personnel:
Ahmed Ahmed Sadek El Sewedy *(Mng Dir)*
Amr Mohamed Labib *(CFO)*

Board of Directors:
Sadek Ahmed El Sewedy
Hany Gamal El Din Mohamed
Mohamed Assem El Gohary
Hesham El Khezindar
Ahmed Ahmed Sadek El Sewedy
Mohamed Ahmed Sadek El Sewedy
Amr Mohamed Labib

Subsidiaries:

Arab Cables Company (1)
14 Baghdad Street
El-Korba Heliopolis, Cairo, Egypt (99.99%)
Tel.: (20) 2 22909430
Fax: (20) 22917078
E-Mail: acc@elsewedy.com
Web Site: www.elsewedycables.com
Mfr of Power Cables, Control Cables & Overhead Transmission Lines
S.I.C.: 3357
N.A.I.C.S.: 335921
Mahmoud Shawky *(Mgr-Sls)*

Egytec Cables Company (1)
Plot No 27 1st District 5th Settlement
New Cairo, Cairo, Egypt (99.98%)
Tel.: (20) 2 27599700
Fax: (20) 2 25799739
E-Mail: egy@elsewedy.com
Web Site: www.elsewedyelectric.com
Cable Networks
S.I.C.: 4841
N.A.I.C.S.: 515210
Ashraf Ahmed *(Mgr-Sls)*

United Metals Company (1)
Plot no 27 1st District 5th Settlement New Cairo
Cairo, Egypt (99.8%)
Tel.: (20) 27599700
Fax: (20) 2759946
E-Mail: umc@elsewedy.com
Web Site: www.elsewedyelectric.com
Current-Carrying Wiring Device Mfr
S.I.C.: 3643
N.A.I.C.S.: 335931
Amro Labib *(Gen Mgr)*

Non-U.S. Subsidiaries:

Jeddah Cable Company (1)
Indus City Phase 3
PO Box 31248
Jeddah, 21497, Saudi Arabia (100%)
Tel.: (966) 26360770
Fax: (966) 26364695
E-Mail: info@jeddah-cable.com
Web Site: www.jeddah-cable.com
Emp.: 800
Mfr. of Cables
S.I.C.: 3351
N.A.I.C.S.: 331420
Halel El Sewedy *(Chm)*

Sudanese Egyptian Electric Industries Company Ltd (1)
El Kwaitia Buildings - 4th tower 7th stage
Khartoum, Sudan (69.97%)
Tel.: (249) 183764118
Fax: (249) 183764116
E-Mail: m.giad@yahoo.com
Emp.: 10
Copper Foundries
S.I.C.: 3369
N.A.I.C.S.: 331529
Hassan Osman *(Gen Mgr)*

EL TIGRE SILVER CORP.

Suite 1000 355 Burrard Street The Marine Building
Vancouver, BC, V6C 2G8, Canada
Tel.: (604) 639-0044
Fax: (604) 608-6163
E-Mail: rgrace@eltigresilvercorp.com
Web Site: www.eltigresilvercorp.com
ELS—(DEU OTC TSXV)
Assets: $6,337,982
Liabilities: $147,853
Net Worth: $6,190,129
Earnings: ($2,710,686)
Fiscal Year-end: 12/31/12

Business Description:
Silver Mining Services
S.I.C.: 1044
N.A.I.C.S.: 212222

Personnel:
Stuart R. Ross *(Pres & CEO)*
Grant T. Smith *(CFO)*

Board of Directors:
Wade Anderson
Kenneth D. Booth
Stuart R. Ross
Jeffrey L. Wilson

Legal Counsel:
McCullough O'Connor Irwin LLP
Suite 2600 Oceanic Plaza 1066 West Hastings Street
Vancouver, BC, Canada

Transfer Agent:
Computershare Trust Company of Canada
510 Burrard St 2nd Fl
Vancouver, BC, Canada

Non-U.S. Subsidiary:

Pacemaker Silver Mining, S.A. de C.V. (1)
Avenida Doctor Aguilar 162 Prados del Centenario
Hermosillo, Sonora, 83250, Mexico
Tel.: (52) 662 2131554
Fax: (52) 6622131559
Silver Ore Mining Services
S.I.C.: 1044
N.A.I.C.S.: 212222

ELAF ISLAMIC BANK

Hai Al-Wehda Mahala 902 Street 99-Building 14 Alwieh
PO Box 3440
Baghdad, Iraq
Tel.: (964) 17184601
Fax: (964) 17183766
E-Mail: info@elaf-islamic-bank.com
Web Site: www.eib-iq.yolasite.com
Year Founded: 2001
BELF—(IRAQ)

Business Description:
Banking Services
S.I.C.: 6029
N.A.I.C.S.: 522110

Personnel:
A. Alhussain Qasim *(Chm)*
Emad Qassim Salman *(Vice Chm)*

Board of Directors:
A. Alhussain Qasim
A. Alrazzaq Ali Fared
Aqeel Muften Khafeef
Hassan A. Ameer Mahdi
Ahmed A. Alhussain Qasim
Akram Matloob Rasheed
Emad Qassim Salman

ELAN CONSTRUCTION LIMITED

100 3639 27 St NE
Calgary, AB, T1Y 5E4, Canada
Tel.: (403) 291-1165
Fax: (403) 291-5396
E-Mail: elan@elanconstruction.com
Web Site: www.elanconstruction.com
Year Founded: 1978
Rev.: $69,643,671
Emp.: 70

Business Description:
Building Construction Services
S.I.C.: 1542
N.A.I.C.S.: 236220

Personnel:
Gregg W. Aicken *(Pres)*
David C. Poulsen *(CEO)*

ELAN CORPORATION, PLC

(Merged with Perrigo Company to form Perrigo Company plc)

ELAND OIL & GAS LTD

17 Abercrombie Court Prospect Road
Westhill, Aberdeen, AB32 6FE, United Kingdom
Tel.: (44) 1224 737 300
Web Site: www.elandoilandgas.com
ELA—(AIM)

Business Description:
Oil & Gas Exploration
S.I.C.: 1311
N.A.I.C.S.: 211111
Personnel:
Leslie Blair *(CEO)*
George Maxwell *(CFO)*
Board of Directors:
Leslie Blair
George Maxwell
Pieter van der Groen
Harry Wilson

ELANGO INDUSTRIES LIMITED

5 Ranganathan Gardens Anna Nagar
Chennai, 600 040, India
Tel.: (91) 44 4217 2116
Fax: (91) 44 4217 2118
E-Mail: info@elangoindustries.com
Web Site: www.elangoindustries.com
Year Founded: 1989
513452—(BOM)
Rev.: $28,162
Assets: $1,038,675
Liabilities: $97,876
Net Worth: $940,800
Earnings: ($71,002)
Fiscal Year-end: 03/31/13
Business Description:
Electric Power Generation Services
S.I.C.: 4939
N.A.I.C.S.: 221118
Personnel:
S. Elangovan *(Chm & Mng Dir)*
N. Ashokan *(Compliance Officer & Sec)*
Board of Directors:
S. Elangovan
V. Narayanan
S. A. Premkumar
R. Ramesh
K. S. Shanmugam
V. R. Subramanian
Transfer Agent:
Cameo Corporate Services Limited
No 1 Club House Road
Chennai, India

ELARG AGRICULTURAL LAND OPPORTUNITY FUND REIT

16 Nikola Vaptsarov Blvd
1164 Sofia, Bulgaria
Tel.: (359) 2 868 1 868
E-Mail: office@elarg.bg
Web Site: www.elarg.bg
4EC—(DEU)
Sales Range: $1-9.9 Million
Business Description:
Agricultural Investment Services
S.I.C.: 6211
N.A.I.C.S.: 523999
Personnel:
Dimitar Valkov *(Chm)*
Board of Directors:
Dimitar Valkov
Ivo Gadev
Dobromir Hristov
Andrey Kruglyikhin
Stefan Stefanov

ELARS SA

Strada Industriei Nr 4 Ramnicu Sarat
5250 Buzau, Romania
Tel.: (40) 238 564322
Fax: (40) 238 565171
E-Mail: office@elars.ro
Web Site: www.elars.ro
Year Founded: 1990
ELAR—(BUC)
Sales Range: Less than $1 Million
Emp.: 56
Business Description:
Fastener Mfr
S.I.C.: 3965
N.A.I.C.S.: 339993
Personnel:
Felicia Enescu Livia *(Gen Mgr)*

ELASTRON S.A.

Ag Ioannis Ave Ag Ioannis
Aspropyrgos, 19300, Greece
Tel.: (30) 2105515000
Fax: (30) 2105515015
E-Mail: elastron@elastron.gr
Web Site: www.elastron.gr
ELSTR—(ATH)
Sls.: $93,765,627
Assets: $183,358,975
Liabilities: $85,108,287
Net Worth: $98,250,689
Earnings: ($5,360,570)
Emp.: 169
Fiscal Year-end: 12/31/12
Business Description:
Steel & Steel Products Trading Services
S.I.C.: 5051
N.A.I.C.S.: 423510
Personnel:
Panagiotis Simos *(Chm)*
Elvira Kalpini *(Vice Chm)*
Athanasios Kalpinis *(Mng Dir)*
Stilianos Koutsothanasis *(Deputy Mng Dir)*
Board of Directors:
Panagiotis Simos
Anastasios Binioris
Elvira Kalpini
Andreas Kalpinis
Athanasios Kalpinis
Gianniris Konstantinos
Stilianos Koutsothanasis
Vasilios Malalitzoglou
Demetrios Paparisteidis
Christos Sakellariou

ELATERAL LTD.

Elateral House Crosby Way
Farnham, GU9 7XX, United Kingdom
Tel.: (44) 1252740740
Fax: (44) 1252740741
E-Mail: info@elateral.com
Web Site: www.elateral.com
Sales Range: $10-24.9 Million
Emp.: 50
Business Description:
Marketing Software Development Services
S.I.C.: 7372
N.A.I.C.S.: 511210
Personnel:
Paul Goater *(CEO)*
Angus de Watteville *(CFO & COO)*
Peter Blackburn *(CTO)*
Board of Directors:
Bryan Taylor
Peter Blackburn
Angus de Watteville
John Elkins
Paul Goater
Perry Kamel
Jamie Szpiro
Robert Whitby-Smith

U.S. Subsidiary:

Elateral, Inc. (1)
1 Westbrook Corporate Ctr Ste 300
Westchester, IL 60154
Tel.: (708) 236-1716
Fax: (630) 563-9720
Toll Free: (877) 914-0789
E-Mail: infousa@elateral.com
Emp.: 5
Software Publisher
S.I.C.: 7372
N.A.I.C.S.: 511210
Perry Kamel *(Pres)*

ELAUT INTERNATIONAL N.V.

Passtraat 223
9100 Saint-Niklaas, Belgium
Tel.: (32) 37809480
Fax: (32) 37780561
E-Mail: info@elaut.be
Web Site: www.elaut.com
Year Founded: 1959
Emp.: 40
Business Description:
Holding Company; Coin-Operated Amusement & Gaming Equipment Mfr & Concessionaire
S.I.C.: 6719
N.A.I.C.S.: 551112
Personnel:
Patrick Magendans *(Mgr-Intl Sls)*

Subsidiary:

Elaut N.V. (1)
Passtraat 223
9100 Saint-Niklaas, Belgium BE
Tel.: (32) 37809480 (100%)
Fax: (32) 37780561
E-Mail: info@elaut.be
Web Site: www.elaut.com
Emp.: 45
Coin-Operated Amusement & Gaming Equipment Mfr & Concessionaire
S.I.C.: 3999
N.A.I.C.S.: 339999
Eric Verstraeten *(Mgr-Intl Sls)*

U.S. Subsidiary:

Elaut USA, Inc. (1)
1000 Towbin Ave
Lakewood, NJ 08701 NJ
Tel.: (732) 364-9900
Fax: (732) 364-7949
Web Site: www.elautusa.com
Amusement Park Coin-Operated Equipment Concessionaire
S.I.C.: 5099
N.A.I.C.S.: 423990
Michael Carle *(CFO)*
Steve Paris *(COO)*

ELB GROUP LIMITED

345 Rivonia Road
Rivonia, South Africa
Mailing Address:
PO Box 565
Boksburg, 1460, South Africa
Tel.: (27) 113060700
Fax: (27) 119187208
E-Mail: sales@elb.co.za
Web Site: www.elb.co.za
ELR—(JSE)
Sls.: $221,679,485
Assets: $181,513,617
Liabilities: $101,691,122
Net Worth: $79,822,496
Earnings: $13,175,350
Emp.: 412
Fiscal Year-end: 06/30/13
Business Description:
Engineered Products Mfr & Related Services In Mining & Process Industries
S.I.C.: 8711
N.A.I.C.S.: 541330
Personnel:
Anthony Garth Fletcher *(Chm)*
Stephen John Meijers *(CEO)*
Peter John Blunden *(CEO-Equipment)*
Board of Directors:
Anthony Garth Fletcher
Peter John Blunden
Theunis de Bruyn
Michael Craig Easter
John Paul Herselman
Stephen John Meijers
Mollo Victor Ramollo
Ian Alan Richard Thomson
Transfer Agent:
Computershare Investor Services (Pty) Limited
70 Marshall Street
PO Box 61051
2107 Marshalltown, South Africa

Subsidiaries:

ELB Capital Investments (Pty) Limited (1)
55-6th Rd Hyde Park
Sandton, Johannesburg, Gauteng, 2196, South Africa
Tel.: (27) 117721400
Fax: (27) 113256680
Web Site: www.masterguardfpsa.co.za
Emp.: 100
Investment Management Services
S.I.C.: 6211
N.A.I.C.S.: 523999

ELB Engineering Services (Pty) Limited (1)
55-6th Rd Hyde Park
Sandton, Johannesburg, Gauteng, 2196, South Africa
Tel.: (27) 117721400
Fax: (27) 113256680
E-Mail: sales@elb.co.za
Emp.: 110
Engineering Services
S.I.C.: 8711
N.A.I.C.S.: 541330
Stephen John Meijers *(CEO)*

ELB Equipment Holdings Limited (1)
4 Parin Rd
Ravensmead, Cape Town, 7493, South Africa
Tel.: (27) 113060700
Fax: (27) 119187208
E-Mail: grahamj@elb.co.za
Investment Holding Services
S.I.C.: 6719
N.A.I.C.S.: 551112
Graham Jones *(Sec)*

ELB Equipment Limited (1)
14 Atlas Rd
Anderbolt, Boksburg, Gauteng, 1459, South Africa
Tel.: (27) 113060700
Fax: (27) 119187208
E-Mail: elb@elbquip.co.za
Web Site: www.elbequipment.com
Emp.: 120
Construction & Mining Equipments Distr
S.I.C.: 5082
N.A.I.C.S.: 423810
Peter John Blunden *(CEO)*

Divisions:

ELB Equipment Limited - Construction Equipment Division (2)
14 Atlas Rd
Boksburg, Gauteng, 1508, South Africa
Tel.: (27) 113060700
Fax: (27) 119187285
Web Site: www.elbquip.co.za
Construction Equipment Distr
S.I.C.: 7353
N.A.I.C.S.: 532412

ELB Equipment Limited - Earthmoving Equipment Division (2)
14 Atlas Road
Boksburg, 1459, South Africa
Tel.: (27) 113060704
Fax: (27) 119187208
E-Mail: elb@elbquip.co.za
Web Site: www.elbequipment.com
Emp.: 200
Earth Moving Equipments Distr
S.I.C.: 7359
N.A.I.C.S.: 532412
Peter Blunden *(CEO)*
Graham Jones *(Sec)*

ELB Equipment Limited - Mining & Quarrying Equipment Division (2)
14 Atlas Rd
Boksburg, Gauteng, 1459, South Africa
Tel.: (27) 113060705
Fax: (27) 119187208
E-Mail: elb@elbquip.co.za
Web Site: www.elbequipment.com
Emp.: 250
Mining Equipments Distr
S.I.C.: 5082
N.A.I.C.S.: 423810
Peter Blunden *(Mng Dir)*

ELB Power Systems Limited (1)
PO Box 565
Boksburg, Gauteng, 1460, South Africa

ELB GROUP LIMITED—(Continued)

Tel.: (27) 132351200
Fax: (27) 117721400
Electrical Contracting Services
S.I.C.: 1731
N.A.I.C.S.: 238210

ELBAR INDUSTRIAL LIMITED

Syston Lane
Grantham, Lincs, NG32 2LY, United Kingdom
Tel.: (44) 01476581300
Fax: (44) 1476581310
E-Mail: d.edwards@autocraftuk.com
Sales Range: $50-74.9 Million
Emp.: 150

Business Description:
Automotive Parts Mfr
S.I.C.: 3714
N.A.I.C.S.: 336390

Personnel:
Steve Harris *(Mng Dir)*

ELBISCO HOLDING S.A.

21st km Marathonas Ave
19009 Pikermi, Greece
Tel.: (30) 2106039712
Fax: (30) 2106233050
E-Mail: ir@elbisco.gr
Web Site: www.elbisco.gr
Year Founded: 1987
Sales Range: $150-199.9 Million
Emp.: 1,240

Business Description:
Cereal Products Mfr
S.I.C.: 2041
N.A.I.C.S.: 311211

Personnel:
Kiriakos Filippou *(Chm)*
Helen Filippou-Coumantarou *(Vice Chm)*
Dimosthenis Ramandanis *(CEO)*
Aglaia Sklavi *(CFO)*

Board of Directors:
Kiriakos Filippou
Helen Filippou-Coumantarou
Eleftheria Koutsioumpa
Periklis Mazarakis
Charalampos Parmagos
Dimosthenis Ramandanis

Subsidiary:

ELBISCO INDUSTRIAL & COMMERCIAL S.A. (1)
21 Km Marathonos Pikermi Attikee
Athens, 19009, Greece
Tel.: (30) 2106039712
Fax: (30) 2106039083
Web Site: www.elbisco.com.gr
Baked Goods Distr
S.I.C.: 5461
N.A.I.C.S.: 445291

Non-U.S. Subsidiary:

Zito Luks A.D. (1)
Bld Makedonsko Kosovska Brigada no 44
1000 Skopje, Macedonia MK
Tel.: (389) 2 5270 000 (53.79%)
E-Mail: zitoluks@zitoluks.com.mk
Web Site: www.zitoluks.com.mk
ZILU—(MAC)
Sls.: $28,554,694
Assets: $34,082,882
Liabilities: $17,535,040
Net Worth: $16,547,842
Earnings: ($948,136)
Emp.: 383
Fiscal Year-end: 12/31/12
Bakery Products Mfr
S.I.C.: 2051
N.A.I.C.S.: 311812
Dimosthenis Ramandanis *(Chm-Mng Bd & Mng Dir)*
Dimitrios Plakoutsis *(Deputy Chm-Mng Bd & Deputy Gen Mgr)*
Nada Vujic *(Member-Mng Bd & Mgr Fin)*
Natasa Cerekovikj *(Member-Mng Bd-Comml & Technical Affairs)*
Emilija Dubardzieva *(Member-Mng Bd-HR)*
Daniela Nonkulovska *(Member-Mng Bd-Quality, R&D & Mill)*

ELBIT SYSTEMS LIMITED

Advanced Technology Center
PO Box 539
Haifa, 31053, Israel
Tel.: (972) 48316404
Fax: (972) 48550002
E-Mail: corporate@elbitsystems.com
Web Site: www.elbitsystems.com
Year Founded: 1966
ESLT—(NASDAQ TAE)
Rev.: $2,925,151,000
Assets: $3,933,168,000
Liabilities: $2,738,999,000
Net Worth: $1,194,169,000
Earnings: $191,419,000
Emp.: 11,674
Fiscal Year-end: 12/31/13

Business Description:
Upgrading Services for Existing Airborne, Ground & Naval Defense Platforms, Development, Manufacture, Integration & Marketing of High Value-added, High Performance Defense Electronics Systems & Subsystems; 40% owned by Federmann Enterprises, Ltd.
S.I.C.: 3492
N.A.I.C.S.: 332912

Personnel:
Michael Federmann *(Chm)*
Joseph Ackerman *(Pres & CEO)*
Joseph Gaspar *(CFO & Exec VP)*
Itzhak Dvir *(COO & Exec VP)*
David Block Temin *(Chief Legal Officer, Chief Compliance Officer & Exec VP)*
Jonathan Ariel *(Chief Legal Officer & Exec VP)*
Elad Aharonson *(Exec VP & Gen Mgr-UAS Div)*
Adi Dar *(Exec VP & Gen Mgr-Electro-Optics Elop Div)*
Yoram Shmuely *(Exec VP & Gen Mgr-Aerospace Div)*
Udi Vered *(Exec VP & Gen Mgr-Land & C4I Div)*
Zeev Gofer *(Exec VP-Strategic & Bus Dev-North America)*
Dalia Gonen *(Exec VP-HR)*
Ilan Pacholder *(Exec VP-Merger & Acq, Offset & Financing)*
Marco Rosenthal *(Exec VP-Corp Shared Svcs)*
Haim Rousso *(Exec VP-Engrg & Tech Excellence)*
Gideon Sheffer *(Exec VP-Strategic Plng & Bus Dev-Israel)*

Board of Directors:
Michael Federmann
Moshe Arad
Avraham Asheri
Rina Baum
David Federmann
Yehoshua Gleitman
Yigal Ne'eman
Dov Ninveh
Dalia Rabin

Transfer Agent:
American Stock Transfer & Trust Company
40 Wall St., 46th Fl.
New York, NY 10005
Tel.: (718) 921-8200

Subsidiaries:

Elbit Security Systems Ltd. (1)
Industrial Park Sderot
Sderot, 80100, Israel
Tel.: (972) 8 689 1691
Fax: (972) 8 689 1695
Security Device Mfr
S.I.C.: 3669
N.A.I.C.S.: 334290

Elbit Systems Cyclone Ltd. (1)
Bar Lev Industrial Park
PO B 114
Karmiel, 20100, Israel
Tel.: (972) 4 996 0700
Fax: (972) 4 996 2220
E-Mail:
Web Site: www.elbitsystems.com
Aircraft Component Mfr
S.I.C.: 3728
N.A.I.C.S.: 336413
Cohen Eitan *(Dir-Bus Dev & Mktg)*

Elbit Systems Electro-Optics ELOP Ltd. (1)
Advanced Technology Park
PO B 1165
Rehovot, 76111, Israel
Tel.: (972) 8 9386211
Fax: (972) 8 9386237
Web Site: www.elbitsystems.com
Electro Optics Systems Mfr & Distr
S.I.C.: 3679
N.A.I.C.S.: 334419
Gabi Gefen *(Dir-Bus Dev & Mktg)*

Elbit Systems EW and SIGINT - Elisra Ltd (1)
48 Mivtza Kadesh St
Bene Beraq, 51203, Israel
Tel.: (972) 3 6175 111
Fax: (972) 3 6175 850
Defence Electronic System Mfr
S.I.C.: 3679
N.A.I.C.S.: 334419

Elbit Systems Land and C4I Ltd. (1)
2 Ha'Machshev St
Netanya, 42507, Israel
Tel.: (972) 9 8898080
Fax: (972) 9 8898231
Web Site: www.elbitsystems.com
Electronic Products Mfr & Whslr
S.I.C.: 3679
N.A.I.C.S.: 334419

Kinetics Ltd. (1)
Golan Street Airport City
Ben-Gurion Airport, 79100, Israel
Tel.: (972) 39720200
E-Mail: Kinetics@elbitsystems.com
Web Site: www.kinetics.co.il
Automotive Parts Mfr
S.I.C.: 3714
N.A.I.C.S.: 336390

U.S. Subsidiaries:

Elbit Systems of America Company (1)
4700 Marine Creek Pkwy
Fort Worth, TX 76179 (100%)
Tel.: (817) 234-6799
E-Mail: info@elbitsystems-us.com
Web Site: www.elbitsystems-us.com
Emp.: 500
Advanced Avionics & Electro-optic Instruments & Systems Mfr
Import Export
S.I.C.: 3812
N.A.I.C.S.: 334511
Raanan Horowitz *(Pres & CEO)*

Subsidiaries:

EFW Inc. (2)
4700 Marine Creek Pkwy
Fort Worth, TX 76179
Tel.: (817) 234-6600
Fax: (817) 234-6768
E-Mail:
Electronic Products Mfr & Distr
S.I.C.: 3679
N.A.I.C.S.: 334419
Tim Taylor *(Pres & CEO)*

Innovative Concepts, Inc. (2)
8200 Greensboro Dr Ste 700
McLean, VA 22102
Tel.: (703) 893-2007
Fax: (703) 893-5890
Rev.: $7,500,000
Emp.: 74
Communication Equipment Mfr
S.I.C.: 3663
N.A.I.C.S.: 334220
Raanan Horowitz *(Pres)*
Bill Augat *(Treas)*

International Enterprises, Inc. (2)
108 Allen St
Talladega, AL 35160
Tel.: (256) 362-8562
Fax: (256) 362-6736
Toll Free: (866) 362-8562
E-Mail: sales@ieionline.com
Web Site: www.ieionline.com
Emp.: 100
Electronic Component Mfr
S.I.C.: 3679
N.A.I.C.S.: 334419
Jimmy Johns *(VP-Ops)*

KMC Systems Inc. (2)
220 Daniel Webster Hwy
Merrimack, NH 03054-4898
Tel.: (603) 886-2611
Fax: (603) 594-7022
E-Mail: info@kmcsystems.com
Web Site: www.kmcsystems.com
Emp.: 200
Provider of Contract Services for the Ddevelopment & Manufacture of Electro-mechanical Instruments for the Medical Industry
Import Export
S.I.C.: 3812
N.A.I.C.S.: 334511
Patrick W. McNallen *(Pres)*

Kollsman, Inc. (2)
220 Daniel Webster Hwy
Merrimack, NH 03054-4844
Tel.: (603) 889-2500
Fax: (603) 889-7966
Navigation Equipment Mfr
S.I.C.: 3812
N.A.I.C.S.: 334511

M7 Aerospace LP (2)
10823 NE Entrance Rd
San Antonio, TX 78216-6001
Tel.: (210) 824-9421
Web Site: www.m7aerospace.com
Emp.: 500
Aircrafts Designer & Mfr
S.I.C.: 5088
N.A.I.C.S.: 423860
Philip O'Connor *(VP-HR)*

Real-Time Laboratories, LLC (2)
990 S Rogers Cir Ste 5
Boca Raton, FL 33487
Tel.: (561) 988-8826
Fax: (561) 988-6997
E-Mail: sales@real-timelabs.com
Web Site: www.real-timelabs.com
Aerospace Hydraulic Assembly Mfr
S.I.C.: 3812
N.A.I.C.S.: 334511

Non-U.S. Subsidiaries:

AEL Sistemas S.A. (1)
Av Sertorio 4400
91040-620 Porto Alegre, Rio Grande do Sul, Brazil
Tel.: (55) 51 2101 1200
Fax: (55) 51 3361 2773
E-Mail: marketing@ael.com.br
Web Site: www.ael.com.br
Emp.: 300
Aircraft Electronic Products Mfr & Distr
S.I.C.: 3714
N.A.I.C.S.: 336320
Paulo Renato Jotz *(Dir-Mktg)*

Elbit Systems of Australia Pty Ltd. (1)
235 Ingles Street
Port Melbourne, Melbourne, VIC, 3207, Australia
Tel.: (61) 3 86441600
Fax: (61) 3 86441698
Web Site: www.elbitsystems-au.com
Emp.: 45
Aircraft Electronic Parts Mfr
S.I.C.: 3728
N.A.I.C.S.: 336413
Warren Smith *(Mgr-Ops)*

Ferranti Technologies (Group) Limited (1)
Cairo House Greenacres Road
Oldham, Lancashire, OL4 3JA, United Kingdom
Tel.: (44) 161 624 0281
Fax: (44) 161 624 5244

E-Mail: sales@ferranti-technologies.co.uk
Web Site: www.ferranti-technologies.co.uk
Aerospace Engineering Services
S.I.C.: 8711
N.A.I.C.S.: 541330
Gillian Booth *(Mgr-Mktg)*

OIP N.V. **(1)**
Westerring 21
9700 Oudenaarde, Belgium (100%)
Tel.: (32) 55333811
Fax: (32) 55333802
E-Mail: sales@oip.be
Web Site: www.oip.be
Sls.: $21,808,800
Emp.: 100
Mfr. of Holographics & Night Vision Equipment
S.I.C.: 3827
N.A.I.C.S.: 333314
Freddy Versluys *(CEO-OIP Sensor Sys)*

Telefunken Radio Communications Systems GmbH **(1)**
Eberhard-Finckkh-Str 55
89075 Ulm, Germany
Tel.: (49) 731 1553 0
Fax: (49) 731 1553 112
E-Mail: info@tfk-racoms.com
Web Site: www.tfk-racoms.com
Radio Communication Equipment Mfr
S.I.C.: 3663
N.A.I.C.S.: 334220
Thomas Nuetzel *(Mng Dir)*

UAV ENGINES LTD. **(1)**
Lynn Lane
Shenstone, Lichfield, WS14 0DT, United Kingdom
Tel.: (44) 1543 481819
Fax: (44) 1543 487393
E-Mail: uav@uavenginesltd.cu.uk
Web Site: www.uavenginesltd.co.uk
Wankel Engine Mfr
S.I.C.: 3724
N.A.I.C.S.: 336412

ELBIT VISION SYSTEMS LTD.

7 Bareket Street Industrial Park
PO Box 3047
Caesarea, Israel 38900
Tel.: (972) 4 610 7600
Fax: (972) 4 610 7626
E-Mail: info@evs.co.il
Web Site: www.evs.co.il
EVSNF—(OTC)
Rev.: $6,708,000
Assets: $4,207,000
Liabilities: $4,481,000
Net Worth: ($274,000)
Earnings: $824,000
Emp.: 14
Fiscal Year-end: 12/31/12

Business Description:
Automatic Visual Inspection & Monitoring Systems for the Textile & Fabric Industries
S.I.C.: 3823
N.A.I.C.S.: 334513

Personnel:
Yossi Ran *(Chm)*
Sam Cohen *(CEO)*
Yaron Menashe *(CFO & VP-Fin)*

Board of Directors:
Yossi Ran
Sam Cohen
Yaron Menashe
Amos Uzani

Subsidiary:

ScanMaster Systems (IRT), Ltd. **(1)**
5 B Ha'Nagar Street
Neve Ne'Eman B
Hod Hasharon, 45800, Israel
Tel.: (972) 97475400
Fax: (972) 97475444
Web Site: www.scanmaster-irt.com
Instrumentation, Automated Ultrasonic Inspection & Imaging Systems & Transducers Mfr
S.I.C.: 3827
N.A.I.C.S.: 333314

U.S. Subsidiary:

EVS US Inc. **(1)**
319 Garlington Rd Ste B4
Greenville, SC 29615
Tel.: (864) 288-9777
Fax: (864) 288-9799
E-Mail: info@elbitvisionsystems.com
Web Site: www.elbitvisionsystems.com
Emp.: 5
Visual Inspection Instruments
S.I.C.: 3823
N.A.I.C.S.: 334513
John Belew *(VP-Sls & Mktg)*

ELBROOK CASH & CARRY LTD.

105 Bond Rd
Mitcham, Surrey, CR4 3HG, United Kingdom
Tel.: (44) 208 646 6502
Fax: (44) 208 646 6503
E-Mail: info@elbrookcc.co.uk
Web Site: www.elbrookcashandcarry.com
Year Founded: 1984
Sales Range: $200-249.9 Million
Emp.: 66

Business Description:
Cash & Carry Management Services
S.I.C.: 6159
N.A.I.C.S.: 522293

Personnel:
Fukhera Khalid *(Mng Dir)*

ELCA HOLDING SA

Av de la Harpe 22 24
Case postale 519
1001 Lausanne, Switzerland
Tel.: (41) 21 613 21 11
Fax: (41) 21 613 21 00
Web Site: www.elca.ch
Sales Range: $75-99.9 Million
Emp.: 500

Business Description:
IT Services
S.I.C.: 8999
N.A.I.C.S.: 541690

Personnel:
Daniel Gorostid *(CEO)*
Laurent Wassenberg *(CFO)*

ELCO HOLDINGS LTD.

Electra Tower Yigal Alon 98
Tel Aviv, 67891, Israel
Tel.: (972) 36939696
Fax: (972) 36913252
E-Mail: nechemia@elco.co.il
Web Site: www.elco.co.il
Year Founded: 1949
ELCO—(TAE)
Rev.: $1,818,815,000
Assets: $2,737,879,000
Liabilities: $2,206,952,000
Net Worth: $530,927,000
Earnings: ($3,021,000)
Emp.: 7,100
Fiscal Year-end: 12/31/12

Business Description:
Electrical Appliance Mfr
S.I.C.: 3675
N.A.I.C.S.: 334416

Personnel:
Mordechai Friedman *(Chm)*
Michael Gershon Salkind *(Mng Dir)*
Eliezer Vessely *(CFO)*
Itamar Deutscher *(CEO-Electra)*
Yaron Sorek *(CEO-Electra Construction)*
Ya'akov Vadmani *(CEO-Electra Consumer Products)*
Bruno Vendroux *(CEO-ACE SAS)*
Nechemia Chazkelevitz *(Sec)*

Board of Directors:
Mordechai Friedman
Gabriella Heller
Emanuel Lazovik
Daniel Salkind
Gershon Salkind
Michael Gershon Salkind
Meir Srebernik

Subsidiaries:

Elco Contracting & Services (1973) Ltd. **(1)**
4 Haomanut Kiryat Nordau
Netanya, 42504, Israel
Tel.: (972) 98630888
Fax: (972) 98655020
Electric Equipment Mfr
S.I.C.: 3699
N.A.I.C.S.: 335999
Haim Arie *(Gen Mgr)*

Electra Consumer Products (1970) Ltd. **(1)**
1 Yosef Sapir St
75 704 Rishon le Zion, Israel (70%)
Tel.: (972) 3 9530530
Fax: (972) 3 9530630
E-Mail: Info@ecp.co.il
Web Site: www.electra-consumer.co.il
ECP—(TAE)
Sales Range: $650-699.9 Million
Emp.: 3,500
Residential & Industrial Air-Conditioners & Air-Conditioning Systems Mfr & Whslr
S.I.C.: 3585
N.A.I.C.S.: 333415
Yaki Vadmani *(CEO & Gen Mgr)*
Nehemia Hazkelevic *(Sec)*

Subsidiaries:

Electra Air Conditioning Industries 2006 Limited **(2)**
1 Sapir Yosef New I Z
Rishon le Zion, 75704, Israel
Tel.: (972) 732220400
Fax: (972) 39530665
Consumer Electronics Distr
S.I.C.: 5064
N.A.I.C.S.: 423620

Electra Ltd. **(1)**
7th Jabotinski Str Aviv Tower
Ramat Gan, 52520, Israel (69%)
Tel.: (972) 37535666
Fax: (972) 37535601
E-Mail: electra@electra.co.il
Web Site: www.electra.co.il
ELTR—(TAE)
Rev.: $858,218,000
Assets: $871,319,000
Liabilities: $647,257,000
Net Worth: $224,062,000
Earnings: $28,690,000
Emp.: 400
Fiscal Year-end: 12/31/12
Manufacture, Installation & Servicing of Central Air-Conditioning Systems, Elevators, Plumbing & Electrical Systems; Owner & Developer of Real Estate
S.I.C.: 1711
N.A.I.C.S.: 238220
Michael Gershon Salkind *(Chm)*
Itamar Deutscher *(CEO)*
Eyal Shadmi *(CEO-ALD Environment)*
Ronit Barzilai *(Legal Counsel & VP)*

Subsidiary:

Electra Real Estate Ltd. **(2)**
98 Yigal Alon St
Tel Aviv, 67891, Israel (80%)
Tel.: (972) 3 710 1700
Fax: (972) 3 710 1720
E-Mail: info@ere.co.il
Web Site: www.ere.co.il
ELCRE—(TAE)
Rev.: $57,134,802
Assets: $952,915,534
Liabilities: $770,621,259
Net Worth: $182,294,275
Earnings: ($42,265,782)
Fiscal Year-end: 12/31/12
Real Estate Developer
S.I.C.: 6531
N.A.I.C.S.: 531390
Georg Salkind *(Chm)*
Shai Weinberg *(CEO)*
Zvi Duskin *(CFO & VP)*

Non-U.S. Subsidiary:

Electech Holding BV **(2)**
Stadhouderskade 125hs
Amsterdam, 1074 AV, Netherlands
Tel.: (31) 205730810
Fax: (31) 205730820
Emp.: 1
Construction Engineering Services
S.I.C.: 8711
N.A.I.C.S.: 541330
Henry Meyer *(Gen Mgr)*

Iliasi Ltd. **(1)**
21 Hamel Shaul Blvd
Tel Aviv, 64367, Israel
Tel.: (972) 36939671
Fax: (972) 36939689
Construction Engineering Services
S.I.C.: 8711
N.A.I.C.S.: 541330

U.S. Subsidiary:

Elco Landmark Residential Holdings LLC **(1)**
3505 Frontage Rd Ste 150
Tampa, FL 33607
Tel.: (813) 281-2907
Fax: (813) 287-2178
E-Mail: corporate@landmarkresidential.com
Web Site: www.landmarkresidential.com
Apartment Leasing Services
S.I.C.: 6513
N.A.I.C.S.: 531110
Joseph G. Lubeck *(CEO & Mng Partner)*
Joan Copeland *(Exec VP-Ops)*

Non-U.S. Subsidiaries:

ACE SAS **(1)**
1 B Avenue Du 8 Mai 1945
Guyancourt, 78284, France
Tel.: (33) 139447800
Fax: (33) 139441155
Air Conditioners Mfr
S.I.C.: 3585
N.A.I.C.S.: 333415
Bruno Vendroux *(Gen Mgr)*

Airwell Industrie France SAS **(1)**
1 Bis Ave 8 Du Mai 1945
78284 Guyancourt, France
Tel.: (33) 139447800
Fax: (33) 139447879
Web Site: www.airwell.com
Emp.: 140
Air Conditioners & Electrical Appliances Mfr
S.I.C.: 3585
N.A.I.C.S.: 333415
Guy Wrobel *(Pres)*

U.S. Subsidiaries:

Airwell-Fedders North America, Inc. **(2)**
2 Centre Dr
Monroe Township, NJ 08831
Tel.: (609) 662-5300
Fax: (609) 662-5301
Web Site: www.fedders.com
Heating & Air Conditioning Equipment Distr
S.I.C.: 3585
N.A.I.C.S.: 333415

Non-U.S. Subsidiaries:

AAC Services CIS **(2)**
Avangardnaja Office 14 Pui
125493 Moscow, Russia
Tel.: (7) 4956450216
Fax: (7) 4956450217
Web Site: www.airwell.com
Emp.: 3
Air Conditioners & Electrical Appliances Mfr
S.I.C.: 3585
N.A.I.C.S.: 333415
Alexey Dyutin *(Mgr)*

Airwell Deutschland GmbH **(2)**
Berner strasse 43
D-60437 Frankfurt, Germany
Tel.: (49) 69507020
Fax: (49) 695070250
E-Mail: info@airwell.de
Web Site: www.airwell.de
Air Conditioners & Electrical Appliances Mfr
S.I.C.: 3585
N.A.I.C.S.: 333415
B Brinkmann *(Mng Dir)*

Elco Holdings Ltd.—(Continued)

Airwell Iberica S.A. (2)
Calle Procion 1-3 2A
28023 Madrid, Spain
Tel.: (34) 91 710 0460
Fax: (34) 91 710 9196
Air Conditioners & Electrical Appliances Mfr
S.I.C.: 3585
N.A.I.C.S.: 333415

Elco Holland B.V. (1)
Strawinskylaan 3501
Amsterdam, 1077 ZX, Netherlands
Tel.: (31) 207105000
Consumer Electronics Distr
S.I.C.: 5064
N.A.I.C.S.: 423620

Non-U.S. Joint Venture:

FagorBrandt SAS (1)
89-91 Bd Franklin Roosevelt CS 30002
92854 Rueil-Malmaison, Cedex, France
Tel.: (33) 1 47 16 65 65
Fax: (33) 1 47 16 68 07
Web Site: www.fagorbrandt.com
Emp.: 300
Mfr. of Large Household Appliances; Joint Venture of Elco-Holdings Ltd.(90%) & Fagor Electrodomesticos(10%)
S.I.C.: 3639
N.A.I.C.S.: 335228

ELCOM TECHNOLOGY PTY LTD

SE 7101 2 Locomotive Street
Eveleigh, Sydney, NSW, 2015, Australia
Tel.: (61) 2 8064 0999
E-Mail: info@elcomCMS.com
Web Site: www.elcomcms.com
Year Founded: 1996
Sales Range: $10-24.9 Million
Business Description:
Software Publisher
S.I.C.: 7372
N.A.I.C.S.: 511210
Personnel:
John Anstey *(CEO)*

ELCORA RESOURCES CORP.

1969 Upper Water Street Suite 2108
Halifax, NS, B3J 3R7, Canada
Tel.: (902) 446-2000
Fax: (902) 446-2001
E-Mail: glenn@jessome.com
Year Founded: 2011
ERA.P—(TSXV)
Business Description:
Investment Services
S.I.C.: 6211
N.A.I.C.S.: 523999
Personnel:
Troy Grant *(Pres & CEO)*
Theo van der Linde *(CFO)*
Board of Directors:
John Cumming
Troy Grant
Gregory Isenor
Theo van der Linde
Transfer Agent:
Computershare Investor Services Inc.
Montreal, QC, Canada

ELDAN ELECTRONIC CO. LTD.

8 Hashiloach Street
PO Box 7641
7641 Petah Tiqwa, Israel
Tel.: (972) 39371103
Fax: (972) 39371100
E-Mail: info@eldan.biz
Web Site: www.eldan.biz
Year Founded: 1960
Sales Range: $10-24.9 Million
Emp.: 90
Business Description:
Equipment, Instrumentation & Services for Scientific Research & Medical Fields
S.I.C.: 3826
N.A.I.C.S.: 334516
Personnel:
Moshe Ben Simon *(Deputy Gen Mgr)*

ELDECO HOUSING & INDUSTRIES LTD

Eldeco Corporate Chamber I 2nd Floor Vibhuti Khand Opp Mandi Parishad
Gomti Nagar, Lucknow, Uttar Pradesh, 226010, India
Tel.: (91) 5224039999
Fax: (91) 5224039900
E-Mail: enquiry@eldecohousing.co.in
Web Site: www.eldecogroup.com
523329—(BOM)
Rev.: $19,273,000
Assets: $43,675,703
Liabilities: $31,858,186
Net Worth: $11,817,516
Earnings: $1,783,992
Fiscal Year-end: 03/31/13
Business Description:
Real Estate Development Services
S.I.C.: 6531
N.A.I.C.S.: 531210
Personnel:
S. K. Garg *(Chm)*
Pankaj Bajaj *(Mng Dir)*
Shruti Gupta *(Compliance Officer & Sec)*
Board of Directors:
S. K. Garg
Rahul Aggarwal
Arvind Bajaj
Pankaj Bajaj
Ashish Jain
Shrikant Jajodia
Ranjit Khattar
Anil Tewari
Transfer Agent:
Skyline Financial Services Pvt Ltd.
D 153A 1st Floor Okhla Industrial Area Phase 1
New Delhi, India

ELDER HEALTH CARE LTD.

C-9 Dalia Industrial Estate Off New Link Road
Andheri W, Mumbai, 400 058, India
Tel.: (91) 22 2673 0058
Fax: (91) 22 2673 0051
E-Mail: corporate.ehcl@elderindia.com
Web Site: www.elderhealthcare.in
524830—(BOM)
Rev.: $27,711,108
Assets: $16,790,899
Liabilities: $14,425,900
Net Worth: $2,364,999
Earnings: $366,350
Emp.: 1,000
Fiscal Year-end: 03/31/13
Business Description:
Skin Care Products Mfr
S.I.C.: 5122
N.A.I.C.S.: 446120
Personnel:
Jagdish Saxena *(Chm)*
Anuj Saxena *(Mng Dir)*
Vijendra Jain *(Sec & Deputy Gen Mgr-Fin)*
Board of Directors:
Jagdish Saxena
B. L. Gupta
Joginder Singh Juneja
Kishan A. Rao
Alok Saxena
Anuj Saxena
Urvashi Saxena
Transfer Agent:
Adroit Corporate Services Pvt. Ltd.
19, Jaferbhoy Industrial Estate 1st Floor
Makwana Road
Marol Naka Andheri E, 400 059 Mumbai, India

ELDER PHARMACEUTICALS LTD.

C 9 Dalia Industrial Estate Off Veera Desai Road
Mumbai, 400 053, India
Tel.: (91) 2226730058
Fax: (91) 22 2673 0051
E-Mail: corporate@elderindia.com
Web Site: www.elderindia.com
Year Founded: 1989
532322—(BOM)
Sales Range: $150-199.9 Million
Emp.: 3,215
Business Description:
Pharmaceutical & Medical Device Mfr
S.I.C.: 2834
N.A.I.C.S.: 325412
Personnel:
Jagdish Saxena *(Chm)*
Alok Saxena *(CEO & Mng Dir)*
S. P. Date *(Sec & Chief Compliance Officer)*
Board of Directors:
Jagdish Saxena
Michael Bastian
Farid Gulmohamed
S. Jayaram
Joginder Singh Juneja
Yusuf Karim Khan
Sailendra Narain
Alok Saxena
Urvashi Saxena
Saleem Shervani
R. Srinivasan
Transfer Agent:
Link Intime India Private Limited
C-13 Pannalal Silk Mills Compound L.B.S. Marg Bhandup
Mumbai, India

Non-U.S. Subsidiary:

NeutraHealth plc (1)
180 Lifford Lane
Kings Norton, B30 3NU, United Kingdom
Tel.: (44) 2075491608
Fax: (44) 2075491611
E-Mail: info@neutrahealthplc.com
Web Site: www.neutrahealthplc.com
Sales Range: $50-74.9 Million
Emp.: 243
Holding Company
S.I.C.: 6719
N.A.I.C.S.: 551112
Robin D. Hilton *(Sec & Dir-Fin)*

Subsidiaries:

BioCare Limited (2)
Lakeside 180 Lifford Lane
Kings Norton, W Midlands, B30 3NU, United Kingdom
Tel.: (44) 1214333727
Fax: (44) 1214338705
E-Mail: biocare@biocare.co.uk
Web Site: www.biocare.co.uk
Emp.: 50
Pharmaceutical Products Whslr
S.I.C.: 5912
N.A.I.C.S.: 446110
Ema Ellis *(Mng Dir)*

Brunel Healthcare Manufacturing Limited (2)
William Nadin Way
Swadlincote, Derbys, DE11 0BB, United Kingdom
Tel.: (44) 1283228300
Fax: (44) 1283228328
E-Mail: info@bruhealth.co.uk
Web Site: www.brunelhealthcare.co.uk
Emp.: 300
Nutraceutical Products Mfr & Sales
S.I.C.: 2834
N.A.I.C.S.: 325412
Ray Myers *(Mng Dir)*

ELDER PROJECTS LIMITED

Plot No A-38/1 Patalganga Industrial Area Village Khaire
District - Raigad, Khalapur, Maharashtra, 410 220, India
Tel.: (91) 2192 250020
Fax: (91) 2192 250019
Web Site: www.elderprojectsindia.com
Year Founded: 1985
524788—(BOM)
Business Description:
Pharmaceutical Preparation Mfr
S.I.C.: 2834
N.A.I.C.S.: 325412
Personnel:
Anuj Saxena *(Mng Dir)*
Board of Directors:
Alok Saxena
Anuj Saxena
Jagat Varma
Transfer Agent:
Adroit Corporate Services (P) Limited.
19 Jaferbhoy Industrial Estate 1st Floor
Makwana Road Marol Naka
Andheri E, Mumbai, 400059, India
Tel.: (91) 22 28590942
Fax: (91) 22 28581132

ELDERS LIMITED

Level 3 27 Currie Street
Adelaide, SA, 5000, Australia
Tel.: (61) 884254999
Fax: (61) 884101597
E-Mail: information@elders.com.au
Web Site: www.elders.com.au
ELD—(ASX)
Rev.: $2,298,213,555
Assets: $1,608,045,630
Liabilities: $1,020,397,800
Net Worth: $587,647,830
Earnings: ($61,102,245)
Emp.: 4,504
Fiscal Year-end: 09/30/12
Business Description:
Automotive Components, Agricultural Products, Real Estate, Forestry & Investments
S.I.C.: 6531
N.A.I.C.S.: 531210
Personnel:
Malcolm Geoffrey Jackman *(CEO & Mng Dir)*
Mark G. Hosking *(CFO)*
Nina Margaret Abbey *(Co-Sec)*
Sarah Jane Graves *(Co-Sec)*
Peter Gordon Hastings *(Co-Sec)*
Board of Directors:
Mark Charles Allison
Malcolm Geoffrey Jackman
James Hutchison Ranck
Josephine Rozman
Subsidiaries:

Acehill Investments Pty. Ltd. (1)
27 Currie Street
Adelaide, SA, 5000, Australia
Tel.: (61) 884254999
Fax: (61) 884108597
E-Mail: reception.adelaide@elders.com.au
Web Site: www.elders.com.au
Investment Management Services
S.I.C.: 6799
N.A.I.C.S.: 523920
Peter Gordon Hastings *(Sec)*

Agricultural Land Management Limited (1)
Level 3 27 Currie Street
Adelaide, SA, 5000, Australia
Tel.: (61) 884255100
Web Site: www.agriculturallandtrust.com.au
Investment Management Services
S.I.C.: 6282
N.A.I.C.S.: 523920
Peter Zachert *(Chm)*
Ian Wigg *(COO, Co-Sec & Mgr)*
Sarah Graves *(Co-Sec)*

Ashwick (Vic) No 102 Pty. Ltd. (1)
27 Currie Street
Adelaide, SA, 5000, Australia
Tel.: (61) 884254000

Fax: (61) 884254000
E-Mail: reception.adelaide@elders.com.au
Web Site: www.elders.com.au
Emp.: 100
Real Estate Property Holding Services
S.I.C.: 6531
N.A.I.C.S.: 531210
Malcolm Geoffrey Jackman *(CEO)*

Charlton Feedlot Pty. Ltd. (1)
Seven Mile Road
Yeungroon, VIC, 3525, Australia
Tel.: (61) 354916266
Fax: (61) 354916277
Emp.: 35
Cattle Feedlot Operation Services
S.I.C.: 0211
N.A.I.C.S.: 112112
Stephen Reynolds *(Mgr)*

Elders Real Estate (NSW) Pty. Ltd. (1)
Level 1 174 Brisbane Street
Dubbo, NSW, 2830, Australia
Tel.: (61) 268843700
Fax: (61) 268841172
Emp.: 13
Real Estate Management Services
S.I.C.: 6531
N.A.I.C.S.: 531312
John Burke *(Reg Mgr)*

Elders Real Estate (QLD) Pty. Ltd. (1)
109 Melbourne Street
Brisbane, QLD, 4101, Australia
Tel.: (61) 738405555
Fax: (61) 738449649
Web Site: www.elder.com.au
Real Estate Management Services
S.I.C.: 6531
N.A.I.C.S.: 531311
Malcolm Jackman *(Mng Dir)*

Elders Real Estate (Tasmania) Pty. Ltd. (1)
50 Invermay Road
Launceston, TAS, 7250, Australia
Tel.: (61) 363312022
Fax: (61) 363344199
Web Site: www.elders.com.au/northtas/
Real Estate Management Services
S.I.C.: 6531
N.A.I.C.S.: 531312
Malcam Jackman *(CEO)*

Elders Real Estate (WA) Pty. Ltd. (1)
179 St Georges Terrace
Perth, WA, 6000, Australia
Tel.: (61) 894222444
Fax: (61) 8 94222443
Real Estate Management Services
S.I.C.: 6531
N.A.I.C.S.: 531312

Elders Rural Services Australia Limited (1)
109 Melbourne Street
Brisbane, QLD, 4101, Australia
Tel.: (61) 7 3840 5522
Fax: (61) 7 3844 9649
E-Mail: robyn.murray@elders.com.au
Web Site: www.eldersrealestate.com.au
Real Estate Management Services
S.I.C.: 6531
N.A.I.C.S.: 531312
John Burke *(Mgr-Real Estate)*

Elders Rural Services Limited (1)
Corner Milaham Street Fairey Road
Windsor, NSW, 2756, Australia
Tel.: (61) 24577370
Fax: (61) 245775827
E-Mail: windsor@elders.com.au
Web Site: www.elders.com.au
Emp.: 12
Farm Management Services
S.I.C.: 0762
N.A.I.C.S.: 115116
Adam King *(Mgr-Stores)*

Subsidiary:

Elders Real Estate Franchise (Vic) Pty. Ltd. (2)
Level 5 120 Clarence St
Sydney, NSW, 2000, Australia
Tel.: (61) 293206666
Fax: (61) 92793791
Emp.: 6
Real Estate Property Development Services
S.I.C.: 6531
N.A.I.C.S.: 531390

Elders Wool International Pty. Ltd. (1)
Level 3 27 Currie Street
Adelaide, SA, 5000, Australia
Tel.: (61) 884254438
Fax: (61) 884254444
E-Mail: elders@elders.com.au
Emp.: 5
Wool Broking Services
S.I.C.: 5159
N.A.I.C.S.: 424590
John Roberts *(Mgr)*

Futuris Automotive Pty. Ltd. (1)
80 Turner Street
Port Melbourne, Melbourne, VIC, 3207, Australia
Tel.: (61) 396444222
Fax: (61) 396453292
E-Mail: info@futurisautomotive.com
Web Site: www.futurisautomotive.com
Emp.: 200
Motor Vehicle Parts Mfr
S.I.C.: 3751
N.A.I.C.S.: 336991

Jetoleaf Pty. Ltd. (1)
70 Smith St
Darwin, NT, 0800, Australia
Tel.: (61) 889811822
Fax: (61) 89814074
Real Estate Management Services
S.I.C.: 6531
N.A.I.C.S.: 531311

Killara Feedlot Pty. Ltd. (1)
Pine Ridge Road
PO Box 348
Quirindi, NSW, 2343, Australia
Tel.: (61) 267461700
Fax: (61) 267462243
Emp.: 30
Cattle Feedlot Services
S.I.C.: 0211
N.A.I.C.S.: 112112
Tony Fitzgerald *(Mgr)*

North Australian Cattle Company Pty. Ltd. (1)
U 1/15 54 Cullen Bay Cres
Larrakeyah, Darwin, NT, 0820, Australia
Tel.: (61) 889814033
Fax: (61) 889811191
Web Site: www.elders.com.au
Emp.: 3
Livestock Breeding Services
S.I.C.: 0752
N.A.I.C.S.: 115210
Ashley James *(Mgr)*

Pitt Son & Keene Pty. Ltd. (1)
101 Kelly Street
Scone, NSW, 2337, Australia
Tel.: (61) 2 6545 1588
Fax: (61) 2 6545 2254
E-Mail: scone@elders.com.au
Web Site: www.elders.com.au
Emp.: 10
Real Estate Management Services
S.I.C.: 6531
N.A.I.C.S.: 531311
Mary Hodge *(Sec)*

Primac Pty. Ltd. (1)
109 Melbourne Street
Brisbane, QLD, 4350, Australia
Tel.: (61) 738405506
Fax: (61) 738464995
E-Mail: elders@elders.com.au
Real Estate Property Development Services
S.I.C.: 6531
N.A.I.C.S.: 531210

Therm Air Australia Pty. Ltd. (1)
27 Currie St
Adelaide, SA, 5000, Australia
Tel.: (61) 884254999
E-Mail: informationelders@elders.com.au
Motor Vehicle Parts Mfr
S.I.C.: 3714
N.A.I.C.S.: 336390
Mark de Wit *(Mng Dir)*

Non-U.S. Subsidiaries:

Elders Fine Foods (Shanghai) Company (1)
No T52-4 Building 1201 Gui Qiao Road
JinQiao Industrial Park, Shanghai, 201206, China
Tel.: (86) 2138720368
Fax: (86) 2138720358
E-Mail: elders.china@elders.com.cn
Web Site: www.elders.com.cn
Emp.: 60
Convenience Foods Distr
S.I.C.: 5411
N.A.I.C.S.: 445120
Adam Thomson *(Head-Comm)*

Futuris Automotive Interiors Trading (Shanghai) Co. Ltd. (1)
No 228 Room 305-308 Meiyuan Road
Shanghai, 200070, China
Tel.: (86) 2161670838
Fax: (86) 2161670662
E-Mail: rmahon@futurisautomotive.com
Web Site: www.futurisautomotive.com.cn
Emp.: 35
Automotive Interiors Distr
S.I.C.: 5013
N.A.I.C.S.: 423120
Ross Mahon *(Mng Dir)*

JS Brooksbank & Co Australasia Ltd. (1)
Level 3 125 Featherston Street
6011 Wellington, New Zealand
Tel.: (64) 43851055
Fax: (64) 43844634
E-Mail: jsb@jsbrooksbank.co.nz
Emp.: 7
Wool Whslr
S.I.C.: 5159
N.A.I.C.S.: 424590
Richard Carroll *(Controller-Fin)*

PT Elders Indonesia (1)
Wisma Raharja Lantai 8 Jl Letjen TB Simatupang Kav 1
Pasar Minggu Jakarta Selatan, Jakarta, 12560, Indonesia
Tel.: (62) 2178840708
Fax: (62) 2178840709
E-Mail: elders@elders.com.id
Web Site: www.elders.com.id
Emp.: 12
Chilled & Frozen Beef Distr
S.I.C.: 5147
N.A.I.C.S.: 424470
Richard Slaney *(Mng Dir)*

ELDERSTREET INVESTMENTS LTD.

32 Bedford Row
London, WC1 R4HE, United Kingdom
Tel.: (44) 2078315088
Fax: (44) 2078315077
E-Mail: admin@elderstreet.com
Web Site: www.elderstreet.com
Year Founded: 1990
Emp.: 10

Business Description:
Investment Services
S.I.C.: 6282
N.A.I.C.S.: 523930

Personnel:
Michael Edward Wilson Jackson *(Founder & Chm)*
Paul Frew *(Partner)*
Vin Murria *(Partner)*
Barnaby Terry *(Partner)*

Board of Directors:
Michael Edward Wilson Jackson
David Taylor

ELDON GROUP

P de la Finca 1 Edificio 13
Madrid, 28223, Spain
Tel.: (34) 917997135
Fax: (34) 917995233
E-Mail: eldon.HQ@eldon.com
Web Site: www.eldon.com
Emp.: 700

Business Description:
Holding Company
S.I.C.: 6719
N.A.I.C.S.: 551112

Personnel:
Fredrik Wikstrom *(CEO)*
Philip Tyden *(CFO)*

Non-U.S. Subsidiary:

Eldon AB (1)
Egnahemsgatan 39
SE 571 83 Nassjo, Sweden SE
Tel.: (46) 105559500
Telex: 8355001
Fax: (46) 105559590
E-Mail: eldon.se@eldon.com
Web Site: www.eldon.se
Emp.: 424
Electronic Enclosures, Relays, Timers, Electric Housing, Electric Boxes, Electric Cabinets & Switchgear Mfr
S.I.C.: 3613
N.A.I.C.S.: 335313
FredriK Strom *(Gen Mgr)*

Non-U.S. Subsidiaries:

Eldon Espana S.A.U. (2)
Ctra De Fuensanta Km 12
Poligono Industrial, Martos, 23600, Spain (100%)
Tel.: (34) 953551000
Fax: (34) 953551539
E-Mail: info.es@eldon.com
Web Site: www.eldon.es
Emp.: 75
Electronic Enclosures, Relays, Timers, Electric Housing, Electric Boxes, Electric Cabinets & Switchgear Mfr
S.I.C.: 3624
N.A.I.C.S.: 335991
Inigo Cano *(Mng Dir)*

Eldon GmbH (2)
Rhoen Strasse 2A
64521 Buttelborn, Germany (100%)
Tel.: (49) 615298155
Fax: (49) 6152981572
E-Mail: eldon.de@eldon.com
Web Site: www.eldon.de
Emp.: 18
Electronic Enclosures, Relays, Timers, Electric Housing, Electric Boxes, Electric Cabinets & Switchgear Mfr
S.I.C.: 3624
N.A.I.C.S.: 335991
Fredrik Wikstrom *(Pres)*

Eldon N.V. (2)
Tussendiepen 64 - 66
PO Box 38 9200
Drachten, Friesland, 9206AE, Netherlands (100%)
Tel.: (31) 512580123
Fax: (31) 512517117
E-Mail: info.nl@eldon.com
Emp.: 35
Electronic Enclosures, Relays, Timers, Electric Housing, Electric Boxes, Electric Cabinets & Switchgear Mfr
S.I.C.: 3624
N.A.I.C.S.: 335991
Mark Houweling *(Mng Dir)*

ELDORADO GOLD CORPORATION

Suite 1188 550 Burrard Street
Vancouver, BC, V6C 2B5, Canada
Tel.: (604) 687-4018
Fax: (604) 687-4026
Toll Free: (888) 353-8166
E-Mail: info@eldoradogold.com
Web Site: www.eldoradogold.com
EGO—(NYSE)
Sls.: $1,147,541,000
Assets: $7,928,129,000
Liabilities: $1,714,794,000
Net Worth: $6,213,335,000
Earnings: $318,058,000
Emp.: 7,024
Fiscal Year-end: 12/31/12

Business Description:
Holding Company; Gold Ore Exploration & Mining

Eldorado Gold Corporation—(Continued)

S.I.C.: 6719
N.A.I.C.S.: 551112
Personnel:
Norman S. Pitcher *(Pres)*
Paul N. Wright *(CEO)*
Fabiana Chubbs *(CFO)*
Paul J. Skayman *(COO)*
Dawn L. Moss *(Sec & Exec VP-Admin)*
Board of Directors:
Robert Russell Gilmore
Timothy C. Baker
K. Ross Cory
Geoffrey Arthur Handley
Wayne D. Lenton
Michael Allan Price
Jonathan Arn Rubenstein
Donald Myron Shumka
Transfer Agent:
Valiant Trust Company
Suite 2950, 130 King Street West
Toronto, ON, Canada

Non-U.S. Subsidiaries:

Deva Gold SA (1)
89 Principala Str
Certeju de Sus, 337190, Romania
Tel.: (40) 254233680
Fax: (40) 254233682
E-Mail: devagold@smart.ro
Web Site: www.eldoradogold.com
Gold Mining Services
S.I.C.: 1041
N.A.I.C.S.: 212221
Nicolae Stanca *(VP & Gen Mgr)*

Eldorado Gold Yukon Corp. (1)
Suite 200 Financial Plaza 204 Lambert Street
Whitehorse, YT, Y1A 3T2, Canada YT
Tel.: (416) 907-6226
E-Mail:
Web Site: www.eldoradogold.com
Sales Range: $25-49.9 Million
Emp.: 260
Holding Company; Gold Exploration & Mining Services
S.I.C.: 6719
N.A.I.C.S.: 551112
David Cather *(COO & Sr VP)*
Steve Sharpe *(Sr VP-Bus Dev)*

Subsidiary:

European Goldfields (Services) Limited (2)
Level 3 11 Berkeley Street
London, W1J 8DS, United Kingdom UK
Tel.: (44) 2074089534
Fax: (44) 2074089535
E-Mail:
Emp.: 15
Mineral Resources Mfr
S.I.C.: 1041
N.A.I.C.S.: 212221
Morgan Wynne *(CEO)*

Tuprag Metal Madencilik Sanayi ve Ticaret Limited Sirketi (1)
Iran Caddesi Turan Emeksiz Sok No 1
Ankara, Turkey (100%)
Tel.: (90) 3124684536
Fax: (90) 3124682646
E-Mail: tuprag@tuprag.com.tr
Web Site: www.tuprag.com.tr
Emp.: 50
Gold Exploration
S.I.C.: 1041
N.A.I.C.S.: 212221
David Tickford *(Dir Gen)*

Unamgen Mineracao e Metalurgia S/A (1)
Avenida Olegario Maciel 1846
Santo Agostinho, Belo Horizonte, Minas Gerais, Brazil 30180-112
Tel.: (55) 31 2101 3750
Fax: (55) 31 2101 3758
Web Site: www.eldoradogold.com
Emp.: 25
Gold Mining Services
S.I.C.: 1041
N.A.I.C.S.: 212221
Lincoln Silva *(Gen Mgr)*

Subsidiary:

Sao Bento Mineracao SA (2)
Rua Dr Geraldo De Campos Moreira
Barao de Cocais, Brazil
Tel.: (55) 31 3837 7180
Fax: (55) 31 837 1670
Gold Mining Services
S.I.C.: 1041
N.A.I.C.S.: 212221

ELECNOR, S.A.

Paseo de la Castellana 95 Planta 17
Edificio Torre Europa
28046 Madrid, Spain
Tel.: (34) 914 179 900
Fax: (34) 915 971 440
E-Mail: elecnor@elecnor.com
Web Site: www.elecnor.es
Year Founded: 1958
ENO—(BAR)
Rev.: $2,599,066,573
Assets: $4,894,193,537
Liabilities: $4,081,950,906
Net Worth: $812,242,631
Earnings: $122,700,703
Emp.: 12,527
Fiscal Year-end: 12/31/12
Business Description:
Civil Engineering Services
S.I.C.: 8711
N.A.I.C.S.: 541330
Personnel:
Fernando Azaola Arteche *(Chm)*
Jaime Real de Asua Arteche *(Deputy Chm)*
Jose Maria Prado Garcia *(Deputy Chm)*
Rafael Martin de Bustamante *(CEO)*
Joaquin Gomez de Olea y Mendaro *(Sec)*
Board of Directors:
Fernando Azaola Arteche
Rafael Prado Aranguren
Cristobal Gonzalez de Aguilar Enrile
Jaime Real de Asua Arteche
Rafael Martin de Bustamante
Joaquin Gomez de Olea y Mendaro
Gabriel de Oraa y Moyua
Fernando Leon Domecq
Gonzalo Cervera Earle
Jose Maria Prado Garcia
Miguel Morenes Giles
Juan Landecho Sarabia

U.S. Subsidiary:

Hawkeye, LLC (1)
100 Marcus Blvd Ste 1
Hauppauge, NY 11788
Tel.: (631) 447-3100
Fax: (631) 447-3830
E-Mail: info@hawkeyellc.com
Web Site: www.hawkeyellc.com
Oil & Gas Pipeline Construction Services
S.I.C.: 1629
N.A.I.C.S.: 237120
Rich Weyer *(Pres)*

ELECO PLC

66 Clifton Street
London, EC2A 4HB, United Kingdom
Tel.: (44) 20 7422 8000
E-Mail: info@eleco.com
Web Site: www.eleco.com
ELCO—(AIM)
Sales Range: $75-99.9 Million
Emp.: 548
Business Description:
Building Supplies Mfr & Distr
S.I.C.: 3271
N.A.I.C.S.: 327331
Personnel:
John Ketteley *(Chm)*
Michael McCullen *(CEO-Software)*
Ivor A. Barton *(Sec)*
Board of Directors:
John Ketteley
Jonathan Cohen
Jonathan Edwards
Michael McCullen
Matthew Turner
Legal Counsel:
Berwin Leighton Paisner
Adelaide House London Bridge
London, EC4R 9HA, United Kingdom
Tel.: (44) 71 623 3144
Telex: 886420 (lond)
Fax: (44) 71 623 3144
Transfer Agent:
Capita Registrars
The Registry 34 Beckenham Road
Beckenham, United Kingdom

Subsidiaries:

Bell & Webster Concrete Ltd. (1)
Alma Pk Rd
Grantham, Lincs, NG31 9SE, United Kingdom
Tel.: (44) 01476562277
Fax: (44) 1476562944
E-Mail: cad.bellandwebster@eleco.com
Web Site: www.eleco.com
Emp.: 50
Engineered Concrete Systems
S.I.C.: 3272
N.A.I.C.S.: 327390
John Stothard *(Mng Dir)*

Downer Cladding Systems Ltd. (1)
Oaksmere Business Park
Yaxley, Eye, Suffolk, IP23 8BW, United Kingdom
Tel.: (44) 01379787215
Fax: (44) 1379788161
E-Mail: downer@eleco.com
Web Site: www.eleco.com
Emp.: 10
Rain Screen Systems Mfr
S.I.C.: 5082
N.A.I.C.S.: 423810
Andy Folkes *(Gen Mgr)*

Eleco Software Limited (1)
Lower Barn 4 Hillside Road
Aldershot, Hampshire, GU11 3NB, United Kingdom
Tel.: (44) 1252334695
Web Site: www.3dhomesoftware.co.uk/index.php/about
Construction Industry Software Developer
S.I.C.: 7372
N.A.I.C.S.: 511210
Simon Payne *(Mgr-Dev)*

Subsidiary:

Asta Development plc (2)
Kingston House 5 Goodsons Mews
Wellington Street
Thame, Oxon, OX9 3BX, United Kingdom UK
Tel.: (44) 1844261700
Fax: (44) 1844261314
E-Mail: enquires@astadev.com
Web Site: www.astadev.com
Emp.: 40
Project Management Software Development Services
S.I.C.: 7371
N.A.I.C.S.: 541511
Paul Bamforth *(Mng Dir)*

Non-U.S. Subsidiary:

Asta Development GmbH (3)
Gablonzer Strasse 4
76185 Karlsruhe, Germany
Tel.: (49) 721 9525 0
Fax: (49) 721 9525 100
E-Mail: info@astadev.de
Web Site: www.astadev.de
Business Management Software Publisher
S.I.C.: 7372
N.A.I.C.S.: 511210
Xaver Theis *(Chm-Mgmt Bd)*
Michael McCullen *(Member-Mgmt Bd)*

Non-U.S. Subsidiaries:

Eleco Software GmbH (2)
Deifteralle 18
31785 Hameln, Germany
Tel.: (49) 5151822390
Fax: (49) 51518223929
E-Mail: info@arcon-eleco.ge
Web Site: www.arcon-eleco.ge
Emp.: 13
Construction Software Developer
S.I.C.: 7372
N.A.I.C.S.: 511210
Jurgen Kruger *(CEO-Germany)*

ESIGN Software GmbH (2)
Warmbuechen Strasse 17
30159 Hannover, Germany
Tel.: (49) 51185614340
Fax: (49) 51185614343
E-Mail: info@e-sign.com
Web Site: www.e-sign.com
Flooring Industry Software Developer
S.I.C.: 7372
N.A.I.C.S.: 511210

Eleco Timber Frame Ltd. (1)
Goodlass Road
Speke, Liverpool, L24 9HJ, United Kingdom
Tel.: (44) 01514480055
Fax: (44) 01514480066
E-Mail: etf.enquiries@eleco.com
Web Site: www.elecotimberframe.com
Emp.: 50
Engineered Timber Products
S.I.C.: 2439
N.A.I.C.S.: 321213
Paul Taylor *(Mng Dir)*

Gang-Nail (1)
Christy Estate Ivy Road
Aldershot, Hants, GU12 4XG, United Kingdom
Tel.: (44) 01252334691
Fax: (44) 1252334562
E-Mail: gang-nail@eleco.com
Web Site: www.eleco.com
Emp.: 50
Timber Engineering Services
S.I.C.: 2439
N.A.I.C.S.: 321213
Paul Baron *(Mng Dir)*

Milbury Systems Limited (1)
Milbury Precast Lydney Industrial Estate
Harbour Road
Lydney, Glos, GL15 4EJ, United Kingdom
Tel.: (44) 1594 847500
Fax: (44) 1594 847501
E-Mail: sales@milbury.com
Web Site: www.milbury.com
Concrete Products Mfr
S.I.C.: 3272
N.A.I.C.S.: 327390

Prompt Profiles Ltd. (1)
Liberator House Bidwell Road
Rackhearth Industrial Estate, Norwich, NR13 6PT, United Kingdom
Tel.: (44) 01603720090
Fax: (44) 1603720202
E-Mail: promptprofiles@eleco.com
Web Site: www.eleco.com
Emp.: 10
Sheet Metal Products Mfr
S.I.C.: 3444
N.A.I.C.S.: 332322
Barrie Brightman *(Mgr-Sls)*

SpeedDeck Building Systems Ltd. (1)
Yaxley
Eye, Suffolk, IP23 8BW, United Kingdom
Tel.: (44) 01379788166
Fax: (44) 1379788161
E-Mail: speeddeck@eleco.com
Web Site: www.speeddeck.com
Emp.: 25
Metal Roofing & Cladding Systems Mfr
S.I.C.: 3466
N.A.I.C.S.: 332119
Bob Shum *(Dir-Sls & Mktg)*

Stramit Industries Ltd. (1)
Oaksmere Business Park
Eye, Suffolk, IP23 8BW, United Kingdom
Tel.: (44) 01379783465, ext. 1379783465
Fax: (44) 1379783659
E-Mail: stramit@eleco.com
Web Site: www.eleco.com
Emp.: 40
Partitioning Products Mfr
S.I.C.: 1629
N.A.I.C.S.: 236210
Liam O'hara *(Gen Mgr)*

Non-U.S. Subsidiaries:

Consultec Group AB (1)
Lasarettsvagen 35
Box 709
931 27 Skelleftea, Sweden
Tel.: (46) 910 878 00
Fax: (46) 910 878 09
E-Mail: info@consultec.se
Web Site: www.consultec.se
Emp.: 4
Construction Software Development Services
S.I.C.: 7371
N.A.I.C.S.: 541511
Tomas Astroem *(Mng Dir)*

Subsidiaries:

Consultec Arkitekter & Konstruktorer AB (2)
Lasarettsvagen 35
Box 709
931 27 Skelleftea, Sweden
Tel.: (46) 910 878 00
Fax: (46) 910 878 09
E-Mail: info@consultec.se
Web Site: www.consultec.se/OmCons/OmCons.asp?PageID=2004&link=About%20Consultec&Hilite=4
Building Software Development Services
S.I.C.: 7371
N.A.I.C.S.: 541511

Consultec Byggprogram AB (2)
Lasarettsvagen 35
Box 709
931 27 Skelleftea, Sweden
Tel.: (46) 910 87878
Fax: (46) 910 87809
E-Mail: info@consultec.se
Web Site: www.consultec.se/OmCons/OmCons.asp?PageID=2002&link=About%20Consultec&Hilite=2
Construction Software Development Services
S.I.C.: 7371
N.A.I.C.S.: 541511

Consultec System AB (2)
Lasarettsvagen 35
Box 709
931 27 Skelleftea, Sweden
Tel.: (46) 910 878 00
Fax: (46) 910 878 09
E-Mail: info@consultec.se
Web Site: www.consultec.se/OmCons/OmCons.asp?PageID=2003&link=About%20Consultec&Hilite=3
Construction Software Development Services
S.I.C.: 7371
N.A.I.C.S.: 541511

Eleco Bauprodukte (1)
Erdingerstrasse 82 A
85359 Munich, Germany
Tel.: (49) 8161879620
Fax: (49) 8161879633
E-Mail: info@eleco.de
Web Site: www.eleco.de
Emp.: 8
Timber Engineering Services
S.I.C.: 2499
N.A.I.C.S.: 321999
Vitus Rottmuller *(Mng Dir)*

International Truss Systems (Pty) Limited (1)
28 Bisset Road
Boksburg, Gauteng, 1469, South Africa
Tel.: (27) 11 397 4441
Fax: (27) 11 397 4929
E-Mail: its@eleco.com
Engineering Software Design Services
S.I.C.: 7371
N.A.I.C.S.: 541511
Emmanuel Piyackis *(Mng Dir)*

Lubekonsult AB (1)
Instrumentvagen 29
Hagersten, Stockholm, 126 53, Sweden
Tel.: (46) 8 18 63 40
Fax: (46) 8 19 63 66
Web Site: www.lube.se
Building Design Software Development Services
S.I.C.: 7371
N.A.I.C.S.: 541511

ELECOM CO., LTD.

4-1-1 Fushimi-machi
Chuo-ku, Osaka, 541-8765, Japan
Tel.: (81) 6 6229 1418
Fax: (81) 6 6229 8030
Web Site: www.elecom.co.jp
6750—(JAS TKS)

Business Description:
Computer Products Mfr & Distr
S.I.C.: 3577
N.A.I.C.S.: 334118
Personnel:
Junji Hada *(Pres)*

ELECON ENGINEERING COMPANY LTD.

Anand Sojitra Road
Vallabh Vidyanagar, 388120 Anand, Gujarat, India
Tel.: (91) 2692 236513
E-Mail: infogear@elecon.com
Web Site: www.elecon.com
Sales Range: $200-249.9 Million
Emp.: 200

Business Description:
Material Handling Equipment Mfr
S.I.C.: 5088
N.A.I.C.S.: 423860
Personnel:
Gurmuk Kalra *(CEO-MHE Div)*
V.B. Kalyankar *(CEO-Gear Div)*
Paresh M. Shukla *(Sec)*

Non-U.S. Subsidiary:

Benzler Antriebstechnik Ges. mbH (1)
Hoheneggstrasse 2
5550 Radstadt, Austria AT
Tel.: (43) 7229 61891 (100%)
Fax: (43) 7229 61884
E-Mail: mail@benzlers.com
Web Site: www.benzlers.com
Sales Range: $150-199.9 Million
Emp.: 600
Speed Changers, Drivers & Gears Mfr
S.I.C.: 3566
N.A.I.C.S.: 333612

ELECTRA GOLD LTD.

Unit 5 2330 Tyner Street
Port Coquitlam, BC, V3C 2Z1, Canada
Tel.: (604) 696-1022
Fax: (604) 944-6102
E-Mail: info@electragoldltd.com
Web Site: www.electragoldltd.com
Year Founded: 1978
ELT.V—(OTC TSXV)
Sls.: $837,660
Assets: $1,465,269
Liabilities: $1,609,225
Net Worth: ($143,956)
Earnings: ($710,467)
Emp.: 5
Fiscal Year-end: 12/31/12

Business Description:
Gold Mining Services
S.I.C.: 1041
N.A.I.C.S.: 212221
Personnel:
Johan T. Shearer *(Pres)*
Ron J. Savelieff *(CFO & Sec)*
Board of Directors:
Keith Hannan
Tom Nelson
Ron J. Savelieff
Johan T. Shearer
Transfer Agent:
Computershare Trust Company of Canada
510 Burrard St 3rd Fl
Vancouver, BC, V6C 3B9, Canada

Subsidiary:

Suquash Coal Ltd. (1)
1165 Burdett Ave
Victoria, BC, V8V 3H3, Canada
Tel.: (250) 381-6768
E-Mail: hburke@islandnet.com
Web Site: www.suquash.com
Emp.: 10
Coal Mining Services
S.I.C.: 1222
N.A.I.C.S.: 212112
Jo Shearer *(Mgr)*

ELECTRA PARTNERS LLP

Paternoster House 65 Saint Paul's Churchyard
London, Ec4M 8AB, United Kingdom
Tel.: (44) 20 7214 4200
Fax: (44) 20 7214 4201
E-Mail: info@electrapartners.com
Web Site: www.electrapartners.com

Business Description:
Private Equity Fund Management Services
S.I.C.: 6282
N.A.I.C.S.: 523920
Personnel:
Hugh Mumford *(Mng Partner)*
Alex Cooper-Evans *(Partner-Investment)*
Rhian Davies *(Partner)*
Philip Dyke *(Partner)*
Charles Elkington *(Partner-Investment)*
Nigel Elsley *(Partner-Property Investment)*
Alex Fortescue *(Chief Partner-Investment)*
Chris Hanna *(Partner-Investment)*
Stephen Ozin *(CFO)*

Affiliate:

Electra Private Equity plc (1)
Paternoster House 65 Saint Paul's Churchyard
London, EC4M 8AB, United Kingdom UK
Tel.: (44) 20 7214 4200
Fax: (44) 20 7214 4201
E-Mail: info@electraequity.com
Web Site: www.electraequity.com
ELTA—(LSE)
Rev.: $226,102,262
Assets: $1,963,396,017
Liabilities: $522,746,216
Net Worth: $1,440,649,801
Earnings: $149,692,970
Fiscal Year-end: 09/30/12
Private Equity Investment Trust
S.I.C.: 6726
N.A.I.C.S.: 525990
Colette Bowe *(Chm)*

Holding:

Axio Data Group Limited (2)
Ludgate House 245 Blackfriars Road
London, SE1 9UY, United Kingdom
Tel.: (44) 20 7975 1600
Web Site: www.axiogroup.net
Sales Range: $250-299.9 Million
Emp.: 1,830
Business-to-Business Information Solutions
S.I.C.: 7389
N.A.I.C.S.: 519190
Hans Gieskes, *(Chm)*
Henry Elkington *(CEO)*
Chris Bradley *(CFO)*

Subsidiary:

OAG Holdings Limited (3)
450 Capability Green
Luton, Bedfordshire, LU1 3LU, United Kingdom UK
Tel.: (44) 1582 695050
Fax: (44) 1582 695230
E-Mail: contactus@oag.com
Web Site: www.oag.com
Sales Range: $50-74.9 Million
Emp.: 150
Travel & Transportation Guide & Magazine Publisher; Online Information Services
S.I.C.: 2721
N.A.I.C.S.: 511120
Stephen Bray *(Mng Dir)*
John Grant *(Exec VP)*

Subsidiary:

OAG Aviation Group Limited (4)
(Formerly UBM Aviation Group Limited)
450 Capability Green
Luton, Bedfordshire, LU1 3LU, United Kingdom
Tel.: (44) 1582 695050
Fax: (44) 1582 695230
Web Site: www.ubmaviation.com
Emp.: 5
Data Consulting Services
S.I.C.: 7374
N.A.I.C.S.: 518210
Peter Von Moltke *(CEO)*
Mike Malik *(Chief Comml Officer)*
Stephen Bray *(Exec VP-Fleets)*
Dirk de Rooij *(Exec VP-Cargo)*
John Grant *(Exec VP-Networks)*
Angel McGovern *(Exec VP-HR)*
David Stroud *(Exec VP-Airports)*

U.S. Subsidiary:

OAG Worldwide Limited (4)
3025 Highland Pkwy Ste 200
Downers Grove, IL 60515-5561
Tel.: (630) 515-5300
Fax: (630) 515-3251
Toll Free: (800) 342-5624
E-Mail: contactus@oag.com
Web Site: www.oag.com
Emp.: 50
Publisher of Travel & Transportation Guides, Online Information & Magazines
S.I.C.: 2741
N.A.I.C.S.: 511199
Stephen Bray *(Mng Dir)*

Non-U.S. Subsidiary:

Inforwarding BV (4)
Hoofdstraat 275
2171 BE Sassenheim, Netherlands
Tel.: (31) 252527431
Fax: (31) 252527602
E-Mail: sales@inforwarding.com
Web Site: www.inforwarding.com
Emp.: 4
Community Portal for Forwarders & Airlines
S.I.C.: 2741
N.A.I.C.S.: 519130

U.S. Subsidiaries:

JOC Group Inc. (3)
2 Penn Plaza
Newark, NJ 07105
Tel.: (973) 776-8660
Toll Free: (800) 952-3839
Web Site: www.joc.com
Periodicals & Directories Publisher
S.I.C.: 2721
N.A.I.C.S.: 511120
Gavin Carter *(CEO)*
Ian Blackman *(CFO)*
Rhiannon James *(COO)*
Peter Tirschwell *(Chief Content Officer & Exec VP)*

Subsidiaries:

Journal of Commerce, Inc. (4)
2 Penn Plaza
Newark, NJ 07105-2251 DE
Tel.: (973) 776-8660
Fax: (973) 848-7165
Toll Free: (800) 223-0243
E-Mail: editor@joc.com
Web Site: www.joc.com
Emp.: 160
Journals for the Shipping & the Airline Industries
S.I.C.: 2721
N.A.I.C.S.: 511120
Tony Stein *(Publr)*

PIERS Global Intelligence Solutions (4)
2 Penn Plaza E 12th Fl
Newark, NJ 07105
Tel.: (800) 952-3839
Web Site: www.piers.com
Import & Export Trade Information
S.I.C.: 2741
N.A.I.C.S.: 519130
Gavin Carter *(CEO)*

RISI, Inc (3)
4 Alfred Cir
Bedford, MA 01730

Electra Partners LLP—(Continued)

Tel.: (866) 271-8525
Fax: (781) 271-0337
Toll Free: (866) 271-8525
E-Mail: info@risi.com
Web Site: www.risiinfo.com
Emp.: 80
Forestry Products Information Services
S.I.C.: 7389
N.A.I.C.S.: 519190
Mike Coffey *(CEO)*
Adrian King *(CFO)*
Iain Murray *(COO)*
Matt Graves *(Sr VP-Pulp & Paper Div)*

ELECTRA PRIVATE EQUITY PLC

(See Under Electra Partners LLP)

ELECTRECORD SA

Bd Corenliu Coposu 11
Bucharest, Romania
Tel.: (40) 21 313 4850
Web Site: www.electrecord.ro
ELRD—(BUC)
Business Description:
Recorded Media Reproduction
S.I.C.: 7313
N.A.I.C.S.: 541840
Personnel:
Corneliea Andreescu *(Pres & Gen Mgr)*

ELECTRIC KHODRO SHARGH COMPANY

7 Th Km Asian Highway
Mashhad, Iran
Tel.: (98) 511 6514390
Fax: (98) 511 6514445
E-Mail: info@eks.co.ir
Web Site: www.eks.co.ir
Year Founded: 1997
KHSH—(THE)
Business Description:
Wire Harness Mfr
S.I.C.: 3999
N.A.I.C.S.: 339999
Personnel:
Mohammad Hossein Shahhosseini *(Mng Dir)*

ELECTRIC METALS INC.

Suite 302 750 West Pender Street
Vancouver, BC, V6C 2T7, Canada
Tel.: (604) 681-0084
Fax: (604) 681-0094
E-Mail: info@electricmetalsinc.com
Web Site: www.electricmetalsinc.com
Year Founded: 1988
EMI—(TSXV)
Int. Income: $12,856
Assets: $1,508,783
Liabilities: $205,799
Net Worth: $1,302,984
Earnings: ($1,318,989)
Fiscal Year-end: 12/31/12
Business Description:
Metal Mining Services
S.I.C.: 1099
N.A.I.C.S.: 212299
Personnel:
Tony M. Ricci *(Pres & CEO)*
Zula Kropivnitski *(CFO)*
Desmond M. Balakrishnan *(Sec)*
Board of Directors:
Gilles Arseneau
Donald J. Currie
Patrick McAndless
Tony M. Ricci
Transfer Agent:
Computershare Investor Services Inc
100 University Avenue 9th Floor North Tower
Toronto, ON, Canada

ELECTRIC POWER DEVELOPMENT CO., LTD.

(d/b/a J-Power)
15-1 Ginza 6 Chome Chuo-ku
Tokyo, 104 8165, Japan
Tel.: (81) 335462211
Fax: (81) 335469532
E-Mail: webmaster@jpower.co.jp
Web Site: www.jpower.co.jp/english/
Year Founded: 1952
9513—(OTC TKS)
Rev.: $7,216,616,000
Assets: $23,868,999,000
Liabilities: $18,876,264,000
Net Worth: $4,992,735,000
Earnings: $327,888,000
Emp.: 7,156
Fiscal Year-end: 03/31/13
Business Description:
Electric Power Whslr
S.I.C.: 4931
N.A.I.C.S.: 221122
Personnel:
Yasuo Maeda *(Chm)*
Masayoshi Kitamura *(Pres)*
Naori Fukuda *(Exec Mng Dir)*
Seigo Mizunuma *(Exec Mng Dir)*
Hitoshi Murayama *(Exec Mng Dir)*
Junji Nagashima *(Exec Mng Dir)*
Kuniharu Takemata *(Exec Mng Dir)*
Masato Uchiyama *(Exec Mng Dir)*
Koichiro Kikuchi *(Exec Mng Officer)*
Itaru Nakamura *(Exec Officer)*
Shirou Otsuka *(Exec Mng Officer)*
Akihito Urashima *(Exec Officer)*
Minoru Hino *(Exec VP)*
Yoshihiko Sakanashi *(Exec VP)*
Toshifumi Watanabe *(Exec VP)*
Board of Directors:
Yasuo Maeda
Naori Fukuda
Minoru Hino
Go Kajitani
Masayoshi Kitamura
Seigo Mizunuma
Hitoshi Murayama
Junji Nagashima
Yoshihiko Sakanashi
Kuniharu Takemata
Masato Uchiyama
Toshifumi Watanabe

Subsidiaries:

Bay Side Energy Co., Ltd. **(1)**
6-15-1 Ginza
Chuo-Ku, Tokyo, 104-0061, Japan
Tel.: (81) 335462211
Electric Power Generation Services
S.I.C.: 4911
N.A.I.C.S.: 221111

Dream-Up Tomamae Co., Ltd. **(1)**
14 Uehira Tomamaecho
Tomamae-Gun, Hokkaido, 078-3712, Japan
Tel.: (81) 335469615
Fax: (81) 164696611
Web Site: www.Epower.co.jp
Emp.: 1,000
Electric Power Generation Services
S.I.C.: 4931
N.A.I.C.S.: 221118
Akira Mihoya *(Pres)*

EPDC CoalTech and Marine Co., Ltd. **(1)**
Building 4-1-6 Nihonbashi Muromachi
Chuo-ku, Tokyo, 103-0022, Japan
Tel.: (81) 352032506
Fax: (81) 352032384
Emp.: 100
Marine Transportation Services
S.I.C.: 4412
N.A.I.C.S.: 483111
Hirata Katsufumi *(Chm)*

Fresh Water Miike Co., Ltd. **(1)**
74 Aobamachi
Omuta, Fukuoka, 836-0897, Japan
Tel.: (81) 944572003
Water Supply Services
S.I.C.: 4971
N.A.I.C.S.: 221310

Green Power Kuzumaki Co., Ltd. **(1)**
20-18-4 Kuzumaki
Kuzumaki-Machi, Iwate, 028-5402, Japan
Tel.: (81) 195663611
Fax: (81) 195663615
Emp.: 4
Electric Power Generation Services
S.I.C.: 4931
N.A.I.C.S.: 221118
Hiroshi Hayashi *(Mng Dir)*

Ichihara Power Co., Ltd. **(1)**
1 Yawatakaigandoori Mitsui Zosen Chiba Jigyosho-Nai
Ichihara, Chiba, 290-0067, Japan
Tel.: (81) 436411561
Fax: (81) 436411563
Emp.: 10
Electric Power Generation Services
S.I.C.: 4911
N.A.I.C.S.: 221118

J-Power EnTech, Inc. **(1)**
No 7 Toyokaiji Bldg 2-8-11 Nishi-shibashi
Minato-ku, Tokyo, 105-0003, Japan (100%)
Tel.: (81) 335972761
Fax: (81) 335972765
E-Mail: mail-box@jp-entech.co.jp
Web Site: www.jpower.co.jp/entech_e
Engineering Relating to Equipment for Removal of Atmospheric & Water Pollutants
S.I.C.: 8711
N.A.I.C.S.: 541330
Kenji Aiso *(Pres)*
Chisato Nishiyama *(Pres)*

J-Power Resources Co., Ltd. **(1)**
Ginza 6
4-chome
Chuo-ku, Tokyo, 103-0022, Japan (100%)
Tel.: (81) 351481315
Fax: (81) 8135647213
E-Mail: kato@eoc.co.jp
Web Site: www.eoc.co.jp
Emp.: 20
Coal Surveying, Prospecting, Development & Related Investments
S.I.C.: 1222
N.A.I.C.S.: 212112
Takayukishi Yamamura *(Pres)*

Japan Network Engineering Co., Ltd. **(1)**
7-15-5 Ginza Kyodo Building 6F
Chuo-ku, Tokyo, 104-0061, Japan
Tel.: (81) 335241721
Fax: (81) 335241725
E-Mail: info@jne.co.jp
Web Site: www.jne.co.jp
Telecommunication Engineering Services
S.I.C.: 4899
N.A.I.C.S.: 517919

JP Business Service Corporation **(1)**
2-2-18 Fukagawa
Tokyo, 135-8451, Japan
Tel.: (81) 336429771
Fax: (81) 336429464
E-Mail: kataoka@jpbs.co.jp
Web Site: www.jpbs.co.jp
Emp.: 700
General Administration, Industrial Relations, Business Development & Accounting Services
S.I.C.: 7389
N.A.I.C.S.: 561499

JPD (J-POWER Design) Co., Ltd. **(1)**
16 No 2 No 2-chome
Chiyoda-ku, Tokyo, 101-0021, Japan
Tel.: (81) 332556211
Fax: (81) 332556248
Web Site: www.jpde.co.jp
Emp.: 80
Power Generation Plant Construction Services
S.I.C.: 1623
N.A.I.C.S.: 237130
Masayuki Hori *(Pres)*

JPec Co., Ltd. **(1)**
6 No 4 - chome Nihonbashi Muromachi
Chuo-ku, Tokyo, 103-0022, Japan
Tel.: (81) 352030361
Fax: (81) 3 5203 0380
Web Site: www.jpec.co.jp
Thermal & Nuclear Power Plant Construction & Engineering Services
S.I.C.: 1623
N.A.I.C.S.: 237130

JPHYTEC Co., Ltd. **(1)**
Kudankita Symbiosis Ichigaya Building 4-2-5
Chiyoda-ku, Tokyo, 102-0073, Japan
Tel.: (81) 332372323
Fax: (81) 32372319
E-Mail: masahiro_satou@jphytec.co.jp
Web Site: www.jphytec.co.jp
Emp.: 200
Power Plant Construction Services
S.I.C.: 1629
N.A.I.C.S.: 237990
Takahisa Nagai *(Gen Mgr)*

Kaihatsu Hiryo Co., Ltd. **(1)**
2-1-1 Tadanouminagahama
Takehara, Hiroshima, 729-2315, Japan
Tel.: (81) 84 624 1601
Fax: (81) 84 624 1603
Fertilizers Mfr
S.I.C.: 2873
N.A.I.C.S.: 325311

KEC Corporation **(1)**
1-37-6 Hakusan
Bunkyo-ku, Tokyo, Japan
Tel.: (81) 338168211
Fax: (81) 338168220
E-Mail: info@kec.co.jp
Web Site: www.kec.co.jp
Emp.: 375
Installation & Maintenance of Electronic & Communications Equipment
S.I.C.: 7699
N.A.I.C.S.: 811310
Munemitsu Yamada *(Mgr)*

U.S. Subsidiary:

J-POWER USA Development Co., Ltd. **(1)**
1900 E Golf Rd Ste 1030
Schaumburg, IL 60173-5076
Tel.: (847) 908-2800
Fax: (847) 908-2888
E-Mail: contact@jpowerusa.com
Web Site: www.jpowerusa.com
Electric Power Generation Services
S.I.C.: 4911
N.A.I.C.S.: 221112
Mark Condon *(VP & CFO)*
Hirofumi Kasa *(Sr VP & COO)*
Yasunobu Ito *(Sec & Treas)*

Non-U.S. Subsidiaries:

J-POWER AUSTRALIA PTY. LTD. **(1)**
Riverside Centre 123 Eagle Street
Brisbane, QLD, 4000, Australia
Tel.: (61) 732117055
Fax: (61) 732117044
Coal Mining Services
S.I.C.: 1241
N.A.I.C.S.: 213113

J-POWER Holdings (Thailand) Co., Ltd. **(1)**
388 Sukhumvit Rd
Klong Toei, Bangkok, 10110, Thailand
Tel.: (66) 22598258
Fax: (66) 026637652
Emp.: 30
Investment Management Services
S.I.C.: 6799
N.A.I.C.S.: 523920

ELECTRIC TRACTOR CORP.

59 Hunter Road
Niagara-on-the-Lake, ON, L0S 1J0, Canada
Tel.: (905) 467-5531
E-Mail: inquiry@electrictractor.com
Web Site: www.electrictractor.com
Year Founded: 2006
Assets: $10,000
Liabilities: $119,232
Net Worth: ($109,232)
Earnings: ($56,106)
Emp.: 1
Fiscal Year-end: 12/31/12

Business Description:
Electric Tractor Mfr
S.I.C.: 3537
N.A.I.C.S.: 333924
Personnel:
Donald Carr *(Pres)*
Richard A. Zirger *(CEO)*
Board of Directors:
Richard A. Zirger

ELECTRIC WORD PLC
33-41 Dallington Street
London, EC1V 0BB, United Kingdom
Tel.: (44) 2079543400
Fax: (44) 2072519050
E-Mail: info@electricworldplc.com
Web Site: www.electricwordplc.com
ELE—(AIM)
Rev.: $22,632,805
Assets: $24,141,027
Liabilities: $10,750,227
Net Worth: $13,390,800
Earnings: $358,499
Emp.: 140
Fiscal Year-end: 11/30/12
Business Description:
Magazine, Book & Website Publisher
S.I.C.: 2721
N.A.I.C.S.: 511120
Personnel:
Julian J.C. Turner *(CEO)*
G. L. Jones *(Sec)*
Board of Directors:
Andrew Brode
Will Fawbert
Steven Routledge
Julian J.C. Turner
Legal Counsel:
Memery Crystal
44 Southampton Buildings
WC2A 1AP London, United Kingdom
Subsidiaries:

IGaming Business Limited (1)
33-41 Dallington St
London, EC1V 0BB, United Kingdom
Tel.: (44) 2079543480
Fax: (44) 2079543511
E-Mail: info@igamingbusiness.com
Web Site: www.igamingbusiness.com
Emp.: 130
Information Publishing Services
S.I.C.: 2741
N.A.I.C.S.: 519130
Alex Pratt *(Publr)*

Incentive Plus Limited (1)
Unit C5 Sunningdale House Caldecotte Lake Business Park
Milton Keynes, MK7 8LF, United Kingdom
Tel.: (44) 1908326940
Fax: (44) 1908278297
E-Mail: info@incentiveplus.co.uk
Web Site: www.incentiveplus.co.uk
Emp.: 20
Social & Emotional Skills Promoting Resources Provider
S.I.C.: 8299
N.A.I.C.S.: 611430

Optimus Professional Publishing Limited (1)
No 33 41 Dallington St
London, EC1V 0BB, United Kingdom
Tel.: (44) 2079543433
Fax: (44) 8454506410
Web Site: www.optimus-education.com
Emp.: 100
Professional Publishing Services
S.I.C.: 2731
N.A.I.C.S.: 511130
Julian Turner *(Mng Dir)*

P2P Publishing Limited (1)
33-41 Dallington St
London, EC1V 0BB, United Kingdom
Tel.: (44) 2079543424
Fax: (44) 8454506403
E-Mail: pp@sports-performance.com
Web Site: www.pponline.co.uk
Emp.: 100
Sports Science Publishing Services
S.I.C.: 2741
N.A.I.C.S.: 519130

Speechmark Publishing Limited (1)
70 Alston Dr Bradwell Abbey
Milton Keynes, MK13 9HG, United Kingdom
Tel.: (44) 1908326944
Fax: (44) 1908326960
E-Mail: info@speechmark.net
Web Site: www.speechmark.net
Emp.: 6
Resources Publishing Services
S.I.C.: 2741
N.A.I.C.S.: 511199
Liz Lane *(Mng Dir)*

ELECTRICAL CONSTRUCTION & MAINTENANCE AUSTRALIA PTY LTD
31 Canvale Rd
Canning Vale, WA, 6970, Australia
Tel.: (61) 894552944
Fax: (61) 894552945
E-Mail: ecandm@ecandm.com.au
Web Site: www.ecandm.com.au
Emp.: 500
Business Description:
Electrical Contractor
S.I.C.: 1731
N.A.I.C.S.: 238210
Personnel:
Michael Hender *(Mng Dir)*

ELECTRICITE DE FRANCE S.A.
(d/b/a EDF Group)
22-30 Avenue de Wagram
75008 Paris, Cedex 8, France
Tel.: (33) 140422222
Fax: (33) 140427940
E-Mail: actionnaires@edf.fr
Web Site: www.edf.com
Year Founded: 1946
EDF—(EUR)
Sls.: $97,905,597,930
Assets: $336,701,348,060
Liabilities: $295,357,775,020
Net Worth: $41,343,573,040
Earnings: $4,788,326,690
Emp.: 156,168
Fiscal Year-end: 12/31/12
Business Description:
Electric Power Producer & Distr
Import Export
S.I.C.: 4911
N.A.I.C.S.: 221122
Personnel:
Henri Proglio *(Chm & CEO)*
Jean-Louis Mathias *(COO-Integration & Deregulated Ops-France)*
Dominique Lagarde *(Chief HR & Comm Officer)*
Marianne Laigneau *(Sec & Sr Exec VP)*
Jean-Pierre Benque *(Sr Exec VP-Customers-North American Activities)*
Bernard Dupraz *(Sr Exec VP-Generation)*
Philippe Huet *(Sr Exec VP-Strategy & Coordination)*
Anne Le Lorier *(Sr Exec VP-Corp Fin & Treasury)*
Gerard Wolf *(Sr Exec VP-Intl Ops & Grp Synergies)*
Board of Directors:
Henri Proglio
David Azema
Bruno Bezard
Julien Dubertret
Alexandre Grillat
Michael Jay
Bruno Lafont
Marie-Christine Lepetit
Francois Loos
Pierre Mariani
Jean-Paul Rignac
Pierre Sellal
Maxime Villota
Subsidiaries:

Dunkerque LNG SAS (1)
30 Rue Lhemitte Centre Tertiaire Des Trois Ponts
59140 Dunkerque, France
Tel.: (33) 3 28 24 16 63
Fax: (33) 6 12 81 58 45
Web Site: dunkerqueing.com
Liquefied Natural Gas Terminal Construction Services
S.I.C.: 5171
N.A.I.C.S.: 424710

EDF Energies Nouvelles S.A. (1)
Coeur Defense Immeuble 1
92933 Paris, La Defense, France FR
Tel.: (33) 0140902300
Fax: (33) 0140902366
E-Mail: accueil.defense@edfen.com
Web Site: www.edf-energies-nouvelles.com
Sales Range: $400-449.9 Million
Emp.: 2,839
Electric Services
S.I.C.: 4931
N.A.I.C.S.: 221118
David Corchia *(CEO)*
Laurence Juin *(Deputy CEO-Southern & Europe)*
Philippe Crouzat *(CFO)*
Yvon Andre *(Co-COO-France & New Bus)*
Christophe Geffray *(Co-COO-Indus)*
Olivier Paquier *(Co-COO-Distributed Energies)*

U.S. Subsidiary:

enXco, Inc. (2)
15445 Innovation Dr
San Diego, CA 92128-3432
Mailing Address:
PO Box 581043
North Palm Springs, CA 92258
Tel.: (760) 740-7022
Fax: (858) 527-3333
E-Mail: info@enxco.com
Web Site: www.enxco.com
Emp.: 200
Wind Energy Developer, Mfr & Operator
S.I.C.: 4939
N.A.I.C.S.: 221122
James A. Walker *(Vice Chm)*
Tristan Grimbert *(Pres & CEO)*
Robert F. Miller *(Gen Counsel, Sec & Exec VP)*
Larry Barr *(Exec VP-Ops & Maintenance)*
Joseph Fahrendorf *(Exec VP-Bus Dev)*
Deborah Gronvold *(Exec VP-Implementation & Generation)*

EDF Holding SAS (1)
22-30 Ave De Wagram
Paris, 75008, France
Tel.: (33) 143692200
Electric Power Distribution Services
S.I.C.: 4939
N.A.I.C.S.: 221122

EDF International S.A (1)
20 Place De La Defense Cedex Courbevoie
Paris, 92050, France
Tel.: (33) 156651111
Electric Power Distribution Services
S.I.C.: 4911
N.A.I.C.S.: 221122

Fahrenheit (1)
1 Rue Du Commerce
Cosne-Cours-sur-Loire, 58200, France
Tel.: (33) 386266014
Electric Power Generation & Distribution Services
S.I.C.: 4911
N.A.I.C.S.: 221122

Protertia FM (1)
Tour Edf 20 Pl De La Defense
Puteaux, 92800, France
Tel.: (33) 141454201
Fax: (33) 141454250
E-Mail: contact@protertia.fr
Web Site: www.protertia.com
Emp.: 50
Facilities Management Services
S.I.C.: 8744
N.A.I.C.S.: 561210
Thierry Millet *(Mng Dir)*

Societe pour le Conditionnement des Dechets et Effluents Industriels (1)
Socodei
BP 54181
Bagnols-sur-Ceze, France
Tel.: (33) 4 66 50 58 00
Fax: (33) 4 66 50 58 36
E-Mail: socodei@socodei.fr
Web Site: www.socodei.fr
Rev.: $99,106,000
Emp.: 196
Industrial Waste Management Services
S.I.C.: 4959
N.A.I.C.S.: 562998

Sofinel (1)
Blvd Du Docteur Postel
27400 Louviers, France
Tel.: (33) 232251085
Fax: (33) 232251288
Engineering Services
S.I.C.: 8711
N.A.I.C.S.: 541330

Joint Venture:

Total Infrastructures Gaz France SA (1)
49 avenue Dufau
BP 522
64010 Pau, Cedex, France FR
Tel.: (33) 5 59 13 34 00
Fax: (33) 5 59 13 35 60
E-Mail: frontoffice@tigf.fr
Web Site: www.tigf.fr
Sales Range: $400-449.9 Million
Emp.: 500
Natural Gas Transportation & Storage Services
S.I.C.: 4922
N.A.I.C.S.: 486210
Bernard Clement *(Chm)*
Monique Delamare *(CEO)*

U.S. Subsidiary:

Madisonville LA (1)
1916 Hwy 22 W
Madisonville, LA 70447
Tel.: (985) 898-6343
Fax: (985) 898-6331
Toll Free: (888) 898-6343
E-Mail: sales@peigroup.com
Web Site: www.peigroup.com
Industrial Equipment Sales & Services
S.I.C.: 7699
N.A.I.C.S.: 811310

U.S. Joint Venture:

Constellation Energy Nuclear Group, LLC (1)
100 Constellation Way
Baltimore, MD 21202 MD
Tel.: (410) 470-2800
Web Site: www.cengllc.com
Holding Company; Nuclear Power Plants Operator
S.I.C.: 6719
N.A.I.C.S.: 551112
Maria G. Korsnick *(COO, Chief Nuclear Officer & Acting CEO)*
Bernard Minvielle *(CFO & Sr VP)*
Steve Miller, Sr. *(Gen Counsel & Sec)*
Sue Collins *(Sr VP-HR)*
Gene Van Slyke *(Sr VP-Support Svcs)*

Subsidiary:

R.E. Ginna Nuclear Power Plant, LLC (2)
1503 Lake Rd
Ontario, NY 14519 MD
Tel.: (585) 771-5402
Web Site: www.cengllc.com
Nuclear Power Plant Operator
S.I.C.: 4939
N.A.I.C.S.: 221113

Non-U.S. Subsidiaries:

DEMASZ Primavill Halozatszerelo Ipari Kft (1)
Pulcz Utca 42
Szeged, 6724, Hungary
Tel.: (36) 62565565
Fax: (36) 62498979
Electric Power Distribution Services
S.I.C.: 4911

Electricite de France S.A.—(Continued)

N.A.I.C.S.: 221122
Istvan Korponai *(Mng Dir)*

EC Krakow S.A (1)
Ul Cieplownicza 1
31-587 Krakow, Poland
Tel.: (48) 126466333
Fax: (48) 12 644 41 74
E-Mail: info@eckrakow.pl
Web Site: www.eckrakow.pl
Electric Power Distribution Services
S.I.C.: 4931
N.A.I.C.S.: 221122
Marian Augustyn *(Pres)*

Subsidiaries:

EKOPLUS Sp. z o.o. (2)
Ul Cieplownicza 1
31-587 Krakow, Poland
Tel.: (48) 126466407
Fax: (48) 126466293
Web Site: www.ekoplus.krakow.pl
Heating Equipment Mfr
S.I.C.: 3433
N.A.I.C.S.: 333414

Przedsiebiorstwo Handlowo-Uslugowe ENERGOKRAK Sp. z o.o. (2)
Ul Cieplownicza 1
31-587 Krakow, Poland
Tel.: (48) 126466740
Fax: (48) 12 64 66 720
Web Site: www.energokrak.pl
Emp.: 70
Electric Power Generation Services
S.I.C.: 4911
N.A.I.C.S.: 221118
Marian Augustyn *(Chm-Supervisory Bd)*
Manfred Ersing *(Vice Chm-Supervisory Bd)*
Adam Bochenski *(Pres & Mng Dir)*
Mariusz Frystacki *(Member-Mgmt Bd)*

EC Wybrzeze S.A (1)
Ul Swojska 9
80-867 Gdansk, Poland
Tel.: (48) 583474200
Fax: (48) 583474203
Web Site: www.ecwybrzeze.pl
Emp.: 670
Electric Power Distribution Services
S.I.C.: 4931
N.A.I.C.S.: 221122
Hendrik Dworakowska *(Pres)*

EDF DEMASZ Partner Kft (1)
Kossuth Lajos Sugarut 64-66
Szeged, 6724, Hungary
Tel.: (36) 62565565
Fax: (36) 62452057
Emp.: 500
Electric Power Distribution Services
S.I.C.: 4939
N.A.I.C.S.: 221122
Jozsef Toth *(Mng Dir)*

EDF Energy plc (1)
40 Grosvenor Place
London, SW1X 7EN, United Kingdom
Tel.: (44) 2072429050
E-Mail: info@edfenergy.com
Web Site: www.edfenergy.com
Emp.: 20,000
Gas & Electricity Supplier
S.I.C.: 4911
N.A.I.C.S.: 221118
Pierre Gadonneix *(Chm)*
Jean MacDonald *(Gen Counsel & Company Sec)*

Subsidiary:

British Energy Group plc (2)
GSO Business Park
East Kilbride, G74 5PG, United Kingdom UK
Tel.: (44) 1355846000
Fax: (44) 1355846001
E-Mail: comp.sec@british-energy.com
Web Site: www.edfenergy.com
Sales Range: $5-14.9 Billion
Emp.: 6,121
Electricity Generation & Distribution Services
S.I.C.: 4911
N.A.I.C.S.: 221113
Jean MacDonald *(Gen Counsel)*
Robert Armour *(Sec)*

Subsidiaries:

British Energy Generation Limited (3)
Barnett Way Barnwood
Gloucester, GL4 3RS, United Kingdom
Tel.: (44) 1452652222
Fax: (44) 01452652776
E-Mail: info@edfenergy.com
Web Site: www.edfenergy.com
Emp.: 2,000
Nuclear Power Stations Owner & Operator; Electricity Supplier
S.I.C.: 4931
N.A.I.C.S.: 221113
Andrew Spurr *(Mng Dir)*
Stuart Crooks *(CTO-Existing Nuclear)*
Brian Cowell *(Chief Nuclear Officer-Existing Nuclear-Reg 1)*
Peter Prozesky *(Chief Nuclear Officer-Existing Nuclear-Reg 3)*
Matt Sykes *(Chief Nuclear Officer-Existing Nuclear-Reg 2)*

EDF Trading Limited (3)
3rd Floor Cardinal Place
80 Victoria Street, London, SW1E 5JL, United Kingdom
Tel.: (44) 2070614000
Fax: (44) 2070615000
E-Mail: enquiries@edftrading.com
Web Site: www.edftrading.com
Emp.: 2,000
Energy Trading
S.I.C.: 7389
N.A.I.C.S.: 425120
Pierre Lederer *(Chm)*
John Rittenhouse *(CEO)*
Beatrice Bigois *(CFO)*
Justin Rowland *(COO)*
Philippe Torrion *(Exec VP-Trading)*

Eggborough Power Limited (3)
Barnett Way
Barnwood, Glos, GL4 3RS, United Kingdom
Tel.: (44) 1452652000
Fax: (44) 1452652776
E-Mail: info@britishenergy.com
Web Site: www.britishenergy.com
Emp.: 100
Electricity Generation
S.I.C.: 4939
N.A.I.C.S.: 221118

EDF Energy UK Ltd (1)
40 Grosvenor Place Victoria
London, SW1X 7EN, United Kingdom
Tel.: (44) 2072429050
E-Mail: customerbunchprocurement@edfenergy.com
Web Site: www.edfenergy.com
Electric Power Generation & Distribution Services
S.I.C.: 4939
N.A.I.C.S.: 221118
Simone Rossi *(CFO)*

EDF Polska Sp. z o.o. (1)
Ul Nowy Swiat 19
00-029 Warsaw, Poland
Tel.: (48) 22 55 65 300
Fax: (48) 22 55 65 320
E-Mail: edf@edf.pl
Web Site: www.polska.edf.com
Electric Power Generation & Distribution Services
S.I.C.: 4931
N.A.I.C.S.: 221118
Philippe Castanet *(Pres)*

EDF Production UK Ltd (1)
1B Blake Mews
Richmond, TW9 3GA, United Kingdom
Tel.: (44) 208 439 8810
Electric Power Generation & Distribution Services
S.I.C.: 4939
N.A.I.C.S.: 221118

Edison S.p.A. (1)
Foro Buonaparte 31
20121 Milan, Italy IT
Tel.: (39) 0262221
Fax: (39) 0262227379
E-Mail: info.affarisocietari@edison.it
Web Site: www.edison.it
Rev.: $17,290,207,480
Assets: $20,021,586,410
Liabilities: $10,346,662,620
Net Worth: $9,674,923,790
Earnings: $115,770,620
Emp.: 3,248
Fiscal Year-end: 12/31/12
Electric Power Generation & Distr
S.I.C.: 4931
N.A.I.C.S.: 221122
Bruno Lescoeur *(CEO & CFO)*
Pierre Vergerio *(COO)*
Roberto Poti *(Chief Dev Officer)*
Pier Giuseppe Biandrino *(Gen Counsel)*

Fenice S.p.A. (1)
Via del Lavoro 1
36078 Valdagno, Vicenza, Italy
Tel.: (39) 0445424888
Fax: (39) 0445403607
E-Mail: info@fenice.com
Web Site: www.fenice.com
Emp.: 100
Specialty Chemicals Mfr
S.I.C.: 2819
N.A.I.C.S.: 325180
Pisi Giuseppe *(Mgr)*

Oceane Re SA (1)
534 Rue de Neudorf
2220 Luxembourg, Luxembourg
Tel.: (352) 26684575
Fax: (352) 26 09 41 18
Electric Power Distribution Services
S.I.C.: 4911
N.A.I.C.S.: 221122

SPE-Luminus n.v. (1)
Markiesstraat 1
1000 Brussels, Belgium
Tel.: (32) 22291950
Fax: (32) 2 218 61 34
E-Mail: info@luminus.be
Web Site: www.luminus.be
Hydroelectric Power Generation Services
S.I.C.: 4931
N.A.I.C.S.: 221111

UTE Norte Fluminense S.A. (1)
Av Almirante Barroso 52/17 Andar Centro
20031-000 Rio de Janeiro, Brazil BR
Tel.: (55) 21 3974 6100
Fax: (55) 21 2220 3998
E-Mail: contato@ute.com.br
Web Site: www.utenortefluminense.com.br
Emp.: 30
Electric Power Generation & Distribution Services
S.I.C.: 4911
N.A.I.C.S.: 221122
Patrick Simon *(Mgr)*

Non-U.S. Joint Venture:

Dalkia NV-SA (1)
Quai Fernand Demets 52
1070 Brussels, Belgium
Tel.: (32) 25251002
Fax: (32) 25200000
E-Mail: info@dalkia.be
Web Site: www.dalkia.com
Emp.: 1,500
Provider of Energy Management Services
S.I.C.: 4911
N.A.I.C.S.: 221122
Pascal Guillaume *(Mng Dir)*
Patrick Labat *(Mng Dir)*

ELECTRICITY GENERATING PUBLIC CO., LTD.

EGCO Tower 222 Moo 5 Vibhavadi Rangsit Road Tungsonghong
Laksi, Bangkok, 10210, Thailand
Tel.: (66) 29985000
Fax: (66) 29550956
E-Mail: Corp_Com@egco.com
Web Site: www.egco.com
EGCO—(OTC THA)
Sls.: $465,693,143
Assets: $3,621,906,578
Liabilities: $1,358,457,610
Net Worth: $2,263,448,968
Earnings: $365,996,187
Emp.: 422
Fiscal Year-end: 12/31/12

Business Description:
Electric Power Generation
S.I.C.: 4911
N.A.I.C.S.: 221118

Personnel:
Pornchai Rujiprapa *(Chm)*
Sahust Pratuknukul *(Pres)*
Piya Jetasanon *(CFO)*
Pawuth Chaladyam *(IR Officer)*
Kulkanok Leongsoithong *(Sec)*
Niwat Adirek *(Sr Exec VP-Bus Dev-Intl 2)*
John Matthew Palumbo *(Sr Exec VP-Bus Dev-Intl 1)*
Sakul Pochanart *(Sr Exec VP-Strategy & Asset Mgmt)*
Voravit Potisuk *(Sr Exec VP-Bus Dev-Domestic)*
Pikul Srisastra *(Sr Exec VP-Fin & Corp Svcs)*
Gumpanart Bumroonggit *(Exec VP-Asset Mgmt)*
Ngamphis Chitphromphan *(Exec VP)*
Suvapan Chomchalerm *(Exec VP-Acctg)*
Thongchai Chotikajornkiat *(Exec VP-Subsidiaries Acctg & Fin)*
Narong In-Eav *(Exec VP)*
Saranya Kalawantwanich *(Exec VP-Bus Dev-Intl 2)*
Pantipa Moolasart *(Exec VP)*
Pornsak Pornchanadham *(Exec VP-Project Mgmt)*
Wimolwan Sasanawin *(Exec VP-Bus Dev-Intl 1)*
Danuja Simasathien *(Exec VP-Bus Dev-Domestic)*
Vasana Vongpromek *(Exec VP-Pres Office)*
Somsiri Yoosook *(Exec VP-Fin)*
Pannee Booncharoensombut *(Sr VP & Controller)*
Paiboon Anawatchamongkol *(Sr VP-HR)*
Sirobon Danudomkit *(Sr VP-Acctg & Budget)*
Jutatip Mahavera *(Sr VP-Internal Audit)*
Chantima Rugpong *(Sr VP-Procurement & Admin)*
Wuthichai Sithipreedanant *(Sr VP-Corp Comm)*
Winchai Tattamanas *(Sr VP-Legal)*

Board of Directors:
Pornchai Rujiprapa
Piboon Buacham
Chotchai Charoenngam
Shigeru Inano
Toshiro Kudama
Pongstorn Kunanusorn
Hideo Kuramochi
Thanapich Mulapruk
Pansiri Prapawat
Sahust Pratuknukul
Mongkol Sakulkao
Phaiboon Siripanoosatien
Kulit Sombatsiri
Surasak Supavititpatana
Pasan Teparak
Satoshi Yajima

Subsidiaries:

BLCP Power Ltd. (1)
No 9 I-8 Rd
PO Box 92
Map Ta Phut Industrial Estate, 21150
Bangkok, Royang, Thailand (50%)
Tel.: (66) 38925100
Fax: (66) 38925199
Web Site: www.blcp.co.th
Emp.: 300
Electric Power Generation
S.I.C.: 4911
N.A.I.C.S.: 221118
Nitikon Tintitshum *(Mng Dir)*

Egco Engineering & Service Co., Ltd (1)
35 Rayong Highway No 3191
Huay Pong, 21150 Rayong, Amphur Muang, Thailand (99.99%)
Tel.: (66) 386826114
Fax: (66) 38691375
E-Mail: rattinan.tha@egco.com
Web Site: www.egco.co.th/en/career_oppo rtunity.asp#link_focus
Emp.: 300
Electric Bulk Power Transmission & Control
S.I.C.: 4911
N.A.I.C.S.: 221121
Ratchada Tont *(Mng Dir)*
Rasda Pongpaew *(Mng Dir)*

Subsidiary:

Agro Energy Co., Ltd (2)
EGCO Tower
Bangkok, Thailand
Tel.: (66) 2998 5000
Fax: (66) 2955 0956
Electric Power Generation Services
S.I.C.: 4939
N.A.I.C.S.: 221118

EGCO Green Energy Co., Ltd (1)
EGCO Tower
Bangkok, Thailand
Tel.: (66) 2998 5000
Fax: (66) 2955 0956
Electric Power Generation Services
S.I.C.: 4911
N.A.I.C.S.: 221118

Khanom Electricity Generating Co., Ltd. (1)
112 Mu 8 Thongnien
80210 Bangkok, Thailand (99.99%)
Tel.: (66) 75529173
Fax: (66) 75528358
E-Mail: chankij.jea@egco.com
Emp.: 105
Electric Power Generation
S.I.C.: 4931
N.A.I.C.S.: 221118
Chankij Jearrephunt *(Chm & Mng Dir)*

Rayong Electricity Generating Co., Ltd. (1)
222 Mu 5 vibhavadi Rangsit Rd
Kwaeng Tungsonghong Khet Laksi, 10210
Bangkok, Thailand (99.99%)
Tel.: (66) 38681012
Fax: (66) 38681784
Web Site: www.egco.co.th
Emp.: 102
Electric Power Generation
S.I.C.: 4939
N.A.I.C.S.: 221118
Chumsak Desudjit *(Dir-Rayong Power Plant)*

Roi-Et Green Co., Ltd. (1)
222 Moo 5 Vibhavadi Rangsit Rd
Tungsonghong Laksi, Bangkok, 10210, Thailand (95%)
Tel.: (66) 29985000
Fax: (66) 29950956
E-Mail: siriluk.soo@egco.com
Web Site: www.egco.co.th/en/corperate_pro file_busin_group_roiet_green.asp
Emp.: 6
Power Generation
S.I.C.: 4931
N.A.I.C.S.: 221122
Chankij Jearapsunt *(Mng Dir)*

Joint Ventures:

B. Grimm & Co., R.O.P. (1)
9th Floor Dr Gerhard Link Building 88
Krungthepkreetha Rd
Huamark, 10240 Bangkok, Bangkapi, Thailand (50%)
Tel.: (66) 27103000
Fax: (66) 23794224
E-Mail: ssariman@amesco.co.th
Web Site: www.bgrimmgroup.com
Electric Bulk Power Transmission
S.I.C.: 4939
N.A.I.C.S.: 221121

Gulf Electric Public Co., Ltd. (1)
87 M Thai Tower 11th FL All Seasons Place
Wireless Road
Lumpini Pathumwan, 10330 Bangkok, Thailand (50%)
Tel.: (66) 26105555
Fax: (66) 26105566
Web Site: www.gulf.co.th
Emp.: 200
Power Plant Operations
S.I.C.: 4911
N.A.I.C.S.: 221122

Non-U.S. Subsidiary:

New Growth B.V (1)
De Lairessestraat 154
Amsterdam, 1075 HL, Netherlands
Tel.: (31) 88 560 9950
Fax: (31) 88 560 9960
Electric Power Generation Services
S.I.C.: 4931
N.A.I.C.S.: 221118

ELECTRO ACO ALTONA S.A.

Rua Eng Paul Werner 925
Blumenau, SC, 89030-900, Brazil
Tel.: (55) 47 3321 7788
Fax: (55) 47 3321 7799
E-Mail: ri@altona.com.br
Web Site: www.altona.com.br
Year Founded: 1924
EALT3—(BRAZ)
Sales Range: $75-99.9 Million
Emp.: 638
Business Description:
Steel Casting Mfr
S.I.C.: 3321
N.A.I.C.S.: 331511
Personnel:
Cacidio Girardi *(Pres & IR Officer)*
Duncan Roderick Mc Kay *(Member-Exec Bd)*

ELECTRO OPTIC SYSTEMS HOLDINGS LIMITED

Suite 2 Level 12 75 Elizabeth Street
Sydney, NSW, 2000, Australia
Tel.: (61) 292333915
Fax: (61) 292323411
E-Mail: contact@eos-aus.com
Web Site: www.eos-aus.com
Year Founded: 1983
EOS—(ASX)
Rev.: $22,842,569
Assets: $14,114,187
Liabilities: $11,312,182
Net Worth: $2,802,005
Earnings: ($10,608,394)
Fiscal Year-end: 12/31/12
Business Description:
Electro Optic Products Mfr
S.I.C.: 3679
N.A.I.C.S.: 334419
Personnel:
Ben Greene *(CEO)*
Scott Lamond *(Acting CFO)*
Mark Bornholt *(CEO-EOS Defence Sys Bus Dev Exec)*
Hugo Keyner *(CEO-EOS Bus-US)*
Craig Smith *(CEO-Space Bus)*
Ian Dennis *(Sec)*
Board of Directors:
Fred Bart
Ian Dennis
Ben Greene
Peter Leahy
Kevin Norbert Scully
Mark Ureda

ELECTRO SONIC INC.

55 Renfrew Drive Suite 100
Markham, ON, L3R 8H3, Canada
Tel.: (905) 946-0100
Fax: (905) 946-1900
Web Site: www.e-sonic.com
Year Founded: 1952
Rev.: $38,935,881
Emp.: 210
Business Description:
Electronic Components & Equipment Distr
S.I.C.: 5065
N.A.I.C.S.: 423690
Personnel:
Eric J. Taylor *(Pres)*
Joel Rosenthal *(Mng Dir)*

ELECTROAPARATAJ S.A.

Calea Campulung nr 121 C7
Targoviste, Dambovita, Romania
Tel.: (40) 21 316 64 16
Fax: (40) 21 316 78 40
E-Mail: office@electroaparataj.ro
Web Site: www.electroaparataj.ro
Year Founded: 1948
ELJ—(BUC)
Rev.: $4,544,343
Assets: $6,180,128
Liabilities: $963,612
Net Worth: $5,216,516
Earnings: $190,286
Emp.: 116
Fiscal Year-end: 12/31/12
Business Description:
Low Voltage Switching Equipment Mfr
S.I.C.: 3699
N.A.I.C.S.: 335999
Personnel:
Adrian Ioan Rus *(Pres)*
Board of Directors:
Chitu Gheorghe
Adrian Ioan Rus

ELECTROARGES SA

12 Albesti St
115300 Arges, Romania
Tel.: (40) 248724000
Fax: (40) 248724004
E-Mail: electroarges@electroarges.ro
Web Site: www.electroarges.ro
ELGS—(BUC)
Rev.: $44,855,844
Assets: $20,809,651
Liabilities: $6,993,543
Net Worth: $13,816,108
Earnings: $4,044,728
Emp.: 468
Fiscal Year-end: 12/31/12
Business Description:
Household Appliances & Electrical Portable Tools Mfr
S.I.C.: 3999
N.A.I.C.S.: 335210
Personnel:
Ion Gavrila *(Vice Dir Gen)*
Sergiu Burca *(Gen Dir)*

ELECTROCOMPONENTS PLC

International Management Centre
8050 Oxford Business Park North
Oxford, OX4 2HW, United Kingdom
Tel.: (44) 1865204000
Fax: (44) 1865207400
E-Mail: queries@electrocomponents.com
Web Site: www.electrocomponents.com
Year Founded: 1937
ECM—(LSE OTC)
Rev.: $1,951,370,724
Assets: $1,357,715,613
Liabilities: $758,217,129
Net Worth: $599,498,484
Earnings: $99,337,341
Emp.: 6,307
Fiscal Year-end: 03/31/13
Business Description:
Distribution of Component Parts & Original Equipment for Electronic, Electrical & Mechanical Devices
S.I.C.: 5063
N.A.I.C.S.: 423610
Personnel:
Peter Johnson *(Chm)*
Ian Mason *(CEO)*
Ian Haslegrave *(Gen Counsel & Sec)*
Board of Directors:
Peter Johnson
Adrian Auer
Simon Boddie
Karen Jane Guerra
Paul Hollingworth
Ian Mason
John Pattullo
Rupert C. Soames
Legal Counsel:
Linklaters LLP
One Silk Street
London, EC2Y 8HQ, United Kingdom
Tel.: (44) 2074562000
Fax: (44) 2074562222
Transfer Agent:
Equiniti Limited
Aspect House Spencer Road
Lancing, West Sussex, BN99 6DA, United Kingdom
Tel.: (44) 121 415 7005
Fax: (44) 871 384 2100

Subsidiaries:

Electrocomponents UK Limited (1)
International Managment Centre 8050
Oxford Business Park North
Oxford, OX4 2HW, United Kingdom
Tel.: (44) 1865 204000
Fax: (44) 1865 207400
Electronic Component Mfr & Distr
S.I.C.: 3679
N.A.I.C.S.: 334419

RS Components Holdings Limited (1)
International Management Center 8050
Oxford Business North
Oxford, OX4 2HW, United Kingdom
Tel.: (44) 1865 204000
Investment Management Services
S.I.C.: 6211
N.A.I.C.S.: 523999

RS Components Ltd. (1)
Birchington Road
Corby, Northants, NN17 9RS, United Kingdom (100%)
Tel.: (44) 1536201234
Fax: (44) 1536405678
E-Mail: general@rs-components.com
Web Site: www.rswww.com
Emp.: 2,250
Supplier of Electronic Components
S.I.C.: 5065
N.A.I.C.S.: 423690

U.S. Subsidiary:

Allied Electronics Inc. (1)
7151 Jack Newell Blvd S
Fort Worth, TX 76118 (100%)
Tel.: (817) 595-3500
Fax: (817) 595-6444
Web Site: www.alliedelec.com
Emp.: 475
Supplier of Electrical Components
S.I.C.: 5065
N.A.I.C.S.: 423690
Scott McLendon *(Pres)*

Non-U.S. Subsidiaries:

Allied Electronics (Canada) Inc. (1)
1155 Lola St Ste 6
Ottawa, ON, K1K 4C1, Canada (100%)
Tel.: (613) 228-1964
Fax: (613) 228-8006
E-Mail: info@alliedelec.com
Web Site: www.alliedelec.com
Sls.: $200,000,000
Emp.: 12
Distributor of Electronic Components
S.I.C.: 3679
N.A.I.C.S.: 334419
Scott Easeaquette *(Gen Mgr)*

Amidata S.A. (1)
Avda De Europa 19
28224 Madrid, Spain
Tel.: (34) 915005093
Fax: (34) 902100611
E-Mail: pedidos@rs-components.com
Web Site: www.rsonline.com
Emp.: 70
Distributors of Electronic Components & Providers of Logistics Support

Electrocomponents plc—(Continued)

S.I.C.: 3679
N.A.I.C.S.: 334419

Amidata S.A. (1)
Carrer Comte Borrell 115
E 08015 Barcelona, Spain (100%)
Tel.: (34) 902100711
Fax: (34) 902100611
Web Site: www.amidata.es
Emp.: 50
Distributors of Electronic Components & Providers of Logistics Support
S.I.C.: 3679
N.A.I.C.S.: 334419

Electrocomponents France SARL (1)
Rue Norman King
60031 Beauvais, Oise, France
Tel.: (33) 3 44 10 15 00
Fax: (33) 825345000
Web Site: www.rs.ww.fr
Emp.: 50
Electronic Component Distr
S.I.C.: 5065
N.A.I.C.S.: 423690
Maffli Stephane *(Mng Dir)*

Radionics Ltd. (1)
Glenview Indus Est Herberton Rd
Rialto, Dublin, 12, Ireland (100%)
Tel.: (353) 014153123, ext. 14153123
Fax: (353) 14153111
E-Mail: enquiries@radionics.ie
Web Site: www.radionics.ie
Emp.: 70
Provider of Electric Equipment
S.I.C.: 5734
N.A.I.C.S.: 443142
John Fitzgerald *(Gen Mgr)*

Radiospares SAS (1)
Rue Norman King
P O Box 453
60031 Beauvais, France (100%)
Tel.: (33) 344101500
Telex: 145759
Fax: (33) 0811651611
E-Mail: question.mail@radiospares.fr
Web Site: www.radiospares.fr
Emp.: 550
Distribution of Electronic & Electrical Components
S.I.C.: 5064
N.A.I.C.S.: 423620
Gigier Goguelin *(Mng Dir)*

RS Componentes Electronicos Limitada (1)
Ave Americo Vespucio 2290
El Cortijo
Conchali, Santiago, Chile (100%)
Tel.: (56) 26681400
Fax: (56) 26681410
E-Mail: ventas@rschile.cl
Web Site: www.rschile.cl
Emp.: 20
Provider of Electronic Equipment
S.I.C.: 5734
N.A.I.C.S.: 443142

RS Components A/S (1)
Vibevej 11
DK 2400 Copenhagen, Denmark (100%)
Tel.: (45) 38169900
Fax: (45) 38333310
E-Mail: salg@rsonline.dk
Web Site: www.rsonline.dk
Emp.: 60
Distribution Equipment for Electronic, Electrical & Mechanical Devices
S.I.C.: 5064
N.A.I.C.S.: 423620
Alberto Dipolla *(Mgr-Mktg)*

RS Components AB (1)
PO BoX 21058, Malmo, 20021, Sweden (100%)
Tel.: (46) 84458900
Fax: (46) 86871152
E-Mail: order@rsonline.se
Web Site: www.rsonline.se
Emp.: 4
Distributor of Electronic Components
S.I.C.: 3679
N.A.I.C.S.: 334419

RS Components AS (1)
Hvamsvingen 24
Skjetten, 2013, Norway
Tel.: (47) 64834000
Fax: (47) 64834010
Web Site: www.no.rs-online.com
Emp.: 6
Electronic Component Distr
S.I.C.: 5065
N.A.I.C.S.: 423690
Gitte Maya Elsing *(Gen Mgr)*

RS Components B.V. (1)
Bingerweg 19
2031 AZ Haarlem, Netherlands (100%)
Tel.: (31) 235166555
Fax: (31) 235166566
E-Mail: orders@rsonline.nl
Web Site: www.rsonline.nl
Emp.: 45
Distribution Equipment for Electronic, Electrical & Mechanical Devices
S.I.C.: 5064
N.A.I.C.S.: 423620
Remco Tolsma *(Gen Mgr)*

RS Components B.V. (1)
Bd Paepsemlaan 22
1070 Anderlecht, Belgium (100%)
Tel.: (32) 25280788
Fax: (32) 25280780
E-Mail: orders@rsonline.be
Web Site: www.rsonline.be
Emp.: 20
Distributor of Electronic Components
S.I.C.: 3679
N.A.I.C.S.: 334419
Hans Devras *(Mgr-Sls)*

RS Components GesmbH (1)
Albrechtser Str 11
PO Box 79
A 3950 Gmund, 3160, Austria (100%)
Tel.: (43) 285253765
Fax: (43) 285254650
E-Mail: verkauf@rs-components.at
Web Site: www.rs-components.at
Emp.: 80
Distributor of Electronic Components
S.I.C.: 3679
N.A.I.C.S.: 334419
Doras Klutz *(Sec)*

RS Components GmbH (1)
Hessenring 13 B Morfelden-Walldorf
D 64546 Walldorf, Germany (100%)
Tel.: (49) 6105401234
Fax: (49) 6105401100
E-Mail: rs-gmbh@rsonline.com
Web Site: www.rsonline.de
Emp.: 300
Distribution of Electronic Components for Electronic, Electrical & Mechanical Devices
S.I.C.: 5064
N.A.I.C.S.: 423620
Gurgen Lamprot *(Mng Dir)*

RS Components Handelsges.m.b.H. (1)
Albrechtser Strasse 11
3950 Gmund, Austria
Tel.: (43) 2852 53765 0
Fax: (43) 2852 54650
E-Mail: admin@rs-components.at
Web Site: www.at.rs-online.com
Electronic Component Distr
S.I.C.: 5065
N.A.I.C.S.: 423690

RS Components KK (1)
West Tower 12th Floor Yokohama Business Park
Hodogaya-ku, Yokohama, 240 0005, Japan (100%)
Tel.: (81) 453358550
Fax: (81) 453358554
E-Mail: webmaster.jp@rs-components.com
Web Site: www.rswww.co.jp
Emp.: 140
Distributor of Electronic Components
S.I.C.: 3679
N.A.I.C.S.: 334419
Kapstsukuni Hyodo *(Gen Mgr)*

RS Components Ltd (1)
10th Fl No 3 Min Sheng Rd Sec 1
PO Box 1
Hsien, 220, Taiwan (100%)
Tel.: (886) 229579902
Fax: (886) 229599844
E-Mail: sallywong@rs-Components.com
Web Site: www.rstaiwan.com
Emp.: 19
Distributors of Electronic Components & Providers of Logistics Support
S.I.C.: 3679
N.A.I.C.S.: 334419
David Lee *(Gen Mgr)*

RS Components Ltd. (1)
Unit 30-31 761 Great South Road
Penrose, Auckland, 1006, New Zealand (100%)
Tel.: (64) 95261600
Fax: (64) 95791700
E-Mail: nzorder@rs-components.com
Web Site: www.rsnewzealand.com
Emp.: 20
Distribution of Electronic Components
S.I.C.: 7389
N.A.I.C.S.: 561499
Ian Mason *(Gen Mgr)*

RS Components Ltd. (1)
Ste 1601 Level 16 Twr 1 Kowloon Commerce Ctr
51 Kwai Cheong Rd, Kwai Chung, China (Hong Kong) (100%)
Tel.: (852) 26106350
Fax: (852) 26102991
E-Mail: hkenquiry@rs-components.com
Web Site: www.rshongkong.com.hk
Emp.: 100
Distributor of Electronic Components
S.I.C.: 4731
N.A.I.C.S.: 541614
Rebecca Wohewong *(Mng Dir)*

RS Components Pte Ltd (1)
1A International Business Park Levels 2 & 3
Singapore, 609933, Singapore (100%)
Tel.: (65) 6865 3433
Fax: (65) 6865 3444
E-Mail: orders.sa@rs-components.com
Web Site: www.singapore.rs-online.com
Emp.: 90
Distr of Electronic Components
S.I.C.: 3679
N.A.I.C.S.: 334419
Jones Leung *(VP-Sls-Asia Pacific South)*

RS Components Pty Ltd (1)
25 Pavesi Street
Smithfield, NSW, 2164, Australia (100%)
Tel.: (61) 296818555
E-Mail: orders.australia@rs-components.com
Web Site: www.rsaustralia.com
Emp.: 150
Distributor of Electronic Components
S.I.C.: 3679
N.A.I.C.S.: 334419
Jereny Edwards *(Country Mgr)*

RS Components SA (1)
20 Indianapolis Street
Kyalami Business Park, Kyalami, 1685, South Africa (100%)
Tel.: (27) 116919300
Fax: (27) 114661577
E-Mail: sales.za@rs-components.com
Web Site: www.rssouthafrica.com
Emp.: 70
Electronic Components Distr
S.I.C.: 3679
N.A.I.C.S.: 334419
Brian Andrew *(Gen Mgr)*

RS Components SAS (1)
Rue Norman King
60031 Beauvais, France
Tel.: (33) 344101500
Fax: (33) 344101600
E-Mail: commercial@rs-components.com
Emp.: 50
Electronic Component Distr
S.I.C.: 5065
N.A.I.C.S.: 423690
Maffli Stephane *(Mng Dir)*

RS Components Sdn Bhd (1)
Lot 12 Jalan Pensyarah U1 28
Hicom Glenmarie Industrial Pk, 40150 Shah Alam, Selangor, 40150, Malaysia (100%)
Tel.: (60) 350321133
Fax: (60) 350322133
E-Mail: orders.my@rs-components.com
Web Site: www.rsmalaysia.com
Emp.: 35
Distributor of Electronic Components
S.I.C.: 3679
N.A.I.C.S.: 334419

RS Components (Shanghai) Company Limited (1)
Suite 23 A-C East Sea Business Centre Phase 2
Shanghai, 200001, China
Tel.: (86) 21 5385 4238
Fax: (86) 21 6427 7692
E-Mail: prcenquiry@rs-components.com
Emp.: 10
Electronic Component Distr
S.I.C.: 5065
N.A.I.C.S.: 423690

RS Components SpA (1)
Via De Vizzi 93 95
20092 Cinisello Balsamo, Milan, Italy (100%)
Tel.: (39) 02660581
Fax: (39) 0266058051
Web Site: www.rswww.it
Emp.: 250
Distributor of Electronic Equipment
S.I.C.: 3699
N.A.I.C.S.: 335999

Non-U.S. Joint Venture:

RS Components & Controls (India) Ltd. (1)
B 74 Sector 60
Noida, 201 301, India (50%)
Tel.: (91) 1204519100
Fax: (91) 120451919899
E-Mail: sales@rs-components.co.in
Web Site: in.rsdelivers.com
Sls.: $3,571,416
Emp.: 80
Distr of Electronic Components; Joint Venture of Electrocomponents plc (50%) & Controls & Switchgear Company Ltd. (50%)
S.I.C.: 3679
N.A.I.C.S.: 334419
Shiv Bhambri *(CEO)*

ELECTROMAGNETIC GEOSERVICES ASA

Stiklestadveien 1
Pb 1878 Lade
7041 Trondheim, Norway
Tel.: (47) 73568810
Fax: (47) 73568811
E-Mail: emgs@emgs.com
Web Site: www.emgs.com
EMGS—(OSL)
Rev.: $200,831,000
Assets: $199,188,000
Liabilities: $88,801,000
Net Worth: $110,387,000
Earnings: $11,895,000
Emp.: 272
Fiscal Year-end: 12/31/12

Business Description:
Oil & Gas Exploration Services
S.I.C.: 1311
N.A.I.C.S.: 211111

Personnel:
Svein Ellingsrud *(Co-Founder & Dir-Technical-Multi-Client)*
Terje Eidesmo *(Co-Founder & VP)*
Bjarte Bruheim *(Chm)*
Roar Bekker *(CEO)*
Svein Knudsen *(CFO)*
David Neser *(COO & CTO)*
Giles Denby *(Pres-Asia Pacific)*
David Hicks *(Pres-EMGS Global Multi-Client & Acting Pres-North South America)*
Bjorn Petter Lindhom *(Acting Pres-Muli-client)*
Jon Nicholls *(Pres-Europe, Africa & Middle East)*
Anette Mellbye *(Legal Counsel)*
Dave Ridyard *(Exec VP-Strategic Dev & Bus Dev)*

Board of Directors:
Bjarte Bruheim
Lodve Berre
Svein Ellingsrud
Jeffrey A. Harris
Magni Hofstad
Christel Pedersen

Stig Eide Sivertsen
Berit Svendsen

Subsidiary:

EMGS AS (1)
Stiklestadveien 1
7041 Trondheim, Norway
Tel.: (47) 73568810
Fax: (47) 73568811
E-Mail: emgs@emgs.com
Emp.: 120
Electromagnetic Geophysical Surveying Services
S.I.C.: 8713
N.A.I.C.S.: 541360

U.S. Subsidiary:

EMGS Americas Inc. (1)
15021 Katy Freeway Ste 500
Houston, TX 77094
Tel.: (281) 920-5601
Fax: (281) 920-5611
E-Mail: emgsamericas@emgs.com
Web Site: www.emgs.com
Emp.: 30
Geophysical Surveying Services
S.I.C.: 8713
N.A.I.C.S.: 541360
Michael A. Vigeant *(VP-Fin)*

Non-U.S. Subsidiaries:

EMGS Asia Pacific Sdn Bhd (1)
Unit E-15 2-4 15th Floor East Wing Wisma Rohas Perkasa
No 8 Jalan Perak, 50450 Kuala Lumpur, Malaysia
Tel.: (60) 321660613
Fax: (60) 321712613
E-Mail: info@emgs.com
Emp.: 20
Electromagnetic Geophysical Surveying Services
S.I.C.: 8713
N.A.I.C.S.: 541360
Giles Denby *(Pres)*

EMGS do Brasil Ltda. (1)
Praia de Botafogo 501 2 andar
Rio de Janeiro, 22250-040, Brazil
Tel.: (55) 21 2546 9936
Electromagnetic Geophysical Surveying Services
S.I.C.: 8713
N.A.I.C.S.: 541360

EMGS International BV (1)
Rokin 55
1012 KK Amsterdam, North Holland, Netherlands
Tel.: (31) 206278983
Business Consulting Services
S.I.C.: 8742
N.A.I.C.S.: 541611

ELECTROMAGNETICA S.A.

266 268 Calea Rahovei
Bucharest, Romania
Tel.: (40) 214042102
Fax: (40) 214042195
Web Site: www.electromagnetica.ro
ELMA—(BUC)
Sls.: $138,446,378
Assets: $86,474,362
Liabilities: $11,814,262
Net Worth: $74,660,100
Earnings: $4,909,311
Emp.: 538
Fiscal Year-end: 12/31/12

Business Description:
Electric & Electronic Devices Mfr
S.I.C.: 3825
N.A.I.C.S.: 334515

Personnel:
Eugen Scheusan *(Gen Dir)*

ELECTROMETALS TECHNOLOGIES LIMITED

Suite 603 The Rocket 203 Robina Town Centre Dr
Robina, QLD, 4226, Australia
Tel.: (61) 7 5562 2294
Fax: (61) 7 5562 2315
Web Site: www.electrowinning.com
EMM—(ASX)
Sls.: $1,873,296
Assets: $4,056,271
Liabilities: $2,334,499
Net Worth: $1,721,772
Earnings: ($1,928,911)
Fiscal Year-end: 12/31/12

Business Description:
Metal Recovery Services
S.I.C.: 3341
N.A.I.C.S.: 331492

Personnel:
R. Gregory Melgaard *(Chm)*
Ian D. Ewart *(CEO)*
D. J. Foster *(CFO)*
Kevin G. Powell *(Sec & Dir-Comml)*

Board of Directors:
R. Gregory Melgaard
Ian D. Ewart
R. J. H. Mills
Kevin G. Powell

Legal Counsel:
Thomsons Lawyers
Level 16 Waterfront Place 1 Eagle Street
Brisbane, Australia

ELECTRONIC BUSINESS SYSTEM

100 rue de Paris
91300 Massy, France
Tel.: (33) 164472150
Fax: (33) 1 69 32 09 85
E-Mail: ebs.mail@wanadoo.fr
Emp.: 25

Business Description:
Postal Printing Engineering
S.I.C.: 4311
N.A.I.C.S.: 491110

Subsidiary:

Societe de Services de Maintenance Industriels (1)
ZI Du Sous Biscain
Villers Sous St Leu, 60340 Saint Leu d'Esserent, France (100%)
Tel.: (33) 344568570
Fax: (33) 344568579
E-Mail: contact@ssmi.fr
Web Site: www.ssmi.fr
Emp.: 20
Provider of Maintenance Services
S.I.C.: 7699
N.A.I.C.S.: 811412

ELECTRONIC DATA PROCESSING PLC

4th Floor Fountain Precinct Balm Green
Sheffield, S1 2JA, United Kingdom
Tel.: (44) 114 262 2000
Fax: (44) 114 278 1262
Web Site: www.edp.co.uk
EDP—(LSE)
Rev.: $9,167,778
Assets: $18,103,401
Liabilities: $8,201,253
Net Worth: $9,902,148
Earnings: ($90,020)
Emp.: 68
Fiscal Year-end: 09/30/12

Business Description:
Electronic Data Processing Services
S.I.C.: 3652
N.A.I.C.S.: 334614

Personnel:
Julian H. Wassell *(CEO)*
James M. Storey *(Sec & Dir-Fin)*

Board of Directors:
Michael A. Heller
Peter A. Davey
Paul J. Davies
Andrew R. Heller
Chris R. Spicer
James M. Storey
Julian H. Wassell

Legal Counsel:
Wake Smith LLP
68 Clarkehouse Road
Sheffield, United Kingdom

Irwin Mitchell LLP
Riverside East 2 Millsands
Sheffield, United Kingdom

Transfer Agent:
Capita Registrars
The Registry 34 Beckenham Road
Beckenham, United Kingdom

Subsidiaries:

BCT Software Solutions Limited (1)
The Barns
Stretton Road Stretton, Warrington, Cheshire, WA4 4NP, United Kingdom
Tel.: (44) 1925732300
Fax: (44) 1925730828
Emp.: 8
Software Solutions & Services to Merchants, Distributors & Wholesalers
S.I.C.: 7372
N.A.I.C.S.: 511210
Mark Jowitt *(Dir-Mktg)*

BML (Office Computers) Limited (1)
Garland Court Garland Road
East Grinstead, West Sussex, RH19 1DN, United Kingdom
Tel.: (44) 13423131
Fax: (44) 1342311092
E-Mail: info@edp.co.uk
Web Site: www.edp.co.uk
Emp.: 20
Software Solutions for Engineering, Fastener & Food Industries
S.I.C.: 3652
N.A.I.C.S.: 334614
Mark Jowitt *(Dir-Mktg)*

Disys Associates Limited (1)
Sunrise Parkway
Linford Wood, Milton Keynes, MK14 6LJ, United Kingdom
Tel.: (44) 1908665522
Fax: (44) 1908 690069
Web Site: www.edp.co.uk/contacts/disys.html
Software Solutions
S.I.C.: 7372
N.A.I.C.S.: 511210
Mark Jowitt *(Dir-Mktg)*

Electronic Data Processing Systems Ltd (1)
Beauchief Hall Beauchief
Sheffield, S Yorkshire, S8 7BA, United Kingdom
Tel.: (44) 1142621621
Fax: (44) 1142621126
Emp.: 15
Enterprise Resource Planning Software Development Services
S.I.C.: 7371
N.A.I.C.S.: 541511
Julian Wassell *(CEO)*

ELECTRONICPARTNER HANDEL SE

Mundelheimer Weg 40
D-40472 Dusseldorf, Germany
Tel.: (49) 211 4156 0
Fax: (49) 211 4156 310
E-Mail: info@electronicpartner.com
Web Site: www.electronicpartner.com
Year Founded: 1937

Business Description:
Holding Company; Electronics, Information Technology & Telecommunications Products Wholesale Trade Distr & Retailer
S.I.C.: 6719
N.A.I.C.S.: 551112

Personnel:
Jorg Ehmer *(CEO & Chm-Mgmt Bd)*
Michael Haubrich *(CFO & Member-Mgmt Bd)*
Karl Trautmann *(Chief Pur Officer & Member-Mgmt Bd)*

Supervisory Board of Directors:
Ralf Deuber
Michael Engl
Fred Pahl
Jacqueline Posner
Thiemo Schmitz

Subsidiary:

ElectronicPartner GmbH (1)
Mundelheimer Weg 40
40472 Dusseldorf, Germany De
Tel.: (49) 211 4156 0
Fax: (49) 211 4156 310
E-Mail: info@electronicpartner.de
Web Site: www.electronicpartner.com
Electronics, Information Technology & Telecommunications Products Wholesale Trade Distr & Retailer
S.I.C.: 5064
N.A.I.C.S.: 423620
Jorg Ehmer *(CEO & Chm-Mgmt Bd)*
Michael Haubrich *(CFO & Member-Mgmt Bd)*
Karl Trautmann *(Chief Pur Officer & Member-Mgmt Bd)*

ELECTRONICS INDUSTRY PUBLIC COMPANY LIMITED

65 68 Soi Chalongkrung 31 I-EA-T Free Zone Lat Krabang
Lat Krabang Industrial Estate, Bangkok, 10520, Thailand
Tel.: (66) 2 326 1234
Fax: (66) 2 326 1020
E-Mail: eic@eicsemi.com
Web Site: www.eicsemi.com
Year Founded: 1984
EIC—(THA)
Rev.: $4,670,058
Assets: $20,550,040
Liabilities: $633,972
Net Worth: $19,916,069
Earnings: ($184,457)
Emp.: 192
Fiscal Year-end: 12/31/12

Business Description:
Semiconductor Device Mfr
S.I.C.: 3674
N.A.I.C.S.: 334413

Personnel:
Sarawuth Jinwuth *(Chm)*
Tippawan Chakphet *(Vice Mng Dir)*
Withaya Chakphet *(Mng Dir)*
Wilaiphorn Buddar *(Sec & Mgr-Exec Office)*

Board of Directors:
Sarawuth Jinwuth
Prateep Buphaintr
Tippawan Chakphet
Withaya Chakphet
Kamol Juntima
Wisut Thitiroongruang
Sanga Wanasinchai

U.S. Subsidiary:

EIC Semiconductor, Inc. (1)
15705 Arrow Hwy Ste 4 & 5
Irwindale, CA 91706
Tel.: (626) 960-0877
Fax: (626) 960-0871
E-Mail: sales@eicsemi.com
Semiconductor Distr
S.I.C.: 5065
N.A.I.C.S.: 423690

Non-U.S. Subsidiary:

EIC International Co., Ltd (1)
Room 702 Block B Hoi Luen Industrial Centre 55 Hoi Yuen Road
Kowloon, Hong Kong, China (Hong Kong)
Tel.: (852) 2341 6681
Fax: (852) 2343 9959
Semiconductor Distr
S.I.C.: 5065
N.A.I.C.S.: 423690

ELECTRONICS LINE 3000 LTD.

14 Hachoma St
75655 Jerusalem, Israel

Electronics Line 3000 Ltd.—(Continued)

Tel.: (972) 3 9637777
Fax: (972) 3 9616584
E-Mail: info@electronics-line.com
Web Site: www.electronics-line.com
ELN—(DEU)
Rev.: $14,331,000
Assets: $7,100,000
Liabilities: $3,440,000
Net Worth: $3,660,000
Earnings: $1,079,000
Emp.: 34
Fiscal Year-end: 12/31/12
Business Description:
Security Solutions Services
S.I.C.: 7382
N.A.I.C.S.: 561621
Personnel:
Moshe Alkelai *(Chm)*
Douglas Luscombe *(CEO)*
Ilan Koren *(Exec VP-R&D & Engrg-RISCO Grp)*
Hezi Shabetay *(Exec VP-Svc-RISCO Grp)*
Board of Directors:
Moshe Alkelai
Mazal Alkelai
Raphael Durst
Dan Elnathan
Yigal Fatran
Sharon Sheep

ELECTROPRECIZIA S.A.

Str Parcului nr 18
Sacele, Brasov, 505600, Romania
Tel.: (40) 268 273 333
Fax: (40) 268 273031
E-Mail: marketing@electroprecizia.ro
Web Site: www.electroprecizia.ro
Year Founded: 1936
ELZY—(BUC)
Business Description:
Electric Motor Mfr
S.I.C.: 3714
N.A.I.C.S.: 336390
Personnel:
Dumitru Matei *(Pres & Gen Mgr)*
Board of Directors:
Laurentiu Ciocirlan
Dumitru Matei
Dragos Zavarache

ELECTROPUTERE S.A.

Str Calea Bucuresti Nr 80 Dolj
200440 Craiova, Romania
Tel.: (40) 251437700
Fax: (40) 251437730
E-Mail: electroputere@electroputere.ro
Web Site: www.electroputere.ro
EPT—(BUC)
Rev.: $39,357,618
Assets: $122,566,487
Liabilities: $127,881,047
Net Worth: ($5,314,560)
Earnings: ($17,471,514)
Emp.: 1,152
Fiscal Year-end: 12/31/12
Business Description:
Railway Transport Electrotechnical Equipments Mfr
S.I.C.: 3621
N.A.I.C.S.: 335312
Personnel:
Manfred Klepacz *(Chm)*
Adrian Dumitriu *(CEO)*
Daraban Marius Costin *(CFO)*
Board of Directors:
Manfred Klepacz
Fahti Mahmoud Taher Mohammad Ahmad
Alexandru Bunea
Abdur Razzak Ladha
Hans-Joachim Schmidt

ELECTROSTEEL CASTINGS LTD

GK Tower 19 Camac Street
Kolkata, 700 017, India
Tel.: (91) 3322839990
Fax: (91) 3322894339
Web Site: www.electrosteel.com
500128—(BOM)
Rev.: $428,191,553
Assets: $943,188,776
Liabilities: $528,805,667
Net Worth: $414,383,109
Earnings: $16,428,016
Fiscal Year-end: 03/31/13
Business Description:
Ductile Iron Spun Pipes Mfr
S.I.C.: 3931
N.A.I.C.S.: 339992
Personnel:
Mayank Kejriwal *(Mng Dir)*
Umang Kejriwal *(Mng Dir)*
Kavita Bhavsar *(Sec)*
Board of Directors:
Pradip Kumar Khaitan
Naresh Chandra
Jamshed Jiji Irani
Mahendra Kumar Jalan
Mayank Kejriwal
Uddhav Kejriwal
Umang Kejriwal
Binod Khaitan
S. Y. Rajagopalan
Vyas Mitre Ralli
M. B. N. Rao
Rama Shankar Singh
Transfer Agent:
Karvy Computershare Private Limited
Plot No 17 to 24 Vittalrao Nagar Madhapur
Hyderabad, India

U.S. Subsidiary:

Electrosteel USA, LLC (1)
270 Doug Baker Blvd
Birmingham, AL 35242
Tel.: (205) 516-8154
Web Site: www.electrosteelusa.com
Emp.: 25
Ductile Iron Pipes Mfr
S.I.C.: 3321
N.A.I.C.S.: 331511
Danny Swalley *(Mgr)*

Non-U.S. Subsidiaries:

Chesterfield Ductile Group Ltd (1)
Ambrose Yard Broombank Rd Trading Estate
Chesterfield, Derbyshire, S41 9QJ, United Kingdom
Tel.: (44) 1246264222
Fax: (44) 1246264224
E-Mail: sales@electrosteel.co.uk
Web Site: www.electrosteel.co.uk
Ductile Iron Pipes Mfr
S.I.C.: 3322
N.A.I.C.S.: 331511
Steve Young *(Mgr)*

Electrosteel Algerie SPA (1)
Rue El Hadi Haouassine N 16 Kaouch Cheraga
Algiers, 16, Algeria
Tel.: (213) 21364423
Fax: (213) 21364429
E-Mail: contact@electrosteel-dz.com
Web Site: www.electrosteel.fr
Emp.: 14
Ductile Iron Pipes Mfr
S.I.C.: 3322
N.A.I.C.S.: 331511
Azizz Chadly *(Gen Mgr)*

Electrosteel Castings (UK) Limited (1)
Ambrose Yard Broombank Trading Estate Broombank Rd
Off Carrwood Rd, Chesterfield, Derbyshire, S41 9QJ, United Kingdom
Tel.: (44) 1246264222
Fax: (44) 1246264224
Web Site: www.electrosteel.co.uk
Emp.: 50
Ductile Iron Pipes Mfr
S.I.C.: 3322
N.A.I.C.S.: 331511
Glenn Wheeler *(Mgr-Sls)*

Electrosteel Europe S.A. (1)
Edificio Forum Ctra de Sant Cugat a Rubi 40
Barcelona, 08190, Spain
Tel.: (34) 935830522
Fax: (34) 935897093
Emp.: 20
Ductile Iron Pipes Mfr
S.I.C.: 3321
N.A.I.C.S.: 331511

Singardo International Pte Ltd (1)
116 Lavender St 02-04 Pek Chuan Bldg
Singapore, 338730, Singapore
Tel.: (65) 62945875
Fax: (65) 62970238
E-Mail: info@singardo.com.sg
Web Site: www.singardo.com.sg
Emp.: 15
Ductile Iron Pipes Mfr
S.I.C.: 3322
N.A.I.C.S.: 331511
Alan Chua *(Pres)*

ELECTROSTEEL STEELS LIMITED

G K Towers 19 Camac Street 2nd & 3rd Floor
Kolkata, 700 017, India
Tel.: (91) 3322839990
Fax: (91) 22839990
E-Mail: eil.investors@electrosteel.com
Web Site: electrosteel.com
Year Founded: 2006
ESL—(BOM NSE)
Rev.: $33,983,375
Assets: $1,902,414,948
Liabilities: $1,570,418,482
Net Worth: $331,996,466
Earnings: ($51,914,317)
Fiscal Year-end: 03/31/13
Business Description:
Iron Pipes Mfr
S.I.C.: 3317
N.A.I.C.S.: 331210
Personnel:
Vikram Saraogi *(Compliance Officer & Sec)*
Board of Directors:
Nigam Chander Bahl
Sunil V. Diwakar
Jinendra Kumar Jain
Umang Kejriwal
Naresh Pachisia
Rama Shankar Singh
Lalit Kumar Singhi
Amrendra Prasad Verma
Transfer Agent:
Karvy Computershare Private Limited
Plot No 17-24 Vittal Rao Nagar Madhapur
Hyderabad, 500 081, India
Tel.: (91) 40 2342 0818

ELECTROTECHNIQUE DE NORMANDIE

5 Rue Nicephore Niepce
BP 278
76300 Rouen, France
Tel.: (33) 232915151
Fax: (33) 232915170
Web Site: www.france-elec.com
Sls.: $24,800,000
Emp.: 44
Business Description:
Electrical Apparatus & Equipment
S.I.C.: 5063
N.A.I.C.S.: 423610
Personnel:
Bertrand Bidard *(Mng Partner)*
Valerie Geiger *(Mng Partner)*
Francine Turlan *(Mng Partner)*
Guillaume Turlan *(Mng Partner)*
Herve Turlan *(Mng Partner)*

ELECTROTHERM INDIA LTD

A1 Skylark Apt Satellite Road
380015 Ahmedabad, Gujarat, India
Tel.: (91) 02717660550
Fax: (91) 7926768855
Web Site: www.electrotherm.com
526608—(BOM)
Sales Range: $500-549.9 Million
Emp.: 2,607
Business Description:
Electrical & Steel Equipment Mfr
S.I.C.: 3677
N.A.I.C.S.: 334416
Personnel:
Mukesh Bhandari *(Chm & CTO)*
Shailesh Bhandari *(Mng Dir)*
Jigar Shah *(Officer-Compliance & Sec)*
Board of Directors:
Mukesh Bhandari
Narendra Dalal
Nilesh Desai
Naveen Nakra
Pradeep Krishna Prasad
Harish Sharma
Ram Singh
Ravi Trehan
Transfer Agent:
Link Intime India Private Limited
211 Sudarshan Complex Near Mithakhali Underbridge Navrangpura
Ahmedabad, India

Divisions:

Electrotherm India Ltd - Electric Vehicle Division (1)
72 Palodia
Ahmedabad, Gujarat, 382116, India
Tel.: (91) 2717660550
Fax: (91) 2717234616
E-Mail: ho@electrotherm.com
Electric Vehicle Component Mfr
S.I.C.: 3714
N.A.I.C.S.: 336390

Electrotherm India Ltd - Engineering & Project Division (1)
Surv No 72 Vlg Palodia Taluka Kalol Dist
Gandhinagar, Gujarat, 382 115, India
Tel.: (91) 2717234553
Fax: (91) 2717234616
E-Mail: ho@electrotherm.com
Web Site: www.electrotherm.com
Emp.: 2,500
Induction Furnace Mfr
S.I.C.: 3567
N.A.I.C.S.: 333994
Shailesh Bhandari *(Mng Dir)*

Unit:

Electrotherm India Ltd - Electrotherm Renewables (1)
Surv No 72 Palodia Via Thaltej
Ahmedabad, Gujarat, 382 115, India
Tel.: (91) 2717660550
Fax: (91) 2717234616
E-Mail: ho@electrotherm.com
Web Site: www.etrenewables.com
Emp.: 2,000
Electricity Generation Services
S.I.C.: 4931
N.A.I.C.S.: 221118
Sanjai Joshi *(Gen Mgr)*

ELECTROVAYA INC.

2645 Royal Windsor Drive
Mississauga, ON, L5J 1K9, Canada
Tel.: (905) 855-4610
Fax: (905) 822-7953
Toll Free: (800) 388-2865
Web Site: www.electrovaya.com
EFL—(TSX)
Rev.: $9,854,000
Assets: $21,173,000
Liabilities: $11,743,000
Net Worth: $9,430,000
Earnings: ($3,872,000)
Emp.: 57
Fiscal Year-end: 09/30/12

Business Description:
Rechargeable Battery Mfr
S.I.C.: 3692
N.A.I.C.S.: 335912
Personnel:
Sankar Das Gupta *(Co-Founder, Chm & CEO)*
James K. Jacobs *(Co-Founder)*
Paul L. Hart *(CFO & Sec)*
Board of Directors:
Sankar Das Gupta
Bejoy DasGupta
Bernard Fleet
Michael L. Gopikanth
Alexander McLean
Transfer Agent:
CIBC Mellon Trust Company
PO Box 7010
Adelaide Street Postal Station, Toronto, ON, M5C 2W9, Canada
Tel.: (416) 643-5500
Fax: (416) 643-5501
Toll Free: (800) 387-0825

Subsidiary:

Electrovaya Corp., (1)
2645 Royal Windsor Dr
Mississauga, ON, L5J 1K9, Canada
Tel.: (905) 855-4610
Fax: (905) 822-7953
Toll Free: (800) 388-2865
E-Mail: sales@electrovaya.com
Web Site: www.electrovaya.com
Battery Design & Mfr
S.I.C.: 3692
N.A.I.C.S.: 335912
Amit Majumdar *(Mgr-Bus Dev)*

U.S. Subsidiaries:

Electrovaya Company (1)
107 Hermes Rd Ste 100 Malta
New York, NY 12020
Tel.: (518) 899-7300
Fax: (518) 899-7301
Toll Free: (800) 388-2865
E-Mail: sales@electrovaya.com
Emp.: 3
BatteryDesign & Mfr
S.I.C.: 3692
N.A.I.C.S.: 335912
Shankar Das Gupta *(Pres)*

Electrovaya USA Inc. (1)
107 Hermes Rd Ste 100
Malta, NY 12020
Tel.: (518) 899-7300
Fax: (518) 899-7301
Toll Free: (800) 388-2865
E-Mail: sales@electrovaya.com
Web Site: www.electrovaya.com
Emp.: 2
Battery Design & Mfr
S.I.C.: 3692
N.A.I.C.S.: 335912
Sankar Das Gupta *(CEO)*

ELECTRUM MINING RESOURCES LTD.
314 Regents Park Road
London, N3 2JX, United Kingdom
Tel.: (44) 20 31378011
E-Mail: admin@emrmining.co.uk
Web Site: electrummr.com
TXK—(DEU)
Business Description:
Mining Resources
S.I.C.: 1241
N.A.I.C.S.: 213113
Personnel:
Anthony Lawerence *(Mng Dir)*
David Venus *(Sec)*

ELEFIRST SCIENCE AND TECHNOLOGY CO., LTD.
86 Runqi Road Dongshan Street
Jiangning District, Nanjing, China
Tel.: (86) 25 68531928
Fax: (86) 25 68531868
Web Site: www.elefirst.com
300356—(CHIN)
Sales Range: $50-74.9 Million
Business Description:
Electricity Signals Testing Instruments & Meter Reading Systems Software & Hardware
S.I.C.: 3825
N.A.I.C.S.: 334515
Personnel:
Changming Long *(Chm)*

ELEGANCE INTERNATIONAL HOLDINGS LTD
B2 B4 8/F Block B Mai Hing Industrial Bldg 16-18 Hing Yip St
Kwun Tong, Kowloon, China (Hong Kong)
Tel.: (852) 23420826
Fax: (852) 23416536
E-Mail: info@elegance-group.com
Web Site: www.elegance-group.com
0907—(HKG)
Rev.: $46,610,009
Assets: $65,567,980
Liabilities: $9,793,753
Net Worth: $55,774,228
Earnings: ($8,144,869)
Emp.: 3,773
Fiscal Year-end: 03/31/13
Business Description:
Medical Devices & Diagnostics
S.I.C.: 3827
N.A.I.C.S.: 333314
Personnel:
Leung Wah Hui *(Co-Founder, Chm & Mng Dir)*
Shu Sum Leung *(Co-Founder)*
Connie Choi Yee Tsui *(Sec & Controller-Fin)*
Board of Directors:
Leung Wah Hui
Maurizio De Gasperis
Shu Sum Leung
Barbara Lissi
Ronald Kwok Fai Poon
Sui Hong Poon
Tommy Hok Lam Tam
Ben Chung Mat Wong

Codan Services Limited
Clarendon House 2 Church Street
Hamilton, Bermuda

Subsidiaries:

Elegance Optical Investments Limited (1)
Rm 2 8 F Mai Hing Indus Bldg Block B 16-18 Hing Yip St
Kwun Tong, Kowloon, China (Hong Kong)
Tel.: (852) 23420826
Fax: (852) 23416536
E-Mail: info@Elegance-group.com
Web Site: www.Elegance-group.com
Investment Holding Services
S.I.C.: 6719
N.A.I.C.S.: 551112
Donald Tsang *(Gen Mgr)*

Elegance Optical Manufactory Limited (1)
Rm B2 & B4 8 Fl Mai Hing Indus Bldg 16-18 Hing Yip St
Kwun Tong, Kowloon, China (Hong Kong)
Tel.: (852) 23420826
Fax: (852) 23416536
E-Mail: info@elegance-group.com
Optical Frames Mfr & Sales
S.I.C.: 3851
N.A.I.C.S.: 339115

Gold Strong Industrial Limited (1)
Rm B2-4 8 F Mai Hing Indus Bldg 16-18 Hing Yip St
Kwun Tong, Kowloon, China (Hong Kong)
Tel.: (852) 23420826
Fax: (852) 23416536
E-Mail: goldstrong@elegance-group.com
Optical Frames Whslr
S.I.C.: 5048
N.A.I.C.S.: 423460

Sandwalk Far East Limited (1)
B1 B2 6 F Block B Mai Hing Indus Bldg 16-18 Hing Yip St
Kwun Tong, Kowloon, China (Hong Kong)
Tel.: (852) 2951 6074
Fax: (852) 2951 7464
E-Mail: mail@sandwalkstudio.com
Web Site: www.sandwalkstudio.com
Leather Accessories Sales
S.I.C.: 5948
N.A.I.C.S.: 448320

ELEGANT MARBLES & GRANI INDUSTRIES LTD.
Elegant House Raghuvanshi Mills Compound Senapati Bapat Marg
Lower Parel West, Mumbai, Maharastra, 400013, India
Tel.: (91) 2224960771
Fax: (91) 2224939676
E-Mail: elegantmarbles@gmail.com
Web Site: www.elegantmarbles.com
Year Founded: 1984
526705—(BOM)
Rev.: $4,671,583
Assets: $11,248,447
Liabilities: $1,999,864
Net Worth: $9,248,582
Earnings: $651,187
Fiscal Year-end: 03/31/13
Business Description:
Marbles & Granites Mfr
S.I.C.: 3281
N.A.I.C.S.: 327991
Personnel:
Rajesh Agarwal *(Chm & Co-Mng Dir)*
Rakesh Agarwal *(Co-Mng Dir)*
Hitesh Kothari *(Compliance Officer)*
Virendra G. Bhat *(Sec)*
Board of Directors:
Rajesh Agarwal
Radhey Shyam Agarwal
Rakesh Agarwal
Ram Chawla
Rajkumar Mittal
Transfer Agent:
Universal Capital Securities Pvt. Ltd
21 Shakil Niwas Mahakali Caves Road Andheri East
Mumbai, India

ELEKEIROZ S.A.
Rua Dr Edgardo de Azevedo Soares 392
Varzea Paulista, Sao Paulo, SP, 13224 030, Brazil
Tel.: (55) 1145968800
E-Mail: export@elekeiroz.com.br
Web Site: www.elekeiroz.com.br
Year Founded: 1894
Sales Range: $300-349.9 Million
Emp.: 770
Business Description:
Chemicals & Synthetic Resin Mfr
S.I.C.: 2899
N.A.I.C.S.: 325998
Personnel:
Alfredo A. Villela Filho *(Vice Chm)*

ELEKTA AB
Kungstensgatan 18
113 75 Stockholm, Sweden
Mailing Address:
PO Box 7593
SE-103 93 Stockholm, Sweden
Tel.: (46) 858725400
Fax: (46) 858725500
E-Mail: info@elekta.com
Web Site: www.elekta.com
EKTA B—(OMX OTC)
Sls.: $1,600,477,200
Assets: $2,524,323,600
Liabilities: $1,663,635,600
Net Worth: $860,688,000
Earnings: $209,134,800
Emp.: 3,488
Fiscal Year-end: 04/30/13
Business Description:
Medical Radiation Treatment Equipment Mfr
S.I.C.: 3841
N.A.I.C.S.: 339112
Personnel:
Laurent Leksell *(Chm)*
Tomas Puusepp *(Pres & CEO)*
Hakan Bergstrom *(CFO)*
Johan Sedihn *(COO)*
Ian Alexander *(Exec VP-Europe, Africa, Latin America & Middle East)*
Asa Hedin *(Exec VP-Neuroscience)*
James P. Hoey *(Exec VP-North America)*
John Lapre *(Exec VP-Brachytherapy)*
Todd Powell *(Exec VP-Software)*
Gilbert Wai *(Exec VP-Asia Pacific)*
Bill Yaeger *(Exec VP-Oncology)*
Board of Directors:
Laurent Leksell
Hans M. Barella
Luciano Cattani
Birgitta Stymne Goransson
Siaou-Sze Lien
Tomas Puusepp
Wolfgang Reim
Jan Secher

Subsidiary:

Elekta Instrument AB (1)
Kungstensgatan 18
PO Box 7593
103 93 Stockholm, Sweden
Tel.: (46) 8 587 254 00
Fax: (46) 8 587 255 00
E-Mail: info@elekta.com
Web Site: www.elekta.com
Medical & Surgical Instrument Mfr
S.I.C.: 3841
N.A.I.C.S.: 339112
Angelica Goldring *(Gen Mgr)*

U.S. Subsidiaries:

Elekta / IMPAC Medical Systems, Inc. (1)
13723 Riverport Dr Ste 100
Maryland Heights, MO 63043 MO
Tel.: (314) 993-0003
Fax: (314) 993-0075
Toll Free: (800) 878-4267
E-Mail: info.america@elekta.com
Web Site: www.elekta.com
Emp.: 100
Radiation Treatment Planning Systems Mfr Export
S.I.C.: 3841
N.A.I.C.S.: 339112
Tomas Puusepp *(Pres & CEO)*
James P. Hoey *(Exec VP)*

Non-U.S. Subsidiaries:

CMS GmbH (2)
Heinrich von Stephan Str 5 b
79100 Freiburg, Germany
Tel.: (49) 761881880
Fax: (49) 7618818811
E-Mail: sales-europe@cmsrtp.com
Web Site: www.cms-euro.com
Emp.: 30
Radiation Treatment Planning Software Mfr
S.I.C.: 3841
N.A.I.C.S.: 339112
Olof Sanden *(Mng Dir)*

CMS Japan K.K. (2)
Nagatacho Bldg 2 4 3 Nagata cho
Chiyoda Ku, Tokyo, 100-0014, Japan
Tel.: (81) 3 3580 7100
Fax: (81) 3 3580 7120
E-Mail: sales-japan@cmsrtp.com
Emp.: 30
Radiation Treatment Planning Software Mfr
S.I.C.: 3841
N.A.I.C.S.: 339112
Yasuo Ashino *(Pres)*

Elekta Inc. (1)
4775 Peachtree Industrial Blvd Bldg 300 Ste 300
Norcross, GA 30092

Elekta AB—(Continued)

Tel.: (770) 300-9725
Fax: (770) 448-6338
E-Mail: info.america@elekta.com
Web Site: www.elekta.com
Emp.: 200
Medical Technology Systems & Solutions
S.I.C.: 3841
N.A.I.C.S.: 339112
Peter Gaccione *(VP-Global Mktg)*

IMPAC Medical Systems, Inc. **(1)**
100 Methilda Pl
Sunnyvale, CA 94086 CA
Tel.: (650) 623-8800
Fax: (408) 830-8003
Web Site: www.impac.com
Emp.: 200
Computer Software Development
Export
S.I.C.: 7372
N.A.I.C.S.: 511210
James P. Hoey *(Co-Founder & COO)*
Scott T. Soehl *(Sr VP-Oncology Sls)*

Subsidiary:

IMPAC Global Systems **(2)**
100 Mathilda Pl Fl 5
Sunnyvale, CA 94086
Tel.: (650) 623-8800
Fax: (408) 830-8003
E-Mail: info.america@elekta.com
Web Site: www.impac.com
Emp.: 200
Computer Software Development
S.I.C.: 7372
N.A.I.C.S.: 511210

Non-U.S. Subsidiary:

Elekta IMPAC Software **(2)**
Linac House Fleming Way
Crawley, W Sussex, RH10 9RR, United Kingdom (100%)
Tel.: (44) 1293544422
Fax: (44) 1293654321
Web Site: www.impac.com
Emp.: 15
Computer Software Developer
S.I.C.: 3652
N.A.I.C.S.: 334614

Non-U.S. Subsidiaries:

3D Line Research and Development S.r.l. **(1)**
Via Bernardo Rucellai 23
Milan, 20126, Italy
Tel.: (39) 022550161
Fax: (39) 0225501642
E-Mail: info@3dline.com
Web Site: www.3dline.com
Medical Equipment Research & Development Services
S.I.C.: 8731
N.A.I.C.S.: 541712

Elekta Asia Ltd **(1)**
16/F The Hennessy 256 Hennessy Road
Wanchai, China (Hong Kong)
Tel.: (852) 2891 2208
Fax: (852) 2575 7133
E-Mail: info.hongkong@elekta.com
Surgical Equipment Distr
S.I.C.: 5047
N.A.I.C.S.: 423450
Mona Lee *(Reg Mgr-Sls)*

Elekta BMEI (Beijing) Medical Equipment Co., Ltd **(1)**
No 21 Chuang Xin Road Science Park
Chang Ping, Beijing, 102200, China
Tel.: (86) 1080125012
Fax: (86) 1080125000
E-Mail: gilbert.way@elekta.com
Web Site: www.elekta.com
Emp.: 115
Medical Radiation Therapy Equipment Mfr & Sales
S.I.C.: 3841
N.A.I.C.S.: 339112
Gilbert Way *(Gen Mgr)*

Elekta B.V. **(1)**
De Maas 26
5684 PL Best, Netherlands
Tel.: (31) 499336161
Fax: (31) 499336160
E-Mail: eos_nl@eos.elekta.com
Web Site: www.elekta.com
Emp.: 18
Medical Radiation Therapy Equipment Mfr & Sales
S.I.C.: 3841
N.A.I.C.S.: 339112
Peter Schoor *(VP)*

Elekta GmbH **(1)**
Alsterdorfer Markt 4
22297 Hamburg, Germany
Tel.: (49) 40 59 38 30
Fax: (49) 40 59 38 31 11
E-Mail: info.germany@elekta.com
Web Site: www.elekta.com
Pharmaceutical Products Mfr
S.I.C.: 2834
N.A.I.C.S.: 325412

Elekta GmbH **(1)**
Klostergasse 4
A 6020 Innsbruck, Austria
Tel.: (43) 512560220
Fax: (43) 512560222
E-Mail: austria-switzerland@elekta.com
Web Site: www.elekta.com
Emp.: 15
Medical Radiation Therapy Equipment Mfr & Sales
S.I.C.: 3841
N.A.I.C.S.: 339112

Elekta Instrument (Shanghai) Ltd **(1)**
B2 No 1000 Jihai Road
Pudong, Shanghai, 201206, China
Tel.: (86) 2158997200
Fax: (86) 2158997220
Emp.: 100
Medical Radiation Therapy Equipment Mfr & Sales
S.I.C.: 3841
N.A.I.C.S.: 339112
Gelpert Ywii *(Mng Dir)*

Elekta KK **(1)**
3-9-1 Shibaura
Minato-Ku, 108-0023 Tokyo, Japan
Tel.: (81) 3 6722 3800
Fax: (81) 3 6722 4231
E-Mail: info.japan@elekta.com
Web Site: www.elekta.com
Medical Equipment Sales & Maintenance
S.I.C.: 5047
N.A.I.C.S.: 423450

Elekta Limited **(1)**
Linac House Fleming Way
Crawley, W Sussex, RH10 9RR, United Kingdom
Tel.: (44) 1293544422
Fax: (44) 1293654321
E-Mail: info@elekta.com
Emp.: 600
Medical Radiation Treatment Equipment Mfr & Sales
S.I.C.: 3841
N.A.I.C.S.: 339112

Elekta Limited **(1)**
No 824 Mikeum Park Building 150
Geumgok-Dong
463-805 Seongnam, Gyeonggi-Do, Korea (South)
Tel.: (82) 31 716 0080
Fax: (82) 31 716 0402
Surgical & Medical Equipment Mfr
S.I.C.: 3841
N.A.I.C.S.: 339113

Elekta Medical S.A. **(1)**
Manuel Tovar 43
28034 Madrid, Spain
Tel.: (34) 915562025
Fax: (34) 915973519
E-Mail: elekta.spain@elekta.com
Web Site: www.elekta.com
Emp.: 40
Medical Radiation Therapy Equipment Mfr & Sales
S.I.C.: 3841
N.A.I.C.S.: 339112

Elekta Medical Systems Comercio e Prestacao de Servicos para Radiologia, Radiocirurgia e Radioterapia Ltda. **(1)**
Rua Carneiro da Cunha Sau de
Sao Paulo, 4144000, Brazil
Tel.: (55) 11 50513186
Emp.: 5
Medical & Surgical Equipment Distr
S.I.C.: 5047
N.A.I.C.S.: 423450
Antonio Ponce *(Gen Mgr)*

Elekta Medical Systems India PVT. Ltd. **(1)**
302 3rd Floor Block 4 Corporate Park DLF Face 3
Haryana, Gurgaon, 122 002, India
Tel.: (91) 1244633222
Fax: (91) 01244933233
Web Site: www.elekta.com
Emp.: 65
Medical Radiation Therapy Equipment Mfr & Sales
S.I.C.: 3841
N.A.I.C.S.: 339112
Brendan Vahey *(Mng Dir)*

Elekta Neuromag Oy **(1)**
Siltasaarenkatu 18 20 A
00530 Helsinki, Finland
Tel.: (358) 97562400
Fax: (358) 975624011
Web Site: www.elekta.com
Emp.: 20
Medical Imaging Equipment Mfr & Sales
S.I.C.: 3841
N.A.I.C.S.: 339112
Juha Hamalainen *(Gen Mgr)*

Elekta (Pty) Ltd (Southern Africa) **(1)**
1221 Edgehill Ln
PO Box 12585
Queenswood, Pretoria, 0186, South Africa
Tel.: (27) 123331740
Fax: (27) 123331974
E-Mail: jeanette.gagiano@elekta.com
Web Site: www.elekta.com
Emp.: 7
Medical Radiation Therapy Equipment Mfr & Sales
S.I.C.: 3841
N.A.I.C.S.: 339112
Jeanette Gagiano *(Mng Dir)*

Elekta Pty. Ltd. **(1)**
Ste 2 Level 14 168 Walker St
North Sydney, NSW, 2060, Australia
Tel.: (61) 299393255
Fax: (61) 289071802
Web Site: www.elekta.com
Emp.: 13
Medical Radiation Therapy Equipment Mfr & Sales
S.I.C.: 3841
N.A.I.C.S.: 339112
Andrew Wilson *(Mng Dir)*

Elekta S.A./N.V. **(1)**
Imperiastraat 8
1930 Zaventem, Belgium
Tel.: (32) 2 721 2010
Fax: (32) 2 721 2090
E-Mail: info.europe@elekta.com
Emp.: 9
Medical & Surgical Equipment Distr
S.I.C.: 5047
N.A.I.C.S.: 423450

Elekta SA **(1)**
Immeuble Le Diderot 39 rue du Gouverneur General Felix Eboue
92130 Issy-les-Moulineaux, France
Tel.: (33) 1 55 95 83 40
Fax: (33) 1 55 95 83 57
E-Mail: contact.fr@elekta.com
Emp.: 5
Medical Device Mfr & Distr
S.I.C.: 3841
N.A.I.C.S.: 339112

Elekta S.p.A. **(1)**
Centro Direzionale Colleoni Palazzo Andromeda Ingr 3
200 41 Agrate Brianza, Italy
Tel.: (39) 039 6570011
Fax: (39) 039 65700131
E-Mail: elektaitalia@elekta.com
Web Site: www.elekta.com
Surgical & Medical Equipment Distr
S.I.C.: 5047
N.A.I.C.S.: 423450

Medical Intelligence Medizintechnik GmbH **(1)**
Robert Bosch Strasse 8
86830 Schwabmunchen, Germany
Tel.: (49) 823296920
Fax: (49) 82329692800
E-Mail: company@medint.de
Web Site: www.elekta.de
Emp.: 60
Medical Radiation Therapy Equipment Mfr
S.I.C.: 3841
N.A.I.C.S.: 339112
Chris Snook *(CEO)*
Lutz Schaefer *(CFO)*

Nucletron B.V. **(1)**
Waardgelder 1
3905 TH Veenendaal, Netherlands NL
Mailing Address:
PO Box 930
3900 AX Veenendaal, Netherlands
Tel.: (31) 318 557280
Fax: (31) 318550485
E-Mail: info@nl.nucletron.com
Web Site: www.nucletron.com
Sales Range: $150-199.9 Million
Emp.: 400
Cancer Treatment Device Mfr, Sales & Service
S.I.C.: 3841
N.A.I.C.S.: 339112
Jos Lamers *(CEO)*

U.S. Subsidiary:

Nucletron Corporation **(2)**
7021 Columbia Gateway Dr
Columbia, MD 21046-2289
Tel.: (410) 312-4100
Fax: (410) 872-4434
Toll Free: (800) 336-2249
E-Mail: info@nucusa.com
Web Site: www.nucletron.com
Emp.: 110
Cancer Treatment Device Mfr & Sales
S.I.C.: 3841
N.A.I.C.S.: 339112

Non-U.S. Subsidiaries:

Nucletron A/S **(2)**
Fyrstikkalleen 3A
Postboks 6651
0609 Oslo, Norway
Tel.: (47) 2270 7970
Fax: (47) 2270 7971
Web Site: www.nucletron.com
Emp.: 20
Cancer Treatment Device Mfr & Sales
S.I.C.: 3841
N.A.I.C.S.: 339112
Kjell Lundenw *(Mng Dir)*

Nucletron Asia Pacific Ltd. **(2)**
Room 1005 Tower II Silvercord
30 Canton Rd Tsim Sha Tsui, Kowloon, China (Hong Kong)
Tel.: (852) 23112683
Fax: (852) 23113672
E-Mail: general@nucletron.com.hk
Web Site: www.nucletron.com.hk
Emp.: 25
Cancer Treatment Device Mfr & Sales
S.I.C.: 3841
N.A.I.C.S.: 339112

Nucletron Canada Inc. **(2)**
411 Legget Drive Suite 502
Kanata, ON, K2K 3C9, Canada
Tel.: (613) 886-1100
Fax: (613) 592-6559
Toll Free: (800) 826-2258
E-Mail: oncosupport@ca.nucletron.com
Emp.: 7
Cancer Treatment Device Mfr & Sales
S.I.C.: 3841
N.A.I.C.S.: 339112
Cathi Nault *(Gen Mgr)*

Nucletron Poland SP z.o.o. **(2)**
Oddzial w Warszawie
Al Krakowska 285, 02 133 Warsaw, Poland
Tel.: (48) 228681782
Fax: (48) 22 868 2216
E-Mail: serwis21@nucletron.com.pl
Cancer Treatment Device Mfr & Sales
S.I.C.: 3841
N.A.I.C.S.: 339112

Nucletron Pty. Ltd. **(2)**
1b Little Commodore Street
Newtown, NSW, 2042, Australia AU
Tel.: (61) 295171300
Fax: (61) 295171311

E-Mail: sales@au.nucletron.com
Web Site: www.nucletron.com
Emp.: 9
Cancer Treatment Device Mfr & Sales
S.I.C.: 3841
N.A.I.C.S.: 339112
Peter Douglas *(Mng Dir)*

Nucletron S.A. (2)
Avda de Castilla 2 Parque Empresarial San Fernando
Edificio Francia Planta 2 E
San Fernando de Henares, 28830 Madrid, Spain ES
Tel.: (34) 918250068
Fax: (34) 918250069
E-Mail: nucletron@nucletron.es
Web Site: www.nucletron.es
Emp.: 11
Cancer Treatment Device Mfr & Sales
S.I.C.: 3841
N.A.I.C.S.: 339112

Nucletron SAS (2)
Parc d'Activites Bernard Vergnaud
15 Rue Paul Langevin, 93274 Sevran, Cedex, France FR
Tel.: (33) 149362060
Fax: (33) 143833638
E-Mail: info@nucletron.fr
Web Site: www.nucletron.com
Emp.: 18
Cancer Treatment Device Mfr & Sales
S.I.C.: 3841
N.A.I.C.S.: 339112

Nucletron Scandinavia AB (2)
Klostergatan 10
Box 1704
751 47 Uppsala, Sweden
Tel.: (46) 18565000
E-Mail: info@elekta.com
Web Site: www.se.nucletron.com
Emp.: 40
Cancer Treatment Device Mfr & Sales
S.I.C.: 3841
N.A.I.C.S.: 339112
Mats Hogberg *(Mng Dir)*

Nucletron UK Ltd. (2)
Nucletron House Chowley Oak
Tattenhall, Chester, CH3 9EX, United Kingdom UK
Tel.: (44) 1829771111
Fax: (44) 1829770979
E-Mail: sales@nucletron.co.uk
Web Site: www.nucletron.com
Emp.: 26
Cancer Treatment Device Mfr & Sales
S.I.C.: 3841
N.A.I.C.S.: 339112
Mark Hitchman *(Mng Dir)*

Nuclital Srl (2)
Centro Dirziomale Colleni
2864 Milan, Italy
Tel.: (39) 039322848
Fax: (39) 396429131
Web Site: www.elatka.com
Cancer Treatment Device Mfr & Sales
S.I.C.: 3841
N.A.I.C.S.: 339112
Massimo Abbiti *(Mng Dir)*

Theranostic Medizintechnik GmbH (2)
Obere Dammstrasse 8 10
42653 Solingen, Germany DE
Tel.: (49) 2125875153
Fax: (49) 2125875269
E-Mail: info@theranostic.de
Web Site: www.theranostic.de
Emp.: 50
Cancer Treatment Device Mfr & Sales
S.I.C.: 3841
N.A.I.C.S.: 339112
Heinz Meyer *(Controller)*

ELEKTRIM S.A.

Panska 77/79 St
00-834 Warsaw, Poland
Tel.: (48) 224328801
Fax: (48) 224328959
E-Mail: info@elektrim.pl
Web Site: www.elektrim.pl
Year Founded: 1945
Sales Range: $200-249.9 Million
Emp.: 15

Business Description:
Holding Company;
Telecommunications, Energy & Cables
S.I.C.: 3357
N.A.I.C.S.: 335929
Personnel:
Wojciech Piskorz *(Gen Mgr)*

Subsidiaries:

Elektrim-Megadex S.A. (1)
Mickiewicza 63
Warsaw, 010625, Poland (99%)
Tel.: (48) 225605700
Fax: (48) 225605766
E-Mail: emsa@emsa.pl
Web Site: www.emsa.com.pl
Emp.: 20
S.I.C.: 1731
N.A.I.C.S.: 238210
Thomas Halls *(Pres)*

Elektrim-Volt S.A. (1)
ul Panska 85
00-834 Warsaw, Poland (100%)
Tel.: (48) 224378655
Fax: (48) 224378682
E-Mail: sekretariat@elektrim-volt.eu
Web Site: www.elektrim-volt.eu
S.I.C.: 1731
N.A.I.C.S.: 238210

ELEKTRISOLA DR. GERD SCHILDBACH GMBH & CO. KG

PO Box 2120
D 51574 Reichshof, Eckenhagen, Germany
Tel.: (49) 2265120
Fax: (49) 22651222
E-Mail: u.gester@elektrisola.de
Web Site: www.elektrisola.com
Emp.: 300

Business Description:
Wire Mfr
S.I.C.: 3354
N.A.I.C.S.: 331318
Personnel:
Detlef Schildbach *(Mng Dir)*

U.S. Subsidiary:

Elektrisola Inc. (1)
126 High St
Boscawen, NH 03303-2808 NH
Tel.: (603) 796-2114
Fax: (603) 796-2111
E-Mail: sales@elektrisola-usa.com
Web Site: www.elektrisola.com
Emp.: 170
Provider of Nonferrous Wiredrawing & Insulating Services
Import Export
S.I.C.: 3357
N.A.I.C.S.: 335929
George Downing *(Exec VP)*

ELEKTRO BIJELJINA A.D. BIJELJINA

Majevicka 97
Bijeljina, Bosnia & Herzegovina
Tel.: (387) 55 226 700
Fax: (387) 55 210 304
E-Mail: elektrobn@teol.net
Web Site: www.elektrobijeljina.com
Year Founded: 2006
ELBJ—(BANJ)
Emp.: 850

Business Description:
Electric Power Distr
S.I.C.: 4931
N.A.I.C.S.: 221122
Personnel:
Aleksandar Bugarinovic *(Chm-Supervisory Bd)*
Zivan Delic *(Vice Chm-Supervisory Bd)*
Supervisory Board of Directors:
Aleksandar Bugarinovic
Zivan Delic
Slavko Lazic
Mladen Mirkovic
Milorad Solakovic

ELEKTRO MACK GMBH

Kiesgrubenstr 18
88255 Baindt, Germany
Tel.: (49) 750294010
Fax: (49) 7502940150
E-Mail: info@elektro-mack.com
Web Site: www.elektro-mack.com
Year Founded: 1973
Rev.: $10,000,000
Emp.: 75

Business Description:
Industrial Electric Installation Services
S.I.C.: 4931
N.A.I.C.S.: 221122
Personnel:
Karl Mack *(Co-Mng Dir)*
Karl-Heinz Mack *(Co-Mng Dir)*

ELEKTRO SLOVENIA D.O.O.

Hajdrihova Ulica 2
1000 Ljubljana, Slovenia
Tel.: (386) 14743000
Fax: (386) 14742552
E-Mail: info@eles.si
Web Site: www.eles.si
Sales Range: $200-249.9 Million
Emp.: 500

Business Description:
Electric Power Transmission Services
S.I.C.: 4939
N.A.I.C.S.: 221122
Personnel:
Srecko Lesjak *(Dir-CPS Electric Power Transmission)*
Supervisory Board of Directors:
Andrej Aplenc
Jure Cater
Leon Cizeli
Matiaz Dolinar
Rado Ferlic
Janez Hrovat
Franc Lavric

Subsidiaries:

Borzen, d.o.o. (1)
Dunajska 128a
1000 Ljubljana, Slovenia
Tel.: (386) 16207600
Fax: (386) 16207601
E-Mail: info@borzen.si
Web Site: www.borzen.si
Emp.: 26
Electricity Trading
S.I.C.: 6231
N.A.I.C.S.: 523210

Education Centre of the Slovenian Electric Power Authority (1)
Hajdrihova Ulica 2
1000 Ljubljana, Slovenia
Tel.: (386) 014742631
Fax: (386) 14742632
E-Mail: info@ices.se
Web Site: www.ices.se
Emp.: 3
Personnel Training
S.I.C.: 8999
N.A.I.C.S.: 541612
Andreja Nardenrepensek *(Gen Mgr)*

Eles-Gen, d.o.o. (1)
Hajdrihova Ulica 2
1000 Ljubljana, Slovenia
Tel.: (386) 014743000
Fax: (386) 14742502
E-Mail: vitoslav.turk@eles.si
Web Site: www.eles.si/
Emp.: 537
Electric Power Generation
S.I.C.: 4931
N.A.I.C.S.: 221121
Vitoslav Turk *(CEO & Mng Dir)*

ELEKTROBIT CORPORATION

Tutkijantie 8
FIN 90570 Oulu, Finland
Mailing Address:
PO Box 45
FIN 90461 Oulunsalo, Finland
Tel.: (358) 403442000
Fax: (358) 8343032
E-Mail: arto.pietila@elektrobit.com
Web Site: www.elektrobit.com
EBC1V—(HEL)
Sls.: $249,593,380
Assets: $191,734,993
Liabilities: $98,711,954
Net Worth: $93,023,039
Earnings: $4,403,322
Emp.: 1,870
Fiscal Year-end: 12/31/12

Business Description:
Embedded Hardware & Software Solutions For Automotive & Wireless Technology
S.I.C.: 7373
N.A.I.C.S.: 541512
Personnel:
Jukka Harju *(CEO)*
Veli-Pekka Paloranta *(CFO)*
Paivi Timonen *(Chief Legal Officer)*
Arto Pietila *(Sr VP)*
Antti Sivula *(Sr VP-Wireless Comm Tool)*
Board of Directors:
Jorma Halonen
Juha Hulkko
Staffan Simberg
Erkki Veikkolainen

Subsidiaries:

Elektrobit Technologies Oy (1)
Automaatiotie 1
PO Box 45
90570 Oulunsalo, Finland (100%)
Tel.: (358) 403442000
Fax: (358) 82432032
E-Mail: info@elektrobit.com
Web Site: www.elektrobit.com
Emp.: 500
Real Estate Property Lessors
S.I.C.: 6519
N.A.I.C.S.: 531190
Pertti Korhonen *(CEO)*

Elektrobit Wireless Communications Oy (1)
Tugkijantieh
Oulunsalo, 90570, Finland (100%)
Tel.: (358) 403442000
Fax: (358) 8343032
E-Mail: info@elektrobit.com
Emp.: 160
Engineering Services
S.I.C.: 8711
N.A.I.C.S.: 541330
Pertti Korhonen *(CEO)*

U.S. Subsidiaries:

EB Automotive Inc (1)
2020 Marion Quimby Dr
Stevensville, MD 21666-2581
Tel.: (410) 643-3716
Fax: (410) 643-3893
Software Systems Development Services
S.I.C.: 7371
N.A.I.C.S.: 541511

Elektrobit Inc (1)
22745 29th Dr SE Ste 200
Bothell, WA 98021
Tel.: (425) 686-3100
Fax: (425) 686-3102
Web Site: www.elektrobit.com
Research & Development in the Physical Engineering & Life Sciences
S.I.C.: 8731
N.A.I.C.S.: 541712

Elektrobit Production Solutions, Inc. (1)
8100 Jetstar Dr Ste 100
Irving, TX 75063
Tel.: (972) 393-5564
Sales Range: $1-9.9 Million
Emp.: 99
Conveyor & Conveying Equipment Mfr
S.I.C.: 3535

Elektrobit Corporation—(Continued)

N.A.I.C.S.: 333922
Brian Bagby *(Gen Mgr)*

Non-U.S. Subsidiaries:

Elektrobit AG (1)
Rosswiesstrasse 29
8608 Bubikon, Switzerland
Tel.: (41) 552532060
Fax: (41) 552532070
Engineering Services
S.I.C.: 8711
N.A.I.C.S.: 541330
Johans Kaufmann *(Mng Dir)*

Elektrobit Austria GmbH (1)
Kaiserstrabe 45-2
1070 Vienna, Austria
Tel.: (43) 1599830
Fax: (43) 15998318
Web Site: www.elektrobit.com
Emp.: 45
Software Development Services
S.I.C.: 7371
N.A.I.C.S.: 541511
Alexander Kocher *(Gen Mgr)*

Elektrobit Automotive GmbH (1)
Am Wolfsmantel 46
91058 Erlangen, Germany (79.92%)
Tel.: (49) 913177010
Fax: (49) 913177016333
E-Mail: info@elektrobit.com
Web Site: www.elektrobit.com
Emp.: 870
Custom Computer Programming Services
S.I.C.: 7371
N.A.I.C.S.: 541511

Elektrobit Automotive Software (Shanghai) Ltd. (1)
Zhangjiang High-tech Park Building 2 401-402 No 690 Bibo Road
Shanghai, 201203, China
Tel.: (86) 10 6781 7020
Fax: (86) 10 6781 7009
Web Site: www.elektrobit.com
Wireless Communications Services
S.I.C.: 4812
N.A.I.C.S.: 517210

Elektrobit France SAS (1)
8 Avenue Eiffel
78420 Carrieres-sur-Seine, France
Tel.: (33) 139760814
Fax: (33) 130157801
E-Mail: ebfrance@elektrobit.com
Web Site: www.elektrobit.com
Emp.: 25
Wireless Telecommunication Services
S.I.C.: 4812
N.A.I.C.S.: 517210
Abou Bruno *(Gen Mgr)*

Elektrobit Nippon K.K. (1)
4th Floor Hiro Building 2-24-10
Minami Aoyama Minato-ku, Tokyo, 107-0062, Japan
Tel.: (81) 357756160
Fax: (81) 357756161
E-Mail: info-jp@elektrobit.com
Web Site: www.elektrobit.com
Electronic Component Mfr
S.I.C.: 3679
N.A.I.C.S.: 334419

Elektrobit Technology (Beijing) Ltd (1)
Building A 2 Beijing Guo Sheng Sci-Tech Par
No 1Yizhuang Economic Technolo, 100176
Beijing, China (100%)
Tel.: (86) 1067817020
Fax: (86) 1067817009
Emp.: 200
Electrical Apparatus & Equipment Wiring Supplies & Related Equipment Merchant Whslr
S.I.C.: 5063
N.A.I.C.S.: 423610
Veli-Pekka Paloranta *(CFO)*

Elektrobit Wireless (Beijing) Ltd (1)
Building A2 Beijing Guo Sheng Sci-tech Park No 1 Kang Ding Street
Beijing, 100176, China
Tel.: (86) 1067817020
Fax: (86) 1067817009
Web Site: www.elektrobit.com
Wireless Communication Services
S.I.C.: 4812
N.A.I.C.S.: 517210

ELEKTROBUDOWA S.A.

ul Porcelanowa 12
40-246 Katowice, Poland
Tel.: (48) 322590100
Fax: (48) 322052760
E-Mail: elbudowa@elbudowa.com.pl
Web Site: www.elbudowa.com.pl
ELB—(WAR)
Rev.: $326,441,571
Assets: $221,685,921
Liabilities: $112,384,529
Net Worth: $109,301,392
Earnings: $12,639,533
Emp.: 2,205
Fiscal Year-end: 12/31/12

Business Description:
Power Engineering Construction & Installation Services
S.I.C.: 1796
N.A.I.C.S.: 238290

Personnel:
Dariusz Manko *(Chm-Supervisory Bd)*
Jacek Faltynowicz *(Chm-Mgmt Bd & CEO)*
Karol Zbikowski *(Vice Chm-Supervisory Bd)*
Ariusz Bober *(Member-Mgmt Bd & Dir-Power Distr Div)*
Janusz Juszczyk *(Member-Mgmt Bd & Dir-Power Generation Div)*
Jaroslaw Tomaszewski *(Member-Mgmt Bd & Dir-Fin)*
Arkadiusz Klimowicz *(Member-Mgmt Bd)*

Supervisory Board of Directors:
Dariusz Manko
Agnieszka Godlewska
Eryk Karski
Tomasz Mosiek
Ryszard Rafalski
Pawel Tarnowski
Karol Zbikowski

ELEKTROKRAJINA A.D. BANJA LUKA

Kralja Petra Karadordevica No 95
Banja Luka, Bosnia & Herzegovina
Tel.: (387) 51 246 300
Fax: (387) 51 215 610
E-Mail: info@elektrokrajina.com
Web Site: www.elektrokrajina.com
Year Founded: 1947
EKBL—(BANJ)
Rev.: $126,894,016
Assets: $436,750,579
Liabilities: $140,706,066
Net Worth: $296,044,513
Earnings: $817,004
Emp.: 1,514
Fiscal Year-end: 12/31/12

Business Description:
Electric Energy Distr
S.I.C.: 4911
N.A.I.C.S.: 221122

Personnel:
Miroslav Bobek *(Chm-Supervisory Bd)*
Dujko Komljenovic *(Deputy Chm-Supervisory Bd & Exec Dir-Legal Issues)*

Supervisory Board of Directors:
Miroslav Bobek
Dujko Komljenovic
Milena Majstorovic
Milivoj Markovic
Zeljko Travar

ELEKTROMOTIVE GROUP LIMITED

18 Boon Lay Way 10-96/97
TradeHub21
Singapore, 609966, Singapore
Tel.: (65) 62920300
Fax: (65) 62921800
E-Mail: corp.info@lexicon.com.sg
Web Site: www.lexicon.com.sg
5KX—(SES)
Rev.: $5,959,245
Assets: $12,592,953
Liabilities: $6,555,979
Net Worth: $6,036,974
Earnings: ($2,956,142)
Emp.: 65
Fiscal Year-end: 03/31/13

Business Description:
Printing & Publication Services
S.I.C.: 2741
N.A.I.C.S.: 519130

Personnel:
Ricky Gee Hing Ang *(Vice Chm & Mng Dir)*
Hwee Ling Ng *(CFO)*
Chye Wan Chong *(Pres-Publ-Malaysia)*
Lynnette Lim *(Pres-Publ-Singapore & Intl)*
Poh Kuan Chan *(Co-Sec)*
Abdul Jabbar Karam Din *(Co-Sec)*

Board of Directors:
James Ghee Ann Ang
Ricky Gee Hing Ang
Kong Seng Chou
Roy Chung Yee Ling
Kesavan Nair
Chong Chai Tan
Choon Wee Tan

Legal Counsel:
Chancery Law Corporation
55 Market Street 08-01
Singapore, 048941, Singapore

Subsidiaries:

Lexicon F&B Pte Ltd (1)
1 HarbourFront Walk 01-52
Singapore, Singapore
Tel.: (65) 6376 9681
E-Mail: mob@lexicon.com.sg
Cafes & Restaurants Operation Services
S.I.C.: 5812
N.A.I.C.S.: 722511

Lifestyle Magazines Publishing Pte Ltd (1)
18 Boon Lay Way TradeHub 21 10-96-97
Singapore, 609966, Singapore
Tel.: (65) 62920300
E-Mail: editorial@wdemedia.com
Web Site: www.wineanddine.com.sg
Emp.: 18
Lifestyle & Special Interest Magazine Publishers
S.I.C.: 2759
N.A.I.C.S.: 323111
Ricky Ang *(Vice Chm)*

Panpac Marketing & Circulation Pte Ltd (1)
50 Raffles Place 30-00 Singapore Land Tower
Singapore, 048623, Singapore
Tel.: (65) 62920300
Fax: (65) 62921866
Newspaper & Magazine Ciruclation Services
S.I.C.: 5963
N.A.I.C.S.: 454390
Ricky Gee Hing Ang *(Mng Dir)*

Wine and Dine Experience Pte Ltd (1)
18 Boon Lay Way Ste 10-96/97 TradeHub 21
Singapore, 609966, Singapore
Tel.: (65) 62920300
Fax: (65) 62921866
E-Mail: circulation@lexicon.com.sg
Web Site: www.wineanddine.com.sg
Emp.: 30
Gourmet Lifestyle Magazine Publishing Services
S.I.C.: 2721
N.A.I.C.S.: 511120
Swee Mei Lan *(Chief HR Officer)*

ELEKTRON TECHNOLOGY PLC

Broers Building JJ Thomson Avenue
Cambridge, CB3 0FA, United Kingdom
Tel.: (44) 1223 371000
Fax: (44) 1223 350642
E-Mail: europe@elektron-technology.com
Web Site: www.elektron-technology.com
EKT—(AIM)
Rev.: $87,966,453
Assets: $48,800,061
Liabilities: $26,216,214
Net Worth: $22,583,847
Earnings: ($631,716)
Emp.: 1,014
Fiscal Year-end: 01/31/13

Business Description:
Engineered Products Mfr
S.I.C.: 3575
N.A.I.C.S.: 334118

Personnel:
Keith Antony Daley *(Chm)*
John Wilson *(CEO)*
Martin Reeves *(Sec)*

Board of Directors:
Keith Antony Daley
Simon Acland
Anthony Gordon Harris
Richard John Piper
Andrew Weatherstone
John Wilson

Legal Counsel:
Birketts LLP
Brierly Place New London Road
Chelmsford, CM2 0AP, United Kingdom

Subsidiaries:

Bulgin Components Plc (1)
Melville Court
Spilsby Road, Romford, Essex, RM3 8SB, United Kingdom
Tel.: (44) 1708 336300
Fax: (44) 1708 374616
E-Mail: europe@elektron-technology.com
Web Site: www.bulgin.co.uk
Electromechanical Components Mfr & Distr
S.I.C.: 3613
N.A.I.C.S.: 335313

Carnation Designs Limited (1)
Ponderosa Business Park Unit 1 Smithies Lane
Heckmondwike, W Yorkshire, WF16 0PR, United Kingdom
Tel.: (44) 1924411211
Fax: (44) 1924413380
E-Mail: sales@carnationdesigns.co.uk
Web Site: www.carnationdesigns.co.uk
Electric Management System Software Development Services
S.I.C.: 7371
N.A.I.C.S.: 541511
Mark Wilson *(Mng Dir)*

Digitron Instrumentation Limited (1)
Woodland Road
Torquay, Devon, TQ2 7AY, United Kingdom
Tel.: (44) 1803407700
Fax: (44) 1803 407699
E-Mail: info@digitron.com
Web Site: www.digitron.com
Emp.: 3
Measuring Instruments Mfr
S.I.C.: 3825
N.A.I.C.S.: 334515

Elektron Components Ltd. (1)
29 Central Avenue
West Molesey, Surrey, KT8 2RF, United Kingdom
Tel.: (44) 2089793232
Fax: (44) 2089792565
E-Mail: info@arcoswitch.co.uk

Web Site: www.arcolectric.co.uk
Emp.: 80
Appliance Switches & Indicator Lights Mfr & Distr
S.I.C.: 3613
N.A.I.C.S.: 335313
John Wilson *(Mng Dir)*

Hartest Holdings plc (1)
5 Lakeside Business Pk
Sandhurst, Berkshire, GU47 9DN, United Kingdom
Tel.: (44) 1252749530
Fax: (44) 1252877288
E-Mail: info@hartest-holdings.com
Web Site: www.hartest-holdings.com
Sales Range: $25-49.9 Million
Emp.: 162
Holding Company; Medical Equipment Mfr & Distr
S.I.C.: 6719
N.A.I.C.S.: 551112

Subsidiaries:

Agar Scientific Limited (2)
Unit 7 M11 Business Link Parsonage Lane
Stansted, Essex, CM248GF, United Kingdom
Tel.: (44) 01279813519
Fax: (44) 1279815106
E-Mail: websales@agarscientific.com
Web Site: www.agarscientific.com
Emp.: 20
Accessories & Consumables Mfr
S.I.C.: 3826
N.A.I.C.S.: 334516
Lynne Joyce *(Mgr-Sls & Mktg)*

Cross Technologies plc (2)
5 Lakeside Business Park
Swan Lane, Sandhurst, Berkshire, GU47 9DN, United Kingdom
Tel.: (44) 01252749500
Fax: (44) 1252877288
E-Mail: info@crosstechplc.co.uk
Web Site: www.qados.co.uk
Emp.: 25
Digital Radiography Systems, Medical Lasers, Aesthetic Lasers & Skin Cooling Devices Mfr
S.I.C.: 5047
N.A.I.C.S.: 423450
Dawn Broadhead *(Mng Dir)*

Division:

QADOS (3)
5 Lakeside Business Park
Swan Lane, Sandhurst, Berkshire, GU47 9DN, United Kingdom
Tel.: (44) 1252878999
Fax: (44) 1252877288
E-Mail: sales@qados.co.uk
Web Site: www.qados.co.uk
Emp.: 20
Radiotherapy & X-Ray Imaging Equipment Mfr
S.I.C.: 5047
N.A.I.C.S.: 423450

Hartest Precision Instruments Limited (1)
2 Gatton Park Business Centre Wells Place
Redhill, Surrey, RH1 3LG, United Kingdom
Tel.: (44) 1737 649300
Fax: (44) 1737 649301
E-Mail: info@h-pi.co.uk
Web Site: www.h-pi.co.uk
Emp.: 70
Industrial Control & Precision Measurement Machinery Mfr
S.I.C.: 3829
N.A.I.C.S.: 334519
Nigel Rose *(Mng Dir)*

Titman Tip Tools Limited (1)
Valley Road
Clacton-on-Sea, Essex, CO15 6PP, United Kingdom
Tel.: (44) 1255220123
Fax: (44) 1255 221422
E-Mail: sales@titman.co.uk
Web Site: www.titman.co.uk
Emp.: 60
Machine Tools Mfr
S.I.C.: 3542
N.A.I.C.S.: 333517
Roger McCoy *(Mng Dir)*

Non-U.S. Subsidiary:

Titman Tip Tools GmbH (2)
Munsterstrasse 52a
Wolbeck, 48167 Munster, Germany
Tel.: (49) 250685040
Fax: (49) 2506 85051
E-Mail: titman.gmbh@t-online.de
Web Site: www.titman.de
Tungsten Carbide Component Whslr
S.I.C.: 5199
N.A.I.C.S.: 424990

U.S. Subsidiaries:

Elektron Components Corporation (1)
31-315 Plantation Dr
Thousand Palms, CA 92276 (100%)
Tel.: (760) 343-3650
Fax: (760) 343-3445
E-Mail: info@arcolectric.com
Web Site: www.arcolectric.com
Switches, Indicator Lights & Fuse Holders Mfr & Distr
S.I.C.: 3613
N.A.I.C.S.: 335313
Matt McElreath *(Mgr-Distr)*

Titman Tip Tools Ltd (1)
31-315 Plantation Dr
Thousand Palms, CA 92276
Tel.: (760) 799-5668
Fax: (562) 927-7633
Tungsten Carbide Component Mfr
S.I.C.: 3999
N.A.I.C.S.: 339999

Non-U.S. Subsidiaries:

Elektron Components Tunisie Sarl (1)
13 Rue 62128 Zone Industrielle Ibn Khaldoun Citie Ettahir
2042 Tunis, Tunisia
Tel.: (216) 71 923 600
Fax: (216) 71 924 142
Electromechanical Component Mfr
S.I.C.: 3679
N.A.I.C.S.: 334419

Hartest Precision Instruments India Private Limited (1)
304 Plot No 7 Mahajan Tower Shreshtha Vihar
New Delhi, 110092, India
Tel.: (91) 1122152150
Fax: (91) 1122152152
Emp.: 2
Industrial Control & Precision Measurement Machinery Mfr
S.I.C.: 3829
N.A.I.C.S.: 334519
Rajesh Vijay *(Mng Dir)*

ELEKTROPORCELAN A.D.

Marka Miljanova 15
21000 Novi Sad, Serbia
Tel.: (381) 21 6615 556
Fax: (381) 21 423 782
E-Mail: elektroporcelan.ns@neobee.net
Web Site: www.elektroporcelan.co.rs
Year Founded: 1922
ELPO—(BEL)
Business Description:
Insulator Mfr
S.I.C.: 5033
N.A.I.C.S.: 423330
Personnel:
Momir Stojkovic *(Gen Mgr)*

ELEKTROTIM S.A.

ul Stargardzka 8
54-156 Wroclaw, Poland
Tel.: (48) 713882480
Fax: (48) 713514839
E-Mail: sekratiriat@elektrotim.pl
Web Site: www.elektrotim.pl
ELT—(WAR)
Rev.: $67,034,622
Assets: $46,530,265
Liabilities: $18,829,277
Net Worth: $27,700,988
Earnings: $2,096,864
Fiscal Year-end: 12/31/12
Business Description:
Electric Installations & Automatic Systems
S.I.C.: 1731
N.A.I.C.S.: 238210
Personnel:
Krzysztof Folta *(Chm-Supervisory Bd)*
Andrzej Diakun *(Chm-Mgmt Bd)*
Jan Walulik *(Vice Chm-Supervisory Bd)*
Sawomir Ciesla *(Member-Mgmt Bd)*
Zbigniew Pawlik *(Member-Mgmt Bd)*
Supervisory Board of Directors:
Krzysztof Folta
Stefan Dziedziul
Wojciech Szymon Kowalski
Mateusz Rodzynkiewicz
Jan Walulik

ELEKTROWNIA BELCHATOW S.A.

Rogowiec 5
97-406 Belchatow, Poland
Tel.: (48) 446325132
Fax: (48) 447352211
Year Founded: 1960
Sales Range: $900-999.9 Million
Emp.: 5,000
Business Description:
Electric Services
S.I.C.: 4911
N.A.I.C.S.: 221122
Subsidiaries:

Bot Elektrowina Turow SA (1)
ul Mlodych Energetykow 12
Bogatynia, 59-916 Warsaw, Poland
Tel.: (48) 757734900
Fax: (48) 757734002
Web Site: www.elturow.bot.pl
Other Electric Power Generation
S.I.C.: 4931
N.A.I.C.S.: 221118

Bot Gornictwo I Energetyka SA (1)
Al J Pilsudskiego 12
90-051 Lodz, Poland
Tel.: (48) 422828000
Fax: (48) 422828002
E-Mail: bot@bot.pl
Web Site: www.bot.pl
Emp.: 150
Other Holding Companies Offices
S.I.C.: 6719
N.A.I.C.S.: 551112
Antoni Piepkiewipz *(Pres)*

ELBIS Sp. z o.o. (1)
97-427 Rogowiec
ul Instalacyjna, 97-427 Bielsko-Biala, Poland
Tel.: (48) 447353320
Fax: (48) 447353322
Web Site: www.elb2.pl
Electric Power Distribution
S.I.C.: 4931
N.A.I.C.S.: 221122

ELEMENT 79 CAPITAL INC.

1250 Boulevard Rene-Levesque West Suite 2500
Montreal, QC, H3B 4Y1, Canada
Tel.: (514) 562-1374
E-Mail: eierfino@gmail.com
Year Founded: 2013
EMS.P—(TSXV)
Business Description:
Investment Services
S.I.C.: 6211
N.A.I.C.S.: 523999
Personnel:
Edward Ierfino *(Pres)*
William Waks *(CFO)*
Kosta Kostic *(Sec)*
Board of Directors:
Edward Ierfino
Kosta Kostic
Andre Laferriere
Transfer Agent:
Computershare Investor Services Inc.
Montreal, QC, Canada

ELEMENT FINANCIAL CORP.

161 Bay Street Suite 4600
Toronto, ON, M5J 2S1, Canada
Tel.: (416) 386-1067
Fax: (888) 772-8129
Toll Free: (888) 772-8129
E-Mail: info@elementfinancial.ca
Web Site: www.elementfinancial.ca
Year Founded: 2007
EFN—(TSX)
Int. Income: $48,812,346
Assets: $1,499,868,826
Liabilities: $1,078,975,907
Net Worth: $420,892,919
Earnings: ($6,381,608)
Fiscal Year-end: 12/31/12
Business Description:
Equipment Finance Services
S.I.C.: 7353
N.A.I.C.S.: 532412
Personnel:
Steven Hudson *(Chm & CEO)*
Steven Small *(Vice Chm)*
Bradley Nullmeyer *(Pres)*
Michel Beland *(CFO)*
Bruce Smith *(Pres-Canada & COO)*
Steve Sands *(Chief Credit Officer)*
Troy Campbell *(Pres-Transportaction Lease Systems Inc)*
Chris Marshall *(Sr Legal Counsel & Sec)*
Issid Issid *(Legal Counsel)*
Karen Martin *(Treas)*
Tony Bergeron *(Exec VP)*
Todd Hudson *(Exec VP-Originations)*
Christian De Broux *(Sr VP-Risk Mgmt)*
John Sadler *(Sr VP-Corp Affairs & IR)*
Board of Directors:
Steven Hudson
Philip Arthur
Harold D. Bridge
Gordon Griffin
Michael D. Harris
Pierre Lortie
Stephens B. Lowden
Steven Small
Paul J. Stoyan
Transfer Agent:
Computershare Investor Services Inc.
Toronto, ON, Canada

ELEMENTAL HOLDING S.A.

ul Traugutta 42
05-825 Grodzisk Mazowiecki, Poland
Tel.: (48) 22 390 91 35
Fax: (48) 22 390 91 36
E-Mail: inwestor@elemental.biz
Web Site: www.elemental-holding.pl
EMT—(WAR)
Business Description:
Recycling Services & Recyclable Materials Distr
S.I.C.: 4959
N.A.I.C.S.: 562998
Personnel:
Pawel Jarski *(Chm-Mgmt Bd)*

ELEMENTAL MINERALS LIMITED

9 Mulberry Hill Office Park
Broadacres Drive
Dainfern, Gauteng, 2055, South Africa
Mailing Address:
PO Box 4983
Dainfern, Gauteng, 2174, South Africa

Elemental Minerals Limited—(Continued)

Tel.: (27) 11 4699140
Fax: (27) 86 6132973
Web Site: www.elementalminerals.com.au
ELM—(ASX TSX)
Business Description:
Potash Mining Services
S.I.C.: 1474
N.A.I.C.S.: 212391
Personnel:
Sam Middlemas *(Interim Chm)*
Ian MacPherson *(CEO)*
Board of Directors:
Sam Middlemas
Michael Barton
Robert Geoffrey Franklyn
Ian MacPherson
Ian Stalker

ELEMENTIS PLC

10 Albermarle Street
London, W1S 4HH, United Kingdom
Tel.: (44) 2074089300
Fax: (44) 2074932194
E-Mail: info@elementis-eu.com
Web Site: www.elementisplc.com
Year Founded: 1908
ELM—(LSE)
Rev.: $757,000,000
Assets: $863,200,000
Liabilities: $381,000,000
Net Worth: $482,200,000
Earnings: $107,100,000
Emp.: 1,323
Fiscal Year-end: 12/31/12
Business Description:
Specialty Chemicals, Pigments & Chromium Mfr
Import Export
S.I.C.: 2899
N.A.I.C.S.: 325998
Personnel:
David Dutro *(CEO)*
Ken Morris *(CIO)*
Walker Allen *(Chief Compliance Officer & Gen Counsel)*
Greg McClatchy *(Pres-Elementis Specialty Products & Elementis Surfactants)*
Dennis Valentino *(Pres-Elementis Chromium)*
Wai Wong *(Sec)*
Board of Directors:
Ian Brindle
Andrew Christie
David Dutro
Kevin Matthews
Brian Taylorson
Legal Counsel:
Lovells
65 Holborn Viaduct
London, EC1A 2DY, United Kingdom
Subsidiary:

Elementis Chromium **(1)**
Eaglescliffe
Stockton-on-Tees, TS16 0QG, United Kingdom UK
Tel.: (44) 1642780682 (100%)
Fax: (44) 1642791866
E-Mail: chromium.uk@elementis.com
Web Site: www.elementischromium.com
ELMB—(LSE)
Sales Range: $650-699.9 Million
Emp.: 180
Chromium Chemicals Sales; Financial & IT Services
S.I.C.: 2899
N.A.I.C.S.: 325998
Dennis Valentino *(Pres)*

U.S. Subsidiaries:

Elementis Chromium, LP **(1)**
3800 Buddy Lawrence Dr
Corpus Christi, TX 78407 DE
Tel.: (361) 880-7706 (100%)
Fax: (361) 880-7760
E-Mail: chromium.usa@elementis-na.com
Web Site: www.elementischromium.com
Sls.: $30,000,000
Emp.: 50
Chromium Chemicals Mfr
S.I.C.: 2819
N.A.I.C.S.: 325180
Jim Marcinko *(Gen Mgr)*

Elementis LTP, LT **(1)**
546 S Water St
Milwaukee, WI 53204-1646 (100%)
Tel.: (414) 278-8844
Fax: (414) 278-0848
Web Site: www.elementischromium.com
Emp.: 10
Leather Tanning Product Mfr
S.I.C.: 2819
N.A.I.C.S.: 325180
Adel Hanna *(VP)*

Elementis Specialties, Inc. **(1)**
329 Wyckoffs Mills Rd
Hightstown, NJ 08520-1007
Tel.: (609) 443-2500
Fax: (609) 443-2422
Toll Free: (800) 866-6800
E-Mail: info@elementis-specialties.com
Web Site: www.elementis-specialties.com
Emp.: 250
Specialty Chemical Mfr
S.I.C.: 2851
N.A.I.C.S.: 325510
Greg McClatchy *(Pres)*

Subsidiary:

Hi-Mar Specialty Chemicals, LLC **(2)**
3939 W McKinley Ave
Milwaukee, WI 53208 WI
Tel.: (414) 342-5443
Fax: (414) 342-7871
E-Mail: infoandsamples@hi-mar.net
Web Site: www.hi-mar.net
Sales Range: $10-24.9 Million
Emp.: 28
Surface Active Agent Mfr
S.I.C.: 2843
N.A.I.C.S.: 325613
Albert Hernandez *(VP-Sls)*

ELEMENTOS LIMITED

Level 8 26 Wharf Street
PO Box 10555
Brisbane, QLD, 4000, Australia
Tel.: (61) 7 3221 7770
Fax: (61) 7 3221 7773
E-Mail: admin@elementos.com.au
Web Site: www.elementos.com.au
ELT—(ASX)
Rev.: $33,989
Assets: $2,559,575
Liabilities: $325,490
Net Worth: $2,234,085
Earnings: ($9,756,959)
Emp.: 9
Fiscal Year-end: 06/30/13
Business Description:
Metal Mining Services
S.I.C.: 1099
N.A.I.C.S.: 212299
Personnel:
Calvin Treacy *(Mng Dir)*
Linda Scott *(CFO & Co-Sec)*
Paul Crawford *(Co-Sec)*
Board of Directors:
Corey Nolan
Richard Seville
Calvin Treacy

EL.EN. S.P.A.

Via Baldanzese 17
50041 Calenzano, FI, Italy
Tel.: (39) 0558826807
Fax: (39) 0558832884
E-Mail: info@elengroup.com
Web Site: www.elengroup.com
Year Founded: 1981
ELN—(ITA)
Rev.: $207,274,722
Assets: $264,149,148
Liabilities: $96,822,035
Net Worth: $167,327,114
Earnings: $31,229,238
Emp.: 812
Fiscal Year-end: 12/31/12
Business Description:
Developer of Laser Systems for Medical, Industrial & Scientific Applications
S.I.C.: 3542
N.A.I.C.S.: 333517
Personnel:
Gabriele Clementi *(Chm)*
Barbara Bazzocchi *(Mng Dir)*
Andrea Cangioli *(Mng Dir)*
Board of Directors:
Gabriele Clementi
Barbara Bazzocchi
Paolo Blasi
Andrea Cangioli
Michele Legnaioli
Stefano Modi
Alberto Pecci
Subsidiaries:

AQL Srl **(1)**
Via Iv Novembre 116
Solbiate Olona, Italy
Tel.: (39) 0331375385
Fax: (39) 330331367815
E-Mail: quanta@quantasystem.com
Web Site: www.quantasystem.com
Emp.: 80
Measuring & Controlling Device Mfr
S.I.C.: 3829
N.A.I.C.S.: 334519
Ferrareo Angelo *(Pres)*

ASA Srl **(1)**
Via A Volta 9
36057 Arcugnano, Vicenza, Italy
Tel.: (39) 0444 289200
Fax: (39) 0444 289080
E-Mail: asalaser@asalaser.com
Web Site: www.asalaser.com
Laser Treatment Services
S.I.C.: 8099
N.A.I.C.S.: 621999
Lucio Zaghetto *(Pres & CEO)*
Roberto Marchesini *(Mng Dir)*

Cutlite Penta Srl **(1)**
Via Baldanzese 17
50041 Calenzano, FI, Italy
Tel.: (39) 055 8826919
Fax: (39) 055 8873843
E-Mail: info@cutlitepenta.com
Web Site: www.cutlitepenta.com
Laser Cutting Machine Mfr
S.I.C.: 3545
N.A.I.C.S.: 333515

Deka M.E.L.A. Srl **(1)**
Via Baldanzese 17
50041 Calenzano, FI, Italy
Tel.: (39) 0558874942
Fax: (39) 0558832884
E-Mail: info@dekalaser.com
Web Site: www.dekalaser.com
Surgical & Medical Instrument Mfr
S.I.C.: 3841
N.A.I.C.S.: 339112
Mauro Galli *(Gen Mgr)*

Esthelogue Srl **(1)**
Via Baldanzese 17
50041 Calenzano, FI, Italy
Tel.: (39) 055 77 66 691
Fax: (39) 055 77 66 692
E-Mail: info@esthelogue.com
Web Site: www.esthelogue.com
Health Care Services
S.I.C.: 8099
N.A.I.C.S.: 621999
Alessandra Cafiero *(Mgr-Mktg)*

Lasit SpA **(1)**
Via Solferino 4
Torre Annunziata, Italy
Tel.: (39) 0815368855
Fax: (39) 0818027676
E-Mail: sales@lasit.it
Web Site: www.lasit.it
Emp.: 55
Laser Marking Systems Mfr
S.I.C.: 3559
N.A.I.C.S.: 333249
Marco Ievoli *(Gen Mgr)*

Ot-las Srl **(1)**
Via Baldanzese 24
50041 Calenzano, FI, Italy
Tel.: (39) 558811232
Fax: (39) 0558873864
E-Mail: info@otlas.com
Web Site: www.otlas.com
Laser Marking Systems Mfr
S.I.C.: 3559
N.A.I.C.S.: 333249

Quanta System S.p.A. **(1)**
Via IV Novembre 116
21058 Solbiate Olona, VA, Italy
Tel.: (39) 0331376797
Fax: (39) 0331367815
E-Mail: quanta@quantasystem.com
Web Site: www.quantasystem.com
Emp.: 57
Measuring & Controlling Device Mfr
S.I.C.: 3829
N.A.I.C.S.: 334519
Paolo Salvadeo *(Gen Mgr)*

Raylife Srl **(1)**
Via Dante Alighieri 8
50041 Calenzano, FI, Italy
Tel.: (39) 055 7766696
Fax: (39) 055 7766695
E-Mail: info@raylife.it
Web Site: www.raylife.it
Laser Treatment & Health Care Services
S.I.C.: 8099
N.A.I.C.S.: 621999

Sotras Srl **(1)**
Via Donatello 13
Borgaro Torinese, 10071 Turin, Italy
Tel.: (39) 0558811232
Fax: (39) 0558873864
Web Site: www.sotras.com
Emp.: 110
Machine Tool & Metal Cutting Types Mfr
S.I.C.: 3541
N.A.I.C.S.: 333517

Valfivre Italia Srl **(1)**
Via Baldanzese 17
50041 Calenzano, FI, Italy
Tel.: (39) 0558874942
Fax: (39) 0558832884
E-Mail: elen@elen.it
Web Site: www.elengroup.com
Machine Tool Mfr
S.I.C.: 3541
N.A.I.C.S.: 333517

U.S. Subsidiaries:

Deka Laser Technologies LLC **(1)**
2720 Loker Ave W Ste C
Carlsbad, CA 92010
Tel.: (760) 918-0297
Fax: (760) 918-9216
Toll Free: (877) 303-5273
E-Mail: info@dekalasers.com
Web Site: www.dekalaser.com
Medical Dental & Hospital Equipment & Supplies Whslr
S.I.C.: 5047
N.A.I.C.S.: 423450
Ted Hurley *(Mgr-Ops)*

Deka Medical Inc **(1)**
665 3rd St
San Francisco, CA 94107-1926
Tel.: (877) 844-5552
E-Mail: info@dekamedinc.com
Web Site: www.dekamedinc.com
Medical Laser Equipment Mfr
S.I.C.: 3841
N.A.I.C.S.: 339112
Dale Koop *(Co-Pres & CEO)*

Lasercut Inc. **(1)**
69 N Branford Rd
Branford, CT 06405-2810
Tel.: (203) 488-0031
Web Site: www.lasercutinc.com
Electronic Components Mfr
S.I.C.: 3679
N.A.I.C.S.: 334419

Lasercut Technologies Inc. **(1)**
69 N Branford Rd
Branford, CT 06405
Tel.: (203) 488-0031

Fax: (203) 483-0463
E-Mail: sales@lasercutinc.com
Web Site: www.lasercutinc.com
Laser Cutting Machinery Mfr
S.I.C.: 3559
N.A.I.C.S.: 333249

Lasit USA Inc. (1)
69 N Branford Rd
Branford, CT 06405
Tel.: (508) 528-2542
Fax: (203) 483-0463
Web Site: www.lasitusa.com
Emp.: 58
Laser Treatment Devices Mfr
S.I.C.: 3841
N.A.I.C.S.: 339112
Robin Barbero *(Gen Mgr)*

Non-U.S. Subsidiaries:

Asclepion Laser Technologies GmbH (1)
Brusseler Str 10
Jena, 07747, Germany
Tel.: (49) 36417700100
Fax: (49) 36417700102
E-Mail: info@asclepion.com
Web Site: www.asclepion.com
Electrical Equipment & Component Mfr
S.I.C.: 3699
N.A.I.C.S.: 335999
Daniel Leggieri *(Gen Mgr)*

Cutlite do Brasil Ltda (1)
Rua General Osorio 4 584 Galpao 16
Bairro da Velha
Blumenau, Brazil
Tel.: (55) 4732210800
E-Mail: vendas@cutlite.com.br
Web Site: www.cutlite.com.br
Laser Cutting Machinery Mfr
S.I.C.: 3542
N.A.I.C.S.: 333517

Cynosure GmbH (1)
Robert Bosch Str 11a
63225 Langen, Germany
Tel.: (49) 61032011100
Fax: (49) 6103 2011111
Web Site: www.cynosure.de
Emp.: 3
Medical Equipment & Supplies Mfr
S.I.C.: 3841
N.A.I.C.S.: 339112
Viana Smith *(Gen Mgr)*

Cynosure KK (1)
25-6 Taito 2-chome
Taito-Ku, Tokyo, 150-0031, Japan
Tel.: (81) 3 58072761
Fax: (81) 3 5807 2762
Web Site: www.cynosure.co.jp
Medical Equipment & Supplies Mfr
S.I.C.: 3841
N.A.I.C.S.: 339112

Cynosure Korea Limited (1)
1 St F Seung Min B/D 56-11 Nonhyun-Dong
Kangnam Gu, Seoul, Korea (South)
Tel.: (82) 2 517 6267
Fax: (82) 2 517 6260
E-Mail: cynosure@cynosure.co.kr
Web Site: www.cynosure.co.kr
Laser Treatment & Health Care Services
S.I.C.: 8099
N.A.I.C.S.: 621999

Cynosure Sarl (1)
Energy Park Batiment 6 132-134 Avenue de Verdun
92400 Courbevoie, France
Tel.: (33) 146672250
Laser Systems Equipment Mfr
S.I.C.: 3845
N.A.I.C.S.: 334510

Cynosure Spain S.L. (1)
Avenue Manoteras 22 3 Floor Office 95-96
28050 Madrid, Spain
Tel.: (34) 91 383 40 00
Fax: (34) 91 383 31 67
E-Mail: info@cynosurespain.com
Web Site: www.cynosurespain.com
Laser Treatment Services
S.I.C.: 8099
N.A.I.C.S.: 621999

Cynosure UK Ltd (1)
The Old Barn Offices Lower Mount Farm
Cookham, Berkshire, SL6 9EE, United Kingdom
Tel.: (44) 1628522252
Fax: (44) 1628520525
E-Mail: info@cynosureuk.com
Web Site: www.cynosureuk.com
Emp.: 7
Medical Equipments Mfr
S.I.C.: 3845
N.A.I.C.S.: 334510
Michael R. Davin *(Chm, Pres & CEO)*
Neil Wolfenden *(Mng Dir)*
Timothy W. Baker *(Exec-VP & CFO & Treas)*
Rafael Sierra *(CTO)*
Douglas J. Delaney *(Exec VP-Sls)*
William T. Kelley *(Sr VP-Intl Sls)*

Deka Japan Co. Ltd (1)
Minamiaoyama 2-21
Minato-Ku, Tokyo, 107-0062, Japan
Tel.: (81) 364200231
Fax: (81) 364200232
E-Mail: info@dekajapan.jp
Web Site: www.dekajapan.jp
Emp.: 10
Medical Equipment Sales & Maintenance Services
S.I.C.: 5047
N.A.I.C.S.: 423450
Mariko Yuki *(Pres)*

Deka Lasertechnologie GmbH (1)
Prielmayerstrasse 3
84048 Mainburg, Germany
Tel.: (49) 8751846156
E-Mail: info@dekalaser.de
Web Site: www.dekalaser.de
Medical Laser Equipment Mfr
S.I.C.: 3841
N.A.I.C.S.: 339112

Deka LMS GmbH (1)
Auhofstrasse 11
63741 Frankfurt, Germany
Tel.: (49) 60213696648
Fax: (49) 60213696649
Machine Tool & Metal Cutting Types Mfr
S.I.C.: 3541
N.A.I.C.S.: 333517
Stephan Gruner *(Gen Mgr)*

Deka Technologies Laser Sarl (1)
99 cours Gambetta
69003 Lyon, France
Tel.: (33) 478627148
Fax: (33) 478626637
E-Mail: administration@deka.fr
Web Site: www.deka.fr
Emp.: 8
Medical Laser Equipments Mfr
S.I.C.: 3841
N.A.I.C.S.: 339112
Igor Pellissier *(Dir-Comml & Mktg)*

ELEPHANT TALK COMMUNICATIONS CORP.

Schiphol Boulevard 249
1118 BH Schiphol, Netherlands
Tel.: (31) 20 653 5916
Fax: (31) 20 653 3846
E-Mail: investorrelations@elephanttalk.com
Web Site: www.elephanttalk.com
Year Founded: 1994
ETAK—(NYSEMKT)
Rev.: $29,202,188
Assets: $37,475,541
Liabilities: $17,326,055
Net Worth: $20,149,486
Earnings: ($23,131,936)
Emp.: 131
Fiscal Year-end: 12/31/12

Business Description:
Telecommunications Software
S.I.C.: 7372
N.A.I.C.S.: 511210

Personnel:
Steven van der Velden *(Chm, Pres & CEO)*
Mark Nije *(CFO)*
Martin Zuurbier *(CTO)*
Alexander Vermeulen *(Gen Counsel)*
Phil D'Angio *(Sr VP-Global Sls-ValidSoft Limited)*

Board of Directors:
Steven van der Velden
Johan Dejager
Rijkman W.J. Groenink
Charles E. Levine

Non-U.S. Subsidiary:

ValidSoft Ltd. (1)
Donegal Suite Castle Buildings
Tara Street, Tullamore, Co Offaly, Ireland IE
Tel.: (353) 57 937 0800 (100%)
Web Site: www.validsoft.com
Telecommunications-Based Credit Card Fraud Identification & Detection Software & Solutions
S.I.C.: 7372
N.A.I.C.S.: 511210
Patrick M. Carroll *(Chm)*
Paul Burmester *(CEO)*

Non-U.S. Subsidiaries:

ValidSoft (Australia) Pty Limited (2)
Level 3 50 York Street
Sydney, NSW, 2000, Australia AU
Tel.: (61) 411 22 22 45 (100%)
Telecommunications-Based Credit Card Fraud Identification & Detection Software & Solutions
S.I.C.: 7372
N.A.I.C.S.: 511210

ValidSoft (UK) Limited (2)
9 Devonshire Square
London, EC2M 4YF, United Kingdom UK
Tel.: (44) 20 31708125 (100%)
Fax: (44) 20 31783221
Web Site: www.validsoft.com
Emp.: 17
Telecommunications-Based Credit Card Fraud Identification & Detection Software & Solutions
S.I.C.: 7372
N.A.I.C.S.: 511210

ELEROM S.A. ROMAN

Str Uzinei de Tevi nr 2
611161 Roman, Neamt, Romania
Tel.: (40) 233 748169
E-Mail: elerom_sa@yahoo.com
Web Site: elerom.150m.com
Year Founded: 1960
ELER—(BUC)

Business Description:
Transformer Mfr
S.I.C.: 3677
N.A.I.C.S.: 334416

Personnel:
Iosif Mihoc *(Pres)*

Board of Directors:
Petre Dumea
Iosif Mihoc

ELETROBRAS PARTICIPACOES S.A

Av Presidente Vargas 409/13 andar
Rio de Janeiro, 20071-003, Brazil
Tel.: (55) 2125145151
Web Site: www.eletrobras.com
LIPR3—(BRAZ)

Business Description:
Telecommunication Services
S.I.C.: 4899
N.A.I.C.S.: 517919

Personnel:
Jorge Jose Teles Rodrigues *(Dir-IR)*

ELEVATION CAPITAL CORP.

1320 885 West Georgia Street
Vancouver, BC, V6C 3E8, Canada
Tel.: (604) 682-7314
Fax: (604) 682-7317
E-Mail: greg@chathamltd.ca
Year Founded: 2012
ELE.P—(TSXV)

Business Description:
Investment Services
S.I.C.: 6211
N.A.I.C.S.: 523999

Personnel:
Greg Andrews *(Pres & CEO)*
Larry Timlick *(CFO & Sec)*

Board of Directors:
Greg Andrews
Lawrence Lee
Marcus New
Larry Timlick

Transfer Agent:
Computershare Investor Services Inc.
510 Burrard St
Vancouver, BC, V6C 3B9, Canada

ELEXIS AG

(See Under SMS Holding GmbH)

ELEXXION AG

Schutzenstrasse 84
78315 Radolfzell, Germany
Tel.: (49) 7732 82299 0
Fax: (49) 7732 82299 77
E-Mail: info@elexxion.com
Web Site: www.elexxion.de
E8X—(DEU)
Sales Range: $1-9.9 Million
Emp.: 21

Business Description:
Dental Laser System Mfr & Distr
S.I.C.: 3845
N.A.I.C.S.: 334510

Personnel:
Oswald Gasser *(Chm-Supervisory Bd)*
Per Liljenqvist *(CEO)*

Supervisory Board of Directors:
Oswald Gasser
Philip Hjelmer

ELGAR ELECTRIC LTD.

7728 134 Street
Surrey, BC, V3W 6Y5, Canada
Tel.: (604) 590-2771
Fax: (604) 594-7822
Web Site: www.elgarelectric.com
Year Founded: 1955
Rev.: $13,924,559
Emp.: 80

Business Description:
Electrical Contractors
S.I.C.: 1731
N.A.I.C.S.: 238210

Personnel:
Robert Klein *(Pres & Gen Mgr)*

ELGEKA S.A.

DA 13 OT B Phase
SindoyDelta, 57022 Thessaloniki, Greece
Tel.: (30) 2310 779 700
Fax: (30) 2310 752 335
E-Mail: info@elgeka.gr
Web Site: www.elgeka.gr
ELGEK—(ATH)
Sls.: $451,259,069
Assets: $384,833,656
Liabilities: $311,245,273
Net Worth: $73,588,383
Earnings: ($15,060,950)
Emp.: 1,689
Fiscal Year-end: 12/31/12

Business Description:
Food Products Distr
S.I.C.: 5142
N.A.I.C.S.: 424420

Personnel:
Elli Drakopoulou *(Chm)*
Harry Papantonopoulos *(CEO)*
Alexander G. Katsiotis *(Mng Dir)*
Anthimos V. Misailidis *(Grp CFO & IR Officer)*
Katerina Argiraki *(Shareholders Svc Officer)*

Board of Directors:
Elli Drakopoulou

ELGEKA S.A.—(Continued)

Michael E. Fandridis
Alexander G. Katsiotis
Anthimos V. Misailidis
Kyriakos S. Sachanidis
Stylianos M. Stephanou
Leonidas T. Theoklitos

ELGI EQUIPMENTS LIMITED

ELGI Industrial Complex Trichy Road
Singanallur, Coimbatore, 641 005, India
Tel.: (91) 422 2589555
Fax: (91) 422 2573697
E-Mail: enquiry@elgi.com
Web Site: www.elgi.com
Year Founded: 1960
ELGIEQUIP—(BOM NSE)
Rev.: $215,204,348
Assets: $195,586,618
Liabilities: $115,199,032
Net Worth: $80,387,586
Earnings: $11,158,670
Emp.: 2,057
Fiscal Year-end: 03/31/13

Business Description:
Air Compressors & Automotive Service Station Equipment Mfr
S.I.C.: 3563
N.A.I.C.S.: 333912

Personnel:
Jairam Vardaraj *(Mng Dir)*
S. Sriram *(CFO)*
R. Syam Kumar *(Sec)*

Board of Directors:
Ganesh Devaraj
T. Balaji Naidu
N. Mohan Nambiar
M. Ramprasad
Sudarsan Varadaraj
Jairam Vardaraj
B. Vijaykumar

Transfer Agent:
Link Intime India Private Limited
Surya 35 May Flower Avenue Behind Senthil Nagar Souripalayam Road
Coimbatore, India

U.S. Subsidiary:

Patton's, Inc. **(1)**
3201 South Blvd
Charlotte, NC 28209 NC
Tel.: (704) 523-4122
Fax: (704) 525-5148
E-Mail: info@pattonsinc.com
Web Site: www.pattonsinc.com
Sales Range: $25-49.9 Million
Emp.: 130
Compressed Air, Gas & Vacuum Systems Mfr & Distr
S.I.C.: 5084
N.A.I.C.S.: 423830
John Charles Patton *(CEO)*
Joe Pool *(Treas)*

Non-U.S. Subsidiaries:

Elgi Compressores do Brazil Ltda **(1)**
Av Emilio Chechinatto 4195-B
Bairro Sao Roque da Chave, Itupeva, Sao Paulo, 13295 000, Brazil
Tel.: (55) 11 4496 5519
E-Mail: contato@elgi.com.br
Web Site: www.elgi.com.br
Compressors Sales, Distr & Repair
S.I.C.: 5084
N.A.I.C.S.: 423830

Elgi Compressors Trading (Shanghai) Co., Ltd **(1)**
Room 402 No 19 Lane 1500 South Lianhua Road
Min Hang District, Shanghai, 201108, China
Tel.: (86) 21 33581191
Fax: (86) 21 33581190
E-Mail: enquiry.cn@elgi.com
Air Compressors & Automotive Service Station Equipment Distr
S.I.C.: 5084
N.A.I.C.S.: 423830

Elgi Gulf FZE **(1)**
PO Box 120695
Q4-081 Saif Zone, Sharjah, United Arab Emirates
Tel.: (971) 6 557 9970
Fax: (971) 6 557 9980
E-Mail: senthil@elgi.com
Compressors Sales, Distr & Repair
S.I.C.: 5046
N.A.I.C.S.: 423440

ELGIN MINING INC.

201-750 West Pender Street
Vancouver, BC, V6C 2T7, Canada
Tel.: (604) 682-3366
Fax: (604) 682-3363
E-Mail: info@elginmining.com
Web Site: www.elginmining.com
ELG—(TSX)
Rev.: $74,984,728
Assets: $153,220,047
Liabilities: $45,446,267
Net Worth: $107,773,780
Earnings: ($2,569,284)
Emp.: 117
Fiscal Year-end: 12/31/12

Business Description:
Gold Mining Services
S.I.C.: 1041
N.A.I.C.S.: 212221

Personnel:
John Huxley *(Chm)*
Patrick Downey *(Pres & CEO)*
Peter Tam *(CFO)*
James A. Currie *(COO)*

Board of Directors:
John Huxley
Robert Mackay Buchan
Glen Dale Dickson
Patrick Downey
Ronald A. Ewing
David F. Mullen
Alistair Murray Sinclair, Jr.
Ravi Sood
Robert G. Wardell

Legal Counsel:
Greenebaum Doll & McDonald PLLC
Louisville, KY 40202

Cassels, Brock & Blackwell LLP
2100 Scotia Plaza 40 King St W
Toronto, ON, M5H 3C2, Canada
Tel.: (416) 869-5300
Telex: 6-23415
Fax: (416) 360-8877

Transfer Agent:
Computershare Trust Company of Canada
510 Burrard St 2nd Fl
Vancouver, BC, Canada

U.S. Subsidiary:

Renfro Equipment Inc. **(1)**
1740 Continental Dr
Madisonville, KY 42431-9534
Tel.: (270) 821-6742
Mining Equipment Distr
S.I.C.: 5082
N.A.I.C.S.: 423810

Non-U.S. Subsidiary:

Bjorkdalsgruvan AB **(1)**
Kage
Skelleftea, 934 94, Sweden
Tel.: (46) 9 10 72 57 50
Emp.: 120
Gold Mining Services
S.I.C.: 1041
N.A.I.C.S.: 212221
Ulf Lindstrom *(Gen Mgr)*

Subsidiary:

Bjorkdal Exploration AB **(2)**
Bjorkdalsgruvan 1
Skelleftea, 934 94, Sweden
Tel.: (46) 910725750
Fax: (46) 91092112
E-Mail: mats.lindegren@bjorkdal.com
Web Site: www.bjorkdalsgruvan.se
Emp.: 75
Gold Mining Services
S.I.C.: 1041
N.A.I.C.S.: 212221
Mats Lindegren *(Mng Dir)*

ELHIM ISKRA JSC

9 Iskra str
Pazardzhik, 4400, Bulgaria
Tel.: (359) 34 444 548
Fax: (359) 34 443 438
E-Mail: elhimiskra@mbox.digsys.bg
Web Site: www.elhim-iskra.com
Year Founded: 1960
52E—(BUL)

Business Description:
Motor Vehicle Equipment Mfr
S.I.C.: 3714
N.A.I.C.S.: 336320

Personnel:
Albena Slaveykova Dimitrova *(Dir-IR)*

ELIA SYSTEM OPERATOR SA

boulevard de l'Empereur 20
1000 Brussels, Belgium
Tel.: (32) 25467011
Fax: (32) 25467010
E-Mail: info@elia.be
Web Site: www.elia.be
ELI—(EUR)
Rev.: $1,653,096,760
Assets: $8,328,753,790
Liabilities: $5,490,354,345
Net Worth: $2,838,399,445
Earnings: $208,656,350
Emp.: 1,917
Fiscal Year-end: 12/31/12

Business Description:
Electric Power Distr
S.I.C.: 4911
N.A.I.C.S.: 221122

Personnel:
Luc Van Nevel *(Chm)*
Jacques Vandermeiren *(Chm-Mgmt Bd & CEO)*
Francis Vermeiren *(Vice Chm)*
Thierry Willemarck *(Vice Chm)*
Jan Gesquiere *(Vice Chm-Mgmt Bd & CFO)*
Markus Berger *(Chief Officer-Asset Mgmt)*
Roel Goethals *(Chief Officer-European Activities & Participations)*
Hubert Lemmens *(Chief Innovation Officer)*
Frank Vandenberghe *(Chief Officer-Energy & Sys Mgmt)*
Catherine Vandenborre *(Chief Corp Officer)*
Gregory Pattou *(Sec)*

Board of Directors:
Luc Van Nevel
Clement De Meersman
Jacques de Smet
Jennifer Debatisse
Cecile Flandre
Claude Gregoire
Philip Heylen
Jean-Marie Laurent Josi
Miriam Maes
Jane Murphy
Steve Stevaert
Francis Vermeiren
Thierry Willemarck

Ernst & Young Bedrijfsrevisoren BCVBA
De Kleetlaan 2
Diegem, Belgium

Subsidiaries:

Elia Asset SA **(1)**
boulevard de l'Empereur 20
1000 Brussels, Belgium
Tel.: (32) 2 546 70 11
Fax: (32) 2 546 70 10
Web Site: elia.be/CorporateInfo.aspx?language=EN
Asset Management Services
S.I.C.: 6799
N.A.I.C.S.: 523920

Elia Engineering SA **(1)**
boulevard de l'Empereur 20
1000 Brussels, Belgium
Tel.: (32) 2 5467711
Fax: (32) 2 5467860
Electrical Engineering Services
S.I.C.: 8711
N.A.I.C.S.: 541330

Non-U.S. Subsidiaries:

50Hertz Transmission GmbH **(1)**
Eichenstrasse 3A
12435 Berlin, Germany
Tel.: (49) 30 5150 0
Fax: (49) 30 5150 4477
E-Mail: info@50hertz.com
Web Site: www.50hertz.com
Emp.: 700
Power Transmission Grid Operation & Maintenance Services
S.I.C.: 4931
N.A.I.C.S.: 221121
Boris Schucht *(CEO)*
Udo Giegerich *(CFO)*
Frank Golletz *(CTO)*
Hans-Joerg Dorny *(Chief HR Officer)*
Dirk Biermann *(Chief Markets & System Ops Officer)*

Subsidiary:

50Hertz Offshore GmbH **(2)**
Eichenstr 3a
Berlin, 12435, Germany
Tel.: (49) 3051502401
Fax: (49) 3051502405
Emp.: 800
Offshore Power Structure Installation Services
S.I.C.: 1623
N.A.I.C.S.: 237130

Eurogrid GmbH **(1)**
Eichenstrasse 3A
12435 Berlin, Germany
Tel.: (49) 30 5150 3201
Fax: (49) 30 5150 3205
E-Mail: info@eurogrid-gmbh.de
Web Site: www.eurogrid-gmbh.de
Rev.: $1,051,826,440
Electric Utility Asset Investment Services
S.I.C.: 6282
N.A.I.C.S.: 523920
Werner Keschl *(Co-Mng Dir)*
Bert Maes *(Co-Mng Dir)*

ELIANCE (PTY) LIMITED

Eliance House Glen Gables Building c/o Lynnwood Road & January Masilela Dr, Pretoria, 0040, South Africa
Tel.: (27) 124712500
Fax: (27) 123486080
E-Mail: career@eliance.co.za
Web Site: www.eliance.co.za
Emp.: 84

Business Description:
Software Consulting & Web Hosting Services
S.I.C.: 7374
N.A.I.C.S.: 518210

Personnel:
Marthinus Strydom *(CEO)*

ELICA S.P.A.

Via Dante 288
60044 Fabriano, Italy
Tel.: (39) 07326101
Fax: (39) 0732610249
E-Mail: info@elica.com
Web Site: www.elicagroup.com
ELC—(ITA)
Sales Range: $450-499.9 Million
Emp.: 2,300

Business Description:
Kitchen Cooker Hoods, Boiler Motors & Home Heating Systems Mfr

S.I.C.: 3631
N.A.I.C.S.: 335221
Personnel:
Francesco Casoli *(Chm)*
Vincenzo Maragliano *(CFO)*
Marco Scippa *(Chief HR Officer)*
Board of Directors:
Francesco Casoli
Giovanni Frezzotti
Gennaro Pieralisi
Gianna Pieralisi
Stefano Romiti

Subsidiary:

Fime (1)
Via Jesina 56
60022 Castelfidardo, Italy
Tel.: (39) 7172041
Fax: (39) 0717204209
E-Mail: info@elica.com
Web Site: www.elica.it
Emp.: 300
Cooker Hood Motors Mfr
S.I.C.: 3631
N.A.I.C.S.: 335221
Samanta Simonetti *(Mgr-Comml)*

Non-U.S. Subsidiaries:

Elica Group Polska (1)
Spring 14 2
53 017 Wroclaw, Poland
Tel.: (48) 713386530
Fax: (48) 713386555
Web Site: www.elicagroup.com
Cooker Hoods & Motor Assembly Sets Mfr
S.I.C.: 3714
N.A.I.C.S.: 336390

Elicamex (1)
Jose Maria Arteaga No 57
76220 Queretaro, Mexico
Tel.: (52) 4421531300
Fax: (52) 4421531310
Furniture Mfr
S.I.C.: 2514
N.A.I.C.S.: 337124

The Gutmann Company (1)
Muhlacker Strasse 77
Muhlacker, 75417, Germany
Tel.: (49) 704188241
Fax: (49) 704146882
Exhaust Hoods Mfr
S.I.C.: 2514
N.A.I.C.S.: 337124

ELINI BVBA
Vestingstraat 49
2018 Antwerp, Belgium
Tel.: (32) 032318640
Fax: (32) 032319509
E-Mail: info@elini.com
Web Site: www.elini.com
Year Founded: 1989
Emp.: 700
Business Description:
Jewelry Mfr, Designer, Marketer & Sales
Export
S.I.C.: 5944
N.A.I.C.S.: 448310
Personnel:
Nisso Barokas *(Owner)*

U.S. Subsidiary:

Elini Designs Corp. (1)
7950 Nw 53rd St Ste 215
Miami, FL 33166-4638
Tel.: (305) 466-7855
Fax: (305) 466-7297
E-Mail: info@elini.com
Web Site: www.elini.com
Jewelry Retailer
S.I.C.: 5944
N.A.I.C.S.: 448310

ELINOIL S.A.
33 Pigon St
Kifisia, 14564 Athens, Greece
Tel.: (30) 210 6241 500
Fax: (30) 210 6241 509
E-Mail: investor.relations@elin.gr
Web Site: www.elin.gr
Year Founded: 1989
ELIN—(ATH)
Emp.: 270
Business Description:
Fuel, Lubricant & Gas Distr
S.I.C.: 5172
N.A.I.C.S.: 424720
Personnel:
Georgios Tsounias *(Vice Chm)*
Giannis Aligizakis *(CEO)*
Board of Directors:
Charalambos P. Kynigos
Giannis Aligizakis
Giannis C. Courouclis
Leonidas P. Drollas
Rodolfos Papaioannou
Nikolaos G. Skorinis
Polydeukis G. Tsiontsis
Georgios Tsounias

ELISA CORPORATION
Ratavartijankatu 5
PO Box 1
Helsinki, 00061, Finland
Tel.: (358) 1026000
Fax: (358) 1026060
E-Mail: investor.relations@elisa.fi
Web Site: www.elisa.com
ELMUF—(OTC)
Rev.: $2,091,140,478
Assets: $2,705,667,083
Liabilities: $1,559,537,945
Net Worth: $1,146,129,138
Earnings: $280,676,445
Emp.: 3,867
Fiscal Year-end: 12/31/12
Business Description:
Telecommunication, Mobile & Voice Services
S.I.C.: 4812
N.A.I.C.S.: 517210
Personnel:
Raimo Lind *(Chm)*
Ari Lehtoranta *(Vice Chm)*
Veli-Matti Mattila *(CEO)*
Jari Kinnunen *(CFO)*
Asko Kansala *(Exec VP-Consumer Customers)*
Timo Katajisto *(Exec VP-Production)*
Pasi Maenpaa *(Exec VP-Corp Customers)*
Katiye Vuorela *(Exec VP-Comm)*
Sami Ylikortes *(Exec VP-Admin)*
Board of Directors:
Raimo Lind
Ari Lehtoranta
Leena Niemisto
Eira Palin-Lehtinen
Jaakko Uotila
Mika Vehvilainen

Subsidiaries:

Ecosite Oy (1)
Kutomotie 18
00380 Helsinki, Finland
Tel.: (358) 1026056
Fax: (358) 1026056
Web Site: www.ecosite.fi
Radio Transmitting Tower Construction Services
S.I.C.: 1629
N.A.I.C.S.: 237130

Electur Oy (1)
Suopurontie 3b 4
02920 Espoo, Finland
Tel.: (358) 407 646 438
Web Site: www.electur.com
Software Consulting & Support Services
S.I.C.: 7372
N.A.I.C.S.: 511210
Sami Seppanen *(CEO)*

Kiinteisto Oy Raision Luolasto (1)
Kuninkaanvayla 3
21200 Raisio, Finland
Tel.: (358) 10 26 000
Real Estate Management Services
S.I.C.: 6531
N.A.I.C.S.: 531390

Saunalahti Group Oyj (1)
Ratabartikankatu 3
00520 Helsinki, Finland
Tel.: (358) 942430001
Fax: (358) 942430829
E-Mail: kontaktit@saunalahti.com
Web Site: www.saunalahti.fi
Cellular & Wireless Telecommunications
S.I.C.: 4812
N.A.I.C.S.: 517210
Panu Lehti *(VP)*

Tampereen Tietoverkko Oy (1)
Nasinlinnankatu 41
33200 Tampere, Finland
Tel.: (358) 103095300
Fax: (358) 103095302
Web Site: www.ttv.fi
Cable Television Distribution Services
S.I.C.: 4813
N.A.I.C.S.: 517110
Matias Castren *(Pres)*

Videra Oy (1)
Elektroniikkatie 2 B
90590 Oulu, Finland
Tel.: (358) 424 6761
Fax: (358) 8 557 8051
E-Mail: videra@videra.com
Web Site: www.videra.com
Video Conferencing Services
S.I.C.: 7389
N.A.I.C.S.: 561499
Harri Martinmaeki *(Mng Dir)*

Xenetic Oy (1)
Mannerheiminaukio 1B
00100 Helsinki, Finland
Tel.: (358) 106178500
Fax: (358) 106178100
E-Mail: sales@xenetic.fi
Web Site: www.xenetic.fi
Emp.: 30
Data Storage Services
S.I.C.: 7379
N.A.I.C.S.: 518210
Ari-Pekka Syvaenne *(CEO)*

Non-U.S. Subsidiaries:

Elisa Eesti As (1)
Sopruse Pst 145
13417 Tallinn, Estonia
Tel.: (372) 681 1963
Fax: (372) 681 1961
E-Mail: info@elisa.ee
Web Site: www.elisa.ee
Emp.: 300
Mobile Phone Network Operation Services
S.I.C.: 4812
N.A.I.C.S.: 517210
Marika Raiski *(Head-PR)*

LNS Kommunikation AB (1)
Lindetorpsvagen 19
Johanneshov, 12163 Stockholm, Sweden (100%)
Tel.: (46) 854490650
Fax: (46) 854490655
Web Site: www.lnscom.net
Telecommunications
S.I.C.: 4899
N.A.I.C.S.: 517919

OOO LNR (1)
15 Liter A Ul Chapaeva
Saint Petersburg, Russia
Tel.: (7) 8123323108
Fax: (7) 812 332 3109
E-Mail: welcome@lnr.elisa.fi
Web Site: www.elisa.ru
Emp.: 15
Telecommunications Software Development Services
S.I.C.: 7371
N.A.I.C.S.: 541511
Olga Valentinovna Kaledina *(Dir Gen)*

ELISSA RESOURCES LTD.
2060 777 Hornby Street
Vancouver, BC, V6Z 1T7, Canada
Tel.: (604) 669-7330
Fax: (604) 642-2629
E-Mail: info@elissaresources.com
Web Site: www.elissaresources.com
Year Founded: 2007
ELI—(OTC TSXV)
Rev.: $20,835
Assets: $3,475,559
Liabilities: $46,988
Net Worth: $3,428,571
Earnings: ($1,128,141)
Fiscal Year-end: 12/31/12
Business Description:
Gold, Lithium & Other Metal Mining Services
S.I.C.: 1099
N.A.I.C.S.: 212299
Personnel:
G. Arnold Armstrong *(Chm)*
Paul Tavis McKenzie *(Pres & CEO)*
Daniel Frederiksen *(CFO)*
Shauna Lynn Hartman *(Sec)*
Board of Directors:
G. Arnold Armstrong
Garry Clark
Daniel Frederiksen
Mel Klohn
Paul Tavis McKenzie
Kerry Suffolk

ELITE BASIC INC.
535-55 Gasan-dong
Geumcheon-gu, Seoul, Korea (South)
Tel.: (82) 232798015
Fax: (82) 232798080
Web Site: www.elitebasic.co.kr
093240—(KRS)
Business Description:
Apparel Mfr
S.I.C.: 2399
N.A.I.C.S.: 315990
Personnel:
Jong Soon Hong *(CEO)*

ELITE BMW
1040 Ogilvie Road
Ottawa, ON, K1J 8G9, Canada
Tel.: (613) 749-7700
Fax: (613) 749-7181
E-Mail: info@elitebmw.com
Web Site: www.elite.bmw.ca
Rev.: $18,519,274
Emp.: 40
Business Description:
New & Used Car Dealers
S.I.C.: 5511
N.A.I.C.S.: 441110
Personnel:
Steve Simard *(Gen Mgr-Sls)*

ELITE EMAIL INC.
5511 Steeles Ave W Suite 200
Toronto, ON, M9L 1S7, Canada
Tel.: (416) 747-6111
Toll Free: (877) 789-3548
Web Site: www.eliteemail.com
Sales Range: $10-24.9 Million
Business Description:
Email Marketing Software, Website Hosting, Website Design & Search Engine Optimization
S.I.C.: 7372
N.A.I.C.S.: 511210
Personnel:
Robert Burko *(Pres)*
Jeffrey Horn *(CTO)*

ELITE KSB HOLDINGS LIMITED
6 Senoko Way
Singapore, 758029, Singapore
Tel.: (65) 6757 2121
Fax: (65) 6756 2121
E-Mail: info@eliteksb.com
Web Site: www.eliteksb.com
550—(SES)
Sales Range: $50-74.9 Million

Elite KSB Holdings Limited—(Continued)

Business Description:
Chicken Processing Services & Meat Products Distr
S.I.C.: 2015
N.A.I.C.S.: 311615
Personnel:
Ghim Bok Chew *(CEO)*
Keng Wah Chew *(COO)*
Lee Fang Tan *(Sec & VP-Fin)*
Board of Directors:
Kenneth Mei Kwang Chew
Ghim Bok Chew
Keng Wah Chew
Peter Boon Huan Tan
Phyllis Sau Bek Wong
Transfer Agent:
Boardroom Corporate & Advisory Services Pte. Ltd.
50 Raffles Place 32-01 Singapore Land Tower
Singapore, Singapore

ELITE MATERIAL CO., LTD.
18 Ta- Tung 1st Rd Kuan-Yin Industrial District
328 Taoyuan, Taiwan
Tel.: (886) 34837937
Fax: (886) 34837949
Web Site: www.emctw.com
2383—(TAI)
Sales Range: $200-249.9 Million
Business Description:
Copper Clad Laminates Mfr
S.I.C.: 3679
N.A.I.C.S.: 334419
Personnel:
Tsai-Fei Liang *(Chm)*
Plants:

Elite Material Co., Ltd. - Hsinchu Plant (1)
No 14 Wunhua Road Hukou Hsiage
Hsin-chu, 30352, Taiwan
Tel.: (886) 3 5981688
Fax: (886) 3 5981556
Web Site: www.emctw.com
Printed Circuit Boards Mfr
S.I.C.: 3672
N.A.I.C.S.: 334412

Elite Material Co., Ltd. - Taoyuan Plant (1)
18 Ta-Tung First Road Kuan-Yin Industrial District
Taoyuan, 32849, Taiwan
Tel.: (886) 34837937
Fax: (886) 34837949
E-Mail: sales@mail.emctw.com
Web Site: www.emctw.com
Emp.: 500
Printed Circuit Boards Mfr
S.I.C.: 3679
N.A.I.C.S.: 334418

Non-U.S. Plant:

Elite Electronic Material Co., Ltd. - Kunshan Plant (1)
368 You Bi Road
Zhou Shi Town, Kunshan, Jiangsu, 215300, China
Tel.: (86) 51257663671
Fax: (86) 51257663558
E-Mail: chiao@emctw.com
Emp.: 500
Printed Circuit Boards Mfr
S.I.C.: 3672
N.A.I.C.S.: 334412
kuan Kenny *(Gen Mgr)*

ELITE SEMICONDUCTOR MEMORY TECHNOLOGY INC.
No 23 Industry E Rd IV Science-Based Industrial Park
300 Hsinchuang, Taiwan
Tel.: (886) 35781970
Fax: (886) 35644432
Web Site: www.esmt.com.tw
3006—(TAI)
Sales Range: $125-149.9 Million
Business Description:
Integrated Circuit Mfr
S.I.C.: 3672
N.A.I.C.S.: 334412
Personnel:
Hsing-Hai Chen *(Chm)*

ELITE SPORTSWEAR & AWARDS LTD.
14703 118th Avenue
Edmonton, AB, T5L 2M7, Canada
Tel.: (780) 454-9775
Fax: (780) 451-1034
Toll Free: (866) 454-7944
E-Mail: info@elitesportswear.com
Web Site: www.elitesportswear.com
Year Founded: 1952
Rev.: $13,407,400
Emp.: 110
Business Description:
Sportswear Supplier
S.I.C.: 5999
N.A.I.C.S.: 453998
Personnel:
Drew Schamehorn *(Pres)*

ELITE SURFACE TECHNOLOGIES PTY. LTD.
13 Graham Rd
Clayton, 3169, Australia
Tel.: (61) 3 9548 3661
Fax: (61) 3 9548 2703
Web Site: www.elitesurtech.com
Business Description:
Metal Finishing Services
S.I.C.: 5051
N.A.I.C.S.: 423510
Personnel:
Anne Yozin *(Mng Dir)*

ELITE WORKWEAR UK LIMITED
Unit 50 Pillared House Ln
Gainsborough, Lincs, DN21 1HX, United Kingdom
Tel.: (44) 1427810555
Fax: (44) 1427 678204
E-Mail: info@vureuse-it.net
Web Site: www.eliteworkwearuk.co.uk/
Year Founded: 2006
Emp.: 7
Business Description:
Health & Safety Consulting Services
S.I.C.: 8748
N.A.I.C.S.: 541618
Personnel:
Colin Emerson *(Co-Owner & Gen Mgr)*
Phill Emerson *(Co-Owner)*

ELITE WORLD S.A.
28 Boulevard d'Avranches
L-1160 Luxembourg, Luxembourg
Tel.: (352) 1 40443222
Fax: (352) 1 40443280
E-Mail: ir@elitemodel-world.com
Web Site: www.elitemodelworld.com
E1M—(DEU)
Rev.: $70,591,556
Assets: $44,699,692
Liabilities: $48,275,587
Net Worth: ($3,575,895)
Earnings: ($11,873,078)
Fiscal Year-end: 12/31/12
Business Description:
Human Resource Consulting Services
S.I.C.: 8999
N.A.I.C.S.: 541612
Personnel:
Stefania Valenti *(CEO)*
Andrew Gleeson *(CFO)*
Board of Directors:
Silvio Scaglia
Paolo Barbieri
Andrew Gleeson
Paul Johnston
Serge Marion
Stefania Valenti
Non-U.S. Subsidiaries:

Angels Model Management SARL (1)
34 rue du Faugbourg Saint Honore
75008 Paris, France
Tel.: (33) 42 68 24 44
Fax: (33) 42 68 29 99
Web Site: www.angels-models.com
Model Management Services
S.I.C.: 7389
N.A.I.C.S.: 711410

Elite Licensing Company S.A. (1)
Route Des Arsenaux 15
1700 Fribourg, Switzerland
Tel.: (41) 263224815
Model Management Services
S.I.C.: 7389
N.A.I.C.S.: 711410

Elite Management S.A. (1)
Paseo de Gracia 81 4-2
08008 Barcelona, Spain
Tel.: (34) 93 272 09 09
Fax: (34) 93 492 31 71
E-Mail: barcelona@elitemodel.es
Web Site: www.elitemodel.es
Model Management Services
S.I.C.: 7389
N.A.I.C.S.: 711410
Anna Vicent *(Mgr-Acctg)*

Elite Model Management Amsterdam B.V. (1)
Keizersgracht 448
1016 GD Amsterdam, Netherlands
Tel.: (31) 20 627 9929
E-Mail: office@elitemodel.nl
Web Site: www.elitemodel.nl
Emp.: 4
Model Management Services
S.I.C.: 7389
N.A.I.C.S.: 711410
Manon Kosterman, *(Head-Acctg)*

Elite Model Management Bratislava Sro. (1)
Klemensova 4
811 09 Bratislava, Slovakia
Tel.: (421) 252 968 300
Fax: (421) 252 927 098
E-Mail: elite@elitemodels.sk
Web Site: www.elitemodels.cz
Model Management Services
S.I.C.: 7389
N.A.I.C.S.: 711410

Elite Model Management Copenhagen (1)
Bredgade 23B 4th Floor
1260 Copenhagen, Denmark
Tel.: (45) 33151414
Web Site: www.elitemodelmanagement.dk
Emp.: 6
Model Management Services
S.I.C.: 7389
N.A.I.C.S.: 711410

Elite Model Management London Ltd. (1)
3-5 Islington High Street
London, N1 9LQ, United Kingdom
Tel.: (44) 207 841 3288
Fax: (44) 207 841 3289
E-Mail: info@elitemodellondon.co.uk
Web Site: www.elitemodellondon.co.uk
Emp.: 22
Model Management Services
S.I.C.: 7389
N.A.I.C.S.: 711410
Michelangelo Chiacchio, *(Mng Dir)*

Elite Model Management Prague Sro (1)
Na Perstyne 2
110 00 Prague, Czech Republic
Tel.: (420) 222 212 394
Fax: (420) 222 211 734
E-Mail: elite@elitemodel.cz
Web Site: www.elitemodel.cz
Emp.: 6
Model Management Services
S.I.C.: 7389
N.A.I.C.S.: 711410

Elite Model Management SARL (1)
via Tortona 35
20144 Milan, Italy
Tel.: (39) 02 467 521
Fax: (39) 02 481 9058
E-Mail: elite@elitemodel.it
Web Site: www.elitemodel.it
Model Management Services
S.I.C.: 7389
N.A.I.C.S.: 711410
Roberto Valensin *(Mng Dir)*

Elite Model Management SARL (1)
19 avenue George V
75008 Paris, France
Tel.: (33) 1 4044 3222
Fax: (33) 1 4044 3280
E-Mail: info@elitemodel.fr
Web Site: management.elitemodel.fr
Model Management Services
S.I.C.: 7389
N.A.I.C.S.: 711410

Inmod AG (1)
Route Des Arsenaux 15
Fribourg, 1700, Switzerland
Tel.: (41) 263232775
Model Management Services
S.I.C.: 7389
N.A.I.C.S.: 711410

ELITECH GROUP
12-12 bis rue Jean-Jaures
92800 Puteaux, France
Tel.: (33) 141450710
Fax: (33) 141450719
Web Site: www.elitechgroup.com
Year Founded: 2005
Emp.: 360
Business Description:
Diagnostic Products Distr
S.I.C.: 5122
N.A.I.C.S.: 424210
Personnel:
Pierre Debiais *(Pres)*
U.S. Subsidiaries:

Wescor, Inc. (1)
370 W 1700 S
Logan, UT 84321
Tel.: (435) 752-6011
Fax: (435) 752-4127
E-Mail: wescor@wescor.com
Web Site: www.wescor.com
Emp.: 90
Mfr., Developer & Marketer Instrumentation & Other Products for Medicine, Science & Industry
S.I.C.: 3841
N.A.I.C.S.: 339112
Dennis Briscoe *(VP-Mfg)*

Division:

Epoch Biosciences Inc. (2)
21720 23rd Dr SE Ste 150
Bothell, WA 98021
Tel.: (425) 482-5555
Fax: (425) 482-5550
Toll Free: (800) 562-5544
Emp.: 20
Diagnostic Products Mfr
S.I.C.: 3826
N.A.I.C.S.: 334516
Walt Mahoney *(Sr VP-R&D)*

Non-U.S. Subsidiaries:

Nanogen Advanced Diagnostics, S.r.l. (1)
Via C Colombo 49
Trezzano sul Naviglio, 20090 Trezzano San Naviglio, Italy IT
Tel.: (39) 0248403542
Fax: (39) 024455482
E-Mail: end.info@elitechgroup.com
Web Site: www.elitechgroup.com

Emp.: 70
Distr of Diagnostic Systems for Biomedical Research
S.I.C.: 5047
N.A.I.C.S.: 423450
Ermanno Tagliabue *(Mgr-Export)*

Vital Scientific NV (1)
Van Rensselaerweg 4
Spankeren, 6956 AC Dieren, Netherlands DE
Mailing Address:
PO Box 100
NL-6950 AC Dieren, Netherlands
Tel.: (31) 313430500
Fax: (31) 313427807
E-Mail: info.vital@elitechgroup.com
Web Site: www.vitalscientific.com
Emp.: 90
Scientific Instruments Distr
S.I.C.: 5047
N.A.I.C.S.: 423450
Al Tink *(Mng Dir)*

ELITETELE.COM HOLDINGS PLC

(d/b/a Elite Telecom)
Dawson House Matrix Business Park
Chorley, Lancashire, PR7 7NA, United Kingdom
Tel.: (44) 844 875 8880
Fax: (44) 871 423 8000
E-Mail: sales@elitetele.com
Web Site: www.elitetele.com
Year Founded: 2000
Sales Range: $10-24.9 Million
Emp.: 170
Fiscal Year-end: 03/31/13
Business Description:
Telecommunications Services
S.I.C.: 4899
N.A.I.C.S.: 517919
Personnel:
Matt Newing *(CEO)*

ELIXENS S.A.

83-85 Boulevard Vincent Auriol
75013 Paris, France
Tel.: (33) 1 56617280
Fax: (33) 1 56617299
E-Mail: contact@elixens.com
Web Site: www.elixens.com
Year Founded: 1987
Sales Range: $25-49.9 Million
Emp.: 200
Business Description:
Organic Molecular Chemicals Mfr & Sales
S.I.C.: 2869
N.A.I.C.S.: 325199
Personnel:
Emmanuel Alves *(Chm & CEO)*
Carole Abdelli *(Mng Dir)*

ELIXIR PETROLEUM LIMITED

Level 3 89 St Georges Terrace
Perth, WA, 6000, Australia
Mailing Address:
PO Box Z5187
St Georges Terrace, Perth, WA, 6831, Australia
Tel.: (61) 8 9226 2111
Fax: (61) 8 9226 2099
E-Mail: info@elixirpetroleum.com
Web Site: www.elixirpetroleum.com
EXR—(ASX DEU)
Rev.: $298,666
Assets: $6,117,793
Liabilities: $1,638,147
Net Worth: $4,479,646
Earnings: ($2,175,074)
Fiscal Year-end: 06/30/13
Business Description:
Oil & Gas Exploration Services
S.I.C.: 1311
N.A.I.C.S.: 211111
Personnel:
Matthew Szwedzicki *(COO)*
Nicholas Chen Chik Ong *(Sec)*
Board of Directors:
Alan Watson
Mark O'Clery
Michael Price
John Robertson
Matthew Szwedzicki
Sam Willis

BDO Audit (WA) Pty Ltd
38 Station Street
Subiaco, WA, Australia
Legal Counsel:
Bond Pearce, LLP
Oceana House 39-49 Commercial Road
Southampton, SO15 1GA, United Kingdom

Blakiston & Crabb
1202 Hay Street
West Perth, Australia

ELIZA TINSLEY LTD.

Potters Lane
Wednesbury, W Midlands, WS10 0AS, United Kingdom
Tel.: (44) 1215020055
Fax: (44) 1215027348
E-Mail: info@elizatinsley.co.uk
Web Site: www.elizatinsley.co.uk
Sales Range: $125-149.9 Million
Emp.: 100
Business Description:
Assemblies Designer & Mfr; Chains, Ropes & Related Flexible Connectors Distr
S.I.C.: 3499
N.A.I.C.S.: 332999
Personnel:
Rythm Jain *(CEO)*

ELIZADE NIGERIA LIMITED

Elizade Toyota Plaza 322A Ikorodu Road AnthonyVillage
Maryland, Lagos, Nigeria
Tel.: (234) 17603012
E-Mail: elizade@elizade.net
Web Site: www.elizade.net
Emp.: 300
Business Description:
Automobile Dealership Operator
S.I.C.: 5511
N.A.I.C.S.: 441110
Personnel:
Michael Ade-Ojo *(Founder)*
Herbert Ademola Ajayi *(Chm)*
Adeola A. Sagoe *(Vice Chm)*
Ademola Ade-Ojo *(Mng Dir)*
Board of Directors:
Herbert Ademola Ajayi
Ademola Ade-Ojo
Michael Ade-Ojo
Adeola A. Sagoe
Olu Tikolo
Subsidiary:

Toyota Nigeria Limited (1)
Plot 2 Block G Oshodi Isolo Expressway Oshodi
Lagos, Nigeria (75%)
Tel.: (234) 1 4528320
Fax: (234) 1 4524637
E-Mail: tnl@toyotanigeria.com
Web Site: www.toyotanigeria.com
Sales Range: $200-249.9 Million
Emp.: 120
Automobile Distr
S.I.C.: 5012
N.A.I.C.S.: 423110
Michael Ade-Ojo *(Chm)*
C. K. Thampy *(Mng Dir)*

ELK PETROLEUM LIMITED

Suite 4 Level 9 341 George Street
Sydney, NSW, 2000, Australia
Tel.: (61) 2 9299 9690
Fax: (61) 2 9299 9629
E-Mail: info@elkpet.com
Web Site: www.elkpet.com
ELK—(ASX OTC)
Rev.: $415,748
Assets: $17,158,184
Liabilities: $9,001,381
Net Worth: $8,156,803
Earnings: ($5,831,240)
Emp.: 7
Fiscal Year-end: 06/30/13
Business Description:
Oil Exploration
S.I.C.: 1311
N.A.I.C.S.: 211111
Personnel:
Neale Taylor *(Chm)*
J. Scott Hornafius *(CEO)*
Robert Cook *(Mng Dir)*
Andrew William Bursill *(Co-Sec)*
David Franks *(Co-Sec)*
Board of Directors:
Neale Taylor
Robert Cook
Matthew Healy
Barry Smith
Tony Strasser
Legal Counsel:
Steinepreis Paganin
Level 4 The Read Building 16 Milligan Street
Perth, WA, 6000, Australia
Tel.: (61) 8 9321 4000
Fax: (61) 8 9321 4333
U.S. Subsidiary:

Elk Petroleum Inc (1)
123 W 1st St
Casper, WY 82601
Tel.: (307) 265-3328
Fax: (307) 265-3312
Emp.: 15
Oil & Gas Production Services
S.I.C.: 1311
N.A.I.C.S.: 211111
Chris Mullen *(Pres)*

ELKWATER RESOURCES LTD.

2000 840 7th Ave SW
Calgary, AB, T2P 3T8, Canada
Tel.: (403) 262-0242
Fax: (403) 262-0339
E-Mail: info@elkwater.ca
Year Founded: 2000
ELW—(TSXV)
Rev.: $2,516,475
Assets: $10,728,948
Liabilities: $6,322,198
Net Worth: $4,406,750
Earnings: $18,350
Fiscal Year-end: 12/31/12
Business Description:
Oil & Natural Gas Exploration Services
S.I.C.: 1389
N.A.I.C.S.: 213112
Personnel:
Don J. Brown *(Pres & CEO)*
Jana L. Lillies *(CFO)*
Board of Directors:
Don J. Brown
Michael R. Clarke
Kathleen Dorey
Legal Counsel:
Burstall Winger LLP
Calgary, AB, Canada
Transfer Agent:
CIBC Mellon Trust Company
Calgary, AB, Canada

ELLAKTOR S.A.

25 Ermou Str
GR 14564 Athens, Greece
Tel.: (30) 2108185000
Fax: (30) 2108185001
E-Mail: info@ellaktor.com
Web Site: www.ellaktor.com
ELLAKTOR—(ATH OTC)
Sls.: $1,659,581,261
Assets: $5,860,813,598
Liabilities: $4,171,156,207
Net Worth: $1,689,657,391
Earnings: $43,443,598
Emp.: 3,972
Fiscal Year-end: 12/31/12
Business Description:
Holding Company
S.I.C.: 6719
N.A.I.C.S.: 551112
Personnel:
Anastasios P. Kallitsantsis *(Chm)*
Leonidas G. Bobolas *(CEO & Mng Dir)*
Board of Directors:
Anastasios P. Kallitsantsis
Iordanis Aivazis
Leonidas G. Bobolas
Loukas I. Giannakoulis
Angelos Giokaris
Dimitrios Hatzigrigoriadis
Dimitrios P. Kallitsantsis
Dimitrios A. Koutras
Theodoros N. Pantalakis
Edward Sarantopoulos
Subsidiaries:

AEOLIKI KANDILIOU SA (1)
25 Ermou St Athens - Lamia National Road
Olympic Village Interchange, 145 64 Nea Kifissia, Greece
Tel.: (30) 210 8184600
Fax: (30) 210 8184601
E-Mail: energy@ellaktor.com
Electric Power Generation Services
S.I.C.: 4911
N.A.I.C.S.: 221118

AEOLIKI OLYMPUS EVIA S.A. (1)
25 Ermou St Athens Lamia National Road
Olympic Village Interchange
14564 Nea Kifissia, Greece
Tel.: (30) 2108184600
Fax: (30) 210 8184601
E-Mail: info@ellaktor.com
Web Site: en.ellaktor.gr/article.asp?catid=21867
Real Estate & Construction Management Services
S.I.C.: 6531
N.A.I.C.S.: 531390
Theodore Sietis *(Mng Dir)*

AEOLIKI PARNONOS SA (1)
25 Ermou St Athens - Lamia National Road
Olympic Village Interchange, 145 64 Nea Kifissia, Greece
Tel.: (30) 2108184600
Fax: (30) 210 8184601
E-Mail: info@ellaktor.com
Construction Engineering Services
S.I.C.: 8711
N.A.I.C.S.: 541330

AKTOR FACILITY MANAGEMENT S.A. (1)
25 Ermou Str Athens - Lamia National Road
Olympic Village Interchange, 145 64 Nea Kifissia, Greece
Tel.: (30) 2108185261
Fax: (30) 2108184948
E-Mail: aktorfm@etae.com
Emp.: 60
Construction Engineering Services
S.I.C.: 8711
N.A.I.C.S.: 541330
Kelpies Mitosis *(Pres)*

Aktor S.A. (1)
25 Ermou Str
Nea Kifissia, 145 64 Athens, Greece
Tel.: (30) 2108184000
Fax: (30) 2108184001
E-Mail: info@aktor.gr
Web Site: www.aktor.gr
Sls.: $1,216,893,256
Assets: $1,808,925,361
Liabilities: $1,243,154,341
Net Worth: $565,771,020
Earnings: $9,670,885
Emp.: 4,000
Fiscal Year-end: 12/31/12
Construction Services

ELLAKTOR S.A.—(Continued)

S.I.C.: 1611
N.A.I.C.S.: 237310
Dimitrios Koutras *(Chm)*
Dimitrios Kallitsantsis *(Mng Dir)*
Georgios Koutsopodiotis *(CFO)*

Subsidiaries:

AKTOR CONCESSIONS S.A (2)
25 Ermou Street
Kifissia, 14564, Greece
Tel.: (30) 2108184000
Fax: (30) 2108185101
E-Mail: info@aktor.gr
Web Site: www.aktor.gr
Construction Engineering Services
S.I.C.: 8711
N.A.I.C.S.: 541330
Dimitris Koutras *(Gen Mgr)*

HELLENIC QUARRIES SA (2)
25 Ermou Str Lamia National Road Olympic Village Interchange
145 64 Nea Kifissia, Greece
Tel.: (30) 2108184350
Fax: (30) 2108184351
Web Site: www.ellakt.gr
Emp.: 500
Real Estate & Construction Management Services
S.I.C.: 6531
N.A.I.C.S.: 531390
vassilis Lambos *(Gen Mgr)*

Kastor S.A. (2)
25 Ermou Str
14564 Kifissia, Greece
Tel.: (30) 2108184300
Fax: (30) 2108184301
E-Mail: info@kastor.gr
Web Site: www.kastor.gr
Sales Range: $1-9.9 Million
Emp.: 50
Construction Services
S.I.C.: 1623
N.A.I.C.S.: 237110
Kare Fylakif Molen *(Pres)*

Trigonon S.A. (2)
93 Othonos & Amalias Str
GR 262 22 Patras, Greece
Tel.: (30) 2610310606
Fax: (30) 2610340294
Sales Range: $1-9.9 Million
Building Construction Services;
Construction Machinery & Vehicles Sales
S.I.C.: 1629
N.A.I.C.S.: 237110

Non-U.S. Subsidiary:

AKTOROM SRL (2)
11 Preciziei Blvd the 6th district
Bucharest, Romania
Tel.: (40) 213141943
Fax: (40) 213141943
E-Mail: office@aktor.ro
Real Estate & Construction Management Services
S.I.C.: 6531
N.A.I.C.S.: 531390
Patros Katias *(Gen Mgr)*

ALPHA AEOLIKI MOLAON LAKONIA S.A (1)
25 Ermou St Athens - Lamia National Road Olympic Village Interchange, 145 64 Nea Kifissia, Greece
Tel.: (30) 210 8184600
Fax: (30) 210 8184601
E-Mail: info@ellaktor.com
Web Site: www.en.ellaktor.gr/article.asp?catid=21867
Construction Engineering Services
S.I.C.: 8711
N.A.I.C.S.: 541330

ANEMOS ATALANTIS SA (1)
25 Ermou St Athens Lamia National Rd Olympic Village Interchange, 145 64 Nea Kifissia, Greece
Tel.: (30) 210 8184600
Fax: (30) 210 8184601
Web Site: www.en.ellaktor.gr
Construction Engineering Services
S.I.C.: 8711
N.A.I.C.S.: 541330

ANEMOS THRAKIS SA (1)
25 Ermou St
GR 145 64 Nea Kifissia, Greece
Tel.: (30) 210 8184600
Fax: (30) 210 8184601
E-Mail: info@ellaktor.com
Web Site: en.ellaktor.gr/article.asp?catid=21867
Real Estate & Construction Management Services
S.I.C.: 6531
N.A.I.C.S.: 531390

APOTEFROTIRAS SA (1)
12 Gravias St
16345 Argyroupolis, Greece
Tel.: (30) 2105595591
Fax: (30) 2105596463
E-Mail: apotefr@otenet.gr
Web Site: www.apotefrotiras.gr
Medical Waste Transportation & Disposal Services
S.I.C.: 4959
N.A.I.C.S.: 562998
Georgios Bouboukas *(Plant Mgr)*

ATTIKI ODOS S.A (1)
41 9 Klm Of Attiki Odos
190 02 Peania, Greece
Tel.: (30) 2106682200
Fax: (30) 21060250 60
Emp.: 1,000
Construction Engineering Services
S.I.C.: 8711
N.A.I.C.S.: 541330

BIOSAR ENERGY SA (1)
25 Ermou st Athinon Lamias National Road Olympic Village Junction, 145 64 Kifissia, Greece
Tel.: (30) 2108185200
Fax: (30) 210 8185201
E-Mail: biosar@biosar.gr
Web Site: www.biosar.gr
Solar Power System Construction Services
S.I.C.: 1623
N.A.I.C.S.: 237130
Aris Polychronopoulos *(Gen Mgr)*

D. Kougioumtzopoulos SA (1)
Vathi Avlidas Chalkida Mnima Kati Evias 34100
PO Box 244
Schimatari Chalkidas, 32009 Athens, Greece
Tel.: (30) 22620 73070
Fax: (30) 22620 73076
E-Mail: info@dkougioumtzopoulos.gr
Web Site: www.dkougioumtzopoulos.gr
Road Safety Products Mfr
S.I.C.: 3999
N.A.I.C.S.: 339999

DIMITRA SA (1)
4 km Alexandroupoli-Anthia
Alexandroupoli, Evros, Greece 68100
Tel.: (30) 25510 51388
Fax: (30) 25510 51166
E-Mail: info@dimitra-sa.gr
Web Site: www.dimitra-sa.gr
Emp.: 25
Pet Food Mfr
S.I.C.: 2047
N.A.I.C.S.: 311111
George Pazarliotis *(Gen Mgr)*

ELLINIKI TECHNODOMIKI ANEMOS S.A (1)
25 Ermou St Athens - Lamia National Road Olympic Village Interchange, 145 64 Nea Kifissia, Greece
Tel.: (30) 2108184600
Fax: (30) 210 8184601
E-Mail: info@ellaktor.com
Construction Engineering Services
S.I.C.: 8711
N.A.I.C.S.: 541330

ELLINIKI TECHNODOMIKI ENERGIAKI S.A (1)
25 Ermou Str Athens - Lamia National Road Olympic Village Interchange, 145 64 Nea Kifissia, Greece
Tel.: (30) 2108184600
Fax: (30) 210 8184601
E-Mail: info@ellaktor.com
Construction Engineering Services
S.I.C.: 8711
N.A.I.C.S.: 541330

EOLIKI ZARAKA METAMORFOSSIS SA (1)
25 Ermou St Athens - Lamia National Road Olympic Village Interchange, 145 64 Nea Kifissia, Greece
Tel.: (30) 210 8184600
Fax: (30) 210 8184601
E-Mail: energy@ellaktor.com
Web Site: www.en.ellaktor.gr/article.asp?catid=21867
Electric Power Generation Services
S.I.C.: 4939
N.A.I.C.S.: 221118
Theodore Sietis *(Mng Dir)*

European Finance Associates S.A. (1)
7 Stratigi Street
154 51 Psychiko, Greece
Tel.: (30) 2106772281
Investment Banking Services
S.I.C.: 6211
N.A.I.C.S.: 523110
Evangelos Boutlas *(Mgr)*

HELECTOR SA (1)
25 Ermou str N
145 64 Kifissia, Greece
Tel.: (30) 210 8184700
Fax: (30) 210 8184701
E-Mail: helector@helector.gr
Web Site: www.helector.gr
Emp.: 40
Electric Power Generation Services
S.I.C.: 4939
N.A.I.C.S.: 221118
Bobolas Leonidas *(Chm)*
Katris Athanasios *(Vice Chm & Mng Dir)*

Pantechniki A.E. (1)
Ermou 25 Str
Kato Kifissia, 145 64 Athens, Greece
Tel.: (30) 2106260600
Fax: (30) 2108184451
E-Mail: info@pantechniki.gr
Web Site: www.pantechniki.gr
Sales Range: $150-199.9 Million
Emp.: 1,070
Construction Services
S.I.C.: 1622
N.A.I.C.S.: 237310
Constantinos I. Sarantopoulos *(Vice Chm & CEO)*
Christos A. Giokaris *(Pres & Gen Mgr)*

Subsidiaries:

Promas S.A (2)
7 Kavalieratou Str Kifisia
14564 Athens, Greece
Tel.: (30) 2108003885
Fax: (30) 2108003856
Web Site: www.promas.gr
Specialty Trade Contractors
S.I.C.: 1799
N.A.I.C.S.: 238990
Atros Savoulibis *(Mng Dir)*

PANTECNIKI SA (1)
25 Ermou St
145 64 Athens, Greece
Tel.: (30) 2108184450
Fax: (30) 2108184451
Web Site: www.pantechniki.gr
Construction Engineering Services
S.I.C.: 8711
N.A.I.C.S.: 541330
Angelos Diokalis *(Mng Dir)*

STATHMOI PANTECHNIKI SA (1)
25 Ermou Str Athens-Lamia National Road Olympic Village Interchange, 145 64 Nea Kifissia, Greece
Tel.: (30) 2108184455
Fax: (30) 2108184945
Construction Engineering Services
S.I.C.: 8711
N.A.I.C.S.: 541330

TOMI SA (1)
25 Ermou Str Athens - Lamia National Road Olympic Village Interchange, 145 64 Nea Kifissia, Greece
Tel.: (30) 2108184500
Fax: (30) 2108184501
E-Mail: info@aktor.gr
Construction Engineering Services
S.I.C.: 8711
N.A.I.C.S.: 541330
Loukas Giannakoulis *(Mng Dir)*

VIOTIKOS ANEMOS SA (1)
25 Ermou St Athens - Lamia National Road Olympic Village Interchange, 145 64 Nea Kifissia, Greece
Tel.: (30) 210 8184600
Fax: (30) 210 8184601
E-Mail: info@ellaktor.com
Web Site: www.en.ellaktor.gr/article.asp?catid=21867
Emp.: 35
Electric Power Generation Services
S.I.C.: 4931
N.A.I.C.S.: 221118

Non-U.S. Subsidiaries:

AKTOR BULGARIA SA (1)
Maritsa Garden Complex Block 10 Office 1
Plovdiv, 4003, Bulgaria
Tel.: (359) 32396760
Fax: (359) 32396762
E-Mail: aktor@aktor.bg
Emp.: 45
Building Construction & Mining Services
S.I.C.: 1542
N.A.I.C.S.: 236220
Simos Banagiogis *(Gen Mgr)*

AKTOR KUWAIT WLL (1)
Fahed Al Salem Street Sheraton Round About Kuwait Flag Plaza
AKTOR Site Office, Kuwait, Kuwait
Tel.: (965) 24921068
E-Mail: aktorkuwaitwll@aktorkw.com
Web Site: en.aktor.gr/article.asp?catid=20112
Road Construction Services
S.I.C.: 1611
N.A.I.C.S.: 237310

CORREA HOLDING LTD (1)
9A Falirou Str Pallouriotissa
1046 Nicosia, Cyprus
Tel.: (357) 22751555
Fax: (357) 22751200
E-Mail: centralmail@demaservices.com
Financial Management Consulting Services
S.I.C.: 8742
N.A.I.C.S.: 541611

HELECTOR BULGARIA LTD (1)
Gurko Street 47
1000 Sofia, Bulgaria
Tel.: (359) 2 988 18 36
Fax: (359) 2 981 95 78
Web Site: www.ellaktor.gr
Emp.: 4
Building Construction & Mining Services
S.I.C.: 1541
N.A.I.C.S.: 236210
Dimitiris Grammatas *(Gen Mgr)*

HELECTOR CYPRUS (1)
33 Vas Freiderikis Str Palais D Ivoire Office 403-404
1066 Nicosia, Cyprus
Tel.: (357) 22818494
Fax: (357) 22873565
E-Mail: helector.cyprus@etae.com
Emp.: 91
Waste Treatment Services
S.I.C.: 4959
N.A.I.C.S.: 562998
Ioannis Kokotsis *(Gen Mgr)*

HELECTOR GMBH (1)
Kalkgraben 2
35606 Solms, Germany
Tel.: (49) 64 42 207 0
Fax: (49) 64 42 207 233
E-Mail: info@helector.de
Web Site: www.helector.de
Emp.: 200
Waste Management Services
S.I.C.: 4959
N.A.I.C.S.: 562998

HERHOF RECYCLING CENTER OSNABRUCK GMBH (1)
Furstenauer Weg 73
49090 Osnabruck, Germany
Tel.: (49) 541349790
Waste Management Services
S.I.C.: 4959
N.A.I.C.S.: 562998

KARTEREDA HOLDING LTD (1)
9A Falirou Str Pallouriotissa
1046 Nicosia, Cyprus

Tel.: (357) 22751555
Fax: (357) 22751200
Web Site: en.ellaktor.gr/article.asp?catid=21547
Financial Management Consulting Services
S.I.C.: 8742
N.A.I.C.S.: 541611

PROFIT CONSTRUCT SRL (1)
Splaiul Unirii nr 96 Etaj 2 ap 10 Sector 4
Bucharest, Romania
Tel.: (40) 213137742
Fax: (40) 213137746
Real Estate & Construction Management Services
S.I.C.: 6531
N.A.I.C.S.: 531390

SC CLH ESTATE SRL (1)
11 Preciziei Bld Sector 6 3rd Floor
Bucharest, 62203, Romania
Tel.: (40) 213137742
Fax: (40) 213137742
E-Mail: clh@etae.com
Web Site: en.ellaktor.gr/article.asp?catid=21552
Emp.: 3
Real Estate & Construction Management Services
S.I.C.: 6531
N.A.I.C.S.: 531390

ELLENBARRIE INDUSTRIAL GASES LIMITED

3A Ripon Street
Kolkata, 700 016, India
Tel.: (91) 33 2249 1922
Fax: (91) 33 22493396
E-Mail: ellenbarrie@vsnl.com
Web Site: www.ellenbarrie.com
Year Founded: 1976
590087—(BOM)
Sales Range: $1-9.9 Million

Business Description:
Industrial Gas Mfr
S.I.C.: 2813
N.A.I.C.S.: 325120

Personnel:
Anjan Kumar Bandyopadhyay *(Compliance Officer & Sec)*

Board of Directors:
Padam Agarwala
Indrajit Mookerjee

ELLERINE HOLDINGS LTD.

14 Charles Cresent Eastgate Ext. 14
PO Box 122
2148 Sandton, South Africa
Tel.: (27) 102012000
Web Site: www.ellerines.co.za
Sales Range: $300-349.9 Million
Emp.: 200

Business Description:
Holding Company
S.I.C.: 6719
N.A.I.C.S.: 551112

Personnel:
Toni Fourie *(CEO)*
August van Heerden *(CFO)*
Marc Moca *(COO)*
Ian Child *(CIO)*
Louis Carstens *(CEO-Strategy)*
Robert Dodds *(Grp Exec-Shared Svcs)*
Paul Marsh *(Grp Exec-Comml)*

ELLERMAN INVESTMENTS LTD.

20 Saint James Street 3rd Floor
London, SW1A 1ES, United Kingdom
Tel.: (44) 12 2435 0733
Fax: (44) 20 7930 9131

Business Description:
Holding Company
S.I.C.: 6719
N.A.I.C.S.: 551112

Personnel:
David Barclay *(Co-Owner)*
Frederick Barclay *(Co-Owner)*

Subsidiary:

The Ritz Hotel (London) Limited **(1)**
150 Piccadilly
London, W1J 9BR, United Kingdom (100%)
Tel.: (44) 2074938181
Telex: 267200 RITZ G
Fax: (44) 2074932687
E-Mail: enquire@theritzlondon.com
Web Site: www.theritzlondon.com
Emp.: 300
Hotel Operator
S.I.C.: 7011
N.A.I.C.S.: 721199
Stephen Boxall *(Mng Dir)*

ELLEX MEDICAL LASERS LIMITED

82 Gilbert Street
Adelaide, SA, 5000, Australia
Tel.: (61) 881045200
Fax: (61) 81045231
E-Mail: reception@ellex.com
Web Site: www.ellex.com
ELX—(ASX)
Rev.: $44,607,091
Assets: $49,339,267
Liabilities: $17,212,366
Net Worth: $32,126,901
Earnings: ($850,354)
Emp.: 201
Fiscal Year-end: 06/30/13

Business Description:
Lasers & Diagnostic Ultrasound Systems Mfr
S.I.C.: 3845
N.A.I.C.S.: 334510

Personnel:
Victor Previn *(Chm)*
Tom Spurling *(CEO)*
Bill Swaim *(Pres-Ellex USA Inc & VP-Sls, Distr & Svcs-Americas)*
Yukitaka Isoda *(Pres-Sls-Japan)*
Maria Maieli *(Sec & Controller-Fin)*

Board of Directors:
Victor Previn
Giuseppe Canala
Rahmon Coupe
Alex Sundich
Meera Verma

Legal Counsel:
Thomsons Lawyers
Level 7 19 Gouger Street
Adelaide, Australia

Subsidiaries:

Ellex Australia Pty. Ltd. (1)
82 Gilbert St
Adelaide, SA, 5000, Australia AU (100%)
Tel.: (61) 294821100
Fax: (61) 810845231
E-Mail: info@ellex.com
Emp.: 120
Diagnostic Ultrasound System Marketing Services
S.I.C.: 5047
N.A.I.C.S.: 423450
Tom Spurling *(CEO)*

Ellex Medical Pty Ltd. (1)
82 Gilbert St
Adelaide, SA, 5000, Australia
Tel.: (61) 881045200
Fax: (61) 881045231
E-Mail: info@ellex.com.au
Emp.: 120
Diagnostic Systems Mfr
S.I.C.: 3845
N.A.I.C.S.: 334510
Tom Spurling *(CEO)*

U.S. Subsidiaries:

Ellex (USA) Inc. (1)
7138 Shady Oak Rd
Minneapolis, MN 55344-3517
Tel.: (952) 881-9100
Fax: (952) 941-5511
Toll Free: (800) 824-7444
E-Mail: info@ellex.com
Emp.: 8
Diagnostic Ultrasound System Sales
S.I.C.: 5047
N.A.I.C.S.: 423450
Bill Swaim *(Pres)*

Non-U.S. Subsidiaries:

Clarion Medical Technologies Inc. (1)
125 Fleming Dr
Cambridge, ON, N1T 2B8, Canada
Tel.: (519) 620-3900
Fax: (519) 621-0313
E-Mail: clarion.medical@clarionmedical.com
Web Site: www.clarionmedical.com
Emp.: 60
Diagnostic Equipment Mfr & Sales
S.I.C.: 3845
N.A.I.C.S.: 334510
Dan Webb *(CEO)*

Ellex Deutschland Gmbh (1)
Ostring 45
63533 Mainhausen, Hesse, Germany
Tel.: (49) 6182929295
Fax: (49) 6182929290
E-Mail: info@ellex.com
Emp.: 7
Diagnostic Ultrasound Systems Sales & Services
S.I.C.: 5047
N.A.I.C.S.: 423450
Andreas Zahl *(Mng Dir)*

Ellex (Japan) Corporation (1)
Hara Building 2 3 Floor 4-11-4
Minato-ku, Tokyo, 108-0014, Japan
Tel.: (81) 354847742
Fax: (81) 354847743
E-Mail: hr@ellex.com
Web Site: www.ellex.jp
Emp.: 25
Diagnostic Ultrasound System Sales & Services
S.I.C.: 5047
N.A.I.C.S.: 423450
Yukitaka Isoda *(Pres)*

Ellex Services Europe S.A.R.L (1)
555 Chemin Du Bois
69140 Rillieux-la-Pape, France
Tel.: (33) 473341855
Fax: (33) 482910459
E-Mail: info@ellex.com
Emp.: 7
Diagnostic Ultrasound Systems Mfr
S.I.C.: 3845
N.A.I.C.S.: 334510
Philippe Maury *(Office Mgr)*

ELLIES HOLDINGS LIMITED

94 Eloff Street Ext Village Deep
P O Box 57076
Johannesburg, 2001, South Africa
Tel.: (27) 114903800
Fax: (27) 114932392
E-Mail: holdings@ellies.co.za
Web Site: www.elliesholdings.com
Year Founded: 1979
ELI—(JSE OTC)
Rev.: $222,959,120
Assets: $189,010,809
Liabilities: $81,950,045
Net Worth: $107,060,764
Earnings: $25,115,298
Emp.: 1,811
Fiscal Year-end: 04/30/13

Business Description:
Electronic Component Mfr & Whslr
S.I.C.: 3679
N.A.I.C.S.: 334419

Personnel:
Ellie R. Salkow *(Founder & Chm)*
Wayne M. G. Samson *(CEO)*
Michael F. Levitt *(CFO)*

Board of Directors:
Ellie R. Salkow
Raymond H. Berkman
Andrew C. Brooking
Oliver D. Fortuin
Malcolm Goodford
Michael F. Levitt
Fikile Sharon Mkhize
Manogaran Moodley
Ryan E. Otto
Wayne M. G. Samson

Legal Counsel:
Java Capital (Pty) Ltd
2nd Floor 2 Arnold Road
2196 Rosebank, South Africa

Transfer Agent:
Link Market Services South Africa (Proprietary) Limited
5th Floor 11 Diagonal Street
PO Box 4844
Johannesburg, South Africa

Subsidiaries:

Archsat Investments (Gauteng)(Pty) Ltd (1)
94 Eloff St Ext
Johannesburg, Gauteng, 2190, South Africa
Tel.: (27) 114903800
Fax: (27) 114932392
Electronic Products Mfr
S.I.C.: 3679
N.A.I.C.S.: 334419

Archsat Investments (Natal) (Pty) Ltd (1)
94 Ellof Street
Johannesburg, Gauteng, South Africa
Tel.: (27) 114903959
Fax: (27) 114903958
Emp.: 30
Electronic Product Mfr
S.I.C.: 3679
N.A.I.C.S.: 334419

Ellies Electronics (Bloemfontein)(Pty) Ltd (1)
27 Grey Street
Bloemfontein, Free State, 9301, South Africa
Tel.: (27) 514035220
Fax: (27) 514470773
Electronic Products Mfr
S.I.C.: 3679
N.A.I.C.S.: 334419

Ellies Electronics (Cape)(Pty) Ltd (1)
47 Morningside Rd
Maitland, Western Cape, 7405, South Africa
Tel.: (27) 215328400
Fax: (27) 215322221
Electronic Products Mfr
S.I.C.: 3679
N.A.I.C.S.: 334419

Ellies Electronics (Natal)(Pty) Ltd (1)
911 Umngeni Road
Durban, Kwazulu-Natal, 4001, South Africa
Tel.: (27) 313033298
Fax: (27) 313031508
Electronic Products Mfr
S.I.C.: 3679
N.A.I.C.S.: 334419

Ellies Electronics (Nelspruit)(Pty) Ltd (1)
45 Bester Street
Nelspruit, Mpumalanga, 1201, South Africa
Tel.: (27) 137553000
Fax: (27) 137553007
Electronic Products Mfr
S.I.C.: 3679
N.A.I.C.S.: 334419

Ellies Electronics (Pietersburg)(Pty) Ltd (1)
Gypsum Tagore Street Nirvana
Polokwane, South Africa
Tel.: (27) 152921096
Fax: (27) 152921027
Electronic Products Mfr
S.I.C.: 3679
N.A.I.C.S.: 334419
Gavin Melville *(Exec Dir)*

Ellies (Pty) Ltd (1)
94 Eloff Street Ext
Village Deep, Johannesburg, South Africa
Tel.: (27) 11 490 3800
Fax: (27) 11 493 0630
Web Site: www.ellies.co.za
Emp.: 100
Electronic Product Mfr
S.I.C.: 3679
N.A.I.C.S.: 334419
Wayne Samson *(CEO)*

Ellies Holdings Limited—(Continued)

Subsidiary:

Megatron Holdings (Pty) Ltd. **(2)**
232 Element Road
Kempton Park, 1624, South Africa
Tel.: (27) 11 976 3003
Fax: (27) 11 393 5816
E-Mail: info@megatronfederal.com
Web Site: www.megatronfederal.com
Emp.: 200
Power Generation & Distribution Services
S.I.C.: 4939
N.A.I.C.S.: 221118
Carlos Fidalgo *(Gen Mgr)*

ELLINAS FINANCE PUBLIC COMPANY LTD

6 Theotoki Str
1055 Nicosia, Cyprus
Tel.: (357) 22 349801
Fax: (357) 22 349744
Web Site: www.ellinasfinance.com
Year Founded: 1992
ELF—(CYP)

Business Description:
Financial Services
S.I.C.: 6211
N.A.I.C.S.: 523999

Personnel:
Emilios Ellinas *(Chm)*
Demetris Petrides *(Vice Chm)*

Board of Directors:
Emilios Ellinas
Andreas Gregoriou
Alexandros M. Iakovidis
Demetris Petrides
Yiannis Pitsilos

ELLIOTT MATSUURA CANADA, INC.

2120 Buckingham Road
Oakville, ON, Canada L6H 5X2
Tel.: (905) 829-2211
Fax: (905) 829-5600
E-Mail: sales@elliottmachinery.com
Web Site: www.elliottmachinery.com
Year Founded: 1950
Rev.: $16,019,231
Emp.: 60

Business Description:
Industrial Equipment Whslr
S.I.C.: 5084
N.A.I.C.S.: 423830

Personnel:
Frank Haydar *(Pres)*
Vince D'Alessio *(Exec VP)*

ELLIPSIZ LTD.

29 Woodlands Industrial Park E1 04-01/03 NorthTech Bldg Lobby 1
Singapore, 757716, Singapore
Tel.: (65) 65182200
Fax: (65) 6269 2628
E-Mail: info@ellipsiz.com
Web Site: www.ellipsiz.com
Year Founded: 1992
E13—(SES)
Rev.: $100,588,166
Assets: $113,632,111
Liabilities: $27,484,588
Net Worth: $86,147,523
Earnings: $4,010,345
Emp.: 100
Fiscal Year-end: 06/30/13

Business Description:
Probe Card Designer & Mfr, Silicon Wafer Reclaim Services, Semiconductor Manufacturing Equipment Distr & Test Systems Integration
S.I.C.: 3679
N.A.I.C.S.: 334419

Personnel:
Melvin Wai Leong Chan *(CEO)*
Suat Lian Ong *(CFO)*
Kevin Kurtz *(Pres/CEO-Probe Card Solutions)*
Yuen Leng Chan *(Co-Sec)*
Anne Choo *(Co-Sec)*

Board of Directors:
Xavier Fook Choy Chong
Melvin Wai Leong Chan
Amos Leong
Wai Meng Phoon
Jeffrey Staszak

Transfer Agent:
M & C Services Private Limited
112 Robinson Road 05-01
Singapore, 068902, Singapore

Division:

SV Probe Pte. Ltd. **(1)**
29 Woodlands Industrial Park E1
#04-01 NorthTech Lobby 1, Singapore, 757716, Singapore SG
Tel.: (65) 67698233 (100%)
Fax: (65) 67658183
Web Site: www.svprobe.com
Emp.: 15
Holding Company; Probe Card Designer, Mfr & Distr
S.I.C.: 6719
N.A.I.C.S.: 551112
Kevin M. Kurtz *(Pres & CEO)*

U.S. Subsidiary:

SV Probe, Inc. **(2)**
2120 W Guadalupe Ste 112
Gilbert, AZ 85233 (100%)
Tel.: (480) 635-4700
Fax: (480) 558-7440
Web Site: www.svprobe.com
Probe Card Designer, Mfr & Distr
S.I.C.: 3679
N.A.I.C.S.: 334419
Kevin M. Kurtz *(Pres & CEO)*

Non-U.S. Subsidiary:

SV Probe Technology S.A.S **(3)**
17 Sq Edouard VII
Paris, 75009, France
Tel.: (33) 144399514
Fax: (33) 970064901
E-Mail: fdrucke@svprobe.com
Web Site: www.svprobe.com
Emp.: 2
Electronic Component Mfr & Distr
S.I.C.: 3679
N.A.I.C.S.: 334419
Kevin Kurez *(Pres)*

Non-U.S. Subsidiaries:

SV Probe (SIP) Co., Ltd **(2)**
No B1-3 Weiting Industrial Square Weixin Road Suzhou Industrial Park
Suzhou, Jiangsu, 215122, China
Tel.: (86) 51262752330
Fax: (86) 51262752275
Web Site: www.svprobe.com
Probe Cards Mfr
S.I.C.: 3674
N.A.I.C.S.: 334413

SV Probe Technology Taiwan Co. Ltd **(2)**
3F No 33 Sintai Road
Jhubei, 302, Taiwan
Tel.: (886) 36565188
Fax: (886) 35544150
Semiconductor Devices Mfr
S.I.C.: 3674
N.A.I.C.S.: 334413

SV Probe Vietnam Co., Ltd **(2)**
37 A Vsip Street 6 Vietnam Singapore Industrial Park
Thuan An, Binh Duong, 72500, Vietnam
Tel.: (84) 650 3784301
Fax: (84) 650 3784304
Web Site: www.svprobe.com
Electronic Component Mfr
S.I.C.: 3679
N.A.I.C.S.: 334419

Subsidiaries:

Ellipsiz Singapore Pte Ltd **(1)**
29 Woodlands Industrial Park E1 04-01/06 NorthTech Lobby 1
Singapore, 757716, Singapore
Tel.: (65) 63118500
Fax: (65) 62690838
Semiconductor Devices Mfr
S.I.C.: 3674
N.A.I.C.S.: 334413

Subsidiary:

E+HPS Pte. Ltd **(2)**
152 Paya Lebar Road 06-03 Citipoint Paya Lebar
Singapore, 409020, Singapore
Tel.: (65) 6841 4833
Fax: (65) 6841 0838
E-Mail: admin.ehps@ellipsiz.com
Web Site: www.ehps.com.sg
Emp.: 20
Electronic Components Distr
S.I.C.: 5065
N.A.I.C.S.: 423690
Jeffrey Choon Leng Koh *(Mng Dir)*

Non-U.S. Subsidiary:

E+HPS Engineering (Suzhou) Co., Ltd **(3)**
Unit 14 3F No 5 XingHan Street Block A
Suzhou, Jiangsu, 215021, China
Tel.: (86) 512 6767 2671
Fax: (86) 512 6767 2673
E-Mail: admin.ehps@ellipsiz.com
Web Site: www.ehps.com.sg/contact_china.html
Electronic Components Mfr
S.I.C.: 3674
N.A.I.C.S.: 334413

Ellipsiz Testlab Pte. Ltd. **(1)**
Midview City Block 22 03-60
Singapore, 738960, Singapore SG
Tel.: (65) 64826121 (91.89%)
Fax: (65) 64824191
Web Site: www.ellipsiz.com
Emp.: 5
Electronic Components Testing Services
S.I.C.: 8734
N.A.I.C.S.: 541380

FMB Industries Pte. Ltd **(1)**
56 Sg Kadut Drive 01-05
729573 Singapore, Singapore
Tel.: (65) 6365 1555
Fax: (65) 6365 5541
E-Mail: accounts@fmb.com.sg
Web Site: www.fmb.com.sg
Emp.: 10
Pharmaceutical Products Distr
S.I.C.: 5122
N.A.I.C.S.: 424210
Susan Lim *(Gen Mgr)*

iNETest Resources Pte. Ltd **(1)**
29 Woodlands Industrial Park E1 NorthTech Lobby 1 04-01/06
Singapore, 757716, Singapore
Tel.: (65) 65182200
Fax: (65) 65182222
Web Site: www.inetest.com
Electronic Equipments Mfr
S.I.C.: 3679
N.A.I.C.S.: 334419
Melvin Chan *(CEO)*

Subsidiary:

Testel Solutions Pte. Ltd **(2)**
1200 Depot Road 07-01/06 Telok Blangah Industrial Park
Singapore, 109675, Singapore
Tel.: (65) 6271 3688
Fax: (65) 6271 8866
E-Mail: enquiry@testel.com.sg
Web Site: www.testel.com.sg
Semiconductor Devices Mfr & Distr
S.I.C.: 3674
N.A.I.C.S.: 334413

Non-U.S. Subsidiaries:

ATE Technology (Shanghai) Inc **(3)**
No 4645 Caoan Road Huangdu Town Jiading Area
Jia Ding District, Shanghai, 201804, China
Tel.: (86) 2159597388
Fax: (86) 2159597390
Emp.: 50
Semiconductor Devices Mfr
S.I.C.: 3674
N.A.I.C.S.: 334413

iNETest International Trading (Shanghai) Co., Ltd **(3)**
No 4645 Caoan Road Huangdu Town Jiading Area
Shanghai, 201804, China
Tel.: (86) 2159597388
Fax: (86) 2159597390
Web Site: www.inetest.com
Electronic Products Mfr
S.I.C.: 3825
N.A.I.C.S.: 334515

Non-U.S. Subsidiaries:

iNETest Resources (China) Co., Ltd **(2)**
Unit K 19F Hua Min Empire Plaza No 726 Yan An Road
Shanghai, 200050, China
Tel.: (86) 21 5238 3300
Fax: (86) 21 5238 3301
Web Site: www.inetest.com
Emp.: 32
Electronic Products Mfr
S.I.C.: 3825
N.A.I.C.S.: 334515
Tony Kung *(Gen Mgr)*

iNETest Resources (Suzhou) Co., Ltd **(2)**
Unit 13-14 3F Building A 5 Xing Han Street
Suzhou, Jiangsu, 215021, China
Tel.: (86) 512 6762 3789
Fax: (86) 512 6762 3790
E-Mail: kao.fiddy@ellipsiz.com
Web Site: www.ellipiz.com
Electronic Products Mfr
S.I.C.: 3825
N.A.I.C.S.: 334515

iNETest Resources (Thailand) Ltd **(2)**
719 Kpn Tower 4th Floor Rama 9 Road
Bangkapi Huaykwang
Bangkok, 10310, Thailand
Tel.: (66) 27171400
Fax: (66) 2717 1422
Electronic Component Mfr
S.I.C.: 3679
N.A.I.C.S.: 334419
Banjong Orachunka *(Gen Mgr)*

Oriental International Technology Limited **(2)**
Room 2507 25F Billion Trade Center 31 Hung To Road
Kwun Tong, Kowloon, China (Hong Kong)
Tel.: (852) 27903350
Fax: (852) 29514004
E-Mail: info@itrader.piz
Emp.: 20
Electronic Components Distr
S.I.C.: 3674
N.A.I.C.S.: 334413
Paul Ong *(Gen Mgr)*

Non-U.S. Subsidiaries:

Ellipsiz Communications (NZ) Limited **(1)**
Pencarrow House level 7 1-3 Willeston St
PO Box 9348
Wellington, New Zealand
Tel.: (64) 4 495 8941
Fax: (64) 4 495 8950
E-Mail: sales@ellipsiz-comms.com
Web Site: www.ellipsiz.com
Emp.: 4
Electronic Components Distr
S.I.C.: 3679
N.A.I.C.S.: 334419
Cheryl Brown *(Mgr)*

Ellipsiz Communications Taiwan Ltd **(1)**
8F No 96 Section 1 Jianguo North Road
Jhongshan District, Taipei, 10489, Taiwan
Tel.: (886) 225159596
Fax: (886) 2 2500 0055
Emp.: 25
Electronic Components Distr
S.I.C.: 5065
N.A.I.C.S.: 423690

Ellipsiz Second Source Inc **(1)**
251 Chen Ju Road Lin 9 Ta Tso Li Chunan
Chen Miaoli
35057 Miao-li, Taiwan
Tel.: (886) 37460087

Fax: (886) 37463360
Pump Sales & Refurbishment Services
S.I.C.: 5084
N.A.I.C.S.: 423830

Ellipsiz Semilab (Shanghai) Co., Ltd (1)
4F No 2 Jia Li Building 201 Keyuan Road
Zhang Jiang Hi-Tech Park
Pudong, Shanghai, 201203, China
Tel.: (86) 21 5027 0969
Fax: (86) 21 5027 0968
Web Site: www.ellipsiz.com
Semiconductor Devices Mfr
S.I.C.: 3674
N.A.I.C.S.: 334413

Ellipsiz (Shanghai) International Ltd (1)
4 F No 2 Jia Li Building 201 Keyuan Road
Zhang Jiang Hi-tech Park
Pudong, Shanghai, 201203, China
Tel.: (86) 2150270969
Fax: (86) 21 5027 0968
Web Site: www.ellipsiz.com
Emp.: 25
Semiconductor Devices Mfr & Distr
S.I.C.: 5065
N.A.I.C.S.: 423690
Goh Ray *(Gen Mgr)*

iNETest Malaysia Sdn. Bhd (1)
50 Persiaran Bayan Indah Bayan Bay
11900 Bayan Lepas, Penang, Malaysia
Tel.: (60) 46448572
Fax: (60) 6046429035
Web Site: www.inetest.com
Emp.: 40
Electronic Testing Instrument Mfr
S.I.C.: 3825
N.A.I.C.S.: 334515
G. P. Boey *(Country Mgr)*

ELLISDON CORPORATION

89 Queensway Ave W Ste 800
Mississauga, ON, L5B 2V2, Canada
Tel.: (905) 896-8900
Fax: (905) 896-8911
Web Site: www.ellisdon.com
Year Founded: 1951
Sales Range: $1-4.9 Billion
Emp.: 1,500

Business Description:
General Contractor & Construction Services
S.I.C.: 1542
N.A.I.C.S.: 236220

Personnel:
Spencer Lanthier *(Chm)*
Geoffrey Smith *(Pres & CEO)*
Vince Davoli *(Sr VP-Western Canada)*

Board of Directors:
Spencer Lanthier
Brendan Calder
Beatrix Dart
Randall J. Findlay
Linda Hohol
George Schott
Gerald Slemko
Geoffrey Smith
Michael Smith

Corporate Headquarters:

EllisDon Corporation (1)
2045 Oxford St
London, ON, N5V 2Z7, Canada
Tel.: (519) 455-6770
Fax: (519) 455-2944
Web Site: www.ellisdon.com
Emp.: 100
General Contractor
S.I.C.: 1542
N.A.I.C.S.: 236220
Geoffrey Smith *(Pres & CEO)*

Branches:

EllisDon Construction Services Inc. (2)
300 7330 Fisher St SE
Calgary, AB, T2H 2H8, Canada
Tel.: (403) 259-6627
Fax: (403) 253-4191
Emp.: 50
General Contractor
S.I.C.: 1542
N.A.I.C.S.: 236220
Vince Davoli *(VP)*

EllisDon Corporation (2)
7071 Bayers Rd Ste 5007
Halifax, NS, B3O 2C2, Canada
Tel.: (902) 422-4587
Fax: (902) 422-8967
Web Site: www.ellisdon.com
Emp.: 28
General Contractor
S.I.C.: 1542
N.A.I.C.S.: 236220
Brian Strecko *(VP)*

EllisDon Corporation (2)
150 Isabella Street Suite 300
Ottawa, ON, K1S 1V7, Canada
Tel.: (613) 565-2680
Fax: (613) 565-9267
Web Site: www.ellisdon.com
Emp.: 50
General Contractor
S.I.C.: 1542
N.A.I.C.S.: 236220
Mark Fazio *(VP)*

EllisDon Corporation (2)
555 Burrard Street Suite 205
Vancouver, BC, V7X 1M7, Canada
Tel.: (604) 683-5555
Fax: (604) 683-5550
Web Site: www.ellisdon.com
General Contractor
S.I.C.: 1542
N.A.I.C.S.: 236220

Oxford Builders Supplies (2)
2045 Oxford St E
London, ON, N5V 2Z7, Canada
Tel.: (519) 455-6109
Fax: (519) 455-6699
E-Mail: rentals@oxfordbuilders.ca
Web Site: www.oxfordbuilders.ca
Emp.: 20
Building Supplies
S.I.C.: 5085
N.A.I.C.S.: 423840
Mike Demelo *(VP-Svc)*

Non-U.S. Branches:

EllisDon Construction Inc. (2)
Pergamou 3
Nea Smyrni, GR-171 21 Athens, Greece
Tel.: (30) 2109313372
Fax: (30) 2109313378
General Contractor
S.I.C.: 1542
N.A.I.C.S.: 236220

EllisDon Construction Inc. (2)
Office No 501 Al Barsha Business Centre
PO Box 112208
Dubai, United Arab Emirates
Tel.: (971) 45153400
Fax: (971) 45153401
Web Site: www.ellisdon.com
Emp.: 150
General Contractor
S.I.C.: 1542
N.A.I.C.S.: 236220
Paul Kirby *(VP-Intl)*

Windjammer Landing Villa Beach Resort & Spa (2)
Labrelotte Bay
PO Box 1504
Labrelotte Bay, 758 Castries, Saint Lucia
Tel.: (758) 4569000
Fax: (758) 4529454
Web Site: www.windjammer-landing.com
Resort & Spa Hotel
S.I.C.: 7011
N.A.I.C.S.: 721110
Anthony Bowen *(Mng Dir & VP)*

ELLISON TRAVEL & TOURS LTD.

311 Main Street
Exeter, ON, N0M 1S7, Canada
Tel.: (519) 235-2000
Fax: (519) 235-2061
Toll Free: (800) 265-7022
E-Mail: vacations@ettravel.com
Web Site: www.ettravel.com
Year Founded: 1980
Sales Range: $10-24.9 Million
Emp.: 60

Business Description:
Tour & Travel Services
S.I.C.: 4724
N.A.I.C.S.: 561510

Personnel:
Doug Ellison *(Pres)*
Don Ellison *(CFO)*

ELLOMAY CAPITAL LTD.

9 Rothschild Boulevard 2nd Floor
Tel Aviv, 66881, Israel
Tel.: (972) 37971108
Fax: (972) 37971122
E-Mail: anatb@ellomay.com
Web Site: www.ellomay.com
ELLO—(NYSEMKT)
Rev.: $8,890,000
Assets: $128,740,000
Liabilities: $45,626,000
Net Worth: $83,114,000
Earnings: ($2,133,000)
Emp.: 11
Fiscal Year-end: 12/31/12

Business Description:
Holding Company
S.I.C.: 6719
N.A.I.C.S.: 551112

Personnel:
Shlomo Nechama *(Chm)*
Ran Fridrich *(CEO)*
Kalia Weintraub *(CFO)*
Eran Zupnik *(Exec VP-Bus Dev)*

Board of Directors:
Shlomo Nechama
Oded Akselrod
Barry Ben-Zeev
Ran Fridrich
Anita Leviant
Alon Lumbroso
Menahem Hemi Raphael

Non-U.S. Subsidiary:

Encre Consumables B.V. (1)
Locatellikade 1 parnassustrn
1076 Amsterdam, North Holland, Netherlands
Tel.: (31) 205408989
Printer Mfr & Services
S.I.C.: 3575
N.A.I.C.S.: 334118

ELM TREE MINERALS INC.

(Name Changed to Ximen Mining Corp.)

ELMA ELECTRONIC AG

Hofstrasse 93
8620 Wetzikon, Switzerland
Tel.: (41) 449334111
Telex: 875401
Fax: (41) 449334215
E-Mail: edwin.wild@elma.ch
Web Site: www.elma.com
Year Founded: 1960
ELMN—(SWX)
Sls.: $119,924,325
Assets: $69,712,199
Liabilities: $45,972,556
Net Worth: $23,739,643
Earnings: $850,504
Emp.: 682
Fiscal Year-end: 12/31/12

Business Description:
Electronic Packaging, Precision Rotary Switches & Other Products Mfr
S.I.C.: 3571
N.A.I.C.S.: 334111

Personnel:
Martin Wipfli *(Chm)*
David Schnell *(Vice Chm)*
Fred Ruegg *(CEO)*
Edwin Wild *(CFO)*

Board of Directors:
Martin Wipfli
Walter Hausermann
David Schnell
Rudolf W. Weber

U.S. Subsidiaries:

Elma Bustronic Corp. (1)
44350 Grimmer Blvd
Fremont, CA 94538 (100%)
Tel.: (510) 490-7388
Fax: (510) 490-1853
E-Mail: info@bustronic.com
Web Site: www.bustronic.com
Emp.: 50
Bare Printed Circuit Board Mfr
S.I.C.: 3672
N.A.I.C.S.: 334412
Boris Micha *(Gen Mgr)*

Elma Electronic Inc. (1)
44350 Grimmer Blvd
Fremont, CA 94538
Tel.: (510) 656-3400
Fax: (510) 653-3783
E-Mail: sales@elma.com
Web Site: www.elma.com
Emp.: 155
Electronic Enclosure & Passive Electronic Component Designer & Mfr
S.I.C.: 3571
N.A.I.C.S.: 334111
Shan Morgan *(Pres)*
Fred Ruegg *(Grp CEO)*

Optima Eps Corp (1)
1775 MacLeod Dr
Lawrenceville, GA 30043 (100%)
Tel.: (770) 496-4000
Fax: (770) 496-4041
E-Mail: sales@optimaeps.com
Web Site: www.optimaeps.com
Emp.: 50
Electronic Parts & Equipment Whslr
S.I.C.: 5065
N.A.I.C.S.: 423690

Non-U.S. Subsidiaries:

Elma Asia Pacific Pte. Ltd. (1)
115-A Commonwealth Drive 03-14 Tanglin Halt Industrial Estate
Singapore, 149596, Singapore
Tel.: (65) 64798552
Fax: (65) 64798662
E-Mail: sales.elmaap@elma.com
Web Site: www.elma.com
Emp.: 3
Back Planes & Rotary Component Mfr
S.I.C.: 3499
N.A.I.C.S.: 332999
Matthias Andermatt *(Mng Dir)*

Elma Electronic (China) Co., Ltd. (1)
8F 355 Fu Te Road West 1 Wai Gao Qiao Free Trade Zone
Pudong District, Shanghai, 200131, China
Tel.: (86) 21 5866 5908
Fax: (86) 21 5866 5918
E-Mail: sales@elmachina.com
Web Site: www.elma.com
Back Planes & Rotary Component Mfr
S.I.C.: 3499
N.A.I.C.S.: 332999

Elma Electronic France SASU (1)
ZA du Buisson Rond
Villemoirieu, 38460 Lyon, France (100%)
Tel.: (33) 437062110
Fax: (33) 437062119
E-Mail: sales@elma-electronic.fr
Web Site: www.elma-electronic.fr
Emp.: 11
Electronic Parts & Equipment Whslr
S.I.C.: 5065
N.A.I.C.S.: 423690
Boris Micha *(Mng Dir)*

Elma Electronic Israel Ltd (1)
34 Modin St
Sgula Petach Tikva, 49271 Petah Tiqwa, Israel (100%)
Tel.: (972) 39305025
Fax: (972) 39313134
E-Mail: avigail@elma.co.il

Elma Electronic AG—(Continued)

Web Site: www.elma.co.il
Emp.: 80
Electronic Parts & Equipment Whslr
S.I.C.: 5065
N.A.I.C.S.: 423690
Moshe Eisenkraft *(Mgr-Israel)*

Elma Trenew Electronic GmbH (1)
Stuttgarter Strasse 11
75179 Pforzheim, Germany (100%)
Tel.: (49) 723197340
Fax: (49) 7231973495
E-Mail: info@elma.de
Web Site: www.elma.de
Emp.: 90
Electronic Component Mfr
S.I.C.: 3679
N.A.I.C.S.: 334419

ELMA HANS SCHMIDBAUER GMBH & CO. KG
Kolpingstr 1 7
D-78224 Singen, Germany
Tel.: (49) 77318820
Fax: (49) 7731882266
E-Mail: info@elma-ultrasonic.com
Web Site: www.elma-ultrasonic.com
Year Founded: 1948
Rev.: $24,584,970
Emp.: 15
Business Description:
Cleaning Equipment Mfr
S.I.C.: 3699
N.A.I.C.S.: 335999
Personnel:
Manfred H. Schmidbauer *(Mng Dir)*

ELMA HOLDINGS PUBLIC COMPANY LTD
54 Grivas Digenis Avenue
1096 Nicosia, Cyprus
Tel.: (357) 22020200
Fax: (357) 22664966
Web Site: www.elma.com.cy
ELMA—(CYP)
Business Description:
Investment Management Services
S.I.C.: 6211
N.A.I.C.S.: 523999
Personnel:
Michalakis Ioannides *(Chm)*
Antonis Kallis *(Sec)*
Board of Directors:
Michalakis Ioannides
Costas Constantinides
Constantinos Damtsas
Yiannos Ioannides
Efi Kalli
Doros Ktorides
Kikis Lefkaritis
Demosthenis Severis

ELMAT - SCHLAGHECK GMBH & CO. KG
Alte Ziegelei 27
51491 Overath, Germany
Tel.: (49) 220494810
Fax: (49) 2204948161
E-Mail: info@elmat.de
Web Site: www.elmat.de
Rev.: $31,144,351
Emp.: 32
Business Description:
Cable Mfr
S.I.C.: 3496
N.A.I.C.S.: 332618
Personnel:
Bodo Schlagheck *(Mng Partner)*

ELMO D.D.
Vojkova ulica 58
1000 Ljubljana, Slovenia
Tel.: (386) 15308800
Fax: (386) 1 5308848
Web Site: www.elmo.si
IELG—(LJU)
Sales Range: $10-24.9 Million
Emp.: 80
Business Description:
Electric Power Transmission Line Engineering & Maintenance Services
S.I.C.: 1629
N.A.I.C.S.: 237130
Personnel:
Majda Andoljsek *(Chm-Mgmt Bd)*

ELMOS SEMICONDUCTOR AG
Heinrich Hertz Strasse 1
44227 Dortmund, Germany
Tel.: (49) 23175490
Fax: (49) 2317549149
E-Mail: info@elmos.com
Web Site: www.elmos.com
Year Founded: 1984
ELG—(DEU)
Sls.: $242,464,063
Assets: $366,408,628
Liabilities: $110,569,019
Net Worth: $255,839,609
Earnings: $11,169,172
Emp.: 1,034
Fiscal Year-end: 12/31/12
Business Description:
Integrated Circuits Mfr
S.I.C.: 3674
N.A.I.C.S.: 334413
Personnel:
Gunter Zimmer *(Chm-Supervisory Bd)*
Burkhard Dreher *(Vice Chm-Supervisory Bd)*
Anton Mindl *(CEO & Member-Mgmt Bd)*
Nicolaus Graf von Luckner *(CFO & Member-Mgmt Bd)*
Peter Geiselhart *(Member-Mgmt Bd-Sls & Dev)*
Reinhard Senf *(Member-Mgmt Bd-Production)*
Supervisory Board of Directors:
Gunter Zimmer
Burkhard Dreher
Klaus Egger
Thomas Lehner
Sven-Olaf Schellenberg
Klaus G. Weyer
Subsidiaries:

Elmos Central IT Services GmbH & Co. KG (1)
Heinrich-Hertz-Str 1
44227 Dortmund, Germany (100%)
Tel.: (49) 23175490
Fax: (49) 2317549149
Computer Programming Services
S.I.C.: 7371
N.A.I.C.S.: 541511

Elmos Facility Management GmbH & Co. KG (1)
Heinrich-Hertz-Str 1
44227 Dortmund, Germany (100%)
Tel.: (49) 23175490
Fax: (49) 2317549149
Web Site: www.elmos.com
Emp.: 700
Regulation & Administration Communications Electric Gas & Utilities
S.I.C.: 9631
N.A.I.C.S.: 926130
Mindl Anton *(Mng Dir)*

ELMOS Semiconductor Sud GmbH (1)
Heinrich-Hertz-Str 1
Dortmund, 44227, Germany (100%)
Tel.: (49) 23175490
Fax: (49) 2317549149
E-Mail: info@elmos.com
Emp.: 800
Electronic Components Mfr
S.I.C.: 3679
N.A.I.C.S.: 334419
Anton Mindl *(Mgr)*

GED Gartner Electronic Design GmbH (1)
Im Technologiepark 27
15236 Frankfurt, Germany (100%)
Tel.: (49) 3355572050
Fax: (49) 3355572055
E-Mail: info@ged.de
Web Site: www.ged.de
Emp.: 35
Computer Systems Design Services
S.I.C.: 7373
N.A.I.C.S.: 541512
Ged Gartner *(Mng Dir)*

IndustrieAlpine Bautrager GmbH (1)
Am Geflugelhof 12
85716 Unterschleissheim, Germany
Tel.: (49) 893183700
Fax: (49) 89 31837031
Semiconductor Mfr
S.I.C.: 3674
N.A.I.C.S.: 334413

Mechaless GmbH (1)
Albert-Nestler-Str 10
Karlsruhe, Germany (51%)
Tel.: (49) 721626980
Fax: (49) 7216269811
E-Mail: info@mechaless.com
Web Site: www.mechaless.com
Emp.: 20
Research & Development in the Physical Engineering & Life Sciences
S.I.C.: 8731
N.A.I.C.S.: 541712
Uwe Hall *(Mng Dir)*

U.S. Subsidiaries:

ELMOS N.A. Inc (1)
32255 Northwestern Hwy Ste 45
Farmington Hills, MI 48334
Tel.: (248) 865-3200
Fax: (248) 865-3203
E-Mail: elna-sales@elmosna.com
Web Site: www.elmosna.com
Semiconductor Devices Mfr
S.I.C.: 3674
N.A.I.C.S.: 334413
Gunter Zimmer *(Chm-Supervisory Bd)*
Anton Mindl *(CEO)*
Nicolaus Graf von Luckner *(CFO)*
Jurgen Hollisch *(Member-Mgmt Bd)*
Reinhard Senf *(Member-Mgmt Bd)*

Silicon Microstructures Inc. (1)
1701 McCarthy Blvd
Milpitas, CA 95035 (100%)
Tel.: (408) 577-0100
Fax: (408) 577-0123
Web Site: www.si-micro.com
Emp.: 100
Relay & Industrial Control Mfr
S.I.C.: 3625
N.A.I.C.S.: 335314
Rainer Cholewa *(Pres & CEO)*

Non-U.S. Subsidiaries:

Elmos Advanced Packaging BV (1)
Microweg 1-11
6545 CL Nijmegen, Netherlands
Mailing Address:
PO Box 566
6500 AN Nijmegen, Netherlands
Tel.: (31) 24 377 0406
Web Site: www.elmos.de/ueber-uns/standorte/nijmegen-nl.html
Integrated Circuit Assembly
S.I.C.: 3674
N.A.I.C.S.: 334413

Elmos Design Services B.V. (1)
Microweg 1
6545CL Nijmegen, Netherlands (100%)
Tel.: (31) 243714499
Fax: (31) 243770406
E-Mail: info@elmosap.nl
Web Site: www.elmos.eu
Emp.: 85
Trusts Estates & Agency Accounts
S.I.C.: 6733
N.A.I.C.S.: 525920
John Pleumeekers *(Mng Dir)*

ELMOS Korea Ltd (1)
1907 Park Pieww Office Tower 6 Jeong Jatong
Bundang-Gu, Seongnam, Kyonggi-do, 463825, Korea (South)
Tel.: (82) 317141131
Fax: (82) 27040155169
Web Site: www.elmos.com
Emp.: 7
Semiconductor Equipment Distr
S.I.C.: 5065
N.A.I.C.S.: 423690
Jin-Koo Lee *(Mgr)*

Elmos Quality Services B.V. (1)
Microweg 1
6545CL Nijmegen, Netherlands (100%)
Tel.: (31) 243714499
Fax: (31) 243770406
E-Mail:
Web Site: www.elmos.com
Emp.: 100
Business Services
S.I.C.: 7389
N.A.I.C.S.: 561499
John Pleumeekers *(Mng Dir)*

Elmos Services B.V. (1)
Microweg 1
6545 CL Nijmegen, Netherlands (100%)
Tel.: (31) 243714499
Fax: (31) 243770406
E-Mail: info@elmosap.nl
Web Site: www.elmos.de/englisch/about-us/locations.html
Emp.: 80
Footwear Whslr
S.I.C.: 5139
N.A.I.C.S.: 424340
John Pleumeekers *(Mng Dir)*

European Semiconductor Assembly (eurasem) B.V. (1)
Microweg 1
6545CL Nijmegen, Netherlands (100%)
Tel.: (31) 243714499
Fax: (31) 243770406
E-Mail: info@elmosap.nl
Web Site: www.elmosap.nl
Emp.: 100
Electronic Components Mfr
S.I.C.: 3679
N.A.I.C.S.: 334419
John Pleumeekers *(Mng Dir)*

ELNA CO., LTD.
3-8-11 Shin-Yokohama Kohoku-ku
Yokohama, Kanagawa, Japan
Tel.: (81) 454707251
Fax: (81) 454707261
E-Mail: info@elna.co.jp
Web Site: www.elna.co.jp
Year Founded: 1937
6972—(TKS)
Sls.: $316,558,000
Assets: $269,973,000
Liabilities: $222,739,000
Net Worth: $47,234,000
Earnings: $5,819,000
Emp.: 604
Fiscal Year-end: 12/31/12
Business Description:
Aluminum & Tantalum Solid-State Electrolytic Capacitors, Electric Double Layer Capacitors, Build-Up PCBs, Multilayer PCBs & Double-Sided PCBs
S.I.C.: 3676
N.A.I.C.S.: 334416
Personnel:
Hidetoshi Yashida *(Pres)*
Motohiro Kuno *(Exec Officer)*
Kenichiro Murata *(Exec Officer)*
Board of Directors:
Masanao Ando
Shunichi Suzuki
Tokuo Tatai
Hidetoshi Yashida
Futoshi Yasueda
Subsidiaries:

Elna Components Co., Ltd. (1)
KDX Shin Yokohama Bldg 3-8-11 Shin Yokohama
Kouhoku-ku, Yokohama, Kanagawa, Japan
Tel.: (81) 47 470 7251
Fax: (81) 45 470 7261

Web Site: www.elna.co.jp/en/company/group.html
Electronic Component Mfr
S.I.C.: 3679
N.A.I.C.S.: 334419
Okubo Satochei *(Mng Dir)*

Elna Matsumoto Co., Ltd. **(1)**
4130-5 Azusagawayamato
Matsumoto, Nagano, 390-1701, Japan
Tel.: (81) 263784631
Fax: (81) 263784638
Web Site: www.elna.co.jp/en/company/group.html
Bare Printed Circuit Board Mfr
S.I.C.: 3672
N.A.I.C.S.: 334412

Elna Tohoku Co., Ltd. **(1)**
1-349-1 Okonoki Kuroishi
Aomori, 036-0357, Japan
Tel.: (81) 172524166
Fax: (81) 172534609
Emp.: 300
Electronic Resistor Mfr
S.I.C.: 3675
N.A.I.C.S.: 334416

Plants:

Elna Co., Ltd. - Shiga Factory **(1)**
30 Ta-cho
Nagahama, Shiga, 529-0142, Japan
Tel.: (81) 749 73 3021
Fax: (81) 749 73 8071
Web Site: www.elna.co.jp/en/company/data.html
Capacitor & Printed Circuit Board Mfr
S.I.C.: 3675
N.A.I.C.S.: 334416

Elna Co., Ltd. - Shirakawa Factory **(1)**
9-32 Aza-sugiyama Oaza-yone
Nishigo-mura, Fukushima, 961-8031, Japan
Tel.: (81) 248 25 5311
Fax: (81) 248 25 5314
Capacitor & Printed Circuit Board Mfr
S.I.C.: 3672
N.A.I.C.S.: 334412

U.S. Subsidiary:

Elna America, Inc. **(1)**
5770 Warland Dr Bldg #B
Cypress, CA 90630
Tel.: (714) 761-8600
Fax: (714) 761-9188
E-Mail: mail@elna-america.com
Web Site: www.elna-america.com
Emp.: 20
Electronic Capacitor Mfr
S.I.C.: 3675
N.A.I.C.S.: 334416
Kent Sterrett *(VP-Sls & Ops)*

Non-U.S. Subsidiaries:

Elna Electronics (S) Pte. Ltd. **(1)**
103 Kallang Avenue
04-01 AIS Industrial Building, 339504
Singapore, Singapore
Tel.: (65) 62930181
Fax: (65) 62966716
Emp.: 16
Electronic Parts & Equipment Whslr
S.I.C.: 5065
N.A.I.C.S.: 423690
Bernard Chang *(Mng Dir)*

Elna (HK) Co., Ltd. **(1)**
Unit 11 1-F Mirror Tower 61 Mody Rd
Tsimshatsui East, Kowloon, China (Hong Kong)
Tel.: (852) 27234285
Fax: (852) 27234623
E-Mail: kikuchi@elna.co.jp
Web Site: www.egco.co.th
Emp.: 1
Electronic Parts & Equipment Whslr
S.I.C.: 5065
N.A.I.C.S.: 423690
Kikuchi Isao *(Mng Dir)*

Elna PCB (M) Sdn. Bhd. **(1)**
Plot 558 Lorong Perusahaan 4 Ftz
Prai Industrial Estate, 13600 Penang, Malaysia
Tel.: (60) 43973934
Fax: (60) 43973932
E-Mail: hr@elnapcb.com
Web Site: www.elnapcb.com
Emp.: 600
Bare Printed Circuit Board Mfr
S.I.C.: 3291
N.A.I.C.S.: 327910
Suzuki Hiroyuki *(Mng Dir)*

Elna (Shanghai) Co., Ltd. **(1)**
Rm 6203 Rui Jin Hotel Business Center
118 Rui Jin 2 Rd, 200 020 Shanghai, China
Tel.: (86) 2164452269
Fax: (86) 2164452271
E-Mail: esh006@elna-sh.com
Web Site: www.elna.co.jp/en/company/group.html
Emp.: 8
Electronic Parts & Equipment Whslr
S.I.C.: 5065
N.A.I.C.S.: 423690
Moriyama Hiroyuki *(Gen Mgr)*

Elna-Sonic Sdn. Bhd. **(1)**
2473 Tingkat Perusahaan 6
Free Trade Zone Prai Industria, 13600
Penang, Malaysia
Tel.: (60) 43992916
Fax: (60) 43992925
E-Mail: khteh@elnasonic.com.my
Web Site: www.elna.com
Emp.: 75
Electronic Capacitor Mfr
S.I.C.: 3675
N.A.I.C.S.: 334416
Masaki Omoda *(Mng Dir)*

Tanin Elna Co., Ltd. **(1)**
88 90 Chalermphrakiat Rama 9 Road
Nongborn Pravest, Bangkok, 10250, Thailand
Tel.: (66) 23985333
Fax: (66) 23985337
E-Mail: prayong@taninelna.com
Emp.: 800
Electronic Capacitor Mfr
S.I.C.: 3675
N.A.I.C.S.: 334416
Tsuki Katsuyuki *(Pres)*

ELNET TECHNOLOGIES LIMITED

Elnet Software City TS 140 Block No 2 & 9 Rajiv Gandhi Salai Taramani
Chennai, Tamil Nadu, 600 113, India
Tel.: (91) 4422541337
Fax: (91) 4422541955
E-Mail: elnet@md4.vsnl.net.in
Web Site: www.elnettechnologies.com
ELNET—(NSE)
Rev.: $4,021,721
Assets: $10,668,549
Liabilities: $3,658,900
Net Worth: $7,009,649
Earnings: $999,122
Emp.: 15
Fiscal Year-end: 03/31/13
Business Description:
Business Process Outsourcing Services
S.I.C.: 7389
N.A.I.C.S.: 561990
Personnel:
Unnamalai Thiagarajan *(Mng Dir)*
C. Venkataramanan *(Compliance Officer)*
G. Porselvam *(Sec)*
Board of Directors:
Atul Anand
V. Dharmalingam
R. Ganapathi
K. Kasim
P. S. Kumar
K. Padmanaban
S. Paulraj
C. Ramachandran
J. Ravi
G. Senrayaperumal
H. Karthik Seshadri
Unnamalai Thiagarajan
Transfer Agent:
Cameo Corporate Services Limited
Subramanian Building V Floor 1 Club House Road
Chennai, India

ELOF HANSSON AB

Forsta Langgatan 17
SE 413 80 Gothenburg, Sweden
Tel.: (46) 31856000
Fax: (46) 31126735
E-Mail: info@elofhansson.com
Web Site: www.elofhansson.com
Year Founded: 1897
Sales Range: $700-749.9 Million
Emp.: 120
Business Description:
Mfr. of Electronics, Appliances, Electric Tools, Textiles, Wood Products, Building Materials, Railway Materials, Forgings & Castings, Steel, Tubes, Pulp & Paper Machinery, Packaging & Converting Machinery Import Export
S.I.C.: 3699
N.A.I.C.S.: 335999
Personnel:
Robert Sandberg *(Chm)*

U.S. Subsidiary:

Elof Hansson Inc. **(1)**
565 Taxter Rd
Elmsford, NY 10523-2300 NY
Tel.: (914) 345-8380 (100%)
Fax: (914) 345-8112
E-Mail:
Web Site: www.elofhansson.com
Emp.: 50
Paper & Wood Pulp
S.I.C.: 5113
N.A.I.C.S.: 424130
Thomas Driscoll *(CFO)*

Subsidiaries:

Elof Hansson Paper & Board, Inc. **(2)**
400 Tech Centre Dr Ste 220
Milford, OH 45150 (100%)
Tel.: (513) 965-5090
Fax: (513) 965-9091
E-Mail: paper@us.elofhansson.com
Emp.: 25
Paper & Board
S.I.C.: 5113
N.A.I.C.S.: 424130

ELONEX

Z I Rousset 85 Avenue De La Plaine
13790 Rousset, Bouches-du-Rhone, France
Tel.: (33) 442535400
Fax: (33) 442535429
E-Mail: lco-n@trsp.net
Web Site: www.elonex.fr/
Sls.: $39,600,000
Emp.: 55
Business Description:
Computer Equipment
S.I.C.: 5045
N.A.I.C.S.: 423430
Personnel:
Veronique Gardy *(Dir-Mktg)*

ELORO RESOURCES LTD.

20 Adelaide Street East Suite 301
Toronto, ON, M5C 2T6, Canada
Tel.: (416) 868-9168
Fax: (416) 361-1333
Toll Free: (800) 360-8006
E-Mail: info@elororesources.com
Web Site: www.elororesources.com
Year Founded: 1975
ELO—(TSXV)
Sales Range: Less than $1 Million
Emp.: 5
Business Description:
Gold Mining & Exploration Services
S.I.C.: 1041
N.A.I.C.S.: 212221
Personnel:
Thomas G. Larsen *(Chm, Pres & CEO)*
Miles Nagamatsu *(CFO)*
Jorge Estepa *(Treas, Sec & VP)*
Martin Bourgoin *(Exec VP)*
Board of Directors:
Thomas G. Larsen
Alexander S. Horvath
Jean Lafleur
Miles Nagamatsu
Denis Potvin
Francis Sauve

ELOS AB

Nya Stadens Torg 10
531 31 Lidkoping, Sweden
Tel.: (46) 510484360
Fax: (46) 51068004
E-Mail: info@elos.se
Web Site: www.elos.se
ELOS B—(OMX)
Sls.: $67,144,964
Assets: $82,931,623
Liabilities: $49,818,665
Net Worth: $33,112,958
Earnings: $1,261,775
Emp.: 424
Fiscal Year-end: 12/31/12
Business Description:
Medical & Precision Technology Products
S.I.C.: 3841
N.A.I.C.S.: 339112
Personnel:
Stig-Arne Blom *(Chm)*
Goran Brorsson *(Pres & CEO)*
Ulrica Ehn *(CFO)*
Patrick Juslin *(CTO)*
Board of Directors:
Stig-Arne Blom
Goran Brorsson
Erik Lowenadler
Jeppe Magnusson
Mats Nilsson
Thomas Oster
Agneta Bengtsson Runmarker
Subsidiaries:

Elos Fixturlaser AB **(1)**
Ostergardsgatan 9
Box 7
SE-431 21 Molndal, Sweden (100%)
Tel.: (46) 317062800
Fax: (46) 317062850
E-Mail: info@fixturlaser.se
Web Site: www.fixturlaser.se
Emp.: 35
Measuring & Controlling Device Mfr
S.I.C.: 3829
N.A.I.C.S.: 334519
Hans Svensson *(Pres)*

Elos Medtech Timmersdala AB **(1)**
Backedalsvagen 5
Box 45
54016 Timmersdala, Sweden
Tel.: (46) 511440600
Fax: (46) 511440690
E-Mail: info@elosmedical.se
Web Site: www.elosmedical.se
Emp.: 11
Surgical & Medical Instrument Mfr
S.I.C.: 3841
N.A.I.C.S.: 339112
Kjell-Erik Johansson *(VP)*

Non-U.S. Subsidiaries:

Elos Medtech Tianjin Co. Ltd. **(1)**
D5-3 Rong Cheng San Zhi Lu Xeda
International Industrial City
300385 Tianjin, China
Tel.: (86) 22 23 82 86 60
Fax: (86) 22 23 82 86 62
E-Mail: info.tianjin@elosmedtech.com

Elos AB—(Continued)

Web Site: www.elos.se/web/Site_Tianjin_1.aspx
Medical Instruments Mfr
S.I.C.: 3841
N.A.I.C.S.: 339112

Elos Medtech Pinol A/S (1)
Engvej 33
3330 Gorlose, Denmark (100%)
Tel.: (45) 48216400
Fax: (45) 48216469
E-Mail: pinol@elos-pinol.dk
Web Site: www.elos-pinol.dk
Emp.: 150
Surgical & Medical Instrument Mfr
S.I.C.: 3841
N.A.I.C.S.: 339112
Soren Oleson *(VP)*

ELPRO INTERNATIONAL LTD.

17th Floor Nirmal Nariman Point
Mumbai, 400 021, India
Tel.: (91) 22023075
Fax: (91) 22027995
E-Mail: mkt@elpro.co.in
Web Site: www.elpro.co.in
Year Founded: 1962
504000—(BOM)
Rev.: $6,420,680
Assets: $70,020,537
Liabilities: $35,435,650
Net Worth: $34,584,887
Earnings: $1,125,341
Fiscal Year-end: 03/31/13

Business Description:
Electrical Equipment Mfr
S.I.C.: 3699
N.A.I.C.S.: 335999

Personnel:
Ram Swaroop Dabriwala *(Chm)*
R. Mukherjee *(CEO)*
Sambhaw Jain *(CFO & Compliance Officer)*
Rashmi Patkar *(Sec)*

Board of Directors:
Ram Swaroop Dabriwala
Narayan T. Atal
Surbhit Dabriwala
Ashok Kumar Jain
Anil Kumar Poddar

Transfer Agent:
Sharex Dynamic (India) Pvt. Ltd.
Unit-1 Luthra Ind Premises Safed Pool Andheri Kurla Rd Andheri (E)
Mumbai, India

Subsidiary:

Elpro Estates Limited (1)
The Metro Pliitan Chapekar Chowk
Chinchwad, Pune, 411 019, India
Tel.: (91) 20 32319113
E-Mail: info@elpro.co.in
Apartment Construction Services
S.I.C.: 1522
N.A.I.C.S.: 236116
Mayur Khandeparkar *(CEO)*

ELPROM-ZEM AD

41 Rozhen Blvd
Sofia, 1271, Bulgaria
Tel.: (359) 2 936 0753
Fax: (359) 2 936 0347
E-Mail: zem@elprom-zem.com
Web Site: www.elprom-zem.com
55E—(BUL)

Business Description:
Electric Motor Mfr
S.I.C.: 3621
N.A.I.C.S.: 335312

Personnel:
Nasya Todorova Aleksandrova *(Dir-IR)*

ELRINGKLINGER AG

Max Eyth Strasse 2
72581 Dettingen an der Erms, Germany
Tel.: (49) 71237240
Fax: (49) 71237249006
E-Mail: info@elringklinger.com
Web Site: www.elringklinger.de
ZIL2—(DEU)
Rev.: $1,517,378,593
Assets: $1,707,739,146
Liabilities: $845,847,073
Net Worth: $861,892,073
Earnings: $120,350,290
Emp.: 6,263
Fiscal Year-end: 12/31/12

Business Description:
Exhaust Equipment Mfr
S.I.C.: 3714
N.A.I.C.S.: 336310

Personnel:
Walter Herwarth Lechler *(Chm-Supervisory Bd)*
Stefan Wolf *(Chm-Mgmt Bd & CEO)*
Markus Siegers *(Deputy Chm-Supervisory Bd)*
Sabrina Haufler *(IR Officer)*
Theo Becker *(Member-Mgmt Bd-Specialty Gaskets & Plastic Housing Modules)*
Karl Schmauder *(Member-Mgmt Bd-Equipment Sls & New Bus Areas)*

Supervisory Board of Directors:
Walter Herwarth Lechler
Gert Bauer
Paula Maria de Castro Monteiro Munz
Armin Diez
Klaus Eberhardt
Pasquale Formisano
Margarete Haase
Thomas Klinger-Lohr
Hans-Ulrich Sachs
Markus Siegers
Manfred Strauss
Gerhard Wick

Subsidiaries:

Elring Klinger Motortechnik GmbH (1)
Richard-Klinger-Strasse 8
65510 Idstein, Hesse, Germany
Tel.: (49) 612622305
Fax: (49) 612622342
Automotive Engineering Services
S.I.C.: 7542
N.A.I.C.S.: 811192
Gerald Eifler *(Gen Mgr)*

ElringKlinger Kunststofftechnik GmbH (1)
Etzelstrasse 10
74321 Bietigheim-Bissingen, Baden-Wuerttemberg, Germany
Tel.: (49) 71425830
Fax: (49) 7142583200
E-Mail: ekt-info@elringklinger.com
Web Site: www.elringklinger.com
Emp.: 570
Polytetrafluoroethylene Products Mfr
S.I.C.: 3714
N.A.I.C.S.: 336310
Stefan Schmid *(Mng Dir)*

Non-U.S. Subsidiaries:

Elring Gaskets (Pty) Ltd. (2)
83 Mimetes Rd
Denver, Johannesburg, Gauteng, 2094, South Africa
Tel.: (27) 116225660
Fax: (27) 116228920
Emp.: 12
Gaskets Retailer
S.I.C.: 5085
N.A.I.C.S.: 423840
Grant Stevens *(Gen Mgr)*

Elring Klinger do Brasil Ltda. (2)
Rua Francisco Carlos de Castro Neves 945
,13422 170 Piracicaba, Sao Paulo, Brazil
Tel.: (55) 1931249000
Fax: (55) 19 3124 9001
Web Site: www.elringklinger.com.br
Emp.: 350
Gaskets Mfr
S.I.C.: 3053
N.A.I.C.S.: 339991
Hans Guenther Eckert *(Gen Dir)*

ElringKlinger Engineered Plastics (Qingdao) Commercial Co., Ltd. (2)
2-1 Ke Yuan Wei San St
Laoshan Dist, 266061 Qingdao, Shandong, China
Tel.: (86) 5 32 88 70 63 26
Fax: (86) 5 32 88 70 63 28
E-Mail: info@elringklinger-ep.cn
Web Site: www.elringklinger-ep.cn
Plastic Products Mfr
S.I.C.: 3089
N.A.I.C.S.: 326199

ElringKlinger Logistic Service GmbH (1)
Mercedesstrasse 40
72108 Rottenburg am Neckar, Baden-Wurttemberg, Germany
Tel.: (49) 7457956010
Fax: (49) 74579560166
E-Mail: info@ek-ls.de
Web Site: www.ek-ls.de
Emp.: 1,500
Cylinder Head Gaskets Supplier
S.I.C.: 5085
N.A.I.C.S.: 423840
Thilo Muller *(Mng Dir)*

Non-U.S. Subsidiaries:

EKASER, S.A. de C.V. (1)
Mz 9 L-13 Y 14
50200 Toluca, Mexico
Tel.: (52) 17222731912
Fax: (52) 1 722 2 73 19 18
Automobile Parts Mfr & Distr
S.I.C.: 3714
N.A.I.C.S.: 336390

Elring Klinger (Great Britain) Ltd. (1)
Kirkleatham Bus Park
Redcar, N Yorkshire, TS10 5RX, United Kingdom
Tel.: (44) 1642492492
Fax: (44) 16 42 49 62 00
E-Mail: elringklinger@ekgb.co.uk
Cylinder Head Gaskets Mfr
S.I.C.: 3053
N.A.I.C.S.: 339991

Elring Klinger Mexico, S.A. de C.V. (1)
Alfonso Gomez de Orozco No 122 Col Exportec II
Toluca, Estado de Mexico, 50200, Mexico
Tel.: (52) 7222622800
Fax: (52) 7222731918
E-Mail: global@elringklinger.com.mx
Web Site: www.elringklinger.com
Gaskets & Shielding Parts Mfr
S.I.C.: 3624
N.A.I.C.S.: 335991
Salvador Cervantes *(Gen Mgr)*

Elring Parts Ltd. (1)
Unit 2 Derwent Ct Earlsway Team Vly Trading Estate
Gateshead, Tyne and Wear, NE11 0TF, United Kingdom
Tel.: (44) 1914915678
Fax: (44) 1914875001
E-Mail: sales@elringparts.co.uk
Web Site: www.elringparts.co.uk
Emp.: 29
Gaskets Distr
S.I.C.: 5085
N.A.I.C.S.: 423840
Dave Masterman *(Mng Dir)*

ElringKlinger Abschirmtechnik (Schweiz) AG (1)
Schildstr 20
9475 Sevelen, Switzerland
Tel.: (41) 817501210
Fax: (41) 817501225
E-Mail: info@elringklinger.ch
Web Site: www.elringklinger.ch
Emp.: 400
Industrial Engineering Services
S.I.C.: 8711
N.A.I.C.S.: 541330
Bruno Malinek *(Mng Dir)*

ElringKlinger Automotive Components (India) Pvt. Ltd. (1)
Plot No G2 Ranjangaon Ind Area
Tal Shirur Dist, Pune, Maharashtra, 412220, India
Tel.: (91) 2138671700
Fax: (91) 2138671701
E-Mail: info@elringklinger.in
Web Site: www.elringklinger.in
Emp.: 120
Automotive Components Distr
S.I.C.: 5013
N.A.I.C.S.: 423120

ElringKlinger Canada, Inc. (1)
1 Seneca Rd RR 4
Leamington, ON, N8H 5P2, Canada
Tel.: (519) 326-6113
Fax: (519) 326-3396
E-Mail: info@elringklinger.ca
Web Site: www.elringklinger.ca
Emp.: 130
Injection Molding Automotive Parts Mfr
S.I.C.: 3714
N.A.I.C.S.: 336390
Ninan Mathew *(Mgr-Engrg)*

PT Natarang Mining (1)
Jalan Ciputat Raya No 16 Pondok Pinang Kebayoran Lama
Jakarta Selatan, Jakarta, 12310, Indonesia
Tel.: (62) 21 751 0125
Fax: (62) 21 769 2783
Gold Mining Services
S.I.C.: 1041
N.A.I.C.S.: 212221

ELRON ELECTRONIC INDUSTRIES LTD.

3 Azrieli Center 42nd Floor
Tel Aviv, Israel 6702301
Tel.: (972) 36075555
Fax: (972) 36075556
E-Mail: elron@elron.net
Web Site: www.elron.com
Year Founded: 1962
ELRN—(TAE)
Rev.: $9,197,000
Assets: $212,902,000
Liabilities: $13,087,000
Net Worth: $199,815,000
Earnings: $16,930,000
Emp.: 5
Fiscal Year-end: 12/31/13

Business Description:
Technology Investment Services
S.I.C.: 6211
N.A.I.C.S.: 523999

Personnel:
Arie Mientkavich *(Chm)*
Zvika Slovin *(Co-CEO, VP-Medical & Life Sciences)*
Ari Bronshtein *(Co-CEO)*
Yaron Elad *(CFO)*

Board of Directors:
Arie Mientkavich
Gad Arbel
Avraham Asheri
Gabi Barbash
Ari Bronshtein
Rona Dankner
Ami Erel
Avraham Fischer
Yaacov Goldman
Shay Livnat
Dori Manor
Arie Ovadia

ELSAN LTD.

Bellbrook Park
Uckfield, Sussex, TN22 1QF, United Kingdom
Tel.: (44) 825748200
Telex: 957236 elsan g
Fax: (44) 825761212
E-Mail: sales@elsan.co.uk
Web Site: www.elsan.co.uk
Year Founded: 1924
Sales Range: $1-9.9 Million
Emp.: 20

Business Description:
Chemical Sanitation Products Mfr & Supplier
Import Export

S.I.C.: 2842
N.A.I.C.S.: 325612
Personnel:
Peter Warwick-Smith *(Mng Dir)*

Subsidiaries:

Horton Hygiene Co. **(1)**
Bellbrook Pk
Uckfield, Sussex, TN22 4LW, United Kingdom
Tel.: (44) 825748200
Fax: (44) 1825761212
Import Export
S.I.C.: 2842
N.A.I.C.S.: 325612

The Trailerbarrow Co. **(1)**
Buxted
Uckfield, Sussex, TN22 4LW, United Kingdom
Tel.: (44) 825733291
Fax: (44) 825733617
Import Export
S.I.C.: 3792
N.A.I.C.S.: 336214

ELSMORE RESOURCES LIMITED

Suite 1306 Level 13 370 Pitt Street
Sydney, NSW, 2000, Australia
Tel.: (61) 2 92670004
Fax: (61) 2 92670009
E-Mail: info@elsmore.com.au
Web Site: www.elsmore.com.au
ELR—(ASX)
Business Description:
Tin & Gems Mining & Exploration
S.I.C.: 1099
N.A.I.C.S.: 212299
Personnel:
John Patrick Gaffney *(Chm)*
Board of Directors:
John Patrick Gaffney
Gregory Hilton Artup
Joseph Tong Hong Chung
Zoran Nedimovic

ELTE

80 Ronald Ave
Toronto, ON, M6E 5A2, Canada
Tel.: (416) 785-7885
Fax: (416) 785-9157
Toll Free: (888) 276-3583
Web Site: www.elte.com
Year Founded: 1919
Rev.: $50,051,310
Emp.: 150
Business Description:
Home Furnishing Retailer
S.I.C.: 5023
N.A.I.C.S.: 423220
Personnel:
Alan Goldberg *(Pres)*
Ken Metrick *(CEO)*

ELTEC ELEKTRONIK AG

Galileo Galilei Strasse 11
55129 Mainz, Germany
Tel.: (49) 61319180
Fax: (49) 6131918195
E-Mail: info@eltec.de
Web Site: www.eltec.de
Year Founded: 1978
Rev.: $13,535,019
Emp.: 40
Business Description:
Electronic Devices Mfr
S.I.C.: 3679
N.A.I.C.S.: 334419
Personnel:
Klaus Bax *(Chm-Supervisory Bd)*
Dieter Gebert *(CEO)*
Supervisory Board of Directors:
Klaus Bax
Fritz-Wilhelm Kruger
Gunter Nahs

ELTEK ASA

Graterudveien 8
3036 Drammen, Norway
Tel.: (47) 32203200
Fax: (47) 32203210
E-Mail: eltek@eltek.com
Web Site: www.eltek.com
ELT—(OSL)
Sls.: $631,528,407
Assets: $534,590,163
Liabilities: $320,062,716
Net Worth: $214,527,447
Earnings: $74,893,662
Emp.: 2,492
Fiscal Year-end: 12/31/12
Business Description:
Electronic Solutions for Wired & Wireless Telecommunications
S.I.C.: 3679
N.A.I.C.S.: 334419
Personnel:
Erik Thorsen *(Chm)*
Colin Howe *(CEO)*
Bjorn Wigstrom *(CFO)*
Morten Schoyen *(CMO)*
Reidar Hagen *(CTO)*
Frode Vagen *(Chief Quality Officer)*
Lars Dousa *(Exec VP-Indus)*
Michel Fraisse *(Exec VP-Sls & Mktg-Telecom, Renewable & E-Vehicles)*
Bengt Lundberg *(Exec VP-Global Ops)*
Board of Directors:
Erik Thorsen
Anne Jorun Aas
Birgitte Feginn Angelil
William H. Crown
Anders Hvide
Hugo Maurstad
Dia S. Weil

Subsidiary:

Eltek Valere AS **(1)**
Graterudveien 8
PB 2340
Stromso, 3036 Drammen, Norway
Tel.: (47) 32203200
Fax: (47) 3220 3210
E-Mail: eltek@eltekvalere.com
Web Site: www.eltekvalere.com
Telecommunication Power Transmission Equipment Mfr
S.I.C.: 3669
N.A.I.C.S.: 334290
Morten Schoyen *(CMO)*
Reidar Hagen *(CTO)*

U.S. Subsidiary:

Eltek Valere **(1)**
1303 E Arapaho Rd
Richardson, TX 75081-2444
Tel.: (469) 330-9100
Fax: (469) 330-2955
E-Mail: info@valerepower.com
Web Site: www.eltekvalere.com
Sales Range: $500-549.9 Million
Emp.: 135
Supplier of Telecommunication Infrastructure Energy Systems
S.I.C.: 4899
N.A.I.C.S.: 517919
Rune Finne *(CEO)*

Non-U.S. Subsidiary:

Eltek Energy AS **(2)**
Graterudveien 8
3036 Drammen, Norway
Tel.: (47) 32203200
Fax: (47) 32203210
E-Mail: elket@elket.com
Web Site: www.elket.com
Sales Range: $400-449.9 Million
Emp.: 200
Supplier of Telecommunication Energy Systems
S.I.C.: 4899
N.A.I.C.S.: 517919
Colin Howe *(Mng Dir)*

Non-U.S. Subsidiary:

Eltek Energy Pte. Ltd. **(3)**
No 3 Teban Gardens Crescent
608920 Singapore, Singapore
Tel.: (65) 67732326
Fax: (65) 67753602
E-Mail: singapore.eltek@eltek.com
Web Site: www.eltekvalere.com.br
Sales Range: $100-124.9 Million
Emp.: 80
Supplier of Telecommunication Energy Systems
S.I.C.: 4899
N.A.I.C.S.: 517919
Kenneth Bodahl *(Reg Pres)*

Non-U.S. Subsidiaries:

Eltek Argentina S.R.L. **(1)**
1300 Maipu St 23rd Floor Dept J
Buenos Aires, Argentina
Tel.: (54) 11 52366646
Telecommunication Power Transmission Equipment Mfr
S.I.C.: 3663
N.A.I.C.S.: 334220

Eltek Egypt ASA **(1)**
15 Salah Salem Road El Estad El Bahary Building Entrance 2 Flat 7
Cairo, Egypt
Tel.: (20) 224052327
Fax: (20) 24033055
Web Site: www.eltekvalere.com
Emp.: 9
Telecommunication Power Transmission Equipment Mfr
S.I.C.: 3568
N.A.I.C.S.: 333613
Mahmoud Morsy *(Mng Dir)*

Eltek Energy International de Mexico. S. de R.L. de C.V. **(1)**
Av Gustavo Baz No 401 Col Hacienda del Cristo
53138 Naucalpan, Mexico
Tel.: (52) 55 53 74 1842
E-Mail: sales.mexico@eltekvalere.com
Web Site: www.eltekvalere.com
Telecommunication Power Transmission Equipment Mfr
S.I.C.: 3568
N.A.I.C.S.: 333613

Eltek Energy (M) Sdn. Bhd. **(1)**
Axis Business Park No 10 Block E Jalan Bersatu 13/4 Seksyen 13
46200 Petaling Jaya, Selangor, Malaysia
Tel.: (60) 379553558
Fax: (60) 3 79543558
Emp.: 30
Telecommunication Power Transmission Equipment Mfr
S.I.C.: 3568
N.A.I.C.S.: 333613

Eltek Energy SA **(1)**
Z I de Bastillac-Nord
65000 Tarbes, France
Tel.: (33) 5623 40930
Fax: (33) 5623 45869
E-Mail: froffice@eltek.com
Emp.: 40
Telecommunication Power Transmission Equipment Mfr
S.I.C.: 3568
N.A.I.C.S.: 333613
Isabelle Giraud *(Gen Mgr)*

Eltek Energy Technology Ltd **(1)**
2nd Sovyetskaya House 7 Office 102
193036 Saint Petersburg, Russia
Tel.: (7) 812 3321 117
Fax: (7) 812 3321 116
E-Mail: eltek@eltek.ru
Web Site: www.eltek.ru
Emp.: 35
Telecommunication Power Transmission Equipment Mfr
S.I.C.: 3568
N.A.I.C.S.: 333613
Allan Christiansen *(Gen Mgr)*

Eltek Holding AB **(1)**
Sjoangsvagen 9
Sollentuna, 192 72, Sweden
Tel.: (46) 86266420
Fax: (46) 8 626 64 30
Telecommunication Power Transmission Equipment Mfr
S.I.C.: 3568
N.A.I.C.S.: 333613

Eltek SGS Pvt. Ltd. **(1)**
362 Sector 37 Pace City II
Gurgaon, Haryana, 122 001, India
Tel.: (91) 124 221 0018
Fax: (91) 124 221 0017
E-Mail: eltek@eltekvalere.in
Telecommunication Equipment Distr
S.I.C.: 5065
N.A.I.C.S.: 423690

Eltek Sistemas de Energia Industria e Comercio S.A. **(1)**
Avenida Guinle 2047 Cidade Industrial Satelite
Guarulhos, Sao Paulo, 07221-070, Brazil
Tel.: (55) 11 2465 5656
Fax: (55) 11 2465 5689
Web Site: www.eltekvalere.com
Telecommunication Power Transmission Equipment Mfr
S.I.C.: 3669
N.A.I.C.S.: 334290
Lois Camagnani *(Mng Dir)*

Eltek Valere AB **(1)**
Dagvindsgatan 9
652 21 Karlstad, Sweden
Tel.: (46) 54 688150
Fax: (46) 54 688151
Telecommunication Power Transmission Equipment Mfr
S.I.C.: 3669
N.A.I.C.S.: 334290
Peter Larnemark *(Gen Mgr)*

Eltek Valere Deutschland GmbH **(1)**
Ferdinand Porsche Str 45
60386 Frankfurt am Main, Germany
Tel.: (49) 69 42002 0
Fax: (49) 69 42002 389
E-Mail: info@eltekvalere.de
Web Site: www.eltek-valere.de
Power Systems Distr
S.I.C.: 5063
N.A.I.C.S.: 423610
Volker Rossmann *(CEO)*
Gunter Schmitt *(COO)*

Eltek Valere Energy Technology (Dongguan) Ltd. **(1)**
Technology Park City Zone Shilong Road
Dongguan, Guangdong, 523119, China
Tel.: (86) 76922651108
Fax: (86) 76922296797
Emp.: 400
Switchgear & Switchboard Apparatus Mfr
S.I.C.: 3613
N.A.I.C.S.: 335313

Eltek Valere Inc. **(1)**
0302 3rd Floor Orient Square Building Emerald Avenue
Ortigas, Pasig, Manila, Philippines
Tel.: (63) 2 910 6355
Fax: (63) 2 910 6358
Emp.: 18
Telecommunication Power Transmission Equipment Mfr
S.I.C.: 3568
N.A.I.C.S.: 333613
Thadeo Pulian *(Gen Mgr)*

Eltek Valere Industrial Systems GmbH **(1)**
Schillerstrasse 16
32052 Herford, Germany
Tel.: (49) 52211708200
Fax: (49) 52 21 17 08 222
E-Mail: info.industrial@eltekvalere.com
Web Site: www.eltekvalere.com
Emp.: 40
Telecommunication Power Transmission Equipment Mfr
S.I.C.: 3568
N.A.I.C.S.: 333613
Volker Pallatzky *(Gen Mgr)*

Eltek Valere Italia S.r.l. **(1)**
Via Zoe Fontana 220 Palazzina B2 Scala A
131 Rome, Italy
Tel.: (39) 06 41 91 227
Fax: (39) 06 41 405 890
E-Mail: info-it@eltek.com
Web Site: www.eltek.com
Emp.: 5

Eltek ASA—(Continued)

Telecommunication Power Transmission Equipment Mfr
S.I.C.: 3663
N.A.I.C.S.: 334220
Alessandro Casicci *(CEO)*

Eltek Valere MEA DMCC UAE (1)
Office 1401 14th Floor Saba Tower 1
Jumeirah Lake Towers
Dubai, United Arab Emirates
Tel.: (971) 44404966
Fax: (971) 4 4404965
E-Mail: salesmea@eltekvalere.com
Telecommunication Power Transmission Equipment Mfr
S.I.C.: 3568
N.A.I.C.S.: 333613

Eltek Valere Montage GmbH (1)
Ferdinand Porsche Str 45
Frankfurt am Main, Hessen, 60386, Germany
Tel.: (49) 6942002310
Fax: (49) 6942002109
Telecommunication Power Transmission Equipment Mfr
S.I.C.: 3568
N.A.I.C.S.: 333613

Eltek Valere Oy (1)
Kuminatie 16 A
1300 Vantaa, Finland
Tel.: (358) 207 798 820
Fax: (358) 207 798 829
E-Mail: sales.fi@eltek.com
Web Site: www.eltek.com
Emp.: 5
Telecommunication Support Services
S.I.C.: 4899
N.A.I.C.S.: 517919
Allan Christiansen *(Mng Dir)*

Eltek Valere Pacific Pty. Ltd (1)
22 Narabang Way
Belrose, NSW, 2085, Australia
Tel.: (61) 294794200
Fax: (61) 294794292
E-Mail: admin.au@eltek.com
Web Site: eltek.com
Emp.: 50
Power Transmission Equipment Mfr
S.I.C.: 3568
N.A.I.C.S.: 333613
Neil Ewen *(Mng Dir)*

Eltek Valere Pakistan (Pvt) Ltd. (1)
House no 4 Street no 89 Ataturk Avenue G-6/3
Islamabad, 44000, Pakistan
Tel.: (92) 51 111 537 537
Fax: (92) 51 8314 594
E-Mail: info@eltek.com.pk
Web Site: www.eltek.com
Emp.: 13
Telecommunication & Power Transmission Supplies Whslr
S.I.C.: 5065
N.A.I.C.S.: 423690
Benno Klocke *(CEO)*

Eltek Valere Pte. Ltd. (1)
No 3 Teban Gardens Crescent
608920 Singapore, Singapore
Tel.: (65) 67732326
Fax: (65) 67753602
E-Mail: singapore.eltek@eltek.com
Telecommunication Power Transmission Equipment Mfr
S.I.C.: 3568
N.A.I.C.S.: 333613

Eltek Valere Saudi Arabia Ltd. (1)
2nd Floor Building 4040 Al Urouba Road Al Wurood
PO Box 54124
11514 Riyadh, Saudi Arabia
Tel.: (966) 14196996
Fax: (966) 14196996
Web Site: www.eltekvalere.com
Telecommunication Power Transmission Equipment Mfr
S.I.C.: 3669
N.A.I.C.S.: 334290
Salman Amin *(Gen Mgr)*

Eltek Valere Sp. z.o.o. (1)
Ul Gorlicka 2
71-042 Szczecin, Poland
Tel.: (48) 914852440
Fax: (48) 914834986
E-Mail: eltek@eltek.com.pl
Web Site: www.eltek.pl
Emp.: 60
Telecommunication Power Transmission Equipment Mfr
S.I.C.: 3669
N.A.I.C.S.: 334290
Bartek Wawrzyniak *(Gen Mgr)*

Eltek Valere s.r.o. (1)
Palenica 53/79
033 17 Liptovsky Hradok, Slovakia
Tel.: (421) 4452 33211
Fax: (421) 4452 33231
Web Site: www.eltekvalere.com
Emp.: 400
Telecommunication Power Transmission Equipment Mfr
S.I.C.: 3568
N.A.I.C.S.: 333613
Stefan Kuric *(Gen Mgr)*

Eltek Valere (UK) Ltd. (1)
Eltek House Cleaveland Road
Hemel Hempstead, Hertfordshire, HP2 7EY, United Kingdom
Tel.: (44) 1442 219355
Fax: (44) 1442 245894
E-Mail: Sales.GB@eltek.com
Web Site: www.eltek.com
Emp.: 50
Telecommunication Power Transmission Equipment Mfr
S.I.C.: 3568
N.A.I.C.S.: 333613
Colin Howe *(CEO)*

Valere Power Europe AB (1)
Hammarbacken 4 A
191 49 Sollentuna, Sweden
Tel.: (46) 8 626 64 20
Fax: (46) 8 626 64 30
Telecommunication Power Transmission Equipment Mfr
S.I.C.: 3568
N.A.I.C.S.: 333613

Valere Power S.R.L. (1)
General Suarez No 1086
Miraflores, Lima, Peru
Tel.: (51) 1 2427766
Fax: (51) 1 4477571
Web Site: www.eltekvalere.com
Telecommunication Power Transmission Equipment Mfr
S.I.C.: 3568
N.A.I.C.S.: 333613

ELTEK LIMITED
(Acquired by Nistec Ltd.)

ELTEX ENTERPRISES 2002 LTD.
211- 14770 64th Avenue
Surrey, BC, V3S 1X7, Canada
Tel.: (604) 599-5088
Fax: (604) 599-5065
E-Mail: eltex@telus.net
Web Site: www.eltex.ca
Year Founded: 1988
Rev.: $16,385,920
Emp.: 80
Business Description:
Drywall & Insulation Contracting Services
S.I.C.: 1742
N.A.I.C.S.: 238310
Personnel:
James Hatch *(Founder)*

ELTON INTERNATIONAL TRADING COMPANY S.A.
Draseza Place Industrial Park
Avlonas, 19011 Athens, Greece
Tel.: (30) 22950 29350
Fax: (30) 22950 29305
E-Mail: info@elton.gr
Web Site: www.elton.gr
Year Founded: 1981
ELTON—(ATH)
Sls.: $119,384,323
Assets: $97,729,760
Liabilities: $45,051,866
Net Worth: $52,677,894
Earnings: $4,308,467
Emp.: 180
Fiscal Year-end: 12/31/12
Business Description:
Chemical Products Distr
S.I.C.: 5169
N.A.I.C.S.: 424690
Personnel:
Nestor Dimitris Papathanasiou *(Pres & Mng Dir)*
Board of Directors:
Kaiti Ioannis Andreou
Michalis Georgiou Chatzis
Alkistis Nestor Papathanasiou
Electra Nestor Papathanasiou
Nestor Dimitris Papathanasiou
Christos Constatinos Poulis

ELTRAK S.A.
15 Thivaidos St
14564 Nea Kifissia, Athens, Greece
Tel.: (30) 2108196800
Fax: (30) 2108078214
E-Mail: info@eltrak.gr
Web Site: www.eltrak.gr
ELTRK—(ATH)
Sls.: $116,599,861
Assets: $148,673,707
Liabilities: $71,427,780
Net Worth: $77,245,927
Earnings: ($2,870,034)
Emp.: 343
Fiscal Year-end: 12/31/12
Business Description:
Machinery & Motor Vehicle Spare Parts Distr
S.I.C.: 5013
N.A.I.C.S.: 423120
Personnel:
Anastasios Polites *(Chm)*
George Kollias *(CEO, Mng Dir & VP)*
Harris Hatzidakis *(CFO)*
Board of Directors:
Anastasios Polites
Charalambos Chatzidakis
George Covas
Natasha Covas-Kneiss
George Kollias
Alexandros Kyparissis
Stefanos Malamas
Alexandra Polites
Aggelos Tsichrintzis

Subsidiary:

Elastrak S.A. (1)
15 Thivaidos St
Nea Kifissia, 14564 Athens, Greece
Tel.: (30) 2108196800
Fax: (30) 2108077818
E-Mail: info@elastrak.gr
Emp.: 80
Tires Distr
S.I.C.: 5014
N.A.I.C.S.: 423130
Stacey Polites *(Chm)*
Takis Diamantopoulos *(Mng Dir)*

Non-U.S. Subsidiary:

Eltrak Bulgaria Ltd. (1)
439 Evropa Boulevard
1331 Sofia, Bulgaria
Tel.: (359) 28183000
Fax: (359) 28083060
E-Mail: info@eltrakbulgaria.com
Web Site: www.eltrakbulgaria.com
Emp.: 53
Construction & Mining Equipment Mfr
S.I.C.: 3531
N.A.I.C.S.: 333120
Plamen Stoychev *(Gen Mgr)*

ELUMATEC GMBH
Pinacher Strasse 61
D 75417 Muhlacker, Germany
Tel.: (49) 7041140
Fax: (49) 704114280
E-Mail: mail@elumatec.de
Web Site: www.elumatec.com
Year Founded: 1928
Rev.: $50,627,400
Emp.: 419
Business Description:
Industrial Cutting Machines Mfr
S.I.C.: 3545
N.A.I.C.S.: 333515
Personnel:
Roland Donath *(Co-Mng Dir)*
Bernd Renz *(Co-Mng Dir)*

ELVAL S.A.
Athens Tower Building B 2 4
Messogion Ave
115 27 Athens, Greece
Tel.: (30) 22620 53111
Fax: (30) 22620 53686
E-Mail: info@elval.vionet.gr
Web Site: www.elval.gr
ELL—(DEU)
Sls.: $1,432,028,978
Assets: $1,388,221,579
Liabilities: $588,191,897
Net Worth: $800,029,682
Earnings: $28,423,105
Emp.: 2,090
Fiscal Year-end: 12/31/12
Business Description:
Aluminium Products Mfr
S.I.C.: 3355
N.A.I.C.S.: 331318
Personnel:
Dimitrios Kyriakopoulos *(Vice Chm)*
Giazizoglou Aggelos *(Investment Liaison Officer & Mgr-Shareholder Svcs)*
Board of Directors:
Miltiadis Lidoriki
Konstantinos Bakouris
Gerard Decoster
Konstantinos Katsaros
Nikolaos Koudounis
Konstantinos Kouklelis
Dimitrios Kyriakopoulos
Andreas Sotiriou Kyriazis
Abraham Megir
Michael Stasinopoulos
Reinhold Wagner

ELVE S.A.
Agios Andreas
Peramos, 64007 Thessaloniki, Greece
Tel.: (30) 25940 23600
Fax: (30) 25940 23604
E-Mail: elve@otenet.gr
Web Site: www.elvesa.gr
Year Founded: 1987
ELBE—(ATH)
Emp.: 426
Business Description:
Apparel Mfr & Distr
S.I.C.: 2389
N.A.I.C.S.: 315240
Personnel:
Ronald Barkshire *(Vice Chm)*
Telemachos Kitsikopoulos *(Pres & Mng Dir)*
Board of Directors:
Ronald Barkshire
Paschalis Kitsikopoulos
Telemachos Kitsikopoulos
Alkiviadis Papadimitriou
Aggelos Tsatsoulis

ELY GOLD & MINERALS INC.
680 - 789 West Pender Street
Vancouver, BC, V6C 1H2, Canada
Tel.: (604) 488-1104
Fax: (604) 488-1105

E-Mail: info@elygoldandminerals.com
Web Site: www.elygoldandminerals.com
Year Founded: 1996
ELY—(OTC TSXV)
Int. Income: $70,366
Assets: $3,053,918
Liabilities: $2,918,552
Net Worth: $135,366
Earnings: ($1,363,632)
Fiscal Year-end: 12/31/12
Business Description:
Gold Exploration Services
S.I.C.: 1041
N.A.I.C.S.: 212221
Personnel:
John Brownlie *(Chm)*
Trey Wasser *(Pres & CEO)*
Scott Kelly *(CFO & Sec)*
Board of Directors:
John Brownlie
Marco Antonio Galindo
Ron K. Husband
Stephen Patrick Kenwood
Trey Wasser
Subsidiary:

DHI Minerals Ltd. (1)
789 Pender St W
Vancouver, BC, V6C 1H2, Canada
Tel.: (604) 488-1104
Fax: (604) 488-1105
Emp.: 5
Property Development Services
S.I.C.: 6531
N.A.I.C.S.: 531312

ELYSIUM FUND MANAGEMENT LIMITED

1st Floor Royal Chambers Saint Julian's Avenue
PO Box 650
Saint Peter Port, GY1 3JX, Guernsey
Tel.: (44) 1481 810 100
Fax: (44) 1481 810 120
E-Mail: elysium@elysiumfundman.com
Web Site: www.elysiumfundman.com
Year Founded: 2006
Business Description:
Investment Management Services
S.I.C.: 6282
N.A.I.C.S.: 523920
Personnel:
Andrew Duquemin *(Chm)*
Joanna Duquemin Nicolle *(CEO)*
Sadie Morrison *(Mng Dir)*

ELZAY READY WEAR MANUFACTURING COMPANY

Rusaifeh-Awajan Main Street
PO Box 3151
Amman, 11181, Jordan
Tel.: (962) 53740200
Fax: (962) 53746001
E-Mail: info@elzay.com
Web Site: www.elzay.com
Year Founded: 1992
ELZA—(AMM)
Sales Range: $10-24.9 Million
Emp.: 1,087
Business Description:
Mens Apparel Mfr & Distr
S.I.C.: 5699
N.A.I.C.S.: 315220
Personnel:
Qustandi Yagnem *(Gen Mgr)*

EMA INDIA LTD.

C-37 Panki Industrial Area PO Udyog Nagar
Kanpur, 208 022, India
Tel.: (91) 512 2691210
Fax: (91) 512 2691214
E-Mail: emain@sancharnet.in
Web Site: www.emainduction.com
522027—(BOM)
Rev.: $656,284
Assets: $1,315,409
Liabilities: $205,096
Net Worth: $1,110,313
Earnings: ($131,915)
Fiscal Year-end: 03/31/13
Business Description:
Induction Heating Equipment Mfr
S.I.C.: 3433
N.A.I.C.S.: 333414
Personnel:
Pradip K. Bhargava *(Founder, Chm & Mng Dir)*
Saket Sharma *(Sec)*
Board of Directors:
Pradip K. Bhargava
Rakshita Bhargava
Ranjana Bhargava
Krishna Das Gupta
Atul Kapoor
Alok Nagory
Transfer Agent:
Alankit Assignments Ltd
Alankit House 2E/21, Jhandewalan Extension
New Delhi, India

EMA S.A.R.

Baltagului Street No 1
Piatra Neamt, Neamt, Romania
Tel.: (40) 233 214020
Fax: (40) 233 216990
E-Mail: office@ema.ro
Web Site: www.ema.ro
Year Founded: 1907
EPN—(BUC)
Business Description:
Knit Wear Mfr
S.I.C.: 2259
N.A.I.C.S.: 313240
Personnel:
Silvia Iftime *(Pres & Gen Mgr)*

EMAAR PROPERTIES PJSC

PO Box 9440
Dubai, United Arab Emirates
Tel.: (971) 43673333
Fax: (971) 43673000
E-Mail: customercare@emaar.ae
Web Site: www.emaar.com
EMAAR—(DFM)
Rev.: $2,242,743,603
Assets: $16,644,131,166
Liabilities: $7,711,365,927
Net Worth: $8,932,765,239
Earnings: $573,462,574
Emp.: 600
Fiscal Year-end: 12/31/12
Business Description:
Real Estate Services
S.I.C.: 6531
N.A.I.C.S.: 531210
Personnel:
Mohamed Ali Rashed Alabbar *(Chm)*
Shravan Gupta *(Vice Chm/Mng Dir-Emaar MGF Land Private Limited)*
Hussain Ahmad Dhaen Al Qemzi *(Vice Chm)*
Abdulla Lahej *(Grp CEO)*
Ahmad Thani Rashed Al Matrooshi *(Mng Dir)*
Amit Jain *(CFO & Exec Dir-Fin)*
Kenneth Foong *(CIO)*
Mohamed El Dahan *(CEO-Emaar Misr & Exec Officer-Bus Dev & Ops)*
Ali H. Odeh *(Chm/CEO-Turner International Middle East LLC)*
Fahad Al-Rasheed *(CEO/Mng Dir-King Abdullah Economic City)*
Mohammad Saeed Al Raqbani *(CEO-Emaar Industries & Invesments PVT LLC)*
Arif AlHarmi *(CEO-Amlak Finance PJSC)*
Robert D. Booth *(CEO-Emaar Dubai Real Estate)*
Yves Delmar *(CEO-Emaar Morocco)*
Fred Durie *(CEO-Emaar International)*
Khurram Noor *(CEO-Emaar DHA Islamabad Limited)*
Nasser Rafi *(CEO-Emaar Malls Group LLC)*
Faran Umar *(CEO-Emaar Giga Karachi Limited)*
Ayman Hamdy *(Sec & Exec Dir-Legal)*
Board of Directors:
Mohamed Ali Rashed Alabbar
Marwan Iqbal Mohammad Abdullah Abedin
Abdul Rahman Hareb Rashed Al Hareb
Ahmad Thani Rashed Al Matrooshi
Arif Obaid Saeed Al Dehail Al Mehairi
Hussain Ahmad Dhaen Al Qemzi
Fadhel Abdulbaqi Abualhasan Alali
Jamal Hamed Almarri
Ahmed Jamal Hassan Jawa
Abdullah Saeed Majed Belyoahah
Jamal Majed Khalfan Thaniyeh
Subsidiaries:

Amlak Finance PJSC (1)
PO Box 2441
Dubai, United Arab Emirates AE
Tel.: (971) 4 4274747
Fax: (971) 4 4274502
E-Mail: info@amlakfinance.com
Web Site: www.amlakfinance.com
AMLAK—(EMI)
Sales Range: $1-9.9 Million
Financial Management Services
S.I.C.: 6211
N.A.I.C.S.: 523999
Arif AlHarmi *(CEO)*
Max Hamidi *(CFO & Exec VP-Fin, Treasury & Corp Investments)*
Adnan Edris Al Awadhi *(Exec VP & Head-Retail Bus)*
Narendra Gajria *(Exec VP-Ops & Corp Svcs)*

Emaar Hospitality Group LLC (1)
Down Town Burj Khalifa Emaar Square Building 3 Level 2
PO Box 9440
Dubai, United Arab Emirates
Tel.: (971) 4 3673392
Fax: (971) 4 3673699
E-Mail: infohospitality@emaar.com
Web Site: www.emaar.com
Hospital & Leisure Facility Development & Management Services
S.I.C.: 1542
N.A.I.C.S.: 236220
Josef Kufer *(COO)*

Emaar Hotels & Resorts LLC (1)
Building 3 Emaar Buisness Park Sheikh Zayed Road
PO Box 9440
Dubai, United Arab Emirates
Tel.: (971) 43673392
Fax: (971) 43673000
Hotel & Resort Management Services
S.I.C.: 7011
N.A.I.C.S.: 721110

Emaar Malls Group LLC (1)
Burj Dubai Square Building 3 Floor 2
PO Box 9440
Dubai, United Arab Emirates
Tel.: (971) 43675588
Fax: (971) 4 367 5501
E-Mail: emaarmalls@emaar.com
Mall Property Development Services
S.I.C.: 1542
N.A.I.C.S.: 236220
Naseer Rasi *(COO)*

Subsidiaries:

Emaar International Malls LLC (2)
Downtown Burj Dubai Emaar Square
PO Box 90807
Dubai, United Arab Emirates
Tel.: (971) 43673333
Commercial Property Management Services
S.I.C.: 6531
N.A.I.C.S.: 531312

Emaar Retail LLC (2)
Emaar Square Building 3 Near Bur Dubai
Dubai, United Arab Emirates
Tel.: (971) 43673333
Mall Property Development Services
S.I.C.: 1542
N.A.I.C.S.: 236220

U.S. Subsidiary:

Emaar USA (1)
5505 Cancha de Golf
Rancho Santa Fe, CA 92091
Tel.: (858) 755-0216, ext. 121
Fax: (858) 779-9098
Web Site: www.emaar.com
Property Development Services
S.I.C.: 6531
N.A.I.C.S.: 531390

Non-U.S. Subsidiaries:

Emaar International Jordan (1)
Al Rabia Towers Fifth Floor
PO Box 4434
Amman, 11953, Jordan
Tel.: (962) 65501800
Fax: (962) 65543948
E-Mail: info@emaar.jo
Web Site: www.emaar.jo
Emp.: 22
Real Estate Management Services
S.I.C.: 6531
N.A.I.C.S.: 531390
H. E. Mohamed Ali Alabbar *(Chm)*
Lowai Mohamed Belhoul *(Vice Chm)*

Emaar Lebanon S.A. (1)
PO Box 16-6622
Beirut, Lebanon
Tel.: (961) 1212121
Fax: (961) 1212021
E-Mail: info@beitmisk.com
Residential Property Development Services
S.I.C.: 1522
N.A.I.C.S.: 236116

Emaar Pakistan Group (1)
Canyon Views Emaar Sales Centre
Islamabad Highway DHA Phase II
Islamabad, 44000, Pakistan
Tel.: (92) 512803188
Fax: (92) 512803133
E-Mail: salespk@emaar.ae
Web Site: www.emaar.com
Property Development Services
S.I.C.: 6531
N.A.I.C.S.: 531390
Matt Cronje *(CEO)*
Muhammad Naeem Aslam *(Sec & Dir-Corp Svcs)*

Emaar Properties Canada LTD (1)
Suite 1420 Guiness Twr 1055 West Hasting Street
Vancouver, BC, V6E 2E9, Canada
Tel.: (604) 630-2008
Fax: (604) 630-2009
E-Mail: customercare@emaarcanada.com
Web Site: www.emaarcanada.com
Property Development Services
S.I.C.: 6519
N.A.I.C.S.: 531190
Robert D. Booth *(Mng Dir)*

Emaar Turkey (1)
Maslak Mah Bilim Sok No 5 Sun Plaza Kat 20
Sisli, 34398 Istanbul, Turkey
Tel.: (90) 212 850 83 00
Fax: (90) 212 850 83 01
E-Mail: ccihaner@emaar.ae
Web Site: www.emaar.com.tr
Real Estate Property Development Services
S.I.C.: 6531
N.A.I.C.S.: 531390

Non-U.S. Joint Venture:

Emaar MGF Land Limited (1)
ECE House 1st Floor 28 Kasturba Gandhi Marg
New Delhi, 110 001, India
Tel.: (91) 1141521155
Fax: (91) 1141524619

Emaar Properties PJSC—(Continued)

E-Mail: myhome@emaarmgf.com
Web Site: www.emaarmgf.com
Emp.: 80
Real Estate Services
S.I.C.: 6531
N.A.I.C.S.: 531390
Shravan Gupta *(Vice Chm & Mng Dir)*

EMAE - EMPRESA METROPOLITANA DE AGUAS E ENERGIA S.A.

Av Nossa Senhora do Sabara 5312 - Vila Emir
04447-902 Sao Paulo, Brazil
Tel.: (55) 11 5613 2100
Fax: (55) 11 5612 3124
E-Mail: riemae@emae.com.br
Web Site: www.emae.com.br
Year Founded: 1899
EMAE3—(BRAZ)
Emp.: 550
Business Description:
Electric Power Generation Services
S.I.C.: 4931
N.A.I.C.S.: 221111
Personnel:
Paulo Roberto Fares *(Dir-IR)*

EMAK S.P.A.

Via E Fermi 4 Bagnolo in Piano
42011 Reggio nell'Emilia, Italy
Tel.: (39) 522956611
Fax: (39) 522951555
E-Mail: info@emakgroup.com
Web Site: www.emak.it
EM—(ITA)
Sls.: $477,594,193
Assets: $473,180,101
Liabilities: $277,930,258
Net Worth: $195,249,843
Earnings: $11,630,909
Emp.: 1,576
Fiscal Year-end: 12/31/12
Business Description:
Garden Machinery & Equipment Mfr
S.I.C.: 3524
N.A.I.C.S.: 333112
Personnel:
Fausto Bellamico *(Chm & CEO)*
Aimone Burani *(Deputy Chm & Fin Reporting Oficer)*
Board of Directors:
Fausto Bellamico
Ivano Accorsi
Carlo Baldi
Andrea Barilli
Luigi Bartoli
Gian Luigi Basini
Paola Becchi
Aimone Burani
Giuliano Ferrari
Giacomo Ferretti
Stefano Slanzi
Vilmo Spaggiari
Guerrino Zambelli
Subsidiary:

Comet S.p.A. (1)
Via G Dorso 4
IT-42124 Reggio nell'Emilia, Italy IT
Tel.: (39) 0522 386 111
Fax: (39) 0522 930 272 (Svc Support)
E-Mail: info@comet.re.it
Web Site: www.comet.re.it
Pumps & Pumping Equipment Mfr & Distr
S.I.C.: 3561
N.A.I.C.S.: 333911

U.S. Subsidiary:

Comet USA, Inc. (2)
12571 Oliver Ave Ste 300
Burnsville, MN 55337 MN
Tel.: (952) 707-1894
Web Site: www.cometpump.com
Pump & Pumping Equipment Mfr & Distr
S.I.C.: 3561
N.A.I.C.S.: 333911
Randall J. Rowan *(CEO)*

Subsidiary:

Valley Industries, LLP (3)
123 Industrial Loop Rd E
Paynesville, MN 56362 MN
Mailing Address: (90%)
PO Box 226
Paynesville, MN 56362
Tel.: (320) 243-8500
Fax: (320) 243-8030
Toll Free: (800) 864-1649
E-Mail: info@valleyind.com
Web Site: www.valleyind.com
Sales Range: $10-24.9 Million
Industrial Fluid Components, Agricultural Parts & Pressure Washer Accessories Mfr & Distr
S.I.C.: 3492
N.A.I.C.S.: 332912
Jeffrey Savage *(Gen Mgr)*

EMAKINA GROUP S.A.

64A Rue Middelbourg
1170 Brussels, Belgium
Tel.: (32) 2 400 40 00
Fax: (32) 2 400 40 01
E-Mail: investor@emakina.com
Web Site: www.emakina.com
Year Founded: 2001
ALEMK—(EUR)
Rev.: $65,670,297
Assets: $40,920,015
Liabilities: $27,896,361
Net Worth: $13,023,655
Earnings: ($612,635)
Emp.: 450
Fiscal Year-end: 12/31/12
Business Description:
Website Development Services
S.I.C.: 7374
N.A.I.C.S.: 518210
Personnel:
Brice Le Blevennec *(Pres & Chief Visionary Officer)*
Denis Steisel *(CEO)*
Pierre Gatz *(Partner)*
Frederic Desonnay *(CFO)*
John Deprez *(CTO)*
Board of Directors:
Pierre Cattoir
Karim Chouikri
John Deprez
Daisy Foquet
Pierre Gatz
Francois Gillet
Brice Le Blevennec
Anne Pinchart
Denis Steisel

EMAMI LTD

Emami Tower 687 Anandapur E M Bypass
Kolkata, West Bengal, 700107, India
Tel.: (91) 3366136264
Fax: (91) 3366136600
E-Mail: contact@emamigroup.com
Web Site: www.emamigroup.com
531162—(BOM)
Rev.: $325,335,081
Assets: $225,477,584
Liabilities: $81,325,247
Net Worth: $144,152,338
Earnings: $58,352,796
Emp.: 2,500
Fiscal Year-end: 03/31/13
Business Description:
Health Care Consumer Products
S.I.C.: 5122
N.A.I.C.S.: 424210
Personnel:
R. S. Agarwal *(Co-Founder & Chm)*
R. S. Goenka *(Co-Founder)*
Sushil K. Goenka *(Mng Dir)*
R. K. Surana *(Pres-Ops & Comml)*
N. H. Bhansali *(CEO-Fin, Strategy & Bus Dev)*
Punita Kalra *(CEO-R&D & Innovation)*
Chandra Kant Katiyar *(CEO-Technical-Healthcare Div)*
Krishna Mohan *(CEO-Sls, Supply Chain & Human Capital)*
Shyam Sutaria *(CEO-Intl Bus)*
A. K. Joshi *(Sec & Asst VP-Legal)*
Board of Directors:
R. S. Agarwal
Aditya V. Agarwal
Harsha V. Agarwal
Sajjan Bhajanka
Vaidya S. Chaturvedi
Amit Kiran Deb
S. B. Ganguly
Mohan Goenka
R. S. Goenka
Sushil K. Goenka
Pradip Kumar Khaitan
K. N. Memani
Priti Sureka
Y. P. Trivedi
Transfer Agent:
Maheshwari Datamatics Pvt. Ltd.
6 Mangoe Lane 2nd Fl
Kolkata, 700 001, India
Tel.: (91) 33 22435029
Fax: (91) 913322484787
Subsidiaries:

Emami Paper Mills Ltd. (1)
687 Anandapur 4th Floor E M Byepass
Kolkata, 700 107, India
Tel.: (91) 33 6613 6264
Fax: (91) 33 6613 6400
E-Mail: emamipaper@emamipaper.in
Web Site: www.emamipaper.in
533208—(BOM)
Rev.: $94,892,188
Assets: $147,903,796
Liabilities: $99,757,826
Net Worth: $48,145,970
Earnings: $2,142,260
Fiscal Year-end: 03/31/13
Newsprint Mfr
S.I.C.: 2621
N.A.I.C.S.: 322122
A. V. Agarwal *(Chm)*
G. Saraf *(Compliance Officer, Sec & VP-Fin)*

Emami Realty Limited (1)
8-2-598 Ground Fl Uma Dev Raj Villa Rd No 10
Banjara Hills, Hyderabad, 500034, India
Tel.: (91) 4040262889
Fax: (91) 4040174562
Health Care Products Mfr
S.I.C.: 2833
N.A.I.C.S.: 325411

Subsidiary:

Orbit Projects Private Limited (2)
1 Near Nicco House
Garstin Pl, Kolkata, 700001, India
Tel.: (91) 3340119050
Fax: (91) 3322101256
E-Mail: info@orbitgroup.net
Web Site: www.orbitgroup.net
Emp.: 50
Real Estate Consultants
S.I.C.: 6531
N.A.I.C.S.: 531390
Basant Parakh *(Mng Dir)*

Non-U.S. Subsidiary:

Emami International FZE (1)
Bel Rasheed Towers Ofc No 1203
PO Box 77884
Sharjah, United Arab Emirates
Tel.: (971) 65754774
Fax: (971) 65754775
Web Site: www.emamigroup.com
Emp.: 30
Health Care Products Mfr
S.I.C.: 2833
N.A.I.C.S.: 325411

EMANUEL UNGARO

2 Avenue Montaigne
75008 Paris, France
Tel.: (33) 153570000
Fax: (33) 0153570008
E-Mail: info@ungaro.com
Web Site: www.emanuelungaro.com
Sales Range: $25-49.9 Million
Emp.: 40
Business Description:
Perfume, Clothing & Accessories Designer & Retailer
S.I.C.: 2399
N.A.I.C.S.: 315990
Personnel:
Mary Fornier *(CEO)*

EMAS KIARA INDUSTRIES BERHAD

Block A4-3-8 Solaris Dutamas No 1
Jalan Dutamas 1
50480 Kuala Lumpur, Malaysia
Tel.: (60) 362053933
Fax: (60) 362053911
E-Mail: marketing@emaskiara.com
Web Site: www.emaskiara.com
EKIB—(KLS)
Rev.: $14,902,955
Assets: $38,422,353
Liabilities: $11,100,427
Net Worth: $27,321,926
Earnings: ($2,001,602)
Fiscal Year-end: 12/31/12
Business Description:
Polyester Textile Mfr
S.I.C.: 2299
N.A.I.C.S.: 313110
Personnel:
Kamaruzzaman Shariff *(Chm)*
Kong Foo Wong *(Deputy Chm)*
Hooi Mooi Lim *(Co-Sec)*
Wai Foong Wong *(Co-Sec)*
Board of Directors:
Kamaruzzaman Shariff
Abd Talib Baba
Yew Hoe Lim
Kah Toong Siew
Kong Foo Wong
Yahya Ya'acob
Subsidiaries:

Emas Kiara Marketing Sdn. Bhd. (1)
Lot 13A Jalan RP 3 Rawang Industrial Estate
48000 Rawang, Selangor, Malaysia
Tel.: (60) 360929898
Fax: (60) 360926602
E-Mail: marketing@emaskiara.com
Emp.: 30
Nonwoven Fabrics Mfr
S.I.C.: 2297
N.A.I.C.S.: 313230
Lim Yew Hoe *(Dir-Mktg)*

Emas Kiara Sdn. Bhd. (1)
Lot 13A Rawang Industrial Estate
48000 Rawang, Selangor, Malaysia
Tel.: (60) 360926881
Fax: (60) 360926602
Emp.: 40
Textile Products Mfr
S.I.C.: 2399
N.A.I.C.S.: 314999
Roger Kong Foo Wong *(Mng Dir)*

Khidmat Edar (M) Sdn. Bhd. (1)
Lot 13A Jalan RP3 Rawang Industrial Estate
48000 Rawang, Selangor, Malaysia
Tel.: (60) 360913271
Fax: (60) 360926602
E-Mail: info@emaskiara.com
Web Site: www.kiaratex.com
Emp.: 50
Building Materials Distr
S.I.C.: 5211
N.A.I.C.S.: 444190
Roger Wong *(Mng Dir)*

Non-U.S. Subsidiary:

Kiaratex Exports Pte. Ltd. (1)
11 Bishan Street 21 Unit 04-03
573943 Singapore, Singapore

Tel.: (65) 63535511
Fax: (65) 63542668
Web Site: www.emaskiara.com
Emp.: 3
Nonwoven Fabrics Distr
S.I.C.: 5136
N.A.I.C.S.: 424320
R. Douglas *(Mng Dir)*

EMATEC II S. DE R. L. DE C.V.

Avenida Isidoro Sepulveda 540
Apodaca, NL, 66603, Mexico
Tel.: (52) 81 81312500
Fax: (52) 81 81312542
Web Site: www.ematec.com.mx
Emp.: 480
Business Description:
Molded Fiber Packaging Mfr
S.I.C.: 2821
N.A.I.C.S.: 325211
Personnel:
Alejandro Paez Jimenez *(CEO)*

Plant:

Ematec - Cuernavaca Plant (1)
Paseo de los clavelaes #74
Col Bugambilias, Jiutepec, Morelos, Mexico MX
Tel.: (52) 777 3295900
Web Site: www.ematec.com.mx
Emp.: 100
Molded Fiber Packaging Mfr
S.I.C.: 2821
N.A.I.C.S.: 325211

EMBELTON LIMITED

147 Bakers Road
Coburg, VIC, 3058, Australia
Tel.: (61) 3 9353 4811
Fax: (61) 3 9353 4855
E-Mail: gpevic@embelton.com
Web Site: www.embelton.com
EMB—(ASX)
Rev.: $33,884,165
Assets: $16,984,402
Liabilities: $5,128,056
Net Worth: $11,856,346
Earnings: $1,092,344
Fiscal Year-end: 06/30/13
Business Description:
Flooring Product Mfr
S.I.C.: 2421
N.A.I.C.S.: 321918
Personnel:
George Embelton *(Chm)*
James Embelton *(Mng Dir)*
E. P. Galgano *(Sec)*
Board of Directors:
George Embelton
Ross Baldwin
James Embelton

EMBERCLEAR CORP.

620-12th Avenue SW Suite 400
Calgary, AB, T2R 0H5, Canada
Tel.: (403) 264-8817
Fax: (403) 266-8886
Web Site: www.emberclear.com
EMB—(TSXV)
Rev.: $288,471
Assets: $35,145,795
Liabilities: $16,312,470
Net Worth: $18,833,325
Earnings: ($47,428,820)
Fiscal Year-end: 06/30/13
Business Description:
Energy Development Services
S.I.C.: 4931
N.A.I.C.S.: 221112
Personnel:
Albert Lin *(Chm)*
Raj Suri *(Pres & CFO)*
David G. Anderson *(CEO)*
Nick Cohen *(COO)*
James Palumbo *(Pres-Fppi & Emberclear Reserves)*
Karen Tanaka *(Sec & Exec VP)*
Board of Directors:
Albert Lin
David G. Anderson
Mike Anglin
Keith Calder
Peter H. Kinash
Raj Suri
Transfer Agent:
Olympia Trust Company inc.
2300 125 - 9th Avenue SE
Calgary, AB, Canada

Subsidiary:

EmberClear Inc. (1)
224 15 Ave Sw
Calgary, AB, T2R 0P7, Canada
Tel.: (403) 264-8817
Electric Power Generation Services
S.I.C.: 4911
N.A.I.C.S.: 221112

U.S. Subsidiaries:

Future Fuels LLC (1)
7322 SW Freeway Ste 1100
Houston, TX 77074
Tel.: (888) 452-9978
Fax: (888) 452-9979
Electric Power Generation Services
S.I.C.: 4911
N.A.I.C.S.: 221112

Future Power PA Inc. (1)
72 Genmaura National
Moosic, PA 18507-2133
Tel.: (281) 989-0903
Electric Power Generation Services
S.I.C.: 4911
N.A.I.C.S.: 221118

EMBLAZE LTD.

9 Hamenofim Street
PO Box 2216
Herzliya Pituach, 46725, Israel
Tel.: (972) 9 7699 333
Fax: (972) 9 7699 800
E-Mail: contactus@emblaze.com
Web Site: www.emblaze.com
BLZ—(LSE)
Rev.: $2,149,000
Assets: $147,137,000
Liabilities: $4,643,000
Net Worth: $142,494,000
Earnings: $886,000
Emp.: 561
Fiscal Year-end: 12/31/12
Business Description:
Technology Holding Company
S.I.C.: 6719
N.A.I.C.S.: 551112
Personnel:
Abraham Wolff *(Chm)*
Yossi Schneorson *(Vice Chm & CEO)*
Board of Directors:
Abraham Wolff
Keren Arad-Leiboviz
Shimon Laor
Yossi Schneorson
Yosef Schvinger
Zvi Shur
Chanoch Winderboim
Legal Counsel:
Berwin Leighton Paisner LLP
Adelaide House London Bridge
London, United Kingdom
Transfer Agent:
Capita Registrars
The Registry 34 Beckenham Road
Beckenham, United Kingdom

Subsidiaries:

ELSE Ltd (1)
Emblaze House 1 Emblaze Square
Industrial Area
PO Box 2220
43662 Ra'anana, Israel
Tel.: (972) 97699302
Fax: (972) 97699665
E-Mail: info@else.bz
Web Site: www.elsemobile.com
Cell Phones Mfr
S.I.C.: 3669
N.A.I.C.S.: 334290

Emblaze Mobile Ltd. (1)
1 Emblaze Square Emblaze House
PO Box 2220
43662 Ra'anana, Israel (100%)
Tel.: (972) 97699302
Fax: (972) 97699665
E-Mail: contactus@emblazemobile.com
Web Site: www.emblazemobile.com
Developer of Mobile Devices & Mobile Related Technologies
S.I.C.: 4812
N.A.I.C.S.: 517210
Eli Reisman *(CEO)*

emoze Ltd. (1)
Hamenofim St Ste 9
PO Box 2216
Herzliyya, 43725, Israel (100%)
Tel.: (972) 97699333
Fax: (972) 97699800
E-Mail: azi@emoze.com
Web Site: www.emoze.com
Emp.: 30
Push E-mail & Personal Information Management Services
S.I.C.: 4812
N.A.I.C.S.: 517210
Moshe Levy *(CEO)*

EMBOTELLADORA ANDINA S.A.

Miraflores 9153 7th Floor
Renca, Santiago, Chile
Tel.: (56) 2 338 0520
Fax: (56) 2 338 0530
E-Mail: ir@koandina.com
Web Site: www.koandina.com
Year Founded: 1946
AKO.A—(NYSE SGO)
Sls.: $2,485,260,772
Assets: $3,264,453,022
Liabilities: $1,370,010,589
Net Worth: $1,894,442,433
Earnings: $187,130,645
Emp.: 10,952
Fiscal Year-end: 12/31/12
Business Description:
Producer & Bottler of Soft-Drinks
S.I.C.: 2086
N.A.I.C.S.: 312112
Personnel:
Juan G. Claro *(Chm)*
Jaime Cohen *(Chief Legal Officer)*
Board of Directors:
Juan G. Claro
Jose Antonio Garces
Gonzalo Said
Salvador Said
Heriberto Urzua Sanchez

Subsidiaries:

Andina Bottling Investments SA (1)
Miraflores Renca
Santiago, Chile (99.9%)
Tel.: (56) 23380520
Fax: (56) 23380530
E-Mail: andina.ir@koandina.com
Web Site: www.embotelladoraandina.com
Holding Company
S.I.C.: 6719
N.A.I.C.S.: 551112
Miguel Peirano *(CEO)*

Non-U.S. Subsidiary:

Embotelladora del Atlantico S.A. (2)
Ruta Nacional 19 Km 3 7
Cordoba, Argentina (99.97%)
Tel.: (54) 3514968888
Fax: (54) 3514962490
Web Site: www.cocacola-edasa.com.ar
Emp.: 1,350
Soft Drink Mfr
S.I.C.: 2086
N.A.I.C.S.: 312111
Jose Luis Solorzano *(Gen Mgr)*

Servicios Multivending Ltda. (1)
Miraflores 8953 Renca
Santiago, Chile (99.9%)
Tel.: (56) 26772700
Fax: (56) 26010685
Web Site: www.andina.com
Service Establishment Equipment & Supplies Merchant Whslr
S.I.C.: 5087
N.A.I.C.S.: 423850
Ricardo Solar *(Mng Dir)*

Affiliates:

Envases Central S.A. (1)
Ave Miraflores No 8755
Renca, Santiago, Chile (49.91%)
Tel.: (56) 25999300
Fax: (56) 25509303
E-Mail: bourys@koandina.com
Web Site: www.koandina.com
Emp.: 60
Metal Can Mfr
S.I.C.: 3411
N.A.I.C.S.: 332431
Janet Bourises *(Mgr-Sls)*

Envases CMF S.A. (1)
La Martina 0390
Santiago, 906 0045, Chile (50%)
Tel.: (56) 25448222
Fax: (56) 25448200
E-Mail: info@cmf.cl
Web Site: www.envases-cmf.cl
Emp.: 200
All Other Plastics Product Mfr
S.I.C.: 3089
N.A.I.C.S.: 326199

Non-U.S. Subsidiary:

Rio de Janeiro Refrescos Ltda. (1)
Rua Andre Rocha 2299 Taquara
Jacarepagua, Rio de Janeiro, Brazil (99.99%)
Tel.: (55) 2124291700
Fax: (55) 2124291558
E-Mail: dcappadona@koandina.com
Web Site: www.rjrefrescos.com.br
Emp.: 300
Production & Sale of Alcoholic & Non-Alcoholic Beverages
S.I.C.: 2086
N.A.I.C.S.: 312112
Aleandro Feuereisen *(Gen Mgr)*

EMBRAER S.A.

Avenida Brigadeiro Faria Lima 2170
12227 901 Sao Jose dos Campos, Sao Paulo, Brazil
Tel.: (55) 1239271000
Fax: (55) 1239271420
E-Mail: investor.relations@embraer.com.br
Web Site: www.embraer.com.br
Year Founded: 1969
ERJ—(BRAZ NYSE)
Rev.: $6,177,900,000
Assets: $9,490,400,000
Liabilities: $6,140,100,000
Net Worth: $3,350,300,000
Earnings: $348,600,000
Emp.: 20,150
Fiscal Year-end: 12/31/12
Business Description:
Commercial Aircraft Mfr
Import Export
S.I.C.: 3721
N.A.I.C.S.: 336411
Personnel:
Hermann Heinemann *(Chm)*
Frederico Pinheiro Fleury Curado *(Pres & CEO)*
Luiz Carlos Affonso *(Exec VP-Exec Jets)*
Luiz Carlos S. Aguiar *(Exec VP-Defense & Security Market)*
Artur Aparecido Valerio Coutinho *(Exec VP-Ops)*
Paulo Cesar De Souza e Silva *(Exec VP-Airline Market)*
Antonio Julio Franco *(Exec VP-Org Dev & Personnel)*
Mauro Kern, Jr. *(Exec VP-Engrg & Tech)*
Board of Directors:

Embraer S.A.—(Continued)

Hermann Heinemann
Vitor Paulo Camargo Goncalves
Joao Cox Neto
Claudemir Marques De Almeida
Aprigio Eduardo de Moura Azevedo
Sergio Eraldo de Salles Pinto
Wilson Carlos Duarte Delfino
Josue Christiano Gomes da Silva
Alexandre Goncalves Silva
Israel Vainboim
Samir Zraick

Transfer Agent:
Banco Itau S.A.
Rua Boa Vista, 185-7 Andar
01092-900 Sao Paulo, SP, Brazil
Tel.: (55) 11 237 5151
Fax: (55) 11 237 5756

Division:

Eleb-Embraer (1)
Rua Itabaiana 40 Parque Industrial
12237 540 Sao Jose dos Campos, SP, Brazil (51%)
Tel.: (55) 1239355494
Telex: 1233441 ebae br
Fax: (55) 1239355284
Web Site: www.eleb.net
Emp.: 500
Production of Landing Gears & Pylons, Wheels, Brakes & Hydraulic System Components
S.I.C.: 3593
N.A.I.C.S.: 333995

Subsidiaries:

ECC do Brasil Cia de Seguros (1)
av Faria Lima Brig 2170 Prd F 56 Sl Eixo C 15
Jd da Granja, Sao Jose dos Campos, Sao Paulo, 12227-901, Brazil
Tel.: (55) 12 3927 1040
General Insurance Services
S.I.C.: 6411
N.A.I.C.S.: 524298

ELEB Equipamentos Ltda. (1)
Rua Itabaiana 40
Sao Jose dos Campos, Sao Paulo, 12237-540, Brazil
Tel.: (55) 12 3935 5211
Fax: (55) 12 3935 5284
E-Mail: gora.almida@eleb.net
Web Site: www.eleb.net
Emp.: 60
Aerospace Component Mfr
S.I.C.: 3812
N.A.I.C.S.: 334511
Jose Luiz Fragnan *(Mng Dir)*

Orbisat Industria e Aerolevantamento S.A. (1)
Avenida Jose de Souza Campos 1815 / An 6
Cambui, 12244-000 Campinas, Sao Paulo, Brazil
Tel.: (55) 19 3295 8844
Electronic Equipment Mfr
S.I.C.: 3679
N.A.I.C.S.: 334419

Joint Venture:

Liebherr-Aerospace Brasil Ltda. (1)
Rua Dr Hans Liebherr 1 Unidade Industrial A Vila Bela
CEP 12522-640 Guaratingueta, SP, Brazil
Tel.: (55) 12 2131 4000
Fax: (55) 12 2131 4102
E-Mail: info.lli@liebherr.com
Web Site: www.liebherr.com.br
Emp.: 25
Joint Venture of Embraer-Empresa Brasileira de Aeronautica S/A (60%) & Liebherr-International AG (40%)
S.I.C.: 3491
N.A.I.C.S.: 332911

U.S. Subsidiary:

Embraer Aircraft Holding Inc. (1)
276 SW 34th St
Fort Lauderdale, FL 33315-3603
Tel.: (954) 359-3700
Fax: (954) 359-3701
Web Site: www.embraer.com
Emp.: 300
Aircraft Mfr
S.I.C.: 5088
N.A.I.C.S.: 423860
Mauricio Botelho *(Chm)*
Frederico Pinheiro Fleury Curado *(Pres & CEO)*
Antonio Manso *(CFO)*
Carlos Villela *(Gen Counsel & VP)*
Romualdo Barros *(Exec VP-Defense Market)*
Horacio Forjaz *(Exec VP-Corp Comm)*
Satoshi Yokota *(Exec VP-Dev)*

Subsidiaries:

Embraer Aircraft Customer Services, Inc. (2)
276 SW 34th St
Fort Lauderdale, FL 33315
Tel.: (954) 359-3700
Fax: (954) 359-8170
Aircraft Parts Mfr
S.I.C.: 3728
N.A.I.C.S.: 336413

Embraer Aircraft Maintenance Services, Inc. (2)
10 Airways Blvd
Nashville, TN 37217
Tel.: (615) 367-2100
Fax: (615) 367-4327
Aircraft Maintenance Services
S.I.C.: 4581
N.A.I.C.S.: 488190

Embraer Executive Aircraft, Inc. (2)
1205 General Aviation Dr
Melbourne, FL 32935-6309
Tel.: (321) 426-2623
Aircraft Mfr
S.I.C.: 3721
N.A.I.C.S.: 336411

Embraer Executive Jet Services, LLC (2)
276 SW 34th St
Fort Lauderdale, FL 33315-3603
Tel.: (954) 359-3700
Fax: (954) 359-3701
Web Site: www1.embraerexecutivejets.com
Emp.: 200
Aircraft Mfr
S.I.C.: 3721
N.A.I.C.S.: 336411
Marco Tulio Pellegrini *(Pres & CEO)*
Scott Kalister *(VP & Mng Dir)*

Embraer Services, Inc. (2)
276 SW 34th St
Fort Lauderdale, FL 33315-3603
Tel.: (954) 359-3700
Fax: (954) 359-3701
Aircraft Mfr
S.I.C.: 3721
N.A.I.C.S.: 336411

Non-U.S. Subsidiaries:

EAI-Embraer Aviation International (1)
33 Rue Des Vanesses
Paris Nord 2 - Bat Eddington
93420 Villepinte, France (100%)
Tel.: (33) 149384400
Telex: 23569 f
Fax: (33) 149384401
Web Site: www.embraer.com
Rev.: $17,237,000
Emp.: 2,050
Sales, Support, Assistance
S.I.C.: 7389
N.A.I.C.S.: 425120
Louis Fuchs *(Sr VP)*

Embraer Aviation Europe SAS (1)
33 rue des Vanesses Paris Nord 2 Bat Eddington Roissy CDG
Villepinte, 95943, France
Tel.: (33) 1 49 38 44 00
Fax: (33) 1 49 38 44 01
Aircraft Repair & Maintenance Services
S.I.C.: 4581
N.A.I.C.S.: 488190

Subsidiary:

Embraer Aviation International SAS (2)
33 Rue Des Vanesses
Villepinte, 93420, France
Tel.: (33) 1 49 38 44 00
Fax: (33) 1 49 38 44 01
Aircraft Repair & Maintenance Services
S.I.C.: 4581
N.A.I.C.S.: 488190

Embraer China (1)
Suite 1806 Tower 2 China Central Place Office Bldg No 79 Jianguo Rd
100025 Beijing, Chaoyang District, China (100%)
Tel.: (86) 10 6598 9988
Fax: (86) 10 6598 9986
E-Mail:
Web Site: www.embraer.com
Emp.: 120
Aircraft & Flight Operations
S.I.C.: 3721
N.A.I.C.S.: 336411
Guan Dongyuan *(Pres)*

Embraer Netherlands B.V. (1)
Evert van de Beekstraat 47
Schiphol, 1118 CL Amsterdam, Netherlands
Tel.: (31) 20 4054747
Finance Management Services
S.I.C.: 6211
N.A.I.C.S.: 523999

Non-U.S. Subsidiary:

Embraer Asia Pacific Pte-Limited (2)
391B Orchard Rd Tower B 24-02
Ngee Ann City, Singapore, 238874, Singapore
Tel.: (65) 6734 4321
Fax: (65) 6734 8255
Emp.: 65
Aircraft Mfr & Whslr
S.I.C.: 3721
N.A.I.C.S.: 336411
Ricardo Pesce *(Mng Dir)*

Embraer Spain Holding Co., SL (1)
Rambla Catalunya 135
Barcelona, Spain
Tel.: (34) 934150522
Financial Management Services
S.I.C.: 6211
N.A.I.C.S.: 523999

Non-U.S. Subsidiary:

ECC Leasing Company Ltd. (2)
202 Q House 76 Furze Road
Sandyford, Dublin, Ireland
Tel.: (353) 1 245 3980
Fax: (353) 1 293 9404
Web Site: www.eccleasing.com
Aircraft Leasing Services
S.I.C.: 7359
N.A.I.C.S.: 532411
Mauro Kern *(Exec VP)*

OGMA - Industria Aeronautica De Portugal S.A. (1)
Parque Aeronautico de Alverca
2615-173 Lisbon, Portugal
Tel.: (351) 219579000
Fax: (351) 219580401
E-Mail: geral@ogma.pt
Web Site: www.ogma.pt
Emp.: 1,600
Aircraft Mfr
S.I.C.: 3721
N.A.I.C.S.: 336411
Almir Borges *(Pres)*
Ladislau Cid *(CFO)*

EMBRUDIS

La Clapiere
05200 Embrun, Hautes Alpes, France
Tel.: (33) 492432850
Fax: (33) 492437140
Sls.: $22,600,000
Emp.: 49

Business Description:
Grocery Stores
S.I.C.: 5411
N.A.I.C.S.: 445110

Personnel:
Alain Vappereau *(Pres)*

EMBRY HOLDINGS LIMITED

7/F Wyler Centre II 200 Tai Lin Pai Road
Kwai Chung, China (Hong Kong)
Tel.: (852) 2418 8222
Fax: (852) 2418 8288
E-Mail: marketing@embryform.com
Web Site: www.embryform.com
1388—(HKG)
Rev.: $257,301,156
Assets: $245,184,885
Liabilities: $59,853,303
Net Worth: $185,331,582
Earnings: $23,670,320
Emp.: 8,430
Fiscal Year-end: 12/31/12

Business Description:
Women's Clothing Retailer
S.I.C.: 5621
N.A.I.C.S.: 448120

Personnel:
Man Tai Cheng *(Founder & Chm)*
Liza Pik Ho Cheng *(CEO)*
Katie Kam Lai Fung *(CFO)*
Ka Man So *(Sec)*

Board of Directors:
Man Tai Cheng
Liza Pik Ho Cheng
Siu Ki Lau
Kwan Hung Lee
Tien-sheng Lee
Ming Chu Ngok

Royal Bank of Canada Trust Company (Cayman) Limited
4th Floor Royal Bank House 24 Shedden Road
Georgetown, Cayman Islands

Transfer Agents:
Tricor Investor Services Limited
26th Floor Tesbury Centre 28 Queens Road East
Wanchai, China (Hong Kong)

Royal Bank of Canada Trust Company (Cayman) Limited
4th Floor Royal Bank House 24 Shedden Road
Georgetown, Cayman Islands

EMC LIMITED

Constantia Office Complex 11 Dr U N Brahmachari Street
8th Floor South Block, Kolkata, 700017, India
Tel.: (91) 33 22893122
Fax: (91) 33 22893121
E-Mail: info@emcpower.com
Web Site: www.emcpower.com
Year Founded: 1953
Rev.: $384,389,105
Assets: $289,702,980
Liabilities: $237,908,447
Net Worth: $51,794,533
Earnings: $17,126,095
Emp.: 1,500
Fiscal Year-end: 03/31/13

Business Description:
Power Transmission & Distribution
S.I.C.: 4931
N.A.I.C.S.: 221121

Personnel:
Sunder Lal Dugar *(Chm)*
Ramesh Chandra Bardia *(Co-Mng Dir)*
Manoj Toshniwal *(Co-Mng Dir)*
Chandra Sekhar Adhikary *(Compliance Officer & Sec)*

Board of Directors:
Sunder Lal Dugar
Ramesh Chandra Bardia
Saubir Bhattacharyya
Durga Prasad Sharma
Suraj Mall Singhi
Manoj Toshniwal

Transfer Agent:
Maheshwari Datamatics Pvt. Ltd.
6 Mangoe Lane 2nd Floor
Kolkata, 700001, India

EMC PUBLIC COMPANY LIMITED
ITF Tower 140/66-67 28-30 Floor
Silom Road Suriyawong
Bangrak, Bangkok, 10500, Thailand
Tel.: (66) 26156100
Fax: (66) 26156128
Web Site: www.emc.co.th
Year Founded: 1979
EMC—(THA)
Rev.: $130,052,824
Assets: $96,154,766
Liabilities: $65,800,335
Net Worth: $30,354,431
Earnings: $398,237
Emp.: 924
Fiscal Year-end: 12/31/12
Business Description:
Engineering Services Contractor
S.I.C.: 1731
N.A.I.C.S.: 238210
Personnel:
Chanachai Leenabanchong *(Chm & CEO)*
Chirdsak Vitooraporn *(Mng Dir)*
Somphop Prompanapitak *(CFO, Sr Exec VP & Sec)*
Thongchai Reanprasert *(Sr Exec VP-Electrical Engrg)*
Vinij Jearsathawong *(Exec VP-Civil Engrg 1)*
Vitoon Kanasaeng *(Exec VP-Civil Engrg 2)*
Pinit Karntikul *(Exec VP-Technical Engrg)*
Korkiat Nipatnantaporn *(Exec VP-Civil Engrg 4)*
Krisana Sa-Ngar-Sang *(Exec VP-Mechanical & Electrical Estimate)*
Pornchai Suwanban *(Exec VP-Civil Engrg 3)*
Board of Directors:
Chanachai Leenabanchong
Neeranuch Na-ranong
Trin Pimhataivoot
Somphop Prompanapitak
Sunee Sornchaitanasuk
Pannathee Sriwongthai
Boonchai Surapakpinyo
Chupong Tanasettagorn
Paiboon Thong-Ra-Ar
Jurairat Uhaka
Chirdsak Vitooraporn
Siriphong Vongvuttipornchai
Legal Counsel:
Soonthornthep & Partners Co Ltd
6 Floor Silom Condominium 52/16 Soi Saladaeng 2 Silom Road Bangrak
Bangkok, Thailand
Siam Premier International Law Office Limited
26th Floor The Offices at Central World 999/9 Rama I Road Pathumwan
Bangkok, 10330, Thailand
IT Law & Accounting Co Ltd
38/2 Soi Ladprao 94 Ladprao Road
Wangthonglang, Bangkok, Thailand
FarEast International Legal Co Ltd
24 Floor RS Tower 121/75 Ratchadaphisek Road DinDaeng
Bangkok, Thailand
Chinnadej & Associates Co Ltd
12 Floor ITF Tower 140/22 Silom Road
Suriyawong Bangrak
Bangkok, Thailand

EMCO INDUSTRIES LIMITED
119-E/1 Hali Road Gulberg III
PO Box 36
Lahore, Pakistan
Tel.: (92) 42 3587 2181
Fax: (92) 42 3587 2191
E-Mail: info@emco.com.pk
Web Site: www.emco.com.pk
Year Founded: 1954
EMCO—(ISL)
Sls.: $15,760,332
Assets: $22,816,553
Liabilities: $16,510,352
Net Worth: $6,306,200
Earnings: ($343,765)
Emp.: 795
Fiscal Year-end: 06/30/13
Business Description:
Insulators Mfr
S.I.C.: 3699
N.A.I.C.S.: 335999
Personnel:
Tariq Rehman *(CEO & Mng Dir)*
Mansoor Jamal Butt *(CFO)*
Board of Directors:
Usman Haq
Ahsan Suhail Mannan
Suhail Mannan
Haris Noorani
Salem Rehman
Tariq Rehman
Javaid Shafiq Siddiqi
Shafiq A. Siddiqi

EMCO LTD.
N-104 MIDC Area
Mehrun, Jalgaon, Maharashtra, 425003, India
Tel.: (91) 2572272462
Fax: (91) 2572272598
E-Mail: emco.jalgaon1@emcoindia.com
Web Site: www.emcoindia.com
EMCO—(NSE)
Rev.: $146,979,780
Assets: $279,659,640
Liabilities: $187,820,805
Net Worth: $91,838,836
Earnings: ($1,670,714)
Fiscal Year-end: 03/31/13
Business Description:
Power Transmission Equipment Mfr & Distr
S.I.C.: 3568
N.A.I.C.S.: 333613
Personnel:
Rajesh S. Jain *(Chm)*
Ram Narayan Mundra *(CFO)*
Praveen Kumar *(Compliance Officer & Sec)*
Board of Directors:
Rajesh S. Jain
T. N. V. Ayyar
Sanjay Bhatnagar
Bheru Choudhary
S. V. Deo
Shailesh S. Jain
K. Narsim Shenoy
Chaturvedi & Shah
Mumbai, India
Transfer Agent:
Link Intime India Private Limited
C-13 Pannalal Silk Mills Compound L.B.S. Marg Bhandup
Mumbai, India

EMCOM HOLDINGS CO., LTD.
KSS Gotanda Building 5F 1-21-8 Nishigotanda
Shinagawa-ku, Tokyo, 141-0031, Japan
Tel.: (81) 50 3155 4370
Fax: (81) 3 5719 4630
Web Site: www.hd.emcom.jp
Year Founded: 1974
7954—(JAS)
Sales Range: $25-49.9 Million
Emp.: 397
Business Description:
Business Strategy Support Services
S.I.C.: 7389
N.A.I.C.S.: 561499
Personnel:
Hakmin Kim *(Pres)*
Board of Directors:
Hakmin Kim
Jungsun Lee
Tetsuo Yamamoto
Yanji Yang
Subsidiary:

EMCOM ENTERTAINMENT Co., Ltd. **(1)**
Kojimachi Center Building 3F 3-5-8 Kojimachi
Chiyoda-ku, Tokyo, 102-0083, Japan
Tel.: (81) 50 3155 4368
Business Management Services
S.I.C.: 8742
N.A.I.C.S.: 541611
Yanji Yang, *(Pres)*

EMD MUSIC S.A.
boulevard General Wahis 16a
1030 Brussels, Belgium
Tel.: (32) 2 745 09 70
Fax: (32) 2 745 09 97
E-Mail: info@emdmusic.com
Web Site: www.emdmusic.com
EMD—(EUR)
Sales Range: $50-74.9 Million
Emp.: 120
Business Description:
Musical Instrument Distr
S.I.C.: 5099
N.A.I.C.S.: 423990
Personnel:
Leonardo Baldocci *(Chm & CEO)*
Marc Lepage *(CFO)*

EME CAPITAL LLP
32 St James Street
London, SW1A 1HD, United Kingdom
Tel.: (44) 20 3468 1900
E-Mail: info@eme-capital.com
Web Site: www.eme-capital.com
Business Description:
Private Equity Firm
S.I.C.: 6211
N.A.I.C.S.: 523999
Personnel:
Richard Bryant *(Partner)*
Ahmad Salam *(Partner)*
Subsidiary:

Theo Fennell PLC **(1)**
169 Fulham Road
London, SW3 6SP, United Kingdom
Tel.: (44) 2075915000
Fax: (44) 2075915001
E-Mail: customerservice@theofennell.com
Web Site: www.theofennell.com
Sls.: $16,908,417
Assets: $13,737,838
Liabilities: $5,718,189
Net Worth: $8,019,649
Earnings: ($1,387,589)
Emp.: 55
Fiscal Year-end: 03/31/13
Jewelry Designer, Mfr & Retailer
S.I.C.: 3911
N.A.I.C.S.: 339910
Rupert Nicholas Hambro *(Chm)*
Alister Theodore Fennell *(Interim Mng Dir & Dir-Creative)*
Alasdair Kinloch Hadden-Paton *(Sec & Dir-Fin)*

EME S.P.A.
(d/b/a Electric Motors Europe)
Zona Industriale
IT-32030 Arsie, BL, Italy
Tel.: (39) 0439750067
Fax: (39) 0439750070
E-Mail: info@orange1.eu
Web Site: www.emespa.it
Year Founded: 1971
Sales Range: $75-99.9 Million
Emp.: 450
Business Description:
Electric Motor Mfr
S.I.C.: 3621
N.A.I.C.S.: 335312
Personnel:
Armando Donazzan *(Pres & CEO)*
Subsidiaries:

CEG S.r.l. **(1)**
Via A Grandi 23
IT-47030 San Mauro Pascoli, FC, Italy IT
Tel.: (39) 0541815611
Fax: (39) 0541815684
E-Mail: info@ceg.it
Web Site: www.ceg.it
Electric Motor Mfr
S.I.C.: 3621
N.A.I.C.S.: 335312
Paolo Giorgi *(Plant Mgr)*

Unielectric S.p.A. **(1)**
Via Edison 17
42049 Sant'Ilario d'Enza, RE, Italy IT
Tel.: (39) 0522 904 011 (100%)
Fax: (39) 0522 904 000
E-Mail: info@unielectric.com
Web Site: www.unielectric.com
Sales Range: $25-49.9 Million
Emp.: 100
Electric Motor Design & Engineering Services
S.I.C.: 7389
N.A.I.C.S.: 541990
Paolo George *(Mgr-Pur)*

Non-U.S. Subsidiary:

EME Kft. **(1)**
Csengery ut 119
8800 Nagykanizsa, Hungary HU
Tel.: (36) 93313036 (100%)
Fax: (36) 93312027
E-Mail: eme@eme-europe.com
Web Site: www.eme-europe.com
Electric Motor Mfr
S.I.C.: 3621
N.A.I.C.S.: 335312
Mauro Grana *(Mng Dir & Mgr-Ops-Global)*

EMECO HOLDINGS LIMITED
Level 3 71 Walters Drive
Osborne Park, WA, 6017, Australia
Mailing Address:
PO Box 1341
Osborne Park, WA, 6916, Australia
Tel.: (61) 8 9420 0222
Fax: (61) 8 9420 0205
E-Mail: corporate@emecogroup.com
Web Site: www.emecogroup.com
Year Founded: 1972
EHL—(ASX)
Rev.: $458,200,949
Assets: $1,173,427,526
Liabilities: $536,521,016
Net Worth: $636,906,510
Earnings: $6,256,768
Emp.: 624
Fiscal Year-end: 06/30/13
Business Description:
Mining Equipment Rental & Maintenance Services
S.I.C.: 7359
N.A.I.C.S.: 532412
Personnel:
Ken Lewsey *(CEO & Mng Dir)*
Stephen Gobby *(CFO)*
Ian Testrow *(Pres-New & Dev Bus)*
Mike Kirkpatrick *(Sec & Gen Mgr-Corp Svcs)*
Board of Directors:
Alec Brennan
Robert Bishop
John Cahill
Stephen Gobby
Mike Kirkpatrick
Peter Richards
Erica Smyth

EMED MINING PUBLIC LIMITED
1 Lambousa Street
Nicosia, 1095, Cyprus
Tel.: (357) 2244 2705
Fax: (357) 2242 1956

EMED Mining Public Limited—(Continued)

E-Mail: info@emed-mining.com
Web Site: www.emed-mining.com
Year Founded: 2004
EMED—(AIM TSX)
Rev.: $169,617
Assets: $107,145,709
Liabilities: $21,059,483
Net Worth: $86,086,225
Earnings: ($15,447,301)
Emp.: 50
Fiscal Year-end: 12/31/12
Business Description:
Gold & Copper Mining Services
S.I.C.: 1041
N.A.I.C.S.: 212221
Personnel:
Aristidis Anagnostaras-Adams *(Co-Founder)*
Ronnie Beevor *(Co-Founder)*
Rod Halliday *(Interim CEO)*
John Leach *(CFO & Dir-Fin)*
William Enrico *(COO)*
Rob Williams *(Dev Officer)*
Board of Directors:
Ronnie Beevor
Roger Davey
Robert Francis
Rod Halliday
John Leach
Hui Liu
Jose Nicolas Sierra Lopez
Ashwath Mehra
Jose Sierra

Moore Stephens Stylianou & Co
Iris Tower 58 Arch Makarios III Avenue 6th Floor, Office 602
Nicosia, Cyprus

Computershare Investor Services Inc.
100 University Ave 9th Floor
Toronto, ON, Canada

Transfer Agents:
Computershare Investor Services plc
2nd Floor Vintners Place 68 Upper Thames Street
London, United Kingdom

Computershare Investor Services Inc.
100 University Ave 9th Floor
Toronto, ON, Canada

Non-U.S. Subsidiaries:

Eastern Mediterranean Resources (Slovakia) SRO **(1)**
Zelezniciarska 1724/11
96901 Banska Stiavnica, Slovakia
Tel.: (421) 456720069
Fax: (421) 45 679 07 75
Web Site: www.emed-slovakia.com
Emp.: 7
Gold Ore Mining Services
S.I.C.: 1041
N.A.I.C.S.: 212221
Demetrios Constantinides *(Mng Dir)*

EMED Tartessus S.L.U. **(1)**
La Dehesa Minas s/n
21660 Minas de Riotinto, Huelva, Spain
Tel.: (34) 959592850
Fax: (34) 959 591 860
Web Site: www.emed-tartessus.com
Copper Ores Mining Services
S.I.C.: 1021
N.A.I.C.S.: 212234
Jose Sierra *(Chm)*

EMED.COM TECHNOLOGIES LIMITED

8-2-87/89 4th Floor Left Hand Side Srinivasa Plaza Srinagar Colony Main Road, Hyderabad, Andhra Pradesh, 500 082, India
Tel.: (91) 40 23734690
E-Mail: info@emedtechno.com
Web Site: www.emedtechno.com
Year Founded: 1989
524588—(BOM)
Rev.: $97,595
Assets: $930,708
Liabilities: $180,357
Net Worth: $750,351
Earnings: ($18,855)
Fiscal Year-end: 03/31/13
Business Description:
Medical Equipment Mfr & Software Development Services
S.I.C.: 3842
N.A.I.C.S.: 339113
Personnel:
Kamlesh Dharsibhai Korodiya *(Compliance Officer)*
Board of Directors:
Sunil Ganesh Bhave
Parth Dinesh Kanabar
Kamlesh Dharsibhai Korodiya
Shashank Vijay Pawar
Transfer Agent:
Skyline Financial Services Private Limited
8-2-87/89 4th Floor Left Hand Side Srinivasa Plaza Srinagar Colony
Main Road, Hyderabad, Andhra Pradesh, 500 082, India

EMERA, INC.

1223 Lower Water Street
PO Box 910
Halifax, NS, B3J 3S8, Canada
Tel.: (902) 450-0507
Fax: (902) 428-6112
Toll Free: (888) 450-0507
E-Mail: investors@emera.com
Web Site: www.emera.com
Year Founded: 1998
EMA—(OTC TSX)
Rev.: $2,046,289,572
Assets: $7,482,187,344
Liabilities: $5,218,008,588
Net Worth: $2,264,178,756
Earnings: $244,131,312
Emp.: 3,500
Fiscal Year-end: 12/31/12
Business Description:
Holding Company; Electric Power Generation
S.I.C.: 6719
N.A.I.C.S.: 551112
Personnel:
John Thomas McLennan *(Chm)*
Christopher G. Huskilson *(Pres & CEO)*
Scott C. Balfour *(CFO & Exec VP)*
Robert R. Bennett *(COO & Exec VP)*
Bruce Marchand *(Chief Legal Officer)*
Barbara Meens Thistle *(Chief HR Officer)*
Robert Hanf *(Pres/CEO-Nova Scotia Power Inc)*
Sarah MacDonald *(Pres-Emera Caribbean Ltd & Pres/CEO-Grand Bahama Power Company)*
Gerry Chasse *(Pres/COO-Bangor Hydro Electric Company)*
Dan Muldoon *(Pres/COO-Emera Utility Services Inc)*
Judy Steele *(Pres/COO-Emera Energy Inc)*
Nancy G. Tower *(CEO-Newfoundland & Labrador & Exec VP-Bus Dev)*
Stephen Aftanas *(Sec)*
Board of Directors:
John Thomas McLennan
Robert S. Briggs
Sylvia D. Chrominska
Allan L. Edgeworth
James D. Eisenhauer
Christopher G. Huskilson
B. Lynn Loewen
Donald A. Pether
Andrea Sarah Rosen
Richard P. Sergel
Jacqueline Mary Sheppard
Transfer Agent:
Computershare Trust Company of Canada
Vancouver, BC, Canada
Tel.: (604) 661-9400
Fax: (604) 669-1548
Subsidiaries:

Emera Brunswick Pipeline Co Ltd **(1)**
1 Germain St Ste 1204
Saint John, NB, E2L 4V1, Canada
Tel.: (506) 693-4214
Fax: (506) 658-0199
Toll Free: (888) 410-2220
Web Site: www.brunswickpipeline.com
Natural Gas Distribution Services
S.I.C.: 4923
N.A.I.C.S.: 486210
Susan Layton *(Dir-Regulatory Affairs & Govt Rels)*

Emera Energy **(1)**
1894 Barrington St 17th Fl
Halifax, NS, B3J 2A8, Canada (100%)
Tel.: (866) 474-7800
Fax: (902) 428-6118
Web Site: www.emeraenergy.com
Energy Marketing & Trading Services
S.I.C.: 7389
N.A.I.C.S.: 561499
Judy Steele *(Pres & COO)*

Emera Utility Services Inc. **(1)**
31 Dominion Crescent
PO Box 40
Lakeside, NS, B3T 1M0, Canada
Tel.: (902) 832-7999
Fax: (902) 832-7998
E-Mail: shauna.ernst@emera.com
Web Site: www.emerautilityservices.com
Emp.: 30
Electrical Engineering Services
S.I.C.: 1731
N.A.I.C.S.: 238210
Dan Muldoon *(Pres & COO)*
Sarah MacDonald *(CEO)*

Nova Scotia Power, Inc. **(1)**
1223 Lower Water Street
Halifax, NS, B3J 3S8, Canada NS
Tel.: (902) 428-6230 (100%)
Fax: (902) 428-6108
Toll Free: (800) 428-6230
E-Mail: home@nspower.ca
Web Site: www.nspower.ca
Rev.: $1,229,801,544
Assets: $3,930,553,884
Liabilities: $3,191,003,004
Net Worth: $739,550,880
Earnings: $133,099,278
Emp.: 1,900
Fiscal Year-end: 12/31/12
Electricity Production, Transmission & Distribution
S.I.C.: 4939
N.A.I.C.S.: 221122
James D. Eisenhauer *(Chm)*
Robert J. S. Hanf *(Pres & CEO)*
Scott C. Balfour *(CFO & Exec VP)*
Rick Janega *(COO & Exec VP)*
Bruce A. Marchand *(Chief Legal Officer)*
Sarah MacDonald *(Pres-Emera Utility Services & VP-HR-Emera Inc)*
Robert R. Bennett *(COO-Emera & Exec VP)*
Stephen D. Aftanas *(Sec)*
Robin McAdam *(Exec VP-Strategic Bus & Customer Svcs)*
Wayne O'Connor *(Exec VP-Ops)*

U.S. Subsidiary:

Bangor Hydro-Electric Company **(1)**
970 Illinois Ave
Bangor, ME 04401 ME
Mailing Address: (100%)
PO Box 932
Bangor, ME 04402-0932
Tel.: (207) 945-5621
Fax: (207) 990-6995
Toll Free: (800) 499-6600
E-Mail: communication@bhe.com
Web Site: www.bhe.com
Emp.: 600
Operator of Electricity Transmission & Distribution System
S.I.C.: 4911
N.A.I.C.S.: 221121
Christopher G. Huskilson *(Chm)*
Gerard Chasse *(Pres & COO)*
Robert Hanf *(CEO)*
Susan E. Faloon *(Comm Officer)*
Peter Dawes *(VP-Fin & Treas)*

Divisions:

Bangor Hydro-Electric Company-Hancock County Division **(2)**
PO Box 932
Bangor, ME 04402
Tel.: (207) 947-2414
Fax: (207) 990-6955
E-Mail: customerservice@bhe.com
Web Site: www.bhe.com
Emp.: 100
Electric Services
S.I.C.: 4931
N.A.I.C.S.: 221121

Bangor Hydro-Electric Company-Northern Division **(2)**
PO Box 932
Bangor, ME 04402
Mailing Address:
PO Box 932
Bangor, ME 04401
Tel.: (207) 945-5621
Fax: (207) 973-2980
Toll Free: (800) 499-6600
E-Mail: sfloon@bhe.com
Web Site: www.bhe.com
Emp.: 272
Electric Services
S.I.C.: 4911
N.A.I.C.S.: 221121
Gerald Chaffe *(Pres & COO)*
Robert Hanf *(Pres & COO)*

Bangor Hydro-Electric Company-Washington County Division **(2)**
PO Box 932
Bangor, ME 04402-0139
Tel.: (207) 945-5621
Fax: (207) 973-2980
E-Mail: communications@bhe.com
Web Site: www.bhe.com
Emp.: 300
Electric Services
S.I.C.: 4931
N.A.I.C.S.: 221121
Gerry Chasse *(Pres & COO)*
Bob Hans *(CEO)*

Subsidiaries:

Maine & Maritimes Corporation **(2)**
209 State St
Presque Isle, ME 04769 ME
Tel.: (207) 760-2499
Fax: (207) 760-2419
Toll Free: (877) 272-1523
Web Site: www.mainepublicservice.com
Sales Range: $25-49.9 Million
Emp.: 138
Holding Company
S.I.C.: 4911
N.A.I.C.S.: 221112
Richard G. Daigle *(Chm)*
Nathan L. Grass *(Vice Chm)*
Brent M. Boyles *(Pres & CEO)*
Michael I. Williams *(CFO, Treas, Sr VP & Asst Sec)*
Patrick C. Cannon *(Gen Counsel, Sec & VP)*

Subsidiary:

Maine Public Service Company **(3)**
209 State St
Presque Isle, ME 04769-2655 ME
Mailing Address:
PO Box 1209
Presque Isle, ME 04769-1209
Tel.: (207) 760-2300
Fax: (207) 764-2300
E-Mail: info@mainepublicservice.com
Web Site: www.mainepublicservice.com
Electrical Power Distr
S.I.C.: 4931
N.A.I.C.S.: 221122
Brent M. Boyles *(Pres & CEO)*
Michael I. Williams *(Sr VP)*

Non-U.S. Subsidiary:

Grand Bahama Power Company Limited **(1)**
PO Box F-40888
Freeport, Grand Bahama Island, Bahamas (80.4%)
Tel.: (242) 350 8900
Fax: (242) 351 8008
Web Site: www.gb-power.com

Emp.: 200
Electricity Supplier
S.I.C.: 4911
N.A.I.C.S.: 221122
Alan Kelley *(CEO & Pres)*
Antonio Lopez *(CFO & VP-Admin Svcs)*

EMERALD AIRWAYS LTD.

Speke Hall Avenue
Liverpool John Lennon Airport,
Liverpool, Merseyside, L24 1YW,
United Kingdom
Tel.: (44) 151 448 0844
Fax: (44) 151 448 0549
E-Mail: mail@emerald-airways.co.uk
Web Site: www.emerald-airways.co.uk
Year Founded: 1987
Emp.: 250
Business Description:
Air Transportation Services
S.I.C.: 4731
N.A.I.C.S.: 488510

EMERALD BAY ENERGY INC.

1A 4015 1st Street SE
Calgary, AB, T2G 4X7, Canada
Tel.: (403) 262-6000
Fax: (403) 263-6001
E-Mail: info@emeraldbayenergy.com
Web Site: www.emeraldbayenergy.com
Year Founded: 1997
EBY—(TSXV)
Rev.: $169,192
Assets: $2,987,002
Liabilities: $4,542,013
Net Worth: ($1,555,011)
Earnings: ($1,802,827)
Emp.: 5
Fiscal Year-end: 12/31/12
Business Description:
Oil & Natural Gas Exploration & Development Services
S.I.C.: 1311
N.A.I.C.S.: 211111
Personnel:
Shelby D. Beattie *(Pres & CEO)*
Michael Rice *(CFO & VP-Ops)*
Gibson C. Scott *(COO)*
Board of Directors:
Shelby D. Beattie
Kendall Dilling
Gibson C. Scott
Conrad K. Wagenaar
Legal Counsel:
Tingle, Merrett LLP
Suite 1250, Standard Life Building 639-5th Avenue S.W.
Calgary, AB, Canada
Transfer Agent:
Computershare Trust Company
Suite 600 530 8th Avenue SW
Calgary, AB, Canada

EMERALD OIL & GAS NL

Ground Floor 20 Kings Park Road
West Perth, WA, 6005, Australia
Tel.: (61) 8 9389 2111
Fax: (61) 8 9389 2199
E-Mail: info@emeraldoilandgas.com
Web Site: www.emeraldoilandgas.com
EMR—(ASX)
Rev.: $112,420
Assets: $14,621,081
Liabilities: $66,719
Net Worth: $14,554,361
Earnings: ($8,130,834)
Fiscal Year-end: 06/30/13
Business Description:
Petroleum Exploration & Production Services
S.I.C.: 1311
N.A.I.C.S.: 211111
Personnel:
Graeme Smith *(Sec)*
Board of Directors:
Jeremy D. Shervington
Tim Kestell
Peter Pynes
Ross Williams
Legal Counsel:
Jeremy Shervington
52 Ord Street
West Perth, WA, 6005, Australia
Davis Graham & Stubbs, LLP
1550 Seventeenth St Ste 500
Denver, CO 80202
Allison and Shoemaker, LLP
7887 San Felipe Ste 200
Houston, TX 77063

EMERALD PLANTATION HOLDINGS LIMITED

Room 3801 38/F Sun Hung Kai Centre
30 Harbour Road, Wanchai, China (Hong Kong)
Tel.: (852) 2877 0078
Fax: (852) 2877 0062
E-Mail: info@emerald-plantation.com
Web Site: www.emeraldplantationholdings.com
EMEXF—(OTC)
Business Description:
Holding Company; Wood & Wood-Based Products Distr; Plantations & Downstream Manufacturing Operator
S.I.C.: 6719
N.A.I.C.S.: 551112
Personnel:
Paul Jeremy Brough *(Chm)*
Board of Directors:
Paul Jeremy Brough
Gene Davis
Barry Field
Colin Denis Keogh
Eddie Wang
Subsidiaries:

Greenheart Group Limited (1)
16F Dah Sing Financial Centre 108 Gloucester Road
Wanchai, China (Hong Kong) (64%)
Tel.: (852) 2598 0380
Fax: (852) 2598 0369
E-Mail: info@greenheartgroup.com
Web Site: www.greenheartgroup.com
0094—(HKG)
Rev.: $63,859,393
Assets: $258,704,648
Liabilities: $104,880,580
Net Worth: $153,824,068
Earnings: ($18,617,414)
Emp.: 532
Fiscal Year-end: 12/31/12
Forestry Services
S.I.C.: 0851
N.A.I.C.S.: 115310
Paul Jeremy Broug *(Interim CEO)*
Daphne Tse *(CFO)*
Andy Fyfe *(COO)*
Ty Wilkinson *(CEO-Greenheart Forest Technologies & Dir-Suriname)*

Sino-Panel (Asia) Inc. (1)
3815-29 Sun Hung Kai Centre 30 Harbour Road
Wanchai, China (Hong Kong)
Tel.: (852) 2877 0078
Fax: (852) 2877 0062
E-Mail: sinopanel-trade@sinoforest.com
Web Site: www.sinopanel.com
Emp.: 30
Wood Products Mfr
S.I.C.: 2426
N.A.I.C.S.: 321918

Sino-Wood Partners Limited (1)
Room 3815-29 38th Floor Sun Hung Kai Centre
30 Harbour Road, Wanchai, China (Hong Kong)
Tel.: (852) 28770078
Fax: (852) 28770062
E-Mail: info@sinoforest.com
Web Site: www.sinoforest.com
Durable Goods Whslr
S.I.C.: 5099
N.A.I.C.S.: 423990
Kai Kit Poon *(Pres)*

Sinowood Limited (1)
3129-40 31/F Sun Hung Kai Centre 30 Harbour Road
Wanchai, China (Hong Kong)
Tel.: (852) 28770078
Fax: (852) 2877 0062
Emp.: 100
Forestry Services
S.I.C.: 0851
N.A.I.C.S.: 115310
James Lau *(VP)*

Non-U.S. Subsidiaries:

Guangzhou Panyu Dacheng Wood Co., Ltd. (1)
Dashi Street
Panyu District, Guangzhou, Guangdong, 510000, China
Tel.: (86) 2084780089
Fax: (86) 2084794689
Engineered Wood Veneer Mfr
S.I.C.: 2435
N.A.I.C.S.: 321211

Jiafeng Wood (Suzhou) Co., Ltd. (1)
No 28 East Shihu Road Wuzhong Economic Development Zone
Suzhou, Jiangsu, 215128, China
Tel.: (86) 51265655365
Fax: (86) 512 65853533
Wood Flooring Mfr
S.I.C.: 2426
N.A.I.C.S.: 321918

Jiangxi Jiachang Forestry Development Co., Ltd. (1)
2-A Jingwei Mansion No 37 Erjing Road
Nanchang, China
Tel.: (86) 7916827143
Fax: (86) 7916827247
Wood Products Mfr
S.I.C.: 2499
N.A.I.C.S.: 321999

Sino-Forest (Suzhou) Trading Co., Ltd. (1)
Room 6018 Business Building No 3
Zhangjiagang Port, Suzhou, Jiangsu, 215633, China
Tel.: (86) 512 58700861
Timber Products Whslr
S.I.C.: 5099
N.A.I.C.S.: 423990
Cui de Heng *(Mgr)*

Sino-Maple (Shanghai) Co., Ltd. (1)
Room 302 Fenghuang Mansion Building 19
No 1515 Gumei Road Xuhui
Shanghai, 200233, China
Tel.: (86) 2161281800
Fax: (86) 2161276216
Wood Flooring Mfr
S.I.C.: 2431
N.A.I.C.S.: 321918

Sino-Maple (Shanghai) Trading Co., Ltd. (1)
No 28 East Shihu Road Wuzhong Economic Development Zone
Suzhou, Jiangsu, 215128, China
Tel.: (86) 51265655365
Fax: (86) 512 6585 3533
Wood Flooring Sales
S.I.C.: 5031
N.A.I.C.S.: 423310

Sino-Panel (China) Investments Limited (1)
767 Dongfeng
510600 Guangzhou, China
Tel.: (86) 20 3836 1982
Fax: (86) 20 3836 1216
E-Mail: info@sinopanel.com
Wood Products Mfr
S.I.C.: 2499
N.A.I.C.S.: 321999

Sino-Panel (Guangxi) Limited (1)
Beihai Road West
Beihai, Guangxi, 536000, China
Tel.: (86) 779 3928068
Fax: (86) 779 3928000
Forestry Services
S.I.C.: 0851
N.A.I.C.S.: 115310

Sino-Panel (Guangzhou) Limited (1)
767 Dongfeng
510600 Guangzhou, Guangdong, China
Tel.: (86) 2038361982
Fax: (86) 2038361216
Forestry Services
S.I.C.: 0851
N.A.I.C.S.: 115310

Sino-Wood Trading Limited (1)
2nd Floor R G Hodge Plaza
Road Town, Tortola, Virgin Islands (British)
Tel.: (284) 284 494 4693
Fax: (284) 284 494 4627
Wood Fiber Products Mfr
S.I.C.: 2499
N.A.I.C.S.: 321999

EMERAM CAPITAL PARTNERS GMBH

Muhlbaurstrasse 1
81677 Munich, Germany
Tel.: (49) 89 41999 67 0
E-Mail: info@emeram.com
Web Site: www.emeram.com
Business Description:
Private Investment Firm
N.A.I.C.S.: 523999
Personnel:
Eckhard Cordes *(Partner)*
Korbinian Knoblach *(Partner)*
Kal Koppen *(Partner)*
Christia Nather *(Partner)*
Kai Obring *(PArtner)*
Volker Schmidt *(Partner)*

EMERCHANTS LIMITED

Level 2 26 Commercial Road
Newstead, QLD, 4006, Australia
Tel.: (61) 7 3607 0100
Fax: (61) 7 3607 0111
E-Mail: info@emerchants.com.au
Web Site: www.emerchants.com.au
EML—(ASX)
Rev.: $5,245,532
Assets: $15,564,859
Liabilities: $1,336,555
Net Worth: $14,228,304
Earnings: ($5,584,688)
Fiscal Year-end: 06/30/13
Business Description:
Financial Services
S.I.C.: 6141
N.A.I.C.S.: 522210
Personnel:
Robert Browning *(Chm)*
Tom Cregan *(CEO & Mng Dir)*
Bruce Stewart *(CFO & Interim Sec)*
James Ingham *(CTO)*
Richard Anderson *(Chief Comml Officer)*
Andrew Betts *(Chief Risk Officer)*
Board of Directors:
Robert Browning
Tony Adcock
David Liddy
Peter Martin
John Toms
Legal Counsel:
McKenzie Moncrieff Lawyers
Level 5 37 St Georges Terrace
Perth, WA, 6000, Australia

EMERGE RESOURCES CORP.

(Formerly Beatrix Ventures Inc.)
Suite 615 800 West Pender Street
Vancouver, BC, V6C 2V6, Canada
Tel.: (604) 687-2038
Fax: (604) 687-3141
E-Mail: info@emerge-resources.com
Web Site: www.emerge-resources.com
Year Founded: 2009
EME—(TSXV)

Emerge Resources Corp.—(Continued)

Int. Income: $4
Assets: $269,541
Liabilities: $197,827
Net Worth: $71,715
Earnings: ($425,723)
Fiscal Year-end: 05/31/13

Business Description:
Gold Exploration Services
S.I.C.: 1041
N.A.I.C.S.: 212221

Personnel:
Heye Daun *(Pres & CEO)*
Florence Luong *(CFO)*

Board of Directors:
Eugene Beukman
Heye Daun
Alan Friedman
Gerry Goldberg
Ari Levy

Legal Counsel:
Boughton Law Corporation
Suite 1000 595 Burrard Street
Vancouver, BC, V7X 1S8, Canada

Transfer Agent:
Valiant Trust Company
700 Cambie Street Suite 600
Vancouver, BC, V6B 0A2, Canada
Tel.: (604) 699-4880

EMERGENCY ASSISTANCE JAPAN CO., LTD.

NRK Koishikawa Building 1-21-14
Koishikawa Bunkyo-ku
Tokyo, 112-0002, Japan
Tel.: (81) 338118121
Web Site: www.emergency.co.jp
6063—(JAS)
Sls.: $20,812,000
Assets: $11,572,000
Liabilities: $5,445,000
Net Worth: $6,127,000
Earnings: $825,000
Emp.: 227
Fiscal Year-end: 12/31/12

Business Description:
Emergency Medical Services
S.I.C.: 8322
N.A.I.C.S.: 624230

Personnel:
Kazumasa Yoshida *(CEO)*

U.S. Subsidiary:

Emergency Assistance Japan (U.S.A), Inc. **(1)**
7200 Glen Forest Dr Ste 300
Richmond, VA 23226
Tel.: (804) 249-9907
Fax: (804) 249-9906
Medical Assistance Services
S.I.C.: 8322
N.A.I.C.S.: 624229

Non-U.S. Subsidiaries:

Emergency Assistance Japan (Singapore), Pte. Ltd **(1)**
137 Telok Ayer Street 04-08
Singapore, 068602, Singapore
Tel.: (65) 6732 5810
Fax: (65) 6736 2083
Emp.: 10
Medical Assistance Services
S.I.C.: 8322
N.A.I.C.S.: 624229
Shinichi Tajima *(Mgr)*

Emergency Assistance Thailand Co., Ltd **(1)**
9th Floor Prime Building 24 Sukhumvit Soi 21 Asoke Klongtoey-Nua
Wattana, Bangkok, 10110, Thailand
Tel.: (66) 2 665 7280
Fax: (66) 2 665 7283
Medical Assistance Services
S.I.C.: 8322
N.A.I.C.S.: 624229

EMERGENT RESOURCES LIMITED

Level 1 33 Ord Street
West Perth, WA, 6005, Australia
Tel.: (61) 8 9420 9300
Fax: (61) 8 9420 9399
E-Mail: info@emergentresources.com.au
Web Site: www.emergentresources.com.au
EMG—(ASX)
Rev.: $151,299
Assets: $7,518,609
Liabilities: $46,470
Net Worth: $7,472,138
Earnings: ($1,521,510)
Fiscal Year-end: 06/30/13

Business Description:
Iron, Copper, Lead, Zinc, Gold, Nickel & Uranium Exploration & Mining Services
S.I.C.: 1011
N.A.I.C.S.: 212210

Personnel:
Patrick Burke *(Sec)*

Board of Directors:
Jian-Hua Sang
Patrick Burke
Wolfgang Fischer
Andrew Tunks
Sai Kit Wong

Legal Counsel:
Steinepreis Paganin
Level 4 The Read Building 16 Milligan Street
Perth, WA, 6000, Australia
Tel.: (61) 8 9321 4000
Fax: (61) 8 9321 4333

EMERGEO SOLUTIONS WORLDWIDE INC.

1001 1166 Alberni Street
Vancouver, BC, V6E 3Z3, Canada
Tel.: (604) 336-8120
Fax: (604) 623-4837
Toll Free: (888) 577-0911
E-Mail: sales@emergeo.com
Web Site: www.emergeo.com
Year Founded: 1997
EMG—(TSXV)
Sales Range: $1-9.9 Million

Business Description:
Security Software Solution Services
S.I.C.: 7371
N.A.I.C.S.: 541511

Personnel:
Allan Larmour *(Chm)*
Mike Morrow *(Pres)*
Rick MacDonald *(CEO)*
Timothy Webb *(CTO & VP)*

Board of Directors:
Allan Larmour
B. J. Cowan
Timothy Webb

EMERGING GLORY SDN BHD

Lot 2.08 2nd Floor Wisma Westcourt
126 Jalan Kelang Lama, Kuala Lumpur, 58000, Malaysia
Tel.: (60) 3 7980 1304
Fax: (60) 3 7982 1636

Business Description:
Investment Holding Company
S.I.C.: 6719
N.A.I.C.S.: 551112

Personnel:
Bong Wong Lau *(Co-Owner)*
Chia Nguang Lau *(Co-Owner)*
Eng Guang Lau *(Co-Owner)*
Tuang Nguang Lau *(Co-Owner)*

Subsidiary:

Leong Hup Holdings Berhad **(1)**
2nd Fl Wisma Westcourt No 126 Jalan Kelang Lama
58000 Kuala Lumpur, Malaysia
Tel.: (60) 379801304
Fax: (60) 379821636
E-Mail: lhhb@lhhb.com
Web Site: www.lhhb.com
Sales Range: $300-349.9 Million
Holding Company; Poultry Farming Services
S.I.C.: 6719
N.A.I.C.S.: 551112
Bong Wong Lau *(Chm)*
Shew Meng Kang *(Co-Sec)*
Meng Lim *(Co-Sec)*
Fei San Seow *(Co-Sec)*

Holding:

Teo Seng Capital Berhad **(2)**
Lot PTD 25740 Batu 4 Jalan Air Hitam
Yong Peng, 83700 Johor, Malaysia (51%)
Tel.: (60) 74672289
Fax: (60) 74672923
E-Mail: tscb@teoseng.com.my
Web Site: www.teoseng.com.my
7252—(KLS)
Sales Range: $75-99.9 Million
Emp.: 900
Holding Company; Poultry Farming Services; Egg Tray & Animal Feeds Mfr & Distr; Pet Food, Medicine & Other Related Products Distr
S.I.C.: 6719
N.A.I.C.S.: 551112
Jui Peng Lau *(Chm)*
Yok San Nam *(Mng Dir)*
Meng Bin Lim *(Co-Sec)*
Bee Hwee Tan *(Co-Sec)*
Wei Fong Wong *(Co-Sec)*

Subsidiaries:

Ritma Prestasi Sdn Bhd **(3)**
Lot 21 & 23 Jalan TTP 5/13 Seksyen 5
Taman Perindustrian, 47100 Puchong, Selangor Darul Ehsan, Malaysia (100%)
Tel.: (60) 380619330
Fax: (60) 380619331
E-Mail: ritmapres@teoseng.com.my
Web Site: www.ritmapets.com
Emp.: 30
Veterinary Products Whslr
S.I.C.: 0742
N.A.I.C.S.: 541940
Tim Nam Ya Jun *(Asst Mgr)*

Success Century Sdn Bhd **(3)**
No 8 Jln Sutera 1
Johor Bahru, Malaysia (100%)
Tel.: (60) 74681982
Poultry Farming Services
S.I.C.: 0254
N.A.I.C.S.: 112340

Teo Seng Farming Sdn Bhd **(3)**
Lot 7850 Mukim Tanjung Sembrong Batu 1 Jalan Muar
Yong Peng, 83700 Johor, Malaysia (100%)
Tel.: (60) 7 4672289
Fax: (60) 74672923
E-Mail: tsgc@tm.net.my
Web Site: www.lhhb.com
Emp.: 450
Egg Production & Marketing
S.I.C.: 0252
N.A.I.C.S.: 112310
Wee Ching Loh *(Dir-Mktg)*

Teo Seng Feedmill Sdn Bhd **(3)**
Lot 7850 Mukim Tanjung Sembrong Batu 1 Jalan Muar Yong Peng, 83700 Johor, Malaysia (100%)
Tel.: (60) 74681690
Fax: (60) 74681695
E-Mail: tsgc@tm.net.my
Web Site: www.lhhb.com
Emp.: 700
Poultry Feedmill
S.I.C.: 2048
N.A.I.C.S.: 311119
Hiok Joo Nam *(Gen Mgr)*

Teo Seng Paper Products Sdn Bhd **(3)**
Lot 7850 Mukim Tanjung Sembrong Batu 1Jalan Muar
Yong Peng, 83700 Johor, Malaysia
Tel.: (60) 74672289
Fax: (60) 74671366
E-Mail: tsgc@tm.net.my
Web Site: www.teoseng.com.my/profile.html
Emp.: 100
Paper Products Mfr
S.I.C.: 2679
N.A.I.C.S.: 322299
Laujui Peng *(CEO)*

Non-U.S. Holding:

Kendo Trading Pte. Ltd. **(2)**
233 Panda Loop
Singapore, 128421, Singapore
Tel.: (65) 6778 7477
Fax: (65) 6779 3314
E-Mail: kendo@kendo.com.sg
Web Site: www.kendo.com.sg
Poultry Distr
S.I.C.: 5144
N.A.I.C.S.: 424440

Subsidiaries:

Safa Gourmet Food Pte Ltd **(3)**
6 Senoko Way
Singapore, Singapore
Tel.: (65) 65553838
Fax: (65) 67523838
E-Mail: safa@eliteksb.com
Emp.: 20
Marinated Chicken Distr
S.I.C.: 5144
N.A.I.C.S.: 424440
Steven Tan *(Mgr-Bus Dev)*

Soonly Food Processing Industries Pte Ltd **(3)**
Senoko Industrial Estate 4 Senoko Way
Singapore, 758028, Singapore
Tel.: (65) 67572121
Fax: (65) 67562121
E-Mail:
Chicken Processing Services
S.I.C.: 2015
N.A.I.C.S.: 311615
Steven Tan *(Gen Mgr)*

EMERGING LEADERS INVESTMENTS LIMITED

Level 23 Symantec House 207 Kent Street
Sydney, NSW, 2000, Australia
Tel.: (61) 292590200
Fax: (61) 292590222
E-Mail: elil@ausbil.com.au
Web Site: www.elil.com.au
Year Founded: 2003
ELI—(ASX)
Sales Range: $1-9.9 Million

Business Description:
Personal Investment Services
S.I.C.: 7299
N.A.I.C.S.: 812990

Personnel:
Mark Reilly *(Sec)*

Board of Directors:
John R. Evans
John Skippen
Paul Xiradis

EMERISQUE BRANDS UK LIMITED

53 Davies St
London, W1K 5JH, United Kingdom
Tel.: (44) 2071526347
Fax: (44) 2071526348
Web Site: www.emerisque.com
Year Founded: 2009

Business Description:
Private Equity Firm
S.I.C.: 6211
N.A.I.C.S.: 523999

Personnel:
Ajay Khaitan *(Founder & Principal)*
Andrew Gardner *(Principal)*
Andy Rigg *(Principal)*

EMERITA GOLD CORP.

Suite 2150 885 West Georgia Street
Vancouver, BC, V6C 3E8, Canada
Tel.: (604) 683-0564
Fax: (604) 602-9311
E-Mail: cwatt@bed-rock.com

Year Founded: 2009
EMO—(TSXV)
Business Description:
Investment Services
S.I.C.: 6211
N.A.I.C.S.: 523999
Personnel:
David Patterson *(CEO)*
Colin Watt *(CFO)*
Board of Directors:
Salman Jamal
Jeffrey Lightfoot
David Patterson
Colin Watt
Transfer Agent:
Computershare Investor Services Inc.
2nd Fl 510 Burrard St
Vancouver, BC, Canada

EMERSON DEVELOPMENTS (HOLDINGS) LIMITED

(d/b/a Emerson Group)
Emerson House Hayes Lane
Alderley Edge, Cheshire, SK9 7LF, United Kingdom
Tel.: (44) 1625 588400
Fax: (44) 1625 585791
E-Mail: info@emerson.co.uk
Web Site: www.emerson.co.uk
Year Founded: 1959
Sales Range: $250-299.9 Million
Emp.: 600
Business Description:
Residential & Commercial Property Developer
S.I.C.: 6552
N.A.I.C.S.: 237210
Personnel:
Peter Emerson Jones *(Chm)*
Alan White *(Deputy Chm)*
Anne Weatherby *(Sec)*
Board of Directors:
Peter Emerson Jones
John Allen
Peter Baren
Paul Burgess
Mark Emerson Jones
Tony Emerson Jones
Lord Lee of Tafford
Mark Royle
Anne Weatherby
Alan White
Simon Wilson

U.S. Subsidiary:

Emerson International, Inc. **(1)**
370 CenterPointe Cir Ste 1136
Altamonte Springs, FL 32701
Tel.: (407) 834-9560
Fax: (407) 834-4023
Web Site: www.emerson-us.com
Residential & Commercial Property Developer
S.I.C.: 6552
N.A.I.C.S.: 237210
Jonathan Claber *(Acting Pres)*

EMFRONTIER INC.

14 F Poonglim Bldg 823 Yeoksam 1 Dong
Gangnam-Gu, Seoul, 135784, Korea (South)
Tel.: (82) 2 3016 7300
Fax: (82) 2 3016 7346
E-Mail: kbk015@emfrontier.com
Web Site: www.emfrontier.com
Year Founded: 2000
Emp.: 150
Business Description:
Information Technology Consulting Services
S.I.C.: 7373
N.A.I.C.S.: 541512
Personnel:
Jae Hwan Ahn *(CEO)*

EMGOLD MINING CORPORATION

Suite 1010-789 West Pender St
Vancouver, BC, V6H 1H2, Canada
Tel.: (778) 375-3106
Fax: (778) 375-3109
Toll Free: (888) 267-1400
E-Mail: info@emgold.com
Web Site: www.emgold.com
EMR—(DEU TSXV)
Assets: $1,677,936
Liabilities: $1,125,067
Net Worth: $552,869
Earnings: ($375,731)
Emp.: 3
Fiscal Year-end: 12/31/12
Business Description:
Gold Exploration Services
S.I.C.: 1041
N.A.I.C.S.: 212221
Personnel:
David G. Watkinson *(Pres & CEO)*
Grant T. Smith *(CFO)*
Lisa Maxwell *(Sec)*
Board of Directors:
Allen Leschert
Andrew MacRitchie
David G. Watkinson
Stephen J. Wilkinson
William J. Witte
Kenneth R. Yurichuk
Transfer Agent:
Computershare
3rd Floor 510 Burrard Street
Vancouver, BC, Canada

EMICO HOLDINGS BERHAD

18 Lebuhraya Kampung Jawa Bayan Lepas
1900 Penang, Malaysia
Tel.: (60) 46443843
Fax: (60) 46438563
E-Mail: info@emico.com.my
Web Site: www.emico.com.my
EMICO—(KLS)
Rev.: $25,462,854
Assets: $27,323,364
Liabilities: $14,184,473
Net Worth: $13,138,890
Earnings: ($749,757)
Fiscal Year-end: 03/31/13
Business Description:
Property Development & Management Services
S.I.C.: 6531
N.A.I.C.S.: 531312
Personnel:
Patrick Teik Hian Lim *(Chm)*
Jimmy Chin Keng Ong *(Mng Dir)*
Peng Loon Lee *(Co-Sec)*
Chiew Keem P'ng *(Co-Sec)*
Board of Directors:
Patrick Teik Hian Lim
Azalan A. Kadir
Francis Teck Chye Lim
Jacky Chee Kong Ng
Jimmy Chin Keng Ong
Sew Yun Wong
Thai Sun Wong

Subsidiaries:

Emico Asia Sdn. Bhd. **(1)**
18 Lebuhraya Kampong Jawa
11900 Bayan Lepas, Penang, Malaysia
Tel.: (60) 46443888
Fax: (60) 46469195
E-Mail: info@emico-asia.com
Web Site: www.emicoasia.com
Emp.: 8
Household Products Distr
S.I.C.: 5722
N.A.I.C.S.: 443141
Lucinda Lim *(Dir-Bus Dev)*

Emico Development Sdn. Bhd. **(1)**
741 Jalan 1/1 Bandar Mutiara Jalan Lencong Timur
08000 Sungai Petani, Kedah Darul Aman, Malaysia
Tel.: (60) 44480888
Fax: (60) 44480448
E-Mail: sales@emicoproperty.com
Web Site: www.emicoproperty.com
Emp.: 10
Residential Building Construction Services
S.I.C.: 1522
N.A.I.C.S.: 236116

Emico Marketing Sdn. Bhd. **(1)**
Plot 18 Lebuhraya Kampung Jawa
11900 Bayan Lepas, Penang, Malaysia
Tel.: (60) 46448202
Fax: (60) 46446557
Emp.: 200
Trophies Distr
S.I.C.: 5199
N.A.I.C.S.: 424990
Jimmy Ong *(Mng Dir)*

Emico Melaka Sdn. Bhd. **(1)**
41-D Jalan Ong Kim Wee
75300 Melaka, Malaysia
Tel.: (60) 62847880
Fax: (60) 62847884
E-Mail: emicomlk@streamyx.com
Emp.: 4
Clothing Apparels Retailer
S.I.C.: 5651
N.A.I.C.S.: 448140
Yeong Cheau Ling *(Mgr)*

Emico Penang Sdn. Bhd. **(1)**
18 Lebuhraya Kampung Jawa
11900 Bayan Lepas, Penang, Malaysia
Tel.: (60) 46448202
Fax: (60) 46438360
E-Mail: info@emico.com.my
Web Site: www.emicopenang.com
Emp.: 200
Plastic Products Mfr
S.I.C.: 3089
N.A.I.C.S.: 326199
Tracey Lim *(Mgr-Bus Dev)*

EMINENCE ORGANIC SKIN CARE INC.

Ste 300 530 W Bdwy
Vancouver, BC, V5Z 1E9, Canada
Tel.: (604) 602-4787
Fax: (604) 602-4731
Toll Free: (888) 747-6342
E-Mail: info@eminenceorganics.com
Web Site: www.eminenceorganics.com
Year Founded: 1958
Emp.: 200
Business Description:
Beauty Products Mfr
S.I.C.: 2844
N.A.I.C.S.: 325620
Personnel:
Boldijarre Koronczay *(Founder)*

EMIRA PROPERTY FUND

Optimum House 1st Floor Epsom Office Park 13 Sloane Street
Bryanston, South Africa
Tel.: (27) 117751000
Fax: (27) 117751001
E-Mail: info@emira.co.za
Web Site: www.emira.co.za
EMI—(JSE)
Sales Range: $125-149.9 Million
Business Description:
Property Trust Fund Services
S.I.C.: 6726
N.A.I.C.S.: 525990
Personnel:
James William Andrew Templeton *(CEO)*
Peter John Thurling *(CFO)*
Martin E. Harris *(Sec)*
Board of Directors:
Benedict James van der Ross
Michael Simpson Aitken
Bryan Hugh Kent
Vusumuzi Mahlangu
Nocawe Eustacia Makiwane
Wayne McCurrie
Matthys Stefanus Benjamin Neser
Vuyisa Nkonyeni
James William Andrew Templeton
Peter John Thurling
Ulana van Biljon
Legal Counsel:
DLA Cliffe Dekker Hofmeyr Inc
6 Sandown Valley Crescent Sandown
Sandton, South Africa
Transfer Agent:
Computershare Investor Services (Pty) Ltd.
70 Marshall Street
Johannesburg, 2001, South Africa
Tel.: (27) 11 370 5000
Fax: (27) 11 370 5487

EMIRATE INTEGRATED TELECOMMUNICATIONS COMPANY PJSC

Al Salam Tower Dubai Media City
P O Box 502666
Dubai, United Arab Emirates
Tel.: (971) 43600000
Fax: (971) 43604440
Web Site: www.du.ae
DUE—(DFM)
Rev.: $2,678,663,825
Assets: $3,789,338,680
Liabilities: $1,740,471,341
Net Worth: $2,048,867,339
Earnings: $538,791,469
Emp.: 2,000
Fiscal Year-end: 12/31/12
Business Description:
Telecommunication Services Provider
S.I.C.: 4899
N.A.I.C.S.: 517410
Personnel:
Ahmad Byat *(Chm)*
Abdulhamid Saeed *(Vice Chm)*
Osman Sultan *(CEO)*
Mark Shuttleworth *(CFO)*
Farid Faraidooni *(COO)*
Raghu Venkataraman *(Chief Strategy Officer & Chief Investments Officer)*
Yatindar Mahajan *(CTO)*
Fahad Al Hassawi *(Chief Comml Officer)*
Ananda Bose *(Chief Corp Affairs Officer)*
Ahmed Hassan Al Hosni *(Exec VP-IT)*
Saleem M. Al-Balooshi *(Exec VP-Customer Ops)*
Hala Badri *(Exec VP-Brand & Comm)*
Hatem Bamatraf *(Exec VP-Enterprise Bus Comml)*
Subra Das *(Exec VP-Mktg & Customer Experience)*
Rashid El Sheikh *(Exec VP-Corp Svcs)*
Andrew Grenville *(Exec VP-Investments-Special Project)*
Amir Al Gergawi *(Sr VP-Internal Control)*
Ayman Eldessouky *(Sr Vp-Sls)*
Dirk Jungnickel *(Sr VP-Program Mgmt & Analytics)*
Walid Kamel *(Sr VP-IT)*
RamaKrishana Krovvidi *(Sr VP-Org Dev)*
Yaser Obaid *(Sr VP-HR)*
Niel Pope *(Sr VP-Fin Control)*
Anneliese Reinhold *(Sr VP-Legal & Regulatory Affairs)*
Anis Tabka *(Sr VP-Sourcing Contracts & Supply Chain Mgmt)*
Georgios Vergopoulos *(Sr VP-Corp Strategy & Plng)*
Board of Directors:
Ahmad Byat

Emirate Integrated Telecommunications Company PJSC—(Continued)

Fadhel Al Ali
Waleed Al Muhairi
Hana Al Rostamani
Abdulla Al Shamsi
Eissa Mohamed Ghanem Al Suwaidi
Saeed Rashed Al Yateem
Jassem Mohamed Al Zaabi
Ziad Galadari
Abdulhamid Saeed

EMIRATES ALUMINIUM COMPANY LIMITED
PO Box 111023
Abu Dhabi, United Arab Emirates
Tel.: (971) 2 509 2222
Fax: (971) 2 509 3333
E-Mail: info@emal.ae
Web Site: www.emal.ae
Business Description:
Aluminium Smelter Operations
S.I.C.: 3339
N.A.I.C.S.: 331410
Personnel:
Saeed Fadhel Al Mazrooei *(Pres & CEO)*

THE EMIRATES GROUP
PO Box 686
Dubai, United Arab Emirates
Tel.: (971) 4708 1111
Fax: (971) 42864066
E-Mail: media.relations@emirates.com
Web Site: www.theemiratesgroup.com
Rev.: $19,368,056,620
Assets: $25,803,480,540
Liabilities: $19,534,630,780
Net Worth: $6,268,849,760
Earnings: $655,409,440
Emp.: 47,678
Fiscal Year-end: 03/31/13
Business Description:
Airlines Holding Company
S.I.C.: 6719
N.A.I.C.S.: 551112
Personnel:
Ahmed Saeed Al Maktoum *(Chm & CEO)*
Adel Ahmad Al Redha *(COO & Exec VP)*
Thierry Antinori *(Chief Comml Officer & Exec VP)*
Gary Chapman *(Pres-Grp Svcs & Dnata)*
Tim Clark *(Pres-Airline)*
Abdulaziz Al Ali *(Exec VP-HR)*
Ali Mubarak Al Soori *(Exec VP-Facilities, Projects Mgmt & P&L)*
Ismail Ali Albanna *(Exec VP-Dnata)*
Nigel Hopkins *(Exec VP-Svc Dept)*
Orhan Abbas *(Sr VP-Comml Ops-Latin America, Central & Southern Africa)*
Division:

Dnata **(1)**
Dubai Airline Ctr Shaik Zayed Rd
PO Box 1515
1st Fl Dnata Agencies, Dubai, United Arab Emirates (100%)
Tel.: (971) 43166704
Fax: (971) 4 316 6006
E-Mail: info@dnata.com
Web Site: www.dnata.com
Emp.: 4,926
Travel Management Services such as Aircraft & Cargo Handling Provisions, Information Technology Services, Engineering Services & Sales of Tickets on Behalf of Airlines
S.I.C.: 4581
N.A.I.C.S.: 488119
Ahmed bin Saeed Al-Maktoum *(Chm)*
Gary Chapman *(Pres)*
Mark Edwards *(CEO-Singapore)*
Gary Morgan *(CEO-UK)*
Ismail Ali Albanna *(Exec VP)*
Jean-Pierre de Pauw *(Sr VP-Dnata Cargo)*
Tom Lewis *(Sr VP)*
Derek Swan *(Sr VP-Dnata Airport Projects)*

Non-U.S. Subsidiary:

Alpha Flight Group Limited **(2)**
Building 319 World Cargo Centre
Manchester Airport, Manchester, M90 5EX, United Kingdom UK
Tel.: (44) 20 8476 7777
Fax: (44) 20 8476 5791
Web Site: www.alpha-group.com
Emp.: 5,800
Holding Company; In-Flight Catering & Retail Services
S.I.C.: 6719
N.A.I.C.S.: 551112
Lionel Wilton *(CEO & Mng Dir-Middle East)*

Subsidiary:

Alpha Flight UK Limited **(3)**
Building 319 World Cargo Centre
Manchester Airport, Manchester, M90 5EX, United Kingdom UK
Tel.: (44) 20 8476 7777
Fax: (44) 20 8476 5791
E-Mail:
Web Site: www.alpha-group.com
In-Flight Catering & Retail Services
S.I.C.: 5812
N.A.I.C.S.: 722320
Lionel Wilton *(CEO & Mng Dir-Middle East)*
Ken Adamson *(Mng Dir)*

EMIRATES INSURANCE COMPANY
Emirates Insurance Co Building
Tourist Club Area
PO Box 3856
Abu Dhabi, United Arab Emirates
Tel.: (971) 26440400
Fax: (971) 26445227
E-Mail: info@eminsco.com
Web Site: www.eminsco.com
Year Founded: 1982
EIC—(ABU)
Premiums: $175,608,909
Assets: $440,123,141
Liabilities: $222,467,649
Net Worth: $217,655,492
Earnings: $27,373,934
Emp.: 200
Fiscal Year-end: 12/31/12
Business Description:
Insurance Services
S.I.C.: 6399
N.A.I.C.S.: 524128
Personnel:
Abdullah Mohamed Mazrui *(Chm)*
Fadel Saeed Al Darmaki *(Deputy Chm)*
Jason Light *(CEO)*
Thomas Varghese *(Deputy CEO)*
Aart Lehmkuhl *(CFO)*
Samir Al Kassim *(Deputy CMO)*
Suresh George *(CMO)*
Dermot Dick *(Chief Underwriting Officer-Intl)*
Ganesh Ram *(Deputy Chief Underwriting Officer)*
Andy Woodward *(Chief Underwriting Officer)*
Board of Directors:
Abdullah Mohamed Mazrui
Ahmed Saeed Al Badi
Fadel Saeed Al Darmaki
Mohammed Abdul Jalil Al Fahim
Mohamed Obeid Khalifa Al Jabr
Mohamed Ahmed Saeed Al Qasimi
Hussai Ali Al Sayegh
Mohammed Rashed Al-Nasseri
Abdullah A. Al-Saadi

EMIRATES INTEGRATED TELECOMMUNICATION COMPANY PJSC
Al Salam Tower
PO Box 502666
Dubai, United Arab Emirates
Tel.: (971) 4 360 00 00
Web Site: www.du.ae
Year Founded: 2006
DU—(DFM)
Rev.: $2,678,663,825
Assets: $3,789,338,680
Liabilities: $1,740,471,341
Net Worth: $2,048,867,339
Earnings: $538,791,469
Emp.: 120
Fiscal Year-end: 12/31/12
Business Description:
Telecommunication Services
S.I.C.: 4899
N.A.I.C.S.: 517919
Personnel:
Ahmad Byat *(Chm)*
Younis Al Khoori *(Vice Chm)*
Osman Sultan *(CEO)*
Mark Shuttleworth *(CFO)*
Farid Faraidooni *(COO)*
Fahad Al Hassawi *(Chief Comml Officer)*
Ananda Bose *(Chief Corp Affairs Officer)*
Saleem M. Al-Balooshi *(Exec VP-Customer Ops)*
Hala Badri *(Exec VP-Brand & Comm)*
Rashid El Sheikh *(Exec VP-Corp Svcs)*
Amir Al Gergawi *(Sr VP-Internal Control)*
Dirk Jungnickel *(Sr VP-Corp Program Mgmt & Analytics)*
Walid Kamal *(Sr VP-IT)*
Ramakrishna Krovvidi *(Sr VP-Organization Dev)*
Yaser Obaid *(Sr VP-HR)*
Neil Pope *(Sr VP-Fin Control)*
Anneliese Reinhold *(Sr VP-Legal & Regulatory Affairs)*
Anis Tabka *(Sr VP-Sourcing Contracts & Supply Chain Mgmt)*
Georgios Vergopoulos *(Sr VP-Corp Strategy & Plng)*
Board of Directors:
Ahmad Byat
Fadel Al Ali
Younis Al Khoori
Waleed Al Muhairi
Abdulla Al Shamsi
Eissa Al Suwaidi
Jassem Al Zaabi
Ziad Galadari
Abdulhamid Saeed

EMIRATES INVESTMENT & DEVELOPMENT COMPANY PSC
(d/b/a Emivest)
PO Box 62220
Dubai, United Arab Emirates
Tel.: (971) 4 3217686
Fax: (971) 4 3217687
Web Site: www.emivest.ae
Year Founded: 1997
Business Description:
Private Equity Investment Services
S.I.C.: 6211
N.A.I.C.S.: 523999
Personnel:
Buti Saeed Al Ghandi *(Chm)*
Anthony Power *(Chief Investment Officer)*
U.S. Subsidiary:

Emivest Aerospace Corporation **(1)**
1770 Skyplace Blvd
San Antonio, TX 78216 DE
Tel.: (210) 258-3900
Fax: (210) 258-3917
Toll Free: (888) JET7530
E-Mail: ssacsj30@aol.com
Web Site: www.emivestaerospace.com
Emp.: 300
Aircraft Designer & Mfr
Export
S.I.C.: 3721
N.A.I.C.S.: 336411
Buti Saeed Al Ghandi *(Chm)*

EMIRATES ISLAMIC BANK PJSC
Dubai Healthcare City Building 16
Executive Building
Dubai, United Arab Emirates
Tel.: (971) 43160101
Fax: (971) 42227321
E-Mail: info@emiratesislamicbank.ae
Web Site: www.emiratesislamicbank.ae
EIB—(DFM)
Rev.: $365,690,705
Assets: $10,142,450,197
Liabilities: $9,428,787,704
Net Worth: $713,662,492
Earnings: $22,077,064
Emp.: 1,097
Fiscal Year-end: 12/31/12
Business Description:
Banking Solutions
S.I.C.: 6029
N.A.I.C.S.: 522110
Personnel:
Hesham Abdulla Al Qassim *(Chm)*
Buti Obaid Buti Al Mulla *(Vice Chm)*
Jamal Saeed Ghalaita *(CEO)*
Faisal Aqil *(Deputy CEO-Consumer Wealth Mgmt)*
Abdulla Showaiter *(Deputy CEO-Wholesale Banking)*
Ahmad Fayez Al Shamsi *(CFO)*
Board of Directors:
Hesham Abdulla Al Qassim
Mohamed Hadi Ahmad Abdullah Al Hussaini
Buti Obaid Buti Al Mulla
Abdulla Sultan Mohamed Al Owais
Mohamed Hamad Obaid Al Shehi
Shoaib Mir Hashem Khoory
Richard Anthony Pudner

EMIRATES NATIONAL OIL COMPANY LIMITED
Shakira Sideroad
PO Box 6442
Dubai, United Arab Emirates
Tel.: (971) 43374400
Fax: (971) 43134503
E-Mail: webmaster@enoc.com
Web Site: www.enoc.com
Emp.: 2,000
Business Description:
Producer of Oil & Related Products
S.I.C.: 1389
N.A.I.C.S.: 213112
Personnel:
Ahmad Altayer *(Vice Chm)*
Hamdan Bin Rahid Al Maktoum *(Chm)*
Subsidiary:

Dragon Oil Plc **(1)**
ENOC House II 3rd Floor Right Wing
Sheikh Rashid Road
PO Box 34666
Dubai, United Arab Emirates (66.7%)
Tel.: (971) 43053600
Fax: (971) 43356954
E-Mail: info@dragonoil.com
Web Site: www.dragonoil.com
DGO—(ISE OTC)
Rev.: $1,155,143,000
Assets: $3,843,093,000
Liabilities: $983,777,000
Net Worth: $2,859,316,000

Earnings: $600,046,000
Emp.: 1,368
Fiscal Year-end: 12/31/12
Oil & Gas Production & Exploration
S.I.C.: 1389
N.A.I.C.S.: 213112
Abdul Jaleel Al Khalifa *(CEO)*
Hussain Al Ansari *(COO)*
Julian Hicks *(Gen Counsel & Sec)*
Annisa Loadwick *(Sr Legal Counsel)*

EMIRATES NBD PJSC

Beniyas Road
PO Box 777
Deira, United Arab Emirates
Tel.: (971) 42256256
Fax: (971) 42230031
Web Site: www.emiratesnbd.com
Year Founded: 2007
EMIRATESNBD—(DFM)
Int. Income: $2,513,938,584
Assets: $83,912,100,815
Liabilities: $73,977,918,400
Net Worth: $9,934,182,416
Earnings: $695,152,891
Fiscal Year-end: 12/31/12

Business Description:
Banking & Financial Services
S.I.C.: 6712
N.A.I.C.S.: 551111

Personnel:
Ahmed Saeed Al Maktoum *(Chm)*
Hesham Abdulla Al Qassim *(Vice Chm)*
Rick Pudner *(CEO)*
Surya Subramanian *(CFO)*
Abdulla Qassem *(COO)*
Arjuna Mahendran *(Chief Investment Officer-Wealth Mgmt Div)*
Suhail Tarraf *(CEO-Tanfeeth)*
Aazar Ali Khwaja *(Treas)*
Saeed Yousuf *(Sec & Gen Mgr-Corp Svcs)*

Board of Directors:
Ahmed Saeed Al Maktoum
Mohamed Hadi Ahmad Abdullah Al Hussaini
Khalid Juma Al Majid
Buti Obaid Buti Al Mulla
Ali Humaid Ali Abdalla Al Owais
Hesham Abdulla Al Qassim
Hussain Hassan Mirza Al Sayegh
Mohamed Hamad Obaid Khamis Al Shehi
Shoaib Mir Hashem Khoory

Subsidiaries:

DINERS CLUB UAE LLC **(1)**
12th Floor Office Tower Burjuman Center
PO Box 4487
Bur Dubai, Dubai, United Arab Emirates
Tel.: (971) 4 316 0355
Fax: (971) 4 344 5695
Web Site: www.dinersclubuae.com
Credit Card Issuing Services
S.I.C.: 6141
N.A.I.C.S.: 522210

Emirates Bank International PJSC **(1)**
Beniyas Rd
PO Box 2923
Deira, Dubai, United Arab Emirates
Tel.: (971) 42256256
Fax: (971) 042264302
E-Mail: info@emiratesnbd.com
Web Site: www.emiratesbank.com
Sales Range: $400-449.9 Million
Emp.: 1,700
Provider of Banking Services
S.I.C.: 6029
N.A.I.C.S.: 522110
Ahmed Humaid Al Tayer *(Chm)*
Rick Pudner *(CEO)*
Anis Al Jallaf *(Mng Dir)*

Subsidiaries:

Emirates Investment Services Ltd **(2)**
Prince Mohamed bin Abdul Aziz St
PO Box 341777
Mansouriah Commercial Center, Riyadh, 11333, Saudi Arabia
Tel.: (966) 12993600
Fax: (966) 12993666
E-Mail: info@eisksa.com
Web Site: www.eisksa.com
Securities Brokerage
S.I.C.: 6211
N.A.I.C.S.: 523120
Khalid Jassim Bin Kalban *(Chm)*

Network International LLC **(2)**
PO Box 4487
Dubai, United Arab Emirates
Tel.: (971) 43032428
Fax: (971) 43420392
E-Mail: nibdunited@network.ae
Web Site: www.network.ae
Commercial Banking
S.I.C.: 6029
N.A.I.C.S.: 522110
Abdulla Qassem *(Chm)*
Bhairav Trivedi *(CEO)*

Union Properties PJSC **(2)**
PO Box 24649
Dubai, United Arab Emirates
Tel.: (971) 48851555
Fax: (971) 48852666
E-Mail: contactus@up.ae
Web Site: www.up.ae
Sales Range: $100-124.9 Million
Emp.: 9,110
Property Investment & Development Services
S.I.C.: 6513
N.A.I.C.S.: 531110
Anis Al Jallaff *(Chm)*
Fardan Bin Ali Alfardan *(Vice Chm)*

Subsidiary:

Edara L.L.C. **(3)**
P O Box 27642
Dubai, United Arab Emirates
Tel.: (971) 44028106
Fax: (971) 43406881
E-Mail: contactus@edara.ae
Web Site: www.edara.ae
Emp.: 100
Project Management Services
S.I.C.: 8748
N.A.I.C.S.: 541618
Phill Edmondson *(Gen Mgr)*

Emirates NBD Asset Management Ltd **(1)**
Level 8 Gate Building Dubai International Financial Center East Wing
Dubai, United Arab Emirates
Tel.: (971) 43700022
Fax: (971) 43700034
E-Mail: assetmanagement@emiratesnbd.com
Web Site: www.emiratesnbd.com
Emp.: 50
Asset Management Services
S.I.C.: 8748
N.A.I.C.S.: 541618
Deon Vernooy *(Head-Asset Mgmt)*

Emirates NBD Capital Ltd. **(1)**
Dubai International Financial Centre Gate Village 5 Level 5
Dubai, United Arab Emirates
Tel.: (971) 4 303 2800
Fax: (971) 4 323 0095
Investment Banking Services
S.I.C.: 6211
N.A.I.C.S.: 523110

Emirates NBD Securities LLC **(1)**
2nd Fl Emirates NBD Bldg Dubai Police Training Academy Al Wasl Road
PO Box 9409
Dubai, United Arab Emirates
Tel.: (971) 4 303 2233
Fax: (971) 7143856746
E-Mail: brokerage@emiratesnbd.com
Web Site: www.eisecurities.ae
Emp.: 37
Securities Brokerage Services
S.I.C.: 6211
N.A.I.C.S.: 523120
Fardan Ali Fardan Alfardan *(Chm)*
Randa Kreidieh *(COO)*

E.T.F.S L.L.C. **(1)**
PO Box 46046
Bur Dubai, Dubai, United Arab Emirates
Tel.: (971) 4 237 3344
Fax: (971) 4 237 3030
Web Site: www.etfs.ae
Investment Banking Services
S.I.C.: 6211
N.A.I.C.S.: 523110
Graham Clarke *(Gen Mgr)*

National Bank of Dubai PJSC **(1)**
Baniyas Road Deira
PO Box 777
Dubai, United Arab Emirates
Tel.: (971) 43100101
Fax: (971) 4 2283000
E-Mail: recruit@nbd.com
Web Site: www.nbd.com
Emp.: 1,540
Banking Services
S.I.C.: 6029
N.A.I.C.S.: 522110
Ahmed Humaid Al Tayer *(Chm)*

Non-U.S. Subsidiaries:

Emirates NBD Capital KSA LLC **(1)**
Prince Mohamed bin Abdul Aziz Street
PO Box 341777
Mansouriah Commercial Center, Riyadh, 11333, Saudi Arabia
Tel.: (966) 1 299 3900
Fax: (966) 1 299 3955
E-Mail: info@emiratesnbdcapital.com.sa
Web Site: www.emiratesnbdcapital.com.sa
Securities Brokerage Services
S.I.C.: 6211
N.A.I.C.S.: 523120
Khalid Jassim Kalban *(Chm)*
Mohamed Suliman Alhegelan *(Deputy Chm)*

Emirates NBD Fund Managers (Jersey) Limited **(1)**
C/o Standard Bank House 47-49 La Motte Street
PO Box 583
Saint Helier, JE4 8XR, Jersey
Tel.: (44) 153 4881 188
Asset Management Services
S.I.C.: 6282
N.A.I.C.S.: 523920

Emirates NBD Trust Company (Jersey) Limited **(1)**
RBC Trust Company International Limited La Motte Chambers
JE1 1PB Saint Helier, Jersey
Tel.: (44) 1534501000
Fax: (44) 153 4501 926
Investment Banking Services
S.I.C.: 6211
N.A.I.C.S.: 523110

EMIRATES POST

Deira Main Post Office
PO Box 99999
Dubai, United Arab Emirates
Tel.: (971) 42622222
Fax: (971) 42031372
E-Mail: custservice@emiratespost.ae
Web Site: www.emiratespost.gov.ae
Emp.: 1,500

Business Description:
Postal Services
S.I.C.: 4311
N.A.I.C.S.: 491110

EMIRATES REFRESHMENTS (P.S.C.)

Ras Al Khor Industrial Estate Aweer Behind Oman Transport
PO Box 5567
Dubai, United Arab Emirates
Tel.: (971) 4 3335566
Fax: (971) 4 3335558
E-Mail: info@erc.ae
Web Site: www.erc.ae
Year Founded: 1980
ERC—(DFM)
Rev.: $15,151,694
Assets: $20,481,473
Liabilities: $9,090,360
Net Worth: $11,391,113
Earnings: $208,878
Fiscal Year-end: 12/31/12

Business Description:
Mineral Water Mfr & Whslr
S.I.C.: 2086
N.A.I.C.S.: 312112

Personnel:
Michael Staley *(Gen Mgr)*

Board of Directors:
Mohamed Salim Rashid Abdalla Al Owais
Abdullah Al Qubaisi
Talal Ahmad Sayed Ibrahim Alhashemi
Huraiz Almur Mohamed Huraiz

EMIRATES TECHNOLOGY COMPANY (EMITAC)

Emitac Bldg Al Ghroud
PO Box 8391
Dubai, United Arab Emirates
Tel.: (971) 42827577
Telex: 893-48710
Fax: (971) 42827836
E-Mail: reception@emitac.ae
Web Site: www.emitac.ae
Sales Range: $250-299.9 Million
Emp.: 400

Business Description:
Computer Technology Services
S.I.C.: 3577
N.A.I.C.S.: 334118

Personnel:
Bratisankar Ghosh *(CFO)*

Board of Directors:
Salah Bukhatir
Nawaf Ghobash
Saqr Ghobash

Non-U.S. Subsidiary:

Qatar Datamation Systems **(1)**
PO Box 13856
Doha, Qatar
Tel.: (974) 4439900
Telex: 497-4833
Fax: (974) 4432154
E-Mail: mohammada@qdsnet.com
Emp.: 50
Computer Technology Services
S.I.C.: 3575
N.A.I.C.S.: 334118
Mohammad Alam *(Gen Mgr)*

EMIRATES TELECOMMUNICATIONS CORPORATION

(d/b/a Etisalat)
Etisalat Building Sheikh Rashid Bin Saeed Al Marktoum Street
PO Box 3838
Abu Dhabi, United Arab Emirates
Tel.: (971) 2 6283333
Fax: (971) 2 6317000
E-Mail: info@etisalat.ae
Web Site: www.etisalat.com
Year Founded: 1976
ETISALAT—(ABU)
Rev.: $8,967,323,934
Assets: $21,814,237,081
Liabilities: $9,219,146,775
Net Worth: $12,595,090,306
Earnings: $1,788,697,826
Fiscal Year-end: 12/31/12

Business Description:
Provider of Telecommunications Services
S.I.C.: 4813
N.A.I.C.S.: 517110

Personnel:
Eissa Mohamed Ghanem Al Suwaidi *(Chm)*
Khalaf Ahmed Al Otaiba *(Vice Chm)*

Emirates Telecommunications Corporation—(Continued)

Ahmad Abdulkarim Julfar *(CEO)*
Serkan Okandan *(CFO)*
Ali Al Sharhan *(CIO)*
Abdulrahim Al Nooryani *(Chief Admin Officer)*
Daniel Jurg Ritz *(Chief Strategy Officer)*
Abdul Aziz Ahmed Saleh Al Sawaleh *(Chief HR Officer)*
Rainer Rathgeber *(Chief Comml Officer)*
Saeed Al Bahhar *(Chief Carrier Svcs Officer)*
Essa Al Haddad *(Chief Reg Officer)*
Khalifa Al Shamsi *(Chief Digital Svcs Officer)*
Jamal Aljarwan *(Chief Reg Officer-Asia Cluster)*
Obaid Bokisha *(Chief Procurement Officer)*
Nasser Obood *(Chief Govt Rels & Corp Comm Officer)*
Amaru Chavez Pujol *(Chief Network Officer)*
Kamal Shehadi *(Chief Legal & Regulatory Officer)*
John Wilkes *(Chief Internal Control Officer)*
Paul Werne *(Gen Counsel)*
Hasan Al Hosani *(Sec)*
Ahmed Bin Ali *(Sr VP-Corp Comm)*
Board of Directors:
Eissa Mohamed Ghanem Al Suwaidi
Khalaf Ahmed Al Otaiba
Abdulla Salem Al Dhaheri
Mohamed Hadi Ahmad Abdullah Al Hussaini
Mubarak Rashed Al Mansoori
Mana Mohamed Saeed Al Mulla
Abdelmonem Eisa Nasser Alserkal
Essa Abdul Fattah Kazim
Shoaib Mir Hashim Khoory
Ahmed Mohammad Sultan Suroor Al Dhaheri

Deloitte & Touche (M.E.)
Bin Ghanim Tower 10th Floor Hamdan Street
PO Box 990
Abu Dhabi, United Arab Emirates
Tel.: (971) 2 676 0606
Fax: (971) 2 676 0644

Subsidiary:

Emirates Telecommunications & Marine Services FZE **(1)**
PO Box 17422
Jebel Ali Free Zone, Dubai, United Arab Emirates
Tel.: (971) 48814433
Fax: (971) 48814422
Web Site: www.emarine.ae
Telecommunications Services
S.I.C.: 4899
N.A.I.C.S.: 517919

EMIS GROUP PLC

Rawdon House Green Lane Yeadon
Leeds, LS19 7BY, United Kingdom
Tel.: (44) 113 3803000
Fax: (44) 113 3803439
Web Site: www.emis-online.com
Year Founded: 1987
EMIS—(AIM)
Rev.: $136,344,844
Assets: $166,158,680
Liabilities: $64,981,466
Net Worth: $101,177,214
Earnings: $30,691,922
Emp.: 1,116
Fiscal Year-end: 12/31/12
Business Description:
Medical Software
S.I.C.: 7372
N.A.I.C.S.: 511210
Personnel:
Chris M. K. Spencer *(CEO)*
Peter Southby *(CFO & Dir-Fin)*
Caroline L. Farbridge *(Sec)*
Board of Directors:
Mike O'Leary
Andy McKeon
Sean D. Riddell
Peter Southby
David L. Stables
Robin Taylor
Legal Counsel:
DWF LLP
Bridgewater Place Water Lane
Water Lane, Leeds, LS11 5DY, United Kingdom
Tel.: (44) 113 261 6000
Fax: (44) 870 094 0939

Subsidiary:

Egton Medical Information Systems Ltd **(1)**
EMIS Rawdon House Green Lane
Leeds, Yeadon, LS19 7BY., United Kingdom
Tel.: (44) 1132591122
Fax: (44) 1132390162
E-Mail: emis@e-mis.com
Emp.: 500
Healthcare Software Development Services
S.I.C.: 7371
N.A.I.C.S.: 541511
Christopher McGarry *(Gen Mgr-Sys Integration Dept)*

Division:

Egton Medical Information Systems Ltd - Egton **(2)**
Rawdon House Green Lane Rawdon
Rawdon, Leeds, W Yorkshire, LS19 7BY, United Kingdom
Tel.: (44) 1132591122
Fax: (44) 1132390162
E-Mail: emis@e-mis.com
Web Site: www.egton.net
Emp.: 500
Health Care Software Development Services
S.I.C.: 7371
N.A.I.C.S.: 541511
Steve Wilcock *(Dir-Comm)*

EMIVEST BERHAD

Lot 13A Jalan PBR 1 Fasa 1
Kawasan Perindustrian Bukit Rambai
75250 Melaka, Malaysia
Tel.: (60) 63512992
Fax: (60) 63512997
E-Mail: gtmcca@po.jaring.my
Web Site: www.emivest.com.my
EMIVEST—(KLS)
Sales Range: $150-199.9 Million
Business Description:
Livestock Feed Mfr
S.I.C.: 2048
N.A.I.C.S.: 311119
Personnel:
Bong Wong Lau *(Chm & Mng Dir)*
Shew Meng Kang *(Co-Sec)*
Lai Hock Lee *(Co-Sec)*
Fei San Seow *(Co-Sec)*
Board of Directors:
Bong Wong Lau
Kim Chui Koh
Low Koh
Eng Guang Lau
Joo Hong Lau
Kim Hwa Sim

Subsidiaries:

Beaming Agrotrade Sdn. Bhd. **(1)**
No 9569 Jln Pbr 6 Fasa 1 Kaw
Perindustrian Bkt Ramba
75260 Melaka, Malaysia
Tel.: (60) 63512616
Animal Feeds Mfr
S.I.C.: 2048
N.A.I.C.S.: 311119

Gymtech Feedmill (M) Sdn. Bhd. **(1)**
Lot 13a Jalan Pbr 1 Phase 1 Kawasan
Perindustrian Bukit Rambai
75250 Melaka, Malaysia
Tel.: (60) 63512992
Fax: (60) 63512998
E-Mail: gtmcca@po.jaring.my
Web Site: www.gym-tech.com
Emp.: 150
Livestock Feeds Mfr
S.I.C.: 2048
N.A.I.C.S.: 311119
Lau Bong Wong *(Mng Dir)*

Ideal Multifeed (Malaysia) Sdn Berhad **(1)**
9578 9578 Kaw Perindustrian Tangga Bt
Tanjong Kling
76400 Melaka, Malaysia
Tel.: (60) 63518303
Fax: (60) 63518541
E-Mail: idmulti@po.jarind.my
Emp.: 100
Livestock Feed Mfr
S.I.C.: 2048
N.A.I.C.S.: 311119
Eddie Eng Guan Low *(Mng Dir)*

Prima Anjung Sdn. Bhd. **(1)**
29 Jln Gopeng Gopeng Industrial Park
Gopeng, Perak, 31600, Malaysia
Tel.: (60) 53576088
Fax: (60) 53578088
E-Mail: prima.anjung@gmail.com
Emp.: 70
Animal Farming Services
S.I.C.: 0752
N.A.I.C.S.: 115210
Law Jui Peng *(Mng Dir)*

Non-U.S. Subsidiary:

United Global Resources Limited **(1)**
1st 2nd and Pent Floor 86 A Allen Avenue
Ikeja, Lagos, Nigeria
Tel.: (234) 17900854
Fax: (234) 12704012
E-Mail: ho@ugrl.net
Web Site: www.ugrl.net
Computer Education & Training Services
S.I.C.: 8243
N.A.I.C.S.: 611420

EMKA-BESCHLAGTEILE GMBH & CO. KG

Langenberger Str 32
42551 Velbert, Germany
Tel.: (49) 20512730
Fax: (49) 2051273128
E-Mail: info@emka.com
Web Site: www.emka.com
Year Founded: 1932
Emp.: 1,050
Business Description:
Lock & Security Systems Mfr
S.I.C.: 7382
N.A.I.C.S.: 561621
Personnel:
Friedhelm Runge *(Mng Dir)*

Non-U.S. Subsidiary:

Fort Securite s.a. **(1)**
Route des Roches
BP 12
F-41100 Bourre, Loir-et-Cher, France
Tel.: (33) 387 29 6666
Fax: (33) 387 90 8181
E-Mail: fort@emka-france.com
Web Site: www.emka-france.com
Emp.: 50
Security Systems Mfr
S.I.C.: 3429
N.A.I.C.S.: 332510
Dominic Ferhtler *(Gen Mgr)*

EMKA JSC

30 Nikola Petkov Str
5400 Sevlievo, Bulgaria
Tel.: (359) 675 3 28 68
Fax: (359) 675 3 28 70
E-Mail: emka@nat.bg
Web Site: www.emka-bg.com
Year Founded: 1936
57E—(BUL)
Business Description:
Cable & Wires Mfr
S.I.C.: 3496
N.A.I.C.S.: 332618
Personnel:
Snezhana Vasileva Stoyanova *(Dir-IR)*

EMKAY GLOBAL FINANCIAL SERVICES LIMITED

7th Floor The Ruby Senapati Bapat Marg
Dadar - West, Mumbai, 400028, India
Tel.: (91) 2266121212
Fax: (91) 2266121299
E-Mail: compliance@emkayglobal.com
Web Site: www.emkayglobal.com
Year Founded: 1995
532737—(BOM)
Rev.: $18,525,443
Assets: $50,168,764
Liabilities: $25,408,222
Net Worth: $24,760,543
Earnings: ($2,740,031)
Emp.: 550
Fiscal Year-end: 03/31/13
Business Description:
Securities Brokerage & Investment Banking Services
S.I.C.: 6211
N.A.I.C.S.: 523120
Personnel:
Krishna Kumar Karwa *(Co-Mng Dir & CFO)*
Prakash Kacholia *(Co-Mng Dir)*
Rajesh Sharma *(COO)*
Divya Gandhi *(Principal Officer & Head-Gen Insurance)*
Vaibhav Purohit *(Sec)*
Board of Directors:
Gian Prakash Gupta
Prakash Kacholia
Krishna Kumar Karwa
R. K. Krishnamurthi
S. K. Saboo
G. C. Vasudeo
Transfer Agent:
Link Intime India Pvt. Ltd
C-13 Pannalal Silk Mills Compound LBS Marg
Bhandup (West)
Mumbai, India

EMLAK KONUT GAYRIMENKUL YATIRIM ORTAKLIGI AS

Ataturk Mah Citlenbik Cad No 4
Atasehir, Istanbul, Turkey
Tel.: (90) 216 579 15 15
Fax: (90) 216 456 48 75
E-Mail: info@emlakkonut.com.tr
Web Site: www.emlakkonut.com.tr
Year Founded: 1953
EKGYO—(IST)
Business Description:
Residential Property Developer & Investment Services
S.I.C.: 6552
N.A.I.C.S.: 237210
Personnel:
Murat Kurum *(Gen Mgr)*

EMMAR INVESTMENTS & REAL ESTATE DEVELOPMENT COMPANY

Zahran Street-6th Circle-Emmar Towers The building east A
PO Box 17384
the 2nd floor, Amman, 11195, Jordan
Tel.: (962) 6 5777 251
Fax: (962) 6 5777 254
E-Mail: Info@Emmar.com.jo
Web Site: www.emmar.jo
Year Founded: 2005
EMAR—(AMM)
Rev.: $543,555
Assets: $38,252,352
Liabilities: $9,087,698

Net Worth: $29,164,654
Earnings: ($974,675)
Emp.: 16
Fiscal Year-end: 12/31/12
Business Description:
Real Estate Development Services
S.I.C.: 6531
N.A.I.C.S.: 531390
Personnel:
Mohamed Al-allawi *(Gen Mgr)*

EMMBI INDUSTRIES LIMITED
(Formerly Emmbi Polyarns Limited)
601-604 Hari Om Chambers 6th Floor off New Link Road
Andheri West, Mumbai, 400 053, India
Tel.: (91) 22 6784 5555
Fax: (91) 22 6784 5506
E-Mail: makrand.appalwar@emmbi.com
Web Site: www.wovensackindia.com
Year Founded: 1994
EMMBI—(BOM NSE)
Rev.: $25,991,411
Assets: $23,585,846
Liabilities: $13,504,536
Net Worth: $10,081,310
Earnings: $613,489
Emp.: 150
Fiscal Year-end: 03/31/13
Business Description:
Jumbo Bags & Woven Sacks Mfr & Sales
S.I.C.: 2394
N.A.I.C.S.: 314910
Personnel:
Makrand Appalwar *(Chm & Mng Dir)*
Kaushal Patvi *(Compliance Officer)*
Board of Directors:
Makrand Appalwar
Mitravinda Appalwar
Rinku Appalwar
Venkatesh Joshi
Prashant Lohiya
Sanjay Rathi

EMMBI POLYARNS LIMITED
(Name Changed to Emmbi Industries Limited)

EMMEGI S.P.A.
Via Archimede n 10
Frazione Limidi, 41010 Soliera, Italy
Tel.: (39) 59 895411
Fax: (39) 59 566286
E-Mail: info@emmegi.com
Web Site: www.emmegi.com
Business Description:
Aluminium Cutting Machines Mfr
N.A.I.C.S.: 811310
Personnel:
Alberto Geremia *(Mgr-Sls)*
Subsidiary:

Cifin S.r.l. **(1)**
Via Archimede n 10
Frazione Limid, 41010 Soliera, Italy
Tel.: (39) 59 895411
Fax: (39) 59 566286
Aluminium Cutting Machines Mfr
N.A.I.C.S.: 423830

Subsidiary:

CIPI S.p.A **(2)**
Via Lorenteggio 259
20152 Milan, Italy
Tel.: (39) 024832981
Fax: (39) 024123450
E-Mail: info@cipi.it
Web Site: www.cipi.it
Commercial Printing Services
S.I.C.: 2759
N.A.I.C.S.: 323111

EMMENDINGER MASCHINENBAU GMBH
Am Elzdamm 32
79312 Emmendingen, Germany
Tel.: (49) 764192420
Fax: (49) 7641924270
E-Mail: info@emmendinger.de
Web Site: www.emmendinger.de
Year Founded: 1957
Rev.: $12,414,600
Emp.: 75
Business Description:
Engineering Parts Mfr
S.I.C.: 5065
N.A.I.C.S.: 423690
Personnel:
Walter Haberstroh *(Owner & Gen Mgr)*

EMMERSON RESOURCES LIMITED
3 Kimberley Street
Leederville, WA, 6007, Australia
Mailing Address:
PO Box 1573
West Perth, WA, 6872, Australia
Tel.: (61) 893817838
Fax: (61) 893815375
E-Mail: info@emmersonresources.com.au
Web Site: www.emmersonresources.com.au
ERM—(ASX)
Rev.: $313,655
Assets: $30,215,915
Liabilities: $1,039,647
Net Worth: $29,176,268
Earnings: ($4,994,385)
Emp.: 20
Fiscal Year-end: 06/30/13
Business Description:
Mineral Exploration
S.I.C.: 1481
N.A.I.C.S.: 213115
Personnel:
Robert Bills *(CEO & Mng Dir)*
Trevor Verran *(CFO & Sec)*
Board of Directors:
Andrew McIlwain
Simon Andrew
Robert Bills
Timothy Kestell
Legal Counsel:
Ward Keller
Level 7 NT House
22 Mitchell Street, Darwin, NT, 0807, Australia

Steinepreis Paganin
Level 4 Next Building 16 Milligan St
Perth, Australia

EMMESSAR BIOTECH & NUTRITION LTD.
29 Kamer Building 4th Floor 38
Cawasji Patel Street Fort
Mumbai, 400 001, India
Tel.: (91) 2266356209
Fax: (91) 2266370190
E-Mail: contact@ebnl.co.in
Web Site: www.ebnl.co.in
524768—(BOM)
Rev.: $122,835
Assets: $912,384
Liabilities: $550,557
Net Worth: $361,827
Earnings: ($34,210)
Fiscal Year-end: 03/31/13
Business Description:
Chemical Products Mfr
S.I.C.: 2819
N.A.I.C.S.: 325180
Personnel:
M. S. Raghavan Ayyangar *(CEO & Mng Dir)*
I. J. Pereira *(Compliance Officer)*
Dinesh Deora *(Sec)*
Board of Directors:
Ashok M. Kadakia
Vijay K. Agrawal
M. S. Raghavan Ayyangar
Ajay I. Bora
Arvind M. Shah
Manoj M. Shah
Transfer Agent:
Link Intime India Pvt. Ltd
C-13 Pannalal Silk Mills Compound LBS Marg
Bhandup (West)
Mumbai, India

EMMI AG
Habsburgerstrasse 12
6002 Lucerne, Switzerland
Tel.: (41) 412272727
Fax: (41) 412272737
E-Mail: info@emmi.ch
Web Site: www.emmi.ch
EMMN—(SWX)
Sls.: $3,217,656,911
Assets: $2,506,782,221
Liabilities: $1,249,249,220
Net Worth: $1,257,533,001
Earnings: $114,662,640
Emp.: 5,074
Fiscal Year-end: 12/31/12
Business Description:
Dairy & Creamery Products Producer
S.I.C.: 0241
N.A.I.C.S.: 112120
Personnel:
Konrad Graber *(Chm)*
Thomas Oehen-Buhlmann *(Vice Chm)*
Urs Riedener *(CEO)*
Robert Muri *(Deputy CEO & Head-Dairy Products Div)*
Jorg Riboni *(CFO)*
Board of Directors:
Konrad Graber
Christian Arnold-Fassler
Stephan Baer
Monique Bourquin
Hans Herzog
Niklaus Meier
Thomas Oehen-Buhlmann
Josef Schmidli
Diana Strebel

EMMSONS INTERNATIONAL LIMITED
2637 First Floor Naya Bazar
Delhi, 110006, India
Tel.: (91) 1123929341
Fax: (91) 1123924234
E-Mail: corporate@emmsons.com
Web Site: www.emmsons.com
532038—(BOM)
Rev.: $12,874,547
Assets: $4,844,131
Liabilities: $4,358,569
Net Worth: $485,563
Earnings: $17,984
Emp.: 76
Fiscal Year-end: 03/31/13
Business Description:
Food Products Distr
S.I.C.: 2099
N.A.I.C.S.: 311999
Personnel:
Rajesh Monga *(Founder)*
Anil Monga *(Mng Dir)*
Hamant Paul *(CFO & Gen Mgr-Fin)*
Vinay Gujral *(Compliance Officer & Sec)*
Board of Directors:
Satish Chander Gupta
Vijay Kumar Kakkar
Viresh Shankar Mathur
Anil Monga
Rajesh Monga
Shivaz Monga
Transfer Agent:
Link Intime India Private Limited
44 Community Centre 2nd Floor Naraina
Industrial Area Phase-I
Near PVR Naraina, New Delhi, India
Non-U.S. Subsidiary:

Emmsons Asia Pte. Ltd. **(1)**
150 Cecil St 07-01 AXA Life Bldg
Singapore, 069543, Singapore
Tel.: (65) 62212090
Fax: (65) 62221290
Grain Farming Services
S.I.C.: 0119
N.A.I.C.S.: 111199

EMNET INC.
7th Floor Dae-ryung 3 Guro-dong
Guro-gu
Seoul, Korea (South)
Tel.: (82) 2 22778877
Fax: (82) 2 22775508
E-Mail: webmaster@emnet.co.kr
Web Site: www.emnet.co.kr
Year Founded: 2000
123570—(KRS)
Emp.: 280
Business Description:
Advertising Agency
S.I.C.: 7311
N.A.I.C.S.: 541810
Personnel:
Yeong-won Kim *(CEO)*

EMO CAPITAL CORP.
115 He Xiang Road
Bai He Village
Qing Pu, Shanghai, 200000, China
Tel.: (86) 13521503777
Year Founded: 2006
NUVI—(OTCB)
Liabilities: $33,850
Net Worth: ($33,850)
Earnings: ($5,554)
Fiscal Year-end: 07/31/13
Business Description:
Investment Services; Health & Beauty Care Website Operator
S.I.C.: 6211
N.A.I.C.S.: 523999
Personnel:
Juanming Fang *(Pres, CEO, Treas & Sec)*
Board of Directors:
Juanming Fang

EMORI & CO., LTD.
1-6-23 Keya
Fukui, 918-8510, Japan
Tel.: (81) 776361133
Fax: (81) 776364002
Web Site: www.emori.co.jp
Year Founded: 1958
9963—(TKS)
Sls.: $1,591,425,000
Assets: $788,304,000
Liabilities: $629,684,000
Net Worth: $158,620,000
Earnings: $21,109,000
Emp.: 1,002
Fiscal Year-end: 03/31/13
Business Description:
Fine Chemicals & Textile Whlslr
S.I.C.: 5169
N.A.I.C.S.: 424690
Personnel:
Kiyotaka Emori *(Pres & CEO)*
Yasumaro Agehara *(Co-Mng Dir)*
Norio Kurose *(Co-Mng Dir)*
Noboru Yamamoto *(Co-Mng Dir)*
Board of Directors:
Yasumaro Agehara
Yoshihide Chikugo
Kiyotaka Emori
Hiroki Hayashi

Emori & Co., Ltd.—(Continued)

Norio Kurose
Noboru Yamamoto

Subsidiaries:

Brain Co., Ltd. (1)
3-5-22 Kitahama Chuo-ku
Osaka, 541-0041, Japan
Tel.: (81) 66203 3018
Fax: (81) 6 6203 2900
Web Site: www.emori.co.jp
Software Development & Sales
S.I.C.: 7372
N.A.I.C.S.: 511210
Takaharu Hirokane *(Pres)*

Emori Engineering Co., Ltd. (1)
1 25 20 Hanando Higashi
Fukui, 918-8013, Japan
Tel.: (81) 776366100
Fax: (81) 776367603
Web Site: www.emori.co.jp/en/e_ab_office.html
Engineering Services
S.I.C.: 1629
N.A.I.C.S.: 237990

Emori Logistics Co., Ltd. (1)
1-25-20 Hanando Higashi
Fukui, 918-8013, Japan
Tel.: (81) 776368400
Fax: (81) 776343554
Logistics Management Services
S.I.C.: 4731
N.A.I.C.S.: 541614

Emori Paint Co., Ltd. (1)
1-25-20 Hanando Higashi
Fukui, 918-8013, Japan
Tel.: (81) 776366600
Fax: (81) 776352125
Web Site: www.emori.co.jp/en/e_ab_office.html
Painting Materials Mfr
S.I.C.: 2851
N.A.I.C.S.: 325510

Emori System Co., Ltd. (1)
1-6 Soft Park Fukui Maruoka-cho
Sakai, Fukui, 910-0347, Japan
Tel.: (81) 776677650
Fax: (81) 0076677604
Web Site: www.emori.co.jp/en/e_ab_office.html
Compound Chemicals Mfr
S.I.C.: 2869
N.A.I.C.S.: 325199

Hokuriku Chemical Industrial Co., Ltd. (1)
29 22 17 Koshikidani-cho
Fukui, 910-3613, Japan
Tel.: (81) 776984670
Fax: (81) 776984546
Chemicals Mfr
S.I.C.: 2899
N.A.I.C.S.: 325998

Hokuriku Color Co., Ltd. (1)
1-25-20 Hanando Higashi
Fukui, 918-8013, Japan
Tel.: (81) 776357415
Fax: (81) 776357462
Emp.: 11
Chemical Colours Mfr
S.I.C.: 2819
N.A.I.C.S.: 325130
Koji Hirakawa *(Mgr)*

ITS Corporation (1)
2nd Fl Sumitomo Syoji Bldg
1 2 2 Shinsenrinishimachi, Toyonaka, Osaka, 560-0083, Japan
Tel.: (81) 661552000
Fax: (81) 661552011
Web Site: www.emori.co.jp/en/e_ab_office.html
Chemicals Mfr & Supplier
S.I.C.: 2819
N.A.I.C.S.: 325130
Yoshimiru Matiyama *(Gen Mgr)*

Nichie-Kosan Co., Ltd. (1)
1 6 23 Keya
Fukui, 918-8510, Japan
Tel.: (81) 776366617
Fax: (81) 776364054
Chemicals Mfr & Supplier
S.I.C.: 2816
N.A.I.C.S.: 325130

Non-U.S. Subsidiaries:

Emori & Co., (Hong Kong) Ltd. (1)
Unit 2003 Level 20 Tower II Metroplaza No 223 Hing Fong Rd
Kwai Chung, China (Hong Kong)
Tel.: (852) 24556711
Fax: (852) 24556168
E-Mail: kylie@emori-hk.com
Emp.: 4
Chemicals Mfr
S.I.C.: 2899
N.A.I.C.S.: 325998
Hideyuki Nakata *(Mng Dir)*

Emori Poland Sp. z.o.o. (1)
ul Krochmalna 32a lok 1a
Masovian, 00-864 Warsaw, Poland
Tel.: (48) 224020768
Fax: (48) 22 402 0738
E-Mail: agata@emori.pl
Web Site: www.emori.co.jp
Emp.: 3
Chemicals Mfr & Supplier
S.I.C.: 5169
N.A.I.C.S.: 424690
Kiyotaka Emori *(Pres)*

Emori (Thailand) Co., Ltd. (1)
10th Fl Boonmitr Bldg 138 Silom Rd
Suriyawongse Bangrak, Bangkok, 10500, Thailand
Tel.: (66) 22382606
Fax: (66) 22382608
E-Mail: yamazaki@emori.co.th
Web Site: www.emori.co.jp/en/e_ab_office.html
Emp.: 32
Chemicals Whslr
S.I.C.: 5169
N.A.I.C.S.: 424690
Yoshiaki Yamazaki *(Mng Dir)*

P.T. Emori Indonesia (1)
Permata Plz Bldg 10th Fl No 1006
JL M H Thamrin 57, Jakarta, 10350, Indonesia
Tel.: (62) 213903272
Fax: (62) 213903274
Emp.: 10
Chemicals Distr
S.I.C.: 5169
N.A.I.C.S.: 424690

EMPEE DISTILLERIES LIMITED

Empee Tower No 59 Harris Road
Pudupet
Chennai, 600 002, India
Tel.: (91) 44 2853 1111
Fax: (91) 44 2855 5163
E-Mail: info@empeegroup.co.in
Web Site: www.empeegroup.co.in
EDL—(NSE)
Rev.: $202,063,085
Assets: $249,551,626
Liabilities: $210,312,995
Net Worth: $39,238,631
Earnings: ($2,128,930)
Fiscal Year-end: 03/31/13

Business Description:
Alcoholic Beverages Mfr
S.I.C.: 2085
N.A.I.C.S.: 312140

Personnel:
M. P. Purushothaman *(Chm)*
Nisha Purushothaman *(Vice Chm & Mng Dir)*

Board of Directors:
M. P. Purushothaman
M. P. Mehrotra
M. K. Mohan
Nisha Purushothaman
Shaji Purushothaman
T. S. Raghavan

Subsidiary:

EDL Properties Limited (1)
59 Harris Road
Pudupet, Chennai, 600 002, India
Tel.: (91) 44 28522510
Fax: (91) 44 28522510
E-Mail: info@edlproperties.in
Web Site: www.edlproperties.in
Emp.: 4
Residential & Commercial Property Development Services
S.I.C.: 1531
N.A.I.C.S.: 236117
N. C. Somaiah *(Chm & Mng Dir)*

EMPEE SUGARS AND CHEMICALS LIMITED

Ayyapareddipalam
Nellore Dist, Chennai, 524 126, India
Tel.: (91) 8623248150
Fax: (91) 8623248172
Web Site: www.empeegroup.co.in
EMPEESUG—(NSE)
Sales Range: $75-99.9 Million

Business Description:
Sugar & Alcoholic Beverages Mfr
S.I.C.: 2061
N.A.I.C.S.: 311314

Personnel:
M. P. Purushothaman *(Chm & Mng Dir)*
Sheeju Purushothaman *(Mng Dir)*
S. S. K. Swarup *(Compliance Officer, Sec & Gen Mgr-F&A)*

Board of Directors:
M. P. Purushothaman
M. P. Mehrotra
Shankar Menon
M. K. Mohan
Nisha Purushothaman
Sheeju Purushothaman
T. S. Raghavan

Transfer Agent:
Cameo Corporate Services Limited
Subramanian Building V Floor 1 Club House Road
Chennai, India

EMPERIA HOLDING S.A

Ul Metalurgiczna 7-9
20 952 Lublin, Poland
Tel.: (48) 817485555
Fax: (48) 817463289
E-Mail: emperia@emperia.pl
Web Site: www.emperia.pl
Year Founded: 2002
EMP—(WAR)
Sales Range: $550-599.9 Million
Emp.: 13,814

Business Description:
Food Products Whslr & Retailer
S.I.C.: 5499
N.A.I.C.S.: 445299

Personnel:
Piotr Laskowski *(Chm-Supervisory Bd)*
Artur Kawa *(Chm-Mgmt Bd)*
Tomasz Krysztofiak *(Vice Chm-Supervisory Bd)*
Dariusz Kalinowski *(Vice Chm-Mgmt Bd)*
Grzegorz Wawerski *(Vice Chm-Mgmt Bd)*
Jaroslaw Wawerski *(Vice Chm-Mgmt Bd)*
Marek Wesolowski *(Vice Chm-Mgmt Bd)*

Supervisory Board of Directors:
Piotr Laskowski
Piotr Dlugosz
Tomasz Krysztofiak
Artur Laskowski
Ireneusz Zieba

Subsidiaries:

Ambra Sp. z o.o. (1)
Ul Hutnicza 7
43-502 Czechowice-Dziedzice, Silesian, Poland
Tel.: (48) 322144340
Fax: (48) 32 214 43 41
E-Mail: market@ambra-czechowice.pl
Web Site: www.ambra-czechowice.pl
Cosmetics Distr
S.I.C.: 5199
N.A.I.C.S.: 424990

Detal Koncept Sp. z o.o. (1)
ul Melgiewska 7-9
20-952 Lublin, Poland
Tel.: (48) 817465757
Fax: (48) 81 746 35 09
E-Mail: biuro@detalkoncept.pl
Web Site: www.detalkoncept.pl
Fast Moving Consumer Goods Distr
S.I.C.: 7389
N.A.I.C.S.: 425120
Bozek Dariusz Pawel *(Chm)*

Emperia Info Sp. z o.o. (1)
Ul Melgiewska 7-9
20-952 Lublin, Poland
Tel.: (48) 817450024
Fax: (48) 817450020
E-Mail: emperia@emperia.pl
Web Site: www.dls.pl
Emp.: 108
Enterprise Management Software Development Services
S.I.C.: 7371
N.A.I.C.S.: 541511
Jacek Dudzik *(Pres)*

Euro Sklep S.A. (1)
Ul Bystrzanska 94/A
43-309 Bielsko-Biala, Silesian, Poland
Tel.: (48) 338150204
Fax: (48) 338150204
E-Mail: biuro@eurosklep.eu
Web Site: www.eurosklep.eu
Delicatessens Retailer
S.I.C.: 5411
N.A.I.C.S.: 445110

Groszek Sp.z.o.o (1)
Melgiewska 7-9
20-952 Lublin, Poland (100%)
Tel.: (48) 817465757
Fax: (48) 817463509
E-Mail: buro@detalkoncept.pl
Web Site: www.groszek.com.pl/
Supermarkets & Grocery Stores
S.I.C.: 5411
N.A.I.C.S.: 445110

Infinite Sp.z.o.o (1)
Ceramiczna St 8
Lublin, Poland (100%)
Tel.: (48) 817451750
Fax: (48) 817485405
E-Mail: b2b@infinite.pl
Web Site: www.infinite.pl
Emp.: 100
Computer Systems Design Services
S.I.C.: 7373
N.A.I.C.S.: 541512
Arcadiusz Wujdiuk *(Gen Mgr)*

Lewiatan Czestochowa Sp. z o.o. (1)
Ul Wreczycka 22 /26
42-200 Czestochowa, Silesian, Poland
Tel.: (48) 343694013
Supermarkets Operation Services
S.I.C.: 5411
N.A.I.C.S.: 445110

Lewiatan Holding S.A. (1)
ul Kilinskiego 10
87-800 Wloclawek, Wloclawek, Poland
Tel.: (48) 544127821
Fax: (48) 544127841
E-Mail: sekretariat@lewiatan.pl
Web Site: www.lewiatan.pl
Emp.: 40
Grocery Stores Operation Services
S.I.C.: 5411
N.A.I.C.S.: 445110
Wojciech Kruszewski *(Pres)*

Lewiatan Kujawy Sp. z o.o. (1)
Komunalna 6
87-800 Wloclawek, Kuyavian-Pomeranian, Poland
Tel.: (48) 54 411 30 45
Fax: (48) 54 411 30 25
E-Mail: wolclawek@lewiatan.com.pl
Web Site: www.kujawy.lewiatan.pl
Grocery Stores Operation Services
S.I.C.: 5411
N.A.I.C.S.: 445110

Waldemar Nowakowski *(Chm)*
Jan Wojciech Kruszewski *(Pres)*

Lewiatan-Orbita Sp.z o.o. (1)
Ul Lubelska 33
10-680 Olsztyn, Warmian-Masurian, Poland
Tel.: (48) 895328242
Fax: (48) 895328242
E-Mail: olsztyn@lewiatan.com.pl
Web Site: www.orbita.lewiatan.pl
Grocery Stores Operation Services
S.I.C.: 5411
N.A.I.C.S.: 445110

Lewiatan Slask Sp. z o.o. (1)
Ul Lenartowicza 39
41-219 Sosnowiec, Silesian, Poland
Tel.: (48) 322947025
Fax: (48) 322947026
E-Mail: biuro@slask.lewiatan.pl
Web Site: www.slask.lewiatan.pl
Emp.: 30
Grocery Stores Operation Services
S.I.C.: 5411
N.A.I.C.S.: 445110
Krzysztof Strobel *(Chm)*

Maro Markety Sp. z o.o. (1)
Ul Skwierzynska 20
61-615 Poznan, Poland
Tel.: (48) 618204204
Fax: (48) 61 8204 204
E-Mail: biuro@maromarkety.pl
Web Site: www.maromarkety.pl
Emp.: 400
Delicatessens Retailer
S.I.C.: 5411
N.A.I.C.S.: 445110
Gulczynski Przemyslaw *(Chm)*

Subsidiaries:

Lewiatan Opole Sp. z o.o. (2)
ul Swiatowida 2
45-325 Opole, Poland
Tel.: (48) 774416505
Fax: (48) 774416890
E-Mail: opole@lewiatan.pl
Web Site: www.opole.lewiatan.pl
Emp.: 15
Grocery Stores Operation Services
S.I.C.: 5411
N.A.I.C.S.: 445110
Szabat Wieslaw Slawomir *(Pres)*

Lewiatan Wielkopolska Sp. z o.o. (2)
Winiary 54
60-479 Poznan, Poland
Tel.: (48) 618460890
Fax: (48) 618479014
E-Mail: wielkopolska@lewiatan.com.pl
Web Site: www.wielkopolska.lewiatan.pl
Emp.: 15
Grocery Stores Operation Services
S.I.C.: 5411
N.A.I.C.S.: 445110
Jolanta Rewers *(Mgr)*

Spolem Tychy Sp. z o.o. (1)
Ul Ks Damrota 72
43-100 Tychy, Silesian, Poland
Tel.: (48) 322272210
Fax: (48) 322274961
E-Mail: informatyka@spolem.tychy.pl
Web Site: www.spolem.tychy.pl
Emp.: 411
Vegetables & Fruits Retailer
S.I.C.: 5148
N.A.I.C.S.: 424480
Gdowski Stanislaw Zbigniew *(Chm)*

Subsidiary:

Piccolo Sp. z o.o. (2)
Grota Roweckiego 60 A
43-100 Tychy, Silesian, Poland
Tel.: (48) 323283639
Fax: (48) 322276639
Baked Goods Retailer
S.I.C.: 5461
N.A.I.C.S.: 445291

Stokrotka Sp.z.o.o (1)
Melgiewska 7-7
Lublin, Poland (100%)
Tel.: (48) 817460725
Fax: (48) 817460938
E-Mail: stokrotka@stokrotka.pl
Web Site: www.stokrotka.pl
Emp.: 700
Supermarkets & Grocery Stores
S.I.C.: 5411
N.A.I.C.S.: 445110
Mareusz Myszak *(Gen Mgr)*

EMPEROR CAPITAL GROUP LIMITED

23-24 F Emperor Group Center 288
Hennessy Road
Wanchai, China (Hong Kong)
Tel.: (852) 29192919
Fax: (852) 28931540
Web Site: www.emperorcapital.com
HQF—(DEU)
Rev.: $28,859,139
Assets: $245,450,006
Liabilities: $84,275,530
Net Worth: $161,174,476
Earnings: $8,171,690
Emp.: 198
Fiscal Year-end: 09/30/12
Business Description:
Financial Services
S.I.C.: 6211
N.A.I.C.S.: 523999
Personnel:
Daisy Yeung *(Mng Dir)*
Louisa Suk Hing Choi *(Sec)*
Board of Directors:
Pearl Chan
Shek Wah Chan
Raymond Wing Keung Cheng
Louisa Suk Hing Choi
Kar Wing Chu
Vincent Chi Sun Kwok
Daisy Yeung

Butterfield Fulcrum Group (Bermuda) Limited
26 Burnaby Street
Hamilton, HM 11, Bermuda

EMPEROR INTERNATIONAL HOLDINGS LIMITED

28/F Emperor Group Centre 288
Hennessy Rd
Wanchai, China (Hong Kong)
Tel.: (852) 28356688
Fax: (852) 28938707
Web Site: www.emperor.com.hk
0163—(HKG)
Sales Range: $650-699.9 Million
Emp.: 1,332
Business Description:
Real Estate Industry
S.I.C.: 6552
N.A.I.C.S.: 237210
Personnel:
Vanessa Man Seung Fan *(Mng Dir)*
Chi Fai Wong *(Mng Dir)*
Ivy Fung Lin Mok *(Sec)*
Board of Directors:
Semon Siu Man Luk
Eric Man Hon Chan
Ping Keung Cheung
Vanessa Man Seung Fan
Michael Ka Ming Law
Hing Hung Liu
Ivy Fung Lin Mok
Chi Fai Wong

Butterfield Fund Services (Bermuda) Limited
Rosebank Centre 11 Bermudiana Rd
Pembroke, Bermuda

EMPEROR OIL LTD.

Suite 1600 144 4th Avenue
Southwest
Calgary, AB, T2P 3N4, Canada
Tel.: (403) 695-1794
E-Mail: info@emperoroil.com
Web Site: www.emperoroil.com
8CV—(DEU TSXV)
Rev.: $1,575
Assets: $9,018,173
Liabilities: $7,833,150
Net Worth: $1,185,023
Earnings: ($2,517,558)
Fiscal Year-end: 01/31/13
Business Description:
Oil & Gas Exploration Services
S.I.C.: 1311
N.A.I.C.S.: 211111
Personnel:
Andrew McCarthy *(Pres & CEO)*
Matthew Hamilton *(CFO)*
Board of Directors:
Mark Bloom
Andrew McCarthy
John G. F. McLeod
A. R. O. Abdel Rahman

EMPEROR WATCH & JEWELLERY LIMITED

25/F Emperor Group Centre 288
Hennessey Road
Wanchai, China (Hong Kong)
Tel.: (852) 2522 2918
E-Mail: enquiry@emperorwj.com
Web Site: www.emperorwatchjewellery.com
0887—(HKG)
Rev.: $842,233,572
Assets: $576,097,278
Liabilities: $47,316,268
Net Worth: $528,781,010
Earnings: $52,137,967
Emp.: 1,079
Fiscal Year-end: 12/31/12
Business Description:
Watches & Jewelry Retailer
S.I.C.: 5944
N.A.I.C.S.: 448310
Personnel:
Cindy Yeung *(Chm & Mng Dir)*
Frina Ho Ying Chung *(Sec)*
Board of Directors:
Cindy Yeung
Hon Piu Chan
Hung Ming Chan
Vanessa Man Seung Fan
May Ka Fung Lai
Chi Fai Wong
Kam Man Yip

Subsidiary:

Emperor Watch & Jewellery (HK) Company Limited (1)
G F & Bsmt Comm House
35 Queen, Hong Kong, China (Hong Kong)
Tel.: (852) 28100988
Fax: (852) 25267626
E-Mail: ewjctl@emperor.com.hk
Web Site: www.emperor.com.hk
Jewelry & Watch Mfr & Retailer
S.I.C.: 3829
N.A.I.C.S.: 334519
Cindy Yeung *(Mng Dir)*

EMPICA LTD.

1 Lyons Ct Long Ashton Bus Park
Yanley Ln
Long Ashton, Bristol, BS41 9LB, United Kingdom
Tel.: (44) 1275 394400
Fax: (44) 1275 393933
E-Mail: info@empica.com
Web Site: www.empica.com
Year Founded: 1989
Emp.: 8
Business Description:
Advertising Services
S.I.C.: 7311
N.A.I.C.S.: 541810
Personnel:
Martin Powell *(Mng Dir)*

EMPIRE AB

Kungsgatan 37
SE-114 56 Stockholm, Sweden
Tel.: (46) 8 586 30 400
Fax: (46) 8 661 07 40
E-Mail: info@empirenordic.com
Web Site: www.empire.se
EMP B—(OMX)
Sales Range: $50-74.9 Million
Emp.: 60
Business Description:
Household Appliances & Hair Care Products
S.I.C.: 5064
N.A.I.C.S.: 423620
Personnel:
Ian Wachtmeister *(Chm)*
Per Bjorkman *(CEO)*
Johanna Alm *(CFO)*
Board of Directors:
Ian Wachtmeister
Per Bjorkman
Ulf Christensen
Asa Mitsell
Hans Risberg
Bengt Stillstrom

Subsidiary:

Empire Sweden AB (1)
Ostermalmsgatan 87A
114 59 Stockholm, Sweden
Tel.: (46) 858630400
Fax: (46) 86610740
E-Mail: info@empire.se
Household Products Distr
S.I.C.: 5064
N.A.I.C.S.: 423620
Per Bjorkman *(CEO)*

Non-U.S. Subsidiaries:

Empire Denmark APS (1)
Virkeholm 3 B
2730 Herlev, Denmark
Tel.: (45) 43 600 609
Fax: (45) 43 600 605
E-Mail: info@sodastream.dk
Web Site: www.empiredenmark.dk
Emp.: 11
Household Appliance Retailer
S.I.C.: 5722
N.A.I.C.S.: 443141
Kare Jensen *(Gen Mgr)*

Empire Finland OY (1)
Ayritie 12 C
01510 Vantaa, Finland
Tel.: (358) 9 77400 100
Fax: (358) 9 77400 101
E-Mail: info.fi@empire.se
Web Site: www.empire.se/fi
Emp.: 5
Household Appliance Distr
S.I.C.: 5064
N.A.I.C.S.: 423620
David Solomon *(Gen Mgr)*

SIA Empire Baltics (1)
Udens 20/22
1007 Riga, Latvia
Tel.: (371) 673 21 205
E-Mail: info@sodastream.lv
Web Site: www.sodastream.lv
Emp.: 6
Household Appliance Distr
S.I.C.: 5021
N.A.I.C.S.: 423210

EMPIRE COMPANY LIMITED

115 King Street
Stellarton, NS, B0K 1S0, Canada
Tel.: (902) 755-4440
Telex: 19-36536
Fax: (902) 755-6477
E-Mail: paul.sobey@sobeys.ca
Web Site: www.empireco.ca
Year Founded: 1963
EMP.A—(TSX)
Sls.: $17,507,376,054
Assets: $7,097,402,202
Liabilities: $3,362,372,052
Net Worth: $3,735,030,150
Earnings: $391,544,478
Emp.: 47,000
Fiscal Year-end: 05/04/13

Empire Company Limited—(Continued)

Business Description:
Holding Company; Supermarkets, Food Distr, Movie Theaters & Real Estate
Import
S.I.C.: 5411
N.A.I.C.S.: 445110

Personnel:
Robert P. Dexter *(Chm)*
Paul David Sobey *(Pres & CEO)*
Paul V. Beesley *(CFO & Exec VP)*
Karin McCaskill *(Sec)*

Board of Directors:
Robert P. Dexter
Bonnie Brooks
Cynthia J. Devine
David S. Ferguson
Edward C. Harsant
David A. Leslie
Kevin G. Lynch
Marc Poulin
Melvin A. Rhinelander
Stephen J. Savidant
David F. Sobey
Donald R. Sobey
Frank C. Sobey
John R. Sobey
Karl R. Sobey
Paul David Sobey
Robert G. C. Sobey
Martine Turcotte

Legal Counsel:
Stewart McKelvey
Halifax, NS, Canada

Transfer Agent:
CST Trust Company
PO Box 700
Postal Station B, Montreal, QC, Canada

Subsidiaries:

Crombie REIT (1)
115 King Street
Stellarton, NS, B0K 1S0, Canada (100%)
Tel.: (902) 755-8100
Fax: (902) 755-6477
E-Mail: j.morris@crombiereit.ca
Web Site: www.crombiereit.ca
CRR.UN—(TSX)
Rev.: $254,490,988
Assets: $2,122,848,992
Liabilities: $1,345,524,358
Net Worth: $777,324,634
Earnings: $39,497,385
Emp.: 344
Fiscal Year-end: 12/31/12
Shopping Center Developers
S.I.C.: 1542
N.A.I.C.S.: 236220
Frank C. Sobey *(Chm)*
Donald E. Clow *(Pres & CEO)*
Glenn R. Hynes *(CFO & Sec)*
Scott R. MacLean *(Sr VP-Ops-Atlantic Reg)*

ECL Developments Limited (1)
115 King St
Stellarton, NS, B0K 1S0, Canada
Tel.: (902) 755-4440
Fax: (902) 755-6477
Web Site: www.empirecompany.com
Emp.: 99
Real Estate Development Services
S.I.C.: 6531
N.A.I.C.S.: 531390
Donald Clow *(Pres & CEO)*

Empire Theaters Limited (1)
610 E River Rd.
New Glasgow, NS, B2H 3S2, Canada Ca
Tel.: (902) 755-7620 (100%)
Fax: (902) 755-7640
E-Mail: empire@empiretheaters.com
Web Site: www.empiretheaters.com
Emp.: 40
Movie Theaters
S.I.C.: 7833
N.A.I.C.S.: 512132
Stuart G. Fraser *(Pres & CEO)*
Paul W. Wigginton *(CFO & VP-Fin)*
Valerie J. Ryan *(COO)*

Subsidiary:

ECL Western Holdings limited (2)
115 King St
Stellarton, NS, B0K 1S0, Canada
Tel.: (902) 755-4440
Fax: (902) 752-5136
Emp.: 88
Investment Management Services
S.I.C.: 6282
N.A.I.C.S.: 523920
Donald Clow *(Gen Mgr)*

Sobeys Capital Incorporated. (1)
115 King St
Stellarton, NS, B0K 1S0, Canada
Tel.: (902) 752-8371
Fax: (902) 928-1671
Web Site: www.sobeys.com
Packaging Services
S.I.C.: 7389
N.A.I.C.S.: 561910

Subsidiary:

Sobeys Group Inc (2)
115 King St
Stellarton, NS, B0K 1S0, Canada
Tel.: (902) 752-8371
Fax: (902) 752-2960
Emp.: 400
Pharmaceutical & Health Care Products Distr
S.I.C.: 5122
N.A.I.C.S.: 424210
Lorne Maclean *(Gen Mgr)*

Sobeys Inc. (1)
115 King Street
Stellarton, NS, B0K 1S0, Canada Ca
Tel.: (902) 752-8371 (72.1%)
Fax: (902) 752-2960
E-Mail: customer.service@sobeys.ca
Web Site: www.sobeys.ca
Sls.: $17,242,072,116
Assets: $5,878,833,084
Liabilities: $2,962,378,404
Net Worth: $2,916,454,680
Earnings: $363,115,506
Emp.: 124,000
Fiscal Year-end: 05/04/13
Food Distribution & Retail Services
Import
S.I.C.: 5149
N.A.I.C.S.: 424490
Robert P. Dexter *(Chm)*
Marc Poulin *(Pres & CEO)*
Francois Vimard *(Interim CFO)*
Simon Gagne *(Chief HR Officer)*
Jason Potter *(Pres-Multi-Format Ops)*
Claude Tessier *(Pres-IGA Ops)*
Karin McCaskill *(Gen Counsel, Sec & Sr VP)*
Clinton Keay *(Exec VP-Fin)*
Stewart Mahoney *(Sr VP-Treasury & IR)*
Andrew Walker *(Sr VP-Comm & Corp Affairs)*

Divisions:

Lawtons Drug Stores Limited (2)
236 Brownlow Ave Ste 270
Dartmouth, NS, B3B 1V5, Canada (100%)
Tel.: (902) 468-1000
Fax: (902) 468-1100
E-Mail: info@lawtons.ca
Web Site: www.lawtons.ca
Emp.: 130
Operator of Drug Stores
S.I.C.: 5912
N.A.I.C.S.: 446110
Vivek Sood *(Gen Mgr)*

Sobeys Ontario Division (2)
6355 Viscount Rd
Mississauga, ON, L4V 1W2, Canada (100%)
Tel.: (905) 672-6633
Fax: (905) 672-6066
Web Site: www.sobeysweb.com
Emp.: 500
S.I.C.: 5541
N.A.I.C.S.: 447110
David Jeff *(Pres-Ops)*

Sobeys Quebec Division (2)
11281 Albert Hudon
Montreal, QC, H1G 3J5, Canada (100%)
Tel.: (514) 324-1010
Fax: (514) 324-7089
E-Mail: info@sobeys.com
Web Site: www.sobeys.com
Emp.: 1,000
Distributor of Groceries
S.I.C.: 5149
N.A.I.C.S.: 424490
Marc Poulin *(Pres-Ops)*

Sobeys West, Inc. (2)
13140 San Albert Trl NW
Edmonton, AB, T5L 4P6, Canada
Tel.: (780) 486-4800
Fax: (780) 486-4882
E-Mail: pwreception@sobeys.com
Web Site: www.sobeys.com
Emp.: 200
S.I.C.: 5541
N.A.I.C.S.: 447110

Subsidiaries:

Canada Safeway Limited (2)
1020 64th Ave NE
Calgary, AB, T2E 7V8, Canada
Tel.: (403) 730-3500
Fax: (403) 730-3888
E-Mail: info@safeway.com
Web Site: www.safeway.com
Sales Range: $1-4.9 Billion
Emp.: 30,000
Operators of Retail Food Stores
S.I.C.: 5499
N.A.I.C.S.: 445299

Thrifty Foods Inc. (2)
6649 Butler Cres
Saanichton, BC, V8M 1Z7, Canada
Tel.: (250) 483-1600
Fax: (250) 483-1601
E-Mail: info@thriftyfoods.com
Web Site: www.thriftyfoods.com
Sales Range: $10-24.9 Million
Emp.: 300
Grocery Store Owner & Operator
S.I.C.: 5411
N.A.I.C.S.: 445110
Jim Jimtores *(Pres)*

EMPIRE EAST LAND HOLDINGS, INC.

21/F The World Centre 330 Sen Gil Puyat Avenue Extension
Makati, 1200, Philippines
Tel.: (63) 28678351
Fax: (63) 28678013
E-Mail: empire@empire-east.com
Web Site: www.empire-east.com
ELI—(PHI)
Rev.: $61,782,236
Assets: $783,159,584
Liabilities: $237,837,598
Net Worth: $545,321,986
Earnings: $5,763,687
Emp.: 477
Fiscal Year-end: 12/31/12

Business Description:
Real Estate Services
S.I.C.: 1522
N.A.I.C.S.: 236118

Personnel:
Andrew L. Tan *(Chm)*
Gerardo C. Garcia *(Vice Chm)*
Anthony Charlemagne C. Yu *(Pres & CEO)*
Giovanni C. Ng *(Treas)*
Dennis E. Edano *(Sec)*
Ricky S. Libago *(Sr VP-Property Dev)*

Board of Directors:
Andrew L. Tan
Evelyn G. Cacho
Gerardo C. Garcia
Enrique Santos L. Sy
Katherine L. Tan
Alejo L. Villanueve Jr.
Anthony Charlemagne C. Yu

EMPIRE ENERGY GROUP LIMITED

Level 7 151 Macquarie Street
Sydney, NSW, 2000, Australia

Mailing Address:
PO Box R356
Royal Exchange, Sydney, NSW, 1225, Australia
Tel.: (61) 292511846
Fax: (61) 292510244
E-Mail: info@empiregp.net
Web Site: www.empireenergygroup.net
Year Founded: 1984
EEG—(ASX OTC)
Rev.: $27,690,528
Assets: $120,439,576
Liabilities: $69,325,901
Net Worth: $51,113,675
Earnings: ($203,577)
Emp.: 30
Fiscal Year-end: 12/31/12

Business Description:
Oil & Gas Exploration
S.I.C.: 1311
N.A.I.C.S.: 211111

Personnel:
Bruce William McLeod *(Chm)*
Rachel V. Ryan *(Co-Sec & Gen Mgr-Ops)*
David Laurence Hughes *(Co-Sec)*

Board of Directors:
Bruce William McLeod
David Henry Sutton
Kevin Anthony Torpey

Nexia Court & Co
Level 16 1 Market Street
Sydney, NSW, 2000, Australia

Legal Counsel:
K&L Gates LLP
K&L Gates Ctr 210 6th Ave
Pittsburgh, PA 15222-2613

Clifford Chance
Level 16 No 1 O'Connell Street
Sydney, NSW, 2000, Australia

EMPIRE INDUSTRIES LTD.

717 Jarvis Avenue
Winnipeg, MB, R2W 3B4, Canada
Tel.: (204) 589-9300
Fax: (204) 582-8057
E-Mail: invest@empind.com
Web Site: www.empireindustriesltd.com
EIL—(TSXV)
Rev.: $83,189,534
Assets: $36,082,926
Liabilities: $28,925,982
Net Worth: $7,156,944
Earnings: ($621,262)
Emp.: 340
Fiscal Year-end: 12/31/12

Business Description:
Holding Company; Fabricated Structural Steel & Engineered Products Mfr
S.I.C.: 6719
N.A.I.C.S.: 551112

Personnel:
Guy Nelson *(Chm, Pres & CEO)*
Micheal Martin *(CFO)*

Board of Directors:
Guy Nelson
Bruce Jackson
Ian MacDonald
Robert Marshall
Campbell McIntyre
Terry Quinn

Transfer Agent:
CIBC Mellon
Suite 600 333-7th Avenue SW
Calgary, AB, Canada

Subsidiaries:

Empire Iron Works Ltd. (1)
21104 107th Avenue
Edmonton, AB, T5S 1X2, Canada
Tel.: (780) 447-4650
Fax: (780) 447-4005
E-Mail: edmonton@empireiron.com

Web Site: www.empireiron.com
Emp.: 100
Fabricated Structural Steel Products Mfr & Construction Services
S.I.C.: 3441
N.A.I.C.S.: 332312
Campbell McIntyre *(Pres)*

Subsidiaries:

Empire Dynamic Structures Ltd. (2)
(Formerly Dynamic Structures Ltd.)
1515 Kingsway Ave
Port Coquitlam, BC, V3C 1S2, Canada
Tel.: (604) 941-9481
Fax: (604) 941-7447
E-Mail:
Web Site: www.empireds.com
Sales Range: $10-24.9 Million
Emp.: 110
Movable Steel Structure Design & Fabrication Services
S.I.C.: 3441
N.A.I.C.S.: 332312
David Halliday *(Pres)*

George Third & Son Partnership (2)
6010 Trapp Ave
Burnaby, BC, V3N 2V4, Canada
Tel.: (604) 639-1708
Fax: (604) 639-1746
E-Mail: info@gthird.com
Web Site: www.gthird.com
Structural & Architectural Steel Fabrication
S.I.C.: 1791
N.A.I.C.S.: 238120
Brett Third *(Co-Pres)*
Rob Third *(Co-Pres)*

Subsidiary:

KWH Constructors Corp. (3)
2792 Norland Ave
Burnaby, BC, V5B 3A6, Canada
Tel.: (604) 299-7969
Fax: (604) 294-4550
E-Mail: info@kwhconstructors.com
Web Site: www.kwhconstructors.com
Emp.: 100
Specialty Engineering & Contract Construction Services
S.I.C.: 1791
N.A.I.C.S.: 238120
Peter Saunderson *(Dir-Engrg)*

Parr Metal Fabricators Ltd (2)
717 Jarvis Ave
Winnipeg, MB, R2W 3B4, Canada
Tel.: (204) 586-8121
Fax: (204) 956-1748
E-Mail: parr@parrmetal.com
Web Site: www.parrmetal.com
Emp.: 20
Pressure Vessel & Tank Mfr
S.I.C.: 3443
N.A.I.C.S.: 332420
Cesare Sacco *(Gen Mgr)*

Ward Industrial Equipment Ltd (2)
2 Broadway Ave
PO Box 511
Welland, ON, L3B 5R3, Canada
Tel.: (905) 732-7591
Fax: (905) 732-3310
Web Site: www.wardequipment.com
Material Handling & Air Purification Equipment Mfr
S.I.C.: 3535
N.A.I.C.S.: 333922
Ridhard Christoper *(Project Mgr)*

Petrofield Industries Inc (1)
Suite 611 7015 MacLeod Trl SW
Calgary, AB, T2H 2K6, Canada
Tel.: (403) 204-6394
Fax: (403) 204-6366
E-Mail: info@petrofield.com
Web Site: www.petrofield.com
Emp.: 60
Oilfield Equipments Mfr
S.I.C.: 3443
N.A.I.C.S.: 332420
Bill Rollins *(Gen Mgr)*

EMPIRE MAINTENANCE INDUSTRIES INC.

695 90e Avenue
LaSalle, Montreal, QC, H8R 3A4, Canada
Tel.: (514) 341-6161
Fax: (514) 342-7899
Toll Free: (800) 501-2501
E-Mail: empire@empiremaintenance.ca
Web Site: www.empiremaintenance.ca
Year Founded: 1938
Rev.: $72,826,310
Emp.: 4,000
Business Description:
Janitorial Services
S.I.C.: 7349
N.A.I.C.S.: 561720
Personnel:
Mario W. Levasseur *(Pres & CEO)*
Glenn R. Leduc *(CFO)*

EMPIRE MINING CORPORATION

(Name Changed to Columbus Copper Corporation)

EMPIRE OIL & GAS NL

229 Stirling Highway
Claremont, WA, 6010, Australia
Tel.: (61) 892846422
Fax: (61) 892846588
E-Mail: info@empireoil.com.au
Web Site: www.empireoil.com.au
EGO—(ASX)
Rev.: $1,307,621
Assets: $67,076,985
Liabilities: $31,350,999
Net Worth: $35,725,986
Earnings: ($8,305,720)
Emp.: 6
Fiscal Year-end: 06/30/13
Business Description:
Oil & Gas Producer
S.I.C.: 1389
N.A.I.C.S.: 213112
Personnel:
Tony Iannello *(Chm)*
Kent Quinlan *(Acting CEO)*
J. L. Craig Marshall *(Mng Dir)*
Geoff Beer *(CFO)*
Kim A. Hogg *(Sec)*
Board of Directors:
Tony Iannello
Stuart Brown
Neil K. Joyce
Jeffrey MacDonald
J. L. Craig Marshall
Legal Counsel:
Mizen & Mizen
69 Mount Street
Perth, Australia
Subsidiaries:

Empire Services Pty Ltd. (1)
Ste 7 & 8 154 Hampden Rd
Nedlands, WA, 6009, Australia
Tel.: (61) 863892687
Fax: (61) 893866812
E-Mail: info@empireoil.com.au
Emp.: 7
Oil & Gas Exploration Services
S.I.C.: 1311
N.A.I.C.S.: 211111
J. L. Craig Marshall *(Mng Dir)*

Rough Range Oil Pty Ltd. (1)
Ste 7 & 8 154 Hampden Rd
Nedlands, WA, 6009, Australia
Tel.: (61) 863892687
Fax: (61) 893866812
E-Mail: info@empireoil.com.au
Emp.: 7
Oil & Gas Exploration Services
S.I.C.: 1389
N.A.I.C.S.: 213112
Craig Marshall *(Mng Dir)*

EMPIRE RESOURCES LIMITED

53 Canning Highway
Victoria Park, WA, 6100, Australia
Tel.: (61) 8 9361 3100
Fax: (61) 8 9361 3184
E-Mail: info@resourcesempire.com.au
Web Site: www.resourcesempire.com.au
ERL—(ASX)
Rev.: $10,548
Assets: $794,860
Liabilities: $160,597
Net Worth: $634,263
Earnings: ($1,648,787)
Emp.: 2
Fiscal Year-end: 06/30/13
Business Description:
Mineral Exploration
S.I.C.: 1481
N.A.I.C.S.: 213115
Personnel:
David Sargeant *(Mng Dir)*
Simon Jonathan Storm *(Sec)*
Board of Directors:
Thomas Revy
Adrian Jessup
David Sargeant

EMPIRED LTD

Level 13 Septimus Roe Square 256 Adelaide Terrace
Perth, WA, 6000, Australia
Mailing Address:
PO Box Y3116
Perth, WA, 6892, Australia
Tel.: (61) 8 9223 1234
Fax: (61) 8 9223 1230
E-Mail: info@empired.com
Web Site: www.empired.com
EPD—(ASX)
Rev.: $48,455,820
Assets: $32,571,569
Liabilities: $16,753,584
Net Worth: $15,817,985
Earnings: $1,615,088
Emp.: 53
Fiscal Year-end: 06/30/13
Business Description:
Software Sevices
S.I.C.: 7372
N.A.I.C.S.: 511210
Personnel:
Russell Baskerville *(CEO & Mng Dir)*
Mark Waller *(CFO & Sec)*
Rob McCready *(COO)*
Greg Leach *(CTO-Enablement & Mktg)*
Board of Directors:
Mel Ashton
John Bardwell
Russell Baskerville
Richard Bevan
Legal Counsel:
Jackson Macdonald
140 St Georges Terrace
Perth, Australia

EMPORIS PROJECTS LIMITED

209 Sarthik 2 Opp Rajpath Club S G Highway
Ahmedabad, Gujarat, India
Tel.: (91) 79 2687 3250
Fax: (91) 79 2687 3252
E-Mail: info@emporisprojects.com
Web Site: www.emporisprojects.com
531470—(BOM)
Sales Range: Less than $1 Million
Business Description:
Real Estate Development & Power Generation Services
S.I.C.: 6531
N.A.I.C.S.: 531390
Personnel:
Jayantibhai Patel *(Chm, Mng Dir & Compliance Officer)*
Board of Directors:
Jayantibhai Patel
Limbadri V. Bommer
Parul Chauhan
Hemant Manjrekar
Chintan Dilipkumar Shah
Brijbhushan S. Singh

EMPOWER TECHNOLOGIES CORPORATION

130 - 3751 Shell Road Airport Executive Park
Richmond, BC, V6X 2W2, Canada
Tel.: (604) 278-3100
Fax: (604) 278-3102
E-Mail: info@empowertechnologies.com
Web Site: www.empowertechnologies.com
Year Founded: 2003
EPT—(TSXV)
Rev.: $113,302
Assets: $64,500
Liabilities: $5,484,456
Net Worth: ($5,419,956)
Earnings: ($1,445,079)
Fiscal Year-end: 12/31/12
Business Description:
Software Development
S.I.C.: 7372
N.A.I.C.S.: 511210
Personnel:
Paul Leung *(Chm, Pres & CEO)*
Amy Chan *(CFO, VP-Ops & Gen Mgr)*
Board of Directors:
Paul Leung
Edward Bagg
Amy Chan
Subsidiary:

Empower Technologies (Canada) Inc. (1)
5600 Parkwood Way Ste 405
Richmond, BC, V6V 2M2, Canada
Tel.: (604) 278-3100
Fax: (604) 278-3102
Software Development Services
S.I.C.: 7371
N.A.I.C.S.: 541511

U.S. Subsidiary:

Empower Technologies, Inc. (1)
8201 164 Ave NE
Redmond, WA 98052
Tel.: (425) 881-0909
Fax: (425) 881-0889
E-Mail: info@empowertechnologies.com
Web Site: www.empowertechnologies.com
Linux-Based Software
S.I.C.: 5045
N.A.I.C.S.: 423430

EMPRESA DE ENERGIA DE BOGOTA S.A. E.S.P.

Cra 9 73-44 Piso 6
Bogota, Colombia
Tel.: (57) 1 3268000
Fax: (57) 1 3268010
E-Mail: webmaster@eeb.com.co
Web Site: www.eeb.com.co
EEB—(COLO)
Rev.: $887,658,800
Assets: $8,226,248,800
Liabilities: $2,515,926,000
Net Worth: $5,710,322,800
Earnings: $386,792,560
Fiscal Year-end: 12/31/12
Business Description:
Electricity Generation & Distribution Services; Natural Gas Distr
S.I.C.: 4931
N.A.I.C.S.: 221112
Personnel:
Gustavo Petro *(Chm)*
Sandra Stella Fonseca Arenas *(Pres)*
Mario Trujillo Hernandez *(Gen Sec)*
Board of Directors:

Empresa de Energia de Bogota S.A. E.S.P.—(Continued)

Gustavo Petro
Alberto Jose Merlano Alcocer
Fernando Arbelaez Bolanos
Diego Bravo Borda
Claudia Lucia Castellanos
Saul Kattan Cohen
Guillermo Raul Asprilla Coronado
Gustavo Ramirez Galindo
Boris Villa Gallo
Mauricio Cabrera Galvis
Jenifer Ruiz Gonzalez
Luis Carlos Sarmiento Gutierrez
Maria Victoria Duque Lopez
Maria Fernanda Rojas Mantilla
Susana Muhamad
Mauricio Cardenas Muller
Carlos Fidel Simancas Narvaez
Jorge Luis Penuela Ramos
Claudia Lucia Castellanos Rodriguez
Maria Fernanda Rojas
Fernando Sanclemente
Carlos Fidel Simancas
Mauricio Trujillo Uribe
Jorge Reinel Pulecio Yate

EMPRESA DISTRIBUIDORA Y COMERCIALIZADORA NORTE S.A.

(d/b/a Edenor)
Avenida Del Libertador 6363 Ciudad de Buenos Aires
C1428ARG Buenos Aires, Argentina
Tel.: (54) 11 4346 5000
Fax: (54) 11 4346 5325
E-Mail: investor@edenor.com
Web Site: www.edenor.com.ar
Year Founded: 1992
EDN—(BUE NYSE)
Rev.: $749,968,538
Assets: $1,369,265,901
Liabilities: $1,270,762,441
Net Worth: $98,503,460
Earnings: ($204,020,909)
Emp.: 3,656
Fiscal Year-end: 12/31/12

Business Description:
Electric Power Distr
S.I.C.: 4939
N.A.I.C.S.: 221122

Personnel:
Ricardo Alejandro Torres *(Chm)*
Gustavo Mariani *(Vice Chm)*
Edgardo Alberto Volosin *(CEO)*
Leandro Carlos Montero *(CFO)*
Victor Augusto Ruiz *(Chief Acctg Officer)*

Board of Directors:
Ricardo Alejandro Torres
Emmanuel Alvarez Agis
Patricia Charvay
Maximiliano Alejandro Fernandez
Daniel Eduardo Flaks
Eduardo Llanos
Gustavo Mariani
Valeria Martofel
Marcos Marcelo Mindlin
Marcela Sacavini
Edgardo Alberto Volosin
Victoria Von Storch

EMPRESA NACIONAL DE COMERCIO REDITO E PARTICIPACOES, S.A.-ENCORPAR

R Aimores 981
30140071 Belo Horizonte, MG, Brazil
Tel.: (55) 31 2129 9877
Fax: (55) 31 2129 9877
ECPR3—(BRAZ)
Sales Range: $1-9.9 Million
Emp.: 1,614

Business Description:
Investment Management Services
S.I.C.: 6799
N.A.I.C.S.: 523920

Personnel:
Joao Batista Da Cunha Bomfim *(Dir-IR)*

EMPRESARIA GROUP PLC

Old Church House Sandy Lane
Crawley Down, Crawley, West Sussex, RH10 4HS, United Kingdom
Tel.: (44) 1342 711430
Fax: (44) 1342 711449
E-Mail: info@empresaria.com
Web Site: www.empresaria.com
EMR—(LSE)
Rev.: $306,856,047
Assets: $99,021,483
Liabilities: $61,118,523
Net Worth: $37,902,960
Earnings: $3,000,651
Emp.: 834
Fiscal Year-end: 12/31/12

Business Description:
Recruitment Services
S.I.C.: 8999
N.A.I.C.S.: 541612

Personnel:
Joost Kreulen *(CEO)*
Anne-Marie Clarke *(Sec)*

Board of Directors:
Anthony Martin
Penny Freer
Joost Kreulen
Zach Miles
Spencer Wreford

Legal Counsel:
Osborne Clarke
2 Temple Back East Temple Quay
Bristol, United Kingdom

Subsidiaries:

2nd City Resourcing Limited (1)
37 - 39 Ludgate Hill St Pauls Square
Birmingham, B3 1EH, United Kingdom
Tel.: (44) 1216656768
Fax: (44) 12163330527
E-Mail: info@2ndcityresourcing.com
Web Site: www.2ndcityresourcing.com
Emp.: 5
Employment Placement Agencies
S.I.C.: 7361
N.A.I.C.S.: 561311
Kathryn Gallan *(Mng Dir)*

Fast Track Management Services (London) Limited (1)
Unit 4 Century Court
Tolpits Lane
Watford, WD18 9RS, United Kingdom
Tel.: (44) 08450659999
Fax: (44) 08450656666
E-Mail: enquiries@ftrack.co.uk
Web Site: www.ftrack.co.uk
Emp.: 100
Industrial Building Construction
S.I.C.: 1629
N.A.I.C.S.: 236210

Fast Track Management Services (Midlands) Limited (1)
The Saturn Centre
101 Lockhurst Lane, Coventry, CV65SF, United Kingdom
Tel.: (44) 2476708110
Fax: (44) 2476708111
E-Mail: shopfitting@ftrackmidlands.co.uk
Web Site: www.ftrack.co.uk
Industrial Building Construction
S.I.C.: 1629
N.A.I.C.S.: 236210

Greycoat Placements Limited (1)
Grosvenor Gardens House
35-37 Grosvenor Gardens, London, SW1W0BS, United Kingdom
Tel.: (44) 2072339950
Fax: (44) 2075920096
E-Mail: info@greycoatlumleys.co.uk
Web Site: www.greycoatplacements.co.uk
Emp.: 25
Employment Placement Agencies
S.I.C.: 7361
N.A.I.C.S.: 561311
Debbie Salter *(Mng Dir)*

HEC Resources Limited (1)
Suite 2 James Yard 480 Larkshall Road
Highams Park, London, E4 9UA, United Kingdom (100%)
Tel.: (44) 20 8523 3561
Web Site: www.hecresources.com
Human Resources & Executive Search Consulting Services
S.I.C.: 8999
N.A.I.C.S.: 541612

Lindsay Morgan Associates Ltd. (1)
Ground Floor Prince Rupert House
64 Queen Street, London, EC4R 1Ad, United Kingdom
Tel.: (44) 2072364999
Fax: (44) 2072365999
E-Mail: reception@lmarecruitment.com
Web Site: www.lmassoc.com
Emp.: 18
Recruitment Services
S.I.C.: 8999
N.A.I.C.S.: 541612
Russell Thompson *(Mng Dir)*

LMA Recruitment Limited (1)
Pellipar House 9 Cloak Lane
London, EC4R 2RU, United Kingdom (80%)
Tel.: (44) 2072364999
Fax: (44) 2072365999
E-Mail: info@lmarecruitment.com
Web Site: www.lmarecruitment.com
Emp.: 20
Human Resources & Executive Search Consulting Services
S.I.C.: 8999
N.A.I.C.S.: 541612
Russell Thompson *(Mng Dir)*

Mansion House Recruitment Ltd. (1)
Ground Floor Pellipar House
9 Cloak Lane, London, EC4R 2RU, United Kingdom
Tel.: (44) 207 332 5870
E-Mail: london@mansionhouse.co.uk
Web Site: www.mansionhouse.co.uk
Emp.: 15
Recruitment Services
S.I.C.: 8999
N.A.I.C.S.: 541612
Jayne Coles *(Mng Dir)*

McCall Limited (1)
Pellipar House 9 Cloak Ln
London, EC4R2RU, United Kingdom
Tel.: (44) 8704050100
Fax: (44) 1992631448
E-Mail: info@mccall.co.uk
Web Site: www.mccall.co.uk
Emp.: 10
Vocational Rehabilitation Services
S.I.C.: 8331
N.A.I.C.S.: 624310
Julie O'Neill *(Mng Dir)*

MVP (Search And Selection) Limited (1)
Priory House Friar Street
Droitwich, Worcestershire, WR9 8ED, United Kingdom (69%)
Tel.: (44) 1905773370
Fax: (44) 1905773378
E-Mail: info@mvp-search.com
Web Site: www.mvpsearch.com
Emp.: 11
Human Resources & Executive Search Consulting Services
S.I.C.: 8999
N.A.I.C.S.: 541612
Andy Rimington *(Mng Dir)*

The Recruitment Business Limited (1)
17-18 Henrietta Street
London, WC2E 8QH, United Kingdom
Tel.: (44) 20 7240 0088
Fax: (44) 20 7240 0089
E-Mail: info@becomeuk.com
Web Site: www.becomeuk.com
Emp.: 14
Human Resource Consulting Services
S.I.C.: 8999
N.A.I.C.S.: 541612
Sue Pilgrim *(Mng Dir)*

Reflex HR Limited (1)
Delta House Bridge Road
Haywards Heath, West Sussex, RH16 1UA, United Kingdom
Tel.: (44) 1444414164
Fax: (44) 1444414168
E-Mail: sales@reflexrecruitment.co.uk
Web Site: www.reflexhr.co.uk
Emp.: 12
Industrial Building Construction
S.I.C.: 1541
N.A.I.C.S.: 236210
Simon Lanaway *(Mng Dir)*

Resolve Interim Solutions Limited (1)
Oakhurst 23 Harrogate Road
Chapel Allerton, Leeds, LS73PD, United Kingdom
Tel.: (44) 1133836207
Fax: (44) 1133836201
E-Mail: leeds@resolveltd.co.uk
Web Site: www.resolveltd.co.uk
Emp.: 5
Employment Placement Agencies
S.I.C.: 7361
N.A.I.C.S.: 561311
Phillip Wagstaff *(Mng Dir)*

Social Work Associates Limited (1)
16 Brune Street
004 Coppergate House, London, E17NJ, United Kingdom (100%)
Tel.: (44) 2079537878
Fax: (44) 2079537888
Web Site: www.socialworkassociates.co.uk
Emp.: 4
Employment Placement Agencies
S.I.C.: 7361
N.A.I.C.S.: 561311
Sue Pilgrin *(Mng Dir)*

Teamsales Limited (1)
25 Princess Road
Primrose Hill, London, NW1 8JR, United Kingdom (100%)
Tel.: (44) 2072092499
Fax: (44) 2072092491
E-Mail: temps@team-sales.co.uk
Web Site: www.team-sales.co.uk
Emp.: 12
Employment Placement Agencies
S.I.C.: 7361
N.A.I.C.S.: 561311
Paul Brennan *(Mng Dir)*

Non-U.S. Subsidiaries:

Headway Holding GmbH (1)
Hofmark-Aich 28
84030 Landshut, Germany
Tel.: (49) 871 9 75 28 0
Fax: (49) 871 9 75 28 13
E-Mail: info@headwayholding.com
Web Site: www.headwayholding.com
Emp.: 18
Employment Agency Services
S.I.C.: 7361
N.A.I.C.S.: 561311

Interactive Manpower Solutions Private Limited (1)
301 President Plaza Near Thaltej Cross Road S G Highway S G Road
Ahmedabad, Gujarat, 380054, India
Tel.: (91) 7930114444
Fax: (91) 7926854231
Web Site: www.imspeople.com
Emp.: 14
Human Resource Consulting Services
S.I.C.: 8999
N.A.I.C.S.: 541612
Amit Somaiya *(CEO)*

ITC Apt Sp. Z.o.o. (1)
ul Kurniki 4
31-156 Krakow, Poland
Tel.: (48) 126192822
Human Resources & Executive Search Consulting Services
S.I.C.: 8999
N.A.I.C.S.: 541612

ITC Cs Sp. Z.o.o. (1)
ul Kurniki 4
31-156 Krakow, Poland
Tel.: (48) 12 357 22 88
E-Mail: csie@itcgrupa.pl

Web Site: www.itcpraca.pl/c/8/kontakt.html
Human Resources & Executive Search Consulting Services
S.I.C.: 8999
N.A.I.C.S.: 541612

Marketing y Promociones S.A. (1)
Alcalde Jorge Monckeberg 77
Nunoa, Santiago, Chile
Tel.: (56) 2 482 3800
E-Mail: informaciones@alternattiva.cl
Temporary Staffing Services
S.I.C.: 7363
N.A.I.C.S.: 561320

Mediradix Oy (1)
World Trade Center Veistamonaukio 1-3
20100 Turku, Finland
Tel.: (358) 2 281 3150
Fax: (358) 2 281 3159
E-Mail: info@mediradix.fi
Web Site: www.mediradix.fi
Emp.: 20
Healthcare Staffing Services
S.I.C.: 7363
N.A.I.C.S.: 561320
Merle Kikas *(Sec)*
Eneli Tukiainen *(Sec-HR)*

Monroe Consuliting Group Pty Limited (1)
BT Tower 1 Mark Street Suite 1903 Level 19
Sydney, NSW, 2000, Australia
Tel.: (61) 282267111
Fax: (61) 282267171
E-Mail: info@monroeconsulting.com
Web Site: www.monroeconsulting.com.au
Investment Banking & Securities Dealing
S.I.C.: 6211
N.A.I.C.S.: 523110

Monroe Consulting Group (1)
Wisma Kemang - 2nd Floor Jl Kemang Selatan Raya No 1
Kemang, 12560 Jakarta, Indonesia
Tel.: (62) 21 781 7040
E-Mail: technology@monroeconsulting.com
Web Site: www.monroeconsulting.com
Emp.: 30
Human Resource Consulting Services
S.I.C.: 8999
N.A.I.C.S.: 541612
Bagus Hendrayano *(Deputy Country Mgr)*

Monroe Recruitment Consulting Group Co Limited (1)
8th Floor Unit 4-4 K Tower A
209 Sukhumvit 21 Asoke Rd Klon, 10110
Bangkok, Thailand
Tel.: (66) 266440149
Fax: (66) 026644013
E-Mail: asia@monroeconsulting.co.th
Web Site: www.monroeconsulting.com
Emp.: 13
Commercial Banking
S.I.C.: 6029
N.A.I.C.S.: 522110
Tolmie John *(Gen Mgr)*

PT. Learning Resources (1)
Jl Wijaya I No 71 Kebayoran Baru
Jakarta Selatan, Jakarta, 12170, Indonesia
Tel.: (62) 21 723 2388
Fax: (62) 21 723 2389
Web Site: www.learningresources.co.id
Professional Training Services
S.I.C.: 8299
N.A.I.C.S.: 611430

Skillhouse Staffing Solutions K.K. (1)
Tomoecho Annex No 2 Building 7th Floor
3-8-27 Toranomon Minato-ku, Tokyo, 1052401, Japan
Tel.: (81) 354085070
Fax: (81) 354080506
E-Mail: info@skillhouse.co.jp
Web Site: www.skillhouse.co.jp
Sales Range: $10-24.9 Million
Emp.: 150
Employment Placement Agencies
S.I.C.: 7361
N.A.I.C.S.: 561311
Mark Smith *(Pres)*

EMPRESAS CMPC S.A.

Agustinas 1343
Santiago, Chile
Tel.: (56) 24412000
Fax: (56) 26721115
E-Mail: investorrelations@cmpc.cl
Web Site: www.cmpc.cl
Year Founded: 1920
CMPC—(SGO)
Rev.: $4,759,320,000
Assets: $14,046,077,000
Liabilities: $6,061,043,000
Net Worth: $7,985,034,000
Earnings: $202,410,000
Emp.: 15,068
Fiscal Year-end: 12/31/12

Business Description:
Paper & Paper Product Mfr
S.I.C.: 2652
N.A.I.C.S.: 322121

Personnel:
Eliodoro Matte Larrain *(Chm)*
Hernan Rodriguez Wilson *(CEO)*
Luis Llanos Collado *(CFO)*
Gonzalo Garcia Balmaceda *(Sec)*

Board of Directors:
Eliodoro Matte Larrain
Martin Costabel Llona
Erwin Hahn Huber
Jorge Gabriel Larrain Bunster
Arturo Mackenna Iniguez
Jorge Marin Correa
Bernardo Matte Larrain

Subsidiaries:

Chilena de Moldeados S.A. (1)
Jose Luis Coo 01162 Puente Alto Apartado 208
Santiago, Chile
Tel.: (56) 2 2433 1900
Fax: (56) 2 850 3110
E-Mail: chimolsa@chimolsa.cmpc.cl
Web Site: www.chimolsa.cl
Emp.: 150
Molded Pulp Packaging Production Services
S.I.C.: 2611
N.A.I.C.S.: 322110

CMPC Celulosa S.A. (1)
Agustina 1343 Piso 3
PO Box 297 Correo Central
Santiago, 562, Chile
Tel.: (56) 24412030
Fax: (56) 26982179
E-Mail: sales@celulosa.cmpc.cl
Web Site: www.cmpccelulosa.cl
Emp.: 1,000
Pulp Milling Services
S.I.C.: 2611
N.A.I.C.S.: 322110
Sergio T. Colvin *(Mng Dir)*

CMPC Papeles S.A. (1)
Agustinas 1343 Piso 5 Correo Central
PO Box 297
6500587 Santiago, Chile
Tel.: (56) 24412000
Fax: (56) 26955290
E-Mail: cmpc.papeles@gerencia.cmpc.cl
Web Site: www.cmpc.cl
Emp.: 500
Folding Boxboard, Corrugating Materials & Newsprint Mfr & Marketer
S.I.C.: 2621
N.A.I.C.S.: 322122
Hernan Rodriguez *(Mng Dir)*
Washington B. Williamson *(Mng Dir)*

CMPC Productos de Papel S.A. (1)
Agustinas 1343 Piso 6
PO Box 297
Santiago, Chile
Tel.: (56) 24412000
Fax: (56) 26723252
E-Mail: fruiztagle@gerencia.cmpc.cl
Web Site: www.cmpc.cl
Emp.: 6
Corrugated Box Mfr
S.I.C.: 2653
N.A.I.C.S.: 322211
Francisco E. Ruiz-Tagle *(Mng Dir)*

CMPC Tissue S.A. (1)
Agustinia 1343 Piso 6
Santiago, Chile
Tel.: (56) 24412000
Fax: (56) 24412568
Web Site: www.cmpctissue.cl
Toilet Paper, Paper Towels, Napkins, Disposable Handkerchiefs & Disposable Diaper Mfr
S.I.C.: 2676
N.A.I.C.S.: 322291
Jorge B. Morel *(Mng Dir)*

Envases Impresos S.A. (1)
Camino Alto Jahuel 0360
Buin, Santiago, Chile
Tel.: (56) 24711300
Fax: (56) 24711323
E-Mail: rruiz@envases.cmpc.cl
Web Site: www.envases.cl
Emp.: 360
Paperboard Mill
S.I.C.: 2631
N.A.I.C.S.: 322130
Ricardo Ruiz *(Mng Dir)*

Envases Roble Alto Ltda. (1)
Lo Echevers 221
Quilicura, Santiago, Chile
Tel.: (56) 24442400
Fax: (56) 2 444 2445
E-Mail: contacto@roblealto.cmpc.cl
Web Site: www.envases.cl/contactos.htm
Emp.: 135
Packaging Products Mfr
S.I.C.: 2657
N.A.I.C.S.: 322212

Forestal Mininco S.A. (1)
Agustinas 1343 Piso 4
PO Box 297
Correo Central, Santiago, Chile
Tel.: (56) 24412000
Fax: (56) 26729054
Emp.: 7
Forest Management Services
S.I.C.: 0851
N.A.I.C.S.: 115310
Francisco Ruiz-Tagle *(Mng Dir)*

Forestal y Agricola Monteaguila S.A. (1)
Avenida Francisco Encina s/n
PO Box 32-D
Pallihue, Los Angeles, Chile
Tel.: (56) 43 631 000
Fax: (56) 43 320 497
E-Mail: fmontea@famasa.cmpc.cl
Flour Milling Services
S.I.C.: 2041
N.A.I.C.S.: 311211

Industrias Forestales S.A. (1)
Agustinas 1357 Piso 9
PO Box 9201
Correo Central, Santiago, Chile
Tel.: (56) 24412050
Fax: (56) 24412890
E-Mail: gerencia@inforsa.cmpc.cl
Web Site: www.inforsa.cl
Emp.: 1,000
Newsprint & Wood-Containing Paper Mfr
S.I.C.: 2621
N.A.I.C.S.: 322122
Andreas Larain *(Gen Mgr)*

U.S. Subsidiary:

CMPC USA, Inc. (1)
1050 Crown Point Pkwy Ste 1590
Atlanta, GA 30338
Tel.: (770) 551-2640
Fax: (770) 551-2641
E-Mail: cmpcusa@cmpc.cl
Web Site: www.cmpcmaderas.com
Emp.: 10
Paper Products Sales
S.I.C.: 5113
N.A.I.C.S.: 424130
Pablo Sufan *(Gen Mgr)*

Non-U.S. Subsidiaries:

CMPC Europe Limited (1)
5 Dukes Gate Acton Lane Chiswick
London, W4 5DX, United Kingdom
Tel.: (44) 2089969960
Fax: (44) 2089969967
E-Mail: info@cmpc.co.uk
Web Site: www.cmpc.co.uk
Emp.: 3
Paper Products Sales
S.I.C.: 5113
N.A.I.C.S.: 424130
Claudio Ojedo Strauch *(Mng Dir)*

FABI Bolsas Industriales S.A. (1)
Virasoro 2656 Edificio Uruguay III
B1643HDB Buenos Aires, Argentina
Tel.: (54) 1147371001
Fax: (54) 1147371001
E-Mail: fabi@cmpc.com.ar
Web Site: www.fabi.com.ar
Emp.: 180
Corrugated & Solid Fiber Box Mfr
S.I.C.: 2653
N.A.I.C.S.: 322211
Adrian Saj *(Mgr)*

EMPRESAS ICA S.A.B. DE C.V.

Blvd Manuel Avila Camacho 36 Col
Lomas de Chapultepec
Del Miguel Hidalgo, 11000 Mexico, Mexico
Tel.: (52) 55 5272 9991
Fax: (52) 55 5227 5012
E-Mail: comunicacion@ica.com.mx
Web Site: www.ica.com.mx
Year Founded: 1947
ICA—(MEX NYSE)
Rev.: $3,740,670,494
Assets: $8,551,554,373
Liabilities: $6,925,891,030
Net Worth: $1,625,663,343
Earnings: $134,346,415
Emp.: 34,363
Fiscal Year-end: 12/31/12

Business Description:
Engineering & Construction for Public & Private Sectors
Import Export
S.I.C.: 1629
N.A.I.C.S.: 237990

Personnel:
Bernardo Quintana Isaac *(Chm)*

Board of Directors:
Bernardo Quintana Isaac
Salvador Alva Gomez
Emilio Carrillo Gamboa
Elsa Beatriz Garcia Bojorges
Margarita Hugues Velez
Carlos Mendez Bueno
Alonso Quintana Kawage
Diego Quintana Kawage
Lorenzo H. Zambrano Trevio

Legal Counsel:
Cleary, Gottlieb, Steen & Hamilton
153 E. 53rd St.
New York, NY 10022-4611
Tel.: (212) 572-5353
Fax: (212) 572-5399

Subsidiaries:

Aeropuerto Acapulco S.A. de C.V. (1)
Blvd De las Naciones s/n Poblado de Los Amates
Acapulco, Guerrero, 39931, Mexico
Tel.: (52) 744 435 2060
E-Mail: acapulco@oma.aero
Airport Management Services
S.I.C.: 4581
N.A.I.C.S.: 488119

Aeropuerto Chihuahua, S.A. de C.V. (1)
Blvd Juan Pablo II Km 14
Chihuahua, 31390, Mexico
Tel.: (52) 614 420 5104
E-Mail: chihuahua@oma.aero
Web Site: www.oma.aero/en/contact-us/airport-directory.htm
Emp.: 90
Airport Management Services
S.I.C.: 4581
N.A.I.C.S.: 488119
Mario Calderon *(Gen Mgr)*

Aeropuerto Ciudad Juarez, S.A. de C.V. (1)
Carretera Panamericana Km 18 5
Ciudad Juarez, Chihuahua, 32690, Mexico
Tel.: (52) 6566330734
E-Mail: cdjuarez@oma.aero
Web Site: www.oma.aero/en/contact-us/airport-directory.htm

Empresas ICA S.A.B. de C.V.—(Continued)

Airport Operating Services
S.I.C.: 4581
N.A.I.C.S.: 488119

AEROPUERTO CULIACAN, S.A. DE C.V. (1)
Carret A Navolato Km 4 5 Col Bachilaguato
Culiacan, Sinaloa, 80130, Mexico
Tel.: (52) 667 480 7000
E-Mail: culiacan@oma.aero
Airport Management Services
S.I.C.: 4581
N.A.I.C.S.: 488119

Aeropuerto Durango (1)
Autopista Gomez Palacios Dgo km 15 5
Durango, 34304, Mexico
Tel.: (52) 618 118 7012
E-Mail: durango@oma.aero
Airport Management Services
S.I.C.: 4581
N.A.I.C.S.: 488119

AEROPUERTO MAZATLAN, S.A. DE C.V. (1)
Carretera Internacional al Sur S/N
Mazatlan, Sinaloa, 82000, Mexico
Tel.: (52) 669 982 23 99
Web Site: www.oma.aero/en/contact-us/airport-directory.htm
Airport Management Services
S.I.C.: 4581
N.A.I.C.S.: 488119
Enrique Navarro Manjarrez *(Mng Dir)*

Aeropuerto Monterrey (1)
Carretera Miguel Aleman km 24
Apodaca, Nuevo Leon, 66600, Mexico
Tel.: (52) 81 82 88 7700
Airport Management Services
S.I.C.: 4581
N.A.I.C.S.: 488119

AEROPUERTO REYNOSA SA DE CV (1)
Carretera a Matamoros-Mazatlan
Reynosa, Tamaulipas, 88780, Mexico
Tel.: (52) 899 478 7000
E-Mail: reynosa@oma.aero
Airport Management Services
S.I.C.: 4581
N.A.I.C.S.: 488119

Aeropuerto Tampico, S. A. de C. V. (1)
Blvd Adolfo Lopez Mateos No 1001
Tampico, 89339, Mexico
Tel.: (52) 833 478 7000
E-Mail: tampico@oma.aero
Airport Management Services
S.I.C.: 4581
N.A.I.C.S.: 488119
Luis Roberto Alves *(Gen Mgr)*

AEROPUERTO TORREON S.A. DE C.V. (1)
Carretera Torreon San Pedro km 9 S/N
Torreon, Coahuila, 27016, Mexico
Tel.: (52) 871 4787000
E-Mail: torreon@oma.aero
Web Site: www.oma.aero/en/contact-us/airport-directory.htm
Airport Operating Services
S.I.C.: 4581
N.A.I.C.S.: 488119

Aeropuerto Zacatecas, S.A. de C.V. (1)
Carretera Panamericana Zacatecas-Fresnillo Km 23
98000 Zacatecas, Mexico
Tel.: (52) 478 985 0338
E-Mail: zacatecas@oma.aero
Airport Management Services
S.I.C.: 4581
N.A.I.C.S.: 488119

Asesoria Tecnica y Gestion Administrativa, S.A. de C.V. (1)
Mineria No 145 Edificio F P B
Mexico, 11800, Mexico
Tel.: (52) 5552729991
Fax: (52) 5552729991
Business Management Consulting Services
S.I.C.: 8742
N.A.I.C.S.: 541611

Autovia Mitla- Tehuantepec, S.A. de C.V. (1)
Blvd Manuel Avila Camacho No 36 Lomas de Chapultepec
Delegacion Miguel Hidalgo, Mexico, DF, 11000, Mexico
Tel.: (52) 55 5272 9991
Construction Material Whslr
S.I.C.: 5039
N.A.I.C.S.: 423390

Autovia Paradores y Servicios, S.A. de C.V. (1)
Blvd Manuel Avila Camacho No 36
Col Lomas de Chapultepec, Mexico, 11000, Mexico
Tel.: (52) 55 52729991
Construction Material Whslr
S.I.C.: 5039
N.A.I.C.S.: 423390

Caminos y Carreteras del Mayab, S.A.P.I. de C.V. (1)
Blvd Manuel Avila Camacho No 36 Lomas de Chapultepec
Seccion Miguel Hidalgo, Mexico, 11000, Mexico
Tel.: (52) 55 5272 9991
Construction Material Whslr
S.I.C.: 5039
N.A.I.C.S.: 423390

Carceri e Infraestructura, S.A.P.I. de C.V. (1)
Blvd Manuel Avila Camacho No 36 Lomas de Chapultepec
Seccion Miguel Hidalgo, Mexico, 11000, Mexico
Tel.: (52) 55 5272 9991
Construction Material Whslr
S.I.C.: 5039
N.A.I.C.S.: 423390

Centro Sur, S.A. de C.V. (1)
Mineria No 145 Escandon
Seccion Miguel Hidalgo, Mexico, 11800, Mexico
Tel.: (52) 55 52729991
Investment Management Services
S.I.C.: 6799
N.A.I.C.S.: 523920

Compania Hidroelectrica La Yesca, S.A. de C.V. (1)
Manuel Avila Camacho No 36 Piso 2
Mexico, 11000, Mexico
Tel.: (52) 5552729991
Industrial Construction Services
S.I.C.: 1542
N.A.I.C.S.: 236220

Compania Integradora Mercantil Agricola, S.A. de C.V. (1)
Mineria 145 Edif G 3o Piso Escandon
Seccion Miguel Hidalgo, Mexico, 11800, Mexico
Tel.: (52) 5552729991
Agricultural Product Whslr
S.I.C.: 9641
N.A.I.C.S.: 926140

Concesionaria de Ejes Terrestres de Coahuila, S.A. de C.V. (1)
Mineria 145 Edif F Planta Baja Escandon
Seccion Miguel Hidalgo, Mexico, 11800, Mexico
Tel.: (52) 5552275000
Road Construction Services
S.I.C.: 1629
N.A.I.C.S.: 237990

Constructora de Proyectos Hidroelectricos, S.A. de C.V. (1)
Manuel Avila Camacho No 36 Piso 2
Mexico, 11000, Mexico
Tel.: (52) 5552729991
Industrial Construction Services
S.I.C.: 1542
N.A.I.C.S.: 236220

Constructora El Cajon, S.A. de C.V. (1)
Mineria No 145 Edif G 3o piso Escandon
Seccion Miguel Hidalgo, Mexico, 11800, Mexico
Tel.: (52) 5552729991
Industrial Construction Services
S.I.C.: 1542
N.A.I.C.S.: 236220

Constructora Hidroelectrica La Yesca, S.A. de C.V. (1)
Manuel Avila Camacho No 36 Piso 2
Mexico, 11000, Mexico
Tel.: (52) 5552729991
Industrial Plant Construction Services
S.I.C.: 1629
N.A.I.C.S.: 237990

Constructoras ICA, S. A. de C. V. (1)
Blvd Manuel Avila Camacha No 36 Tower 2 Fl 9
Miguel Hidalgo, Mexico, 11870, Mexico
Tel.: (52) 555 272 9991
Emp.: 70
Construction Engineering Services
S.I.C.: 8711
N.A.I.C.S.: 541330
Bernardo Quintana Isaac *(Pres)*

Construexport, S.A. de C.V. (1)
Mineria No 145 Escandon
11800 Mexico, Mexico
Tel.: (52) 55 52729991
Industrial Building Construction Services
S.I.C.: 1629
N.A.I.C.S.: 236210

Controladora de Empresas de Vivienda, S. A. de C. V. (1)
Mineria No 145 Edif G 3o piso Escandon
Miguel Hidalgo, 11800, Mexico
Tel.: (52) 5552729991
Industrial Construction Services
S.I.C.: 1542
N.A.I.C.S.: 236220

Controladora de Operaciones de Infraestructura, S. A. de C. V. (1)
Blvd Manuel Avila Camacha No 36 Tower 2 Fl 9
Mexico, 11800, Mexico
Tel.: (52) 5552729991
Fax: (52) 5552777126
Emp.: 70
Investment Management Services
S.I.C.: 6282
N.A.I.C.S.: 523920
Bernardo Quintana Isaac *(Pres)*

Grupo Aeroportuario Centro Norte, S.A. de C.V. (1)
Carretera Miguel Aleman S/N Km 24
Apodaca, 66600, Mexico
Tel.: (52) 8186254300
Airport Management Services
S.I.C.: 4581
N.A.I.C.S.: 488119

Ica Construccion Civil, S.A. de C.V. (1)
Mineria 145 Colonia Escandon Edificio B Piso 2
Delegacion Miguel Hidalgo, Mexico, DF, 11800, Mexico
Tel.: (52) 5552729991
Fax: (52) 5552275060
Industrial Construction Services
S.I.C.: 1542
N.A.I.C.S.: 236220

Ica Infraestructura, S.A. de C.V. (1)
Mineria No 145
Mexico, 11800, Mexico
Tel.: (52) 5552729991
Fax: (52) 55 5277 5045
Industrial Construction Services
S.I.C.: 1542
N.A.I.C.S.: 236220

Ica Ingenieria, S.A. de C.V. (1)
Mineria No 145 Edif A Piso 3
Mexico, 11800, Mexico
Tel.: (52) 5552729991
Industrial Construction Services
S.I.C.: 1542
N.A.I.C.S.: 236220

Ica Propiedades Inmuebles, S.A. de C.V. (1)
Manuel Avila Camacho 36
Mexico, 11800, Mexico
Tel.: (52) 5552729991
Real Estate Development Services
S.I.C.: 6531
N.A.I.C.S.: 531390

Ica Servicios de Direccion Corporativa, S.A. de C.V. (1)
Minera No 145
Mexico, 11800, Mexico
Tel.: (52) 5552729991
Construction Engineering Services
S.I.C.: 8711
N.A.I.C.S.: 541330

Icapital, S.A. de C.V. (1)
Mineria No 145 Escandon
Seccion Miguel Hidalgo, Mexico, 11800, Mexico
Tel.: (52) 55 52729991
Industrial Construction Services
S.I.C.: 1542
N.A.I.C.S.: 236220

Ingenieros Civiles Asociados, S. A. de C. V. (1)
Mineria 145 Edificio Central
Mexico, 11800, Mexico
Tel.: (52) 5 272 9991
Fax: (52) 5 227 5065
Civil Engineering Construction Services
S.I.C.: 1629
N.A.I.C.S.: 237990

Inmobiliaria Baja, S.A. de C.V. (1)
Blvd Manuel Avila Camacho No 36
Mexico, 11000, Mexico
Tel.: (52) 5552729991
Real Estate Management Services
S.I.C.: 6531
N.A.I.C.S.: 531390

Libramiento ICA La Piedad, S.A. de C.V. (1)
Manuel Avila Camacho No 36
Mexico, 11000, Mexico
Tel.: (52) 5552729991
Industrial Construction Services
S.I.C.: 1542
N.A.I.C.S.: 236220

Operadora de la Autopista del Occidente, S.A. de C.V. (1)
Blvd Manuel Avila Camacho No 36
Mexico, 11000, Mexico
Tel.: (52) 5552729991
Fax: (52) 5552734315
Commercial Building Construction Services
S.I.C.: 1542
N.A.I.C.S.: 236220
Ramon Martinez Solorio *(Mgr)*

Prefabricados y Transportes, S.A. de C.V. (1)
Blvd Manuel Avila Camacho No 36 5o Piso Lomas de Chapultepec
Mexico, 11000, Mexico
Tel.: (52) 5552729991
Industrial Construction Services
S.I.C.: 1542
N.A.I.C.S.: 236220

Promotora e Inversora Adisa, S.A. de C.V. (1)
Mineria No 145 Edif G 3er Piso
Mexico, 11800, Mexico
Tel.: (52) 5552729991
Investment Management Services
S.I.C.: 6282
N.A.I.C.S.: 523920

Tuneles Concesionados de Acapulco, S.A. de C.V. (1)
Domicilio Conocido Caseta de Cobro
Las Cruces, Coyuca de Catalan, Guerrero, 39760, Mexico
Tel.: (52) 7444411766
Industrial Construction Services
S.I.C.: 1542
N.A.I.C.S.: 236220

Viveica, S.A. de C.V. (1)
Mineria 145 Edif D 4to Piso Col Escandon
Miguel Hidalgo, Mexico, 11800, Mexico
Tel.: (52) 656 681 7295
Fax: (52) 656 647 2603
Web Site: www.viveica.com.mx
Real Estate Management Services
S.I.C.: 6531
N.A.I.C.S.: 531390

U.S. Subsidiaries:

Ica Construction Corporation (1)
908 Town & Country Blvd
Houston, TX 77024
Tel.: (713) 984-7628
Emp.: 4
Construction Engineering Services
S.I.C.: 8711

N.A.I.C.S.: 541330
Ulises Vidal *(CEO)*

Ica- Miramar Corporation (1)
444 Calle De Diego Ste 105
San Juan, PR 00923
Tel.: (787) 622-3040
Highway & Street Construction Services
S.I.C.: 1611
N.A.I.C.S.: 237310

Ica- Miramar Metro San Juan Corp. (1)
Carr 2 Km 6 4
Guaynabo, PR 00966
Tel.: (787) 782-9711
Highway Construction Services
S.I.C.: 1622
N.A.I.C.S.: 237310

Non-U.S. Subsidiaries:

Ica Construccion Civil de Venezuela, S.A. (1)
Av Colombia Torre Loreto II B Ph
Valencia, Venezuela
Tel.: (58) 414 272 4601
Civil Engineering Construction Services
S.I.C.: 1629
N.A.I.C.S.: 237990

Ingenieros Civiles Asociados Mexico, S.A. (1)
Cl 102 A 50 49
Bogota, Colombia
Tel.: (57) 12574079
Residential Building Construction Services
S.I.C.: 1522
N.A.I.C.S.: 236116

Rodio Cimentaciones Especiales, S.A. (1)
Velazquez 50 6th Fl
28001 Madrid, Spain (100%)
Tel.: (34) 915624610
Fax: (34) 915641440
E-Mail: rodio@rodio.com
Web Site: www.rodio.com
Emp.: 80
S.I.C.: 1622
N.A.I.C.S.: 237310
Jose Luex Rogo *(Gen Mgr)*

San Martin Contratistas Generales S.A. (1)
Av Pedro Miotta 103
San Juan de Miraflores, Lima, Peru
Tel.: (51) 511 450 1999
Fax: (51) 511 276 9851
Web Site: www.sanmartinperu.pe
Mining Engineering Services
S.I.C.: 8711
N.A.I.C.S.: 541330

Sondagens Rodio Ltda. (1)
Avenida Dos Combatientes No 52 Apartado 112-Abrunheira
2710 Sintra, Portugal
Tel.: (351) 219158210
Fax: (351) 21 915 16 07
E-Mail: rodio@rodio.pt
Web Site: www.rodio.pt
Emp.: 70
Civil Engineering & Construction
S.I.C.: 1622
N.A.I.C.S.: 237310

EMPRESAS JUAN YARUR S.A.C.

125 Av El Golf Las Condes
Santiago, Chile
Tel.: (56) 2 692 7000
Web Site: www.bci.cl
Emp.: 2,000

Business Description:
Holding Company: Banking Services
S.I.C.: 6712
N.A.I.C.S.: 551111

Personnel:
Luis Enrique Yarur Rey *(Chm)*

Subsidiary:

Banco de Credito e Inversiones (1)
Avenida El Golf 125
Las Condes, Santiago, Chile (53.73%)
Tel.: (56) 2 692 7000
E-Mail: investor_relations_bci@bci.cl
Web Site: www.bci.cl
BCI—(SGO)
Int. Income: $2,389,295,120
Assets: $38,004,345,360
Liabilities: $34,994,036,520
Net Worth: $3,010,308,840
Earnings: $575,062,720
Emp.: 10,595
Fiscal Year-end: 12/31/12
Commercial Banking Services
S.I.C.: 6029
N.A.I.C.S.: 522110
Luis Enrique Yarur Rey *(Chm)*
Andres Bianchi Larre *(Vice Chm)*
Lionel Olavarria Leyton *(CEO)*

Subsidiary:

BCI Seguros Generales S.A. (2)
Huerfanos 1189 Piso 3 Fl 2 4
Santiago, Chile
Tel.: (56) 26799350
Fax: (56) 26799480
E-Mail: sinustros@bciseguros.cl
Web Site: www.bciseguros.cl
Emp.: 500
Life Insurance
S.I.C.: 6311
N.A.I.C.S.: 524113
Mario Gaitua *(Gen Mgr)*

EMPRESAS PETROLEO IPIRANGA

Av Dolores Alcaraz Caldas 90
CEP 901-180 Porto Alegre, RS, Brazil
Tel.: (55) 5132164411
Web Site: www.ipiranga.com.br
Emp.: 384

Business Description:
Oil & Gas Exploration & Development Services
S.I.C.: 1311
N.A.I.C.S.: 211111

EMPRESAS POLAR

2 Da Avenida De Los Cortijos
Ed Centro Empresarial Polar,
Caracas, 1071, Venezuela
Tel.: (58) 212202311
Fax: (58) 212202709
E-Mail: webmaster@empresas-polar.com
Web Site: www.empresas-polar.com
Emp.: 10,001

Business Description:
Holding Company
S.I.C.: 6719
N.A.I.C.S.: 551112

Subsidiary:

Mavesa, S.A. (1)
Avenida Principal De Los Ruces Centro Ed Centro Empresarial Polar, Caracas, 1071, Venezuela
Tel.: (58) 2122023111
Fax: (58) 580212000
Web Site: www.empresas-polar.com
Emp.: 1,800
Mfr. & Distributor of Consumer Products such as Food, Soaps & Cleaning Products
S.I.C.: 2034
N.A.I.C.S.: 311423

EMPTEEZY LTD

Muir Rd
Houstoun Industrial Estate,
Livingston, W Lothian, EH54 5DR, United Kingdom
Tel.: (44) 506430309
Fax: (44) 506441466
Web Site: www.empteezy.co.uk
Emp.: 60

Business Description:
Engineered Storage & Waste Handling Solutions
S.I.C.: 4959
N.A.I.C.S.: 562998

Personnel:
Bruce Wishart *(Mng Dir)*

Non-U.S. Subsidiary:

Schoeller Industries (1)
Z I Rue De La Maziere
67130 Wisches, France FR
Tel.: (33) 388473500
Fax: (33) 388473380
E-Mail: info@schoellerindustries.fr
Web Site: www.schoellerindustries.fr
Emp.: 32
Engineered Papers & Specialized Printing Papers Mfr
S.I.C.: 2621
N.A.I.C.S.: 322122
Bruce Wishart *(Mng Dir)*

EMPYREAN ENERGY PLC

200 Strand
London, WC2R 1DJ, United Kingdom
Tel.: (44) 2071821746
E-Mail: enquiries@empyreanenergy.com
Web Site: www.empyreanenergy.com
EME—(LSE)
Rev.: $9,306,756
Assets: $36,939,593
Liabilities: $10,761,282
Net Worth: $26,178,311
Earnings: $3,180,690
Fiscal Year-end: 03/31/13

Business Description:
Energy Resource Exploration & Development In Geopolitically Stable Environments
S.I.C.: 9611
N.A.I.C.S.: 926110

Personnel:
Tom Kelly *(CEO)*
Amanda Wilton-Heald *(Sec & Controller-Fin)*

Board of Directors:
Patrick Cross
Frank Brophy
Tom Kelly
John Laycock

Legal Counsel:
Kerman & Co. LLP
200 Strand
London, EC1V 9EE, United Kingdom

EMS-CHEMIE HOLDING AG

Fuederholzstrasse 34
8704 Herrliberg, Switzerland
Tel.: (41) 44 915 7000
Fax: (41) 44 915 7002
E-Mail: info@ems-group.com
Web Site: www.ems-group.com
EMSN—(SWX)
Rev.: $1,950,508,248
Assets: $1,809,945,167
Liabilities: $567,480,552
Net Worth: $1,242,464,615
Earnings: $294,448,210
Emp.: 2,371
Fiscal Year-end: 12/31/12

Business Description:
Polymer Plastics & Fiber Mfr
S.I.C.: 3089
N.A.I.C.S.: 326199

Personnel:
Ulf Berg *(Chm)*
Magdalena Martullo-Blocher *(Vice Chm & CEO)*
Peter Germann *(CFO)*
Conrad Gericke *(Sec Gen & Head-Corp Admin)*

Board of Directors:
Ulf Berg
Urs Fankhauser
Magdalena Martullo-Blocher
Joachim Streu

Subsidiaries:

Eftec AG (1)
Hofstrasse 31
PO Box 46
CH 9323 Romanshorn, 8590, Switzerland (100%)
Tel.: (41) 714664300
Fax: (41) 714664301
E-Mail: h.vogel@strtest.ch
Web Site: www.eftec.ch
Sales Range: $25-49.9 Million
Emp.: 100
Adhesives, Sealants & Coatings Mfr for the Automotive Industry
S.I.C.: 2891
N.A.I.C.S.: 325520
R. Holderegger *(Mng Dir)*
T. Zahner *(Mng Dir)*

Non-U.S. Subsidiaries:

Changchun EFTEC Chemical Products Ltd. (2)
No 808 Chuangxin Rd New & High Tech Ind
Development Zone, Changchun, 130012, China
Tel.: (86) 43185080800
Fax: (86) 43185080808
Web Site: www.eftec.com
Emp.: 16
S.I.C.: 3089
N.A.I.C.S.: 326199
Han Qingguo *(Gen Mgr)*

D Plast-Eftec a.s. (2)
Utescomy 206
76001 Zlin, Czech Republic CZ
Tel.: (420) 577004411 (52%)
Fax: (420) 577004444
E-Mail: zlin@dplast-eftec.cz
Web Site: www.dplast-eftec.cz
Sales Range: $500-549.9 Million
Emp.: 85
Mfr. of Automotive Products & Parts
S.I.C.: 3714
N.A.I.C.S.: 336340
Jiri Drag *(Gen Mgr)*

D Plast-Eftec NN (2)
ul Kovpaka 1
603 053 Nizhniy Novgorod, Russia
Tel.: (7) 8312530515
Fax: (7) 8312530515
E-Mail: vvvsnab@sandy.ru
Web Site: www.ems-group.com
S.I.C.: 3089
N.A.I.C.S.: 326199

D PLAST-EFTEC RO S.R.L. (2)
Budeasa Mare Arges
117-151 Budeasa, Romania
Tel.: (40) 248 236 377
Fax: (40) 248 236 325
E-Mail: ion.cazan@dplast-eftec.eu
Adhesives, Sealants & Coatings Mfr
S.I.C.: 2891
N.A.I.C.S.: 325520

D PLAST-EFTEC UA (2)
Gorkeho 27/29
69063 Zaporizhzhya, Ukraine
Tel.: (380) 612138568
Fax: (380) 612 138 568
E-Mail: plastol@comint.net
Web Site: www.eftec.com
Adhesives, Sealants & Coatings Mfr
S.I.C.: 2891
N.A.I.C.S.: 325520

Eftec Asia Pte. Ltd. (2)
15 Beach Road
#03-07 Beach Centre, Singapore, 189677, Singapore (100%)
Tel.: (65) 65458201
Fax: (65) 63372806
Web Site: www.ems-group.com
Sales Range: $700-749.9 Million
Emp.: 6
Plastic Products Mfr
S.I.C.: 3089
N.A.I.C.S.: 326199

EFTEC Brasil Ltda. (2)
Av Charles Goodyear 521 Cururuquara
CEP 06524-115 Santana de Parnaiba, SP, Brazil
Tel.: (55) 11 4193 1353
Fax: (55) 11 4193 1148
Adhesives, Sealants & Coatings Mfr
S.I.C.: 2891
N.A.I.C.S.: 325520

EFTEC China Ltd. (2)
3313-3317 Jardine House
1 Connaught Place, Central, China (Hong Kong)

EMS-Chemie Holding AG—(Continued)

Tel.: (852) 2526 4868
Fax: (852) 2526 6568
Adhesives, Sealants & Coatings Mfr
S.I.C.: 2891
N.A.I.C.S.: 325520

Eftec Engineering AB (2)
Spangatan 3
28121 Hassleholm, Sweden (100%)
Tel.: (46) 45188000
Web Site: www.eftec.se
Sales Range: $10-24.9 Million
Emp.: 40
Mfr of Adhesives, Sealants & Coatings for the Automotive Industry
S.I.C.: 3084
N.A.I.C.S.: 326199

EFTEC Engineering GmbH (2)
Dornierstrasse 7
88677 Markdorf, Germany
Tel.: (49) 7544 9200
Fax: (49) 7544 920200
Adhesives, Sealants & Coatings Mfr
S.I.C.: 2891
N.A.I.C.S.: 325520

EFTEC Guangzhou Automotive Materials Co. Ltd. (2)
Room 516-517 Jing Xing Building
No 89 Linhe Road West
Tian He District, Guangzhou, 510620, China
Tel.: (86) 20 3877 2815
Fax: (86) 50 3877 2963
Adhesives, Sealants & Coatings Mfr
S.I.C.: 2891
N.A.I.C.S.: 325520

EFTEC (India) Pvt. Ltd. (2)
G-9 MIDC Arena Ranjangaon
Tal Shirur, 412 210 Pune, India
Tel.: (91) 2138 663 400
Fax: (91) 2138 663401
Web Site: www.eftec.com
Emp.: 5
Adhesives, Sealants & Coatings Mfr
S.I.C.: 2891
N.A.I.C.S.: 325520
Elise Vaillant *(Gen Mgr)*

Eftec Ltd. (2)
Treherbert Road Rhigos
Aberdare, M Glam, CF44 9UE, United Kingdom (100%)
Tel.: (44) 1685815400
Fax: (44) 1685813997
E-Mail: enquiries@eftec.comcom
Web Site: www.eftec.com
Emp.: 30
Mfr of Adhesives, Sealants & Coatings for the Automotive Industry
S.I.C.: 3084
N.A.I.C.S.: 326199
Steve Reynolds *(Mng Dir)*

Eftec Market GmbH (2)
Pyrmonter Strasse 76
Lugde, 32676, Germany (100%)
Tel.: (49) 5281982980
Fax: (49) 52819829860
E-Mail: service@eftec.de
Web Site: www.eftec.de
Sls.: $10,396,854
Emp.: 65
Mfr. of Polymer Plastics & Fiber
S.I.C.: 3089
N.A.I.C.S.: 326199
Edmond Robeyn *(Mng Dir)*

Eftec N.V. (2)
Henry Fordlaan 1
Genk, Limburg, 3600, Belgium (99%)
Tel.: (32) 89612786
Fax: (32) 89612793
E-Mail: info@ems-group.com
Web Site: www.ems-group.com
Emp.: 100
Mfr. of Polymer Plastics & Fiber
S.I.C.: 3089
N.A.I.C.S.: 326199
Chrestel Martens *(Mgr-Pur)*

EFTEC-PLACOSA (2)
Calle 56 sur #11 CIVAC
62578 Jiutepec, Morelos, Mexico
Tel.: (52) 777 319 3477
Fax: (52) 777 320 4240
Adhesives, Sealants & Coatings Mfr
S.I.C.: 2891
N.A.I.C.S.: 325520

Eftec S.A. (2)
Carretera Logrono Km 29 Pt 2
Figueruelas, Zaragoza, 50639, Spain (100%)
Tel.: (34) 976656269
Fax: (34) 976656270
E-Mail: info@ems-group.com
Web Site: www.ems-group.com
Emp.: 35
Mfr of Adhesives, Sealants & Coatings for the Automotive Industry
S.I.C.: 3089
N.A.I.C.S.: 326199

Eftec S.a.r.l. (2)
Les Marches de l'Oise Batiment Copenhague
100 rue Louis Blanc, F 60765 Montataire, Cedex, France
Tel.: (33) 344241918
Fax: (33) 344249710
Web Site: www.eftec.ch/index.cfm?id=20#
Sales Range: $125-149.9 Million
Emp.: 8
Mfr of Polymer Plastics & Fiber
S.I.C.: 3089
N.A.I.C.S.: 326199
Jean- Francis Rommes *(Mng Dir)*

Eftec Shroff India Limited (2)
Plot No 645-646 4th FL Oberoi Chambers II
New Link Road, Mumbai, 400053, India (49%)
Tel.: (91) 2226747900
Fax: (91) 2226736218
E-Mail: esil@eftecindia.com
Web Site: www.eftec.com
Sales Range: $700-749.9 Million
Emp.: 120
Bonding, Coating, Sealing & Damping Systems
S.I.C.: 3053
N.A.I.C.S.: 339991
Abdul Gambir *(Gen Mgr)*

Eftec (Thailand) Co. Ltd. (2)
E Seaboard Industrial Est 109-10 Moo 4 Pluakdaeng
Rayong, 21140, Thailand (100%)
Tel.: (66) 38954271
Fax: (66) 38954270
E-Mail: info@eftec.com
Web Site: www.eftec.com
Sales Range: $25-49.9 Million
Emp.: 20
Mfr of Adhesives, Sealants & Coatings for the Automotive Industry
S.I.C.: 3089
N.A.I.C.S.: 326199
Patrick Janssen *(Gen Mgr)*

Shanghai Eftec Chemical Products Ltd. (2)
521 Guang Hua Rd Hu Min Rd
Shanghai, 201 108, China (60%)
Tel.: (86) 2164891122
Fax: (86) 2164891199
Web Site: www.eftec.com
Sales Range: $10-24.9 Million
Emp.: 70
Sealant, Adhesive & Coating Mfr
S.I.C.: 2851
N.A.I.C.S.: 325510

Wuhu EFTEC Chemical Products Ltd. (2)
Yinhu North Road East
Wuhu, Anhui, 241009, China
Tel.: (86) 553 596 5152
Fax: (86) 553 596 5151
Adhesives, Sealants & Coatings Mfr
S.I.C.: 2891
N.A.I.C.S.: 325520

EMS-Chemie AG (1)
Reichenauer Strasse
Domat/Ems, 7013, Switzerland (100%)
Tel.: (41) 816326111
Fax: (41) 816327401
E-Mail: welcome@emschem.com
Web Site: www.emschem.com
Emp.: 1,600
S.I.C.: 3084
N.A.I.C.S.: 326199
Morf Christian *(VP-Sls & Mktg)*

EMS-PATENT AG (1)
Via Innovativa
7013 Domat/Ems, Switzerland
Tel.: (41) 81 632 6826
Fax: (41) 81 632 7440
E-Mail: info@emspatent.com
Web Site: www.emspatent.com
Plastics Products Mfr
S.I.C.: 3089
N.A.I.C.S.: 326199
Magdalena Martullo *(Gen Mgr)*

U.S. Subsidiary:

EMS-Chemie (North America) Inc. (1)
2060 Corporate Way
Sumter, SC 29150-1717 (100%)
Tel.: (803) 481-9173
Fax: (803) 481-6121
E-Mail: welcome@us.emschem.com
Web Site: www.emschem.com
Emp.: 100
Mfr. of Polyhydrocarbonic Chemicals
S.I.C.: 2821
N.A.I.C.S.: 325211
Guido Hobi *(CEO)*

Non-U.S. Subsidiaries:

EMS-CHEMIE (China) Ltd. (1)
227 Songbei Road Suzhou Industrial Park
Suzhou, Jiangsu, 215126, China
Tel.: (86) 512 8666 8180
Fax: (86) 512 8666 6180
E-Mail: welcome@cn.emsgrivory.com
Polymer Plastics & Fiber Mfr
S.I.C.: 3089
N.A.I.C.S.: 326199

EMS-Chemie (Deutschland) GmbH (1)
Warthweg 14
Gross-Umstadt, Hessen, 64823, Germany (100%)
Tel.: (49) 60787830
Fax: (49) 6078783416
E-Mail: welcome@de.emschem.com
Web Site: www.ems-group.com
Emp.: 150
S.I.C.: 3089
N.A.I.C.S.: 326199
Habbet Back *(Gen Mgr)*

EMS-Chemie (France) S.A. (1)
73-77 Rue De Sevres
PO Box 52
F 92105 Boulogne-Billancourt, France (100%)
Tel.: (33) 141100610
Fax: (33) 148255607
E-Mail: welcome@fr.emsgrivory.com
Web Site: www.emsgrivory.com
Emp.: 25
Chemical Polymers Mfr
S.I.C.: 2819
N.A.I.C.S.: 325180
Christian Morf *(VP-Sls & Mktg)*

EMS-CHEMIE (Japan) Ltd. (1)
EMS Building 2-11-20 Higashi-koujiya
Ota-ku, Tokyo, 144 0033, Japan (70%)
Tel.: (81) 357350611
Fax: (81) 357350614
E-Mail: welcome@jp.emsgrivory.com
Web Site: www.ems-group.com
Emp.: 15
Performance Polymers & Fine Chemicals/ Engineering
S.I.C.: 2899
N.A.I.C.S.: 325199

EMS-CHEMIE (Korea) Ltd. (1)
#1226 Dong Gwan Doosan Venturedigm
126-1 Pyeong Chon-dong
Dong An-gu, Anyang, Gyeong Gi, 431-070, Korea (South)
Tel.: (82) 31 478 3159
Fax: (82) 31 478 3157
Polymer Plastics & Fiber Mfr
S.I.C.: 3089
N.A.I.C.S.: 326199

EMS-CHEMIE (Neumunster) GmbH Co. KG (1)
Tungendorfer Str 10
24536 Neumunster, Germany
Tel.: (49) 4321 302500
Fax: (49) 4321 302511
E-Mail: info@de.emsgriltech.com
Polymer Plastics & Fiber Mfr
S.I.C.: 3089
N.A.I.C.S.: 326199

EMS-CHEMIE (Suzhou) Ltd. (1)
227 Songbei Road Suzhou Industrial Park
Suzhou, Jiangsu, 215126, China
Tel.: (86) 512 8666 8181
Fax: (86) 512 8666 8183
E-Mail: welcome@cn.emsgrivory.com
Polymer Plastics & Fiber Mfr
S.I.C.: 3089
N.A.I.C.S.: 326199

EMS-CHEMIE (Taiwan) Ltd. (1)
36 Kwang Fu South Road
Hsin Chu Industrial Park
Fu Kou Hsiang, Hsin-chu, Hsien, 30351, Taiwan (100%)
Tel.: (886) 35985335
Fax: (886) 35985345
E-Mail: welcome@tw.emsgrivory.com
Web Site: www.ems-group.com
Emp.: 65
Polymer Plastics & Fiber Mfr
S.I.C.: 3089
N.A.I.C.S.: 326199

EMS-Chemie (UK) Ltd. (1)
Darfin House Priestly Ct Stafford Technology Park
Stafford, ST180LQ, United Kingdom (100%)
Tel.: (44) 8458385180
Fax: (44) 1785283722
E-Mail: welcome@uk.emschem.com
Web Site: www.ems-group.com
Emp.: 10
S.I.C.: 3089
N.A.I.C.S.: 326199
Christin Mors *(VP-Sls & Mktg)*

EMS-INTERNATIONAL FINANCE (Guernsey) Ltd. (1)
Trafalger Court 3rd Floor West Wing
Saint Peter Port, GY1 2JA, Guernsey
Tel.: (44) 1481 712704
Fax: (44) 1481 712705
Financial Services
S.I.C.: 7389
N.A.I.C.S.: 561499

EMS-PATVAG s.r.o. (1)
Brankovice 350
Brankovice, 683 33, Czech Republic (100%)
Tel.: (420) 517302200
Fax: (420) 517302222
E-Mail: welcome@emspatvag.com
Web Site: www.emspatvag.com
Emp.: 180
Systems Engineering
S.I.C.: 7373
N.A.I.C.S.: 541512
Urs Ulrich Britt *(Mng Dir)*

EMS-UBE Ltd. (1)
1978-10 Kogushi
Ube, Yamaguchi, 755-8633, Japan
Tel.: (81) 836 310213
Fax: (81) 836 310214
E-Mail: uems1k3@ube-ind.co.jp
Polymer Plastics & Fiber Mfr
S.I.C.: 3089
N.A.I.C.S.: 326199

EMS ENERGY LIMITED

10 Tuas Avenue 11
Singapore, 639076, Singapore
Tel.: (65) 68621062
Fax: (65) 68615512
E-Mail: mail@emsenergy.com.sg
Web Site: www.emsenergy.com.sg
5DE—(SES)
Rev.: $15,132,110
Assets: $40,141,505
Liabilities: $28,448,916
Net Worth: $11,692,589
Earnings: ($12,485,266)
Emp.: 100
Fiscal Year-end: 12/31/12

Business Description:
Marine, Oil & Gas Engineering Services & Mfr
S.I.C.: 1629
N.A.I.C.S.: 237990

Personnel:
Teck Jin Ting *(Chm & CEO)*
Patsy Mah *(CFO)*
Gwendolyn Jong Yuh Gn *(Sec)*
Board of Directors:
Teck Jin Ting
Poh Boon Lim
Siong Sheng Lim
Gim Sei Ung
Legal Counsel:
ShookLin & Bok LLP
1 Robinson Road 18 00 AIA Tower
Singapore, Singapore
Transfer Agent:
M & C Services Private Limited
112 Robinson Road 05-01
Singapore, Singapore
Subsidiaries:

EMS Offshore Pte Ltd (1)
10 Tuas Ave 11
Singapore, 639076, Singapore
Tel.: (65) 68621062
Fax: (65) 68621368
E-Mail: mail@emsenergy.com.sg
Web Site: www.emsenergy.com.sg/con_energyservices.html
Vessel Products Mfr
S.I.C.: 2652
N.A.I.C.S.: 322219
Ting Teck Jin *(CEO)*

Subsidiaries:

Engineering & Marine Services (Pte) Ltd (2)
10 Tuas Ave 11
Singapore, 639076, Singapore
Tel.: (65) 68621062
Fax: (65) 68615655
E-Mail: mail@emsenergy.com.sg
Web Site: www.emsenergy.com.sg
Offshore Natural Gas Production Services
S.I.C.: 1311
N.A.I.C.S.: 211111

Oilfield Services & Supplies Pte Ltd (2)
No 11 Joo Koon Rd
Singapore, 628974, Singapore
Tel.: (65) 65425933
Fax: (65) 65426355
E-Mail: posk@ossapi.com
Web Site: www.ossapi.com
Emp.: 45
Oil & Gas Drilling Services
S.I.C.: 1381
N.A.I.C.S.: 213111
Peter Ong *(Mng Dir)*

EMS Water Pte Ltd (1)
10 Tuas Ave 11
Singapore, Singapore
Tel.: (65) 68621062
Fax: (65) 68984056
E-Mail: enquiry@emswater.com.sg
Web Site: www.emsenergy.com.sg/eco_products.html
Emp.: 30
General Trading Company
S.I.C.: 1799
N.A.I.C.S.: 238990
Jayaraj Neyak *(Mgr)*

EMU NICKEL NL
(Name Changed to Emu NL)

EMU NL
(Formerly Emu Nickel NL)
10 Walker Avenue
West Perth, WA, 6005, Australia
Mailing Address:
PO Box 1112
West Perth, WA, 6872, Australia
Tel.: (61) 892264266
Fax: (61) 894852840
E-Mail: info@emunl.com.au
Web Site: www.emunl.com.au
EMU—(ASX)
Rev.: $341,499
Assets: $4,581,678
Liabilities: $48,531
Net Worth: $4,533,148
Earnings: ($138,046)
Emp.: 10
Fiscal Year-end: 06/30/13
Business Description:
Diamond Mining Services
S.I.C.: 1411
N.A.I.C.S.: 212311
Personnel:
Peter Thomas *(Chm)*
Greg Steemson *(Mng Dir)*
Board of Directors:
Peter Thomas
Gavin Rutherford
Greg Steemson
Legal Counsel:
Smyth & Thomas
10 Walker Avenue
Perth, Australia

EMUGE-WERK RICHARD GLIMPEL GMBH & CO. KG
Nurnberger Str 96-100
91207 Lauf an der Pegnitz, Germany
Tel.: (49) 91231860
Fax: (49) 912314313
E-Mail: info@emuge.de
Web Site: www.emuge.de
Rev.: $100,696,200
Emp.: 761
Business Description:
Threading Equipments Mfr
S.I.C.: 3541
N.A.I.C.S.: 333517
Personnel:
Helmut Glimpel *(Mng Dir)*

EMW
459-24 Gozan-dong
Seoul, Geumcheon-gu, Korea (South)
Tel.: (82) 221075500
Fax: (82) 28376351
Web Site: www.emw.co.kr
Year Founded: 1988
079190—(KRS)
Business Description:
Electronic Device Mfr
S.I.C.: 3679
N.A.I.C.S.: 334419
Personnel:
Byung-Hoon Ryu *(CEO)*

EMX ENTERPRISES LIMITED
250 Granton Drive
Richmond Hill, ON, L4B 1H7, Canada
Tel.: (905) 764-0040
Fax: (905) 764-0076
Web Site: www.emx.ca
Year Founded: 1970
Sales Range: $25-49.9 Million
Emp.: 36
Business Description:
Printed Circuit Supplies & Electronic Components Whslr
S.I.C.: 5065
N.A.I.C.S.: 423690
Personnel:
Arthur Legiehn *(Founder)*

EN-JAPAN INC.
Shinjuku I-land Tower 6-5-1 Nishi-Shinjuku Shinjuku-ku
Tokyo, 163-1335, Japan
Tel.: (81) 3 3342 3386
Fax: (81) 3 3342 3324
Web Site: corp.en-japan.com
Year Founded: 2000
4849—(JAS)
Sls.: $149,200,502
Assets: $203,103,868
Liabilities: $35,041,424
Net Worth: $168,062,444
Earnings: $17,004,548
Emp.: 8,505
Fiscal Year-end: 03/31/13
Business Description:
Recruitment Consultation Services
S.I.C.: 8748
N.A.I.C.S.: 541618
Personnel:
Michikatsu Ochi *(Chm)*
Takatsugu Suzuki *(Pres)*
Subsidiaries:

Cbase corporation (1)
Fukuriku bldg 8F 1-14-6 Uchikanda
Chyoda-ku, Tokyo, 101-0047, Japan
Tel.: (81) 3 5282 3554
Web Site: www.cbase.co.jp
Recruitment Services
S.I.C.: 7361
N.A.I.C.S.: 561311

en world Japan K.K. (1)
6F Kojun Building 6-8-7 Ginza
Chuo-ku, Tokyo, 104-0061, Japan
Tel.: (81) 3 3289 3101
Fax: (81) 3 3289 3102
E-Mail: info@enworld.com
Web Site: www.enworld.com
Emp.: 180
Employment Placement Agency
S.I.C.: 7361
N.A.I.C.S.: 561311
Craig Saphin, *(Pres)*
Neal Walters *(Exec VP)*

Non-U.S. Subsidiaries:

Calibrate Recruitment Pty Ltd (1)
Level 1 1 Chandos Street
Saint Leonards, NSW, 2065, Australia
Tel.: (61) 2 9431 6500
Fax: (61) 2 9901 3811
Web Site: www.calibrate.com.au
Recruitment Services
S.I.C.: 7361
N.A.I.C.S.: 561311
Geoff Cooper, *(Mng Dir)*

The Capstone Group Recruitment and Consulting (Thailand) Ltd. (1)
Trendy Building 7th Floor Sukhumvit Soi 13
Bangkok, Thailand
Tel.: (66) 2 168 7070
E-Mail: info@thecapstonegroup.com
Web Site: www.thecapstonegroup.com
Employment Placement Agency
S.I.C.: 7361
N.A.I.C.S.: 561311

en world Hong-Kong Limited. (1)
Level 27 World Wide House 19 Des Voeux Road
Central, China (Hong Kong)
Tel.: (852) 3972 6580
Fax: (852) 3182 7316
E-Mail: hongkong@enworld.com
Web Site: www.enworld.com
Recruitment Services
S.I.C.: 7361
N.A.I.C.S.: 561311
Robert England, *(Pres)*

en world Korea Co., Ltd (1)
10F Seoul Finance Center 136 Sejong-Daero
Jung-gu, Seoul, 100-768, Korea (South)
Tel.: (82) 2 3782 4680
Fax: (82) 2 3782 4555
E-Mail: korea@enworld.com
Web Site: www.enworld.com
Recruitment Services
S.I.C.: 7361
N.A.I.C.S.: 561311
Simon Kim, *(Pres)*

en world SINGAPORE PTE. LTD. (1)
30 Raffles Place Unit 13-02 Chevron House
Singapore, 048622, Singapore
Tel.: (65) 6420 0570
Fax: (65) 6534 1143
E-Mail: singapore@enworld.com
Web Site: www.enworld.com
Employment Placement Agency
S.I.C.: 7361
N.A.I.C.S.: 561311
Brian Richards, *(Pres)*

Navigos Group Joint Stock Company (1)
130 Suong Nguyet Anh St
District 1, Ho Chi Minh City, Vietnam
Tel.: (84) 8 3925 5000
Fax: (84) 8 3925 5111
E-Mail: contact@navigosgroup.com
Web Site: www.navigosgroup.com
Recruitment Services
S.I.C.: 7361
N.A.I.C.S.: 561311
Jonah Founder & Chm *(Founder & Chm)*
Carlton Pringle *(CEO)*

Subsidiary:

Navigos Search (2)
6th Floor V-Building 125 -127 Ba Trieu Street
Hai Ba Trung District, Hanoi, Vietnam
Tel.: (84) 4 3974 3033
Fax: (84) 4 3974 3032
E-Mail: contact@navigossearch.com
Web Site: www.navigossearch.com
Employment Placement Agency
S.I.C.: 7361
N.A.I.C.S.: 561311
Jonah Levey, *(Founder & Chm)*
Nguyen Thi Van Anh *(Mng Dir)*

ENABLENCE TECHNOLOGIES INC.
390 March Road Suite 119
Ottawa, ON, K2K 0G7, Canada
Tel.: (613) 656-2850
Fax: (613) 656-2855
E-Mail: investors@enablence.com
Web Site: www.enablence.com
ENA—(TSXV)
Rev.: $7,879,000
Assets: $15,039,000
Liabilities: $20,806,000
Net Worth: ($5,767,000)
Earnings: ($15,558,000)
Fiscal Year-end: 06/30/13
Business Description:
Optical Components Mfr
S.I.C.: 3827
N.A.I.C.S.: 333314
Personnel:
Louis De Jong *(Chm)*
Jacob Sun *(CEO)*
Tao Zhang *(CFO)*
Evan Chen *(Chief Strategy Officer)*
Board of Directors:
Louis De Jong
Zhiyin Gao
John Roland
Jim Seto
Jacob Sun
Tao Zhang
Shengyin Zhu
Legal Counsel:
Fasken Martineau DuMoulin LLP
55 Metcalfe Street Suite 1300
Ottawa, ON, Canada
Transfer Agent:
Computershare Investor Services Inc.
100 University Avenue 8th Floor
Toronto, ON, M5J 2Y1, Canada
Tel.: (514) 982-7555

ENABLES IT GROUP PLC
Unit 5 Mole Business Park Randalls Road
Leatherhead, Surrey, KT22 7BA, United Kingdom
Tel.: (44) 845 676 0650
Fax: (44) 845 676 0659
E-Mail: info@enablesit.co.uk
Web Site: www.enablesit.com
EIT—(AIM)
Rev.: $6,749,276
Assets: $2,112,886
Liabilities: $1,763,175
Net Worth: $349,712
Earnings: ($161,928)
Emp.: 69
Fiscal Year-end: 09/30/12
Business Description:
Information Technology Services
S.I.C.: 7373

Enables IT Group Plc—(Continued)

N.A.I.C.S.: 541512
Personnel:
Michael Dean Walliss *(CEO)*
Mark Elliott *(CFO)*
Board of Directors:
Miles Johnson
Mark Barney Battles
Mark Elliott
Michael Dean Walliss
Marcus Yeoman
Legal Counsel:
Brown Rudnick LLP
8 Clifford Street
London, W1K 3SQ, United Kingdom
Subsidiary:

Enables IT (UK) Limited (1)
120 Moorgate
London, EC2M 6UR, United Kingdom
Tel.: (44) 8451303595
Fax: (44) 8701374300
E-Mail:
Emp.: 10
Information Technology Solutions
S.I.C.: 7373
N.A.I.C.S.: 541512
Andy Duncan *(Mng Dir)*

U.S. Subsidiaries:

Enables IT, Inc. (1)
4 Industrial Pkwy Ste 101
Brunswick, ME 04011
Tel.: (207) 319-1100
Fax: (207) 725-8552
Sales Range: $10-24.9 Million
Emp.: 41
Computer Software Development & Applications
S.I.C.: 7371
N.A.I.C.S.: 541511
Patrick Jones *(Pres-North America)*

Nerd Force Franchise Company (1)
97 New Dorp Plz 2nd Fl
Staten Island, NY 10306-2903
Tel.: (718) 370-6147
Fax: (718) 370-6731
Toll Free: (800) 979-6373
E-Mail: support@nerdforce.com
Web Site: www.nerdforce.com
Computer & Technology Support Services
S.I.C.: 7373
N.A.I.C.S.: 541512
Boris Adlam *(Pres)*
Ilir Sela *(Mng Dir)*

ENAGAS, S.A.

Paseo de los Olmos 19
28005 Madrid, Spain
Tel.: (34) 90 244 3700
Fax: (34) 91 709 9328
E-Mail: contacta@enagas.es
Web Site: www.enagas.es
Year Founded: 1972
ENG—(MAD)
Rev.: $1,588,560,024
Assets: $10,881,688,463
Liabilities: $8,182,908,386
Net Worth: $2,698,780,077
Earnings: $510,882,284
Emp.: 1,118
Fiscal Year-end: 12/31/12
Business Description:
Pipeline Infrastructure Construction & Operation & Natural Gas Transportation & Storage
S.I.C.: 4923
N.A.I.C.S.: 486210
Personnel:
Antonio Llarden Carratala *(Chm)*
Marcelino Oreja Arburua *(CEO)*
Diego de Reina Lovera *(CFO)*
Francisco Javier Gonzalez Julia *(COO & Chief Technical Sys Mgmt Officer)*
Rafael Piqueras Bautista *(Gen Sec)*
Board of Directors:
Antonio Llarden Carratala
Sultan Hamed Khamis Al Burtamani
Marcelino Oreja Arburua
Federico Ferrer Delso
Rosa Rodriguez Diaz
Jose Riva Francos
Isabel Sanchez Garcia
Teresa Garcia-Mila Lloveras
Dionisio Martinez Martinez
Miguel Angel Lasheras Merino
Jesus David Alvarez Mezquiriz
Jesus Maximo Pedrosa Ortega
Marti Parellada Sabata
Ramon Perez Simarro
Luis Javier Navarro Vigil
Subsidiary:

Naturgas Energia Grupo, S.A. (1)
Plz de Pio Baroja 3
48001 Bilbao, Spain
Tel.: (34) 944035700
Fax: (34) 944242325
E-Mail: telefonoazul@naturgasenergia.com
Web Site: www.naturgasenergia.com
Emp.: 200
Gas & Electricity Marketing & Supply
S.I.C.: 4924
N.A.I.C.S.: 221210
Manuel Menendez Menendez *(Pres)*

Subsidiaries:

Naturgas Energia Comercializadora, S.A. (2)
Plaza Pio Baroja 3
Bilbao, 48001, Spain
Tel.: (34) 944 03 57 00
Fax: (34) 944 24 27 36
Natural Gas Distribution Services
S.I.C.: 4924
N.A.I.C.S.: 221210

Naturgas Energia Comercializadoras Ultimo Recurso, S.A. (2)
Plaza Pio Baroja 3-2
Bilbao, 48001, Spain
Tel.: (34) 944035700
Natural Gas Distribution Services
S.I.C.: 4924
N.A.I.C.S.: 221210

Naturgas Energia Distribucion, S.A.U. (2)
Plaza Pio Baroja 3-1
Bilbao, 48001, Spain
Tel.: (34) 944035700
Fax: (34) 944242325
Natural Gas Distribution Services
S.I.C.: 4924
N.A.I.C.S.: 221210

Naturgas Energia Participaciones, S.A.U. (2)
Plaza Pio Baroja 3
Bilbao, 48001, Spain
Tel.: (34) 944035700
Fax: (34) 944242325
Natural Gas Distribution Services
S.I.C.: 4924
N.A.I.C.S.: 221210

Naturgas Energia Servicios Comunes, S.A. (2)
General Concha 20
Bilbao, 48010, Spain
Tel.: (34) 944035700
Fax: (34) 944242325
E-Mail: recepcion@edpenergia.es
Web Site: www.edpenergia.es
Electric Power Generation Services
S.I.C.: 4931
N.A.I.C.S.: 221118

Naturgas Energia Servicios, S.A. (2)
Plaza Pio Baroja 3-2
Bilbao, 48001, Spain
Tel.: (34) 944035700
Fax: (34) 944242325
E-Mail: recepcion@naturgasenergia.com
Emp.: 200
Electric Power Generation Services
S.I.C.: 4931
N.A.I.C.S.: 221118

Naturgas Energia Transporte, S.A.U. (2)
Plaza Pio Baroja 3
Bilbao, 48001, Spain
Tel.: (34) 944 03 57 00
E-Mail: recepcion@naturgasenergia.com
Natural Gas Transportation Services
S.I.C.: 4922
N.A.I.C.S.: 486210

Joint Venture:

Bahia de Bizkaia Gas, S.L. (1)
Explanda de Punta Ceballos 2
Atraque De Punta Lucero, 48508 Zierbena, Spain ES
Tel.: (34) 946366020
Fax: (34) 946366150
E-Mail: info@bbg.es
Web Site: www.bbg.es
Emp.: 71
Natural Gas Distr
S.I.C.: 4924
N.A.I.C.S.: 221210
Guillermo Gonzalez *(Gen Mgr)*

ENBIO HOLDINGS INC.

3F Tachotakakyu Building 2-11 Kandata-cho
Chiyoda-ku, Tokyo, 101-0046, Japan
Tel.: (81) 3 5297 7155
Web Site: www.enbio-holdings.com
Rev.: $14,574,793
Fiscal Year-end: 03/31/13
Business Description:
Environmental Services
S.I.C.: 8999
N.A.I.C.S.: 541620
Personnel:
Minoru Nishimura *(Pres)*

ENBRIDGE INCOME FUND HOLDINGS INC.

3000 Fifth Avenue Place 425 - 1st Street SW
Calgary, AB, T2P 3L8, Canada
Tel.: (403) 231-3900
Fax: (403) 231-3920
Web Site: www.enbridgeincomefund.com
Year Founded: 2010
ENF—(TSX)
Rev.: $59,477,187
Assets: $1,246,739,645
Liabilities: $37,048,120
Net Worth: $1,209,691,525
Earnings: $59,470,229
Fiscal Year-end: 12/31/12
Business Description:
Financial Investment Services
S.I.C.: 6211
N.A.I.C.S.: 523999
Personnel:
Gordon G. Tallman *(Chm)*
John K. Whelen *(Pres)*
Colin K. Gruending *(CFO)*
Board of Directors:
Gordon G. Tallman
Richard H. Auchinleck
J. Richard Bird
M. Elizabeth Cannon
Charles W. Fischer
Ernest F. H. Roberts
Bruce G. Waterman
Transfer Agent:
CIBC Mellon Trust Company
600 333 7th Avenue S W
Calgary, AB, Canada

ENBRIDGE, INC.

3000 Fifth Avenue Place 425-1st Street SW
Calgary, AB, T2P 3L8, Canada
Tel.: (403) 231-3900
Fax: (403) 231-3920
Toll Free: (800) 481-2804
E-Mail: webmaster-corp@enbridge.com
Web Site: www.enbridge.com
Year Founded: 1949
ENB—(NYSE TSX)
Rev.: $32,721,150,360
Assets: $57,223,743,360
Liabilities: $39,818,453,160
Net Worth: $17,405,290,200
Earnings: $491,045,880
Emp.: 8,607
Fiscal Year-end: 12/31/13
Business Description:
Energy Transportation, Distribution & Services
S.I.C.: 3822
N.A.I.C.S.: 334512
Personnel:
David A. Arledge *(Chm)*
Albert Monaco *(Pres & CEO)*
J. Richard Bird *(CFO & Exec VP-Corp Dev)*
Leon Zupan *(COO)*
B. D. Poohkay *(CIO & VP)*
David T. Robottom *(Exec VP & Chief Legal Officer)*
D. Guy Jarvis *(Chief Comml Officer-Liquids Pipelines & Exec VP)*
Glenn Beaumont *(Pres-Enbridge Gas Distribution)*
C. Gregory Harper *(Pres-Gas Pipelines & Processing)*
Janet Holder *(Exec VP-Western Access)*
Karen Radford *(Exec VP-People & Partners)*
John K. Whelen *(Sr VP & Controller)*
Byron C. Neiles *(Sr VP-Major Projects)*
Board of Directors:
David A. Arledge
James Johnston Blanchard
J. Lorne Braithwaite
James Herbert England
Charles Wayne Fischer
V. Maureen Kempston Darkes
David A. Leslie
Albert Monaco
George K. Petty
Charles E. Shultz
Dan C. Tutcher
Catherine L. Williams
Computershare
480 Washington Blvd
Jersey City, NJ 07310
Transfer Agents:
CST Trust Company
PO Box 700 Station B
Montreal, QC, Canada
Computershare
480 Washington Blvd
Jersey City, NJ 07310
Subsidiaries:

Enbridge Gas Distribution (1)
500 Consumers Road
North York, ON, M2J 1P8, Canada (100%)
Tel.: (416) 492-5100
Fax: (905) 762-3616
E-Mail: customercare@enbridge.com
Web Site: www.enbridge.com
Emp.: 100
Natural Gas Distribution
S.I.C.: 4924
N.A.I.C.S.: 221210

Enbridge Pipelines, Inc. (1)
10201 Jasper Avenue
Edmonton, AB, T5J 2J9, Canada (100%)
Mailing Address:
PO Box 398
Edmonton, AB, T5J 2J9, Canada
Tel.: (780) 420-5210
Fax: (780) 420-5140
Web Site: www.enbridge.com
Emp.: 425
Crude Oil & Liquid Hydrocarbons Transportation
S.I.C.: 4612
N.A.I.C.S.: 486110
D. Guy Jarvis *(Exec VP)*

U.S. Subsidiaries:

Enbridge Energy Company, Inc. (1)
1100 Louisiana St Ste 3300
Houston, TX 77002-5217 TX
Tel.: (713) 650-8900
Fax: (713) 650-3232
E-Mail: info@enbridge.us.com
Web Site: www.enbridge.us.com
Emp.: 500
Natural Gas Pipeline Company
S.I.C.: 4924
N.A.I.C.S.: 221210
Jeffrey A. Connelly *(Chm)*
Mark Andrew Maki *(Pres)*
Terrance L. McGill *(CEO)*
Stephen J. Neyland *(CFO & VP-Fin)*
Janet L. Coy *(Dir-Mktg)*
Leon A. Zupan *(Exec VP-Gas Pipelines)*

U.S. Affiliate:

Enbridge Energy Partners, L.P. (1)
1100 Louisiana St Ste 3300
Houston, TX 77002 DE
Tel.: (713) 821-2000
Fax: (719) 821-2230
Web Site: www.enbridgepartners.com
EEP—(NYSE)
Rev.: $7,117,100,000
Assets: $14,901,500,000
Liabilities: $7,204,100,000
Net Worth: $7,697,400,000
Earnings: $160,400,000
Fiscal Year-end: 12/31/13
Oil Transportation
S.I.C.: 5088
N.A.I.C.S.: 423860
Jeffrey A. Connelly *(Chm)*
Mark Andrew Maki *(Pres)*
Leon A. Zupan *(Exec VP-Gas Pipelines)*

Subsidiaries:

Dufour Petroleum, LP (2)
1374 Hwy 11 N
Petal, MS 39465-1184 MS
Mailing Address: (100%)
PO Box 1184
Petal, MS 39465-1184
Tel.: (601) 583-9991
Fax: (601) 583-9881
Web Site: www.dufourpetroleum.com
Emp.: 95
Marketer & Transporter of Natural Gas, Petroleum Products & Chemicals
S.I.C.: 5172
N.A.I.C.S.: 424720

Enbridge G & P (North Texas) L P (2)
451 Jones Rd
Weatherford, TX 76088
Tel.: (817) 598-5828
Business Support Services
S.I.C.: 7389
N.A.I.C.S.: 561499

Enbridge Pipeline Corporation (2)
PO Box 157
Duncanville, AL 35456-0157 AL
Tel.: (205) 758-5926 (100%)
Fax: (205) 758-7147
Natural Gas Pipeline
S.I.C.: 4924
N.A.I.C.S.: 221210

Enbridge Pipelines (Alatenn) L.L.C. (2)
3230 Second St
Muscle Shoals, AL 35661-1252 AL
Tel.: (256) 383-3631 (100%)
Fax: (256) 381-2858
Emp.: 9
Interstate Natural Gas Pipeline
S.I.C.: 4924
N.A.I.C.S.: 221210

Enbridge Pipelines (Tennessee River) L.L.C. (2)
3230 2nd St
Muscle Shoals, AL 35661-1252 AL
Tel.: (256) 383-3631 (100%)
Fax: (256) 381-2858
Emp.: 10
S.I.C.: 4924
N.A.I.C.S.: 221210

U.S. Joint Venture:

Vector Pipeline, L.P. (1)
38705 7th Mile Rd Ste 490
Livonia, MI 48152
Tel.: (734) 462-0234
Fax: (734) 462-0231
Toll Free: (866) 538-2867
Web Site: www.vector-pipeline.com
Emp.: 10
Gas Pipeline; Owned 50% by DTE Energy Company & 50% by Enbridge, Inc.
S.I.C.: 4922
N.A.I.C.S.: 486210
Craig R. Fishbeck *(Pres)*

ENBW ENERGIE BADEN-WURTTEMBERG AG

Durlacher Allee 93
76131 Karlsruhe, Germany
Tel.: (49) 7216300
Fax: (49) 7216312672
E-Mail: kontakt@enbw.com
Web Site: www.enbw.com
Year Founded: 1997
EBK—(DEU)
Rev.: $27,099,882,887
Assets: $49,498,536,283
Liabilities: $39,828,458,705
Net Worth: $9,670,077,578
Earnings: $719,931,716
Emp.: 18,912
Fiscal Year-end: 12/31/12

Business Description:
Holding Company; Electricity, Heat & Natural Gas
S.I.C.: 4911
N.A.I.C.S.: 221122

Personnel:
Claus Dieter Hoffmann *(Chm-Supervisory Bd)*
Frank Mastiaux *(Chm-Mgmt Bd & CEO)*
Dietrich Herd *(Deputy Chm-Supervisory Bd)*
Thomas Kusterer *(CFO & Member-Mgmt Bd)*
Hans-Josef Zimmer *(CTO & Member-Mgmt Bd)*
Birte Mossner *(Chief Compliance Officer)*
Bernhard Beck *(Chief Personnel Officer & Member-Mgmt Bd)*
Dirk Erich Mausbeck *(Chief Comml Officer & Member-Mgmt Bd)*

Supervisory Board of Directors:
Claus Dieter Hoffmann
Gunther Cramer
Dirk Gaerte
Stefan Paul Hamm
Dietrich Herd
Silke Krebs
Marianne Kugler-Wendt
Wolfgang Lang
Hans Hubert Lienhard
Sebastian Maier
Aichwald Arnold Messner
Bodo Moray
Gunda Rostel
Nils Schmid
Klaus Schornich
Heinz Seiffert
Gerhard Stratthaus
Dietmar Weber
Kurt Widmaier
Bernd-Michael Zinow

Subsidiaries:

AWISTA Logistik GmbH (1)
Hoherweg 222
Dusseldorf, 40233, Germany
Tel.: (49) 180 1831831
E-Mail: mail@awista-logistik.de
Web Site: www.awista-logistik.de
Waste Collection & Transportation Services
S.I.C.: 4959
N.A.I.C.S.: 562998

Elektrizitatswerk Aach eG, (1)
Eltastr 1-5
78532 Tuttlingen, Germany
Tel.: (49) 74617090
Fax: (49) 7461 709 298
E-Mail: DL-mailbox@ew-aach.de
Web Site: www.ew-aach.de
Electric Power Generation Services
S.I.C.: 4931
N.A.I.C.S.: 221111

EnBW Akademie Gesellschaft fur Personal- und Managemententwicklung mbH (1)
Schelmenwasenstr 15
70567 Stuttgart, Germany
Tel.: (49) 711 289 69222
Fax: (49) 711 289 69269
E-Mail: akademie@enbw.com
Emp.: 2,000
Natural Gas Distr
S.I.C.: 4924
N.A.I.C.S.: 221210
Woyde Koehler *(Gen Mgr)*

EnBW Baltic 1 GmbH & Co. KG (1)
Kronenstr. 26
Stuttgart, Baden-Wurttemberg, 70173, Germany
Tel.: (49) 71112800
Electric Power Generation Services
S.I.C.: 4931
N.A.I.C.S.: 221118

EnBW Baltic 1 Verwaltungs gesellschaft mbH (1)
Durlacher Allee 93
Karlsruhe, Germany
Tel.: (49) 7216307
Electric Power Generation Services
S.I.C.: 4931
N.A.I.C.S.: 221111

EnBW EnergyWatchers GmbH (1)
Friedrichstr 13
70174 Stuttgart, Germany
Tel.: (49) 7111283683
Fax: (49) 711 128 48365
E-Mail: energywatchers@enbw.com
Emp.: 20
Electric Power Distribution Services
S.I.C.: 4939
N.A.I.C.S.: 221122
Melanie Bunke *(Gen Mgr)*

EnBW Gasnetz GmbH (1)
Talstrasse 117
70188 Stuttgart, Germany
Tel.: (49) 711 289 46883
Fax: (49) 711 289 46883
E-Mail: Gastransport.enbw.gasnetz@enbw.com
Web Site: www.enbw.com
Gas Distribution Services
S.I.C.: 4924
N.A.I.C.S.: 221210

EnBW Kernkraft GmbH (1)
Kraftwerkstrasse 1
Obrigheim, 74847, Germany
Tel.: (49) 6261650
Fax: (49) 62616533390
Electrcity & Natural Gas
S.I.C.: 4911
N.A.I.C.S.: 221122

EnBW Kommunale Beteiligungen GmbH (1)
Schelmenwasenstrasse 15
70567 Stuttgart, Germany
Tel.: (49) 711 289 44710
Fax: (49) 711 289 44792
E-Mail: beteiligungen@enbw.com
Electric Power Distr
S.I.C.: 4911
N.A.I.C.S.: 221122
Ulrich Kleine *(Member-Exec Bd)*

EnBW Kraftwerke AG (1)
Schelmenwasenstrasse 15
70567 Stuttgart, Germany
Tel.: (49) 7112181500
Fax: (49) 71128989505
E-Mail: kontakt@enbw.com
Web Site: www.enbw.com
Emp.: 72
Power Stations Operator
S.I.C.: 4931
N.A.I.C.S.: 221122
Udo Brockmeier *(CEO)*

EnBW Omega Dreiundzwanzigste Verwaltungsgesellschaft mbH (1)
Durlacher Allee 93
Karlsruhe, Baden-Wurttemberg, 76131, Germany
Tel.: (49) 7216300
Electric Power Generation Services
S.I.C.: 4931
N.A.I.C.S.: 221118

EnBW Omega Elfte Verwaltungsgesellschaft mbH (1)
Durlacher Allee 93
Karlsruhe, Baden-Wurttemberg, 76131, Germany
Tel.: (49) 7216300
Electric Power Generation Services
S.I.C.: 4931
N.A.I.C.S.: 221118

EnBW Omega Siebzehnte Verwaltungsgesellschaft mbH (1)
Durlacher Allee 93
Karlsruhe, Baden-Wurttemberg, 76131, Germany
Tel.: (49) 7216307
Fax: (49) 7216312725
E-Mail: info@enbw.com
Energy Consulting Services
S.I.C.: 8999
N.A.I.C.S.: 541690

EnBW Ostwurttemberg DonauRies AG (1)
Unterer Bruhl 2
73479 Ellwangen, Germany
Tel.: (49) 79 61 82 0
Fax: (49) 79 61 82 38 80
E-Mail: info@odr.de
Web Site: www.odr.de
Electric Power & Natural Gas Distr
S.I.C.: 4939
N.A.I.C.S.: 221122

EnBW Systeme Infrastruktur Support GmbH (1)
Durlacher Allee 93
76131 Karlsruhe, Germany
Tel.: (49) 721 63 00
E-Mail: kontakt@enbw.com
Web Site: www.enbw.com
Energy Consulting Services
S.I.C.: 8999
N.A.I.C.S.: 541690
Bernhard Beck *(Chm)*
Jochen Adenau *(Member-Exec Bd)*
Hans-Guenther Meier *(Member-Exec Bd)*

EnBW Trading GmbH (1)
Durlacher Allee 93
D-76131 Karlsruhe, Germany (100%)
Tel.: (49) 7216307
Fax: (49) 7216312725
E-Mail: info@enbw.com
Web Site: www.enbw.com
Risk Management Services; Trades in Electricity, Gas, Coal & Oil
S.I.C.: 7389
N.A.I.C.S.: 561499
Ralf Klopfer *(CEO-Risk Mgmt Div)*

EnBW Transportnetze AG (1)
Kriegsbergstrasse 32
70174 Stuttgart, Germany
Tel.: (49) 7 21 63 00
Fax: (49) 7216312725
E-Mail: kontakt@enbw.com
Web Site: www.enbw.com
Energy Consulting Services
S.I.C.: 8999
N.A.I.C.S.: 541690
Christian Buchel *(Chm)*
Rainer Joswig *(Member-Mgmt Bd)*
Rainer Pflaum *(Member-Mgmt Bd)*

EnBW Vertrieb GmbH (1)
Schelmenwasenstrasse 15
70567 Stuttgart, Germany
Tel.: (49) 800 3629 000
Fax: (49) 800 3629 111
E-Mail: kontakt@enbw.com
Web Site: www.enbw.com
Electric Power Distribution Services
S.I.C.: 4939
N.A.I.C.S.: 221122
Hans-Peter Villis *(Chm-Supervisory Bd)*
Gerhard Kleih *(Member-Exec Bd)*
Joerg Luedorf *(Member-Exec Bd)*
Klaus Rohatsch *(Member-Exec Bd)*

Energieversorgung Gaildorf OHG der EnBW Kommunale Beteiligungen GmbH (1)
Burg 2
Gaildorf, Baden-Wurttemberg, 74405, Germany

EnBW Energie Baden-Wurttemberg AG—(Continued)

Tel.: (49) 7971260920
Fax: (49) 79712609299
E-Mail: service@ev-gaildorf.de
Web Site: www.ev-gaildorf.de
Electric Power Distr
S.I.C.: 4911
N.A.I.C.S.: 221122

Erdgas-Beteiligungsgesellschaft Sud mbH (1)
Am Wallgraben 135
Stuttgart, Baden-Wurttemberg, 70565, Germany
Tel.: (49) 71178121303
Fax: (49) 71178121376
Electric Power Distribution Services
S.I.C.: 4911
N.A.I.C.S.: 221122

Erdgas Sudwest GmbH (1)
Siemensstrasse 9
76275 Ettlingen, Germany
Tel.: (49) 800 3629 379
Fax: (49) 800 3629 401
E-Mail: info@erdgas-suedwest.de
Web Site: www.erdgas-suedwest.de
Natural Gas Distr
S.I.C.: 4924
N.A.I.C.S.: 221210
Ralf Biehl *(Gen Mgr)*

Facilma Grundbesitzmanagement und -service GmbH & Co. Besitz KG (1)
Kraftwerkstr 1
Obrigheim, 74847, Germany
Tel.: (49) 7216300
Fax: (49) 7216312725
Real Estate Management Services
S.I.C.: 6531
N.A.I.C.S.: 531390

GasVersorgung Suddeutschland GmbH (1)
Am Wallgraben 135
70565 Stuttgart, Germany
Tel.: (49) 711 7812 0
Fax: (49) 711 7812 1411
E-Mail: info@gvs-erdgas.de
Web Site: www.gvs-erdgas.de
Emp.: 200
Natural Gas Distr
S.I.C.: 4924
N.A.I.C.S.: 221210
Hans-Peter Villis *(Chm-Supervisory Bd)*

Gasversorgung Unterland GmbH (1)
Weipertstrasse 41
74076 Heilbronn, Germany
Tel.: (49) 7131610821
Fax: (49) 7131 610 1350
E-Mail: info@gasversorgung-unterland.de
Web Site: www.gasversorgung-unterland.de
Natural Gas Distr
S.I.C.: 4924
N.A.I.C.S.: 221210

Grunwerke GmbH (1)
Hoherweg 200
40233 Dusseldorf, Germany
Tel.: (49) 211 821 8088
Fax: (49) 211 821 3358
E-Mail: info@gruenwerke.de
Web Site: www.gruenwerke.de
Emp.: 10
Solar Power Plant Construction Services
S.I.C.: 1623
N.A.I.C.S.: 237130
Ralf Zischke *(Gen Mgr)*

GVS Netz GmbH (1)
Schulze Delitzsch Strasse 7
70565 Stuttgart, Germany
Tel.: (49) 71178120
Fax: (49) 71178121296
E-Mail: info@gvs-netz.de
Web Site: www.gvs-netz.de
Oil & Gas Field Engineering Services
S.I.C.: 1389
N.A.I.C.S.: 213112

Kernkraftwerk Obrigheim GmbH (1)
Kraftwerkstrasse 1
Obrigheim, 74847, Germany
Tel.: (49) 6261650
Fax: (49) 626165500
Electric Power Generation Services
S.I.C.: 4911
N.A.I.C.S.: 221111
Joseph Zimmer *(Gen Mgr)*

KMS Kraftwerke Grundbesitzmanagement und -service GmbH & Co. KG (1)
Durlacher Allee 93
Karlsruhe, Baden-Wurttemberg, 76131, Germany
Tel.: (49) 7216304
Fax: (49) 7216312725
E-Mail: info@enbw.com
Emp.: 2,000
Electric Power Generation Services
S.I.C.: 4911
N.A.I.C.S.: 221111
Hans Peter Velles *(CEO)*

KNG Kraftwerks- und Netzgesellschaft mbH (1)
Am Kuhlturm 1
18147 Rostock, Germany
Tel.: (49) 381 67 02 250
Fax: (49) 381 67 02 203
E-Mail: post@kng.de
Web Site: www.kraftwerk-rostock.de
Emp.: 121
Electric Power Generation Services
S.I.C.: 4931
N.A.I.C.S.: 221111
Lars Eigenmann *(Mgr-Tech)*

MSE Mobile Schlammentwasserungs GmbH (1)
Auf der Hub 35-39
Karlsbad, 76307 Ittersbach, Germany
Tel.: (49) 724892700
Fax: (49) 723278577
E-Mail: info@mse-mobile.de
Web Site: www.mse-mobile.de
Emp.: 60
Sewage Disposal Services
S.I.C.: 4953
N.A.I.C.S.: 562219
Michael Part *(Mng Dir)*

NeckarCom Telekommunikation GmbH (1)
Stockachstr 48
70190 Stuttgart, Germany
Tel.: (49) 711 22 55 78 0
Fax: (49) 711 22 55 78 20678
E-Mail: support@neckarcom.de
Web Site: www.neckarcom.de
Telecommunication Services
S.I.C.: 4899
N.A.I.C.S.: 517919

Netzgesellschaft Ostwurttemberg GmbH (1)
Unterer Bruhl 2
73479 Ellwangen, Germany
Tel.: (49) 7961 9336 0
Fax: (49) 7961 9336 1415
E-Mail: info@ng-o.com
Web Site: www.ng-o.com
Electric Power Distribution Services
S.I.C.: 4911
N.A.I.C.S.: 221122

Netzgesellschaft Steinheim GmbH & Co. KG (1)
Hauptstr 24
Steinheim, Baden-Wurttemberg, 89555, Germany
Tel.: (49) 796193360
Electric Power Distribution Services
S.I.C.: 4911
N.A.I.C.S.: 221122

Netzgesellschaft Steinheim Verwaltungsgesellschaft mbH. (1)
Unterer Bruhl 2
Ellwangen, Baden-Wurttemberg, 73479, Germany
Tel.: (49) 796193360
Electric Power Distribution Services
S.I.C.: 4911
N.A.I.C.S.: 221122

NHF Netzgesellschaft Heilbronn-Franken mbH (1)
Weipertstrasse 39
Heilbronn, Germany
Tel.: (49) 7131 27758 30
Fax: (49) 7131 27758 50
E-Mail: info@n-hf.de
Web Site: www.n-hf.de
Electric Power Distribution Services
S.I.C.: 4911
N.A.I.C.S.: 221122

ODR Technologie Services GmbH (1)
Unterer Bruhl 2
73479 Ellwangen, Germany
Tel.: (49) 1805 637 874
Fax: (49) 7961 82 6445
E-Mail: tsg@odr.de
Web Site: www.tsg.odr.de
Telecommunication Services
S.I.C.: 4899
N.A.I.C.S.: 517919

OSD SCHAFER GmbH (1)
Greschbachstrasse 1
76229 Karlsruhe, Germany
Tel.: (49) 721 98597 70
Fax: (49) 721 9859780
E-Mail: mail@osd-schaefer.com
Web Site: www.osd-schaefer.com
Corporate Security Consulting Services
S.I.C.: 8999
N.A.I.C.S.: 541690

RBS wave GmbH (1)
Kriegsbergstrasse 32
70174 Stuttgart, Germany
Tel.: (49) 71128951300
Fax: (49) 711 289 51308
E-Mail: info@rbs-wave.de
Web Site: www.rbs-wave.de
Emp.: 100
Engineering Services
S.I.C.: 8711
N.A.I.C.S.: 541330

Rheinkraftwerk Iffezheim GmbH (1)
Lautenschlagerstr 20
Stuttgart, Baden-Wurttemberg, 70173, Germany
Tel.: (49) 7229188300
Fax: (49) 7229188310
Electric Power Generation Services
S.I.C.: 4931
N.A.I.C.S.: 221111

Rieger Beteiligungs-GmbH (1)
Friedrichstr 16
72805 Lichtenstein, Germany
Tel.: (49) 712992510
Electric Power Distr
S.I.C.: 4911
N.A.I.C.S.: 221122

Stadtwerke Dusseldorf AG (1)
Hoherweg 100
40233 Dusseldorf, Germany
Tel.: (49) 211 821 821
Fax: (49) 211 821 3821
E-Mail: info@swd-ag.de
Web Site: www.swd-ag.de
Emp.: 3,500
Electric Power Distribution Services
S.I.C.: 4939
N.A.I.C.S.: 221122
Udo Brockmeier *(Gen Mgr)*

Stadtwerke Dusseldorf Netz GmbH, (1)
Hoherweg 200
40233 Dusseldorf, Germany
Tel.: (49) 211 821 6389
E-Mail: netznutzung@swd-netz.de
Web Site: www.swd-netz.de
Electric Power Distribution Services
S.I.C.: 4939
N.A.I.C.S.: 221122

Stadtwerke Sinsheim Verwaltungs GmbH (1)
Neulandstr 6
Sinsheim, Baden-Wurttemberg, 74889, Germany
Tel.: (49) 7261404301
Electric Power Distribution Services
S.I.C.: 4931
N.A.I.C.S.: 221122

T-plus GmbH (1)
Am Erlengraben 5
76275 Ettlingen, Germany
Tel.: (49) 72435057890
Fax: (49) 72435057899
E-Mail: info@tplusgmbh.de
Web Site: www.tplusgmbh.de
Emp.: 11
Waste Materials Disposal Services
S.I.C.: 4959
N.A.I.C.S.: 562998
Gerd Uhlenbrauck *(Gen Mgr)*

Thermogas Gas- und Geratevertriebs-GmbH (1)
Talstr 117
70188 Stuttgart, Germany
Tel.: (49) 711 289 41700
Fax: (49) 711 289 41740
E-Mail: thermogas@thermogas.de
Web Site: www.thermogas.de
Liquefied Petroleum Gas Distr
S.I.C.: 5172
N.A.I.C.S.: 424720

Watt Deutschland GmbH (1)
Lyoner Strasse 44-48
60528 Frankfurt am Main, Germany
Tel.: (49) 800 9 28 87 87
Fax: (49) 800 9 28 87 88
E-Mail: info@watt.de
Web Site: www.watt.de
Energy Consulting Services
S.I.C.: 8999
N.A.I.C.S.: 541690

Watt Synergia GmbH (1)
Lyoner Strasse 44-48
60528 Frankfurt am Main, Germany
Tel.: (49) 69 244 371 88 112
Fax: (49) 69 244 371 86 112
E-Mail: info@wattsynergia.de
Web Site: www.wattsynergia.de
Emp.: 10
Energy Consulting Services
S.I.C.: 8999
N.A.I.C.S.: 541690
Michael Georgi *(CEO & CFO)*

Yello Strom GmbH (1)
Am Grauen Stein 27
51105 Cologne, Germany
Tel.: (49) 800 99 998 90
Fax: (49) 800 99 999 74
E-Mail: immerda@yellostrom.de
Web Site: www.yellostrom.de
Electric Power Distribution Services
S.I.C.: 4931
N.A.I.C.S.: 221122

Yello Strom Verwaltungsgesellschaft mbH (1)
Durlacher Allee 93
Karlsruhe, Baden-Wurttemberg, 76131, Germany
Tel.: (49) 8001900019
Fax: (49) 8009999974
Electric Power Distr
S.I.C.: 4939
N.A.I.C.S.: 221122

ZEAG Energie AG (1)
Weipertstrasse 41
74076 Heilbronn, Germany
Tel.: (49) 7131 610 0
Fax: (49) 7131 610 183
E-Mail: info@zeag-energie.de
Web Site: www.zeag-energie.de
Electric Power Distribution Services
S.I.C.: 4931
N.A.I.C.S.: 221122

ZEAG Zementwerk Lauffen-Elektrizitaetswerk Heilbronn AG (1)
Badstrasse 41
74076 Heilbronn, Germany
Tel.: (49) 71316100
Fax: (49) 610183
E-Mail: info@zeagenergy.de
Web Site: www.zeagenergy.de
Sales Range: $75-99.9 Million
Emp.: 235
Provider of Cement & Electricity Services
S.I.C.: 4931
N.A.I.C.S.: 221122

U.S. Subsidiary:

Leoni Cable Inc (1)
336 Main St Ste A
Rochester, MI 48307
Tel.: (248) 650-3328
Fax: (248) 650-3365
Web Site: www.leoni.com
Fiber Optic Cables Mfr
S.I.C.: 3357
N.A.I.C.S.: 335921
Mary DeCook *(Acct Mgr)*

Non-U.S. Subsidiaries:

EnAlpin AG (1)
Bahnhofplatz 1b
CH 3930 Visp, Switzerland
Tel.: (41) 279457500
Fax: (41) 279457501
E-Mail: info@enalpin.com
Web Site: www.enalpin.com
Emp.: 50
Utility Company Generating & Distributing Electricity
S.I.C.: 4911
N.A.I.C.S.: 221122
Rane Derran *(Mng Dir)*

Subsidiaries:

Energie De Sion Region SA (2)
Rue De La Industrie 43
1950 Sion, Switzerland
Tel.: (41) 273240111
Fax: (41) 273240250
E-Mail: info@esr.ch
Web Site: www.esr.ch
Emp.: 250
Services & Natural Gas Distribution
S.I.C.: 4924
N.A.I.C.S.: 221210
David Michellod *(Mng Dir)*

ERAG Elektrizitatswerk Rheinau AG (2)
Parkstrasse 23
8462 Rheinau, Switzerland
Tel.: (41) 523191454
Power Station
S.I.C.: 4931
N.A.I.C.S.: 221122

Gaznat SA (2)
28 Ave Du General Guisan
1800 Vevey, Switzerland
Tel.: (41) 219258484
Fax: (41) 219258485
E-Mail: info@gaznat.ch
Web Site: www.gaznat.ch
Emp.: 10
Services & Natural Gas Distribution
S.I.C.: 4924
N.A.I.C.S.: 221210
Mouehet Daniel *(Chm)*
Morael Wigner *(CFO)*

RHOWAG Rhonewerke AG (2)
PO Box 91
3966 Chiasso, Switzerland
Tel.: (41) 274516201
Fax: (41) 274516256
Web Site: www.snv.sw
Emp.: 35
Power Station
S.I.C.: 4911
N.A.I.C.S.: 221122

RKN Rheinkraftwerk Neuhausen AG (2)
c/o EnAlpine AG
Bahnhofplatz 1b
Visp, 3930, Switzerland
Tel.: (41) 27 945 7500
Power Station
S.I.C.: 4939
N.A.I.C.S.: 221122

EnBW Benelux B.V. (1)
Schouwburgplein 30-34
Rotterdam, 3012 CL, Netherlands
Tel.: (31) 102245333
Fax: (31) 334517390
Energy Consulting Services
S.I.C.: 8999
N.A.I.C.S.: 541690

EnBW Holding A.S. (1)
Gumussuyu No 43/9 Inonu Cad
Istanbul, 34437, Turkey
Tel.: (90) 2122455015
Fax: (90) 2122455025
Electric Power Generation Services
S.I.C.: 4911
N.A.I.C.S.: 221111

EnergieDienst Holding AG (1)
Baslerstrasse 44
CH-5080 Laufenburg, Switzerland CH
Tel.: (41) 62 869 2510
Fax: (41) 62 869 2200
E-Mail: info@energiedienst.de
Web Site: www.energiedienst.de
EDHN—(SWX)
Sales Range: $1-4.9 Billion
Emp.: 770
Holding Company; Hydroelectric Power Generation Services
S.I.C.: 6719
N.A.I.C.S.: 551112
Martin Steiger *(Chm-Mgmt Bd)*
Christian Bersier *(CFO)*
Michael Schwery *(Member-Mgmt Bd)*

Non-U.S. Subsidiary:

Energiedienst AG (2)
Rheinbruckenstrasse 5/7
Rheinfelden, 79618, Germany
Tel.: (49) 7623 92 0
Fax: (49) 7623 92 3434
E-Mail: info@energiedienst.de
Web Site: www.energiedienst.de
Hydroelectric Power Generation Services
S.I.C.: 4931
N.A.I.C.S.: 221111

Subsidiaries:

ED Immobilien GmbH & Co. KG (3)
Rheinbruckstr 5/7
79618 Rheinfelden, Germany
Tel.: (49) 776381 2640
Fax: (49) 776381 2581
Natural Gas Distr
S.I.C.: 4924
N.A.I.C.S.: 221210

Energiedienst Netze GmbH (3)
Rheinbruckstrasse 5/7
79618 Rheinfelden, Germany
Tel.: (49) 7623920
Fax: (49) 7623 92 3303
E-Mail: info@energiedienst.de
Web Site: www.energiedienst-netze.de
Emp.: 750
Energy Consulting Services
S.I.C.: 8999
N.A.I.C.S.: 541690
Martin Steiger *(Gen Mgr)*

Energiedienst Support GmbH (3)
Rheinbruckstrasse 5-7
Rheinfelden, Baden-Wurttemberg, 79618, Germany
Tel.: (49) 7623920
Fax: (49) 7623923333
Electric Power Distribution Services
S.I.C.: 4911
N.A.I.C.S.: 221122
Martin Steiger *(Gen Mgr)*

NaturEnergie AG (3)
Am Wasserkraftwerk 49
D-79639 Grenzach-Wyhlen, Germany De
Tel.: (49) 762490803140
Fax: (49) 7624 9080 3149
E-Mail: service@naturenergie.de
Web Site: www.naturenergie.de
Hydroelectric Power Generation Services
S.I.C.: 4931
N.A.I.C.S.: 221111
Achim Geigle *(Mng Dir)*

Hidiv Elektrik Enerjisi Toptan Satis A.S (1)
Purtelas Hasan Mah Meclisi Mebusan Cd N 35 K 7
Istanbul, Turkey
Tel.: (90) 2123935297
Fax: (90) 2123935261
Electric Power Generation Services
S.I.C.: 4911
N.A.I.C.S.: 221111

Intepe Elektrik Uretim Ve Tic. A.S (1)
Purtelas Hasan Mah Meclisi Mebusan Cad No 35 K 7
Istanbul, Turkey
Tel.: (90) 2123935200
Electric Power Generation Services
S.I.C.: 4931
N.A.I.C.S.: 221111

KIC InnoEnergy S.E. (1)
High Tech Campus 69
5656 AG Eindhoven, Netherlands
Tel.: (31) 40 800 22 80
Fax: (31) 40 800 22 89
E-Mail: info@kic-innoenergy.com
Web Site: www.innoenergy-initiative.com
Educational Services
S.I.C.: 8299
N.A.I.C.S.: 611710
Diego Pavia *(CEO)*

Maya Enerji Yatirimlari A.S. (1)
Buyukdere Caddesi No 112
Esentepe, Istanbul, 34394, Turkey
Tel.: (90) 2123402760
Fax: (90) 2122726180
Electric Power Generation Services
S.I.C.: 4939
N.A.I.C.S.: 221111

ENCANA CORP.

Suite 4400 500 Centre Street S E
PO Box 2850
Calgary, AB, T2P 2S5, Canada
Tel.: (403) 645-2000
Fax: (403) 645-3400
E-Mail: investor.relations@encana.com
Web Site: www.encana.com
Year Founded: 1973
ECA—(NYSE TSX)
Rev.: $5,858,000,000
Assets: $17,648,000,000
Liabilities: $12,501,000,000
Net Worth: $5,147,000,000
Earnings: $236,000,000
Emp.: 3,303
Fiscal Year-end: 12/31/13

Business Description:
Oil & Gas Exploration, Production, Gas Storage & Processing
Export
S.I.C.: 1311
N.A.I.C.S.: 211111

Personnel:
Clayton H. Woitas *(Chm)*
Douglas James Suttles *(Pres & CEO)*
Sherri A. Brillon *(CFO & Exec VP)*
Michael G. McAllister *(COO)*
Terry Hopwood *(Gen Counsel & Exec VP)*
David Hill *(Exec VP-Exploration & Bus Dev)*
Renee Zemljak *(Exec VP-Midstream Mktg & Fundamentals)*

Board of Directors:
Clayton H. Woitas
Peter A. Dea
Claire Scobee Farley
Fred J. Fowler
Suzanne P. Nimocks
Jane L. Peverett
Allan P. Sawin
Douglas James Suttles
Bruce G. Waterman

Computershare
480 Washington Blvd
Jersey City, NJ 07310

Transfer Agents:
CST Trust Company
PO Box 700 Station B
Montreal, QC, Canada

Computershare
480 Washington Blvd
Jersey City, NJ 07310

Branch:

EnCana Corporation-Eastern Canada Office (1)
Founders Square Suite 700 1701 Hollis Street
Halifax, NS, B3J 3M8, Canada (100%)
Tel.: (902) 422-4500
Fax: (902) 425-2766
Web Site: www.encana.com
Sales Range: $1-9.9 Million
Emp.: 45
Oil & Gas Exploration, Production, Pipelining & Gas Storage & Processing
S.I.C.: 1311
N.A.I.C.S.: 211111
Robert Macqueen *(Mgr-Comml)*

U.S. Subsidiaries:

EnCana Energy Resources Inc. (1)
Republic Plz 370 17th St Ste 1700
Denver, CO 80202
Tel.: (303) 623-2300
Fax: (303) 623-2400
Web Site: www.encana.com
Emp.: 600
Oil & Gas Exploration, Production, Pipelining & Gas Storage & Processing
S.I.C.: 1311
N.A.I.C.S.: 211111

Encana Marketing (USA) Inc. (1)
370 - 17th St Ste 1700
Denver, CO 80202
Tel.: (303) 623-2300
Fax: (303) 623-2400
Emp.: 991
Natural Gas Distribution Services
S.I.C.: 4924
N.A.I.C.S.: 221210

EnCana Oil & Gas (USA) Inc. (1)
Republic Plz 370 17th St Ste 1700
Denver, CO 80202 DE
Tel.: (303) 623-2300 (100%)
Fax: (303) 623-2400
Web Site: www.encana.com
Emp.: 1,400
Oil & Gas Exploration & Production
S.I.C.: 1311
N.A.I.C.S.: 211111
Mike Graham *(Exec VP & Pres-Canadian Div)*

Division:

EnCana Gulf of Mexico (2)
370 17th St Ste 1700
Denver, CO 80202-5632
Tel.: (303) 623-2300
Fax: (303) 623-2400
Web Site: www.encana.com
Oil & Gas Exploration, Production, Pipelining & Gas Storage & Processing
S.I.C.: 4939
N.A.I.C.S.: 221122

ENCANTO POTASH CORP.

Suite 450 800 W Pender Street
PO Box 6
Vancouver, BC, V6C 2V6, Canada
Tel.: (604) 683-2402
Fax: (604) 683-2484
Toll Free: (866) 918-0824
E-Mail: jwalchuck@encantopotash.com
Web Site: www.encantopotash.com
EPO—(OTC TSXV)
Int. Income: $44,303
Assets: $31,072,740
Liabilities: $5,223,143
Net Worth: $25,849,597
Earnings: ($6,153,039)
Emp.: 1
Fiscal Year-end: 12/31/12

Business Description:
Potash Exploration Services
S.I.C.: 1474
N.A.I.C.S.: 212391

Personnel:
Gordon Bruce Keep *(Chm)*
James Walchuck *(Pres & CEO)*
Robert G. McMorran *(CFO & Sec)*

Board of Directors:
Gordon Bruce Keep
Hamad Al-Wazzan
Tyler D. Cran
Aref Kanafani
Robert G. McMorran
John Douglas Reynolds
Jamie Schwitzer
Brian G. Thurston
James Walchuck

Legal Counsel:
Anfield, Sujir, Kennedy & Durno
1600 609 Granville Street
Vancouver, BC, V7Y 1C3, Canada

Transfer Agent:
Computershare Trust Company
510 Burrard Street 2nd Floor
Vancouver, BC, Canada

Subsidiary:

Encanto Resources Ltd (1)
Ste 380 580 Hornby St
Vancouver, BC, V6C 3B6, Canada

Encanto Potash Corp.—(Continued)

Tel.: (604) 683-2402
Fax: (604) 683-2484
Emp.: 3
Potash Mining Services
S.I.C.: 1474
N.A.I.C.S.: 212391
James Walchuck *(Pres)*

ENCE, ENERGIA Y CELULOSA, S.A.

(Formerly Grupo Empresarial ENCE, S.A.)
Paseo de la Castellana 35
28046 Madrid, Spain
Tel.: (34) 91 337 8500
Telex: 23564 ENCESE
Fax: (34) 91 337 8556
Web Site: www.ence.es
Year Founded: 1957
Rev.: $1,114,060,676
Assets: $1,855,088,222
Liabilities: $879,486,515
Net Worth: $975,601,707
Earnings: $57,927,041
Emp.: 1,271
Fiscal Year-end: 12/31/12

Business Description:
Cellulose & Wood Products Producer
S.I.C.: 0831
N.A.I.C.S.: 113210

Personnel:
Juan Luis Arregui Ciarsolo *(Chm)*
Ignacio Colmenares y Brunet *(CEO)*
Diego Maus Lizariturry *(CFO)*
Jose Antonio Escalona de Molina *(Sec)*

Board of Directors:
Juan Luis Arregui Ciarsolo
Fernando Abril-Martorell Hernandez
Javier Arregui Abendivar
Pedro Barato Triguero
Gustavo Matias Clavero
Ignacio Colmenares y Brunet
Jose Carlos del Alamo Jimenez
Javier Echenique Landiribar
Pascual Fernandez Martinez
Jesus Ruano Mochales
Jose Manuel Serra Peris
Jose Guillermo Zubia Guinea

Subsidiaries:

Celulosa Energia, S.L. (1)
Carretera A-5000 Km 7.5
Apartado 223, 21007 Huelva, Spain
Tel.: (34) 959367700
Fax: (34) 959367628
Web Site: www.ence.es
Electric Power Generation
S.I.C.: 4931
N.A.I.C.S.: 221118

Celulosas de Asturias, S.A. (1)
Calle Armental
Navia, 33710 Asturias, Spain
Tel.: (34) 985630200
Fax: (34) 985473280
Emp.: 300
Pulp Mills
S.I.C.: 2611
N.A.I.C.S.: 322110
Diec Arto *(Mng Dir)*

Non-U.S. Subsidiaries:

Iberflorestal - Comercio E ServiCos Florestais, S A (1)
Avenida Antonio Augusto De Aguiar130 2
2nd Fl, Lisbon, Portugal
Tel.: (351) 217800269
Fax: (351) 217800270
Emp.: 20
Forest Nurseries & Gathering
S.I.C.: 0831
N.A.I.C.S.: 113210
ALexandro Oliveros *(Mng Dir)*

Ibersilva, S.A.U. (1)
Avenida Antonio Augusto De Aguiar 130 St 2
1050 020 Lisbon, Portugal
Tel.: (351) 217800269
Fax: (351) 217800270
E-Mail: geral@ibersilva.pt
Web Site: www.ibersilva.es
Emp.: 17
Forestry
S.I.C.: 0851
N.A.I.C.S.: 115310
Louis Gomes *(Gen Mgr)*

ENCO SPOL. S R.O.

Michalska 7
811 01 Bratislava, Slovakia
Tel.: (421) 254435144
Fax: (421) 254434768
E-Mail: enco@enco.sk
Web Site: www.enco.sk
Year Founded: 1993
Sales Range: $150-199.9 Million
Emp.: 600

Business Description:
Sheet Metal Processor; Large Pressing Tools & Moulded Rubber Products Mfr for the Automotive Industry
S.I.C.: 3444
N.A.I.C.S.: 332322

Personnel:
Jozef Medved *(Mng Dir)*

Joint Venture:

KUKA ENCO Werkzeugbau spol. s r.o. (1)
Sturova 1
018 41 Dubnica nad Vahom, Slovakia
Tel.: (421) 424402102
Fax: (421) 424402114
E-Mail: eng@kukaenco.sk
Web Site: www.kukaenco.sk
Sls.: $5,915,819
Emp.: 147
Large Pressing Tools Mfr for Automotive Industry; Owned by Enco Spol. s r.o. & by KUKA Sweissanlagen GmbH
S.I.C.: 3544
N.A.I.C.S.: 333514

Subsidiary:

METALLFORM, s.r.o. (1)
Tovarenska 422
018 61 Belusa, Slovakia
Tel.: (421) 424459204
Fax: (421) 424459209
E-Mail: budjacova@metallform.sk
Web Site: www.enco.sk/en/dcerske
Emp.: 150
Automotive Rubber & Plastic Composites Mfr
S.I.C.: 3069
N.A.I.C.S.: 326299
Monica Budjacova *(Gen Mgr)*

ENCORE ART GROUP

Unit 110, 6311 Westminster Hwy
Richmond, BC, V7C 4V4, Canada
Tel.: (604) 276-4551
Fax: (604) 276-4552
Toll Free: (800) 663-1166
E-Mail: sales@encoreartgroup.com
Web Site: www.encoreartgroup.com
Emp.: 40

Business Description:
Fine Art Reproductions, Limited Edition Prints, Imprints, Monoprints & Upscale Posters Publisher
S.I.C.: 2741
N.A.I.C.S.: 511199

Personnel:
Hall Krieger *(Pres)*

Divisions:

Canadian Art Prints, Inc. (1)
6311 Westminster Hwy Ste 110
Richmond, BC, V7C 4V4, Canada
Tel.: (604) 276-4551
Fax: (604) 276-4552
E-Mail: sales@encoreartgroup.com
Web Site: www.canadianartprints.com
Emp.: 60
Art Publisher
S.I.C.: 2741
N.A.I.C.S.: 511140
Lisa Krieger *(Pres)*
Joseph Halby Krieger *(CEO)*

Winn Devon Art Group (1)
Unit 110 6311 Westminster Hwy
Richmond, BC, V7C 4V4, Canada
Tel.: (604) 276-4551
Fax: (604) 276-4552
Toll Free: (800) 663-1166
E-Mail: sales@encoreartgroup.com
Web Site: www.winndevon.com
Emp.: 50
Fine Art Reproductions, Limited Edition Prints, Imprints, Monoprints & Upscale Posters Publisher
S.I.C.: 2741
N.A.I.C.S.: 511199

ENCORE SALES

333 North Rivermede Rd
Concord, ON, L4K 3N7, Canada
Tel.: (905) 738-8888
Fax: (905) 738-5435
Toll Free: (800) 387-3736
E-Mail: custserv@encoresales.com
Web Site: www.encoresales.com
Year Founded: 1964
Rev.: $37,648,380
Emp.: 280

Business Description:
Stationery Products Distr & Whslr
S.I.C.: 5399
N.A.I.C.S.: 452990

Personnel:
Irving Bloomberg *(Pres)*

ENCORE SOFTWARE LTD.

6th Floor Leo Complex 44 & 45 Residency Road
Bengaluru, Karnataka, 560 025, India
Tel.: (91) 8040808080
Fax: (91) 8025587690
Web Site: www.ncoretech.com
531750—(BOM)
Rev.: $479,670
Assets: $230,698
Liabilities: $4,363,945
Net Worth: ($4,133,247)
Earnings: ($340,544)
Fiscal Year-end: 03/31/13

Business Description:
Software Services
S.I.C.: 5731
N.A.I.C.S.: 443142

Personnel:
Vinay L. Deshpande *(Founder, Chm & CEO)*
Chhanda Deshpande *(Compliance Officer)*

Board of Directors:
Vinay L. Deshpande
Chhanda Deshpande
Ramesh Rao
J. Suri

Transfer Agent:
Integrated Enterprises (India) Limited
30 Ramana Residency 4th Cross Sampige Road
560003 Bengaluru, India

ENCORIUM GROUP, INC.

Keilaranta 10
FI 02150 Espoo, Finland
Tel.: (358) 20 751 8200
E-Mail: hq@encorium.com
Web Site: www.encorium.com
Year Founded: 1989
ENCO—(OTC)
Sales Range: $10-24.9 Million
Emp.: 141

Business Description:
Contract Pharmaceutical Research Services
Import Export
S.I.C.: 8731
N.A.I.C.S.: 541712

Personnel:
Shahab Fatheazam *(Chm)*
Kai E. Lindevall *(CEO)*
Niklas Tevajari *(Chief Acctg Officer)*
Renee E. Moore *(Pres-Corp & Bus Dev-Germany)*

Board of Directors:
Shahab Fatheazam
Kai E. Lindevall
David Morra

Non-U.S. Subsidiaries:

Encorium Denmark ApS (1)
Danish Science Pk Venlighedsvej 6
DK-2970 Horsholm, Denmark
Tel.: (45) 45768555
Fax: (45) 45765848
E-Mail: denmark@encorium.com
Web Site: www.encorium.com
Sales Range: $75-99.9 Million
Emp.: 100
Contract Pharmaceutical Research Services
S.I.C.: 8731
N.A.I.C.S.: 541712

Encorium Estonia OU (1)
Kreutzwaldi 12
EST-10124 Tallinn, Estonia
Tel.: (372) 6830356
Fax: (372) 6830357
E-Mail: estonia@encorium.com
Web Site: www.encorium.com
Sales Range: $75-99.9 Million
Emp.: 5
Contract Pharmaceutical Research Services
S.I.C.: 8731
N.A.I.C.S.: 541712

Encorium Germany GmbH (1)
Am Hermeshof 8
Erftstadt Cologne, DE-50374, Germany
Tel.: (49) 2235688672
Fax: (49) 2235 688 746
E-Mail: germany@encorium.com
Web Site: www.encorium.com
Sales Range: $75-99.9 Million
Contract Pharmaceutical Research Services
S.I.C.: 8731
N.A.I.C.S.: 541712
Renee E. Moore *(Pres-Corp & Bus Dev)*
Klaus-Dieter Albrecht *(Exec VP-Affiliates & Admin)*

Encorium Limited Ankara Turkiye Subesi (1)
Silikon Binasi 1 kat
06531 Ankara, Turkey
Tel.: (90) 3122101535
Fax: (90) 3122101531
E-Mail: turkey@encorium.com
Web Site: www.encorium.com
Sales Range: $75-99.9 Million
Emp.: 10
Contract Pharmaceutical Research Services
S.I.C.: 8731
N.A.I.C.S.: 541712

Encorium Oy (1)
Keilaranta 16
FI-02150 Espoo, Finland
Tel.: (358) 207518200
Fax: (358) 207518250
E-Mail: johanna.garainen@encorium.com
Web Site: www.encorium.com
Sales Range: $75-99.9 Million
Contract Pharmaceutical Research Services
S.I.C.: 8731
N.A.I.C.S.: 541712
Kai E. Lindevall *(Chm, Pres & CEO)*

Divisions:

Encorium Mankkaa (2)
Sinimaentie 14B
FI-02630 Espoo, Finland
Tel.: (358) 207518200
Fax: (358) 207518253
E-Mail: kailin.devall@encorium.com
Web Site: www.encorium.com
Sales Range: $75-99.9 Million
Contract Pharmaceutical Research Services
S.I.C.: 8731
N.A.I.C.S.: 541712
Kailin Devall *(Gen Mgr)*

Encorium Oulu (2)
Kiilakiventie 1 4 krs
FI-90250 Oulu, Finland

Tel.: (358) 207518310
Fax: (358) 207518360
E-Mail: info@encorium.com
Web Site: www.encorium.com
Sales Range: $25-49.9 Million
Emp.: 100
Contract Pharmaceutical Research Services
S.I.C.: 8731
N.A.I.C.S.: 541712
Kai E. Lindevall *(Gen Mgr)*

Encorium Tampere (2)
Itsenaisyydenkatu Bldg 2
FI-33100 Tampere, Finland
Tel.: (358) 207518400
Fax: (358) 207518450
E-Mail: eu@encorium.com
Web Site: www.encorium.com
Sales Range: $25-49.9 Million
Emp.: 100
Contract Pharmaceutical Research Services
S.I.C.: 8731
N.A.I.C.S.: 541712

Encorium Turku (2)
Keilaranta 10
FI-02150 Espoo, Finland
Tel.: (358) 207518300
Fax: (358) 207518350
E-Mail: eu@encorium.com
Web Site: www.encorium.com
Sales Range: $25-49.9 Million
Emp.: 150
Contract Pharmaceutical Research Services
S.I.C.: 8731
N.A.I.C.S.: 541712
Kai Lindevall *(Gen Mgr)*

Encorium Poland Sp.z o.o. (1)
ul Goledzinowska 10
03-30 Warsaw, Poland
Tel.: (48) 225100970
Fax: (48) 225100971
E-Mail: poland@encorium.com
Web Site: www.encorium.com
Sales Range: $10-24.9 Million
Emp.: 15
Contract Pharmaceutical Research Services
S.I.C.: 8731
N.A.I.C.S.: 541712

Encorium Romania srl (1)
35 Jean Monnet Street
Apt 2 District 1, 011956 Bucharest, Romania
Tel.: (40) 213196070
Fax: (40) 213196090
E-Mail: romania@encorium.com
Web Site: www.encorium.com
Sales Range: $10-24.9 Million
Emp.: 50
Contract Pharmaceutical Research Services
S.I.C.: 8731
N.A.I.C.S.: 541712
Sergei Nicora *(Gen Mgr)*

Encorium Sweden AB (1)
Torshamnsgatan 28a
SE-164 40 Kista, Sweden
Tel.: (46) 856488270
Fax: (46) 856488279
E-Mail: sweden@encorium.com
Web Site: www.encorium.se
Sales Range: $1-9.9 Million
Emp.: 200
Contract Pharmaceutical Research Services
S.I.C.: 8742
N.A.I.C.S.: 541611

UAB Encorium Lithuania (1)
Senasis Ukmerges kel 4 Avizieniu sen
LT-14013 Vilnius, Lithuania
Tel.: (370) 52101252
Fax: (370) 52755059
E-Mail: lithuania@encorium.com
Web Site: www.encorium.com
Sales Range: $75-99.9 Million
Emp.: 7
Contract Pharmaceutical Research Services
S.I.C.: 8731
N.A.I.C.S.: 541712
Egle Lukaitiene *(Gen Mgr)*

ENCORP BERHAD

Level 2 Block B-59 Taman Sri Sarawak Mall Jalan Tunku Abdul Rahman
93100 Kuching, Sarawak, Malaysia
Tel.: (60) 82 428 626
Fax: (60) 82 423 626
E-Mail: enquiry@encorp.com.my
Web Site: www.encorp.com.my
ENCORP—(KLS)
Rev.: $130,025,257
Assets: $656,557,630
Liabilities: $525,196,095
Net Worth: $131,361,536
Earnings: $8,083,146
Emp.: 170
Fiscal Year-end: 12/31/12

Business Description:
Property Development & Construction Management Services
S.I.C.: 1542
N.A.I.C.S.: 236220

Personnel:
Mohd Effendi Norwawi *(Chm)*
Soo Ann Yeoh *(CEO)*
Mohd Ibrahim Masrukin *(COO)*
Michael Chan *(CMO)*
Steven Hooi *(CEO-Construction)*
Lay Hong Lee *(Sec & Gen Mgr-Legal & Corp Svcs)*

Board of Directors:
Mohd Effendi Norwawi
Kong Seng Chew
Joo Chung Fong
Marcus Kok Fei Kam
Hamzah Kassim
Efeida Mohd Effendi
Philip Ding Ing Ting
Soo Ann Yeoh

Subsidiaries:

Encorp Construct Sdn Bhd (1)
No 25 1st Floor Jalan Bukit Mata
Kuching, Sarawak, 93100, Malaysia
Tel.: (60) 82236050
Fax: (60) 82238050
Web Site: www.encorpberhad.com
Emp.: 14
Property Development Services
S.I.C.: 6531
N.A.I.C.S.: 531390
Pui Chee Khian *(Project Mgr)*

Must Ehsan Development Sdn Bhd (1)
No 46G Jalan PJU 5/22 The Strand Encorp
Kota Damansara PJU 5, 47180 Petaling Jaya, Selangor, Malaysia
Tel.: (60) 361423777
Fax: (60) 361424777
E-Mail: michael.wong@encsp.com.my
Emp.: 150
Property Development Services
S.I.C.: 6531
N.A.I.C.S.: 531390
Michael Wong *(Gen Mgr)*

ENCOUNTER RESOURCES LIMITED

Level 7 600 Murray Street
West Perth, WA, 6005, Australia
Mailing Address:
PO Box 273
West Perth, WA, 6872, Australia
Tel.: (61) 8 9486 9455
Fax: (61) 8 6210 1578
E-Mail: contact@enrl.com.au
Web Site: www.enrl.com.au
Year Founded: 2004
ENR—(ASX)
Rev.: $321,843
Assets: $24,182,007
Liabilities: $816,611
Net Worth: $23,365,395
Earnings: ($1,632,188)
Emp.: 11
Fiscal Year-end: 06/30/13

Business Description:
Mineral Exploration Services
S.I.C.: 1099
N.A.I.C.S.: 212299

Personnel:
William Robinson *(Mng Dir)*
Kevin Hart *(Co-Sec)*
Dan Travers *(Co-Sec)*

Board of Directors:
Paul Chapman
Peter Bewick
Jonathan Hronsky
William Robinson

ENCOURAGE TECHNOLOGIES CO., LTD.

Tornare Nihonbashi Hamacho 7F 3-3-2 Nihonbashi Hama-cho
Chhuo-ku, Tokyo, 103-0007, Japan
Tel.: (81) 3 56232622
Web Site: www.et-x.jp
Year Founded: 2002
3682—(TKS)
Rev.: $10,069,411
Emp.: 60
Fiscal Year-end: 03/31/13

Business Description:
Security Software
S.I.C.: 7372
N.A.I.C.S.: 511210

Personnel:
Shinya Ishii *(Pres & CEO)*
Yoshihiro Maruyama *(CTO)*

Board of Directors:
Shinya Ishii
Hisao Kawashima
Yoshihiro Maruyama
Takashi Omori

ENCRES DUBUIT SA

1 Rue Isaac Newton ZI Mitry-Compans
77292 Mitry-Mory, France
Tel.: (33) 164674167
Fax: (33) 164674189
E-Mail: export@encresdubuit.com
Web Site: www.encresdubuit.net
DBT—(EUR)
Sales Range: $25-49.9 Million

Business Description:
Screen Printing Services
S.I.C.: 2759
N.A.I.C.S.: 323113

Personnel:
Chystelle Ferrari *(CFO)*

ENDAVA LIMITED

125 Old Broad Street
London, EC2N 1AR, United Kingdom
Tel.: (44) 2073671000
E-Mail: info.london@endava.com
Web Site: www.endava.com
Year Founded: 2000
Sales Range: $25-49.9 Million
Emp.: 750

Business Description:
IT Services
S.I.C.: 7373
N.A.I.C.S.: 541512

Personnel:
John Cotterell *(CEO)*
Graham Lee *(Sec)*

Board of Directors:
Mike Kinton
Andy Allan
John Cotterell
Graham Lee
Nick Lonsdale
Trevor Smith
Robert Spittal

Divisions:

Endava Limited (1)
3rd Floor 151 West George Street
Glasgow, G2 2JJ, United Kingdom
Tel.: (44) 20 7367 1000
IT Services
S.I.C.: 7373
N.A.I.C.S.: 541512

Endava Limited (1)
The Stables 112 Preston
Crowmarsh, Wallingford, Oxon, OX10 6SL, United Kingdom
Tel.: (44) 1491 820900
E-Mail: info.oxford@endava.com
IT Services
S.I.C.: 7373
N.A.I.C.S.: 541512

Non-U.S. Subsidiary:

Endava Limited (1)
75B Nicolae Caramfil St Floor 2-3 Sector 1
14142 Bucharest, Romania
Tel.: (40) 372 363 291
E-Mail: info.bucharest@endava.com
Web Site: www.endava.com
IT Services
S.I.C.: 7373
N.A.I.C.S.: 541512
Marian V. Popa *(Mng Dir)*

ENDEAVOUR FINANCIAL LTD.

37 Lombard St
London, EC3V 9BQ, United Kingdom
Tel.: (44) 2075902720
Fax: (44) 2075902721
Web Site: www.endeavourfinancial.com
Year Founded: 1988

Business Description:
Debt Finance & Merger Advisory Services
S.I.C.: 6159
N.A.I.C.S.: 522294

Personnel:
David Rhodes *(Mng Partner)*
Steve Smith *(Mng Partner)*
George Pyper *(Partner)*

ENDEAVOUR MINING CORPORATION

Regatta Office Park Windward 3
Suite 240
PO Box 1793
Georgetown, Grand Cayman, Cayman Islands
Tel.: (345) 7697250
Fax: (345) 7697256
E-Mail: investor@endeavourmining.com
Web Site: www.endeavourmining.com
Year Founded: 1988
EDV—(ASX OTC TSX)
Rev.: $346,097,000
Assets: $1,755,813,000
Liabilities: $618,418,000
Net Worth: $1,137,395,000
Earnings: ($8,556,000)
Emp.: 1,575
Fiscal Year-end: 12/31/12

Business Description:
Holding Company; Gold & Other Mineral Exploration & Mining
S.I.C.: 6719
N.A.I.C.S.: 551112

Personnel:
Michael E. Beckett *(Chm)*
Neil Woodyer *(Pres & CEO)*
Christian Milau *(CFO & Exec VP)*
Adriaan Roux *(COO)*
Morgan Carroll *(Gen Counsel, Sec & Sr VP-Corp Fin)*
Douglas Bowlby *(Exec VP-Corp Dev)*
David Laing *(Exec VP-Technical Svcs)*
Don Dudek *(Sr VP-Technical Svcs)*
Jeremy Langford *(Sr VP-Projects)*
Doug Reddy *(Sr VP-Technical Svcs)*

Board of Directors:
Michael E. Beckett
Ian David Cockerill
Jorge L. Gamarci
Frank Giustra
Antony Harwood
Ian Henderson

Endeavour Mining Corporation—(Continued)

Wayne McManus
Miguel A. Rodriguez
Neil Woodyer

Transfer Agent:
Computershare Trust Company of Canada
Vancouver, BC, Canada
Tel.: (604) 661-9400
Fax: (604) 669-1548

ENDEAVOUR SILVER CORP.

301- 700 West Pender Street
Vancouver, BC, V6C 1G8, Canada
Tel.: (604) 685-9775
Fax: (604) 685-9744
Toll Free: (877) 685-9775
E-Mail: info@edrsilver.com
Web Site: www.edrsilver.com
EXK—(DEU NYSE TSX)
Rev.: $208,079,000
Assets: $477,527,000
Liabilities: $137,331,000
Net Worth: $340,196,000
Earnings: $42,117,000
Emp.: 950
Fiscal Year-end: 12/31/12

Business Description:
Silver Mining & Production Services
S.I.C.: 1044
N.A.I.C.S.: 212222

Personnel:
Geoffrey Arthur Handley *(Chm)*
Godfrey J. Walton *(Pres & COO)*
Bradford James Cooke *(CEO)*
Dan Dickson *(CFO)*

Board of Directors:
Geoffrey Arthur Handley
Ricardo Moreno Campoy
Bradford James Cooke
Leonard J. Harris
Rex John McLennan
Kenneth William Pickering
Mario D. Szotlender
Godfrey J. Walton

Legal Counsel:
Koffman Kalef LLP
19th Fl 885 W Georgia St
Vancouver, BC, Canada

Computershare Investor Services Inc.
510 Burrard Street 2nd Floor
Vancouver, BC, V6C 3B9, Canada

Transfer Agents:
Computershare Investor Services Inc.
Montreal, QC, Canada

Computershare Investor Services Inc.
510 Burrard Street 2nd Floor
Vancouver, BC, V6C 3B9, Canada

Non-U.S. Subsidiary:

Minera Santa Cruz y Garibaldi SA de CV **(1)**
Miguel De Cervantes Saavedra No 106 Sur Centro
Durango, Mexico
Tel.: (52) 6188114668
Fax: (52) 6748845100
Silver Mining Services
S.I.C.: 1044
N.A.I.C.S.: 212222
Emilio Rivero *(Dir Gen)*

ENDLESS LLP

3 Whitehall Quay
Leeds, LS1 4BF, United Kingdom
Tel.: (44) 113 210 4000
Web Site: www.endlessllp.com
Year Founded: 2005
Managed Assets: $789,645,000

Business Description:
Private Equity Firm
S.I.C.: 6211
N.A.I.C.S.: 523999

Personnel:
Peter Yendell *(Chm)*
Garry Wilson *(Mng Partner)*
Darren Forshaw *(Partner)*
Christopher Clegg *(Mng Dir)*

Holding:

Cinesite (Europe) Limited **(1)**
Medius House 2 Sheraton Street
London, W1F 8BH, United Kingdom
Tel.: (44) 2079734000
Fax: (44) 2079734040
E-Mail: press@cinesite.co.uk
Web Site: www.cinesite.com
Sales Range: $50-74.9 Million
Emp.: 200
Digital Imaging Services
S.I.C.: 7829
N.A.I.C.S.: 512120
Antony Hunt *(Mng Dir)*

ENDO INTERNATIONAL PLC

25-28 North Wall Quay International Financial Services Centre
Dublin, 1, Ireland
Tel.: (353) 1 649 2000
Web Site: www.endo.com
Year Founded: 2013
ENDP—(NASDAQ TSX)
Sales Range: $1-4.9 Billion

Business Description:
Holding Company; Pharmaceutical Mfr & Distr
S.I.C.: 6719
N.A.I.C.S.: 551112

Personnel:
Roger Hartley Kimmel *(Chm)*
Rajiv De Silva *(Pres & CEO)*
Suketu P. Upadhyay *(CFO & Exec VP)*
Caroline B. Manogue *(Chief Legal Officer, Sec & Exec VP)*
Susan T. Hall *(Chief Scientific Officer, Exec VP & Global Head-R&D & Quality)*

Board of Directors:
Roger Hartley Kimmel
Rajiv De Silva
John J. Delucca
Arthur Joseph Higgins
Nancy J. Hutson
Michael Hyatt
William P. Montague
Jill D. Smith
William F. Spengler

U.S. Subsidiary:

Endo Health Solutions Inc. **(1)**
1400 Atwater Dr
Malvern, PA 19355 DE
Tel.: (484) 216-0000
Web Site: www.endo.com
Rev.: $2,616,907,000
Assets: $6,571,856,000
Liabilities: $5,986,640,000
Net Worth: $585,216,000
Earnings: ($632,414,000)
Emp.: 3,371
Fiscal Year-end: 12/31/13
Holding Company for Pharmaceutical Mfr
S.I.C.: 2834
N.A.I.C.S.: 325412
Rajiv De Silva *(Pres & CEO)*
Suketu P. Upadhyay *(CFO & Exec VP)*
Caroline B. Manogue *(Chief Legal Officer, Sec & Exec VP)*
Jon Smollen *(Chief Compliance Officer & Exec VP)*
Camille Farhat *(Pres-American Medical Sys)*
Larry Cunningham *(Exec VP-HR)*
Denise Hudson *(Exec VP-Enterprise Quality & Supply Chain)*

Subsidiaries:

American Medical Systems Holdings, Inc. **(2)**
10700 Bren Rd W
Minnetonka, MN 55343-9679 DE
Tel.: (952) 930-6000
Fax: (952) 930-6373
Toll Free: (800) 328-3881
E-Mail: info@americanmedicalsystems.com
Web Site: www.americanmedicalsystems.com
Emp.: 1,255
Medical Device Mfr
S.I.C.: 3841
N.A.I.C.S.: 339112
Anthony P. Bihl, III *(Grp Pres)*
Mark A. Heggestad *(CFO & Exec VP)*
Joe W. Martin *(Sr VP & Gen Mgr-BPH Therapy)*
John F. Nealon *(Sr VP & Gen Mgr-Women's Health)*
Randall Ross *(Sr VP-HR)*

Subsidiary:

American Medical Systems, Inc. **(3)**
10700 Bren Rd W
Minnetonka, MN 55343-9679
Tel.: (952) 930-6000
Fax: (952) 930-6157
Toll Free: (800) 328-33881
Web Site: www.americanmedicalsystems.com
Sales Range: $75-99.9 Million
Emp.: 500
Urological Devices Mfr
S.I.C.: 3841
N.A.I.C.S.: 339113
Anthony P. Bihl, III *(Grp Pres)*

Branch:

American Medical Systems, Inc.-San Jose **(4)**
3052 Orchard Dr
San Jose, CA 95134-2011 CA
Tel.: (408) 943-0636
Fax: (408) 943-9630
Web Site: www.americanmedicalsystems.com
Sales Range: $75-99.9 Million
Emp.: 296
Medical Laser Equipment & Systems Designer, Mfr, Sales & Servicer Export
S.I.C.: 3845
N.A.I.C.S.: 334510

Non-U.S. Subsidiaries:

American Medical Systems Canada Inc. **(3)**
381 Elmira N
PO Box 461
Guelph, ON, N1H 6K9, Canada
Tel.: (519) 826-5333
Fax: (519) 821-1356
Medical Devices Distr
S.I.C.: 5047
N.A.I.C.S.: 423450

American Medical Systems Deutschland GmbH **(3)**
Voss Strasse 20
10117 Berlin, Germany
Tel.: (49) 302064390
Fax: (49) 3020643999
E-Mail: contact@americanmedicalsystems.de
Web Site: www.americanmedicalsystems.de
Medical Therapy Apparatus & Medical Devices Mfr
S.I.C.: 5047
N.A.I.C.S.: 423450
Michael Krumbiegel *(Country Mgr)*

American Medical Systems Europe B.V. **(3)**
Haarlerbergweg 23 G
1101 CH Amsterdam, Netherlands
Tel.: (31) 205938800
Fax: (31) 205938830
Web Site: www.americanmedicalsystems.nl
Medical Therapy Apparatus & Medical Devices Mfr
S.I.C.: 5047
N.A.I.C.S.: 423450

American Medical Systems France S.A.S **(3)**
19 Avenue de Norvege
91953 Courtaboeuf, France
Tel.: (33) 169599700
Fax: (33) 169599729
E-Mail: csFrance@ammd.com
Emp.: 30
Medical Device Mfr
S.I.C.: 3841
N.A.I.C.S.: 339112
Frederic Pette *(Mng Dir)*

American Medical Systems Iberica S.L. **(3)**
C / Joaquin Turina 22 Planta Primera Oficina 6
28224 Pozuelo de Alarcon, Spain
Tel.: (34) 917994970
Fax: (34) 917157526
E-Mail: csIberica@ammd.com
Medical Therapy Apparatus & Devices Mfr
S.I.C.: 3841
N.A.I.C.S.: 339112

American Medical Systems UK Limited **(3)**
Capital Court Capital Interchange Way
Brentford, TW8 0EX, United Kingdom
Tel.: (44) 2089963100
Fax: (44) 2089953720
E-Mail: amsuk@ammd.com
Web Site: www.americanmedicalsystems.co.uk
Emp.: 40
Medical Therapy Apparatus & Medical Devices Mfr
S.I.C.: 5047
N.A.I.C.S.: 423450

AMS - American Medical Systems do Brasil Produtos Urologicos e Ginecologicos Ltda. **(3)**
Av Ibirapuera 2907 Conj 1212
Sao Paulo, 04029-200, Brazil
Tel.: (55) 1150919753
Fax: (55) 1150919755
E-Mail: amsbrazil@ammg.com
Emp.: 6
Medical Therapy Apparatus & Medical Devices Mfr
S.I.C.: 5047
N.A.I.C.S.: 423450
Jorge Bukalil *(Mgr-Natl Sls)*

AMS Medical Systems Ireland Limited **(3)**
Unit A Garrycastle Business Park
Athlone, Westmeath, Ireland
Tel.: (353) 906465300
Medical Therapy Apparatus & Medical Devices Mfr
S.I.C.: 5047
N.A.I.C.S.: 423450

CPEC LLC **(2)**
3326 Hwy 51 N
Fort Mill, SC 29715 DE
Tel.: (803) 548-4348
Pharmaceutical Product Mfr
S.I.C.: 2834
N.A.I.C.S.: 325412

Endo Pharmaceuticals Solutions Inc. **(2)**
100 Endo Blvd
Chadds Ford, PA 19317 DE
Tel.: (610) 558-9800
Fax: (610) 558-8979
Web Site: www.endo.com
Sales Range: $75-99.9 Million
Emp.: 246
Pharmaceuticals Mfr
S.I.C.: 2834
N.A.I.C.S.: 325412

Unit:

Endo Pharmaceuticals Solutions Inc. - New Jersey **(3)**
7 Clarke Dr
Cranbury, NJ 08512
Tel.: (609) 409-9010
Fax: (609) 409-1650
Toll Free: (888) 262-8855
Web Site: www.endo.com
Sales Range: $25-49.9 Million
Emp.: 101
Pharmaceuticals Mfr
S.I.C.: 2834
N.A.I.C.S.: 325412

Qualitest Pharmaceuticals, Inc. **(2)**
130 Vintage Dr
Huntsville, AL 35811
Tel.: (800) 444-4011
E-Mail: info@qualitestrx.com
Web Site: www.qualitestrx.com

Emp.: 1,000
Generic Pharmaceutical Mfr
S.I.C.: 2834
N.A.I.C.S.: 325412
Kathryn Weingart *(Dir-Quality Assurance)*

Subsidiary:

Boca Pharmacal, LLC **(3)**
3550 NW 126th Ave
Coral Springs, FL 33065 FL
Tel.: (954) 426-1919
Toll Free: (800) 354-8460
E-Mail: info@bocapharmacal.com
Web Site: www.bocapharmacal.com
Generic Pharmaceutical Mfr
S.I.C.: 2834
N.A.I.C.S.: 325412
Robert Edwards *(Pres & CEO)*

Non-U.S. Subsidiary:

Paladin Labs Inc. **(2)**
100 Blvd Alexis Nihon Suite 600
Saint Laurent, QC, H4M 2P2, Canada Ca
Tel.: (514) 340-1112
Fax: (514) 344-4675
Toll Free: (888) 376-7830
E-Mail: info@paladinlabs.com
Web Site: www.paladinlabs.com
Rev.: $208,943,004
Assets: $600,901,988
Liabilities: $153,081,068
Net Worth: $447,820,920
Earnings: $58,006,037
Emp.: 403
Fiscal Year-end: 12/31/12
Biotechnological & Pharmaceutical Products Mfr
S.I.C.: 2834
N.A.I.C.S.: 325412
Mark Beaudet *(Interim Pres & Interim CEO)*
Samira Sakhia *(CFO)*

Non-U.S. Subsidiary:

Labopharm Europe Limited **(3)**
5 Seapoint Building 44 Clomtars
3 Dublin, Ireland IE
Tel.: (353) 018540140 (100%)
Fax: (353) 018540144
E-Mail: europe@labopharm.com
Web Site: www.labopharm.com
Emp.: 12
Pharmaceutical Research & Development
S.I.C.: 8731
N.A.I.C.S.: 541712
Samira Sakhia *(Mng Dir)*

ENDO MANUFACTURING CO., LTD.

987 Higashiota
Tsubame, Niigata, 959 1289, Japan
Tel.: (81) 256636111
Fax: (81) 256626118
E-Mail: e-mail@endo-mfg.co.jp
Web Site: www.endo-mfg.co.jp
Year Founded: 1950
7841—(JAS)
Sls.: $192,346,000
Assets: $204,886,000
Liabilities: $62,260,000
Net Worth: $142,626,000
Earnings: $5,324,000
Emp.: 2,851
Fiscal Year-end: 03/31/13

Business Description:
Golf Club Heads, Stainless Products & Forged Products Mfr & Sales
S.I.C.: 3499
N.A.I.C.S.: 332999

Personnel:
Ken Shigematsu *(Pres & CEO)*

Subsidiary:

EPON GOLF CORPORATION **(1)**
5-3 Chuo-dori
Tsubame, Niigata, 959-1244, Japan
Tel.: (81) 256645551
Fax: (81) 256645553
E-Mail: contact@eponforged-international.com
Web Site: www.epongolf.co.jp
Emp.: 13
Golf Clubs Mfr & Distr
S.I.C.: 3949
N.A.I.C.S.: 339920
Kenji Kobayashi *(Pres)*

Non-U.S. Subsidiaries:

Endo Forging (Thailand) Co. Ltd. **(1)**
179-1 Moo 7 Gate Way Industrial Estate
High Way 311 Road, 24190 Chachoengsao, Thailand (100%)
Tel.: (66) 38575223
Fax: (66) 38575221
Web Site: www.endo-mfg.co.jp/contents/guide/factory/forging/index.html
Emp.: 130
All Other Motor Vehicle Parts Mfr
S.I.C.: 3714
N.A.I.C.S.: 336390
Kenji Koboyashi *(CEO)*

Endo Stainless Steel (Thailand) Co. Ltd. **(1)**
179 Moo 7 Gateway Industrial Estate
Export Zone
Plangyao District, 24190 Chachoengsao, Thailand (100%)
Tel.: (66) 8575016
Fax: (66) 8575035
Web Site: www.endo-mfg.co.jp/contents/guide/factory/steel/index.html
Emp.: 90
Structural Steel Erection Contractors
S.I.C.: 1791
N.A.I.C.S.: 238120
Kenji Koboyashi *(CEO)*

ENDO STAINLESS STEEL (VIETNAM) CO., LTD. **(1)**
Plot 74 - Noi Bai Industrial Zone Quang Tien
Soc Son District, Hanoi, Vietnam
Tel.: (84) 435824784
Fax: (84) 435823912
Stainless Steel Products Mfr
S.I.C.: 3312
N.A.I.C.S.: 331110

Endo Thai Co.Ltd. **(1)**
179-1 Moo 9 Gate Way City Industrial Estat
Plangyao, 24190 Chachoengsao, Thailand (100%)
Tel.: (66) 23260342
Fax: (66) 7394985
E-Mail: endothai@endolkb.com
Web Site: www.endothai.com
Emp.: 80
Sporting & Athletic Goods Mfr
S.I.C.: 3949
N.A.I.C.S.: 339920
Koboyashi Sang *(Pres)*
Kenji Koboyashi *(CEO)*

ENDOCEUTICS INC.

2989 de la Promenade
Quebec, QC, G1W 2J5, Canada
Tel.: (418) 652-0197
Fax: (418) 651-1856
E-Mail: info@endoceutics.com
Web Site: www.endoceutics.com
Sales Range: $1-9.9 Million
Emp.: 1

Business Description:
Hormone Therapy Biopharmaceutical Product Developer
S.I.C.: 2834
N.A.I.C.S.: 325412

Personnel:
Fernand Labrie *(Pres, CEO & Chief Scientific Officer)*
Claude Dore *(CFO)*

Board of Directors:
Donald R. Conklin
Michel Dallaire
Eric Dupont
Jean-Pierre Gayral
Fernand Labrie
Pierre Seccareccia
Jerome F. Strauss, III

ENDOCOAL LIMITED

(Acquired & Absorbed by Yima Coal Industry Group Co., Ltd. & Daton Group Australia Limited)

ENDOMINES AB

Hovslagargatan 5B
SE-111 48 Stockholm, Sweden
Tel.: (46) 8 611 66 45
Fax: (46) 8 611 47 30
Web Site: www.endomines.com
ENDO—(HEL OMX)
Rev.: $36,393,480
Assets: $77,895,360
Liabilities: $56,889,000
Net Worth: $21,006,360
Earnings: $2,925,720
Fiscal Year-end: 12/31/12

Business Description:
Gold Mining
S.I.C.: 1041
N.A.I.C.S.: 212221

Personnel:
Staffan Simberg *(Chm)*
Markus Ekberg *(CEO)*
Borje Linden *(CFO)*
Jaakko Liikanen *(CTO)*
Fredrik Dahlstrom *(IR Officer)*

Board of Directors:
Staffan Simberg
Timo Lindborg
Stefan Mansson
Rauno Pitkanen
Mati Sallert
Meg Tiveus

ENDRESS+HAUSER (INTERNATIONAL) HOLDING AG

Kagenstrasse 2
CH 4153 Reinach, Switzerland
Tel.: (41) 61 7 15 75 75
Fax: (41) 61 7 15 27 75
E-Mail: info@ii.endress.com
Web Site: www.endress.com
Year Founded: 1953
Sales Range: $800-899.9 Million
Emp.: 9,000

Business Description:
Industrial Process Control Devices & Systems Mfr
S.I.C.: 3823
N.A.I.C.S.: 334513

Personnel:
Klaus Endress *(CEO)*
Luc Schultheiss *(CFO)*
Michael Ziesemer *(COO)*

Board of Directors:
Klaus Endress
Michael Ziesemer

Subsidiaries:

Endress+Hauser Consult AG **(1)**
Kaegenstrasse 2
4153 Reinach, Switzerland
Tel.: (41) 617157575
Fax: (41) 617152775
E-Mail: info@holding.endress.com
Web Site: www.ch.endress.com
Emp.: 425
Management Consulting Services
S.I.C.: 8748
N.A.I.C.S.: 541618
Klaus Endress *(CEO)*

Endress+Hauser Metso AG **(1)**
Kaegenstrasse 2
4153 Reinach, Switzerland
Tel.: (41) 617157575
Fax: (41) 617152888
E-Mail: info@ch.endress.com
Web Site: www.ch.endress.com
Emp.: 120
Industrial Machinery & Equipment Whslr
S.I.C.: 5084
N.A.I.C.S.: 423830
Klaus Endress *(Gen Mgr)*

U.S. Subsidiaries:

Endress+Hauser Inc. **(1)**
2350 Endress Pl
Greenwood, IN 46143
Tel.: (317) 535-7138
Fax: (317) 535-8498
E-Mail: info@us.endress.com
Web Site: www.us.endress.com
Emp.: 250
Instruments & Related Products Mfr for Measuring Displaying & Controlling Industrial Process Variables
S.I.C.: 3823
N.A.I.C.S.: 334513
Codd Lucey *(Gen Mgr)*

Kaiser Optical Systems, Inc. **(1)**
371 Parkland Plz
Ann Arbor, MI 48103 MI
Tel.: (734) 665-8083 (100%)
Fax: (734) 665-8199
E-Mail: sales@kosi.com
Web Site: www.kosi.com
Sales Range: $10-24.9 Million
Emp.: 70
Spectrographic Instrumentation & Applied Holographic Technology
S.I.C.: 3827
N.A.I.C.S.: 333314
Bruno Lenain *(Dir-Europe)*

SpectraSensors, Inc. **(1)**
4333 W Sam Houston Pkwy Ste 100
Houston, TX 77043
Tel.: (713) 300-2700
Fax: (713) 856-6623
Toll Free: (800) 619-2861
E-Mail: sales@spectrasensors.com
Web Site: www.spectrasensors.com
Sales Range: $10-24.9 Million
Emp.: 80
Laser-Based Test Instruments for Natural Gas & Petrochemical Companies
S.I.C.: 3826
N.A.I.C.S.: 334516
George Balogh *(Chm & CEO)*
Mike Dyar *(CFO)*

Non-U.S. Subsidiaries:

EMC Industrial Group Limited **(1)**
56 Tarndale Grove Albany
PO Box 101-444
0632 Auckland, New Zealand
Tel.: (64) 94155110
Fax: (64) 94155115
E-Mail: sales@emc.co.nz
Web Site: www.emc.co.nz
Emp.: 25
Inorganic Chemical Mfr
S.I.C.: 2819
N.A.I.C.S.: 325180
Russell P. Mason *(Mgr-Mktg)*

Endress y Hauser, S.A. **(1)**
Constitucio 3 A
08960 Barcelona, Spain
Tel.: (34) 934803366
Fax: (34) 934733839
E-Mail: info@es.endress.com
Web Site: www.es.endress.com
Emp.: 52
Electrical Appliance Television & Radio Set Whslr
S.I.C.: 5064
N.A.I.C.S.: 423620
Antonio Carrillo *(Gen Mgr)*

Endress+Hauser A/S **(1)**
Poppelgardvej 10-12
2860 Soborg, Denmark
Tel.: (45) 70131132
Fax: (45) 70132133
E-Mail: info@dk.endress.com
Web Site: www.dk.endress.com
Emp.: 30
Electrical Appliance Television & Radio Set Whslr
S.I.C.: 5064
N.A.I.C.S.: 423620
Felix Langkjaer *(Mng Dir)*

Endress+Hauser AB **(1)**
PO Box 3107
16903 Solna, Sweden
Tel.: (46) 855511600
Fax: (46) 855511655
E-Mail: info@se.endress.com
Web Site: www.se.endress.com
Emp.: 25
Industrial Machinery & Equipment Whslr
S.I.C.: 5084
N.A.I.C.S.: 423830
Stefan Bgo Rkegrem *(Mgr-Sls)*

Endress+Hauser (International) Holding AG—(Continued)

Endress+Hauser Argentina S.A. (1)
Av Ruiz Huidobro 4771
1430 Buenos Aires, Argentina
Tel.: (54) 1145434500
Fax: (54) 1145432400
E-Mail: info@ar.endress.com.ar
Web Site: www.ar.endress.com
Industrial Machinery & Equipment Whslr
S.I.C.: 5084
N.A.I.C.S.: 423830

Endress+Hauser Australia Pty Ltd. (1)
Level 1 16 Giffnock Avenue
North RydeLink Business Park, Macquarie Park, NSW, 2113, Australia
Tel.: (61) 288777000
Fax: (61) 288777099
E-Mail: info@au.endress.com
Web Site: www.endress.com.au
Emp.: 40
Engineering Services
S.I.C.: 8711
N.A.I.C.S.: 541330
Chris Gailer *(Mng Dir)*

Endress+Hauser B.V. (1)
Nikkelstraat 6-12
PO Box 5102
1410AC Naarden, Netherlands
Tel.: (31) 356958611
Fax: (31) 356958825
E-Mail: info@nl.endress.com
Web Site: www.nl.endress.com
Emp.: 125
Warm Air Heating & Air-Conditioning Equipment & Supplies Whslr
S.I.C.: 5075
N.A.I.C.S.: 423730
R. Homnersen *(Gen Mgr)*

Endress+Hauser Canada Ltd. (1)
1075 Sutton Drive
L7L5Z8 Burlington, ON, Canada
Tel.: (905) 681-9292
Fax: (905) 681-9444
E-Mail: info@ca.endress.com
Web Site: www.ca.endress.com
Emp.: 125
Industrial Machinery & Equipment Whslr
S.I.C.: 5084
N.A.I.C.S.: 423830
Richard Lewandowski *(Gen Mgr)*

Endress+Hauser Chile Ltd. (1)
Maria Luisa Santander 0447
Providencia, 7500859 Santiago, Chile
Tel.: (56) 27849800
Fax: (56) 27849801
E-Mail: info@cl.endress.com
Web Site: www.cl.endress.com
Emp.: 43
Electrical Apparatus & Equipment Wiring Supplies & Construction Material Whslr
S.I.C.: 5063
N.A.I.C.S.: 423610
Susana Torres *(Gen Mgr)*

Endress+Hauser Conducta GmbH+Co. KG (1)
Dieselstrasse 24
70839 Gerlingen, Germany
Tel.: (49) 71562090
Fax: (49) 715628158
E-Mail: info@conducta.endress.com
Web Site: www.conducta.endress.com
Industrial Liquid Analysis
S.I.C.: 7389
N.A.I.C.S.: 541990
Manfred Jagiella *(CEO)*

Endress+Hauser Controle e Automacao Ltda. (1)
Av Ibirapuera 2033 3Fl Andar Moema
04029-100 Sao Paulo, Brazil
Tel.: (55) 1150334333
Fax: (55) 1150334334
E-Mail: info@br.endress.com.br
Web Site: www.br.endress.com
Emp.: 60
Industrial Machinery & Equipment Whslr
S.I.C.: 5084
N.A.I.C.S.: 423830
Carlos Behrends *(Gen Mgr)*

Endress+Hauser Czech S.r.o. (1)
Olbrachtova 2006-9
14000 Prague, Czech Republic
Tel.: (420) 241080450
Fax: (420) 41080460
E-Mail: info@cz.endress.com
Web Site: www.cz.endress.com
Emp.: 24
Industrial Machinery & Equipment Whslr
S.I.C.: 5084
N.A.I.C.S.: 423830

Endress+Hauser D.o.o. (1)
Froudeova 94
10020 Zagreb, Croatia
Tel.: (385) 16591780
Fax: (385) 16591790
E-Mail: info@hr.endress.com
Web Site: www.endress.com
Emp.: 9
Management Consulting Services
S.I.C.: 8748
N.A.I.C.S.: 541618
Drazen Kolenc *(Mng Dir)*

Endress+Hauser Ges.m.b.H. (1)
Lehnergasse 4
PO Box 173
1230 Vienna, Austria
Tel.: (43) 1880560
Fax: (43) 188056335
E-Mail: info@at.endress.com
Web Site: www.at.endress.com
Emp.: 60
Instrument Mfr for Measuring & Testing Electricity & Electrical Signals
S.I.C.: 3825
N.A.I.C.S.: 334515
Adel Smayer *(Mng Dir)*

Endress+Hauser (Hellas) S.A. (1)
4 Leoforoskimis Ilektras 4B
Marousi, 15122 Athens, Greece
Tel.: (30) 2108002320
Fax: (30) 2106208386
E-Mail: info@gr.endress.com
Web Site: www.endress.com
Emp.: 10
Electrical Apparatus & Equipment Wiring Supplies & Construction Material Whslr
S.I.C.: 5063
N.A.I.C.S.: 423610
George Karageorges *(Gen Mgr)*

Endress+Hauser (H.K.) Ltd. (1)
Unit 1211 12th-Floor Tower I Silvercord
30 Canton Road Tsimshatsui, Kowloon, China (Hong Kong)
Tel.: (852) 25283120
Fax: (852) 28654171
E-Mail: info@hk.endress.com
Web Site: www.hk.endress.com
Emp.: 13
Inorganic Chemical Mfr
S.I.C.: 2819
N.A.I.C.S.: 325180
Ken Wong *(Dir-Mktg)*

Endress+Hauser (India) Pvt. Ltd. (1)
5th Floor Wing A and B Raj Plaza
LBS Marg Vikhroli - West, 400083 Mumbai, India
Tel.: (91) 2266481111
Fax: (91) 2266938330
E-Mail: info@in.endress.com
Web Site: www.in.endress.com
Emp.: 80
Industrial Machinery & Equipment Whslr
S.I.C.: 5084
N.A.I.C.S.: 423830
Sajiv Nath *(Mng Dir)*

Endress+Hauser (Ireland) Ltd. (1)
Industrial Instrumentation Centre
Kilcock Rd Clane Business Pk, Kildare, Ireland
Tel.: (353) 45868615
Fax: (353) 45868182
E-Mail: info@ie.endress.com
Web Site: www.ie.endress.com
Emp.: 24
Engineering Services
S.I.C.: 8711
N.A.I.C.S.: 541330
Christophe Roche *(Gen Mgr)*

Endress+Hauser Italia S.p.A. (1)
Via Donat Cattin 2-a
Cernusco, 20063 Milan, Italy
Tel.: (39) 02921921
Fax: (39) 0292192362
E-Mail: info@it.endress.com
Web Site: www.it.endress.com
Emp.: 144
Environmental Consulting Services
S.I.C.: 8999
N.A.I.C.S.: 541620
Ivano Mazzoletti *(Mng Dir)*

Endress+Hauser Japan Co.,Ltd. (1)
5-70-3 Nisshincho Fuchu-shi
Tokyo, 183-0036, Japan
Tel.: (81) 423141911
Fax: (81) 423141907
E-Mail: info@jp.endress.com
Web Site: www.jp.endress.com
Emp.: 154
Industrial Machinery & Equipment Whslr
S.I.C.: 5084
N.A.I.C.S.: 423830
Sito Yujiro *(Pres)*

Endress+Hauser Korea Co., Ltd. (1)
5th Floor Kocom Building
260-7 Yeomchang-dong Kangseo-g, 157-040 Seoul, Korea (South)
Tel.: (82) 226587200
Fax: (82) 226592838
E-Mail: info@rok.endress.com
Web Site: www.endress.co.kr
Emp.: 40
Industrial Machinery & Equipment Whslr
S.I.C.: 5084
N.A.I.C.S.: 423830
Is Kim *(Gen Mgr)*

Endress+Hauser Ltd. (1)
Floats Rd
Manchester, M239NF, United Kingdom
Tel.: (44) 1612865000
Fax: (44) 1619981841
E-Mail: info@uk.endress.com
Web Site: www.uk.endress.com
Emp.: 190
Instruments & Related Products Mfr for Measuring Displaying & Controlling Industrial Process Variables
S.I.C.: 3823
N.A.I.C.S.: 334513
David Newell *(Mng Dir)*

Endress+Hauser (M) Sdn. Bhd. (1)
Lot 10 4th Floor
Jalan Astaka U8-84 Seksyen U8, Shah Alam, Selangor, 40150, Malaysia
Tel.: (60) 378433888
Fax: (60) 378433800
E-Mail: infomy@endress.com
Web Site: www.my.endress.com
Emp.: 55
Industrial Machinery & Equipment Whslr
S.I.C.: 5084
N.A.I.C.S.: 423830
Chow Nunkang *(Mng Dir)*

Endress+Hauser Polska Sp. Z o.o. (1)
ul J Pilsudskiego 49-57
50-032 Wroclaw, Poland
Tel.: (48) 717803700
Fax: (48) 717803760
E-Mail: info@pl.endress.com
Web Site: www.pl.endress.com
Emp.: 69
Totalizing Fluid Meter & Counting Device Mfr
S.I.C.: 3824
N.A.I.C.S.: 334514
Andrzej Frosztega *(Gen Mgr)*

Endress+Hauser Portugal, Lda (1)
Condominio Empresarial da Moita
Fraccao K, 2860-579 Moita, Portugal
Tel.: (351) 214253070
Fax: (351) 214253079
E-Mail: info@pt.endress.com
Web Site: www.endress.com
Emp.: 15
Warm Air Heating & Air-Conditioning Equipment & Supplies Whslr
S.I.C.: 5075
N.A.I.C.S.: 423730
Fandro Silva *(Mng Dir)*

Endress+Hauser (Pty.) Ltd. (1)
5 Commerce Crescent West Eastgate Ext 13
PO Box 783996
2146 Sandton, South Africa
Tel.: (27) 112628000
Fax: (27) 112628062
E-Mail: info@za.endress.com
Web Site: www.za.endress.com
Emp.: 80
Electrical Appliance Television & Radio Set Whslr
S.I.C.: 5064
N.A.I.C.S.: 423620
Rob MacKenzie *(Mng Dir)*

Endress+Hauser Romania SRL (1)
319C Splaiul Independentei
060044 Bucharest, Romania
Tel.: (40) 213159067
Fax: (40) 213159063
E-Mail: info@ro.endress.com
Web Site: www.endress.com
Emp.: 13
Industrial Machinery & Equipment Whslr
S.I.C.: 5084
N.A.I.C.S.: 423830
Rudolf Moos *(Mng Dir)*

Endress+Hauser sa/nv (1)
Rue Carli Straat 13
1140 Brussels, Belgium
Tel.: (32) 22480600
Fax: (32) 22480553
E-Mail: info@be.endress.com
Web Site: www.be.endress.com
Emp.: 55
Electrical Apparatus & Equipment Wiring Supplies & Construction Material Whslr
S.I.C.: 5063
N.A.I.C.S.: 423610

Endress+Hauser (SEA) Pte Ltd. (1)
1 International Business Park
#01-11-12 The Synergy, 609917 Singapore, Singapore
Tel.: (65) 65668222
Fax: (65) 65666848
E-Mail: info@sg.endress.com
Web Site: www.sg.endress.com
Emp.: 38
Industrial Machinery & Equipment Whslr
S.I.C.: 5084
N.A.I.C.S.: 423830
Neal Watmough *(Mng Dir)*

Endress+Hauser Shanghai Automation Equipment Co. Ltd. (1)
No 458 East Jiang Chuan Road
200241 Shanghai, China
Tel.: (86) 2124039600
Fax: (86) 2124039607
E-Mail: info@cn.endress.com
Web Site: www.cn.endress.com
Emp.: 170
Industrial Machinery & Equipment Whslr
S.I.C.: 5084
N.A.I.C.S.: 423830
Yu Guantjin *(Mgr)*

Endress+Hauser (Slovenija) D.o.o. (1)
Bravnicarjeva 20
1000 Ljubljana, Slovenia
Tel.: (386) 15140250
Fax: (386) 15192298
Web Site: www.si.endress.com
Emp.: 7
Instrument Mfr for Measuring & Testing Electricity & Electrical Signals
S.I.C.: 3825
N.A.I.C.S.: 334515
Bozo Vihar *(Gen Mgr)*

Endress+Hauser (Thailand) Ltd. (1)
111 Moo 4 Bangkruai - Jongthanom Road
Mahasawat Bangkruai, 11130 Nonthaburi, Thailand
Tel.: (66) 244769009
Fax: (66) 2244769201
E-Mail: infobkk@th.endress.com
Web Site: www.th.endress.com
Emp.: 44
Instrument Mfr for Measuring & Testing Electricity & Electrical Signals
S.I.C.: 3825
N.A.I.C.S.: 334515
Suphot Pokpattanakul *(Gen Mgr)*

Metso Endress+Hauser Oy (1)
Laippatie 4C
Helsinki, Finland
Tel.: (358) 20483160
Fax: (358) 20483161
E-Mail: info.metsoendress@metsoendress.com
Web Site: www.metsoendress.com
Emp.: 100

Electronic Parts & Equipment Whslr
S.I.C.: 5065
N.A.I.C.S.: 423690
Tuomo Saukkonen *(Gen Mgr)*

ENDRICH BAUELEMENTE VERTRIEBS GMBH

Hauptstrasse 56
72202 Nagold, Germany
Tel.: (49) 745260070
Fax: (49) 7452600770
E-Mail: endrich@endrich.com
Web Site: www.endrich.com
Year Founded: 1976
Rev.: $88,675,606
Emp.: 106
Business Description:
Electrochemical Components Whlsr
S.I.C.: 3679
N.A.I.C.S.: 334419
Personnel:
Ursula Endrich *(Co-Founder & Co-CEO)*
Wolfgang Endrich *(Co-Founder & Co-CEO)*

ENDURANCE GOLD CORPORATION

Suite 1700 - 750 West Pender Street
Vancouver, BC, V6C 2T8, Canada
Tel.: (604) 682-2707
Fax: (604) 681-0902
E-Mail: info@endurancegold.com
Web Site: www.endurancegold.com
Year Founded: 2003
EDG—(TSXV)
Int. Income: $5,518
Assets: $3,027,379
Liabilities: $139,295
Net Worth: $2,888,084
Earnings: ($341,983)
Fiscal Year-end: 12/31/12
Business Description:
Mineral Exploration Services
S.I.C.: 1081
N.A.I.C.S.: 213114
Personnel:
Robert T. Boyd *(Pres & CEO)*
Teresa Cheng *(CFO & Sec)*
Board of Directors:
H. Ross Arnold
Robert T. Boyd
Richard Gilliam
J. Christopher Mitchell
Robert Bruce Pease
Legal Counsel:
Vector Corporate Finance Lawyers
Suite 1040 - 999 West Hastings Street
Vancouver, BC, Canada
Transfer Agent:
Computershare Investor Services Inc.
3rd Floor 510 Burrard St
V6C 3B9 Vancouver, BC, Canada

ENDURANCE SPECIALTY HOLDINGS LTD.

Wellesley House 90 Pitts Bay Road
Pembroke, HM 08, Bermuda
Tel.: (441) 278 0400
Fax: (441) 278 0401
Web Site: www.endurance.bm
ENH—(NYSE)
Premiums: $2,665,244,000
Assets: $8,978,122,000
Liabilities: $6,091,573,000
Net Worth: $2,886,549,000
Earnings: $311,915,000
Emp.: 920
Fiscal Year-end: 12/31/13
Business Description:
Commercial Insurance & Reinsurance
S.I.C.: 6351
N.A.I.C.S.: 524126
Personnel:
John R. Charman *(Chm & CEO)*
Michael J. Mcguire *(CFO)*
Catherine A. Kalaydjian *(COO)*
Mark K. Silverstein *(CIO-Endurance Svcs Limited)*
Carrie Rosorea *(Chief Acctg Officer)*
Joan deLemps *(Chief Underwriting Officer)*
Jerome Faure *(CEO-Global Reinsurance)*
John A. Kuhn *(CEO-Global Insurance)*
John V. Del Col *(Gen Counsel, Sec & Exec VP-Acq)*
Fred Cooper *(Exec VP & Head-Fin Institutions Insurance-US)*
Joseph C. O'Donnell *(Exec VP & Head-Fin & Pro Lines)*
Daniel Wadley *(Exec VP & Head-Pro Insurance Unit)*
Steven Dresner *(Exec VP-Global Insurance Distr)*
Judy Hart *(Exec VP)*
David Bigley *(Sr VP & Head-Property Catastrophe Reinsurance-US)*
Dennis Stokes *(Sr VP)*
Board of Directors:
John R. Charman
John T. Baily
Norman Barham
Galen R. Barnes
William H. Bolinder
Susan S. Fleming Cabrera
Scott D. Moore
Brendan R. O'Neill
William John Raver
Robert A. Spass

U.S. Subsidiaries:

Endurance American Insurance Company **(1)**
767 3rd Ave 5th Fl
New York, NY 10017
Tel.: (212) 209-6500
Fax: (212) 209-6501
Web Site: www.endurance.com
Direct Title Insurance Carriers
S.I.C.: 6361
N.A.I.C.S.: 524127
Douglas M. Worman *(CEO & Exec VP)*

Endurance American Specialty Insurance Company **(1)**
767 3 Ave 5th Fl
New York, NY 10017
Tel.: (212) 209-6500
Fax: (212) 309-6501
E-Mail: info@enduranceamericanspeciality.com
Web Site: www.enduranceamericanspeciality.com
Direct Title Insurance Carriers
S.I.C.: 6361
N.A.I.C.S.: 524127

Endurance Reinsurance Corporation of America **(1)**
750 3 Ave Fl 18 & 19
New York, NY 10017
Tel.: (212) 471-2800
Fax: (212) 471-1748
Web Site: www.endurance.bm/locations.html
Emp.: 80
Direct Title Insurance Carriers
S.I.C.: 6361
N.A.I.C.S.: 524127
Christopher Donelan *(Pres & Chief Underwriting Officer)*
James D'Onofrio *(Exec VP & Head-Reinsurance)*
Michael Fokken *(Exec VP-Underwriting Ops-North America)*
Tracy Thomson *(Exec VP-Underwriting Ops-North America)*

Galileo Weather Risk Management Advisors LLC **(1)**
810 7th Ave 17th Fl
New York, NY 10019
Tel.: (212) 382-1482
Fax: (212) 382-1155
Web Site: www.galileoweather.com
Emp.: 6
Weather Risk Management Services
S.I.C.: 6411
N.A.I.C.S.: 524298
Martin Malinow *(Co-Founder & CEO)*
Scott Edwards *(Co-Founder & CFO)*

Non-U.S. Subsidiary:

Galileo Weather Risks Advisors Limited **(2)**
Golden Cross House 8 Duncannon Street
Strand, London, WC2N 4JF, United Kingdom
Tel.: (44) 20 7043 5184
Fax: (44) 20 7692 7951
E-Mail: dtomlinson@galileoweather.com
Web Site: www.galileoweather.com
Weather Risk Management Services
S.I.C.: 6411
N.A.I.C.S.: 524298
Dan Tomlinson *(Mng Dir)*

Non-U.S. Subsidiary:

Endurance Worldwide Insurance Limited **(1)**
7th Fr 2 Minster Court
London, EC3R7BB, United Kingdom
Tel.: (44) 2073372800
Fax: (44) 2073372900
E-Mail: londonfd@enduranceww.com
Emp.: 35
Direct Health & Medical Insurance Carriers
S.I.C.: 6321
N.A.I.C.S.: 524114
Graham Evans *(CEO-Intl Insurance)*
Ian Bowler *(Sr VP)*

ENE TECHNOLOGY INC.

4F-1 9 Prosperity Road I
Science-Based Industrial Park, Hsinchu, 300, Taiwan
Tel.: (886) 36662888
Fax: (886) 36662999
E-Mail: investors@ene.com.tw
Web Site: www.ene.com.tw
Year Founded: 1998
6243—(TAI)
Sales Range: $25-49.9 Million
Emp.: 130
Business Description:
Integrated Circuits Mfr & Distr
S.I.C.: 3672
N.A.I.C.S.: 334412
Personnel:
Jiaxiang Weng *(Chm)*

ENEA AB

Jan Stenbecks Torg 17
PO Box 1033
SE-164 21 Kista, Sweden
Tel.: (46) 8 5071 4000
Fax: (46) 8 5071 4040
E-Mail: info@enea.se
Web Site: www.enea.se
EMEA—(OMX)
Sls.: $81,969,232
Assets: $71,164,656
Liabilities: $14,319,929
Net Worth: $56,844,727
Earnings: $16,517,624
Emp.: 400
Fiscal Year-end: 12/31/12
Business Description:
Software Developer
S.I.C.: 7372
N.A.I.C.S.: 511210
Personnel:
Anders Skarin *(Chm)*
Anders Lidbeck *(Pres & CEO)*
Hakan Rippe *(CFO)*
Tobias Lindquist *(CTO)*
Adrian Leufven *(Sr VP-Software Sls)*
Karl Morner *(Sr VP-Products)*
Bogdan Putinica *(Sr VP-Global Svcs)*
Board of Directors:
Anders Skarin
Robert W. Andersson
Kjell Duveblad
Asa Landen Ericsson
Mats Lindoff
Torbjorn Nilsson
Eva Swedberg

U.S. Subsidiary:

Enea TekSci Inc. **(1)**
1711 W Greentree Dr Ste 108
Tempe, AZ 85284 WA
Tel.: (480) 753-9200
Fax: (480) 753-6400
Web Site: www.enea.com
Sales Range: $10-24.9 Million
Emp.: 65
Software Design Services
S.I.C.: 7371
N.A.I.C.S.: 541511
Anders Lidbeck *(CEO)*

Non-U.S. Subsidiary:

Enea Services Romania SRL **(1)**
319 Splaiul Independentei OB403A District 6
Bucharest, Romania 060044
Tel.: (40) 21 311 43 00
Fax: (40) 21 311 43 01
E-Mail: contact-romania@enea.com
Web Site: www.enea.ro
Emp.: 200
Computer Systems Design Services
S.I.C.: 7373
N.A.I.C.S.: 541512
Bogdan Putinica *(CEO)*
Marius Dutu *(CFO)*
Daniel Bogdan *(CTO)*

ENEA S.A.

ul Gorecka 1
60-201 Poznan, Poland
Tel.: (48) 618845300
Fax: (48) 618845955
E-Mail: enea@enea.pl
Web Site: www.enea.pl
ENA—(WAR)
Rev.: $3,263,432,290
Assets: $4,665,128,814
Liabilities: $1,196,269,541
Net Worth: $3,468,859,273
Earnings: $225,672,562
Emp.: 10,126
Fiscal Year-end: 12/31/12
Business Description:
Electric Power Distr & Generator
S.I.C.: 4911
N.A.I.C.S.: 221122
Personnel:
Wojciech Chmielewski *(Chm-Supervisory Bd)*
Krzysztof Zamasz *(Chm-Mgmt Bd)*
Jeremi Mordasewicz *(Vice Chm-Supervisory Bd)*
Dalida Gepfert *(Member-Mgmt Bd-Fin Affairs)*
Grzegorz Kinelski *(Member-Mgmt Bd-Comml Affairs)*
Pawel Orlof *(Member-Mgmt Bd-Corp Affairs)*
Krzysztof Zborowski *(Member-Mgmt Bd-Energy Generation)*
Supervisory Board of Directors:
Wojciech Chmielewski
Malgorzata Aniolek
Slawomir Brzezinski
Michal Kowalewski
Przemyslaw Lyczynski
Sandra Malinowska
Tadeusz Miklosz
Jeremi Mordasewicz
Torbjorn Wahlborg

Subsidiaries:

Elektrownia Kozienice S.A. **(1)**
Swierze Upper Vlg Kozienice
26 900 Kozienice, Masovian, Poland
Tel.: (48) 486141627
Fax: (48) 486143516
Web Site: www.elko.com.pl
Electric Power Distribution Services
S.I.C.: 4931

ENEA S.A.—(Continued)

N.A.I.C.S.: 221122

Elektrownie Wodne Sp. z o.o. (1)
Samociazek 92
86 010 Koronowo, Kuyavian-Pomeranian, Poland
Tel.: (48) 523825800
Fax: (48) 523825840
E-Mail: ew@ew.koronowo.pl
Web Site: www.ew.koronowo.pl
Emp.: 176
Electric Power Generation Services
S.I.C.: 4931
N.A.I.C.S.: 221118
Janusz Herder *(CEO)*

ENEA Operator Sp. z o.o. (1)
Strzeszynska 58
60 479 Poznan, Poland
Tel.: (48) 618561999
Fax: (48) 618561907
E-Mail: kontakt@operator.enea.pl
Web Site: www.operator.enea.pl
Electricity Distribution Services
S.I.C.: 4931
N.A.I.C.S.: 221122

Energetyka Poznanska Przedsiebiorstwo Uslug Energetycznych Energobud Leszno Sp. z o.o. (1)
Gronowko 30
64111 Lipno, Poland
Tel.: (48) 655256900
Fax: (48) 655294416
E-Mail: energobud@energobud.pl
Web Site: www.energobud.pl
Emp.: 100
Energy Consulting Services
S.I.C.: 8999
N.A.I.C.S.: 541690
Rafal Sieracki *(Mgr)*

Energetyka Poznanska Zaklad Obslugi Socjalnej ENERGO-TOUR Sp. z o.o. (1)
Glogowska 55 57
60 738 Poznan, Poland
Tel.: (48) 618561630
E-Mail: turystyka@energo-tour.com.pl
Web Site: www.energo-tour.com.pl
Airline Ticket Services
S.I.C.: 4729
N.A.I.C.S.: 561599

Energomiar Sp. z o.o. (1)
Ul Strzeszynska 58
60479 Poznan, Poland
Tel.: (48) 618561730
Fax: (48) 618561727
E-Mail: energomiar@energomiar.pl
Web Site: www.energomiar.pl
Emp.: 200
Power Supplier Services
S.I.C.: 4931
N.A.I.C.S.: 221122
Wanda Mucha *(Mgr)*

EnergoPartner Sp. z o.o. (1)
Ul Warszawska 43
61028 Poznan, Poland
Tel.: (48) 618561050
Fax: (48) 616503102
E-Mail: energopartner@energopartner.com.pl
Web Site: www.energopartner.com.pl
Emp.: 12
Electricity Mfr
S.I.C.: 4911
N.A.I.C.S.: 221118
Marek Hensler *(Mng Dir)*

Kozienice II Sp. z o.o. (1)
Swierze Gorne
26 900 Kozienice, Masovian, Poland
Tel.: (48) 486141097
Fax: (48) 486141675
E-Mail: biuro@kozienice2.com.pl
Web Site: www.kozienice2.com.pl
Emp.: 10
Electricity Distribution Services
S.I.C.: 4911
N.A.I.C.S.: 221122
Marek Rozycki *(Mng Dir)*

Miejska Energetyka Cieplna Sp. z o.o. (1)
Armii Krajowej 81
78 400 Szczecinek, Poland
Tel.: (48) 943726680
Fax: (48) 943726659
E-Mail: mec@mec-szczecinek.com.pl
Web Site: www.mec-szczecinek.com.pl
Heating System Distr
S.I.C.: 4961
N.A.I.C.S.: 221330

Przedsiebiorstwo Energetyki Cieplnej - Gozdnica Sp. z o.o. (1)
Wybudowanie 56
64 600 Oborniki, Poland
Tel.: (48) 612961519
Fax: (48) 61961519
Web Site: www.picoborniki.pl
Heating System Distr
S.I.C.: 4961
N.A.I.C.S.: 221330

Przedsiebiorstwo Energetyki Cieplnej Sp. z o.o. (1)
ul. Nasienna 6
PO Box 69
73-110 Stargard Szczecinski, Poland
Tel.: (48) 915788400
Fax: (48) 915788452
E-Mail: obsluga_odbiorcy@pec.stargard.pl
Web Site: www.pec.stargard.pl
Steam Heat Distr
S.I.C.: 4961
N.A.I.C.S.: 221330
Richard Richard *(CEO)*

Zaklad Handlowo-Uslugowy Auto-Styl Zielonogorskich Zakladow Energetycznych S.A. sp. z o.o. (1)
Zacisze 15
65 775 Gora Zielona, Lubusz, Poland
Tel.: (48) 683281913
Fax: (48) 683272916
Vehicle Repair & Service Station
S.I.C.: 7539
N.A.I.C.S.: 811198

Zaklad Uslug Teleinformatycznych ZZE S.A. ITSERWIS sp. z o.o. (1)
Zacisze 28
65 792 Gora Zielona, Lubusz, Poland
Tel.: (48) 683281898
Fax: (48) 683281798
E-Mail: biuro@itserwis.com.pl
Web Site: www.itserwis.com.pl
Emp.: 100
Telecommunications Services
S.I.C.: 4899
N.A.I.C.S.: 517919
Miroslow Jatota *(Pres)*

ENEABBA GAS LIMITED

Suite 2/12 Parliament Place
West Perth, WA, 6005, Australia
Tel.: (61) 894820555
Fax: (61) 894820505
E-Mail: info@eneabbagas.com.au
Web Site: www.eneabbagas.com.au
ENB—(ASX)
Rev.: $127,588
Assets: $5,868,297
Liabilities: $40,857
Net Worth: $5,827,441
Earnings: $114
Emp.: 5
Fiscal Year-end: 06/30/13

Business Description:
Mineral Exploration & Electricity Generation
S.I.C.: 1629
N.A.I.C.S.: 237990

Personnel:
Brett Tucker *(Sec)*

Board of Directors:
Greg Allen
Morgan Barron
Thomas L. Goh

Legal Counsel:
Hardy Bowen Lawyers
1 / 28 Ord Street
West Perth, WA, 6005, Australia

Subsidiary:

Eneabba Energy Pty Ltd (1)
L 1 30 Ord St
West Perth, WA, 6005, Australia
Tel.: (61) 893210099
Fax: (61) 893210299
E-Mail: admin@eneabbagas.com.au
Emp.: 7
Power Generation Services
S.I.C.: 4931
N.A.I.C.S.: 221112
Thomas Goh *(Mng Dir)*

ENEGEX N.L.

Level 21 500 Collins Street
Melbourne, VIC, 3000, Australia
Tel.: (61) 3 8610 4703
Fax: (61) 3 8610 4799
Year Founded: 2012
ENX—(ASX)

Business Description:
Oil & Natural Gas Exploration
S.I.C.: 1389
N.A.I.C.S.: 213112

Personnel:
Graeme Alan Menzies *(Chm)*
Robert John Wright *(CFO & Sec)*

Board of Directors:
Graeme Alan Menzies
Robert John Coppin
Brett Dean Maltz

ENEGI OIL PLC

44 Peter Street
Manchester, M2 5GP, United Kingdom
Tel.: (44) 161 817 7460
E-Mail: info@enegioil.com
Web Site: www.enegioil.com
Year Founded: 2007
ENEG—(LSE)
Rev.: $290,589
Assets: $12,689,595
Liabilities: $5,306,414
Net Worth: $7,383,181
Earnings: ($4,919,488)
Emp.: 10
Fiscal Year-end: 06/30/13

Business Description:
Oil & Gas Exploration Services
S.I.C.: 1389
N.A.I.C.S.: 213112

Personnel:
Alan Minty *(Chm & CEO)*
Damian Minty *(CFO)*
Derek Cochrane *(COO)*
Tejvinder Minhas *(Sec)*

Board of Directors:
Alan Minty
Derek Cochrane
Frank Jackson
Alex Lamb
Damian Minty

Legal Counsel:
Stewart McKelvey
100 New Gower Street
Saint John's, NL, A1C 5V3, Canada

Gowlings (UK) LLP
15th Floor 125 Old Broad Street
London, EC2N 1AR, United Kingdom

ENEL S.P.A.

Viale Regina Margherita 137
00198 Rome, Italy
Tel.: (39) 0683051
Fax: (39) 0683057940
E-Mail: ufficiostampa@enel.it
Web Site: www.enel.com
Year Founded: 1963
ENEL—(ITA)
Rev.: $114,275,025,130
Assets: $231,078,157,520
Liabilities: $159,518,452,660
Net Worth: $71,559,704,860
Earnings: $2,793,302,750
Emp.: 73,702
Fiscal Year-end: 12/31/12

Business Description:
Electricity Generator & Distr; Natural Gas Distr
S.I.C.: 4939
N.A.I.C.S.: 221112

Personnel:
Paolo Andrea Colombo *(Chm)*
Fulvio Conti *(CEO & Gen Mgr)*
Luigi Ferraris *(CFO)*
Roberta Vivenzio *(Intl Press Officer)*
Francesco Starace *(CEO-Enel Green Power & Dir-Renewable Energies Div)*

Board of Directors:
Paolo Andrea Colombo
Alessandro Banchi
Lorenzo Codogno
Fulvio Conti
Mauro Miccio
Pedro Solbes Mira
Fernando Napolitano
Angelo Taraborrelli
Gianfranco Tosi

Subsidiaries:

Deval SpA (1)
Via Clavalite 8
11100 Aosta, Italy
Tel.: (39) 0165647211
Fax: (39) 0165647333
Electric Power Distribution Service
S.I.C.: 4931
N.A.I.C.S.: 221122

Enel Energy Europe SL (1)
Viale Regina Margherita 137
Rome, 00198, Italy
Tel.: (39) 0683057378
Fax: (39) 0800900150
Electric Power Generation Services
S.I.C.: 4911
N.A.I.C.S.: 221118

Enel Green Power, S.p.A. (1)
Viale Regina Margherita 125
00198 Rome, Italy (70%)
Tel.: (39) 06 83058721
Fax: (39) 06 83052700
Web Site: www.enelgreenpower.com
EGPW—(ITA)
Rev.: $3,629,274,320
Assets: $21,705,645,080
Liabilities: $10,973,977,840
Net Worth: $10,731,667,240
Earnings: $660,969,470
Emp.: 3,512
Fiscal Year-end: 12/31/12
Renewable Energy Generation Services
S.I.C.: 4939
N.A.I.C.S.: 221111
Luigi Ferraris *(Chm)*
Francesco Starace *(CEO & Gen Mgr)*
Giulio Carone *(CFO & Head-Admin, Fin & Control)*
Camillo Catarci *(Intl Press Officer)*
Marco Spaccino *(Intl Press Officer)*
Roberta Vivenzio *(Intl Press Officer)*
Francesco Venturini *(Pres/CEO-North America)*

Subsidiary:

Taranto Solar Srl (2)
Viale Regina Margherita 125
00198 Rome, Italy
Tel.: (39) 06 83059104
Fax: (39) 06 83057200
Solar Electric Power Generation Services
S.I.C.: 4939
N.A.I.C.S.: 221118
Donatella Izzo *(Gen Mgr)*

Enel M@P Srl (1)
Via Ombrone 2
198 Rome, Italy
Tel.: (39) 0683051
Electric Power Generation Services
S.I.C.: 4939
N.A.I.C.S.: 221118

Subsidiary:

Concert Srl (2)
Via Adamello 5
20099 Sesto San Giovanni, Italy
Tel.: (39) 02 23202460
Fax: (39) 02 23202168
Emp.: 15
Electric Power Generation Sevices

S.I.C.: 4911
N.A.I.C.S.: 221118
Sencer Aydin *(Pres)*
Carmelo Michelizzi *(CEO & Mng Dir)*

Enel Produzione SpA (1)
Viale Regina Margherita 125
Rome, 198, Italy
Tel.: (39) 0683051
Thermal Electric Power Generation Services
S.I.C.: 4931
N.A.I.C.S.: 221118

Non-U.S. Subsidiary:

Slovenske elektrarne AS (2)
Mlynske nivy 47
821 09 Bratislava, Slovakia
Tel.: (421) 2 5866 1111
Fax: (421) 2 5341 7525
E-Mail: infoseas@enel.com
Web Site: www.seas.sk
Nuclear Electric Power Generation Services
S.I.C.: 4931
N.A.I.C.S.: 221113
Paolo Ruzzini *(Chm)*
Robert Mistrik *(Chm-Supervisory Bd)*
Branislav Strycek *(Vice Chm)*

Subsidiary:

Ochrana A Bezpecnost Se AS (3)
Seas 83538
935 39 Mochovce, Slovakia
Tel.: (421) 36 6355 811
Fax: (421) 36 6355 819
E-Mail: info@oabse.sk
Emp.: 46
Nuclear Electric Power Generation Services
S.I.C.: 4911
N.A.I.C.S.: 221113

Non-U.S. Subsidiary:

Slovenske elektrarne Finance BV (3)
Herengracht 471
Amsterdam, 1017 BS, Netherlands
Tel.: (31) 205218777
Fax: (31) 205218799
Web Site: www.seas.sk
Emp.: 3
Financial Investment Services
S.I.C.: 6211
N.A.I.C.S.: 523999
Tran Nhat Minh *(Gen Mgr)*

Enel Servizio Elettrico SpA (1)
Viale Regina Margherita 125
Rome, 198, Italy
Tel.: (39) 0683051
Fax: (39) 683058948
Web Site: www.enel.it
Electric Power Distribution Services
S.I.C.: 4939
N.A.I.C.S.: 221122

Hydrogen Park Marghera Per L'idrogeno Scrl (1)
Via Delle Industrie 19
Marghera, 30175 Venice, Italy
Tel.: (39) 041 5499152
Fax: (39) 041 935601
E-Mail: info@hydrogenpark.com
Web Site: www.hydrogenpark.com
Hydroelectric Power Generation & Distribution Services
S.I.C.: 4931
N.A.I.C.S.: 221111
Adriano Pinelli *(Chm)*
Nelson Persello *(Vice Chm)*

Nuove Energie Srl (1)
Via Della Meccanica 23/25
36100 Vicenza, Italy
Tel.: (39) 0444963453
Fax: (39) 0444960959
E-Mail: info@nuoveenergie.it
Web Site: www.nuoveenergie.com
Emp.: 2
Micro Filter Mfr
S.I.C.: 3564
N.A.I.C.S.: 333413

Water & INDUSTRIAL Services Company SpA (1)
Via Borgazzi 27
Monza, 20052, Italy
Tel.: (39) 0392096411
Fax: (39) 0392002728
E-Mail: info@yisco.it
Emp.: 23
Sewage Treatment Services
S.I.C.: 4952
N.A.I.C.S.: 221320

U.S. Subsidiaries:

Boott Hydropower Inc. (1)
1 Tech Dr Ste 220
Andover, MA 01810
Tel.: (978) 454-8074
Hydroelectric Power Generation Services
S.I.C.: 4911
N.A.I.C.S.: 221111
Wayne Pincence *(Mgr)*

Bypass Power Company (1)
1 Tech Dr
Andover, MA 01810-2453
Tel.: (828) 452-5346
Management Consulting Services
S.I.C.: 8742
N.A.I.C.S.: 541611

Subsidiaries:

CHI Operations Inc. (2)
97 Industrial Ave
Sanford, ME 04073-5820
Tel.: (207) 490-1980
Fax: (207) 490-2600
Sales Range: $10-24.9 Million
Emp.: 10
Hydro Electric Services
Import Export
S.I.C.: 4911
N.A.I.C.S.: 221122

Consolidated Hydro New York Inc (2)
Pine St
Schuylerville, NY 12871
Tel.: (518) 695-3035
Hydro Electric Power Generation Services
S.I.C.: 4939
N.A.I.C.S.: 221111

Hydro Development Group Inc. (2)
16472 NYS Route 12F
Dexter, NY 13634
Tel.: (315) 639-6700
Fax: (315) 639-3880
Web Site: www.enel.com
Sls.: $8,600,000
Emp.: 40
Hydro Electric Power Generation
Import Export
S.I.C.: 4939
N.A.I.C.S.: 221118

TKO Power Inc. (2)
9485 Deschutes Rd
Palo Cedro, CA 96073-9758
Tel.: (203) 425-8850
Sls.: $2,500,000
Emp.: 11
Electric Services
Import Export
S.I.C.: 4939
N.A.I.C.S.: 221122

Chi West Inc. (1)
20020 Tamarack Rd
Burney, CA 96013
Tel.: (530) 335-4305
Fax: (530) 335-4635
Emp.: 5
Electric Power Generation Services
S.I.C.: 4931
N.A.I.C.S.: 221118
Patrick Strickland *(Gen Mgr)*

Consolidated Hydro Mountain States Inc. (1)
2283 Wright Ave Ste D
Twin Falls, ID 83301-6028
Tel.: (208) 734-0551
Fax: (208) 734-0553
Emp.: 10
Hydroelectric Power Generation Services
S.I.C.: 4911
N.A.I.C.S.: 221111
Brad Platt *(Reg Mgr)*

Consolidated Hydro Southeast Inc. (1)
11 Anderson St
Piedmont, SC 29673
Tel.: (978) 681-1900
Fax: (978) 681-7727
Hydroelectric Power Generation Services
S.I.C.: 4939
N.A.I.C.S.: 221111

Enel Cove Fort LLC (1)
1 Main St
Beaver, UT 84713
Tel.: (978) 681-1900
Hydroelectric Power Generation Services
S.I.C.: 4911
N.A.I.C.S.: 221111

Enel North America, Inc. (1)
1 Tech Dr Ste 220
Andover, MA 01810 DE
Tel.: (978) 681-1900
Fax: (978) 681-7727
Web Site: www.enel.com
Emp.: 60
Renewable Energy Plants Owner & Operator
S.I.C.: 4931
N.A.I.C.S.: 221118
Toni Volpe *(Pres & CEO)*
Daniel S. Pease *(COO & Sr VP)*
Derek Deblois *(Treas, VP & Controller)*
Lisa Zarek *(Treas, VP & Controller)*
Michael I. Storch *(Exec VP-Strategy & Corp Dev)*

Enel Stillwater LLC (1)
4785 Lawrence Ln
Fallon, NV 89406
Tel.: (775) 423-0322
Hydroelectric Power Generation Services
S.I.C.: 4939
N.A.I.C.S.: 221111

Enel Washington Dc Lld (1)
816 Connecticut Ave NW Ste 600
Washington, DC 20006
Tel.: (202) 609-7798
Fuelelectric Power Generation Services
S.I.C.: 4931
N.A.I.C.S.: 221112

Hydro Energies Corporation (1)
Deweys Mills Rd
Quechee, VT 05059
Tel.: (802) 295-1490
Electric Power Distribution Services
S.I.C.: 4931
N.A.I.C.S.: 221122

Northwest Hydro Inc. (1)
31 Cougar Creek Rd
Stevenson, WA 98648
Tel.: (509) 427-5081
Electric Power Generation Services
S.I.C.: 4911
N.A.I.C.S.: 221118

Ottauquechee Hydro Company Inc. (1)
One Tech Dr Ste 220
Andover, MA 01810
Tel.: (978) 681-1900
Hydroelectric Power Generation Services
S.I.C.: 4911
N.A.I.C.S.: 221118

Smoky Hills Wind Farm LLC (1)
223 N Hwy 14
Lincoln, KS 67455
Tel.: (978) 681-1900
Fax: (978) 681-7727
Electric Power Generation Services
S.I.C.: 4911
N.A.I.C.S.: 221118

Smoky Hills Wind Project II LLC (1)
16105 W 113th St Ste 105
Shawnee Mission, KS 66219-2307
Tel.: (978) 681-1900
Wind Farm Electric Power Generation Services
S.I.C.: 4939
N.A.I.C.S.: 221118

Snyder Wind Farm LLC (1)
1 Tech Dr Ste 220
Andover, MA 01810-2452
Tel.: (978) 296-6827
Wind Farm Electric Power Generation Services
S.I.C.: 4931
N.A.I.C.S.: 221118

Non-U.S. Subsidiaries:

Bolonia Real Estate SL (1)
Calle Ribera Del Loira 60
Madrid, 28042, Spain
Tel.: (34) 912131000
Fax: (34) 912131000
Real Estate Management Services
S.I.C.: 6531
N.A.I.C.S.: 531390

Carvemagere Manutencao e Energias Renovaveis Lda (1)
Lugar Pedreira
4750-625 Braga, Portugal
Tel.: (351) 253860030
Natural Gas Mfr
S.I.C.: 2813
N.A.I.C.S.: 325120

Central Geradora Termeletrica Fortaleza SA (1)
Rodovia Ce 422 s/n Km 1 Complexo Industrial Do Pecem
Caucaia, Ceara, 61600-000, Brazil
Tel.: (55) 85 3464 4100
Fax: (55) 8534624115
Web Site: www.endesabrasil.com.br
Electric Power Generation Services
S.I.C.: 4911
N.A.I.C.S.: 221118
Martelo Falcucci *(Office Mgr)*

Central Termica do Estuario Lda (1)
Avenida Sidonio Pais 379 2
4100-468 Porto, Portugal
Tel.: (351) 226 080 180
Fax: (351) 226 080 189
Fuel Electric Power Generation Services
S.I.C.: 4931
N.A.I.C.S.: 221112

Chi Hydroelectric Company Inc. (1)
1255 University St Suite 1204
Montreal, QC, H3B 3W9, Canada
Tel.: (514) 397-0463
Fax: (514) 397-0284
Emp.: 4
Hydroelectric Power Generation Services
S.I.C.: 4931
N.A.I.C.S.: 221111
Pascal J. Brun *(Pres)*

Subsidiary:

St-Felicien Cogeneration (2)
1250 Rue De L Energie
Saint-Felicien, QC, G8K 3J2ca, Canada
Tel.: (418) 630-3800
Fax: (418) 630-3803
Electric Power Distribution Services
S.I.C.: 4939
N.A.I.C.S.: 221122

Chi S F LP (1)
1255 University St Bureau 1204
Montreal, QC, H3B 3W9, Canada
Tel.: (514) 397-0463
Fax: (514) 397-0284
Electric Power Generation Services
S.I.C.: 4911
N.A.I.C.S.: 221118

Empreendimentos Eolicos de Viade Lda (1)
Avenida Sidonio Pais 379 - 2Andar
Porto, 4100-468, Portugal
Tel.: (351) 226198400
Fax: (351) 226198410
Electric Power Generation Services
S.I.C.: 4939
N.A.I.C.S.: 221118

Empresa Carbonifera del Sur SA (1)
Calle Ribera Del Loira 60
Madrid, 28042, Spain
Tel.: (34) 912131165
Fax: (34) 912131711
Electric Power Generation Services
S.I.C.: 4911
N.A.I.C.S.: 221118

Endesa Generacion Portugal SA (1)
Quinta Da Fonte Edificio Dom Manuel I
Piso Ala B
Paco d'Arcos, 2770-192, Portugal
Tel.: (351) 211102700
Fax: (351) 211102727
E-Mail: geral@endesaportugal.pt
Emp.: 12

Enel S.p.A.—(Continued)

Electric Power Generation Services
S.I.C.: 4931
N.A.I.C.S.: 221118
Pedro Fernandes *(Gen Mgr)*

Endesa Ingenieria SLU (1)
C/Inca Garcilaso s/n Edif EXPO Isla de la Cartuja
41092 Seville, Spain
Tel.: (34) 954 48 71 02
Fax: (34) 954 48 84 03
E-Mail: info@endesaingenieria.es
Web Site: www.endesaingenieria.es
Emp.: 160
Electric Power Generation & Distribution Services
S.I.C.: 4911
N.A.I.C.S.: 221118

Endesa, S.A. (1)
Ribera del Loira 60
Campo de las Naciones, 28042 Madrid, Spain (92%)
Tel.: (34) 912131000
Telex: 22917 ENE
Fax: (34) 915638181
Web Site: www.endesa.es
ELE—(MAD)
Sales Range: $25-49.9 Billion
Emp.: 27,019
Electric Utility Services
S.I.C.: 4939
N.A.I.C.S.: 221122
Borja Prado Eulate *(Chm & Pres)*
Fulvio Conti *(Deputy Chm & VP)*
Andrea Brentan *(CEO)*
Salvador Montejo Velilla *(Sec)*
Francisco de Borja Acha Besga *(Sr VP-Legal Affairs)*

Subsidiaries:

Carboex, S.A. (2)
Manuel Cortina 2 2
Madrid, Spain (100%)
Tel.: (34) 915668800
Fax: (34) 914452407
Emp.: 23
Coal Supply Services
S.I.C.: 5052
N.A.I.C.S.: 423520

Endesa Desarrollo SL (2)
Calle Ribera Del Loira 60
Madrid, 28042, Spain
Tel.: (34) 912131000
Fax: (34) 915638181
Electric Power Generation Services
S.I.C.: 4931
N.A.I.C.S.: 221118

Endesa Financiacion Filiales SA (2)
Calle Ribera Del Loira 60
Madrid, 28042, Spain
Tel.: (34) 912131000
Financial Management Services
S.I.C.: 3291
N.A.I.C.S.: 327910

Non-U.S. Subsidiary:

Sociedad Inversora Dock Sud SA (3)
Debenedetti 1636
Dock Sud, Buenos Aires, 1871, Argentina
Tel.: (54) 1142018011
Electric Power Generation Services
S.I.C.: 4931
N.A.I.C.S.: 221118

Endesa Latinoamerica SA (2)
Ribera Del Loira 60
Madrid, 28042, Spain
Tel.: (34) 912 13 10 00
Fax: (34) 912 13 18 70
Electric Power Generation Services & Distr
S.I.C.: 4939
N.A.I.C.S.: 221118

Endesa Red SA (2)
Av Del Paralelo 51
Barcelona, 08004, Spain
Tel.: (34) 91 566 88 00
Fax: (34) 91 213 48 49
Electric Power Distribution Services
S.I.C.: 4939
N.A.I.C.S.: 221122

Subsidiary:

Distribuidora de Energia Electrica del Bages SA (3)
Bda Riera 1
Rajadell, Barcelona, 8289, Spain
Tel.: (34) 938368000
Electric Power Distribution Services
S.I.C.: 4931
N.A.I.C.S.: 221122

Endesa Servicios SL (2)
Calle Ribera del Loira 60
Madrid, 28042, Spain
Tel.: (34) 91 213 10 00
Fax: (34) 91 213 10 72
Consulting Management Services
S.I.C.: 8742
N.A.I.C.S.: 541611

Subsidiary:

Endesa Network Factory SL (3)
Avenida Paral Lel 51
Barcelona, Spain
Tel.: (34) 912131000
Electric Power Transmission Services
S.I.C.: 4939
N.A.I.C.S.: 221122

Non-U.S. Subsidiaries:

Enersis S.A. (2)
Santa Rosa 76
Santiago, 8330099, Chile (60%)
Tel.: (56) 2 353 4639
Fax: (56) 2 378 4789
Web Site: www.enersis.cl
ENI—(MAD NYSE SGO)
Rev.: $13,944,654,706
Assets: $28,233,807,317
Liabilities: $13,470,617,931
Net Worth: $14,763,189,385
Earnings: $1,894,351,402
Emp.: 11,087
Fiscal Year-end: 12/31/12
Electricity Generator & Distr
S.I.C.: 4911
N.A.I.C.S.: 221122
Pablo Yrarrazabal Valdes *(Chm)*
Ignacio Alvear Antonanzas *(CEO)*
Alfredo Ergas Segal *(CFO)*
Ramiro Alfonsin Balza *(Officer-Plng & Control)*
Francisco Silva Bafalluy *(Officer-HR)*

Subsidiaries:

Chilectra S.A. (3)
Santa Rosa 76 Piso 8
Santiago, Chile (99%)
Tel.: (56) 2 3534680
Fax: (56) 3534522
E-Mail: rrpp@chilectra.cl
Web Site: www.chilectra.cl
Sales Range: $1-4.9 Billion
Emp.: 720
Electric Power Distr
S.I.C.: 4911
N.A.I.C.S.: 221122
Jorge Rosenblut Ratinoff *(Chm)*
Jose Maria Calvo Sotelo Ibanez-Martin *(Vice Chm)*
Rafael Lopez Rueda *(CEO)*

Subsidiary:

Compania Electrica Tarapaca SA (4)
Santa Rosa 76 Piso 13
Santiago, 8330099, Chile
Tel.: (56) 2 630 9448
Fax: (56) 2 635 5389
Electric Power Generation & Distribution Services
S.I.C.: 4939
N.A.I.C.S.: 221118

Empresa Nacional de Electricidad S.A. (3)
Santa Rosa 76
Santiago, Chile CL
Tel.: (56) 2 630 9000 (60%)
Fax: (56) 26354720
Web Site: www.endesa.cl
EOC—(MAD NYSE SGO)
Rev.: $5,023,099,113
Assets: $13,756,022,639
Liabilities: $6,474,578,535
Net Worth: $7,281,444,103
Earnings: $888,370,691
Emp.: 2,533
Fiscal Year-end: 12/31/12
Electricity Generation & Distribution
S.I.C.: 4911
N.A.I.C.S.: 221122
Jorge Ratinoff Rosenblut *(Chm)*
Paolo Bondi *(Vice Chm)*
Joaquin Galindo Velez *(CEO)*
Jose Venegas Maluenda *(Officer-Trading & Commercialization)*

Subsidiaries:

Empresa Electrica Pehuenche, S.A. (4)
Santa Rosa 76 Piso 16
Santiago, Chile (92.65%)
Tel.: (56) 2 63090009
Fax: (56) 26965568
PEHUENCHE—(SGO)
Sales Range: $400-449.9 Million
Electricity Generation & Distribution
S.I.C.: 4939
N.A.I.C.S.: 221122
Claudio Iglesis Guillard *(Chm)*
Alan Fischer Hill *(Vice Chm)*
Lucio Castro Marquez *(CEO)*

Endesa Eco SA (4)
Avda Santa Rosa 76 Piso 12
Santiago, Chile
Tel.: (56) 26309000
Fax: (56) 26353938
Electric Power Generation Services
S.I.C.: 4911
N.A.I.C.S.: 221118

Non-U.S. Subsidiary:

Southern Cone Power Argentina SA (4)
Avenida Costanera Espana 3301 Ciudad de 1107
Buenos Aires, Argentina
Tel.: (54) 1143073040
Electric Power Generation Services
S.I.C.: 4911
N.A.I.C.S.: 221118

Non-U.S. Subsidiary:

Endesa Argentina SA (4)
Avenida Espana 3301
Buenos Aires, C1107ANA, Argentina
Tel.: (54) 1143073040
Fax: (54) 1143073043
Electric Power Generation Services
S.I.C.: 4931
N.A.I.C.S.: 221118

Subsidiary:

Endesa Cemsa SA (5)
Ing Enrique Butty 220 Piso 16
C1001AFB Buenos Aires, Argentina
Tel.: (54) 11 4875 0600
Fax: (54) 11 4875 0618
Web Site: www.endesacemsa.com
Electric Power Distribution Services
S.I.C.: 4911
N.A.I.C.S.: 221122

Inmobiliaria Manso de Velasco Ltda (3)
Calle Miraflores 383 Fl 29
Piso, Santiago, 8320149, Chile
Tel.: (56) 2 378 4700
Fax: (56) 2 378 4702
Emp.: 34
Real Estate Development Services
S.I.C.: 6531
N.A.I.C.S.: 531390
Andres Salas *(Gen Mgr)*

Non-U.S. Subsidiaries:

Empresa Distribucion Electrica de Lima Norte S.A.A. (3)
Cesar Lopez Rojas 201
Urbanizacion Maranga Etapa VII
San Miguel, Lima, Peru (60%)
Tel.: (51) 15612001
Fax: (51) 15610451
E-Mail: enlinea@edelnor.com.pe
Web Site: www.edelnor.com.pe
Emp.: 625
Electricity Generation & Distribution
S.I.C.: 4911
N.A.I.C.S.: 221122
Reynaldo Llosa Barber *(Chm)*
Ignacio Blanco Fernandez *(Vice Chm & CEO)*
Jose Otarola *(Chief Comm Officer)*
Walter Sciutto Brattoli *(CTO)*
Carlos Solis Pino *(Chief Comml Officer)*
Rocio Pachas Soto *(Chief Org & HR Officer)*
Luis Salem Hone *(Chief Legal & Regulation Officer)*
Juan Yamamoto Shishido *(Chief Admin & Control Officer)*

Empresa Distribuidora Sur S.A. (3)
San Jose 140
1076 Buenos Aires, Argentina (65.39%)
Tel.: (54) 1143703700
Fax: (54) 11 4381 0708
E-Mail: emailservicio@edesur.com.ar
Web Site: www.edesur.com.ar
Emp.: 2,400
Electricity Distribution
S.I.C.: 4939
N.A.I.C.S.: 221122
Joao Becerra de Souza *(Chm)*
Rafael Lopez Rueda *(Vice Chm)*
Jose Maria Hidalgo Martin-Mateos *(CEO)*
Daniel Martini *(Chief Comm Officer)*
Jose Maria Gottig *(Chief Environ Quality & Sustainable Dev Officer)*
Jorge Lukaszczuk *(Chief Internal Auditing Officer)*

Endesa Brasil S.A. (3)
Praca Leoni Ramos 1 Sao Domingos
24210-200 Rio de Janeiro, Niteroi, Brazil (53.9%)
Tel.: (55) 2136079500
Fax: (55) 2136079555
Web Site: www.endesabrasil.com.br/Default.aspx?id=42&strLang=en
Holding Company
S.I.C.: 6719
N.A.I.C.S.: 551112
Mario Fernando de Melo Santos *(Chm)*
Francisco Bugallo *(Vice CEO)*
Marcelo Llevenes Rebolledo *(CEO)*
Luis Carlos Lorens Ortins *(CFO)*

Subsidiaries:

Ampla Energia e Servicos, S.A. (4)
Praca Leoni Ramos No 1
Sao Domingos Niteroi, Rio de Janeiro, Brazil BR
Tel.: (55) 2126137000 (99.64%)
Fax: (55) 2126137123
Web Site: www.ampla.com.br —(BRAZ)
Emp.: 1,500
Electricity Distribution
S.I.C.: 4931
N.A.I.C.S.: 221122
Mario Fernando de Melo Santos *(Chm)*
Cristian Eduardo Fierro Montes *(Pres)*

Companhia Energetica do Ceara, S.A. (4)
Av Barao de Studart 2917 83
Bairro Dionisio Torres, Fortaleza, Ceara, Brazil (58.87%)
Tel.: (55) 85 3216 1350
Fax: (55) 85 3216 1247
Web Site: www.coelce.com.br
COCE3—(BRAZ)
Sales Range: $1-4.9 Billion
Emp.: 1,297
Electric Power Distribution
S.I.C.: 4931
N.A.I.C.S.: 221122
Mario Melo Santos *(Chm)*
Marcelo Andres Llevenes Rebolledo *(Vice Chm)*
Abel Alves Rochinha *(CEO)*
Luiz Carlos Laurens Ortins Bettencourt *(CFO & Chief IR Officer)*
Jose Tavora Batista *(CTO)*
Aurelio Ricardo Bustilho de Oliveira *(Plng & Control Officer)*
Olga Jovanna Carranza Salazar *(Comml Officer)*
Jose Alves de Mello Franco *(Regulation Officer)*
Jose Renato Ferreira Barreto *(HR Officer)*
Jose Nunes de Almeida Neto *(Comm & Institutional Officer)*
Silvia Cunha Saraiva Pereira *(Legal Officer)*

Synapsis Argentina Ltda (3)
Azopardo 1335
Buenos Aires, 1095, Argentina

Tel.: (54) 11 4021 8300
E-Mail: info@synapsis-sa.com.ar
Web Site: www.synapsis.com.ar
Information Technology Services
S.I.C.: 7373
N.A.I.C.S.: 541512
Fernando Marsha Dano *(Gen Mgr)*

International Endesa BV **(2)**
Herengracht 471
Amsterdam, 1017BS, Netherlands
Tel.: (31) 20 521 8771
Fax: (31) 20 521 8799
Emp.: 2
Financial Management Services
S.I.C.: 6211
N.A.I.C.S.: 523999
Ernesto Di Giacomo *(Mng Dir)*

Enel Brasil Participacoes Ltda **(1)**
Praca Leoni Ramos andar bloco 2
20090 010 Niteroi, Brazil
Tel.: (55) 21 2206 5600
Fax: (55) 21 2206 5610
E-Mail: reception.brazil@enel.com
Emp.: 20
Electric Power Generation & Distribution Services
S.I.C.: 4931
N.A.I.C.S.: 221118

Enel de Costa Rica SA **(1)**
200 Mts Sur del Parqueo de CineMark Multiplaza Escazu
Edificio Terraforte 2do Piso, San Jose, San Jose, Costa Rica
Tel.: (506) 2201 4500
Fax: (506) 2201 5150
E-Mail: comunicacion.externa@enel.com
Emp.: 6
Electric Power Generation Services
S.I.C.: 4911
N.A.I.C.S.: 221118
Joseph Benavidez *(Gen Mgr)*

Enel Finance International NV **(1)**
Herengracht 471
Amsterdam, 1017 BS, Netherlands
Tel.: (31) 205218777
Fax: (31) 25218799
Web Site: www.enel.com
Emp.: 1
Financial Management Services
S.I.C.: 6211
N.A.I.C.S.: 523999
Ernesto Di Giacomo *(COO)*
Ralf Thiehofe *(COO)*

Enel Green power France Sas **(1)**
Le Bonnel - 20 rue de la Villette
39003 Lyon, France
Tel.: (33) 4 78 92 68 70
Fax: (33) 4 78 42 03 44
E-Mail: info_egpfrance@enel.com
Web Site: www.enelgreenpower.com
Emp.: 5
Wind Farm Electric Power Generation Services
S.I.C.: 4931
N.A.I.C.S.: 221118
Lamberto Dai Pra *(Gen Mgr)*

Enel Green power Romania SRL **(1)**
62-64 Strada Buzesti Et 6 Sector 1
Bucharest, 427206, Romania
Tel.: (40) 263350298
Fax: (40) 372872710
E-Mail: contact@enel.com
Emp.: 50
Hydro Electric Power Generation Services
S.I.C.: 4931
N.A.I.C.S.: 221111
Francesco Lazzeri *(Gen Mgr)*

Enel Guatemala SA **(1)**
Diagonal 6 10-65 Zona 10 Centro Gerencial Las Margaritas
Torre I Nivel 8 Oficina 801, 1010
Guatemala, Guatemala
Tel.: (502) 23277000
Fax: (502) 23393176
E-Mail: comunicacion.externa@latinamerica.enel.it
Emp.: 4
Hydroelectric Power Generation Services
S.I.C.: 4911
N.A.I.C.S.: 221111

Enel Panama SA **(1)**
C/O Maud & Maud Torre Dresdner Latinoamerica Calle 50 Piso 7 Y 9
Panama, Panama
Tel.: (507) 2693555
Fax: (507) 2638804
Electric Power Generation Services
S.I.C.: 4939
N.A.I.C.S.: 221118

Enercampo - Producao Porto de Energia Lda **(1)**
Rua Eng Ferreira Dias 161
Porto, 4100-247, Portugal
Tel.: (351) 226198400
Fax: (351) 226198410
Electric Power Generation Services
S.I.C.: 4931
N.A.I.C.S.: 221118

Energia Nueva Energia Limpia Mexico Srl de Cv **(1)**
Miguel De Cervantes Saavedra No 193 9th Fl Office 901
Mexico, 11520, Mexico
Tel.: (52) 5552809361
Fax: (52) 5552809371
Web Site: www.enelgreenpower.com
Emp.: 10
Electric Power Generation Services
S.I.C.: 4939
N.A.I.C.S.: 221118
Nicola Melchiotti *(Mng Dir)*

Energias de Graus SL **(1)**
Argualas street 1 Edificio Torreon 1 Planta
Barcelona, 50012, Spain
Tel.: (34) 976760011
Fax: (34) 976050564
E-Mail: javier.derez@enel.com
Web Site: www.enelgreenpower.com
Emp.: 20
Fuel Electric Power Generation Services
S.I.C.: 4931
N.A.I.C.S.: 221112
Sai-Ubol Noparat *(Gen Mgr)*

Eolcinf - Producao de Energia Eolica Lda **(1)**
Av Sidonio Pais Nr 379 2
Porto, 4100-247, Portugal
Tel.: (351) 226080180
Fax: (351) 226080189
E-Mail: egp_portugal.nl@enel.com
Web Site: www.enel.com
Electric Power Generation Services
S.I.C.: 4939
N.A.I.C.S.: 221118
Mischa Knight *(Gen Mgr)*

Eolflor - Producao de Energia Eo lica Lda **(1)**
Avenida Sidonio Pais 379 - 2 Andar
Porto, 4100-468, Portugal
Tel.: (351) 226080180
Fax: (351) 226080189
E-Mail:
Web Site: www.enel.com
Emp.: 3
Wind Farm Electric Power Generation Services
S.I.C.: 4911
N.A.I.C.S.: 221118
Rue Nevis *(Gen Mgr)*

Explotaciones Eolicas Zaragoza de Escucha SA **(1)**
Calle San Miguel Zaragoza 10
Zaragoza, 50001, Spain
Tel.: (34) 976760011
Fax: (34) 976050564
Solar Electric Power Generation Services
S.I.C.: 4931
N.A.I.C.S.: 221118

Fermicaise SA de Cv **(1)**
Reforma No 873 San Nicolas Tolentino Iztapalapa
Mexico, 9850, Mexico
Tel.: (52) 5556322235
Electric Power Generation Services
S.I.C.: 4939
N.A.I.C.S.: 221118

Gas y Electricidad Generacion SAU **(1)**
Calle Sant Joan De Deu 1
Palma de Mallorca, 7007, Spain
Tel.: (34) 971467711
Fax: (34) 971462361
Electric Power Generation Services
S.I.C.: 4939
N.A.I.C.S.: 221118

Gasoducto Atacama Argentina SA **(1)**
Av Isidora Goyenechea 3365 Piso 8
Las Condes, Santiago, 7550120, Chile
Tel.: (56) 23663800
Fax: (56) 23663801
E-Mail: info@gasatacama.cl
Web Site: www.gasatacama.cl
Emp.: 5
Natural Gas Distribution & Transmission Services
S.I.C.: 4924
N.A.I.C.S.: 221210
Dawn Hancock *(Office Mgr)*

Generadora de Occidente Ltda **(1)**
Diagonal 6 10-65 Zona 10 Fl 8
Guatemala, 1010, Guatemala
Tel.: (502) 23277017
Fax: (502) 23393176
E-Mail: comunicacion.gt@enel.com
Web Site: www.enelgreenpower.com
Emp.: 12
Electric Power Generation Services
S.I.C.: 4931
N.A.I.C.S.: 221118
Andrew Gunn *(Gen Mgr)*

Gesa Gas SAU **(1)**
Calle Juan Maragall 16
07006 Palma de Mallorca, Spain
Tel.: (34) 971 467 711
Fax: (34) 971 770 225
Natural Gas Distr
S.I.C.: 4924
N.A.I.C.S.: 221210

Hidroelectricidad del Pacifico Srl de Cv **(1)**
Boulevard Miguel De Cervantes Saavedra No 193 901 Granada
Miguel Hidalgo, Mexico, 11520, Mexico
Tel.: (52) 5552809361
Fax: (52) 5552809371
Emp.: 6
Electric Power Generation Services
S.I.C.: 4931
N.A.I.C.S.: 221118

Hydromac Energy BV **(1)**
Herengracht 471
Amsterdam, 1017 BS, Netherlands
Tel.: (31) 205218777
Fax: (31) 205218799
Web Site: www.enel.it
Emp.: 4
Investment Management Services
S.I.C.: 6211
N.A.I.C.S.: 523999
Romain Bausch *(CEO)*

Non-U.S. Subsidiary:

Enel Latin America (Chile) Ltda. **(2)**
Rosario Norte 530
Las Condes, Santiago, Chile
Tel.: (56) 2 8999200
Fax: (56) 2 4700084
Electric Power Generation Services
S.I.C.: 4939
N.A.I.C.S.: 221118

International Wind Parks of Achaia SA **(1)**
4 Gravias
Maroussi, 15125, Greece
Tel.: (30) 2111808500
Fax: (30) 2111808515
E-Mail: officesupport.enelgreece@enel.com
Emp.: 7
Wind Farm Turbine Mfr
S.I.C.: 3511
N.A.I.C.S.: 333611
Georgios Stassis *(CEO)*

Minas de Estercuel SA **(1)**
Cl Ribera Del Loira 60
Madrid, 28042, Spain
Tel.: (34) 976 228 504
Mineral Mining Services
S.I.C.: 1499
N.A.I.C.S.: 212399

Minas Gargallo SL **(1)**
Calle Ribera Del Loira 60
Madrid, 28042, Spain
Tel.: (34) 912131165
Fax: (34) 912131711
Electric Power Generation Services
S.I.C.: 4911
N.A.I.C.S.: 221118
Juan Carlos Alonso *(Gen Mgr)*

Newind Group Inc. **(1)**
1255 Rue University Bureau 1204
Montreal, QC, H3B 3W9, Canada
Tel.: (514) 397-0463
Fax: (514) 397-0284
Web Site: www.enel.com
Electric Power Generation Services
S.I.C.: 4939
N.A.I.C.S.: 221118
Christian Calisti *(Office Mgr)*

O&M Cogeneration Inc. **(1)**
1255 Rue University Bureau 120
Montreal, QC, H3B 3W9, Canada
Tel.: (514) 397-0463
Fax: (418) 630-3803
Emp.: 3
Electric Power Distribution Services
S.I.C.: 4939
N.A.I.C.S.: 221122
Daniel Munger *(Gen Mgr)*

Planta Eolica Europea SA **(1)**
Calle Balbino Marron 1
Seville, 41018, Spain
Tel.: (34) 954171101
Fax: (34) 954170691
Electric Power Generation Services
S.I.C.: 4911
N.A.I.C.S.: 221118

Proyectos Eolicos Valencianos SA **(1)**
Plaza America 2
46004 Valencia, Spain
Tel.: (34) 963 16 21 42
Electric Power Generation Services
S.I.C.: 4911
N.A.I.C.S.: 221118

Sealve - Sociedade Electrica de Alvaiazere SA **(1)**
Avenida Sidonio Pais 379 2
4100-468 Porto, Portugal
Tel.: (351) 226080180
Fax: (351) 226080189
Electric Power Generation Services
S.I.C.: 4939
N.A.I.C.S.: 221118

Suministro de Luz y Fuerza SL **(1)**
Rambla D Anselm Viola 7
17257 Torroella de Montgri, Spain
Tel.: (34) 972 75 92 56
Fax: (34) 972761343
E-Mail: info@suministrodeluzyfuerza.com
Electric Power Distribution Services
S.I.C.: 4931
N.A.I.C.S.: 221122

Synapsis Soluciones y Servicios It Ltda **(1)**
Miraflores 383 piso 27
Santiago, Chile
Tel.: (56) 2 397 6600
Fax: (56) 2 397 6601
E-Mail: info@swww.synapsis.cl
Web Site: www.synapsis-it.com
Information Technology Consulting Services
S.I.C.: 7373
N.A.I.C.S.: 541512

Teploprogress OJSC **(1)**
ul Fryazevskaya 10
111 396 Moscow, Russia
Tel.: (7) 4953032981
E-Mail: info@teploprogress.ru
Heat Exchange Block Mfr
S.I.C.: 3443
N.A.I.C.S.: 332410

Union Electrica de Canarias Generacion SAU **(1)**
Calle Albareda Plaza Woermann 38
Las Palmas, 35008, Spain
Tel.: (34) 928309900
Fax: (34) 928309986
Electric Power Generation Services
S.I.C.: 4939
N.A.I.C.S.: 221118

WP Bulgaria 12 EOOD **(1)**
R-N Triaditsa Distr Floor 5 2 Pl Pozitano
Sofia, 1000, Bulgaria
Tel.: (359) 29032300
Electric Power Plant Construction & Maintenance Services

Enel S.p.A.—(Continued)

S.I.C.: 1629
N.A.I.C.S.: 237130

ENEMONA AD

20 Kosta Lulchev Str
Sofia, 1113, Bulgaria
Tel.: (359) 28054850
Fax: (359) 28524842
E-Mail: office@enemona.com
Web Site: www.enemona.bg
E4A—(DEU)
Rev.: $96,407,675
Assets: $134,334,407
Liabilities: $95,211,550
Net Worth: $39,122,857
Earnings: ($523,561)
Fiscal Year-end: 12/31/12

Business Description:
Engineering Services
S.I.C.: 8711
N.A.I.C.S.: 541330

Personnel:
Dichko Prokopiev *(Chm & CEO)*

Board of Directors:
Dichko Prokopiev
Margarita Dineva
Nikolay Filchev
Emil Manchev
Bogdan Prokopiev

ENERCARE INC.

4000 Victoria Park Avenue
Toronto, ON, M2H 3P4, Canada
Tel.: (416) 649-1860
Fax: (905) 695-7789
Toll Free: (877) 877-0142
E-Mail: investor.relations@enercare.ca
Web Site: www.enercareinc.com
Year Founded: 2002
ECI—(TSX)
Rev.: $255,047,640
Assets: $797,249,765
Liabilities: $702,184,674
Net Worth: $95,065,091
Earnings: ($3,156,013)
Emp.: 87
Fiscal Year-end: 12/31/12

Business Description:
Water Heater & Related Products Investment Services
S.I.C.: 6211
N.A.I.C.S.: 523999

Personnel:
Jim Pantelidis *(Chm)*
John A. MacDonald *(Pres & CEO)*
Evelyn Sutherland *(CFO)*
John Toffoletto *(Gen Counsel, Sec & Sr VP)*

Board of Directors:
Jim Pantelidis
Lisa de Wilde
John A. MacDonald
Grace Palombo
Jerry Patava
Roy J. Pearce
Michael S. Rousseau
William M. Wells

Transfer Agent:
Computershare Investor Services Inc
100 University Avenue
Toronto, ON, Canada

Subsidiaries:

The Consumers Waterheater Operating Trust **(1)**
80 Allstate Pkwy 2nd Fl
Southern Ontario, Markham, ON, L3R 6H3, Canada
Tel.: (905) 943-6229
Fax: (905) 943-6393
Water Heater Rental Services
S.I.C.: 7359
N.A.I.C.S.: 532210
Chris Cawston *(Interim CFO)*

Stratacon Inc. **(1)**
641 Chrislea Rd Unit 8
Woodbridge, ON, Canada
Tel.: (905) 856-4001
Fax: (905) 856-1513
Toll Free: (800) 750-2960
E-Mail: sales@stratacon.ca
Web Site: www.stratacon.ca
Emp.: 30
Residential Metering Devices Mfr
S.I.C.: 3829
N.A.I.C.S.: 334514
Peter R.J. Mills *(Mng Dir)*
Ian D. Stewart *(Mng Dir)*

ENERCHEM INTERNATIONAL, INC.

Bow Valley Square 2. Ste 3900, 205 5th Avenue SW.
Calgary, AB, T2P 2V7, Canada
Tel.: (403) 269-1500
Fax: (403) 269-1559
Web Site: www.enerchem.com
Year Founded: 1988
Sales Range: $100-124.9 Million
Emp.: 55

Business Description:
Mfr & Distr of Hydrocarbon Drilling & Fracturing Fluids & Specialty Solvents for the Oil & Gas Industry
S.I.C.: 2869
N.A.I.C.S.: 325110

Personnel:
Larry B. Phillips *(Chm)*

Board of Directors:
Larry B. Phillips
William D. Burch
Bruce K. Gibson
Gordon J. Hoy
Kenneth A. Klein
Kevin M. Maguire

Transfer Agent:
CIBC Mellon Trust Company
320 Bay Street
PO Box 1
Toronto, ON, M5H 2A6, Canada
Tel.: (416) 643-5500
Fax: (416) 643-5570
Toll Free: (800) 387-0825

Subsidiary:

Millard Trucking Ltd. **(1)**
PO Box 960
Sundre, AB, T0M 1X0, Canada
Tel.: (403) 638-4500
Fax: (403) 638-4987
Emp.: 25
Trucking Services
S.I.C.: 4212
N.A.I.C.S.: 484110
Jody Millard *(Mgr-Transportation)*

ENERCHINA HOLDINGS LTD

28/F Infinitus Plaza 199 Des Voeux Road
Central, China (Hong Kong)
Tel.: (852) 25211181
Fax: (852) 28510970
E-Mail: group@sinolinkhk.com
Web Site: www.enerchina.com.hk
00622—(HKG)
Sales Range: $1-9.9 Million
Emp.: 493

Business Description:
Electricity Generation
S.I.C.: 4911
N.A.I.C.S.: 221118

Personnel:
Yaping Ou *(Chm)*
Wei Chen *(CEO)*
Tai On Lo *(Sec)*

Board of Directors:
Yaping Ou
Wei Chen
Yungang Lu
Francis Yui Man Tang
Bing Xiang
Ya Bo Xiang
Luo Lin Xin

Butterfield Fulcrum Group (Bermuda) Limited
Rosebank Centre 11 Bermudiana Road
Pembroke, Bermuda

Transfer Agents:
Computershare Hong Kong Investor Services Limited
Shops 1712-1716 17th Floor Hopewell Centre
183 Queens Road East
Wanchai, China (Hong Kong)

Butterfield Fulcrum Group (Bermuda) Limited
Rosebank Centre 11 Bermudiana Road
Pembroke, Bermuda

Subsidiaries:

Enerchina Resources Limited **(1)**
28th Floor Vicwood Plaza
Central, China (Hong Kong) (100%)
Tel.: (852) 28518811
Fax: (852) 28510970
E-Mail: group@sinolinkhk.com
Web Site: www.sinolinkhk.com
Emp.: 10
Management Consulting Services
S.I.C.: 8748
N.A.I.C.S.: 541618
Chen Wei *(CEO)*

Sinolink Electric Power Company Limited **(1)**
28th Floor Vicwood Plaza
Central District, Central, China (Hong Kong) (100%)
Tel.: (852) 28518811
Investment Advice
S.I.C.: 6282
N.A.I.C.S.: 523930

Non-U.S. Subsidiaries:

Enerchina Oil and Petrochemical Company Limited **(1)**
C-o Offshore Incorporations Limited
Road Town, Virgin Islands (British)
Tel.: (284) 4948184
Fax: (284) 4945132
Oil & Gas Operations
S.I.C.: 1389
N.A.I.C.S.: 213112

Kenson Investment Limited **(1)**
C/o MMG Trust BVI Corp
Road Town, Tortola, Virgin Islands (British)
Tel.: (284) 494 2011
Fax: (284) 494 2015
Electric Power Generation Services
S.I.C.: 4939
N.A.I.C.S.: 221118

Rado International Limited **(1)**
C/O Morgan & Morgan Trust Corporation Ltd
PO Box 958
Road Town, Virgin Islands (British) (100%)
Tel.: (284) 4942011
Fax: (284) 4942015
Holding Company
S.I.C.: 6719
N.A.I.C.S.: 551112

Roxy Link Limited **(1)**
C/O Offshore Incorporations Limited
PO Box 957
Road Town, Tortola, VG 1110, Virgin Islands (British)
Tel.: (284) 494-8184
Fax: (284) 494-5132
Holding Company
S.I.C.: 6719
N.A.I.C.S.: 551112

Sinolink LPG Investment Limited **(1)**
c/o Offshore Incorporations Limited
Road Town, Virgin Islands (British)
Tel.: (284) 4948184
Fax: (284) 4945132
Holding Company
S.I.C.: 6719
N.A.I.C.S.: 551112

Sinolink Power Investment Ltd **(1)**
C/O Offshore Incorporations Limited
PO Box 116C Sea Meadow House
Road Town, Virgin Islands (British)
Tel.: (284) 4948184
Fax: (284) 4945132
Holding Company
S.I.C.: 6719
N.A.I.C.S.: 551112

ENERES CO., LTD.

4-1 Senju 1-chome Adachi-ku
Tokyo, 120-0034, Japan
Tel.: (81) 3 6657 5453
Web Site: www.eneres.co.jp
6079—(TKS)
Rev.: $56,140,469
Emp.: 90
Fiscal Year-end: 12/31/12

Business Description:
Energy Resource Management Services
S.I.C.: 4911
N.A.I.C.S.: 221122

Personnel:
Motohide Ikeda *(CEO)*

ENERFLEX LTD.

Ste 904 1331 Macleod Trail SE
Calgary, AB, T2G 0K3, Canada
Tel.: (403) 387-6377
Fax: (403) 720-4385
Toll Free: (800) 242-3178
E-Mail: info@enerflex.com
Web Site: www.enerflex.com
Year Founded: 2010
EFX—(TSX)
Rev.: $1,492,703,930
Assets: $1,380,956,201
Liabilities: $499,579,542
Net Worth: $881,376,660
Earnings: $71,344,791
Emp.: 3,300
Fiscal Year-end: 12/31/12

Business Description:
Natural Gas, Oil & CO2 Compression, Production & Processing
S.I.C.: 1311
N.A.I.C.S.: 211111

Personnel:
Stephen. J. Savidant *(Chm)*
J. Blair Goertzen *(Pres & CEO)*
D. James Harbilas *(CFO & VP)*
Greg Stewart *(CIO & VP)*
Bradley Beebe *(Pres-Gas Drive)*
Jerry Fraelic *(Pres-Americas)*
Bill Moore *(Pres-Intl)*

Board of Directors:
Stephen. J. Savidant
Robert S. Boswell
Kenneth R. Bruce
W. Byron Dunn
J. Blair Goertzen
Wayne S. Hill
H. Stanley Marshall
Michael A. Weill

Transfer Agent:
Canadian Stock Transfer Company Inc.
320 Bay Street
PO Box 1
M5H4A6 Toronto, ON, Canada

U.S. Subsidiary:

Enerflex Energy Systems Inc. **(1)**
10815 Telge Rd
Houston, TX 77095-5038 DE
Tel.: (281) 345-9300 (100%)
Fax: (281) 345-7434
E-Mail: jfraelic@enerflex.com
Web Site: www.enerflex.com
Emp.: 300
Gas Compression Units & Commercial Refrigeration Systems Mfr
S.I.C.: 3563
N.A.I.C.S.: 333912
Jerry Fraelic *(Pres)*

Subsidiary:

Enerflex Energy Systems (Wyoming) Inc. (2)
2289 Renauna Ave
Casper, WY 82605 DE
Tel.: (307) 237-7118 (100%)
E-Mail: iheidecker@enerflex.com
Web Site: www.enerflex.com
Gas Compression Units & Commercial Refrigeration Systems Mfr
S.I.C.: 3563
N.A.I.C.S.: 333912

ENERFLOW INDUSTRIES INC.
4800 27th Street SE
Calgary, AB, T2B 3M4, Canada
Tel.: (403) 279-9696
Fax: (403) 279-9633
E-Mail: info@enerflow.com
Web Site: www.enerflow.com
Year Founded: 2003
Rev.: $51,007,704
Emp.: 300
Business Description:
Oilfield Equipment Mfr
S.I.C.: 3533
N.A.I.C.S.: 333132
Personnel:
Larry Lindholm *(Co-Founder)*
Mark Williamson *(Co-Founder)*

ENERGETIC SERVICES INC.
Mile 54 Alaska Hwy
PO Box 6639
Fort Saint John, BC, V1J 4J1, Canada
Tel.: (250) 785-4761
Fax: (250) 785-9980
Toll Free: (877) 785-4769
Web Site: www.energeticservices.com
Rev.: $12,259,238
Emp.: 68
Business Description:
Transportation Services
S.I.C.: 4789
N.A.I.C.S.: 488999
Personnel:
Brennan Ross *(Pres)*

ENERGETICKY A PRUMYSLOVY HOLDING, A.S.
(d/b/a EP Holding)
Parizska 26
CZ-110 00 Prague, 1, Czech Republic
Tel.: (420) 232 005 300
E-Mail: info@epholding.cz
Web Site: www.epholding.cz
Year Founded: 2009
Business Description:
Energy & Industrial Investment Holding Company
S.I.C.: 6719
N.A.I.C.S.: 551112
Personnel:
Daniel Kretinsky *(Chm)*
Ladislav Bartonicek *(Chm-Supervisory Bd)*
Board of Directors:
Daniel Kretinsky
Marek Janca
Marek Spurny
Supervisory Board of Directors:
Ladislav Bartonicek
Milos Badida
Martin Fedor
Ivan Jakabovic
Robert Sevela
Martin Stefunko

Non-U.S. Holdings:

Mitteldeutsche Braunkohlengesellschaft mbH (1)
Glueck-Auf-Strasse 1
Zeitz, 06711, Germany De
Tel.: (49) 34416840
Fax: (49) 3441684425
Web Site: www.mibrag.de
Sales Range: $500-549.9 Million
Emp.: 2,000
Coal Mining
S.I.C.: 1221
N.A.I.C.S.: 212111
Wilhelm Hans Beermann *(Chm-Supervisory Bd)*
Joachim Geisler *(Chm-Mgmt Bd & CEO)*
Ralf Bartels *(Deputy Chm-Supervisory Bd)*
Heinz Junge *(Mng Dir-HR & Member-Mgmt Bd)*
Horst Schmidt *(Mng Dir-Technical & Member-Mgmt Bd)*

Przedsiebiorstwo Gornicze SILESIA Sp. z o.o. (1)
ul Gornicza 60
PL-43 502 Czechowice-Dziedzice, Poland PL
Tel.: (48) 32 737 3311
Fax: (48) 32 215 2144
E-Mail: info@pgsilesia.pl
Web Site: www.pgsilesia.pl
Coal Mining
S.I.C.: 1221
N.A.I.C.S.: 212111
Jiri Pastika *(Dir Gen)*

ENERGETIX GROUP PLC
Capenhurst Technology Park
Chester, CH1 6EH, United Kingdom
Tel.: (44) 2031374466
Fax: (44) 1513482101
E-Mail: info@energetixgroup.com
Web Site: www.energetixgroup.com
EGX—(LSE)
Rev.: $17,372
Assets: $43,013,542
Liabilities: $5,352,214
Net Worth: $37,661,329
Earnings: ($7,896,450)
Emp.: 43
Fiscal Year-end: 12/31/12
Business Description:
Alternative Energy Products Development
S.I.C.: 1623
N.A.I.C.S.: 237130
Personnel:
Adrian Charles Hutchings *(Founder)*
Anthony David Stiff *(CEO & Mng Dir-Flow Energy)*
P. M. Barry *(Sec)*
Board of Directors:
Clare Mary Joan Spottiswoode
Henry J. Cialone
David K. Grundy
Anthony David Stiff
Legal Counsel:
Atticus Legal LLP
Third Floor Castlefield House Liverpool Road Castlefield
Manchester, United Kingdom

Subsidiaries:

Energetix Genlec Limited (1)
Capenhurst Tech Park
Capenhurst, Chester, Cheshire, M2 4JU, United Kingdom
Tel.: (44) 151 348 2110
Fax: (44) 151 348 2101
E-Mail: info@genlec.com
Web Site: www.flowenergy.uk.com
Emp.: 40
Heat Boilers Mfr
S.I.C.: 3433
N.A.I.C.S.: 333414
Peter Richardson *(Mng Dir)*

Energetix (Pnu) Power Limited (1)
Capenhurst Technology Park Capenhurst
Chester, Chester, CH1 6EH, United Kingdom
Tel.: (44) 1513482107
Fax: (44) 1513482101
E-Mail: info@energetixgroup.com
Web Site: www.energetixgroup.com
Emp.: 10
Compressed Air Back Up Power Systems Mfr
S.I.C.: 3699
N.A.I.C.S.: 335999
James Derby *(Gen Mgr)*

ENERGIA MINERALS LIMITED
Suite 6 Level 2 20 Kings Park Road
West Perth, WA, 6005, Australia
Mailing Address:
PO BOX 1785
West Perth, WA, 6872, Australia
Tel.: (61) 8 9321 5000
Fax: (61) 8 9321 7177
E-Mail: info@energiaminerals.com
Web Site: www.energiaminerals.com
EMX—(ASX)
Rev.: $770,605
Assets: $3,740,984
Liabilities: $423,634
Net Worth: $3,317,349
Earnings: ($3,567,591)
Emp.: 6
Fiscal Year-end: 06/30/13
Business Description:
Uranium Exploration Services
S.I.C.: 1094
N.A.I.C.S.: 212291
Personnel:
Kim Robinson *(Mng Dir)*
Max D. J. Cozijn *(Sec)*
Board of Directors:
Antonino Iannello
Max D. J. Cozijn
Kim Robinson
Ian W. Walker
Legal Counsel:
Deacons
Level 39 Bankwest Tower 108 St Georges Terrace
Perth, WA, 6000, Australia
Tel.: (61) 08 9426 3222
Fax: (61) 08 8372 6666

ENERGIE AG
Boehmerwaldstrasse 3
PO Box 298
A 4021 Linz, Austria
Tel.: (43) 7090000
Fax: (43) 800818001
E-Mail: service@energieag.at
Web Site: www.energieag.at
Sls.: $2,806,342,447
Assets: $4,866,050,520
Liabilities: $3,093,484,061
Net Worth: $1,772,566,459
Earnings: $85,119,451
Emp.: 7,781
Fiscal Year-end: 09/30/12
Business Description:
Electric Power & Water Distr; Waste Disposal Services
S.I.C.: 4931
N.A.I.C.S.: 221122
Personnel:
Gerhard Falch *(Chm-Supervisory Bd)*
Leo Windtner *(Chm-Mgmt Bd & CEO)*
Hermann Kepplinger *(First Deputy Chm-Supervisory Bd)*
Ludwig Scharinger *(Second Deputy Chm-Supervisory Bd)*
Andreas Kolar *(CFO & Member-Mgmt Bd)*
Werner Steinecker *(COO & Member-Mgmt Bd)*
Supervisory Board of Directors:
Gerhard Falch
Alois Froschauer
Franz Gasselsberger
Anna Maria Hochhauser
Michaela Keplinger-Mitterlehner
Hermann Kepplinger
Manfred Klicnik
Ruperta Lichtenecker
Maria Theresia Niss
Manfred Polzer
Ludwig Scharinger
Viktor Sigl
Michael Strugl
Bruno Wallnofer

ENERGIE EUROPE SERVICE SA
22 avenue de la Grande Armee
75017 Paris, France
Tel.: (33) 1 55 37 46 00
Fax: (33) 1 55 37 46 36
E-Mail: contact@ees.homeip.net
Web Site: www.energie-europeservice.com
MLEES—(EUR)
Business Description:
Solar, Electric & Thermal Power Energy Producer
S.I.C.: 4931
N.A.I.C.S.: 221118
Personnel:
Pierre Samaha *(Pres)*

ENERGIO LIMITED
(Name Changed to Kogi Iron Limited)

ENERGISA S.A.
Praca Rui Barbosa 80 Cataguases
Gerais, 36770 901, Brazil
Tel.: (55) 3234296000
Fax: (55) 3234296317
Web Site: www.energisa.com.br
ENGI3—(BRAZ)
Rev.: $1,435,865,769
Assets: $2,488,654,985
Liabilities: $1,750,207,582
Net Worth: $738,447,403
Earnings: $143,171,963
Emp.: 5,016
Fiscal Year-end: 12/31/12
Business Description:
Electric Power Distr
S.I.C.: 4911
N.A.I.C.S.: 221121
Personnel:
Ivan Muller Botelho *(Chm)*
Ricardo Perez Botelho *(Vice Chm & CEO)*
Mauricio Perez Botelho *(CFO & IR Officer)*
Daniele Araujo Salomao Castelo *(HR Officer)*
Danilo de Souza Dias *(Strategic & Regulatory Affairs Officer)*
Jose Marcelo Goncalves Reis *(Supplies & Logistics Officer)*
Board of Directors:
Ivan Muller Botelho
Ricardo Perez Botelho
Omar Carneiro da Cunha Sobrinho
Antonio Jose de Almeida Carneiro
Marcilio Marques Moreira

ENERGISER INVESTMENTS PLC
2 Anglo Office Park 67 White Lion Road
Amersham, Bucks, HP7 9FB, United Kingdom
Tel.: (44) 1494762450
Fax: (44) 1494765897
E-Mail: info@energiserinvestments.co.uk
Web Site: www.energiserinvestments.co.uk
ENGI—(AIM)
Rev.: $235,314
Assets: $4,087,203
Liabilities: $3,820,303
Net Worth: $266,900
Earnings: ($270,059)
Emp.: 3
Fiscal Year-end: 12/31/12
Business Description:
Investment Services
S.I.C.: 6211

Energiser Investments plc—(Continued)

N.A.I.C.S.: 523999
Personnel:
Nishith Malde *(Sec)*
Board of Directors:
William Jeremy Weston
Nishith Malde
Legal Counsel:
Dorsey & Whitney
21 Wilson Street
London, United Kingdom

ENERGIZER RESOURCES INC.

520 - 141 Adelaide Street West
Toronto, ON, M5H 3L5, Canada
Tel.: (416) 364-4911
Fax: (416) 364-2753
Toll Free: (800) 818-5442
E-Mail: info@energizerresources.com
Web Site: www.energizerresources.com
EGZ—(OTC OTCB TSX)
Rev.: $307,992
Assets: $1,220,436
Liabilities: $803,130
Net Worth: $417,306
Earnings: ($7,824,248)
Emp.: 7
Fiscal Year-end: 06/30/13
Business Description:
Vanadium Mining & Exploration Services
S.I.C.: 1094
N.A.I.C.S.: 212291
Personnel:
Vernon Peter Harder *(Chm)*
John P. Sanderson *(Vice Chm)*
Craig Scherba *(Pres & COO)*
Richard E. Schler *(CEO)*
Peter D. Liabotis *(CFO, Sec & Sr VP)*
Robin Borley *(Sr VP-Mine Dev)*
Brent Nykoliation *(Sr VP-Corp Dev)*
Board of Directors:
Vernon Peter Harder
Robin Borley
Johann K. de Bruin
J. A. Kirk McKinnon
John P. Sanderson
Craig Scherba
Richard E. Schler
Albert Adolph Thiess, Jr.
Quentin Yarie
Legal Counsel:
Fraser Milner Casgrain
First Canadian Place
P.O. Box 100
Toronto, ON, M5X 1B2, Canada
Tel.: (416) 863-4511
Telex: 6-219825
Fax: (416) 863-4592
Transfer Agent:
Equity Transfer & Trust Company
Toronto, ON, Canada

ENERGIZER TENNIS INC.

Suite 3 219 Bow Road
Docklands, London, E3 2SJ, United Kingdom
Tel.: (44) 203 086 8131
Web Site: www.energizertennis.com
Year Founded: 2011
EZRT—(OTC OTCB)
Assets: $31,201
Liabilities: $23,677
Net Worth: $7,524
Earnings: ($49,989)
Emp.: 1
Fiscal Year-end: 04/30/13
Business Description:
Online Tennis Information & Instruction
S.I.C.: 2741
N.A.I.C.S.: 519130
Personnel:
Alexander Farquharson *(Chm, Pres & CEO)*
Ella German *(CFO, Sec & Treas)*
Board of Directors:
Alexander Farquharson
Ella German

ENERGO-PRO A.S.

Nam Miru 62/39
CZ-568 02 Svitavy, Czech Republic
Tel.: (420) 510000000
Fax: (420) 510000001
E-Mail: info@energo-pro.com
Web Site: www.energo-pro.com
Year Founded: 1994
Emp.: 5,900
Business Description:
Holding Company; Hydroelectric Power Plant Operator, Construction & Maintenance Services
S.I.C.: 6719
N.A.I.C.S.: 551112
Personnel:
Jiri Krushina *(Chm)*

Subsidiary:

ENERGO-PRO Czech s.r.o. **(1)**
Edisonova 5
CZ-612 00 Brno, Czech Republic CZ
Tel.: (420) 510 000 050
Fax: (420) 510 000 011
E-Mail: info@energo-pro.com
Web Site: www.energo-pro.com
Hydroelectric Power Plant Operator, Construction & Maintenance Services
S.I.C.: 4911
N.A.I.C.S.: 221111
Jiri Krushina *(Chm)*

Non-U.S. Subsidiaries:

ENERGO-PRO Bulgaria EAD **(1)**
2 Pozitano Sq 5th Floor
1000 Sofia, Bulgaria BG
Tel.: (359) 29817050
Fax: (359) 29817021
E-Mail: bulgaria@energo-pro.com
Web Site: www.energo-pro.com
Hydroelectric Power Plant Operator, Construction & Maintenance Services
S.I.C.: 4939
N.A.I.C.S.: 221111

ENERGO-PRO Georgia JSC **(1)**
1 Sandro Euli Str
0186 Tbilisi, Georgia GE
Tel.: (995) 32319800
Fax: (995) 32 319 801
E-Mail: info@energo-pro.ge
Web Site: www.energo-pro.ge
Hydroelectric Power Plant Operator, Construction & Maintenance Services
S.I.C.: 4911
N.A.I.C.S.: 221111

ENERGO-PRO EAD **(1)**
Varna Towers Tower G
258 Vladislav Varnenchik Bul, 9009 Varna, Bulgaria (100%)
Tel.: (359) 700 161 61
E-Mail: service@energo-pro.bg
Web Site: www.energo-pro.bg
Electric Power Distr
S.I.C.: 4931
N.A.I.C.S.: 221122
Guenther Schubert *(Chm)*
Hoobert Lechner *(Sr VP-Law)*

ENERGOINSTAL S.A.

Al Rozdzienskiego 188d
40-203 Katowice, Poland
Tel.: (48) 327357200
Fax: (48) 327357257
E-Mail: energoinstal@energoinstal.pl
Web Site: www.energoinstal.pl
ENI—(WAR)
Rev.: $105,997,848
Assets: $78,711,349
Liabilities: $35,588,329
Net Worth: $43,123,020
Earnings: $4,545,107
Fiscal Year-end: 12/31/12
Business Description:
Power Boilers Mfr
S.I.C.: 3443
N.A.I.C.S.: 332410
Personnel:
Stanislaw Wiecek *(Chm-Supervisory Bd)*
Michal Wiecek *(Chm-Mgmt Bd)*
Jaroslaw Wiecek *(Vice Chm-Mgmt Bd)*
Lucjan Noras *(Gen Dir & Member-Mgmt Bd)*
Supervisory Board of Directors:
Stanislaw Wiecek
Henryk Kawalski
Wladyslaw Komarnicki
Andrzej Kowalski
Artur Olszewski

ENERGOINVEST - RASKLOPNA OPREMA A.D.

Vuka Karadzica 17
71123 Sarajevo, Bosnia & Herzegovina
Tel.: (387) 57 342 180
Fax: (387) 57 340 357
E-Mail: office@e-raop.com
Web Site: www.e-raop.com
Year Founded: 1954
RAOP—(BANJ)
Emp.: 271
Business Description:
Electrical Equipment Mfr
S.I.C.: 3699
N.A.I.C.S.: 335999
Personnel:
Zoran Kukobat *(Gen Mgr)*

ENERGOLD DRILLING CORP.

543 Granville Street Suite 1100
Vancouver, BC, V6C 1X8, Canada
Tel.: (604) 681-9501
Fax: (604) 681-6813
E-Mail: info@energold.com
Web Site: www.energold.com
Year Founded: 1973
EGD—(DEU OTC TSXV)
Rev.: $140,667,746
Assets: $171,782,560
Liabilities: $42,698,129
Net Worth: $129,084,431
Earnings: ($8,598,273)
Emp.: 1,200
Fiscal Year-end: 12/31/12
Business Description:
Diamond Drilling
S.I.C.: 1411
N.A.I.C.S.: 212311
Personnel:
James Hayward Coleman *(Chm)*
Frederick W. Davidson *(Pres & CEO)*
Steven Gold *(Interim CFO)*
Nicolas F. Rodrigo *(Pres/CEO-E-Global Drilling Corp)*
Board of Directors:
James Hayward Coleman
Michael J. Beley
Frederick W. Davidson
Wayne D. Lenton
H. Walter Sellmer
Legal Counsel:
Norton Rose Canada LLP
Suite 3700 400 3 Avenue SW
Calgary, AB, Canada

Boughton Law Corporation
Suite 700 595 Burrard Street
Vancouver, BC, Canada
Transfer Agent:
Computershare Trust Company of Canada
510 Burrard St 2nd Fl
Vancouver, BC, Canada

Non-U.S. Subsidiaries:

E Global Drilling Corp **(1)**
PO Box 11004
Alcester, Warwickshire, B49 6WE, United Kingdom
Tel.: (44) 1926650376
Fax: (44) 1926 650 106
Web Site: www.eglobaldrilling.com
Oil & Gas Wells Drilling Services
S.I.C.: 1381
N.A.I.C.S.: 213111

Energold de Mexico S.A. de C.V. **(1)**
Neiva 949 Lindavista Gustavo A Madero
Mexico, 7300, Mexico
Tel.: (52) 15555862523
Fax: (52) 15555862559
Diamond Mining Services
S.I.C.: 1499
N.A.I.C.S.: 212399

ENERGOMONTAJ S.A.

103-105 Calea Dorobantilor
010561 Bucharest, Romania
Tel.: (40) 213189303
Fax: (40) 213189330
E-Mail: saem@saem.ro
Web Site: www.saem.ro
Year Founded: 1949
Emp.: 5,897
Business Description:
Power Station Installation & Construction Services
S.I.C.: 1629
N.A.I.C.S.: 237990
Personnel:
Florin Kessler *(Chm & Mng Dir)*
Iosif Falup *(Vice Chm & VP)*
Board of Directors:
Florin Kessler
Dumitru Budianu
Iosif Falup
Gheorghe Nicolau
Adrian Popescu
Vasile Radutoiu
Tudorel Sibianu
Manea Simion
Nestor Zidaroiu

Divisions:

Energomontaj S.A. - Electrical, Automation & Telecommunication Installations Division **(1)**
103-105 Calea Dorobantilor
District 1, 010561 Bucharest, Romania
Tel.: (40) 213460238
Fax: (40) 213460261
E-Mail: home@iea-saem.ro
Web Site: www.saem.ro/en
Emp.: 1,300
Telecommunication Installation, Repair & Technical Assistance Services
S.I.C.: 1629
N.A.I.C.S.: 237130
Florin Kessler *(Pres)*

Energomontaj S.A. - FEE **(1)**
103-105 Calea Dorobantilor
District 1, 10561 Bucharest, Romania
Tel.: (40) 21 3469449
E-Mail: saemfeeb@arexim.ro
Web Site: www.saem.ro/en/fabrica.htm
Emp.: 350
Metallic Structures, Protective Coatings, Machine Tools & Equipment Mfr
S.I.C.: 3441
N.A.I.C.S.: 332312

Energomontaj S.A. - Hidro Division **(1)**
103-105 Calea Dorbantilor
District 1, 010561 Bucharest, Romania
Tel.: (40) 213189310
Fax: (40) 213189335
E-Mail: hidro@saem.ro
Emp.: 1,100
Hydro Mechanical & Power Equipment Installer & Mfr
S.I.C.: 3568
N.A.I.C.S.: 333613
Viorel Popoescu *(Mgr-Div)*

Energomontaj S.A. - Thermo Division (1)
103-105 Calea Dorbbantilor Dt 1
010561 Bucharest, Romania
Tel.: (40) 213189300
Fax: (40) 213189302
E-Mail: export@saem.ro
Web Site: www.saem.ro/en/termo.htm
Emp.: 200
Water & Gas Power Plant Engineering Services
S.I.C.: 1629
N.A.I.C.S.: 237990
Iosif Falup *(Division Mgr)*

ENERGOMONTAZ POLNOC SA

(See Under Polimex-Mostostal S.A.)

ENERGOMONTAZA A.D.

Zivojina Zujovica 14
11050 Belgrade, Serbia
Tel.: (381) 11 3814 900
Fax: (381) 11 3809 692
E-Mail: office@energomontaza.com
Web Site: www.energomontaza.com
Year Founded: 1958
EGMN—(BEL)
Emp.: 432

Business Description:
Electric Power Transmission Lines Design & Construction
S.I.C.: 4911
N.A.I.C.S.: 221122

Personnel:
Mladen Zujkovic *(Mng Dir)*
Aleksandar Ristic *(CFO)*
Milenko Babic *(CTO)*

ENERGONI AD

No 115 G Tsarigradsko shose blvd
4-th fl
Mladost Region, 1784 Sofia, Bulgaria
Tel.: (359) 2 48 900 418
Fax: (359) 2 87 87 003
Web Site: www.energoni.com
Year Founded: 2007
2EL—(BUL)

Business Description:
Electric Power Generation
S.I.C.: 4911
N.A.I.C.S.: 221118

Personnel:
Yavor Rusinov *(Dir-IR)*

ENERGOPROJEKT HOLDING A.D.

Bulevar Mihaila Pupina 12
Belgrade, 11070, Serbia
Tel.: (381) 112142108
Fax: (381) 113111979
E-Mail: ep@energoprojekt.rs
Web Site: www.energoprojekt.rs
ENHL—(BEL)
Rev.: $316,240,315
Assets: $327,594,725
Liabilities: $175,042,825
Net Worth: $152,551,899
Earnings: $10,754,359
Emp.: 2,385
Fiscal Year-end: 12/31/12

Business Description:
Civil Engineering Services
S.I.C.: 8711
N.A.I.C.S.: 541330

Personnel:
Ivar Berger *(Chm-Supervisory Bd)*
Vladimir Milovanovic *(CEO)*

Supervisory Board of Directors:
Ivar Berger
Dragan Aleksic
Aleksandar Glisic
Slobodan Jovanovic
Vladimir Sekulic
Jovan Serbanovic
Milun Trivunac

Subsidiaries:

Energoprojekt Energodata a.d. (1)
Bulevar Mihaila Pupina 12
11070 Belgrade, Serbia
Tel.: (381) 113113351
Fax: (381) 113114780
E-Mail: energodata@energodata.rs
Web Site: www.energodata.rs
Emp.: 80
Financial Software Development Services
S.I.C.: 7371
N.A.I.C.S.: 541511
Milos Milinovic *(Mng Dir)*

Energoprojekt Garant a.d.o. (1)
Bulevar Mihaila Pupina 12
11070 Belgrade, Serbia
Tel.: (381) 113101066
Fax: (381) 113112107
Web Site: www.garant.rs
Emp.: 15
General Insurance Services
S.I.C.: 6351
N.A.I.C.S.: 524126
Mirjana Bogicevic *(CEO)*
Violeta Nikolic *(CEO-Fin & Acct)*

Energoprojekt Hidroinzenjering a.d. (1)
Bulevar Mihaila Pupina 12
11070 Belgrade, Serbia
Tel.: (381) 11 311 28 85
Fax: (381) 11 311 19 79
E-Mail: info@ephydro.com
Web Site: www.ephydro.com
Emp.: 211
Engineering Consulting Services
S.I.C.: 8711
N.A.I.C.S.: 541330
Bogdan Uzelac *(Exec Dir-Project Implementation)*

Energoprojekt Niskogradnja Joint Stock Co. (1)
12 Bulevar Mihaila Pupina
11070 Belgrade, Serbia
Tel.: (381) 11 214 64 24
Fax: (381) 11 311 24 93
E-Mail: info@niskogradnja.rs
Web Site: www.niskogradnja.rs
Public Utility Construction & Engineering Services
S.I.C.: 1629
N.A.I.C.S.: 237110
Ljubisav Popovic *(Pres)*
Stojan Colakov *(Mng Dir)*
Dragan Antonijevic *(Sec)*

Energoprojekt Oprema a.d. (1)
Bulevar Mihaila Pupina 12
11070 Belgrade, Serbia
Tel.: (381) 113101600
Fax: (381) 113112660
E-Mail: ep-oprema@ep-oprema.com.rs
Web Site: www.energoprojekt-oprema.com
Emp.: 300
Electrical & Mechanical Engineering Services
S.I.C.: 8711
N.A.I.C.S.: 541330
Mladen Simovic *(Chm)*
Pavle Tomasevic *(Mng Dir)*

EP Industrija a.d. (1)
Bulevar Mihaila Pupina 12
11070 Belgrade, Serbia
Tel.: (381) 11 310 14 01
Fax: (381) 11 311 07 26
E-Mail: office@ep-industry.com
Web Site: www.ep-industry.com
Emp.: 130
Industrial Plants & Facilities Engineering Services
S.I.C.: 1541
N.A.I.C.S.: 236210
Ljubisav Popovic *(Gen Mgr)*

EP Urbanizam i arh. a.d. (1)
Bulevar Mihaila Pupina 12
11070 Belgrade, Serbia
Tel.: (381) 11 311 33 45
Fax: (381) 11 311 53 91
E-Mail: ep-arh@eunet.yu
Web Site: www.eparhitektura.rs
Emp.: 170
Architectural Design Services
S.I.C.: 8712
N.A.I.C.S.: 541310
Svetislav B. Simovic *(Mng Dir)*

Holding:

Energoprojekt - Entel a.d. (1)
Bulevar Mihajla Pupina 12
PO Box 20
11070 Belgrade, Serbia
Tel.: (381) 113101200
Fax: (381) 113101292
E-Mail: office@ep-entel.com
Web Site: www.ep-entel.com
EPEN—(BEL)
Sales Range: $25-49.9 Million
Emp.: 192
Consulting, Engineering, Design & Project Management Services
S.I.C.: 8711
N.A.I.C.S.: 541330
Mladen Simovic *(Mng Dir)*

Non-U.S. Subsidiaries:

302 Enlisa S.A. (1)
Amador Merino Reyna 460 piso 17
San Isidro, Lima, Peru
Tel.: (51) 14429033
Fax: (51) 144299036
Web Site: eng.energoprojekt.rs
Emp.: 32
Construction Engineering Services
S.I.C.: 8711
N.A.I.C.S.: 541330
Goran Doradobeac *(Mgr)*

Encom GmbH (1)
Zeppelinallee 71
60487 Frankfurt am Main, Hesse, Germany
Tel.: (49) 699706050
Fax: (49) 69700123
E-Mail: info@encom-ffm.de
Web Site: www.encom.info
Engineering Consulting Services
S.I.C.: 8711
N.A.I.C.S.: 541330

Energo Consult L.L.C. (1)
Hamadan Street Al Qubaissi Building
PO Box 52473
Abu Dhabi, United Arab Emirates
Tel.: (971) 26763554
Fax: (971) 26763559
E-Mail: energoad@emirates.net.ae
Emp.: 40
Energy Consulting Services
S.I.C.: 8999
N.A.I.C.S.: 541690
Vladimir Milosevic *(Mgr)*

Energo Nigerija Ltd. (1)
Plot 699 Aminu Kano Cresent Wuse II FCT
Abuja, Nigeria
Tel.: (234) 94611362
Fax: (234) 94611364
E-Mail: office.abuja@energonigeria.com
Web Site: www.energonigeria.com
Emp.: 200
Construction Engineering Services
S.I.C.: 8711
N.A.I.C.S.: 541330
A. A. Abubakar *(Chm)*
Dejan Jerotic *(Mng Dir)*
Ademokun Adeyinka *(Sec)*

EP-Holding Guinee S.A. (1)
Rue MA-019 Coleah
BP 251
Matam, Conakry, Guinea
Tel.: (224) 63 403 525
Fax: (224) 30 464 809
Construction Engineering Services
S.I.C.: 8711
N.A.I.C.S.: 541330
Dragi Kraljevski *(Mgr)*

INEC ENGINEERING CO. Ltd. (1)
73 Mornington Street
London, NW1 7QE, United Kingdom
Tel.: (44) 2073832385
Fax: (44) 2073833471
E-Mail: inecenergo@aol.com
Construction Engineering Services
S.I.C.: 8711
N.A.I.C.S.: 541330

ENERGOPROJEKT INDUSTRIJA A.D.

Bulevar Mihajla Pupina 12
11070 Belgrade, Serbia
Tel.: (381) 11 310 14 01
Fax: (381) 11 311 07 26
E-Mail: office@ep-industry.com
Web Site: www.ep-industry.com
EPIN—(BEL)

Business Description:
Engineering Services
S.I.C.: 8711
N.A.I.C.S.: 541330

Personnel:
Ljubisav Popovic *(Gen Mgr)*

ENERGOREMONT HOLDING JSC

No 14 Kozloduy Str
1202 Sofia, Bulgaria
Tel.: (359) 2 8133577
Fax: (359) 2 8133506
E-Mail: info@erhold.bg
Web Site: www.erhold.bg
6EG—(BUL)
Sales Range: $10-24.9 Million

Business Description:
Engineering Services
S.I.C.: 8711
N.A.I.C.S.: 541330

Personnel:
Valentin Dimitrov *(Chm-Supervisory Bd)*
Ivan Lichev *(Chm-Mgmt Bd)*
Nikolai Raichev *(Deputy Chm-Supervisory Bd)*
Hristo Dimitrov *(Deputy Chm-Mgmt Bd)*
Teodor Rosenov Osikovski *(Member-Mgmt Bd)*

Supervisory Board of Directors:
Valentin Dimitrov
Alipi Alipiev
Nikolai Raichev

Subsidiary:

Energoremont Bobov Dol AD (1)
2635 Golemo selo
Kyustendil, Bulgaria
Tel.: (359) 701 501 01
Fax: (359) 701 501 48
E-Mail: er.bd@abv.bg
Web Site: www.erhold.bg
6EB—(BUL)
Electric Machinery Repair Services
S.I.C.: 7539
N.A.I.C.S.: 811118
Snejana Lazarova Bojilova *(Dir-IR)*

ENERGULF RESOURCES INC.

4005 - 1011 West Cordova Street
Vancouver, BC, V6C 0B2, Canada
Tel.: (604) 408-1990
Fax: (604) 608-4822
E-Mail: info@energulf.com
Web Site: www.energulf.com
ENG—(TSXV)
Rev.: $42,908
Assets: $22,849,661
Liabilities: $929,269
Net Worth: $21,920,392
Earnings: ($1,396,561)
Fiscal Year-end: 02/28/13

Business Description:
Oil & Gas Exploration Services
S.I.C.: 1389
N.A.I.C.S.: 213112

Personnel:
Jeff Greenblum *(Chm, Pres & CEO)*
Albert Ongendangenda *(Dir Gen-EnerGulf Congo SARL)*
Jonathan Chu *(CFO)*

Board of Directors:
Jeff Greenblum
Anu Dhir
Peter Gianulis

Transfer Agent:
Computershare Investor Services Inc.
100 University Ave 9th Floor
Toronto, ON, Canada

ENERGY ABSOLUTE PUBLIC COMPANY LIMITED

888 I- Tower Building 9th Floor Zone D Vibhavadi Rangsit Rd
Bangkok, 10900, Thailand
Tel.: (66) 25549238
Fax: (66) 25549243
Web Site: www.energyabsolute.co.th
EA—(THA)
Business Description:
Biodiesel Production
S.I.C.: 2999
N.A.I.C.S.: 324199
Personnel:
Somchainuek Engtrakun *(Chm)*
Board of Directors:
Michael Young
David Cornell
Julian Tapp

ENERGY ACTION LIMITED

Level 5 56 Station St
Parramatta, NSW, 2150, Australia
Tel.: (61) 2 9633 6400
Fax: (61) 2 9475 0954
Web Site: www.energyaction.com.au
Year Founded: 2000
EAX—(ASX)
Rev.: $23,098,911
Assets: $19,920,592
Liabilities: $6,109,691
Net Worth: $13,810,901
Earnings: $4,560,291
Emp.: 9
Fiscal Year-end: 06/30/13
Business Description:
Energy Procurement & Management Services
S.I.C.: 1389
N.A.I.C.S.: 213112
Personnel:
Scott Wooldridge *(CEO)*
Nathan Francis *(CFO, Sec & Exec Dir-Fin)*
Board of Directors:
Ronald Watts
Murray Bleach
Paul Meehan
Steve Twaddell
Legal Counsel:
Greenwich Legal
Level 11 50 Margaret Street
Sydney, Australia
Subsidiary:
Energy Action (Australia) Pty Limited **(1)**
Level 5 56 Station St
Parramatta, NSW, 2150, Australia
Tel.: (61) 298916911
Fax: (61) 294750954
Emp.: 40
Electric Power Generation Services
S.I.C.: 4911
N.A.I.C.S.: 221118
Kroy Davids *(Gen Mgr)*

ENERGY & MINERALS AUSTRALIA LIMITED

Ground Floor 25 Richardson Street
West Perth, WA, 6005, Australia
Tel.: (61) 893892700
Fax: (61) 893892722
E-Mail: admin@eama.com.au
Web Site: www.eama.com.au
EMA—(ASX)
Rev.: $71,357
Assets: $2,680,950
Liabilities: $19,548,813
Net Worth: ($16,867,863)
Earnings: ($15,983,697)
Emp.: 15
Fiscal Year-end: 06/30/13
Business Description:
Uranium Exploration
S.I.C.: 1094
N.A.I.C.S.: 212291
Personnel:
Julian Tapp *(CEO)*
Shane McBride *(CFO & Sec)*

ENERGY DEVELOPMENT CORPORATION

38/F One Corporate Centre Julia Vargas corner Meralco Ave Ortigas Ctr
Pasig, 1605, Philippines
Tel.: (63) 26677332
E-Mail: pubrels@energy.com.ph
Web Site: www.energy.com.ph
EDC—(OTC PHI)
Rev.: $694,745,840
Assets: $2,309,487,502
Liabilities: $1,441,712,396
Net Worth: $867,775,106
Earnings: $254,101,062
Emp.: 2,478
Fiscal Year-end: 12/31/12
Business Description:
Power Generation Services
S.I.C.: 4939
N.A.I.C.S.: 221111
Personnel:
Federico R. Lopez *(Chm & CEO)*
Richard B. Tantoco *(Pres & COO)*
Nestor H. Vasay *(CFO, Treas & Sr VP)*
Ferdinand B. Poblete *(CIO & VP-Info Svcs)*
Agnes C. de Jesus *(Compliance Officer & Sr VP-Environment & External Rels)*
Erudito S. Recio *(IR & Corp Info Officer)*
Teodorico Jose R. Delfin *(Sec)*
Ernesto B. Pantangco *(Exec VP)*
Dominic M. Camu *(Sr VP-Power Generation)*
Danilo C. Catigtig *(Sr VP-Strategic Initiatives Office)*
Manuel S. Ogena *(Sr VP-Technical Svcs)*
Marcelino M. Tongco *(Sr VP-Strategic Contracting)*
Board of Directors:
Federico R. Lopez
Edgar O. Chua
Peter D. Garrucho Jr.
Elpidio L. Ibanez
Francisco Ed. Lim
Ernesto B. Pantangco
Francis Giles B. Puno
Jonathan C. Russell
Richard B. Tantoco
Arturo T. Valdez

ENERGY EARTH PUBLIC COMPANY LIMITED

889 Thai CC Tower 125-128 F12
South Sathorn Road
Bangkok, 10120, Thailand
Tel.: (66) 2 673 9631 3
Fax: (66) 2 673 9634
Web Site: www.energyearth.co.th
1EE—(DEU)
Sls.: $344,760,032
Assets: $291,981,919
Liabilities: $190,066,085
Net Worth: $101,915,834
Earnings: $42,421,037
Fiscal Year-end: 12/31/12
Business Description:
Bituminous Coal Whslr
S.I.C.: 5052
N.A.I.C.S.: 423520
Personnel:
Phisudhi Phihakendr *(Chm)*
Parada Bunnag *(Vice Chm)*
Paiboon Assawasiriwong *(Asst Mng Dir)*
Board of Directors:
Phisudhi Phihakendr
Suriyaporn Bunchai
Parada Bunnag
Kanchana Chakvichitsopon
Khajohnpong Khamdee
Phiboon Phihakendr
Phipat Phihakendr
Phiroon Phihakendr
Thanawat Pratoomsuwan
Nugoon Sri-in
Somkiat Sukdheva
Eknarin Thammaraks
Thongchai Watanasoponwong

ENERGY FUELS INC.

2 Toronto Street Suite 500
Toronto, ON, M5C 2B6, Canada
Tel.: (303) 974-2140
Fax: (303) 974-2141
Toll Free: (888) 864-2125
E-Mail: investorinfo@energyfuels.com
Web Site: www.energyfuels.com
UUUU—(NYSEMKT TSX)
Rev.: $25,027,610
Assets: $239,808,070
Liabilities: $55,710,399
Net Worth: $184,097,671
Earnings: $16,973,227
Emp.: 255
Fiscal Year-end: 09/30/12
Business Description:
Uranium & Vanadium Mining Services
S.I.C.: 1094
N.A.I.C.S.: 212291
Personnel:
J. Birks Bovaird *(Chm)*
Stephen P. Antony *(Pres & CEO)*
Daniel G. Zang *(Interim CFO)*
Harold R. Roberts *(COO & Exec VP)*
David C. Frydenlund *(Gen Counsel, Sec & Sr VP-Regulatory Affairs)*
Gary R. Steele *(Sr VP-Corp Mktg)*
Board of Directors:
J. Birks Bovaird
Stephen P. Antony
Paul A. Carroll
W. Robert Dengler
Lawrence A. Goldberg
Mark E. Goodman
Bruce D. Hansen
Ronald F. Hochstein
Sheldon Inwentash
Richard J. Patricio
Transfer Agent:
Canadian Stock Transfer Company Inc
Toronto, ON, Canada

ENERGY INFORMATION CENTRE LTD

(Acquired by Utilitywise plc)

ENERGY INTERNATIONAL INVESTMENTS HOLDINGS LIMITED

Unit 1508 15th Floor The Center 99 Queen's Road Central
Hong Kong, China (Hong Kong)
Tel.: (852) 2169 3104
Fax: (852) 2169 3300
E-Mail: info@energyintl.com.hk
Web Site: energyintl.todayir.com
353—(HKG)
Rev.: $39,604,542
Assets: $350,412,212
Liabilities: $96,885,680
Net Worth: $253,526,532
Earnings: ($43,021,460)
Emp.: 445
Fiscal Year-end: 12/31/12
Business Description:
Investment Management Services
S.I.C.: 6799
N.A.I.C.S.: 523920
Personnel:
Joe Siu Keung Wong *(Sec)*
Board of Directors:
Kwok Wing Chan
Wai Cheung Chan
Chi Fai Choi
Nianru Luo
Donghai Wang
Jinghua Wang
Meiyan Wang
Guangming Yang
Legal Counsel:
Hui & Lam Solicitors
Rooms 1505-6 The Center 99 Queen's Road Central, China (Hong Kong)
Conyers Dill & Pearman
2901 One Exchange Square 8 Connaught Place
Central, China (Hong Kong)
HSBC Trustee (Cayman) Limited
HSBC House 68 West Bay Road
PO Box 484
Georgetown, Cayman Islands
Transfer Agents:
Tricor Tengis Limited
26/F Tesbury Centre, 28 Queens Road East
Hong Kong, China (Hong Kong)
HSBC Trustee (Cayman) Limited
HSBC House 68 West Bay Road
PO Box 484
Georgetown, Cayman Islands

ENERGY METALS LIMITED

Ground Floor 10 Kings Park Road
West Perth, WA, 6005, Australia
Tel.: (61) 893226904
Fax: (61) 893215240
E-Mail: enquiry@energymetals.net
Web Site: www.energymetals.net
EME—(ASX)
Rev.: $9,866,904
Assets: $50,855,895
Liabilities: $2,124,069
Net Worth: $48,731,827
Earnings: $87,801
Fiscal Year-end: 12/31/12
Business Description:
Uranium Exploration
S.I.C.: 1094
N.A.I.C.S.: 212291
Personnel:
Weidong Xiang *(Mng Dir)*
Bin Cui *(CFO & Controller-Fin)*
Xuekun Li *(Sec)*
Board of Directors:
Zuyuan He
Lindsay George Dudfield
Yunfei Jin
Geoffrey Michael Jones
Xinjian Peng
Weidong Xiang
Yu Zhong
Legal Counsel:
Minter Ellison
Allendale Square 77 St Georges Terrace
Perth, WA, 6000, Australia

ENERGY ONE LIMITED

Level 14 71 Macquarie St
Sydney, NSW, 2000, Australia
Mailing Address:
GPO Box 3968
Sydney, NSW, 2001, Australia
Tel.: (61) 2 8252 9898
Fax: (61) 2 8252 9888
E-Mail: enquiries@energyone.com.au
Web Site: www.energyone.com.au
EOL—(ASX)
Rev.: $1,921,628
Assets: $4,860,617
Liabilities: $1,282,280
Net Worth: $3,578,337
Earnings: ($219,611)
Fiscal Year-end: 06/30/13
Business Description:
Software Development Services

S.I.C.: 7371
N.A.I.C.S.: 541511
Personnel:
Shaun Ankers *(CEO & Mng Dir)*
Reena Minhas *(CFO & Sec)*
Board of Directors:
Ottmar Weiss
Shaun Ankers
Andrew Bonwick
Vaughan Busby
Ian Douglas Ferrier
Legal Counsel:
Johnson Winter & Slattery
Level 25 20 Bond Street
Sydney, NSW, 2000, Australia

ENERGY POWER SYSTEMS AUSTRALIA PTY. LTD.

47 51 Westpool Dr
Hallam, VIC, 3803, Australia
Tel.: (61) 397034000
Fax: (61) 397034004
E-Mail: epsa@energypower.com.au
Web Site: www.energypower.com.au
Year Founded: 1992
Sales Range: $500-549.9 Million
Emp.: 120
Business Description:
Medium-Speed Engine & High-Speed Diesel Engine Supplier
S.I.C.: 5013
N.A.I.C.S.: 423120
Personnel:
Phil Canning *(Mng Dir)*
Haydn Vella *(CFO)*

Subsidiary:

Energy Power Systems PNG Limited (1)
Spring Garden Road
Port Moresby, Hohola, Papua New Guinea
Tel.: (675) 3008358
Fax: (675) 3235324
Web Site: www.energysystems.com.au
Emp.: 50
S.I.C.: 3531
N.A.I.C.S.: 333120
Stuart Honey *(Country Mgr)*

ENERGY SOURCE NATURAL GAS SERVICES INC.

102 75 Farquhar St
Guelph, ON, Canada N1H 3N4
Tel.: (519) 826-0777
Fax: (519) 837-0006
Toll Free: (866) 218-8694
Web Site: www.energysource.ca
Rev.: $80,032,798
Emp.: 11
Business Description:
Natural Gas Distr
S.I.C.: 4924
N.A.I.C.S.: 221210
Personnel:
Dave Cornies *(Pres)*

ENERGY TECHNIQUE PLC

47 Central Avenue
West Molesey, Surrey, KT8 2QZ, United Kingdom
Tel.: (44) 2087830033
Fax: (44) 2087830140
E-Mail: diffusion@etenv.co.uk
Web Site: www.energytechniqueplc.co.uk
ETQ—(LSE)
Rev.: $11,923,640
Assets: $5,454,868
Liabilities: $3,036,975
Net Worth: $2,417,893
Earnings: $254,266
Emp.: 69
Fiscal Year-end: 03/31/13
Business Description:
Air Conditioning & Heating Solutions Distr
S.I.C.: 3564
N.A.I.C.S.: 333413
Personnel:
R. M. Unsworth *(Sec)*
Board of Directors:
Walter K. Goldsmith
Martin M. Reid
Leigh A. Stimpson
Legal Counsel:
Sherrards Solicitors LLP
7 Swallow Place
London, United Kingdom

ENERGY TECHNOLOGIES LIMITED

Unit 2 35-41 Waterloo Road
North Ryde, NSW, 2113, Australia
Tel.: (61) 298707277
Fax: (61) 298707299
Web Site: www.dulhuntypower.com
EGY—(ASX)
Sales Range: $10-24.9 Million
Emp.: 167
Business Description:
Energy Infrastructure Products Mfr
S.I.C.: 8711
N.A.I.C.S.: 541330
Personnel:
Anthony J. Wingrove *(Mng Dir)*
Gregory R. Knoke *(CFO & Sec)*
Board of Directors:
Alfred J. Chown
Michael D. Butcherine
Philip W. Dulhunty
Richard K. Llewellyn
Martin H. Thomas
Anthony J. Wingrove

Subsidiary:

Dulhunty Power (Aust) Pty Limited (1)
Unit 2 35 Waterloo Rd
North Ryde, New South Wales, 2113, Australia
Tel.: (61) 298707277
Fax: (61) 298707299
E-Mail: jessica.elms@dulhuntypower.com
Web Site: www.dulhuntypower.com
Emp.: 26
Electricity Transmission & Distribution Products Mfr
S.I.C.: 3641
N.A.I.C.S.: 335110
Jack Roughan *(CEO)*

Non-U.S. Subsidiary:

Dulhunty Power (NZ) Limited (2)
PO Box 281
Whangaparaoa, 0943 Auckland, New Zealand
Tel.: (64) 94247295
Fax: (64) 94280577
E-Mail: brian@dulhunty.com
Web Site: www.dulhuntypower.com
Emp.: 1
Transmission & Disribution Equipment Mfr
S.I.C.: 3612
N.A.I.C.S.: 335311
Richard Buisson *(Gen Mgr)*

Non-U.S. Subsidiary:

Dulhunty Power (Thailand) Limited (1)
3 2 Moo 7 Suwintawong Rd
Klongluangpang, Chachoengsao, 24000, Thailand
Tel.: (66) 38845675
Fax: (66) 38845674
E-Mail: pana@dulhunty.co.th
Web Site: www.dulhuntypower.com
Emp.: 30
Electricity Transmission & Distribution Products Mfr
S.I.C.: 3641
N.A.I.C.S.: 335110
Pana Pong Pairoj *(Gen Mgr)*

ENERGY VENTURES LIMITED

Level 1 8 Colin Street
West Perth, WA, 6005, Australia
Mailing Address:
PO Box 886
West Perth, WA, 6872, Australia
Tel.: (61) 864655500
Fax: (61) 864655599
E-Mail: info@energyventures.com.au
Web Site: www.energyventures.com.au
EVE—(ASX)
Rev.: $6,227
Assets: $7,535,979
Liabilities: $72,306
Net Worth: $7,463,673
Earnings: ($15,914,633)
Fiscal Year-end: 06/30/13
Business Description:
Uranium Exploration
S.I.C.: 1094
N.A.I.C.S.: 212291
Personnel:
Alasdair Cooke *(Chm)*
Steven Jackson *(Sec)*
Board of Directors:
Alasdair Cooke
Michael Curnow
Gregory Fry
Legal Counsel:
Fairweather Corporate Lawyers
595 Stirling Highway
Cottesloe, Australia

ENERGY WORLD CORPORATION LTD

Suite 08 34th Floor Sun Hung Kai Centre 30 Harbour Road
Hong Kong, China (Hong Kong)
Tel.: (852) 2528 0082
Fax: (852) 2528 0966
Web Site: www.energyworldcorp.com
Year Founded: 1985
EWW—(DEU)
Rev.: $132,904,000
Assets: $1,139,947,000
Liabilities: $557,597,000
Net Worth: $582,350,000
Earnings: $16,716,000
Fiscal Year-end: 06/30/13
Business Description:
Oil & Gas Exploration Services
S.I.C.: 1311
N.A.I.C.S.: 211111
Personnel:
Stewart W. G. Elliott *(Chm, CEO & Mng Dir)*
Ian W. Jordan *(Sec)*
Board of Directors:
Stewart W. G. Elliott
Brian J. Allen
Leslie J. Charles
James D. Dewar
Ian W. Jordan
Brian D. Littlechild
Bruce Macfarlane
Michael P. O'Neill
K. S. Virk
Legal Counsel:
Hogan Lovells
11/F One Pacific Place 88 Queensway
Hong Kong, China (Hong Kong)
Corrs Chambers Westgarth
Governor Philip Tower 1 Farrer Place
Sydney, NSW, 2000, Australia

ENERGY XXI (BERMUDA) LIMITED

Canon's Court 22 Victoria Street
PO Box HM 1179
Hamilton, HM EX, Bermuda
Tel.: (441) 295 2244
Web Site: www.energyxxi.com
Year Founded: 2005
EXXI—(AIM NASDAQ)
Rev.: $1,208,845,000
Assets: $3,611,711,000
Liabilities: $2,174,465,000
Net Worth: $1,437,246,000
Earnings: $162,081,000
Emp.: 271
Fiscal Year-end: 06/30/13
Business Description:
Oil & Gas Exploration Services
S.I.C.: 1389
N.A.I.C.S.: 213112
Personnel:
John D. Schiller, Jr. *(Chm & CEO)*
David West Griffin *(CFO)*
Hugh A. Menown *(CIO, Chief Acctg Officer & VP)*
Ben Marchive *(Exec VP-Exploration & Production)*
Antonio De Pinho *(Sr VP-M&A, Joint Ventures & Tech)*
Todd Reid *(Sr VP-Mktg & Risk Mgmt)*
Board of Directors:
John D. Schiller, Jr.
William Colvin
Paul Davison
David Mooris Dunwoody
Cornelius Dupre, II
Hill Arnold Feinberg
Kevin Sean Flannery

U.S. Subsidiaries:

Energy XXI GOM, LLC (1)
1021 Main St Ste 2626
Houston, TX 77002
Tel.: (713) 351-3000
Fax: (713) 351-3300
Oil & Gas Exploration Services
S.I.C.: 1389
N.A.I.C.S.: 213112

Energy XXI, Inc. (1)
1021 Main Ste 2626
Houston, TX 77002
Tel.: (713) 351-3000
Fax: (713) 351-3300
Oil & Natural Gas Exploration Services
S.I.C.: 1311
N.A.I.C.S.: 211111

Energy XXI Onshore, LLC (1)
1021 Main St Ste 2626
Houston, TX 77002
Tel.: (713) 351-3000
Emp.: 100
Oil & Gas Exploration Services
S.I.C.: 1389
N.A.I.C.S.: 213112

Energy XXI Services, LLC (1)
1021 Main St No 2626
Houston, TX 77002-6516
Tel.: (713) 351-3000
Oil & Gas Exploration Services
S.I.C.: 1389
N.A.I.C.S.: 213112
Ben Marchive *(CEO)*

Energy XXI Texas Onshore, LLC (1)
1021 Main St Ste 2626
Houston, TX 77002
Tel.: (713) 351-3000
Emp.: 300
Oil & Gas Exploration Services
S.I.C.: 1389
N.A.I.C.S.: 213112

Energy XXI USA, Inc (1)
Co Ste 2626 1021 Main
Houston, TX 77002 DE
Tel.: (713) 351-3000
Fax: (713) 351-3300
Web Site: www.energyxxi.com
Oil & Gas Exploration Services
S.I.C.: 3533
N.A.I.C.S.: 333132
Ben Marchive *(Exec VP-Exploration & Production)*

Non-U.S. Subsidiary:

Energy XXI Gulf Coast, Inc (2)
Canon's Court 22 Victoria Street
Hamilton, HM 12, Bermuda
Tel.: (441) 295 2244
Oil & Gas Exploration Services
S.I.C.: 1389
N.A.I.C.S.: 213112

ENERJI LIMITED
Ground Floor 10 Ord Street
West Perth, WA, 6005, Australia
Mailing Address:
PO Box 1933
West Perth, WA, 6872, Australia
Tel.: (61) 8 9268 3800
Web Site: www.enerji.com.au
ERJ—(ASX OTC)
Rev.: $27,429
Assets: $12,286,835
Liabilities: $4,580,982
Net Worth: $7,705,853
Earnings: ($7,624,830)
Fiscal Year-end: 12/31/12
Business Description:
Electric Power Generation
S.I.C.: 4939
N.A.I.C.S.: 221118
Personnel:
Colin Stonehouse *(Inteirm Chm, CEO & Mng Dir)*
Gregory Douglas Pennefather *(CEO)*
Board of Directors:
Colin Stonehouse
Justin Audcent
Rolf Hasselstrom
Gregory Douglas Pennefather
Legal Counsel:
Steinepreis Paganin
Level 4 16 Milligan Street
Perth, WA, 6000, Australia

ENERKEM INC.
1010 Sherbrooke Street West Suite 1610
Montreal, QC, H3A 2R7, Canada
Tel.: (514) 875-0284
Fax: (514) 875-0835
E-Mail: enerkem@enerkem.com
Web Site: www.enerkem.com
Sales Range: $1-9.9 Million
Emp.: 136
Business Description:
Chemical Mfr
S.I.C.: 2899
N.A.I.C.S.: 325998
Personnel:
Joshua Ruch *(Chm)*
Vincent Chornet *(Pres & CEO)*
Patrice Ouimet *(CFO & Sr VP)*
Jocelyn Auger *(Gen Counsel & VP-Legal)*
Dirk Andreas *(Sr VP-Bus Dev)*
Board of Directors:
Joshua Ruch
Bruce Aitken
Anton de Vries
Larry A. MacDonald
Carl Rush
Neil S. Suslak

ENERO GROUP LIMITED
Level 3 1 Buckingham Street
Surry Hills, NSW, 2010, Australia
Tel.: (61) 2 8213 3031
Fax: (61) 2 8213 3030
E-Mail: info@enero.com
Web Site: www.enero.com
Year Founded: 2000
EGG—(ASX)
Rev.: $258,409,537
Assets: $149,858,148
Liabilities: $46,546,439
Net Worth: $103,311,710
Earnings: ($85,633,525)
Emp.: 700
Fiscal Year-end: 06/30/13
Business Description:
Advertising Services
S.I.C.: 7311
N.A.I.C.S.: 541810
Personnel:
Matthew Melhuish *(CEO)*
Eleni North *(Gen Counsel & Sec)*
Board of Directors:
John C. Porter
Roger Amos
Max Johnston
Susan McIntosh
Matthew Melhuish
Legal Counsel:
Gilbert & Tobin
Two Park Street
Sydney, NSW, 2000, Australia
Subsidiaries:

Ausrep Pty Ltd (1)
11B Clarice Road
Box Hill South, Melbourne, VIC, 3128, Australia
Tel.: (61) 3 9876 8822
Fax: (61) 3 9897 1750
E-Mail: ausrep@ausrep.com.au
Web Site: www.ausrep.com.au
Emp.: 100
Hardware Retailer
S.I.C.: 5251
N.A.I.C.S.: 444130
Tony Fantasia *(Mng Dir)*

BMF Advertising Pty Limited (1)
Level 2 63 Miller Street
Pyrmont, NSW, 2009, Australia
Tel.: (61) 2 9552 7000
Fax: (61) 2 9552 7060
E-Mail: agency@bmf.com.au
Web Site: www.bmf.com.au
Emp.: 200
Advertising Agency Services
S.I.C.: 7311
N.A.I.C.S.: 541810
Warren Brown *(Founder-Creative)*
Matthew Melhuish *(Chm)*
Chris Kay *(Mng Partner)*
Martin Rippon *(Mng Dir)*

BMF (1)
Level 2 63 Miller St
Pyrmont, NSW, 2009, Australia
Tel.: (61) 2 9552 7000
Fax: (61) 2 95557060
E-Mail: agency@bmf.com.au
Web Site: www.bmf.com.au
Sales Range: $75-99.9 Million
Emp.: 230
S.I.C.: 7311
N.A.I.C.S.: 541810
Warren Brown *(Founder & Exec Dir-Creative)*
Matthew Melhuish *(Chm)*
Dominic Stinton *(CEO)*
Stephen McArdle *(Mng Partner)*
Ricci Meldrum *(Mng Partner)*
Simon Halfhide *(COO)*

City Public Relations Pty Limited (1)
Level 6 155 George Street
Sydney, NSW, 2000, Australia
Tel.: (61) 2 8916 4848
Fax: (61) 2 9251 1825
Web Site: www.citypublicrelations.com.au
Public Relations Services
S.I.C.: 8743
N.A.I.C.S.: 541820
Tim Allerton *(Mng Dir)*

CPR Communications and Public Relations Pty Limited (1)
Level 2 70 Pirie St
Adelaide, SA, 5006, Australia
Tel.: (61) 884187500
Fax: (61) 884187599
E-Mail: cpr@cprcomm.com.au
Web Site: www.cprcomm.com.au
Public Relations Services
S.I.C.: 8743
N.A.I.C.S.: 541820
Jayne Dullard *(Mng Dir-Melbourne)*

Dark Blue Sea Limited (1)
Level 10 243 Edward St
4000 Brisbane, QLD, Australia AU
Mailing Address:
GPO Box 278
QLD C3 4001 Brisbane, Australia
Tel.: (61) 730070000
Fax: (61) 730070001
E-Mail: privacy@darkbluesea.com
Web Site: www.darkbluesea.com
Sales Range: $10-24.9 Million
Online Direct Navigation Supplier
Export
S.I.C.: 7319
N.A.I.C.S.: 541890
Lee Taylor *(Sec)*

Subsidiaries:

Darkblue.com Pty Limited (2)
Level 1 91 Bridge St
Fortitude Valley, QLD, 4006, Australia
Tel.: (61) 7 3007 0070
Fax: (61) 7 3007 0075
E-Mail: enquires@darkbluesea.com
Web Site: www.darkbluesea.com
Emp.: 4
Online Marketing Services
S.I.C.: 8742
N.A.I.C.S.: 541613
Peter Stevenson *(Mgr-Ops)*

DBS Administration Pty Limited (2)
Level 1 91 Birch Street
PO Box 278
Brisbane, QLD, 4006, Australia
Tel.: (61) 730070000
Fax: (61) 3007 0001
E-Mail: enquires@au.darkbluesea.com
Web Site: www.darkbluesea.com
Emp.: 4
Online Marketing Services
S.I.C.: 8742
N.A.I.C.S.: 541613
Peter Stevenson *(Mgr-Ops)*

Domain Active Pty Limited (2)
Level 10 243 Edward St
PO Box 262
Clayfield, Brisbane, QLD, 4000, Australia
Tel.: (61) 730185100
Fax: (61) 730185101
Emp.: 4
Online Marketing Services
S.I.C.: 8742
N.A.I.C.S.: 541613

Fabulous.com Pty Limited (2)
Level 10 243 Edward St
Brisbane, Queensland, Australia
Tel.: (61) 7 3007 0070
Fax: (61) 7 3007 0075
E-Mail: support@fabulous.com
Web Site: www.fabulous.com
Emp.: 25
Online Marketing Services
S.I.C.: 8742
N.A.I.C.S.: 541613

Roar.com Pty Limited (2)
Level 10
243 Edward St, Brisbane, Queensland, 4000, Australia
Tel.: (61) 7 3007 0070
Fax: (61) 7 3007 0075
E-Mail: customercare@roar.com
Web Site: www.roar.com
Emp.: 25
Online Marketing Services
S.I.C.: 8742
N.A.I.C.S.: 541613

Whois Privacy Services Pty Limited (2)
PO Box 1717
Brisbane, Queensland, Australia
Tel.: (61) 730070090
Fax: (61) 730070091
Web Site: www.whoisprivacyservices.com.au
Domain Privacy Services
S.I.C.: 7374
N.A.I.C.S.: 518210
Sandra Meurer *(Head-Editorial Svc)*

Frank PR Australia Pty Limited (1)
Flr 6 2-12 Foveaux St
Surry Hills, Sydney, NSW, 2010, Australia
Tel.: (61) 2 8202 0555
E-Mail: info@frankpr.com.au
Web Site: www.frankpr.com.au
Emp.: 20
Public Relations Consulting Services
S.I.C.: 8743
N.A.I.C.S.: 541820
Graham Goodkind *(Founder & Chm)*

ImageBox Group Pty Limited (1)
135-141 York St
South Melbourne, Melbourne, VIC, 3205, Australia
Tel.: (61) 3 96969022
Fax: (61) 3 96969322
E-Mail: sales@imagebox.com.au
Web Site: www.imagebox.com.au
Emp.: 22
Graphic Design Services
S.I.C.: 7336
N.A.I.C.S.: 541430
David Asker *(Gen Mgr)*

ISS Marketing Pty Limited (1)
Suite 102 490 Crown Street
Surry Hills, NSW, 2010, Australia
Tel.: (61) 2 9018 8730
E-Mail: info@issmarketing.com.au
Web Site: www.issmarketing.com.au
Emp.: 5
Marketing Consulting Services
S.I.C.: 8742
N.A.I.C.S.: 541613
Michael Blumberg *(Mng Dir)*

The Leading Edge Market Research Consultants Pty Limited (1)
Level 6 76 Commonwealth Street
Millers Point, Sydney, NSW, 2010, Australia
Tel.: (61) 2 9258 4444
Fax: (61) 2 9258 4455
E-Mail: solutions@theleadingedge.com
Web Site: www.theleadingedge.com.au
Emp.: 4
Marketing Research Services
S.I.C.: 8732
N.A.I.C.S.: 541910
Tim Riches *(Mng Dir)*
Clive Yoxall *(Mng Dir)*

Love Pty Limited (1)
L 8 155 George St
Sydney, NSW, 2000, Australia
Tel.: (61) 289164800
Fax: (61) 292522040
Advertising Agency Services
S.I.C.: 7311
N.A.I.C.S.: 541810

Naked Communications Australia Pty Limited (1)
Level 5 / 2-12 Foveaux St
Surry Hills, NSW, 2010, Australia
Tel.: (61) 2 9213 3400
E-Mail: hello@nakedcomms.com.au
Web Site: www.nakedcommunications.com.au
Marketing Consulting Services
S.I.C.: 8742
N.A.I.C.S.: 541613
Carl Ratcliff *(CEO)*
Joe Lugo *(Grp COO)*
Paul Ward *(Grp Chief Production Officer-Sydney)*

Non-U.S. Subsidiary:

Naked NZ Limited (2)
150 Karangahape Rd Suite 602
Auckland, 1010, New Zealand
Tel.: (64) 9 307 3860
Emp.: 10
Business Consulting Services
S.I.C.: 8748
N.A.I.C.S.: 541618
Matt Osullivan *(Gen Mgr)*

Photon Group (US) Pty Limited (1)
L 6 155 George St
Sydney, NSW, 2000, Australia
Tel.: (61) 282133031
Fax: (61) 282133030
Emp.: 20
Marketing Consulting Services
S.I.C.: 8742
N.A.I.C.S.: 541613
Matthew Melhuish *(CEO)*

Precinct (1)
6 Bond St
Yarra, VIC 3141, Australia
Tel.: (61) 3 9856 2977
Fax: (61) 3 9856 2979
E-Mail: sean@precinct.com.au
Web Site: www.precinct.com.au
S.I.C.: 7311
N.A.I.C.S.: 541810
Craig Lindsay *(Pres)*
Sean Langdon *(CEO)*
Bob Withers *(CIO)*

U.S. Subsidiaries:

Findology Interactive Media (1)
1158 26th St Ste 464
Santa Monica, CA 90403

Tel.: (310) 556-4440
Fax: (310) 556-4441
Toll Free: (888) 632-8640
E-Mail: info@findology.com
Web Site: www.findology.com
Emp.: 20
S.I.C.: 7319
N.A.I.C.S.: 541890
George Coo *(Mgr-Mktg)*

OB Media LLC (1)
5718 Westheimer Ste 1240
Houston, TX 77057
Tel.: (713) 850-0607
E-Mail: compliance@obmedia.com
Web Site: www.obmedia.com
Online Advertising Services
S.I.C.: 8742
N.A.I.C.S.: 541613

Non-U.S. Subsidiaries:

The Bailey Group UK Limited (1)
Photon House Old Bracknell Lane West
Bracknell, Berkshire, RG12 7FS, United Kingdom
Tel.: (44) 1344 418 570
Fax: (44) 1344 418 571
Web Site: www.thebaileygroupuk.com
Marketing Agency & Research Services
S.I.C.: 8732
N.A.I.C.S.: 541910
Julia Collis *(Mng Dir)*

DVL Smith Limited (1)
Suite 3 Jamaica Wharf 2 Shad Thames
London, SE1 2YU, United Kingdom
Tel.: (44) 203 397 2550
E-Mail: info@dvlsmith.com
Web Site: www.dvlsmith.com
Marketing Consulting Services
S.I.C.: 8742
N.A.I.C.S.: 541613

Frank PR Limited (1)
Centro 4 20-23 Mandela St
London, NW1 0DU, United Kingdom
Tel.: (44) 207 693 6999
Fax: (44) 207 693 6998
E-Mail: contactus@frankpr.it
Web Site: www.frankpr.it
Emp.: 70
Public Relations Agency Services
S.I.C.: 8743
N.A.I.C.S.: 541820
Graham Goodkind *(Gen Mgr)*

Hotwire Public Relations GmbH (1)
Friedensstr 6-10
60311 Frankfurt, Germany
Tel.: (49) 69 25 66 93 70
Fax: (49) 69 25 66 93 93
Web Site: www.hotwirepr.de
Public Relation Consulting Services
S.I.C.: 8743
N.A.I.C.S.: 541820
Manuela Moore *(Mng Dir)*
Isabel Fox *(CEO-US)*

Non-U.S. Subsidiaries:

33 Digital Limited (2)
Scriptor Court 155-157 Farringdon Road
London, EC1R 3AD, United Kingdom
Tel.: (44) 20 7000 4000
Fax: (44) 20 7608 2600
E-Mail: mscommunity@33-digital.com
Web Site: www.33-digital.com
Emp.: 10
Digital Public Relation & Marketing Agency Services
S.I.C.: 8743
N.A.I.C.S.: 541820
Drew Benvie *(Mng Dir)*

Hotwire Public Relation Italy S.R.L. (2)
Via Conservatorio 22
20122 Milan, Italy
Tel.: (39) 02 77 29 968
Fax: (39) 02 77 29 40
Web Site: www.hotwirepr.it
Emp.: 4
Public Relation Consulting Services
S.I.C.: 8743
N.A.I.C.S.: 541820
Alessia Bulani *(Country Mgr)*

Hotwire Public Relations Limited (2)
33/41 Dallington Street
London, EC1V 0BB, United Kingdom
Tel.: (44) 20 7608 2500
Fax: (44) 20 7608 2600
E-Mail: info@hotwirepr.com
Web Site: www.hotwirepr.com
Emp.: 50
Public Relations Consulting Services
S.I.C.: 8743
N.A.I.C.S.: 541820
Kristin Syltevik *(Co-Founder & Chm)*
Anthony Wilson *(Co-Founder & Grp CFO)*
Drew Benvie *(Grp Mng Dir)*
Andy West *(Grp Mng Dir-Global Client Dev)*

Hotwire Public Relations SL (2)
C/ Javier Ferrero 12 2nd Fl left Side
Madrid, 28002, Spain
Tel.: (34) 91 744 12 65
Web Site: www.hotwirepr.es
Emp.: 1
Public Relations Consulting Services
S.I.C.: 8743
N.A.I.C.S.: 541820
Yashim Zavaleta *(Country Mgr)*

Hotwire Public Relations SARL (1)
51 Rue le Peletier
75009 Paris, France
Tel.: (33) 1 43 12 55 55
Web Site: www.hotwirepr.fr
Public Relations Agency Services
S.I.C.: 8743
N.A.I.C.S.: 541820
Christophe Goudy *(Grp Mng Dir)*
Isabel Fox *(CEO-USA)*

Naked Communications Ltd. (1)
159-173 Saint John St
5th Fl, London, EC1V 4QY, United Kingdom
Tel.: (44) 207 336 8084
Fax: (44) 207 336 8009
E-Mail: hello@nakedcomms.com
Web Site: www.nakedcomms.com
Emp.: 60
Advertising Agency
S.I.C.: 7311
N.A.I.C.S.: 541810
Jon Wilkins *(Founder)*
Nigel Long *(CEO)*
Will Collin *(Partner)*

Branches

Naked Communications Nordic (2)
Fred Olsens Gate 3B
N-0152 Oslo, Norway
Tel.: (47) 2299 2150
E-Mail: passion@nakedcomms.com
Web Site: nakedcomms.no
Emp.: 10
S.I.C.: 7311
N.A.I.C.S.: 541810
Eddie D'Sa *(Founder)*
Ornulf Johnsen *(Mng Partner)*
Edward Lee *(CFO)*

Non-U.S. Subsidiary:

Naked Communications Sweden AB (3)
Malarvarvsbacken 8
117 33 Stockholm, Sweden
Tel.: (46) 8 720 35 00
Web Site: www.nakedcomms.se
Emp.: 20
Commuhication Consulting Services
S.I.C.: 8748
N.A.I.C.S.: 541618
Johan Falk *(Mng Partner)*
Fredrik Svensson *(Mng Partner)*

Ne Kid Paris (2)
8 Rue du Grand Prieure
75011 Paris, France
Tel.: (33) 1 43 38 15 48
Fax: (33) 1 43 38 15 42
E-Mail: paris@nekidcomms.fr
Web Site: www.nekid.fr
Emp.: 10
S.I.C.: 7311
N.A.I.C.S.: 541810
Eric de Rugy *(Founder)*
Gabriel Saenz De Buruaga *(Co-CEO)*
Olivier du Chayla *(Mng Partner)*

Subsidiary:

Lunch Communications Limited (2)
Second Floor 159-173 Saint John Street
London, EC1V 4QJ, United Kingdom
Tel.: (44) 20 7663 1650
E-Mail: info@lunchcomms.com
Web Site: www.lunchcomms.com
Marketing Consulting Services
S.I.C.: 8742
N.A.I.C.S.: 541613
Malcolm Cox *(Founder & Partner)*

U.S. Subsidiary:

Naked New York LLC (2)
96 Greene St Fl 3
New York, NY 10012-5221
Tel.: (212) 625-3082
Fax: (212) 625-3087
Emp.: 35
Advertising Agency Services
S.I.C.: 7311
N.A.I.C.S.: 541810
Troy Kelley *(CEO)*

North By Northwest Group Limited (1)
33-41 Dallington Street
London, EC1V 0BB, United Kingdom
Tel.: (44) 20 7608 2500
Fax: (44) 20 7608 2600
Web Site: www.northbynorthwestgroup.com
Public Relations Consulting Services
S.I.C.: 8743
N.A.I.C.S.: 541820

Photon Group Singapore Pte Limited (1)
28 Maxwell Road 04-08 Reddot Traffic
Singapore, 069120, Singapore
Tel.: (65) 64356116
Fax: (65) 63274666
Marketing Research Services
S.I.C.: 8732
N.A.I.C.S.: 541910

Resource Experience Limited (1)
Blue Print House Old Bracknell Lane West
Bracknell, Berkshire, RG12 7FS, United Kingdom
Tel.: (44) 1344 418383
Fax: (44) 1344 418384
E-Mail: sales@relfm.com
Web Site: www.relfm.com
Emp.: 100
Marketing Consulting Services
S.I.C.: 8742
N.A.I.C.S.: 541613
Stephen Gordon *(Mng Dir)*
Rebecca Mason *(Mng Dir)*

Retail Insight Limited (1)
Parkshot House 5 Kew Road
Richmond, Surrey, TW9 2PR, United Kingdom
Tel.: (44) 208 334 8079
E-Mail: enquiries@retailinsight.uk.com
Web Site: www.retailinsight.uk.com
Marketing Consulting Services
S.I.C.: 8742
N.A.I.C.S.: 541613

Sledge (1)
5-12 Mandela Street
London, NW1 0DU, United Kingdom
Tel.: (44) 20 7380 4380
Fax: (44) 20 7387 3777
E-Mail: info@sledge.co.uk
Web Site: www.sledge.co.uk
Billings: $22,000,000
Emp.: 30
Advertising Agency
S.I.C.: 7311
N.A.I.C.S.: 541810
Nick Cooper *(CEO)*

ENERPLUS CORPORATION

The Dome Tower 3000 333 7th Avenue SW
Calgary, AB, T2P 2Z1, Canada
Tel.: (403) 298-2200
Fax: (403) 298-2211
Toll Free: (800) 319-6462
E-Mail: investorrelations@enerplus.com
Web Site: www.enerplus.com
Year Founded: 1986
ERF—(NYSE TSX)
Rev.: $1,178,689,909
Assets: $3,311,225,931
Liabilities: $1,573,410,127
Net Worth: $1,737,815,804
Earnings: $43,147,216
Emp.: 707
Fiscal Year-end: 12/31/13

Business Description:
Oil & Gas Refining
S.I.C.: 1311
N.A.I.C.S.: 211111

Personnel:
Douglas R. Martin *(Chm)*
Ian C. Dundas *(Pres & CEO)*
Robert J. Waters *(CFO & Sr VP)*
Edward L. McLaughlin *(Pres-USA)*
David A. Mccoy *(Gen Counsel, Sec & VP-Corp Svcs)*
Raymond J. Daniels *(Sr VP-Ops)*
Eric Le Dain *(Sr VP-Corp Dev & Comml)*

Board of Directors:
Douglas R. Martin
Edwin V. Dodge
Ian C. Dundas
James Berkeley Fraser
Robert Bruce Hodgins
Donald J. Nelson
David P. O'Brien
Elliott Pew
Glen D. Roane
Sheldon B. Steeves

Transfer Agents:
Computershare Trust Company of Canada
Calgary, AB, Canada

Computershare Trust Company, N.A.
Golden, CO 80401

U.S. Subsidiary:

Enerplus Resources (USA) Corporation (1)
950 17th St Ste 2200
Denver, CO 80202-2805 DE
Tel.: (720) 279-5500 (100%)
Fax: (720) 279-5550
Web Site: www.enerplus.com
Sales Range: $1-9.9 Million
Emp.: 25
Oil & Gas Refining
S.I.C.: 1311
N.A.I.C.S.: 211111
Edward L. McLaughlin *(Pres)*

ENERSOURCE CORPORATION

3240 Mavis Rd
Mississauga, ON, L5C 3K1, Canada
Tel.: (905) 273-9050
Fax: (905) 566-2737
E-Mail: info@enersource.com
Web Site: www.enersource.com
Year Founded: 1917
Sales Range: $800-899.9 Million
Emp.: 600

Business Description:
Water Utility
S.I.C.: 4931
N.A.I.C.S.: 221111

Personnel:
Norman B. Loberg *(Chm)*
Peter Gregg *(Pres & CEO)*
Norm Wolff *(CFO & Exec VP)*
Dan Pastoric *(COO & Exec VP)*
John Stirling *(Gen Counsel)*

Board of Directors:
Norman B. Loberg
Gerald E. Beasley
Rick Byers
Hasan Imam
Robert MacCallum
Katie Mahoney
Hazel McCallion
Pat Saito
Ronald E. Starr

Subsidiaries:

Enersource Hydro Mississauga Services Inc. (1)
3240 Mavis Road
Mississauga, ON, L5C 3K1, Canada

Enersource Corporation—(Continued)

Tel.: (905) 273-7425
Fax: (905) 566-2731
E-Mail: info@enersource.com
Web Site: www.enersource.com
Hydro Distr
S.I.C.: 4941
N.A.I.C.S.: 221310
Dan Pastoric *(COO & Exec VP)*

Enersource Technologies (1)
3240 Mavis Rd
Mississauga, ON, L5C 3K1, Canada
Tel.: (905) 803-6467
Fax: (905) 566-2731
E-Mail: technologiesservices@enersource.com
Energy Solutions
S.I.C.: 4911
N.A.I.C.S.: 221122

ENERTOPIA CORP.

950-1130 West Pender Street
Vancouver, BC, V6E 4A4, Canada
Tel.: (604) 602-1675
Fax: (604) 685-1602
E-Mail: mcallister@utopia2030.com
Web Site: www.enertopia.com
Year Founded: 2004
ENRT—(OTCB)
Assets: $54,469
Liabilities: $525,918
Net Worth: ($471,449)
Earnings: ($730,904)
Emp.: 1
Fiscal Year-end: 08/31/13
Business Description:
Oil & Gas Exploration & Other Related Services
S.I.C.: 1311
N.A.I.C.S.: 211111
Personnel:
Robert G. McAllister *(Pres, CEO, Sec & Treas)*
Baljinder Bhullar *(CFO)*
Matthew Chadwick *(Sr VP-Marijuana Ops)*
Board of Directors:
Matthew Chadwick
Donald James Findlay
Robert G. McAllister
John Alan Thomas
Transfer Agent:
Olympia Trust Company
Suite 1003-750 West Pender Street
Vancouver, BC, Canada

ENERTRONICA SPA

Via Armando Fabi 339
03100 Frosinone, Italy
Tel.: (39) 0775 292273
Fax: (39) 0775 0199402
E-Mail: info@enertronica.it
Web Site: www.enertronica.it
ENT—(ITA)
Sales Range: $10-24.9 Million
Emp.: 40
Business Description:
Solar Power Plant Construction
S.I.C.: 1623
N.A.I.C.S.: 237130
Personnel:
Gerardo Plocco *(Chm & CEO)*

ENERVIT S.P.A.

Viale Monte Rosa 96
20149 Milan, Italy
Tel.: (39) 02485631
Fax: (39) 024984727
Web Site: www.enervit.com
Year Founded: 1954
ENV—(ITA)
Sales Range: $50-74.9 Million
Emp.: 140
Business Description:
Sports Nutrition Products Researcher, Developer, Mfr & Marketer
S.I.C.: 2099
N.A.I.C.S.: 311999
Personnel:
Alberto Sorbini *(Chm, CEO & Mng Dir)*
Giuseppe Maurizia Sorbini *(Chm & CEO)*
Board of Directors:
Giuseppe Maurizia Sorbini
Alberto Sorbini
Nerio Alessandri
Carlo Capelli
Maurizio Cereda
Stefano Clini
Maurizia Sorbini

ENERXY AG

Colorado-Turm Industriestrasse 4
70565 Stuttgart, Germany
Tel.: (49) 711 49047 860
Fax: (49) 711 49047 865
E-Mail: info@enerxy.com
Web Site: www.enerxy.com
EXJ—(DEU)
Sales Range: $10-24.9 Million
Business Description:
Energy Consulting Services
S.I.C.: 8999
N.A.I.C.S.: 541690
Personnel:
Matthias Gaebler *(Chm-Supervisory Bd)*
Michael Xiao Ting Zhang *(CEO)*
Christian Hoelscher *(CFO)*
Supervisory Board of Directors:
Matthias Gaebler
Dirk Bildhauser
Carl-Christian Fricker

ENEXOMA AG

Otto-Brenner-Str 209
33604 Bielefeld, Germany
Tel.: (49) 5219276226
Fax: (49) 5219276227
E-Mail: info@enexoma.de
Web Site: www.enexoma.de
EK3—(DEU)
Emp.: 15
Business Description:
Software Publisher
S.I.C.: 7372
N.A.I.C.S.: 511210
Personnel:
Nikolaus Brakowski *(Mng Dir)*

ENF TECHNOLOGY CO., LTD.

3F Susan B/D 205-5 Nonhyeon-dong
Gangnam-gu, Seoul, 135-010, Korea (South)
Tel.: (82) 2 3440 4300
Fax: (82) 2 546 3387
Web Site: www.enftech.com
Year Founded: 2000
102710—(KRS)
Sls.: $216,144,090
Assets: $146,424,780
Liabilities: $52,584,060
Net Worth: $93,840,720
Earnings: $12,331,800
Emp.: 262
Fiscal Year-end: 12/31/12
Business Description:
Chemical Product Mfr
S.I.C.: 2899
N.A.I.C.S.: 325998
Personnel:
Yong-Seok Chi *(CEO)*

ENFIELD EXPLORATION CORP.

2408 Pine Street
Vancouver, BC, V6J 0A9, Canada
Tel.: (604) 721-3000
Year Founded: 2013
EXP—(CNSX)
Business Description:
Metal Mining
S.I.C.: 1099
N.A.I.C.S.: 212299
Personnel:
John Bevilacqua *(Pres & CEO)*

ENFINITY N.V.

Henri Lebbestraat 188
Waregem, 8790, Belgium
Tel.: (32) 56288888
Fax: (32) 56288899
E-Mail: info@enfinity.be
Web Site: www.enfinity.be
Year Founded: 2005
Sales Range: $100-124.9 Million
Emp.: 200
Business Description:
Renewable Energy Project Development, Management & Financing Services
S.I.C.: 1629
N.A.I.C.S.: 237130
Personnel:
Patrick Decuyper *(Founder)*
Rik Missault *(CEO)*
U.S. Subsidiary:

Enfinity Corporation (1)
1414 S St
Sacramento, CA 95814 DE
Tel.: (916) 339-7003 (100%)
Fax: (916) 880-5633
E-Mail: info@enfinitycorp.com
Web Site: www.enfinitycorp.com
Renewable Energy Project Development, Management & Financing Services
S.I.C.: 1623
N.A.I.C.S.: 237130
Rafael Dobrzynski *(CEO)*

ENFO OYJ

Viestikatu 7
PO Box 1582
70600 Kuopio, Finland
Tel.: (358) 2054321
Fax: (358) 205432355
E-Mail: info@enfo.fi
Web Site: www.enfo.fi
Sls.: $195,404,653
Assets: $152,724,333
Liabilities: $87,966,825
Net Worth: $64,757,508
Earnings: $5,931,225
Emp.: 792
Fiscal Year-end: 12/31/12
Business Description:
Information Technology & Information Logistics Services
S.I.C.: 7373
N.A.I.C.S.: 541512
Personnel:
Tapio Hakakari *(Chm)*
Hannu Isotalo *(Deputy Chm)*
Arto Herranen *(CEO)*
Tero Kosunen *(CFO)*
Sebastian Linko *(CIO)*
Ulla Louhisuo *(Sec)*
Lars Aabol *(Exec VP-Consulting Svcs)*
Nina Annila *(Exec VP-Indus Verticals)*
Tero Saksman *(Exec VP-Info Logistics)*
Osmo Wilska *(Exec VP-Outsourcing Svcs)*
Maria Lundell *(Sr VP-HR)*
Board of Directors:
Tapio Hakakari
Hannu Isotalo
Marja Liisa Kaario
Timo Karkkainen
Ossi Saksman
Non-U.S. Subsidiary:

Enfo AB (1)
Anders Carlssons Gata 9
nind hollnstiren 3B, 417 55 Gothenburg, Sweden
Tel.: (46) 774404400
Fax: (46) 031510105
E-Mail: infosweden@info.se
Web Site: www.enfo.se
Emp.: 1,000
IT Infrstructure & Integration Services
S.I.C.: 7372
N.A.I.C.S.: 511210
Devordeer Gohan *(Mng Dir)*

Subsidiaries:

Zingle by Enfo AB (2)
Anders Carlssons Gata 9
PO Box 8792
402 76 Gothenburg, Sweden
Tel.: (46) 774404400
Fax: (46) 31510105
E-Mail: info@enfo.se
Web Site: www.zingle.se
Emp.: 350
IT User Integration
S.I.C.: 7379
N.A.I.C.S.: 541519
Peter Lorincz *(CEO)*

Zipper by Enfo AB (2)
Lindholmspiren 4B
417 55 Gothenburg, Sweden
Tel.: (46) 774404400
Fax: (46) 31510501
E-Mail: info@zipper.se
Web Site: www.zipper.se
Emp.: 120
IT Infrastructure
S.I.C.: 7372
N.A.I.C.S.: 511210
Ulf Borjel *(CEO)*

Zystems by Enfo AB (2)
Anders Carlssons Gata 9
402 76 Gothenburg, Sweden
Tel.: (46) 774404400
Fax: (46) 31510105
E-Mail: info@zystems.se
Web Site: www.zystems.se/en
Emp.: 300
Computer Systems Integration
S.I.C.: 7379
N.A.I.C.S.: 541519
Karin Nordstrom *(Reg Mgr)*

ENG KAH CORPORATION BERHAD

Plot 95 97 Hala Kampung Jawa 2
Kawasan Perindustrian Bayan Lepas
11900 Bayan Lepas, Penang, Malaysia
Tel.: (60) 46435180
Fax: (60) 46442101
E-Mail: engkahpg@engkahp.com.my
Web Site: www.eng-kah.com
ENGKAH—(KLS)
Rev.: $27,643,729
Assets: $30,476,871
Liabilities: $4,781,240
Net Worth: $25,695,631
Earnings: $4,261,692
Fiscal Year-end: 12/31/12
Business Description:
Personal Care Products Mfr
S.I.C.: 2844
N.A.I.C.S.: 325620
Personnel:
Eng Kah Ewe *(Chm & Mng Dir)*
Lay Hoon Ch'ng *(Sec)*
Board of Directors:
Eng Kah Ewe
Ahmad Badry Azahari
Kim Siang Ewe
Wee Ting Ewe
Wei Ru Ewe
Kim Nam Ong
Muttaqin Othman

Subsidiaries:

Eng Kah Enterprise (KL) Sdn. Bhd. (1)
PT16777 Jalan Permata 1 Arab Malaysia Industrial Park
Nilai, Negeri Sembilan, 71800, Malaysia
Tel.: (60) 67999121
Fax: (60) 67990807
E-Mail: info@eng-kah.com
Web Site: www.eng-kah.com
Household Cosmetic Products Mfr
S.I.C.: 2844
N.A.I.C.S.: 325620
Bat Wong *(Mgr-Fin & Admin)*

Eng Kah Enterprise Sdn. Bhd. (1)
Plot 95 & 97 Hala Kampung Jawa 2
Kawasan Perindustrian Bayan Lepas
11900 Bayan Lepas, Penang, Malaysia
Tel.: (60) 46435180
Fax: (60) 46442101
E-Mail: info@eng-kah.com
Emp.: 400
Household Cosmectics Mfr
S.I.C.: 2844
N.A.I.C.S.: 325620
Lim Mei Ning *(Gen Mgr)*

ENG KONG HOLDINGS LIMITED

13 Tuas Avenue 11
Jurong, 639079, Singapore
Tel.: (65) 68616355
Fax: (65) 66615195
E-Mail: enquiry@engkong.com
Web Site: www.engkong.com
Year Founded: 1978
E06—(SES)
Sales Range: $50-74.9 Million
Emp.: 600

Business Description:
Warehouse & Container Services
S.I.C.: 4731
N.A.I.C.S.: 541614

Personnel:
Eddie Hung Li *(Co-Chm)*
Paul Kam Ming Ng *(Co-Chm)*
Tee Hien Teoh *(CEO)*

Board of Directors:
Eddie Hung Li
Paul Kam Ming Ng
Godfrey Wai Kuen Leung
Tee Hien Teoh

Subsidiaries:

Eng Kong Container Agencies (Pte) Ltd (1)
8A Tuas Ave 13
Singapore, Singapore
Tel.: (65) 68610843
Fax: (65) 68619780
General Warehousing Services
S.I.C.: 4225
N.A.I.C.S.: 493110

PCL (Pte) Ltd (1)
13 Tuas Ave 11
Singapore, 639079, Singapore
Tel.: (65) 65587106
Fax: (65) 65587109
E-Mail: pclpl@engkong.com
Web Site: www.engkong.com
Emp.: 2
Container Sales
S.I.C.: 5085
N.A.I.C.S.: 423840
Henry Heng *(Exec Dir)*

Reefertec Pte Ltd (1)
13 Tuas Ave 11
Singapore, 639079, Singapore
Tel.: (65) 68620400
Fax: (65) 68620466
E-Mail: nuramirah@muhayat.com
Web Site: www.engkong.com
Emp.: 15
Refrigeration Equipment Repair & Maintenance Services
S.I.C.: 5085
N.A.I.C.S.: 423840
Michael Ho *(Gen Mgr)*

Smartz Pte Ltd (1)
13 Tuas Ave 11
Singapore, 639079, Singapore
Tel.: (65) 68978577
Fax: (65) 68978578
Web Site: www.engkong.com.sg
Emp.: 200
Container Parts Whslr
S.I.C.: 5085
N.A.I.C.S.: 423840
Terry Chan *(Mng Dir)*

Non-U.S. Subsidiaries:

Eng Kong Container Services (Johor) Sdn Bhd (1)
PLO 704 Jalan Keluli Pasir Gudang Indust Area
81700 Pasir Gudang, Johor Bahru, Malaysia
Tel.: (60) 72551870
Fax: (60) 72527036
Container Sales & Services
S.I.C.: 5085
N.A.I.C.S.: 423840

Eng Kong Container Services (Penang) Sdn Bhd. (1)
Lot 1332 Mukim 14 Jalan Bagan Lallang Mak Mandin Indus Estate
13400 Butterworth, Penang, Malaysia
Tel.: (60) 43249268
Fax: (60) 43249261
Emp.: 200
Container Sales & Services
S.I.C.: 5085
N.A.I.C.S.: 423840
Ronny Tan *(Mng Dir)*

Eng Kong Container Services (Shenzhen) Company Limited (1)
1st Gang Cheng Rd Mawan Gang Ave
Shekou, Shenzhen, Guangdong, 518067, China
Tel.: (86) 75526451148
Fax: (86) 75526391770
Container Services
S.I.C.: 4214
N.A.I.C.S.: 484110

Eng Kong- FASA Vietnam Co., Ltd (1)
161 Ky Con St Nguyen Thai
Binh Ward, Ho Chi Minh City, Vietnam
Tel.: (84) 838213333
Fax: (84) 838213999
Emp.: 20
Transportation Support Services
S.I.C.: 4789
N.A.I.C.S.: 488999
Thi My Linh *(Mng Dir)*

Grand Pacific Warehouse Limited (1)
Unit 508-509 Hutchison Logistics Ctr 18 Container Port Rd
Kwai Chung, China (Hong Kong)
Tel.: (852) 26152228
Fax: (852) 26151333
E-Mail: enquiry@engkong.com
Web Site: www.ekh-gpw.com.hk
Emp.: 25
Warehousing & Container Freight Services
S.I.C.: 4214
N.A.I.C.S.: 484110
Alan Ho *(Gen Mgr)*

Ming Fung Container Limited (1)
16-26 Kwai Tak St Golden Indus Bldg 5th Fl Rm 12
Kwai Chung, New Territories, China (Hong Kong)
Tel.: (852) 24182882
Fax: (852) 24810208
Emp.: 80
Refrigeration Equipment Maintenance Services
S.I.C.: 7699
N.A.I.C.S.: 811310
Danny Hung *(Gen Mgr & Mng Dir)*

New Eng Kong Container Logistic Services (M) Sdn Bhd (1)
Lot 4 Lingkaran Sultan Muhamed 1
Kawasan Perusahaan
Bandar Sultan Suleiman, 42000 Port Klang, Selangor Darul Ehsan, Malaysia
Tel.: (60) 331764142
Fax: (60) 331768730
Web Site: www.engkong.com
Emp.: 30
Container & Logistics Consulting Services
S.I.C.: 4731
N.A.I.C.S.: 541614
Ronny Tan *(Gen Mgr)*

PCL Container Services Limited (1)
Unit 310-311A Hutchison Logistics Ctr 18 Container Port Rd
Kwai Chung, New Territories, China (Hong Kong)
Tel.: (852) 24022180
Fax: (852) 2413 0353
Container Depot Services
S.I.C.: 4225
N.A.I.C.S.: 493110

Shanghai Eng Kong Container Services Ltd (1)
1800-1 Yun Chuan Rd
Bao Shan, Shanghai, China
Tel.: (86) 2156497060
Fax: (86) 2156497066
E-Mail: xia.chang@engkong.com
Container Trucking Services
S.I.C.: 4214
N.A.I.C.S.: 484110

Techni-con Container Survey Limited (1)
1800-1 Yun Chuan Rd
Bao Shan, Shanghai, 201901, China
Tel.: (86) 2166760090
Fax: (86) 2166760087
E-Mail: technicon@engkong.com.sg
Web Site: www.engkong.com.sg
Emp.: 17
Container Surveying Services
S.I.C.: 4212
N.A.I.C.S.: 484110
Molin Ohou *(Mgr)*

Tricool Reefer Sdn Bhd (1)
Lot 51 & 52 Jalan Perigi Nanas 8/7 Taman Perindustrian
42920 Pulau Indah, Selangor, Malaysia
Tel.: (60) 331012678
Fax: (60) 331012677
E-Mail: tricool@streamyx.com
Emp.: 8
Reefer Repair Services
S.I.C.: 7699
N.A.I.C.S.: 811310
Ong Ngun Son *(Pres)*

ENG. SHABAH AL-SHAMMERY & PARTNERS CO.

Al-Mansoor Al-Ameerat St
District 609 St 1 House 21, Baghdad, Iraq
Tel.: (964) 15412787
Fax: (964) 15418155
E-Mail: sapco_iraq@shammery.com
Web Site: www.shammery.com
Emp.: 260

Business Description:
General Trading Services
S.I.C.: 7389
N.A.I.C.S.: 425120

ENG TEKNOLOGI HOLDINGS BHD.

Plot 69-70 Pesara Kampung Jawa
Bayan Lepas Industrial Zone, Bayan Lepas, Penang, 11900, Malaysia
Tel.: (60) 46440122
Fax: (60) 46423430
E-Mail: info@engtek.com
Web Site: www.engtek.com
Sales Range: $150-199.9 Million

Business Description:
Engineering Solutions & Services
S.I.C.: 8711
N.A.I.C.S.: 541330

Personnel:
Yeong Keat Teh *(Chm)*
Yong Khoon Teh *(CEO)*
Hock Leong Chee *(CFO)*
Woei En Teng *(COO)*
Sook Fun Thum *(Sec)*

Board of Directors:
Yeong Keat Teh
Mohd Suhaimi Abdullah
Aziz Anuar
Hock Leong Chee
Danny Siew Cheang Goon
Hee Choo Lim
Shaharom Md Shariff
Yong Khoon Teh
Woei En Teng

Legal Counsel:
Salina Lim Kim Chuan & Co.
51-15-C2 Menara BHL Jalan Sultan Ahmad Shah
Penang, Malaysia

Presgrave & Matthews
1st Floor Standard Chartered Bank Chambers
No. 2 Lebuh Pantai
Penang, Malaysia

Subsidiaries:

Altum Precision Sdn. Bhd. (1)
Plo 185 Jalan Siber 9 Kawasan Perindustrian Senai IV
81400 Senai, Johor, Malaysia
Tel.: (60) 75989928
Fax: (60) 75988034
Web Site: www.altumjb.com.my
Automated Die Castings Mfr
S.I.C.: 3364
N.A.I.C.S.: 331523

Eng Hardware Engineering Sdn. Bhd. (1)
Plot 69-70 Pesara Kampung Jawa Bayan Lepas Industrial Zone
11900 Bayan Lepas, Penang, Malaysia
Tel.: (60) 46440122
Fax: (60) 46413992
Emp.: 600
Engineering Services
S.I.C.: 8711
N.A.I.C.S.: 541330
Choo Yong Tee *(Mng Dir)*

Eng Teknologi Sdn. Bhd. (1)
Plot 69-70 Pesara Kampung Jawa Bayan Lepas Industrial Zone
11900 Bayan Lepas, Penang, Malaysia
Tel.: (60) 46449760
Fax: (60) 46423430
E-Mail: info@engtek.com
Web Site: www.engtek.com
Emp.: 400
Precision Components Mfr & Distr
S.I.C.: 3451
N.A.I.C.S.: 332721
Teh Yong Khoon *(CEO)*

Selekta Inovatif (M) Sdn. Bhd. (1)
800 Jalan Perindustrian Bukit Minyak
Kawasan Perindustrian, 14000 Bukit Mertajam, Penang, Malaysia
Tel.: (60) 45023688
Fax: (60) 45022068
Emp.: 50
Magnet Plates Mfr
S.I.C.: 3499
N.A.I.C.S.: 332999
Y. T. Choo *(Mng Dir)*
Teh Yoong Khoon *(COO)*

Non-U.S. Subsidiaries:

Altum Precision Co., Ltd. (1)
146 Moo 1 Hi-Tech Industrial Estate Asia-Nakornsawan Road
Nakhon Si, Ayutthaya, 13160, Thailand
Tel.: (66) 35729100
Fax: (66) 35314192
Emp.: 1,300
Automotive Mechanical Components Mfr
S.I.C.: 3714
N.A.I.C.S.: 336310
Bamroong Koolawonk *(Mng Dir)*

Engtek International Limited (1)
16/F Flat 1612 Cheung Fung Industrial Building
23-39 Pak Tin Par Street, Tsuen Wan, China (Hong Kong)
Tel.: (852) 24024618
Fax: (852) 24908396
Precision Machine Components Mfr
S.I.C.: 3999
N.A.I.C.S.: 339999

Eng Teknologi Holdings Bhd.—(Continued)

Engtek Precision Philippines, Inc. (1)
L10 Phase II-A Special Export Processing Zone II
Carmelray Industrial Park I, Calamba, Laguna, 4027, Philippines
Tel.: (63) 495491748
Fax: (63) 495491327
Precision Engineering Components Mfr
S.I.C.: 3699
N.A.I.C.S.: 335999

Engtek (Thailand) Co., Ltd. (1)
2/6 Moo 5 Rojana Industrial Park Rojana Road
Ayutthaya, 13210, Thailand
Tel.: (66) 35719579
Fax: (66) 35719583
Electronic Components Mfr
S.I.C.: 3676
N.A.I.C.S.: 334416

ENGEL CONSTRUCTION & DEVELOPMENT GROUP
85 Medinat Hyhudin
Herzliyya, 46140, Israel
Tel.: (972) 99707000
Fax: (972) 99580202
E-Mail: rachelk@engel.co.il
Web Site: www.engel.co.il
Emp.: 70

Business Description:
Provider of Building & Housing Construction Services
S.I.C.: 1542
N.A.I.C.S.: 236220

Personnel:
Yael Miller *(CEO)*

Subsidiary:

Engel General Developers Ltd. (1)
66 Hahistadrut Avenue
Haifa, 32960, Israel
Tel.: (972) 48422777
Fax: (972) 4 841 9333
Emp.: 52
Residential Construction Services
S.I.C.: 1521
N.A.I.C.S.: 236115

Non-U.S. Subsidiary:

Kimberly Enterpises N.V. (2)
Keizersgracht 616
1017 ER Amsterdam, Netherlands (68.35%)
Tel.: (31) 20 778 4141
Fax: (31) 20 330 5444
Web Site: www.kimberly-enterprises.com
KBE—(AIM)
Rev.: $3,491,965
Assets: $78,558,443
Liabilities: $96,213,462
Net Worth: ($17,655,020)
Earnings: ($8,953,377)
Fiscal Year-end: 12/31/12
Residential Property Development
S.I.C.: 6531
N.A.I.C.S.: 531311
Gad Raveh *(CEO)*
Assaf Vardimon *(CFO)*

ENGENCO LIMITED
Level 22 535 Bourke Street
Melbourne, VIC, 3000, Australia
Tel.: (61) 3 8620 8900
Fax: (61) 3 8620 8999
E-Mail: investor.relations@engenco.com.au
Web Site: www.engenco.com.au
EGN—(ASX)
Rev.: $184,800,804
Assets: $147,174,741
Liabilities: $54,397,620
Net Worth: $92,777,121
Earnings: ($95,367,781)
Emp.: 520
Fiscal Year-end: 06/30/13

Business Description:
Engineering Services
S.I.C.: 8711
N.A.I.C.S.: 541330

Personnel:
Ross Dunning *(Interim Mng Dir)*
Kevin Pallas *(CFO, COO & Co-Sec)*
Josephine Tan *(Chief Legal Officer & Co-Sec)*
Geoff Thorn *(CEO-Gemco Rail)*

Board of Directors:
Dale Brendon Elphinstone
Vincent De Santis
Ross Dunning
Donald Hector

Subsidiaries:

Centre for Excellence in Rail Training Pty. Ltd. (1)
1359 Albany Highway
PO Box 270
Maddington, Cannington, WA, 6107, Australia
Tel.: (61) 892518080
Fax: (61) 894521513
E-Mail: infowest@certrail.com
Web Site: www.certrail.com
Emp.: 7
Training & Assessment Services
S.I.C.: 8299
N.A.I.C.S.: 611430
Andy Marsh *(CEO)*

Convair Engineering Pty. Ltd. (1)
93 Miller St
Epping, VIC, 3076, Australia
Tel.: (61) 394087255
Fax: (61) 94086820
E-Mail: sales@convair.com.au
Web Site: www.convair.com.au
Emp.: 35
Pneumatic Bulk Tanker Mfr
S.I.C.: 3443
N.A.I.C.S.: 332420
Peter Swann *(Gen Mgr)*

Coote Logistics Pty. Ltd. (1)
627-635 Bickley Rd
Maddington, Perth, Western Australia, 6989, Australia
Tel.: (61) 892518000
Fax: (61) 894522186
Web Site: www.coote.com.au/default.aspx?MenuID=7
Freight Trucking Services
S.I.C.: 4213
N.A.I.C.S.: 484121
Peter Wilson *(Gen Mgr)*

Subsidiary:

Asset Kinetics Pty. Ltd. (2)
6 Sandhill St
Wedgefield, Port Hedland, Western Australia, 6721, Australia
Tel.: (61) 891722255
Fax: (61) 891722288
Emp.: 5
Transport & Logistics Services
S.I.C.: 4731
N.A.I.C.S.: 541614
Jeff Coote *(Mng Dir)*

Drivetrain Australia Pty. Ltd. (1)
Bldg B 12 Loyalty Rd
North Rocks, New South Wales, 2151, Australia
Tel.: (61) 296048566
Fax: (61) 288385501
E-Mail: sales@drivetrainpower.com
Web Site: www.drivetrainpower.com
Emp.: 30
Industrial Equipment Repair & Maintenance Services
S.I.C.: 7699
N.A.I.C.S.: 811310
Glenn Parrett *(Mng Dir)*

U.S. Subsidiary:

Eden Cryogenics LLC (2)
8500 Rausch Dr
Plain City, OH 43064-8067
Tel.: (614) 873-3949
Fax: (614) 873-6295
Toll Free: (877) 273-4660
E-Mail: info@edencryogenics.com
Web Site: www.edencryogenics.com
Emp.: 50
Cryogenic Product & Equipment Mfr
S.I.C.: 3443
N.A.I.C.S.: 332420
Steve L. Hensley *(Pres)*

Non-U.S. Subsidiaries:

Drivetrain Philippines Inc. (2)
325 Gregorio Araneta Ave
Quezon City, Manila, Philippines
Tel.: (63) 27145820
Fax: (63) 27146850
E-Mail: sales@drivetrainpower.com
Web Site: www.drivetrainpower.com
Emp.: 4
Engine Repair & Maintenance Services
S.I.C.: 7539
N.A.I.C.S.: 811198
Glenn Parratt *(CEO)*

Drivetrain Singapore Pte. Ltd. (2)
69N Tuas Sth Ave 1
No 02-07 Eunos Technolink, Singapore, 637504, Singapore
Tel.: (65) 67495117
Fax: (65) 67429722
E-Mail: drivetrain@singnet.com.sg
Web Site: www.drivetrainpower.com
Emp.: 4
Industrial Equipment Repair & Maintenance Services
S.I.C.: 7699
N.A.I.C.S.: 811310

Drivetrain Power and Propulsion Pty. Ltd. (1)
Level 8 15 Talavera Rd
North Ryde, New South Wales, 2113, Australia
Tel.: (61) 298054000
Fax: (61) 298054055
E-Mail: info@drivetrainpower.com
Web Site: www.drivetrainpower.com.au
Emp.: 100
Engine Maintenance & Repair Services
S.I.C.: 7539
N.A.I.C.S.: 811198
Glenn Parrott *(CEO)*

PC Diesel Pty. Ltd. (1)
Unit 1 15 Colin Jamieson Dr
PO Box 167
Welshpool, WA, 6106, Australia
Tel.: (61) 893583003
Fax: (61) 892587009
E-Mail: sales@pcdiesel.com
Web Site: www.industrial-powertrain.com.au
Emp.: 13
Diesel Engine Equipment Mfr
S.I.C.: 3519
N.A.I.C.S.: 333618
Peter Crosswell *(CEO)*

Subsidiary:

Industrial Powertrain Pty. Ltd. (2)
857 Abernethy Road, Forrestfield WA 6058
Bassendean, Western Australia, 6054, Australia
Tel.: (61) 893771880
Fax: (61) 862547177
E-Mail: service@industrial-powertrain.com.au
Web Site: www.industrial-powertrain.com.au
Emp.: 24
Industrial Equipment Repair & Maintenance Services
S.I.C.: 7699
N.A.I.C.S.: 811310
Brian Honeywood *(Gen Mgr)*

Total Momentum Pty. Ltd. (1)
867 Abernethy Road
Kewdale, WA, 6105, Australia
Mailing Address:
PO Box 191
Cloverdale, WA, 6985, Australia
Tel.: (61) 893608200
Fax: (61) 397329642
E-Mail: info@momentumrail.com
Web Site: www.momentumrail.com
Railroad Construction Services
S.I.C.: 4011
N.A.I.C.S.: 482111
Andy Marsh *(CEO)*

Non-U.S. Subsidiary:

Hedemora Investments AB (1)
Sturegatan 2
77635 Hedemora, Dalarna, Sweden
Tel.: (46) 225595800
Fax: (46) 225595801
E-Mail: spareparts@hedemoradiesel.se
Web Site: www.hedemoradiesel.se
Emp.: 25
Engine Maintenance & Repair Services
S.I.C.: 7539
N.A.I.C.S.: 811118
Greg Northeast *(Mng Dir)*

Subsidiary:

Hedemora Diesel AB (2)
Sturegatan 2
776 35 Hedemora, Dalarna, Sweden
Tel.: (46) 225595800
Fax: (46) 225595801
E-Mail: spareparts@hedemoradiesel.se
Web Site: www.hedemoradiesel.se
Emp.: 28
Diesel Engine Mfr
S.I.C.: 3519
N.A.I.C.S.: 333618
Greg Northeast *(Mng Dir)*

ENGHOUSE SYSTEMS LIMITED
80 Tiverton Court Suite 800
Markham, ON, L3R 0G4, Canada
Tel.: (905) 946-3200
Fax: (905) 946-3201
E-Mail: info@enghouse.com
Web Site: www.enghouse.com
Year Founded: 1984
ESL—(TSX)
Rev.: $136,062,536
Assets: $239,173,050
Liabilities: $81,586,835
Net Worth: $157,586,214
Earnings: $20,826,244
Emp.: 820
Fiscal Year-end: 10/31/12

Business Description:
Automated Mapping & Facilities Management Through Geographic Information Systems Engineering Software Products
S.I.C.: 7373
N.A.I.C.S.: 541512

Personnel:
Stephen J. Sadler *(Chm & CEO)*
Todd M. May *(Gen Counsel & VP)*
Douglas C. Bryson *(Sec & VP-Fin & Admin)*

Board of Directors:
Stephen J. Sadler
Eric A. Demirian
Reid Drury
John G. Gibson
Pierre Lassonde
Paul J. Stoyan

Legal Counsel:
Lang Michener LLP
Brookfield Place 181 Bay Street Suite 2500
Toronto, ON, Canada

Transfer Agent:
Equity Financial Trust Company
200 University Avenue Suite 400
Toronto, ON, M5H 4H1, Canada
Tel.: (416) 361-0152
Fax: (416) 361-0470
Toll Free: (866) 393-4891

Subsidiaries:

Enghouse Transportation LLC (1)
205 - 2150 Islington Ave
Toronto, ON, M9P 3V4, Canada
Tel.: (416) 915-9593
Fax: (416) 915-9594
E-Mail: info@transched.com
Web Site: www.transched.com
Transportation Software Development Services
S.I.C.: 7371
N.A.I.C.S.: 541511

Moore Resource Systems (Ontario) Limited (1)
80 Tiverton Crt Ste 800
Markham, ON, L3R 0G4, Canada
Tel.: (905) 854-1607

Fax: (905) 854-1608
Software Development Services
S.I.C.: 7371
N.A.I.C.S.: 541511

Pulse Teleservice Inc. (1)
90 Nolan Crt
Markham, ON, L3R 4L9, Canada
Tel.: (905) 695-3500
Telecommunication Servicesb
S.I.C.: 4899
N.A.I.C.S.: 517919

Pulse Voice Inc (1)
90 Nolan Ct Ste 1A
Markham, ON, L3R 4L9, Canada
Tel.: (905) 754-4100
Toll Free: (888) 777-8573
E-Mail: sales@pulsenetworks.com
Web Site: www.pulsenetworks.com
Enterprise Software Development Services
S.I.C.: 7371
N.A.I.C.S.: 541511
A. S. Tony Cassetta *(Chm)*
Mohan Markandaier *(CEO)*

U.S. Subsidiaries:

CustomCall Data Systems, Inc. (1)
1009 S Whitney Way
Madison, WI 53711 WI
Tel.: (608) 274-3009
Fax: (608) 274-8583
Web Site: www.customcall.com
Emp.: 40
Billing, OSS & Business Process Management Solutions
S.I.C.: 7379
N.A.I.C.S.: 541519
Frank D. Peregrine *(Chm & CEO)*

Information Access Technology, Inc. (1)
6671 South Redwood Rd
West Jordan, UT 84084
Fax: (801) 265-8880
Toll Free: (800) 574-8801
Web Site: www.iat-cti.com
Sales Range: $1-9.9 Million
Emp.: 30
Software Publishers
S.I.C.: 7372
N.A.I.C.S.: 511210
Randy Cooper *(Chm)*
David Rudd *(Pres & CEO)*

Syntellect, Inc. (1)
2095 W Pinnacle Peak Rd Ste 110
Phoenix, AZ 85027 DE
Tel.: (602) 789-2800
Fax: (602) 789-2768
Toll Free: (800) 788-9733
E-Mail: info@syntellect.com
Web Site: www.syntellect.com
Emp.: 85
Speech-Enabled Customer, Employee & Supply-Chain Self-Service Software Solutions & Hosted Services
Export
S.I.C.: 3571
N.A.I.C.S.: 334111
Mike Dalton *(VP)*

Subsidiaries:

CosmoCom Inc. (2)
121 Broadhollow Rd
Melville, NY 11747
Tel.: (631) 940-4200
Fax: (631) 940-4500
E-Mail: info@cosmocom.com
Web Site: www.cosmocom.com
Sales Range: $10-24.9 Million
Emp.: 75
Software Publishers
S.I.C.: 7372
N.A.I.C.S.: 511210
Benjamin Eisner *(Pres & COO)*
Stephen Dellutri *(CTO)*

Syntellect Technology Corp. (2)
Ste 110 30 Mansell Ct
Roswell, GA 30076-1580
Toll Free: (800) 788-9733
Mfr. of Telephone Systems
S.I.C.: 8721
N.A.I.C.S.: 541219

Teloquent Communications Corp. (2)
2095 W Pinnacle Peak Rd Ste 110
Phoenix, AZ 85027
Tel.: (602) 789-2800
Fax: (602) 789-2899
E-Mail: info@synpellect.com
Web Site: www.synpellect.com
Sales Range: $10-24.9 Million
Emp.: 78
Computer Software Development
S.I.C.: 7371
N.A.I.C.S.: 541511
Anga Allen *(Controller)*

Non-U.S. Subsidiary:

Syntellect Ltd (2)
Technology House Fleetwood Pk
Barley Way Fleet, Hampshire, GU51 2QJ, United Kingdom (100%)
Tel.: (44) 256685100
Fax: (44) 01252618899
E-Mail: info@syntellect.com
Web Site: www.syntellect.com
Emp.: 45
S.I.C.: 3679
N.A.I.C.S.: 334418
Andy Clune *(Mng Dir)*

Non-U.S. Subsidiaries:

Enghouse (U.K.) Limited (1)
Enterprise House Ocean Village
Southampton, Hampshire, SO14 3XB, United Kingdom
Tel.: (44) 2380 488752
Emp.: 1
Computer Software Development Services
S.I.C.: 7371
N.A.I.C.S.: 541511

Gamma Projects Ltd. (1)
The Brewery
Magor, Monmouthshire, NP26 3DJ, United Kingdom
Tel.: (44) 1633 883000
Fax: (44) 1633 882990
E-Mail: info@gammaprojects.com
Web Site: www.gammaprojects.com
Telecommunication Software Consulting Services
S.I.C.: 7373
N.A.I.C.S.: 541512

Mettoni Ltd. (1)
Progression House Pincents Lane
Reading, Berks, RG31 4UH, United Kingdom
Tel.: (44) 118 972 8400
Web Site: www.mettoni.com
Sales Range: $25-49.9 Million
Emp.: 150
Voice Application Software Solutions
S.I.C.: 7372
N.A.I.C.S.: 511210
Iain McKenzie *(Mng Dir)*
Alex Black *(CTO)*

Subsidiaries:

Arc Solutions (International) Limited (2)
Innovation House Turnhams Green Park
Pincents Lane
Reading, Berkshire, RG31 4UH, United Kingdom
Tel.: (44) 1189139200
Fax: (44) 1189439201
E-Mail: info@arcsolutions.com
Web Site: www.arcsolutions.com
Software Development Services
S.I.C.: 7371
N.A.I.C.S.: 541511

Datapulse Limited (2)
Progression House Pincents Lane
Reading, Berkshire, RG31 4UH, United Kingdom
Tel.: (44) 1189728400
Fax: (44) 8704424423
E-Mail: dpsales@datapulse.com
Web Site: www.datapulse.co.uk
Emp.: 10
Information Technology Consulting Services
S.I.C.: 7373
N.A.I.C.S.: 541512
Iain McKenzie *(Grp Mng Dir-EMEA)*

Exxcom Limited (2)
Kingsmede House 1 Southbridge Street
Shefford, Bedfordshire, SG17 5DB, United Kingdom
Tel.: (44) 1462 850912
Fax: (44) 1462 850922
E-Mail: sales@exxcom.co.uk
Web Site: www.exxcom.co.uk
Web Hosting Services
S.I.C.: 7374
N.A.I.C.S.: 518210

U.S. Subsidiary:

Telrex LLC (2)
8525 120th Ave NE Ste 203
Kirkland, WA 98033 WA
Tel.: (425) 827-6156
Fax: (425) 803-3323
Toll Free: (800) 788-9730
Web Site: www.telrex.com
Sales Range: $1-9.9 Million
Emp.: 45
Call Recording & Call Center Optimization Software Solutions
S.I.C.: 7372
N.A.I.C.S.: 511210
Dan Boehm *(VP)*

Trio Danmark A/S (1)
Rodkaervej 18
Sabro, 8471 Arhus, Denmark
Tel.: (45) 4488 0050
Fax: (45) 4488 0051
E-Mail: danmark@trio.com
Web Site: www.trio.com
Communication Software Development Services
S.I.C.: 7371
N.A.I.C.S.: 541511

Trio Enterprise AB (1)
St Eriksgatan 117
Box 6795
113 85 Stockholm, Sweden
Tel.: (46) 8 457 30 00
Fax: (46) 8 31 87 00
E-Mail: info@trio.com
Web Site: www.trio.com
Emp.: 45
Telephony System Software Development Services
S.I.C.: 7371
N.A.I.C.S.: 541511
Michael Stubbing *(CEO)*

Trio Norge AS (1)
Fornebuvn 46
PB 493
1327 Lysaker, Norway
Tel.: (47) 67 83 00 80
Fax: (47) 67 83 00 81
E-Mail: norge@trio.com
Communication Software Development Services
S.I.C.: 7371
N.A.I.C.S.: 541511

ENGINEERED NANOPRODUCTS GERMANY AG

Goethestrasse 30
64347 Griesheim, Germany
Tel.: (49) 6332 48192 0
Fax: (49) 6332 48192 44
E-Mail: email@e-p-g.de
Web Site: www.e-p-g.de
Q9Z—(DEU)
Sales Range: $1-9.9 Million
Business Description:
Nanotechnology Product Mfr
S.I.C.: 3999
N.A.I.C.S.: 339999
Personnel:
Andreas Zimmermann *(Member-Mgmt Bd)*

ENGINEERING INGEGNERIA INFORMATICA S.P.A.

(d/b/a Gruppo Engineering)
Via San Martino della Battaglia 56
00185 Rome, Italy
Tel.: (39) 06492011
Fax: (39) 4453278
E-Mail: info@eng.it
Web Site: www.eng.it
Year Founded: 1980
ENG—(ITA)
Rev.: $1,036,604,848
Assets: $1,273,821,617
Liabilities: $812,922,731
Net Worth: $460,898,886
Earnings: $56,814,910
Emp.: 6,844
Fiscal Year-end: 12/31/12
Business Description:
Engineering Services
S.I.C.: 8711
N.A.I.C.S.: 541330
Personnel:
Michele Cinaglia *(Chm)*
Rosario Amodeo *(Vice Chm)*
Tommaso Amodeo *(Vice Chm)*
Paolo Pandozy *(CEO)*
Luca Sabelli *(Sec)*
Board of Directors:
Michele Cinaglia
Rosario Amodeo
Tommaso Amodeo
Alberto De Nigro
Giuliano Mari
Marilena Menicucci
Paolo Pandozy
Massimo Porfiri
Dario Schlesinger

Subsidiaries:

Engineering Tributi S.p.A (1)
Via San Martino Della Battaglia 56
Rome, 00185, Italy
Tel.: (39) 06492011
Fax: (39) 064453278
Information Technology Services
S.I.C.: 7373
N.A.I.C.S.: 541512

Engineering.IT S.p.A (1)
Via Carlo Maria Viola 76
Pont San Martin, Aosta, 11026, Italy
Tel.: (39) 683074240
Fax: (39) 0125810200
Information Technology Services
S.I.C.: 7373
N.A.I.C.S.: 541512

Subsidiary:

Sitel S.r.l (2)
Via XXIV Maggio 143
31015 Conegliano, Italy
Tel.: (39) 043832248
Fax: (39) 043835865
E-Mail: info@sitelsrl.com
Web Site: www.sitelsrl.com
Telecommunications & Networking Services
S.I.C.: 4899
N.A.I.C.S.: 517919

Engiweb Security S.R.L. (1)
Via San Martino della Battaglia 56
00185 Rome, Italy (100%)
Tel.: (39) 06492011
Fax: (39) 0649201389
E-Mail: info@engiweb.com
Web Site: www.engiweb.com
Emp.: 23
Business Security Software Applications
S.I.C.: 7382
N.A.I.C.S.: 561621

EngO S.p.A (1)
Via San Martino Della Battaglia 56
Rome, 00185, Italy
Tel.: (39) 0683074240
Fax: (39) 064453278
E-Mail: info@eng-o.it
Web Site: www.eng-o.it
Business Processing Outsourcing Services
S.I.C.: 7389
N.A.I.C.S.: 561499
Alfredo Belsito *(Pres)*
Gabriele Corno *(CEO)*

Neta S.p.A. (1)
Via Edison 2
Osimo, 60027 Ancona, Italy (98%)
Tel.: (39) 0717202050
E-Mail: infomarketing@netanet.it
Web Site: www.netanet.it
Emp.: 275
Utilities IT Solutions & Services
S.I.C.: 7379
N.A.I.C.S.: 541519

Engineering Ingegneria Informatica S.p.A.—(Continued)

Nexen S.p.A (1)
Corso Stati Uniti 23/C
35127 Padua, Italy
Tel.: (39) 0498283411
Fax: (39) 0498702624
E-Mail: info@nexen.it
Web Site: www.nexen.it
Business Consulting Services
S.I.C.: 7389
N.A.I.C.S.: 561499

Overit S.r.l. (1)
Via Bassi 81
Fiume Veneto, 33080 Pordenone, Italy (80%)
Tel.: (39) 0434562911
Fax: (39) 0434562964
E-Mail: info@overit.it
Web Site: www.overit.it
Emp.: 60
Software & IT Services
S.I.C.: 7379
N.A.I.C.S.: 541519
Marco Zanuttini *(Mng Dir)*

Softlab Sp.A. (1)
Via V Mazzola 66
00142 Rome, Italy (99.95%)
Tel.: (39) 06510391
Fax: (39) 065035929
E-Mail: softlab@soft.it
Web Site: www.soft.it
Emp.: 580
IT Services
S.I.C.: 7379
N.A.I.C.S.: 541519
Raffaele Rubinacci *(Mng Dir)*

Affiliate:

Engineering Progetti Speciali S.r.l. (1)
Guido Lfami 29
00135 Rome, Italy (55%)
Tel.: (39) 0645438469
Fax: (39) 0644360682
E-Mail: info@eng-ps.it
Web Site: www.eng-ps.it
Software Solutions
S.I.C.: 7379
N.A.I.C.S.: 541519

Non-U.S. Subsidiaries:

Engineering International Belgium SA (1)
Rue de la Loi 81/A
1040 Brussels, Belgium
Tel.: (32) 2 2305707
Fax: (32) 2 2304391
Information Technology Consulting Services
S.I.C.: 7373
N.A.I.C.S.: 541512

Engitech Ltd (1)
Jassamine House Main St
Celbridge, Kildare, Ireland (100%)
Tel.: (353) 1 5058500
Fax: (353) 1 5058524
E-Mail: info@engitech.ie
Web Site: www.engitech.ie
Emp.: 19
IT Products & Services
S.I.C.: 7379
N.A.I.C.S.: 541519
Francesco Bonino *(Mng Dir)*

ENGINEERING.COM INCORPORATED

5285 Solar Drive Suite 101
Mississauga, ON, L4W 5B8, Canada
Tel.: (905) 273-9991
Fax: (905) 273-6691
Toll Free: (877) 997-9917
E-Mail: info@engineering.com
Web Site: www.engineering.com
Year Founded: 2000
Rev.: $1,861,537
Assets: $841,182
Liabilities: $632,805
Net Worth: $208,377
Earnings: ($155,434)
Emp.: 7
Fiscal Year-end: 12/31/12

Business Description:
Online Engineering Information & Resource Services
S.I.C.: 2741
N.A.I.C.S.: 519130

Personnel:
Frank G. Baldesarra *(Chm, CEO, Treas & Sec)*
John Hayes *(Pres & CFO)*

Board of Directors:
Frank G. Baldesarra
G. Ron Baldesarra
Hugo J. Blasutta
C. James Cooper
Brian W. Semkiw
Dennis Semkiw

Transfer Agent:
Equity Financial Trust Company
200 University Avenue Suite 400
Toronto, ON, M5H 4H1, Canada
Tel.: (416) 361-0152
Fax: (416) 361-0470
Toll Free: (866) 393-4891

ENGINEERS INDIA LTD.

Engineers India Bhawan 1 Bhikaiji Cama Place RK Puram
New Delhi, 110066, India
Tel.: (91) 11 26762121
Fax: (91) 11 26186245
E-Mail: eil.mktg@eil.co.in
Web Site: www.engineersindia.com
Year Founded: 1965
532178—(BOM NSE)
Rev.: $527,616,826
Assets: $724,414,180
Liabilities: $298,877,407
Net Worth: $425,536,773
Earnings: $117,209,398
Emp.: 3,379
Fiscal Year-end: 03/31/13

Business Description:
Heavy Engineering Services
S.I.C.: 1629
N.A.I.C.S.: 237990

Personnel:
A. K. Purwaha *(Chm & Mng Dir)*
R. Mohan *(COO)*
Rajan Kapur *(Compliance Officer & Sec)*

Board of Directors:
A. K. Purwaha
Bijoy Chatterjee
Ajay N. Deshpande
J. P. Gupta
Sanjay Gupta
Adit Jain
Archana S. Mathur
Deepak Moudgil
R. K. Shevgaonkar
Ram Singh
Veena Swarup

Transfer Agent:
Karvy Computershare Private Limited
305 New Delhi House 27 Barakhamba Road
Connaught Pl
New Delhi, India

ENGINES ENGINEERING S.R.L.

Via Pasquali 6
Castenaso, Bologna, 40055, Italy
Tel.: (39) 516050312
Fax: (39) 0516050049
E-Mail: info@engineseng.com
Web Site: www.enginesengineering.com
Year Founded: 1979
Sales Range: $10-24.9 Million
Emp.: 50

Business Description:
Motorcycles Mfr
S.I.C.: 3751
N.A.I.C.S.: 336991

Personnel:
Alberto Strazzari *(Pres & Mng Dir)*

ENGLISH NATIONAL OPERA

The London Coliseum
London, WC2N 4ES, United Kingdom
Tel.: (44) 2078360111
Fax: (44) 2078459270
E-Mail: feedback@eno.org
Web Site: www.eno.org
Year Founded: 1931
Sales Range: $25-49.9 Million
Emp.: 500

Business Description:
Music Producer
S.I.C.: 7929
N.A.I.C.S.: 711130

Personnel:
Peter Bazalgette *(Deputy Chm)*
Vernon Ellis *(Pres)*
Loretta Tomasi *(CEO)*
John Cooke *(Sec)*

Board of Directors:
Nicholas Allan
Gyln Barker
Peter Bazalgette
Harry Brunjes
David Buchler
John Cooke
Anthony Fry
Ffion Hague
David Harrel
Nicholas Kenyon
Anthony Lilley
Janis Susskind

ENGLOBE CORP.

4495 Wilfrid-Hamel Blvd Suite 100
Quebec, QC, G1P 2J7, Canada
Tel.: (418) 781-0191
Fax: (418) 653-3583
E-Mail: info@englobecorp.com
Web Site: www.englobecorp.com
Year Founded: 2000
Sales Range: $125-149.9 Million
Emp.: 346

Business Description:
Environmental Services & Waste Management
S.I.C.: 4959
N.A.I.C.S.: 562998

Personnel:
Michael D. Harris *(Chm)*
Andre Heroux *(Pres & CEO)*
Georges Szaraz *(Sr VP-Organic Waste Mgmt)*
Marie-Chantal Turcotte *(Sr VP-Legal Affairs, HR & Corp Comm)*

Board of Directors:
Michael D. Harris
Allen Clarke
Andre Heroux

Legal Counsel:
Aird & Berlis
Toronto, ON, Canada

Transfer Agent:
Equity Transfer
120 Adelaide St Ste 800
Toronto, ON, M5H 3V1, Canada
Tel.: (416) 361-0152

Subsidiaries:

Biogenie S.R.D.C. Inc. (1)
350 Franquet Street
Quebec, QC, G1P 4P3, Canada
Tel.: (418) 653-2074
Fax: (418) 653-2675
Toll Free: (877) 653-2074
E-Mail: marketing@biogenie-env.com
Web Site: www.biogenie-env.com
Sales Range: $25-49.9 Million
Site Assessments
S.I.C.: 9511
N.A.I.C.S.: 924110
Jean-Pierre Dutil *(Gen Mgr)*

GSI Environnement (1)
1501 Lionel-Boulet Blvd
Varennes, QC, J3X 1P7, Canada
Tel.: (450) 929-4949
Fax: (450) 929-1659
E-Mail: montreal@gsienv.ca
Web Site: www.gsienv.ca
Emp.: 20
Environmental Management Services
S.I.C.: 8999
N.A.I.C.S.: 541620
Alain Danis *(CFO)*

Tanknology Canada Inc. (1)
3295 Mainway Unit No 6
Burlington, ON, L7M 1A6, Canada
Tel.: (905) 681-5542
Fax: (905) 681-6473
Toll Free: (800) 465-1577
E-Mail: info@tanknology.ca
Web Site: www.tanknology.ca
Emp.: 20
Construction of Building & Civil Engineering Work
S.I.C.: 1611
N.A.I.C.S.: 237310
Peter Sutherland *(Pres)*

ENGRO CORPORATION LIMITED

8th Floor Harbor Front Building HC 3
Marine Drive Block 4 Clifton
Karachi, 74000, Pakistan
Tel.: (92) 2135297501
Fax: (92) 2135810669
E-Mail: info@engro.com
Web Site: www.engro.com
ENGRO—(KAR)
Sls.: $1,267,782,385
Assets: $1,920,513,291
Liabilities: $1,482,418,284
Net Worth: $438,095,007
Earnings: $18,205,910
Emp.: 3,794
Fiscal Year-end: 12/31/12

Business Description:
Fertilizer Mfr
S.I.C.: 2875
N.A.I.C.S.: 325314

Personnel:
Hussain Dawood *(Chm)*
Muhammad Aliuddin Ansari *(Pres & CEO)*
Naz Khan *(CFO)*
Khalid Siraj Subhani *(Pres/CEO-Engro Polymer & Chemical Limited)*
Imran ul-Haque *(Pres/CEO-Engro Vopak Terminal Limited)*
Shamsuddin A. Shaikh *(CEO-Sindh Engro Coal Mining Company)*
Andalib Alavi *(Sec & Gen Mgr-Legal)*
Tahir Jawaid *(Sr VP)*

Board of Directors:
Hussain Dawood
Afnan Ahsan
Muhammad Aliuddin Ansari
Abdul Samad Dawood
Shahzada Dawood
Shabbir Hashmi
Khawaja Iqbal Hassan
Ruhail Mohammed
Shahid Hamid Pracha
Saad Raja
Sarfaraz Ahmed Rehman
Khalid Siraj Subhani

Engro Fertilizers Limited (1)
7th & 8th Floors Harbor Front Building
Marine Drive Block 4
Clifton, Karachi, Pakistan
Tel.: (92) 21 111211211
Fax: (92) 21 35810669
Web Site: www.engrofertilizers.com
EFERT—(KAR LAH)
Sls.: $310,246,648
Assets: $987,751,583
Liabilities: $827,717,569
Net Worth: $160,034,014
Earnings: ($29,727,245)
Emp.: 1,160
Fiscal Year-end: 12/31/12
Fertilizers Mfr & Distr
S.I.C.: 2875
N.A.I.C.S.: 325314

Muhammad Aliuddin Ansari *(Chm)*
Ruhail Mohammed *(Pres & CEO)*

Engro Foods Limited (1)
5 & 6th Floor Harbor Front Building Marine Drive Block 4
Clifton, Karachi, 75600, Pakistan (100%)
Tel.: (92) 21 111 211 211
Fax: (92) 35295961
Rev.: $243,759,000
Emp.: 1,223
Dairy Products Mfr
S.I.C.: 0241
N.A.I.C.S.: 112120
Muhammed Affnen Ahsan *(CEO)*

Engro Polymers & Chemicals Limited (1)
16th Floor The Harbour Front Building HC-3 Marine Drive Block 4
Scheme-5 Clifton, Karachi, 75600, Pakistan (56.2%)
Tel.: (92) 2135293871
Fax: (92) 2135293886
E-Mail: epcl-info@engro.com
Web Site: www.engropolymer.com
EPCL-PRO (KAR)
Rev.: $208,734,738
Assets: $254,175,517
Liabilities: $190,072,837
Net Worth: $64,102,681
Earnings: $780,101
Emp.: 574
Fiscal Year-end: 12/31/12
Plastics Material & Resin Mfr
S.I.C.: 2821
N.A.I.C.S.: 325211
Muhammad Aliuddin Ansari *(Chm)*
Khalid Siraj Subhani *(Pres & CEO)*
Haseeb Hafeezuddeen *(CFO)*
Kaleem Ahmad *(Sec)*

Joint Venture:

Engro Vopak Terminal Ltd (1)
1st Floor Bahria Complex 1 M T Khan Rd
74000 Karachi, Pakistan
Tel.: (92) 21111311311
Fax: (92) 215611394
E-Mail: evtl@engro.com
Web Site: www.vopak.com
Emp.: 80
Other Chemical & Allied Products Merchant Whslr
S.I.C.: 5169
N.A.I.C.S.: 424690
Imran Ul-Haque *(Pres & CEO)*

ENGRO CORPORATION LIMITED

29 International Business Park 08 05 06 Acer Building Tower B
Singapore, 609923, Singapore
Tel.: (65) 65617978
Telex: sancem rs26203
Fax: (65) 65619770
Web Site: www.engro-global.com
Year Founded: 1973
S44—(SES)
Rev.: $111,365,816
Assets: $175,470,611
Liabilities: $24,185,951
Net Worth: $151,284,660
Earnings: $9,172,055
Fiscal Year-end: 12/31/12

Business Description:
Cement Mfr
S.I.C.: 3241
N.A.I.C.S.: 327310

Personnel:
Cheng Gay Tan *(Chm & CEO)*
Jimmy Ho *(COO)*
Joanna Lan Sim Lim *(Co-Sec)*
Siew Tian Low *(Co-Sec)*

Board of Directors:
Cheng Gay Tan
Tat Pun Ng
Kim Soon Soh
Yok Koon Tan
Ronnie Heng Hock Teo

Subsidiaries:

Resin & Pigment Technologies Pte Ltd (1)
1 Banyan Place
Jurong Island, Singapore, 627841, Singapore
Tel.: (65) 68624588
Fax: (65) 68624353
E-Mail: sales@resinpts.com
Web Site: www.resinpts.com
Emp.: 60
Polymer Processing & Compounding Services
S.I.C.: 3087
N.A.I.C.S.: 325991
Chi Tsung Wong *(Mng Dir)*

Sancem Investment Pte Ltd (1)
29 International Business Park Acer Building Tower B
Singapore, 609923, Singapore
Tel.: (65) 6561 7978
Investment Management Services
S.I.C.: 6211
N.A.I.C.S.: 523999

SsangYong Cement (S) Pte Ltd (1)
Acer Building
Singapore, 609923, Singapore
Tel.: (65) 65617978
Fax: (65) 656179770
E-Mail: info@engro-global.com
Web Site: www.engro-global.com
Emp.: 200
Construction Materials Sales
S.I.C.: 5032
N.A.I.C.S.: 423320
Cheng Gay Tan *(CEO)*

SsangYong Cement Singapore (China) Pte Ltd (1)
Acer Building 29 International Business Park
Singapore, 609923, Singapore
Tel.: (65) 65617978
Cement Mfr
S.I.C.: 3241
N.A.I.C.S.: 327310

SsangYong LTI Pte Ltd (1)
29 International Business Park Acer Building
Singapore, 609923, Singapore
Tel.: (65) 6561 7978
Fax: (65) 619770
Web Site: www.engro-global.com
Investment Management Services
S.I.C.: 8741
N.A.I.C.S.: 551114

Top Mix Concrete Pte Ltd (1)
29 Intl Business Pk
Acer Bldg Tower B # 08-05/06, Singapore, 609923, Singapore SG (100%)
Tel.: (65) 65617978
Telex: sancem rs 26203
Fax: (65) 65619770
Emp.: 53
Concrete Mfr
S.I.C.: 3273
N.A.I.C.S.: 327320
Tan Cheng Gay *(CEO)*

Non-U.S. Subsidiary:

Shanghai S3 Building Materials Co Ltd (1)
18 Nan Wen Zao Bang Road Ye Qiao
Baoshan District, Shanghai, 200435, China
Tel.: (86) 21 5641 3366
Fax: (86) 21 5643 0624
Web Site: www.s3tasia.com
Building Materials Mfr & Distr
S.I.C.: 2891
N.A.I.C.S.: 325520

ENGTEX GROUP BERHAD

Lot 36 Jalan BRP 9/2B Putra Indus Pk Bukit Rahman Putra
47000 Sungai Buloh, Selangor Darul Ehsan, Malaysia
Tel.: (60) 361401111
Fax: (60) 361401919
E-Mail: enquiry@engtex.com.my
Web Site: www.engtex.com.my
ENGTEX—(KLS)
Rev.: $301,836,587
Assets: $253,796,307
Liabilities: $146,869,138
Net Worth: $106,927,170
Earnings: $10,132,400
Fiscal Year-end: 12/31/12

Business Description:
Hardware Distr & Precision Components Mfr
S.I.C.: 5251
N.A.I.C.S.: 444130

Personnel:
Hook Ng *(Mng Dir)*
Chong Keong Khoo *(Sec)*
Seck Wah Lim *(Sec)*
Chi Hoe Tang *(Sec)*

Board of Directors:
Ismail Hamzah
Mee Foon Chin
Chooi Guan Ng
Hook Ng
Yik Soon Ng
Chee Ghee Teh
Seng Kuan Yap

Subsidiaries:

Allpipes Technology Sdn. Bhd. (1)
Lot 36 Jalan Brp 9/2B PUTRA Industrial park Bkt rahman Putra
47000 Sungai Buloh, Selangor, Malaysia
Tel.: (60) 361401111
Fax: (60) 361404545
Emp.: 100
Iron Pipe Fittings & Mfr
S.I.C.: 3321
N.A.I.C.S.: 331511
Cheah Hock Kee *(Mgr-Sls)*

Subsidiaries:

Canova Manufacturing Sdn. Bhd. (2)
Lot 3757 29 Batu Jalan Kl-Ipoh
Serendah, Selangor, 48200, Malaysia
Tel.: (60) 360813836
Fax: (60) 360813845
E-Mail: allpipes@engtex.com.my
Emp.: 150
Steel Water Tank & Pipe Fittings Mfr
S.I.C.: 3321
N.A.I.C.S.: 331511
Cheah Hock Kee *(Gen Mgr)*

Nagasari Bitumen Products Sdn. Bhd. (2)
Lot 3757 Batu 29 Jalan KL Ipoh
48200 Serendah, Selangor, Malaysia
Tel.: (60) 360813836
Fax: (60) 360813845
Iron Pipe & Fittings Mfr
S.I.C.: 3321
N.A.I.C.S.: 331511
Cheah Hock Kee *(Gen Mgr)*

Benton Corporation Sdn. Bhd. (1)
No 6 Jln Brp 9/2B Taman Industri Putra
47000 Sungai Buloh, Malaysia
Tel.: (60) 361575757
Fax: (60) 361571188
Emp.: 8
Iron Pipe Fittings Mfr
S.I.C.: 3322
N.A.I.C.S.: 331511
Chong Keong Khoo *(Acct Mgr-Fin)*

East Coast Manufacturing Sdn. Bhd. (1)
Lot 10769 Jln Gebeng 1/2 Kaw Perindustrian Gebeng
26080 Kuantan, Pahang, Malaysia
Tel.: (60) 95839898
Fax: (60) 95839889
E-Mail: ecm_khorcl@yahoo.com
Web Site: www.engtexgroup.com
Emp.: 50
Steel Products Mfr
S.I.C.: 3312
N.A.I.C.S.: 331221
Cl Khor *(Gen Mgr)*

East Coast Metals Sdn. Bhd. (1)
Lot 10769 Jln Gebeng 1/2
26080 Kuantan, Pahang, Malaysia
Tel.: (60) 95662833
Fax: (60) 95839889
E-Mail: ecm.liowzw@yahoo.com
Iron Pipe Fittings Mfr
S.I.C.: 3498
N.A.I.C.S.: 332996

Eng Lian Hup Trading Sdn. Bhd. (1)
No 910 Jln Perindustrian Bukit Minyak
14000 Bukit Mertajam, Penang, Malaysia
Tel.: (60) 45082666
Fax: (60) 45082555
E-Mail: elht@tm.net.my
Iron Pipe Fittings Mfr
S.I.C.: 3317
N.A.I.C.S.: 331210

Subsidiary:

Apsonic Sdn. Bhd. (2)
910 Jalan Perindustrian Bukit Minyak
Mukim 13 Kawasan Perindustrian
Bukit Minyak, 14100 Bukit Mertajam, Penang, Malaysia
Tel.: (60) 45071222
Fax: (60) 45021222
Financial & Real Estate Planning Services
S.I.C.: 6211
N.A.I.C.S.: 523999
Boon Yew Yong *(Mgr)*

Engtex Ductile Iron Pipes Industry Sdn. Bhd. (1)
Lot 68 Kawasan Perindustrian Gebeng
26080 Kuantan, Pahang, Malaysia
Tel.: (60) 95837822
Fax: (60) 95837827
E-Mail: edip@engtex.com.my
Emp.: 100
Iron Pipe Fittings Mfr
S.I.C.: 3494
N.A.I.C.S.: 332919
Simon Quah *(Mng Dir)*

Engtex Metals Sdn. Bhd. (1)
Lot 443 Off Jalan Abdul Aziz Batu 30
Jalan Kuala Selangor, 45600 Kuala Lumpur, Malaysia
Tel.: (60) 361401554
Fax: (60) 361404545
E-Mail: engtexmetals@engtex.com.my
Web Site: www.engtex.com.my/CorporateDirectory.html
Emp.: 70
Iron Pipe Fittings Mfr
S.I.C.: 3317
N.A.I.C.S.: 331210
Wong Ah Choo *(Gen Mgr)*

Engtex Properties Sdn. Bhd. (1)
No 2 Level 10 Wisma Menjalara Jalan 7A/62A
Bandar Manjalara, Kuala Lumpur, Federal Territory, 52200, Malaysia
Tel.: (60) 362801594
Fax: (60) 362779532
Web Site: www.engtexproperties.com.my
Emp.: 15
Property Development Services
S.I.C.: 6531
N.A.I.C.S.: 531390
Geok Ai Lee *(Gen Mgr)*

LYE Marketing Sdn. Bhd. (1)
Lot 36 Jalan BRP 9/2B Putra Industrial Park Bukit Rahman Putra
47000 Sungai Buloh, Selangor, Malaysia
Tel.: (60) 361403131
Fax: (60) 361405858
E-Mail: enquiry@lye.com.my
Web Site: www.lye.com.my
Emp.: 200
Valves Mfr & Distr
S.I.C.: 3491
N.A.I.C.S.: 332911
Ng Chooi Guan *(Mng Dir)*

Mega Alliance Builder Supplies Sdn. Bhd. (1)
Lot 36 Jalan BRP 9/2B Putra Industrial Park Bukit Rahman Putra
Sungai Buloh, Selangor, 47000, Malaysia
Tel.: (60) 361403722
Fax: (60) 361414215
Emp.: 12
Iron Pipe Fittings Mfr
S.I.C.: 3321
N.A.I.C.S.: 331511

Non-U.S. Subsidiary:

Engtex (S) Pte. Ltd. (1)
No 32 Tuas South Street 3
Singapore, 638029, Singapore

Engtex Group Berhad—(Continued)

Tel.: (65) 67950779
Fax: (65) 65587885
Web Site: www.engtex.com.my/CorporateDirectory.html
Emp.: 13
Ductile Iron Pipe Fittings Mfr
S.I.C.: 3494
N.A.I.C.S.: 332919
Goh Wai Keong *(Gen Mgr)*

ENGYCO PLC

22 Grenville Street
Saint Helier, JE4 8PX, Jersey
Tel.: (44) 1534609556
Fax: (44) 1534635875
E-Mail: info@engyco.com
Web Site: www.engyco.com
Business Description:
Solar Power
S.I.C.: 4931
N.A.I.C.S.: 221118
Personnel:
John Roberts *(Chm)*
Alexander Voigt *(Vice Chm)*
Thomas Krupke *(CEO)*
Mark Kirkland *(CFO)*
Ulrich Prochaska *(CTO)*
Board of Directors:
John Roberts
John Danilovich
Charles Gave
Mark Kirkland
Thomas Krupke
Pedro Mielgo
Martin Negre
Ulrich Prochaska
Thomas van Aubel
Alexander Voigt

ENHANCE SKIN PRODUCTS INC.

100 King Street West 56th Floor
Toronto, ON, M5X 1C9, Canada
Tel.: (416) 644-8318
Toll Free: (800) 817-7161
E-Mail: info@visibleyouth.com
Web Site: www.enhanceskinproducts.com
Year Founded: 2006
EHSK—(OTC OTCB)
Rev.: $3,089
Assets: $34,543
Liabilities: $384,586
Net Worth: ($350,043)
Earnings: ($244,748)
Fiscal Year-end: 04/30/13
Business Description:
Cosmetics Mfr
S.I.C.: 2844
N.A.I.C.S.: 325620
Personnel:
Samuel S. Asculai *(Chm & Chief Scientific Officer)*
Donald Nicholson *(Pres, CEO & CFO)*
Drasko Puseljic *(Gen Counsel)*
Board of Directors:
Samuel S. Asculai
Frode Botnevik
Donald Nicholson
Transfer Agent:
Globex Transfer, LLC
789 Deltona Blvd
Deltona, FL 32725

ENI S.P.A.

1 piazzale Enrico Mattei
00144 Rome, Italy
Tel.: (39) 0659821
Fax: (39) 06 5982 2141
E-Mail: investor.relations@eni.it
Web Site: www.eni.com
Year Founded: 1953
E—(ITA NYSE)
Rev.: $173,340,926,220
Assets: $187,980,524,970
Liabilities: $103,558,165,760
Net Worth: $84,422,359,210
Earnings: $11,675,332,410
Emp.: 77,838
Fiscal Year-end: 12/31/12
Business Description:
Petroleum & Natural Gas Products & Services
S.I.C.: 1311
N.A.I.C.S.: 211111
Personnel:
Giuseppe Recchi *(Chm)*
Paolo Scaroni *(CEO)*
Massimo Mondazzi *(CFO)*
Salvatore Sardo *(COO)*
Massimo Mantovani *(Gen Counsel-Legal Affairs & Sr Exec VP)*
Stefano Lucchini *(Sr Exec VP-Public Affairs & Comm)*
Leonardo Maugeri *(Sr Exec VP-Strategies & Dev)*
Roberto Ulissi *(Sr Exec VP-Corp Affairs & Governance)*
Giulio Bozzini *(Exec VP-Plng & Control)*
Board of Directors:
Giuseppe Recchi
Carlo Cesare Gatto
Alessandro Lorenzi
Paolo Marchioni
Roberto Petri
Alessandro Profumo
Mario Resca
Paolo Scaroni
Francesco Taranto
Transfer Agent:
The Bank of New York Mellon
PO Box 358516
Pittsburgh, PA 15122

Division:

Eni S.p.A. - Gas & Power Division **(1)**
Villa De Gasperi 16 San Donato Milanese
20097 Milan, San Donato Milanese, Italy (100%)
Tel.: (39) 025201
Telex: 310246ENI-I
Fax: (39) 0252031935
Rev.: $9,500,000,000
Emp.: 100
Purchaser, Transporter, Distributor & Seller of Imported & Domestic Natural Gas; Oil Transportation by Sea & Land; Gasoline & Oil Pipeline
S.I.C.: 4924
N.A.I.C.S.: 221210

Subsidiary:

Immobiliare Metanopoli S.p.A. **(2)**
Via Martiri di Cefalonia N 67
20097 San Donato Milanese, Italy (90.39%)
Tel.: (39) 0252054014
Fax: (39) 02 5204 4303
Emp.: 6
Provider of Real Estate Services
S.I.C.: 6531
N.A.I.C.S.: 531210

Affiliates:

Acquedotto di Domodossola S.p.A. **(2)**
Via San Quintono 14
Turin, Italy (25.84%)
Tel.: (39) 01155941
Water Transport & Distribution
S.I.C.: 4971
N.A.I.C.S.: 221310

Acquedotto di Savona S.p.A. **(2)**
Largo Folconi 3
17100 Savona, Italy (26.29%)
Tel.: (39) 019 840171
Fax: (39) 019 84017220
Emp.: 34
Water Transport & Distribution
S.I.C.: 4941
N.A.I.C.S.: 221310

Acquedotto Monferrato S.p.A. **(2)**
Corso Re Umberto N 9 Bis
10121 Turin, Italy (26.29%)
Tel.: (39) 01155941
Fax: (39) 0115629730
Web Site: www.eni.it
Water Transport & Distribution
S.I.C.: 4971
N.A.I.C.S.: 221310

Societa Italiana Per Il Gas **(2)**
Via XX Settembre 41
10121 Turin, Italy (100%)
Tel.: (39) 01123941
Telex: 221595 ITALGAS
Fax: (39) 0112394799
Web Site: www.italgas.it
Sales Range: $700-749.9 Million
Emp.: 5,165
Hydrocarbon Transport & Gas Distribution
S.I.C.: 4924
N.A.I.C.S.: 221210

Subsidiary:

Toscana Energia S.p.A. **(3)**
Via dei Neri 25
50122 Florence, Italy
Tel.: (39) 055 43801
Fax: (39) 55 216390
Web Site: www.toscanaenergia.eu
Sls.: $898,089,192
Emp.: 347
Hydrocarbons Transport & Gas Distribution; Owned by Italgas S.p.A. (41.75%) & Snam S.p.A. (9.28%)
S.I.C.: 4924
N.A.I.C.S.: 221210
Lorenzo Becattini *(Pres)*

Veneziana Gas S.p.A. **(2)**
Forte Marghera 140 Mestre
30173 Venice, Italy (64%)
Tel.: (39) 0412389111
Fax: (39) 0412389222
Sls.: $75,235,317
Emp.: 244
Hydrocarbons Transport & Gas Distribution
S.I.C.: 4924
N.A.I.C.S.: 221210

Non-U.S. Subsidiaries:

Scogat SA Societe Pour la Construction du Gazoduc Transt **(2)**
Centre Urbain Du Nord Boulevard 7 Novembre 1082
Tunis, Tunisia (100%)
Tel.: (216) 71 238522
Fax: (216) 71 237224
E-Mail: info@greenstreambv.com
Web Site: www.ttpc.it
Sls.: $8,867,000
Emp.: 48
Pipeline Construction
S.I.C.: 1629
N.A.I.C.S.: 237120
Agrebe Mohamed *(Gen Mgr)*

Subsidiaries:

Agenzia Giornalistica Italia SpA **(1)**
Via Ostiense 72
154 Rome, Italy
Tel.: (39) 06519961
Fax: (39) 0651996362
E-Mail: info@agi.it
Web Site: www.agenziaitalia.it
Emp.: 82
News Agency Management Services
S.I.C.: 7383
N.A.I.C.S.: 519110
Gianni Di Giovanni *(CEO)*

Agip S.p.A. **(1)**
Via Emilia 1
20097 San Donato Milanese, Italy (100%)
Tel.: (39) 025201
Telex: 310246-ENI
Fax: (39) 025261846
Web Site: www.agip.it
Rev.: $5,986,000,000
Hydrocarbon Exploration & Production
S.I.C.: 2911
N.A.I.C.S.: 324110

Subsidiary:

Eni S.p.A. - Refining & Marketing Division **(2)**
Via Laurentina 449
I 00142 Rome, Italy (100%)
Tel.: (39) 0659881
Telex: 614031
Fax: (39) 0659885700
Web Site: www.agippetroli.it
Petroleum Refining; Operator of Service Stations
S.I.C.: 1311
N.A.I.C.S.: 211111
Angelo Fanelli *(COO)*

U.S. Subsidiaries:

Eni Petroleum **(3)**
1201 Louisiana St Ste 3500
Houston, TX 77002-5617 DE
Tel.: (504) 593-7000
Fax: (504) 593-7225
Web Site: www.enipetroleum.it
Emp.: 407
Energy Exploration & Production
S.I.C.: 1389
N.A.I.C.S.: 213112
Kevin Guilbeau *(Sr VP & Gen Mgr)*

Non-U.S. Subsidiaries:

Agip (Africa) Ltd. **(3)**
Appt B 3 2 7 Rue Chott Errommen
PO Box 1073
Montplaisir, Tunis, 1073, Tunisia (100%)
Tel.: (216) 71 90 3141
Fax: (216) 71 90 9426
E-Mail: tunisia@agip.com
Web Site: www.agip.com
Emp.: 6
Intellectual Property Development
S.I.C.: 7372
N.A.I.C.S.: 511210
Fathi Abu-Nimeh *(Gen Mgr)*

Agip (Suisse) S.A. **(3)**
World Trade Ctr Lausanne
PO Box 512
Av De Gratta Paille 1, CH 1000 Lausanne, Switzerland (100%)
Tel.: (41) 216443111
Fax: (41) 216443101
E-Mail: info@agip.ch
Web Site: www.agip.ch
Sls.: $245,000,000
Emp.: 80
Petroleum Wholesaling
S.I.C.: 5172
N.A.I.C.S.: 424720
Riccardo Piunti *(Gen Mgr)*

Eni Ceska Republika, s.r.o. **(3)**
Sokolovska 394/17
CZ 186 00 Prague, 8, Czech Republic (100%)
Tel.: (420) 224495111
Fax: (420) 224495226
E-Mail: info@agip.cz
Web Site: www.eniceska.cz
Emp.: 80
Crude Oil Processor & Petroleum Products Mfr
S.I.C.: 1311
N.A.I.C.S.: 211111
Massimo Bechi *(Mng Dir)*

Eni Deutschland GmbH **(3)**
Sonnenstrasse 23
D 80331 Munich, Germany (100%)
Tel.: (49) 8959070
Fax: (49) 89596303
Web Site: www.eni.com
Sales Range: $1-4.9 Billion
Emp.: 100
Petroleum Refining & Wholesaling
S.I.C.: 2911
N.A.I.C.S.: 324110

Subsidiary:

Bronberger & Kessler Handelsgesellschaft GmbH **(4)**
Dreimuhlen Strasse
82065 Munich, Germany (100%)
Tel.: (49) 8972901
Fax: (49) 897290250
E-Mail: info@bronberger-kessler.de
Web Site: www.bronberger-kessler.de
Emp.: 20
S.I.C.: 1311
N.A.I.C.S.: 211111
Tobias Schweiger *(Mng Dir)*

Eni Magyarorszagon **(3)**
Agip Komplexum
1 PF 164 H 2041 Dell Oldal Pos, 2040
Budapest, Hungary (65%)

Tel.: (36) 23415550
Fax: (36) 23415556
E-Mail:
Web Site: www.eni.com
Emp.: 50
Petroleum & Natural Gas
S.I.C.: 1311
N.A.I.C.S.: 211111

Compagnia Napoletana di illuminazione e Scaldamento col Gas SpA (1)
Via Galileo Ferraris 66/F
80142 Naples, Italy
Tel.: (39) 081 5831 909
Fax: (39) 081 5831 418
E-Mail: napoletanagas.concessioni@pec.eni.it
Natural Gas Distribution Services
S.I.C.: 4924
N.A.I.C.S.: 221210

Costiero Gas Livorno SpA (1)
Via Leonardo Da Vinci 23
Livorno, 57123, Italy
Tel.: (39) 0586244111
Fax: (39) 0586406221
Oil & Gas Exploration Services
S.I.C.: 1389
N.A.I.C.S.: 213112

Eni Corporate University SpA (1)
Via S Salvo 1
20097 San Donato Milanese, Milan, Italy
Tel.: (39) 025201
Fax: (39) 0252047945
E-Mail: info@enicorporateuniversity.eni.it
Human Resource Consulting Services
S.I.C.: 8999
N.A.I.C.S.: 541612

Eni Fuel Nord SpA (1)
26 V Maritano
San Donato Milanese, Milan, 20097, Italy
Tel.: (39) 02 5201
Fax: (39) 02 52056677
Heating Fuel Whslr
S.I.C.: 5989
N.A.I.C.S.: 454310

EniPower Mantova SpA (1)
Via Taliercio 14
46100 Mantua, Italy
Tel.: (39) 025201
Electric Power Generation Services
S.I.C.: 4931
N.A.I.C.S.: 221118

EniPower SpA (1)
Piazza Vanoni 1
San Donato Milanese, Milan, 20097, Italy
Tel.: (39) 025201
Fax: (39) 0252031804
Electric Power Generation & Distribution Services
S.I.C.: 4931
N.A.I.C.S.: 221118

LNG Shipping SpA (1)
Piazza Vanoni 1
20097 San Donato Milanese, Milan, Italy
Tel.: (39) 02 52041375
Fax: (39) 02 52041380
E-Mail: Operations@lng.eni.it
Web Site: www.eni.com
Natural Gas Transportation Services
S.I.C.: 4922
N.A.I.C.S.: 486210
Emil Montia *(Gen Mgr)*

Petrolig Srl (1)
Calata Canzio
16126 Genoa, Italy
Tel.: (39) 010 265178
Fax: (39) 010 255952
Oil & Gas Exploration Services
S.I.C.: 1389
N.A.I.C.S.: 213112

Polimeri Europa SpA (1)
Piazza Boldrini 1
20097 San Donato Milanese, Milano, Italy
Tel.: (39) 02 520 1
Fax: (39) 02 5204 2814
E-Mail: info@polimerieuropa.com
Web Site: www.polimerieuropa.com
Petrochemical Product Mfr & Distr
S.I.C.: 2869
N.A.I.C.S.: 325110

Saipem S.p.A. (1)
Via Martiri di Cefalonia 67
20097 San Donato Milanese, Italy IT
Tel.: (39) 025201 (43%)
Telex: 310246
Fax: (39) 0252044415
E-Mail: info@saipem.com
Web Site: www.saipem.eni.it
SPM—(ITA)
Rev.: $18,019,831,620
Assets: $23,147,393,150
Liabilities: $15,672,111,140
Net Worth: $7,475,282,010
Earnings: $1,286,938,520
Emp.: 44,980
Fiscal Year-end: 12/31/12
Offshore Construction, Pipe Laying & Drilling
S.I.C.: 8711
N.A.I.C.S.: 541330
Umberto Vergine *(CEO)*
Hugh James O'Donnell *(Deputy CEO)*
Stefano Goberti *(CFO)*
Erika Mandraffino *(Sr VP-Pub Affairs & Comm)*

U.S. Subsidiary:

Saipem America, Inc. (2)
15950 Park Row
Houston, TX 77084
Tel.: (281) 552-5600
Fax: (281) 552-5915
E-Mail: inquiry@saipemamerica.com
Web Site: www.saipemamerica.com
Emp.: 300
Engineering Services
S.I.C.: 8711
N.A.I.C.S.: 541330
Mauro Piasere *(Pres)*

Non-U.S. Subsidiaries:

Moss Maritime A/S (2)
Lysaker Torg 8
PO Box 120
N 1366 Lysaker, Norway (100%)
Tel.: (47) 67526250
Telex: 11578 kmt n
Fax: (47) 67526298
E-Mail: mossmaritime@mossww.com
Web Site: www.mossww.com
Emp.: 70
Gas Technology, Gas Carriers & Rigs Mfr
S.I.C.: 4924
N.A.I.C.S.: 221210
Ida Husem *(Pres)*

Petrex S.A. (2)
Avenida Republica de Panama 3050 San Isidro
Lima, 27, Peru
Tel.: (51) 12215050
Fax: (51) 12225644
Web Site: www.petrex.com.pe
Emp.: 1,200
Oilfield Services
S.I.C.: 1389
N.A.I.C.S.: 213112

Saipem (Malaysia) Sdn. Bhd. (2)
Office Suite 19-21-1 Level 21 UOA Centre
No 19 Jalan Pinang, 50450 Kuala Lumpur, Malaysia
Tel.: (60) 321642466
Fax: (60) 321625657
Oilfield Services
S.I.C.: 1389
N.A.I.C.S.: 213112

Saipem S.A. (2)
Energies 1/7 Av San Fernando
78884 Montigny-le-Bretonneux, St Quentin Yvelines, Cedex, France (100%)
Tel.: (33) 1 61 378888
Telex: 204 420
E-Mail: contact@saipem-sa.com
Web Site: www.saipem.fr
Emp.: 2,200
On/Offshore Sea & River Projects
S.I.C.: 4412
N.A.I.C.S.: 483111

Saipem UK Ltd (2)
Saipem House Station Rd
Motspur Park, New Malden, Surrey, KT3 6JJ, United Kingdom
Tel.: (44) 2082965000
Emp.: 100
Oilfield Services, Construction & Engineering
S.I.C.: 8711
N.A.I.C.S.: 541330
Stefano Porcari *(Mng Dir)*

Sonsub Ltd. (2)
Tern Place Denmore Rd
Bridge of Don, Aberdeen, AB23 8JX, United Kingdom
Tel.: (44) 1224843434
Fax: (44) 1224843435
E-Mail: enquiries@sonsub.saipem.eni.it
Web Site: www.sonsub.com
Emp.: 500
Subsea Construction & Engineering Services
S.I.C.: 1629
N.A.I.C.S.: 237120
Hugh James O'Donnell *(Deputy CEO & Mng Dir)*

Servizi Aerei SpA (1)
Via Carlo Simeoni Snc
Ciampino, Rome, 40, Italy
Tel.: (39) 0679348601
Fax: (39) 0679348637
E-Mail: ops.operazioni@serviziaerei.eni.it
Web Site: www.eni.com
Emp.: 58
Electric Power Distribution Services
S.I.C.: 4931
N.A.I.C.S.: 221122
Daniele Martinelli *(Acct Mgr)*

Snam S.p.A. (1)
Piazza Santa Barbara 7
20097 San Donato Milanese, MI, Italy (50.18%)
Tel.: (39) 0237031
Fax: (39) 0237039227
E-Mail: relazioni.esterne@snam.it
Web Site: www.snam.it
SRG—(ITA)
Rev.: $5,311,986,820
Assets: $30,401,903,280
Liabilities: $22,419,115,180
Net Worth: $7,982,788,100
Earnings: $1,048,666,430
Emp.: 6,051
Fiscal Year-end: 12/31/12
Holding Company; Natural Gas Pipeline Management, Storage & Distribution Services
S.I.C.: 6719
N.A.I.C.S.: 551112
Lorenzo Bini Smaghi *(Chm)*
Carlo Malacarne *(CEO)*

Subsidiaries:

GNL Italia S.p.A. (2)
Piazza S Barbara 7
20097 San Donato Milanese, Italy (100%)
Tel.: (39) 025201
Web Site: www.gnlitalia.it/english/tools/contatti.html
Natural Gas Pipeline Transportation
S.I.C.: 4923
N.A.I.C.S.: 486210

Padana assicurazioni S.p.A. (2)
via Cassinis 21
20139 Milan, Italy
Tel.: (39) 025201
Fax: (39) 0252055240
Web Site: www.padanaassicurazioni.it
Insurance Related Activities
S.I.C.: 6411
N.A.I.C.S.: 524298

Serfactoring S.p.A. (2)
Via Maastricht 1
San Donato Milanese, Italy
Tel.: (39) 0252045690
Credit Intermediation
S.I.C.: 6099
N.A.I.C.S.: 522390

Snam Rete Gas S.p.A. (2)
Piazza Santa Barbara 7
20097 San Donato Milanese, MI, Italy IT
Tel.: (39) 0237031
Fax: (39) 0237039227
Web Site: www.snamretegas.it
Natural Gas Pipeline Transportation Services
S.I.C.: 4922
N.A.I.C.S.: 486210
Carlo Malacarne *(Chm)*
Francesco Iovane *(CEO)*

Stoccaggi Gas Italia S.p.A. (2)
Via Dell Unione Europea 4
20097 San Donato Milanese, Italy
Tel.: (39) 025201
Fax: (39) 02252055006
Natural Gas Distribution
S.I.C.: 4924
N.A.I.C.S.: 221210

Non-U.S. Joint Venture:

Total Infrastructures Gaz France SA (2)
49 avenue Dufau
BP 522
64010 Pau, Cedex, France FR
Tel.: (33) 5 59 13 34 00
Fax: (33) 5 59 13 35 60
E-Mail: frontoffice@tigf.fr
Web Site: www.tigf.fr
Sales Range: $400-449.9 Million
Emp.: 500
Natural Gas Transportation & Storage Services
S.I.C.: 4922
N.A.I.C.S.: 486210
Bernard Clement *(Chm)*
Monique Delamare *(CEO)*

Sofidsim S.p.A. (1)
Via M Ghetaldi 64
143 Rome, Italy (100%)
Tel.: (39) 645474547
Fax: (39) 0659822263
Web Site: www.sofidsim.it
Emp.: 50
S.I.C.: 1311
N.A.I.C.S.: 211111

Syndial S.p.A. (1)
Villa De Gasperi 16 San Donato Milanese
20097 Milan, Italy (100%)
Tel.: (39) 025201
Fax: (39) 0252032300
E-Mail: info@syndial.it
Web Site: www.syndial.it
Sales Range: $200-249.9 Million
Emp.: 64,000
S.I.C.: 1311
N.A.I.C.S.: 211111

Trans Tunisian Pipeline Co Ltd (1)
Piazza Ezio Vanoni 1
20097 San Donato Milanese, Milan, Italy
Tel.: (39) 02 520 59089
Fax: (39) 02 520 59090
E-Mail: info@ttpc.com
Web Site: www.ttpc.it
Oil & Gas Pipeline Transportation Services
S.I.C.: 4619
N.A.I.C.S.: 486990

U.S. Subsidiary:

Eni USA Inc (1)
1201 La St Ste 3500
Houston, TX 77002
Tel.: (713) 393-6100
Fax: (713) 393-6206
Oil & Gas Exploration Services
S.I.C.: 1389
N.A.I.C.S.: 213112
Windle Martin *(Gen Mgr)*

Subsidiaries:

Eni Oil & Gas Inc (2)
1201 La St 3500
Houston, TX 77002
Tel.: (713) 393-6100
Management Consulting Services
S.I.C.: 8742
N.A.I.C.S.: 541611

Eni Trading & Shipping Inc (2)
1221 Lamar St Ste 500
Houston, TX 77010
Tel.: (713) 393-6100
Web Site: www.eni.com
Petroleum Product Whslr
S.I.C.: 5172
N.A.I.C.S.: 424720

Eni US Operating Co Inc (2)
1201 Louisiana St 350
Houston, TX 77002-5604
Tel.: (713) 393-6100
Fax: (713) 393-6205

Eni S.p.A.—(Continued)

Crude Petroleum & Natural Gas Extraction Services
S.I.C.: 1311
N.A.I.C.S.: 211111

Eni USA R&M Co Inc (2)
539 Marwood Rd
Cabot, PA 16023-9526
Tel.: (724) 352-4451
Fax: (724) 352-9543
Oil Refinery Services
S.I.C.: 2911
N.A.I.C.S.: 324110

Non-U.S. Subsidiaries:

Agip Caspian Sea BV (1)
Strawinskylaan 1725
Amsterdam, 1077 XX, Netherlands
Tel.: (31) 205707100
Fax: (31) 205707170
Oil & Gas Production Services
S.I.C.: 1311
N.A.I.C.S.: 211111

Banque Eni SA (1)
Rue Guimard 1
Brussels, 1040, Belgium
Tel.: (32) 25510380
Fax: (32) 3225511990
Web Site: www.eni.com
Emp.: 4
Oil & Gas Exploration Services
S.I.C.: 1629
N.A.I.C.S.: 237120

Distrigas LNG Shipping SA (1)
Rue Guimard 1a
Brussels, 1040, Belgium
Tel.: (32) 25573001
Fax: (32) 25573112
E-Mail: info@distrigas.be
Web Site: www.distrigas.be
Emp.: 50
Natural Gas Distr
S.I.C.: 4924
N.A.I.C.S.: 221210
John Peuteman *(CEO)*

Dunastyr Polisztirolgyarto Zartkoruen Mukodo Reszvenytarsasag (1)
Arpad Fejedelem Utja 26-28
Budapest, 1023, Hungary
Tel.: (36) 1 345 7171
Fax: (36) 1 335 0684
Shock Resistant Polystyrene Mfr & Distr
S.I.C.: 5169
N.A.I.C.S.: 424690

Dunastyr Polystyrene Manufacturing Co. Ltd. (1)
26-28 Arpad Sejedelem Utca
H 1023 Budapest, Hungary (56.9%)
Tel.: (36) 013457171
Fax: (36) 13350684
E-Mail: pe.dunastyr@polimerieuropa.com
Web Site: www.polimerieuropa.com
Emp.: 140
S.I.C.: 1311
N.A.I.C.S.: 211111
Franco Andrea Ossona *(Mng Dir)*

Non-U.S. Subsidiary:

Polimeri Europa Benelux S.A. (2)
Rue De Ilndustrie 8
1400 Nivelles, Belgium (100%)
Tel.: (32) 67880611
Fax: (32) 67218678
E-Mail: pe.benelux@polimerieuropa.com
Web Site: www.polimerieuropa.co.it
Emp.: 50
S.I.C.: 1311
N.A.I.C.S.: 211111
Giuseppa La Scola *(Pres)*

Eni Algeria Production BV (1)
Strawinskylaan 1725
Amsterdam, 1077 XX, Netherlands
Tel.: (31) 20719600
Fax: (31) 205570170
Web Site: www.eni.com
Emp.: 2
Liquid & Gas Whslr
S.I.C.: 5989
N.A.I.C.S.: 454310
David Colombo *(Mgr-Fin)*

Eni Angola Exploration (1)
Strawinskylaan 1725
Amsterdam, 1077 XX, Netherlands
Tel.: (31) 20719600
Fax: (31) 7196000
Emp.: 3
Oil & Gas Exploration Services
S.I.C.: 1389
N.A.I.C.S.: 213112
Davide Maria Colombo *(Mgr-Fin)*

Eni Australia Ltd (1)
10 Ebury Bridge Road
London, SW1W 8PZ, United Kingdom
Tel.: (44) 20 73446000
Fax: (44) 2075906044
Oil & Gas Exploration Services
S.I.C.: 1389
N.A.I.C.S.: 213112

Eni Austria GmbH (1)
Millennium Tower Handelskai 94-96
1200 Vienna, Osterreich, Austria
Tel.: (43) 1 24070 0
Fax: (43) 1 24070 3017
E-Mail: info@eniaustria.at
Oil Refining & Distr
S.I.C.: 1389
N.A.I.C.S.: 213112
Ricardo Piunti *(Gen Mgr)*

Eni Austria Marketing GmbH (1)
Millennium Tower Handelskai 94-96
1200 Vienna, Austria
Tel.: (43) 1 24070 0
Fax: (43) 1 24070 3017
E-Mail: info@eniaustria.at
Oil Refining Services & Distr
S.I.C.: 2911
N.A.I.C.S.: 324110
Mario Silla *(Mng Dir)*

Eni Austria Tankstellenbetrieb GmbH (1)
Millennium Tower Handelskai 94-96
1200 Vienna, Austria
Tel.: (43) 1 24070 0
Fax: (43) 1 2407010
E-Mail: info@eniaustria.at
Emp.: 180
Natural Gas Product Mfr & Distr
S.I.C.: 4924
N.A.I.C.S.: 221210

Eni BTC Ltd (1)
10 Ebury Bridge Road
London, SW1W 8PZ, United Kingdom
Tel.: (44) 20 73446000
Fax: (44) 20 7606 2893
Oil & Gas Exploration Services
S.I.C.: 1389
N.A.I.C.S.: 213112

Eni Croatia BV (1)
Strawinskylaan 1725
Amsterdam, 1077 XX, Netherlands
Tel.: (31) 205707100
Fax: (31) 205707170
Oil & Gas Exploration Services
S.I.C.: 1389
N.A.I.C.S.: 213112

Eni Finance International SA (1)
Rue Guimard 1a
Brussels, 1040, Belgium
Tel.: (32) 25510380
Fax: (32) 025511990
Emp.: 40
Financial Services
S.I.C.: 6211
N.A.I.C.S.: 523999
Domenica Rapone *(Gen Mgr)*

Eni Gas & Power Belgium SA (1)
Guimardstraat 1A Rue Guimard
BE-1040 Brussels, Belgium
Tel.: (32) 25112344
Fax: (32) 25028242
Web Site: www.eni.it/en_IT/eni-world/belgium/where-we-are/where-we-are.shtml
Gas & Power Services
S.I.C.: 1389
N.A.I.C.S.: 213112
Fabio Marchetti *(Mng Dir)*

Subsidiaries:

Distrigas S.A. (2)
Guimurdstraat 1A
B 1000 Brussels, Belgium
Tel.: (32) 25573001
Fax: (32) 25573112
E-Mail: info@distri.be
Web Site: www.distrigas.be
Emp.: 150
Natural Gas Sales & Trading
S.I.C.: 4924
N.A.I.C.S.: 221210
Erwin Van Bruysel *(CEO)*
Jadran Trevisan *(CFO)*

Nuon Belgium N.V. (2)
Medialaan 34
1800 Vilvoorde, Belgium
Tel.: (32) 22909400
Fax: (32) 22909401
E-Mail: info@eni.be
Web Site: www.eni.com
Emp.: 150
Electricity Generation & Distribution
S.I.C.: 4939
N.A.I.C.S.: 221122

Eni Gas & Power GmbH (1)
Zollhof 2
40221 Dusseldorf, Germany
Tel.: (49) 211 520660
Fax: (49) 21152066200
E-Mail: enigp@enigp.ge
Oil & Gas Exploration Services
S.I.C.: 1389
N.A.I.C.S.: 213112

Eni Hungaria Zrt (1)
Agip u 4
2040 Budaors, Hungary
Tel.: (36) 23 505 500
Fax: (36) 23 415 556
E-Mail: agip@agip.hu
Web Site: www.eni.com
Emp.: 80
Oil Product Refining & Distr
S.I.C.: 1389
N.A.I.C.S.: 213112
Alessio Lilli *(Mng Dir)*

Eni Indonesia Ltd. (1)
Atrium Mulia Building 3 and 3A Floors
Jl HR Rasuna Said Kav B10-11, Jakarta, 12910, Indonesia UK
Tel.: (62) 2130003200 (100%)
Fax: (62) 2130003230
Web Site: www.eni.com
Oil & Gas Exploration & Production
S.I.C.: 1311
N.A.I.C.S.: 211111

Eni International B.V. (1)
Strawinskylaan 1725
1077 XX Amsterdam, Netherlands (54%)
Tel.: (31) 205707100
Fax: (31) 0205707170
Web Site: www.eni.it/en_IT/eni-world/the-netherlands/where-we-are/where-we-are.shtml
Emp.: 40
Holding Company
S.I.C.: 6719
N.A.I.C.S.: 551112
Giuseppina Fusco *(Chm)*
Roberto Castriota *(Mng Dir)*

Non-U.S. Subsidiary:

Snam International Holding A.G. (2)
Banhofstrasse 18
Zurich, Switzerland
Owned by Eni International Holding B.V. (51%) & Snam S.p.A. (49%); Joint Venture
S.I.C.: 6719
N.A.I.C.S.: 551112

Eni International Resources Ltd (1)
80 Cardinal Place Victoria Street
London, SW1E 5JL, United Kingdom
Tel.: (44) 20 7344 4100
Fax: (44) 20 7344 4123
E-Mail: info@eni-irl.com
Emp.: 7
Employee Assessment Consulting Services
S.I.C.: 8999
N.A.I.C.S.: 541612

Eni JPDA 06-105 Pty Ltd (1)
226 Adelaide Terrace
Perth, WA, 6000, Australia
Tel.: (61) 8 9320 1111
Fax: (61) 8 9320 1100
E-Mail: info@eniaustralia.com.au
Web Site: www.eni.com
Emp.: 20
Oil & Gas Exploration Services
S.I.C.: 1389
N.A.I.C.S.: 213112
Michael Pirner *(Gen Mgr)*

Eni Mali BV (1)
Strawinskylaan 1725
1077 XX Amsterdam, Netherlands
Tel.: (31) 20 5707100
Fax: (31) 20 5707170
Oil & Gas Exploration Services
S.I.C.: 1389
N.A.I.C.S.: 213112

Eni Norge AS (1)
Vestre Svanholmen 12
4313 Sandnes, Norway
Tel.: (47) 52 87 48 00
Fax: (47) 52 87 49 30
E-Mail: firmapost@eninorge.com
Web Site: www.eninorge.com
Oil & Gas Exploration Serevices
S.I.C.: 1389
N.A.I.C.S.: 213112
Franco Magnani *(Chm)*
Guido Michelotti *(Vice Chm)*
Andrea Forzoni *(Mng Dir)*

Eni Polska spolka z ograniczona odpowiedzialnoscia (1)
Armii Ludowej 26
Warsaw, 60900, Poland
Tel.: (48) 223517207
Fax: (48) 224173147
Emp.: 25
Oil & Gas Exploration Services
S.I.C.: 2992
N.A.I.C.S.: 324191

Eni Romania Srl (1)
Bl A Sector 1 169a Calea Floreasca
Bucharest, 10146, Romania
Tel.: (40) 316 206 300
Fax: (40) 316 206 304
E-Mail: agip@agip.ro
Lubricant Station Operating Services
S.I.C.: 5171
N.A.I.C.S.: 424710

Eni Schmiertechnik GmbH (1)
Paradiesstr 14
Wurzburg, 97080, Germany
Tel.: (49) 931900980
Fax: (49) 93198442
Oil & Gas Exploration Services
S.I.C.: 1389
N.A.I.C.S.: 213112

Eni Slovenija doo (1)
3 Trg Republike
Ljubljana, 1000, Slovenia
Tel.: (386) 12528790
Fax: (386) 12528798
E-Mail: info@agip.si
Web Site: www.eni.com
Emp.: 11
Petroleum Products Distr
S.I.C.: 5172
N.A.I.C.S.: 424720
Alessio Lilli *(Gen Mgr)*

Eni Slovensko Spol Sro (1)
Prievozska 2/A
811 09 Bratislava, Slovakia
Tel.: (421) 250700411
Fax: (421) 250700460
E-Mail: info@agip.sk
Emp.: 5
Oil & Gas Exploration Services
S.I.C.: 1389
N.A.I.C.S.: 213112
Massimo Bechi *(Gen Mgr)*

Eni Trading & Shipping BV (1)
Strawinskylaan 1641 - Tower C/16
1077 XX Amsterdam, Netherlands
Tel.: (31) 20 719 5500
Fax: (31) 20 679 4796
Crude Oil Distr
S.I.C.: 5172
N.A.I.C.S.: 424720

Eni Tunisia BV (1)
Rue Du Lac Tanganyika
Les Berges Du Lac, Tunis, Tunisia
Tel.: (216) 71860011
Fax: (216) 71861641
Oil & Gas Exploration Services
S.I.C.: 1389

N.A.I.C.S.: 213112

Eni ULT Ltd (1)
ENI House 10 Ebury Bridge Road
Westminster, London, SW1W 8PZ, United Kingdom
Tel.: (44) 20 7344 6000
Fax: (44) 20 7344 6044
Web Site: www.eni.it
Investment Management Services
S.I.C.: 6211
N.A.I.C.S.: 523999

Eni ULX Ltd (1)
Eni House 10 Ebury Bridge Road
London, SW1W 8PZ, United Kingdom
Tel.: (44) 2073446372
Fax: (44) 2071733001
Oil & Gas Exploration Services
S.I.C.: 1389
N.A.I.C.S.: 213112

Eni UK Holding Plc (1)
Eni House 10 Ebury Bridge Road
London, SW1W 8PZ, United Kingdom
Tel.: (44) 20 7344 6000
Investment Management Services
S.I.C.: 6211
N.A.I.C.S.: 523999

Eni UK Ltd (1)
Eni House
10 Ebury Bridge Rd, London, SW1W 8PZ, United Kingdom (100%)
Tel.: (44) 2073446000
Fax: (44) 2073446044
Web Site: www.eni.it
Emp.: 200
Holding Company for Exploration & Production of Oil & Gas
S.I.C.: 6719
N.A.I.C.S.: 551112
Philip Hemmens *(Mng Dir)*

Subsidiary:

Burren Energy (2)
Kierran Cross 2nd Fl
London, WC2N 5HR, United Kingdom
Tel.: (44) 2074841900
Fax: (44) 2074841910
Web Site: www.burren.co.uk
Emp.: 75,862
Exploration & Production Services
S.I.C.: 8713
N.A.I.C.S.: 541360

Subsidiary:

Burren Energy (Services) Limited (3)
11 Strand
WC2N 5HR London, United Kingdom
Tel.: (44) 2074841900
Fax: (44) 2074841910
E-Mail: burren@burren.co.uk
Web Site: www.burren.co.uk/
Oil & Gas Field Machinery & Equipment Mfr
S.I.C.: 3533
N.A.I.C.S.: 333132
Atul Gupta *(CEO)*

Non-U.S. Subsidiaries:

Burren Resources Petroleum Limited (3)
Business Centre
Archabil Shayoly 41, 744000 Ashkhabad, Turkmenistan
Tel.: (993) 12488522
Fax: (993) 12488519
E-Mail: burren@burren.co.uk
Emp.: 1,000
Oil & Gas Field Machinery & Equipment Mfr
S.I.C.: 3533
N.A.I.C.S.: 333132

Ieoc Production BV (3)
1 Road 204 Deglia Square
PO Box 52
Maadi, 11742 Cairo, Egypt
Tel.: (20) 27057171
Web Site: www.eni.com
Oil & Gas Field Machinery & Equipment Mfg
S.I.C.: 3533
N.A.I.C.S.: 333132

Non-U.S. Subsidiaries:

Eni Venezuela (2)
Av Orinoco con Calle Mucuchies Edif 448
Calle Los Chaguaramos, Las Mercedes, 1060, Venezuela (100%)
Tel.: (58) 2123182000
Fax: (58) 2123182034
E-Mail: maria.parise@eni.com.ve
Emp.: 70
Oil & Gas Exploration
S.I.C.: 1311
N.A.I.C.S.: 211111
Biagio Pietraroia *(Gen Mgr)*

Polimeri Europa France SAS (1)
Rte Des Dunes
Mardyck, 59279, France
Tel.: (33) 328627400
Fax: (33) 328627500
E-Mail: pe.france@polimerieuropa.com
Web Site: www.eni.com
Emp.: 450
Oil & Gas Exploration Services
S.I.C.: 1389
N.A.I.C.S.: 213112
Protopapa Antonio *(Mng Dir)*

Polimeri Europa GmbH (1)
Dusseldorfer Str 13
65760 Eschborn, Germany
Tel.: (49) 6196 4920
Fax: (49) 6196 492218
E-Mail: pe.handel@polimerieuropa.com
Web Site: www.polimerieuropa.com
Emp.: 40
Petrochemical Products Distr
S.I.C.: 5172
N.A.I.C.S.: 424720
Massimo Favilli *(Gen Mgr)*

Polimeri Europa Iberica SA (1)
Avenida Diagonal 652-656 Edificio A 3
08034 Barcelona, Spain
Tel.: (34) 93 4012300
Fax: (34) 93 2803050
E-Mail: pe.iberica@polimerieuropa.com
Web Site: www.eni.com
Chemical Product Mfr
S.I.C.: 2899
N.A.I.C.S.: 325998

Polimeri Europa UK Ltd (1)
Cadland Road Hardley - Hythe
Inghilterra, Southampton, SO45 3YY, United Kingdom
Tel.: (44) 23 80387000
Fax: (44) 23 80387306
E-Mail: pe.uk@polimerieuropa.com
Web Site: www.eni.com
Natural Gas Distribution Services
S.I.C.: 4924
N.A.I.C.S.: 221210

ENIRO AB

Gustav IIIs Boulevard 40
169 87 Stockholm, Sweden
Tel.: (46) 855331000
Fax: (46) 858509037
E-Mail: info@eniro.com
Web Site: www.eniro.com
ENRO—(OMX)
Rev.: $621,212,400
Assets: $1,384,531,200
Liabilities: $836,074,800
Net Worth: $548,456,400
Earnings: $07,920,000
Emp.: 3,187
Fiscal Year-end: 12/31/12

Business Description:
Directories, Directory Assistance, Internet & Mobile Information Services
S.I.C.: 2741
N.A.I.C.S.: 511140

Personnel:
Lars-Johan Jarnheimer *(Chm)*
Johan Lindgren *(Pres & CEO)*
Mattias Lundqvist *(CFO)*
Katarina Lindgren *(Chief Legal Officer)*
Magdalena Bonde *(CEO-Sweden)*
Bozena Chmielarczyk *(CEO-Poland)*
Stefan Kercza *(CEO-Denmark)*
Annica Elmehagen Lundquist *(Sr VP & Dir-Corp Comm)*
Krister Skalberg *(Sr VP-Svc Delivery)*
Martina Smedman *(Sr VP-HR)*

Board of Directors:
Lars-Johan Jarnheimer
Fredrik Arnander
Thomas Axen
Ketil Eriksen
Leif Aa. Fredsted
Jennie Hallberg
Bengt Herkules
Susanne Olin Jonsson
Jonas Svensson
Cecilia Daun Wennborg

Subsidiaries:

Din Del AB (1)
Gustav III Boulevard 40
Stockholm, 16987, Sweden
Tel.: (46) 8 58 50 23 00
Fax: (46) 58509037
E-Mail: kontakt@dindel.se
Web Site: www.dindel.se
Directory & Periodical Publishing Services
S.I.C.: 2741
N.A.I.C.S.: 511140
Markus Rosenlund *(Gen Mgr)*

Subsidiary:

Din Del Forsaljning AB (2)
Gustav III S Boulevard 40
169 87 Solna, Sweden
Tel.: (46) 8 585 023 00
Fax: (46) 8 585 090 37
Advertising Agency Services
S.I.C.: 7311
N.A.I.C.S.: 541810
Johan Lindgren *(Gen Mgr)*

Eniro 118 118 AB (1)
Gustav Iii s Boulevard 40
16973 Solna, Sweden (100%)
Tel.: (46) 855331000
Fax: (46) 858509037
E-Mail:
Web Site: www.eniro.com
Emp.: 1,000
Wired Telecommunications Carriers
S.I.C.: 4813
N.A.I.C.S.: 517110
Johan Lindgren *(Gen Mgr)*

Eniro Emfas AB (1)
Gustav Lii S Boulevard 40
16987 Stockholm, Sweden (100%)
Tel.: (46) 855331000
Fax: (46) 858509623
Web Site: www.eniro.com
Emp.: 1,500
Book Publishers
S.I.C.: 2731
N.A.I.C.S.: 511130
Johan Lindgren *(Pres & CEO)*

Eniro International AB (1)
Gustav IIIs Boulevard 40
Solna, SE-169 87 Stockholm, Sweden (100%)
Tel.: (46) 855331000
Fax: (46) 858509037
E-Mail: info@eniro.com
Web Site: www.eniro.com
Holding Company
S.I.C.: 6719
N.A.I.C.S.: 551112

Non-U.S. Subsidiaries:

1880 Nummeropplysning AS (2)
Ringvegen 3
2815 Gjovik, Norway (100%)
Tel.: (47) 93435829
Fax: (47) 62956001
Emp.: 150
Information Services
S.I.C.: 7389
N.A.I.C.S.: 519190
Roar Johansen *(Mng Dir)*

Bedriftskatalogen AS (2)
Olaf Helsets Vei 5
Oslo, Norway
Tel.: (47) 81544418
Fax: (47) 22771641
Book Publishers
S.I.C.: 2731
N.A.I.C.S.: 511130
Wenche Holen *(Mng Dir)*

Ditt Distrikt AS (2)
Olaf Helsets Vei 5
Oslo, Norway
Tel.: (47) 81544418
Fax: (47) 22771502
Web Site: www.dittdistrikt.no/oslo/
Book Publishers
S.I.C.: 2731
N.A.I.C.S.: 511130
Hamp Terning *(Mng Dir)*

Editorium AS (2)
Gjerdrums Vei 19
Oslo, Norway (100%)
Tel.: (47) 21508000
Web Site: www.findexaforlag.no/om-oss
Book Publishers
S.I.C.: 2731
N.A.I.C.S.: 511130

Eniro Danmark A/S (2)
Sydmarken 44a
2860 Soborg, Denmark
Tel.: (45) 88383800
Fax: (45) 88383810
E-Mail: info@eniro.dk
Web Site: www.eniro.dk
Sales Range: $75-99.9 Million
Emp.: 510
Directories, Directory Assistance, Internet & Mobile Information Services
S.I.C.: 2741
N.A.I.C.S.: 511140
Stefan Kercza *(Pres)*
Mathias Wedar *(Pres)*

Eniro Norge AS (2)
Olaf Helsets Vei 5
Oslo, Norway
Mailing Address:
PO Box 6705
Etterstad, 0609 Oslo, Norway
Tel.: (47) 81544418
Fax: (47) 22771502
Web Site: www.eniro.no
Emp.: 800
S.I.C.: 2711
N.A.I.C.S.: 511110

Eniro Polska Sp. z.o.o (2)
Domaniewska 41
02672 Warsaw, Poland
Tel.: (48) 223142000
Fax: (48) 222892001
E-Mail: eniro@eniro.pl
Web Site: www.eniropolska.pl
Emp.: 300
Books Printing
S.I.C.: 2732
N.A.I.C.S.: 323117
Roger Asplund *(Gen Mgr)*

Eniro Sentraali Oy (2)
Valimotie 9-11
380 Helsinki, Finland
Tel.: (358) 29 0100 100
Fax: (358) 29 0100 101
E-Mail: asiakaspalvelu@sentraali.fi
Web Site: www.sentraali.fi
Emp.: 50
Directory Assistance & Mobile Search Services
S.I.C.: 2741
N.A.I.C.S.: 511140
Kaj Lindholm *(CEO)*

Findexa Forlag AS (2)
Sandakerveien 116 D
Oslo, Nydalen, 0484, Norway (100%)
Tel.: (47) 21508000
Fax: (47) 21508001
E-Mail: post@findexaforlag.no
Web Site: www.findexaforlag.no
Book Publishers
S.I.C.: 2731
N.A.I.C.S.: 511130
Parj Enstne *(Mng Dir)*

Grenseguiden AS (2)
Olaf Helsets Vei 5
Oslo, Norway
Tel.: (47) 81544418
Fax: (47) 22771641
Book Publishers
S.I.C.: 2731
N.A.I.C.S.: 511130

Gule Sider AS (2)
Olaf Helsets Vei 5
Oslo, Norway
Tel.: (47) 81544448
Fax: (47) 22770831
Web Site: www.gulesider.no/andre/kontakt.html

Eniro AB—(Continued)

Book Publishers
S.I.C.: 2731
N.A.I.C.S.: 511130
Wenche Holen *(Mng Dir)*

Subsidiary:

Gule Sider Internett AS (3)
Olaf Helsets Vei 5
Oslo, Norway
Tel.: (47) 81544418
Fax: (47) 22771641
Web Site: www.gulesider.no
Book Publishers
S.I.C.: 2731
N.A.I.C.S.: 511130

Index Publishing AS (2)
Gjerdrums Vei 19
Oslo, Norway (100%)
Tel.: (47) 21508000
Book Publishers
S.I.C.: 2731
N.A.I.C.S.: 511130

Proff AS (2)
Olaf Helsets Vei 5
Oslo, Norway
Tel.: (47) 81544428
Fax: (47) 22771641
E-Mail: info@proff.no
Web Site: www.proff.no
Book Publishers
S.I.C.: 2731
N.A.I.C.S.: 511130
Wenche Holen *(Mng Dir)*

Scandinavia Online AS (2)
Postboks 858 Sentrum
N 0104 Oslo, Norway (100%)
Tel.: (47) 21508000
Web Site: www.sol.no/
News Website
S.I.C.: 4899
N.A.I.C.S.: 517919

Telefonkatalogens Gule Sider AS (2)
Olaf Helsets Vei 5
Oslo, Norway
Tel.: (47) 81544448
Fax: (47) 22771641
Web Site: www.eniro.no/no/Norge/Konta kt/Telefonkatalogen/
Book Publishers
S.I.C.: 2731
N.A.I.C.S.: 511130
Wenche Holen *(Mng Dir)*

TeleMedia International BV (2)
Locatellikade 1 Parnassustrn
1076 Amsterdam, Netherlands
Tel.: (31) 205408989
Fax: (31) 205408909
Trusts Estates & Agency Accounts
S.I.C.: 6733
N.A.I.C.S.: 525920

Eniro Sverige AB (1)
Guftav 3 Boulevard 40
16973 Solna, Sweden (100%)
Tel.: (46) 855331000
Fax: (46) 0858509037
E-Mail: fredrik.brandel@enrio.com
Web Site: www.enrio.com
Emp.: 1,550
Advertising Agencies
S.I.C.: 7311
N.A.I.C.S.: 541810
Matthias Wedrar *(Mng Dir)*

Subsidiaries:

Eniro Gula Sidorna AB (2)
Gustav III S Boulevard 40
Stockholm, 169 87, Sweden
Tel.: (46) 85533 1000
Fax: (46) 858509037
Web Site: www.eniro.com
Directory Publishing Services
S.I.C.: 2741
N.A.I.C.S.: 511140

Subsidiary:

Eniro Gula Sidorna Forsaljning AB (3)
Gustav III S Boulevard 40
Solna, SE-169 87 Stockholm, Sweden SE
Tel.: (46) 8 55331000
Fax: (46) 8 58509037
E-Mail: info@eniro.com
Web Site: www.eniro.se
Directory Sales
S.I.C.: 5192
N.A.I.C.S.: 424920
Mattisa Wedar *(CEO)*

Eniro Passagen AB (2)
Gustav Iii S Boulevard 40
Solna, 169 87, Sweden
Tel.: (46) 8 55331000
Fax: (46) 8 58509037
Web Site: www.eniro.se
Advertising Agency Services
S.I.C.: 7311
N.A.I.C.S.: 541810
Johan Lindgren *(Gen Mgr)*

Eniro Sverige Forsaljning AB (2)
Justav 3rd Blvd 40
16973 Solna, Sweden
Tel.: (46) 855331000
Fax: (46) 08253110
E-Mail: johan.lindgren@eniro.com
Web Site: www.eniro.se
Emp.: 2,000
Advertising Agencies
S.I.C.: 7311
N.A.I.C.S.: 541810
Martin Carlefund *(Mng Dir)*

Kataloger I Norr AB (1)
Hornellgatan 17
93130 Skelleftea, Sweden (100%)
Tel.: (46) 910714350
Fax: (46) 910714359
Web Site: www.katalogerinorr.se
Plate Work Mfr
S.I.C.: 3443
N.A.I.C.S.: 332313
Per-Olof Ahlbin *(Mng Dir)*

Leta Information Eniro AB (1)
Gustav Iii S Boulevard 40
Solna, 169 73, Sweden
Tel.: (46) 855331000
Directory Publishing Services
S.I.C.: 2741
N.A.I.C.S.: 511140

ENISH INC.

6F/8F Fujikikai Hiroo Building 1-13-1 Hiroo
Shibuya-ku, Tokyo, 150-0012, Japan
Tel.: (81) 3 57912131
Fax: (81) 3 57912132
Web Site: www.enish.jp
Year Founded: 2009
3667—(TKS)
Sales Range: $25-49.9 Million
Emp.: 71

Business Description:
Social Gaming Software
S.I.C.: 7372
N.A.I.C.S.: 511210
Personnel:
Masanori Sugiyama *(Pres)*

ENJAZ FOR DEVELOPMENT & MULTI PROJECTS COMPANY P.L.C.

Sukareyah Commercial buliding Number 45 Third floor Office number 302
PO Box 910776
Al Suwefieh, Amman, 11191, Jordan
Tel.: (962) 6 5817576
Fax: (962) 6 5885621
E-Mail: injaz@jab-group.com
Year Founded: 1976
LIPO—(AMM)
Rev.: $3,599,838
Assets: $25,406,433
Liabilities: $6,880,108
Net Worth: $18,526,325
Earnings: $3,098,673
Emp.: 4
Fiscal Year-end: 12/31/12

Business Description:
Real Estate Development Services
S.I.C.: 6531
N.A.I.C.S.: 531390
Personnel:
Hazem Mohammad Al-Qadi *(Gen Mgr)*

ENJOY MONTPELLIER

Le Corum Esplanade Charles De Gaulle
34000 Montpellier, Herault, France
Tel.: (33) 467616761
Fax: (33) 467616700
Web Site: www.enjoy-montpellier.com
Rev.: $24,200,000
Emp.: 101

Business Description:
Theatrical Producers & Services
S.I.C.: 7389
N.A.I.C.S.: 711410
Personnel:
Federik Lopez *(Chm)*
Board of Directors:
Alain Formentn

ENK DRUCK & MEDIA GMBH

Drinkstegge 33
46395 Bocholt, Germany
Tel.: (49) 287124800
Fax: (49) 2871248024
E-Mail: info@enk-media.de
Web Site: www.enk-media.de
Emp.: 80

Business Description:
Printing Services
S.I.C.: 2759
N.A.I.C.S.: 323111
Personnel:
Richard Benning *(Mng Dir)*
Franz-Hermann Enk *(Mng Dir)*

ENK PLC

(Acquired by DMCI Holdings, Inc.)

ENKA INSAAT VE SANAYI A.S.

Balmumcu Mah Zincirlikuyu Yolu No 10
34349 Istanbul, Turkey
Tel.: (90) 2123761000
Fax: (90) 2122728869
E-Mail: enka@enka.com
Web Site: www.enka.com
Year Founded: 1957
ENKAI—(IST)
Rev.: $5,745,762,000
Assets: $8,237,506,000
Liabilities: $2,878,003,000
Net Worth: $5,359,503,000
Earnings: $657,716,000
Emp.: 21,290
Fiscal Year-end: 12/31/12

Business Description:
Industrial Building Construction
S.I.C.: 1542
N.A.I.C.S.: 236220
Personnel:
M. Sinan Tara *(Chm)*
A. Mehmet Tara *(Chm-Exec Bd & Gen Mgr-Engrg, Personnel, HR & Environment)*
Haluk Gercek *(Vice Chm & Gen Mgr)*
M. Gokhan Sagnaklar *(Vice Chm-Exec Bd)*
Alp Doguoglu *(Member-Exec Bd-Energy Projects)*
Zafer Gur *(Member-Exec Bd-Special Projects)*
C. San Gurdamar *(Member-Exec Bd-Oman)*
Ozger Inal *(Member-Exec Bd-Infrastructure Projects)*
S. Oguz Kirkgoz *(Member-Exec Bd-Oil & Gas Projects)*
B. Burak Ozdogan *(Member-Exec Bd-Moscow Projects)*
Asaf Yener *(Member-Exec Bd)*
Board of Directors:
M. Sinan Tara
E. Melih Araz
Haluk Gercek
Veli Ergin Imre
A. Mehmet Tara
Erdogan Turgut

Subsidiaries:

Adapazari Elektrik Uretim Limited Sirketi (1)
Hayriye Konak No 2
Bestekar Sevki Bey Caddesi, 34349
Istanbul, Turkey (100%)
Tel.: (90) 2122889998
Fax: (90) 902122752461
E-Mail: info@enkapower.com
Web Site: www.enkapower.com
Emp.: 100
Heavy & Civil Engineering Construction
S.I.C.: 1629
N.A.I.C.S.: 237990

Airenka Hava Tasimaciligi A.S. (1)
Bestekar Sevki Bey Sokak Enka 1 Bina Zemin Kat
Balmumcu, Besiktas, Istanbul, Turkey
Tel.: (90) 212 274 25 40
Fax: (90) 212 274 09 57
E-Mail: airenka@enka.com
Air Taxi Operator
S.I.C.: 4522
N.A.I.C.S.: 481211

Cimtas Borulama Sanayi ve Ticaret Ltd. Sti. (1)
Bursa Serbest Bolgesi Liman Yolu Hisar Mevkii
Bursa, 16600, Turkey
Tel.: (90) 2245248731
Fax: (90) 2245248739
Industrial Pipe Distr
S.I.C.: 5084
N.A.I.C.S.: 423830

Cimtas Celik Imalat Montaj Ve Tesisat A.S. (1)
Enka 2 Binasi Kat 3
Bestekar Sevkibey Sokak, Istanbul, Turkey
Tel.: (90) 2123403535
Fax: (90) 212 340 36 96
E-Mail: cimtas@cimtas.com.tr
Web Site: www.cimtas.com.tr
Emp.: 1,000
Fabricated Structural Metal Mfr
S.I.C.: 3441
N.A.I.C.S.: 332312
Asa Yener *(Gen Mgr)*

Non-U.S. Subsidiary:

IBH Engineering GmbH (2)
Donnersbergweg 2
Ludwigshafen, 67059, Germany
Tel.: (49) 621659010
Fax: (49) 62165901220
E-Mail: info@ibh-engineers.de
Web Site: www.ibh-engineers.de
Emp.: 10
Business Support Services
S.I.C.: 7389
N.A.I.C.S.: 561990
Siegfried Muench *(CEO & Gen Mgr)*
Martin Becker *(CFO)*

Cimtas Gemi Insa Sanayi ve Ticaret A.S. (1)
2 Ada Kocaeli Serbest Bolgesi
41275 Izmit, Kocaeli, Turkey
Tel.: (90) 2623414282
Fax: (90) 2623414284
E-Mail: info@cimtasshipyard.com
Web Site: www.cimtasshipyard.com
Emp.: 50
Civil Engineering Construction Services
S.I.C.: 1629
N.A.I.C.S.: 237990
Marco Fossataro *(Gen Mgr)*

Enka Finansal Kiralama A.S. (1)
Ata 4 Carsi Plaza K 3 No 39 Atasehir
Kadikoy, Istanbul, Turkey
Tel.: (90) 216 455 10 00
Fax: (90) 216 455 20 27

E-Mail: info@enkafk.com.tr
Emp.: 16
Automotive Financial Leasing Services
S.I.C.: 6159
N.A.I.C.S.: 522220
Fikri Aca *(Gen Mgr)*

Enka Teknik A.S. (1)
Istanbul Ataturk Hava Limani Serbest
Bolg Plaza Ofis N 710, Istanbul, Turkey
Tel.: (90) 2122741800
Fax: (90) 2122664699
E-Mail: headoffice@enkateknik.com
Web Site: www.enkateknik.com
Emp.: 85
New Single-Family Housing Construction
S.I.C.: 1521
N.A.I.C.S.: 236115
Hamelt Orhun *(Gen Mgr)*

Enka Teknik Genel Muteahhitlik Bakim Isletme Sevk ve Idare Anonim Sirketi (1)
Enka Ii Binasi 8 Bestekar Sevki Bey Sokak
Istanbul, 34349, Turkey
Tel.: (90) 2122741800
Fax: (90) 2122664699
Civil Engineering Construction Services
S.I.C.: 1629
N.A.I.C.S.: 237990

Entas Nakliyat ve Turizm Anonim Sirketi (1)
Enka Binasi No 108 A
Buyukdere Caddesi, Istanbul,
Turkey (99.93%)
Tel.: (90) 2123542424
Fax: (90) 2123542499
Web Site: www.entas.com.tr
Emp.: 50
Travel Agencies
S.I.C.: 4724
N.A.I.C.S.: 561510

Gebze Elektrik Uretim Limited Sirketi (1)
Hayriye Konak No 2
Bestekar Sevki Bey Caddesi, Istanbul,
Turkey (100%)
Tel.: (90) 2122889998
Fax: (90) 2122752461
E-Mail: info@enkapower.com
Web Site: www.enkapower.com
Emp.: 33
Heavy & Civil Engineering Construction
S.I.C.: 1629
N.A.I.C.S.: 237990
Inan Soydan *(Gen Mgr)*

Izmir Elektrik Uretim Limited Sirketi (1)
Hayriye Konak No 2 8
Sevkibey Caddesi, 34349 Istanbul,
Turkey (100%)
Tel.: (90) 2123558100
Fax: (90) 2122752461
E-Mail: info@encapower.com
Web Site: www.enca.com
Emp.: 22
Electric Power Generation
S.I.C.: 4931
N.A.I.C.S.: 221118

Kasktas Kayar Kalip Altyapi Sondaj Kazik ve Tecrit Anonim Sirketi (1)
E Ismail Hakki Bey Sok No 31
Balmumcu, 34349 Istanbul, Turkey
Tel.: (90) 212 274 58 42
Fax: (90) 212 266 33 93
E-Mail: kasktas@kasktas.com.tr
Web Site: www.kasktas.com.tr
Emp.: 50
Geotechnical Engineering Services
S.I.C.: 8711
N.A.I.C.S.: 541330
Mehmet Ibrahimiye *(Gen Mgr)*

Metra Akdeniz Dis Ticaret A.S. (1)
Istasyon Mah Araplar Cad No 6
Tuzla, Istanbul, 34940, Turkey
Tel.: (90) 216 44 66 464
Fax: (90) 2163951340
E-Mail: istanbul@enka.tr
Web Site: www.metra-akdeniz.com
Civil Engineering Construction Services
S.I.C.: 1629
N.A.I.C.S.: 237990

Pimas Plastik Insaat Malzemeleri A.S. (1)
No 29 Beylikbagi Mevkii
kocaeli, Gebze, 1420, Turkey
Tel.: (90) 2626777777
Fax: (90) 2626777700
E-Mail: pimas@pimas.com.pr
Web Site: www.pimas.com
Emp.: 500
Plastics Product Mfr
S.I.C.: 3089
N.A.I.C.S.: 326199

Non-U.S. Subsidiary:

Pimapen Logistic Center Srl (2)
B-dul Iuliu Maniu 220 Obiectiv 52 A
Sector 6, Bucharest, Romania
Tel.: (40) 214340238
Fax: (40) 214340516
E-Mail: office@pimapen.com.ro
Web Site: www.pimapen.com
Emp.: 4
Nondurable Goods Whslr
S.I.C.: 5199
N.A.I.C.S.: 424990
Nicolae Irinoiu *(Mng Dir)*

Titas Toprak Insaat ve Taahhut Anonim Sirketi (1)
Balmumcu Besiktas Apartment 525
Besiktas, 80700 Istanbul, Turkey
Tel.: (90) 2122742342
Fax: (90) 2122754050
Civil Engineering Construction Services
S.I.C.: 1629
N.A.I.C.S.: 237990

Non-U.S. Subsidiaries:

Cimtas (Ningbo) Steel Processing Company Ltd. (1)
No 17 Xing Ye Zhong Lu East Park Ningbo
Free Trade Zone
Beilun, Ningbo, China
Tel.: (86) 574 86 82 10 20
Fax: (86) 574 86 82 10 29
E-Mail: cimtasnbo@cimtasnbo.com
Web Site: www.cimtasnbo.com
Fabricated Steel Pipe Mfr
S.I.C.: 3317
N.A.I.C.S.: 331210

Enka Holding B.V. (1)
Evert van de Beekstraat 310
1118 CX Schiphol, Netherlands NL
Tel.: (31) 206541938 (100%)
Holding Company; Real Estate Investment Trusts
S.I.C.: 6719
N.A.I.C.S.: 551112

Subsidiaries:

Capital City Investment B.V. (2)
Evert van de Beekstraat 310
1118 CX Schiphol, Netherlands (100%)
Tel.: (31) 206541938
Real Estate Investment Trusts
S.I.C.: 6726
N.A.I.C.S.: 525990

Covet B.V. (2)
Evert van de Beekstraat 310
1118 CX Schiphol, Netherlands
Tel.: (31) 206541938
Construction Engineering Services
S.I.C.: 8711
N.A.I.C.S.: 541330

Edco Investment B.V. (2)
Evert van de Beekstraat 310
1118 CX Schiphol, Netherlands (100%)
Tel.: (31) 206541938
Real Estate Investment Trusts
S.I.C.: 6726
N.A.I.C.S.: 525990

Enka Adapazari Power Investment B.V. (2)
Evert van de Beekstraat 310
1118 CX Schiphol, Netherlands NL
Tel.: (31) 206541938 (100%)
Real Estate Investment Trust
S.I.C.: 6726
N.A.I.C.S.: 525990

Enka Construction & Development B.V. (2)
Evert van de Beekstraat 310
1118 CX Schiphol, Netherlands (100%)
Tel.: (31) 206541938
Real Estate Investment Trusts
S.I.C.: 6726
N.A.I.C.S.: 525990

Enka Gebze Power Investment B.V. (2)
Evert van de Beekstraat 310
1118 CX Schiphol, Netherlands NL
Tel.: (31) 206541938 (100%)
Real Estate Investment Trust
S.I.C.: 6726
N.A.I.C.S.: 525990

Enka Izmir Power Investment B.V. (2)
Evert van de Beekstraat 310
1118 CX Schiphol, Netherlands NL
Tel.: (31) 206541938 (100%)
Real Estate Investment Trust
S.I.C.: 6726
N.A.I.C.S.: 525990

Enka Power Investment B.V. (2)
Evert van de Beekstraat 310
1118 CX Schiphol, Netherlands NL
Tel.: (31) 206541938 (100%)
E-Mail:
Real Estate Investment Trust
S.I.C.: 6726
N.A.I.C.S.: 525990

Enru Development B.V. (2)
Evert van de Beekstraat 310
1118 CX Schiphol, Netherlands (100%)
Tel.: (31) 206541938
Real Estate Investment Trusts
S.I.C.: 6726
N.A.I.C.S.: 525990

Far East Development B.V. (2)
Evert van de Beekstraat 310
1118 CX Schiphol, Netherlands
Tel.: (31) 206541938
Real Estate Investment Trust
S.I.C.: 6726
N.A.I.C.S.: 525990

Enka TC LLC (1)
Presnenskaya Nab 10 Block C Floor 58
Moscow, 123317, Russia
Tel.: (7) 499 922 35 00
Fax: (7) 499 922 35 01
Shopping Mall Operating Services
S.I.C.: 6512
N.A.I.C.S.: 531120

Enmar Trading Ltd (1)
10 Coldbath Square
London, EC1R 5HL, United Kingdom
Tel.: (44) 2081331920
Fax: (44) 1689868124
E-Mail: info@enka.com
Emp.: 1
Nondurable Goods Merchant Whslr
S.I.C.: 5199
N.A.I.C.S.: 424990
Paul Denby *(Gen Mgr)*

Enwin Rus Ltd. (1)
Ul Fedoseenko 55
Nizhniy Novgorod, 603037, Russia
Tel.: (7) 831225 95 95
Plastic Products Mfr
S.I.C.: 3089
N.A.I.C.S.: 326199

MCC Investment SA. (1)
C/o Fidinam Geneve Sa Avenue Blanc 53
Geneva, 1202, Switzerland
Tel.: (41) 227051130
Fax: (41) 223295161
Investment Management Services
S.I.C.: 6211
N.A.I.C.S.: 523999

Mosenka OAO (1)
Str 3 25 Bul Tsvetnoi Blvd
127051 Moscow, Russia
Tel.: (7) 4957872288
Fax: (7) 4957872292
E-Mail: support@mosenka.ru
Emp.: 50
Heavy & Civil Engineering Construction
S.I.C.: 1629
N.A.I.C.S.: 237990
Viczeki Isin *(Gen Dir)*

Rumos S.A. (1)
Campo Grande 56
1700-093 Lisbon, Portugal
Tel.: (351) 217 824 100
Fax: (351) 217 971 568
E-Mail: info@rumos.pt
Web Site: www.rumos.pt
Information Technology Consulting Services
S.I.C.: 7373
N.A.I.C.S.: 541512
Andy Thomson *(Mng Dir)*

ENKEI WHEELS (INDIA) LTD.

Gat No 1425 Shikrapur Tal-Shirur
Pune, 412208, India
Tel.: (91) 2137618700
Fax: (91) 2137618720
E-Mail: info@enkei.in
Web Site: www.enkei.in
Year Founded: 2009
533477—(BOM)
Rev.: $59,607,711
Assets: $65,479,461
Liabilities: $63,227,797
Net Worth: $2,251,664
Earnings: $806,509
Fiscal Year-end: 03/31/13

Business Description:
Auto Parts & Equipment Mfr
S.I.C.: 5012
N.A.I.C.S.: 423110

Personnel:
Masakatsu Uchiyama *(Mng Dir)*
C. S. K. Rao *(CFO)*
Omkar Kaulgud *(Compliance Officer & Sec)*

Board of Directors:
Satyavara Prasad Garimella
Shailendrajit Rai
Haresh B. Shah
Junichi Suzuki
Masakatsu Uchiyama

Transfer Agent:
Universal Capital Securities Pvt. Ltd
21 Shakil Niwas Mahakali Caves Road Andheri East
Mumbai, India

ENL LIMITED

ENL House Vivea Business Park
Moka, Mauritius
Tel.: (230) 404 95 00
Fax: (230) 404 95 65
E-Mail: info@enl.mu
Web Site: www.enl.mu
Year Founded: 1944
ENL—(MAU)
Sls.: $250,799,586
Assets: $1,239,605,400
Liabilities: $409,701,088
Net Worth: $829,904,312
Earnings: $107,715,368
Emp.: 5,600
Fiscal Year-end: 06/30/13

Business Description:
Holding Company; Agricultural Services; Manufacturing Services; General Business Services
S.I.C.: 6719
N.A.I.C.S.: 551112

Personnel:
Hector Espitalier-Noel *(Chm & CEO)*
Paul Tsang *(CFO)*
Eric Espitalier-Noel *(CEO-Commercial)*
Gilbert Espitalier-Noel *(CEO-Property)*
Jean-Raymond Hardy *(CEO-Agribus)*
Laowmila Burrun-Arlandoo *(Co-Sec)*
Preety P. Gopaul *(Co-Sec)*

Board of Directors:
Hector Espitalier-Noel
Patrice de Robillard
Andre Espitalier-Noel
Christian Espitalier-Noel
Eduoard Espitalier-Noel
Eric Espitalier-Noel
Gilbert Espitalier-Noel
Philippe Espitalier-Noel

ENL Limited—(Continued)

Robert Espitalier-Noel
Roger Espitalier-Noel

Transfer Agent:
MCB Registry & Securities Ltd
Raymond Lamusse Building 9-11 Sir William Newton Street
Port Louis, Mauritius

Subsidiaries:

Enex (Mauritius) Limited (1)
7th Floor Swan Group Centre
Intendance Street, Port Louis, Mauritius
Tel.: (230) 213 3800
Fax: (230) 208 0968
E-Mail: info@enl.mu
Business Support Services
S.I.C.: 7389
N.A.I.C.S.: 561499

Enfyn Management Limited (1)
Stone House Mon Desert Alma
Saint Pierre, Mauritius
Tel.: (230) 433 2929
Fax: (230) 433 8812
E-Mail: enlproperty@enl.mu
Real Estate Services
S.I.C.: 6531
N.A.I.C.S.: 531390

ENL Commercial Limited (1)
7th Floor Swan Group Centre
Intendance Street, Port Louis, Mauritius
Tel.: (230) 213 3800
Fax: (230) 208 0968
E-Mail: ericnoel@enl.mu
Holding Company
S.I.C.: 6719
N.A.I.C.S.: 551112
Eric Espitalier-Noel *(CEO)*
Olivier Lagesse *(COO)*

Subsidiaries:

Axess Limited (2)
Grewals Lane
Les Pailles, Mauritius
Tel.: (230) 206 4300
Fax: (230) 286 5121
E-Mail: axess@axess.mu
Web Site: www.axess.mu
Automobile Sales
S.I.C.: 5571
N.A.I.C.S.: 441228
Antoine M. d'Unienville *(Mgr)*

Charabia Ltd. (2)
Virgile Naz Street
Curepipe, Mauritius
Tel.: (230) 696 2772
Fax: (230) 696 4623
E-Mail: charabia@intnet.mu
Web Site: www.charabia.mu
Emp.: 9
Decorator Fabric Sales
S.I.C.: 5719
N.A.I.C.S.: 442299
Nathalie Hardy *(Gen Mgr)*

Cogir Limitee (2)
Grewals Lane
Les Pailles, Mauritius (56%)
Tel.: (230) 286 5633
Fax: (230) 286 5633
E-Mail: cogirltee@intnet.mu
Building & Civil Engineering Construction Services
S.I.C.: 1542
N.A.I.C.S.: 236220
Benoit Hardy *(CEO)*

Grewals (Mauritius) Limited (2)
Grewals Lane
Les Pailles, Mauritius
Tel.: (230) 286 6619
Fax: (230) 286 8649
E-Mail: info@grewals.mu
Lumbering & Saw Mill Operations
S.I.C.: 2421
N.A.I.C.S.: 321912
Denis Gallet *(Mgr)*

Subsidiary:

Grewals Rodrigues Ltd. (3)
Camp de Roi
Rodrigues, Mauritius
Tel.: (230) 831 0178
Fax: (230) 831 0177
Lumbering & Milling Services
S.I.C.: 2421
N.A.I.C.S.: 321912
Dennis Gallet *(Mgr)*

Pack Plastics Limited (2)
Anse Courtois
Les Pailles, Mauritius
Tel.: (230) 286 2826
Fax: (230) 286 6584
E-Mail: info@pack.mu
Web Site: www.elit_spationery.com
Emp.: 10
Plastics Products Mfr
S.I.C.: 3089
N.A.I.C.S.: 326199
Arnaud Boulle *(Mgr)*

Packestate Limited (2)
Anse Courtois
Les Pailles, Mauritius
Tel.: (230) 286 2826
Fax: (230) 286 6584
E-Mail: info@pack.mu
Plastics Products Mfr
S.I.C.: 3089
N.A.I.C.S.: 326199
Arnaud Boulle *(Mgr)*

Plastinax Austral Limitee (2)
Industrial Zone
Saint Pierre, Mauritius
Tel.: (230) 433 4638
Fax: (230) 433 4639
E-Mail: npark@plastinax.com
Sunglasses & Reading Glasses Mfr
S.I.C.: 3851
N.A.I.C.S.: 339115
Nicolas Park *(Mgr)*

Plastinax Madagascar Ltd. (2)
Industrial Zone
Saint Pierre, Mauritius
Tel.: (230) 433 4638
Fax: (230) 433 4639
E-Mail: npark@plastinax.com
Sunglasses & Reading Glasses Mfr
S.I.C.: 3851
N.A.I.C.S.: 339115
Nicholas Park *(Mgr)*

Plastintco International Ltd. (2)
Industrial Zone
Saint Pierre, Mauritius
Tel.: (230) 433 4638
Fax: (230) 433 4839
E-Mail: npark@plastinax.com
Web Site: www.plastinax.com
Sunglasses & Reading Glasses Mfr
S.I.C.: 3851
N.A.I.C.S.: 339115
Nicolas Park *(Mgr)*

Rennel Limited (2)
Grewals Lane
Les Pailles, Mauritius
Tel.: (230) 286 5914
Fax: (230) 286 4948
E-Mail: info@rennel.mu
Web Site: www.fedex.com
Emp.: 35
Air Courier Services
S.I.C.: 4513
N.A.I.C.S.: 492110
Michel Prefumo *(Mgr)*

Savi Shop Ltd. (2)
7th Floor Swan Group Centre
Intendance Street, Port Louis, Mauritius
Tel.: (230) 213 3800
Fax: (230) 208 0968
E-Mail: info@enl.com
Business Support Services
S.I.C.: 7389
N.A.I.C.S.: 561499

Versatech Limited (2)
Anse Courtois
Les Pailles, Mauritius
Tel.: (230) 286 2826
Fax: (230) 286 6584
E-Mail: aboulle@pack.mu
Emp.: 3
Water Purifier Rental Services
S.I.C.: 4971
N.A.I.C.S.: 221310
Arnaud Boulle *(Mgr)*

ENL Finance Limited (1)
7th Floor Swan Group Centre
Intendance Street, Port Louis, Mauritius
Tel.: (230) 213 3800
Fax: (230) 208 0968
Financial Services
S.I.C.: 7389
N.A.I.C.S.: 561499

ENL Foundation (1)
Railway Square Minissy
Moka, Mauritius
Tel.: (230) 433 4231
Fax: (230) 433 9261
E-Mail: csroffice@enl.mu
Community Support Services
S.I.C.: 7389
N.A.I.C.S.: 561499
Mario Radegonde *(Mgr)*

ENL House Limited (1)
Vivea Business Park Saint Pierre
Intendance Street
Port Louis, Mauritius
Tel.: (230) 213 3800
Fax: (230) 4049565
E-Mail: info@enl.mu
Web Site: www.enl.mu
Emp.: 4
Business Support Services
S.I.C.: 7389
N.A.I.C.S.: 561499
Pascal Grosse *(Gen Mgr)*

ENL Investment Limited (1)
7th Floor Swan Group Centre 10
Intendance Street
Port Louis, Mauritius
Tel.: (230) 213 38 00
Fax: (230) 208 09 68
Web Site: www.enl.mu/en/enl_investment/enl_investment.aspx
ENIT—(MAU)
Investment Management Services
S.I.C.: 6211
N.A.I.C.S.: 523999
Hector Espitalier-Noel *(Chm)*

Subsidiary:

ENL Portfolio Managers Ltd. (2)
7th Floor Swan Group Centre
Intendance Street, Port Louis, Mauritius
Tel.: (230) 213 3800
Fax: (230) 208 0968
E-Mail: info@enl.mu
Investment Services
S.I.C.: 6211
N.A.I.C.S.: 523999

ENL Land Ltd (1)
7th Floor Swan Group Centre 10
Intendance Street
Port Louis, Mauritius
Tel.: (230) 213 380
Fax: (230) 208 096
E-Mail: info@enl.mu
Web Site: www.enl.mu
SAVA—(MAU)
Crop Farming Services
S.I.C.: 0191
N.A.I.C.S.: 111998
Gilbert Espitalier-Noel *(Exec Dir)*

Subsidiary:

ENL Agri Limited (2)
Royal Road
Saint Pierre, Mauritius
Tel.: (230) 433 4304
Fax: (230) 433 4143
E-Mail: info@enlagri.mu
Agricultural Services
S.I.C.: 5193
N.A.I.C.S.: 424930
Jean-Raymond Hardy *(CEO)*

Subsidiaries:

Agrex Limited (3)
Royal Road
Henrietta, Vacoas, Mauritius
Tel.: (230) 684 7146
Fax: (230) 684 2915
E-Mail: info@agrex.mu
Web Site: www.agrex.mu
Flower Grower & Exporter
S.I.C.: 5193
N.A.I.C.S.: 424930
Alban Doger de Speville *(Gen Mgr)*

Anthurium and Orchids Limited (3)
Royal Road
Henrietta, Vacoas, Mauritius
Tel.: (230) 684 7147
Fax: (230) 684 2915
E-Mail: jhardy@enlagri.mu
Flower Grower & Exporter
S.I.C.: 5193
N.A.I.C.S.: 424930

Enquickfix Limited (3)
Royal Road
Saint Pierre, Mauritius
Tel.: (230) 433 4304
Fax: (230) 433 4143
E-Mail: info@enlagri.mu
Agricultural Services
S.I.C.: 9641
N.A.I.C.S.: 926140

ESP Landscapers Ltd. (3)
Vivea Business Park
Moka, Mauritius
Tel.: (230) 433 3445
Fax: (230) 433 3445
E-Mail: bmariette@esplandscapers.com
Web Site: www.esplandscapers.com
Landscaping Services
S.I.C.: 0782
N.A.I.C.S.: 561730
Benoit Mariette *(Mgr)*

Exotiflors Limited (3)
Henrietta
Vacoas, Mauritius
Tel.: (230) 684 7147
Fax: (230) 684 2915
E-Mail: jhardy@enlagri.mu
Flower Growing Services
S.I.C.: 5193
N.A.I.C.S.: 424930

Mon Desert-Alma Sugar Milling Company Limited (3)
7th Floor Swan Group Centre
Intendance Street, Port Louis, Mauritius
Tel.: (230) 433 4304
Fax: (230) 433 4143
E-Mail: info@enlagri.mu
Sugar Refining Services
S.I.C.: 2062
N.A.I.C.S.: 311314

The Savannah Sugar Milling Company Ltd. (3)
Royal Road
Saint Pierre, Mauritius
Tel.: (230) 433 4304
Fax: (230) 433 4143
E-Mail: info@enlagri.mu
Sugar Milling Services
S.I.C.: 2062
N.A.I.C.S.: 311314

Soled Limited (3)
Henrietta
Vacoas, Mauritius
Tel.: (230) 684 7147
Fax: (230) 684 2915
E-Mail: jrhardy@enlagri.mu
Web Site: www.enlagri.mu
Emp.: 21
Agricultural Services
S.I.C.: 5193
N.A.I.C.S.: 424930

ENL Property Limited (1)
Stone House Mon Desert Alma
Saint Pierre, Mauritius
Tel.: (230) 433 2929
Fax: (230) 433 8812
E-Mail: eniproperty@eni.mu
Property Management Services
S.I.C.: 6531
N.A.I.C.S.: 531390
Gilbert Espitalier-Noel *(CEO)*

Subsidiaries:

Bagaprop Limited (2)
Stone House Mon Desert Alma
Saint Pierre, Mauritius
Tel.: (230) 433 2929
Fax: (230) 433 8812
E-Mail: enlproperty@ent.mu
Real Estate Services
S.I.C.: 6531
N.A.I.C.S.: 531390

Bagatelle Hotel Operation Limited (2)
Stone House Mon Desert Alma
Saint Pierre, Mauritius

Tel.: (230) 433 2939
Fax: (230) 433 8812
E-Mail: rstedman@enl.mu
Hotel Owner & Operator
S.I.C.: 7011
N.A.I.C.S.: 721110
Roux Gerber *(Mgr-Dev)*

Ensejour Ltd. (2)
Stone House Mon Desert Alma
Saint Pierre, Mauritius
Tel.: (230) 433 2929
Fax: (230) 433 8812
E-Mail: enlproperty@eni.mu
Real Estate Services
S.I.C.: 6531
N.A.I.C.S.: 531390

Enstyle Management Limited (2)
7th Floor Swan Group Centre
Intendance Street, Port Louis, Mauritius
Tel.: (230) 213 3800
Fax: (230) 208 0968
E-Mail: info@eni.mu
Property Management Services
S.I.C.: 6531
N.A.I.C.S.: 531390

Espral Ltd. (2)
6th Floor Anglo-Mauritius House
Intendance Street, Port Louis, Mauritius
Tel.: (230) 210 8669
Fax: (230) 211 1727
E-Mail: info@espral.com
Land Management Services
S.I.C.: 6552
N.A.I.C.S.: 237210
Nicolas Eynaud *(Mgr)*

Subsidiaries:

Espral International Ltd. (3)
Old Factory
Saint Pierre, Mauritius
Tel.: (230) 433 4030
Fax: (230) 433 3601
E-Mail: info@espral.com
Land Management Services
S.I.C.: 6552
N.A.I.C.S.: 237210

International Valuers Ltd. (3)
6th Floor Anglo-Mauritius House
Intendance Street, Port Louis, Mauritius
Tel.: (230) 210 8669
Fax: (230) 211 1727
E-Mail: info@espral.com
Real Estate Services
S.I.C.: 6531
N.A.I.C.S.: 531390
Thierry Rey *(Mgr)*

The Gardens of Bagatelle Ltd. (2)
Stone House Mon Desert Alma
Saint Pierre, Mauritius
Tel.: (230) 433 2929
Fax: (230) 433 8812
E-Mail: enlproperty@eni.mu
Real Estate Management Services
S.I.C.: 6531
N.A.I.C.S.: 531390

Helvetia Sport Ltd. (2)
Stone House Mon Desert Alma
Saint Pierre, Mauritius
Tel.: (230) 433 2929
Fax: (230) 433 8812
E-Mail: eniproperty@eni.mu
Real Estate Management Services
S.I.C.: 6531
N.A.I.C.S.: 531390

Kendra Saint Pierre Limited (2)
Stone House Mon Desert Alma
Saint Pierre, Mauritius
Tel.: (230) 433 2929
Fax: (230) 433 8812
E-Mail: eniproperty@eni.mu
Real Estate Management Services
S.I.C.: 6531
N.A.I.C.S.: 531390

Les Allees D'Helvetia Commercial Centre Limited (2)
Stone House Mon Desert Alma
Saint Pierre, Mauritius
Tel.: (230) 433 2929
Fax: (230) 433 8812
E-Mail: eniproperty@enl.mu
Real Estate Management Services
S.I.C.: 6531
N.A.I.C.S.: 531390

Mall of (Mauritius) at Bagatelle Ltd. (2)
Stone House Mon Desert Alma
Saint Pierre, Mauritius
Tel.: (230) 433 2929
Fax: (230) 433 8812
E-Mail: eniproperty@eni.mu
Real Estate Management Services
S.I.C.: 6531
N.A.I.C.S.: 531390

MDA Properties Ltd. (2)
Stone House Mon Desert Alma
Saint Pierre, Mauritius
Tel.: (230) 433 2929
Fax: (230) 433 8812
E-Mail: eniproperty@eni.mu
Real Estate Management Services
S.I.C.: 6531
N.A.I.C.S.: 531390

The Old Factory Limited (2)
Stone House Mon Desert Alma
Saint Pierre, Mauritius
Tel.: (230) 433 2929
Fax: (230) 433 8812
E-Mail: enlproperty@enl.mu
Real Estate Management Services
S.I.C.: 6531
N.A.I.C.S.: 531390

Robin's Nest Interiors (Mauritius) Ltd. (2)
Place Dumoulin Coastal Road
Bel Ombre, Mauritius
Tel.: (230) 623 5620
Fax: (230) 623 5461
E-Mail: subi@robinsnestisland.com
Web Site: robinsnestmauritius.com
Emp.: 11
Interior Design Services
S.I.C.: 7389
N.A.I.C.S.: 541410
Subi Ramburrun *(Mgr)*

Savannah Properties Limited (2)
Stone House Mon Desert Alma
Saint Pierre, Mauritius
Tel.: (230) 433 2929
Fax: (230) 433 8812
E-Mail: eniproperty@eni.mu
Real Estate Services
S.I.C.: 6531
N.A.I.C.S.: 531390

SB Cattle Ltd. (2)
Stone House Mon Desert Alma
Saint Pierre, Mauritius
Tel.: (230) 433 2929
Fax: (230) 433 6812
E-Mail: eniproperty@eni.mu
Real Estate Development Services
S.I.C.: 6531
N.A.I.C.S.: 531390

Valetta Locoshed Offices Ltd. (2)
Stone House Mon Desert Alma
Saint Pierre, Mauritius
Tel.: (230) 433 2929
Fax: (230) 433 8812
Real Estate Management Services
S.I.C.: 6531
N.A.I.C.S.: 531390

Societe Reunion (1)
7th Floor Swan Group Centre
Intendance Street, Port Louis, Mauritius
Tel.: (230) 213 3800
Fax: (230) 208 0968
E-Mail: info@eni.mu
Business Services
S.I.C.: 7389
N.A.I.C.S.: 561499

ENM HOLDINGS LIMITED

Suites 3301-03 33/F Tower 2 Nina Tower 8 Yeung Uk Road
Tsuen Wan, New Territories, China (Hong Kong)
Tel.: (852) 25940600
Fax: (852) 28271491
E-Mail: comsec@enmholdings.com
Web Site: www.enmholdings.com
0128—(HKG OTC)
Rev.: $43,487,227
Assets: $164,855,612
Liabilities: $10,776,352
Net Worth: $154,079,260
Earnings: $2,928,841
Emp.: 286
Fiscal Year-end: 12/31/12

Business Description:
Resort & Recreation Club Holding Company
S.I.C.: 6719
N.A.I.C.S.: 551112

Personnel:
Joseph Wing Kong Leung *(Chm & Acting CEO)*
Regina Wai Man Lam *(COO)*
Pui Man Cheng *(Sec)*

Board of Directors:
Joseph Wing Kong Leung
Raymond Siu Wing Chan
Jen Chen
Victor Yiu Keung Chiang
Derek Wai Choi Leung
David Kwok Kwei Lo
Ian Grant Robinson
Chi Keung Wong
Wing Tung Yeung

Subsidiaries:

Hill Top Country Club Limited (1)
10 Hilltop Rd Lo Wai Vlg
Tsuen Wan, New Territories, China (Hong Kong)
Tel.: (852) 24120201
Fax: (852) 24122089
E-Mail: info@hilltopcountryclub.com
Web Site: www.hilltopcountryclub.com
Country Club Services
S.I.C.: 7999
N.A.I.C.S.: 713910
Cail Chan *(Mgr)*

The Swank Shop Limited (1)
Shop B51-54 The Landmark Basement
Central, China (Hong Kong)
Tel.: (852) 28100769
Fax: (852) 28683096
E-Mail: info@swank.com.hk
Web Site: www.swank.com.hk
Emp.: 150
Fashion Apparels Retailer
S.I.C.: 5651
N.A.I.C.S.: 448140
David Hong *(Mng Dir)*

Non-U.S. Subsidiary:

The Swank Shop (Beijing) Limited (2)
Shop 210-211 Jinbao Pl Shopping Ctr 88 Jinbao St
Dong Cheng Dist, Beijing, 100005, China
Tel.: (86) 1085221398
Fashion Wears Retailer
S.I.C.: 5651
N.A.I.C.S.: 448140

ENMAX CORPORATION

141- 50th Ave SE
Calgary, AB, T2G 4S7, Canada
Tel.: (403) 514-3000
Fax: (403) 514-2061
E-Mail: info@enmax.com
Web Site: www.enmax.com
Year Founded: 1904
Rev.: $3,141,202,602
Assets: $4,791,076,998
Liabilities: $2,642,105,160
Net Worth: $2,148,971,838
Earnings: $223,654,500
Emp.: 1,830
Fiscal Year-end: 12/31/12

Business Description:
Holding Company; Energy Distribution, Transmission & Support Services
S.I.C.: 6719
N.A.I.C.S.: 551112

Personnel:
Gregory Melchin *(Chm)*
Gianna Manes *(Pres & CEO)*
David Halford *(CFO, Chief Risk Officer & Exec VP-Fin & Plng)*
Helen Bremner *(Exec VP-Residential Markets & Customer Care)*
Robert Hemstock *(Exec VP-Regulatory & Legal Svcs)*
Dale McMaster *(Exec VP-Transmission & Distr Svcs)*
Dave Rehn *(Exec VP-Generation, IT & Supply Chain Mgmt)*

Board of Directors:
Gregory Melchin
Neil Camarta
James F. Hankinson
Michael D. Harris
Donald L. Lenz
Gord Lowe
Sarah Morgan-Silvester
Robert Page
Brian Pincott
Kathleen E. Sendall
Richard Shaw

Divisions:

ENMAX Energy Corporation (1)
141 50th Ave SE
Calgary, AB, T2G 4S7, Canada (100%)
Tel.: (403) 514-3000
Fax: (403) 514-3247
Web Site: www.enmax.com
Emp.: 1,500
Electric Power Generation, Retail & Wholesale Energy Distribution & Transmission Services
S.I.C.: 4911
N.A.I.C.S.: 221122
Gianna Manes *(CEO)*
Dale McMaster *(Exec VP-Transmission & Distr Svcs)*
Dave Rehn *(Exec VP-Generation & Wholesale)*

Subsidiaries:

ENMAX Commercial Energy Marketing Inc. (2)
141 50th Ave SE
Calgary, AB, T2G 4S7, Canada (100%)
Tel.: (403) 514-3000
Fax: (403) 514-1826
Toll Free: (877) 571-7111
E-Mail: info@enmax.com
Emp.: 800
Commercial Electric Power & Natural Gas Wholesale Transmission
S.I.C.: 4939
N.A.I.C.S.: 221121
Gianna Manes *(Pres & CEO)*

ENMAX Energy Marketing Inc. (2)
141 50th Avenue SE
Calgary, AB, T2G 4S7, Canada (100%)
Tel.: (403) 514-3000
Fax: (403) 514-1366
E-Mail: info@enmax.com
Emp.: 1,800
Electric Power & Natural Gas Wholesale Transmission
S.I.C.: 4939
N.A.I.C.S.: 221121
Gianna Manes *(CEO)*

ENMAX Green Power Inc. (2)
141 50 Avenue Southeast
ENMAX Place, Calgary, AB, T2G 4S7, Canada (100%)
Tel.: (403) 689-6150
Emp.: 100
Electric Power Generation
S.I.C.: 4931
N.A.I.C.S.: 221118
Gary Holden *(CEO)*

ENMAX Power Corporation (1)
141 50 Avenue Southeast
Calgary, AB, T2G 4S7, Canada (100%)
Tel.: (403) 514-3000
Fax: (403) 514-1366
Web Site: www.enmax.com
Emp.: 800
Holding Company; Electricity Distribution & Transmission Network Owner & Operator
S.I.C.: 6719
N.A.I.C.S.: 551112

ENMAX Corporation—(Continued)

Gianna Manes *(CEO)*

Subsidiaries:

ENMAX Encompass Inc. (1)
141 50th Ave SE
Calgary, AB, T2G 4S7, Canada (100%)
Tel.: (403) 514-3000
Fax: (403) 514-1366
E-Mail: residential@enmax.com
Web Site: www.enmax.com
Emp.: 1,200
Energy Billing & Customer Care Services
S.I.C.: 7389
N.A.I.C.S.: 561499
Gianna Manes *(CEO)*

ENMAX Envision Inc. (1)
141 50th Ave SE
Calgary, AB, T2G 4S7, Canada (100%)
Tel.: (403) 514-3900
E-Mail: envision@enmax.com
Web Site: www.enmax.com
Emp.: 100
Commercial High-Speed Internet & Data Services
S.I.C.: 4813
N.A.I.C.S.: 517911
Gary Holden *(CEO)*

ENN ENERGY HOLDINGS LIMITED

BuildingA ENN Industrial Park
Xinyuan Dong Road Economic Technological
Development Zone, Langfang, Hebei, 065001, China
Tel.: (86) 316 2598100
Fax: (86) 316 2598585
E-Mail: enn@ennenergy.com
Web Site: www.ennenergy.com
2688—(HKG)
Rev.: $2,863,588,950
Assets: $4,907,353,050
Liabilities: $3,212,423,550
Net Worth: $1,694,929,500
Earnings: $316,588,050
Emp.: 23,771
Fiscal Year-end: 12/31/12

Business Description:
Gas Distr
S.I.C.: 4924
N.A.I.C.S.: 221210

Personnel:
Yusuo Wang *(Chm)*
Yip Sang Cheung *(CEO)*
Shengli Zhao *(COO)*

Board of Directors:
Yusuo Wang
Yip Sang Cheung
Zhongqiu Jiang
Yongsheng Jin
Dongzhi Wang
Guangtian Wang
Yuyu Yan
Jianchao Yu
Baoju Zhao
Jinfeng Zhao
Shengli Zhao

Legal Counsel:
Woo, Kwan, Lee & Lo
26 F Jardine House 1 Connaught Place
Hong Kong, China (Hong Kong)

Computershare Hong Kong Investor Services Limited
Rooms 1712-1716 17/F Hopewell Centre 183 Queen's Road East
Wanchai, China (Hong Kong)
Tel.: (852) 2862 8628
Fax: (852) 2865 0990

Transfer Agents:
Royal Bank of Canada Trust Company (Cayman) Limited
4th Floor Royal Bank House 24 Shedden Road
Georgetown, Cayman Islands

Computershare Hong Kong Investor Services Limited
Rooms 1712-1716 17/F Hopewell Centre 183 Queen's Road East
Wanchai, China (Hong Kong)
Tel.: (852) 2862 8628
Fax: (852) 2865 0990

Non-U.S. Subsidiary:

Liaocheng Xinao Gas Company Limited (1)
N Section Of Changyun Rd
Dongchangfu, Liaocheng, Shandong, China 252000
Tel.: (86) 635 8467188
Gas Mfr
S.I.C.: 1629
N.A.I.C.S.: 237120

ENNO ROGGEMANN GMBH & CO. KG

Ahrens Strasse 4
28197 Bremen, Germany
Tel.: (49) 42151850
Fax: (49) 421518550
E-Mail: email@enno-roggemann-bremen.de
Web Site: www.roggemann.de
Year Founded: 1948
Sales Range: $150-199.9 Million
Emp.: 220

Business Description:
Lumber Whslr
S.I.C.: 5031
N.A.I.C.S.: 423310

Personnel:
Jurgen Roggemann *(Mng Dir)*

Subsidiary:

Sperrholz Koch GmbH (1)
Otterkamp 11
48653 Coesfeld, Germany De (100%)
Tel.: (49) 25418090
Fax: (49) 254180925
E-Mail: email@sperrholzkoch.de
Web Site: www.sperrholzkoch.de
Sales Range: $10-24.9 Million
Emp.: 75
Based Panel Products & Flush Doors Whslr
S.I.C.: 5031
N.A.I.C.S.: 423310
Juergen Roggemann *(CEO)*

ENNORE COKE LTD.

85 A Sarat Bose Road Flat 3A & B
3rd floor
Kolkata, 700026, India
Tel.: (91) 3324851697
Fax: (91) 3324851698
E-Mail: info@ennorecoke.com
Web Site: www.ennorecoke.com
512369—(BOM)
Rev.: $66,530,929
Assets: $150,926,389
Liabilities: $148,866,726
Net Worth: $2,059,663
Earnings: ($7,376,928)
Fiscal Year-end: 03/31/13

Business Description:
Metallurgical Coke Mfr
S.I.C.: 5052
N.A.I.C.S.: 423520

Personnel:
Ganesh Natarajan *(Pres & CEO)*
K. Rajagopal *(CFO & Sec)*
Vivek Sharma *(COO)*

Board of Directors:
Rajeev Agarwal
Ganesh Natarajan
R. Ramakrishnan
K. U. Sivadas
M. Aravind Subramanian

Transfer Agent:
Cameo Corporate Services Limited
Subramanian Building No 1 Club House Road
5th Floor
Chennai, India

ENO S.A.S.

(d/b/a Groupe ENO)
95 rue de la Terraudiere
F-79000 Niort, France
Tel.: (33) 549286001
Fax: (33) 549332684
Web Site: www.eno.fr
Year Founded: 1909
Sales Range: $10-24.9 Million
Emp.: 80

Business Description:
Home & Marine Heating & Cooking Equipment Designer, Mfr & Distr
S.I.C.: 3585
N.A.I.C.S.: 333415

Personnel:
Antoine Thomas *(Mng Dir)*

Non-U.S. Subsidiary:

Force 10 Manufacturing Corporation (1)
Unit A 19169 21st Ave
Surrey, BC, V3S 3M3, Canada BC
Tel.: (604) 536-0379
Fax: (604) 535-1210
Toll Free: (800) 663-8515
E-Mail: sales@force10.com
Web Site: www.force10.com
Sales Range: $1-9.9 Million
Emp.: 20
Gas & Electric Cooking Appliances Mfr
S.I.C.: 3631
N.A.I.C.S.: 335221
Brad Clark *(VP)*

ENOMOTO CO., LTD.

8154-19 Uenohara
Uenohara City, Yamanashi, 409-0198, Japan
Tel.: (81) 554625111
Fax: (81) 554 63 4193
Web Site: www.enomoto.co.jp
Year Founded: 1967
6928—(JAS)
Sls.: $180,455,000
Assets: $203,456,000
Liabilities: $102,047,000
Net Worth: $101,409,000
Earnings: ($14,300,000)
Emp.: 1,100
Fiscal Year-end: 03/31/13

Business Description:
Electronic Parts Mfr & Sales
S.I.C.: 3679
N.A.I.C.S.: 334419

Personnel:
Maasaki Enomoto *(Pres)*

Board of Directors:
Maasaki Enomoto
Ikkei Ito
Yukinori Narita
Shiro Ozawa
Nobuo Sakurai
Homare Shiratori
Nobuyuki Takeuchi
Hiroyuki Yamazaki

Non-U.S. Subsidiaries:

Enomoto Hong Kong Co.Ltd. (1)
Room 1805 Star House No 3 Salisbury Rd
Kowloon, China (Hong Kong)
Tel.: (852) 21997848
Fax: (852) 21997918
E-Mail: anna@enomoto.com.hk
Emp.: 4
Other Electronic Component Mfr
S.I.C.: 3679
N.A.I.C.S.: 334419

Enomoto Philippine Manufacturing Inc. (1)
PEZA-Gateway Business Park Javalera Gen
4107 Cavite, Philippines
Tel.: (63) 464330263
Fax: (63) 464330264
Web Site: www.enomoto.co.gp
Emp.: 500
Semiconductor & Related Device Mfr
S.I.C.: 3674
N.A.I.C.S.: 334413
Hitoshi Sakamoco *(Sr VP)*

Enomoto Precision Engineering (S) Pte.Ltd (1)
30 Loyang Drive
508945 Singapore, Singapore
Tel.: (65) 65424542
Fax: (65) 65422484
E-Mail: precision@enomoto.com.cn
Web Site: www.enomoto.com.cn
Emp.: 70
Mfg & Indus Building Construction
S.I.C.: 1629
N.A.I.C.S.: 236210
Akama Yosinavo *(Mng Dir)*

Zhong Shan Enomoto Co. Ltd. (1)
Yixian Industrial District Zhangjiabian
Zhongshan, Guangdong, China
Tel.: (86) 7605335111
Fax: (86) 7605335113
Web Site: www.enomoto.com.cn
Emp.: 200
Semiconductor & Related Device Mfr
S.I.C.: 3674
N.A.I.C.S.: 334413

ENOTECA CO., LTD.

5-14-15 B1F Minami Azabu
Minato-ku, Tokyo, 106-0047, Japan
Tel.: (81) 332806388
Fax: (81) 332806293
E-Mail: import@enoteca.co.jp
Web Site: www.enoteca.jp/english/company/index.html
Year Founded: 1988
Sales Range: $100-124.9 Million
Emp.: 300

Business Description:
Wine Retailer, Importer, E-Commerce & Mail Order Sales
S.I.C.: 5921
N.A.I.C.S.: 445310

Personnel:
Yasuhisa Hirose *(Pres & CEO)*
Kentaro Abe *(Mng Dir)*

ENOVOS INTERNATIONAL S.A.

2 Rue Thomas Edison
1445 Strassen, Luxembourg
Tel.: (352) 27371
Fax: (352) 27379100
E-Mail: info@enovos.eu
Web Site: www.enovos.eu
Emp.: 745

Business Description:
Electricity Generation & Distribution Services
S.I.C.: 4911
N.A.I.C.S.: 221112

Personnel:
Etienne Schneider *(Chm)*
Fernand Felzinger *(Co-Vice Chm)*
Marco Hoffmann *(Co-Vice Chm)*
Claude Seywert *(Co-Vice Chm)*
Romain Becker *(Member-Exec Bd)*
Hanno Dornseifer *(Member-Mgmt Bd)*
Jean Lucius *(Member-Exec Bd)*

Board of Directors:
Marco Hoffmann
Etienne Schneider
Eric Bosman
Fernand Felzinger
Peter Frankenberg
Andre Gilbertz
Tim Hartmann
Charles Hutmacher
Jean-Claude Knebeler
Arnold Neudeck
Peter Pichl
Pierre Rauchs
Gaston Reinesch
Claude Seywert
Nico Wietor

Subsidiary:

Enovos Luxembourg S.A. (1)
2 rue Thomas Edison
L-2089 Strassen, Luxembourg

Tel.: (352) 27371
Fax: (352) 27376111
E-Mail: info@enovos.eu
Emp.: 111
Gas & Electricity Distr
S.I.C.: 4931
N.A.I.C.S.: 221122
Marco Hoffmann *(Chm)*
Claude Seywert *(Vice Chm)*
Jean Lucius *(CEO)*

Subsidiary:

Cegedel Participations S.A. (2)
Rue Thomas Edison 2
Strassen, Luxembourg (100%)
Tel.: (352) 27371
Fax: (352) 27376111
E-Mail: mail@enovo.eu
Web Site: www.enovo.eu
Emp.: 100
Holding Company
S.I.C.: 6719
N.A.I.C.S.: 551112
Jean Lucius *(CEO)*

Subsidiary:

LuxEnergie S.A. (3)
23 avenue John F Kennedy
Luxembourg, 5326, Luxembourg (60.35%)
Tel.: (352) 2254741
Fax: (352) 225477
E-Mail: info@luxenergie.lu
Web Site: www.luxenergie.lu
Emp.: 60
Power Plant Design Services
S.I.C.: 8711
N.A.I.C.S.: 541330
W. Ees *(Mng Dir)*

Non-U.S. Subsidiary:

Enovos Deutschland AG (1)
Am Halberg 3
66121 Saarbrucken, Germany
Tel.: (49) 681810500
Fax: (49) 6818105232
Web Site: www.enovos.eu/index.php?id=16
Emp.: 150
Gas & Electricity Distr
S.I.C.: 4911
N.A.I.C.S.: 221122
Etienne Schneider *(Chm)*
Marco Hoffmann *(Vice Chm)*
Arnold Neudeck *(Co-Vice Chm)*
Hanno Dornseifer *(Mng Dir)*

ENOX BIOPHARMA, INC.

1687 West Broadway Suite 303
Vancouver, BC, V6J 1X2, Canada
Tel.: (604) 637-9744
Fax: (888) 224-7259
Web Site: www.enoxbiopharma.com
Year Founded: 2007
Business Description:
Biopharmaceutical Developer & Mfr
S.I.C.: 2834
N.A.I.C.S.: 325412
Personnel:
Yossef Av-Gay *(Founder & Pres)*
Amir Avniel *(Chm)*
Itamar David *(CFO)*
David Greenberg *(Chief Medical Officer)*
Razi Mizrahi *(Treas & Sec)*
Board of Directors:
Amir Avniel
Yossef Av-Gay
David Greenberg
Razi Mizrahi

ENPAR TECHNOLOGIES INC.

70 Southgate Drive Unit 4
Guelph, ON, N1G 4P5, Canada
Tel.: (519) 836-6155
Fax: (519) 836-5683
Toll Free: (800) 811-6216
E-Mail: info@enpar-tech.com
Web Site: www.enpar-tech.com
ENP—(TSXV)
Rev.: $201,755
Assets: $928,968
Liabilities: $422,117
Net Worth: $506,852
Earnings: ($1,508,721)
Fiscal Year-end: 12/31/12
Business Description:
Waste Water Treatment Services
S.I.C.: 4959
N.A.I.C.S.: 562998
Personnel:
Gene S. Shelp *(Co-Founder, Pres & CEO)*
Barry J. Shelp *(Co-Founder & Sec)*
Edward Tsang *(Interim CFO)*
Board of Directors:
Sunil Ghorawat
Iurie Pargaru
Barry J. Shelp
Gene S. Shelp
Edward Tsang
Transfer Agent:
Equity Financial Trust Company
200 University Avenue Suite 400
Toronto, ON, Canada
Non-U.S. Subsidiary:

Blue Print Technologies (Pty) Ltd. (1)
394 Aries Street Waterkloof Ridge
Pretoria, 0181, South Africa
Tel.: (27) 12 460 8922
Fax: (27) 12 346 8866
E-Mail: info-sa@enpar-tech.com
Web Site: www.enpar-tech.com
Water Treatment Services
S.I.C.: 4971
N.A.I.C.S.: 221310
J. A. du Plessis *(Mng Dir)*

ENPLAS CORPORATION

2-30-1 Namiki
Kawaguchi, Saitama, 332-0034, Japan
Tel.: (81) 482533131
Fax: (81) 482551688
E-Mail: webmaster@enplas.co.jp
Web Site: www.enplas.com
6961—(TKS)
Sls.: $288,690,402
Assets: $425,276,159
Liabilities: $55,178,860
Net Worth: $370,097,299
Earnings: $61,995,384
Emp.: 300
Fiscal Year-end: 03/31/13
Business Description:
Plastics Mfr
S.I.C.: 3089
N.A.I.C.S.: 326199
Personnel:
Daisuke Yokota *(Pres)*
Board of Directors:
Ichiro Hasegawa
Yutaka Kikuchi
Ryoji Maruyama
Takashi Sakai
Noboru Sugawara
Yoshio Tamiya
Daisuke Yokota
Divisions:

Enplas Corporation - Engineering Plastics Products Division (1)
2-30-1 Namiki
Kawaguchi, Saitama, 332-0034, Japan
Tel.: (81) 48 497 2986
Fax: (81) 48 253 5809
E-Mail: ep-sales@enplas.co.jp
Web Site: www.enplas.com
Engineering Plastics Products Mfr
S.I.C.: 3089
N.A.I.C.S.: 326199

Enplas Corporation - LED Business Division (1)
2-30-1 Namiki
Kawaguchi, Saitama, 332-0034, Japan
Tel.: (81) 482501334
Fax: (81) 482580520
E-Mail: lc-sales@enplas.co.jp
Web Site: www.enplas.co.jp
Emp.: 250
Light Enhancer Cap Module Mfr
S.I.C.: 3648
N.A.I.C.S.: 335129
Daisuae Yokoca *(Pres)*

Enplas Corporation - Plastic Optics Division (1)
2-30-1 Namiki
Kawaguchi, Saitama, 332-0034, Japan
Tel.: (81) 482501310
Fax: (81) 482580520
E-Mail: op-sales@enplas.co.jp
Web Site: www.enplas.com
Emp.: 200
Optical Fiber Components Whslr
S.I.C.: 3357
N.A.I.C.S.: 335921
Masanori Watanabe *(Gen Mgr)*

Subsidiaries:

Enplas Seiki Corporation (1)
827-3 Moro
Kanuma, Tochigi, 322-0026, Japan
Tel.: (81) 289765315
Fax: (81) 289 76 2069
Web Site: www.enplas.co.jp/english/company/network.html
Semiconductor Peripherals Mfr
S.I.C.: 3674
N.A.I.C.S.: 334413

Enplas Semiconductor Peripheral Corporation (1)
1-19-57 Kamiaoki
Kawaguchi, Saitama, 333-0844, Japan
Tel.: (81) 482506680
Fax: (81) 482557258
E-Mail: sp-gwedi@enplas.com
Web Site: www.enplas.com
Emp.: 85
Semiconductor Peripherals Mfr
S.I.C.: 3674
N.A.I.C.S.: 334413
Ryoji Maruyama *(Pres)*

QMS Co., Ltd. (1)
1-3-12 Kamiaoki
Kawaguchi, Saitama, 333-0844, Japan
Tel.: (81) 482550051
Fax: (81) 482514398
E-Mail: info@qms-co.com
Web Site: www.qms-co.com
Emp.: 50
Sockets Mfr
S.I.C.: 3699
N.A.I.C.S.: 335999
Takeo Shimane *(Pres)*

Plant:

Enplas Corporation - Kanuma Plant (1)
7-2 Satsuki-Cho
Kanuma, Tochigi, 322-0014, Japan
Tel.: (81) 289720600
Fax: (81) 289766621
Web Site: www.enplas.co.jp
Emp.: 157
Engineering Plastic Products Mfr
S.I.C.: 3089
N.A.I.C.S.: 326199
Daifuki Yokota *(Pres)*

U.S. Subsidiaries:

Enplas Tesco, Inc. (1)
765 N Mary Ave
Sunnyvale, CA 94085-2909
Tel.: (408) 749-8124
Fax: (408) 749-8125
E-Mail: info@enplas-ets.com
Web Site: www.enplas-ets.com
Emp.: 11
Sockets Mfr
S.I.C.: 3699
N.A.I.C.S.: 335999
John Ambrosini *(Reg Sls Mgr)*

Enplas (U.S.A.), Inc. (1)
1901 W Oak Cir
Marietta, GA 30062
Tel.: (770) 795-1100
Fax: (770) 795-1190
E-Mail: sale@enplasusa.com
Web Site: www.enplasusa.com
Emp.: 50
Injection Molding Solutions
S.I.C.: 3544
N.A.I.C.S.: 333511
Jerry Mullis *(Gen Mgr-HR & Gen Affairs)*

Non-U.S. Subsidiaries:

Enplas (Hong Kong) Limited (1)
Ste 515 5 F World Com Ctr Harbour City 11 Canton Rd
Tsim Sha Tsui, Kowloon, China (Hong Kong)
Tel.: (852) 23698661
Fax: (852) 27392808
E-Mail: y-satoh@enplas-hk.com
Web Site: www.enplas.com
Emp.: 4
Optical Devices Mfr & Whslr
S.I.C.: 3572
N.A.I.C.S.: 334112
Yoshihiko Sato *(Mgr)*

Enplas Hy-cad Electronic (Shanghai) Co., Ltd. (1)
Fl 1 Standard Indus Bldg 3 No 253 Ai Du Rd Shanghai Waigaoqiao
Free Trade Zone, Shanghai, 200131, China
Tel.: (86) 2150461685
Fax: (86) 2150461207
E-Mail: salesinquiry@enplas-hycad.com
Web Site: www.enplasusa.com
Emp.: 100
Engineering Plastics Products Mfr
S.I.C.: 3052
N.A.I.C.S.: 326220
Ogura Takashi *(Mng Dir)*

Enplas Niching Technology Corporation (1)
4F-1 No 27 Puding Rd
Hsin-chu, 300, Taiwan
Tel.: (886) 35637305
Fax: (886) 35670254
E-Mail: emily@enplas.com.tw
Web Site: www.enplas.com
Emp.: 7
Testing Equipments Mfr
S.I.C.: 3825
N.A.I.C.S.: 334515
Akio Kurihara *(Mng Dir)*

Enplas Precision (Malaysia) Sdn. Bhd. (1)
No 9 & 9A Jalan Hasil 2 Kawasan Perindustrian
Jalan Hasil, 81200 Johor Bahru, Johor, Malaysia
Tel.: (60) 72365253
Fax: (60) 72365243
Plastic Engineering Products Mfr
S.I.C.: 3089
N.A.I.C.S.: 326199

Enplas Precision (Thailand) Co., Ltd. (1)
Hi-Tech Indus Estate 104 Moo 1 Bhan Lain
Bangpa-in, Ayutthaya, 13160, Thailand
Tel.: (66) 35350990
Fax: (66) 35350989
E-Mail: weerapong@enplas.com
Web Site: www.enplas.co.jp
Emp.: 150
Plastic Injection Molding Machines Mfr
S.I.C.: 3089
N.A.I.C.S.: 326199
Morikazu Kubota *(Mng Dir)*

Enplas (Vietnam) Co., Ltd. (1)
K-3 Plot Thang Long Indus Park Dong Anh Dist
Hanoi, Vietnam
Tel.: (84) 439516485
Fax: (84) 439516486
Web Site: www.enplas.co.jp/english/company/network.html
Optical & Semiconductor Peripherals Mfr
S.I.C.: 3827
N.A.I.C.S.: 333314

Guangzhou Enplas Mechatronics Co., Ltd. (1)
Standard Bldg 1 Hexing Industry Park 10 Yongsheng Rd Yong He Econ Zone
Guangzhou Econ & Tech Dev Dist,
Guangzhou, 511356, China
Tel.: (86) 2032225678
Fax: (86) 2032225686

ENPLAS CORPORATION—(Continued)

Web Site: www.enplas.com
Emp.: 70
Engineering Plastics Products Mfr
S.I.C.: 3089
N.A.I.C.S.: 326199

EN+ GROUP LTD.
1a Granatny Lane
123001 Moscow, Russia
Tel.: (7) 4956427937
Fax: (7) 4956427938
E-Mail: info@enplus.ru
Web Site: www.enplus.ru
Sales Range: $15-24.9 Billion
Emp.: 100,000
Business Description:
Holding Company; Electricity, Coal, Uranium, Aluminum & Silicon
S.I.C.: 6719
N.A.I.C.S.: 551112
Personnel:
Vladislav Soloviev *(CEO)*
Jivko Savov *(Deputy CEO)*
Alexander Popov *(CFO)*

ENQUEST PLC
4th Floor Rex House 4-12 Regent Street
London, SW1Y 4PE, United Kingdom
Tel.: (44) 20 7925 4900
Fax: (44) 20 7925 4936
E-Mail: communications@enquest.com
Web Site: www.enquest.com
ENQ—(LSE OMX)
Emp.: 220
Business Description:
Oil & Natural Gas Exploration & Production Services
S.I.C.: 1311
N.A.I.C.S.: 211111
Personnel:
James W. Buckee *(Chm)*
Amjad Bseisu *(CEO)*
Jonathan Swinney *(CFO)*
Nigel Hares *(COO)*
Neil McCulloch *(Pres-North Sea)*
Stefan Ricketts *(Gen Counsel & Sec)*
Board of Directors:
James W. Buckee
Amjad Bseisu
Nigel Hares
Helmut Langanger
Jock Fyfe Lennox
Phil Nolan
Clare Mary Joan Spottiswoode
Jonathan Swinney

ENR ASSET MANAGEMENT INC.
1 Westmount Square Suite 1400
Westmount, QC, H3Z 2P9, Canada
Tel.: (514) 989-8027
Fax: (514) 989-7060
Toll Free: (877) 989-8027
Web Site: www.enrassetmanagement.com
Year Founded: 1991
Managed Assets: $303,176,100
Business Description:
Investment Advisory & Management Services
S.I.C.: 6282
N.A.I.C.S.: 523930
Personnel:
Eric N. Roseman *(Founder, Pres & Chief Investment Officer)*

ENR RUSSIA INVEST SA
2-4 Place du Molard
Case Postale 3458
1211 Geneva, Switzerland
Tel.: (41) 227161000
Fax: (41) 227161001
E-Mail: contact@enr.ch
Web Site: www.enr.ch
Year Founded: 1995
RUS—(SWX)
Rev.: $24,970,284
Assets: $131,713,241
Liabilities: $3,879,135
Net Worth: $127,834,106
Earnings: $21,758,144
Fiscal Year-end: 12/31/12
Business Description:
Investment Services
S.I.C.: 6282
N.A.I.C.S.: 523930
Personnel:
Urs Maurer-Lambrou *(Chm)*
Board of Directors:
Urs Maurer-Lambrou
Walter Fetscherin
Gustav Stenbolt

ENRO ENERGIE SE
Huyssenallee 86-88
45128 Essen, Germany
Tel.: (49) 2012453615
Fax: (49) 2012453639
E-Mail: info@enro-se.de
Web Site: www.enro-energie.de
EEO—(DEU)
Business Description:
Power Distr
S.I.C.: 4911
N.A.I.C.S.: 221122
Personnel:
Thomas Neu *(Mng Dir)*

ENS TOYOTA
285 Venture Crescent
Saskatoon, SK, S7K 6N8, Canada
Tel.: (306) 653-5611
Fax: (306) 664-6965
E-Mail: reception@enslexustoyota.ca
Web Site: www.enslexustoyota.ca
Rev.: $35,299,650
Emp.: 72
Business Description:
New & Used Car Dealers
S.I.C.: 5511
N.A.I.C.S.: 441110
Personnel:
Josh Ens *(VP)*

ENSA STEEL INDUSTRIES LIMITED
43 Atlanta
Nariman Point, Mumbai, Maharashtra, 400 021, India
Tel.: (91) 22 66306732
Fax: (91) 22 22041954
Web Site: www.ensasteel.com
512135—(BOM)
Rev.: $126,387
Assets: $12,160,850
Liabilities: $29,702
Net Worth: $12,131,148
Earnings: ($142,424)
Fiscal Year-end: 06/30/13
Business Description:
Iron & Steel Product Whslr
S.I.C.: 5051
N.A.I.C.S.: 423510
Personnel:
R. B. Dixit *(Compliance Officer)*
Board of Directors:
Sanjay Chohan
R. B. Dixit
J. C. Sandesara
R. J. Sandesara
T. R. Thakkar

ENSCO PLC
6 Chesterfield Gardens
London, W1J 5BQ, United Kingdom
Tel.: (44) 207 659 4660
Telex: 166304
E-Mail: ir.hdqrs@enscoplc.com
Web Site: www.enscoplc.com
Year Founded: 1987
ESV—(NYSE)
Rev.: $4,919,800,000
Assets: $19,472,900,000
Liabilities: $6,674,000,000
Net Worth: $12,798,900,000
Earnings: $1,427,900,000
Emp.: 9,000
Fiscal Year-end: 12/31/13
Business Description:
Offshore Drilling Services
Export
S.I.C.: 1381
N.A.I.C.S.: 213111
Personnel:
Daniel W. Rabun *(Chm, Pres & CEO)*
James W. Swent, III *(CFO & Exec VP)*
John Mark Burns *(COO, Exec VP & Sr VP-Western Hemisphere)*
William S. Chadwick Jr. *(COO & Exec VP)*
Robert W. Edwards, III *(Chief Acctg Officer & Controller)*
Brady K. Long *(Gen Counsel, Sec & VP)*
David Hensel *(Sr VP-Mktg)*
John S. Knowlton *(Sr VP-Tech)*
Patrick Carey Lowe *(Sr VP-Eastern Hemisphere)*
Board of Directors:
Daniel W. Rabun
David A. B. Brown
J. Roderick Clark
Roxanne J. Decyk
Mary E. Francis
C. Christopher Gaut
Gerald W. Haddock
Francis S. Kalman
Keith O. Rattie
Paul E. Rowsey, III
Legal Counsel:
Baker & McKenzie
Lock Box No. 163 4500 LTV Center, 2001 Ross Ave.
Dallas, TX 75201
Tel.: (214) 978-3000
Transfer Agent:
American Stock Transfer & Trust Company
40 Wall St
New York, NY 10005
Tel.: (212) 936-5100
Subsidiaries:

ENSCO Marine Co. (1)
620 Moulin Rd
Broussard, LA 70518-5041 TX
Tel.: (337) 837-8500 (100%)
Fax: (337) 837-7863
Toll Free: (800) 227-9583
E-Mail: marine@enscous.com
Web Site: www.enscous.com
Rev.: $36,100,000
Emp.: 400
Petroleum & Natural Gas & Marine Transportation
S.I.C.: 4432
N.A.I.C.S.: 483113
Stan Rayburn *(CEO)*
Jay W. Swent *(Sr VP & CFO)*
J. Mark Burns *(Sr VP-Western Hemisphere)*
P. Carey Lowe *(Sr VP-Eastern Hemisphere)*

ENSCO Offshore Company (1)
620 Moulin Rd
Broussard, LA 70518-5041
Tel.: (337) 837-8500
Fax: (337) 837-8501
Toll Free: (800) 322-8217
Web Site: www.enscoplc.com
Sales Range: $50-74.9 Million
Emp.: 75
Drilling Oil & Gas Wells
S.I.C.: 1381
N.A.I.C.S.: 213111
Unit:

ENSCO Offshore Company - Marketing & Contracts (2)
16340 Park Ten Pl Ste 350
Houston, TX 77084-5147
Tel.: (281) 920-6440
Fax: (281) 920-6441
Web Site: www.enscous.com
Sales Range: $10-24.9 Million
Emp.: 5
Contract Drilling Services
S.I.C.: 1389
N.A.I.C.S.: 213112

ENSCO Services Limited (1)
Badentoy Ave
Aberdeen, Aberdeenshire, AB12 4YB, United Kingdom
Tel.: (44) 1224780400
Fax: (44) 1224783483
E-Mail: marketing.eu@enscoplc.com
Offshore Drilling Services
S.I.C.: 1381
N.A.I.C.S.: 213111

U.S. Division:

Ensco (1)
5847 San Felipe St Ste 3300
Houston, TX 77057-3195 DE
Tel.: (713) 789-1400
Fax: (713) 789-1430
Web Site: www.enscoplc.com
Sales Range: $1-4.9 Billion
Emp.: 3,900
International Oil & Gas Contract Drilling Services
S.I.C.: 1311
N.A.I.C.S.: 211111
David Douglas *(Dir-Sls & Mktg-Deepwater)*

Subsidiaries:

Larcom Insurance, Ltd. (2)
5847 San Felipe St Ste 3300
Houston, TX 77057-3195 (100%)
Tel.: (713) 789-1400
Fax: (713) 789-1430
Sales Range: $250-299.9 Million
Insurance Services
S.I.C.: 6411
N.A.I.C.S.: 524298

Non-U.S. Subsidiary:

Pride Forasol-Foramer S.A. (2)
16 bis rue Grange Dame Rose
PO Box 100
Velizy-Villacoublay, 78143 Paris, France FR
Tel.: (33) 130705807 (100%)
Telex: FORAS 698047
Fax: (33) 130705998
Sales Range: $50-74.9 Million
Emp.: 60
Drillings & Ancillary Services for Oil Industry
Export
S.I.C.: 1381
N.A.I.C.S.: 213111

Non-U.S. Subsidiaries:

ENSCO Asia Pacific (Singapore) Pte. Ltd. (1)
300 Beach Rd Ste 10 01 03
The Concourse, Singapore, 199555, Singapore SG
Tel.: (65) 63943100 (100%)
Fax: (65) 63943105
E-Mail: drilling.ap@enscous.com
Sales Range: $25-49.9 Million
Emp.: 11
Provider of Oil & Gas Drilling & Marine Transportation
S.I.C.: 1381
N.A.I.C.S.: 213111

ENSCO Australia Pty. Ltd. (1)
GF 10 Kings Pk Rd
Perth, WA, 6005, Australia AU
Tel.: (61) 892113388 (100%)
Fax: (61) 892113390
E-Mail: contact@enscous.com.au
Web Site: www.enscous.com.au
Sls.: $56,000,000
Emp.: 10
Provider of Oil & Gas Drilling Transportation
S.I.C.: 1381
N.A.I.C.S.: 213111

Paul Howe *(Office Mgr)*

ENSCO Drilling Company (Nigeria) Ltd. **(1)**
Plot 184C Trans Amadi Industrial Layout
Port Harcourt, Nigeria NG
Tel.: (234) 8423 1322 (99%)
Sales Range: $250-299.9 Million
Petroleum & Natural Gas Drilling & Extraction
S.I.C.: 1381
N.A.I.C.S.: 213111

ENSCO Drilling (Venezuela), S.A. **(1)**
Muelle Terminales Maracaibo
Los Morochas, Edo Zulia, 4019, Venezuela (100%)
Tel.: (58) 2656312287
Telex: 29642 CONSE VC
Fax: (58) 2656311435
E-Mail: southamerica@enscous.com
Sales Range: $150-199.9 Million
Oil & Gas Drilling
S.I.C.: 1381
N.A.I.C.S.: 213111

ENSCO Gerudi (M) Sdn. Bhd. **(1)**
5th Flr Angkasa Raya Bldg
Jalan Ambang, 50450 Kuala Lumpur, Malaysia MY
Tel.: (60) 321402205 (49%)
Fax: (60) 321402214, ext. 21483909
Sales Range: $10-24.9 Million
Emp.: 7
Provider of Oil & Gas Drilling Transportation
S.I.C.: 1381
N.A.I.C.S.: 213111

ENSCO Offshore UK Ltd. **(1)**
ENSCO House Badentoy Ave Badentoy Pk
Aberdeen, Portlethen, AB12 4YB, United Kingdom UK
Tel.: (44) 224780400 (100%)
Fax: (44) 1224780444
E-Mail: Drilling.eu@enscous.com
Sales Range: $50-74.9 Million
Emp.: 50
Provider of Oil & Gas Drilling & Marine Transportation
S.I.C.: 1381
N.A.I.C.S.: 213111

P.T. ENSCO Sarida Offshore **(1)**
Wahana Graha 3rd Floor JL Warung Buncit Raya 2
Mampang Prapatan, Jakarta, 12790, Indonesia
Tel.: (62) 217989080
Fax: (62) 217989081
Emp.: 20
Offshore Drilling Services
S.I.C.: 1381
N.A.I.C.S.: 213111
Raymond Pachtiar *(Gen Mgr)*

ENSECO ENERGY SERVICES CORPORATION

800-138 4th Ave SE
Calgary, AB, T2G 4Z6, Canada
Tel.: (403) 806-0088
Fax: (403) 806 0004
Toll Free: (866) 806-0088
E-Mail: dhawkins@enseco.ca
Web Site: www.enseco.com
ENS—(TSXV)
Sales Range: $75-99.9 Million

Business Description:
Energy Related Services & Rentals to the Oil & Gas Industries
S.I.C.: 1389
N.A.I.C.S.: 213112

Personnel:
M. Scott Ratushny *(Chm)*
Kent M. Devlin *(Pres)*
Blair B. Layton *(CFO & VP-Fin)*

Board of Directors:
M. Scott Ratushny
John A. Brussa
Stan G. P. Grad
Gregory T. Tisdale

Transfer Agent:
Olympia Trust Company
Calgary, AB, Canada

ENSEMBLE SYSTEMS INC.

2268 - 13353 Commerce Parkway
Richmond, BC, Canada V6V 3A1
Tel.: (604) 231-9510
Fax: (604) 231-9545
Toll Free: (877) 290-2662
E-Mail: sales@ensemble.com
Web Site: www.ensemble.com
Year Founded: 1995
Rev.: $10,172,559
Emp.: 86

Business Description:
Software Development & Services
S.I.C.: 5734
N.A.I.C.S.: 443142

Personnel:
Mike Bacinschi *(Pres)*
Ray Blaak *(CTO)*

ENSHU LIMITED

4888 Takatsuka-cho
Minami-ku, Hamamatsu, Shizuoka, 432-8522, Japan
Tel.: (81) 53 447 2111
Fax: (81) 53 448 6718
Web Site: www.enshu.co.jp
Year Founded: 1920
6218—(TKS)

Business Description:
Machine Tool Mfr & Whslr
S.I.C.: 3542
N.A.I.C.S.: 333517

Personnel:
Takashi Tsuchiya *(Pres)*

ENSIGN CHRYSLER DODGE JEEP

1061 Yates Street
Victoria, BC, V8V3M5, Canada
Tel.: (250) 386-2411
Fax: (250) 381-7444
Toll Free: (888) 269-1505
E-Mail: ensign@ensignchrysler.com
Web Site: www.ensignchrysler.com
Year Founded: 1957
Rev.: $28,700,000
Emp.: 52

Business Description:
New & Used Car Dealers
S.I.C.: 5511
N.A.I.C.S.: 441110

Personnel:
Kevin Knight *(Owner)*

ENSIGN ENERGY SERVICES INC.

1000 400 5th Avenue SW
Calgary, AB, T2P 0L6, Canada
Tel.: (403) 262-1361
Fax: (403) 262-8215
E-Mail: info@ensignenergy.com
Web Site: www.ensignenergy.com
ESI—(TSX)
Rev.: $2,184,181,020
Assets: $3,052,612,558
Liabilities: $1,205,765,146
Net Worth: $1,846,847,411
Earnings: $216,221,218
Emp.: 8,276
Fiscal Year-end: 12/31/12

Business Description:
Drilling, Well Servicing, Manufacturing & Production Service
S.I.C.: 1381
N.A.I.C.S.: 213111

Personnel:
N. Murray Edwards *(Chm)*
Selby W. Porter *(Vice Chm)*
Robert H. Geddes *(Pres & COO)*
Glenn O. J. Dagenais *(CFO & Exec VP-Fin)*
Suzanne Davies *(Gen Counsel & Sec)*
Edward D. Kautz *(Exec VP-US & Intl Oilfield Svcs)*

Board of Directors:
N. Murray Edwards
Robert H. Geddes
James B. Howe
Len O. Kangas
Selby W. Porter
John G. Schroeder
Kenneth J. Skirka
Gail D. Surkan
Barth E. Whitham

Legal Counsel:
Burnet, Duckworth & Palmer LLP
Suite 1400 350 7th Avenue Southwest
Calgary, AB, T2P 3N9, Canada
Tel.: (403) 263-3050

Transfer Agent:
Computershare Trust Company of Canada
100 University Avenue 9th Floor
Toronto, ON, M5J 2Y1, Canada
Tel.: (416) 663-9097
Fax: (416) 263-9694

Division:

Enhanced Petroleum Services Partnership - Chandel Equipment Rentals Division **(1)**
1000 400-5th Ave SW
Calgary, AB, T2P 0L6, Canada
Tel.: (403) 262-1361
Fax: (403) 264-9376
Toll Free: (877) 262-1361
Web Site: www.ensign.com
Drilling Equipment Rental Services
S.I.C.: 7359
N.A.I.C.S.: 532412
Dave Fyhn *(Office Mgr)*

Subsidiaries:

Champion Drilling, Inc. **(1)**
1 Tree Rd
Brooks, AB, T1R1B9, Canada (100%)
Mailing Address:
PO Box 1090
Brooks, AB, T1R 1B9, Canada
Tel.: (403) 362-4400
Fax: (403) 793-8686
E-Mail: info@ensigngroup.com
Web Site: www.ensignenergy.com
Emp.: 525
Provider of Drilling, Well Servicing, Manufacturing & Production Services to Crude Oil & Natural Gas Industry
S.I.C.: 1381
N.A.I.C.S.: 213111

Continuous Tubing **(1)**
Ste 1000 400 5th Ave SW
Calgary, AB, T2P 0L6, Canada (100%)
Tel.: (403) 265-6361
Fax: (403) 262-8215
E-Mail: info@ensignenergy.com
Emp.: 30
S.I.C.: 1311
N.A.I.C.S.: 211111
Bob Geddes *(Pres)*

Enhanced Petroleum Services Partnership **(1)**
1000 400-5th Avenue SW
Calgary, AB, T2P 0L6, Canada
Tel.: (403) 262-1361
Fax: (403) 262-8215
Toll Free: (877) 262-1361
Web Site: www.ensignenergy.com
Oil & Gas Well Drilling Services
S.I.C.: 1381
N.A.I.C.S.: 213111

Ensign Drilling, Inc. **(1)**
Ste 1000 400 5th Ave SW
Calgary, AB, T2P 0L6, Canada (100%)
Tel.: (403) 262-1361
Fax: (403) 262-8215
E-Mail: info@ensignenergy.com
Web Site: www.ensignenergy.com
Sales Range: $1-4.9 Billion
Emp.: 150
Provider of Drilling, Well Servicing, Manufacturing & Production Services to Crude Oil & Natural Gas Industry
S.I.C.: 1381
N.A.I.C.S.: 213111
Selby Porter *(Vice Chm)*
Glenn Dagenais *(CFO & Exec VP-Fin)*

Divisions:

Ensign Drilling Partnership - Encore Coring & Drilling Division **(2)**
1345 Highfield Crescent SE
Calgary, AB, T2G 5N2, Canada
Tel.: (403) 287-0123
Fax: (403) 243-6158
Emp.: 15
Oil & Gas Well Drilling Services
S.I.C.: 1381
N.A.I.C.S.: 213111
Tom Connors *(Gen Mgr)*

Ensign Drilling Partnership - Engineering, Procurement & Construction Division **(2)**
2000-5th Street
Nisku, AB, T9E 7X3, Canada
Tel.: (780) 955-8808
Fax: (780) 955-7208
Engineering Services
S.I.C.: 8711
N.A.I.C.S.: 541330

Ensign Drilling Partnership - Ensign Atlantic Directional Services Division **(2)**
14 10672-46th St SE
Calgary, AB, T2C 1G1, Canada
Tel.: (403) 290-1570
Fax: (403) 290-1540
E-Mail: eadsales@ensignenergy.com
Web Site: www.ensignenergy.com
Oil & Gas Well Drilling Services
S.I.C.: 1381
N.A.I.C.S.: 213111

Ensign Drilling Partnership - Ensign Canadian Drilling Division **(2)**
2000-5th Street
Nisku, AB, T9E 7X3, Canada
Tel.: (780) 955-8808
Fax: (780) 955-7208
Toll Free: (877) 262-1361
Oil & Gas Well Drilling Services
S.I.C.: 1381
N.A.I.C.S.: 213111

Ensign Drilling Partnership - Ensign Directional Services Division **(2)**
14 10672-46th Street SE
Calgary, AB, T2C 1G1, Canada
Tel.: (403) 290-1570
Fax: (403) 290-1540
E-Mail: eadsales@ensignenergy.com
Web Site: www.ensignenergy.com
Oil & Gas Well Drilling Services
S.I.C.: 1381
N.A.I.C.S.: 213111

Subsidiary:

Ensign Drilling, Inc.-Nisku Operations Centre **(2)**
2000 5th St
Nisku, AB, T9E 7X3, Canada (100%)
Tel.: (780) 955-8808
Fax: (780) 955-7208
E-Mail: hr@ensignenergy.com
Web Site: www.ensignenergy.com
Emp.: 100
Provider of Drilling, Well Servicing, Manufacturing & Production Services to Crude Oil & Natural Gas Industry
S.I.C.: 1381
N.A.I.C.S.: 213111
Bob Zanusso *(VP)*

Ensign Rockwell Services **(1)**
6302 53rd Ave
Lloydminster, AB, T9V 2E2, Canada
Tel.: (780) 875-5278
Fax: (403) 262-0026
Web Site: www.ensignenergy.com
Emp.: 100
Provider of Oil Well Services
S.I.C.: 1381
N.A.I.C.S.: 213111
Dave Shyn *(Office Mgr)*

Opsco Energy Industries Ltd. **(1)**
1000 400 5th Avenue SW
Calgary, AB, T2P 0L6, Canada
Tel.: (403) 272-2206
Fax: (403) 272-6414
E-Mail: opsco_info@ensignenergy.com
Web Site: www.ensignenergy.com
Emp.: 20

Ensign Energy Services Inc.—(Continued)

Provider of Drilling, Well Servicing, Manufacturing & Production Services to Crude Oil & Natural Gas Industry
S.I.C.: 1381
N.A.I.C.S.: 213111

Rockwell Service (1)
52 Hwy 39 E
Estevan, SK, S4A 2A5, Canada (100%)
Tel.: (403) 267-1463
Fax: (306) 634-3238
E-Mail: info@ensignenergy.com
Web Site: www.ensignenergy.com
Emp.: 60
Provider of Drilling, Well Servicing, Manufacturing & Production Services to Crude Oil & Natural Gas Industry
S.I.C.: 1381
N.A.I.C.S.: 213111

Rockwell Servicing, Inc. (1)
1000 400 5th Ave SW
Calgary, AB, T2P 0L6, Canada (100%)
Tel.: (403) 265-6361
Fax: (403) 262-0026
E-Mail: rsp@ensignenergy.com
Web Site: www.ensignenergy.com
Emp.: 25
Provider of Drilling, Well Servicing, Manufacturing & Production Services to Crude Oil & Natural Gas Industry
S.I.C.: 1381
N.A.I.C.S.: 213111
Bryan Toth *(Gen Mgr)*

Tri-City Drilling (1968) Ltd. (1)
Nisku Operations Centre
2000 5th St, Nisku, AB, T9E 7X3, Canada
Tel.: (780) 955-8808
Fax: (780) 955-7208
E-Mail: info@ensignenergy.com
Web Site: www.ensignenergy.com
Emp.: 20
Drilling, Well Servicing, Manufacturing & Production Services to Crude Oil & Natural Gas Industry
S.I.C.: 1381
N.A.I.C.S.: 213111
Roch Currier *(Gen Mgr)*

U.S. Subsidiaries:

Ensign International Energy Services Inc. (1)
450 Gears Rd Ste 777
Houston, TX 77065
Tel.: (281) 872-7770
Fax: (281) 227-7312
E-Mail: marketing@ensignsa.com
Web Site: www.ensignenergy.com
Oil & Gas Drilling Services
S.I.C.: 1381
N.A.I.C.S.: 213111

Division:

Ensign International Energy Services Inc. - Latin America Division (2)
450 Gears Rd Ste 777
Houston, TX 77067
Tel.: (281) 872-7770
Fax: (281) 872-4700
E-Mail: marketing@ensignsa.com
Web Site: www.ensignenergy.com
Emp.: 25
Oil & Gas Well Drilling Services
S.I.C.: 1381
N.A.I.C.S.: 213111
Anthony Bellgrove *(Gen Mgr)*

Ensign Operating Company Inc. (1)
1225 17th St Ste 1900
Denver, CO 80202 CO
Tel.: (303) 293-9999
Fax: (303) 295-6168
Emp.: 40
Crude Petroleum Production
S.I.C.: 1389
N.A.I.C.S.: 213112

Ensign United States Drilling-California (1)
7001 Charity Ave
Bakersfield, CA 93308-5824
Tel.: (661) 589-0111
Fax: (661) 589-0283
Toll Free: (800) 443-5925
Web Site: www.ensignusd.com
Emp.: 500
Drilling, Well Servicing, Manufacturing & Production Services to Crude Oil & Natural Gas Industry
S.I.C.: 1381
N.A.I.C.S.: 213111

Divisions:

Ensign United States Drilling (California) Inc. - Ensign California Well Services Division (2)
3701 Fruitvale Ave
Bakersfield, CA 93308
Tel.: (661) 387-8400
Fax: (661) 387-8028
Emp.: 350
Oil & Gas Well Drilling Services
S.I.C.: 1381
N.A.I.C.S.: 213111
Richard Green *(Gen Mgr)*

Ensign United States Drilling (California) Inc. - West Coast Oilfield Rentals Divison (2)
7001 Charity Ave
Bakersfield, CA 93308
Tel.: (661) 589-0111
Fax: (661) 589-0283
Toll Free: (800) 443-5925
Emp.: 1,000
Oil & Gas Well Drilling Services
S.I.C.: 1381
N.A.I.C.S.: 213111
Larry Lorenz *(Mgr-Ops-West Coast)*

Ensign United States Drilling, Inc. (1)
1700 Broadway Ste 777
Denver, CO 80290
Tel.: (303) 292-1206
Fax: (800) 886-3898
Toll Free: (866) 866-8739
E-Mail: infousd@ensignenergy.com
Web Site: www.ensignusd.com
Emp.: 95
Drilling, Well Servicing, Manufacturing & Production Services
S.I.C.: 1381
N.A.I.C.S.: 213111
Tom Schledwitz *(Sr VP-Ops)*

Divisions:

Ensign United States Drilling Inc. - Ensign Directional Drilling Services Division (2)
1700 Broadway Ste 777
Denver, CO 80290
Tel.: (303) 292-1206
Fax: (800) 886-3898
Toll Free: (866) 866-8739
Web Site: www.ensignenergy.com
Oil & Gas Well Drilling Services
S.I.C.: 1381
N.A.I.C.S.: 213111

Ensign United States Drilling Inc. - Ensign Well Services Division (2)
1700 Broadway Ste 777
Denver, CO 80290
Tel.: (303) 292-1206
Fax: (800) 886-3898
Toll Free: (866) 866-8739
E-Mail: infousd@ensignenergy.com
Web Site: www.ensignenergy.com
Oil & Gas Well Drilling Services
S.I.C.: 1381
N.A.I.C.S.: 213111

Ensign United States Drilling Inc. - Rocky Mountain Oilfield Rentals Division (2)
1700 Broadway Ste 777
Denver, CO 80290
Tel.: (303) 292-1206
Fax: (800) 886-3898
Web Site: www.ensignenergy.com
Emp.: 95
Oil & Gas Well Drilling Services
S.I.C.: 1381
N.A.I.C.S.: 213111
Tom Schledwitz *(Sr VP-Ops)*

Ensign US Southern Drilling LLC (1)
450 Gears Rd Ste 777
Houston, TX 77065
Tel.: (281) 872-7770
Fax: (281) 872-4700
Oil & Gas Wells Drilling Services
S.I.C.: 1381
N.A.I.C.S.: 213111

Opsco Energy Industries (USA) Ltd. (1)
1700 Broadway Ste 777
Denver, CO 80290
Tel.: (303) 292-1206
Fax: (800) 886-3898
Web Site: www.ensignenergy.com
Oil & Gas Well Drilling Services
S.I.C.: 1381
N.A.I.C.S.: 213111

Non-U.S. Division:

Ensign Energy Services International Limited - Eastern Hemisphere Division (1)
15-17 Westport Road Edinburgh North
Edinburgh North, Adelaide, SA, 5113, Australia
Tel.: (61) 8 8255 3011
Fax: (61) 8 8252 0272
E-Mail: adel@ensignenergy.com
Web Site: www.ensignenergy.com
Emp.: 7
Oil & Gas Exploration Services
S.I.C.: 1389
N.A.I.C.S.: 213112
Gene Gaz *(VP-Intl Ops)*

Non-U.S. Subsidiaries:

Ensign Argentina S.A. (1)
Cerrito 836 Piso 9 Office 22
C1010AAR Buenos Aires, Argentina
Tel.: (54) 11 4816 0067
Fax: (54) 11 4816 5388
Emp.: 5
Oil & Gas Well Drilling Services
S.I.C.: 1381
N.A.I.C.S.: 213111
Ricardo Lopez Olaciregu *(Gen Mgr)*

Ensign Australia Pty Limited (1)
461 Greenwattle Street
Toowoomba, QLD, 4350, Australia AU
Tel.: (61) 746991888
Fax: (61) 746991800
E-Mail:
Web Site: www.ensignenergy.com
Emp.: 15
Oil, Gas & Geothermal Drillings Import Export
S.I.C.: 1381
N.A.I.C.S.: 213111
Gene Gaz *(CEO)*

Subsidiary:

Ensign International Energy Services (2)
Level 1 5 Elizabeth Street
15 17 West Court Rd Elizabeth, Sydney, NSW, 2000, Australia AU
Tel.: (61) 292233755 (100%)
Fax: (61) 0882520272
E-Mail: adel@ensignint.com
Web Site: www.ensignint.com
Emp.: 4
Oil & Gas Drilling Services
S.I.C.: 1381
N.A.I.C.S.: 213111
Kenneth John Picard *(CEO)*

Ensign de Venezuela C.A. (1)
Av Espana Cruce con Penalver Salida hacia
Puerto La Cruz, Estado Anzoategui, 6050, Venezuela
Tel.: (58) 283 500 5000
Fax: (58) 283 500 5004
Web Site: www.ensignenergy.com
Oil & Gas Well Drilling Services
S.I.C.: 1381
N.A.I.C.S.: 213111

Ensign Energy Services International Limited (1)
15-17 Westport Rd Edinburgh North
Elizabeth West, Adelaide, SA, 5113, Australia
Tel.: (61) 8 8255 3011
Fax: (61) 882520272
E-Mail: adel@ensignenergy.com
Web Site: www.ensignenergy.com
Emp.: 7
Oil & Gas Exploration Services
S.I.C.: 1389
N.A.I.C.S.: 213112
Gene Gaz *(Gen Mgr)*

Ensign Europa Sp. Z.O.O. (1)
Horizon Business Centre Entrance A Floor
5 Domaniewska Street
39A Room 501, Warsaw, 02-672, Poland
Tel.: (48) 22 208 2756
Emp.: 3
Oil & Gas Exploration Services
S.I.C.: 1389
N.A.I.C.S.: 213112
Dein Hills *(Gen Mgr)*

ENSINGER GMBH

Rudolf-Diesel-Str 8
71154 Nufringen, Germany
Tel.: (49) 70328190
Fax: (49) 7032819100
E-Mail: info@ensinger-online.com
Web Site: www.ensinger-online.com
Emp.: 600

Business Description:
Laminated Plastics Mfr
S.I.C.: 3083
N.A.I.C.S.: 326130

U.S. Subsidiary:

Ensinger, Inc. (1)
365 Meadowlands Blvd
Washington, PA 15301
Tel.: (724) 746-6050
Fax: (724) 746-9209
E-Mail: shopforplastics@ensinger-ind.com
Web Site: www.shopforplastics.com
Emp.: 100
Laminated Plastics Mfr
S.I.C.: 3083
N.A.I.C.S.: 326130
Peter Fowler *(Controller)*

Subsidiaries:

Ensinger-Hyde (2)
1 Main St
Grenloch, NJ 08032
Tel.: (856) 227-0500
Fax: (856) 232-1754
Emp.: 80
Custom OEM Plastic Injection Molding, Extruded Mill Shapes
S.I.C.: 3083
N.A.I.C.S.: 326130
Dennis Palladino *(Controller)*

ENSO SECUTRACK LIMITED

13-6-436/A/26 Tyche House Lakshmi Nagar Colony Mehdipatnam
Hyderabad, Andhra Pradesh, 500028, India
Tel.: (91) 4023525436
Fax: (91) 4023525403
E-Mail: info@enso-secutrack.com
Web Site: ensosecutrack.com
532984—(BOM)
Sales Range: $1-9.9 Million

Business Description:
Surveillance & Tracking Solutions
S.I.C.: 3812
N.A.I.C.S.: 334511

Personnel:
Sabari S. Kambli *(Compliance Officer)*

Board of Directors:
Kanhaiya Lal Bothra
Pradeep Chauhan
Sabari S. Kambli
Rabi Paul
Hanuman Mal Tater

Transfer Agent:
XL Softech Systems Limited
3 Sagar Society Road No. 2 Banjara Hills
Hyderabad, India

ENSOR HOLDINGS PLC

Ellard House Dallimore Road
Manchester, M23 9NX, United Kingdom

Tel.: (44) 1619455953
Fax: (44) 1619455851
E-Mail: mail@ensor.co.uk
Web Site: www.ensor.co.uk
ESR—(LSE)
Rev.: $51,753,333
Assets: $34,788,600
Liabilities: $20,672,906
Net Worth: $14,115,694
Earnings: $2,618,463
Emp.: 252
Fiscal Year-end: 03/31/13

Business Description:
Holding Company; Building & Packaging Products Mfr
S.I.C.: 6719
N.A.I.C.S.: 551112

Personnel:
Kenneth A. Harrison *(Chm)*
A. Roger Harrison *(CEO)*
Marcus A. Chadwick *(Sec & Dir-Fin)*

Board of Directors:
Kenneth A. Harrison
Marcus A. Chadwick
Anthony E. Coyne
A. Roger Harrison
Christine M. Harrison

Legal Counsel:
Westhouse Securities Limited
One Angel Court
London, EC2R 7HJ, United Kingdom

Subsidiaries:

CMS Tools Limited (1)
Don Pedro Close Normanton Industrial Estate
Normanton, West Yorkshire, WF6 1TD, United Kingdom
Tel.: (44) 1924895999
Fax: (44) 1924 896999
E-Mail: info@cmstools.co.uk
Web Site: www.cmstools.co.uk
Emp.: 6
Roofing Tools & Accessories Distr
S.I.C.: 5033
N.A.I.C.S.: 423330
Steven Smith *(Mng Dir)*

Ellard Limited (1)
Ellard House
Dallimore Rd, Manchester, M23 9NX, United Kingdom
Tel.: (44) 1619454561
Fax: (44) 1619454566
E-Mail: sales@ellard.co.uk
Web Site: www.ellard.co.uk
Emp.: 30
Electric Door & Shutter Drive Mfr
S.I.C.: 3699
N.A.I.C.S.: 335999

Ensor Building Products Limited (1)
Blackamoor Road
Guide, Blackburn, Lancs, BB1 2LQ, United Kingdom
Tel.: (44) 125452244
Fax: (44) 1254682371
E-Mail: info@ensorbuilding.com
Web Site: www.ensorbuilding.com
Emp.: 22
Drainage, Building & Natural Slate Roofing Products
S.I.C.: 5211
N.A.I.C.S.: 444190
Philip Brooke *(Mng Dir)*

OSA Door Parts Limited (1)
Ashville Insustrial Estate
Runcorn, Cheshire, WA7 3EZ, United Kingdom
Tel.: (44) 1928 703 580
Fax: (44) 1928 759 984
E-Mail: sales@osadoorparts.co.uk
Web Site: www.osadoorparts.co.uk
Industrial Doors Mfr & Distr
S.I.C.: 3442
N.A.I.C.S.: 332321

SRC Limited (1)
Buckingham Rd Heaton Moor
Stockport, Greater Manchester, SK4 4QZ, United Kingdom
Tel.: (44) 161 432 3222
Fax: (44) 161 443 2025
E-Mail: mail@src.ltd.uk
Web Site: www.src.ltd.uk
Emp.: 11
Recycled Rubber Products Distr
S.I.C.: 5099
N.A.I.C.S.: 423990
Adrian France *(Gen Mgr)*

Woods Packaging Limited (1)
Unit D4 Whitwood Enterprise Pk Speedwell Rd
WF10 5PX Castleford, W Yorkshire, United Kingdom
Tel.: (44) 1977604050
Fax: (44) 1977604440
E-Mail: sales@woods-packaging.co.uk
Web Site: www.woods-packaging.co.uk
Emp.: 7
Packaging Products Mfr
S.I.C.: 2671
N.A.I.C.S.: 322220
Anthony Wood *(CEO)*

ENSPERT INC.

2F 7F Daewha Bldg 169 Samsung-Dong
Gangnam-Gu, Seoul, Korea (South)
Tel.: (82) 260039300
Fax: (82) 260039322
Web Site: www.enspert.com

Business Description:
Software Development Services
S.I.C.: 7371
N.A.I.C.S.: 541511

Personnel:
Sang Soo Lee *(Pres)*
Chang-Seok Lee *(CEO)*

ENSSOLUTIONS GROUP INC.

4306 Bartlett Rd
Beamsville, ON, L0R 1B1, Canada
Tel.: (905) 312-8422
Fax: (905) 312-8565
E-Mail: info@enssolutions.com
Web Site: www.enssolutions.com
ENV—(OTC TSXV)
Rev.: $2,132,795
Assets: $1,253,491
Liabilities: $701,475
Net Worth: $552,016
Earnings: ($841,811)
Fiscal Year-end: 12/31/12

Business Description:
Soil Stabilization Emulsions
S.I.C.: 0711
N.A.I.C.S.: 115112

Personnel:
James Lincoln *(Chm)*
Phillip Moruzi *(Interim CEO)*
Darren Dierich *(CFO)*

Board of Directors:
James Lincoln
Michael M. Cone
James C. Griffiths
David C. Lincoln

Transfer Agent:
Equity Financial Trust Company
200 University Avenue Suite 400
Toronto, ON, Canada

Subsidiary:

EnsSolutions Ltd. (1)
450 Sherman Avenue North
Hamilton, ON, L8L 8J6, Canada
Tel.: (905) 312-8422
Fax: (905) 312-8565
Toll Free: (866) 306-2489
E-Mail: info@enssolutions.com
Web Site: www.enssolutions.com
Construction Equipment & Supplies Distr
S.I.C.: 5082
N.A.I.C.S.: 423810

ENSTAR GROUP LIMITED

Windsor Place 3rd Floor 18 Queen Street
PO Box HM 2267
Hamilton, HM JX, Bermuda
Tel.: (441) 292 3645
Fax: (441) 296 0895
E-Mail: enquiries@enstargroup.bm
Web Site: www.enstargroup.com
ESGR—(NASDAQ)
Rev.: $416,570,000
Assets: $8,620,155,000
Liabilities: $6,642,632,000
Net Worth: $1,977,523,000
Earnings: $223,822,000
Emp.: 739
Fiscal Year-end: 12/31/13

Business Description:
Insurance Acquisitions & Management
S.I.C.: 6411
N.A.I.C.S.: 524298

Personnel:
Robert Johnson Campbell *(Chm)*
Dominic F. Silvester *(CEO)*
Richard J. Harris *(CFO)*
Paul J. O'Shea *(Co-COO & Exec VP)*
Nicholas A. Packer *(Co-COO & Exec VP)*
Roger Thompson *(Chief Investment Officer-Bermuda)*
David Rocke *(Exec VP)*
Orla Gregory *(Sr VP-Mergers & Acq)*
Gareth Nokes *(Sr VP-Fin)*

Board of Directors:
Robert Johnson Campbell
Charles Thomas Akre, Jr.
T. Whit Armstrong
Kenneth J. LeStrange
Paul J. O'Shea
Sumit Rajpal
Dominic F. Silvester

U.S. Subsidiaries:

American Concept Insurance Company (1)
475 Kilvert St 330
Warwick, RI 02886
Tel.: (401) 453-7000
Toll Free: (800) 264-4000
Reinsurance Services
S.I.C.: 6399
N.A.I.C.S.: 524130

Cranmore (US) Inc. (1)
7901 4th St N Ste 204
Saint Petersburg, FL 33702
Tel.: (727) 471-0438
Fax: (727) 578-5469
E-Mail: mail@cranadj.com
Web Site: www.cranadj.com
Reinsurance Services
S.I.C.: 6399
N.A.I.C.S.: 524130
Steven Norrington *(CEO & Pres)*
Ed Holland *(Exec VP)*

Enstar (US) Inc. (1)
7901 4th St Ste 203
Saint Petersburg, FL 33702
Tel.: (727) 576-1632
Fax: (727) 576-3627
Investment Management Services
S.I.C.: 6799
N.A.I.C.S.: 523920
Linda Reinking *(VP-Claims)*

U.S. Subsidiary:

SeaBright Holdings, Inc. (1)
1501 4th Ave Ste 2600
Seattle, WA 98101 DE
Tel.: (206) 269-8500
Fax: (206) 269-8903
Toll Free: (888) 636-1580
Web Site: www.sbic.com
Sales Range: $250-299.9 Million
Emp.: 325
Insurance Services; Holding Company
S.I.C.: 6331
N.A.I.C.S.: 524126
John G. Pasqualetto *(Chm, Pres & CEO)*
Neal Andrew Fuller *(CFO, Sr VP & Asst Sec)*
Richard J. Gergasko *(COO)*
Marc B. Miller *(Sr VP & Chief Medical Officer)*
Philip Romney *(Principal Acctg Officer & VP-Fin)*
Craig Pankow *(Pres-PointSure Insurance Svcs)*
D. Drue Wax *(Gen Counsel, Sec & Sr VP)*
Richard W. Seelinger *(Sr VP-Policyholder Svcs)*
Jeffrey C. Wanamaker *(Sr VP-Underwriting)*

Subsidiaries:

Point Sure Insurance Services, Inc. (2)
1501 4th Ave Ste 2050 PO Box 2045
Seattle, WA 98111 (100%)
Mailing Address:
PO Box 2045
Seattle, WA 98111-2045
Tel.: (206) 269-8600
Fax: (206) 269-8907
Toll Free: (888) 636-1575
Sales Range: $10-24.9 Million
Emp.: 12
Insurance Services
S.I.C.: 6399
N.A.I.C.S.: 524128

SeaBright Insurance Company (2)
1501 4th Ave Ste 2600
Seattle, WA 98101
Tel.: (206) 269-8500
Fax: (206) 269-8903
Toll Free: (800) 372-2255
Web Site: www.sbic.com
Sales Range: $75-99.9 Million
Emp.: 115
Workers' Compensation Insurance Services
S.I.C.: 6351
N.A.I.C.S.: 524126
John G. Pasqualetto *(Chm, Pres & CEO)*
Marc B. Miller *(Sr VP & Chief Medical Officer)*
Richard W. Seelinger *(Sr VP-Policyholder Svcs)*
Jeffrey C. Wanamaker *(Sr VP-Underwriting)*

Non-U.S. Subsidiaries:

Cranmore (Asia) Pte Limited (1)
Asia Square Tower 1 Ste 07-04
8 Marina View, Singapore, 18960, Singapore
Tel.: (65) 64071027
E-Mail: mail@cranmore-asia.com
Web Site: www.cranmore-asia.com
Reinsurance Services
S.I.C.: 6399
N.A.I.C.S.: 524130
Ian Belcher *(Mng Dir)*

Enstar (EU) Limited (1)
Avaya House
2 Cathedral Hill, Guildford, Surrey, GU2 7YL, United Kingdom
Tel.: (44) 1483452622
Fax: (44) 1483452644
E-Mail: enquiries@enstargroup.com
Web Site: www.enstargroup.com
Emp.: 10
Reinsurance Services
S.I.C.: 6399
N.A.I.C.S.: 524130

Forsakringsaktiebolaget Assuransinvest MF (1)
Wallingatan 33
10397 Stockholm, Sweden
Tel.: (46) 856219930
Fax: (46) 856219939
Reinsurance Services
S.I.C.: 6399
N.A.I.C.S.: 524130
Turel Jonsson *(Office Mgr)*

Kinsale Brokers Limited (1)
America House 2 America Square
London, EC3N 2LU, United Kingdom
Tel.: (44) 2076804141
Fax: (44) 2076804111
E-Mail: mail@kinsalebroker.com
Web Site: www.kinsalebrokers.co.uk
Emp.: 10
Direct Insurance Services
S.I.C.: 6399
N.A.I.C.S.: 524128
Philip Hernon *(Mng Dir)*
Steven Western *(CFO)*

Shelbourne Group Limited (1)
America House
London, EC3N 2LU, United Kingdom
Tel.: (44) 2076804123

Enstar Group Limited—(Continued)

Fax: (44) 2076804111
Emp.: 10
Direct Insurance Services
S.I.C.: 6399
N.A.I.C.S.: 524128

ENTA TECHNOLOGIES LIMITED

(d/b/a Entagroup)
Stafford Park 6
Telford, Shropshire, TF3 3AT, United Kingdom
Tel.: (44) 3331018888
Fax: (44) 3331019484
E-Mail: sales@entagroup.com
Web Site: www.entagroup.com
Sales Range: $150-199.9 Million
Emp.: 250

Business Description:
Holding Company; Information Technology Products & Services
S.I.C.: 6719
N.A.I.C.S.: 551112

Personnel:
Jason Tsai *(Founder & CEO)*

Subsidiaries:

EntaMedia Ltd. (1)
Stafford Park 6
Telford, Shropshire, TF3 3AT, United Kingdom UK
Tel.: (44) 333 101 5000
Web Site: www.entamedia.com
Digital Media Design & Marketing Services
S.I.C.: 7336
N.A.I.C.S.: 541430
Ryan Lee, *(Mng Dir)*

Entatech UK Ltd. (1)
Stafford Park 6
Telford, Shropshire, TF3 3AT, United Kingdom UK
Tel.: (44) 333 101 0000
Web Site: www.enta.net
Information Technology Components, Systems & Software Distr
S.I.C.: 5045
N.A.I.C.S.: 423430
Jon Atherton, *(VP)*

ENTAGROUP

(See Under Enta Technologies Limited)

ENTANET INTERNATIONAL LTD.

Stafford Park 6
Telford, Shropshire, TF3 3AT, United Kingdom
Tel.: (44) 333 101 0000
E-Mail: info@enta.net
Web Site: www.enta.net
Year Founded: 1996
Sales Range: $25-49.9 Million
Emp.: 75

Business Description:
Voice & Data Telecommunications Services
S.I.C.: 4813
N.A.I.C.S.: 517911

Personnel:
Jason Tsai *(Founder)*
Elsa Chen *(Mng Dir)*
Steve Lalonde *(CTO)*

ENTE VASCO DE LA ENERGIA

Alameda de Urquijo 36 1
Edificio Plz Bizkaia, 48011 Bilbao, Spain
Tel.: (34) 944035600
Fax: (34) 944035699
E-Mail: publicaciones@eve.es
Web Site: www.eve.es
Sls.: $123,253,979
Assets: $547,122,527
Liabilities: $97,159,820
Net Worth: $449,962,707
Earnings: $69,347,948
Emp.: 75
Fiscal Year-end: 12/31/12

Business Description:
Energy Services
S.I.C.: 4911
N.A.I.C.S.: 221121

Personnel:
Arantza Tapia Otaegui *(Chm)*
Jose Ignacio Garcia de Motiloa Ubis *(Deputy Chm)*
Pilar Urruticoechea Uriarte *(Gen Mng Dir)*
Alvaro Colon Barriocanal *(Sec)*

Board of Directors:
Arantza Tapia Otaegui
Inigo Marco-Gardoqui Alcala-Galiano
Joseba Andoni Alcalde Amutxategi
Jose Ignacio Garcia de Motiloa Ubis
Juan Ignacio Lopez Gandasegui
Arantza Mendizabal Gorostiaga
Jose Ignacio Arrieta Heras
Estibaliz Hernaez Lavina
Xabier Viteri Solaun
Pilar Urruticoechea Uriarte
Javier Zarraonandia Zuloaga

Joint Ventures:

Bahia de Bizkaia Electricidad S.L. (1)
Punta Ceballos 8
48508 Zierbena, Spain ES
Tel.: (34) 94 636 6000
Fax: (34) 94 636 6004
E-Mail: info@bbe.es
Web Site: www.bbe.es
Electricity Generation Services
S.I.C.: 4911
N.A.I.C.S.: 221112

Bahia de Bizkaia Gas, S.L. (1)
Explanda de Punta Ceballos 2
Atraque De Punta Lucero, 48508 Zierbena, Spain ES
Tel.: (34) 946366020
Fax: (34) 946366150
E-Mail: info@bbg.es
Web Site: www.bbg.es
Emp.: 71
Natural Gas Distr
S.I.C.: 4924
N.A.I.C.S.: 221210
Guillermo Gonzalez *(Gen Mgr)*

ENTEGRA LIMITED.

4th Floor Harchandrai House
Maharshi Karve Road Marine Lines E
Mumbai, 400002, India
Tel.: (91) 2266044242
Fax: (91) 2266550320
Web Site: www.entegra.co.in
ENTEGRA—(NSE)
Rev.: $192,164
Assets: $850,847,641
Liabilities: $794,864,820
Net Worth: $55,982,821
Earnings: ($23,691,937)
Fiscal Year-end: 03/31/13

Business Description:
Electric Power Generation Services
S.I.C.: 4911
N.A.I.C.S.: 221118

Personnel:
Mukul S. Kasliwal *(Founder)*
Sanjay Gopalan *(CFO)*
Rekha Jagdale *(Compliance Officer, Pres-Corp Affiars & Sec)*

Board of Directors:
Mukul S. Kasliwal
Jagdish Capoor
Pradeep V. Goyal
Ashish S. Jalan
Ajit C. Kapadia
Warij A. Kasliwal
Hiten A. Khatau
Prabhakar L. Nene
Alok N. Sinha

Transfer Agent:
Bigshare Services Private Limited
E-2 Ansa Industrial Estate Sakivihar Road Saki Naka Andheri (E)
Mumbai, India

ENTEK ENERGY LIMITED

338 Hay Street
Subiaco, WA, 6008, Australia

Mailing Address:
PO Box 1381
West Perth, WA, 6872, Australia
Tel.: (61) 892134388
Fax: (61) 892134399
E-Mail: info@entekenergy.com.au
Web Site: www.entekenergy.com.au
ETE—(ASX OTC)
Rev.: $5,193,454
Assets: $36,810,298
Liabilities: $2,587,519
Net Worth: $34,222,780
Earnings: ($3,491,491)
Fiscal Year-end: 06/30/13

Business Description:
Oil & Gas Exploration
S.I.C.: 1311
N.A.I.C.S.: 211111

Personnel:
Trent Benjamin Spry *(CEO & Mng Dir)*
Andrew Gastevich *(CFO & Sec)*

Board of Directors:
Graham Douglas Riley
Alexander Forcke
Andrew J. Padman
Trent Benjamin Spry

Legal Counsel:
Norton Rose Fulbright
1200 17th Street Suite 1000
Denver, CO 80202-5835

Gilbert & Tobin
1202 Hay Street
West Perth, Australia

Andrews Kurth
600 Travis Suite 4200
Houston, TX 77002

ENTELLECT LIMITED

Level 1 61 Spring Street
Melbourne, VIC, 3000, Australia
Tel.: (61) 3 9286 7500
Fax: (61) 3 9662 1472
E-Mail: info@entellect.com.au
Web Site: www.entellect.com.au
ESN—(ASX)
Rev.: $18,680
Assets: $220,624
Liabilities: $1,368,236
Net Worth: ($1,147,612)
Earnings: ($2,158,654)
Emp.: 2
Fiscal Year-end: 06/30/13

Business Description:
Software Publisher
S.I.C.: 7372
N.A.I.C.S.: 511210

Personnel:
James Kellett *(CEO)*
Sophie Karzis *(Sec)*

Board of Directors:
Andrew Plympton
Jeffrey Bennett
James Kellett

Legal Counsel:
HWL Ebsworth
Level 26 530 Collins Street
Melbourne, VIC, 3000, Australia

Subsidiaries:

MXL Consolidated Pty. Limited (1)
Level 19 9 Hunter St
Sydney, New South Wales, 2000, Australia
Tel.: (61) 2 8249 0000
Fax: (61) 2 8249 0099
E-Mail: enquiries@mxl.com
Emp.: 35
Management Software Publishers
S.I.C.: 7372
N.A.I.C.S.: 511210
Joe Younane *(CEO)*

Schoolmate.Net Pty. Limited (1)
Level 1 261 George St
Sydney, New South Wales, 2000, Australia
Tel.: (61) 2 8249 0000
Fax: (61) 2 8249 0099
E-Mail: enquiries@schoolmate.net.au
Web Site: www.schoolmate.net.au
Management Software Design & Publishers
S.I.C.: 7372
N.A.I.C.S.: 511210

Virtual Communications International Pty. Limited (1)
22A Muriel Ave
Innaloo, Perth, Western Australia, 6018, Australia
Tel.: (61) 8 9242 8380
Web Site: www.virtualcommunications.com.au
Computer Software Publishers
S.I.C.: 7372
N.A.I.C.S.: 511210

ENTEQ UPSTREAM PLC

The Courtyard High Street
Ascot, Berkshire, SL5 7HP, United Kingdom
Tel.: (44) 7710 160177
E-Mail: mperry@enteq.com
Web Site: www.enteq.com
NTQ—(AIM)

Business Description:
Oil & Gas Exploration Services
S.I.C.: 1311
N.A.I.C.S.: 211111

Personnel:
Neil William Warner *(Chm)*
Martin Gordon Perry *(CEO)*
Raymond Garcia *(COO)*

Board of Directors:
Neil William Warner
Raymond Garcia
Iain Stayton Paterson
Martin Gordon Perry
Robin Hunter Pinchbeck

ENTERPRISE CAPITAL CORPORATION

(See Under Ecuador Gold and Copper Corp.)

ENTERPRISE DEVELOPMENT HOLDINGS LIMITED

Suites 904-5 9/F Great Eagle Centre
23 Harbour Road
Wanchai, China (Hong Kong)
Tel.: (852) 29076111
Fax: (852) 29076123
E-Mail: spella@uni-1.com.hk
Web Site: www.1808.com.hk
1808—(HKG)
Sls.: $20,967,406
Assets: $23,902,001
Liabilities: $4,106,431
Net Worth: $19,795,569
Earnings: ($4,753,269)
Emp.: 100
Fiscal Year-end: 12/31/12

Business Description:
Wire Mfr & Sales
S.I.C.: 3559
N.A.I.C.S.: 333249

Personnel:
Bowei Jia *(Chm)*
Kwan Sing Lam *(CEO)*
Stella Yuen Ying Chan *(Sec)*

Board of Directors:
Bowei Jia
Gin Ing Hu
Pak Fu King
Kwan Sing Lam

Ting Lok Lam
Xiaoman Zhang
Computershare Hong Kong Investor Services Limited
Shops 1712-1716 17th Floor Hopewell Centre
183 Queens Road East
Wanchai, China (Hong Kong)
Butterfield Fund Services (Cayman) Limited
Butterfield House 68 Fort Street PO Box 705
Georgetown, Cayman Islands
Transfer Agents:
Royal Bank of Canada Trust Company (Cayman) Limited
4th Floor Royal Bank House 24 Shedden Road
Georgetown, Cayman Islands
Computershare Hong Kong Investor Services Limited
Shops 1712-1716 17th Floor Hopewell Centre
183 Queens Road East
Wanchai, China (Hong Kong)

ENTERPRISE ENERGY RESOURCES LTD.

(Acquired & Absorbed by Esrey Energy Ltd)

ENTERPRISE GROUP, INC.

64 Riel Dr Ste 2
Saint Albert, AB, T8N 5B3, Canada
Tel.: (780) 418-4400
Fax: (780) 418-1941
Toll Free: (888) 303-3361
E-Mail: contact@enterpriseoil.ca
Web Site: www.enterpriseoil.ca
Year Founded: 2004
E—(TSX)
Rev.: $18,389,370
Assets: $28,279,869
Liabilities: $16,321,808
Net Worth: $11,958,061
Earnings: $2,489,000
Emp.: 220
Fiscal Year-end: 12/31/12
Business Description:
Pipeline Construction & Maintenance Services
S.I.C.: 1623
N.A.I.C.S.: 237120
Personnel:
Leonard D. Jaroszuk *(Chm, Pres & CEO)*
Warren Cabral *(CFO)*
Douglas C. Bachman *(COO)*
Desmond O'Kell *(Sec & VP)*
Board of Directors:
Leonard D. Jaroszuk
Desmond O'Kell
John Pinsent
Fredy Ramsoondar
Keir B. Reynolds
Legal Counsel:
Borden Ladner Gervais
Calgary, AB, Canada
Transfer Agent:
Valiant Trust
Edmonton, AB, Canada
Subsidiaries:

Enterprise Energy Services Inc. **(1)**
900 8th St NW
PO Box 652
Slave Lake, AB, T0G 2A0, Canada
Tel.: (780) 849-3865
Fax: (780) 849-3630
Emp.: 15
Energy Supply Services
S.I.C.: 8999
N.A.I.C.S.: 541690
Leonard Jaroszuk *(Pres)*

Enterprise Pipeline Company Inc. **(1)**
64 Riel Dr Unit 2
Saint Albert, AB, T8N 5B3, Canada
Tel.: (780) 418-4400
Fax: (718) 418-1941
E-Mail: des.okell@enterpriseoil.ca
Emp.: 8
Pipeline Transportation Services
S.I.C.: 4619
N.A.I.C.S.: 486990
Leonard Jaroszuk *(Pres)*

U.S. Subsidiary:

Pro Tech Construction, Inc. **(1)**
7429 ACC Blvd Ste 109
Raleigh, NC 27617
Tel.: (919) 848-9035
E-Mail: info@protechconstruction.net
Web Site: protechconstruction.net
Sales Range: $10-24.9 Million
Emp.: 16
Commercial & Institutional Building Construction Services
S.I.C.: 1542
N.A.I.C.S.: 236220
Linda Wilkerson *(Pres)*
Mike Wilkerson *(Sec & Treas)*

ENTERPRISE GROUP LIMITED

Enterprise House No 11 High Street
GP 50
Accra, Ghana
Tel.: (233) 302 663 710
Fax: (233) 302 670 306
Web Site: www.enterprisegroup.net.gh
EIC—(GHA)
Rev.: $12,442,900
Assets: $88,321,089
Liabilities: $46,245,090
Net Worth: $42,075,998
Earnings: $11,807,030
Emp.: 85
Fiscal Year-end: 12/31/12
Business Description:
Insurance Services
S.I.C.: 6411
N.A.I.C.S.: 524298
Personnel:
Trevor Trefgarne *(Chm)*
George Otoo *(CEO)*
Abena Ponma Bonsu *(Head-Legal Svcs & Sec)*
Board of Directors:
Trevor Trefgarne
Martin Eson-Benjamin
Keli Gadzekpo
Emmanuel Idun
Ken Ofori-Atta
George Otoo
Legal Counsel:
Sam Okudzeto & Associates
Total House 3rd Floor Liberia Road
PO Box 5520
Accra, Ghana

ENTERPRISE INNS PLC

3 Monkspath Hall Road
Solihull, W Midlands, B90 4SJ, United Kingdom
Tel.: (44) 1217337700
Fax: (44) 1217336447
E-Mail: enquiries@enterpriseinns.plc.uk
Web Site: www.enterpriseinns.com
ETI—(LSE)
Rev.: $1,061,660,160
Assets: $7,532,968,960
Liabilities: $5,203,630,080
Net Worth: $2,329,338,880
Earnings: ($6,645,760)
Emp.: 508
Fiscal Year-end: 09/30/13
Business Description:
Pub Leasing & Management Services
S.I.C.: 5813
N.A.I.C.S.: 722410
Personnel:
W. Simon Townsend *(CEO)*
Neil R. Smith *(CFO)*
Loretta Togher *(Sec)*
Board of Directors:
Robert M. Walker
Peter J. Baguley
Adam P. Fowle
David Ossian Maloney
Neil R. Smith
W. Simon Townsend
Legal Counsel:
CMS Cameron McKenna LLP
Mitre House 160 Aldersgate Street
London, United Kingdom
Transfer Agent:
Computershare Investor Services PLC
The Pavilions Bridgewater Road
PO Box 82
Bristol, BS13 8AE, United Kingdom
Tel.: (44) 870 702 0000
Fax: (44) 870 703 6119
Subsidiary:

Unique Pub Properties Limited **(1)**
3 Monkspath Hall Rd Solihull
Shirley, West Midlands, B90 4SJ, United Kingdom
Tel.: (44) 1217337700
Fax: (44) 1217336447
E-Mail: enquires@enterpriseinn.com
Web Site: www.enterpriseinn.com
Emp.: 300
Real Estate Management Services
S.I.C.: 6531
N.A.I.C.S.: 531390
G Tuppen *(CEO)*
Neil Smith *(CFO)*

ENTERPRISE INSURANCE CO. LTD.

(See Under Enterprise Group Limited)

ENTERPRISE INVESTMENT FUND SLHF.

Lagmuli 9
108 Reykjavik, Iceland
Tel.: (354) 571 7080
Fax: (354) 571 7089
E-Mail: framtakssjodur@framtakssjodur.is
Web Site: www.framtakssjodur.is
Year Founded: 2009
Business Description:
Investment Management Services
S.I.C.: 6211
N.A.I.C.S.: 523999
Personnel:
Brynjolfur Bjarnason *(CEO)*
Holdings:

Advania hf **(1)**
Gudrunartun 10
105 Reykjavik, Iceland IS (73.95%)
Tel.: (354) 440 9000
Fax: (354) 4409001
E-Mail: advania@advania.com
Web Site: www.advania.com
Emp.: 1,100
Information Technology Services
S.I.C.: 7379
N.A.I.C.S.: 541519
Gestur G. Gestsson, *(CEO)*

Icelandic Group HF **(1)**
Borgartun 27
105 Reykjavik, Iceland IS (100%)
Tel.: (354) 5607800
Fax: (354) 5621252
E-Mail: info@icelandic.is
Web Site: www.icelandic.is
Sales Range: $1-4.9 Billion
Emp.: 4,941
Holding Company
S.I.C.: 6719
N.A.I.C.S.: 551112
Herdis Drofn Fjeldsted *(Chm)*
Magnus Bjarnason *(Pres & CEO)*
Jon Gardar Gudmundsson *(Deputy CEO & Member-Mgmt Bd)*
Johann Gunnar Johannsson *(CFO & Member-Mgmt Bd)*
Jonas Engilbertsson *(Mng Dir-Procurement & Member-Mgmt Bd)*
Jon Thor Klemensson *(Mng Dir-Fiskval & Member-Mgmt Bd)*
Frank Tierenteyn *(Mng Dir-Gadus & Member-Mgmt Bd)*
Hjorleifur Asgeirsson *(Member-Mgmt Bd)*
Malcolm Eley *(Member-Mgmt Bd)*
Eythor Eyjolfsson *(Member-Mgmt Bd)*
Magni Thor Geirsson *(Member-Mgmt Bd)*
Simon Smith *(Member-Mgmt Bd)*

Non-U.S. Subsidiaries:

Icelandic Germany GmbH **(2)**
Osterbekstrasse 90 B
D 22083 Hamburg, Germany (100%)
Tel.: (49) 402783940
Fax: (49) 4027839444
E-Mail: icelandic@icelandic.de
Web Site: www.icelandic.de
Sales Range: $1-9.9 Million
Emp.: 20
Importer, Wholesaler & Supplier of Frozen Seafood Products to Industry & Retail
S.I.C.: 5421
N.A.I.C.S.: 445220

Icelandic Iberica SA **(2)**
Edificio Muntadas
Parque Empresarial Mas Blau, Llobregat, 08820, Spain (100%)
Tel.: (34) 934788000
Fax: (34) 934788001
E-Mail: iberica@icelandic.is
Web Site: www.icelandic.com
Emp.: 14
Distributor of Frozen Seafood Products
S.I.C.: 5421
N.A.I.C.S.: 445220
Hjorleifur Asgeirsson *(Mng Dir)*

Icelandic Japan KK **(2)**
Landic Toranomon Bldg 6F 3 7 10
Toranomon
Minato Ku, Tokyo, 105 0001, Japan (100%)
Tel.: (81) 354720450
Fax: (81) 354720451
Web Site: www.icelandic.is
Emp.: 10
Trader of Frozen Fish
S.I.C.: 5421
N.A.I.C.S.: 445220
Eythor Eyjolfsson *(Mng Dir)*

Icelandic UK Limited **(2)**
Estate Rd No 2 S Humberside
Industrial Estate, Grimsby, DN31 2TG, United Kingdom UK (100%)
Tel.: (44) 1472582900
Fax: (44) 1472582920
E-Mail: iuk@icelandic.is
Web Site: www.icelandic.co.uk
Sales Range: $450-499.9 Million
Emp.: 1,500
Seller & Distributor of Frozen Seafood Products
S.I.C.: 5421
N.A.I.C.S.: 445220
Malcolm Eley *(CEO)*
Magni Thor Geirsson *(Mng Dir-Procurement & Deputy CEO)*

Subsidiaries:

Coldwater Seafood (UK) Limited **(3)**
Est Rd No 2 S Humberside Industrial Est
N E Limcs, DN312TG Grimsby, United Kingdom (100%)
Tel.: (44) 472321100
Fax: (44) 472321220
E-Mail: reception@coldwater.co.uk
Web Site: www.coldwater.co.uk/
Emp.: 600
Producer of Frozen Seafood
S.I.C.: 2092
N.A.I.C.S.: 311710
Penny Wood *(Head-Innovation)*

IFP Trading Ltd. **(3)**
Estate Road No 2
South Humberside Ind Est, Grimsby, NE Lincolnshire, DN31 2TG, United Kingdom UK (100%)
Tel.: (44) 224878099
Fax: (44) 224878438
Emp.: 180
Fish Processing
S.I.C.: 2092
N.A.I.C.S.: 311710

Promens hf. **(1)**
Hlidasmari 1
201 Kopavogur, Iceland IS

Enterprise Investment Fund slhf.—(Continued)

Tel.: (354) 5805550
Fax: (354) 5805551
E-Mail: promens@promens.com
Web Site: www.promens.com
Sales Range: $1-4.9 Billion
Emp.: 3,800
Plastic Products Mfr
S.I.C.: 3089
N.A.I.C.S.: 326199
Hermann M. Thorisson *(Chm)*
Jakob Sigurdsson *(Pres & CEO)*
Adrian Platt *(CFO)*
Jeroen Hooft *(Chief Bus Officer)*
Jon Sigurdsson *(Sr VP-Procurement)*
Gestur Thorisson *(Sr VP-Bus Dev)*

Subsidiaries:

Promens Dalvik ehf. (2)
Gunnarsbraut 12
620 Dalvik, Iceland IS
Tel.: (354) 4605000
Fax: (354) 4605001
E-Mail: sales.dalvik@promens.com
Web Site: www.promens.is/dalvik
Emp.: 250
Mfr of Plastic Molded Tubs for Fish Storage & Marine Flotation Devices
S.I.C.: 3089
N.A.I.C.S.: 326199
Hermann M. Thorisson *(Chm)*
Dadi Valdirmarsson *(Mng Dir)*
Jon Sigurosson *(Sr VP-Procurement)*

Promens Tempra ehf. (2)
Ishella 8
221 Hafnarfjordur, Iceland
Tel.: (354) 5205400
Fax: (354) 5642500
E-Mail: tempra@promens.com
Web Site: www.promens.com
Emp.: 15
Housing Insulation & Packaging Products Mfr
S.I.C.: 3089
N.A.I.C.S.: 326199
Halldor Jonsson *(Coord-Sls)*

Non-U.S. Divisions:

LLC Promens Yekaterinburg (2)
al Bazovyi 21
Mailbox 171
620089 Yekaterinburg, Russia
Tel.: (7) 343 351 00 32
Fax: (7) 343 351 00 34
Plastic Products Mfr
S.I.C.: 3089
N.A.I.C.S.: 326199

Promens A/S (2)
Gl Donsvej 12
6000 Kolding, Denmark
Tel.: (45) 76322400
Fax: (45) 76322451
E-Mail: sales.kolding@promens.com
Web Site: www.promens.com
Emp.: 75
Plastic Bottles Mfr
S.I.C.: 3085
N.A.I.C.S.: 326160
Henrick Ludvigsen *(Mgr-Sls)*

Promens Aalesund AS (2)
Tverrevegen 37
PO Box 23
6020 Alesund, Norway
Tel.: (47) 71401900
Fax: (47) 71401919
E-Mail: mail@saeplast.no
Web Site: www.saeplast.no
Plastic Products Distr
S.I.C.: 5162
N.A.I.C.S.: 424610
Dadi Valdimarsson *(Dir-Sls & Mktg)*

Promens AS - Kambo (2)
Brevikveien 535
Boks 3054
Kambo, N-1506 Moss, Norway
Tel.: (47) 69279500
Fax: (47) 69279501
E-Mail: sales.kambo@promens.com
Web Site: www.promens.com
Emp.: 110
Plastic Bottles Mfr
S.I.C.: 3085
N.A.I.C.S.: 326160
Yngve Jacobsen *(Coord-Sls & Pkg)*

Promens AS - Kristiansand (2)
Stadionveien 15
PO Box 1514
Lundsiden, 4688 Kristiansand, Norway
Tel.: (47) 38144000
Fax: (47) 38144044
E-Mail: foodpackaging@promens.com
Web Site: www.promens.com
Emp.: 75
Plastic Food Packaging Mfr
S.I.C.: 3089
N.A.I.C.S.: 326199
Svein Harald Egestad *(VP-Food & Beverage Pkg)*

Promens a.s. (2)
Priluky 38
760 01 Zlin, Czech Republic
Tel.: (420) 577051101
Fax: (420) 577051137
E-Mail: sales.zlin@promens.com
Web Site: www.zlin.promens.com
Emp.: 200
Plastic Product Mfr
S.I.C.: 3089
N.A.I.C.S.: 326199

Promens AS (2)
Tehase 4
61001 Rongu, Estonia
Tel.: (372) 7307230
Fax: (372) 7371818
E-Mail: eesti@promens.com
Web Site: www.promens.com
Emp.: 250
Plastic Crates & Trays Mfr
S.I.C.: 3089
N.A.I.C.S.: 326199
Indrek Ojamaa *(Gen Mgr)*

Promens Bjaeverskov A/S (2)
Industrivej 3
4632 Bjaeverskov, Denmark
Tel.: (45) 70266810
Fax: (45) 70266811
E-Mail: sales.bjaverskov@promens.com
Web Site: www.promens.com
Emp.: 50
Plastic Products Mfr
S.I.C.: 3089
N.A.I.C.S.: 326199
Lasse Pedersen *(Mgr-Sls)*

Promens B.V. (2)
Einsteinstraat 22
PO Box 131
NL-6900 AC Zevenaar, Netherlands
Tel.: (31) 316586100
Fax: (31) 316586111
E-Mail: sales.zevenaar@promens.com
Web Site: www.promens.com
Emp.: 200
Industrial Plastic Component Parts Mfr
S.I.C.: 3089
N.A.I.C.S.: 326199
Richard Diepeveen *(Gen Mgr)*

Promens Deventer B.V. (2)
Zweedsestraat 61010
7418 BG Deventer, Netherlands
Tel.: (31) 570660706
Fax: (31) 570660719
E-Mail: deventer@promens.com
Web Site: www.promens.com
Emp.: 70
Plastic Material Handling Products Mfr
S.I.C.: 3085
N.A.I.C.S.: 326160
Peter Baken *(Mng Dir)*

Promens Farum A/S (2)
Lucernemarken 6
3520 Farum, Denmark
Tel.: (45) 44975133
Fax: (45) 44974466
E-Mail: sales.farum@promens.com
Web Site: www.promens.com
Emp.: 1
Plastics Products Distr
S.I.C.: 5162
N.A.I.C.S.: 424610
Charles Jorgensen *(Mgr-Sls)*

Promens Firenze S.R.L. (2)
Via delle Bertesche 11M
I-50050 San Mauro a Signa, Italy
Tel.: (39) 055894261
Fax: (39) 0558996408
E-Mail: sales.florence@promens.com
Plastic Bottle & Container Mfr
S.I.C.: 3085
N.A.I.C.S.: 326160

Promens Hockenheim GmbH (2)
4 Industriestrasse 18
D-68766 Hockenheim, Germany
Tel.: (49) 620520990
Fax: (49) 62052099227
E-Mail: mail.hockenheim@promens.com
Web Site: www.promens.com
Emp.: 180
Plastic Container Mfr
S.I.C.: 3089
N.A.I.C.S.: 326199
Klaus Uhlenbrok *(Coord-Sls)*

Promens Iberia S.A. (2)
Poligono Industrial 15
36880 La Caniza, Spain
Tel.: (34) 986663091
Fax: (34) 986663314
E-Mail: sales.iberia@promens.com
Web Site: www.promens.com
Emp.: 50
Plastic Container Mfr
S.I.C.: 3089
N.A.I.C.S.: 326199
Dorian Xerri *(Mgr-Sls)*

Promens India Pvt. Ltd. (2)
601 Venus Atlantic Corporate Park
Anandnagar Road
Prahladnagar, Ahmedabad, Gujarat, 380 015, India
Tel.: (91) 79 4007 3880
Fax: (91) 79 4007 3885
E-Mail: info@promens.in
Web Site: www.promens.com
Plastics Product Mfr
S.I.C.: 3089
N.A.I.C.S.: 326199

Promens Lainate S.R.L. (2)
Via Canova 49
Lainate, Milan, 20020, Italy
Tel.: (39) 029370669
Fax: (39) 0293570617
E-Mail: paola.moroni@promens.com
Web Site: www.promens.com
Emp.: 32
Plastic Bottle & Container Mfr
S.I.C.: 3089
N.A.I.C.S.: 326199
Giovanna Mazzola *(Sls Coord)*

Promens Lidkoping AB (2)
Skogvaktarevagen 2
PO Box 794
SE-531 17 Lidkoping, Sweden
Tel.: (46) 510310000
Fax: (46) 51021117
E-Mail: sales.lidkoping@promens.com
Web Site: www.promens.com
Emp.: 80
Plastic Packaging Mfr
S.I.C.: 3089
N.A.I.C.S.: 326199
Claes Nystroem *(Mgr-Sls)*

Promens Medical Packaging A/S (2)
Industrivej 6
DK-5550 Langeskov, Denmark
Tel.: (45) 63381000
Fax: (45) 63381001
E-Mail: sales.langeskov@promens.com
Emp.: 50
Plastic Packaging Mfr
S.I.C.: 3089
N.A.I.C.S.: 326199
Christian Holmskov *(Area Mgr-Sls)*

Promens Munchen GmbH (2)
Klausnerring 8
D-85551 Kirchheim, Germany
Tel.: (49) 899919320
Fax: (49) 8999193222
E-Mail: info@promens.com
Web Site: www.promens.com
Emp.: 40
Plastic Component Mfr
S.I.C.: 3089
N.A.I.C.S.: 326199
Jeroen Bloom *(Gen Mgr)*

Promens Nitra, s.r.o. (2)
Praska 33
949 01 Nitra, Slovakia
Tel.: (421) 918940370
Fax: (421) 376556295
E-Mail: boris.pevny@promens.com
Web Site: www.promens.com
Emp.: 1
Plastic Component Parts Mfr
S.I.C.: 3089
N.A.I.C.S.: 326199
Boris Pevny *(Mgr-Fin)*

Promens N.V. (2)
Begoniastraat 44
Eke-Nazareth, 9810 Gent, Belgium
Tel.: (32) 93822222
Fax: (32) 93822220
E-Mail: sales.gent@promens.com
Emp.: 62
Plastic Packaging Container Mfr
S.I.C.: 3089
N.A.I.C.S.: 326199
Kurt Thienpont *(Gen Mgr)*

Promens Oy (2)
Vanha Tampereentie 260
FIN-20380 Turku, Finland
Tel.: (358) 2489555
Fax: (358) 24895511
E-Mail: Sales.turku@promens.com
Web Site: www.promens.com
Emp.: 100
Plastic Bottles & Closures Mfr
S.I.C.: 3085
N.A.I.C.S.: 326160
Krister Sigfrids *(Mng Dir)*

Promens Packaging GmbH - Ettlingen (2)
Hertzstrasse 22
D-76275 Ettlingen, Germany
Tel.: (49) 724358660
Fax: (49) 7243586613
E-Mail: sales.germany@promens.com
Web Site: www.promens.com
Emp.: 82
Plastic Container Mfr
S.I.C.: 3089
N.A.I.C.S.: 326199
Herr Bernd Bsonek *(Controller)*

Promens Packaging GmbH - Gorzke (2)
Chausseestr 56
D-14828 Gorzke, Germany
Tel.: (49) 338476990
Fax: (49) 3384769920
E-Mail: sales.germany@promens.com
Web Site: www.promens.com
Emp.: 24
Plastic Bottle Mfr
S.I.C.: 3085
N.A.I.C.S.: 326160
Dragan Stjepanovic *(Gen Mgr)*

Promens Packaging GmbH - Neumunster (2)
Gadelander Str 137
DE-24539 Neumunster, Germany
Tel.: (49) 432198780
Fax: (49) 4321987810
E-Mail: info@promens.com
Web Site: www.promens.com
Emp.: 300
Plastic Bottle Mfr
S.I.C.: 3085
N.A.I.C.S.: 326160
Alexandra Erdmann *(Mgr-Sls)*

Promens Packaging GmbH - Winsen (2)
Moorweg 1-15
21423 Winsen, Germany
Tel.: (49) 41717060
Fax: (49) 4171706130
E-Mail: sales.germany@promens.com
Web Site: www.promens.com
Emp.: 30
Industrial Plastic Container Mfr
S.I.C.: 3089
N.A.I.C.S.: 326199

Promens Packaging GmbH - Witzenhausen (2)
Ludwigsteinstr 63
37214 Witzenhausen, Germany
Tel.: (49) 55429540
Fax: (49) 5542954155
E-Mail: yen.lueck@promens.com
Web Site: www.promens.com
Emp.: 40
Plastic Bottle & Container Mfr

S.I.C.: 3089
N.A.I.C.S.: 326199
Yen Lueck *(Mgr)*

Promens Packaging Ltd. - Beccles (2)
Ellough
Beccles, Suffolk, NR34 7TB, United Kingdom
Tel.: (44) 1502718400
Fax: (44) 1502718450
Web Site: www.promens.com
Emp.: 220
Rigid Plastic Packaging Container Mfr
S.I.C.: 3089
N.A.I.C.S.: 326199
David Learner *(Mng Dir)*

Promens Packaging Ltd. - Deeside (2)
Engineer Park
Deeside, CH5 2QD, United Kingdom
Tel.: (44) 1244537555
Fax: (44) 1244526645
E-Mail: sales.deeside@promens.com
Web Site: www.promens.com
Industrial Plastic Packaging Mfr
S.I.C.: 3089
N.A.I.C.S.: 326199
Clive Saunders *(Mng Dir)*

Promens Packaging Ltd. - Thetford (2)
Brunel Way
Thetford, Norfolk, IP24 1HP, United Kingdom
Tel.: (44) 1842760600
Fax: (44) 1842760601
E-Mail: sales.thetford@promens.com
Web Site: www.promens.com
Emp.: 31
Plastic Bottle Mfr
S.I.C.: 3085
N.A.I.C.S.: 326160
Dave Lambert *(Gen Mgr)*

Promens Packaging S.A. (2)
Pol Ind Can Roca
Barcelona, 8292, Spain
Tel.: (34) 937772448
Fax: (34) 937772252
E-Mail: info@promens.com
Web Site: www.promens.com
Emp.: 100
Plastics Product Mfr
S.I.C.: 3089
N.A.I.C.S.: 326199

Promens Rijen B.V. (2)
Provincienbaan 21
5121 DK Rijen, Netherlands
Tel.: (31) 161222330
Fax: (31) 161220626
E-Mail: info.rijen@promens.com
Web Site: www.saeplast.is
Emp.: 110
Plastic Products Mfr
S.I.C.: 3089
N.A.I.C.S.: 326199

Promens S.A. - Bellignat (2)
5 rue Castellion
01117 Oyonnax, France
Tel.: (33) 474817481
Fax: (33) 474730475
E-Mail: packaging.france@promens.com
Web Site: www.promens.com
Emp.: 100
Plastic Container & Closure Mfr
S.I.C.: 3089
N.A.I.C.S.: 326199
Pierre Sabatier *(Mng Dir)*

Promens S.A. - Geovreisset (2)
Route d'oyonnax
01104 Oyonnax, France
Tel.: (33) 474817481
Fax: (33) 474734063
Web Site: www.promens.com
Emp.: 63
Plastic Packaging Mfr
S.I.C.: 3089
N.A.I.C.S.: 326199

Promens S.A. - L'Aigle (2)
ZI n1 route de Crulai
BP 214
61306 L'Aigle, France
Tel.: (33) 233843499
Fax: (33) 233843500
E-Mail: packaging.france@promens.com
Web Site: www.promens.com
Emp.: 80
Plastic Packaging Mfr
S.I.C.: 3089
N.A.I.C.S.: 326199
Arnaud Bodier *(Dir-Production)*

Promens S.a.r.l. (2)
ZI de la Balme 481 rue des Voirons
BP 145
74805 La Roche-sur-Foron, France
Tel.: (33) 450251700
Fax: (33) 450031119
E-Mail: packaging.france@promens.com
Emp.: 60
Plastic Container Mfr
S.I.C.: 3089
N.A.I.C.S.: 326199

Promens St. John Inc. (2)
100 Industrial Drive
PO Box 2087
Saint John, NB, E2L 3T5, Canada
Tel.: (506) 633-0101
Fax: (506) 658-0227
Toll Free: (800) 567-3966
E-Mail: info@promensstjohn.ca
Web Site: www.promens.com
Plastic Products Mfr
S.I.C.: 3089
N.A.I.C.S.: 326199
Mike Kilpatrick *(Coord-Sls-East Coast)*

Promens Stilling A/S (2)
Industrivej 12
Stilling, 8660 Skanderborg, Denmark
Tel.: (45) 87935300
Fax: (45) 86572521
Web Site: www.promens.com
Emp.: 100
Plastic Container Mfr
S.I.C.: 3089
N.A.I.C.S.: 326199

Promens Tunisia Sarl (2)
Zi Route De Khniss BP81
5060 Monastir, Tunisia
Tel.: (216) 73530823
Fax: (216) 73530822
E-Mail: sales.monastir@promens.com.tn
Emp.: 80
Molded Plastic Components Mfr
S.I.C.: 3089
N.A.I.C.S.: 326199
Walid Hamza *(Gen Mgr)*

Promens Warszawa sp. z o.o. (2)
Batorego 6
Otwock, Warsaw, 05-400, Poland
Tel.: (48) 22 7199900
Fax: (48) 22 7199926
E-Mail: sales.otwock@promens.com
Web Site: www.promens.com
Emp.: 200
Industrial Plastic Container Packaging Mfr
S.I.C.: 3089
N.A.I.C.S.: 326199
Jan Jaszczuk *(Mng Dir)*

ENTERPRISE INVESTORS SP ZOO

Warsaw Financial Center
Emilii Plater 53 31st floor, 00-113
Warsaw, Poland
Tel.: (48) 224588500
Fax: (48) 224588555
E-Mail: info@ei.com.pl
Web Site: www.ei.com.pl
Sales Range: $1-9.9 Million
Emp.: 60
Fiscal Year-end: 12/31/12

Business Description:
Private Equity Firm
S.I.C.: 6211
N.A.I.C.S.: 523999

Personnel:
Robert Faris *(Chm)*
Jacek Siwicki *(Pres)*
Robert Manz *(Mng Partner)*
Dariusz R. Pronczuk *(Mng Partner)*
Michal Rusiecki *(Mng Partner)*

ENTERPRISE METALS LIMITED

Level 1 640 Murray Street
West Perth, WA, 6005, Australia
Tel.: (61) 894369200
Fax: (61) 894369220
E-Mail: info@enterprisemetals.com.au
Web Site: www.enterprisemetals.com.au
ENT—(ASX)
Rev.: $3,158,558
Assets: $22,299,109
Liabilities: $389,101
Net Worth: $21,910,008
Earnings: ($5,576,629)
Emp.: 2
Fiscal Year-end: 06/30/13

Business Description:
Uranium Producer
S.I.C.: 2819
N.A.I.C.S.: 325180

Personnel:
Dermot Ryan *(Mng Dir)*
Damian Delaney *(CFO & Sec)*

Board of Directors:
Jingbin Wang
Paul Hallam
Anna Mao
Dermot Ryan
Allan Trench

Legal Counsel:
Hilary Macdonald
Suite 29 18 Stirling Highway
6009 Nedlands, Australia

ENTERPRISE URANIUM LIMITED

Level 1 640 Murray Street
West Perth, WA, 6005, Australia
Mailing Address:
PO Box 1906
West Perth, WA, 6872, Australia
Tel.: (61) 8 9436 9240
Fax: (61) 8 9436 9220
E-Mail: info@enterpriseuranium.com.au
Web Site: www.enterpriseuranium.com.au
Year Founded: 2012
ENU—(ASX)

Business Description:
Uranium Mining
S.I.C.: 1094
N.A.I.C.S.: 212291

Personnel:
Anna Mao *(Chm)*
Dennis William Wilkins *(CFO & Sec)*

Board of Directors:
Anna Mao
Michael Atkins
Zhen Huang
Dermot Ryan

ENTERTAINMENT MAGPIE LIMITED

(d/b/a musicMagpie.co.uk)
Black & White House Hulley Rd
Hurdsfield Industrial Estate
Macclesfield, SK10 2AF, United Kingdom
Tel.: (44) 870 495 1283
E-Mail: enquiries@musicmagpie.co.uk
Web Site: www.musicmagpie.co.uk
Year Founded: 2007
Sales Range: $100-124.9 Million
Emp.: 750

Business Description:
Online CD, DVD & Video Game Trading Services
S.I.C.: 7999
N.A.I.C.S.: 713990

Personnel:
Steve Oliver *(Co-Founder & CEO)*
Walter Gleeson *(Co-Founder & COO)*
Allan L. Leighton *(Chm)*

ENTERTAINMENT ONE LTD.

175 Bloor Street East Suite 1400
North Tower
Toronto, ON, M4W 3RB, Canada
Tel.: (416) 646-2400
Fax: (416) 979-9255
E-Mail: info@entertainmentone.ca
Web Site: www.entertainmentone.ca
ETO—(AIM)
Rev.: $993,531,339
Assets: $1,554,179,289
Liabilities: $1,031,750,157
Net Worth: $522,429,132
Earnings: $1,737,219
Emp.: 1,169
Fiscal Year-end: 03/31/13

Business Description:
Retail Entertainment Distr
S.I.C.: 3652
N.A.I.C.S.: 512220

Personnel:
Darren D. Throop *(CEO)*
Giles Kirkley Willits *(CFO)*
Patrice Theroux *(Pres-Film)*

Board of Directors:
James Corsellis
Bob Allan
Ronald Atkey
Clare R. Copeland
Garth M. Girvan
Mark Opzoomer
Patrice Theroux
Darren D. Throop
Giles Kirkley Willits

Legal Counsel:
Osler, Hoskin & Harcourt LLP
100 King Street West 1 First Canadian Place
Toronto, ON, Canada

Mayer Brown International LLP
201 Bishopsgate
London, United Kingdom

Subsidiaries:

E1 Films Canada Inc (1)
175 Bloor St E Ste 1400
Toronto, ON, M4W 3R8, Canada
Tel.: (416) 646-2400
Fax: (416) 646-2399
Web Site: www.e1films.com
Photographic Films & Chemical Mfr
S.I.C.: 3861
N.A.I.C.S.: 325992
David Reckziegel *(Pres-North America)*
Dylan Wiley *(Sr VP & Gen Mgr-US)*

E1 Television International Ltd. (1)
175 Bloor Street East Ste 1400 North Tower
Toronto, ON, M4W 3R8, Canada
Tel.: (416) 646-2400
Fax: (416) 646-6998
Emp.: 150
Entertainment Services
S.I.C.: 7929
N.A.I.C.S.: 711510
Peter Emerson *(Pres)*

E1 Television Productions Inc (1)
175 Bloor St E Ste 1400 N Tower
Toronto, ON, M4W 3R8, Canada
Tel.: (416) 646-2400
Fax: (416) 646-2588
Web Site: www.Eonetv.com
Emp.: 125
Film Production Services
S.I.C.: 7812
N.A.I.C.S.: 512110
Noreen Halpern *(Pres)*
John Morayniss *(CEO)*

Entertainment One Limited Partnership (1)
5014 49th St
Yellowknife, NT, X1A 3R7, Canada
Tel.: (867) 873-4112
Fax: (867) 873-4112
Emp.: 4
Music Entertainment Services
S.I.C.: 7929
N.A.I.C.S.: 711130

Seville Pictures Inc (1)
400 De Maisonneuve Blvd W 11th Fl
Montreal, QC, H3A 1L4, Canada

Entertainment One Ltd.—(Continued)

Tel.: (514) 841-1910
Fax: (514) 841-8030
E-Mail: info@filmsseville.com
Web Site: www.sevillepictures.com
Emp.: 40
Film Entertainment Services
S.I.C.: 7812
N.A.I.C.S.: 512110
Frederic Verdy *(Mgr-HR)*

Videoglobe 1 Inc (1)
6000 Ch De La Cote-De-Liesse
Saint Laurent, QC, PQ H4T 1E3, Canada
Tel.: (514) 738-6665
Fax: (514) 738-3923
Web Site: www.eonedistribution.ca
Emp.: 150
Electronic Parts & Equipment Services
S.I.C.: 8299
N.A.I.C.S.: 611519
Karim Trottier *(Gen Mgr)*

Subsidiary:

Seville Entertainment Inc (2)
147 Rue Saint-Paul Ouest Ste 200
Montreal, QC, H2Y 1Z5, Canada
Tel.: (514) 841-1910
Fax: (514) 841-8030
Film Mfr & Distr
S.I.C.: 5043
N.A.I.C.S.: 423410

Non-U.S. Subsidiaries:

Eone Holding Holland B.V. (1)
Bergweg 46
Hilversum, 1217 SC, Netherlands
Tel.: (31) 356251200
Fax: (31) 356251254
E-Mail: receptie@entonegroup.com
Web Site: www.entertainmentone.nl
Emp.: 45
Music Entertainment Services
S.I.C.: 5099
N.A.I.C.S.: 423990
Jan Kouwenhocen *(Mng Dir)*

Entertainment One Benelux (1)
46 Mountain Road
Hilversum, 1217 SC, Netherlands
Mailing Address:
PO Box 142
1200 AC Hilversum, Netherlands
Tel.: (31) 356 25 12 00
Fax: (31) 356 25 12 84
E-Mail: customer.care@entonegroup.com
Web Site: www.entertainmentone.nl
Emp.: 30
Entertainment Services
S.I.C.: 7829
N.A.I.C.S.: 512120
Jim Calmer *(Mgr-Logistics)*

ENTIE COMMERCIAL BANK, LTD.

40F Taipei 101 Tower 7 Sec 5 Xin Yi Rd
Taipei, Taiwan
Tel.: (886) 281012233
Fax: (886) 227187625
E-Mail: entiefmail@entiebank.com.tw
Web Site: www.entiebank.com.tw
2849—(TAI)
Rev.: $294,530,506
Assets: $12,179,875,305
Liabilities: $11,350,234,092
Net Worth: $829,641,213
Earnings: $138,066,110
Emp.: 1,866
Fiscal Year-end: 12/31/12
Business Description:
Commercial Bank Services
S.I.C.: 6029
N.A.I.C.S.: 522110
Personnel:
Mark Zoltan Chiba *(Chm)*
Wen-Hsien Tsai *(Vice Chm)*
Jesse Ding *(Pres)*
Andrew Lee *(CFO)*
Eddie Chen *(Chief Risk Officer)*
Board of Directors:
Mark Zoltan Chiba
Jesse Ding
Philippe Espinasse
Charles Huang
Henry Lee
Steven Lin
Wen-Hsien Tsai
Harukazu Yamaguchi
Chien-San Yen
Supervisory Board of Directors:
Bor-Yi Huang
Samuel Wu
Transfer Agent:
Capital Securities Corporation
B2 97 Tun Hwa S Rd
Taipei, Taiwan

ENTIRE TECHNOLOGY CO., LTD.

No 12 Kung-Yeh 5th Rd Ping-Zhen Industrial Park
32459 Taoyuan, Taiwan
Tel.: (886) 32623311
Fax: (886) 32623377
Web Site: www.entire.com.tw
3573—(TAI)
Sales Range: $50-74.9 Million
Business Description:
Liquid Crystal Display Mfr
S.I.C.: 3679
N.A.I.C.S.: 334419
Personnel:
Jan-Feng Huang *(Chm)*
Hsieh-Ju Peng *(CFO)*

ENTOURAGE METALS LTD.

Suite 1500 409 Granville Street
Vancouver, BC, V6C 1T2, Canada
Tel.: (604) 484-7855
Fax: (604) 484-7155
Toll Free: (866) 284-2296
E-Mail: info@entouragemetals.com
Web Site: www.entouragemetals.com
Year Founded: 2010
EMT—(TSXV)
Int. Income: $1,126
Assets: $1,302,485
Liabilities: $139,338
Net Worth: $1,163,148
Earnings: ($1,929,149)
Fiscal Year-end: 03/31/13
Business Description:
Gold Mining Services
S.I.C.: 1041
N.A.I.C.S.: 212221
Personnel:
Robert McLeod *(Chm)*
Jeff Sundar *(Pres & CEO)*
Cale Moodie *(CFO)*
Board of Directors:
Robert McLeod
Adrian Fleming
John Florek
Jeff Sundar
Michael Williams
Legal Counsel:
DuMoulin Black
10th Floor, 595 Howe Street
Vancouver, BC, V6C 2T5, Canada
Transfer Agent:
Computershare
3rd Floor 510 Burrard Street
Vancouver, BC, Canada

ENTOURAGE MINING LTD.

Suite 614-475 Howe Street
Vancouver, BC, V6C 2B3, Canada
Tel.: (604) 669-4367
Fax: (604) 669-4368
E-Mail: info@entouragemining.com
Web Site: www.entouragemining.com
Year Founded: 1995
ENMGF—(OTCB)
Assets: $5,780
Liabilities: $244,911
Net Worth: ($239,130)
Earnings: ($50,734)
Fiscal Year-end: 12/31/12
Business Description:
Mineral Exploration Services
S.I.C.: 1481
N.A.I.C.S.: 213115
Personnel:
Paul Shatzko *(Chm & Sec)*
Gregory F. Kennedy *(Pres & CEO)*
Pradeep Varshney *(CFO)*
Board of Directors:
Paul Shatzko
Gregory F. Kennedy
James A. Turner
Transfer Agent:
Computershare Trust Company of Canada
510 Burrard St 3rd Fl
Vancouver, BC, V6C 3B9, Canada

ENTR RATIONNELLE INSTALLATION ELECTRIQUE

102 B Rue Danielle Casanova
93300 Aubervilliers, France
Tel.: (33) 148113750
Fax: (33) 148337597
E-Mail: entr@entr.fr
Web Site: www.entr.fr
Rev.: $23,000,000
Emp.: 178
Business Description:
Special Trade Contractors
S.I.C.: 1799
N.A.I.C.S.: 238990
Personnel:
Christine Desbrueres *(Dir-Pur)*

ENTREC CORPORATION

(Formerly Entrec Transportation Services Ltd.)
100 Diamond Avenue
PO Box 3490
Spruce Grove, AB, T7X 3A7, Canada
Tel.: (780) 962-5630
Fax: (780) 962-1722
E-Mail: jvandenberg@entrec.com
Web Site: www.entrec.com
Year Founded: 2009
ENT—(TSXV)
Rev.: $131,698,704
Assets: $263,782,093
Liabilities: $148,483,726
Net Worth: $115,298,368
Earnings: $12,039,570
Emp.: 600
Fiscal Year-end: 12/31/12
Business Description:
Cargo Transport Services
S.I.C.: 4731
N.A.I.C.S.: 488510
Personnel:
Rodney F. Marlin *(Chm)*
John M. Stevens *(Pres & CEO)*
Jason Vandenberg *(CFO)*
Joe Brennan *(Sec)*
Terris Chorney *(Exec VP-Bus Dev)*
Glen Fleming *(Exec VP-Ops)*
Chris Good *(Exec VP-Mktg)*
Alan Swagerman *(Exec VP-Ops-Crane Svcs)*
Board of Directors:
Rodney F. Marlin
Joe Brennan
Peter Alan Lacey
Carolyn Mains
Chris Porter
Chuck Sanders
John M. Stevens
Brian W.L. Tod
Legal Counsel:
Shea Nerland Calnan LLP
Calgary, AB, Canada
Transfer Agent:
Olympia Trust Company
125 9th Avenue SE Suite 2300
Calgary, AB, T2G 0P6, Canada
Tel.: (403) 261-0900

ENTREC TRANSPORTATION SERVICES LTD.

(Name Changed to ENTREC Corporation)

ENTREE GOLD INC.

Suite 1201- 1166 Alberni Street
Vancouver, BC, V6E 3Z3, Canada
Tel.: (604) 687-4777
Fax: (604) 687-4770
E-Mail: info@entreegold.com
Web Site: www.entreegold.com
EGI—(DEU NYSEMKT TSX)
Int. Income: $190,449
Assets: $64,173,530
Liabilities: $15,845,620
Net Worth: $48,327,910
Earnings: ($15,196,129)
Emp.: 72
Fiscal Year-end: 12/31/12
Business Description:
Gold & Copper Mining Services
S.I.C.: 1041
N.A.I.C.S.: 212221
Personnel:
Gregory G. Crowe *(Pres & CEO)*
Bruce Colwill *(CFO)*
Mona M. Forster *(Sec & VP)*
Board of Directors:
Michael Howard
Mark H. Bailey
Lindsay Richard Bottomer
Gregory G. Crowe
Alan R. Edwards
James L. Harris
Peter M. Meredith, Jr.
Transfer Agent:
Computershare Investor Services Inc.
3rd Floor 510 Burrard St
V6C 3B9 Vancouver, BC, Canada

U.S. Subsidiary:

Entree Gold (US) Inc. (1)
Reindeer Cir
Franktown, CO 10510
Tel.: (303) 663-8875
Fax: (303) 663-8701
E-Mail: jbensing@bensingassociates.com
Web Site: www.entreegold.com
Emp.: 2
Mineral Resources Exploration Services
S.I.C.: 1479
N.A.I.C.S.: 212393
Tom Watkins *(VP)*

Non-U.S. Subsidiaries:

Beijing Entree Minerals Technology Company Limited (1)
2705 Tower 12 Bldg Technology Company Limited Jianguo Rd
Wanda Plz Chaoyong District, 100022
Beijing, China
Tel.: (86) 1058203099
Fax: (86) 1058205779
E-Mail: xyong@entreegold.com
Emp.: 30
Mineral Resources Exploration Services
S.I.C.: 1479
N.A.I.C.S.: 212393
Yan Zhu *(Gen Mgr)*

Entree LLC (1)
Ste 201 202 Jamyan Gun St 5 Ar Mongol Travel Bldg
Sukhbaatar District 1st county, 97611
Ulaanbaatar, Mongolia
Tel.: (976) 11318562
Fax: (976) 11319426
Emp.: 10
Mineral Resources Exploration Services
S.I.C.: 1479
N.A.I.C.S.: 212393

Kelly Peterson *(Mng Dir)*

PacMag Metals Limited (1)
Level 2 33 Ord St
West Perth, WA, 6005, Australia
Tel.: (61) 894812997
Fax: (61) 893210070
E-Mail: info@pacmag.com.au
Web Site: www.pacmag.com.au
Sales Range: Less than $1 Million
Copper, Gold & Molybdenum Mining Services
S.I.C.: 1041
N.A.I.C.S.: 212221
Rodney Michael Joyce *(Chm)*
Bruce Richard Acutt *(Sec)*

ENTREPRENDRE SA

53 rue du Chemin Vert
92100 Boulogne-Billancourt, France
Tel.: (33) 1 46 10 21 21
Fax: (33) 1 46 10 21 22
Web Site: www.entreprendre.fr
ALENR—(EUR)
Sales Range: $25-49.9 Million
Business Description:
Magazine Publisher
S.I.C.: 2721
N.A.I.C.S.: 511120
Personnel:
Robert Lafont *(Chm & CEO)*
Didier Delignou *(CFO)*

ENTREPRISE BOYER

16 Rue De La Mairie
77167 Poligny, France
Tel.: (33) 164785700
Fax: (33) 164292895
Web Site: www.entreprises.com
Rev.: $23,600,000
Emp.: 184
Business Description:
Nonresidential Construction
S.I.C.: 1542
N.A.I.C.S.: 236220
Personnel:
Claude Boyer *(Pres-Supervisory Bd)*
Gilles Boyer *(Pres)*

ENTREPRISE G BATAILLE

Rue Jean Bertin
76330 Le Havre, France
Tel.: (33) 235386099
Fax: (33) 235314733
E-Mail: info@bataille-sa.fr
Web Site: www.bataille-sa.fr
Rev.: $23,800,000
Emp.: 360
Business Description:
Business Services
S.I.C.: 7349
N.A.I.C.S.: 561790
Personnel:
Philippe Dentu *(Chm)*
Board of Directors:
Philippe Dentu
Arnaud Debris

ENTREPRISE GUIBAN SA

Z I Kerpont-Bras Rue De Kerlo
56850 Caudan, France
Tel.: (33) 297760588
Fax: (33) 297764470
E-Mail: secretariat@guiban.com
Web Site: www.guiban.com
Sales Range: $10-24.9 Million
Emp.: 50
Business Description:
Plumbing, Heating, Air-conditioning
S.I.C.: 1711
N.A.I.C.S.: 238220
Personnel:
Lionel Guiban *(Mng Dir)*

ENTREPRISE GUILLERM

Le Gueven 5
29420 Plouvorn, France
Tel.: (33) 298613022
Fax: (33) 298613600
Web Site: www.guillerm.fr/contact.php
Rev.: $20,300,000
Emp.: 108
Business Description:
Nonresidential Construction
S.I.C.: 1542
N.A.I.C.S.: 236220
Personnel:
Alain Guillerm *(Pres)*

ENTREPRISE HUBERT ROUGEOT

Route Nationale 74
Meursault, 21190 Beaune, France
Tel.: (33) 380216909
Rev.: $24,800,000
Emp.: 144
Business Description:
Highway & Street Construction
S.I.C.: 1611
N.A.I.C.S.: 237310
Personnel:
Christophe Rougeot *(Pres)*

ENTREPRISE MINIERE ET CHIMIQUE SA

(d/b/a EMC)
62 Rue Jeanne d'Arc
F 75641 Paris, Cedex 13, France
Tel.: (33) 144065200
Telex: 200 191 F
Fax: (33) 1 44 06 54 00
E-Mail: dircom.emc@mail.groupe-emc.com
Year Founded: 1967
Sales Range: $1-4.9 Billion
Emp.: 2,270
Business Description:
Holding Company; Producer of Potash, Derivatives & Chemicals; Environment & Waste Management Import Export
S.I.C.: 1474
N.A.I.C.S.: 212391

Subsidiaries:

Societe Commerciale des Potasses et de L'azote (1)
2 Pl Du General De Gaulle
BP 1170
F 68053 Mulhouse, Cedex, France (100%)
Tel.: (33) 389363600
Fax: (33) 389363626
E-Mail: dai@scpa.fr
Web Site: www.scpa.com
S.I.C.: 1474
N.A.I.C.S.: 212391

ENTREPRISE PAUL CALIN

25 Rue Voltaire
Harchechamp, 88300 Nancy, France
Tel.: (33) 329069009
Web Site: www.paul-calin.fr
Sales Range: $10-24.9 Million
Emp.: 113
Business Description:
Mixed Concrete
S.I.C.: 3273
N.A.I.C.S.: 327320
Personnel:
Guy Calin *(Mng Dir)*

ENTREPRISE ROBERT THIBERT INC.

200 Saint Jean Baptiste Boulevard
Mercier, QC, J6R 2L2, Canada
Tel.: (450) 699-0560
Fax: (450) 691-4387
Toll Free: (800) 361-9805
E-Mail: info@rtxwheels.com
Web Site: www.rthibert.com
Year Founded: 1976
Rev.: $50,000,000
Emp.: 200
Business Description:
Automotive Parts & Components Distr
S.I.C.: 5013
N.A.I.C.S.: 441310
Personnel:
Robert Thibert *(Pres)*

ENTREPRISES LANG

28 Rue De Cardurand
44600 Saint Nazaire, Loire Atlantique, France
Tel.: (33) 240225543
Fax: (33) 240668394
E-Mail: contact@langbtp.com
Web Site: www.lang-entreprise.com
Rev.: $22,200,000
Emp.: 109
Business Description:
Nonresidential Construction
S.I.C.: 1542
N.A.I.C.S.: 236220
Personnel:
Edouard Chambon *(Pres)*

ENUSTECH, INC.

3rd Floor 1197-2 Gaepo
Gangnam, Seoul, 135-962, Korea (South)
Tel.: (82) 2 5650782
Fax: (82) 2 34523603
E-Mail: leo@enus.co.kr
Web Site: www.enus.co.kr
109960—(KRS)
Business Description:
Wireless Product Mfr
S.I.C.: 3663
N.A.I.C.S.: 334220
Personnel:
Hwi Jang *(CEO)*

ENVESTRA LIMITED

Level 10 81 Flinders Street
Adelaide, SA, 5000, Australia
Tel.: (61) 8 8227 1500
Fax: (61) 8 8227 1511
E-Mail: envestra@envestra.com.au
Web Site: www.envestra.com.au
Year Founded: 1997
ENV—(ASX DEU)
Rev.: $528,865,750
Assets: $3,373,173,490
Liabilities: $2,495,933,710
Net Worth: $877,239,780
Earnings: $112,338,380
Emp.: 15
Fiscal Year-end: 06/30/13
Business Description:
Natural Gas Distribution Services
S.I.C.: 4924
N.A.I.C.S.: 221210
Personnel:
John Geoffrey Allpass *(Chm)*
Ian Bruce Little *(Mng Dir)*
Des Petherick *(Sec)*
Board of Directors:
John Geoffrey Allpass
Eric Fraser Ainsworth
Dominic Loi Shun Chan
Ivan Kee Ham Chan
Ross Murray Gersbach
Ian Bruce Little
Michael Joseph McCormack
Olaf Brian O'Duill

ENVICONTROL-ENVITEC N.V.

Nijverheidsweg 10
Merelbeke, 9820, Belgium
Tel.: (32) 92320203
Fax: (32) 92320283
E-Mail: info@envicontrol.com
Web Site: www.envicontrol.com
Year Founded: 1978
Sales Range: $10-24.9 Million
Emp.: 10
Fiscal Year-end: 12/31/12
Business Description:
Measuring Instruments Mfr
S.I.C.: 3829
N.A.I.C.S.: 334519
Personnel:
Eric Callaert *(Mng Dir)*

ENVIPCO HOLDING N.V.

Utrechtseweg 102
3818 EP Amersfoort, Netherlands
Tel.: (31) 332851773
Fax: (31) 332851774
E-Mail: info@envipco.com
Web Site: www.envipco.com
Year Founded: 1998
ENV—(EUR)
Rev.: $69,786,799
Assets: $54,561,616
Liabilities: $38,921,813
Net Worth: $15,639,803
Earnings: ($5,556,990)
Emp.: 226
Fiscal Year-end: 12/31/12
Business Description:
Reverse Vending Machines Mfr
S.I.C.: 3559
N.A.I.C.S.: 333249
Personnel:
Bhajun Santchurn *(CEO)*
Dilraj S. Chawla *(CFO & VP-Fin)*
Haissam Dib *(Pres/CEO-Plastics Recycling-France)*
Robert Lincoln *(Pres-USA)*
Michael Wellman *(Pres-Collection Svcs Div-USA)*
Board of Directors:
Gregory Steven Garvey
Alexandre F. Bouri
Christian Yves Louis Pierre Crepet
David Francis D'Addario
Guy Arthur Jean Marie Louis Edmond Lefebvre
Bhajun Santchurn
Theodorus Jozef Maria Stalenhoef

Holding:

Posada Holding B.V. (1)
Herengracht 458
1017 CA Amsterdam, Netherlands
Tel.: (31) 20 521 6342
Investment Management Services
S.I.C.: 6282
N.A.I.C.S.: 523920

U.S. Subsidiary:

Envipco Pickup & Processing Services Inc. (1)
99 Great Hill Rd
Naugatuck, CT 06770
Tel.: (203) 720-4059
Fax: (203) 720-9302
Logistics Consulting Services
S.I.C.: 4731
N.A.I.C.S.: 541614

Non-U.S. Subsidiaries:

Envipco Automaten GmbH (1)
Gartenkamp 8C
49492 Westerkappeln, Germany
Tel.: (49) 54 04 917 980
Fax: (49) 54 04 917 9820
Material Recycling Services
S.I.C.: 4953
N.A.I.C.S.: 562920

Sorepla Industrie S.A. (1)
100 Chemin de Grety
BP 89
Rebeuville, 88300 Neufchateau, Cedex, France
Tel.: (33) 3 29 06 11 80
Fax: (33) 3 29 06 11 93
Web Site: www.sorepla.com
Plastic Recycling Services
S.I.C.: 4953

Envipco Holding N.V.—(Continued)

N.A.I.C.S.: 562920

ENVIPRO HOLDINGS INC.

3507-19 Yamamiya
Fujinomiya-shi, Shizuoka, 418-0111, Japan
Tel.: (81) 544 58 0521
Web Site: www.envipro.jp
5698—(TKS)
Rev.: $417,665,006
Emp.: 20
Business Description:
Holding Company; Solid Waste Services
S.I.C.: 6719
N.A.I.C.S.: 551112
Personnel:
Tomikazu Sano *(Pres)*

ENVIREAU TECHNOLOGIES INC.

(See Under OCION Water Sciences Group Ltd.)

ENVIRO ENERGY INTERNATIONAL HOLDINGS LIMITED

(d/b/a EnviroEnergy)
Unit 806 Level 8 Core D Cyberport 3
100 Cyberport Road
Hong Kong, China (Hong Kong)
Tel.: (852) 26766631
Fax: (852) 27906616
E-Mail: inquiry@enviro-energy.com.hk
Web Site: www.enviro-energy.com.hk
1102—(HKG)
Rev.: $8,898
Assets: $175,098,110
Liabilities: $38,843,351
Net Worth: $136,254,760
Earnings: ($9,589,109)
Emp.: 29
Fiscal Year-end: 12/31/12
Business Description:
Up-Stream Petroleum & Natural Gas Developer
S.I.C.: 2999
N.A.I.C.S.: 324199
Personnel:
Kenny W. Chan *(Chm & CEO)*
Adrian Chan *(CFO)*
Christie Kam Sheung Mok *(Gen Counsel & Sec)*
Donald O. Downing *(Sr VP)*
Board of Directors:
Kenny W. Chan
Arthur Ross Gorrell
Chi Kit Lo
Hang Chuen Tam
David Tsoi

Royal Bank of Canada Trust Company (Cayman) Limited
4th Floor Royal Bank House 24 Shedden Road
Georgetown, Cayman Islands

Transfer Agents:
Tricor Tengis Limited
26th Floor Tesbury Centre 28 Queen's Road East
Wanchai, China (Hong Kong)
Tel.: (852) 29801333
Fax: (852) 28108185

Royal Bank of Canada Trust Company (Cayman) Limited
4th Floor Royal Bank House 24 Shedden Road
Georgetown, Cayman Islands

ENVIRO-HUB HOLDINGS LTD.

No 3 Tuas Avenue 2
Singapore, 639443, Singapore
Tel.: (65) 68632100
Fax: (65) 68612100
E-Mail: info@enviro-hub.com
Web Site: www.enviro-hub.com
L23—(SES)
Rev.: $27,107,005
Assets: $81,861,675
Liabilities: $31,532,503
Net Worth: $50,329,171
Earnings: ($12,392,837)
Fiscal Year-end: 12/31/12
Business Description:
Environmental Services
S.I.C.: 8711
N.A.I.C.S.: 541330
Personnel:
Raymond Ah Hua Ng *(Chm)*
Wei Hsiung Lee *(Co-Sec)*
Joanna Lan Sim Lim *(Co-Sec)*
Board of Directors:
Raymond Ah Hua Ng
Wilfried Kofmehl
Huen Poh Lai
Samuel Hon Thang Poon
Gim Soo Tan
Kok Hiang Tan
Legal Counsel:
ShookLin & Bok LLP
1 Robinson Road 18 00 AIA Tower
Singapore, Singapore
Transfer Agent:
Boardroom Corporate & Advisory Services Pte. Ltd.
50 Raffles Place 32-01 Singapore Land Tower
Singapore, Singapore

Subsidiaries:

Cimelia Resource Recovery Pte. Ltd. **(1)**
No 3 Tuas Avenue 2
Singapore, 639443, Singapore SG
Tel.: (65) 68980808
Fax: (65) 68980888
E-Mail: info@cimeliaglobal.com
Web Site: www.cimeliaglobal.com
Emp.: 50
Electronic Waste Management & Recycling Services
S.I.C.: 4959
N.A.I.C.S.: 562998
Mohamed Gani Mohamed Ansari *(Exec Dir)*

Enviro-Metals Pte Ltd **(1)**
No 3 Tuas Avenue 2
Singapore, 339443, Singapore
Tel.: (65) 68632100
Fax: (65) 68612100
E-Mail: info@enviro-hub.com
Web Site: www.enviro-hub.com
Emp.: 100
Metal Wastes Recycling Services
S.I.C.: 4953
N.A.I.C.S.: 562920
Mai Tan Lay *(Controller-Fin)*

HLS Electronics Pte Ltd **(1)**
99 12B Drive
Singapore, 637426, Singapore
Tel.: (65) 67925333
Fax: (65) 67927555
E-Mail: info@hls.com.sg
Web Site: www.hls.com.sg
Electronic Waste Recycling Services
S.I.C.: 4953
N.A.I.C.S.: 562920
Jess Tai *(Mgr-Fin)*

Leong Hin Piling (Pte) Ltd **(1)**
No 3 Tuas Avenue 2
Singapore, 639443, Singapore
Tel.: (65) 6863 2100
Fax: (65) 68612100
Web Site: www.leonghin.com
Emp.: 130
Piling Contractors
S.I.C.: 1799
N.A.I.C.S.: 238190

ENVIROMISSION LIMITED

Ground Floor 3 Raglan Street
South Melbourne, VIC, 3205, Australia
Tel.: (61) 396935666
Fax: (61) 396997566
E-Mail: communications@enviromission.com.au
Web Site: www.enviromission.com.au
EVM—(ASX OTC)
Rev.: $392,464
Assets: $3,335,565
Liabilities: $4,207,750
Net Worth: ($872,185)
Earnings: ($1,480,535)
Emp.: 15
Fiscal Year-end: 06/30/13
Business Description:
Solar Tower Technology
S.I.C.: 9631
N.A.I.C.S.: 926130
Personnel:
Roger Chalmers Davey *(Chm & CEO)*
Andrew J. Draffin *(CFO & Sec)*
Board of Directors:
Roger Chalmers Davey
Andrew J. Draffin
David Norman Galbally
Legal Counsel:
DLA Piper Australia
Level 21 140 William Street
Melbourne, Australia

Subsidiary:

Pure Solar Power (IP) Pty. Ltd. **(1)**
3 Raglan Street
Melbourne, VIC, 3205, Australia
Tel.: (61) 396935666
Fax: (61) 396997566
Emp.: 1
Solar Tower Development Services
S.I.C.: 1623
N.A.I.C.S.: 237130
Roger Davey *(Mng Dir)*

ENVIRON GROUP (INVESTMENTS) PLC

5 Furlong Parade Burslem
Stoke-on-Trent, Staffs, United Kingdom
Tel.: (44) 1782 826939
E-Mail: enquiries@environgroup.co.uk
Web Site: www.environgroup.co.uk
Sales Range: $25-49.9 Million
Emp.: 288
Business Description:
Holding Company; Investment Services
S.I.C.: 6719
N.A.I.C.S.: 551112
Personnel:
Mark Sims *(CEO)*
Michael Anthony Clough *(Sec & Dir-Fin)*
Board of Directors:
Chris Arnott
Neil Chapman
Michael Anthony Clough
Paul John Richardson
Mark Sims
Legal Counsel:
Memery Crystal LLP
44 Southampton Buildings Memery
London, WC2A 1AP, United Kingdom

Subsidiaries:

Fenhams Ltd. **(1)**
James Richardson House Gosforth Pkwy
Gosforth Bus Park, Newcastle upon Tyne, Tyne and Wear, NE12 8DG, United Kingdom
Tel.: (44) 1912561066
Fax: (44) 1912560160
E-Mail: enquiries@fenhams.com
Web Site: www.fenhams.com
Emp.: 175
Heating System Installation & Plumbing Services
S.I.C.: 1711
N.A.I.C.S.: 238220
Jonathon Stephens *(Controller-Fin)*

Intumescent Protective Coatings Limited **(1)**
2 Jupiter Ct Orion Bus Park
North Shields, Tyne & Wear, NE29 7SN, United Kingdom
Tel.: (44) 1912728225
Fax: (44) 1912728226
E-Mail: sales@ipcl.co.uk
Web Site: www.ipcl.co.uk
Emp.: 5
Fire Protection Services
S.I.C.: 9224
N.A.I.C.S.: 922160
Claire L Chapman *(Sec)*

Ronald Thompson Limited **(1)**
Albany Rd E Gateshead Indus Estate
Gateshead, Tyne & Wear, NE8 3EH, United Kingdom
Tel.: (44) 191 477 8000
Fax: (44) 191 477 8010
E-Mail: info@ronaldthompson.co.uk
Web Site: www.ronaldthompson.co.uk
Emp.: 20
Electrical & Mechanical Contractors
S.I.C.: 1731
N.A.I.C.S.: 238210
Moira L Leonard *(Sec)*

ENVIRONMENT ECOLOGY HOLDING COMPANY OF CHINA

391 Hua Yu Lane Dong Xin Street
Xi'an, Shaanxi, China
Tel.: (86) 29 88265109
Year Founded: 1989
EVEH—(OTC)
Sales Range: $25-49.9 Million
Emp.: 68
Business Description:
Landscape Architectural Services
S.I.C.: 0781
N.A.I.C.S.: 541320
Personnel:
Sheng Li Liu *(Chm & Pres)*
Shun Cheng Ma *(CFO)*
Board of Directors:
Sheng Li Liu
Hong Mei Ding
Wei Sheng Lu
Shun Cheng Ma
Wei Tian

ENVIRONMENTAL CLEAN TECHNOLOGIES LIMITED

Level 7 530 Little Collins Street
Melbourne, VIC, 3000, Australia
Tel.: (61) 399097684
Fax: (61) 399236566
E-Mail: info@ectltd.com.au
Web Site: www.ectltd.com.au
ESI—(ASX)
Rev.: $1,370,272
Assets: $9,042,204
Liabilities: $4,474,180
Net Worth: $4,568,023
Earnings: ($5,673,385)
Emp.: 48
Fiscal Year-end: 06/30/13
Business Description:
Waste Management Services
S.I.C.: 9511
N.A.I.C.S.: 924110
Personnel:
Glenn Fozard *(Chm)*
Ashley Moore *(Mng Dir)*
Adam Giles *(Sec & Mgr-Ops)*
Board of Directors:
Glenn Fozard
Stephen Carter
Iain McEwin
Ashley Moore
Lloyd Thomson
Legal Counsel:
Norton Rose Fulbright
RACV Tower 485 Bourke Street
Melbourne, VIC, 3000, Australia

THE ENVIRONMENTAL GROUP LIMITED
Unit 1A 9 Packard Avenue
Castle Hill, NSW, 2154, Australia
Tel.: (61) 288583499
Fax: (61) 298993463
E-Mail: mail@environmental.com.au
Web Site: www.environmental.co m.au
EGL—(ASX)
Rev.: $14,912,929
Assets: $11,435,778
Liabilities: $4,914,869
Net Worth: $6,520,909
Earnings: ($829,144)
Emp.: 2
Fiscal Year-end: 06/30/13
Business Description:
Designing & Building Gas Cleaning Systems
S.I.C.: 3443
N.A.I.C.S.: 332420
Personnel:
Ellis Richardson *(Chm)*
Allan Fink *(Sec)*
Board of Directors:
Ellis Richardson
Tim Hargreaves
Louis A. Niederer
Giles Woodgate
Subsidiaries:

EGL Management Services Pty Limited (1)
Unit 1A 9 Packard Ave
Castle Hill, New South Wales, 2154, Australia
Tel.: (61) 288583499
Fax: (61) 298993463
E-Mail: mail@environmental.com.au
Web Site: www.environmental.com.au
Emp.: 15
Sewage Treatment Services
S.I.C.: 4952
N.A.I.C.S.: 221320
Frank Placko *(Mgr)*

Mine Assist Pty Limited (1)
20 Enterprise Crescent
PO Box 3107
Singleton, New South Wales, Australia
Tel.: (61) 265723220
Fax: (61) 265723095
E-Mail: info@mineassist.com.au
Web Site: www.mineassist.com.au
Emp.: 100
Construction Management Services
S.I.C.: 1629
N.A.I.C.S.: 237990
Greg Hunt *(Mgr)*

Total Air Pollution Control Pty Limited (1)
4 Prince of Wales Ave
Unanderra, New South Wales, 2526, Australia
Tel.: (61) 242725233
Fax: (61) 242725633
E-Mail: sales@tapc.com.au
Web Site: www.tapc.com.au
Emp.: 10
Environment Control Management Services
S.I.C.: 8999
N.A.I.C.S.: 541620
Gary Hardie *(Mgr)*

ENVIRONMENTAL RECYCLING TECHNOLOGIES PLC
Keble House Church End South Leigh
Witney, Oxon, OX29 6UR, United Kingdom
Tel.: (44) 8450711394
Fax: (44) 1993776480
E-Mail: info@ertplc.com
Web Site: www.ertplc.com
ENRT—(AIM)
Rev.: $63,172
Assets: $6,290,312
Liabilities: $4,687,333
Net Worth: $1,602,979
Earnings: ($5,898,648)
Emp.: 5
Fiscal Year-end: 12/31/12
Business Description:
Plastic Waste Recycling Technology Developer
S.I.C.: 4959
N.A.I.C.S.: 562998
Personnel:
Kenneth W. Brooks *(Chm)*
Roger Baynham *(Mng Dir)*
Lee Anthony Clayton *(COO)*
R. E. Sims *(Sec)*
Board of Directors:
Kenneth W. Brooks
Jeremy Allen
Roger Baynham
Lee Anthony Clayton
Divyash Patel
David Shepley-Cuthbert
Legal Counsel:
Rickerbys LLP
Ellenborough House Wellington Street
Cheltenham, United Kingdom

ENVIRONMENTAL RESOURCES INVESTMENT PLC
450 Taj Samudra Hotel 25 Galle Face Centre Rd
3 Colombo, Sri Lanka
Tel.: (94) 115379100
Fax: (94) 115745193
E-Mail: info@erlanka.com
Web Site: www.erlanka.com
GREG—(COL)
Sales Range: Less than $1 Million
Business Description:
Investment Management Services
S.I.C.: 6282
N.A.I.C.S.: 523920
Personnel:
Lalith Heengama *(Chm)*
Kosala Heengama *(Deputy Chm)*
Board of Directors:
Lalith Heengama
H. B. Dissanayake
Kosala Heengama
Gamini Sarath Munasinghe
Gregory Scott Newsome

ENVIRONMENTAL WASTE INTERNATIONAL INC.
360 Frankcom Street
Ajax, ON, L1S 1R5, Canada
Tel.: (905) 686-8689
Fax: (905) 428-8730
Toll Free: (800) 399-2366
Web Site: www.ewi.ca
Year Founded: 1992
EWS—(TSXV)
Rev.: $129,379
Assets: $4,482,434
Liabilities: $4,073,374
Net Worth: $409,060
Earnings: ($2,839,826)
Fiscal Year-end: 12/31/12
Business Description:
Waste Treatment Services
S.I.C.: 4959
N.A.I.C.S.: 562998
Personnel:
Emanuel Gerard *(Chm)*
Daniel Kaute *(Pres & CEO)*
Michael Abrams *(CFO)*
Steve Kantor *(CTO)*
Board of Directors:
Emanuel Gerard
William E. Bateman
Sam Geist
Daniel Kaute
Valdis Martinsons
Thomas Russell
Stephen P. Simms
Transfer Agent:
Equity Transfer & Trust Company
200 University Avenue Ste 400
Toronto, ON, M5H 4H1, Canada
Tel.: (416) 361-0152
Fax: (416) 361-0470
Subsidiary:

Ellsin Environmental Ltd. (1)
405 Fairall St
Ajax, ON, L1S 1R8, Canada
Tel.: (905) 686-8689
Fax: (905) 428-8730
Toll Free: (800) 399-2366
Web Site: www.ellsin.com
Emp.: 8
Tire Recycling Services
S.I.C.: 4953
N.A.I.C.S.: 562920
Steven Simms *(Pres)*

Plant:

Ellsin Environmental Ltd. - Ellsin Plant 1 (2)
Sault Ste Marie Facility 155 Yates Avenue
Sault Sainte Marie, ON, P6C 1G1, Canada
Tel.: (705) 575-4662
Fax: (705) 575-6689
E-Mail: clint.Wardlaw@ellsin.com
Web Site: www.ellsin.com
Emp.: 1
Tire Recycling Services
S.I.C.: 4953
N.A.I.C.S.: 562920
John Clinton Wardlaw *(Gen Mgr)*

ENVIRONNEMENT S.A.
111 boulevard Robespierre
78300 Poissy, France
Tel.: (33) 1 39 22 38 00
Fax: (33) 1 39 65 38 08
E-Mail: info@environnement-sa.com
Web Site: www.environnement-sa. com
Year Founded: 1978
ALTEV—(EUR)
Emp.: 200
Business Description:
Environment Monitoring Instrument Mfr & Whslr
S.I.C.: 3823
N.A.I.C.S.: 334513
Personnel:
Francois Gourdon *(Founder, Chm & Pres)*
Christophe Chevillion *(CEO)*
Stephane Kempenar *(CFO)*

ENVITEC BIOGAS AG
Industriering 10a
49393 Lohne, Germany
Tel.: (49) 444280168100
Fax: (49) 4442801698100
E-Mail: info@envitec-biogas.de
Web Site: www.envitec-biogas.com
ETG—(DEU)
Rev.: $268,093,758
Assets: $474,920,760
Liabilities: $226,581,697
Net Worth: $248,339,063
Earnings: $1,590,422
Emp.: 462
Fiscal Year-end: 12/31/12
Business Description:
Tank Construction
S.I.C.: 1799
N.A.I.C.S.: 238990
Personnel:
Bernard Ellmann *(Chm-Supervisory Bd)*
Olaf von Lehmden *(Chm-Mgmt Bd-Legal Affairs, HR Strategy & CEO)*
Hans-Joachim Jung *(Deputy Chm-Supervisory Bd)*
Joerg Fischer *(CFO & Member-Mgmt Bd-Controlling, Fin, IT, IR, Mktg & PR)*
Roel Slotman *(Chief Compliance Officer & Member-Mgmt Bd-Intl Sls & Domestic Sls)*
Jurgen Tenbrink *(CTO & Member-Mgmt Bd-Tech, R&D, Pur Mgmt & Quality Mgmt)*
Supervisory Board of Directors:
Bernard Ellmann
Michael Boging
Hans-Joachim Jung
Subsidiaries:

A3 Water Solutions GmbH (1)
Magdeburger Strasse 16a
45881 Gelsenkirchen, Nordrhein-Westfalen, Germany
Tel.: (49) 20998099809
Fax: (49) 20998099801
E-Mail: info@a3-gmbh.com
Web Site: www.a3-gmbh.com
Emp.: 25
Water Treatment Equipment Mfr & Wastewater Treatment Services
S.I.C.: 1629
N.A.I.C.S.: 237110
Ulrich Bruess *(Mng Dir)*

Subsidiary:

MaxFlow Membran Filtration GmbH (2)
Magdeburger Str 16a
45881 Gelsenkirchen, Nordrhein-Westfalen, Germany
Tel.: (49) 20998099860
Fax: (49) 20998099865
E-Mail: info@maxflow-gmbh.com
Web Site: www.maxflow-gmbh.com
Emp.: 10
Filtration Membrane Modules Distr
S.I.C.: 5113
N.A.I.C.S.: 424130
Ulrich Bruess *(CEO)*

Biogas Friedland GmbH & Co. KG (1)
Industriering 10a
49393 Lohne, Nordrhein-Westfalen, Germany
Tel.: (49) 444280650
Biogas Mfr & Distr
S.I.C.: 4924
N.A.I.C.S.: 221210

Biogas Herzberg GmbH & Co. KG (1)
Industriering 10a
49393 Lohne, Nordrhein-Westfalen, Germany
Tel.: (49) 444280650
Fax: (49) 44428065110
E-Mail: info@envitec-biogas.com
Web Site: www.envitec-biogas.com
Emp.: 100
Biogas Mfr
S.I.C.: 2911
N.A.I.C.S.: 324110
Olaf von Lehmden *(Mgr)*

Biogas Nieheim GmbH & Co. KG (1)
Steinheimer Strasse 99
33039 Nieheim, Nordrhein-Westfalen, Germany
Tel.: (49) 527495840
Fax: (49) 5274 95842
Biogas Mfr
S.I.C.: 2911
N.A.I.C.S.: 324110

EnviTec Green Power GmbH & Co. KG (1)
Industriering 10a
49393 Lohne, Nordrhein-Westfalen, Germany
Tel.: (49) 44428065100
Fax: (49) 44428065110
E-Mail: info@envitech-biogas.de
Web Site: www.envitech-biogas.de
Emp.: 420
Biogas Mfr
S.I.C.: 2911
N.A.I.C.S.: 324110
Olaf von Lehmden *(Mgr)*

EnviTec Biogas AG—(Continued)

EnviTec Green Power Verwaltungs GmbH (1)
Industriering 10a
49393 Lohne, Nordrhein-Westfalen, Germany
Tel.: (49) 44428065100
Fax: (49) 44428065110
E-Mail: info@envitec-biogas.de
Web Site: www.envitec-biogas.de
Emp.: 100
Biogas Mfr
S.I.C.: 2911
N.A.I.C.S.: 324110
Olaf von Lehmden *(CEO)*

EnviTec Service GmbH (1)
Industriering 10a
49393 Lohne, Nordrhein-Westfalen, Germany
Tel.: (49) 444280650
Fax: (49) 44428065100
E-Mail: info@envitec-biogas.de
Web Site: www.envitec-biogas.de
Industrial Equipments & Machinery Maintenance Services
S.I.C.: 7699
N.A.I.C.S.: 811310

ETFT EnviTec Filtration Technik GmbH (1)
Industriering 10a
49393 Lohne, Nordrhein-Westfalen, Germany
Tel.: (49) 444280650
Fax: (49) 4442806510
Emp.: 2
Biogas Mfr
S.I.C.: 2911
N.A.I.C.S.: 324110

RePro Beber GmbH & Co. KG (1)
Industriering 10 a
49393 Lohne, Nordrhein-Westfalen, Germany
Tel.: (49) 444280650
Fax: (49) 4442 806510
Biogas Mfr
S.I.C.: 2911
N.A.I.C.S.: 324110

Zweite EnviTec Beteiligungs GmbH & Co. KG (1)
Industriering 10a
49393 Lohne, Nordrhein-Westfalen, Germany
Tel.: (49) 44428065100
Fax: (49) 44428065110
Web Site: www.enviTec-biogas.de
Emp.: 400
Biogas Mfr
S.I.C.: 1311
N.A.I.C.S.: 211111
Olaf Lehmden *(CEO)*

Non-U.S. Subsidiaries:

EnviTec Biogas Baltic SIA (1)
Atmodas iela 19
Jelgava, 3001, Latvia
Tel.: (371) 27507497
Fax: (371) 52 33 98 47
E-Mail: r.riskus@envitec-biogas.com
Biogas Mfr
S.I.C.: 2813
N.A.I.C.S.: 325120

EnviTec Biogas Baltics SIA (1)
Mokslininku Str 9A-16
Vilnius, Lithuania
Tel.: (370) 64055888
Fax: (370) 52339847
E-Mail: r.riskus@envitec-biogas.com
Emp.: 10
Biogas Mfr
S.I.C.: 2911
N.A.I.C.S.: 324110

EnviTec Biogas Central Europe s.r.o. (1)
Prumyslova 2051
594 01 Velke Mezirici, Czech Republic
Tel.: (420) 566520800
Fax: (420) 566688499
E-Mail: info@envitec-biogas.cz
Web Site: www.envitec-biogas.cz
Emp.: 25
Biogas Mfr
S.I.C.: 2911
N.A.I.C.S.: 324110
Hendrik Van der Tol *(Mng Dir)*

EnviTec Biogas France S.A.R.L. (1)
Rue Croix Denis
22590 Tregueux, Cotes-d Armor, France
Tel.: (33) 962062840
Fax: (33) 0256766170
E-Mail: info@envitec-biogas.fr
Web Site: www.envitec-biogas.fr
Emp.: 3
Biogas Mfr
S.I.C.: 2911
N.A.I.C.S.: 324110

EnviTec Biogas Nederland B.V. (1)
Bornerbroekseweg 1d
7468 RM Enter, Overijssel, Netherlands
Tel.: (31) 54 73 80 523
Fax: (31) 54 73 81 161
E-Mail: info@envitec-biogas.nl
Emp.: 300
Biogas Mfr
S.I.C.: 2911
N.A.I.C.S.: 324110
Roel G Slotman *(CEO)*

EnviTec Biogas Romania S.R.L (1)
Str Corneliu Coposu 9
310003 Arad, Romania
Tel.: (40) 357445946
Fax: (40) 257289394
E-Mail: info@envitec-biogas.ro
Web Site: www.envitec-biogas.ro
Emp.: 5
Biogas Mfr
S.I.C.: 2911
N.A.I.C.S.: 324110

EnviTec Biogas South East Europe Ltd. (1)
62 Cegledi Str
6000 Kecskemet, Bacs-Kiskun, Hungary
Tel.: (36) 76505590
Fax: (36) 70505591
E-Mail: info@envitec-biogas.hu
Web Site: www.envitec-biogas.hu
Emp.: 10
Biogas Mfr
S.I.C.: 2911
N.A.I.C.S.: 324110
Sandor Kiss *(Mng Dir)*

EnviTec Biogas UK Ltd. (1)
Colton Rd
Rugeley, Staffordshire, WS15 3HF, United Kingdom
Tel.: (44) 1889584459
Fax: (44) 1889578088
E-Mail: info@envitec-biogas.com
Web Site: www.envitec-biogas.de
Emp.: 4
Biogas Plant Construction Management Services
S.I.C.: 1623
N.A.I.C.S.: 237120
John Day *(Mgr-Sls)*

Kiinteisto Oy Piispanpiha 5 (1)
Korkeavuorenkatu 45
00130 Helsinki, Finland
Tel.: (358) 400 472272
Fax: (358) 20 4313333
Biogas Plant Construction Services
S.I.C.: 1623
N.A.I.C.S.: 237120

ENWAVE CORPORATION

Suite 2000 1066 West Hastings Street
Vancouver, BC, V6E 3X2, Canada
Tel.: (604) 806-6110
Fax: (604) 806-6112
Web Site: www.enwave.net
Year Founded: 1996
ENW—(TSXV)
Rev.: $4,899,845
Assets: $15,880,013
Liabilities: $3,201,057
Net Worth: $12,678,955
Earnings: ($7,095,840)
Fiscal Year-end: 09/30/13
Business Description:
Dehydrated Food Mfr
S.I.C.: 2034
N.A.I.C.S.: 311423
Personnel:
Timothy D. Durance *(Founder, Chm & Co-CEO)*
John McNicol *(Pres & Co-CEO)*
Salvador Miranda *(CFO & Sec)*
Beenu Anand *(Exec VP)*
Board of Directors:
Timothy D. Durance
Beenu Anand
Hugh McKinnon
John McNicol
Salvador Miranda
Stewart Ritchie
Gary Sandberg
J. Hugh Wiebe
Transfer Agent:
Computershare Investor Services Inc.
100 University Ave 9th Floor
Toronto, ON, Canada

Non-U.S. Subsidiary:

Hans Binder Maschinenbau GmbH (1)
Isarstrasse 8
Freising, Marzling, 85417, Germany
Tel.: (49) 816196810
Fax: (49) 8161968111
E-Mail: info@hans-binder.de
Web Site: www.binder-trockner.de
Emp.: 3
Belt Dryer Mfr
S.I.C.: 3535
N.A.I.C.S.: 333922
Fred Hoen *(Mng Dir)*

ENZAL CHEMICALS (INDIA) LTD.

159 1st Fl Bldg 6 Mittal Industrial Estate Sir MV Rd
Kalina Santa Cruz E, Mumbai, 400 098, India
Tel.: (91) 2256926478
Fax: (91) 2256926472
E-Mail: enzal@vsnl.com
Web Site: www.enzal.com
Year Founded: 1992
Sales Range: $10-24.9 Million
Emp.: 200
Business Description:
Specialty Drug Intermediates Mfr
S.I.C.: 2834
N.A.I.C.S.: 325412
Personnel:
Arun Gupta *(Chm & Mng Dir)*

ENZYCHEM LIFESCIENCES CORPORATION

Daechi-Dong 890-47 Miso Building 10th Floor
Gangnam-gu, Seoul, 135-280, Korea (South)
Tel.: (82) 2 501 1084
Fax: (82) 2 501 1201
Web Site: www.enzychem.com
Year Founded: 1999
183490—(KRS)
Sales Range: $10-24.9 Million
Business Description:
Pharmaceutical Products Mfr
S.I.C.: 2834
N.A.I.C.S.: 325412
Personnel:
Ki-Young Sohn *(Chm & CEO)*
Hye-Kyung Kim *(Co-Pres)*
Wan-Hee Lee *(Co-Pres)*
Tae-Seok Lee *(CTO)*
Board of Directors:
Ki-Young Sohn
Se-Heon Ah
Hye-Kyung Kim
Jae-Yong Lee
Tae-Seok Lee
Wan-Hee Lee
Joo-Cheol Moon

ENZYMOTEC LTD.

Sagi 2000 Industrial Area
PO Box 6
2310001 Migdal Ha'Emeq, Israel
Tel.: (972) 74 717 7177
Fax: (972) 74 717 7001
E-Mail: info@enzymotec.com
Web Site: www.enzymotec.com
Year Founded: 1998
ENZY—(NASDAQ)
Rev.: $64,975,000
Assets: $136,373,000
Liabilities: $18,470,000
Net Worth: $117,903,000
Earnings: $11,395,000
Emp.: 158
Fiscal Year-end: 12/31/13
Business Description:
Nutritional Ingredients & Medical Foods Mfr
S.I.C.: 2099
N.A.I.C.S.: 311999
Personnel:
Steve Dubin *(Chm)*
Yoav Doppelt *(Vice Chm)*
Ariel Katz *(Pres & CEO)*
Oren Bryan *(CFO & VP)*
Yoni Twito *(COO)*
Boaz Noy *(Sr VP-BioActive Ingredients)*
Board of Directors:
Yoav Doppelt
Jacob Bachar
Nir Belzer
Steve Dubin
Gilead Fortuna
Dov Pekelman
Yossi Peled
Michal Silverberg
Joseph Tenne
Imanuel Wasserman

EO TECHNICS CO., LTD.

91 Dongpyeonro
Anyang, Korea (South) 431-803
Tel.: (82) 31 422 2501
Fax: (82) 31 422 2502
E-Mail: sales@eotechnics.com
Web Site: www.eotechnics.com
Year Founded: 1989
039030—(KRS)
Business Description:
Laser Equipment Mfr
S.I.C.: 3541
N.A.I.C.S.: 333517
Personnel:
Kyu Dong Sung *(CEO)*

EO2 S.A.

26 rue Jacques Dulud
92200 Neuilly-sur-Seine, France
Tel.: (33) 1 55620662
Fax: (33) 1 55620663
E-Mail: gd@eo2.fr
Web Site: www.eo2.fr
ALEO2—(EUR)
Business Description:
Wood Pellets Mfr
S.I.C.: 2499
N.A.I.C.S.: 321999
Personnel:
Guillaume Poizat *(Pres & Gen Dir)*

EOC LIMITED

15 Hoe Chiang Road 28-01 Tower Fifteen
Singapore, 089316, Singapore
Tel.: (65) 63498535
Fax: (65) 6224 9756
E-Mail: investor_relations@emasoffshore-cnp.com
Web Site: www.emasoffshore-cnp.com
EOC—(OSL)

Rev.: $43,071,000
Assets: $549,664,000
Liabilities: $373,879,000
Net Worth: $175,785,000
Earnings: $11,092,000
Fiscal Year-end: 08/31/13
Business Description:
Offshore Construction Services
S.I.C.: 1311
N.A.I.C.S.: 211111
Personnel:
Jonathan Michael Dunstan *(Acting CEO & COO)*
Jason Goh *(CFO)*
Keng Nien Yeo *(Sec)*
Board of Directors:
Kian Soo Lee
Dale Bruce Alberda
Cuthbert I. J. Charles
Lionel Chye Tek Lee
Kai Yuen Wang

EOH HOLDINGS LIMITED

EOH Business Park Gillooly's View
Osborne Lane
Bedfordview, 2007, South Africa
Mailing Address:
PO Box 59
Bruma, Johannesburg, 2026, South Africa
Tel.: (27) 116078100
Fax: (27) 116169929
E-Mail: info@eoh.co.za
Web Site: www.eoh.co.za
EOH—(JSE)
Rev.: $568,103,854
Assets: $386,141,538
Liabilities: $205,106,333
Net Worth: $181,035,206
Earnings: $37,012,800
Emp.: 6,000
Fiscal Year-end: 07/31/13
Business Description:
Business & Technology Solutions Provider
S.I.C.: 7374
N.A.I.C.S.: 518210
Personnel:
Asher Bohbot *(CEO)*
Adri Els *(Sec)*
Board of Directors:
Sandile Zungu
Pumeza Bam
Asher Bohbot
Lucky Khumalo
John King
Danny Mackay
Tshilidzi Marwala
Thoko Mnyango
Dion Dominic Ramoo
Tebogo Skwambane
Robert Michael Maria Sporen
Jane Sinclair Thomson

Subsidiaries:

CA Southern Africa (Pty) Limited (1)
Block F Gilloolys View Ofc Park 1 Osborne Ln
Bedfordview, Gauteng, 2007, South Africa
Tel.: (27) 114178699
Fax: (27) 114178694
E-Mail: info@caafrica.co.za
Web Site: www.caafrica.co.za
Emp.: 60
Business Management Software Solutions
S.I.C.: 7371
N.A.I.C.S.: 541511
Gary Lawrence *(Mng Dir)*

E-Secure (Pty) Limited (1)
Block C Cent Park 400 16th Rd
Randjespark, Midrand, Gauteng, 1685, South Africa
Tel.: (27) 115456200
Fax: (27) 115456210
E-Mail: contact@edst.co.za
Web Site: www.esecuredist.co.za
Emp.: 9
Secured Software Applications Development Services
S.I.C.: 7371
N.A.I.C.S.: 541511
John Hindley *(Mgr)*

Enterprise Softworks (Pty) Limited (1)
Block F Gillooly
Johannesburg, Gauteng, 2007, South Africa
Tel.: (27) 116078299
Fax: (27) 116078428
E-Mail: info@esoftworx.co.za
Web Site: www.esoftworx.co.za
Emp.: 81
Business & Information Technology Solutions
S.I.C.: 7373
N.A.I.C.S.: 541512
Crystal Smith *(Mgr-HR)*

Enterweb (Pty) Limited (1)
Gillooly View Ofc Pk 1 Osborne Ln
Bedfordview, South Africa
Tel.: (27) 116078400
Fax: (27) 116168108
E-Mail: andries.louw@eoh.co.za
Business & Information Technology Solutions
S.I.C.: 7373
N.A.I.C.S.: 541512
Asher Bobhot *(CEO)*

EOH Consulting Services (Eastern Cape) (Pty) Limited (1)
36 Pickerling St
Port Elizabeth, Eastern Cape, 6045, South Africa
Tel.: (27) 413930700
Fax: (27) 413654050
Web Site: www.eoh.com
Emp.: 51
Business Software Consulting Services
S.I.C.: 7373
N.A.I.C.S.: 541512

EOH Consulting Services (Western Cape) (Pty) Limited (1)
Block C The Estuaries Oxbow Ln Century Ave
Century City, Cape Town, Western Cape, 7441, South Africa
Tel.: (27) 215056800
Fax: (27) 215257201
Business Software Consulting Services
S.I.C.: 7373
N.A.I.C.S.: 541512

EOH Mthombo (Pty) Limited (1)
1 Osborne Rd Block F Gilloolys View
Bedfordview, Gauteng, 2007, South Africa
Tel.: (27) 116078100
Fax: (27) 116169929
E-Mail: sugeshmi.subroyen@eoh.co.za
Emp.: 3,000
Information Technology Solutions
S.I.C.: 7373
N.A.I.C.S.: 541512
Asher Bohbot *(Gen Mgr)*

Subsidiary:

Bromide Technologies (Pty) Ltd (2)
Block C Cent Park 400 16th Rd
Randjespark, Midrand, Gauteng, 1685, South Africa
Tel.: (27) 115456000
Fax: (27) 118059169
E-Mail: info@bromide.co.za
Web Site: www.bromide.co.za
Emp.: 100
Business Management Software Solutions
S.I.C.: 7371
N.A.I.C.S.: 541511
Delfim Alves *(Mng Dir)*

Intellient (Pty) Limited (1)
Block D Gilloolys View Ofc Park 1 Osborne Ln
Bedfordview, Gauteng, 2007, South Africa
Tel.: (27) 116078200
Fax: (27) 116078219
E-Mail: info@intellient.co.za
Web Site: www.intellient.co.za
Business Management Software Solutionsde Villiers
S.I.C.: 7371
N.A.I.C.S.: 541511
Andrew Krause *(Mng Dir-EOH Oracle Svcs)*

Mthombo IT Services (Pty) Limited (1)
Block E Gilloolys View Ofc Park 1 Osborne Ln
Bedfordview, Gauteng, 2007, South Africa
Tel.: (27) 114796300
Fax: (27) 114796400
E-Mail: info@mit.co.za
Web Site: www.mit.co.za
Emp.: 500
Business Management Services
S.I.C.: 8741
N.A.I.C.S.: 561110
Nkosinathi Khumalo *(Chm)*
Lucky Khumalo *(CEO)*
Eben Klynsmith *(CFO)*

Non-U.S. Subsidiary:

EOH Consulting (Pty) Limited (1)
Plot 67977 Fairgrounds Park
Private Bag BR 97 CP40
Gaborone, Botswana
Tel.: (267) 3191039
Fax: (267) 3191040
E-Mail: info@eoh.co.bw
Web Site: www.eoh.co.bw
Emp.: 18
Business Management Consulting Services
S.I.C.: 8742
N.A.I.C.S.: 541611
Kenneth Molosi *(CEO)*
Asad Petkar *(COO)*

EON ELECTRIC LTD.

B-88 Sector 83
Noida, 201305, India
Tel.: (91) 120 3096700
Fax: (91) 120 3096800
E-Mail: corporate@eonelectric.com
Web Site: www.eonelectric.com
532658—(BOM NSE)
Rev.: $30,519,650
Assets: $40,267,646
Liabilities: $10,208,279
Net Worth: $30,059,367
Earnings: ($3,669,997)
Fiscal Year-end: 03/31/13
Business Description:
Lighting Equipment Mfr
S.I.C.: 3646
N.A.I.C.S.: 335122
Personnel:
V. P. Mahendru *(Chm & Mng Dir)*
Kumar Indramani *(Compliance Officer, Sec & Sr Mgr-Legal)*
Board of Directors:
V. P. Mahendru
R. C. Bansal
A. K. Ghosh
Vinay Mahendru
Vivek Mahendru
Ranjan Sarkar
Transfer Agent:
Alankit Assignments Limited
2E/21 Alankit House Jhandewalan Extension
New Delhi, India

Plants:

Indo Asian Fusegear Ltd - Haridwar Lighting Plant (1)
B-88 Sector-83
Noida, 201305, India
Tel.: (91) 1203042222
Fax: (91) 1203096800
E-Mail: corporate@indoasian.com
Web Site: www.indoasian.com
Emp.: 173
Electric Power Generation Services
S.I.C.: 4911
N.A.I.C.S.: 221118
Olivier Lefloch *(Pres)*

Indo Asian Fusegear Ltd - Indo Simon Plant Haridwar (1)
Plot No 26 Sector 4
Sidcul, Haridwar, Uttarakhand, 249 403, India
Tel.: (91) 1334329801
Electric Power Generation Services
S.I.C.: 4931
N.A.I.C.S.: 221118

Indo Asian Fusegear Ltd - Jalandhar Switchgear Plant (1)
By Ln Nakodar Rd
Jalandhar, Punjab, 144 003, India
Tel.: (91) 1814639900
Fax: (91) 1814639925
E-Mail: jalandhar@indoasian.com
Electric Power Generation Services
S.I.C.: 4931
N.A.I.C.S.: 221118

Indo Asian Fusegear Ltd - Noida Lighting Plant (1)
B-88 Sector 83
Noida, Uttar Pradesh, 201 301, India
Tel.: (91) 1203042222
Fax: (91) 1203096800
E-Mail: sales@indoasian.com
Emp.: 210
Electric Power Generation Services
S.I.C.: 4939
N.A.I.C.S.: 221118
Samir Saxena *(VP-Mktg)*

E.ON SE

E ON Platz 1
40479 Dusseldorf, Germany
Tel.: (49) 21145790
Fax: (49) 2114579501
E-Mail: info@eon.com
Web Site: www.eon.com
Year Founded: 1929
EOAN—(BER DEU EUR ITA OTC)
Sls.: $180,382,741,490
Assets: $189,037,268,420
Liabilities: $136,780,295,190
Net Worth: $52,256,973,230
Earnings: $3,555,234,970
Emp.: 72,083
Fiscal Year-end: 12/31/12
Business Description:
Energy Holding Company
Import Export
S.I.C.: 6719
N.A.I.C.S.: 551112
Personnel:
Werner Wenning *(Chm-Supervisory Bd)*
Johannes Teyssen *(Chm-Mgmt Bd & CEO)*
Ulrich Lehner *(Deputy Chm-Supervisory Bd)*
Erhard Ott *(Deputy Chm-Supervisory Bd)*
Stephen Asplin *(Chief Comml Officer-Power & Gas Trading-E.ON Global Commodities)*
David Finch *(Chief Comml Officer-Global Trading-Coal, Oil, LNG & Freight-EGC)*
David Port *(Chief Risk Officer-E.ON Global Commodities)*
Damian Bunyan *(Chief Process Officer-E.ON Global Commodities)*
Maxim Shirokov *(CEO-Russia)*
Jorgen Kildahl *(Member-Mgmt Bd)*
Klaus-Dieter Maubach *(Member-Mgmt Bd)*
Bernhard Reutersberg *(Member-Mgmt Bd)*
Marcus Schenck *(Member-Mgmt Bd)*
Regine Stachelhaus *(Member-Mgmt Bd)*
Mike Winkel *(Member-Mgmt Bd)*
Supervisory Board of Directors:
Werner Wenning
Karen M. A. de Segundo
Gabriele Gratz
Baroness Denise Kingsmill
Ulrich Lehner
Eugen-Gheorghe Luha
Rene Obermann
Erhard Ott
Klaus Dieter Raschke
Eberhard Schomburg
Theo Siegert
Willem Vis

E.ON SE—(Continued)

Subsidiaries:

Arena One GmbH (1)
Leopoldstr 175
80804 Munich, Germany
Tel.: (49) 89 350 948 0
Fax: (49) 9350948199
E-Mail: info@arena-one.com
Web Site: www.arena-one.com
Rev.: $87,211,740
Emp.: 454
Event Organizing & Catering Management Services
S.I.C.: 7999
N.A.I.C.S.: 711310
Frank Wassermann *(Co-Mng Dir & Head-Catering & Arena)*
Stephan Thewalt *(Co-Mng Dir)*

AWP GmbH (1)
Tegelweg 25
33102 Paderborn, Germany
Tel.: (49) 52 51 5 03 62 57
Fax: (49) 52 51 5 03 62 58
E-Mail: info@awp-ewh.de
Web Site: www.awp-gmbh.net
Emp.: 13
Sewage & Drinking Water Treatment Services
S.I.C.: 4952
N.A.I.C.S.: 221320
Markus Schmitt *(Mgr)*

Bioenergie Merzig GmbH (1)
Waldwieser Str B
66663 Merzig, Germany
Tel.: (49) 6869 911760
Bio Gas Production Services
S.I.C.: 1389
N.A.I.C.S.: 213112

Bioerdgas Hallertau GmbH (1)
Kellerstrasse 1
Wolnzach, 85283, Germany
Tel.: (49) 87 54 96 09 80
Fax: (49) 87 54 96 09 60
E-Mail: info@bioerdgas-hallertau.de
Web Site: www.bioerdgas-hallertau.de
Natural Gas Extraction & Production Services
S.I.C.: 1321
N.A.I.C.S.: 211112

Biogas Ducherow GmbH (1)
Karl-Marx-Srasse 23
17398 Ducherow, Germany
Tel.: (49) 39726 25860
Natural Gas Distr
S.I.C.: 4924
N.A.I.C.S.: 221210

Biomasseheizkraftwerk Emden GmbH (1)
Zum Kraftwerk
Emden, Germany
Tel.: (49) 4921 8921
Fax: (49) 4921 892325
Steam Heat Distribution Services
S.I.C.: 4961
N.A.I.C.S.: 221330

CEC Energieconsulting GmbH (1)
Bahnhofstrasse 40
32278 Kirchlengern, Germany
Tel.: (49) 52 23 8 21 49 70
Fax: (49) 52 23 8 21 49 79
E-Mail: info@cec-energie.de
Web Site: www.cec-energie.de
Energy Consulting Services
S.I.C.: 8999
N.A.I.C.S.: 541690

Donau-Wasserkraft Aktiengesellschaft (1)
Blutenburgstr 20
Munich, Bavaria, 80636, Germany
Tel.: (49) 89992220
Fax: (49) 8999222199
E-Mail: info@rmd.de
Web Site: www.rmd.de
Emp.: 15
Electric Power Generation Services
S.I.C.: 4931
N.A.I.C.S.: 221118
Albrecht Schleich *(Gen Mgr)*

E WIE EINFACH Strom & Gas GmbH (1)
Salierring 47-53
Cologne, 50677, Germany
Tel.: (49) 221 17737 0
Fax: (49) 221 17737 210
E-Mail: service@e-wie-einfach.de
Web Site: www.e-wie-einfach.de
Electric Power & Gas Distribution Services
S.I.C.: 4911
N.A.I.C.S.: 221122

EAV Beteiligungs-GmbH (1)
Reutlinger Str 30
76228 Karlsruhe, Baden-Wurttemberg, Germany
Tel.: (49) 721 2010338
Management Consulting Services
S.I.C.: 8748
N.A.I.C.S.: 541618

EBY Gewerbeobjekt GmbH (1)
Lilienthalstr 7
Regensburg, Bayern, 93049, Germany
Tel.: (49) 941 201 0
Fax: (49) 941 201399
Management Consulting Services
S.I.C.: 8748
N.A.I.C.S.: 541618

EBY Port 3 GmbH (1)
Lilienthalstr 7
93049 Regensburg, Germany
Tel.: (49) 941 38393350
Fax: (49) 941 38393353
Management Consulting Services
S.I.C.: 8748
N.A.I.C.S.: 541618

EBY Port 5 GmbH (1)
Heinkelstrasse 1
93049 Regensburg, Bayern, Germany
Tel.: (49) 941 38393426
Fax: (49) 941 38393423
Management Consulting Services
S.I.C.: 8748
N.A.I.C.S.: 541618

e.dialog GmbH (1)
Am Kanal 2-3
14467 Potsdam, Germany
Tel.: (49) 331 979198 2401
Fax: (49) 331 979198 2402
E-Mail: info@edialog.de
Web Site: www.edialog.de
Emp.: 1,000
Marketing Consulting Services
S.I.C.: 8742
N.A.I.C.S.: 541613

e.discom Telekommunikation GmbH (1)
Hauptsitz Erich-Schlesinger-Strasse 37
18059 Rostock, Germany
Tel.: (49) 381 3824800
Fax: (49) 381 3824809
E-Mail: ihrwunschname@ediscom.de
Web Site: www.ediscom.de
Emp.: 10
Data Transfer & Telecommunication Services
S.I.C.: 4899
N.A.I.C.S.: 517919
Andreas Wuensch *(Mgr-IT)*

e.distherm Warmedienstleistungen GmbH (1)
Am Kanal 2-3
14467 Potsdam, Germany
Tel.: (49) 3 31 2 34 32 30
Fax: (49) 3 31 2 34 31 41
E-Mail: info@eon-edis.com
Electric Power Distr
S.I.C.: 4931
N.A.I.C.S.: 221122

Energienetze Bayern GmbH (1)
Frankenthaler Strasse 2
81539 Munich, Germany
Tel.: (49) 89 68003 352
Fax: (49) 89 68003 419
E-Mail: info@energienetze-bayern.de
Web Site: www.energienetze-bayern.de
Emp.: 35
Natural Gas Distribution Services
S.I.C.: 4924
N.A.I.C.S.: 221210

Energienetze Schaafheim GmbH (1)
Heinkelstrasse 1
93049 Regensburg, Germany
Tel.: (49) 9 41 38 39 36 42
Fax: (49) 9 41 38 39 31 13
E-Mail: info@energienetze-schaafheim.com
Web Site: www.energienetze-schaafheim.com
Natural Gas Distribution Services
S.I.C.: 4924
N.A.I.C.S.: 221210

Energos Deutschland GmbH (1)
Schoninger Str 2-3
Helmstedt, Niedersachsen, 38350, Germany
Tel.: (49) 5351182383
Fax: (49) 5351182522
Electric Power Distributing Services
S.I.C.: 4931
N.A.I.C.S.: 221122

E.ON Academy GmbH (1)
Ehrenhof 3
40479 Dusseldorf, Germany
Tel.: (49) 21145797317
Fax: (49) 21145797321
E-Mail: eon-academy@eon.com
Web Site: www.academy.eon.com
Emp.: 30
Educational & Corporate Training Services
S.I.C.: 9411
N.A.I.C.S.: 923110
Anja Jerussulam *(Mgr-Program)*

E.ON Anlagenservice GmbH (1)
Zentrale Bergmannsglueckstrasse 41-43
45896 Gelsenkirchen, Germany
Tel.: (49) 2096015050
Fax: (49) 2096015353
E-Mail: anlagenservice@eon-as.de
Web Site: www.eon-anlagenservice.com
Process Plant Technology, Electrical Engineering, Steam Generation, Mechanical Engineering, Instrumentation & Control
S.I.C.: 7699
N.A.I.C.S.: 811310
Gerhard Dewender *(Gen Mgr-Market & Admin)*

E.ON Avacon Vertrieb GmbH (1)
Schillerstrasse 3
Helmstedt, Niedersachsen, 38350, Germany
Tel.: (49) 53511230
Fax: (49) 535112340019
E-Mail: netzkundenservice@eon-avacon.com
Electricity & Natural Gas Distribution Services
S.I.C.: 4931
N.A.I.C.S.: 221122

E.ON Avacon Warme GmbH (1)
Jacobistreet 3
31157 Sarstedt, Germany
Tel.: (49) 5 066 830
Fax: (49) 5 066 834 0442
E-Mail: waermeservice@eon-avacon-waerme.com
Web Site: www.eon.de/de/eonde/gk/produkteUndPreise/Waerme/index.htm
Heating Equipment Distr
S.I.C.: 5075
N.A.I.C.S.: 423730

E.ON Bayern Warme 1. Beteiligungs-GmbH (1)
Lilienthalstr 7
93049 Regensburg, Bayern, Germany
Tel.: (49) 941 3839 0
Fax: (49) 941 3839 3399
Management Consulting Services
S.I.C.: 8748
N.A.I.C.S.: 541618

E.ON Bayern Warme GmbH (1)
Lilienthalstrasse 7
93049 Regensburg, Germany
Tel.: (49) 9 41 2 01 00
Fax: (49) 9 41 2 01 20 00
E-Mail: info@eon-bayern-waerme.com
Web Site: www.eon-bayern.com
Electricity & Natural Gas Distribution Services
S.I.C.: 4939
N.A.I.C.S.: 221122

E.ON Best Service GmbH (1)
Steindamm 100
20149 Hamburg, Germany
Tel.: (49) 402533450
Web Site: www.eon-best-service.com
Emp.: 600
Electric Power Distr
S.I.C.: 4931
N.A.I.C.S.: 221122
Patrick Mombaur *(CEO)*

E.ON Beteiligungsverwaltungs GmbH (1)
E On-Platz 1
Dusseldorf, Nordrhein-Westfalen, 40479, Germany
Tel.: (49) 21145790
Fax: (49) 2114579501
Administrative Management Consulting Services
S.I.C.: 8742
N.A.I.C.S.: 541611

E.ON Bioerdgas GmbH (1)
Ruhrallee 307-309
Essen, 45136, Germany
Tel.: (49) 201 184 7831
Fax: (49) 201 184 7837
Web Site: www.eon-ruhrgas.com
Bio Gas Production & Distr
S.I.C.: 1389
N.A.I.C.S.: 213112
Fritz Wolf *(Mng Dir)*

E.ON Climate & Renewables GmbH (1)
Brusseler Platz 1
45131 Essen, Germany
Tel.: (49) 211 4579 0
Fax: (49) 211 4579 501
Electric Power Generation Services
S.I.C.: 4931
N.A.I.C.S.: 221118
Mike Winkel *(CEO)*
Cord Landsmann *(CFO)*

Non-U.S. Subsidiary:

E.ON Renovables, S.L. (2)
Torre Picasso Pl 42 Pza Pablo Ruiz Picasso s/n
Madrid, 28020, Spain
Tel.: (34) 9 1418 4400
E-Mail: informacion@eon.com
Wind Electric Power Generation Services
S.I.C.: 4911
N.A.I.C.S.: 221118
Wulf H. Bernotat *(CEO)*
Nikolaj Harbo *(Mng Dir)*

E.ON Direkt GmbH (1)
Brusseler Platz 1
45131 Essen, Germany
Tel.: (49) 2 01 1 84 74 32
Fax: (49) 2 01 1 84 20 16
E-Mail: kontakt@eon-direkt.de
Web Site: www.eon.com
Emp.: 2
Electric Power Distribution Services
S.I.C.: 4931
N.A.I.C.S.: 221122
Uwe Krause *(Acct Mgr)*

E.ON edis AG (1)
Langewahler Strasse 60
15517 Furstenwalde, Germany
Tel.: (49) 33 61 70 0
Fax: (49) 33 61 70 3105
E-Mail: info@eon-edis.com
Web Site: www.eon-edis.com
Power & Natural Gas Distribution Services
S.I.C.: 4931
N.A.I.C.S.: 221122

Subsidiaries:

E.ON edis Vertrieb GmbH (2)
Langewahler Str 60
Furstenwalde Spree, Brandenburg, 15517, Germany
Tel.: (49) 3361700
Fax: (49) 3361703105
E-Mail: info@eon-edis-vertrieb.com
Web Site: www.eon-edis-vertrieb.com
Electric Power & Natural Gas Distribution Services
S.I.C.: 4939
N.A.I.C.S.: 221122

Netzservice Mecklenburg-Vorpommern (NMV) GmbH (2)
Werkstr 708
Schwerin, 19061, Germany
Tel.: (49) 385202855203
Fax: (49) 385202855241
Natural Gas Distribution Services
S.I.C.: 4924
N.A.I.C.S.: 221210

E.ON edis Contracting GmbH (1)
Langewahler Str 60
Furstenwalde, 15517, Germany
Tel.: (49) 3361702022
Electric Power Distribution Services
S.I.C.: 4931
N.A.I.C.S.: 221122

E.ON Energie 31. Beteiligungsgesellschaft mbH Munchen (1)
Brienner Str 40
Munich, 80333, Germany
Tel.: (49) 89125401
E-Mail: info@eonenergie.com
Web Site: www.eonenergie.com
Financial Management Services
S.I.C.: 6211
N.A.I.C.S.: 523999
Ingo Luge *(Gen Mgr)*

E.ON Energie 39. Beteiligungs-GmbH (1)
Brienner Str 40
Munich, Bayern, 80333, Germany
Tel.: (49) 89125401
Fax: (49) 12543906
E-Mail: info@eon-energy.com
Web Site: www.eon-energy.com
Energy Consulting Services
S.I.C.: 8999
N.A.I.C.S.: 541690
Ingo Luge *(CEO)*

E.ON Energie AG (1)
Brienner Strasse 40
80333 Munich, Germany (100%)
Tel.: (49) 89125401
Telex: 922756
Fax: (49) 8912543906
E-Mail: info@eon-energie.com
Web Site: www.eon-energie.com
Emp.: 700
Production & Distribution of Electric Power; Heating, Gas & Water Supply Services
S.I.C.: 4931
N.A.I.C.S.: 221122
Klaus-Dieter Maubach *(Chm)*
Bernhard Fischer *(Mng Dir & CTO)*
Karl-Michael Fuhr *(Mng Dir)*
Walter Hohlefelder *(Mng Dir)*
Bernd Romeike *(Mng Dir)*

Subsidiaries:

Amrumbank-West GmbH (2)
Denisstr 2
Munich, Germany
Tel.: (49) 89 1254 01
Fax: (49) 89 1254 30 36
Electric Power Generation Services
S.I.C.: 4911
N.A.I.C.S.: 221118

BauMineral GmbH Herten (2)
Hiberniastrasse 12
D 45699 Herten, Germany (100%)
Tel.: (49) 23665090
Fax: (49) 2366509256
E-Mail: info@baumineral.de
Web Site: www.baumineral.de
Emp.: 100
Treatment & Marketing of Power Station By-products
S.I.C.: 1623
N.A.I.C.S.: 237130
Burkhardt Jakob Uss *(Mng Dir)*

Energiewerke Rostock AG (2)
Bleicherstrasse 1
2500 Rostock, Germany (100%)
Tel.: (49) 3813820
Electrical Distribution Services
S.I.C.: 4911
N.A.I.C.S.: 221122

E.ON Avacon AG (2)
Schillerstrasse 3
38350 Helmstedt, Germany (67.2%)
Tel.: (49) 53511230
Fax: (49) 535112340361
E-Mail: pr@eon-avacon.com
Web Site: www.eon-avacon.com
Emp.: 500
Electricity Services
S.I.C.: 4931
N.A.I.C.S.: 221122
Thomas Koenig *(Mng Dir)*

E.ON Bayern AG (2)
Henkel Strasse 1
93049 Regensburg, Germany (100%)
Tel.: (49) 8952080
Fax: (49) 94138393399
E-Mail: info@eon-bayern.com
Web Site: www.eon-bayern.com
Emp.: 250
Electric Services
S.I.C.: 7389
N.A.I.C.S.: 561990
Peter Deml *(CEO)*

Branch:

E.ON Bayern AG (3)
Prufeninger Strasse 20
D-93049 Regensburg, Bayern, Germany
Tel.: (49) 94120100
Fax: (49) 9412012000
Web Site: www.eon-bayern.com
Emp.: 500
Electricity Services
S.I.C.: 3825
N.A.I.C.S.: 334515
Maximillian Binde *(Mng Dir)*

E.ON Bayern Vertrieb GmbH (2)
Luitpoldplatz 5
95444 Bayreuth, Germany (90.7%)
Tel.: (49) 9212850
Fax: (49) 92128852565
Web Site: www.eon-netz.com
Energy Services
S.I.C.: 4911
N.A.I.C.S.: 221122

E.ON Czech Holding AG (2)
Denisstr 2
Munich, Bayern, 80335, Germany
Tel.: (49) 8912543156
Fax: (49) 8912543989
Web Site: www.eon.cz
Emp.: 8
Investment Management Services
S.I.C.: 6211
N.A.I.C.S.: 523999
Michael Fehn *(Gen Mgr)*

E.ON Energy Projects GmbH (2)
Denisstrasse 2
80335 Munich, Germany
Tel.: (49) 89125409
Fax: (49) 8912544582
E-Mail: info@eon-energie.com
Web Site: www.eon-energyprojects.com
Emp.: 60
Electricity, Heat Generation, Compressed Air & Water & Renewable Energies Project Developer, Financer & Plant Operator
S.I.C.: 4911
N.A.I.C.S.: 221122
Harry Schmitz *(Mng Dir)*

Subsidiary:

KGW-Kraftwerk Grenzach-Wyhlen GmbH (3)
Arnulfstr 56
Munich, 80335, Germany
Tel.: (49) 89125409
Fax: (49) 8912541599
Electric Power Generation Services
S.I.C.: 4939
N.A.I.C.S.: 221118

E.ON Energy Sales GmbH (2)
Brusseler Platz 1
45131 Essen, Germany
Tel.: (49) 2 01 1 84 27 56
Fax: (49) 2 01 1 84 46 32
E-Mail: info-ees@eon-energie.com
Web Site: www.eon-energy-sales.com
Electric Power & Natural Gas Distribution Services
S.I.C.: 4911
N.A.I.C.S.: 221122

E.ON Facility Management GmbH (2)
Denisstrasse 2
80335 Munich, Germany (100%)
Tel.: (49) 89125408
Fax: (49) 8912542742
E-Mail: info@facility-management.com
Web Site: www.eon-facilitymanagement.com
Emp.: 1,200
Facility Management Services
S.I.C.: 8744
N.A.I.C.S.: 561210
Wolfgang Titz *(Mng Dir)*

E.ON Hanse AG (2)
Schlesweg Heinges Platz 1
Postfach 260
Dreigborn, 25450 Quickborn, Germany (73.8%)
Tel.: (49) 4331180
Fax: (49) 41066293940
E-Mail: info@eon-hanse.com
Web Site: www.eonhanse.com
Sales Range: $100-124.9 Million
Emp.: 1,000
Distr. of Electric Power & Gas
S.I.C.: 4931
N.A.I.C.S.: 221122
Uber Kukes *(Gen Mgr)*

E.ON IS Furstenwalde (2)
Langewahler Strasse 60
D-15517 Furstenwalde, Germany (70%)
Tel.: (49) 180 12 13 14 0
E-Mail: info@eon-edis.com
Web Site: www.eon-edis.com
Gas Services
S.I.C.: 1389
N.A.I.C.S.: 213112

E.ON IS GmbH (2)
Humboldtstrasse 33
30169 Hannover, Germany (60%)
Tel.: (49) 51112178505
Fax: (49) 511000000
E-Mail: eon-it@eon-is.com
Web Site: www.eon-is.com
Sales Range: $400-449.9 Million
Emp.: 1,521
IT Services
S.I.C.: 7379
N.A.I.C.S.: 541519

Non-U.S. Subsidiary:

E.ON IS Hungary Kft. (3)
Corvin ter 10
H-1011 Budapest, Hungary
Tel.: (36) 014878200
Fax: (36) 014878201
E-Mail: info@eon-is.hu
Web Site: www.eon-is.hu
Emp.: 350
IT Services; Owned 51% by E.ON IS GmbH & 49% by E.ON Hungaria Zrt.
S.I.C.: 7379
N.A.I.C.S.: 541519
Josef Guggenhuber *(Mng Dir)*

E.ON Kernkraft GmbH (2)
Tresckowstrasse 5
PO Box 4849
30457 Hannover, Germany (100%)
Tel.: (49) 05114390
Fax: (49) 05114392375
E-Mail: info@eon-energie.com
Web Site: www.eon-kernkraft.com
Nuclear Fuels
S.I.C.: 2819
N.A.I.C.S.: 325180
Erich Steiner *(Chm)*

E.ON Kraftwerke GmbH (2)
Bergmannsgluckstrasse 41-43
45896 Gelsenkirchen, Germany (100%)
Tel.: (49) 20960102
Fax: (49) 02096018145
Web Site: www.eon-kraftwerke.com
Sales Range: $150-199.9 Million
Emp.: 5,058
Energy Services
S.I.C.: 8999
N.A.I.C.S.: 541690
Dirk Eckei *(Head-Materials & Economics)*

Subsidiaries:

enertech Energie und Technik GmbH (3)
Wasastrasse 50
01445 Radebeul, Germany (50%)
Tel.: (49) 3518398610
Fax: (49) 3518398640
Web Site: www.enertech-eut.de/kontakt/index.php?id=12
Planning of Fossil-fired Thermal Power Stations, Hydroelectric Power Stations, Disposal Plants & Natural Gas Pipelines & Compressor Plants
S.I.C.: 5084
N.A.I.C.S.: 423830

E.ON Engineering GmbH (3)
Bergmannsgluckstrasse 41 43
45896 Gelsenkirchen, Germany (100%)
Tel.: (49) 020960105
Fax: (49) 02096015011
E-Mail: info.engineering@eon-energie.com
Web Site: www.eon-engineering.com
Emp.: 500
Portfolio Management & Operation of Power Station Units Scholven G & H at Gelsenkirchen-Buer
S.I.C.: 6799
N.A.I.C.S.: 523920
Wolfgang Knyhala *(Chm)*

E.ON Fernwaerme GmbH (3)
Bergmannsgluckstrasse 41-43
45896 Gelsenkirchen, Germany (100%)
Tel.: (49) 2096015071
Fax: (49) 2096015761
E-Mail: info@eon-fernwaerme.com
Web Site: www.eon-fernwaerme.com
Emp.: 130
Operation of a District Heating Line between the VKR Power Station Shamrock & the VEW Power Station Bochum
S.I.C.: 1623
N.A.I.C.S.: 237130
Fritz Henjes *(Mng Dir)*

E.ON Kraftwerke GmbH (3)
Tresckowstrasse 5
30457 Hannover, Germany (100%)
Tel.: (49) 5114394774
Fax: (49) 5114394711
E-Mail: info@eon-kraftwerke.com
Web Site: www.eon-kraftwerke.com
Conventional Power Plants, District Heating Plants & Thermal Waste-Treatment Services
S.I.C.: 4931
N.A.I.C.S.: 221112

Subsidiaries:

Kraftwerk Mehrum GmbH (4)
Triftstrasse 25
31249 Hohenhameln, Germany (50.1%)
Tel.: (49) 5128740
Fax: (49) 512874335
Web Site: www.kraftwerk-mehrum.de
Sls.: $73,000,000
Emp.: 140
Production of Electric Power
S.I.C.: 3699
N.A.I.C.S.: 335999
Bernhard Michels *(Gen Mgr)*

Fernwarmeversorgung Herne GmbH (3)
Grenzweg 18
4690 Herne, 1, Germany (50%)
Tel.: (49) 2349600
Fax: (49) 2349601009
Web Site: www.stadtwerke-bochum.de
Emp.: 200
Construction & Operation of a District Heating Network in the Urban Area of Herne 1
S.I.C.: 1542
N.A.I.C.S.: 236220

Kraftwerk Schkopau GmbH (3)
Glueckaufstr 56
45896 Gelsenkirchen, Germany (100%)
Tel.: (49) 2096016272
Fax: (49) 2096016538
E-Mail: gerd.franzen@eon-energie.com
Construction, Acquisition & Operation of Power Stations; Distribution of Electricity, Steam & Heat
S.I.C.: 1629
N.A.I.C.S.: 237110

OEWA Wasser und Abwasser GmbH (3)
Walter Kohn Strasse 1A
D-04356 Leipzig, Germany (50%)
Tel.: (49) 3415285430
Fax: (49) 3414962443
Web Site: www.wa-gruppe.de
Financing, Planning, Construction & Operation of Water Supply & Waste Water Disposal Plants
S.I.C.: 6159
N.A.I.C.S.: 522298

VEBA Fernheizung Wanne-Eickel GmbH (3)
Bergmannsgluckstrasse 41-43
Alexander Hunbolet 1, 45896
Gelsenkirchen, Germany (100%)

E.ON SE—(Continued)

Tel.: (49) 2096011
Fax: (49) 2096015150
E-Mail: info@vebaengineering.com
Web Site: www.vebaengineering.com
Emp.: 800
District Heating
S.I.C.: 5075
N.A.I.C.S.: 423730

E.ON Metering GmbH (2)
Carl-von-Linde-Strasse 38
85716 Unterschleissheim, Germany
Tel.: (49) 89 12 54 04
Fax: (49) 89 12 54 53 59
E-Mail: info@eon-metering.com
Emp.: 3
Electric Power Distribution Services
S.I.C.: 4911
N.A.I.C.S.: 221122
Robert Pfluegl *(Co-Mng Dir)*
Lars Weber *(Co-Mng Dir)*

E.ON Mitte AG (2)
Monteverdistrasse 2
34131 Kassel, Germany (73%)
Tel.: (49) 5619330
Fax: (49) 9332500
E-Mail: wolf.hatje@eon-mitte.com
Web Site: www.eon-mitte.com
Sls.: $800,000,000
Emp.: 400
Gas Distribution Services
S.I.C.: 4924
N.A.I.C.S.: 221210
Hendry Wilckens *(Mng Dir)*

Subsidiary:

E.ON Mitte Vertrieb GmbH (3)
Monteverdistr 2
Kassel, Hessen, 34131, Germany
Tel.: (49) 56193301
Fax: (49) 5619332509
E-Mail: info@eon-mitte-vertrieb.com
Emp.: 45
Electric Power Distribution Services
S.I.C.: 4939
N.A.I.C.S.: 221122

E.ON Netz GmbH (2)
Regionalleitung Oberfranken
Luitpoldplatz 5, 95444 Bayreuth, Germany (100%)
Web Site: www.eon-netz.com
Energy Services Provider
S.I.C.: 4911
N.A.I.C.S.: 221122

E.ON Portfolio Solution GmbH (2)
Holzstrasse 6
40221 Dusseldorf, Germany
Tel.: (49) 2 117 3275 2530
Fax: (49) 2 117 3275 2529
E-Mail: info@eon-portfolio-solution.com
Web Site: www.eon-portfolio-solution.com
Emp.: 15
Portfolio Management Services
S.I.C.: 6282
N.A.I.C.S.: 523920
Hakan Larsson *(Member-Mgmt Bd)*

E.ON Wasserkraft GmbH (2)
Luitpoldstr 27
84034 Landshut, Germany (100%)
Tel.: (49) 87169402
E-Mail: info.wasserkraft@eon-energie.com
Web Site: www.eon-wasserkraft.com
Emp.: 120
Energy Services
S.I.C.: 4931
N.A.I.C.S.: 221122
Christof Gattermann *(Mng Dir-Comml)*

E.ON Westfalen Weser AG (2)
Tegelweg 25
33102 Paderborn, Germany (62.8%)
Tel.: (49) 52515030
Fax: (49) 52515036278
E-Mail: nicol.korn@eon-westfalenweser.com
Web Site: www.eon-westfalenweser.com
Energy Services
S.I.C.: 4939
N.A.I.C.S.: 221122

Subsidiaries:

E.ON Westfalen Weser Vertrieb GmbH (3)
Rolandsweg 80
Paderborn, Nordrhein-Westfalen, 33102, Germany
Tel.: (49) 52515030
Fax: (49) 52515037308
E-Mail: widerruf@eon-westfalenweser-vertrieb.com
Web Site: www.eon.de/de/eonde/pk/ueberEon/Unternehmen/Vertriebsgesellschaften/EON_Westfalen_Weser_Vertrieb/index.htm
Emp.: 1,000
Electric Power Distribution Services
S.I.C.: 4911
N.A.I.C.S.: 221122
Henning Probst *(Gen Mgr)*

Kraftverkehrsgesellschaft Paderborn mbH (3)
Barkhauser Strasse 6
33106 Paderborn, Germany
Tel.: (49) 5251 76545
Fax: (49) 5251 503 6028
Web Site: www.kvp-paderborn.de
Transportation Services
S.I.C.: 4789
N.A.I.C.S.: 488999

Gemeinschaftskernkraftwerk Grohnde GmbH (2)
PO Box 1230
31860 Emmerthal, Germany (100%)
Tel.: (49) 5155671
Fax: (49) 5155672380
E-Mail: krastwerksleatung@eon-energy.com
Web Site: www.eon.com
Sls.: $200,000,000
Emp.: 300
Production of Electric Power
S.I.C.: 3699
N.A.I.C.S.: 335999
York Borneman *(Mng Dir)*

Gemeinschaftskraftwerk Kiel GmbH (2)
Hasselfelde 40
24149 Kiel, Germany (50%)
Tel.: (49) 43120020
Fax: (49) 4312002341
Web Site: www.eon-kraftwerke.com
Emp.: 120
Production of Electric Power
S.I.C.: 3699
N.A.I.C.S.: 335999
Klaus Nieder Hoff *(Gen Mgr)*

Kernkraftwerk Brokdorf GmbH (2)
Osterende 999
25576 Brokdorf, Germany (80%)
Tel.: (49) 48297501616
Fax: (49) 48291666
Web Site: www.eon-kernkraft.com
Sales Range: $350-399.9 Million
Production of Electric Power
S.I.C.: 3699
N.A.I.C.S.: 335999

Kernkraftwerk Unterweser GmbH (2)
Dedesdorser Str 2
Postfach 4849
26935 Stadland, Germany (100%)
Tel.: (49) 4732801
Fax: (49) 4732802085
E-Mail: info@eon-kernkraft.com
Web Site: www.eon-kernkraft.com
Emp.: 300
Production of Electric Power
S.I.C.: 3699
N.A.I.C.S.: 335999
Kars Ramler *(Plant Mgr)*

Rhein-Main-Donau AG (2)
Blutenburg Strasse 20
80636 Munich, Germany
Tel.: (49) 89992220
Fax: (49) 8999222199
E-Mail: info@rmd.de
Web Site: www.rmd.de
Emp.: 150
Operator of Canals & Hydroelectric Power Stations
S.I.C.: 4911
N.A.I.C.S.: 221111
Bernhard Fischer *(Chm)*

Subsidiary:

Mittlere Donau Kraftwerke Aktiengesellschaft (3)
Blutenburgstr 20
80636 Munich, Bayern, Germany
Tel.: (49) 89 992220
Fax: (49) 89 99222299
E-Mail: info@rnd.de
Web Site: www.rnd.de
Emp.: 15
Electric Power Generation Services
S.I.C.: 4939
N.A.I.C.S.: 221118
Allen Carlson *(Gen Mgr)*

Affiliates:

Berliner Kraft-und Licht (Bewag) AG (2)
Puschkinallee 52
12435 Berlin, Germany (10%)
Tel.: (49) 302670
Fax: (49) 30 12727
Web Site: www.bewag.de
Energy Services
S.I.C.: 4911
N.A.I.C.S.: 221122

Elektrizitaetswerk Minden-Ravensberg (2)
Postfach 15 42
32005 Herford, Germany (25.1%)
Web Site: www.emr.de
Distribution of Electric Power
S.I.C.: 4911
N.A.I.C.S.: 221122

Energieobjektgesellschaft mbH-EOG (2)
Allee der Kosmonauten 29
12681 Berlin, Germany (20.9%)
Electric Distribution Services
S.I.C.: 4931
N.A.I.C.S.: 221122

LSW LandE-Stadtwerke Wolfsburg GmbH & Co. KG (2)
Hesslinger Strasse 1-5
38432 Wolfsburg, Germany (25%)
Tel.: (49) 5361189
Fax: (49) 5361189574
E-Mail: info@lsw.de
Web Site: www.lsw.de
Emp.: 600
Electric Power & Gas Services
S.I.C.: 4931
N.A.I.C.S.: 221122
Walter Rangette *(Mng Dir)*

Ueberlandwerk Leinetal GmbH (2)
Am Eltwerk 1
31028 Gronau, Germany (48%)
Mailing Address:
Postfach 1353
Leine, Gronau, 31023, Germany
Tel.: (49) 51825880
Fax: (49) 518258825
E-Mail: info@uewl.de
Web Site: www.uewl.de
Sales Range: $25-49.9 Million
Electric Power Distribution
S.I.C.: 4911
N.A.I.C.S.: 221122

Joint Venture:

KKK GmbH & Co OHV (2)
Elbuferstrasse 82
21502 Geesthacht, Germany
Tel.: (49) 4152150
Fax: (49) 4152152008
E-Mail: kkk@kkv.krummel.de
Nuclear Power Plant; Production of Electric Power
S.I.C.: 4939
N.A.I.C.S.: 221113
Torsten Fricke *(Gen Mgr)*

Non-U.S. Subsidiaries:

E.ON Benelux B.V. (2)
Capelseweg 400
Postbus 84065
3009 Rotterdam, Netherlands (100%)
Tel.: (31) 102895089
Fax: (31) 102895088
E-Mail: info@eon-benelux.com
Web Site: www.eon-benelux.com
Emp.: 600
Holding Company; Energy Services
S.I.C.: 6719
N.A.I.C.S.: 551112
Joost F.M. van Dijk *(CEO & Mng Dir)*
Markus Bokelmann *(Mng Dir)*

Subsidiaries:

E.ON Benelux Generation B.V. (3)
Coloradoweg 10
3199 LA Rotterdam, Maasvlakte, Netherlands (100%)
Tel.: (31) 181362222
Fax: (31) 181363992
Web Site: www.eon-benelux.com
Emp.: 150
Energy Services
S.I.C.: 4911
N.A.I.C.S.: 221122
J. Dijk *(CEO)*

E.ON Benelux Generation N.V. (3)
Capelseweg 400
PO Box 909
3068 AX Rotterdam, 3009 AP, Netherlands (100%)
Tel.: (31) 102895711
Fax: (31) 102895039
E-Mail: info@eon-benelux.com
Web Site: www.eon-benelux.com
Emp.: 600
Energy Services
S.I.C.: 4931
N.A.I.C.S.: 221122
Jost F.M. Van Dek *(Mng Dir)*

E.ON Ceska republika, s.r.o. (2)
F. A. Gerstnera 2151/6
370 49 Ceske Budejovice, Czech Republic CZ (100%)
Tel.: (420) 387862303
Fax: (420) 387862900
E-Mail: vladimir.vacha@eon.cz
Web Site: www.eon.cz
Emp.: 2,700
Electricity Production & Sales
S.I.C.: 4939
N.A.I.C.S.: 221122
Michael Fehn *(Chm)*
Lorenz Pronnet *(Vice Chm)*
Karel Dietrich-Nespesny *(CEO)*

Subsidiaries:

E.ON Distribuce, a.s. (3)
Lannova 205/16
370 49 Ceske Budejovice, Czech Republic (100%)
Tel.: (420) 840111333
E-Mail: info@eon.cz
Web Site: www.eon-distribuce.cz/cs/o-spolecnosti/kontakty/index.shtml
Electric Power Distr
S.I.C.: 4911
N.A.I.C.S.: 221122
Josef Havel *(Chm)*
Zdenek Bauer *(Vice Chm)*

E.ON Energie, a.s. (3)
Lannova 205/16
370 49 Ceske Budejovice, Czech Republic
Tel.: (420) 840 111 333
E-Mail: info@eon.cz
Web Site: www.eon.cz/cs/contact.shtml
Electric Power Distr
S.I.C.: 4911
N.A.I.C.S.: 221122
Michael Safar *(Chm)*
Radek Lucky *(Vice Chm)*

E.ON Hungaria Zrt. (2)
Szechenyi Istvan ter 7-8
1051 Budapest, Hungary
Tel.: (36) 14722300
Fax: (36) 14722301
Web Site: www.eon-hungaria.com
Rev.: $1,498,077,056
Emp.: 600
Energy Services
S.I.C.: 4939
N.A.I.C.S.: 221122
Konrad Kreuzer *(Chm)*
Eric Depluet *(CEO)*

Subsidiaries:

Energetikai es Tavkozlesi Halozatepito es Szerelo Kft. (3)
Kando Kalman utca 11-13
9027 Gyor, Hungary
Tel.: (36) 696521188
Web Site: www.eon.com
Cable & Free Power Line Construction; Station & Switching Equipment Construction; Network Operational Malfunctions Elimination; Energy &

Telecommunications Operation & Maintenance; Owned 51% by E.ON Hungria Zrt. & 49% by E.ON Eszak Dunantuli Aramszolgltato Zrt.
S.I.C.: 1629
N.A.I.C.S.: 237130

E.ON Del-dunantuli Aramszolgaltato Zrt. (3)
Rakoczi ut 73/b.
7626 Pecs, Hungary (100%)
Tel.: (36) 72 501 000
E-Mail: sajtoszoba@eon-hungaria.com
Web Site: www.eon-hungaria.com
Emp.: 100
Electricity Distribution Services
S.I.C.: 4911
N.A.I.C.S.: 221122

E.ON Del-dunantuli Gazszolgaltato Zrt. (3)
Bzza tir 8/a
H-7626 Pecs, Hungary (99.94%)
Tel.: (36) 40 220 220
Web Site: hungaria.com
Gas Supplies, System Operations, Network Development & Maintenance
S.I.C.: 4924
N.A.I.C.S.: 221210
Lajos Gelenscer *(Chm)*
Konrad Kreuzer *(Chm-Supervisory Bd)*

E.ON Energiakereskedo Kft. (3)
Szechenyi rkp 8
H-1054 Budapest, Hungary (100%)
Tel.: (36) 13542660
Fax: (36) 13543890
E-Mail: info@eon-energiakereskedo.com
Web Site: www.eon-energiakereskedo.com
Rev.: $142,366,829
Energy Services
S.I.C.: 4911
N.A.I.C.S.: 221122

E.ON Eszak-Dunantuli Aramszolgaltato Zrt. (3)
Kando Kalman utca 11-13
H-9027 Gyor, Hungary (100%)
Tel.: (36) 96521000
E-Mail: info-eszakdunatul@eon-hungaria.com
Web Site: www.eon-eszakdunantul.com
Electric Power Distr
S.I.C.: 4931
N.A.I.C.S.: 221122
Gelenczer Lajos *(Chm)*

E.ON Szolgaltato Kft. (3)
Kando Kando u 11-13
9027 Gyor, Hungary
Tel.: (36) 696521637
Fax: (36) 696521172
Property & Vehicles Operator
S.I.C.: 7389
N.A.I.C.S.: 561499

E.ON Tiszantuli Aramszolgaltato Rt. (3)
Kossuth Ut 41
4024 Debrecen, Hungary (83.1%)
Tel.: (36) 52511100
Fax: (36) 52414031
E-Mail: info@eon-tiszantul.com
Web Site: www.eon-tiszantul.com
Sales Range: $250-299.9 Million
Emp.: 1,400
Electric Power Supplier
S.I.C.: 4931
N.A.I.C.S.: 221122
Dezso Rubint *(Chm)*

KOGAZ Rt. (3)
Zrinyi Miklos utca 32
H-8800 Nagykanizsa, Hungary (98.11%)
Tel.: (36) 93321300
Fax: (36) 93 313 077
Web Site: www.eon-hungaria.com
Pipeline Gas Supplier
S.I.C.: 4924
N.A.I.C.S.: 221210
Laszlo Patay *(Chm)*

E.ON Moldova-Furnizare (2)
Strasse Stefan Cel Mare nr 22
Bacau, 600359, Romania (51%)
Tel.: (40) 235 305 555
Fax: (40) 234 205 704
E-Mail: sesozari@eon-romania.ro
Web Site: www.eon-moldova.com
Electric Power Distr
S.I.C.: 4911
N.A.I.C.S.: 221122

E.ON New Build & Technology Limited (2)
Technology Centre Ratcliffe-on-Soar
Nottingham, NG11 0EE, United Kingdom
Tel.: (44) 24 76 19 25 60
Fax: (44) 1159025012
E-Mail: ent-info@eon.com
Emp.: 40
Engineering Consulting Services
S.I.C.: 8711
N.A.I.C.S.: 541330
Fiona Wingate *(Engr-Electrical)*

E.ON Polska Sp. z o.o. (2)
Ul Nabielaka 6
00-743 Warsaw, Poland
Tel.: (48) 228406466
Fax: (48) 228406468
E-Mail: info@eon-polska.com
Web Site: www.eon-polska.com
Emp.: 4
Electric Power Distr
S.I.C.: 4911
N.A.I.C.S.: 221122
Krzysztof Borowiec *(Mng Dir)*

Non-U.S. Joint Venture:

Zapadoslovenska energetika, a.s. (2)
Culenova 6
816 47 Bratislava, Slovakia
Tel.: (421) 252961741
Fax: (421) 252925314
E-Mail: kontakt@zse.sk
Web Site: www.zse.sk
Sales Range: $800-899.9 Million
Emp.: 1,413
Electric Power Distr; Owned 51% by National Property Fund of the Slovak Republic & 49% by E.ON Energie AG
S.I.C.: 4931
N.A.I.C.S.: 221122
Konrad Kreuzer *(Chm)*
Walter Hohlefelder *(Vice Chm-Supervisory Bd)*
Peter Vlasaty *(Vice Chm)*

E.ON Energy from Waste Grossraschen GmbH (1)
Bergmannstrasse 29
1983 Grossraschen, Germany
Tel.: (49) 3 57 53 3 77 50
Fax: (49) 3 57 53 3 77 52
E-Mail: info@eon-energyfromwaste.com
Electric Power Generation Services
S.I.C.: 4911
N.A.I.C.S.: 221118

E.ON Energy from Waste Hannover GmbH (1)
Moorwaldweg 310
30659 Hannover, Germany
Tel.: (49) 5 11 33 63 97 0
Fax: (49) 5 11 33 63 97 90
Web Site: www.eon-energyfromwaste.com
Emp.: 50
Electric Power Generation Services
S.I.C.: 4911
N.A.I.C.S.: 221118
Hans Koerte *(Gen Mgr)*

E.ON Energy from Waste Helmstedt GmbH (1)
An der B244
38350 Helmstedt, Germany
Tel.: (49) 53 51 18 45 63
Fax: (49) 53 51 18 46 50
E-Mail: info@eon-energyfromwaste.com
Electric Power Generation Services
S.I.C.: 4939
N.A.I.C.S.: 221118

E.ON Energy from Waste Heringen GmbH (1)
In Der Aue 3
36266 Heringen, Germany
Tel.: (49) 66 24 54 21 00 0
Fax: (49) 66 24 54 21 02 0
Natural Gas Extraction Services
S.I.C.: 1321
N.A.I.C.S.: 211112

E.ON Energy from Waste Saarbrucken GmbH (1)
Heitersheimer Strasse 2
79427 Eschbach, Germany
Tel.: (49) 76 34 50 79 122
Fax: (49) 76 34 50 79 135
Web Site: www.eon-energyfromwaste.com
Electric Power Distribution Services
S.I.C.: 4939
N.A.I.C.S.: 221122
Martin Bentz *(Chm-Supervisory Bd-Works Council)*

E.ON Energy from Waste Stapelfeld GmbH (1)
Ahrensburger Weg 4
22145 Stapelfeld, Germany
Tel.: (49) 40 6757 60
Fax: (49) 40 6757 6500
E-Mail: frank.ehlers@eew-energyfromwaste.com
Emp.: 7
Waste Management Services
S.I.C.: 4959
N.A.I.C.S.: 562998
Frank Ehlers *(Mgr-Technical)*

E.ON Energy Trading Holding GmbH (1)
E On-Platz 1
Dusseldorf, Nordrhein-Westfalen, 40479, Germany
Tel.: (49) 211732750
Fax: (49) 2114579501
E-Mail: info@eon-energy-trading.com
Web Site: www.eon.com
Investment Management Services
S.I.C.: 6211
N.A.I.C.S.: 523999

E.ON Gruga Geschaftsfuhrungsgesellschaft mbH (1)
E On-Platz 1
40479 Dusseldorf, Nordrhein-Westfalen, Germany
Tel.: (49) 211 45790
Fax: (49) 211 4579501
Business Management Consulting Services
S.I.C.: 8742
N.A.I.C.S.: 541611

E.ON Gruga Objektgesellschaft mbH & Co. KG (1)
E ON-Platz 1
40479 Dusseldorf, Nordrhein-Westfalen, Germany
Tel.: (49) 211 45790
Fax: (49) 211 4579501
Real Estate Management Services
S.I.C.: 6531
N.A.I.C.S.: 531390

E.ON Hanse Vertrieb GmbH (1)
Kuuhnehofe 1 - 5
Hamburg, 22761, Germany
Tel.: (49) 40 6 05 90 00 00
Fax: (49) 40 6 05 90 00 05
E-Mail: kundenbetreuung@eon.de
Web Site: www.eon.de/de/hanse/pk/services/Kontakt_Servicenummern/index.htm
Eelectricity & Natural Gas Distribution Services
S.I.C.: 4931
N.A.I.C.S.: 221122

E.ON Hanse Warme GmbH (1)
Am Radeland 25
21079 Hamburg, Germany
Tel.: (49) 40 23 78 27 325
Fax: (49) 40 23 78 27 910
E-Mail: info@eon-hanse-waerme.com
Web Site: www.eon-hanse-waerme.com
Solar Thermal Heating & Storage Services
S.I.C.: 1711
N.A.I.C.S.: 238220

E.ON Human Resources International GmbH (1)
Brienner Str 40
Munich, 80333, Germany
Tel.: (49) 89125401
Fax: (49) 8912544131
E-Mail: info@eon-energy.com
Human Resource Consulting Services
S.I.C.: 8999
N.A.I.C.S.: 541612

E.ON Iberia Holding GmbH (1)
E On-Platz 1
Dusseldorf, Nordrhein-Westfalen, 40479, Germany
Tel.: (49) 21145790
Fax: (49) 2114579501
Investment Management Services
S.I.C.: 6282
N.A.I.C.S.: 523920

E.ON Inhouse Consulting GmbH (1)
Grafinger Strasse 2
Munich, 81671, Germany
Tel.: (49) 89 418 601 185
Fax: (49) 89 41 86 01 180
Emp.: 100
Business Management Consulting Services
S.I.C.: 8742
N.A.I.C.S.: 541611
Sebastian Luehrs *(Project Mgr)*

E.ON Invest GmbH (1)
Nordliche Munchner Strasse 14
82031 Grunwald, Bavaria, Germany
Tel.: (49) 8964913672021
Investment Management Services
S.I.C.: 6211
N.A.I.C.S.: 523999

E.ON Mitte Natur GmbH (1)
Maybachstrasse 7
35683 Dillenburg, Germany
Tel.: (49) 27 71 873 2030
Fax: (49) 27 71 873 2035
E-Mail: info@eon-mitte-natur.com
Web Site: www.eon-mitte-natur.com
Emp.: 14
Fuel Electric Power Generation Services
S.I.C.: 4931
N.A.I.C.S.: 221112
Hans-Ulrich Terschueren *(Gen Mgr)*

E.ON Mitte Warme GmbH (1)
Monteverdistrasse 2
34131 Kassel, Germany
Tel.: (49) 561 933 03
Fax: (49) 561 933 24 50
E-Mail: info.waerme@eon-mitte.com
Web Site: www.eon-mitte-waerme.com
Electric Power Distribution Services
S.I.C.: 4931
N.A.I.C.S.: 221122

E.ON New Build & Technology GmbH (1)
Alexander-von-Humboldt-Strasse 1
45896 Gelsenkirchen, Germany
Tel.: (49) 2 09 601 50 10
Engineering & Scientific Services
S.I.C.: 8711
N.A.I.C.S.: 541330
Martin Krimphove *(Deputy Chm-Supervisory Bd)*

Subsidiary:

HGC Hamburg Gas Consult GmbH (2)
Heidenkampsweg 99
20097 Hamburg, Germany
Tel.: (49) 40 23 53 30
Fax: (49) 40 23 66 37 30
E-Mail: info@hgc-hamburg.de
Web Site: www.hgc-hamburg.de
Emp.: 50
Gas & Heat Supply Engineering Services
S.I.C.: 8711
N.A.I.C.S.: 541330
Peter Uhl *(Mng Dir)*

E.ON Risk Consulting GmbH (1)
Kennedydamm 17
Dusseldorf, Nordrhein-Westfalen, 40476, Germany
Tel.: (49) 21147970
Fax: (49) 2114797207
Emp.: 3
Insurance Risk Management Services
S.I.C.: 6411
N.A.I.C.S.: 524298

E.ON Ruhrgas AG (1)
Brueissilir Platz
45131 Essen, Germany
Tel.: (49) 20118400
Telex: 857299 O rgd
Fax: (49) 2011843766
E-Mail: info@eon-ruhrgas.com
Web Site: www.eon-ruhrgas.com
Sales Range: $10-24.9 Million
Emp.: 11,520
Natural Gas Distr
S.I.C.: 4924
N.A.I.C.S.: 221210

E.ON SE—(Continued)

Jorgen Kildahl *(Chm-Supervisory Bd)*
Gabriele Gratz *(Vice Chm-Supervisory Bd)*
Klaus Schaefer *(Pres)*
Klaus Schafer *(CEO)*
Achim Middelschulte *(Member-Exec Bd)*

Subsidiaries:

E.ON Gas Mobil GmbH (2)
Brusseler Platz 1
Essen, Nordrhein-Westfalen, 45131, Germany
Tel.: (49) 201 18400
Fax: (49) 201 1843766
Natural Gas Distribution Services
S.I.C.: 4924
N.A.I.C.S.: 221210

E.ON Ruhrgas International AG (2)
Huttropstrasse 60
45138 Essen, Germany (100%)
Tel.: (49) 20118400
Fax: (49) 2011843766
E-Mail: info@eon.com
Web Site: www.eon.com
Emp.: 200
Gas Production & Distr
S.I.C.: 4924
N.A.I.C.S.: 221210
Ulrich Schoeler *(Chm & Mng Dir)*
Stephan Kamphues *(Mng Dir)*
Juergen Schneider *(Mng Dir)*

Erdgasversorgungsgesellschaft Thuringen-Sachsen mbH (2)
Juri-Gagarin-Ring 162
99084 Erfurt, Germany
Tel.: (49) 361 5673 01
Fax: (49) 361 5673 119
E-Mail: evg@evg-thueringen.de
Web Site: www.evg-thueringen.de
Emp.: 25
Natural Gas Distribution Services
S.I.C.: 4924
N.A.I.C.S.: 221210

Ferngas Nordbayern GmbH (2)
Further Strasse 13
90429 Nuremberg, Bavaria, Germany (53.1%)
Tel.: (49) 911277700
Fax: (49) 9112777280
E-Mail: info@ferngasnordbayern.de
Web Site: www.ferngas-nordbayern.de
Rev.: $820,253,184
Emp.: 35
Gas Supplier.
S.I.C.: 4924
N.A.I.C.S.: 221210
Peter Lauaer *(Mng Dir)*

Gas-Union GmbH (2)
Kurmainzer Strasse 2
65929 Frankfurt am Main, Germany
Tel.: (49) 6930030
Fax: (49) 693003129
E-Mail: gu@gas-union.de
Web Site: www.gas-union.de
Emp.: 50
S.I.C.: 4924
N.A.I.C.S.: 221210
Hugo Wiemer *(Mng Dir)*

Harterei VTN Witten GmbH (2)
Rusbergs Plz 75
58456 Witten, Germany (100%)
Tel.: (49) 232493420
Fax: (49) 2324934240
E-Mail: info@haertereivtn.com
Web Site: www.haertereivtn.com
Emp.: 120
Supplier of Heating Appliances.
S.I.C.: 5074
N.A.I.C.S.: 423720
Andreas Ludes *(Mgr-Sls)*

LOI Thermprocess GmbH (2)
Am Lichtbogen 29
45141 Essen, Germany (100%)
Tel.: (49) 20118911
Fax: (49) 2011891321
E-Mail: info@loi.de
Web Site: www.loi.de
Sales Range: $50-74.9 Million
Emp.: 300
S.I.C.: 4924
N.A.I.C.S.: 221210
Hermann Stumpp *(Mng Dir)*

Lubmin-Brandov Gastransport GmbH (2)
Norbertstrasse 85
Essen, Nordrhein-Westfalen, 45131, Germany
Tel.: (49) 20143999992
Fax: (49) 20163278904
E-Mail: info@lbtg.de
Web Site: www.lbtg.de
Gas Transportation Services
S.I.C.: 4922
N.A.I.C.S.: 486210
Oliver Giese *(Mng Dir)*

NGT Neue Gebaudetechnik GmbH (2)
Haengebank 13
45307 Essen, Germany (100%)
Tel.: (49) 20185220
Fax: (49) 2018522144
E-Mail: infor@ngt-essen.de
Web Site: www.ruhrgas.de
Emp.: 135
S.I.C.: 4924
N.A.I.C.S.: 221210

PLEcon Pipeline Engineering Consulting GmbH (2)
Gurtel Strasse 29 A 30
10247 Berlin, Germany (85%)
Tel.: (49) 30293855
Fax: (49) 3029401621
E-Mail: info@plecon.de
Web Site: www.ple.de
Sales Range: $1-9.9 Million
Emp.: 60
Gas Exploration
S.I.C.: 4924
N.A.I.C.S.: 221210

TGT GmbH (2)
Goldbacharstrasse 37
99867 Gotha, Germany (100%)
Tel.: (49) 36213820
Fax: (49) 3621382111
E-Mail: info@tgt.de
Sales Range: $1-9.9 Million
Emp.: 35
Natural Gas
S.I.C.: 4924
N.A.I.C.S.: 221210

E.ON Ruhrgas E & P Agypten GmbH (1)
Brusseler Platz 1
45138 Essen, Nordrhein-Westfalen, Germany
Tel.: (49) 201 18400
Fax: (49) 201 1843766
E-Mail: info@eon.com
Web Site: www.eon.com
Emp.: 200
Electric Power Generation Services
S.I.C.: 4911
N.A.I.C.S.: 221118

E.ON Ruhrgas E & P GmbH (1)
Brusseler Platz 1
45131 Essen, Germany
Tel.: (49) 2 01 1 84 44 43
Oil & Gas Exploration Services
S.I.C.: 1389
N.A.I.C.S.: 213112

E.ON Ruhrgas GGH GmbH (1)
Brusseler Platz 1
Essen, Nordrhein-Westfalen, 45131, Germany
Tel.: (49) 20118400
Fax: (49) 18400 3766
E-Mail: info@eon.com
Web Site: www.eon.com
Emp.: 200
Natural Gas Distribution Services
S.I.C.: 4924
N.A.I.C.S.: 221210
Guy Creten *(CEO)*

E.ON Ruhrgas GPA GmbH (1)
Brusseler Platz 1
Essen, Nordrhein-Westfalen, 45131, Germany
Tel.: (49) 20118400
Oil & Gas Exploration Services
S.I.C.: 1389
N.A.I.C.S.: 213112

E.ON Ruhrgas Personalagentur GmbH (1)
Brusseler Platz 1
Essen, Nordrhein-Westfalen, 45131, Germany
Tel.: (49) 20118400
Fax: (49) 20118424272
Oil & Gas Exploration Services
S.I.C.: 1389
N.A.I.C.S.: 213112

E.ON Russia Holding GmbH (1)
E ON-Platz 1
Dusseldorf, '40479, Germany
Tel.: (49) 211 45790
Fax: (49) 211 4579501
Electric Power Generation & Distributing Services
S.I.C.: 4931
N.A.I.C.S.: 221118

E.ON Service GmbH (1)
Brusseler Platz 1
45131 Essen, Germany
Tel.: (49) 2 01 1 84 00
Fax: (49) 2 01 1 84 21 83
E-Mail: info@eon-service.com
Web Site: www.eon-service.com
Human Resource Consulting Services
S.I.C.: 8999
N.A.I.C.S.: 541612

E.ON Vertrieb Deutschland GmbH (1)
Karlstrasse 68
80335 Munich, Germany
Tel.: (49) 89 12 54 01
Fax: (49) 89 12 54 39 06
E-Mail: info@eon-vertrieb.com
Electric Power Distribution Services
S.I.C.: 4911
N.A.I.C.S.: 221122
Stefan Vogg *(Gen Mgr)*

E.ON Westfalen Weser 2. Vermogensverwaltungs-GmbH (1)
Bielefelder Str 3
32051 Herford, Nordrhein-Westfalen, Germany
Tel.: (49) 5221 1830
Fax: (49) 5221 1834152
E-Mail: service-center@eon-westfalenweser.com
Business Management Consulting Services
S.I.C.: 8742
N.A.I.C.S.: 541611
Michael Heidkamp *(Gen Mgr)*

E.ON Zwanzigste Verwaltungs GmbH (1)
E On-Platz 1
Dusseldorf, Nordrhein-Westfalen, 40479, Germany
Tel.: (49) 211 4579501
Management Consulting Services
S.I.C.: 8748
N.A.I.C.S.: 541618

ERKA Vermogensverwaltungsgesellschaft mbH (1)
E ON-Platz 1
40479 Dusseldorf, Nordrhein-Westfalen, Germany
Tel.: (49) 211 4 57 92 08
Asset Management Services
S.I.C.: 6282
N.A.I.C.S.: 523920

Evantec GmbH (1)
Marsstr 42
80335 Munich, Germany
Tel.: (49) 89 51566 0
Fax: (49) 8951566122
E-Mail: info@evantec.de
Web Site: www.evantec.de
Emp.: 40
Radiation Protection Services
S.I.C.: 7218
N.A.I.C.S.: 812332
Gunter Frenzel *(Gen Mgr)*

FITAS Verwaltung GmbH & Co. REGIUM-Objekte KG (1)
Emil-Riedl-Weg 6
82049 Pullach, Bavaria, Germany
Tel.: (49) 815793410
Fax: (49) 8157934120
Administrative Management Services
S.I.C.: 8742
N.A.I.C.S.: 541611

FITAS Verwaltung GmbH & Co. Vermietungs-KG (1)
Emil-Riedl-Weg 6
Pullach, Bayern, 82049, Germany
Tel.: (49) 8951200
Real Estate Development Services
S.I.C.: 6531
N.A.I.C.S.: 531390

Gasversorgung im Landkreis Gifhorn GmbH (1)
Hinterm Hagen 13
38442 Wolfsburg, Germany
Tel.: (49) 5362 12 0
Fax: (49) 5362 12 399
E-Mail: aktiv@lsw.de
Web Site: www.glg-gmbh.de
Natural Gas Distribution Services
S.I.C.: 4924
N.A.I.C.S.: 221210

Subsidiary:

GLG Netz GmbH (2)
Hinterm Hagen 13
38442 Wolfsburg, Germany
Tel.: (49) 5362 12 0
Fax: (49) 5362 12 4855
E-Mail: info@glg-netz.de
Web Site: www.glg-netz.de
Natural Gas Distribution Services
S.I.C.: 4924
N.A.I.C.S.: 221210

Gelsenberg Verwaltungs GmbH (1)
E On-Platz 1
Dusseldorf, Nordrhein-Westfalen, 40479, Germany
Tel.: (49) 2093895421
Fax: (49) 2093895450
Business Management Consulting Services
S.I.C.: 8742
N.A.I.C.S.: 541611

Gemeinschaftskernkraftwerk Grohnde Management GmbH (1)
Kraftwerksgelande
Emmerthal, Niedersachsen, 31860, Germany
Tel.: (49) 5155671
Fax: (49) 5155672380
Electric Power Generation Services
S.I.C.: 4939
N.A.I.C.S.: 221118

Gemeinschaftskernkraftwerk Isar 2 GmbH (1)
Dammstr 32
Bessenbach, Bayern, 84051, Germany
Tel.: (49) 8702384420
Fax: (49) 8702384957
Electric Power Generation Services
S.I.C.: 4931
N.A.I.C.S.: 221118

Gemeinschaftskraftwerk Veltheim Gesellschaft mit beschrankter Haftung (1)
Mollberger Strasse 387
32457 Porta Westfalica, Germany
Tel.: (49) 5706 399 0
Fax: (49) 5706 399 381
E-Mail: info@gk-veltheim.de
Web Site: www.gk-veltheim.de
Electric Power Generation Services
S.I.C.: 4911
N.A.I.C.S.: 221118

Gesellschaft fur Energie und Klimaschutz Schleswig- Holstein GmbH (1)
Boschstrasse 1
24118 Kiel, Germany
Tel.: (49) 4 31 98 05 8 00
Fax: (49) 4 31 98 05 8 88
E-Mail: info@eksh.org
Web Site: www.eksh.org
Environmental Protection Science & Research Services
S.I.C.: 8999
N.A.I.C.S.: 541620

GGG Gesellschaft fur Grundstucks- und Gebaudenutzung mbH (1)
Huttropstrasse 60
45138 Essen, Germany

Tel.: (49) 201 18400
Real Estate Development Services
S.I.C.: 6531
N.A.I.C.S.: 531390

GHD E.ON Bayern AG & Co. KG (1)
Lilienthalstr 7
Regensburg, Bayern, 93049, Germany
Tel.: (49) 9412010
Fax: (49) 941201399
Electric Power Generation Services
S.I.C.: 4939
N.A.I.C.S.: 221118

GreyLogix GmbH (1)
Conrad-Rontgen-Str 1
24941 Flensburg, Germany
Tel.: (49) 461 505487 0
Fax: (49) 461 505487 100
E-Mail: info@greylogix.com
Web Site: www.greylogix.com
Emp.: 30
Automation Technology Services
S.I.C.: 7373
N.A.I.C.S.: 541512
Lars Malter *(Co-Mng Dir)*
Gerd Witzel *(Co-Mng Dir)*

Hamburg Netz GmbH (1)
Ausschlager Elbdeich 127
20539 Hamburg, Germany
Tel.: (49) 40 53 79 93 98
Fax: (49) 1 80 5 23 66 23
E-Mail: info@hh-netz.com
Web Site: www.hh-netz.com
Natural Gas Pipeline Transportation Services
S.I.C.: 4923
N.A.I.C.S.: 486210

Hamburger Hof Versicherungs-Aktiengesellschaft (1)
Kennedydamm 17
Dusseldorf, Nordrhein-Westfalen, 40476, Germany
Tel.: (49) 21147970
Fax: (49) 2114797207
Web Site: www.eon.com
Insurance Management Services
S.I.C.: 6411
N.A.I.C.S.: 524298
Klaus Greimel *(Gen Mgr)*

Hermann Seippel-Unterstutzungseinrichtung GmbH (1)
Brusseler Platz 1
45131 Essen, Nordrhein-Westfalen, Germany
Tel.: (49) 201 18400
Management Consulting Services
S.I.C.: 8748
N.A.I.C.S.: 541618

ILSE Bergbau-GmbH (1)
Georg-von-Boeselager-Str 25
D-53117 Bonn, Germany (100%)
Tel.: (49) 22855201
Fax: (49) 2285522977
Chemical Mineral Mining Company
S.I.C.: 1479
N.A.I.C.S.: 212393

Induboden GmbH & Co. Industriewerte OHG (1)
E On-Platz 1
40479 Dusseldorf, Nordrhein-Westfalen, Germany
Tel.: (49) 211 45791
Electric Power Generation Services
S.I.C.: 4911
N.A.I.C.S.: 221118

Interargem GmbH (1)
Schelpmilser Weg 30
33609 Bielefeld, Germany
Tel.: (49) 521 3398 106
Fax: (49) 521 3398 199
E-Mail: info@interargem.de
Web Site: www.interargem.de
Emp.: 20
Waste Disposal Services
S.I.C.: 4953
N.A.I.C.S.: 562219
Peter Beranek *(Gen Mgr)*

Subsidiary:

Enertec Hameln GmbH (2)
Heinrich-Schoormann-Weg 1
31789 Hameln, Germany
Tel.: (49) 5 151 81 2901
Fax: (49) 5 151 81 2922
E-Mail: info@enertec-hameln.de
Electric Power Generation Services
S.I.C.: 4931
N.A.I.C.S.: 221118

Kernkraftwerk Stade GmbH & Co. oHG (1)
Bassenflether Chaussee
Stade, Niedersachsen, 21683, Germany
Tel.: (49) 41 41 77 0
Fax: (49) 41 41 77 3312
Nuclear Electric Power Generation Services
S.I.C.: 4931
N.A.I.C.S.: 221113

Kernkraftwerke Isar Verwaltungs GmbH (1)
Dammstr 33
Bessenbach, Bayern, 84051, Germany
Tel.: (49) 8702380
Fax: (49) 8702384218
Nuclear Electric Power Generation Services
S.I.C.: 4939
N.A.I.C.S.: 221113
Christian Reilein *(Mng Dir)*

KommEnergie GmbH (1)
Bahnhofstrasse 1
82223 Eichenau, Germany
Tel.: (49) 8141 53 72 52 2
Fax: (49) 8141 53 72 58 5
E-Mail: info@kommenergie.de
Web Site: www.kommenergie.de
Electric Power Distribution Services
S.I.C.: 4939
N.A.I.C.S.: 221122

Kraftwerk Schwedt Verwaltungsgesellschaft mbH (1)
Kuhheide 34
16303 Schwedt an der Oder, Germany
Tel.: (49) 3332 581285
Electric Power Generation Services
S.I.C.: 4939
N.A.I.C.S.: 221118

Kurgan Grundstucks-Verwaltungsgesellschaft mbH & Co. oHG (1)
Tolzer Str 15
82031 Grunwald, Bayern, Germany
Tel.: (49) 89 64143 0
Fax: (49) 89 64143 594
Real Estate Management Services
S.I.C.: 6531
N.A.I.C.S.: 531390

LandE GmbH (1)
Hinterm Hagen 13
38442 Wolfsburg, Niedersachsen, Germany
Tel.: (49) 5362 120
Fax: (49) 5362 124820
E-Mail: info@lsw.de
Web Site: www.lsw.de
Electric Power Generation & Distribution Services
S.I.C.: 4931
N.A.I.C.S.: 221118
Horst Finkendey *(Mng Dir)*

Landwehr Wassertechnik GmbH (1)
Schwarzer Weg 2A
38170 Schoppenstedt, Germany
Tel.: (49) 53 32 96 87 0
Fax: (49) 53 32 96 87 199
E-Mail: info@landwehr-wt.de
Web Site: www.landwehr-wt.de
Emp.: 80
Water Treatment Plant Construction Services
S.I.C.: 1629
N.A.I.C.S.: 237110
Andreas Walenczyk *(Gen Mgr)*

Line WORX GmbH (1)
Halterner Str 125
46284 Dorsten, Nordrhein-Westfalen, Germany
Tel.: (49) 2362 938678
Fax: (49) 2362 938702
Management Consulting Services
S.I.C.: 8748
N.A.I.C.S.: 541618

LSW LandE-Stadtwerke Wolfsburg Verwaltungs-GmbH (1)
Hesslinger Str 1-5
Wolfsburg, 38440, Germany
Tel.: (49) 5361189662
Fax: (49) 5361189303
Business Management Consulting Services
S.I.C.: 8742
N.A.I.C.S.: 541611

Mainkraftwerk Schweinfurt Gesellschaft mit beschrankter Haftung (1)
Blutenburgstrasse 20
80636 Munich, Germany
Tel.: (49) 89 992220
Fax: (49) 89 99222 129
E-Mail: info@rmd.de
Web Site: www.rmd.de
Emp.: 35
Electric Power Generation Services
S.I.C.: 4911
N.A.I.C.S.: 221118
Albrecht Schleich *(Mng Dir)*

MEGAL Verwaltungs-GmbH (1)
Kallenbergstr 7
Essen, Nordrhein-Westfalen, 45141, Germany
Tel.: (49) 20128953780
Fax: (49) 201364212409
Business Management Consulting Services
S.I.C.: 8742
N.A.I.C.S.: 541611

MEON Verwaltungs GmbH (1)
Nordliche Munchner Str 14
Grunwald, Bayern, 82031, Germany
Tel.: (49) 8964143398
Business Management Consulting Services
S.I.C.: 8742
N.A.I.C.S.: 541611

METHA-Methanhandel GmbH (1)
Brusseler Platz 1
45131 Essen, Nordrhein-Westfalen, Germany
Tel.: (49) 201 1844205
Fax: (49) 201 1842115
Natural Gas Distribution Services
S.I.C.: 4924
N.A.I.C.S.: 221210

MVA Bielefeld-Herford GmbH (1)
Schelpmilser Weg 30
33609 Bielefeld, Germany
Tel.: (49) 521 3398 0
Fax: (49) 521 3398 199
Web Site: www.interargem.de/Kontakte.php
Waste Recycling & Treatment Services
S.I.C.: 4959
N.A.I.C.S.: 562998

Netz Veltheim GmbH (1)
Mollberger Strasse 387
32457 Porta Westfalica, Germany
Tel.: (49) 5706 900 49 0
Fax: (49) 5706 900 49 31
E-Mail: info@netz-veltheim.de
Web Site: www.netz-veltheim.de
Electric Power Distributing Services
S.I.C.: 4911
N.A.I.C.S.: 221122

Netzgesellschaft Herrenwald Verwaltung GmbH (1)
Bahnhofstr 2
Stadtallendorf, Hessen, 35260, Germany
Tel.: (49) 64287070
Electric Power Generation Services
S.I.C.: 4939
N.A.I.C.S.: 221118

NORD-direkt GmbH (1)
Bismarckstrasse 67 - 69
24534 Neumunster, Germany
Tel.: (49) 43 21 49 90 200
Fax: (49) 43 21 49 90 299
E-Mail: info@norddirekt.de
Web Site: www.norddirekt.de
Environmental Consulting Services
S.I.C.: 8999
N.A.I.C.S.: 541620

Norddeutsche Gesellschaft zur Ablagerung von Mineralstoffen mbH (1)
Schoninger Strasse 2-3
38350 Helmstedt, Germany
Tel.: (49) 5351 1838 93
Fax: (49) 5351 1838 90
E-Mail: info@norgam.de
Web Site: www.norgam.de
Waste Management & Disposal Services
S.I.C.: 4959
N.A.I.C.S.: 562998
Hans-Ulrich Terschueren *(Mng Dir)*

Nordzucker Bioerdgas Verwaltung-GmbH (1)
Kuchenstr 9
Braunschweig, Niedersachsen, 38100, Germany
Tel.: (49) 5312411100
Oil & Gas Exploration Services
S.I.C.: 1389
N.A.I.C.S.: 213112

Obere Donau Kraftwerke Aktiengesellschaft (1)
Kraftwerk Faimingen Romerstrasse 1
Lauingen, 89415, Germany
Tel.: (49) 9072 2096
Fax: (49) 9072 6411
Electric Power Generation Services
S.I.C.: 4931
N.A.I.C.S.: 221118

Open Grid Service GmbH (1)
Ruhrallee 307-309
45136 Essen, Germany
Tel.: (49) 20136420
Fax: (49) 201364213900
E-Mail: info@open-grid-service.com
Web Site: www.open-grid-service.com
Gas Transmission Services
S.I.C.: 4922
N.A.I.C.S.: 486210
Jean-Michel Douret *(Mng Dir)*

PADES Personalservice GmbH (1)
Marsstr 42
80335 Munich, Germany
Tel.: (49) 89 51566 251
Fax: (49) 89 51566 259
E-Mail: pades@pades.eu
Web Site: www.pades.eu
Human Resources Consulting Services
S.I.C.: 8999
N.A.I.C.S.: 541612

Peissenberger Kraftwerksgesellschaft mit beschrankter Haftung (1)
Bergwerkstr 14
82380 Peissenberg, Germany
Tel.: (49) 8803 496 0
Fax: (49) 8803 496 77
E-Mail: info@pkg-peissenberg.de
Web Site: www.pkg-peissenberg.de
Electric Power Generation Services
S.I.C.: 4911
N.A.I.C.S.: 221118

Purena GmbH (1)
Halchtersche Strasse 33
38304 Wolfenbuttel, Germany
Tel.: (49) 5331 88263 0
Fax: (49) 5331 88263 38813
E-Mail: direkt@purena.de
Web Site: www.purena.de
Water Treatment Services
S.I.C.: 4941
N.A.I.C.S.: 221310

Rappold, Hermann & Co. GmbH (1)
Zollhausstr 121
D 52353 Duren, Germany (100%)
Tel.: (49) 242184070
Fax: (49) 2421840799
Equipment for Iron & Steel Mills, Power Plants & Ceramic Burners
S.I.C.: 3547
N.A.I.C.S.: 333519

Rauschbergbahn Gesellschaft mit beschrankter Haftung (1)
Rathausstrasse 12
Ruhpolding, 83324, Germany
Tel.: (49) 8663 5945
Fax: (49) 8663 8828 33
E-Mail: rauschbergbahn@t-online.de
Web Site: www.rauschbergbahn.com
Cable Car Operating Services
S.I.C.: 4522
N.A.I.C.S.: 487990

RDE Regionale Dienstleistungen Energie GmbH & Co. KG (1)
Bismarckstr 9 - 11
97080 Wurzburg, Germany
Tel.: (49) 9 31 3 00 22 30
Fax: (49) 9 31 3 00 24 81
E-Mail: info@rde-dienstleistungen.de
Web Site: www.rde-dienstleistungen.de

E.ON SE—(Continued)

Electric Power Distribution Services
S.I.C.: 4911
N.A.I.C.S.: 221122

RDE Verwaltungs-GmbH (1)
Bismarckstr 9-11
97080 Wurzburg, Baravia, Germany
Tel.: (49) 9313002230
Fax: (49) 9313002481
Management Consulting Services
S.I.C.: 8748
N.A.I.C.S.: 541618

RMD-Consult GmbH Wasserbau und Energie (1)
Blutenburgstrasse 20
80636 Munich, Germany
Tel.: (49) 89 99 222 402
Fax: (49) 89 99 222 409
E-Mail: mail@rmd-consult.de
Web Site: www.rmd-consult.de
Emp.: 4
Electric Power Generation Services
S.I.C.: 4911
N.A.I.C.S.: 221118
Franz Zimmermann *(Mng Dir)*

RMD Wasserstrassen GmbH (1)
Blutenburgstrasse 20
80636 Munich, Germany
Tel.: (49) 89 99 222 0
Fax: (49) 89 99 222 303
E-Mail: info@rmd-wasserstrassen.de
Web Site: www.rmd-wasserstrassen.de
Emp.: 15
Hydraulic Engineering Services
S.I.C.: 8711
N.A.I.C.S.: 541330
Albrecht Schleich *(Co-Mng Dir)*

Safetec Entsorgungs- und Sicherheitstechnik GmbH (1)
Kurpfalzring 98a
Postfach 120651
69123 Heidelberg, Germany
Tel.: (49) 6221 65175 0
Fax: (49) 6221 65175 10
E-Mail: strahlenschutz@safetec-hd.de
Web Site: www.safetec-strahlenschutz.de
Emp.: 80
Radiation Protection & Nuclear Engineering Services
S.I.C.: 8711
N.A.I.C.S.: 541330
Jurgen Fleischhacker *(Gen Mgr)*

Schleswig-Holstein Netz Verwaltungs-GmbH (1)
Schleswag-HeinGas-Platz 1
25451 Quickborn, Schleswig-Holstein, Germany
Tel.: (49) 4106 6489090
Electric Power Distributing Services
S.I.C.: 4939
N.A.I.C.S.: 221122

SERVICE plus GmbH (1)
Bismarckstr 67-69
24534 Neumunster, Germany
Tel.: (49) 4321 49 90 100
Fax: (49) 4321 49 90 101
E-Mail: info@service-plus-gmbh.de
Web Site: www.service-plus-gmbh.de
Information Technology Consulting Services
S.I.C.: 7371
N.A.I.C.S.: 541511

SKW Stickstoffwerke Piesteritz GmbH (1)
Moellensdorfer Strasse 13
06886 Lutherstadt Wittenberg, Germany (50%)
Tel.: (49) 3491680
Fax: (49) 3491684300
E-Mail: office@av-halle.com
Web Site: www.skwp.de
Sls.: $287,902,880
Emp.: 65
Agricultural & Industrial Chemicals
S.I.C.: 2879
N.A.I.C.S.: 325320
Rudiger Giesrick *(Mng Dir)*

Stadtwerke Gelnhausen GmbH (1)
Philipp-Reis-Strasse 1-3
63571 Gelnhausen, Germany
Tel.: (49) 6051 838 01
Fax: (49) 6051 838 4756
E-Mail: info@stadtwerke-gelnhausen.de
Web Site: www.stadtwerke-gelnhausen.de
Emp.: 4
Electric Power Distribution Services
S.I.C.: 4931
N.A.I.C.S.: 221122
Martin Severin *(Gen Mgr)*

Strom Germering GmbH (1)
Barenweg 13
82110 Germering, Germany
Tel.: (49) 89 50 05 99 44
Fax: (49) 89 50 05 99 45
E-Mail: info@strom-germering.de
Web Site: www.strom-germering.de
Electric Power Distribution Services
S.I.C.: 4911
N.A.I.C.S.: 221122

Stromversorgung Ahrensburg GmbH (1)
Kurt-Fischer-Str 52
22926 Ahrensburg, Germany
Tel.: (49) 4102 99 49 010
Fax: (49) 4102 99 49 011
E-Mail: info@stromversorgung-ahrensburg.de
Web Site: www.stromversorgung-ahrensburg.de
Electric Power Distribution Services
S.I.C.: 4939
N.A.I.C.S.: 221122

Stromversorgung Ruhpolding Gesellschaft mit beschrankter Haftung (1)
Rathausstrasse 12
83324 Ruhpolding, Germany
Tel.: (49) 8663 88280
Fax: (49) 8663 882833
E-Mail: stromversorgung@strom-ruhpolding.de
Web Site: www.strom-ruhpolding.de
Emp.: 13
Electric Power Distribution Services
S.I.C.: 4939
N.A.I.C.S.: 221122
Rolf Stieler *(Gen Mgr)*

SVO Vertrieb GmbH (1)
Sprengerstrasse 2
29223 Celle, Germany
Tel.: (49) 51 41 975 0
Fax: (49) 1411633395
E-Mail: info@svo-vertrieb.de
Web Site: www.svo.de
Emp.: 30
Electric Power Distribution Services
S.I.C.: 4939
N.A.I.C.S.: 221122
Kersten Koschoreck *(Gen Mgr)*

TEN Thuringer Energienetze GmbH (1)
Schwerborner Strasse 30
99087 Erfurt, Germany
Tel.: (49) 3641691888
Fax: (49) 36173901292
E-Mail: info@thueringer-energienetze.com
Web Site: www.thueringer-energienetze.com
Electric Power Transmission Services
S.I.C.: 4911
N.A.I.C.S.: 221121

Terrakomp GmbH (1)
Schoninger Str 2-3
38350 Helmstedt, Germany
Tel.: (49) 5351 183888
Fax: (49) 5351 183890
E-Mail: info@terrakomp-helmstedt.de
Web Site: www.terrakomp-helmstedt.de
Emp.: 14
Organic Waste Recycling Services
S.I.C.: 4953
N.A.I.C.S.: 562920
Sophie Dutordoir *(Gen Mgr)*

THB Thuringer Breitband GmbH (1)
Schwanseestr 13
99423 Weimar, Germany
Tel.: (49) 361 73900
Information Technology Consulting Services
S.I.C.: 8748
N.A.I.C.S.: 541618

Thuringer Energie Netzservice Geschaftsfuhrungsgesellschaft mbH (1)
Schwerborner Str 30
99087 Erfurt, Thuringen, Germany
Tel.: (49) 361 652 0
Fax: (49) 361 652 3480
Electric Power Distribution Services
S.I.C.: 4911
N.A.I.C.S.: 221122

Subsidiary:

Iridium Services Deutschland GmbH (2)
Jaegerhofstrabe 19 - 20
40479 Dusseldorf, Germany (100%)
Tel.: (49) 2114973176
Sales Range: $1-9.9 Million
Electric Services
S.I.C.: 4939
N.A.I.C.S.: 221122

VEBACOM GmbH (1)
Am Bonneshof 35
40474 Dusseldorf, Germany (55%)
Web Site: www.vebacom.de
Sales Range: $200-249.9 Million
Emp.: 1,219
Electricity Distribution Services
S.I.C.: 4911
N.A.I.C.S.: 221122

Versorgungsbetriebe Helgoland GmbH (1)
Kurpromenade
27498 Heligoland, Schleswig-Holstein, Germany
Tel.: (49) 4725 8180
Fax: (49) 4725 81829
Electric Power Generation Services
S.I.C.: 4911
N.A.I.C.S.: 221118

VIAG Telecom Beteilgungs GmbH (1)
Munich, Munich, Germany (100%)
Web Site: www.viag.de
Telecommunication Services
S.I.C.: 4813
N.A.I.C.S.: 517110

VR Telecommunications GmbH & Co. (1)
Norderfriedrichskoog, Husum, Germany (51.2%)
Telecommunications Company
S.I.C.: 4813
N.A.I.C.S.: 517110

Warmeversorgungsgesellschaft Konigs Wusterhausen mbH (1)
Schillerstr 7
15711 Konigs Wusterhausen, Brandenburg, Germany
Tel.: (49) 3375 256110
Fax: (49) 3375 256111
Electric Power Distributing Services
S.I.C.: 4931
N.A.I.C.S.: 221122

WBG GmbH (1)
Sudstrasse 22
38350 Helmstedt, Germany
Tel.: (49) 5351 18 2226
Fax: (49) 5351 18 2219
E-Mail: dialog@wbg-helmstedt.de
Web Site: www.wbg-helmstedt.de
Property Management Services
S.I.C.: 6531
N.A.I.C.S.: 531311

Weissmainkraftwerk Rohrenhof Aktiengesellschaft (1)
Luitpoldplatz 5
95444 Bayreuth, Germany
Tel.: (49) 921 285 2863
Fax: (49) 921 285 2898
E-Mail: weissmainkraftwerk@t-online.de
Web Site: www.weissmainkraftwerk.de
Emp.: 7
Hydroelectric Power Generation Services
S.I.C.: 4931
N.A.I.C.S.: 221118
Konrad Walter *(CEO)*

WEVG Salzgitter GmbH & Co. KG (1)
Albert-Schweitzer-Strasse 7-11
38226 Salzgitter, Germany
Tel.: (49) 5341 408 0
Fax: (49) 5341 408 200
Electric Power & Gas Distribution Services
S.I.C.: 4939
N.A.I.C.S.: 221122

WEVG Verwaltungs GmbH (1)
Albert-Schweitzer-Str 7-11
Salzgitter, 38226, Germany
Tel.: (49) 5341 408 0
Fax: (49) 5341 408200
E-Mail: info@wevg.vom
Web Site: www.wevg.com
Emp.: 26
Electric Power & Natural Gas Distribution Services
S.I.C.: 4939
N.A.I.C.S.: 221122
Rainer Krause *(Mng Dir)*

Windpark Mutzschen OHG (1)
Am Kanal 2-3
Potsdam, Brandenburg, 14467, Germany
Tel.: (49) 3312342903
Fax: (49) 3312343015
Electric Power Generation Services
S.I.C.: 4939
N.A.I.C.S.: 221118

Windpark Naundorf OHG (1)
Am Kanal 2-3
Potsdam, Brandenburg, 14467, Germany
Tel.: (49) 331 2340
Fax: (49) 331 2343301
Electric Power Generation Services
S.I.C.: 4931
N.A.I.C.S.: 221118

U.S. Subsidiaries:

Anacacho Wind Farm, LLC (1)
353 N Clark St Fl 30
Chicago, IL 60654-4704
Tel.: (312) 245-3035
Electric Power Generation Services
S.I.C.: 4931
N.A.I.C.S.: 221118

Champion Wind Farm, LLC (1)
53 N Clark St Fl 30
Chicago, IL 60654
Tel.: (312) 923-9463
Fax: (312) 923-9469
Electric Power Generation Services
S.I.C.: 4931
N.A.I.C.S.: 221118
Steven Trenholm *(Pres)*

Cordova Wind Farm, LLC (1)
220 W Main St Ste 500
Louisville, KY 40202-5324
Tel.: (502) 627-2000
Electric Power Generation Services
S.I.C.: 4931
N.A.I.C.S.: 221118

EC&R NA Solar PV, LLC (1)
353 N Clark St
Chicago, IL 60654-4704
Tel.: (312) 245-3035
Electric Power Generation Services
S.I.C.: 4939
N.A.I.C.S.: 221118

EC&R Panther Creek Wind Farm I&II, LLC (1)
401 N Michigan Ave 1720
Chicago, IL 60611-4255
Tel.: (432) 398-5309
Wind Electric Power Generation Services
S.I.C.: 4939
N.A.I.C.S.: 221118

EC&R Panther Creek Wind Farm III, LLC (1)
353 N Clark St 30th Fl
Chicago, IL 60654
Tel.: (312) 923-9463
Fax: (312) 923-9469
Electric Power Generation Services
S.I.C.: 4931
N.A.I.C.S.: 221118
Steven Trenholm *(Pres)*

EC&R Papalote Creek I, LLC (1)
401 N Michigan Ave Ste 1720
Chicago, IL 60611-4255
Tel.: (312) 923-9463
Fax: (312) 923-9469
Electric Power Generation Services
S.I.C.: 4939
N.A.I.C.S.: 221118

EC&R Papalote Creek II, LLC (1)
812 San Antonio St Ste 201
Austin, TX 78701

Tel.: (512) 482-4045
Fax: (512) 494-9581
Electric Power Generation & Distribution Services
S.I.C.: 4911
N.A.I.C.S.: 221118

EC&R QSE, LLC (1)
353 N Clark St Fl 30
Chicago, IL 60654
Tel.: (312) 923-9463
Fax: (312) 923-9469
Electric Power Generation Services
S.I.C.: 4931
N.A.I.C.S.: 221118
Steve Trenholm *(Pres)*

EC&R Services, LLC (1)
353 N Clark St Fl 30
Chicago, IL 60654-4704
Tel.: (312) 923-9463
Fax: (312) 923-9469
Electric Power Generation Services
S.I.C.: 4939
N.A.I.C.S.: 221118
Steven Trenholm *(Pres)*

E.ON Climate & Renewables North America LLC (1)
353 N Clark St Fl 30
Chicago, IL 60654
Tel.: (312) 923-9463
Fax: (312) 923-9469
Web Site: www.eoncrna.com
Emp.: 75
Electric Power Generation Services
S.I.C.: 4939
N.A.I.C.S.: 221118
Paul Dowling *(CEO)*
Brian Hurley *(CTO)*
Ciaran O'Brien *(Sr VP)*

Subsidiary:

EC&R Energy Marketing, LLC (2)
353 N Clark St Fl 30
Chicago, IL 60611
Tel.: (312) 923-9463
Fax: (312) 923-9469
Management Consulting Services
S.I.C.: 8748
N.A.I.C.S.: 541618

E.ON NA Capital LLC (1)
2751 Centerville Rd Ste 231
Wilmington, DE 19808
Tel.: (302) 996-9020
Fax: (302) 996-9080
Financial Management Services
S.I.C.: 6211
N.A.I.C.S.: 523999

EZH-Systems Inc. (1)
220 W Main St Ste 500
Louisville, KY 40202-5324
Tel.: (502) 627-2000
Management Consulting Services
S.I.C.: 8748
N.A.I.C.S.: 541618

Flatlands Wind Farm, LLC (1)
220 W Main St Ste 500
Louisville, KY 40202-5324
Tel.: (502) 627-2000
Electric Power Generation Services
S.I.C.: 4939
N.A.I.C.S.: 221118

Forest Creek WF Holdco, LLC (1)
220 W Main St Ste 500
Louisville, KY 40202-5324
Tel.: (502) 627-2000
Electric Power Generation Services
S.I.C.: 4931
N.A.I.C.S.: 221118

Forest Creek Wind Farm, LLC (1)
812 San Antonio St Ste 201
Austin, TX 78701
Tel.: (512) 482-4042
Fax: (512) 494-9581
Emp.: 9
Wind Electric Power Generation Services
S.I.C.: 4911
N.A.I.C.S.: 221118
John Franklin *(Gen Mgr)*

Inadale WF Holdco, LLC (1)
220 W Main St Ste 500
Louisville, KY 40202-5324
Tel.: (502) 627-2000
Electric Power Generation Services
S.I.C.: 4911
N.A.I.C.S.: 221118

Inadale Wind Farm, LLC (1)
353 N Clark St Fl 30
Chicago, IL 60654
Tel.: (312) 923-9463
Electric Power Generation Services
S.I.C.: 4939
N.A.I.C.S.: 221118
Steve Trenholm *(Pres)*

Munnsville Investco, LLC (1)
220 W Main St Ste 500
Louisville, KY 40202-5324
Tel.: (502) 627-2000
Electric Power Generation Services
S.I.C.: 4911
N.A.I.C.S.: 221118

Pyron Wind Farm, LLC (1)
353 N Clark St Fl 30
Chicago, IL 60654-4704
Tel.: (325) 766-3083
Fax: (312) 923-9469
E-Mail: ecrna@eon.com
Emp.: 650
Electric Power Generation Services
S.I.C.: 4911
N.A.I.C.S.: 221118
Steve Trenholm *(CEO)*

Roscoe Wind Farm, LLC (1)
401 N Michigan Ave 1720
Chicago, IL 60611-4255
Tel.: (312) 923-9463
Fax: (312) 923-9469
Electric Power Generation Services
S.I.C.: 4911
N.A.I.C.S.: 221118

Sand Bluff Wind Farm, LLC (1)
812 San Antonio St Ste 201
Austin, TX 78701
Tel.: (512) 482-4042
Fax: (512) 494-9581
Web Site: www.eoncrna.com
Emp.: 7
Electric Power Generation Services
S.I.C.: 4931
N.A.I.C.S.: 221118
John Franklin *(Gen Mgr)*

Settlers Trail Wind Farm, LLC (1)
353 N Clark St Fl 30
Chicago, IL 60654-4704
Tel.: (312) 245-3035
Electric Power Generation Services
S.I.C.: 4911
N.A.I.C.S.: 221118

Stony Creek WF Holdco, LLC (1)
353 N Clark St Fl 30
Chicago, IL 60654-4704
Tel.: (312) 245-3035
Electric Power Generation Services
S.I.C.: 4911
N.A.I.C.S.: 221118

Stony Creek Wind Farm, LLC (1)
353 N Clark St Fl 30
Chicago, IL 60654
Tel.: (312) 923-9463
Fax: (312) 923-9469
Electric Power Generation Services
S.I.C.: 4911
N.A.I.C.S.: 221118

Venado Wind Farm, LLC (1)
353 N Clark St Fl 30
Chicago, IL 60654-4704
Tel.: (312) 245-3035
Electric Power Generation Services
S.I.C.: 4939
N.A.I.C.S.: 221118

Non-U.S. Subsidiaries:

ANCO Sp. z o.o. (1)
ul Grunwaldzka 219
80-266 Gdansk, Poland
Tel.: (48) 58 557 31 18
Fax: (48) 58 345 80 93
E-Mail: anco@anco.com.pl
Web Site: www.anco.com.pl
Emp.: 4
Safety Equipment Distr
S.I.C.: 5084
N.A.I.C.S.: 423830
Agnieszka Owczarczak *(Gen Dir)*

Barras Electricas Galaico-Asturianas, S.A. (1)
Calle Cidade De Viveiro 4 - 1
Lugo, 27002, Spain
Tel.: (34) 982222200
Fax: (34) 982243635
Web Site: www.begasa.es
Electric Power Generation & Distribution Services
S.I.C.: 4931
N.A.I.C.S.: 221118
Luis Garcia Santalla *(Gen Mgr)*

Barras Electricas Generacion, S.L. (1)
Calle Cidade De Viveiro 4 - 1
Lugo, 27002, Spain
Tel.: (34) 982222200
Fax: (34) 982243635
Electric Power Generation Services
S.I.C.: 4939
N.A.I.C.S.: 221118

Debreceni Kombinalt Ciklusu Eromu Kft. (1)
Mikepercsi ut 1
Debrecen, 4030, Hungary
Tel.: (36) 52512800
Fax: (36) 52512813
Electric Power Generation Services
S.I.C.: 4939
N.A.I.C.S.: 221118

Distribuidora de Gas del Centro S.A. (1)
Avenida Hipolito Yrigoyen 475
Cordoba, 5000, Argentina
Tel.: (54) 3514688154
Fax: (54) 3514688111
E-Mail: compras@ecogas.com.ar
Web Site: www.ecogas.com.ar
Emp.: 30
Natural Gas Distribution Services
S.I.C.: 4924
N.A.I.C.S.: 221210

Dutchdelta Finance SARL (1)
Grand Rue 99
1661 Luxembourg, Luxembourg
Tel.: (352) 2686851
Financial Management Services
S.I.C.: 6211
N.A.I.C.S.: 523999

EC Serwis Sp. z o.o. (1)
ul Kulczynskiego 6
Slupsk, 76 200, Poland
Tel.: (48) 59 8474480
Fax: (48) 59 8474499
E-Mail: sekretariat.ecserwis@ecslupsk.pl
Web Site: www.ecserwis.eu
Emp.: 1
Electrical Equipment Installation Services
S.I.C.: 1711
N.A.I.C.S.: 238220
Izabela Drzal *(Mng Dir)*

ELICA S.R.L. (1)
Traversa II Priv S Croce A Orsolone 18
Naples, Italy
Tel.: (39) 0815466592
Management Consulting Services
S.I.C.: 8748
N.A.I.C.S.: 541618

Enel Viesgo (1)
Calle Medio 12
39003 Santander, Spain
Tel.: (34) 942246000
Fax: (34) 942246030
Web Site: www.eon-espana.com
Emp.: 1,000
Electric Utility Services
S.I.C.: 4939
N.A.I.C.S.: 221122

Energest S.r.l. (1)
Via dei Remi 26
Rome, 122, Italy
Tel.: (39) 06 56305680
Fax: (39) 06 23328544
E-Mail: info@energest.it
Web Site: www.energest.it
Electric Power & Natural Gas Distribution Services
S.I.C.: 4931
N.A.I.C.S.: 221122

Energetika Malenovice, a.s. (1)
Trida 3 Kvetna
cp 1173
763 02 Zlin, Czech Republic
Tel.: (420) 577 533 111
Fax: (420) 577 103 306
E-Mail: eng@energetikamalenovice.cz
Web Site: www.energetikamalenovice.cz
Emp.: 2
Electric Power Distribution Services
S.I.C.: 4939
N.A.I.C.S.: 221122
George Stedl *(Chm)*

ENERGETIKA SERVIS s.r.o. (1)
Krizikova 1690
370 01 Ceske Budejovice, Czech Republic
Tel.: (420) 38 635 60 55
Fax: (420) 38 635 64 22
E-Mail: info@energetika-servis.cz
Web Site: www.energetika-servis.cz
Electric Power Generation & Distribution Services
S.I.C.: 4911
N.A.I.C.S.: 221118

E.ON Austria GmbH (1)
Niederhofstr 37
1010 Vienna, Austria
Tel.: (43) 1 5 32 29 65
Fax: (43) 1 5 32 29 65 10
E-Mail: office@eon-austria.at
Emp.: 12
Electric Power Distribution Services
S.I.C.: 4911
N.A.I.C.S.: 221122
Sven Schlotz *(Gen Mgr)*

E.ON Belgium N.V. (1)
Kunstlaan 40
1040 Brussels, Belgium
Tel.: (32) 2 743 33 33
Fax: (32) 2 743 33 39
E-Mail: salesbelgium@eon-benelux.com
Web Site: www.eon.com
Emp.: 15
Electric Power & Gas Distribution Services
S.I.C.: 4931
N.A.I.C.S.: 221122
Rob Oudshoorn *(CEO)*

E.ON Benelux CCS Project B.V. (1)
Capelseweg 400
Rotterdam, 3068 AX, Netherlands
Tel.: (31) 102895097
Fax: (31) 102825039
Electric Power Distribution Services
S.I.C.: 4911
N.A.I.C.S.: 221122

E.ON Benelux Levering b.v. (1)
Dr Holtroplaan 2-28
Eindhoven, 5652 XR, Netherlands
Tel.: (31) 40 257 7600
Fax: (31) 40 257 7755
E-Mail: zakelijk@eon.nl
Web Site: www.eon.nl
Electric Power & Natural Gas Distribution Services
S.I.C.: 4939
N.A.I.C.S.: 221122
Patrick Nanninga *(Gen Mgr)*

E.ON Bulgaria Grid AD (1)
Varna Towers Tower E 258 Vladislav Varnenchik Blvd
9009 Varna, Bulgaria
Tel.: (359) 70016161
Fax: (359) 52577565
E-Mail: service@energo-pro.bg
Web Site: www.energo-pro.bg
Electric Power Distribution Services
S.I.C.: 4931
N.A.I.C.S.: 221122
Werner Haberkorn *(Chm-Mgmt Bd)*
Martin Mirchev *(Member-Mgmt Bd)*
Anatoli Tokmakchiev *(Member-Mgmt Bd)*

E.ON Climate & Renewables Italia S.r.l. (1)
Via Amerigo Vespucci 2
20124 Milan, Italy
Tel.: (39) 02 89448301
Fax: (39) 02 89448822
Web Site: www.eon-italia.com
Emp.: 3
Electric Power Generation Services
S.I.C.: 4939
N.A.I.C.S.: 221118
Roberta Benedetti *(Mng Dir)*

E.ON Comercializadora de Ultimo Recurso S.L. (1)
Calle Medio 12
Santander, 39003, Spain

E.ON SE—(Continued)

Tel.: (34) 942 24 60 00
Electric Power Distributing Services
S.I.C.: 4931
N.A.I.C.S.: 221122

E.ON Danmark A/S (1)
Norrelundvej 10
2730 Herlev, Denmark
Tel.: (45) 44854100
Fax: (45) 44854101
E-Mail: kundecenter@eon.dk
Web Site: www.eon.dk
Sls.: $6,169,500
Emp.: 60
Electric Power Distr
S.I.C.: 4931
N.A.I.C.S.: 221122
Joean Maesen *(Mng Dir)*
Toi Harris *(Mng Dir)*

Subsidiary:

E.ON Varme Danmark ApS (2)
Dirch Passers Alle 76
2000 Frederiksberg, Denmark
Tel.: (45) 44854100
E-Mail: kundecenter@eon.dk
Emp.: 5
Electric Power Distribution Services
S.I.C.: 4931
N.A.I.C.S.: 221122
Tore Harritshoj *(Mng Dir)*

E.ON Elektrarne s.r.o. (1)
SPP Kompresorova Stanica 3
919 33 Trakovice, Slovakia
Tel.: (421) 33 32 35 101
Fax: (421) 33 32 35 403
E-Mail: elektrarne@eon-energie.com
Web Site: www.eon-elektrarne.sk
Emp.: 35
Electric Power Generation & Distribution Services
S.I.C.: 4931
N.A.I.C.S.: 221118
Vladimir Pestun *(Mng Dir)*

E.ON Energiatermelo Kft. (1)
Mikepercsi Utca 1
Debrecen, 4030, Hungary
Tel.: (36) 52512800
Fax: (36) 52512813
Electric Power Distribution Services
S.I.C.: 4931
N.A.I.C.S.: 221122

E.ON Energie Odnawialne Sp. z o.o. (1)
Plac Rodla 8
70-419 Szczecin, Poland
Tel.: (48) 913594281
Fax: (48) 913594282
Web Site: www.eon.pl
Emp.: 1
Electric Power Distribution Services
S.I.C.: 4939
N.A.I.C.S.: 221122
Nihat Hunerle *(Gen Mgr)*

E.ON Energie Romania S.A. (1)
Justitiei Nr 12
Tirgu Mures, Mures, 540069, Romania
Tel.: (40) 365403302
Fax: (40) 365403312
E-Mail: office.eero@eon-romania.ro
Web Site: www.eon-romania.ro
Electric Power & Natural Gas Distribution Services
S.I.C.: 4939
N.A.I.C.S.: 221122
Frank Hajdinjak *(Chm)*
Dan Morari *(Gen Dir)*

E.ON Energihandel Nordic AB (1)
Carl Gustafs vag 1
205 09 Malmo, Skane, Sweden
Tel.: (46) 40 255000
Gas & Electric Power Distributing Services
S.I.C.: 4924
N.A.I.C.S.: 221210

E.ON Energy from Waste Delfzijl B.V. (1)
Oosterhorn 38
9936 HD Farmsum, Netherlands
Tel.: (31) 5 96 67 40 00
Fax: (31) 5 96 67 43 94
Web Site: www.eew-energyfromwaste.com
Electric Power Generation Services
S.I.C.: 4931
N.A.I.C.S.: 221118
Horst Bieber *(CEO)*

E.ON Energy from Waste Polska Sp. z o.o. (1)
ul Krolowej Marysienki 10
02-954 Warsaw, Poland
Tel.: (48) 22 858 14 50
Waste Management & Electric Power Generation Services
S.I.C.: 4953
N.A.I.C.S.: 562219

E.ON Energy Trading Bulgarien EOOD (1)
Varna Towers Tower G 258 Vladislav Varnenchik Blvd
Varna, 9009, Bulgaria
Tel.: (359) 52577000
E-Mail: service@eon-bulgaria.com
Electric Power Distribution Services
S.I.C.: 4911
N.A.I.C.S.: 221122
Boyko Dimitrachkov *(Co-Mng Dir)*
Kaloyan Kanev *(Co-Mng Dir)*

E.ON Energy Trading NL Staff Company B.V. (1)
Capelseweg 400
Rotterdam, Zuid-Holland, 3068 AX, Netherlands
Tel.: (31) 102895711
Fax: (31) 102895519
E-Mail: info@eon-benelux.com
Emp.: 9
Electric Power Distribution Services
S.I.C.: 4911
N.A.I.C.S.: 221122

E.ON Eromuvek Termelo es Uzemelteto Kft (1)
Roosevelt ter 7-8
1051 Budapest, Hungary
Tel.: (36) 1 373 3529
Electric Power Distributing Services
S.I.C.: 4911
N.A.I.C.S.: 221122

E.ON Espana, S.L. (1)
Ed Torre Picasso Pl 19 Pza Pablo Ruiz Picasso s/n
28020 Madrid, Spain
Tel.: (34) 91 4184400
Fax: (34) 91 4184424
E-Mail: informacion@eon.com
Web Site: www.eonespana.com
Emp.: 18
Electric Power Generation & Distribution Services
S.I.C.: 4939
N.A.I.C.S.: 221118
Anders Svensson *(Chm & Pres)*
Miguel Antonanzas *(Chm)*
Manuel Sanchez *(Gen Dir & Mgr-Infrastructures)*
Javier Anzola *(Gen Dir-Liberalized Markets)*

Subsidiaries:

E.ON Distribucion, S.L. (2)
Calle del Medio 12
Santander, 39003, Spain
Tel.: (34) 942 24 60 00
Fax: (34) 942 24 60 34
Electric Power Distributing Services
S.I.C.: 4931
N.A.I.C.S.: 221122

E.ON Energia, S.L. (2)
Calle Medio 12
Santander, 39003, Spain
Tel.: (34) 942 24 60 00
Fax: (34) 942 24 60 31
Electric Power Distributing Services
S.I.C.: 4911
N.A.I.C.S.: 221122

E.ON Iberia Services, S.L. (2)
Avenida Juan Lopez De Penalver 17
Malaga, 29590, Spain
Tel.: (34) 952020381
Management Consulting Services
S.I.C.: 8748
N.A.I.C.S.: 541618

E.ON Red S.L. (2)
C Medio 12
Santander, Cantabria, Spain
Tel.: (34) 942246000
Electric Power Distribution Services
S.I.C.: 4911
N.A.I.C.S.: 221122

E.ON Servicios, S.L. (2)
Carrta Poblado S/N
Central Termica, 14220 Sagunto, Spain
Tel.: (34) 942246000
Electric Power Generation & Distribution Services
S.I.C.: 4931
N.A.I.C.S.: 221118

Northeolic Montebuno, S.L. (2)
Calle Goya 4 Plt 4
Madrid, Spain
Tel.: (34) 914320606
Electric Power Distribution Services
S.I.C.: 4931
N.A.I.C.S.: 221122

SINERGIA ARAGONESA, S.L. (2)
Av Academia General Militar 52
Zaragoza, 50015, Spain
Tel.: (34) 97 6216735
Engineering Services
S.I.C.: 8711
N.A.I.C.S.: 541330

Sociedad Eolica Salmantina, S.L (2)
C Gran Via 2 2 a
Salamanca, Spain
Tel.: (34) 915562866
Fax: (34) 915972139
Electric Power Generation Services
S.I.C.: 4939
N.A.I.C.S.: 221118

E.ON Europa, S.L. (1)
Ribera Del Loira 60
Madrid, 28042, Spain
Tel.: (34) 915 66 88 00
Fax: (34) 915 63 81 81
Electricity Production & Distribution Services
S.I.C.: 4911
N.A.I.C.S.: 221118
Bogas Galvez Jose Damian *(CEO)*

E.ON First Future Energy Holding B.V. (1)
Capelseweg 400
Rotterdam, Zuid-Holland, 3068 AX, Netherlands
Tel.: (31) 102895711
Investment Management Services
S.I.C.: 6282
N.A.I.C.S.: 523920

E.ON France Management S.A.S. (1)
5 Rue Athenes
75009 Paris, France
Tel.: (33) 144633998
Fax: (33) 144633999
Web Site: www.eon.de
Emp.: 15
Electric Power Generation & Distribution Services
S.I.C.: 4931
N.A.I.C.S.: 221118

E.ON France S.A.S. (1)
5 Rue d'Athenes
75009 Paris, France
Tel.: (33) 1 44 63 39 98
Fax: (33) 1 44 63 39 99
E-Mail: acceul.hotesse@eon.com
Web Site: www.eon-france.com
Rev.: $2,625,601,930
Emp.: 885
Electric Power & Gas Distribution Services
S.I.C.: 4939
N.A.I.C.S.: 221122
Luc Poyer *(Chm)*
Stephan Parthier *(Member-Mgmt Bd)*

E.ON Gaz Distributie S.A. (1)
Piata Trandafirilor No 21
540049 Tirgu Mures, Mures, Romania
Tel.: (40) 365 40 36 00
Fax: (40) 265 26 04 18
E-Mail: office@eon-gaz-distributie.ro
Web Site: www.eon-gaz-distributie.ro
Emp.: 5,600
Natural Gas Distribution Services
S.I.C.: 4924
N.A.I.C.S.: 221210
George Cristodorescu *(Chm)*
Virgil Metea *(Gen Dir)*

E.ON Gazdasagi Szolgaltato Kft. (1)
Kando Kalman Utca 11-13
Gyor, 9027, Hungary
Tel.: (36) 96521841
Fax: (36) 96521938
Emp.: 50
Financial Management Services
S.I.C.: 6211
N.A.I.C.S.: 523999
Zsolt Temesvary *(Gen Mgr)*

E.ON Halozati Szolgaltato Kft. (1)
Malomvolgyi Utca 2
Pecs, 7636, Hungary
Tel.: (36) 72501000
Fax: (36) 72501228
Water & Sewer Line Construction Services
S.I.C.: 1629
N.A.I.C.S.: 237110

E.ON INTERNATIONAL FINANCE B.V. (1)
Capelseweg 400
Rotterdam, 3068 AX, Netherlands
Tel.: (31) 10 289 5640
Financial Management Services
S.I.C.: 6211
N.A.I.C.S.: 523999
Eric Choy *(Gen Mgr)*

E.ON IT Bulgaria EOOD (1)
Varna Towers 258 Vladislav Varnenchik
Varna, 9009, Bulgaria
Tel.: (359) 52577000
Fax: (359) 52577761
Information Technology Consulting Services
S.I.C.: 7373
N.A.I.C.S.: 541512
Rudolf Willig *(Mng Dir)*

E.ON IT Czech Republic s.r.o. (1)
F A Gerstnera 2151/6
Ceske Budejovice, 370 01, Czech Republic
Tel.: (420) 387 867 717
Fax: (420) 387 867 719
E-Mail: info@eon-is.cz
Web Site: www.eon-is.cz
Information Technology Consulting Services
S.I.C.: 7373
N.A.I.C.S.: 541512

E.ON IT Hungary Kft. (1)
Szechenyi Istvan Ter 7-8
Budapest, 1051, Hungary
Tel.: (36) 14722300
Fax: (36) 14878251
Information Technology Consulting Services
S.I.C.: 7373
N.A.I.C.S.: 541512

E.ON IT Italia S.r.l. (1)
Via Amerigo Vespucci 2
Milan, 20124, Italy
Tel.: (39) 0289448001
Fax: (39) 0141968518
Information Technology Consulting Services
S.I.C.: 7373
N.A.I.C.S.: 541512

E.ON IT Netherlands B.V. (1)
Capelseweg 400
Rotterdam, Zuid-Holland, 3068 AX, Netherlands
Tel.: (31) 102895711
Information Technology Consulting Services
S.I.C.: 7373
N.A.I.C.S.: 541512

E.ON IT Slovakia s.r.o. (1)
Culenova 5
811 09 Bratislava, Slovakia
Tel.: (421) 2 5061 2212
E-Mail: info-sk@eon.com
Web Site: www.eon-it.sk
Information Technology Consulting Services
S.I.C.: 7373
N.A.I.C.S.: 541512

E.ON IT Sverige AB (1)
Carl Gustavs vag 1
205 09 Malmo, Sweden
Tel.: (46) 40 25 50 00
Information Technology Consulting Services
S.I.C.: 8748
N.A.I.C.S.: 541618

E.ON IT UK Limited (1)
Westwood Way
Coventry, CV4 8LG, United Kingdom
Tel.: (44) 24 7642 4000

Information Technology Consulting Services
S.I.C.: 8748
N.A.I.C.S.: 541618

E.ON Italia (1)
Via Amerigo Vespucci
2-20124 Milan, Italy
Tel.: (39) 0289448001
Fax: (39) 0289448318
Web Site: www.eon-italia.com
Energy Services Management
S.I.C.: 4939
N.A.I.C.S.: 221112
Luca Dasl Fabbro *(CEO)*

Subsidiaries:

E.ON Climate & Renewables Italia Solar S.r.l. (2)
Via Amerigo Vespucci 2
20124 Milan, Italy
Tel.: (39) 02 89448001
E-Mail: info.italia@eon.com
Electric Power Generation Services
S.I.C.: 4911
N.A.I.C.S.: 221118

E.ON Energia S.p.A. (2)
Via E Fermi 15
37135 Verona, Italy
Tel.: (39) 0458251300
Fax: (39) 0458251333
E-Mail: info@italia.eon.com
Web Site: www.italia.eon.com
Emp.: 100
Energy Services
S.I.C.: 4911
N.A.I.C.S.: 221122
Massimo Bonato *(Dir-Admin)*

E.ON Produzione S.p.A (2)
Via Giuseppe Mangili 9
00197 Rome, Italy
Tel.: (39) 6830686611
Fax: (39) 683068562
Web Site: www.eon-italia.com
Electric Power Distribution
S.I.C.: 4911
N.A.I.C.S.: 221122
Alvaro Quiralte Abello *(Mng Dir)*

E.ON Kainuu Oy (1)
Ahontie 1 PL 5
87101 Kajaani, Finland
Tel.: (358) 1022 6000
Fax: (358) 1022 61226
E-Mail: info@eon.fi
Web Site: www.eon.fi
Electricity Power Distribution & Transmission Services
S.I.C.: 4911
N.A.I.C.S.: 221122

E.ON Kozep-dunantuli Gazhalozati Zrt. (1)
Zrinyi Miklos Utca 32
Nagykanizsa, 8800, Hungary
Tel.: (36) 93503600
Fax: (36) 93313077
Oil & Gas Exploration Services
S.I.C.: 1389
N.A.I.C.S.: 213112

E.ON Produktion Danmark A/S (1)
Norrelundvej 10
2730 Herlev, Denmark
Tel.: (45) 44 85 41 00
Fax: (45) 44 85 41 01
E-Mail: kundecenter@eon.dk
Web Site: www.eon.dk/Om-EON/Om-selskabet/
Emp.: 50
Electric Power Generation Services
S.I.C.: 4931
N.A.I.C.S.: 221118
Tore Harritshoj *(Mgr)*

E.ON Produzione Centrale Livorno Ferraris S.p.A. (1)
SP 7 Km 430
13046 Livorno Ferraris, Vercelli, Italy
Tel.: (39) 0161 1985201
Electric Power Production Services
S.I.C.: 4931
N.A.I.C.S.: 221118

E.ON Regenerabile Romania S.R.L (1)
146-150 Ciurchi Str
Iasi, 700359, Romania
Tel.: (40) 232405076
Fax: (40) 232405077
E-Mail: regenerabile@eon.com
Emp.: 6
Electric Power Generation Services
S.I.C.: 4931
N.A.I.C.S.: 221118

E.ON Renovaveis Portugal, SGPS S.A. (1)
Avenida Dom Joao II Lote 1 06 2 3 7 B
1990-095 Lisbon, Portugal
Tel.: (351) 211 554 944
Fax: (351) 218949006
Emp.: 4
Electric Power Generation Services
S.I.C.: 4911
N.A.I.C.S.: 221118

E.ON Romania S.R.L. (1)
Justitiei nr 12
540069 Tirgu Mures, Romania
Tel.: (40) 365 40 35 46
Fax: (40) 265 26 04 18
E-Mail: office@eon-romania.ro
Web Site: www.eon-romania.ro
Natural Gas & Electricity Distribution Services
S.I.C.: 4924
N.A.I.C.S.: 221210
Frank Hajdinjak *(Gen Dir)*

E.ON Ruhrgas Austria GmbH (1)
Kantgasse 1
Vienna, 1010, Austria
Tel.: (43) 15322963
Fax: (43) 1532296310
E-Mail: kontakt@eon-ruhrgas-austria.at
Web Site: www.eon-ruhrgas-austria.at
Emp.: 13
Oil & Gas Exploration Services
S.I.C.: 1389
N.A.I.C.S.: 213112
Sven Schlotz *(Mgr)*

E.ON Ruhrgas BBL B.V. (1)
Capelseweg 400
Rotterdam, 3068 AX, Netherlands
Tel.: (31) 10 2 89 57 91
Fax: (31) 10 2 89 50 90
Natural Gas Distr
S.I.C.: 4924
N.A.I.C.S.: 221210

E.ON Ruhrgas Dutch Holding B.V. (1)
Capelseweg 400
3068 AX Rotterdam, Zuid-Holland, Netherlands
Tel.: (31) 104780855
Fax: (31) 104769867
Investment Management Services
S.I.C.: 6799
N.A.I.C.S.: 523920

E.ON Servisni, s.r.o. (1)
F A Gerstnera 2151/6
370 49 Ceske Budejovice, Czech Republic
Tel.: (420) 387 861 111
Fax: (420) 387 862 900
Web Site: www.eon-servisni.cz
Electric Power & Gas Distribution Services
S.I.C.: 4911
N.A.I.C.S.: 221122

E.ON Suomi Oy (1)
Itamerenkatu 1
00180 Helsinki, Finland
Tel.: (358) 0102265500
Fax: (358) 102265555
E-Mail: markku.ryymin@eon.fi
Web Site: www.eonsuomi.fi
Emp.: 4
Energy Services
S.I.C.: 4931
N.A.I.C.S.: 221122
Markku Ryymin *(Mgr)*

E.ON Sverige AB (1)
Carl Gustafs Vaeg 1
205 09 Malmo, Sweden
Tel.: (46) 40255000
E-Mail: info@eon.se
Web Site: www.eon.se
Rev.: $170,000,000
Emp.: 5,000
Electric Power Distr
S.I.C.: 4931
N.A.I.C.S.: 221122
Wulf H. Bernotat *(Chm & CO-CEO)*
Jonas Abrahamsson *(CEO)*

Subsidiaries:

E.ON Biofor Sverige AB (2)
Nobelvagen 66
Malmo, 212 15, 212 15, Sweden
Tel.: (46) 40255000
Gasoline Whslr
S.I.C.: 5172
N.A.I.C.S.: 424720

E.ON Elnat Stockholm AB (2)
Carl Gustafs vag 1
Malmo, Sweden
Tel.: (46) 40 255000
Fax: (46) 40 255424
Electric Power Distributing Services
S.I.C.: 4931
N.A.I.C.S.: 221122

E.ON Elnat Sverige AB (2)
Nobelvagen 66
205 09 Malmo, Sweden
Tel.: (46) 40 25 50 00
Fax: (46) 40 24 40 11
Web Site: www.eon.se
Electric Power Distribution Services
S.I.C.: 4931
N.A.I.C.S.: 221122
Tom Nagy *(Project Mgr)*

E.ON Fastigheter Sverige AB (2)
Carl Gustavs v 1
205 09 Malmo, Sweden
Tel.: (46) 40 25 50 00
Fax: (46) 40 25 53 20
Real Estate Development Services
S.I.C.: 6531
N.A.I.C.S.: 531390

E.ON Forsaljning Sverige AB (2)
Carl Gustafs Vag 4
205 09 Malmo, Sweden
Tel.: (46) 40 25 50 00
E-Mail: kundservice@eon.se
Emp.: 30
Electric Power Distribution Services
S.I.C.: 4931
N.A.I.C.S.: 221122
Siegfried Ruckriegel *(CEO)*

E.ON Gas Sverige AB (2)
Nobelvagen 66
205 09 Malmo, Skane, Sweden
Tel.: (46) 40 25 50 00
Fax: (46) 40 24 40 11
Web Site: www.eon.se/om-eon/Om-foretaget/Dotterbolag/EON-Gas-Sverige-AB/
Natural Gas Transmission Services
S.I.C.: 4923
N.A.I.C.S.: 486210
Anna Grauers *(Head-Customer Rels)*

E.ON Gashandel Sverige AB (2)
Carl Gustafs vag 1
Malmo, Skane, 205 09, Sweden
Tel.: (46) 40255000
Natural Gas Distr
S.I.C.: 4924
N.A.I.C.S.: 221210

E.ON Gasification Development AB (2)
Carl Gustafs Vag 1
Malmo, Skane, 205 09, Sweden
Tel.: (46) 40255000
Web Site: www.eon.se
Emp.: 150
Gas Storage Services
S.I.C.: 4922
N.A.I.C.S.: 486210
Bjoern Fredriksson *(Project Mgr)*

E.ON Karnkraft Sverige AB (2)
Carl Gustafs vag 1
205 09 Malmo, Skane, Sweden
Tel.: (46) 40 25 50 00
Electric Power Generation Services
S.I.C.: 4911
N.A.I.C.S.: 221118

E.ON Kundsupport Sverige AB (2)
Carl Gustafs Vag 4
205 09 Malmo, Skane, Sweden
Tel.: (46) 40 25 50 00
Customer Support Management Services
S.I.C.: 8742
N.A.I.C.S.: 541613

E.ON Trading Nordic AB (2)
Carl Gustafs vaeg 1
20509 Malmo, Sweden
Tel.: (46) 40255000
Fax: (46) 40125520
E-Mail: portfolio.trading@eon.se
Web Site: www.eon.se
Emp.: 8
Energy Trading Services
S.I.C.: 7389
N.A.I.C.S.: 425120
Jonas Abrahamsson *(CEO)*

E.ON Varme Sverige AB (2)
Carl Gustafs Vag 1
205 09 Malmo, Sweden
Tel.: (46) 40 25 50 00
Heating Equipment Distr
S.I.C.: 5075
N.A.I.C.S.: 423730

E.ON Varmekraft Sverige AB (2)
Turbingatan 10
30245 Halmstad, Sweden
Tel.: (46) 706256548
Management Consulting Services
S.I.C.: 8748
N.A.I.C.S.: 541618

E.ON Vind Sverige AB (2)
Carl Gustafs Vag 1
205 09 Malmo, Sweden
Tel.: (46) 40 25 50 00
E-Mail: vind@eon.se
Emp.: 8
Wind Electric Power Generation Services
S.I.C.: 4939
N.A.I.C.S.: 221118
Marten Larson *(Project Coord-Offshore)*

HEMAB Elforsaljning AB (2)
Vastra Ringvagen 125
871 42 Harnosand, Sweden
Tel.: (46) 61155 75 26
Fax: (46) 79140 79 80
Electronic Equipment Whslr
S.I.C.: 5065
N.A.I.C.S.: 423690

Karlshamn Kraft AB (2)
Munkahusvagen 181
Karlshamn, 374 21, Sweden
Tel.: (46) 454 850 00
E-Mail: karlshamnkraft@eon.se
Web Site: www.karlshamnkraft.se
Emp.: 10
Electric Power Generation Services
S.I.C.: 4911
N.A.I.C.S.: 221118
Karin Jarl-Mansson *(Mgr)*

Sakab Sellbergs AB (2)
O Dravsan
Rattvik, 795 90, Sweden
Tel.: (46) 24810433
Waste Management Services
S.I.C.: 4959
N.A.I.C.S.: 562998

Joint Venture:

Baltic Cable AB (2)
Nobelvaegen 66
205 09 Malmo, Sweden
Tel.: (46) 40256130
Fax: (46) 40256140
E-Mail: info@balticcable.com
Web Site: www.balticcable.com
Rev.: $34,549,200
Emp.: 3
Telecommunications Services; Owned 66.7% by Statkraft Energy Europe AS & 33.3% by E.ON Sverige AB
S.I.C.: 4813
N.A.I.C.S.: 517110
Jan Brewitz *(Mng Dir)*

E.ON Trend s.r.o. (1)
FA Gerstnera 2151/6
370 49 Ceske Budejovice, Czech Republic
Tel.: (420) 387 867 512
Fax: (420) 387 867 517
E-Mail: info@eon.cz
Electric Power Generation & Distribution Services
S.I.C.: 4911
N.A.I.C.S.: 221118
Tomas Turek *(Mng Dir)*

Subsidiary:

Teplarna Otrokovice a.s. (2)
Objizdna 1777
765 39 Otrokovice, Czech Republic

E.ON SE—(Continued)

Tel.: (420) 577 649 111
Fax: (420) 577 921 600
E-Mail: info@tot.cz
Web Site: www.tot.cz
Electric Power Generation & Distribution Services
S.I.C.: 4931
N.A.I.C.S.: 221118

E.ON UK plc (1)
Westwood Way Westwood Business Park
Coventry, West Midlands, CV4 8LG, United Kingdom UK
Tel.: (44) 2476424000 (100%)
Fax: (44) 2476425432
Web Site: www.eon-uk.com
Sales Range: $15-24.9 Billion
Emp.: 17,000
Electric Generation, Retail Energy Distribution & Support Services
S.I.C.: 4911
N.A.I.C.S.: 221112
Brian Tear *(CFO)*

Subsidiaries:

CHN Group Ltd (2)
HN House Straits Road Lower Gornal
Dudley, DY3 2UY, United Kingdom
Tel.: (44) 1384 212 992
Fax: (44) 1384 456 773
Plumbing & Heating Equipment Installation Services
S.I.C.: 1711
N.A.I.C.S.: 238220

Subsidiaries:

CHN Contractors Limited (3)
Larch House 241 High Street
Kingswinford, West Midlands, DY6 8BN, United Kingdom
Tel.: (44) 1384 245999
Plumbing Equipment Installation Services
S.I.C.: 1711
N.A.I.C.S.: 238220

CHN Electrical Services Limited (3)
7 Zoar Street Lower Gornal
Dudley, DY3 2PA, United Kingdom
Tel.: (44) 1384217860
Electrical Contracting Services
S.I.C.: 1731
N.A.I.C.S.: 238210

Citigen (London) Limited (2)
47-53 Charterhouse Street
London, EC1M 6PB, United Kingdom
Tel.: (44) 20 7553 7400
Fax: (44) 20 7553 7446
E-Mail: cr@eon-uk.com
Web Site: www.eon-uk.com
Emp.: 21
Electric Power Generation & Distribution Services
S.I.C.: 4931
N.A.I.C.S.: 221118
Carl-Johan Falk *(Gen Mgr)*

E.ON Climate & Renewables UK Biomass Limited (2)
Westwood Way Westwood Business Park
Coventry, West Midlands, CV4 8LG, United Kingdom
Tel.: (44) 24 7642 4000
Fax: (44) 24 7642 4443
Electric Power Generation Services
S.I.C.: 4939
N.A.I.C.S.: 221118

E.ON Climate & Renewables UK London Array Limited (2)
Westwood Way Westwood Business Park
Coventry, West Midlands, CV4 8LG, United Kingdom
Tel.: (44) 24 7642 4000
Electric Power Distributing Services
S.I.C.: 4911
N.A.I.C.S.: 221122

E.ON Climate & Renewables UK Offshore Wind Limited (2)
Westwood Way Westwood Business Park
Coventry, West Midlands, CV4 8LG, United Kingdom
Tel.: (44) 24 7642 4000
Fax: (44) 24 7642 4443
Electric Power Generation Services
S.I.C.: 4911
N.A.I.C.S.: 221118

E.ON Climate & Renewables UK Robin Rigg West Limited (2)
Westwood Way Westwood Business Park
Coventry, West Midlands, CV4 8LG, United Kingdom
Tel.: (44) 24 7642 4000
Electric Power Distributing Services
S.I.C.: 4939
N.A.I.C.S.: 221122

E.ON Climate & Renewables UK Wind Limited (2)
Westwood Way Westwood Business Park
Coventry, West Midlands, CV4 8LG, United Kingdom
Tel.: (44) 24 7642 4000
Fax: (44) 24 7642 4443
Electric Power Generation Services
S.I.C.: 4911
N.A.I.C.S.: 221118

E.ON Energy From Waste UK Limited (2)
Westwood Way
Coventry, West Midlands, CV4 8LG, United Kingdom
Tel.: (44) 24 7642 4000
Waste Management & Electric Power Generation Services
S.I.C.: 4953
N.A.I.C.S.: 562219

E.ON Energy UK Limited (2)
Westwood Way
Coventry, West Midlands, CV4 8LG, United Kingdom
Tel.: (44) 24 7642 4000
Electric Power Distributing Services
S.I.C.: 4931
N.A.I.C.S.: 221122

E.ON Ruhrgas UK E&P Limited (2)
Davis Ho
London, SW1V 1JZ, United Kingdom
Tel.: (44) 20 3004 3700
Fax: (44) 2030043710
E-Mail: info@eon-ruhrgas.com
Upstreaming Oil & Gas Services
S.I.C.: 1389
N.A.I.C.S.: 213112

Subsidiary:

E.ON Ruhrgas UK North Sea Limited (3)
7th Floor Davis House 129 Wilton Road
London, SW1V1JZ, United Kingdom
Tel.: (44) 2030043700
Fax: (44) 2030043710
E-Mail: info@eon-ruhrgas.com
Natural Gas Exploration Services
S.I.C.: 1311
N.A.I.C.S.: 211111

E.ON UK CHP Limited (2)
Winnington Lane
Winnington, Northwich, Cheshire, CW8 4GX, United Kingdom
Tel.: (44) 1606 723700
Fax: (44) 1606 783195
Emp.: 5
Electric Power Generation Services
S.I.C.: 4931
N.A.I.C.S.: 221118
Steve Wheat *(Project Mgr)*

E.ON UK Energy Services Limited (2)
Westwood Way Westwood Business Park
Coventry, West Midlands, CV4 8LG, United Kingdom
Tel.: (44) 24 7642 4000
Fax: (44) 24 7642 5432
Electric Power Generation & Distributing Services
S.I.C.: 4931
N.A.I.C.S.: 221118

E.ON UK Energy Solutions Limited (2)
Westwood Way Westwood Business Park
Coventry, West Midlands, CV4 8LG, United Kingdom
Tel.: (44) 24 7642 4000
Fax: (44) 1623 788 566
Management Consulting Services
S.I.C.: 8748
N.A.I.C.S.: 541618

E.ON UK Holding Company Limited (2)
Westwood Way
Coventry, West Midlands, CV4 8LG, United Kingdom
Tel.: (44) 24 7642 4000
Fax: (44) 24 7642 5432
Investment Management Services
S.I.C.: 6211
N.A.I.C.S.: 523999

E.ON UK Power Technology Limited (2)
Ratcliffe-on-Soar
Nottingham, NG11 0EE, United Kingdom
Tel.: (44) 115 936 2000
Fax: (44) 115 936 2711
Electric Power Generation Services
S.I.C.: 4911
N.A.I.C.S.: 221118

E.ON UK Property Services Limited (2)
241 High Street
Kingswinford, West Midlands, DY6 8BN, United Kingdom
Tel.: (44) 1384 217860
Fax: (44) 1384 217866
Emp.: 5,000
Property Management Services
S.I.C.: 6531
N.A.I.C.S.: 531390
Adrian Harvey *(Mng Dir)*

E.ON UK Technical Services Limited (2)
17 Camp Road Rutherglen
Glasgow, Lanarkshire, G73 1EW, United Kingdom
Tel.: (44) 141 613 1119
Fax: (44) 1416470222
Central Heating Equipment Installation & Maintenance Services
S.I.C.: 1711
N.A.I.C.S.: 238220

Holford Gas Storage Limited (2)
Westwood Way Westwood Business Park
Coventry, West Midlands, CV4 8LG, United Kingdom
Tel.: (44) 24 7642 4000
Fax: (44) 24 7642 5432
Gas Storage & Transmission Services
S.I.C.: 4226
N.A.I.C.S.: 493190

Lighting for Staffordshire Limited (2)
A B B Business Centre Oulton Road
Stone, Staffordshire, ST15 0RS, United Kingdom
Tel.: (44) 904 049 8229
Street Light Maintaining Services
S.I.C.: 1731
N.A.I.C.S.: 238210

Midlands Power (UK) Limited (2)
Whittington Hall
Worcester, Worcestershire, WR5 2RA, United Kingdom
Tel.: (44) 800590866
Electric Power Generation Services
S.I.C.: 4939
N.A.I.C.S.: 221118

Power Technology Limited (2)
First Avenue
Scunthorpe, South Humberside, DN15 8SE, United Kingdom
Tel.: (44) 1724 282500
Fax: (44) 1724 282 064
Electric Power Generation & Distributing Services
S.I.C.: 4911
N.A.I.C.S.: 221118

Statco Six Limited (2)
Wilford Road
Nottingham, Nottinghamshire, NG2 1EB, United Kingdom
Tel.: (44) 115 986 3471
Electric Power Generation Services
S.I.C.: 4931
N.A.I.C.S.: 221118

TXU Warm Front Limited (2)
Suffolk House Civic Drive
Ipswich, IP1 2AE, United Kingdom
Tel.: (44) 800 952 1555
Management Consulting Services
S.I.C.: 8748
N.A.I.C.S.: 541618

EPS Polska Holding Sp. z o.o. (1)
Krolowej Marysienki 10
02-954 Warsaw, Poland
Tel.: (48) 22 858 14 50
Fax: (48) 22 858 14 51
E-Mail: d.majewska@epspolska.pl
Emp.: 1
Investment Management Services
S.I.C.: 6211
N.A.I.C.S.: 523999
Monika Stypulkowska *(Mng Dir)*

Subsidiary:

EPS Polska Sp. z o.o. (2)
ul Krolowej Marysienki 10
Warsaw, 02-954, Poland
Tel.: (48) 22 858 14 50
Fax: (48) 22 858 14 51
Electric Power Distributing Services
S.I.C.: 4939
N.A.I.C.S.: 221122

EZH-SEON b.v. (1)
Capelseweg 400
3068 AX Rotterdam, Netherlands
Tel.: (31) 10 2895711
Management Consulting Services
S.I.C.: 8748
N.A.I.C.S.: 541618

Generale Servizi S.r.l. (1)
Via Cilea 106
20151 Milan, Italy
Tel.: (39) 02 35 34 258
Fax: (39) 02 35 39 149
E-Mail: info@generaleservizisrl.com
Web Site: www.generaleservizisrl.com
Building Maintenance Services
S.I.C.: 0783
N.A.I.C.S.: 561730

HEUREKA-Gamma AG (1)
Husmatt 1
5405 Baden-Dattwil, Switzerland
Tel.: (41) 56 484 70 60
Fax: (41) 56 484 70 69
E-Mail: info@heureka-gamma.ch
Web Site: www.heureka-gamma.ch
Emp.: 4
Human Resource Consulting Services
S.I.C.: 8999
N.A.I.C.S.: 541612
Dieter Bader *(Gen Mgr)*

Holland Chemical International N.V. (1)
Haagsbergweg 3 17 E
1101 BP Amsterdam, Netherlands (99.4%)
S.I.C.: 2851
N.A.I.C.S.: 325998

Industry Development Services Limited (1)
Unit 2 Bloomfield Pk Bloomfield Road
Tipton, West Midlands, DY4 9AH, United Kingdom
Tel.: (44) 121 5226969
Web Site: www.eon-uk.com
Industrial Training & Development Services
S.I.C.: 8299
N.A.I.C.S.: 611430
Tammy Ristow *(Mgr-Trng)*

Informacni sluzby - energetika, a.s. (1)
U Plynarny 500
141 00 Prague, Czech Republic
Tel.: (420) 267 172 903
Fax: (420) 267 174 903
E-Mail: ise@ise.cz
Web Site: www.ise.cz
Emp.: 45
Information Technology Consulting Services
S.I.C.: 7373
N.A.I.C.S.: 541512

Lobeska Energetyka Cieplna Sp. z o.o. (1)
ul Magazynowa 16
Lobez, Poland
Tel.: (48) 91 397 33 97
Fax: (48) 91 397 49 76
E-Mail: sekretariat@leclobez.pl
Web Site: www.leclobez.pl

Thermal Electric Power Generation Services
S.I.C.: 4931
N.A.I.C.S.: 221118

Maasvlakte I b.v. (1)
Capelseweg 400
3068 AX Rotterdam, Zuid-Holland, Netherlands
Tel.: (31) 102895711
Electric Power Distribution Services
S.I.C.: 4911
N.A.I.C.S.: 221122

OAO Shaturskaya Upravlyayushchaya Kompaniya (1)
4 Pr Konny
140700 Shatura, Russia
Tel.: (7) 4964523317
Electric Power Generation Services
S.I.C.: 4911
N.A.I.C.S.: 221118

OKG AB (1)
Simpevarp
Oskarshamn, 572 83, Sweden
Tel.: (46) 4 91 78 60 00
Fax: (46) 4 91 78 60 90
E-Mail: info@okg.eon.se
Web Site: www.okg.se
Rev.: $444,390,000
Emp.: 850
Electric Power Generation Services
S.I.C.: 4939
N.A.I.C.S.: 221118

OOO E.ON Russia Power (1)
18 Nab Krasnopresnenskaya
Moscow, 123317, Russia
Tel.: (7) 4957821461
Fax: (7) 4957821351
Electric Power Generation Services
S.I.C.: 4939
N.A.I.C.S.: 221118

Powergen Limited (1)
Westwood Way Westwood Business Park
Coventry, CV4 8LG, United Kingdom
Tel.: (44) 24 7642 4000
Fax: (44) 24 7642 5432
Electric Power & Gas Distribution Services
S.I.C.: 4911
N.A.I.C.S.: 221122

Powergen Luxembourg Holdings SARL (1)
17 Boulevard prince Henri
1724 Luxembourg, Luxembourg
Tel.: (352) 26 86 85 1
Investment Management Services
S.I.C.: 6211
N.A.I.C.S.: 523999
Paul De Haan *(Mgr)*

Powergen UK Limited (1)
PO Box 111
Immingham, South Humberside, DN40 3NG, United Kingdom
Tel.: (44) 1469 541155
Electric Power Generation Services
S.I.C.: 4911
N.A.I.C.S.: 221118

Powergen US Holdings Limited (1)
Westwood Way Westwood Business Park
Coventry, CV4 8LG, United Kingdom
Tel.: (44) 2476424000
Investment Management Services
S.I.C.: 6799
N.A.I.C.S.: 523920

Powergen US Investments (1)
Westwood Way Westwood Business Park
Coventry, West Midlands, CV4 8LG, United Kingdom
Tel.: (44) 24 7642 4000
Fax: (44) 1268 653 627
Investment Management Services
S.I.C.: 6282
N.A.I.C.S.: 523920

Powergen US Securities Limited (1)
Westwood Way
Coventry, West Midlands, CV4 8LG, United Kingdom
Tel.: (44) 24 7642 4000
Fax: (44) 24 7642 5432
Investment Management Services
S.I.C.: 6799
N.A.I.C.S.: 523920

Prazska plynarenska Distribuce, a.s. (1)
U Plynarny 500
145 08 Prague, Czech Republic
Tel.: (420) 267 171 111
Fax: (420) 267 171 030
E-Mail: dispecink@ppdistribuce.cz
Web Site: www.ppdistribuce.cz
Natural Gas Distribution Services
S.I.C.: 4924
N.A.I.C.S.: 221210

Prazska plynarenska Holding a.s. (1)
U Plynarny 500
Prague, 140 00, Czech Republic
Tel.: (420) 2 6717 1111
Fax: (420) 2 6717 1030
E-Mail: info@ppas.cz
Emp.: 800
Investment Management Services
S.I.C.: 6211
N.A.I.C.S.: 523999

Prazska plynarenska Servis distribuce, a.s. (1)
U Plynarny 1450/2a
Michle, 140 00 Prague, Czech Republic
Tel.: (420) 267 171 111
Fax: (420) 267 174 245
E-Mail: info@ppsd.cz
Web Site: www.ppsd.cz
Emp.: 140
Natural Gas Distribution Services
S.I.C.: 4924
N.A.I.C.S.: 221210

Prazska plynarenska Sprava majetku, s.r.o. (1)
U Plynarny 500
4-Michle, 145 08 Prague, Czech Republic
Tel.: (420) 267 171 111
Fax: (420) 267 173 438
E-Mail: info@ppsm.cz
Web Site: www.ppsm.cz
Emp.: 70
Asset Management Services
S.I.C.: 6282
N.A.I.C.S.: 523920
Lenka Poklopova *(Gen Mgr)*

Promec Sp. z o.o. (1)
ul Prusa 4
26-110 Skarzysko-Kamienna, Poland
Tel.: (48) 41 25 28 994
E-Mail: promec@promec.pl
Web Site: www.promec.pl
Real Estate Management Services
S.I.C.: 6531
N.A.I.C.S.: 531390

Przedsiebiorstwo Energetyki Cieplnej w Barlinku Sp. z o.o. (1)
ul Przemyslowa 7
74-320 Barlinek, Poland
Tel.: (48) 95 746 26 51
Fax: (48) 95 746 26 51
Electric Power Generation Services
S.I.C.: 4931
N.A.I.C.S.: 221118

Q-Energie b.v. (1)
Beemdstraat 23
5653 MA Eindhoven, Netherlands
Tel.: (31) 40 70 70 700
Fax: (31) 40 70 70 701
E-Mail: info@q-energy.nl
Web Site: www.q-energy.nl
Electric Power Generation Services
S.I.C.: 4911
N.A.I.C.S.: 221118

Sakab AB (1)
Norrtorp
Kumla, 692 85, Sweden
Tel.: (46) 19 30 51 00
Fax: (46) 19 57 70 27
E-Mail: info@sakab.se
Web Site: www.sakab.se
Emp.: 15
Waste Treatment & Disposal Services
S.I.C.: 4953
N.A.I.C.S.: 562211
Johanna Telander *(Mgr-Intl Sls)*

S.C. Salgaz S.A. (1)
Ion Creanga 18
Salonta, Romania
Tel.: (40) 259374014
Fax: (40) 259373786
Web Site: www.salgaz.ro
Emp.: 25
Gaseous Fuels & Natural Gas Distribution Services
S.I.C.: 5989
N.A.I.C.S.: 454310
Ghita Adrian *(Gen Mgr)*

SEC Energia Sp. z o.o. (1)
Ul Dembowskiego 6
Szczecin, 71-533, Poland
Tel.: (48) 914250800
Fax: (48) 914554311
Electric Power Generation Services
S.I.C.: 4939
N.A.I.C.S.: 221118

SEE-Sul Energia Eolica, Lda (1)
Parque Eolico Espinhaco Cao-Aljezur
Aljezur, 8670-120, Portugal
Tel.: (351) 282688117
Electric Power Generation Services
S.I.C.: 4911
N.A.I.C.S.: 221118

Sisyphus Quebec Limited (1)
10 Newhall Street
Birmingham, B3 3LX, United Kingdom
Tel.: (44) 7973 212 269
Electric Power Distributing Services
S.I.C.: 4911
N.A.I.C.S.: 221122

SO.MET. ENERGIA S.r.l. (1)
Sede in Via G Testore 12
14055 Costigliole d'Asti, Asti, Italy
Tel.: (39) 0141962311
Fax: (39) 0141961355
Electric Power Generation Services
S.I.C.: 4939
N.A.I.C.S.: 221118

Surschiste, S.A. (1)
Rue Auguste Mariette ZI La Croisette
62300 Lens, France
Tel.: (33) 3 21 45 73 73
E-Mail: contact@surschiste.com
Web Site: www.surschiste.com
Electric Power Generation Services
S.I.C.: 4931
N.A.I.C.S.: 221118

Sydkraft EC Slupsk Sp. z o.o. (1)
ul Koszalinska 3D
76-200 Slupsk, Poland
Tel.: (48) 59 84 86 300
Fax: (48) 59 84 22 061
E-Mail: sekretariat@ecslupsk.pl
Web Site: www.ecslupsk.pl
Emp.: 70
Electric Power & Natural Gas Distribution Services
S.I.C.: 4931
N.A.I.C.S.: 221122
Agnieszka Jeziorska *(CFO)*

Sydkraft Polen AB (1)
Carl Gustafs Vag 1
Malmo, Skane, 217 42, Sweden
Tel.: (46) 40255000
Electric Power Distributing Services
S.I.C.: 4939
N.A.I.C.S.: 221122

Sydkraft Term Sp. z o.o. (1)
ul Za Dworcem 3
77-400 Zlotow, Poland
Tel.: (48) 67 263 35 44
Fax: (48) 67 263 35 44
Web Site: www.sydkraftterm.pl
Heat Energy Generation & Distribution Services
S.I.C.: 4961
N.A.I.C.S.: 221330

Sydkraft Zlotow Sp. z o.o. (1)
ul Za Dworcem 3
77-400 Zlotow, Poland
Tel.: (48) 67 263 29 69
Fax: (48) 67 263 31 07
Web Site: www.sydkraft.zlotow.com
Electricity Production & Distribution Services
S.I.C.: 4931
N.A.I.C.S.: 221118

Szczecinska Energetyka Cieplna Sp. z o.o. (1)
ul Dembowskiego 6
71-533 Szczecin, Poland
Tel.: (48) 91 42 50 800
Fax: (48) 91 45 54 311
E-Mail: sec@sec.szczecin.pl
Web Site: www.sec.szczecin.pl
Electric Power Distribution Services
S.I.C.: 4911
N.A.I.C.S.: 221122

Teplarna Kyjov, a.s. (1)
Havlickova 180/18
697 01 Kyjov, Czech Republic
Tel.: (420) 518 698 712
Fax: (420) 518 698 713
Emp.: 20
Electric Power Generation & Distribution Services
S.I.C.: 4911
N.A.I.C.S.: 221118

Teplarna Tabor, a.s. (1)
U Cihelny 2128
Tabor, 39049, Czech Republic
Tel.: (420) 381417202
Fax: (420) 381417268
E-Mail: info@teplarna.tabor.cz
Electric Power Generation & Distribution Services
S.I.C.: 4931
N.A.I.C.S.: 221118

Utilities Center Maasvlakte Leftbank b.v. (1)
Capelseweg 400
Rotterdam, Zuid-Holland, 3068 AX, Netherlands
Tel.: (31) 703820028
Fax: (31) 104769867
Electric Power Generation Services
S.I.C.: 4911
N.A.I.C.S.: 221118

Veszprem-Kogeneracio Energiatermelo Zrt. (1)
Kando Kalman Utca 13
9027 Gyor, Hungary
Tel.: (36) 96521118
Fax: (36) 96521706
Emp.: 8
Electric Power Generation Services
S.I.C.: 4911
N.A.I.C.S.: 221118

Non-U.S. Affiliate:

BKW FMB Energie AG (1)
Viktoriaplatz 2
CH 3000 Bern, 25, Switzerland (20%)
Tel.: (41) 313305797
Fax: (41) 313305635
E-Mail: investor.relations@bkw-fmb.ch
Web Site: www.bkw-fmb.ch
Sales Range: $1-4.9 Billion
Emp.: 400
Energy Services
S.I.C.: 4939
N.A.I.C.S.: 221122
Urs Gasche *(Chm)*

Non-U.S. Joint Venture:

Enerjisa Enerji A.S. (1)
Sabanci Center Kule 2 Kat 4
Levent, 34330 Istanbul, Turkey TR
Tel.: (90) 2123395500
Fax: (90) 2122841842
Web Site: www.enerjisa.com.tr
Holding Company; Electric Power Generation, Distr & Natural Gas Distr
S.I.C.: 6719
N.A.I.C.S.: 551112
Selahattin Hakman *(Chm)*
Gunther Rabensteiner *(Vice Chm)*
Yetik K. Mert *(CEO)*
Bernhard Raberger *(CFO)*

Subsidiaries:

Enerjisa Baskent Elektrik Dagitim A.S. (2)
Sabanci Center Kule 2
Levent, 34330 Istanbul, Turkey TR
Tel.: (90) 212 385 85 92
Fax: (90) 212 281 05 74
Web Site: www.enerjisa.com.tr
Retail Electric Power Distr
S.I.C.: 4939
N.A.I.C.S.: 221122
Gerhard Neubauer *(CEO)*

Enerjisa Electrik Enerjisi Toptan Satis A.S. (2)
Sabanci Center Kule 2 Kat 4
Levent, 34330 Istanbul, Turkey TR

E.ON SE—(Continued)

Tel.: (90) 212 385 88 28
Fax: (90) 2123859142
E-Mail: enerji.enerji@enerjisa.com
Web Site: www.enerjisa.com.tr
Electric Power Whslr & Natural Gas Distr
S.I.C.: 4911
N.A.I.C.S.: 221122
Kiran Madisetti *(CEO)*
Fuat Oksuz *(CFO)*

Enerjisa Enerji Uretim A.S. **(2)**
Sabanci Center Kule 2 Kat 5
Levent, 34330 Istanbul, Turkey TR
Tel.: (90) 212 385 88 66
Fax: (90) 212 385 88 55
Web Site: www.enerjisa.com.tr
Geothermal, Hydro & Wind Electric Power Generation Services
S.I.C.: 4931
N.A.I.C.S.: 221118
Yetik K. Mert *(Chm)*
Bernhard Raberger *(Vice Chm)*
Erich Wagner *(CEO)*
Veli Balat *(Chief Project Officer)*

Plants:

Enerjisa Enerji Uretim A.S. - Canakkale Power Plant **(3)**
Akcansa Fabrikasi Yani Ezine
Canakkale, Turkey
Tel.: (90) 286 628 77 78
Fax: (90) 286 628 77 98
Web Site: www.enerjisa.com.tr
Geothermal & Wind Electric Power Generation Services
S.I.C.: 4911
N.A.I.C.S.: 221116

Enerjisa Enerji Uretim A.S. - Kentsa Power Plant **(3)**
Kentsa
Alikahya, 41220 Izmit, Turkey
Tel.: (90) 262 315 10 00
Fax: (90) 262 364 71 70
E-Mail: billur.oztejin@enerjisa.com
Web Site: www.enerjisa.com.tr
Emp.: 20
Geothermal Electric Power Generation Services
S.I.C.: 4931
N.A.I.C.S.: 221116
Franck Degeorgio *(Plant Mgr)*

Enerjisa Enerji Uretim A.S. - Mersin Power Plant **(3)**
Cimsa Fabrikasi Yani Yenitaskent
Mersin, Turkey
Tel.: (90) 324 241 16 00
Fax: (90) 324 241 16 40
Web Site: www.enerjisa.com.tr
Geothermal Electric Power Generation Services
S.I.C.: 4931
N.A.I.C.S.: 221116

E.ON THURINGER ENERGIE AG

Schwerborner Strasse 30
99087 Erfurt, Germany
Tel.: (49) 3616520
Fax: (49) 3616523490
E-Mail: info@eon-thueringerenergie.com
Web Site: www.eon-thueringerenergie.com
Sales Range: $1-4.9 Billion
Emp.: 1,362

Business Description:
Energy Services
S.I.C.: 8999
N.A.I.C.S.: 541690

Personnel:
Olaf Werner *(Mng Dir-PR & Editor)*

Subsidiaries:

Energie- und Medienversorgung Schwarza GmbH (EMS) **(1)**
Breitscheidstrasse 160
Rudolstadt, 07407, Germany
Tel.: (49) 3672 48900
Fax: (49) 3672 489019
E-Mail: info@ems-schwarza.de
Web Site: www.ems-schwarza.de
Emp.: 38
Electric Power Distribution Services
S.I.C.: 4931
N.A.I.C.S.: 221122

E.ON Thuringer Energie Dritte Vermogensverwaltungs-GmbH **(1)**
Schwerborner Strasse 30
99087 Erfurt, Germany
Tel.: (49) 361 652 0
Fax: (49) 3616523490
Management Consulting Services
S.I.C.: 8748
N.A.I.C.S.: 541618

Thuringer Netkom GmbH **(1)**
Schwanseestrasse 13
99423 Weimar, Germany
Tel.: (49) 36 43 21 30 01
Fax: (49) 36 43 21 30 09
E-Mail: info@netkom.de
Web Site: www.netkom.de
Emp.: 6
Telecommunication Services
S.I.C.: 4899
N.A.I.C.S.: 517919
Karsten Kluge *(Mgr)*

EONMETALL GROUP BERHAD

Lot 1258 Mk 12 Jalan Seruling
Kawasan Perusahaan Valdor
14200 Sungai Bakap, Penang, Malaysia
Tel.: (60) 45828323
Fax: (60) 45821525
E-Mail: info@eonmetall.com
Web Site: www.eonmetall.com
EMETALL—(KLS)
Rev.: $47,506,987
Assets: $80,015,508
Liabilities: $32,820,894
Net Worth: $47,194,614
Earnings: $534,181
Emp.: 250
Fiscal Year-end: 12/31/12

Business Description:
Cold Rolled Steels Mfr
S.I.C.: 3399
N.A.I.C.S.: 331110

Personnel:
Cheng Chye Yeoh *(CEO & Mng Dir)*
Hong Kent Goh *(COO & Exec Dir)*
Tze-En Ong *(Co-Sec)*
Yit Chan Tai *(Co-Sec)*

Board of Directors:
Mohd Desa Pachi
Cheng Huat Goh
Hong Kent Goh
Kee Seng Goh
Wahab Hamid
Ibrahim Mahdi Phee
Siew Hoong Soong
Yin Kham Tang
Cheng Chye Yeoh

Subsidiaries:

Eonmetall Industries Sdn. Bhd. **(1)**
1258 Mk12 Jalan Seruling
14200 Sungai Bakap, Pulau Pinang, Malaysia
Tel.: (60) 45828323
Fax: (60) 45821525
E-Mail: info@eonmetall.com
Web Site: www.eonmetall.com
Emp.: 200
Steel Products Mfr & Distr
S.I.C.: 3399
N.A.I.C.S.: 331110

Eonmetall Systems Sdn. Bhd. **(1)**
Lot 1258 Mk12 Jalan Seruling Kawasan Perusahaan Valdor
Sungai Bakap, Pulau Pinang, 14200, Malaysia
Tel.: (60) 45828323
Fax: (60) 45821525
E-Mail: info@eonmetall.com
Emp.: 200
Steel Products Mfr & Distr
S.I.C.: 3317
N.A.I.C.S.: 331210
Goh Cheng Suat *(Mng Dir)*

Eonmetall Technology Sdn. Bhd. **(1)**
Lot 1258 Mk12 Jalan Seruling Kawasan Perusahaan Valdor
Sungai Jawi, Pulau Pinang, 14200, Malaysia
Tel.: (60) 45828322
Fax: (60) 45821525
E-Mail: info@eonmetall.com
Emp.: 200
Metalworks Machinery Mfr
S.I.C.: 3541
N.A.I.C.S.: 333517
Cheng Huat Goh *(Pres)*

Eontarr IT Solutions Sdn. Bhd. **(1)**
Lot 1258 MK 12 Jalan Seruling Kawasan Perusahaan Valdor
14200 Sungai Bakap, Penang, Malaysia
Tel.: (60) 45828323
Fax: (60) 45821525
E-Mail: info@eonmetall.com
Emp.: 2
Software Development Services
S.I.C.: 7371
N.A.I.C.S.: 541511
Yeoh Cheng Chye *(COO)*

Norimax Sdn. Bhd. **(1)**
No 2 Jalan TPP 5/17 Taman Perindustrian Seksyen 5
47100 Puchong, Selangor Darul Ehsan, Malaysia
Tel.: (60) 380602334
Fax: (60) 380622334
E-Mail: sales@norimax.com.my
Web Site: www.norimax.com.my
Emp.: 40
Corrosion Control Products Mfr
S.I.C.: 3999
N.A.I.C.S.: 339999
Junaidy Abdulla *(Gen Mgr)*

EOS GMBH ELECTRO OPTICAL SYSTEMS

Robert Stirling Ring 1
82152 Krailling, Germany
Tel.: (49) 89893360
Fax: (49) 8989336285
E-Mail: info@eos.info
Web Site: www.eos.info
Rev.: $89,173,000
Emp.: 280

Business Description:
Optical Instruments & Lenses Mfr
S.I.C.: 3827
N.A.I.C.S.: 333314

Personnel:
Hans Langer *(Founder & CEO)*
Johann Oberhofer *(COO)*
Peter Klink *(Exec VP-Sls)*

U.S. Subsidiary:

EOS of North America, Inc. **(1)**
28970 Cabot Dr Ste 700
Novi, MI 48377-2978
Tel.: (248) 306-0143
Fax: (248) 306-0298
E-Mail: info-US@eos.info
Emp.: 25
Laser Sintering System & Equipment Mfr
S.I.C.: 3441
N.A.I.C.S.: 332312
Tim Morris *(VP)*

Non-U.S. Subsidiaries:

Electro Optical Systems Nordic AB **(1)**
Stena Center 1 C
41292 Gothenburg, Sweden
Tel.: (46) 31 760 46 40
Fax: (46) 31 772 80 88
Emp.: 7
Laser Sintering System & Equipment Mfr
S.I.C.: 3441
N.A.I.C.S.: 332312
Micael Amandusson, *(Reg Mgr-Sls)*

EOS Electro Optical Systems Ltd. **(1)**
The Innovation Centre Warwick Technology Park
Warwick, CV34 6UW, United Kingdom
Tel.: (44) 19 26 62 31 07
Fax: (44) 19 26 62 31 08
Emp.: 12
Laser Sintering System & Equipment Mfr
S.I.C.: 3441
N.A.I.C.S.: 332312
Stuart Jackson *(Reg Mgr)*

EOS Singapore Pte Ltd **(1)**
8 Admiralty Street 06-12/13 Admirax
Singapore, 757438, Singapore
Tel.: (65) 6430 0552
Fax: (65) 6430 0549
Laser Sintering System & Equipment Mfr
S.I.C.: 3441
N.A.I.C.S.: 332312
Kevin Teo, *(Area Mgr-Sls)*

EOS s.r.l. Electro Optical Systems **(1)**
Via Gallarate 94
20151 Milan, Italy
Tel.: (39) 02 33 40 16 59
Fax: (39) 02 33 49 89 19
Laser Sintering System & Equipment Mfr
S.I.C.: 3441
N.A.I.C.S.: 332312

EOS Taiwan **(1)**
3F No 150 Zhuangjing N Road
Jhubei, Hsinchu, Taiwan 30264
Tel.: (886) 936 40 96 61
Fax: (886) 3 6576385
Laser Sintering System & Equipment Mfr
S.I.C.: 3441
N.A.I.C.S.: 332312

EOS IMAGING S.A.

10 rue Mercoeur
75008 Paris, France
Tel.: (33) 1 55 25 60 60
Fax: (33) 1 55 25 60 61
E-Mail: contact@eos-imaging.com
Web Site: www.eos-imaging.com
EOSI—(EUR)

Business Description:
Medical Imaging Products
S.I.C.: 3841
N.A.I.C.S.: 339112

Personnel:
Michael J. Dormer *(Chm)*
Marie Meynadier *(CEO)*
Anne Renevot *(CFO)*
Fabienne Hirigoyenberry-Lanson *(Chief Medical Officer)*

Board of Directors:
Michael J. Dormer
Eric Beard
Aris Constantinides
Olivier Denigot
Marie-Laure Garrigues
Herve Legrand
Marie Meynadier
Marie-Helene Plais
Philip Whitehead
Raphael Wisniewski

U.S. Subsidiary:

EOS Imaging Inc. **(1)**
185 Alewife Brook Pkwy #410
Cambridge, MA 02138
Tel.: (678) 564-5400
Fax: (678) 564-5399
Toll Free: (866) 933-5301
Web Site: www.eos-imaging.com
Medical Imaging Products
S.I.C.: 3841
N.A.I.C.S.: 339112
Herve Legrand *(VP-Sls & Mktg)*

Non-U.S. Subsidiaries:

EOS Imaging Canada **(1)**
3630 Montee Saint Hubert
Saint-Hubert, QC, J3Y 4J7, Canada
Tel.: (514) 875-0300
E-Mail: salescanada@eos-imaging.com
Medical Imaging Products
S.I.C.: 3841
N.A.I.C.S.: 339112

EOS Imaging GmbH **(1)**
Dieselstrasse 12
64347 Griesheim, Germany

Tel.: (49) 6155 89811 10
E-Mail: germany@eos-imaging.com
Medical Imaging Products
S.I.C.: 3841
N.A.I.C.S.: 339112

EP MANUFACTURING BHD.

No 8 10 Jalan Jurutera U1/23
Seksyen U1
Kawasan Perindustrian Hicom
Glenmarie, 40150 Shah Alam,
Selangor Darul Ehsan, Malaysia
Tel.: (60) 378036663
Fax: (60) 378049761
Web Site: www.epmb.com.my
EPMB—(KLS)
Rev.: $171,355,252
Assets: $203,384,838
Liabilities: $99,384,354
Net Worth: $104,000,484
Earnings: $9,693,643
Fiscal Year-end: 12/31/12
Business Description:
Automotive Parts Mfr
S.I.C.: 5531
N.A.I.C.S.: 441310
Personnel:
Hamidon Abdullah *(Chm)*
Li Li Tay *(Sec)*
Board of Directors:
Hamidon Abdullah
Aidan Hamidon
Johan Hamidon
Linden Hamidon
Shaari Haron
Ikmal Hijaz Hashim
Voon Foo Hew
Ismail Shahudin
Subsidiaries:

Circle Ring Network Sdn Bhd **(1)**
No 8 & 10 Jalan Jurutera U1/23 Seksyen U1
Shah Alam, Selangor, 40150, Malaysia
Tel.: (60) 378054441
Fax: (60) 378042141
Electronic Water Meters Mfr & Distr
S.I.C.: 3679
N.A.I.C.S.: 334419
Hamidon Abdullah *(Chm)*
Ahmad Kamaruzaman Mohamed Baria *(Mng Dir)*
Li Li Tay *(Sec)*

EP Polymers (M) Sdn Bhd **(1)**
No 8 & 10 Jalan Jurutera U1/23 Seksyen U1
Shah Alam, Selangor, 40150, Malaysia
Tel.: (60) 378036663
Fax: (60) 378049761
E-Mail: roslihr@epmb.com.my
Emp.: 100
Automotive Parts Whslr
S.I.C.: 5013
N.A.I.C.S.: 423120
Hamidon Abdullah *(CEO)*

PEPS - JV (M) Sdn Bhd **(1)**
Lot 1403 1406 & 1409 Batu 29 Jalan Ipoh
Batang Kali, Selangor, 44300, Malaysia
Tel.: (60) 360753190
Fax: (60) 360751637
Emp.: 900
Automotive Parts Distr
S.I.C.: 5013
N.A.I.C.S.: 423120
Hong Hung Moon *(Sr Gen Mgr)*

EP6

Z d'Amenagement Concerte Sud
1 B rue de Saint Louis, 57150
Creutzwald, Moselle, France
Tel.: (33) 387937161
Fax: (33) 387936295
E-Mail: contact@ep6.fr
Sls.: $22,300,000
Emp.: 16
Business Description:
Durable Goods
S.I.C.: 5099
N.A.I.C.S.: 423990
Personnel:
Evelyne Muller *(Mng Partner)*

E.P.B. HOLDINGS LIMITED

Launton Road
Bicester, Oxon, OX26 4UR, United Kingdom
Tel.: (44) 1869363636
Fax: (44) 01869363618
E-Mail: custemerservices@barrus.co.uk
Web Site: www.barrus.co.uk/contact_form.php
Year Founded: 1997
Sales Range: $25-49.9 Million
Emp.: 186
Business Description:
Holding Company
S.I.C.: 6719
N.A.I.C.S.: 551112
Personnel:
Robert D. Glen *(Chm)*
Board of Directors:
Robert D. Glen
Subsidiary:

E.P. Barrus Limited **(1)**
Launton Rd
Bicester, Oxon, OX26 4UR, United Kingdom
Tel.: (44) 1869363636
Fax: (44) 1869363618
E-Mail: customerservices@barrus.co.uk
Web Site: www.barrus.co.uk
Emp.: 150
Vehicles & Engines Distr for Garden, Marine & Road Use
Import
S.I.C.: 5251
N.A.I.C.S.: 444210
Robert D. Glen *(Mng Dir)*
Robert Richard Muir *(Mng Dir)*

EPC GROUPE

61 rue Galilee
75008 Paris, France
Tel.: (33) 1 40 69 80 00
Fax: (33) 1 40 69 80 50
E-Mail: contact@epc-groupe.com
Web Site: www.epc-groupe.com
Year Founded: 1893
EXPL—(EUR)
Emp.: 1,729
Business Description:
Explosive Mfr & Distr
S.I.C.: 2892
N.A.I.C.S.: 325920
Personnel:
Paul Brancion *(Chm)*
Olivier Obst *(CEO)*
Charles-Ernest Armand *(CFO)*

EPC INDUSTRIES LIMITED

(d/b/a PolyCello)
12 Tupper Blvd
Amherst, NS, B4H 4S7, Canada
Tel.: (902) 667-7241
Fax: (902) 667-7698
Web Site: www.polycello.com
Year Founded: 1956
Rev.: $23,408,000
Emp.: 350
Business Description:
Flexographic Packaging Services
S.I.C.: 7389
N.A.I.C.S.: 561910
Personnel:
Stephen Emmerson *(Pres & CEO)*

EPCOR UTILITIES, INC.

2000 10423 101 Street NW
Edmonton, AB, T5H 0E8, Canada
Tel.: (780) 412-3414
Fax: (780) 412-3192
E-Mail: Supplychainmanagement@epcor.com
Web Site: www.epcor.com
Year Founded: 1995
Rev.: $1,947,285,180
Assets: $5,391,564,480
Liabilities: $3,170,923,800
Net Worth: $2,220,640,680
Earnings: $17,892,360
Emp.: 2,749
Fiscal Year-end: 12/31/12
Business Description:
Electric Power & Water Solutions
S.I.C.: 4939
N.A.I.C.S.: 221122
Personnel:
Hugh John Bolton *(Chm)*
Sheila Christine Weatherill *(Vice Chm)*
David Stevens *(Pres & CEO)*
Guy Alfred Bridgeman *(CFO & Sr VP-Strategic Plng)*
Mark Donovan Wiltzen *(CFO & Sr VP)*
Wray Steedsman *(CIO & Sr VP-Bus Svcs)*
Samuel William Theodore Myers *(Treas)*
Doreen Alexandra Cole *(Sr VP-Electricity Svcs)*
Joseph George Gysel *(Sr VP-EPCOR Water (USA) Inc)*
Ronald John Liteplo *(Sr VP-Corp Svcs)*
Robert Petryk *(Sr VP-Comml Svcs)*
Stephen John Stanley *(Sr VP-Water Svcs)*
Board of Directors:
Hugh John Bolton
James Edward Clarke Carter
Vito Culmone
Alexander Mackay Davidson
Allister John McPherson
Douglas Harding Mitchell
Michael Barrett Percy
Robert Lawrence Phillips
Laurence Malcolm Pollock
Helen Katrina Sinclair
Wesley Robert Twiss
Sheila Christine Weatherill
Transfer Agent:
BNY Trust Company of Canada
Toronto, ON, Canada
Subsidiaries:

EPCOR Energy **(1)**
10423 101 St NW
Edmonton, AB, T5H 2R8, Canada
Tel.: (780) 412-3414
Fax: (780) 310-4295
Web Site: www.epcor.com
Sales Range: $1-9.9 Million
Emp.: 20
Regulated Electricity Services
S.I.C.: 4931
N.A.I.C.S.: 221122

EPCOR Merchant & Capital, L.P. **(1)**
EPCOR Place 505 2nd Street Southwest 8th Floor
Calgary, AB, T2P 1N8, Canada
Tel.: (403) 717-4600
Fax: (403) 717-4601
E-Mail: emc@epcor.com
Web Site: www.epcor.com
Emp.: 200
Non-regulated Electricity Services
S.I.C.: 4911
N.A.I.C.S.: 221122

EPCOR Power Development Corporation **(1)**
10065 Jasper Avenue Northwest
Edmonton, AB, Canada
Tel.: (780) 412-3492
Fax: (780) 412-3192
Web Site: www.epcor.com
Sales Range: $1-9.9 Million
Emp.: 2,000
Developing, Constructing & Operating Non-regulated Power Plants
S.I.C.: 4939
N.A.I.C.S.: 221122

EPCOR Water Services, Inc. **(1)**
215 10451 Shellbridge Way
Richmond, BC, V6X 2W8, Canada
Tel.: (604) 270-9236
Sales Range: $1-9.9 Million
Emp.: 20
Water & Wastewater Services
S.I.C.: 9511
N.A.I.C.S.: 924110

U.S. Subsidiaries:

Arizona-American Water Company **(1)**
19820 N 7th St Ste 201
Phoenix, AZ 85024 AZ
Tel.: (623) 445-2400
Fax: (623) 445-2454
Toll Free: (800) 383-0834
Web Site: www.amwater.com
Emp.: 50
Water Utility
S.I.C.: 4941
N.A.I.C.S.: 221310
Paul Townsley *(Pres)*

New Mexico American Water **(1)**
1005 N Norris St
Clovis, NM 88101-6372 NM
Tel.: (575) 763-5538
Fax: (575) 762-1642
Toll Free: (866) 430-0824
Emp.: 17
Water Supply
S.I.C.: 4971
N.A.I.C.S.: 221310
Daniel Bailet *(Gen Mgr)*

Primary Energy Ventures LLC **(1)**
2000 York Rd Ste 129
Oak Brook, IL 60523
Tel.: (630) 371-0505
E-Mail: investorinfo@epcorusa.com
Web Site: www.epcorusa.com
Emp.: 200
Investment Services
S.I.C.: 6211
N.A.I.C.S.: 523999
Mark Hall *(Sr VP-External & Environ Affairs)*

Subsidiary:

Portside Energy Corp. **(2)**
6290 US Hwy 12
Portage, IN 46368 IN
Mailing Address:
PO Box 209
Portage, IN 46368-0209
Tel.: (219) 763-7426
Fax: (219) 764-4516
Emp.: 15
Provider of Electric Services
S.I.C.: 4911
N.A.I.C.S.: 221118

EPCYLON TECHNOLOGIES, INC.

(Formerly Mobile Integrated Systems, Inc.)
Suite 502 25 Adelaide Street
Toronto, ON, M5C 3A1, Canada
Tel.: (416) 479-0880
Web Site: www.mobileintegratedsystems.com
Year Founded: 2009
PRFC—(OTC OTCB)
Rev.: $34,827
Assets: $304,736
Liabilities: $769,210
Net Worth: ($464,474)
Earnings: ($2,092,380)
Fiscal Year-end: 05/31/13
Business Description:
Algorithmic Securities Trading Systems Developer; Software & Interactive Games Developer
S.I.C.: 7372
N.A.I.C.S.: 511210
Personnel:
Todd Alan Halpern *(Chm)*
Cato Kemmler *(Pres)*
Kyle Appleby *(CFO)*
Board of Directors:

epcylon Technologies, Inc.—(Continued)

Todd Alan Halpern
Cato Kemmler
Douglas McKay

EPI ENVIRONMENTAL TECHNOLOGIES INC.

Suite 801 1788 West Broadway
Vancouver, BC, V6J 1Y1, Canada
Tel.: (604) 738-6281
Fax: (604) 738-7839
Toll Free: (866) 738-6281
E-Mail: info@epi-global.com
Web Site: www.epi-global.com
Year Founded: 2005
Rev.: $6,807,281
Assets: $7,303,494
Liabilities: $1,963,436
Net Worth: $5,340,058
Earnings: $464,014
Fiscal Year-end: 12/31/12
Business Description:
Chemical Additives Mfr & Distr
S.I.C.: 2899
N.A.I.C.S.: 325998
Personnel:
Joseph G. Gho *(Chm & CEO)*
Henry Poon *(CFO)*
Evon Siu *(Sec)*
Board of Directors:
Joseph G. Gho
Reginald Allen
Sam Wang
Sheng Wang
Transfer Agent:
Computershare Investor Services Inc.
510 Burrard St 2nd Floor
Vancouver, BC, V6C 3B9, Canada
Tel.: (604) 661-9400

Subsidiary:

EPI Environmental Products Inc. **(1)**
Unit 210 - 27090 Gloucester Way
Langley, BC, V4W 3Y5, Canada
Tel.: (604) 856-8812
Fax: (604) 856-8189
E-Mail: info@epi-global.com
Degradable & Biodegradable Chemical Additives Mfr
S.I.C.: 2899
N.A.I.C.S.: 325998

U.S. Subsidiary:

EPI Environmental Products Inc. **(1)**
Unit 207 102 Grover St
Lynden, WA 98264
Tel.: (604) 738-6281
Fax: (604) 738-7839
Web Site: www.epi-global.com
Degradable & Biodegradable Chemical Additives Mfr
S.I.C.: 2899
N.A.I.C.S.: 325998

Non-U.S. Subsidiary:

EPI (Europe) Limited **(1)**
McLintocks Summer Lane
Barnsley, South Yorkshire, S70 2NZ, United Kingdom
Tel.: (44) 1629760168
Fax: (44) 1629760857
E-Mail: epieurope@epi-global.com
Web Site: www.epi-global.com
Emp.: 1
Degradable & Biodegradable Chemical Additives Distr
S.I.C.: 5169
N.A.I.C.S.: 424690
Ted Aguirre *(Mgr-Bus Dev)*

EPI (HOLDINGS) LIMITED

Room 1401 14F Bank of East Asia Harbour View Centre 56 Gloucester Road
Wanchai, China (Hong Kong)
Tel.: (852) 26163689
Fax: (852) 24812902
E-Mail: enquiries@epiholdings.com
Web Site: www.epiholdings.com
0689—(HKG)
Rev.: $11,177,644
Assets: $146,578,368
Liabilities: $59,717,390
Net Worth: $86,860,978
Earnings: ($432,245,558)
Emp.: 24
Fiscal Year-end: 12/31/12
Business Description:
Telecommunication Equipment
S.I.C.: 3669
N.A.I.C.S.: 334290
Personnel:
Robert Kwok Chi Chu *(Chm & CEO)*
Board of Directors:
Robert Kwok Chi Chu
Yuk Ming Cheung
Zhi Hui Qian
Tiansheng Zhu
Butterfield Fulcrum Group (Bermuda) Limited
Rosebank Centre 11 Bermudiana Rd
Pembroke, Bermuda

EPI S.A.

1 rue de l'Europe
67520 Marlenheim, France
Tel.: (33) 388592989
Fax: (33) 388592849
E-Mail: info@epi.fr
Web Site: www.epi.fr
Sales Range: $250-299.9 Million
Emp.: 770
Business Description:
Household Furniture & Flooring Mfr & Distr
S.I.C.: 2511
N.A.I.C.S.: 337122
Personnel:
Gerard Voirin *(Chm-Exec Bd)*
Antonio Clemente *(CEO)*

EPIC DATA INTERNATIONAL INC.

(Acquired by Sylogist Ltd.)

EPIC ENERGY LTD.

304 - A Wing Winsway Complex Old Police Lane
Andheri, Mumbai, 400 069, India
Tel.: (91) 2226848347
Fax: (91) 2226848347
E-Mail: info@epicenergy.biz
Web Site: www.epicenergy.biz
530407—(BOM)
Sales Range: $1-9.9 Million
Business Description:
Renewable Energy Devices Mfr
S.I.C.: 3568
N.A.I.C.S.: 333613
Personnel:
Nikhil Morsawala *(Chm)*
Sraban Khan *(Sec)*
Board of Directors:
Nikhil Morsawala
V. Chandrasekhar
Sanjay Gugale
Zubin Patel

Unit:

Epic Energy Ltd. - Navi Mumbai Works **(1)**
119 Patil Wadi Station Road Rabale West
Navi Mumbai, 400 701, India
Tel.: (91) 22 27692611
Fax: (91) 22 27693706
E-Mail: info@epicenrgy.biz
Solar Product Mfr
S.I.C.: 3433
N.A.I.C.S.: 333414

EPIC GROUP

52 Old Steine
Brighton, E Sussex, BN1 1NH, United Kingdom
Tel.: (44) 1273728686
Fax: (44) 1273821567
E-Mail: contactenquiries@epic.co.uk
Web Site: www.epic.co.uk
Year Founded: 1996
Sales Range: $25-49.9 Million
Emp.: 143
Business Description:
E-learning & Knowledge Solutions
S.I.C.: 8299
N.A.I.C.S.: 611710
Personnel:
Jonathan Satchell *(CEO)*

U.S. Subsidiary:

Epic Learning Inc. **(1)**
11 Broadway Ste 466
New York, NY 10004
Tel.: (212) 574-8233
E-Mail: contactus@epiclearninggroup.com
Web Site: www.epiclearninggroup.com
Online Learning Software Development Services
S.I.C.: 7371
N.A.I.C.S.: 541511
David Rogers *(Mgr-Production)*

Non-U.S. Subsidiary:

EpicBrasil **(1)**
Av das Americas 3500-Ed Hong Kong 1 000-Bl 5-Loja B
Rio de Janeiro, 22640-102, Brazil
Tel.: (55) 21 3282 5249
Web Site: www.epicbrasil.com
Emp.: 20
Online Learning Services
S.I.C.: 2741
N.A.I.C.S.: 519130
Richard Vasconcelos *(CEO)*

EPIC RESOURCES LIMITED

(Name Changed to Ascot Resources Limited)

EPICENTRE HOLDINGS LIMITED

39 Ubi Road 1 08-01 World Publications Building
Singapore, 408695, Singapore
Tel.: (65) 6601 9100
Fax: (65) 6601 9111
E-Mail: info@epicentreorchard.com
Web Site: www.epicentreasia.com
Year Founded: 2002
5MQ—(CAT)
Rev.: $144,359,467
Assets: $26,109,751
Liabilities: $16,198,458
Net Worth: $9,911,293
Earnings: ($3,131,842)
Emp.: 50
Fiscal Year-end: 06/30/13
Business Description:
Computer & Computer Products Retailer & Distr
S.I.C.: 5946
N.A.I.C.S.: 443142
Personnel:
Jimmy Teck Loon Fong *(Chm & CEO)*
Kok Liang Chew *(Co-Sec)*
Chee Keen Yun *(Co-Sec)*
Board of Directors:
Jimmy Teck Loon Fong
Azman Hisham Jaafar
Joshua Chee Keong Siow
Ron Aik Ti Tan
Brenda Yeo
Transfer Agent:
Boardroom Corporate & Advisory Services Pte. Ltd.
50 Raffles Place 32-01 Singapore Land Tower
Singapore, Singapore

Subsidiaries:

EpiCentre Pte. Ltd. **(1)**
545 Orchard Rd Far E Shopping Ctr No 12-11
Singapore, 238882, Singapore
Tel.: (65) 62389376
Fax: (65) 62387681
Computer Peripherals Mfr
S.I.C.: 3575
N.A.I.C.S.: 334118

EpiCentre Solutions Pte. Ltd. **(1)**
Far E Shopping Ctr
545 Orchard Rd No 12-11, Singapore, 238882, Singapore
Tel.: (65) 62389376
Computer Peripherals Mfr
S.I.C.: 3575
N.A.I.C.S.: 334118
Joanne Lee Sieu Wei *(Mgr)*

Non-U.S. Subsidiary:

Afor Sdn. Bhd. **(1)**
No 34 17th Fl Cent Plz
Jln Sultan Ismail, 50250 Kuala Lumpur, Malaysia
Tel.: (60) 321411781
Fax: (60) 321413787
Web Site: www.epicentreasia.com
Emp.: 9
Computer Peripherals Mfr
S.I.C.: 3575
N.A.I.C.S.: 334118
Ling Chuan Goh *(Gen Mgr)*

EPIGENOMICS AG

Kleine Praesidentenstrasse 1
10178 Berlin, Germany
Tel.: (49) 30243450
Fax: (49) 3024345555
E-Mail: contact@epigenomics.com
Web Site: www.epigenomics.com
ECX—(DEU OTC)
Rev.: $1,398,671
Assets: $9,258,957
Liabilities: $3,661,582
Net Worth: $5,597,375
Earnings: ($16,419,235)
Emp.: 39
Fiscal Year-end: 12/31/12
Business Description:
In Vitro Diagnostic Tests For Cancer Screening & Specialty Applications
S.I.C.: 8734
N.A.I.C.S.: 541380
Personnel:
Heino von Prondzynski *(Chm-Supervisory Bd)*
Thomas Taapken *(CEO & CFO)*
Uwe Staub *(COO)*
Noel Doheny *(CEO-Epigenomics Inc)*
Andrew Sledziewski *(Sr VP-Res)*
Albert Weber *(Sr VP-Fin, Acctg & Controlling)*
Supervisory Board of Directors:
Heino von Prondzynski
Ann Clare Kessler
Gunther Reiter

EPILEDS TECHNOLOGIES, INC.

5F 2 Chuangye Rd Tainan Science Park
Sinshih Township, T'ainan, 74147, Taiwan
Tel.: (886) 6 5050101
Fax: (886) 6 5056533
E-Mail: sales@epileds.com.tw
Web Site: www.epileds.com.tw
Year Founded: 2006
4956—(TAI)
Sales Range: $25-49.9 Million
Emp.: 351
Business Description:
LED Wafer & Chip Mfr
S.I.C.: 3674
N.A.I.C.S.: 334413
Personnel:
Shui-Shu Hung *(Chm)*
Chin-Fu Ku *(Pres)*

EPINAL AUTO

91 Rue D Alsace
88000 Epinal, Vosges, France

Tel.: (33) 329291515
Fax: (33) 329353000
E-Mail: epinalauto@groupuchouk.com
Web Site: www.epinalauto.peugeot.fr/
Sls.: $31,000,000
Emp.: 78
S.I.C.: 5511
N.A.I.C.S.: 441110
Personnel:
Johann Choux *(Dir-Pur)*

EPISIL TECHNOLOGIES, INC.

3 Innovation Road 1 Science Based Industrial Park
Hsin-chu, R.O.C., 300, Taiwan
Tel.: (886) 35779245
Fax: (886) 35776289
E-Mail: sales@episil.com
Web Site: www.episil.com
Year Founded: 1985
Sales Range: $100-124.9 Million
Business Description:
Semiconductor Component Mfr
S.I.C.: 3679
N.A.I.C.S.: 334419
Personnel:
Amy Fan *(CFO)*

EPISTAR CORPORATION

5 Li-hsin 5th Road
Science Industrial Park, Hsin-chu, 300, Taiwan
Tel.: (886) 3 5678000
Fax: (886) 35783080
E-Mail: sales@epistar.com.tw
Web Site: www.epistar.com.tw
Year Founded: 1996
2448—(TAI)
Sales Range: $250-299.9 Million
Emp.: 4,000
Business Description:
Optoelectronic Light Emitting Diode Products Developer, Mfr & Marketer
S.I.C.: 3648
N.A.I.C.S.: 335129
Personnel:
Biing-Jye Lee *(Co-Founder, Chm & Chief Strategy Officer)*
Ming-Jiunn Jou *(Co-Founder & Pres)*
Subsidiaries:

Huga Optotech Inc. (1)
22 Keya Rd Central Taiwan Science Park
Taichung, Taiwan
Tel.: (886) 4 25598999
Fax: (886) 4 25658803
E-Mail: mktcom.huga@hugaopto.com.tw
Web Site: www.hugaopto.com.tw
Sales Range: $150-199.9 Million
Emp.: 1,200
Light Emitting Diode (LED) Semiconductor Device Mfr
S.I.C.: 3674
N.A.I.C.S.: 334413
T.P. Chen *(Chm)*
Chao Nien Huang *(Pres)*

EPISTEM HOLDINGS PLC

48 Grafton Street
Manchester, M13 9XX, United Kingdom
Tel.: (44) 1616067258
Fax: (44) 1616067348
E-Mail: info@epistem.co.uk
Web Site: www.epistem.co.uk
EHP—(AIM)
Rev.: $8,458,677
Assets: $22,223,769
Liabilities: $3,185,428
Net Worth: $19,038,341
Earnings: ($1,836,714)
Emp.: 65
Fiscal Year-end: 06/30/13
Business Description:
Biotechnology Stem Cell Researcher & Developer
S.I.C.: 8731
N.A.I.C.S.: 541712
Personnel:
Matthew H. Walls *(CEO)*
Hugh John Joseph Rylands *(Sec & Dir-Fin)*
Board of Directors:
David E. Evans
Catherine Booth
Roger Lloyd
Robert Nolan
Hugh John Joseph Rylands
Matthew H. Walls
Legal Counsel:
McGrigors LLP
Princes Exchange 1 Earl Grey St
Edinburgh, United Kingdom
Subsidiary:

Epistem Limited (1)
48 Grafton St
Manchester, Lancashire, M13 9XX, United Kingdom
Tel.: (44) 1616067258
Fax: (44) 1616067348
E-Mail: info@epistem.co.uk
Web Site: www.epistem.co.uk/contactus.asp
Emp.: 55
Biotechnology Research & Development Services
S.I.C.: 8731
N.A.I.C.S.: 541711
Jeff Moore *(Mng Dir)*

EPISURF MEDICAL AB

Roslagstulllsbacken 11
114 21 Stockholm, Sweden
Tel.: (46) 763 989 666
E-Mail: ir@episurf.com
Web Site: www.episurf.com
EPIS B—(OMX)
Business Description:
Implants & Surgical Instruments Mfr
S.I.C.: 3841
N.A.I.C.S.: 339112
Personnel:
Saeid Esmaeilzadeh *(Chm)*
Nina Bake *(CEO & Mng Dir)*
Board of Directors:
Saeid Esmaeilzadeh
Thomas Nortoft
Leif Ryd

EPM GLOBAL SERVICES INC.

195 Royal Crest Court
Markham, ON, L3R 9X6, Canada
Tel.: (905) 479-6203
Fax: (905) 479-6990
Toll Free: (800) 965-4446
E-Mail: inquirygeneral@epmglobal.com
Web Site: www.epmglobal.com
Year Founded: 1993
Rev.: $22,616,084
Emp.: 190
Business Description:
Electronic Components Mfr
S.I.C.: 3679
N.A.I.C.S.: 334419
Personnel:
James McColl *(Pres & CEO)*
Lianne Bastien *(CFO)*
Cyril Fernandes *(Sr VP-Mktg & Corp Dev)*
John Kouzoukas *(Sr VP)*

EPOCH CO. LTD.

2-2 Komagata 2 chome
Taitoku, Tokyo, 111 8618, Japan
Tel.: (81) 338438812
Fax: (81) 338438856
Web Site: www.epoch.jp
Year Founded: 1958
Emp.: 14
Business Description:
Toy & Game Mfr
S.I.C.: 3944
N.A.I.C.S.: 339930
Personnel:
Michihiro Maeda *(Pres & CEO)*
U.S. Subsidiary:

International Playthings, LLC (1)
75D Lackawanna Ave
Parsippany, NJ 07054
Tel.: (973) 316-5883
Toll Free: (800) 445-8347
E-Mail: info@intplay.com
Web Site: www.intplay.com
Toy Developer & Supplier
S.I.C.: 5092
N.A.I.C.S.: 423920
Michael Varda *(CEO)*

EPOCH HOLDING CORPORATION

(Acquired by The Toronto-Dominion Bank)

EPPENDORF AG

Barkhausenweg 1
22339 Hamburg, Germany
Tel.: (49) 40538010
Fax: (49) 4053801556
E-Mail: eppendorf@eppendorf.de
Web Site: www.eppendorf.com
Year Founded: 1945
Sls.: $700,330,135
Assets: $809,878,757
Liabilities: $321,548,859
Net Worth: $488,329,898
Earnings: $95,015,371
Emp.: 2,650
Fiscal Year-end: 12/31/12
Business Description:
Medical Equipment & Supplies Whslr
S.I.C.: 3841
N.A.I.C.S.: 339112
Personnel:
Klaus Fink *(Chm-Supervisory Bd)*
Dirk Ehlers *(Chm-Mgmt Bd)*
Philipp von Loeper *(Vice Chm-Supervisory Bd)*
Detmar Ammermann *(CFO & Member-Mgmt Bd)*
Michael Schroeder *(CMO, Chief Sls Officer & Member-Mgmt Bd)*
Heinz Gerhard Kohn *(CTO, Chief Production Officer & Member-Mgmt Bd)*
Supervisory Board of Directors:
Klaus Fink
Adrian Deteindre
Hans Hinz
Marlis Kripke
Peter Schmidt
Philipp von Loeper
Subsidiary:

Eppendorf Vertrieb Deutschland GmbH (1)
Peter-Henlein-Str 2
50389 Wesseling, Germany (100%)
Tel.: (49) 22324180
Fax: (49) 2232418155
E-Mail: vertrieb@eppendorf.de
Web Site: www.eppendorf.de
Emp.: 60
Laboratory Apparatus & Furniture Mfr
S.I.C.: 3559
N.A.I.C.S.: 333249
Klaus Ambos *(Mng Dir)*

U.S. Subsidiaries:

Brinkmann Instruments, Inc. (1)
1 Cantiague Rock Rd
Westbury, NY 11590-2826 DE
Mailing Address:
102 Motor Pkwy Ste 410
Hauppauge, NY 11788-5178
Tel.: (516) 334-7500
Fax: (516) 334-7506
Toll Free: (800) 645-3050
E-Mail: info@brinkmann.com
Web Site: www.brinkmann.com
Sales Range: $75-99.9 Million
Emp.: 260
Importer & Distributor of Scientific Instruments Used in Laboratories, for Quality Control of Manufacturing Processes & for Environmental Monitoring
Import Export
S.I.C.: 5049
N.A.I.C.S.: 423490
Susan Garfinkel *(Mgr)*

Non-U.S. Subsidiary:

Brinkmann Instruments (Canada), Ltd. (2)
6670 Campobello Rd
Mississauga, ON, L5N 2L8, Canada (100%)
Tel.: (905) 826-5525
Fax: (905) 826-5424
E-Mail: canada@brinkmann.com
Web Site: www.brinkmann.com
Emp.: 30
U.S. & Canadian Distribution & Marketing of Scientific Instruments Such as Laboratory Analysis Equipment; Distribution & Marketing of Process & Quality Control Equipment
S.I.C.: 5049
N.A.I.C.S.: 423490
Edward Colihan *(VP-Mktg)*

Eppendorf North America, Inc. (1)
1 Cantiague Rd
Westbury, NY 11590
Tel.: (516) 334-7500
Fax: (516) 334-7506
Web Site: www.eppendorf.de/int/index.php?l=131&action=corporate&contentid=12&sitemap=7.14
Emp.: 250
Laboratory Apparatus & Furniture Mfr
S.I.C.: 3826
N.A.I.C.S.: 334516
Martin Farb *(Mng Dir)*

Eppendorf Scientific, Inc. (1)
102 Motor Pkwy
Hauppauge, NY 11788
Tel.: (516) 334-7500
Fax: (516) 334-7506
Toll Free: (800) 645-3050
E-Mail: custserv@eppendorf.com
Web Site: www.eppendorf.com
Emp.: 70
Analytical Laboratory Instrument Mfr
S.I.C.: 3826
N.A.I.C.S.: 334516
Martin Farb *(Pres)*

New Brunswick Scientific Co., Inc. (1)
44 Talmadge Rd
Edison, NJ 08817-3319 NJ
Mailing Address:
PO Box 4005
Edison, NJ 08818-4005
Tel.: (732) 287-1200
Fax: (732) 287-4222
Toll Free: (800) 631-5417
E-Mail: bioinfo@nbsc.com
Web Site: www.nbsc.com
Sales Range: $75-99.9 Million
Emp.: 437
Designer, Mfr & Marketer of High-Technology Equipment & Instruments for Research & Development to Produce Therapeutic Drugs, Enzymes, Biochemicals, Antibiotics, Vaccines & Other Biological Products
Import Export
S.I.C.: 3826
N.A.I.C.S.: 334516
James T. Orcutt *(Pres & CEO)*

Non-U.S. Subsidiaries:

New Brunswick Scientific B.V. (2)
Kerkenbos 1101
6546 BC Nijmegen, Netherlands
Mailing Address:
PO Box 6826
6503 GH, Nijmegen, Netherlands
Tel.: (31) 243717600
Fax: (31) 243717640
E-Mail: sales@nbsbv.nl

Eppendorf AG—(Continued)

Web Site: www.nbsc.com
Emp.: 25
Laboratory Equipment Sales & Service
S.I.C.: 5049
N.A.I.C.S.: 423490

New Brunswick Scientific Co., Inc. (2)
9 Building Qijiayuan No 9-42 Diplomatic Compound
9 Jianguomenwai Dajie, Beijing, 100600, China
Tel.: (86) 1085325665
Fax: (86) 1085325675
E-Mail: nbsbj@public.bta.net.cn
Web Site: www.nbsc.com
Emp.: 4
Pharmaceutical Mfr
S.I.C.: 2834
N.A.I.C.S.: 325412
Jia Fu *(Mng Dir)*

New Brunswick Scientific GmbH (2)
In der Au 14
D 72622 Nurtingen, Germany
Tel.: (49) 7022932490
Fax: (49) 7022 32486
E-Mail: sales@nbsgmbh.de
Web Site: www.nbsgmbh.de
Emp.: 15
Laboratory Equipment Sales & Services
S.I.C.: 5049
N.A.I.C.S.: 423490
Frau Brigitte Mayer *(Gen Mgr)*

New Brunswick Scientific (UK) Ltd. (2)
17 Alban Pk Hatfield Road
Saint Albans, AL4 0JJ, United Kingdom UK
Tel.: (44) 1727853855
Fax: (44) 1727835666
E-Mail: contact@nbsuk.co.uk
Web Site: www.nbsuk.co.uk
Sls.: $1,632,685
Emp.: 20
Laboratory Equipment Sales & Services
S.I.C.: 5049
N.A.I.C.S.: 423490
Pisa Gollsa *(Gen Mgr)*

New Brunswick Scientific (2)
903 Yin Hai Building Suite A903
250 Cao Xi Road, Shanghai, 200051, China
Tel.: (86) 2164845955
Fax: (86) 2164845933
E-Mail: nbschc@vip.163.com
Web Site: www.nbschc.com
Emp.: 50
Pharmaceutical Mfr
S.I.C.: 2834
N.A.I.C.S.: 325412
Lisa Chen *(Gen Mgr)*

USA Scientific, Inc. (1)
346 SW 57th Ave
Ocala, FL 34474-9345
Tel.: (352) 237-6288
Fax: (352) 351-2057
Toll Free: (800) 522-8477
E-Mail: infoline@usascientific.com
Web Site: www.usascientific.com
Emp.: 50
Surgical & Medical Instrument Mfr
S.I.C.: 3841
N.A.I.C.S.: 339112
Bob Declerk *(Pres)*

Non-U.S. Subsidiaries:

Eppendorf Biotechnology International Trade (Shanghai) Company Ltd. (1)
Shanghai Pudong Century Boulevard
1600 Pohang Business Plaza 151, 200122
Shanghai, China
Tel.: (86) 2168760880
Fax: (86) 2150815371
Professional Equipment & Supplies Whslr
S.I.C.: 5049
N.A.I.C.S.: 423490

Eppendorf China Ltd. (1)
Pu Jian Road
International Plaza No 76, 200127
Shanghai, Pudong, China
Tel.: (86) 2138560500
Fax: (86) 2138560555
E-Mail: market.info@eppendorf.cn
Web Site: www.eppendorf.cn
Emp.: 50
Professional Equipment & Supplies Whslr
S.I.C.: 5047
N.A.I.C.S.: 423450

Eppendorf Co., Ltd. (1)
Horisho Building
Higashi-Kanda 2-4-5 Chiyoda-ku, 101-0031
Tokyo, Japan (100%)
Tel.: (81) 358252361
Fax: (81) 358252365
E-Mail: info@eppendorf.jp
Web Site: www.eppendorf.com.jp
Professional Equipment & Supplies Whslr
S.I.C.: 5049
N.A.I.C.S.: 423490

Eppendorf do Brasil Ltda. (1)
Rua Ferreira de Araujo 221 Conj 15
05428-000 Sao Paulo, SP, Brazil (100%)
Tel.: (55) 1130959344
Fax: (55) 1130959340
E-Mail: eppendorf@eppendorf.com.br
Web Site: www.eppendorf.com.br
Emp.: 6
Medical Dental & Hospital Equipment & Supplies Whslr
S.I.C.: 5047
N.A.I.C.S.: 423450
Algaro Alvarev *(Gen Mgr)*

Eppendorf France S.A.R.L. (1)
60 Route de Sartrouville
78230 Le Pecq, France (100%)
Tel.: (33) 130156740
Fax: (33) 130156745
E-Mail: eppendorf@eppendorf.fr
Web Site: www.eppendorf.com
Emp.: 20
Medical Dental & Hospital Equipment & Supplies Whslr
S.I.C.: 5047
N.A.I.C.S.: 423450
Arnaud Aladenise *(Mng Dir)*

Eppendorf Iberica S.L. (1)
Avda Tenerife 2
Edificio 1 Planta 3, 28700 Madrid, Spain (100%)
Tel.: (34) 916517694
Fax: (34) 916518144
E-Mail: eppendorf@eppendorf.es
Web Site: www.eppendorf.es
Emp.: 14
Laboratory Apparatus & Furniture Mfr
S.I.C.: 3826
N.A.I.C.S.: 334516
Francis Chabari *(Gen Mgr)*

Eppendorf India Ltd. (1)
Doshi Towers 4th Floor
156 Poonamallee High Road Kilp, 600010
Chennai, India (100%)
Tel.: (91) 4442111341
Fax: (91) 4442187405
E-Mail: info@eppendorf.co.in
Web Site: www.eppendorf.co.in
Emp.: 22
Surgical & Medical Instrument Mfr
S.I.C.: 3841
N.A.I.C.S.: 339112
V. Sankaranarayanan *(CEO)*

Eppendorf Middle East FZ-LLC (1)
Al Thuraya Tower 1 - Office 901 Media
PO Box 502019
Dubai, United Arab Emirates
Tel.: (971) 43692954
Fax: (971) 43688260
E-Mail: info-dubai@eppendorf.ae
Web Site: www.eppendorf.ae
Emp.: 5
Medical Dental & Hospital Equipment & Supplies Whslr
S.I.C.: 5047
N.A.I.C.S.: 423450
Nabil Faza *(Mng Dir)*

Eppendorf Nordic ApS (1)
Slotsmarken 15
2970 Horsholm, Denmark (100%)
Tel.: (45) 70222970
Fax: (45) 45767370
E-Mail: nordic@eppendorf.dk
Web Site: www.eppendorf.dk
Emp.: 5
Industrial Supplies Whslr
S.I.C.: 5085
N.A.I.C.S.: 423840
Liselotte Schmidt *(Gen Mgr)*

Eppendorf South Pacific Pty. Ltd. (1)
Unit 4 112 Talavera Road
North Ryde, NSW, 2113, Australia
Tel.: (61) 298895000
Fax: (61) 298895111
E-Mail: info@eppendorf.com.au
Web Site: www.eppendorf.com.au
Emp.: 23
Professional Equipment & Supplies Whslr
S.I.C.: 5049
N.A.I.C.S.: 423490
Jason Fiwcett *(Mgr)*

Eppendorf S.r.l. (1)
Via Zante 14
20138 Milan, Italy
Tel.: (39) 02554041
Fax: (39) 0258013438
E-Mail: eppendorf@eppendorf.it
Web Site: www.eppendorf.it
Emp.: 55
Electrical Apparatus & Equipment Wiring Supplies & Construction Material Whslr
S.I.C.: 5063
N.A.I.C.S.: 423610
Alberto Musti *(Mng Dir)*

Eppendorf UK Ltd. (1)
Endurance House
Vision Park Histon, Cambridge, CB249ZR, United Kingdom (100%)
Tel.: (44) 1223200440
Fax: (44) 1223200441
E-Mail: sales@eppendorf.co.uk
Web Site: www.eppendorf.co.uk
Emp.: 17
Measuring & Controlling Device Mfr
S.I.C.: 3829
N.A.I.C.S.: 334519
Albrecht Wiener *(Mng Dir)*

EPS CO., LTD.

Tsuruya Building 2-23
Shimomiyabicho
Shinjuku-ku, Tokyo, 162-0822, Japan
Tel.: (81) 3 5684 7797
E-Mail: info@eps.co.jp
Web Site: www.eps.co.jp
Year Founded: 1991
4282—(TKS)
Sales Range: $350-399.9 Million
Emp.: 3,094

Business Description:
Medical & Pharmaceutical Testing & Research Services
S.I.C.: 8731
N.A.I.C.S.: 541712

Personnel:
Yan Hao *(Pres & CEO)*

Board of Directors:
Hiroaki Abe
Hidetaka Ando
Yan Hao
Tatsuhiko Ichiki
Koichi Jingu
Yasuharu Tamai

Subsidiaries:

All Right Software Inc. (1)
3rd Fl Takara Bldg
4 18 13 Iidabashi Chiyoda ku, Tokyo, 102 0072, Japan
Tel.: (81) 352262581
Fax: (81) 352262587
E-Mail: info@allrightsoftware.com
Web Site: www.allrightsoft.co.jp
Emp.: 120
Software Reproducing
S.I.C.: 3652
N.A.I.C.S.: 334614
Hao Yan *(Pres)*

E -Trial Co., Ltd. (1)
9th Fl Tsuruya Bldg 2-23 Shimomiyabi-cho
Shinjuku-ku, Tokyo, 162-0822, Japan
Tel.: (81) 352259771
Fax: (81) 352259776
Web Site: www.e-trial.co.jp
Emp.: 20
Software Reproducing
S.I.C.: 3652
N.A.I.C.S.: 334614

EMS Co., Ltd (1)
1-2-5 Higashishinagawa
Shinagawa-ku, Tokyo, 140-0002, Japan
Tel.: (81) 3 6711 3203
Web Site: www.eps.co.jp/en/company/group/index.html
Business Process Outsourcing Services
S.I.C.: 7389
N.A.I.C.S.: 561499

EP-Mint Co., Ltd. (1)
Sumitomo Fudousan Otowa Bldg
2-9-3 Otsuka Bunkyo-ku, Tokyo, 112-0012, Japan (62.64%)
Tel.: (81) 353193530
Fax: (81) 3 5319 3450
Web Site: www.epmint.co.jp
6052—(JAS)
Sales Range: $25-49.9 Million
Emp.: 535
Medical Development Support & Associated Services
S.I.C.: 2834
N.A.I.C.S.: 325412
Shinro Tashiro *(Pres)*

EPMate Co., Ltd. (1)
3rd Floor S&S Building
6-36 Shin Ogawa-cho
Shinjuku-ku, 162-0814 Tokyo, Japan
Tel.: (81) 352298992
Fax: (81) 352298993
Web Site: www.epmate.co.jp
Temporary Help Services
S.I.C.: 7363
N.A.I.C.S.: 561320

EPMedical Co., Ltd. (1)
5th Floor Ishikinnihonbashi Building
4-14-7 Nihonbashi-honcho
Chuo-ku, 103-0023 Tokyo, Japan
Tel.: (81) 358477725
Fax: (81) 358477727
Web Site: www.epmedical.co.jp
Emp.: 92
Testing Laboratories
S.I.C.: 8734
N.A.I.C.S.: 541380

EPS International Co., Ltd. (1)
9th Fl Tsuruya Bldg
2-23 Shimomiyabi-cho Shinjuku, Tokyo, 1620822, Japan
Tel.: (81) 356847882
Fax: (81) 352257972
Web Site: www.eps.co.jp
Emp.: 1,000
Chemical & Allied Products Merchant Whslr
S.I.C.: 5169
N.A.I.C.S.: 424690
Hao Yan *(Pres & CEO)*

Non-U.S. Subsidiary:

Taiwan Total Management Consulting Ltd. (2)
4F-2 No 26 Sec 3 Zhung-Shan N Road
Taipei, Taiwan
Tel.: (886) 2 25866090
Fax: (886) 2 25866333
E-Mail: service@ttmc.com.tw
Web Site: www.ttmc.com.tw
Site Management Organization Services
S.I.C.: 8748
N.A.I.C.S.: 541618

LSG Co., Ltd. (1)
S And S Bldg 6-36 Shin Ogawa-cho
Shinjuku-ku, Tokyo, 162-0814, Japan
Tel.: (81) 335136533
Fax: (81) 335136535
E-Mail: info@lsg.co.jp
Web Site: www.lsg.co.jp
Emp.: 18
Surface Active Agent Mfr
S.I.C.: 2843
N.A.I.C.S.: 325613
Takeshi Tadano *(Pres)*

Medical Line Co., Ltd. (1)
Ikebukuro Westpark Bldg 3-27-12
Nishiikebukuro
Toshima-ku, Tokyo, 171-0021, Japan
Tel.: (81) 359798128
Fax: (81) 353915730
E-Mail: ml@medicalline.co.jp
Web Site: www.medicalline.co.jp

Sales Range: $10-24.9 Million
General Medical Services
S.I.C.: 8011
N.A.I.C.S.: 621491

PHARMA NETWORK Co., Ltd (1)
3rd Floor Shionogihonchokyodo Building
4-14-7 Nihonbashihoncho
Chuo-ku, Tokyo, 103-0023, Japan
Tel.: (81) 3 5614 4880
Fax: (81) 3 5614 4889
E-Mail: p-mark@pharmanetwork.jp
Web Site: www.pharmanetwork.jp
Pharmaceutical Training Services
S.I.C.: 8299
N.A.I.C.S.: 611430

Non-U.S. Subsidiary:

EPS China Co., Ltd. (1)
Floor 5 Building 5 B No 329 Tianyaoqiao Road
Xuhui District, Shanghai, 200030, China
Tel.: (86) 2133632793
Fax: (86) 2133632784
E-Mail: contact@epscn.com
Web Site: www.epscn.com
Contract Research Services
S.I.C.: 8731
N.A.I.C.S.: 541712
Ping Xu *(Chm)*

EPSILON ENERGY LTD.

150 Jardin Drive Suite 9
Concord, ON, L4K 3P9, Canada
Tel.: (905) 738-7877
Fax: (905) 669-8220
E-Mail: information@epsilonenergyltd.com
Web Site: www.epsilonenergyltd.com
Year Founded: 2005
EPS—(TSX)
Rev.: $43,076,784
Assets: $169,943,821
Liabilities: $64,766,591
Net Worth: $105,177,230
Earnings: ($4,129,664)
Emp.: 16
Fiscal Year-end: 12/31/12

Business Description:
Oil & Natural Gas Exploration Services
S.I.C.: 1311
N.A.I.C.S.: 211111

Personnel:
Zoran Arandjelovic *(Founder)*
John V. Lovoi *(Chm)*
Michael Raleigh *(CEO)*
B. Lane Bond *(CFO & Dir-Fin)*

Board of Directors:
John V. Lovoi
Matthew W. Dougherty
Adrian Montgomery
Nick Orlando
Michael Raleigh
Ryan Roebuck

Transfer Agent:
Computershare Trust Company of Canada
Toronto, ON, Canada

U.S. Subsidiary:

Epsilon Energy USA Inc. (1)
10700 North Fwy Ste 930
Houston, TX 77037-1142
Tel.: (231) 922-0467
Fax: (231) 922-0431
Toll Free: (866) 384-8774
Emp.: 15
Oil & Gas Exploration Services
S.I.C.: 1311
N.A.I.C.S.: 211111

EPSOM PROPERTIES LIMITED

Regency House 2A Second Floor
250/7 Anna Salai Teynampet
Chennai, 600 006, India
Tel.: (91) 4424350676
E-Mail: epsomproperties@gmail.com
Web Site: www.epsom.in
Year Founded: 1987
531155—(BOM)
Rev.: $19,276
Assets: $206,807
Liabilities: $18,412
Net Worth: $188,394
Earnings: ($10,543)
Fiscal Year-end: 03/31/13

Business Description:
Construction Services
S.I.C.: 1542
N.A.I.C.S.: 236220

Personnel:
C. Sivakumar Reddy *(Mng Dir)*
K. V. Narasimhan *(Compliance Officer & Sec)*

Board of Directors:
T. S. Raju
C. Sivakumar Reddy
K. Bhakthavatsala Reddy
Mohan Swami
Gomathi A. Vaidyanathan

Transfer Agent:
Cameo Corporate Services Limited
Subramanian Building No 1 Club House Road
5th Floor
Chennai, India

EPWIN (HOLDINGS) LIMITED

Manor Park Business Centre
MacKenzie Way, Cheltenham, GL51 9TX, United Kingdom
Tel.: (44) 1242 243444
Fax: (44) 1242 233548
E-Mail: info@epwin.co.uk
Web Site: www.epwin.co.uk
Sales Range: $250-299.9 Million
Emp.: 2,500

Business Description:
Extruder of PVC-U & Roofline Products; Windows & Doors Mfr
S.I.C.: 3089
N.A.I.C.S.: 326199

Personnel:
Jim Rawson *(Chm)*

Board of Directors:
Jim Rawson
Brian Kennedy

Subsidiaries:

Swish Building Products Limited (1)
Pioneer House
Lichfield Road Indl Estate, Tamworth, Staffordshire, B79 7TF, United Kingdom
Tel.: (44) 1827 317200
Fax: (44) 1827 317201
PVC Windows, Doors & Conservatory Systems Mfr
S.I.C.: 3089
N.A.I.C.S.: 326199

Ultraframe (UK) Ltd. (1)
Enterprise Works Salthill Rd
Clitheroe, Lancs, BB7 1PE, United Kingdom UK
Tel.: (44) 1200443311
Fax: (44) 1200425455
E-Mail: export@ultraframe.co.uk
Web Site: www.ultraframe.co.uk
Sales Range: $150-199.9 Million
Emp.: 250
Conservatory Roofing Systems Mfr
S.I.C.: 2541
N.A.I.C.S.: 337212
Mark Hanson *(Mgr-Mktg)*

Subsidiary:

Four Seasons Sunroom (2)
5005 Veterans Memorial Hwy
Holbrook, NY 11741-4506 NY
Tel.: (631) 563-4000
Fax: (631) 563-4010
Toll Free: (800) 368-7732
E-Mail: info@fourseasonssunrooms.com
Web Site: www.four-seasons-sunrooms.com
Emp.: 200
Mfr. & Distr of Sunrooms, Enclosures & Large-Scale Skylights
Import Export
S.I.C.: 3448
N.A.I.C.S.: 332311
Shaun Kennedy *(CEO)*

Subsidiary:

Fisher Skylights, Inc. (3)
5005 Veterans Memorial Hwy
Holbrook, NY 11741-4506 NY
Tel.: (631) 563-4001
Fax: (631) 563-3399
Toll Free: (800) 431-1586
Web Site: www.fisherskylights.com
Emp.: 150
Mfr. of Custom Metal Framed Skylights
Export
S.I.C.: 3448
N.A.I.C.S.: 332311

EQ INC.

(Formerly Cyberplex Inc.)
(d/b/a EQ Works)
1255 Bay Street Suite 400
Toronto, ON, M5R 2A9, Canada
Tel.: (416) 597-8889
Fax: (416) 597-2345
Toll Free: (866) 962-9764
E-Mail: press@eqworks.com
Web Site: www.eqworks.com
EQ—(TSX)
Rev.: $13,425,234
Assets: $11,871,581
Liabilities: $3,868,726
Net Worth: $8,002,855
Earnings: $1,552,659
Fiscal Year-end: 12/31/12

Business Description:
Internet Software Development Services
S.I.C.: 7372
N.A.I.C.S.: 511210

Personnel:
Vernon F. Lobo *(Chm)*
Geoffrey Rotstein *(Pres & CEO)*
Dilshan Kathiarachchi *(CTO-Adv Ops)*
Greg Pogue *(CTO)*
David Katz *(Gen Counsel & Exec VP-Corp Dev)*

Board of Directors:
Vernon F. Lobo
John Fisher
Marc Lavine
Geoffrey Rotstein
Anthony Tjan

Transfer Agent:
Equity Financial Holdings Inc
200 University Avenue Suite 400
Toronto, ON, Canada

U.S. Subsidiary:

Cyberplex Inc.-Boston (1)
15 Dartmouth Pl
Boston, MA 02116-6106
Tel.: (617) 859-9361
Fax: (617) 859-9363
E-Mail: chris.degrace@cyberplex.com
Provider of Internet Advertising Services
S.I.C.: 4899
N.A.I.C.S.: 517919

Subsidiary:

WebAffairs Inc (1)
1255 Bay St Ste 400
Toronto, ON, M5R 2A9, Canada (100%)
Tel.: (416) 597-8889
Fax: (416) 597-2345
E-Mail: info@webaffairs.ca
Web Site: www.webaffairs.ca
Emp.: 20
Data Processing & Hosting Services
S.I.C.: 7379
N.A.I.C.S.: 518210
Jesse Rothstein *(Mng Dir)*

EQ OYJ

(d/b/a eQ Group)
Mikonkatu 9 4th Floor
00100 Helsinki, Finland
Tel.: (358) 96878777
Fax: (358) 968178766
E-Mail: eqinfo@eq.fi
Web Site: www.eq.fi
EQV1V—(HEL)
Sls.: $21,995,072
Assets: $113,507,708
Liabilities: $14,424,212
Net Worth: $99,083,497
Earnings: $4,558,132
Emp.: 103
Fiscal Year-end: 12/31/12

Business Description:
Investment Services
S.I.C.: 6211
N.A.I.C.S.: 523999

Personnel:
Ole Johansson *(Chm)*
Janne Larma *(CEO)*
Mikko Koskimies *(CEO-eQ Asset Management Ltd)*
Annamaija Peltonen *(CEO-eQ Fund Management Company Ltd)*
Juha Surve *(Gen Counsel)*

Board of Directors:
Ole Johansson
Nicolas Berner
Christina Dahlblom
Georg Ehrnrooth
Jussi Seppala

Subsidiaries:

Amanda Advisors Ltd (1)
Mikonkatu 0
00100 Helsinki, Finland
Tel.: (358) 96829600
Fax: (358) 0968178749
E-Mail: amandainfo@eq.fi
Web Site: www.eq.fi/www/page/669
Emp.: 50
Equity Investment Management & Consulting Services
S.I.C.: 8748
N.A.I.C.S.: 541618
Janne Larma *(Mng Dir)*

Subsidiaries:

Amanda III Eastern GP Ltd (2)
Aleksanterinkatu 15 A VI Fl
00100 Helsinki, Finland
Tel.: (358) 96829600
Equity Investment Management & Consulting Services
S.I.C.: 8748
N.A.I.C.S.: 541618

Amanda IV West GP Ltd (2)
Mikonkatu 9
00100 Helsinki, Finland
Tel.: (358) 96829600
Fax: (358) 968296030
E-Mail: investors@eq.fi
Web Site: www.eq.fi
Emp.: 6
Equity Investment Management & Consulting Services
S.I.C.: 8748
N.A.I.C.S.: 541618
Jyrky Orpna *(Deputy Mng Dir)*

Amanda GP I and II Ltd (1)
Mikonkatu 9
100 Helsinki, Finland
Tel.: (358) 96829600
Fax: (358) 968296020
E-Mail: emmi.lehponen@eq.fi
Web Site: www.eq.fi
Emp.: 70
Equity Investment Management & Consulting Services
S.I.C.: 8748
N.A.I.C.S.: 541618

Amanda Warehousing GP Ltd (1)
Mikonkatu 9
00101 Helsinki, Finland
Tel.: (358) 96829600
Fax: (358) 0968178748
Emp.: 60
Equity Investment Management & Consulting Services
S.I.C.: 8748
N.A.I.C.S.: 541618
Janne Larma *(CEO)*

EQOLOGY ASA
Kirkeveien 59b
1363 Hovik, Norway
Tel.: (47) 67102190
Fax: (47) 67102199
E-Mail: ir@eqology.com
Web Site: www.eqology.com
Year Founded: 2010
EQO—(OSL)
Business Description:
Health & Skincare Products
S.I.C.: 2844
N.A.I.C.S.: 325620
Personnel:
Karstein Gjersvik *(Chm)*
Frank Erikstad Bjordal *(CEO)*
Board of Directors:
Karstein Gjersvik
Anne Margrete Borjesson
Christian Krefting
Marit Lambrechts
Erik Langaker

EQS GROUP AG
(Formerly EquityStory AG)
Seitzstrasse 23
D-80538 Munich, Germany
Tel.: (49) 89 21 02 98 0
Fax: (49) 89 21 02 98 49
E-Mail: info@eqs.com
Web Site: www.eqs.com
EQS—(DEU MUN)
Sls.: $19,142,537
Assets: $21,816,031
Liabilities: $2,813,495
Net Worth: $19,002,536
Earnings: $2,980,420
Emp.: 170
Fiscal Year-end: 12/31/12
Business Description:
Online Communication Services
S.I.C.: 2741
N.A.I.C.S.: 519130
Personnel:
Rony Vogel *(Chm-Supervisory Bd)*
Achim Weick *(Chm-Exec Bd & CEO)*
Robert Wirth *(Member-Exec Bd)*
Supervisory Board of Directors:
Rony Vogel
Peter Conzatti
Christian Goetz

EQSTRA HOLDINGS LIMITED
61 Maple Street
Pomona, Kempton Park, 1619, South Africa
Mailing Address:
PO Box 1050
Bedfordview, 2008, South Africa
Tel.: (27) 11 966 2000
Fax: (27) 86 532 2967
Web Site: www.eqstra.co.za
EQS—(JSE OTC)
Rev.: $1,015,241,300
Assets: $1,485,721,700
Liabilities: $1,119,904,200
Net Worth: $365,817,500
Earnings: $43,563,000
Emp.: 7,878
Fiscal Year-end: 06/30/13
Business Description:
Holding Company; Construction, Mining & Industrial Equipment & Passenger Vehicle Distr, Leasing & Rental Services
S.I.C.: 6719
N.A.I.C.S.: 551112
Personnel:
Walter Stanley Hill *(CEO)*
Jannie Lodewyk Serfontein *(CFO)*
Denish Venhod Haripal *(CIO)*
Gavin Edgar Bantam *(Exec-Corp Affairs)*
Jacqueline Veronica Carr *(CEO-Fleet Mgmt & Logistics)*
Erich Clarke *(CEO-Contract Mining & Plant Rental)*
Gary Derek Neubert *(CEO-Indus Equipment)*
Paul Siddall *(Treas)*
Liezl Moller *(Sec)*
Board of Directors:
Nkateko Peter Mageza
Erich Clarke
Marthinus Johannes Croucamp
Salukazi Dakile-Hlongwane
Grant Glenn Gelink
Walter Stanley Hill
Veli Joseph Mokoena
Sankie Dolly Mthembi-Mahanyele
Anthony John Phillips
Timothy Dacre Aird Ross
Jannie Lodewyk Serfontein
Legal Counsel:
Tugendhaft Wapnick Banchetti & Partners
20th Floor Sandton City Office Towers 5th Street
2146 Sandton, South Africa
Transfer Agent:
Computershare Investor Services (Proprietary) Limited
70 Marshall Street
Johannesburg, South Africa

Subsidiaries:

600SA Holdings (Pty) Ltd. (1)
17 Derrick Road
Spartan, Kempton Park, 1619, South Africa ZA
Mailing Address:
PO Box 600
Kempton Park, 1620, South Africa
Tel.: (27) 11 573 2300
Fax: (27) 11 573 2331
E-Mail: info@600sa.co.za
Web Site: www.eiegroup.co.za/600sa/about
Emp.: 100
Mfr & Distr of Vehicle Utilization Equipment for Lifting & Loading
S.I.C.: 5084
N.A.I.C.S.: 423830
Brendan Londt *(Gen Mgr)*

Eqstra NH Equipment (Pty) Limited (1)
9 Brewery Road
Isando, Gauteng, 1600, South Africa
Tel.: (27) 119778300
Fax: (27) 119778150
E-Mail: reception@nhconstruction.co.za
Web Site: www.nhconstruction.co.za
Construction & Mining Equipments Distr
S.I.C.: 5082
N.A.I.C.S.: 423810
Renier Botha *(Reg Mgr)*

MCC Contracts (Pty) Limited (1)
60 Radio Pl Comml Midran Industrial Park
Halfway House, Johannesburg, Gauteng, 1683, South Africa
Tel.: (27) 119906600
Fax: (27) 113101988
Emp.: 200
Contract Mining Services
S.I.C.: 1081
N.A.I.C.S.: 213114

Mutual Construction Company Transvaal (Pty) Limited (1)
60 Radio Pl Comml
Midrand Industrial Park, Johannesburg, Gauteng, 1685, South Africa
Tel.: (27) 119906600
Fax: (27) 0113101988
E-Mail: mccgroup@mccgroup.co.za
Web Site: www.mccgroup.co.za
Emp.: 397
Commercial Building Construction Services
S.I.C.: 1542
N.A.I.C.S.: 236220

Non-U.S. Subsidiary:

Impact Fork Trucks Limited (1)
Earl St Indus Estate Brunel Rd
Corby, Northamptonshire, NN17 4JW, United Kingdom
Tel.: (44) 1536463900
Fax: (44) 1536402400
Web Site: www.impact-handling.com
Emp.: 60
Forklift Trucks Retailer
S.I.C.: 3711
N.A.I.C.S.: 336120
Marcus Knight *(Gen Mgr)*

EQT PARTNERS AB
Hovslagargatan 3
PO Box 16409
SE 103 27 Stockholm, Sweden
Tel.: (46) 850655300
Fax: (46) 850655319
E-Mail: reception@eqt.se
Web Site: www.eqt.se
Year Founded: 1994
Emp.: 220
Business Description:
Private Equity Firm
S.I.C.: 6211
N.A.I.C.S.: 523999
Personnel:
Conni Jonsson *(CEO & Mng Partner)*
Thomas Ramsay *(Partner & Head-Finland)*
Christian Sinding *(Partner & Head-Equity)*
Tomas Aubell *(Partner-Germany)*
Lennart Blecher *(Partner)*
Piotr Czapski *(Partner-Poland)*
Patrick De Muynck *(Partner)*
Simon Griffiths *(Partner-Singapore)*
Asa Hallert Riisberg *(Partner)*
Morten Hummelmose *(Partner-Denmark)*
Samir Kamal *(Partner)*
Harry Klagsbrun *(Partner)*
Glen T. Matsumoto *(Partner-USA)*
Martin Mok *(Partner)*
Jens Moritz *(Partner-Frankfurt)*
Jan Stahlberg *(Partner)*
Thomas Von Koch *(Partner)*
Johan Bygge *(COO)*
Board of Directors:
Jan Stahlberg
Josef Ackermann
Johan Bygge
Conni Jonsson
Leif Ostling
Finn Rausing
Marcus Wallenberg

Subsidiaries:

EQT Northern Europe Private Equity Funds (1)
Hovflagar Jagas 3
Stockholm, 10327, Sweden (100%)
Tel.: (46) 84405300
Fax: (46) 84405319
E-Mail: info@eqt.se
Web Site: www.eqt.fi
Emp.: 80
Provider of Equity Management & Funding
S.I.C.: 6722
N.A.I.C.S.: 525910
Conni Jonsson *(CEO)*
Caspar Callerstrom *(Partner)*

EQT Scandinavian Partners Ltd. (1)
Hovslagargatan 3
PO Box 16409
Stockholm, 11148, Sweden (100%)
Tel.: (46) 850655300
Fax: (46) 850655319
E-Mail: reception@eqt.se
Emp.: 70
Portfolio Management
S.I.C.: 6282
N.A.I.C.S.: 523920
Thomas Von Koch *(Partner)*
Conni Jonsson *(Mng Dir)*

Holdings:

Anticimex International AB (1)
Lovholmsvagen 61
117 65 Stockholm, Sweden SE
Mailing Address: (92%)
PO Box 47025
100 74 Stockholm, Sweden
Tel.: (46) 8517 633 00
Fax: (46) 8517 634 42
Web Site: www.anticimex.com
Sls.: $316,875,600
Emp.: 1,338
Fiscal Year-end: 12/31/12
Holding Company; Hygiene, Pest Control, Safety & Fire Protection Services
S.I.C.: 6719
N.A.I.C.S.: 551112
Olof Sand *(Pres & CEO)*
Christer Holmen *(CFO)*
Thomas Hilde *(Pres-Norway)*
Mikael Roos *(Pres-Sweden)*
Mats Samuelsson *(Pres-Insurance)*

Subsidiaries:

Anticimex AB (2)
Lovholmsvagen 61
100 74 Stockholm, Sweden SE
Tel.: (46) 8517 633 00
Fax: (46) 8517 634 42
E-Mail: info@anticimex.se
Web Site: www.anticimex.com
Sales Range: $250-299.9 Million
Emp.: 70
Hygiene, Pest Control, Safety & Fire Protection Services
S.I.C.: 7342
N.A.I.C.S.: 561710
Mikael Roos *(Pres)*
Olof Sand *(CEO)*
Magnus Holgersson *(CFO)*

Subsidiary:

Anticimex Forsakringar AB (3)
Lovholmsvagen 61
117 65 Stockholm, Sweden
Mailing Address:
PO Box 47025
100 74 Stockholm, Sweden
Tel.: (46) 8517 633 00
Fax: (46) 8517 634 42
Web Site: www.anticimex.com
Insurance Services
S.I.C.: 6411
N.A.I.C.S.: 524298
Mats Samuelsson *(Pres)*
Thomas Akerfelt *(CFO)*

Non-U.S. Subsidiaries:

Anticimex A/S (2)
Pilestredet 28
0166 Oslo, Norway NO
Tel.: (47) 815 48 250
Fax: (47) 2254 2890
Hygiene, Pest Control, Safety & Fire Protection Services
S.I.C.: 7342
N.A.I.C.S.: 561710
Thomas Hilde *(Pres)*

Anticimex AS (2)
Kvaglundvej 82
6705 Esbjerg, Denmark DK
Tel.: (45) 7514 5822
Fax: (45) 7514 5825
E-Mail: info@anticimex.dk
Web Site: www.anticimex.com
Hygiene, Pest Control, Safety & Fire Protection Services
S.I.C.: 7342
N.A.I.C.S.: 561710

Anticimex Benelux B.V. (2)
Schapenweide 6
4824 AN Breda, Netherlands NL
Mailing Address:
PO Box 3420
4800 DK Breda, Netherlands
Tel.: (31) 76 548 6660
Fax: (31) 76 542 4230
E-Mail: info@anticimex.nl
Web Site: www.anticimex.com
Emp.: 56
Hygiene, Pest Control, Safety & Fire Protection Services
S.I.C.: 7342
N.A.I.C.S.: 561710
Sascha Suijkerbuijk *(Mng Dir)*
Koen Zijlmans-Smits *(CFO)*

Anticimex GmbH & Co. KG (2)
Havighorster Weg 8d
21031 Hamburg, Germany De
Tel.: (49) 40 739 245 0
Fax: (49) 40 739 245 29

E-Mail: info@anticimex.de
Web Site: www.anticimex.com
Hygiene, Pest Control, Safety & Fire Protection Services
S.I.C.: 7342
N.A.I.C.S.: 561710

Anticimex Oy (2)
Vetotie 3 A
01610 Vantaa, Finland FI
Tel.: (358) 207 495 500
Fax: (358) 207 495 600
E-Mail: asiakaspalvelu@racx.fi
Web Site: www.raksystems-anticimex.fi
Emp.: 180
Hygiene, Pest Control, Safety & Fire Protection Services
S.I.C.: 7342
N.A.I.C.S.: 561710
Marko Malmivaara *(Mng Dir)*

Atos Medical AB (1)
PO Box 183
SE 242 22 Horby, Sweden
Tel.: (46) 41519800
Fax: (46) 41519898
E-Mail: info@atosmedical.com
Web Site: www.atosmedical.com
Emp.: 120
Voice & Pulmonary Rehabilitation Products Mfr
S.I.C.: 3841
N.A.I.C.S.: 339112
Tommy Hedberg *(CEO)*

Munksjo Oyj (1)
Klarabergsviadukten 70 D5
PO Box 70365
107 24 Stockholm, Sweden SE
Tel.: (46) 10 250 10 00
Fax: (46) 36 12 90 58
E-Mail: info@munksjo.com
Web Site: www.munksjo.com
MUNK1—(HEL)
Rev.: $822,297,600
Assets: $906,044,400
Liabilities: $639,788,400
Net Worth: $266,256,000
Earnings: ($14,086,800)
Emp.: 1,802
Fiscal Year-end: 12/31/12
Specialty Paper Mfr
S.I.C.: 2621
N.A.I.C.S.: 322121
Peter Seligson *(Chm)*
Jan Astrom *(Pres & CEO)*
Kim Henriksson *(CFO & Exec VP)*
Daniele Borlatto *(Pres-Release Liners & Exec VP)*
Dan Adrianzon *(Pres-Indus Applications)*
Roland Le Cardiec *(Pres-Graphics & Pkg)*
Gustav Adlercreutz *(Gen Counsel & Sr VP)*
Anna Bergqvist *(Sr VP-Streategic Dev)*
Asa Fredriksson *(Sr VP-HR & Comm)*

U.S. Subsidiary:

Munksjo Paper Inc. (2)
642 River St
Fitchburg, MA 01420-2957 DE
Tel.: (978) 342-1080
Fax: (978) 345-4268
Web Site: www.munksjo.se
Emp.: 18
Decor Base Paper Mfr
S.I.C.: 2671
N.A.I.C.S.: 322220
Andrew Rice *(VP-Fin & Admin)*

Non-U.S. Subsidiary:

Ahlstrom Brasil Industria e Comercio de Papeis Especiais Ltda. (2)
770 Rua Armando Steck Bairro Capivari
CEP-13290-000 Louveira, SP, Brazil BR
Tel.: (55) 12 2127 9378
Fax: (55) 12 2127 9580
Web Site: www.ahlstrom.com
Mfr & Sales of Specialty Fiber-Based Materials
S.I.C.: 2621
N.A.I.C.S.: 322121

Plant:

Ahlstrom Brasil Industria e Comercio de Papeis Especiajs Ltda - Paulinia Plant (3)
Av Paris 2120 - Cascata
13140-000 Paulinia, Sao Paulo, Brazil
Tel.: (55) 1938441502
Web Site: www.ahlstrom.com
Paper Products Mfr
S.I.C.: 2679
N.A.I.C.S.: 322299

Scandic Hotels AB (1)
Halsingegatan 40
PO Box 3
SE 102 33 Stockholm, Sweden
Tel.: (46) 851735000
Fax: (46) 851751711
E-Mail: info@scandic-hotels.se
Web Site: www.scandic-hotels.com
Sales Range: $800-899.9 Million
Emp.: 6,600
Hotel Operator
S.I.C.: 7011
N.A.I.C.S.: 721110
Vagn Sorensen *(Chm)*
Frank Fiskers *(CEO)*
Lars Axelson *(CFO & Sr VP-Fin)*
Martin Creydt *(Chief Dev Officer & Sr VP)*
Nevio Sagberg *(Gen Counsel & Sr VP-Bus Dev)*
Roger Olofsson *(Sr VP-HR)*

Non-U.S. Subsidiaries:

Scandic Hotel Deutschland GmbH (2)
Ferdinand-Sauerbruch-Strasse 14
56073 Koblenz, Germany
Tel.: (49) 26 1947 310
Fax: (49) 26 1947 3133
Hotel Operator
S.I.C.: 7011
N.A.I.C.S.: 721110

Scandic Hotels A/S (2)
173 Skoyen
0212 Oslo, Norway
Tel.: (47) 23155050
Fax: (47) 23155111
E-Mail: sjoayst@scandichotels.com
Web Site: www.scandichotels.no
Emp.: 30
Hotel Operator
S.I.C.: 7011
N.A.I.C.S.: 721110

Scandic Hotels A/S (2)
Nansensgade 19 7th Fl
DK 1366 Copenhagen, Denmark
Tel.: (45) 23680461
Fax: (45) 33917600
E-Mail: info@scandichotels.com
Web Site: www.scandichotels.dk
Emp.: 20
Hotel Operator
S.I.C.: 7011
N.A.I.C.S.: 721110
Tonny Poulsen *(Dir-Fin)*

Scandic Hotels Oy (2)
Lars Sonckin Kaari 10
02600 Espoo, Finland
Tel.: (358) 207664107
Fax: (358) 98521978
E-Mail: espoo@scandic-hotels.com
Web Site: www.scandic-hotels.fi
Emp.: 30
Hotel Operator
S.I.C.: 7011
N.A.I.C.S.: 721110
Aarne Hallama *(VP-Finland & Baltic States)*

Non-U.S. Subsidiary:

Scandic Hotels Eesti AS (3)
Vabaduse Valjak House 3
10141 Tallinn, Estonia
Tel.: (372) 6407300
Fax: (372) 6407299
E-Mail: palace@scandichotels.com
Web Site: www.scandichotels.com
Emp.: 30
Hotel Operator
S.I.C.: 7011
N.A.I.C.S.: 721110
Kati Saluoks *(Gen Mgr)*

Swedegas AB (1)
Basagacan 36
PO Box 824
101 36 Stockholm, Sweden (96%)
Tel.: (46) 87963800
Fax: (46) 87963840
E-Mail: kontrollrum@swedegas.se
Web Site: www.swedegas.com
Sales Range: $50-74.9 Million
Emp.: 33
Natural Gas Distribution Services
S.I.C.: 4924
N.A.I.C.S.: 221210
Lars Frithiof *(Chm)*
Lars Gustafsson *(CEO)*
Anna Borg *(CFO)*

Joint Venture:

Gambro Holding AB (1)
Magistratsvgen 16
PO Box 7373
111 57 Stockholm, Sweden SE (51%)
Tel.: (46) 86136500
Fax: (46) 86112830
E-Mail: info@gambro.com
Web Site: www.gambro.com
Emp.: 1,000
Holding Company
S.I.C.: 6719
N.A.I.C.S.: 551112
Ulf Mattsson *(CEO)*

U.S. Holdings:

Synagro Technologies, Inc. (1)
1800 Bering Dr Ste 1000
Houston, TX 77057-3169 DE
Tel.: (713) 369-1700
Fax: (713) 369-1750
Toll Free: (800) 370-0035
E-Mail: info@synagro.com
Web Site: www.synagro.com
Sales Range: $300-349.9 Million
Emp.: 966
Waste Water Treatment & Residual Management Services
S.I.C.: 4953
N.A.I.C.S.: 562219
Tom Rabaut *(Chm)*
Eric Zimmer *(Pres & CEO)*
Tricia Papile *(CFO)*

Westway Group, LLC (1)
(Formerly Westway Group, Inc.)
365 Canal St Ste 2900
New Orleans, LA 70130 DE
Tel.: (504) 525-9741
Fax: (504) 636-4316
E-Mail: sharon.karrigan@westway.com
Web Site: www.westway.com
Emp.: 495
Holding Company; Liquid Animal Feed Products Mfr & Bulk Liquid Storage Services
S.I.C.: 6719
N.A.I.C.S.: 551112
Gene McClain *(CEO)*
Thomas A. Masilla, Jr. *(CFO)*

Subsidiary:

Westway Terminal Company LLC (2)
365 Canal St Ste 2900
New Orleans, LA 70130 DE
Tel.: (504) 525-9741
Fax: (504) 522-1638
Web Site: www.westwayterminals.com
Bulk Liquid Storage & Other Related Services
S.I.C.: 4226
N.A.I.C.S.: 493190
Gene McClain *(CEO)*

Non-U.S. Subsidiary:

Westway Netherlands Cooperatief U.A. (3)
Kabelweg 57
1014 BA Amsterdam, Netherlands NL
Tel.: (31) 20 581 8180
Web Site: www.westwayterminals.com
Holding Company; Regional Managing Office
S.I.C.: 6719
N.A.I.C.S.: 551112
Bert van Holst *(Dir-Ops-Europe)*

Subsidiary:

Westway Terminals Nederland B.V. (4)
Kabelweg 57
1014 BA Amsterdam, Netherlands NL
Tel.: (31) 20 581 8180
Web Site: www.westwayterminals.com
Bulk Liquid Storage & Other Related Services
S.I.C.: 4226
N.A.I.C.S.: 493190
Bert van Holst *(Dir-Ops-Europe)*

Non-U.S. Holdings:

Aker Well Service AS (1)
Lagerveien 30
NO-4066 Stavanger, Norway NO
Mailing Address:
PO Box 281
NO-4066 Stavanger, Norway
Tel.: (47) 51951600
E-Mail: kjetil.drag@akersolutions.com
Web Site: www.akersolutions.com
Rev.: $69,922,448
Emp.: 389
Wireline, Tractor & Cased Hole Logging Services Supplier
S.I.C.: 1389
N.A.I.C.S.: 213112
Ole Petter Thomesen *(Pres)*

BSN medical GmbH (1)
Quickbornstrasse 24
D 20253 Hamburg, Germany De
Tel.: (49) 404909909
Fax: (49) 4049096666
E-Mail: info@bsnmedical.com
Web Site: www.bsnmedical.com
Sales Range: $750-799.9 Million
Emp.: 3,400
Medical Devices Mfr & Distr
S.I.C.: 3841
N.A.I.C.S.: 339112
Claus-H. Wiegel *(CEO)*
Steve Brown *(CFO)*
Ann Maitland *(Sr VP-Ops)*

Subsidiary:

BSN-Jobst GmbH (2)
Beiersdorfstrasse 1
D 46446 Emmerich am Rhein, Germany DE
Tel.: (49) 28226070
Fax: (49) 2822607191
E-Mail: jobst@bsnmedical.com
Web Site: www.bsnmedical.de
Emp.: 200
Compression Bandages & Garments Mfr
S.I.C.: 2389
N.A.I.C.S.: 315280
Gerhard Krimmel *(Mng Dir)*
Ute Weir *(Sec)*

U.S. Subsidiaries:

BSN-Jobst, Inc. (2)
5825 Carnegie Blvd
Charlotte, NC 28209-4633
Tel.: (704) 554-9933
Fax: (704) 551-8583
Toll Free: (800) 221-7573
E-Mail: jobst.customerservice@bsnmedical.com
Web Site: www.jobst-usa.com
Emp.: 250
Medical Compression Stockings & Bandages Mfr
S.I.C.: 3845
N.A.I.C.S.: 334510
Darrell Jenkins *(Pres)*

BSN medical, Inc. (2)
5825 Carnegie Blvd
Charlotte, NC 28209
Tel.: (704) 331-0600
Fax: (704) 331-8785
Toll Free: (800) 552-1157
E-Mail: bsnorthopaedics@bsnmedical.com
Web Site: www.bsnmedical.com
Emp.: 250
Orthopaedic Supplies Distr
S.I.C.: 3845
N.A.I.C.S.: 334510
Claus-H. Wiegel *(CEO)*

FLA Orthopedics, Inc. (2)
2881 Corporate Way
Miramar, FL 33025-3973
Mailing Address:
PO Box 277810
Miramar, FL 33027-7810
Tel.: (954) 704-4484
Fax: (954) 431-8781
Toll Free: (800) 327-4110
E-Mail: marketing@flaorthopedics.com

EQT Partners AB—(Continued)

Web Site: www.flaorthopedics.com
Rev.: $15,500,000
Orthopedic, Sports Medicine & Occupational Support Mfr
S.I.C.: 3841
N.A.I.C.S.: 339113
Rhonda Machin *(VP-Mktg)*

E.ON Energy from Waste AG (1)
Schoninger Strasse 2 - 3
38350 Helmstedt, Germany
Tel.: (49) 53 51 1 80
Fax: (49) 53 51 18 25 22
E-Mail: info@eon-energyfromwaste.com
Web Site: www.eon-energyfromwaste.com
Sales Range: $700-749.9 Million
Emp.: 20
Waste Management Power Generation Services
S.I.C.: 4931
N.A.I.C.S.: 221118
Carsten Stablein *(CEO)*
Detlef Hartmann *(Member-Mgmt Bd)*
Markus Hauck *(Member-Mgmt Bd)*
Karl-Heinz Muller *(Member-Mgmt Bd)*

Subsidiaries:

E.ON Energy from Waste Goppingen GmbH (2)
Iltishofweg 40
73037 Goppingen, Germany
Tel.: (49) 71 61 67 16 1 21
Fax: (49) 71 61 67 16 2 10
Web Site: www.eon-energyfromwaste.com
Electric Power Generation Services
S.I.C.: 4939
N.A.I.C.S.: 221118

E.ON Energy from Waste Premnitz GmbH (2)
Dr Herbert-Rein-Strasse 1
14727 Premnitz, Germany
Tel.: (49) 33 86 2 13 87 33 70
Fax: (49) 33 86 2 13 87 33 52
Web Site: www.eon-energyfromwaste.com
Emp.: 50
Electric Power Generation Services
S.I.C.: 4939
N.A.I.C.S.: 221118
Klaus Piefke *(Gen Mgr)*

Mullheizkraftwerk Rothensee GmbH (2)
Kraftwerk-Privatweg 07
39126 Magdeburg, Germany
Tel.: (49) 391 587 2534
Fax: (49) 391 587 1764
E-Mail: info@mhkw-rothensee.de
Web Site: www.mhkw-rothensee.de
Emp.: 90
Electric Power Generation & Distribution Services
S.I.C.: 4911
N.A.I.C.S.: 221118
Guido Luecker *(Dir-Tech)*

PSM International Ltd. (1)
14 Barton Industrial Estate
Etruria Way Mount Pleasant
Bilston, Wolverhampton, WV14 7LH, United Kingdom
Tel.: (44) 1902 407 370
Telex: 338565
Fax: (44) 1902 407 380
E-Mail: info@psminternational.com
Web Site: www.psminternational.com
Sls.: $37,000,000
Emp.: 600
Industrial Fastener Systems, Spring Steel & Plastic Fasteners, Wire Thread Inserts & Automated Assembly Equipment
S.I.C.: 3452
N.A.I.C.S.: 332722
Ian Atkinson *(Mng Dir)*

Subsidiary:

BAS Components Limited (2)
Ferry Lane
Pembroke, Pembrokeshire, SA71 4RE, United Kingdom (100%)
Tel.: (44) 1646 683501
Fax: (44) 1646 687251
E-Mail: info@bas-components.co.uk
Web Site: www.bas-components.co.uk
Emp.: 113
Aerospace & Commercial Fasteners & Components
S.I.C.: 3499
N.A.I.C.S.: 332999

U.S. Subsidiary:

BAS Components Inc. (3)
1100 N Meridian Rd
Youngstown, OH 44515 (100%)
Tel.: (330) 793-9650
Fax: (330) 793-9620
E-Mail: sales@psminternational.com
Web Site: www.psminternational.com
Emp.: 2
Fasteners, Components & Fastening Systems Whslr
S.I.C.: 5051
N.A.I.C.S.: 423510
Bob Mangapora *(Gen Mgr)*

Springer Science+Business Media S.A. (1)
Heidelberger Platz 3
14197 Berlin, Germany LU
Tel.: (49) 30827875434
Fax: (49) 30827875707
E-Mail: corporate-communication@springer.com
Web Site: www.springer.com
Sales Range: $1-4.9 Billion
Emp.: 5,708
Holding Company; Scientific & Business Book & Journal Publisher
S.I.C.: 6719
N.A.I.C.S.: 551112
Derk J. Haank *(CEO)*
Ulrich Vest *(CFO)*
Martin Mos *(COO)*
Gregor Karolus *(Pres-HR)*

Co-Headquarters:

Springer Science+Business Media Deutschland GmbH (2)
Heidelberger Platz 3
D-14197 Berlin, Germany De
Mailing Address: (100%)
PO Box 140201
D-14302 Berlin, Germany
Tel.: (49) 30827870
Fax: (49) 308214091
Web Site: www.springer-sbm.com
Scientific & Business Book & Journal Publisher
S.I.C.: 9131
N.A.I.C.S.: 921140
Ulrich Vest *(CFO)*
Gregor Karolus *(Grp Pres-HR)*
Eric Merkel-Sobotta *(Exec VP-Corp Comm)*

Subsidiary:

Springer Verlag GmbH (3)
Tiergartenstrasse 17
69121 Heidelberg, Germany De
Tel.: (49) 62214870 (100%)
Telex: 183 319 spbln d
Fax: (49) 62214878366
E-Mail: scsc-books@springer.com
Web Site: www.springer.com
Emp.: 500
Scientific & Business Book & Journal Publisher
S.I.C.: 2731
N.A.I.C.S.: 511130
Ralf Birkelbach *(Mng Dir & Exec VP-Pro Bus & Tech)*
Olaf Ernst *(Grp Pres-eProduct Mgmt & Innovation)*
Andreas Kosters *(Pres-STM Asia/Local Americas & Europe/Pharma)*
Joachim Krieger *(Grp Exec VP-Prof Transport-Bus Media)*
Eric Schmitt *(Exec VP-Customer Svc, Fulfillment & Logistics)*
Harm van Maanen *(Grp Exec VP-Prof Medicine Div)*

Subsidiaries:

GWV Fachverlage GmbH (4)
Abraham-Lincoln-Strasse 46
D-65189 Wiesbaden, Germany De
Tel.: (49) 61178780 (100%)
Fax: (49) 6117878400
Web Site: www.gwv-fachverlage.de
Emp.: 400
Business-to-Business, Technology & Transportation Book Publisher
S.I.C.: 2731
N.A.I.C.S.: 511130
Ralf Birkelbach *(Chm-Mgmt Bd & Mng Dir)*
Albrecht F. Shirmacher *(Head-Info Mgmt)*

Spektrum Akademischer Verlag GmbH (4)
Slevoggstrasse 3-5
69126 Heidelberg, Germany De
Tel.: (49) 62214870 (100%)
Telex: 461842
Fax: (49) 62214878366
Web Site: www.spektrum-verlag.de
Emp.: 40
Scientific Textbook & Journal Publisher
S.I.C.: 2731
N.A.I.C.S.: 511130

Springer Transport Media GmbH (4)
Neumarkter Strasse 18
D-81673 Munich, Germany De
Tel.: (49) 8943720 (100%)
Fax: (49) 8943722879
Web Site: www.springertransportmedia.de
Transportation & Logistics Book & Journal Publisher
S.I.C.: 2731
N.A.I.C.S.: 511130
Joachim Krieger *(Mng Dir)*

U.S. Subsidiary:

Springer Science+Business Media, LLC (4)
233 Spring St
New York, NY 10013 MA
Tel.: (212) 460-1500
Fax: (212) 460-1575
Toll Free: (800) SPRINGER
E-Mail: service-ny@springer.com
Web Site: www.springer.com
Emp.: 200
Scientific & Business Book & Journal Publisher
S.I.C.: 2731
N.A.I.C.S.: 511130
Syed Hasan *(Pres-STM Sls Academic & Govt)*

Springer Science+Business Media Netherlands B.V. (2)
Prins Hendrikstraat 17
NL-7001 GK Doetinchem, Netherlands NL
Tel.: (31) 314376040 (100%)
Fax: (31) 314325768
Web Site: www.springer-sbm.com
Scientific & Business Book & Journal Publisher
S.I.C.: 9131
N.A.I.C.S.: 921140
Derk Haank *(CEO)*
Martin Mos *(COO)*
Milan Wielinga *(Exec VP-Mergers & Acq)*

Subsidiary:

Springer Science+Business Media B.V. (3)
Van Godewijckstraat 30
3311 GX Dordrecht, Netherlands NL
Tel.: (31) 786576000 (100%)
Fax: (31) 786576555
E-Mail: info@springer-sbm.com
Web Site: www.springer-sbm.com
Rev.: $1,227,500,800
Emp.: 250
Scientific & Business Book & Journal Publisher
S.I.C.: 2731
N.A.I.C.S.: 511130
Peter Hendriks *(Pres-STM Global Publ & Mktg)*
Yvonne Campfens *(Grp Exec VP-eOps)*
Jan-Erik de Boer *(Grp Exec VP-IT)*
Arjan Grootenboer *(Grp Exec VP-Production)*
Wim van der Stelt *(Grp Exec VP-Bus Dev)*
Michael Veen *(Grp Exec VP-B2B-Netherlands)*

Subsidiary:

Springer Uitgeverij B.V. (4)
Het Spoor 2
NL-3994 AK Houten, Netherlands NL
Tel.: (31) 306383736 (100%)
Web Site: www.springeruitgeverij.nl
Emp.: 250
Trade Periodical Publisher
S.I.C.: 2721
N.A.I.C.S.: 511120
Michel Veen *(Mng Dir)*

Non-U.S. Joint Ventures:

Carl Zeiss Vision International GmbH (1)
Gartenstrasse 97
73430 Aalen, Germany
Fax: (49) 7361 55578 1299
E-Mail: optics@zeiss.de
Web Site: www.vision.zeiss.com
Sales Range: $1-4.9 Billion
Emp.: 10,000
Mfr of Eyeglasses & Lenses
S.I.C.: 3827
N.A.I.C.S.: 333314
Michael Hoffmann *(CEO)*

Subsidiary:

Carl Zeiss Vision GmbH (2)
Turnstrasse 27
73430 Aalen, Germany
Tel.: (49) 7361 598 5000
Fax: (49) 7361 591 480
Web Site: vision.zeiss.com
Emp.: 8
Eyeglass Lenses Mfr
S.I.C.: 3827
N.A.I.C.S.: 333314
Spiller Rudols *(Gen Mgr)*

U.S. Subsidiary:

Carl Zeiss Vision Inc. (2)
12121 Scripps Summit Dr
San Diego, CA 92130-4682 DE
Tel.: (858) 790-7700
Fax: (858) 790-7590
Web Site: www.vision.zeiss.com
Sales Range: $650-699.9 Million
Emp.: 6,634
Plastic & Glass Eyeglass Lenses Mfr & Sales
Import Export
S.I.C.: 3851
N.A.I.C.S.: 339115
Susan Armstrong *(VP)*

Subsidiaries:

Great Lakes Coating Laboratory (3)
1784 Larchwood Dr
Troy, MI 48083-2223
Tel.: (248) 524-0550
Fax: (248) 524-0808
Web Site: www.carl-zeiss.com
Emp.: 120
Optical Goods Mfr & Sales
S.I.C.: 3827
N.A.I.C.S.: 333314

Kansas City Opthalmics LLC (3)
13731 E 42nd Ter
Independence, MO 64055
Tel.: (816) 478-4901
Emp.: 6
Optical Services
S.I.C.: 5995
N.A.I.C.S.: 446130
David Jochims *(CEO)*

Non-U.S. Subsidiaries:

Alpha Lens Company Ltd. (2)
76-77 Capitol Industrial Park Capitol Way
London, NX9 0EW, United Kingdom
Tel.: (44) 2089491901
Emp.: 50
Ophthalmic Products Mfr & Supply
S.I.C.: 3827
N.A.I.C.S.: 333314

Carl Zeiss Vision Australia Ltd. (2)
24 Heath St
Lonsdale, SA, 5160, Australia
Mailing Address:
PO Box 244
Morphett Vale, SA, 5162, Australia
Tel.: (61) 883928899
Fax: (61) 883928875
Web Site: www.vision.zeiss.com.au
Emp.: 700
Eyeglass Lense Mfr
S.I.C.: 3827
N.A.I.C.S.: 333314

Nobert Gorny *(Pres)*

Carl Zeiss Vision Brasil Industria Optica Ltda. (2)
Rua Luiz Winter 222 Duarte da Silveira
25665-431 Petropolis, RJ, Brazil
Tel.: (55) 24 2233 7012
Fax: (55) 24 2233 7096
E-Mail: andrea.costa@vision.zeiss.com
Web Site: www.lenteszeiss.com.br
Eyeglass Lenses Mfr
S.I.C.: 3827
N.A.I.C.S.: 333314
Andrea Costa *(Dir-Mktg)*

Carl Zeiss Vision (Guangzhou) Ltd. (2)
No 1389 Jui Fo West Road
Baiyun District, Guangzhou, 510555, China
Tel.: (86) 2087490088
Fax: (86) 20 8749 0733
Web Site: www.joffray.com
Eyeglass Lenses Mfr
S.I.C.: 3827
N.A.I.C.S.: 333314

Carl Zeiss Vision Ireland Ltd. (2)
Whitemill Industrial Estate
Wexford, Ireland
Tel.: (353) 5363700
Fax: (353) 5341671
Emp.: 450
Optical Lense Services
S.I.C.: 5995
N.A.I.C.S.: 446130

Carl Zeiss Vision Italia SPA (2)
Via SEP Mazzucchelli No 17
Castiglione Olona, 21043 Varese, Lombardia, Italy
Tel.: (39) 0331851111
Fax: (39) 0331850720
E-Mail: marketing@vision.zeiss.com
Web Site: www.zeiss.it/
Emp.: 450
Eyeglass Lenses & Magnifying Vision Mfr
S.I.C.: 3827
N.A.I.C.S.: 333314
Michele D'adamo *(Gen Mgr)*

Carl Zeiss Vision Swiss AG (2)
Helsinkistrasse 9
Basel, 4142, Switzerland
Tel.: (41) 613388100
Fax: (41) 613388101
E-Mail: info@americanoptical.ch
Web Site: www.americanoptical.ch
Emp.: 15
Optical Products Mfr & Sales
S.I.C.: 3827
N.A.I.C.S.: 333314

Carl Zeiss Vision UK Ltd. (2)
Unit 9 Holford Way
Holford, Birmingham, B6 7AX, United Kingdom
Tel.: (44) 1213324404
Fax: (44) 121 356 5618
Web Site: www.vision.zeiss.co.uk
Emp.: 279
Eyeglass Lenses Mfr
S.I.C.: 3827
N.A.I.C.S.: 333314
Andrew Leonsson *(Mng Dir)*

Carl Zeiss Vision Venezuela Industria Optica C.A. (2)
Av Francisco de Miranda
Centro Profesional Miranda
piso 2 ofc 2C, Caracas, 1060, Venezuela
Mailing Address:
PO Box 3982
Caracas, 1010-A, Venezuela
Tel.: (58) 212 264 6231
Fax: (58) 212 264 5108
Web Site: www.solaven.com
Emp.: 5
Eyeglass Lenses Mfr
S.I.C.: 3827
N.A.I.C.S.: 333314

Carl Zeiss Vision (2)
5th Fl Nissei Fushimi Machi Building
4 4 1 Fushimi Machi Chuo Ku, Osaka, 541 0044, Japan
Tel.: (81) 662022672
Fax: (81) 662022675
Emp.: 100
Eyeglass Lenses Mfr
S.I.C.: 3827
N.A.I.C.S.: 333314

Carl Zeiss Vision (2)
Avenida San Andres Atoto 165-B
Naucalpan de Juarez, Mexico, 53550, Mexico
Tel.: (52) 5555767033
Fax: (52) 5553583576
Web Site: www.aolens.com
Emp.: 100
Optical Lense Services
S.I.C.: 3827
N.A.I.C.S.: 333314

Carl Zeiss Vision (2)
Calle 7 Sur No 1111
Tijuana, 22500, Mexico
Tel.: (52) 6646233734
Fax: (52) 6646233734
Optical Lense Services
S.I.C.: 5995
N.A.I.C.S.: 446130

ISS Holding A/S (1)
Bredgade 30
DK-1260 Copenhagen, Denmark DK
Tel.: (45) 38170000
Fax: (45) 38170011
Web Site: www.issworld.com
Sales Range: $5-14.9 Billion
Emp.: 520,000
Holding Company
S.I.C.: 6719
N.A.I.C.S.: 551112
Jeff Olsen Gravenhorst *(CEO)*
Charles Allen *(Chm-ISS World Services A/S)*

Subsidiary:

ISS A/S (2)
Bredgade 30
DK-1260 Copenhagen, Denmark DK
Tel.: (45) 38170000
Fax: (45) 38170011
E-Mail: info@group.issworld.com
Web Site: www.issworld.com
Rev.: $14,330,323,440
Assets: $9,723,568,320
Liabilities: $8,817,620,040
Net Worth: $905,948,280
Earnings: ($80,079,840)
Emp.: 534,200
Fiscal Year-end: 12/31/12
Holding Company; Commercial Facility Maintenance & Business Support Services
S.I.C.: 6719
N.A.I.C.S.: 551112
Charles Allen *(Chm)*
Jeff Gravenhors *(CEO)*
Henrik Andersen *(CFO & COO-Europe)*
Luis Andrade *(CEO-Iberia & Latin America & Sr VP)*
Troels Bjerg *(CEO-CEO Nordic & Eastern Europe & Sr VP)*
Jacob Gotzsche *(CEO-Central Europe & Sr VP)*
Thomas Hinnerskov *(CEO-APAC & Sr VP)*
Henrik Langebaek *(CFO-Europe & Procurement & Sr VP)*
Jens Ebbe Olesen *(Exec VP & Head-Grp Mergers & Acq)*
Magnus Akerberg *(Sr VP & Head-Corp Clients)*
Daniel Patrick Brennan *(Sr VP & Head-HR)*
Barbara Plucnar Jensen *(Sr VP & Head-Treasury)*
Todd O'Neill *(Sr VP & Head-Strategy & Corp Dev)*
Andrew Price *(Sr VP & Head-Global Corp Clients)*
Henrik Trepka *(Sr VP & Head-IT)*

Subsidiary:

ISS Global A/S (3)
Bredgade 30
DK-1260 Copenhagen, Denmark DK
Tel.: (45) 38170000
Fax: (45) 38170011
Web Site: www.issworld.com
Sales Range: $50-74.9 Million
Emp.: 125
Holding Company
S.I.C.: 6719
N.A.I.C.S.: 551112
Barbara Plucnar *(Mng Dir)*
Henrik Andersen *(Grp CFO & Grp COO-Europe)*
Jeff Olsen Gravenhorst *(COO)*
Christian K. Jakobsen *(Treas & Sr VP)*

Subsidiary:

ISS Facility Services A/S (4)
Montmestervej 31
2400 Copenhagen, Denmark DK
Tel.: (45) 38171717
Fax: (45) 38331211
E-Mail: kundeservice@dk.iss.com
Web Site: www.issworldservices.com
Emp.: 11,000
Commercial Facility Maintenance & Business Support Services
S.I.C.: 8744
N.A.I.C.S.: 561210
Maarten van Engeland *(Mng Dir)*
Flemming Bendt *(Dir-Fin)*

U.S. Subsidiary:

ISS Facility Services, Inc. (4)
1019 Central Pkwy N Ste 100
San Antonio, TX 78232-5027 DE
Tel.: (210) 495-6021
Fax: (210) 495-6071
E-Mail: info@us.issworld.com
Web Site: www.us.issworld.com
Sales Range: $300-349.9 Million
Emp.: 10,000
Commercial Facility Maintenance & Support Services
S.I.C.: 8744
N.A.I.C.S.: 561210
Ed Walsh *(Gen Mgr)*

Branches:

ISS Facility Services, Inc. - Austin Regional Office (5)
8101 Cameron Rd Ste 304
Austin, TX 78754-3818
Tel.: (512) 836-9516
Fax: (512) 836-7721
Web Site: www.us.issworld.com
Emp.: 170
Commercial Facility Maintenance & Support Services
S.I.C.: 8744
N.A.I.C.S.: 561210
Trent Harr *(Gen Mgr)*

ISS Facility Services, Inc. - Dallas Regional Office (5)
1448 Halsey Way Ste 100
Carrollton, TX 75007-4441
Tel.: (972) 446-1223
Fax: (972) 446-1318
Web Site: www.us.issworld.com
Sales Range: $125-149.9 Million
Emp.: 400
Commercial Facility Maintenance & Support Services
S.I.C.: 8744
N.A.I.C.S.: 561210
Dave Howarter *(Gen Mgr)*

ISS Facility Services, Inc. - Greensboro Regional Office (5)
18-A Oak Branch Dr
Greensboro, NC 27407
Tel.: (336) 855-8480
Fax: (336) 855-7018
Web Site: www.us.issworld.com
Emp.: 218
Commercial Facility Maintenance & Support Services
S.I.C.: 8744
N.A.I.C.S.: 561210
Randy Jordan *(Gen Mgr)*

ISS Facility Services, Inc. - Houston Regional Office (5)
6137 Westview Dr
Houston, TX 77055-5421
Tel.: (713) 956-2277
Fax: (713) 956-2851
E-Mail: info@us.issworld.com
Web Site: www.us.issworld.com
Sales Range: $25-49.9 Million
Emp.: 14
Commercial Facility Maintenance & Support Services
S.I.C.: 8744
N.A.I.C.S.: 561210
Jim Roll *(Gen Mgr)*

ISS Facility Services, Inc. - Kansas City Regional Office (5)
1225 E 18th St
Kansas City, MO 64108
Tel.: (816) 421-8088
Fax: (816) 421-7572
Web Site: www.us.issworld.com
Sls.: $58,400,000
Emp.: 1,850
Commercial Facility Maintenance & Support Services
S.I.C.: 8744
N.A.I.C.S.: 561210
John Combs *(Mgr-Bus Dev)*

ISS Facility Services, Inc. - Las Vegas Regional Office (5)
4155 N Rancho Dr Ste 150
Las Vegas, NV 89130
Tel.: (702) 822-2133
Fax: (702) 822-2136
Web Site: www.us.issworld.com
Emp.: 440
Commercial Facility Maintenance & Support Services
S.I.C.: 8744
N.A.I.C.S.: 561210
Don Dun *(Gen Mgr)*

ISS Facility Services, Inc. - Memphis Regional Office (5)
3043 Broad Ave
Memphis, TN 38112-3003
Tel.: (901) 452-3770
Fax: (901) 452-0954
Web Site: www.us.issworld.com
Sales Range: $25-49.9 Million
Emp.: 10
Commercial Facility Maintenance & Support Services
S.I.C.: 8744
N.A.I.C.S.: 561210
Ed Walsh *(Gen Mgr)*

ISS Facility Services, Inc. - Phoenix Regional Office (5)
4811 N 7th St Ste 100
Phoenix, AZ 85014
Tel.: (602) 222-2555
Fax: (602) 997-7770
Web Site: www.us.issworld.com
Commercial Facility Maintenance & Support Services
S.I.C.: 8744
N.A.I.C.S.: 561210
Karon Smedley *(Gen Mgr)*

ISS Facility Services, Inc. - San Antonio Regional Office (5)
8506 Speedway Dr
San Antonio, TX 78230-5331
Tel.: (210) 349-4647
Fax: (210) 349-4669
Web Site: www.us.issworld.com
Sales Range: $250-299.9 Million
Emp.: 800
Commercial Facility Maintenance & Support Services
S.I.C.: 8744
N.A.I.C.S.: 561210
Russell Tadd Marler *(Gen Mgr)*

Subsidiary:

ISS TMC Services, Inc. (5)
81 Dorsa Ave
Livingston, NJ 07039
Tel.: (973) 740-0032
Fax: (973) 740-9261
Web Site: www.us.issworld.com
Sls.: $40,000,000
Emp.: 1,000
Commercial Facility Maintenance & Support Services
S.I.C.: 8744
N.A.I.C.S.: 561210
Joe Caprio *(Gen Mgr)*

Non-U.S. Subsidiaries:

ISS Abilis France S.A.S. (4)
65-67 rue Ordener
F-75899 Paris, Cedex 18, France FR
Tel.: (33) 144924848
Fax: (33) 144924800
E-Mail: jeanpierre.henner@fr.issworld.com
Web Site: www.fr.issworld.com
Emp.: 43,000
Commercial Facility Maintenance & Support Services
S.I.C.: 8744
N.A.I.C.S.: 561210
Jean-Pierre Henner *(Pres)*

EQT Partners AB—(Continued)

ISS Facility Services A/S (4)
PO Box 132 Skoyen
0509 Oslo, Norway NO
Tel.: (47) 22885000
Fax: (47) 22885400
Web Site: www.no.issworld.com
Emp.: 16,000
Commercial Facility Maintenance & Business Support Services
S.I.C.: 8744
N.A.I.C.S.: 561210
Bjorn Nilsen *(Mng Dir)*

Subsidiary:

ISS Personalhuset (5)
Skippergata 33
0154 Oslo, Norway
Tel.: (47) 98295200
Fax: (47) 22410729
E-Mail: personalhuset@personalhuset.no
Web Site: www.personalhuset.no
Emp.: 81
Recruitment Services
S.I.C.: 7361
N.A.I.C.S.: 561311
Chatrine Haug *(Mgr)*

ISS Facility Services AB (4)
Arstaangsvagen 11
SE-117 43 Stockholm, Sweden SE
Mailing Address:
PO Box 47635
SE-117 94 Stockholm, Sweden
Tel.: (46) 86816000
Fax: (46) 86816390
Web Site: www.se.issworld.com
Sales Range: $450-499.9 Million
Emp.: 12,000
Commercial Facility Maintenance & Business Support Services
S.I.C.: 8744
N.A.I.C.S.: 561210
Marcus Kristiansson *(Mng Dir)*

ISS Facility Services A.E. (4)
14 Thrasimachou Str
GR-104 42 Athens, Greece GR
Tel.: (30) 2102705600
Fax: (30) 2102723625
E-Mail: iss@gr.issworld.com
Web Site: www.gr.issworld.com
Sales Range: $75-99.9 Million
Emp.: 100
Commercial Facility Maintenance & Business Support Services
S.I.C.: 8744
N.A.I.C.S.: 561210
Nick Boutsiarakos *(CFO)*

ISS Facility Services Australia Limited (4)
Units 1 & 2 12 Mars Road
Lane Cove, NSW, 2066, Australia AU
Tel.: (61) 286449700
Fax: (61) 286449821
Web Site: www.au.issworld.com
Sales Range: $600-649.9 Million
Emp.: 21,000
Commercial Facility Maintenance & Business Support Services
S.I.C.: 8744
N.A.I.C.S.: 561210
Charles Blinkworth *(CEO)*
Ian Scanlon *(CFO)*

ISS Facility Services GmbH (4)
Brunner Strasse 85
A 1210 Vienna, Austria AT
Tel.: (43) 5 7400
Telex: 47 134162 issoma
E-Mail: office@at.issworld.com
Web Site: www.at.issworld.com
Sales Range: $75-99.9 Million
Emp.: 7,500
Commercial Facility Maintenance & Business Support Services
S.I.C.: 8744
N.A.I.C.S.: 561210
Erich Steinreiber *(Mng Dir)*

ISS Facility Services GmbH (4)
Wanheimer Strasse 92
D-40468 Dusseldorf, Germany De
Tel.: (49) 21130278O
Fax: (49) 21130278222
E-Mail: info@de.issworld.com
Web Site: www.de.issworld.com
Sales Range: $350-399.9 Million
Emp.: 12,500
Commercial Facility Maintenance & Business Support Services
S.I.C.: 8744
N.A.I.C.S.: 561210
Martin Gieser *(CFO, Mng Dir, Country Mgr)*

ISS Facility Services Lda. (4)
Rua Moinho da Barrunchada 4 1st Dt
PT-2790-109 Carnaxide, Portugal PT
Tel.: (351) 214246760
Fax: (351) 214246786
E-Mail: info@pt.issworld.com
Web Site: www.pt.issworld.com
Sales Range: $900-999.9 Million
Emp.: 9,000
Commercial Facility Maintenance & Business Support Services
S.I.C.: 8744
N.A.I.C.S.: 561210
Luis Andrade *(Dir Gen)*

ISS Facility Services Limited (4)
18/F Warwick House West
Taikoo Place 979 King's Road, Quarry Bay, China (Hong Kong) HK
Tel.: (852) 28269166
Fax: (852) 28691441
E-Mail: info@hk.issworld.com
Web Site: www.hk.issworld.com
Sales Range: $1-4.9 Billion
Emp.: 12,000
Holding Company; Commercial Facility Maintenance & Business Support Services
S.I.C.: 6719
N.A.I.C.S.: 551112
Keith Futcher *(CEO)*
William Fung *(CFO)*

Subsidiary:

ISS EastPoint Facility Services Limited (5)
18/F Warwick House West
Taikoo Place 979 King's Road, Quarry Bay, China (Hong Kong) HK
Tel.: (852) 28269166
Fax: (852) 28691441
E-Mail: info@hk.issworld.com
Web Site: www.hk.issworld.com
Sales Range: $50-74.9 Million
Emp.: 300
Commercial Facility Maintenance & Support Services
S.I.C.: 8744
N.A.I.C.S.: 561210
Keith Futcher *(CEO)*
Barry Chan *(CFO)*

ISS Facility Services S.A. (4)
Rue Christophe Plantin 5
L-2339 Gasperich, Luxembourg LU
Tel.: (352) 4246201
Fax: (352) 42462020
E-Mail: martina.szart@lu.issworld.com
Web Site: www.lu.issworld.com
Sales Range: $75-99.9 Million
Emp.: 600
Commercial Facility Maintenance & Business Support Services
S.I.C.: 8744
N.A.I.C.S.: 561210
Kris Cloots *(Country Mgr)*

ISS Facility Services spol. s r.o. (4)
Mokran Zahon 2
SK-821 04 Bratislava, Slovakia Sk
Tel.: (421) 232630111
Fax: (421) 232630199
E-Mail: iss.slovakia@sk.issworld.com
Web Site: www.sk.issworld.com
Sales Range: $75-99.9 Million
Emp.: 60
Commercial Facility Maintenance & Business Support Services
S.I.C.: 8744
N.A.I.C.S.: 561210
Jan Bohacek *(Mng Dir)*

ISS Facility Services s.r.o. (4)
Antala Staska 38/510
CZ-140 00 Prague, 4 - Krc, Czech Republic CZ
Tel.: (420) 261392311
Fax: (420) 261392320
E-Mail: iss@cz.issworld.com
Web Site: www.cz.issworld.com
Sales Range: $50-74.9 Million
Emp.: 200
Commercial Facility Maintenance & Business Support Services
S.I.C.: 8744
N.A.I.C.S.: 561210
Jan Bohacek *(Country Mgr)*

ISS Ireland Ltd. (4)
3007 Lake Drive
Citywest Business Campus, Dublin, 24, Ireland IE
Tel.: (353) 1 468 2900
Fax: (353) 1 468 2901
E-Mail: enquiries@iss.ie
Web Site: www.ie.issworld.com
Emp.: 3,700
Commercial Facility Maintenance & Business Support Services
S.I.C.: 8744
N.A.I.C.S.: 561210
Paul Lynch *(Mng Dir)*

ISS Island ehf. (4)
Armula 40
IS-108 Reykjavik, Iceland IS
Tel.: (354) 5800600
Fax: (354) 5800 666
Web Site: www.is.issworld.com
Sales Range: $200-249.9 Million
Emp.: 900
Commercial Facility Maintenance & Business Support Services
S.I.C.: 8744
N.A.I.C.S.: 561210
Gudmundur Gudmundsson *(Country Mgr)*

ISS Nederland B.V. (4)
Rijnzathe 8
NL-3454 PV De Meern, Utrecht, Netherlands
Tel.: (31) 302424344
Telex: 44 79430 issse nl
Fax: (31) 302413947
E-Mail: info@iss.nlworld.com
Web Site: www.nl.issworld.com
Sales Range: $200-249.9 Million
Emp.: 21,000
Commercial Facility Maintenance & Business Support Services
S.I.C.: 8744
N.A.I.C.S.: 561210

Subsidiaries:

De Loge Schoonmaakdiensten B.V. (5)
Van Deventerlaan 30-40
NL-3528 AE Utrecht, Netherlands NL
Tel.: (31) 30 242 4344
Fax: (31) 30 241 3947
Web Site: www.nl.issworld.com
Sales Range: $75-99.9 Million
Facility Janitorial & Specialty Cleaning Services
S.I.C.: 7349
N.A.I.C.S.: 561720
Ronald Boesjes *(Dir-Comml)*

Subsidiary:

ISS Food Hygiene B.V. (6)
Rijnzathe 8
3454 PV, De Meern, Netherlands NL
Tel.: (31) 302424344
Telex: 44 79430 issse nl
Fax: (31) 302413947
E-Mail: info@nl.issworld.com
Web Site: www.nl.issworld.com
Sales Range: $50-74.9 Million
Emp.: 200
Food Industry Facility Sanitizing & Maintenance Services
S.I.C.: 8744
N.A.I.C.S.: 561210
Peter Vorm *(Gen Mgr)*

ISS Integrated Facility Services B.V. (5)
Rijnzathe 8
NL-3528 De Meern, Netherlands NL
Tel.: (31) 302424344
Fax: (31) 30 241 3947
E-Mail: info@nl.issworld.com
Web Site: www.nl.issworld.com
Sales Range: $50-74.9 Million
Integrated Facility Support Management Services
S.I.C.: 8742
N.A.I.C.S.: 541611
Morten Andreasen *(CFO)*

Subsidiary:

ISS Hospital Services B.V. (6)
Rijnzathe 8
3454 PV De Meern, Netherlands NL
Tel.: (31) 302424800
Telex: 44 79430 issse nl
Fax: (31) 302413947
Web Site: www.nl.issworld.com
Emp.: 200
Management of Integrated Hospital Support Services
S.I.C.: 8742
N.A.I.C.S.: 541611
Peter ten Hoedt *(Dir-Ops)*

ISS N.V. (4)
Steenstraat 20-1
BE-1800 Vilvoorde, Belgium BE
Tel.: (32) 22636611
Telex: 62 410 ISS BRU B
Fax: (32) 22636612
E-Mail: info@be.issworld.com
Web Site: www.be.issworld.com
Sales Range: $75-99.9 Million
Emp.: 500
Commercial Facility Maintenance & Business Support Services
S.I.C.: 8744
N.A.I.C.S.: 561210
Kris Cloots *(Mng Dir)*

ISS Palvelut Oy (4)
Rajatorpantie 8 A
PO Box 100
FI-01055 Vantaa, Finland FI
Tel.: (358) 20515500
Telex: 5 7 12 26 46 servi sf
Fax: (358) 205150155
Web Site: www.fi.issworld.com
Sales Range: $550-599.9 Million
Emp.: 12,000
Commercial Facility Maintenance & Business Support Services
S.I.C.: 8744
N.A.I.C.S.: 561210
Kari Virta *(Mng Dir)*

ISS Schweiz AG (4)
Buckhauserstrasse 22
Postfach
CH-8010 Zurich, Switzerland CH
Tel.: (41) 587878000
Fax: (41) 587878011
E-Mail: info@ch.issworld.com
Web Site: www.ch.issworld.com
Sales Range: $400-449.9 Million
Emp.: 300
Holding Company; Facility Support Services
S.I.C.: 6719
N.A.I.C.S.: 551112
Andre Nauer *(CEO)*
Robert Fuchs *(CFO)*

Subsidiary:

ISS Facility Services AG (5)
Buckhauserstrasse 22
Postfach
CH-8010 Zurich, Switzerland CH
Tel.: (41) 587878000
Fax: (41) 587878011
E-Mail: info@ch.issworld.com
Web Site: www.iss.ch
Sales Range: $75-99.9 Million
Emp.: 300
Commercial Facility Support Services
S.I.C.: 8744
N.A.I.C.S.: 561210
Andre Nauer *(CEO)*

ISS Servisystem do Brasil Ltda. (4)
Estrada Kaiko 8 Embu
06843-195 Sao Paulo, Brazil BR
Tel.: (55) 1121353700
Telex: 11 71 843 issl br
Fax: (55) 1147046252
Web Site: www.br.issworld.com
Sales Range: $25-49.9 Million
Commercial Facility Maintenance & Business Support Services
S.I.C.: 8744
N.A.I.C.S.: 561210
Jorge Luis Lima *(Pres)*

ISS Servisystem d.o.o. (4)
Ptujska Cesta 95
SI-2000 Maribor, Slovenia SI
Tel.: (386) 24503300
Fax: (386) 24503338

E-Mail: info@si.issworld.com
Web Site: www.si.issworld.com
Sales Range: $10-24.9 Million
Emp.: 1,300
Commercial Facility Maintenance & Business Support Services
S.I.C.: 8744
N.A.I.C.S.: 561210
Rudi Zupan *(Mng Dir)*

ISS Servisystem Kft. (4)
Peterdy u 15
HU-1071 Budapest, Hungary HU
Tel.: (36) 1 413 3140
Fax: (36) 1 413 3141
E-Mail: office@hu.issworld.com
Web Site: www.hu.issworld.com
Sales Range: $75-99.9 Million
Commercial Facility Maintenance & Business Support Services
S.I.C.: 8744
N.A.I.C.S.: 561210
Sutka Pal *(Dir-Bus Dev)*

ISS UK Limited (4)
ISS House Genesis Bus Pk Albert Dr
Woking, Surrey, GU21 5RW, United Kingdom UK
Tel.: (44) 8450576500
Fax: (44) 8714296500
E-Mail: info@uk.issworld.com
Web Site: www.uk.issworld.com
Sales Range: $1-4.9 Billion
Emp.: 43,500
Holding Company; Commercial Facility Maintenance & Business Support Services
S.I.C.: 6719
N.A.I.C.S.: 551112
Philip Leigh *(Mng Dir)*
Matthew Brabin *(CFO)*
Andrew Price *(COO)*

Subsidiary:

ISS Facility Services Limited (5)
ISS House Genesis Business Park
Albert Drive, Woking, Surrey, GU21 5RW, United Kingdom UK
Tel.: (44) 8450576400
Fax: (44) 8714296400
E-Mail: isshouse@uk.issworld.com
Web Site: www.uk.issworld.com
Sales Range: $750-799.9 Million
Commercial Facility Maintenance & Business Support Services
S.I.C.: 8744
N.A.I.C.S.: 561210

Branch:

ISS Facility Services Ltd. - London (6)
9- 10- 11th Fl South Keuy Plz
London, E14 9FH, United Kingdom
Tel.: (44) 8449361030
Fax: (44) 2074039386
E-Mail: iss.uk@issworld.com
Web Site: www.uk.issworld.com
Sales Range: $50-74.9 Million
Emp.: 250
Commercial Facility Maintenance & Support Services
S.I.C.: 8744
N.A.I.C.S.: 561210

EQUAL EXPERTS UK LTD.

1 Kingdom Street
London, W2 6BD, United Kingdom
Tel.: (44) 203 603 7830
E-Mail: hellouk@equalexperts.com
Web Site: www.equalexperts.com
Year Founded: 2007
Sales Range: $10-24.9 Million
Emp.: 140
Business Description:
Software Development Services
S.I.C.: 7371
N.A.I.C.S.: 541511
Personnel:
Thomas Granier *(Mng Dir)*
Board of Directors:
Thomas Granier
Ryan Sikorsky

EQUAMINERAL HOLDINGS LIMITED

Level 6 66 Kings Park Road
West Perth, WA, 6005, Australia
Tel.: (61) 8 6141 3500
Fax: (61) 8 6141 3599
E-Mail: info@equamineral.com
Web Site: www.equamineral.com
EQH—(ASX)
Rev.: $54,189
Assets: $1,912,152
Liabilities: $123,954
Net Worth: $1,788,199
Earnings: ($684,563)
Fiscal Year-end: 06/30/13
Business Description:
Mineral Exploration Services
S.I.C.: 1099
N.A.I.C.S.: 212299
Personnel:
Keith Coughlan *(CEO & Mng Dir)*
Julia Beckett *(Co-Sec)*
James Cole *(Co-Sec)*
Board of Directors:
Robert Timmins
Keith Coughlan
Colin Ikin
David Porter
Legal Counsel:
Steinepreis Paganin
Level 4 The Read Building 16 Milligan Street
Perth, WA, 6000, Australia
Tel.: (61) 8 9321 4000
Fax: (61) 8 9321 4333

Maples & Calder
Sea Meadow House Road Town
PO Box 173
Tortola, Virgin Islands (British)

EQUATION CORP LIMITED

Redhill Industrial Estate Blk 1001
Jalan Bukit Merah 06-11
Singapore, 159455, Singapore
Tel.: (65) 62707080
Fax: (65) 62707106
Web Site: www.equcorp.com
532—(SES)
Rev.: $12,675,540
Assets: $42,677,423
Liabilities: $21,534,249
Net Worth: $21,143,174
Earnings: ($15,306,191)
Fiscal Year-end: 06/30/13
Business Description:
Electronic Products Distr
S.I.C.: 7379
N.A.I.C.S.: 518210
Personnel:
Eddie Weng Wah Chng *(CEO)*
Hui Chee Lim *(CFO)*
Larry Sou Chian Chow *(CEO-Disa Digital Safety Pte Ltd)*
Wei Hsiung Lee *(Co-Sec)*
Joanna Lan Sim Lim *(Co-Sec)*
Board of Directors:
Hock Ghim Toh
Eddie Weng Wah Chng
Ah Chye Kan
Kay Heng Lau
Legal Counsel:
TSMP Law Corporation
6 Battery Road #33-01
Singapore, Singapore
Subsidiaries:

Disa Digital Safety Pte. Ltd. (1)
300 Jalan Bukit Ho Swee
Singapore, Singapore
Tel.: (65) 62709268
Fax: (65) 6270 9067
Web Site: www.digital-safety.sg
Digital Security Systems Retailer
S.I.C.: 5999
N.A.I.C.S.: 453998
Eddie Weng Wah Chng *(Chm)*
Han Yang Kwang *(Pres)*
Larry Sou Chian Chow *(CEO)*

Equation Energy Pte. Ltd. (1)
19 Jalan Kilang Barat 02-05 Acetech Ctr
Singapore, Singapore
Tel.: (65) 62707500
Fax: (65) 62707978
Web Site: www.equcorp.com
Energy Consulting Services
S.I.C.: 8999
N.A.I.C.S.: 541690

Equation Recycling Pte. Ltd. (1)
6B Jalan Papan
Singapore, Singapore
Tel.: (65) 68982220
Fax: (65) 68982221
E-Mail: enquiry@equrecycling.com.sg
Web Site: www.equrecycling.com.sg
Electronic Waste Recycling Services
S.I.C.: 7389
N.A.I.C.S.: 561990
Hai Chin Peh *(Gen Mgr)*

Equation Resources Pte. Ltd. (1)
300 Jalan Bukit Ho Swee
Singapore, Singapore
Tel.: (65) 62707080
Fax: (65) 6270 7106
Web Site: www.equcorp.com
Construction Materials Whslr
S.I.C.: 5032
N.A.I.C.S.: 423320

Non-U.S. Subsidiary:

M3 Electronic GmbH (1)
Lyoner Street 44-48
60528 Frankfurt am Main, Hesse, Germany
Tel.: (49) 69 2713 86 0
Fax: (49) 69 2713 86 27
E-Mail: info@m3-electronic.de
Web Site: www.m3-electronic.com
Electronic Equipment Mfr & Whslr
S.I.C.: 3651
N.A.I.C.S.: 334310
Matthias Claus *(Mng Dir)*

Subsidiary:

Disa Digital Safety GmbH (2)
Lyoner Strassee 48
60528 Frankfurt am Main, Germany
Tel.: (49) 69 66 11 9731
Fax: (49) 69 66 11 9213
Web Site: www.digital-safety.de
Storage Device Mfr & Security Software Distr
S.I.C.: 3572
N.A.I.C.S.: 334112
Uwe Bremeyer *(Co-Mng Dir)*
Matthias Claus *(Co-Mng Dir)*

EQUATORIAL ENERGIA SA

Av Borges de Medeiros 633 708
22430 041 Rio de Janeiro, Brazil
Tel.: (55) 2132066600
Fax: (55) 2132066601
E-Mail: ry@equatorialenergia.com.br
Web Site: www.equatorialenergia.com.br
EQTL3—(BRAZ)
Sales Range: $1-4.9 Billion
Emp.: 10
Business Description:
Electric Energy Distr
S.I.C.: 4931
N.A.I.C.S.: 221122
Personnel:
Carlos Augusto Leone Piani *(Chm)*
Gilberto Sayao da Silva *(Vice Chm)*
Firmino Ferreira Sampaio Neto *(CEO)*
Eduardo Haiama *(CFO & Officer-IR)*
Tinn Freire Amado *(Exec Officer)*
Ana Marta Horta Veloso *(Exec Officer)*
Board of Directors:
Carlos Augusto Leone Piani
Alexandre Goncalves da Silva
Gilberto Sayao da Silva
Paulo Jeronimo Bandeira de Mello Pedrosa
Alessandro Monteiro Morgado Horta
Firmino Ferreira Sampaio Neto
Celso Fernandez Quintella
Subsidiaries:

CEMAR - Companhia Energetica do Maranhao (1)
Al A Qda Sqs Loteamento Quitandinha
65071680 Sao Luis, MA, Brazil
Tel.: (55) 98 3217 8000
Fax: (55) 98 3217 8000
E-Mail: ri@cemar-ma.com.br
Web Site: www.cemar-ma.com.br
ENMA3B—(BRAZ)
Emp.: 1,250
Electrical Power Distribution Services
S.I.C.: 4911
N.A.I.C.S.: 221122
Eduardo Haiama *(Dir-IR)*

Centrais Eletricas do Para S.A. - CELPA (1)
Rod Augusto Montenegro - Km 8 5
66823010 Belem, PA, Brazil
Tel.: (55) 11 3216 1201
Fax: (55) 11 3216 1419
CELP3—(BRAZ)
Sales Range: $1-4.9 Billion
Emp.: 2,136
Electric Power Generation & Distribution Services
S.I.C.: 4911
N.A.I.C.S.: 221118
Leonardo Da Silva Lucas Tavares de Lima, *(Dir-IR)*

EQUATORIAL PALM OIL PLC

94 Jermyn Street
London, SW1Y 6JE, United Kingdom
Tel.: (44) 2077667555
Fax: (44) 2077667599
E-Mail: enquiries@epoil.co.uk
Web Site: www.epoil.co.uk
PAL—(AIM)
Rev.: $420,000
Assets: $20,219,000
Liabilities: $183,000
Net Worth: $20,036,000
Earnings: ($3,814,000)
Emp.: 8
Fiscal Year-end: 12/31/12
Business Description:
Crude Palm Oil Producer
S.I.C.: 0119
N.A.I.C.S.: 111120
Personnel:
Michael Frayne *(Chm)*
Tim Daniel *(CFO)*
John Bottomley *(Sec)*
Board of Directors:
Michael Frayne
Geoffrey Brown
Anthony Samaha
Shankar Varadharajan
Legal Counsel:
Pierre, Tweh & Associates
Palm Hotel Building Broad & Randall Streets
PO Box 10-2536
Monrovia, 1000, Liberia

Kerman & Co. LLP
200 Strand
London, EC1V 9EE, United Kingdom

EQUATORIAL RESOURCES LIMITED

Level 2 BGC Centre 28 The Esplanade
Perth, WA, 6000, Australia
Tel.: (61) 8 9466 5030
Fax: (61) 8 9466 5029
E-Mail: info@equatorialresources.com.au
Web Site: www.equatorialresources.com.au
EQX—(ASX)
Rev.: $3,188,677
Assets: $68,207,975
Liabilities: $3,643,481
Net Worth: $64,564,495
Earnings: ($34,136,784)
Fiscal Year-end: 06/30/13
Business Description:
Iron Ore Exploration & Development Services
S.I.C.: 1011
N.A.I.C.S.: 212210

Equatorial Resources Limited—(Continued)

Personnel:
John Welborn *(CEO & Mng Dir)*
Brad Farrington *(CFO)*
Greg Swan *(Sec)*
Board of Directors:
Ian Middlemas
Mark Laurence Pearce
John Welborn
Peter Woodman
Legal Counsel:
Hardy Bowen Lawyers
PO Box 1364
West Perth, Australia
Tel.: (61) 8 9211 3600
Fax: (61) 8 6211 3690

EQUINE CAPITAL BERHAD
(Name Changed to Global Oriental Berhad)

EQUINOX COPPER CORP.
(Name Changed to Anfield Resources Inc.)

EQUINOX EXPLORATION CORP.
(Name Changed to Anfield Resources Inc.)

EQUIOM (ISLE OF MAN) LIMITED
Jubilee Buildings Victoria Street
Douglas, IM1 2SH, Isle of Man
Tel.: (44) 1624 699000
Fax: (44) 1624 699001
E-Mail: enquiries@equiom.im
Web Site: www.equiom.im
Emp.: 70
Business Description:
Business Management Services
S.I.C.: 7389
N.A.I.C.S.: 561499
Personnel:
Larry Kearns *(Chm)*
Sheila Dean *(Grp Mng Dir)*
Board of Directors:
Larry Kearns
Clive Stanford
Non-U.S. Subsidiaries:

Equiom Marine & Aviation Services (Jersey) Limited (1)
1st Floor Channel House Green Street
Saint Helier, JE2 4UH, Jersey
Tel.: (44) 1534 720555
Fax: (44) 1534 720554
E-Mail: enquiries@equiom.je
Business Management Services
S.I.C.: 7389
N.A.I.C.S.: 561499

Equiom Trust Company (Cyprus) Limited (1)
18 Spyrou Kyprianou Avenue 2nd & 3rd Floors
1075 Nicosia, Cyprus
Mailing Address:
PO Box 27163
1642 Nicosia, Cyprus
Tel.: (357) 22 451317
Fax: (357) 22 451322
E-Mail: enquiries@equiom.com.cy
Business Management Services
S.I.C.: 7389
N.A.I.C.S.: 561499

EQUIOM TRUST COMPANY LIMITED
(See Under Equiom (Isle of Man) Limited)

EQUIPCERAMIC, S.A.
Ctra de la Pobla 64
08788 Vilanova del Cami, Spain
Tel.: (34) 938070717
Fax: (34) 938070720
E-Mail: info@equipceramic.com
Web Site: www.equipceramic.com
Year Founded: 1998
Emp.: 85
Business Description:
Industrial Machinery Mfr
S.I.C.: 3559
N.A.I.C.S.: 333249
Personnel:
Francisco Pain *(Mng Dir)*

EQUIPEMENTS PIERRE CHAMPIGNY LTEE
280 Bonin Street
Acton Vale, QC, J0H 1A0, Canada
Tel.: (450) 546-0999
Fax: (450) 546-0888
Toll Free: (800) 561-7610
Web Site: www.novilicad.com
Year Founded: 1989
Rev.: $16,495,116
Emp.: 18
Business Description:
Automotive Dealers
S.I.C.: 7532
N.A.I.C.S.: 811121

EQUIPMENT HOLDING COMPANY K.S.C.C.
99 Shuwaikh Industrial Area Block 2 Street 12
PO Box 192
13002 Kuwait, Kuwait
Tel.: (965) 1802440
Fax: (965) 24819562
E-Mail: agm@equipcokuwait.com
Web Site: www.equipcokuwait.com
EQUIPMENT—(KUW)
Sales Range: $75-99.9 Million
Business Description:
Investment Services
S.I.C.: 6211
N.A.I.C.S.: 523999
Personnel:
Mahmoud Khaled Ahmad Al-Khenah *(Chm)*
Abdullah Bader Abdulmohsen Al-Mokhezem *(Vice Chm, Mng Dir & Gen Mgr)*
Board of Directors:
Mahmoud Khaled Ahmad Al-Khenah
Abdullah Bader Abdulmohsen Al-Mokhezem
Hamad Mubarak Jaber Al-Ahmad Al-Sabah
Nasser Abdullah Mohammad Al-Sanose
Abdullah Fuad Abdullah Al-Thaqeb
Subsidiary:

Equipment Co. W.L.L. (1)
99 Shuwaikh Industrial Area
PO Box 192
Safat, 13002 Kuwait, Kuwait
Tel.: (965) 24812400
Fax: (965) 24819562
E-Mail: agm@equipcokuwait.com
Web Site: www.equipcokuwait.com
Construction & Industrial Machines & Spare Parts Distr
S.I.C.: 5084
N.A.I.C.S.: 423830

EQUIPMENT WORLD INC.
988 Alloy Drive
Thunder Bay, ON, P7B 6A5, Canada
Tel.: (807) 623-9561
Fax: (807) 623-2943
Toll Free: (800) 465-6955
E-Mail: info@equipworld.com
Web Site: www.equipworld.com
Year Founded: 1973
Rev.: $12,495,232
Emp.: 63
Business Description:
Industrial Machinery Whslr
S.I.C.: 5084
N.A.I.C.S.: 423830
Personnel:
Lyle Knudsen *(VP-Ops)*

EQUISNZAROO CO., LTD.
4BA 204HO 728-3 Sunggok-dong
Danwon-Gu, Ansan, Gyeonggi, Korea (South)
Tel.: (82) 314958262
Fax: (82) 314947005
Web Site: www.equispharm.com
058530—(KRS)
Business Description:
Printed Circuit Board Mfr
S.I.C.: 3672
N.A.I.C.S.: 334412
Personnel:
Nam Wook Lee *(CEO)*

EQUISTONE PARTNERS EUROPE LIMITED
Condor House Saint Paul's Churchyard
London, EC4M 8AL, United Kingdom
Tel.: (44) 2076535300
Fax: (44) 2076535301
E-Mail: rob.myers@equistonepe.com
Web Site: www.equistonepe.com
Sales Range: $5-14.9 Billion
Emp.: 35
Business Description:
Private Equity Firm
S.I.C.: 6211
N.A.I.C.S.: 523999
Personnel:
Guillaume Jacqueau *(Mng Partner & Head-Paris)*
Andrew Backen *(Partner)*
Sam Breuning *(Partner)*
Joyce Church *(Partner)*
Phil Griesbach *(Partner)*
Paul Harper *(Partner)*
Steve O'hare *(Partner)*
Steven Silvester *(Partner)*
Tim swales *(Partner)*
Owen Clarke *(Chief Investment Officer & Mng Dir)*
Rob Myers *(Mng Dir & Head-UK)*
Simon Brown *(CFO)*
Sue Woodman *(Gen Counsel)*
Non-U.S. Holdings:

APEM S.A. (1)
Centre d'Affaires Paris Nord Tour Continental
Le Blanc Mesnil, 93153 Paris, Cedex, France
Tel.: (33) 148149265
Fax: (33) 148149284
E-Mail: commercial@apem.fr
Web Site: www.apem.com
Sales Range: $75-99.9 Million
Emp.: 1,145
Switch, Keyboard & Integrated Assemblies Mfr
S.I.C.: 3679
N.A.I.C.S.: 334419

U.S. Subsidiary:

APEM Components Inc. (2)
63 Neck Rd
Haverhill, MA 01835
Tel.: (978) 372-1602
Fax: (978) 245-4531
Web Site: www.apem.com
Emp.: 50
Electronic Components Mfr
S.I.C.: 3679
N.A.I.C.S.: 334419

Non-U.S. Subsidiaries:

Apem AB (2)
Isafjordsgatan 35
16440 Kista, Sweden
Tel.: (46) 86263800
Fax: (46) 86268249
E-Mail: info@apem.se
Web Site: www.apem.se
Emp.: 7
Electrical Apparatus & Equipment Wiring Supplies & Construction Material Whslr
S.I.C.: 5063
N.A.I.C.S.: 423610
Stefan Steiner *(Mng Dir)*

Apem Bauelemente GmbH (2)
Gewerbehof Giesing
Paulsdorfferstr 34 2 OG, 81549 Munich, Germany
Tel.: (49) 894599110
Fax: (49) 89481039
E-Mail: info@apem.de
Web Site: www.apem.de
Emp.: 18
Electronic Parts & Equipment Whslr
S.I.C.: 5064
N.A.I.C.S.: 423620
Michael Schulza *(Mng Dir)*

Apem Benelux NV/SA (2)
Ave Excelsiorlaan 21
1930 Zaventem, Belgium
Tel.: (32) 27250500
Fax: (32) 27252200
E-Mail: sales@apemswitches.be
Web Site: www.apemswitches.be
Emp.: 10
Electronic Parts & Equipment Whslr
S.I.C.: 5064
N.A.I.C.S.: 423620
Ves Foccart *(Mng Dir)*

APEM Components Ltd. (2)
Drakes Dr
Long Crendon, Aylesbury, HP18 9BA, United Kingdom
Tel.: (44) 1844202400
Fax: (44) 1844202500
E-Mail: sales@apem.co.uk
Web Site: www.apem.co.uk
Emp.: 100
Electrical Equipment & Component Mfr
S.I.C.: 3699
N.A.I.C.S.: 335999
James Clemenger *(Mng Dir)*
Tony West *(Mng Dir)*

Apem Italia S.r.l. (2)
Via Marconi 147G
Marene, 12030 Cuneo, Italy
Tel.: (39) 0172743170
Fax: (39) 0172743171
E-Mail: apem.italia@apem.it
Web Site: fr.apem.com
Fabricated Metal Product Mfr
S.I.C.: 3499
N.A.I.C.S.: 332999

MEC A/S (2)
Industrieparken 23
Ballerup, DK-2750, Denmark
Tel.: (45) 44973366
Fax: (45) 44681514
E-Mail: danmec@mec.dk
Web Site: www.mec.dk/contact/mec
Emp.: 36
Electronic Switches Components Mfr
S.I.C.: 3679
N.A.I.C.S.: 334419
Soren Mollekaer *(Mng Dir)*

CU Chemie Uetikon GmbH (1)
Raiffeisenstrasse 4
D 77933 Lahr, Germany
Tel.: (49) 7821 585 0
Fax: (49) 7821 585 230
E-Mail: info@uetikon.com
Web Site: www.uetikon.com
Sales Range: $10-24.9 Million
Emp.: 108
Active Pharmaceutical Ingredients & Fine Chemicals Mfr
S.I.C.: 2899
N.A.I.C.S.: 325998
Heinz Sieger *(Chm-Supervisory Bd)*
Thomas Seeler *(CEO)*

Konrad Hornschuch AG (1)
Salinenstrasse 1
74679 Weissbach, Germany
Tel.: (49) 7947810
Fax: (49) 7947 81 300
E-Mail: info@hornschuch.de
Web Site: www.hornschuch.com

Sales Range: $300-349.9 Million
Emp.: 1,200
Producer & Marketer of Films, Foils & Artificial Leather for the Home Decoration, Fashion, Furniture, Automotive & Construction Related Markets
S.I.C.: 3081
N.A.I.C.S.: 326113
Michael H. Bork *(Chm-Supervisory Bd)*
Rolf J. Gemmersdorfer *(CEO)*
Hans-Hinrich Kruse *(COO)*

U.S. Subsidiary:

O'Sullivan Films, Inc. **(2)**
1944 Valley Ave
Winchester, VA 22601-6306 VA
Tel.: (540) 667-6666
Fax: (540) 722-2695
Toll Free: (800) 336-9882
Web Site: www.osul.com
Sales Range: $75-99.9 Million
Emp.: 350
Manufactures & Sells Vinyl & Alloy Films & Embossing, Laminating & Painting Equipment for Vinly Processing
S.I.C.: 3081
N.A.I.C.S.: 326113
Denis Belzile *(CEO)*

Meilleurtaux SA **(1)**
19/29 rue du Capitaine Guynemer
92903 Paris, la Defense Cedex, France
Tel.: (33) 1 41 97 98 99
Fax: (33) 1 41 97 98 91
Web Site: www.meilleurtaux.com
Sales Range: $50-74.9 Million
Emp.: 400
Investment Related Services Through Online
S.I.C.: 6163
N.A.I.C.S.: 522310
Herve Hatt *(CEO)*

Parkeon S.A.S. **(1)**
Le Barjac 1 boulevard Victor
F-75015 Paris, France FR
Tel.: (33) 158098110
Fax: (33) 158098126
Web Site: www.parkeon.com
Sales Range: $200-249.9 Million
Emp.: 1,100
Electronic Parking & Transport Management Systems Developer, Mfr & Distr
S.I.C.: 3824
N.A.I.C.S.: 334514
Yves Chambeau *(Chm & CEO)*

U.S. Subsidiary:

Parkeon, Inc. **(2)**
40 Twosome Dr Ste 7
Moorestown, NJ 08057 DE
Tel.: (856) 234-8000
Fax: (856) 234-7178
Web Site: www.parkeon.com
Emp.: 50
Electronic Parking & Transport Management Systems Mfr & Distr
S.I.C.: 3829
N.A.I.C.S.: 334514
Lisa Monte Carlo *(Mgr-HR)*

Non-U.S. Subsidiary:

Parkeon Limited **(2)**
10 Willis Way
Fleets Industrial Estate, Poole, Dorset, BH15 3SS, United Kingdom UK
Tel.: (44) 1202339494
Fax: (44) 1202667293
Web Site: www.parkeon.com
Holding Company; Electronic Parking & Transport Management Systems Mfr & Distr
S.I.C.: 6719
N.A.I.C.S.: 551112
Owen Griffith *(Mng Dir)*

Subsidiaries:

Parkeon Transit Limited **(3)**
10 Willis Way Fleets Industrial Estate
Poole, Dorset, BH15 3SS, United Kingdom UK
Tel.: (44) 1202339494
Fax: (44) 1202667293
E-Mail: sales_uk@parkeon.com
Web Site: www.parkeon.com
Emp.: 120
Electronic Parking & Transport Management Systems Developer, Mfr & Distr
S.I.C.: 3824
N.A.I.C.S.: 334514
Owen Griffith *(Mng Dir)*

UNITHER Pharmaceuticals SAS **(1)**
41 Rue de la Chaussee d'Antin
75009 Paris, France FR
Tel.: (33) 1 4463 5170
Web Site: www.unither-pharma.com
Sales Range: $200-249.9 Million
Emp.: 850
Pharmaceutical Mfr
S.I.C.: 2834
N.A.I.C.S.: 325412
Eric Goupil *(CEO)*

EQUITA MANAGEMENT GMBH

Inge Quandt Haus
Am Pilgerrain 15, 61352 Bad Homburg, Germany
Tel.: (49) 617294410
Fax: (49) 617294410299
E-Mail: info@equita.de
Web Site: www.equita.de
Emp.: 10
Business Description:
Private Equity Company
S.I.C.: 6211
N.A.I.C.S.: 523999
Personnel:
Michael Honig *(Partner)*
Hans J. Moock *(Mng Dir)*
Hansjoerg Schnabel *(Mng Dir)*
Hans Jurgen Wiemker *(CFO & Dir-Investment)*

EQUITABLE GROUP INC.

30 St Clair Avenue West Suite 700
Toronto, ON, M4V 3A1, Canada
Tel.: (416) 515-7000
Fax: (416) 515-7001
E-Mail: gicinfo@equitabletrust.com
Web Site: www.equitablegroup.ca
ETC—(TSX)
Rev.: $473,677,369
Assets: $11,532,063,389
Liabilities: $11,033,491,783
Net Worth: $498,571,605
Earnings: $80,721,382
Emp.: 271
Fiscal Year-end: 12/31/12
Business Description:
Mortgage Financing
S.I.C.: 6163
N.A.I.C.S.: 522310
Personnel:
Austin Beutel *(Chm)*
Andrew Moor *(Pres & CEO)*
Tim Wilson *(CFO & VP)*
Dan Ruch *(Chief Compliance Officer & VP)*
William Edmunds *(Sr VP & Chief Risk Officer-Equitable Trust)*
Drew Berman *(Gen Counsel, Sec & VP)*
Nicholas Strube *(Treas-Equitable Trust)*
Board of Directors:
Austin Beutel
Eric Beutel
Joseph Dickstein
Eric Kirzner
David Malcolm Balfour LeGresley
Lynn McDonald
Andrew Moor
Katherine A. Rethy
Lionel Robins
Morris Shohet
Michael Shulman
Transfer Agent:
Computershare Investor Services Inc.
100 University Ave 9th Floor
Toronto, ON, Canada

THE EQUITABLE LIFE INSURANCE COMPANY OF CANADA

(d/b/a Equitable Life of Canada)
1 Westmount Road North
PO Box 1603
Waterloo, ON, N2J 4C7, Canada
Tel.: (519) 886-5110
Fax: (519) 883-7404
Toll Free: (800) 265-8878
E-Mail: head-office@equitable.ca
Web Site: www.equitable.ca
Year Founded: 1920
Rev.: $575,734,396
Assets: $2,916,646,526
Liabilities: $2,555,251,668
Net Worth: $361,394,857
Earnings: $44,388,957
Emp.: 500
Fiscal Year-end: 12/31/12
Business Description:
Life Insurance Services
S.I.C.: 6311
N.A.I.C.S.: 524113
Personnel:
Douglas W. Dodds *(Chm)*
Ronald E. Beettam *(Pres & CEO)*
David Bennett *(CFO & Sr VP)*
Cam Crosbie *(CIO & VP-IT)*
Randy Howell *(Sec & VP-Legal)*
Michael M. Dawe *(Sr VP-Individual)*
Paul English *(Sr VP-Investments)*
Karen Mason *(Sr VP)*
Board of Directors:
Douglas W. Dodds
Douglas S. Alexander
Robert Badun
Rita Burak
Douglas L. Derry
Maureen A. Farrow
A. David Pelletier
Craig Richardson
Donald N. Stevens
C. Lee F. Watchorn
David S. Weinberg

Subsidiary:

262695 Holdings Limited **(1)**
25 Westmount Rd N Suite 101
Waterloo, ON, N2L 5G7, Canada
Tel.: (519) 886-5210
Life Insurance Services
S.I.C.: 6311
N.A.I.C.S.: 524113

EQUITAS RESOURCES CORP.

1450 - 789 W Pender St
Vancouver, BC, V6C 1H2, Canada
Tel.: (604) 681-1568
Toll Free: (877) 377-6222
E-Mail: info@equitasresources.com
Web Site: www.equitasresources.com
EQT—(TSXV)
Assets: $2,203,888
Liabilities: $136,705
Net Worth: $2,067,184
Earnings: ($505,483)
Fiscal Year-end: 02/28/13
Business Description:
Gold Mining Services
S.I.C.: 1041
N.A.I.C.S.: 212221
Personnel:
David Hodge *(Pres & CEO)*
Jody Bellefleur *(CFO)*
Board of Directors:
Chris Grove
Jay Roberge
Quangjie Wang
Steve Williams

EQUITORIAL EXPLORATION CORP.

1818 - 701 W Georgia Street
Vancouver, BC, V7Y 1C6, Canada
Tel.: (604) 689-1799
Fax: (604) 689-8199
E-Mail: info@equitorial.ca
Web Site: www.equitorial.ca
Year Founded: 2010
EXX—(TSXV)
Int. Income: $2
Assets: $451,443
Liabilities: $13,066
Net Worth: $438,377
Earnings: ($65,914)
Fiscal Year-end: 12/31/12
Business Description:
Metal Mining Services
S.I.C.: 1099
N.A.I.C.S.: 212299
Personnel:
Dean Pekeski *(Pres)*
Patrick Power *(CEO & Sec)*
Troy Nikolai *(CFO)*
Board of Directors:
Frank D. Hegner
Troy Nikolai
Dean Pekeski
Patrick Power
Jorge Patricio Varas
Transfer Agent:
Computershare Investor Services Inc.
3rd Floor 510 Burrard Street
Vancouver, BC, Canada

EQUITY BANK LIMITED

Upper Hill - Hospital Road Equity Centre 9th Floor
00200 Nairobi, Kenya
Tel.: (254) 202744000
Fax: (254) 202737276
E-Mail: info@equitybank.co.ke
Web Site: www.equitybank.co.ke
EQTY—(NAI)
Rev.: $346,423,040
Assets: $2,730,799,100
Liabilities: $2,248,852,420
Net Worth: $481,946,680
Earnings: $135,658,400
Fiscal Year-end: 12/31/12
Business Description:
Personal Banking Services
S.I.C.: 6141
N.A.I.C.S.: 522291
Personnel:
James Mwangi *(CEO & Mng Dir)*
Julius Kipng'etich *(COO)*
Maurice A. Ewing *(Chief Risk Officer)*
John Staley *(Chief Officer-Fin, Innovation & Tech)*
Mary Wamae *(Sec & Dir-Corp Strategy)*
Board of Directors:
Peter Munga
Dennis Aluanga
Helen Gichohi
Julius Kipng'etich
Temitope Lawani
Fredrick Muchoki
James Mwangi
Alykhan Nathoo
Ernest Nzovu
Babatunde Soyoye
Benson I. Wairegi
Legal Counsel:
Coulson Harney Advocates
1st Floor Block A Nairobi Business Park Ngong Road
PO Box 10643 00100
Nairobi, Kenya

U.S. Subsidiary:

Equity Investment services Ltd **(1)**
301 S Tubb St Ste G
Oakland, FL 34760
Tel.: (407) 573-0711
Fax: (407) 573-0710
E-Mail: Info@EISRE.com
Web Site: www.equityinvestmentservices.com

Equity Bank Limited—(Continued)

Investment Banking Services
S.I.C.: 6211
N.A.I.C.S.: 523999
Christopher M. Savino *(Mng Dir)*

EQUITY FINANCIAL HOLDINGS INC.

200 University Avenue Suite 400
Toronto, ON, M5H 4H1, Canada
Tel.: (416) 361-0152
Fax: (416) 361-0470
Toll Free: (866) 393-4891
E-Mail: investor@equityfinancialtrust.com
Web Site: www.equityfinancialholdings.com
Year Founded: 2003
EQI—(TSX)
Int. Income: $7,725,523
Assets: $249,938,377
Liabilities: $197,983,934
Net Worth: $51,954,443
Earnings: $530,807
Emp.: 114
Fiscal Year-end: 12/31/12
Business Description:
Holding Company; Trust, Mortgage, Deposit & Foreign Exchange Services
S.I.C.: 6719
N.A.I.C.S.: 551112
Personnel:
Paul G. Smith *(Founder)*
Donald A. Wright *(Chm)*
Michael Jones *(Interim CEO)*
Josh Reusing *(CFO)*
Michael Ecclestone *(Chief Compliance Officer & Gen Counsel)*
Darryl J. Ivan *(Chief Risk Officer & VP-Risk Mgmt)*
Deborah Robinson *(Chief People Officer)*
Nick Kyprianou *(CEO-Equity Financial Trust Company)*
Phil Braginetz *(Treas & VP-Mortgage Ops)*
James Gould *(Sec & VP-Compliance)*
Board of Directors:
Donald A. Wright
Stephen J. Griggs
Wesley J. Hall
Michael Jones
Bradley R. Kipp
Michele McCarthy
F. David Roundthwaite
Glen Silvestri
Thomas R. Spencer
Transfer Agent:
Equity Financial Trust Company
Toronto, ON, Canada
Subsidiary:

Equity Financial Trust Company (1)
200 University Avenue Suite 400
Toronto, ON, M5H 4H1, Canada (100%)
Tel.: (416) 361-0152
Fax: (416) 361-0470
Toll Free: (866) 393-4891
E-Mail: investor@equitytransfer.com
Web Site: www.equityfinancialtrust.com
Emp.: 100
Trust, Mortgage & Deposit Services
S.I.C.: 6099
N.A.I.C.S.: 523991
Michael Jones *(Pres & Interim CEO)*
Terry Martinuk *(Pres-Transfer Agent & Trust Svcs)*
Nick Kyprianou *(CEO)*

EQUITY TRUSTEES LIMITED

Level 2 575 Bourke Street
Melbourne, VIC, 3000, Australia
Mailing Address:
GPO Box 2307
Melbourne, VIC, 3001, Australia
Tel.: (61) 386235000
Fax: (61) 386235200
E-Mail: equity@eqt.com.au
Web Site: www.eqt.com.au
EQT—(ASX)
Rev.: $49,480,778
Assets: $73,332,395
Liabilities: $8,107,356
Net Worth: $65,225,039
Earnings: $9,036,467
Emp.: 110
Fiscal Year-end: 06/30/13
Business Description:
Financial Services.
S.I.C.: 6099
N.A.I.C.S.: 522320
Personnel:
Robin B. O. Burns *(Mng Dir)*
Terry Ryan *(CFO & Co-Sec)*
George Boubouras *(Chief Investment Officer)*
Philip B. Maddox *(Co-Sec & Head-Legal Risk Mgmt & Compliance)*
Board of Directors:
James A. Killen
Robin B. O. Burns
Kevin J. Eley
David F. Groves
Jeffrey Gibb Kennett
Anne M. O'Donnell
Alice J. M. Williams

EQUITYSTORY AG

(Name Changed to EQS Group AG)

EQUUS MINING LIMITED

(Formerly Caspian Oil & Gas Limited)
Level 2 66 Hunter Street
Sydney, NSW, 2000, Australia
Tel.: (61) 2 9300 3366
Fax: (61) 2 9221 6333
E-Mail: equus@equusmining.com
Web Site: www.equusmining.com
EQE—(ASX)
Rev.: $2,084,200
Assets: $12,907,482
Liabilities: $654,259
Net Worth: $12,253,223
Earnings: ($3,741,793)
Emp.: 10
Fiscal Year-end: 06/30/13
Business Description:
Copper & Gold Mining
S.I.C.: 1021
N.A.I.C.S.: 212234
Personnel:
Norman Seckold *(Chm)*
Edward Leschke *(Mng Dir)*
Marcelo Mora *(Sec)*
Board of Directors:
Norman Seckold
Edward Leschke
Juerg Walker

EQVITEC PARTNERS OY

PO Box 65
00131 Helsinki, Finland
Tel.: (358) 50 66563
E-Mail: jukka.makinen@eqvitec.com
Web Site: www.eqvitec.com
Business Description:
Private Equity Firm
S.I.C.: 6211
N.A.I.C.S.: 523999
Personnel:
Jukka Makinen *(Mng Dir)*
Holding:

Ecocat Oy (1)
PI 330
00101 Helsinki, Finland
Tel.: (358) 108611717
Fax: (358) 108621119
E-Mail: erez@mennenmedical.co.il
Web Site: www.mennenmedical.com
Sales Range: $50-74.9 Million
Emp.: 150
Catalytic Converters Mfr
S.I.C.: 3714
N.A.I.C.S.: 336390
Harry Harrikerminen *(Mng Dir)*

Non-U.S. Subsidiary:

Ecocat Italia S.r.l. (2)
Via Colano 9A/14D
I 16162 Genoa, GE, Italy
Tel.: (39) 0107261653
Catalytic Converters Mfr & Distr
S.I.C.: 3714
N.A.I.C.S.: 336390

ER&GE GMBH

Halberstadter Strasse 75
33106 Paderborn, Germany
Tel.: (49) 525117560
Fax: (49) 5251175640
E-Mail: info@ergeplas.de
Web Site: www.ergeplas.de
Year Founded: 1982
Rev.: $14,843,516
Emp.: 29
Business Description:
Plastic Products Mfr
S.I.C.: 3089
N.A.I.C.S.: 326199
Personnel:
Christian Raatz *(Mng Dir)*

E.R. CAPITAL HOLDING GMBH & CIE. KG

Hohe Bleichen 12
20354 Hamburg, Germany
Tel.: (49) 40 3008 0
E-Mail: info@er-capital.com
Web Site: www.er-capital.com
Business Description:
Holding Company
S.I.C.: 6719
N.A.I.C.S.: 551112
Personnel:
Erck R.C. Rickmers *(Founder & Chm-Supervisory Bd)*
Nicholas Teller *(CEO & Chm-Mgmt Bd)*
Frank Bergert *(CFO & Member-Mgmt Bd)*
Jochen Klosges *(COO, CEO-Designate & Member-Mgmt Bd)*
Hermann J. Klein *(Member-Mgmt Bd)*
Subsidiaries:

Equitrust GmbH (1)
Hohe Bleichen 12
20354 Hamburg, Germany De
Tel.: (49) 40 3008 1431
Web Site: www.equitrust.de
Private Equity Fund Management Services
S.I.C.: 6799
N.A.I.C.S.: 523920
Florian Maack *(Chm-Mgmt Bd)*
Anke Hennings *(Member-Mgmt Bd)*

E.R. SCHIFFAHRT GmbH & Cie. KG (1)
Hohe Bleichen 12
20354 Hamburg, Germany De
Tel.: (49) 40 3008 1100
Fax: (49) 40 3008 1000
E-Mail: info@er-ship.com
Web Site: www.er-ship.com
Freight Shipping Services
S.I.C.: 4412
N.A.I.C.S.: 483111
Hermann J. Klein *(CEO & Member-Exec Bd)*
Nils Aden *(Mng Dir & Member-Exec Bd)*
Willem Dekker *(Mng Dir & Member-Exec Bd)*
Frank Bergert *(CFO & Member-Exec Bd)*

Subsidiary:

E.R. OFFSHORE GmbH & Cie. KG (2)
Hohe Bleichen 12
20354 Hamburg, Germany De
Tel.: (49) 40 3008 0
Fax: (49) 40 3008 1000
Web Site: www.er-ship.com
Offshore Supply Vessels Operator
S.I.C.: 4499
N.A.I.C.S.: 488390
Kai Naumann *(Mng Dir)*
Ian Perrott *(Mng Dir)*

Nordcapital GmbH (1)
Hohe Bleichen 12
20354 Hamburg, Germany De
Tel.: (49) 40 3008 0
Fax: (49) 40 3008 1000
E-Mail: info@nordcapital.com
Web Site: www.nordcapital.com
Investment Holding Company
S.I.C.: 6719
N.A.I.C.S.: 551112
Florian Maack *(Co-CEO & Member-Mgmt Bd)*
Felix von Buchwaldt *(Co-CEO & Member-Mgmt Bd)*
Frank Bergert *(CFO & Member-Mgmt Bd)*

E.R. PROBYN LTD.

Ste 350 601 6th St
New Westminster, BC, V3L 3C1, Canada
Tel.: (604) 526-8545
Fax: (604) 526-0891
E-Mail: info@probyngroup.com
Web Site: www.probyngroup.com
Emp.: 30
Business Description:
Logging, Wholesale Forest Products, Manufacturer of Cedar Fencing & Specialty Cedar Products
S.I.C.: 2448
N.A.I.C.S.: 321920
Personnel:
Edward Probyn *(Chm)*
Subsidiaries:

E.R. Probyn Export Ltd. (1)
350 601 63
New Westminster, BC, V3L 3C1, Canada (100%)
Tel.: (604) 526-8546
Fax: (604) 526-8565
Web Site: www.probynexport.com
Emp.: 8
Export Lumber
S.I.C.: 5031
N.A.I.C.S.: 423310
Rod McCoy *(Gen Mgr)*

Probyn Log, Ltd. (1)
Ste 350 601 6th St
New Westminster, BC, V3O 3C1, Canada (100%)
Tel.: (604) 526-8545
Fax: (604) 526-0891
Web Site: www.probynlog.com
Emp.: 25
Logging Sales
S.I.C.: 2411
N.A.I.C.S.: 113310
Peter Sotraseher *(Pres)*

U.S. Subsidiary:

TMI Forest Products Inc. (1)
PO Box U
Morton, WA 98356-0110 (100%)
Tel.: (360) 496-6777
Fax: (360) 496-5252
Web Site: www.tubafor.com
Emp.: 150
Mfr. of Cedar Fencing
S.I.C.: 2421
N.A.I.C.S.: 321113
Mike Pedersen *(Gen Mgr)*

ERA CARBON OFFSETS LTD.

(Name Changed to Offsetters Climate Solutions Inc.)

ERA D.O.O.

Presernova 10
SI-3320 Velenje, Slovenia
Tel.: (386) 3 62 03100

Fax: (386) 3 89 60396
E-Mail: info@era.si
Web Site: www.era.si/
Year Founded: 1951
Sales Range: $350-399.9 Million
Emp.: 2,676
Business Description:
Wholesale Food Procurement Agencies
S.I.C.: 5411
N.A.I.C.S.: 452910
Personnel:
Gvido Omladic *(CEO)*
Non-U.S. Subsidiary:

Eko Energetika DOO (1)
Belasica 2
PO Box 356
1000 Skopje, Macedonia
Tel.: (389) 2 3218 388
Fax: (389) 2 3218 375
Electric Power Generation & Distribution Services
S.I.C.: 4939
N.A.I.C.S.: 221114

ERA INFRA ENGINEERING LIMITED

370-371/2 Sahi Hospital Road
Jungpura
Bhogal, New Delhi, 110 014, India
Tel.: (91) 1143637000
Fax: (91) 1124378784
Web Site: www.eragroup.co.in
ERAINFRA—(NSE)
Rev.: $868,846,880
Assets: $1,685,672,874
Liabilities: $1,339,843,955
Net Worth: $345,828,919
Earnings: $20,311,349
Emp.: 3,722
Fiscal Year-end: 03/31/13
Business Description:
Real Estate Development Services
S.I.C.: 6531
N.A.I.C.S.: 531390
Personnel:
H. S. Bharana *(Chm & Mng Dir)*
Sanjay Gupta *(CFO)*
Rajiv Kumar *(Compliance Officer & Sec)*
R. K. Gupta *(Pres-Design, Engrg, Plng & Power)*
Alok Khanna *(COO-Infrastructure Mgmt & Resources Dev & Sr VP)*
Board of Directors:
H. S. Bharana
Tulsi Dass Arora
S. D. Kapoor
A. K. Mehta
Arvind Pande
S. D. Sharma
Transfer Agent:
Beetal Financial & Computer Services Pvt Limited
99 Madangir Behind Local Shopping Centre
Near Dada Harsukhdas Mandir
New Delhi, 110062, India
Subsidiary:

Era T&D Limited (1)
C-56/41 Sector-62
Noida, 201307, India
Tel.: (91) 120 4145139
Fax: (91) 120 4145152
Emp.: 20
Electric Power Generation Services
S.I.C.: 4931
N.A.I.C.S.: 221118
Virendra Swarup *(Mgr)*

ERAMET SA

(d/b/a Eramet Group)
Tour Maine Montparnasse 33 Avenue du Maine
75755 Paris, Cedex 15, France
Tel.: (33) 145384242
Fax: (33) 145384128
E-Mail: info.france@eramet-international.com
Web Site: www.eramet.com
ERA—(EUR)
Sls.: $4,640,247,990
Assets: $8,506,448,230
Liabilities: $3,322,347,560
Net Worth: $5,184,100,670
Earnings: $56,539,140
Emp.: 15,000
Fiscal Year-end: 12/31/12
Business Description:
Nonferrous Metals & Chemical Derivatives Producer
S.I.C.: 3356
N.A.I.C.S.: 331491
Personnel:
Patrick Buffet *(Chm & CEO)*
Jean-Didier Dujardin *(CFO)*
Georges Duval *(CEO-Alloys Div)*
Bertrand Madelin *(CEO-Nickel Div)*
Philippe Vecten *(CEO-Manganese)*
Michel Carnec *(Exec VP-HR, Hygiene, Health & Safety)*
Catherine Tissot-Colle *(Exec VP-Comm & Sustainable Dev)*
Board of Directors:
Patrick Buffet
Claire Cheremetinski
Thomas Devedjian
Cyrille Duval
Edouard Duval
Georges Duval
Patrick Duval
Caroline Gregoire Sainte Marie
Thierry Le Henaff
Manoelle Lepoutre
Louis Mapou
Michel Quintard
Michel Somnolet
Claude Tendil
Antoine G. Treuille
Divisions:

Eramet Alloys (1)
Tour Maine Montparnesse
33 Avenue du Maine, Paris, Cedex 15, France
Tel.: (33) 145386300
Fax: (33) 145383860
E-Mail: accueil-alleajes.tmm@eramet-aubertduvil.com
Web Site: www.eramet.fr/us/Site/Template/CONTACT.aspx?SELECTID=178&ID=125
Emp.: 100
Steel Products Mfr
S.I.C.: 3462
N.A.I.C.S.: 332111
Patrick Busset *(Pres)*
Georges Duval *(CEO)*

Subsidiaries:

Aubert & Duval (2)
Tour Maine Montparnesse
33 avenue du Maine, Paris, Cedex 15, France
Tel.: (33) 145383888
Fax: (33) 0145383860
E-Mail: accueil-alliages.tmm@eramet-aubertduval.com
Web Site: www.aubertduval.fr
Emp.: 30
Steel Alloy Products Mfr
S.I.C.: 3462
N.A.I.C.S.: 332111
Xavier Chastel *(CEO)*

Plants:

Aubert & Duval SAS - Firminy Plant (3)
Rue du Colonel Riez
BP 141
42704 Firminy, Loire, France
Tel.: (33) 477403606
Fax: (33) 477403699
Web Site: www.aubertduval.com
Emp.: 320
Fabricated Steel Products Mfr
S.I.C.: 3399
N.A.I.C.S.: 331110
Denis Hugelmann *(Gen Mgr)*

Aubert & Duval SAS - Gennevilliers Plant (3)
22 rue Henri Vuillemin
BP 63
92233 Gennevilliers, Hauts-de-Seine, France
Tel.: (33) 1 55 02 58 00
Fax: (33) 1 55 02 58 01
Fabricated Steel Products Mfr
S.I.C.: 3399
N.A.I.C.S.: 331110

Aubert & Duval SAS - Imphy Plant (3)
Avenue Jean Jaures
BP 02
58160 Imphy, Nievre, France
Tel.: (33) 3 86 90 74 00
Fax: (33) 3 86 90 74 10
Fabricated Steel Products Mfr
S.I.C.: 3399
N.A.I.C.S.: 331110

Aubert & Duval SAS - Issoire Interforge Plant (3)
Zone Artisanale Maze
BP 45
63502 Issoire, Puy-de-Dome, France
Tel.: (33) 473555400
Fax: (33) 473555401
Fabricated Steel Products Mfr
S.I.C.: 3312
N.A.I.C.S.: 331110

Aubert & Duval SAS - Les Ancizes Plant (3)
BP 1
63770 Les Ancizes-Comps, Puy-de-Dome, France
Tel.: (33) 4 73 67 30 00
Fax: (33) 4 73 67 33 00
Fabricated Steel Products Mfr
S.I.C.: 3399
N.A.I.C.S.: 331110

Aubert & Duval SAS - Pamiers Plant (3)
75 boulevard de la Liberation
BP 173
09102 Pamiers, Ariege, France
Tel.: (33) 5 61 68 44 00
Fax: (33) 5 61 60 02 31
Metal Stampings Mfr
S.I.C.: 3466
N.A.I.C.S.: 332119

Erasteel SAS (2)
Tour Maine-Montparnasse
33 Avenue du Maine, 75755 Paris, Cedex 15, France
Tel.: (33) 145386300
Fax: (33) 145386330
E-Mail: info.erasteel@eramet.fr
Web Site: www.erasteel.com
Steel Products Mfr
S.I.C.: 3499
N.A.I.C.S.: 332117
Victor Polard *(CEO)*

Plants:

Erasteel SAS - Champagnole Plant (3)
23 rue G Clemenceau
BP 104
39 300 Champagnole, Jura, France
Tel.: (33) 3 84 52 64 44
Fax: (33) 3 84 52 61 25
Web Site: www.erasteel.com
Emp.: 40
Steel Products Mfr
S.I.C.: 3312
N.A.I.C.S.: 331110
Olivier Louis *(Mgr)*

Erasteel SAS- Commentry Plant (3)
1 place Martenot
BP 1
03600 Commentry, Allier, France
Tel.: (33) 4 70 28 78 00
Fax: (33) 4 70 28 78 93
Web Site: www.erasteel.com
Steel Products Mfr
S.I.C.: 3312
N.A.I.C.S.: 331110

Non-U.S. Subsidiaries:

ERASTEEL KLOSTER AB (3)
Bruksplan 1
PO Box 100
815 82 Soderfors, Tierp, Sweden
Tel.: (46) 29354300
Fax: (46) 29330770
E-Mail: oscar.lunddal@eramed-erasteel.com
Emp.: 400
Steel Products Mfr
S.I.C.: 3312
N.A.I.C.S.: 331110
Perre Blanchard *(Gen Mgr)*

ERASTEEL STUBS LTD. (3)
Causeway Avenue
Warrington, Cheshire, WA4 6QB, United Kingdom
Tel.: (44) 1925653939
Fax: (44) 192 541 3870
Emp.: 50
Steel Products Mfr
S.I.C.: 3312
N.A.I.C.S.: 331110

Eramet Manganese (1)
Tour Maine-Montparnasse
33 Avenue du Maine, 75755 Paris, Cedex, France (100%)
Tel.: (33) 153912400
Fax: (33) 145384128
E-Mail: info@erametgroup.com
Web Site: www.erachem-comilog.com
Emp.: 6,800
Manganese Chemicals Production & Supplier; Copper Recycling
S.I.C.: 2899
N.A.I.C.S.: 325998
Philippe Vecten *(CEO)*

Non-U.S. Plant:

Eramet SA - ERAMET Manganese Division - Tyssedal Plant (2)
Naustbakken 7
Tyssedal, 5770 Odda, Norway
Tel.: (47) 53 65 00 50
Fax: (47) 53 65 00 51
Managanese Alloys Mfr
S.I.C.: 3312
N.A.I.C.S.: 331110

Eramet Nickel (1)
Tour Maine Montparnasse
33 Avenue du Maine, 75755 Paris, Cedex 15, France
Tel.: (33) 145384200
Fax: (33) 145387348
Web Site: www.eramet.com
Emp.: 200
Nickel Production
S.I.C.: 1021
N.A.I.C.S.: 212234
Bertrand Madelin *(CEO)*

U.S. Subsidiary:

Gulf Chemical & Metallurgical Corporation (1)
302 Midway Road
Freeport, TX 77542-2290
Tel.: (979) 415-1500
Fax: (979) 415-1600
E-Mail: info@eramet-gulf.com
Web Site: www.gulfchem.com
Spent Ptroleum Catalysts Recycling & Ferroalloys Mfr
S.I.C.: 3399
N.A.I.C.S.: 331110
Francois Bour *(Chm)*
David J. Pacella *(CEO)*

Non-U.S. Subsidiary:

PT Weda Bay Nickel (1)
Wisma Pondok Indah 2 11th Floor Suites
1101 Jl Sultan Iskandar Muda
Kav V-TA Pondok Indah, Jakarta, 12310, Indonesia
Tel.: (62) 2175922802
Fax: (62) 21 75922803
Web Site: www.wedabay.co.id
Nickel Ore Mine Site Development Services
S.I.C.: 1021
N.A.I.C.S.: 212234

ERARING ENERGY PTY LTD.

(Acquired by Origin Energy Ltd.)

ERATAT LIFESTYLE LIMITED
Liupu Industrial Park Yangdai
Chendai Town
Jingjiang, Fujian, China 362218
Tel.: (86) 595 85086888
Fax: (86) 595 85083388
E-Mail: ir@eratatgroup.com
Web Site: www.eratatgroup.com
FO8—(SES)
Rev.: $163,893,646
Assets: $162,586,787
Liabilities: $11,812,880
Net Worth: $150,773,907
Earnings: $22,486,647
Fiscal Year-end: 12/31/12
Business Description:
Sports Footwear & Apparel Designer, Mfr & Distr
S.I.C.: 2389
N.A.I.C.S.: 316210
Personnel:
Jiancheng Lin *(Chm & CEO)*
Ker Chern Ho *(CFO)*
Cher Liang Tan *(Sec)*
Board of Directors:
Jiancheng Lin
Peck Heng Lam
Yeow Hua Lim
Yeoh Chi Tao
Sanzhi Ye

THE ERAWAN GROUP PUBLIC COMPANY LIMITED
Ploenchit Center 6th Floor 2
Sukhumvit Soi 2 Road
Klong Toey, Bangkok, 10110, Thailand
Tel.: (66) 22574588
Fax: (66) 22574577
E-Mail: info@theerawan.com
Web Site: www.theerawan.com
Year Founded: 1982
ERW—(THA)
Rev.: $144,571,360
Assets: $425,192,169
Liabilities: $302,142,006
Net Worth: $123,050,163
Earnings: $5,524,901
Emp.: 2,000
Fiscal Year-end: 12/31/12
Business Description:
Hotel Developer & Operator
S.I.C.: 1542
N.A.I.C.S.: 236220
Personnel:
Prakit Pradipasen *(Chm)*
Kamonwan Wipulakorn *(Pres)*
Kasama Punyagupta *(CEO)*
Krailuck Asawachatroj *(CFO & Exec VP)*
Kanokwan Thongsiwarugs *(Sec)*
Petch Krainukul *(Exec VP & Head-Hotel Investment)*
Apichan Mapaisansin *(Exec VP & Head-Project Dev & Mgmt)*
Navarat Tamsuwan *(Asst Exec VP-Project Dev & Mgmt)*
Anuphong Wangphongsawasd *(Exec VP-Bus Dev)*
Board of Directors:
Prakit Pradipasen
Manop Bongsadadt
Dej Bulsuk
Ekasith Jotikasthira
Banyong Pongpanich
Kasama Punyagupta
Panida Thepkanjana
Chanin Vongkusolkit
Gavin Vongkusolkit
Vitoon Vongkusolkit
Supol Wattanavekin
Kamonwan Wipulakorn
Sansern Wongcha-um

ERBUD S.A.
ul Pulawska 300A
02-819 Warsaw, Poland
Tel.: (48) 225487000
Fax: (48) 225487020
E-Mail: info@erbud.pl
ERB—(WAR)
Rev.: $439,051,897
Assets: $259,949,241
Liabilities: $180,209,123
Net Worth: $79,740,119
Earnings: $5,875,468
Emp.: 1,630
Fiscal Year-end: 12/31/12
Business Description:
Construction Services
S.I.C.: 1542
N.A.I.C.S.: 236220
Personnel:
Udo Berner *(Chm-Supervisory Bd)*
Jozef Olszynski *(Vice Chm-Supervisory Bd)*
Dariusz Grzeszczak *(Member-Exec Bd)*
Jozef Adam Zubelewicz *(Member-Exec Bd)*
Supervisory Board of Directors:
Udo Berner
Albert Durr
Zofia Dzik
Gabriel Glowka
Jozef Olszynski
Michal Otto
Lech Wysokinski

ERCO INTERIEURBOUW B.V.
JF Kennedylaan 51
PO Box 175
5550 AD Valkenswaard, Netherlands
Tel.: (31) 402084222
Fax: (31) 402084223
E-Mail: info@erco-ib.nl
Web Site: www.erco-ib.nl
Sales Range: $10-24.9 Million
Business Description:
Office Furnishings Designer & Mfr
S.I.C.: 2522
N.A.I.C.S.: 337214

ERCROS SA
Avda Diagonal 595
08014 Barcelona, Spain
Tel.: (34) 934393009
Fax: (34) 934308073
E-Mail: ercros@ercros.es
Web Site: www.ercros.es
Year Founded: 1989
ECR—(MAD)
Rev.: $941,080,524
Assets: $814,675,161
Liabilities: $580,616,583
Net Worth: $234,058,578
Earnings: ($17,500,210)
Emp.: 1,620
Fiscal Year-end: 12/31/12
Business Description:
Chemicals, Plastics & Pharmaceuticals Mfr
S.I.C.: 2899
N.A.I.C.S.: 325998
Personnel:
Antonio Zabalza Marti *(Chm & CEO)*
Pedro Rodriguez Sanchez *(CFO)*
Jose Luis Muniz Alvarez *(COO)*
Santiago Mayans Sintes *(Legal Counsel)*
Board of Directors:
Antonio Zabalza Marti
Laureano Roldan Aguilar
Ramon Blanco Balin
Eduardo Sanchez Morrondo
Luis Fernandez-Goula Pfaf

Divisions:

Ercros SA - Animal Feed Division (1)
Avda Diagonal 595
08014 Barcelona, Spain
Tel.: (34) 934393009
Fax: (34) 934 308 073
E-Mail: alimentacionanimal@ercros.es
Animal Feeds Mfr
S.I.C.: 2048
N.A.I.C.S.: 311119

Plants:

Ercros SA - Animal Feed Division - Cartagena Factory (2)
C Los Parales S N Valle de Escombreras
30350 Cartagena, Murcia, Spain
Tel.: (34) 968 333 400
Fax: (34) 968 333 408
E-Mail: cartagena@ercros.es
Web Site: www.ercros.es
Animal Feeds Mfr
S.I.C.: 2048
N.A.I.C.S.: 311119

Ercros SA - Animal Feed Division - Flix Factory (2)
Calle Afores S N
43750 Flix, Tarragona, Spain
Tel.: (34) 93 439 3009
Fax: (34) 977 410 537
E-Mail: flix@ercros.es
Web Site: www.ercros.es
Emp.: 245
Phosphates Mfr
S.I.C.: 2819
N.A.I.C.S.: 325180
Antonio Llena Estruch *(Dir-Animal Feed)*

Ercros SA - Basic Chemicals Division (1)
Avda Diagonal 595
08014 Barcelona, Spain
Tel.: (34) 934393009
Fax: (34) 934308073
E-Mail: quimicabasica@ercros.es
Emp.: 100
Basic Chemicals Mfr
S.I.C.: 2833
N.A.I.C.S.: 325411
Jose Luismuniz *(Gen Mgr)*

Plants:

Ercros SA - Basic Chemicals Division - Flix Factory (2)
C Afores S N
43750 Flix, Tarragona, Spain
Tel.: (34) 977 410 125
Fax: (34) 977 548 011
E-Mail: flix@ercros.es
Chlorine Compounds Mfr
S.I.C.: 2819
N.A.I.C.S.: 325180

Ercros SA - Basic Chemicals Division - Palos de la Frontera Factory (2)
Apartado de correos 284
21080 Huelva, Spain
Tel.: (34) 959 369 200
Fax: (34) 959 369 193
E-Mail: palos@ercros.es
Emp.: 152
Chloromethanes Mfr
S.I.C.: 2899
N.A.I.C.S.: 325199

Ercros SA - Basic Chemicals Division - Sabinanigo Factory (2)
C/ Serrablo 102
22600 Sabinanigo, Huesca, Spain
Tel.: (34) 974498000
Fax: (34) 974 498 006
E-Mail: sabinanigo@ercros.es
Emp.: 219
Chlorine Derivatives Mfr
S.I.C.: 2819
N.A.I.C.S.: 325180

Ercros SA - Basic Chemicals Division - Tarragona Factory (2)
Apartado de Correos 450
43080 Tarragona, Spain
Tel.: (34) 977548011
Fax: (34) 977547300
E-Mail: complejotarragona@ercros.es
Chemicals Mfr
S.I.C.: 2833
N.A.I.C.S.: 325411
Antonio Ferrer *(Gen Mgr)*

Ercros SA - Basic Chemicals Division - Vila-seca I Factory (2)
Autovia Tarragona-Salou C-31 B Km 6
43480 Vila-seca, Tarragona, Spain
Tel.: (34) 977370354
Fax: (34) 977370407
E-Mail: complejotarragona@ercros.es
Chemicals Mfr
S.I.C.: 2869
N.A.I.C.S.: 325199

Ercros SA - Intermediate Chemicals Division (1)
Avda Diagonal 595
08014 Barcelona, Spain
Tel.: (34) 934 393 009
Fax: (34) 932 321 460
E-Mail: quimicaintermedia@ercros.es
Formaldehyde & Derivatives Mfr
S.I.C.: 2869
N.A.I.C.S.: 325199
Cerda Ignacio *(Product Mgr)*

Plants:

Ercros SA - Intermediate Chemicals Division - Cerdanyola Factory (2)
C Santa Anna 105
08290 Cerdanyola del Valles, Barcelona, Spain
Tel.: (34) 935803353
Fax: (34) 935805409
E-Mail: cerdanyola@ercros.es
Web Site: www.ercros.com
Emp.: 90
Chemicals & Resins Mfr
S.I.C.: 2821
N.A.I.C.S.: 325211
Angel Punzano *(Mng Dir)*

Ercros SA - Intermediate Chemicals Division - Tortosa Factory (2)
Poligono Indus Baix Ebre Calle A
43897 Tortosa, Tarragona, Spain
Tel.: (34) 977454022
Fax: (34) 977597101
E-Mail: tortosa@ercros.es
Emp.: 101
Organic Compounds Mfr
S.I.C.: 2869
N.A.I.C.S.: 325199
Santiago Rodriguez *(Gen Mgr)*

Ercros SA - Pharmaceutical Division-Fyse (1)
Paseo del Deleite S N
28300 Aranjuez, Madrid, Spain
Tel.: (34) 918 090 344
Fax: (34) 918 923 560
E-Mail: fyse@ercros.es
Web Site: www.ercros.es
Emp.: 200
Generic Pharmaceutical Products Mfr & Distr
S.I.C.: 2834
N.A.I.C.S.: 325412
Antonio Zabalza *(Mgr)*

Ercros SA - Plastics Division (1)
Avda Diagonal 595
8014 Barcelona, Spain
Tel.: (34) 933 230 554
Fax: (34) 933 237 921
E-Mail: plasticos@ercros.es
Web Site: www.ercros.es
Plastics Mfr
S.I.C.: 3089
N.A.I.C.S.: 326199
Jose Miguel Falcon *(Gen Mgr)*

Ercros SA - Water Treatment Division (1)
Avda Diagonal 595
08014 Barcelona, Spain
Tel.: (34) 934532179
Fax: (34) 934 537 350
E-Mail: tratamientoaguas@ercros.es
Web Site: www.ercros.es
Emp.: 30
Swimming Pool Chemicals Mfr
S.I.C.: 2899
N.A.I.C.S.: 325998
Natalia Torrents *(Mgr-Sls)*

Plant:

Ercros SA - Water Treatment Division - Sabinanigo Factory (2)
C Serrablo 102
22600 Sabinanigo, Huesca, Spain
Tel.: (34) 974498000
Fax: (34) 974498006
E-Mail: sabinanigo@ercros.es
Swimming Pool Chemicals Mfr
S.I.C.: 2899
N.A.I.C.S.: 325998
Aosel Beraes *(Mgr)*

ERDENE RESOURCE DEVELOPMENT CORP.

Metropolitan Place 99 Wyse Road
Suite 1480
Dartmouth, NS, B3A 4S5, Canada
Tel.: (902) 423-6419
Fax: (902) 423-6432
Toll Free: (800) 261-1422
E-Mail: info@erdene.com
Web Site: www.erdene.com
Year Founded: 2002
ERD—(TSX)
Rev.: $95,806
Assets: $13,235,336
Liabilities: $635,277
Net Worth: $12,600,058
Earnings: ($7,301,882)
Emp.: 6
Fiscal Year-end: 12/31/12
Business Description:
Metal Mining & Exploration Services
S.I.C.: 1099
N.A.I.C.S.: 212299
Personnel:
Peter C. Akerley *(Pres & CEO)*
Kenneth W. MacDonald *(CFO & VP-Bus Strategy)*
D. Suzan Frazer *(Sec)*
Board of Directors:
Peter C. Akerley
William B. Burton
John P. Byrne
David S. B. Carnell
J. C. Cowan
Kenneth W. MacDonald
Philip L. Webster
Legal Counsel:
McInnes Cooper & Robertson
1601 Lower Water Street
P.O. Box 730
Halifax, NS, B3J 2V1, Canada
Transfer Agent:
Computershare Trust Company of Canada
Purdy's Wharf Tower II 2008-1969 Upper Water Street
Halifax, NS, Canada

ERDENET MINING CORPORATION

Amariin Square 1
Erdenet, 213900, Mongolia
Tel.: (976) 135273501
Fax: (976) 70353002
Web Site: www.erdenetmc.mn
Emp.: 5,900
Business Description:
Mining Services
S.I.C.: 1099
N.A.I.C.S.: 212299
Personnel:
H. Narankhuu *(Gen Dir)*

EREDENE CAPITAL PLC

Fifth Floor 16 Eastcheap
London, EC3M 1BD, United Kingdom
Tel.: (44) 2074488000
Fax: (44) 2071499832
E-Mail: info@eredene.com
Web Site: www.eredene.com
ERE—(LSE)
Rev.: $7,471,621
Assets: $126,463,226
Liabilities: $23,670,399
Net Worth: $102,792,828
Earnings: ($14,343,112)
Emp.: 60
Fiscal Year-end: 03/31/13
Business Description:
Investment Management
S.I.C.: 6282
N.A.I.C.S.: 523920
Personnel:
Alastair J. N. King *(Founder & CEO)*
Richard Kendall *(Legal Counsel)*
Gary D. Varley *(Sec & Dir-Fin)*
Board of Directors:
D. D. Struan Robertson
Robert J. Arnold
Christopher J. Benson
Charles W. Cayzer
Paul A. Gismondi
Alastair J. N. King
Gary D. Varley
Legal Counsel:
SJ Berwin LLP
10 Queen Street Place
EC4R 1BE London, United Kingdom
Faegre & Benson LLP
7 Pilgrim Street
London, United Kingdom
Non-U.S. Subsidiary:

MJ Logistic Services Ltd. (1)
A-227 Okhla Indus Area Phase 1
New Delhi, 110020, India
Tel.: (91) 1140718800
Fax: (91) 1140718899
E-Mail: contact@mjlsl.com
Web Site: www.mjlsl.com
Logistics & Warehousing Services
S.I.C.: 4225
N.A.I.C.S.: 493110
Anil Arora *(Founder & Mng Dir)*
Sarvjit Singh *(Pres)*

EREGLI DEMIR VE CELIK FABRIKALARI T.A.S.

Hosdere Caddesi Piyade Sokak No 27
06650 Ankara, Turkey
Tel.: (90) 312 409 1400
Fax: (90) 312 442 2923
E-Mail: erdinfo@erdemir.com.tr
Web Site: www.erdemir.com.tr
Year Founded: 1960
EREGL—(IST OTC)
Rev.: $5,408,518,292
Assets: $7,426,611,038
Liabilities: $3,235,656,641
Net Worth: $4,190,954,397
Earnings: $256,992,574
Emp.: 12,969
Fiscal Year-end: 12/31/12
Business Description:
Steel Producer
S.I.C.: 3462
N.A.I.C.S.: 332111
Personnel:
Fatih Osman Tar *(Chm, Acting CEO & Mng Dir)*
Nihat Karadag *(Deputy Chm & Mng Dir)*
Dinc Kizildemir *(Mng Dir)*
Sami Nezih Tunalitosunoglu *(CFO & Exec VP)*
Mucteba Bekcan *(Exec VP-Technical Svcs & Investments)*
Kaan Boke *(Exec VP-HR & Admin Affairs)*
Esat Gunday *(Exec VP-Ops)*
Board of Directors:
Fatih Osman Tar
Atilla Tamer Alptekin
Ertugrul Aydin
Fatma Canli
Nazmi Demir
Nihat Karadag
Dinc Kizildemir
Oguz N. Ozgen
Ali Aydn Pandir
Mehmet Saritas
Subsidiaries:

Celbor Celik Cekme Boru Sanayi Ve Ticaret A.S. (1)
Kayseri yolu 7 km PK 21
71300 Kirikkale, Turkey
Tel.: (90) 3182254696
Fax: (90) 3182242871
E-Mail: bkayaoglu.celbor@erdenir.com.tr
Web Site: www.celbor.com.tr
Emp.: 100
Iron & Steel Pipe & Tube Mfr from Purchased Steel
S.I.C.: 3317
N.A.I.C.S.: 331210
Feranuz Guleryuz *(Gen Mgr)*

Erdemir Lojistik A.S. (1)
19 Mayis Mah Ataturk Cad Sitki Bey Plaza No 82 K 8
Kozyatagi-Kadikoy, Istanbul, Turkey
Tel.: (90) 2164688090
Fax: (90) 2164688091
E-Mail: info@erdemirlojistik.com.tr
Web Site: www.erdemirlojistik.com.tr
Emp.: 20
Activities for Transportation
S.I.C.: 4789
N.A.I.C.S.: 488999
Dinc Kizildemir *(Chm)*

Erdemir Madencilik Sanayi Ve Ticaret A.S. (1)
Curek Yolu 5 Km
58330 Divrigi, Sivas, Turkey
Tel.: (90) 3464191126
Fax: (90) 3464191150
E-Mail: ermaden@erdemirmaden.com.tr
Web Site: www.erdemirmaden.com.tr
Emp.: 300
Iron & Steel Mills
S.I.C.: 3399
N.A.I.C.S.: 331110
Sedat Oktan *(Gen Mgr)*

Erdemir Muhendislik Yonetim Ve Danismanlik Hizmetleri A.S. (1)
Merdivenkoy Yolu Cad No 2
Kucukbakkalkoy, 34750 Istanbul, Atasehir, Turkey
Tel.: (90) 2165788000
Fax: (90) 2164694837
E-Mail: erenco@erenco.com.tr
Web Site: www.erenco.com.tr
Emp.: 200
Engineering Services
S.I.C.: 8711
N.A.I.C.S.: 541330
Ilhami Acar *(Gen Mgr)*

Iskenderun Demir Ve Celik A.S. (1)
Karayilan Beldesi
Genel Mudurlugu, 31319 Iskenderun, Hatay, Turkey
Tel.: (90) 3267583000
Fax: (90) 3267551184
E-Mail: info@isdemir.com.tr
Web Site: www.isdemir.com.tr
Emp.: 6,037
Steel Foundries
S.I.C.: 3325
N.A.I.C.S.: 331513
Ismail Acakakmak *(Pres)*

Non-U.S. Subsidiary:

Erdemir Romania S.R.L. (1)
18 Soseaua Gaesti
Dimbovita Targoviste, 130087 Arges, Romania
Tel.: (40) 245607100
Fax: (40) 245606070
E-Mail: office@erdemir.ro
Web Site: www.erdemir.ro
Emp.: 300
Iron & Steel Mills
S.I.C.: 3312
N.A.I.C.S.: 331110
Gunay Irdogan *(Gen Mgr)*

EREN GROUPE SA

25B Boulevard Royal
2449 Luxembourg, Luxembourg
Tel.: (352) 46 83 28
Fax: (352) 26 47 83 01
Web Site: www.eren-groupe.lu
Business Description:
Holding Company
S.I.C.: 6719
N.A.I.C.S.: 551112
Personnel:
Paris Mouratoglou *(Founder)*
Non-U.S. Subsidiary:

Orege SA (1)
1 rue Pierre Vaudenay
78350 Jouy-en-Josas, France
Tel.: (33) 139466432
Fax: (33) 139467064
E-Mail: info@orege.com
Web Site: www.orege.com
OREGE—(EUR)
Rev.: $1,418,863
Emp.: 30
Fiscal Year-end: 12/31/12
Water Treatment Solutions
S.I.C.: 4941
N.A.I.C.S.: 221310
Pascal Gendrot *(Chm & CEO)*
Patrice Capeau *(CFO)*

Division:

Orege - Scientific Division (2)
645 Rue Mayor de Montricher TechIndus Batiment C
Zone d Activite Aix les Milles, 13854 Aix-en-Provence, France
Tel.: (33) 442262816
Fax: (33) 442262869
Web Site: www.oregonscientific.com
Emp.: 18
Waste Water Treatment Services
S.I.C.: 4952
N.A.I.C.S.: 221320
Pascal Gendrot *(Gen Mgr)*

ERG S.P.A.

WTC Building Via De Marini 1
16149 Genoa, Italy
Mailing Address:
Torre WTC
via De Marini 1, 16149 Genoa, Italy
Tel.: (39) 01024011
Fax: (39) 0102401585
E-Mail: info@erg.it
Web Site: www.erg.it
Year Founded: 1938
ERG—(ITA)
Rev.: $11,157,191,577
Assets: $3,343,482,429
Liabilities: $690,046,742
Net Worth: $2,653,435,687
Earnings: $269,099,383
Emp.: 613
Fiscal Year-end: 12/31/12
Business Description:
Renewable Sources of Energy Production, Management & Services
Import Export
S.I.C.: 4939
N.A.I.C.S.: 221118
Personnel:
Edoardo Garrone *(Chm)*
Alessandro Garrone *(Deputy Chm)*
Luca Bettonte *(CEO)*
Massimo Derchi *(CEO-ERG Renew)*
Gian Raffaele Rivanera *(Gen Counsel)*
Board of Directors:
Edoardo Garrone
Massimo Belcredi
Luca Bettonte
Lino Cardarelli
Alessandro Careri
Marco Costaguta
Alessandro Garrone
Antonio Guastoni
Paola Francesco Lanzoni
Graziella Merello
Giovanni Mondini
Umberto Quadrino

ERG S.p.A.—(Continued)

Subsidiary:

ERG Renew S.p.A. (1)
Torre WTC via de Marini 1
16149 Genoa, Italy (100%)
Tel.: (39) 01024011
Fax: (39) 0102401490
E-Mail: info@ergrenew.it
Web Site: www.ergrenew.it
Rev.: $239,051,522
Assets: $1,686,114,272
Liabilities: $946,089,623
Net Worth: $740,024,649
Earnings: $38,236,613
Emp.: 34
Fiscal Year-end: 12/31/12
Waste Disposal & Renewable Energy Services
S.I.C.: 4959
N.A.I.C.S.: 562998
Alessandro Garrone *(Chm)*
Vittorio Garrone *(Vice Chm)*
Massimo Derchi *(CEO)*
Danilo Lodola *(Sec)*

Subsidiaries:

Enercombustibili Srl (2)
Via Casilina Km 57
03018 Frosinone, Frosinone, Italy
Tel.: (39) 0775705553
Fax: (39) 0775538775
Clay & Ceramic & Refractory Minerals Mining
S.I.C.: 3259
N.A.I.C.S.: 327120

Eolo Srl (2)
Via Broile 545
Atina, 03042 Frosinone, Frosinone, Italy (51%)
Tel.: (39) 776610413
Fax: (39) 0776610972
E-Mail: silvio.mancini@mancini.biz
Land Subdivision
S.I.C.: 6552
N.A.I.C.S.: 237210
Silvio Mancini *(Mgr)*

ERG Eolica Italia Srl (2)
Torre WTC via De Marini 1
16149 Genoa, Italy IT
Tel.: (39) 01024011
Fax: (39) 0102401585
E-Mail:
Emp.: 4,000
Electric Power Generating Wind Turbines Operator
S.I.C.: 4911
N.A.I.C.S.: 221115
Alessandro Garrone *(Gen Mgr)*

Omnia Srl (2)
Via Gramsci 14
Giarre, 95014 Catania, Italy
Tel.: (39) 0957796006
E-Mail: info@omnia.it
Web Site: www.omnia.it/
Curtain & Drapery Mills
S.I.C.: 2391
N.A.I.C.S.: 314120

Sodai Italia SpA (2)
Corso Di Porta Nuova 13-15
20121 Milan, Italy (51%)
Tel.: (39) 026268861
Fax: (39) 0263618218
E-Mail: sodai@enertad.it
Web Site: www.ergrenew.it/site/1883.php
Emp.: 10
Other Heavy & Civil Engineering Construction
S.I.C.: 1629
N.A.I.C.S.: 237990

U.S. Subsidiaries:

TCT Stainless Steel Inc (2)
6300 19 Mile Rd
Sterling Heights, MI 48314
Tel.: (586) 254-5333
Fax: (586) 731-0729
Web Site: www.tctstainless.com
Metal Service Centers & Offices
S.I.C.: 5051
N.A.I.C.S.: 423510
Andrea Mazzarini *(Gen Mgr)*

TCT Stainless Steel of Nashville Inc (2)
711 Maddox Simpson Pkwy
Lebanon, TN 37090
Tel.: (615) 443-4657
Fax: (615) 449-6079
Web Site: www.tctstainless.com
Emp.: 15
Metal Service Centers & Offices
S.I.C.: 5051
N.A.I.C.S.: 423510
Sherry Shaub *(Gen Mgr)*

Non-U.S. Subsidiaries:

Fim Inox Sas (2)
15 Avenue des Morillons - ZI les Doucettes
Garges-Les-Gonesse, 95140 Paris, France
Tel.: (33) 134452323
Fax: (33) 139861936
E-Mail: fiminox@fiminox.fr
Web Site: www.fiminox.fr
Emp.: 70
Metal Service Centers & Offices
S.I.C.: 5051
N.A.I.C.S.: 423510
David Sims *(Pres)*

Sorepla Srl (2)
BP 89 - Chemin de Grety - Rebeuville
Neufchateau, 88300 Nancy, France
Tel.: (33) 329061180
Fax: (33) 329061193
E-Mail: contact@sorepla.com
Web Site: www.sorepla.com
Emp.: 86
All Other Plastics Product Mfr
S.I.C.: 3089
N.A.I.C.S.: 326199
Christian Cretet *(Mng Dir)*

TAD Inox Service BV (2)
Sourethweg 5
6422PC Heerlen, Netherlands
Tel.: (31) 455436161
Fax: (31) 455422636
E-Mail: sales@tadinox.nl
Web Site: www.tadinox.nl
Emp.: 100
Metal Service Centers & Offices
S.I.C.: 5051
N.A.I.C.S.: 423510
Maureceo Rota *(Mng Dir)*

Non-U.S. Subsidiary:

TAD Inox Service GmbH (3)
Ewald-Renz-Str 1
76669 Bad Schonborn, Germany
Tel.: (49) 725380200
Fax: (49) 7253802022
E-Mail: info@tadinox.de
Web Site: www.tadinox.de
Emp.: 30
Metal Service Centers & Offices
S.I.C.: 5051
N.A.I.C.S.: 423510
Murrasso Trovanne *(Mng Dir)*

ERGIS-EUROFILMS S.A.

ul Tamka 16
00-349 Warsaw, Poland
Tel.: (48) 228280410
Fax: (48) 228280414
E-Mail: mail@ergis-eurofilms.eu
Web Site: www.ergis.plastech.biz
EEF—(WAR)
Sales Range: $150-199.9 Million
Emp.: 798

Business Description:
Polyethylene Stretch Films & Laminated Fabrics Mfr
S.I.C.: 3081
N.A.I.C.S.: 326113

Personnel:
Marek Gorski *(Chm-Supervisory Bd)*
Tadeusz Nowicki *(Chm-Mgmt Bd)*
Jacek Korpala *(Vice Chm-Supervisory Bd)*
Stanislaw Mazgaj *(Vice Chm-Supervisory Bd)*
Jan Polaczek *(Vice Chm-Mgmt Bd)*

Supervisory Board of Directors:
Marek Gorski
Zenon Dabrowski
Maciej Olaf Grelowski
Pawel Kaczorowski
Jacek Korpala
Beata Kurbiel
Stanislaw Mazgaj

ERGO-FIT GMBH & CO. KG

Blocksbergstrasse 165
66955 Pirmasens, Germany
Tel.: (49) 633124610
Fax: (49) 6331246155
E-Mail: info@ergo-fit.de
Web Site: www.ergo-fit.de
Year Founded: 1947
Rev.: $16,552,800
Emp.: 100

Business Description:
Fitness Products Supplier
S.I.C.: 7991
N.A.I.C.S.: 713940

Personnel:
Michael Resch *(Mng Dir)*

ERGON ENERGY CORPORATION LIMITED

PO Box 1090
Townsville, QLD, 4810, Australia
Tel.: (61) 749216001
E-Mail: customerservice@ergon.com.au
Web Site: www.ergon.com.au
Rev.: $3,138,805,200
Assets: $11,942,466,000
Liabilities: $8,071,064,500
Net Worth: $3,871,401,500
Earnings: $452,271,400
Emp.: 4,435
Fiscal Year-end: 06/30/13

Business Description:
Electric Power Distr
S.I.C.: 4939
N.A.I.C.S.: 221122

Personnel:
Ian McLeod *(CEO)*
John Hooper *(CFO)*
Peter Effeney *(CEO-SPARQ Solutions)*
Graeme Finlayson *(Gen Counsel & Sec)*

Board of Directors:
Malcolm Hall-Brown
Annabel Dolphin
John Gardner
Gary Humphrys
John Love
Rowena McNally

ERGORESEARCH LTD.

2101 Le Carrefour Suite 200
Laval, QC, H7S 2J7, Canada
Tel.: (450) 973-6700
Fax: (450) 973-1299
E-Mail: info@ergoresearch.com
Web Site: www.ergoresearch.com
ERG—(TSXV)
Rev.: $13,388,801
Assets: $30,583,131
Liabilities: $8,024,592
Net Worth: $22,558,538
Earnings: $11,855,570
Fiscal Year-end: 06/30/13

Business Description:
Orthopedic Products Mfr
S.I.C.: 3851
N.A.I.C.S.: 339115

Personnel:
Sylvain Boucher *(Pres & CEO)*

Board of Directors:
Danielle Boucher
Sylvain Boucher
Catherine Chamouton
Gilles Laporte
Michel Pierron
Francois Tollier

Transfer Agent:
Equity Transfer & Trust Company
200 University Avenue Ste 400
Toronto, ON, M5H 4H1, Canada
Tel.: (416) 361-0152
Fax: (416) 361-0470

Subsidiary:

Victhom Bionique Humaine Inc. (1)
5365 Jean-Talon East Suite 204
Montreal, QC, H1S 3G2, Canada AB
Tel.: (438) 380-5244
Fax: (438) 381-1530
E-Mail: karine.tendland@victhom.com
Web Site: www.victhom.com
Sales Range: Less than $1 Million
Emp.: 74
Human Bionic Devices Developer & Mfr
S.I.C.: 8731
N.A.I.C.S.: 541711
Normand Rivard *(Pres & CEO)*

ERGYCAPITAL S.P.A.

Via Salaria 226
00198 Rome, Italy
Tel.: (39) 06 96036900
Fax: (39) 06 62298484
E-Mail: info@ergycapital.com
Web Site: www.ergycapital.com
Year Founded: 2007
ECA—(ITA)

Business Description:
Investment Management Services
S.I.C.: 6211
N.A.I.C.S.: 523999

Personnel:
Vincenzo Cannatelli *(Chm & CEO)*
Francesco Cursano *(CFO)*

Board of Directors:
Vincenzo Cannatelli
Nicolo Dubini
Gian Carlo Losi
Diva Moriani
Fabio Tomassini

ERI HOLDINGS CO., LTD.

6F Akasaka DS Bldg 8-5-26 Akasaka
Minato-ku, Tokyo, 107-0052, Japan
Tel.: (81) 3 3796 0223
Web Site: www.h-eri.co.jp
Year Founded: 2013
6083—(TKS)
Sales Range: $125-149.9 Million
Emp.: 873

Business Description:
Holding Company; Building Inspection Services
S.I.C.: 6719
N.A.I.C.S.: 551112

Personnel:
Yoshiki Nakazawa *(Pres)*

Subsidiary:

Japan ERI Co., Ltd. (1)
6F Akasaka DS Bldg 8-5-26 Akasaka
Minato-ku, Tokyo, 107-0052, Japan JP
Tel.: (81) 3 3796 0223
Fax: (81) 3 57751841
E-Mail: info@j-eri.co.jp
Web Site: www.j-eri.co.jp
Building Inspection Services
S.I.C.: 7389
N.A.I.C.S.: 541350
Yoshiki Nakazawa *(Pres)*
Akiyo Masuda *(Sr Mng Dir & Exec Officer)*
Toshihiko Umano *(Sr Mng Dir & Exec Officer)*
Junsuke Doyama *(Sr Exec Officer)*
Yoshio Fukada *(Sr Exec Officer)*
Takao Izumo *(Sr Exec Officer)*
Kazuo Konokawa *(Sr Exec Officer)*
Hiroaki Yokose *(Sr Exec Officer)*
Takao Fujimuta *(Exec Officer)*
Hiroshi Fujioka *(Exec Officer)*
Kazunobu Minamide *(Exec Officer)*
Shigeki Miyatake *(Exec Officer)*
Shuichi Yoshida *(Exec Officer)*

ERICH NETZSCH GMBH & CO. HOLDING KG

Gebruder Netzsch Strasse 19
95100 Selb, Bayern, Germany

Tel.: (49) 9287750
Fax: (49) 928775208
E-Mail: info@netzsch.com
Web Site: www.netzsch.com
Year Founded: 1873
Sales Range: $200-249.9 Million
Emp.: 2,000

Business Description:
Mfr. of Industrial Machinery, Pumps, Filtration System Equipment, Grinding & Dispersing Equipment & Thermal Analysis Equipment
S.I.C.: 3561
N.A.I.C.S.: 333911

Personnel:
Dietmar Bolkart *(Chm)*
Katja Hoppe *(Sec)*

Subsidiaries:

NETZSCH-Feinmahltechnik GmbH (1)
Sedanstrasse 70
PO Box 1460
95100 Selb, Germany (100%)
Tel.: (49) 92877970
Fax: (49) 9287797149
E-Mail: info@nft.netzsch.com
Web Site: www.netzschgrinding.com
Emp.: 100
Mfr. of Industrial Machinery, Pumps, Filtration System Equipment, Grinding & Dispersing Equipment & Thermal Analysis Equipment
S.I.C.: 3561
N.A.I.C.S.: 333911
Makrakis Demitrios *(Mng Dir)*
Dimitrios Makrakis *(Mng Dir)*

NETZSCH Geratebau GmbH (1)
Wittelsbacher Str 42
95100 Selb, Bavaria, Germany (100%)
Tel.: (49) 92878810
Fax: (49) 92878811505
E-Mail: at@net.com
Web Site: www.ngb.netzsch.com
Emp.: 200
Industrial Machinery, Pumps, Filtration System Equipment, Grinding & Dispersing Equipment & Thermal Analysis Equipment Mfr
S.I.C.: 3561
N.A.I.C.S.: 333911
Thomas Denner *(Mng Dir)*

NETZSCH-Oilfield Products GmbH (1)
Gebrueder Netzsch Str 19
95100 Selb, Germany (100%)
Tel.: (49) 928775424
Fax: (49) 928775427
E-Mail: nop@netzsch.com
Web Site: www.oil.netzsch.com
Emp.: 20
Mfr. of Industrial Machinery, Pumps, Filtration System Equipment, Grinding & Dispersing Equipment & Thermal Analysis Equipment
S.I.C.: 3561
N.A.I.C.S.: 333911
Holger Hartwig *(Mng Dir)*

NETZSCH Werbe- und Service-GmbH (1)
Gebruder-Netzsch-Strasse 19
PO Box 1460
95100 Selb, Germany (100%)
Tel.: (49) 928775163
Fax: (49) 928775166
E-Mail: info@nws.netzsch.com
Web Site: www.netzsch.com
Sales Range: $200-249.9 Million
Emp.: 700
Mfr. of Industrial Machinery, Pumps, Filtration System Equipment, Grinding & Dispersing Equipment & Thermal Analysis Equipment
S.I.C.: 3561
N.A.I.C.S.: 333911
Otto Max Schaefer *(Chm)*
Hammf-Peter Oho *(CFO)*

U.S. Subsidiaries:

NETZSCH Instruments, Inc. (1)
129 Middlesex Tpke
Burlington, MA 01803
Tel.: (781) 272-5353
Fax: (781) 272-5225
E-Mail: nib-sales@netzsch.com
Web Site: www.nib.netzsch.us
Emp.: 30
Mfr of Monitoring Instrumentation
S.I.C.: 3823
N.A.I.C.S.: 334513
Dave Shepard *(Reg Mgr-Sls)*

NETZSCH Pumps North America, LLC (1)
119 Pickering Way
Exton, PA 19431-1393 PA
Tel.: (610) 363-8010
Fax: (610) 363-0971
E-Mail: netzsch@netzschusa.com
Web Site: www.netzschusa.com
Sales Range: $25-49.9 Million
Emp.: 60
Mfr of Special Industrial Machinery, Pumps, Grinding & Filtration System Equipments Import Export
S.I.C.: 3561
N.A.I.C.S.: 333911
Julio C. Ferreira *(VP-Sls)*

Non-U.S. Subsidiaries:

NETZSCH Argentina S. A. (1)
Ruta Panamericana Km 33 5 Ramal Escobar
Grand Bourg Partido De Islas, 1615
Buenos Aires, Argentina (100%)
Tel.: (54) 3327444935
Fax: (54) 3327444934
E-Mail: info@nar.netzsch.com.ar
Web Site: www.netzsch.com
Sales Range: $200-249.9 Million
Emp.: 23
Mfr. of Industrial Machinery, Pumps, Filtration System Equipment, Grinding & Dispersing Equipment & Thermal Analysis Equipment
S.I.C.: 3561
N.A.I.C.S.: 333911
Sretz Kraupner *(Mgr)*

NETZSCH Asia Pacific PTE Ltd. (1)
7 Toh Guan Road East unit 07-01/02
Alpha Industrial Building, 608599
Singapore, Singapore
Tel.: (65) 68634453
Fax: (65) 68634483
E-Mail: info@nap.netzsch.com
Web Site: www.netzsch.com.sg
Emp.: 19
Mfr. of Industrial Machinery, Pumps, Filtration System Equipment, Grinding & Dispersing Equipment & Thermal Analysis Equipment
S.I.C.: 3561
N.A.I.C.S.: 333911
Edwin Chng *(Gen Mgr)*

NETZSCH do Brasil Ltda. (1)
Rua Hermann Weege 2383
PO Box 51
BR 89107-000 Pomerode, SC, Brazil (100%)
Tel.: (55) 47 3387 8222
Fax: (55) 47 3387 8400
E-Mail: info@ndb-netzsch.com.br
Web Site: www.netzsch.com.br
Sales Range: $1-9.9 Million
Emp.: 100
Mfr of Industrial Machinery, Pumps, Filtration System Equipment, Grinding & Dispersing Equipment & Thermal Analysis Equipment
S.I.C.: 3561
N.A.I.C.S.: 333911

NETZSCH Espana S.A. (1)
Poligono Industrial Norte
C Provenza 194, Terrassa, 8226, Spain (99%)
Tel.: (34) 937355065
Fax: (34) 937354551
E-Mail: info@neb.netzsch.com
Web Site: www.netzsch.com
Emp.: 10
Mfr. of Industrial Machinery, Pumps, Filtration System Equipment, Grinding & Dispersing Equipment & Thermal Analysis Equipment
S.I.C.: 3561
N.A.I.C.S.: 333911
Santiago Requena *(Mng Dir)*

NETZSCH Freres S.a.r.l. (1)
32 34 Av Des Chardons
77348 Paris, France (100%)
Tel.: (33) 164435400
Fax: (33) 160295726
E-Mail: info@netzsch.fr
Emp.: 15
Mfr. of Industrial Machinery, Pumps, Filtration System Equipment, Grinding & Dispersing Equipment & Thermal Analysis Equipment
S.I.C.: 3561
N.A.I.C.S.: 333911
Catherine Stoganoysk *(Mng Dir)*

NETZSCH Instruments Sp.zo.o. (1)
Halicka 9
31065 Krakow, Poland
Tel.: (48) 124240920
Fax: (48) 124240939
E-Mail: warszawa@netzsch.pl
Web Site: www.netzsch.com.pl
Emp.: 10
Mfr of Industrial Machinery, Pumps, Filtration System Equipment, Grinding & Dispersing Equipment & Thermal Analysis Equipment
Import Export
S.I.C.: 3561
N.A.I.C.S.: 333911
Grzegorz Seniuta *(Mng Dir)*

NETZSCH Korea Co. Ltd (1)
5 F Jaeneung Bldg No 1294 3 Beaksuk Dong
ROK Ilsan Gu Koyang, Seoul, 410816, Korea (South) (100%)
Tel.: (82) 319073193
Fax: (82) 9312388
E-Mail: info@nks.netzsch.com
Web Site: www.netzsch.com
Emp.: 25
Mfr. of Industrial Machinery, Pumps, Filtration System Equipment, Grinding & Dispersing Equipment & Thermal Analysis Equipment
S.I.C.: 3561
N.A.I.C.S.: 333911
Steven Min *(Mng Dir)*

NETZSCH Lanzhou Pumps Co. Ltd. (1)
506 Liu Jia Tan Lanzhou High Development Zone
730000 Lanzhou, Gansu, China
Tel.: (86) 9318555000
Fax: (86) 9318556650
E-Mail: info@nlp.netzsch.com
Web Site: www.netzsch.com.cn
Mfr. of Industrial Machinery, Pumps, Filtration System Equipment, Grinding & Dispersing Equipment & Thermal Analysis Equipment
S.I.C.: 3561
N.A.I.C.S.: 333911
Guangda Li *(Gen Mgr-Ops Process)*

NETZSCH Malaysia Sdn.Bhd (1)
No 49 2 Jalan PJU 1 37
Dataran Prima, Petaling Jaya, Kuala Lumpur, 47301, Malaysia (100%)
Tel.: (60) 378800882
Fax: (60) 378800855
E-Mail: info@nmk.netzsch.com
Web Site: www.netzsch-pumps.com
Emp.: 4
Mfr. of Industrial Machinery, Pumps, Filtration System Equipment, Grinding & Dispersing Equipment & Thermal Analysis Equipment
S.I.C.: 3561
N.A.I.C.S.: 333911
Edwin Chng *(Gen Mgr)*

NETZSCH Mastermix Ltd. (1)
23 Lombard Street
Lichfield, Staffordshire, WS13 6DP, United Kingdom
Tel.: (44) 1543418938
Fax: (44) 1543418926
E-Mail: info@nmx.netzsch.com
Web Site: www.netzsch-grinding.com
Emp.: 15
Mfr. of Industrial Machinery, Pumps, Filtration System Equipment, Grinding & Dispersing Equipment & Thermal Analysis Equipment
S.I.C.: 3561
N.A.I.C.S.: 333911
David Tomlinson *(Mng Dir)*

NETZSCH Milantecnica S.R.L. (1)
Via Fleming 17
37135 Verona, Italy (100%)
Tel.: (39) 0458200755
Fax: (39) 0458200807
E-Mail: info@nmv.netzsch.com
Web Site: www.netzsch.com
Emp.: 12
Industrial Machinery, Pumps, Filtration System Equipment, Grinding & Dispersing Equipment & Thermal Analysis Equipment Mfr
S.I.C.: 3561
N.A.I.C.S.: 333911

NETZSCH (Shanghai) Machinery and Instruments Co. Ltd. (1)
8 Yuan Da Rd An Ting
201805 Shanghai, China (100%)
Tel.: (86) 2169576008
Fax: (86) 2169576005
E-Mail: info.nsc@netzsch.com
Web Site: www.netzschgrinding.com.cn
Sls.: $1,480,577
Emp.: 80
Mfr. of Industrial Machinery, Pumps, Filtration System Equipment, Grinding & Dispersing Equipment & Thermal Analysis Equipment
S.I.C.: 3561
N.A.I.C.S.: 333911
Martin Rahm *(Mng Dir)*

NETZSCH Thailand Ltd. (1)
1559 Town in Town Soi Srivara (Ladprow 94)
Ladprow Road Wangthonglang, 10310
Bangkok, Thailand
Tel.: (66) 23073858
Fax: (66) 25307384
E-Mail: info@ntb.netzsch.com
Web Site: www.netzsch.com
Mfr. of Industrial Machinery, Pumps, Filtration System Equipment, Grinding & Dispersing Equipment & Thermal Analysis Equipment
S.I.C.: 3561
N.A.I.C.S.: 333911
Somchai Udomvidhayathorn *(Mng Dir)*

ERICH UTSCH AG

Marienhutte 49
57080 Siegen, Germany
Tel.: (49) 27131910
Fax: (49) 2713191103
E-Mail: info@utsch.com
Web Site: www.utsch.com
Year Founded: 1961
Rev.: $62,769,671
Emp.: 196

Business Description:
License Plate Mfr
S.I.C.: 3443
N.A.I.C.S.: 332313

Personnel:
Helmut Jungbluth *(CEO)*
Wolfgang Bilger *(COO)*
Stephan Wustefeld *(Chief Strategy Officer)*

ERICH WESJOHANN GMBH & CO. KG

Norddollen 51
49429 Visbek, Germany
Tel.: (49) 44459700
Emp.: 4,800

Business Description:
Poultry Breeding Services
S.I.C.: 0254
N.A.I.C.S.: 112340

Non-U.S. Subsidiary:

Aviagen Limited (1)
11 Lothend Rd
Newbridge, Midlothian, EH28 8SZ, United Kingdom
Tel.: (44) 313331056, ext. 1313331056
Fax: (44) 1313333296
E-Mail: infoworldwide@aviagen.com
Web Site: www.aviagen.com

Erich Wesjohann GmbH & Co. KG—(Continued)

Emp.: 150
Poultry Producer
S.I.C.: 0259
N.A.I.C.S.: 112390
Ben Thompson *(Pres)*
Ian Hamilton *(Mng Dir)*

U.S. Subsidiary:

Aviagen Incorporated **(2)**
Cummings Research Park 5015 Bradford Dr NW
Huntsville, AL 35805-1943
Tel.: (256) 890-3800
Fax: (256) 890-3919
E-Mail: info@aviagen.com
Web Site: www.aviagen.com
Emp.: 80
Poultry Breeders
S.I.C.: 0259
N.A.I.C.S.: 112390
Randall Ennis *(CEO)*

Subsidiaries:

CWT Farms International, Inc. **(3)**
1180 Airport Industrial Park
Gainesville, GA 30501
Mailing Address:
PO Box 1396
Gainesville, GA 30503
Tel.: (770) 532-3181
Fax: (770) 531-0555
Toll Free: (800) 253-1242
E-Mail: cwt@aviagen.com
Web Site: www.cwt.aviagen.com
Emp.: 30
Egg Production Services
S.I.C.: 0259
N.A.I.C.S.: 112390
Vicky Ferbeyre *(VP-Hatching Eggs)*

Aviagen Inc. **(3)**
31186 Midland Trl
Lewisburg, WV 24901 CA
Tel.: (304) 793-2680
Telex: 510-746-9267
Fax: (304) 793-2684
E-Mail: turkeysinc@aviagen.com
Web Site: www.aviagen.com
Emp.: 486
Turkey Breeding & Genetic Research
S.I.C.: 0253
N.A.I.C.S.: 112330

ERICKSEN NISSAN

10982 101 Street
Edmonton, AB, T5H 2S8, Canada
Tel.: (780) 429-4611
Toll Free: (888) 375-5985
E-Mail: info@ericksennissan.com
Web Site: www.ericksennissan.com
Rev.: $25,747,905
Emp.: 35
Business Description:
New & Used Car Dealers
S.I.C.: 5511
N.A.I.C.S.: 441110
Personnel:
Heather G. Hartmann *(Controller)*

ERICOM TELEKOMUNIKASYON VE ENERJI TEKNOLOJILERI A.S.

Buyukdere Cd No 15/A Hur Han B Blok Kat 3
Maslak, Istanbul, 34381, Turkey
Tel.: (90) 212 330 05 40
Fax: (90) 212 330 05 43
E-Mail: info@ericom.com.tr
Web Site: www.ericom.com.tr
Sales Range: $1-9.9 Million
Emp.: 70
Fiscal Year-end: 12/31/12
Business Description:
Energy & Communications Products Mfr
S.I.C.: 3691
N.A.I.C.S.: 335911
Personnel:
Ilker Aydin *(Chm & Gen Mgr)*
Mustafa Unal *(Vice Chm)*
Board of Directors:
Ilker Aydin
Soner Bahcuvan
Jamie Fleetwood
Mustafa Unal

ERICPOL SP. Z O.O.

Targowa 9A
90-042 Lodz, Poland
Tel.: (48) 42 6642500
Fax: (48) 42 6642555
E-Mail: office@ericpol.com
Web Site: www.ericpol.com
Year Founded: 1991
Sales Range: $50-74.9 Million
Emp.: 1,001
Business Description:
Telecommunication Consultancy Services
S.I.C.: 8748
N.A.I.C.S.: 541618
Personnel:
Jan Smela *(Founder, Owner & Pres)*
Pawel Szczerkowski *(CEO)*
Stefan Znarowski *(Deputy CEO)*
Marcin Knap *(CFO)*
Anna Smela-Kjellin *(Exec VP)*

ERIK THUN AB

Ostra Hamnen 7
Lidkoping, Sweden
Tel.: (46) 510 848 00
Fax: (46) 510 848 55
E-Mail: info@thun.se
Web Site: www.thun.se
Business Description:
Marine Cargo Handling, Aircraft Leasing, Real Estate Management Services; Processed Meat Mfr
S.I.C.: 4491
N.A.I.C.S.: 488320
Personnel:
Anders Kallsson *(CEO)*

ERIMA GMBH

Carl Zeiss Strasse 10
72793 Pfullingen, Germany
Tel.: (49) 71213420
Fax: (49) 7121342340
E-Mail: info@erima.de
Web Site: www.erima.de
Sales Range: $25-49.9 Million
Emp.: 200
Business Description:
Sports Apparel
S.I.C.: 3949
N.A.I.C.S.: 339920
Personnel:
Wolfram Mannherz *(Mng Dir)*

ERIN DODGE CHRYSLER LTD.

2365 Motorway Boulevard
Mississauga, ON, L5L 2M4, Canada
Tel.: (905) 828-2004
Fax: (905) 828-6172
Toll Free: (888) 606-2308
E-Mail: admin@erindodge.com
Web Site: www.erindodge.com
Year Founded: 1983
Rev.: $37,065,598
Emp.: 75
Business Description:
New & Used Car Dealer
S.I.C.: 5511
N.A.I.C.S.: 441110
Personnel:
Paul Kaye *(Pres)*
Debra Jones *(Treas & Sec)*

ERIN PARK AUTOMOTIVE PARTNERSHIP

2360 Motorway Boulevard
Mississauga, ON, L5L 1X3, Canada
Tel.: (905) 828-7727
Fax: (905) 828-9282
Toll Free: (888) 211-7173
Web Site: www.erinparklexus.com
Rev.: $70,084,137
Emp.: 138
Business Description:
New & Used Car Dealers
S.I.C.: 5511
N.A.I.C.S.: 441110
Personnel:
Emily Lee *(Bus Mgr)*

ERIN VENTURES INC.

645 Fort Street Suite 203
Victoria, BC, V8W 1G2, Canada
Tel.: (250) 384-1999
Fax: (250) 384-6761
Toll Free: (888) 289-3746
E-Mail: info@erinventures.com
Web Site: www.erinventures.com
Year Founded: 1993
EV—(TSXV)
Assets: $6,413,019
Liabilities: $371,693
Net Worth: $6,041,327
Earnings: ($1,379,970)
Fiscal Year-end: 06/30/13
Business Description:
Mineral Exploration Services
S.I.C.: 1081
N.A.I.C.S.: 213114
Personnel:
Tim Daniels *(Pres, CEO, Treas & Sec)*
Blake Fallis *(CFO & Gen Mgr)*
Board of Directors:
Paolo Bonini
Tim Daniels
Dragoljub Jujic
Vladan Milosevic
Legal Counsel:
Chamberlain Hutchison
Edmonton, AB, Canada
Transfer Agent:
Computershare Trust Company of Canada
9th Floor 100 University Avenue
Toronto, ON, Canada

ERINMOTORWAY INVESTMENTS LIMITED

(d/b/a Mississauga Honda)
2380 Motorway Blvd
Mississauga, ON, L5L 1X3, Canada
Tel.: (905) 828-2336
Fax: (905) 828-0136
Toll Free: (866) 928-1587
Web Site: www.mississaugahonda.com
Rev.: $54,340,594
Emp.: 105
Business Description:
New & Used Car Dealers
S.I.C.: 5511
N.A.I.C.S.: 441110
Personnel:
Bryndon Davies *(Pres)*

ERITH GROUP

Erith House Queen St
Erith, Kent, DA8 1RP, United Kingdom
Tel.: (44) 8709508800
Fax: (44) 8709508808
Web Site: www.enith.net
Sales Range: $75-99.9 Million
Emp.: 200
Business Description:
Demolition & Civil Engineering Services
S.I.C.: 1629
N.A.I.C.S.: 237990
Personnel:
Steve Darsey *(Chm)*

ERM POWER LIMITED

Level 52 111 Eagle St
Brisbane, QLD, 4000, Australia
Mailing Address:
GPO Box 7152
Brisbane, QLD, 4001, Australia
Tel.: (61) 7 3020 5100
Fax: (61) 7 3220 6110
E-Mail: astbaker@ermpower.com.au
Web Site: www.ermpower.com.au
Year Founded: 1980
EPW—(ASX)
Rev.: $1,635,648,897
Assets: $1,008,481,854
Liabilities: $725,194,264
Net Worth: $283,287,590
Earnings: $40,088,545
Emp.: 336
Fiscal Year-end: 06/30/13
Business Description:
Electric Power & Natural Gas Distribution & Generation Services
S.I.C.: 9631
N.A.I.C.S.: 926130
Personnel:
Trevor St Baker *(Founder)*
Philip St Baker *(CEO & Mng Dir)*
Graeme Walker *(CFO & Co-Sec)*
William Anderson *(CEO-Electricity Sls)*
Derek McKay *(CEO-Generation)*
Peter Jans *(Gen Counsel & Co-Sec)*
Board of Directors:
Anthony Bellas
Martin Greenberg
Brett Heading
Antonino Mario Iannello
Philip St Baker
Trevor St Baker

ERMENEGILDO ZEGNA HOLDITALIA S.P.A.

(d/b/a Gruppo Ermenegildo Zegna)
Via Savona 56/A
20144 Milan, Italy
Tel.: (39) 2422091
Fax: (39) 0242209101
Web Site: www.zegna.com
Emp.: 5,000
Business Description:
High-End Menswear & Sportswear Mfr
S.I.C.: 5699
N.A.I.C.S.: 315220
Personnel:
Paulo Zegna *(Pres)*

ERMENEGILDO ZEGNA HOLDITALIA S.P.A.

Via Roma 99-100
Trivero, 13835 Biella, Italy
Tel.: (39) 01575911
Fax: (39) 015756139
Web Site: www.zegna.com
Emp.: 5,000
Business Description:
Men's & Boys' Clothing Mfr & Retailer
S.I.C.: 2329
N.A.I.C.S.: 315220
Personnel:
Paolo Zegna *(Pres)*
Ermenegildo Zegna *(Co-CEO)*
Lynda Tyler-Cagni *(Exec VP)*

ERMEWA GROUP SA

Rue du Mont-Blanc 7
Geneva, 1211, CP 1464, Switzerland
Tel.: (41) 229060400
Fax: (41) 229060496
E-Mail: info@ermewa.com
Web Site: www.ermewa.com

Sales Range: $300-349.9 Million
Emp.: 510
Business Description:
Tank Container Services
S.I.C.: 4731
N.A.I.C.S.: 488510
Personnel:
Josef Kuttel *(CEO)*
Alain A. Stocker *(CFO)*
Olivier Ghesquiere *(COO)*

Non-U.S. Branches:

Ermewa France (1)
Le Stratege 172 rue de la Republique
92817 Puteaux, Cedex, France
Tel.: (33) 1 4907 2531
Fax: (33) 1 4907 2548
Web Site: www.ermewa.com
Sales Range: $25-49.9 Million
Emp.: 16
Tank Container Services
S.I.C.: 4731
N.A.I.C.S.: 488510
Pascal Le Quere *(Mgr-Admin & Legal)*

Eurotainer SA (1)
Le Stratege 172 Rue De La Republique
92817 Puteaux, France
Tel.: (33) 0149072410
Fax: (33) 149072411
E-Mail: head-paris@eurotainer.com
Web Site: www.eurotainer.com
Emp.: 25
Tank Container Services
S.I.C.: 4731
N.A.I.C.S.: 488510
Vincent Martin *(Mng Dir)*

ERMO GROUP
Zone Artisanale
BP 15
53440 Marcille-la-Ville, France
Tel.: (33) 2 43 00 71 22
Fax: (33) 2 43 00 65 20
E-Mail: contact@ermo-group.com
Web Site: www.ermo-group.com
Year Founded: 1979
ERMO—(EUR)
Emp.: 175
Business Description:
Injection Molding Machinery Mfr
S.I.C.: 3559
N.A.I.C.S.: 333249
Personnel:
Jean-Yves Pichereau *(Chm, CEO & Dir-Publ)*
Bertrand Hugain *(CFO)*

ERNEST DOE & SONS LIMITED
Ulting
Maldon, Essex, CM9 6QH, United Kingdom
Tel.: (44) 1245380311
Fax: (44) 1245381194
E-Mail: info@ernestdoe.com
Web Site: www.ernestdoe.com
Rev.: $139,118,781
Emp.: 526
Business Description:
Agricultural Machinery Distr
S.I.C.: 5083
N.A.I.C.S.: 423820
Personnel:
Colin Doe *(Mng Dir)*

ERNI ELECTRONICS GMBH
Seestrasse 9
D-73099 Adelberg, Germany
Tel.: (49) 7166500
Fax: (49) 716650282
E-Mail: info@erni.com
Web Site: www.erni.com
Year Founded: 1956
Sales Range: $200-249.9 Million
Emp.: 650
Business Description:
Telecommunications & Information Technology Interconnect Products Designer, Mfr & Distr
S.I.C.: 3678
N.A.I.C.S.: 334417
Personnel:
Martin Seidenfuss *(CEO)*

U.S. Subsidiary:

ERNI Electronics, Inc. (1)
2201 Westwood Ave
Richmond, VA 23230 VA
Tel.: (804) 228-4100
Fax: (804) 228-4099
E-Mail: info.usa@erni.com
Web Site: www.erni.com
Sales Range: $10-24.9 Million
Emp.: 30
Telecommunications & Information Technology Interconnect Products Designer, Mfr & Distr
S.I.C.: 3678
N.A.I.C.S.: 334417
Michael Singer *(Dir-Mktg)*

ERNST & YOUNG GLOBAL LIMITED
1 More London Place
London, SE1 2AF, United Kingdom
Tel.: (44) 20 7951 2000
Telex: 760 7796
Fax: (44) 20 7951 1345
Web Site: www.ey.com
Year Founded: 1989
Sales Range: $15-24.9 Billion
Emp.: 152,000
Business Description:
Accounting, Audit, Tax & Financial Advisory Services Organization
S.I.C.: 8621
N.A.I.C.S.: 813920
Personnel:
Mark A. Weinberger *(Chm & CEO)*
Beth A. Brooke *(Vice Chm-Pub Policy)*
Norman Lonergan *(Vice Chm-Advisory)*
Pip McCrostie *(Global Vice Chm-Transaction Advisory Svcs)*
Christian Mouillon *(Global Vice Chm-Assurance)*
Victoria Cochrane *(Mng Partner-Quality & Risk Mgmt-Global)*
Mike Cullen *(Global Mng Partner-People)*
Peter Griffith *(Global Mng Partner-Ops & Fin)*
Steve Howe *(Mng Partner-Americas)*
Yoshitaka Kato *(Mng Partner-Japan)*
John Murphy *(Mng Partner-Markets-Global)*
Mark Otty *(Mng Partner-Europe, Middle East, India & Africa)*
Lou Pagnutti *(Mng Partner-Asia Pacific)*
John Ferraro *(COO)*

ERNST & YOUNG GMBH WIRTSCHAFTSPRUFUNGS GESELLSCHAFT
Mittlerer Pfad 5
70499 Stuttgart, Germany
Tel.: (49) 711 9881 0
Fax: (49) 711 9881 550
E-Mail: info@de.ey.com
Web Site: www.ey.com
Business Description:
Accounting, Tax Preparation & Consulting Services
S.I.C.: 8721
N.A.I.C.S.: 541211
Personnel:
Georg Graf Waldersee *(Mng Partner & Chm-Mgmt Bd)*
Ute Benzel *(Member-Mgmt Bd)*
Rudolf Krammer *(Member-Mgmt Bd)*
Alexander Kron *(Member-Mgmt Bd)*
Norbert Pfitzer *(Member-Mgmt Bd)*
Gunther Ruppel *(Member-Mgmt Bd)*
Markus T. Schweizer *(Member-Mgmt Bd)*
Mark Smith *(Member-Mgmt Bd)*
Claus-Peter Wagner *(Member-Mgmt Bd)*
Peter Wollmert *(Member-Mgmt Bd)*

Subsidiary:

Ernst & Young J&M Management Consulting GmbH (1)
Willy-Brandt-Platz 5
68161 Mannheim, Germany De
Tel.: (49) 621 1247 690
Fax: (49) 621 1247 6920
E-Mail: info@jnm.de
Web Site: www.jnm.de
Sales Range: $50-74.9 Million
Emp.: 320
Supply Chain Management Consulting Services
S.I.C.: 4731
N.A.I.C.S.: 541614
Andreas Muller *(Co-Founder, Mng Partner & Member-Mgmt Bd)*
Frank Jenner *(Co-Founder & Mng Partner)*
Sven Hahnel *(Member-Mgmt Bd)*
Markus Heinen *(Member-Mgmt Bd)*

ERNST & YOUNG INC.
Ernst and Young Twr 222 Bay St
Toronto, ON, M5K 1J7, Canada
Mailing Address:
P.O.Box 251
Toronto, ON, M5K 1J7, Canada
Tel.: (416) 864-1234
Fax: (416) 864-1174
Web Site: www.ey.com
Year Founded: 1989
Emp.: 2,000
Business Description:
Auditing & Accounting Services
S.I.C.: 8721
N.A.I.C.S.: 541211
Personnel:
Trent Henry *(Chm & CEO)*
Fiona Macfarlane *(Mng Partner-Western Canada & Chief Inclusiveness Officer)*
Jeff Charriere *(Mng Partner-Markets)*
Anne-Marie Hubert *(Mng Partner-Advisory)*
Jay Hutchison *(Mng Partner-Tax)*
Tom Kornya *(Mng Partner-Assurance)*
Murray McDonald *(Mng Partner-Transaction Advisory Svcs)*
Eric F. Rawlinson *(Mng Partner-Greater Toronto Area)*
Stephen Shea *(Mng Partner-People)*
Sylvain Vincent *(Mng Partner-Eastern Canada)*
Fred Withers *(Chief Dev Officer)*

ERNST DELLO GMBH & CO. KG
Nedderfeld 75
22529 Hamburg, Germany
Tel.: (49) 40 4712 0
Fax: (49) 40 4712 23
E-Mail: service-eppendorf@dello.de
Web Site: www.dello.de
Year Founded: 1898
Emp.: 900
Business Description:
Holding Company; New & Used Car Dealerships Owner & Operator
S.I.C.: 6719
N.A.I.C.S.: 551112
Personnel:
Michael Babick *(CEO)*
Kurt Kroger *(Mng Dir)*

ERNST KLETT AG
Rotebuhlstrasse 77
70178 Stuttgart, Germany
Tel.: (49) 7 11 66 72 18 97
Fax: (49) 7 11 66 72 20 68
Web Site: www.klett-gruppe.de
Year Founded: 1897
Sales Range: $600-649.9 Million
Emp.: 2,763
Business Description:
Educational Material Publisher
S.I.C.: 2731
N.A.I.C.S.: 511130
Personnel:
Philipp Haussmann *(CEO)*

ERNSTING'S FAMILY GMBH & CO. KG
Industriestrasse 1
48653 Coesfeld, Lette, Germany
Tel.: (49) 25 4677 0
Fax: (49) 25 4677 2890
Web Site: www.ernstings-family.de
Sales Range: $1-4.9 Billion
Emp.: 9,000
Business Description:
Clothing Retailer
S.I.C.: 5651
N.A.I.C.S.: 448140
Personnel:
Dietmar Bollmann *(Mng Dir)*
Johannes Ehling *(Mng Dir)*
Dagmar Heuer *(Mng Dir)*

ERO MINING LIMITED
(Name Changed to Tychean Resources Limited)

ERONGO ENERGY LIMITED
Level 1 Suite 5 The Business Centre
55 Salvado Road
Subiaco, WA, 6008, Australia
Tel.: (61) 863801333
Fax: (61) 893806781
Web Site: www.erongoenergy.com.au
ERN—(ASX)
Rev.: $23,740
Assets: $1,023,306
Liabilities: $31,658
Net Worth: $991,648
Earnings: ($7,000,643)
Emp.: 4
Fiscal Year-end: 06/30/13
Business Description:
Uranium & Mineral Sands
S.I.C.: 1094
N.A.I.C.S.: 212291
Personnel:
Paul Jurman *(Sec)*
Board of Directors:
Ron Gajewski
Mark Calderwood
Paul Jurman
Transfer Agent:
Advanced Share Registry Services
150 Stirling Hwy
PO Box 1156
Nedlands, WA, Australia

EROS INTERNATIONAL PLC
Fort Anne
Douglas, Isle of Man IM1 5PD
Tel.: (44) 1624638300
Fax: (44) 2079355656
E-Mail: jamie.kirkwood@erosintl.com
Web Site: www.erosplc.com
EROS—(AIM NYSE)
Rev.: $215,346,000
Assets: $798,657,000
Liabilities: $312,481,000
Net Worth: $486,176,000
Earnings: $33,665,000
Emp.: 287
Fiscal Year-end: 03/31/13
Business Description:
Film Production & Distribution Services

Eros International Plc—(Continued)

S.I.C.: 7812
N.A.I.C.S.: 512110
Personnel:
Kishore Lulla *(Chm)*
Sunil Lulla *(Vice Chm/Mng Dir-Eros International Media)*
Vijay Ahuja *(Vice Chm)*
Jyoti Deshpande *(CEO & Mng Dir)*
Andrew Heffernan *(CFO)*
Sean Hanafin *(Chief Strategy Officer & Chief Corp Officer)*
Pranab Kapadia *(Pres-United Kingdom, Europe & Africa Ops)*
Ken Naz *(Pres-America Ops)*
Surender Sadhwani *(Pres-Middle East Ops)*
Rishika Lulla *(CEO-Eros Digital)*
Richard Vanderplank *(Sec)*
Board of Directors:
Kishore Lulla
Vijay Ahuja
Naresh Chandra
Jyoti Deshpande
Michael James Kirkwood
Sunil Lulla
Dilip Thakkar

Non-U.S. Subsidiaries:

Ayngaran International Ltd. **(1)**
Unit 19 Riverside Bus Park Lyon Rd
Wimbledon, London, SW19 2 RL, United Kingdom
Tel.: (44) 2085434477
Fax: (44) 208 543 44 66
E-Mail: sales@ayngaran.com
Web Site: www.ayngaran.com
Emp.: 12
Tamil Movies Production & Distribution Services
S.I.C.: 7812
N.A.I.C.S.: 512110
Rohan Manickavasagar *(Head-Ops)*

Non-U.S. Subsidiaries:

Ayngaran International Films Pvt. Ltd. **(2)**
901-902 9th Floor Supreme Chambers Veera Desai Road
400 053 Mumbai, Andheri West, India
Tel.: (91) 22 66021500
Fax: (91) 22 66021540
E-Mail: india@aynagaran.com
Web Site: www.erosplc.com
Tamil Film Production & Distribution Services
S.I.C.: 7812
N.A.I.C.S.: 512110

Ayngaran International Media Pvt. Ltd. **(2)**
No 147 11 3rd Fl Rajparis Trimeni Towers G N Chetty Rd
T Nagar, Chennai, Tamil Nadu, 600 017, India
Tel.: (91) 4428153344
Fax: (91) 4428153355
E-Mail: india@ayngaran.com
Web Site: www.ayngaran.com
Emp.: 25
Film Production & Distribution Services
S.I.C.: 7812
N.A.I.C.S.: 512110
Arun Pandiyan *(Mng Dir)*

Ayngaran International SARL. **(2)**
29 rue Philippe De Girard
75010 Paris, France
Tel.: (33) 142055212
Fax: (33) 142055214
E-Mail: ayngaran_paris@hotmail.com
Emp.: 4
Tamil Film Production & Distribution Services
S.I.C.: 7812
N.A.I.C.S.: 512110
Balasingham Ayngaran *(Mng Dir)*

Big Screen Entertainment Pvt. Limited **(1)**
201 Kailash Plz Plot No A-12 Opp Laxmi Indus Estate Link Rd
Andheri W, Mumbai, Maharashtra, 400 058, India
Tel.: (91) 2266918500
Fax: (91) 2226732586
E-Mail: contact@bigscreen.co.in
Web Site: www.bigscreen.co.in
Emp.: 50
Movies Production & Distribution Services
S.I.C.: 7812
N.A.I.C.S.: 512110
Kumar Mangat *(Mng Dir)*

Eros International Ltd. **(1)**
Milner House 13 Manchester Sq
London, W1U 3PP, United Kingdom
Tel.: (44) 2079352727
Fax: (44) 207 935 5656
E-Mail: UK-business@erosintl.co.uk
Web Site: www.erosentertainment.com
Emp.: 20
Film Production & Distribution Services
S.I.C.: 7812
N.A.I.C.S.: 512110
Kishore Lulla *(Mng Dir)*

Eros International Media Ltd. **(1)**
9th Floor Supreme Chambers Off Veera Desai Road
Mumbai, Maharashtra, 400 053, India
Tel.: (91) 22 66021500
Fax: (91) 22 66021540
E-Mail: india-business@erosintl.com
Web Site: www.erosentertainment.com
EROSMEDIA—(BOM NSE)
Rev.: $199,184,490
Assets: $334,641,438
Liabilities: $150,318,612
Net Worth: $184,322,826
Earnings: $28,887,174
Emp.: 160
Fiscal Year-end: 03/31/13
Movie Production & Distribution Services
S.I.C.: 7812
N.A.I.C.S.: 512110
Sunil Lulla *(Vice Chm & Mng Dir)*
Kamal Jain *(CFO)*
Dimple Mehta *(Compliance Officer & Sec)*
Kumar Ahuja *(Pres-Bus Dev)*
Nandu Ahuja *(Sr VP-India Theatrical)*

Eros Network Limited **(1)**
Unit 23 Sovereign Park Coronation Rd
Park Royal, London, NW10 7QP, United Kingdom
Tel.: (44) 20 89653025
Fax: (44) 20 89630154
Film Production & Distribution Services
S.I.C.: 7812
N.A.I.C.S.: 512110
Jyoti Deshpande *(Mng Dir)*

Eros Pacific Limited **(1)**
92 Kennedy Ave
PO Box 1802
Nadi, Fiji
Tel.: (679) 6707722
E-Mail: erosspecific@connect.com.fj
Web Site: www.erosentertainment.com
Emp.: 3
Film Production & Distribution Services
S.I.C.: 7812
N.A.I.C.S.: 512110
Jack Raniga *(Mng Dir)*

Eros Worldwide FZ LLC **(1)**
529 Bldg No 8 Dubai Media City
PO Box 502121
Dubai, United Arab Emirates
Tel.: (971) 43902825
Fax: (971) 43908867
E-Mail: vijay.chand@erosintl.com
Web Site: www.erosentertainment.com
Emp.: 7
Film Production & Distribution Services
S.I.C.: 7812
N.A.I.C.S.: 512110
Surender Sadhwani *(Mng Dir)*

EyeQube Studios Pvt. Ltd. **(1)**
Ground Fl Satyadev Bldg Off New Link Rd
Andheri W, Mumbai, Maharashtra, 400053, India
Tel.: (91) 2240538600
Fax: (91) 2240538611
E-Mail: sales@eyeqube.com
Web Site: www.eyeqube.com
Emp.: 150
Movie Visual Effects Creation Services
S.I.C.: 7812
N.A.I.C.S.: 512110
Charles H. Darby *(Dir-Creative)*

U.S. Subsidiary:

Eros Entertainment, Inc. **(1)**
550 County Ave
Secaucus, NJ 07094
Tel.: (201) 558-9001
Fax: (201) 558-9002
E-Mail: us-business@erosentertainment.com
Film Production & Distribution Services
S.I.C.: 7812
N.A.I.C.S.: 512110
Kishore Lulla *(Pres)*

ERPSOFT SYSTEMS LIMITED

Plot No 10A Tranquill Nest Kama Koti Nagar Extension Pallikarani
Chennai, 600100, India
Tel.: (91) 44 22461154
E-Mail: info@erpsoft.com
Web Site: www.erpsoft.com
Year Founded: 1994
530909—(BOM)
Rev.: $6,233,262
Assets: $4,820,264
Liabilities: $2,804,842
Net Worth: $2,015,422
Earnings: $139,591
Fiscal Year-end: 03/31/13
Business Description:
Information Technology Consulting Services
S.I.C.: 7373
N.A.I.C.S.: 541512
Personnel:
Kallurupalli Parvathi *(Mng Dir)*
Sivkumar Reddy Duvvuru *(CFO)*
R. Kamala Mohan *(Compliance Officer)*
Pavan Srinivas *(Sec)*
Board of Directors:
R. Kamala Mohan
Kallurupalli Parvathi
K. Radha Krishna Reddy
D. Sarojanamma
Pavan Srinivas
Transfer Agent:
Cameo Corporate Services Limited
Subramaniam Building First Floor 1 Club House Road
Chennai, India

ERRECINQUE S.R.L.

Via Meucci 31/A
10040 Turin, TO, Italy
Tel.: (39) 011 99 69 260
Fax: (39) 011 99 69 243
E-Mail: info@errecinque.it
Web Site: www.errecinque.it
Year Founded: 1981
Sales Range: $25-49.9 Million
Emp.: 160
Business Description:
Rubber & Plastic Hose Mfr
S.I.C.: 3052
N.A.I.C.S.: 326220
Personnel:
Piero Lovera *(CEO)*

ERRIA A/S

Amager Strandvej 390 2nd Kastrup
2770 Copenhagen, Denmark
Tel.: (45) 33364400
Fax: (45) 33364401
E-Mail: info@erria.dk
Web Site: www.erria.dk
Year Founded: 1992
ERRIA—(CSE)
Sales Range: $1-9.9 Million
Emp.: 69
Business Description:
Cargo Handling Services
S.I.C.: 4491
N.A.I.C.S.: 488320
Personnel:
Kaare Vagner *(Chm)*
Finn Buus Nielsen *(Deputy Chm)*
Henrik N. Andersen *(CEO & Mng Dir)*
Board of Directors:
Kaare Vagner
Peter Jein
Claus Jarlgaard Jensen
Finn Buus Nielsen

Subsidiary:

K/S Maria J. **(1)**
Amager Strandvej 390 C/O Erria A/S Floors 2
Kastrup, Arhus, 2770, Denmark
Tel.: (45) 33364400
Fax: (45) 36334401
Transportation Services
S.I.C.: 4789
N.A.I.C.S.: 488999
Henrik Normann Andersen *(Mng Dir)*

Non-U.S. Subsidiary:

Ibex Maritime Ltd **(1)**
Bagdat Caddesi Gokce Sok Toksoy Apt No 10/17-18
Caddebostan, 34728 Kadikoy, Istanbul, Turkey
Tel.: (90) 216 302 5900
Fax: (90) 216 302 8999
E-Mail: operations@ibexmaritime.com
Web Site: www.ibexmaritime.com
Ship Chartering Services
S.I.C.: 4412
N.A.I.C.S.: 483111
Gokce Atay *(Mgr-Ops)*

ERSTE ABWICKLUNGSANSTALT

Elisabethstrasse 65
40217 Dusseldorf, Germany
Tel.: (49) 211 826 7800
Fax: (49) 211 826 7883
E-Mail: info@aa1.de
Web Site: www.aa1.de
Business Description:
Corporate Restructuring & Winding-up Services
S.I.C.: 6726
N.A.I.C.S.: 525990
Personnel:
Rudiger Messal *(Chm-Supervisory Bd)*
Joachim Stapf *(Vice Chm-Supervisory Bd)*
Markus Bolder *(Member-Mgmt Bd)*
Matthias Wargers *(Member-Mgmt Bd)*
Supervisory Board of Directors:
Rudiger Messal
Karlheinz Bentele
Gunter Borgel
Ralf Fleischer
Henning Giesecke
Wilfried Groos
Wolfgang Kirsch
Hans Martz
Joachim Stapf
Michael Stolting
Jurgen Wannhoff
Uwe Zimpelmann

ERSTE GROUP BANK AG

Graben 21
A-1010 Vienna, Austria
Tel.: (43) 5010010100
Fax: (43))50100 910100
E-Mail: erstegroup@erstegroup.com
Web Site: www.erstegroup.com
Year Founded: 2007
EBS—(BUC OTC PRA VIE)
Rev.: $11,839,730,729
Assets: $287,843,448,695
Liabilities: $265,849,025,919
Net Worth: $21,994,422,776
Earnings: $849,446,732
Emp.: 49,381
Fiscal Year-end: 12/31/12
Business Description:
Bank Holding Company
S.I.C.: 6712
N.A.I.C.S.: 551111

Personnel:
Friedrich Rodler *(Chm-Supervisory Bd)*
Andreas Treichl *(Chm-Mgmt Bd-Comm, IT, HR, Audit & Brands)*
Theresa Jordis *(Second Vice Chm-Supervisory Bd)*
George Winckler *(First Vice Chm-Supervisory Bd)*
Franz Hochstrasser *(Deputy Chm-Mgmt Bd-Res, Investment Banking & Large Corp Banking)*
Manfred Wimmer *(CFO, Chief Performance Officer & Member-Mgmt Bd)*
Linda Michalech *(Grp Press Officer)*
Michaela Riediger *(Press Officer-Austrian)*
Carmen Staicu *(Grp Press Officer)*
Herbert Juranek *(Member-Mgmt Bd-Grp Org, IT, Banking Ops & Svcs)*
Gernot Mittendorfer *(Member-Mgmt Bd-Strategic, Corp & Retail Risk Mgmt & Corp Workout)*
Supervisory Board of Directors:
Friedrich Rodler
Bettina Breiteneder
Jan Homan
Theresa Jordis
Andreas Lachs
Friedrich Lackner
Bertram Mach
Juan Maria Nin Genova
Brian Deveraux O'Neill
Wilhelm G. Rasinger
Barbara Smrcka
John James Stack
Werner Tessmar-Pfohl
George Winckler
Karin Zeisel

Ernst & Young Wirtschaftsprufungsgesellschaft m.b.H.
Vienna, Austria

Subsidiaries:

Bad Leonfelden Hotelbetriebs Gesellschaft mbH (1)
Wallseerstr 10
4190 Leonfelden, Austria
Tel.: (43) 7213 20687
Fax: (43) 7213 20687900
Financial Management Services
S.I.C.: 6211
N.A.I.C.S.: 523999

Balance Resort AG (1)
Panoramaweg 1
Stegersbach, Burgenland, 7551, Austria
Tel.: (43) 332655155
Fax: (43) 332655150
E-Mail: balanceresort@falkenstenier.com
Web Site: www.falkensteiner.com
Financial Investment Management Services
S.I.C.: 6211
N.A.I.C.S.: 523999
Peter Kogelbauer *(Gen Mgr)*

CITY REAL Immobilienbeteiligungs- und Verwaltungsgesellschaft mbH & Co KG (1)
Albrechtgasse 1
Graz, 8010, Austria
Tel.: (43) 5010035044
Fax: (43) 50100935044
Financial Management Services
S.I.C.: 6211
N.A.I.C.S.: 523999

CSSC Customer Sales Service Center GmbH (1)
Ernst-Melchior-Gasse 24
1020 Vienna, Austria
Tel.: (43) 5010055000
Customer Care Services
S.I.C.: 7389
N.A.I.C.S.: 561422

DIE ERSTE Immobilienvermietungsgesellschaft m.b.H. (1)
Graben 21
Vienna, 1010, Austria
Tel.: (43) 5010020111
Fax: (43) 5010920111
Investment Management Services
S.I.C.: 6211
N.A.I.C.S.: 523999
Hans Flackel *(Mgr)*

EB-Restaurantsbetriebe Ges.m.b.H. (1)
Petersplatz 4
1010 Vienna, Austria
Tel.: (43) 5 0100 18129
Fax: (43) 5 0100 13043
E-Mail: verwaltung@ebr.at
Web Site: www.ebr.at
Emp.: 85
Restaurant Operation Services
S.I.C.: 5812
N.A.I.C.S.: 722511
Renate Tomaschek *(Mng Dir)*

EBB Hotelbetriebs GmbH (1)
Teilwiesen 1
6460 Imst, Tyrol, Austria
Tel.: (43) 5412 66415
Fax: (43) 5412 66415 133
Financial Management Services
S.I.C.: 6211
N.A.I.C.S.: 523999
Thomas Steel *(Gen Mgr)*

EBV-Beteiligungen GmbH (1)
Linke Wienzeile 120
Vienna, 1061, Austria
Tel.: (43) 5010076700
Fax: (43) 501009610
Web Site: www.ebv-leasing.at
Emp.: 150
Investment Management Services
S.I.C.: 6211
N.A.I.C.S.: 523999
Michael Steiner *(Gen Mgr)*

EBV - Leasing Gesellschaft m.b.H. & Co. KG. (1)
Linke Wienzeile 120
1061 Vienna, Austria
Tel.: (43) 5 0100 76700
Fax: (43) 5 0100 9 76607
Web Site: www.ebv-leasing.at
Emp.: 130
Automobile Finance Leasing Services
S.I.C.: 6153
N.A.I.C.S.: 522220
Tanja Burger *(Mgr-Mktg)*

EGB e-business Holding GmbH (1)
Mariahilferstrasse 121b
Vienna, 1060, Austria
Tel.: (43) 1536890
Fax: (43) 15368913550
Emp.: 100
Financial Management Services
S.I.C.: 6211
N.A.I.C.S.: 523999
Wolfgang Siegl *(Gen Mgr)*

Erste Asset Management GmbH (1)
Habsburgergasse 2
1010 Vienna, Austria
Tel.: (43) 5010019777
Fax: (43) 50100919777
E-Mail: office@erste-am.com
Web Site: www.ersteassetmanagement.com
Asset Management Services
S.I.C.: 6799
N.A.I.C.S.: 523920
Heinz Bedner *(CEO)*
Gerold Permoser *(Chief Investment Officer)*

Non-U.S. Subsidiary:

Asset Management Slovenskej sporitelne sprav spol a s. (2)
Tomasikova 48
832 65 Bratislava, Slovakia
Tel.: (421) 850 111 888
E-Mail: amslsp@slsp.sk
Web Site: www.amslsp.sk
Asset Management Services
S.I.C.: 6282
N.A.I.C.S.: 523920
Roman Vlcek *(Chm & CEO)*

Erste Bank der oesterreichischen Sparkassen AG (1)
Graben 21
1010 Vienna, Austria AT
Tel.: (43) 5010010100
Fax: (43) 50100910100
Web Site: www.sparkasse.at
Sales Range: $100-149.9 Billion
Emp.: 14,332
Retail, Commercial & Investment Banking Services
S.I.C.: 6029
N.A.I.C.S.: 522110
Andreas Treichl *(Chm-Supervisory Bd)*
Heinz Kessler *(Vice Chm-Supervisory Bd)*
Thomas Uher *(Deputy Chm-Mgmt Bd)*
Peter Bosek *(Member-Mgmt Bd)*

Subsidiaries:

Erste Bank AG (2)
Graben 21
2020 Vienna, Austria AT
Tel.: (43) 5 0100 25800
Fax: (43) 5 0100 25801
Retail & Commercial Banking Services
S.I.C.: 6035
N.A.I.C.S.: 522120
Walter Schmidt *(Chm-Supervisory Bd)*
Andreas Kaim *(Chm-Mgmt Bd)*
Volker Dahlhausen *(Second Vice Chm-Supervisory Bd)*
Christian Wilhelm *(Member-Mgmt Bd)*

Salzburger Sparkasse Bank AG (2)
Alter Markt 3
Postfach 180
A-5021 Salzburg, Austria AT
Tel.: (43) 5010041000
Fax: (43) 50100941000
E-Mail: info@salzburg.sparkasse.at
Web Site: www.sparkasse.at/salzburg
Retail & Commercial Banking Services
S.I.C.: 6035
N.A.I.C.S.: 522120
Elisabeth Bleyleben-Koren *(Chm-Supervisory Bd)*
Regina Ovesny-Straka *(Chm-Mgmt Bd)*
Thomas Uher *(Vice Chm-Supervisory Bd)*
Johann Lassacher *(Member-Mgmt Bd)*
Christoph Paulweber *(Member-Mgmt Bd)*

Sparkasse Hainburg-Bruck-Neusiedl AG (2)
Hauptplatz 1
A-2410 Hainburg, Austria AT
Tel.: (43) 5010020216
Fax: (43) 50100926600
E-Mail: info@sparkasse.hbn.at
Web Site: www.sparkasse.at/hainburg
Retail & Commercial Banking Services
S.I.C.: 6036
N.A.I.C.S.: 522120
Walter Schmidt *(Chm-Supervisory Bd)*
Helmut Rattinger *(First Vice Chm-Supervisory Bd)*
Gerald Leder *(Second Vice Chm-Supervisory Bd)*
Wolfgang Dinhof *(Member-Mgmt Bd)*
Josef Preschitz *(Member-Mgmt Bd)*

Tiroler Sparkasse Bank AG (2)
Sparkassenplatz 1
Postfach 245
A-6010 Innsbruck, Austria AT
Tel.: (43) 5010070000
Fax: (43) 004350100970232
E-Mail: sparkasse@tirolersparkasse.at
Web Site: www.sparkasse.at/tirolersparkasse
Retail & Commercial Banking Services
S.I.C.: 6035
N.A.I.C.S.: 522120
Elisabeth Bleyleben-Koren *(Chm-Supervisory Bd)*
Markus Jochum *(Chm-Mgmt Bd)*
Bruno Wallnofer *(Vice Chm-Supervisory Bd)*
Wolfgang Hechenberger *(Member-Mgmt Bd)*
Karl Obernosterer *(Member-Mgmt Bd)*

ERSTE-SPARINVEST Kapitalanlagegesellschaft m.b.H. (1)
Habsburgergasse 1a
1010 Vienna, Austria
Tel.: (43) 5010019881
Fax: (43) 50100917102
E-Mail: erste@sparinvest.com
Web Site: www.erstesparinvest.com
Emp.: 350
Financial Management Services
S.I.C.: 6211
N.A.I.C.S.: 523999
Heinz Bednar *(CEO)*

ESPA-Financial Advisors GmbH (1)
Habsburgergasse 1a
1010 Vienna, Austria
Tel.: (43) 5010011490
Financial Management Services
S.I.C.: 6211
N.A.I.C.S.: 523999

Flottenmanagement GmbH (1)
Linke Wienzeile 120
1060 Vienna, Austria
Tel.: (43) 5010027652
Fax: (43) 5 0100 27753
E-Mail: flottenmanagement@s-autoleasing.at
Web Site: www.flottenmanagement.co.at
Fleet Leasing Services
S.I.C.: 7515
N.A.I.C.S.: 532112
Engrad Angerer *(Gen Mgr)*

good.bee Holding GmbH (1)
Friedrichstrasse 10 4th Level
1010 Vienna, Austria
Tel.: (43) 5010016364
Fax: (43) 50100916364
E-Mail: office@goodbee.com
Web Site: www.goodbee.com
Financial Support Services
S.I.C.: 6726
N.A.I.C.S.: 525990
H. C. Mult Karl Korinek *(Chm-Supervisory Bd)*
Andreas Treichl *(Chm-Mgmt Bd)*

Hochkonig Bergbahnen Ges.m.b.H (1)
Schloglberg 63
5505 Muhlbach am Hochkonig, Austria
Tel.: (43) 64677214
Fax: (43) 64677595
E-Mail: office@hochkonig-bergbahnen.at
Web Site: www.hochkonig.at
Emp.: 100
Financial Investment Management Services
S.I.C.: 6211
N.A.I.C.S.: 523999
Peter Nadeje *(Gen Mgr)*

IMMORENT Aktiengesellschaft (1)
Windmuhlgasse 22-24
1060 Vienna, Austria
Tel.: (43) 5010027000
Fax: (43) 50100 9 27104
Web Site: www.immorent.at
Real Estate Management Services
S.I.C.: 6531
N.A.I.C.S.: 531390

Immorent-Mobilienvermietungsgesellschaft m.b.H. & Co Leasing 89 KG (1)
Windmuhlgasse 22-24
Vienna, 1060, Austria
Tel.: (43) 1588940
Fax: (43) 1588944000
E-Mail: office.vienna@immorent.com
Web Site: www.erstegroup.com
Emp.: 200
Financial Management Services
S.I.C.: 6211
N.A.I.C.S.: 523999
Richard Wilkinson *(Pres)*

IMMORENT-RAMON Grundverwertungsgesellschaft m.b.H. (1)
Windmuhlgasse 22-24
Vienna, 1060, Austria
Tel.: (43) 1588940
Fax: (43) 1588944000
E-Mail: office.veene@immorent.com
Web Site: www.erstegroupimmorent.vom
Investment Management Services
S.I.C.: 6211
N.A.I.C.S.: 523999

IMMORENT S-Immobilienmanagement GesmbH (1)
Windmuhlgasse 22-24
1060 Vienna, Austria
Tel.: (43) 5 0100 27000
Fax: (43) 5 0100 27204
Financial Management Services
S.I.C.: 6211
N.A.I.C.S.: 523999

Erste Group Bank AG—(Continued)

Immorent - Sud Gesellschaft m.b.H., S-Leasing Kg. (1)
Andreas Hofer Platz 17
Graz, 8010, Austria
Tel.: (43) 5010027365
Fax: (43) 5010027369
Web Site: www.s-leasing.at
Emp.: 13
Automobile Finance Leasing Services
S.I.C.: 6153
N.A.I.C.S.: 522220
Robert Brettenthaler *(Gen Mgr)*

Immorent-Sud Gesellschaft m.b.H. (1)
Landhausgasse 12/Ii
Graz, Styria, 8010, Austria
Tel.: (43) 5010027365
Fax: (43) 50100927365
Web Site: www.immorent.at
Emp.: 15
Commercial Banking Services
S.I.C.: 6029
N.A.I.C.S.: 522110
Heinz Moser *(Gen Mgr)*

Informations Technologie Austria SK spol. s r.o. (1)
Lassallestrabe 5
Vienna, 1020, Austria
Tel.: (43) 12171730
Commercial Banking Services
S.I.C.: 6029
N.A.I.C.S.: 522110

OM Objektmanagement GmbH (1)
Traungasse 12
1030 Vienna, Austria
Tel.: (43) 5 0100 13025
Fax: (43) 5 0100 9 13025
Web Site: www.objektmanagement.at
Emp.: 220
Facilities Management Services
S.I.C.: 8744
N.A.I.C.S.: 561210

PARAGON Hotelbetriebs GmbH (1)
Paragonstrabe 1
1110 Vienna, Austria
Tel.: (43) 17431777
Fax: (43) 17431888
Web Site: www.roomshotels.com
General Insurance Services
S.I.C.: 6411
N.A.I.C.S.: 524210
Bernard Haselsteiner *(Gen Mgr)*

RINGTURM Kapitalanlagegesellschaft m.b.H. (1)
Habsburgergasse 2
1010 Vienna, Austria
Tel.: (43) 5010019709
Fax: (43) 50100919709
E-Mail: office@ringturm.at
Web Site: www.ringturm.at
Emp.: 17
Mutual Funds Management Services
S.I.C.: 6799
N.A.I.C.S.: 523920
Michael Kukacka *(Gen Mgr)*

s Autoleasing GmbH (1)
Linke Wienzeile 120
1061 Vienna, Austria
Tel.: (43) 5010027700
Fax: (43) 5 0100 9 27700
Web Site: www.s-autoleasing.at
Emp.: 120
Automobile Finance Leasing Services
S.I.C.: 6153
N.A.I.C.S.: 522220
Michael Steiner *(Mgr-Site)*

S-Immobilien Weinviertler Sparkasse GmbH (1)
Hauptplatz 10
Hollabrunn, 2020, Austria
Tel.: (43) 5010025800
Fax: (43) 5010025801
Financial Management Services
S.I.C.: 6211
N.A.I.C.S.: 523999

s Proserv Austria - Procurement Services GmbH (1)
Am Heumarkt 4
1030 Vienna, Austria
Tel.: (43) 5 0100 28300
Fax: (43) 5 0100 9 28300
Emp.: 100
Procurement Services
S.I.C.: 7389
N.A.I.C.S.: 561990
Leopold Ivan *(Mng Dir)*

S-Tourismusfonds Management Aktiengesellschaft (1)
Fleischmarkt 18/14
1010 Vienna, Austria
Tel.: (43) 5010025251
Fax: (43) 5010025299
E-Mail: info@s-tourismusfonds.at
Web Site: www.s-tourismusfonds.at
Emp.: 12
Tourism Funding Services
S.I.C.: 6726
N.A.I.C.S.: 525990
Johann Lassachaer *(Mng Dir)*

s Wohnbaubank AG (1)
Graben 21
1010 Vienna, Austria
Tel.: (43) 5 0100 29361
Fax: (43) 5 0100 9 29361
Web Site: www.swohnbaubank.at
Commercial Banking Services
S.I.C.: 6029
N.A.I.C.S.: 522110
Ernst Karner *(Gen Mgr)*

s Wohnbautrager GmbH (1)
Graben 21
1010 Vienna, Austria
Tel.: (43) 50 100 294 64
Investment Management Services
S.I.C.: 6211
N.A.I.C.S.: 523999
Hans Mueller *(Gen Mgr)*

s Wohnfinanzierung Beratungs GmbH (1)
Beatrixgasse 27
1030 Vienna, Austria
Tel.: (43) 5 0100 39030
Fax: (43) 5 0100 9 39030
E-Mail: office@swohnfinanz.at
Web Site: www.swohnfinanz.at
Financial Investment Management Services
S.I.C.: 6211
N.A.I.C.S.: 523999
Ines Stampf *(Mgr-Site)*

Sparkasse Kremstal Pyhrn Aktiengesellschaft (1)
Hauptplatz 18
4560 Kirchdorf am Inn, Austria
Tel.: (43) 5010049126
Fax: (43) 50100949126
Web Site: www.sparkasse.at/kremstal-pyhrn/
Asset Management Services
S.I.C.: 6282
N.A.I.C.S.: 523920

Sparkasse Muhlviertel West Bank Aktiengesellschaft (1)
Markt 17
Ulrichsberg, 416, Austria
Tel.: (43) 72882226
Commercial Banking Services
S.I.C.: 6029
N.A.I.C.S.: 522110

Sparkassenbeteiligungs und Service AG fur Oberosterreich und Salzburg (1)
Promenade 11-13
4020 Linz, Austria
Tel.: (43) 73273912725
Fax: (43) 501 0094 0000
Financial Management Services
S.I.C.: 6211
N.A.I.C.S.: 523999

SPV-Druck Gesellschaft m.b.H (1)
Grimmelshausengasse 1
1030 Vienna, Austria
Tel.: (43) 5010028203
Books Printing Services
S.I.C.: 2732
N.A.I.C.S.: 323117
Werner Muhlbachler *(Gen Mgr)*

Tirolinvest Kapitalanlagegesellschaft mbH. (1)
Sparkassenplatz 1
Innsbruck, Tyrol, 6020, Austria
Tel.: (43) 5010070094
Web Site: www.tirolinvest.at
Asset Management Services
S.I.C.: 6799
N.A.I.C.S.: 523920

Non-U.S. Subsidiaries:

Banca Comerciala Romana Chisinau S.A. (1)
Street A Puskin nr 60/2
Chisinau, 2005, Moldova
Tel.: (373) 22 85 20 00
Fax: (373) 22 26 50 02
Web Site: www.bcr.md
Commercial Banking Services
S.I.C.: 6029
N.A.I.C.S.: 522110
Soren Andrei *(Pres)*

Banca Comerciala Romana S.A. (1)
5 Regina Elisabeta Blvd
RO-030016 Bucharest, 3, Romania RO
Tel.: (40) 213131246 (69%)
Fax: (40) 213111819
E-Mail: investors.relations@bcr.ro
Web Site: www.bcr.ro
Sales Range: $900-999.9 Million
Emp.: 9,012
Retail & Commercial Banking Services
S.I.C.: 6029
N.A.I.C.S.: 522110
Andreas Treichl *(Chm-Supervisory Bd)*
Dominic Bruynseels *(Chm-Mgmt Bd & CEO)*
Manfred Wimmer *(Vice Chm-Supervisory Bd)*
Paul Ursaciuc *(COO)*
Helmuth Hintringer *(Exec VP-Risk Mgmt, Acctg & Legal)*
Oana Petrescu *(Exec VP-Org & IT)*
Wolfgang Schoiswohl *(Exec VP-Corp Banking & Treasury & Capital Markets)*
Martin Skopek *(Exec VP-Retail Div & Private Banking)*

BCR Procesare SRL (1)
18-20 Str Lipscani
Bucharest, 030153, Romania
Tel.: (40) 213112761
Financial Management Services
S.I.C.: 6211
N.A.I.C.S.: 523999

Ceska Sporitelna a.s. (1)
Olbrachtova 1929/62
140 00 Prague, Czech Republic CZ
Tel.: (420) 956711111 (97.99%)
Fax: (420) 261073006
E-Mail: csas@csas.cz
Web Site: www.csas.cz
Rev.: $1,982,782,690
Assets: $48,385,585,710
Liabilities: $43,480,173,870
Net Worth: $4,905,411,840
Earnings: $862,305,710
Emp.: 10,556
Fiscal Year-end: 12/31/12
Retail, Commercial & Investment Banking Services
S.I.C.: 6029
N.A.I.C.S.: 522110
Pavel Kysilka *(Chm & CEO)*
Manfred Wimmer *(Chm-Supervisory Bd)*
Dusan Baran *(Vice Chm & First Deputy CEO)*
Peter Bosek *(Vice Chm-Supervisory Bd)*
Daniel Heler *(Deputy CEO)*
Heinz Knotzer *(Deputy CEO)*
Jiri Skorvaga *(Deputy CEO)*

Subsidiary:

Penzijni fond Ceske sporitelny, a.s (2)
PO Box 30
140 21 Prague, Czech Republic
Tel.: (420) 800207207
E-Mail: info@pfcs.cz
Web Site: www.pfcs.cz
Pension Fund Management Services
S.I.C.: 6371
N.A.I.C.S.: 525110
Ales Poklop *(Chm)*
Milan Hasek *(Chm-Supervisory Bd)*
Veronika Matuskova *(Vice Chm & Dir-Fin Mgmt)*
Petr Kudrna *(Vice Chm-Supervisory Bd)*

Czech TOP Venture Fund B.V. (1)
Postweg 11
Groesbeek, Gelderland, 6561 KJ, Netherlands
Tel.: (31) 243977577
Investment Management Services
S.I.C.: 6211
N.A.I.C.S.: 523999

Erste Alapkezelo Zrt. (1)
Nepfurdo U 24-26 9 Em
Budapest, 1138, Hungary
Tel.: (36) 12355100
Fax: (36) 12355889
Securities Brokerage Services
S.I.C.: 6211
N.A.I.C.S.: 523120

Erste & Steiermarkische Bank d.d. (1)
Jadranski trg 3a
HR-51000 Rijeka, Croatia HR
Tel.: (385) 62375000 (51.4%)
Fax: (385) 62376000
E-Mail: erstebank@erstebank.hr
Web Site: www.erstebank.hr
Sales Range: $200-249.9 Million
Emp.: 2,265
Retail, Commercial & Investment Banking Services
Export
S.I.C.: 6029
N.A.I.C.S.: 522110
Herbert Juranek *(Chm-Supervisory Bd)*
Petar Radakovic *(Chm-Mgmt Bd)*
Franz Kerber *(Deputy Chm-Supervisory Bd)*
Tomislav Vuic *(Deputy Chm-Mgmt Bd-Retail Div/HR/Mktg)*
Boris Centner *(Member-Mgmt Bd-Corp Div/ Fin Markets/Investment Banking Div)*
Sladana Jagar *(Member-Mgmt Bd)*

ERSTE BANK AD NOVI SAD (1)
Bulevar Oslobodenja 5
21000 Novi Sad, Serbia
Tel.: (381) 60 79 79 000
Fax: (381) 21 201 5070
E-Mail: netbanking@erstebank.rs
Web Site: www.erstebank.rs
Commercial Banking Services
S.I.C.: 6029
N.A.I.C.S.: 522110

ERSTE BANK AD PODGORICA (1)
Marka Miljanova 46
81000 Podgorica, Montenegro
Tel.: (382) 20440440
Fax: (382) 20 440 432
E-Mail: info@erstebank.me
Web Site: www.erstebank.me
Commercial Banking Services
S.I.C.: 6029
N.A.I.C.S.: 522110
Ortner Reinhard *(Chm)*
Lukic Aleksa *(CEO)*

Erste Bank d.d. (1)
Bulevar oslobodenja 5
21000 Novi Sad, Serbia RS
Tel.: (381) 214873510
Fax: (381) 212015070
E-Mail: info@erstebank.rs
Web Site: www.erstebank.rs
Emp.: 909
Retail & Commercial Banking Services
S.I.C.: 6029
N.A.I.C.S.: 522110
Andreas Klingen *(Chm-Supervisory Bd)*
Slavko Caric *(Chm-Mgmt Bd)*
Suzan Tanriyar *(Member-Mgmt Bd-Acctg & Controlling/IT & Org/Ops)*
Jasna Terzic *(Member-Mgmt Bd-Retail Banking/HR/Mktg)*

Erste Bank Hungary Nyrt. (1)
Nepfurdo ut 24-26
H-1138 Budapest, Hungary HU
Mailing Address: (99.95%)
PO Box 1933
Budapest, Hungary
Tel.: (36) 12980221
Fax: (36) 13732499
E-Mail: uszolg@erstebank.hu
Web Site: www.erstebank.hu
Sales Range: $300-349.9 Million
Emp.: 3,181
Retail, Commercial & Investment Banking Services
S.I.C.: 6029

N.A.I.C.S.: 522110
Manfred Wimmer *(Chm-Supervisory Bd)*
Edit Papp *(Chm-Mgmt Bd & CEO)*
Laszlo Pelle *(Member-Mgmt Bd-IT/Back Office/Org)*
Imre Sztano *(Member-Mgmt Bd-Retail Div)*
Jonathan William Till *(Member-Mgmt Bd-Risk Mgmt/Acctg/Fin)*

Erste Bank (Malta) Limited (1)
72 Regent House Bisazza Street
Sliema, SLM 1641, Malta
Tel.: (356) 21347161
Fax: (356) 21347159
Emp.: 5
Commercial Banking Services
S.I.C.: 6029
N.A.I.C.S.: 522110
Martin Sadleder *(Mng Dir)*

ERSTE CARD CLUB d.d. (1)
Praska 5
10 000 Zagreb, Croatia
Tel.: (385) 1 4929 000
Fax: (385) 1 4920 400
E-Mail: info@erstecardclub.hr
Web Site: www.erstecardclub.hr
Emp.: 250
Credit Card Issuing Services
S.I.C.: 6153
N.A.I.C.S.: 522210
Zeljko Menalo *(Pres)*

Erste Corporate Finance, a.s. (1)
Na Perstyne 1/342
11000 Prague, Czech Republic
Tel.: (420) 224 995 166
E-Mail: prague@erste-cf.com
Commercial Banking Services
S.I.C.: 6029
N.A.I.C.S.: 522110

ERSTE DMD d.o.o. (1)
Ulica Ivana Lucica 2/a
Zagreb, 10000, Croatia
Tel.: (385) 14877381
Fax: (385) 14877370
Emp.: 4
Commercial Banking Services
S.I.C.: 6029
N.A.I.C.S.: 522110
Senka Klemen *(Mng Dir)*

Erste Faktor Penzugyi Szolgaltato Zrt. (1)
Vaci ut 48
1132 Budapest, Hungary
Tel.: (36) 40 222 228
Fax: (36) 327 07 49
E-Mail: faktor@erstefaktor.hu
Financial Management Services
S.I.C.: 6211
N.A.I.C.S.: 523999

Erste Kereskedohaz Kft. (1)
Nepfurdo Utca 24-26
Budapest, 1138, Hungary
Tel.: (36) 12684139
Fax: (36) 12684399
Investment Management Services
S.I.C.: 6211
N.A.I.C.S.: 523999

ERSTE NEKRETNINE d.o.o. (1)
Ivana Lucica 2
10000 Zagreb, Croatia
Tel.: (385) 62 37 2950
Fax: (385) 62 37 2951
Web Site: www.erstenekretnine.hr
Real Estate Development Services
S.I.C.: 6531
N.A.I.C.S.: 531390

Erste Private Equity Limited (1)
68 Cornhill
London, EC3V 3QE, United Kingdom
Tel.: (44) 2076215000
Emp.: 50
Security Brokerage Services
S.I.C.: 6211
N.A.I.C.S.: 523120
Aduard Oxwald *(Gen Mgr)*

Erste Securities Istanbul Menkul Degerler AS (1)
Buyukdere Cad No 14 Kanyon Ofis Blogu
34394 Istanbul, Levent, Turkey
Tel.: (90) 2123712500
Fax: (90) 212 371 25 02
Web Site: www.erstesecuritiesistanbul.com.tr
Emp.: 20
Mutual Fund Management Services
S.I.C.: 6371
N.A.I.C.S.: 524292
Franz Bichler *(Chm)*
Robert Cselovszki *(Deputy Chm)*

Erste Securities Polska S.A. (1)
ul Krolewska 16
00-103 Warsaw, Poland
Tel.: (48) 22 538 62 00
Fax: (48) 22 538 62 02
E-Mail: erste.securities@esp.pl
Web Site: www.esp.pl
Securities Brokerage Services
S.I.C.: 6211
N.A.I.C.S.: 523120
Piotr Prazmo *(CFO)*
Marin Hresic *(Member-Mgmt Bd)*
Andrzej Tabor *(Member-Mgmt Bd)*

Erste Securities Zagreb d.o.o. (1)
Ivana Lucica 2a/20
Zagreb, 10000, Croatia
Tel.: (385) 62372814
Fax: (385) 62372801
Securities Brokerage Services
S.I.C.: 6211
N.A.I.C.S.: 523120

ERSTE SPARINVEST Deutschland Ges.m.b.H. (1)
Zugspitzstra And Szlige 2a
85591 Vaterstetten, Germany
Tel.: (49) 8106210160
Fax: (49) 8106 210 16 20
E-Mail: deutschland@sparinvest.com
Mutual Fund Management Services
S.I.C.: 6371
N.A.I.C.S.: 524292

F&S Finance and Service Leasing GmbH (1)
Blumenstrasse 22
70736 Fellbach, Germany
Tel.: (49) 711 933 83 0
Fax: (49) 711 933 83 298
E-Mail: info@fs-leasing.com
Web Site: www.finance-and-service.com
Financial Leasing Services
S.I.C.: 6159
N.A.I.C.S.: 522220

Factoring Ceske sporitelny a.s. (1)
Budejovicka 1518 B
140 00 Prague, Czech Republic
Tel.: (420) 956 770 711
Fax: (420) 224 641 614
E-Mail: marketing@factoringcs.cz
Web Site: www.factoringcs.cz
Factoring Services
S.I.C.: 6159
N.A.I.C.S.: 522298
Petra Kozarova *(Dir-Ops)*

Financiara SA (1)
15 Calea Victoriei
Bucharest, 030023, Romania
Tel.: (40) 213130154
Fax: (40) 21132759
Financial Management Services
S.I.C.: 6211
N.A.I.C.S.: 523999

good.bee Service RO SRL (1)
6C Timisoara Blv 3rd Floor Sector 6
Bucharest, 061328, Romania
Tel.: (40) 21 266 77 01
Fax: (40) 21 266 77 02
E-Mail: office@goodbee.ro
Web Site: www.goodbee.ro
Financial Transaction Services
S.I.C.: 6099
N.A.I.C.S.: 522320
Catalan Moisie *(Gen Mgr)*

GRANTIKA Ceske sporitelny, a.s. (1)
Jakubske nam 127/5
602 00 Brno, Czech Republic
Tel.: (420) 542210148
Fax: (420) 542210242
E-Mail: info@grantikacs.com
Web Site: www.grantikacs.cz
Emp.: 40
Commercial Banking Services
S.I.C.: 6029
N.A.I.C.S.: 522110
Lukas Nemec *(Gen Mgr)*

IMMORENT BETA, leasing druzba, d.o.o. (1)
Cesta v Klece 15
Ljubljana, 1000, Slovenia
Tel.: (386) 1 513 88 00
Fax: (386) 1 513 88 14
E-Mail: office.si@immorent.com
Commercial Banking Services
S.I.C.: 6029
N.A.I.C.S.: 522110

Luitpoldpark-Hotel Betriebs- und Vermietungsgesellschaft mbH (1)
Bahnhofstr 1-3
87629 Fussen, Germany
Tel.: (49) 83629040
Fax: (49) 8362904678
E-Mail: fuessen@luitpoldpark-hotel.de
Web Site: www.luitpoldpark-hotel.de
Emp.: 50
Hotel Management Services
S.I.C.: 7011
N.A.I.C.S.: 721110

Public Company Erste Bank (1)
Polova 24 D
Kiev, Ukraine
Tel.: (380) 44 593 00 00
Fax: (380) 44 585 92 97
Web Site: www.erstebank.ua
Commercial Banking Services
S.I.C.: 6029
N.A.I.C.S.: 522110

REICO investicni spolecnost Ceske sporitelny, a.s. (1)
Budejovicka alej Antala Staska 79
140 00 Prague, Czech Republic
Tel.: (420) 221 516 500
Fax: (420) 221 516 513
E-Mail: nemofond@reicofunds.cz
Web Site: www.reicofunds.cz
Emp.: 9
Real Estate Fund Management Services
S.I.C.: 6159
N.A.I.C.S.: 522292
Martin Skalicky *(Gen Mgr)*

RUTAR INTERNATIONAL trgovinska d.o.o. (1)
15 Cesta V Klece
Ljubljana, 1000, Slovenia
Tel.: (386) 15138800
Fax: (386) 15138814
E-Mail: ofiice.com@immornt.com
Web Site: www.earthgroupimmorant.com
Emp.: 8
Real Estate Leasing Services
S.I.C.: 6519
N.A.I.C.S.: 531190
Andreja Tonin *(Gen Mgr)*

s Autoleasing a.s. (1)
Budejovicka 1518/13B
140 00 Prague, Czech Republic
Tel.: (420) 266 095 111
Fax: (420) 266 095 777
E-Mail: info@sautoleasing.cz
Web Site: www.sautoleasing.cz
Finance Leasing Services
S.I.C.: 6141
N.A.I.C.S.: 522220

s IT Solutions CZ, s.r.o. (1)
Antala Staska 32/1292
Prague, 14000, Czech Republic
Tel.: (420) 956 783 102
Web Site: www.s-itsolutions.at/en/Company/Locations/CID~0901481b8006b7b2/main0render/CP
Emp.: 600
Information Technology Consulting Services
S.I.C.: 7373
N.A.I.C.S.: 541512
Christian Gosch *(Mng Dir)*
Martin Hornig *(Mng Dir)*

s IT Solutions HR drustvo s ogranicenom odgovornoscu za usluge informacijskih tehnologija (1)
Jurja Haulika 19A
43000 Bjelovar, Croatia
Tel.: (385) 62 37 3388
Fax: (385) 62 37 3891
E-Mail: s-itsolutions@s-itsolutions.hr
Web Site: www.s-itsolutions.hr
Emp.: 90
Information Technology Consulting Services
S.I.C.: 7373
N.A.I.C.S.: 541512
Sinisa Jurkovic *(Gen Mgr)*

S MORAVA Leasing, a.s. (1)
Horni namesti 264/18
669 02 Znojmo, Czech Republic
Tel.: (420) 515200511
Fax: (420) 515200512
E-Mail: info@smorava.cz
Web Site: www.smorava.cz
Emp.: 60
Financial Leasing Services
S.I.C.: 6141
N.A.I.C.S.: 522220
Mrna Zdenek *(Mng Dir)*

s Proserv Hungary - Procurement Services HU Kft. (1)
Nepfurdo str 24-26
1138 Budapest, Hungary
Tel.: (36) 13732780
Fax: (36) 1 373 2703
Emp.: 11
Real Estate Development Services
S.I.C.: 6531
N.A.I.C.S.: 531390
Nikoletta Kovacs *(Mng Dir)*
Calin Valcea *(Mng Dir)*

s Proserv Slovakia - Procurement Services SK, s.r.o. (1)
Mileticova 60
816 10 Bratislava, Slovakia
Tel.: (421) 2 5850 6610
Fax: (421) 2 5850 6091
Real Estate Development Services
S.I.C.: 6531
N.A.I.C.S.: 531390
Ivan Ujcek *(Mng Dir)*

S-Real Morava spol. s.r.o. (1)
Horni Namesti 264/18
Znojmo, 66902, Czech Republic
Tel.: (420) 515261950
Financial Management Services
S.I.C.: 6211
N.A.I.C.S.: 523999

s Real Sparkasse d.o.o. (1)
Cesta v Klece 1515
1000 Ljubljana, Slovenia
Tel.: (386) 15832330
Fax: (386) 1 583 23 70
E-Mail: info@sreal.si
Web Site: www.sreal.si
Real Estate Management Services
S.I.C.: 6531
N.A.I.C.S.: 531390

S Servis, s.r.o. (1)
Horni Namesti 3561/14
669 02 Znojmo, Czech Republic
Tel.: (420) 222 711 399
E-Mail: info@s-servis.cz
Web Site: www.s-servis.eu
Insurance Brokerage Services
S.I.C.: 6411
N.A.I.C.S.: 524210

SAI Erste Asset Management S.A. (1)
14 Uruguay Street
Bucharest, Romania
Tel.: (40) 372 269 999
Fax: (40) 372 870 995
E-Mail: office@erste-am.ro
Web Site: www.erste-am.ro
Asset Management Services
S.I.C.: 6799
N.A.I.C.S.: 523920
Heinz Bednar *(Chm-Supervisory Bd)*
Dragos Neacsu *(Chm-Mgmt Bd & CEO)*
Valentina Berevoianu *(CFO)*

SC Bucharest Financial Plazza SRL (1)
Calea Victoriei 15
Bucharest, Romania
Tel.: (40) 213104020
Fax: (40) 3104017
Financial Management Services
S.I.C.: 6211
N.A.I.C.S.: 523999
Roxana Aldea *(Gen Mgr)*

Slovenska Sporitelna, a.s. (1)
Tomasikova 48
SK 83237 Bratislava, Slovakia Sk
Tel.: (421) 258268111 (100%)

Erste Group Bank AG—(Continued)

Fax: (421) 258268670
E-Mail: info@slsp.sk
Web Site: www.slsp.sk
Sales Range: $350-399.9 Million
Emp.: 4,238
Retail, Commercial & Investment Banking Services
S.I.C.: 6029
N.A.I.C.S.: 522110
Franz Hochstrasser *(Chm-Supervisory Bd)*
Stefan Maj *(Deputy Chm & First Deputy CEO-Property Mgmt/Control/Banking Ops)*
Wolfgang Schopf *(Deputy Chm-Supervisory Bd)*
Frank-Michael Beitz *(Deputy CEO-Risk Mgmt)*
Peter Krutil *(Deputy CEO-Corp Banking & Capital Markets)*
Martin Pilecky *(Deputy CEO-IT, Payments & Org)*

ERWEKA GMBH

Ottostrasse 20-22
D- 63150 Heusenstamm, Germany
Tel.: (49) 610469030
Fax: (49) 6104690340
E-Mail: sales@erweka.com
Web Site: www.erweka.com
Year Founded: 1951
Rev.: $17,448,261
Emp.: 75
Business Description:
Pharmaceutical Testing Equipment Mfr
S.I.C.: 3841
N.A.I.C.S.: 339112
Personnel:
Werner G. Muller *(Owner & Mng Dir)*

ERWIN HALDER KG

Erwin Halder Strasse 5-9
88480 Achstetten, Germany
Tel.: (49) 739270090
Fax: (49) 73927009160
E-Mail: info@halder.de
Web Site: www.halder.de
Year Founded: 1938
Rev.: $40,107,434
Emp.: 180
Business Description:
Industrial Products Distr
S.I.C.: 5085
N.A.I.C.S.: 423840
Personnel:
Stefan Halder *(Mng Dir)*

ERWIN MULLER GRUPPE GMBH

Breslauer Strasse 34
49808 Lingen, Germany
Tel.: (49) 5919400
Web Site: www.erwin-mueller-gruppe.de
Year Founded: 1949
Emp.: 758
Business Description:
Mfr. of Art, Photo, Presentation & Office Products
S.I.C.: 5943
N.A.I.C.S.: 453210
Personnel:
Harald Muller *(Owner)*

Subsidiaries:

Dahle Burotechnik GmbH (1)
Karchestrasse 3 7
Coburg, 96450, Germany
Tel.: (49) 95612780
Fax: (49) 9561278333
E-Mail: dahle@dahle.de
Web Site: www.dahle.de
Emp.: 190
Mfr. of Art, Photo, Presentation & Office Products
S.I.C.: 5112
N.A.I.C.S.: 453210
Truno Ghibely *(Mng Dir)*

U.S. Subsidiary:

Dahle USA (2)
49 Vose Farm Rd
Peterborough, NH 03458-1792 CT
Tel.: (603) 924-0003
Fax: (603) 924-1616
Toll Free: (800) 243-8145
E-Mail: info@dahle.com
Web Site: www.dahle.com
Emp.: 15
Mfr. of Art & Photo Tools & Other Office Related Products
Import Export
S.I.C.: 3589
N.A.I.C.S.: 333318
Scott Prokop *(VP & Gen Mgr)*

Novus GmbH & Co. KG (1)
Breslauer Strasse 34-38
D-49803 Lingen, Germany
Web Site: www.novus.de
Mfr. of Art, Photo, Presentation & Office Products
S.I.C.: 5943
N.A.I.C.S.: 453210

ERYPLAST SA

Zoning industriel des haut-Sarts
2eme Avenue 16
4040 Herstal, Belgium
Tel.: (32) 4 247 57 71
Fax: (32) 4 247 57 69
E-Mail: info@eryplast.com
Web Site: www.eryplast.be
Year Founded: 1993
ERY—(EUR)
Sales Range: $1-9.9 Million
Business Description:
Plastic Product Mfr
S.I.C.: 3089
N.A.I.C.S.: 326199
Personnel:
Dominique Rykers *(CEO)*
Dryvers-Rykers Bernadette *(Gen Sec)*

ES-CON JAPAN LTD.

4F Uchikanda 282 Building 2-15-9 Uchinkanda
Chiyoda-ku, Tokyo, 101-0047, Japan
Tel.: (81) 3 52976161
Fax: (81) 3 52976162
Web Site: www.es-conjapan.co.jp
Year Founded: 1995
8892—(JAS)
Sls.: $112,024,000
Assets: $54,010,000
Liabilities: $7,678,000
Net Worth: $46,332,000
Earnings: $4,312,000
Emp.: 54
Fiscal Year-end: 12/31/12
Business Description:
Real Estate Services
S.I.C.: 6531
N.A.I.C.S.: 531390
Personnel:
Takatoshi Ito *(Pres & CEO)*
Transfer Agent:
Sumitomo Mitsui Trust Bank Limited
1-4-1 Marunouchi Chiyoda-ku
Tokyo, Japan

E.S. FOX LIMITED

9127 Montrose Road
PO Box 1010
Niagara Falls, ON, L2E 7J9, Canada
Tel.: (905) 354-3700
Fax: (905) 354-5599
Toll Free: (866) 233-8933
E-Mail: esfox@esfox.com
Web Site: www.esfox.com
Year Founded: 1934
Rev.: $152,346,927
Emp.: 1,000
Business Description:
Engineering Services
S.I.C.: 8711
N.A.I.C.S.: 541330
Personnel:
E. Spencer Fox *(Pres)*
Rob Arsenault *(CFO & VP)*
Denis Carrier *(COO & Sr VP)*

ES GLOBAL LTD

3 Vyner Street
London, E2 9DG, United Kingdom
Tel.: (44) 20 7055 7200
Fax: (44) 20 7055 7201
E-Mail: info@esglobalsolutions.com
Web Site: www.esglobalsolutions.com
Sales Range: $50-74.9 Million
Business Description:
Outdoor Staging
S.I.C.: 7999
N.A.I.C.S.: 711310
Personnel:
Eugene O'Doherty *(CEO)*

ES GROUP (HOLDINGS) LIMITED

8 Ubi Road 2 06-26 Zervex
Singapore, 408538, Singapore
Tel.: (65) 6748 9111
Fax: (65) 6284 3005
Web Site: www.esgroup.com.sg
Year Founded: 1975
5RC—(SES)
Rev.: $38,709,373
Assets: $56,533,642
Liabilities: $26,934,382
Net Worth: $29,599,260
Earnings: $1,668,997
Fiscal Year-end: 12/31/12
Business Description:
Cargo Handling Services
S.I.C.: 4491
N.A.I.C.S.: 488320
Personnel:
Christopher Chee Leng Low *(CEO)*
Alice Keng Len Chuah *(CFO & Co-Sec)*
Adrian Chan Pengee *(Co-Sec)*
Board of Directors:
Siew Kim Wee
Chee Wee Low
Christopher Chee Leng Low
Eddy Chiang Swee Neo
Jens Rasmussen
Swee Ling Tan
Legal Counsel:
Lee & Lee
50 Raffles Place 06-00 Singapore Land Tower
Singapore, Singapore
Transfer Agent:
Boardroom Corporate & Advisory Services Pte. Ltd.
50 Raffles Place 32-01 Singapore Land Tower
Singapore, Singapore

Subsidiary:

Eng Soon Engineering (1999) Pte Ltd (1)
8 Ubi Road 2 No 06-26 Zervex
Singapore, 408538, Singapore
Tel.: (65) 6752 8017
Fax: (65) 6755 4193
Mechanical Engineering Services
S.I.C.: 8711
N.A.I.C.S.: 541330

Non-U.S. Subsidiary:

Dalian ES Marine & Offshore Engineering Co., Ltd. (1)
Room 1733 Changjiang Square No 123 Changjiang Road
Zhongshan District, Dalian, 116001, China
Tel.: (86) 411 8252 9272
Fax: (86) 411 8252 9810
E-Mail: es-dalian@163.com
Emp.: 20
Marine & Offshore Engineering Services
S.I.C.: 8711
N.A.I.C.S.: 541330
Marco Chanz, *(Gen Mgr)*

ES-SYSTEM S.A.

Ul Przemyslowa 2
30-701 Krakow, Poland
Tel.: (48) 126563633
Fax: (48) 126563649
E-Mail: essystem@essystem.pl
Web Site: www.essystem.pl
ESS—(WAR)
Rev.: $53,697,403
Assets: $60,353,010
Liabilities: $13,055,291
Net Worth: $47,297,720
Earnings: $1,369,367
Emp.: 230
Fiscal Year-end: 12/31/12
Business Description:
Lighting Equipment Mfr
S.I.C.: 3645
N.A.I.C.S.: 335121
Personnel:
Bozena Ciupinska *(Chm-Supervisory Bd)*
Romuald Wojtkowiak *(Chm-Mgmt Bd)*
Leszek Ciupinski *(Deputy Chm-Mgmt Bd-Fin)*
Miroslaw Butryn *(Member-Mgmt Bd)*
Supervisory Board of Directors:
Bozena Ciupinska
Jerzy Burdzy
Arkadiusz Chojnacki
Rafal Maciejewicz
Radoslaw Wojciechowski

Subsidiaries:

ES-SYSTEM Rzeszow sp. z o.o. (1)
Spichlerzowa 42
35322 Rzeszow, Subcarpathia, Poland
Tel.: (48) 178508230
Fax: (48) 178502984
E-Mail: esrzeszow@essystem.pl
Emp.: 76
Lighting Equipment Mfr
S.I.C.: 3645
N.A.I.C.S.: 335121
Jerzy Dyrda *(Pres)*

ES-SYSTEM Wilkasy sp. z o.o. (1)
Wilkasy Ul Olsztynska 2
Gizycko, 11 500, Poland
Tel.: (48) 874299600
Fax: (48) 874299601
Web Site: www.essystem.pl/wilkasy/
Emp.: 500
Lighting Equipment Mfr
S.I.C.: 3646
N.A.I.C.S.: 335122

Non-U.S. Subsidiary:

ES-SYSTEM Scandinavia A.B. (1)
Klarabergsviadukten 92
111 64 Stockholm, Sweden
Tel.: (46) 858500035
Fax: (46) 858500045
E-Mail: info@essystem.se
Web Site: www.essystem.se
Emp.: 4
Lighting Equipment Mfr
S.I.C.: 3648
N.A.I.C.S.: 335129
Chris Erickson *(Mng Dir)*

ESAOTE S.P.A.

Via Siffredi 58
16153 Genoa, Italy
Tel.: (39) 01065471
Fax: (39) 0106547275
E-Mail: esaote@esaote.com
Web Site: www.esaote.com
Sales Range: $350-399.9 Million
Emp.: 1,360
Business Description:
Biomedical Equipment Mfr
S.I.C.: 3845
N.A.I.C.S.: 334510
Personnel:
Carlo Castellano *(Chm, CEO & Mng Dir)*

Fabrizio Landi *(Mng Dir & Gen Mgr-Bus)*
Livio Carniglia *(CFO & Dir-Fin Area)*
Board of Directors:
Carlo Castellano
Luca Arnaboldi
Lorenzo Baraldi
Andrea Bovone
Gabriele Cappellini
Daniele Discepolo
Luciano Hassan
Fabrizio Landi

U.S. Subsidiary:

Esaote North America Inc. (1)
8000 Castleway Dr
Indianapolis, IN 46250
Tel.: (317) 813-6000
Fax: (317) 813-6600
Toll Free: (800) 428-4374
E-Mail: inquire@esaoteusa.com
Web Site: www.esaoteusa.com
Biomedical Equipment Mfr
S.I.C.: 3845
N.A.I.C.S.: 334510
Gordon Parhar *(Gen Mgr)*

Non-U.S. Subsidiaries:

Esaote Asia Pacific Diagnostic Private Limited (1)
F1 Level 1 Global Arcade Near Global Business Park
MG Road, Gurgaon, 122002, India
Tel.: (91) 1244775600
Fax: (91) 1244775699
E-Mail: akacfo@gmail.com
Web Site: www.esaote.com
Emp.: 3
Biomedical Equipment Mfr
S.I.C.: 3845
N.A.I.C.S.: 334510

Esaote Biomedica Deutschland GmbH (1)
Max Planck Str 27 a
Cologne, Germany
Tel.: (49) 22192680000
Fax: (49) 22349679628
E-Mail: esaote@esaote.de
Web Site: www.esaote.de
Emp.: 15
Biomedical Equipment Mfr
S.I.C.: 3845
N.A.I.C.S.: 334510
Wily Luiten *(Mng Dir)*

Esaote China Ltd. (1)
18F 135 Bonham Strand Trade Centre
135 Bonham Strand, Sheung Wan, China (Hong Kong)
Tel.: (852) 25458386
Fax: (852) 25433068
E-Mail: esaote@esaotechina.com
Web Site: www.esaote.com
Biomedical Equipment Mfr
S.I.C.: 3845
N.A.I.C.S.: 334510

Esaote Espana S.A. (1)
Avda San Sebastian sn 08960 Sant Just Desvern
Barcelona, Spain
Tel.: (34) 934732090
Fax: (34) 934732042
E-Mail: info@esaote.es
Web Site: www.esaote.es
Biomedical Equipment Mfr
S.I.C.: 3845
N.A.I.C.S.: 334510

Esaote Europe B.V (1)
Philipsweg 1
6227 AJ Maastricht, Netherlands
Tel.: (31) 433824600
Fax: (31) 433824601
E-Mail: info@esaote.nl
Web Site: www.esaote.com
Emp.: 120
Biomedical Equipment Mfr
S.I.C.: 3845
N.A.I.C.S.: 334510
Anton Esseling *(Gen Mgr)*

Esaote France S.A.R.L. (1)
Za Du Bel Air 10 Ruegetemara
78105 Saint Germain-en-Laye, France
Tel.: (33) 148712525
Fax: (33) 144512420
E-Mail: info@esaote.fr
Web Site: www.esaote.fr
Biomedical Equipment Mfr
S.I.C.: 3845
N.A.I.C.S.: 334510

Esaote Latinoamerica S.A. (1)
San Martin 551 Cuerpo C Piso 8
1004 Buenos Aires, Argentina
Tel.: (54) 1143261832,
Fax: (54) 1143281245
E-Mail: info@esaote.com.ar
Biomedical Equipment Mfr
S.I.C.: 3845
N.A.I.C.S.: 334510

ESAS HOLDING A.S.

Ruzgarlibahce Mah Kavak Sok 3
Beykoz
Istanbul, Turkey
Tel.: (90) 2166818500
Fax: (90) 216 6818560
E-Mail: esas@esas.com.tr
Web Site: www.esas.com.tr
Year Founded: 2000
Business Description:
Investment Holding Company
S.I.C.: 6719
N.A.I.C.S.: 551112
Personnel:
Sevket Sabanci *(Chm)*
Emine S. Kamisli *(Vice Chm)*
Cagatay Ozdogru *(CEO)*
Inan Tanriover *(CFO)*
Board of Directors:
Sevket Sabanci
Emine S. Kamisli
Erhan Kamisli
Ali Ismail Sabanci
Z. Engin Tuncay
Subsidiary:

Pegasus Hava Tasimaciligi A.S. (1)
Aeropark Yenisehir Mah Osmanli Bulvari No:11 34912
Kurtkoy, Istanbul, Turkey
Tel.: (90) 216 560 70 00
Fax: (90) 216 560 71 00
Web Site: www.flypgs.com
PGSUS—(IST)
Emp.: 1,200
Airline
S.I.C.: 4512
N.A.I.C.S.: 481111
Ali Ismail Sabanci *(Chm)*

ESCADA SE

Einsteinring 14-18
85609 Aschheim, Germany
Tel.: (49) 8999440
Fax: (49) 899944111
E-Mail: info@de.escada.com
Web Site: www.escada.com
Year Founded: 1990
Sales Range: $550-599.9 Million
Emp.: 4,118
Business Description:
Women's Clothing & Accessories Mfr Import Export
S.I.C.: 2389
N.A.I.C.S.: 315240
Personnel:
Reinhard Pollath *(Chm-Supervisory Bd)*
Bruno Salzer *(CEO)*
Markus Schurholz *(CFO & Dir-Fin)*
Werner Lackas *(COO)*
Michael Bornicke *(Chief Restructuring Officer)*
Supervisory Board of Directors:
Reinhard Pollath
Rustam Aksenenko
Monika Bader-Janzen
Robert Dissmann
Rainer Fleck
Susanne Hartmann
Gisela Hennig
Jean-Christophe Hocke
Martin Kuhn
Richard Lohner
Britta Munkler
Raffaello Napoleone
Jurgen Wagner
Peter Zuhlsdorff

U.S. Subsidiaries:

Escada USA, New Jersey (1)
1412 Broadway
New York, NY 10018
Tel.: (201) 462-6000
Fax: (201) 462-6440
Web Site: www.escadausa.com
Provider of Women's Clothing & Accessories
S.I.C.: 5137
N.A.I.C.S.: 424330

Escada USA, New York (1)
1412 Broadway
New York, NY 10018-9228
Tel.: (212) 869-8424
Fax: (212) 869-0109
Web Site: www.escada.com
Provider of Women's Apparel & Accessories
S.I.C.: 5621
N.A.I.C.S.: 448120

Non-U.S. Subsidiaries:

Escada Asia Ltd. (1)
24 East Warwick House Taikoo Place 979 King's Road
Quarry Bay, Hong Kong, China (Hong Kong) (100%)
Tel.: (852) 28454321
Fax: (852) 28400667
E-Mail: info@escadaasia.com
Web Site: www.escadaasia.com
Emp.: 30
Provider of Women's Apparel & Accessories
S.I.C.: 2389
N.A.I.C.S.: 315210

Escada Canada Inc. (1)
1412 Broadway
New York, NY 10018 (100%)
Tel.: (212) 852-5300
E-Mail: info@ca.escada.com
Web Site: www.escada.com
Emp.: 12
Women's Clothing Mfr
S.I.C.: 2389
N.A.I.C.S.: 315240
Mohan Sookdeo *(Controller)*

Escada France S.A. (1)
19 32 Paris Ten
75009 Paris, France (100%)
Tel.: (33) 149701521
Fax: (33) 149701500
E-Mail: agnes.gesas@escada.com
Web Site: www.escada.com
Emp.: 80
Provider of Women's Apparel
S.I.C.: 2389
N.A.I.C.S.: 315210

Escada Italia S.r.l. (1)
Via Solferino 19
Milan, 20121, Italy
Tel.: (39) 0229003141
Fax: (39) 026595182
Web Site: www.escada.com
Provider of Women's Apparel
S.I.C.: 2389
N.A.I.C.S.: 315210

Escada Japan Co. Ltd. (1)
550 Nishihonmachi Mitsui Building
1-3-15 Awaza, Osaka, Japan
Web Site: www.escada.com
Provider of Women's Apparel
S.I.C.: 2399
N.A.I.C.S.: 315210

Escada Korea Ltd. (1)
4th & 5th Floors Wookyung Building 98-13 Chungdam-dong
Kangnam-ku, Seoul, Korea (South)
Web Site: www.escada.com
Provider of Women's Apparel
S.I.C.: 2389
N.A.I.C.S.: 315210

Escada UK Ltd. (1)
5 Fl W Shropshire House 2-10 Capper St
Marylebone, London, W1G9NB, United Kingdom (100%)
Tel.: (44) 2075806066
Fax: (44) 2076378749
Web Site: www.escada.com
Emp.: 5
Wholesaler of Ladies Fashion
S.I.C.: 7389
N.A.I.C.S.: 541490

Grupo Escada Espana S.A. (1)
Fonollar 4
Manresa, 8240 Barcelona, Spain (100%)
Tel.: (34) 938751000
Fax: (34) 938753336
E-Mail: mail@grupoescada.es
Web Site: www.grupoescada.es
Provider of Women's Apparel
S.I.C.: 2389
N.A.I.C.S.: 315210

ESCHA BAUELEMENTE GMBH

Elberfelder Str 32
58553 Halver, Germany
Tel.: (49) 2353708800
Fax: (49) 2353708400
E-Mail: info@escha.de
Web Site: www.escha.de
Rev.: $31,726,200
Emp.: 296
Business Description:
Electronic Connectors Mfr
S.I.C.: 3678
N.A.I.C.S.: 334417
Personnel:
Dietrich Turck *(Mng Dir)*

ESCO FINANCIAL & ENGINEERING COMPANY S.A/N.V.

(d/b/a Efeco)
Square de Meeus 38/40
B-1000 Brussels, Belgium
Tel.: (32) 2 717 64 05
Fax: (32) 2 720 38 12
E-Mail: ch.verbeke@efeco.com
Web Site: www.efeco.com
Sales Range: $50-74.9 Million
Emp.: 200
Business Description:
Electric Drive, Inverter, Switch & Control Mfr
S.I.C.: 3625
N.A.I.C.S.: 335314
Personnel:
Thierry Schmidt *(CEO)*

Subsidiaries:

Esco Couplings N.V. (1)
Kouterveld Culliganlaan 3
B 1831 Diegem, Belgium
Tel.: (32) 2 715 65 60
Fax: (32) 2 720 83 62
E-Mail: info@esco-couplings.be
Web Site: www.escocoupling.com
Coupling Mfr
S.I.C.: 3568
N.A.I.C.S.: 333613

Non-U.S. Subsidiary:

Esco Couplings & Transmissions Private Limited (2)
Plot 22/A 1st Stage Peenya Industrial Estate
Bengaluru, 560058, India
Tel.: (91) 80 49256000
Fax: (91) 80 49256060
E-Mail: info@esco-couplings.co.in
Web Site: www.esco-couplings.co.in
Coupling Mfr
S.I.C.: 3568
N.A.I.C.S.: 333613

Esco Drives & Automation N.V. (1)
Kouterveld Culliganlaan 3
1831 Diegem, Flemish Brabant, Belgium
Tel.: (32) 27176432
Fax: (32) 27176431
E-Mail: info@esco-da.be

Esco Financial & Engineering Company S.A/N.V.—(Continued)

Web Site: www.esco.be
Emp.: 9
Automation Electric Controls Mfr
S.I.C.: 3613
N.A.I.C.S.: 335313

Esco Power N.V. (1)
Avenue Ernest Solvay 48
B 1831 Saintes, Belgium
Tel.: (32) 2 717 64 90
Fax: (32) 2 717 64 91
E-Mail: info@escopower.be
Web Site: www.escopower.be
Gearbox & Transmission Equipment Mfr
S.I.C.: 3568
N.A.I.C.S.: 333613

Esco Transmissions N.V. (1)
Kouterveld Culliganlaan 3
B 1831 Diegem, Belgium
Tel.: (32) 2 717 64 60
Fax: (32) 2 717 64 61
E-Mail: info@esco-transmissions.be
Web Site: www.esco-transmissions.be
Transmission Equipment Mfr
S.I.C.: 3568
N.A.I.C.S.: 333613

Non-U.S. Subsidiaries:

Esco Aandrijvingen B.V. (1)
Ondernemingsweg 19
2404 HM Alphen aan den Rijn, Netherlands
Mailing Address:
Postbus 349
2400 AH Alphen aan den Rijn, Netherlands
Tel.: (31) 172 42 33 33
Fax: (31) 172 42 33 42
E-Mail: info@esco-aandrijvingen.nl
Web Site: www.esco-aandrijvingen.nl
Machinery Sales, Distribution Services
S.I.C.: 5084
N.A.I.C.S.: 423830

esco antriebstechnik gmbh (1)
Biberweg 10
D 53842 Troisdorf, Germany
Tel.: (49) 2241 48070
Fax: (49) 2241 480710
E-Mail: esco-antriebstechnik@t-online.de
Web Site: www.esco-antriebstechnik.de
Electrical Drive System Mfr
S.I.C.: 3699
N.A.I.C.S.: 335999

Esco Transmissions S.A. (1)
ZII 34 rue Ferme Saint-Ladre Saint Witz
F 95471 Fosses, France
Tel.: (33) 1 34 31 95 95
Fax: (33) 1 34 31 95 99
E-Mail: info@esco-transmissions.fr
Web Site: www.esco-transmissions.fr
Transmission Equipment Mfr
S.I.C.: 3568
N.A.I.C.S.: 333613

ESCO GLOBAL REALTY CORP.

1081 Cole Harbour Road Suite 6
Dartmouth, NS, B2V 1E8, Canada
Tel.: (902) 434-9381
Fax: (902) 435-5464
Toll Free: (888) 434-9381
Web Site: www.escorealtyspecialists.com
Year Founded: 2003
Sales Range: Less than $1 Million
Emp.: 1
Business Description:
Real Estate Brokerage Services
S.I.C.: 6531
N.A.I.C.S.: 531210
Personnel:
Edward Gaius Carmichael *(CEO & Co-Owner)*
Sara Carmichael *(Co-Owner & Sr Broker)*

ESCORTS INVESTMENT BANK LIMITED

Escorts House 26-Davis Road
Lahore, Pakistan
Tel.: (92) 42 3637 1931
Fax: (92) 42 3637 5950
E-Mail: mailmanager@escortsbank.net
Web Site: www.escortsbank.net
ESBL—(KAR LAH)
Rev.: $2,428,253
Assets: $12,739,682
Liabilities: $9,710,298
Net Worth: $3,029,383
Earnings: ($26,710)
Fiscal Year-end: 06/30/13
Business Description:
Banking Services
S.I.C.: 6029
N.A.I.C.S.: 522110
Personnel:
Shazia Bashir *(Pres & CEO)*
Hamid ur Rehman *(CFO & Sec)*
Malik Shahid Mahmood *(Sr Exec VP & Head-Ops)*
Board of Directors:
Bairam Qureishy
Amjad Mahmood Agha
Mutahir Ahmed
Muhammad Sharif Baqir
Shazia Bashir
Tajamul Hussain Bokharee
Zulfiqar A. Khan

Subsidiary:

Escorts Capital Limited (1)
26 Davis Rd
Lahore, Pakistan
Tel.: (92) 426371931
Fax: (92) 426375950
E-Mail: mailmanager@escortsbank.net
Banking Services
S.I.C.: 6029
N.A.I.C.S.: 522110
Hasan Abidzaidi *(Gen Mgr)*

ESCORTS LIMITED

15/5 Mathura Road
Faridabad, 121 003, India
Tel.: (91) 1292250222
Fax: (91) 1292250009
E-Mail: escortsgroup@escortscorporate.com
Web Site: www.escortsgroup.com
ESCORTS—(NSE)
Rev.: $769,992,156
Assets: $658,370,232
Liabilities: $351,190,242
Net Worth: $307,179,990
Earnings: $13,571,280
Emp.: 5,338
Fiscal Year-end: 09/30/12
Business Description:
Agricultural & Industrial Machinery Mfr & Distr
S.I.C.: 3523
N.A.I.C.S.: 333111
Personnel:
Rajan Nanda *(Chm & Mng Dir)*
Nikhil Nanda *(Mng Dir)*
G. B. Mathur *(Compliance Officer, Sec & Exec VP-Law)*
G. V. R. Murthy *(CEO-Construction Equipment)*
Lalit K. Pahwa *(CEO-Auto Products)*
Vikram Singhal *(CEO-ERP)*
S. Sridhar *(CEO-Agri Machinery)*
Kanwal Kishore Vij *(CEO-ECE)*
Ishan Mehta *(Exec VP-HR & ER)*
Board of Directors:
Rajan Nanda
S. C. Bhargava
S. A. Dave
Nikhil Nanda
P. S. Pritam
Hardeep Singh

ESCRIT INC.

Minami Aoyama City Building 3-2-5
Minami Aoyama
Minato-ku, Tokyo, 107-0062, Japan
Tel.: (81) 354108822
Fax: (81) 354103588
E-Mail: info@escrit.jp
Web Site: www.escrit.jp
2196—(TKS)
Sales Range: $75-99.9 Million
Emp.: 218
Business Description:
Wedding Ceremonies & Wedding Receptions Planner & Operator
S.I.C.: 7299
N.A.I.C.S.: 812990
Personnel:
Hiroshi Iwamoto *(Pres)*

ESCROW AGENT JAPAN, INC.

2-2-1 Yaesu Daiya Yaesuguchi
Building 4F Chuo-ku
Tokyo, 104-0028, Japan
Tel.: (81) 3 6703 0500
Web Site: www.ea-j.jp/
Rev.: $11,416,487
Emp.: 100
Fiscal Year-end: 02/28/13
Business Description:
Real Estate Financial Services
S.I.C.: 6531
N.A.I.C.S.: 531390
Personnel:
Hideaki Homma *(CEO)*

ESCUDO CAPITAL CORPORATION

#3507 1033 Marinaside Crescent
Vancouver, BC, V6Z 3A3, Canada
Tel.: (604) 893-8784
Fax: (604) 266-1840
E-Mail: jboddie@shaw.ca
Web Site: www.escudocapital.ca
Year Founded: 2011
EDO.P—(TSXV)
Business Description:
Investment Services
S.I.C.: 6211
N.A.I.C.S.: 523999
Personnel:
John Boddie *(CEO & Sec)*
Catherine Der *(CFO)*
Board of Directors:
John Boddie
Richard Cohen
Joseph Groia
Transfer Agent:
Olympia Trust Company
125 9th Avenue SE Suite 2300
Calgary, AB, T2G 0P6, Canada
Tel.: (403) 261-0900

ESERVGLOBAL LIMITED

c/o Simpsons Solicitors Level 2 Pier 8/9
23 Hickson Road, Millers Point, NSW, 2000, Australia
Tel.: (61) 2 8014 5050
Fax: (61) 2 8014 5060
E-Mail: info@eservglobal.com
Web Site: www.eservglobal.com
ESV—(AIM ASX)
Rev.: $27,810,311
Assets: $47,708,009
Liabilities: $14,200,724
Net Worth: $33,507,285
Earnings: $9,305,685
Fiscal Year-end: 10/31/13
Business Description:
Mobile Payment Services
S.I.C.: 7389
N.A.I.C.S.: 561499
Personnel:
Stephen John Baldwin *(Acting Chm)*
Paolo Montessori *(CEO & Mng Dir)*
Stephen Blundell *(CFO & Dir-Fin)*
Remi Arame *(Chief Sls Officer)*
James Hume *(CTO)*
Paolo Gagliardi *(Chief Delivery Officer)*
Tom Rowe *(Sec)*
Board of Directors:
Stephen John Baldwin
Francois Barrault
Stephen Blundell
John Conoley
Tom Rowe

Headquarters:

eServGlobal Holdings SAS (1)
244 avenue Pierre Brossolette
92245 Malakoff, Cedex, France
Tel.: (33) 146125885
Fax: (33) 147350788
E-Mail: allstaff@eservglobal.com
Web Site: www.eservglobal.com
Emp.: 70
Telecommunication Services Provider
S.I.C.: 4899
N.A.I.C.S.: 517919
Rahel Kebede *(Gen Mgr)*

Subsidiary:

eServGlobal SAS (2)
244 avenue Pierre Brossolette
92245 Malakoff, Cedex, France
Tel.: (33) 1 4612 5885
Fax: (33) 1 4735 0788
Mobile Payment Solutions
S.I.C.: 7389
N.A.I.C.S.: 561499

Non-U.S. Subsidiaries:

eServGlobal Telecom Romania Srl (3)
Calea Floreasca N 167 Sector 1
Bucharest, 014459, Romania
Tel.: (40) 21 233 2115
Fax: (40) 21 233 1877
Business Support Services
S.I.C.: 7389
N.A.I.C.S.: 561499

P.T. eServGlobal Indonesia (3)
Manara Rajalawali
Kawasan Mega Kuningan, Jakarta, 12950, Indonesia
Tel.: (62) 2157950220
Fax: (62) 2157950660
E-Mail: stellaretratnasari@eservglobal.com
Web Site: www.eservglobal.com
Emp.: 12
Software Programming Services
S.I.C.: 7371
N.A.I.C.S.: 541511
Jean Baptiste Voisin *(Gen Mgr)*

Subsidiary:

eServGlobal (NZ) Pty Limited (1)
Suite 5 30 Florence Street
Newlands, Newstead, QLD 4006, Australia
Tel.: (61) 733020194
Fax: (61) 733020193
Web Site: www.eservglobal.com
Emp.: 65
Telecommunication Services Provider
S.I.C.: 4899
N.A.I.C.S.: 517919
Craig Halliday *(CEO)*

Non-U.S. Subsidiaries:

eServGlobal (HK) Limited (1)
Level 19 2 Intl Fin Ctr
8 Fin St, Central, China (Hong Kong)
Tel.: (852) 22511953
Fax: (852) 22511618
Web Site: www.eservglobal.com
Telecommunication Services Provider
S.I.C.: 4899
N.A.I.C.S.: 517919

eServGlobal NVSA (1)
Gossetlaan 54
1702 Dilbeek, Groot Bijgaarden, Belgium
Tel.: (32) 2 304 3918
Fax: (32) 2 308 0011
Web Site: www.eservglobal.com
Emp.: 50
Telecommunication Services Provider
S.I.C.: 4899
N.A.I.C.S.: 517919

eServGlobal UK Limited (1)
Atrium Court The Ring
Bracknell, Berks, RG12 1BW, United Kingdom
Tel.: (44) 1344 393228
Web Site: www.eservglobal.com
Emp.: 50
Telecommunication Services
S.I.C.: 4899
N.A.I.C.S.: 517919

ESHRAQ PROPERTIES COMPANY (PJSC)
Suite 1201 12th Floor C2 Building
PO Box 108737
Bateen Towers Al Bateen, Abu Dhabi, United Arab Emirates
Tel.: (971) 2 635 4854
Fax: (971) 2 635 4864
E-Mail: info@eshraquae.com
Web Site: www.eshraquae.com
ESHRAQ—(EMI)
Sales Range: $1-9.9 Million
Business Description:
Real Estate Management Services
S.I.C.: 6531
N.A.I.C.S.: 531390
Personnel:
Saleh Mohammed Nasrah Al Amri *(Chm)*
Jamal Hamad Al Sageer *(Mng Dir)*

ESI ENTERTAINMENT SYSTEMS INC.
Unit 130 - 8610 Glenlyon Parkway
Burnaby, BC, V5J 0B6, Canada
Tel.: (604) 299-6922
Fax: (604) 299-3984
E-Mail: info@esi.ca
Web Site: www.esi.ca
Year Founded: 1999
ESY—(CNSX)
Rev.: $2,535,494
Assets: $9,468,558
Liabilities: $12,266,582
Net Worth: ($2,798,023)
Earnings: $1,627,299
Emp.: 18
Fiscal Year-end: 02/28/13
Business Description:
Software Developer
S.I.C.: 7372
N.A.I.C.S.: 511210
Personnel:
Christopher H. Freeman *(Chm)*
Michael R. Meeks *(Pres & CEO)*
Ian H. Franks *(CFO)*
Board of Directors:
Christopher H. Freeman
William L. Koyle
Michael R. Meeks

E.S.I. ENVIRONMENTAL SENSORS INC.
2071C Malaview Avenue
Sidney, BC, V8L 5X6, Canada
Tel.: (250) 655-3211
Fax: (250) 655-3299
Toll Free: (800) 799-6324
E-Mail: info@esica.com
Web Site: www.esica.com
Year Founded: 1973
ESV—(TSXV)
Rev.: $152,357
Assets: $251,263
Liabilities: $1,458,341
Net Worth: ($1,207,077)
Earnings: ($694,590)
Emp.: 6
Fiscal Year-end: 03/31/13
Business Description:
Soil Monitoring Instruments Mfr
S.I.C.: 3823
N.A.I.C.S.: 334513
Personnel:
Stephan Radermacher *(Chm)*
Board of Directors:
Stephan Radermacher
Mateo Beffa
Johan Grandin
Legal Counsel:
Campney & Murphy
#2100-1111 West Georgia Street
Vancouver, BC, V7X 1K9, Canada
Tel.: (604) 688-8022
Transfer Agent:
Computershare Trust Company of Canada
510 Burrard St 4th Floor
Vancouver, BC, Canada

ESI GROUP S.A.
100-102 Avenue de Suffren
75015 Paris, France
Tel.: (33) 153651414
Fax: (33) 153651412
E-Mail: investors@esi-group.com
Web Site: www.esi-group.com
Year Founded: 1973
ESI—(EUR)
Rev.: $146,770,223
Assets: $196,115,430
Liabilities: $91,485,713
Net Worth: $104,629,717
Earnings: $6,759,120
Emp.: 1,000
Fiscal Year-end: 01/31/13
Business Description:
Digital Simulation Software for Product Prototyping & Manufacturing Processes
S.I.C.: 3652
N.A.I.C.S.: 334614
Personnel:
Alain de Rouvray *(Chm & CEO)*
Vincent Chaillou *(COO & Pres-Product Ops)*
Naury Birnbaum *(Chief Strategy Officer)*
Lech Tomasz Kisielewicz *(Exec VP-Svcs Ops)*
Board of Directors:
Alain de Rouvray
Francis Bernard
Vincent Chaillou
Eric d'Hotelans
Michel Barbier de La Serre
Cristel de Rouvray
Charles Helen des Isnards
Jacques Dubois
Othman Laraki
Ernst & Young Audit
Faubourg de l Arche 11 Allee de l Arche
Paris, France
Subsidiary:

ESI France SARL (1)
Le Recamier 70 rue Robert
69458 Lyon, France
Tel.: (33) 478141200
Fax: (33) 478141201
E-Mail: info@esi-group.com
Web Site: www.esi-group.com
Emp.: 60
Digital Simulation Software Development Services
S.I.C.: 7371
N.A.I.C.S.: 541511
Eric Daubourg *(Mng Dir)*

U.S. Subsidiary:

ESI North America, Inc. (1)
32605 W 12 Mile Rd Ste 350
Farmington, MI 48334
Tel.: (248) 203-0642
Fax: (248) 381-8998
Web Site: www.esi-group.com
Emp.: 30
Simulation Software Distr & Sales
S.I.C.: 5045
N.A.I.C.S.: 423430
Michael Bloor *(COO)*

Non-U.S. Subsidiaries:

Calcom ESI SA (1)
Parc Scientifique EPFL
CH-1015 Lausanne, Switzerland
Tel.: (41) 216932918
Fax: (41) 216934740
E-Mail: mail@calcom.ch
Web Site: www.calcom.ch
Emp.: 18
Simulation Software Distr & Sales
S.I.C.: 5045
N.A.I.C.S.: 423430
Alaen Derougray *(Pres)*

ESI CFD Services (1)
K502 MegaCenter Pune Solapur Road
Hadapsar, Pune, Maharashtra, 411013, India
Tel.: (91) 20 26890656
Fax: (91) 20 26890384
E-Mail: info@mindwr-india.com
Web Site: www.esi-group.com
Emp.: 35
Industrial Software Development Services
S.I.C.: 7371
N.A.I.C.S.: 541511

ESI China (1)
Unit 1006-1008 Metropolis Tower No 2 Haidiandongsanjie
Haidian District, Beijing, 100080, China
Tel.: (86) 1065544907
Fax: (86) 1065544911
Web Site: www.esi-group.com
Emp.: 40
Software Development Services
S.I.C.: 7371
N.A.I.C.S.: 541511

ESI GmbH (1)
Mergenthaleralle 15-21
D-65760 Eschborn, Germany
Tel.: (49) 619695830
Fax: (49) 61969583111
E-Mail: abt@esigmbh.de
Web Site: www.esigmbh.de
Emp.: 40
Simulation Software Sales & Technical Services
S.I.C.: 5045
N.A.I.C.S.: 423430

ESI Group Hispania, S.L. (1)
Parque Empresarial Arroyo De La Vega C Francisca Delgado 11 Planta 2
28108 Alcobendas, Madrid, Spain
Tel.: (34) 914840256
Fax: (34) 91 484 02 55
Web Site: www.esi-group.com
Software Development Services
S.I.C.: 7371
N.A.I.C.S.: 541511

ESI Group Netherlands (1)
Radex Innovation Centre Room 4.57
Rotterdamseweg 183 C, 2629 HD Delft, Netherlands
Tel.: (31) 152682501
Fax: (31) 152682514
Web Site: www.esi-group.com
Simulation Software Distr & Sales
S.I.C.: 5045
N.A.I.C.S.: 423430

ESI Italia srl (1)
Via San Donato 191
40127 Bologna, Italy
Tel.: (39) 516335577
Fax: (39) 051 6335601
E-Mail: info.italy@esi-group.com
Web Site: www.esi-italia.it
Emp.: 5
Digital Simulation Software Development Services
S.I.C.: 7371
N.A.I.C.S.: 541511
Denis Luci *(Mng Dir)*

ESI Japan Ltd (1)
16F Shinjuku Green Tower Bldg 6-14-1 Nishi-Shinjuku
Shinjuku-ku, Tokyo, 160-0023, Japan
Tel.: (81) 363818490
Fax: (81) 363818488
E-Mail: mmr@esi.co.jp
Web Site: www.esi.co.jp
Emp.: 50
Digital Simulation Software Development Services
S.I.C.: 7371
N.A.I.C.S.: 541511
Isao Yumoto *(Gen Mgr)*

ESI Software Pvt. Ltd (1)
24-25 27th Cross Banasankari 2nd Stage
560 070 Bengaluru, India
Tel.: (91) 8026719006
Fax: (91) 8041818405
E-Mail: deepa.b@esi-group.com
Web Site: www.esi-group.com
Emp.: 100
Simulation Software
S.I.C.: 3652
N.A.I.C.S.: 334614
Nagesh L. Bysani *(Mng Dir)*

ESI UK Limited (1)
John Eccles House
Robert Robinson Avenue
The Oxford Science Park, Oxford, OX4 4GP, United Kingdom
Tel.: (44) 01865338007
Fax: (44) 01865338100
Web Site: www.esi.com
Simulation Software Distr & Sales
S.I.C.: 5045
N.A.I.C.S.: 423430
Michael Hawley *(Mng Dir)*

Hankook ESI (1)
157-033 5F Misung Building 660-6 Deungchon-3Dong
Gangseo-ku, Seoul, Korea (South)
Tel.: (82) 53300743
Fax: (82) 2 3662 0084
Web Site: www.esi.co.kr
Digital Simulation Software Development Services
S.I.C.: 7371
N.A.I.C.S.: 541511

MECAS ESI s.r.o. (1)
Uslavska 10
32600 Plzen, Czech Republic
Tel.: (420) 377432931
Fax: (420) 377432930
E-Mail: info@mecasesi.cz
Web Site: www.mecasesi.cz
Emp.: 35
Simulation Software Distr & Sales
S.I.C.: 5045
N.A.I.C.S.: 423430
Karel Lunacek *(Mng Dir, Dir-Sls & Mktg)*

The Virtual Try-Out Space S.L. (1)
Edificio IKEA Oficina 311
C/ Estartetxe 5, 48940 Leioa, Bizkaia, Spain
Tel.: (34) 944804760
Fax: (34) 94 4805199
Simulation Software Distr & Sales
S.I.C.: 5045
N.A.I.C.S.: 423430

ESJOT GOLDENBERG
Rue Du Zornhoff
Monswiller, 67700 Saverne, France
Tel.: (33) 388715502
Fax: (33) 3344388916018
E-Mail: Cgillig@esjot-group.com
Web Site: www.esjot-group.com
Sls.: $20,900,000
Emp.: 68
Business Description:
Sheet Metalwork
S.I.C.: 3444
N.A.I.C.S.: 332322
Personnel:
Jean Bonnelye *(Pres)*

ESKANDAR LTD.
134 Lots Rd
London, SW10 0RJ, United Kingdom
Tel.: (44) 2073517333
Fax: (44) 2073517444
E-Mail: info@eskandar.com
Web Site: www.eskandar.com
Sales Range: $10-24.9 Million
Emp.: 50
Business Description:
Clothing & Accessories Retailer
S.I.C.: 5699
N.A.I.C.S.: 448150

Eskandar Ltd.—(Continued)

Personnel:
Eskandar Nabavi *(Mng Dir)*

ESKAY MINING CORPORATION
36 Toronto Street Suite 1000
Toronto, ON, M5H 2V6, Canada
Tel.: (416) 907-6151
E-Mail: info@eskaymining.com
Web Site: www.kenrich-eskay.com
ESK—(TSXV)
Int. Income: $749
Assets: $195,492
Liabilities: $817,796
Net Worth: ($622,304)
Earnings: ($342,394)
Fiscal Year-end: 02/28/13
Business Description:
Metal Mining Services
S.I.C.: 1081
N.A.I.C.S.: 213114
Personnel:
Hugh Mac Balkam *(Pres & CEO)*
Carmelo Marrelli *(CFO)*
Board of Directors:
Hugh Mac Balkam
J. Gordon McMehen
Robert Myhill
Transfer Agent:
Computershare Investor Services Inc.
100 University Avenue 8th Floor
Toronto, ON, M5J 2Y1, Canada
Tel.: (514) 982-7555

ESKER S.A.
10 rue des emeraudes
69006 Lyon, France
Tel.: (33) 472834646
Fax: (33) 472834640
E-Mail: info@esker.fr
Web Site: www.esker.fr
Year Founded: 1985
ALESK—(EUR)
Sls.: $54,196,804
Assets: $44,587,843
Liabilities: $23,652,207
Net Worth: $20,935,636
Earnings: $4,039,856
Emp.: 281
Fiscal Year-end: 12/31/12
Business Description:
Computer Software
S.I.C.: 7372
N.A.I.C.S.: 511210
Personnel:
Marie-Claude Bernal *(Chm-Supervisory Bd)*
Jean-Michel Berard *(Chm-Mgmt Bd & CEO)*
Kleber Beauvillain *(Vice Chm-Supervisory Bd)*
Emmanuel Olivier *(COO & Member-Mgmt Bd)*
Steve Smith *(COO-USA & Member-Mgmt Bd)*
Jean-Jacques Berard *(Member-Mgmt Bd & Exec VP-R&D)*
Eric Thomas *(Member-Mgmt Bd & VP-Bus Dev)*
Eric Bussy *(Member-Mgmt Bd & Dir-Product Mgmt & Mktg)*
Anne Grand-Clement *(Member-Mgmt Bd & Dir-Pro Svcs & Technical Support)*
Supervisory Board of Directors:
Marie-Claude Bernal
Kleber Beauvillain
Thomas Wolfe

Deloitte & Associes
Villeurbanne, France

U.S. Subsidiary:

Esker, Inc. **(1)**
1212 Deming Way Ste 350
Madison, WI 53717-1984 (100%)
Tel.: (608) 828-6000
Fax: (608) 273-8227
Toll Free: (800) 368-5283
E-Mail: info@esker.com
Web Site: www.esker.com
Emp.: 120
Developer of Computer Network Connectivity Software
S.I.C.: 7371
N.A.I.C.S.: 541511
Steve Smith *(COO & Mng Dir)*
Kevin Kniess *(Chief Compliance Officer & Gen Counsel)*

Non-U.S. Subsidiaries:

Esker Australia Pty. Ltd. **(1)**
Unit 13 9 11 Chaplin Dr Lanecove
Sydney, 2066, Australia (100%)
Tel.: (61) 285965100
Fax: (61) 285965175
E-Mail: info@esker.com.au
Web Site: www.esker.com.au
Sales Range: $1-9.9 Million
Emp.: 10
Provider of Computer Software
S.I.C.: 7371
N.A.I.C.S.: 541511
Christophe Dumonet *(Mng Dir)*

Esker Documents Automation Asia Pte Ltd **(1)**
47 Scotts Road 05-04 Goldbell Towers
Singapore, 228233, Singapore
Tel.: (65) 67356882
Fax: (65) 67356889
E-Mail: info@esker.com.sg
Web Site: www.esker.com.sg
Emp.: 5
Document Process Automation Software Development Services
S.I.C.: 7389
N.A.I.C.S.: 561410
Albert Leong *(Mng Dir)*

Esker GmbH **(1)**
Dillwaechterstrasse 5
80686 Munich, Germany De
Tel.: (49) 897008870 (100%)
Fax: (49) 8970088770
E-Mail: info@esker.de
Web Site: www.esker.de
Emp.: 8
Provider of Computer Software
S.I.C.: 7371
N.A.I.C.S.: 541511

Esker Iberica **(1)**
C/ Maudes, 51 6 4
28014 Madrid, Spain (100%)
Tel.: (34) 2 89 20 03 03
Fax: (34) 2 57 51 18 96
E-Mail: info@esker.es
Web Site: www.esker.es
Emp.: 55
Provider of Computer Software
S.I.C.: 7371
N.A.I.C.S.: 541511
Jesus Midon *(Mng Dir)*

Esker Italia S.r.l. **(1)**
Strada 4 Palazzo A2 Assago
20090 Milan, Italy IT
Tel.: (39) 289200303 (100%)
Fax: (39) 257511896
E-Mail: info@esker.it
Web Site: www.esker.it
Emp.: 7
Provider of Computer Software
S.I.C.: 7371
N.A.I.C.S.: 541511
Giovanni Gavioli *(Mng Dir)*

Esker Ltd. **(1)**
Durham Wyvern Business Park Spaniel Way
Shardlow, Derby, Derbyshire, DE72 2GH, United Kingdom (100%)
Tel.: (44) 332548181
Fax: (44) 332548160
E-Mail: info@esker.co.uk
Web Site: www.esker.co.uk
Emp.: 22
Provider of Computer Software
S.I.C.: 7371
N.A.I.C.S.: 541511

ESKMUIR PROPERTIES LTD
8 Queen Anne Street
London, W1G 9LD, United Kingdom
Tel.: (44) 2074362339
Fax: (44) 2074362307
Web Site: www.eskmuir.com
Year Founded: 1990
BD28—(LSE)
Business Description:
Commercial Property Investment Services
S.I.C.: 6531
N.A.I.C.S.: 531390
Personnel:
Paul Hodgson *(Mng Dir)*
Anita Moran *(Sec & Controller-Fin)*

Subsidiary:

Eskmuir Securities Ltd **(1)**
8 Queen Anne Street
W1G 9LD London, United Kingdom
Tel.: (44) 207 436 2339
Fax: (44) 207 436 2307
E-Mail: info@eskmuir.com
Web Site: www.eskmuirproperties.co.uk
Emp.: 5
Securities Brokerage Services
S.I.C.: 6211
N.A.I.C.S.: 523120
Paul Hodgson *(Mng Dir)*

ESKOM HOLDINGS SOC LIMITED
Megawatt Park Maxwell Drive
Sunninghill
Sandton, 2157, South Africa
Tel.: (27) 11 800 8111
Telex: 4 50585 ESKOM
Fax: (27) 11 800 4299
E-Mail: khany.makhaya@eskom.co.za
Web Site: www.eskom.co.za
Year Founded: 1923
ESKDY—(OTC)
Rev.: $14,394,667,300
Assets: $48,257,080,800
Liabilities: $36,066,254,500
Net Worth: $12,190,826,300
Earnings: $578,941,100
Emp.: 46,266
Fiscal Year-end: 03/31/13
Business Description:
Electricity Generation Services
S.I.C.: 4939
N.A.I.C.S.: 221122
Personnel:
Zola A. Tsotsi *(Chm)*
Brian A. Dames *(CEO)*
Bhabalazi E. Bulunga *(Grp Exec-HR)*
Thava Govender *(Grp Exec-Generation)*
Erica L. Johnson *(Grp Exec-Enterprise Dev)*
Steve J. Lennon *(Grp Exec-Sustainability)*
Dan L. Marokane *(Grp Exec-Tech & Comml & Acting Exec-Grp Capital)*
Tsholofelo B. L. Molefe *(Grp Exec-Customer Svc)*
Ayanda Noah *(Grp Exec-Distr)*
Mongezi M. Ntsokolo *(Grp Exec-Transmission)*
B. Mbomvu *(Sec)*
Board of Directors:
Zola A. Tsotsi
Brian A. Dames
Bernard Lewis Fanaroff
R. M. Queendy Gungubele
Caroline Henry
Neo Lesela
Bajabulile Luthuli
Chwayita Mabude
Yasmin Masithela
Marake Collin Matjila
Boni Mehlomakulu
Mafika Edmund Mkhwanazi
S. Phenyane Q. Sedibe
Daitile Elizabeth Lily Zondo

KPMG Inc
85 Empire Road
Parktown, South Africa

Subsidiary:

Rotek Engineering (Pty) Ltd. **(1)**
3 Lower Germiston Road Roshewill
Rosherville, 40099 Johannesburg, South Africa (100%)
Mailing Address:
PO Box 40099
Cleveland, 2022, South Africa
Tel.: (27) 00116294000
Fax: (27) 116262169
E-Mail: theva.govnder@rotekengineering.co.za
Web Site: www.rotekengineering.com
Emp.: 1,500
Maintenance & Service
S.I.C.: 4939
N.A.I.C.S.: 221122
Lef Carlo *(CEO)*

ESO PARTNERS L.P.
Palladium House 2nd Floor 1-4 Argyll Street
London, W1F 7TA, United Kingdom
Tel.: (44) 2070047860
Fax: (44) 2072875157
E-Mail: ad@esocapital.com
Web Site: www.esocapital.com
Emp.: 20
Business Description:
Miscellaneous Investment Management Services
S.I.C.: 6211
N.A.I.C.S.: 523999
Personnel:
Alex Schmid *(CEO)*
Driss Benkirane *(Mng Partner)*

Non-U.S. Holdings:

Ucamco N.V. **(1)**
Bijenstraat 19
9051 Gent, Belgium
Tel.: (32) 92169900
Fax: (32) 92169912
E-Mail: info@ucamco.com
Web Site: www.ucamco.com
Emp.: 40
Designer & Mfr of PCB CAM & Laser Photoplotting Systems
S.I.C.: 3575
N.A.I.C.S.: 334118
Karel Tavernier *(Mng Dir)*

Gardien Pacific Ltd. **(1)**
Ste 1022-23 Level 10 Landmark N 39 Lung Sum Ave, Sheung Shui, China (Hong Kong)
Tel.: (852) 29675980
Fax: (852) 29675990
E-Mail: info.hk@gardien.com
Web Site: www.gardien.com
Emp.: 500
Printed Circuit Board Testing Services
S.I.C.: 8734
N.A.I.C.S.: 541380
Rory Devlin *(Chm)*
Michael Tose *(Vice Chm)*
Jan Lipton *(Pres)*
Alison Chan-Dorr *(CFO)*
Jason Fraser *(Exec VP-Sls & Mktg)*

Non-U.S. Subsidiaries:

Gardien Japan Co., Ltd. **(2)**
2-4-3 Takanodai
177-0033 Tokyo, Nerima Ku, Japan
Tel.: (81) 339046282
Fax: (81) 339046249
Printed Circuit Board Testing Services
S.I.C.: 8734
N.A.I.C.S.: 541380
Masahiro Tateishi *(Gen Mgr)*

Gardien **(2)**
79 Milliken Blvd
Toronto, ON, M1V1V3, Canada
Tel.: (416) 292-0726
Fax: (416) 292-3254
Printed Circuit Board Testing Services
S.I.C.: 8734

N.A.I.C.S.: 541380

ESON PRECISION IND. CO., LTD.

12F-3 No 2 Sec 4 Chungyang Road
Tucheng District, Taipei, Taiwan
Tel.: (886) 2 22673272
Fax: (886) 2 22673292
E-Mail: eson-ir@eson.com.cn
Web Site: www.eson.com.cn
5243—(TAI)
Rev.: $222,446,136
Emp.: 80
Fiscal Year-end: 12/31/12
Business Description:
Consumer Electronics Parts Mfr
S.I.C.: 3679
N.A.I.C.S.: 334419
Personnel:
Jeng-Wu Tai *(Chm)*

ESORFRANKI LIMITED

30 Activia Road Activia Park
1429 Germiston, South Africa
Mailing Address:
PO Box 6478
Dunswart, South Africa 1508
Tel.: (27) 11 776 8700
Fax: (27) 11 822 1158
E-Mail: info@esorfranki.co.za
Web Site: www.esorfranki.co.za
ESR—(JSE)
Rev.: $259,809,509
Assets: $250,630,338
Liabilities: $132,980,972
Net Worth: $117,649,365
Earnings: $9,797,207
Emp.: 4,654
Fiscal Year-end: 02/28/13
Business Description:
Road & Earthwork Construction Services
S.I.C.: 8711
N.A.I.C.S.: 541330
Personnel:
Bernie Krone *(CEO)*
Wessel C. van Zyl *(CFO)*
Board of Directors:
David Thompson
Ethan Dube
Bernie Krone
Malemadutje Mathabathe
Franklin Sonn
Wessel C. van Zyl
Legal Counsel:
Thomson Wilks Inc
23 Impala Road Chislehurston
Parklands, South Africa
Transfer Agent:
Computershare Investor Services (Pty) Limited
Ground Floor 70 Marshall Street
Johannesburg, South Africa
Subsidiaries:

Brookmay Properties (Pty) Limited (1)
33 Setter Rd
Midrand, Gauteng, 1685, South Africa
Tel.: (27) 113101900
Real Estate Property Investment Services
S.I.C.: 6531
N.A.I.C.S.: 531210

Esor Africa (Pty) Limited (1)
30 Activia Rd
Activia Park, Germiston, Gauteng, 1401, South Africa
Tel.: (27) 118223906
Fax: (27) 118223112
E-Mail: info@esor.co.za
Emp.: 28
Civil & Geotechnical Engineering Services
S.I.C.: 8711
N.A.I.C.S.: 541330
Roy McLintock *(Mng Dir)*

Esorfranki Civils (Pty) Limited (1)
33 Setter Rd Midrand Indus Park
Commercia, Midrand, Gauteng, 1685, South Africa
Tel.: (27) 11 310 1901
Fax: (27) 11 310 1911
E-Mail: admin@patula.co.za
Web Site: www.esorfranki.co.za/index.php?option=com_content&view=article&id=29&Itemid=129&bus=ec
Emp.: 1,100
Civil Engineering Services
S.I.C.: 8711
N.A.I.C.S.: 541330
Richard Maynard *(Mng Dir)*

Esorfranki Pipelines (Pty) Limited (1)
30 Activia Road Activia Park
Germiston, South Africa
Mailing Address:
PO Box 6478
Dunswart, 1508, South Africa
Tel.: (27) 11 776 8700
Fax: (27) 11 822 7027
E-Mail: info@esorfranki.co.za
Web Site: www.esorfranki.co.za
Emp.: 30
Construction & Rehabilitation Services of Onshore Pipelines Including Operations in Water, Sewerage & Stormwater Sectors & Gas & Petrochemicals
S.I.C.: 1623
N.A.I.C.S.: 237120
David Gibbons *(Mng Dir)*

Franki Africa (Pty) Limited (1)
688 Main Pretoria Rd Wynberg
Wynberg, Sandton, Gauteng, 2019, South Africa
Tel.: (27) 115312700
Fax: (27) 118870475
E-Mail: info@franki.co.za
Web Site: www.franki.co.za
Geotechnical Engineering Contract Services
S.I.C.: 8711
N.A.I.C.S.: 541330
Roy McLintock *(Mng Dir)*

Geo Compaction Dynamics (Pty) Limited (1)
Unit 9 Hentha Indus Park Wolverhampton St
Benoni, Gauteng, 1504, South Africa
Tel.: (27) 11 422 1219
Fax: (27) 114223643
Emp.: 30
Civil & Geotechnical Engineering Services
S.I.C.: 1771
N.A.I.C.S.: 238140
Sandra Jasen *(Mgr)*

Non-U.S. Subsidiary:

Frankipile International Projects Limited (1)
4th Fl Barkly Whart Ste 410 Le Caudan
Port Louis, Mauritius
Tel.: (230) 2100983
Fax: (230) 2103133
E-Mail: frankipi@bow.intnet.mu
Emp.: 40
Geotechnical Engineering Contract Services
S.I.C.: 1771
N.A.I.C.S.: 238140

Subsidiary:

Frankipile Mauritius International Limited (2)
4th Fl Barkly Whart Ste 410 Le Caudan
Port Louis, Mauritius
Tel.: (230) 2100983
Geotechnical Engineering Contract Services
S.I.C.: 1771
N.A.I.C.S.: 238140

ESP SYSTEX LTD.

68 74 Holderness Road
Hull, HU9 1ED, United Kingdom
Tel.: (44) 1482384500
Fax: (44) 1482384555
E-Mail: info@espsystex.co.uk
Web Site: www.espsystex.co.uk
Year Founded: 1994
Sales Range: $10-24.9 Million
Emp.: 85
Business Description:
Smart Card Solutions
S.I.C.: 7373
N.A.I.C.S.: 541512
Personnel:
Terry Dunn *(Mng Dir)*

ESPACE AUTO BLOIS

13/15 rue des Guignieres
41000 Blois, France
Tel.: (33) 254788844
Fax: (33) 254789840
E-Mail: espaceauto.blois@groupewarsemann.fr
Web Site: www.groupewarsemann.fr/
Sls.: $21,500,000
Emp.: 34
Business Description:
New & Used Car Dealers
S.I.C.: 5511
N.A.I.C.S.: 441110
Personnel:
Laurence Warsemamm *(Pres)*
Board of Directors:
Francois Jarry

ESPACE PRODUCTION INTERNATIONALE S.A.

(See Under EPI S.A.)

ESPARES LTD

13-14 Chelsea Wharf
15 Lots Road, London, SW10 0QJ, United Kingdom
Tel.: (44) 20 7351 1800
Fax: (44) 20 7351 2429
Web Site: www.espares.co.uk
Sales Range: $10-24.9 Million
Emp.: 70
Business Description:
Electrical Appliance Spare Parts, Accessories & Consumables Online Retailer
S.I.C.: 5961
N.A.I.C.S.: 454111
Personnel:
Peter Francis *(Controller)*

ESPEC CORP.

3-5-6 Tenjinbashi Kita Ku
Osaka, 530 8550, Japan
Tel.: (81) 663584741
Fax: (81) 663585500
Web Site: www.espec.co.jp
Year Founded: 1947
6859—(TKS)
Sls.: $338,789,000
Assets: $436,964,000
Liabilities: $101,959,000
Net Worth: $335,005,000
Earnings: $13,409,000
Emp.: 1,318
Fiscal Year-end: 03/31/13
Business Description:
Industrial, Electronic & Semiconductor Machinery, Equipment & Accessories Mfr
S.I.C.: 3559
N.A.I.C.S.: 333249
Personnel:
Masaaki Ishida *(Pres)*
Kunikazu Ishii *(Co-Mng Dir)*
Taneo Shimada *(Co-Mng Dir)*
Board of Directors:
Masaaki Ishida
Kunikazu Ishii
Seiichi Murakami
Kaoru Okeya
Keiji Oshima
Taneo Shimada
Nobuo Shiseki
Transfer Agent:
Mizuho Trust & Banking Co., Ltd.
2-1 Yaesu 1-Chome Chuo-ku
Tokyo, 103 8670, Japan
Tel.: (81) 332788111
Fax: (81) 332816947
Subsidiaries:

ESPEC Engineering Corp. (1)
15-8 Taimahigashi-machi
Neyagawa, Osaka, 572-0072, Japan
Tel.: (81) 728341191
Fax: (81) 663585500
Web Site: www.espec-global.com
Consumer Electronics Repair & Maintenance
S.I.C.: 7629
N.A.I.C.S.: 811211

ESPEC Kyushu Corp. (1)
2-6-15 Katanoshinmachi Kokurakita-ku Kitakyushu
Kitakyushu Hukuoka, Fukuoka, 802-0062, Japan
Tel.: (81) 939411731
Fax: (81) 939212822
E-Mail: info@espec-q.co.jp
Web Site: www.espec-q.co.jp
Emp.: 20
Professional Equipment & Supplies Merchant Whslr
S.I.C.: 5049
N.A.I.C.S.: 423490

ESPEC Mic Corp. (1)
1-233-1 Omido Oguchi-cho Niwa-gun
Aichi, 480-0138, Japan
Tel.: (81) 587956369
Fax: (81) 587954833
E-Mail: info@especmic.co.jp
Web Site: www.especmic.co.jp
Emp.: 40
Florists
S.I.C.: 5992
N.A.I.C.S.: 453110
Maekawa Takeshi *(Sr Mng Dir)*

ESPEC Techno Corp. (1)
5-10-18 Sumiyoshi-miyamachi
Higashinada-ku, Kobe, 658-0053, Japan
Tel.: (81) 788113211
Fax: (81) 788565186
E-Mail: sales@espec-techno.com
Web Site: www.espec-global.com
Emp.: 30
Electrical Apparatus & Equipment Wiring Supplies & Construction Materials Whslr
S.I.C.: 5063
N.A.I.C.S.: 423610
Hiromichi Hukumoto *(Pres)*

Plant:

ESPEC Corp. - FUKUCHIYAMA PLANT (1)
1-7 Osadano-cho
Fukuchiyama, Kyoto, 620-0853, Japan
Tel.: (81) 773 27 3131
Environmental Testing Equipment Mfr
S.I.C.: 3823
N.A.I.C.S.: 334513

U.S. Subsidiary:

ESPEC North America Inc. (1)
4141 Central Pkwy
Hudsonville, MI 49426
Tel.: (616) 896-6100
Fax: (616) 896-6150
Web Site: www.espec.com
Emp.: 155
Environmental Chambers Mfr, Servicer & Sales
S.I.C.: 3822
N.A.I.C.S.: 334512
Ken Walter *(Pres)*

Non-U.S. Subsidiaries:

DAINAN TECH (S) PTE LTD (1)
66 Tannery Lane 01-01B Sindo Building
Singapore, 347805, Singapore
Tel.: (65) 68978977
Fax: (65) 68977077
E-Mail: dainan@singnet.com.sg
Web Site: www.dainan.com.sg
Emp.: 27
Environmental Testing Services
S.I.C.: 8734
N.A.I.C.S.: 541380
Theng Tat Ong *(Gen Mgr)*

DEVICE ENG CO., LTD. (1)
3-13 Samgeo-ri Eumbong-myeon
Asan, Chungcheongnam-do, Korea (South)

ESPEC Corp.—(Continued)

Tel.: (82) 32789028
Fax: (82) 41 629 5209
Web Site: www.deviceeng.co.kr
Industrial Supplies Distr
S.I.C.: 5085
N.A.I.C.S.: 423840

ENVIRONMATE TECH CORP. (1)
Unit 3 Sycamore Arcs 2 Buencamino Street
Corner Alabang-Zapote Road
Muntinlupa, 1770, Philippines
Tel.: (63) 2 842 6195
Fax: (63) 2 807 0367
E-Mail: mail@environmate.com
Web Site: www.environmate.com
Emp.: 12
Environmental Test Chambers Distr
S.I.C.: 5084
N.A.I.C.S.: 423830
Lilia Duma-o *(Mgr-HR)*

ESPEC (CHINA) LIMITED (1)
Suite 618 6th F Ocean Centre
Harbour City, Kowloon, China (Hong Kong)
Tel.: (852) 2620 0830
Fax: (852) 2620 0788
Web Site: www.espec-global.com
Environmental Test Chamber Distr
S.I.C.: 5084
N.A.I.C.S.: 423830
Kimura Hiromitsu *(Gen Mgr)*

ESPEC Environmental Equipment (Shanghai) Co , Ltd. (1)
5th Fl ShenHua Financial Bldg No1 Ning Bo Rd
Huangpu District, 200002 Shanghai, China
Tel.: (86) 2151036677
Fax: (86) 2163372237
E-Mail: shpnghai@espec.cn
Web Site: www.espec-global.com
Emp.: 40
Residential Commercial & Appliance Use Automatic Environmental Control Mfr
S.I.C.: 3822
N.A.I.C.S.: 334512
Hao Yang *(VP)*

ESPEC Europe GmbH (1)
Dachauer Str 11
80335 Munich, Germany
Tel.: (49) 8918939630
Fax: (49) 89189396379
E-Mail: info@espec.de
Web Site: www.espec.de
Emp.: 5
Analytical Laboratory Instrument Mfr
S.I.C.: 3826
N.A.I.C.S.: 334516
Yoshinobu Matsumura *(Gen Mgr)*

ESPEC Korea Corp. (1)
452-3 Hyeongok-Ri Chongbuk-Myeon
Pyeongtaek, Gyeonggi-do, 451-831, Korea (South)
Tel.: (82) 5 641 37 65
Fax: (82) 31 686 8526
Environmental Test Chamber Mfr
S.I.C.: 3822
N.A.I.C.S.: 334512

ESPEC (Malaysia) Sdn. Bhd. (1)
No 10-1 Jalan Dagang SB 4-2
Taman Sungai Besi Indah Off Ja, 43300
Seri Kembangan, Selangor, Malaysia
Tel.: (60) 389451377
Fax: (60) 389451287
E-Mail: info@espec.com.my
Web Site: www.espec.com.my
Emp.: 6
Electronic Parts & Equipment Whslr
S.I.C.: 5065
N.A.I.C.S.: 423690
Ming Huei Niam *(Mgr-Sls)*

ESPEC SOUTH EAST ASIA SDN. BHD. (1)
No 10-1 Jalan Dagang SB 4/2 Taman Sungai Besi Indah
Off Jalan Sungai Besi, 43300 Seri Kembangan, Selangor, Malaysia
Tel.: (60) 3 8945 1377
Fax: (60) 3 8945 1287
Web Site: www.espec.dm1beta.com
Electronic Chambers Distr
S.I.C.: 5084
N.A.I.C.S.: 423830
Shuhei Okabe *(Gen Mgr)*

ESPEC Test Technology (Shanghai) Co., Ltd. (1)
Room 106 Building 8 No 3000 Shanghai
Zhangjiang Longdong Avenue
Pudong New Area, 201203 Shanghai, China
Tel.: (86) 2168798008
Fax: (86) 2168798088
E-Mail: vhusun@espec.cn
Web Site: www.espec.com
Emp.: 8
Analytical Laboratory Instrument Mfr
S.I.C.: 3826
N.A.I.C.S.: 334516
Yang Hao *(Pres)*

EST-SMT LLC (1)
404G 1 Novgorodskaya st
Moscow, Russia 127576
Tel.: (7) 495 988 4648
Fax: (7) 495 988 4648
E-Mail: info@est-smt.ru
Web Site: www.est-smt.ru
Electronic Component Distr
S.I.C.: 5065
N.A.I.C.S.: 423690

FURNACE ENGINEERING PTY LTD (1)
50 Howleys Rd
Notting Hill, VIC, 3168, Australia
Tel.: (61) 395442922
Fax: (61) 395442723
E-Mail: info@furnace.com.au
Web Site: www.furnace.com.au
Emp.: 90
Furnaces & Industrial Oven Mfr
S.I.C.: 3567
N.A.I.C.S.: 333994

H. BENTZ ELECTRONICS LTD. (1)
2 Faran St
Yavne, Israel
Tel.: (972) 8 9422923
Fax: (972) 8 9422988
E-Mail: hbentz@netvision.net.il
Web Site: www.hbentz.com
Emp.: 15
Electronic Equipment Mfr
S.I.C.: 3699
N.A.I.C.S.: 335999
H. Bentz *(Gen Mgr)*

HIELKEMA TESTEQUIPMENT B.V. (1)
Vluchtoord 23
5406 XP Uden, Netherlands
Tel.: (31) 413255243
Fax: (31) 413 255289
E-Mail: info@hielkematest.nl
Web Site: www.hielkematest.nl
Emp.: 10
Environmental Test Chambers Distr
S.I.C.: 5084
N.A.I.C.S.: 423830
Peter Hielkema *(Gen Mgr)*

J&S ENGINEERING CORP. (1)
Rm 501 Sudo Building 160-18 Samsung-Dong
Gangnam-ku, Seoul, Korea (South) 135-881
Tel.: (82) 2 557 0505
Fax: (82) 2 557 2253
E-Mail: jsec148@unitel.co.kr
Environmental Test Chamber Distr
S.I.C.: 5084
N.A.I.C.S.: 423830

JSC VO MASHPRIBORINTORG (1)
19 Tkatskaya st
Moscow, 105318, Russia
Tel.: (7) 495 363 2327
Fax: (7) 495 644 3303
E-Mail: svb@est-smt.ru
Web Site: www.espec-global.com
Electronic Equipment Distr
S.I.C.: 5065
N.A.I.C.S.: 423690

OSTEC ENTERPRISE Ltd. (1)
Moldavskaya str 5/2
Moscow, 121467, Russia
Tel.: (7) 495 788 44 44
Fax: (7) 495 788 44 42
E-Mail: info@ostec-group.ru
Web Site: www.ostec-group.ru
Emp.: 200
Engineering Consulting Services
S.I.C.: 8711
N.A.I.C.S.: 541330

PRECISE TECH ELECTRONICS LTD. (1)
Unit 910 9/F Chevalier Commercial Centre
8 Wang Hoi Road
Kowloon, China (Hong Kong)
Tel.: (852) 21239023
Fax: (852) 21239022
E-Mail: enquiry@precisetech-hk.com
Environmental Test Chambers Distr
S.I.C.: 5084
N.A.I.C.S.: 423830

PSP BRASIL (1)
Rua Machado Bittencourt 190 cj 203
Vila Clementino, 04044-903 Sao Paulo, Brazil
Tel.: (55) 11 5087 9433
Fax: (55) 11 5574 7983
E-Mail: pspbrasil@pspbrasil.com.br
Web Site: www.pspbrasil.com.br
Emp.: 10
Printed Circuit Boards Distr
S.I.C.: 5065
N.A.I.C.S.: 423690

SAMS ADVANCE CLIMATIC TECHNOLOGIES (1)
Plot No 646 Sri Swamy Ayyappa Society
Madhapur, Hyderabad, 500 081, India
Tel.: (91) 40 4466 1212
Fax: (91) 40 4466 1200
E-Mail: info@samsact.com
Web Site: www.samsact.com
Emp.: 2
Environmental Test Chambers Distr
S.I.C.: 5084
N.A.I.C.S.: 423830
Geeth Kiran *(Mgr)*

SCHOELLER INSTRUMENTS, S.R.O. (1)
Videnska 1398/124
148 00 Prague, Czech Republic
Tel.: (420) 261009111
Fax: (420) 261009112
E-Mail: mail@schoeller.cz
Web Site: www.schoeller.cz
Industrial Equipment Distr
S.I.C.: 5084
N.A.I.C.S.: 423830

SENECO SRL (1)
Via Marcello Prestinari 4
Milan, 20158, Italy
Tel.: (39) 0239313031
Fax: (39) 0239313044
E-Mail: info@seneco.it
Web Site: www.seneco.it
Laboratory & Scientific Instruments Mfr
S.I.C.: 3826
N.A.I.C.S.: 334516
Ettore Senes *(Gen Mgr)*

Shanghai ESPEC Environmental Equipment Co., Ltd. (1)
1518 Hao Hua Xin Zhen Hua Zhi Road
Qing Pu Qu
Shanghai, 201708, China
Tel.: (86) 21 69791178
Fax: (86) 21 69791213
E-Mail: sespec@guomai.sh.cn
Web Site: www.sh-espec.com
Environmental Test Chambers Mfr
S.I.C.: 3559
N.A.I.C.S.: 333249

THERMOTEC Weilburg GmbH & Co. KG (1)
Mittlere Friedenbach 8
35781 Weilburg, Germany
Tel.: (49) 647162930
Fax: (49) 6471629310
E-Mail: info@ttwe.de
Web Site: www.thermotec-weilburg.de
Emp.: 25
Environmental Test Chamber Mfr
S.I.C.: 3559
N.A.I.C.S.: 333249
Karl-Heinz Habich *(Deputy Mgr)*

UNITEMP LIMITED (1)
Unit 14 Treadaway Technical Centre
Treadaway Hill Loudwater
High Wycombe, Buckinghamshire, HP10 9RS, United Kingdom
Tel.: (44) 1628 850611
Fax: (44) 1628 850608
E-Mail: info@unitemp.co.uk
Web Site: www.unitemp.co.uk
Emp.: 7
Environmental Test Chambers Mfr
S.I.C.: 3559
N.A.I.C.S.: 333249
Ron Brown *(Gen Mgr)*

ESPERA-WERKE GMBH
Moltkestrasse 17 33
D-47058 Duisburg, Germany
Tel.: (49) 20330540
Fax: (49) 2033054275
E-Mail: info@espera.de
Web Site: www.espera-gmbh.de
Year Founded: 1924
Rev.: $23,449,800
Emp.: 125

Business Description:
Labelling Machine Mfr
S.I.C.: 3565
N.A.I.C.S.: 333993

Personnel:
Marcus Korthauer *(Mng Dir)*

ESPERANCE MINERALS LIMITED
Suite 605 Level 6 50 Clarence Street
Sydney, NSW, 2000, Australia
Tel.: (61) 2 9299 9580
Fax: (61) 2 9299 9501
E-Mail: manager@esperanceminerals.com
Web Site: www.esperanceminerals.com
ESM—(ASX)
Rev.: $34,984
Assets: $1,025,608
Liabilities: $539,917
Net Worth: $485,691
Earnings: ($1,787,923)
Fiscal Year-end: 06/30/13

Business Description:
Oil & Gas Investment Services
S.I.C.: 6211
N.A.I.C.S.: 523999

Personnel:
Kris Knauer *(Chm)*
Robert Lees *(CFO & Sec)*

Board of Directors:
Kris Knauer
Vincent Fayad
Jacob Khouri

ESPERANZA RESOURCES CORP.
(Acquired & Absorbed by Alamos Gold Inc.)

ESPIAL GROUP INC.
200 Elgin Street Suite 900
Ottawa, ON, K2P 1L5, Canada
Tel.: (613) 230-4770
Fax: (613) 230-8498
Toll Free: (888) 437-7425
Web Site: www.espial.com
ESP—(TSX)
Rev.: $13,201,100
Assets: $18,362,841
Liabilities: $9,407,616
Net Worth: $8,955,225
Earnings: ($2,690,950)
Emp.: 91
Fiscal Year-end: 12/31/12

Business Description:
On-Demand Television Software & Services
S.I.C.: 7372
N.A.I.C.S.: 511210

Personnel:
Peter Seeligsohn *(Chm)*
Jaison Dolvane *(Pres & CEO)*
Carl Smith *(CFO)*

Kumanan Yogaratnam *(CTO & VP-Engrg)*
Nemer D. Abourizk *(Gen Counsel)*
Board of Directors:
Peter Seeligsohn
Tawfiq Arafat
Jaison Dolvane
Michael Lee
Kumanan Yogaratnam
Transfer Agent:
Computershare Investor Services Inc.
Montreal, QC, Canada
Non-U.S. Subsidiary:

Espial (UK) Limited (1)
New Bond House 124 New Bond Street
London, W1S 1DX, United Kingdom UK
Tel.: (44) 121 2882 575 (100%)
Web Site: www.espial.com
On-Demand Television Software Whslr
S.I.C.: 5045
N.A.I.C.S.: 423430

Subsidiary:

ANT Limited (2)
First Floor 335 Cambridge Science Park
Milton Road
Cambridge, CB4 0WN, United Kingdom UK
Tel.: (44) 1223716400
E-Mail: info@antplc.com
Web Site: www.antplc.com
Emp.: 50
Holding Company; Television Industry Software Developer & Services
S.I.C.: 6719
N.A.I.C.S.: 551112
David Fell *(CTO)*
Mathew Lobo *(Sec & Dir-Comml Ops)*

Subsidiary:

ANT Software Limited (3)
Cambridge Bus Park Cowley Rd
Cambridge, CB4 0WZ, United Kingdom
Tel.: (44) 1223716400
Fax: (44) 1223716401
E-Mail: info@antplc.com
Web Site: www.antlimited.com
Emp.: 50
Software Development Services
S.I.C.: 7371
N.A.I.C.S.: 541511
John Anderson *(Dir-Product Mktg)*

ESPIGA CAPITAL GESTION S.G.E.C.R, S.A.

Alfonso XII 22 4 Izquierda
28014 Madrid, Spain
Tel.: (34) 91 531 7277
Fax: (34) 91 531 2552
E-Mail: contact@espiga.com
Web Site: www.espiga.com
Emp.: 6
Business Description:
Private Equity Firm
S.I.C.: 6211
N.A.I.C.S.: 523999
Personnel:
Juan Carvajal *(Mng Partner)*
Carlos Prado *(Mng Partner)*
Holding:

Industrial Veterinaria, S.A. (1)
Carrer de l'Esmaragda 19
8950 Esplugues de Llobregat, Spain (91%)
Tel.: (34) 93 470 62 71
Fax: (34) 933727556
E-Mail: invesa_int@invesagroup.eu
Web Site: www.invesagroup.eu
Emp.: 13
Veterinary Pharmaceutical Product Mfr
S.I.C.: 2834
N.A.I.C.S.: 325412
Patrick Mochel *(Gen Mgr)*

ESPIRITO SANTO FINANCIAL GROUP S.A.

22/24 Boulevard Royal
L-2449 Luxembourg, Luxembourg
Tel.: (352) 43494524
Fax: (352) 43494541
Web Site: www.esfg.com
Year Founded: 1984
ESTL—(EUR LSE LUX)
Rev.: $5,516,175,232
Assets: $117,889,572,350
Liabilities: $106,955,943,264
Net Worth: $10,933,629,087
Earnings: $500,376,774
Emp.: 14,889
Fiscal Year-end: 12/31/12
Business Description:
Bank Holding Company
S.I.C.: 6712
N.A.I.C.S.: 551111
Personnel:
Ricardo Espirito Santo Silva Salgado *(Chm)*
Jose Manuel Pinheiro Espirito Santo Silva *(Vice Chm)*
Gerard Laffineur Petracchini *(CEO)*
Filipe Worsdell *(CFO & Sr VP)*
Jean-Luc Schneider *(Chief Acctg Officer & Sr VP)*
Teresa de Souza *(Sec & Sr VP)*
Erich Daehler *(Sr VP)*
Jorge Manuel Amaral Penedo *(Chief Prudential Reporting Officer & Sr VP)*
Board of Directors:
Ricardo Espirito Santo Silva Salgado
Bernard Basecqz
Jackson Behr Gilbert
Othman Benjelloun
Jose Carlos Cardoso Castella
Anibal da Costa Reis Oliveira
Jose Manuel Ruivo da Pena
Carlos Augusto Machado de Almeida Freitas
Manuel Antonio Ribeiro Serzedelo de Almeida
Patrick Monteiro de Barros
Pedro Guilherme Beauvillain de Brito e Cunha
Luis Antonio Burnay Pinto de Carvalho Daun e Lorena
Manuel Fernando de Moniz Galvao Espirito Santo Silva
Jose Maria Espirito Santo Silva Ricciardi
Manuel Guerrero Peman
Philippe Guiral
Roger H. Hartmann
Yves Alain Marie Morvan
Mario Mosqueira do Amaral
Fernando Pedro Braga Pereira Coutinho
Gerard Laffineur Petracchini
Antonio Luis Roquette Ricciardi
Jose Manuel Pinheiro Espirito Santo Silva
Jose Pedro Torres Garcia Caldeira Da Silva

Subsidiary:

ESFIL - Espirito Santo Financiere S.A. (1)
22/24 boulevard Royal
2520 Luxembourg, Luxembourg LU
Tel.: (352) 434945 (100%)
Fax: (352) 43494531
Rev.: $120,546,134
Assets: $1,568,283,948
Liabilities: $1,326,999,317
Net Worth: $241,284,631
Earnings: $28,596,276
Emp.: 15
Fiscal Year-end: 12/31/12
Investment Holding Company
S.I.C.: 6719
N.A.I.C.S.: 551112
Jose Manuel da Fonseca Antunes *(Chm)*
Joao Manuel Baptista do Nascimento Bruno *(Mng Dir)*

Non-U.S. Holdings:

Banque Espirito Santo et de la Venetie S.A. (2)
45 avenue Georges Mandel
F-75116 Paris, France FR
Tel.: (33) 144344800 (44.8%)
Telex: 205 711 F
Fax: (33) 144344848
E-Mail: besv@besv.fr
Web Site: www.besv.fr
Emp.: 150
Corporate & Private Banking
S.I.C.: 6211
N.A.I.C.S.: 523110
Philippe Gilles Fernand Guiral *(Pres)*

Banque Privee Espirito Santo S.A. (2)
Avenue General Guisan 70a
Case Postale 107, 1009 Pully, Switzerland CH
Tel.: (41) 216195555 (100%)
Fax: (41) 216195556
E-Mail: mail@espiritosanto.com
Web Site: www.espiritosanto.com
Sales Range: $50-74.9 Million
Emp.: 158
Investment Banking & Asset Management Services
S.I.C.: 6211
N.A.I.C.S.: 523110
Jose Manuel Pinheiro Espirito Santo Silva *(Chm)*
Jose Pedro Torres Garcia Caldeira da Silva *(CEO)*

Non-U.S. Subsidiaries:

Avistar, SGPS, S.A. (1)
Praca Marques De Pombal 3 20
Lisbon, 1250-161, Portugal
Tel.: (351) 213517129
Fax: (351) 213501180
Emp.: 6
Financial Management Services
S.I.C.: 6211
N.A.I.C.S.: 523999
Rodrigo Franca *(Gen Mgr)*

Banco Espirito Santo Cabo Verde (1)
Avenida Cidade de Lisboa CP 35
Praia, Santiago, Cape Verde
Tel.: (238) 260 26 26
Fax: (238) 260 26 34
E-Mail: bescv@bescv.cv
Web Site: www.bescv.cv
Emp.: 3
Commercial Banking Services
S.I.C.: 6029
N.A.I.C.S.: 522110
Bengt Ino Martens *(Gen Mgr)*

BES Africa, SGPS, S.A. (1)
Rua Braamcamp 2 50
Lisbon, 1250-050, Portugal
Tel.: (351) 213518132
Fax: (351) 213518133
Emp.: 5
Financial Management Services
S.I.C.: 6211
N.A.I.C.S.: 523999
Alberto Diniz *(Mng Dir)*

BES Securities do Brasil, S.A. (1)
Av Brigadeiro Faria Lima 3729 Mezanino - Itaim Bibi
04538-905 Sao Paulo, Brazil
Tel.: (55) 11 3074 7444
Fax: (55) 11 3074 7562
E-Mail: bessecurities@bessecurities.com.br
Security Brokerage Services
S.I.C.: 6211
N.A.I.C.S.: 523120

BESPAR, SGPS, S.A. (1)
Rua De Sao Bernardo 62
Lisbon, 1200-826, Portugal
Tel.: (351) 213915700
Fax: (351) 213979777
Investment Management Services
S.I.C.: 6211
N.A.I.C.S.: 523999
Pedro Lorenzo *(Gen Mgr)*

Capital mais - Assessoria Financeira, S.A. (1)
Avenida De Alvares Cabral 41
Lisbon, 1250-015, Portugal
Tel.: (351) 213810800
Fax: (351) 213810837
Financial Management Services
S.I.C.: 6211
N.A.I.C.S.: 523999

Cliria - Hospital Privado de Aveiro, S.A. (1)
Rua do Brazil No 21
Aveiro, 3800-009, Portugal
Tel.: (351) 23 440 0700
Fax: (351) 23 440 0739
Web Site: www.cliria.pt
Emp.: 249
Health Care Hospital Operating Services
S.I.C.: 8062
N.A.I.C.S.: 622110
Zose Loreto da Costa *(Gen Mgr)*

Companhia de Seguros Tranquilidade, S.A. (1)
Avenida da Liberdade 242
1250-149 Lisbon, Portugal PT
Tel.: (351) 213503500 (100%)
Fax: (351) 21 358 4232
E-Mail: infogeral@tranquilidade.pt
Web Site: www.tranquilidade.pt
Emp.: 100
Non-Life Insurance Products & Services
S.I.C.: 6331
N.A.I.C.S.: 524126
Pedro Guilherme Beauvillain de Brito e Cunha *(Chm)*

Subsidiary:

Seguros LOGO S.A. (2)
R D Manuel II 290
4001-809 Porto, Portugal PT
Tel.: (351) 213306605 (100%)
Fax: (351) 213584214
E-Mail: geral@logo.pt
Web Site: www.logo.pt
Home & Automotive Insurance Products & Services
S.I.C.: 6351
N.A.I.C.S.: 524126

ES Bank (Panama), S.A. (1)
Calle 53 Marbella Edificio World Trade Center Oficina 1902
0832-0847 Panama, Panama Pa
Tel.: (507) 265-3174 (100%)
Fax: (507) 265-8142
E-Mail: esbank@esbpanama.com
Web Site: www.esbpanama.com
Sales Range: $50-74.9 Million
Retail & Commercial Banking
S.I.C.: 6029
N.A.I.C.S.: 522110

ES Bankers (Dubai) Limited (1)
Gate Village Building 1 1st Floor Unit 7
Dubai Intl Financial Centre
PO Box 506627
Dubai, United Arab Emirates AE
Tel.: (971) 47090000
Fax: (971) 43230200
E-Mail: contact@esbankersdubai.com
Web Site: www.esbankersdubai.com
Emp.: 17
Investment Banking & Asset Management Services
S.I.C.: 6211
N.A.I.C.S.: 523110
Ricardo Espirito Santo Silva Salgado *(Chm)*
Yves Alain Marie Morvan *(Vice Chm)*

ES Concessions International Holding, BV (1)
Prins Bernhardplein 200
1097 JB Amsterdam, Netherlands
Tel.: (31) 20 5214777
Investment Management Services
S.I.C.: 6211
N.A.I.C.S.: 523999

ES Recuperacao de Credito, ACE (1)
Rua Castilho 50 6
1250-071 Lisbon, Portugal
Tel.: (351) 218 50 30 00
Fax: (351) 218 50 30 99
E-Mail: recuperacao.enterna@bes.pt
Financial Collection Services
S.I.C.: 7322
N.A.I.C.S.: 561440

ES Tech Ventures, S.G.P.S., S.A. (1)
Avenida Da Liberdade 195
Lisbon, 1250-142, Portugal

Espirito Santo Financial Group S.A.—(Continued)

Tel.: (351) 213106490
Fax: (351) 213106425
Venture Capital Management Services
S.I.C.: 6799
N.A.I.C.S.: 523910

ESAF - Espirito Santo Participacoes Internacionais SGPS, S.A. (1)
Avenida Alvares Cabral 41
Lisbon, 1250-015, Portugal
Tel.: (351) 213810800
Fax: (351) 213810838
E-Mail: contacto@esaf.pt
Emp.: 3
Investment Management Services
S.I.C.: 6799
N.A.I.C.S.: 523920
Pedro Costa *(Gen Mgr)*

Espirito Santo Fundos de Investimentos Mobiliarios, S.A. (1)
Av Alvares Cabral 41 R/c 1st Floor
Lisbon, 1250-015, Portugal
Tel.: (351) 21 381 0800
Fax: (351) 21 3810837
Investment Management Services
S.I.C.: 6211
N.A.I.C.S.: 523999

Espirito Santo Gestao de Patrimonios, S.A. (1)
Avenida Alvares Cabral 41 R/C
Lisbon, 1250-015, Portugal
Tel.: (351) 213810800
Fax: (351) 213810837
Financial Management Services
S.I.C.: 6211
N.A.I.C.S.: 523999

Espirito Santo Informatica, ACE (1)
Rua da Barruncheira 4
2790-034 Carnaxide, Portugal
Tel.: (351) 21 425 86 86
Fax: (351) 21 425 86 88
E-Mail: info@esi.pt
Information Technology Consulting Services
S.I.C.: 7373
N.A.I.C.S.: 541512

Espirito Santo Investment sp. z.o.o (1)
59th Zlota Street Floor V
00-120 Warsaw, Poland
Tel.: (48) 223474000
Fax: (48) 223476098
Investment Banking Services
S.I.C.: 6211
N.A.I.C.S.: 523110
Christian Georges Jacques Minzolini *(Gen Mgr)*

Espirito Santo Securities India Private Limited (1)
1203A Tower-2A Floor 12A One Indiabulls Centre 841 Senapati Bapat Marg
Elphiston Road, Mumbai, 400 013, India
Tel.: (91) 22 43156800
Fax: (91) 22 24216327
Web Site: www.espiritosantoib.co.uk
Emp.: 4
Securities Brokerage Services
S.I.C.: 6211
N.A.I.C.S.: 523120
Nick Paulson-Ellis *(CEO)*

Espirito Santo Servicos Financeiros Distribuicao de Titulos e V.M., S.A. (1)
Rua Leopoldo Couto Magalhaes Jr 758 20 Andar - Parte
Sao Paulo, 04542-000, Brazil
Tel.: (55) 1130736262
Fax: (55) 1130736274
Financial Management Services
S.I.C.: 6211
N.A.I.C.S.: 523999

Espirito Santo - Unidades de Saude e de Apoio a Terceira Idade, S.A. (1)
Rua Carlos Alberto Da Mota Pinto 17 9Fl
Lisbon, 1070-313, Portugal
Tel.: (351) 213138260
Fax: (351) 213530292
E-Mail: geral@essaude.pt
Web Site: www.essaude.pt
Emp.: 7
Hospital Management Services
S.I.C.: 8062
N.A.I.C.S.: 622110
Isabel Vaz *(CEO)*

Esumedica - Prestacao de Cuidados medicos, S.A. (1)
Rua Rodrigues Sampaio 103 1 & 2 pisos
1150-005 Lisbon, Portugal
Tel.: (351) 213503615
Fax: (351) 218647389
E-Mail: infogeral@esumedica.pt
Web Site: www.esumedica.pt
Emp.: 5
Health Care Services
S.I.C.: 8082
N.A.I.C.S.: 621610
Ernie Delfos *(Gen Mgr)*

Execution Holdings Limited (1)
10 Paternoster Square
London, EC4M 7AL, United Kingdom
Tel.: (44) 20 7456 9191
Fax: (44) 20 7456 9189
E-Mail: info@espiritosantoib.co.uk
Investment Management Services
S.I.C.: 6211
N.A.I.C.S.: 523999

Execution Noble & Company Limited (1)
10 Paternoster Square Mona Street
London, EC4M 7AL, United Kingdom
Tel.: (44) 20 7456 9191
Fax: (44) 20 7375 2007
Emp.: 200
Accounting Services
S.I.C.: 8721
N.A.I.C.S.: 541219

Execution Noble (Hong Kong) Limited (1)
15/F St John's Building 33 Garden Road
Central, China (Hong Kong)
Tel.: (852) 3181 4000
Web Site: www.execution-noble.com
Securities Brokerage Services
S.I.C.: 6211
N.A.I.C.S.: 523120

Execution Noble Limited (1)
91 Brick Lane The Old Truman Brewery Block D
London, E1 6QL, United Kingdom
Tel.: (44) 20 7456 9191
E-Mail: info@executionlimited.com
Web Site: www.execution-noble.com
Emp.: 150
Investment Banking Services
S.I.C.: 6211
N.A.I.C.S.: 523110
Nick Finegold *(Co-Chm)*
Luis Luna Vaz *(Exec Vice Chm & CEO)*
Charles Ashton *(CFO)*
Jennifer Owens *(Gen Counsel & Sec)*

Hospital da Arrabida - Gaia, S.A. (1)
Pcta Henrique Moreira 150
4400-346 Vila Nova de Gaia, Portugal
Tel.: (351) 223 776 800
Fax: (351) 223 776 899
Web Site: www.hospitaldaarrabida.pt
Hospital Management Services
S.I.C.: 8062
N.A.I.C.S.: 622110

Hospital da Luz, S.A. (1)
Avenida Lusiada 100
Lisbon, 1500-650, Portugal
Tel.: (351) 217104400
Fax: (351) 217104409
Web Site: www.hospitaldaluz.pt
Hospital Management Services
S.I.C.: 8062
N.A.I.C.S.: 622110
Manuel Cabral *(Dir-Customer Svc)*

HOSPOR - Hospitais Portugueses, S.A. (1)
Rua D Manuel I 183
Povoa de Varzim, 4490-592, Portugal
Tel.: (351) 252690900
Fax: (351) 252615353
E-Mail: hospor@hospor.pt
Web Site: www.clipovoa.pt
Emp.: 100
Health Care Hospital Operating Services
S.I.C.: 8062
N.A.I.C.S.: 622110
Lima Cardoso *(Gen Mgr)*

Instituto de Radiologia Dr. Idalio de Oliveira - Centro de radiologia Medica, S.A. (1)
Avenida Sidonio Pais 18 C/V Esq
Lisbon, 1050-215, Portugal
Tel.: (351) 213150404
Fax: (351) 213541179
E-Mail: abatata@hospitaldaluz.pt
Web Site: www.hospitaldaluz.pt
Emp.: 2
Hospital Management Services
S.I.C.: 8062
N.A.I.C.S.: 622110
Miguel Rio Tinto *(Gen Mgr)*

Marignan Gestion S.A. (1)
45 Avenue Georges Mandel
75116 Paris, France
Tel.: (33) 142663989
Fax: (33) 142662461
E-Mail: contact@marigest.com
Portfolio Management Services
S.I.C.: 6282
N.A.I.C.S.: 523920

OBLOG Consulting S.A. (1)
Rua da Barruncheira 4
2790-034 Carnaxide, Portugal
Tel.: (351) 21 425 86 86
Fax: (351) 21 425 86 88
E-Mail: info@oblog.pt
Web Site: www.oblog.pt
Emp.: 4
Information Technology Consulting Services
S.I.C.: 7373
N.A.I.C.S.: 541512
Miroslav Krpec *(Gen Mgr)*

Parsuni - Sociedade Unipessoal, SGPS Lda. (1)
Avenida Arriaga 42b
Funchal, 9000-064, Portugal
Tel.: (351) 213501000
Fax: (351) 218830386
Investment Management Services
S.I.C.: 6211
N.A.I.C.S.: 523999

Quinta dos Conegos- Sociedade Imobiliaria, S.A. (1)
Rua Souto 363
Maia, 4470-215, Portugal
Tel.: (351) 229444100
Fax: (351) 229444079
Real Estate Management Services
S.I.C.: 6531
N.A.I.C.S.: 531390

RML - Residencia Medicalizada de loures, SGPS, S.A. (1)
Rua Carlos Alberto Da Mota Pinto 17 90
Lisbon, 1070-313, Portugal
Tel.: (351) 213138260
Financial Management Services
S.I.C.: 6211
N.A.I.C.S.: 523999

Sociedade Gestora do Hospital de loures, S.A. (1)
Avenida Carlos Teixeira 3
Loures, 2670-000, Portugal
Tel.: (351) 219847200
Fax: (351) 219847250
Hospital Management Services
S.I.C.: 8062
N.A.I.C.S.: 622110

Socur, S.A. (1)
Avenida 18 De Julio
1317 Montevideo, Uruguay
Tel.: (598) 2908 0000
Fax: (598) 29016626
E-Mail: pdercony@creditel.com.uy
Web Site: www.creditel.com.uy
Consumer Lending Services
S.I.C.: 6141
N.A.I.C.S.: 522291

Vila Lusitano - Unidades de Saude, S.A. (1)
Rua Carlos Alberto Mota Pinto 17 90
Lisbon, 1070-313, Portugal
Tel.: (351) 213138260
Fax: (351) 213530292
E-Mail: geral@essaude.pt
Web Site: www.essaude.pt
Emp.: 3
Hospital Management Services
S.I.C.: 8062
N.A.I.C.S.: 622110
Vishaal Gupta *(Gen Mgr)*

Non-U.S. Affiliate:

Espirito Santo Saude S.G.P.S., S.A. (1)
R Carlos Alberto da Mota Pinto 17 9th andar
1070-313 Lisbon, Portugal PT
Tel.: (351) 213138260 (37.9%)
Fax: (351) 213530292
E-Mail: lmartins@essaude.pt
Web Site: www.essaude.pt
ESS—(EUR)
Sales Range: $400-449.9 Million
Emp.: 70
Holding Company; Hospital, Out-Patient Clinic & Senior Care Facility Operator & Healthcare Services
S.I.C.: 6719
N.A.I.C.S.: 551112
Ricardo Espirito Santo Silva Salgado *(Chm)*

Subsidiary:

Surgicare - Unidades de Saude, S.A. (2)
Rua Carlos Alberto Da Mota Pinto 17 9th Flr
Lisbon, 1070-313, Portugal
Tel.: (351) 213138260
Fax: (351) 213530292
E-Mail: geral@cppoetas.pt
Web Site: www.cppoetas.pt
Emp.: 100
Health Practitioner Services
S.I.C.: 8049
N.A.I.C.S.: 621399
Isabel Vaz *(CEO)*

Non-U.S. Joint Ventures:

BESPAR - Sociedade Gestora de Participacoes Sociais, S.A. (1)
Rua de Sao Bernardo 62
PT-1200 826 Lisbon, Portugal PT
Tel.: (351) 213915700
Fax: (351) 213978646
Web Site: www.esfg.com
Sales Range: $5-14.9 Billion
Bank Holding Company; Owned 67% by Espirito Santo Financial Group & 33% by Credit Agricole S.A.
S.I.C.: 6712
N.A.I.C.S.: 551111
Rui Manuel Duarte Sousa da Silveira *(Chm)*
Maria Madalena Franca e Silva Quintanilha Mantas Moura *(Vice Chm)*
Francisco Marques da Cruz Vieira da Cruz *(Sec)*

Holding:

Banco Espirito Santo, S.A. (2)
Avenida Da Liberdade 195
1250-142 Lisbon, Portugal PT
Mailing Address:
PO Box 8135
1802-001 Lisbon, Portugal
Tel.: (351) 213501000
Fax: (351) 218557491
E-Mail: info@bes.pt
Web Site: www.bes.pt
BES—(EUR LSE LUX)
Int. Income: $5,269,056,113
Assets: $112,662,081,929
Liabilities: $102,252,493,938
Net Worth: $10,409,587,990
Earnings: $161,319,628
Emp.: 9,944
Fiscal Year-end: 12/31/12
Retail, Commercial & Investment Banking Services
S.I.C.: 6029
N.A.I.C.S.: 522110
Bruno Bernard Marie Joseph de Laage de Meux *(Vice Chm)*
Ricardo Espirito Santo Silva Salgado *(Vice Chm)*
Artur Miguel Marques da Rocha Gouveia *(Deputy Sec)*
Eugenio Fernando Quintais Lopes *(Sec)*

Subsidiaries:

Banco Espirito Santo de Investimento, S.A. (3)
Edificio Quartzo Sede Rua Alexandre Herculano 38

1269-161 Lisbon, Portugal PT
Tel.: (351) 213196900 (100%)
Fax: (351) 213309500
Web Site: www.espiritosantoib.com
Rev.: $460,635,143
Assets: $8,725,689,515
Liabilities: $7,775,286,764
Net Worth: $950,402,751
Earnings: $27,653,024
Emp.: 853
Fiscal Year-end: 12/31/12
Investment Banking, Private Equity, Financial Advisory & Asset Management Services
S.I.C.: 6211
N.A.I.C.S.: 523110
Ricardo Espirito Santo Silva Salgado *(Chm)*
Jose Manuel Macedo Pereira *(Chm-Supervisory Bd)*
Jose Maria Espirito Santo Silva Ricciardi *(Vice Chm & CEO)*
Francisco Ravara Cary *(Vice Chm, Deputy CEO & CFO)*
Rafael Caldeira de Castel-Branco Valverde *(Vice Chm)*
Miguel Antonio Igrejas Horta e Costa *(Vice Chm)*
Ricardo Abecassis Espirito Santo Silva *(Vice Chm)*
Jose Luis de Saldanha Ferreira Pinto Basto *(Sr Mng Dir)*
Alan do Amaral Fernandes *(Sr Mng Dir)*
Pedro Miguel Cordovil Toscano Rico *(Sr Mng Dir)*
Jose Miguel Alecrim Duarte *(Sec)*

Subsidiaries:

Espirito Santo Capital - Sociedade de Capital de Risco, S.A. (4)
Edificio Quartzo Rua Alexandre Herculano 38
1269-161 Lisbon, Portugal PT
Tel.: (351) 213515840 (100%)
Fax: (351) 213515846
Web Site: www.escapital.pt
Emp.: 14
Equity Investment Firm
S.I.C.: 6211
N.A.I.C.S.: 523999
Joao Arantes *(Gen Mgr)*

U.S. Branch:

Espirito Santo Investment - New York Branch (4)
340 Madison Ave 12th Fl
New York, NY 10173
Tel.: (212) 351-6000
Fax: (212) 351-6099
Web Site: www.esinvestment.com
Emp.: 60
Investment Banking & Securities Brokerage Services
S.I.C.: 6211
N.A.I.C.S.: 523110
Moses Dodo *(CEO)*

Non-U.S. Branches:

Banco Espirito Santo de Investimento, S.A. - Sucursal en Espana (4)
Calle Serrano 88 4th Planta
ES-28006 Madrid, Spain
Tel.: (34) 914005000
Fax: (34) 914352283
Emp.: 300
Investment Banking & Securities Brokerage Services
S.I.C.: 6211
N.A.I.C.S.: 523110
Felix Aguirre Cabanyes *(CEO)*

Banco Espirito Santo de Investimento, S.A. - UK (4)
10 Paternoster Square 3rd Floor
London Stock Exchange Building, London, EC4M 7AL, United Kingdom
Tel.: (44) 2072460180
Fax: (44) 2072460190
Web Site: www.esinvestment.com
Emp.: 150
Investment Banking & Securities Brokerage Services
S.I.C.: 6211
N.A.I.C.S.: 523110
Rafael Caldeira de Castel-Branco Valverde *(CEO)*

Non-U.S. Subsidiaries:

BES Investimento do Brasil S.A. (4)
Avenida Brigadeiro Faria Lima 3729 6th andar
04538-905 Sao Paulo, SP, Brazil BR
Tel.: (55) 1130747444 (80%)
Fax: (55) 1130747462
Web Site: www.besinvestimento.com.br
Investment Banking
S.I.C.: 6211
N.A.I.C.S.: 523110
Jose Maria Espirito Santo Silva Ricciardi *(Chm)*
Ricardo Abecassis Espirito Santo Silva *(Pres)*

Espirito Santo Investment Sp. z o.o. (4)
59th Zlota Street Floor V
PL-00-120 Warsaw, Poland PL
Tel.: (48) 223474000 (100%)
Fax: (48) 223474099
E-Mail: info@esinvesment.pl
Web Site: www.esinvestment.com
Emp.: 50
Investment Banking & Securities Brokerage Services
S.I.C.: 6211
N.A.I.C.S.: 523110
Christian Georges Jacques Minzolini *(CEO)*

Espirito Santo Investment Plc (4)
Spencer House 4th Floor 71/73 Talbot Street
Dublin, 1, Ireland IE
Tel.: (353) 18560699
Fax: (353) 18134366
Emp.: 3
Investment Banking & Securities Brokerage Services
S.I.C.: 6211
N.A.I.C.S.: 523110
John Madigan *(Mng Dir)*

Banco Espirito Santo dos Acores S.A. (3)
Rua Hintze Ribeiro 2-8
9500-049 Ponta Delgada, Sao Miguel - Acores, Portugal PT
Tel.: (351) 296307000
Fax: (351) 296307054
Web Site: www.besdosacores.pt
Retail & Commercial Banking
S.I.C.: 6029
N.A.I.C.S.: 522110
Maria Lopes Estrela *(Gen Mgr)*

Besleasing e Factoring - Instituicao Financeira de Credito, S.A. (3)
Av Alvares Cabral 27 1st Fl
1269 140 Lisbon, Portugal PT
Tel.: (351) 213821100
Fax: (351) 213872461
Web Site: www.besleasing.pt
Emp.: 100
Commercial Property & Equipment Leasing & Factoring Services
S.I.C.: 6159
N.A.I.C.S.: 522298

BEST - Banco Electronico de Servico Total, S.A. (3)
Praca Marques de Pombal 3 - 3rd andar
1250-161 Lisbon, Portugal PT
Tel.: (351) 218839252
Fax: (351) 218839370
E-Mail: rp@bancobest.pt
Web Site: www.bancobest.pt
Emp.: 300
Online Investment Banking Services
S.I.C.: 6211
N.A.I.C.S.: 523110
Ricardo Espirito Santo Silva Salgado *(Chm)*
Isabel Maria Ferreira Possantes Rodrigues Cascao *(CEO)*

ESAF - Espirito Santo Activos Financeiros S.G.P.S., S.A. (3)
Avenida Alvares Cabral 41
1249-140 Lisbon, Portugal PT
Tel.: (351) 213810800 (90%)
Fax: (351) 213810849
E-Mail: gerald@esaf.pt
Web Site: www.esaf.pt
Emp.: 100
Asset Management & Private Banking Services
S.I.C.: 6099
N.A.I.C.S.: 523991
Fernando Coelho *(Chm)*
Jose Maria Espirito Santo Silva Ricciardi *(Vice Chm)*
Tim Sherwood *(CEO)*

Espirito Santo Ventures - Sociedade de Capital de Risco, S.A. (3)
Rua Alexandre Herculano 38 5th piso
1250-011 Lisbon, Portugal PT
Tel.: (351) 213106490 (100%)
Fax: (351) 213106425
E-Mail: info@es-ventures.com
Web Site: www.es-ventures.com
Managed Assets: $269,298,000
Emp.: 12
Equity Investment Firm
S.I.C.: 6211
N.A.I.C.S.: 523999
Joaquim Servulo Rodrigues *(CEO)*
Joao Paulo Alpendre *(CFO)*
Jose Guerreiro de Sousa *(Principal)*
Duarte Mineiro *(Principal)*
Pedro Ribeiro Santos *(Principal)*

U.S. Subsidiaries:

Espirito Santo Bank (3)
1395 Brickell Ave
Miami, FL 33131-3012 FL
Tel.: (305) 539-7700 (98.45%)
E-Mail: info@esbf.com
Web Site: www.esbf.com
Emp.: 50
Investment Banking & Financial Advisory Services
S.I.C.: 6211
N.A.I.C.S.: 523110
G. Frederick Reinhardt *(Chm & CEO)*
Mark North *(Pres)*
Carlos Modia *(CFO)*
Andrew Methven *(COO)*
T. Douglas Hollowell *(Gen Counsel & Exec VP)*
Rafael Madan *(Sr VP & Head-Wealth Mgmt)*
Maggie Angulo-Levine *(Sr VP-Credit)*
Miguel Burelo *(Sr VP-Trade Fin)*
Ricardo Martin *(Sr VP-Comml Banking & Comml Real Estate Lending)*
Nuno Poppe *(Sr VP-Treasury)*
Martin Prego *(Sr VP-Compliance)*
Raul Vidal *(Sr VP-Residential Real Estate Lending)*

Subsidiary:

E.S. Financial Services, Inc. (4)
1395 Brickell Ave
Miami, FL 33131-3012 FL
Tel.: (305) 810-2024 (84.15%)
Fax: (305) 371-4556
Web Site: www.esbf.com
Sales Range: $25-49.9 Million
Investment Advisory & Wealth Management Services
S.I.C.: 6282
N.A.I.C.S.: 523930
Lia Yaffar *(Pres)*
Mark North *(CEO)*

Non-U.S. Branch:

Banco Espirito Santo, S.A. - Sucursal en Espana (3)
Calle Serrano 88 7th Planta
ES-28006 Madrid, Spain
Tel.: (34) 914005000
Telex: 22179 BESSA E
Fax: (34) 914005072
E-Mail: bancoespiritosanto@groupobes.es
Web Site: www.bes.es
Emp.: 500
S.I.C.: 6159
N.A.I.C.S.: 522298
Pedra Escudero *(Mng Dir)*

Non-U.S. Subsidiaries:

Banco Espirito Santo Angola S.A.R.L. (3)
1 Congresso St 27 31
Luanda, 6947, Angola AO
Tel.: (244) 222693600 (51.94%)
Fax: (244) 222693689
Web Site: www.besa.ao
Sales Range: $300-349.9 Million
Emp.: 500
Retail, Commercial & Investment Banking
S.I.C.: 6029
N.A.I.C.S.: 522110
Pedro Manuel de Castro Simoes Ferreira Neto *(CEO)*

Banco Espirito Santo do Oriente S.A. (3)
Av Dr Mario Soares N 323 Edificio Banco da China
28th Floor Units E & F, Macau, China (Macau) Mo
Tel.: (853) 28785222 (99.75%)
Fax: (853) 28785228
E-Mail: besor@macau.ctm.net
Emp.: 13
Retail & Commercial Banking
S.I.C.: 6029
N.A.I.C.S.: 522110
Jose Morgato *(CEO)*

Bank Espirito Santo International Ltd. (3)
Grand Pavilion Commercial Ctr 802 W Bay Rd Ste 1
PO Box 10507
Georgetown, Grand Cayman, KY1-1005, Cayman Islands Ky
Tel.: (345) 9493128 (100%)
Fax: (345) 9496911
Web Site: www.bes.pt
Emp.: 2
Retail & Commercial Banking
S.I.C.: 6029
N.A.I.C.S.: 522110
Jofe Leal de faria *(Mng Dir)*

Europ Assistance - Companhia Portuguesa de Seguros de Assistencia, S.A. (1)
Avda Columbano Bordalo Pinheiro 75 10th andar
1070-061 Lisbon, Portugal PT
Tel.: (351) 213860003
Fax: (351) 213860308
E-Mail: velculos.eap@europassistance.pt
Web Site: www.europassistance.pt
Emp.: 2,000
Medical, Travel & Automobile Assistance Services; Owned 53% by Assicurazioni Generali S.p.A. & 47% by Espirito Santo Financial Group S.A.
S.I.C.: 7389
N.A.I.C.S.: 541990
Manrico Iachia *(CEO)*

ESPLANADE LIMITED

Medina Avenue
Newport, Isle of Wight, PO30 1HG, United Kingdom
Tel.: (44) 1983523232
Fax: (44) 1983532661
E-Mail: info@esplanade.co.uk
Web Site: www.esplanade.co.uk
Year Founded: 1946
Rev.: $10,701,972
Emp.: 39

Business Description:
New & Used Car Dealer
S.I.C.: 5511
N.A.I.C.S.: 441110

Personnel:
Peter Dorley-Brown *(Founder)*
Nick Dorley-Brown *(Mng Dir)*

ESPRINET SPA

Via Energy Park
20-20871 Vimercate, Italy
Tel.: (39) 0240498800
Fax: (39) 0240496800
E-Mail: Elisabetta.Eredi@esprinet.com
Web Site: www.esprinet.com
PRT—(ITA MAD)
Sls.: $2,600,665,823
Assets: $921,925,871
Liabilities: $599,013,342
Net Worth: $322,912,529
Earnings: $31,416,915
Emp.: 971
Fiscal Year-end: 12/31/12

Business Description:
IT Hardware & Software
S.I.C.: 5045

Esprinet SpA—(Continued)

N.A.I.C.S.: 423430
Personnel:
Francesco Monti *(Chm)*
Maurizio Rota *(Vice Chm & Co-CEO)*
Alessandro Cattani *(Co-CEO)*
Board of Directors:
Francesco Monti
Giuseppe Cali
Stefania Cali
Valerio Casari
Alessandro Cattani
Andrea Cavaliere
Cristina Galbusera
Mario Massari
Chiara Mauri
Marco Monti
Umberto Giovanni Quilici
Maurizio Rota

Subsidiaries:

Comprel S.r.l. (1)
Via Tuscolana 1381
A 00173 Rome, Italy (100%)
Tel.: (39) 0672630700
Fax: (39) 067234504
Web Site: www.comprel.it
Computer Components
S.I.C.: 3577
N.A.I.C.S.: 334118

Nilox (1)
Via G Saragat 4
20054 Nova Milanese, Italy (100%)
Tel.: (39) 03624961
Fax: (39) 0362496800
E-Mail: marketing@nilox.com
Web Site: www.nilox.com
Emp.: 800
IT Hardware & Software
S.I.C.: 5045
N.A.I.C.S.: 423430
Andrea Sala *(Mgr)*

ESPRIT HOLDINGS LIMITED

43/F Enterprise Square Three 39 Wang Chiu Road
Kowloon Bay, Kowloon, China (Hong Kong)
Tel.: (852) 27654321
Fax: (852) 23625576
E-Mail: contact.hk@esprit.com
Web Site: www.esprit.com
0330—(HKG)
Sls.: $3,340,062,900
Assets: $2,997,829,600
Liabilities: $857,775,400
Net Worth: $2,140,054,200
Earnings: ($565,832,600)
Emp.: 10,700
Fiscal Year-end: 06/30/13
Business Description:
Holding Company; Clothing, Accessories, Footwear & Housewares
Import Export
S.I.C.: 5136
N.A.I.C.S.: 424320
Personnel:
Jose Manuel Martinez Gutierrez *(CEO)*
Thomas Wing Yung Tang *(CFO)*
Jose Antonio Ramos *(Chief Comml Officer)*
Juan Antonio Chaparro Vazquez *(Chief Supply Chain Officer)*
Armin F. Broger *(Pres-edc Brand)*
Florence Wai Yin Ng *(Sec)*
Ernst-Peter Vogel *(Exec VP-Global Fin & IT)*
Julia Merkel *(Sr VP & Head-Global HR)*
Arnd Mueller *(Sr VP & Head-Global Mktg)*
Elena Lazcanotegui Larrarte *(Sr VP-Trend)*
Board of Directors:
Raymond Ching Fai Or
Eva Kam Fun Cheng Li
Paul Ming Fun Cheng
Jurgen Alfred Rudolph Friedrich
Alexander Reid Hamilton
Carmelo Ka Sze Lee
Jose Manuel Martinez Gutierrez
Norbert Adolf Platt
Thomas Wing Yung Tang

Butterfield Fulcrum Group (Bermuda) Limited
26 Burnaby Street
Hamilton, HM 11, Bermuda

Subsidiaries:

Esprit Asia (Distribution) Limited (1)
43/F Enterprise Square Three 39 Wang Chiu Road
Kowloon Bay, Kowloon, China (Hong Kong) (100%)
Tel.: (852) 27654232
Fax: (852) 27641723
Quality & Lifestyle Products Sourcing, Retail & Wholesale
Import Export
S.I.C.: 5621
N.A.I.C.S.: 448120
Fookaun Chew *(CFO)*

Esprit de Corp (Far East) Limited (1)
43F Enterprise Sq Three 39 Wang Chiu Rd
Kowloon Bay, Kowloon, China (Hong Kong)
Tel.: (852) 27654321
E-Mail: contact.hk@esprit.com
Casual Apparel Retailer
S.I.C.: 5651
N.A.I.C.S.: 448140

Esprit (Hong Kong) Limited (1)
43/f Enterprise Sq Three 39 Wang Chiu Rd
Kowloon Bay, Kowloon, China (Hong Kong)
Tel.: (852) 23779114
Clothing Apparels Retailer
S.I.C.: 5699
N.A.I.C.S.: 448150

Esprit Regional Services Limited (1)
40F Enterprise Square Three 39 Wang Chiu Road
Kowloon Bay, Kowloon, China (Hong Kong)
Tel.: (852) 35113511
Fax: (852) 23039083
E-Mail: contact.hk@esprit.com
Clothing Apparels Retailer
S.I.C.: 5699
N.A.I.C.S.: 448150
Fook Aun Chew *(CEO)*

U.S. Subsidiaries:

Esprit International GP, Inc. (1)
1370 Broadway Fl 16
New York, NY 10018 DE
Tel.: (212) 401-1122
Sales Range: $1-9.9 Million
Emp.: 15
Holding Company
S.I.C.: 6719
N.A.I.C.S.: 551112

Esprit US Online Shop Limited (1)
1370 Broadway 16th Fl
New York, NY 10018
Tel.: (212) 401-1125
Fax: (212) 401-1130
Toll Free: (877) 377-7488
E-Mail: service@espritshop.com
Web Site: www.espritshop.com
Online Apparels Retailer
S.I.C.: 5961
N.A.I.C.S.: 454111

Non-U.S. Subsidiaries:

ESP Clothing Finland OY (1)
Kornetintie 6
00380 Helsinki, Finland
Tel.: (358) 941700700
Fax: (358) 941700770
Emp.: 24
Apparels Retailer
S.I.C.: 5699
N.A.I.C.S.: 448150
Piia Rossi *(Mng Dir)*

Esprit Belgie Retail N.V. (1)
Hessenstraatje 19
2000 Antwerp, Belgium
Tel.: (32) 32336020
Fax: (32) 3 2253002
E-Mail: info@esprit.be
Web Site: www.esprit.be
Emp.: 400
Apparels Retailer
S.I.C.: 5699
N.A.I.C.S.: 448150
Cinthia De Meyer *(Mng Dir)*

Esprit Canada Distribution Limited (1)
135 Liberty St Ste 300
Toronto, ON, M6K 1A7, Canada
Tel.: (416) 913-0505
Fax: (416) 913-0606
Casual Apparels Distr
S.I.C.: 2399
N.A.I.C.S.: 315990
Finn Simpler *(VP-Fin)*

Esprit Canada Retail Limited (1)
1 Bass Pro Mills Dr
Vaughan, ON, L4K 5W4, Canada
Tel.: (905) 738-2218
Fax: (905) 738-2217
Casual Apparels Retailer
S.I.C.: 2389
N.A.I.C.S.: 315210

Esprit Canada Wholesale Inc. (1)
2452 Chomedey A-13 O
Laval, QC, H7X 4G8, Canada
Tel.: (450) 689-3613
Clothing Apparels Retailer
S.I.C.: 5699
N.A.I.C.S.: 448150

Esprit Card Services GmbH (1)
Esprit-Allee
40882 Ratingen, Nordrhein-Westfalen, Germany
Tel.: (49) 21021230/
Fax: (49) 210212345100
Emp.: 1,500
Apparels Retailer
S.I.C.: 5621
N.A.I.C.S.: 448120

Esprit de Corp Danmark A/S (1)
Pohjoisesplanadi 33a
00100 Helsinki, Finland
Tel.: (358) 9780781
Apparels Retailer
S.I.C.: 5699
N.A.I.C.S.: 448150

Esprit de Corp France S.A.S. (1)
N 29 Au 33 29 Rue du Louvre
Paris, 75002, France
Tel.: (33) 140285500
Fax: (33) 140285090
E-Mail: olivierwesterlinck@esprit.com
Apparels Retailer
S.I.C.: 5699
N.A.I.C.S.: 448150
Gotz-Henning Gerbaulet *(Gen Dir)*

Esprit de Corp. (Spain) S.L. (1)
Calle Jose Abascal 45 5th Floor
Madrid, 28003, Spain
Tel.: (34) 914292213
Fax: (34) 914203058
E-Mail: recepcion.s@esprit.com
Web Site: www.esprit.com
Emp.: 30
Apparels Retailer
S.I.C.: 5699
N.A.I.C.S.: 448150
Tamara Reach *(Asst Mgr)*

Esprit Design & Product Development GmbH (1)
Esprit Allee 1
40882 Ratingen, Nordrhein-Westfalen, Germany
Tel.: (49) 210212345780
Fax: (49) 210212315100
Web Site: www.esprit.com
Emp.: 1,300
Apparels Retailer
S.I.C.: 5699
N.A.I.C.S.: 448150
Ronald Ronald *(Mng Dir)*

Esprit Europe B.V. (1)
Marktstraat 6
5211 SL 's-Hertogenbosch, Noord-Brabant, Netherlands
Tel.: (31) 736241244
Fax: (31) 736241244
Apparels Retailer
S.I.C.: 5699
N.A.I.C.S.: 448150
Elf Wingerden *(Mng Dir)*

Esprit GB Limited (1)
178-182 Regent Street
London, W1B 5TH, United Kingdom
Tel.: (44) 2070257700
Fax: (44) 2078339109
Clothing Apparels Retailer
S.I.C.: 5699
N.A.I.C.S.: 448150

Esprit Handelsgesellschaft mbH. (1)
Carl-Zuckmayer strasse 38
5020 Salzburg, Austria
Tel.: (43) 6624547700
Fax: (43) 6624547704
E-Mail: info@esprit.com
Web Site: www.esprit.at
Emp.: 60
Clothing Apparels Retailer
S.I.C.: 5699
N.A.I.C.S.: 448150
Thomas Kainz *(Mng Dir)*

Esprit Italy Distribution S.R.L. (1)
Via Morimondo 30
Milan, 20143, Italy
Tel.: (39) 0281881701
Fax: (39) 0281881799
E-Mail: info.espiritiitaly@espirit.com
Web Site: www.espirit.com
Emp.: 34
Apparels & Accessories Distr
S.I.C.: 5131
N.A.I.C.S.: 424310
Marco Bonanni *(Gen Mgr)*

Esprit Luxembourg S.a.r.L. (1)
Grand-Rue 23-25
1661 Luxembourg, Luxembourg
Tel.: (352) 26262176
Fax: (352) 2626217676
E-Mail: info@espirit.com
Web Site: www.espirit.com
Emp.: 15
Apparels Retailer
S.I.C.: 5699
N.A.I.C.S.: 448150
Kruse Weller *(Mgr-Store)*

Esprit Macao Commercial Offshore Limited (1)
Room A-C L-N 15F Edi Zhu Kuan Avenida Xian Xing Hai
Macau, China (Macau)
Tel.: (853) 87913600
Fax: (853) 28755020
E-Mail: hrmo@esprit.com
Emp.: 70
Casual Apparels Retailer
S.I.C.: 5651
N.A.I.C.S.: 448140
Ronnie Fok *(Asst Mgr-Logistics)*

Esprit Retail B.V. & Co. KG. (1)
Esprit Allee
40882 Ratingen, Nordrhein-Westfalen, Germany
Tel.: (49) 1805037467
Fax: (49) 1805 805777
E-Mail: service@esprit.de
Web Site: www.esprit.de
Online Apparels Retailer
S.I.C.: 5961
N.A.I.C.S.: 454111
Juergen Michelberger *(Mgr-Global Bus-ECommerce)*

Esprit Retail Pte. Ltd. (1)
70 Bendemeer Road 05-01 Luzerne
Singapore, Singapore 339940
Tel.: (65) 62971211
Fax: (65) 62963120
Emp.: 200
Casual Apparels Retailer
S.I.C.: 5651
N.A.I.C.S.: 448140
S. T. Ang *(Gen Mgr)*

Esprit (Retail) Proprietary Limited (1)
Unit 9-11 2 Pyrmont Bridge Road
Pyrmont, NSW, 2009, Australia
Tel.: (61) 285860444
Fax: (61) 295187040
E-Mail: reception.edc@esprit.com
Web Site: www.esprit.com.au

Emp.: 40
Casual Apparels Retailer
S.I.C.: 5651
N.A.I.C.S.: 448140
Sophia Hwang-Judiesch *(Gen Mgr)*

Esprit Switzerland Distribution AG (1)
Thurgauerstrasse 113
8152 Glattbrugg, Zurich, Switzerland
Tel.: (41) 448281616
Fax: (41) 848000453
Web Site: www.espirit.com
Emp.: 50
Apparel & Accessories Wholesale Distribution Services
S.I.C.: 5137
N.A.I.C.S.: 424330
Ulrich Hess *(Country Mgr)*

Esprit Switzerland Retail AG (1)
Thurgauerstrasse 113
8152 Glattbrugg, Zurich, Switzerland
Tel.: (41) 448281616
Fax: (41) 448102603
Emp.: 80
Apparel & Accessories Retailer
S.I.C.: 5699
N.A.I.C.S.: 448150
Ulrich Hess *(Country Mgr)*

ESPRIT MAILLE

100 rue Reaumur
75002 Paris, France
Tel.: (33) 142214220
Sls.: $22,200,000
Emp.: 15
Business Description:
Piece Goods & Notions
S.I.C.: 5131
N.A.I.C.S.: 424310
Personnel:
Marc Policcino *(Chm)*

ESPRO INFORMATION TECHNOLOGIES LTD.

(d/b/a Espro Acoustiguide Group)
17 Atir Yeda Street
Kfar Saba, 44643, Israel
Tel.: (972) 9 763 4400
Fax: (972) 9 763 4411
E-Mail: customersolutions@espro.com
Web Site: www.acoustiguide.com
Business Description:
Multimedia Guide Production Services
S.I.C.: 7812
N.A.I.C.S.: 512110
Personnel:
Israel Gal *(Pres & CEO)*
Nadav Karni *(CFO)*
Eyal Ben Gigi *(COO)*
Shmuel Shalem *(CTO)*

U.S. Subsidiary:

Acoustiguide Inc. (1)
102 W 38th St
New York, NY 10018 NY
Tel.: (212) 279-1300
Fax: (212) 575-6574
E-Mail: operations@acoustiguide.com
Web Site: www.acoustiguide.com
Emp.: 12
Multimedia Guide Production Services
S.I.C.: 7812
N.A.I.C.S.: 512110
Julie Twitmyer *(Mng Dir-Americas)*

Non-U.S. Subsidiaries:

Acoustiguide GmbH (1)
Martin Luther Strasse 111
D 10825 Berlin, Germany
Tel.: (49) 30 78 77 36 0
Fax: (49) 30 78 77 36 36
E-Mail: info@acoustiguide.de
Web Site: www.acoustiguide.de
Emp.: 3
Multimedia Guide Production Services
S.I.C.: 7812
N.A.I.C.S.: 512110
Jorg Bruckner *(Mng Dir)*

Acoustiguide Ltd. (1)
2 3 North Mews
London, WC1N 2JP, United Kingdom
Tel.: (44) 20 7269 5150
Fax: (44) 20 7404 7715
E-Mail: info@acoustiguide.co.uk
Web Site: www.acoustiguide.co.uk
Multimedia Guide Production Services
S.I.C.: 7812
N.A.I.C.S.: 512110
Louisa Matthews *(Mng Dir)*

Espro Acoustiguide SAS (1)
9 Rue de Clichy
7500 Paris, France
Tel.: (33) 1 4260 6968
Fax: (33) 1 4260 6967
E-Mail: esprofrance@espro.com
Multimedia Guide Production Services
S.I.C.: 7812
N.A.I.C.S.: 512110
Fella Myara *(Mng Dir)*

ESREY ENERGY LTD

(Formerly LNG Energy Ltd.)
Suite 250 - 1075 West Georgia Street
Vancouver, BC, V6E 3C9, Canada
Tel.: (778) 373-0103
Fax: (604) 484-1487
E-Mail: info@esreyenergy.com
Web Site: www.esreyenergy.com
Year Founded: 2000
EEL—(TSXV)
Int. Income: $36,003
Assets: $23,120,225
Liabilities: $6,343,876
Net Worth: $16,776,350
Earnings: ($3,760,000)
Fiscal Year-end: 09/30/13
Business Description:
Oil & Gas Exploration & Development Services
S.I.C.: 1389
N.A.I.C.S.: 213112
Personnel:
David Cohen *(Chm)*
David R. Nelson *(Pres & CEO)*
Shayne Dyrdal *(CFO)*
Board of Directors:
David Cohen
Richard Green
Paul Anthony Larkin
Legal Counsel:
Fasken Martineau
2900-550 Burrard Street
Vancouver, BC, Canada
Transfer Agent:
Computershare Investor Services Inc.
100 University Avenue 8th Floor
Toronto, ON, M5J 2Y1, Canada
Tel.: (514) 982-7555

ESS DEE ALUMINIUM LTD

Ess Dee House Akurli Road Kandivali East
Mumbai, 400101, India
Tel.: (91) 2266908200
Fax: (91) 2266908396
E-Mail: info@essdee.in
Web Site: www.essdee.in
532787—(BOM)
Rev.: $140,812,283
Assets: $268,381,072
Liabilities: $115,416,283
Net Worth: $152,964,789
Earnings: $13,614,386
Emp.: 442
Fiscal Year-end: 03/31/13
Business Description:
Aluminium Foil Packaging Laminates Provider
S.I.C.: 3353
N.A.I.C.S.: 331315
Personnel:
Indrajit Chaudhuri *(Co-Pres)*
M. S. R. Srinivasa *(Co-Pres)*
Bijoy Kumar Pansari *(CEO & Mng Dir)*
Satya Ray *(CMO & Chief Sls Officer)*
Haresh Vala *(Compliance Officer & Sec)*
Ashis Bhattacharya *(Pres-Ops)*
Soumitra Maitra *(Pres-Consumer Div)*
Board of Directors:
Sudip Dutta
Ramdas Baxi
Ashis Bhattacharya
Tara Shankar Bhattacharya
Vinaya Desai
Madan Mohan Jain
Gautam Mukherjee
Bijoy Kumar Pansari
Dilip Phatarphekar
Legal Counsel:
Kanga & Co.
Readymoney Mansion 43 Veer Nariman Rd
Mumbai, India
Transfer Agent:
Bigshare Services Private Limited
E 2/3 Ansa Industrial Estate Sakivihar Road Sakinaka Andheri(E)
Mumbai, India

ESSANELLE HAIR GROUP AG

Niederkasseler Lohweg 20
40547 Dusseldorf, Germany
Tel.: (49) 21117480
Fax: (49) 2111748290
Web Site: www.essanelle-hair-group.de
EHX—(DEU)
Sales Range: $150-199.9 Million
Emp.: 2,326
Business Description:
Hairdressing Industry
S.I.C.: 7241
N.A.I.C.S.: 812111
Personnel:
Fritz Kuhn *(Chm-Supervisory Bd)*
Achim Mansen *(Chm-Mgmt Bd-Fin)*
Peter-Michael Herold *(Deputy Chm-Supervisory Bd)*
Dieter Bonk *(Member-Mgmt Bd-Sls)*
Dirk Wietholter *(Member-Mgmt Bd-HR)*
Supervisory Board of Directors:
Fritz Kuhn
Silvia Altenberger
Michael Eberhard
Cornelia Glass
Peter-Michael Herold
Ursel Lohmuller
Olaf Rogowski
Werner Schneider
Hiltrud Seggewib
Jurgen Trondle
Andreas Tscherner
Barbara Wietusch

ESSAR GLOBAL LIMITED

(d/b/a Essar Group)
Essar House 11 Keshavrao Khadya Marg
Mahalaxmi, Mumbai, 400 034, India
Tel.: (91) 2266601100
Fax: (91) 2256601809
E-Mail: corporatecommunications@essar.com
Web Site: www.essar.com
Sales Range: $5-14.9 Billion
Emp.: 20,000
Business Description:
Holding Company
S.I.C.: 6719
N.A.I.C.S.: 551112
Personnel:
Shashi Ruia *(Chm)*
Ravi Ruia *(Vice Chm)*
Arvind Chopra *(Grp Pres-Assurance & Cost Control)*
Prashant Ruia *(CEO)*
Adil Malia *(Pres-HR)*
Alwyn Bowden *(CEO-Projects Bus Grp)*
Naresh Nayyar *(CEO-Energy Bus Grp)*
Rajiv Sawhney *(CEO-Telecom Bus Grp)*
Board of Directors:
Shashi Ruia
Smiti Kanodia
Anshuman Ruia
Prashant Ruia
Ravi Ruia
Rewant Ruia

Subsidiaries:

Essar Ports Limited (1)
Administrative Building Essar Refinery Complex Okha Highway
Taluka Khambhalia, Jamnagar, Gujarat, 361 305, India
Tel.: (91) 2833661449
Fax: (91) 2833662929
E-Mail: corporatecommunications@essar.com
Web Site: www.essarports.com
500630—(BOM NSE)
Rev.: $265,982,126
Assets: $1,772,426,039
Liabilities: $1,263,143,660
Net Worth: $509,282,379
Earnings: $61,468,703
Emp.: 150
Fiscal Year-end: 03/31/13
Ports & Terminals, Logistics Services, Sea Transportation & Oilfield Drilling Services
S.I.C.: 4491
N.A.I.C.S.: 488310
Rajiv Agarwal *(Co-CEO & Mng Dir)*
K. K. Sinha *(Co-CEO)*
Manoj Contractor *(Compliance Officer & Sec)*

Subsidiaries:

Essar International Ltd. (2)
Equinox Business Park off Bandra Kurla Complex LBS Marg Kurla West
Mumbai, Maharashtra, 400 070, India
Tel.: (91) 22 6733 5000
Fax: (91) 22 666 01809
Web Site: www.essar.com
Ports & Harbor Operations
S.I.C.: 4491
N.A.I.C.S.: 488310
Rakesh Kankanala *(Mgr-Fin)*

Essar Oil Limited (2)
Equinox Business Park off Bandra Kurla Complex LBS Marg Kurla West
Mumbai, 400 070, India
Tel.: (91) 22 6733 5000
Fax: (91) 22 6708 2183
Web Site: www.essar.com
Oil Operations
S.I.C.: 1381
N.A.I.C.S.: 213111
Lalit Kumar Gupta *(Mng Dir & CEO)*

Subsidiary:

Essar (3)
Essar House 11 Keshavrao Khadye Marg
Mahalaxmi, Mumbai, 400 034, India
Tel.: (91) 22 5001 1100
Fax: (91) 22 6660 1809
Web Site: www.essar.com
Crude Oil & Petroleum Products, Storage, Handling & Terminalling
S.I.C.: 1389
N.A.I.C.S.: 213112
K. K. Sinha *(CEO)*

Essar Port & Terminals Ltd. (2)
11 Keshavrao Khadye Marg Mahalaxmi
Mumbai, 400 034, India
Tel.: (91) 22 2495 0606
Port & Terminal Operations
S.I.C.: 4491
N.A.I.C.S.: 488310
K. K. Sinha *(CEO)*

Essar Power Ltd. (1)
Essar House 11 Keshavrao Khadya Marg Opp Race Course Mahalakshmi, Mumbai, 400 034, India
Tel.: (91) 22673350

Essar Global Limited—(Continued)

Fax: (91) 2223544490
E-Mail: essarpower@essar.com
Power Generation
S.I.C.: 1311
N.A.I.C.S.: 211111
V. Suresh *(CFO)*
Sumant Nayak *(Gen Counsel)*
T. S. Bhatt *(Sr VP-Ops)*

Essar Steel Ltd. (1)
Essar House 11 Keshavrao Khadye Marg
Opposite Mahalaxmi, Mumbai, 400 034, India In
Tel.: (91) 2266601100
Fax: (91) 22 2492 8896
E-Mail: steel@essar.com
Web Site: www.essarsteel.com
Sales Range: $300-349.9 Million
Steel Production & Export
S.I.C.: 3462
N.A.I.C.S.: 332111
Shashi Ruia *(Chm)*
Firdose Vandrevala *(Vice Chm)*
Ashutosh Agarwala *(CFO & Dir-Fin)*
Shivramkrishnan Hariharan *(Chief Comml Officer)*
Rajendra Mittal *(CEO-Odisha)*
Dilip Oommen *(CEO-India)*
Narottam B. Vyas *(Sec)*

U.S. Subsidiary:

Essar Steel Minnesota LLC (2)
555 W 27th St
Hibbing, MN 55746
Tel.: (218) 263-3331
Fax: (218) 262-1497
E-Mail: Corporatecommunications@minnesotasteel.com
Web Site: www.essarsteelmn.com
Emp.: 20
Steel Mining
S.I.C.: 3462
N.A.I.C.S.: 332111
Madagu Vuppuluri *(Pres & CEO)*

Non-U.S. Subsidiaries:

Essar Steel Algoma Inc. (2)
105 West Street
Sault Sainte Marie, ON, P6A 7B4, Canada ON
Tel.: (705) 945-2351
Fax: (705) 945-2203
E-Mail: sales@algoma.com
Web Site: www.algoma.com
Rev.: $1,854,443,712
Assets: $1,866,371,952
Liabilities: $2,164,776,756
Net Worth: ($298,404,804)
Earnings: ($202,084,266)
Emp.: 3,200
Fiscal Year-end: 03/31/13
Rolled Sheet & Plate Steel Mfr Export
S.I.C.: 3399
N.A.I.C.S.: 331221
Kalyan Ghosh *(CEO)*
Pramod Kumar Shukla *(COO)*
J. Robert Sandoval *(Gen Counsel & Sec)*

PT Essar Indonesia (2)
Bekasi Fajar Industrial Estate
Industri 3 Area Kav #B1, Bekasi, 17520, Indonesia
Tel.: (62) 218980152
Fax: (62) 218980150
E-Mail: marketing@essar.co.id
Web Site: www.essar.co.id
Emp.: 400
Cold Rolled Steel
S.I.C.: 3312
N.A.I.C.S.: 331221
K. B. Trivedi *(Pres)*

Essar Teleholding Ltd. (1)
Equinox Business Park off Bandra Kurla Complex LBS Marg Kurla West
Mumbai, Maharashtra, 400 070, India
Tel.: (91) 22 6733 5000
Fax: (91) 22 67082183
Web Site: www.essar.com
Telecommunications
S.I.C.: 4899
N.A.I.C.S.: 517919
Rajiv Sawhney *(CEO)*
S. Subramaniam *(CFO)*

Subsidiary:

The MobileStore Ltd. (2)
Essar Techno Park Building 'B' 1st Floor
Pyramid Infotech Park
Swan Mill Compound LBS Marg, Mumbai, Kurla (W), 400 070, India
Tel.: (91) 2260006363
E-Mail: mobicares@mytms.in
Web Site: www.themobilestore.in
Mobile Phones & Equipment Stores
S.I.C.: 4899
N.A.I.C.S.: 517919
Himanshu Chakrawarti *(CEO)*

Holding:

Aegis BPO Services Ltd. (1)
Essar House
PO Box No 7945
Mahalaxmi, Mumbai, 400 034, India
Tel.: (91) 2266601100
Business Process Outsourcing
S.I.C.: 7361
N.A.I.C.S.: 561311
Agarup Sengupta *(CEO & Mng Dir)*

Subsidiaries:

Aegis Limited (2)
Essar House 13th Floor
11 KK Marg Mahalaxmi, Mumbai, 400 034, India
Tel.: (91) 2266601100
Fax: (91) 2223544490
Web Site: www.aegiscomgroup.com
Business Process Outsourcing
S.I.C.: 8742
N.A.I.C.S.: 541611
Rajiv Ahuja *(Pres)*
Agarup Sengupta *(Global CEO & Mng Dir)*
C. M. Sharma *(CFO)*
Sudhir Agarwal *(COO)*
Sandeep Sen *(Global CMO & Global Head-Sls)*
Ishita Swaroop *(Chief Legal Officer)*
Rahul Kamlakar *(CTO)*
Peter Bloom *(Pres-Global Quality & Customer Experience)*
S. M. Gupta *(Exec VP-Corp HR)*

Subsidiaries:

Aegis Services (3)
Essar House 13th FL 11KK Marg Mahalaxmi
Mumbai, Maharashtra, 400034, India
Tel.: (91) 2266601100
Fax: (91) 22 2354 4490
Web Site: www.aegisbpo.com
Customer Contact Management Services
S.I.C.: 8748
N.A.I.C.S.: 541618
Sudhir Agarwal *(Pres)*
Sandip Sen *(Interim CEO)*
C. M. Sharma *(CFO)*
Rahul Kamalakar *(CTO)*
Neeti Khaitan *(Chief Relationship Officer)*
Rajiv Ahuja *(Pres-Asean & ANZ)*

AGC Networks Limited (3)
Equinox Business Park Tower A Peninsula Techno Park
Off Bandra Kurla Complex LBS Marg Kurla West, Mumbai, Maharashtra, 400070, India In
Tel.: (91) 22 66617272
Fax: (91) 22 67045888
E-Mail: info@agcnetworks.com
Web Site: www.agcnetworks.com
500463—(BOM)
Rev.: $205,701,300
Assets: $223,073,280
Liabilities: $166,415,040
Net Worth: $56,658,240
Earnings: ($4,060,260)
Emp.: 1,124
Fiscal Year-end: 03/31/13
Communications Systems, Applications & Services
S.I.C.: 4899
N.A.I.C.S.: 517919
Satya K. Jha *(CEO & Mng Dir)*
Srinivasa Raghavan V. *(CFO)*
Greg Forrest *(Pres-AGC Networks Inc-North America)*
Sanjeev Verma *(Pres-Global Sls & Bus Ops)*
Pratik Bhanushali *(Sec)*

U.S. Subsidiary:

AGC Networks, Inc. (4)
222 W Las Colinas Blvd Ste 200 N Tower
Irving, TX 75039
Fax: (214) 445-4099
Toll Free: (888) 960-3792
E-Mail: info_us@agcnetworks.com
Web Site: www.agcnetworks.com
Telecommunications Network Integration Services
S.I.C.: 7373
N.A.I.C.S.: 541512
Greg Forrest, *(Pres)*
Mike Carney *(Sr VP-Corp Strategy & Dev)*
Rick Hirsh *(Sr VP-Bus Dev)*

Subsidiary:

Transcend United Technologies LLC (5)
460 E Swedesford Rd Ste 1080
Wayne, PA 19087 DE
Tel.: (484) 654-1500
Fax: (484) 654-1501
E-Mail: info@transcendunited.com
Web Site: www.transcendunited.com
Sales Range: $25-49.9 Million
Emp.: 120
Technical Consulting
S.I.C.: 7389
N.A.I.C.S.: 541990
Stephen Benson *(Sr VP-Managed Svcs)*

U.S. Subsidiary:

Aegis Communications, Inc. (3)
8201 Ridgepoint Dr
Irving, TX 75063 DE
Tel.: (972) 830-1800
Fax: (972) 830-1801
Toll Free: (800) 332-0266
E-Mail: info@aegiscomgroup.com
Web Site: www.aegiscomgroup.com
Sales Range: $50-74.9 Million
Emp.: 3,700
Customer Lifecycle Management & Business Process Outsourcing
S.I.C.: 7361
N.A.I.C.S.: 561311

Branches:

Aegis Communications (4)
1225 W 11 Court
Broomfield, CO 80020
Tel.: (303) 410-0554
Telemarketing Services
S.I.C.: 7389
N.A.I.C.S.: 561422

Aegis Communications (4)
504 Plaza Dr
Woodbridge, NJ 07095
Tel.: (732) 634-1542
Fax: (732) 634-1542
E-Mail: anilm@aegiscomm.com
Web Site: www.aegiscommunications.com
Telemarketing Services
S.I.C.: 7389
N.A.I.C.S.: 561422

Subsidiary:

Aegis PeopleSupport, Inc. (4)
2049 Century Park E Ste 300
Los Angeles, CA 90067
Tel.: (310) 824-6200
Fax: (310) 824-6299
Toll Free: (877) 914-5999
Sales Range: $125-149.9 Million
Emp.: 8,550
Global Labor Management Services
S.I.C.: 7361
N.A.I.C.S.: 561311
Lance Rozensweig *(Founder, Chm & CEO)*
Caroline Rook *(CFO)*
Jesper Rathje *(Chief Acctg Officer)*

Non-U.S. Subsidiary:

Aegis PeopleSupport, Inc. (Cebu) (5)
Aegis Tower 1, Asiatown IT Park Apas
Cebu, 6000, Philippines
Tel.: (63) 322348200
Fax: (63) 322348248
E-Mail: info@aegisglobal.com
Web Site: www.aegisbpo.com
Emp.: 3,904
Business Process Outsourcing Services
S.I.C.: 7361
N.A.I.C.S.: 561311
Faye Cadungog *(Mgr-HR Recruitment)*

Non-U.S. Branch:

Aegis Communications (4)
Essar House
11 Keshavrao Khadye Marg, Mumbai, 400 034, India
Tel.: (91) 9819730611
Telemarketing Services
S.I.C.: 7389
N.A.I.C.S.: 561422

Non-U.S. Subsidiary:

Symphony BPO Solutions Sdn. Bhd. (3)
Level 8 Symphony House Pusat Dagangan Dana 1
Jalan PJU 1A/46, 47301 Petaling Jaya, Selangor Darul Ehsan, Malaysia
Tel.: (60) 378418000
Fax: (60) 378418008
E-Mail: bposales@symphony.com.my
Emp.: 1,000
Business Process Outsourcing Services
S.I.C.: 7389
N.A.I.C.S.: 561499
Vilaashini Balakrishnan *(Mgr-HR)*

Joint Venture:

Hutchison Essar Limited (1)
Hutch House Peninsula Corporate Park
Ganpatrao Kdam Marg
Lower Parel, Mumbai, 400 013, India
Tel.: (91) 2256661200
Wireless Telecommunications Services; Owned by Cheung Kong (Holdings) Limited & Essar Group
S.I.C.: 4812
N.A.I.C.S.: 517210
Naveen Chopra *(VP-Corp Mktg)*

Non-U.S. Subsidiary:

Essar Energy plc (1)
Essar House 10 Frere Felix de Valois Street
Port Louis, Mauritius UK
Tel.: (230) 405 1400 (78.02%)
Web Site: www.essarenergy.com
ESSR—(LSE OTC)
Rev.: $27,257,700,000
Assets: $17,805,100,000
Liabilities: $14,514,900,000
Net Worth: $3,290,200,000
Earnings: ($175,000,000)
Emp.: 3,951
Fiscal Year-end: 03/31/13
Holding Company; Petroleum Exploration, Production, Refining & Marketing Services; Power Generation & Transmission Services
S.I.C.: 6719
N.A.I.C.S.: 551112
Prashant Ruia *(Chm)*
Sushil K. Maroo *(CEO)*
Deepak Maheshwari *(CFO)*
P. Sampath *(Pres-Bus Optimisation & Improvement)*
Lalit K. Gupta *(CEO-Essar Oil)*
Iftikhar Nasir *(CEO-E&P Bus)*
Volker Schultz *(CEO-Essar Oil UK)*

Non-U.S. Subsidiaries:

Essar Exploration & Production Ltd. (2)
Equinox Business Park off Bandra Kurla Complex LBS Marg Kurla West
Mumbai, 400 070, India
Tel.: (91) 22 6733 5000
Web Site: www.essarenergy.com
Gas Exploration
S.I.C.: 1389
N.A.I.C.S.: 213112
Naresh Nayyar *(Deputy Chm & CEO)*

Essar Oil Limited (2)
Khambalia Post
PO Box 24
Jamnagar, Gujarat, 361 305, India
Tel.: (91) 2833661444
Fax: (91) 2833662929
E-Mail: corporatecommunications@essar.com
Web Site: www.essar.com
500134—(BOM NSE)

Rev.: $16,535,251,260
Assets: $8,818,708,590
Liabilities: $8,613,502,308
Net Worth: $205,206,282
Earnings: ($218,853,576)
Emp.: 1,659
Fiscal Year-end: 03/31/13
Oil & Gas Exploration, Production & Marketing Services
S.I.C.: 1311
N.A.I.C.S.: 211111
Lalit Kumar Gupta *(CEO & Mng Dir)*
Suresh Jain *(CFO)*
Vikas Prabhu *(CIO)*
Shaffi S. Sheikh *(Compliance Officer, Sec & Head-Legal)*
V. Ramachandran *(Pres-CRG)*
K. Govindarajan *(CEO-Projects)*
Iftikhar Nasir *(CEO-Exploration & Production)*
S. Thangapandian *(CEO-Mktg & Intl Supply & Trading)*

ESSAR SECURITIES LIMITED

Essar House 11 Keshavrao Khadye Marg
Mahalaxmi, Mumbai, Maharashtra, 400 034, India
Tel.: (91) 2250011100
Fax: (91) 2266601809
E-Mail: corporatecommunications@essar.com
Web Site: www.essar.com
533149—(BOM)
Sales Range: $1-9.9 Million
Business Description:
Financial Services
S.I.C.: 9311
N.A.I.C.S.: 921130
Personnel:
A. S. Ruia *(Chm)*
Girish K. Sathe *(Compliance Officer & Sec)*
Board of Directors:
A. S. Ruia
S. M. Lodha
Dhanpat Nahata
Vikash Saraf
Sujay Sheth
S. V. Venkatesan
Transfer Agent:
Data Software Research Company Pvt Ltd
Sree Sovereign Complex No 22 4th Cross St
Trustpuram Kodambakkam
Chennai, India

ESSECO GROUP SRL

28069 San Martino Trecate
via S. Cassiano 99, Trecate, 28069, Italy
Tel.: (39) 03217901
Fax: (39) 0321779646
E-Mail: esseco@esseco.it
Web Site: www.essecogroup.com
Year Founded: 1982
Sales Range: $1-4.9 Billion
Business Description:
Holding Company; Chemicals Research & Development & Mfr
S.I.C.: 2819
N.A.I.C.S.: 325180
Personnel:
Fabrizio Zenone *(Owner)*
Piero Nulli *(Chm & CEO)*
Alberto Cambieri *(CFO)*

Non-U.S. Subsidiary:

Brotherton Esseco Limited **(1)**
Calder Vale Road
Wakefield, W Yorkshire, WF1 5PH, United Kingdom (100%)
Tel.: (44) 1924371919
Telex: 556320 BROKEM G
Fax: (44) 1924290408
E-Mail: info@brothertonesseco.com
Web Site: www.brotherton.co.uk
Sales Range: $10-24.9 Million
Emp.: 55
Mfr. of Ammonium Compounds
S.I.C.: 2819
N.A.I.C.S.: 325180
Roger Perry *(Mng Dir)*

ESSEL CORPORATE RESOURCES PVT. LTD.

(d/b/a Essel Group)
135 Continental Building
Dr Annie Besant Road Worli, Mumbai, 400 018, India
Tel.: (91) 22 2490 3926
Fax: (91) 22 2490 3926
Web Site: www.esselgroup.com
Rev.: $60,185,475
Assets: $67,861,962
Liabilities: $28,410,511
Net Worth: $39,451,451
Earnings: $4,480,747
Emp.: 8,000
Fiscal Year-end: 03/31/13
Business Description:
Holding Company
S.I.C.: 6719
N.A.I.C.S.: 551112
Personnel:
Punit Goenka *(Mng Dir)*
Dinesh Garg *(CFO)*
Pushpal Sanghavi *(Sec)*

Subsidiaries:

Essel Propack Ltd. **(1)**
Top Floor Times Tower Kamala City
Senapati Bapat Marg Lower Parel
Mumbai, 400 013, India
Tel.: (91) 22 248 19000
Fax: (91) 22 249 63137
E-Mail: info@ep.esselgroup.com
Web Site: www.esselpropack.com
500135—(BOM)
Rev.: $349,186,050
Assets: $402,700,818
Liabilities: $226,442,281
Net Worth: $176,258,537
Earnings: $15,009,491
Emp.: 3,513
Fiscal Year-end: 03/31/13
Specialty Packaging Products Mfr
S.I.C.: 2671
N.A.I.C.S.: 322220
Ashok Kumar Goel *(Vice Chm & Mng Dir)*
A. V. Ganapathy *(CFO)*
Prakash Dharmani *(CIO)*
Ajay N. Thakkar *(Compliance Officer, Sec & VP-Legal)*
M. R. Ramasamy *(Pres-Americas & EAP)*
Cherian Kenneth Thomas *(CEO-Packaging India Pvt Ltd)*

Siti Cable Network Ltd. **(1)**
(Formerly Wire & Wireless India Ltd.)
135 Continental Building Dr Annie Besant Road
Worli, Mumbai, 400 018, India
Tel.: (91) 22 6697 1234
Fax: (91) 22 2490 0302
Web Site: www.wwil.net
532795—(BOM)
Rev.: $63,558,272
Earnings: ($17,587,971)
Emp.: 350
Fiscal Year-end: 03/31/13
Cable Television Services
S.I.C.: 4813
N.A.I.C.S.: 517110
Subhash Chandra *(Chm)*
Sanjay Goyal *(CFO)*
Anil Malhotra *(COO)*
Sanjay Jindal *(CTO)*

Subsidiaries:

Central Bombay Cable Network Limited **(2)**
Essel House B-10 Lawrence Road Industrial Area
New Delhi, 110 035, India
Tel.: (91) 1127101145
Fax: (91) 1127186561
Web Site: www.wwil.net
Cable Television Services
S.I.C.: 4813
N.A.I.C.S.: 517110

Indian Cable Net Company Limited **(2)**
J 1/15 Block EP 4th Floor Sector V
Saltlake Electronics Complex, Kolkata, 700 091, India
Tel.: (91) 33 22828169
Fax: (91) 33 23577640
Web Site: www.wwil.net
Cable Television Services
S.I.C.: 4813
N.A.I.C.S.: 517110

Master Channel Community Network Private Limited **(2)**
T-4 Vijaya Apartments Jammichettu Centre
Mogalrajpuram, Vijayawada, 520 010, India
Tel.: (91) 866 2491955
Fax: (91) 866 2496767
E-Mail: mccnvja@gmail.com
Web Site: www.wwil.net
Emp.: 10
Cable Television Services
S.I.C.: 4813
N.A.I.C.S.: 517110
B. Nagamani *(Mgr-Sls)*

Siticable Broadband South Limited **(2)**
United Mansions 3rd Floor
39 Mahatma Gandhi Road, Bengaluru, 560 001, India
Tel.: (91) 8025581234
Fax: (91) 8025580099
Web Site: www.wwil.net
Cable Television Services
S.I.C.: 4813
N.A.I.C.S.: 517110

Wire and Wireless Tisai Satellite Limited **(2)**
3rd Floor TISAI House opp Ashirwad Hospital
Poona Link Road, Kalyan, East, 421 306, India
Tel.: (91) 2512356255
Web Site: www.wwil.net
Cable Television Services
S.I.C.: 4813
N.A.I.C.S.: 517110

Zee Entertainment Enterprises Ltd. **(1)**
135 Continental Building Dr Annie Besant Road
Worli, Mumbai, 400018, India
Tel.: (91) 2266971234
Fax: (91) 22 24900302
Web Site: www.zeetelevision.com
505537—(BOM)
Rev.: $712,992,780
Assets: $937,345,320
Liabilities: $211,541,400
Net Worth: $725,803,920
Earnings: $133,413,840
Emp.: 1,630
Fiscal Year-end: 03/31/13
Television Broadcasting
S.I.C.: 4833
N.A.I.C.S.: 515120
Subodh Kumar *(Vice Chm)*
Punit Goenka *(CEO & Mng Dir)*
Bharat Ranga *(Chief Creative Officer & Chief Content Officer)*
M. Lakshminarayanan *(Chief Compliance Officer, Sec & Exec VP)*
Ashish Sehgal *(Chief Sls Officer)*
Mihir Modi *(Chief Fin & Strategy Officer)*
Rajesh Sethi *(CEO-Sports Bus)*
Hitesh Vakil *(CEO-Svc Excellence)*
Mona Jain *(Exec VP & Head-Cluster)*
Sharada Sunder *(Exec VP-Reg Channels)*
Rahul Sharma *(Sr VP & Natl Head-Sls)*

Subsidiary:

ETC Networks Ltd. **(2)**
Continental Building 135
Dr Annie Besant Road Worli, Mumbai, 400 018, India
Tel.: (91) 2266971234
Fax: (91) 2224900302
Web Site: www.etc.in
Emp.: 400
Television Broadcasting Services
S.I.C.: 4833
N.A.I.C.S.: 515120
Subhash Chandra *(Chm)*
Deepak Bondre *(CFO-ETC)*
Rahul Neogi *(Sec)*

Divisions:

ETC Networks Ltd.-Broadcasting Division **(3)**
7B Shah Industrial Estate
Off Veera Desai Road Andheri, 40053 Mumbai, India
Tel.: (91) 2267813737
Fax: (91) 222673203
Web Site: www.etc.in
Emp.: 200
Television Broadcasting Services
S.I.C.: 4833
N.A.I.C.S.: 515120

ETC Networks Ltd.-Education Division **(3)**
3rd Floor Valecha Chambers Plot B6
Andheri Link Road Andheri, Mumbai, 400 053, India
Tel.: (91) 2226743900
Fax: (91) 26743422
Web Site: www.zeelearn.com
Educational Television Programming & Broadcasting Services
S.I.C.: 4833
N.A.I.C.S.: 515120
Nitya Ramaswamy *(Gen Mgr-Academics)*

Joint Venture:

Zee Turner Limited **(2)**
2nd Floor Plot 9
Film City Sector 16 A, Noida, 201301, India
Tel.: (91) 1206766466
Fax: (91) 1206766465
Web Site: www.zeeturner.com
Sales Range: $200-249.9 Million
Television Broadcasting Services; Owned 74% by Zee Entertainment Enterprises Ltd. & 26% by Turner Broadcasting System, Inc.
S.I.C.: 4833
N.A.I.C.S.: 515120
Virad Kaul *(CEO)*
Viresh Dhaibar *(Sec & VP-Legal)*

Non-U.S. Subsidiaries:

Asia Today Limited **(2)**
2nd Fl Ebene House 33 Cybercity
Ebene City, Ebene, Mauritius
Tel.: (230) 4642222
Fax: (230) 4644040
E-Mail: asiatoday@intnet.mu
Web Site: www.zeetelevision.com
Television Broadcasting Services
S.I.C.: 4833
N.A.I.C.S.: 515120

Non-U.S. Subsidiary:

Zee TV South Africa Pty. Ltd. **(3)**
110 Atrium Terraces
272 Oak Avenue, Randburg, RSA 2194, South Africa
Mailing Address:
PO Box 1392
Randburg, RSA 2125, South Africa
Tel.: (27) 117813352
Fax: (27) 117813347
E-Mail: info@zeetv.co.za
Web Site: www.zeetv.co.za
Emp.: 8
Television Broadcasting Services
S.I.C.: 4833
N.A.I.C.S.: 515120
Vishwa Mohan *(Head-Territory)*

Taj Television Ltd. **(2)**
Dubai Media City ten sports Bld
PO Box 502018
Dubai Media City, Dubai, United Arab Emirates AE
Tel.: (971) 4 426 4100
Fax: (971) 4 362 5386
E-Mail: info@tensports.com
Web Site: www.tensports.com
Emp.: 150
Sports Television Broadcasting
S.I.C.: 4833
N.A.I.C.S.: 515120
Rajesh Sethi *(CEO)*
Sanjay Raina *(COO)*
Subhadip Bhattacharyya *(Exec VP-Distr)*

Zee Multimedia Worldwide Limited **(2)**
2nd Fl Ebene House 33 Cybercity Ebene City
Port Louis, Mauritius

Essel Corporate Resources Pvt. Ltd.—(Continued)

Tel.: (230) 4642222
Fax: (230) 4644040
E-Mail: zeetv@ingnet.nu
Web Site: www.zeetelevision.com
Emp.: 13
Holding Company; Television Broadcasting Services
S.I.C.: 6719
N.A.I.C.S.: 551112

U.S. Subsidiary:

Zee TV USA, Inc. (3)
701 Highlander Blvd Ste 200
Arlington, TX 76015-7480 (100%)
Mailing Address:
PO Box 569
West New York, NJ 07093-0569
Tel.: (817) 524-6400
Fax: (817) 524-6464
Web Site: www.zeetvusa.com
Sales Range: $10-24.9 Million
Emp.: 19
Theatrical Producers & Services
S.I.C.: 5812
N.A.I.C.S.: 711110
Subroto Bhattacharya *(CEO)*

Zee Media Corporatiion Ltd. (1)
(Formerly Zee News Limited)
Continental Building 135 Dr Annie Besant Road Worli
Mumbai, 400 018, India In
Tel.: (91) 22 6697 1234 (53.34%)
Fax: (91) 22 2490 0302
E-Mail: irZNL@zeenetwork.com
Web Site: www.zeenews.india.com
ZEENEWS—(NSE)
Rev.: $54,121,968
Assets: $63,202,860
Liabilities: $25,542,558
Net Worth: $37,660,302
Earnings: $4,505,220
Emp.: 1,268
Fiscal Year-end: 03/31/13
Television Broadcasting Services
S.I.C.: 4833
N.A.I.C.S.: 515120
Alok Agrawal *(CEO)*
Punit Goenka *(Mng Dir)*
Dinesh Garg *(CFO)*
Jitesh Rajdeo *(Chief Sls Officer)*
Geetanjali Pandit Gupta *(Chief People Officer)*
Bhaskar Das *(CEO-News Cluster)*
Pushpal Sanghavi *(Sec)*

U.S. Subsidiary:

Natural Wellness USA, Inc. (1)
701 Highlander Blvd Ste 200
Arlington, TX 76015
Mailing Address:
PO Box 569
West New York, NJ 07093-0569
Tel.: (817) 804-4650
Fax: (817) 524-6464
Web Site: www.veria.com
Emp.: 40
Holding Company; Natural Health Center Operator & Health Food & Herbal Supplement Whslr
S.I.C.: 6719
N.A.I.C.S.: 551112
Subhash Chandra *(Chm)*

Subsidiary:

Natural Wellness Corporation Ltd. (2)
701 Highlander Blvd Ste 200
Arlington, TX 76015
Tel.: (817) 804-4650
Fax: (817) 524-6464
Toll Free: (866) 918-3742
E-Mail: info@veria.com
Web Site: www.veria.com
Emp.: 50
Natural Health Center Operator & Health Food & Supplement Whslr
S.I.C.: 7991
N.A.I.C.S.: 713940
Subroto Bhattacharya *(CEO)*

ESSEN SUPPLEMENTS INDIA LIMITED
(Name Changed to Square Four Projects India Limited)

ESSENCE DIGITAL LIMITED
Academy House 36 Poland Street
London, W1F 7LU, United Kingdom
Tel.: (44) 20 7758 4200
E-Mail: contact@essencedigital.com
Web Site: www.essencedigital.com
Sales Range: $100-124.9 Million
Emp.: 250
Business Description:
Digital Advertising Services
S.I.C.: 7319
N.A.I.C.S.: 541890
Personnel:
Andy Bonsall *(Founder & Partner)*
Andrew Shebbeare *(Founder & Partner)*
Matt Isaacs *(Global CEO & Partner)*
Christian Juhl *(CEO-North America)*

ESSENDEN PLC
3rd Floor 2-4 St Georges Road
Wimbledon
London, SW19 4DP, United Kingdom
Tel.: (44) 2088793932
Fax: (44) 2034 410 700
Web Site: www.essenden.com
Year Founded: 2000
ESS—(AIM ISDX)
Rev.: $74,395,614
Assets: $71,191,235
Liabilities: $52,726,176
Net Worth: $18,465,059
Earnings: ($1,361,348)
Emp.: 975
Fiscal Year-end: 12/30/12
Business Description:
Bowling Center Owner & Operator
S.I.C.: 7933
N.A.I.C.S.: 713950
Personnel:
Nick Basing *(CEO)*
Richard Darwin *(Sec & Dir-Fin)*
Board of Directors:
Rory MacNamara
Nick Basing
Richard Darwin
Christopher Harwood Bernard Mills
Nicholas Oppenheim
Kailayapillai Ranjan
Legal Counsel:
Herbert Smith LLP
Exchange House Primrose Street
London, EC2A 2HS, United Kingdom

ESSENT GROUP LTD.
Clarendon House 2 Church Street
Hamilton, HM 11, Bermuda
Tel.: (441) 297 9901
Web Site: www.essent.us
Year Founded: 2008
ESNT—(NYSE)
Premiums: $186,200,000
Assets: $853,970,000
Liabilities: $131,829,000
Net Worth: $722,141,000
Earnings: $65,413,000
Emp.: 289
Fiscal Year-end: 12/31/13
Business Description:
Holding Company; Mortgage Insurance Services
S.I.C.: 6411
N.A.I.C.S.: 524298
Personnel:
Mark A. Casale *(Pres & CEO)*
Lawrence E. McAlee *(CFO & Sr VP)*
Mary Lourdes Gibbons *(Chief Legal Officer, Sr VP & Asst Sec)*
Vijay Bhasin *(Chief Risk Officer & Sr VP)*
David Weinstock *(Chief Acctg Officer)*
Adolfo F. Marzol *(Exec VP)*
Board of Directors:
Mark A. Casale
Aditya Dutt
Robert E. Glanville
Allan Levine
Douglas J. Pauls
William Spiegel
Vipul Tandon
Andrew Turnbull

ESSENTIAL ENERGY SERVICES LTD.
Livingston Place West 1100 250 2 Street SW
Calgary, AB, T2P 0C1, Canada
Tel.: (402) 263-6778
Fax: (402) 263-6737
E-Mail: service@essentialenergy.ca
Web Site: www.essentialenergy.ca
ESN—(TSX)
Rev.: $346,495,492
Assets: $404,420,019
Liabilities: $103,823,401
Net Worth: $300,596,618
Earnings: $21,732,259
Emp.: 1,140
Fiscal Year-end: 12/31/12
Business Description:
Oilfield Services
S.I.C.: 1389
N.A.I.C.S.: 213112
Personnel:
James A. Banister *(Chm)*
Garnet K. Amundson *(Pres & CEO)*
Allan Mowbray *(CFO & VP-Fin)*
Don A. K. Webster *(COO)*
Jeff B. Newman *(Corp Sr VP)*
Board of Directors:
James A. Banister
Garnet K. Amundson
Michael J. Black
Robert T. German
Roderick W. Graham
Nicholas G. Kirton
Robert B. Michaleski
Andrew B. Zaleski
Transfer Agent:
Olympia Trust Company
2300 125 9 Avenue SW
Calgary, AB, Canada

ESSENTIAL INNOVATIONS TECHNOLOGY CORP.
15/F Radio City 505-511 Hennessy Road
Causeway Bay, China (Hong Kong)
Tel.: (852) 2910-7828
Fax: (852) 29107000
E-Mail: pubcoconsultingservice@yahoo.ca
Web Site: www.eximiusenvironmental.com
Year Founded: 2001
ESIV—(OTC OTCB)
Assets: $82,424
Liabilities: $1,006,241
Net Worth: ($923,817)
Earnings: ($801,805)
Fiscal Year-end: 10/31/13
Business Description:
Industrial Products Mfr
S.I.C.: 3559
N.A.I.C.S.: 333249
Personnel:
Jason McDiarmid *(Pres, CEO, CFO & Treas)*
Board of Directors:
Jason McDiarmid

ESSENTRA PLC
(Formerly Filtrona plc)
Avebury House 201-249 Avebury Boulevard
Milton Keynes, MK9 1AU, United Kingdom
Tel.: (44) 1908 359 100
Fax: (44) 1908 359 120
E-Mail: enquiries@filtrona.com
Web Site: www.filtrona.com
FLTR—(LSE)
Rev.: $1,047,700,986
Assets: $983,739,741
Liabilities: $604,236,354
Net Worth: $379,503,387
Earnings: $84,492,015
Emp.: 4,075
Fiscal Year-end: 12/31/12
Business Description:
Specialty Plastic & Fiber Products Mfr
S.I.C.: 3089
N.A.I.C.S.: 326199
Personnel:
Colin R. Day *(CEO)*
Russ Rogers *(Pres-Porous Technologies)*
Jon Green *(Gen Counsel & Sec)*
Board of Directors:
Jeff Harris
Colin R. Day
Paul Drechsler
Jon Green
Matthew Gregory
Terry Twigger
Legal Counsel:
Slaughter & May
One Bunhill Row
London, EC1Y 8YY, United Kingdom
Tel.: (44) 20 7600 1200
Fax: (44) 20 7600 0289

Subsidiaries:

Filtrona United Kingdom Ltd. (1)
201-249 Avebury Boulevard
Milton Keynes, Buckinghamshire, MK9 1AU, United Kingdom
Tel.: (44) 1908359100
Fax: (44) 1908359120
E-Mail: filtersenquiries@filtrona.com
Web Site: www.filtronafilters.com
Cigarette Filters Mfr
S.I.C.: 2679
N.A.I.C.S.: 322299
Puthen Thermedam Sreekumar *(Mng Dir)*

Moss Plastic Parts Ltd. (1)
Langford Locks
Kidlington, Oxon, OX5 1HX, United Kingdom
Tel.: (44) 1865844572
Fax: (44) 1865844487
E-Mail: sales@mossplastics.com
Web Site: www.mossplastics.com
Emp.: 350
Industrial Plastic Products Mfr & Distr
S.I.C.: 3089
N.A.I.C.S.: 326199
Scot Fawcett *(Mng Dir)*

Non-U.S. Subsidiaries:

Moss Ceska republika s.r.o. (2)
Skrobarenska 8
617 00 Brno, Czech Republic
Tel.: (420) 545221660
Fax: (420) 545221877
E-Mail: czechsales@mossplastics.com
Web Site: www.mossplastics.cz
Emp.: 16
Industrial Plastic Products Distr
S.I.C.: 5162
N.A.I.C.S.: 424610
Andrej Skatulla *(Gen Mgr)*

Moss Kunststof Produkten B.V. (2)
Den Belleman 9
5571 NR Bergeijk, North Brabant, Netherlands
Tel.: (31) 497572002
Fax: (31) 497574185
E-Mail: beneluxsales@mossexpress.com
Web Site: www.mossexpress.com
Emp.: 20
Industrial Plastic Products Distr
S.I.C.: 5162
N.A.I.C.S.: 424610
E. Daris *(Mgr)*

Moss Kunststoffprodukte GmbH (2)
Herrenpfad Sud 36
41334 Nettetal, Nordrhein-Westfalen, Germany

Tel.: (49) 215789690
Fax: (49) 2157896989
E-Mail: sales@mossplastics.de
Web Site: www.mossplastics.de
Emp.: 30
Industrial Plastic Products Distr
S.I.C.: 5162
N.A.I.C.S.: 424610
Alphons van Hove *(Mng Dir)*

Moss Pieces Plastiques S.A.R.L. **(2)**
Strategic Parc 1 Rue du Gue
77990 Le Mesnil-Amelot, Seine-et-Marne, France
Tel.: (33) 160038484
Fax: (33) 160038499
E-Mail: sales@mossexpress.fr
Web Site: www.mossexpress.fr
Emp.: 14
Industrial Plastic Products Distr
S.I.C.: 5162
N.A.I.C.S.: 424610
Fawcet Scotch *(Pres)*

Moss Polska Sp. z o.o. **(2)**
ul P Gojawiczynskiej 22
92-237 Lodz, Poland
Tel.: (48) 426395264
Fax: (48) 426395266
E-Mail: mosspolska@mossplastics.pl
Web Site: www.mossplastics.pl
Emp.: 20
Industrial Plastic Products Distr
S.I.C.: 3089
N.A.I.C.S.: 326199
Tom S. Zalasa *(Mgr)*

Payne Security **(1)**
Wildmere Road
Banbury, Oxon, OX16 3JU, United Kingdom
Tel.: (44) 1295265601
Fax: (44) 1295251109
E-Mail: banbury@payne-worldwide.com
Web Site: www.payne-security.com
Emp.: 50
Brand Protection & Document Security Services
S.I.C.: 7382
N.A.I.C.S.: 561621

Branch:

Payne Security - Nottingham **(2)**
Giltway
Giltbrook, Nottingham, Nottinghamshire, NG16 2GT, United Kingdom
Tel.: (44) 1159759000
Fax: (44) 1159759001
E-Mail: nottingham@payne-worldwide.com
Web Site: www.payne-worldwide.com
Emp.: 160
Document Protection Services
S.I.C.: 7381
N.A.I.C.S.: 561612
Martin Dallas *(Mng Dir-Pkg Solutions)*

U.S. Subsidiary:

Payne Richmond Inc. **(2)**
1625 Ashton Park Dr
Colonial Heights, VA 23834
Tel.: (804) 518-1803
Fax: (804) 518-1809
Toll Free: (800) 849-0634
E-Mail: richmond@payne-worldwide.com
Web Site: www.payne-worldwide.com
Emp.: 39
Tear Tapes & Coated Films Distr
S.I.C.: 5112
N.A.I.C.S.: 424120
Hugh Ross *(Pres)*

Non-U.S. Subsidiaries:

Payne (Asia) PTE. LTD. **(2)**
238A Thomson Rd 25-04/05 Novena Sq
Singapore, 307684, Singapore
Tel.: (65) 65429993
Fax: (65) 65429996
E-Mail: singapore@essentrapackaging.com
Web Site: www.essentrapackaging.com
Emp.: 6
Tear Tapes & Coated Films Distr
S.I.C.: 5112
N.A.I.C.S.: 424120
Bertrand Tellier *(Mng Dir)*

Payne (India) Private Limited **(2)**
Survey No 46 Jala Hobli Doddajala Village
Bangalore North, Bengaluru, Karnataka, 562157, India
Tel.: (91) 8028010900
Fax: (91) 8028010930
E-Mail: bangalore@payne-worldwide.com
Web Site: www.payne-security.com
Emp.: 20
Tear Tapes & Coated Films Distr
S.I.C.: 5112
N.A.I.C.S.: 424120
Hamish Arthur Macrae Pitt *(Chm & Mng Dir)*

Payne **(1)**
Cypress Drive St Mellons
Cardiff, South Glamorgan, CF3 0EG, United Kingdom
Tel.: (44) 29 2077 8500
Fax: (44) 29 2077 8388
E-Mail: cardiff@payne-worldwide.com
Emp.: 35
Self Adhesive Label Printing Services
S.I.C.: 7389
N.A.I.C.S.: 561910
Jackie Evans *(Mgr-Mktg)*

U.S. Subsidiaries:

Filtrona Holdings Corp. **(1)**
1625 Ashton Park Dr Ste A
Colonial Heights, VA 23834-5908 DE
Tel.: (804) 518-0322
Fax: (804) 518-1814
Web Site: www.filtronaporoustechnologies.com
Holding Company; Regional Managing Office
S.I.C.: 6719
N.A.I.C.S.: 551112
Russell P Rogers *(Pres)*

Divisions:

Filtrona Fibertec **(2)**
1625 E Ashton Park Dr
Colonial Heights, VA 23834 VA
Tel.: (804) 524-4983
Fax: (804) 518-1802
Web Site: www.filtronaporoustechnology.com
Emp.: 10
Liquid Handling Components Mfr
Export
S.I.C.: 3089
N.A.I.C.S.: 326199
Russell P. Rogers *(Pres)*
Jeffrey R. Green *(Exec VP-Bus Dev)*
Susan W. Lipp *(Exec VP-Fin)*
B. Jeff Shugart *(Exec VP-Comml Dev)*

Filtrona Porous Technologies **(2)**
1625 Ashton Park Dr
Colonial Heights, VA 23834
Tel.: (804) 524-4983
Fax: (804) 518-0105
E-Mail: fpt-usa@filtrona.com
Web Site: www.filtronaporoustechnologies.com
Fluid & Vapor Handling Components Mfr
S.I.C.: 3492
N.A.I.C.S.: 332912
Russell P. Rogers *(Pres)*

Subsidiaries:

Alliance Plastics **(2)**
3123 Station Rd
Erie, PA 16510
Tel.: (814) 899-7671
Fax: (814) 898-1638
Toll Free: (800) 832-8677
E-Mail: service@allianceplastics.com
Web Site: www.allianceplastics.com
Emp.: 210
Custom Moulded Plastic Product Mfr
S.I.C.: 3089
N.A.I.C.S.: 326199
Mike Conley *(Pres)*

Duraco, Inc. **(2)**
7400 W Industrial Dr
Forest Park, IL 60130-2514
Tel.: (708) 488-1025
Fax: (708) 488-1215
Toll Free: (888) 500-5805
E-Mail: info@duracoinc.com
Web Site: www.duracoinc.com
Emp.: 120
Adhesive Tapes Mfr & Distr
S.I.C.: 3999
N.A.I.C.S.: 339999
Mark Hefty *(CEO)*

Non-U.S. Subsidiary:

Moss Plastic Products Trading (Ningbo) Co., Ltd. **(3)**
99 Huanghai Road
Beilun Dist, Ningbo, Zhejiang, 315800, China
Tel.: (86) 57426863666
Fax: (86) 57426863677
Web Site: www.mossplastics.cn
Emp.: 21
Adhesive Tapes Distr
S.I.C.: 5169
N.A.I.C.S.: 424690
Lola Chen *(Mgr-Customer Svc)*

MSI Oilfield Products **(2)**
9035 Solon Rd
Houston, TX 77064
Tel.: (281) 890-4595
Fax: (281) 890-0543
E-Mail: sales@msiproducts.com
Web Site: www.msiproducts.com
Emp.: 100
Drilling Thread & Pipe Protection Products Mfr
S.I.C.: 3533
N.A.I.C.S.: 333132
John Boben *(Pres)*

Reid Supply Company **(2)**
2265 Black Creek Rd
Muskegon, MI 49444
Tel.: (231) 777-3951
Fax: (231) 773-4485
Toll Free: (800) 253-0421
E-Mail: mail@reidsupply.com
Web Site: www.reidsupply.com
Emp.: 200
Industrial Components Whslr
S.I.C.: 5085
N.A.I.C.S.: 423840
Greg Palmer *(Dir-Mktg & Interim Dir-Sls)*

Richco, Inc. **(2)**
8145 River Dr
Morton Grove, IL 60053 IL
Tel.: (773) 539-4060
Fax: (773) 539-6770
Toll Free: (800) 466-8301
E-Mail: customerservice@richco-inc.com
Web Site: www.richco-inc.com
Emp.: 300
Plastic Installation Hardware Mfr
Import Export
S.I.C.: 3089
N.A.I.C.S.: 326199
Samantha Richardson *(Owner & Chm)*
Jim Fegen *(Vice Chm)*

John R. Lyman Company **(1)**
2255 Westover Rd
Chicopee, MA 01014 MA
Mailing Address:
2255 Westover Rd
Chicopee, MA 01022
Tel.: (413) 598-8344
Fax: (413) 592-4112
Toll Free: (800) 628-8606
E-Mail: jrlcsales@johnrlyman.com
Web Site: www.johnrlyman.com
Sales Range: $10-24.9 Million
Emp.: 120
Specialty Wipes Mfr
Import Export
S.I.C.: 2392
N.A.I.C.S.: 314120
William McCormick *(Controller)*

Subsidiary:

Lymtech Scientific **(2)**
2255 Westover
Chicopee, MA 02022 MA
Tel.: (413) 592-4111 (100%)
Fax: (413) 592-4112
Toll Free: (800) 628-8606
E-Mail: sales@lymtech.com
Web Site: www.lymtech.com
Sales Range: $25-49.9 Million
Emp.: 100
Lint Free Wiping Cloths Mfr
S.I.C.: 2392
N.A.I.C.S.: 314120
Michael Burzynski *(VP-Ops)*

Non-U.S. Subsidiaries:

Enitor B.V. **(1)**
Beatrixstraat 7/9
9285 TV Buitenpost, Friesland, Netherlands
Tel.: (31) 511541700
Fax: (31) 511543332
E-Mail:
Web Site: www.essentraextrusion.com
Emp.: 450
Plastic Extrusions Mfr & Distr
S.I.C.: 3089
N.A.I.C.S.: 326199
J. Schootstra *(Principal)*

Filtrona BV **(1)**
Beatrixstraat 7-9
9285 TV Buitenpost, Friesland, Netherlands
Tel.: (31) 511541700
Fax: (31) 511543332
E-Mail: info@enitar.com
Web Site: www.enitar.com
Emp.: 200
Plastic Products Mfr
S.I.C.: 3089
N.A.I.C.S.: 326199
J. Schoodstra *(Mgr)*

Filtrona Fibertec GmbH **(1)**
Gutenbergstrasse 5 9
D 21465 Reinbek, Germany
Tel.: (49) 4072707219
Fax: (49) 4072707248
E-Mail: fibertec-europe@filtrona.com
Web Site: www.filtronaporoustechnologies.com
Emp.: 180
Liquid Handling Components Mfr
S.I.C.: 3089
N.A.I.C.S.: 326199
Andreas Schneekloth *(Dir-EMEA)*

Essentra Pipe Protection Technologies **(1)**
(Formerly Filtrona Mexico S. de R.L. de C.V.)
Lote 1 MZNA 4 AV Framboyanes Esq
Almendros CD Industrial
Bruno Pagliai, Veracruz, VER, CP 91697, Mexico
Tel.: (52) 229 989 6731
Fax: (52) 229 981 1839
Web Site: www.essentra.com
Emp.: 87
Component & Protection Solutions & Pipe Mfr
S.I.C.: 3498
N.A.I.C.S.: 332996
Rafael Villegas *(Gen Mgr)*

Filtrona Porous Technologies Japan Co., Ltd. **(1)**
6-4-1508 Akashicho
Chuo-ku, Tokyo, 104-0044, Japan
Tel.: (81) 9057954334
Fax: (81) 368090950
E-Mail: FPT-Japan@filtrona.com
Fluid & Vapor Handling Components Mfr
S.I.C.: 3492
N.A.I.C.S.: 332912

Filtrona Special Fiber Products Ningbo Co., Ltd. **(1)**
99 Huanghai Road
Beilun District, Ningbo, Zhejiang, 315800, China
Tel.: (86) 574 2688 3377
Fax: (86) 574 2688 6944
E-Mail: fpt-asia@filtrona.com.cn
Web Site: www.filtronaporoustechnologies.com
Emp.: 80
Fluid & Vapor Handling Components Mfr
S.I.C.: 3492
N.A.I.C.S.: 332912
Chai Philip *(Mgr-Ops)*

P.T. Filtrona Indonesia **(1)**
Jalan Berbek Industri I No 18-20 Surabaya Industrial Estate
Rungkut, Surabaya, East Java, 61256, Indonesia
Tel.: (62) 318432017
Fax: (62) 318495217
E-Mail: filtersenquiries@filtrona.com
Cigarette Filters Mfr
S.I.C.: 2131
N.A.I.C.S.: 312230
Eko Suhartono *(Gen Mgr)*

Skiffy B.V. **(1)**
Transformatorweg 37
1014 AJ Amsterdam, North Holland, Netherlands

Essentra PLC—(Continued)

Tel.: (31) 206868711
Fax: (31) 206822567
E-Mail: info@skiffy.com
Web Site: www.skiffy.com
Emp.: 235
Industrial Plastic & Metal Products Mfr & Distr
S.I.C.: 3082
N.A.I.C.S.: 326121
J. R. Purcell *(Principal)*

Non-U.S. Subsidiaries:

FPFP Sp. z o.o. Oddzial Skiffy (2)
Slasska 12126D
90-562 Lodz, Poland
Tel.: (48) 426372419
Fax: (48) 426372431
E-Mail: skiffypl@skiffy.com
Web Site: www.skiffy.com
Emp.: 20
Industrial Plastic & Metal Products Distr
S.I.C.: 5051
N.A.I.C.S.: 423510
Wojciech Olejniczak *(Gen Mgr)*

Skiffy GmbH (2)
Memelerstrasse 26
42781 Haan, Nordrhein-Westfalen, Germany
Tel.: (49) 212994313
Fax: (49) 2129943144
E-Mail: infode@skiffy.com
Web Site: www.skiffy.com
Metal Screws Mfr
S.I.C.: 3452
N.A.I.C.S.: 332722
Karen J. Arlow *(Gen Mgr)*

Skiffy Ltd. (2)
Unit 12 Old Forge Trading Estate Dudley Road
Stourbridge, DY9 8EL, United Kingdom
Tel.: (44) 1902894658
Fax: (44) 138444348
E-Mail: infouk@skiffy.com
Web Site: www.skiffy.com
Emp.: 3
Transmission Equipments Mfr
S.I.C.: 3568
N.A.I.C.S.: 333613

Skiffy S.A. (Pty) Ltd. (2)
Unit 2 Corner Suni & Tsessebe Streets
Sage Corporate Park South
Randjiesfontein, Midrand, Gauteng, 1685, South Africa
Tel.: (27) 113148750
Fax: (27) 113148759
E-Mail: infosa@skiffy.com
Web Site: www.skiffy.com
Emp.: 5
Industrial Plastic & Metal Products Distr
S.I.C.: 5051
N.A.I.C.S.: 423510
Andrew Falkner *(Gen Mgr)*

Skiffy S.A.S. (2)
7 allee des Foulons
BP 305
67832 Lingolsheim, Bas-Rhin, France
Tel.: (33) 388789130
Fax: (33) 3 88 78 91 40
E-Mail: infofr@skiffy.com
Web Site: www.skiffy.com
Industrial Plastic & Metal Products Mfr
S.I.C.: 3082
N.A.I.C.S.: 326121
Christain Alt *(Dir-Pur)*

ESSEX ANGEL CAPITAL INC.

720 Ouellette Avenue Suite 516
Windsor, ON, N9A 1C2, Canada
Tel.: (519) 997-2851
Fax: (519) 973-7073
E-Mail: info@essexangelcapital.com
Web Site: www.essexangelcapital.com
Year Founded: 2010
EXC.P—(TSXV)
Assets: $873,480
Liabilities: $219,551
Net Worth: $653,929
Earnings: ($1,094,436)
Fiscal Year-end: 08/31/13

Business Description:
Investment Services
S.I.C.: 6211
N.A.I.C.S.: 523999
Personnel:
Richard J. Galdi *(Chm, Pres & CEO)*
Julian Hawkins *(CFO)*
Michael L. Labiak *(COO, Sec & Exec VP)*
Board of Directors:
Richard J. Galdi
Jason Krueger
Michael Magnus
Legal Counsel:
Wildeboer Dellelce
Suite 800 Wildeboer Dellelce Place 365 Bay Street
Toronto, ON, M5H 2V1, Canada
Transfer Agent:
Equity Financial Trust Company
200 University Avenue Suite 400
Toronto, ON, Canada

ESSEX BIO-TECHNOLOGY LIMITED

2818 China Merchants Tower Shun Tak Centre 168-200 Connaught Road Central, China (Hong Kong)
Tel.: (852) 25877838
Fax: (852) 25877363
E-Mail: essex@essexbio.com
Web Site: www.essexbio.com
1061—(HKG)
Sls.: $34,462,554
Assets: $42,778,278
Liabilities: $17,468,887
Net Worth: $25,309,391
Earnings: $5,028,423
Emp.: 409
Fiscal Year-end: 12/31/12
Business Description:
Biopharmaceutical Mfr
S.I.C.: 2834
N.A.I.C.S.: 325412
Personnel:
Patrick Mia Je Ngiam *(Chm)*
Hai Zhou Fang *(Mng Dir & Gen Mgr)*
Lai Man Yau *(Sec)*
Board of Directors:
Patrick Mia Je Ngiam
Hai Zhou Fang
Chi Ying Fung
Benoit Jean Marie Mauffrey
Mee Mooi Yeow
Sheng Zhong
Hong Kong Registrars Limited
Shops 1712-1716 17/F Hopewell Centre 183 Queen's Road East
Wanchai, China (Hong Kong)
Transfer Agent:
Royal Bank of Canada Trust Company (Cayman) Limited
4th Floor Royal Bank House 24 Shedden Road
Georgetown, Cayman Islands

ESSEX SERVICES GROUP PLC

Viking Business Centre Danes Road
Romford, Essex, RM7 0HL, United Kingdom
Tel.: (44) 1708 708 888
E-Mail: info@esgplc.com
Web Site: www.esgplc.com
Year Founded: 1975
Business Description:
Mechanical, Electrical & Maintenance Services Contractor
S.I.C.: 1731
N.A.I.C.S.: 238990
Personnel:
John Sampson *(CEO)*
Mark Sampson *(Mng Dir)*

ESSILOR INTERNATIONAL, S.A.

147 rue de Paris
94220 Charenton-le-Pont, France
Tel.: (33) 149774224
Fax: (33) 149774420
E-Mail: invest@essilor.com
Web Site: www.essilor.com
Year Founded: 1971
EI—(EUR)
Rev.: $6,715,833,474
Assets: $9,298,296,386
Liabilities: $4,020,313,820
Net Worth: $5,277,982,566
Earnings: $848,657,876
Emp.: 50,668
Fiscal Year-end: 12/31/12
Business Description:
Eyeglass Lenses & Other Ophthalmic Products Mfr & Whslr
Export
S.I.C.: 3827
N.A.I.C.S.: 333314
Personnel:
Hubert Sagnieres *(Chm & CEO)*
Geraldine Picaud *(CFO)*
Paul du Saillant *(Co-COO)*
Laurent Vacherot *(Co-COO)*
Bernard Duverneuil *(CIO)*
Jayanth Bhuvaraghan *(Chief Corp Mission Officer)*
Norbert Gorny *(Pres-Satisloh & Sr VP-Alemannic Zone)*
Thomas Bayer *(Pres-Latin America)*
Eric Bernard *(Pres-China)*
Jean Carrier-Guillomet *(Pres-Essilor of America)*
Patrick Cherrier *(Pres-AMERA)*
Real Goulet *(Pres-Essilor Laboratories of America)*
Eric Leonard *(Pres-Europe)*
Kevin A. Rupp *(CFO/Exec VP-Fin & Admin-Essilor of America)*
Eric Perrier *(Exec VP-Global R&D)*
Tadeu Alves *(Sr VP-Latin America)*
Claude Brignon *(Sr VP-Worldwide Ops)*
Lucia Dumas *(Sr VP-Corp Comm)*
Marc Fracois-Brazier *(Sr VP-HR)*
Patrick Poncin *(Sr VP-Global Engrg)*
Bertrand Roy *(Sr VP-Strategic Partnerships)*
Eric Thoreux *(Sr VP-Strategic Mktg)*
Henri Vidal *(Sr VP-Equipment & Instruments)*
Carol Xueref *(Sr VP-Legal Affairs & Dev)*
Board of Directors:
Hubert Sagnieres
Philippe Alfroid
Benoit Bazin
Yves Chevillotte
Mireille Faugere
Xavier Fontanet
Louise Frechette
Yves Gillet
Yi He
Bernard Hours
Maurice Marchand-Tonel
Aicha Mokdahi
Olivier Pecoux
Michel Rose
Mazars
61 rue Henri-Regnault
Paris, France
Subsidiaries:

BBGR S.A. (1)
22 Rue De Montmorency
75003 Paris, France FR
Tel.: (33) 0144783100 (99.99%)
Telex: 670220
Fax: (33) 144783179
E-Mail: accueilt@bbgr.fr
Web Site: www.bbgr.fr
Emp.: 70
Glass & Plastic Lenses Mfr & Marketer
S.I.C.: 3827
N.A.I.C.S.: 333314
Lauren Schmitt *(Pres)*

BNL Eurolens SA (1)
ZI Avenue Paul Langevin
1200 Bellegarde-sur-Valserine, France
Tel.: (33) 4 50 48 02 80
Fax: (33) 4 50 48 03 33
E-Mail: sales@bnl-eurolens.com
Web Site: www.bnl-eurolens.com
Emp.: 6
Polarized Lenses Mfr
S.I.C.: 3851
N.A.I.C.S.: 339115
Frank Ledien *(Gen Mgr)*

Essor SAS (1)
Zi Les malalonnes 12 Boulevard Jacques Monod
26700 Pierrelatte, France
Tel.: (33) 4 75 96 49 72
Fax: (33) 4 75 96 49 71
Optical Lens Distr
S.I.C.: 5048
N.A.I.C.S.: 423460

Mont-Royal Sarl (1)
Pole De Dynamisation Territori 6 Bd Bertrand De Lassus
Montrejeau, Haute Garonne, 31210, France
Tel.: (33) 561958574
Optical Lens Distr
S.I.C.: 5048
N.A.I.C.S.: 423460

OMI (1)
101 Boulevard Des Liberateurs
13011 Marseille, Bouches-du-Rhone, France
Tel.: (33) 491892601
Fax: (33) 491185608
E-Mail: o.m.i@wanadoo.fr
Emp.: 4
Optical Lens Mfr
S.I.C.: 3827
N.A.I.C.S.: 333314

U.S. Subsidiary:

Essilor of America, Inc. (1)
13555 N Stemmons Fwy
Dallas, TX 75234 (100%)
Tel.: (214) 496-4000
Fax: (972) 241-1162
Toll Free: (800) THE-EYES
Web Site: www.essilorusa.com
Eyeglass Lenses & Other Ophthalmic Products Mfr & Whslr
Import Export
S.I.C.: 3827
N.A.I.C.S.: 333314
Jean Carrier-Guillomet *(Pres)*
Kevin A. Rupp *(CFO & Sr VP-Fin & Admin)*
Bob Colucci *(Pres-Independent Distr Div)*
Carl Bracy *(Sr VP-Mktg & New Bus)*

Subsidiaries:

Cherry Optical, Inc. (2)
1640 Fire Ln Dr
Green Bay, WI 54311 WI
Tel.: (920) 469-2559
Fax: (800) 469-5171
Toll Free: (800) 469-4211
E-Mail:
Web Site: www.cherryoptical.com
Sales Range: $1-9.9 Million
Emp.: 28
Manufacturer of Prescription Eyeglass Lenses
S.I.C.: 5049
N.A.I.C.S.: 423490
Adam Cherry *(Pres)*

Dioptics Medical Products Inc. (2)
1327 Archer St
San Luis Obispo, CA 02917
Tel.: (800) 959-9038
Fax: (805) 781-3302
E-Mail: dmpinfo@fgxi.com
Web Site: www.diopticssunwear.com
Sunwear Optical Mfr
S.I.C.: 3827
N.A.I.C.S.: 333314
Henry Lane *(CEO & Pres)*

ELOA California Acquisition Corp. (2)
2101 S Atlantic Blvd
Commerce, CA 90040-1319

Tel.: (323) 266-3030
Fax: (323) 266-3039
Eyewear Products Distr
S.I.C.: 5048
N.A.I.C.S.: 423460

Essilor Laboratories of America, Inc. (2)
13555 N Stemmons Fwy
Dallas, TX 75234
Tel.: (214) 496-4000
Fax: (800) 877-0328
Toll Free: (800) 215-7249
Web Site: www.eloa.com
Optical Laboratory Services
S.I.C.: 8071
N.A.I.C.S.: 621511
Rick Long *(Sr VP-Partner Lab Div)*

Subsidiaries:

Advance Optical (3)
37 Goodway Dr
Rochester, NY 14623
Tel.: (585) 427-0800
Fax: (585) 272-1602
Toll Free: (800) 828-6331
E-Mail: advance@advanceoptical.com
Web Site: www.advanceoptical.com
Emp.: 30
Optical Goods Mfr & Distr
S.I.C.: 3827
N.A.I.C.S.: 333314
Brian Bartlett *(Mgr-Ops)*

Apex Optical Company Inc. (3)
306 Goodland St
Orlando, FL 32811
Tel.: (407) 298-1200
Fax: (800) 432-8496
Toll Free: (800) 432-8605
Emp.: 9
Ophthalmic Lenses Mfr & Whslr
S.I.C.: 3851
N.A.I.C.S.: 339115
Michele Freeman *(Gen Mgr)*

Beitler McKee Company (3)
160 S 22nd St
Pittsburgh, PA 15203
Tel.: (800) 989-4700
Fax: (412) 488-1024
E-Mail: contactus@beitlermckee.com
Web Site: www.beitlermckee.com
Optical Products Mfr & Whslr
S.I.C.: 3827
N.A.I.C.S.: 333314
Richard Hughes *(Pres)*

BSA Industries Inc (3)
6510 Huntley Rd
Columbus, OH 43229-1012
Tel.: (614) 846-5750
Fax: (614) 846-6063
Ophthalmic Goods Mfr & Whslr
S.I.C.: 3851
N.A.I.C.S.: 339115

Classic Optical Laboratories, Inc. (3)
3710 Belmont Ave
Youngstown, OH 44505 FL
Mailing Address:
PO Box 1341
Youngstown, OH 44501-1341
Tel.: (330) 759-8245
Fax: (330) 759-8300
Toll Free: (888) 522-2020
Web Site: www.classicoptical.com
Sales Range: $10-24.9 Million
Emp.: 170
Ophthalmic Goods Mfr
S.I.C.: 3851
N.A.I.C.S.: 339115
Dawn Friedkin *(COO)*

Collard Rose (3)
12402 Philadelphia
Whittier, CA 90601
Tel.: (562) 698-2286
Fax: (562) 693-2087
Toll Free: (800) 242-2020
E-Mail: info@collardrose.com
Web Site: www.collardrose.com
Optical Laboratory Services
S.I.C.: 8734
N.A.I.C.S.: 541380
Robby Hernandez *(CEO & Pres)*

CSC Laboratories, Inc. (3)
180 Westgate Dr
Watsonville, CA 95076 CA
Tel.: (831) 763-6931
Fax: (800) 888-3291
Toll Free: (800) 288-2721
E-Mail: custserve@yahoo.com
Web Site: www.csclabs.com
Sales Range: $25-49.9 Million
Emp.: 200
Eyeglass Lens & Frame Mfr & Distr
S.I.C.: 3851
N.A.I.C.S.: 339115
D. K. Kim *(Pres & CEO)*

Custom Optical (3)
661 Duling Ave
Jackson, MS 39216
Tel.: (601) 362-6675
Fax: (601) 362-5767
E-Mail: customoptical@hotmail.com
Web Site: www.customoptical.net
Optical Goods Distr
S.I.C.: 5995
N.A.I.C.S.: 446130

Dunlaw Optical Laboratories Inc. (3)
1313 Sw A Ave
Lawton, OK 73501
Tel.: (580) 355-8410
Fax: (580) 365-3409
Emp.: 14
Optical Goods Mfr & Whslr
S.I.C.: 3851
N.A.I.C.S.: 339115
Jeffrey Foster *(Gen Mgr)*

Empire Optical of California Inc (3)
7633 Varna Ave
North Hollywood, CA 91605
Tel.: (818) 997-6474
Fax: (818) 997-7816
Toll Free: (800) 767-6784
E-Mail: info@empireoptical.org
Web Site: www.empireoptical.org
Emp.: 50
Optical Laboratory Equipment Whslr
S.I.C.: 5046
N.A.I.C.S.: 423440
Noel Diaz *(Pres)*

Eye Care Express Lab Inc. (3)
6119 Clarewood Dr
Houston, TX 77081
Tel.: (713) 774-2314
Fax: (713) 774-2491
Toll Free: (800) 441-2811
E-Mail: info@eye-care-express-lab.com
Web Site: www.eye-care-express-lab.com
Emp.: 30
Optical Glasses Mfr
S.I.C.: 3231
N.A.I.C.S.: 327215
Ty Dinh *(Founder & Pres)*

Focus Optical Labs, Inc. (3)
1665 Quincy Unit 171
Naperville, IL 60540
Tel.: (630) 428-0800
Fax: (888) 319-3937
Toll Free: (800) 244-7090
Testing Laboratory Operating Services
S.I.C.: 8734
N.A.I.C.S.: 541380

Homer Optical Company, Inc. (3)
2401 Linden Ln
Silver Spring, MD 20910
Tel.: (301) 585-9060
Fax: (301) 585-5934
Toll Free: (800) 627-2710
E-Mail: sales@homeroptical.com
Web Site: www.homeroptical.com
Optical Laboratory Lens Whslr
S.I.C.: 5048
N.A.I.C.S.: 423460
Candi Levri *(Pres)*

Interstate Optical Co Inc (3)
680 Lindaire Ln
Mansfield, OH 44901
Tel.: (419) 529-6800
Fax: (419) 529-6801
Toll Free: (800) 472-5790
E-Mail: info@interstateoptical.com
Web Site: www.interstateoptical.com
Emp.: 150
Optical Laboratory Equipment Whslr
S.I.C.: 5046
N.A.I.C.S.: 423440
John Art *(Pres)*
Debbie Art *(Sec & Treas)*

Jorgenson Optical Supply Cy. (3)
1901 S Union Ave B1001
Tacoma, WA 98405-1879
Tel.: (253) 572-4522
Fax: (253) 627-0787
Optical Goods Retailer
S.I.C.: 5995
N.A.I.C.S.: 446130
John Jorgenson *(Pres)*

Katz & Klein (3)
1909 H St
Sacramento, CA 95811 CA
Tel.: (916) 444-2024
Fax: (916) 441-5943
Toll Free: (800) 698-5265
E-Mail: info@katzandklein.com
Web Site: www.katzandklein.com
Sales Range: $1-9.9 Million
Emp.: 45
Ophthalmic Goods Mfr
S.I.C.: 3851
N.A.I.C.S.: 339115
Mike Francesconi *(VP)*

KBco, The Polarized Lens Company (3)
7328 S Revere Pkwy Unit 208
Centennial, CO 80112
Tel.: (303) 253-6600
Fax: (303) 253-6610
Toll Free: (800) 722-8776
E-Mail: info@kbco.net
Web Site: www.kbco.net
Sales Range: $25-49.9 Million
Emp.: 50
Polarized Optical Lens Mfr & Whslr
S.I.C.: 3827
N.A.I.C.S.: 333314
Kurt Hollinger *(Pres)*

McLeodd Optical Company Inc. (3)
50 Jefferson Park Rd
Warwick, RI 02888
Tel.: (401) 467-3000
Fax: (401) 467-9410
Toll Free: (800) 288-5367
E-Mail: mcleod@mcleodoptical.com
Web Site: www.mcleodoptical.com
Laboratory Equipment Whslr
S.I.C.: 5047
N.A.I.C.S.: 423450
Scott MacLeod *(Pres)*

NEA Optical LLC (3)
1426 E Washington
Jonesboro, AR 72401
Tel.: (800) 535-7774
Fax: (800) 527-0290
Web Site: www.neaoptical.com
Emp.: 20
Ophthalmic Goods Mfr
S.I.C.: 3851
N.A.I.C.S.: 339115
Jim Evans *(Mng Dir)*

Omega Optical Holdings Inc. (3)
13515 N Stemmons Fwy
Dallas, TX 75234-5765
Tel.: (972) 241-4141
Fax: (972) 241-1162
Investment Management Services
S.I.C.: 6211
N.A.I.C.S.: 523999

OMNI Optical Lab (3)
3255 Executive Blvd Ste 100
Beaumont, TX 77705
Tel.: (409) 842-4113
Fax: (800) 324-3291
Toll Free: (800) 324-5221
Web Site: www.omnioptical.com
Rev.: $1,500,000
Emp.: 40
Optical Goods Stores
S.I.C.: 5995
N.A.I.C.S.: 446130
Tony Ash *(Chm)*

Optical One Inc (3)
1751 Houret Ct
Milpitas, CA 95035
Tel.: (408) 263-0933
Fax: (408) 263-0186
Toll Free: (800) 223-3200
Web Site: www.opticalone.com
Eyewear Lens & Frames Mfr
S.I.C.: 3851
N.A.I.C.S.: 339115
Edward Deblasio *(Pres)*

Ozarks Optical Laboratories Inc (3)
1845 W Arbor Ct
Springfield, MO 65807
Tel.: (417) 890-5367
Fax: (417) 890-0365
E-Mail:
Optical Lens Whslr
S.I.C.: 5995
N.A.I.C.S.: 446130
Paul Yutesler *(Mgr-HR)*

Peninsula Optical Lab Inc. (3)
1631 NE Franklin Ave
Bremerton, WA 98311
Tel.: (800) 540-4640
Fax: (888) 478-8992
E-Mail: poinfo@peninsula-optical.com
Web Site: www.peninsula-optical.com
Optical Goods Distr
S.I.C.: 5048
N.A.I.C.S.: 423460
Blayne Rollman *(Principal)*
Pat Rollman *(Principal)*

Perferx Optical Co. Inc. (3)
25 Downing 3
Pittsfield, MA 01201
Tel.: (800) 649-2550
Fax: (877) 484-1933
Web Site: www.perferxoptical.com
Eyewear Products Mfr
S.I.C.: 3827
N.A.I.C.S.: 333314
John Enright *(Pres & Founder)*

Plunkett Optical, Inc. (3)
1705 N A St
Fort Smith, AR 72901 AR
Tel.: (479) 783-2001
Sales Range: $1-9.9 Million
Emp.: 26
Ophthalmic Goods Merchant Whslr
S.I.C.: 5048
N.A.I.C.S.: 423460
Bill Plunkett *(Pres)*

Precision Optical Lab Inc. (3)
225 Overton Rd
Gallaway, TN 38036
Tel.: (901) 867-2991
Fax: (901) 867-9583
Toll Free: (800) 238-6828
Web Site: www.preclabtn.com
Emp.: 36
Optical Laboratory Equipment Whslr
S.I.C.: 5049
N.A.I.C.S.: 423490
Linda Brittoon *(Gen Mgr)*

Professional Ophthalmic Laboratories, Inc. (3)
2126 Winston Ave SW
Roanoke, VA 24014 VA
Tel.: (540) 345-7303
Fax: (800) 476-0167
Toll Free: (800) 476-8770
Sales Range: $1-9.9 Million
Emp.: 25
Ophthalmic Goods Developer & Distr
S.I.C.: 3851
N.A.I.C.S.: 339115
Diane Strickler *(Pres, Sec & Treas)*

RD Cherry, Inc. (3)
2429 Oakwood Blvd
Melvindale, MI 48122 MI
Tel.: (313) 388-7622
Fax: (313) 388-9474
Toll Free: (800) 537-2831
Web Site: www.cherryoptical.com
Sales Range: $1-9.9 Million
Emp.: 23
Ophthalmic Goods Mfr
S.I.C.: 3851
N.A.I.C.S.: 339115
Richard Cherry *(Pres)*

Southwest Lens Corp. (3)
4735 Memphis St
Dallas, TX 75207
Tel.: (214) 634-8109
Fax: (214) 637-4303
Toll Free: (800) 662-2251
E-Mail: info@southwestlens.com
Web Site: www.southwestlens.com
Optical Lens Mfr
S.I.C.: 3827
N.A.I.C.S.: 333314

Essilor International, S.A.—(Continued)

Matthew Herod *(Gen Mgr)*

Stereo Optical Co. Inc. (3)
8623 W Bryn Mawr Ave Ste 502
Chicago, IL 60631
Tel.: (773) 867-0380
Fax: (773) 867-0388
Toll Free: (800) 344-9500
E-Mail: sales@stereooptical.com
Web Site: www.stereooptical.com
Vision Testing Equipment Whslr
S.I.C.: 5049
N.A.I.C.S.: 423490
Mackenzie Rakers *(Mgr-Sls-Natl Mktg)*

Sutherlin Optical Company (3)
1941 Central Ave
Kansas City, MO 64108
Tel.: (816) 421-0369
Fax: (816) 471-4090
Toll Free: (800) 999-8193
Web Site: www.sutherlinoptical.com
Sales Range: $10-24.9 Million
Emp.: 150
Eyeglass Lens Mfr
S.I.C.: 3827
N.A.I.C.S.: 333314
Steve Sutherlin *(Pres)*
John Sutherlin *(Treas & Sec)*

Tri Supreme Optical LLC (3)
91 Carolyn Blvd
Farmingdale, NY 11735
Tel.: (631) 249-2020
Fax: (631) 249-0577
Toll Free: (800) 321-1100
Web Site: www.trisupreme.com
Emp.: 10
Ophthalmic Product Whslr
S.I.C.: 5995
N.A.I.C.S.: 446130
Jay Graber *(Pres & CEO)*

VIP Optical Laboratories, Inc. (3)
325 Dalziel Rd
Linden, NJ 07036-6229 NJ
Tel.: (908) 523-1422
Fax: (908) 523-1423
Web Site: www.vipopticallabs.com
Sales Range: $1-9.9 Million
Ophthalmic Goods Mfr
S.I.C.: 3851
N.A.I.C.S.: 339115
Robert Renta *(Mgr-Lab)*

FGX International, Inc. (2)
500 George Washington Hwy
Smithfield, RI 02917 VG
Tel.: (401) 231-3800
Fax: (401) 231-7235
Toll Free: (800) 283-3090
E-Mail: crinfo@fgxi.com
Web Site: www.fgxi.com
Sales Range: $250-299.9 Million
Emp.: 500
Non-Prescription Reading Glasses, Sunglasses & Costume Jewelry Designer & Marketer
Import Export
S.I.C.: 3842
N.A.I.C.S.: 339113
John H. Flynn, Jr. *(Pres)*
Cesar Melo *(CEO)*
Anthony Di Paola *(CFO & Exec VP)*
Jeffrey J. Giguere *(Gen Counsel, Sec & Exec VP)*
Steven Crellin *(Exec VP-North America)*
Robert Grow *(Exec VP-Product Dev)*
Gerald Kitchen *(Exec VP-Ops)*

Subsidiaries:

Corinne McCormark, Inc (3)
7 W 36th St
New York, NY 10018
Tel.: (212) 868-7919
Fax: (212) 868-9808
E-Mail: corinne@corinnemccormack.com
Web Site: www.corinnemccormack.com
Emp.: 9
Optical Accessories Mfr & Whslr
S.I.C.: 3827
N.A.I.C.S.: 333314

Non-U.S. Subsidiaries:

FGX Canada-FosterGrant (3)
555 Richmond St W Ste 1005
PO Box 201
Toronto, ON, M5V 3B1, Canada Ca
Tel.: (416) 504-5533
Fax: (416) 504-4073
Web Site: www.fgxi.com
Sales Range: $100-124.9 Million
Non-Prescription Eyewear Mfr
S.I.C.: 3827
N.A.I.C.S.: 333314
Diane Pooles *(Pres)*

FGX Europe, Ltd. (3)
Longbridge Hayes Road Longport
Stoke-on-Trent, ST6 4DS, United Kingdom UK
Tel.: (44) 1782577055
Fax: (44) 1782575115
Web Site: www.fostergrant.co.uk
Sales Range: $10-24.9 Million
Emp.: 40
Non-Prescription Eyewear Mfr
S.I.C.: 3827
N.A.I.C.S.: 333314
Chris Jones *(Mng Dir)*

FGX International Limited China (3)
Rm 1004 Block A Carrianna Friendship Sq
Chun Feng Rd, Shenzhen, Luo Hu District, China HK
Tel.: (86) 75582219328
Fax: (86) 75582219002
E-Mail: achan@fgxi.com
Web Site: www.fgxi.com
Sales Range: $100-124.9 Million
Emp.: 50
Non-Prescription Eyewear Mfr
S.I.C.: 3827
N.A.I.C.S.: 333314
James Mg *(Gen Mgr)*

Suntech Optics Inc. (3)
758 Harbourside Drive
North Vancouver, BC, V7P 3R7, Canada
Tel.: (604) 929-8141
Fax: (604) 929-6174
Sales Range: $10-24.9 Million
Emp.: 80
Eye Wears & Lenses
S.I.C.: 3827
N.A.I.C.S.: 333314

Frames For America Inc (2)
3100 S Gessner Rd Ste 329
Houston, TX 77063
Tel.: (713) 914-0011
Fax: (713) 914-0099
Toll Free: (800) 248-9427
Web Site: www.framesforamerica.com
Eyewear Product Whslr
S.I.C.: 5049
N.A.I.C.S.: 423490

Future Optics FL Inc (2)
13191 Starkey Rd Ste 9
Largo, FL 33773-1438
Tel.: (727) 533-0505
Fax: (727) 528-8810
Lab Optical Instruments Mfr
S.I.C.: 3827
N.A.I.C.S.: 333314

Gentex Optics, Inc. (2)
324 Main St
Simpson, PA 18407-1182 (100%)
Mailing Address:
PO Box 336
Carbondale, PA 18407-0336
Tel.: (570) 282-3550
Fax: (570) 282-8538
E-Mail: info@essilorusa.com
Web Site: www.gentexoptics.com
Sls.: $20,000,000
Emp.: 200
Mfr. Optical Products, Safety Lenses, Welding Filter Plates, Polycarbonate RX Lenses
S.I.C.: 3851
N.A.I.C.S.: 339115
L. Peter Frieder, Jr. *(Chm)*
R. Nahmias *(Exec VP)*

Plant:

Gentex Optics, Inc. (3)
183 W Main St
Dudley, MA 01571-0307 (100%)
Tel.: (508) 943-3860
Fax: (508) 949-3701
E-Mail: info@gentexoptics.com
Web Site: www.gentexoptics.com
Emp.: 500
Manufacturing Plant for Lenses
S.I.C.: 3827
N.A.I.C.S.: 333314
Bill Van Wieren *(Plant Mgr)*

MOC Acquisition Corporation (2)
2360 59th St
Saint Louis, MO 63110-2812
Tel.: (314) 533-2020
Fax: (800) 356-5038
Emp.: 200
Ophthalmic Goods Equipment Mfr & Whslr
S.I.C.: 3851
N.A.I.C.S.: 339115
Craig Hausmann *(CMO)*

OOGP, Inc. (2)
557 Westbrook Way PO Box 724
Grants Pass, OR 97528 (80%)
Tel.: (541) 479-4743
Fax: (888) 654-0618
Toll Free: (800) 654-3829
E-Mail: oogp@oogp.com
Web Site: www.oogp.com
Sales Range: $25-49.9 Million
Emp.: 125
Contact Lenses & Other Ophthalmic Products Distr
S.I.C.: 5048
N.A.I.C.S.: 423460
Kenji Hamada *(Pres)*

Optical Dimension Inc (2)
6750 Airport Blvd Ste A
Mobile, AL 36608-3792
Tel.: (251) 342-1905
Ophthalmic Goods Mfr
S.I.C.: 3851
N.A.I.C.S.: 339115
Richard Kirsammer *(Pres)*

Optifacts Inc. (2)
18 Riverside Ave S Ste 100
Sartell, MN 56377
Tel.: (320) 258-3559
Fax: (320) 258-3880
Toll Free: (800) 678-4322
E-Mail: support@optifacts.com
Web Site: www.optifacts.com
Emp.: 14
Optical Laboratory Software Management Services
S.I.C.: 7371
N.A.I.C.S.: 541511
Steve Morris *(Pres)*

Quantum Direct LLC (2)
500 Washington Hwy
Smithfield, RI 02917
Tel.: (401) 231-3800
Fax: (401) 232-7236
E-Mail: quantumcs@fgxi.com
Optical Goods Mfr & Whslr
S.I.C.: 5048
N.A.I.C.S.: 423460

Satisloh North America Inc (2)
N116 W18111 Morse Dr
Germantown, WI 53022
Tel.: (262) 255-6001
Fax: (262) 255-6002
E-Mail: info.usa@satisloh.com
Web Site: www.satisloh.com
Ophthalmic Lens Mfr & Distr
S.I.C.: 5048
N.A.I.C.S.: 423460

Signet Armorlite, Inc. (2)
1001 Armorlite Dr
San Marcos, CA 92069-1431 CA (100%)
Tel.: (760) 744-4000
Fax: (760) 471-6255
Toll Free: (800) 759-4630
E-Mail: info@signetarmorlite.com
Web Site: www.signetarmorlite.com
Sales Range: $125-149.9 Million
Emp.: 200
Ophthalmic Lenses Mfr
S.I.C.: 3851
N.A.I.C.S.: 339115
Brad Staley *(Pres)*
Edward P. DeRosa *(Exec VP-Global Bus Ops)*
Francois Glon *(Exec VP-Mktg-Global & Sls-US Brand)*
Beverly Marquez *(Exec VP-North America)*

Non-U.S. Subsidiary:

Crossbows Optical Ltd (3)
Unit 1 Halfpenny Valley Industrial Estate
Craigavon, Lurgan, Co Armagh, BT66 8TP, United Kingdom
Tel.: (44) 28 3832 2301
Fax: (44) 28 3832 8923
E-Mail: general@crossbowsoptical.com
Web Site: www.crossbowsoptical.com
Emp.: 3
Optical Lens Mfr
S.I.C.: 3827
N.A.I.C.S.: 333314
Mervyn McCrea *(Mng Dir)*

Skaggs and Gruber, Ltd (2)
2970 Sutro St
Reno, NV 89512-1616
Tel.: (775) 359-6667
Fax: (800) 245-6667
Toll Free: (800) 248-2501
Optical Goods Distr
S.I.C.: 5048
N.A.I.C.S.: 423460
Jeffrey Skaggs *(Pres)*

Specialty Optical Services, Inc. (2)
4139 S 88th East Ave
Tulsa, OK 74145
Tel.: (918) 627-0593
Fax: (918) 627-7842
Toll Free: (800) 767-8545
Web Site: www.emagineoptical.com
Sales Range: $10-24.9 Million
Emp.: 18
Optical Instrument & Lens Mfr
S.I.C.: 3827
N.A.I.C.S.: 333314
Beverly Yancy *(VP)*

Joint Venture:

Transitions Optical, Inc. (2)
9251 Belcher Rd
Pinellas Park, FL 33782-4200
Mailing Address:
PO Box 700
Pinellas Park, FL 33782
Tel.: (727) 545-0400
Fax: (727) 546-4732
Toll Free: (800) 533-2081
Web Site: www.transitions.com
Sls.: $250,000,000
Emp.: 1,200
Lightweight Sundarkening Lenses Mfr
Export
S.I.C.: 3827
N.A.I.C.S.: 333314
Dave Cole *(Pres)*
Richard Elias *(CEO)*

Non-U.S. Subsidiaries:

20 20 Optics Pvt Ltd (1)
Plot No A 30 2nd Floor Shankar Towers
Near Allahabad Bank
Apiie Main Road Bala Nagar, Hyderabad, Andhra Pradesh, 500037, India
Tel.: (91) 40 64633922
Fax: (91) 40 23771025
Emp.: 70
Optical Lens Mfr
S.I.C.: 3827
N.A.I.C.S.: 333314
Ratan Kumar *(Gen Mgr)*

Amico (1)
Dubai Healthcare City
PO Box 55320
Dubai, United Arab Emirates
Tel.: (971) 4 3624727
Fax: (971) 4 3624725
E-Mail: info@amicogroup.com
Web Site: www.amicogroup.com
Emp.: 80
Medical Equipment Whslr
S.I.C.: 5047
N.A.I.C.S.: 423450
Ashok Dewan *(Gen Mgr)*

Aries Optical Ltd. (1)
77 Stonebridge Ct
Fredericton, NB, E3A 1J4, Canada
Tel.: (506) 458-1902
Fax: (506) 450-2869
Toll Free: (800) 463-9701
Web Site: www.ariesoptical.ca
Ophthalmic Laboratory Services
S.I.C.: 8734
N.A.I.C.S.: 541380

BBGR GmbH (1)
Von-Ketteler-Str 1
96050 Bamberg, Germany
Tel.: (49) 951 1860

Fax: (49) 951 1861920
E-Mail: info@brillenglas.de
Emp.: 35
Investment Management Services
S.I.C.: 6211
N.A.I.C.S.: 523999
Steven Landry *(Gen Mgr)*

BBGR Skandinaviska AB (1)
Krossverksgatan 11b
Limhamn, Malmo, 216 16, Sweden
Tel.: (46) 40 36 38 60
Fax: (46) 40 16 28 81
E-Mail: info@bbgr.se
Web Site: www.bbgr.se
Emp.: 15
Optical Products Mfr
S.I.C.: 3851
N.A.I.C.S.: 339115
Olivier Rabeyrin *(Gen Mgr)*

Canoptec Inc. (1)
371 Deslauriers
Saint Laurent, QC, H4N 1W2, Canada
Tel.: (514) 337-0673
Fax: (514) 337-2377
Toll Free: (800) 361-9491
E-Mail: receptionmtl@essilor.ca
Web Site: www.canoptecservices.ca
Ophthalmic Lenses Whslr
S.I.C.: 5048
N.A.I.C.S.: 423460
Ronald Pepin *(Mgr)*

Cascade Optical Ltd (1)
7475 Hedley Ave Ste 206
Burnaby, BC, V5E 2R1, Canada
Tel.: (604) 437-3937
Fax: (604) 437-3938
Optical Lens Distr
S.I.C.: 5048
N.A.I.C.S.: 423460

City Optical Pty Ltd. (1)
10 Marlow Rd
Keswick, Adelaide, SA, 5035, Australia
Tel.: (61) 1800882176
Fax: (61) 883711429
Ophthalmic Photographic Equipment Mfr
S.I.C.: 3579
N.A.I.C.S.: 333316

De Ceunynck & Co nv (1)
Kontichsesteenweg 36
Aartselaar, 2630, Belgium
Tel.: (32) 3 870 37 11
Fax: (32) 3 887 19 20
E-Mail: contact@deceunynck.be
Web Site: www.deceunynck.be
Emp.: 80
Glass Mfr
S.I.C.: 3211
N.A.I.C.S.: 327211
Stefan Laridon *(Mng Dir)*

Eastern Optical Laboratories Ltd. (1)
101 Ilsley Avenue
PO Box 115
Dartmouth, NS, B3B 1S8, Canada
Tel.: (902) 468-4567
Fax: (902) 468-4371
Toll Free: (800) 565-7538
Web Site: www.easternoptical.ca
Emp.: 3
Optical Lenses Mfr
S.I.C.: 3827
N.A.I.C.S.: 333314
Tom Allen *(Gen Mgr)*

Easy Vision (1)
Hope Street 78
George, Western Cape, 6530, South Africa
Tel.: (27) 448744210
Fax: (27) 448744114
E-Mail: orders1@easyvision.co.za
Web Site: www.easy.co.za
Emp.: 2
Contact Lens Whslr
S.I.C.: 5048
N.A.I.C.S.: 423460
Brian Randall *(Gen Mgr)*

Non-U.S. Subsidiary:

Optodev, Inc. (2)
Block 2 Lot 2 Star Avenue corner Interstar Street
LIIP Mamplasan, Laguna,
Philippines (99.99%)
Fax: (63) 49 539 0975
E-Mail: elhr@optodev.essilor.com.ph
Mfr. & Sales of Ophthalmic Goods
S.I.C.: 3842
N.A.I.C.S.: 339113

Non-U.S. Joint Venture:

Nikon-Essilor Co., Ltd. (2)
4th Fl Sumitomo Fudosan Ryogoku Bldg
10 8 Ryogoku 2 Chome Sumida Ku, Tokyo, 130-0026, Japan
Tel.: (81) 356003511
Fax: (81) 356003525
Web Site: www.nikon-essilor.co.jp
Emp.: 150
Developer, Manufacturer & Sales of Ophthalmic Lenses & Related Products; Joint Venture of Essilor International S.A. (50%) & Nikon Corporation (50%)
S.I.C.: 3827
N.A.I.C.S.: 333314
Serge Zins *(CFO)*

Essilor AB (1)
Fagerstagatan 21
Box 8169
163 08 Spanga, Sweden
Tel.: (46) 86212600
Fax: (46) 87609591
E-Mail: info@essilor.se
Optical Goods Distr
S.I.C.: 5048
N.A.I.C.S.: 423460

Essilor Asia Pacific Pte Ltd. (1)
215 Kallang Bahru 06-00 Essilor Building
Singapore, 339346, Singapore SG
Tel.: (65) 62936801 (100%)
Fax: (65) 62920245
E-Mail: enquiry@essilor.com
Web Site: www.essilor.com.sg
Sales Range: $300-349.9 Million
Emp.: 8,752
Eyeglass Lenses & Other Ophthalmic Products Mfr & Whslr
S.I.C.: 3827
N.A.I.C.S.: 333314
Patrick Cherrier *(Reg Pres)*

Essilor Austria Gmbh (1)
Liebermann Street 1 A01/401
2355 Brunn, Austria
Tel.: (43) 2236 680 0
Fax: (43) 2236 680 209
E-Mail: frage@essilor.at
Web Site: www.essilor.at
Emp.: 3
Optical Instruments Whslr
S.I.C.: 5048
N.A.I.C.S.: 423460
Christian Kirchmeyer *(Gen Mgr)*

Essilor Canada Ltd. (1)
371 Rue Deslauriers
Saint Laurent, QC, H4N 1W2,
Canada (100%)
Tel.: (514) 337-2943
Fax: (514) 337-5679
E-Mail: information@essilor.ca
Web Site: www.essilor.ca
Emp.: 200
Mfr. of Optical Lens
S.I.C.: 3842
N.A.I.C.S.: 339113
Gerard Malledant *(Chm & Pres)*

Essilor Danmark A.S. (1)
Hassellunden 13
2765 Smorum, Denmark
Tel.: (45) 70 20 84 44
Fax: (45) 70 20 84 45
Optical Instruments Mfr & Whslr
S.I.C.: 3851
N.A.I.C.S.: 339115

Essilor D.O.O (1)
22 Zagrebska Cesta
Maribor, 2000, Slovenia
Tel.: (386) 22283620
Fax: (386) 22518422
E-Mail: office@essilor.si
Optical Lens Mfr
S.I.C.: 3827
N.A.I.C.S.: 333314

Essilor European Shared Service Center Ltd. (1)
St Lukes House Emerson Way Emersons Green
Bristol, Avon, BS16 7AR, United Kingdom
Tel.: (44) 117 970 9618
Fax: (44) 117 970 9629
Accounting Services
S.I.C.: 8721
N.A.I.C.S.: 541219
Andrew Cheatham *(Gen Mgr)*

Essilor India Pvt Ltd (1)
No 71/1 S C Road Brigade Plaza 6th Floor
Anand Rao Circle Gandhinagar
Bengaluru, Karnataka, 560009, India
Tel.: (91) 80 40921800
Fax: (91) 80 22250286
E-Mail: essilor@essilorindia.com
Web Site: www.essilorindia.com
Optical Lens Mfr
S.I.C.: 3827
N.A.I.C.S.: 333314

Essilor Ireland Ltd. (1)
Bay 1 Raheen Industrial Park
Raheen, Limerick, Ireland IE
Tel.: (353) 61227533 (100%)
Telex: 70135
Fax: (353) 61229313
Web Site: www.essilor.ie
Emp.: 70
Eyeglass Lenses Mfr
S.I.C.: 3827
N.A.I.C.S.: 333314

Essilor Lens & Spects P Ltd (1)
Shed No 2 Chashmawala Compound
Behind Vihar Cinema
Pratap Nagar, Vadodara, Gujarat, 390004, India
Tel.: (91) 265 2439006
Optical Goods Distr
S.I.C.: 5048
N.A.I.C.S.: 423460

Essilor Ltd. (1)
Cooper Road
Thornbury, Bristol, BS35 3UW, United Kingdom (100%)
Tel.: (44) 1454417100
Telex: ORMAOP 44218
Fax: (44) 1454423365
E-Mail: orders@essilor.co.uk
Web Site: www.essilor.co.uk
Emp.: 500
Ophthalmic Lenses
S.I.C.: 3827
N.A.I.C.S.: 333314
Steve Nussbaumer *(Mng Dir)*

Essilor Logistik GmbH (1)
Voltastrasse 12
63457 Hanau, Germany
Tel.: (49) 6181 50010
Fax: (49) 6181 500122
Logistics Consulting Services
S.I.C.: 4731
N.A.I.C.S.: 541614

Essilor Mexico S.A DE CV (1)
sevilla 40 floor 5 colonial juarez
Mexico, 6000, Mexico
Tel.: (52) 55 5130 7310
Fax: (52) 51307310
E-Mail: reception@essilor.com.mx
Web Site: www.essilor.com.mx
Emp.: 10
Ophthalmic Lens Whslr
S.I.C.: 5048
N.A.I.C.S.: 423460
Harm Dressan *(Dir-Logistics)*

Essilor Nederland BV (1)
Luchthavenweg 18f
Eindhoven, 5657 EB, Netherlands
Tel.: (31) 402065858
Fax: (31) 402065828
Web Site: www.essilor.nl
Emp.: 3
Optical Goods Distr
S.I.C.: 5048
N.A.I.C.S.: 423460
R. de Bruijn *(VP)*

Essilor Nederland Holding BV (1)
Luchthavenweg 18f
Eindhoven, 5657 EB, Netherlands
Tel.: (31) 402065858
Fax: (31) 402065828
E-Mail: info@essilor.com
Web Site: www.essilor.com
Investment Management Services
S.I.C.: 6211
N.A.I.C.S.: 523999

Essilor Norge A.S. (1)
Hermann Foss Gate 4
Kongsberg, 3611, Norway
Tel.: (47) 32726000
Fax: (47) 32726200
E-Mail: info@essilor.no
Web Site: www.essilor.no
Emp.: 31
Eyeglass & Frame Whslr
S.I.C.: 5048
N.A.I.C.S.: 423460

Essilor Optical laboratory Polska Sp. Z.o.o. (1)
Annopol 3
Warsaw, 03-236, Poland
Tel.: (48) 225105900
Fax: (48) 225105901
Corrective Lens Mfr
S.I.C.: 3827
N.A.I.C.S.: 333314
Sielicki Witold *(Gen Mgr)*

Essilor Polonia Sp. z o.o (1)
Biuro Centralne Ul Annopol 3
03-236 Warsaw, Poland
Tel.: (48) 225 10 59 00
Fax: (48) 22 510 59 60
Eyeglass & Contact Lenses Mfr
S.I.C.: 3851
N.A.I.C.S.: 339115

Essilor Romania SRL (1)
266-268 Calea Rahovei
Bucharest, 10011, Romania
Tel.: (40) 214048244
Fax: (40) 214048251
E-Mail: office@Essilor.ro
Web Site: www.Essilor.ro
Emp.: 3
Optical Glasses Mfr & Whslr
S.I.C.: 3827
N.A.I.C.S.: 333314
Jery Pascal *(Gen Mgr)*

Essilor S.A. (1)
Rue des Avouil 30
Les Acacias, Gland, 1196, Switzerland
Tel.: (41) 228274727
Fax: (41) 228274797
Ophthalmic Lenses Mfr
S.I.C.: 3851
N.A.I.C.S.: 339115

Essilor South Africa (Pty) Ltd. (1)
137 Kuschke St
Edenvale, 1614, South Africa
Tel.: (27) 114531602
Fax: (27) 114541705
Emp.: 25
Optical Lens Mfr
S.I.C.: 3827
N.A.I.C.S.: 333314
Darren Duggan *(Gen Mgr)*

FGX Canada Corp (1)
555 Richmond St W Suite 1005
Toronto, ON, M5V 3B1, Canada
Tel.: (416) 504-5533
Fax: (416) 504-4073
Emp.: 3
Sunglasses Whlsr
S.I.C.: 3851
N.A.I.C.S.: 339115
Alli Cambridge *(Pres)*

Groupe Vision Optique (1)
551 Boulevard Laurier Suite 100
Beloeil, QC, J3G 4J1, Canada
Tel.: (450) 446-9898
Fax: (450) 446-8114
Ophthalmic Lenses Mfr
S.I.C.: 3851
N.A.I.C.S.: 339115

Holland Optical Instruments BV (1)
Verrijn Stuartweg 42
1112 AX Diemen, Netherlands
Tel.: (31) 205696555
Fax: (31) 205696593
E-Mail: info@hoisite.nl
Quality Lenses Distr
S.I.C.: 5048
N.A.I.C.S.: 423460

Horizon Optical Company Ltd (1)
9-11 Apex Business Centre Boscombe Road
Dunstable, LU5 4SA, United Kingdom
Tel.: (44) 1582 472733

Essilor International, S.A.—(Continued)

Fax: (44) 1582 472837
E-Mail: info@horizonoptical.co.uk
Web Site: www.horizonoptical.co.uk
Emp.: 6
Eyeglass Mfr & Whslr
S.I.C.: 3851
N.A.I.C.S.: 339115
Ian Wooster *(Mng Dir)*

Infield Safety GmbH (1)
Nordstrasse 10 a
42719 Solingen, Germany
Tel.: (49) 2 12 23 23 40
Fax: (49) 2 12 23 23 499
E-Mail: info@infield-safety.de
Web Site: www.infield-safety.de
Emp.: 3
Optical Products Distr
S.I.C.: 5048
N.A.I.C.S.: 423460
Stefan Find *(Mng Dir)*

Infield safety UK, Ltd. (1)
Unit 1-7 Apollo Olympus Park
Quedgeley, Gloucester, GL2 4NF, United Kingdom
Tel.: (44) 1223 836222
Fax: (44) 1223 836201
E-Mail: info@infield-safety.co.uk
Web Site: www.infield-safety.co.uk
Protective Eyewear Mfr & Whslr
S.I.C.: 3851
N.A.I.C.S.: 339115
Chris Stewart *(Gen Mgr)*

Integrated Lens Technology Pte Ltd (1)
Block 50 Ubi Ave 3 03-19 Frontier
Singapore, 408866, Singapore
Tel.: (65) 6554 2242
Fax: (65) 6554 2272
E-Mail: sales@iltoptics.com
Web Site: www.iltoptics.com
Emp.: 3
Optical Lens Mfr & Distr
S.I.C.: 3851
N.A.I.C.S.: 339115

K & W Optical Ltd. (1)
1770 Courtwood Crescent
Ottawa, ON, K2C 2B5, Canada
Tel.: (800) 361-1106
Fax: (866) 231-2908
Web Site: www.kwoptical.ca
Ophthalmic Products Mfr
S.I.C.: 3851
N.A.I.C.S.: 339115

Kaleido Vision Pte Ltd (1)
164 Kallang Way 04-37/38/39
Singapore, 349248, Singapore
Tel.: (65) 62961551
Fax: (65) 62973996
Emp.: 80
Optical Goods Distr
S.I.C.: 5048
N.A.I.C.S.: 423460

Omega Optix S.R.O. (1)
Komenskeho 12B
974 01 Banska Bystrica, Slovakia
Tel.: (421) 48 411 30 74
Fax: (421) 48 281 20 07
E-Mail: objednavky@omega-optix.sk
Web Site: www.omega-optix.sk
Emp.: 11
Spectacle Lenses Mfr & Distr
S.I.C.: 3827
N.A.I.C.S.: 333314
Jiri Peterka *(Mgr-Sls)*

OPSG Ltd. (1)
2100 Oxford Street East Unit 27 & 29
London, ON, N5V 4A4, Canada
Tel.: (519) 451-9943
Fax: (519) 451-4211
Web Site: www.opsg.ca
Emp.: 6
Optical Laboratory Equipment Whslr
S.I.C.: 5046
N.A.I.C.S.: 423440
Tom Anstett *(Gen Mgr)*

Optical Laboratories Ltd. (1)
Unit 1 76 Porana Road
Glenfield, Auckland, 627, New Zealand
Tel.: (64) 3 3666420
Optical Laboratory Services
S.I.C.: 8734
N.A.I.C.S.: 541380

Optikos SP Zoo (1)
Traugutta 24-3
Krakow, 30-549, Poland
Tel.: (48) 126562769
Fax: (48) 122632105
Optical Goods Whslr
S.I.C.: 5048
N.A.I.C.S.: 423460

Optique Cristal Inc (1)
197 Avenue Riverin
Chicoutimi, Saguenay, QC, G7H 4R2, Canada
Tel.: (418) 545-8556
Fax: (418) 545-8633
Optical Lens Mfr
S.I.C.: 3827
N.A.I.C.S.: 333314

Optique de l'Estrie Inc (1)
417-T Rue Bel Vedere S
Sherbrooke, QC, J1H-4B7, Canada
Tel.: (819) 569-5533
Fax: (819) 565-5501
Web Site: www.essilor.ca
Emp.: 2
Ophthalmic Lens Mfr & Whslr
S.I.C.: 3851
N.A.I.C.S.: 339115
Tom Enge Winger *(Office Mgr)*

Optique Lison Inc. (1)
6980 rue Dalpe
Trois Rivieres, QC, G9A 5C9, Canada
Tel.: (819) 691-4110
Optical Products Whslr
S.I.C.: 5048
N.A.I.C.S.: 423460

Perspectics (1)
1393 Border St Unit 1
Winnipeg, MB, R3H 0N1, Canada
Tel.: (204) 474-2684
Fax: (204) 474-2731
Toll Free: (800) 465-3235
E-Mail: dmagonwski@essilor.ca
Web Site: www.perspectics.ca
Emp.: 15
Lens & Frames Mfr
S.I.C.: 3827
N.A.I.C.S.: 333314
Volker Hues *(Gen Mgr)*

Pioneer Optical Inc. (1)
100-2825 Saskatchewan Dr
Regina, SK, S4T 1H3, Canada
Tel.: (306) 525-5201
Fax: (306) 569-6010
Emp.: 6
Ophthalmic Lens Whslr
S.I.C.: 5048
N.A.I.C.S.: 423460
Don Kuhnie *(Gen Mgr)*

Pro Optic Canada Inc. (1)
551 Boulevard Laurier Suite 100
Laval, QC, H7L 5C7, Canada
Tel.: (800) 361-4010
Fax: (450) 625-4545
Emp.: 40
Optical Lens Mfr
S.I.C.: 3827
N.A.I.C.S.: 333314
Claude Perreault *(Gen Mgr)*

Non-U.S. Subsidiary:

Satisloh do Brasil Ltda (2)
Rua Caramuru 525 - Cj Saude
Sao Paulo, 04138-001, Brazil
Tel.: (55) 11 5589 8607
Fax: (55) 11 5594 2871
Emp.: 1
Optical Lenses Whslr
S.I.C.: 5048
N.A.I.C.S.: 423460
Walke Rainer *(Gen Mgr)*

R & R Optical Laboratory Ltd. (1)
4500 Sheppard Avenue East Unit 43
Scarborough, ON, M1S 3R6, Canada
Tel.: (416) 291-8811
Fax: (416) 291-0338
Toll Free: (800) 268-3511
Web Site: www.rroptical.ca
Emp.: 2
Lens Whslr
S.I.C.: 5048
N.A.I.C.S.: 423460
Ed Mcgrath *(Gen Mgr)*

Rupp & Hubrach Optik Gmbh (1)
Von-Ketteler-Str 1
96050 Bamberg, Germany
Tel.: (49) 951 186 2400
Fax: (49) 9511861920
E-Mail: info@rh-brillenglas.de
Web Site: www.rh-brillenglas.de
Emp.: 50
Spectacle Lenses Mfr
S.I.C.: 3851
N.A.I.C.S.: 339115
Ralf Thiehofe *(Mng Dir)*

Satisloh AG (1)
Neuhofstrasse 12
6340 Baar, Switzerland
Tel.: (41) 766 16 16
Fax: (41) 766 16 10
E-Mail: info@satisloh.com
Web Site: www.satisloh.com
Emp.: 505
Optical Goods Mfr
S.I.C.: 3827
N.A.I.C.S.: 333314

Satisloh Asia Ltd. (1)
Room 21 3/F Sino Industrial Plaza 9 Kai Cheung Road
Kowloon Bay, Kowloon, China (Hong Kong)
Tel.: (852) 2756 7711
Fax: (852) 2796 6175
E-Mail: info.asia@satisloh.com
Web Site: www.satisloh.com
Emp.: 100
Optical Goods Mfr
S.I.C.: 3827
N.A.I.C.S.: 333314
Holger Zunft *(Pres & CEO)*

Satisloh Gmbh (1)
Wilhelm-Loh-Str 2-4
35578 Wetzlar, Germany
Tel.: (49) 6441 912 0
Fax: (49) 6441 912 0
E-Mail: info.de@satisloh.com
Web Site: www.satisloh.com
Optical Lenses Mfr
S.I.C.: 3851
N.A.I.C.S.: 339115
Albrecht Bachus *(Gen Mgr)*

Satisloh Iberica SL (1)
Les Sagraments 22 Pol Ind Sant Ermengol
08630 Abrera, Barcelona, Spain
Tel.: (34) 93 773 80 28
Fax: (34) 93 770 26 52
E-Mail: info.es@satisloh.com
Optical Lens Mfr
S.I.C.: 3827
N.A.I.C.S.: 333314
Jan Pohl *(Gen Mgr)*

Satisloh Italy Spa (1)
Via Campaccio 0013
Settimo Milanese, Milan, 20019, Italy
Tel.: (39) 02 335561
Fax: (39) 02 33501200
E-Mail: info.it@satisloh.com
Web Site: www.satisloh.com
Emp.: 7
Optical Lens Mfr
S.I.C.: 3827
N.A.I.C.S.: 333314

Satisloh Photonics AG (1)
Neugasse 10
8810 Horgen, Switzerland
Tel.: (41) 43 244 15 44
Fax: (41) 43 244 15 40
E-Mail: satisloh.photonics@satisloh.com
Optical Instrument & Machine Tool Mfr
S.I.C.: 3542
N.A.I.C.S.: 333517
Marc Peter *(Head-R&D Photonics)*

Satisloh Zhongshan Ltd (1)
Ground Floor 4th Building Sinda-Jiahu Industrial Park Jiang Wei Tou
Hi-Tech Development Zone, Zhongshan, Guangdong, 528437, China
Tel.: (86) 760 8858 0781
Fax: (86) 760 8858 0787
E-Mail: info.china.zs@satisloh.com
Web Site: www.satisloh.com
Optical Lens Mfr
S.I.C.: 3827
N.A.I.C.S.: 333314

Sentralslip AS (1)
Gladengveien 3B
Oslo, 601, Norway
Tel.: (47) 23 12 24 00
Fax: (47) 22 68 71 74
E-Mail: post@sentralslip.no
Web Site: www.sentralslip.no
Emp.: 9
Optical Lens Distr
S.I.C.: 5048
N.A.I.C.S.: 423460
Bert Jan Koekoek *(Mgr)*

Shamir Optical Industry Ltd. (1)
Kibbutz Shamir
Shamir, Upper Galilee, 12135, Israel II
Tel.: (972) 4 694 7810 (50%)
Fax: (972) 4 695 1302
E-Mail: shamir_opt@shamir.co.il
Web Site: www.shamir.com
Sales Range: $150-199.9 Million
Emp.: 1,764
Progressive Eyeglass Lenses Mfr
S.I.C.: 3827
N.A.I.C.S.: 333314
Amos Netzer *(Pres & CEO)*
Yagen Moshe *(CFO)*
Nir Shmuel *(CIO)*
Dan Katzman *(CTO & VP-R & D)*

Subsidiary:

Eyal Optical Ind. Ltd. (2)
Kibbutz Eyal
Hasharon Hatihon, 45840, Israel
Tel.: (972) 97639000
Fax: (972) 97494508
E-Mail: eyal_opt@eyaloptica.com
Web Site: www.shamir.co.il
Emp.: 200
Optical Lens Mfr
S.I.C.: 3827
N.A.I.C.S.: 333314
Amos Nezer *(Mng Dir)*

U.S. Subsidiaries:

Shamir Insight, Inc. (2)
9938 Via Pasar
San Diego, CA 92126 CA
Tel.: (858) 514-8330 (100%)
Fax: (877) 285-4863
Toll Free: (877) 514-8330
E-Mail: information@shamirlens.com
Web Site: www.shamirlens.com
Emp.: 40
Optical Lens Marketing & Distribution Services
S.I.C.: 3827
N.A.I.C.S.: 333314
Raanan Naftalovich *(CEO)*

Shamir USA, Inc. (2)
30077 Agoura Rd Ste 220
Agoura Hills, CA 91301-2713
Tel.: (818) 889-6292
Fax: (818) 889-6293
E-Mail: michael@shamirusa.com
Web Site: www.shamir.co.il/world.asp
Emp.: 3
Optical Lens Research, Development, Mfr & Marketing
S.I.C.: 3827
N.A.I.C.S.: 333314
Michael Latzer *(Pres)*

Non-U.S. Subsidiary:

Shamir Optic GmbH (2)
Philipp-Reis-Strasse 4a
61130 Nidderau, Germany
Tel.: (49) 618792500
Fax: (49) 6187925035
E-Mail: bestellungen@shamir-optic.de
Web Site: www.shamiroptic.de
Holding Company for European Marketing & Distribution Activities
S.I.C.: 3827
N.A.I.C.S.: 333314

Non-U.S. Subsidiaries:

Altra Optik Sanayi ve Ticaret A.S. (3)
4 Yan y Cumhuriyet Cad Senem Sok
Istanbul, Turkey
Tel.: (90) 2164516630
Fax: (90) 2163770775

E-Mail: info@altraoptik.com.tr
Web Site: www.altraoptik.com.tr
Emp.: 120
Optical Lens Mfr & Distr
S.I.C.: 3827
N.A.I.C.S.: 333314
Ekim Somer *(Gen Mgr)*

Shamir Optical Espana S.L. (3)
Calle Sagasta 30
28004 Madrid, Spain
Tel.: (34) 918373440
E-Mail: shamir@shamir.es
Web Site: www.shamir.es
Emp.: 41
Optical Lens & Opthalmic Goods Distr
S.I.C.: 5995
N.A.I.C.S.: 446130
Jesus Lopez *(Gen Mgr)*

Shamir Portugal Lda. (3)
Rua do Cego 100
Vilar, 4485 814 Vila do Conde, Portugal
Tel.: (351) 229287510
Fax: (351) 229287518
E-Mail: info@shamir.pt
Web Site: www.shamir.pt
Optical Lens Mfr & Distr
S.I.C.: 3827
N.A.I.C.S.: 333314
Luis F. Feijo *(Mng Dir)*

Shamir UK Limited (3)
Bar Hill
PO Box 76
Cambridge, CB23 8AP, United Kingdom
Tel.: (44) 1954785100
Fax: (44) 1954785101
E-Mail: info@shamirlens.co.uk
Web Site: www.shamirlens.co.uk
Emp.: 40
Optical Lens & Opthalmic Goods Distr
S.I.C.: 5995
N.A.I.C.S.: 446130
Philip Pareham *(Mng Dir)*

Signet Armorlite (Asia) Pte Ltd (1)
215 Kallang Bahru 06-00
Singapore, 349281, Singapore
Tel.: (65) 6293 6801
Fax: (65) 6292 0245
Web Site: www.signetarmorlite.com
Emp.: 100
Optical Goods Mfr & Whslr
S.I.C.: 3827
N.A.I.C.S.: 333314

Signet Armorlite Canada, Inc (1)
349 Evans Avenue
Etobicoke, ON, M8Z 1K2, Canada
Tel.: (905) 828-8798
Fax: (905) 828-4187
Optical Goods Mfr & Whslr
S.I.C.: 3851
N.A.I.C.S.: 339115

Signet Armorlite Germany Holding GmbH (1)
Bevenroder Str 150
Braunschweig, 38108, Germany
Tel.: (49) 531370020
Fax: (49) 5313700218
Emp.: 4
Financial Investment Services
S.I.C.: 6211
N.A.I.C.S.: 523999
Stephan Find *(Gen Mgr)*

Signet Armorlite (Holland) BV (1)
Parellaan 56
Hoofddorp, 2132 WS, Netherlands
Tel.: (31) 235650304
Fax: (31) 235627336
E-Mail: sales@saeurope.nl
Ophthalmic Lens Mfr
S.I.C.: 3851
N.A.I.C.S.: 339115
Robert Dirks *(Acct Mgr)*

Signet Armorlite Iberica SA (1)
Calle Manuel Tovar 7
28034 Madrid, Spain
Tel.: (34) 913581513
Fax: (34) 913584936
E-Mail: info@signetiberica.com
Optical Lens Mfr
S.I.C.: 3827
N.A.I.C.S.: 333314

Signet Armorlite Optic Gmbh (1)
Bevenroder Str 150
38108 Braunschweig, Germany
Tel.: (49) 531 37 002 20
Fax: (49) 531 37002 16
E-Mail: info@signet-armorlite.de
Web Site: www.signet-armorlite.de
Emp.: 10
Optical Instrument Mfr
S.I.C.: 3827
N.A.I.C.S.: 333314
Mario Bracci *(Gen Mgr)*

Spherical Optics (Pty) Ltd. (2)
10 The Avenue Orchards
2196 Johannesburg, South Africa
Tel.: (27) 114833584
E-Mail: shamiroptics@ibi.co.za
Web Site: www.shamir.co.il
Emp.: 20
Optical Lens Distr
S.I.C.: 3827
N.A.I.C.S.: 333314
Philip Rabinowitz *(Mng Dir)*

Tasmanian Optical Cy Pty LTD (1)
71 Murray St
Hobart, TAS, 7000, Australia
Tel.: (61) 3 6234 5044
Optical Goods Whslr
S.I.C.: 5995
N.A.I.C.S.: 446130

UAB JZP Optika Lituania (1)
Savanoriu Pr 187
Vilnius, 2300, Lithuania
Tel.: (370) 52653704
Fax: (370) 852653449
Emp.: 6
Optical Goods Distr
S.I.C.: 5048
N.A.I.C.S.: 423460
Donatas Guzys *(Gen Mgr)*

Wholesale Lens Corporation Limited (1)
73-77 Gloucester Road
Croydon, Surrey, CR0 2DL, United Kingdom
Tel.: (44) 20 8683 2902
Fax: (44) 20 8684 8826
E-Mail: orders@wlclens.co.uk
Web Site: www.wlclens.co.uk
Emp.: 4
Optical Goods Distr
S.I.C.: 5048
N.A.I.C.S.: 423460
David Spencer Lever *(Mng Dir)*

ESSTRA INDUSTRIES INC.

218 - 10458 Mayfield Road
Edmonton, AB, T5P 4P4, Canada
Tel.: (780) 484-3794
Fax: (780) 484-4230
Year Founded: 1996
ESS—(TSXV)
Rev.: $9,639
Assets: $1,710,926
Liabilities: $221,974
Net Worth: $1,488,952
Earnings: ($578,943)
Fiscal Year-end: 05/31/13

Business Description:
Financial Investment Services
S.I.C.: 6211
N.A.I.C.S.: 523999

Personnel:
Peter G. Dickson *(CEO)*
Sharon Lewis *(CFO)*

EST IMPRIMERIE

Z D"activite Tournebride Zone De Tournebride
57160 Metz, France
Tel.: (33) 387383400
Fax: (33) 387383939
E-Mail: est-Imprimerie@est-imprimerie.fr
Web Site: www.est-imprimerie.fr/
Rev.: $21,300,000
Emp.: 64

Business Description:
Commercial Printing
S.I.C.: 2759
N.A.I.C.S.: 323111

Personnel:
Gilles Peltier *(Chm)*

Board of Directors:
Gilles Peltier
Joel Perez

ESTABLISSEMENTEN FRANZ COLRUYT N.V.

(d/b/a COLRUYT)
Wilgenveld Edingensesteenweg 196
1500 Halle, Belgium
Tel.: (32) 23601040
Fax: (32) 23600207
E-Mail: info@colruyt.be
Web Site: www.colruytgroup.com
COLR—(EUR)
Rev.: $11,188,826,572
Assets: $4,635,267,161
Liabilities: $2,221,718,968
Net Worth: $2,413,548,193
Earnings: $476,005,712
Emp.: 24,287
Fiscal Year-end: 03/31/13

Business Description:
Management of Chain Stores;
Catalog Sales & Distribution;
Computer Applications & Graphics Distribution
Export
S.I.C.: 5999
N.A.I.C.S.: 453998

Personnel:
Jef Colruyt *(Chm & COO-Svcs)*
Marc Hofman *(CFO)*
Wim Biesemans *(CEO-Parkwind NV)*

Board of Directors:
Jef Colruyt
Koen Baetens
Dirk Berteloot
Wim Biesemans
Dries Colpaert
Frans Colruyt
Koen Demaesschalck
Dirk Depoorter
Marc Hofman
Luc Rogge
Chris Van Wetterre
Peter Vanbellingen

Subsidiaries:

Alvocol N.V. (1)
Wilgenveld 196
Halle, Vlaams Brabant, 1500, Belgium
Tel.: (32) 23601040
Logistics Consulting Services
S.I.C.: 4731
N.A.I.C.S.: 541614

Bio-Planet N.V. (1)
Victor Desmesmaekerstraat 167
1500 Halle, Belgium
Tel.: (32) 2 363 50 10
Fax: (32) 2 363 50 20
E-Mail: bio-planet@bio-planet.be
Web Site: www.bioplanet.be
Emp.: 163
Supermarket Operator
S.I.C.: 5411
N.A.I.C.S.: 445110

BODEGAS BVBA (1)
Rijksweg 10 A
2880 Bornem, Belgium
Tel.: (32) 3 899 38 55
Fax: (32) 3 825 46 42
E-Mail: info@bodegas.be
Web Site: www.bodegas.be
Beverage Mfr
S.I.C.: 2084
N.A.I.C.S.: 312130
Marc de Parade *(Gen Mgr)*

Collivery N.V. (1)
Edingensesteenweg 196
1500 Halle, Belgium
Tel.: (32) 2 333 88 88
Fax: (32) 2 333 88 89
E-Mail: collivery@collivery.be
Web Site: www.collivery.be
Emp.: 399
Food Product Whslr
S.I.C.: 5149
N.A.I.C.S.: 424490

Colruyt Mobile (1)
Edingensesteenweg 196
1500 Halle, Belgium
Tel.: (32) 491 87 19 72
Web Site: www.colruytmobile.be
Cellular Phone Whslr
S.I.C.: 5065
N.A.I.C.S.: 423690

DATS24 N.V. (1)
Edingensesteenweg 196
1500 Halle, Belgium
Tel.: (32) 2 363 51 52
Fax: (32) 2 360 02 07
E-Mail: dats24@colruyt.be
Web Site: www.dats24.be
Petroleum Bulk Station Operator
S.I.C.: 5171
N.A.I.C.S.: 424710

DreamBaby N.V. (1)
August Demaeghtlaan 279
1500 Halle, Belgium
Tel.: (32) 2 361 39 15
E-Mail: advieslijn@dreambaby.be
Web Site: www.dreambaby.collishop.be
Baby Product Retailer
S.I.C.: 5945
N.A.I.C.S.: 451120

DreamLand N.V. (1)
Edingensesteenweg 196
1500 Halle, Belgium
Tel.: (32) 2 363 56 56
E-Mail: dreamland@dreamland.be
Web Site: www.dreamland.be
Supermarket Operator
S.I.C.: 5411
N.A.I.C.S.: 445110

E-Logistics N.V. (1)
Leuvensesteenweg 375
1930 Zaventem, Belgium
Tel.: (32) 2 720 85 27
Logistics Management Services
S.I.C.: 4731
N.A.I.C.S.: 541614

Foodinvest N.V. (1)
Rijksweg 6
2880 Bornem, Belgium
Tel.: (32) 3 633 23 30
Fax: (32) 3 633 02 42
E-Mail: info@foodinvest.com
Web Site: www.foodinvest.com
Food Product Retailer
S.I.C.: 5411
N.A.I.C.S.: 445110

Foodlines B.V.B.A. (1)
Rijksweg 6
Bornem, 2880, Belgium
Tel.: (32) 3 637 53 57
Fax: (32) 3 637 53 51
Supermarket Operator & Catering Services
S.I.C.: 5411
N.A.I.C.S.: 445110

Intrion N.V. (1)
Vaucampslaan 28
1654 Huizingen, Belgium
Tel.: (32) 2 360 14 15
Fax: (32) 2 360 28 80
E-Mail: info@intrion.com
Web Site: www.intrion.com
Industrial Automation Equipment Mfr
S.I.C.: 3559
N.A.I.C.S.: 333249

SPAR retail NV (1)
Industrielaan 23
1740 Ternat, Belgium
Tel.: (32) 2 583 11 11
Fax: (32) 2 582 73 23
E-Mail: info@sparretail.be
Web Site: www.sparretail.be
Emp.: 255
Food Product Retailer & Distr
S.I.C.: 5411
N.A.I.C.S.: 445110
Dirk Depoorter *(Gen Mgr)*

Symeta N.V. (1)
Beertsestraat 273
1500 Halle, Belgium
Tel.: (32) 2 360 01 90
Fax: (32) 2 360 03 35
E-Mail: info@symeta.com

Establissementen Franz Colruyt N.V.—(Continued)

Web Site: www.symeta.com
Emp.: 125
Printing Services
S.I.C.: 2759
N.A.I.C.S.: 323111
Jo Van De Weghe, *(Mgr-Sls & Mktg)*

Non-U.S. Subsidiaries:

Aubepine S.A.R.L. **(1)**
12 route de Saint-Omer
59285 Arneke, France
Tel.: (33) 328482607
E-Mail: contact@aubepineflandre.fr
Web Site: www.aubepineflandre.fr
Flower Retailer
S.I.C.: 5992
N.A.I.C.S.: 453110

Blin Etablissements S.A.S. **(1)**
11 Bis r Moulin Florent
51420 Witry-les-Reims, France
Tel.: (33) 3 26 84 32 32
Fax: (33) 3 26 84 32 33
Supermarket Operator
S.I.C.: 5411
N.A.I.C.S.: 445110

Codi-France S.A.S. **(1)**
4 Rue des Entrepots
39700 Rochefort-sur-Nenon, France
Tel.: (33) 3 84 70 74 00
Fax: (33) 3 84 70 64 39
E-Mail: contact.rochefort@codifrance.fr
Web Site: www.codifrance.fr
Supermarket Operator
S.I.C.: 5411
N.A.I.C.S.: 445110

Colruyt Luxembourg S.A. **(1)**
Av JF Kennedy 46A
1855 Luxembourg, Luxembourg
Tel.: (352) 26 32 27 29
Fax: (352) 26 32 27 40
E-Mail: help@colruyt.lu
Web Site: www.colruyt.lu
Supermarket Operator
S.I.C.: 5411
N.A.I.C.S.: 445110

Dimaco UK Limited **(1)**
1 Wolseley Business Park
Kempston, Bedford, MK42 7PN, United Kingdom
Tel.: (44) 1234 851515
Fax: (44) 1234 851514
E-Mail: sales@dimaco.co.uk
Web Site: www.dimaco.co.uk
Food Inspection Services
S.I.C.: 7389
N.A.I.C.S.: 561499

Immoco S.A.S. **(1)**
1 Faubourg de Belfort
68700 Cernay, France
Tel.: (33) 8 99 18 06 82
Supermarket Operator
S.I.C.: 5411
N.A.I.C.S.: 445110

Intrion NL B.V. **(1)**
Satellietbaan 17 C
2181 MG Hillegom, Netherlands
Tel.: (31) 252 53 10 30
E-Mail: info@intrion.nl
Industrial Automation Equipment Mfr
S.I.C.: 3559
N.A.I.C.S.: 333249

Pro a Pro Distribution Nord S.A.S. **(1)**
18 Rue Andre Petit
Chalette-sur-Loing, 45120, France
Tel.: (33) 238890060
Food Product Distr
S.I.C.: 5149
N.A.I.C.S.: 424490

Pro a Pro Distribution Sud S.A.S. **(1)**
Zone Industrielle Nord 3 Rue Voltaire
82032 Montauban, CEDEX, France
Tel.: (33) 5 63 21 44 38
E-Mail: support@proapro.fr
Web Site: www.proapro.fr
Food Product Distr
S.I.C.: 5149
N.A.I.C.S.: 424490

Subsidiary:

Codifrais S.A.S. **(2)**
ZAC Paris Oise
Longueil-Sainte-Marie, 60126, France
Tel.: (33) 3 44 38 60 00
Fax: (33) 3 44 38 60 09
E-Mail: commercial@codifrais.com
Web Site: www.codifrais.com
Dairy Product Whslr
S.I.C.: 5143
N.A.I.C.S.: 424430

S.A.S Colruyt Distribution France **(1)**
4 Rue des Entrepots
39700 Rochefort-sur-Nenon, France
Tel.: (33) 3 84 70 74 00
Fax: (33) 3 84 70 64 39
E-Mail: contact@colruytfrance.fr
Web Site: www.colruyt.fr
Emp.: 2,000
Supermarket Operator
S.I.C.: 5411
N.A.I.C.S.: 445110

Unifrais Distribution S.A.S. **(1)**
Agropole Alphagro B
47310 Estillac, France
Tel.: (33) 5 53 77 08 60
Fax: (33) 5 53 68 30 22
Food Product Distr
S.I.C.: 5149
N.A.I.C.S.: 424490

ESTATIA AG

Gubelstrasse 17
6304 Zug, Switzerland
Tel.: (41) 223628852
Business Description:
Holding Company
S.I.C.: 6719
N.A.I.C.S.: 551112
Personnel:
Jostein Eikeland *(Founder & Chm)*
John Skjevesland *(Chief Dev Dir)*

Non-U.S. Subsidiary:

Meridian Technologies Inc. **(1)**
25 MacNab Ave
Strathroy, ON, N7G 4H6, Canada
Tel.: (519) 246-9600
Fax: (519) 245-6605
Web Site: www.meridian-mag.com
Sales Range: $350-399.9 Million
Emp.: 1,350
Magnesium Die Casting Designer & Mfr
S.I.C.: 3364
N.A.I.C.S.: 331523
Eric Showalter *(Pres & CEO)*
Jim Mallak *(CFO)*

Division:

Meridian Technologies Inc. - Global Technology Center **(2)**
25 Mac Nab Ave
Strathroy, ON, N7G 4H6, Canada
Tel.: (519) 245-4040
Fax: (519) 245-4620
E-Mail: jmoyer@meridian-mag.com
Web Site: www.meridian-mag.com
Emp.: 500
Magnesium Die Casting Technology Services
S.I.C.: 3364
N.A.I.C.S.: 331523
Jeffrey Moyer *(VP-Bus Dev & Engrg)*

U.S. Divisions:

Magnesium Products of America **(2)**
2001 Industrial Dr
Eaton Rapids, MI 48827
Tel.: (517) 663-2700
Fax: (517) 663-2714
Web Site: www.meridian-mag.com
Magnesium Mfr
S.I.C.: 3499
N.A.I.C.S.: 332999
Debbie Hutchison *(Dir-HR)*

Meridian Technologies Inc. - Business Development **(2)**
352 N Main St
Plymouth, MI 48170
Tel.: (734) 416-8600
Fax: (734) 416-8632
E-Mail: meridian.nafta@meridian-mag.com
Web Site: www.meridian.com
Emp.: 15
Magnesium Die Casting Sales
S.I.C.: 5051
N.A.I.C.S.: 423510

Non-U.S. Divisions:

Magnesium Products of Italy s.r.l. **(2)**
Via Glair 41
11029 Verres, Italy
Tel.: (39) 0125 922 111
Fax: (39) 0125 922 220
E-Mail: meridian-italy@meridian-mag.com
Web Site: www.meridian-mag.com
Emp.: 220
Magnesium Die Casting Services
S.I.C.: 5051
N.A.I.C.S.: 423510
Adrianna Lachello *(Acct Mgr)*

Meridian Deutschland GmbH **(2)**
Koenigstrasse 10c
D-70173 Stuttgart, Germany
Tel.: (49) 6227380780
Fax: (49) 6227389620
E-Mail: meridian.germany@meridian-mag.com
Web Site: www.meridian-mag.com
Emp.: 4
Magnesium Die Casting Services
S.I.C.: 3364
N.A.I.C.S.: 331523
Christian Frantz *(Acct Mgr)*

Meridian Technologies Inc. - Business Development **(2)**
Sano Bldg 6F 1-5-12 Nishishinbashi
Minato-ku, Tokyo, 105-0003, Japan
Tel.: (81) 335196668
Fax: (81) 335196669
E-Mail: meridian.japan@meridian-mag.com
Web Site: www.meridian-mag.com
Emp.: 8
Magnesium Die Casting Services
S.I.C.: 5051
N.A.I.C.S.: 423510

Meridian Technologies Inc. - United Kingdom **(2)**
Orchard Way Calladine Park
Sutton in Ashfield, Nottinghamshire, NG17 1JU, United Kingdom
Tel.: (44) 1623444920
Fax: (44) 1623444921
E-Mail: meridian.uk@meridian-mag.com
Web Site: www.meridian-mag.com
Emp.: 90
Rotary Machining, Drilling & Assembly Center; Business Development Services
S.I.C.: 3599
N.A.I.C.S.: 332710
Steve Brown *(Mgr)*

Shanghai Meridian Magnesium Products Limited **(2)**
777 Taishun Road Anting Town
Jiading District, Shanghai, 201814, China
Tel.: (86) 2159502388
Fax: (86) 2159502399
Web Site: www.meridian-mag.com
Emp.: 150
Magnesium Product Mfr & Services
S.I.C.: 3364
N.A.I.C.S.: 331523
John Chen *(Gen Mgr)*

ESTAVIS AG

Uhlandstrasse 165
D-10719 Berlin, Germany
Tel.: (49) 308871810
Fax: (49) 3088718111
E-Mail: mail@estavis.de
Web Site: www.estavis.de
E7S—(BER BOA DEU DUS STU)
Rev.: $160,036,728
Assets: $272,857,890
Liabilities: $183,159,890
Net Worth: $89,697,999
Earnings: $2,017,909
Emp.: 30
Fiscal Year-end: 06/30/13
Business Description:
Real Estate Investment Services
S.I.C.: 6531
N.A.I.C.S.: 531390
Personnel:
Karl-Josef Stohr *(Chm-Supervisory Bd)*
Rolf Elgeti *(Deputy Chm-Supervisory Bd)*
Torsten Cejka *(Member-Mgmt Bd)*
Jacopo Mingazzini *(Member-Mgmt Bd)*
Supervisory Board of Directors:
Karl-Josef Stohr
Rolf Elgeti
Philipp K. Wagner

Subsidiaries:

B & V Bautrager und Vertriebsgesellschaft fur Immobilien mbh **(1)**
Uhland Strasse 165
10719 Berlin, Germany
Tel.: (49) 3086391910
Fax: (49) 30863919111
E-Mail: info@bv-immobilien.com
Web Site: www.bv-immobilien.com
Emp.: 20
Real Estate Agencies
S.I.C.: 6531
N.A.I.C.S.: 531210
Jacqueline Schlaffke *(CEO)*

CWI Real Estate AG **(1)**
Mainstrabe 5
95444 Bayreuth, Bavaria, Germany
Tel.: (49) 921789080
Fax: (49) 9217890810
E-Mail: info@cwi.de
Web Site: www.cwi.de
Emp.: 5
Immovable Property Trading Services
S.I.C.: 6531
N.A.I.C.S.: 531312
Albrecht Spindler *(CEO)*

Estavis Property Management GmbH **(1)**
Uhlandstr 165
10719 Berlin, Germany
Tel.: (49) 3088718168
Fax: (49) 3088718111
Property Management Services
S.I.C.: 6531
N.A.I.C.S.: 531312

Hamburgische Immobilien Invest SUCV AG **(1)**
Neuer Wall 34
20354 Hamburg, Germany
Tel.: (49) 4036807790
Fax: (49) 40368077979
E-Mail: info@hamburgische-ag.de
Web Site: www.hamburgische-ag.de
Emp.: 3
Real Estate Development & Management Services
S.I.C.: 6531
N.A.I.C.S.: 531311
Alexander Kersteng *(Gen Mgr)*

Subsidiaries:

15. CWI Wohnen GmbH & Co. KG **(2)**
Mainstr 5
95444 Bayreuth, Germany
Tel.: (49) 9217890801
E-Mail: info@cwi.de
Web Site: www.cwi.de
Property Management Services
S.I.C.: 6531
N.A.I.C.S.: 531311

CWI Consult GmbH **(2)**
Landshuter St 21-23
Straubing, Bavaria, 94315, Germany
Tel.: (49) 942192490
Computer Software Solutions
S.I.C.: 7371
N.A.I.C.S.: 541511
John Haslbeck *(CEO)*

CWI Immobilien AG **(2)**
Uhlandstr 171
10719 Berlin, Germany

Tel.: (49) 30 88719780
Real Estate Development & Management Services
S.I.C.: 6531
N.A.I.C.S.: 531311

Hanseatische Immobilienborse HIB GmbH (2)
Neuer Wall 34
20354 Hamburg, Germany
Tel.: (49) 406887463
Fax: (49) 4068874654
E-Mail: info@hib-gmbh.de
Web Site: www.hib-gmbh.de
Real Estate Management Services
S.I.C.: 6531
N.A.I.C.S.: 531390

SIAG Funfundzwanzigste Wohnen GmbH & Co. KG (1)
Uhlandstr 165
Berlin, Germany
Tel.: (49) 308871810
Fax: (49) 3088718111
E-Mail: mail@estavis.de
Web Site: www.estavis.de
Real Estate Agents & Managers
S.I.C.: 6531
N.A.I.C.S.: 531210
Jacopo Mingazzini *(Gen Mgr)*

SIAG Neunzehnte Wohnen GmbH & Co. KG (1)
Uhlandstr 165
10719 Berlin, Germany
Tel.: (49) 30 88718139
Fax: (49) 30 88718111
Real Estate Management Services
S.I.C.: 6531
N.A.I.C.S.: 531312

ESTEC SYSTEMS CORP.

2nd Flr 17510 102 Avenue
Edmonton, AB, T5S 1K2, Canada
Tel.: (780) 483-7120
Fax: (780) 489-9557
E-Mail: investor@estec.com
Web Site: www.estec.com
Year Founded: 1989
ESE—(TSXV)
Rev.: $5,543,139
Assets: $2,821,055
Liabilities: $2,609,269
Net Worth: $211,786
Earnings: $350,307
Fiscal Year-end: 06/30/13

Business Description:
Engineering Services
S.I.C.: 8711
N.A.I.C.S.: 541330

Personnel:
Anthony B. Nelson *(Pres & CEO)*
Mark Bamford *(CFO)*

Board of Directors:
Barbara E. Fraser
Allan R. Nelson
Anthony B. Nelson
David E. Wright

Legal Counsel:
Ogilvie LLP
14th Floor 10303 Jasper Avenue
Edmonton, AB, Canada
Tel.: (780) 421-1818

Transfer Agent:
Computershare Investor Services Inc.
510 Burrard St
Vancouver, BC, V6C 3B9, Canada

Subsidiary:

Allan R. Nelson Engineering (1997) Inc (1)
2nd Fl 17510-102nd Ave
Edmonton, AB, T5S 1K2, Canada
Tel.: (780) 483-3436
Fax: (780) 489-9557
E-Mail: sales@arneng.ab.ca
Web Site: www.arneng.ab.ca
Emp.: 20
Mechanical Engineering Services
S.I.C.: 8711
N.A.I.C.S.: 541330
Tony Nelson *(Pres)*

U.S. Subsidiary:

Encore Electronics, Inc. (2)
4400 Route 50
Saratoga Springs, NY 12866 NY
Tel.: (518) 584-5354
Fax: (518) 584-5963
Toll Free: (866) 936-2673
E-Mail: info@encore-elec.com
Web Site: www.encore-elec.com
Emp.: 22
Instrument Mfr for Measuring & Testing Electricity & Electrical Signals
S.I.C.: 3825
N.A.I.C.S.: 334515
Brian Crawford *(Mgr-Sls)*

ESTECHPHARMA CO., LTD.

34BL-10 11 Boran Regional industrial Complex 1407-9 Hagil-ri
Hyangnam-eup, Hwaseong, Gyenggi-do, 445-992, Korea (South)
Tel.: (82) 31 831 4800
Fax: (82) 31 831 4801
E-Mail: estech@estechpharma.com
Web Site: www.estechpharma.com
Year Founded: 1996
041910—(KRS)

Business Description:
Pharmaceutical Product Mfr & Distr
S.I.C.: 2834
N.A.I.C.S.: 325412

Personnel:
Jason Jae Chul Kim *(Pres & CEO)*

ESTEEM BIO ORGANIC FOOD PROCESSING LTD

49 Gujrawala Town Part II
New Delhi, 110009, India
Tel.: (91) 11 32961926
E-Mail: info@esteembioorganic.com
Web Site: www.esteembioorganic.com
534927 534927—(BOM)
Emp.: 13

Business Description:
Farm Management & Food Processing
S.I.C.: 0762
N.A.I.C.S.: 115116

Personnel:
Jai Kumar *(Exec Dir-Gen Plng & Mgmt)*

Board of Directors:
Vinod Kumar Garg
Jai Kumar
Neeraj Mittal
Brij Kishore Sabharwal

ESTER INDUSTRIES LTD

Plot No-11-A Infocity -1 Sector - 33-34
Gurgaon, Haryana, 122001, India
Tel.: (91) 1244572100
Fax: (91) 1244572199
E-Mail: info@ester.in
Web Site: www.esterindustries.com
ESTER—(BOM NSE)
Rev.: $177,730,262
Assets: $120,965,528
Liabilities: $73,180,606
Net Worth: $47,784,922
Earnings: ($979,097)
Fiscal Year-end: 03/31/13

Business Description:
Polyester Films & Plastics Production & Marketing
S.I.C.: 3081
N.A.I.C.S.: 326113

Personnel:
Pradeep Kumar Rustagi *(CFO)*
Sunil Kumar Soni *(CIO)*
Rahul Bhatia *(CMO)*
Diwaker Dinesh *(Sec)*

Board of Directors:
Arvind Kumar Singhania
Ashok Kumar Agarwal
Anand Chand Burman
P. S. Dasgupta
V. B. Haribhakti
Dinesh Kothari
Ashok K. Newatia
M. S. Ramachandran
Pradeep Kumar Rustagi

Transfer Agent:
MCS Limited
F-65 Okhla Industrial Area Phase-I
New Delhi, India

ESTERAD INVESTMENT COMPANY BSC

Almoayyed Tower 5th Floor Suite 503
Seef District
PO Box 1080
Manama, Bahrain
Tel.: (973) 17 585400
Fax: (973) 17 585444
E-Mail: mail@esterad.net
Web Site: www.esterad.net
Year Founded: 1973
ESTERAD—(BAH)
Rev.: $6,281,923
Assets: $138,764,738
Liabilities: $30,318,595
Net Worth: $108,446,143
Earnings: ($859,650)
Emp.: 10
Fiscal Year-end: 12/31/12

Business Description:
Equity Investment Services
S.I.C.: 6211
N.A.I.C.S.: 523999

Personnel:
Nooruddin A. Nooruddin *(Chm)*
Rashid Ismail Almeer *(Deputy Chm)*
Faisal Yousif Janahi *(CEO)*
Khalid El-Ali *(Asst CEO)*
Abdulrahman M. S. Jamsheer *(Mng Dir)*
Jamshir M. Nasimi *(CFO & Compliance Officer)*

Board of Directors:
Nooruddin A. Nooruddin
Hussain Mohamed Aamer
Mazen Ibrahim Abdulkarim
Adnan Al Bassam
Hussain Al Hussaini
Yusuf Al Saleh
Rashid Ismail Almeer
Abdulla Ebrahim Jamsheer
Abdulrahman M. S. Jamsheer

ESTERCHEM LTD.

Brooklands Way Basford Lane Industrial Estate
Leekbrook, Leek, ST13 7QF, United Kingdom
Tel.: (44) 1538383997
Fax: (44) 1538386855
E-Mail: mail@esterchem.co.uk
Web Site: www.esterchem.co.uk
Year Founded: 1998
Rev.: $15,554,198
Emp.: 35

Business Description:
Chemical Products Mfr
S.I.C.: 2869
N.A.I.C.S.: 325199

Personnel:
Andy Barwell *(Dir-Technical)*

Board of Directors:
Adam Bray
Paul Bray

ESTHETICS INTERNATIONAL GROUP BERHAD

Lot 11 Jalan Astaka U8/88 Bukit Jelutong
40150 Shah Alam, Selangor, Malaysia
Tel.: (60) 378096688
Fax: (60) 378096699
E-Mail: investorrelations@estheticsgroup.com
Web Site: www.estheticsgroup.com
EIG—(KLS)
Rev.: $44,077,039
Assets: $50,359,002
Liabilities: $11,805,120
Net Worth: $38,553,882
Earnings: $2,377,748
Emp.: 750
Fiscal Year-end: 03/31/13

Business Description:
Skincare Product Mfr
S.I.C.: 7231
N.A.I.C.S.: 812112

Personnel:
Eddy Ing Huong Chieng *(Chm)*
Roderick Ngee Kai Chieng *(CEO & Mng Dir)*
Wai Ngan Lee *(Sec)*

Board of Directors:
Eddy Ing Huong Chieng
Mohd Ismail Che Rus
Brian Ngee Wen Chieng
Roderick Ngee Kai Chieng
Siew Mun Chu
Felicia Chang Ching Lim

Subsidiaries:

AsterSpring International Sdn. Bhd. (1)
Lot 11 Jalan Astaka U8/88 Bukit Jelutong Seksyen U8
40150 Shah Alam, Malaysia
Tel.: (60) 355129088
E-Mail: asterspring@estheticsgroup.com
Web Site: www.asterspring.com
Skin Care Services
S.I.C.: 7231
N.A.I.C.S.: 812112

EIG Pharma Asia Sdn. Bhd. (1)
Lot 11 Jalan Astaka U8/88 Bukit Jelutong Seksyen U8
40150 Shah Alam, Selangor, Malaysia
Tel.: (60) 3 7809 6612
Fax: (60) 3 7809 6620
Pharmaceutical Products Distr
S.I.C.: 5122
N.A.I.C.S.: 424210
Susan Siok Wee Lim *(Sr Gen Mgr)*

Esthetics and Wellness International Sdn. Bhd. (1)
Lot 11 Jalan Astaka U8/88 Bukit Jelutong Seksyen U8
Shah Alam, Selangor, 40150, Malaysia
Tel.: (60) 3 78096688
Fax: (60) 3 78096699
Web Site: www.estheticsgroup.com
Emp.: 100
Educational Support Services
S.I.C.: 8299
N.A.I.C.S.: 611710
Eddy Chieng *(Mng Dir)*

Esthetics Concept Sdn.Bhd. (1)
Lot 11 Jalan Astaka U8/88 Seksyen U8 Bukit Jelutong
40150 Shah Alam, Selangor, Malaysia
Tel.: (60) 378096688
Fax: (60) 78096736
E-Mail: hr@estheticsgroup.com
Web Site: www.estheticsgroup.com
Emp.: 200
Cosmectics Products Distr
S.I.C.: 5122
N.A.I.C.S.: 424210
Mitchell Lam *(Gen Mgr)*

Klientec International Sdn. Bhd. (1)
Lot 11 Jalan Astaka U8/88 Bukit Jelutong Seksyen U8
40150 Shah Alam, Selangor, Malaysia
Tel.: (60) 378096689
Fax: (60) 3 7809 6663
E-Mail: sales@klientec.com
Web Site: www.klientec.com
Marketing Automation Solutions
S.I.C.: 7379
N.A.I.C.S.: 518210
Peck Ong Goh *(Gen Mgr)*

Esthetics International Group Berhad—(Continued)

Leonard Drake (M) Sdn. Bhd. (1)
Lot 11 Jalan Astaka U8/88 Bukit Jelutong
Seksyen U8
40150 Shah Alam, Malaysia
Tel.: (60) 3 78096666
Fax: (60) 3 78096699
E-Mail: leonarddrake.my@estheticsgroup.com
Web Site: www.leonarddrake.com.my
Emp.: 400
Cosmetic Products Mfr
S.I.C.: 2844
N.A.I.C.S.: 325620
Michelle Lam *(Gen Mgr)*

Medklinn International Sdn. Bhd. (1)
22 Jalan Pengacara U1/48 Temasya
Industrial Park
40150 Shah Alam, Malaysia
Tel.: (60) 3 5567 0788
Fax: (60) 3 5567 0780
E-Mail: info@medklinn.com
Web Site: www.medklinn.com
Healthcare Products Distr
S.I.C.: 5122
N.A.I.C.S.: 424210
Peter Tham *(Gen Mgr)*

Non-U.S. Subsidiaries:

EIG Global (China) Co. Ltd. (1)
Room Unit 04 15th Floor Teem Tower No
208 Tianhe Road
Tianhe District, Guangzhou, China
Tel.: (86) 2038103628
Web Site: www.estheticsgroup.com
Skin & Hair Care Products Distr
S.I.C.: 5122
N.A.I.C.S.: 424210

EIG Global (HK) Ltd. (1)
3/F Kaiseng Commercial Centre 4-6
Hankow Road
Tsim Tsa Tsui, Kowloon, China (Hong Kong)
Tel.: (852) 28816169
Fax: (852) 2881 7612
Web Site: www.estheticsgroup.com
Cosmetics Distr
S.I.C.: 5122
N.A.I.C.S.: 424210

EIG GLOBAL PTE LTD (1)
70 Bendemeer Road 02-08 Luzerne
Singapore, 339940, Singapore
Tel.: (65) 6271 4733
Fax: (65) 6274 4889
Web Site: www.estheticsgroup.com
Health Care Products Distr
S.I.C.: 5122
N.A.I.C.S.: 424210

Ina Gail Pte. Ltd. (1)
1 Pasir Ris Central Street 3 03-20 White
Sands Shopping Centre
Singapore, 518457, Singapore
Tel.: (65) 65817887
Fax: (65) 65850575
Skin & Hair Care Products Distr
S.I.C.: 5122
N.A.I.C.S.: 424210

Leonard Drake (HK) Ltd. (1)
HK Pacific Centre Fl 9
Tsim Tsa Tsui, Kowloon, China (Hong Kong)
Tel.: (852) 31151132
Fax: (852) 23763370
Hair & Skin Care Services
S.I.C.: 7231
N.A.I.C.S.: 812112

ESTIC CORPORATION

2-5-9 Hashibahigashino-cho
Moriguchi, Osaka, 570-0031, Japan
Tel.: (81) 6 6993 8855
Fax: (81) 6 6993 8881
Web Site: www.estic.co.jp
Year Founded: 1993
6161—(TKS)
Sales Range: $25-49.9 Billion
Emp.: 70
Business Description:
Electric Power Tool Mfr & Whslr
S.I.C.: 3546
N.A.I.C.S.: 333991
Personnel:
Hiroshi Suzuki *(Pres & CEO)*
Isamu Isejima *(Mng Dir & Gen Mgr-Admin)*
Board of Directors:
Masashi Hashimoto
Yasuhiro Ikeda

ESTNATION INC.

6-10-2 Roppongi Minato-ku 1F-2F
Keyakizaka Complex Roppongi Hills
Tokyo, 106-0032, Japan
Tel.: (81) 3 5159 7800
E-Mail: info@estnation.co.jp
Web Site: www.estnation.co.jp
Year Founded: 2000
Sales Range: $25-49.9 Million
Emp.: 200
Business Description:
Clothing, Accessories, Sundries & Gift Items Retailer
S.I.C.: 5611
N.A.I.C.S.: 448110
Personnel:
Shunsuki Nagaoka *(CEO)*

ESTONIAN AIR A.S.

Lennujaama St 13
11101 Tallinn, Estonia
Tel.: (372) 6401101
Fax: (372) 6016092
E-Mail: ov@estonian-air.ee
Web Site: www.estonian-air.ee
Year Founded: 1991
Sales Range: $50-74.9 Million
Emp.: 347
Business Description:
Air Transportation Services
S.I.C.: 4522
N.A.I.C.S.: 481111
Personnel:
Andrus Aljas *(Deputy Chm & Pres)*
Rauno Barras *(Chief Comml Officer & VP-Comml)*
Board of Directors:
Andrus Aljas
Rauno Barras

Subsidiary:

AS Estonian Air Regional (1)
Lennujaama tee 13
11101 Tallinn, Estonia
Tel.: (372) 6401 101
Fax: (372) 6016 092
E-Mail: ov@estonian-air.ee
Emp.: 200
Air Transportation Services
S.I.C.: 4512
N.A.I.C.S.: 481111
Jan Palmer *(CEO)*

ESTORE CORPORATION

SumitomoSeimei Nishi-Shinbashi
Bldg 1-10-2 Nishi-Shinbashi Minato-ku
Tokyo, 105-0003, Japan
Tel.: (81) 3 3595 1106
Fax: (81) 3 3595 2711
Web Site: estore.co.jp
Year Founded: 1999
4304—(JAS)
Sls.: $65,582,000
Assets: $48,774,000
Liabilities: $25,454,000
Net Worth: $23,320,000
Earnings: $4,279,000
Fiscal Year-end: 03/31/13
Business Description:
Internet Related Services
S.I.C.: 4899
N.A.I.C.S.: 517919
Personnel:
Kenichi Ishimura *(Pres)*
Board of Directors:
Kenichi Ishimura
Fumiya Iwamura
Seiji Takasaki
Youichi Yanagida

ESTORIL SOL, SGPS, S.A.

Av Dr Stanley Ho Edificio do Casino Estoril
Estoril, 2765-190 Cascais, Portugal
Tel.: (351) 214667700
Fax: (351) 214667966
Web Site: www.estoril-solsgps.com
ESON—(EUR)
Rev.: $264,628,485
Assets: $311,261,970
Liabilities: $218,905,425
Net Worth: $92,356,545
Earnings: ($12,096,892)
Emp.: 883
Fiscal Year-end: 12/31/12
Business Description:
Investment Management Services
S.I.C.: 6282
N.A.I.C.S.: 523920
Personnel:
Stanley Hung Sun Ho *(Chm)*
Patrick Wing Ming Huen *(Deputy Chm)*
Mario Alberto Neves Assis Ferreira *(Deputy Chm)*
Carlos Alberto Francisco Farinha *(Sec)*
Board of Directors:
Stanley Hung Sun Ho
Antonio Jose de Melo Vieira Coelho
Miguel Antonio Dias Urbano de Magalhaes Queiroz
Vasco Esteves Fraga
Choi Man Hin
Pansy Catilina Chiu King Ho
Patrick Wing Ming Huen
Calvin ka Wing Chann
Mario Alberto Neves Assis Ferreira
Ambrose So
Jorge Armindo Teixeira

ESTRELLA GOLD CORPORATION

Suite 410 325 Howe Street
Vancouver, BC, V6C 1Z7, Canada
Tel.: (604) 687-3520
Fax: (604) 688-3392
Toll Free: (888) 889-4874
E-Mail: info@estrellagold.com
Web Site: www.estrellagold.com
Year Founded: 1996
EST—(TSXV)
Int. Income: $11,519
Assets: $5,688,461
Liabilities: $267,137
Net Worth: $5,421,324
Earnings: ($6,172,589)
Emp.: 20
Fiscal Year-end: 12/31/12
Business Description:
Gold Mining & Exploration Services
S.I.C.: 1041
N.A.I.C.S.: 212221
Personnel:
Gregory R. Harris *(Chm)*
John R. Wilson *(Pres & CEO)*
Winnie Wong *(CFO & Sec)*
Board of Directors:
Gregory R. Harris
Mark Thomas Brown
Fernando Pickmann
Donald R. Taylor

Non-U.S. Subsidiaries:

Anderson Peru Mining and Exploration S.A.C. (1)
Av Malecon Cisneros 1270 Int 1402
Lima, Miraflores, Peru
Tel.: (51) 1 1243 32 57
Mineral Resource Exploration Services
S.I.C.: 1481
N.A.I.C.S.: 213115

Compania Minera Canadian Shield Peru S.A.C. (1)
Calle Dos De Mayo No 472
Lima, Miraflores, Peru
Tel.: (51) 17196152
Fax: (51) 14461194
E-Mail:
Emp.: 4
Mineral Resource Exploration Services
S.I.C.: 1481
N.A.I.C.S.: 213115

ESTRELLA GROUP LTD

Number 7 Mill Pool Nash Lane
Belbroughton, Stourbridge, W
Midlands, DY9 9AF, United Kingdom
Tel.: (44) 1562 730871
Fax: (44) 1562 731919
E-Mail: steve.hayes@estrellagroup.co.uk
Web Site: www.estrellagroup.co.uk
Sales Range: $50-74.9 Million
Emp.: 270
Business Description:
Engineering Services
S.I.C.: 8711
N.A.I.C.S.: 541330
Personnel:
Steve Hayes *(Chm)*

ESTRELLA INTERNATIONAL ENERGY SERVICES LTD.

Carlos Pellegrini 1023 Piso 1st Floor
C1009ABU Buenos Aires, Argentina
Tel.: (54) 11 5217 5250
Fax: (54) 11 5217 5280
E-Mail: info@estrellasp.com
Web Site: www.estrellasp.com
Year Founded: 2007
EEN—(TSXV)
Rev.: $62,654,000
Assets: $123,745,000
Liabilities: $71,103,000
Net Worth: $52,642,000
Earnings: ($28,997,000)
Emp.: 439
Fiscal Year-end: 12/31/12
Business Description:
Investment Services
S.I.C.: 6211
N.A.I.C.S.: 523999
Personnel:
Carlos Valencia *(CEO)*
Javier Vedoya *(CFO)*

ESTRELLA RESOURCES LIMITED

Level 17 15 Castlereagh Street
Sydney, NSW, 2000, Australia
Mailing Address:
PO Box R514
Royal Exchange, Sydney, NSW, 1225, Australia
Tel.: (61) 2 9993 4475
Fax: (61) 2 9993 4433
E-Mail: admin@estrellaresources.com.au
Web Site: www.estrellaresources.com.au
ESR—(ASX)
Business Description:
Gold & Copper Mining
S.I.C.: 1041
N.A.I.C.S.: 212221
Personnel:
Gavin Solomon *(Chm)*
Jason Berton *(Mng Dir)*
Justin Clyne *(Sec)*
Board of Directors:
Gavin Solomon
Julian Bavin
Simon Kidston

Non-U.S. Subsidiary:

Estrella Resources (Chile) SpA (1)
Av Vitacura 5250 Oficina 802
Vitacura, Santiago, Chile
Tel.: (56) 2 242 1157
Fax: (56) 2 784 7401
Gold & Copper Mining
S.I.C.: 1041
N.A.I.C.S.: 212221
Juan Pablo Vargas de la Vega *(Gen Mgr)*

ESTSOFT CORP
Banpo-daero 3 Seocho-gu
Seoul, Korea (South) 137-867
Tel.: (82) 25834620
Fax: (82) 25834628
Web Site: www.estsoft.com
47560—(KRS)
Sls.: $29,128,530
Assets: $76,511,100
Liabilities: $49,788,480
Net Worth: $26,722,620
Earnings: ($7,277,250)
Emp.: 370
Fiscal Year-end: 12/31/12
Business Description:
Software Products
S.I.C.: 3652
N.A.I.C.S.: 334614
Personnel:
Jang Joong Kim *(CEO)*

ESUN HOLDINGS LIMITED
Yeung Kam Hoi 11th Fl Lai Sun
Commercial Centre
680 Cheung Sha Wan Rd
Kowloon, China (Hong Kong)
Tel.: (852) 27410391
Fax: (852) 27852775
E-Mail: advpr@laisun.com
Web Site: www.laisun.com
0571—(HKG)
Sales Range: $50-74.9 Million
Emp.: 270
Business Description:
Holding Company
S.I.C.: 6719
N.A.I.C.S.: 551112
Personnel:
Chee Keong Low *(Chm)*
Richard Siu Tsuen Lui *(CEO)*
Siu Man Kwok *(Sec)*
Board of Directors:
Chee Keong Low
Fook Aun Chew
Lester Hau Yin Lam
Peter Kin Ngok Lam
David Kwok Kwei Lo
Richard Siu Tsuen Lui
Carmen Lai Man Ng
Po Chu U
Andrew Y. Yan
Alfred Donald Yap
Legal Counsel:
Vincent T. K. Cheung, Yap & Co.
11th Floor Central Building 1-3 Pedder Street
Central, China (Hong Kong)
Richards Butler
20/F Alexandra House 16-20 Chater Road
Central, China (Hong Kong)
Tel.: (852) 2810 8008
Fax: (852) 2810 0664
Conyers Dill & Pearman
2901 One Exchange Square 8 Connaught Place
Central, China (Hong Kong)
Butterfield Fund Services (Bermuda) Limited
Rosebank Centre 11 Bermudiana Rd
Pembroke, Bermuda
Transfer Agents:
Tricor Tengis Limited
26/F Tesbury Centre, 28 Queens Road East
Hong Kong, China (Hong Kong)
Butterfield Fund Services (Bermuda) Limited
Rosebank Centre 11 Bermudiana Rd
Pembroke, Bermuda

Subsidiary:

Kadokawa Intercontinental Publishing (Asia) Ltd. (1)
Unit 1 20/F Wyler Center Phase 2 200 Tai Lin Pai Road
Kwai Chung, NT, China (Hong Kong)
Tel.: (852) 36532888
Fax: (852) 24181331
E-Mail: Contact_kipa@kadokawa.com.hk
Web Site: www.hongkongwalker.com
Emp.: 40
Entertainment Services
S.I.C.: 7812
N.A.I.C.S.: 512110

ESURE INSURANCE LTD.
The Observatory
Reigate, Surrey, RG2 0SG, United Kingdom
Tel.: (44) 1737 222222
Fax: (44) 1737 235000
E-Mail: pr@esure.com
Web Site: www.esure.com
Year Founded: 2000
Sales Range: $800-899.9 Million
Emp.: 1,500
Business Description:
Insurance Services
S.I.C.: 6411
N.A.I.C.S.: 524298
Personnel:
Peter Wood *(Founder & Exec Chm)*
Stuart Vann *(COO)*

ETA ELECTRIC INDUSTRY CO., LTD.
2-16-10 Hon-Haneda Ohta-Ku
Tokyo, 144-8611, Japan
Tel.: (81) 3 3745 7771
Fax: (81) 3 3745 2423
Web Site: www.eta.co.jp
Year Founded: 1979
6891—(JAS)
Sls.: $34,815,000
Assets: $48,939,000
Liabilities: $46,255,000
Net Worth: $2,684,000
Earnings: ($3,861,000)
Emp.: 87
Fiscal Year-end: 03/31/13
Business Description:
Customized Power Production & Sales
S.I.C.: 4939
N.A.I.C.S.: 221122
Personnel:
Hiroshi Kitagawa *(Chm)*
Hiroyuki Yamamoto *(Pres & CEO)*
Takashi Toshida *(COO)*
Board of Directors:
Hiroshi Kitagawa
Hiroshi Ishihara
Hiroshi Takahashi
Hiroyuki Yamamoto

Non-U.S. Subsidiary:

ETA-POWER EUROPE LTD. (1)
Sennweidstrasse 45
6312 Steinhausen, Switzerland
Tel.: (41) 41 747 0111
Fax: (41) 41 740 0122
Web Site: www.etapower.com
Power Conversion Device Mfr
S.I.C.: 3699
N.A.I.C.S.: 335999

U.S. Subsidiary:

ETA-USA Inc. (1)
16170 Vineyard Blvd Ste 180
Morgan Hill, CA 95037
Tel.: (408) 778-2793
Fax: (408) 779-2753
Toll Free: (800) 382-7697
E-Mail: info@eta-usa.com
Web Site: www.eta-usa.com
Electronic Equipment Mfr
S.I.C.: 3699
N.A.I.C.S.: 335999

ETABLISSEMENTS ALLIN
28 Rue De Cardurand
44600 Saint Nazaire, Loire Atlantique, France
Tel.: (33) 549350003
Fax: (33) 549350264
Web Site: www.allin.fr
Rev.: $22,200,000
Emp.: 100
Business Description:
Wood Products
S.I.C.: 2499
N.A.I.C.S.: 321999

ETABLISSEMENTS CHAZAUD
ZI N 2 Les Grands Danjons
2 Allee Evariste Galois, 18000
Bourges, France
Tel.: (33) 248505050
Sales Range: $10-24.9 Million
Emp.: 23
Business Description:
Meat Packing Plants
S.I.C.: 2011
N.A.I.C.S.: 311611
Personnel:
Herve Puigrenier *(Chm)*
Board of Directors:
Herve Puigrenier

ETABLISSEMENTS EMILE GEORGET
Z D''activite Tournebride Zone De Tournebride
57160 Metz, France
Tel.: (33) 549200088
Sales Range: $10-24.9 Million
Emp.: 64
Business Description:
New & Used Car Dealers
S.I.C.: 5511
N.A.I.C.S.: 441110
Personnel:
Focazanf Denes *(Pres)*

ETABLISSEMENTS EMILE LLAU
ZI du Couserans Voie Haussmann
09160 Caumont, France
Tel.: (33) 561044444
Fax: (33) 561044445
E-Mail: valerie.lau@saica.com
Sls.: $24,100,000
Emp.: 35
Business Description:
Scrap & Waste Materials
S.I.C.: 5093
N.A.I.C.S.: 423930
Personnel:
Valerie Llau *(Dir-Personnel & HR)*

ETABLISSEMENTS GASCHEAU
895 Rue Louis Saillant
26800 Portes-les-Valence, France
Tel.: (33) 475577074
Sales Range: $10-24.9 Million
Emp.: 168
Business Description:
Nonresidential Construction
S.I.C.: 1542
N.A.I.C.S.: 236220
Personnel:
Jean-Pierre Fernandes *(Chm)*
Board of Directors:
Jean-Pierre Fernandes
Jean-Louis Morel

ETABLISSEMENTS GOUTOULY ET FILS
Le Bearnais
47330 Saint-Quentin, France
Tel.: (33) 553368283
Sls.: $23,900,000
Emp.: 46
Business Description:
Canned Fruits & Specialties
S.I.C.: 2033
N.A.I.C.S.: 311421
Personnel:
Nadine Giroud *(DP Mgr)*
Board of Directors:
Mathieu Wincker

ETABLISSEMENTS MARTINENQ
2 rue Georges Charpak
ZAC Universite Gare, 77127
Lieusaint, France
Tel.: (33) 1 60 188900
Fax: (33) 1 60 188901
E-Mail: impmartinenq@martinenq.com
Web Site: www.martinenq.com
Year Founded: 1921
Rev.: $20,800,000
Emp.: 120
Business Description:
Commercial Printing
S.I.C.: 2759
N.A.I.C.S.: 323111
Personnel:
Jean-Christophe Martinenq *(Dir Gen)*

ETABLISSEMENTS MAUREL & PROM S.A.
51 rue d'Anjou
75008 Paris, France
Tel.: (33) 1 53 83 16 00
Fax: (33) 1 53 83 16 05
Web Site: www.maureletprom.fr
Year Founded: 1813
MAU—(EUR)
Sls.: $635,532,242
Assets: $2,212,391,356
Liabilities: $1,175,899,687
Net Worth: $1,036,491,669
Earnings: $77,971,513
Emp.: 341
Fiscal Year-end: 12/31/12
Business Description:
Oil & Gas Exploration Services
S.I.C.: 1389
N.A.I.C.S.: 213112
Personnel:
Jean-Francois Henin *(Chm)*
Michel Hochard *(CFO)*
Board of Directors:
Jean-Francois Henin
Gerard Andreck
Xavier Blandin
Emmanuel de Marion de Glatigny
Nathalie Delapalme
Roman Gozalo
A. B. C. Orjiako
Alexandre Vilgrain

Non-U.S. Subsidiary:

Panther Eureka Srl (1)
Viale Dei Platani 34/B
97100 Ragusa, Italy
Tel.: (39) 0932251892
Fax: (39) 0932259514
Emp.: 2
Gas Exploration Services
S.I.C.: 1389
N.A.I.C.S.: 213112
Jean-Francois Henin, *(Chm & CEO)*

ETABLISSEMENTS R. BLANCHET
17 rue de l'Esperance
Les Hautes Rivieres, 08800
Charleville-Mezieres, France
Tel.: (33) 254310182
Fax: (33) 254311030
Sales Range: $10-24.9 Million

Etablissements R. Blanchet—(Continued)

Emp.: 141
Business Description:
Trucking, Except Local
S.I.C.: 4213
N.A.I.C.S.: 484121
Personnel:
Emmanuelle Pilon *(Mng Partner)*

ETABLISSEMENTS R. LEGRAND
91 Rue Jean Chossegros
69270 Lyon, France
Tel.: (33) 478222696
Rev.: $23,500,000
Emp.: 188
Business Description:
Water, Sewer & Utility Lines
S.I.C.: 1623
N.A.I.C.S.: 237110
Personnel:
Michel Gros *(Pres)*

ETABLISSEMENTS ROCHE ET COMPAGNIE
105 Rue Basse Saint Martin
16100 Cognac, Charente, France
Tel.: (33) 478788210
Sales Range: $10-24.9 Million
Emp.: 216
Business Description:
Painting & Paper Hanging
S.I.C.: 1721
N.A.I.C.S.: 238320
Personnel:
Patrick Roche *(Chm)*

ETALON GROUP LIMITED
Ogier House St Julian's Avenue
Saint Peter Port, Guernsey GY1 1WA
Tel.: (44) 20 8123 1328
Fax: (44) 20 8123 1328
E-Mail: info@etalongroup.com
Web Site: www.etalongroup.com
Year Founded: 1987
ETLN—(LSE)
Rev.: $889,384,580
Assets: $2,431,174,120
Liabilities: $1,172,430,710
Net Worth: $1,258,743,410
Earnings: $165,350,000
Emp.: 4,000
Fiscal Year-end: 12/31/12
Business Description:
Real Estate Development Services
S.I.C.: 6531
N.A.I.C.S.: 531390
Personnel:
Viacheslav Zarenkov *(Co-Founder, Chm & Pres)*
Dmitri Zarenkov *(Co-Founder & First VP)*
Anton Evdokimov *(CFO)*
Board of Directors:
Viacheslav Zarenkov
Dmitri Boulkhoukov
Michael John Calvey
Martin Cocker
Anton Evdokimov
Alexei Kalinin
Anton Poriadine
Boris Svetlichniy
Peter Touzeau
Dmitri Zarenkov

ETALON-LENSPETSSMU CONSTRUCTION HOLDING COMPANY
2 lit a Bogatyrskiy Prospect
Saint Petersburg, 197348, Russia
Tel.: (7) 812 3493840
Fax: (7) 8123800529
Web Site: www.finance.lenspecsmu.ru
Sales Range: $550-599.9 Million
Business Description:
Holding Company; Real Estate Services
S.I.C.: 6719
N.A.I.C.S.: 551112
Personnel:
Viacheslav A. Zarenkov *(Chm)*
Dmitry V. Zarenkov *(Pres & CEO)*
Anton V. Evdokimov *(CFO & VP)*

ETAM DEVELOPPEMENT SCA
(d/b/a Etam Groupe)
78 rue de Rivoli
75004 Paris, France
Tel.: (33) 1 55 90 70 70
Fax: (33) 1 55 90 79 26
Web Site: www.etamdeveloppement.fr
TAM—(EUR)
Sls.: $1,638,235,043
Assets: $1,367,902,568
Liabilities: $947,093,865
Net Worth: $420,808,703
Earnings: $18,060,217
Emp.: 19,147
Fiscal Year-end: 12/31/12
Business Description:
Women's Clothing Mfr & Retailer
S.I.C.: 2389
N.A.I.C.S.: 315240
Personnel:
Laurent Milchior *(Gen Partner & Mgr)*
Pierre Milchior *(Gen Partner & Mgr)*
Marie-Claire Tarica *(Gen Partner & Mgr)*
Vanessa Milchior *(Gen Partner)*

Constantin Associes
185 Avenue Charles-de-Gaulle
Neuilly-sur-Seine, France

Non-U.S. Subsidiary:

Etam Italia Srl **(1)**
Centro Direzionale Colleoni Palazzo Andromeda 2
20041 Agrate Brianza, Italy
Tel.: (39) 039 68 92 236
Web Site: www.etam.it
Women's Clothing Retailer
S.I.C.: 5621
N.A.I.C.S.: 448120

ETEC E&C LIMITED
2-5Fl Jei Tower 538 Sinsa Dong
Gangnam Gu
Seoul, Korea (South)
Tel.: (82) 25105600
Fax: (82) 25105824
E-Mail: kele@etecenc.com
Web Site: www.etecenc.com
Year Founded: 1967
016250—(KRS)
Sls.: $730,554,060
Assets: $443,533,740
Liabilities: $274,535,070
Net Worth: $168,998,670
Earnings: $18,431,670
Emp.: 380
Fiscal Year-end: 12/31/12
Business Description:
Construction Services
S.I.C.: 1629
N.A.I.C.S.: 237990
Personnel:
Bok-Young Lee *(Chm)*
Chang-Suk Oh *(Pres)*

ETEM SA
1-4, Iroom Politechniou Str
19018 Magoula, Attica, Greece
Tel.: (30) 2104898605
Fax: (30) 2104898500
E-Mail: etem@etem.gr
Web Site: www.etem.gr
ETEM—(ATH)
Sales Range: $125-149.9 Million
Emp.: 939
Business Description:
Extruded Aluminum Products Mfr
S.I.C.: 3355
N.A.I.C.S.: 331318
Personnel:
Markos Kallergis *(Chm)*
Dimitrios Pavlakis *(Vice Chm & Mng Dir)*
Grigorios Symeonidis *(Quality Control Officer)*
Board of Directors:
Markos Kallergis
Antonios Kallergis
Ioannis Oikonomou
Charalambos Papanicolaou
Dimitrios Pavlakis
Efstathios Striber

Plant:

Etem SA - OINOFYTA PLANT **(1)**
Madaro
32011 Oinofita, Viotia, Greece
Tel.: (30) 2262053584
Fax: (30) 22620 53560
Web Site: www.etem.gr/default.asp?siteid=1&pageid=71&langID=2
Composite Panels Mfr
S.I.C.: 3999
N.A.I.C.S.: 339999

Non-U.S. Subsidiaries:

Alu Build S.R.L **(1)**
Via C Carra 64
Zona Ind Corte Tegge, 42100 Reggio nell'Emilia, Italy (100%)
Tel.: (39) 0522941218
Fax: (39) 0522941264
E-Mail: info@alubuild.it
Web Site: www.alubuild.it/fiere.php
Metal Service Centers & Offices
S.I.C.: 5051
N.A.I.C.S.: 423510

Etem Scg **(1)**
Marsala Tita 206
Dobanovci, Belgrade, Serbia (100%)
Tel.: (381) 112696117
Web Site: www.etem.gr/default.asp?siteID=3&pageid=49&langid=2
Aluminum Extruded Product Mfr
S.I.C.: 3354
N.A.I.C.S.: 331318

ETEM SYSTEMS LLC **(1)**
7 Zdolbunivska Street
02081 Kiev, Ukraine
Tel.: (380) 44 499 07 87
Fax: (380) 44 499 07 86
Aluminum Extruded Product Mfr
S.I.C.: 3355
N.A.I.C.S.: 331318

Etem Systems S.R.L. **(1)**
Str Prelungirea Giurgiului nr 33 A
Loc Jilava Jud Llfon, Bucharest, Romania (51%)
Tel.: (40) 214570176
Fax: (40) 214570176
E-Mail: office@steelmet.ro
Web Site: www.etem.gr/default.asp?siteID=1&langID=2&pageID=65
Aluminum Extruded Product Mfr
S.I.C.: 3354
N.A.I.C.S.: 331318

MOPPETS LTD. **(1)**
77 Queens Road
PO12 1LG Gosport, Hampshire, United Kingdom
Tel.: (44) 23 9252 2941
Child Day Care Services
S.I.C.: 8351
N.A.I.C.S.: 624410

ETERNAL BEST INDUSTRIAL LIMITED
(d/b/a Eternal Best Industries)
Room F 16th Floor Block 2 Sheung Shui Centre
Sheung Shui New Territories, Kowloon, China (Hong Kong)
Tel.: (852) 26722348
Fax: (852) 2668 1230
Business Description:
Holding Company
S.I.C.: 6719
N.A.I.C.S.: 551112

Non-U.S. Holding:

Shelly's Shoes Limited **(1)**
6th Floor 4 Great Portland Street
London, W1W 8QJ, United Kingdom UK (100%)
Tel.: (44) 2033262590
Fax: (44) 2073236864
E-Mail: info@shellys.com
Web Site: www.shellys.com
Sales Range: $1-9.9 Million
Emp.: 5
Women's Shoes & Accessories Retailer
S.I.C.: 5661
N.A.I.C.S.: 448210
Lynsey Hand *(Mng Dir)*

ETERNAL CHEMICAL CO., LTD.
578 Chien-Kung Rd
807 Kaohsiung, Taiwan
Tel.: (886) 73838181
Fax: (886) 73830816
Web Site: www.eternal.com.tw
1717—(TAI)
Sales Range: $550-599.9 Million
Business Description:
Electronic Chemical Materials & Special Chemicals Mfr
S.I.C.: 3541
N.A.I.C.S.: 333517
Personnel:
Kuo-Lun Kao *(Chm)*

Plants:

Eternal Chemical Co., Ltd. - PING-NAN Plant **(1)**
23 Pingnan Road Ping-Nan Industrial Park
Fang-liao, Pingtung, 940, Taiwan
Tel.: (886) 88669009
Fax: (886) 88669808
Web Site: www.eternal.com.tw/en/service_1_1.html
Synthetic Resins Mfr
S.I.C.: 2821
N.A.I.C.S.: 325211

Eternal Chemical Co., Ltd. - TA-FA Plant **(1)**
30 Yumin St Ta-Fa Industrial Pk
Taliao, Kaohsiung, 831, Taiwan
Tel.: (886) 77873645
Fax: (886) 77707167
Web Site: www.eternal.com.tw/en/service_1_5.html
Emp.: 400
Dry Film Photoresist Mfr
S.I.C.: 3861
N.A.I.C.S.: 325992
Johnny Liao *(Mgr)*

U.S. Subsidiaries:

Eternal Technology Corporation **(1)**
1800 Touchstone Rd
Colonial Heights, VA 23834
Tel.: (804) 524-8555
Fax: (804) 524-8556
Web Site: www.eternal.com.tw
Emp.: 40
Dry Film Photoresist Distr
S.I.C.: 5044
N.A.I.C.S.: 423420
Jim Tesimale *(Mgr-Logistics & Distr)*

Non-U.S. Subsidiaries:

Changhe International Trading (GZFTZ) Co,. Ltd. **(1)**
Floor 1 1st Building Scientech Park
Chuangyie Road GETDD
Guangzhou, Guangdong, 510730, China
Tel.: (86) 2082221885
Fax: (86) 2082221884
Web Site: www.eternal-group.com
Copper Clad Laminates & Speciality Chemicals Mfr
S.I.C.: 3861

N.A.I.C.S.: 325992

ESCO Specialty Coatings (Guangzhou) Co., Ltd. (1)
182 Junda Road Eastern Zone GETDD
Guangzhou, Guangdong, 510530, China
Tel.: (86) 20 2820 7118
Fax: (86) 20 2820 7001
Web Site: www.eternal.com.tw/en/service_3_ch.html#00
Specialty Chemical Coating Services
S.I.C.: 3479
N.A.I.C.S.: 332812

Eternal Chemical (Guangdong) Co., Ltd. (1)
Dalang Bay Industrial Zone
Nanshui Town, Zhuhai, Guangdong, 519050, China
Tel.: (86) 756 726 5566
Fax: (86) 756 398 5577
Web Site: www.eternal.com.tw/en/service_3_ch.html#00
Emp.: 200
Resins Mfr
S.I.C.: 2821
N.A.I.C.S.: 325211
King Huang *(Mgr)*

Eternal Chemical (Guangzhou) Co., Ltd. (1)
Fl 2 1st Bldg Scientech Pk Chuangyie Rd GETDD
Guangzhou, Guangdong, 510730, China
Tel.: (86) 2082221885
Fax: (86) 2082221884
Web Site: www.eternal.com.tw/en/service_3_ch.html#00
Emp.: 400
Dry Film Photoresist Mfr
S.I.C.: 3861
N.A.I.C.S.: 325992

Eternal Chemical (Japan) Co., Ltd. (1)
Kijmon Building 5F 6-26-9 Haramachida
Machida, Tokyo, 194-0013, Japan
Tel.: (81) 427241745
Fax: (81) 427298039
E-Mail: aya@eternailj.com
Emp.: 6
Resins Mfr
S.I.C.: 2821
N.A.I.C.S.: 325211
Abba Yo *(Mgr-Mktg)*

Eternal Electronic Material (Thailand) Co., Ltd. (1)
335/8 Moo 9 T Bangchalong
Bang Phli, Samut Prakan, 10540, Thailand
Tel.: (66) 27509086
Fax: (66) 27509096
Industrial Chemicals Mfr
S.I.C.: 2911
N.A.I.C.S.: 324110

Eternal Optical Material (Suzhou) Co., Ltd. (1)
111 Songshan Road SND
Suzhou, Jiangsu, China
Tel.: (86) 51268050026
Fax: (86) 51268050025
Web Site: www.eternal.com.tw/en/service_3_ch.html#00
Optical Materials Mfr
S.I.C.: 3827
N.A.I.C.S.: 333314

Eternal Photoelectric Material Industry (Yingkou) Co., Ltd. (1)
1 East Xinlian Street Yingkou Coastal Industrial Base
Yingkou, Liaoning, 115000, China
Tel.: (86) 51257663857
Fax: (86) 512 5766 8779
Web Site: www.eternal-group.com
Industrial Chemicals Mfr
S.I.C.: 2869
N.A.I.C.S.: 325199

Eternal Specialty Chemical (Zhuhai) Co., Ltd. (1)
Biyang Road Gaolan Petrochemical Sector of Harbor Industrial Zone
Zhuhai, Guangdong, 519060, China
Tel.: (86) 7563985888
Fax: (86) 756 398 5111
Web Site: www.eternal.com.tw/en/service_3_ch.html#00
Monomer Specialty & OPV Mfr
S.I.C.: 2821
N.A.I.C.S.: 325211

Eternal Technologies (Shanghai) Co., Ltd. (1)
1397 Yishan Rd
Shanghai, 200233, China
Tel.: (86) 2164016000
Fax: (86) 2164063225
Web Site: www.eternal.com.tw/en/service_3_ch.html#00
Chemicals Research & Development Services
S.I.C.: 8731
N.A.I.C.S.: 541711

Nichigo-Morton Company, Ltd. (1)
3F Chokokan16 3 Nakamachi 1chome
Machida-shi, Osaka, 194-0021, Japan JP
Tel.: (81) 42 722 7310
Fax: (81) 42 722 7320
Web Site: www.nichigo-morton.co.jp
Emp.: 75
Printed Circuit Boards Mfr
S.I.C.: 3679
N.A.I.C.S.: 334418

ETERNIT S.A.

Rua Dr Fernandes Coelho 85 8
Andar Pinheiros
05423 040 Sao Paulo, Brazil
Tel.: (55) 1130383838
Fax: (55) 1138162782
E-Mail: ri@eternit.com.br
Web Site: www.eternit.com.br
ETER3—(BRAZ OTC)
Sales Range: $450-499.9 Million
Emp.: 1,672

Business Description:
Construction Materials Mfr
S.I.C.: 3271
N.A.I.C.S.: 327331

Personnel:
Sergio Alexandre Melleiro *(Chm)*
Elio Antonio Martins *(Chm-Exec Bd & Dir-IR)*

Board of Directors:
Sergio Alexandre Melleiro
Victor Adler
Marcelo Munhoz Auricchio
Guilherme Affonso Ferreira
Luiz Barsi Filho
Mario Fleck
Elio Antonio Martins
Lirio Albino Parisotto
Luis Terepins

Subsidiaries:

Precon Goias Industrial Ltda. (1)
Distrito Indus de Anapolis
Quadra Anapolis, Goias, Brazil
Tel.: (55) 62 3328 4444
Fax: (55) 62 3328 4412
Asbestos Cement Sheets Mfr
S.I.C.: 3299
N.A.I.C.S.: 327999

Sama S.A. (1)
Cana Brava Mine
PO Box 01
76450000 Minacu, Goias, Brazil
Tel.: (55) 62 3379 8100
Fax: (55) 62 3379 8181
E-Mail: sama@sama.com.br
Web Site: www.sama.com.br
Emp.: 530
Asbestos Mining Services
S.I.C.: 1499
N.A.I.C.S.: 212399
Wagener Calvo *(Gen Mgr)*

ETERNITY HEALTHCARE INC.

8755 Ash Street Suite 1
Vancouver, BC, V6P 6T3, Canada
Tel.: (855) 324-1110
Web Site: www.eternityhealthcare.com
Year Founded: 2009
ETAH—(OTC)
Sls.: $16,175
Assets: $189,605
Liabilities: $767,211
Net Worth: ($577,606)
Earnings: ($252,039)
Emp.: 1
Fiscal Year-end: 04/30/13

Business Description:
In-Home Medical Diagnostic Kits Mfr & Distr
S.I.C.: 3841
N.A.I.C.S.: 339112

Personnel:
Hassan Salari *(Chm, Pres, CEO, CFO, Treas & Sec)*

Board of Directors:
Hassan Salari
Dominique F. Borrelly
Bin Huang

Transfer Agent:
Island Stock Transfer
15500 Roosevelt Blvd Ste 301
Clearwater, FL 33760

ETHANE PIPELINE INCOME FUND

Locked Bag A14
Sydney, NSW, 1235, Australia
Tel.: (61) 282807106
Fax: (61) 292870303
Web Site: www.ethanepipeline.com.au
EPX—(ASX)
Rev.: $27,853,249
Assets: $94,879,037
Liabilities: $13,620,247
Net Worth: $81,258,790
Earnings: $8,320,126
Fiscal Year-end: 06/30/13

Business Description:
Investors Service
S.I.C.: 6799
N.A.I.C.S.: 523910

Personnel:
Mark T. Knapman *(Sec)*

Board of Directors:
Robert J. Wright
Rick Coles
Nancy Fox

ETHANOL TECHNOLOGIES LIMITED

73-81 Lannercost St
Ingham, QLD, 4850, Australia
Tel.: (61) 747765300
Fax: (61) 747765392
Web Site: www.ethtec.com.au

Business Description:
Ethanol Fuel Mfr
S.I.C.: 2869
N.A.I.C.S.: 325193

Personnel:
Robert Carey *(Chm)*
Russell Reeves *(Mng Dir)*

ETHERSTACK PLC

1st Floor 80 Abercrombie Street
Sydney, NSW, 2008, Australia
Tel.: (61) 2 8399 7500
Fax: (61) 2 8399 7507
Web Site: www.etherstack.com
ESK—(ASX)

Business Description:
Radio & Wireless Communications Software
S.I.C.: 7372
N.A.I.C.S.: 511210

Personnel:
David Deacon *(CEO)*

ETHIAS INSURANCE

Rue des Croisiers 24
Liege, 4000, Belgium
Tel.: (32) 42203111
Fax: (32) 42203005
E-Mail: info@ethias.be
Web Site: www.ethias.be
Sales Range: $1-4.9 Billion
Emp.: 1,800

Business Description:
Insurance
S.I.C.: 6411
N.A.I.C.S.: 524210

Personnel:
Bernard Thiry *(Gen Dir)*

Board of Directors:
Eric Ancion
Jean-Paul Parmentier
Dirk van Berlaer

Subsidiary:

Nateus NV (1)
Posthofbrug 16
2600 Antwerp, Belgium
Tel.: (32) 32473511
Fax: (32) 473590
E-Mail: info@nateus.be
Web Site: www.nateus.be
Life Insurance Carrier
S.I.C.: 6311
N.A.I.C.S.: 524113
Hans Verstraete *(Pres)*

ETHIOPIAN AIRLINES ENTERPRISE

Bole International Airport
PO Box 1755
Addis Ababa, 1755, Ethiopia
Tel.: (251) 116652222
Fax: (251) 11611474
E-Mail: Publicrelations@ethiopianairlines.com
Web Site: www.ethiopianairlines.com
Year Founded: 1945
Sales Range: $350-399.9 Million
Emp.: 4,587

Business Description:
Airline Services
S.I.C.: 4512
N.A.I.C.S.: 481111

Personnel:
Tewolde Gebremariam *(CEO)*
Kassim Geressu *(CFO)*
Mesfin Tassew *(COO)*
Kemeredin Bedru *(CIO)*
Gobena Michael *(Chief Comml Officer)*
Rahel Zerihun *(VP & Gen Counsel)*
Essayas Wolde Mariam *(Sr VP-Sls)*

ETHIOPIAN POTASH CORP.

200 Bay Street Suite 3800
Royal Bank Plaza South Tower,
Toronto, ON, M5J 2Z4, Canada
Tel.: (416) 907-9422
Fax: (416) 848-1768
Web Site: www.ethiopianpotash.com
FED—(OTC TSXV)
Assets: $83,243
Liabilities: $3,813,807
Net Worth: ($3,730,564)
Earnings: ($46,189,613)
Emp.: 6
Fiscal Year-end: 09/30/12

Business Description:
Potash Mining Services
S.I.C.: 1474
N.A.I.C.S.: 212391

Personnel:
George Roach *(Chm & CEO)*
Michael Galloro *(CFO)*

Board of Directors:
George Roach
Paul DesLauriers
Michael Galloro
Pamela Hueston
Antonino Vella
Binh Vu

Ethiopian Potash Corp.—(Continued)

Transfer Agent:
Olympia Trust Company
1900 925 W Georgia Street
Vancouver, BC, V6C 3L2, Canada

ETHOS GOLD CORP.

Suite 480 - 789 West Pender Street
Vancouver, BC, V6C 1H2, Canada
Tel.: (604) 682-4750
Fax: (604) 682-4809
E-Mail: info@ethosgold.com
Web Site: www.ethosgold.com
ECC—(OTC TSXV)
Rev.: $252,766
Assets: $9,236,127
Liabilities: $91,547
Net Worth: $9,144,579
Earnings: ($8,234,988)
Fiscal Year-end: 12/31/12
Business Description:
Gold Mining Services
S.I.C.: 1041
N.A.I.C.S.: 212221
Personnel:
Gary R. Freeman *(Pres & CEO)*
Peter G. Wong *(CFO)*
Dayna Leigh *(Sec)*
Board of Directors:
Mark D. Cruise
Gary R. Freeman
Peter Mordaunt
Chris Theodoropoulos
Hendrick Van Alphen
Godfrey J. Walton
Legal Counsel:
Bull, Housser & Tupper LLP
3000 Royal Centre, 1055 West Georgia Street
Vancouver, BC, V6E 3R3, Canada
Tel.: (604) 687-6575
Fax: (604) 641-4949
Transfer Agent:
Computershare Investor Services Inc.
3rd Floor 510 Burrard Street
Vancouver, BC, Canada

ETHOS PRIVATE EQUITY (PROPRIETARY) LIMITED

35 Fricker Road
Illovo, 2196, South Africa
Mailing Address:
PO Box 9773
Johannesburg, 2000, South Africa
Tel.: (27) 11 328 7400
Fax: (27) 11 328 7410
Web Site: www.ethos.co.za
Year Founded: 1984
Business Description:
Private Equity Firm
S.I.C.: 6211
N.A.I.C.S.: 523999
Personnel:
Andre Roux *(CEO & Partner)*
Craig Dreyer *(CFO & Partner)*
Ngalaah Chuphi *(Partner & Head-IR)*
Bill Ashmore *(Partner)*
Garry Boyd *(Partner)*
Anthonie de Beer *(Partner)*
Stuart MacKenzie *(Partner)*
Christo Roos *(Partner)*
Shaun Zagnoev *(Partner)*
Board of Directors:
Peter Mageza
Garry Boyd
Ngalaah Chuphi
Craig Dreyer
Kelly Moylan
Andre Roux

Joint Ventures:

Universal Industries Corporation (Pty) Limited **(1)**
16 Precision Street
Kyasand
2125 Randburg, South Africa
Tel.: (27) 114622130
Fax: (27) 114622621
E-Mail: darylp@insulated.co.za
Web Site: www.universalindustries.co.za
Sales Range: $100-124.9 Million
Emp.: 790
Display Cases & Polyurethane Insulated Panels Mfr
S.I.C.: 5078
N.A.I.C.S.: 423740
Daryl Paynter *(CEO)*

Subsidiaries:

Colcab (Pty) Ltd. **(2)**
Buttskop Rd
Blackheath, 7580 Cape Town, Western Province, South Africa
Tel.: (27) 219072800
Fax: (27) 219072850
E-Mail: info.cpt@colcabct.co.za
Web Site: www.colcab.co.za
Emp.: 250
Refrigerated Display Cabinets Mfr
S.I.C.: 3585
N.A.I.C.S.: 333415
Ivor Morgan *(CEO)*

Insulated Structures (1989) (Pty) Limited **(2)**
16 Precision St Kya Sands
Randburg, Johannesburg, Gauteng, South Africa
Tel.: (27) 114622130
Fax: (27) 114622621
E-Mail: sales@insulated.co.za
Web Site: www.insulatedstructures.co.za
Emp.: 150
Panels & Refrigerated Cabinets Mfr & Supplier
S.I.C.: 3585
N.A.I.C.S.: 333415
Mike Constable *(Dir-Sls)*

Macadams International (Pty) Ltd. **(2)**
Macadams Bus Park School St
Blackheath, Cape Town, Western Cape, 7581, South Africa
Tel.: (27) 219071000
Fax: (27) 219071111
E-Mail: info@macadams.co.za
Web Site: www.macadams.co.za
Emp.: 300
Bakery Equipment Mfr & Supplier
S.I.C.: 3556
N.A.I.C.S.: 333241
Karien Donnelly *(Mgr-Food Production)*

Waco International Ltd. **(1)**
No 2 Harrowdene Office Park
128 Western Services Road, Woodmead, 2148, South Africa ZA
Mailing Address:
Private Bag X23
Gallo Manor, 2052, South Africa
Tel.: (27) 11 461 1400
Fax: (27) 11 4611450
Web Site: www.wacointernational.com
Sales Range: $750-799.9 Million
Emp.: 4,000
Holding Company; Scaffolding & Modular Building Mfr & Contractor Services
S.I.C.: 6719
N.A.I.C.S.: 551112
Stephen J. M. Goodburn *(CEO)*
Mark R. Towler *(Sec)*

Subsidiary:

Waco Africa Pty. Ltd. **(2)**
181 Barbara Road Cnr Barbara & Tunney Roads
Elandsfontein, Gauteng, South Africa ZA
Mailing Address:
PO Box 669
Isando, Gauteng, 1600, South Africa
Tel.: (27) 118424000
Fax: (27) 118424280
E-Mail: info@wacoafrica.co.za
Web Site: www.wacoafrica.co.za
Holding Company; Formwork, Shoring & Scaffolding Products
S.I.C.: 6719
N.A.I.C.S.: 551112
Stephen J.M. Goodburn *(Chm)*
Michael Graham Els *(CEO)*

Non-U.S. Subsidiary:

Waco UK Limited **(2)**
Catfoss Lane
Brandesburton, Driffield, E Yorkshire, YO25 8EJ, United Kingdom UK
Tel.: (44) 1964 545 000
Fax: (44) 1964 545 054
E-Mail: sales@waco.co.uk
Web Site: www.waco.co.uk
Sales Range: $50-74.9 Million
Emp.: 300
Commercial & Institutional Modular Buildings Mfr
S.I.C.: 1542
N.A.I.C.S.: 236220
Eugenio de Sa *(Mng Dir)*

ETI ELEKTROELEMENT, D.D.

(d/b/a ETI, d.d.)
Obrezija 5
1411 Izlake, Slovenia
Tel.: (386) 35657570
Fax: (386) 35673629
E-Mail: eti@eti.si
Web Site: www.eti.si
Year Founded: 1950
Sales Range: $50-74.9 Million
Emp.: 1,860
Business Description:
Electrical Equipment & Supplies
S.I.C.: 3548
N.A.I.C.S.: 333992
Personnel:
Marjan Kramar *(Chm-Supervisory Bd)*
Tomaz Berginc *(Pres & CEO)*
Maja Opresnik-Kovacic *(CFO)*
Supervisory Board of Directors:
Marjan Kramar
Martina Oberzan

Subsidiaries:

ETI Gum d.o.o. **(1)**
Obrezija 5
1145 Izlake, Slovenia
Tel.: (386) 35657590
Fax: (386) 35674195
E-Mail: etigum@eti.si
Web Site: www.etigum.si
Emp.: 71
Plastic Products Mfr
S.I.C.: 3089
N.A.I.C.S.: 326199
Thomas Balginc *(Mng Dir)*

Non-U.S. Subsidiaries:

ETI B **(1)**
Pancevacki put 85
11210 Belgrade, Serbia
Tel.: (381) 112712943
Fax: (381) 112711220
Web Site: www.etigroup.eu
Electrical Equipment & Supplies
S.I.C.: 3699
N.A.I.C.S.: 335999

ETI DE GmbH **(1)**
Dorfwiesenweg 13
63828 Kleinkahl, Bavaria, Germany
Tel.: (49) 6024639710
Fax: (49) 6024639729
E-Mail: roland.glaab@eti-de.de
Web Site: www.eti-de.de/kontakt.aspx
Electrical Equipment & Supplies
S.I.C.: 3699
N.A.I.C.S.: 335999
Roland Glaab *(Mng Dir)*

ETI ELB s.r.o. **(1)**
Potocna 42
District of Pezinok, 90084 Bahon, Bratislava Region, Slovakia
Tel.: (421) 3364552
Fax: (421) 336455139
E-Mail: etielb@etielb.sk
Web Site: www.eti.szm.sk/index6.html
Emp.: 73
Switchgear & Switchboard Apparatus Mfr
S.I.C.: 3613
N.A.I.C.S.: 335313

ETI Polam Sp.zo.o. **(1)**
ul Jana Pawla II 18
06 100 Warsaw, Poland
Tel.: (48) 236919300
Fax: (48) 236919360
E-Mail: etipolam@etipolam.com.pl
Web Site: www.etipolam.com.pl
Sales Range: $1-9.9 Million
Emp.: 100
Electrical Apparatus & Equipment Whslr
S.I.C.: 5063
N.A.I.C.S.: 423610

ETI Sarajevo d.o.o. **(1)**
Hifzi Bjelevca 13
71 000 Sarajevo, Bosnia & Herzegovina
Tel.: (387) 33775250
Fax: (387) 33 45 20 94
E-Mail: etisa@bih.net.ba
Web Site: www.etigroup.eu/concern_eti/organization_of_concern/subsidiaries.aspx
Electrical Equipment & Supplies
S.I.C.: 3699
N.A.I.C.S.: 335999

ETI Ukraine Ltd. **(1)**
19 Tupoleva Str of 214
Kiev, Ukraine
Tel.: (380) 44 494 2180
Fax: (380) 44 494 2182
E-Mail: office@eti.ua
Web Site: www.eti.ua
Electrical Equipment & Supplies
S.I.C.: 5063
N.A.I.C.S.: 423610

ETIBALTUS UAB **(1)**
Tilzes 41a
47187 Kaunas, Lithuania
Tel.: (370) 37261582
Fax: (370) 37261583
E-Mail: info@etibaltus.lt
Web Site: www.etibaltus.lt
Emp.: 4
Electrical Equipment & Supplies
S.I.C.: 5063
N.A.I.C.S.: 423610
Rumunas Gumis *(Mng Dir)*

ETIHAD AIRWAYS P.J.S.C.

Khailfa City A
PO Box 35566
Abu Dhabi, United Arab Emirates
Tel.: (971) 25110000
Fax: (971) 25111200
Web Site: www.etihadairways.com
Year Founded: 2003
Sales Range: $1-4.9 Billion
Emp.: 9,000
Business Description:
Air Transportation Services
S.I.C.: 4512
N.A.I.C.S.: 481111
Personnel:
Hamed bin Zayad Al Nahyan *(Chm)*
Khaled bin Zayed Al Nahyan *(Vice Chm)*
James Hogan *(Pres & CEO)*
James Rigney *(CFO)*
Richard Hill *(COO)*
Peter Baumgartner *(Chief Comml Officer)*
Ray Gammell *(Chief People & Performance Officer)*
Juliana Kfouri *(Sr VP-Corp Strategy & Special Projects)*
James Mueller *(Sr VP-Sls)*
Gordon Penfold *(Sr VP-IT)*
Board of Directors:
Hamed bin Zayad Al Nahyan
Mohamed Mubarak Fadel Al Mazrouie
Mubarak Hamad Al Muhairy
Khaled bin Zayed Al Nahyan
Ahmed Ali Al Sayegh
Hamad Abdullah Al Shamsi
Khalifa Sultan Al Suwaidi

ETIHAD ETISALAT COMPANY

26th Floor The Kingdom Tower
PO Box 9979
Riyadh, 11423, Saudi Arabia
Tel.: (966) 560314099
Fax: (966) 560316605

E-Mail: investorcontact@mobily.com.sa
Web Site: www.mobily.com.sa
7020—(SAU)
Rev.: $6,295,900,018
Assets: $10,285,330,997
Liabilities: $4,718,122,849
Net Worth: $5,567,208,149
Earnings: $1,602,500,994
Fiscal Year-end: 12/31/12
Business Description:
Mobile Network Service Providers
S.I.C.: 3663
N.A.I.C.S.: 334220
Personnel:
Abdulaziz Saleh Alsaghyir *(Chm)*
Khaled Omar Al Kaf *(CEO & Mng Dir)*
Thamer Al Hosani *(CFO)*
Nasser Al Nasser *(COO)*
Medhat Amer *(CIO)*
Karl Michael Henneking *(CMO & Chief Corp Strategy)*
Mohammed Beseiso *(Chief Sls Officer & Chief Customer Relations Officer)*
Abdulrahman Ghaleb *(Chief Contracts & Admin Officer)*
Mohammed Basafi *(CTO-Fixed & Broadband Network)*
Marwan Al Ahmadi *(Chief Bus Officer)*
Hamad Al Hashemi *(Chief HR Officer)*
Eyas Al Hajery *(Chief Bus Support Officer)*
Abdulaziz Al Tamami *(Chief Corp Governance Officer)*
Board of Directors:
Abdulaziz Saleh Alsaghyir
Abdulrahman Abdullah Al Fehaid
Essa Mohammed Al Haddad
Saleh Nasser Al Jasser
Abdulaziz Hamad Al Jomaih
Khaled Omar Al Kaf
Mohammed Ibrahim Al Mansour
Mubarak Rashed Al Mansouri
Ibrahim Mohammed Al Saif
Ahmed Abdulkarim Julfar

ETIKA INTERNATIONAL HOLDINGS LIMITED
4 Shenton Way 17-01 SGX Centre II
Singapore, 068807, Singapore
Tel.: (65) 6361 9883
Fax: (65) 6538 0877
E-Mail: enquiry@etika-intl.com
Web Site: www.etika-intl.com
5FR—(SES)
Rev.: $297,802,417
Assets: $262,733,829
Liabilities: $179,745,168
Net Worth: $82,988,661
Earnings: $1,546,983
Emp.: 2,200
Fiscal Year-end: 09/30/13
Business Description:
Condensed Milk
S.I.C.: 2023
N.A.I.C.S.: 311514
Personnel:
Kamal Y. P. Tan *(CEO)*
Billy Yew Thoon Lim *(CFO)*
Christopher Weng Choong Mah *(COO, Mng Dir-Dairies Div & Dir-Pkg Div)*
Sin Kok Khor *(Deputy COO & Dir-Ops-Dairies Div & Pkg Div)*
Mor Keat Kok *(Co-Sec)*
S. Surenthiraraj *(Co-Sec)*
Board of Directors:
Jaya J. B. Tan
Sam Seng Hui Goi
Sin Kok Khor
John Hian Woon Lyn
Christopher Weng Choong Mah
Kamal Y. P. Tan
Chee Seng Teo

Non-U.S. Subsidiaries:

Etika Beverages Sdn Bhd **(1)**
Lot 17225 Jalan Haruan 6 Kawasan Perindustrian Oakland
70300 Seremban, Negeri Sembilan, Malaysia
Tel.: (60) 67677830
Fax: (60) 6 767 7831
Emp.: 54
Canned Beverages Mfr
S.I.C.: 2086
N.A.I.C.S.: 312111
Wong Swee Peng *(Gen Mgr)*

Etika Dairies NZ Limited **(1)**
44 Johnston Way Hastings
Hastings, Hawkes Bay, 4140, New Zealand
Tel.: (64) 6 650 3000
Emp.: 8
Fruit Juice Mfr
S.I.C.: 2037
N.A.I.C.S.: 311411
Neil McGarva *(Gen Mgr)*

Etika Dairies Sdn Bhd **(1)**
Lot LS-1 Persiaran Satu Meru Industrial Park
Off Persiaran Hamzah Alang, 42200 Kelang, Selangor, Malaysia
Tel.: (60) 333922988
Fax: (60) 333931688
E-Mail: info@etikadairies.com
Web Site: www.etikadairies.com
Emp.: 340
Dairy Products Mfr & Distr
S.I.C.: 2023
N.A.I.C.S.: 311514
Sin Kok Khor *(Exec Dir)*

Subsidiary:

Pok Brothers Sdn Bhd **(2)**
No 2 Jalan U1/24 Hicom Glenmarie Industrial Park
40150 Shah Alam, Selangor, Malaysia
Tel.: (60) 378051100
Fax: (60) 378053628
E-Mail: pokbros@pokbrothers.com
Web Site: www.etika.com
Emp.: 220
Frozen Foods Whslr
S.I.C.: 5142
N.A.I.C.S.: 424420
Lawrence York Keaw Pok *(Mng Dir)*

Subsidiaries:

De-Luxe Food Services Sdn Bhd **(3)**
No 9 Jalan Korporat KU9
Taman Perindustrian Meru, 42200 Kelang, Selangor, Malaysia
Tel.: (60) 3 3393 1001
Fax: (60) 3 3393 1002
Web Site: www.de-luxefood.com
Emp.: 50
Processed Meats Mfr
S.I.C.: 5147
N.A.I.C.S.: 311612
Tan San May *(Deputy CEO)*

Pok Brothers (Penang) Sdn Bhd **(3)**
1L Jalan Sungai Kelian Taman Seaview
Tanjung Bungah, 11200 George Town, Penang, Malaysia
Tel.: (60) 4 890 2563
Frozen Foods Whslr
S.I.C.: 5142
N.A.I.C.S.: 424420

Etika Global Resources Sdn Bhd **(1)**
Suite B 12-01 Plaza Mon T Kiara No 2 Jalan Kiara
Mont Kiara, 50480 Kuala Lumpur, Malaysia
Tel.: (60) 3 6203 1727
Fax: (60) 3 3393 1688
Dairy Products Distr
S.I.C.: 5143
N.A.I.C.S.: 424430
Mah Weng Choong *(Mng Dir)*

Family Bakery Sdn Bhd **(1)**
No 33 Jalan Meru Indah 20 Taman Perindustrian Meru Indah
42200 Kelang, Selangor, Malaysia
Tel.: (60) 333931436
Fax: (60) 333931435
E-Mail: admin@familybakery.co.my
Emp.: 250
Bakery Products Mfr & Distr
S.I.C.: 2052
N.A.I.C.S.: 311812
Simon Chua *(Gen Mgr)*

General Packaging Sdn Bhd **(1)**
Lot 3 Jalan 203
46050 Petaling Jaya, Selangor, Malaysia
Tel.: (60) 377813462
Fax: (60) 377810818
Tin Cans Mfr
S.I.C.: 3411
N.A.I.C.S.: 332431
Chen Sheong *(Mng Dir)*

Naturalac Nutrition Limited **(1)**
Level 2 18 Normanby Road Mount Eden
Symonds Street
PO Box 8645
Auckland, 1024, New Zealand
Tel.: (64) 96385320
Fax: (64) 96383899
E-Mail: info@horleys.com
Web Site: www.horleys.com
Emp.: 11
Dietary Supplement Products Mfr
S.I.C.: 2023
N.A.I.C.S.: 311514
Margaret Orourke *(Mgr-Supply Chain)*

PT Sentraboga Intiselera **(1)**
Jl Raya Gn Gangsir Km 4 5
Malang, East Java, 67155in, Indonesia
Tel.: (62) 343656986
Fax: (62) 34 365 6908
Instant Noodles Mfr Distr
S.I.C.: 2098
N.A.I.C.S.: 311824

Quality Wines Sdn Bhd **(1)**
Lot 560 Jalan Subang 3 Off Persiaran Subang
Sungei Penaga Industrial Park, 47500 Subang Jaya, Selangor, Malaysia
Tel.: (60) 3 5636 8833
Fax: (60) 3 5636 0086
Emp.: 50
Alcoholic Beverages Whslr
S.I.C.: 2084
N.A.I.C.S.: 312130
Cheng Leong Tan *(Mng Dir)*

Susu Lembu Asli (Johor) Sdn Bhd **(1)**
Plot 169 Jalan Angkasa Mas 3 Kawasan Perindustrian Tebrau II
81100 Johor Bahru, Johor, Malaysia
Tel.: (60) 73525584
Fax: (60) 73516709
Web Site: www.goodday.com.my
Emp.: 50
Dairy Products Distr
S.I.C.: 5143
N.A.I.C.S.: 424430

Susu Lembu Asli (Marketing) Sdn Bhd **(1)**
Lot 31 Jalan 213 Section 51
46050 Petaling Jaya, Selangor, Malaysia
Tel.: (60) 377858811
Fax: (60) 377851811
Web Site: www.goodday.com.my
Emp.: 20
Dairy Products Mfr & Whslr
S.I.C.: 2023
N.A.I.C.S.: 311514
Lee Song Yong *(Founder)*

ETIMEX GMBH
Martin Adolff Strasse 44
D 89165 Dietenheim, Germany
Tel.: (49) 7347670
Fax: (49) 734767369
E-Mail: marketing@etimex-pp.com
Web Site: www.etimex.de
Emp.: 900
Business Description:
Plastics Mfr
S.I.C.: 3089
N.A.I.C.S.: 326199
Personnel:
Michael Joy *(Mng Dir)*

Subsidiary:

ETIMEX Technical Components GmbH **(1)**
Ehinger Strasse 30
D-89616 Rottenacker, Germany
Tel.: (49) 7393 52 0
Fax: (49) 7393 52 130
Web Site: www.etimex-tc.com
Molded Plastic Components & Assemblies Mfr
S.I.C.: 3089
N.A.I.C.S.: 326199

U.S. Subsidiary:

Etimex USA, Inc. **(1)**
10925 Westlake Dr
Charlotte, NC 28273
Tel.: (704) 583-0002
Fax: (704) 583-0110
E-Mail: nick.pignatiello@etimex-usa.com
Web Site: www.etimex-tc.com
Sales Range: $10-24.9 Million
Emp.: 37
Plastic Products Mfr
S.I.C.: 3089
N.A.I.C.S.: 326199
Paul L. Mastroianni *(COO)*

ETOBICOKE IRONWORKS LIMITED
141 Rivalda Road
Weston, ON, M9M 2M6, Canada
Tel.: (416) 742-7111
Fax: (416) 742-2737
E-Mail: info@eiw-ca.com
Web Site: www.eiw.ca
Year Founded: 1955
Rev.: $26,651,142
Emp.: 160
Business Description:
Structural Steel Fabricator & Scaffolds Mfr
S.I.C.: 3446
N.A.I.C.S.: 332323
Personnel:
John G. Brasil *(Pres & COO)*

ETON PROPERTIES PHILIPPINES, INC.
8th Floor Allied Bank Center 6754 Ayala Ave
Makati, Philippines
Tel.: (63) 2845 3866
Fax: (63) 27502233
Web Site: www.eton.com.ph
ETON—(PHI)
Rev.: $65,993,430
Assets: $445,848,759
Liabilities: $280,688,976
Net Worth: $165,159,783
Earnings: $1,029,486
Emp.: 241
Fiscal Year-end: 12/31/12
Business Description:
Real Estate Services
S.I.C.: 6531
N.A.I.C.S.: 531210
Personnel:
Lucio C. Tan *(Chm)*
Harry C. Tan *(Vice Chm)*
Josephine A. Martinez *(CFO)*
Juanita T. Tan Lee *(Treas)*
Ma. Cecilia L. Pesayco *(Sec)*
Rhoel Alberto B. Nolido *(Sr VP-Bus Dev & Comml)*
Board of Directors:
Lucio C. Tan
Antonino L. Alindogan Jr.
Juanita T. Tan Lee
Reynaldo A. Maclang
Wilfrido E. Sanchez
Harry C. Tan
Lucio K. Tan Jr.
Michael G. Tan
Wilson T. Young

ETRATECH INC.
1047 Cooke Boulevard
Burlington, ON, Canada L7T 4A8
Tel.: (905) 681-7544
Fax: (905) 681-7601
Toll Free: (866) 681-7544
E-Mail: info@etratech.com
Web Site: www.etratech.com
Year Founded: 1989
Rev.: $32,304,879
Emp.: 150
Business Description:
Electronic Parts Mfr
S.I.C.: 3625
N.A.I.C.S.: 335314
Personnel:
Michael Desnoyers *(Pres & CEO)*
Mike Lamontagne *(CFO & Exec VP)*
John Bielby *(COO)*

ETRION CORPORATION
Rue du Stand 60-62
1204 Geneva, Switzerland
Tel.: (41) 227152090
Fax: (41) 227152099
E-Mail: info@etrion.com
Web Site: www.etrion.com
Year Founded: 1996
ETX—(OMX OTC TSX)
Rev.: $55,662,000
Assets: $452,777,000
Liabilities: $467,423,000
Net Worth: ($14,646,000)
Earnings: ($8,458,000)
Emp.: 27
Fiscal Year-end: 12/31/12
Business Description:
Power Plant Operator
S.I.C.: 4911
N.A.I.C.S.: 221118
Personnel:
Ian H. Lundin *(Chm)*
Marco A. Northland *(CEO)*
Cheryl Eversden *(CFO)*
David Knight *(Sec)*
Giora Salita *(Exec VP-Bus Dev & M&A)*
Board of Directors:
Ian H. Lundin
Aksel Azrac
Tom Dinwoodie
C. Ashley Heppenstall
Marco A. Northland
Garrett Soden
Legal Counsel:
Norton Rose Canada
Toronto, ON, Canada
Transfer Agent:
Computershare
Vancouver, BC, Canada

ETRO S.P.A.
Via Spartaco 3
20135 Milan, Italy
Tel.: (39) 2550201
Fax: (39) 0255020281
E-Mail: etro@etro.com
Web Site: www.etro.com
Year Founded: 1968
Sales Range: $150-199.9 Million
Emp.: 250
Business Description:
Textile Goods Mfr
S.I.C.: 2399
N.A.I.C.S.: 313210
Personnel:
Gerolamo Etro *(Pres)*
U.S. Subsidiary:

ETRO USA Inc. (1)
41 W 56th St
New York, NY 10019
Tel.: (212) 247-1200
Fax: (212) 317-1550
Leather Goods Mfr & Distr
S.I.C.: 3199
N.A.I.C.S.: 316998
Marco Pievani, *(Gen Mgr)*

ETROPAL JSC
191 Rusky Blvd
Etropole, 2180, Bulgaria
Tel.: (359) 720 63422
Fax: (359) 720 67098
E-Mail: etropal2002@yahoo.com
Web Site: www.etropal.eu
Year Founded: 1976
5EO—(BUL)
Business Description:
Medical Products Mfr
S.I.C.: 5047
N.A.I.C.S.: 423450
Personnel:
Maya Stefanova *(Dir-IR)*

ETS MOUSSIER
21 avenue de Fontcouverte
84036 Avignon, Cedex, France
Tel.: (33) 490132120
Fax: (33) 490885682
Web Site: www.moussier.com
Sls.: $28,100,000
Emp.: 74
Business Description:
Electrical Appliances Sales
S.I.C.: 5064
N.A.I.C.S.: 423620
Personnel:
Patricia Giraud *(Pres)*

ETS RAYMOND BARRE
17 rue de l'Esperance
Les Hautes Rivieres, 08800
Charleville-Mezieres, France
Tel.: (33) 324534218
Rev.: $22,900,000
Emp.: 141
Business Description:
Metal Stampings
S.I.C.: 3469
N.A.I.C.S.: 332119
Personnel:
Gerard Barre *(Mng Dir)*

ETTEPLAN OYJ
Muovitie 1
15860 Hollola, Finland
Tel.: (358) 103070
Fax: (358) 103071012
E-Mail: info@etteplan.com
Web Site: www.etteplan.com
ETT1V—(HEL)
Rev.: $181,031,595
Assets: $102,805,657
Liabilities: $69,584,873
Net Worth: $33,220,783
Earnings: $7,518,359
Emp.: 1,776
Fiscal Year-end: 12/31/12
Business Description:
Software Design & Development Services
S.I.C.: 7373
N.A.I.C.S.: 541512
Personnel:
Heikki Hornborg *(Chm)*
Juha Nakki *(Pres & CEO)*
Per-Anders Gadin *(CFO & Sr VP)*
Robert Berg *(Sr VP-Solutions & Bus Dev)*
Veikko Lamminen *(Sr VP)*
Outi-Maria Liedes *(Sr VP-Comm & Ops Dev)*
Mikael Vatn *(Sr VP)*
Board of Directors:
Heikki Hornborg
Tapio Hakakari
Robert Ingman
Pertti Nupponen
Satu Rautavalta
Teuvo Rintamaki
Subsidiaries:

Ette-Consulting Oy (1)
Terveystie 18
15860 Hollola, Finland (100%)
Tel.: (358) 103070
Fax: (358) 103071021
E-Mail: info@ette.com
Web Site: www.ette.com
Emp.: 100
Engineering Services
S.I.C.: 8711
N.A.I.C.S.: 541330
Natti Shyytiainen *(Mng Dir)*

Ette-Engineering Oy (1)
Terveystie 18
15860 Hollola, Finland (100%)
Tel.: (358) 103070
Fax: (358) 38729010
E-Mail: info@ette.com
Web Site: www.ette.com
Emp.: 100
Engineering Services
S.I.C.: 8711
N.A.I.C.S.: 541330
Vesa Juntilla *(Mng Dir)*

Ette-Ins Oy (1)
Terveystie 18
15860 Hollola, Finland (100%)
Tel.: (358) 103070
Fax: (358) 38729010
E-Mail: info@ette.com
Web Site: www.ette.com
Emp.: 100
Engineering Services
S.I.C.: 8711
N.A.I.C.S.: 541330
Vesa Juntilla *(Mng Dir)*

Etteplan Design Center Oy (1)
Terveystie 18
15860 Hollola, Finland
Tel.: (358) 103071010
Fax: (358) 103071012
Web Site: www.etteplan.com
Emp.: 75
Engineering Design Services
S.I.C.: 8711
N.A.I.C.S.: 541330

Non-U.S. Subsidiaries:

Cool Engineering AB (1)
Arods Industrivag 60
422 43 Hisings Backa, Sweden
Tel.: (46) 31 744 90 80
Fax: (46) 31 744 90 89
Web Site: www.cool-engineering.se
Emp.: 50
Product Testing & Consulting Services
S.I.C.: 8734
N.A.I.C.S.: 541380
Arvo Siosteen *(CEO)*

Etteplan Consulting (Shanghai) Co., Ltd (1)
Suite 14 C 14 F No 1555 Lian Hua Road
Min Hang District, Shanghai, 200233, China
Tel.: (86) 21 6480 4828
Fax: (86) 21 6480 6435
Industrial Engineering Services
S.I.C.: 8711
N.A.I.C.S.: 541330

Etteplan Industriteknik AB (1)
Gjuterigatan 28
65221 Karlstad, Sweden (100%)
Tel.: (46) 54852600
Fax: (46) 54854770
E-Mail: info.karlstad@ette.com
Web Site: www.etteplan.se
Emp.: 27
Engineering Services
S.I.C.: 8711
N.A.I.C.S.: 541330
Anders Magnusson *(Mng Dir-Sweden)*

Etteplan Industry AB (1)
Iggebygatan 12
PO Box 1089
721 27 Vasteras, Sweden
Tel.: (46) 21 171 000
Fax: (46) 21 414 585
E-Mail: info@etteplan.se
Web Site: www.etteplan.com
Emp.: 100
Mechanical Engineering Services
S.I.C.: 8711
N.A.I.C.S.: 541330
Mikael Vatn *(Gen Mgr)*

Etteplan Technical Systems AB (1)
Stora Torget 3
44130 Alingsas, Sweden (100%)
Tel.: (46) 322669900
Fax: (46) 322669940
E-Mail: info@etteplan.com
Web Site: www.etteplan.com
Emp.: 20
Engineering Services
S.I.C.: 8711
N.A.I.C.S.: 541330
Uls Aiff *(Mng Dir)*

Etteplan (1)
Stora Varvsgatan 19
21119 Malmo, Sweden (80%)
Tel.: (46) 406646700
Fax: (46) 406646719
E-Mail: kontakt@etteplan.com
Web Site: www.etteplan.se
Emp.: 20
Engineering Services
S.I.C.: 8711
N.A.I.C.S.: 541330
Larry Falk *(VP)*

Innovation Team Sweden AB (1)
Sperlingsgatan 5
302 48 Halmstad, Sweden
Tel.: (46) 35 17 47 00
Fax: (46) 35 17 47 50
E-Mail: info@innovationteam.se
Web Site: www.innovationteam.se
Emp.: 50
Medical Equipment Mfr
S.I.C.: 3841
N.A.I.C.S.: 339112
Anders Rosengren *(Mng Dir)*

Lutab AB (1)
Gavlegatan 22
113 30 Stockholm, Sweden
Tel.: (46) 86741200
Fax: (46) 8 6741201
E-Mail: info@lutab.se
Web Site: www.lutab.se
Emp.: 45
Technical Consulting Services
S.I.C.: 8999
N.A.I.C.S.: 541690
Fredrik Bergner *(Mgr-Sls)*

ProTang AB (1)
Iggebygatan 12
1089
72127 Vasteras, Sweden (73.16%)
Tel.: (46) 21171000
Fax: (46) 21414585
Web Site: www.protang.se
Emp.: 200
Other Scientific & Technical Consulting Services
S.I.C.: 8999
N.A.I.C.S.: 541690
Tom Anderson *(Mng Dir)*

ProTang Teknikinformation Ab (1)
Iggebygatan 12 1089
72127 Vasteras, Sweden (100%)
Tel.: (46) 21171000
Fax: (46) 21171760
Web Site: www.protang.se
Emp.: 250
Other Management Consulting Services
S.I.C.: 8748
N.A.I.C.S.: 541618
Tom Anderson *(Mng Dir)*

EU SUPPLY PLC
26 Red Lion Square
London, WC1R 4AG, United Kingdom
Tel.: (44) 20 7127 4545
Fax: (44) 20 7127 5141
E-Mail: info@eu-supply.com
Web Site: www.eu-supply.com
EUSP—(AIM)
Business Description:
Electronic Tender Management & Contract Management Solutions
S.I.C.: 7372
N.A.I.C.S.: 511210

Personnel:
David Richard Cutler *(Chm)*
Thomas Bo Beergrehn *(CEO)*
Mark Westcombe Elliott *(CFO)*
Board of Directors:
David Richard Cutler
Thomas Bo Beergrehn
Mark Westcombe Elliott
Steffen Patrik Karlsson

EU YAN SANG INTERNATIONAL LTD.

Eu Yan Sang Centre 21 Tai Seng Drive
Singapore, 535223, Singapore
Tel.: (65) 62253211
Fax: (65) 62258276
E-Mail: info@euyansang.com
Web Site: www.euyansang.com
Year Founded: 1879
E02—(SES)
Rev.: $264,701,395
Assets: $297,950,904
Liabilities: $176,760,431
Net Worth: $121,190,473
Earnings: $14,724,840
Fiscal Year-end: 06/30/13
Business Description:
Holding Company; Traditional Chinese Medicinal Products Mfr & Distr
S.I.C.: 6719
N.A.I.C.S.: 551112
Personnel:
Robert Yee Sang Eu *(Chm & Mng Dir-China)*
Richard Yee Ming Eu *(CEO)*
Chee Weng Lam *(CFO)*
Anne Eu *(Chm-Malaysia)*
Byron Patching *(Chm-Australia)*
Clifford Yee Fong Eu *(Mng Dir-Intl & Co-Sec)*
Yock Miin Tang *(Co-Sec & Gen Mgr-Legal & Corp Secretariat)*
Board of Directors:
Robert Yee Sang Eu
Matthew J. Estes
Clifford Yee Fong Eu
Richard Yee Ming Eu
Shin Ein Ng
Daniel Chung Hian Soh
Subsidiaries:

Eu Yan Sang Integrative Health Pte. Ltd. (1)
269A South Bridge Road
Singapore, 058818, Singapore
Tel.: (65) 6225 1887
Fax: (65) 6227 4312
E-Mail: enquiry@ihealth.com.sg
Web Site: www.ihealth.com.sg
General Medical Services
S.I.C.: 8011
N.A.I.C.S.: 621111
Caryn Peh *(Gen Mgr)*

Eu Yan Sang Marketing Pte Ltd (1)
269A South Bridge Road
Singapore, 58818, Singapore
Tel.: (65) 6225 3211
Fax: (65) 6221 1861
Medicinal Products Marketer
S.I.C.: 8732
N.A.I.C.S.: 541910
Richard Eu *(CEO)*

Eu Yan Sang (Singapore) Pte Ltd (1)
21 Ubi Road 1 03-01
Singapore, 408724, Singapore
Tel.: (65) 6749 8830
Fax: (65) 6749 8692
E-Mail: info@euyansang.com
Traditional Chinese Medicinal Products Mfr & Distr
S.I.C.: 2833
N.A.I.C.S.: 325411
Vincent Lim *(Mng Dir)*

EYS KangHong Herbal Pte Ltd (1)
269a South Bridge Road
Singapore, 58818, Singapore
Tel.: (65) 62253211
Fax: (65) 62258276
E-Mail: customersvc@euyansang.com
Emp.: 45
Herbal Products Whslr
S.I.C.: 5122
N.A.I.C.S.: 424210
Richard Yee Ming Eu *(CEO)*

Yin Yang Spa Products Pte Ltd (1)
151 Lorong Chuan 05-05/06 New Tech Park Lobby E
Singapore, 556741, Singapore
Tel.: (65) 6749 8830
Fax: (65) 6749 8692
E-Mail: contact@yinyangspa.com.sg
Web Site: www.yinyangspa.com.sg
Traditional Chinese Medicinal Products Mfr
S.I.C.: 2833
N.A.I.C.S.: 325411

Non-U.S. Subsidiaries:

Bod International Pty. Limited (1)
316 Horsley Rd
PO Box 4034
Milperra, NSW, 2214, Australia
Tel.: (61) 297727155
Fax: (61) 297730075
E-Mail: info@bod.com.au
Web Site: www.bod.com.au
Emp.: 5
Healthcare Products Mfr & Sales
S.I.C.: 5999
N.A.I.C.S.: 446199
Bruce Angun *(Brand Mgr)*

Eu Yan Sang (Hong Kong) Limited (1)
Eu Yan Sang Centre 10 Wang Lee Street
Yuen Long Industrial Park
Yuen Long, New Territories, China (Hong Kong)
Tel.: (852) 2544 3268
Fax: (852) 2850 6785
E-Mail: info@euyansang.com.hk
Health Care Products Distr
S.I.C.: 5122
N.A.I.C.S.: 424210

Healthy Life Group Pty. Ltd. (1)
Locked Bag 6270
Regents Park, NSW, 2143, Australia
Tel.: (61) 1300 135 900
Fax: (61) 1300 135 700
Health Food Stores
S.I.C.: 5122
N.A.I.C.S.: 446191
Ian Houlton *(Gen Mgr-Sls & Mktg)*

Synco (H.K.) Limited (1)
3 On Yip Street 3/F Block D Sunview Industrial Building
Chai Wan, China (Hong Kong)
Tel.: (852) 2556 0157
Fax: (852) 2897 2582
Web Site: www.synco-pharma.com
Pharmaceutical Products Mfr & Distr
S.I.C.: 2834
N.A.I.C.S.: 325412

Vistern Health Sdn. Bhd. (1)
L2-01 And L2-12 2nd Floor Shaw Parade
Changkat Thambi Dollah
55100 Kuala Lumpur, Malaysia
Tel.: (60) 3 2143 1509
Fax: (60) 3 2116 8201
E-Mail: info@purehoney2u.com
Web Site: www.purehoney2u.com
Honey Products Mfr & Distr
S.I.C.: 2099
N.A.I.C.S.: 311999
Eric Chiu *(Deputy Mng Dir)*

Weng Li Sdn. Bhd. (1)
No 2 And 4 Persiaran 1/118C Fasa 2 Desa Tun Razak Industrial Park
Cheras, 56000 Kuala Lumpur, Malaysia MY (100%)
Tel.: (60) 3 9173 1984
Fax: (60) 3 9173 1987
E-Mail: info@wengli.com.my
Web Site: www.wengli.com.my
Medicinal Herbal Soups & Teas Mfr
S.I.C.: 2833
N.A.I.C.S.: 325411

EUCATEX S.A. INDUSTRIA E COMERCIO

Av Juscelino Kubitschek 1830 - Ri
04543-900 Sao Paulo, SP, Brazil
Tel.: (55) 11 3049 2473
Fax: (55) 11 3049 2284
E-Mail: ri@eucatex.com.br
Web Site: www.eucatex.com.br
Year Founded: 1951
EUCA3—(BRAZ)
Sales Range: Less than $1 Million
Emp.: 2,430
Business Description:
Insulating Material Mfr & Whslr
S.I.C.: 2499
N.A.I.C.S.: 321999
Personnel:
Otavio Maluf *(Pres & Vice Chm)*
Flavio Maluf *(CEO & VP)*
Jose Antonio Goulart de Carvalho *(IR Officer & Exec VP)*
Board of Directors:
Heitor Aquino Ferreira
Miguel Jorge
Flavio Maluf
Otavio Maluf
Antonio Delfim Netto
Dacio Antonio Pereira Oliveira
Marcelo Faria Parodi

EUCODIS BIOSCIENCE GMBH

Campus Vienna Biocenter II
Viehmarktgasse 2 a/ 2 OG, 1030
Vienna, Austria
Tel.: (43) 18900804
Fax: (43) 1890080411
E-Mail: office@eucodisbioscience.com
Web Site: www.eucodisbioscience.com
Business Description:
Biotechnology Researcher & Developer
S.I.C.: 8731
N.A.I.C.S.: 541711
Personnel:
Thomas Fischer *(CEO)*
Henryk Kalisz *(Chief Scientific Officer)*
Bhupinder Hundle *(Sr VP-Sls)*

EUCON HOLDING LIMITED

80 Marine Parade Road 11-02
Parkway Parade
Singapore, 449269, Singapore
Tel.: (65) 63456078
Fax: (65) 63456079
Web Site: www.euconholding.com
E27—(SES)
Rev.: $63,556,641
Assets: $97,488,711
Liabilities: $60,683,897
Net Worth: $36,804,814
Earnings: ($20,225,806)
Fiscal Year-end: 12/31/12
Business Description:
Printed Circuit Boards Mfr
S.I.C.: 3672
N.A.I.C.S.: 334412
Personnel:
Yao-Long Wen *(Co-Founder, Chm & CEO)*
Yao-Chou Wen *(Co-Founder)*
Wan-Hsin Chien *(CFO)*
Cheng Siew Tan *(Sec)*
Board of Directors:
Yao-Long Wen
Kwong Wah Er
Sim Ho Ong
Winston Han Chiang Seow
Yao-Chou Wen
Non-U.S. Subsidiaries:

LGANG Optronics Technology Co., Ltd. (1)
19 Her-Jun North Road Chung-Li Industrial Park
Chung-li, Taoyuan, 32061, Taiwan
Tel.: (886) 34340771
Fax: (886) 34340770
Web Site: www.euconholding.com
Emp.: 110
Laser Drilling Services
S.I.C.: 8711
N.A.I.C.S.: 541330
Yao Lung Wen *(CEO)*

Shanghai Zhuo Kai Electronic Technology Co., Ltd. (1)
399 Baoqian Road Xuhang Industrial Park
Jiading District, Shanghai, China
Tel.: (86) 2139533226
Fax: (86) 2139533205
Laser Drilling Services & Printed Circuit Boards Mfr
S.I.C.: 7389
N.A.I.C.S.: 561990

Subsidiaries:

Shanghai Yaolong Electronic Technology Co., Ltd (2)
188 Yuwan Road
Jiading District, Shanghai, 201809, China
Tel.: (86) 21 3997 7791
Fax: (86) 21 3997 7793
Laser Drilling & Circuit Boards Mfr
S.I.C.: 3672
N.A.I.C.S.: 334412

Shanghai Zeng Kang Electronic Co., Ltd. (2)
1150 Caoxin Road Xuhang Town
Jiading District, Shanghai, China
Tel.: (86) 2159949019
Fax: (86) 2159949126
Mechanical & Laser Drilling Services
S.I.C.: 7389
N.A.I.C.S.: 561990

EUGEN LAGLER GMBH

Kappelrain 2
74363 Guglingen, Germany
Tel.: (49) 713598900
Fax: (49) 7135989098
E-Mail: info@laegler.de
Web Site: www.laegler.de
Year Founded: 1956
Rev.: $20,691,000
Emp.: 60
Business Description:
Floor Sanding Machines Mfr
S.I.C.: 3589
N.A.I.C.S.: 333318
Personnel:
Karleugen Lagler *(Mng Dir)*

EUGENE ALLARD INC

2244 Chapais Street
Jonquiere, QC, Canada G7X 7W8
Tel.: (418) 547-6654
Fax: (418) 547-5770
Toll Free: (800) 463-9199
E-Mail: service@eugeneallard.com
Web Site: www.eugeneallard.com
Year Founded: 1933
Rev.: $24,969,732
Emp.: 45
Business Description:
Packaging & Maintenance Products Distr
S.I.C.: 5113
N.A.I.C.S.: 424130
Personnel:
Daniel Blackburn *(VP-Admin)*

EUGENE INVESTMENT & SECURITIES CO., LTD.

23-9 Yeouido-Dong Yeongdeungpo-Gu
Seoul, 150 710, Korea (South)
Tel.: (82) 23686000
Fax: (82) 23689703
Web Site: www.eugenefn.com
Year Founded: 1954
001200—(KRS)
Emp.: 883

Eugene Investment & Securities Co., Ltd.—(Continued)

Business Description:
Investment Banking & Brokerage
S.I.C.: 6211
N.A.I.C.S.: 523110
Personnel:
Chang-Su Rue *(CEO & Vice Chm)*
Board of Directors:
Young-Min Joo
Byung-Kook Kim
Jae-Sik Kim
Chang-Su Rue
Kwan-Hee Yoo
Jae-Hoon Youh

Subsidiaries:

Eugene Investment & Futures Co., Ltd. **(1)**
A23-9 Yeouido-Dong Yeongdeungpo-Gu
Seoul, 150 710, Korea (South)
Tel.: (82) 237718721
Fax: (82) 23771870
E-Mail: packoffice@eugenefutures.com
Web Site: eng.eugenefutures.com
Emp.: 80
Brokerage & Investment Services
S.I.C.: 6211
N.A.I.C.S.: 523120

Hanil Investment Trust Management **(1)**
23 9 Yoido Dong Yungdeungpo Gu
Seoul, 150 710, Korea (South)
Tel.: (82) 221293300
Fax: (82) 27837105
E-Mail: ks@eugenefn.com
Web Site: www.hitmc.co.kr
Emp.: 35
Asset Management
S.I.C.: 6211
N.A.I.C.S.: 523999
Tong Gun Kim *(Co-CEO)*

EUGENE TECHNOLOGY CO., LTD.

42 Chugye-Ro Yangii-myeon
Cheoin-gu, Yongin, Gyeonggi-do, Korea (South)
Tel.: (82) 31 323 5700
Fax: (82) 31 333 1681
Web Site: www.eugenetech.co.kr
Year Founded: 2000
084370—(KRS)
Business Description:
Semiconductor Machinery Mfr
S.I.C.: 3559
N.A.I.C.S.: 333242
Personnel:
Pyung Yong Um *(CEO)*

EUGLENA CO., LTD.

7F University of Tokyo Entrepreneur Plaza 7-3-1 Hongo
Bunkyo-ku, Tokyo, 113-0033, Japan
Tel.: (81) 3 5800 4907
Web Site: www.euglena.jp
Year Founded: 2005
2931—(TKS)
Sales Range: $10-24.9 Million
Emp.: 40
Business Description:
Bio-Fuel Production & Research
S.I.C.: 2999
N.A.I.C.S.: 324199
Personnel:
Mitsuru Izumo *(Pres)*

Subsidiary:

Yaeyama Shokusan Co., Ltd. **(1)**
287-14 Shiraho
Ishigaki, Okinawa, 907-0242, Japan
Tel.: (81) 980 86 7154
Fax: (81) 980 86 7509
E-Mail: yaechlo@ruby.ocn.ne.jp
Web Site: www.yaeyamachlorella.com
Emp.: 30
Pharmaceutical Product Mfr
S.I.C.: 2834
N.A.I.C.S.: 325412
Ansei Shikiya *(Pres & CEO)*

EUMERALLA RESOURCES LIMITED

3/91 Aberdeen Street
Northbridge, Perth, WA, 6003, Australia
Tel.: (61) 8 9328 6262
Fax: (61) 8 9227 6390
E-Mail: info@eumerallaresources.com
Web Site: www.eumerallaresources.com
Year Founded: 2011
EUM—(ASX)
Business Description:
Metal Mining
S.I.C.: 1099
N.A.I.C.S.: 212299
Personnel:
Jack Robert James *(Chm & Sec)*
Michael John Hynes *(CEO)*
Board of Directors:
Jack Robert James
Michael John Hynes

EUMUNDI GROUP LIMITED

Level 15 10 Market Street
Brisbane, QLD, 4000, Australia
Tel.: (61) 732297222
Fax: (61) 732118222
E-Mail: mail@eumundi-ltd.com.au
Web Site: www.eumundi-ltd.com.au
EBG—(ASX)
Rev.: $21,499,565
Assets: $53,047,058
Liabilities: $35,423,063
Net Worth: $17,623,995
Earnings: ($1,339,098)
Emp.: 24
Fiscal Year-end: 06/30/13
Business Description:
Investment Properties Services
S.I.C.: 6799
N.A.I.C.S.: 523920
Personnel:
Suzanne Jacob-Lee *(CEO)*
Rhianna Mikkelsen *(CFO)*
Leni Pia Stanley *(Sec)*
Board of Directors:
Joseph Michael Ganim
Gilbert De Luca
Charles Russel McCart
Vernon Alan Wills
Legal Counsel:
Hopgood Ganim
Level 8 1 Eagle Street
Brisbane, QLD, 4000, Australia

EUNETWORKS GROUP LIMITED

50 Raffles Place 32-01 Singapore Land Tower
Singapore, 048623, Singapore
Tel.: (65) 65365355
Fax: (65) 65361360
E-Mail: info@eunetworks.com
Web Site: www.eunetworks.com
H23—(SES)
Rev.: $127,616,916
Assets: $360,100,475
Liabilities: $82,789,455
Net Worth: $277,311,020
Earnings: $40,115,866
Emp.: 208
Fiscal Year-end: 12/31/12
Business Description:
Internet Connectivity Services
S.I.C.: 4813
N.A.I.C.S.: 517110
Personnel:
John Scarano *(Vice Chm & Exec VP-Fin, Ops & Corp Dev)*
Brady Rafuse *(CEO)*
Joachim Piroth *(CFO)*
Uwe Nickl *(CMO)*
Richard Taylor *(Gen Counsel)*
Ming Fai Yip *(Sec)*
Board of Directors:
Nicholas George
Daniel Aegerter
Jason Booma
Neil Hobbs
Simon Koenig
Kwok Chong Lam
Duncan Lewis
Uwe Nickl
Joachim Piroth
Brady Rafuse
Kai-Uwe Ricke
John Scarano
John Siegel

Non-U.S. Subsidiaries:

euNetworks BV **(1)**
Paul van Vlissingenstraat 16
1096 BK Amsterdam, Netherlands
Tel.: (31) 20 354 8080
Fax: (31) 20 653 5791
E-Mail: info@eunetworks.com
Fiber Networks & Communications Infrastructure & Networking Solutions
S.I.C.: 4899
N.A.I.C.S.: 517919
Brady Rafuse *(CEO)*

euNetworks (BVI) Limited **(1)**
Trident Chambers
Road Town, Tortola, Virgin Islands (British)
Tel.: (284) 4942434
Fax: (284) 4943547
Investment Management Services
S.I.C.: 6211
N.A.I.C.S.: 523999

euNetworks Fiber UK Limited **(1)**
15 Worship Street
London, EC2A 2DT, United Kingdom
Tel.: (44) 20 7952 1300
Fax: (44) 20 7256 5859
Web Site: www.eunetworks.com
Fiber Networks & Communications Infrastructure & Networking Solutions
S.I.C.: 4899
N.A.I.C.S.: 517919
Brady Rafuse *(CEO)*

euNetworks GmbH **(1)**
Ludwig Landmann Strasse 405
60489 Frankfurt am Main, Hesse, Germany
Tel.: (49) 69 90554 0
Fax: (49) 69 90554 111
E-Mail: marketing@euNetworks.com
Internet Service Provider
S.I.C.: 4899
N.A.I.C.S.: 517919
Joachim Piroth *(Mng Dir)*

Subsidiary:

LambdaNet Communications Deutschland GmbH **(2)**
Gunther-Wagner-Allee 13
30177 Hannover, Lower Saxony, Germany
Tel.: (49) 51184880
Fax: (49) 511 84 88 15 09
E-Mail: info@lambdanet.net
Web Site: www.lambdanet.net
Sales Range: $50-74.9 Million
Emp.: 90
Telecommunications & Internet Services
S.I.C.: 4813
N.A.I.C.S.: 517110
Brady Rafuse *(Chm-Supervisory Bd)*
Uwe Nickl *(CEO)*
James Thomas *(CFO)*
John Franklin *(COO)*
Uwe Knoke *(CMO)*

euNetworks Ireland - Private Fiber Limited **(1)**
Suite D16 2nd Floor M The Cubes Offices
Beacon South Quarter
Sandyford, Dublin, 18, Ireland
Tel.: (353) 1 652 1200
Fax: (353) 1 652 1201
E-Mail: info@eunetworks.com
Internet Connectivity Services
S.I.C.: 4899
N.A.I.C.S.: 517919
Brady Rafuse *(CEO)*

euNetworks Pte. Limited **(1)**
50 Raffles Place 32-01 Singapore Land Tower
Singapore, 048623, Singapore
Tel.: (65) 6536 5355
Fax: (65) 6536 1360
E-Mail: info@eunetworks.com
Web Site: www.eunetworks.com
Internet Protocol Services
S.I.C.: 4899
N.A.I.C.S.: 517919

EUPE CORPORATION BERHAD

5th Floor Wisma Ria Taman Ria
08000 Sungai Petani, Kedah Darul Aman, Malaysia
Tel.: (60) 44414888
Fax: (60) 44414548
E-Mail: sales@eupe.com.my
Web Site: www.eupe.com.my
EUPE—(KLS)
Rev.: $48,085,657
Assets: $136,670,363
Liabilities: $48,169,459
Net Worth: $88,500,904
Earnings: $5,473,375
Fiscal Year-end: 02/28/13
Business Description:
Property Development Services
S.I.C.: 6531
N.A.I.C.S.: 531312
Personnel:
Huck Lee Beh *(Mng Dir)*
Bee Lian Ng *(Sec)*
Board of Directors:
Rasli Basir
Huck Lee Beh
Jaafar Jamaludin
Jenny Kek
Ismail Shafie
Muhamad Faisal Tajudin
Hiang Joo Tan
Choon Boay Teoh

Subsidiaries:

Esteem Glory Sdn. Bhd. **(1)**
94 Lorong Ria 5/2 Taman Ria Padang Serai
09400 Kulim, Kedah, Malaysia
Tel.: (60) 44855884
Fax: (60) 44853290
Residential Building Construction Services
S.I.C.: 1531
N.A.I.C.S.: 236117

Eupe Golf Management Bhd. **(1)**
No 552 Taman Ria
08000 Sungai Petani, Kedah, Malaysia
Tel.: (60) 44414666
Fax: (60) 44415600
E-Mail: cintasayang@cintasayangresort.com
Web Site: www.cintasayangresort.com
Emp.: 200
Golf Club Management Services
S.I.C.: 7999
N.A.I.C.S.: 713910
Chris Deleon *(Mgr)*

Ria Food Centre Sdn. Bhd. **(1)**
57-61 Lrg 2 Taman Ria
08000 Sungai Petani, Kedah, Malaysia
Tel.: (60) 44412705
Fax: (60) 44422218
Emp.: 15
Operator of Complex for Rental of Stalls
S.I.C.: 6531
N.A.I.C.S.: 531312
Beh Huck Boon *(Mng Dir)*

Riacon Sdn. Bhd. **(1)**
5th Floor Wisma Ria Taman Ria
08000 Sungai Petani, Kedah, Malaysia
Tel.: (60) 44414888
Fax: (60) 44414548
Emp.: 150
Residential Construction Services
S.I.C.: 1522
N.A.I.C.S.: 236116
Law Seuw Ching *(Sec)*

EURASIA DESIGN, INC.
(Name Changed to Luve Sports Inc.)

EURASIA DRILLING COMPANY LIMITED
Boundary Hall Cricket Square
PO Box 1111
Georgetown, Grand Cayman, Ky1-1102, Cayman Islands
Tel.: (345) 19495122
Web Site: www.eurasiadrilling.com
EDCL—(LSE)
Rev.: $3,237,333,000
Assets: $3,035,055,000
Liabilities: $1,372,429,000
Net Worth: $1,662,626,000
Earnings: $382,009,000
Fiscal Year-end: 12/31/12
Business Description:
Oil & Gas Exploration
S.I.C.: 1389
N.A.I.C.S.: 213112
Personnel:
Alexander Djaparidze *(CEO)*
Richard W. Anderson *(CFO)*
Murat Sampiev *(COO)*
Douglas S. Stinemetz *(Gen Counsel & Sec)*
Edward Redd *(Sr VP-Offshore Ops)*
Board of Directors:
Patrick James Gillford
Richard W. Anderson
Maurice Dijols
Alexander Djaparidze
Martin E. Hansen
Rene Huck
Anatoliy Kozyrev
Richard Matzke
Alexander Shokhin

Non-U.S. Subsidiary:

BKE Shelf Ltd. (1)
ul N Kachuevskoy 9
Astrakhan, 414000, Russia
Tel.: (7) 8512 391008
Fax: (7) 8512 391009
E-Mail: shelf@bkeshelf.ru
Web Site: www.bkeshelf.ru
Emp.: 200
Offshore Drilling Contract Services
S.I.C.: 1381
N.A.I.C.S.: 213111
Gagaev K. Yuri *(Dir Gen)*
Sergey Polousov *(Deputy Dir Gen)*

EURASIA GROUPE SA
72 Rue de la Haie Coq
93300 Aubervilliers, France
Tel.: (33) 148392161
Fax: (33) 148391664
E-Mail: contact@eurasiagroupe.com
Web Site: www.eurasiagroupe.com
ALEUA—(EUR)
Sales Range: $10-24.9 Million
Business Description:
Commercial Real Estate Owner & Manager
S.I.C.: 6531
N.A.I.C.S.: 531312
Personnel:
Hsuehsheng Wang *(Chm)*

EURASIA MINING PLC
Suite 139 Grosvenor Garden House 35-37
Grosvenor Gardens, London, SW1W 0BS, United Kingdom
Tel.: (44) 2079320418
Fax: (44) 2079766283
E-Mail: info@eurasiamining.co.uk
Web Site: www.eurasiamining.co.uk
EUA—(AIM)
Rev.: $98,268
Assets: $6,865,194
Liabilities: $217,470
Net Worth: $6,647,724
Earnings: ($2,145,619)
Emp.: 19
Fiscal Year-end: 12/31/12
Business Description:
Gold & Metals Exploration
S.I.C.: 1041
N.A.I.C.S.: 212221
Personnel:
Christian Schaffalitzky *(CEO & Mng Dir)*
Michael J. de Villiers *(CFO & Sec)*
Board of Directors:
Michael Peter Martineau
Gary FitzGerald
Christian Schaffalitzky
Dmitry Suschov
Legal Counsel:
Gowlings (UK) LLP
15th Floor 125 Old Broad Street
London, EC2N 1AR, United Kingdom

EURASIAN BANK JSC
56 Kunaev Str
050002 Almaty, Kazakhstan
Tel.: (7) 727 2445379
Fax: (7) 727 2508697
E-Mail: investors@eubank.kz
Web Site: www.eurasian-bank.kz
Year Founded: 1994
EUBN—(KAZ)
Int. Income: $330,038,459
Assets: $3,081,844,161
Liabilities: $2,768,857,632
Net Worth: $312,986,530
Earnings: $64,399,947
Emp.: 4,001
Fiscal Year-end: 12/31/12
Business Description:
Banking Services
S.I.C.: 6029
N.A.I.C.S.: 522110
Personnel:
Alexander Mashkevitch *(Chm-Supervisory Bd)*
Michael Eggleton *(Chm-Mgmt Bd & CEO)*
Roman Aleksander Maszczyk *(Deputy Chm-Mgmt Bd, Deputy CEO & Chief Risk Officer)*
Zain Majidulla *(First Deputy Chm-Mgmt Bd & COO)*
Yerkeblan Okayev *(First Deputy Chm-Mgmt Bd)*
Talgat Abdukhalikov *(Deputy CEO-Ops)*
Nurbek Ayazbayev *(Deputy CEO)*
Ayaz Bakassov *(Deputy CEO-Private Banking)*
Anna Bichurina *(Deputy CEO-Fin & Admin Block)*
Seitzhan Yermekbayev *(Deputy CEO-Corp & SME Bus)*
Supervisory Board of Directors:
Alexander Mashkevitch
Ruslan Adylon
Michael Eggleton
Alijan Ibragimov
Nikolay Radostovets
Olga Rozmanova
Patokh Shodiyev
Boris Umanov

Subsidiary:

Insurance Company Eurasia JSC (1)
Zheltoksan St 59
050004 Almaty, Kazakhstan
Tel.: (7) 7272584336
Fax: (7) 7272584338
E-Mail: info@theeurasia.kz
Web Site: www.theeurasia.kz
Insurance Services
S.I.C.: 6411
N.A.I.C.S.: 524210

Non-U.S. Subsidiary:

Eurasian Capital B.V (1)
Schouwburgplein 30-34
3012 Rotterdam, Netherlands
Tel.: (31) 10 2245333
Banking Services
S.I.C.: 6211
N.A.I.C.S.: 523110

EURASIAN DEVELOPMENT BANK
220 Dostyk ave
Almaty, 050051, Kazakhstan
Tel.: (7) 7272444044
Fax: (7) 7272508158
E-Mail: info@eabr.org
Web Site: www.eabr.org
EABRK280414—(KAZ)
Int. Income: $186,311,000
Assets: $3,884,008,000
Liabilities: $2,174,926,000
Net Worth: $1,709,082,000
Earnings: $11,988,000
Emp.: 274
Fiscal Year-end: 12/31/12
Business Description:
Commercial Banking Services
S.I.C.: 6029
N.A.I.C.S.: 522110
Personnel:
Sergey Glazyev *(Chm-Supervisory Bd)*
Igor Valentinovich Finogenov *(Chm-Mgmt Bd)*
Viktor Bolyasnikov *(Deputy Chm-Mgmt Bd)*
Marat Djaukenov *(Deputy Chm-Mgmt Bd)*
Kanat Dosmukametov *(Deputy Chm-Mgmt Bd)*
Sergey I. Shatalov *(Deputy Chm-Mgmt Bd)*
Gennady Zhuzhlev *(Deputy Chm-Mgmt Bd)*
Sergey Elagin *(Member-Mgmt Bd & Mng Dir-Treasury)*
Dmitry Krasilnikov *(Member-Mgmt Bd & Mng Dir-Corp Fin)*
Berik Mukhambetzhanov *(Member-Mgmt Bd & Mng Dir-Fin)*
Vladimir Yasinsky *(Member-Mgmt Bd & Mng Dir-Res & Strategy)*
Supervisory Board of Directors:
Sergey Glazyev
Sailau Baizakov
Valery Geets
Mikhail Gelvanovsky
Viktor Ivanter
Ivan Korolev
Alexandr Libman
Leonid Limonov
Dmitry Travin
Andrey Tur
Vyacheslav Vashanov
Sergey Vassilyev
Vladimir Yassinsky
Oraz Zhandossov
Vladimir Zuev

EURASIAN MINERALS INC.
Suite 501 - 543 Granville Street
Vancouver, BC, V6C 1X8, Canada
Tel.: (604) 688-6390
Fax: (604) 688-1157
E-Mail: info@eurasianminerals.com
Web Site: www.eurasianminerals.com
Year Founded: 2001
EMXX—(NYSEMKT TSXV)
Rev.: $1,740,504
Assets: $81,982,582
Liabilities: $14,022,757
Net Worth: $67,959,824
Earnings: ($20,777,059)
Emp.: 58
Fiscal Year-end: 12/31/12
Business Description:
Mineral Exploration Services
S.I.C.: 1081
N.A.I.C.S.: 213114
Personnel:
Michael D. Winn *(Chm)*
David M. Cole *(Pres & CEO)*
Christina Cepeliauskas *(CFO)*
M. Stephen Enders *(COO)*
Jan N. Steiert *(Chief Legal Officer)*
Valerie Barlow *(Corp Sec)*
Board of Directors:
Michael D. Winn
Brian Eric Bayley
David M. Cole
M. Stephen Enders
Brian K. Levet
George K.C. Lim
James Andrew Morris
Legal Counsel:
Northwest Law Group
Suite 950 Scotia Tower 650 West Georgia Street
11587
Vancouver, BC, Canada
Transfer Agent:
Computershare Investor Services Inc.
510 Burrard Street 2nd Floor
Vancouver, BC, V6C 3B9, Canada

EURASIAN NATURAL RESOURCES CORPORATION PLC
16 Saint James's Street
London, SW1A 1ER, United Kingdom
Tel.: (44) 2073891440
Fax: (44) 2073891441
E-Mail: reception@enrc.com
Web Site: www.enrc.com
ENRC—(LSE OTC)
Rev.: $6,320,000,000
Assets: $20,164,000,000
Liabilities: $9,614,000,000
Net Worth: $10,550,000,000
Earnings: ($852,000,000)
Emp.: 78,484
Fiscal Year-end: 12/31/12
Business Description:
Diversified Natural Resource Holding Company
S.I.C.: 6719
N.A.I.C.S.: 551112
Personnel:
Felix J. Vulis *(CEO)*
Zaure Zaurbekova *(CFO)*
Almaz Ibragimov *(Pres-JSC Aluminium-Kazakhstan)*
Bereke Mukhametkaliev *(Pres-JSC Zhairem GOK)*
Abduazim Rustambayev *(Pres-JSC Eurasian Energy Corp)*
Victor V. Till *(Pres-JSC Kazchrome)*
Mukhamejan Turdakhunov *(Pres-SSGPO)*
Arif Shadiev *(Gen Dir-ENRC Logistics)*
Beat Ehrensberger *(Gen Counsel)*
Paul Waller *(Treas)*
Victoria Penrice *(Sec)*
Board of Directors:
Marat Beketayev
Felix J. Vulis
Zaure Zaurbekova
Legal Counsel:
Jones Day
21 Tudor Street
London, EC4Y 6DA, United Kingdom
Denton Wilde Sapte
Ken Dala Business Centre 38 Dostyk Avenue
Almaty, Kazakhstan
Subsidiaries:

ENRC Management (UK) Limited (1)
2nd Fl 16 St James
London, SW1A 1ER, United Kingdom

Eurasian Natural Resources Corporation PLC—(Continued)

Tel.: (44) 2073891440
Fax: (44) 2073891441
Web Site: www.enrc.com
Emp.: 70
Business Management Services
S.I.C.: 7389
N.A.I.C.S.: 561499
Felix J. Vulis *(CEO)*

Non-U.S. Subsidiaries:

ENRC Leasing BV (1)
Jan Luijkenstraat 8
1071 CM Amsterdam, Netherlands
Tel.: (31) 205707590
Financial Management Services
S.I.C.: 6282
N.A.I.C.S.: 523920

ENRC Logistics LLP (1)
76 Abai Ave
Almaty, 050057, Kazakhstan
Tel.: (7) 7272582858
Fax: (7) 7272597119
E-Mail: resception@logistics.enrc.com
Freight Transportation Services
S.I.C.: 4522
N.A.I.C.S.: 481212
Shadiyev Orifjan *(Chm)*

ENRC Marketing AG (1)
Balz Zimmermann Strasse 7
Zurich, 8058, Switzerland
Tel.: (41) 434994100
Fax: (41) 434994199
Emp.: 80
Transportation Services
S.I.C.: 4512
N.A.I.C.S.: 481112

TransCom LLP (1)
76 Abai Ave
050057 Almaty, Kazakhstan
Tel.: (7) 7272509952
Fax: (7) 7272509952
Web Site: www.transsystem.kz/eng/rooteng.asp?idx=65&lang=eng
Freight Transportation Services
S.I.C.: 4522
N.A.I.C.S.: 481212

Universal Service LLP (1)
76 Abai Ave
050057 Almaty, Kazakhstan
Tel.: (7) 7272582188
Fax: (7) 7272582188
E-Mail: info-el@logistics.enrc.com
Web Site: www.transsystem.kz
Freight Transportation Services
S.I.C.: 4522
N.A.I.C.S.: 481212
Khader Sargey *(Mng Dir)*

EURAZEO S.A.

32 rue de Monceau
75008 Paris, France
Tel.: (33) 144150111
Fax: (33) 147668441
E-Mail: Eurazeo_investor_relations@eurazeo.com
Web Site: www.eurazeo.com
RF—(DEU EUR LSE)
Rev.: $5,951,075,643
Assets: $18,181,171,441
Liabilities: $13,014,774,252
Net Worth: $5,166,397,188
Earnings: ($362,107,614)
Emp.: 29,540
Fiscal Year-end: 12/31/12

Business Description:
Investment Services
S.I.C.: 6211
N.A.I.C.S.: 523999

Personnel:
Michel David-Weill *(Chm-Supervisory Bd)*
Patrick Sayer *(Chm-Exec Bd)*
Jean Laurent *(Vice Chm-Supervisory Bd)*
Bruno Keller *(Deputy CEO & Member-Exec Bd)*
Philippe Audouin *(CFO & Member-Exec Bd)*
Virginie Morgon *(Chief Investment Officer & Member-Exec Bd)*
Fabrice de Gaudemar *(Member-Exec Bd)*
Nicolas Huet *(Gen Counsel)*

Supervisory Board of Directors:
Michel David-Weill
Richard Goblet d'Alviella
Victoire de Margerie
Roland du Luart de Montsaulnin
Olivier Merveilleux du Vignaux
Anne Lalou
Jean Laurent
Michel Mathieu
Stephane Pallez
Georges Pauget
Jean-Pierre Richardson
Kristen van Riel
Jacques Veyrat

Mazars
61 rue Henri Regnault
Courbevoie, France

Subsidiaries:

Elis SA (1)
31 Rue Voltaire
92803 Puteaux, France
Tel.: (33) 141254500
Fax: (33) 1 47 28 80 65
Web Site: www.elis.com
Emp.: 10,000
Consumer Goods Rental Services
S.I.C.: 7359
N.A.I.C.S.: 532299
Xavier Martire *(Gen Mgr)*

Eurazeo PME (1)
32 rue de Monceau
75008 Paris, France
Tel.: (33) 1 53 83 81 65
E-Mail: omillet@eurazeo-pme.com
Web Site: www.eurazeo-pme.com
Investment Management
S.I.C.: 6211
N.A.I.C.S.: 523999
Olivier Millet *(Chm-Mgmt Bd)*

Holding:

Financiere Dessange SASU (2)
39 avenue Franklin Roosevelt
75008 Paris, France
Tel.: (33) 1 53 83 99 10
Holding Company
S.I.C.: 6719
N.A.I.C.S.: 551112
Jacques Dessange *(Chm)*

Holding:

DESSANGE International SA (3)
39 avenue Franklin Roosevelt
75008 Paris, France
Tel.: (33) 1 53 83 99 10
Fax: (33) 1 42 89 13 54
Sales Range: $1-4.9 Billion
Hair Salons
S.I.C.: 7231
N.A.I.C.S.: 812112
Benjamin Dessange *(Chm-Exec Bd)*

U.S. Subsidiary:

Fantastic Sams International Corporation (4)
50 Dunham Rd 3rd Fl
Beverly, MA 01915
Tel.: (978) 232-5600
Fax: (978) 232-5601
Toll Free: (888) 263-4432
Web Site: www.fantasticsams.com
Sales Range: $10-24.9 Million
Emp.: 48
Hair Salon Operator
S.I.C.: 7231
N.A.I.C.S.: 812112
Allyson Hurley King *(CEO)*
Tom Boitz *(COO)*

Fonroche Energie SAS (1)
Zac Des Champs De Lescaze
47310 Roquefort, France
Tel.: (33) 553772131
Fax: (33) 5 53 77 21 51
E-Mail: contact@fonroche.fr
Web Site: www.fonroche.fr
Emp.: 28
Semiconductor Device Mfr
S.I.C.: 3674
N.A.I.C.S.: 334413

OFI Private Equity Capital SCA (1)
32 Rue de Monceau
75008 Paris, France (52.5%)
Tel.: (33) 1 53 83 81 60
Fax: (33) 153838174
Web Site: www.eurazeopme.com
Sales Range: $450-499.9 Million
Emp.: 13
Investment Banking & Securities Services
S.I.C.: 6211
N.A.I.C.S.: 523110
Virginia Morgon *(Chm-Supervisory Bd)*
Olivier Millet *(Chm-Exec Bd)*

Holdings:

3S Photonics S.A.S. (1)
Route de Villejust
F 91625 Nozay, France (86%)
Tel.: (33) 169805750
Fax: (33) 169805883
E-Mail: contact@3spgroup.com
Web Site: www.3spgroup.com
Sales Range: $50-74.9 Million
Emp.: 400
Optical & Optoelectronic Components Mfr
S.I.C.: 3827
N.A.I.C.S.: 333314
Alexandre Krivine *(Pres & CEO)*
Jean-Michel Bonard *(Sec)*
Eric Delevaque *(Exec VP-Mktg & Bus Dev)*
Michel Privat *(Exec VP-Sls)*
Didier Sauvage *(Exec VP-Tech)*

Branch:

3S Photonics S.A.S - Marcoussis (2)
Batiment A1
Route de Nozay, F-91460 Marcoussis, France
Tel.: (33) 169805830
Fax: (33) 169805884
Electronic Components Mfr
S.I.C.: 3679
N.A.I.C.S.: 334418
Alexandre Krivine *(Pres & CEO)*

Europcar Groupe S.A. (1)
19 Rue du Moulin Quignon
80100 Picardie, Abbeville, France (84.5%)
Tel.: (33) 130449000
Fax: (33) 130449445
Web Site: www.europcar.fr
Sales Range: $1-4.9 Billion
Emp.: 7,689
Holding Company
S.I.C.: 6719
N.A.I.C.S.: 551112
Jean-Charles Pauze *(Chm)*
Roland Keppler *(CEO)*
Charles Desmartis *(CFO)*
Didier Fenix *(COO)*

Holding:

Europcar International S.A. (2)
3 Ave Du Centre
Les Quadrants, 78881 Saint-Quentin-en-Yvelines, France (100%)
Tel.: (33) 130449000
Fax: (33) 130441279
E-Mail: contact@europcar.com
Web Site: www.europcar.com
Sales Range: $1-4.9 Billion
Emp.: 60
Car Rental Services
S.I.C.: 7514
N.A.I.C.S.: 532111
Philip Gheaaeppe *(CEO)*
Charles Desmartis *(CFO)*

Subsidiaries:

Europcar France S.A. (3)
3 Ave Du Centre
Les Quadrants, 78881 Saint-Quentin-en-Yvelines, France (99.9%)
Tel.: (33) 130449000
Fax: (33) 130441279
E-Mail: evelynenercier@europcar.com
Web Site: www.europcar.fr
Emp.: 500
Car Rental Services
S.I.C.: 7514
N.A.I.C.S.: 532111
Roland Keppler *(Gen Mgr)*

Non-U.S. Subsidiaries:

Europcar IB, S.A. (4)
Av del Partenon 16 18
Campo de las Naciones, 28042 Madrid, Spain (100%)
Tel.: (34) 917226200
Fax: (34) 917226201
E-Mail: es-customerservice@europcar.com
Web Site: www.europcar.es
Car Rental Services
S.I.C.: 7514
N.A.I.C.S.: 532111

Europcar International S.A. & Co. OHG (4)
Tangstedter Landstrasse 81
22415 Hamburg, Germany (99%)
Tel.: (49) 40520180
Fax: (49) 40520182610
E-Mail: infomaster@mail.europcar.com
Web Site: www.europcar.de
Emp.: 430
Car Rental Services
S.I.C.: 7514
N.A.I.C.S.: 532111
Orland Keppler *(Mng Dir)*

Subsidiary:

Europcar Autovermietung GmbH (5)
Tangstedter Landstrasse 81
22415 Hamburg, Germany DE
Tel.: (49) 40520180
Telex: 2 174 346
Fax: (49) 40520182610
E-Mail: info@mail.europcar.com
Web Site: www.europcar.com
Emp.: 1,000
Car Rental Services
S.I.C.: 7514
N.A.I.C.S.: 532111
Andrea Weichert *(Dir-Fin)*

Europcar Holding S.A.S. (3)
Parc d'affaires Le val Saint Quentin 2 rue Rene Caudron
Les Quadrants, 78881 Voisins-le-Bretonneux, France (100%)
Tel.: (33) 130449000
Fax: (33) 130441279
Web Site: www.europcar.fa
Holding Company
S.I.C.: 6719
N.A.I.C.S.: 551112
Kippler Holang *(Gen Mgr)*

Non-U.S. Subsidiaries:

Europcar Italia S.p.A. (4)
Via Cesare Giulio Viola 48
Parco De Medici, 00148 Rome, Italy(100%)
Tel.: (39) 06967091
Fax: (39) 06 520 5806
Car Rental Services
S.I.C.: 7514
N.A.I.C.S.: 532111

Europcar S.A. (4)
Weiveldlaan 8
1930 Zaventem, Brussels, Belgium (99.9%)
Tel.: (32) 27097100
Fax: (32) 27097110
E-Mail: customer.servicesbelgium@europcar.com
Web Site: www.europcar.com
Sales Range: $25-49.9 Million
Emp.: 70
Car Rental Services
S.I.C.: 7514
N.A.I.C.S.: 532111

Europcar UK Limited (4)
Europcar House
Aldenham Road, Watford, WD23 2QQ, United Kingdom (100%)
Tel.: (44) 1923811000
Fax: (44) 1923811010
Web Site: www.europcar.co.uk
Emp.: 100
Car Rental Services
S.I.C.: 7514
N.A.I.C.S.: 532111
Keen McCall *(Mng Dir)*

Non-U.S. Subsidiary:

APCOA Parking AG (1)
Flughafenstrasse 34
PO Box 23 04 63
70624 Stuttgart, Germany
Tel.: (49) 711947910
Fax: (49) 711 947 91 59
E-Mail: info@apcoa.eu
Web Site: www.apcoa-europe.com
Emp.: 950
Parking Facility Management Services
S.I.C.: 8744
N.A.I.C.S.: 561210
Ralf Bender *(CEO)*

Subsidiary:

APCOA Autoparking GmbH (2)
Flughafenstr 34
70629 Stuttgart, Germany
Tel.: (49) 711 947 91 0
Fax: (49) 711 947 91 860
E-Mail: service@apcoa.de
Web Site: www.apcoa.de
Emp.: 150
Automobile Parking Services
S.I.C.: 7521
N.A.I.C.S.: 812930
Peter Schneck *(Gen Mgr)*

Non-U.S. Subsidiaries:

APCOA Belgium N.V. (2)
Brusselstraat 59
2018 Antwerp, Belgium
Tel.: (32) 32339423
Fax: (32) 32339553
Web Site: www.apcoa.be
Parking Facility Management Services
S.I.C.: 8744
N.A.I.C.S.: 561210
Luc Verduyckt *(Gen Mgr)*

APCOA d.o.o. (2)
Adamiceva 13 III
51000 Rijeka, Croatia
Tel.: (385) 51212418
Fax: (385) 51322072
Web Site: www.apcoa.hr
Parking Facility Management Services
S.I.C.: 8744
N.A.I.C.S.: 561210
James Andreas Toal *(Gen Mgr)*

APCOA Parking Austria GmbH (2)
Landstrasser Hauptstrasse 146-13 A
1030 Vienna, Austria
Tel.: (43) 1 717 16 0
Fax: (43) 1 717 16 35
Web Site: www.apcoa.at
Emp.: 163
Parking Facility Management Services
S.I.C.: 8744
N.A.I.C.S.: 561210
James Toal *(Mng Dir)*

APCOA Parking Espana S.A. (2)
C/Colombia n63 - 7A
28016 Madrid, Spain
Tel.: (34) 917030447
Fax: (34) 913508791
E-Mail: info@apcoa.es
Web Site: www.apcoa.es
Parking Facility Management Services
S.I.C.: 7521
N.A.I.C.S.: 812930
Jesus Maria Salinero *(Mng Dir)*

APCOA Parking Ireland Ltd. (2)
Unit 11 Millbank Business Pk Lower Rd
Lucan Village, Dublin, Ireland
Tel.: (353) 16516900
Fax: (353) 16516909
E-Mail: info@apcoa.ie
Web Site: www.apcoa.ie
Parking Facility Management Services
S.I.C.: 8744
N.A.I.C.S.: 561210
Neil Cunningham *(Mng Dir)*

APCOA Parking Italia S.p.A. (2)
Via Chiassi 20 D
46100 Mantua, Italy
Tel.: (39) 376221677
Fax: (39) 0376 22 16 79
E-Mail: info@apcoa.it
Web Site: www.apcoa.it
Emp.: 25
Water Treatment Services
S.I.C.: 4941
N.A.I.C.S.: 221310
Friedrich Schock *(Chm)*
Arturo Benigna *(Mng Dir & Gen Mgr)*

APCOA Parking Nederland B.V. (2)
Westblaak 88
3012 KM Rotterdam, Netherlands
Tel.: (31) 102331984
Fax: (31) 102331955
E-Mail: info@apcoa.nl
Web Site: www.apcoa.nl
Parking Facility Management Services
S.I.C.: 8744
N.A.I.C.S.: 561210
Henk de Bruin *(Gen Mgr)*

APCOA Parking Polska Sp.z o.o. (2)
Rondo ONZ 1
00-124 Warsaw, Poland
Tel.: (48) 22 354 83 80
Fax: (48) 22 354 83 90
Web Site: www.apcoa.pl
Emp.: 120
Parking Facility Management Services
S.I.C.: 8744
N.A.I.C.S.: 561210
Marie Zawadzki *(Mng Dir)*

APCOA Parking Switzerland AG (2)
Buckhauserstrasse 11
8048 Zurich, Switzerland
Tel.: (41) 44 49 52 401
Web Site: www.apcoa.ch
Emp.: 50
Parking Facilities Management Services
S.I.C.: 8744
N.A.I.C.S.: 561210
Hamit Beganaj *(Mgr-Ops-Biel / Bienne)*

APCOA Parking Turkey (2)
ParkSistem Buyukdere Caddesi M Dervis Ibrahim
Gayrettepe, 34394 Istanbul, Turkey
Tel.: (90) 2122752030
Fax: (90) 212 275 20 30
Web Site: www.apcoa.com.tr
Parking Facility Management Services
S.I.C.: 8744
N.A.I.C.S.: 561210

APCOA Parking (UK) Ltd (2)
Wellington House 4-10 Cowley Road
Uxbridge, London, Middlesex, UB8 2XW, United Kingdom
Tel.: (44) 1895272500
Fax: (44) 1895454200
E-Mail: support@apcoa.co.uk
Web Site: www.apcoa.co.uk
Emp.: 80
Parking Facility Management Services
S.I.C.: 8744
N.A.I.C.S.: 561210
Christopher Pullen *(Mng Dir)*

EUREKA DESIGN PUBLIC COMPANY LIMITED

19 Moo 11 Tambon Ladsawai
Amphoe Lamlukka, Pathumthani, 12150, Thailand
Tel.: (66) 21923737
Fax: (66) 21923741
Web Site: www.eurekadesign.co.th
Year Founded: 2002
EUREKA—(THA)
Sales Range: $10-24.9 Million
Emp.: 120
Business Description:
Automotive Machinery Mfr
S.I.C.: 3714
N.A.I.C.S.: 336390
Personnel:
Adisorn Prakunhangsit *(Chm)*
Narakorn Ratchapolsitte *(Mng Dir)*

EUREKA GROUP HOLDINGS LIMITED

Unit 7 486 Scottsdale Drive
Varsity Lakes, QLD, 4227, Australia
Tel.: (61) 7 3840 3111
Fax: (61) 7 3840 3199
E-Mail: corporate@scvgroup.com.au
Web Site: www.scvgroup.com.au
EGH—(ASX)
Rev.: $11,336,422
Assets: $9,775,965
Liabilities: $5,589,311
Net Worth: $4,186,654
Earnings: $78,087
Emp.: 12
Fiscal Year-end: 06/30/13
Business Description:
Retirement Facilities Property Asset Management & Catering Services
S.I.C.: 6531
N.A.I.C.S.: 531390
Personnel:
Troy Nunan *(CFO & Sec)*
Kerry Potter *(COO)*
Board of Directors:
Lachlan McIntosh
Paul Fulloon
Nirmal Hansra
Kerry Potter
Greg Rekers
Legal Counsel:
HWL Ebsworth
Level 2 Brisbane 500 Queen St
Brisbane, Australia

EUREKA RESOURCES, INC.

1000 355 Burrard Street
Vancouver, BC, V6C 2G8, Canada
Tel.: (604) 608-6154
Fax: (604) 602-1989
E-Mail: info@eurekaresourcesinc.com
Web Site: www.eurekaresourcesinc.com
Year Founded: 1981
EUK—(TSXV)
Int. Income: $131
Assets: $124,332
Liabilities: $215,061
Net Worth: ($90,729)
Earnings: ($20,357)
Fiscal Year-end: 10/31/12
Business Description:
Mineral Exploration Services
S.I.C.: 1081
N.A.I.C.S.: 213114
Personnel:
John Jack O'Neill *(Pres & CEO)*
Sheryl A. Jones *(CFO)*
Terence O'Neill *(Sec)*
Board of Directors:
John Jack O'Neill
Lawrence B. O'Neill
Mark Rozenberg
Kristian Whitehead
Legal Counsel:
Fraser Milner Casgrain
15th Floor 1040 West Georgia Street
Vancouver, BC, Canada
Transfer Agent:
Computershare Trust Company of Canada
2nd Floor 510 Burrard Street
V6C3B9 Vancouver, BC, Canada

EUREMIS HOLDING SA

Avenue Greiner 1
4100 Seraing, Belgium
Tel.: (32) 498442411
E-Mail: pierre.meyers@skynet.be
Emp.: 3,500
Business Description:
Holding Company
S.I.C.: 6719
N.A.I.C.S.: 551112
Personnel:
Pierre Meyers *(CEO & Mng Dir)*
Holding:

Cockerill Maintenance & Ingenierie SA (1)
Ave Greiner 1
4100 Seraing, Belgium BE
Tel.: (32) 43302243 (80.65%)
Fax: (32) 43302582
E-Mail: welcome@cmigroupe.com
Web Site: www.cmigroupe.com
Sales Range: $750-799.9 Million
Emp.: 2,700
Designs, Maintains, Engineers & Supplies Technical Equipment, Including Boilers, Weapon Systems, Processing Lines, Chemical & Thermal Process Systems for Energy, Defence & Industry Sectors
S.I.C.: 3568
N.A.I.C.S.: 333613
Bernard Serin *(Chm & Mng Dir)*
Yves Honhon *(CFO & Chief Admin Officer)*
Paul Neirinck *(Chief Dev Officer)*
Jean-Francois Levaux *(Chief Sls & Legal Officer)*
Brigitte Coppens *(Chief Comm Officer)*
Jean-Luc Taelman *(Chief HR Officer)*
Jean-Marc Kohlgruber *(Pres-Indus-Engrg)*
Pierre Melin *(Pres-Sls Energy)*
Franck Pasqualini *(Pres-Indus-Maintenance)*
Milan Peter *(Pres-Energy)*
Paul Thonon *(Pres-Defence)*

Subsidiary:

CMI Nesa (2)
Rue Edouard Belin 1
Box 4
1435 Mont-Saint-Guibert, Belgium
Tel.: (32) 10 47 5611
Telex: 59228
Fax: (32) 10450401
E-Mail: nesa@cmigroupe.com
Web Site: www.cmigroupe.com
Emp.: 75
Engineering Services
S.I.C.: 8711
N.A.I.C.S.: 541330

U.S. Holding:

CMI Industry Americas Inc. (2)
435 W Wilson St
Salem, OH 44460
Tel.: (330) 332-4661
Fax: (330) 332-1853
E-Mail: efco@cmigroupe.com
Web Site: www.cmigroupe.com
Sales Range: $300-349.9 Million
Emp.: 973
Industrial Furnace Mfr; Designs, Modernizes & Supplies Cold Steel-Making Complexes
S.I.C.: 3567
N.A.I.C.S.: 333994
Thomas Walfraffe *(CEO)*

Non-U.S. Subsidiary:

CMI FPE Ltd. (2)
Mehta House 64 Road no 13 MIDC
Andheri E, Mumbai, 400 093, India
Tel.: (91) 22 6676 2727
Fax: (91) 22 6676 2737
E-Mail: sales@cmifpe.com
Web Site: www.cmifpe.com
500147—(BOM)
Rev.: $103,334,933
Assets: $100,046,809
Liabilities: $72,124,252
Net Worth: $27,922,556
Earnings: ($184,213)
Emp.: 562
Fiscal Year-end: 03/31/13
Metal Processing Equipment Mfr
S.I.C.: 3559
N.A.I.C.S.: 333249
Sanjoy Kumar Das *(Mng Dir)*
Akash Ohri *(CFO)*
Vijay Karayi *(CIO & Dir-Mgmt Assurance & QMS)*
Sanjay Kumar Mutha *(Compliance Officer & Sec)*

EURINNOV SA

25 boulevard Malheserbes
75008 Paris, France
Tel.: (33) 1 40980345
Fax: (33) 1 42662352
E-Mail: gaelle.leturdu@eurinnov.com
Web Site: www.eurinnov.com
Year Founded: 2001
MLERI—(EUR)
Sales Range: $1-9.9 Million
Emp.: 30

Eurinnov SA—(Continued)

Business Description:
Financial Consulting Services
S.I.C.: 8742
N.A.I.C.S.: 541611
Personnel:
Michel Moreau *(Pres)*

EURO ARAB INSURANCE
PO Box 1435
Amman, 11953, Jordan
Tel.: (962) 65518935
Fax: (962) 65518956
E-Mail: info@euroarabins.com
Web Site: www.euroarabins.com
Year Founded: 1996
AMMI—(AMM)
Sales Range: $10-24.9 Million
Emp.: 45
Business Description:
Insurance Services
S.I.C.: 6411
N.A.I.C.S.: 524298
Personnel:
Fouad Bajjali *(Chm)*
Ramez Bajjali *(Vice Chm)*
Board of Directors:
Fouad Bajjali
Mohammad Al Farrayeh
Ramez Bajjali
Rosie Bajjali
Hani Rabie
Mousa Rizk

EURO ASIA PREMIER REAL ESTATE COMPANY LIMITED
Jian Hong East Street Number 316
Weifang, China
Tel.: (86) 536 2222276
Fax: (86) 536 8258686
E-Mail: euasia@eu-asia.net
Web Site: www.eu-asia.net
JT9—(DEU)
Sales Range: $25-49.9 Million
Business Description:
Property Development Services
S.I.C.: 1542
N.A.I.C.S.: 236220
Personnel:
Xiyi Sun *(Chm)*
Patrick P. L. Chan *(CEO)*
Dingxiang Chan *(CFO)*
Board of Directors:
Xiyi Sun
Patrick P. L. Chan
Han Wei Guo
Haitao Sun
Cong Yu

EURO CERAMICS LTD
Euro House Chincholi Bunder Road
Behind Inorbit Mall Malad West
Mumbai, 400064, India
Tel.: (91) 2240194019
Fax: (91) 2240194020
E-Mail: sales@eurovitrified.com
Web Site: www.eurovitrified.com
532823—(BOM)
Rev.: $18,618,895
Assets: $111,741,278
Liabilities: $118,641,832
Net Worth: ($6,900,555)
Earnings: ($20,960,653)
Emp.: 1,000
Fiscal Year-end: 03/31/13
Business Description:
Ceramic Tiles Mfr
S.I.C.: 3297
N.A.I.C.S.: 327120
Personnel:
Nenshi L. Shah *(Chm & Mng Dir)*
V. Annapurneswary *(Compliance Officer)*
Board of Directors:
Nenshi L. Shah
Mahendra V. Modi
Amit Nandu
Karan Rajput
Paresh K. Shah
Transfer Agent:
Link Intime India Private Limited
C-13 Pannalal Silk Mills Compound L.B.S. Marg
Bhandup
Mumbai, India
Subsidiary:

Euro Merchandise (India) Limited **(1)**
Chincholi Bunder Rd near Inorbit Mall Opp
HSBC bank 3F Malad W
Mumbai, Maharashtra, 400064, India
Tel.: (91) 2240194019
Fax: (91) 2240194020
E-Mail: sales@eurotilesindia.com
Web Site: www.eurotilesindia.com
Emp.: 50
Wall & Floor Tiles Mfr
S.I.C.: 3259
N.A.I.C.S.: 327120
Nitesh P Shah *(Mng Dir)*

EURO DISNEY S.C.A.
Disneyland Paris
BP 100
77777 Marne-la-Vallee, Cedex 04, France
Tel.: (33) 1 64 745855
Fax: (33) 1 64 745636
E-Mail: dlp.communication.institutionnelle@disney.com
Web Site: www.eurodisney.com
EDL—(EUR)
Sales Range: $1-4.9 Billion
Emp.: 11,820
Business Description:
Owner & Operator of Theme Parks & Resorts
S.I.C.: 7996
N.A.I.C.S.: 713110
Personnel:
Antoine Jeancourt-Galignani *(Chm-Supervisory Bd)*
Philippe Geslin *(CEO)*
Joe Schott *(COO & Sr VP)*
Francois Pinon *(Gen Counsel & VP)*
Dominique Cocquet *(Sr VP-Strategic Project Consulting & Dev)*
Federico J. Gonzalez *(Sr VP-Mktg & Sls)*
Norbert Stiekema *(Sr VP-Sls & Distr)*
Supervisory Board of Directors:
Antoine Jeancourt-Galignani
Valerie Irene Amelie Monique Bernis
Gerard Bouche
Michel Corbiere
Philippe Geslin
Philippe Labro
James A. Rasulo
Anthony Martin Robinson
Thomas O. Staggs
Subsidiaries:

EDL Hotels SCA **(1)**
BP 100
Marne-la-Vallee, France (100%)
Tel.: (33) 164744000
Fax: (33) 160456533
Hotels & Motels
S.I.C.: 7011
N.A.I.C.S.: 721110

Euro Disney Associes SCA **(1)**
Route Nationale 34
Immeubles Administratifs, 77700 Chessy, France
Tel.: (33) 160302020
Fax: (33) 164746161
Web Site: www.disneylandparis.com
Emp.: 12,000
Amusement & Theme Parks
S.I.C.: 7996
N.A.I.C.S.: 713110

Euro Disney SAS **(1)**
Route Nationale 34
Immeubles Administratifs, 77700 Chessy, France
Tel.: (33) 164745855
Fax: (33) 1 64 745636
Web Site: corporate.disneylandparis.com
Amusement & Theme Parks
S.I.C.: 7996
N.A.I.C.S.: 713110
Karl Holz *(Pres)*

Euro Disney SAS **(1)**
Route Nationale 34
Immeubles Administratifs, 77700 Chessy, France
Tel.: (33) 160302020
Fax: (33) 164744543
E-Mail: resources.humaines@disneyland.com
Web Site: corporate.disneylandparis.com
Amusement & Theme Parks
S.I.C.: 7996
N.A.I.C.S.: 713110
Philippe Gas *(CEO)*

EURO-FINANCE LTD.
43 Christopher Columbus Blvd
1592 Sofia, Bulgaria
Tel.: (359) 29805657
Fax: (359) 29811496
E-Mail: contact@euro-fin.com
Web Site: www.euro-fin.com
Sales Range: Less than $1 Million
Emp.: 30
Business Description:
Financial Services
S.I.C.: 6726
N.A.I.C.S.: 525990
Personnel:
Jordan Popov *(Head-HR & Exec Dir)*

EURO HOLDINGS BERHAD
Wisma Euro Lot 21 Rawang Industrial Estate
48000 Rawang, Selangor Darul Ehsan, Malaysia
Tel.: (60) 360926666
Fax: (60) 3 6092 3000
E-Mail: corporate@eurochairs.com
Web Site: www.eurochairs.com
EURO—(KLS)
Rev.: $33,832,162
Assets: $42,321,027
Liabilities: $20,058,538
Net Worth: $22,262,489
Earnings: $482,698
Emp.: 664
Fiscal Year-end: 12/31/12
Business Description:
Office Furniture Mfr
S.I.C.: 2521
N.A.I.C.S.: 337211
Personnel:
Fatt Sin Lew *(Founder & Mng Dir)*
Hooi Chin Lim *(Co-Sec)*
Keat Chai Tai *(Co-Sec)*
Board of Directors:
Mohd Haniff Abd Aziz
Muhamad Abdul Kadir
Yuen Keong Choong
Yein Teng Foong
Sim Shee Law
Fatt Sin Lew
Hin Lew
Wai Pin Ng
Kah Ho Pua
Poh Ling Tan
Hock Toh Teh
Subsidiaries:

Euro Chairs Manufacturer (M) Sdn Bhd. **(1)**
Wisma Euro Lot 21 Rawang Industrial Estate
Rawang, Selangor, 48000, Malaysia
Tel.: (60) 360926666
Fax: (60) 360923000
Emp.: 300
Office Furniture Mfr & Distr
S.I.C.: 2522
N.A.I.C.S.: 337214
Law Sim Shee *(Mng Dir)*

Euro Space Industries (M) Sdn Bhd **(1)**
Wisma Euro Lot 21 Rawang Industrial Estate
Rawang, Selangor, Malaysia
Tel.: (60) 360927777
Fax: (60) 360925000
Office Furniture Mfr & Distr
S.I.C.: 2522
N.A.I.C.S.: 337214

EURO-M FLEXIBLE PACKAGING S.A.
Parc Industriel de Ghlin Baudour Nord
B 7011 Mons, Belgium
Tel.: (32) 65760000
Fax: (32) 65760028
E-Mail: info@eurom.de
Sales Range: $10-24.9 Million
Emp.: 65
Business Description:
Mfr of Flexible Packaging Products
S.I.C.: 2671
N.A.I.C.S.: 326112
Personnel:
Silvio Pignone *(Mng Dir)*
Non-U.S. Joint Venture:

AEP Industries Nederland B.V. **(1)**
Laan Van Westenenk 11
PO Box 66
7300 AB Apeldoorn, 7336 AZ, Netherlands NL
Tel.: (31) 555996600
Fax: (31) 555996550
E-Mail: info@afpholland.com
Web Site: www.afpholland.com
Emp.: 230
Plastic Pallet Wrapping Material & Flexible Packaging Mfr; Owned 51% by Ghlin S.r.l. & 49% by Euro-M Flexible Packaging S.A.
S.I.C.: 3089
N.A.I.C.S.: 326199
Paul ten Brink *(Mng Dir)*

EURO MECHANICAL & ELECTRICAL CONTRACTORS LTD.
(d/b/a EMEC)
1st Floor Moh'd Al Hurr Al Suweidi Bldg
PO Box 46153
Abu Dhabi, 46153, United Arab Emirates
Tel.: (971) 26781133
Fax: (971) 26781953
E-Mail: sales@euromechanical.com
Web Site: www.euromechanical.com
Year Founded: 1976
Emp.: 500
Business Description:
Mechanical & Electrical Contractor
S.I.C.: 1731
N.A.I.C.S.: 238210
Personnel:
John Manna *(Founder & Chm)*

EURO-MED LABORATORIES PHIL., INC.
2nd Floor PPL Bldg UN Avenue
corner San Marcelino St
Manila, Philippines
Tel.: (63) 25240091
Fax: (63) 25260977
E-Mail: corporate@euromedlab.net
Web Site: www.euromedlab.net
EURO—(PHI)
Rev.: $110,179,590
Assets: $220,747,828
Liabilities: $98,663,632
Net Worth: $122,084,196
Earnings: $16,051,835
Fiscal Year-end: 12/31/12
Business Description:
Intravenous Fluids Mfr
S.I.C.: 2834

N.A.I.C.S.: 325412
Personnel:
William G. Padolina *(Chm)*
Johnny C. Yap *(Vice Chm, Treas, Exec VP & Asst Sec)*
Georgiana S. Evidente *(Pres)*
Jancie R. Ong *(Sec)*
Evangeline V. Baviera *(Exec VP)*
Jose A. Emiterio *(Sr VP)*
Arnold D. Ong *(Sr VP)*
Board of Directors:
William G. Padolina
Evangeline V. Baviera
Georgiana S. Evidente
Edwin Feist
Teodara D. Tan
Johnny C. Yap
Michael Vincent Y. Yap

EURO MULTIVISION LTD.
Euro House, Chincholi Bunder Road, Behind Inorbit Mall,
Malad W, Mumbai, 400 064, India
Tel.: (91) 2240364036
Fax: (91) 2240364037
E-Mail: euro@euromultivision.com
Web Site: www.euromultivision.com
EUROMULTI—(BOM NSE)
Emp.: 5,000
Business Description:
Interior & Exterior Building Materials Mfr & Distr
S.I.C.: 2499
N.A.I.C.S.: 321999
Personnel:
Nenshi Shah *(Chm)*
Hitesh Shah *(Mng Dir)*
Board of Directors:
Nenshi Shah
Mahendra Modi
Chirag Shah
Hitesh Shah

EURO-PRO CORPORATION
4400 Bois Franc
Saint Laurent, QC, H4S IA7, Canada
Tel.: (514) 842-8691
Fax: (514) 842-6985
Toll Free: (800) 361-4639
Web Site: www.euro-pro.com
Year Founded: 1950
Emp.: 100
Business Description:
Vacuum Cleaner & Household Appliance Designer, Mfr & Distr
S.I.C.: 3639
N.A.I.C.S.: 335210

EURO RESSOURCES S.A.
Suite 3200 320 Bay Street
PO Box 153
Toronto, ON, M5H 2Y4, Canada
Tel.: (416) 360-4710
Fax: (416) 360-4710
E-Mail: Phillips@euroressources.net
Web Site: www.euroressources.fr
EUR—(EUR)
Rev.: $55,805,477
Assets: $38,684,887
Liabilities: $3,101,576
Net Worth: $35,583,312
Earnings: $33,776,751
Fiscal Year-end: 12/31/12
Business Description:
Gold Mining Services
S.I.C.: 1041
N.A.I.C.S.: 212221
Personnel:
David Harold Watkins *(Chm)*
Brian Trnkus *(CEO)*
Susanne Hermans *(Deputy CEO & VP-Fin)*
Benjamin Little *(Dir Gen)*
Board of Directors:
David Harold Watkins
Ian L. Boxall
Benjamin Little
Phillip Marks
Paul Olmsted
Ian Kingsley B. Smith
Transfer Agent:
BNP Paribas Securities Services S.A.
Paris, France

EURO-RITE CABINETS LTD.
1610 Industrial Avenue
Port Coquitlam, BC, V3C 6N3, Canada
Tel.: (604) 464-5060
Fax: (604) 464-7210
Toll Free: (888) 464-5063
E-Mail: info@eurorite.com
Web Site: www.eurorite.com
Year Founded: 1986
Rev.: $16,961,032
Emp.: 115
Business Description:
Kitchen Cabinets & Accessories Mfr
S.I.C.: 2434
N.A.I.C.S.: 337110
Personnel:
Bill Longman *(Founder & Owner)*

EURO TECH HOLDINGS COMPANY LIMITED
18/F Gee Chang Hong Centre 65
Wong Chuk Hong Road
Hong Kong, China (Hong Kong)
Tel.: (852) 2814 0311
Fax: (852) 2873 4887
E-Mail: euro-tech@euro-tech.com
Web Site: www.euro-tech.com
Year Founded: 1971
CLWT—(NASDAQ)
Rev.: $21,645,000
Assets: $24,947,000
Liabilities: $7,191,000
Net Worth: $17,756,000
Earnings: ($120,000)
Emp.: 138
Fiscal Year-end: 12/31/12
Business Description:
Analytical Instruments Distr Import
S.I.C.: 3589
N.A.I.C.S.: 333318
Personnel:
T. C. Leung *(Chm & CEO)*
Jerry Wong *(CFO)*
Board of Directors:
T. C. Leung
Ka Chong Cheang
Y. K. Liang
Alex Sham
Li Da Weng
Jerry Wong
Transfer Agent:
American Stock Transfer & Trust Co.
59 Maiden Ln
New York, NY 10038
Tel.: (212) 936-5100
Fax: (718) 236-2641

Subsidiary:

Euro Tech (Far East) Ltd. **(1)**
65 Wong Chuk Hang Road
65 Wong Chuk Hong Road, Hong Kong, China (Hong Kong)
Tel.: (852) 28140311
Fax: (852) 28734887
E-Mail: euro-tech@euro-tech.com
Analytical Instruments Distr
S.I.C.: 3823
N.A.I.C.S.: 334513

Non-U.S. Subsidiary:

Shanghai Euro Tech Ltd. **(1)**
2F Block C 501 Jingqiao Export Processing Zone
201206 Shanghai, PR, China (100%)
Tel.: (86) 2158347460
Fax: (86) 2158545673
E-Mail: factory.sh@euro-tech.com
Web Site: www.euro-tech.com
Business Support Services
S.I.C.: 7389
N.A.I.C.S.: 561499

EUROAMERICA SEGUROS DE VIDA, S.A.
Agustinas 1127 3rd Floor
Santiago, 8340418, Chile
Tel.: (56) 27827000
Fax: (56) 4799428
Toll Free: 80020-VIDA
E-Mail: info@euroamerica.cl
Web Site: www.euroamerica.cl
Year Founded: 1900
Sales Range: $50-74.9 Million
Emp.: 400
Business Description:
Insurance & Financial Products
S.I.C.: 6399
N.A.I.C.S.: 524128
Personnel:
Nicolas Di Salvo *(CEO)*
Jose Miguel Infante *(Sec)*
Board of Directors:
Jose Miguel Infante

EUROBANK ERGASIAS SA
20 Amalias Av
10557 Athens, Greece
Tel.: (30) 2109555000
E-Mail: info@eurobank.gr
Web Site: www.eurobank.gr
Year Founded: 1990
EUROB—(ATH)
Int. Income: $5,485,642,750
Assets: $91,072,439,010
Liabilities: $91,954,180,360
Net Worth: ($881,741,350)
Earnings: ($1,938,484,800)
Emp.: 17,427
Fiscal Year-end: 12/31/12
Business Description:
Banking Services
S.I.C.: 6029
N.A.I.C.S.: 522110
Personnel:
George A. David *(Chm)*
Efstratios-Georgios A. Arapoglou *(Vice Chm)*
Byron N. Ballis *(Deputy CEO & Head-Retail Banking & Insurance Activities.)*
Michael H. Colakides *(Deputy CEO & Head-Risk Mgmt)*
Nikolaos V. Karamouzis *(Deputy CEO & Head-Corp & Investment Banking & Capital Markets)*
Paula N. Hadjisotiriou *(CFO & Gen Mgr)*
Board of Directors:
George A. David
Efstratios-Georgios A. Arapoglou
Michael H. Colakides
Dimitrios A. Georgoutsos
George C. Gondicas
Spyros L. Lorentziadis
Christos I. Megalou
Dimitrios Th. Papalexopoulos
Kenneth Howard K. Prince-Wright

Subsidiaries:

Be-Business Exchanges S.A. **(1)**
6 Siniosoglou Street & Al Panagouli Street
Nea Ionia, 142 34 Athens, Greece
Tel.: (30) 210 352 3525
Fax: (30) 210 352 3599
E-Mail: info@be24.gr
Web Site: www.be24.gr
Emp.: 10
Ecommerce Services
S.I.C.: 7389
N.A.I.C.S.: 425110
Alkiviadis Trigas *(CEO)*

EFG Eurobank Ergasias Leasing S.A. **(1)**
34-36 Panepistimiou Str & Ipokratous
106 79 Athens, Greece
Tel.: (30) 210 366 0800
Fax: (30) 210 352 3811
E-Mail: efgleasing@eurobank.gr
Web Site: www.eurobank.gr/online/home/generic.aspx?id=724&mid=333=en
Emp.: 57
Financial Leasing Services
S.I.C.: 6211
N.A.I.C.S.: 523999
Konstantinos Kanakis *(CEO)*

EFG Eurolife General Insurance S.A. **(1)**
209-211 Syngrou Avenue
Nea Smyrni, 171 21 Athens, Greece
Tel.: (30) 210 930 3900
Fax: (30) 210 930 3980
E-Mail: info@eurolife.gr
Web Site: www.eurolife.gr
General Insurance Services
S.I.C.: 6311
N.A.I.C.S.: 524113
Alexander Sarrigeorgiou *(CEO)*

EFG Insurance Services S.A. **(1)**
190 Syngrou Ave
Nea Smyrni, 17671 Athens, Greece
Tel.: (30) 2109303850
Fax: (30) 2109303971
E-Mail: info@efginsurancebrokers.gr
Web Site: www.efginsurancebrokers.gr
Emp.: 30
Insurance Brokerage Services
S.I.C.: 6411
N.A.I.C.S.: 524210
Anna Tryfon *(CEO)*

Eurobank EFG Asset Management Investment Firm S.A. **(1)**
10 Stadiou St
10564 Athens, Greece
Tel.: (30) 2103710500
Fax: (30) 2103352850
E-Mail: efgaebak@eurobank.gr
Web Site: www.eurobank.gr/online/home/generic.aspx?id=724&mid=333=en
Emp.: 60
Asset Management Services
S.I.C.: 6794
N.A.I.C.S.: 533110

Eurobank EFG Business Services S.A. **(1)**
21 Kallirois Street
117 43 Athens, Greece
Tel.: (30) 2109008500
Fax: (30) 2109008600
E-Mail: info@efgbs.gr
Web Site: www.efgbs.gr
Emp.: 60
Payroll Processing Services
S.I.C.: 8721
N.A.I.C.S.: 541214
Katerina Triviza *(CEO)*

Eurobank EFG Equities Investment Firm S.A. **(1)**
10 Filellinon Street & Xenofontos Street
105 57 Athens, Greece
Tel.: (30) 210 372 00
Fax: (30) 210 372 0001
E-Mail: info@eurobankequities.gr
Web Site: www.eurobankequities.gr
Equities Investment Services
S.I.C.: 6513
N.A.I.C.S.: 531110
Nikolaos Andrianopoulos *(CEO & Pres)*

Eurobank EFG Factors S.A. **(1)**
16 Laodikias and 1-3 Nymfeou St
115 28 Athens, Greece
Tel.: (30) 2106078000
Fax: (30) 2106078020
E-Mail: efgfactors@efgfactors.gr
Web Site: www.efgfactors.gr
Emp.: 50
Factoring & Forfaiting Services
S.I.C.: 6159
N.A.I.C.S.: 522298
Andreas Chasapis *(Pres)*
George Karagiannopoulos *(CEO)*
Athanasios Daflos *(CIO)*

Eurobank EFG Financial Planning Services S.A. **(1)**
19-21 Kyprou Street & Archimidous Street
183 46 Athens, Greece

Eurobank Ergasias SA—(Continued)

Tel.: (30) 210 484 7000
Fax: (30) 210 484 7982
E-Mail: fps_cv@eurobank-fps.gr
Web Site: eurobankfps.applymycv.gr
Financial Planning Services
S.I.C.: 6211
N.A.I.C.S.: 523999

Eurobank EFG Mutual Funds Management Company S.A. (1)
10 Stadiou St
105 64 Athens, Greece
Tel.: (30) 2103352800
Fax: (30) 2103352850
Web Site: www.eurobank.gr/online/home/generic.aspx?id=724&mid=333=en
Mutual Fund Management Services
S.I.C.: 6722
N.A.I.C.S.: 525910
Aristides Xenofos *(CEO)*

Eurobank Fin and Rent S.A. (1)
34 El Venizelou
106 79 Athens, Greece
Tel.: (30) 210 366 0800
Fax: (30) 210 352 3813
E-Mail:
Web Site: www.eurobank.gr
Automobile Leasing Services
S.I.C.: 7515
N.A.I.C.S.: 532112
Konstantinos Kanakis *(CEO)*

Open 24 S.A. (1)
188 Syngrou Avenue
176 71 Kallithea, Athens, Greece
Tel.: (30) 210 955 8100
Fax: (30) 210 955 8150
Web Site: www.open24.gr
Financial & Insurance Services
S.I.C.: 6141
N.A.I.C.S.: 522291
Ritsa Nikolopoulou *(CEO)*

TT Hellenic Postbank S.A. (1)
2-6 Pesmazoglou Street
101 75 Athens, Greece
Tel.: (30) 2103704000
Fax: (30) 2103704107
E-Mail: investor_relations@ttbank.gr
Web Site: www.ttbank.gr
TT—(ATH)
Sales Range: $750-799.9 Million
Emp.: 2,510
Banking Services
S.I.C.: 6029
N.A.I.C.S.: 522110
Kleanthis A. Papadopoulos *(Chm)*
Spyros C. Pantelias *(Vice Chm)*
Filipdes Amgelos *(CEO)*
Athansios Dionas *(Dir-Fin Svcs)*
George Xifaras *(CFO)*
Andreas Taprantzis *(COO)*

Subsidiary:

TT ELTA AEDAK (2)
Vasileos Konstantinou 38.
Athens, 11635, Greece
Tel.: (30) 2103316644
Fax: (30) 2103316648
E-Mail: secretariat@tteltaaedak.gr
Web Site: www.tteltaaedak.gr
Emp.: 8
Mutual Fund Management Services
S.I.C.: 6733
N.A.I.C.S.: 525190
Politis Spyros *(Gen Mgr)*

Non-U.S. Subsidiaries:

Bancpost S.A. (1)
6A Dimitrie Pompeiu Boulevard Sector 2
020337 Bucharest, Romania
Tel.: (40) 213020789
Fax: (40) 213300285
E-Mail: fastbanking@bancpost.ro
Web Site: www.bancpost.ro
Emp.: 3,500
Commercial Banking Services
S.I.C.: 6029
N.A.I.C.S.: 522110
Mihai Bogza *(Chm)*
Dimitris Damkalidis *(Deputy Chm)*
Peter Weiss *(CEO)*

EFG Business Services d.o.o. Beograd (1)
Eurobank EFG Centar 10 Vuka Karadzica Str
11000 Belgrade, Serbia
Tel.: (381) 11 320 7572
Fax: (381) 11 262 9299
Payroll Processing Services
S.I.C.: 8721
N.A.I.C.S.: 541214
Dragan Obradovi *(Gen Mgr)*

EFG Eurobank Finance S.A. (1)
America House 4-8 Nicolae Titulescu Blvd
West Wing 4th Floor, 011141 Bucharest, Romania
Tel.: (40) 212062300
Fax: (40) 212062310
E-Mail: office@efgfinance.ro
Web Site: www.efgfinance.ro
Emp.: 2
Financial Advisory Services
S.I.C.: 6282
N.A.I.C.S.: 523930
Bogdan Erdeli *(Head-Investment Banking)*

EFG Eurobank Property Services S.A. (1)
6A Dimitrie Pompeiu Blvd Olympus House Fifth Fl
District 2, 020337 Bucharest, Romania
Tel.: (40) 213086100
Fax: (40) 213276954
E-Mail: info@efgpropertyservices.ro
Web Site: www.efgpropertyservices.ro
Emp.: 25
Real Estate Management Services
S.I.C.: 6531
N.A.I.C.S.: 531210
Dimitra Marini *(Gen Mgr)*

EFG Leasing IFN S.A. (1)
6A Dimitrie Pompeiu Boulevard Sector 2 5 th Floor
020337 Bucharest, Romania
Tel.: (40) 213086121
Fax: (40) 213230613
E-Mail: sales@efgleasing.ro
Web Site: www.efgleasing.ro
Financial Leasing Services
S.I.C.: 6159
N.A.I.C.S.: 522220
Sorin Manolescu *(Gen Dir)*
Constantin Gina *(Principal)*

EFG Leasing Poland Sp. z o.o (1)
19 Mokotowska Street
00-560 Warsaw, Poland
Tel.: (48) 22 347 75 30
Fax: (48) 22 347 73 81
E-Mail: leasing@polbankefg.pl
Web Site: www.efgleasing.com.pl
Financial Leasing Services
S.I.C.: 6159
N.A.I.C.S.: 522220
Periklis Donta *(Gen Mgr)*

EFG Property Services d.o.o. Belgrade (1)
10 Vuka Karadzica Str
11000 Belgrade, Serbia
Tel.: (381) 11 3207 580
Fax: (381) 11 2185 843
E-Mail: info@efgpropertyservices.rs
Web Site: www.efgpropertyservices.rs
Real Estate Management Services
S.I.C.: 6531
N.A.I.C.S.: 531210
Ladislav Tomasevic *(Gen Mgr)*

EFG Property Services Polska Sp.z.o.o. (1)
Mokotowska 19
00 560 Warsaw, Poland
Tel.: (48) 22 343 8084
Fax: (48) 22 343 8081
E-Mail: efgpropertyservices@polbankefg.pl
Web Site: www.efgpropertyservices.pl
Real Estate Management Services
S.I.C.: 6531
N.A.I.C.S.: 531210
Jacek Zych *(Mgr)*

EFG Property Services Ukraine LLC (1)
54/19 Avtozavodska Street
04114 Kiev, Ukraine
Tel.: (380) 443915604
Fax: (380) 443915887
E-Mail: efgpropertyservices@universalbank.com.ua
Web Site: www.efgpropertyservices.net.ua
Emp.: 10
Real Estate Management Services
S.I.C.: 6531
N.A.I.C.S.: 531210
George Vasilantonakis *(Gen Mgr)*

EFG Retail Services IFN S.A. (1)
6A Dimitrie Pompeiu Boulevard Sector 2
3rd & 4th Floor
020337 Bucharest, Romania
Tel.: (40) 21 308 4000
Fax: (40) 21 320 9040
Web Site: www.euroline-cards.ro
Credit Cards Issuing Services
S.I.C.: 6141
N.A.I.C.S.: 522210
Aristeidis Papathoma *(Gen Dir)*
Aurora Tomiuc *(Principal)*

Eurobank Bulgaria AD (1)
(Formerly Eurobank EFG Bulgaria AD)
14 Tsar Osvoboditel Blvd
1048 Sofia, Bulgaria
Tel.: (359) 28166000
Fax: (359) 29888110
E-Mail: contact@postbank.bg
Web Site: www.postbank.bg/
Sales Range: $350-399.9 Million
Emp.: 2,998
Banking Services
S.I.C.: 6029
N.A.I.C.S.: 522110
Anthony C. Hassiotis *(Chm-Mgmt Bd & CEO)*
Petia Dimitrova *(Member-Mgmt Bd)*
Ilian Raychev *(Member-Mgmt Bd)*
Iordan Souvandjiev *(Member-Mgmt Bd)*
Yiannis Vouyioukas *(Member-Mgmt Bd)*

Subsidiaries:

EFG Auto Leasing E.O.O.D. (2)
Okolovrasten pat 260 Building C 5th Floor
1715 Sofia, Bulgaria
Tel.: (359) 2 937 5810
Fax: (359) 2 974 2756
E-Mail: office@efgleasing.bg
Web Site: www.postbank.bg/TransformationService.asmx/XHTML?strXML=/en-US/Leasing/08Feedback/
Emp.: 30
Automobile Leasing Services
S.I.C.: 7515
N.A.I.C.S.: 532112
Gergana Gerdzhikova *(Gen Mgr)*

EFG Securities Bulgaria E.A.D. (2)
14 Tzar Osvoboditel Boulevard
1048 Sofia, Bulgaria
Tel.: (359) 2 811 6601
Fax: (359) 2 988 8150
Securities Brokerage Services
S.I.C.: 6211
N.A.I.C.S.: 523120
Dragomir Velikov *(Exec Dir)*

Eurobank EFG A.D. Belgrade (1)
10 Vuka Karadzica Street
11000 Belgrade, Serbia
Tel.: (381) 11 2023 353
Fax: (381) 11 3027 536
E-Mail: office@eurobankefg.rs
Web Site: www.eurobankefg.rs
Commercial Banking Services
S.I.C.: 6029
N.A.I.C.S.: 522110
Slavica Pavlovic *(Member-Exec Bd & CFO)*
George Michalakopoulos *(Member-Exec Bd-Ops)*
Natasa Strugarevic *(Member-Exec Bd-HR)*
Michalis Tsagalakis *(Member-Exec Bd-Corp Banking Div)*
Vuk Zecevic *(Member-Exec Bd-Treasury)*

Subsidiary:

EFG Leasing A.D. Belgrade (2)
Vuka Karadzica 10
11000 Belgrade, Serbia
Tel.: (381) 113027555
Fax: (381) 112622350
E-Mail: administration@efgleasing.rs
Web Site: www.eurobankefg.rs/the_bank/related_companies/efg_leasing.1108.html
Emp.: 30
Financial Leasing Services
S.I.C.: 6141
N.A.I.C.S.: 522220
Milos Kaludjerovic *(Mng Dir)*

Eurobank EFG Cyprus Ltd. (1)
41 Arch Makarios Avenue
CY-1065 Nicosia, Cyprus
Tel.: (357) 22 20 8000
Fax: (357) 22 87 5456
E-Mail: info@eurobank.com.cy
Web Site: www.eurobank.com.cy
Emp.: 70
Commercial Banking Services
S.I.C.: 6029
N.A.I.C.S.: 522110
Koullis Hadjigavriel *(Mgr-Nicosia Banking Centre)*

Eurobank EFG Fund Management Company (Luxembourg) S.A. (1)
5 rue Jean Monnet Str
PO Box 438
2180 Luxembourg, Luxembourg
Tel.: (352) 2609151
Fax: (352) 26091555
E-Mail: info@eurobankefg-fmc.lu
Web Site: www.eurobankefg-fmc.lu
Emp.: 10
Mutual Fund Management Services
S.I.C.: 6722
N.A.I.C.S.: 525910
Agamemnon Kotrozos *(Gen Mgr)*

Eurobank EFG Private Bank Luxembourg S.A. (1)
5 rue Jean Monnet
2180 Luxembourg, Luxembourg
Tel.: (352) 4207241
Fax: (352) 420724650
E-Mail: info@eurobankefg.lu
Web Site: www.eurobankefg.lu
Private Banking & Investment Advisory Services
S.I.C.: 6029
N.A.I.C.S.: 522110
Ries Francois *(Chm)*
Lena Lascari *(Mng Dir)*

P.J.S.C. Universal Bank (1)
54/19 Avtozavodska Str
04114 Kiev, Ukraine
Tel.: (380) 443915777
Fax: (380) 44 391 5770
E-Mail: contact@universalbank.com.ua
Web Site: www.universalbank.com.ua
Commercial Banking Services
S.I.C.: 6029
N.A.I.C.S.: 522110
Miltiadis Papanikolao *(Chm & CEO)*

SC EFG Eurolife Asigurari de Viata S.A. (1)
6A Dimitrie Pompeiu Boulevard Sector 2
Olympus House 5 Floor
020337 Bucharest, Romania
Tel.: (40) 314184083
Fax: (40) 314184084
E-Mail: asigurari@efgeurolife.ro
Web Site: www.efgeurolife.ro/asigurari-de-viata
Emp.: 12
Life Insurance Services
S.I.C.: 6311
N.A.I.C.S.: 524113
Anita Laura Nitulescu *(Gen Dir)*

SC EFG Eurolife Asigurari Generale S.A. (1)
6A Dimitrie Pompeiu Boulevard Sector 2
020337 Bucharest, Romania
Tel.: (40) 21 320 0640
Fax: (40) 31 418 4084
E-Mail: asigurari@eurolife.gr
Web Site: www.efgeurolife.ro/asigurari-generale
Emp.: 17
General Insurance Services
S.I.C.: 6411
N.A.I.C.S.: 524210
Simona Roxana Petrach *(Gen Mgr)*

EUROBANK PROPERTIES REIC

117 Kifissias Ave Agiou Konstantinou
15124 Maroussi, Greece
Tel.: (30) 2108129600
Fax: (30) 2108129670
E-Mail: eurobankproperties@eurobank.gr

Web Site: www.eurobankpropertie s.gr
EUPRO—(ATH)
Rev.: $52,325,628
Assets: $967,544,880
Liabilities: $123,531,290
Net Worth: $844,013,590
Earnings: ($37,773,530)
Emp.: 19
Fiscal Year-end: 12/31/12
Business Description:
Real Estate Property Services
S.I.C.: 6531
N.A.I.C.S.: 531210
Personnel:
Nikolaos A. Bertsos *(Chm)*
Stelios Probonas *(CFO)*
Board of Directors:
Nikolaos A. Bertsos
Odisseas Athanassiou
Wade Burton
George Chryssikos
Nikolaos Galetas
George Katsibris
Georgios Papazoglou

EUROBEX MANUFACTURING LTD.

(See Under EXM Manufacturing Ltd.)

EUROBROKERS S.A.

100 Kifissias Av Marathonodromou 83
Marousi, 15125 Athens, Greece
Tel.: (30) 210 8123800
Fax: (30) 210 6140201
E-Mail: info@eurobrokers.gr
Web Site: www.eurobrokers.gr
Year Founded: 1992
EUBRK—(ATH)
Emp.: 50
Business Description:
Insurance Brokerage & Advisory Services
S.I.C.: 6411
N.A.I.C.S.: 524210
Personnel:
G. Koumbas *(Chm)*
W. Abdo *(Mng Dir & VP)*
Board of Directors:
G. Koumbas
W. Abdo
K. Karakostas
Th. Kirlis
A. Tsironis

EUROCASTLE INVESTMENT LIMITED

Regency Court Glategny Esplanade
Saint Peter Port, GY1 1WW, Guernsey
Tel.: (44) 2072905600
Fax: (44) 1481 716868
Web Site: www.eurocastleinv.com
ECT—(EUR)
Int. Income: $32,173,463
Assets: $3,569,636,297
Liabilities: $3,176,403,886
Net Worth: $393,232,411
Earnings: ($109,944,396)
Fiscal Year-end: 12/31/12
Business Description:
Investment Sevices
S.I.C.: 6211
N.A.I.C.S.: 523999
Personnel:
Stephen Charlton *(CFO)*
Board of Directors:
Keith Dorrian
Randal Alan Nardone
Udo Scheffel
Peter M. Smith
Simon J. Thornton
Legal Counsel:
SNR Denton
1221 Avenue of the Americas
New York, NY 10020

Linklaters LLP
One Silk Street
London, EC2Y 8HQ, United Kingdom
Tel.: (44) 2074562000
Fax: (44) 2074562222

Carey Olsen
Carey House Les Banques
PO Box 98
GY1 4BZ Saint Peter Port, Guernsey
Transfer Agent:
Anson Registrars Limited
Anson Place Mill Courtq
PO Box 426
La Charroterie, Saint Peter Port, Guernsey

EUROCHEM MINERAL CHEMICAL COMPANY, OJSC

(d/b/a EuroChem Group)
53 6 Dubininskaya Street
115054 Moscow, Russia
Tel.: (7) 4957952527
Fax: (7) 4957952532
E-Mail: info@eurochem.ru
Web Site: www.eurochem.ru
Year Founded: 2001
Sls.: $5,505,418,498
Assets: $7,845,861,568
Liabilities: $4,314,099,891
Net Worth: $3,531,761,677
Earnings: $1,077,061,791
Emp.: 22,073
Fiscal Year-end: 12/31/12
Business Description:
Holding Company; Fertilizer Mfr
S.I.C.: 6719
N.A.I.C.S.: 551112
Personnel:
Dmitry Strezhnev *(CEO)*
Andrey Ilyin *(CFO)*
Board of Directors:
Andrey Melnichenko
Nikolay Pilipenko
Richard Sheath
Vladimir Stolin
Dmitry Strezhnev
Andrea Wine

Subsidiaries:

EuroChem - Belorechenskie Minudobrenia, LLC **(1)**
Chemical Site
352636 Belorechensk, Krasnodar, Russia (100%)
Tel.: (7) 86155 2 31 31
Web Site: www.eurochem.ru/about-eurochem-2/operations/production/eurochem-bmu
Phosphate & Compound Fertilizers Mfr
S.I.C.: 2874
N.A.I.C.S.: 325312

Nevinomysskiy Azot, OJSC **(1)**
1 Nizyaeva St
7 Nevinnomyssk, Stavropol, 357107, Russia (100%)
Tel.: (7) 86554 4 42 65
Fax: (7) 86554 7 95 77
E-Mail: nevinazot@eurochem.ru
Web Site: www.eurochem.ru/about-eurochem-2/operations/production/nevinomysskiy-azot
Nitrogen Fertilizers Mfr
S.I.C.: 2873
N.A.I.C.S.: 325311

Novomoskovskiy Azot, OJSC **(1)**
10 Svyasi St
Novomoskovsk, Moscow, Tula Region, 31660, Russia
Tel.: (7) 48762 2 22 22
E-Mail: novomoskovsk@eurochem.ru
Web Site: www.eurochem.ru/about-eurochem-2/operations/production/nak-azot
Ammonia & Nitrogen Fertilizer Mfr
S.I.C.: 2873
N.A.I.C.S.: 325311

Phosphorit Industrial Group, LLC **(1)**
Phosphorit Industrial Site
Kingisepp, Leningrad Region, 188452, Russia (100%)
Tel.: (7) 81375 9 53 12
Fax: (7) 81375 2 87 27
E-Mail: info_ksp@eurochem.ru
Web Site: www.eurochem.ru/about-eurochem-2/operations/production/phosphorit
Phosphate Fertilizers & Feed Phosphates Mfr
S.I.C.: 2874
N.A.I.C.S.: 325312

U.S. Subsidiary:

EuroChem Trading USA Corp. **(1)**
2701 N Rocky Point Dr Ste 1100
Tampa, FL 33607 (100%)
Tel.: (813) 549-3400
Fax: (813) 549-3401
E-Mail: sales@eurochemusa.com
Web Site: www.eurochem.ru/about-eurochem-2/operations/sales
Sales of Fertilizers
S.I.C.: 5169
N.A.I.C.S.: 424690
Kathie Ditri *(Mgr)*

Non-U.S. Subsidiaries:

EuroChem Antwerpen NV **(1)**
Scheldelaan 600
B-2040 Antwerp, 4, Belgium (100%)
Tel.: (32) 3 561 52 86
Fax: (32) 3 561 36 80
Web Site: www.eurochem.ru/about-eurochem-2/operations/production
Emp.: 330
Fertilizer Mfr
S.I.C.: 2875
N.A.I.C.S.: 325314

EuroChem Trading GmbH **(1)**
Bundesstrasse 5
6301 Zug, Switzerland CH (100%)
Tel.: (41) 41 727 7608
Fax: (41) 41 727 7606
E-Mail: info@eurochem-trading.ch
Web Site: www.eurochem.ru/about-eurochem-2/operations/sales
Sales of Fertilizers
S.I.C.: 5169
N.A.I.C.S.: 424690

Non-U.S. Subsidiaries:

EuroChem Agro GmbH **(2)**
Reichskanzler-Mueller-Strasse 23
68165 Mannheim, Germany (100%)
Tel.: (49) 621 87209 0
Fax: (49) 621 87209 101
E-Mail: info@eurochemagro.com
Web Site: www.ks-nitrogen.com
Nitrogenous Fertilizer Mfr
S.I.C.: 2873
N.A.I.C.S.: 325311
Rudolf Graf von Plettenberg *(Gen Mgr)*

EuroChem Agro Iberia, S.L. **(2)**
Joan dAustria 39-47 6 planta
08005 Barcelona, Spain (100%)
Tel.: (34) 932247222
Fax: (34) 932259291
E-Mail: nitrogen@eurochemagro.com
Web Site: es.eurochemagro.com
Nitrogenous Fertilizer Mfr
S.I.C.: 2873
N.A.I.C.S.: 325311

EuroChem Comercio de Produtos Quimicos Ltda **(2)**
888 Rua Tabapua 2nd Floor
Sao Paulo, 04533 003, Brazil (50%)
Tel.: (55) 11 3562 1486
E-Mail: francisco.alves@eurochem-trading.com.br
Web Site: www.eurochem.ru/about-eurochem-2/operations/sales
Sales of Fertilizers
S.I.C.: 5169
N.A.I.C.S.: 424690
Francisco Alves *(Mgr)*

Lifosa AB **(1)**
Juodkiskio str 50
LT 57502 Kedainiai, Lithuania (96.35%)
Tel.: (370) 347 66483
Fax: (370) 347 66166
E-Mail: info@lifosa.com
Web Site: www.lifosa.com
Fertilizers Mfr
S.I.C.: 2873
N.A.I.C.S.: 325311
Juozas Baniota *(Dir-Admin)*

EUROCLEAR S.A./N.V.

1 boulevard du Roi Albert II
1210 Brussels, Belgium
Tel.: (32) 23261211
Telex: 61025 MGTEC B
Fax: (32) 23261287
E-Mail: info@euroclear.com
Web Site: www.euroclear.com
Year Founded: 1968
Rev.: $1,852,317,804
Assets: $27,548,643,464
Liabilities: $23,360,153,972
Net Worth: $4,188,489,492
Earnings: $293,353,328
Emp.: 3,688
Fiscal Year-end: 12/31/12
Business Description:
Securities Settlement Services
S.I.C.: 6231
N.A.I.C.S.: 523210
Personnel:
Marc Antoine Autheman *(Chm)*
Jean-Jacques Verdickt *(Deputy Chm)*
Timothy Howell *(CEO)*
Andre Rolland *(CFO)*
Frederic Hannequart *(Chief Bus Dev Officer)*
Lieve Mostrey *(Chief Tech & Svcs Officer)*
Board of Directors:
Marc Antoine Autheman
Joseph C. Antonellis
Michael Berthezene
Stephen Davies
Drew Douglas
Erik Dralans
Mary M. Fenoglio
Mark S. Garvin
Frederic Hannequart
Tsutomu Hattori
William Higgins
Mathias Hlubek
Toru Horie
Timothy Howell
Peter T. Johnston
Francis J. La Salla
Vivien Levy-Garboua
Francois Marion
Neil Martin
Lieve Mostrey
Nils-Fredrik Nyblaeus
Bruno Prigent
Martin Slumbers
John Stewart
Jean-Jacques Verdickt
Clare Woodman
Eddy Wymeersch

Subsidiaries:

Calar Belgium S.A./N.V. **(1)**
1 Blvd Du Roi Albert II
B 1210 Brussels, Belgium (100%)
Tel.: (32) 22241211
Fax: (32) 22244045
Emp.: 3,000
Financial Services
S.I.C.: 6282
N.A.I.C.S.: 523930

TradeGO S.A./N.V. **(1)**
1 Boulevard du Roi Albert II
B-1210 Brussels, Belgium
Investment Banking Services
S.I.C.: 6211
N.A.I.C.S.: 523110

Non-U.S. Subsidiary:

Euroclear UK & Ireland **(1)**
33 Cannon St
London, EC4M 5SB, United Kingdom
Tel.: (44) 2078490000
Fax: (44) 2078490134

Euroclear S.A./N.V.—(Continued)

E-Mail: info@euroclear.com
Web Site: www.euroclear.com
Emp.: 500
Provider of Securities Settlement Services
S.I.C.: 6231
N.A.I.C.S.: 523210

EUROCOM CORPORATION

148 Colonnade Rd
Nepean, ON, K2E 7R4, Canada
Tel.: (613) 224-6122
Fax: (613) 224-2511
Toll Free: (877) 387-6266
E-Mail: sales@eurocom.com
Web Site: www.eurocom.com
Year Founded: 1989
Rev.: $123,000,000
Emp.: 15
Business Description:
Computer Mfr
S.I.C.: 3571
N.A.I.C.S.: 334111
Personnel:
Mark Bialic *(Pres)*

EUROCOMMERCIAL PROPERTIES N.V.

Herengracht 469
1017 BS Amsterdam, Netherlands
Tel.: (31) 205306030
Fax: (31) 205306040
E-Mail: info@eurocommercialproperties.com
Web Site: www.eurocommercialproperties.com
ECMPA—(EUR)
Rev.: $273,936,172
Assets: $3,889,121,477
Liabilities: $2,050,167,102
Net Worth: $1,838,954,375
Earnings: $165,469,870
Emp.: 64
Fiscal Year-end: 06/30/13
Business Description:
Real Estate Investment Services
S.I.C.: 6531
N.A.I.C.S.: 531210
Personnel:
Willem G. van Hassel *(Chm-Supervisory Bd)*
Jeremy P. Lewis *(Chm-Mgmt Bd & CEO)*
Evert Jan van Garderen *(Member-Mgmt Bd & Dir-Fin)*
Supervisory Board of Directors:
Willem G. van Hassel
Carlo Croff
Pieter W. Haasbroek
Jan-Ake Persson
Andre E. Teeuw

Subsidiaries:

Boleto B.V. (1)
Herengracht 469
1017 BS Amsterdam, Netherlands (100%)
Tel.: (31) 205306030
Fax: (31) 205306040
E-Mail: info@eurocommercialproperties.com
Emp.: 50
Real Estate Investment Trusts
S.I.C.: 6726
N.A.I.C.S.: 525990
Kate Goode *(Gen Mgr)*

Sentinel Holdings B.V. (1)
Herengracht 469
Amsterdam, 1017 BS, Netherlands
Tel.: (31) 20 530 6030
Investment Management Services
S.I.C.: 6211
N.A.I.C.S.: 523999

Sentinel Holdings II B.V. (1)
Herengracht 469
1017BS Amsterdam, Netherlands (100%)
Tel.: (31) 205306030
Fax: (31) 205306040
E-Mail: info@ecpnv.com
Web Site: www.ecpnv.com
Emp.: 12
Real Estate Investment Trusts
S.I.C.: 6726
N.A.I.C.S.: 525990
J. Louis *(Mng Dir)*

Non-U.S. Subsidiaries:

Aktiebolaget Norrkoping Silvret 1 (1)
PO Box 1147
11181 Stockholm, Sweden
Tel.: (46) 84535046
Fax: (46) 84535060
Miscellaneous Financial Investment Activities
S.I.C.: 6211
N.A.I.C.S.: 523999

Bergvik Kopet 3 K.B. (1)
Timmergatan 1
65115 Karlstad, Sweden
Tel.: (46) 54220000
Fax: (46) 54220318
Other Real Estate Property Lessors
S.I.C.: 6519
N.A.I.C.S.: 531190

Burlov Centre Fastighets A.B. (1)
PO Box 1147
11181 Stockholm, Sweden
Tel.: (46) 84535046
Fax: (46) 84535060
Other Real Estate Property Lessors
S.I.C.: 6519
N.A.I.C.S.: 531190
Martin Bjoorn *(Mng Dir)*

ECP Karlskrona AB (1)
Norrlandsgatan 22
Stockholm, 111 43, Sweden
Tel.: (46) 86785360
Fax: (46) 86785370
E-Mail: info@ecpnb.com
Web Site: www.ecpnb.com
Emp.: 8
Investment Management Services
S.I.C.: 6211
N.A.I.C.S.: 523999
Patrick Cornell *(Gen Mgr)*

ECP Moraberg K.B. (1)
PO Box 1147
11181 Stockholm, Sweden
Tel.: (46) 84535046
Fax: (46) 84535060
Web Site: www.eurocommercialproperties.com
Other Real Estate Property Lessors
S.I.C.: 6519
N.A.I.C.S.: 531190
Martin Bjoorn *(Mng Dir)*

Eurocommercial Properties Azur S.a.r.l (1)
66 Avenue des Champs Elysees (Chez Abc Liv)
75008 Paris, France
Tel.: (33) 140687002
Miscellaneous Financial Investment Activities
S.I.C.: 6211
N.A.I.C.S.: 523999

Eurocommercial Properties Caumartin S.N.C. (1)
107 Rue Saint Lazare
Paris, 75009, France
Tel.: (33) 153219672
Properties Leasing Services
S.I.C.: 6519
N.A.I.C.S.: 531190

Eurocommercial Properties Italia S.r.l. (1)
Via Vecchio Politecnico 3
Milan, Italy (100%)
Tel.: (39) 027607591
Fax: (39) 0276016180
E-Mail: infoit@ecpnv.com
Web Site: www.eurocommercialproperties.com
Emp.: 15
Real Estate Investment Trusts
S.I.C.: 6726
N.A.I.C.S.: 525990
Tim Samtini *(Mng Dir)*

Eurocommercial Properties Ltd (1)
4 Carlton Gardens
SW1Y5AB London, United Kingdom
Tel.: (44) 2079257860
Fax: (44) 2079257888
Web Site: www.eurocommercialproperties.com
Emp.: 82
Miscellaneous Financial Investment Activities
S.I.C.: 6211
N.A.I.C.S.: 523999
Kate Spiro *(Mgr-IR)*

Eurocommercial Properties Sweden AB (1)
Norrlandsgatan 22
11143 Stockholm, Sweden
Tel.: (46) 86785360
Fax: (46) 86785370
E-Mail: info@eurocommercialproperties.com
Web Site: www.eurocommercialproperties.com
Emp.: 5
Other Real Estate Property Lessors
S.I.C.: 6519
N.A.I.C.S.: 531190
Jeremi Lewis *(CEO)*

Halla Shopping Fastighets AB (1)
Hallagatan 14
72134 Vasteras, Sweden
Tel.: (46) 21186207
Electronic Shopping
S.I.C.: 5961
N.A.I.C.S.: 454111

Kronan Fastigheter i Karlskrona AB (1)
Box 1147
111 81 Stockholm, Sweden
Tel.: (46) 45510755
Property Leasing Services
S.I.C.: 6519
N.A.I.C.S.: 531190

Samarkandfastigheter AB (1)
PO Box 1147
11181 Stockholm, Sweden
Tel.: (46) 84535046
Fax: (46) 84535060
Other Real Estate Property Lessors
S.I.C.: 6519
N.A.I.C.S.: 531190
Martin Bjoorn *(Mng Dir)*

EUROCONSULTANTS S.A.

21 Antonis Tritsis St
Thermi, Thessaloniki, 57001, Greece
Tel.: (30) 2310 804000
Fax: (30) 2310 804100
E-Mail: info@euroconsultants.com.gr
Web Site: www.euroconsultants.gr
Year Founded: 1993
EUROC—(ATH)
Emp.: 40
Business Description:
Business Managment Consulting Services
S.I.C.: 8748
N.A.I.C.S.: 541618
Personnel:
Paris Kokorotsikos *(Chm)*

EUROCONTROL TECHNICS GROUP INC.

130 Adelaide Street West Suite 1010
Toronto, ON, M5H 3P5, Canada
Tel.: (416) 861-2808
Fax: (416) 364-5400
E-Mail: info@eurocontrol.ca
Web Site: www.eurocontrol.ca
EUO—(TSXV)
Rev.: $4,978,092
Assets: $8,198,002
Liabilities: $3,056,939
Net Worth: $5,141,063
Earnings: ($1,359,553)
Fiscal Year-end: 12/31/12
Business Description:
Oil Products Mfr
S.I.C.: 2999
N.A.I.C.S.: 324199
Personnel:
W. Bruce Rowlands *(Chm, Pres & CEO)*
Andres Tinajero *(CFO)*
Gadi Gonen *(COO)*
Board of Directors:
W. Bruce Rowlands
James Fairbairn
Gadi Gonen
Michael Rose
Kenneth Wawrew
Paul Wood
Eli Zahavi

Non-U.S. Subsidiaries:

Xenemetrix Ltd. (1)
Ramat Gabriel Industrial Zone 6 Hatikshoret St
Migdal Ha'Emeq, 23000, Israel
Mailing Address:
POB 997
Migdal Ha'Emeq, 23100, Israel
Tel.: (972) 4 9891313
Fax: (972) 4 9891323
E-Mail: info@xenemetrix.com
Web Site: www.xenemetrix.com
Emp.: 30
Spectrometer Mfr
S.I.C.: 3829
N.A.I.C.S.: 334519
Doron Reinis, *(CEO)*

XwinSys Ltd (1)
Ramat Gabriel Industrial Zone 6 Hatikshoret St
Migdal Ha'Emeq, 23000, Israel
Mailing Address:
POB 997
23100 Migdal Ha'Emeq, Israel
Tel.: (972) 4 9891313
Fax: (972) 4 9891323
E-Mail: info@xwinsys.com
Web Site: www.xwinsys.com
Semiconductor Mfr & Whslr
S.I.C.: 3674
N.A.I.C.S.: 334413

EURODEV BV

(d/b/a European Business Development Group)
Windmolen 22
7609 NN Almelo, Netherlands
Tel.: (31) 546 660 000
Fax: (31) 546 660 010
Web Site: www.eurodev.com
Emp.: 73
Business Description:
Business Services
S.I.C.: 7389
N.A.I.C.S.: 561499
Personnel:
Mark de Vries *(Co-Owner & CEO)*
Edward Nijland *(Co-Owner & Partner)*
Dirk-Jan Vorgers *(Mng Partner-Mergers & Acq)*

Non-U.S. Subsidiary:

EuroDev SARL (1)
Villantipolis Bat 5 Rez de chaussee
473 route des Dolinas, 06560 Sophia-Antipolis, France
Tel.: (33) 4 92 91 07 91
Fax: (33) 4 92 96 01 70
Business Services
S.I.C.: 7389
N.A.I.C.S.: 561499

EUROESPES S.A.

Santa Marta de Babio s/n
Bergondo, 15165 La Coruna, Spain
Tel.: (34) 981 780 505
E-Mail: info@euroespes.com
Web Site: www.euroespes.com
Year Founded: 1991
EEP—(MAD)
Emp.: 40
Business Description:
Pharmaceutical Researcher, Developer & Mfr
S.I.C.: 2834
N.A.I.C.S.: 325412

Personnel:
Ramon Cacabelos *(Pres)*

EUROFIMA
Rittergasse 20
PO Box 1764
CH-4001 Basel, Switzerland
Tel.: (41) 612873340
Fax: (41) 41612873240
E-Mail: info@eurofima.org
Web Site: www.eurofima.org
Year Founded: 1956
Rev.: $1,367,359,563
Assets: $33,791,625,260
Liabilities: $32,137,266,783
Net Worth: $1,654,358,477
Earnings: $36,098,969
Emp.: 31
Fiscal Year-end: 12/31/12
Business Description:
Holding Company
S.I.C.: 6719
N.A.I.C.S.: 551112
Personnel:
Alain Picard *(Chm)*
Michel Alle *(Vice Chm)*
Luigi Lenci *(Vice Chm)*
Harry Muller *(Vice Chm)*
Wolfgang Reuter *(Vice Chm)*
Andre Bovet *(CEO)*
Martin Fleischer *(CFO)*
Patrick Tschudin *(COO & Chief Risk Officer)*
Marco Termignone *(CIO)*
Susanne Honegger *(Sec)*
Board of Directors:
Alain Picard
Anita Wetterlof Ajaxon
Michel Alle
Manuel Fresno
Luigi Lenci
Milovan Markovic
Harry Muller
Alfredo Vicente Pereira
Wolfgang Reuter
Engelhardt Robbe
Panagiotis Theofanopoulos
Marc Wengler

EUROFINS SCIENTIFIC S.A.
Rue Pierre Adolphe Bobierre
44323 Nantes, France
Tel.: (33) 251832100
Fax: (33) 251832111
E-Mail: eurofinsfr@eurofins.com
Web Site: www.eurofins.com
ERF—(EUR OTC)
Rev.: $1,405,351,672
Assets: $1,560,340,262
Liabilities: $1,054,016,110
Net Worth: $506,324,153
Earnings: $86,017,571
Emp.: 10,890
Fiscal Year-end: 12/31/12
Business Description:
Bioanalytical Services
S.I.C.: 8731
N.A.I.C.S.: 541712
Personnel:
Gilles G. Martin *(Chm & CEO)*
Dirk Bontridder *(Exec VP-Pharmaceutical Svcs)*
Markus Brandmeier *(Exec VP-Food Testing)*
Xavier Dennery *(Exec VP-Environ Testing)*
Matthias-Wilbur Weber *(Exec VP-Asia Pacific & Global Product Testing)*
Board of Directors:
Gilles G. Martin
Stuart Anderson
Valerie Hanote
Yves-Loic Martin
Wicher Wichers

Subsidiaries:

ADME Bioanalyses SAS (1)
75 Chemin de Sommieres
30310 Vergeze, France
Tel.: (33) 466731773
Fax: (33) 466731774
E-Mail: adme@eurofins.com
Emp.: 53
Research & Development in the Physical Engineering & Life Sciences
S.I.C.: 8731
N.A.I.C.S.: 541712
Patrick Duchene *(Pres)*

Agrisearch France SARL (1)
Les Herbonnes
Meauzac, 82290 Toulouse, France (100%)
Tel.: (33) 563316444
Fax: (33) 563315185
E-Mail: christophe.narboux@agrisearch.eu.com
Web Site: www.eurofins-agrisearch.com
Emp.: 40
Scientific Research Services, Product Development & Technical Support to the Crop Protection Industry
S.I.C.: 8734
N.A.I.C.S.: 541380
Claudio Lama *(Mng Dir)*

Chemtox SAS (1)
3 rue Gruninger - Parc d'Innovation
67400 Illkirch-Graffenstaden, France
Tel.: (33) 3 90 400 540
Fax: (33) 3 90 400 541
E-Mail: labochemtox@labochemtox.com
Web Site: www.labochemtox.com
Emp.: 12
Laboratory Testing Services
S.I.C.: 8734
N.A.I.C.S.: 541380
Vincent Cirimele *(CEO)*

Eurofins ADME Bioanalyses SAS (1)
75 chemin de Sommieres
30310 Vergeze, France
Tel.: (33) 4 66 73 17 73
Fax: (33) 4 66 73 17 74
Web Site: www.eurofinsadmebioanalyses.com
Biotechnology Research & Development Services
S.I.C.: 8731
N.A.I.C.S.: 541711
Patrick Duchene *(Founder & CEO)*

Eurofins Agroscience Services France SAS (1)
19 Rue Du Verger
56860 Sene, France
Tel.: (33) 297683499
Fax: (33) 297684231
Emp.: 1
Agricultural Chemical Research Services
S.I.C.: 8731
N.A.I.C.S.: 541711

Eurofins Agrosciences Services SAS (1)
Les Herbonnes
82290 Meauzac, France
Tel.: (33) 5 63 31 64 44
Fax: (33) 5 63 31 51 85
Web Site: www.eurofins.com
Emp.: 15
Environmental Testing Services
S.I.C.: 8734
N.A.I.C.S.: 541380

Eurofins Air a l'Emission France SAS (1)
557 Route de Noyelles PA du Pommier
62110 Henin-Beaumont, France
Tel.: (33) 3 21 08 80 20
Fax: (33) 3 21 08 80 01
E-Mail: environnement@eurofins.com
Bio Analytical Testing Services
S.I.C.: 8734
N.A.I.C.S.: 541380

Eurofins Analyses pour l'Environnement France SAS (1)
5 rue d'Otterswiller
67700 Saverne, France
Tel.: (33) 3 88 02 15 69
Fax: (33) 3 88 91 65 31
E-Mail: environnement@eurofins.com
Web Site: www.eurofins.fr/fr-fr/contacts/eurofins-analyses-pour-lenvironnement-france-saverne.aspx
Laboratory Testing Services
S.I.C.: 8734
N.A.I.C.S.: 541380

Eurofins Analytics France SAS (1)
Rue Pierre Adolphe Bobierre
BP 42301
44323 Nantes, France
Tel.: (33) 251832100
Fax: (33) 251832111
E-Mail: eurofinsfr@eurofins.com
Web Site: www.eurofins.com
Emp.: 400
Laboratory Testing Services
S.I.C.: 8734
N.A.I.C.S.: 541380

Eurofins Ascal Environnement SAS (1)
Parc Europa
57602 Forbach, France
Tel.: (33) 3 87 83 48 00
Fax: (33) 3 87 83 48 35
E-Mail: hydrologie@eurofins.com
Web Site: www.eurofins.com
Ground & Waste Water Testing Services
S.I.C.: 8734
N.A.I.C.S.: 541380

Subsidiaries:

Eurofins Ascal Batiment Nord SAS (2)
557 Route de Noyelles PA du Pommier
62110 Henin-Beaumont, France
Tel.: (33) 3 21 13 49 70
Fax: (33) 3 21 13 49 74
E-Mail: batiment@eurofins.com
Web Site: www.eurofins.fr/fr-fr/contacts/eurofins-ascal-batiment-nord.aspx
Asbestos Testing Services
S.I.C.: 8734
N.A.I.C.S.: 541380

Eurofins Ascal Batiment Sud Est SAS (2)
Route de St Genis
BP 18
69610 Sainte-Foy-l'Argentiere, France
Tel.: (33) 4 74 72 26 40
Fax: (33) 4 74 26 15 59
E-Mail: batiment@eurofins.com
Web Site: www.eurofins.com
Emp.: 22
Laboratory Testing Services
S.I.C.: 8734
N.A.I.C.S.: 541380
Sarah Thevenet *(Gen Mgr)*

Eurofins ATS SAS (1)
Z I des Milles Actimart 1140 rue Ampere
13851 Aix-en-Provence, France
Tel.: (33) 4 42 39 78 08
Fax: (33) 4 42 39 77 81
E-Mail: ats@eurofins.com
Web Site: www.eurofins.com
Laboratory Testing Services
S.I.C.: 8734
N.A.I.C.S.: 541380
Yann Agustin *(Gen Mgr)*

Eurofins Biosciences Cervac Consulting (1)
ZA des Chabauds Nord
64 Rue Eugene Schneider, F-13320
Marseille, Bouc Bel Air, France (100%)
Tel.: (33) 442943530
Fax: (33) 442943548
E-Mail: chrestinechaix@eurofins.com
Web Site: www.eurofins.fr
Emp.: 17
Management Consulting Services
S.I.C.: 8748
N.A.I.C.S.: 541618
Fabrice Marcel *(Mgr)*

Eurofins Biosciences SAS (1)
Z I de Courtaboeuf 9 Avenue de Laponie
91978 Les Ulis, France
Tel.: (33) 1 69 10 88 88
Fax: (33) 1 69 10 88 99
E-Mail: servicecommercialhygiene@eurofins.com
Web Site: www.eurofins.com
Biotechnology Research & Development Services
S.I.C.: 8731
N.A.I.C.S.: 541711

Eurofins Certification SARL (1)
9 Ave de la Laponie
Z A I de Courtaboeuf, 91940 Les Ulis, France (100%)
Tel.: (33) 169108888
Fax: (33) 169130001
E-Mail: certification@eurofins.com
Web Site: www.eurofins.com
Emp.: 80
Testing Laboratories
S.I.C.: 8734
N.A.I.C.S.: 541380
Faycal Bellatif *(Mng Dir)*

Eurofins Cervac Audit SAS (1)
64 rue Eugene Schneider
13320 Toulon, France (100%)
Tel.: (33) 442943500
Fax: (33) 442943548
Web Site: www.eurofins.fr/contacts.aspx
Emp.: 100
Management Consulting Services
S.I.C.: 8748
N.A.I.C.S.: 541618
Francois Vigneau *(Mng Dir)*

Eurofins Cervac Sud SAS (1)
64 rue Eugene Schneider
13320 Toulon, France (100%)
Tel.: (33) 442943500
Fax: (33) 442943548
Web Site: www.eurofins.com
Testing Laboratories
S.I.C.: 8734
N.A.I.C.S.: 541380
Francois Vigneau *(Mng Dir)*

Eurofins Eaux Residuaires SAS (1)
1 rue du Professeur Calmette
59046 Lille, France
Tel.: (33) 3 27 86 95 60
Fax: (33) 3 27 87 24 67
E-Mail: hydrologie@eurofins.com
Web Site: www.eurofins.com
Waste Water Testing Services
S.I.C.: 8734
N.A.I.C.S.: 541380

Eurofins Environnement & Sante SAS (1)
9 Av de la Laponie
Z A I de Courtaboeuf, 91940 Orleans, France (100%)
Tel.: (33) 169108888
Fax: (33) 169108899
E-Mail: standardulis@eurofins.com
Emp.: 50
Testing Laboratories
S.I.C.: 8734
N.A.I.C.S.: 541380
Jilles Martin *(Gen Mgr)*

Eurofins Environnement SAS (1)
9 Av de la Laponie
Z A I de Courtaboeuf, 91967 Courtaboeuf, France (100%)
Tel.: (33) 169108888
Fax: (33) 1691088996
E-Mail: info@eurofins.com
Web Site: www.eurofins.fr
Emp.: 80
Testing Laboratories
S.I.C.: 8734
N.A.I.C.S.: 541380
Gilles G. Martin *(CEO)*

Eurofins Genomics SAS (1)
9 Avenue de Laponie Les Ulis
Les Ulis, 91978 Courtaboeuf, France
Tel.: (33) 1 69 10 88 97
Fax: (33) 1 69 10 88 84
E-Mail: info-fr@eurofins.com
Web Site: www.eurofins.com
Emp.: 9
Pharmaceutical Product Research Services
S.I.C.: 8731
N.A.I.C.S.: 541711
Nicolas Rouquet *(Mng Dir)*

Eurofins Hydrologie France SAS (1)
ZAI de Courtaboeuf 9 Avenue de Laponie
91978 Les Ulis, France
Tel.: (33) 1 69 10 88 88
Fax: (33) 1 69 10 88 99
E-Mail: hydrologie@eurofins.com
Water Treatment Services
S.I.C.: 4971
N.A.I.C.S.: 221310

Eurofins Scientific S.A.—(Continued)

Eurofins Hygiene des lieux de Travail SAS (1)
5 Rue d Otterswiller
67700 Saverne, France
Tel.: (33) 3 88 91 19 11
Fax: (33) 3 88 91 65 31
E-Mail: environnement@eurofins.com
Laboratory Testing Services
S.I.C.: 8734
N.A.I.C.S.: 541380

Eurofins Hygiene du Batiment Paris SAS (1)
20 Rue Du Kochersberg
67700 Saverne, France
Tel.: (33) 3 88 91 19 11
Fax: (33) 3 88 91 65 31
E-Mail: batiment@eurofins.com
Real Estate Management Services
S.I.C.: 6531
N.A.I.C.S.: 531390

Eurofins IPL Environnement SAS (1)
20 Rue du Kochersberg
67701 Saverne, France
Tel.: (33) 820 20 05 25
Fax: (33) 820 20 90 32
Environmental Consulting Services
S.I.C.: 8999
N.A.I.C.S.: 541620

Subsidiaries:

Eurofins IPL Est SAS (2)
Rue Lucien Cuenot - Site Saint Jacques II
BP 51 005
54521 Maxeville, France
Tel.: (33) 3 83 50 36 00
Fax: (33) 3 83 56 84 22
E-Mail: hydrologie@eurofins.com
Water Treatment Services
S.I.C.: 4941
N.A.I.C.S.: 221310

Eurofins IPL Ile de France SAS (2)
9 Avenue de Laponie - ZAI de Courtaboeuf
91940 Les Ulis, France
Tel.: (33) 1 69 10 88 88
Fax: (33) 1 69 10 88 99
E-Mail: scandardures@urofins.com
Web Site: www.eurofins.com
Water Testing Services
S.I.C.: 8734
N.A.I.C.S.: 541380

Eurofins IPL Sud SAS (2)
778 rue de la Croix Verte
34196 Montpellier, France
Tel.: (33) 4 67 84 74 27
Fax: (33) 4 67 04 17 67
E-Mail: hydrologie@eurofins.com
Web Site: www.eurofins.com
Water Testing Services
S.I.C.: 8734
N.A.I.C.S.: 541380

IPL Sante Environnement Durable Atlantique SAS (2)
1 Rue du Professeur Vezes
33300 Bordeaux, France
Tel.: (33) 5 56 01 84 00
Fax: (33) 5 57 87 11 63
Laboratory Testing Services
S.I.C.: 8734
N.A.I.C.S.: 541380

LCAM SAS (2)
7 Rue de l'Abbe Gregoire
57050 Metz, France
Tel.: (33) 3 87 37 40 60
Fax: (33) 3 87 36 74 80
E-Mail: ServiceClientsMetz@eurofins.com
Web Site: www.eurofins.com
Biological Testing Services
S.I.C.: 8734
N.A.I.C.S.: 541380

Eurofins Laboratoire Centre SAS (1)
ZAC Les Esses Galerne
45760 Vennecy, France
Tel.: (33) 2 38 77 21 22
Fax: (33) 2 38 77 48 50
E-Mail: serviceclientelc@eurofins.com
Web Site: www.eurofins.com
Emp.: 30
Laboratory Testing Services
S.I.C.: 8734
N.A.I.C.S.: 541380

Eurofins Laboratoire de Microbiologie Est SAS (1)
16 rue Clement Ader
68127 Sainte-Croix-en-Plaine, France
Tel.: (33) 3 89 22 27 70
Fax: (33) 3 89 22 27 71
E-Mail: microbiofrance@eurofins.com
Web Site: www.eurofins.com
Microbiological Testing Services
S.I.C.: 8734
N.A.I.C.S.: 541380

Eurofins Laboratoire de Pathologie Vegetale SAS (1)
81 Bis Rue Bernard Palissy
62750 Loos-en-Gohelle, France
Tel.: (33) 3 21 28 10 76
Fax: (33) 3 27 87 24 67
E-Mail: ServiceClientelpv@eurofins.com
Pathological Testing Laboratory Services
S.I.C.: 8734
N.A.I.C.S.: 541380

Eurofins Laboratoire Nord SAS (1)
Rue Maurice Caullery ZI Douai Dorignies
59500 Douai, France
Tel.: (33) 3 27 86 95 60
Fax: (33) 3 27 87 24 67
E-Mail: info@eurofins.fr
Web Site: www.eurofins.fr/fr-fr/contacts/eurofins-laboratoire-nord.aspx
Microbiological Testing Services
S.I.C.: 8734
N.A.I.C.S.: 541380

Eurofins Laboratoires de Microbiologie Ouest SAS (1)
11 Rue Pierre Adolphe Bobierre CS 12352
44300 Nantes, France
Tel.: (33) 2 51 83 79 50
Fax: (33) 2 51 83 79 90
E-Mail: MicrobioFrance@eurofins.com
Web Site: www.eurofins.com
Food Product Testing Services
S.I.C.: 8734
N.A.I.C.S.: 541380

Eurofins Lara SA (1)
1 Impasse De Lisieux
31025 Toulouse, France
Tel.: (33) 5 61 16 15 00
Fax: (33) 5 61 16 15 15
Laboratory Testing Services
S.I.C.: 8734
N.A.I.C.S.: 541380

Eurofins Lem SAS (1)
20 Rue du Kochersberg
67701 Saverne, France
Tel.: (33) 388710867
Fax: (33) 388916531
Web Site: www.eurofins.com
Emp.: 100
Management Consulting Services
S.I.C.: 8748
N.A.I.C.S.: 541618

Eurofins LHCF Environment (1)
117 Quai de Valmy
F 75010 Paris, France (100%)
Tel.: (33) 140370303
Fax: (33) 140371512
E-Mail: Communicationlem@eurofins.com
Web Site: www.eurofins.fr
Emp.: 17
Testing Laboratories
S.I.C.: 8734
N.A.I.C.S.: 541380
Gildas Leray *(Dir-Tech)*

Eurofins Marketing Research SAS (1)
5 Rue Cadet
75009 Paris, France
Tel.: (33) 1 53 34 17 47
Fax: (33) 1 53 34 00 08
E-Mail: marketingresearchparis@eurofins.com
Web Site: www.eurofins-marketing-research.com
Emp.: 50
Marketing Research Services
S.I.C.: 8732
N.A.I.C.S.: 541910
Jean-Marc Legall *(Gen Mgr)*

Eurofins Medinet SAS (1)
48-52 rue de la Gare
BP 11, 78372 Plaisir, France (100%)
Tel.: (33) 130546000
Fax: (33) 130546151
E-Mail: info@eurofinsmedinet.com
Web Site: www.eurofins-medinet.com
Emp.: 6
Medical Laboratories
S.I.C.: 8071
N.A.I.C.S.: 621511
Eric Mal-Erbe *(Gen Mgr)*

Eurofins MWG Biotech France S.A. (1)
9 Av de la Laponie
Z A I de Courtaboeuf, 91978 Les Ulis, France (100%)
Tel.: (33) 169108888
Fax: (33) 169108899
E-Mail: info@mwg-biotech.sa
Web Site: www.mwg-biotech.sa
Emp.: 80
Testing Laboratories
S.I.C.: 8734
N.A.I.C.S.: 541380

Eurofins NDSC Food France SAS (1)
Rue Pierre Adolphe Bobierre
44300 Nantes, France
Tel.: (33) 251832100
Fax: (33) 251832111
E-Mail: eurofinsfr@eurofins.com
Food Product Testing Services
S.I.C.: 8734
N.A.I.C.S.: 541380

Eurofins NSC Developpement France SAS (1)
20 Rue Du Kochersberg
67700 Saverne, France
Tel.: (33) 3 88 91 19 11
Biotechnology Research & Development Services
S.I.C.: 8731
N.A.I.C.S.: 541711

Eurofins Optimed Lyon SAS (1)
Centre Hospitalier Lyon Sud Pavillon 40
165 Chemin du Grand Revoyet
69310 Pierre-Benite, France
Tel.: (33) 4 78 86 65 26
Fax: (33) 4 78 86 65 27
Web Site: www.optimed-recrutement.com
Biotechnology Research & Development Services
S.I.C.: 8731
N.A.I.C.S.: 541711

Eurofins Optimed SAS (1)
1 rue des Essarts
38610 Gieres, France
Tel.: (33) 4 38 37 27 40
Fax: (33) 4 38 37 27 41
E-Mail: contact@optimed.fr
Web Site: www.optimed.fr
Emp.: 80
Clinical Research & Biometry Services
S.I.C.: 8734
N.A.I.C.S.: 541380
Yves Donazzolo *(Pres, CEO & Dir-Medical)*

Eurofins Pharma Control SAS (1)
9 Av de la Laponie
Z A I de Courtaboeuf, 91940 Les Ulis, France (100%)
Tel.: (33) 169108888
Fax: (33) 1691088996
Web Site: www.eurofins.fr/contacts/eurofins-pharma-control-ace.aspx
Emp.: 80,000
Testing Laboratories
S.I.C.: 8734
N.A.I.C.S.: 541380
Luc Leroy *(CEO)*

Eurofins Pharma Quality Control SAS (1)
Rue Clement Ader
68127 Sainte-Croix-en-Plaine, France
Tel.: (33) 3 89 22 27 74
Fax: (33) 3 89 22 27 75
Pharmaceutical Product Laboratory Testing Services
S.I.C.: 8734
N.A.I.C.S.: 541380

Eurofins Scientific AgroGene SARL (1)
Rue Pierre Adolphe Bobierre
BP 42301, 44323 Nantes, France (100%)
Tel.: (33) 251832100
Fax: (33) 251832111
E-Mail: eurofinsfr@eurofins.com
Web Site: www.eurofins.com
Emp.: 200
Research & Development in the Physical Engineering & Life Sciences
S.I.C.: 8731
N.A.I.C.S.: 541712
Francois Vigneau *(Mng Dir)*

Eurofins Scientific Analytics SAS (1)
9 Rue Pierre Adolphe Bobierre
Nantes, France (100%)
Tel.: (33) 251832100
Fax: (33) 251832111
E-Mail: eurofinssr@eurofins.com
Emp.: 300
Scientific & Technical Consulting Services
S.I.C.: 8999
N.A.I.C.S.: 541690

Eurofins Scientific Biosciences SAS (1)
9 avenue de la Laponie
Z I de Courtaboeuf, 91978 Les Ulis, France (100%)
Tel.: (33) 169108888
Fax: (33) 169108899
E-Mail: microbiofrance@eurofins.com
Web Site: www.eurofins.com
Emp.: 60
Testing Laboratories
S.I.C.: 8734
N.A.I.C.S.: 541380
Nicolas Karam *(Gen Mgr)*

Eurofins Scientific Test Center SAS (1)
5 Rue Cadet
75009 Paris, France (100%)
Tel.: (33) 153341747
Fax: (33) 153340008
E-Mail: jeanmarclegall@eurofins.com
Web Site: www.eurofins.com
Emp.: 20
Testing Laboratories
S.I.C.: 8734
N.A.I.C.S.: 541380
Jean-Marc Le Gall *(Mgr)*

Eurofins Test Center SAS (1)
64 Rue Eugene Schneider
Z A I de Courtaboeuf Bouc-Bel, 13320 Toulon, France (100%)
Tel.: (33) 442943500
Fax: (33) 442943548
Web Site: www.eurofins.com
Testing Laboratories
S.I.C.: 8734
N.A.I.C.S.: 541380
Francois Vigneau *(Mng Dir)*

GAB France SARL (1)
58 rue des Ateliers
67220 Saint-Pierre, France (100%)
Tel.: (33) 388089943
Fax: (33) 388081649
E-Mail: eass@eurofins.com
Web Site: www.eurofins.com
Emp.: 10
Research & Development in the Physical Engineering & Life Sciences
S.I.C.: 8731
N.A.I.C.S.: 541712
Claugio Lama *(Mng Dir)*

IFEG SAS (1)
Rue Pierre Adolphe Bobierre
BP 42301, 44323 Nantes, France (100%)
Tel.: (33) 251832100
Fax: (33) 251832111
E-Mail: IFEG@eurofins.com
Emp.: 200
Research & Development in the Physical Engineering & Life Sciences
S.I.C.: 8731
N.A.I.C.S.: 541712
Francois Vigneau *(Mng Dir)*

LCN SAS (1)
9 Av de la Laponie
Z A I de Courtaboeuf, 91940 Les Ulis, France (100%)
Tel.: (33) 169108888
Fax: (33) 1069108899
E-Mail: milleneguzbens@eurofins.com
Web Site: www.eurofins.com
Emp.: 80

Testing Laboratories
S.I.C.: 8734
N.A.I.C.S.: 541380
Zelles Malge *(Chm)*

Optimed S.A. **(1)**
1 Rue des Essarts
Gieres, 38610 Grenoble, France (100%)
Tel.: (33) 438372740
Fax: (33) 438372741
E-Mail: contact@optimed.fr
Web Site: www.optimed.fr
Emp.: 80
Testing Laboratories
S.I.C.: 8734
N.A.I.C.S.: 541380
Yves Donazzolo *(Mng Dir)*

Toxlab SAS **(1)**
7 Rue Jacques Cartier
75018 Paris, France
Tel.: (33) 1 58 59 28 06
Fax: (33) 1 58 59 28 01
E-Mail: contact@labotoxlab.com
Web Site: www.labotoxlab.com
Emp.: 35
Laboratory Testing Services
S.I.C.: 8734
N.A.I.C.S.: 541380
Marc Deveaux *(CEO)*

U.S. Subsidiaries:

Eurofins Agroscience Services Inc. **(1)**
150 Industrial Park Dr
Forsyth, GA 31029
Tel.: (478) 994-1092
Fax: (478) 994-5066
Web Site: www.eurofins.com
Emp.: 60
Laboratory Testing Services
S.I.C.: 8734
N.A.I.C.S.: 541380
Randy Fuller *(Mgr-Quality Assurance)*

Eurofins Analytical Testing Center Inc. **(1)**
401 W State St Rm T235B
Jacksonville, FL 32202
Tel.: (904) 359-0947
Web Site: www.eurofins.com
Analytical Laboratory Testing Services
S.I.C.: 8734
N.A.I.C.S.: 541380
Michelle Lovett *(Gen Mgr)*

Eurofins AvTech Laboratories, Inc. **(1)**
6859 Quality Way
Kalamazoo, MI 49002 (100%)
Tel.: (269) 323-3366
Fax: (269) 323-8774
Emp.: 21
Testing Laboratories
S.I.C.: 8734
N.A.I.C.S.: 541380

Eurofins Central Analytical Laboratories Inc. **(1)**
2315 N Causeway Blvd Ste 150
Metaire, LA 70001
Tel.: (504) 297-3400
Fax: (504) 297-3410
E-Mail: info@centralanalytical.com
Web Site: www.centralanalytical.com
Food & Chemical Testing Services
S.I.C.: 8734
N.A.I.C.S.: 541380
John Reuther *(Pres)*
Gilles G. Martin *(CEO)*
Markus Brandmeier *(Exec VP)*
Xavier Dennery *(Exec VP)*

Eurofins DQCI LLC **(1)**
5205 Quincy St
Mounds View, MN 55112
Tel.: (763) 785-0484
Fax: (763) 785-0584
E-Mail: info@DQCI.com
Web Site: www.dqci.com
Dairy Product Laboratory Testing Services
S.I.C.: 8734
N.A.I.C.S.: 541380
Dave Berkley *(VP-Sls & Mktg)*

Eurofins GeneScan USA Inc. **(1)**
2315 N Causeway Blvd Ste 200
Metairie, LA 70001 (100%)
Tel.: (504) 297-4330
Fax: (504) 297-4335
E-Mail: info@gmotesting.com
Web Site: www.eurofinsus.com
Emp.: 20
Testing Laboratories
S.I.C.: 8734
N.A.I.C.S.: 541380
Frank Spiegel Halter *(Controller)*

Eurofins Medinet Inc. **(1)**
14100 Park Meadow Dr Ste 110
Chantilly, VA 20151 (100%)
Tel.: (703) 480-2500
Fax: (703) 480-2670
Emp.: 90
Medical Laboratories
S.I.C.: 8071
N.A.I.C.S.: 621511
Daniel F. Sahm *(Mng Dir)*

Eurofins MWG Operon Inc. **(1)**
2211 Seminole Dr Ste 201
Huntsville, AL 35805
Tel.: (256) 704-8200
Fax: (256) 704-8189
Toll Free: (800) 688-2248
E-Mail: oligo-us@eurofins.com
Web Site: www.operon.com
Emp.: 100
Biological Testing Services
S.I.C.: 8734
N.A.I.C.S.: 541380
Martin Kunz *(CEO)*

Eurofins Product Safety Labs Inc. **(1)**
2394 US Hwy 130
Dayton, NJ 08810-1500 (100%)
Tel.: (732) 438-5100
Fax: (732) 355-3275
Web Site: www.productsafetylabs.com
Testing Laboratories
S.I.C.: 8734
N.A.I.C.S.: 541380
Gary Wnorowski *(Pres)*

Eurofins Scientific Inc. **(1)**
2200 Rittenhouse St Ste 150
Des Moines, IA 50321-3155 TN
Tel.: (515) 280-8378
Fax: (515) 280-7075
Web Site: www.eurofins.com
Emp.: 120
Testing Laboratories
S.I.C.: 8731
N.A.I.C.S.: 541712
Lars Reimann *(Chief Scientific Officer)*

Subsidiary:

Eurofins Scientific **(2)**
14100 Park Meadow Dr
Chantilly, VA 20151
Tel.: (703) 480-2500
Fax: (703) 480-2670
Toll Free: (877) 480-2500
Web Site: www.eurofinsmedinet.com
Sales Range: $50-74.9 Million
Emp.: 70
Medical Data & Testing Services & Diagnostic Products Mfr
S.I.C.: 8071
N.A.I.C.S.: 621511

Eurofins STA Laboratories Inc. **(1)**
1821 Vista View Dr
Longmont, CO 80504
Tel.: (303) 651-6417
Fax: (303) 772-4003
Toll Free: (800) 426-9124
E-Mail: stacoinfo@eurofinsus.com
Web Site: www.stalabs.com
Emp.: 25
Agricultural Chemical Testing Services
S.I.C.: 8734
N.A.I.C.S.: 541380
John R. Mizicko *(Pres & Mgr-Seed Quality Svcs Div)*

Lancaster Laboratories, Inc. **(1)**
2425 New Holland Pike
Lancaster, PA 17601 (100%)
Tel.: (717) 656-2300
Fax: (717) 656-2681
E-Mail: webmaster@lancasterlabs.com
Web Site: www.lancasterlabs.com
Sales Range: $100-124.9 Million
Emp.: 800
Research & Analytical Laboratory Services
S.I.C.: 8732
N.A.I.C.S.: 541720
Wilson Hershey *(Chm)*
Timothy Oostdyk *(Pres)*
Thomas E. Wolgemuth *(CFO)*

MWG Biotech Inc. **(1)**
2211 Seminole Dr
Huntsville, AL 35805 (100%)
Tel.: (336) 812-9995
Fax: (251) 252-7794
Web Site: www.mwg-biotech.com
Emp.: 100
In-Vitro Diagnostic Substance Mfr
S.I.C.: 2835
N.A.I.C.S.: 325413
Dale Harrison *(Mng Dir)*

Non-U.S. Subsidiaries:

Agrisearch Ltd **(1)**
Slade Lane Wilson
Melbourne, Derbyshire, DE73 8AG, United Kingdom
Tel.: (44) 1332 864800
Fax: (44) 1332 864763
Pesticide & Agricultural Chemical Mfr
S.I.C.: 2879
N.A.I.C.S.: 325320

Agrisearch UK Ltd. **(1)**
Slade Lane Wilson
Melbourne, Derbyshire, DE738AG, United Kingdom (100%)
Tel.: (44) 1332864800
Fax: (44) 1332864763
E-Mail: info@eurofins.com
Web Site: www.eurofins.com
Emp.: 110
Agricultural Marketing & Commodities Regulation
S.I.C.: 9641
N.A.I.C.S.: 926140
Chris Harrison *(Dir-Ops)*

Analytico BV **(1)**
Bergschot 71
PO Box 5510
4817 PA Breda, Netherlands (100%)
Tel.: (31) 765737373
Fax: (31) 765737777
E-Mail: info@eurofins.com
Web Site: www.eurofins.com
Emp.: 200
Testing Laboratories
S.I.C.: 8734
N.A.I.C.S.: 541380
Zaan Erp *(Mng Dir)*

Analytico Milieu NV **(1)**
Fotografielaan 43
2610 Antwerp, Belgium (100%)
Tel.: (32) 38275111
Fax: (32) 38279832
E-Mail: info@eurofins.be
Web Site: www.eurofins.be
Emp.: 50
Testing Laboratories
S.I.C.: 8734
N.A.I.C.S.: 541380
Bart van Boven *(Mng Dir)*

Bacteriologisch Controle Station BV **(1)**
Heerenveg 7
Katwijk, 2222AM Hague, Netherlands (100%)
Tel.: (31) 714024234
Research & Development in the Physical Engineering & Life Sciences
S.I.C.: 8731
N.A.I.C.S.: 541712

Biolab Espagnola de Analisis e Investigacion SL **(1)**
Baldiri Reixac 4-6
Barcelona, 08028, Spain
Tel.: (34) 934034555
Fax: (34) 934034510
Biotechnology Research & Development Services
S.I.C.: 8731
N.A.I.C.S.: 541711

Biolab Espanola De Analisis E Investigacion S.L. **(1)**
Parc Cientific de Barcelona
C- Baldiri Reixac 4-6, 8028 Barcelona, Spain (100%)
Tel.: (34) 934034555
Fax: (34) 934034555
E-Mail: biolab.spain@biolab.it
Web Site: www.biolab.es
Emp.: 9
Testing Laboratories
S.I.C.: 8734
N.A.I.C.S.: 541380
Luca Salvi *(Mng Dir)*

Chemical Control Srl **(1)**
Via Celdit 2
Madonna dell Olmo-Cuneo, 12100 Cuneo, Italy (100%)
Tel.: (39) 0171412470
Fax: (39) 0171411826
E-Mail: info@chemicalcontrol.it
Web Site: www.chemicalcontrol.it
Emp.: 50
Research & Development in the Physical Engineering & Life Sciences
S.I.C.: 8731
N.A.I.C.S.: 541712
Giuseppe Chiappetta *(Mgr)*

Chemiphar NV **(1)**
Lieven Bauwensstraat 4 6
8200 Brugge, Belgium
Tel.: (32) 50 31 02 52
Fax: (32) 50 31 02 54
E-Mail: info@chemiphar.com
Web Site: www.chemiphar.com
Analytical Laboratory Testing Services
S.I.C.: 8734
N.A.I.C.S.: 541380

CPA Laboratories Ltd. **(1)**
318 Worple Road
Raynes Park, London, SW20 8QU, United Kingdom (100%)
Tel.: (44) 2089468621
Fax: (44) 2089471206
Web Site: www.cpalaboratories.com
Emp.: 10
Biological Product Mfr
S.I.C.: 2836
N.A.I.C.S.: 325414
Alex Snashall *(Gen Mgr)*

CRL Medinet BV **(1)**
Bergschot 69-71
PO Box 5510
4817PA Breda, Netherlands (100%)
Tel.: (31) 765737373
Fax: (31) 765737777
E-Mail: info@crlmedinet.com
Web Site: www.crlmedinet.com
Testing Laboratories
S.I.C.: 8734
N.A.I.C.S.: 541380

Dr. Appelt Beteiligungs GmbH **(1)**
Taubchenweg 28
04317 Leipzig, Germany
Tel.: (49) 341 64966 0
Fax: (49) 341 64966 99
E-Mail: info@wqlpz.de
Emp.: 100
Laboratory Testing Services
S.I.C.: 8734
N.A.I.C.S.: 541380
Nadine Slomma *(Mgr)*

Subsidiaries:

Institut Dr. Appelt Hilter GmbH & Co. KG **(2)**
Munsterstrasse 9-11
49171 Hilter, Germany
Tel.: (49) 5424 22 637 0
Fax: (49) 5424 226399
E-Mail: info@wqh-appelt.de
Web Site: www.appelt-laboratorien.de/en/contact/Hilter.php
Laboratory Testing Services
S.I.C.: 8734
N.A.I.C.S.: 541380

Institut Dr. Appelt Thuringen GmbH & CO. KG **(2)**
Talstrasse 50
98544 Zella-Mehlis, Germany
Tel.: (49) 3682 89 65 0
Fax: (49) 3682 89 65 65
E-Mail: info@wqt-appelt.de
Web Site: www.appelt-laboratorien.de/de/kontakt/Zella-Mehlis.php
Emp.: 20
Testing Laboratory Services
S.I.C.: 8734
N.A.I.C.S.: 541380
Andreas Mueller *(Mng Dir)*

Environmental Laboratories BV (1)
Koopvaardijweg 34
4906CV Oosterhout, Netherlands (100%)
Tel.: (31) 235677950
Web Site: www.eurofins.com
Testing Laboratories
S.I.C.: 8734
N.A.I.C.S.: 541380

Eurofins 1. Verwaltungsgesellschaft mbH (1)
Grossmoorbogen 25
21079 Hamburg, Germany
Tel.: (49) 40 30086201
Bio Analytical Testing Services
S.I.C.: 8734
N.A.I.C.S.: 541380

Eurofins 2. Verwaltungsgesellschaft mbH (1)
Stenzelring 14b
21107 Hamburg, Germany
Tel.: (49) 40 49294 0
Fax: (49) 40 704412111
Management Consulting Services
S.I.C.: 8748
N.A.I.C.S.: 541618

Eurofins A/S (1)
Smedeskovvej 38
Galten, 8464 Arhus, Denmark (100%)
Tel.: (45) 70224266
Fax: (45) 70224255
E-Mail: miljo@eurofins.dk
Web Site: www.eurofins.dk
Emp.: 750
Analytical Laboratory Instrument Mfr
S.I.C.: 3826
N.A.I.C.S.: 334516
Svend Aage Linde *(Mng Dir)*

Eurofins-Agrisearch (1)
Via Vinca 6 San Giorgio di Piano
40016 Bologna, Italy (100%)
Tel.: (39) 0516650637
Fax: (39) 0516655119
Web Site: www.eurofins-agrisearch.com
Management Consulting Services
S.I.C.: 8748
N.A.I.C.S.: 541618
Claudio Lama *(Gen Mgr)*

Eurofins Agroscience Services EcoChem GmbH (1)
Eutingerstr 24
75223 Niefern-Oschelbronn, Germany
Tel.: (49) 7 2339 6270
Fax: (49) 7 2339 62768
E-Mail: easinfo@eurofins.com
Web Site: www.eurofins.com
Emp.: 115
Agricultural Chemical Testing Services
S.I.C.: 8734
N.A.I.C.S.: 541380
Martin Feyerabend *(Mng Dir)*

Eurofins Agroscience Services GmbH (1)
Carl-Goerdeler-Weg 5
21684 Stade, Germany
Tel.: (49) 4141 80030
Fax: (49) 4141 800320
E-Mail: info@eurofins.com
Web Site: www.eurofins.com
Emp.: 40
Laboratory Testing Services
S.I.C.: 8734
N.A.I.C.S.: 541380
P. Joerg *(Head-Sls & Mktg)*

Non-U.S. Subsidiary:

Eurofins Agroscience Services Sp. z.o.o. (2)
Galowo ul Wierzbowa 12
64-500 Szamotuly, Poland
Tel.: (48) 61 29 27 08 1
Fax: (48) 61 62 42 98 2
Web Site: www.eurofins.com
Chemical Testing Services
S.I.C.: 8734
N.A.I.C.S.: 541380

Eurofins Agroscience Services Kft (1)
Uj Varalja sor 16
8000 Szekesfehervar, Hungary
Tel.: (36) 22 501 684
Fax: (36) 22 501 685
Web Site: www.eurofins.hu
Emp.: 13
Agricultural Chemical Testing Services
S.I.C.: 8734
N.A.I.C.S.: 541380
Jozsef Pardi *(Mng Dir)*

Eurofins Agroscience Services Ltd (1)
Slade Lane Wilson
Melbourne, Derby, DE73 8AG, United Kingdom
Tel.: (44) 1332 86 48 00
Fax: (44) 1332 86 47 63
Emp.: 100
Agricultural Chemical Mfr
S.I.C.: 2879
N.A.I.C.S.: 325320

Eurofins Agroscience Services SL (1)
Pol PISA C/ Brujula 39 Mairena del Aljarafe
41927 Seville, Spain
Tel.: (34) 954 18 70 14
Fax: (34) 954 18 42 96
Web Site: www.eurofins.com
Agricultural Chemical Testing Services
S.I.C.: 8734
N.A.I.C.S.: 541380

Eurofins Agrosciences Services Srl (1)
Sede Operativa Via XXV Aprile 8/3
40016 San Giorgio di Piano, Bologna, Italy
Tel.: (39) 051 66 50 637
Fax: (39) 051 66 55 119
Web Site: www.eurofins.com
Emp.: 20
Pesticide & Agricultural Chemical Mfr
S.I.C.: 2879
N.A.I.C.S.: 325320
Dario Rinaldi *(Project Mgr)*

Eurofins Analytical Services India Pvt Ltd (1)
183 1st floor Gayathri Tech Park EPIP 2nd Phase
Whitefield, 560 066 Bengaluru, India
Tel.: (91) 80 3070 6666
Fax: (91) 80 4168 0405
E-Mail: foodindia@eurofins.com
Web Site: www.eurofins.com
Emp.: 35
Analytical Laboratory Testing Services
S.I.C.: 8734
N.A.I.C.S.: 541380
Ramesh Jampala *(Mgr-Food Lab)*

Eurofins Analytico Food BV (1)
Leeuwarderstraatweg 129
PO Box 766
8441 PK Heerenveen, Netherlands (100%)
Tel.: (31) 888310000
Fax: (31) 888310100
E-Mail: service@eurofins.nl
Web Site: www.eurofins.nl
Emp.: 250
Research & Development in the Physical Engineering & Life Sciences
S.I.C.: 8731
N.A.I.C.S.: 541712
Sabine Meersseman *(Mng Dir)*

Eurofins Analytico (1)
Gildeweg 44-46
3771 NB Barneveld, Netherlands (100%)
Mailing Address:
PO Box 459
3770 AL Barneveld, Netherlands
Tel.: (31) 342426300
Fax: (31) 342426399
E-Mail: nl_nez@eurofins.com
Web Site: www.analytico.com
Emp.: 270
Research & Development in the Physical Engineering & Life Sciences
S.I.C.: 8731
N.A.I.C.S.: 541712
Hans Wart *(Gen Mgr)*

Eurofins Analytik GmbH (1)
Grossmoorbogen 25
21079 Hamburg, Germany (100%)
Tel.: (49) 4030086200
Fax: (49) 40881448101
E-Mail: specht@eurofins.de
Web Site: www.eurofins.de
Emp.: 130
Testing Laboratories
S.I.C.: 8734
N.A.I.C.S.: 541380
Manfred Linkerhaegner *(Mng Dir)*

Subsidiary:

Eurofins Umwelt West GmbH (2)
Lachener Strasse 88
67433 Neustadt, Germany (100%)
Tel.: (49) 632191780
Fax: (49) 6321917840
E-Mail: info.neustadt@eurofins-umwelt.de
Web Site: www.eurofins.de
Testing Laboratories
S.I.C.: 8734
N.A.I.C.S.: 541380

Eurofins avd. Moss (1)
Postboks 3055
Kambo, NO-1506 Moss, Norway (100%)
Tel.: (47) 69005200
Fax: (47) 69272340
E-Mail: miljo@eurofins.no
Web Site: www.eurofins.no
Testing Laboratories
S.I.C.: 8734
N.A.I.C.S.: 541380

Eurofins Becewa NV (1)
Venecoweg 5
9810 Nazareth, Belgium
Tel.: (32) 9 222 77 59
Fax: (32) 9 220 56 50
E-Mail: info@eurofins.be
Biotechnology Research & Development Services
S.I.C.: 8731
N.A.I.C.S.: 541711

Eurofins Belgium NV (1)
Parc Crealys CRI Cassiopee Rue Jean Jonet 21 bte 1
Isnes, 5032 Gembloux, Belgium
Tel.: (32) 81 72 88 50
Fax: (32) 81 72 88 59
E-Mail: info@eurofins.be
Web Site: www.eurofins.be
Laboratory Testing Services
S.I.C.: 8734
N.A.I.C.S.: 541380
Frederic Dupont *(CEO)*

Eurofins C Mark BV (1)
Leeuwarderstraatweg 129
PO Box 766
8441PK Heerenveen, Netherlands (100%)
Tel.: (31) 888310000
Fax: (31) 888310101
E-Mail: service@eurofins.nl
Web Site: www.eurofins.nl
Emp.: 120
Research & Development in the Physical Engineering & Life Sciences
S.I.C.: 8731
N.A.I.C.S.: 541712
Caspar Pronk *(Mng Dir)*

Eurofins Consult GmbH (1)
Grossmoorbogen 25
21079 Hamburg, Germany (100%)
Tel.: (49) 4030086200
Fax: (49) 4049294699
Emp.: 30
Management Consulting Services
S.I.C.: 8748
N.A.I.C.S.: 541618
Helga Neumann *(Mng Dir)*

Eurofins Danmark A/S (1)
Smedeskovvej 38
Galten, 8464 Arhus, Denmark (100%)
Tel.: (45) 70224266
Fax: (45) 70224255
E-Mail: info@eurofins.dk
Web Site: www.eurofins.dk
Emp.: 100
Analytical Laboratory Instrument Mfr
S.I.C.: 3826
N.A.I.C.S.: 334516
Coston Yanson *(Mng Dir)*

Eurofins do Brasil Analise de Alimentos Ltda (1)
Rodovia Engenheiro Emilio de Oliviera Penteado
Km 57 7 Marginal Norte Condomi, Sao Paulo, Brazil (100%)
Tel.: (55) 1938755502
Fax: (55) 1939342434
Web Site: www.eurofins.com.br
Emp.: 32
Testing Laboratories
S.I.C.: 8734
N.A.I.C.S.: 541380
Pablo Molloy *(Mng Dir)*

Eurofins Dr. Specht Express GmbH (1)
Grossmoorbogen 25
21079 Hamburg, Germany
Tel.: (49) 40 88 14 48 511
Fax: (49) 40 88 14 48 599
Web Site: www.eurofins.de/de-de/kontakt/dr-specht-express-gmbh.aspx
Scientific & Technical Consulting Services
S.I.C.: 8999
N.A.I.C.S.: 541690

Eurofins Eastern Ventures BV (1)
Bergschot 69-71
4801 DM Breda, Netherlands
Tel.: (31) 765737373
Venture Capital Management Services
S.I.C.: 6799
N.A.I.C.S.: 523910

Non-U.S. Subsidiary:

Eurofins Steins Laboratorium Sp. z.o.o. (2)
Aleja Wojska Polskiego 90A
82-200 Malbork, Poland
Tel.: (48) 55 272 04 73
Fax: (48) 55 272 04 75
E-Mail: info@eurofins.pl
Laboratory Testing Services
S.I.C.: 8734
N.A.I.C.S.: 541380

Eurofins Environment Testing Norway AS (1)
Mollebakken 50
1538 Moss, Norway
Tel.: (47) 23 05 05 00
Fax: (47) 69272340
E-Mail: miljo@eurofins.no
Web Site: www.eurofins.no/om-oss-/eurofins-environment-testing-norway-as.aspx
Environmental Testing Services
S.I.C.: 8734
N.A.I.C.S.: 541380
Christina W. Haug *(CEO)*

Eurofins Environment Testing Sweden Holding AB (1)
Sjohagsgatan 3
Box 737
531 17 Lidkoping, Sweden
Tel.: (46) 10 4908100
Fax: (46) 10 4908390
E-Mail: info.environment@eurofins.se
Emp.: 100
Environmental Testing & Consulting Services
S.I.C.: 8999
N.A.I.C.S.: 541620
Thomas Kiratsopoulos *(Mng Dir)*

Subsidiary:

Eurofins Environment Testing Sweden AB (2)
Sjohagsgatan 3 Port 1
531 40 Lidkoping, Sweden
Tel.: (46) 10 490 8100
Fax: (46) 10 490 8390
E-Mail: info.environment@eurofins.se
Web Site: www.eurofins.se/kontakta-oss/lidkoping_miljo.aspx
Emp.: 100
Environmental Testing Services
S.I.C.: 8734
N.A.I.C.S.: 541380
Cecilia Frendius *(Controller-Bus)*

Eurofins Food & Agro Testing Sweden AB (1)
Estrids Vag 1
291 65 Kristianstad, Sweden
Tel.: (46) 10 490 83 00
Fax: (46) 10 490 84 70
E-Mail: info@eurofins.se
Web Site: www.eurofins.se/kontakta-oss/kristianstad.aspx
Food Product Testing Services
S.I.C.: 8734
N.A.I.C.S.: 541380

Fredrik Westerberg *(Mgr)*

Eurofins Food Denmark Holding A/S (1)
Smedeskovvej 38
8464 Galten, Denmark
Tel.: (45) 70224266
Investment Management Services
S.I.C.: 6211
N.A.I.C.S.: 523999

Subsidiary:

Eurofins Steins Laboratorium A/S (2)
Hjaltesvej 8
7500 Holstebro, Denmark
Tel.: (45) 70 22 42 86
Fax: (45) 70 22 42 95
E-Mail: steins@eurofins.dk
Web Site: www.eurofins.dk/dk/f0devarer-agro/kontakt.aspx
Laboratory Testing Services
S.I.C.: 8734
N.A.I.C.S.: 541380

Eurofins Food GmbH (1)
Am Neulander Gewerbepark 1
21079 Hamburg, Germany
Tel.: (49) 40 49 29 47 99
Fax: (49) 40 49 29 47 39
E-Mail: info@eurofins.de
Web Site: www.eurofins.de
Laboratory Testing Services
S.I.C.: 8734
N.A.I.C.S.: 541380

Subsidiaries:

Eurofins CTC GmbH (2)
Am Neulaender Gewerbepark 1
21079 Hamburg, Germany
Tel.: (49) 40 49294 600
Fax: (49) 40 49294 99 609
E-Mail: conferences@eurofins.com
Web Site: www.eurofins.de/conferences/kontakt.aspx
Conference & Training Services
S.I.C.: 8299
N.A.I.C.S.: 611430

Eurofins Fintelmann und Meyer GMP GmbH (2)
Grossmoorbogen 25
21079 Hamburg, Germany
Tel.: (49) 40 49 29 46 70
Fax: (49) 40 49 29 46 99
E-Mail: fintelmann-meyer@eurofins.de
Web Site: www.eurofins.de/fintelmann-meyer-de.aspx
Emp.: 30
Microbiological Testing Services
S.I.C.: 8734
N.A.I.C.S.: 541380
Veronika Stoll *(Mgr-Analytical Svc)*

Eurofins Global Control GmbH (2)
Grossmoorbogen 25
21079 Hamburg, Germany
Tel.: (49) 40 49294 717
Fax: (49) 40 49294 782
E-Mail: global@eurofins.de
Web Site: www.global-testing.de
Emp.: 6
Food Product Testing Services
S.I.C.: 8734
N.A.I.C.S.: 541380
Werner Nader *(Mng Dir)*

Sofia GmbH (2)
Rudower Chaussee 29
12489 Berlin, Germany
Tel.: (49) 30 677 98560
Fax: (49) 30 677 98588
E-Mail: sofia@sofia-gmbh.de
Web Site: www.sofia-gmbh.de
Emp.: 65
Vegetable & Animal Feed Testing Services
S.I.C.: 8734
N.A.I.C.S.: 541380
Juergen Lipinski *(Co-CEO)*
Helmut Rost *(Co-CEO)*

Eurofins Food Ireland Limited (1)
Unit D13 North City Business Park North Road
Finglas, Dublin, Ireland
Tel.: (353) 1 4311 306
Fax: (353) 1 4311 308
E-Mail: info@eurofins.ie
Web Site: www.eurofins.ie
Emp.: 30
Laboratory Testing Services
S.I.C.: 8734
N.A.I.C.S.: 541380
Michelle Fitzgerald *(Mng Dir)*

Eurofins Food Testing Netherlands Holding BV (1)
Leeuwarderstraatweg 129
8441 PK Heerenveen, Netherlands
Tel.: (31) 88 8310000
Fax: (31) 88 8310100
E-Mail: service@eurofins.nl
Emp.: 175
Investment Management Services
S.I.C.: 6211
N.A.I.C.S.: 523999
Sabine Meersseman *(Gen Mgr)*

Subsidiaries:

C-mark BV (2)
Hoflaan 7
7383 CD Voorst, Netherlands
Tel.: (31) 88 831 05 00
E-Mail: info@c-mark.nl
Web Site: www.c-mark.nl
Drinking Water Testing Services
S.I.C.: 8734
N.A.I.C.S.: 541380

Eurofins Food Netherlands BV (2)
Bijdorpplein 21-23
PO Box 510
2992 LB Barendrecht, Netherlands
Tel.: (31) 88 831 04 61
Fax: (31) 88 831 01 00
Food Testing Services
S.I.C.: 8734
N.A.I.C.S.: 541380

Eurofins Food US Holdings I BV (1)
Argusvlinder 14
4814 SP Breda, Netherlands
Tel.: (31) 765737373
Investment Management Services
S.I.C.: 6282
N.A.I.C.S.: 523920

Eurofins Food US Holdings II BV (1)
Bergschot 71
4817PA Breda, Netherlands
Tel.: (31) 765737373
Investment Management Services
S.I.C.: 6211
N.A.I.C.S.: 523999

Eurofins-GAB GmbH (1)
Eutingerstrasse 24
75223 Niefern-Oschelbronn, Germany (100%)
Tel.: (49) 723396270
Fax: (49) 7233962780
E-Mail: info@eurofins-gab.com
Web Site: www.eurofins-gab.com
Emp.: 60
Management Consulting Services
S.I.C.: 8748
N.A.I.C.S.: 541618
Marcus Calluss *(Mng Dir)*

Non-U.S. Subsidiary:

GAB Poland Sp. Z.o.o. (2)
Galowo ul Wierzbowa 12
Szamotuly, 64500 Poznan, Poland (100%)
Tel.: (48) 612927081
Fax: (48) 612927081
E-Mail: office.poland@eurofins.com
Web Site: www.gab-biotech.de/comp410.htm
Emp.: 20
Management Consulting Services
S.I.C.: 8748
N.A.I.C.S.: 541618
Christophe Rozalski *(Mng Dir)*

Eurofins GeneScan GmbH (1)
Engesserstrasse 4
BioTech Park, 79108 Freiburg, Germany (100%)
Tel.: (49) 7615038100
Fax: (49) 7145803211
E-Mail: info@genescan.com
Web Site: www.genescan.com
Emp.: 16
Testing Laboratories
S.I.C.: 8734
N.A.I.C.S.: 541380

Eurofins GeneScan Holding GmbH (1)
Engesserstrasse 4
79108 Freiburg, Baden-Wurttemberg, Germany
Tel.: (49) 761 50380
Fax: (49) 761 5038111
Emp.: 60
Food Testing Services
S.I.C.: 8734
N.A.I.C.S.: 541380
Nicholas Krohn *(Gen Mgr)*

Eurofins Genomics BV (1)
Bergschot 71
4817 PA Breda, Netherlands
Tel.: (31) 765737373
Fax: (31) 765737777
Laboratory Testing Services
S.I.C.: 8734
N.A.I.C.S.: 541380

U.S. Subsidiary:

Eurofins Genomics Inc. (2)
2211 Seminole Dr
Huntsville, AL 35805
Tel.: (800) 688-2248
Fax: (251) 252-7794
Emp.: 100
Laboratory Testing Services
S.I.C.: 8734
N.A.I.C.S.: 541380
Martin Kunz *(Gen Mgr)*

Eurofins Genomics India Pvt Ltd (1)
183 1st Floor Gayathri Tech Park EPIP 2nd Phase
Whitefield, Bengaluru, 560 066, India
Tel.: (91) 80 30706666
Fax: (91) 80 41680405
E-Mail: infoindia@eurofhins.com
Web Site: www.eurofinsgenomics.co.in
Scientific & Technical Consulting Services
S.I.C.: 8999
N.A.I.C.S.: 541690

Eurofins GfA GmbH (1)
Stenzelring 14b
21107 Hamburg, Germany (100%)
Tel.: (49) 406970960
Fax: (49) 4069709699
E-Mail: info.umyelt-hamburg@eurofins.de
Web Site: www.ergo-enviro.de/englisch/start_en.htm
Emp.: 20
Air Testing & Monitoring Services
S.I.C.: 7389
N.A.I.C.S.: 541990
Gerd Volkmer *(Mng Dir)*

Eurofins Hong Kong Ltd. (1)
Unit F 8th Fl Caliant Industri Ctr St No 2 12 Au Pui Wan
Shaiin, Hong Kong, China (Hong Kong) (100%)
Tel.: (852) 26363288
Fax: (852) 26360211
Web Site: www.eurofins.cn
Emp.: 100
Professional Scientific & Technical Services
S.I.C.: 7389
N.A.I.C.S.: 541990
Enders Wong *(Mgr-Sls)*

Eurofins I Verwaltungsgesellschaft GmbH (1)
Stenzelring 14 b
21107 Hamburg, Germany
Tel.: (49) 40 7527090
Business Management Consulting Services
S.I.C.: 8742
N.A.I.C.S.: 541611
Dietrich Roettger *(Gen Mgr)*

Subsidiary:

Institut fur Lebensmittel-, Wasser- und Umweltanalytik Nurnberg GmbH (2)
Bucher Hauptstrasse 25
90427 Nuremberg, Germany
Tel.: (49) 911 383860
Fax: (49) 911 3838610
Emp.: 15
Laboratory Testing Services
S.I.C.: 8734
N.A.I.C.S.: 541380
Andreas Mueller *(Mng Dir)*

Eurofins Institut Jager GmbH (1)
Ernst-Simon-Strasse 2-4
72072 Tubingen, Germany
Tel.: (49) 7 071 70 07 0
Fax: (49) 7 071 70 07 77
E-Mail: info.tuebingen@eurofins-umwelt.de
Web Site: www.eurofins.de/umwelt/standorte/eurofins-institut-jager.aspx
Emp.: 30
Microbiological Testing Services
S.I.C.: 8734
N.A.I.C.S.: 541380
Matthias Hamann *(Gen Mgr)*

Eurofins International Holdings LUX SARL (1)
Rue Henri M Schnadt 10 A
2530 Luxembourg, Luxembourg
Tel.: (352) 2618531
Fax: (352) 2618530
Investment Management Services
S.I.C.: 6282
N.A.I.C.S.: 523920

Subsidiaries:

Eurofins Environment Testing LUX Holding SARL (2)
Rue Henri M Schnadt 10 A
2530 Luxembourg, Luxembourg
Tel.: (352) 26185341
Fax: (352) 26185330
Investment Management Services
S.I.C.: 6282
N.A.I.C.S.: 523920

Subsidiary:

Eurofins Industrial Testing Lux SARL (3)
Rue Henri M Schnadt 10 A
2530 Luxembourg, Luxembourg
Tel.: (352) 2618531
Industrial Testing Services
S.I.C.: 8734
N.A.I.C.S.: 541380

Non-U.S. Subsidiaries:

Eurofins Environment II DE GmbH (3)
Am Neulander Gewerbepark 1
21079 Hamburg, Germany
Tel.: (49) 40 49294100
Fax: (49) 40 49294369
Environmental Consulting Services
S.I.C.: 8999
N.A.I.C.S.: 541620

Eurofins Environment Testing Netherlands Holding BV (3)
Bergschot 71
4817 PA Breda, Netherlands
Tel.: (31) 76 573 73 73
Investment Management Services
S.I.C.: 6282
N.A.I.C.S.: 523920

Eurofins Environmental Services Ltd (3)
28-32 Westway Estate
Acton, London, W3 7XR, United Kingdom
Tel.: (44) 2082 22 60 70
Fax: (44) 2082 22 60 80
E-Mail: info@eurofins.co.uk
Web Site: www.eurofins.co.uk
Environmental Consulting Services
S.I.C.: 8999
N.A.I.C.S.: 541620

Eurofins GSC LUX SARL (2)
10A Rue Henri Schnadt
2530 Luxembourg, Luxembourg
Tel.: (352) 26 18 53 41
Fax: (352) 26 18 53 30
E-Mail: info@eurofins.com
Laboratory Testing Services
S.I.C.: 8734
N.A.I.C.S.: 541380

Eurofins Japan KK (1)
Ota Ward Hamashima Miyako
Tokyo, 143-0003, Japan
Tel.: (81) 3 5492 7344
Fax: (81) 3 5492 7219
E-Mail: info@eurofins.co.jp
Web Site: www.eurofins.co.jp
Laboratory Testing Services
S.I.C.: 8734

Eurofins Scientific S.A.—(Continued)

N.A.I.C.S.: 541380

Eurofins Laboratories Ltd. (1)
Charter House Woodlands Road
Ashburton Road West Trafford P,
Altrincham, WA14 1HF, United
Kingdom (100%)
Tel.: (44) 1618687600
Fax: (44) 1618687699
E-Mail: info@eurofins.co.uk
Web Site: www.eurofins.co.uk
Emp.: 5
Business Support Services
S.I.C.: 7389
N.A.I.C.S.: 561499
Derek Hepburn *(Mng Dir)*

Eurofins Laborservices GmbH (1)
Kobelweg 12 1/6
86156 Augsburg, Germany
Tel.: (49) 821 240 920
Fax: (49) 821 240 9229
E-Mail: laboaugsburg@eurofins.com
Web Site: www.eurofins.de/lebensmittel/kontakt.aspx
Laboratory Testing Services
S.I.C.: 8734
N.A.I.C.S.: 541380
Andreas Mueller *(Mgr)*

Eurofins Medigenomix GmbH (1)
Anzinger Str 7a
D 85560 Ebersberg, Germany (100%)
Tel.: (49) 80928289200
Fax: (49) 8092221084
E-Mail: info@medigenomix.de
Web Site: www.medigenomix.de
Emp.: 200
Research & Development in the Physical Engineering & Life Sciences
S.I.C.: 8731
N.A.I.C.S.: 541712
Brigitte Obermaier *(Mng Dir)*

Eurofins Medinet BV (1)
Bergschot 71
PO Box 5510
4801 PA Breda, DM, Netherlands (100%)
Tel.: (31) 765737373
Fax: (31) 765737777
E-Mail: info@eurofinsmedinet.com
Web Site: www.eurofins-medinet.com
Emp.: 251
Research & Development in the Physical Engineering & Life Sciences
S.I.C.: 8731
N.A.I.C.S.: 541712
Rene Van Erp *(Mng Dir)*

Eurofins Medinet Pte. Ltd. (1)
1 International Business Park
Unit 01-16 The Synergy, 609917 Singapore,
Singapore (100%)
Tel.: (65) 65623858
Fax: (65) 63047389
E-Mail: info@eurofins.com
Web Site: www.eurofins-medinet.com
Emp.: 10
Testing Laboratories
S.I.C.: 8734
N.A.I.C.S.: 541380

Eurofins Mikro Kemi AB (1)
Seminariegatan 29
Box 15018
750 15 Uppsala, Sweden
Tel.: (46) 18 57 22 00
Fax: (46) 18 57 22 22
E-Mail: info.mikrokemi@eurofins.se
Web Site: www.mikrokemi.se
Emp.: 20
Pharmaceutical Product Testing Services
S.I.C.: 8734
N.A.I.C.S.: 541380
Ilya Zelikman *(Pres & Mgr-Mktg & Ops)*
Karin Engstroem *(Sec)*

Eurofins Miljo A/S (1)
Smedeskovvej 38
Galten, 8464 Arhus, Denmark (100%)
Tel.: (45) 70224266
Fax: (45) 70224255
E-Mail: miljo@eurofins.dk
Web Site: www.eurofins.dk
Emp.: 600
Analytical Laboratory Instrument Mfr
S.I.C.: 3826
N.A.I.C.S.: 334516
Svend Aage Linde *(Mng Dir)*

Eurofins Miljo (Galten) (1)
Smedeskovvej 38
Galten, DK 8464 Arhus, Denmark (100%)
Tel.: (45) 70224276
Fax: (45) 70224255
E-Mail: product-testing@eurofins.dk
Web Site: www.eurofins.dk
Testing Laboratories
S.I.C.: 8734
N.A.I.C.S.: 541380
Svend Aage Linde *(Mng Dir)*

Eurofins (NI) Limited (1)
Room 74 4th Floor
16 Donegall Square South, Belfast,
BT15JJ, United Kingdom (100%)
Tel.: (44) 2890321691
Fax: (44) 2890439604
E-Mail: info@eurofins.co.uk
Web Site: www.eurofins.co.uk
Emp.: 6
Marketing Consulting Services
S.I.C.: 8742
N.A.I.C.S.: 541613
David Bailie *(Mgr)*

Eurofins Norsk Matanalyse AS (1)
Nils Hansens Vei 4
0602 Oslo, Norway
Tel.: (47) 23 05 05 00
Fax: (47) 23 05 05 20
Laboratory Testing Services
S.I.C.: 8734
N.A.I.C.S.: 541380

Eurofins Norsk Miljoanalyse AS (1)
Sandviksvn 110
Postboks 17
Sandviken, Bergen, 5035, Norway
Tel.: (47) 55 54 92 92
Laboratory Testing Services
S.I.C.: 8734
N.A.I.C.S.: 541380

Eurofins NSC Denmark A/S (1)
Smedeskovvej 38
8464 Galten, Denmark
Tel.: (45) 70224266
Fax: (45) 70224255
Emp.: 100
Business Management Consulting Services
S.I.C.: 8748
N.A.I.C.S.: 541618

Eurofins NSC Finance Germany GmbH (1)
Stenzelring 14 b
21107 Hamburg, Germany
Tel.: (49) 40 73 44 12 100
Fax: (49) 40 49 29 43 69
E-Mail: bewerbung@eurofins.de
Financial Consulting Services
S.I.C.: 8742
N.A.I.C.S.: 541611
Dietrich Roettger *(Gen Mgr)*

Eurofins NSC Netherlands BV (1)
Koopvaardijweg 32-34
4906 CV Oosterhout, Noord-Brabant,
Netherlands
Tel.: (31) 76 5737373
Fax: (31) 76 5737777
Laboratory Testing Services
S.I.C.: 8734
N.A.I.C.S.: 541380

Eurofins NSC UK & Ireland Ltd (1)
Room 139 Woodthorne Wergs Road
Wolverhampton, WV6 8TQ, United Kingdom
Tel.: (44) 1902693215
Laboratory Testing Services
S.I.C.: 8734
N.A.I.C.S.: 541380

Eurofins - Ofi Lebensmittelanalytik GmbH (1)
Brehmstrasse 14a
1110 Vienna, Austria
Tel.: (43) 1 904 3344 0
Fax: (43) 1 904 3344 105
E-Mail: office@eurofins.at
Web Site: www.eurofins.at
Food Testing Services
S.I.C.: 8734
N.A.I.C.S.: 541380
Ayse Atak *(Mgr-Analytical Svc)*

Eurofins Pharma Quality Control Denmark A/S (1)
Smedeskovvej 38
8464 Galten, Denmark
Tel.: (45) 70 22 42 96
Fax: (45) 70 22 42 55
Pharmaceutical Product Mfr
S.I.C.: 2834
N.A.I.C.S.: 325412

Eurofins Pharma Services India Pvt Ltd (1)
183 1st Floor Gayatri Tech Park PIP 2nd Phase
Whitefield, Bengaluru, 560066, India
Tel.: (91) 80 3070 6666
Fax: (91) 80 4168 0405
Web Site: www.pharma.eurofins.cn/en/contact-us.aspx
Pharmaceutical Product Testing Services
S.I.C.: 8734
N.A.I.C.S.: 541380

Eurofins Pharma US Holdings BV (1)
Bergschot 71
4817 PA Breda, Netherlands
Tel.: (31) 765737373
Investment Management Services
S.I.C.: 6282
N.A.I.C.S.: 523920

Eurofins Product Service (Thailand) Co., Ltd (1)
344/2 Soi Soonvijai 4 Rama9 Rd
Bangkapi Huaykwang, 10310 Bangkok,
Thailand
Tel.: (66) 27 16 85 30
Fax: (66) 2716 85 37
E-Mail: producttesting-th@eurofins.com
Electrical Product Laboratory Testing Services
S.I.C.: 8734
N.A.I.C.S.: 541380

Eurofins Product Testing Denmark A/S (1)
Smedeskovvej 38
8464 Galten, Denmark
Tel.: (45) 7022 4276
Fax: (45) 7022 4275
E-Mail: product-testing@eurofins.dk
Web Site: www.eurofins.com
Laboratory Testing Services
S.I.C.: 8734
N.A.I.C.S.: 541380

Eurofins Product Testing Service (Shanghai) Co., Ltd (1)
No 395 Jiangchangxi Rd
Zhabei district, 200436 Shanghai, China
Tel.: (86) 216 1819 181
Fax: (86) 216 1819 180
E-Mail: info.sh@eurofins.com
Web Site: www.eurofins.com
Laboratory Testing Services
S.I.C.: 8734
N.A.I.C.S.: 541380

Eurofins Product Testing Services Ltd (1)
D3 Broadoak Business Park Ashburton Road West
Trafford Park, Manchester, M17 1RW,
United Kingdom
Tel.: (44) 161 868 7600
Fax: (44) 161 868 7699
E-Mail: producttesting-uk@eurofins.com
Web Site: www.product-testing.eurofins.com
Emp.: 7
Laboratory Testing Services
S.I.C.: 8734
N.A.I.C.S.: 541380
Derek Hepburn *(Mng Dir)*

Eurofins Product Testing Verwaltungs GmbH (1)
Grossmoorbogen 25
21079 Hamburg, Germany
Tel.: (49) 40 49294360
Fax: (49) 40 49294369
Laboratory Testing Services
S.I.C.: 8734
N.A.I.C.S.: 541380

Subsidiary:

Eurofins Consumer Product Testing GmbH (2)
Mendelssohnstrasse 15D
22761 Hamburg, Germany
Tel.: (49) 40 57 01 04 100
Fax: (49) 40 57 01 04 199
E-Mail: ProductTesting-HH@eurofins.de
Web Site: www.eurofins.com
Consumer Product Testing Services
S.I.C.: 8734
N.A.I.C.S.: 541380

Eurofins Regulatory AG (1)
Weidenweg 15
4310 Rheinfelden, Switzerland
Tel.: (41) 61 83 620 80
Fax: (41) 61 83 620 88
Web Site: www.eurofins.com
Emp.: 12
Agricultural Chemical Testing Services
S.I.C.: 8734
N.A.I.C.S.: 541380
Andreas Wais *(Mng Dir)*

Eurofins Scientific AG (1)
Parkstrasse 10
5012 Schonenwerd, Switzerland (100%)
Tel.: (41) 628587100
Fax: (41) 628587109
E-Mail: info@eurofins.ch
Web Site: www.eurofins.ch
Emp.: 20
Research & Development in the Physical Engineering & Life Sciences
S.I.C.: 8731
N.A.I.C.S.: 541712
Klaus Fuchs *(Mgr)*

Eurofins Scientific BV (1)
Bergschot 69-71
PO Box 5510
4801 DM Breda, Netherlands (100%)
Tel.: (31) 765737373
Fax: (31) 765737777
Web Site: www.eurofinsmedinet.com
Emp.: 700
Testing Laboratories
S.I.C.: 8734
N.A.I.C.S.: 541380

Eurofins Scientific CZ S.r.o. (1)
Schr 41 Nechvilova 1821
CA 14800 Prague, Czech Republic (100%)
Tel.: (420) 271 911 344
Fax: (420) 271 911 344
Web Site: www.eurofins.com
Testing Laboratories
S.I.C.: 8734
N.A.I.C.S.: 541380

Eurofins Scientific GmbH (1)
Am Neulander Gewerbepark 1
21079 Hamburg, Germany (100%)
Tel.: (49) 4049 294360
Fax: (49) 4049 29499350
E-Mail: info@eurofins.de
Web Site: www.eurofins.de
Emp.: 60
Laboratory Testing Services
S.I.C.: 8734
N.A.I.C.S.: 541380
Markus Brandmeier *(Mng Dir)*

Subsidiaries:

Eurofins Deutsches Institut fur Lebensmitteluntersuchung GmbH (2)
Neulander Kamp 1
21079 Hamburg, Germany
Tel.: (49) 40 492 94 0
Fax: (49) 40 492 94 759
E-Mail: dilu@eurofins.de
Web Site: www.eurofins.de/lebensmittel/kontakt.aspx
Food Product Testing Services
S.I.C.: 8734
N.A.I.C.S.: 541380

Eurofins Dr. Specht Laboratorien GmbH (2)
Grossmoorbogen 25
21079 Hamburg, Germany
Tel.: (49) 40 88 14 48 0
Fax: (49) 40 88 14 48 101
E-Mail: pesticides@eurofins.de
Web Site: www.eurofins.com
Emp.: 150
Laboratory Testing Services
S.I.C.: 8734
N.A.I.C.S.: 541380
Manfred Linkerhagner *(Gen Mgr)*

Eurofins GfA Lab Service GmbH (2)
Otto-Hahn-Strasse 22
48161 Munster, Germany

Tel.: (49) 25 34 80 70
Fax: (49) 25 34 80 71 10
E-Mail: gfa@eurofins.de
Web Site: www.eurofins.de/gfa-en.aspx
Laboratory Testing Services
S.I.C.: 8734
N.A.I.C.S.: 541380
Jochen Schulte *(Mng Dir)*

Eurofins Information Systems GmbH (2)
Am Neulander Gewerbepark 1
21079 Hamburg, Germany
Tel.: (49) 40 492947 99
Fax: (49) 40 492947 39
Data Processing Services
S.I.C.: 7374
N.A.I.C.S.: 518210

Eurofins IT-infrastructure GmbH (2)
Am Neulander Gewerbepark 1
Hamburg, 21079, Germany
Tel.: (49) 4049294360
Fax: (49) 4049294729
E-Mail: info@eurofins.com
Information Technology Consulting Services
S.I.C.: 7373
N.A.I.C.S.: 541512

Eurofins Scientific (Ireland) Limited (1)
Unit D13 North City Business Park,
North Road, Dublin, Finglas, 11,
Ireland (100%)
Tel.: (353) 429328333
E-Mail: info@eurofins.ie
Web Site: www.eurofins.ie
Emp.: 3
Testing Laboratories
S.I.C.: 8734
N.A.I.C.S.: 541380
Michelle Fitzgerald *(Mng Dir)*

Eurofins Scientific Italia Srl (1)
Via Bruno Buozzi 2
20090 Vimodrone, Italy
Tel.: (39) 022507151
Fax: (39) 0225071 599
E-Mail: info@biolab.it
Emp.: 100
Laboratory Testing Services
S.I.C.: 8734
N.A.I.C.S.: 541380
Sebastiano Drago *(Mgr-IT)*

Subsidiaries:

Eurofins Biolab Srl (2)
Via Bruno Buozzi 2
20090 Vimodrone, Milan, Italy
Tel.: (39) 02 250715 1
Fax: (39) 02 25071599
E-Mail: InfoFarma@eurofins.com
Web Site: www.biolab.it
Laboratory Testing Services
S.I.C.: 8734
N.A.I.C.S.: 541380

Eurofins Chemical Control Srl (2)
Via Celdit 2
12100 Cuneo, Italy
Tel.: (39) 0171 41 24 70
Fax: (39) 0171 41 18 26
E-Mail: chemicalcontrolsrl@eurofins.com
Web Site: www.eurofins.com
Emp.: 50
Chemical Product Research & Development Services
S.I.C.: 8731
N.A.I.C.S.: 541712

Eurofins Consulting Italia Srl (2)
Via Cuorgne 21
10156 Turin, Italy
Tel.: (39) 011 22 22 228
Fax: (39) 011 22 22 226
E-Mail: customerservicesconsulting@eurofins.com
Web Site: www.consulting.eurofins.com
Laboratory Testing Services
S.I.C.: 8734
N.A.I.C.S.: 541380

Eurofins Environment Testing Italy Srl (2)
Via Austria 25B
35127 Padua, Italy
Tel.: (39) 049 87 01 192
Fax: (39) 049 76 29 935
E-Mail: infoenvironmentitaly@eurofins.com
Web Site: www.eurofins.it/contatti/eurofins-environment-testing-italy.aspx
Environmental Testing Services
S.I.C.: 8734
N.A.I.C.S.: 541380
Fabio Spinelli *(Mgr-Sustainability Sls)*

Eurofins Modulo Uno SpA (2)
Via Cuorgne 21
Turin, 10156, Italy
Tel.: (39) 011 22 22 225
Fax: (39) 011 22 22 226
E-Mail: info@modulouno.it
Web Site: www.modulouno.it
Emp.: 100
Testing & Inspection Services
S.I.C.: 8734
N.A.I.C.S.: 541380
Paolo Trisoglio *(Mng Dir)*

Eurofins Scientific Japan K.K. (1)
Shimouma 4-16-21
Setagaya-ku, Tokyo, 154-0002,
Japan (100%)
Tel.: (81) 5055396350
Management Consulting Services
S.I.C.: 8748
N.A.I.C.S.: 541618

Eurofins Scientific Services S.A. (1)
Chaussee de Malines 455
Kraainem, Brussels, B 1950,
Belgium (100%)
Tel.: (32) 27661620
Fax: (32) 27661639
E-Mail: info@eurofins.com
Web Site: www.eurofins.com
Emp.: 50
Testing Laboratories
S.I.C.: 8734
N.A.I.C.S.: 541380
Gilles G. Martin *(CEO)*

Eurofins Technology Service (Suzhou) Ltd. (1)
10 B1 Long Shan Road
215163 Suzhou, Jiangsu, China (100%)
Tel.: (86) 51268785300
Fax: (86) 5126680173
Web Site: www.eurofins.cn
Professional Scientific & Technical Services
S.I.C.: 7389
N.A.I.C.S.: 541990

Eurofins Technology Services (Suzhou) Co., Ltd (1)
B1 SSTT No 10 LongShan Road SND
Suzhou, Jiangsu, 215163, China
Tel.: (86) 400 828 5088
Fax: (86) 512 6878 5966
E-Mail: info@eurofins.cn
Web Site: www.eurofins.cn
Emp.: 50
Analytical Testing Services
S.I.C.: 8734
N.A.I.C.S.: 541380
Mark Ralph *(Gen Mgr)*

Eurofins Testing A/S (1)
Smedeskovvej 38
Galten, 6600 Arhus, Denmark (100%)
Tel.: (45) 70224266
Fax: (45) 70224266
E-Mail: info@eurofins.dk
Web Site: www.eurofins.dk
Emp.: 800
Analytical Laboratory Instrument Mfr
S.I.C.: 3826
N.A.I.C.S.: 334516
Svend Aage Linde *(Mng Dir)*

Eurofins Testing Technology (Shenzhen) Co., Ltd (1)
Rm 03A Block F16 Tianfa Building Tian'an Cyber Park
Futian District, Shenzhen, 518040, China
Tel.: (86) 755 8358 5700
Fax: (86) 755 8358 5701
E-Mail: producttesting-sz@eurofins.com
Web Site: www.product-testing.eurofins.cn
Laboratory Testing Services
S.I.C.: 8734
N.A.I.C.S.: 541380
Flora Wei *(Mgr-HR)*

Eurofins Umwelt Ost GmbH (1)
Lobstedter Strasse 78
07749 Jena, Germany
Tel.: (49) 3641 4649 0
Fax: (49) 3641 4649 19
E-Mail: info_jena@eurofins.de
Web Site: www.eurofins-umwelt-ost.de
Scientific & Technical Consulting Services
S.I.C.: 8999
N.A.I.C.S.: 541690

Eurofins WEJ Agro Nutrition GmbH (1)
Fahrenheitstr 1
28359 Bremen, Germany
Tel.: (49) 421 24 40 62 0
Fax: (49) 421 24 40 62 28
Food Product Laboratory Testing Services
S.I.C.: 8734
N.A.I.C.S.: 541380

Eurofins WEJ Contaminants GmbH (1)
Neulander Kamp 1
21079 Hamburg, Germany
Tel.: (49) 40 49 29 47 77
Fax: (49) 40 49 29 91 13
E-Mail: wej-contaminants@eurofins.de
Web Site: www.eurofins.de/wej-contaminants-en.aspx
Emp.: 100
Food Testing Services
S.I.C.: 8734
N.A.I.C.S.: 541380
Markus Brandmeier *(Exec Dir)*

GFA GmbH (1)
Otto-Hahn-Strasse 22
48161 Munster, Germany (100%)
Tel.: (49) 25348070
Fax: (49) 2534807110
E-Mail: info.munster@eurofins-umwelt.de
Web Site: www.eurofins-umwelt.de
Emp.: 25
Testing Laboratories
S.I.C.: 8734
N.A.I.C.S.: 541380
Gerhard Volkmer *(Mng Dir)*

INLAB GmbH Institut fur Lebensmittelmikrobiologie (1)
Balkenstrasse 17-19
44137 Dortmund, Germany
Tel.: (49) 231 9520560
Fax: (49) 231 952056556
E-Mail: asm-inlab@eurofins.de
Web Site: www.inlab-dortmund.de
Emp.: 50
Microbiological Testing Services
S.I.C.: 8734
N.A.I.C.S.: 541380

Innolab do Brasil Ltda. (1)
Rua Sacadura Cabral 236 Saude
20221-161 Rio de Janeiro, Brazil
Tel.: (55) 21 3509 1750
Fax: (55) 21 2233 4621
E-Mail: comercial.pedropaulo@innolab.com.br
Web Site: www.innolab.com.br
Emp.: 80
Laboratory Testing Services
S.I.C.: 8734
N.A.I.C.S.: 541380

Institut Dr. Rothe GmbH (1)
Freudenbergstrasse 41-43
44809 Bochum, Germany
Tel.: (49) 2 34 9 52 72 0
Fax: (49) 2 34 9 52 72 99
E-Mail: info@instro.de
Web Site: www.instro.de
Laboratory Testing Services
S.I.C.: 8734
N.A.I.C.S.: 541380

Institut Prof. Dr. Jager GmbH (1)
Robert-Bosch-Strasse 18
78467 Konstanz, Germany (100%)
Tel.: (49) 753150343
Fax: (49) 753150262
E-Mail: info.kuatuebingen@eurofins-umyyelt.de
Web Site: www.eurofins.de
Research & Development in the Physical Engineering & Life Sciences
S.I.C.: 8731
N.A.I.C.S.: 541712
Matthias Hamann *(Mng Dir)*
Matthias Hartung *(Mng Dir)*

JACS Ltd. (1)
Unit 16 Hercules Way
Bowerhill Ind Est, Melksham, Wiltshire,
SN12 6TS, United Kingdom (100%)
Tel.: (44) 1225700202
Fax: (44) 1225792586
E-Mail: administrator@jacsuk.com
Web Site: www.jacsuk.com
Emp.: 5
Plastics Materials & Basic Forms & Shapes Merchant Whslr
S.I.C.: 5162
N.A.I.C.S.: 424610
Jeff Payne *(Owner)*

Medinet International BV (1)
Bergschot 71
PO Box 5510
4817PA Breda, Netherlands (100%)
Tel.: (31) 765737373
Fax: (31) 765737777
E-Mail: info@eurofinsmedinet.com
Web Site: www.eurofinsmedinet.com
Emp.: 250
Research & Development in the Physical Engineering & Life Sciences
S.I.C.: 8731
N.A.I.C.S.: 541712
Rene Zanerp *(Gen Mgr)*

MV Genetix GmbH (1)
Anzinger Str 7a
D-85560 Ebersberg, Germany (100%)
Tel.: (49) 898998920
Fax: (49) 80928289201
E-Mail: info@medigenomix.de
Web Site: www.medigenomix.de
Emp.: 60
Research & Development in the Physical Engineering & Life Sciences
S.I.C.: 8731
N.A.I.C.S.: 541712
Brigitte Obermaier *(Mng Dir)*

MWG Biotech AG (1)
Anzinger Strasse 7A
Ebersberg, 85560 Augsburg,
Germany (100%)
Tel.: (49) 809282890
Fax: (49) 809221084
E-Mail: info-eu@eurofins.com
Web Site: www.eurofinsdna.com
Emp.: 150
Biological Product Mfr
S.I.C.: 2836
N.A.I.C.S.: 325414
Bruno Poddevin *(Mng Dir)*

Subsidiaries:

Eurofins MWG GmbH (2)
Anzinger Str 7a
85560 Ebersberg, Germany
Tel.: (49) 8092 8289 0
Fax: (49) 8092 21084
E-Mail: info-eu@eurofins.com
Web Site: www.eurofinsdna.com
Emp.: 150
Laboratory Testing Services
S.I.C.: 8734
N.A.I.C.S.: 541380
Jutta Huber *(Co-Mng Dir)*
Peter Persigehl *(Co-Mng Dir)*

Eurofins MWG Synthesis GmbH (2)
Anzinger Str 7a
Ebersberg, Bavaria, 85560, Germany
Tel.: (49) 809282890
Fax: (49) 809221084
Chemical Product Mfr
S.I.C.: 2899
N.A.I.C.S.: 325998

MWG Biotech Pvt Ltd. (1)
No 17 5th Cross Vidya Nagar Opp M/S
SKF Bearings Hosur Main Road
560100 Bengaluru, India (100%)
Tel.: (91) 80 307 06666
E-Mail: infoindia@eurofins.com
Web Site: www.eurofinsdna.com
Biological Product Mfr
S.I.C.: 2836
N.A.I.C.S.: 325414

New Zealand Laboratory Services Ltd (1)
85 Port Road Seaview Lower Hutt
Moera, 1061 Wellington, New Zealand
Tel.: (64) 4 576 5016
E-Mail: info@eurofins.co.nz
Web Site: www.eurofins.co.nz
Laboratory Testing Services
S.I.C.: 8734
N.A.I.C.S.: 541380

Eurofins Scientific S.A.—(Continued)

Terry Manning *(Mng Dir)*

O.C.B. NV (1)
Lieven Bauwensstraat 12 B
Sint-Andries, 8200 Brugge, Belgium
Tel.: (32) 50 31 02 52
Fax: (32) 50 31 02 54
Emp.: 5
Laboratory Testing Services
S.I.C.: 8734
N.A.I.C.S.: 541380
David Demuynck *(Plant Mgr)*

OEKOMETRIC GmbH (1)
Bernecker Str 17-21
95448 Bayreuth, Germany
Tel.: (49) 921726330
Fax: (49) 9217263399
E-Mail: info@oekometric.de
Web Site: www.oekometric.de
Emp.: 20
Analytical Testing Services
S.I.C.: 8734
N.A.I.C.S.: 541380
Markus Brandmeier *(Mng Dir)*

Pro Monitoring BV (1)
Mercuriusweg 37
3771 NC Barneveld, Netherlands
Tel.: (31) 342 400606
Fax: (31) 342 401220
E-Mail: promonitoring@eurofins.com
Web Site: www.promonitoring.nl
Emp.: 14
Air Emission Monitoring & Testing Services
S.I.C.: 8734
N.A.I.C.S.: 541380

ProMonitoring BV (1)
Mercuriusweg 37
3771NC Barneveld, Netherlands (100%)
Tel.: (31) 342400606
E-Mail: dosteus@promonitoring.nl
Web Site: www.promonitoring.nl
Emp.: 15
Professional Scientific & Technical Services
S.I.C.: 7389
N.A.I.C.S.: 541990
Wim Meijer *(Mng Dir)*

Public Analyst Scientific Services Ltd (1)
28-32 Brunel Road Westway Estate
Acton, W3 7XR London, United Kingdom
Tel.: (44) 20 8222 6070
Fax: (44) 20 8222 6080
E-Mail: info@publicanalystservices.co.uk
Web Site: www.publicanalystservices.co.uk
Analyst Scientific & Laboratory Testing Services
S.I.C.: 8734
N.A.I.C.S.: 541380
Alan Richards, *(Head-Scientific Svcs)*

Public Analyst Scientific Services (NI) Ltd (1)
Room 74 4th Floor 16 Donegal Square South
BT1 5JJ Belfast, United Kingdom
Tel.: (44) 28 9032 1691
Fax: (44) 28 9043 9604
E-Mail: info@publicanalystservices.co.uk
Web Site: www.publicanalystservices.co.uk
Analytical Laboratory Testing Services
S.I.C.: 8734
N.A.I.C.S.: 541380
Alan Richards *(Head-Scientific Svcs)*

SNiP Biotech GmbH & Co. KG (1)
Fraunhoferstr 22
Bundesrepublik Planegg, 82152
Martinsried, Germany (100%)
Tel.: (49) 898998920
Fax: (49) 8989989290
Emp.: 60
Professional Scientific & Technical Services
S.I.C.: 7389
N.A.I.C.S.: 541990
Brigitte Obermaier *(Mng Dir)*
Engelbert Precht *(Mng Dir)*

Steins Laboratorium Sp. Z.o.o. (1)
Aleja Wojska Polskiego 90 A
Malbork, 82 200 Malbork, Pomorskie, Poland (100%)
Tel.: (48) 552720473
Fax: (48) 552720475
E-Mail: info@eurofins.pl
Web Site: www.eurofins.pl
Emp.: 30
Testing Laboratories
S.I.C.: 8734
N.A.I.C.S.: 541380
Marcin Czupa *(Mng Dir)*

EUROFLACO COMPIEGNE
7 Ave Louis Barbillon
60200 Compiegne, France
Tel.: (33) 344382525
Fax: (33) 344382526
Web Site: www.alpla.com
Sls.: $23,900,000
Emp.: 35
Business Description:
Plastics Products
S.I.C.: 3089
N.A.I.C.S.: 326199
Personnel:
Georg Fruh *(Mng Partner)*

EUROGAS INTERNATIONAL INC.
Suites 205-207 Dowell House
Roebuck & Palmetto Streets
Bridgetown, Barbados
Tel.: (246) 4367967
Fax: (246) 2285756
E-Mail: avt@gwpco.com.bb
Web Site: www.eurogasinternational.com
EI—(CNSX)
Assets: $9,048,243
Liabilities: $41,068,887
Net Worth: ($32,020,644)
Earnings: ($2,060,674)
Fiscal Year-end: 12/31/12
Business Description:
Oil & Gas Exploration & Mining Services
S.I.C.: 1311
N.A.I.C.S.: 211111
Personnel:
Daniel T. Goodman *(Chm)*
Jaffar Khan *(Pres & CEO)*
Donald Christopher Hope *(CFO)*
Andrew V. Thornhill *(Sec)*
Board of Directors:
Daniel T. Goodman
John William Ivany
Jaffar Khan
Mark Rachovides
Christopher J. Sinclair

EUROGERM SA
Parc d'activites bois Guillaume 2 rue Champ Dore
21850 Saint Apollinaire, France
Tel.: (33) 3 80 730 777
Fax: (33) 3 80 730 770
E-Mail: contact@eurogerm.com
Web Site: www.eurogerm.com
Year Founded: 1989
ALGEM—(EUR)
Emp.: 212
Business Description:
Flour Corrector & Bread Making Improver Mfr
S.I.C.: 2099
N.A.I.C.S.: 311999
Personnel:
Jean-Philippe Girard *(Chm, CEO & Mng Dir)*
Benoit Huvet *(Deputy CEO)*

EUROGOLD LIMITED
Unit B1 Tempo Building 431 Roberts Road
Subiaco, WA, 6008, Australia
Tel.: (61) 893819550
Fax: (61) 893887559
E-Mail: info@eurogold.com.au
Web Site: www.eurogold.com.au
EUG—(ASX)
Rev.: $7,868
Assets: $4,404,059
Liabilities: $1,364,200
Net Worth: $3,039,860
Earnings: ($10,957,910)
Emp.: 2
Fiscal Year-end: 06/30/13
Business Description:
Gold Mining
S.I.C.: 1041
N.A.I.C.S.: 212221
Personnel:
Pauline Collinson *(Sec)*
Board of Directors:
Peter L. Gunzburg
Arthur Dew
Carlisle C. Procter
Legal Counsel:
Hardy Bowen
Level 1 28 Ord Street
West West Perth, WA, 6005, Australia

EUROHOLD BULGARIA AD
Christopher Columbus Blvd 43
Eurohold Business Centre, Sofia, 1592, Bulgaria
Tel.: (359) 2 9651651
Fax: (359) 2 9651652
E-Mail: office@eurohold.bg
Web Site: www.eurohold.bg
Year Founded: 1995
4EH—(BUL WAR)
Rev.: $338,568,308
Assets: $461,634,533
Liabilities: $303,266,900
Net Worth: $158,367,634
Earnings: ($6,037,355)
Emp.: 1,710
Fiscal Year-end: 12/31/12
Business Description:
Holding Company; Financial Services, Leasing, Insurance & Car Sales
S.I.C.: 6719
N.A.I.C.S.: 551112
Personnel:
Assen Christov *(Chm-Supervisory Bd)*
Kiril Iwanow Boshov *(Chm-Mgmt Bd)*
Dimitar Dimitrov *(Vice Chm-Supervisory Bd)*
Assen Minchev *(CEO & Member-Mgmt Bd)*
Assen Assenov *(Member-Mgmt Bd)*
Velislav Christov *(Member-Mgmt Bd)*
Dimitar Kirilov Dimitrov *(Member-Mgmt Bd)*
Supervisory Board of Directors:
Assen Christov
Dimitar Dimitrov
Krassimir Katev
Ivan Mankov

Subsidiaries:

Avto Union AD (1)
Christopher Columbus blvd 43 Eurohold Business Centre
Sofia, 1592, Bulgaria
Tel.: (359) 2 462 11 88
Fax: (359) 2 462 11 37
E-Mail: office@avtounion.bg
Web Site: www.avto-union.bg
Emp.: 20
New Car Dealer
S.I.C.: 5511
N.A.I.C.S.: 441110
Assen Asenov *(CEO)*
Katrin Kutsarova *(CFO)*
Ivaylo Stoyanov *(COO)*

Subsidiaries:

Auto Italia EAD (2)
43 Hristophor Kolumb Blvd 1592
Sofia, Bulgaria
Tel.: (359) 2 462 11 11
Fax: (359) 2 462 11 49
Web Site: www.autoitalia.bg
New Car Dealer
S.I.C.: 5511
N.A.I.C.S.: 441110
Stoyan Mihov *(CEO)*

Autoplaza EAD (2)
84 Orion Str - next to Bulvaria Lulin 7
Sofia, Bulgaria
Tel.: (359) 8 9999 2273
E-Mail: west@autoplaza.bg
Web Site: www.autoplaza.bg
New Car Sales & Leasing Services
S.I.C.: 5511
N.A.I.C.S.: 441110
Stoyan Mihov, *(Mgr)*

Bulvaria Holding EAD (2)
84 Orion Str
Sofia, 1324, Bulgaria
Tel.: (359) 2 926 77 77
Investment Management Services
S.I.C.: 6799
N.A.I.C.S.: 523920

Bulvaria Varna EOOD (2)
Yanush Hunyadi St 7
Varna, Bulgaria
Tel.: (359) 700 10799
Financial Investment Services
S.I.C.: 6211
N.A.I.C.S.: 523999

Daru Car AD (2)
Druzhba 1 2 Ilia Beshkov Str
Sofia, 1592, Bulgaria
Tel.: (359) 29 60 16 03
Fax: (359) 29 60 16 13
Web Site: www.darucar.bg
New & Used Car Dealer
S.I.C.: 5511
N.A.I.C.S.: 441110

Gransport Auto EOOD (2)
43 Hristofor Kolumb Blvd
Sofia, 1592, Bulgaria
Tel.: (359) 2 462 11 60
E-Mail: sales@maserati.bg
Web Site: www.maserati.bg
New Car Dealer
S.I.C.: 5511
N.A.I.C.S.: 441110
Peter Dochev, *(Brand Mgr)*

Nissan Sofia EAD (2)
Bul Nikola Vaptsarov 47
Sofia, 1407, Bulgaria
Tel.: (359) 2 93760100
Fax: (359) 2 93760111
E-Mail: service_vt@nissan-sofia.bg
Web Site: www.nissan-sofia.bg
Emp.: 25
Car Leasing Services
S.I.C.: 7515
N.A.I.C.S.: 532112
Danail Danailov *(CEO)*

Euro Lease Auto AD (1)
16 GM Dimitrov Blvd
Sofia, 1797, Bulgaria
Tel.: (359) 2 965 15 55
Fax: (359) 2 965 16 87
Web Site: www.euroleaseauto.bg
Car Leasing Services
S.I.C.: 7515
N.A.I.C.S.: 532112

Euroins Insurance Group AD (1)
43 Hristofor Kolumb Blvd
Sofia, 1540, Bulgaria
Tel.: (359) 29 65 15 00
Fax: (359) 29 65 15 26
E-Mail: eig@euroins.bg
Web Site: www.eig.bg
Emp.: 25
General Insurance Services
S.I.C.: 6411
N.A.I.C.S.: 524210
Dessislava Elenkova *(Mgr-Mktg & Comm)*

Subsidiary:

Euroins Health Insurance EAD (2)
43 Christopher Columbus Blvd
1592 Sofia, Bulgaria
Tel.: (359) 2 9651 650
Fax: (359) 2 9651 562
E-Mail: office@euroins-zo.bg
Web Site: www.euroins-zo.bg
Health Insurance Services
S.I.C.: 6321

N.A.I.C.S.: 524114

Non-U.S. Subsidiaries:

EUROINS INSURANCE AD Skopje (2)
Centraina Agencija 02
Skopje, Macedonia
Tel.: (389) 2 3216 983
Web Site: www.euroins.com.mk
General Insurance Services
S.I.C.: 6411
N.A.I.C.S.: 524298
Janko Georgiev Nikolov *(Exec Dir & Member-Mgmt Bd)*
Violeta Pop Vasileva, *(Exec Dir & Member-Mgmt Bd)*

SC Euroins Romania Insurance Reinsurance SA (2)
Bucuresti North Road nr 10 Global City Business Park
O23 Building 4th floor, Voluntari, Ilfov, 077190, Romania
Tel.: (40) 21 317 07 11
Fax: (40) 21 317 07 14
E-Mail: receptie@euroins.ro
Web Site: www.euroins.ro
General Insurance Services
S.I.C.: 6411
N.A.I.C.S.: 524210
Kiril Boshov, *(Pres)*
Iulius Alin Bucsa *(Co-CEO)*
Milena Guentcheva *(Co-CEO)*

Eurolease Group EAD (1)
Christopher Columbus blvd 43 Fl 10 Avto Union Centre
Sofia, 1540, Bulgaria
Tel.: (359) 2 9651 651
Fax: (359) 2 9651 652
E-Mail: office@eurohold.bg
Web Site: www.euroleasegroup.com
Financial Investment Services
S.I.C.: 6211
N.A.I.C.S.: 523999

EUROIMPLANT SA

ul Krucza 13
Rybie gm, 05-090 Raszyn, Poland
Tel.: (48) 22 8861568
Fax: (48) 22 7202487
E-Mail: biuro@euroimplant.com.pl
Web Site: www.euroimplant.com.pl
EUI—(WAR)
Emp.: 20
Business Description:
Biotechnology Researcher & Developer
S.I.C.: 8731
N.A.I.C.S.: 541711
Personnel:
Andrzej Kisielinski *(Chm)*

EUROINS INSURANCE PLC

Christopher Columbus blvd 43
1592 Sofia, Bulgaria
Tel.: (359) 2 9651 525
Fax: (359) 2 9651 526
E-Mail: office@euroins.bg
Web Site: www.euroins.bg
5IC—(BUL)
Business Description:
Insurance Services
S.I.C.: 6411
N.A.I.C.S.: 524298
Personnel:
Violeta Darakova *(Chm-Supervisory Bd)*
Supervisory Board of Directors:
Violeta Darakova
Todor Danailov
Radi Georgiev

EUROKAI KG AA

Kurt-Eckelmann-Strasse 1
D-21129 Hamburg, Germany
Tel.: (49) 4074052055
Fax: (49) 40740511
E-Mail: eckelmann@eurokai.com
Web Site: www.eurokai.de
EUK2—(DEU)
Rev.: $812,949,371
Assets: $1,426,071,920
Liabilities: $793,075,863
Net Worth: $632,996,057
Earnings: $38,893,544
Emp.: 4,212
Fiscal Year-end: 12/31/12
Business Description:
Dock Constructors
S.I.C.: 1629
N.A.I.C.S.: 237990
Personnel:
Winfried Steeger *(Chm-Supervisory Bd)*
Thomas H. Eckelmann *(Chm-Mgmt Bd)*
Bertram R. C. Rickmers *(Deputy Chm-Supervisory Bd)*
Cecilia E. M. Eckelmann *(Member-Mgmt Bd)*
Supervisory Board of Directors:
Winfried Steeger
Sebastian Biedenkopf
Jochen Dohle
Raetke H. Muller
Bertram R. C. Rickmers
Max M. Warburg

EUROLLS S.P.A.

Via Malignani 14
33040 Attimis, Italy
Tel.: (39) 0432796511
Fax: (39) 0432796501
E-Mail: info@eurolls.com
Web Site: www.eurolls.com
Year Founded: 1987
Business Description:
Tube Forming & Wire Production
S.I.C.: 3315
N.A.I.C.S.: 331222
Personnel:
Renato Railz *(Pres)*

Non-U.S. Subsidiary:

Teurema SL (1)
Poligono Txirrita Maleo 10
Errenteria, E 20100 Guipuzcoa, Spain ES
Tel.: (34) 943341919
Fax: (34) 943518807
E-Mail: teurema@teurema.com
Web Site: www.teurema.com
Sales Range: $1-9.9 Million
Emp.: 25
Designs & Mfr Equipment for the Wire industry
S.I.C.: 3548
N.A.I.C.S.: 333992
Renato Railz *(Pres)*

EUROMARK POLSKA S.A.

ul Modlinska 244 A
03-152 Warsaw, Poland
Tel.: (48) 225041860
Fax: (48) 226768738
E-Mail: sekretariat@euromark.pl
Web Site: www.euromark.pl
EMK—(WAR)
Business Description:
Outdoor Clothes, Footwear & Equipment Mfr & Distr
S.I.C.: 5941
N.A.I.C.S.: 451110
Personnel:
Timothy Mark Roberts *(Chm-Mgmt Bd)*
Aleksander Romanowski *(Vice Chm-Supervisory Bd)*
Rafal Lysakowski *(Member-Mgmt Bd & Dir-Fin)*
Agnieszka Piotrowska *(Member-Mgmt Bd)*
Supervisory Board of Directors:
Daniel Jagodzinski
Adam Piekarski
Aleksander Romanowski
Teresa Warburton

EUROMAX RESOURCES LTD.

10th Floor 595 Howe Street
Vancouver, BC, V6C 2T5, Canada
Tel.: (604) 669-5999
Fax: (604) 682-2802
Web Site: www.euromaxresources.com
EOX—(OTC TSXV)
Rev.: $140,723
Assets: $20,302,487
Liabilities: $744,738
Net Worth: $19,557,749
Earnings: ($5,424,934)
Fiscal Year-end: 12/31/12
Business Description:
Gold Mining
S.I.C.: 1041
N.A.I.C.S.: 212221
Personnel:
Steve Sharpe *(Pres & CEO)*
Varshan Gokool *(CFO)*
Patrick William Forward *(COO)*
Deborah Paxford *(Sec & VP-Legal Affairs)*
Dimitar Lazarov Dimitrov *(Sr VP-Exploration)*
Board of Directors:
Martyn Konig
Patrick William Forward
Varshan Gokool
Randal J. Matkaluk
Timothy M. Morgan-Wynne
Steve Sharpe
Legal Counsel:
DuMoulin Black LLP
10th Floor 595 Howe St
Vancouver, BC, Canada

EUROMEDIC INTERNATIONAL B.V.

Vaci Street 2224
1051 Budapest, Hungary
Tel.: (36) 18153504
Fax: (36) 18153510
E-Mail: info@euromedic.com
Web Site: www.euromedic.com
Emp.: 5,000
Business Description:
Medical Services
S.I.C.: 8092
N.A.I.C.S.: 621492
Personnel:
Janos Meszaros *(Chm)*
Dimitris Moulavasilis *(CEO)*
Michael Leahy *(VP-Ops & Sec)*
Board of Directors:
Janos Meszaros
Jurg Ambuhl
Rodrigo Galvao
Nico Helling
Matthew Turner
Supervisory Board of Directors:
Jacques Theurillat

EUROMEZZANINE CONSEIL

11 rue Scribe
75009 Paris, France
Tel.: (33) 153302330
Fax: (33) 153302340
E-Mail: contact@euromezzanine.com
Web Site: www.euromezzanine.com
Managed Assets: $963,673,920
Emp.: 13
Business Description:
Equity Investment Firm
S.I.C.: 6211
N.A.I.C.S.: 523999
Personnel:
Thierry Raiff *(Pres)*
Marie-Cecile Matar *(Partner)*
Francois Carre *(Mng Dlr)*
Bruno Froideval *(Mng Dir)*
Thierry Raiss *(Mng Dir)*

EUROMICRON AG

Zum Laurenburger Hof 76
60594 Frankfurt am Main, Germany
Tel.: (49) 696315830
Fax: (49) 6963158317
E-Mail: info@euromicron.de
Web Site: www.euromicron.de
EUC—(DEU)
Sls.: $444,276,485
Assets: $382,148,047
Liabilities: $221,894,586
Net Worth: $160,253,461
Earnings: $11,883,989
Emp.: 1,699
Fiscal Year-end: 12/31/12
Business Description:
Network & Fiber Optics Technology
S.I.C.: 7373
N.A.I.C.S.: 541512
Personnel:
Franz-Stephan von Gronau *(Chm-Supervisory Bd)*
Willibald Spath *(Chm-Exec Bd)*
Josef Martin Ortolf *(Deputy Chm-Supervisory Bd)*
Thomas Hoffmann *(Member-Exec Bd)*
Supervisory Board of Directors:
Franz-Stephan von Gronau
Andreas de Forestier
Josef Martin Ortolf

Subsidiaries:

Cteam Consulting & Anlagenbau GmbH (1)
Im Stocken 6
88444 Ummendorf, Baden-Wurttemberg, Germany
Tel.: (49) 7351440980
Fax: (49) 73514409899
E-Mail: info@cteam.de
Web Site: www.cteam.de
Emp.: 200
Communication Tower Construction Services
S.I.C.: 1629
N.A.I.C.S.: 237130
Helmut Locher *(Mng Dir)*
Tanya Kirchner *(Sec)*

ELABO GmbH (1)
Rossfelder Strasse 56
74564 Crailsheim, Baden-Wurttemberg, Germany
Tel.: (49) 79513070
Fax: (49) 795130766
E-Mail: info@elabo.de
Web Site: www.elabo.de
Emp.: 170
Education & Laboratory & Test Systems Development & Installation Services
S.I.C.: 7373
N.A.I.C.S.: 541512
Juergen Nehler *(CEO)*

euromicron solutions GmbH (1)
Essenstrsse 157
55129 Mainz, Rhineland-Palatinate, Germany
Tel.: (49) 6131958590
Fax: (49) 61319585920
E-Mail: info@euromicron-solutions.de
Web Site: www.euromicron-solutions.com
Emp.: 250
Information Technology Solutions
S.I.C.: 7373
N.A.I.C.S.: 541512
Oliver Thome *(Gen Mgr)*

euromicron systems GmbH (1)
II Hagen 7
45127 Essen, Nordrhein-Westfalen, Germany
Tel.: (49) 2016491220
Fax: (49) 20164912229
E-Mail: info@euromicron-systems.de
Web Site: www.euromicron-systems.de
Emp.: 250
Communication Equipments Mfr
S.I.C.: 3669
N.A.I.C.S.: 334290
Marc Lutzenkirchen *(Mng Dir)*

euromicron AG—(Continued)

EUROMICRON Werkzeuge GmbH (1)
Zur Dornheck 32-34
Fleisbach, 35764 Sinn, Hesse, Germany
Tel.: (49) 2772575590
Fax: (49) 27725755929
E-Mail: info@euromicron-fo.de
Web Site: www.euromicron-fo.de
Emp.: 50
Fiber Optic Components Mfr
S.I.C.: 3678
N.A.I.C.S.: 334417
Alexander Thome *(Mng Dir)*

LWL-Sachsenkabel GmbH (1)
Auerbacher Strasse 24
Erzgebirge, 09390 Gornsdorf, Saxony, Germany
Tel.: (49) 372139880
Fax: (49) 3721398816
E-Mail: info@sachsenkabel.de
Web Site: www.sachsenkabel.de
Emp.: 70
Fiber Optic Cable Mfr
S.I.C.: 3357
N.A.I.C.S.: 335921
Henry Drechsel *(Co-CEO)*

Microsens GmbH & Co. KG (1)
Kueferstr 16
59067 Hamm, Nordrhein-Westfalen, Germany
Tel.: (49) 238194520
Fax: (49) 23819452100
E-Mail: info@microsens.de
Web Site: www.microsens.com
Emp.: 75
Fiber Optic Conversion & Transmission Products Mfr
S.I.C.: 3678
N.A.I.C.S.: 334417
Dirk Herppich *(Mgr-Sls)*

NetWays Network Consulting GmbH (1)
Am Erlengraben 10
76275 Ettlingen, Baden-Wurttemberg, Germany
Tel.: (49) 72439497900
Fax: (49) 72439497999
E-Mail: info@netways-gmbh.de
Web Site: www.netways-gmbh.de
Emp.: 15
Network Consulting Services
S.I.C.: 7373
N.A.I.C.S.: 541512
Stefan Simon *(Mng Dir)*
Sandra Rapp *(Sec)*
Renate Zoller *(Sec)*

SKM Delwave GmbH (1)
Borsteler Chaussee 51
22453 Hamburg, Germany
Tel.: (49) 4069694580
Fax: (49) 4069694582
E-Mail: info@skm-delwave.de
Web Site: www.skm-delwave.de
Emp.: 30
Data Communication & Networking Equipment Distr
S.I.C.: 5065
N.A.I.C.S.: 423690
Torsten Gross *(Mng Dir)*

Non-U.S. Subsidiary:

euromicron Holding GmbH (1)
Gewerbestrasse 2
5201 Seekirchen, Salzburg, Austria
Tel.: (43) 621230000
Fax: (43) 6212300009100
E-Mail: oofice@euromicron-austria.at
Web Site: www.euromicron-austria.at
Emp.: 15
Management Services
S.I.C.: 8741
N.A.I.C.S.: 551114

EURONA WIRELESS TELECOM, S.A.

Ctra Hospitalet 11 Nau 4
09840 Cornella de Llobregat, Barcelona, Spain
Tel.: (34) 902906359
Fax: (34) 934670520
E-Mail: atencionalcliente@eurona.net
Web Site: www.eurona.net
EWT—(MAD)
Rev.: $7,313,742
Fiscal Year-end: 12/31/12

Business Description:
Wireless Communications Services
S.I.C.: 4812
N.A.I.C.S.: 517210

Personnel:
Jaume Sanpera Izoard *(Pres & CEO)*
Joaquin Gali *(Mng Dir)*
Alejandro Garcia Moncayo *(CFO)*

EURONAV NV

Belgica House De Gerlachkaai 20
B 2000 Antwerp, Belgium
Tel.: (32) 32474411
Fax: (32) 32474409
E-Mail: admin@euronav.com
Web Site: www.euronav.com
EURN—(EUR)
Sls.: $410,701,000
Assets: $2,362,879,000
Liabilities: $1,495,859,000
Net Worth: $867,020,000
Earnings: ($118,931,000)
Emp.: 1,600
Fiscal Year-end: 12/31/12

Business Description:
Freight Transportation Services
S.I.C.: 4731
N.A.I.C.S.: 488510

Personnel:
Marc Saverys *(Chm)*
Peter G. Livanos *(Vice Chm)*
Patrick Rodgers *(CEO)*
Hugo De Stoop *(CFO & Head-IR)*
Alex Staring *(Chief Offshore Officer)*
Egied Verbeeck *(Gen Counsel & Sec Gen)*

Board of Directors:
Marc Saverys
Daniel Rochfort Bradshaw
Ludwig Criel
Alice Wingfield Digby
Nicolas G. Kairis
Peter G. Livanos
Patrick Rodgers
Virginie Saverys
William Thomson

Non-U.S. Subsidiaries:

Euronav Hong Kong Ltd (1)
Room 3206 32nd Floor Lippo Centre Tower Two No 89
Queensway, Hong Kong, China (Hong Kong)
Tel.: (852) 2861 3880
Fax: (852) 2861 3881
Crude Oil Shipping Services
S.I.C.: 4499
N.A.I.C.S.: 488330

Euronav Ltd. (1)
20 The Slipway
Port Solent, Portsmouth, Hampshire, PO6 4TR, United Kingdom
Tel.: (44) 2392988806
Fax: (44) 23 9232 5800
E-Mail: sales@euronav.co.uk
Web Site: www.euronav.co.uk
Marine Navigation & Electronic Charting Products Mfr
S.I.C.: 3812
N.A.I.C.S.: 334511
Guy Morris *(Gen Mgr)*

Euronav Luxembourg SA (1)
20 rue de Hollerich
PO Box 2255
Luxembourg, 1022, Luxembourg
Tel.: (352) 482850
Fax: (352) 482871
Marine Shipping Services
S.I.C.: 4412
N.A.I.C.S.: 483111
Ludo Beersmans *(Gen Mgr)*

Euronav SaS (1)
15 Quai Ernest Renaud
Nantes, 44104, France
Tel.: (33) 228034250
E-Mail: crw@euronav.com
Emp.: 9
Marine Shipping Services
S.I.C.: 4412
N.A.I.C.S.: 483111
Gacques Moizan *(Gen Mgr)*

Euronav Ship Management (Hellas) Ltd (1)
69 Akti Miaouli
Piraeus, GR 18537, Greece
Tel.: (30) 2104558000
Fax: (30) 2104558010
E-Mail: admin.gr@euronav.com
Emp.: 35
Ship Transportation Services
S.I.C.: 4412
N.A.I.C.S.: 483111
Stan Atis Bourboulis *(Gen Mgr)*

Euronav Ship Management SaS (1)
15 Quai Ernest Renaud
44000 Nantes, France
Tel.: (33) 228034250
Fax: (33) 228034279
E-Mail: admin.fr@euronav.com
Emp.: 9
Marine Shipping Services
S.I.C.: 4412
N.A.I.C.S.: 483111
Moizan Jacques *(Gen Mgr)*

EURONICS INTERNATIONAL BV

Transpolis Commerce Center
Schiphol Airport
Polarisavenue 83a, 2132 JH Hoofddorp, Netherlands
Tel.: (31) 23 56851 40
Fax: (31) 23 56851 41
E-Mail: info@euronics.com
Web Site: www.euronics.com
Rev.: $21,378,580,000
Emp.: 50,000

Business Description:
Consumer Electronics Retailer
S.I.C.: 5734
N.A.I.C.S.: 443142

Non-U.S. Subsidiaries:

Euronics Austria reg. Genossenschaft m.b.H. (1)
Georg-Humbhandl-Gasse 7
2362 Biedermannsdorf, Austria
Tel.: (43) 2236 47 140
Fax: (43) 2236 47 140 65
E-Mail: office@redzac.at
Web Site: www.redzac.at
Emp.: 16
Consumer Electronics Retailer
S.I.C.: 5734
N.A.I.C.S.: 443142
Alexander Klaus *(Gen Mgr)*

Euronics Baltic OU (1)
Taamsaare 134B
12918 Tallinn, Estonia
Tel.: (372) 651 2222
E-Mail: epood@euronics.ee
Web Site: www.euronics.ee
Consumer Electronics Retailer
S.I.C.: 5731
N.A.I.C.S.: 443142

Euronics CR a.s. (1)
Zapsana u Krajskeho soudu v Brne oddil B vlozka 3059
Prstne - Kutiky 637, 760 01 Zlin, Czech Republic
Tel.: (420) 577 055 171
Fax: (420) 577055111
E-Mail: dotazy@euronics.cz
Web Site: www.euronics.cz
Emp.: 25
Consumer Electronics Retailer
S.I.C.: 5731
N.A.I.C.S.: 443142
Sandor Mucsi *(Gen Mgr)*

Euronics Deutschland eG (1)
Berblingerstr 1
71254 Ditzingen, Germany
Tel.: (49) 71 56 93 30
Fax: (49) 71 56 93 31 390
E-Mail: info@euronics.de
Web Site: www.euronics.de
Emp.: 37
Consumer Electronics Retailer
S.I.C.: 5734
N.A.I.C.S.: 443142
Benedict Kober *(Mng Dir)*
Michael Niederfuhr *(Mng Dir)*

Euronics Espana (1)
Madre Vedruna 38
50008 Zaragoza, Spain
Tel.: (34) 976 226 313
Fax: (34) 976 239 811
E-Mail: ven@euronics.es
Web Site: www.euronics.es
Consumer Electronics Retailer
S.I.C.: 5946
N.A.I.C.S.: 443142

Euronics Ireland (1)
Unit 4H Six Cross Roads Business Park Lacken
Kilbarry, Waterford, Ireland
Tel.: (353) 51 372135
Fax: (353) 51 372139
E-Mail: enquiries@euronics.ie
Web Site: www.euronics.ie
Emp.: 4
Consumer Electronics Retailer
S.I.C.: 5731
N.A.I.C.S.: 443142
David Benes *(Gen Mgr)*

Euronics Kft. (1)
Petzval Jozsef u 35-37
1119 Budapest, Hungary
Tel.: (36) 1 480 1188
Web Site: www.euronics.hu
Consumer Electronics Retailer
S.I.C.: 5731
N.A.I.C.S.: 443142

Euronics Latvia SIA (1)
Ieriku Str 3 Korpus 2B 309
LV 1003 Riga, Latvia
Tel.: (371) 67218560
E-Mail: eshop@euronics.lv
Web Site: www.euronics.lv
Consumer Electronics Retailer
S.I.C.: 5946
N.A.I.C.S.: 443142

Euronics Norge AS (1)
Postboks 1417
1602 Fredrikstad, Norway
Tel.: (47) 815 00 635
E-Mail: kundeservice@euronics.no
Web Site: www.euronics.no
Consumer Electronics Retailer
S.I.C.: 5731
N.A.I.C.S.: 443142

Euronics Portugal (1)
Rua do Arquitecto Cassiano Barbosa 112 D Office Number 7
112 D Esc 7, 4100-009 Porto, Portugal
Tel.: (351) 22 605 78 20
Fax: (351) 22 605 78 29
E-Mail: geral@euronics.pt
Web Site: www.euronics.pt
Consumer Electronics Retailer
S.I.C.: 5731
N.A.I.C.S.: 443142

EUROPA APOTHEEK VENLO BV

Dirk Hartogweg 14
NL-5928 LV Venlo, Netherlands
Tel.: (31) 77 850 59 00
E-Mail: info@europa-apotheek.com
Web Site: www.europa-apotheek.com
Year Founded: 2001
Emp.: 400

Business Description:
Pharmacy Services
S.I.C.: 5912
N.A.I.C.S.: 446110

Personnel:
Michael Kohler *(CEO)*

Subsidiary:

Europa Apotheek Service Venlo B.V. (1)
Dirk Hartogweg 14
NL-5928 LV Venlo, Netherlands

Tel.: (31) 778505900
E-Mail: info@europa-apotheek.com
Web Site: www.europa-apotheek.com
Medical Laboratories
S.I.C.: 8071
N.A.I.C.S.: 621511

EUROPA OIL & GAS (HOLDINGS) PLC

6 Porter Street
London, W1U 6DD, United Kingdom
Tel.: (44) 20 7224 3770
E-Mail: mail@europaoil.com
Web Site: www.europaoil.com
EOG—(LSE)
Rev.: $7,111,543
Assets: $13,897,752
Liabilities: $10,892,363
Net Worth: $3,005,389
Earnings: ($159,508)
Emp.: 13
Fiscal Year-end: 07/31/13

Business Description:
Hydrocarbons Exploration & Production
S.I.C.: 1321
N.A.I.C.S.: 211112

Personnel:
Hugh Mackay *(CEO)*
Phil Greenhalgh *(Sec & Dir-Fin)*

Board of Directors:
Bill H. Adamson
William Ahlefeldt
Roderick Corrie
Phil Greenhalgh
Hugh Mackay

Legal Counsel:
Charles Russell LLP
5 Fleet Place
London, EC4M 7RD, United Kingdom

Subsidiary:

Europa Oil & Gas Limited **(1)**
11 Chambers Vineyard
Abingdon, Oxfordshire, OX14 3PX, United Kingdom
Tel.: (44) 1235553266
Fax: (44) 1235467369
E-Mail: mail@europaoil.com
Emp.: 4
Oil & Gas Field Exploration Services
S.I.C.: 1389
N.A.I.C.S.: 213112
Philip Greenhalgh *(Sec)*

EUROPA SUPPORT SERVICES LTD.

(Acquired by Bilfinger SE)

EUROPACKAGING LTD.

20 Brickfield Rd
Yardley, Birmingham, B25 8HE, United Kingdom
Tel.: (44) 1217066181
Fax: (44) 1217066514
E-Mail: info@europackaging.co.uk
Web Site: www.europackaging.co.uk
Year Founded: 1974
Emp.: 375

Business Description:
Packaging Products Mfr
S.I.C.: 3089
N.A.I.C.S.: 326199

Non-U.S. Division:

Europackaging Ltd. - Euro Packaging Luxury Division **(1)**
Morgenstrasse 129
3018 Bern, Switzerland
Tel.: (41) 31 991 8790
Fax: (41) 31 991 8791
E-Mail: info@europackagingluxury.co.uk
Web Site: www.europackagingluxury.co.uk
Packaging Product Mfr & Whslr
S.I.C.: 3089
N.A.I.C.S.: 326199

Non-U.S. Subsidiary:

Euro Packaging Europe **(1)**
395 rue Paradis
13008 Marseille, France
Tel.: (33) 491 800 527
Fax: (33) 491786102
E-Mail: info@europackaging.co.uk
Emp.: 7
Packaging Product Mfr & Whslr
S.I.C.: 3089
N.A.I.C.S.: 326199

EUROPACORP

20 rue Ampere
93413 Saint Denis, France
Tel.: (33) 1 53 83 03 03
Fax: (33) 1 53 83 03 04
E-Mail: investors@europacorp.com
Web Site: www.europacorp-corporate.com
Year Founded: 1999
ECP—(EUR)
Emp.: 150

Business Description:
Film Production & Distribution Services
S.I.C.: 7812
N.A.I.C.S.: 512110

Personnel:
Luc Besson *(Chm)*
Charles Milhaud *(Vice Chm)*
Christophe Lambert *(CEO)*

Board of Directors:
Luc Besson
Patrice Gassenbach
Didier Kunstlinger
Christophe Lambert
Charles Milhaud
Eugenio Minvielle
Francoise Nyssen

EUROPE ISRAEL (M.M.S.) LTD.

8 kineret Street
Bnei Brak, 51201, Israel
Tel.: (972) 36086000
Fax: (972) 36086054
Web Site: www.elbitimaging.com
Emp.: 35

Business Description:
Holding Company
S.I.C.: 6719
N.A.I.C.S.: 551112

Personnel:
Mordechay Zisser *(Owner & Pres)*
Shimon Yitzhaki *(Chm)*

Subsidiary:

Elbit Imaging Ltd. **(1)**
8 Kinneret Street
Bnei Brak, 51261, Israel
Tel.: (972) 3 6086000
Fax: (972) 3 6086050
Web Site: www.elbitimaging.com
EMITF—(NASDAQ TAE)
Sls.: $671,086,000
Assets: $7,094,411,000
Liabilities: $5,673,282,000
Net Worth: $1,421,129,000
Earnings: ($455,500,000)
Emp.: 1,225
Fiscal Year-end: 12/31/12
Shopping Mall Construction & Management Services; Hotel Management Services; Medical Imaging Product Mfr
S.I.C.: 7011
N.A.I.C.S.: 721110
Shimon Yitzhaki *(Chm)*
Mordechay Zisser *(Pres & CEO)*
Doron Moshe *(CFO)*
Dudi Machluf *(CEO-Elbit Plaza USA)*
Ran Shtarkman *(CEO-PC)*
Zvi Maayan *(Gen Counsel)*

Subsidiaries:

Elscint Limited **(2)**
Kinert 8 Bneibrak
Tel Aviv, 67442, Israel
Tel.: (972) 36086020
Fax: (972) 36962022
E-Mail: info@elbitimaging.com
Web Site: www.elbitimaging.com
Sales Range: $50-74.9 Million
Emp.: 1,100
Hotel Owner & Operator
S.I.C.: 7011
N.A.I.C.S.: 721110
Doron Moshe *(CFO)*

InSightec Ltd. **(2)**
5 Nahum Heth St
PO Box 2059
Tirat Karmel, 39120, Israel (52%)
Tel.: (972) 48131313
E-Mail: info@insightec.com
Web Site: www.insightec.com
Emp.: 160
Magnetic Resonance Imaging Equipment Mfr
S.I.C.: 3845
N.A.I.C.S.: 334510
Jackob Vortman *(Founder & CEO)*
Mordechay Zisser *(Exec Chm)*
Robert Sigal *(Pres & Chief Comml Officer)*
Oded Tamir *(COO)*

EUROPEAN AERONAUTIC DEFENCE & SPACE COMPANY EADS N.V.

(Name Changed to Airbus Group N.V.)

EUROPEAN BANK FOR RECONSTRUCTION & DEVELOPMENT

1 Exchange Square
London, EC2A 2JN, United Kingdom
Tel.: (44) 2073386000
Fax: (44) 2073386100
E-Mail: newbusiness@ebrd.com
Web Site: www.ebrd.com
Year Founded: 1991
Rev.: $1,400,016,800
Assets: $68,926,596,340
Liabilities: $50,066,754,640
Net Worth: $18,859,841,700
Earnings: $1,117,321,100
Emp.: 1,611
Fiscal Year-end: 12/31/12

Business Description:
Transition Bank
S.I.C.: 6011
N.A.I.C.S.: 521110

Personnel:
Suma Chakrabarti *(Pres)*
Manfred Schepers *(CFO & VP)*
Philip Bennett *(COO & First VP)*
Enery Quinones *(Chief Compliance Officer)*
Emmanuel Maurice *(Gen Counsel)*
Axel Van Nederveen *(Treas)*
Enzo Quattrociocche *(Sec Gen)*

Board of Directors:
Memduh Akcay
Claire Dansereau
Alain de Cointet
Toshiyuki Furui
Michel Grilli
Werner Gruber
Zbigniew Hockuba
Ole Hovland
James Hudson
Andras Karman
Giorgio Leccesi
Vassili Lelakis
Abel Mateus
Bob McMullan
Pedro Moriyon
Denis Stanislavovich Morozov
Jonathan Ockenden
Eoin Ryan
Joachim Schwarzer
Jean-Louis Six
Eva Srejber
Paul Vlaanderen

EUROPEAN CENTRAL BANK

Kaiserstrasse 29
60311 Frankfurt am Main, Germany
Tel.: (49) 6913440
Telex: 411 144 ecb d
Fax: (49) 6913446000
E-Mail: info@ecb.europa.eu
Web Site: www.ecb.int
Year Founded: 1998
Rev.: $14,696,146,139
Assets: $279,042,104,637
Liabilities: $268,743,286,690
Net Worth: $10,298,817,946
Earnings: $1,343,518,900
Emp.: 1,609
Fiscal Year-end: 12/31/12

Business Description:
Central Banking Institution for the European Union & the Euro Currency
S.I.C.: 6011
N.A.I.C.S.: 521110

Personnel:
Mario Draghi *(Pres & Member-Exec Bd)*
Andreas Adriano *(Pres Officer)*
Niels Bunemann *(Press Officer)*
Andrea Jurges *(Press Officer)*
Wiktor Krzyzanowski *(Press Officer)*
William Lelieveldt *(Press Officer)*
Eszter Miltenyi *(Press Officer)*
Stefano Nardelli *(Press Officer)*
Philippe Rispal *(Press Officer)*
Martina Solcanyiova *(Press Officer)*
Vitor Manuel Ribeiro Constancio *(VP & Member-Exec Bd)*
Jorg Asmussen *(Member-Exec Bd)*
Benoit Coeure *(Member-Exec Bd)*
Yves Mersch *(Member-Exec Bd)*
Peter Praet *(Member-Exec Bd)*

EUROPEAN COLOUR PLC

Hempshaw Ln
Stockport, Cheshire, SK1 4LG, United Kingdom
Tel.: (44) 614803891
Fax: (44) 8706089469
E-Mail: mail@ecplc.com
Web Site: www.ecplc.com
Year Founded: 1900
Sales Range: $25-49.9 Million
Emp.: 199

Business Description:
Specialty Chemical & Pigments Mfr
S.I.C.: 2899
N.A.I.C.S.: 325998

Personnel:
Steve Smith *(Chm)*

Board of Directors:
Steve Smith

Legal Counsel:
Addleshaw Booth & Co.
100 Barbirolli Square
Manchester, M2 3AR, United Kingdom

Subsidiary:

European Colour (Pigments) Limited **(1)**
Hempshaw Lane
Stockport, Cheshire, SK1 4LG, United Kingdom
Tel.: (44) 1614803891
Fax: (44) 1614809852
E-Mail: enquiries@ecpigments.com
Web Site: www.ecpigments.com
Emp.: 5
Pigment Mfr
S.I.C.: 2816
N.A.I.C.S.: 325130
Steve Smith *(Mng Dir)*

EUROPEAN DIRECTORIES S.A.

Gustav Mahlerplein 68
1082 MA Amsterdam, Netherlands
Mailing Address:
PO Box 75191
1070 AD Amsterdam, Netherlands

European Directories S.A.—(Continued)

Tel.: (31) 204873688
Fax: (31) 204086400
E-Mail: info@europeandirectories.com
Web Site: www.europeandirectories.com
Sales Range: $650-699.9 Million
Emp.: 11
Business Description:
Publisher of Online & Printed Directories
S.I.C.: 2741
N.A.I.C.S.: 511140
Personnel:
Stuart Ross *(CFO)*
Non-U.S. Subsidiary:

TDC Forlag A/S (1)
Rodovrejev 241
2610 Rodovre, Denmark
Tel.: (45) 80363636
Fax: (45) 70113636
Web Site: www.degulesider.dk
Sales Range: $200-249.9 Million
Emp.: 50
Publisher of Print & Online Directories
S.I.C.: 2741
N.A.I.C.S.: 511140

EUROPEAN DRINKS S.A.

Complex Transylvania Street
Treatului Nr 1-2
PO Box 306
410020 Oradea, Romania
Tel.: (40) 259407200
Fax: (40) 259470005
E-Mail: marketing@europeandrinks.ro
Web Site: www.europeandrinks.ro
Sales Range: $1-9.9 Million
Emp.: 1,000
Fiscal Year-end: 03/31/13
Business Description:
Soft Drink & Mineral Water Bottler & Mfr
S.I.C.: 2086
N.A.I.C.S.: 312111
Personnel:
Ioan Micula *(Co-Pres)*
Viorel Micula *(Co-Pres)*
Subsidiaries:

European Food (1)
Complex Transylvania Str Treatului 1-2
PO Box 306
410020 Oradea, Romania
Tel.: (40) 259407200
Fax: (40) 259470005
E-Mail: contact@europeanfood.ro
Web Site: www.europeanfood.ro
Snack Foods, Cereal, Biscuits & Ketchup
S.I.C.: 2052
N.A.I.C.S.: 311919
Ioan Micula *(Co-Pres)*
Viorel Micula *(Co-Pres)*

Scandic Distilleries (1)
Complex Transylvania Str Treatului 1-2
PO Box 306
410020 Oradea, Romania
Tel.: (40) 259407200
Fax: (40) 259470005
E-Mail: mailbox@scanicdistilleries.ro
Web Site: www.scandicdistilleries.ro
Emp.: 1,200
Distillery
S.I.C.: 2085
N.A.I.C.S.: 312140
Ioan Micula *(Co-Founder)*
Viorel Micula *(Co-Founder)*

EUROPEAN ENERGY LIMITED

Level 2 BGC Centre 28 The Esplanade
Perth, WA, 6000, Australia
Tel.: (61) 8 9486 4422
Fax: (61) 8 9486 4433
Web Site: www.europeanenergy.com.au
Business Description:
Oil & Gas Exploration Services
S.I.C.: 1311
N.A.I.C.S.: 211111
Personnel:
William Paul Brooks *(Chm)*
Gerald Johnson *(Mng Dir)*
Board of Directors:
William Paul Brooks
Gerald Johnson
Keith Vuleta
Ildiko Wowesny
Legal Counsel:
Steinepreis Paganin
Level 4 The Read Buildings 16 Milligan Street
Perth, Australia

EUROPEAN FINE WINES LTD.

11-13 Bromley Common
Bromley, BR2 9LS, United Kingdom
Tel.: (44) 203 236 0100
Fax: (44) 20 3236 0111
E-Mail: info@efwines.com
Web Site: www.efwines.com
Year Founded: 2005
Sales Range: $25-49.9 Million
Emp.: 55
Business Description:
Wine Distribution Services
S.I.C.: 5182
N.A.I.C.S.: 424820
Personnel:
Scott Assemakis *(Founder)*

EUROPEAN INVESTMENT BANK

98-100 boulevard Konrad Adenauer
L- 2950 Luxembourg, Luxembourg
Tel.: (352) 35243791
Fax: (352) 352437704
E-Mail: press@eib.org
Web Site: www.eib.org
Rev.: $34,408,525,205
Assets: $685,080,209,325
Liabilities: $643,389,914,048
Net Worth: $41,690,295,278
Earnings: $3,831,714,057
Emp.: 2,188
Fiscal Year-end: 12/31/12
Business Description:
Investment Bank of the European Union
S.I.C.: 6211
N.A.I.C.S.: 523110
Personnel:
Werner Hoyer *(Pres)*
Gerhard Hutz *(Chief Compliance Officer & Dir Gen)*
Nicola Barr *(Dir Gen & Gen Counsel)*
Patrick Klaedtke *(Dir Gen & Controller-Fin)*
Tamsyn Barton *(Dir Gen)*
Pierluigi Gilibert *(Dir Gen)*
Christopher Hurst *(Dir Gen)*
Jean-Christophe Laloux *(Dir Gen)*
Jean-Marie Magnette *(Dir Gen)*
Laurent Mautort *(Dir Gen)*
Klaus Tromel *(Dir Gen)*
Francesco Mantegazza *(Deputy Chief Compliance Officer)*
Alfonso Querejeta *(Gen Sec)*
Board of Directors:
Konstantin Andreopoulos
Sanita Bajare
Anna Brandt
Clara Crespo
Peter Curwen
Claudiu Doltu
Jacek Dominik
Sandrine Gaudin
Franciscus Godts
Jan Gregor
Arsene Jacoby
Kyriacos Kakouris
Karina Karaivanova
Katarina Kaszasova
Pedro Machado
Carlo Monticelli
John Moran
Wolfgang Nitsche
Kristina Sarjo
Ivar Sikk
Julie Sonne
Gerassimos Thomas
Migle Tuskiene
Zoltan Urban
Jan Willem van den Wall Bake
Thomas Westphal
Subsidiary:

European Investment Fund (1)
15 avenue JF Kennedy
2968 Luxembourg, Luxembourg (61.9%)
Tel.: (352) 4266881
Fax: (352) 426688200
E-Mail: info@eif.org
Web Site: www.eif.org
Emp.: 250
Equity Investments in Venture Capital Funds & Guarantees to Financial Institutions
S.I.C.: 6211
N.A.I.C.S.: 523999
Richard Pelly *(CEO)*
Maria Leander *(Sec & Head-Legal)*

THE EUROPEAN INVESTMENT TRUST PLC

Beaufort House 51 New North Road
Exeter, EX4 4EP, United Kingdom
Tel.: (44) 2076288000
Fax: (44) 2076288188
Web Site: www.edinburghpartners.com
Year Founded: 1972
EUT—(LSE NZE)
Sales Range: $10-24.9 Million
Business Description:
Investment Trust Services
S.I.C.: 6211
N.A.I.C.S.: 523999
Personnel:
Douglas C.P. McDougall *(Chm)*
Board of Directors:
Douglas C.P. McDougall
William D. Eason
Ralph Kanza
Michael B. Moule
Legal Counsel:
Dickson Minto
16 Charlotte Square
Edinburgh, United Kingdom

Computershare Investor Serivces Limited
159 Hurstmere Rd Takapuna N Shore City
Auckland, New Zealand
U.S. Subsidiary:

Edinburgh Partners North America Inc (1)
445 Park Ave Ste 1026
New York, NY 10022
Tel.: (212) 906-9080
Fax: (917) 322-2105
E-Mail: enquiries@edpam.com
Investment Management Services
S.I.C.: 6799
N.A.I.C.S.: 523920

EUROPEAN INVESTOR RELATIONS SA

20 Rue Adrien-Lachenal
1207 Geneva, 6, Switzerland
Tel.: (41) 22 591 22 66
Fax: (41) 22 591 22 67
E-Mail: info@eir.ch
Web Site: www.voxia.ch
Sales Range: $10-24.9 Million
Business Description:
Marketing & Communication Agency
S.I.C.: 8742
N.A.I.C.S.: 541613
Personnel:
Laurent Ashenden *(Founding Partner)*
Michel Donath *(Partner)*
Alexandre Bonnard *(Mng Dir)*
Board of Directors:
Laurent Ashenden
Alain Guttmann
Robert Zwartendijk
Subsidiary:

Rochat & Partners SA (1)
Rue Adrien-Lachenal 20
1211 Geneva, 6, Switzerland
Mailing Address:
PO Box 6374
Geneva, 6, Switzerland
Tel.: (41) 22 591 22 66
E-Mail: contact@voxia.ch
Web Site: www.rochat-pr.ch
Emp.: 9
Communication & Public Relations Services
S.I.C.: 8743
N.A.I.C.S.: 541820
Michel Donath *(Partner)*

Branches

Rochat & Partners (2)
Parkring 59
8002 Zurich, Switzerland
Tel.: (41) 43 3449 848
Fax: (41) 43 3449 849
E-Mail: contact@voxia.ch
Web Site: www.rochat-pr.ch
Emp.: 5
Public Relations
S.I.C.: 8743
N.A.I.C.S.: 541820
Michel Donath *(Partner)*

EUROPEAN ISLAMIC INVESTMENT BANK PLC

Milton Gate 60 Chiswell Street
London, EC1Y 4SA, United Kingdom
Tel.: (44) 2078479900
Fax: (44) 2078479901
E-Mail: reception@eiib.co.uk
Web Site: www.eiib.co.uk
EIIB—(LSE)
Rev.: $3,978,990
Assets: $271,156,899
Liabilities: $67,536,565
Net Worth: $203,620,334
Earnings: ($17,405,227)
Emp.: 84
Fiscal Year-end: 12/31/12
Business Description:
Investment Management
S.I.C.: 6799
N.A.I.C.S.: 523920
Personnel:
Zulfi Caar Hydari *(CEO)*
Al-Harith Sinclair *(Sec)*
Board of Directors:
H. E. Abdallah Al-Mouallimi
Mohammed Abdul Aziz Ibrahim Al Sarhan
Aabed Al Zeera
Martin Gilbert Barrow
Zulfi Caar Hydari
Michael Toxvaerd
John Robertson Wright
Legal Counsel:
Berwin Leighton Paisner LLP
Adelaide House London Bridge
London, United Kingdom

EUROPEAN METAL RECYCLING LIMITED

Sirius House Delta Crescent
Westbrook, Warrington, WA5 7NS, United Kingdom
Tel.: (44) 1925 715 400
Fax: (44) 1925 713 470
E-Mail: info@emrltd.com
Web Site: www.emrltd.com
Year Founded: 1994
Sales Range: $1-4.9 Billion

Emp.: 2,300
Business Description:
Holding Company; Recycling Services & Recycled Materials Whslr
S.I.C.: 6719
N.A.I.C.S.: 551112
Personnel:
Colin Liles *(CEO)*
U.S. Subsidiary:

Southern Recycling, LLC (1)
902 Julia St
New Orleans, LA 70113 LA
Tel.: (504) 636-7200
Fax: (504) 636-7221
E-Mail: info@sorec-emr.com
Web Site: www.sorec-emr.com
Sls.: $110,000,000
Emp.: 330
Metal Recycling Services & Materials Whslr
Import Export
S.I.C.: 4953
N.A.I.C.S.: 562920
Joel Dupre *(Pres & CEO)*
David Farnsworth *(CFO)*

Subsidiaries:

Auto Shred Recycling, LLC (2)
1000 Myrick St
Pensacola, FL 32505-8061 LA (100%)
Tel.: (850) 432-0977
Fax: (850) 433-4814
E-Mail: info@sorec-emr.com
Web Site: www.sorec-emr.com
Emp.: 45
Scrap & Waste Materials
Import Export
S.I.C.: 5093
N.A.I.C.S.: 423930
Steve Harris *(Gen Mgr)*

Isco Metals & Supply, LLC (2)
10062 S Park Dr
Gulfport, MS 39503 LA
Tel.: (228) 896-7888
Fax: (228) 896-7775
Emp.: 7
Metal Distributor
Import Export
S.I.C.: 5093
N.A.I.C.S.: 423930

Resource Recycling, LLC (2)
13130 56th Ct Ste 604
Clearwater, FL 33760 LA
Tel.: (727) 573-2482
Fax: (727) 573-2527
Web Site: www.resourcerecycling.com
Sales Range: $10-24.9 Million
Emp.: 35
Ash Processing & Metal Recovery Systems Developer & Installation Services
S.I.C.: 3567
N.A.I.C.S.: 333994
William Lensmyer *(Gen Mgr)*

Southern Recycling Sales, LLC (2)
902 Julia St
New Orleans, LA 70113 LA (100%)
Tel.: (504) 636-7200
Fax: (504) 636-7221
E-Mail: sales@sorec-emr.com
Web Site: www.sorec-emr.com
Sls.: $1,400,000
Emp.: 5
Recycled Metal Materials Whslr
Export
S.I.C.: 5093
N.A.I.C.S.: 423930
Joel Dupre *(CEO)*

Southern Scrap Material Co., LLC (2)
902 Julia St
New Orleans, LA 70113 LA
Tel.: (504) 636-7200
Fax: (504) 636-7221
E-Mail: info@sorec-emr.com
Web Site: www.sorec-emr.com
Emp.: 150
Scrap & Waste Materials Recycling
S.I.C.: 4953
N.A.I.C.S.: 562920
Joel Dupre *(CEO)*

Southern Scrap Recycling Morgan City, LLC (2)
222 S Railroad St
Morgan City, LA 70380-6054 LA
Tel.: (985) 384-1960
Fax: (985) 385-4844
E-Mail: info@sorec-emr.com
Web Site: www.sorec-emr.com
Sales Range: $10-24.9 Million
Emp.: 20
Scrap & Waste Materials
Import Export
S.I.C.: 5093
N.A.I.C.S.: 423930
Darryl Himel *(Gen Mgr)*

SSX, L.C. (2)
6847 Scenic Hwy
Baton Rouge, LA 70807-6254 LA (100%)
Tel.: (225) 355-4453
E-Mail: info@sorec-emr.com
Web Site: www.sorec-emr.com
Sls.: $40,000,000
Emp.: 73
Metal Recycling & Merchant Whslr
S.I.C.: 4953
N.A.I.C.S.: 562920
Chip Hunter *(Pres)*

U.S. Holding:

Smith Industries, Inc. (1)
2001 Kenilworth Ave
Capitol Heights, MD 20743 MD (50%)
Tel.: (301) 773-1266
Fax: (301) 773-7346
E-Mail: info@smithindustries.us
Web Site: www.smithindustries.us
Sls.: $21,400,000
Emp.: 2
Holding Company; Scrap Metal Processing, Recycling & Materials Whslr
S.I.C.: 6719
N.A.I.C.S.: 551112
R. Paul Smith *(Pres)*

Subsidiary:

Joseph Smith & Sons, Inc. (2)
2001 Kenilworth Ave
Capitol Heights, MD 20743 DE
Tel.: (301) 773-1266
Fax: (301) 773-7346
Web Site: www.smithindustries.us
Scrap Metal Processing, Recycling & Materials Whslr
S.I.C.: 4953
N.A.I.C.S.: 562920
R. Paul Smith *(Pres)*

EUROPEAN REAL ESTATE INVESTMENT TRUST LIMITED

Sarnia House Le Truchot
Saint Peter Port, Guernsey GY1 4NA
Tel.: (44) 1481 737600
Web Site: www.ereit.co.uk
Year Founded: 2005
ERET—(LSE)
Rev.: $46,271,618
Assets: $407,245,195
Liabilities: $306,061,664
Net Worth: $101,183,531
Earnings: ($8,193,357)
Fiscal Year-end: 12/31/12
Business Description:
Real Estate Investment Services
S.I.C.: 6519
N.A.I.C.S.: 531190
Personnel:
Crispian Collins *(Chm)*
Board of Directors:
Crispian Collins
Stephen Coe
Wessel Hamman
Roger Phillips
Jan van der Vlist

Computershare Investor Services (Jersey) Limited
Queensway House Hilgrove Street
Saint Helier, JE1 1ES, Jersey
Tel.: (44) 1534 281814

EUROPEAN RELIANCE GENERAL INSURANCE S.A.

274 Kifisias Avenue
Halandri, Athens, Greece
Tel.: (30) 2106829601
Fax: (30) 21068424780
E-Mail: info@europisti.gr
Web Site: www.europisti.gr
EUPIC—(ATH)
Sales Range: $50-74.9 Million
Emp.: 1,800
Business Description:
Fire, Marine, & Casualty Insurance
S.I.C.: 6331
N.A.I.C.S.: 524126
Personnel:
Konstantinos Tsokas *(Vice Chm)*
Christos Georgakopoulos *(CEO)*

EUROPEAN TRUST BANK

Building 4 1 Srednyi Ovchinnikovskiy per
115184 Moscow, Russia
Tel.: (7) 4957455979
Fax: (7) 4959592002
E-Mail: seb@etrust.ru
Web Site: www.etrust.ru
Year Founded: 1994
Sales Range: $10-24.9 Million
Emp.: 309
Business Description:
Banking Services
S.I.C.: 6029
N.A.I.C.S.: 522110
Personnel:
Andrey V. Krysin *(Chm)*
Board of Directors:
Andrey V. Krysin
Anatoliy P. Artsebarskiy
Stanislav V. Chemakin
Boris Yu. Shtern
Leonid V. Tyagachev

EUROPEAN URANIUM RESOURCES LTD.

Unit 1 - 15782 Marine Drive
White Rock, BC, Canada V4B 1E6
Tel.: (604) 536-2711
Fax: (604) 536-2788
Web Site: www.euresources.com
EUU—(TSXV)
Business Description:
Uranium Exploration & Development Services
S.I.C.: 1094
N.A.I.C.S.: 212291
Personnel:
Michael J. Hopley *(Chm)*
Dorian L. Nicol *(Pres & CEO)*
Doris Meyer *(CFO & Corp Sec)*
Board of Directors:
Michael J. Hopley
Peter Bojtos
David Hutchins
Rex McLennan
David Montgomery
Dorian L. Nicol
Hein Poulus
Ronald Shorr
Philip Williams
Legal Counsel:
Stikeman Elliott LLP
Suite 1700 Park Place 666 Burrard Street
Vancouver, BC, Canada V6C 2X8
Tel.: (604) 631-1300
Fax: (604) 681-1825
Transfer Agent:
Computershare Investor Services Inc.
510 Burrard St
Vancouver, BC, V6C 3B9, Canada

EUROPEJSKIE CENTRUM ODSZKODOWAN S.A.

M Kolbego 18
59-220 Legnica, Poland
Tel.: (48) 76 723 98 00
Fax: (48) 76 723 98 50
E-Mail: biuro@euco.pl
Web Site: www.euco.pl
Year Founded: 2004
EUC—(WAR)
Emp.: 60
Business Description:
Claims Recovery Services
S.I.C.: 6411
N.A.I.C.S.: 524291
Personnel:
Daniel Kubach *(Chm-Supervisory Bd)*
Krzysztof Lewandowski *(Chm-Mgmt Bd)*
Pawel Filipiak *(Vice Chm-Supervisory Bd)*
Adam Wszolek *(Vice Chm-Mgmt Bd)*
Jolanta Zendran *(Mng Dir)*
Joanna Tylko *(Sec)*
Supervisory Board of Directors:
Daniel Kubach
Pawel Filipiak
Wanda Ronka-Chmielowiec
Joanna Smereczanska-Smulczyk
Joanna Tylko

EUROPLASMA SA

ZA de Cantegrit Est 471 route de Cantegrit Est
BP 23
40110 Morcenx, France
Tel.: (33) 556497000
Fax: (33) 556497019
E-Mail: contact@europlasma.com
Web Site: www.europlasma.com
Year Founded: 1992
ALEUP—(EUR)
Sales Range: $25-49.9 Million
Emp.: 217
Business Description:
Torches & Complete Plasma Torch Waste Treatment Systems
S.I.C.: 4953
N.A.I.C.S.: 562211
Personnel:
Didier Pineaut *(Pres & CEO)*
Pierre Bellman *(COO-Europe Environment Grp)*
Jean-Claude Rebischung *(CEO-Europe Environ Grp)*
Board of Directors:
Roger Ammoun
Kim Ying Lee
Jean-Claude Rebischung
Subsidiaries:

Europe Environment S.A. (1)
1 Rue des Pins
Aspach-le-Haut, 68700 Thann, Haut-Rhin, France
Tel.: (33) 389374141
Fax: (33) 389374730
E-Mail: info@europe-environnement.com
Web Site: www.europe-environnement.com
Emp.: 95
Environmental Control Systems Mfr
S.I.C.: 3822
N.A.I.C.S.: 334512
Pierre Bellmann *(Mng Dir)*

Inertam SAS (1)
471 Route de Cantegrit Est
BP 23
40110 Morcenx, Landes, France
Tel.: (33) 558041749
Fax: (33) 5 58 04 17 50
E-Mail: amiante@inertam.fr
Web Site: www.inertam.fr
Emp.: 42
Asbestos Disposal Services
S.I.C.: 1799
N.A.I.C.S.: 562910

EUROPTRONIC GROUP LTD

60 Kaki Bukit Place 01-10 Eunos Techpark
Singapore, 415979, Singapore
Tel.: (65) 64472037
Fax: (65) 64471582
Web Site: www.europtronic.com
E23—(SES)

Europtronic Group Ltd—(Continued)

Rev.: $42,735,000
Assets: $77,401,000
Liabilities: $64,596,000
Net Worth: $12,805,000
Earnings: ($20,783,000)
Fiscal Year-end: 12/31/12

Business Description:
Film Capacitors Mfr
S.I.C.: 3676
N.A.I.C.S.: 334416

Personnel:
Shih-An Huang *(Co-Founder & Chm)*
Chuang Shueh-Ou Huang *(Co-Founder & Vice Chm)*
Justin Chien-Hung Huang *(CEO)*
Chee Chong Seng *(CFO)*
Busarakham Kohsikaporn *(Co-Sec)*
Lei Mui Toh *(Co-Sec)*

Board of Directors:
Shih-An Huang
Toon Bah Ho
Chuang Shueh-Ou Huang
Justin Chien-Hung Huang
Chien Lin
Sek Khee Tan

Subsidiaries:

Europtronic Green Energy Pte Ltd **(1)**
60 Kakidukit Place Unit No 01-10 Eunon Tech Park
Singapore, 415979, Singapore
Tel.: (65) 64472037
Fax: (65) 64471582
Web Site: www.europtronicgroup.com
Emp.: 26
Plantlets Breeding Services
S.I.C.: 7389
N.A.I.C.S.: 561990
Justin Hoang *(Gen Mgr)*

Europtronic Investment Pte Ltd **(1)**
60 Kaki Bukit Place Eunos Techpark 01-10
Singapore, 415979, Singapore
Tel.: (65) 64472037
Fax: (65) 6447 1582
Web Site: www.europtronicgroup.com
Emp.: 20
Investment Management Services
S.I.C.: 6211
N.A.I.C.S.: 523999
Huang Chien Hung *(CEO)*

Europtronic (Singapore) Pte Ltd **(1)**
60 Kaki Bukit Place Eunos Techpark 60-10
Singapore, 415979, Singapore
Tel.: (65) 63485558
Fax: (65) 64471582
Web Site: www.europtronic.com
Emp.: 25
Electronic Components Mfr & Distr
S.I.C.: 3676
N.A.I.C.S.: 334416
Han Yee Neng *(Mgr)*

UPT Component (S) Pte Ltd **(1)**
60 Kaki Bukit Pl Eunos Techpark 05-10
Singapore, 415979, Singapore
Tel.: (65) 63485558
Fax: (65) 64471582
Web Site: www.europtronic.com
Emp.: 25
Electronic Components Distr
S.I.C.: 5065
N.A.I.C.S.: 423690
Mei Theng Leong *(Controller-Fin)*

Non-U.S. Subsidiaries:

Europtronic Electronic (Shenzhen) Co., Ltd. **(1)**
Block 19 8/F Shatoujiao Free Trade Zone
Shenzhen, 518081, China
Tel.: (86) 75525260670
Fax: (86) 75525260672
Web Site: www.europtronic.com
Electronic Components Mfr
S.I.C.: 3675
N.A.I.C.S.: 334416

Europtronic (HK) Company Limited **(1)**
Unit 11A Phase 1 Goodman Shatin Logistics Centre 6 Wong Chuk Yeung Street Fotan, Sha Tin, New Territories, China (Hong Kong)
Tel.: (852) 27564786
Fax: (852) 27564876
Electronic Components Whslr
S.I.C.: 5065
N.A.I.C.S.: 423690

Europtronic (Suzhou) Co., Ltd. **(1)**
No 1618 Yundongdadao Wujiang Economic Development Zone
Suzhou, Jiangsu, 215200, China
Tel.: (86) 51263401650
Fax: (86) 512 6340 1648
Web Site: www.europtronic.com
Electronic Components Mfr
S.I.C.: 3675
N.A.I.C.S.: 334416

Europtronic (Taiwan) Ind. Corp. **(1)**
10F-4 No 2 Lane 258 Rueiguang Road
Neihu District, Taipei, 114, Taiwan
Tel.: (886) 287523118
Fax: (886) 2 8752 3116
Emp.: 20
Electronic Components Mfr
S.I.C.: 3676
N.A.I.C.S.: 334416
Shih An Huang *(Pres)*

Subsidiary:

Housing Technology Corp. **(2)**
No 8 Lane 646 Po Ai Street
Chupei, Hsin-chu, 302, Taiwan
Tel.: (886) 35533280
Fax: (886) 35533282
Chip Inductors & Chip Beads Mfr
S.I.C.: 3674
N.A.I.C.S.: 334413

Europtronic Technology (UK) Limited **(1)**
5 Kerry Ave
Stanmore, Middlesex, HA7 4NJ, United Kingdom
Tel.: (44) 208 954 9798
Fax: (44) 208 954 8918
Web Site: www.europtronic.com
Emp.: 5
Electronic Components Mfr & Distr
S.I.C.: 3675
N.A.I.C.S.: 334416
Justin Huang *(Mng Dir)*

UPT Crypson Component (Shanghai) Co., Ltd. **(1)**
Room 1301 No 333 Zhao Jia Bang Road
Shanghai, 200032, China
Tel.: (86) 2164162909
Fax: (86) 2164167138
Web Site: www.europtronicgroup.com
Emp.: 20
Electronic Components Whslr
S.I.C.: 5065
N.A.I.C.S.: 423690
Shih an Huang *(Chm)*

EUROQUARZ GMBH

Sudwall 15
46282 Dorsten, Germany
Tel.: (49) 236220050
Fax: (49) 2362200599
E-Mail: post@euroquarz.de
Web Site: www.euroquarz.com
Year Founded: 1897
Rev.: $54,648,804
Emp.: 101

Business Description:
Silica Products Distr
S.I.C.: 5169
N.A.I.C.S.: 424690

Personnel:
Rolf Wildforster *(CEO)*

EUROSCREEN S.A.

Route de Lennik 802
01070 Brussels, Belgium
Tel.: (32) 71348500
Fax: (32) 71348519
E-Mail: info@euroscreen.be
Web Site: www.euroscreen.be
Emp.: 44

Business Description:
BioPharmaceutical Services
S.I.C.: 2834
N.A.I.C.S.: 325412

Personnel:
Jean Combalbert *(Pres & CEO)*

Board of Directors:
Michel Alle
Jean Combalbert
Philippe Degive
Guy Heynen
Raf Moons
Alain Parthoens
Yves Ribeill

EUROSEAS LTD.

4 Messogiou and Evropis Street
151 25 Maroussi, Greece
Tel.: (30) 211 1804005
Fax: (30) 211 1804097
Web Site: www.euroseas.gr
Year Founded: 2005
ESEA—(NASDAQ)
Rev.: $54,921,697
Assets: $278,312,797
Liabilities: $68,686,651
Net Worth: $209,626,146
Earnings: ($13,198,741)
Fiscal Year-end: 12/31/12

Business Description:
Deep Sea Transportation Services
S.I.C.: 4412
N.A.I.C.S.: 483111

Personnel:
Aristides J. Pittas *(Chm & CEO)*
Aristides P. Pittas *(Vice Chm)*
Anastasios Aslidis *(CFO & Treas)*
Stephania Karmiri *(Sec)*

Board of Directors:
Aristides J. Pittas
Anastasios Aslidis
Panagiotis Kyriakopoulos
Aristides P. Pittas
George Skarvelis
George I. Taniskidis
Gerald Turner

Non-U.S. Subsidiary:

Eternity Shipping Company **(1)**
Rm 1302 Shun Tak Centre
W Tower Connaught Rd, 168 200 Hong Kong, China (Hong Kong)
Tel.: (852) 25451212
Fax: (852) 2541 2085
E-Mail: eternity@esal.com.hk
Shipping Services
S.I.C.: 4731
N.A.I.C.S.: 488510
Jimmy Tse *(Mgr)*

EUROSIC S.A.

49 Avenue d'Iena
75116 Paris, France
Tel.: (33) 1 4502 2338
Fax: (33) 1 4754 2324
E-Mail: info@eurosic.fr
Web Site: www.eurosic.fr
ERSC—(EUR)
Rev.: $140,095,912
Earnings: $7,969,326
Fiscal Year-end: 12/31/12

Business Description:
Real Estate Investment Trust
S.I.C.: 6726
N.A.I.C.S.: 525990

Personnel:
Yan Parchet *(Chm & Dir Gen)*

Board of Directors:
Yan Parchet
Gerard Aubert
Francois Couchou-Meillot
Francoise Debrus
Philippe Depoux
Marie-Francoise Dubail
Francois Morrisson
Philippe Narzul
Charles Ruggieri
Jean Paul Sorand
Francois Thomazeau

EUROSPAN HOLDINGS BERHAD

35 1st Floor Jalan Kelisa Emas 1
Taman Kelisa Emas Seberang Jaya
13700 Penang, Malaysia
Tel.: (60) 43976672
Fax: (60) 43976675
E-Mail: enquiry@eurospan.com.my
Web Site: www.eurospan.com.my
EUROSP—(KLS)
Rev.: $19,971,016
Assets: $17,951,055
Liabilities: $4,153,812
Net Worth: $13,797,243
Earnings: $1,061,456
Fiscal Year-end: 05/31/13

Business Description:
Home Furnishings Mfr
S.I.C.: 2512
N.A.I.C.S.: 337121

Personnel:
Kok Beng Guan *(Chm & Mng Dir)*
Kim Teck Lim *(Sec)*

Board of Directors:
Kok Beng Guan
Kim Heng Guan
Shaw Kee Guan
Shaw Yin Guan
Chee Kong Ng
Yee Fuan Sim

Subsidiaries:

Dynaspan Furniture Sdn. Bhd. **(1)**
Lot 14 Kawasan Perindustrian
09000 Kulim, Kedah, Malaysia
Tel.: (60) 44892070
Fax: (60) 44892072
Web Site: www.eurospan.com.my
Emp.: 80
Furniture Mfr
S.I.C.: 2519
N.A.I.C.S.: 337125
K. P. Andy *(Sr Mgr-Production)*

Eurospan Furniture Sdn. Bhd. **(1)**
1168 Kampung Teluk Sungai Dua Kawasan Perusahaan Sungai Lokan
13800 Butterworth, Penang, Malaysia
Tel.: (60) 43563727
Fax: (60) 43561728
Emp.: 300
Furniture Mfr
S.I.C.: 3559
N.A.I.C.S.: 333249
Guan Kok Beng *(Mng Dir)*

EUROSPORTS GLOBAL LIMITED

30 Teban Gardens Crescent
Singapore, 608927, Singapore
Tel.: (65) 6565 5995
Fax: (65) 6567 5515
E-Mail: customerservice@eurosportsauto.com.sg
Web Site: www.eurosportsglobal.com
5G1—(CAT)
Rev.: $69,956,352
Emp.: 60
Fiscal Year-end: 03/31/13

Business Description:
Luxury Automobile Distr
S.I.C.: 5012
N.A.I.C.S.: 423110

Personnel:
Melvin Goh *(Chm & CEO)*
Andy Goh *(Deputy CEO)*
Yeung Sau Siu *(CFO)*
Dennis Yung Kang Yang *(COO)*

Board of Directors:
Melvin Goh
Andy Goh
Kim Quee Lim
Tiak Soon Ng

Calvin Siok Sing Tan

EUROSTAR INTERNATIONAL LTD

Times House
5 Bravingtons Walk, London, N1 9AW, United Kingdom
Tel.: (44) 2078435172
Fax: (44) 2078435720
E-Mail: info@eurostar.com
Web Site: www.eurostar.com
Year Founded: 1994
Sales Range: $450-499.9 Million
Emp.: 1,376
Business Description:
Train Services
S.I.C.: 4011
N.A.I.C.S.: 482111
Personnel:
Clare Hollingsworth *(Chm)*
Nicolas Petrovic *(CEO)*
James Cheesewright *(CFO)*

EUROTECH S.P.A.

Via Fratelli Solari 3/a
Amaro, 33020 Udine, Italy
Tel.: (39) 0433485411
Fax: (39) 0433485499
E-Mail: support.it@eurotech.com
Web Site: www.eurotech.com
Year Founded: 1992
ETH—(ITA)
Rev.: $127,124,218
Assets: $242,931,184
Liabilities: $81,159,243
Net Worth: $161,771,941
Earnings: ($3,746,391)
Emp.: 420
Fiscal Year-end: 12/31/12
Business Description:
Information Technology Research & Development; Computer Hardware & Software
S.I.C.: 7379
N.A.I.C.S.: 541519
Personnel:
Roberto Siagri *(Chm & CEO)*
Sandro Barazza *(CFO)*
Giampietro Tecchiolli *(CTO)*
Giovanni Bertolone *(Exec VP-Ops)*
Board of Directors:
Roberto Siagri
Sandro Barazza
Giovanni Bertolone
Giancarlo Grasso
Chiara Mio
Maria Cristina Pedicchio
Cesare Pizzul
Giovanni Soccodato
Giampietro Tecchiolli
Subsidiaries:

EthLab S.R.L. (1)
Viale Dante 78
Pergine Valsugana, Trento, 38057, Italy
Tel.: (39) 0461538358
Fax: (39) 0433485499
E-Mail: info@ethLab.com
Web Site: www.eurotech.com
Emp.: 10
Computer Related Research & Development Services
S.I.C.: 8731
N.A.I.C.S.: 541712
Giampietro Tecchiolli *(Pres)*

I.P.S. Sistemi Programmabili S.R.L. (1)
Via Piave 54
21040 Caronno Varesino, VA, Italy
Tel.: (39) 0331980669
Fax: (39) 0331980476
E-Mail: info@ipssistemi.com
Web Site: www.ipssistemi.com
Industrial Computers Designer & Mfr
S.I.C.: 3571
N.A.I.C.S.: 334111
Danilo Zimaldi *(Dir-Sls & Admin)*

U.S. Subsidiaries:

Dynatem, Inc. (1)
23263 Madero St Ste C
Mission Viejo, CA 92691 CA
Tel.: (949) 855-3235
Fax: (949) 770-3481
Toll Free: (800) 543-3830
E-Mail: sales@dynatem.com
Web Site: www.dynatem.com
Emp.: 20
Computer Equipment Mfr
S.I.C.: 3571
N.A.I.C.S.: 334111
Robert Anslow *(Dir-Ops)*

Eurotech Inc. (1)
10260 Old Columbia Rd
Columbia, MD 21046
Tel.: (301) 490-4007
Fax: (301) 490-4582
Toll Free: (800) 541-2003
E-Mail: sales.us@eurotech.com
Web Site: www.eurotech-inc.com
Emp.: 45
Single Board Computer Mfrs
S.I.C.: 3577
N.A.I.C.S.: 334118
Greg Nicoloso *(CEO)*
Leann Zawodniak *(CFO)*
Ben Roderique *(COO)*

Subsidiary:

Eurotech Inc. (2)
7500 W 161st St
Overland Park, KS 66085
Tel.: (913) 549-1000
Fax: (913) 549-1001
Web Site: www.eurotech-inc.com
Emp.: 12
Single Board Computer Mfr
S.I.C.: 3575
N.A.I.C.S.: 334118

Non-U.S. Subsidiaries:

Advanet Inc. (1)
616-4 Tanaka
Kita-ku, Okayama, 700-0951, Japan
Tel.: (81) 862452861
Fax: (81) 86 2452860
E-Mail: sales@advanet.jp
Web Site: www.advanet.co.jp
Sls.: $43,214
Emp.: 67
Computer Software Publishers
S.I.C.: 7372
N.A.I.C.S.: 511210

Subsidiary:

Spirit 21 Inc. (2)
134-1 Yonegura
Minami-ku, Okayama, 700-0954, Japan
Tel.: (81) 862432340
Fax: (81) 862438351
E-Mail: sales@spirit21.co.jp
Web Site: www.spirit21.co.jp
Emp.: 105
Computer Boards Mfr
S.I.C.: 3575
N.A.I.C.S.: 334118

Chengdu Vantron Technology Inc. (1)
4th Fl No 16 Gao Peng Ave
Hi-Tech Zone, Chengdu, Sichuan, China
Tel.: (86) 2885123930
Fax: (86) 2885123935
E-Mail: sales@vantrontech.com.cn
Web Site: www.vantrontech.com.cn
Emp.: 60
Computer Software Publishers
S.I.C.: 7372
N.A.I.C.S.: 511210

Eurotech Finland Oy (1)
Kantelettarenkuja 1
PO Box 73
00420 Helsinki, Uusimaa, Finland
Tel.: (358) 94778880
Fax: (358) 947788899
E-Mail: info@eurotech.fi
Web Site: www.eurotech.fi
Emp.: 2
Computer Boards Mfr
S.I.C.: 3575
N.A.I.C.S.: 334118
Tomi Hanninen *(Mng Dir)*

Eurotech France S.A.S. (1)
33 Ave du Docteur Georges Levy
Parc du Moulin a Vent Bat 33 1, 69693 Venissieux, Rhone, France
Tel.: (33) 472890090
Fax: (33) 478700824
E-Mail: sales-fr@eurotech.com
Web Site: www.eurotech.com
Emp.: 15
Computer Boards Mfr
S.I.C.: 3577
N.A.I.C.S.: 334118
Isabelle Garneau *(Gen Mgr)*

Eurotech Ltd. (1)
3 Clifton Ct
Cambridge, CB1 7BN, United Kingdom
Tel.: (44) 1223403410
Fax: (44) 1223410457
E-Mail: sales.uk@eurotech.com
Web Site: www.eurotech.com
Emp.: 25
Mfr of Industrial Controls Devices
S.I.C.: 3823
N.A.I.C.S.: 334513

EUROTERRA BULGARIA AD

1 Vitosha Ave
Sofia, 1000, Bulgaria
Tel.: (359) 2 9816606
E-Mail: info@euroterrabulgaria.bg
Web Site: www.euroterrabulgaria.bg
4EJ—(BUL)
Business Description:
Real Estate Services
S.I.C.: 6531
N.A.I.C.S.: 531210
Personnel:
Michael Therianos *(Chm & CEO)*
Olga Therianou *(Vice Chm)*
Lidia Gerdjikova *(CFO)*
Board of Directors:
Michael Therianos
Angelos Paraschakis
Olga Therianou

EUROTEX INDUSTRIES & EXPORTS LIMITED

809 Raheja Chambers 12th floor 213 Nariman Point, Mumbai, 400021, India
Tel.: (91) 22 22041408
Fax: (91) 22 22044139
E-Mail: companysecretary@eurotexgroup.com
Web Site: www.eurotexgroup.com
Year Founded: 1989
521014—(BOM)
Rev.: $52,572,531
Assets: $35,629,673
Liabilities: $23,704,656
Net Worth: $11,925,017
Earnings: ($333,011)
Fiscal Year-end: 03/31/13
Business Description:
Cotton Yarn Mfr & Distr
S.I.C.: 2299
N.A.I.C.S.: 313110
Personnel:
Krishan Kumar Patodia *(Chm, CEO & Mng Dir)*
Narayan Patodia *(Mng Dir)*
Rahul Rawat *(Compliance Officer & Sec)*
Board of Directors:
Krishan Kumar Patodia
M. L. Bagaria
P. P. Dundh
A. R. Garde
V. K. Gupta
D. K. Patel
Gopal Patodia
Narayan Patodia
Rajiv Patodia
Dharam Paul
Hariprasad Siotia

Transfer Agent:
Datamatics Financial Services Ltd
Plot No B 5 Part B Crosslane MIDC Marol Andheri East
Mumbai, India

EUROTIN INC.

25 Adelaide Street East Suite 818
Toronto, ON, M5C 3A1, Canada
Tel.: (416) 603-8706
Fax: (416) 603-8119
Year Founded: 2008
TIN—(TSXV)
Int. Income: $19,190
Assets: $15,154,949
Liabilities: $904,273
Net Worth: $14,250,676
Earnings: ($2,194,623)
Fiscal Year-end: 03/31/13
Business Description:
Metal Mining Services
S.I.C.: 1099
N.A.I.C.S.: 212299
Personnel:
Trevor Richardson *(Pres & CEO)*
Carlos Pinglo *(CFO)*
Board of Directors:
David C. Danziger
John Walter Wallen Hick
Colin Jones
Peter Miller
Trevor Richardson
Legal Counsel:
Chitiz Pathak LLP
320 Bay Street, Suite 1600
Toronto, ON, Canada
Transfer Agent:
Equity Financial Holdings Inc
200 University Avenue Suite 400
Toronto, ON, Canada

EUROVESTECH PLC

29 Curzon Street
London, W1J 7TL, United Kingdom
Tel.: (44) 20 7478 9070
Fax: (44) 20 7478 9079
E-Mail: enquiries@eurovestech.com
Web Site: www.eurovestech.com
Year Founded: 2000
Sales Range: $10-24.9 Million
Emp.: 71
Business Description:
Venture Capital Investment Services
S.I.C.: 6211
N.A.I.C.S.: 523999
Personnel:
Richard Philip Bernstein *(CEO)*
Board of Directors:
Richard Henry Grogan
Richard Philip Bernstein
David G. Ristow
Quentin-Colin Maxwell Solt
Holding:

Kalibrate Technologies PLC (1)
(Formerly Knowledge Support Systems Limited)
7th Floor Saint James's Buildings 79 Oxford Street
Manchester, M1 6SS, United Kingdom UK
Tel.: (44) 161 228 0040 (60%)
Fax: (44) 161 236 6305
E-Mail: info@kssfuels.com
Web Site: www.kalibratetech.com
KLBT—(AIM)
Sales Range: $10-24.9 Million
Emp.: 90
Petroleum Retail Industry Software & Consulting Services
S.I.C.: 7372
N.A.I.C.S.: 511210
Phlip James Lawler *(Chm)*
Bob Stein *(Pres & CEO)*
Brad Ormsby *(CFO)*
Adrian Preston *(CTO)*
Mark Hawtin *(Sr VP-Bus Dev, Strategy & Mktg)*

Eurovestech Plc—(Continued)

Gail Hay *(Sr VP-HR & Data Svcs)*
Scott Stein *(Sr VP-Pro Svcs)*
Ian Thompson *(Sr VP-Strategy)*

U.S. Subsidiaries:

Knowledge Support Systems Inc. **(2)**
Ste 200 25 B Hanover Rd
Florham Park, NJ 07932
Tel.: (973) 549-1850
Web Site: www.kssg.com
Pricing Analytics, Price Management, Rules-Based Pricing, & Optimization Technology & Services
S.I.C.: 8742
N.A.I.C.S.: 541613
Bob Stein *(Pres & CEO)*

Market Planning Solutions Inc. **(2)**
4343 S 118th E Ave Ste C
Tulsa, OK 74146 DE
Tel.: (918) 877-6774
Fax: (918) 877-6960
Toll Free: (800) 727-6774
E-Mail: info@mpsisolutions.com
Web Site: www.mpsisolutions.com
Sales Range: $10-24.9 Million
Emp.: 67
Fuel Pricing, Retail Network Planning & Data Analytics Services
S.I.C.: 8732
N.A.I.C.S.: 541910
Bob Stein *(CEO)*

Non-U.S. Holding:

MPSI Systems Ltd. **(3)**
7th Floor St James Buildings
79 Oxford Street, Manchester, M1 6SS, United Kingdom (100%)
Tel.: (44) 161 228 0040
Fax: (44) 161 236 6305
E-Mail: info@kssfuels.com
Web Site: www.kssfuels.com
Emp.: 50
Fuel Pricing, Retail Network Planning & Data Analytics Services
S.I.C.: 8732
N.A.I.C.S.: 541910
Bob Stein *(Mng Dir)*

Non-U.S. Subsidiary:

Audionamix SA **(1)**
114 Ave de Flandre
75019 Paris, France
Tel.: (33) 140055511
E-Mail: info@audionamix.com
Web Site: www.audionamix.com
Audio Mixing Services
S.I.C.: 7389
N.A.I.C.S.: 512290
Olivier Attia *(CEO)*
Pierre Leveau *(Chief Scientific Officer)*

EUROZ LIMITED

Level 18 Alluvion 58 Mounts Bay Road
Perth, WA, 6000, Australia
Tel.: (61) 894881400
Fax: (61) 894881477
E-Mail: info@euroz.com.au
Web Site: www.euroz.com.au
EZL—(ASX)
Rev.: $40,035,796
Assets: $134,260,590
Liabilities: $11,551,081
Net Worth: $122,709,508
Earnings: $6,569,953
Emp.: 45
Fiscal Year-end: 06/30/13

Business Description:
Funds Management Services
S.I.C.: 6282
N.A.I.C.S.: 523920

Personnel:
Andrew McKenzie *(Chm)*
Chris Webster *(Sec)*

Board of Directors:
Andrew McKenzie
Greg Chessell
Jay Hughes
Russell Kane
Simon Yeo
Doug Young

Subsidiaries:

Westoz Funds Management Pty. Ltd. **(1)**
Level 1 Ernst & Young Bldg
11 Mounts Bay Rd, Perth, Western Australia, 6000, Australia
Tel.: (61) 893217877
Fax: (61) 893218288
E-Mail: prees@westozfunds.com.au
Web Site: www.westozfunds.com.au
Emp.: 2
Investment Fund Management Services
S.I.C.: 6722
N.A.I.C.S.: 525910
Peter Diamond *(Chm)*

Zero Nominees Pty. Ltd. **(1)**
St Georges Terrace
PO Box Z5036
Perth, Western Australia, 6831, Australia
Tel.: (61) 894881400
Fax: (61) 894881477
E-Mail: info@euroz.com.au
Web Site: www.euroz.com.au
Emp.: 60
Business Consulting Services
S.I.C.: 8742
N.A.I.C.S.: 541611
Andrew McKenzie *(CEO)*

EUTELSAT COMMUNICATIONS SA

70 rue Balard
75502 Paris, Cedex 15, France
Tel.: (33) 1 53 98 4747
Fax: (33) 1 53 98 3700
Web Site: www.eutelsat.com
ETL—(EUR OTC)
Rev.: $1,728,616,897
Assets: $7,545,282,850
Liabilities: $4,875,558,506
Net Worth: $2,669,724,344
Earnings: $497,813,666
Emp.: 822
Fiscal Year-end: 06/30/13

Business Description:
Holding Company
S.I.C.: 4812
N.A.I.C.S.: 517210

Personnel:
Michel de Rosen *(Chm & CEO)*
John Birt *(Vice Chm)*
Michel Azibert *(Deputy CEO)*
Antoine Castarede *(CFO)*
Ariane Rossi *(Deputy CFO)*
Yohann Leroy *(Deputy CTO & Dir-Engrg)*
Jacques Dutronc *(Chief Dev Officer & Chief Innovation Officer)*
Manuel Calvo *(Deputy CTO & Dir-Ops)*
Raphael Mussalian *(CTO)*
Francesco Cataldo *(Deputy Chief Comml Officer)*
Jean-Francois Leprince-Ringuet *(Chief Comml Officer)*
Ignacio Gonzalez Nunez *(Chief Risk Officer)*
Edouard Silverio *(Gen Counsel & Sec)*
Andrew Jordan *(Exec VP-Strategic Projects)*

Board of Directors:
Michel de Rosen
John Birt
Jean-Paul Brillaud
Miriem Bensalah Chaqroun
Thomas Devedjian
Bertrand Mabille
Ross McInnes
Elisabetta Oliveri
Carole Piwnica

Ernst & Young et Autres
1-2 Place des Saisons Paris La Defense 1
92400 Courbevoie, France

Subsidiaries:

Eutelsat Communications Finance S.A.S. **(1)**
70 Rue Balard
75015 Paris, France
Tel.: (33) 153984747
Fax: (33) 153983700
Telecommunication Services
S.I.C.: 4812
N.A.I.C.S.: 517210

Eutelsat S.A. **(1)**
70 Rue Balard
F 75502 Paris, Cedex 15, France FR
Tel.: (33) 153984747
Fax: (33) 153983700
E-Mail: accueil@eutelsat.fr
Web Site: www.eutelsat.com
Emp.: 500
Satellite Telecommunications Services
S.I.C.: 4899
N.A.I.C.S.: 517919
Giuliano Berretta *(Chm & CEO)*
Jean-Paul Brillaud *(Deputy CEO & Dir-Corp Dev)*
Sylvie Lallement *(Gen Counsel & Sec)*

Subsidiary:

Eutelsat VAS S.A.S. **(2)**
70 Rue Balard
75015 Paris, France
Tel.: (33) 153984747
Fax: (33) 153983700
Telecommunication Services
S.I.C.: 4812
N.A.I.C.S.: 517210

U.S. Subsidiary:

Eutelsat Inc. **(2)**
1776 I St 9th Fl
Washington, DC 20006
Tel.: (202) 756-4870
Web Site: www.eutelsat.com
Emp.: 100
Satellite Communications Services
S.I.C.: 4899
N.A.I.C.S.: 517410
Ron Samuel *(COO)*

Division:

Eutelsat America Corp. **(3)**
1776 I St 9th FL
Washington, DC 20006
Tel.: (202) 756-4870
Web Site: www.eutelsat.com
Satellite Telecommunication Sales
S.I.C.: 4899
N.A.I.C.S.: 517410
Tony Rayner *(Mgr-Sls)*

Non-U.S. Subsidiaries:

Eutelsat do Brasil SA **(2)**
Avenida Presidente Wilson 113 9 Fl
Rio de Janeiro, 20030-020, Brazil
Tel.: (55) 2125240894
Fax: (55) 2122158480
E-Mail: eutelsat@eutelsat.com.br
Web Site: www.eutelsat.com.br
Emp.: 2
Satellite Communications Services
S.I.C.: 4899
N.A.I.C.S.: 517410
Eloi Stivalletti *(Dir-Sls Ops)*

Eutelsat GmbH **(2)**
Im Mediapark 6
50670 Cologne, Germany
Tel.: (49) 2216500450
Fax: (49) 22165004529
E-Mail: koeln@eutelsat.de
Web Site: www.eutelsat.de
Emp.: 15
Satellite Communications Services
S.I.C.: 4899
N.A.I.C.S.: 517410
Volker Steiner *(Pres & Gen Mgr)*

Eutelsat Polska s.p.z.o. **(2)**
Ul Panska 81/83
Warsaw, 834, Poland
Tel.: (48) 224328030
Fax: (48) 224328475
E-Mail: biuro@eutelsat.sr
Web Site: www.eutelsat.pl
Emp.: 4
Satellite Communications Services
S.I.C.: 4899
N.A.I.C.S.: 517410
Jikub Brzeczkowske *(Dir-Comml)*

Eutelsat Services und Beteiligungen GmbH **(2)**
Spichernstrasse 73
Cologne, 50672, Germany De
Tel.: (49) 221 6500 45 0
Fax: (49) 221 6500 4529
Telecommunication Services
S.I.C.: 4812
N.A.I.C.S.: 517210

Eutelsat UK Ltd. **(2)**
Marble Arch Tower
55 Bryanston Street, London, W1H7AJ, United Kingdom
Tel.: (44) 2078688873
Fax: (44) 2078688782
E-Mail: admin@eutelsat.co.uk
Web Site: www.eutelsat.com
Emp.: 5
Satellite Communications Services
S.I.C.: 4899
N.A.I.C.S.: 517410

Satelites Mexicanos S.A de C.V **(2)**
Avenida Paseo de la Reforma 222 Piso 20 y 21
Colonia Juarez, 06600 Mexico, Mexico
Tel.: (52) 55 2629 5800
Fax: (52) 55 2629 5865
Web Site: www.satmex.com.mx
Rev.: $139,407,000
Assets: $746,014,000
Liabilities: $444,404,000
Net Worth: $301,610,000
Earnings: $41,319,000
Emp.: 210
Fiscal Year-end: 12/31/12
Satellite Services
S.I.C.: 4899
N.A.I.C.S.: 517410
Josiah Rotenberg *(Chm)*
Patricio E. Northland *(CEO)*
Juan Garcia-Gayou Facha *(CFO)*
Veronica Gutierrez Zamora Garcia *(Gen Counsel)*
Alejandro Sainz Orantes *(Sec)*

Skylogic Mediterraneo S.r.l **(2)**
Via Gianquinto De Gioannis 25 A
Cagliari, 09125, Italy
Tel.: (39) 070247645
Fax: (39) 0115585444
E-Mail: noc.cgl@skylogic.it
Web Site: www.skylogic.it
Television Broadcasting Services
S.I.C.: 4833
N.A.I.C.S.: 515120

Skylogic Polska sp Zoo **(2)**
Panska 81-463
Warsaw, 00-834, Poland
Tel.: (48) 224328030
Fax: (48) 224328475
Satellite Telecommunication Services
S.I.C.: 4899
N.A.I.C.S.: 517410

Skylogic S.p.A. **(2)**
Piazza Lagrange 2
10123 Turin, Italy
Tel.: (39) 0115585400
Fax: (39) 0115585444
E-Mail: skylogic@skylogic.it
Web Site: www.skylogic.com
Emp.: 100
Broadband Satellite Communications Services
S.I.C.: 4899
N.A.I.C.S.: 517410
Arduino Patacchini *(Pres)*
Jean-Francois Fenech *(CEO)*

Wins Ltd **(2)**
Business Centre 217 Parilja St
Santa Vennera, SVR 1936, Malta
Tel.: (356) 2149 8680
Fax: (356) 2149 8679
E-Mail: info@winssystems.com
Web Site: www.winssystems.com
Emp.: 10
Telecommunications Services
S.I.C.: 4899
N.A.I.C.S.: 517919
Tony Mejlaq *(Chm & CEO)*
Jean-Noel Colcy *(Mng Dir)*

EVA PRECISION INDUSTRIAL HOLDINGS LIMITED
Unit 8 6th Floor Greenfield Tower
Concordia Plaza
No 1 Science Museum Road,
Kowloon, China (Hong Kong)
Tel.: (852) 26206488
Fax: (852) 21919978
Web Site: www.eva-group.com
0838—(HKG)
Rev.: $305,227,616
Assets: $493,070,628
Liabilities: $225,412,208
Net Worth: $267,658,420
Earnings: $8,975,952
Emp.: 7,595
Fiscal Year-end: 12/31/12
Business Description:
Metals Industry
S.I.C.: 3542
N.A.I.C.S.: 333517
Personnel:
Hwo Jie Zhang *(Chm)*
Jian Hua Zhang *(Vice Chm)*
Yaohua Zhang *(CEO)*
Francis Hoi Chu Wong *(CFO & Sec)*
Te Min Ll *(Chief Strategic Officer)*
Shou Sheng Wen *(Pres-Labour Union)*
Board of Directors:
Hwo Jie Zhang
Tak Ho Choy
Hiu Lo Lam
Tai Chiu Leung
Jian Hua Zhang
Yaohua Zhang
Computershare Hong Kong Investor Services Limited
Shops 1712-1716 17th Floor Hopewell Centre
183 Queens Road East
Wanchai, China (Hong Kong)
Transfer Agents:
HSBC Trustee (Cayman) Limited
HSBC House 68 West Bay Road
PO Box 484
Georgetown, Grand Cayman, Cayman Islands
Computershare Hong Kong Investor Services Limited
Shops 1712-1716 17th Floor Hopewell Centre
183 Queens Road East
Wanchai, China (Hong Kong)

EVANCE WIND TURBINES LTD.
Unit 6 Weldon Road
Loughborough, Leicestershire, LE11 5RN, United Kingdom
Tel.: (44) 1509 215669
Fax: (44) 1509 267722
Web Site: www.evancewind.com
Year Founded: 2000
Sales Range: $10-24.9 Million
Emp.: 38
Business Description:
Wind Turbine Mfr
S.I.C.: 3511
N.A.I.C.S.: 333611
Personnel:
Kevin Parslow *(CEO)*

EVATHERM LTD.
Hintermattlistrasse 3
CH-5506 Magenwil, Switzerland
Tel.: (41) 62 889 79 00
Fax: (41) 62 889 79 01
E-Mail: info@evatherm.com
Web Site: www.evatherm.com
Business Description:
Evaporation & Crystallization Technology & Services
S.I.C.: 3559
N.A.I.C.S.: 333249
Personnel:
Peter Kondorosy *(Chm)*
Eors Kondorosy *(Mng Dir)*
Non-U.S. Subsidiaries:

EVATHERM GmbH (1)
Dubener Strasse 17
D-06774 Muldestausee, Germany
Tel.: (49) 342 08 71 295
Fax: (49) 342 08 71 297
Evaporation & Crystallization Technology & Services
S.I.C.: 3559
N.A.I.C.S.: 333249

EVATHERM Kft. (1)
Beregszaszter 16
H-1118 Budapest, Hungary
Tel.: (36) 1 246 37 77
Fax: (36) 1 246 37 87
Evaporation & Crystallization Technology & Services
S.I.C.: 3559
N.A.I.C.S.: 333249

EVEN CONSTRUTORA E INCORPORADORA S.A.
Rua Hungria 1 400 - 3 andar
01455-000 Jardim America, Sao Paulo, Brazil
Tel.: (55) 11 3377 3699
Fax: (55) 11 3377 3780
E-Mail: ri@even.com.br
Web Site: www.even.com.br
Year Founded: 2002
EVEN3—(BRAZ)
Rev.: $1,063,584,234
Assets: $1,856,235,947
Liabilities: $968,328,751
Net Worth: $887,907,196
Earnings: $133,087,726
Emp.: 2,009
Fiscal Year-end: 12/31/12
Business Description:
Real Estate Development Services
S.I.C.: 6531
N.A.I.C.S.: 531390
Personnel:
Carlos Eduardo Terepins *(Chm & CEO)*
Michel Jacques Levy *(Vice Chm)*
Dany Muszkat *(CFO & IR Officer)*
Joao Eduardo de Azevedo Silva *(Chief Dev Officer)*
Silvio Luiz Gava *(CTO)*
Paulo Otavio Goncalves de Moura *(Officer)*
Board of Directors:
Carlos Eduardo Terepins
Fabio Alperowitch
Nicolau Ferreira Chacur
Roberto de Aguiar Attuch, Jr.
Michel Jacques Levy
Luis Terepins

EVENT MARKETING SERVICE GMBH
Geusaugasse 9
A-1030 Vienna, Austria
Tel.: (43) 1 714 88 77 0
Fax: (43) 1 714 88 77 10
E-Mail: contact@event-marketing.com
Web Site: www.event-marketing.com
Sales Range: $1-9.9 Million
Business Description:
Touring Shows, Exhibits & Event Marketing
S.I.C.: 7929
N.A.I.C.S.: 711190
Personnel:
Christoph Rahofer *(CEO)*

EVENTA ENTERTAINMENT GROUP LTD.
118 Queens Road
Brighton, BN1 3XG, United Kingdom
Tel.: (44) 1273 225 071
Fax: (44) 1273 202 500
E-Mail: contact@theeventagroup.com
Web Site: www.theeventagroup.com
Year Founded: 2002
Sales Range: $10-24.9 Million
Emp.: 50
Business Description:
Event Organising Services
S.I.C.: 7999
N.A.I.C.S.: 711310
Personnel:
Hen Heaven *(Mng Dir)*

EVER-GLORY INTERNATIONAL GROUP INC.
Ever-Glory Commercial Center 509
Chengxin Road
Jiangning Development Zone,
Nanjing, Jiangsu, China
Tel.: (86) 25 5209 6875
E-Mail: info@everglorygroup.com
Web Site: www.everglorygroup.com
Year Founded: 1994
EVK—(NYSEMKT)
Sls.: $279,633,212
Assets: $151,170,455
Liabilities: $121,212,608
Net Worth: $29,957,847
Earnings: $12,802,942
Emp.: 5,100
Fiscal Year-end: 12/31/12
Business Description:
Men's, Women's & Children's Casual Wear, Sportswear & Outerwear Mfr
S.I.C.: 2389
N.A.I.C.S.: 315280
Personnel:
Edward Yihua Kang *(Chm, Pres & CEO)*
Jiansong Wang *(CFO & Sec)*
JiaJun Sun *(COO)*
Board of Directors:
Edward Yihua Kang
Changyu Qi
JiaJun Sun
Merry Tang
Zhixue Zhang

EVER LOTUS ENTERPRISE CO., LTD.
No 89 Yu Ping Road
T'ainan, 70843, Taiwan
Tel.: (886) 62999757
Fax: (886) 62999765
E-Mail: elotus99@ms34.hinet.net
Web Site: www.everlotus.com
Year Founded: 1996
Business Description:
Plastic Computerware & Accessories
S.I.C.: 3089
N.A.I.C.S.: 326199
Personnel:
Jenifer Chang *(CEO)*

EVERARDS BREWERY LTD
Castle Acres
Narborough, Leicestershire, LE19 1BY, United Kingdom
Tel.: (44) 1162014100
Fax: (44) 1162814199
E-Mail: mail@everards.co.uk
Web Site: www.everards.co.uk
Year Founded: 1849
Rev.: $49,937,748
Emp.: 110
Business Description:
Brewing Services
S.I.C.: 2084
N.A.I.C.S.: 312130
Personnel:
Richard Everard *(Chm)*

EVERBRIGHT SECURITIES CO., LTD.
No 1508 Xinzha Road Jing'an District
Shanghai, 200040, China
Tel.: (86) 21 2216 9999
Fax: (86) 21 2216 9964
Web Site: www.ebscn.com
601788—(SHG)
Sales Range: $700-749.9 Million
Emp.: 1,965
Business Description:
Securities Brokerage Services
S.I.C.: 6211
N.A.I.C.S.: 523120
Personnel:
Changqing Yuan *(Chm)*

EVEREADY EAST AFRICA LIMITED
MCFL Logistics Centre 1st Floor
Mombasa Road
PO Box 44765
00100 Nairobi, Kenya
Tel.: (254) 202980000
Fax: (254) 20343213
E-Mail: info@eveready.co.ke
Web Site: www.eveready.co.ke
EVRD—(NAI)
Rev.: $15,138,880
Assets: $12,922,687
Liabilities: $8,997,925
Net Worth: $3,924,761
Earnings: $787,043
Emp.: 250
Fiscal Year-end: 09/30/12
Business Description:
Alkaline Batteries Mfr
S.I.C.: 3692
N.A.I.C.S.: 335912
Personnel:
Jackson K. Mutua *(Mng Dir)*
Issa Timamy *(Sec)*
Board of Directors:
A. Moody Awori
Akif H. Butt
Susan Mudhune
Jackson K. Mutua
Catherine Ngahu
Isaac Olentiki
Paul Scott
Fauzia B. Shah
Legal Counsel:
Mukite Musangi & Company Advocates
PO Box 149
Nairobi, Kenya
Kemboy & Ogola Advocates
PO Box 19500
Nairobi, Kenya
Kaplan & Stratton
PO Box 40111
Nairobi, Kenya

EVEREADY INDUSTRIES INDIA LTD
2 Rainey Park
Kolkata, West Bengal, 700019, India
Tel.: (91) 3324864961
Fax: (91) 3324864673
E-Mail: feedback@eveready.co.in
Web Site: www.evereadyindustries.com
531508—(BOM)
Rev.: $193,697,948
Assets: $203,966,846
Liabilities: $95,668,254
Net Worth: $108,298,592
Earnings: $941,165
Emp.: 2,500
Fiscal Year-end: 03/31/13
Business Description:
Battery, Lantern, Tea & Insect Repellant Mfr
S.I.C.: 3691
N.A.I.C.S.: 335911
Personnel:
Tehnaz Punwani *(Sec & Sr Gen Mgr-Legal)*
Board of Directors:

Eveready Industries India Ltd—(Continued)

Brij Mohan Khaitan
Subir Ranjan Dasgupta
Sanjiv Goenka
Aditya Khaitan
Amritanshu Khaitan
Deepak Khaitan
Puranam Hayagreeva Ravikumar
Suvamoy Saha
Ajay Saraf
Sudipto Sarkar

Transfer Agent:
Maheshwari Datamatics Private Limited
6 Mangoe Lane
Kolkata, India

Non-U.S. Subsidiary:

Idea Power Limited (1)
Room 1009 10/F Block A Hoi Luen Industrial Centre 55 Hoi Yuen Road
Kwun Tong, Kowloon, China (Hong Kong)
Tel.: (852) 27931191
Fax: (852) 27931181
E-Mail: info@uniross.com.hk
Rechargeable Batteries Mfr & Distr
S.I.C.: 3691
N.A.I.C.S.: 335911

Non-U.S. Subsidiaries:

Everfast Rechargeables Limited (1)
Room 1605 Stelux House 698 Prince Edward Road East
SanpoKong, Kowloon, China (Hong Kong)
Tel.: (852) 31523687
Fax: (852) 31522986
E-Mail: marketing@everfast.com.hk
Web Site: www.everfast.com.hk
Emp.: 5
Rechargeable Batteries Distr
S.I.C.: 5063
N.A.I.C.S.: 423610
Julien Ceran *(Gen Mgr)*

Industrial - Uniross Batteries (PTY) Ltd. (1)
Unit 63 Capital Hill Commercial Estate Corner K101 & Le Loux Avenue
Midrand, Gauteng, 1685, South Africa
Tel.: (27) 11 312 0016
Fax: (27) 11 312 0079
E-Mail: info@uniross.co.za
Web Site: www.uniross.co.za
Emp.: 20
Batteries Mfr
S.I.C.: 3691
N.A.I.C.S.: 335911
Michael Rogers *(Mng Dir)*

Uniross SA (1)
ZI de la Madeleine
77185 Lognes, France
Tel.: (33) 160950040
Fax: (33) 160950058
E-Mail: info@uniross.com
Web Site: www.uniross.com
Electronic Device Battery & Battery Charger Designer, Mfr & Distr
S.I.C.: 3692
N.A.I.C.S.: 335912
Cristophe Gurtner *(Chm & CEO)*
Craig Taylor *(Pres)*

Subsidiary:

Uniross Batteries SAS (2)
Zone Industrielle De La Madeleine 27 Rue De La Maison Rouge
Seine Et Marne, Lognes, France
Tel.: (33) 160950040
Fax: (33) 160950058
E-Mail: irene.daoug@uniross.com
Web Site: www.uniross.com
Rechargeable Batteries Mfr & Distr
S.I.C.: 3691
N.A.I.C.S.: 335911
Christophe Gurtner *(Gen Mgr)*

U.S. Subsidiaries:

Uniross Batteries HK Ltd. (2)
10 State St Ste 1c
Woburn, MA 01801-6820
Tel.: (914) 241-9510
Fax: (978) 945-8786
E-Mail: eddie@multiplier.com
Web Site: www.uniross.com
Electronic Device Battery & Battery Charger Mfr & Distr
S.I.C.: 3692
N.A.I.C.S.: 335912

Zhongshan Uniross Industry Co. Limited (1)
39 Middle Industrial Main Road
528415 Zhongshan, Guangdong, China
Tel.: (86) 76022139808
Fax: (86) 22268675
Web Site: www.uniross.com
Rechargeable Batteries Mfr
S.I.C.: 3691
N.A.I.C.S.: 335911
Fredric Poupeau *(Gen Mgr)*

EVEREST BANK LIMITED

EBL House Lazimpath
PO Box 13384
Kathmandu, Nepal
Tel.: (977) 14443377
Fax: (977) 14443160
E-Mail: ebl@mos.com.np
Web Site: www.everestbankltd.com
EBL—(NEP)
Sales Range: $25-49.9 Million

Business Description:
Investment Banking Services
S.I.C.: 6211
N.A.I.C.S.: 523110

Personnel:
B. K. Shrestha *(Chm)*
P. K. Mohapatra *(CEO)*
Pramod Raj Sharma *(Sec)*

Board of Directors:
B. K. Shrestha
Bal Gopal Baidhya
B. J. Gupta
P. K. Mohapatra
Arun Man Sherchan
K. C. Shivasharan
Muskan Shrestha
Ved K. Shrestha

EVEREST FINANCE LIMITED

Narayan Path Rupendehi
Siddharthanagar, 32907, Nepal
Tel.: (977) 71 526507
Fax: (977) 71 526508
E-Mail: efl@ntc.net.np
Web Site: www.efl.com.np
EFL—(NEP)

Business Description:
Financial Services
S.I.C.: 6211
N.A.I.C.S.: 523999

Personnel:
Govind Ballav Bhatt *(Chm)*
Khim Bahadur Karki *(Mng Dir)*
Bhuvan Rana *(Acct Officer)*
Bikash Shrestha *(Loan Officer)*

Board of Directors:
Govind Ballav Bhatt
Khim Bahadur Karki
Arjun Jung Rana
Rajan Jung Rana
Rameshwar Shrestha
Bishnu Prasad Upadhyay

EVEREST FINANCIAL GROUP LIMITED

Level 35 AMP Centre 50 Bridge St
Sydney, NSW, 2000, Australia
Tel.: (61) 280019100
Fax: (61) 280019200
E-Mail: info@everest.com.au
Web Site: www.everest.com.au
Sales Range: $1-9.9 Million

Business Description:
Investment Services
S.I.C.: 6282
N.A.I.C.S.: 523920

Personnel:
Wilson Leung *(CFO)*
Michael Sutherland *(Sec & Gen counsel)*

Board of Directors:
Michael Sutherland

EVEREST INDUSTRIES LTD

Gat No 152 Lakhmapur Taluka Dindori
Nasik, Maharashtra, 422 202, India
Tel.: (91) 2557250375
Fax: (91) 2557250376
E-Mail: info@everestind.com
Web Site: www.everestind.com
508906—(BOM)
Rev.: $199,811,123
Assets: $130,014,142
Liabilities: $76,290,320
Net Worth: $53,723,822
Earnings: $9,733,444
Emp.: 1,609
Fiscal Year-end: 03/31/13

Business Description:
Industrial, Commercial & Residential Construction Requirements Provider
S.I.C.: 1542
N.A.I.C.S.: 236220

Personnel:
A. V. Somani *(Chm)*
Manish Sanghi *(Mng Dir)*
Neeraj Kohli *(Compliance Officer, Sec & Head-Legal)*
Rakesh Kumar Gupta *(Sr VP-Fin)*

Board of Directors:
A. V. Somani
Mohanlal Bhandari
M. L. Gupta
Sandeep Hemendra Junnarkar
Amitabh Das Mundhra
M. L. Narula
Y. Srinivasa Rao
Manish Sanghi
B. L. Taparia

Transfer Agent:
MCS Limited
F-65 Okhla Industrial Area Phase-I
New Delhi, India

EVEREST INSURANCE COMPANY LTD.

Hattisar
PO Box 10675
Kathmandu, Nepal
Tel.: (977) 1 4425758
Fax: (977) 1 4444366
E-Mail: info@eic.com.np
Web Site: www.everestinsurance.com
EIC—(NEP)

Business Description:
Insurance Services
S.I.C.: 6411
N.A.I.C.S.: 524298

Personnel:
Rajendra K. Khetan *(Chm)*
Ratan Lal Sanghai *(Vice Chm)*
Kewal Krishna Shrestha *(CEO)*

Board of Directors:
Rajendra K. Khetan
Madhu Sudhan Agrawal
Prasad Gyawali
Prem Prakash Khetan
Ratan Lal Sanghai
Birendra K. Shah
Om Prakash Sikaria
Niranjan Tibrewala
Rabi K. Tibrewala

EVEREST KANTO CYLINDER LIMITED

204 Raheja Centre Free Press Journal Marg 214 Nariman Point
Mumbai, 400 021, India
Tel.: (91) 2230268300
Fax: (91) 2222870720
Web Site: www.everestkanto.com
532684—(BOM)
Rev.: $103,696,408
Assets: $240,447,355
Liabilities: $124,967,758
Net Worth: $115,479,597
Earnings: ($24,438,130)
Emp.: 1,200
Fiscal Year-end: 03/31/13

Business Description:
Gas Cylinders Mfr
S.I.C.: 3443
N.A.I.C.S.: 332420

Personnel:
Prem Kumar Khurana *(Chm & Mng Dir)*
Vipin Chandok *(CFO)*
Kanika Sharma *(Compliance Officer & Sec)*

Board of Directors:
Prem Kumar Khurana
Krishen Dev
Mohan Jayakar
Puneet Khurana
Pushkar Khurana
Naresh Oberoi
Vyomesh Shah

Transfer Agent:
Link Intime India Pvt. Ltd
C-13 Pannalal Silk Mills Compound LBS Marg
Bhandup (West)
Mumbai, India

Subsidiary:

Medical Engineers (I) Pvt. Ltd. (1)
B-69 2 Dsidc Complex
Wazirpur Indus Area, New Delhi, 110052, India
Tel.: (91) 1142474916, ext. 43363100
Fax: (91) 1127377530
Web Site: www.everestkanto.con
Medical Equipments Supplier
S.I.C.: 5047
N.A.I.C.S.: 423450

U.S. Subsidiary:

CP Industries Holdings, Inc (1)
2214 Walnut St
McKeesport, PA 15132-7054
Tel.: (412) 664-6639
Fax: (412) 664-6653
Web Site: www.cp-industries.com
Emp.: 118
Ultra Large Seamless Cylinders Mfr
S.I.C.: 3443
N.A.I.C.S.: 332313
Roger L Seese *(CFO)*

EVEREST RE GROUP, LTD.

Wessex House 2nd Floor 45 Reid Street
PO Box HM 845
Hamilton, D0, HM DX, Bermuda
Tel.: (441) 2950006
Fax: (441) 295-4828
Toll Free: 8002330686
E-Mail: info@everestregroup.com
Web Site: www.everestre.com
Year Founded: 1999
RE—(NYSE)
Rev.: $5,640,836,000
Assets: $19,808,036,000
Liabilities: $12,839,760,000
Net Worth: $6,968,276,000
Earnings: $1,265,260,000
Emp.: 1,063
Fiscal Year-end: 12/31/13

Business Description:
Insurance Holding Company
S.I.C.: 6331
N.A.I.C.S.: 524126

Personnel:
Joseph V. Taranto *(Chm & CEO)*
Dominic J. Addesso *(Pres)*
Craig W. Howie *(CFO & Exec VP)*

Barry H. Smith *(Chief Admin Officer & Exec VP)*
Jack Nelson *(Chief Investment Officer & Sr VP)*
Sanjoy Mukherjee *(Chief Comml Officer, Gen Counsel, Sec & Sr VP)*
John P. Doucette *(Chief Underwriting Officer & Exec VP)*
Daryl W. Bradley *(Pres-Natl Insurance Company & Exec VP)*
Frank N. Lopapa *(Treas & Sr VP)*
Robert E. Capicchioni *(Exec VP)*
Dennis Alba *(Sr VP)*
Ronald D. Diaz *(Sr VP)*
James H. Foster *(Sr VP)*
Linda Mitchell *(Sr VP)*
Gail Van Beveren *(Sr VP)*
Board of Directors:
Joseph V. Taranto
Dominic J. Addesso
John J. Amore
John R. Dunne
William F. Galtney, Jr.
John P. Phelan
Roger M. Singer
John A. Weber

Subsidiaries:

Everest Reinsurance (Bermuda), Ltd. **(1)**
Wessex House
PO Box HM 845
45 Reid Street 2nd Floor, Hamilton, HM DX, Bermuda BM
Tel.: (441) 278 6267 (100%)
Fax: (441) 295 4828
E-Mail: Mark.deSaram@everestrebermuda.bm
Web Site: www.everestre.com
Property & Casualty Insurance & Reinsurance Products
S.I.C.: 6331
N.A.I.C.S.: 524126
Mark de Saram *(CEO & Mng Dir)*

U.S. Subsidiaries:

Everest Global Services, Inc. **(1)**
477 Martinsville Rd
Liberty Corner, NJ 07938-0830
Tel.: (908) 604-3000
Fax: (908) 604-3369
Insurance & Reinsurance Services
S.I.C.: 6331
N.A.I.C.S.: 524126

Subsidiaries:

Everest Indemnity Insurance Company **(2)**
477 Martinsville Rd
Liberty Corner, NJ 07938 DE
Mailing Address: (100%)
PO Box 830
Liberty Corner, NJ 07938-0830
Tel.: (908) 604-3000
Fax: (908) 604-3450
Web Site: www.everestre.com
Emp.: 300
Provider of Excess & Surplus Lines Insurance Products
S.I.C.: 6411
N.A.I.C.S.: 524210
Daryl Bradley *(Pres)*

Everest National Insurance Company **(2)**
477 Martinsville Rd
Liberty Corner, NJ 07938-0830 AZ
Tel.: (908) 604-3000 (100%)
Fax: (908) 604-3322
Toll Free: (800) 269-6660
Web Site: www.everestnational.com
Sales Range: $100-124.9 Million
Emp.: 450
Property & Casualty Insurance Services
S.I.C.: 6411
N.A.I.C.S.: 524210
Darryl Bradley *(Pres)*

Everest Reinsurance Company **(2)**
477 Martinsville Rd
Liberty Corner, NJ 07938 DE
Tel.: (908) 604-3000 (100%)
Fax: (908) 604-3322
Toll Free: (800) 438-4375
Web Site: www.everestnational.com
Emp.: 300
Provider of Property & Casualty Insurance & Reinsurance Products
S.I.C.: 6351
N.A.I.C.S.: 524126
Scott P. Callahan *(Exec VP-US Treaty Property)*

Non-U.S. Subsidiary:

Everest Reinsurance Company - Escritorio de Representa cao No Brasil Ltda. **(3)**
Av Rio Branco No 1 sala 1501
Centro, Rio de Janeiro, Brazil 20090-003
Tel.: (55) 2125163511
Property & Casualty Insurance Services
S.I.C.: 6331
N.A.I.C.S.: 524126

Subsidiary:

Everest National **(3)**
300 Vestavia Pkwy Ste 2305
Birmingham, AL 35216 AL
Mailing Address: (100%)
PO Box 830
Liberty Corner, NJ 07938-0830
Tel.: (205) 795-2070
Fax: (908) 604-3344
Web Site: www.everestnational.com
Emp.: 3
Workers Compensation
S.I.C.: 8742
N.A.I.C.S.: 541611

Everest Security Insurance Company **(2)**
925 North Point Pkwy
Alpharetta, GA 30005 GA
Tel.: (678) 942-2300 (100%)
Fax: (678) 942-2310
Toll Free: (800) 545-7742
E-Mail: custserve@esicinsurance.com
Web Site: www.esicinsurance.com
Emp.: 35
Provider of Property & Casualty Insurance Products
S.I.C.: 6311
N.A.I.C.S.: 524113

Mt. McKinley Managers, LLC **(2)**
477 Martinsville Rd
Liberty Corner, NJ 07938 NJ
Mailing Address: (99%)
PO Box 830
Liberty Corner, NJ 07938
Tel.: (908) 604-3000
Fax: (908) 604-3322
Toll Free: (800) 438-4375
Web Site: www.everestre.com
Emp.: 450
Insurance Policy Management Services
S.I.C.: 6411
N.A.I.C.S.: 524210
Joseph Taranto *(CEO)*

Subsidiary:

WorkCare Southeast of Georgia, Inc. **(3)**
PO Box 1620
Alpharetta, GA 30009-1623 GA
Tel.: (678) 942-2300 (100%)
Fax: (678) 942-2310
Toll Free: (800) 545-7746
Web Site: www.esicinsurance.com
Emp.: 50
Property & Casualty Insurance Agency
S.I.C.: 6411
N.A.I.C.S.: 524210
Chip Craze *(Sr VP)*

Non-U.S. Subsidiary:

Everest Reinsurance Company **(2)**
The Exchange Tower 130 King Street West Suite 2520
PO Box 431
Toronto, ON, M5X 1E3, Canada Ca
Tel.: (416) 862-1228 (100%)
Fax: (416) 366-5899
E-Mail: info@everestre.com
Web Site: www.everestre.com
Sales Range: $100-124.9 Million
Emp.: 25
Provider of Property & Casualty Insurance Products
S.I.C.: 6351
N.A.I.C.S.: 524126
Jim Camerino *(VP-Treaty & Facultative-Canada)*

Everest Reinsurance Holdings, Inc. **(1)**
477 Martinsville Rd
Liberty Corner, NJ 07938 DE
Tel.: (908) 604-3000 (100%)
Fax: (908) 604-3322
Toll Free: (800) 269-6660
Web Site: www.everestre.com
Rev.: $2,483,881,000
Assets: $15,087,950,000
Liabilities: $11,609,344,000
Net Worth: $3,478,606,000
Earnings: $520,329,000
Emp.: 450
Fiscal Year-end: 12/31/12
Reinsurance Services; Holding Company
S.I.C.: 6331
N.A.I.C.S.: 524126
Keith T. Shoemaker *(VP & Controller)*

Subsidiaries:

Everest Specialty Underwriters, LLC **(2)**
461 5th Ave 20th FL
New York, NY 10017-6234
Tel.: (646) 746-1990
Fax: (646) 746-1991
Insurance Underwriting Services
S.I.C.: 6321
N.A.I.C.S.: 524114
John Iannotti *(Sr VP)*

Heartland Crop Insurance, Inc. **(2)**
120 S E 6th Ave Ste 2-210
Topeka, KS 66601
Tel.: (785) 235-5566
Fax: (785) 235-5577
Toll Free: (888) 789-5566
E-Mail: Heartland@HeartlandCropInsurance.com
Web Site: www.heartlandcropinsurance.com
Crop Insurance Services
S.I.C.: 6411
N.A.I.C.S.: 524210
Mike Miller *(CEO)*
Jim Eastburn *(CFO & VP)*
Trent Nauholz *(COO & VP)*
Mike Hartquist *(CIO & VP)*
Wade Shuler *(Exec VP)*

Non-U.S. Subsidiaries:

Everest Advisors (UK), Ltd. **(1)**
40 Lime Street
London, EC3M 5BS, United Kingdom
Tel.: (44) 2074504282
Fax: (44) 2076235967
Emp.: 30
Insurance & Reinsurance Services
S.I.C.: 6331
N.A.I.C.S.: 524126
Paul Tester *(Chief Underwriting Officer)*

Everest Insurance Company of Canada **(1)**
130 Bloor Street West Suite 602
Toronto, ON, M5S 1N5, Canada
Tel.: (416) 487-3900
Fax: (416) 487-0311
Property & Casualty Insurance Services
S.I.C.: 6331
N.A.I.C.S.: 524126
Bradley Bradley *(Chm)*
David Crozier *(CEO)*

Subsidiary:

Premiere Insurance Underwriting Services **(2)**
130 Bloor Street West Suite 602
Toronto, ON, Canada
Tel.: (416) 487-3900
Fax: (416) 487-0311
Web Site: premiereins.com
Insurance Underwriting Services
S.I.C.: 6331
N.A.I.C.S.: 524126
Mark Teitelbaum *(Pres)*

Everest Reinsurance Company (Ireland), Limited **(1)**
5th Floor Hainault House 69-71 St Stephens Green, Dublin, Ireland
Tel.: (353) 14180300
Insurance & Reinsurance Services
S.I.C.: 6331
N.A.I.C.S.: 524126
Graham Waite *(Chief Underwriting Officer)*

EVEREST TEXTILE CO., LTD.

256 Ming Ho Tsun Shansan Hsiang
T'ainan, Taiwan
Tel.: (886) 65782561
Fax: (886) 65782864
Web Site: www.everest.com.tw
1460—(TAI)
Sales Range: $75-99.9 Million
Business Description:
Textile Fabric Mfr
S.I.C.: 2299
N.A.I.C.S.: 313210
Personnel:
Jar-Yi Hsi *(Chm)*

Non-U.S. Subsidiary:

Everest Textile (HK) Co. Ltd. **(1)**
Unit 3006 Laws Commercial Plaza 9
Cheung Sha Wan Road
Cheung Sha Wan, Kowloon, China (Hong Kong)
Tel.: (852) 023081938
Fax: (852) 27876803
Emp.: 1
Woven Fabrics Mfr
S.I.C.: 2241
N.A.I.C.S.: 313220
Carol Chang *(Mgr)*

Non-U.S. Plants:

Everest Textile Co., Ltd. - Shanghai Factory **(1)**
No 197 Baisha Road Xinghuo Development Zone
Fengxian, Shanghai, 201419, China
Tel.: (86) 2157502111
Fax: (86) 2157504166
Garments Mfr
S.I.C.: 2389
N.A.I.C.S.: 315280

Everest Textile Co., Ltd. - Thailand Factory **(1)**
49 Moo 1 Taladnadwadsoita Road Ban Muang Subdistrict
Banpong District, Ratchaburi, 70110, Thailand
Tel.: (66) 32 354070
Fax: (66) 32 354071
Nylon Fabrics Mfr
S.I.C.: 2252
N.A.I.C.S.: 315110

EVERFOCUS ELECTRONICS CO., LTD.

12F-1 No 79 Section 1 Shin-Tai Wu Road
Hsi-chieh, Taipei, Hsien, Taiwan
Tel.: (886) 226982334
Fax: (886) 226982380
Web Site: www.everfocus.com.tw
5484—(TAI)
Sales Range: $25-49.9 Million
Emp.: 615
Business Description:
Closed Circuit Camera Mfr
S.I.C.: 3812
N.A.I.C.S.: 334511
Personnel:
Zhongliang Li *(Chm & CMO)*
Jiaming Huang *(Vice Chm & Chief R&D Officer)*
James Weng *(Pres)*
Board of Directors:
Zhongliang Li
Jiaming Huang
James Weng
Yongshun Zhuang

U.S. Subsidiary:

EverFocus Electronics Corp. **(1)**
1801 Highland Ave Unit A
Duarte, CA 91010

EverFocus Electronics Co., Ltd.—(Continued)

Tel.: (626) 844-8888
Fax: (626) 844-8838
Toll Free: (888) 884-9154
E-Mail: techsupport@everfocus.com
Web Site: www.everfocus.com
Emp.: 45
Surveillance System Mfr
S.I.C.: 3679
N.A.I.C.S.: 334419
John Lee *(Chm)*
James Weng *(Pres)*

Non-U.S. Subsidiaries:

EverFocus Electronics AG (1)
Albert Einstein Street 1
46446 Emmerich am Rhein, Nordrhein-Westfalen, Germany
Tel.: (49) 282293940
Fax: (49) 2822939495
E-Mail: info@everfocus.de
Web Site: www.everfocus.de
Emp.: 21
Surveillance System Mfr
S.I.C.: 3812
N.A.I.C.S.: 334511
James Weng *(Chm)*
Dirk Reinders *(Mng Dir)*

EverFocus Electronics (Beijing) Co., Ltd. (1)
Room 609 Kemao Mansion Shangdi Xinxi Road
Haidian District, Beijing, 100085, China
Tel.: (86) 1062973336
Fax: (86) 1062971423
Electronic Products Mfr
S.I.C.: 3679
N.A.I.C.S.: 334419
Jiaming Huang *(Mgr-Taipei)*

Everfocus Electronics (India) Private Ltd. (1)
Suite 803 8th Floor Housefin Bhavan C 21
Bandra Kurla Complex
Bandra, Mumbai, 400 051, India
Tel.: (91) 2261288700
Fax: (91) 2261288705
E-Mail: sales@everfocus.in
Web Site: www.everfocus.in
Emp.: 12
Surveillance System Mfr
S.I.C.: 3812
N.A.I.C.S.: 334511
Vivek Rajpurkar *(CEO)*

Everfocus Electronics Ltd. (1)
Unit 12 Spitfire Business Park 1 Hawker Rd
Croydon, Surrey, CR0 4WD, United Kingdom
Tel.: (44) 2086499757
Fax: (44) 2086880603
E-Mail: uk.support@EverFocus.com
Web Site: www.uk.everfocus.com
Emp.: 8
Surveillance System Mfr
S.I.C.: 3669
N.A.I.C.S.: 334290
Basil Singh *(Gen Mgr)*

Subsidiary:

SCT-Security Consultancy & Technical Ltd. (2)
Unit 12 Spitfire Business Park Hawker Road
Croydon, Surrey, CR0 4WD, United Kingdom
Tel.: (44) 2086499757
Fax: (44) 20 8649 9907
E-Mail: sales@sctltd.co.uk
Web Site: www.sctltd.co.uk
Emp.: 7
Surveillance Systems Import & Distr
S.I.C.: 5065
N.A.I.C.S.: 423690

EverFocus Japan Corp. (1)
5F Kinshicho City Building 2-13-4 Koto-Bashi
Sumida-ku, Tokyo, 130-0022, Japan
Tel.: (81) 356258188
Fax: (81) 356258189
E-Mail: info@everfocus.co.jp
Web Site: www.everfocus.co.jp
Emp.: 8
Surveillance Equipment Mfr & Sales
S.I.C.: 3812
N.A.I.C.S.: 334511
John Lee *(Pres)*

EVERFRONT VENTURES CORP.

55 York Street Suite 403
Toronto, ON, M5J 1R7, Canada
Tel.: (416) 479-8623
Fax: (416) 361-6022
E-Mail: josh@everfrontcapital.com
Year Founded: 2011
EVC.P—(TSXV)
Business Description:
Investment Services
S.I.C.: 6211
N.A.I.C.S.: 523999
Personnel:
Joshua Gerstein *(Pres & CEO)*
Linda Dundas *(CFO & Sec)*
Board of Directors:
Linda Dundas
Eric Fredrickson
Joshua Gerstein
Leonidas Karabelas
Transfer Agent:
Equity Financial Trust Company
Toronto, ON, Canada

EVERGRANDE REAL ESTATE GROUP LIMITED

Evergrande Center No 78 Huangpu Avenue W
Tianhe, Guangzhou, 510060, China
Tel.: (86) 2088883333
Fax: (86) 2038302233
E-Mail: evergrandeir@evergrande.com
Web Site: www.evergrande.com
3333—(HKG)
Rev.: $10,366,684,116
Assets: $37,963,649,026
Liabilities: $31,340,982,050
Net Worth: $6,622,666,976
Earnings: $1,458,548,151
Emp.: 38,463
Fiscal Year-end: 12/31/12
Business Description:
Large-Scale Residential Property Developer
S.I.C.: 1522
N.A.I.C.S.: 236116
Personnel:
Ka Yan Hui *(Chm)*
Haijun Xia *(Vice Chm, Pres & CEO)*
Gang Li *(Vice Chm & Exec VP)*
Wai Wah Tse *(CFO & VP)*
Weiqiao Yu *(Chm-Guangdong & VP)*
Jimmy Kar Chun Fong *(Sec & VP)*
Board of Directors:
Ka Yan Hui
David Shing Yim Chau
Miaoling He
Qi He
Lixin Lai
Gang Li
Wai Wah Tse
Haijun Xia
Hongxi Xie
Wen Xu

EVERGREEN BAMBOO INTERNATIONAL LIMITED

1/F Winner Mansion 691A Nathan Road
Mong Kok, Kowloon, China (Hong Kong)
Tel.: (852) 35829570
E-Mail: info@evergreenbambooint l.com
Web Site: www.evergreenbambooint l.com
LBT—(DEU)
Business Description:
Nutraceutical Products Mfr
S.I.C.: 2833
N.A.I.C.S.: 325411
Personnel:
Hong Hua Liu *(Chm)*
Nixon Lau *(Pres & CEO)*
Shao Bing Liu *(CTO)*

EVERGREEN EQUIPMENT LTD.

Hwy 873 North of Brooks
Brooks, AB, T1R 1B7, Canada
Tel.: (403) 362-3486
Fax: (403) 362-4301
E-Mail: brooks@evergreenequipment.ca
Web Site: www.evergreenimplements.com
Rev.: $11,611,500
Emp.: 30
Business Description:
Miscellaneous Retail Stores
S.I.C.: 5999
N.A.I.C.S.: 453998
Personnel:

EVERGREEN FIBREBOARD BERHAD

PLO 22 Parit Raja Industrial Estate
86400 Parit Raja
80400 Batu Pahat, Johor, Malaysia
Tel.: (60) 74541933
Fax: (60) 74542933
E-Mail: efb@tm.net.my
Web Site: www.evergreengroup.com.my
EVERGRN—(KLS)
Rev.: $338,302,478
Assets: $445,043,026
Liabilities: $165,759,592
Net Worth: $279,283,435
Earnings: $8,382,808
Fiscal Year-end: 12/31/12
Business Description:
Wooden Furniture Mfr
S.I.C.: 2499
N.A.I.C.S.: 321999
Personnel:
Wen Chi Kuo *(Deputy Chm)*
Jen Chang Kuo *(CEO)*
Jen Chiu Kuo *(COO)*
Siew Foong Leong *(Sec)*
Board of Directors:
Jonathan Ngee Song Law
Izuan Kamarulbahrin
Jen Chang Kuo
Jen Chiu Kuo
Wen Chi Kuo
Mary Henerietta Kim Neo Lim
Kok Fong Yong
Legal Counsel:
Nik Saghir & Ismail
Aras G2 Mezzanine Floor Plaza Permata No 6
Jalan Kampar
Kuala Lumpur, Malaysia
Keah & Choo
No 29-13B Jalan Rahmat Batu Pahat
Johor, Malaysia
Subsidiaries:

Allgreen Timber Products Sdn. Bhd. (1)
Plot 202 Segamat Industrial Area II
85000 Segamat, Johor, Malaysia
Tel.: (60) 79279933
Fax: (60) 79270033
E-Mail: admin@agtb.com.my
Emp.: 200
Particleboard Mfr
S.I.C.: 3999
N.A.I.C.S.: 339999
Tan Meng How *(Mgr-Ops)*

Evergreen Adhesive & Chemicals Sdn. Bhd. (1)
Plot 22 Parit Raja Industrial Estate Parit Raja
86400 Batu Pahat, Johor, Malaysia
Tel.: (60) 74541933
Fax: (60) 74542933
Emp.: 15
Adhesives Mfr
S.I.C.: 2891
N.A.I.C.S.: 325520

Evergreen Fibreboard (JB) Sdn. Bhd. (1)
11 1/2 Miles Jalan Masai
58200 Masai, Johor, Malaysia
Tel.: (60) 73874980
Fax: (60) 73874995
E-Mail: efb@tm.net.my
Emp.: 240
Fibreboard Mfr
S.I.C.: 3999
N.A.I.C.S.: 339999
Zuhairi Ozir *(Mgr)*

Non-U.S. Subsidiaries:

PT Hijau Lestari Raya Fibreboard (1)
Desa Pematang Palas Kecamatan Banyuasin I
Palembang, South Sumatera, Indonesia
Tel.: (62) 711373459
Fax: (62) 711373473
E-Mail: pth@hijaulestari.co.id
Web Site: www.hijaulestari.co.id
Emp.: 200
Fibreboard Mfr
S.I.C.: 3999
N.A.I.C.S.: 339999
Christopher B. M. *(Mgr)*

Siam Fibreboard Company Limited (1)
417/112-113 Karnchanavanich Road
Amphur Haadyai, Songkhla, Tumbol Patong, 90230, Thailand
Tel.: (66) 74291111
Fax: (66) 743702534
E-Mail: office@siamfibreboard.com
Web Site: evergreengroup.com.my
Emp.: 600
Fibreboard Mfr
S.I.C.: 2653
N.A.I.C.S.: 322211
Jen Chang Kuo *(Chm)*
Heng Nang Chieng *(Deputy Mng Dir)*

EVERGREEN INTERNATIONAL HOLDINGS LIMITED

Room 1305-1307 13/F New East Ocean Centre 9 Science Museum Road
Tsim Sha Tsui East, Kowloon, China (Hong Kong)
Tel.: (852) 27122288
Fax: (852) 26718738
E-Mail: admin@evergreen-intl.com
Web Site: www.evergreen-intl.com
238—(HKG)
Rev.: $118,994,694
Assets: $273,953,981
Liabilities: $47,600,038
Net Worth: $226,353,943
Earnings: $24,661,780
Emp.: 1,239
Fiscal Year-end: 12/31/12
Business Description:
Menswear Clothing Stores
S.I.C.: 5611
N.A.I.C.S.: 448110
Personnel:
Yuk Ming Chan *(Chm)*
Kwong Yeung To *(CFO)*
Sau Ling Chan *(Sec)*
Board of Directors:
Yuk Ming Chan
Minwen Chen
Yunan Chen
Andrew King Hoi Cheng
Felix Wo Fong
Vincent Chi Sun Kwok
Appleby Trust (Cayman) Limited
Clifton House 75 Fort Street PO Box Box 1350
Georgetown, Cayman Islands

Transfer Agents:
Computershare Hong Kong Investor Services Limited
Shops 1712-1716 17th Floor Hopewell Centre
183 Queens Road East
Wanchai, China (Hong Kong)
Appleby Trust (Cayman) Limited
Clifton House 75 Fort Street PO Box Box 1350
Georgetown, Cayman Islands

EVERGREEN MARINE CORPORATION (TAIWAN) LTD.

166 Sec 2 Minsheng East Road
Taipei, 104, Taiwan
Tel.: (886) 225057766
Fax: (886) 225001090
E-Mail: cbdbcd@evergreen-marine.com
Web Site: www.evergreen-marine.com
Year Founded: 1968
2603—(TAI)
Rev.: $4,776,622,695
Assets: $5,259,937,773
Liabilities: $3,145,472,928
Net Worth: $2,114,464,845
Earnings: ($14,179,235)
Emp.: 4,966
Fiscal Year-end: 12/31/12

Business Description:
Container Shipping Services
S.I.C.: 4412
N.A.I.C.S.: 483111

Personnel:
Chung-Jinn Wang *(Chm)*

Board of Directors:
Chung-Jinn Wang
Cheng-Yung Chang
Yung-Fa Chang
Chih-Chien Hsieh
Long-Hwa Lin
Sun-San Lin
Jiin-Chyuan Tai

Supervisory Board of Directors:
Lee-Ching Ko
Mei-Hsueh Ku Lai

Subsidiaries:

EVA Airways Corporation (1)
376 sector 1 Hsien Nan Rd
Luchu, Taoyuan, Hsien, 330, Taiwan
Tel.: (886) 33515151
Fax: (886) 3510025
E-Mail: vickylien@evaair.com
Web Site: www.evaair.com
Emp.: 4,300
Air Transportation
S.I.C.: 4512
N.A.I.C.S.: 481111
Kung-Yeun Jeng *(Chm)*
Chang Kuo-Wei *(Pres)*
Cheng Chuan-Yi *(Exec VP-Project Div)*
Tsao Buo-Yen *(Exec VP-Engrg & Maintenance)*
Sun Chia-Ming *(Exec VP-Cargo Div)*
Ho Ching-Sheng *(Exec VP-Flight Safety Div)*
Fang Gwo-Shiang *(Exec VP-Computer Div)*
Yuen Ping-Yu *(Exec VP-Flight Ops Div)*
Li Shyn-Liang *(Exec VP-Passenger Div)*
Tsai Ta-Wei *(Exec VP-Fin Div)*
Chen Yeou-Yuh *(Exec VP-Ops Mgmt)*
Yang Yong-Heng *(Exec VP-Airport Div)*
Y.Y. Chen *(Sr VP)*
Yu Ching-Hsi *(Deputy Sr VP-Gen Affairs)*
Wu Chun-Hung *(Deputy Sr VP-Personnel Div)*
Yang Hsiu-Huey *(Deputy Sr VP-Svc Coordination Div)*
Chang Lih-Lih *(Sr VP-Cabin Svc Div)*
Li Ping-Yin *(Sr VP-Auditing Div)*
Liu Ying *(Sr VP-Cabin Crew Div)*

Subsidiary:

Evergreen Aviation Technologies Corp. (2)
6 Harng-Jann South Road
Tayuan, Taoyuan, Hsien 33758, Taiwan
Tel.: (886) 33519004
Fax: (886) 33931037
E-Mail: bowen.tsao@mail.egat.com.tw
Web Site: www.egat.com.tw
Emp.: 2,000
Aircraft Upgrade & Maintenance Services
S.I.C.: 7389
N.A.I.C.S.: 561990
Bowen Tsao *(Sr VP)*

Taiwan Terminal Service Corporation Ltd. (1)
10 Chi Chin 1st Road
Kaohsiung, Taiwan
Tel.: (886) 75718963
Fax: (886) 75718954
E-Mail: ttsscsup@taiwan-terminal.com
Marine Shipping Services
S.I.C.: 4499
N.A.I.C.S.: 488330
Ta Wei Chiang *(Mgr)*

U.S. Subsidiary:

Hemlock Equipment LLC (1)
Pierce County Terminal
Tacoma, WA 98421
Tel.: (253) 896-0189
Construction Equipments Rental Services
S.I.C.: 1799
N.A.I.C.S.: 238910

Non-U.S. Subsidiaries:

Evergreen Agency (South Africa) (PTY) Ltd. (1)
No 9B Riley Road
Bedfordview, 2008 Johannesburg, Guateng, South Africa
Tel.: (27) 112849000
Fax: (27) 112849010
E-Mail: bizjnb@evergreen-shipping.co.za
Web Site: www.evergreen-shipping.co.za
Emp.: 50
Marine Shipping Services
S.I.C.: 4412
N.A.I.C.S.: 483111
Raj Bunsee *(Mng Dir)*

Evergreen Heavy Industrial Corp (M) Berhad (1)
Lot 139 Jalan Ceasir Phase 2 Free Trade Zone Johor Port Authority
81700 Pasir Gudang, Johor, Malaysia
Tel.: (60) 72510432
Fax: (60) 72510433
E-Mail: janlis@evergreen-heavy.com.my
Web Site: www.evergreen-heavy.com.my
Emp.: 400
Cargo Containers Mfr
S.I.C.: 3999
N.A.I.C.S.: 339999
Chu Wang June *(Mng Dir)*

Evergreen Shipping Agency (UK) Limited (1)
Evergreen House 160 Euston Road
London, NW1 2DX, United Kingdom
Tel.: (44) 2075598241
Fax: (44) 2075598406
E-Mail: ibdbcd@uk.evergreen-line.com
Emp.: 100
Marine Shipping Services
S.I.C.: 4412
N.A.I.C.S.: 483111
Raymond Lin *(Mng Dir)*

Evergreen Shipping Agency (Australia) Pty. Ltd. (1)
Level 13 181 Miller Street
North Sydney, Sydney, NSW, 2060, Australia
Tel.: (61) 299365700
Fax: (61) 299365710
E-Mail: sydemcbiz@evergreen-shipping.com.au
Web Site: www.evergreen-line.com
Emp.: 20
Marine Shipping Services
S.I.C.: 4412
N.A.I.C.S.: 483111
Alex Kotnoa *(Mgr)*

Evergreen Shipping Agency (Deutschland) GmbH (1)
Amsinckstr 55
20097 Hamburg, Germany
Tel.: (49) 40237080
Fax: (49) 40234875
E-Mail: hpg@evergreen-shipping.de
Web Site: www.evergreen-shipping.de
Emp.: 130
Marine Shipping Services
S.I.C.: 4412
N.A.I.C.S.: 483111
Roger Huang *(Mng Dir)*

Evergreen Shipping Agency France S.A. (1)
Tour Franklin La Defense 8
La Defense, 92042 Paris, France
Tel.: (33) 158580222
Fax: (33) 158580220
E-Mail: biz@evergreen-shipping.com.fr
Web Site: www.evergreen-line.com
Emp.: 90
Marine Shipping Services
S.I.C.: 4412
N.A.I.C.S.: 483111
Martine Toulet *(Mng Dir)*

Evergreen Shipping Agency (Ireland) Ltd. (1)
22 Fitzwilliam Place 2
Dublin, Leinster, 2, Ireland
Tel.: (353) 16612095
Fax: (353) 16612110
E-Mail: dbl@evergreen-shipping.co.uk
Web Site: www.evergreen-line.com
Emp.: 12
Marine Shipping Services
S.I.C.: 4412
N.A.I.C.S.: 483111
Alex Quo *(Gen Mgr)*

Evergreen Shipping Agency (Italy) S.p.A. (1)
Scali Cerere 9
Livorno, 57122, Italy
Tel.: (39) 586413111
Fax: (39) 0586413112
E-Mail: biz@evergreen-shipping.it
Web Site: www.evergreen-shipping.it
Emp.: 60
Marine Shipping Services
S.I.C.: 4499
N.A.I.C.S.: 488330
Antonio Maneschil *(Chm)*

Evergreen Shipping Agency (Netherlands) B.V. (1)
Portcity II - Havennummer 2235 Waalhaven zz 19
3089 JH Rotterdam, South Holland, Netherlands
Tel.: (31) 102311000
Fax: (31) 104383049
E-Mail: egn@evergreen-shipping.nl
Web Site: www.evergreen-shipping.nl
Emp.: 120
Marine Shipping Services
S.I.C.: 4412
N.A.I.C.S.: 483111
P. Lugtigheid *(Mgr-DP)*

Evergreen Shipping Agency (Poland) SP. ZO. O (1)
Ul Solec 22
00-382 Warsaw, Poland
Tel.: (48) 225222286
Fax: (48) 225222291
E-Mail: wwx@evergreen-shipping.pl
Web Site: www.shipmentlink.com
Emp.: 10
Marine Shipping Services
S.I.C.: 4412
N.A.I.C.S.: 483111
Robert Kacprzak *(Mgr)*

Evergreen Shipping Agency (Singapore) PTE. Ltd. (1)
200 Cantonment Rd Level 12-02 Southpoint
Singapore, 089763, Singapore
Tel.: (65) 63477320
Fax: (65) 62273045
E-Mail: hr@evergreen-shipping.com.sg
Web Site: www.evergreen-shipping.com.sg
Emp.: 100
Marine Shipping Services
S.I.C.: 4499
N.A.I.C.S.: 488330
Patrick Ang *(Mng Dir)*
Patrick Phoon *(Deputy Mng Dir)*

Evergreen Shipping Agency (Thailand) Co., Ltd. (1)
3656/81 24-25th Floor Green Tower Rama IV Road Klongtoey
Bangkok, 10110, Thailand
Tel.: (66) 22299999
Fax: (66) 2 3673556
E-Mail: biz@evergreen-shipping.co.th
Web Site: www.evergreen-shipping.co.th
Marine Shipping Services
S.I.C.: 4731
N.A.I.C.S.: 488510
Nivat Changariyavong *(Mng Dir)*

Evergreen Shipping Agency (Vietnam) Corp. (1)
11 Fl Fideco Tower No 81-85 Ham Nghi Street
Nguyen Thai Binh Ward Dist 1, Ho Chi Minh City, Vietnam
Tel.: (84) 839111023
Fax: (84) 8 39111012
E-Mail: egv@evergreen-shipping.com.vn
Marine Shipping Services
S.I.C.: 4412
N.A.I.C.S.: 483111
Pham van Thuan *(Chm)*

Evergreen Shipping (Spain) S.L. (1)
Calle Siete Aguas 11 Entlo
46023 Valencia, Spain
Tel.: (34) 960451280
Fax: (34) 960451373
E-Mail: biz@evergreen-shipping.es
Web Site: www.shipmentlink.com
Emp.: 50
Marine Shipping Servicesd
S.I.C.: 4412
N.A.I.C.S.: 483111
Albert Ko *(Mgr)*

P.T. Evergreen Shipping Agency Indonesia (1)
Mega Plaza Building 9th Floor Jl H R Rasuna Kav C 3
Jakarta, Indonesia
Tel.: (62) 215212310
Fax: (62) 215212890
E-Mail: dktbizias@evergreen-shipping.co.id
Web Site: www.evergreen-line.com
Emp.: 35
Marine Shipping Services
S.I.C.: 4499
N.A.I.C.S.: 488330
Terrence Wu *(VP)*

P.T. Multi Bina Pura International (1)
Jl Raya Cakung Cilincing Km 4 Jakarta Utara
Jakarta, 14260, Indonesia
Tel.: (62) 214406403
Fax: (62) 21 4406268
E-Mail: tmncys@mbpi.co.id
Web Site: www.mbpi.co.id
Warehousing & Freight Forwarding Services
S.I.C.: 4731
N.A.I.C.S.: 488510

P.T. Multi Bina Transport (1)
Jl Raya Cakung Cilincing Km 4 Jakarta Utara
Jakarta, 14260, Indonesia
Tel.: (62) 214406405
Fax: (62) 214406268
Freight Forwarding Services
S.I.C.: 4731
N.A.I.C.S.: 488510

Shenzhen Greentrans Transportation Co., Ltd. (1)
Sanjiaolong Warehouse & Storage Zone Fukang Road
Henggang Town, Shenzhen, Guangdong, 518115, China
Tel.: (86) 75528863245
Fax: (86) 755 2886 2974
E-Mail: szyrys@public.szptt.net.cn
Freight Forwarding Services
S.I.C.: 4731
N.A.I.C.S.: 488510

EVERLIGHT ELECTRONICS CO., LTD.

No 25 Ln 76 Sec 3 Chung Yang Rd
236 Tucheng, Taipei, Taiwan
Tel.: (886) 222672000
Fax: (886) 222676244
E-Mail: fn@everlight.com
Web Site: www.everlight.com
2393—(TAI)
Sales Range: $550-599.9 Million
Emp.: 8,225

Everlight Electronics Co., Ltd.—(Continued)

Business Description:
Electronic Products Mfr
S.I.C.: 3674
N.A.I.C.S.: 334413
Personnel:
Robert Yeh *(CEO)*

U.S. Subsidiary:

Everlight Americas, Inc. **(1)**
3220 Commander Dr Ste 100
Carrollton, TX 75006
Tel.: (972) 490-4008
Fax: (972) 490-5009
E-Mail: salesmarketing@everlightamericas.com
Web Site: www.everlight.com
Emp.: 20
Lighting Fixtures Distr
S.I.C.: 5063
N.A.I.C.S.: 423610
Robert Yeh *(CEO)*

Non-U.S. Subsidiary:

Everlight Canada, Inc. **(2)**
1011 Upper Middle Road
PO Box 86056
Oakville, ON, L7L 6A3, Canada
Tel.: (905) 315-5050
Fax: (905) 336-0040
E-Mail: everlightcanada@everlight.com
Lighting Fixtures Distr
S.I.C.: 5063
N.A.I.C.S.: 423610

Non-U.S. Subsidiaries:

E&E Components (HK) Limited **(1)**
Unit 613-613A 6F Ocean Centre 5 Canton Road
Tsim Tsa Tsui, Kowloon, China (Hong Kong)
Tel.: (852) 31889701
Fax: (852) 3 188 9704
E-Mail: eehk@eehk.com.hk
Web Site: www.everlight.com
Light Emitting Diodes Distr
S.I.C.: 5065
N.A.I.C.S.: 423690
Jeremy Kwan-Mo Ho *(Mgr-Sls)*

Everlight Electronics (China) Co., Ltd. **(1)**
Binhe Road 1388 X2 Creative Block 3A-608
Suzhou, Jiangsu, 215011, China
Tel.: (86) 51268631358
Fax: (86) 512 6802 1303
Electronic Components Distr
S.I.C.: 5946
N.A.I.C.S.: 443142

Everlight Electronics (Europe) GmbH **(1)**
Siemensallee No 84 Building No 7302 5th Floor
76187 Karlsruhe, Baden-Wurttemberg, Germany
Tel.: (49) 721824473
Fax: (49) 7218244740
E-Mail: info@everlight-eu.de
Web Site: www.everlight.com
Emp.: 20
Electronic Components Distr
S.I.C.: 5946
N.A.I.C.S.: 443142
Bernd Kammerer *(Gen Mgr)*

Everlight Electronics (Suzhou) Ltd. **(1)**
Binhe Rd 1388 X2 Creative Block A-608
Suzhou, Jiangsu, China
Tel.: (86) 51268021303
Fax: (86) 51268021302
Light Emitting Diode Displays Mfr
S.I.C.: 3679
N.A.I.C.S.: 334419
Kevin Li *(Mgr)*

Everlight Optoelectronics (M) Sdn Bhd **(1)**
B 04-20 Krystal Point 303 Jalan Sultan Azlan Shah
11900 Bayan Lepas, Penang, Malaysia
Tel.: (60) 46464233
Fax: (60) 6046465233
E-Mail: inquiry@everlight-pg.com.my
Web Site: www.everlight.com
Emp.: 2
Electronic Components Distr
S.I.C.: 5946
N.A.I.C.S.: 443142

Evlite Electronics Co., Ltd. **(1)**
Unit 1606-08 16F Prosperity Place 6 Shing Yip Street
Kwun Tong, Kowloon, China (Hong Kong)
Tel.: (852) 23880602
Fax: (852) 23881127
E-Mail: hkcm@everlight.com
Web Site: www.everlight.com
Emp.: 50
Light Emitting Diode Components Distr
S.I.C.: 5065
N.A.I.C.S.: 423690
Kevin Tse *(Mgr-Sls)*

Guangzhou Yi-Liang Trading Co., Ltd. **(1)**
No 708 No 88 LiWan North Road
Guangzhou, Guangdong, China
Tel.: (86) 2081947439
Electronic Components Distr
S.I.C.: 5065
N.A.I.C.S.: 423690

Yi-Liang International Trade (Shanghai) Ltd. **(1)**
Rm 3F-A1 No 825 Zhao Jiao Babg Rd
Shanghai, 200030, China
Tel.: (86) 2164036237
E-Mail: xnw@sohu.com
Electronic Components Distr
S.I.C.: 5065
N.A.I.C.S.: 423690
William Shu *(Gen Mgr)*

Zenaro Lighting GmbH **(1)**
Carl-Friedrich-Gauss-Str 64
47475 Kamp-Lintfort, Nordrhein-Westfalen, Germany
Tel.: (49) 2842908110
Fax: (49) 28 4290 811 100
E-Mail: info@zenarolighting.com
Web Site: www.zenarolighting.com
Lighting Fixtures Mfr & Distr
S.I.C.: 3645
N.A.I.C.S.: 335121
Bernd Kammerer *(Mgr)*

EVERLON SYNTHETICS LTD.

67 Regent Chambers Nariman Point
Mumbai, 400 021, India
Tel.: (91) 2222049233
Fax: (91) 2222870540
E-Mail: info@everlon.in
Web Site: www.everlon.in
514358—(BOM)
Rev.: $8,917,313
Assets: $1,920,818
Liabilities: $1,603,313
Net Worth: $317,506
Earnings: $34,643
Emp.: 21
Fiscal Year-end: 03/31/13
Business Description:
Textile Products Mfr
S.I.C.: 2269
N.A.I.C.S.: 313310
Personnel:
Jitendra K. Vakharia *(Mng Dir)*
Board of Directors:
Kamlesh C. Sanghavi
Dinesh P. Turakhia
Jitendra K. Vakharia
Varsha J. Vakharia
Transfer Agent:
Sharex Dynamic (India) Pvt. Ltd.
Unit-1 Luthra Ind Premises Safed Pool Andheri Kurla Rd Andheri (E)
Mumbai, India

EVERMASTER GROUP BERHAD

Ste 11 05B Level 11 The Gardens S Tower
Mid Valley City Lingkaran Syed Putra
59200 Kuala Lumpur, Malaysia
Tel.: (60) 322793080
Fax: (60) 322793090
E-Mail: evermas@po.jaring.my
Web Site: www.evermaster.com.my
EVERMAS—(KLS)
Sales Range: $10-24.9 Million
Business Description:
Timber Plywood Mfr
S.I.C.: 2439
N.A.I.C.S.: 321213
Personnel:
Piak How Lim *(Chm)*
Ching Chi Tsai *(Mng Dir)*
Voon Wah Chong *(Co-Sec)*
Tong Lang Tan *(Co-Sec)*
Board of Directors:
Piak How Lim
Hin Fatt Lai
Hou Loo Thong
Ching Chi Tsai

EVERMORE CHEMICAL INDUSTRY CO., LTD.

7 Industrial S 2nd Rd Nangang
Industiral Park
Nant'ou, Taiwan
Tel.: (886) 492255356
Fax: (886) 492255358
E-Mail: cannie@twemc.com.tw
Web Site: www.twemc.com
1735—(TAI)
Sales Range: $75-99.9 Million
Business Description:
Coagulated Polyurethane Resins Mfr
S.I.C.: 2821
N.A.I.C.S.: 325211
Personnel:
Wen-Chieh Ho *(Chm)*

EVERONN EDUCATION LIMITED

Everonn House Plot 96-99 Industrial Estate Perungudi
Chennai, Tamil Nadu, 600096, India
Tel.: (91) 4442968400
Fax: (91) 4424962800
E-Mail: everonn@everonn.com
Web Site: www.everonn.com
532876—(BOM NSE)
Rev.: $23,108,126
Assets: $200,062,359
Liabilities: $151,746,396
Net Worth: $48,315,963
Earnings: ($60,830,426)
Fiscal Year-end: 03/31/13
Business Description:
Education & Training Services
S.I.C.: 8299
N.A.I.C.S.: 611710
Personnel:
Susha John *(Founder)*
A. Srinivasan *(Mng Dir)*
Ganapathy H. Puranik *(CFO)*
N. P. Mathi Lingan *(Compliance Officer & Sec)*
Board of Directors:
Lakdawala Turab Mohd Hussein
C. N. Radhakrishnan
Natarajan Ranganathan
A. Srinivasan
Dino Sunny Varkey
Transfer Agent:
Cameo Corporate Services Limited
Subramanian Bldg No 1 Club House Road
Chennai, 600 002, India
Tel.: (91) 44 2846 0390
Fax: (91) 44 2846 0129

EVERPIA VIETNAM JOINT STOCK COMPANY

Duong xa
Gia lam District, Hanoi, Vietnam
Tel.: (84) 4 3827 6490
Fax: (84) 4 3 827 6492
E-Mail: info@everpia.vn
Web Site: www.everpia.vn
Year Founded: 1993
EVE—(HOSE)
Sales Range: $25-49.9 Million
Emp.: 1,138
Business Description:
Bedding & Padding Services
S.I.C.: 7389
N.A.I.C.S.: 561990
Personnel:
Jae Eun Lee *(Chm & CEO)*
Jean-Charles Belliol *(Member-Mgmt Bd)*
Thi Thu Hien Le *(Member-Mgmt Bd)*
Phuong Chi Ngo *(Member-Mgmt Bd)*
Board of Directors:
Jae Eun Lee
Jean-Charles Belliol
Yong Hwan Cho
Thi Thu Hien Le
Je Won Lee
Phuong Chi Ngo
Soon O. Park
Nguyen Van Dao

EVERSENDAI CORPORATION BERHAD

Lot 19956 Jalan Industri 3/6 Rawang Integrated Indusl Park
Kuala Selangor, 48000, Malaysia
Tel.: (60) 3 6091 2575
Fax: (60) 3 6091 2577
E-Mail: eversendai@eversendai.com
Web Site: www.eversendai.com
SENDAI—(KLS)
Rev.: $334,889,284
Assets: $486,005,969
Liabilities: $227,249,544
Net Worth: $258,756,425
Earnings: $39,840,968
Emp.: 10,026
Fiscal Year-end: 12/31/12
Business Description:
Structural Steel Construction & Engineering Services
S.I.C.: 1791
N.A.I.C.S.: 238120
Personnel:
A. K. Nathan *(Chm & Mng Dir)*
Fook Kwong Chan *(CFO)*
Nadarajan Rohan Raj *(COO)*
Kim Chee Cheok *(Co-Sec)*
Pramila Kaur *(Co-Sec)*
Board of Directors:
A. K. Nathan
Mohammad Nizar Idris
Rastam Mohd Isa
Sunthara Moorthy
Narish Nathan
Seing Liong Ng
Nadarajan Rohan Raj
Narla Srinivasa Rao

EVERSTONE CAPITAL ADVISORS PVT. LTD.

One Indiabulls Centre 16th Floor
Tower 2A Senapati Bapat Marg
Elphinstone Road, Mumbai, 400013, India
Tel.: (91) 22 4043 6000
Web Site: www.everstonecapital.com
Year Founded: 2006
Managed Assets: $1,800,000,000
Emp.: 100
Business Description:
Private Equity Firm
S.I.C.: 6211
N.A.I.C.S.: 523999
Personnel:
Atul Kapur *(Co-Founder & Mng Partner)*
Sameer Sain *(Co-Founder & Mng Partner)*
Dhanpal Jhaveri *(Partner & CEO)*
Rajesh Jaggi *(Mng Partner-Real Estate)*
Brian Oravec *(Partner)*

Non-U.S. Subsidiaries:

Everstone Capital Asia Pte. Ltd. **(1)**
250 North Bridge Road
12-03 Raffles City Tower, Singapore, 179101, Singapore SG
Tel.: (65) 6511 6888
Web Site: www.everstonecapital.com
Private Equity Firm
S.I.C.: 6211
N.A.I.C.S.: 523999
Atul Kapur *(Co-Founder & Mng Partner)*
Sameer Sain *(Co-Founder & Mng Partner)*

Everstone Capital Limited **(1)**
3rd Floor Raffles Tower 19 Cybercity
Ebene, Mauritius MU
Tel.: (230) 467 7986
Web Site: www.everstonecapital.com
Private Equity Firm
S.I.C.: 6211
N.A.I.C.S.: 523999

Non-U.S. Holding:

Harry's Holdings Ltd. **(1)**
77 High Street 07-09/11 High Street Plaza
Singapore, 179433, Singapore
Tel.: (65) 63370657
Fax: (65) 63349832
E-Mail: marketing@harrys.com.sg
Web Site: www.harrys.com.sg
Sales Range: $25-49.9 Million
Bars, Restaurants, Night Clubs, Children's Play Centers, Hotel & Catering
S.I.C.: 5813
N.A.I.C.S.: 722410
Mohan Mulani *(Chm)*
Ai Ling Chang *(Sec)*

Subsidiaries:

Harry s Esplanade Pte. Ltd. **(2)**
8 Raffles Ave
01-05 07 Esplanade Mal, Singapore, 179433, Singapore
Tel.: (65) 6334 0132
Restaurant Operation Services
S.I.C.: 5812
N.A.I.C.S.: 722511

Harry s International Pte. Ltd **(2)**
77 High Street 07-09/11
High Street Plaza, Singapore, 179433, Singapore
Tel.: (65) 6337 0657
Fax: (65) 63349832
E-Mail: hr@harrys.com.sg
Web Site: www.harrys.com.sg
Emp.: 40
Restaurant Operation Services
S.I.C.: 5812
N.A.I.C.S.: 722511
Philip Walters *(CEO)*

EVERTECHNO CO., LTD.

139-1 Sandong-ri Eumbong-myun
Asan, Chungcheongnam-do, Korea (South)
Tel.: (82) 41 580 6600
Fax: (82) 41 580 6616
Web Site: www.evertechno.co.kr
Year Founded: 2000
070480—(KRS)
Sales Range: $200-249.9 Million
Business Description:
Electronic Component Mfr
S.I.C.: 3679
N.A.I.C.S.: 334419
Personnel:
Back-Woon Jung *(CEO)*

EVERTON RESOURCES INC.

205 2742 St Joseph Boulevard
Orleans, ON, K1C 1G5, Canada
Tel.: (613) 241-2332
Fax: (613) 834-8166
Toll Free: (800) 778-0263
E-Mail: andre@evertonresources.com
Web Site: www.evertonresources.com
EVR—(OTC TSXV)
Rev.: $8,182
Assets: $23,775,501
Liabilities: $583,468
Net Worth: $23,192,033
Earnings: ($5,662,127)
Fiscal Year-end: 10/31/12
Business Description:
Gold & Other Metal Mining Services
S.I.C.: 1041
N.A.I.C.S.: 212221
Personnel:
Andre D. Audet *(Chm, Pres & CEO)*
Board of Directors:
Andre D. Audet
Salvador Brouwer
Daniel F. Hachey
Hugh Brooke Macdonald
David W. Massola
Steven M. Mintz
John Hamilton Paterson
Keith J. Stein
Transfer Agent:
Computershare Trust Company of Canada
1500 University St 7th Floor
Montreal, QC, Canada

EVERTOP WIRE CABLE CORPORATION

No 1 Ln 91 Ren-Ai Rd Sec 2
Taipei, Taiwan
Tel.: (886) 223218855
Fax: (886) 223213236
Web Site: www.evertop.com
1616—(TAI)
Sales Range: $50-74.9 Million
Business Description:
Electronic Wire & Power Cords Mfr
S.I.C.: 3496
N.A.I.C.S.: 332618
Personnel:
Michael M. C. Chang *(Chm)*
Robert Hung *(Mng Dir)*

Plant:

Evertop Wire Cable Corporation - Chungli Plant **(1)**
No 32 Lane 363 Chung Cheng Rd Section 2
Chung-li, Taoyuan, 320, Taiwan
Tel.: (886) 34253111
Fax: (886) 34221991
E-Mail: sales1@evertop.com
Web Site: www.evertop.com
Emp.: 118
Cables & Power Cords Mfr
S.I.C.: 3351
N.A.I.C.S.: 331420

EVERTRADE (PTY) LTD.

2nd Floor Eurocentre South 363 Rivonia Road
Johannesburg, 2191, South Africa
Tel.: (27) 11 807 5345
Business Description:
Home Furnishings & Kitchenware Whslr & Distr
S.I.C.: 5023
N.A.I.C.S.: 423220

Subsidiary:

Goldenmarc (Pty) Ltd. **(1)**
Stand No 13 & 14 Angus Crescent
Longmeadow East, Edenvale, 1644, South Africa ZA
Tel.: (27) 118423800
Fax: (27) 118423801
E-Mail: info@sale.co.za
Emp.: 90
Home Textiles & Party Products Distr
S.I.C.: 5023
N.A.I.C.S.: 423220
Walter Fillinger *(Gen Mgr)*

EVERTZ MICROSYSTEMS LTD.

5292 John Lucas Dr
Burlington, ON, L7L 5Z9, Canada
Tel.: (905) 335-3700
Fax: (905) 335-0909
Toll Free: (877) 995-3700
Web Site: www.evertz.com
Sales Range: $250-299.9 Million
Emp.: 800
Business Description:
Motion Picture Editing & Projection Hardware
S.I.C.: 3651
N.A.I.C.S.: 334310
Personnel:
Romolo Magarelli *(CEO)*

EVERYMAN MEDIA GROUP PLC

5 Holly Bush Vale
Hempstead, London, NW3 6TX, United Kingdom
Tel.: (44) 203 145 0500
Web Site: www.everymancinema.com
EMAN—(AIM)
Sales Range: $10-24.9 Million
Emp.: 180
Business Description:
Movie Theater Owner & Operator
S.I.C.: 7832
N.A.I.C.S.: 512131
Personnel:
Paul Wise *(Chm)*
Andrew Myers *(CEO)*
Board of Directors:
Paul Wise
Charles Dorfman
Philip Jacobson
Adam Kaye
Andrew Myers
Michael Rosehill

EVERYMATRIX LTD.

Vincenti Buildings Suite 712 14/19 Strait Street
Valletta, VLT 1432, Malta
Tel.: (356) 2557 2424
Fax: (356) 2557 2474
E-Mail: info@everymatrix.com
Web Site: www.everymatrix.com
Year Founded: 2008
Emp.: 70
Business Description:
Gaming Industry Software Publisher & Content Hosting Services
S.I.C.: 7372
N.A.I.C.S.: 511210
Personnel:
Stian Hornsletten *(Co-Owner & Chm)*
Ebbe Groes *(Co-Owner & CEO)*

EVERYTHING FOR A DOLLAR STORE (CANADA), INC.

600 Alden Road Suite 305
Markham, ON, L3R 0E7, Canada
Tel.: (905) 513-6744
Fax: (905) 513-6746
Rev.: $31,600,800
Emp.: 300
Business Description:
Retail Stores
S.I.C.: 5399
N.A.I.C.S.: 452990
Personnel:
Mohammed Q. Choksi *(Pres)*

EVIIVO LTD.

Commercial House Commercial Street
Sheffield, S1 2AT, United Kingdom
Tel.: (44) 20 8576 5600
Fax: (44) 20 8576 5601
E-Mail: info@eviivo.com
Web Site: www.eviivo.com
Year Founded: 2004
Sales Range: $10-24.9 Million
Emp.: 80
Business Description:
Hospitality Industry Software Developer
S.I.C.: 7372
N.A.I.C.S.: 511210
Personnel:
Michele Fitzpatrick *(CEO)*

EVINIX ACCESSORIES LTD.

KH43 Sector 45 Mewla Maharajpur
Faridabad, Haryana, 121003, India
Tel.: (91) 129 2439654
Fax: (91) 129 2437582
E-Mail: evinix@evinix.in
Web Site: www.evinix.in
532818—(BOM)
Sales Range: $25-49.9 Million
Business Description:
Fashion Accessories & Garment Mfr
S.I.C.: 7389
N.A.I.C.S.: 541490
Personnel:
Raujeev Taneja *(Mng Dir)*
Arun K. Goela *(CFO)*
Board of Directors:
Rajeev Aggarwal
A. K. Doshi
K. M. Gupta
Sanjay Kumar Jain
Deepak Malhotra
Raujeev Taneja

EVN AG

EVN Platz
A-2344 Maria Enzersdorf, Austria
Tel.: (43) 22362000
Fax: (43) 22362002030
E-Mail: info@evn.at
Web Site: www.evn.at
EVN—(EUR)
Rev.: $3,783,854,750
Assets: $9,754,379,245
Liabilities: $5,542,694,820
Net Worth: $4,211,684,425
Earnings: $217,279,790
Emp.: 7,497
Fiscal Year-end: 09/30/13
Business Description:
Electricity, Natural Gas, Heat, Water & Related Services Distr
S.I.C.: 4911
N.A.I.C.S.: 221122
Personnel:
Burkhard Hofer *(Chm-Supervisory Bd)*
Stefan Schenker *(Vice Chm-Supervisory Bd)*
Willi Stiowicek *(Vice Chm-Supervisory Bd)*
Peter Layr *(Member-Exec Bd)*
Stefan Szyszkowitz *(Member-Exec Bd)*
Supervisory Board of Directors:
Burkhard Hofer
Monika Fraissl
Norbert Griesmayr
Franz Hemm
Paul Hofer
Thomas Kusterer
Dieter Lutz
Otto Mayer
Reinhard Meissl
Bernhard Muller
Edwin Rambossek
Stefan Schenker
Willi Stiowicek
Angela Stransky
Manfred Weinrichter

Subsidiaries:

Allplan GmbH **(1)**
Schwindgasse 10
1040 Vienna, Austria (50%)
Tel.: (43) 1505370794

EVN AG—(Continued)

Fax: (43) 1505370727
E-Mail: wien@allplan.at
Web Site: www.allplan.at
Emp.: 45
Engineering Services
S.I.C.: 8711
N.A.I.C.S.: 541330
Klaus Reisinger *(Mng Dir)*

AVN Abfallverwertung Niederosterreich GmbH (1)
Evn Platz
2345 Enzersdorf, Niederosterreich, Austria (100%)
Tel.: (43) 22362000
Fax: (43) 22362002030
E-Mail: info@evn.at
Web Site: www.evn-abfallverwertung.at/en/kontakt/anfahrtdirektion.asp
Emp.: 600
Solid Waste Combustors & Incinerators
S.I.C.: 4953
N.A.I.C.S.: 562213
Burkhard Hofer *(CEO)*

EVN Business Service GmbH (1)
Evn Platz
2344 Maria Enzersdorf, Niederosterreich, Austria (100%)
Tel.: (43) 22362000
Fax: (43) 22362002030
E-Mail: info@evn.at
Web Site: www.evn.at/SpecialPages/Kontakt.aspx
Restaurant
S.I.C.: 5812
N.A.I.C.S.: 722511

EVN Energievertrieb GmbH & Co Kg (1)
Evn Platz
2344 Maria Enzersdorf, Niederosterreich, Austria (100%)
Tel.: (43) 22362000
Fax: (43) 22362002030
E-Mail: info@evn.at
Web Site: www.evn.at/SpecialPages/Kontakt.aspx
Emp.: 5,000
Electrical Apparatus & Equipment Wiring Supplies & Related Equipment Merchant Whslr
S.I.C.: 5063
N.A.I.C.S.: 423610
Burkhart Hoser *(Mng Dir)*

EVN Finanzservice GmbH (1)
Maria Evn Platz
2344 Enzersdorf, Niederosterreich, Austria (100%)
Tel.: (43) 22362000
Fax: (43) 22362002030
E-Mail: info@evn.at
Emp.: 2,500
Holding Company
S.I.C.: 6719
N.A.I.C.S.: 551112
Burkhart Hofer *(Gen Mgr)*

EVN Geoinfo GmbH (1)
EVN Platz
2344 Maria Enzersdorf, Austria
Tel.: (43) 2236 47079 0
Fax: (43) 2236 47079 14815
E-Mail: office@evn-geoinfo.at
Emp.: 40
Geographic Information Services
S.I.C.: 7389
N.A.I.C.S.: 519190

EVN Kraftwerks- und Beteiligungsgesellschaft mbH (1)
EVN Platz
2344 Maria Enzersdorf, Austria
Tel.: (43) 2236 200 0
Fax: (43) 2236 200 2030
Emp.: 3,000
Electric Power Generation Services
S.I.C.: 4911
N.A.I.C.S.: 221118
Peter Layr *(Gen Mgr)*

evn naturkraft Beteiligungs- und Betriebs-GmbH (1)
EVN Platz
2344 Maria Enzersdorf, Austria
Tel.: (43) 2236 200 0
Fax: (43) 2236 200 2030
Emp.: 5
Electric Power Generation Services
S.I.C.: 4939
N.A.I.C.S.: 221118

evn naturkraft Erzeugungsgesellschaft m.b.H. (1)
EVN Platz
2344 Maria Enzersdorf, Austria
Tel.: (43) 2236 200 0
Fax: (43) 2236 200 2030
E-Mail: info@evn.at
Web Site: www.evn.at
Emp.: 60
Hydroelectric Power Generation Services
S.I.C.: 4931
N.A.I.C.S.: 221111
Jose Galamba *(Gen Mgr)*

EVN Netz GmbH (1)
Evn Platz
2344 Enzersdorf, Niederosterreich, Austria (100%)
Tel.: (43) 22362000
Fax: (43) 22362002030
E-Mail: info@evn-netz.at
Web Site: www.evn-netz.at
Emp.: 2,500
Electrical Apparatus & Equipment Wiring Supplies & Related Equipment Merchant Whslr
S.I.C.: 5063
N.A.I.C.S.: 423610

EVN Projektmanagement GmbH (1)
EVN Platz
2344 Maria Enzersdorf, Austria
Tel.: (43) 22362000
Fax: (43) 2236 200 2030
Electric Power Generation Services
S.I.C.: 4931
N.A.I.C.S.: 221118

EVN Umweltholding Und Betriebs-GmbH (1)
Evn Platz
2344 Enzersdorf, Niederosterreich, Austria (100%)
Tel.: (43) 22362000
Fax: (43) 22362002030
E-Mail: info@evn.at
Web Site: www.evn.at
Emp.: 90
Marketing Consulting Services
S.I.C.: 8742
N.A.I.C.S.: 541613
Stefan Szyszkowitz *(Mng Dir)*

Subsidiaries:

EVN Projektgesellschaft Mullverbrennungsanlage Nr. 3 mbH (2)
EVN Platz
2344 Maria Enzersdorf, Austria
Tel.: (43) 2236 200 0
Fax: (43) 2236 2002030
E-Mail: info@evn.at
Web Site: www.evn.at/
Electric Power Transmission Services
S.I.C.: 4939
N.A.I.C.S.: 221121

EVN Umwelt Beteiligungs und Service GmbH (2)
EVN Platz
23443 Maria Enzersdorf, Austria
Tel.: (43) 2236 200 0
Fax: (43) 2236 200 2030
E-Mail: info@evn.at
Web Site: www.evn.at
Emp.: 300
Environmental Consulting Services
S.I.C.: 8999
N.A.I.C.S.: 541620
Uno Makotsvana *(Mng Dir)*

EVN Umwelt Finanz- und Service-GmbH (2)
EVN Platz
2344 Maria Enzersdorf, Austria
Tel.: (43) 2236 200 0
Fax: (43) 2236 200 2030
E-Mail: info@evn.at
Web Site: www.evn.at
Financial Investment Services
S.I.C.: 6211
N.A.I.C.S.: 523999
Stefan Szyszkowitz *(Gen Mgr)*

Non-U.S. Subsidiary:

WTE Wassertechnik GmbH (2)
Ruhrallee 185
45136 Essen, Germany
Tel.: (49) 201 8968 559
Fax: (49) 201 8968 560
E-Mail: info@wte.de
Web Site: www.wte.de
Emp.: 11
Waste Water Treatment Services
S.I.C.: 4941
N.A.I.C.S.: 221310
Ralf Schroeder *(CEO)*

Subsidiaries:

WTE Projektgesellschaft Kurjanovo mbH (3)
Ruhrallee 185
45136 Essen, Germany
Tel.: (49) 201 8968500
Water Treatment Services
S.I.C.: 4971
N.A.I.C.S.: 221310

Non-U.S. Subsidiaries:

Storitveno podjetje Lasko d.o.o. (3)
Modric 8
3270 Lasko, Slovenia
Tel.: (386) 4 5885 070
Fax: (386) 4 5885 071
E-Mail: info@wte.si
Water Treatment Plant Services
S.I.C.: 4941
N.A.I.C.S.: 221310
Andreas Siegmund *(Gen Mgr)*

UAB WTE Baltic (3)
Savanoriu Pr 192
44151 Kaunas, Lithuania
Tel.: (370) 37 332 681
Fax: (370) 37 332 921
Web Site: www.wte.de/SpecialPages/Kontakt.aspx
Emp.: 12
Water Treatment Services
S.I.C.: 4941
N.A.I.C.S.: 221310
Vidas Jonas Kleinas *(Gen Mgr)*

WTE Projektna druzba Bled d.o.o. (3)
Savska Cesta 23
4260 Bled, Slovenia
Tel.: (386) 4 5885070
Fax: (386) 4 5885071
Water Treatment Services
S.I.C.: 4971
N.A.I.C.S.: 221310
Jim Sinclair *(Mng Dir)*

WTE Projektna druzba Kranjska Gora d.o.o. (3)
Kolodvorska Ulica 1B
4280 Kranjska Gora, Slovenia
Tel.: (386) 4 588 50 70
Fax: (386) 4 574 51 47
E-Mail: info@wte.se
Web Site: www.wte.se
Emp.: 3
Water Treatment Services
S.I.C.: 4941
N.A.I.C.S.: 221310
Freeman Wen *(Gen Mgr)*

EVN Warme GmbH (1)
Evn Platz
Maria Enzersdorf, 2344, Austria
Tel.: (43) 22362000
Fax: (43) 2236 200 2030
E-Mail: info@evn.at
Web Site: www.evn.at
Emp.: 10
Electric Power Generation Services
S.I.C.: 4911
N.A.I.C.S.: 221118
Peter Layr *(Mng Dir)*

EVN Wasser GmbH (1)
Evn Platz
2344 Maria Enzersdorf, Niederosterreich, Austria (100%)
Tel.: (43) 22362000
Fax: (43) 22362002030
E-Mail: info@evnwasser.at
Web Site: www.evn-wasser.at
Emp.: 3,000
Water Supply & Irrigation Systems
S.I.C.: 4971
N.A.I.C.S.: 221310

Kabelsignal AG (1)
Sudstadtzentrum 4
2344 Enzersdorf, Niederosterreich, Austria (100%)
Tel.: (43) 2236455640
Fax: (43) 2236455642030
E-Mail: office@kabelsignal.at
Web Site: www.kabsi.at
Emp.: 70
Radio & Television Broadcasting & Wireless Communications Equipment Mfr
S.I.C.: 3663
N.A.I.C.S.: 334220
Alois Ecker *(Mng Dir)*

RAG-Beteiligungs-Aktiengesellschaft (1)
Schwarzenbergplatz 16
A-1015 Vienna, Austria AT
Tel.: (43) 50724 (50.03%)
Fax: (43) 50724388
Web Site: www.rag-austria.at
Holding Company; Crude Petroleum & Natural Gas Extraction
S.I.C.: 6719
N.A.I.C.S.: 551112

Subsidiary:

Rohol-Aufsuchungs Aktiengesellschaft (2)
Schwarzenbergplatz 16
Postfach 56
1015 Vienna, Austria AT
Tel.: (43) 50724
Fax: (43) 507245238
E-Mail: office@rhe-austria.at
Web Site: www.rhe-austria.at
Emp.: 250
Crude Petroleum & Natural Gas Extraction
S.I.C.: 1311
N.A.I.C.S.: 211111
Rudolf Gruber *(Chm-Supervisory Bd)*
Hans-Peter Floren *(Deputy Chm-Supervisory Bd)*
Markus Mitteregger *(Mng Dir)*
Helmut Sitz *(CFO)*
Kurt Sonnleitner *(CTO)*

Non-U.S. Subsidiary:

RAG Hungary Kft. (3)
Bocskai ut 134-146 Dorottya Udvar Bldg D 3rd Floor
HU-1113 Budapest, Hungary HU
Tel.: (36) 15056800
Fax: (36) 15056899
E-Mail: office@rag-hungary.hu
Web Site: www.rag-austria.at/en/company/international-business/hungary.html
Sales Range: $1-9.9 Million
Emp.: 13
Petroleum Products
S.I.C.: 2911
N.A.I.C.S.: 324110
Ernst Burgschwaiger *(Mng Dir)*
Karoly Varga *(Mng Dir)*

Toplak GmbH (1)
7 HaidequerstraBe 6
1110 Vienna, Austria (50%)
Tel.: (43) 22395058
E-Mail: office@toplak.com
Web Site: www.toplak.com
Emp.: 25
Construction Mining & Forestry Machinery & Equipment Rental & Leasing
S.I.C.: 7353
N.A.I.C.S.: 532412

V&C GmbH (1)
Josef Perger-Str 2 - A-05
3031 Pressbaum, Austria (100%)
Tel.: (43) 223357771
Fax: (43) 22335777115
Web Site: www.vc-austria.com
Emp.: 38
Engineering Services
S.I.C.: 8711
N.A.I.C.S.: 541330
Alfred Nolz *(Mng Dir)*

Non-U.S. Subsidiaries:

EVN Bulgaria Elektrorazpredelenie AD (1)
37 Hristo G Danov street
4000 Plovdiv, Bulgaria

Tel.: (359) 32 627 804
Web Site: www.evn.bg
EV6—(BUL)
Sales Range: $200-249.9 Million
Electricity Distribution Services
S.I.C.: 4911
N.A.I.C.S.: 221122
Johannes Reindl *(Chm-Supervisory Bd)*
Wolfgang Hummer *(Chm-Mgmt Bd)*
Klaus Kohlhuber *(Vice Chm-Supervisory Bd)*
Gocho Chemshirov *(Vice Chm-Mgmt Bd)*
Darina Latinova *(IR Officer)*
Velko Kurshumov *(Member-Mgmt Bd)*
Karl Peter *(Member-Mgmt Bd)*
Lyudmila Tsartseva-Vladimirova *(Member-Mgmt Bd)*
Kostadin Velichkov *(Member-Mgmt Bd)*

EVN Bulgaria Elektrosnabdiavane AD **(1)**
37 Hristo G Danov street
4000 Plovdiv, Bulgaria
Tel.: (359) 32 632 052
Web Site: www.evn.bg
1EV—(BUL)
Sales Range: $400-449.9 Million
Electricity Distribution Services
S.I.C.: 4939
N.A.I.C.S.: 221122
Stefan Szyszkowitz *(Chm-Supervisory Bd)*
Joerg Sollfelner *(Chm-Mgmt Bd)*
Georg Reitter *(Vice Chm-Supervisory Bd)*
Mihaela Mihaylova-Doerfler *(Vice Chm-Mgmt Bd)*
Darina Latinova *(IR Officer)*
Stefan Zamanov *(Member-Mgmt Bd)*

EVN Bulgaria Toplofikatsia EAD **(1)**
37 Hristo G Danov
Plovdiv, 4000, Bulgaria
Tel.: (359) 700 1 7777
Fax: (359) 32 990010
E-Mail: info@evn.bg
Heat Power Generation Services
S.I.C.: 4961
N.A.I.C.S.: 221330

EVN Croatia Plin d.o.o **(1)**
Josipa Marohnica 1
10000 Zagreb, Croatia
Tel.: (385) 1 3094 224
Fax: (385) 1 3094 716
E-Mail: info@evn.hr
Web Site: www.evn.hr
Emp.: 2
Natural Gas Distribution Services
S.I.C.: 4924
N.A.I.C.S.: 221210
Tomas Klapste *(Gen Mgr)*

EVN Trading South East Europe EAD **(1)**
Blvd Tzar Osvoboditel 14
Sofia, 1000, Bulgaria
Tel.: (359) 32 304 987
Fax: (359) 32 278 532
E-Mail: info@evn-trading.com
Web Site: www.evn-trading.com
Emp.: 12
Electric Power Distribution Services
S.I.C.: 4911
N.A.I.C.S.: 221122
Diana Chobanova *(Member-Mgmt Bd)*
Jorg Sollfellner *(Member-Mgmt Bd)*
Klaus Stricker *(Member-Mgmt Bd)*

Non-U.S. Subsidiary:

EVN Trading d.o.o. Beograd **(2)**
3 Cincar Jankova
Belgrade, 11000, Serbia
Tel.: (381) 113208900
Fax: (381) 113208930
Electric Power Distribution Services
S.I.C.: 4911
N.A.I.C.S.: 221122

WTE Betriebsgesellschaft mbH **(1)**
Gansefurth 7-10
39444 Hecklingen, Germany
Tel.: (49) 3925 9269 0
Fax: (49) 3925 282231
E-Mail: info@wteb.de
Web Site: www.wteb.info
Emp.: 5
Water Treatment Services
S.I.C.: 4941
N.A.I.C.S.: 221310
Michael Knus *(Gen Mgr)*

WTE Projektgesellschaft Sud-West Wasser mbH **(1)**
Ruhrallee 185
45136 Essen, Germany
Tel.: (49) 201 8968500
Fax: (49) 201 8968555
Emp.: 10
Water Treatment Services
S.I.C.: 4971
N.A.I.C.S.: 221310
Joerg Koering *(Gen Mgr)*

WTE Projektmanagement GmbH **(1)**
Ruhrallee 185
45136 Essen, Germany
Tel.: (49) 201 8968500
Fax: (49) 201 868968555
E-Mail: info@wte.de
Emp.: 10
Water Supply Services
S.I.C.: 4971
N.A.I.C.S.: 221310
Ralf Schroder *(Mng Dir)*

EVOC INTELLIGENT TECHNOLOGY COMPANY LIMITED

EVOC Technology Building 31
Gaoxin Central Avenue 4th
Nanshan District, Shenzhen, 518057, China
Tel.: (86) 75586255066
Fax: (86) 75586255909
E-Mail: oversea@evoc.com
Web Site: www.evoc.com
Year Founded: 1993
2308—(HKG)
Sls.: $184,545,735
Assets: $602,362,059
Liabilities: $375,529,184
Net Worth: $226,832,876
Earnings: $15,042,777
Emp.: 1,308
Fiscal Year-end: 12/31/12
Business Description:
Advanced Process Automation Product Mfr
S.I.C.: 3625
N.A.I.C.S.: 335314
Personnel:
Zhi Lie Chen *(Chm)*
Jing Pu *(Chm-Supervisory Bd)*
Cheng Shun Tso *(Vice Chm)*
Jun Zhu *(Compliance Officer)*
Chun Kuen Tsui *(Sec)*
Board of Directors:
Zhi Lie Chen
Jian An
Lin Ying Dai
Chun Kwok Ling
Cheng Shun Tso
Zhao Hui Wang
Jun Zhu
Supervisory Board of Directors:
Jing Pu
Lin Xin Dong
Bing Wen
Guo Nian Zhan
Zheng An Zhang
Legal Counsel:
Commerce & Finance Law Offices
27C Shenzhen Te Qu Bao Ye Building
Shenzhen, China
Transfer Agent:
Tricor Abacus Limited
26/F Tesbury Centre 28 Queen's Road East
Hong Kong, China (Hong Kong)

EVOCUTIS PLC

Sandbeck Lane
Wetherby, W Yorkshire, LS22 7TW, United Kingdom
Tel.: (44) 1937 547470
E-Mail: info@evocutis.com
Web Site: www.evocutis.com
EVO—(AIM)
Rev.: $623,820
Assets: $1,860,404
Liabilities: $352,182
Net Worth: $1,508,222
Earnings: ($1,590,345)
Emp.: 16
Fiscal Year-end: 07/31/13
Business Description:
Dermatology Products Research Services
S.I.C.: 2834
N.A.I.C.S.: 325412
Personnel:
Gwyn Humphreys *(CEO)*
Darren Bamforth *(CFO, Sec & Dir-Fin)*
Board of Directors:
Tom Bannatyne
Darren Bamforth
Gwyn Humphreys
Mike Townend
Legal Counsel:
Walker Morris
Kings Court 2 King Streets
Leeds, LS1 2HL, United Kingdom

EVOLEM S.A.

6 quai Saint Antoine
CS 60026
69289 Lyon, Cedex 2, France
Tel.: (33) 472689800
Fax: (33) 472689809
E-Mail: contact@evolem.com
Web Site: www.evolem.fr/
Emp.: 10
Business Description:
Private Equity Firm
S.I.C.: 6211
N.A.I.C.S.: 523999
Personnel:
Bruno Rousset *(Founder & CEO)*

Holdings:

April Group SA **(1)**
114 boulevard Marius Vivier Merle
69439 Lyon, Cedex 03, France (60.32%)
Tel.: (33) 472361898
Fax: (33) 472361879
E-Mail: april.international@april.com
Web Site: www.april.com
APR—(EUR)
Rev.: $1,041,282,688
Assets: $2,038,125,611
Liabilities: $1,344,037,667
Net Worth: $694,087,944
Earnings: $71,898,940
Emp.: 3,960
Fiscal Year-end: 12/31/12
Holding Company; Life Insurance, Property & Casualty Insurance Services
S.I.C.: 6719
N.A.I.C.S.: 551112
Bruno Rousset *(Founder, Chm & CEO)*
Marc Le Doze *(CFO)*

Subsidiaries:

Amt Assurances Sarl **(2)**
14 Quai Marmoutier
37072 Tours, France
Tel.: (33) 810125750
Fax: (33) 247510050
E-Mail: info@amt.tm.fr
Web Site: www.amt.tm.fr
Insurance Agencies & Brokerages
S.I.C.: 6411
N.A.I.C.S.: 524210
Philips Annoncera *(Mng Dir)*

April Corporate Broking Sarl **(2)**
33 Rue Maurice Flandin
69003 Lyon, France
Tel.: (33) 472755471
Fax: (33) 437245279
Web Site: www.aprilcorporate.com
Real Estate Agents & Brokers
S.I.C.: 6531
N.A.I.C.S.: 531210
Bruno Rousset *(CEO)*

April Cover Sarl **(2)**
33 Rue Maurice Flandin
69003 Lyon, France
Tel.: (33) 472367342
Fax: (33) 472367550
E-Mail:
Web Site: www.april.fr/contact
Emp.: 2
Insurance Agencies & Brokerages
S.I.C.: 6411
N.A.I.C.S.: 524210
Bruno Rousset *(CEO)*

April Entreprise Lyon **(2)**
1 Place De Razza No CS 30621
69258 Lyon, Cedex, 9, France
Tel.: (33) 472198700
Fax: (33) 478648755
E-Mail: sepcofi.cd@wanadoo.fr
Web Site: www.aprilgroup.com
Emp.: 15
Insurance Agencies & Brokerages
S.I.C.: 6411
N.A.I.C.S.: 524210

April Iard Sarl **(2)**
27 Rue Maurice Flandin
69404 Lyon, France
Tel.: (33) 437911133
Fax: (33) 437911144
E-Mail: axeria@axeria-iard.fr
Web Site: www.axeria-iard.fr
Emp.: 69
Insurance Agencies & Brokerages
S.I.C.: 6411
N.A.I.C.S.: 524210
Bruno Rousset *(CEO)*

April Marine **(2)**
12 rue Paul Doumer
B.P. 47
850002 La Roche-sur-Yon, France
Tel.: (33) 251372260
Fax: (33) 251379885
E-Mail: laroche@aprilmarine.fr
Web Site: www.aprilmarine.fr
Emp.: 18
Marine Insurance Agencies & Brokerages
S.I.C.: 6411
N.A.I.C.S.: 524210

April Marketing Solutions Sarl **(2)**
Le Bois Des Cotes Bat A 300 Route Nationale 6
69576 Limonest, France
Tel.: (33) 426294316
Web Site: www.aprilgroup.com
Emp.: 155
Insurance Agencies & Brokerages
S.I.C.: 6411
N.A.I.C.S.: 524210

April Patrimoine Sarl **(2)**
27 Rue Maurice Flandin
69395 Lyon, France
Tel.: (33) 472367500
Fax: (33) 472367329
E-Mail: info@april-patrimoine.fr
Web Site: www.april-patrimoine.fr
Insurance Agencies & Brokerages
S.I.C.: 6411
N.A.I.C.S.: 524210

Axeria IRAD **(2)**
129 rue Servient
Tower Credit Lyonnais, 69326 Lyon, France
Tel.: (33) 478637030
Fax: (33) 478637044
E-Mail: axeria@axeria.iard.fr
Web Site: www.axeria-iard.fr
Sls.: $102,289,512
Emp.: 80
Indemnity Insurance
S.I.C.: 6399
N.A.I.C.S.: 524128
Julien Richard-Vitton *(Mgr)*

Axeria Prevoyance Sarl **(2)**
33 Rue Maurice Flandin
69003 Lyon, France
Tel.: (33) 472361794
Fax: (33) 472361791
E-Mail: cbouty@axeria.fr
Web Site: www.axeria-prevoyance.fr
Emp.: 25
Direct Life Insurance Carriers
S.I.C.: 6311
N.A.I.C.S.: 524113
Cathrerine Pigeon *(Pres)*

Cgca Sarl **(2)**
1 Avenue De La Fosse aux Mats
17304 Rochefort, France

Evolem S.A.—(Continued)

Tel.: (33) 546993160
Fax: (33) 546870021
E-Mail: cgca@cgca.fr
Web Site: www.cgca.fr
Emp.: 22
Insurance Agencies & Brokerages
S.I.C.: 6411
N.A.I.C.S.: 524210

Europassur Sarl (2)
33 Rue De Chateaudun
75009 Paris, France
Tel.: (33) 149680720
Fax: (33) 142701135
E-Mail: contact@europassur.com
Web Site: www.europassur.com
Emp.: 9
Insurance Agencies & Brokerages
S.I.C.: 6411
N.A.I.C.S.: 524210
Laurette Fleury *(Asst Dir)*

Gi2a Assurances Sarl (2)
18 Bis Rue Jules Ferry
Fougeres, 35303 Loir-et-Cher, France
Tel.: (33) 299943839
Fax: (33) 299940680
E-Mail: gi2a@gi2a.com
Web Site: www.gi2a.com
Emp.: 85
Insurance Agencies & Brokerages
S.I.C.: 6411
N.A.I.C.S.: 524210
Claugi Guilin *(Mng Dir)*

Habitance Sarl (2)
33 Rue Maurice Flandin
69003 Lyon, France
Tel.: (33) 426293699
Fax: (33) 472367319
Insurance Agencies & Brokerages
S.I.C.: 6411
N.A.I.C.S.: 524210
Bruno Rousset *(CEO)*

Mutant Assurances Sarl (2)
Mlle Frederique Millet-Perriol
41 Rue Garibaldi, 69006 Lyon, France
Tel.: (33) 472822010
Fax: (33) 472822012
Web Site: www.mutant-assurances.fr
Emp.: 500
Insurance Agencies & Brokerages
S.I.C.: 6411
N.A.I.C.S.: 524210
Sebastian Rodriguez *(Dir-Mktg)*

Resolution Sarl (2)
27 Rue Maurice Flandin
69444 Lyon, France
Tel.: (33) 472755460
Fax: (33) 426106919
Emp.: 23
Insurance Agencies & Brokerages
S.I.C.: 6411
N.A.I.C.S.: 524210

Sasco Sarl (2)
81 Rue des Carts
BP 70030
74373 Pringy, Cedex, France
Tel.: (33) 40 50523860
Fax: (33) 40 50523865
Web Site: www.sasco.fr/fr/contactez-nous.html
Emp.: 28
Insurance Agencies & Brokerages
S.I.C.: 6411
N.A.I.C.S.: 524210

Solucia Protection Juridique Sarl (2)
14 Rue Scandicci
93500 Pantin, France
Tel.: (33) 148105400
Fax: (33) 148105414
E-Mail: contact@soluciapj.fr
Web Site: www.soluciapj.fr
Direct Health & Medical Insurance Carriers
S.I.C.: 6324
N.A.I.C.S.: 524114

TMS Contact Sarl (2)
110 Ave de la Republique
75011 Paris, France
Tel.: (33) 73034101
Fax: (33) 1 73 03 41 10
Web Site: www.tmscontact.com
Emp.: 48
Insurance Agencies & Brokerages
S.I.C.: 6411
N.A.I.C.S.: 524210

Non-U.S. Subsidiaries:

April Financial Services AG (2)
Richard Reitzner Allee 1
85540 Haar, Germany
Tel.: (49) 8943607102
Fax: (49) 8943607177
E-Mail: info@apri.de
Web Site: www.april.de
Emp.: 40
Financial Investment Activities
S.I.C.: 6211
N.A.I.C.S.: 523999
Lutz Goehler *(Mng Dir)*

April Germany AG (2)
Richard Reitzner Allee 1
85540 Haar, Germany
Tel.: (49) 8943607400
Fax: (49) 8943607177
E-Mail: info@april-fs.de
Web Site: www.april-fs.de
Emp.: 40
Direct Life Insurance Carriers
S.I.C.: 6311
N.A.I.C.S.: 524113
Volker Stegmann *(Chm)*

April Iberia Sarl (2)
C-Serrano 93 2 E
28006 Madrid, Spain
Tel.: (34) 915643170
Fax: (34) 915633268
E-Mail: contacto@april.iberia.es
Web Site: www.april-iberia.es
Emp.: 2
Insurance Agencies & Brokerages
S.I.C.: 6411
N.A.I.C.S.: 524210

Dierrevi SpA (2)
Via Carducci 38
20123 Milan, Italy
Tel.: (39) 0243319588
Fax: (39) 0243319596
E-Mail: info@dierrevi.it
Web Site: www.dierrevi.it
Emp.: 6
Insurance Agencies & Brokerages
S.I.C.: 6221
N.A.I.C.S.: 523140
Max Piombo *(Member-Exec Board)*

Moral Caraibes Sarl (2)
Immeuble Mirador
97122 La Baie Mahault, Guadeloupe
Tel.: (590) 380636
E-Mail: moral-caraibes@moral-caraibes.fr
Emp.: 32
Insurance Agencies & Brokerages
S.I.C.: 6411
N.A.I.C.S.: 524210
Jean-Louis Favier *(Pres)*

Chemica S.A.S (1)
8 rue Poncetton
42000, Saint-Etienne, France
Tel.: (33) 477492090
Fax: (33) 477 25 79 82
E-Mail: info@chemica.fr
Web Site: www.chemica.fr
Textile Heat Transfer Product Mfr
S.I.C.: 2389
N.A.I.C.S.: 314999

Dufieux Industrie S.A.S. (1)
4 rue Monmousseau
38433 Echirolles, France
Tel.: (33) 4 76 33 26 10
Fax: (33) 4 76 09 67 44
E-Mail: info@dufieux-industrie.com
Web Site: www.dufieux-industrie.com
Machine Tool Mfr
S.I.C.: 3541
N.A.I.C.S.: 333517
Rene Panczuk *(CEO)*

EVOLUTION CAPITAL PUBLIC COMPANY LIMITED

The Offices at Centralworld Unit 1912
999/9 Rama I Road
Pathumwan, Bangkok, 10330, Thailand
Tel.: (66) 2207 2900
Fax: (66) 2207 2929
E-Mail: info@evolution.co.th
Web Site: www.evolution.co.th
E—(THA)
Rev.: $9,918,791
Assets: $52,131,712
Liabilities: $8,368,969
Net Worth: $43,762,742
Earnings: $1,032,662
Fiscal Year-end: 12/31/12

Business Description:
Investment Advisory Services
S.I.C.: 6282
N.A.I.C.S.: 523930

Personnel:
Krit Srichawla *(Chm)*
Simon Gerovich *(CEO)*
Pattama Joednapa *(CFO)*
Sayarm Tongkrabin *(COO)*
Mark Michael Reinecke *(CIO)*
Sanjay Singh *(CEO-Foods Bus Grp)*
Arthur Hugh Napolitano *(Sr VP-Bus Dev)*

Board of Directors:
Krit Srichawla
Hugh Andrew
Krish Detter
Simon Gerovich
Akarat Na Ranong
Mark Michael Reinecke
Sanjay Singh
Amorn Srichawla
Witit Sujjapong
Viroj Tangjetanaporn

EVOLUTION MINING LIMITED

Level 28 175 Liverpool Street
Sydney, NSW, 2000, Australia
Tel.: (61) 2 9696 2900
Fax: (61) 2 9696 2901
E-Mail: admin.sydney@evolutionmining.com.au
Web Site: www.evolutionmining.com.au
Year Founded: 2003
EVN—(ASX)
Rev.: $630,505,931
Assets: $1,073,429,694
Liabilities: $286,280,502
Net Worth: $787,149,193
Earnings: ($320,363,424)
Emp.: 771
Fiscal Year-end: 06/30/13

Business Description:
Gold Exploration & Mining
S.I.C.: 1041
N.A.I.C.S.: 212221

Personnel:
Jake Klein *(Chm)*
Tim Churcher *(CFO & VP-Fin)*
Mark Le Messurier *(COO)*
Evan Elstein *(Sec & VP-IT & Comm Rels)*

Board of Directors:
Jake Klein
James E. Askew
Lawrie Conway
Graham Freestone
Colin Johnstone
Thomas McKeith
John Rowe

Subsidiaries:

Lion Selection Group Limited (1)
Level 4 15 Queen Street
Melbourne, VIC, 3000, Australia
Tel.: (61) 396148008
Fax: (61) 396148009
E-Mail: info@lsg.com.au
Web Site: www.lionselection.com.au
LSX—(ASX)
Rev.: $1,928,927
Assets: $66,520,369
Liabilities: $53,147
Net Worth: $66,467,222
Earnings: ($2,112,337)
Emp.: 1
Fiscal Year-end: 07/31/13
Investment Services
S.I.C.: 6211
N.A.I.C.S.: 523999
Craig K. Smyth *(CEO)*
Jane Rose *(Sec & Mgr-IR)*

EVOLVA HOLDING SA

Duggingerstrasse 23
4153 Reinach, Switzerland
Tel.: (41) 614852000
Fax: (41) 614852001
E-Mail: info@evolva.com
Web Site: www.evolva.com
EVE—(SWX)
Rev.: $7,570,828
Assets: $97,541,127
Liabilities: $31,444,976
Net Worth: $66,096,152
Earnings: ($17,974,527)
Emp.: 82
Fiscal Year-end: 12/31/12

Business Description:
Biopharmaceutical Developer & Mfr
S.I.C.: 2834
N.A.I.C.S.: 325412

Personnel:
Tom McKillop *(Chm)*
Claus Braestrup *(Vice Chm)*
Neil Goldsmith *(CEO & Mng Dir)*
Jakob Dynnes Hansen *(CFO)*
Jogen Hansen *(Chief Scientific Officer)*
Pascal Longchamp *(Chief Bus Officer)*
Panchapagesa Murali *(CEO/Mng Dir-Evolva India)*
Simon Waddington *(CEO-Evolva Nutrition Inc)*

Board of Directors:
Tom McKillop
Claus Braestrup
Martin Gertsch
Neil Goldsmith
Jutta Heim
Ganesh M. Kishore
Stuart Strathdee
Thomas Videbaek

Non-U.S. Subsidiaries:

Evolva A/S (1)
Bulowsvej 25
1870 Frederiksberg, Denmark
Tel.: (45) 35200230
Fax: (45) 35 200 231
Drug Discovery & Development Services
S.I.C.: 2834
N.A.I.C.S.: 325412

Evolva Biotech Private Limited (1)
401-405 Ticel Bio Park Ltd 4th Floor
Taramani Road
Taramani, Chennai, Tamil Nadu, 600 113, India
Tel.: (91) 44 4297 1050
Fax: (91) 44 4297 1060
E-Mail: info@evolva.com
Web Site: www.evolva.com
Emp.: 21
Medical Compound Research & Development Services
S.I.C.: 8731
N.A.I.C.S.: 541712
Panchapagesa Murali *(CEO & Mng Dir)*

Subsidiary:

Evolva SA (1)
Duggingerstrasse 23
4153 Reinach, Basel-Country, Switzerland
Tel.: (41) 614852000
Fax: (41) 614852001
E-Mail: info@evolva.com
Web Site: www.evolva.com
Emp.: 40
Drugs Mfr
S.I.C.: 2834
N.A.I.C.S.: 325412
Neil Goldsmith *(CEO)*
Jakob Dynnes Hansen *(CFO)*

EVOLVE IT AUSTRALIA PTY. LTD.
1/476 Canterbury Road
Forest Hill, VIC, 3131, Australia
Tel.: (61) 3 8872 6000
Web Site: www.evolveit.com.au
Year Founded: 1993
Sales Range: $1-9.9 Million
Business Description:
IT Services
S.I.C.: 7379
N.A.I.C.S.: 541519
Personnel:
Nick Moran *(CEO)*

EVOLVING GOLD CORP.
Suite 605 1166 Alberni Street
Vancouver, BC, V6E 3Z3, Canada
Tel.: (604) 685-6375
Fax: (604) 909-1163
Toll Free: (866) 604-3864
E-Mail: info@evolvinggold.com
Web Site: www.evolvinggold.com
Year Founded: 2003
EVG—(TSX)
Rev.: $56,764
Assets: $45,306,669
Liabilities: $2,398,613
Net Worth: $42,908,056
Earnings: ($15,722,060)
Emp.: 12
Fiscal Year-end: 03/31/13
Business Description:
Gold Mining Services
S.I.C.: 1041
N.A.I.C.S.: 212221
Personnel:
R. Bruce Duncan *(CEO)*
Charles E. Jenkins *(CFO & Sec)*
Board of Directors:
Robert Barker
R. Bruce Duncan
William Francis Lindqvist
William Majcher
Legal Counsel:
McMillan LLP
Royal Centre 1055 West Georgia Street Suite 1500
PO Box 11117
Vancouver, BC, Canada
Baker & Hostetler LLP
303 E 17th Ave Ste 1100
Denver, CO 80203-1264
Computershare Trust Company of Canada
9th Floor 100 University Avenue
Toronto, ON, Canada
Transfer Agents:
Computershare Trust Company of Canada
2nd Floor 510 Burrard Street
V6C3B9 Vancouver, BC, Canada
Computershare Trust Company of Canada
9th Floor 100 University Avenue
Toronto, ON, Canada

EVOTEC AG
Manfred Eigen Campus Essener Bogen 7
22419 Hamburg, Germany
Tel.: (49) 40560810
Fax: (49) 4056081222
E-Mail: info@evotec.com
Web Site: www.evotec.com
EVT—(DEU OTC)
Rev.: $117,473,525
Assets: $303,463,065
Liabilities: $98,108,870
Net Worth: $205,354,195
Earnings: $3,335,809
Emp.: 637
Fiscal Year-end: 12/31/12
Business Description:
Pharmaceutical Developer & Mfr
S.I.C.: 2834
N.A.I.C.S.: 325412
Personnel:
Walter Wenninger *(Chm-Supervisory Bd)*
Werner Lanthaler *(CEO & Member-Mgmt Bd)*
Colin Bond *(CFO & Member-Mgmt Bd)*
Mario Polywka *(COO & Member-Mgmt Bd)*
Cord Dohrmann *(Chief Scientific Officer & Member-Mgmt Bd)*
Supervisory Board of Directors:
Walter Wenninger
Hubert Birner
Claus Braestrup
Roland Oetker
Andreas Pinkwart
Mary C. Tanner
Non-U.S. Subsidiaries:

Evotec (Asia) Private Ltd **(1)**
Nanyang Polytechnic 180 Ang Mo Kio Avenue 8 Q 507
Singapore, 569830, Singapore
Tel.: (65) 6459 1090
Fax: (65) 6459 1449
E-Mail: info@evotec.com
Web Site: www.evotec.com
Emp.: 10
Toxicology Testing Services
S.I.C.: 8071
N.A.I.C.S.: 621511

Evotec (India) Private Ltd. **(1)**
DIL Complex Ghodbunder Road
Majiwada, Thane, Maharashtra, 400610, India
Tel.: (91) 22 6623 0900
Fax: (91) 22 6623 0998
E-Mail: info@evotec.com
Emp.: 160
Pharmaceutical Products Mfr
S.I.C.: 2834
N.A.I.C.S.: 325412
David John *(Sr VP)*

Evotec (UK) Ltd. **(1)**
114 Milton Park
Abingdon, Oxfordshire, OX14 4SA, United Kingdom
Tel.: (44) 1235861561
Fax: (44) 1235863139
E-Mail: info@evotec.com
Web Site: www.evotec.com
Emp.: 250
Pharmaceutical Products Distr
S.I.C.: 5122
N.A.I.C.S.: 424210

Subsidiaries:

Kinaxo Biotechnologies GmbH **(1)**
Am Klopferspitz 19a
Martinsried, 82152 Planegg, Bavaria, Germany
Tel.: (49) 89 461 3363 0
Fax: (49) 89 461 3363 20
E-Mail: office.munic@evotec.com
Web Site: www.kinaxo.de
Emp.: 30
Biotechnology Research & Development Services
S.I.C.: 8731
N.A.I.C.S.: 541711
Andreas Jenne *(Founder & CEO)*
Henrik Daub *(Founder & CTO)*
Hellmut Kirchner *(Co-Founder)*
Axel Ullrich *(Co-Founder)*

EVPU A.S.
Trencianska 19
018 51 Nova Dubnica, Slovakia
Tel.: (421) 424409102
Fax: (421) 424434252
E-Mail: marketing@evpu.sk
Web Site: www.evpu.sk
Emp.: 240
Business Description:
Electric Motors Mfr, Researcher & Developer
S.I.C.: 3714
N.A.I.C.S.: 336320
Personnel:
Igor Gerek *(Chm)*
Jozef Buday *(Mng Dir)*
Board of Directors:
Igor Gerek
Jozef Buday
Vladislav Pavlikovsky

EVRAZ GROUP S.A.
46A Avenue JF Kennedy
PO Box 415
L-1855 Luxembourg, Luxembourg
Tel.: (352) 442078328998
E-Mail: info@evraz.com
Web Site: www.evraz.com
EVR—(LUX)
Sales Range: $5-14.9 Billion
Emp.: 110,000
Business Description:
Holding Company
S.I.C.: 6719
N.A.I.C.S.: 551112
Personnel:
Alexander G. Abramov *(Chm)*
Alexander V. Frolov *(CEO)*
Giacomo Baizini *(CFO & VP-Corp Affairs)*
Pavel S. Tatyanin *(Sr VP & Head-Intl Bus)*
Leonid M. Kachur *(Sr VP-Bus Support & Interregional Relations)*
Board of Directors:
Alexander G. Abramov
Duncan Baxter
Alexander V. Frolov
Karl Gruber
Alexander V. Izosimov
Michael Charles Gerrard Peat
Terry J. Robinson
Eugene Shvidler
Eugene Alexander Tenenbaum
Corporate Headquarters:

EvrazHolding, OOO **(1)**
15 Dolgorukovskaya St Bldg 4-5
Moscow, 127006, Russia RU
Tel.: (7) 4952344631
Fax: (7) 4952344626
E-Mail: info@evraz.com
Web Site: www.evraz.com
Holding Company; Steel Mfg, Iron Ore & Coal Mining
S.I.C.: 6719
N.A.I.C.S.: 551112
Alexander V. Frolov *(Pres)*
Pavel S. Tatyanin *(CFO & Sr VP)*
Leonid M. Kachur *(Sr VP-Bus Security)*

U.S. Subsidiaries:

Evraz Inc. NA **(2)**
1000 SW Broadway Ste 2200
Portland, OR 97205-3074 DE
Mailing Address:
PO Box 5368
Portland, OR 97228-5368
Tel.: (503) 240-5226
Fax: (503) 240-5777
Toll Free: (800) 831-2187
Web Site: www.osm.com
Emp.: 1,750
Steel Products Mfr
Import Export
S.I.C.: 3399
N.A.I.C.S.: 331221
Conrad Winkler *(Pres & CEO)*
Glenda Minor *(CFO)*
Jerry Reed *(Exec VP-Long Products)*
John Zanieski *(Exec VP-Flat Products Grp & Recycling)*
Mike Garcia *(Sr VP-Mfg & Supply Chain)*

Subsidiaries:

C&W Railway Co. **(3)**
2100 S Freeway
Pueblo, CO 81004-3406 CO
Mailing Address:
PO Box 316
Pueblo, CO 81002-0316
Tel.: (719) 561-6358
Fax: (719) 561-6837
E-Mail: hamlerc@cwrailway.com
Emp.: 55
Railroad Plant
S.I.C.: 4011
N.A.I.C.S.: 482111

Evraz Claymont Steel Holdings, Inc. **(3)**
4001 Philadelphia Pike
Claymont, DE 19703 DE
Tel.: (302) 792-5400
Fax: (302) 792-5477
Web Site: www.claymontsteel.com
Emp.: 479
Steel Plate Mfr
S.I.C.: 3399
N.A.I.C.S.: 331110
Randolph Harris *(Gen Mgr-Melting & Casting)*

Subsidiary:

Evraz Claymont Steel **(4)**
4001 Philadelphia Pike
Claymont, DE 19703-2727 (100%)
Tel.: (302) 792-5400
Fax: (302) 791-6650
Web Site: www.claymontsteel.com
Sales Range: $300-349.9 Million
Emp.: 479
Mfr of Custom Discrete Steel Plate
S.I.C.: 3399
N.A.I.C.S.: 331110
Kendra Curtis *(CFO)*

Evraz Inc. NA **(3)**
1612 E Abriendo Ave
Pueblo, CO 81004-3406 CO
Mailing Address:
PO Box 316
Pueblo, CO 81002-0316
Tel.: (719) 561-6000
Fax: (719) 561-6037
E-Mail: info@rmsm.com
Web Site: www.osm.com
Emp.: 1,200
Seamless Casing & Tubing; Rails; Heat Treated Rails; Reinforcing Bars, Hot Rolled Bars & Wire Rods Mfr
Import Export
S.I.C.: 3312
N.A.I.C.S.: 331110
Ben Lutze *(Dir-Ops)*

Joint Venture:

Oregon Feralloy Partners **(3)**
14400 N Rivergate Blvd
Portland, OR 97203
Tel.: (503) 286-8869
Fax: (503) 286-8934
E-Mail: feralloyop@feralloy.com
Web Site: www.feralloy.com
Sales Range: $150-199.9 Million
Emp.: 15
Flat Rolled Steel Products Processor & Distr; Owned 60% by Evraz Oregon Steel Mills, Inc. & 40% by Feralloy Corporation
S.I.C.: 5051
N.A.I.C.S.: 423510
Paul W. Abernethy *(Gen Mgr)*

Non-U.S. Subsidiary:

Evraz Inc. NA **(3)**
5302 39th St
Camrose, AB, T4V 2N8, Canada
Tel.: (780) 672-3116
Fax: (780) 679-0690
E-Mail: kelly.broffarts@evrazincna.com
Web Site: www.osm.com
Sales Range: $50-74.9 Million
Emp.: 350
Mfr. of Steel Pipe
S.I.C.: 3317
N.A.I.C.S.: 331210
Robert Jones *(Gen Mgr)*

Strategic Minerals Corporation **(2)**
4285 Malvern Rd
Hot Springs, AR 71901-8504 CT
Tel.: (203) 790-1555
Fax: (203) 790-5750
E-Mail: info@stratcor.com
Web Site: www.stratcor.com
Sales Range: $200-249.9 Million
Emp.: 543
Primary Nonferrous Metals Producer
Import Export
S.I.C.: 3339

Evraz Group S.A.—(Continued)

N.A.I.C.S.: 331410
Heinrich Enslin *(CEO)*

Subsidiaries:

Stratcor, Inc. (3)
Omega Corporate Ctr 1180 Omega Dr Ste 1180
Pittsburgh, PA 15205-5005
Tel.: (412) 787-4500
Fax: (412) 787-5030
Toll Free: (800) 573-6052
E-Mail: info@stratcor.com
Web Site: www.stratcor.com
Emp.: 5
Vanadium & Tungsten Products Mfr
S.I.C.: 3299
N.A.I.C.S.: 327999
Vincent P. Rocco *(Mgr-Sls-Master Alloys)*

Non-U.S. Division:

Evraz Inc. NA (2)
100 Armour Rd
Regina, SK, S4P 3C7, Canada SK
Mailing Address:
PO Box 1670
Regina, SK, S4P 3C7, Canada
Tel.: (306) 924-7700
Fax: (306) 924-7500
Toll Free: (800) 667-1616
E-Mail: kbrossart@ipsco.com
Web Site: www.evraz.com
Emp.: 600
Steel Production
Import Export
S.I.C.: 3325
N.A.I.C.S.: 331513
Roger Juarez *(VP & Gen Mgr)*

Non-U.S. Subsidiary:

Evraz Highveld Steel & Vanadium Limited (2)
Old Pretoria Road Portion 93 of the farm Schoongezicht
308 JS Witbank, Mpumalanga, South Africa ZA
Mailing Address: (80.9%)
PO Box 111
Witbank, 1035, South Africa
Tel.: (27) 13 690 9911
Fax: (27) 13 690 9293
E-Mail: general@highveld.co.za
Web Site: www.evrazhighveld.co.za
EHS—(JSE OTC)
Rev.: $486,341,800
Assets: $409,603,900
Liabilities: $215,469,300
Net Worth: $194,134,600
Earnings: ($105,333,100)
Emp.: 2,230
Fiscal Year-end: 12/31/12
Steel & Vanadium Products Mfr
S.I.C.: 3325
N.A.I.C.S.: 331513
Michael Dennis Garcia *(CEO)*
Jan Valenta *(CFO & Dir-Fin)*
Jaco S. de Klerk *(Co-COO)*
Franz Holy *(Co-COO)*
Johan Nel *(Deputy COO-Mining & Iron Making)*
Anre Weststrate *(Sec)*

EVRIM RESOURCES CORP.

410-800 West Pender Street
Vancouver, BC, V6C 2V6, Canada
Tel.: (604) 248-8648
Fax: (604) 248-8663
Toll Free: (855) 240-3727
E-Mail: info@evrimresources.com
Web Site: www.evrimresources.com
Year Founded: 2005
EVM—(TSXV)
Rev.: $47,848
Assets: $5,202,439
Liabilities: $286,385
Net Worth: $4,916,054
Earnings: ($1,572,147)
Fiscal Year-end: 12/31/12
Business Description:
Gold Mining Services
S.I.C.: 1041
N.A.I.C.S.: 212221
Personnel:
E. Kenneth Paul *(Chm)*
J. Patrick Nicol *(Pres & CEO)*
Mahesh Liyanage *(CFO)*
Board of Directors:
E. Kenneth Paul
David A. Caulfield
Jack H. L. Miller
J. Patrick Nicol
Paul van Eeden
Legal Counsel:
Fraser Milner Casgrain LLP
20th Floor 250 Howe Street
Vancouver, BC, V6C 3R8, Canada
Transfer Agent:
Olympia Transfer Services Inc.
Suite 920 120 Adelaide Street West
Toronto, ON, Canada

EVROFARMA SA

3 klm Alexandroupolis-Airport
68100 Alexandroupoli, Greece
Tel.: (30) 25510 88120
Fax: (30) 25510 88153
E-Mail: info@evrofarma.gr
Web Site: www.evrofarma.gr
Year Founded: 1991
EVROF—(ATH)
Emp.: 118
Business Description:
Dairy Products Mfr & Distr
S.I.C.: 2023
N.A.I.C.S.: 311514
Personnel:
Athanasios H. Papazilakis *(Pres)*
Pasxalis H. Papazilakis *(Mng Dir & VP)*
Board of Directors:
Anastasios H. Alexandridis
Georgios A. Arabatzis
Vasilios I. Gioftsidis
Athanasios H. Papazilakis
Pasxalis H. Papazilakis

EVRY ASA

Nedre Skoyen vei 26
0276 Oslo, Norway
Mailing Address:
PB 494
Skoyen, NO 0213 Oslo, Norway
Tel.: (47) 23145000
E-Mail: info@evry.com
Web Site: www.evry.com
EVRY—(OSL)
Rev.: $2,304,147,492
Assets: $2,192,440,464
Liabilities: $1,229,193,585
Net Worth: $963,246,879
Earnings: $35,455,941
Emp.: 9,873
Fiscal Year-end: 12/31/12
Business Description:
Information Technology Consulting Services
S.I.C.: 8999
N.A.I.C.S.: 541690
Personnel:
Arve Johansen *(Chm)*
Terje Mjos *(CEO)*
Jan Sandtro *(Chief Legal Officer & Head-Compliance)*
Morten Sogard *(Exec VP-Corp Dev)*
Janne Marie Log *(Sr VP-Corp Comm & Mktg)*
Board of Directors:
Arve Johansen
Eirik Borno
Anders Brandt
Jan Dahlstrom
Lisbeth Gustafsson
Ingrid Lund
Dag Mejdell
Sigmund Orjavik
Hilde Ringereide
Eli Skrovset

Non-U.S. Subsidiaries:

Guide Konsult Stockholm AB (1)
Ekensbergsvagen 113
171 79 Solna, Sweden
Tel.: (46) 105886000
Fax: (46) 105886001
Web Site: www.guide.se
Information Technology Consulting Services
S.I.C.: 8742
N.A.I.C.S.: 541611
Bo Jangvik *(CEO)*

Span Infotech (India) Private Limited (1)
18/2 Vani Vilas Road Basavanagudi
Bengaluru, 560 004, India (51%)
Tel.: (91) 8040219600
Fax: (91) 8040219632
Web Site: www.spansystems.com
Emp.: 1,000
Information Technology Consulting Services
S.I.C.: 7373
N.A.I.C.S.: 541512
Prakash Grama *(Co-Founder & CEO)*
G. L. Pradeep *(Co-Founder & Mng Dir)*
Naganand Doraswamy *(Co-Founder & Exec VP)*
Pramod Grama *(Co-Founder & Exec VP-Engrg)*

U.S. Subsidiary:

Span Systems Corporation Inc. (2)
230 Sherman Ave Ste 9
Berkeley Heights, NJ 07922 IL
Tel.: (908) 665-9100
Fax: (908) 665-9002
Web Site: www.spansystems.com
Sales Range: $1-9.9 Million
Emp.: 20
Information Technology Consulting Services
S.I.C.: 7373
N.A.I.C.S.: 541512
Mysore S. Srinath *(Gen Mgr)*

EVS BROADCAST EQUIPMENT S.A.

16 Rue Bois Saint-Jean
4102 Seraing, Belgium
Tel.: (32) 43617000
Fax: (32) 43617099
E-Mail: info@evs.com
Web Site: www.evs.com
Year Founded: 1994
EVS—(EUR OTC)
Rev.: $185,630,112
Assets: $127,834,996
Liabilities: $37,272,755
Net Worth: $90,562,241
Earnings: $56,193,174
Emp.: 463
Fiscal Year-end: 12/31/12
Business Description:
Digital Equipment & Automation Software Designer, Mfr & Marketer
S.I.C.: 3663
N.A.I.C.S.: 334220
Personnel:
Michel Counson *(Founder & Mng Dir)*
Pierre Rion *(Chm)*
Joop Janssen *(CEO & Mng Dir)*
Jacques Galloy *(CFO, Sec & Exec VP-Corp Svcs)*
Michel De Wolf *(CTO & Sr VP)*
Luc Doneux *(Exec VP-Sports Div)*
Henry Alexander *(Sr VP-Entertainment & News Div)*
Nicolas Bourdon *(Sr VP-Mktg)*
Benoit Fevrier *(Sr VP-Media Div)*
Fred Garroy *(Sr VP-Americas)*
Quentin Grutman *(Sr VP-EMEA)*
Olivier Heurteaux *(Sr VP-APAC)*
Bernard Stas *(Sr VP-Product Strategy)*
Vincent Theunissen *(Sr VP-HR)*
Board of Directors:
Pierre Rion
Francis Bodson
Francoise Chombar
Michel Counson
Jean Dumbruch
Jacques Galloy
Joop Janssen
Christian Raskin
Yves Trouveroy
Legal Counsel:
Tossens & Associes
Avenue W Churchill 237
1180 Brussels, Belgium

Subsidiaries:

Fundamental Acoustic Research (FAR) (1)
Poissonrue 43
4500 Huy, Belgium
Tel.: (32) 85318123
Fax: (32) 85318124
E-Mail: info@far-audio.com
Web Site: www.far-audio.com
Emp.: 3
Acoustic Studio Designer & Mfr
S.I.C.: 7389
N.A.I.C.S.: 512240
Pierre Thomas *(CEO & Mng Dir)*

XDC S.A. (1)
Rue De Mulhouse 36
4020 Liege, Belgium
Tel.: (32) 43641200
Fax: (32) 43641299
E-Mail: info@xdcinema.com
Web Site: www.xdcinema.com
Sales Range: $1-9.9 Million
Emp.: 65
Digital Cinema Service Company
S.I.C.: 7819
N.A.I.C.S.: 512199
Laurent Minguet *(Founder & CEO)*
Jacques Galloy *(CFO)*

U.S. Subsidiary:

XDC Inc. (2)
9 Law Dr Ste 200
Fairfield, NJ 07004
Tel.: (973) 575-7811
Fax: (973) 575-7812
E-Mail: f.garroy@evs.tv
Web Site: www.xdcinema.com
Emp.: 1
Digital Cinema Services
S.I.C.: 7819
N.A.I.C.S.: 512199
Fred Garroy *(Gen Mgr)*

Non-U.S. Subsidiary:

XDC France (2)
Centre d'affaire Val Courcelle 4 Route de la Noue
91196 Gif-sur-Yvette, France
Tel.: (33) 169187120
Fax: (33) 169187129
E-Mail: xdcfrance@xdcinema.com
Web Site: www.xdcinema.com
Digital Cinema Services
S.I.C.: 7819
N.A.I.C.S.: 512199
Alain Remond *(Gen Mgr)*

U.S. Subsidiary:

EVS Inc. (1)
9 Law Dr Ste 200
Fairfield, NJ 07004
Tel.: (973) 575-7811
Fax: (973) 575-7812
E-Mail: usa@evs.tv
Web Site: www.evs-global.com
Emp.: 10
Broadcast Equipments Mfr
S.I.C.: 3663
N.A.I.C.S.: 334220
Fred Garroy *(Gen Mgr)*

Non-U.S. Subsidiaries:

EVS Broadcast Equipment Iberica S.L. (1)
Avenida de Europa 12-2C Edificio Monaco
28109 Alcobendas, Madrid, Spain
Tel.: (34) 914903930
Fax: (34) 914903939
E-Mail: iberica@evs.tv
Web Site: www.evs-global.tv
Emp.: 4
Broadcasting Equipments Mfr
S.I.C.: 3663

N.A.I.C.S.: 334220
Marc Caeymaex *(Mng Dir)*

EVS Broadcast Equipment Ltd. (1)
Room A 35/F Convoy 169 Electric Road
North Point, China (Hong Kong)
Tel.: (852) 29142501
Fax: (852) 2914 2505
E-Mail: sales@evs-asia.com.hk
Web Site: www.evs-global.com
Emp.: 10
Broadcasting Equipment Mfr
S.I.C.: 3663
N.A.I.C.S.: 334220
Olivia Heurteaux *(Gen Mgr)*

EVS Broadcast UK Ltd. (1)
Ashcombe House 5 The Crescent
Leatherhead, Surrey, KT22 8DY, United Kingdom
Tel.: (44) 1372387250
E-Mail: uk@evs.com
Web Site: www.evs.com
Emp.: 10
Broadcasting Equipments Distr
S.I.C.: 5065
N.A.I.C.S.: 423690
Brett Stoneham *(Gen Mgr)*

EVS Canada Inc. (1)
240-1200 Ave Papineau
Montreal, QC, H2K 4R5, Canada
Tel.: (514) 750-7544
Fax: (514) 750-7518
E-Mail: usa@evs.tv
Web Site: www.evs-global.com
Emp.: 3
Television Broadcasting Equipment Mfr
S.I.C.: 3663
N.A.I.C.S.: 334220

EVS Deutschland GmbH (1)
Oskar Schlemmer Strasse 15
80807 Munich, Germany
Tel.: (49) 89 4111 949 00
Fax: (49) 89 4111 949 99
E-Mail: germany@evs.tv
Broadcast Equipment Mfr
S.I.C.: 3663
N.A.I.C.S.: 334220
Jamie Gordon Mitchell *(Mgr-Office)*

EVS France Developpement S.A.R.L. (1)
48 Quai Carnot
92210 Saint-Cloud, Hauts-de-Seine, France
Tel.: (33) 1 41 12 1245
Fax: (33) 1 47 71 1578
E-Mail: france@evs.tv
Web Site: www.evs-global.com
Television Broadcasting Equipment Mfr
S.I.C.: 3663
N.A.I.C.S.: 334220
Pierre L'Hoest *(Mng Dir)*

EVS France S.A. (1)
Avenue Andre Morizet 6bis
92100 Boulogne-Billancourt, Hauts-de-Seine, France
Tel.: (33) 146999000
Fax: (33) 146999009
E-Mail: france@evs.tv
Web Site: www.evs.tv
Emp.: 3
Television Broadcasting Equipment Mfr
S.I.C.: 3663
N.A.I.C.S.: 334220
Eric Karcher *(Gen Mgr)*

EVS Italy S.R.L. (1)
Via Milano 2
25126 Brescia, Italy
Tel.: (39) 030296400
Fax: (39) 0302943650
E-Mail: italy@evs.tv
Emp.: 3
Broadcasting Equipment Mfr
S.I.C.: 3663
N.A.I.C.S.: 334220
Glameris Konstin *(Gen Mgr)*

Network and Broadcast Systems Limited (NBS) (1)
The Idealism Center Tianyi Street 78
Building 4 N 1407
Gaoxin District, Chengdu, Sichuan, China
Tel.: (86) 18981948985
Fax: (86) 85229142505
E-Mail: info@nbsystems.tv
Emp.: 13
Television Broadcasting Equipment Mfr
S.I.C.: 3663
N.A.I.C.S.: 334220
Laurent Champon *(Gen Mgr)*

OpenCube Technologies S.A.S (1)
Parc Technologique du Canal 9 Avenue de l Europe
31520 Ramonville-Saint-Agne, Haute-Garonne, France
Tel.: (33) 561285606
Fax: (33) 561285635
E-Mail: contact@evs-opencube.com
Web Site: www.opencubetech.com
Emp.: 20
Movie Post Production Software Development Services
S.I.C.: 7371
N.A.I.C.S.: 541511
Benoit Fevrier *(Mng Dir)*

EVZ LIMITED

15 Clifford Street
PO Box 1070
Huntingdale, VIC, 3166, Australia
Tel.: (61) 395455288
Fax: (61) 395589944
E-Mail: info@evz.com.au
Web Site: www.evz.com.au
EVZ—(ASX)
Rev.: $59,610,554
Assets: $51,286,371
Liabilities: $25,362,483
Net Worth: $25,923,888
Earnings: $927,227
Emp.: 350
Fiscal Year-end: 06/30/13

Business Description:
Engineering Services
S.I.C.: 8711
N.A.I.C.S.: 541330

Personnel:
Scott Farthing *(CEO)*
Ian Wallace *(CFO & Sec)*

Board of Directors:
Maxwell Findlay
Graham Burns
Robert Edgley
Raelene Murphy

Subsidiaries:

Brockman Engineering Pty Ltd (1)
340 Forest Rd
Corio, Geelong, VIC, 3214, Australia
Tel.: (61) 352741222
Fax: (61) 352751263
E-Mail: enquiries@brockmaneng.com.au
Web Site: www.brockmaneng.com.au
Emp.: 135
Tank Engineering & Steel Fabrication Services
S.I.C.: 3462
N.A.I.C.S.: 332111
Chris Bishop *(Gen Mgr)*

Danum Engineering Pty. Ltd. (1)
17 Seaforth St
North Shore, Geelong, VIC, 3214, Australia
Tel.: (61) 3 5278 4488
Fax: (61) 3 5277 9378
E-Mail: info@danum.com.au
Web Site: www.danum.com.au
Emp.: 100
Engineering Services
S.I.C.: 8711
N.A.I.C.S.: 541330
Bradley Harris *(Mgr-Bus Dev)*

Syfon Systems Pty Ltd (1)
22 Hargreaves St
Huntingdale, VIC, 3166, Australia
Tel.: (61) 3 9542 6000
Fax: (61) 3 9542 606
E-Mail: syfon@syfon.com
Web Site: www.syfon.com
Emp.: 70
Roof Drainage Services
S.I.C.: 1761
N.A.I.C.S.: 238160
Adam Bellgrove *(Mng Dir)*

TSF Engineering Pty Ltd (1)
1 Prosperity Parade
Warriewood, NSW, 2102, Australia
Tel.: (61) 299972200
Fax: (61) 299974077
E-Mail: tsfnsw@tsfeng.com.au
Web Site: www.tsfeng.com.au
Emp.: 30
Power Generation Equipments Mfr
S.I.C.: 4931
N.A.I.C.S.: 221118
Andrew Green *(Mng Dir)*

EWE AKTIENGESELLSCHAFT

Donnerschweer Strasse 22-26
26123 Oldenburg, Lower Saxony, Germany
Tel.: (49) 441 4805 0
E-Mail: info@ewe.de
Web Site: www.ewe.com
Sls.: $11,559,157,939
Assets: $14,093,592,198
Liabilities: $10,772,186,957
Net Worth: $3,321,405,241
Earnings: $186,848,396
Emp.: 800
Fiscal Year-end: 12/31/12

Business Description:
Energy Services
S.I.C.: 4931
N.A.I.C.S.: 221122

Personnel:
Stephan-Andreas Kaulvers *(Chm-Supervisory Bd)*
Werner Brinker *(CEO & Chm-Mgmt Bd)*
Berhard Bramlage *(Fourth Deputy Chm-Supervisory Bd)*
Hans Eveslage *(Third Deputy Chm-Supervisory Bd)*
Rainer Janssen *(First Deputy Chm-Supervisory Bd)*
Frank Mastiaux *(Second Deputy Chm-Supervisory Bd)*
Matthias Bruckmann *(Member-Mgmt Bd-Sls)*
Torsten Kohne *(Member-Mgmt Bd-Power Generation)*
Heiko Sanders *(Member-Mgmt Bd-Fin)*

Supervisory Board of Directors:
Stephan-Andreas Kaulvers
Wolfgang Behnke
Berhard Bramlage
Eckhard Dibke
Hans Eveslage
Gregor Heller
Jurgen Humer
Rainer Janssen
Aloys Kiepe
Peter Marrek
Frank Mastiaux
Peter Meiwald
Johann Pachole
Immo Schlepper
Ulrike Schlieper
Heiner Schonecke
Gerd Schwandner
Thomas Windgassen
Hans-Josef Zimmer

Subsidiaries:

BCC Business Communication Company GmbH (1)
Heinrich-Nordhoff-Str 69
38440 Wolfsburg, Germany
Tel.: (49) 5361 2777 0
Fax: (49) 812255124
E-Mail: info@bcc.de
Web Site: www.bcc.de
Emp.: 100
Information Technology Consulting Services
S.I.C.: 7373
N.A.I.C.S.: 541512

BTC Business Technology Consulting AG (1)
Escherweg 5
26121 Oldenburg, Germany
Tel.: (49) 441 36 12 0
Fax: (49) 441 36 12 3999
E-Mail: office@btc-ag.com
Web Site: www.btc-ag.com
Sls.: $219,829,561
Emp.: 1,512
Information Technology Consulting Services
S.I.C.: 7373
N.A.I.C.S.: 541512
Bulent Uzuner *(CEO)*
Joachim Muller *(Officer-Data Security)*

BTC IT Services GmbH (1)
Escherweg 5
26121 Oldenburg, Germany
Tel.: (49) 441 36 192 0
Fax: (49) 441 36 192 1799
E-Mail: office@btc-it-services.com
Web Site: www.btc-it-services.com
Information Technology Consulting Services
S.I.C.: 7373
N.A.I.C.S.: 541512

E&D Energie- und Dienstleistungs GmbH & Co. KG (1)
Merlostr 10
50668 Cologne, Germany
Tel.: (49) 221 972242 0
Fax: (49) 221 733071
Natural Gas Distr
S.I.C.: 4924
N.A.I.C.S.: 221210

ENRo Ludwigsfelde Energie GmbH (1)
Rudolf-Diesel-Strabe 15 Industriepark
14974 Ludwigsfelde, Germany
Tel.: (49) 3378 82 30
Fax: (49) 3378 82 31 02
E-Mail: info@enro-ludwigsfelde.de
Web Site: www.enro-ludwigsfelde.de
Electric Power, Heat & Natural Gas Distr
S.I.C.: 4911
N.A.I.C.S.: 221122

EWE Biogas GmbH & Co. KG (1)
Isums 45a
26409 Wittmund, Germany
Tel.: (49) 4462 9199 0
Fax: (49) 4462919919
E-Mail: biogasanlage-wittmund@ewe.de
Web Site: www.ewe-biogas.de
Electric Power Generation Services
S.I.C.: 4939
N.A.I.C.S.: 221118

EWE IMMoBILIEN GmbH (1)
Donnerschweer Str 22
26123 Oldenburg, Germany
Tel.: (49) 44148050
Natural Gas Distr
S.I.C.: 4924
N.A.I.C.S.: 221210

EWE TEL GmbH (1)
Cloppenburger Str 310
26133 Oldenburg, Germany
Tel.: (49) 441 8000 2773
E-Mail: info@ewe.de
Telecommunication Services
S.I.C.: 4899
N.A.I.C.S.: 517919

EWE TRADING GmbH (1)
Tirpitzstrabe 39
Oldenburg, Germany
Tel.: (49) 441 35095 0
Fax: (49) 441 35095 419
E-Mail: energyhandel@ewetel.net
Emp.: 65
Electric Power & Natural Gas Distr
S.I.C.: 4939
N.A.I.C.S.: 221122
Malte Neuendorff *(Gen Mgr)*

EWE Urbanisation Dienstleistungs GmbH (1)
Am Weser-Terminal 1
28217 Bremen, Germany
Tel.: (49) 421 696527 0
Fax: (49) 421 696527 19
E-Mail: udg-brv@ewe.de
Web Site: www.udg-ewe.de
Emp.: 1
Residential Building Construction Services
S.I.C.: 1522
N.A.I.C.S.: 236116

EWE VERTRIEB GmbH (1)
Donnerschweer Str 22-26
26123 Oldenburg, Germany
Tel.: (49) 4 41 803 0

EWE Aktiengesellschaft—(Continued)

Fax: (49) 4 41 803 3999
E-Mail: info@ewe.de
Electric Power & Natural Gas Distr
S.I.C.: 4911
N.A.I.C.S.: 221122
Alwin Schlormann *(Bus Dir)*

Subsidiary:

EWE NETZ GmbH (2)
Cloppenburger Str 302
26133 Oldenburg, Germany
Tel.: (49) 441 4808 0
Fax: (49) 441 4808 1195
E-Mail: info-netz@ewe.de
Web Site: www.ewe-netz.de
Emp.: 1,655
Energy Infrastructure Network Operator
S.I.C.: 1623
N.A.I.C.S.: 237130

NaturWatt GmbH (1)
Rummelweg 14
Oldenburg, Germany
Tel.: (49) 441 350910 0
Fax: (49) 441 350910 59
E-Mail: info@naturwatt.de
Web Site: www.naturwatt.de
Electric Power Distr
S.I.C.: 4911
N.A.I.C.S.: 221122

offshore Windpark RIFFGAT GmbH & Co. KG (1)
Tirpitzstrabe 39
26122 Oldenburg, Germany
Tel.: (49) 441 803 4075
Fax: (49) 4418034079
E-Mail: info@riffgat.de
Web Site: www.riffgat.de
Electric Power Generation & Distribution Services
S.I.C.: 4939
N.A.I.C.S.: 221118

PRo CoNSULT Management- und Systemberatung GmbH (1)
Wilhelm-Theodor-Romheld-Strabe 24
55130 Mainz, Germany
Tel.: (49) 6131 27562 0
Web Site: www.proconsult.de
Business Management Consulting Services
S.I.C.: 8742
N.A.I.C.S.: 541611

SoCoN Sonar Control Kavernenvermessung GmbH (1)
Windmuhlenstrabe 41
Emmerke, 31180 Giesen, Germany
Tel.: (49) 5121 998 19 0
Fax: (49) 5121 998 19 88
E-Mail: info@socon.com
Web Site: www.socon.info
Emp.: 60
Cavern Surveying Services
S.I.C.: 8713
N.A.I.C.S.: 541360

swb CREA GmbH (1)
Rickmersstrabe 90
27568 Bremerhaven, Germany
Tel.: (49) 471 958 713 10
Fax: (49) 471 958 713 15
Emp.: 10
Electric Power Generation Services
S.I.C.: 4911
N.A.I.C.S.: 221118

swb Entsorgung GmbH & Co. KG (1)
Otavistr 7-9
28237 Bremen, Germany
Tel.: (49) 421 359 79 333
Fax: (49) 421 359 66 40
E-Mail: info@swb-gruppe.de
Waste Disposal Services
S.I.C.: 4953
N.A.I.C.S.: 562211

swb Erzeugung GmbH & Co. KG (1)
Theodor-Heuss-Allee 20
28215 Bremen, Germany
Tel.: (49) 421 359 3351
Fax: (49) 421 359 3350
E-Mail: info.erzeugung@swb-gruppe.de
Emp.: 500
Electric Power Generation Services
S.I.C.: 4931
N.A.I.C.S.: 221118

swb Messung und Abrechnung GmbH (1)
Theodor-Heuss-Allee 20
28215 Bremen, Germany
Tel.: (49) 421 988 68 0
Fax: (49) 421 988 68 197
E-Mail: info@metacount.de
Web Site: www.metacount.de
Emp.: 180
Utility Metering Services
S.I.C.: 7389
N.A.I.C.S.: 561990

swb Netze Bremerhaven GmbH & Co. KG (1)
Rickmersstrabe 90
27568 Bremerhaven, Germany
Tel.: (49) 471 477 1344
Fax: (49) 471 477 1332
E-Mail: netze-bhv@swb-gruppe.de
Electric Power Generation Services
S.I.C.: 4911
N.A.I.C.S.: 221118

swb Services GmbH & Co. KG (1)
Theodor-Heuss-Allee 20
28215 Bremen, Germany
Tel.: (49) 421 359 3494
Fax: (49) 421 359 3455
E-Mail: info@swb-services.de
Web Site: www.swb-services.de
Emp.: 180
Energy Consulting Services
S.I.C.: 8999
N.A.I.C.S.: 541690

swb Vertrieb Bremen GmbH (1)
Theodor-Heuss-Allee 20
28215 Bremen, Germany
Tel.: (49) 421 359 3590
Fax: (49) 421 359 2499
Electric Power Distr
S.I.C.: 4931
N.A.I.C.S.: 221122

swb Vertrieb Bremerhaven GmbH & Co. KG (1)
Rickmersstrabe 90
27568 Bremerhaven, Germany
Tel.: (49) 471 477 1111
Fax: (49) 471 477 2321
Electric Power Distr
S.I.C.: 4931
N.A.I.C.S.: 221122

Non-U.S. Subsidiaries:

Bursagaz Bursa Sehirici Dogalgaz Dagitim Ticaret ve Taahhut A.S. (1)
Kavaklidere Sk No 15
16265 Bursa, Turkey
Tel.: (90) 444 1 133
Natural Gas Distr
S.I.C.: 4924
N.A.I.C.S.: 221210

EWE Enerji AS (1)
Buyukdere Cad No 127 Astoria Tower A Kat 4
34394 Esentepe, Istanbul, Turkey
Tel.: (90) 212 336 60 10
Fax: (90) 212 336 60 40
E-Mail: info@eweenerji.com.tr
Web Site: www.eweenerji.com.tr
Emp.: 15
Natural Gas Distr
S.I.C.: 4924
N.A.I.C.S.: 221210

EWE Turkey Holding A.S. (1)
Buyukdere Caddesi No 127 Astoria A Blok Kat 25
34394 Esentepe, Istanbul, Turkey
Tel.: (90) 212 355 26 00
Fax: (90) 212 355 26 48
Emp.: 397
Investment Management Services
S.I.C.: 6282
N.A.I.C.S.: 523920

Kayserigaz Kayseri Dogalgaz Dagitim Pazarlama ve Ticaret A.S. (1)
Yeni Mahalle Mustafa Kemal Pasa Bulvari 5 Cadde No 61
Kocasinan, 38090 Kayseri, Turkey
Tel.: (90) 352 207 20 00
Fax: (90) 352 207 20 05
E-Mail: bilgi@kayserigaz.com
Web Site: www.kayserigaz.com
Emp.: 150
Natural Gas Distr
S.I.C.: 4924
N.A.I.C.S.: 221210

EWEIN BERHAD

Plot 317 & 318 Tingkat Perusahaan Tiga Mukim 1
Kawasan Perusahaan Perai, 13600 Perai, Penang, Malaysia
Tel.: (60) 4 3992122
Fax: (60) 4 3997548
E-Mail: info@tekunasas.com
Web Site: www.eweinberhad.com
EWEIN—(KLS)
Rev.: $28,221,458
Assets: $47,505,542
Liabilities: $20,673,666
Net Worth: $26,831,875
Earnings: $1,800,712
Emp.: 400
Fiscal Year-end: 12/31/12

Business Description:
Holding Company; Precision Sheet Metal Fabricated Parts Mfr
S.I.C.: 6719
N.A.I.C.S.: 551112

Personnel:
Swee Kheng Ewe *(Mng Dir)*
Poh Lim Chuah *(Deputy Mng Dir)*
Wai Hong Chee *(Co-Sec)*
Yee Lin Wong *(Co-Sec)*

Board of Directors:
Tiong Hor Ewe
Abdul Rahim Abdul Halim
Poh Lim Chuah
Swee Kheng Ewe
Ah Hua Khor
Tiang Hua Lau
See Wah Wong

Subsidiaries:

Kelpen Resources Sdn Bhd (KRSB) (1)
212 Tkt Perusahaan 4
13600 Prai, Pulau Pinang, Malaysia
Tel.: (60) 43976584
Fax: (60) 43991412
E-Mail:
Emp.: 100
Investment Management Services
S.I.C.: 8748
N.A.I.C.S.: 541618
Sweekheng Eve *(Mng Dir)*

Subsidiary:

Kelpen Plastics Technology Sdn. Bhd (2)
Plot 212 Mukim 1 Tingkat Perusahaan 4
Free Industrial Zone, Prai, Pulau Pinang, 13600, Malaysia
Tel.: (60) 43977255
Fax: (60) 43991412
E-Mail: enquiry@kelpen.com.my
Web Site: www.kelpen.com.my
Emp.: 120
Metal Products Mfr
S.I.C.: 3499
N.A.I.C.S.: 332999
Poh Lim Chuah *(Deputy Mng Dir)*

Precision Press Industries Sdn Bhd (PPISB) (1)
Plot 318 Tingkat Perusahaan 3 Mk 1 Kawasan
Perindustrian Prai, Perai, Penang, 13600, Malaysia
Tel.: (60) 43992122
Fax: (60) 43997548
E-Mail: info@tekunasas.com
Web Site: www.tekunasas.com
Emp.: 10
Metal Stamping Service Provider
S.I.C.: 3466
N.A.I.C.S.: 332119
P. L. Chuah *(Deputy Mng Dir)*

Tekun Asas Sdn Bhd (TASB) (1)
Plot 318 Tingkat Perusahaan Tiga Mukim 1 Kawasan
Perusahaan Perai, 13600 Perai, Pulau Pinang, Malaysia
Tel.: (60) 43992122
Fax: (60) 43997548
E-Mail: info@tekunasas.com
Web Site: www.tekunasas.com
Emp.: 300
Metal Products Mfr
S.I.C.: 3499
N.A.I.C.S.: 332999

EWING PUBLIC RELATIONS, S.R.O.

Smichov Gate Plzenska 3217/16
150 00 Prague, Czech Republic
Tel.: (420) 224 828 065 8
Fax: (420) 224 828 456
E-Mail: ewing@ewingpr.cz
Web Site: www.ewingpr.cz
Year Founded: 1998
Sales Range: $1-9.9 Million
Emp.: 20

Business Description:
Public Relations Agency
S.I.C.: 8743
N.A.I.C.S.: 541820

Personnel:
Jiri Hrabovsky *(Owner)*
Pavlina Rieselova *(Owner)*

EWON COMFORTECH CO., LTD.

127-33 503-beon-gil Wonang-ro
Yeounmu-eup, Nonsan, Chungcheongnam-do, 320-836, Korea (South)
Tel.: (82) 41 742 6688
Fax: (82) 41 742 6744
Web Site: www.ewonseat.co.kr
Year Founded: 1994
088290—(KRS)

Business Description:
Automobile Seat Mfr
S.I.C.: 2396
N.A.I.C.S.: 336360

Personnel:
Seong Mo Kang *(Chm)*

EWORK SCANDINAVIA AB

Klarabergsgatan 60 3tr
111 21 Stockholm, Sweden
Tel.: (46) 850605500
Fax: (46) 50605501
E-Mail: info@ework.se
Web Site: www.ework.se
EWRK—(OMX)
Sls.: $545,678,050
Assets: $169,136,492
Liabilities: $148,167,749
Net Worth: $20,968,744
Earnings: $7,231,018
Emp.: 150
Fiscal Year-end: 12/31/12

Business Description:
IT & Management Consulting Services
S.I.C.: 8999
N.A.I.C.S.: 541690

Personnel:
Magnus Berglind *(Founder)*
Staffan Salen *(Chm)*
Claes Ruthberg *(CEO)*
Magnus Eriksson *(CFO)*
Nils Keife *(CIO)*
Zoran Covic *(CEO-Denmark & Mgr-Malmoe Site)*
Magnus Silen *(CEO-Finland)*
Helge Stromnes *(CEO-Norge)*

Board of Directors:
Staffan Salen
Magnus Berglind
Dan Berlin
Sven Hagstromer
Claes Ruthberg
Anna Storakers
Erik Tornberg

Non-U.S. Subsidiaries:

eWork Danmark ApS (1)
Havnegade 39
1058 Copenhagen, Denmark
Tel.: (45) 88969550
E-Mail: search.dk@eworknordic.com
Web Site: www.eworknordic.com
Emp.: 7
Business Consulting Services
S.I.C.: 8742
N.A.I.C.S.: 541611
Bettina Schwartz Thorkelin *(Mng Dir)*

eWork Nordic OY (1)
Tekniikantie 4B
02150 Espoo, Uusimaa, Finland
Tel.: (358) 207870800
Fax: (358) 207870801
E-Mail: support.fi@eworknordic.com
Web Site: www.eworknordic.com
Emp.: 10
Business Consulting Services
S.I.C.: 8742
N.A.I.C.S.: 541611
Magnus Silen *(Mng Dir)*

eWork Norge AS (1)
Ovre Slottsgate 12B
0157 Oslo, Norway
Tel.: (47) 22403620
Fax: (47) 22403621
E-Mail: info.no@ework.no
Web Site: www.ework.no
Emp.: 10
Business Consulting Services
S.I.C.: 8742
N.A.I.C.S.: 541611
Helge Stromnes *(Gen Mgr)*

EXA E&C INC.

Daerung Post Tower 15F 212-8 Guro-Dong Digitalro 288
Guro-Gu, Seoul, Korea (South)
Tel.: (82) 2 3289 5100
Fax: (82) 2 3289 5261
Web Site: www.exaenc.com
Year Founded: 1988
054940—(KRS)
Sales Range: $100-124.9 Million
Emp.: 240

Business Description:
Interior Design Services
S.I.C.: 7389
N.A.I.C.S.: 541410

Personnel:
Cha Keuk Koo *(Chm & CEO)*

EXACT HOLDING N.V.

Molengraaffsingel 33
P O BOX 566
2629 Delft, 2600, Netherlands
Tel.: (31) 15 711 50 00
Fax: (31) 15 711 50 10
E-Mail: ir@exact.com
Web Site: www.exact.com
Year Founded: 1984
EXACT—(EUR)
Rev.: $292,237,353
Assets: $276,787,360
Liabilities: $140,332,838
Net Worth: $136,454,522
Earnings: $25,150,494
Emp.: 1,653
Fiscal Year-end: 12/31/12

Business Description:
Holding Company; Business Software Publisher & Distr
Export
S.I.C.: 6719
N.A.I.C.S.: 551112

Personnel:
Thierry C. V. Schaap *(Chm-Supervisory Bd)*
Willem Cramer *(Vice Chm-Supervisory Bd)*
Erik van der Meijden *(CEO & Member-Mgmt Bd)*
Onno Krap *(CFO & Member-Mgmt Bd)*
Jelle Zuidema *(PR Officer)*
Mitchell Alcon *(Pres-Americas)*
Marinus ter Laak *(Member-Mgmt Bd & Mng Dir-Bus Solutions)*
Hartmut Wagner *(Member-Mgmt Bd & Mng Dir-Cloud Solutions)*

Supervisory Board of Directors:
Thierry C. V. Schaap
Willem Cramer
Evert Kooistra
Peter van Haasteren

Subsidiaries:

Exact EMEA B.V. (1)
Molengraaffsingel 33
NL-2629 JD Delft, Netherlands NL
Tel.: (31) 157115200 (100%)
Fax: (31) 157115210
E-Mail: emea-sales@exact.com
Web Site: www.exact.com
Emp.: 60
Holding Company; Regional Managing Office
S.I.C.: 6719
N.A.I.C.S.: 551112

Non-U.S. Subsidiaries:

Exact Business Software (Switzerland) AG (2)
Thurgauerstrasse 40
PO Box 6463
8050 Zurich, Switzerland (100%)
Tel.: (41) 443073560
Fax: (41) 443073561
E-Mail: info@switzerland.exactsoftware.com
Web Site: www.exactsoftware.de
Emp.: 1
Software Publishers
S.I.C.: 7372
N.A.I.C.S.: 511210
Sarp Sagnak *(Mng Dir)*

Exact France SARL (2)
18 rue Jules Saulnier
Parc du Colombier Saint-Denis, 93285
Paris, France (100%)
Tel.: (33) 155872020
Fax: (33) 155872040
E-Mail: exactement@france.exactsoftware.com
Web Site: www.exactsoftware.com
Emp.: 15
Industrial Machinery & Equipment Whslr
S.I.C.: 5084
N.A.I.C.S.: 423830
Max Timmer *(Mgr)*

Exact Hungary Software Ltd. (2)
Vaciut 76
1133 Budapest, Hungary (100%)
Tel.: (36) 18874100
Fax: (36) 18874101
E-Mail: exact@exact.hu
Web Site: www.exact.hu
Emp.: 9
Electronic Parts & Equipment Merchant Whslr
S.I.C.: 5065
N.A.I.C.S.: 423690

Exact Portugal Informatica, Lda (2)
CEB-Centro Empresarial de Braga
Lg Estrada da Misericordia, 4705-319
Braga, Portugal (80%)
Tel.: (351) 253339123
Fax: (351) 253674378
Software Publishers
S.I.C.: 7372
N.A.I.C.S.: 511210

Exact Russia OOO (2)
3-ya ul Yamskogo Polya 28 offices 314-315
125040 Moscow, Russia
Tel.: (7) 4957807232
Fax: (7) 4957807233
E-Mail: russia@exactinternational.com
Web Site: www.exactrussia.com
Emp.: 10
Software Publishers
S.I.C.: 7372
N.A.I.C.S.: 511210
Alex Turundaef *(Gen Mgr)*

Exact Software Austria GmbH (2)
Weyringergasse 3 4 Stock
1040 Vienna, Austria (100%)
Tel.: (43) 160221110
Fax: (43) 1602211122
E-Mail: kontakt@exact.com
Web Site: www.exact.com
Emp.: 8
Software Publishers
S.I.C.: 7372
N.A.I.C.S.: 511210
Brian Aiken *(Mng Dir)*

Subsidiary:

Exact Soft-2000 GmbH (3)
Paris-Lodron-Str 19
5020 Salzburg, Austria (100%)
Tel.: (43) 66283760
Fax: (43) 662825482
E-Mail: office@soft-2000.com
Emp.: 30
Software Publishers
S.I.C.: 7372
N.A.I.C.S.: 511210
Brian Aiken *(Mng Dir)*

Exact Software Belgium N.V. (2)
Koningin Astridlaan 166
1780 Wemmel, Belgium (100%)
Tel.: (32) 27111626
Fax: (32) 27111613
E-Mail: sales@exact.com
Web Site: www.exact.be
Emp.: 60
Software Publishers
S.I.C.: 7372
N.A.I.C.S.: 511210
Stefaan Missiaen *(Mng Dir)*

Exact Software Deutschland GmbH (2)
Karl-Hammerschmidt Strasse 40
Muchen-Dornach, 85609 Munich, Germany
Tel.: (49) 89360420
Fax: (49) 8936042299
E-Mail: hotmail@exact.com
Web Site: www.exactsoftware.com
Emp.: 100
Software Publishers
S.I.C.: 7372
N.A.I.C.S.: 511210
Daniel Schalag *(Gen Mgr)*

Subsidiary:

Exact Software GmbH (3)
Barthonia Forum Vogelsanger Strasse 76
50823 Cologne, Germany
Tel.: (49) 221991970
Fax: (49) 22199197250
E-Mail: info@exactsoftware.de
Web Site: www.exactsoftware.com
Emp.: 23
Software Publishers
S.I.C.: 7372
N.A.I.C.S.: 511210

Exact Software Italia S.r.l. (2)
Via A Ponchielli 1
Cernusco Sul Naviglio, 20063 Milan, Italy (100%)
Tel.: (39) 236545375
Fax: (39) 0236545374
E-Mail: infoitalia@exact.com
Web Site: www.exactsoftware.com
Emp.: 8
Software Publishers
S.I.C.: 7372
N.A.I.C.S.: 511210
Julien Anno *(Mng Dir)*

Exact Software Poland Sp. z o.o. (2)
Ul Hankiewicza 2
02103 Warsaw, Poland
Tel.: (48) 225762200
Fax: (48) 225762201
E-Mail: warsaw@exact.com
Web Site: www.exact.pl/Kontakt-166.html
Emp.: 50
Software Publishers
S.I.C.: 7372
N.A.I.C.S.: 511210
Marek Cuz *(Gen Mgr)*

Exact Software Romania S.R.L. (2)
Str Chiscani 25-27 Grant Center-Etaj 4
012241 Bucharest, Romania (100%)
Tel.: (40) 212017968
Fax: (40) 212221693
Web Site: www.exactsoftware.com
Emp.: 100
Software Publishers
S.I.C.: 7372
N.A.I.C.S.: 511210
Stephane Manfroy *(Mng Dir)*

Exact Software Slovakia s.r.o (2)
Leskova 16
81104 Bratislava, Slovakia
Tel.: (421) 257100604
Fax: (421) 257100601
E-Mail: slovakia@exactsoftware.com
Web Site: www.exactsoftware.com
Publishers
S.I.C.: 2741
N.A.I.C.S.: 511199

Exact Software Spain, S.R.L. (2)
Nudo Eisenhower Canada Real de las Merinas 7
28042 Madrid, Spain (100%)
Tel.: (34) 915152141
Fax: (34) 915152144
E-Mail: salv5062@exact.nl
Web Site: www.exactsoftware.com
Emp.: 40
Computer & Computer Peripheral Equipment & Software Merchant Whslr
S.I.C.: 5045
N.A.I.C.S.: 423430

Exact Software (UK) Ltd. (2)
Tamesis The Glanty
Egham, Surrey, TW209AW, United Kingdom UK
Tel.: (44) 1784221200
Fax: (44) 1784221251
E-Mail: infouk@exactsoftware.com
Web Site: www.exactinternational.com
Emp.: 250
Software Publishers
S.I.C.: 7372
N.A.I.C.S.: 511210
Jaime Stewart *(Mng Dir)*

Subsidiaries:

Exact Manufacturing Systems (UK) Ltd (3)
Unit 7 Westleigh Business Park
Blaby, Leicester, LE84EZ, United Kingdom (100%)
Tel.: (44) 1162784888
Fax: (44) 1162784666
E-Mail: emsinfo@exactsoftware.com
Web Site: www.software.com
Emp.: 5
Custom Computer Programming Services
S.I.C.: 7371
N.A.I.C.S.: 541511
Rajesh Patel *(Mng Dir)*

Longview Solutions Ltd (3)
3rd Floor Viewpoint House
Staines-upon-Thames, TW18 4JT, United Kingdom
Tel.: (44) 1784 221270
Fax: (44) 1784 221759
E-Mail: infouk@exactsoftware.com
Web Site: www.longview.com
Emp.: 12
Financial Software Development Services
S.I.C.: 7371
N.A.I.C.S.: 541511
John Power *(CEO)*
Chris Carlstead *(Pres-Tax)*
Gerard Chiasson *(Pres-Corp Performance Mgmt)*

Exact, s.r.o. (2)
Zavodskeho 5
636 00 Brno, Czech Republic (100%)
Tel.: (420) 511 115 501
Fax: (420) 511 115 500
E-Mail: info@exact.cz
Web Site: www.exact.cz
Emp.: 20
Computer & Computer Peripheral Equipment & Software Merchant Whslr
S.I.C.: 5045
N.A.I.C.S.: 423430
Vaclav Urban *(Mng Dir)*

Exact Group B.V (1)
Molengraaffsingel 33
Leidschendam, 2629 JD, Netherlands
Tel.: (31) 157115002
Fax: (31) 157115011
Software Development Services
S.I.C.: 7371
N.A.I.C.S.: 541511

Exact Holding N.V.—(Continued)

Subsidiaries:

Exact Corporate Services B.V. (2)
Molengraaffsingel 33
Delft, 2629 JD, Netherlands
Tel.: (31) 157115000
Fax: (31) 157115110
Software Development Services
S.I.C.: 7371
N.A.I.C.S.: 541511

Exact International Development B.V. (2)
Molengraaffsingel 33
Delft, 2629 JD, Netherlands
Tel.: (31) 152515584
Fax: (31) 157115110
E-Mail: info@exact.com
Web Site: www.exact.com
Emp.: 55
Software Development Services
S.I.C.: 7373
N.A.I.C.S.: 541512
Erik van der Meijden *(CEO)*

Exact Online B.V. (2)
Molengraaffsingel 33
2629 JD Delft, Netherlands
Tel.: (31) 15 711 51 00
Fax: (31) 15 711 51 10
E-Mail: info@exactonline.nl
Online Accounting Software Development Services
S.I.C.: 7371
N.A.I.C.S.: 541511

Exact Nederland B.V. (1)
Molengraaffsingel 33
NL-2926 JD Delft, Netherlands NL (100%)
Tel.: (31) 157115100
Fax: (31) 157115110
E-Mail: info.nl@exact.com
Web Site: www.exact.com
Emp.: 600
Holding Company; Business Software Publisher & Distr
S.I.C.: 6719
N.A.I.C.S.: 551112
Erik Meaven *(Mng Dir)*
Paul Ramakers *(Mng Dir)*

Subsidiaries:

Exact Software Nederland B.V. (2)
Molengraaffsingel 33
2629 JD Delft, Netherlands NL (100%)
Tel.: (31) 157115100
Fax: (31) 157115110
E-Mail: info.nl@exact.com
Web Site: www.exact.com
Emp.: 600
Business Software Publisher
S.I.C.: 7372
N.A.I.C.S.: 511210
Paul Ramakers *(Mng Dir)*

U.S. Subsidiaries:

Exact Holding North America, Inc. (1)
35 Vlg Rd
Middleton, MA 01949
Tel.: (978) 560-6900
Fax: (978) 560-6901
Investment Management Services
S.I.C.: 6211
N.A.I.C.S.: 523999

Exact Software North America, LLC (1)
35 Village Rd
Middleton, MA 01949 DE
Tel.: (978) 560-6900
Fax: (978) 560-6901
Web Site: www.exact.com
Emp.: 30
Business Software Publisher, Distr & Support Services
S.I.C.: 7372
N.A.I.C.S.: 511210
Mitchell Alcon *(Pres)*

Branch:

Exact Software North America - Columbus (2)
8800 Lyra Dr Ste 220
Columbus, OH 43240-2151
Tel.: (614) 410-2600
Toll Free: (800) 468-0834
Web Site: www.exact.com
Emp.: 200
Business Software Publisher, Distr & Support Services
Export
S.I.C.: 7372
N.A.I.C.S.: 511210
Kit Martin *(Mgr-Mktg Comm)*

Non-U.S. Subsidiaries:

Exact Asia Development Centre Sdn. Bhd. (1)
Jalan Tun Razak 199 Suite 8-01 8-02 Level 8 GTower
50400 Kuala Lumpur, Malaysia
Tel.: (60) 3 2179 4242
Fax: (60) 3 2179 4244
Software Development Services
S.I.C.: 7371
N.A.I.C.S.: 541511

Non-U.S. Subsidiary:

Exact Software (International) N.V. (2)
Schottegatweg Oost 82-84 B1
Willemstad, Curacao
Tel.: (599) 9 4650077
Fax: (599) 9 4650082
Web Site: www.exactcaribbean.com
Emp.: 1
Software Development Services
S.I.C.: 7371
N.A.I.C.S.: 541511
Denise Testing *(Gen Mgr)*

Exact Software (Antilles) N.V. (1)
Schottegatweg Oost 82-84 B1
Willemstad, Curacao
Tel.: (599) 9 4650077
Fax: (599) 9 4650082
Emp.: 1
Software Development Services
S.I.C.: 7371
N.A.I.C.S.: 541511
Densie Densie *(Gen Mgr)*

Exact Software Asia Sdn. Bhd. (1)
A-6-1 & A-6-2 Northpoint Mid Valley City
No 1 Medan Syed Putra Utara, 59200
Kuala Lumpur, Malaysia MY (100%)
Tel.: (60) 322822221
Fax: (60) 322823231
Web Site: www.exact.com
Holding Company; Regional Managing Office
S.I.C.: 6719
N.A.I.C.S.: 551112
Roland Rott *(Mng Dir)*

Subsidiary:

Exact Software (Malaysia) Sdn. Bhd. (2)
A-6-1 & A-6-2 Northpoint Mid Valley City
No 1 Medan Syed Putra Utara, 59200
Kuala Lumpur, Malaysia MY
Tel.: (60) 322822221
Fax: (60) 20816900
E-Mail: heej283842@exactsoftware.com
Web Site: www.exact.com
Business Software Developer, Publisher, Distr & Support Services
S.I.C.: 7372
N.A.I.C.S.: 511210
Tan Chor Hoong *(Gen Mgr)*

Exact Software Australia Pty Ltd (1)
Suite 401 Level 4 15 Help Street
Chatswood, Sydney, NSW, 2067, Australia
Tel.: (61) 28448 1900
Fax: (61) 28448 1984
E-Mail: info.au@exact.com
Web Site: www.exactsoftware.com.au
Emp.: 1
Software Development Services
S.I.C.: 7371
N.A.I.C.S.: 541511
Elisabeth Schindler *(Mgr-Territory)*

Exact Software Canada Ltd. (1)
1165 Franklin Blvd Unit E
N1R 8E1 Cambridge, ON, Canada
Tel.: (877) 392-2879
Fax: (519) 624-5732
E-Mail: info@exactsoftware.ca
Web Site: www.exact.com
Software Development Services
S.I.C.: 7371
N.A.I.C.S.: 541511

Exact Software Czech Republic, s.r.o. (1)
Antala Staska 510/38
140 00 Prague, Czech Republic
Tel.: (420) 241 049 011
Fax: (420) 241 049 000
E-Mail: info.cee@exact.com
Web Site: www.exact.co.cz
Emp.: 14
Software Development Services
S.I.C.: 7371
N.A.I.C.S.: 541511

Exact Software de Mexico S.A. de C.V. (1)
Jaime Balmes No 11 Edificio E Mezanine 1A
Seccion Miguel Hidalgo, 11560 Mexico, Mexico
Tel.: (52) 5555573733
Web Site: www.exact.com
Software Development Services
S.I.C.: 7371
N.A.I.C.S.: 541511

Exact Software France Sarl. (1)
18 rue Jules Saulnier
Parc du Colombier, 93 285 Saint Denis, France
Tel.: (33) 1 55 872020
Fax: (33) 1 55 872040
Web Site: www.exact.com
Emp.: 20
Software Development Services
S.I.C.: 7371
N.A.I.C.S.: 541511
Stephanie Malloy *(Gen Mgr)*

Exact Software (Shanghai) Co., Ltd. (1)
Suite 1101 Shanghai CITIC Square No 1168 Nanjing Road West
200041 Shanghai, China
Tel.: (86) 21 52925666
Fax: (86) 21 52925005
E-Mail: marketing.cn@exact.com
Emp.: 25
Software Development Services
S.I.C.: 7371
N.A.I.C.S.: 541511
Patrick Cai *(Gen Mgr)*

Exact Software Singapore PTE Ltd. (1)
7 Temasek Boulevard 08-03 Suntec Tower One
Singapore, 38987, Singapore
Tel.: (65) 62224822
Fax: (65) 62250883
Emp.: 7
Software Development Services
S.I.C.: 7371
N.A.I.C.S.: 541511

Exact Software (Thailand) Ltd. (1)
Unit 2312 195 Empire Tower Unit 2312
South Sathorn Road
Yannawa Sathorn, Bangkok, 10120, Thailand
Tel.: (66) 2 670 1604
Fax: (66) 2 670 1605
Software Development Services
S.I.C.: 7371
N.A.I.C.S.: 541511

Longview Solutions Inc. (1)
65 Allstate Parkway Suite 200
Markham, ON, L3R 9X1, Canada
Tel.: (905) 940-1510
Fax: (905) 940-8310
E-Mail: learning@longview.com
Web Site: www.longview.com
Emp.: 200
Financial Software Development Services
S.I.C.: 7371
N.A.I.C.S.: 541511
John Power *(Pres & CEO)*
Chris Carlstead *(Pres-Tax)*
Gerard Chiasson *(Pres-Corp Performance Mgmt)*
Rob J. Hoevens *(Exec VP-Intl)*
Terence Wallis *(Sr VP-Global Sls & Mktg)*

EXALL ENERGY CORPORATION

400 715 - 5th Avenue SW
Calgary, AB, T2P 2X6, Canada
Tel.: (403) 237-7820
Fax: (403) 262-4723
E-Mail: info@exall.com
Web Site: www.exall.com
EE—(TSX)
Rev.: $31,296,720
Assets: $127,475,113
Liabilities: $73,662,846
Net Worth: $53,812,267
Earnings: $3,611,275
Emp.: 7
Fiscal Year-end: 12/31/12

Business Description:
Oil & Gas Exploration & Services
S.I.C.: 1311
N.A.I.C.S.: 211111

Personnel:
Stephen G. Roman *(Chm)*
Frank S. Rebeyka *(Vice Chm)*
Roger N. Dueck *(Pres & CEO)*
Warren F. E. Coles *(CFO & VP-Fin)*
Wayne Egan *(Sec)*

Board of Directors:
Stephen G. Roman
Roger N. Dueck
Wayne Egan
Bernard Albert Lang
D. Allan Menzies
Roderick Phipps
Frank S. Rebeyka

Legal Counsel:
WeirFoulds LLP
4100 66 Wellington Street West
Toronto, ON, M5K 1B7, Canada

Norton Rose LLP
3700 400 - 3rd Avenue SW
Calgary, AB, T2P 4H2, Canada

Equity Financial Trust Company
200 University Avenue Suite 400
Toronto, ON, M5H 4H1, Canada
Tel.: (416) 361-0152
Fax: (416) 361-0470
Toll Free: (866) 393-4891

Transfer Agents:
Equity Financial Trust Company
505 - 3rd Street SW Suite 850
Calgary, AB, Canada

Equity Financial Trust Company
200 University Avenue Suite 400
Toronto, ON, M5H 4H1, Canada
Tel.: (416) 361-0152
Fax: (416) 361-0470
Toll Free: (866) 393-4891

EXALT RESOURCES LTD.

Level 39 Australia Square 264-278 George Street
Sydney, NSW, 2000, Australia
Tel.: (61) 2 9037 4344
Fax: (61) 2 9037 4324
E-Mail: info@exaltresources.com.au
Web Site: www.exaltresources.com.au
ERD—(ASX)
Rev.: $96,935
Assets: $12,407,425
Liabilities: $829,892
Net Worth: $11,577,533
Earnings: ($3,904,766)
Fiscal Year-end: 06/30/13

Business Description:
Metal Mining Services
S.I.C.: 1099
N.A.I.C.S.: 212299

Personnel:
Richard Sheridan *(CFO)*
Shane Hartwig *(Sec)*

Board of Directors:
Robert Whitton
Robert Crossman
Peter Dykes
Shane Hartwig
Edward Kwong Foo Lee
Romy Soekarno

Legal Counsel:
Gadens Lawyers
Skygarden Building 77 Castlereagh Street
Sydney, NSW, Australia

EXCALIBUR MINING CORPORATION LIMITED

Ground Floor 16 Ord Street
West Perth, WA, 6005, Australia
Tel.: (61) 8 9429 2900
Fax: (61) 8 9486 1011
E-Mail: adminsupport@excaliburmining.com.au
Web Site: www.excaliburmining.com.au
EXM—(ASX)
Rev.: $493,494
Assets: $12,190,219
Liabilities: $1,288,136
Net Worth: $10,902,083
Earnings: ($2,738,832)
Emp.: 1
Fiscal Year-end: 06/30/13
Business Description:
Gold Exploration & Mining Services
S.I.C.: 1041
N.A.I.C.S.: 212221
Personnel:
Alex S. Bajada *(Chm)*
Mark M. J. Smith *(Sec)*
Board of Directors:
Alex S. Bajada
Terrence Jones
Mark M. J. Smith

EXCALIBUR RESOURCES LTD.

20 Adelaide Street East Suite 400
Toronto, ON, M5C 2T6, Canada
Tel.: (416) 987-0298
Fax: (604) 637-5624
E-Mail: info@excaliburresources.ca
Web Site: www.excaliburresources.ca
Year Founded: 2000
XBR—(CNSX OTC)
Int. Income: $15,139
Assets: $6,995,700
Liabilities: $232,018
Net Worth: $6,763,682
Earnings: ($1,004,335)
Fiscal Year-end: 05/31/13
Business Description:
Mining & Exploration Services
S.I.C.: 1499
N.A.I.C.S.: 212399
Personnel:
Timothy Gallagher *(Chm & CEO)*
Donna McLean *(CFO)*
Dianne Marie Szigety *(Sec)*
Board of Directors:
Timothy Gallagher
Charles Beaudry
Oscar Fitch Gomez
David J. Libby
Andrew Robertson
Dianne Marie Szigety
Legal Counsel:
Wildeboer Dellelce, LLP
Suite 800 365 Bay Street
Toronto, ON, Canada
Transfer Agent:
Valiant Trust Company
Suite 600 750 Cambie Street
Vancouver, BC, Canada

EXCEED COMPANY LTD.

Unit F 24/F China Overseas Building
139 Hennessy Road
Wanchai, China (Hong Kong)
Tel.: (852) 2153 2771
Fax: (852) 2153 2775
Web Site: www.ir.xdlong.cn
Year Founded: 2006
EDS—(NASDAQ)
Rev.: $307,354,388
Assets: $292,171,428
Liabilities: $13,264,958
Net Worth: $278,906,470
Earnings: $25,653,571
Emp.: 2,093
Fiscal Year-end: 12/31/12
Business Description:
Acquisition & Investment Services
S.I.C.: 6211
N.A.I.C.S.: 523999
Personnel:
Shuipan Lin *(Founder, Chm & CEO)*
Yau Ting Tai *(CFO & Sec)*
Shulong Yu *(Deputy Fin Officer)*
Dongdong Ding *(Exec Sr VP)*
Board of Directors:
Shuipan Lin
Yea-Mow Chen
Dongdong Ding
Jichun Jin
Xiaozhong Pang

EXCEET GROUP SE

115 avenue Gaston Diderich
L-1420 Luxembourg, Luxembourg
Tel.: (352) 26 00 31 81
Fax: (352) 26 00 31 33
E-Mail: info@exceet.ch
Web Site: www.exceet.ch
EXC—(DEU)
Rev.: $254,092,280
Assets: $241,150,201
Liabilities: $121,396,264
Net Worth: $119,753,937
Earnings: $4,634,863
Emp.: 970
Fiscal Year-end: 12/31/12
Business Description:
Electronic Equipment Mfr
S.I.C.: 3679
N.A.I.C.S.: 334419
Personnel:
Hans Hofstetter *(Chm)*
Ulrich Reutner *(CEO)*
Board of Directors:
Hans Hofstetter
Thomas Brauchli
Hagen Hultzsch
Roland Lienau
Ulrich Reutner
Dirk-Jan Van Ommeren
Non-U.S. Subsidiaries:

AEMtec GmbH (1)
Carl-Scheele-Strasse 16
12489 Berlin, Germany
Tel.: (49) 30 6392 7300
Fax: (49) 30 6392 7302
E-Mail: info@AEMtec.com
Web Site: www.aemtec.com
Emp.: 140
Chip Card Mfr
S.I.C.: 3679
N.A.I.C.S.: 334419
Thomas John, *(Dir-Sls)*

Contec Steuerungstechnik & Automation GmbH (1)
Wildbichler Strasse 2E
6341 Ebbs, Austria
Tel.: (43) 5373 43 1 43 0
Fax: (43) 5373 43 1 43 888
E-Mail: info@contec.at
Web Site: www.contec.at
Electronic Control System Mfr
S.I.C.: 3679
N.A.I.C.S.: 334419

exceet Group AG (1)
Marktplatz 4
Saint Gallen, 9004, Switzerland
Tel.: (41) 41 499 93 33
Fax: (41) 41 499 93 13
E-Mail: l.koeppel@exceet.ch
Emp.: 1,000
Electronic Module Mfr
S.I.C.: 3679
N.A.I.C.S.: 334419

Subsidiaries:

ECR AG (2)
Riedstrasse 1
6343 Rotkreuz, Switzerland
Tel.: (41) 41 798 48 84
Fax: (41) 41 790 01 05
E-Mail: info@ecrag.ch
Web Site: www.ecrag.ch
Electronic Component Mfr
S.I.C.: 3679
N.A.I.C.S.: 334419
David Niederer *(Head-Supply Chain)*

GS Swiss PCB AG (2)
Faennring 8
PO Box 61
6403 Kussnacht, Switzerland
Tel.: (41) 41 854 48 00
Fax: (41) 41 854 48 43
E-Mail: sales@swisspcb.ch
Web Site: www.swisspcb.ch
Emp.: 160
Printed Circuit Board Mfr
S.I.C.: 3672
N.A.I.C.S.: 334412
Danie Puschmann, *(Gen Mgr)*

Mikrap AG (2)
Riedstrasse 1
6343 Rotkreuz, Switzerland
Tel.: (41) 41 799 47 99
Fax: (41) 41 799 47 98
E-Mail: info@mikrap.ch
Web Site: www.mikrap.ch
Electronic Product Mfr
S.I.C.: 3679
N.A.I.C.S.: 334419

Non-U.S. Subsidiaries:

as electronics GmbH (2)
Kantstrasse 10
72663 Grossbettlingen, Germany
Tel.: (49) 7022 4057 0
Fax: (49) 7022 4057 22
E-Mail: info@as-electronics.de
Web Site: www.as-electronics.de
Chip Card Mfr
S.I.C.: 3679
N.A.I.C.S.: 334419
Holger Wussmann, *(Mng Dir)*

exceet Card Group AG (2)
Senefelderstrasse 10
33100 Paderborn, Germany
Tel.: (49) 5251 15 83 123
Fax: (49) 52 51 15 83 250
E-Mail: info@exceet-group.com
Web Site: www.exceet-card-group.com
Emp.: 42
Plastic Card Mfr
S.I.C.: 3089
N.A.I.C.S.: 326199
Andreas Gordes *(Chief Sls Officer)*
Ulrich Reutner *(CEO-Strategy & Mktg)*

Subsidiary:

exceet Card AG (3)
Edisonstrasse 3
Unterschleissheim, 85716 Munich, Germany
Tel.: (49) 89 33034 0
E-Mail: info@exceet-group.com
Web Site: www.exceet-group-card.com
Emp.: 60
Smart Card Mfr
S.I.C.: 3089
N.A.I.C.S.: 326199

Non-U.S. Subsidiaries:

exceet Card Austria GmbH (3)
Industriezone 3
6175 Kematen in Tirol, Austria
Tel.: (43) 5232 206 86
Fax: (43) 5232 206 44
E-Mail: info@exceet-group.com
Emp.: 65
Plastic Card Mfr
S.I.C.: 3089
N.A.I.C.S.: 326199

exceet Card Nederland B.V. (3)
Neutronstraat 8
9743 AM Groningen, Netherlands
Tel.: (31) 50 368 77 77
Fax: (31) 50 368 77 22
E-Mail: verkoop@exceet-group.com
Web Site: www.exceet-card.nl
Emp.: 20
Plastic Card Mfr
S.I.C.: 3089
N.A.I.C.S.: 326199
Bas Timmer *(Acct Mgr-Field Svc)*

idvation GmbH (1)
Otto-Hesse-Strasse 19 / T5
64293 Darmstadt, Germany
Tel.: (49) 6151 4923021
Fax: (49) 6151 3689296
E-Mail: info@idvation.com
Web Site: www.idvation.com
Emp.: 5
Card Reader Mfr
S.I.C.: 3577
N.A.I.C.S.: 334118

Inplastor Graphische Produkte Gesellschaft m.b.H. (1)
Leberstrasse 61
1110 Vienna, Austria
Tel.: (43) 1 6041800
Fax: (43) 1 6041800 15
E-Mail: info@inplastor.at
Web Site: www.inplastor.at
Plastic Card Mfr
S.I.C.: 3089
N.A.I.C.S.: 326199
Walter Balasch, *(Co-CEO)*
Robert Wolny *(Co-CEO)*
Andreas Korger *(COO)*

EXCEL CELL ELECTRONIC CO., LTD.

No 20 25th Rd Taichung Industrial Park
Taichung, Taiwan
Tel.: (886) 423591253
Fax: (886) 423593893
E-Mail: info@mail.ece.com.tw
Web Site: www.ece.com.tw
2483—(TAI)
Sales Range: $25-49.9 Million
Business Description:
Electronic Components Mfr
S.I.C.: 3678
N.A.I.C.S.: 334417
Personnel:
Louis Liao *(CEO)*
U.S. Subsidiary:

Excel Cell Electronic (USA) Corp. (1)
628 Route 10 Unit 12
Whippany, NJ 07981
Tel.: (973) 887-8116
Fax: (973) 887-8117
Toll Free: (800) 416-4660
E-Mail: mail@ece-usa.com
Electronic Components Distr
S.I.C.: 5065
N.A.I.C.S.: 423690

EXCEL CO., LTD.

3-12-10 Nishi-Shinbashi
Minato-ku, Tokyo, 105-0003, Japan
Tel.: (81) 3 5733 8401
Fax: (81) 3 3436 2051
Web Site: www.excelweb.co.jp
Year Founded: 1961
EZ3—(DEU)
Business Description:
Integrated Circuit Mfr & Distr
S.I.C.: 3674
N.A.I.C.S.: 334413
Personnel:
Yoshio Hashimoto *(Pres & CEO)*
Isaku Tanimura *(Sr Mng Dir)*
Nobuaki Ohtaki *(Mng Dir)*
Toyoo Ueda *(Mng Dir)*
Board of Directors:
Yoshio Hashimoto
Nobuaki Ohtaki
Katsuo Ota
Isaku Tanimura
Toyoo Ueda
Naoki Yanagida

EXCEL CROP CARE LIMITED

13/14 Aradhana Industrial
Development Corporation Near

Excel Crop Care Limited—(Continued)

Virwani
Industrial Estate Goregaon East,
Mumbai, 400063, India
Tel.: (91) 2242522200
Fax: (91) 2228713037
Web Site: www.excelcropcare.com
EXCELCROP—(NSE)
Rev.: $153,913,370
Assets: $94,784,341
Liabilities: $48,659,361
Net Worth: $46,124,980
Earnings: $3,946,832
Emp.: 1,066
Fiscal Year-end: 03/31/13

Business Description:
Agrochemical Products Mfr
S.I.C.: 2879
N.A.I.C.S.: 325320

Personnel:
Ninad D. Gupte *(Mng Dir)*
Dipesh K. Shroff *(Mng Dir)*
K. Srinivasan *(CFO)*
Pravin D. Desai *(Sec & VP-Fin & Accts)*

Board of Directors:
Ashwin C. Shroff
Mukul G. Asher
B. V. Bhargava
Deepak Bhimani
Vinayak B. Buch
Ninad D. Gupte
Sandeep Junnarkar
Jagdish R. Naik
Sharad L. Patel
David Pullan
Dipesh K. Shroff

Transfer Agent:
Link Intime India Pvt. Ltd
C-13 Pannalal Silk Mills Compound LBS Marg
Bhandup (West)
Mumbai, India

Non-U.S. Subsidiary:

EXCEL CROP CARE (EUROPE) N V **(1)**
Uitbreidingsstraat 84/3
2600 Antwerp, Belgium
Tel.: (32) 35425722
Fax: (32) 22182020
E-Mail: abishek.gupta@excelcropcare.com
Web Site: www.excelcrop.com
Agricultural Chemicals Mfr
S.I.C.: 2879
N.A.I.C.S.: 325320
Abishek Gupta *(Gen Mgr)*

EXCEL DEVELOPMENT BANK LTD.

Mukti Chowk Anarmani Birtamod
Jhapa
Birtamod, 57203, Nepal
Tel.: (977) 23 543714
Fax: (977) 23 543563
E-Mail: info@edb.com.np
Web Site: www.edb.com.np
EDBL—(NEP)

Business Description:
Banking Services
S.I.C.: 6029
N.A.I.C.S.: 522110

Personnel:
Chet Prasad Bhattarai *(Chm)*
Khagendra Dhungana *(CEO)*

Board of Directors:
Chet Prasad Bhattarai
Kamal bhattari
Hem Raj Dhakal
Mahendra Goyal
Rishikesh Goyal
Nima Devi Karmacharya
Rajan Sharma

EXCEL GLASSES LIMITED

Udayanagar
Pathirapally, Alleppey, Kerala, 688 521, India
Tel.: (91) 4772258671
Fax: (91) 4772258670
E-Mail: mail@excelglasses.com
Web Site: www.excelglasses.com
Year Founded: 1970
502223—(BOM)

Business Description:
Containers & Packaging Mfr
S.I.C.: 3221
N.A.I.C.S.: 327213

Personnel:
Prashant Somani *(Mng Dir)*

Board of Directors:
Surendran Nair
Ramesh Prabhu
Basant Kumar Soni

Transfer Agent:
Sharex Dynamic (India) Pvt. Ltd
17 B Dena Bank Building 2nd Floor Horniman Circle Fort
Mumbai, India

EXCEL INDUSTRIES LIMITED

184-87 SV Road Jogeshwari West
Mumbai, Maharashtra, 400 102, India
Tel.: (91) 2266464200
Fax: (91) 2226783657
E-Mail: excel.mumbai@excelind.com
Web Site: www.excelind.co.in
EXCELINDUS—(NSE)
Rev.: $77,927,384
Assets: $56,063,773
Liabilities: $30,939,033
Net Worth: $25,124,741
Earnings: $2,768,041
Fiscal Year-end: 03/31/13

Business Description:
Speciality Chemicals Mfr
S.I.C.: 2819
N.A.I.C.S.: 325180

Personnel:
A. C. Shroff *(Chm & Mng Dir)*
Usha A. Shroff *(Vice Chm)*
S. K. Singhvi *(Compliance Officer & Sec)*

Board of Directors:
A. C. Shroff
Ramchandra N. Bhogale
Priyam S. Jhaveri
Harish Narendra Motiwalla
Madhukar Balvantray Parekh
Setumadhav Rangrao Potdar
Nilesh Bhaskar Sathe
Atul G. Shroff
Dipesh K. Shroff
Usha A. Shroff

Transfer Agent:
Link Intime India Private Limited
C-13 Pannalal Silk Mills Compound Bhandup W
Mumbai, India

EXCEL INFOWAYS LTD.

New Link Road Andheri West
Mumbai, 400053, India
Tel.: (91) 2240309898
Fax: (91) 2226394248
Web Site: www.excel-infoways.com
533090—(BOM NSE)
Rev.: $5,685,090
Assets: $31,426,551
Liabilities: $1,576,751
Net Worth: $29,849,800
Earnings: $456,682
Emp.: 1
Fiscal Year-end: 03/31/13

Business Description:
Collections, Telemarketing, Customer Care & IT Call Center & Outsourcing Services
S.I.C.: 7389
N.A.I.C.S.: 561422

Personnel:
Lakhmendra Khurana *(Chm & Mng Dir)*
Kamal C. Thaker *(CFO)*
Kumud Harshal Waradkar *(Compliance Officer & Sec)*

Board of Directors:
Lakhmendra Khurana
Binoy Gupta
Ramesh Joshi
Arpit Khurana
Ranjana Khurana
Ravi Prakash Sinha

Transfer Agent:
Link Intime India Private Limited
C-13 Pannalal Silk Mills Compound L.B.S. Marg
Bhandup
Mumbai, India

EXCEL LATIN AMERICA BOND FUND

2000 Argentia Road Suite 280 Plaza 4
Mississauga, ON, L5N 1W1, Canada
Tel.: (905) 813-7111
E-Mail: grant.patterson@excelfunds.com
ELA.UN—(TSX)

Business Description:
Investment Services
S.I.C.: 6211
N.A.I.C.S.: 523999

Personnel:
Bhim D. Asdhir *(Pres & CEO)*
Glenn William Cooper *(CFO)*
Grant Patterson *(Chief Compliance Officer)*

Board of Directors:
Bhim D. Asdhir
Glenn William Cooper
Adrian Herschell

Transfer Agent:
Computershare Investor Services Inc.
Montreal, QC, Canada

EXCEL MACHINE TOOLS LTD.

521 Bukit Batok St 23
Singapore, 659544, Singapore
Tel.: (65) 66650488
Fax: (65) 66653438
Year Founded: 1986
Sales Range: $10-24.9 Million
Emp.: 449

Business Description:
Holding Company
S.I.C.: 6719
N.A.I.C.S.: 551112

Subsidiaries:

Excel Advanced Technology Pte. Ltd. **(1)**
521 Bukit Batok St 23
Singapore, 659544, Singapore (100%)
Tel.: (65) 65643488
Fax: (65) 66653466
E-Mail: excel-hq@excel-ltd.com.sg
Web Site: www.excelaei.com
Emp.: 25
Automators & System Integrators of Laser Marking and Water-Jet Cutting Systems for Industrial Applications
S.I.C.: 3548
N.A.I.C.S.: 333992

Excel Precision (Singapore) Pte. Ltd. **(1)**
521 Bukit Batok St 23
Singapore, 659544, Singapore (100%)
Tel.: (65) 65660488
Fax: (65) 66653455
E-Mail: excel-hq@excel-ltd.com.sg
Web Site: www.excelaei.com
S.I.C.: 5941
N.A.I.C.S.: 451110

U.S. Subsidiary:

America Excel, Inc. **(1)**
Ste F 1740 W Cortland Ct
Addison, IL 60101-4233
Tel.: (847) 229-6180
Fax: (847) 229-6175
Web Site: www.excelaei.com
Emp.: 4
Machine Tools, Metal Cutting Type Import Export
S.I.C.: 5082
N.A.I.C.S.: 423810

Non-U.S. Subsidiaries:

Excel Csepel Machine Tools Ltd **(1)**
Varrogepgyar u 1
1211 Budapest, Hungary (83%)
Tel.: (36) 12785800
Fax: (36) 1 425 7605
E-Mail: sales@excel-csepel.hu
Web Site: www.excel-csepel.hu
Machine Tools Mfr
S.I.C.: 3541
N.A.I.C.S.: 333517

Holding:

Excel Europe Ltd. **(2)**
1751 Budapest
PO Box 200/3
1211 Budapest, Gyepsor u.1., Hungary
Tel.: (36) 1 420 4194
Web Site: www.excelaei.com
S.I.C.: 6512
N.A.I.C.S.: 531120

India Excel Pte. Ltd. **(1)**
14th Floor C Wing Mittal Tower
PO Box 5200
47/6 MG Road, Bengaluru, 560001, India
Tel.: (91) 805591941
Web Site: www.excelaei.com
S.I.C.: 5941
N.A.I.C.S.: 451110

P.T. E-Tech Manufacturing Indonesia **(1)**
Lot 246 Jalan Kenanga Bip Mukakuning
Batam, Indonesia
Tel.: (62) 770612450
Fax: (62) 770 611868
Web Site: www.etechbatam.com
S.I.C.: 3469
N.A.I.C.S.: 332119

EXCEL MARITIME CARRIERS LTD.

c/o 17th Km National Road Athens-Lamia & Finkos Street
145 64 Athens, Nea Kifisia, Greece

Mailing Address:
Par La Ville Place 14 Par-La-Ville Road
Hamilton, HM JX, Bermuda
Tel.: (30) 210 62 09 520
Fax: (30) 210 62 09 528
E-Mail: info@excelmaritime.com
Web Site: www.excelmaritime.com
Year Founded: 1989
EXM—(NYSE)
Sales Range: $350-399.9 Million
Emp.: 1,171

Business Description:
Deep Sea Dry Bulk Cargo Carrier Operator
S.I.C.: 4412
N.A.I.C.S.: 483111

Personnel:
Gabriel Panayotides *(Chm & Pres)*
Pavlos Kanellopoulos *(CFO)*
Ismini Panayotides *(Officer-Bus Dev)*

Board of Directors:
Gabriel Panayotides
Apostolos Kontoyannis
Evangelos S. Macris
Hans J. Mende
Frithjof Stoud Platou
Trevor J. Williams

Legal Counsel:
Seward & Kissel LLP
One Battery Park Plz
New York, NY 10004
Tel.: (212) 574-1200
Fax: (212) 480-8421

Transfer Agent:
American Stock Transfer & Trust Company LLC
59 Maiden Ln
New York, NY 10007

Tel.: (718) 921-8200

Non-U.S. Subsidiaries:

Maryville Maritime Inc. **(1)**
17th km National Rd Athens-Lamia & Finikos St
Nea Kifisia, 145 64 Athens, Greece LR
Tel.: (30) 2106209520 (100%)
Fax: (30) 2108002197
E-Mail: info@excelmaritime.com
Emp.: 150
Vessel Manager & Shipping Services
S.I.C.: 4412
N.A.I.C.S.: 483111

EXCEL TECHNOLOGY INTERNATIONAL HOLDINGS LIMITED

(Name Changed to Hong Kong Jewellery Holding Limited)

EXCEL TRANSPORTATION INC.

333 Ongman Road
Prince George, BC, V2K 4K9, Canada
Tel.: (250) 563-7356
Fax: (250) 563-3201
Rev.: $14,877,247
Emp.: 150
Business Description:
Truck Transportation Services
S.I.C.: 4212
N.A.I.C.S.: 484110
Personnel:
Annie Horning *(Pres)*

EXCELA LIMITED

Level 2 2 Miami Key Broadbeach Waters
Gold Coast, QLD, 4218, Australia
Tel.: (61) 7 5668 5381
Fax: (61) 7 5555 8555
Web Site: www.excela.com.au
EXA—(ASX)
Rev.: $2,646,968
Assets: $4,100,444
Liabilities: $2,379,335
Net Worth: $1,721,108
Earnings: ($3,379,430)
Emp.: 11
Fiscal Year-end: 06/30/13
Business Description:
Investment Management Service
S.I.C.: 6282
N.A.I.C.S.: 523920
Personnel:
Delan Pagliaccio *(CEO)*
Craig Burbury *(CFO & Sec)*
Board of Directors:
John Margerison
Clayton Dempsey
Joseph Goldberg
Delan Pagliaccio
Legal Counsel:
Nick Stretch Legal
Suite 802 530 Little Collins Street
Melbourne, VIC, 3000, Australia

EXCELDOR COOPERATIVE AVICOLE

5700 rue J B Michaud bureau 500
Levis, QC, Canada G6V 0B1
Tel.: (418) 830-5600
Fax: (418) 830-5644
E-Mail: info@exceldor.com
Web Site: www.exceldor.ca
Year Founded: 1945
Rev.: $113,362,304
Emp.: 800
Business Description:
Poultry Products Supplier
S.I.C.: 2015
N.A.I.C.S.: 311615
Personnel:
Jean-Pierre Dube *(Chm)*
Rene Proulx *(Pres & CEO)*

EXCELIAN LIMITED

44 Featherstone St
London, EC1Y 8RN, United Kingdom
Tel.: (44) 2073369595
E-Mail: info@excelian.com
Web Site: www.excelian.com
Year Founded: 2001
Sales Range: $25-49.9 Million
Emp.: 250
Business Description:
IT Consulting Services
S.I.C.: 8999
N.A.I.C.S.: 541690
Personnel:
Stephen Grant *(Chm)*
Adrian Marshall *(Co-CEO)*
Jeremy Ward *(Co-CEO)*
Phil Culbert *(Partner-Commodities Consulting)*
Neil Gourlay *(Partner-Bus Dev, Resourcing & Client Relationship)*
Mark Jolley *(Sr Partner-Managed Svcs)*
Graham Loveitt *(Partner-Capital Markets)*
Phil Roberts *(Sr Partner-Murex Consulting)*
John Seager-Smith *(Partner-Capital Markets)*
Adam Vile *(Sr Partner-Technical Consulting)*
Robert Grant *(COO)*
Board of Directors:
Stephen Grant
Robert Grant
Adrian Marshall
Jeremy Ward

EXCELLENCE REAL ESTATE GROUP LIMITED

(d/b/a Excellence Group)
22nd Floor Excellence Mansion 98 Fuhua First Road
Futian Central District, Shenzhen, Guangdong, 518000, China
Tel.: (86) 75582877000
Fax: (86) 75582912456
E-Mail: ir@exceintl.com
Web Site: www.excegroup.com
Emp.: 1,560
Business Description:
Commercial & Residential Real Estate Developer & Manager
S.I.C.: 1542
N.A.I.C.S.: 236220
Personnel:
Hua Li *(Chm)*
Xiaoping Li *(Pres)*

EXCELLERATE HOLDINGS LTD.

Atholl Square 1st Floor
Cnr Katherine Street & Wierda Road East
Sandton, South Africa
Tel.: (27) 11 523 2980
Fax: (27) 11 523 2990
E-Mail: leonel@excellerate.co.za
Web Site: www.excellerate.co.za
Sales Range: $100-124.9 Million
Emp.: 3,306
Business Description:
Investment Holding Company
S.I.C.: 6719
N.A.I.C.S.: 551112
Personnel:
Nick Christodoulou *(Chm)*
Gordon Hulley *(CEO)*
E. Goodman *(Sec)*
Board of Directors:
Nick Christodoulou
Gordon Hulley
Michael Mohohlo
Athol Stewart
Rudi Stumpf
James Wellsted
Subsidiaries:

Ferrengi Household Products (Pty) Ltd. **(1)**
772 Sixth St
Wynberg, Johannesburg, Gauteng, 2012, South Africa
Tel.: (27) 118872730
Fax: (27) 118872728
E-Mail: johann@ferrengi.co.za
Web Site: www.ferrengi.co.za
Emp.: 60
Kitchen Accessories Mfr & Distr
S.I.C.: 2842
N.A.I.C.S.: 325612
Johann Van Awaswegen *(Mgr-Sls Natl)*

First Park (Pty) Ltd. **(1)**
1 Palm Blvd
Umhlanga, KwaZulu-Natal, 4320, South Africa
Tel.: (27) 315663116
Parking Lot Operation Services
S.I.C.: 7521
N.A.I.C.S.: 812930
Lucas Zondi *(Gen Mgr)*

Foodserv Solutions (Pty) Ltd. **(1)**
No 9 Watkins Street
Denver, Johannesburg, Gauteng, 2001, South Africa
Tel.: (27) 116165183
Fax: (27) 116168287
E-Mail: info@foodserv.co.za
Web Site: www.foodserv.co.za
Emp.: 168
Food Service Equipment Distr
S.I.C.: 5046
N.A.I.C.S.: 423440
Athol C. Stewart *(Mng Dir)*

Interpark (South Africa) (Pty) Ltd. **(1)**
37 Angus Crescent Longmeadow Bus Estate E
Edenvale, Gauteng, 1609, South Africa
Tel.: (27) 118790200
Fax: (27) 118790220
E-Mail: park@interpark.co.za
Web Site: www.interpark.co.za
Emp.: 60
Parking Lot Operation Services
S.I.C.: 7521
N.A.I.C.S.: 812930
Kate Wolfaardt *(Mng Dir)*

Levingers Dry Cleaners (Pty) Ltd. **(1)**
37 Angus Crescent Longmeadow Bus Estate E
Private Bag x782
Edenvale, Gauteng, 1609, South Africa
Tel.: (27) 118790270
Fax: (27) 118790290
E-Mail: barry@levingers.co.za
Web Site: www.levingers.co.za
Dry Cleaning Services
S.I.C.: 7219
N.A.I.C.S.: 812320

EXCELLIUM INC.

1550 Beaulac Street Ville Saint-Laurent
Montreal, QC, H4R 1W8, Canada
Tel.: (514) 798-8899
Fax: (514) 798-8898
Toll Free: (888) 381-2457
E-Mail: info@excellium.ca
Web Site: www.excellium.ca
Year Founded: 2009
XLM—(TSXV)
Rev.: $4,964,881
Assets: $1,459,635
Liabilities: $3,158,990
Net Worth: ($1,699,355)
Earnings: ($3,148,959)
Fiscal Year-end: 12/31/12
Business Description:
Security Solutions Integration Services
S.I.C.: 7382
N.A.I.C.S.: 561621
Personnel:
Jean-Claude Siew *(Pres & CEO)*
Board of Directors:
Monique Imbeault
Bernard Imbeault
Sylvain Lemieux
Claude Roussin
Transfer Agent:
Canadian Stock Transfer Trust Company
320 Bay Street B! Level
Toronto, ON, M5H 4A6, Canada

EXCELLON RESOURCES INC.

20 Victoria Street Suite 900
Toronto, ON, M5C 2N8, Canada
Tel.: (416) 364-1130
Fax: (416) 364-6745
E-Mail: info@excellonresources.com
Web Site: www.excellonresources.com
Year Founded: 1987
EXN—(OTC TSX)
Rev.: $36,273,000
Assets: $71,143,000
Liabilities: $4,014,000
Net Worth: $67,129,000
Earnings: $8,408,000
Emp.: 252
Fiscal Year-end: 12/31/12
Business Description:
Silver, Zinc & Lead Mining & Development Services
S.I.C.: 1044
N.A.I.C.S.: 212222
Personnel:
Peter Alexander Crossgrove *(Chm)*
Brendan Cahill *(Pres)*
Rupy Dhadwar *(CFO)*
Robert D. Moore *(COO)*
Board of Directors:
Peter Alexander Crossgrove
Thor E. Eaton
Oliver Fernandez
Andre Y. Fortier
Alan R. McFarland
Timothy J. Ryan
Legal Counsel:
Heenan Blaikie LLP
Bay Adelaide Centre 333 Bay Street Suite 2900
PO Box 2900
Toronto, ON, M5H 2T4, Canada
Transfer Agent:
Computershare Investor Services Inc.
100 University Ave 9th Floor
Toronto, ON, Canada

EXCELPOINT TECHNOLOGY LTD

15 Changi Business Park Central 1 06-00
Singapore, 486057, Singapore
Tel.: (65) 67418966
Fax: (65) 67418980
Web Site: www.excelpoint.com
E17—(SES)
Rev.: $584,852,000
Assets: $166,257,000
Liabilities: $117,837,000
Net Worth: $48,420,000
Earnings: $5,046,000
Emp.: 500
Fiscal Year-end: 12/31/12
Business Description:
Electronic Components Mfr
S.I.C.: 3269
N.A.I.C.S.: 327110
Personnel:
Albert Yong Hen Phuay *(Founder, Chm & CEO)*
Ivan See Thiam Lee *(CFO)*
Cher Liang Tan *(Co-Sec)*
Yoen Har Wong *(Co-Sec)*
Kwek Hwa Chang *(Sr VP-Ops)*

Excelpoint Technology Ltd—(Continued)

Board of Directors:
Albert Yong Hen Phuay
David Fat Keung Kok
Thiam Hock Kwah
Alan Wai Loen Kwan
Teck Seng Low
Sunny Fook Choy Wong

Subsidiary:

Excelpoint Systems (Pte) Ltd **(1)**
15 Changi Business Park Central 1 06-00
Singapore, 486057, Singapore
Tel.: (65) 6741 8966
Fax: (65) 6741 8980
E-Mail: sales.enquiry@excelpoint.com.sg
Web Site: www.excelpoint.com
Emp.: 150
Electronic Components Distr
S.I.C.: 5065
N.A.I.C.S.: 423690
Albert Yong Hen Phuay *(Chm & Grp CEO)*

Non-U.S. Subsidiary:

Excelpoint Systems Sdn. Bhd. **(2)**
D 5-05 Block D No 5 Ritze Perdana
Business Ctr Jalan PJU 8/2
Bandar Damansara Perdana, 47820
Petaling Jaya, Selangor, Malaysia
Tel.: (60) 377298086
Fax: (60) 377298089
E-Mail: sales.enquiry@excelpoint.com.sg
Web Site: www.excelpoint.com
Emp.: 3
Electronic Components Whslr
S.I.C.: 5065
N.A.I.C.S.: 423690
David Khong *(Mgr)*

Non-U.S. Subsidiary:

Excelpoint Systems (H.K.) Limited **(1)**
Unit 1001 10/F Tower 1 Kowloon Commerce Centre
No 51 Kwai Cheong Road, Kwai Chung, New Territories, China (Hong Kong)
Tel.: (852) 25032212
Fax: (852) 2503 1558
E-Mail: esplhk@excelpoint.com.hk
Web Site: www.excelpoint.com
Electronic Components Whslr
S.I.C.: 5065
N.A.I.C.S.: 423690

Non-U.S. Subsidiaries:

Excelpoint International Trading (Shanghai) Co., Ltd. **(2)**
10F Bosendo Building 686 Jiujiang Road
Shanghai, 200001, China
Tel.: (86) 21 2308 9588
Fax: (86) 21 2308 9599
E-Mail: esplhk@excelpoint.com.hk
Web Site: www.excelpoint.com
Electronic Components Whslr
S.I.C.: 5065
N.A.I.C.S.: 423690

Excelpoint International Trading (Shenzhen) Co., Ltd. **(2)**
Unit A 21F Finance Centre 4003 Shenna Block A World n Road East
Shenzhen, Guangdong, 518008, China
Tel.: (86) 75583640166
Fax: (86) 75525982255
E-Mail: esplhk@excelpoint.com.hk
Web Site: www.excelpoint.com.cn
Emp.: 100
Electronic Components Whslr
S.I.C.: 5065
N.A.I.C.S.: 423690

EXCELSIOR GOLD LIMITED

Unit 2 124 Stirling Highway North Fremantle
Perth, WA, 6159, Australia
Tel.: (61) 8 9335 7770
Fax: (61) 8 9335 6231
E-Mail: admin@excelsiorgold.com.au
Web Site: www.excelsiorgold.com.au
EXG—(ASX)
Rev.: $350,021
Assets: $25,419,174
Liabilities: $495,877
Net Worth: $24,923,297
Earnings: ($1,825,390)
Emp.: 6
Fiscal Year-end: 06/30/13

Business Description:
Gold, Uranium & Other Metal Exploration Services
S.I.C.: 1041
N.A.I.C.S.: 212221

Personnel:
David Alan Hamlyn *(Mng Dir)*
Nicholas Chen Chik Ong *(Sec)*

Board of Directors:
Peter John Bird
David Alan Hamlyn
Nicholas Chen Chik Ong
David Sidney Potter

Legal Counsel:
Kings Park Corporate Lawyers
Suite 8 8 Clive Street
West Perth, Australia

EXCELSIOR HOTEL BEOGRAD

Kneza Milosa 5
11000 Belgrade, Serbia
Tel.: (381) 11 32 31 381
Fax: (381) 11 32 31 951
Web Site: www.hotelexcelsior.co.rs
EXCL—(BEL)

Business Description:
Hotel & Motel Services
S.I.C.: 7011
N.A.I.C.S.: 721110

Personnel:
Christoph Brueckner *(Gen Mgr)*

EXCELSIOR MEDICAL CO., LTD.

17F No 880 Chung Cheng Road
Chunghe, Taipei, Taiwan
Tel.: (886) 2 2225 1888
Fax: (886) 2 2225 8117
Web Site: www.excelsiormedical.com.tw
4104—(TAI)
Sales Range: $500-549.9 Million

Business Description:
Medical Equipment Distr
S.I.C.: 5047
N.A.I.C.S.: 423450

Personnel:
Huidong Fu *(Chm)*

Subsidiary:

RTS Excelsior Co., Ltd. **(1)**
Chongjheng Road
Zhonghe, Taipei, 880, Taiwan
Tel.: (886) 2 2225 7111
Fax: (886) 2 2225 7211
Emp.: 100
General Medical Services
S.I.C.: 8011
N.A.I.C.S.: 621491
Ata Hsu *(Mgr)*

EXCELSIOR MINING CORP.

1240 - 1140 West Pender Street
Vancouver, BC, V6E 4G1, Canada
Tel.: (604) 681-8030
Fax: (604) 681-8039
Toll Free: (866) 683-8030
E-Mail: info@excelsiormining.com
Web Site: www.excelsiormining.com
Year Founded: 2005
MIN—(OTC TSXV)
Rev.: $36,813
Assets: $2,183,270
Liabilities: $332,532
Net Worth: $1,850,737
Earnings: ($5,070,862)
Fiscal Year-end: 12/31/12

Business Description:
Copper Mining Services
S.I.C.: 1021
N.A.I.C.S.: 212234

Personnel:
Mark Joseph Morabito *(Chm)*
Stephen Twyerould *(Pres & CEO)*
Sonya Karur Atwal *(CFO)*
Sheila Paine *(Sec)*

Board of Directors:
Mark Joseph Morabito
V. Roland Goodgame
Colin B. Kinley
James T. Kolbe
Steven W. Lynn
Edward Jay Sujir
Stephen Twyerould
John P. Vettese

Legal Counsel:
Blake, Cassels & Graydon LLP
Suite 2600 Three Bentall Centre 595 Burrard Street
PO Box 49314
Vancouver, BC, Canada

Transfer Agent:
Computershare Investor Services Inc
100 University Avenue 9th Floor
Toronto, ON, Canada

EXCELSIOR TECHNOLOGIES LTD.

Parkway Deeside Industrial Park
Deeside, CH5 2NS, United Kingdom
Tel.: (44) 1244 833230
Fax: (44) 1244 833231
E-Mail: info@exceltechuk.com
Web Site: www.exceltechuk.com
Sales Range: $50-74.9 Million
Emp.: 200

Business Description:
Packaging Product Mfr
S.I.C.: 2671
N.A.I.C.S.: 326112

Personnel:
David Moorcroft *(Mng Dir)*

EXCHANGE INCOME CORPORATION

1067 Sherwin Road
Winnipeg, MB, R3H 0T8, Canada
Tel.: (204) 982-1857
Fax: (204) 982-1855
E-Mail: mpyle@eig.ca
Web Site: www.exchangeincomecorp.ca
Year Founded: 2002
EIF—(TSX)
Rev.: $795,785,573
Assets: $705,127,967
Liabilities: $412,347,329
Net Worth: $292,780,639
Earnings: $25,199,401
Emp.: 3,934
Fiscal Year-end: 12/31/12

Business Description:
Investment Services
S.I.C.: 6211
N.A.I.C.S.: 523999

Personnel:
Gary A. Filmon *(Chm)*
Duncan D. Jessiman *(Vice Chm)*
Michael C. Pyle *(Pres & CEO)*
Adam S. Terwin *(CFO)*
Cindy J. Genyk *(CIO)*
Carmele N. Peter *(Chief Admin Officer)*
Diane M. Spencer *(Sec & Mgr-Compliance)*

Board of Directors:
Gary A. Filmon
Brad Bennett
Gary Buckley
Duncan D. Jessiman
Serena H. Kraayeveld
Michael C. Pyle
Donald Streuber
Edward L. Warkentin
William Wehrle

Legal Counsel:
Aikins, MacAulay & Thorvaldson LLP
Winnipeg, MB, Canada

Transfer Agent:
Canadian Stock Transfer Company Inc
Calgary, AB, Canada

Holdings:

Calm Air International Ltd. **(1)**
90 Thompson Dr
Thompson, MB, R8N 1Y8, Canada
Tel.: (204) 778-6471
Fax: (204) 778-6954
Toll Free: (800) 839-2256 (Canada/US)
E-Mail: mail@calmair.com
Web Site: www.calmair.com
Emp.: 300
Air Transportation Services
S.I.C.: 4512
N.A.I.C.S.: 481111
Gary Beaurivage *(Pres)*

Jasper Tank Ltd **(1)**
200-53016 Hwy 60 Zone 3 200 Ellis Dr
Acheson Industrial Park
Acheson, AB, T7X 5A7, Canada
Tel.: (780) 220-0666
Fax: (780) 962-1499
Toll Free: (888) 813-1760
Web Site: www.jaspertank.com
Truck Mfr
S.I.C.: 3711
N.A.I.C.S.: 336211
Mark Skaley *(Gen Mgr)*

U.S. Subsidiary:

Stainless Fabrication, Inc **(2)**
4455 W Kearney
Springfield, MO 65803
Tel.: (417) 865-5696
Fax: (417) 865-7863
Toll Free: (800) 397-8265
E-Mail: sfi-info@stainlessfab.com
Web Site: www.stainlessfab.com
Emp.: 150
Stainless Steel Tank Mfr
S.I.C.: 3399
N.A.I.C.S.: 331110
Claude Mizell *(Pres)*

Keewatin Air LP **(1)**
50 Morberg Way
Winnipeg, MB, R3H0A4, Canada
Tel.: (204) 888-0100
Fax: (204) 888-3300
Toll Free: (877) 879-8477
Web Site: www.keewatinair.ca
Emp.: 50
Air Transportation Services
S.I.C.: 4512
N.A.I.C.S.: 481111
Wayne McLeod *(Pres & CEO)*
Denis Lavallee *(CFO)*

Overlanders Manufacturing LP **(1)**
30320 Fraser Hwy
Abbotsford, BC, V4X 1G1, Canada
Tel.: (604) 856-6815
Fax: (604) 856-5610
Web Site: www.overlanders.com
Fabricated Metal Products Mfr
S.I.C.: 3441
N.A.I.C.S.: 332312
Claude Lefebvre *(Controller)*

Perimeter Aviation LP **(1)**
626 Ferry Rd Winnipeg International Airport
Winnipeg, MB, R3H 0T7, Canada
Tel.: (204) 786-7031
Fax: (204) 783-7911
Toll Free: (800) 665-8986
E-Mail: charters@perimeter.ca
Web Site: www.perimeter.ca
Air Transportation Services
S.I.C.: 4512
N.A.I.C.S.: 481111
Mark Wehrle *(Pres)*

Water Blast Manufacturing LP **(1)**
3700 - 19 St NE Ste 6
Calgary, AB, T2E 6V2, Canada
Tel.: (403) 717-4280

Fax: (403) 717-4281
Toll Free: (800) 717-8101
E-Mail: wblast@telus.net
Web Site: www.hotsyab.com
Emp.: 8
High Pressure Cleaning Equipments & Pumping Systems Mfr
S.I.C.: 3699
N.A.I.C.S.: 335999
Ray Moyer *(Pres)*

Subsidiary:

Water Blast Manufacturing B.C. Ltd. (2)
20575 Langley Bypass Ste 112
Langley, BC, V3A 5E8, Canada
Tel.: (604) 532-7002
Fax: (604) 532-7010
Toll Free: (800) 328-1555
E-Mail: sales@hotsybc.com
Web Site: www.hotsybc.com
Emp.: 4
Pressure Washers Mfr & Sales
S.I.C.: 3452
N.A.I.C.S.: 332722
Ray Moher *(Pres)*

U.S. Holding:

Regional One, Inc. (1)
6750 NE 4th Ct
Miami, FL 33138 FL
Tel.: (305) 759-0670
Fax: (305) 759-0637
E-Mail: info@regionalone.com
Web Site: www.regionalone.com
Sales Range: $25-49.9 Million
Aircraft Engines & Parts Distr & Aircraft Leasing Services
S.I.C.: 5088
N.A.I.C.S.: 423860
Doron Marom *(Pres)*

EXCLUSIVE CONTRACT SERVICES LIMITED

8-12 Salisbury Square
Hatfield, Hertfordshire, AL9 5AD, United Kingdom
Tel.: (44) 1707264400
Fax: (44) 1707266170
E-Mail: admin@exclusivecontracts.co.uk
Web Site: www.exclusivecontracts.co.uk
Year Founded: 1987
Rev.: $24,320,758
Emp.: 1,723
Business Description:
Commercial Cleaning Services
S.I.C.: 7349
N.A.I.C.S.: 561720
Personnel:
Bill Wilkerson *(Mng Dir)*

EXCO TECHNOLOGIES LIMITED

130 Spy Court
Markham, ON, L3R 5H6, Canada
Tel.: (905) 477-3065
Fax: (905) 477-2449
E-Mail: general@excocorp.com
Web Site: www.excocorp.com
Year Founded: 1952
XTC—(TSX)
Sls.: $241,972,764
Assets: $177,246,077
Liabilities: $33,822,068
Net Worth: $143,424,009
Earnings: $24,394,234
Emp.: 2,213
Fiscal Year-end: 09/30/12
Business Description:
Casting Technologies, Extrusion Tooling For Automotive & Industrial Markets
Export
S.I.C.: 3544
N.A.I.C.S.: 333514
Personnel:
Brian A. Robbins *(Pres & CEO)*
Mary Nguyen *(CFO & VP-Fin)*
Paul Riganelli *(COO & Sr VP)*
Bonnie Cartwright *(Pres-Exco Tooling Solutions Grp)*
Jan M. Tesar *(Pres-Casting Tech)*
William Schroers *(CEO-Automotive Solutions Grp)*
Board of Directors:
Laurie T. F. Bennett
Edward H. Kernaghan
Robert B. Magee
Philip B. Matthews
Brian A. Robbins
Stephen Rodgers
Peter van Schaik
Transfer Agent:
Equity Transfer & Trust Company
200 University Avenue Ste 400
Toronto, ON, M5H 4H1, Canada
Tel.: (416) 361-0152
Fax: (416) 361-0470

Units:

Exco Engineering (1)
1314 Ringwell Drive
Newmarket, ON, L3Y 9C6, Canada
Tel.: (905) 853-8568
Fax: (905) 853-0054
Web Site: www.excoeng.com
High-Pressure Die-Casting Die Mfr
S.I.C.: 3544
N.A.I.C.S.: 333514

Exco Tooling Solutions (1)
130 Spy Court
Markham, ON, L3R 5H6, Canada
Tel.: (905) 477-1208
Fax: (905) 477-6304
Toll Free: (800) 461-6298
E-Mail: ordersexco@etsdies.com
Web Site: www.extrusiontoolinggroup.com
Emp.: 100
Extrusion Die Mfr
S.I.C.: 3544
N.A.I.C.S.: 333514
Bill Ferguson *(Gen Mgr)*

U.S. Subsidiary:

Exco Extrusion Dies, Inc. (2)
56617 N Bay Dr
Chesterfield, MI 48051-3746 MI
Tel.: (586) 749-5400
Fax: (586) 749-7360
Special Die & Tool, Die Set, Jig & Fixture Mfr
S.I.C.: 3544
N.A.I.C.S.: 333514
Bonnie Cartwright *(Pres)*

Neocon (1)
35 Akerley Blvd
Dartmouth, NS, B3B 1J7, Canada
Tel.: (902) 468-6663
Fax: (902) 468-6880
Web Site: www.excoautomotive.com
Automotive Interior Protection & Convenience Products Mfr
S.I.C.: 3089
N.A.I.C.S.: 326199

U.S. Subsidiaries:

BE&H Extrusion Dies, Inc. (1)
400 S Highway 78
Wylie, TX 75098 TX
Tel.: (972) 442-3131
Web Site: www.behdies.com
Sales Range: $1-9.9 Million
Emp.: 20
Extrusion Die Mfr
S.I.C.: 3544
N.A.I.C.S.: 333514
Jerry Buchanan *(Pres)*

EDCO, Inc. (1)
5244 Enterprise Blvd
Toledo, OH 43612 OH
Tel.: (419) 726-1595
E-Mail: edco_info@edcodie.com
Web Site: www.edcodie.com
Industrial Die Mfr
S.I.C.: 3544
N.A.I.C.S.: 333514
Elie Ghanime *(Gen Mgr)*

Exco Automotive Solutions L.P. (1)
1550 W Maple Rd
Troy, MI 48084 TX
Tel.: (248) 822-8111 (100%)
Fax: (248) 822-8862
E-Mail:
Web Site: www.excoautomotive.com
Emp.: 20
Motor Vehicle Interior Trim Component Mfr & Distr
S.I.C.: 3714
N.A.I.C.S.: 336390
William P. Schroers *(Pres & CEO)*
Greg Fadler *(CFO)*

Non-U.S. Subsidiaries:

Allper AG (1)
Industriestrasse 12
PO Box 12
3186 Dudingen, Fribourg, Switzerland
Tel.: (41) 264929660
Fax: (41) 264929661
E-Mail: allper@allper.com
Web Site: www.allper.com
Emp.: 10
Die Casting Materials Mfr
S.I.C.: 3364
N.A.I.C.S.: 331523
Cornelia Jungo *(Sec-Sls)*
Ursula Luthi *(Sec-Sls)*

Polydesign Systems S.A.R.L. (1)
Zone Franche Boukhalef Lot 18B
Tangiers, Morocco
Tel.: (212) 539399400
Fax: (212) 539393524
E-Mail: atika@polydesignsystems.com
Web Site: www.polydesignsystems.com
Emp.: 700
Automotive Interiors Mfr
S.I.C.: 2396
N.A.I.C.S.: 336360
Julianne Furman *(Mgr)*

EXDON TRADING COMPANY LIMITED

20 Western Prabhadevi Building Nr Kismat Cinema
Prabhadevi, Mumbai, Maharashtra, 400004, India
Tel.: (91) 22 24312561
E-Mail: exdontrading@yahoo.co.in
Web Site: www.exdontrading.com
512017—(BOM)
Sls.: $31,703
Assets: $4,837,550
Liabilities: $229,099
Net Worth: $4,608,451
Earnings: $1,094
Fiscal Year-end: 03/31/13
Business Description:
Commodity Trading Services
S.I.C.: 6221
N.A.I.C.S.: 523130
Personnel:
Navneet Singh *(Chm & Compliance Officer)*
Board of Directors:
Navneet Singh
Rakesh Yagnesh Bhatt
Prajyot Yashvant Jambekar
Ashok Hiralal Shah
Amol Atmaram Walkar
Transfer Agent:
PURVA SHAREGISTRY (INDIA) PRIVATE LIMITED
Unite No 9 Shiv Shakti Industrial Estate, Ground Floor JR Boricha Marg
Opp Kasturba Hospital Lower Parel E, Mumbai, 400011, India
Tel.: (91) 22 2301 6761
Fax: (91) 22 2301 2517

EXECUTIVE FLIGHT CENTRE FUEL SERVICES LTD.

200 680 Palmer Rd NE
Calgary, AB, T2E 7R3, Canada
Tel.: (403) 291-2825
Fax: (403) 291-2245
Toll Free: (888) 299-2825
Web Site: www.efcaviation.ca
Rev.: $13,282,870
Emp.: 35
Business Description:
Aviation Services
S.I.C.: 4522
N.A.I.C.S.: 481219
Personnel:
Dennis Cooper *(Owner-Red Deer)*
Rod Dann *(Owner-Prince Rupert)*
Coral Fife *(Owner-Fort Nelson)*
Geoff Price *(Owner-Lethbridge)*
Dean Buckland *(Pres & CEO)*

EXEDY CORPORATION

1-1-1 Kitamotomiya
Neyagawa, Osaka, 572-8570, Japan
Tel.: (81) 72 8221 152
Fax: (81) 72 822 7552
E-Mail: info@exedy.com
Web Site: www.exedy.com
7278—(TKS)
Sls.: $2,224,596,000
Assets: $2,160,125,000
Liabilities: $667,304,000
Net Worth: $1,492,821,000
Earnings: $106,953,000
Emp.: 2,614
Fiscal Year-end: 03/31/13
Business Description:
Drivetrain-Related Products Mfr
S.I.C.: 3714
N.A.I.C.S.: 336340
Personnel:
Haruo Shimizu *(Pres & CEO)*
Koji Akita *(Sr Exec Officer)*
Masahito Baba *(Exec Officer)*
Shinji Fujimoto *(Exec Officer)*
Hidehito Hisakawa *(Sr Exec Mng Officer)*
Makoto Ichikawa *(Sr Exec Officer)*
Yoshio Katayama *(Exec Mng Officer)*
Yoshihiro Kojima *(Exec Officer)*
Hisayasu Masaoka *(Sr Exec Mng Officer)*
Kenji Matsuda *(Sr Exec Officer)*
Masayuki Matsuda *(Sr Exec Mng Officer)*
Tadashi Nakahara *(Exec Officer)*
Shogo Okamura *(Exec Mng Officer)*
Yoshimi Osanai *(Exec Officer)*
Shigeo Tabata *(Exec Officer)*
Hiroshi Toyohara *(Sr Exec Officer)*
Mitsugu Yamaguchi *(Exec Officer)*
Yoshihiro Yamamura *(Exec Officer)*
Tetsuya Yoshinaga *(Exec Officer)*
Board of Directors:
Fumio Fujimori
Kagenori Fukumura
Hidehito Hisakawa
Yoshihiro Kojima
Hisayasu Masaoka
Masayuki Matsuda
Tadashi Nakahara
Haruo Shimizu
Hiroshi Toyohara
Transfer Agent:
Mitsubishi UFJ Trust & Banking Corporation
3-6-3 Fushimimachi, Chuo-ku
Osaka, Japan

Division:

Exedy Corporation - Ueno Division (1)
2418 Ota-cho
Iga, Mie, 518-0825, Japan
Tel.: (81) 595 23 8101
Fax: (81) 595 24 5521
Emp.: 1,974
Automotive Parts Mfr
S.I.C.: 3714
N.A.I.C.S.: 336390

Exedy Corporation—(Continued)

Subsidiaries:

DYNAX Corporation (1)
1053-1 Kamiosatsu
Chitose, Hokkaido, 066-8585, Japan
Tel.: (81) 123 24 3247
Fax: (81) 123 49 2050
Web Site: www.dynax-j.com
Sls.: $667,136,000
Emp.: 1,522
Automotive Parts Mfr & Distr
S.I.C.: 3714
N.A.I.C.S.: 336390
Kagenori Fukumura *(Pres)*

EXEDY Casting Co., Ltd. (1)
112 Haishi
Fukuchiyama, Kyoto, 620-0955, Japan
Tel.: (81) 773 22 1156
Fax: (81) 773 23 8477
Emp.: 48
Automotive Die Casting Parts Mfr
S.I.C.: 3714
N.A.I.C.S.: 336390

EXEDY Hiroshima Co., Ltd. (1)
6-11 Taguchi Kenkyu Danchi
Higashi-hiroshima, Hiroshima, 739-0038, Japan
Tel.: (81) 82 425 3434
Fax: (81) 82 425 3436
Web Site: www.exedy.com
Emp.: 100
Automotive Parts Mfr
S.I.C.: 3714
N.A.I.C.S.: 336390

EXEDY Kyoto Co., Ltd. (1)
15 Kizuogawa
Kizugawa, Kyoto, 619-0214, Japan
Tel.: (81) 774 73 0631
Fax: (81) 774 73 2147
Web Site: www.exedy.com
Emp.: 40
Automotive Parts Mfr
S.I.C.: 3714
N.A.I.C.S.: 336390

EXEDY Logistics Co., Ltd. (1)
1-30-1 Kidamotomiya
Neyagawa, Osaka, 572-0822, Japan
Tel.: (81) 72 822 1462
Fax: (81) 72 822 1174
Emp.: 127
Logistic Consulting Services
S.I.C.: 4731
N.A.I.C.S.: 541614

EXEDY Precision Co., Ltd. (1)
104-1 Joden
Mimasaka, Okayama, 701-2625, Japan
Tel.: (81) 868 74 3501
Fax: (81) 868 74 3503
Web Site: www.exedy.com
Emp.: 109
Automotive Parts Mfr
S.I.C.: 3714
N.A.I.C.S.: 336390

EXEDY Sun Co., Ltd. (1)
1-16-5 Kidamotomiya
Neyagawa, Osaka, 572-0822, Japan
Tel.: (81) 72 822 1147
Fax: (81) 72 824 3871
Web Site: www.exedy.com
Automotive Parts Mfr
S.I.C.: 3714
N.A.I.C.S.: 336390
Naoki Kanatani *(Pres)*

EXEDY Trading Co., Ltd. (1)
1-1-33 Kidamotomiya
Neyagawa, Osaka, 572-0822, Japan
Tel.: (81) 72 824 7633
Fax: (81) 72 822 1016
Emp.: 49
Automotive Parts Distr
S.I.C.: 5013
N.A.I.C.S.: 423120

Plant:

Exedy Corporation - Kawagoe Plant (1)
1-103-25 Yoshinodai
Kawagoe, Saitama, 350-0833, Japan
Tel.: (81) 49 225 0601
Fax: (81) 49 225 0600
Emp.: 138
Automotive Parts Mfr
S.I.C.: 3714
N.A.I.C.S.: 336390

U.S. Subsidiaries:

DYNAX America Corporation (1)
568 East Park Dr
Roanoke, VA 24019
Tel.: (540) 966-6010
Fax: (540) 966-6011
Web Site: dxa.dynax-j.com
Emp.: 360
Automotive Transmission Component Mfr
S.I.C.: 3714
N.A.I.C.S.: 336350
Tetsuo Kuroda *(Pres)*

Exedy-Dynax America Corporation (1)
8601 Haggerty Rd S
Belleville, MI 48111
Tel.: (734) 397-6556
Fax: (734) 397-6566
Web Site: eda.exedy.com
Emp.: 11
Motor Vehicle Supplies & New Parts Whslr
S.I.C.: 5013
N.A.I.C.S.: 423120
Koji Akita *(Pres)*

Exedy Globalparts Corporation (1)
8601 Haggerty Rd S
Belleville, MI 48111
Tel.: (734) 397-3333
Fax: (734) 397-7300
Web Site: www.exedyusa.com
Emp.: 30
Automobile & Motor Vehicle Whslr
S.I.C.: 5012
N.A.I.C.S.: 423110
Takeshi Nakano *(Pres)*

Exedy Holdings of America Corporation (1)
8601 Haggerty Rd S
Belleville, MI 48111
Tel.: (734) 397-3333
Fax: (734) 397-9567
Web Site: www.exedyusa.com
Emp.: 30
Holding Company; Motor Vehicle Supplies & New Parts Whslr
S.I.C.: 6719
N.A.I.C.S.: 551112
Takeshi Nakano *(Pres)*

Non-U.S. Subsidiaries:

Ceekay Daikin Ltd. (1)
NKM International House 4th Floor
178 Babubhai M Chinai Marg, 400020
Mumbai, India
Tel.: (91) 2222020849
Fax: (91) 22043939
E-Mail: ckd@exedyindia.in
Web Site: www.exedyindia.in
Emp.: 10
Motor Vehicle Supplies & New Parts Whslr
S.I.C.: 5013
N.A.I.C.S.: 423120
Pradeep Chinai *(Mng Dir)*

Plant:

Ceekay Daikin Ltd. - Aurangabad Plant (2)
Plot No L-4 M I D C Industrial Area
Chikalthana
Aurangabad, Maharashtra, 431 210, India
Tel.: (91) 24833341
Fax: (91) 24833341
Web Site: www.exedyindia.in/contact.asp
Automotive Transmission Clutch Component Mfr
S.I.C.: 3714
N.A.I.C.S.: 336350

Dynax Industry (Shanghai) Co., Ltd. (1)
No 350 Rongxiang Rd
Songjiang Export Processing Zo, 201613
Shanghai, China
Tel.: (86) 2157748388
Fax: (86) 2157748389
E-Mail: wng-chunmei@dxchina.com.cn
Web Site: www.dxchina.com.cn
Motor Vehicle Parts Mfr
S.I.C.: 3714
N.A.I.C.S.: 336390

Exedy Australia Pty. Ltd. (1)
21 Five ways Boulevard
Keysborough, VIC, 3173, Australia
Tel.: (61) 397015556
Fax: (61) 397015684
Web Site: www.exedy.com.au
Emp.: 100
Motor Vehicle Parts Mfr
S.I.C.: 3714
N.A.I.C.S.: 336390
Kabel James Davis *(Gen Mgr)*

Exedy Chongqing Co., Ltd. (1)
4 Long Ting Rd
Nanan District, Chongqing, 401122, China
Tel.: (86) 2362924439
Fax: (86) 2362900349
E-Mail: guoning@exedy.com.cn
Web Site: www.exedy.com.cn
Motor Vehicle Supplies & New Parts Whslr
S.I.C.: 5013
N.A.I.C.S.: 423120
Yuvuru Hirose *(Pres)*

Exedy Clutch Europe Ltd. (1)
Unit 2 Rokeby Court
Manor Park Runcom, Chester, Cheshire, WA7 1RW, United Kingdom
Tel.: (44) 1928571850
Fax: (44) 1928571852
E-Mail: info@exedy.co.uk
Web Site: www.exedy.co.uk
Emp.: 14
Motor Vehicle Parts Mfr
S.I.C.: 3714
N.A.I.C.S.: 336390
Masaki Urano *(Mgr)*

Exedy Dynax Europe Ltd. (1)
Szarkalab ut 6
2800 Tatabanya, Hungary
Tel.: (36) 34311117
Fax: (36) 34311122
E-Mail: sf_eec@axelero.hu
Web Site: www.exedy.hu
Emp.: 35
Manual Clutch Mfr & Assembler
S.I.C.: 3714
N.A.I.C.S.: 336390
Norifumi Ikeda *(Gen Mgr)*

Exedy Friction Material Co.,Ltd. (1)
700-359 Moo 6
Bangna-Trad Road Tumbon Don Hu, 20000
Chon Buri, Chonburi, Thailand
Tel.: (66) 38743923
Fax: (66) 38743927
Web Site: www.exedy.co.jp
Emp.: 500
Motor Vehicle Supplies & New Parts Whslr
S.I.C.: 5013
N.A.I.C.S.: 423120
Tomoaki Coto *(Pres)*

Exedy Guangzhou Co., Ltd. (1)
No 406 E-Aria Longfu Car Accessories Centre
Hengfu Road, Guangzhou, China
Tel.: (86) 2083489371
Fax: (86) 02083489370
Web Site: www.exedy.com.au/EXEDYWorldwide.aspx
Emp.: 16
Motor Vehicle Supplies & New Parts Whslr
S.I.C.: 5013
N.A.I.C.S.: 423120
Yang Feng Chun *(VP)*

Exedy (Malaysia) Sdn.Bhd. (1)
PT 16748 Jalan Permate 1-5
Arab-Malaysian Industrial Park, 71800 Nilai, Malaysia
Tel.: (60) 67992988
Fax: (60) 67996388
E-Mail: exedy@exedy.com.my
Web Site: www.exedy.com.my
Emp.: 150
Motor Vehicle Supplies & New Parts Whslr
S.I.C.: 5013
N.A.I.C.S.: 423120
Naoki Yoshii *(Mng Dir)*

Exedy Middle East FZCO (1)
Warehouse No ZE5 & ZE6 Jebel Ali Free Zone
PO Box 18199
Dubai, United Arab Emirates
Tel.: (971) 48832244
Fax: (971) 48832500
E-Mail: exedy@exedy.ae
Web Site: www.exedy.ae
Emp.: 17
Motor Vehicle Supplies & New Parts Whslr
S.I.C.: 5013
N.A.I.C.S.: 423120
Toshihiro Abe *(Gen Mgr)*

EXEDY New Zealand Ltd. (1)
151 Wairau Road Glenfield
745 Auckland, New Zealand
Tel.: (64) 9 444 0901
Fax: (64) 9 444 0903
E-Mail: files04@exedy.co.nz
Web Site: www.exedy.com
Emp.: 14
Automotive Clutch Distr
S.I.C.: 5013
N.A.I.C.S.: 423120
Kabel Davis *(Gen Mgr)*

Exedy (Shanghai) Co., Ltd. (1)
1399 Chengqiao Road
Fengxian District, 201400 Shanghai, China
Tel.: (86) 2167109075
Fax: (86) 02137566715
Web Site: www.exedy.co.jp
Emp.: 850
Motor Vehicle Supplies & New Parts Whslr
S.I.C.: 5013
N.A.I.C.S.: 423120
Masayuki Matsuda *(CEO)*

Exedy (Thailand) Co., Ltd. (1)
700-316 Moo 6
Bangna-Trad Road Tumbon Don Hu, 20000
Chon Buri, Chonburi, Thailand
Tel.: (66) 38214423
Fax: (66) 38214422
E-Mail: knomsan@exedy.co.th
Web Site: www.exedy.co.th
Emp.: 800
Motor Vehicle Supplies & New Parts Whslr
S.I.C.: 5013
N.A.I.C.S.: 423120

Exedy Vietnam Co.,Ltd. (1)
Khai Quang Industrial Zone
Vinh Yen Town, Vinh, Vietnam
Tel.: (84) 211721252
Fax: (84) 211721253
Web Site: www.exedy.com.au/EXEDYWorldwide.aspx
Motor Vehicle Supplies & New Parts Whslr
S.I.C.: 5013
N.A.I.C.S.: 423120
Haruo Shimizu *(Pres)*

P.T. Exedy Indonesia (1)
Jalan Pegangsaan Dua Km2 No 64
Kelapa Gading, 14250 Jakarta, Utara, Indonesia
Tel.: (62) 214603353
Fax: (62) 214603355
Web Site: www.exedy.com.au/EXEDYWorldwide.aspx
Motor Vehicle Supplies & New Parts Whslr
S.I.C.: 5013
N.A.I.C.S.: 423120

P.T. Exedy Motorcycle Indonesia (1)
Jl Pulobuaran Raya Kav IIIFF 8-9 Pulo Gadung
13920 Jakarta, Indonesia
Tel.: (62) 214602581
Fax: (62) 214602580
E-Mail: harry@exedy-motorcycle.co.id
Motor Vehicle Supplies & New Parts Whslr
S.I.C.: 5013
N.A.I.C.S.: 423120

Shanghai Dynax Co., Ltd. (1)
No 2 Plant 1399 Chengqiao Rd
Fengxian District, 201400 Shanghai, China
Tel.: (86) 2157437465
Fax: (86) 2157437458
Web Site: www.dxchina.com.cn
Motor Vehicle Supplies & New Parts Whslr
S.I.C.: 5013
N.A.I.C.S.: 423120
Wang Peitan *(CFO)*

EXEL COMPOSITES OYJ

Utelantie 24B
PO Box 29
52701 Mantyharju, Finland
Tel.: (358) 207541200

Fax: (358) 207541202
E-Mail: profiles@exel.fi
Web Site: www.exelcomposites.com
Year Founded: 1960
EXL1V—(HEL)
Sls.: $102,306,228
Assets: $69,330,447
Liabilities: $27,009,555
Net Worth: $42,320,892
Earnings: $2,734,071
Emp.: 427
Fiscal Year-end: 12/31/12

Business Description:
Reinforced Composite Tubes & Profiles Mfr
S.I.C.: 2652
N.A.I.C.S.: 322219

Personnel:
Peter Hofvenstam *(Chm)*
Vesa Korpimies *(Pres & CEO)*
Ilkka Silvanto *(CFO, Sr VP & Dir-Admin)*
Callum Gough *(Sr VP-Ops & Gen Mgr-Bus Unit-Australia)*
Lasse Orre *(Sr VP-Sls)*
Kim Sjodahl *(Sr VP-Product & Tech Dev)*

Board of Directors:
Peter Hofvenstam
Heikki Hiltunen
Goran Jonsson
Reima Kerttula
Heikki Mairinoja

U.S. Subsidiaries:

Exel Sports NA (1)
113 Elm St
Winooski, VT 05454
Tel.: (802) 846-5565
Fax: (802) 846-5561
Web Site: www.nordicwalker.com
Marine Cargo Handling
S.I.C.: 4491
N.A.I.C.S.: 488320

Exel USA Inc. (1)
7210 W Paradise Dr
Peoria, AZ 85345-8903 (100%)
Tel.: (623) 487-5076
Hotels & Motels
S.I.C.: 7011
N.A.I.C.S.: 721110

Non-U.S. Subsidiaries:

Exel Composites (Australia) Pty Ltd (1)
991 Mountain Hwy
Boronia, VIC, Australia (100%)
Tel.: (61) 387279600
Fax: (61) 387279688
E-Mail: office.melbourne@exelcomposite.com
Web Site: www.exelcomposite.com
Emp.: 40
Household Furniture Mfr
S.I.C.: 2519
N.A.I.C.S.: 337125
Kim Slater *(Gen Mgr)*

Exel Composites GmbH (1)
Industriestrasse-West 8
8605 Kapfenberg, Austria (100%)
Tel.: (43) 386233180
Fax: (43) 38623318025
E-Mail: office.kapfenberg@exelcomposites.com
Web Site: www.exelcomposites.com
Emp.: 40
All Other Plastics Product Mfr
S.I.C.: 3089
N.A.I.C.S.: 326199
Joses Lan Maier *(Mng Dir)*

Exel Composites N.V. (1)
Industriepark De Bruwaan 2
9700 Oudenaarde, Belgium
Tel.: (32) 55333011
Fax: (32) 55333050
E-Mail: office.oudenaarde@exelcomposites.com
Web Site: www.exelcomposites.com
Emp.: 100
Other Nonscheduled Air Transportation
S.I.C.: 4522
N.A.I.C.S.: 481219
Eric Moussiaux *(Mng Dir)*

Exel Composites UK Ltd. (1)
Fairoak Lane
Whitehouse Cheshire Runcorn, Runcorn, United Kingdom (100%)
Tel.: (44) 1928701515
Fax: (44) 1928713572
E-Mail: richard.thomas@exelcomposites.com
Web Site: www.exel.com
Emp.: 50
All Other Plastics Product Mfr
S.I.C.: 3089
N.A.I.C.S.: 326199
Richard Thomas *(Mng Dir)*

Exel GmbH (1)
Alte Hunxer Strasse 139
46562 Voerde, Germany
Tel.: (49) 2811641210
Fax: (49) 2811641220
Web Site: www.exelcomposites.com
Emp.: 30
Other Pressed & Blown Glass & Glassware Mfr
S.I.C.: 3229
N.A.I.C.S.: 327212
V. Corpimis *(Mng Dir)*

Exel Sports Sweden AB (1)
Furunasvagen 105
94152 Pitea, Sweden (100%)
Tel.: (46) 91166501
Fax: (46) 91166142
E-Mail: info@gateway.se
Web Site: www.intgateway.se
Emp.: 5
Sporting & Recreational Goods & Supplies Whslr
S.I.C.: 5091
N.A.I.C.S.: 423910
Joacim Bergstrom *(Mng Dir)*

Pacific Composites Pty. Ltd (1)
991 Mountain Highway
Boronia, VIC, 3155, Australia (100%)
Tel.: (61) 387279600
Fax: (61) 0387279688
E-Mail: office.melbourne@exelcomposites.com
Web Site: www.Exelcomposites.com
Emp.: 25
Broadwoven Fabric Mills
S.I.C.: 2299
N.A.I.C.S.: 313210
Ken Slater *(Mng Dir)*

EXEL INDUSTRIES SA

52 rue de la Victoire
75009 Paris, France
Tel.: (33) 1 71 70 49 50
Fax: (33) 1 71 70 49 53
Web Site: www.exel-industries.com
Year Founded: 1987
EXE—(EUR)
Rev.: $1,019,672,629
Assets: $829,344,048
Liabilities: $514,291,099
Net Worth: $315,052,949
Earnings: $38,827,432
Emp.: 3,600
Fiscal Year-end: 08/31/13

Business Description:
Crop Spraying Equipment Mfr
S.I.C.: 3523
N.A.I.C.S.: 333111

Personnel:
M. Patrick Ballu *(Chm)*
Daniel Tragus *(Chm-Matrot & Herriau & Vice Chm-Hardi International)*
Guerric Ballu *(CEO)*
Cyril Ballu *(Deputy CEO)*
Franck Ballu *(Deputy CEO)*
Sylvain Rousseau *(CFO)*
Marie-Pierre du Cray-Sirieix *(Chief Legal Officer)*
Dominique Lagouge *(Chm-Vermorel & CEO-Kremlin-Rexson & Preciculture)*
Marc Ballu *(CEO-Exel GSA & Hozelock)*
Wolfgang Bergmann *(CEO-Halmer Machinenbau Gmbh)*
Laurent de Buyer-Mineure *(CEO-Tecnoma Technologies & CMC)*
Sten Kjelstrup *(CEO-Hardi International)*
Pierre Nieuviarts *(CEO-SAS Herriau & SAS Holmer Exxact)*
Cedric Perres *(CEO-Sames)*
Sebastien Roche *(CEO-Berthoud)*
Christophe Turpin-Invernon *(CEO-Caruelle Nicolas & Ram Environnement)*

Board of Directors:
M. Patrick Ballu
Guerric Ballu
Marc Ballu
Marie-Claude Bernal
Marie-Pierre du Cray-Sirieix
Claude Lopez

Deloitte & Associes
Villeurbanne, France

Subsidiaries:

Berthoud Agricole SAS (1)
1 rue de l'Industrie
BP 202
69220 Le Plessis-Belleville, France
Tel.: (33) 474065050
Fax: (33) 474065077
Web Site: www.berthoud.com
Rev.: $65,126,800
Emp.: 190
Farm Machinery & Equipment Mfr
S.I.C.: 3523
N.A.I.C.S.: 333111
J. M. Perriei *(Mng Dir)*

Non-U.S. Subsidiary:

Berthoud Sprayers Ltd (2)
Waterford Industrial Estate Mill Lane Great Masssingham
King's Lynn, Norfolk, PE32 2HT, United Kingdom
Tel.: (44) 1485 520626
Fax: (44) 1485 520918
E-Mail: sales@berthoud.co.uk
Web Site: www.berthoud.co.uk
Farm Machinery & Equipment Mfr
S.I.C.: 3523
N.A.I.C.S.: 333111

Caruelle-Nicolas SAS (1)
2 Rue de l'Industrie
BP 2
45550 Saint-Denis-de-l'Hotel, France
Tel.: (33) 238463131
Fax: (33) 238463100
E-Mail: contact@caruelle-nicolas.com
Web Site: www.caruelle-nicolas.com
Emp.: 100
Farm Machinery & Equipment Mfr
S.I.C.: 3523
N.A.I.C.S.: 333111

CMC SAS (1)
1 Rue Vincent Ballu
51200 Epernay, France
Tel.: (33) 326511888
Fax: (33) 326518351
Web Site: www.cmc51.com
Emp.: 2
Farm Machinery & Equipment Mfr
S.I.C.: 3523
N.A.I.C.S.: 333111
Joel Thomas *(Mgr-Comml)*

EXEL gsa SAS (1)
Rue de l'abbaye
BP 424
69653 Villefranche-sur-Saone, France
Tel.: (33) 474624848
Fax: (33) 474623751
E-Mail: exelgsa@ecelgsa.com
Web Site: www.exelgsa.fr
Emp.: 130
Spraying Equipment Mfr
S.I.C.: 3523
N.A.I.C.S.: 333111

Hardi Evrard SA (1)
43 rue du Cuivre
BP 59
77542 Savigny-le-Temple, France
Tel.: (33) 164105400
Fax: (33) 1 64 10 54 10
E-Mail: hardi-evrard@hardi-fr.com
Web Site: www.hardi-fr.com
Farm Machinery & Equipment Mfr
S.I.C.: 3523
N.A.I.C.S.: 333111

Kremlin-Rexson SA (1)
150 Ave de Stalingrad
93240 Stains, France
Tel.: (33) 149402525
Fax: (33) 48260716
Web Site: www.kremlinrexson-sames.com
Emp.: 200
Spraying Equipment Distr
S.I.C.: 5084
N.A.I.C.S.: 423830
Dominique Lagouge *(Gen Mgr)*

Subsidiary:

API Technologies SAS (2)
29 Avenue Ashton Under Lyne
52000 Chaumont, France
Tel.: (33) 325011919
Fax: (33) 325011913
Web Site: www.api-technologies.com
Farm Machinery & Equipment Mfr
S.I.C.: 3523
N.A.I.C.S.: 333111

U.S. Subsidiary:

EXEL NORTH AMERICA INC. (2)
45001 5 Mile Rd
Plymouth, MI 48170
Tel.: (734) 979-0100
Fax: (734) 927-0064
Web Site: www.exel-na.com
Farm Machinery & Equipment Mfr
S.I.C.: 3523
N.A.I.C.S.: 333111

Non-U.S. Subsidiaries:

EXEL INDUSTRIAL CANADA INC. (2)
931 Progress Ave Unit 7
Scarborough, ON, M1G 3V5, Canada
Tel.: (416) 431-5017
Fax: (416) 431-9171
Toll Free: (800) 450-0655
E-Mail: order@exel-na.com
Web Site: www.Kremlin-Rexson.com
Emp.: 15
Farm Machinery & Equipment Mfr
S.I.C.: 3523
N.A.I.C.S.: 333111
S. T. Rajan *(VP)*

EXEL INDUSTRIAL E.P.E. LDTA (2)
Avenida Jose Luis Sereno 1200
13212-210 Jundiai, Brazil
Tel.: (55) 11 45 81 63 04
Fax: (55) 11 45 82 00 68
E-Mail: exel.brazil@exel-industrial.com.br
Web Site: www.exel-industrial.com.br
Emp.: 15
Farm Machinery & Equipment Mfr
S.I.C.: 3523
N.A.I.C.S.: 333111
Oscar Simoas *(Gen Mgr)*

EXEL INDUSTRIAL E.P.E., S.A. (2)
C/Botanica 49
8908 L'Hospitalet de Llobregat, Barcelona, Spain
Tel.: (34) 932641540
Fax: (34) 932632829
Farm Machinery & Equipment Mfr
S.I.C.: 3523
N.A.I.C.S.: 333111

EXEL Lackier- und Beschichtungssysteme GmbH (2)
Moselstrasse 19
41464 Neuss, Germany
Tel.: (49) 2131 369 22 00
Fax: (49) 2131 369 22 22
E-Mail: info@exel-gmbh.com
Farm Machinery & Equipment Mfr
S.I.C.: 3523
N.A.I.C.S.: 333111
Hermann Rothe *(Mgr-Sls)*

EXEL S.A. de C.V. (2)
Bernardo Garza Trevino 1715 Col de Maestro
Monterrey, Nuevo Leon, 64180, Mexico

Exel Industries SA—(Continued)

Tel.: (52) 8112571111
Fax: (52) 81 1352 8316
Farm Machinery & Equipment Mfr
S.I.C.: 3523
N.A.I.C.S.: 333111

EXELUSA INDUSTRIAL, LDA (2)
Rua da Silveira 554 - Touria
2410-269 Pousos, Portugal
Tel.: (351) 244848220
Fax: (351) 244 848 229
E-Mail: exel.pt@exel-industrial.pt
Emp.: 6
Farm Machinery & Equipment Mfr
S.I.C.: 3523
N.A.I.C.S.: 333111
Shaher Hasan *(Gen Mgr)*

KREMLIN REXSON India Pvt Ltd (2)
Kothari House Gate No 634 Pune Nagar Road
Wagholi, Pune, 412207, India
Tel.: (91) 20 30472700
Fax: (91) 20 30472710
E-Mail: info@exel-in.com
Web Site: www.kremlinrexson-sames.com
Emp.: 25
Farm Machinery & Equipment Mfr
S.I.C.: 3523
N.A.I.C.S.: 333111
Jyotirmoy Banerjee *(Mng Dir)*

Kremlin Rexson Polska Sp. z o.o. (2)
ul Modlinska 221B
03-120 Warsaw, Poland
Tel.: (48) 225103850
Fax: (48) 225103877
E-Mail: biuro@kremlin.pl
Web Site: www.kremlin-rexson.pl
Emp.: 10
Farm Machinery & Equipment Mfr
S.I.C.: 3523
N.A.I.C.S.: 333111

KREMLIN REXSON PTE LTD (2)
German Centre International Business Park 05-109E
Singapore, 609916, Singapore
Tel.: (65) 65628290
Fax: (65) 68359096
Web Site: www.kremlinrexson-sames.sg
Emp.: 5
Spraying Equipment Mfr
S.I.C.: 7699
N.A.I.C.S.: 811310

KREMLIN REXSON S.p.A (2)
Via F Brunelleschi 16
20146 Milan, Italy
Tel.: (39) 0248952815
Fax: (39) 0248300071
Web Site: www.kremlinrexson-sames.it
Spraying Equipment Mfr
S.I.C.: 3523
N.A.I.C.S.: 333111

Matrot Equipements SAS (1)
116 rue des Pommiers
60480 Noyers-Saint-Martin, France
Tel.: (33) 3 44 80 66 33
Fax: (33) 3 44 80 66 30
E-Mail: info@domaine-matrot.fr
Web Site: www.matrot.fr
Rev.: $38,226,600
Farm Machinery & Equipment Mfr
S.I.C.: 3523
N.A.I.C.S.: 333111

Preciculture SAS (1)
165 rue des Verriers
51230 Fere-Champenoise, France
Tel.: (33) 326424051
Fax: (33) 3 26 42 04 96
Web Site: www.preciculture.fr
Spraying Equipment Distr
S.I.C.: 5084
N.A.I.C.S.: 423830

RAM Environnement SAS (1)
2 Rue de l'Industrie
45550 Saint-Denis-de-l'Hotel, France
Tel.: (33) 238463110
Fax: (33) 238591528
E-Mail: ram@ramenvironnement.com
Web Site: www.ramenvironnement.com
Emp.: 11
Farm Machinery & Equipment Mfr
S.I.C.: 3523
N.A.I.C.S.: 333111
Christophe Turpin *(Mgr)*

Sames Technologies SAS (1)
13 Chemin de Malacher
BP 86
38243 Meylan, France
Tel.: (33) 476416060
Fax: (33) 476416090
E-Mail: accueil@sames.com
Web Site: www.sames.com
Spraying Equipment Distr
S.I.C.: 5084
N.A.I.C.S.: 423830

Tecnoma Technologies SAS (1)
54 rue Marcel Paul
BP 195
51206 Epernay, France
Tel.: (33) 326519999
Fax: (33) 326518351
E-Mail: tecnoma@tecnoma.com
Web Site: www.tecnoma.com
Emp.: 160
Farm Machinery & Equipment Mfr
S.I.C.: 3523
N.A.I.C.S.: 333111
Patrick Ballu *(Owner & Mng Dir)*

Non-U.S. Subsidiaries:

FISCHER New SARL (1)
En Bovery A
Case Postale 184, 1868 Collombey, Switzerland
Tel.: (41) 244735080
Fax: (41) 244735081
Web Site: www.fischer-sarl.ch
Farm Machinery & Equipment Mfr
S.I.C.: 3523
N.A.I.C.S.: 333111

Hardi International AS (1)
Helgeshoj Alle 38
2630 Tastrup, Denmark
Tel.: (45) 4358 8300
Fax: (45) 4371 3355
E-Mail: hardi@hardi-international.com
Web Site: www.hardi-international.com
Emp.: 575
Crop Spraying Services
S.I.C.: 0711
N.A.I.C.S.: 115112
Sten Kjelstrup *(Pres & CEO)*

U.S. Subsidiary:

Hardi North America Inc (2)
1500 W 76th St
Davenport, IA 52806
Tel.: (563) 386-1730
Fax: (563) 386-1710
E-Mail: info@hardi-us.com
Web Site: www.hardi-us.com
Farm Machinery & Equipment Mfr
S.I.C.: 3523
N.A.I.C.S.: 333111
Dave Fraker *(Mgr-OEM Bus)*

Non-U.S. Subsidiaries:

HARDI Australia Pty. Ltd. (2)
534-538 Cross Keys Road
Cavan, SA, 5094, Australia
Tel.: (61) 883439999
Fax: (61) 883439959
E-Mail: info@hardi-aus.com
Web Site: www.hardi.com.au
Farm Machinery & Equipment Mfr
S.I.C.: 3523
N.A.I.C.S.: 333111

HARDI Crop Protection SA LTD. (2)
No 11 Rand Str
Blackheath, Cape Town, Western Cape, 7560, South Africa
Tel.: (27) 21 905 2260
Fax: (27) 21 905 2611
Web Site: www.hardi.co.za
Emp.: 11
Agricultural Equipment Distr
S.I.C.: 5083
N.A.I.C.S.: 423820
Clive Crouse *(Mng Dir)*

Hardi Gmbh (2)
Schaumburger Str 17
30900 Wedemark, Germany
Tel.: (49) 5130 97 68 0
Fax: (49) 5130 97 68 68
E-Mail: hardi@hardi-gmbh.com
Web Site: www.hardi-gmbh.com
Emp.: 10
Farm Machinery & Equipment Mfr
S.I.C.: 3523
N.A.I.C.S.: 333111
Karsten Hemmingsen *(Gen Mgr)*

HARDI GmbH (2)
Werksvertretung Osterreich Nr 56
3662 Munichreith, Austria
Tel.: (43) 664 9232373
Farm Machinery & Equipment Mfr
S.I.C.: 3523
N.A.I.C.S.: 333111

HARDI INC. (2)
337 Sovereign Rd
London, ON, N6M 1A6, Canada
Tel.: (519) 659-2771
Fax: (519) 659-2821
E-Mail: custserv@hardi-us.com
Web Site: www.hardi-us.com
Emp.: 4
Farm Machinery & Equipment Distr
S.I.C.: 5083
N.A.I.C.S.: 423820
Don Hewitt *(Gen Mgr)*

HARDI Kenya Ltd. (2)
PO Box 47409
00100 Nairobi, Kenya
Tel.: (254) 20 85 62 098
Fax: (254) 20 2384206
E-Mail: sales@hardi.co.ke
Web Site: www.hardi.co.ke
Farm Machinery & Equipment Mfr
S.I.C.: 3523
N.A.I.C.S.: 333111
Robinson Ngano *(Mgr-Ops)*

Hardi Ltd (2)
Watling Ste Unit B High Cross Business Park Coventry Rd
Sharnford, LE10 3PG, United Kingdom
Tel.: (44) 1 455 22 22 30
Fax: (44) 1 455 22 22 40
E-Mail: sales@hardi-uk.com
Web Site: www.hardi-uk.com
Emp.: 7
Spraying Equipment Distr
S.I.C.: 5083
N.A.I.C.S.: 423820
Peter Wiles *(Dir-Sls)*

HARDI Spraying Equipment Limited (2)
4 Princes Street
PO Box 24-186
Onehunga, Auckland, New Zealand
Tel.: (64) 9 634 4632
Fax: (64) 9 634 4238
Farm Machinery & Equipment Mfr
S.I.C.: 3523
N.A.I.C.S.: 333111

Svenska Hardi AB (2)
Box 50 444
202 14 Malmo, Sweden
Tel.: (46) 40210250
Fax: (46) 40 210 251
E-Mail: skandinavien@hardi-international.com
Web Site: www.svenskahardi.se
Emp.: 60
Farm Machinery & Equipment Mfr
S.I.C.: 3523
N.A.I.C.S.: 333111
Sten Kjelstrup *(Pres)*

ILEMO HARDI, S.A.U. (1)
Pol Ind El Segre Carrer de l Empresari Josep
Segura i Farre parc 712-713, 25191 Lleida, Spain
Tel.: (34) 973 20 80 12
Fax: (34) 973 20 81 53
E-Mail: ilemo@hardi-es.com
Web Site: www.hardi-es.com
Emp.: 50
Agricultural Spraying Equipment Mfr
S.I.C.: 3523
N.A.I.C.S.: 333111
J. M. Goida *(Gen Mgr)*

Matrot UK Ltd (1)
Mill Lane Great Massingham
King's Lynn, Norfolk, PE32 2HT, United Kingdom
Tel.: (44) 1485520626
Farm Machinery & Equipment Distr
S.I.C.: 5083
N.A.I.C.S.: 423820

Vermorel SRL (1)
3 Strada Pompelor
100411 Ploiesti, Romania
Tel.: (40) 344104178
Fax: (40) 244522152
E-Mail: ru@vermorel.eu
Web Site: www.vermorel.eu
Farm Machinery & Equipment Mfr
S.I.C.: 3523
N.A.I.C.S.: 333111

EXERCISE FOR LIFE SYSTEMS, INC.

92 Gleneagles View
Cochrane, AB, Canada
Tel.: (403) 932-1801
E-Mail: adam@e4lifeonline.com
Web Site: www.e4lifeonline.com
Year Founded: 1996
EFLS—(OTC)
Sales Range: Less than $1 Million

Business Description:
Personal Fitness Training Facilities
S.I.C.: 7991
N.A.I.C.S.: 713940

Personnel:
Benjamin Schaeffer *(Pres, CEO, CFO, Treas & Sec)*

Board of Directors:
Al Hayes
Neil P. Hudd
Gerald Lotterstein
Terry O'Hearn
Benjamin Schaeffer

Transfer Agent:
Guardian Registrar & Transfer, Inc.
7951 SW 6th St Ste 216
Plantation, FL 33324-3276

EXETER PRODUCE & STORAGE CO. LIMITED

215 Thames Road West
Exeter, ON, N0M 1S3, Canada
Tel.: (519) 235-0141
Fax: (519) 235-3515
Toll Free: (800) 881-4861
Web Site: www.exeterproduce.com
Year Founded: 1951
Rev.: $17,937,709
Emp.: 50

Business Description:
Fresh Fruits & Vegetables Whslr
S.I.C.: 5148
N.A.I.C.S.: 424480

Personnel:
Friedhelm Hoffmann *(Mgr-Ops)*

EXETER RESOURCE CORPORATION

999 West Hastings Street Ste 1660
Vancouver, BC, V6C 2W2, Canada
Tel.: (604) 688-9592
Fax: (604) 688-9532
Toll Free: (888) 688-9592
E-Mail: exeter@exeterresource.com
Web Site: www.exeterresource.com
XRA—(DEU NYSEMKT TSX)
Int. Income: $807,144
Assets: $55,988,177
Liabilities: $920,463
Net Worth: $55,067,714
Earnings: ($25,075,149)
Emp.: 24
Fiscal Year-end: 12/31/12

Business Description:
Mineral Exploration Services
S.I.C.: 1041
N.A.I.C.S.: 212221

Personnel:
Bryce Gordon Roxburgh *(Co-Chm)*
Yale R. Simpson *(Co-Chm)*
Wendell Zerb *(Pres & CEO)*
Cecil Bond *(CFO)*

Board of Directors:
Bryce Gordon Roxburgh
Yale R. Simpson
Julian Bavin
Robert Gordon Reynolds
John Simmons
Transfer Agent:
Computershare Investor Services Inc.
510 Burrard Street 2nd Floor
Vancouver, BC, V6C 3B9, Canada
Non-U.S. Subsidiaries:

Cognito Limited (1)
Martin Zapata 445
5500 Mendoza, Argentina VG
Tel.: (54) 2614203415 (100%)
Fax: (54) 2614203415
E-Mail: lucia.costewla@extowre.com
Emp.: 100
Mineral Exploration Services
S.I.C.: 1099
N.A.I.C.S.: 212299
Patricia Inzirillo *(Mgr-Admin & Legal)*

Estelar Resources Limited (1)
Martin Zapata 445
5500 Mendoza, Argentina VG
Tel.: (54) 2614203415 (100%)
Fax: (54) 2614293426
E-Mail: lucia.costewla@extowre.com
Web Site: www.extowre.com
Emp.: 90
Mineral Exploration Services
S.I.C.: 1099
N.A.I.C.S.: 212299
Patricia Inzirillo *(Mgr-Admin & Legal)*

EXFO INC.
400 Godin Avenue
Quebec, QC, G1M 2K2, Canada
Tel.: (418) 683-0211
Fax: (418) 683-2170
Toll Free: (800) 663-3936 (US & Canada)
E-Mail: info@exfo.com
Web Site: www.exfo.com
Year Founded: 1985
EXFO—(NASDAQ TSX)
Sls.: $242,150,000
Assets: $281,538,000
Liabilities: $45,086,000
Net Worth: $236,452,000
Earnings: $1,341,000
Emp.: 1,583
Fiscal Year-end: 08/31/13
Business Description:
Fiber-Optic Test, Measurement & Monitoring Instruments Mfr for Telecommunications Industries
S.I.C.: 3825
N.A.I.C.S.: 334515
Personnel:
Germain Lamonde *(Chm, Pres & CEO)*
Pierre Plamondon *(CFO & VP-Fin)*
Benoit Ringuette *(Gen Counsel & Sec)*
Board of Directors:
Germain Lamonde
Pierre-Paul Allard
Darryl Alexander Edwards
Guy Marier
Claude Seguin
Randy E. Tornes
Transfer Agent:
CST Trust Company
2001 University Street Ste 1600
Montreal, QC, H3A 2A6, Canada
Division:

EXFO Navtel Product Group (1)
160 Drumlin Circle
Concord, ON, L4K 3E5, Canada
Tel.: (905) 738-3741
Fax: (905) 738-3712
Toll Free: (800) 465-9400
E-Mail: info@exfo.com
Web Site: www.exfo.com
Emp.: 35
Network Test Solutions Developer for Mobile & Fixed Network Industries
S.I.C.: 3825
N.A.I.C.S.: 334515
Germain Lamonde *(Chm, Pres & CEO)*

U.S. Subsidiaries:

EXFO America Inc. (1)
3400 Waterview Pkwy Ste 100
Richardson, TX 75080 DE
Tel.: (972) 761-9271
Fax: (972) 761-9067
Toll Free: (800) 663-3936
Sales Range: $1-9.9 Million
Emp.: 60
Fiber-Optic Test, Measurement & Monitoring Instruments Mfr
S.I.C.: 3825
N.A.I.C.S.: 334515

EXFO Service Assurance Inc. (1)
285 Mill Rd
Chelmsford, MA 01824
Tel.: (978) 367-5600
Emp.: 50
Telecommunication Network Quality Assurance Solutions
S.I.C.: 3663
N.A.I.C.S.: 334220
Thomas Pincinco *(Pres)*
Rick Rigoli *(CFO)*
Kaynam Hedayat *(CTO)*

Non-U.S. Subsidiaries:

EXFO Asia Pacific PTE. Ltd. (1)
Room 1207 Office Tower C Global Trade Center No 36 N 3rd Ring East Rd
Dongcheng District, Beijing, PR, 100013, China CN
Tel.: (86) 1058257755 (100%)
Fax: (86) 1058257722
Web Site: www.exfo.com
Sales Distribution of Test & Monitoring Solutions for Network Services
S.I.C.: 3825
N.A.I.C.S.: 334515

EXFO Asia Pacific Pte. Ltd. (1)
Room 2711 Trade Center No 4028 Jintian Road
Futian District, Shenzhen, PR, 518035, China CN
Tel.: (86) 75582032300 (100%)
Fax: (86) 75582032306
Web Site: www.exfo.com
Sales Distribution of Test & Monitoring Solutions for Network Services & Equipment Mfrs
S.I.C.: 3825
N.A.I.C.S.: 334515

EXFO Asia Pacific PTE Ltd. (1)
100 Beach Road 25-01/03 Shaw Tower
Singapore, 189702, Singapore
Tel.: (65) 63338241
Fax: (65) 63338242
E-Mail: info@exfo.com
Web Site: www.exfo.com
Emp.: 10
Mfr of Fiber-Optic Test, Measurement & Monitoring Instruments for Telecommunications Industry
S.I.C.: 3825
N.A.I.C.S.: 334515
Joseph Soo *(VP-Sls)*

Non-U.S. Subsidiaries:

EXFO Electro-Optical Engineering India Private Ltd. (2)
Office No 604 Tower S-4 Cybercity
Magarpatta
Hadapsar, Pune, 411 013, India
Tel.: (91) 20 66040246
Web Site: www.exfo.com
Wireless Telecommunication Services
S.I.C.: 4812
N.A.I.C.S.: 517210

EXFO Telecom Equipment (Shenzhen) Co. Ltd. (2)
2 3/F Block 10 Yusheng Industrial Park
Side Of Gushu Cross
Shenzhen, China
Tel.: (86) 75529553100
Fax: (86) 75529553101
Emp.: 14
Telecommunication Equipment Mfr
S.I.C.: 3669
N.A.I.C.S.: 334290

NetHawk Solutions Pvt. Ltd. (2)
308 3rd Floor Iris Technology Park Sector 48 Sona Road
Gurgaon, 12218, India
Tel.: (91) 9871871633
Fax: (91) 1244868374
E-Mail: sales.india@exfo.com
Web Site: www.exfo.com
Emp.: 12
Wireless Telecommunication Services
S.I.C.: 4812
N.A.I.C.S.: 517210
Olivier Ferret *(Country Mgr)*

EXFO Europe Ltd. (1)
Winchester House School Ln
Chandlers Ford, Chandlers Ford, SO53 4DG, United Kingdom
Tel.: (44) 2380 246 800
Fax: (44) 2380 246 801
E-Mail: Orders.EXFO.Europe@exfo.com
Web Site: www.exfo.com
Emp.: 30
Mfr of Fiber-Optic Test, Measurement & Monitoring Instruments for Telecommunications Industry
S.I.C.: 3825
N.A.I.C.S.: 334515
Jon Bradley *(VP-Intl Sls)*

EXFO Finland Oy (1)
Elektroniikkatie 2
90590 Oulu, Finland
Tel.: (358) 403 010 300
Fax: (358) 8 564 5203
Wireless Network Equipment Mfr
S.I.C.: 3663
N.A.I.C.S.: 334220

EXFO India (1)
7th Floor 701 Building B1
Cerebrum Lt Park Vadgaontri, 14 Pune, 411 001, India In
Tel.: (91) 2040186615 (100%)
Fax: (91) 40186615
Web Site: www.exfo.com
Emp.: 150
Test & Monitoring Solutions for Network Services
S.I.C.: 3825
N.A.I.C.S.: 334515
Sathish Kamath *(Country Head)*

EXFO Japan (1)
4-6-3-202 Akasaka Minato-ku
Tokyo, 107 0052, Japan JP
Tel.: (81) 355625344 (100%)
Fax: (81) 355625777
Web Site: www.exfo.com
Test & Monitoring Solutions for Network Services & Equipment Mfrs
S.I.C.: 3825
N.A.I.C.S.: 334515

NetHawk S.a.r.l (1)
27 rue de Solferino
92100 Boulogne-Billancourt, France
Tel.: (33) 1 46 08 19 53
Fax: (33) 1 46 08 13 96
Wireless Telecommunication Services
S.I.C.: 4812
N.A.I.C.S.: 517210

EXIDE INDUSTRIES LIMITED
Exide House 59E Chowringhee Road
Kolkata, 700020, India
Tel.: (91) 3322832120
Fax: (91) 22832637
Web Site: www.exideindustries.com
EXIDEIND—(NSE)
Rev.: $1,327,365,738
Assets: $2,096,634,834
Liabilities: $1,523,591,244
Net Worth: $573,043,590
Earnings: $100,116,000
Emp.: 4,898
Fiscal Year-end: 03/31/13
Business Description:
Storage Batteries Mfr
S.I.C.: 3691
N.A.I.C.S.: 335911
Personnel:
P. K. Kataky *(CEO & Mng Dir)*
G. Chatterjee *(Mng Dir)*
A. K. Mukherjee *(CFO & Dir-Fin)*
Supriya Coomer *(Compliance Officer, Sec & VP-Legal & Admin)*
Board of Directors:
R. G. Kapadia
Vijay Aggarwal
Subir Chakraborty
Sudhir Chand
G. Chatterjee
Mona N. Desai
P. K. Kataky
Nadeem Kazim
A. K. Mukherjee
R. B. Raheja
S. B. Raheja
W. Wong
Legal Counsel:
A.H. Parpia & Co.
203-204 Prabhat Chambers 92 S V Road Khar West
Mumbai, 400 052, India
Transfer Agent:
C. B. Management Services (P) Ltd
P-22 Bondel Road
700019 Kolkata, India
Subsidiaries:

Caldyne Automatics Limited (1)
Plot No Y-21 Block Ep Sector-5 Salt Lake Electronics Complex
Bidhannagar, Kolkata, West Bengal, 700091, India
Tel.: (91) 3323575851
Fax: (91) 3323577062
E-Mail: info@caldyneautomatics.com
Web Site: www.caldyneautomatics.com
Emp.: 110
High End Industrial Chargers Mfr
S.I.C.: 3691
N.A.I.C.S.: 335911

ING Vysya Life Insurance Company Ltd. (1)
ING Vysya House 5th Floor
22 M G Road
560001 Bengaluru, India
Tel.: (91) 805328000
Fax: (91) 805559764
Web Site: www.ingvysyalife.com
Insurance Services
S.I.C.: 6311
N.A.I.C.S.: 524113

Leadage Alloys India Limited (1)
60 2 Sheethanayakanahalli
Kolar Dist, Malur, Karnataka, 563130, India
Tel.: (91) 8151 233333
Fax: (91) 8151 232222
E-Mail: info@leadage.in
Web Site: www.leadage.in
Lead & Lead Alloys Mfr & Supplier
S.I.C.: 3341
N.A.I.C.S.: 331492
T. Arun Kumar *(CEO & Mng Dir)*
E. Narayanan *(COO)*

Non-U.S. Subsidiaries:

Chloride Batteries S E Asia Pte Limited (1)
106 Neythal Rd
Jurong, 628594, Singapore
Tel.: (65) 62652444
Fax: (65) 62651478
E-Mail: salesdesk@cbsea.com.sg
Web Site: www.cbsea.com.sg
Emp.: 40
Batteries & Chargers Mfr & Distr
S.I.C.: 3699
N.A.I.C.S.: 335999
Winston Kay Wong *(Mng Dir)*

Espex Batteries Limited (1)
Unit 13 Llandough Trading Estate Off Penarth Rd
Cardiff, South Glamorgan, CF11 8RR, United Kingdom
Tel.: (44) 2920705453
Fax: (44) 2920708165
E-Mail: sales@espexbatteries.co.uk
Web Site: www.espexbatteries.co.uk
Emp.: 11
Power Traction Cells & Battery Charges Mfr & Distr

EXIDE INDUSTRIES LIMITED—(Continued)

S.I.C.: 3691
N.A.I.C.S.: 335911
Amit Ghosal *(Gen Mgr)*

EXILLON ENERGY PLC

Fort Anne
Douglas, Isle of Man
Tel.: (44) 43996311
E-Mail: ir@ee.im
Web Site: www.exillonenergy.com
EXI—(LSE WAR)
Rev.: $301,928,000
Assets: $776,463,000
Liabilities: $208,929,000
Net Worth: $567,534,000
Earnings: $12,142,000
Emp.: 376
Fiscal Year-end: 12/31/12

Business Description:
Oil & Gas Exploration Services
S.I.C.: 1311
N.A.I.C.S.: 211111

Personnel:
Mark Martin *(CEO)*
Alexander Suchkov *(Deputy CEO)*
Yuri Ovcharov *(COO)*
Henry Wolski *(Sr VP-Production Ops)*

Board of Directors:
David Herbert
Anne Belveze
Ezio Bracco
L. Stuard Detmer
Sergey Koshelenko
Mark Martin
Alexander Suchkov

Legal Counsel:
Cains Advocates Limited
Fort Anne
Douglas, Isle of Man

Baker & McKenzie LLP
100 New Bridge Street
EC4V6JA London, United Kingdom

EXINI DIAGNOSTICS AB

Scheelevagen 19 A
SE-223 70 Lund, Sweden
Tel.: (46) 462865420
Fax: (46) 462865429
E-Mail: info@exini.com
Web Site: www.exini.com
Year Founded: 1999
EXINI—(OMX)
Emp.: 12

Business Description:
Medical Image Analysis Software
S.I.C.: 7372
N.A.I.C.S.: 511210

Personnel:
Bo Hakansson *(Chm)*
Magnus Aurell *(CEO)*
Klas Themner *(CFO & COO)*

Board of Directors:
Bo Hakansson
Jan Erik Hedborg
Fredrik Herslow
Olof Jarlman
Henrik Perlmutter
Marcus Pramgard

EXIQON A/S

Skelstedet 16
2950 Vedbaek, Denmark
Tel.: (45) 45660888
Fax: (45) 45661888
E-Mail: exiqon@exiqon.com
Web Site: www.exiqon.com
Year Founded: 1995
EXQ—(CSE)
Rev.: $21,174,264
Assets: $22,038,008
Liabilities: $6,830,594
Net Worth: $15,207,414
Earnings: ($2,632,354)
Emp.: 73
Fiscal Year-end: 12/31/12

Business Description:
Pharmaceutical Product Mfr
S.I.C.: 2834
N.A.I.C.S.: 325412

Personnel:
Thorleif Krarup *(Chm)*
Erik Wallden *(Deputy Chm)*
Lars Kongsbak *(CEO)*
Hans Henrik Chrois Christensen *(CFO)*

Board of Directors:
Thorleif Krarup
Michael Nobel
Erik Wallden
Per Wold-Olsen

U.S. Subsidiary:

Exiqon, Inc. **(1)**
12 Gill St Ste 1650
Woburn, MA 01801
Tel.: (781) 376-4150
Fax: (781) 376-4152
Toll Free: (888) 647-2879
Web Site: www.exiqon.com
Pharmaceutical Products Whslr
S.I.C.: 5122
N.A.I.C.S.: 424210
Lars Kongsbak *(CEO)*

EXISTA HF.

(See Under Klakki ehf.)

EXITO ENERGY II INC.

500 1414 8th Street Southwest
Calgary, AB, T2R 1J6, Canada
Tel.: (403) 472-5767
E-Mail: brad@doclaw.ca
Year Founded: 2010
EXI.P—(TSXV)

Business Description:
Investment Services
S.I.C.: 6211
N.A.I.C.S.: 523999

Personnel:
Brad Docherty *(Pres & CEO)*
Eli Abergel *(CFO & Sec)*

Board of Directors:
Eli Abergel
Brad Docherty
Brody Loster
William Matheson
Andrew Oppenheim
Colin Reeves
Christopher Scase

Transfer Agent:
Valiant Trust Company
Suite 310 606 4th Street S.W.
Calgary, AB, Canada

EXM MANUFACTURING LTD.

870 boul Michele-Bohec
Blainville, QC, J7C 5E2, Canada
Tel.: (450) 979-4373
Fax: (450) 979-4626
Toll Free: (800) 363-2423
E-Mail: info@exmweb.com
Web Site: www.exmweb.com
Year Founded: 1975
Sales Range: $10-24.9 Million
Emp.: 30

Business Description:
Cabinets Mfr
S.I.C.: 2434
N.A.I.C.S.: 337110

Personnel:
Maurizio Ciocca *(Pres)*

EXMAR N.V.

De Gerlachekaai 20
B-2000 Antwerp, Belgium
Tel.: (32) 32475611
Fax: (32) 32482740
E-Mail: corporate@exmar.be
Web Site: www.exmar.be
EXM—(EUR)
Rev.: $509,092,000
Assets: $1,370,334,000
Liabilities: $1,003,361,000
Net Worth: $366,973,000
Earnings: $54,628,000
Emp.: 1,571
Fiscal Year-end: 12/31/12

Business Description:
Deep Sea Freight Transportation
S.I.C.: 4412
N.A.I.C.S.: 483111

Personnel:
Nicolas Saverys *(CEO & Mng Dir)*
Miguel de Potter *(CFO)*
Patrick De Brabandere *(COO)*
Paul Young *(CMO)*
Marc Nuytemans *(CEO-Shipmanagement)*
Karel Stes *(Sec)*
Didier Ryelandt *(Exec VP-Exmar Offshore)*

Board of Directors:
Baron Philippe Bodson
Ludwig Criel
Patrick De Brabandere
Francois Gillet
Jens Ismar
Ariane Saverys
Nicolas Saverys
Pauline Saverys
Guy Verhofstadt
Baron Philippe Vlerick

Subsidiaries:

Belgibo N.V. **(1)**
De Gerlachekaai 20
2000 Antwerp, Belgium
Tel.: (32) 32475811
Fax: (32) 32483319
E-Mail: all@belgibo.be
Web Site: www.belgibo.be
Emp.: 45
Insurance Agencies
S.I.C.: 6411
N.A.I.C.S.: 524298
Piarre Derom *(Mng Dir)*

Bexco N.V. **(1)**
Industriepark Zwaarveld 25
9220 Hamme, East Flanders, Belgium
Tel.: (32) 52499306
Fax: (32) 52499380
E-Mail: bexco@bexco.be
Web Site: www.bexco.be
Emp.: 120
Rope Mfr & Suppliers
S.I.C.: 2298
N.A.I.C.S.: 314994
Francis Mottrie *(Gen Mgr)*

EXMAR Marine N.V. **(1)**
De Gerlachekaai 20
2000 Antwerp, Belgium
Tel.: (32) 32475611
Fax: (32) 32482740
E-Mail: corporate@exmar.be
Emp.: 40
Shipping Agencies
S.I.C.: 4412
N.A.I.C.S.: 483111
Nicolas Saverys *(CEO)*

EXMAR Shipmanagement N.V. **(1)**
De Gerlachekaai 20
2000 Antwerp, Belgium
Tel.: (32) 32475011
Fax: (32) 32475091
E-Mail: shipmanagement@exmar.be
Web Site: www.exmar.be/shipmanagement.html
Emp.: 80
Marine Transportation Services
S.I.C.: 4412
N.A.I.C.S.: 483111
Marc Nuytemans *(Mng Dir)*

EXMAR Shipping N.V. **(1)**
De Gerlachekaai 20
2000 Antwerp, Belgium
Tel.: (32) 32475611
Fax: (32) 3 2482740
Web Site: www.exmar.be
Marine Transportation Services
S.I.C.: 4412
N.A.I.C.S.: 483111

Travel Plus N.V. **(1)**
Verviersstraat 2 4
2000 Antwerp, Belgium
Tel.: (32) 32475800
Fax: (32) 32480883
E-Mail: travelplus.business@travelplus.be
Web Site: www.travelplus.be
Emp.: 14
Travel Agencies
S.I.C.: 4724
N.A.I.C.S.: 561510
Christel Daeseleire *(Mng Dir)*

U.S. Subsidiary:

Exmar Offshore Company **(1)**
11511 Katy Fwy Ste 200
Houston, TX 77079 TX
Tel.: (281) 679-3900
Fax: (281) 497-3370
E-Mail: marketing@exmaroffshore.com
Web Site: www.exmaroffshore.com
Emp.: 25
Construction Management Services
S.I.C.: 1629
N.A.I.C.S.: 237990
Otto Da Silva *(Mgr-Engrg)*

Non-U.S. Subsidiaries:

EXMAR Lux SA **(1)**
Jean Pierre Brasseur 6
Luxembourg, 1258, Luxembourg
Tel.: (352) 2638481
Fax: (352) 26259454
Shipping Agencies
S.I.C.: 4412
N.A.I.C.S.: 483111
Brijitte Chouly *(Mgr)*

Exmar Shipmanagement India, Pvt. Ltd. **(1)**
Shop No 405 406 407 Mint Chambers
45 47 Mint Rd Fort, Mumbai, Maharashtra, 400001, India
Tel.: (91) 2222640226
Fax: (91) 2222640230
E-Mail: crew.operations@shipmanagement.exmar.in
Emp.: 10
Marine Transportation Services
S.I.C.: 4412
N.A.I.C.S.: 483111
S. Anand Kapoor *(Gen Mgr-Fleet Personnel)*

EXMAR (UK) Shipping Company Limited **(1)**
Moreau House
112-120 Brompton Rd, London, SW3 1JJ, United Kingdom
Tel.: (44) 2078700400
Fax: (44) 2072251854
Emp.: 10
Shipping Agencies
S.I.C.: 4412
N.A.I.C.S.: 483111

Tecto Cyprus Limited **(1)**
15 Navpliou St 2nd Fl
3025 Limassol, Cyprus
Tel.: (357) 25960114
Fax: (357) 25960200
E-Mail: info@tectocy.com
Marine Shipping Agencies
S.I.C.: 4731
N.A.I.C.S.: 488510
Pampos Papas *(Gen Mgr)*

EXOIL LIMITED

Level 21 500 Collins St
Melbourne, VIC, 3000, Australia
Tel.: (61) 3 8610 4700
Fax: (61) 3 8610 4799
E-Mail: admin@exoil.net
Web Site: www.exoil.net
Year Founded: 1979
EXX—(NSXA)
Sales Range: $1-9.9 Million

Business Description:
Oil & Gas Exploration Services
S.I.C.: 1311
N.A.I.C.S.: 211111

Personnel:
James M. D. Willis *(Chm)*
J. G. Tuohy *(Sec)*
Board of Directors:
James M. D. Willis
E. Geoffrey Albers
Graeme Alan Menzies

EXOMA ENERGY LIMITED
Level 5 40 Creek Street
Brisbane, QLD, 4000, Australia
Tel.: (61) 732265600
Fax: (61) 732265699
E-Mail: info@exoma.net
Web Site: www.exoma.net
EXE—(ASX)
Rev.: $3,314,638
Assets: $14,079,362
Liabilities: $801,003
Net Worth: $13,278,359
Earnings: ($2,056,564)
Emp.: 1
Fiscal Year-end: 06/30/13
Business Description:
Oil & Gas Exploration Services
S.I.C.: 1311
N.A.I.C.S.: 211111
Personnel:
Robert Crook *(CEO)*
Josie King *(Sec)*
Board of Directors:
Brian Barker
Stephen Harrison
Robbert Willink
Legal Counsel:
Corrs Chambers Westgarth
Level 35 Waterfront Place 1 Eagle Street
Brisbane, Australia

EXONHIT THERAPEUTICS SA
(Name Changed to Diaxonhit SA)

EXOR GROUP S.A.
22-24 Blvd Royale
L-2449 Luxembourg, Luxembourg
Tel.: (352) 227840
Fax: (352) 227407
Business Description:
Holding Company
S.I.C.: 6719
N.A.I.C.S.: 551112
Personnel:
Gilbert Cahen d'Anvers *(Chm)*
Non-U.S. Subsidiaries:

Chateau Greysac (1)
18 Route de By
F 33340 Begadan, France (100%)
Tel.: (33) 556732656
Fax: (33) 556732658
E-Mail: info@greysac.com
Web Site: www.greysac.com
Sales Range: $1-9.9 Million
Emp.: 32
Vineyard
S.I.C.: 0172
N.A.I.C.S.: 111332
Brandino Brandolini d'Abba *(Pres)*
Philippe Dambrine *(CEO)*

EXP GLOBAL INC.
56 Queen Street East Suiite 301
Brampton, ON, L6V 4M8, Canada
Tel.: (905) 796-3200
Fax: (905) 793-5533
E-Mail: one@exp.com
Web Site: www.exp.com
Year Founded: 1959
Sales Range: $300-349.9 Million
Business Description:
Building Engineering, Earth & Environmental Engineering, Infrastructure Engineering, Planning & Design, Program Management & Sustainability Services
S.I.C.: 8712
N.A.I.C.S.: 541310
Personnel:
Robert Sheh *(Chm)*
Jeff Kishel *(Pres & CEO)*
Greg Henderson *(CFO & Exec VP)*
Ben Schwartz *(Chief HR Officer & Exec VP)*
David Kleiman *(Gen Counsel, Sec & Exec VP)*
Board of Directors:
Robert Sheh
William G. Davis
Raul Fernandez
Sam Iapalucci
Daniel Johnson
Jeff Kishel
Vlad Stritesky
Murli Tolaney

EXPANSYS PLC
Network House Globe Park
Marlow, Buckinghamshire, SL7 1EY, United Kingdom
Tel.: (44) 618680868
Fax: (44) 618680306
E-Mail: info@expansys.com
Web Site: www.expansys.com
XPS—(LSE)
Rev.: $147,219,835
Assets: $83,334,395
Liabilities: $22,969,194
Net Worth: $60,365,202
Earnings: ($28,316,670)
Emp.: 234
Fiscal Year-end: 04/30/13
Business Description:
High Tech Products Retailer & Distr
S.I.C.: 3829
N.A.I.C.S.: 333997
Personnel:
Anthony Catterson *(CEO)*
Christopher John Rathmell Ogle *(CFO & Sec)*
Board of Directors:
Bob Wigley
Anthony Catterson
Brian Joseph Collie
Graham Dawber
Peter Jones
Christopher John Rathmell Ogle
Stephen Vincent
Legal Counsel:
Eversheds LLP
Eversheds House 70-76 Great Bridgewater Street
Manchester, United Kingdom
U.S. Subsidiary:

eXpansys Inc. (1)
902 IAA Dr
Bloomington, IL 61701
Tel.: (309) 834-0323
Fax: (309) 295-8900
E-Mail: sales@expansys-usa.com
Web Site: www.expansys-usa.com
Emp.: 20
Wireless Technology Products Retailer & Distr
S.I.C.: 5065
N.A.I.C.S.: 423690
Tim Eltze *(Pres)*

Non-U.S. Subsidiaries:

eXpansys (Hong Kong) Limited (1)
Unit C 10f Cdw Bldg 388 Castle Peak Rd
Tsuen Wan, China (Hong Kong)
Tel.: (852) 24166700
Fax: (852) 24111362
E-Mail: info@expansys.com.hk
Web Site: www.expansys.com.hk
Emp.: 30
Wireless Technology Products Retailer & Distr
S.I.C.: 5065
N.A.I.C.S.: 423690
Sean Ho *(Gen Mgr)*

eXpansys SAS (1)
Eureka Pk 256 Rue de Thor
34960 CS 90554 Montpellier, France
Tel.: (33) 467457780
Fax: (33) 467451225
E-Mail: info@expansys.fr
Web Site: www.expansys.fr
Emp.: 55
Wireless Technology Products Sales & Services
S.I.C.: 5065
N.A.I.C.S.: 423690
Pont Frederick *(Mng Dir)*

eXpansys (ShenZhen) Trading Limited (1)
9E Hua Yue Ct Nan Hua Garden Hua Qian S Rd
Futian Dist, Shenzhen, 518031, China
Tel.: (86) 75582182165
Fax: (86) 75582182167
E-Mail: cn-sales@eXpansys.cn
Web Site: www.expansys.cn
Online Electronic Products Sales
S.I.C.: 5961
N.A.I.C.S.: 454111

RCK Communications Limited (1)
Unit C 10 F CDW Bldg 388 Castle Peak Rd
Tsuen Wan, New Territories, China (Hong Kong)
Tel.: (852) 24127858
Fax: (852) 24116727
E-Mail: info@rck.com.hk
Web Site: www.rck.com.hk
Emp.: 120
Branded Electronic Products Sales
S.I.C.: 5731
N.A.I.C.S.: 443142

Subsidiary:

eXpansys UK Limited (1)
Rutherford House 40 Pencroft Way
Manchester Sci Park
Manchester, Greater Manchester, M15 6SZ, United Kingdom
Tel.: (44) 1618680868
Fax: (44) 1618680306
E-Mail: info@expansys.com
Consumer Electronic Products Sales
S.I.C.: 5064
N.A.I.C.S.: 423620
Anthony Catterson *(CEO)*

EXPECT DISTRIBUTION
Unit 2 Premier Point Premier Gate
Staithgate Lane, Bradford, West Yorkshire, BD6 1DW, United Kingdom
Tel.: (44) 1274378220
Fax: (44) 1274378230
E-Mail: info@expectdistribution.com
Web Site: www.expectdistribution.com
Rev.: $19,107,556
Emp.: 144
Business Description:
Transportation & Warehousing Services
S.I.C.: 4731
N.A.I.C.S.: 488510
Personnel:
Robert Rushworth *(Mng Dir)*

EXPEDIT A/S
Toftegaardsvej 4
DK-8370 Hadsten, Denmark
Tel.: (45) 87612200
Fax: (45) 87612300
E-Mail: expedit@expedit.dk
Web Site: www.expedit.eu
EXPB—(CSE)
Rev.: $3,671,228
Assets: $46,733,621
Liabilities: $27,925,139
Net Worth: $18,808,482
Earnings: $701,420
Emp.: 354
Fiscal Year-end: 12/31/12
Business Description:
Supplier of Furnishing & Layout Solutions for Retail Chains, Specialist Stores & Brand Label Outlets
S.I.C.: 2599
N.A.I.C.S.: 337127
Personnel:
Ib Mortensen *(Chm)*
Steen Bodtker *(CEO & Member-Exec Bd)*
Helle Wulff *(CFO & Member-Exec Bd)*
Peter Korning *(Bus Dev Officer)*
Bo Holmlind *(Member-Exec Bd & Mng Dir-Expedit AB)*
Geir Kristian Svendsen *(Member-Exec Bd & Mng Dir-Norway)*
Pekka Haapasalo *(Member-Exec Bd & Mgr-Finland)*
Board of Directors:
Ib Mortensen
Bent Holm
Lars Karstenskov
Berhard Renzhofer
Gottfried Wanzl
Non-U.S. Subsidiaries:

Expedit Finland (1)
Mestarintie 8B
FIN-01730 Vantaa, Finland
Tel.: (358) 207433640
Fax: (358) 207433649
E-Mail: expedit@expedit.fi
Web Site: www.expedit.fi
Emp.: 7
S.I.C.: 2599
N.A.I.C.S.: 337127
Pekki Haapasalo *(Gen Mgr)*

Expedit Norge A/S (1)
Hvamveien 4
PO Box 117
N 2026 Skjetten, Norway (100%)
Tel.: (47) 64831300
Fax: (47) 64831399
E-Mail: post@expedit.no
Web Site: www.expedit.no
Emp.: 8
S.I.C.: 2599
N.A.I.C.S.: 337127
Bjorn Ole Uglem *(Acct Mgr)*

Expedit Retail Solutions AB (1)
Gjuterigatan 9
553 18 Jonkoping, Smaland, Sweden
Tel.: (46) 36173380
Fax: (46) 36 17 33 89
E-Mail: info@expedit.se
Web Site: www.expedit.se/contact-area/where-to-find-expedit.aspx
Shop Fittings Retailer
S.I.C.: 5999
N.A.I.C.S.: 453998

Expedit Sverige AB (1)
Gardsfogdevagen 16
Bromma, 16866, Sweden (100%)
Tel.: (46) 86260770
Fax: (46) 87670211
E-Mail: office@expedit.se
Web Site: www.expedit.se
Emp.: 2
S.I.C.: 2599
N.A.I.C.S.: 337127
Henrik Sorensen *(Gen Mgr)*

Nassjo Inredningar AB (1)
Fredriksdal
571 75 Nassjo, Smaland, Sweden
Tel.: (46) 380 265 00
Fax: (46) 380 265 50
E-Mail: sales@nassjo-inredningar.se
Web Site: www.nassjo-inredningar.se
Emp.: 70
Shop Fittings Mfr & Sales
S.I.C.: 3089
N.A.I.C.S.: 326122
Jam Borgenhede *(VP)*

EXPEDITION MINING INC.
600 595 Howe Street
Vancouver, BC, V6C 2T5, Canada
Tel.: (604) 662-3903
Fax: (604) 662-3904

Expedition Mining Inc.—(Continued)

E-Mail: info@expeditionmining.com
Web Site: www.expeditionmining.com
Year Founded: 1987
EXU—(TSXV)
Int. Income: $19,649
Assets: $2,715,985
Liabilities: $51,276
Net Worth: $2,664,709
Earnings: ($1,888,700)
Emp.: 4
Fiscal Year-end: 09/30/12

Business Description:
Mineral Properties Exploration & Development Services
S.I.C.: 1099
N.A.I.C.S.: 212299

Personnel:
Ronald Atlas *(Chm, Pres & CEO)*
Jorge Avelino *(CFO)*
William Galine *(Exec VP)*

Board of Directors:
Ronald Atlas
Steven Chan
James Chapman
Corry J. Silbernagel
John S. Watt

Transfer Agent:
Computershare Investor Services Inc
100 University Avenue 9th Floor North Tower
Toronto, ON, Canada

EXPERIAN PLC

Newenham House Northern Cross
Malahide Road
Dublin, 17, Ireland
Tel.: (353) 18469100
Fax: (353) 18469150
E-Mail: corporate.communications@uk.experian.com
Web Site: www.experianplc.com
EXPN—(LSE)
Rev.: $4,730,000,000
Assets: $8,195,000,000
Liabilities: $4,971,000,000
Net Worth: $3,224,000,000
Earnings: $406,000,000
Emp.: 17,119
Fiscal Year-end: 03/31/13

Business Description:
Credit Reporting Services, Decision Analytics & Marketing Support Services
S.I.C.: 7323
N.A.I.C.S.: 561450

Personnel:
Don Robert *(Chm)*
Alan Rudge *(Deputy Chm)*
Chris Callero *(Pres & COO)*
Brian J. Cassin *(CEO)*
Ricardo Loureiro *(Chm-Latin America)*
Michael DeVico *(Pres-Mktg Svcs)*
John Gray *(Pres-Automotive Bus Unit)*
Jennifer Schulz *(Grp Pres-Vertical Markets)*
Kerry Williams *(Pres-Global Credit Svcs & North America)*
Joy Griffiths *(CEO-Asia Pacific & Mng Dir-Decision Analytics-Global)*
Victor Nichols *(CEO-North America)*
Robert Nelson *(Gen Counsel & Exec VP)*
Charles Brown *(Sec)*

Board of Directors:
Don Robert
Fabiola R. Arredondo de Vara
Chris Callero
Brian J. Cassin
Roger Davis
Alan Jebson
Deirdre A. Mahlan
George W. Rose
Alan Rudge
Judith A. Sprieser
Paul Walker

Subsidiaries:

Experian Finance Holdings Limited **(1)**
Newenham House Northern Cross Malahide Road
Dublin, Ireland
Tel.: (353) 1 846 9100
Investment Management Services
S.I.C.: 6282
N.A.I.C.S.: 523920

Experian Holdings Ireland Limited **(1)**
Newenham House Northern Cross
Dublin, Ireland
Tel.: (353) 1 846 9100
Investment Management Services
S.I.C.: 6282
N.A.I.C.S.: 523920

U.S. Subsidiaries:

Experian Information Solutions, Inc. **(1)**
475 Anton Blvd
Costa Mesa, CA 92626
Tel.: (714) 830-7000
Web Site: www.experian.com
Sls.: $1,030,211,200
Emp.: 1,200
Decision Support & Outsourcing Services with Information on Consumers, Businesses, Motor Vehicles & Property
S.I.C.: 7323
N.A.I.C.S.: 561450
Chris Callero *(CEO)*
Charles Chung *(Pres-Decision Analytics-North America)*
Genevieve Juillard *(Pres-Consumer Info Svcs-Credit Svcs Grp-North America)*
Hiq Lee *(Pres-Bus Info Svcs-Credit Svcs Grp-North America)*
Lloyd Parker *(Pres-Credit Svcs Grp-North America)*
Peg Smith *(Exec VP-IR)*
Laura DeSoto *(Sr VP-Mktg-Bus Info Svcs-Credit Svcs Grp-North America)*
Michele Pearson *(Sr VP-Indirect Sls-Credit Svcs & Decision Analytics-North America)*

Branch:

Experian Information Solutions, Inc. - Chicago **(2)**
955 American Ln
Schaumburg, IL 60173-4983
Tel.: (224) 698-5600
Fax: (224) 698-3507
Web Site: www.experian.com
Emp.: 568
Information Services, List Development & Enhancement, Mail Production, Database Development & Credit Reports
S.I.C.: 7323
N.A.I.C.S.: 561450

Divisions:

Experian Healthcare **(2)**
5000 Plaza on the Lake Ste 265
Austin, TX 78746
Tel.: (512) 795-0015
Fax: (512) 795-9529
Toll Free: (866) 930-1230
E-Mail:
Web Site: www.experian.com
Emp.: 167
Software Developer for Medical Group Reimbursement Services
S.I.C.: 7372
N.A.I.C.S.: 511210
Tom Stampiglia *(CEO)*
Craig Halley *(CTO & VP-Engrg)*
Dean Paluch *(Sr VP-Sls)*

Branch:

Experian Healthcare **(3)**
601 NW Loop 410 Ste 450
San Antonio, TX 78216 DE
Tel.: (210) 930-1230
Fax: (210) 822-4562
Web Site: www.experian.com
Emp.: 53
Software Developer for Medical Group Reimbursement Services
S.I.C.: 7372
N.A.I.C.S.: 511210
Paul Delbecq *(VP-Sls)*

Subsidiaries:

ConsumerInfo.com, Inc. **(2)**
18500 Von Karman Ave Ste 900
Irvine, CA 92612 CA
Tel.: (888) 888-8553
Fax: (949) 567-5758
E-Mail: feedback@consumerinfo.com
Web Site: www.consumerinfo.com
Credit Reporting Services
S.I.C.: 7323
N.A.I.C.S.: 561450
Ty Taylor *(Pres)*

Passport Health Communications, Inc. **(2)**
700 Cool Springs Blvd
Franklin, TN 37067
Tel.: (615) 661-5657
Fax: (615) 376-3552
Toll Free: (888) 661-5657
Web Site: www.passporthealth.com
Emp.: 170
Internet-Based Financial Management Tools for Healthcare Industry
S.I.C.: 2741
N.A.I.C.S.: 519130
Scott MacKenzie *(CEO)*
Seth Rupp *(CTO)*

Joint Venture:

VantageScore Solutions, LLC **(2)**
107 Elm St Ste 907
Stamford, CT 06902 DE
Tel.: (203) 363-0269
Web Site: www.vantagescore.com
Sales Range: $10-24.9 Million
Emp.: 15
Consumer Credit Scoring Services
S.I.C.: 7323
N.A.I.C.S.: 561450
Barrett Burns *(Pres & CEO)*
Sarah Davies *(Sr VP-Analytics & Product Dev)*

Experian Marketing Solutions, Inc. **(1)**
475 Anton Blvd
Costa Mesa, CA 92626 DE
Tel.: (714) 830-7000
Web Site: www.experian.com
Emp.: 598
Marketing Services
S.I.C.: 8742
N.A.I.C.S.: 541613
Matthew Seeley *(Pres)*

Units:

Experian CheetahMail **(2)**
29 Broadway 6th Fl
New York, NY 10006
Tel.: (212) 809-0825
Fax: (212) 863-4490
E-Mail: info@cheetahmail.com
Web Site: www.experian.com
Online Marketing Research Services
S.I.C.: 8732
N.A.I.C.S.: 541910
Kat Berman *(VP-Client Svcs)*

Experian Hitwise **(2)**
300 Park Ave 9th Fl
New York, NY 10010
Tel.: (212) 380-2900
Fax: (212) 380-2929
Web Site: www.experian.com
Emp.: 220
Competitive Intelligence Services
S.I.C.: 8732
N.A.I.C.S.: 541910
Simon Bradstock *(Sr VP & Gen Mgr)*
Harley Giles *(Sr VP-Product Dev & Ops)*

Experian Simmons **(2)**
600 3rd Ave
New York, NY 10016
Tel.: (212) 883-0407
Toll Free: (800) 918-9064
Web Site: www.experian.com
Market Research Services
S.I.C.: 8732
N.A.I.C.S.: 541910
Ken Wollenberg *(Pres & Gen Mgr)*

Non-U.S. Division:

Experian Decision Analytics **(1)**
Landmark House NG2 Business Pk
Experian Way
Nottingham, NG80 1ZZ, United Kingdom
Tel.: (44) 01159410888
Fax: (44) 1158286522
E-Mail: larrie.scott@experian.com
Web Site: www.experian-da.com
Emp.: 200
Data Intelligence, Predictive Analytics, Strategy Optimisation & Technical Consulting Services
S.I.C.: 7374
N.A.I.C.S.: 518210
Elio Vitucci *(Mng Dir)*
Gary Wood *(Mng Dir)*

Subsidiaries:

Experian Tallyman **(2)**
3110 Great Western Court Hunts Ground Road
Aztec W, Bristol, BS34 8HP, United Kingdom UK
Tel.: (44) 1454441000
Fax: (44) 1454441300
Web Site: www.experian-da.com
Sales Range: $10-24.9 Million
Emp.: 80
IT Solutions
S.I.C.: 3652
N.A.I.C.S.: 334614

Scorex (UK) Limited **(2)**
Scorex House 1 Bolton Rd
Bradford, BD1 4AS, United Kingdom
Tel.: (44) 1274762700
Fax: (44) 1274762701
E-Mail: info@scorex.com
Web Site: www.scorex.com
Emp.: 70
Provider of Credit Risk Analysis & Software Development Services
S.I.C.: 7371
N.A.I.C.S.: 541511
Gary Scott *(Mng Dir)*

U.S. Subsidiary:

Experian Scorex US, LLC **(2)**
5909 Peachtree Dunwoody Rd Ste 1100
Atlanta, GA 30328
Tel.: (678) 731-1100
Fax: (678) 731-1220
Toll Free: (800) 726-4083
Web Site: www.scorex.com
Provider of Credit Risk Analysis & Software Development Services
S.I.C.: 7389
N.A.I.C.S.: 561499

Non-U.S. Subsidiaries:

Experian Decision Analytics **(2)**
6 Georgiou Mpakou Street
11524 Athens, Filothei, Greece
Tel.: (30) 2106930790
Fax: (30) 2106930799
E-Mail: maria.katsifi@experian.com
Web Site: www.experian-da.com
Emp.: 10
Credit Risk Analysis & Software Development Services
S.I.C.: 7371
N.A.I.C.S.: 541511
Spiros Ziourgias *(Mgr-Mktg)*

Experian Deutschland Holding GmbH **(2)**
Circus 2
20359 Hamburg, Germany
Tel.: (49) 408995000
Fax: (49) 4089950280
E-Mail: info@experian.de
Web Site: www.experian.de
Emp.: 35
Provider of Decision Support & Outsourcing Services with Information on Consumers, Businesses, Motor Vehicles & Property
S.I.C.: 3589
N.A.I.C.S.: 333318
David Groom *(Gen Mgr)*

Experian Scorex Espana SRL **(2)**
Calle Ombu 3 Planta 1
28045 Madrid, Spain

Tel.: (34) 917709500
Fax: (34) 915286507
E-Mail: inform@experian-scorex.mc
Web Site: www.experian-da.com
Emp.: 30
Provider of Credit Risk Analysis & Software Development Services
S.I.C.: 7371
N.A.I.C.S.: 541511

Experian-Scorex S.r.l. Italia (2)
Viale Dell Esperanto 71
00144 Rome, Italy
Tel.: (39) 06 59 29 301
Fax: (39) 0065925638
Web Site: www.experian-scorex.com
Credit Risk Analysis & Software Development Services
S.I.C.: 7371
N.A.I.C.S.: 541511
Elio Vitucci *(Mng Dir-Analytics)*

Scorex Scandinavia (2)
Glarmestervej 2
DK 8600 Silkeborg, Denmark
Tel.: (45) 70100107
Fax: (45) 87465601
E-Mail: william@experian.dk
Web Site: www.experian-scorex.com
Emp.: 50
Credit Risk Analysis & Software Development Services
S.I.C.: 7371
N.A.I.C.S.: 541511
Charlotte Muller Andersen *(Gen Mgr)*

Non-U.S. Subsidiaries:

Altovision Inc. (1)
Kataho Building Third Floor 2-16-11 Ginza
Chuo-ku, Tokyo, 104-0061, Japan
Tel.: (81) 3 5550 6440
Fax: (81) 3 5550 6444
E-Mail: info@altovision.co.jp
Web Site: www.altovision.co.jp
Sales Range: $1-9.9 Million
Marketing Consulting Services
S.I.C.: 8742
N.A.I.C.S.: 541613

Experian AS (1)
Sorkedalsveien 10 C
Postboks 5275
Majorstuen, 303 Oslo, Norway
Tel.: (47) 815 55 454
Fax: (47) 22 93 20 80
Web Site: www.experian.no
Marketing Consulting Services
S.I.C.: 8742
N.A.I.C.S.: 541613
Charlotte Moller-Andersen *(Mng Dir)*

Experian Finance plc (1)
Talbot House Talbot St
Nottingham, NG80 1TH, United Kingdom
Tel.: (44) 1159 410888
Fax: (44) 1159 768478
Financial Investment Services
S.I.C.: 6211
N.A.I.C.S.: 523999

Experian Investment Holdings Limited (1)
Landmark House Experian Way NG2 Business Park
Nottingham, NG80 1ZZ, United Kingdom
Tel.: (44) 115 941 0888
Investment Management Services
S.I.C.: 6211
N.A.I.C.S.: 523999

Experian Ltd. (1)
Talbot House
Talbot St, Nottingham, Nottinghamshire, NG80 1TH, United Kingdom UK
Tel.: (44) 01159410888
Fax: (44) 1159344905
E-Mail: corporate.communications@uk.experian.com
Web Site: www.experian.co.uk
Emp.: 1,300
Credit Reporting Services, Decision Analytics & Marketing Support Services
S.I.C.: 7323
N.A.I.C.S.: 561450
Richard Fiddis *(Mng Dir)*

Non-U.S. Subsidiaries:

CreditInform AS (2)
Sorkedalsvn 10C Majorstuen
PO Box 5275
0303 Oslo, Norway
Tel.: (47) 81555454
Fax: (47) 22465390
E-Mail: kundsenper@no.experian.com
Web Site: www.creditinform.no
Emp.: 80
Credit Reporting Services
S.I.C.: 7323
N.A.I.C.S.: 561450
Gabor Molnar *(Mng Dir)*

Experian A/S (2)
Glarmestervej 2
PO Box 259
8600 Silkeborg, Denmark
Tel.: (45) 70100107
Fax: (45) 87465601
E-Mail: Experian@Experian.dk
Web Site: www.Experian.dk
Sales Range: $10-24.9 Million
Emp.: 170
Operates as a Credit & Business Information Group
S.I.C.: 6159
N.A.I.C.S.: 522298
Scharlogge Moeller Amsdersem *(Mng Dir)*

Experian Asia Pacific Pty. Ltd. (2)
Rm 3905-08 39th Fl ACE Twr Windsor House
311 Gloucester Rd, Causeway Bay, China (Hong Kong)
Tel.: (852) 27225037
Fax: (852) 28777803
E-Mail: info@experian.com
Web Site: www.experian.com
Emp.: 60
Provider of Decision Support & Outsourcing Services with Information on Consumers, Businesses, Motor Vehicles & Property
S.I.C.: 3589
N.A.I.C.S.: 333318
Ken Sansom *(Pres)*

Experian Australia Pty. Ltd. - Sydney Office (2)
Level 30 100 Miller Street
Sydney, NSW, 2060, Australia
Tel.: (61) 294099888
Fax: (61) 299545708
E-Mail: info@au.experian.com
Web Site: www.experian.com.au
Emp.: 15
Provider of Decision Support & Outsourcing Services with Information on Consumers, Businesses, Motor Vehicles & Property
S.I.C.: 3589
N.A.I.C.S.: 333318

Experian Australia Pty. Ltd. (2)
Level 6 580 Saint Kilda Road
Melbourne, VIC, 3004, Australia AU
Tel.: (61) 386990100
Fax: (61) 395298907
E-Mail: enquiry@ap.experian.com
Web Site: www.experian.com.au
Emp.: 200
Decision Support & Outsourcing Services with Information on Consumers, Businesses, Motor Vehicles & Property
S.I.C.: 3589
N.A.I.C.S.: 333318
Kim Jenkins *(Gen Mgr)*

Experian Data Services S.r.l. (2)
Cinecitta 2 Palazzo Experian
Via Quintavalle 68, 00173 Rome, Italy IT
Tel.: (39) 6724221
Fax: (39) 0672422480
Web Site: www.experian.it
Decision Support & Outsourcing Services with Information on Consumers, Businesses, Motor Vehicles & Property
S.I.C.: 3589
N.A.I.C.S.: 333318

Experian France (2)
Tour Europlaza 20 Avenue Andre Prothin
92927 Paris, La Defense Cedex, France
Tel.: (33) 1 41 45 10 01
Fax: (33) 141451020
E-Mail: com@experian.fr
Web Site: www.experian.fr
Emp.: 250
Risk Management & Marketing Solutions
S.I.C.: 7389
N.A.I.C.S.: 561499
Thomas Bourayne *(Chm)*

Experian Ireland Ltd. (2)
New enhan Nalhaibe Rd
Dublin, 7, Ireland
Tel.: (353) 18385422
Fax: (353) 35318386897
E-Mail: enquiries@experian.ie
Web Site: www.experian.ie
Emp.: 25
Provider Business and Personal Information Solutions
S.I.C.: 4899
N.A.I.C.S.: 517919

Experian Nederland B.V. (2)
Kantoorgebouw Schip Vrheeskade 25
2521 BE Hague, Netherlands
Mailing Address:
Postbus 13128
2501EC Hague, Netherlands
Tel.: (31) 704404000
Fax: (31) 704404040
E-Mail: nl@experian.com
Web Site: www.nl.experian.com
Emp.: 100
Provider of Decision Support & Outsourcing Services with Information on Consumers, Businesses, Motor Vehicles & Property
S.I.C.: 3589
N.A.I.C.S.: 333318
T. Vink *(Mgr-Fin)*

Experian Singapore Pte. Ltd. (2)
1 Maritime Square
HarbourFront Centre, Singapore, 099253, Singapore SG
Tel.: (65) 65937500
Telex: 33184
Fax: (65) 65937598
Web Site: www.experian.com
Emp.: 50
Credit Reporting Services, Decision Analytics & Marketing Support Services
S.I.C.: 7323
N.A.I.C.S.: 561450

Experian South Africa (2)
Experian House Ballyoaks Office Park
35 Ballyclare Dr, 2021 Bryanston, South Africa
Tel.: (27) 117993400
Fax: (27) 117076726
Web Site: www.experian.co.za
Emp.: 115
Provider of Decision Support & Outsourcing Services with Information on Consumers, Businesses, Motor Vehicles & Property
S.I.C.: 7323
N.A.I.C.S.: 561450
Michelle Beetar *(Mng Dir)*

Garlik Limited (1)
1-3 Halford Road
Richmond, TW10 6AW, United Kingdom
Tel.: (44) 845 862 2441
Fax: (44) 20 8940 4978
E-Mail: partners@garlik.com
Web Site: www.garlik.com
Emp.: 16
Online Security Services
S.I.C.: 2741
N.A.I.C.S.: 519130
Andy Thomas *(Mng Dir)*
Steve Harris *(CTO)*

LM Group Ltd (1)
Prospect House Sherwood E Village
Newark, Nottinghamshire, NG22 9SS, United Kingdom
Tel.: (44) 84 4871 1868
Fax: (44) 16 2386 9998
E-Mail: info@riskdisk.com
Web Site: www.riskdisk.com
Online Credit Checking Services
S.I.C.: 2741
N.A.I.C.S.: 519130

QAS Limited (1)
George W House 2 3 Clapham Common N Side
London, SW4 0QL, United Kingdom UK
Tel.: (44) 2074987777
Fax: (44) 2074980303
E-Mail: uk.info@qas.com
Web Site: www.qas.co.uk
Emp.: 500
Data Accuracy & Identity Management Services
S.I.C.: 7389
N.A.I.C.S.: 519190

Serasa S.A. (1)
Alameda dos Quinimuras 187
04068-900 Sao Paulo, SP, Brazil BR
Tel.: (55) 11 3373 7272 (99.6%)
Fax: (55) 11 2847 9198
Web Site: www.serasaexperian.com.br
Sales Range: $800-899.9 Million
Credit Bureau
S.I.C.: 7323
N.A.I.C.S.: 561450

Techlightenment Limited (1)
3 08 Tea Building 56 Shoreditch High Street
London, E1 6JJ, United Kingdom
Tel.: (44) 20 7033 3567
E-Mail: info@techlightenment.com
Web Site: www.techlightenment.com
Emp.: 40
Marketing Consulting Services
S.I.C.: 8742
N.A.I.C.S.: 541613
Steve Pole *(CTO)*

Virid Interatividade Digital Ltda (1)
Rua Bandeira Paulista 275 - 12 Andar
Itaim Bibi, Sao Paulo, 04532-010, Brazil
Tel.: (55) 11 3708 4000
Fax: (55) 11 3708 4000 3
E-Mail: contato@virtualtarget.com.br
Emp.: 40
Online Marketing Services
S.I.C.: 8742
N.A.I.C.S.: 541613
Conrado Cruz Muller *(Mgr-Sls)*

EXPERT SYSTEM S.P.A.

Via Virgilio 56/Q Staircase 5
41123 Modena, Italy
Tel.: (39) 059 894011
Fax: (39) 059 894099
E-Mail: info@expertsystem.net
Web Site: www.expertsystem.net
EXSY—(ITA)
Sales Range: $10-24.9 Million
Emp.: 100

Business Description:
Semantic Analysis Products & Services
S.I.C.: 7372
N.A.I.C.S.: 511210

Personnel:
Marco Varone *(Chm & CTO)*
Stefano Spaggiari *(CEO)*
Luigi Paraboschi *(CFO)*
Bryan Bell *(Exec VP)*

Board of Directors:
Marco Varone
Paolo Lombardi
Andrea Melegari
Luca Scagliarini
Stefano Roberto Siglienti
Stefano Spaggiari
Alberto Sangiovanni Vincentelli

EXPLICIT FINANCE LIMITED

Office No 305 3rd Floor Sohan Commercial Plaza Opp Shiv Sena Office
Vasai E, Thane, 401210, India
Tel.: (91) 250 3246249
E-Mail: info@explicitfinance.net
Web Site: www.explicitfinance.net
Year Founded: 1994
530571—(BOM)
Rev.: $358,656
Assets: $1,762,263
Liabilities: $119,698
Net Worth: $1,642,566
Earnings: ($4,301)
Fiscal Year-end: 03/31/13

Business Description:
Investment Banking & Securities Dealing Services
S.I.C.: 6211
N.A.I.C.S.: 523110

Personnel:
Gopal Dave *(Mng Dir)*
Avinash Mainkar *(Sec)*

Board of Directors:
Jayesh Jain
Gopal Dave
Avinash Mainkar

EXPLICIT FINANCE LIMITED—(Continued)

Deepak Oza
Satish Pai

Transfer Agent:
Adroit Corporate Services Private Limited
19 Jaferbhoy Industrial Estate Makwana Road
Marol Naka Andheri E
Mumbai, India

EXPLOATARE PORTUARA DROBETA S.A.

2 Tufari Str
225200 Orsova, Romania
Tel.: (40) 252361291
Fax: (40) 252363679
E-Mail: scep@port-orsova.ro
Web Site: www.port-orsova.ro
EXPV—(BUC)
Sales Range: $1-9.9 Million
Emp.: 125

Business Description:
Sea Freight Transportation Services
S.I.C.: 4412
N.A.I.C.S.: 483111

Personnel:
Urdarean Nicolae *(Gen Mgr)*

EXPLOR RESOURCES INC.

15 Gamble St E Suite 204
Rouyn-Noranda, QC, J9X 3B6, Canada
Tel.: (819) 797-4630
Fax: (819) 797-6050
Toll Free: (800) 388-8668
E-Mail: info@explorresources.com
Web Site: www.explorresources.com
Year Founded: 1986
EXS—(OTC TSXV)
Rev.: $32,638
Assets: $38,587,739
Liabilities: $2,262,162
Net Worth: $36,325,577
Earnings: ($1,131,419)
Fiscal Year-end: 04/30/13

Business Description:
Gold Exploration Services
S.I.C.: 1041
N.A.I.C.S.: 212221

Personnel:
Christian Dupont *(Pres & CEO)*
Jacques Frigon *(CFO)*

Board of Directors:
Geoff Carter
Jonathan Challis
Mario Colantonio
Christian Dupont
Jacques Frigon

Transfer Agent:
CST Trust Company
Calgary, AB, Canada

EXPLORATION AURTOIS INC.

1237 3rd Avenue
Val d'Or, QC, J9P 6C3, Canada
Tel.: (819) 874-2115
Fax: (819) 874-2118
E-Mail: info@explorationaurtois.com
Web Site: www.explorationaurtois.com
Year Founded: 2005
EXA—(TSXV)

Business Description:
Gold Mining Services
S.I.C.: 1041
N.A.I.C.S.: 212221

Personnel:
Mario Bisson *(Pres & CEO)*
Christian Caplette *(CFO)*

Board of Directors:
Mario Bisson
Christian Caplette
Frederic Dubois
Andre Dumont
Serge Martel
Ghislain Tourigny

Subsidiary:

Ressources Aurtois Inc. (1)
1470 Rue Begin
Montreal, QC, H4R 1X1, Canada
Tel.: (819) 874-2115
Fax: (450) 786-2013
Metal Mining Services
S.I.C.: 1099
N.A.I.C.S.: 212299

EXPLOREX RESOURCES INC.

214 1118 Homer Street
Vancouver, BC, V6B 6L5, Canada
Tel.: (604) 609-0555
Fax: (604) 609-0565
E-Mail: bill@explorex.ca
Web Site: www.explorex.ca
Year Founded: 2011
EX.P—(TSXV)
Int. Income: $2,489
Assets: $253,388
Liabilities: $32,557
Net Worth: $220,830
Earnings: ($435,056)
Fiscal Year-end: 03/31/13

Business Description:
Metal Exploration Services
S.I.C.: 1499
N.A.I.C.S.: 212399

Personnel:
William E. A. Wishart *(Pres & CEO)*
Patrick Forseille *(CFO)*

Board of Directors:
Gary Schellenberg
William E. A. Wishart
Paul M. Zdebiak

Transfer Agent:
Equity Financial Trust Company
Vancouver, BC, Canada

EXPO GAS CONTAINERS LTD.

150 Sheriff Devji House
Mumbai, 400 003, India
Tel.: (91) 2240339600
Fax: (91) 2223401635
E-Mail: vessels@expogas.com
Web Site: www.expogas.com
Year Founded: 1982
526614—(BOM)
Sales Range: $1-9.9 Million

Business Description:
Engineering & Construction Services
S.I.C.: 8711
N.A.I.C.S.: 541330

Personnel:
Shaukatali S. Mewawala *(Chm & Mng Dir)*

Board of Directors:
Shaukatali S. Mewawala
Syed Abbas Ali
Bhagwan N. Bhardwaj
Vazirali G. Lokhandwalla
Hasanain S. Mewawala
Sajjadhussein Nathani

EXPOBANK LLC

29 Kalanchevskaya Street Building 2
107078 Moscow, Russia
Tel.: (7) 4952311111
Fax: (7) 4952311101
E-Mail: info@expobank.ru
Web Site: www.expobank.ru
Year Founded: 1994

Business Description:
Retail & Commercial Banking
S.I.C.: 6029
N.A.I.C.S.: 522110

Personnel:
Igor V. Kim *(Chm)*
Kirill Nifontov *(CEO)*

Board of Directors:
Igor V. Kim
Alexey Andreev
John McNaughton
Kirill Nifontov
German Tsoy
Juriy Vavilov

EXPONENT PRIVATE EQUITY LLP

12 Henrietta Street
London, WC2E 8LH, United Kingdom
Tel.: (44) 2078458520
Fax: (44) 2078458521
E-Mail: info@exponentpe.com
Web Site: www.exponentpe.com
Emp.: 25

Business Description:
Private Equity Firm
S.I.C.: 6211
N.A.I.C.S.: 523999

Personnel:
Richard Campin *(Co-Founder & Partner)*
Chris Graham *(Co-Founder & Partner)*
Hugh Richards *(Co-Founder & Partner)*
Tom Sweet-Escott *(Co-Founder & Partner)*
Tom Lindell *(Mng Dir)*

Holdings:

Durrants Ltd. (1)
Discovery House
28-42 Banner Street, London, EC1Y 8QE, United Kingdom
Tel.: (44) 2076740200
Fax: (44) 2076740222
E-Mail: sales@durrants.co.uk
Web Site: www.durrants.co.uk
Emp.: 350
Media Planning, Monitoring & Evaluation Services
S.I.C.: 7313
N.A.I.C.S.: 541840
John Moore *(Chm)*
Gordon Young *(CIO)*

Subsidiaries:

Gorkana Limited (2)
Discovery House 28-42 Banner Street
London, EC1Y 8QE, United Kingdom UK
Tel.: (44) 2074206808
Fax: (44) 2074206801
E-Mail: enquiries@gorkana.com
Web Site: www.gorkana.com
Public Relations Services
S.I.C.: 7313
N.A.I.C.S.: 541840
Alexander Northcott *(Co-Founder & CEO)*
Michael Webster *(Co-Founder & Dir)*
Myles Johnson *(CFO)*
Dermot Corrigan *(Chief Comml Officer)*

Portfolio Metrica Ltd. (2)
140 Old Street
London, EC1V 9BJ, United Kingdom UK
Tel.: (44) 20 7664 0800 (100%)
Fax: (44) 20 7664 0801
E-Mail: info@metrica.net
Web Site: ww.metrica.net
Media Analysis Through Public Relations Measurement Products, Services & Consultancy
S.I.C.: 7313
N.A.I.C.S.: 541840
Richard Bagnall *(Mng Dir)*

Marlow Foods Ltd. (1)
Station Road
Stokesley, North Yorkshire, TS9 7AB, United Kingdom
Tel.: (44) 1642710803
Fax: (44) 1642717231
E-Mail: customer.services@marlowfoods.com
Web Site: www.quorn.com
Sales Range: $125-149.9 Million
Emp.: 335
Mfr of Mycoproteins for Meat Substitutes
S.I.C.: 2836
N.A.I.C.S.: 325414
Clive Sharpe *(Chm)*
Kevin Brennan *(CEO)*

Pattonair Limited (1)
Kingsway Business Park Forsyth Road
Sheerwater, Woking, Surrey, GU21 5SA, United Kingdom
Tel.: (44) 1483774600
Fax: (44) 1483774619
E-Mail: sales@pattonair.com
Web Site: www.pattonair.com
Sales Range: $350-399.9 Million
Emp.: 686
Inventory Management Systems & Components for Aerospace & Defense Industries
S.I.C.: 7389
N.A.I.C.S.: 561499
Paul Dunkley *(Chm)*
Wayne Hollinshead *(CEO)*
Kevin Sargent *(Mng Dir)*
Peter Ahye *(CFO)*

Subsidiary:

Ulogistics Limited (2)
Unit 7 Stoney Gate Road
Stoney Cross Spondon, Derby, DE21 7RX, United Kingdom
Tel.: (44) 1332545545
Fax: (44) 1332678008
E-Mail: jread@ulogistics.co.uk
Web Site: www.ulogistics.co.uk
Inventory Management Systems for Aerospace Industry
S.I.C.: 7389
N.A.I.C.S.: 561499
Wayne Hollinshead *(Mng Dir)*

U.S. Subsidiaries:

Abscoa Industries Inc. (2)
1900 Robotics Pl
Fort Worth, TX 76118-7128 DE
Tel.: (817) 284-4449
Fax: (817) 595-1554
Web Site: www.pattonair.com
Emp.: 90
Aerospace & Defense Equipment Distr & Supply Chain Management Services Import Export
S.I.C.: 5072
N.A.I.C.S.: 423710
Paul Fanelli *(Pres)*

Pattonair (2)
1900 Robotics Pl
Fort Worth, TX 76118
Tel.: (817) 284-4449
Fax: (817) 595-1554
Web Site: www.pattonair.com
Component Kitting Services for Overhaul of Military Equipment & Aircraft Systems
S.I.C.: 3795
N.A.I.C.S.: 336992
Aaron Mooi *(Pres & Gen Mgr-Americas)*

Non-U.S. Subsidiaries:

Pattonair Canada, Inc. (2)
1310 55th Ave
Lachine, QC, H8T 3JB, Canada
Tel.: (514) 631-4242
Fax: (514) 422-4126
E-Mail: info@ulogistics.ca
Web Site: www.ulogistics.co.uk
Emp.: 4
Inventory Management Systems for Aerospace Industry
S.I.C.: 7389
N.A.I.C.S.: 561499

Pattonair SAS (2)
Immeuble le Grand Axe
10-12 boulevard de l'Oise
95031 Cergy, Pontoise, Cedex, France
Tel.: (33) 134186100
Fax: (33) 1 3441 2530
E-Mail: ventes@pattonair.com
Inventory Management Systems
S.I.C.: 7389
N.A.I.C.S.: 561499

EXPONENTIAL-E LIMITED

2nd Floor Central House 25 Camperdown Street
London, E1 8DZ, United Kingdom
Tel.: (44) 2070964100
E-Mail: enquiries@exponential-e.com

Web Site: www.exponential-e.com
Year Founded: 2002
Sales Range: $25-49.9 Million
Emp.: 88
Business Description:
Computer Network Design Services
S.I.C.: 7373
N.A.I.C.S.: 541512
Personnel:
Lee Wade *(CEO)*
Mukesh Bavisi *(Mng Dir)*
Adrian Hobbins *(CTO)*

EXPORT DEVELOPMENT CANADA

150 Slater Street
Ottawa, ON, K1A 1K3, Canada
Tel.: (613) 598-2500
Telex: 53-4136
Fax: (613) 594-3858
Toll Free: (866) 996-9995
E-Mail: emergingexporters@edc.ca
Web Site: www.edc.ca
Year Founded: 1944
Sales Range: $1-4.9 Billion
Emp.: 1,071
Business Description:
Provider of Loans & Investments for New Businesses
S.I.C.: 6282
N.A.I.C.S.: 523930
Personnel:
James F. Dinning *(Chm)*
Benoit Daignault *(Pres & CEO)*
Ken Kember *(CFO & Sr VP-Fin)*
Pierre Gignac *(Chief Risk Officer & Sr VP-Enterprise Risk Mgmt)*
Monica Ryan *(Compliance Officer & VP-Internal Audit)*
Jim McArdle *(Sec & Sr VP-Corp Affairs)*
Rajesh Sharma *(Sr VP-Bus Dev & Mgr-Singapore)*
Susanne Laperle *(Sr VP-HR & Comm)*
Derek Layne *(Sr VP-Bus Solutions & Innovation Grp)*
Clive Witter *(Sr VP-Insurance)*
Board of Directors:
James F. Dinning
Norman M. Betts
Jacques Boivin
Jeff Burghardt
Adam Chowaniec
Herbert M. Clarke
Linda M. O. Hohol
Elliot Lifson
Donald A. MacLeod
John Ross Rooney
Jeffrey Steiner
Darlene Thibault

Subsidiary:

Export Development Corporation **(1)**
150 York St Ste 810
PO Box 810
Toronto, ON, M5H 3S5, Canada (100%)
Tel.: (416) 640-7600
Fax: (416) 862-1267
Emp.: 20
Provider of Loans & Investments for New Businesses
S.I.C.: 6282
N.A.I.C.S.: 523930
Ruth Fothergill *(VP-Corp)*

EXPORT IMPORT BANK OF BANGLADESH LIMITED

Symphony Plot SE F 9 Rd 142
Gulshan Avenue
Dhaka, 1212, Bangladesh
Tel.: (880) 29889363
Fax: (880) 28828962
E-Mail: info@eximbankbd.com
Web Site: www.eximbankbd.com
EXIMBANK—(DHA)
Rev.: $213,967,635
Assets: $2,067,434,371
Liabilities: $1,862,542,870
Net Worth: $204,891,501
Earnings: $25,788,546
Fiscal Year-end: 12/31/12
Business Description:
Commercial Banking Services
S.I.C.: 6029
N.A.I.C.S.: 522110
Personnel:
Md. Nazrul Islam Mazumder *(Chm)*
Mohammed Haider Ali Miah *(Mng Dir & CEO)*
Khondoker Rumy Ehsanul Haq *(Deputy Mng Dir)*
Md. Sirajul Islam *(Deputy Mng Dir)*
Sirajul Haque Miah *(Deputy Mng Dir)*
Shah Md. Abdul Bari *(Sr Exec VP)*
Md. Feroz Hossain *(Sr Exec VP)*
A. Y. M. Naimul Islam *(Sr Exec VP)*
Bashirul Islam *(Sr Exec VP)*
Md. Humayun Kabir *(Sr Exec VP)*
Md. Golam Mahbub *(Sr Exec VP)*
Md. Fazlur Rahaman *(Sr Exec VP)*
Moyeen Uddin *(Sr Exec VP)*
Md. Anisul Alam *(Exec VP)*
Mohammad Alamgir *(Exec VP)*
Md. Zoshim Uddin Bhuiyan *(Exec VP)*
Moniruzzaman Chowdhury *(Exec VP)*
Md. Akhtar Hossain *(Exec VP)*
Md. Fakhrul Islam *(Exec VP)*
Md. Mosharraf Hossain Mazumder *(Exec VP)*
Md. Muniruzzaman *(Exec VP)*
Shahidur Rahman *(Exec VP)*
Md Shahidullah *(Exec VP)*
Md. Shahjahan *(Exec VP)*
Board of Directors:
Md. Nazrul Islam Mazumder
Mohammad Abdullah
Khandaker Nurul Afser
Khandakar Mohammed Saiful Alam
Al-haj Md. Nurul Amin
Mohammad Omar Farooque Bhuiyan
Ranjan Chowdhury
Md.Habib Ullah Dawn
Nasreen Islam
Serajul Islam
Muhammad Sekandar Khan
Mohammed Haider Ali Miah
Anjan Kumar Saha
Mohammed Shahidullah
Md. Nazrul Islam Swapan

Non-U.S. Subsidiaries:

Exim Exchange Company (CANADA) Ltd. **(1)**
Unit 2 3096 Danforth Avenue
Toronto, ON, M1L 1B1, Canada
Tel.: (416) 699-5802
Fax: (416) 699-5800
E-Mail: eximexchangeca@eximbankbd.com
Web Site: www.eximexchangeca.com
Emp.: 3
Foreign Currency Exchange Services
S.I.C.: 6221
N.A.I.C.S.: 523130
Mohammad Hanif *(Mgr)*

EXIM Exchange Company (UK) Limited **(1)**
Universal House Ground Floor 88-94 Wentworth Street
London, E1 7SA, United Kingdom
Tel.: (44) 2073772474
Fax: (44) 2073771335
E-Mail: eximexchangeuk@eximbankbd.com
Web Site: www.eximexchange.co.uk
Money Transmission Services
S.I.C.: 6099
N.A.I.C.S.: 522390
Khurrum Ibne Alam *(CEO)*
Ashraf Mahmud Chowdhury *(Officer-Customer Svc)*
Khaled Ahmed Chowdhury *(Officer-Customer Svc)*

THE EXPORT-IMPORT BANK OF KOREA

16-1 Yeouido-dong
Yeongdeungpo-gu, Seoul, 150 996, Korea (South)
Tel.: (82) 3779 6114
Telex: K26595 EXIMBK
Fax: (82) 2 784 1030
E-Mail: iro@koreaexim.go.kr
Web Site: www.koreaexim.go.kr
Sales Range: $900-999.9 Million
Emp.: 600
Business Description:
Provider of International Banking Services
Export
S.I.C.: 6159
N.A.I.C.S.: 522298
Personnel:
Dong Kyu Shin *(Chm & Pres)*
Board of Directors:
Dong Kyu Shin

U.S. Division:

The Export-Import Bank of Korea **(1)**
460 Park Ave Fl 8
New York, NY 10022 (100%)
Tel.: (212) 355-7280
Telex: 428144 eximbank
Fax: (212) 308-6106
Web Site: www.koreaexim.go.kr/kr/about/m06/m06_s03.jsp
Emp.: 3
Banking
S.I.C.: 6159
N.A.I.C.S.: 522298

Non-U.S. Divisions:

The Export-Import Bank Of Korea **(1)**
1 2 2 Hidiya Taikiru Rm No 1904
Chiyoda Ku Uchisaiwaisho, Tokyo, 100 0011, Japan (100%)
Tel.: (81) 335808702
Telex: J29481 eximkra
Fax: (81) 335808705
E-Mail: extokyo@hotmail.com
Web Site: www.koreaexim.co.kr
Emp.: 3
S.I.C.: 6159
N.A.I.C.S.: 522298
Hae Hyun Kim *(Mgr)*

The Export-Import Bank of Korea **(1)**
3rd fl moorgate hall 155moograte
London, EC2M 1JJ, United Kingdom (100%)
Tel.: (44) 2075625500
Telex: 8812140 eximbk
Fax: (44) 02075883642
E-Mail: london@koreaexim.go.kr
Web Site: www.koreaexim.go.kr/uk/etc/contactus.jsp
Emp.: 8
S.I.C.: 6159
N.A.I.C.S.: 522298
Ged Hally *(Gen Mgr)*

The Kexim Asia Ltd. **(1)**
Rm 1805 18 FL Central Plz 18 Harbour Road
1 Connaught Pl, Wanchai, China (Hong Kong) (100%)
Tel.: (852) 28100182
Telex: 63104 EXIMB HX
Fax: (852) 28104460
E-Mail: webmaster@keximasia.com.hk
Emp.: 8
Deposit Banking Services
S.I.C.: 6159
N.A.I.C.S.: 522298

PT Koexim MANDIRI Finance **(1)**
Menara Mulia Twr Ste 2007
JL Jend Gatot Subroto Kav 9 11, Jakarta, 12930, Indonesia
Tel.: (62) 215257261
Telex: 62174 eximbk ia
Fax: (62) 215257260
E-Mail: koexim@cbn.net.id
Web Site: www.kmf.co.id
Emp.: 22
S.I.C.: 6159
N.A.I.C.S.: 522298
Kung Jong Lin *(Pres)*

EXPORT PACKERS COMPANY LIMITED

107 Walker Dr
Brampton, ON, L6T 5K5, Canada
Tel.: (905) 792-9700
Fax: (905) 792-9547
Web Site: www.exportpackers.com
Year Founded: 1937
Sales Range: $550-599.9 Million
Emp.: 150
Business Description:
Agricultural Commodity Trader; Food & Poultry Products Whslr
S.I.C.: 5153
N.A.I.C.S.: 424510
Personnel:
Max Rubenstein *(Chm)*
Daniel Leblanc *(Pres & COO)*
Jeff Rubenstein *(CEO)*
Brian Lampert *(CFO)*
Werter Mior *(Exec VP-Intl Trading)*

EXPOSOFT SOLUTIONS INC.

7895 Tranmere Drive Suite 221
Mississauga, ON, L5S 1V9, Canada
Tel.: (905) 672-7001
Fax: (905) 672-7050
Toll Free: (888) 304-9161
E-Mail: info@exposoft.com
Web Site: www.exposoft.com
Year Founded: 1996
Sales Range: $1-9.9 Million
Emp.: 40
Business Description:
Software Developer & Technical Support for Event Industry-Conferences, Trade Shows & Special Events
S.I.C.: 7372
N.A.I.C.S.: 511210
Personnel:
Bassel Annab *(Pres & CEO)*

EXPRESS CUSTOM TRAILERS MFG. INC.

1365 Alberni Hwy
Parksville, BC, V9P 2B9, Canada
Tel.: (250) 248-2218
Fax: (250) 248-2895
Toll Free: (800) 688-6840
E-Mail: info@expresscustom.com
Web Site: www.expresscustom.com
Year Founded: 1992
Rev.: $10,346,449
Emp.: 60
Business Description:
Aluminum & Steel Trailers Mfr
S.I.C.: 3537
N.A.I.C.S.: 333924
Personnel:
Tony Ethier *(Pres)*

EXPRESSWAY MOTORS LTD

1554 Haysville Rd
New Hamburg, ON, N3A 1A3, Canada
Tel.: (519) 622-3900
Fax: (519) 622-3904
Web Site: www.expressway.dealerconnection.com
Year Founded: 1982
Rev.: $22,692,632
Emp.: 47
Business Description:
New & Used Car Dealers
S.I.C.: 5511
N.A.I.C.S.: 441110
Personnel:
Nelda Brenneman *(Co-Founder)*
Ray Brenneman *(Co-Founder)*
Doug Brenneman *(Partner,Treas & Sec)*

EXPRIVIA SPA

Viale A Olivetti 11/A
70056 Molfetta, Italy
Tel.: (39) 0803382070
Fax: (39) 0803382077
E-Mail: info@exprivia.it
Web Site: www.exprivia.it
XPR—(ITA)
Rev.: $184,993,265
Assets: $251,896,360
Liabilities: $159,440,227
Net Worth: $92,456,133
Earnings: $3,263,764
Emp.: 1,923
Fiscal Year-end: 12/31/12

Business Description:
Software Designer & Developer
S.I.C.: 7372
N.A.I.C.S.: 511210

Personnel:
Domenico Favuzzi *(Chm & CEO)*
Dante Altomare *(Vice Chm & VP-Pub Market Div)*
Gianni Sebastiano *(CFO)*
Pierfilippo Vito Maria Roggero *(CEO-Exprivia Group)*

Board of Directors:
Domenico Favuzzi
Vito Albino
Dante Altomare
Rosa Daloiso
Giorgio De Porcellinis
Giancarlo Di Paola
Marco Forneris
Alessandro Laterza
Pierfilippo Vito Maria Roggero
Valeria Savelli

Subsidiaries:

Exprivia Projects S.p.A **(1)**
Via Cristoforo Colombo 456
00145 Rome, Italy
Tel.: (39) 06598541
Fax: (39) 0659854400
E-Mail: info@exprivia.it
Emp.: 300
Management Consulting Services
S.I.C.: 8742
N.A.I.C.S.: 541611
Gianluca Giorgi *(Acct Mgr)*

GST Gruppo Soluzioni Tecnologiche S r l **(1)**
Via Maccani
5438100 Trento, Italy
Tel.: (39) 0461431333
Fax: (39) 0461431334
E-Mail: info@gsttn.it
Web Site: www.gsttn.it
Emp.: 16
Engineering Consultancy Services
S.I.C.: 8711
N.A.I.C.S.: 541330
Marco Biraghi *(CEO & Gen Mgr)*

Wel.Network S.p.A. **(1)**
Via Emilia Pavese 103
29100 Piacenza, Italy
Tel.: (39) 0523482460
Fax: (39) 0523498907
E-Mail: info@welnetgroup.com
Web Site: www.welnetgroup.com
Emp.: 125
Consultancy Services
S.I.C.: 8711
N.A.I.C.S.: 541330
Stefano Baldini *(Mgr)*

EXTE - EXTRUDERTECHNIK GMBH

Wasserfuhr 4
PO Box 1220
D- 51676 Wipperfurth, Germany
Tel.: (49) 22676870
Fax: (49) 226768788
E-Mail: kontakt@exte.de
Web Site: www.exte.de
Year Founded: 1959
Rev.: $21,159,996
Emp.: 231

Business Description:
Windows & Door Product Services
S.I.C.: 5714
N.A.I.C.S.: 442291

Personnel:
Arn Friedl *(Co-Mng Dir)*
Dan Friedl *(Co-Mng Dir)*

EXTENDICARE INC.

3000 Steeles Avenue East Suite 700
Markham, ON, L3R 9W2, Canada
Tel.: (905) 470-4000
Fax: (905) 470-5588
E-Mail: invest@extendicare.com
Web Site: www.extendicare.com
Year Founded: 1968
EXE—(OTC TSX)
Rev.: $2,025,229,270
Assets: $1,797,104,662
Liabilities: $1,742,771,529
Net Worth: $54,333,133
Earnings: $62,281,317
Emp.: 35,700
Fiscal Year-end: 12/31/12

Business Description:
Long-Term Care Services
S.I.C.: 8051
N.A.I.C.S.: 623110

Personnel:
Timothy L. Lukenda *(Pres & CEO)*
Mark Durishan *(Interim CFO)*
Paul Tuttle *(Pres-Ops-Canada)*
Jillian E. Fountain *(Sec)*

Board of Directors:
Melvin A. Rhinelander
John F. Angus
Margery Cunningham
Howard Dean
Seth B. Goldsmith
Benjamin J. Hutzel
Michael J. L. Kirby
Alvin G. Libin
Timothy L. Lukenda
J. Thomas MacQuarrie

Transfer Agent:
Computershare Trust Company of Canada
100 University Avenue 9th Floor
Toronto, ON, M5J 2Y1, Canada
Tel.: (416) 663-9097
Fax: (416) 263-9694

Subsidiaries:

Extendicare (Canada), Inc. **(1)**
3000 Steeles Ave E Ste 700
Markham, ON, L3R 9W2, Canada
Tel.: (905) 470-4000
Fax: (905) 470-5588
E-Mail: extendicare_canada@extendicare.com
Web Site: www.extendicarecanada.com
Emp.: 160
Nursing Home Services
S.I.C.: 8051
N.A.I.C.S.: 623110
Melvin A. Rhinelander *(Chm)*
Paul Tuttle *(Pres)*
Tim Lukendar *(CEO)*
Jillian E. Fountain *(Sec)*

Extendicare, Inc. **(1)**
3000 Steeles Ave E Ste 700
Markham, ON, L3R 9W2, Canada (100%)
Tel.: (905) 470-4000
Fax: (905) 470-5588
E-Mail: extendicare_canada@extendicare.com
Web Site: www.extendicarecanada.com
Emp.: 160
Provider of Nursing Centers, Home Care Services, Hospital Management & Development, Assisted Living & Retirement Centers, Institutional Pharmacy & Durable Medical Supply Business
S.I.C.: 8082
N.A.I.C.S.: 621610
Melvin A. Rhinelander *(Chm)*
Timothy L. Lukenga *(Pres & CEO)*
J. Douglas Harris *(CFO & Sr VP)*

U.S. Subsidiary:

Extendicare Health Services Inc. **(1)**
111 W Michigan St
Milwaukee, WI 53203-2903 DE
Tel.: (414) 908-8000
Fax: (414) 908-8059
Toll Free: (800) 395-5000
E-Mail: info@extendicare.com
Web Site: www.extendicare.com
Emp.: 450
Skilled Nursing Services
S.I.C.: 8051
N.A.I.C.S.: 623110
Tim Lukulda *(CEO)*
Roch Carter *(Gen Counsel & VP)*
Douglas J. Harris *(CFP, Sr VP & Treas)*

Subsidiary:

Tendercare, Inc. **(2)**
111 W Michigan St
Milwaukee, WI 53203
Tel.: (414) 908-8000
Fax: (906) 635-0212
Toll Free: (866) 719-8706
E-Mail: corp@tendercare.net
Web Site: www.tendercare.net
Emp.: 500
Nursing Care Services
S.I.C.: 8051
N.A.I.C.S.: 623110

EXTENWAY SOLUTIONS INC.

500 chemin Morgan Suite 100
Baie-d'Urfe, QC, H9X 3V1, Canada
Tel.: (514) 694-1916
Fax: (514) 694-4280
Toll Free: (888) 201-0210
E-Mail: sales@extenway.com
Web Site: www.extenway.com
EY—(TSXV)
Rev.: $365,615
Assets: $5,416,143
Liabilities: $8,011,549
Net Worth: ($2,595,406)
Earnings: ($3,314,064)
Emp.: 24
Fiscal Year-end: 04/30/13

Business Description:
Healthcare & Hospitality Solution Services
S.I.C.: 8049
N.A.I.C.S.: 621330

Personnel:
Richard Laferriere *(Chm & Mgr-IR)*
John McAllister *(Pres & CEO)*
David Brown *(CFO)*
Mario Pelletier *(CTO)*
Jacky Chatelais *(Pres-Extenway MD & VP-Ops)*
Carolyn Lassonde *(Sec)*

Board of Directors:
Richard Laferriere
Louis Brunel
Carolyn Lassonde
Francine Laurent
John McAllister
Lorne J. Zakaib

Transfer Agent:
Canadian Stock Transfer
320 Bay Street B1 Level
Toronto, ON, Canada

EXTER B.V.

Gerrit Bolkade 10
1507 BR Zaandam, Netherlands
Tel.: (31) 75 6700041
Fax: (31) 75 6161559
E-Mail: info@exteraroma.com
Web Site: www.exteraroma.com
Sales Range: $10-24.9 Million
Emp.: 50

Business Description:
Development, Production & Trade of Foodstuff Ingredients
S.I.C.: 2899
N.A.I.C.S.: 325998

Personnel:
John Bruggink *(Owner)*

EXTERNET TELECOMMUNICATIONS AND INTERNET SERVICE PROVIDER PUBLIC LIMITED COMPANY

(d/b/a EXTERNET Plc)
Szapary ut 18
HU-5000 Szolnok, Hungary
Tel.: (36) 12371860
Fax: (36) 1 2371869
E-Mail: externet@externet.hu
Web Site: www.externet.hu
EXTERNET—(BUD)
Sales Range: $10-24.9 Million
Emp.: 38

Business Description:
Telecommunications Services
S.I.C.: 4812
N.A.I.C.S.: 517210

Personnel:
Gabor Winkler *(Chm-Supervisory Bd)*
Geza Laszlo *(Chm-Mgmt Bd)*
Andras Porffy *(Vice Chm-Mgmt Bd)*
Ferenc Kocsis *(CEO)*
Istvan Sebok *(Deputy CEO)*
Balazs Nyiri *(CFO)*

Supervisory Board of Directors:
Gabor Winkler
Emese Varga
Istvan Takacs

EXTERRA RESOURCES LIMITED

The Kirrin Centre Level 4 15 Ogilvie Road
Applecross, WA, 6153, Australia
Tel.: (61) 8 9317 9700
Fax: (61) 8 9481 7288
E-Mail: j.davis@exterraresources.com.au
Web Site: www.exterraresources.com.au
EXC—(ASX)
Rev.: $330,203
Assets: $6,728,510
Liabilities: $76,131
Net Worth: $6,652,380
Earnings: ($2,032,338)
Fiscal Year-end: 06/30/13

Business Description:
Gold Mining Services
S.I.C.: 1041
N.A.I.C.S.: 212221

Personnel:
John Davis *(Mng Dir)*
Dennis William Wilkins *(Sec)*

Board of Directors:
Justin Brown
Peter Cole
John Davis
Gary Morgan

Legal Counsel:
Kings Park Corporate Lawyers
8 8 Clive Street
West Perth, WA, 6005, Australia

EXTOL COMMERCIAL LIMITED

20 Bhaveshwar Sadan 207
Sion East, Mumbai, 400 022, India
Tel.: (91) 22 32506927
Fax: (91) 22 24095065
E-Mail: extolcommercial@gmail.com
Web Site: www.extolcommercial.com
512163—(BOM)
Sales Range: Less than $1 Million

Business Description:
Commercial Trading Services
S.I.C.: 5099
N.A.I.C.S.: 423990

Personnel:
Sanjiv Hansraj Kathuria *(Mng Dir)*

Board of Directors:
Jerome D'souza
Sanjiv Hansraj Kathuria
Hemant Tiwari
Transfer Agent:
Bigshare Services Pvt. Ltd.
E-2/3 Ansa Industrial Estate Sakivihar Road
Saki Naka Andheri E
Mumbai, India

EXTRAWELL PHARMACEUTICAL HOLDINGS LTD.

Rom 3409-10 34th Fl China Resources Bldg 26 Harbour Rd
Wanchai, China (Hong Kong)
Tel.: (852) 28561918
Fax: (852) 28563139
E-Mail: info@extrawell.com.hk
Web Site: www.extrawell.com.hk
0858—(HKG)
Sls.: $19,480,219
Assets: $92,536,583
Liabilities: $17,321,080
Net Worth: $75,215,503
Earnings: $1,054,811
Emp.: 294
Fiscal Year-end: 03/31/13
Business Description:
Pharmaceutical Products Mfr
S.I.C.: 2834
N.A.I.C.S.: 325412
Personnel:
Yu Min Mao *(Chm)*
Yi Xie *(CEO)*
Kwok Wah Liu *(Sec & Controller-Fin)*
Board of Directors:
Yu Min Mao
Lin Hu Fang
Song Jin
Yi Lou
Sau Kuen Wong
Yi Xie
Jing Lun Xue
HSBC Securities Services (Bermuda) Limited
6 Front Street
Hamilton, Bermuda
Transfer Agents:
Tricor Tengis Limited
26th Floor Tesbury Centre 28 Queen's Road East
Wanchai, China (Hong Kong)
Tel.: (852) 29801333
Fax: (852) 28108185
HSBC Securities Services (Bermuda) Limited
6 Front Street
Hamilton, Bermuda
Subsidiaries:

Extrawell Enterprises Limited (1)
Rm 09-10 34th Floor China Resources Buillding 26 Harbour Road
Wanchai, China (Hong Kong)
Tel.: (852) 28561918
Fax: (852) 28563139
E-Mail: info@extrawell.com.hk
Web Site: www.extrawell.com.hk
Emp.: 15
Investment Management Services
S.I.C.: 6211
N.A.I.C.S.: 523999

Extrawell Pharmaceutical (HK) Limited (1)
Room 3409-10 34/F China Resources Building 26 Harbour Road
Wanchai, China (Hong Kong)
Tel.: (852) 28561918
Fax: (852) 28563139
Pharmaceutical Products Distr
S.I.C.: 5122
N.A.I.C.S.: 424210

Non-U.S. Subsidiaries:

Changchun Extrawell Pharmaceutical Co., Ltd. (1)
1299 Changchun Economic Development Zone
130033 Changchun, China (68%)
Tel.: (86) 4314634271
Web Site: www.ccepcd.com
Pharmaceutical Products Mfr
S.I.C.: 2834
N.A.I.C.S.: 325412
Lian Bang Chan *(Gen Mgr)*

Jilin Extrawell Changbaishan Pharmaceutical Co., Ltd. (1)
Jilin Changchun Economic Development Zone
940 Shenzhen Street, Changchun, Jilin, 130033, China
Tel.: (86) 43186821498
Fax: (86) 4314664738
E-Mail: Ccwdc@126.com
Web Site: www.jycbs.com
Pharmaceutical Products Mfr
S.I.C.: 2834
N.A.I.C.S.: 325412
Jian Yong Jian Yong *(Gen Mgr)*

EXXARO RESOURCES LTD.

Roger Dyason Road
Pretoria, Gauteng, 0183, South Africa
Mailing Address:
PO Box 9229
Pretoria, 0001, South Africa
Tel.: (27) 123075000
Fax: (27) 123233400
Web Site: www.exxaro.com
EXX—(JSE)
Rev.: $1,365,979,300
Assets: $4,737,978,900
Liabilities: $1,520,348,700
Net Worth: $3,217,630,200
Earnings: $1,077,569,900
Emp.: 7,826
Fiscal Year-end: 12/31/12
Business Description:
Coal, Metal & Mineral Exploration & Mining Services
S.I.C.: 1222
N.A.I.C.S.: 212112
Personnel:
Deenadayalen Konar *(Chm)*
Sipho Abednego Nkosi *(CEO)*
Carina H. Wessels *(Sec)*
Board of Directors:
Deenadayalen Konar
Salukazi Dakile-Hlongwane
Willem Abraham de Klerk
Jurie Johannes Geldenhuys
Norman Bloe Mbazima
Vincent Zwelibanzi Mntambo
Richard Peter Mohring
Sipho Abednego Nkosi
Mohamed Fazel Randera
Nkululeko Leonard Sowazi
Jeffrey van Rooyen
Dalikhaya Rain Zihlangu

Subsidiaries:

Exxaro Base Metals and Industrial Minerals Holdings (Pty) Limited (1)
Exxaro Building Rodger Dyson Road
Pretoria, 0183, South Africa
Tel.: (27) 123075000
Metal Mining Services
S.I.C.: 1099
N.A.I.C.S.: 212299
Sipho Abednego Nkosi *(CEO)*

Exxaro Base Metals (Pty) Limited (1)
Cnr Vogelstruis and Plover Street
Springs, Gauteng, 1559, South Africa
Tel.: (27) 118129500
Fax: (27) 113633293
Metal Mining Services
S.I.C.: 1099
N.A.I.C.S.: 212299
Deon Le Grange *(Gen Mgr)*

Exxaro Coal (Pty) Limited (1)
1 Roger Dyason St
Pretoria, 0183, South Africa
Tel.: (27) 123075000
Fax: (27) 01230750000
Coal Mining Services
S.I.C.: 1222
N.A.I.C.S.: 212112
Sipho Abednego Nkosi *(Mng Dir)*

Exxaro Holdings Sands (Pty) Limited (1)
R34 Melmoth Rd
Empangeni, 3880, South Africa
Tel.: (27) 359027000
Fax: (27) 359027828
Sand Mining Services
S.I.C.: 1442
N.A.I.C.S.: 212321

Exxaro Insurance Company Limited (1)
PO Box 9229
Pretoria, 0001, South Africa
Tel.: (27) 12 307 4550
Fax: (27) 12 3233400
E-Mail: rian.strydon@exxaro.com
Web Site: www.exxaro.com
General Insurance Services
S.I.C.: 6411
N.A.I.C.S.: 524210
Rian Strydom *(Gen Mgr)*

Inyanda Coal (Pty) Limited (1)
Portion 21 284 JS Zaaihoek Road
Witbank, 1034, South Africa
Tel.: (27) 136528534
Fax: (27) 123075236
Emp.: 100
Coal Mining Services
S.I.C.: 1222
N.A.I.C.S.: 212112
Alf Debnam *(Mgr-Sls)*

The Vryheid (Natal) Railway Coal and Iron Company Limited (1)
PO Box 28
Hlobane, 3145, South Africa
Tel.: (27) 34 967 1258
Fax: (27) 34 967 1602
Emp.: 20
Coal & Iron Ore Mining Services
S.I.C.: 1222
N.A.I.C.S.: 212112
Sarel Swart *(Mgr-Rehabilitation)*

Non-U.S. Subsidiaries:

Exxaro Australia Pty Limited (1)
L 2 24 Outram Street
West Perth, WA, 6005, Australia
Tel.: (61) 894865600
Fax: (61) 894865699
Mineral Exploration Services
S.I.C.: 1499
N.A.I.C.S.: 212399

Exxaro Australia Sands Pty Limited (1)
Level 2 24 Outram Street
West Perth, WA, 6005, Australia
Tel.: (61) 894865600
Fax: (61) 894865699
Titanium Dioxide Mfr
S.I.C.: 2819
N.A.I.C.S.: 325180

Exxaro Finance Ireland Ltd (1)
AIB Block IFSC Dublin 1
Dublin, Ireland
Tel.: (353) 1 6701464
Fax: (353) 1 8743050
Consumer Lending Services
S.I.C.: 6141
N.A.I.C.S.: 522291

Exxaro International Coal Trading BV (1)
Strawinskylaan 333b-Tower 3E
Amsterdam, 1077 XX, Netherlands
Tel.: (31) 208804195
Fax: (31) 208804196
Emp.: 2
Coal Distr
S.I.C.: 5052
N.A.I.C.S.: 423520
Ian Jennings *(Mgr-Fin)*

Exxaro International Trading BV (1)
Strawinskylaan 333b-Tower 3e
Amsterdam, Netherlands
Tel.: (31) 208804195
Iron Products Whslr
S.I.C.: 5051
N.A.I.C.S.: 423510

Ticor Resources Pty Limited (1)
L2 24 Outram Street
West Perth, WA, 6005, Australia
Tel.: (61) 894865600
Fax: (61) 894865699
Coal Mining Services
S.I.C.: 1241
N.A.I.C.S.: 213113

EYANG HOLDINGS (GROUP) COMPANY LTD.

8th Fl Tien Chu Commercial Bldg
173 174 Gloucester Rd, Wanchai, China (Hong Kong)
Tel.: (852) 31767266
Fax: (852) 31767300
E-Mail: mlcc@szeyang.com
Web Site: www.szeyang.com
0117—(HKG)
Sales Range: $75-99.9 Million
Emp.: 1,295
Business Description:
Holding Company
S.I.C.: 6719
N.A.I.C.S.: 551112
Personnel:
Weirong Chen *(Chm & CEO)*
Chuncheng Xu *(CFO)*
Wai Chung Leung *(Sec)*
Board of Directors:
Weirong Chen
Hao Chen
Wusheng Cheng
Peleus Kin Wang Chu
Jie Liao
Huanbin Liu
Wei Pan
Mei Shuang
Chuncheng Xu
Zhilin Zhang
Computershare Hong Kong Investor Services Limited
Shops 1712-1716 17th Floor Hopewell Centre
183 Queens Road East
Wanchai, China (Hong Kong)
Transfer Agents:
HSBC Trustee (Cayman) Limited
HSBC House 68 West Bay Road
PO Box 484
Georgetown, Grand Cayman, Cayman Islands
Computershare Hong Kong Investor Services Limited
Shops 1712-1716 17th Floor Hopewell Centre
183 Queens Road East
Wanchai, China (Hong Kong)

EYECARE PARTNERS LIMITED

4A Lord Street
Botany, NSW, 2019, Australia
Tel.: (61) 2 9695 9300
Fax: (61) 2 9316 8892
E-Mail: info@eyecarepartners.com.au
Web Site: www.eyecarepartners.com.au
Emp.: 100
Business Description:
Optical Products Provider
S.I.C.: 7699
N.A.I.C.S.: 811219
Personnel:
Raymond John Fortescue *(Chm)*
Michael Jenkins *(CFO & Sec)*
Board of Directors:
Raymond John Fortescue
Colin Coverdale
Robert Rollinson
Peter Rose
Legal Counsel:
PWC Australia
201 Sussex Street
Sydney, NSW, 2000, Australia
Middletons
Level 25 Rialto South Tower 525 Collins Street
Melbourne, VIC, 3000, Australia
Tel.: (61) 3 9205 2000
Fax: (61) 3 9205 2055

EYECARE PARTNERS LIMITED—(Continued)

Subsidiaries:

EyeQ Optometrists Pty. Ltd. **(1)**
Karrinyup Shopping Ctr Karrinyup Rd
Karrinyup Shop F144, Perth, WA, 6018, Australia
Tel.: (61) 894458870
Fax: (61) 894458875
Web Site: www.eyeq.com.au
Emp.: 15
Optometrist Centers
S.I.C.: 8042
N.A.I.C.S.: 621320

Focus Optics Pty. Ltd. **(1)**
113 Wickham Ter
Brisbane, 4000, Australia
Tel.: (61) 738312900
Fax: (61) 738312905
E-Mail: sales@focusoptics.com.au
Web Site: www.focusoptics.com.au
Emp.: 29
Optical Goods Stores & Services
S.I.C.: 5995
N.A.I.C.S.: 446130
Shelley Mattingley *(Mgr)*

EYEGENE INC.

DMC Building #414 1580 Samgam-dong Mapo-gu
Seoul, 121-270, Korea (South)
Tel.: (82) 2 3221687
Fax: (82) 2 3248059
Web Site: www.eyegene.co.kr
185490—(KRS)

Business Description:
Pharmaceutical Mfr
S.I.C.: 2834
N.A.I.C.S.: 325412
Personnel:
Wonil Yoo *(CEO)*

EYELOGIC SYSTEMS INC.

Suite 160A 340 Midpark Way SE
Calgary, AB, T2X IPI, Canada
Tel.: (403) 264-5896
Fax: (403) 264-9740
Toll Free: (888) 854-7780
E-Mail: info@eyelogic.com
Web Site: www.eyelogic.com
Year Founded: 1986
EYE.A—(TSXV)
Rev.: $837,632
Assets: $1,337,791
Liabilities: $207,089
Net Worth: $1,130,702
Earnings: ($207,435)
Emp.: 50
Fiscal Year-end: 12/31/12

Business Description:
Ophthalmic Equipment Mfr
S.I.C.: 3841
N.A.I.C.S.: 339112
Personnel:
Richard K. Skauge *(Chm & CEO)*
Mark McDonald *(Pres)*
Ryan Hoult *(CFO)*
Board of Directors:
Frank Bailey
Ryan Hoult
Harvey Kraft
Mark McDonald
Kristoffer Moen
Richard K. Skauge
Donald S. Smith
Transfer Agent:
Olympia Trust Company
125 9th Avenue SE Suite 2300
Calgary, AB, T2G 0P6, Canada
Tel.: (403) 261-0900

EZ-COMM TRADE TECHNOLOGIES LIMITED.

Daulatram Mansion 4th Floor St
Kittridge Road
Colaba, Mumbai, Maharashtra, 400005, India
Tel.: (91) 2222825252
E-Mail: hima@ezcommindia.com
Web Site: www.ezcommindia.com
531621—(BOM)
Sales Range: Less than $1 Million

Business Description:
Information Technology Consulting Services
S.I.C.: 7389
N.A.I.C.S.: 519190
Personnel:
Sanjiv Khandelwal *(Chm & Mng Dir)*
Board of Directors:
Sanjiv Khandelwal
Shilpa Khandelwal
Khushrow Shiavax Patel

EZ SYSTEMS AS

Klostergata 30
3732 Skien, Norway
Tel.: (47) 35 58 70 20
E-Mail: info@ez.no
Web Site: www.ez.no
Year Founded: 1999
Sales Range: $10-24.9 Million

Business Description:
Web Content Management Software
S.I.C.: 7372
N.A.I.C.S.: 511210
Personnel:
Aleksander Farstad *(Co-Founder & CEO)*
Bard Farstad *(Co-Founder)*
Michael Longman *(CFO)*
Michael Friedmann *(CIO)*
Ralph Hunermann *(CTO)*

Subsidiary:

eZ Systems Nordics **(1)**
Askergata 1
0158 Oslo, Norway
Tel.: (47) 35 58 70 20
Web Content Management Software
S.I.C.: 7372
N.A.I.C.S.: 511210

Non-U.S. Subsidiaries:

eZ Systems Asia **(1)**
Marina Bay Financial Center Tower 2 Level 39
10 Marina Boulevard, Singapore, 018983, Singapore
Tel.: (65) 6818 6151
Fax: (65) 6818 6152
E-Mail: info.as@ez.no
Web Content Management Software
S.I.C.: 7372
N.A.I.C.S.: 511210

eZ Systems China **(1)**
L24 Tower 3 China Central Place 77 Jianguo Road
Chaoyang District, Beijing, 100025, China
Tel.: (86) 10 8587 2237
Fax: (86) 10 8588 0220
E-Mail: info.cn@ez.no
Web Content Management Software
S.I.C.: 7372
N.A.I.C.S.: 511210

eZ Systems France **(1)**
26 rue de la republique
69002 Lyon, France
Tel.: (33) 1 44 93 15 50
E-Mail: info.fr@ez.no
Web Content Management Software
S.I.C.: 7372
N.A.I.C.S.: 511210

eZ Systems Germany **(1)**
Bonner Strasse 484
50968 Cologne, Germany
Tel.: (49) 221 367 4860
E-Mail: info.de@ez.no
Web Content Management Software
S.I.C.: 7372
N.A.I.C.S.: 511210

eZ Systems Italy **(1)**
Via San Pietro all'Orto 3
20121 Milan, Italy
Tel.: (39) 02 7631 7631
E-Mail: info.it@ez.no
Web Content Management Software
S.I.C.: 7372
N.A.I.C.S.: 511210

eZ Systems Japan **(1)**
Namisho Building 2F 2-3-7 Shinkawa
Chuo-ku, Tokyo, 104-0033, Japan
Tel.: (81) 3 6327 1514
E-Mail: info.jp@ez.no
Web Content Management Software
S.I.C.: 7372
N.A.I.C.S.: 511210

eZ Systems Spain **(1)**
Barcelona Activa c/ Llacuna 162
08018 Barcelona, Spain
Tel.: (34) 93 401 98 77
Content Management Software
S.I.C.: 7372
N.A.I.C.S.: 511210

EZAKI GLICO CO., LTD.

6-5 Utajima 4-Chome
Nishiyodogawa-ku
Osaka, 555-8502, Japan
Tel.: (81) 664778352
Fax: (81) 664778250
Web Site: www.glico.co.jp
Year Founded: 1922
2206—(TKS)
Sls.: $3,223,033,000
Assets: $2,412,993,000
Liabilities: $1,133,176,000
Net Worth: $1,279,817,000
Earnings: $36,157,000
Emp.: 1,101
Fiscal Year-end: 03/31/13

Business Description:
Confectionery & Convenience Food Producer
S.I.C.: 2064
N.A.I.C.S.: 311340
Personnel:
Katsuhisa Ezaki *(Pres & CEO)*
Toshio Monna *(Mng Dir)*
Board of Directors:
Masahiro Azumi
Etsuro Ezaki
Katsuhisa Ezaki
Takatoshi Kato
Takashi Kuriki
Tetsuo Masuda
Munekazu Nakagawa
Nobuhiko Umezaki
Transfer Agent:
Mitsui Sumitomo Trust & Banking Co Ltd
5-33 Kitahama 4-chome Chuo-ku
Osaka, 541-0041, Japan

Subsidiaries:

Glico Dairy Products Co., Ltd. **(1)**
2 14 1 Musashino
Akishima, Tokyo, 196 0021, Japan
Tel.: (81) 425442222
Dairy Products Mfr
S.I.C.: 5149
N.A.I.C.S.: 424490

ICREO Co., Ltd. **(1)**
Aqua City 4F 4-16-23 Shibaura Minato-ku
Tokyo, 108 0023, Japan
Tel.: (81) 337697500
Fax: (81) 337697514
E-Mail: info@icreo.co.jp
Web Site: www.icreo.co.jp
Emp.: 393
Infant Formula Milk & Health Foods Production Services
S.I.C.: 2023
N.A.I.C.S.: 311514
Asaka Masahiro *(Pres)*

Non-U.S. Subsidiaries:

Generale Biscuit Glico France S.A. **(1)**
3 rue Saarinen Silic
Rungis, Val De Marne, F 94150, France
Tel.: (33) 156344000
Fax: (33) 156344400
Dairy Products Whslr
S.I.C.: 5143
N.A.I.C.S.: 424430

Glico Canada Corporation **(1)**
162 5th Ave W
Vancouver, BC, V5Y 1H7, Canada
Tel.: (604) 876-7192
Fax: (604) 876-0578
Confectionery Products Mfr
S.I.C.: 5145
N.A.I.C.S.: 424450

Thai Glico Co., Ltd. **(1)**
Ploenchit Tower 4th Fl
898 Ploenchit Rd, Bangkok, 10330, Thailand
Tel.: (66) 22630510
Fax: (66) 22630518
E-Mail: antl@thaiglico.com
Web Site: www.thaiglico.com
Emp.: 100
Confectionery Products Mfr
S.I.C.: 5145
N.A.I.C.S.: 424450
Akihiko Adachi *(Gen Mgr)*

EZCHIP SEMICONDUCTOR LTD.

1 Hatamar Street
PO Box 527
Yokneam, 20692, Israel
Tel.: (972) 49596666
Fax: (972) 49594166
E-Mail: info@ezchip.com
Web Site: www.ezchip.com
Year Founded: 1989
EZCH—(NASDAQ TAE)
Rev.: $54,707,000
Assets: $286,594,000
Liabilities: $12,949,000
Net Worth: $273,645,000
Earnings: $15,651,000
Emp.: 195
Fiscal Year-end: 12/31/12

Business Description:
Semiconductor Mfr
S.I.C.: 3674
N.A.I.C.S.: 334413
Personnel:
Benny Hanigal *(Chm)*
Eli Fruchter *(Pres & CEO)*
Dror Israel *(CFO)*
Board of Directors:
Benny Hanigal
Eli Fruchter
Ran Giladi
Karen Sarid
Shai Saul
David Schlachet

Subsidiary:

EZchip Technologies **(1)**
1 Hatamar St
PO Box 527
Yokneam, 20692, Israel
Tel.: (972) 49596666
Fax: (972) 49594177
E-Mail: info@ezchip.com
Web Site: www.ezchip.com
Emp.: 110
Fabless Semiconductors
S.I.C.: 3674
N.A.I.C.S.: 334413
Eli Fruchter *(Pres & CEO)*

U.S. Subsidiary:

EZchip Technologies Inc. **(1)**
900 E Hamilton Ave Ste 100
Campbell, CA 95008
Tel.: (408) 879-7355
Fax: (408) 879-7357
E-Mail: info@ezchip.com
Web Site: www.ezchip.com
Emp.: 4
Semiconductor & Related Device Mfr
S.I.C.: 3674
N.A.I.C.S.: 334413
Benny Hanigal *(Chm)*

EZDAN HOLDING GROUP COMPANY (Q.S.C.)
(Formerly Ezdan Real Estate Company L.L.C.)
West Bay - Ezdan Tower
PO Box 3222
Doha, Qatar
Tel.: (974) 44094001
Fax: (974) 44094111
Web Site: www.ezdanholding.qa
Year Founded: 1960
ERES—(QE)
Rev.: $138,867,961
Assets: $10,387,605,273
Liabilities: $2,976,420,837
Net Worth: $7,411,184,436
Earnings: $109,176,324
Fiscal Year-end: 12/31/12
Business Description:
Real Estate Management Services
S.I.C.: 6531
N.A.I.C.S.: 531390
Personnel:
Thani Abdulla Thani Al Thani *(Chm)*
Abdulla Thani Abdulla Thani Al Thani *(Vice Chm)*
Ali Al-Obidli *(CEO)*
Abdul Al Rahman Al-Najjar *(Deputy CEO)*
Khaled Ghazi *(CFO)*
Naser Aljaber *(Chief Logistics & Admin Dev Officer)*
Board of Directors:
Thani Abdulla Thani Al Thani
Jaber Al-Harami
Ali Al-Obidli
Ayed Al-Qahtani
Khaled Thani Abdulla Al Thani
Abdulla Thani Abdulla Thani Al Thani
Mohamed Thani Abdulla Thani Al Thani

EZDAN REAL ESTATE COMPANY L.L.C.
(See Under Ezdan Holding Group Company (Q.S.C.))

EZEATM LIMITED
Unit 1 25 Montgomery Way
Malaga, WA, 6090, Australia
Mailing Address:
PO Box 3344
Malaga, WA, 6945, Australia
Tel.: (61) 8 9249 7422
Fax: (61) 8 9249 7400
E-Mail: atmsupport@ezeatm.com.au
Web Site: www.ezeatm.com.au
EZA—(ASX)
Business Description:
Automatic Teller Machine Owner & Operator
S.I.C.: 6099
N.A.I.C.S.: 522320
Personnel:
Mark Jones *(Chm)*
Todd Zani *(CEO)*
Chad Zani *(Mng Dir)*
Board of Directors:
Mark Jones
Douglas Rose
Zaffer Soemya
Chad Zani
Todd Zani

Subsidiary:

Ezeatm Pty Ltd. (1)
Unit 1 25 Montgomery Way
Malaga, Perth, WA, 6090, Australia
Tel.: (61) 8 9249 7422
Fax: (61) 8 9249 7400
Automatic Teller Machine Mfr
S.I.C.: 3577
N.A.I.C.S.: 334118
Todd Zani *(Mng Dir)*

EZEFLOW, INC.
985 rue Andre-Line
Granby, QC, J2J 1J6, Canada
Tel.: (450) 375-3575
Telex: 5-832524
Fax: (450) 375-3772
Toll Free: (800) 363-6310
E-Mail: ezeflow@sympatico.ca
Web Site: www.ezeflow.com
Emp.: 200
Business Description:
Mfr. of Corrosion Resistant Alloy Pipe Fittings & Flanges
S.I.C.: 3494
N.A.I.C.S.: 332919
Personnel:
Jacques Latendresse *(Pres)*

U.S. Subsidiary:

Flowline Corporation (1)
1400 New Butler Rd
New Castle, PA 16101 DE
Mailing Address:
PO Box 7027
New Castle, PA 16107-7027
Tel.: (724) 658-3711
Fax: (724) 658-6117
Toll Free: (800) 245-0354
E-Mail: sales@flowlinefittings.com
Web Site: www.flowlinefittings.com
Emp.: 120
Pipe Fittings Mfr
Export
S.I.C.: 3498
N.A.I.C.S.: 332996
Marty Capoferri *(Pres)*

Non-U.S. Subsidiary:

Munro & Miller Fittings Ltd. (1)
East Mains Industrial Estate
Broxburn, EH52 5AU, United Kingdom UK
Tel.: (44) 1506853531 (100%)
Fax: (44) 1506856628
E-Mail: info@munro-miller.co.uk
Web Site: www.munro-miller.co.uk
Emp.: 50
Fabricated Pipe Fittings Mfr
S.I.C.: 3498
N.A.I.C.S.: 332996
Jay Barnett *(Mgr-Admin)*

EZI GMBH
Reiherstrasse 2
35708 Haiger, Germany
Tel.: (49) 27738350
Fax: (49) 2773835199
E-Mail: Info@EZI.de
Web Site: www.ezi.de
Rev.: $10,980,024
Emp.: 50
Business Description:
Customs Consulting & Agency Services
S.I.C.: 8748
N.A.I.C.S.: 541618
Personnel:
Adrian F. Gog *(Co-CEO)*
Berit Wagener-Gog *(Co-CEO)*

EZIBUY (NZ) LTD.
208 John F Kennedy Dr
Palmerston North, New Zealand
Tel.: (64) 69522112
Fax: (64) 69522110
E-Mail: sford@ezibuy.co.nz
Web Site: www.ezibuy.co.nz
Year Founded: 1978
Emp.: 700
Business Description:
Clothing Retailer
S.I.C.: 5699
N.A.I.C.S.: 448190
Personnel:
Gerard Gillespie *(Founder & Dir)*

EZION HOLDINGS LIMITED
15 Hoe Chiang Road Tower Fifteen 12-05
Singapore, 089316, Singapore
Tel.: (65) 63090555
Fax: (65) 62227848
E-Mail: ir@ezionholdings.com
Web Site: www.ezionholdings.com
5ME—(OTC SES)
Rev.: $158,669,000
Assets: $1,198,005,000
Liabilities: $645,156,000
Net Worth: $552,849,000
Earnings: $78,841,000
Fiscal Year-end: 12/31/12
Business Description:
Offshore Services
S.I.C.: 3731
N.A.I.C.S.: 336611
Personnel:
Thiam Keng Chew *(CEO)*
Boon Pin Cheah *(CFO & Co-Sec)*
Larry Glenn Johnson *(COO)*
Peter Kon Meng Lee *(Deputy COO)*
David Leong Ching Poh *(Chief Comml Officer)*
Mark Ortega *(Legal Counsel)*
Ka Bee Lim *(Co-Sec)*
Board of Directors:
Kian Soo Lee
Thiam Keng Chew
Larry Glenn Johnson
Thean Ee Lim
Woon Hum Tan
Kai Yuen Wang

Subsidiary:

Teras Offshore Pte Ltd (1)
15 Hoe Chiang Road Tower Fifteen 12-05
Singapore, Singapore
Tel.: (65) 63090555
Fax: (65) 62227848
E-Mail: commercial@terasoffshore.com
Web Site: www.terasoffshore.com
Marine Logistics & Support Services
S.I.C.: 4412
N.A.I.C.S.: 483111
Thiam Keng Chew *(CEO & Exec Dir)*
Boon Pin Cheah *(CFO)*
Larry Glenn Johnson *(COO)*
David Poh *(Chief Comml Officer)*

U.S. Subsidiary:

Teras Cargo Transport (America) LLC (1)
5358 33rd Ave NW Ste 302
Gig Harbor, WA 98335
Tel.: (253) 857-9209
Fax: (253) 857-9172
E-Mail: info@terasamerica.com
Web Site: www.terasamerica.com
Emp.: 15
Marine Logistics Services
S.I.C.: 4491
N.A.I.C.S.: 488320
Kathleen Reed *(Acct Mgr)*

EZRA HOLDINGS LTD.
15 Hoe Chiang Road 28-01 Tower Fifteen
Singapore, 089316, Singapore
Tel.: (65) 6349 8535
Fax: (65) 6345 0139
E-Mail: general@ezraholdings.com
Web Site: www.ezraholdings.com
5DN—(OTC SES)
Rev.: $1,021,868,789
Assets: $2,369,706,650
Liabilities: $1,446,739,463
Net Worth: $922,967,187
Earnings: $51,871,340
Emp.: 3,000
Fiscal Year-end: 08/31/13
Business Description:
Offshore Oil & Gas Operation Support Services
S.I.C.: 1389
N.A.I.C.S.: 213112
Personnel:
Kian Soo Lee *(Founder)*
Lionel Chye Tek Lee *(CEO & Mng Dir)*
Ranjit Singh *(Deputy CEO-EMAS Marine)*
Eugene Chee Mun Cheng *(CFO)*
Adarash Kumar *(COO)*
C. J. D'Cort *(CEO-EMAS AMC)*
Keng Nien Yeo *(Sec)*
Alan Allred *(Sr VP-Global HSSEQ)*
Board of Directors:
Poh Tiong Koh
Philip Heng Nee Eng
Karl Erik Kjelstad
Adarash Kumar
Kian Soo Lee
Lionel Chye Tek Lee
Get Ping Ngo
Hong Teck Soon

Non-U.S. Subsidiary:

Aker Marine Contractors AS (1)
Lilleakerveien 8
Pox Box 247
Oslo, 216, Norway
Mailing Address:
PO Box 247
N-0216 Oslo, Norway
Tel.: (47) 22945000
Fax: (47) 22945900
Emp.: 90
Marine Engineering & Installation Contractor
S.I.C.: 8711
N.A.I.C.S.: 541330
Torgeier Ramstad *(Pres)*

EZTEC EMPREENDIMENTOS E PARTICIPACOES S.A.
Av Republica do Libano 1921 - Ibirapuera
04501-002 Sao Paulo, SP, Brazil
Tel.: (55) 11 5056 8300
Fax: (55) 11 5056 8301
E-Mail: ri@eztec.com.br
Web Site: www.eztec.com.br
Year Founded: 1979
EZTC3—(BRAZ)
Business Description:
Real Estate Development Services
S.I.C.: 6531
N.A.I.C.S.: 531390
Personnel:
Ernesto Zarzur *(Chm)*
Samir Zakkhour El Tayar *(Vice Chm)*
Marcelo Ernesto Zarzur *(CEO & Chief Engrg Officer)*
Antonio Emilio Clemente Fugazzar *(CFO & IR Officer)*
Silvio Ernesto Zarzur *(Chief Dev Officer & Exec VP)*
Mauro Alberto *(Chief Admin Officer)*
Marcos Ernesto Zarzur *(Chief Sls Officer)*
Joao Paulo Flaifel *(Chief New Bus Officer)*
Silvio Hidemi Iamamura *(Real Estate Ops Officer)*
Roberto Mounir Maalouli *(Legal Officer)*
Carlos Eduardo Monteiro *(Plng & Supply Officer)*
Flavio Ernesto Zarzur *(Exec VP)*
Board of Directors:
Ernesto Zarzur
Massimo Bauducco
Mario Guy de Faria Mariz
Nelson de Sampaio Bastos
Samir Zakkhour El Tayar
Gustavo Diniz Junqueira
Flavio Ernesto Zarzur
Silvio Ernesto Zarzur

EZWELFARE CO., LTD.
1401 Kolon Science Valleyb 1 Cha
187-10 Guro-dong Guro-gu
Seoul, 152729, Korea (South)
Tel.: (82) 2 32827900
Web Site: www.ezwelfare.net
090850—(KRS)

Ezwelfare Co., Ltd.—(Continued)

Emp.: 190

Business Description:
Welfare Programs, Benefit Package Programs & Government Support Businesses Software Publisher
S.I.C.: 7372
N.A.I.C.S.: 511210

Personnel:
Sang-Yong Kim *(CEO)*

EZZ STEEL CO. S.A.E.

10 Shehab Street Mohandessin
Cairo, Egypt
Tel.: (20) 233046060
Fax: (20) 233470059
E-Mail: ir@ezzsteel.com
Web Site: www.ezzsteel.com
Year Founded: 1994
AEZD—(LSE)
Sls.: $2,940,977,179
Assets: $3,043,821,373
Liabilities: $2,106,911,264
Net Worth: $936,910,108
Earnings: $37,193,822
Fiscal Year-end: 12/31/12

Business Description:
Steel Products Mfr
S.I.C.: 3312
N.A.I.C.S.: 331110

Personnel:
Paul Philipe Chekaiban *(Chm & Mng Dir)*
Nabil El Khatib *(Corp Procurement Officer)*
Farouk Ibrahim *(Corp Technical Officer)*
George Matta *(Corp Mktg Officer)*
Samir Naaman *(Corp Sls Officer)*

Board of Directors:
Paul Philipe Chekaiban
Fayez Aly
Raed El-Beblawy
Mohammed El-Berry
Mamdouh El-Rouby
Gamal Omar

Subsidiaries:

Al Ezz Dekheila Steel Company Alexandria SAE (1)
Dekheila
Alexandria, Egypt (54.59%)
Tel.: (20) 3 433 2220
Web Site: www.ezzsteel.com
IRAX—(EGX)
Sales Range: $1-4.9 Billion
Emp.: 2,791
Steel Mfr & Exporter
S.I.C.: 3399
N.A.I.C.S.: 331110
Paul Chekaiban *(Chm)*

Al Ezz Flat Steel Company (1)
5th Floor 10 Shehab Street
Giza, Egypt
Tel.: (20) 233030493
Flat Steel Mfr
S.I.C.: 3312
N.A.I.C.S.: 331110

F&A AQUA HOLDINGS, INC.

2-19-10 Kami-Osaki Shinagawa-ku
Tokyo, 141-0021, Japan
Tel.: (81) 357193429
Fax: (81) 357194462
Web Site: www.fa-aqua.co.jp
8008—(TKS)
Sls.: $519,914,934
Assets: $586,250,148
Liabilities: $134,077,119
Net Worth: $452,173,029
Earnings: $30,639,994
Emp.: 3,036
Fiscal Year-end: 02/28/13

Business Description:
Apparel & Accessories Mfr & Sales
S.I.C.: 2389
N.A.I.C.S.: 315990

Personnel:
Saishi Kimura *(Chm)*
Hidenori Suzuki *(Pres)*

Board of Directors:
Saishi Kimura
Nobuyuki Hosoda
Masahiko Iwamori
Satoshi Miyamoto
Masahiko Nishimura
Hidenori Suzuki
Akihiro Takiguchi

Transfer Agent:
Mitsubishi UFJ Trust & Banking Corporation
7-10-11 Higashisuna Koto-ku
Tokyo, Japan

Subsidiaries:

AS'TY Inc. (1)
Shoko Ctr 2-15-1
Nishi-ku, Hiroshima, 733-8641, Japan
Tel.: (81) 822781111
Fax: (81) 822782533
Web Site: www.asty.co.jp
Emp.: 200
Apparel Mfr
S.I.C.: 2389
N.A.I.C.S.: 315990
Satoshi Miyamoto *(Pres)*

F.D.C. Products Inc. (1)
2-19-10 Kami-Osaki Shinagawa-ku
Tokyo, 141-8544, Japan
Tel.: (81) 357194300
Fax: (81) 3 5719 3289
Web Site: www.fdcp.co.jp
Emp.: 1,000
Jewelry Mfr
S.I.C.: 3911
N.A.I.C.S.: 339910
Hideke Tamura *(Pres)*

MISUZU Co., Ltd. (1)
1-11-2 Yoyogi
Shibuya-ku, Tokyo, 151-0053, Japan
Tel.: (81) 333202100
Fax: (81) 333735344
E-Mail: misuzuweb@misuzugp.co.jp
Web Site: www.misuzugp.co.jp
Womens Apparel Mfr & Whslr
S.I.C.: 5621
N.A.I.C.S.: 448120
Ichiro Okafuji *(Pres)*

F&B GROUP

(d/b/a Fashion & Beauty Group)
15 rue Pasteur
F-92300 Levallois-Perret, France
Tel.: (33) 1 4105 5555 (Maesa Group)
Year Founded: 2011

Business Description:
Investment Holding Company
S.I.C.: 6719
N.A.I.C.S.: 551112

Personnel:
Gregory Mager *(Partner)*
Julien Saada *(Partner)*

Holding:

Maesa SA (1)
15 rue Pasteur
92300 Levallois-Perret, France FR
Tel.: (33) 141055555 (96.2%)
Fax: (33) 141055557
E-Mail: manuel.varliette@maesa.com
Web Site: www.maesa.com
ALMAE—(EUR)
Sales Range: $25-49.9 Million
Emp.: 250
Perfume & Cosmetic Products Mfr & Retailer
S.I.C.: 2844
N.A.I.C.S.: 325620
Julien Saada *(Chm & CEO)*
Gregory Mager *(Deputy CEO)*
Sophie Thiolas *(Chief Comm Officer)*

U.S. Subsidiaries:

Maesa Home (2)
3105 E Harcourt St Rancho Dominguez
Compton, CA 90221
Tel.: (310) 639-3999
E-Mail: home-us@maesa.com
Emp.: 35
Cosmetics & Beauty Solutions Whslr
S.I.C.: 5122
N.A.I.C.S.: 424210

Maesa Inc (2)
40 Worth St Rm 705
New York, NY 10013-2994
Tel.: (212) 431-6613
Fax: (212) 431-6614
E-Mail: Beauty-us@maesa.com
Soap & Detergent Mfr
S.I.C.: 2841
N.A.I.C.S.: 325611
Jill Belasco *(Mng Dir)*

Non-U.S. Subsidiary:

Maesa UK Ltd (2)
Crown House 143-147 Regent St
London, W1B 4NR, United Kingdom
Tel.: (44) 20 74946101
E-Mail: beautyandhome-EU@maesa.com
Soap & Detergent Mfr
S.I.C.: 2841
N.A.I.C.S.: 325611

F&C ASSET MANAGEMENT PLC

Exchange House Primrose Street
London, EC2A 2NY, United Kingdom
Tel.: (44) 2076288000
Fax: (44) 2076288188
E-Mail: enquiries@fandc.com
Web Site: www.fandc.com
FCAM—(LSE)
Rev.: $406,509,246
Assets: $1,798,495,452
Liabilities: $935,887,254
Net Worth: $862,608,198
Earnings: $4,737,870
Emp.: 852
Fiscal Year-end: 12/31/12

Business Description:
Asset Management Services
S.I.C.: 6282
N.A.I.C.S.: 523930

Personnel:
Kieran Charles Poynter *(Chm)*
Richard Wilson *(CEO)*
David Logan *(CFO)*
Nick Criticos *(CEO-F&C REIT)*
Toby Hampden-Acton *(CEO-Thames River Capital)*
W. Marrack Tonkin *(Sec & Head-Investment Trusts)*

Board of Directors:
Kieran Charles Poynter
Keith Bedell-Pearce
Keith Jones
David Logan
Derham O'Neill
Keith Percy
Charlie Porter
Ruth Sack
Richard Wilson

Legal Counsel:
Shepperd & Wedderburn LLP
One Exchange Crescent Conference Square
Edinburgh, EH3 8UL, United Kingdom

Norton Rose LLP
3 More London Riverside
London, SE1 2AQ, United Kingdom
Tel.: (44) 20 7283 6000
Fax: (44) 20 7283 6500

Transfer Agent:
Equiniti Limited
34 South Gyle Crescent South Gyle Business Park
Edinburgh, United Kingdom

Subsidiaries:

European Assets Trust NV (1)
Weena 210-212
3012 NJ Rotterdam, Netherlands NL
Tel.: (31) 102013600
Fax: (31) 102013601
E-Mail: info@fandc.com
Web Site: www.europeanassets.eu
EAT—(LSE)
Rev.: $48,077,469
Assets: $193,813,844
Liabilities: $11,695,411
Net Worth: $182,118,434
Earnings: $45,054,343
Fiscal Year-end: 12/31/12
Investment Services
S.I.C.: 6282
N.A.I.C.S.: 523930
John Ward *(Chm-Supervisory Bd)*
Tim Koster *(Member-Mgmt Bd)*
Wilbert van Twuijver *(Member-Mgmt Bd)*
Michael Campbell *(Sec)*

F&C Asset Managers Limited (1)
8th Floor Exchange House Primrose Street
London, EC2A2NY, United Kingdom
Tel.: (44) 1314651000
Fax: (44) 2076288188
Emp.: 800
Management Consulting Services
S.I.C.: 8748
N.A.I.C.S.: 541618
Alain Grisay *(CEO)*

F&C (CI) Limited (1)
8th Floor Exchange House Primrose Street
London, EC2A2NY, United Kingdom
Tel.: (44) 1314651000
Fax: (44) 2076288188
Web Site: www.unitmanagement.co.uk
Emp.: 800
Holding Company
S.I.C.: 6719
N.A.I.C.S.: 551112
Alain Grisay *(CEO)*

F&C Emerging Markets Limited (1)
8th Floor Exchange House Primrose Street
London, EC2A2NY, United Kingdom
Tel.: (44) 2076288000
Fax: (44) 2076288188
E-Mail: info@fandc.com
Emp.: 800
Financial Investment Activities
S.I.C.: 6211
N.A.I.C.S.: 523999
Richard Wilson *(CEO)*

F&C Fund Management Limited (1)
Exchange House Primrose Street
London, EC2A 2NY, United Kingdom
Tel.: (44) 2076288000
Fax: (44) 2076288188
E-Mail: info@fandc.com
Web Site: www.fandc.com
Emp.: 400
Investment Management Services
S.I.C.: 6211
N.A.I.C.S.: 523999
Richard Wilson *(CEO)*

F&C Group (Holdings) Limited (1)
8th Floor Exchange House Primrose Street
London, EC2A2NY, United Kingdom
Tel.: (44) 2076288000
Fax: (44) 2076288188
Emp.: 800
Holding Company
S.I.C.: 6719
N.A.I.C.S.: 551112
Alain Grisay *(CEO)*

F&C Group Management Limited (1)
8th Fl Exchange House Primrose St
London, EC2A2NY, United Kingdom
Tel.: (44) 2076288000
Fax: (44) 2076288188
Web Site: www.unitmanagement.co.uk
Emp.: 800
Holding Company
S.I.C.: 6719
N.A.I.C.S.: 551112

F&C Holdings Limited (1)
8th Fl Exchange House Primrose St
London, EC2A 2NY, United Kingdom
Tel.: (44) 2076288000
Fax: (44) 2076288188
Emp.: 500
Holding Company
S.I.C.: 6719
N.A.I.C.S.: 551112
Richard Wilson *(CEO)*

F&C Investment Services Limited (1)
8th Floor Exchange House Primrose Street
London, EC2A2NY, United Kingdom

Tel.: (44) 2076288000
Fax: (44) 2076288188
E-Mail: info@fandc.com
Web Site: www.fandc.com
Emp.: 800
Health & Welfare Funds
S.I.C.: 6371
N.A.I.C.S.: 525120
Jonanthan Mann *(Head-Emerging Market Debt)*

F&C Management Limited (1)
8th Floor Exchange House Primrose Street
London, United Kingdom
Tel.: (44) 2076288000
Fax: (44) 2076288188
Emp.: 800
Securities & Commodity Exchanges
S.I.C.: 6231
N.A.I.C.S.: 523210
Richard Wilson *(CEO)*

F&C Private Equity Nominees Limited (1)
8th Fl Exchange House Primrose St
London, EC2A2NY, United Kingdom
Tel.: (44) 2076288000
Fax: (44) 2076288188
Emp.: 800
Holding Company
S.I.C.: 6719
N.A.I.C.S.: 551112
Richard Wilson *(CEO)*

F&C Property Limited (1)
8th Floor Exchange House Primrose Street
London, EC2A2NY, United Kingdom
Tel.: (44) 2076288000
Fax: (44) 2076288188
Web Site: www.fandc.com
Emp.: 800
New Housing Operative Builders
S.I.C.: 1531
N.A.I.C.S.: 236117
Alain Grisay *(CEO)*

F&C REIT Asset Management LLP (1)
5 Wigmore Street
London, W1U 1PB, United Kingdom
Tel.: (44) 20 7499 2244
Fax: (44) 20 7499 7700
E-Mail: info@fandcreit.com
Web Site: www.fandcreit.com
Emp.: 80
Real Estate Management Services
S.I.C.: 6531
N.A.I.C.S.: 531390
Leo Noe *(Chm)*
Nick Criticos *(CEO)*
Ivor Smith *(Partner)*

F&C REIT Corporate Finance Limited (1)
5 Wigmore Street
London, W1U 1PB, United Kingdom
Tel.: (44) 20 7499 2244
Real Estate Management Services
S.I.C.: 6531
N.A.I.C.S.: 531390

FP Asset Management Holdings Limited (1)
Park Lodge Pixham End
Dorking, Surrey, RH41QA, United Kingdom (100%)
Tel.: (44) 2076288000
Fax: (44) 2078365124
Holding Company
S.I.C.: 6719
N.A.I.C.S.: 551112

FP Fund Managers Limited (1)
Park Lodge Pixham End
Dorking, Surrey, RH4 1QA, United Kingdom (100%)
Tel.: (44) 8706083678
Fax: (44) 2078365124
E-Mail: hrhelpdesk@friendsprovident.co.uk
Web Site: www.friendsprovident.co.uk
Securities & Commodity Exchanges
S.I.C.: 6231
N.A.I.C.S.: 523210

REIT Asset Management Limited (1)
95 Wigmore St
London, W1U 1QW, United Kingdom
Tel.: (44) 20 7499 2244
Fax: (44) 20 7499 7700
Real Estate Management Services
S.I.C.: 6531
N.A.I.C.S.: 531390

Thames River Capital UK Limited (1)
51 Berkeley Square
London, W1J 5BB, United Kingdom
Tel.: (44) 2073601200
Fax: (44) 2073601300
E-Mail: trc@thamesriver.co.uk
Emp.: 150
Investment Management Services
S.I.C.: 6211
N.A.I.C.S.: 523999
Charlie Porter *(CEO)*

Subsidiary:

Thames River Multi-Capital LLP (2)
51 Berkeley Square
London, W1J 5BB, United Kingdom
Tel.: (44) 20 7360 1200
Fax: (44) 20 7360 1300
Investment Management Services
S.I.C.: 6211
N.A.I.C.S.: 523999

Non-U.S. Subsidiaries:

F&C Ireland Limited (1)
Block 5 Harcourt Centre
Dublin, Ireland
Tel.: (353) 14364000
Fax: (353) 14364001
E-Mail: irelandenquiries@fandc.ie
Web Site: www.fandc.com
Emp.: 16
Business Support Services
S.I.C.: 7389
N.A.I.C.S.: 561499
Grainne Alexander *(Gen Mgr)*

F&C Netherlands B.V. (1)
Jachthavenweg 109 K
1081 KM Amsterdam, Netherlands
Tel.: (31) 205823000
Fax: (31) 205823621
E-Mail: info@fandc.com
Emp.: 60
Investment Advice
S.I.C.: 6282
N.A.I.C.S.: 523930
Ban Kramer *(Mng Dir)*

F&C Portugal Gestao de Patrimonios S.A. (1)
Rua de Campolide 372, 1
1070-040 Lisbon, Portugal
Tel.: (351) 21 003 3200
Fax: (351) 21 003 3229
E-Mail: institutional.enquiries@fandc.com
Emp.: 35
Investment Management Services
S.I.C.: 6211
N.A.I.C.S.: 523999
Joao Pedro Palmela *(Head-Client Svcs)*

REIT Asset Management GmbH & Co KG (1)
Oberanger 34-36
80331 Munich, Germany
Tel.: (49) 89 61 46 51 0
Fax: (49) 89 61 46 51 56
Real Estate Management Services
S.I.C.: 6531
N.A.I.C.S.: 531390
Iris Schoeberl *(Mng Dir)*

F&D SCENE CHANGES LTD.

2B 803 24th Avenue SE
Calgary, AB, T2G 1P5, Canada
Tel.: (403) 233-7633
Fax: (403) 266-7597
E-Mail: info@fdscenechanges.com
Web Site: www.fdscenechanges.com
Year Founded: 1982
Rev.: $12,684,628
Emp.: 120
Business Description:
Prefabricated Design Components Mfr
S.I.C.: 3448
N.A.I.C.S.: 332311
Personnel:
Joe Kondrat *(Mgr-Bus Dev)*

F & J PRINCE HOLDINGS CORPORATION

5th Fl Citibank Ctr 8741 Paseo de Roxas
Makati, Philippines
Tel.: (63) 28927133
Fax: (63) 28927127
E-Mail: prinznet@compass.com.ph
Web Site: www.fjprince.com
FJP—(PHI)
Sales Range: $1-9.9 Million
Business Description:
Investment Services
S.I.C.: 6799
N.A.I.C.S.: 523920
Personnel:
Robert Y. Cokeng *(Chm)*
Francisco Y. Cokeng Jr. *(Vice Chm)*
Johnson U. Co *(Treas & VP)*
Roman G. Pacia Jr. *(Sec)*
Emeterio L. Barcelon *(Sr VP)*
Board of Directors:
Robert Y. Cokeng
Emeterio L. Barcelon
Francis L. Chua
Johnson U. Co
Johnny O. Cobankiat
Francisco Y. Cokeng Jr.
Homer U. Cokeng Jr.
Mary K. Cokeng
Johnson Gui Yee Tan
Rufino B. Tiangco
Robert Y. Ynson

F&M CO., LTD.

23-38 Esaka 1 Chome Suita
Osaka, 564-0063, Japan
Tel.: (81) 663397177
Fax: (81) 663397184
E-Mail: info@fmltd.co.jp
Web Site: www.fmltd.co.jp
Year Founded: 1990
4771—(TKS)
Sales Range: $250-299.9 Million
Emp.: 246
Business Description:
General Affairs, Administrative Consulting Services, Training, Examination Services & ISO Certification Acquisition Support Services
S.I.C.: 7389
N.A.I.C.S.: 561499
Personnel:
Ichiro Morinaka *(CEO)*

F. MCCLURE & SONS LTD.

55 Ouellette Street
Grand Falls, NB, E3Z 0A6, Canada
Tel.: (506) 473-2024
Fax: (506) 473-6140
Toll Free: (888) 812-9900
E-Mail: info@mcclure.toyota.ca
Web Site: www.mccluretoyota.com
Year Founded: 1973
Rev.: $12,496,887
Emp.: 28
Business Description:
New & Used Car Dealers
S.I.C.: 5511
N.A.I.C.S.: 441110
Personnel:
Donald McClure *(Co-Owner)*
Jacques McClure *(Co-Owner)*

F/NAZCA SAATCHI & SAATCHI

Av Republica do Libano
253 Ibirapuera, Sao Paulo, SP, 04501-000, Brazil
Tel.: (55) 11 3059 4800
Telex: 1121749 sgbp br
Fax: (55) 113059 4948
Web Site: www.fnazca.com.br
Year Founded: 1989
Billings: $43,500,239
Emp.: 63
Business Description:
Full Service Advertising
S.I.C.: 7311
N.A.I.C.S.: 541810
Personnel:
Fabio Fernandes *(CEO & Creative Dir)*
Ivan Marques *(Mng Dir)*

F. RAMADA INVESTIMENTOS, SGPS, S.A.

Rua do General Norton de Matos 68 R/C
4050-424 Porto, Portugal
Tel.: (351) 228346502
Fax: (351) 228346503
E-Mail: sede@ramadainvestimento s.pt
Web Site: www.ramadainvestimento s.pt
RAM—(EUR)
Sls.: $134,177,560
Assets: $225,658,862
Liabilities: $154,794,419
Net Worth: $70,864,443
Earnings: $8,304,485
Emp.: 391
Fiscal Year-end: 12/31/12
Business Description:
Holding Company; Steel & Storage Systems
S.I.C.: 6719
N.A.I.C.S.: 551112
Personnel:
Joao Manuel Matos Borges de Oliveira *(Chm)*
Joao da Silva Nataria *(Chm-Supervisory Bd)*
Board of Directors:
Joao Manuel Matos Borges de Oliveira
Ana Rebelo de Carvalho Meneres de Mendonca Mariz Fernandes
Domingos Jose Vieira de Matos
Pedro Macedo Pinto de Mendonca
Pedro Miguel Matos Borges de Oliveira
Paulo Jorge dos Santos Fernandes
Supervisory Board of Directors:
Joao da Silva Nataria
Jacinto da Costa Vilarinho
Manuel Tiago Alves Baldaque de Marinho Fernandes
Cristina Isabel Linhares Fernandes

Subsidiary:

F. Ramada, Acos e Industrias, S.A. (1)
Apartado 10
3884-909 Ovar, Portugal
Tel.: (351) 256 580 400
Fax: (351) 256 580 410
E-Mail: acos.ovar@ramada.pt
Web Site: www.ramada.pt
Emp.: 400
Steel Products Distr
S.I.C.: 5051
N.A.I.C.S.: 423510
Borges de Oliveira *(Gen Mgr)*

Non-U.S. Subsidiary:

NV STORAX BENELUX SA (1)
Au Fonds Race 17
4300 Waremme, Belgium
Tel.: (32) 19 33 86 86
Fax: (32) 19 33 86 80
E-Mail: info@storax-ramada.com
Web Site: www.storax-ramada.com
Emp.: 15
Racking Systems Mfr
S.I.C.: 3559
N.A.I.C.S.: 333249
Philippe Tromme *(Gen Mgr)*

F-SECURE CORPORATION

Tammasaarenkatu 7 PL 24
00181 Helsinki, Finland

F-Secure Corporation—(Continued)

Tel.: (358) 925200700
Fax: (358) 925205001
E-Mail: info@f-secure.com
Web Site: www.f-secure.com
Year Founded: 1988
FSC1V—(HEL)
Sls.: $211,580,231
Assets: $171,428,019
Liabilities: $83,785,621
Net Worth: $87,642,398
Earnings: $18,928,496
Emp.: 940
Fiscal Year-end: 12/31/12

Business Description:
Software Encryption & Security Services
S.I.C.: 7371
N.A.I.C.S.: 541511

Personnel:
Risto Siilasmaa *(Founder & Chm)*
Sari Maritta Baldauf *(Vice Chm)*
Christian Fredrikson *(Pres & CEO)*
Taneli Virtanen *(CFO)*
Pirkka Palomaki *(Chief Strategy Officer)*

Board of Directors:
Risto Siilasmaa
Jussi Arovaara
Sari Maritta Baldauf
Pertti Ervi
Matti Heikkonen
Juho Malmberg
Anu Nissinen

U.S. Subsidiary:

F-Secure Inc. **(1)**
100 Century Center Ct Ste 700
San Jose, CA 95112
Tel.: (408) 938-6700
Fax: (408) 350-2339
Web Site: www.f-secure.com
Emp.: 25
Software Encryption & Security Services
S.I.C.: 7371
N.A.I.C.S.: 541511

Non-U.S. Subsidiaries:

F-Secure AB **(1)**
Gardsvaegen 18
16970 Solna, Sweden
Mailing Address:
PO Box 717
16927 Solna, Sweden
Tel.: (46) 850744000
Fax: (46) 850744001
E-Mail: info@f-secure.se
Web Site: www.f-secure.se
Emp.: 20
Software Encryption & Security Services
S.I.C.: 7371
N.A.I.C.S.: 541511
David Traed *(Country Mgr)*

F-Secure Australia Pty Ltd **(1)**
Suite 09 Level 8 100 Walker Street
North Sydney, NSW, 2060, Australia
Tel.: (61) 284044192
Fax: (61) 28404 4170
E-Mail: australia@f-secure.com
Security Software Development Services
S.I.C.: 7371
N.A.I.C.S.: 541511

F-Secure Belgie **(1)**
Interleuvenlaan 62 Zone 2 Bus 56
3001 Leuven, Belgium
Tel.: (32) 16394735
Web Site: www.f-secure.be
Emp.: 2
Security Software Development Services
S.I.C.: 7371
N.A.I.C.S.: 541511

F-Secure BV BA **(1)**
Interleuvenlaan 62 Zone 2 Bus 56
Heverlee, Leuven, 3001, Belgium
Tel.: (32) 16394735
Fax: (32) 16 39 47 37
Software Development Services
S.I.C.: 7371
N.A.I.C.S.: 541511

F-Secure Corporation **(1)**
Nydalsveien 33
0484 Oslo, Norway
Tel.: (47) 21520062
Fax: (47) 21520010
Web Site: www.fsecure.com
Emp.: 1
Software Encryption & Security Services
S.I.C.: 7371
N.A.I.C.S.: 541511

F-Secure Corporation **(1)**
Via Giovanni da Udine 34
21056 Milan, Italy
Tel.: (39) 0238093590
Fax: (39) 0238093591
E-Mail: italy@f-secure.com
Web Site: www.f-secure.com
Software Encryption & Security Services
S.I.C.: 7371
N.A.I.C.S.: 541511

F-Secure Corporation **(1)**
Ul Prusa 2
00-493 Warsaw, Poland
Tel.: (48) 226570112
Fax: (48) 226570111
Software Encryption & Security Services
S.I.C.: 7371
N.A.I.C.S.: 541511

F-Secure Danmark A/S **(1)**
International House Center Boulevard 5
2300 Copenhagen, Denmark
Tel.: (45) 32473347
Web Site: www.f-secure.com
Emp.: 4
Software Development Services
S.I.C.: 7371
N.A.I.C.S.: 541511

F-Secure GmbH **(1)**
Ganhoferstrasse 29 A
80339 Munich, Germany
Tel.: (49) 8978746700
Fax: (49) 8978746799
E-Mail: germany@f-secure.com
Web Site: www.f-secure.de
Emp.: 15
Software Encryption & Security Services
S.I.C.: 7371
N.A.I.C.S.: 541511
Christian Fredrikson *(Pres)*

F-Secure India Pvt Ltd **(1)**
Office No 117 6-3-1192/1/1 Block 2 212 2nd Fl White House Kundanbagh
Begumpe, Hyderabad, 500016, India
Tel.: (91) 4040133503
Fax: (91) 4040133506
Web Site: www.f-secure.co.in
Security Software Development Services
S.I.C.: 7371
N.A.I.C.S.: 541511
Mahindar Kaur *(Office Mgr)*

F-Secure Malaysia (M) Sdn Bhd **(1)**
Block 3A Horizon Bangsar S No 8 Jalan Kerinchi
59200 Kuala Lumpur, Malaysia
Tel.: (60) 322640200
Fax: (60) 322640299
Web Site: www.f-secure.com
Emp.: 200
Security Software Development Services
S.I.C.: 7371
N.A.I.C.S.: 541511
Ingvar Froiland *(Mng Dir)*

F-Secure Norge **(1)**
Fresjrveen 40
0638 Oslo, Norway
Tel.: (47) 21 52 00 62
Software Development Services
S.I.C.: 7371
N.A.I.C.S.: 541511
Eroels Christensen *(Gen Mgr)*

F-Secure Pte Ltd **(1)**
21 Science Park Road 02-01 The Aquarius
Singapore, 117628, Singapore
Tel.: (65) 81184552
Fax: (65) 22640299
E-Mail: singapore@f-secure.com
Security Software Development Consulting Services
S.I.C.: 8999
N.A.I.C.S.: 541690

F-Secure SARL **(1)**
3 rue Gustave Eiffel
Espace Media - Le Technoparc, 78306
Poissy, Cedex, France
Tel.: (33) 139226419
Fax: (33) 153304161
E-Mail: france@f-secure.com
Web Site: www.f-secure.de
Emp.: 10
Software Encryption & Security Services
S.I.C.: 7371
N.A.I.C.S.: 541511

F-Secure SDC SAS **(1)**
9 Rue Raymond Manaud
33520 Bruges, France
Tel.: (33) 557924720
Fax: (33) 556976422
Emp.: 80
Security Software Development Services
S.I.C.: 7371
N.A.I.C.S.: 541511

F-Secure Sp.z.o.o. **(1)**
Ul Hrubieszowska 6a
01-209 Warsaw, Poland
Tel.: (48) 22 431 82 21
Fax: (48) 22 431 82 20
Web Site: www.f-secure.pl
Emp.: 6
Security Software Development Services
S.I.C.: 7371
N.A.I.C.S.: 541511
Michal Iwan *(Country Mgr)*

F-Secure (UK) Ltd **(1)**
Mercury Park Wycombe Lane
Wooburn Green, High Wycombe, Bucks, HP10 0HH, United Kingdom
Tel.: (44) 8458903300
Fax: (44) 8458903301
E-Mail: uk@f-secure.com
Web Site: www.f-secure.co.uk
Emp.: 15
Software Encryption & Security Services
S.I.C.: 7371
N.A.I.C.S.: 541511

F-TECH INC.

19 Showa-numa Shobu-Cho
Saitama, 346-0194, Japan
Tel.: (81) 480855211
Fax: (81) 480855219
E-Mail: webmaster@ftech.co.jp
Web Site: www.ftech.co.jp
Year Founded: 1947
7212—(TKS)
Sls.: $429,341,000
Assets: $413,017,000
Liabilities: $333,927,000
Net Worth: $79,090,000
Earnings: ($48,114,000)
Emp.: 5,397
Fiscal Year-end: 03/31/13

Business Description:
Automotive Parts, Related Dies, Machinery & Equipment Mfr & Sales
S.I.C.: 3714
N.A.I.C.S.: 336390

Personnel:
Tsuguo Kimura *(Pres & COO)*
Kenichi Ando *(Sr Operating Officer-North America)*
Yuichi Fukuda *(Sr Mng Operating Officer-Japan)*
Yoshinori Furusawa *(Sr Operating Officer-R&D)*
Makoto Hasegawa *(Sr Operating Officer-Sls & Mktg Div)*
Mamoru Sotoyama *(Sr Operating Officer-Asia & Oceania)*
Shigeharu Tobita *(Sr Operating Officer-China)*
Takefumi Toyoshima *(Sr Mng Operating Officer)*

Board of Directors:
Hajime Fujitaki
Akihide Fukuda
Yuichi Fukuda
Tsuguo Kimura
Noriyuki Miyaoka
Masao Toyoda
Takefumi Toyoshima

Transfer Agent:
The Chuo Mitsui Trust & Banking Company Limited
3-33-1 Shiba Minato-ku
Tokyo, Japan

Subsidiaries:

Fukuda Engineering Co., Ltd. **(1)**
3206-3 Koguki
Kazo, Saitama, 347-0111, Japan
Tel.: (81) 480 70 1171
Fax: (81) 480 70 1295
Dies & Die Component Mfr
S.I.C.: 3544
N.A.I.C.S.: 333514

Kyushu F-Tech Inc. **(1)**
4455 Oaza Kubaru
Yamagata, Kumamoto, Japan
Tel.: (81) 968445116
Fax: (81) 968445117
Web Site: www.ftech.co.jp/en/profile/profile_05_n.html
Emp.: 100
Dies & Die Component Mfr
S.I.C.: 3544
N.A.I.C.S.: 333514

Reterra Co., Ltd **(1)**
2703 Ryokamisusuki Ogano-machi
Chichibu-gun, Saitama, 368-0201, Japan
Tel.: (81) 494 79 1300
Fax: (81) 494 79 1305
Web Site: www.reterra.co.jp
Sls.: $5,030,640
Emp.: 215
Automotive Aluminum Die Casting Parts Mfr
S.I.C.: 3714
N.A.I.C.S.: 336390
Hiroaki Fukushima *(CEO)*

Plants:

F-Tech Inc - Kuki Plant **(1)**
19 Showa-numa Shobu-Cho
Kuki, Saitama, Japan
Tel.: (81) 480 85 5215
Fax: (81) 480 855211
Emp.: 350
Automobile Parts Mfr
S.I.C.: 3714
N.A.I.C.S.: 336390
Tsugo Kimura *(Pres)*

F-Tech Inc. - Kameyama Plant **(1)**
395-43 Sagiyama Shiraki-cho
Kameyama, Mie, Japan 519-0169
Tel.: (81) 595 83 2111
Fax: (81) 595 83 2110
Web Site: www.ftech.co.jp/en/profile/profile_04_n.html
Automobile Parts Mfr
S.I.C.: 3714
N.A.I.C.S.: 336390

F-Tech Inc. - Kameyama Wada Plant **(1)**
1370-2 Wada-cho
Kameyama, Mie, Japan
Tel.: (81) 595823321
Fax: (81) 595823325
Precision Machining Tools Mfr
S.I.C.: 3451
N.A.I.C.S.: 332721

U.S. Subsidiaries:

F&P America Mfg., Inc. **(1)**
2101 Corporate Dr
Troy, OH 45373
Tel.: (937) 339-0212
Fax: (937) 339-0065
Web Site: www.fandp.com
Emp.: 600
Automotive Parts Mfr
S.I.C.: 3714
N.A.I.C.S.: 336390
David Harrison *(Mng Dir)*

F&P Georgia Mfg., Inc. **(1)**
88 Enterprise Dr
Rome, GA 30161
Tel.: (706) 291-7550
Fax: (706) 291-7756
E-Mail: info@fandp.com
Web Site: www.fandp.com
Emp.: 375
Automotive Parts Mfr
S.I.C.: 3714

N.A.I.C.S.: 336390
Makoto Hasegawa *(Pres & COO)*

F.tech R&D North America Inc (1)
1191 Horizon West Ct
Troy, OH 45373
Tel.: (937) 339-2777
Fax: (937) 339-4742
Web Site: www.ftech.co.jp/en/profile/profile_06_n.html#4
Emp.: 43
Automotive Component Mfr
S.I.C.: 3714
N.A.I.C.S.: 336320
Takefumi Toyoshima *(Pres & COO)*

Non-U.S. Subsidiaries:

DYNA-MIG Mfg. of Stratford Inc. (1)
275 Wright Blvd
PO Box 1123
Stratford, ON, N5A 7Y1, Canada
Tel.: (519) 272-2188
Fax: (519) 272-0180
E-Mail: info@dynamig.com
Web Site: www.dynamig.com
Emp.: 275
Automotive Parts Mfr
S.I.C.: 3714
N.A.I.C.S.: 336390

F&P Mfg. Inc. (1)
1 Nolan Road
Tottenham, ON, L0G 1W0, Canada
Tel.: (905) 936-3435
Fax: (905) 936-4809
Web Site: www.fandpmfg.com
Emp.: 600
Automotive Parts Mfr
S.I.C.: 3714
N.A.I.C.S.: 336390
Kenichi Ando *(Pres)*

F-tech Philippines Mfg., Inc. (1)
118 N Science Ave
Laguna Technopark, Binan, Philippines
Tel.: (63) 28454001
Fax: (63) 28454003
E-Mail: m.toyoda@f-tech.com.ph
Web Site: www.ftech.com.ph
Emp.: 530
Automotive Parts Mfr
S.I.C.: 3714
N.A.I.C.S.: 336390
Masahiro Toyoda *(Pres & COO)*

F-Tech Zhongshan Inc. (1)
Torch Road Zhongshan Torch Hi-Tech Industrial Development Zone
Zhongshan, Guangdong, China
Tel.: (86) 76085335336
Fax: (86) 760 8533 5007
Web Site: www.ftech.co.jp/en/profile/profile_06_n.html
Automotive Parts Mfr
S.I.C.: 3714
N.A.I.C.S.: 336390

F.E.G. DE QUERETARO S.A. DE C.V (1)
Cerrada de La Noria No 106 Parque Industrial Queretaro
Queretaro, 76220, Mexico
Tel.: (52) 442 229 5100
Fax: (52) 442 229 5103
E-Mail: ventas-mx@fegq.com.mx
Web Site: www.fegq.com.mx
Stamping Parts Mfr
S.I.C.: 3465
N.A.I.C.S.: 336370

F.tech Mfg. (Thailand) Ltd. (1)
99 Moo 3 Tambon Banchang Amphur U-Thai
Ayutthaya, Thailand
Tel.: (66) 3574 6700
Fax: (66) 3574 6710
Web Site: www.ftech.co.jp/en/profile/profile_06_n.html#4
Dies & Die Component Mfr
S.I.C.: 3544
N.A.I.C.S.: 333514

F.tech R&D Philippines Inc (1)
123 North Science Avenue Laguna Technopark
Binan, Laguna, Philippines
Tel.: (63) 25844150
Fax: (63) 25844151
Web Site: www.ftech.co.jp/en/profile/profile_06_n.html#4
Automobile Parts Mfr
S.I.C.: 3714
N.A.I.C.S.: 336390
Maelene Gegarcia *(Gen Mgr)*

F.tech Wuhan Inc. (1)
The Fifth Road Of Gaoqiao
Dongxihu District, Wuhan, Hubei, China
Tel.: (86) 2783068806
Fax: (86) 27 8306 8846
Automobile Parts Mfr
S.I.C.: 3714
N.A.I.C.S.: 336390

F24 AG

Frauenplatz 5
80331 Munich, Germany
Tel.: (49) 89 23236380
Fax: (49) 89 23236386
E-Mail: office@f24.com
Web Site: www.f24.com
Year Founded: 2000
F2Y—(DEU)
Sls.: $6,891,044
Assets: $3,450,234
Liabilities: $620,584
Net Worth: $2,829,649
Earnings: $1,126,744
Emp.: 27
Fiscal Year-end: 12/31/12

Business Description:
Application Service Providers
S.I.C.: 7374
N.A.I.C.S.: 518210

Personnel:
Ralf Meister *(Co-Founder & Chm-Mgmt Bd)*
Christian Gotz *(Co-Founder & Member-Mgmt Bd-Sls, Mktg, PR & HR)*
Rainer Genes *(Chm-Supervisory Bd)*
Karl Schopfel *(Vice Chm-Supervisory Bd)*
Sabine Riess *(PR Officer)*
Jochen Schutte *(Member-Mgmt Bd-Product Mgmt, IT Dev & Ops)*

Supervisory Board of Directors:
Rainer Genes
Oliver Hackl
Karl Schopfel

U.S. Subsidiary:

F24 United States, Inc. (1)
1330 Avenue of the Americas Ste 23A
New York, NY 10019
Tel.: (212) 653-0948
Fax: (212) 653-0950
E-Mail: office_us@f24.com
Emp.: 4
Software Development Services
S.I.C.: 7371
N.A.I.C.S.: 541511
Robert F. Mattes *(Mng Dir)*

Non-U.S. Subsidiaries:

F24 Czech Republic s.r.o. (1)
Vaclavske nam 19/832
110 00 Prague, Czech Republic
Tel.: (420) 234 656 124
Fax: (420) 234 656 138
E-Mail: office_cz@f24.com
Security Alert & Crisis Management Services
S.I.C.: 7382
N.A.I.C.S.: 561621
Michael Funk, *(Mng Dir)*

F24 France SARL (1)
60 Avenue Charles de Gaulle CS 60016
92573 Neuilly-sur-Seine, Cedex, France
Tel.: (33) 1 72 74 55 07
Fax: (33) 1 72 92 05 99
E-Mail: commercial-fr@f24.com
Emp.: 2
Security Alert & Crisis Management Services
S.I.C.: 7382
N.A.I.C.S.: 561621
David Ebel, *(Mng Dir)*

F24 SERVICIOS DE COMUNICACION, S.L.U. (1)
Edif Atica 5 planta 2 Avda Europa 26
Pozuelo de Alarcon, 28224 Madrid, Spain
Tel.: (34) 911 845 925
Fax: (34) 913 511 858
E-Mail: oficina@f24.com
Emp.: 4
Security Alert & Crisis Management Services
S.I.C.: 7382
N.A.I.C.S.: 561621
Juan Manuel Gil Bote, *(Mng Dir)*

F2I SGR SPA

Via San Prospero 1
20121 Milan, Italy
Tel.: (39) 0272179200
Fax: (39) 0272179222
E-Mail: segreteria@f2isgr.it
Web Site: www.f2isgr.it

Business Description:
Infrastructure Investment Services
S.I.C.: 6211
N.A.I.C.S.: 523999

Personnel:
Ettore Gotti Tedeschi *(Chm)*
Vito A. Gamberale *(CEO)*
Carlo Michelini *(Sr Partner)*
Marcello Garolla di Bard *(Sr Partner-Ops)*
Matteo Ambroggio *(Partner)*
Laura Pascotto *(Partner)*
Corrado Santini *(Partner)*

Board of Directors:
Ettore Gotti Tedeschi
Alfredo Checchetto
Vito A. Gamberale
Francesco Lorenzetti
Angelo Maglietta
Davide Mereghetti
Maurizio Pagani
Marco Parlangeli
Vittorio Pignatti Morano
Fausto Savoldi
Maurizio Tamagnini

Subsidiary:

Metroweb S.p.A. (1)
Viale Certosa 2
20155 Milan, Italy (58.8%)
Tel.: (39) 02 7720 1
E-Mail: info@metroweb.it
Web Site: www.metroweb.it
Sales Range: $50-74.9 Million
Emp.: 47
Fiber Optical Network
S.I.C.: 4812
N.A.I.C.S.: 517210
Alberto Trondoli *(CEO)*
Moreno Grassi *(COO)*

FA. ANTON SCHLECKER

Talstrasse 12
D 89579 Ehingen, Germany
Tel.: (49) 73915840
Fax: (49) 73915843
E-Mail: info@schlecker.com
Web Site: www.schlecker.com
Year Founded: 1975
Emp.: 52,000

Business Description:
Discount Drug Stores & Internet Shopping Services
S.I.C.: 5999
N.A.I.C.S.: 453998

Personnel:
Anton Schlecker *(CEO)*

FAB-FORM INDUSTRIES LTD.

Unit 212 6333 148th Street
Surrey, BC, V3S 3C3, Canada
Tel.: (604) 596-3278
Toll Free: (888) 303-3278
E-Mail: info@fab-form.com
Web Site: www.fab-form.com
Year Founded: 1995
FBF—(TSXV)
Sls.: $381,351
Assets: $222,077
Liabilities: $217,068
Net Worth: $5,009
Earnings: $6,051
Fiscal Year-end: 12/31/12

Business Description:
Building Structures Related Services
S.I.C.: 1799
N.A.I.C.S.: 238190

Personnel:
Herbert Bentz *(Chm & CFO)*
Richard N. Fearn *(Pres & CEO)*

Board of Directors:
Herbert Bentz
Bruce Clark
Richard N. Fearn
Chris Mattock

Subsidiary:

Fab-Form Industries (1986) Ltd. (1)
Unit 19 1610 Derwent Way
Delta, BC, V3M 6W1, Canada
Tel.: (604) 596-3278
Toll Free: (888) 303-3278
E-Mail: info@fab-form.com
Web Site: www.fab-form.com
Emp.: 4
Fabricated Concrete Products Mfr
S.I.C.: 3272
N.A.I.C.S.: 327390
Richard Fearn *(Office Mgr)*

FABASOFT AG

Honauerstrase 4
4020 Linz, Austria
Tel.: (43) 7326061620
Fax: (43) 732606162609
E-Mail: office@fabasoft.com
Web Site: www.fabasoft.com
FAA—(DEU)
Rev.: $31,159,797
Assets: $37,237,755
Liabilities: $18,842,341
Net Worth: $18,395,413
Earnings: $354,043
Emp.: 204
Fiscal Year-end: 03/31/13

Business Description:
Software Services
S.I.C.: 7371
N.A.I.C.S.: 541511

Personnel:
Friedrich Roithmayr *(Chm-Supervisory Bd)*
Leopold Bauernfeind *(Member-Mgmt Bd)*
Helmut Fallmann *(Member-Mgmt Bd)*

Supervisory Board of Directors:
Friedrich Roithmayr
Peter Posch
Helmut Schutzeneder
Hans Spitzner

FABBRICA D'ARMI PIETRO BERETTA S.P.A.

Via Pietro Beretta 18
I 25063 Brescia, Gardone Val Trompia, Italy
Tel.: (39) 3083411
Telex: 301523 PB BS I
Fax: (39) 0308341421
E-Mail: info@beretta.com
Web Site: www.beretta.com
Year Founded: 1526
Sales Range: $350-399.9 Million
Emp.: 2,000

Business Description:
Mfr of Firearms & Knives
S.I.C.: 3489
N.A.I.C.S.: 332994

Personnel:
Ugo Gussalli Beretta *(Pres)*

Fabbrica D'Armi Pietro Beretta S.p.A.—(Continued)

Subsidiaries:

Benelli Armi S.p.A. **(1)**
Via della Stazione 50
61029 Urbino, PU, Italy
Tel.: (39) 07223071
Fax: (39) 0722307206
E-Mail: lporreca@benelli.it
Web Site: www.benelli.it
Emp.: 140
Mfr. of Fire Arms
S.I.C.: 3489
N.A.I.C.S.: 332994
Mauro Dellacostanza *(Mng Dir)*

Beretta Holding S.p.A. **(1)**
Via P Beretta 18
25063 Gardone Val Trompia, Italy (100%)
Tel.: (39) 03083411
Fax: (39) 0308341212
Holding Company
S.I.C.: 6719
N.A.I.C.S.: 551112

U.S. Subsidiary:

Benelli USA Corporation **(2)**
17603 Indian Head Hwy Ste 200
Accokeek, MD 20607 (100%)
Tel.: (301) 283-6981
Fax: (301) 283-6988
Toll Free: (800) 264-4962
E-Mail: info@benelliusa.com
Web Site: www.benelliusa.com
Emp.: 66
Mfr. & Supplier of Firearms & Accessories
S.I.C.: 5099
N.A.I.C.S.: 423990
Greg Mooney *(VP & Gen Mgr)*

Subsidiaries:

Stoeger Industries Inc. **(3)**
17603 Indian Head Hwy
Accokeek, MD 20607 (100%)
Tel.: (301) 283-6300
Fax: (301) 283-6988
E-Mail: krandall@benelliusa.com
Web Site: www.stoegerindustries.com
Sls.: $15,000,000
Emp.: 13
Firearms Mfr
S.I.C.: 3484
N.A.I.C.S.: 332994

U.S. Subsidiary:

Beretta U.S.A. Corp. **(1)**
17601 Beretta Dr
Accokeek, MD 20607-9515 (100%)
Tel.: (301) 283-2191
Telex: 829729 BERETTA ACKK
Fax: (301) 283-0435
Toll Free: (800) 636-3420
E-Mail: email@berettausa.com
Web Site: www.berettausa.com
Emp.: 400
Mfr. of Firearms
S.I.C.: 3489
N.A.I.C.S.: 332994

Non-U.S. Subsidiary:

Sako Ltd. **(1)**
P O Box 149
Riihimaki, FI-11101, Finland (100%)
Tel.: (358) 10 830 5200
Fax: (358) 19 720 446
E-Mail: export@sako.fi
Web Site: www.sako.fi
Sales Range: $25-49.9 Million
Emp.: 250
Firearms Mfr
S.I.C.: 3489
N.A.I.C.S.: 332994

FABBRICA ITALIANA LAPIS ED AFFINI S.P.A.

(d/b/a F.I.L.A.)
Via 25 Aprile 5
20016 Pero, Italy
Tel.: (39) 2381051
Fax: (39) 023538546
E-Mail: info@fila.it
Web Site: www.fila.it
Emp.: 380

Business Description:
Pens & Pencils Mfr & Distr
S.I.C.: 3579
N.A.I.C.S.: 339940
Personnel:
Massimo Candela *(Chm & CEO)*

U.S. Subsidiary:

Dixon Ticonderoga Company **(1)**
195 International Pkwy
Heathrow, FL 32746-5007 DE
Tel.: (407) 829-9000
Fax: (407) 829-2574
Toll Free: (800) 824-9430
E-Mail: info@dixonticonderoga.com
Web Site: www.dixonticonderoga.com
Sales Range: $75-99.9 Million
Emp.: 45
Writing & Drawing Materials Mfr & Marketer
Import Export
S.I.C.: 3579
N.A.I.C.S.: 339940
Lillian Gonzales *(Dir-HR)*

Non-U.S. Subsidiaries:

Dixon Europe, Ltd. **(2)**
23 Maxwell Rd
Peterborough, PE2 7JD, United Kingdom UK
Tel.: (44) 733371237
Fax: (44) 733371666
Web Site: www.Dixoneurope.com
Emp.: 25
Stationary & Office Supplies Whslr
S.I.C.: 5112
N.A.I.C.S.: 453210
Tiovinni Colombo *(Mng Dir)*

Dixon Ticonderoga de Mexico, S.A. de C.V. **(2)**
Autopista Mexico-Queretaro 104
Tultitlan, 54940, Mexico MX
Tel.: (52) 5558647900
Fax: (52) 5558647901
E-Mail: rherrera@dixonmexico.com
Web Site: www.dixon.com.mx
Emp.: 60
Writing Instruments Mfr & Sales
S.I.C.: 3579
N.A.I.C.S.: 339940
Diego Cespedes Creixell *(CEO)*

Dixon Ticonderoga Inc. **(2)**
210 Pony Dr Unit 1
Newmarket, ON, L3Y7B6, Canada
Tel.: (905) 895-5122
Fax: (905) 895-9555
Web Site: www.prang.com
Sales Range: $1-9.9 Million
Emp.: 13
Pencils Mfr & Distr
S.I.C.: 3579
N.A.I.C.S.: 339940

FABCHEM CHINA LIMITED

2 Bukit Merah Central 12-03
Singapore, 159835, Singapore
Tel.: (65) 62655918
Fax: (65) 62682447
E-Mail: ir@fabchemchina.com
Web Site: www.fabchemchina.com
I54—(SES)
Rev.: $77,690,517
Assets: $111,339,077
Liabilities: $38,206,284
Net Worth: $73,132,793
Earnings: $5,005,046
Fiscal Year-end: 03/31/13

Business Description:
Boosters Mfr
S.I.C.: 3483
N.A.I.C.S.: 332993
Personnel:
Bowen Sun *(Mng Dir)*
Min-Li Tan *(Sec)*
Board of Directors:
Seck Yeow Lim
Simon Hunter Atkinson
Hongwei Bao
Peter Neville Hogan
Rongguang Jiang
Frankie Manuel Mlcallef
Desmond Tai Tiong Ong
Bowen Sun
Phui Gam Wee
Transfer Agent:
Boardroom Corporate & Advisory Services Pte. Ltd.
50 Raffles Place 32-01 Singapore Land Tower
Singapore, Singapore

Non-U.S. Subsidiary:

Shandong Yinguang Technology Co., Ltd. **(1)**
No 1 Huagong Road
Feixian County, Linyi, Shandong, China
Tel.: (86) 5395039767
Fax: (86) 5395039001
E-Mail: yinguang@163169.net
Web Site: www.sdyg.cc
Explosives Mfr
S.I.C.: 2892
N.A.I.C.S.: 325920

FABEGE AB

Pyramidvagen 7
169 56 Solna, Sweden
Tel.: (46) 855514800
Fax: (46) 855514801
E-Mail: info@fabege.se
Web Site: www.fabege.se
FABG—(OMX OTC)
Rev.: $289,321,200
Assets: $5,218,153,200
Liabilities: $3,452,814,000
Net Worth: $1,765,339,200
Earnings: ($13,622,400)
Emp.: 129
Fiscal Year-end: 12/31/12

Business Description:
Real Estate Agents & Brokerage Services
S.I.C.: 6531
N.A.I.C.S.: 531210
Personnel:
Erik Paulsson *(Chm)*
Christian Hermelin *(CEO)*
Asa Bergstrom *(Deputy CEO & CFO)*
Board of Directors:
Erik Paulsson
Eva Eriksson
Christian Hermelin
Gustaf Hermelin
Martha Josefsson
Par Nuder
Svante Paulsson
Mats Qviberg

Subsidiary:

Fastighets AB Tornet **(1)**
Djaknegatan 23
211 35 Malmo, Sweden (82.4%)
Tel.: (46) 6142680
E-Mail: info@tornet.se
Web Site: www.tornet.se
Emp.: 146
Real Estate Properties Purchase & Acquisition Services
S.I.C.: 6531
N.A.I.C.S.: 531390
Erik Paulsson *(Chm)*
Christian Hermelin *(CEO)*
Roger Johansson *(CFO & Exec VP)*
Anders Hoernqvist *(Exec VP)*

FABER-CASTELL AG

Nuernberger Strasse 2
90546 Stein, Germany
Tel.: (49) 91199650
Fax: (49) 9119965856
E-Mail: info@faber-castell.de
Web Site: www.faber-castell.com
Year Founded: 1761
Sales Range: $350-399.9 Million
Emp.: 5,500

Business Description:
Writing Instruments Mfr
S.I.C.: 3579
N.A.I.C.S.: 339940
Personnel:
Anton Wolfgang von Faber-Castell *(Chm & CEO)*
Antonio C. Perondi *(Mng Dir)*
Yan P. Toh *(Mng Dir)*
Michael Boy *(CFO)*

U.S. Subsidiary:

A.W. Faber-Castell USA Inc **(1)**
9450 Allen Dr
Cleveland, OH 44125
Tel.: (216) 643-4660
Fax: (216) 643-4664
Web Site: www.fabercastell.com
Emp.: 60
Pens Producer
S.I.C.: 3579
N.A.I.C.S.: 339940
Jamie Gallagher *(CEO)*

Non-U.S. Subsidiary:

A.W. Faber-Castell Italia S.r.l. **(1)**
Via Stromboli 14
I-20144 Milan, Italy
Tel.: (39) 02 430 696 01
Fax: (39) 02481 45 66
E-Mail: marketing@faber-castell.it
Web Site: www.faber-castell.it
Quality Writing Tools Mfr & Distr
S.I.C.: 3579
N.A.I.C.S.: 339940

FABER GROUP BERHAD

20th Floor Menara 2 Faber Towers
Jalan Desa Bahagia Taman Desa,
58100 Kuala Lumpur, Malaysia
Tel.: (60) 376282888
Fax: (60) 376282828
E-Mail: info@fabergroup.com.my
Web Site: www.fabergroup.com.my
Year Founded: 1963
FABER—(KLS)
Rev.: $290,628,938
Assets: $313,759,103
Liabilities: $110,347,048
Net Worth: $203,412,055
Earnings: $48,346,557
Emp.: 7,200
Fiscal Year-end: 12/31/12

Business Description:
Holding Company; Hotels; Real Estate; Health Care
S.I.C.: 6719
N.A.I.C.S.: 551112
Personnel:
Adnan Mohammad *(Mng Dir)*
Juliza Jalil *(CFO)*
A. Hamid A. Rahman *(CEO-Faber Medi-Serve Sdn Bhd)*
Riad Ahmad Ramzi *(CEO-Faber LLC)*
Suriati Ashari *(Sec & Head-Legal)*
Board of Directors:
Ikmal Hijaz Hashim
Abdullah Sani Abd Karim
Azmir Merican Azmi Merican
Suhaimi Halim
Mohd Izzaddin Idris
Saimy Ismail
Elakumari Kantilal
Adnan Mohammad
Kim Sun Oh
Robert Bun Poo Tan

Subsidiaries:

Faber Development Holdings Sdn Bhd **(1)**
19th Floor Menara 2 Faber Tower
Jalan Desa Bahagia Tun Desa, 58100 Kuala Lumpur, Malaysia
Tel.: (60) 376282888
Fax: (60) 376205105
E-Mail:
Web Site: www.fabergroup.com
Emp.: 120
Subdividers & Developers
S.I.C.: 6552
N.A.I.C.S.: 237210

Subsidiaries:

Country View Development Sdn Bhd (2)
168 1st Floor Wisma Cosway
Jalan Raja Chulan, 50200 Kuala Lumpur, Malaysia
Tel.: (60) 321456377
Emp.: 50
Subdivider & Developer
S.I.C.: 6552
N.A.I.C.S.: 237210

Rimbunan Melati Sdn. Bhd (2)
Lot 112 1st Floor Faber Towers Jln Desa Bahagia Taman Desa
58100 Kuala Lumpur, Malaysia
Tel.: (60) 3 7628 2833
Fax: (60) 3 7620 5106
Property Management Services
S.I.C.: 6531
N.A.I.C.S.: 531311

Faber Grandview Development (Sabah) Sdn Bhd (2)
20th Floor Menara 2 Faber Tower
Jalan Desa Bahagia Tmn Desa, 58100 Kuala Lumpur, Malaysia
Tel.: (60) 379 838 855
Subdividers & Developers
S.I.C.: 6552
N.A.I.C.S.: 237210

Faber Heights Management Sdn Bhd (2)
20th Floor Menara 2 Faber Tower
Jalan Desa Bahagia Tmn Desa, 58100 Kuala Lumpur, Malaysia
Tel.: (60) 379838855
Subdividers & Developers
S.I.C.: 6552
N.A.I.C.S.: 237210

Faber Union Sdn Bhd (2)
20th Fl Menara 2 Faber Tower
Jalan Desa Bahagia Tmn Desa, 58100 Kuala Lumpur, Malaysia
Tel.: (60) 376282888
Fax: (60) 376282828
Web Site: www.fabergroup.com
Emp.: 126
Subdividers & Developers
S.I.C.: 6552
N.A.I.C.S.: 237210
Khalid Abdul Majid *(Gen Mgr)*

Faber Facilities Sdn. Bhd. (1)
19th Floor Faber Tower Menara 2 Jalan Desa Bahagia Taman Desa
Kuala Lumpur, 58100, Malaysia
Tel.: (60) 376282888
Fax: (60) 376255722
Web Site: www.faberfacilities.com.my
Emp.: 150
Property Management Services
S.I.C.: 6531
N.A.I.C.S.: 531311
Adnan Mohamad *(Mng Dir)*

Faber Healthcare Management Sdn Bhd (1)
18 Jalan 4/109E Desa Business Park
Tmn Desa off Jalan Klang Lama, 58100 Kuala Lumpur, Malaysia
Tel.: (60) 379838855
Holding Company; Health Services
S.I.C.: 6719
N.A.I.C.S.: 551112

Subsidiary:

Faber Medi-Serve Sdn Bhd (2)
10th Floor Menara 2 Faber Tower
Jalan Desa Bahagia, 58100 Kuala Lumpur, Malaysia
Tel.: (60) 376 215 593
Web Site: www.fabergroup.com.my/contacts.html#
Health & Allied Services
S.I.C.: 8099
N.A.I.C.S.: 621999

Subsidiary:

Healthtronics (M) Sdn. Bhd. (3)
Suite P3-03 Building Information Centre Lot 2 Jalan 51a 243
Petaling Jaya, 46100, Malaysia
Tel.: (60) 376252525
Fax: (60) 376252828
E-Mail: info@healthtronics.com.my
Web Site: www.healthtronics.com.my
Emp.: 50
Healthcare Management Services
S.I.C.: 8099
N.A.I.C.S.: 621999
Salleh Tahir *(CEO)*

FABREL AG

Seestrasse 50
6052 Hergiswil, Switzerland
Tel.: (41) 41 632 68 58
Fax: (41) 6326840
Business Description:
Holding Company
S.I.C.: 6719
N.A.I.C.S.: 551112
Personnel:
Hans Muller-Meier *(Mng Partner & Pres)*
Board of Directors:
Jacobi Michael
Marc Muller
Rudolf Muller
Hans Muller-Meier

Subsidiary:

Fabrel Lotos AG (1)
Seestrasse 50
CH 6052 Hergiswil, Switzerland CH
Tel.: (41) 41 632 68 52
Fax: (41) 41 632 68 40
E-Mail: postmaster@fabrellotos.ch
Web Site: www.fabrellotos.ch
Sales Range: $25-49.9 Million
Emp.: 100
Private Equity Firm
S.I.C.: 6211
N.A.I.C.S.: 523999
Martin Maeder *(Mng Partner)*
Juerg Muffler *(Partner)*
Hans-Ulrich von Weissenfluh *(Partner)*

Holding:

Buss AG (2)
Hohenrainstrasse 10
4133 Pratteln, Switzerland
Tel.: (41) 618256600
Fax: (41) 618256688
E-Mail: info@busscorp.com
Web Site: www.busscorp.com
Emp.: 220
Engineering & Machinery for Chemicals & Plastics Plants
S.I.C.: 3589
N.A.I.C.S.: 333318
Marco Senoner *(Mgr-Corp Comm)*

FABRICA DE TECIDOS CARLOS RENAUX S.A.

Av Primeiro de Maio 1283 Centro CP 10
88353-901 Brusque, SC, Brazil
Tel.: (55) 47 3351 0922
Fax: (55) 47 3351 2979
E-Mail: renaux@renaux.com.br
Web Site: www.renaux.com.br
Year Founded: 1892
FTRX3—(BRAZ)
Business Description:
Apparel Fabric Mfr
S.I.C.: 2399
N.A.I.C.S.: 315990
Personnel:
Jorge Paulo Krieger Filho *(Dir-IR)*

FABRIKA MAZIVA FAM A.D. KRUSEVAC

Jug Bogdanova 42 Pos Fah 78
37 000 Krusevac, Serbia
Tel.: (381) 37 422 078
Fax: (381) 37 438 809
E-Mail: office@fam.co.rs
Web Site: www.fam.co.rs
FAMKR—(BEL)
Business Description:
Lubricant Product Mfr
S.I.C.: 2992
N.A.I.C.S.: 324191
Personnel:
Vladica Petrovic *(Mng Dir)*

FABRYKA FARB I LAKIEROW SNIEZKA S.A.

Lubzina 34a
39-102 Lubzina, Poland
Tel.: (48) 146811111
Fax: (48) 146822222
E-Mail: sekretariat@sniezka.com
Web Site: www.sniezka.pl
SKA—(WAR)
Rev.: $182,832,105
Assets: $111,446,776
Liabilities: $46,330,156
Net Worth: $65,116,620
Earnings: $15,048,136
Emp.: 976
Fiscal Year-end: 12/31/12
Business Description:
Paints & Varnishes Mfr
S.I.C.: 2851
N.A.I.C.S.: 325510
Personnel:
Stanislaw Mikrut *(Chm-Supervisory Bd)*
Piotr Mikrut *(Chm-Mgmt Bd)*
Jerzy Pater *(Vice Chm-Supervisory Bd)*
Witold Wasko *(Vice Chm-Mgmt Bd & Dir-Economics)*
Joanna Wrobel-Lipa *(Vice Chm-Mgmt Bd & Dir-Sls)*
Supervisory Board of Directors:
Stanislaw Mikrut
Stanislaw Cymbor
Zbigniew Lapinski
Dariusz Orlowski
Anna Pater
Jerzy Pater

Subsidiary:

Hadrokor sp. z o.o. (1)
ul Smocza 19
87-800 Wloclawek, Poland
Tel.: (48) 544127600
Fax: (48) 54 412 76 60
E-Mail: info@hadrokor.com.pl
Web Site: www.hadrokor.com.pl
Paint & Varnish Mfr
S.I.C.: 2851
N.A.I.C.S.: 325510

Plant:

Powder Paints and Varnishes Plant Ltd. (1)
ul Lesna 5
77-100 Bytow, Pomeranian, Poland
Tel.: (48) 544127600
Fax: (48) 54 412 76 60
Paint & Varnish Mfr
S.I.C.: 2851
N.A.I.C.S.: 325510

FABRYKA WAGONOW GNIEWCZYNA SA

Gniewczyna 591
37-203 Gniewczyna Lancucka, Poland
Tel.: (48) 166488364
Fax: (48) 166488013
E-Mail: anna.gawel@gniewcznya.pl
Web Site: www.gniewcznya.pl
Year Founded: 1982
Sales Range: $10-24.9 Million
Emp.: 750
Fiscal Year-end: 12/31/12
Business Description:
Railway Repair Services
S.I.C.: 7629
N.A.I.C.S.: 811219
Personnel:
Wieslaw Kojder *(Dir-Production)*

FABRYKI MEBLI FORTE S.A.

Biala 1
07 300 Ostrow Mazowiecka, Poland
Tel.: (48) 296442222
Fax: (48) 296442110
E-Mail: forte@forte.com.pl
Web Site: www.forte.com.pl
Year Founded: 1992
FTE—(WAR)
Sales Range: $125-149.9 Million
Emp.: 3,375
Business Description:
Furniture Mfr & Distr
S.I.C.: 2521
N.A.I.C.S.: 337211
Personnel:
Zbigniew M. Sebastian *(Chm-Superviosry Bd)*
Maciej Formanowicz *(Chm-Mgmt Bd)*
Witold S. Dzbenski *(Vice Chm-Supervisory Bd)*
Robert Rogowski *(Vice Chm-Mgmt Bd)*
Gert Coopmann *(Member-Mgmt Bd)*
Klaus Dieter Dahlem *(Member-Mgmt Bd)*
Supervisory Board of Directors:
Witold S. Dzbenski
Zbigniew M. Sebastian

Subsidiary:

Meble Polonia, Ltd. (1)
Brucknera S 25-43
51-411 Wroclaw, Poland (100%)
Tel.: (48) 713255078
E-Mail: marketing@meblepolonia.pl
Web Site: www.meblepolonia.pl
Furniture & Interior Design Sales
S.I.C.: 5021
N.A.I.C.S.: 423210

Non-U.S. Subsidiaries:

FORTE Furniture Ltd. (1)
108 Courtyard Radway Green Business Park
Crewe, CW2 5PR, United Kingdom (100%)
Tel.: (44) 8453510355
Fax: (44) 8453510360
E-Mail: fortefurnitureltd@forte.com.pl
Web Site: www.fortefurniture.co.uk/?section=3
Emp.: 1
Trade Activities
S.I.C.: 7389
N.A.I.C.S.: 425120
Graham Garrod *(CEO)*

FORTE Iberia (1)
Avenida De Aragon
46004 Valencia, Spain (100%)
Tel.: (34) 963818970
Fax: (34) 963818971
E-Mail: forteiberia@forteiberia.es
Web Site: www.forteiberia.es
Emp.: 2
Trade Activities
S.I.C.: 7389
N.A.I.C.S.: 425120
Rosa Santos *(Chm)*

FORTE Mobilier SARL (1)
88 Boulevard de la Villette
75019 Paris, France (100%)
Tel.: (33) 142402040
Fax: (33) 142402500
E-Mail: stephane.polowy@forte.com.pl
Trade Activities
S.I.C.: 7389
N.A.I.C.S.: 425120

FORTE RUS Ltd. (1)
Dobrosielskaja 4-a
600016 Vladimir, Russia
Tel.: (7) 0922211701
E-Mail: forte-rus@mail.ru
Furniture
S.I.C.: 5021
N.A.I.C.S.: 423210

FORTE SK GmbH (1)
Sportova 2757
024 01 Nove Mesto, Slovakia (100%)
Tel.: (421) 414220488
Trade Acitivities
S.I.C.: 7389
N.A.I.C.S.: 425120

Fabryki Mebli Forte S.A.—(Continued)

FORTE UKRAINE, Ltd. (1)
Patrisa Lumumby 95
84-500 Artiomowsk, Ukraine (100%)
Tel.: (380) 627432052
E-Mail: office@forte.com.ua
Web Site: www.forte.com.pl
Furniture
S.I.C.: 5021
N.A.I.C.S.: 423210

Mobelvertrieb FORTE GmbH (1)
Ketteler 5
D-59929 Brilon, Germany (100%)
Tel.: (49) 296196000
E-Mail: info@Moebel-FORTE.de
Web Site: www.moebel-forte.de
Furniture Trade
S.I.C.: 5021
N.A.I.C.S.: 423210

FABRYKI SPRZETU I NARZEDZI GORNICZYCH GRUPA KAPITALOWA FASING S.A.

ul Modelarska 11
40-142 Katowice, Poland
Tel.: (48) 327350000
Fax: (48) 327302260
E-Mail: fasing@fasing.com.pl
FSG—(WAR)
Rev.: $66,453,323
Assets: $69,342,694
Liabilities: $32,435,422
Net Worth: $36,907,272
Earnings: $4,223,854
Fiscal Year-end: 12/31/12
Business Description:
Mining Chains Mfr
S.I.C.: 3449
N.A.I.C.S.: 332323
Personnel:
Tadeusz Demel *(Chm-Supervisory Bd)*
Zdzislaw Bik *(Chm-Mgmt Bd & Gen Dir)*
Jozef Dubinski *(Vice Chm-Supervisory Bd)*
Maksymilian Klank *(Vice Chm-Mgmt Bd & Mng Dir)*
Mariusz Fialek *(Vice Chm-Mgmt Bd & Dir-Tech & Sls)*
Supervisory Board of Directors:
Tadeusz Demel
Stanislaw Bik
Jozef Dubinski
Wlodzimierz Grudzien
Andrzej Matczewski

FACB INDUSTRIES INCORPORATED BERHAD

Etiqa Twins Tower 1 Level 13 11
Jalan Pinang
50450 Kuala Lumpur, Malaysia
Tel.: (60) 321620060
Fax: (60) 321620062
E-Mail: enquiry@facbi.com
Web Site: www.facbi.com
FACBIND—(KLS)
Rev.: $13,794,400
Assets: $64,326,560
Liabilities: $8,757,654
Net Worth: $55,568,906
Earnings: ($2,362,546)
Fiscal Year-end: 06/30/13
Business Description:
Stainless & Carbon Steel Mfr
S.I.C.: 3399
N.A.I.C.S.: 331110
Personnel:
Hock Kee Teo *(Acting CEO)*
Shee Cheng Bong *(CFO)*
Boo Tian Lee *(Sec)*
Board of Directors:
Sulaiman Sujak
Abdul Razak Abdul
Kassim Ahmed
Lip Keong Chen
Yiy Fon Chen
Yiy Hwuan Chen
Chou Sarn Lee
Mun Kee Lim
Subsidiaries:

Dream Products Sdn. Bhd. (1)
Plo 97 Tanjung Agas Industrial Estate
84007 Muar, Johor, Malaysia
Tel.: (60) 69512900
Fax: (60) 69548415
E-Mail: dpm@streamyx.com
Emp.: 30
Bed & Pillow Mfr
S.I.C.: 2515
N.A.I.C.S.: 337910
Winnie Suah *(Mgr)*

Dreamland Corporation (Malaysia) Sdn. Bhd. (1)
56 Kompleks Selayang Taman
Perindustrian Selayang Baru
Batu 8 1/2 Jalan Ipoh, 68100 Batu Caves, Selangor, Malaysia
Tel.: (60) 361380499
Fax: (60) 361380676
Web Site: www.dreamland.com.my
Emp.: 100
Furniture & Mattresses Whslr
S.I.C.: 5021
N.A.I.C.S.: 423210
Gan Lee Peng *(CEO)*

Kanzen Management Sdn. Bhd. (1)
Lot 4 Persiaran Perusahaan Section 23
PO Box 7272
40300 Shah Alam, Selangor, Malaysia
Tel.: (60) 355421400
Fax: (60) 355419777
Web Site: www.kanzen-tedsu.com
Emp.: 320
Management & Secretarial Services
S.I.C.: 0762
N.A.I.C.S.: 115116
Loke Chee Kuang *(Sr Mgr-Production)*

FACILASOL GROUP SA

Les Rolandieres
35120 Dol-de-Bretagne, France
Tel.: (33) 299464943
Fax: (33) 299464944
E-Mail: info@facilasol.fr
Web Site: www.facilasol.fr
MLFAC—(EUR)
Sales Range: $25-49.9 Million
Emp.: 150
Business Description:
Solar Energy Equipment Mfr, Distr & Installer
S.I.C.: 3585
N.A.I.C.S.: 333415
Personnel:
Sergei Hernani *(Chm, Pres & Dir Gen)*
David Hernani *(Dir Gen)*
Jerome Hernani *(Dir Gen)*

FACILITATE DIGITAL HOLDINGS LIMITED

(Acquired by Adslot Ltd.)

FACILITIES SERVICES GROUP LIMITED

Midland House 42 Buckingham Street
Aylesbury, HP20 2LL, United Kingdom
Tel.: (44) 8449802500
Fax: (44) 8449802505
E-Mail: enquiries@fsguk.co.uk
Web Site: www.facilities-services-group.co.uk
Emp.: 270
Business Description:
Facilities Management Services
S.I.C.: 8744
N.A.I.C.S.: 561210
Personnel:
David Simons *(Chm)*
George Lilley *(Mng Dir)*

FACOR ALLOYS LTD.

Shreeramnagar
Garividi District, 535101
Vizianagaram, India
Tel.: (91) 8952282029
Fax: (91) 8952282188
E-Mail: facoralloys@facorgroup.in
Web Site: www.facorgroup.in
532656—(BOM)
Rev.: $42,617,175
Assets: $54,064,809
Liabilities: $27,782,338
Net Worth: $26,282,471
Earnings: $521,159
Emp.: 623
Fiscal Year-end: 03/31/13
Business Description:
Ferro Chrome & Alloys Mfr
S.I.C.: 3312
N.A.I.C.S.: 331110
Personnel:
R. K. Saraf *(Chm & Mng Dir)*
M. D. Saraf *(Vice Chm & Mng Dir)*
M. S. S. Sarma *(CEO)*
Anurag Saraf *(Mng Dir)*
Ashim Saraf *(Mng Dir)*
O. P. Saraswat *(Deputy CFO)*
Dinesh Sardana *(CFO)*
S. S. Sharma *(Compliance Officer, Sec & Gen Mgr-Legal)*
Board of Directors:
R. K. Saraf
Arye Berest
C. N. Harman
A. S. Kapre
Gautam Khaitan
K. L. Mehrotra
Keshaorao Pardhey
P. V. R. K. Prasad
K. Jayabharath Reddy
Anurag Saraf
Ashim Saraf
M. D. Saraf
Transfer Agent:
Link Intime India Private Limited
C 13 Kantilal Maganlal Estate Pannalal Silk Mills Compound
LBS Marg Bhandup West, 400078 Mumbai, India

FACOR STEELS LTD

46 A & B MIDC Industrial Estate
Hingna Road
Nagpur, 440028, India
Tel.: (91) 7104235701
Fax: (91) 7104235709
E-Mail: info@facorsteel.com
Web Site: www.facorsteel.com
532657—(BOM)
Rev.: $50,807,016
Assets: $22,377,354
Liabilities: $20,774,422
Net Worth: $1,602,931
Earnings: ($4,636,594)
Emp.: 664
Fiscal Year-end: 03/31/13
Business Description:
Steel Mfrs
S.I.C.: 1791
N.A.I.C.S.: 238120
Personnel:
Narayandas D. Saraf *(Chm)*
Murlidhar D. Saraf *(Vice Chm & Mng Dir)*
Anurag M. Saraf *(Mng Dir)*
Vinod V. Saraf *(Mng Dir)*
C. Vikram Raghavan *(CFO)*
Amit G. Pandey *(Compliance Officer, Sec & Gen Mgr-Legal)*
S. C. Parija *(Exec VP)*
Board of Directors:
Narayandas D. Saraf
Mohandas Shenoy Adige
Arye Berest
Anand S. Kapre
Achintya Karati
Rajkamal Rao
Anurag M. Saraf
Murlidhar D. Saraf
Vinod V. Saraf
Mahendra B. Thaker
Transfer Agent:
Link Intime India Pvt. Ltd
C-13 Pannalal Silk Mills Compound LBS Marg
Bhandup (West)
Mumbai, India
Division:

Facor Steels Ltd - Export Division (1)
46 A & B MIDC Industrial Estate
Nagpur, Maharastra, 440028, India
Tel.: (91) 7104235701
Fax: (91) 7104235709
E-Mail: info@facorsteel.com
Web Site: www.facorsteel.com
Steel Mfr
S.I.C.: 3399
N.A.I.C.S.: 331110
S.K. Bellary *(Deputy Gen Mgr-Exports)*

Unit:

Facor Steels Ltd - Manufacturing Unit (1)
46 A & B MIDC Industrial Estate
Hingna, Nagpur, Maharashtra, 440028, India
Tel.: (91) 7104235701
Fax: (91) 7104235709
E-Mail: info@facorsteel.com
Web Site: www.facorsteel.com
Emp.: 500
Steel Mfr
S.I.C.: 3312
N.A.I.C.S.: 331110
S. K. Bellare *(Mgr-Export)*

FACT CORPORATION

5614E Burbank Road SE
Calgary, AB, T2H 1Z4, Canada
Tel.: (403) 693-8004
Fax: (403) 272-3620
Toll Free: (888) 410-3228
E-Mail: info@factfoods.com
Web Site: www.factfoods.com
Year Founded: 1982
FCTOA—(DEU OTC)
Sales Range: $1-9.9 Million
Emp.: 3
Business Description:
Holding Company; Bake Mixes Whslr
S.I.C.: 6719
N.A.I.C.S.: 551112
Personnel:
Jacqueline R. Danforth *(Pres, CEO & Treas)*
Jacqueline M. Tucker *(CFO)*
Brad D. Hunsaker *(Acting COO)*
Bryan Hunsaker *(Pres-FACT Products)*
Brian Raines *(Sec)*
Board of Directors:
Jacqueline R. Danforth
Brad D. Hunsaker
Paul H. Litwack
Brian Raines

FACT ENTERPRISE LIMITED

C/208 Crystal Plaza Opp Infinity Mall
New Link Road
Andheri - West, Mumbai, 400 053, India
Tel.: (91) 22 26732223
Fax: (91) 22 26732224
E-Mail: factmedia@ymail.com
Web Site: www.factmediahouse.com
511668—(BOM)

Business Description:
Real Estate Development Services
S.I.C.: 6531
N.A.I.C.S.: 531390
Personnel:
Rajiv Kashyap *(Chm, Mng Dir & Compliance Officer)*
Board of Directors:
Rajiv Kashyap
Varun S. Gautam
Kunal Patil
Praful Sadanand Rane
Transfer Agent:
Big Share Services Pvt Ltd
E-2/3 Ansa industrial Estate Sakivihar Rd Saki naka Andheri(E)
Mumbai, India

FACTOR FORMS LTD
8411 McIntyre Road
Edmonton, AB, Canada T6E 6G3
Tel.: (780) 468-1111
Fax: (780) 469-5141
Toll Free: (800) 661-7243
E-Mail: edmonton@factorforms.com
Web Site: www.factorforms.com
Year Founded: 1971
Rev.: $14,335,392
Emp.: 103
Business Description:
Printing Services
S.I.C.: 2759
N.A.I.C.S.: 323111
Personnel:
Brenda Jane *(Mgr-Sls)*

FACTOR GAS LIQUIDS INC.
840 7th Avenue SW Suite 1260
Calgary, AB, T2P 3G2, Canada
Tel.: (403) 266-8778
Fax: (403) 266-0070
Toll Free: (877) 460-6441
Web Site: www.factorgas.com
Year Founded: 1995
Rev.: $104,748,078
Emp.: 10
Business Description:
Liquefied Petroleum Gas Distr
S.I.C.: 4924
N.A.I.C.S.: 221210
Personnel:
Barry Vosburg *(Pres-Sarnia)*

FAD A.D. GORNJI MILANOVAC
Kneza Aleksandra 210
32 300 Gornji Milanovac, Serbia
Tel.: (381) 32 725 255
Fax: (381) 32 725 878
Web Site: www.fad.rs
FADG—(BEL)
Emp.: 1,500
Business Description:
Motor Vehicle Steering & Suspension Component Mfr
S.I.C.: 3714
N.A.I.C.S.: 336330
Personnel:
Dragisa Ristic *(Mng Dir)*

FAES FARMA, S.A.
Maximo Aguirre 14
Leioa, Vizcaya, 48940, Spain
Tel.: (34) 901120362
Fax: (34) 944818323
E-Mail: accionistas@faes.es
Web Site: www.faes.es
Year Founded: 1933
FAE—(MAD)
Sales Range: $250-299.9 Million
Emp.: 800
Business Description:
Pharmaceutical Drug Developer, Mfr & Sales
S.I.C.: 2834
N.A.I.C.S.: 325412
Personnel:
Eduardo Fernadez de Valderrama y Murillo *(Chm & CEO)*
Mariano Ucar Angulo *(Vice Chm & Sec)*
Antonio Basagoiti Garcia-Tunon *(Vice Chm)*
Subsidiaries:

Biotecnet I Mas D S.A. **(1)**
Cl Alpedrete 24
28045 Madrid, Spain
Tel.: (34) 914680800
Fax: (34) 914685934
Medical Laboratories
S.I.C.: 8071
N.A.I.C.S.: 621511
Francisco Quintailla *(Mng Dir)*

Hispana Dos S.A. **(1)**
Calle Serrano 88
Madrid, Spain
Tel.: (34) 913199800
Web Site: www.faes.es/area_AI/PDF/doc_enviados/AI_20050623_243.pdf
Investment Advice
S.I.C.: 6282
N.A.I.C.S.: 523930

Iquinosa Farma S.A. **(1)**
Cl Alpedrete 24
28045 Madrid, Spain
Tel.: (34) 914680800
Fax: (34) 914685934
E-Mail: aweber@faes.es
Web Site: www.faes.es/advertencia_legal/0_en.lasso
Emp.: 50
Pharmaceutical Preparation Mfr
S.I.C.: 2834
N.A.I.C.S.: 325412
Francisco Quintailla *(Mng Dir)*

Laboratorios Veris S.A. **(1)**
Cl Alpedrete 24
28045 Madrid, Spain
Tel.: (34) 914680800
Fax: (34) 914685934
Medical Laboratories
S.I.C.: 8071
N.A.I.C.S.: 621511
Francisco Quintailla *(Mng Dir)*

Lazlo International SA **(1)**
Cl Alpedrete 24
28045 Madrid, Spain
Tel.: (34) 914680800
Fax: (34) 914685934
E-Mail: heinz.w.pfeifer@novatemporade.com
Web Site: www.deegna.com
Emp.: 80
Pharmaceutical Preparation Mfr
S.I.C.: 2834
N.A.I.C.S.: 325412
Francisco Quintailla *(Mng Dir)*

Non-U.S. Subsidiaries:

Laboratorios Vitoria S.A. **(1)**
Rua Elias Garcia
26 Venda Nova, 2700 Amadora, Portugal (99.83%)
Tel.: (351) 14745333
Fax: (351) 14747070
Web Site: www.faes.es/area_AI/PDF/doc_enviados/AI_20050623_243.pdf
Pharmaceutical Preparation Mfr
S.I.C.: 2834
N.A.I.C.S.: 325412

Olve Farmaceutica Limitada **(1)**
Venda Nova
Amadora, 2700-327, Portugal (100%)
Tel.: (351) 214758300
Fax: (351) 214747070
E-Mail: lab.victory@labvictory.pt
Web Site: www.labvictory.pt
Emp.: 100
Pharmaceutical Preparation Mfr
S.I.C.: 2834
N.A.I.C.S.: 325412

Veris Farmaceutica Limitada **(1)**
Venda Nova
Amadora, Portugal (100%)
Tel.: (351) 214763667
Fax: (351) 214747070
Biological Product (except Diagnostic) Mfr
S.I.C.: 2836
N.A.I.C.S.: 325414

FAG BEARINGS INDIA LIMITED
Nariman Bhavan 8th Floor 227
Backbay Reclamation Nariman Point
Mumbai, Maharashtra, 400 021, India
Tel.: (91) 22 22022144
Fax: (91) 22 22072022
Web Site: www.fag.co.in
FAGBEARING—(NSE)
Sls.: $287,357,022
Assets: $212,034,564
Liabilities: $48,975,264
Net Worth: $163,059,300
Earnings: $29,511,972
Emp.: 1,580
Fiscal Year-end: 12/31/12
Business Description:
Ball & Roller Bearings Mfr
S.I.C.: 3562
N.A.I.C.S.: 332991
Personnel:
Rajendra Anandpara *(Mng Dir)*
Satish Patel *(CFO)*
Raj Sarraf *(Compliance Officer & Sec)*
Board of Directors:
Avinash Gandhi
Rajendra Anandpara
Dharmesh Arora
Wolfgang H. Dangel
Moreshwar Garde
Dietmar Heinrich
Frank Huber
R. Sampath Kumar
Bernhard Steinruecke
Transfer Agent:
Link Intime India Pvt. Ltd.
B-102 & 103 Shangrila Complex First Floor
Near Radhakrishna Char Rasta
Opp.HDFC Bank, Vadodara, India

FAGE DAIRY INDUSTRY S.A.
35 Hermou St
GR 144 52 Metamorfosis, Athens, Greece
Tel.: (30) 2102892555
Telex: 221145 FAGE GR
Fax: (30) 2102828386
E-Mail: info@fage.gr
Web Site: www.fage.gr
Year Founded: 1989
Sales Range: $500-549.9 Million
Emp.: 1,000
Business Description:
Dairy Products Mfr
S.I.C.: 2023
N.A.I.C.S.: 311514
Personnel:
Athanassios-Kyros Filippou *(Chm)*
Athanassios Filippou *(Vice Chm/ CEO-USA & CEO)*
Dimitrios Filippou *(Vice Chm)*
John Filippou *(Pres)*
Christos Koloventzos *(CFO, Chief Admin Officer & Treas-USA)*
Alexis Alexopoulos *(Chief Comml Officer)*
Spyros Gianpapas *(Chief Quality Assurance, R&D & Reg Plants Officer)*
Christos Krommidas *(Chief Athens Plant Officer)*
Robert Shea *(CFO/Sec-USA)*
Ioannis Ravanis *(Exec VP-Mfg & Ops)*
Board of Directors:
Athanassios-Kyros Filippou
Alexis Alexopoulos
Athanassios Filippou
Dimitra Filippou
Dimitrios Filippou
Spyros Gianpapas
Christos Koloventzos
Christos Krommidas
Emmanuel Papaefthimiou
U.S. Subsidiary:

FAGE USA Holdings, Inc. **(1)**
1 Opportunity Dr
Johnstown, NY 12095-3349
Tel.: (518) 762-5912
Dairy Product Mfr & Distr
S.I.C.: 2023
N.A.I.C.S.: 311514

Subsidiary:

FAGE USA Dairy Industry, Inc. **(2)**
1 Opportunity Dr Johnstown Industrial Park
Johnstown, NY 12095
Tel.: (866) 962-5912
Fax: (518) 762-5918
Web Site: www.fageusa.com
Yoghurt Mfr & Distr
S.I.C.: 2023
N.A.I.C.S.: 311514
Robert Shea *(CFO)*

Non-U.S. Subsidiary:

FAGE Italia S.r.l. **(1)**
Via E De Nicola 12
20090 Cesano Boscone, Milan, Italy
Tel.: (39) 02 48 61 03 11
Fax: (39) 02 48 61 03 90
E-Mail: info@fageitalia.it
Web Site: www.fageitalia.it
Emp.: 10
Dairy Product Distr
S.I.C.: 5143
N.A.I.C.S.: 424430
Donatella Cifarelli *(Office Mgr)*

FAGERDALA WORLD FOAMS AB
Odelbergsvagen 11
13482 Gustavsberg, Sweden
Tel.: (46) 857013200
Fax: (46) 857013256
E-Mail: info@fagerdala.se
Web Site: www.fagerdala.com
Emp.: 1,200
Business Description:
Offices of Holding Companies
S.I.C.: 6719
N.A.I.C.S.: 551112
Personnel:
Leif Sparrremo *(CFO)*
Subsidiary:

Fagerdala Singapore Pte. Ltd. **(1)**
6 Penjuru Lane
Jurong, 609187, Singapore
Tel.: (65) 63795000
Fax: (65) 62623721
E-Mail: inquiry@fagerdala.com.sg
Web Site: www.fagerdala.com.sg
Emp.: 55
Plastic & Foam Products
S.I.C.: 3086
N.A.I.C.S.: 326140
Paul Yeo *(Mng Dir)*

U.S. Division:

Fagerdala USA - Lompoc, Inc. **(2)**
1017 W Central Ave
Lompoc, CA 93436-2701 CA
Tel.: (805) 735-5205
Fax: (805) 735-5206
E-Mail: info@fagerdalausa.com
Web Site: www.fagerdalausa.com
Emp.: 65
Plastic & Foam Products
Import Export
S.I.C.: 3089
N.A.I.C.S.: 326199
Jason Montella *(Bus Mgr)*

FAIR FRIEND GROUP
No 186 Yung Chi Road
Xinyi District, Taipei, 110, Taiwan
Tel.: (886) 2 2763 9696

Fair Friend Group—(Continued)

Fax: (886) 2 2768 0639
Web Site: www.ffg-tw.com
Year Founded: 1979

Business Description:
Holding Company; Machine Tool, Printed Circuit Board, Industrial Equipment & Green Energy Technologies Designer, Mfr & Distr
S.I.C.: 6719
N.A.I.C.S.: 551112

Personnel:
Jimmy Chih-Yaung Chu *(Chm)*
Hsiang-Jung Chen *(Gen Mgr)*

Subsidiaries:

Fair Friend Enterprise Co., Ltd. (1)
No 133 Gong 1st Road
Taichung Industrial Park, Taichung, Taiwan TW
Tel.: (886) 4 2359 4075
Fax: (886) 4 2359 4873
Web Site: www.feeler.com
Machine Tools Mfr & Distr
S.I.C.: 3541
N.A.I.C.S.: 333517
Yu-Wei Chu *(Pres)*

Fair Friend Enterprise Group (1)
No 186 Yung Chi Road
Xinyi District, Taipei, 110, Taiwan
Tel.: (886) 2 2763 9696
Fax: (886) 2 2768 0639
Web Site: www.fairfriend.com.tw
Office Administrative Services
S.I.C.: 8741
N.A.I.C.S.: 561110
Jimmy Chih-Yaung Chu, *(Chm)*
Chin-Chen Lee *(CEO)*
Ching-Chang Chen *(CIO)*

Non-U.S. Subsidiary:

FFG Europe S.p.A. (1)
Corso Venezia 16
20121 Milan, Italy IT
Tel.: (39) 02 3659 0824
Fax: (39) 02 7631 9015
Web Site: www.ffgeurope.com
Holding Company; Regional Managing Office
S.I.C.: 6719
N.A.I.C.S.: 551112
Luigi Maniglio *(Chm)*

Subsidiaries:

Jobs Automazione S.p.A. (2)
Via Emilia Parmense 164
29122 Piacenza, Italy IT
Tel.: (39) 0523 549 611
Fax: (39) 0523 549 750
Web Site: www.jobs.it
Automated Machine Tool Mfr & Distr
S.I.C.: 3541
N.A.I.C.S.: 333517
Marco Livelli *(CEO)*

Division:

Jobs Automazione S.p.A. - Sachman Division (3)
Via Masaccio 15/A
42124 Reggio Emilia, Italy
Tel.: (39) 0522 233 311
Fax: (39) 0522 511 7010
Automated Machine Tool Mfr & Distr
S.I.C.: 3541
N.A.I.C.S.: 333517
Marco Livelli *(CEO)*

Sigma Technology S.r.l. (2)
Via San Giovanni 109
27029 Vigevano, Italy IT
Tel.: (39) 0381 3051
Fax: (39) 0381 347864
Web Site: www.sigmaekkon.it
Machine Tool Mfr & Distr
S.I.C.: 3542
N.A.I.C.S.: 333517
Davide Grossi *(CEO)*

Sky Thrive Rambaudi S.r.l. (2)
Via Acqui 10/B
10098 Rivoli, TO, Italy IT
Tel.: (39) 011 957 6254
Fax: (39) 011 950 8517
Web Site: www.ffgrambaudi.it
Machine Tool Mfr & Distr
S.I.C.: 3542
N.A.I.C.S.: 333517

FAIR VALUE REIT-AG

Leopoldstrasse 244
80807 Munich, Germany
Tel.: (49) 89 92 92 8 15 01
Fax: (49) 89 92 92 8 15 15
E-Mail: info@fvreit.de
Web Site: www.fvreit.de
FVI—(DEU)
Sls.: $15,029,988
Assets: $248,826,063
Liabilities: $144,641,928
Net Worth: $104,184,135
Earnings: $1,581,750
Emp.: 4
Fiscal Year-end: 12/31/12

Business Description:
Real Estate Development Services
S.I.C.: 6531
N.A.I.C.S.: 531390

Personnel:
Heinz Rehkugler *(Chm-Supervisory Bd)*
Oscar Kienzle *(Deputy Chm-Supervisory Bd)*
Frank Schaich *(CEO & Member-Mgmt Bd)*

Supervisory Board of Directors:
Heinz Rehkugler
Christian Hopfer
Oscar Kienzle

Subsidiaries:

BBV 10 Geschatsfuhrungs-GmbH & Co. KG (1)
Ohmstrabe 4
85716 Unterschleissheim, Bayern, Germany
Tel.: (49) 89 9292815 01
Fax: (49) 89 929281515
Real Estate Management Services
S.I.C.: 6531
N.A.I.C.S.: 531390

BBV Immobilien-Fonds Nr. 6 GmbH & Co. KG (1)
Ohmstr 4
85716 Unterschleissheim, Bayern, Germany
Tel.: (49) 8955227541
Real Estate Management Services
S.I.C.: 6531
N.A.I.C.S.: 531390

FAIRBORNE ENERGY LIMITED

(Name Changed to Santonia Energy Inc.)

FAIRCOURT GOLD INCOME CORP.

141 Adelaide Street West Suite 1402
Toronto, ON, M5H 3L5, Canada
Tel.: (416) 364-8989
Fax: (416) 360-3466
Year Founded: 2007
FGX—(TSX)
Rev.: $3,578,039
Assets: $45,171,969
Liabilities: $2,920,769
Net Worth: $42,251,200
Earnings: $2,428,728
Fiscal Year-end: 12/31/12

Business Description:
Financial Investment Services
S.I.C.: 6211
N.A.I.C.S.: 523999

Personnel:
Charles Taerk *(Pres & CEO)*

Transfer Agent:
CIBC Mellon Trust Company
PO Box 7010
Adelaide Street Postal Station, Toronto, ON, M5C 2W9, Canada
Tel.: (416) 643-5500
Fax: (416) 643-5501
Toll Free: (800) 387-0825

FAIRCOURT SPLIT TRUST

141 Adelaide Street West Suite 1402
Toronto, ON, M5H 3L5, Canada
Tel.: (416) 364-8989
Fax: (416) 360-3466
Year Founded: 2006
FCS—(TSX)
Rev.: $3,588,455
Assets: $65,602,698
Liabilities: $48,716,945
Net Worth: $16,885,753
Earnings: ($864,120)
Fiscal Year-end: 12/31/12

Business Description:
Financial Investment Services
S.I.C.: 6211
N.A.I.C.S.: 523999

Personnel:
Charles Taerk *(Pres & CEO)*
Douglas Waterson *(CFO & Portfolio Mgr)*

Board of Directors:
Jane Davis
Stephen Kangas
Marshall Miller
Charles Taerk
Douglas Waterson

FAIRDEAL FILAMENTS LTD.

3rd Floor Dawer Chamber Near Sub Jail Ring Road
Surat, Gujarat, 395 002, India
Tel.: (91) 2613090200
Fax: (91) 2612635550
E-Mail: info@fairdealfilaments.com
Web Site: www.shahlon.com
Year Founded: 2005
514474—(BOM)
Rev.: $29,208,528
Assets: $11,908,446
Liabilities: $9,803,896
Net Worth: $2,104,550
Earnings: $152,028
Fiscal Year-end: 03/31/13

Business Description:
Synthetic Fabric Mfr
S.I.C.: 2269
N.A.I.C.S.: 313310

Personnel:
Dhirajlal R. Shah *(Mng Dir)*
Prachi V. Shukla *(Compliance Officer & Sec)*

Board of Directors:
Jayantilal R. Shah
Rajendra K. Desai
Arvind R. Shah
Dhirajlal R. Shah
Manubhai J. Shah
Nandish S. Vin

Transfer Agent:
MCS Limited
Neelam Apartment 88 Sampatrao Colony Abv Chappan Bhog Sweets Alkapuri
Vadodara, India

FAIRFAX FINANCIAL HOLDINGS LIMITED

95 Wellington Street West Suite 800
Toronto, ON, M5J 2N7, Canada
Tel.: (416) 367-4941
Fax: (416) 367-4946
E-Mail: ffhgetinfo@fairfax.ca
Web Site: www.fairfax.ca
Year Founded: 1951
FRFHF—(OTC)
Premiums: $7,294,000,000
Assets: $35,958,800,000
Liabilities: $27,498,300,000
Net Worth: $8,460,500,000
Earnings: ($564,500,000)
Emp.: 10,938
Fiscal Year-end: 12/31/13

Business Description:
Financial Services Holding Company
S.I.C.: 6719
N.A.I.C.S.: 551112

Personnel:
Vivan Prem Watsa *(Chm & CEO)*
Paul C. Rivett *(Pres)*
David Bonham *(CFO)*
Peter Clarke *(VP & Chief Risk Officer)*
Jean Cloutier *(Chief Actuary & VP)*
Ronald Schokking *(Treas & VP)*

Board of Directors:
Vivan Prem Watsa
Anthony Frear Griffiths
Robert J. Gunn
Alan Douglas Horn
Timothy Robert Price
Brandon W. Sweitzer

Legal Counsel:
Tory Tory Deslauriers & Binnington
Maritime Life Tower Ste 3000 TD Centre 79 Wellington St W
PO Box 270
Toronto, ON, M5K 1N2, Canada
Tel.: (416) 865-0040
Fax: (416) 865-7380

Registrar & Transfer Company
10 Commerce Dr
Cranford, NJ 07016
Tel.: (800) 368-5948

Transfer Agents:
Valiant Trust Company
130 King Street West Suite 710 34
Toronto, ON, Canada

Registrar & Transfer Company
10 Commerce Dr
Cranford, NJ 07016
Tel.: (800) 368-5948

Subsidiaries:

Northbridge Financial Corporation (1)
105 Adelaide Street West Suite 700
Toronto, ON, M5H 1P9, Canada
Tel.: (416) 350-4300
Fax: (416) 350-4307
Toll Free: (855) 620-6262
E-Mail: info@nbfc.com
Web Site: www.nbfc.com
Sales Range: $1-4.9 Billion
Emp.: 1,480
Financial Services Holding Company
S.I.C.: 6712
N.A.I.C.S.: 551111
Mark J. Ram *(Vice Chm)*
Silvy Wright *(Pres & CEO)*
Craig Pinnock *(CFO)*
Andrew Wood *(CIO)*
Innes Dey *(Sec & VP-Corp Affairs)*

Subsidiaries:

Federated Insurance Company of Canada (2)
717 Portage Ave
Winnipeg, MB, R3C 3C9, Canada
Tel.: (204) 786-6431
Fax: (204) 783-4443
E-Mail: winnipeg@federated.ca
Web Site: www.federated.ca
Sales Range: $125-149.9 Million
Emp.: 150
Property, Automobile, Liability, Life & Health Insurance
S.I.C.: 6399
N.A.I.C.S.: 524128
John Paisley *(Pres & CEO)*

Northbridge General Insurance Corporation (2)
105 Adelaide St W
Toronto, ON, M5H 1P9, Canada (100%)
Tel.: (416) 350-4400
Fax: (416) 350-4266
Web Site: www.nbins.co
Sales Range: $800-899.9 Million
Emp.: 550
Insurance Services
S.I.C.: 6351
N.A.I.C.S.: 524126

Fabian Richenberger *(Pres)*
Mark J. Ram *(CEO)*
William J. Dunlop *(Gen Counsel)*
Jane M. Gardner *(Exec VP)*
Katharine M. Allan *(Sr VP & Chief Underwriting Officer)*
Peter Aumonier *(Sr VP-Claims)*
Kim H. Tan *(Sr VP)*

Subsidiaries:

Northbridge Commercial Insurance Corporation (3)
55 University Avenue
Toronto, ON, M5J 2H7, Canada
Tel.: (416) 364-7800
Fax: (416) 364-1625
Web Site: www.nbfc.com
Sales Range: $200-249.9 Million
Emp.: 230
Long-Haul Trucking, Property, Liability & Automobile Insurance Carrier
S.I.C.: 6351
N.A.I.C.S.: 524126
Lisa White *(Gen Mgr)*

Northbridge Indemnity Insurance Corporation (3)
Ste 1500 595 Burrard St
PO Box 49115
Vancouver, BC, V7X 1G4, Canada
Tel.: (604) 683-5511
Fax: (604) 683-8968
E-Mail: info@commonw.com
Web Site: www.commonw.com
Emp.: 200
Property, Casualty, Marine & Energy Insurance Carrier
S.I.C.: 6351
N.A.I.C.S.: 524126
Stewart Woo *(CFO)*
Tim Davies *(Chief Underwriting Officer)*
Dennis G. Shave *(Exec VP-Claims)*
Patricia Gibson *(Sr VP-Ops)*
Thomas E. Wilson *(Sr VP-US Property)*

U.S. Subsidiary:

Northbridge Indemnity Insurance Corporation (4)
1700 7th Ave Ste 1850
Seattle, WA 98101-1397
Tel.: (206) 382-6670
Fax: (206) 382-6669
Web Site: www.commonw.com
Emp.: 200
Property, Casualty, Marine & Energy Insurance Carrier
S.I.C.: 6351
N.A.I.C.S.: 524126
Edward P. Hunter *(COO & Exec VP)*

Prime Restaurants Inc. (1)
10 Kingsbridge Garden Circle Suite 600
Mississauga, ON, L5R 3K6, Canada Ca
Tel.: (905) 568-0000 (81.7%)
Fax: (905) 568-0080
Web Site: www.primerestaurants.com
Emp.: 11,850
Hotel Management Services
S.I.C.: 5812
N.A.I.C.S.: 722511
Steven Sharpe *(Chm)*
Nicholas M. Perpick *(Pres & COO)*
John A. Rothschild *(CEO)*
H. Ross R. Bain *(Sec & Exec VP)*
Grant Cobb *(Sr VP-Brand Mgmt)*

Sporting Life Inc. (1)
2665 Yonge Street
Toronto, ON, M4P 2J6, Canada (75%)
Tel.: (416) 485-1611
Fax: (416) 485-7825
Web Site: www.sportinglife.ca
Sales Range: $50-74.9 Million
Emp.: 650
Sporting Goods Store Retailer
S.I.C.: 5941
N.A.I.C.S.: 451110
Jerry Rynda *(Gen Mgr)*

William Ashley China Corporation (1)
55 Bloor St W
Toronto, ON, M4W 3V1, Canada
Tel.: (416) 964-9111
Fax: (416) 960-9348
Toll Free: (800) 268-1122
Web Site: www.williamashley.com
Coins & Gift Products Retailer
S.I.C.: 5947
N.A.I.C.S.: 453220

Joint Venture:

Arbor Memorial Services Inc. (1)
2 Jane Street 3rd Floor
Toronto, ON, M6S 4W8, Canada ON
Tel.: (416) 763-4531
Fax: (416) 763-0381
E-Mail: info@arbormemorial.com
Web Site: www.arbormemorial.com
Sales Range: $250-299.9 Million
Emp.: 1,550
Crematories, Funeral Homes & Cemeteries Operator
S.I.C.: 7261
N.A.I.C.S.: 812220
David Scanlan *(Chm & Sr VP-Sls)*
Brian D. Snowdon *(Pres & CEO)*
Laurel L. Ancheta *(CFO & VP-Fin & Trust Admin)*
Michael J. Scanlan *(Sr VP-Mktg, Ops, Construction & Dev)*

U.S. Subsidiaries:

Crum & Forster Holdings Corp. (1)
305 Madison Ave
Morristown, NJ 07962 DE
Mailing Address: (100%)
PO Box 1973
Morristown, NJ 07962
Tel.: (973) 490-6600
E-Mail: information@cfins.com
Web Site: www.cfins.com
Premiums: $1,529,700,000
Earnings: $29,300,000
Emp.: 1,345
Fiscal Year-end: 12/31/12
Holding Company; Property & Casualty Insurance Services
S.I.C.: 6719
N.A.I.C.S.: 551112
Douglas M. Libby *(Chm & CEO)*
Richard H. Smith *(Vice Chm & Head-Excess & Surplus Lines Casualty)*
Mary Jane Robertson *(CFO, Treas & Exec VP)*
Nicole Bennett *(CIO & Sr VP)*
Jorge A. Echemendia *(CMO)*
Richard Yien *(CTO)*
James V. Kraus *(Sr VP, Gen Counsel & Sec)*
Stephen M. Mulready *(Exec VP)*
Dennis J. Hammer *(Sr VP & Controller)*
Steve Fomchenko *(Sr VP-Property)*
David J. Ghezzi *(Sr VP-Fin Ops)*
Matt Kunish *(Sr VP)*
Chris I. Stormo *(Sr VP-Corp Ops)*

Subsidiaries:

Crum & Forster Insurance Company (2)
305 Madison Ave
Morristown, NJ 07960-6117 (100%)
Tel.: (973) 490-6600
Fax: (973) 490-6940
Web Site: www.cfins.com
Sales Range: $750-799.9 Million
Emp.: 879
Commercial Lines Property & Casualty Insurance
S.I.C.: 6411
N.A.I.C.S.: 524210
Douglas M. Libby *(Chm & CEO)*
Mary Jane Robertson *(CFO, Treas & Exec VP)*
Nicole Bennett *(CIO)*
Ahmed K. Yaknour *(CTO)*
Steve Mulready *(Exec VP)*

Division:

Fairmont Specialty (3)
10350 Richmond Ave Ste 300
Houston, TX 77042
Mailing Address:
PO Box 2807
Houston, TX 77252-2807
Tel.: (713) 954-8100
Fax: (713) 954-8176
E-Mail: consumercomplaints@fairmontspecialty.com
Web Site: www.fairmontspecialty.com
Emp.: 101
Insurance Services
S.I.C.: 6411
N.A.I.C.S.: 524210
Marc Adee *(Pres)*
Lloyd Chaffin *(Exec VP-Hawaii Bus Unit)*
Gary McGeddy *(Exec VP-A & H Bus Unit)*
Lloyd Godbold *(Sr VP-Claims)*

Crum & Forster Insurance (2)
160 Water St
New York, NY 10038 NY
Tel.: (212) 277-1660 (100%)
Fax: (877) 622-6214
E-Mail: info@cfins.com
Web Site: www.cfins.com
Emp.: 20
Insurance
S.I.C.: 6331
N.A.I.C.S.: 524126
Keith McCarthy *(Pres-Metro Reg)*

First Mercury Financial Corporation (2)
26600 Telegraph Rd
Southfield, MI 48034 DE
Tel.: (248) 358-4010
Fax: (248) 358-2459
Toll Free: (800) 762-6837
E-Mail: elaframboise@firstmercury.com
Web Site: www.firstmercury.com
Sales Range: $300-349.9 Million
Emp.: 349
Insurance Services
Import Export
S.I.C.: 6331
N.A.I.C.S.: 524126
Marc Adee *(CEO)*
John A. Marazza *(CFO, Sec & Exec VP)*
E. Edward Camp *(Exec VP & Chief Underwriting Officer)*
Michael Roskiewicz *(Sr VP)*

Subsidiaries:

CoverXSpecialty (3)
26600 Telegraph Rd
Southfield, MI 48033
Tel.: (248) 358-4010
Fax: (248) 358-2459
Toll Free: (800) 762-6837
E-Mail: coverxuw@coverx.com
Web Site: www.coverx.com
Sales Range: $75-99.9 Million
Emp.: 120
Liability Insurance Products
S.I.C.: 6411
N.A.I.C.S.: 524298
Marc Adee *(CEO)*
John Bures *(Sr VP)*

First Mercury Insurance Company (3)
26600 Telegraph Rd
Southfield, MI 48033-2438 (100%)
Tel.: (248) 358-4010
Fax: (248) 357-5036
Web Site: www.coverx.com
Sales Range: $50-74.9 Million
Emp.: 107
Insurance Services
S.I.C.: 6351
N.A.I.C.S.: 524126
Tom Bredahl *(Chief Underwriting Officer)*

The North River Insurance Company (2)
305 Madison Ave
Morristown, NJ 07962 NJ
Tel.: (973) 490-6600 (100%)
Fax: (973) 490-6900
Web Site: www.cfins.com
Emp.: 600
Insurance Company
S.I.C.: 6351
N.A.I.C.S.: 524126

Seneca Insurance Company Inc. (2)
160 Water St Fl 16
New York, NY 10038-5032
Tel.: (212) 344-3000
Fax: (212) 344-4567
E-Mail: kmccarthy@senecainsurance.com
Web Site: www.senecainsurance.com
Emp.: 100
Insurance Services
S.I.C.: 6351
N.A.I.C.S.: 524126
Gary Dubois *(Pres & CEO)*
Marc Wolin *(CFO)*
Ahmed K. Yaknour *(CIO & VP)*
Steve Fomchenko *(Sr VP)*
Keith McCarthy *(Sr VP)*
Ellen O'Connor *(Sr VP)*
Chris Stormo *(Sr VP-Ops)*

United States Fire Insurance Company (2)
305 Madison Ave
Morristown, NJ 07962 NY
Tel.: (973) 490-6600 (100%)
Fax: (877) 622-6191
Web Site: www.cfins.com
Emp.: 600
Fire Insurance
S.I.C.: 6331
N.A.I.C.S.: 524126
Douglas M. Libby *(CEO)*

Subsidiary:

Hartville Group, Inc. (3)
3840 Greentree Ave SW
Canton, OH 44706 NV
Tel.: (330) 484-8166
Fax: (330) 484-8081
Toll Free: (866) 820-7764
E-Mail: ir@hartvillegroup.com
Web Site: www.hartvillegroup.com
Sales Range: $10-24.9 Million
Emp.: 70
Pet Insurance Products & Services
S.I.C.: 6399
N.A.I.C.S.: 524128
Dennis C. Rushovich *(Pres & CEO)*
Christopher R. Sachs *(CFO & Chief Acctg Officer)*
Michael Kalman *(CIO)*
Christopher C. Edgar *(CMO)*
Patricia Downing *(Sec)*

Odyssey Re Holdings Corp. (1)
300 1st Stamford Pl
Stamford, CT 06902 DE
Tel.: (203) 977-8000 (100%)
Fax: (203) 356-0196
Web Site: www.odysseyre.com
Premiums: $2,773,218,000
Assets: $11,217,559,000
Liabilities: $7,538,793,000
Net Worth: $3,678,766,000
Earnings: $282,513,000
Emp.: 721
Fiscal Year-end: 12/31/12
Reinsurance Services
S.I.C.: 6399
N.A.I.C.S.: 524130
Vivan Prem Watsa *(Chm)*
Andrew A. Barnard *(Vice Chm)*
James F. Dowd *(Vice Chm)*
Brian D. Young *(Pres & CEO)*
Jan Christiansen *(CFO & Exec VP)*
Robert S. Bennett *(Chief Actuary & Exec VP)*
Brian D. Quinn *(Chief Underwriting Officer-Reinsurance Ops-North America)*
Christopher L. Gallagher *(CEO-US Insurance)*
Carl A. Overy *(CEO-London Market)*
Lucien Pietropoli *(CEO-EuroAsia Div)*
Peter H. Lovell *(Gen Counsel, Sec & Sr VP)*
Alane R. Carey *(Exec VP & Dir-Global Mktg)*
Michael G. Wacek *(Exec VP-Global Risk Strategies)*
Jeffrey M. Rubin *(Sr VP & Dir-Global Claims)*
Philippe E. Mallier *(Sr VP-Reinsurance Ops-Latin America)*

Subsidiaries:

Hudson Insurance Group (2)
17 State St 29th Fl
New York, NY 10004 DE
Tel.: (212) 978-2800 (100%)
Fax: (212) 344-2973
Web Site: www.hudsoninsgroup.com
Emp.: 30
Specialty Insurance Products; Medical Malpractice & Fire & Marine Casualty Insurance Services
S.I.C.: 6351
N.A.I.C.S.: 524126
Christopher L. Gallagher *(CEO)*
Peter H. Lovell *(Gen Counsel & Sr VP)*

Subsidiaries:

Clearwater Insurance Company (3)
17 State St
New York, NY 10004 DE

FAIRFAX FINANCIAL HOLDINGS LIMITED—(Continued)

Tel.: (212) 978-2800
Fax: (212) 344-2973
Web Site: www.hudsoninsurancecompany.com
Emp.: 117
Reinsurance Services
S.I.C.: 6411
N.A.I.C.S.: 524298
Christopher L. Gallagher *(CEO)*

Clearwater Select Insurance Company (3)
300 1st Stamford Pl
Stamford, CT 06902
Tel.: (203) 977-8000
Fax: (203) 356-0196
E-Mail: info@fairfax.com
Web Site: www.fairfax.com
Emp.: 150
Reinsurance Services
S.I.C.: 6399
N.A.I.C.S.: 524130
Andrew A. Barnard *(Chm & CEO)*

Odyssey America Reinsurance Corporation (2)
300 1st Stamford Pl
Stamford, CT 06902-6765 CT
Tel.: (203) 977-8000 (100%)
Fax: (203) 356-0196
E-Mail: info@odysseyre.com
Web Site: www.odysseyre.com
Emp.: 250
Reinsurance Services
S.I.C.: 6399
N.A.I.C.S.: 524130
Brian D. Young *(COO & Exec VP)*
Brian D. Quinn *(Chief Underwriting Officer-North American Reinsurance Ops)*
Michael G. Wacek *(Exec VP-Global Risk Strategies)*

Odyssey Holdings Latin America, Inc. (2)
1200 Prickle Ave Ste 1550
Miami, FL 33131 DE
Tel.: (203) 977-8000 (100%)
Fax: (203) 356-0196
E-Mail: hr@odysseyre.com
Web Site: www.odysseyre.com
Emp.: 9
Holding Company
S.I.C.: 6399
N.A.I.C.S.: 524130
Michael G. Wacek *(CEO)*

Non-U.S. Division:

Odyssey Reinsurance EuroAsia Division (2)
15 Rue Du 4 Septembre
75002 Paris, France
Tel.: (33) 149261000
Fax: (33) 142963026
Web Site: www.odysseyre.com
Emp.: 62
Reinsurance Services
S.I.C.: 6399
N.A.I.C.S.: 524130
Lucien Pietropoli *(CEO)*

Non-U.S. Subsidiaries:

First Capital Insurance Ltd. (2)
6 Raffles Quay 21-00
Singapore, 048580, Singapore SG
Tel.: (65) 62222311 (100%)
Fax: (65) 62223547
E-Mail: enquiry@first-insurance.com.sg
Web Site: www.first-insurance.com.sg
Emp.: 50
Personal & Commercial Insurance Services
S.I.C.: 6411
N.A.I.C.S.: 524298
Ramasamy Athapan *(CEO)*

Newline Underwriting Management Ltd. (2)
London Underwriting Center
3 Minster Court Suite 4, London, EC3R 7DD, United Kingdom UK
Tel.: (44) 2070901800 (100%)
Fax: (44) 2070901701
Web Site: www.odysseyre.com
Emp.: 95
Holding Company; Insurance Services
S.I.C.: 6719
N.A.I.C.S.: 551112
Carl Overy *(CEO)*

TIG Holdings, Inc. (1)
250 Commercial St Ste 5000
Manchester, NH 03101
Tel.: (972) 831-5000
Fax: (603) 656-2400
Web Site: www.riverstone-group.com
Emp.: 200
Insurance Holding Company
S.I.C.: 6351
N.A.I.C.S.: 524126
Robert Kant *(Mgr-Sys)*

Subsidiary:

TIG Insurance Co. (2)
5205 N O'Connor Blvd
Irving, TX 75039-3707 (100%)
Tel.: (972) 831-5000
Fax: (972) 831-6081
Web Site: www.tiginsurance.com
Emp.: 350
Property & Casualty Insurance; Reinsurance, Specialty, Commercial & Personal Insurance; Underwrites Sports, Leisure & Entertainment Events
S.I.C.: 6351
N.A.I.C.S.: 524126

Zenith National Insurance Corp. (1)
21255 Califa St
Woodland Hills, CA 91367-5005 DE
Mailing Address:
PO Box 9055
Van Nuys, CA 91409-9055
Tel.: (818) 713-1000
Fax: (818) 710-1860
E-Mail: info@thezenith.com
Web Site: www.thezenith.com
Sales Range: $550-599.9 Million
Emp.: 1,400
Holding Company; Property & Casualty Reinsurance & Workers' Compensation Insurance Services
S.I.C.: 6331
N.A.I.C.S.: 524126
Kari L. Van Gundy *(CFO & Exec VP)*
Michael E. Jansen *(Gen Counsel & Exec VP)*
Hyman J. Lee Jr. *(Sec, Sr VP & Asst Gen Counsel)*
Jack D. Miller *(Exec VP)*
Davidson M. Pattiz *(Exec VP)*
Robert E. Meyer *(Sr VP)*
William J. Owen *(Sr VP-IR)*

Subsidiary:

Zenith Insurance Company (2)
21255 Califa St
Woodland Hills, CA 91367 (100%)
Tel.: (818) 713-1000
Fax: (818) 710-1860
Web Site: www.thezenith.com
Emp.: 1,076
Workers' Compensation Underwriting Services
S.I.C.: 6411
N.A.I.C.S.: 524298
Jack D. Miller *(Vice Chm)*
Janet Frank *(Pres & COO)*
Paul Ramont *(Chief Underwriting Officer & Exec VP)*
John J. Tickner *(Gen Counsel, Sec & Sr VP)*
Hyman J. Lee, Jr. *(Sec & VP)*
Davidson M. Pattiz *(Exec VP)*
Craig Thomson *(Exec VP)*
Keith E. Trotman *(Exec VP)*
Robert E. Meyer *(Sr VP)*

U.S. Holding:

Ridley, Inc. (1)
424 N Riverfront Dr PO Box 8500
Mankato, MN 56002-8500 (73.6%)
Tel.: (507) 388-9400
Fax: (507) 388-9415
E-Mail: info@ridleyinc.com
Web Site: www.ridleyinc.com
RCL—(TSX)
Emp.: 876
Livestock Feed Mfr, Hog Breeding & Sales: Livestock Equipment, Animal Health Supplies & Pet Food Distr
S.I.C.: 2048
N.A.I.C.S.: 311119
Bradley P. Martin *(Chm)*
Steven J. VanRoekel *(Pres & CEO)*
Gordon Hildebrand *(CFO)*
Robert E. Frost *(Exec VP & Pres-Block Ops)*
Michael J. Hudspith *(Exec VP & Pres-Feed Ingredients)*
K. Bruce Campbell *(Sec)*

Subsidiary:

Hubbard Feeds Inc. (2)
424 N Riverfront Dr
Mankato, MN 56001 MN
Mailing Address: (100%)
PO Box 8500
Mankato, MN 56002-8500
Tel.: (507) 388-9400
Fax: (507) 388-9415
E-Mail: info@hubbardfeeds.com
Web Site: www.hubbardfeeds.com
Emp.: 550
Feed Mfr & Pet Food Distr
Export
S.I.C.: 2048
N.A.I.C.S.: 311119
Michael Hinton *(Mgr-Mktg-Feed Ops)*

Co-Headquarters:

Ridley Inc. (2)
34 Terracon Place
Winnipeg, MB, R2J 4G7, Canada
Tel.: (204) 956-1717
Fax: (204) 956-1687
E-Mail: info@ridleyinc.com
Web Site: www.ridleyinc.com
Manufactures & Markets Animal Feed, Nutrition & Health Products
S.I.C.: 2048
N.A.I.C.S.: 311119
Bradley P. Martin *(Chm)*
Steven J. VanRoekel *(Pres & CEO)*
Gordon Hildebrand *(CFO)*

Non-U.S. Subsidiaries:

Advent Capital (Holdings) PLC (1)
2nd Floor 2 Minster Court Mincing Lane
London, EC3R 7BB, United Kingdom (100%)
Tel.: (44) 2077438200
Fax: (44) 2077438299
E-Mail: head.office@adventgroup.co.uk
Web Site: www.adventgroup.co.uk
Sales Range: $200-249.9 Million
Emp.: 65
Insurance & Reinsurance Services
S.I.C.: 6351
N.A.I.C.S.: 524126
Brian F. Caudle *(Chm)*
Keith D. Thompson *(CEO)*
Trevor J. Ambridge *(Mng Dir)*
Philip Green *(CFO)*
Neil Ewing *(Sec)*

American Safety Insurance Holdings, Ltd. (1)
31 Queen Street 2nd Floor
Hamilton, HM 11, Bermuda BM
Tel.: (441) 296 8560
Fax: (441) 296 8561
Toll Free: 8003883647
E-Mail: info@americansafetyinsurance.com
Web Site: www.americansafetyinsurance.com
Rev.: $297,122,000
Assets: $1,373,131,000
Liabilities: $1,028,083,000
Net Worth: $345,048,000
Earnings: $13,108,000
Emp.: 242
Fiscal Year-end: 12/31/12
Holding Company; Insurance Products & Services
S.I.C.: 6719
N.A.I.C.S.: 551112
Michael A. Hinojosa *(Chief Claims Officer)*
Ambuj Kumar Jain *(Chief Underwriting Officer)*
Randolph L.M. Hutto *(Gen Counsel & Sec)*
Don Sather *(Sr VP-HR)*

Subsidiaries:

American Safety Assurance Ltd (2)
The Boyle Building 31
Queen Street, Hamilton, Bermuda (100%)
Tel.: (441) 2968560
Fax: (441) 2968561
Web Site: www.amsafety.bm/tabid/834/Default.aspx
All Other Insurance Related Activities
S.I.C.: 6411
N.A.I.C.S.: 524298
Leon Maloney *(Gen Mgr)*

American Safety Reinsurance Ltd. (2)
The Boyle Bldg 31 Queen St 2nd Floor
Hamilton, HM 11, Bermuda BM
Tel.: (441) 296 8560 (100%)
Fax: (441) 296 8561
E-Mail:
Web Site: www.amsafety.bm
Emp.: 8
Reinsurance Carrier
S.I.C.: 6399
N.A.I.C.S.: 524130
Nicholas Pascall *(Chief Underwriting Officer)*

U.S. Subsidiaries:

American Safety Casualty Insurance Company (2)
100 Galleria Pkwy Ste 700
Atlanta, GA 30339 (100%)
Tel.: (770) 916-1908
Fax: (770) 955-8339
Toll Free: (800) 388-3647
E-Mail: info@americansafety.com
Web Site: www.amsafety.com
Emp.: 130
Insurance Agencies & Brokerages
S.I.C.: 6411
N.A.I.C.S.: 524210
Stephen Ray Crim *(CEO)*

American Safety Indemnity Company (2)
100 Galleria Pkwy E700
Atlanta, GA 30339 (100%)
Tel.: (770) 916-0673
Fax: (770) 955-8339
E-Mail: info@amsafety.com
Web Site: www.amsafety.com
Emp.: 75
Mortgage & Nonmortgage Loan Brokers
S.I.C.: 6163
N.A.I.C.S.: 522310
Stephen Ray Crim *(CEO)*
Mark Haushill *(CFO)*

American Safety Insurance Services Inc. (2)
100 Galleria Pkwy SE Ste 700
Atlanta, GA 30339 (100%)
Tel.: (770) 916-1908
Fax: (770) 955-8339
E-Mail: info@amsafety.com
Web Site: www.amsafety.com
Emp.: 180
Insurance Agencies & Brokerages
S.I.C.: 6411
N.A.I.C.S.: 524210
Joseph D. Scollo, Jr. *(Pres & COO)*
Stephen Ray Crim *(CEO)*
Mark William Haushill *(CFO & Treas)*
Ambuj Jain *(Sr VP)*

American Safety Risk Retention Group Inc (2)
100 Galleria Pkwy SE Ste 700
Atlanta, GA 30339 (100%)
Tel.: (770) 916-1908
Fax: (770) 955-8339
E-Mail: info@amsafety.com
Web Site: www.amsafety.com
Emp.: 50
All Other Insurance Related Activities
S.I.C.: 6411
N.A.I.C.S.: 524298
Stephen Ray Crim *(CEO)*
Mark Haushill *(CFO)*

Brit Insurance Limited (1)
55 Bishopsgate
London, EC2N 3AS, United Kingdom UK
Tel.: (44) 2079848500
Fax: (44) 2079848701
E-Mail:
Web Site: www.britinsurance.com
Emp.: 5
Insurance Agencies & Brokerages
S.I.C.: 6411
N.A.I.C.S.: 524210

Fairfax Brasil Seguros Corporativos S.A. (1)
Alamenda Santos 1940 4 Andar
Cerqueira Cesar, Sao Paulo, 01418-200, Brazil
Tel.: (55) 11 3041 3020
Fax: (55) 11 3041 3076
E-Mail: fairfax@fairfax.com.br
Web Site: www.fairfax.com.br
Emp.: 70
Insurance Management Services
S.I.C.: 6411
N.A.I.C.S.: 524298
Jacques Bergman *(CEO)*

Falcon Insurance Company (Hong Kong) Limited (1)
6th Floor DCH Commercial Center
25 Westlands Road, Quarry Bay, China (Hong Kong)
Tel.: (852) 22322888
Fax: (852) 22322899
E-Mail: info@falconinsurance.com.hk
Web Site: www.falconinsurance.com.hk
Emp.: 100
Insurance Services
S.I.C.: 6411
N.A.I.C.S.: 524210
Gobinath Athappan *(CEO)*

nSpire Re Limited (1)
First Floor 25-28 Adelaide Road
Dublin, Ireland
Tel.: (353) 1 642 4000
Fax: (353) 1 642 4001
Insurance Management Services
S.I.C.: 6411
N.A.I.C.S.: 524298

Polskie Towarzystwo Reasekuracji Spolka Akcyjna (1)
Ul Bytomska 4
01 612 Warsaw, Poland
Tel.: (48) 22 832 02 56
Fax: (48) 22 833 02 18
E-Mail: info@polishre.com
Web Site: www.polishre.com
Insurance Management Services
S.I.C.: 6411
N.A.I.C.S.: 524298
Jean Cloutier *(Chm-Supervisory Bd)*
Monika Wozniak-Makarska *(Chm-Mgmt Bd)*
Urszula Palaszek *(Deputy Chm-Supervisory Bd)*

RiverStone Managing Agency Limited (1)
Park Gate 161-163 Preston Road
Brighton, East Sussex, BN1 6AU, United Kingdom
Tel.: (44) 1273562345
Fax: (44) 2074818928
Web Site: www.rsml.co.uk
Emp.: 75
Insurance Management Services
S.I.C.: 6411
N.A.I.C.S.: 524298
Luke Tanzer *(Gen Mgr)*

Thomas Cook (India) Limited (1)
Thomas Cook Building Dr DN Road Fort
Mumbai, 400001, India
Tel.: (91) 2261603333
Fax: (91) 2222871069
E-Mail: sales@thomascook.in
Web Site: www.thomascook.co.in
THOMASCOOK—(NSE)
Rev.: $81,669,825
Assets: $177,109,397
Liabilities: $95,825,813
Net Worth: $81,283,584
Earnings: $9,350,794
Emp.: 2,800
Fiscal Year-end: 12/31/12
Financial Services
S.I.C.: 6211
N.A.I.C.S.: 523999
Debasis Nandy *(Pres & CFO)*
Madhavan Menon *(Mng Dir)*
R. R. Kenkare *(Compliance Officer, Pres/ Head-Legal & Sec)*
Ambreesh Mahajan *(Pres-Ops)*
Mahesh Iyer *(Sr VP & Head-Foreign Exchange)*
Prashant Narayan *(Sr VP & Head-Leisure Travel-Inbound)*
Indiver Rastogi *(Sr VP & Head-Global Enterprise Bus)*
Surinder Singh Sodhi *(Sr VP & Head-Leisure Trave-Inbound)*
Suraj Nair *(Sr VP-Strategy & Plng)*

Non-U.S. Joint Venture:

ICICI Lombard General Insurance Co. Ltd. (1)
South Tower 6th Floor ICICI Towers
Bandra Kurla Complex, Mumbai, 400051, India
Tel.: (91) 2266723800
E-Mail: info@icicilombard.com
Web Site: www.icicilombard.com
Insurance Services
S.I.C.: 6411
N.A.I.C.S.: 524210
Chandra Kochhar *(Chm)*
Bhargav Dasgupta *(CEO & Mng Dir)*

FAIRFAX MEDIA LIMITED

1 Darling Island Rd
Pyrmont, NSW, 2009, Australia
Mailing Address:
GPO 506
Sydney, NSW, 2001, Australia
Tel.: (61) 2 9282 2833
Fax: (61) 2 9282 1633
E-Mail: corporateenquiries@fairfaxmedia.com.au
Web Site: fairfaxmedia.com.au
Year Founded: 1990
FXJ—(ASX)
Rev.: $2,131,500,919
Assets: $3,143,693,691
Liabilities: $1,251,036,882
Net Worth: $1,892,656,810
Earnings: ($1,011,879)
Emp.: 7,043
Fiscal Year-end: 06/30/13
Business Description:
Newspaper, Magazine & Website Publisher
Import
S.I.C.: 2711
N.A.I.C.S.: 511110
Personnel:
Gregory Hywood *(CEO & Mng Dir)*
David Housego *(CFO)*
Andrew Lam-Po-Tang *(CIO & Dir-Svcs)*
Antony Catalano *(CEO-Domain)*
Jack Matthews *(CEO-Metro Media)*
Gail Hambly *(Gen Counsel & Sec)*
Board of Directors:
Roger Campbell Corbett
Michael E. Anderson
Jack Cowin
Gregory Hywood
Sandra McPhee
James Millar
Sam Morgan
Linda Nicholls
Peter Francis Young
Legal Counsel:
Freehill Hollingdale & Page
MLC Centre Martin Place
Sydney, NSW, 2000, Australia
Tel.: (61) 2 225 5000

Subsidiaries:

The Advocate Newspaper Proprietary Limited (1)
56 Mount Street
PO Box 63
Burnie, TAS, 7320, Australia
Tel.: (61) 3 6440 7409
Fax: (61) 3 6440 7470
E-Mail: news@theadvocate.com.au
Web Site: www.theadvocate.com.au
Emp.: 50
Newspaper Publishing Services
S.I.C.: 2711
N.A.I.C.S.: 511110
Jason Purdie *(Gen Mgr)*

The Age Company Ltd. (1)
655 Collins St DockLands
Melbourne, VIC, 3008, Australia (100%)
Tel.: (61) 396004211
E-Mail: primitge@theage.com.au
Web Site: www.theage.com.au
Emp.: 100
Newspaper & Magazine Publishers
S.I.C.: 2711
N.A.I.C.S.: 511110
Andrew Holden *(Editor-in-Chief)*

The Age Print Company Pty Ltd (1)
L 5 1 Darling Island Rd
Pyrmont, NSW, 2009, Australia
Tel.: (61) 292821674
Fax: (61) 292823065
Newspaper Publishing Services
S.I.C.: 2711
N.A.I.C.S.: 511110

Agricultural Publishers Pty Limited (1)
1 Darling Island Rd
Pyrmont, NSW, 2009, Australia
Tel.: (61) 292822833
Fax: (61) 292823253
Newspaper Publishing Services
S.I.C.: 2711
N.A.I.C.S.: 511110
Greg Hywood *(CEO)*

Australian Property Monitors Pty Limited (1)
Level 2 1 Darling Island Road
Pyrmont, NSW, 2009, Australia
Tel.: (61) 1800 817 616
Fax: (61) 8596 4928
E-Mail: enquiries@apm.com.au
Web Site: www.apm.com.au
Property Management Services
S.I.C.: 6531
N.A.I.C.S.: 531311

The Barossa News Pty Limited (1)
Shop 1 119 Murray St
Tanunda, SA, 5352, Australia
Tel.: (61) 885632041
Fax: (61) 85633655
Emp.: 15
Newspaper Publishing Services
S.I.C.: 2711
N.A.I.C.S.: 511110
Robert Davies *(Gen Mgr)*

Border Mail Printing Pty Ltd (1)
1 Mckoy St
Wodonga, VIC, 3689, Australia
Tel.: (61) 260240555
Fax: (61) 260240606
Commercial Printing Services
S.I.C.: 2759
N.A.I.C.S.: 323111

The Border Morning Mail Pty Ltd (1)
1 McKoy Street
PO Box 491
Wodonga, VIC, 3689, Australia
Tel.: (61) 2 6024 0555
Fax: (61) 2 6024 0604
E-Mail: bmm@bordermail.com.au
Web Site: www.bordermail.com.au
Newspaper Publishing Services
S.I.C.: 2711
N.A.I.C.S.: 511110
Heath Harrison *(Editor)*

Bridge Printing Office Pty Limited (1)
110-118 Adelaide Rd
Murray Bridge, SA, 5253, Australia
Tel.: (61) 885328000
Fax: (61) 885321594
E-Mail: office@bridgeprinting.com.au
Web Site: www.bridgeprinting.com.au
Commercial Printing Services
S.I.C.: 3555
N.A.I.C.S.: 333244

Bundaberg Broadcasters Pty Ltd (1)
38 Crofton St
Bundaberg, QLD, 4670, Australia
Tel.: (61) 741512478
Radio Broadcasting Services
S.I.C.: 3663
N.A.I.C.S.: 334220

Carpentaria Newspapers Pty Ltd (1)
112 Camooweal Street
PO Box 777
Mount Isa, QLD, 4825, Australia
Tel.: (61) 747433355
Fax: (61) 747439789
E-Mail: admin@starnews.com.au
Web Site: www.northweststar.com.au
Emp.: 20
Newspaper Publishing Services
S.I.C.: 2711
N.A.I.C.S.: 511110
Peter Baldwin *(Gen Mgr)*

Commerce Australia Pty Ltd (1)
Level 2 8 Parliament Place
West Perth, WA, 6005, Australia
Tel.: (61) 8 9226 0011
Fax: (61) 8 9226 0033
E-Mail: info@ca.com.au
Web Site: www.ca.com.au
Emp.: 2
Software Development Services
S.I.C.: 7371
N.A.I.C.S.: 541511

Country Publishers Pty Ltd (1)
13 Coral St
Victor Harbour, SA, 5211, Australia
Tel.: (61) 885521488
Fax: (61) 85524613
E-Mail: victortimes@ruralpress.com
Web Site: www.victorharbortimes.com.au
Emp.: 16
Newspaper Publishing Services
S.I.C.: 2711
N.A.I.C.S.: 511110

CountryCars.com.au Pty Ltd (1)
PO Box 2297
Orange, NSW, 2800, Australia
Tel.: (61) 1300 737 161
Fax: (61) 2 6369 0621
Web Site: www.countrycars.com.au
Online Advertising Services
S.I.C.: 7319
N.A.I.C.S.: 541890

Cudgegong Newspapers Pty Ltd (1)
9 Perry St
Mudgee, NSW, 2850, Australia
Tel.: (61) 263721455
Fax: (61) 263724127
Emp.: 5
Newspaper Publishing Services
S.I.C.: 2711
N.A.I.C.S.: 511110
Carmel Houlison *(Mgr-Adv)*

The Examiner Newspaper Pty Ltd (1)
71 Paterson St
PO Box 99
Launceston, TAS, 7250, Australia
Tel.: (61) 3 6336 7111
Fax: (61) 3 6331 4858
E-Mail: admin@examiner.com.au
Web Site: www.examiner.com.au
Newspaper Publishing Services
S.I.C.: 2711
N.A.I.C.S.: 511110
Phil Leersen *(Gen Mgr)*

Fairfax Business Media (1)
Level 2 469 LaTrobe St
Melbourne, VIC, 3000, Australia AU
Tel.: (61) 396033888 (100%)
Fax: (61) 396704328
Web Site: www.brw.com.au
Emp.: 75
S.I.C.: 2711
N.A.I.C.S.: 511110
Kevin Chinnery *(Mng Dir)*

Fairfax Community Newspapers Pty. Limited (1)
1 Worth Street
Chullora, NSW, 2190, Australia AU
Tel.: (61) 97356452 (100%)
Fax: (61) 29756499
E-Mail: info@fcnonline.com.au
Web Site: www.fcnonline.com.au
Emp.: 200
Newspaper Publishers
S.I.C.: 2711
N.A.I.C.S.: 511110

Fairfax Community Newspapers Pty. Ltd. (1)
142 144 Dandenong Frankston Rd
3175 Dandenong, VIC, Australia AU
Tel.: (61) 392387777 (100%)
Fax: (61) 392387682
E-Mail: eastnews@yourweekly.com.au
Web Site: www.fairfax.com.au
Emp.: 5,500
S.I.C.: 2711
N.A.I.C.S.: 511110

Fairfax Media Limited—(Continued)

Fairfax Corporation Pty Limited (1)
L 5 1 Darling Island Rd
Pyrmont, NSW, 2009, Australia
Tel.: (61) 292822833
Web Site: fairfaxmedia.com.au
Emp.: 300
Newspaper Publishing Services
S.I.C.: 2711
N.A.I.C.S.: 511110
Kazuya Mori *(CEO)*

Fairfax Digital Australia & New Zealand Pty Ltd (1)
L 5 1 Darling Island Rd
Pyrmont, NSW, 2009, Australia
Tel.: (61) 292822833
Fax: (61) 292821633
Newspaper Publishing Services
S.I.C.: 2711
N.A.I.C.S.: 511110

Fairfax Digital Limited (1)
1 Darling Island Road
Pyrmont, Sydney, NSW, Australia
Tel.: (61) 1800 500 864
E-Mail: newsroom@fairfax.com.au
Web Site: www.fairfax.com.au
Online News & Classified Advertising Services
S.I.C.: 2741
N.A.I.C.S.: 519130
Olivia Baldrocco *(Mgr-Sls-Victoria)*

Fairfax Media Group Finance Pty Limited (1)
L 5 Darling Island Rd
Pyrmont, NSW, 2000, Australia
Tel.: (61) 292822833
Fax: (61) 292823065
Financial Management Services
S.I.C.: 6211
N.A.I.C.S.: 523999
Greg Hywood *(CEO)*

Fairfax Media Management Pty Limited (1)
L5 1 Darling Island Rd
Pyrmont, NSW, 2009, Australia
Tel.: (61) 292822833
Fax: (61) 292823065
Newspaper Publishing Services
S.I.C.: 2711
N.A.I.C.S.: 511110
Brian Cassell *(CEO)*

Fairfax Media Publications Pty Limited (1)
L 5 1 Darling Island Rd
Pyrmont, NSW, 2009, Australia
Tel.: (61) 292822833
Fax: (61) 292823065
Newspaper Publishing Services
S.I.C.: 2711
N.A.I.C.S.: 511110

Fairfax News Network Pty Limited (1)
L 2 1 Darling Island Rd
Pyrmont, NSW, 2009, Australia
Tel.: (61) 0292822833
Fax: (61) 292823253
Web Site: www.fairfaxmedia.com.au
Newspaper Publishing Services
S.I.C.: 2711
N.A.I.C.S.: 511110

Fairfax Printers Pty Limited (1)
1 Worth St
Chullora, NSW, 2190, Australia
Tel.: (61) 297356000
Fax: (61) 297356250
Emp.: 230
Commercial Printing Services
S.I.C.: 2759
N.A.I.C.S.: 323111
Jamie Patterson *(Gen Mgr)*

Fairfax Radio Syndication Pty Limited (1)
170 Pacific Highway
Greenwich, NSW, 2065, Australia
Tel.: (61) 2 9930 9810
Fax: (61) 2 9930 9814
E-Mail: info@fxrs.com.au
Web Site: www.fairfaxradionews.com.au
Radio Programs Distribution Services
S.I.C.: 4832
N.A.I.C.S.: 515112

Fairfax Regional Printers Pty Limited (1)
7 Enterprise Dr
Beresfield, Newcastle, NSW, 2322, Australia
Tel.: (61) 249357435
Fax: (61) 249357444
Emp.: 90
Newspaper Publishing Services
S.I.C.: 2711
N.A.I.C.S.: 511110
Anthony Payne *(Gen Mgr)*

The Federal Capital Press of Australia Pty Limited (1)
9 Pirie Street
Fyshwick, ACT, 2609, Australia
Tel.: (61) 262802122
Fax: (61) 262804959
E-Mail: media.release@canberratimes.com.au
Web Site: www.canberratimes.com.au
Emp.: 400
Newspaper Publishing Services
S.I.C.: 2711
N.A.I.C.S.: 511110
Ken Nicholls *(Gen Mgr)*

Find a Babysitter Pty Limited (1)
Level 2 1 Darling Island Road
Pyrmont, NSW, 2009, Australia
Tel.: (61) 1300789073
Fax: (61) 2 8596 4962
E-Mail: info@findababysitter.com.au
Web Site: www.findababysitter.com.au
Babysitting Services
S.I.C.: 8351
N.A.I.C.S.: 624410
Alicia Melvill *(Mgr-Bus Dev)*

Harris and Company Pty Limited (1)
L 2 39 Alexander St
Burnie, TAS, 7320, Australia
Tel.: (61) 364407409
Newspaper Publishing Services
S.I.C.: 2711
N.A.I.C.S.: 511110

Harris Print Pty Ltd (1)
13 Dunham Road
PO Box 63
Cooee, Burnie, TAS, 7320, Australia
Tel.: (61) 364407414
Fax: (61) 364407419
E-Mail: print@harrisprint.com.au
Web Site: www.harrisprint.com.au
Emp.: 12
Newspaper Publishing Services
S.I.C.: 2711
N.A.I.C.S.: 511110
Fiona van de Worp *(Gen Mgr)*

Hunter Distribution Network Pty Ltd (1)
7 Enterprise Dr
Beresfield, Newcastle, NSW, 2322, Australia
Tel.: (61) 249357488
Fax: (61) 49357444
E-Mail: htn@ruralpress.com
Emp.: 6
Newspaper Publishing Services
S.I.C.: 2711
N.A.I.C.S.: 511110
Michael Roberts *(Gen Mgr)*

Illawarra Newspaper Holdings Pty. Limited (1)
21 Auburn St
PO Box 1215
Wollongong, NSW, 2500, Australia (100%)
Tel.: (61) 242212333
Fax: (61) 2422122338
E-Mail: cos@illawarramercury.com.au
Web Site: www.illawarramercury.com.au
Emp.: 200
Newspaper Publishers
S.I.C.: 2711
N.A.I.C.S.: 511110
Ben Marsh *(Gen Mgr)*

Integrated Publication Solutions Pty Ltd (1)
Level 4 Media House 655 Collins St
Docklands, Melbourne, VIC, 3008, Australia
Tel.: (61) 1800 606 477
Fax: (61) 3 8667 3190
E-Mail: info@publicationsolutions.com.au
Web Site: www.publicationsolutions.com.au
Magazine Publishing Services
S.I.C.: 2721
N.A.I.C.S.: 511120
Adam Gray *(Gen Mgr)*

John Fairfax Limited (1)
1 Darling Island Rd
Pyrmont, NSW, 2009, Australia
Tel.: (61) 292822833
Fax: (61) 292823208
Newspaper Publishing Services
S.I.C.: 2711
N.A.I.C.S.: 511110

John Fairfax Publications Pty. Ltd. (1)
1 Darling Island Road
Island Rd, Pyrmont, NSW, 2009, Australia AU
Tel.: (61) 292822833
Fax: (61) 292823253
E-Mail: hrnsfff@fairfax.com.au
Web Site: www.fairfax.com.au
Emp.: 1,300
S.I.C.: 2711
N.A.I.C.S.: 511110
Greg Hywood *(CEO)*

Milton Ulladulla Publishing Co. Pty Ltd (1)
Suite 29 The Plaza Princes Highway
PO Box 210
Ulladulla, NSW, 2539, Australia
Tel.: (61) 2 4455 1244
Fax: (61) 244554314
E-Mail: mail.mutimes@ruralpress.com
Web Site: www.ulladullatimes.com.au
Emp.: 13
Newspaper Publishing Services
S.I.C.: 2711
N.A.I.C.S.: 511110
Freddie Simon *(Mgr)*

Mountain Press Pty Ltd (1)
274 Macquarie Road
PO Box 21
Springwood, NSW, 2777, Australia
Tel.: (61) 247511955
Fax: (61) 247515556
E-Mail: damien.madigan@fairfaxmedia.com.au
Web Site: www.bluemountainsgazette.com.au
Emp.: 40
Newspaper Publishing Services
S.I.C.: 2711
N.A.I.C.S.: 511110
Steve Ticehurst *(Gen Mgr)*

Newcastle Newspapers Pty. Limited (1)
28-30 Bolton Street
Newcastle, NSW, 2300, Australia (100%)
Tel.: (61) 249795000
Fax: (61) 249795588
E-Mail: news@theherald.com.au
Web Site: www.theherald.com.au
Emp.: 350
Newspaper Publishers
S.I.C.: 2711
N.A.I.C.S.: 511110
Jason King *(Mgr-Special Project)*

Port Lincoln Times Pty Ltd (1)
2-8 Washington Street
PO Box 1672
Port Lincoln, SA, 5606, Australia
Tel.: (61) 8 8682 1055
Fax: (61) 86824417
E-Mail: lincolntimes@ruralpress.com
Web Site: www.portlincolntimes.com.au
Emp.: 20
Newspaper Publishing Services
S.I.C.: 2711
N.A.I.C.S.: 511110
Christopher Coote *(Editor)*

Queensland Community Newspapers Pty Limited (1)
135a Queen St
Cleveland, 4163, Australia
Tel.: (61) 738218333
Newspaper Publishing Services
S.I.C.: 2711
N.A.I.C.S.: 511110

Radio 1278 Melbourne Pty Limited (1)
655 Collins St
Docklands, Melbourne, VIC, 3008, Australia
Tel.: (61) 386673600
E-Mail: feedback@3aw.com.au
Emp.: 200
Radio Broadcasting Services
S.I.C.: 3663
N.A.I.C.S.: 334220
Shane Healy *(Gen Mgr)*

Radio 2UE Sydney Pty Ltd (1)
170 Pacific Hwy
Greenwich, NSW, 2065, Australia
Tel.: (61) 299309954
Fax: (61) 299309479
Web Site: www.2ue.com.au
Emp.: 100
Radio Broadcasting Services
S.I.C.: 3663
N.A.I.C.S.: 334220
Arne Reiler *(Gen Mgr)*

Radio 4BH Brisbane Pty Limited (1)
77 Southgate Avenue
Cannon Hill, Brisbane, 4170, Australia
Tel.: (61) 7 390 882 00
E-Mail: feedback@4bh.com.au
Web Site: www.4bh.com.au
Radio Broadcasting Services
S.I.C.: 3663
N.A.I.C.S.: 334220

Radio 6PR Perth Pty Limited (1)
Level 1/169 Hay Street
East Perth, Perth, WA, 6004, Australia
Tel.: (61) 892201400
Fax: (61) 893252806
E-Mail: news@6pr.com.au
Web Site: www.6pr.com.au
Emp.: 50
Radio Station Operating Services
S.I.C.: 4832
N.A.I.C.S.: 515112
John Solvander *(Program Dir)*

Radio 96FM Perth Pty Limited (1)
Level 1 169 Hay Street
East Perth, Perth, WA, 6004, Australia
Tel.: (61) 893239600
Fax: (61) 893239666
E-Mail: 96fm@96fm.com.au
Web Site: www.96fm.com.au
Emp.: 4
Radio Broadcasting Services
S.I.C.: 3663
N.A.I.C.S.: 334220
Martin Boylen *(Acting Gen Mgr)*

Regional Printers Pty Limited (1)
159 Bells Line Of Rd
North Richmond, Sydney, NSW, 2754, Australia
Tel.: (61) 245704444
Fax: (61) 245704663
Commercial Printing Services
S.I.C.: 2759
N.A.I.C.S.: 323111
Michael Gee *(Gen Mgr)*

Regional Publishers Pty Ltd (1)
Unit 6 555 High St
Maitland, NSW, 2320, Australia
Tel.: (61) 249310100
Fax: (61) 249310154
Web Site: www.maitlandmercury.com.au
Emp.: 50
Newspaper Publishing Services
S.I.C.: 2711
N.A.I.C.S.: 511110
S. Prescott *(Office Mgr)*

Regional Publishers (Western Victoria) Pty Limited (1)
110 Creswick Rd
Ballarat, VIC, 3350, Australia
Tel.: (61) 353201200
Fax: (61) 353201209
Emp.: 100
Newspaper Publishing Services
S.I.C.: 2711
N.A.I.C.S.: 511110
Angela Carey *(Gen Mgr)*

Riverina Newspapers (Griffith) Pty Ltd (1)
32-36 Ulong Street
PO Box 1004
Griffith, NSW, 2680, Australia
Tel.: (61) 2 6962 1733
Fax: (61) 2 6964 1844
E-Mail: classifieds@areanews.com.au
Web Site: www.areanews.com.au

Newspaper Publishing Services
S.I.C.: 2711
N.A.I.C.S.: 511110
Lyn Urquhart *(Gen Mgr)*

RSVP.com.au Pty Limited (1)
GPO Box 506
Sydney, NSW, 2001, Australia
Tel.: (61) 2 9957 1404
Fax: (61) 2 8596 4962
E-Mail: iphonefeedback@rsvp.com.au
Web Site: www.rsvp.com.au
Online Dating Services
S.I.C.: 7299
N.A.I.C.S.: 812990

Rural Press Limited (1)
159 Bells Line of Rd
Richmond, NSW, 2754, Australia
Tel.: (61) 245704444
Fax: (61) 245704663
E-Mail: groupadmin@ruralpress.com
Web Site: www.ruralpress.com
Sales Range: $250-299.9 Million
Emp.: 400
Agricultural & Regional Publisher, Broadcaster & Printer
Export
S.I.C.: 2721
N.A.I.C.S.: 511120
J. B. Fairfax *(Chm)*
Brian McCarthy *(CEO & Mng Dir)*

Subsidiary:

Wimmera Mail Times Pty Ltd (2)
92 Wilson St
PO Box 519
Horsham, VIC, 3400, Australia
Tel.: (61) 353620000
Fax: (61) 353810329
E-Mail: classies@mailtimes.com.au
Web Site: www.mailtimes.com.au
Emp.: 35
Newspaper Publisher
S.I.C.: 2711
N.A.I.C.S.: 511110
Tim Lewis *(Gen Mgr)*

Satellite Music Australia Pty Limited (1)
157-159 Harris Street
Pyrmont, NSW, 2009, Australia
Tel.: (61) 2 9566 7788
E-Mail: sales@sma.net.au
Web Site: www.sma.net.au
Digital Music Publishing Services
S.I.C.: 2741
N.A.I.C.S.: 512230

Stock Journal Publishers Pty Ltd (1)
123 Greenhill Rd
Unley, Adelaide, SA, 5061, Australia
Tel.: (61) 883725222
Fax: (61) 883725279
Emp.: 60
Newspaper Publishing Services
S.I.C.: 2711
N.A.I.C.S.: 511110
Joe Wallman *(Gen Mgr)*

The Wagga Daily Advertiser Pty Ltd (1)
48 Trail Street
Wagga Wagga, NSW, 2650, Australia
Tel.: (61) 269383300
Fax: (61) 269217221
E-Mail: editor@dailyadvertiser.com.au
Web Site: www.dailyadvertiser.com.au
Emp.: 150
Newspaper Publishing Services
S.I.C.: 2711
N.A.I.C.S.: 511110
Crystal Hollis *(Editor-Features)*

The Weather Company Pty Limited (1)
L 5 8 West St
Sydney, NSW, 2060, Australia
Tel.: (61) 299659200
Fax: (61) 299551536
Professional Scientific & Technical Services
S.I.C.: 7389
N.A.I.C.S.: 541990

Western Magazine Pty Ltd (1)
216 Macquarie St
PO Box 311
Dubbo, NSW, 2830, Australia
Tel.: (61) 2 6883 2949
Fax: (61) 2 6884 1695
E-Mail: westernmag@ruralpress.com
Web Site: www.westernmagazine.com.au
Magazines Publishing Services
S.I.C.: 2721
N.A.I.C.S.: 511120

Whyalla News Properties Pty Ltd (1)
21 Forsyth Street
PO Box 183
Whyalla, SA, 5600, Australia
Tel.: (61) 886458088
Fax: (61) 86451045
E-Mail: editor.whyallanews@ruralpress.com
Web Site: www.whyallanewsonline.com.au
Newspaper Publishing Services
S.I.C.: 2711
N.A.I.C.S.: 511110
Sara Garcia *(Editor)*

Units:

Australian Financial Review (1)
1 Darling Island Rd Pyrmon
Sydney, NSW, 2009, Australia AU
Tel.: (61) 292822833 (100%)
Telex: 20121
Fax: (61) 292823137
E-Mail: afrnewsdesk@afr.com.au
Web Site: www.afr.com
Emp.: 100
Business & Financial Newspaper
S.I.C.: 2711
N.A.I.C.S.: 511110
Vicki Aristidopoulos *(Head-Mktg)*

The Sun-Herald (1)
1 Darling Island Rd
PO Box 506
Sydney, NSW, 2001, Australia AU
Mailing Address: (100%)
GPO Box 506
Sydney, NSW, 2001, Australia
Tel.: (61) 292822833
Telex: 20121
Fax: (61) 292822151
E-Mail: shdmedia@fairfaxmedia.com.au
Web Site: www.smh.com.au
Emp.: 200
Sunday Newspaper
S.I.C.: 2711
N.A.I.C.S.: 511110
Brian Cassell *(CFO)*

The Sydney Morning Herald (1)
1 Darling Island Road
Pyrmont, NSW, 2000, Australia AU
Mailing Address: (100%)
GPO Box 506
Sydney, NSW, 2001, Australia
Tel.: (61) 292822018
Telex: AA 20121
Fax: (61) 292823253
E-Mail: newsdesk@smh.com.au
Web Site: www.smh.com.au
Emp.: 100
Morning Newspaper
S.I.C.: 2711
N.A.I.C.S.: 511110
Darren Goodsir *(Editor-in-Chief)*

Warrnambool Standard (1)
575 Rajlin Tirid
Warrnambool, VIC, 3280, Australia (100%)
Tel.: (61) 355631800
Fax: (61) 355631880
E-Mail: ws.editor@standard.fairfax.com
Web Site: www.the.standard.net.au
Emp.: 75
S.I.C.: 2711
N.A.I.C.S.: 511110
Michalla Lumstan *(CFO)*

Non-U.S. Subsidiaries:

Fairfax Business Media Pte Limited (1)
152 Beach Road 11-06/08 Gateway East
Rochor
Singapore, 189721, Singapore
Tel.: (65) 63399382
Fax: (65) 63399281
Periodical Publishing Services
S.I.C.: 2721
N.A.I.C.S.: 511120

Fairfax Media (UK) Limited (1)
3rd Floor 27-29 Berwick Street
London, W1F 8RQ, United Kingdom
Tel.: (44) 207 851 9699
Fax: (44) 207 851 9688
Newspaper Publishing Services
S.I.C.: 2711
N.A.I.C.S.: 511110

Fairfax New Zealand Limited (1)
40 Boulcott St
Wellington, 6140, New Zealand
Mailing Address:
PO Box 2595
Wellington, New Zealand
Tel.: (64) 44969800
Fax: (64) 44740304
E-Mail: news@domcost.co.nz
Web Site: www.fairfaxmedia.co.nz
Emp.: 350
Publisher of Newspapers & Magazines
S.I.C.: 2711
N.A.I.C.S.: 511110
Joan Withers *(CEO)*
Andrew Boyle *(Acting Mng Dir)*
Randall Burt *(CFO)*

Subsidiaries:

The Christchurch Press Co. Ltd. (2)
22 Cathedral Sq
Private Bag 158
Christchurch, 8140, New Zealand (100%)
Tel.: (64) 33790940
Fax: (64) 33648496
E-Mail: editorial@press.co.nz
Web Site: www.press.co.nz
Emp.: 390
Publisher of Newspapers
S.I.C.: 2711
N.A.I.C.S.: 511110
Andrew Boyle *(Gen Mgr)*

The Manawatu Standard Limited (2)
PO Box 3
Palmerston North, 5301, New Zealand
Mailing Address:
PO Box 3
Palmerston, North, New Zealand
Tel.: (64) 63509555
Fax: (64) 63509545
Web Site: www.manawatustandard.co.nz
Emp.: 150
Publisher of Newspapers
S.I.C.: 2711
N.A.I.C.S.: 511110
Michael Cummings *(Editor)*

The Marlborough Express (2)
62 Arthur St
PO Box 242
7240 Blenheim, New Zealand (100%)
Mailing Address:
PO Box 242
Blenheim, New Zealand
Tel.: (64) 35772950
Fax: (64) 52089100
E-Mail: marlexpress@marlboroughexpress.co.nz
Web Site: www.marlboroughexpress.co.nz
Sls.: $8,475,420
Emp.: 75
Publisher of Newspapers
S.I.C.: 2711
N.A.I.C.S.: 511110
Vanessa Watson *(Gen Mgr)*

The Nelson Mail (2)
15 Bridge St
PO Box 244
Nelson, 7001, New Zealand
Mailing Address:
PO Box 244
Nelson, New Zealand
Tel.: (64) 35487079
Fax: (64) 35462802
E-Mail: chiefreporter@nelsonmail.co.nz
Web Site: www.nelsonmail.co.nz
Emp.: 110
Publisher of Newspapers
S.I.C.: 2711
N.A.I.C.S.: 511110
Craig Dennis *(Gen Mgr)*

The Southland Times (2)
67 Esk St
PO Box 805
Invercargill, New Zealand
Mailing Address:
PO Box 805
Invercargill, New Zealand
Tel.: (64) 32111130
Fax: (64) 32111098
E-Mail: executive@stl.co.nz
Web Site: www.stuff.co.nz
Emp.: 150
Publisher of Newspapers
S.I.C.: 2711
N.A.I.C.S.: 511110

Taranaki Newspapers Limited (2)
49 65 Currie St
PO Box 444
Taranaki Mail Ctr, 4340 New Plymouth, 4310, New Zealand (100%)
Mailing Address:
PO Box 444
New Plymouth, New Zealand
Tel.: (64) 67590808
Fax: (64) 67584653
E-Mail: tnlmanagement@dailynews.co.nz
Web Site: www.taranakidailynews.co.nz
Emp.: 125
Publisher of Newspapers
S.I.C.: 2711
N.A.I.C.S.: 511110

Waikato Times (2)
Forman Rd Te Rapa
Private Bag 3086
Hamilton, 3240, New Zealand
Tel.: (64) 78496180
Fax: (64) 78499554
Web Site: www.stuff.co.nz
Emp.: 250
Publisher of Newspapers
S.I.C.: 2711
N.A.I.C.S.: 511110
Gareth Cott *(Gen Mgr)*

NZ Rural Press Limited (1)
Level 1 300 Great South Road
PO Box 4233
Auckland, 1140, New Zealand
Tel.: (64) 95235056
Fax: (64) 95241170
E-Mail: admin.nz@ruralpress.com
Web Site: www.ruralpress.com
Emp.: 12
Commercial Printing Services
S.I.C.: 2759
N.A.I.C.S.: 323111
Craig Chapman *(Gen Mgr)*

FAIRMONT RESOURCES INC.

Suite 810 789 West Pender St
Vancouver, BC, V6C 1H2, Canada
Tel.: (604) 648-0523
Fax: (604) 682-6509
E-Mail: info@fairmontres.com
Web Site: www.fairmontresources.com
Year Founded: 2007
FMR—(TSXV)
Int. Income: $5,307
Assets: $2,121,568
Liabilities: $107,929
Net Worth: $2,013,639
Earnings: ($628,365)
Fiscal Year-end: 10/31/12

Business Description:
Mineral Exploration Services
S.I.C.: 1081
N.A.I.C.S.: 213114

Personnel:
Neil Pettigrew *(Pres & CEO)*
Greg Ball *(CFO)*

Board of Directors:
Greg Ball
John Bevilacqua
Neil Pettigrew
Michael Thompson

Transfer Agent:
Equity Financial Trust Company
200 University Avenue Suite 400
Toronto, ON, Canada

FAIRPLAY SCHLEPPDAMPFSCHIFFS-REEDEREI RICHARD BORCHARD GMBH

Bei den Muhren 1
20457 Hamburg, Germany
Tel.: (49) 403749990
Fax: (49) 4037499949

Fairplay Schleppdampfschiffs-Reederei Richard Borchard GmbH—(Continued)

E-Mail: Info@fairplay-towage.com
Web Site: www.fairplay-towage.com
Year Founded: 1905
Rev.: $19,989,750
Emp.: 70

Business Description:
Towage Services
S.I.C.: 4499
N.A.I.C.S.: 488390

Personnel:
Walter Collet *(Co-Mng Dir)*
Jorg Mainzer *(Co-Mng Dir)*
Mirek Wiater *(Pres-Szczecin)*
Agnieszka Janczynska *(Sec-Szczecin)*

FAIRPOINT GROUP PLC

Fairclough House Church Street
Adlington, Lancashire, PR7 4EX, United Kingdom
Tel.: (44) 8448261209
Fax: (44) 8448261176
E-Mail: info@fairpoint.co.uk
Web Site: www.debtfreedirect.co.uk
Year Founded: 1997
FRP—(AIM)
Rev.: $54,270,722
Assets: $81,961,992
Liabilities: $16,923,672
Net Worth: $65,038,321
Earnings: $12,585,362
Emp.: 410
Fiscal Year-end: 12/31/12

Business Description:
Debt Advisory Services
S.I.C.: 7299
N.A.I.C.S.: 812990

Personnel:
David Terence Digby Harrel *(Chm)*
Christopher Moat *(CEO)*
John Gittins *(Sec & Dir-Fin)*

Board of Directors:
David Terence Digby Harrel
John Allkins
Mike Fletcher
John Gittins
Christopher Moat
Amanda West

Legal Counsel:
Eversheds LLP
Eversheds House 70 Great Bridgewater Street
Manchester, M1 5ES, United Kingdom

Subsidiaries:

Allixium Limited (1)
Eversheds House 70 Great Bridgewater Street
Manchester, Lancashire, M1 5ES, United Kingdom
Tel.: (44) 845 296 0191
Fax: (44) 1257 476 128
Web Site: www.allixium.com
Debt Management Services
S.I.C.: 9311
N.A.I.C.S.: 921130

Clear Start Partnerships Limited (1)
Eversheds House 70 Great Bridgewater Street
Manchester, M1 5ES, United Kingdom
Tel.: (44) 8452960300
Web Site: www.clearstartpartnerships.co.uk
Debt Advisory Services
S.I.C.: 6282
N.A.I.C.S.: 523930

ClearStart UK Limited (1)
PO Box 555
Chorley, Lancashire, PR6 6HF, United Kingdom
Tel.: (44) 800 954 6241
E-Mail: enquiries@clearstart.co.uk
Web Site: www.clearstart.co.uk
Debt Advisory Services
S.I.C.: 6282
N.A.I.C.S.: 523930

Debt Advice Group Limited (1)
70 Great Bridgewater Street
Manchester, M1 5ES, United Kingdom
Tel.: (44) 800 116 4952
Web Site: www.debtadvicegroup.co.uk
Debt Advisory Services
S.I.C.: 6282
N.A.I.C.S.: 523930

Debt Free Direct Limited (1)
Fairclough House Church Street
Adlington, Chorley, Lancashire, PR7 4EX, United Kingdom
Tel.: (44) 8452960137
Fax: (44) 8452964095
E-Mail: customerenquiries@debtfreedirect.co.uk
Web Site: www.debtfreedirect.co.uk
Emp.: 400
Debt Advisory Services
S.I.C.: 6282
N.A.I.C.S.: 523930

Money Tailor Limited (1)
Fairclough House Church Street
Adlington, Lancs, PR7 4EX, United Kingdom
Tel.: (44) 800 5 999 999
E-Mail: info@moneytailor.co.uk
Web Site: www.moneytailor.co.uk
Debt Management Services
S.I.C.: 6211
N.A.I.C.S.: 523999

WKD UK Limited (1)
Crown House Luton Street
Keighley, West Yorkshire, BD21 2LE, United Kingdom
Tel.: (44) 1535 607 788
Debt Advisory Services
S.I.C.: 6282
N.A.I.C.S.: 523930

FAIRSON HOLDINGS LTD.

Flat A-C 9/F Yue Cheung Centre 1-3
Wong Chuk Yeung Street
Fotan, Sha Tin, China (Hong Kong)
Tel.: (852) 26063380
Fax: (852) 26910599
E-Mail: sales@sunfairw.com.hk
Web Site: www.sunfairw.com.hk
8132—(HKG)
Rev.: $22,630,420
Assets: $18,471,813
Liabilities: $10,164,882
Net Worth: $8,306,931
Earnings: ($1,370,712)
Emp.: 941
Fiscal Year-end: 12/31/12

Business Description:
Electric Power Cords & Cables
S.I.C.: 3357
N.A.I.C.S.: 335929

Personnel:
Tin Hung Yeung *(Chm)*
Shing Wai Yeung *(Compliance Officer & Sr Mgr-Fin & Mktg)*
Annie Sui Ping Cheung *(Sec)*

Board of Directors:
Tin Hung Yeung
Kai Wo Chan
Tian Gang Chen
Hoon Chong Chua
Hin Lung Li
Chi Yung Wong
Shing Wai Yeung
Yu Hui Zhou

Codan Trust Company (Cayman) Limited
Cricket Square Hutchins Drive
PO Box 2681
Georgetown, Grand Cayman, Cayman Islands

Transfer Agent:
Tricor Investor Services Limited
26th Floor Tesbury Centre 28 Queens Road East
Wanchai, China (Hong Kong)

FAIRSTAR RESOURCES LIMITED

U3 136 Main Street
PO Box 1520
Osborne Park, WA, 6017, Australia
Tel.: (61) 892425111
Fax: (61) 892425677
E-Mail: admin@fairstarresources.com
Web Site: www.fairstarresources.com
FAS—(ASX)
Rev.: $6,658
Assets: $4,345,292
Liabilities: $11,863,533
Net Worth: ($7,518,241)
Earnings: ($15,740,962)
Emp.: 9
Fiscal Year-end: 06/30/13

Business Description:
Exploration of Oil & Gas
S.I.C.: 1389
N.A.I.C.S.: 213112

Personnel:
Kevin J. Robertson *(Mng Dir)*
Madhukar Bhalla *(Sec)*

Board of Directors:
Constantino Markopoulos
Kevin J. Robertson
Timothy Michael Symons
Wayne Yiu-Wing Wan

Legal Counsel:
Lawton Gillon
Level 11 16 St Georges Terrace
Perth, Australia

FAIRVEST PROPERTY HOLDINGS LIMITED

Office 18003 18th Floor Triangle
House 22 Riebeek Street
Cape Town, 8001, South Africa

Mailing Address:
Postnet Suite 30
Private Bag x 3
Roggebaai, 8012, South Africa
Tel.: (27) 21 276 0800
Fax: (27) 21 276 0899
E-Mail: office@fairvest.co.za
Web Site: www.fairvest.co.za
FVT—(JSE)
Rev.: $6,052,353
Assets: $87,693,324
Liabilities: $87,291,428
Net Worth: $401,897
Fiscal Year-end: 06/30/13

Business Description:
Real Estate Development Services
S.I.C.: 6531
N.A.I.C.S.: 531390

Personnel:
Darren Wilder *(CEO)*
Jacques Kriel *(CFO)*
Adam Marcus *(COO)*

Board of Directors:
Jacques du Toit
Louis Andrag
Martin Epstein
Jacques Kriel
Keneilwe Moloko
Pieter van der Merwe
Darren Wilder

Transfer Agent:
Computershare Investor Services (Proprietary) Limited
Ground Floor 70 Marshall St
Johannesburg, South Africa

FAIRVIEW COVE AUTO LTD

(d/b/a Atlantic Acura)
30 Bedford Highway
Halifax, NS, B3M 2J2, Canada
Tel.: (902) 457-1555
Fax: (902) 443-4284
Toll Free: (800) 458-1555
E-Mail: sales@atlanticacura.ns.ca
Web Site: www.atlanticacura.ns.ca
Year Founded: 1987
Rev.: $13,911,192
Emp.: 30

Business Description:
New & Used Car Dealers
S.I.C.: 5511
N.A.I.C.S.: 441110

Personnel:
Bruce Hill *(Pres)*

FAIRWAY FORD SALES LTD.

236 Main Street
Steinbach, MB, R5G 1Y6, Canada
Tel.: (204) 326-3412
Fax: (204) 326-5996
Toll Free: (800) 668-0200
E-Mail: info@fairwayford.ca
Web Site: www.fairwayford.dealerconnection.com
Rev.: $27,400,000
Emp.: 50

Business Description:
New & Used Car Dealers
S.I.C.: 5511
N.A.I.C.S.: 441110

Personnel:
Mariann Stoesz *(Controller)*

FAIRWEST ENERGY CORPORATION

Ste 800 407 2 St SW
Calgary, AB, T2P 2Y3, Canada
Tel.: (403) 264-4949
Fax: (403) 269-1761
E-Mail: info@fairwestenergy.com
Web Site: www.fairwestenergy.com
FEC—(TSXV)
Sales Range: $1-9.9 Million
Emp.: 18

Business Description:
Oil & Gas Exploration Services
S.I.C.: 1389
N.A.I.C.S.: 213112

Personnel:
Douglas O. McNichol *(Pres & COO)*
Marion D. Mackie *(CFO)*

Board of Directors:
H. Allen Cameron
Sean C. Fauth
David S. Kelcher
Douglas O. McNichol
Carl M. Ravinsky

Legal Counsel:
Heenan Blaikie LLP
Calgary, AB, Canada

Carscallen LLP
Calgary, AB, Canada

Transfer Agent:
Olympia Trust Company
125 9th Avenue SE Suite 2300
Calgary, AB, T2G 0P6, Canada
Tel.: (403) 261-0900

FAIRWOOD HOLDINGS LIMITED

2/F TRP Commercial Centre 18
Tanner Road
North Point, China (Hong Kong)
Tel.: (852) 28567111
Fax: (852) 28805502
Web Site: www.fairwood.com.hk
0052—(HKG)
Sls.: $248,776,014
Assets: $111,155,287
Liabilities: $44,140,101
Net Worth: $67,015,186
Earnings: $17,984,528
Emp.: 4,400
Fiscal Year-end: 03/31/13

Business Description:
Fast Foods Industry
S.I.C.: 5812
N.A.I.C.S.: 722511

Personnel:
Dennis Hoi Yeung Lo *(Chm)*
Chee Shing Chan *(CEO)*
Yee Mei Mak *(Sec)*

Board of Directors:
Dennis Hoi Yeung Lo
Chee Shing Chan
Joseph Kai Nin Chan

Peter Kwok Kuen Lau
Yee Mei Mak
Chi Keung Ng
Tony Tong Hoo Tsoi
Peter Kam To Wan

Computershare Hong Kong Investor Services Limited
Rooms 1712-1716 17th Floor Hopewell Centre
183 Queen's Road East
Wanchai, China (Hong Kong)

Transfer Agents:
HSBC Securities Services (Bermuda) Limited
6 Front Street
Hamilton, Bermuda

Computershare Hong Kong Investor Services Limited
Rooms 1712-1716 17th Floor Hopewell Centre
183 Queen's Road East
Wanchai, China (Hong Kong)

FAISAL ISLAMIC BANK OF EGYPT

3 26th July St
Cairo, Egypt
Tel.: (20) 2 7621285
Fax: (20) 2 7621281
E-Mail: mails@faisalbank.com.eg
Web Site: www.faisalbank.com.eg
Year Founded: 1979
Sales Range: $75-99.9 Million
Emp.: 1,000

Business Description:
Banking Services
S.I.C.: 6029
N.A.I.C.S.: 522110

Board of Directors:
Ibrahim Ben Khalifa Al Khalifa
Amr Mohamed Al-Faisal
Omar Abdi Ali
Mostafa Abo Bakr Azzam
Mohammad Kamal Abdel El-Aziz Hashem
Ziad Hassan El-Rawashdeh
Ahmed Salah Jamjoum
Khalid Abdullah Janahi

FAISAL SPINNING MILLS LIMITED

Umer House Plot 23/1 Sector 23 SM
Farooq Road Korangi Industrial Area
Karachi, 74900, Pakistan
Tel.: (92) 2135115177
Fax: (92) 2135063002
E-Mail: khioff@umergroup.com
Web Site: www.umergroup.com
FASM—(KAR LAH)
Sls.: $85,991,417
Assets: $51,567,461
Liabilities: $21,063,051
Net Worth: $30,504,410
Earnings: $8,086,089
Emp.: 1,026
Fiscal Year-end: 06/30/13

Business Description:
Yarn Mfr
S.I.C.: 2299
N.A.I.C.S.: 313110

Personnel:
Bilal Sharif *(CEO)*
Anwar Hussain *(CFO)*
Asshraf Ali *(Sec)*

Board of Directors:
Mohammad Salim
Mohammad Amin
Khurram Salim
Mohammad Shaheen
Adil Shakeel
Mohammad Shakeel
Bilal Sharif
Mohammad Sharif

FAIST CHEMTEC GMBH

Weinsheimer Strasse 96
67547 Worms, Germany
Tel.: (49) 62 4130 10
Fax: (49) 62 4130 1200
E-Mail: info@faist-chemtec.com
Web Site: www.faist-chemtec.com
Year Founded: 2010
Emp.: 700

Business Description:
Industrial Application Acoustic Reduction Products Developer, Mfr & Whslr
S.I.C.: 3499
N.A.I.C.S.: 332999

Personnel:
Christoph Rotges *(Mng Dir)*

FAITH, INC.

Imon-Meiji-Yasudaseimei Building
566-1 Karasumadori-Oike-Sagaru
Toraya-cho Nakagyo-ku, Kyoto, 604-8171, Japan
Tel.: (81) 752133933
Fax: (81) 752133833
Web Site: www.faith-inc.com
4295—(TKS)
Sls.: $74,058,336
Assets: $248,722,540
Liabilities: $22,644,996
Net Worth: $226,077,544
Earnings: $12,228,436
Emp.: 161
Fiscal Year-end: 03/31/13

Business Description:
Content Delivery & Electronic Money Businesses
S.I.C.: 6099
N.A.I.C.S.: 522390

Personnel:
Hajime Hirasawa *(Pres & CEO)*
Jiro Saeki *(CFO)*
Hiroomi Yazaki *(CTO)*

Board of Directors:
Yasuyuki Higuchi
Hajime Hirasawa
Jiro Saeki
Koji Saeki
Hiroomi Yazaki

Transfer Agent:
Mitsubishi UFJ Trust & Banking Corporation
3-6-3 Fushimi-machi Chuo-ku Osaka-shi
Osaka, Japan

Subsidiaries:

Brave, Inc. (1)
No 23 Sq 3F Ebisu 1-chome
Shibuya-ku, Tokyo, Japan
Tel.: (81) 3 5789 9800
Fax: (81) 3 5789 9801
E-Mail: info@brave.bz
Web Site: www.brave.bz
Digital Content Services
S.I.C.: 2759
N.A.I.C.S.: 323111
Hiroshige Tonomura *(Pres)*

Faith Wonderworks, Inc. (1)
3F Ebisu Sq 1-23-23 Ebisu
Shibuya-ku, Tokyo, Japan
Tel.: (81) 3 5447 8338
Fax: (81) 3 5447 8339
Web Site: www.faith-wonderworks.co.jp
Cellular Phone Services
S.I.C.: 4812
N.A.I.C.S.: 517210
Ishida Yuuzi *(VP)*

Goody Point, Inc. (1)
4-3-24 Osaka Ctr Bldg 2F Samuti
Yodogawa-ku, Osaka, 532-0011, Japan
Tel.: (81) 668388822
Fax: (81) 668388823
E-Mail: info@ml.goody.jp
Web Site: www.goody.co.jp
Emp.: 29
Retail Business Service
S.I.C.: 5999
N.A.I.C.S.: 453998
Mitsuru Morimoto *(Pres)*

Rightsscale, Inc. (1)
3F Ebisu Sq 1-23-23 Ebisu
Shibuya-Ku, Tokyo, 150-0013, Japan
Tel.: (81) 3 5447 2480
Fax: (81) 3 5447 2481
E-Mail: domingo@rightsscale.co.jp
Web Site: www.rightsscale.co.jp
Emp.: 7
Digital Music Distr
S.I.C.: 5099
N.A.I.C.S.: 423990
Mamoru Sukumitsu *(Pres)*

FAIVELEY TRANSPORT S.A.

Le Delage Building Hall Parc - Batiment 6A 6eme etage
3 rue du 19 mars 1962, 92230 Gennevilliers, CEDEX, France
Tel.: (33) 148136500
Fax: (33) 148136554
E-Mail: info@faiveleytransport.com
Web Site: www.faiveleytransport.com
LEY—(EUR)
Sls.: $1,329,620,186
Assets: $1,984,233,041
Liabilities: $1,230,566,305
Net Worth: $753,666,736
Earnings: $85,631,220
Emp.: 5,483
Fiscal Year-end: 03/31/13

Business Description:
Railroad, Transportation & Other Industrial Equipment Mfr
S.I.C.: 3743
N.A.I.C.S.: 336510

Personnel:
Philippe Alfroid *(Chm-Supervisory Bd)*
Thierry Barel *(Chm-Mgmt Bd & CEO)*
Francois Faiveley *(Vice Chm-Supervisory Bd)*
Guillaume Bouhours *(CFO & Member-Mgmt Bd)*
Francois Feugier *(COO)*
Xavier de Lavallade *(Legal Counsel)*

Supervisory Board of Directors:
Philippe Alfroid
Didier Alix
Helele Auriol-Potier
Serge Choumaker
Francois Faiveley
Nicoletta Giadrossi-Morel
Robert Joyeux
Maurice Marchand-Tonel
Christopher Spencer

Expertise Comptable et Audit
Dijon, France

Subsidiaries:

Faiveley Transport Gennevilliers (1)
41 rue Jean Jaures
92230 Gennevilliers, France
Tel.: (33) 1 41 85 43 00
Fax: (33) 141854315
E-Mail: info.ftg@faiveleytransport.com
Web Site: www.faiveleytransport.com
Automotive Braking System Mfr
S.I.C.: 3714
N.A.I.C.S.: 336340

Faiveley Transport N.S.F (1)
ZI Voie Nouvelle rue de Reckem
59960 Neuville-en-Ferrain, France
Tel.: (33) 3 20 45 65 46
Fax: (33) 32 04 56 49 8
Aircraft Equipment Mfr
S.I.C.: 3728
N.A.I.C.S.: 336413

Faiveley Transport S.A. (1)
Le Delage Building Hall Parc Batiment 6A 6eme etage 3 Rue du 19 Mars 1962, 92230 Gennevilliers, Cedex, France
Tel.: (33) 1 48 13 6500
Fax: (33) 1 48 13 6554
Web Site: www.faiveleytransport.com
Railroad Equipment Mfr
S.I.C.: 3743
N.A.I.C.S.: 336510

Subsidiaries:

Faiveley Transport Amiens S.A.S. (2)
Espace Industriel Nord
Rue Andre Durouchez, 80046 Amiens, Cedex 2, France (100%)
Tel.: (33) 322673500
Fax: (33) 322673501
E-Mail: guillaume.lucas@faiveleytransport.com
Web Site: www.faiveley.com
Emp.: 300
Railway Vehicle Components Mfr
S.I.C.: 3442
N.A.I.C.S.: 332321

Non-U.S. Subsidiaries:

Faiveley Transport Witten (2)
Brauckstrasse 26
58454 Witten, Germany (100%)
Tel.: (49) 230227750
Fax: (49) 2277599215
E-Mail: info.wit@faiveleytransport.com
Web Site: www.faiveleytransport.com
Emp.: 300
Mfr of Brake Systems & Brake Components, Wheels, Doors, Air-Conditioning Equipment, Electricity Supply & Light Fittings for Railbound Vehicles
S.I.C.: 3743
N.A.I.C.S.: 336510
Christian Graeve *(Mng Dir)*

Faiveley Transport (2)
Harita
635 109 Hosur, Tamil Nadu, India (100%)
Tel.: (91) 4344276761
Fax: (91) 4344276035
E-Mail: su.in@faiveleytrnsport.com
Web Site: www.faiveleytrnsport.com
Emp.: 600
Railway Vehicle Components Mfr
S.I.C.: 3561
N.A.I.C.S.: 333911
Seshadri Srinivasan *(Mng Dir)*

Faiveley Transport (2)
9 Fl Geumchuk Bldg 889-60 Daechi-dong Gangnam-Gu
128-20 Samsung-Dong Kangnam-Ku, Seoul, 135 839, Korea (South) (100%)
Tel.: (82) 25640325
Fax: (82) 5640328
E-Mail: ji-young.park@faiveleytransport.com
Web Site: www.faiveleytransport.com
Emp.: 8
Railway Vehicle Components Mfr
S.I.C.: 3743
N.A.I.C.S.: 336510
Owonsuk Oh *(Gen Mgr)*

Faiveley Transport (2)
Unit 1 175 James Ruse Drive
Rosehill, Sydney, NSW, 2142, Australia
Mailing Address:
PO Box 6347
2150 Parramatta, NSW, Australia
Tel.: (61) 288634700
Fax: (61) 288634799
E-Mail: info@faiveleytransport.com
Web Site: www.faiveleytransport.com
Emp.: 60
Railway Vehicle Components Mfr
S.I.C.: 3743
N.A.I.C.S.: 336510
Mark Carling *(Mng Dir)*

Faiveley Transport (2)
Unit 4A Leuvensesteenweg 573
B 1930 Zaventem, Belgium (100%)
Tel.: (32) 27597912
Fax: (32) 27593245
E-Mail: su.be@sabwabco.com
Web Site: www.faiveleytransport.com
Emp.: 4
Railway Vehicle Components Mfr Export
S.I.C.: 3442
N.A.I.C.S.: 332321
Yvef De Herde *(Mng Dir)*

Faiveley Transport (2)
Via Volvera 51
IT 10045 Piossasco, Turin, Italy
Tel.: (39) 01190433
Fax: (39) 0119044290
Web Site: www.sabwabco.com
Emp.: 300
Railway Vehicle Components Mfr
S.I.C.: 3442
N.A.I.C.S.: 332321

Faiveley Transport (2)
Rua Mario Regallo Pereira 242
Butanta, 5550 Sao Paulo, Brazil (100%)

Faiveley Transport S.A.—(Continued)

Tel.: (55) 137838100
Fax: (55) 1137838101
E-Mail: subrazil@faiveley.com
Web Site: www.faiveleytransport.com
Emp.: 55
Railway Vehicle Components Mfr
S.I.C.: 3442
N.A.I.C.S.: 332321

Faiveley Transport (2)
Morpeth Wharf Twelve Quays
Birkenhead, Wirral, CH41 1LW, United Kingdom (100%)
Tel.: (44) 1516495000
Telex: 627020
Fax: (44) 1516495001
E-Mail: uk@faiveleytransport.com
Web Site: www.faiveleytransport.com
Emp.: 150
Railway Vehicle Components Mfr
S.I.C.: 3442
N.A.I.C.S.: 332321
Ian Dolman *(Pres)*

Faiveley Transport (2)
2nd Varvsvagen 55
PO Box 515
SE 261 24 Landskrona, Sweden
Tel.: (46) 41854400
Fax: (46) 41810690
E-Mail: info@faiveleytransport.com
Sls.: $180,000,000
Emp.: 136
Mfr. of Brake Systems & Brake Components, Wheels, Doors, Air-Conditioning Equipment, Electricity Supply & Light Fittings for Railbound Vehicles
S.I.C.: 3743
N.A.I.C.S.: 336510
Tarik Khan *(Mng Dir)*

Subsidiary:

Faiveley Transport Nordic A.B (3)
Andra Tvargatan 41
Box 515
261 24 Landskrona, Sweden
Tel.: (46) 41 85 44 00
Fax: (46) 41 81 06 90
E-Mail: su.nordic@faiveleytransport.com
Emp.: 141
Railroad Rolling Stock Mfr
S.I.C.: 3743
N.A.I.C.S.: 336510

Faiveley Transport (2)
Lichnicka 402
538 43 Tremosnice, Czech Republic
Tel.: (420) 469661938
Fax: (420) 469661926
E-Mail: su.cz@faiveleytransport.com
Emp.: 5
Railway Vehicle Components Mfr
S.I.C.: 3714
N.A.I.C.S.: 336340
Yusuf Mateja *(Mng Dir)*

Faiveley Transport (2)
Mar Tirreno 7 And 9
ES 28830 San Fernando de Henares, Spain (50%)
Tel.: (34) 915727100
Fax: (34) 916778582
E-Mail: su.es@sabwabco.com
Web Site: www.sabwabco.com
Emp.: 50
Mfr. of Brake Systems & Brake Components, Wheels, Doors, Air-Conditioning Equipment, Electricity Supply & Light Fittings for Railbound Vehicles
S.I.C.: 3442
N.A.I.C.S.: 332321

Faiveley Transport TOURS SAS (1)
Unite 3 ZI du Bois de Plante Rue Amelia Earhart
BP 43
37700 La Ville-aux-Dames, France
Tel.: (33) 2 47 32 55 55
Fax: (33) 2 47 32 56 61
E-Mail: electronics@faiveleytransport.com
Web Site: www.faiveleytransport.com
Emp.: 50
Railway Rolling Stock Mfr
S.I.C.: 3743
N.A.I.C.S.: 336510
Justin Tibaldi *(Gen Mgr)*

U.S. Subsidiary:

Faiveley Transport USA Inc. (1)
50 Beechtree Blvd
Greenville, SC 29605-5100
Tel.: (864) 277-5000
Fax: (864) 277-4863
Emp.: 300
Railway Transportation Services
S.I.C.: 4789
N.A.I.C.S.: 488210

Non-U.S. Subsidiaries:

FAIVELEY METRO TECHNOLOGY SHANGHAI Ltd. (1)
No 683-1 Baoqi Road
Baoshan Dist, Shanghai, 200444, China
Tel.: (86) 2160820008
Fax: (86) 2160820940
Platform Door & Gate Mfr
S.I.C.: 3442
N.A.I.C.S.: 332321

Faiveley Transport Belgium NV. (1)
Unit 4A Leuvensesteenweg 573
1930 Zaventem, Belgium
Tel.: (32) 27 59 79 12
Fax: (32) 27 59 32 45
E-Mail: su.be@faiveleytransport.com
Web Site: www.faiveleytransport.com
Emp.: 4
Railroad Rolling Stock Mfr
S.I.C.: 3743
N.A.I.C.S.: 336510
Kevin Curran *(Gen Mgr)*

Faiveley Transport Birkenhead Ltd. (1)
Morpeth Wharf
Birkenhead, CH41 1LF, United Kingdom
Tel.: (44) 151 649 5000
Fax: (44) 151 649 5001
Web Site: www.faiveleytransport.com
Emp.: 13
Railway Parts Repair Services
S.I.C.: 7539
N.A.I.C.S.: 811198

Faiveley Transport Far East Ltd (1)
21/F 9 Des Voeux Rd W
Sheung Wan, China (Hong Kong)
Tel.: (852) 28611788
Fax: (852) 28611744
E-Mail: info@faiveley-fareast.com
Web Site: www.faiveley-fareast.com
Emp.: 30
Railway Rolling Stock Mfr
S.I.C.: 3743
N.A.I.C.S.: 336510
Rebecca Lor *(Gen Mgr)*

Faiveley Transport Holding GmbH & Co KG (1)
Brauckstr 26
Witten, 58454, Germany
Tel.: (49) 2302 2775464
Fax: (49) 2302 27759301
Investment Management Services
S.I.C.: 6211
N.A.I.C.S.: 523999

Non-U.S. Subsidiary:

Sab Wabco Uk Ltd (2)
1 Morpeth Wharf
CH41 1NQ Birkenhead, United Kingdom
Tel.: (44) 151 649 50 00
Fax: (44) 151 649 50 01
Automotive Parts Distr
S.I.C.: 5013
N.A.I.C.S.: 423120

Faiveley Transport India Ltd (1)
No 39 Harita
Post Box No 39
Hosur, 635 109, India
Tel.: (91) 43 44 27 67 61
Fax: (91) 43 44 27 60 35
E-Mail: su.in@faiveleytransport.com
Web Site: www.faiveleytransport.com
Emp.: 50
Rail Transportation Equipment Mfr
S.I.C.: 3743
N.A.I.C.S.: 336510
Thomas Descamps *(Mng Dir)*

Faiveley Transport Italia Spa (1)
Via Volvera 51 IT
10045 Piossasco, Turin, Italy
Tel.: (39) 0 11 90 44 1
Fax: (39) 0 11 90 64 39 4
E-Mail: su.it@faiveleytransport.com
Railroad Rolling Stock Mfr
S.I.C.: 3743
N.A.I.C.S.: 336510

Faiveley Transport Leipzig GmbH & Co KG (1)
Industriestr 60
Schkeuditz, 4435, Germany
Tel.: (49) 3420485300
Fax: (49) 3420485302
Emp.: 30
Air Conditioning Equipment Mfr
S.I.C.: 3585
N.A.I.C.S.: 333415
David Bouwens *(Mng Dir)*

Faiveley Transport Lekov a.s (1)
Jirotova 375
336 01 Blovice, Czech Republic
Tel.: (420) 379 207 111
Fax: (420) 379 207 201
E-Mail: lekov@lekov.cz
Web Site: www.faiveleytransport-lekov.cz
Emp.: 26
Transportation Equipment Mfr
S.I.C.: 3799
N.A.I.C.S.: 336999
Thierry Barel *(Chm)*
Anatol Cebotaru *(Mng Dir)*

Faiveley Transport METRO TECHNOLOGY SINGAPORE Ltd. (1)
541 Orchard Road 09-01 Liat Towers
Singapore, 238881, Singapore
Tel.: (65) 62263623
Transportation Equipment Distr
S.I.C.: 5088
N.A.I.C.S.: 423860

Faiveley Transport METRO TECHNOLOGY TAIWAN Ltd. (1)
10F -2 No 560 Sec 4 Zhongxiao E Rd
Xinyi Dist, Taipei, 11017, Taiwan
Tel.: (886) 2 7735 0040
Fax: (886) 2 7735 0030
E-Mail: info@faiveleytransport.com
Platform Screen Door Mfr
S.I.C.: 3442
N.A.I.C.S.: 332321

Faiveley Transport Plzen S.r.o. (1)
Nyrany 1238
Nyrany, 330 23, Czech Republic
Tel.: (420) 379411540
Fax: (420) 379411530
E-Mail:
Web Site: www.aiveleytransport.com
Emp.: 80
Automotive Parts Mfr
S.I.C.: 3714
N.A.I.C.S.: 336390
Gabriela Petkova *(Mgr-Supply Chain)*

Faiveley Transport Tamworth Ltd (1)
21-22 Darwell Park
Tamworth, Staffordshire, B77 4DR, United Kingdom
Tel.: (44) 1827 308430
Fax: (44) 1827 61390
E-Mail: info.tamworth@faiveleytransport.com
Industrial Machinery & Equipment Distr
S.I.C.: 5084
N.A.I.C.S.: 423830

Nowe GmbH (1)
Heilswannenweg 66
31008 Elze, Germany
Tel.: (49) 5068 5506
Fax: (49) 5068 4435
E-Mail: info@nowe.de
Web Site: www.nowe.de
Automotive Electro Pneumatic Mfr
S.I.C.: 3714
N.A.I.C.S.: 336390
Werner Bartling *(Co-Mng Dir)*
Ekkehard Cramer *(Co-Mng Dir)*

SHANGHAI FAIVELEY RAILWAY TECHNOLOGY Co. Ltd. (1)
N 31 Fu Lian Yi Road
Baoshan Dist, Shanghai, 201906, China
Tel.: (86) 21 33 71 88 66
Fax: (86) 21 33 71 99 00
E-Mail: info@china-faiveley.com
Railway Air Conditioning Equipment Mfr
S.I.C.: 3585
N.A.I.C.S.: 333415

FAJARBARU BUILDER GROUP BHD.

No 1 & 1A 2nd Floor Room 2 Jalan Ipoh Kecil
50350 Kuala Lumpur, Malaysia
Tel.: (60) 34043 5750
Fax: (60) 34043 5755
E-Mail: accounts@fb.com.my
Web Site: www.fb.com.my
FAJAR—(KLS)
Rev.: $69,912,857
Assets: $96,745,191
Liabilities: $49,510,941
Net Worth: $47,234,250
Earnings: $1,369,315
Fiscal Year-end: 06/30/13

Business Description:
Property Development Services
S.I.C.: 6531
N.A.I.C.S.: 531311

Personnel:
Peng Ching Kuan *(Chm)*
Sock Cheng Teo *(COO)*
Kok Aun Tan *(Co-Sec)*
Wai Yin Wong *(Co-Sec)*

Board of Directors:
Peng Ching Kuan
Kuan Ming Foong
Keng Kok Low
Zahedi Mohd Zain
Ismail Omar
Leng Chooi Ooi
Chee Heng Wong

Subsidiary:

Fajarbaru Builder Sdn. Bhd. (1)
No 61 & 63 Jalan SS 6/12
Kelana Jaya, 47301 Petaling Jaya, Selangor, Malaysia
Tel.: (60) 378049698
Fax: (60) 378043698
Emp.: 110
Construction Services
S.I.C.: 1629
N.A.I.C.S.: 237990
Teo Sock Cheng *(Exec Dir)*

FAL GROUP OF COMPANIES

PO Box 6600
Sharjah, United Arab Emirates
Tel.: (971) 65286666
Fax: (971) 65281437
Web Site: www.falgroup.com
Emp.: 500

Business Description:
Petroleum Products Marketer & Whslr
S.I.C.: 7389
N.A.I.C.S.: 425120

Personnel:
Abdulla Juma Al Sari *(Chm)*

Board of Directors:
Majid A. Al Sari
Mohammed A. Al Sari

Subsidiaries:

FAL Energy Co., Ltd. (1)
PO Box 6600
Sharjah, United Arab Emirates
Tel.: (971) 65286666
Fax: (971) 65281437
Web Site: www.falgroup.com
Marine Lubes & Bunkers Supplier to Ship Owners & Charterers
S.I.C.: 5172
N.A.I.C.S.: 424720

FAL Oil (1)
PO Box 6600
Sharjah, United Arab Emirates
Tel.: (971) 65286666
Fax: (971) 65281437
E-Mail: sales@faloil.co.ae
Web Site: www.faloil.com
Emp.: 100
Bulk Cargo Oil

S.I.C.: 5172
N.A.I.C.S.: 424720
Abdulla Juma Al Sari *(Chm)*

FAL Shipping Co., Ltd. (1)
PO Box 6600
Sharjah, United Arab Emirates
Tel.: (971) 65286666
Fax: (971) 65281437
E-Mail: interpert@faloil.co.ae
Emp.: 70
Owner & Operator of Tanker Vessels
S.I.C.: 4491
N.A.I.C.S.: 488320
Abdulla Juma Al Sari *(Chm)*

S.A.C.I. FALABELLA

Rosas 1665
Santiago, Chile
Tel.: (56) 23802000
Fax: (56) 23802077
E-Mail: inversionistas@falabella.cl
Web Site: www.falabella.com
FALABELLA—(SGO)
Rev.: $11,641,852,270
Assets: $18,315,145,707
Liabilities: $10,949,474,851
Net Worth: $7,365,670,855
Earnings: $867,827,847
Emp.: 96,286
Fiscal Year-end: 12/31/12
Business Description:
Department Store Owner & Operator
S.I.C.: 5311
N.A.I.C.S.: 452111
Personnel:
Juan Cuneo Solari *(Chm)*
Fernando de Pena Iver *(Exec Vice Chm)*
Carlo Solari Donaggio *(Vice Chm)*
Sandro Solari Donaggio *(CEO)*
Alejandro Gonzalez Dale *(CFO)*
Pablo Meza Martinez *(CTO)*
Jordi Gaju Nicolau *(Chief Dev Officer)*
Pablo Ardanaz *(CEO-Sodimac Argentina)*
Alejandro Arze Safian *(CEO-Seguros Falabella)*
Claudio Cisternas Duque *(CEO-CMR Chile)*
Pedro Colombo Maciel *(CEO-Tottus Chile)*
Juan Fernando Correa Malachowski *(CEO-Tottus Peru)*
Isabella Dallago Munoz *(CEO-Viajes Falabella)*
Bruno Funcke Cibiani *(CEO-Banco Falabella Peru)*
Juan Manuel Matheu *(CEO-Banco Falabella Chile)*
Eduardo Mizon Friedemann *(CEO-Sodimac Chile)*
Juan Xavir Roca Mendenhall *(CEO-Saga Falabella)*
Agustin Solari Alvarez *(CEO-Chile)*
Emilio Van Oordt Martinez *(CEO-Sodimac Peru)*
Jorge Villarroel Barrera *(CEO-Banco Falabella Colombia)*
Ricardo Zimerman Heller *(CEO-CMR Argentina)*
Board of Directors:
Juan Cuneo Solari
Hernan Buchi Buc
Sergio Cardone Solari
Juan Carlos Cortes Solari
Carolina del Rio Goudie
Jose Luis del Rio Goudie
Carlos Heller Solari
Maria Cecilia Karlezi Solari
Carlo Solari Donaggio

FALCK S.P.A.

GE Falck 63
20099 Milan, Italy
Tel.: (39) 224331
Fax: (39) 0224332394
E-Mail: info@falck.it
Web Site: www.falck.it
Year Founded: 1906
Sales Range: $200-249.9 Million
Emp.: 296
Business Description:
Renewable Energy Production & Iron & Steel Mfg
S.I.C.: 3312
N.A.I.C.S.: 331110
Personnel:
Federico Falck *(Chm)*
Ferruccio Marchi *(Vice Chm)*
Achille Colombo *(Mng Dir)*
Fabio Cattaneo *(Sec)*
Board of Directors:
Federico Falck
Angelo Caso
Fabio Cattaneo
Achille Colombo
Guido Corbetta
Enrico Falck
Bruno Isabella
Carlo Marchi
Ferruccio Marchi
Filippo Marchi
Subsidiaries:

Falck Renewables S.p.A. (1)
Via Alberto Falck 4-16
20099 Sesto San Giovanni, MI, Italy (68.7%)
Tel.: (39) 0224331
Fax: (39) 0224333791
E-Mail: investor.falckrenewables@falckgroup.eu
Web Site: www.falckrenewables.eu
FKR—(ITA)
Rev.: $369,662,321
Assets: $1,993,753,156
Liabilities: $1,531,051,642
Net Worth: $462,701,514
Earnings: ($115,053,111)
Emp.: 244
Fiscal Year-end: 12/31/12
Renewable Energy Production
S.I.C.: 4911
N.A.I.C.S.: 221118
Federico Falck *(Chm)*
Guido Rosa *(Deputy Chm)*
Piero Manzoni *(CEO)*
Paolo Rundeddu *(CFO & Dir-Mgmt Svcs)*

Falck Acciai-CNS SpA (1)
Via Lungo Serio 21
Grassobbio, Bergamo, 24050, Italy
Tel.: (39) 035335668
Fax: (39) 035335672
E-Mail: info@falckacciai.it
Web Site: www.falckacciai.it
Iron & Steel Mfr
S.I.C.: 3399
N.A.I.C.S.: 331110

ITLA S.p.A. (1)
Strada provinciale per Dolzago 69
Oggiono Lecco, 22048, Italy
Tel.: (39) 0341 576188
Fax: (39) 0341 578276
Steel Mfr
S.I.C.: 3312
N.A.I.C.S.: 331110

FALCO PACIFIC RESOURCE GROUP INC.

Suite 409 - 1080 Mainland St
Vancouver, BC, V6B 2T4, Canada
Tel.: (604) 732-5840
Fax: (604) 608-3503
E-Mail: info@falcopacific.com
Web Site: www.falcopacific.com
Year Founded: 2010
FPC—(TSXV)
Rev.: $28,909
Assets: $11,684,561
Liabilities: $585,167
Net Worth: $11,099,394
Earnings: ($1,721,665)
Fiscal Year-end: 06/30/13
Business Description:
Exploration & Mining Services
S.I.C.: 1099
N.A.I.C.S.: 212299
Personnel:
Kelly D. Klatik *(Pres & CEO)*
James G. Davidson *(CFO & Sec)*
Board of Directors:
Darin W. Wagner
Michael J. Byron
James G. Davidson
Kelly D. Klatik
Gordon Neal
Legal Counsel:
MOI Solicitors
Vancouver, BC, Canada
Transfer Agent:
Equity Financial Trust Company
1185 West Georgia Street Suite 1620
Vancouver, BC, Canada

FALCO SD HOLDINGS CO. LTD.

346 Shimizu-cho Nijo-agaru
Kawaramachi-dori
Nakagyo-ku, Kyoto, 604-0911, Japan
Tel.: (81) 752578500
Web Site: www.falco.co.jp
Year Founded: 1962
4671—(TKS)
Sales Range: $650-699.9 Million
Emp.: 1,483
Business Description:
Contract Clinical & Genetic Testing Services
S.I.C.: 8734
N.A.I.C.S.: 541380
Personnel:
Hiroharu Akazawa *(Chm)*
Kenjiro Hirasaki *(Pres)*
Toshikazu Shikata *(Mng Dir)*
Subsidiary:

FALCO Clinical Plan, Ltd (1)
346 Shimizucho Kawaramachidori Nijoagaru
Nakagyo-Ku, Kyoto, Japan (100%)
Tel.: (81) 752131621
Fax: (81) 752131653
E-Mail: sec9002@mail.falco.co.jp
Web Site: www.falco-pharm.co.jp/english/03company/index.html
Emp.: 300
Drug Stores & Proprietary Stores
S.I.C.: 5912
N.A.I.C.S.: 446110
Morri Masahiko *(Pres)*

FALCO-SOPRON BUTOR KFT.

Banfalvi ut 27
9400 Sopron, Hungary
Tel.: (36) 99513310
Fax: (36) 99311311
E-Mail: info.sopron@falcosopron.hu
Web Site: www.falcosopron.hu
Year Founded: 1961
Emp.: 100
Business Description:
Office Furnishings Mfr
S.I.C.: 2522
N.A.I.C.S.: 337214
Personnel:
Hulesch Karoly *(Exec Dir)*

FALCON ENERGY GROUP LIMITED

10 Anson Road 33-15 International Plaza
Singapore, 079903, Singapore
Tel.: (65) 65387177
Fax: (65) 65387188
E-Mail: admin@feg.com.sg
Web Site: www.falconenergy.com.sg
5FL—(SES)
Rev.: $116,195,000
Assets: $400,837,000
Liabilities: $192,756,000
Net Worth: $208,081,000
Earnings: $10,381,000
Fiscal Year-end: 03/31/13
Business Description:
Offshore Oil & Gas Operation Support Services
S.I.C.: 1389
N.A.I.C.S.: 213112
Personnel:
Pong Tyea Tan *(Chm & CEO)*
Wah Kwang Gan *(CFO)*
Chin Lee Neo *(COO)*
Mee Fun Lim *(Co-Sec)*
Lei Eng Peh *(Co-Sec)*
Board of Directors:
Pong Tyea Tan
Wenxing Cai
Christopher Guan Ngang Chan
Kait Long Lien
Chin Lee Neo
Mohan Raj

FALCON GOLD CORP.

Suite 322 - 470 Granville St
Vancouver, BC, V6C 1V5, Canada
Tel.: (604) 683-1991
Fax: (905) 681-3648
E-Mail: info@falcongold.ca
Web Site: www.falcongold.ca
Year Founded: 2006
FG—(TSXV)
Assets: $2,622,526
Liabilities: $299,882
Net Worth: $2,322,644
Earnings: ($639,097)
Fiscal Year-end: 06/30/13
Business Description:
Mineral Exploration Services
S.I.C.: 1081
N.A.I.C.S.: 213114
Personnel:
Jamie Lavigne *(Interim Pres & CEO)*
Brian Crawford *(CFO)*
Board of Directors:
David Beilhartz
Peter Clausi
Brian Crawford
James Farley
Jamie Lavigne
Edward Stringer
David Tafel
Legal Counsel:
Perley-Robertson Hill & McDougall LLP
1400 340 Albert Street
Ottawa, ON, Canada
Transfer Agent:
Equity Financial Trust Company
200 University Avenue Suite 400
Toronto, ON, Canada

FALCON MINERALS LIMITED

Suite 19 100 Hay Street
PO Box 8319
Subiaco, WA, 6008, Australia
Tel.: (61) 893821596
Fax: (61) 893824637
E-Mail: fcn@falconminerals.com.au
Web Site: www.falconminerals.com.au
FCN—(ASX)
Rev.: $178,029
Assets: $1,510,403
Liabilities: $86,762
Net Worth: $1,423,641
Earnings: ($547,214)
Emp.: 4
Fiscal Year-end: 06/30/13
Business Description:
Gold Exploration Services
S.I.C.: 3339
N.A.I.C.S.: 331410
Personnel:
Richard Edward Diermajer *(Chm)*
Ronald Smit *(Mng Dir)*
Dean Calder *(Sec)*
Board of Directors:
Richard Edward Diermajer

FALCON MINERALS LIMITED—(Continued)

Ray Muskett
Ronald Smit

Legal Counsel:
Brickhills
Level 1 10 Outram St
Perth, Australia

FALCON OIL & GAS LTD.

5th Floor Styne House Upper Hatch Street
Dublin, 2, Ireland
Tel.: (353) 1 417 1900
E-Mail: info@falconoilandgas.com
Web Site: www.falconoilandgas.com
Year Founded: 1980
FOG—(AIM TSXV)
Sales Range: Less than $1 Million
Emp.: 23

Business Description:
Oil & Gas Exploration Services
S.I.C.: 1389
N.A.I.C.S.: 213112

Personnel:
John Craven *(Chm)*
Philip O'Quigley *(CEO)*
Eoin Grindley *(CFO)*

Board of Directors:
John Craven
Igor Akhmerov
Joachim Conrad
Daryl Harvey Gilbert
David Harris
Gregory Harold Smith
Gyorgy Szabo

Transfer Agent:
Computershare Investor Services Inc.
510 Burrard St 2nd Floor
Vancouver, BC, V6C 3B9, Canada
Tel.: (604) 661-9400

FALCON POWER CO., LTD.

6F No 6 Sec 2 Nanjing E Rd
Jhongshan District
104 Taipei, Taiwan
Tel.: (886) 225237733
Fax: (886) 225411077
Web Site: www.falconpower.com.tw
1516—(TAI)
Sales Range: $1-9.9 Million

Business Description:
Bicycle Parts, Exercise Products & Parts Mfr
S.I.C.: 3949
N.A.I.C.S.: 339920

Personnel:
Zolton Kiss *(CTO)*

FALCON-SOFTWARE COMPANY, INC.

2826 Bryn Maur Road
Victoria, BC, V9B 3T4, Canada
Tel.: (250) 481-1311
Fax: (250) 480-1322
Toll Free: (800) 707-1311
Web Site: www.falcon-software.com
Year Founded: 1993
Sales Range: $1-9.9 Million
Emp.: 20

Business Description:
Software Publisher
S.I.C.: 7372
N.A.I.C.S.: 511210

Personnel:
Gary Eisenstein *(Pres)*

FALCON TYRES LTD.

46 Syed Amir Ali Avenue
Kolkata, 700017, India
Tel.: (91) 3322894747
Fax: (91) 3322893463
Web Site: www.falcontyres.com
Year Founded: 1973
509527—(BOM)
Rev.: $195,777,133
Assets: $224,282,005
Liabilities: $170,001,810
Net Worth: $54,280,195
Earnings: ($11,210,522)
Fiscal Year-end: 09/30/12

Business Description:
Rubber Tyre Mfr
S.I.C.: 3069
N.A.I.C.S.: 326299

Personnel:
Pawan Kumar Ruia *(Chm)*
M. C. Bhansali *(Compliance Officer & Sec)*

Board of Directors:
Pawan Kumar Ruia
Ashok Kumar Agarwal
Ambuj Kumar Jain
Kamal Jewrajka
Prakash P. Mallya
Kokkarne Natarajan Prithviraj
S. Ravi

Transfer Agent:
Integrated Enterprises (India) Ltd
30 Ramana Residency 4th Cross Sampige Road Malleswaram
Bengaluru, India

FALKLAND ISLANDS HOLDINGS PLC

Kenburgh Court 133-137 South Street
Bishop's Stortford, Hertfordshire, CM23 3HX, United Kingdom
Tel.: (44) 279461630
Fax: (44) 279461631
E-Mail: admin@fihplc.com
Web Site: www.fihplc.com
FKL—(LSE)
Rev.: $56,216,407
Assets: $88,789,263
Liabilities: $34,652,781
Net Worth: $54,136,482
Earnings: $2,533,181
Emp.: 287
Fiscal Year-end: 03/31/13

Business Description:
General Trading, Logistics & Storage Service
S.I.C.: 4482
N.A.I.C.S.: 483114

Personnel:
David Hudd *(Chm)*
John Foster *(Mng Dir)*
Carol Bishop *(Sec)*

Board of Directors:
David Hudd
Jeremy Brade
John Foster
Mike Killingley

Legal Counsel:
Bircham Bell and Dyson LLP
50 Broadway
SW1H 0BL London, United Kingdom

Subsidiaries:

Clarence Marine Engineering Limited (1)
Unit 1 Mumby Rd Clarence Wharf
Gosport, Hampshire, PO12 1AJ, United Kingdom
Tel.: (44) 2392511555
Fax: (44) 2392581013
E-Mail: admin@clarence-marine.co.uk
Emp.: 15
Ferry & Launch Repair Services
S.I.C.: 8711
N.A.I.C.S.: 541330
John L Foster *(Mng Dir)*
James B Ivins *(Sec)*

The Falkland Islands Company Limited (1)
Kenburgh Ct 133-137 S St
Bishop's Stortford, Hertfordshire, CM23 3HX, United Kingdom
Tel.: (44) 1279461630
Fax: (44) 1279461631
E-Mail: admin@fihplc.com
Web Site: www.the-falkland-islands-co.com
Emp.: 7
Retail Store Operation Services
S.I.C.: 5411
N.A.I.C.S.: 445110
Ana Crowie *(Controller-Fin-Stanley)*

Gosport Ferry Limited (1)
Bus Sta S St
Gosport, Hampshire, PO12 1EP, United Kingdom
Tel.: (44) 2392524551
Fax: (44) 2392524802
E-Mail: info@gosportferry.co.uk
Web Site: www.gosportferry.co.uk
Emp.: 45
Ferry Passenger Transportation Services
S.I.C.: 4482
N.A.I.C.S.: 483114
John L Foster *(Mng Dir)*
James B Ivins *(Sec)*

Momart Limited (1)
Unit C The Denim Factory 4-6 Davenant St
London, E1 5AQ, United Kingdom
Tel.: (44) 2074263000
Fax: (44) 2074263001
E-Mail: enquiries@momart.co.uk
Web Site: www.momart.co.uk
Emp.: 130
Fine Arts & Antiquities Handling Services
S.I.C.: 4783
N.A.I.C.S.: 488991

Portsea Harbour Company Limited (1)
First Station S St
Gosport, Hampshire, PO12 1EP, United Kingdom
Tel.: (44) 2392524551
E-Mail: admin@gosportferry.co.uk
Emp.: 40
Ferry Passenger Transportation Services
S.I.C.: 4482
N.A.I.C.S.: 483114
John L Foster *(Mng Dir)*

FALKLAND ISLANDS RADIO SERVICE

John Street
FIQQ 1ZZ Stanley, Falkland Islands
Tel.: (500) 27277
Fax: (500) 27279
E-Mail: liz@firs.co.fk
Web Site: www.firs.co.fk
Emp.: 12

Business Description:
Radio Broadcasting Services
S.I.C.: 4832
N.A.I.C.S.: 515112

Personnel:
Liz Elliot *(Program Controller)*

FALKLAND OIL AND GAS LIMITED

32 34 Wigmore Street
London, W1U 2RR, United Kingdom
Tel.: (44) 2075631260
Fax: (44) 2074862330
E-Mail: info@fogl.co.uk
Web Site: www.fogl.com
FOGL—(LSE)
Rev.: $2,807,000
Assets: $302,062,000
Liabilities: $40,961,000
Net Worth: $261,101,000
Earnings: $1,051,000
Emp.: 6
Fiscal Year-end: 12/31/12

Business Description:
Oil & Gas Exploration
S.I.C.: 1389
N.A.I.C.S.: 213112

Personnel:
Richard Liddell *(Chm)*
Tim Bushell *(CEO)*

Board of Directors:
Richard Liddell
Tim Bushell
David Hudd
Timothy Jones
Colin More

Legal Counsel:
Pinsent Masons (Stanley)
56 John Street
Stanley, Falkland Islands

Pinsent Masons LLP
Princes Exchange 1 Earl Grey Street
Edinburgh, United Kingdom

Subsidiary:

Desire Petroleum Plc (1)
Mathon Court Mathon
Malvern, Worcs, WR13 5NZ, United Kingdom
Tel.: (44) 1684892242
Fax: (44) 1684575226
E-Mail: dpl@desireplc.co.uk
Web Site: www.desireplc.co.uk
Rev.: $36,000
Assets: $11,060,000
Liabilities: $322,000
Net Worth: $10,738,000
Earnings: ($3,868,000)
Emp.: 9
Fiscal Year-end: 12/31/12
Oil & Gas Exploration Services
S.I.C.: 1311
N.A.I.C.S.: 211111
Stephen Lawrey Phipps *(Founder & Chm)*
Ian Gordon Duncan *(CEO)*
Anna Ruth Neve *(Sec)*

FALMAC LIMITED

25 International Business Park 04-22/ 26 German Centre
Singapore, 609916, Singapore
Tel.: (65) 62654033
Fax: (65) 62732216
E-Mail: falmacmc@falmac.com
Web Site: www.falmac.com
Sales Range: $1-9.9 Million

Business Description:
Machinery & Components Mfr
S.I.C.: 3559
N.A.I.C.S.: 333249

Personnel:
Charlie Ji Lai Cheng *(CEO)*

Board of Directors:
Xue Jun Fei
Charlie Ji Lai Cheng
David Hai Ge Lu
Jing Lu
Wei Ying Yu

Non-U.S. Subsidiaries:

Falmac Machinery (Tianjin) Ltd. (1)
Ninghe Jingji Kaifa Qu
Ninghe County, Tianjin, Hebei, 301500, China
Tel.: (86) 2269581388
Fax: (86) 2269581088
E-Mail: falmacmc@falmac.com
Web Site: www.falmac.com
Circular Knitting Machinery Mfr & Distr
S.I.C.: 3559
N.A.I.C.S.: 333249
Shuren Zhang *(Gen Mgr)*

Falmac Textile (Tianjin) Ltd. (1)
7 KuanMing Road Lutai
Tianjin, 301500, China
Tel.: (86) 22 6958 8173
Fax: (86) 22 6958 8172
Textile Mfr
S.I.C.: 2299
N.A.I.C.S.: 314999

FALTEC CO., LTD.

580 Horikawa-cho Saiwai-Ku
Kawasaki, Kanagawa-Ken, 212-0013, Japan
Tel.: (81) 44 520 0290
Fax: (81) 44 520 0018
Web Site: www.faltec.co.jp
7215—(TKS)
Sls.: $792,198,000
Assets: $528,858,000
Liabilities: $386,276,000
Net Worth: $142,582,000

Earnings: $22,418,000
Emp.: 2,426
Fiscal Year-end: 03/31/13
Business Description:
Automotive Parts & Accessories Mfr
S.I.C.: 3714
N.A.I.C.S.: 336390
Personnel:
Kazuhiko Toida *(Pres)*
Katsuhiro Takamatsu *(Exec VP)*
Hiroshi Kato *(Sr VP)*
Hiroshi Miki *(Sr VP)*
Tatsuro Sato *(Sr VP)*
Board of Directors:
Hiroshi Kato
Hiroshi Miki
Akisato Saruta
Tatsuro Sato
Katsuhiro Takamatsu
Kazuhiko Toida
Kenichi Tomita
Kenichi Yamamoto

FAM REAL ESTATE INVESTMENT TRUST
309 - 317 Adelaide Street West
Toronto, ON, M5V 1P9, Canada
Tel.: (647) 256-5002
Fax: (647) 256-5001
E-Mail: info@famreit.com
Web Site: www.famreit.com
Year Founded: 2012
F.UN—(TSX)
Business Description:
Real Estate Investment Services
S.I.C.: 6211
N.A.I.C.S.: 523999
Personnel:
Zachary George *(Chm)*
Shant Poladian *(CEO)*
Sandeep Manak *(CFO)*
Transfer Agent:
Computershare Trust Company of Canada
3 rd Floor 510 Burrard Street
Vancouver, BC, V6C 3A8, Canada

FAMILY MEMORIALS INC.
1126 Roland Street
Thunder Bay, ON, P7B 5M4, Canada
Tel.: (807) 577-6463
Fax: (807) 577-5338
E-Mail: familymemorials@tbaytel.net
Web Site: www.family-memorials.ca
Year Founded: 2003
FAM—(TSXV)
Sls.: $2,974,534
Assets: $4,213,530
Liabilities: $4,870,643
Net Worth: ($657,114)
Earnings: ($1,144,690)
Emp.: 10
Fiscal Year-end: 12/31/12
Business Description:
Death Care Business Services
S.I.C.: 7389
N.A.I.C.S.: 561499
Personnel:
Scott C. Kellaway *(Pres & CEO)*
Gary Armstrong *(CFO)*
Board of Directors:
Robert Kellaway
Scott C. Kellaway
Douglas J. Livesey
Kevin Nephin
Transfer Agent:
Computershare
600 530 8th Ave SW
Calgary, AB, Canada
Subsidiaries:

Barber Monuments Ltd. (1)
120 Bunting Road
Saint Catharines, ON, L2P 3G5, Canada
Tel.: (905) 684-7913
Monument & Grave Stone Distr
S.I.C.: 5099
N.A.I.C.S.: 423990

Grajack Industries Ltd. (1)
638 Dundas St W
Belleville, ON, K8N 4Z2, Canada
Tel.: (613) 968-6897
Fax: (613) 968-5364
Toll Free: (800) 563-2628
E-Mail: blemkie@reajh.net
Web Site: www.lonsmemorials.com
Emp.: 1
Monument Retailer
S.I.C.: 5999
N.A.I.C.S.: 453998
Terry Newman *(Office Mgr)*

R.H. Verduyn Granite Co. Ltd. (1)
69 Aylmer St N
Peterborough, ON, K9J 3J4, Canada
Tel.: (705) 742-2715
Monument & Grave Stone Distr
S.I.C.: 5099
N.A.I.C.S.: 423990

Somerville Memorials Ltd. (1)
7134R Fisher St SE
Calgary, AB, T2H 0W5, Canada
Tel.: (403) 265-0780
Fax: (403) 269-5181
Toll Free: (888) 700-0780
E-Mail: info@somervillememorials.com
Web Site: www.somervillememorials.com
Emp.: 1
Monument & Grave Stone Retailer
S.I.C.: 5999
N.A.I.C.S.: 453998
Adolfo Preciado *(Office Mgr)*

FAMILYMART CO., LTD.
Sunshine60 Building 17th Floor1-1
3-1-1 Higashi-Ikebukuro
Toshima-ku, Tokyo, 170-6017, Japan
Tel.: (81) 339896600
Web Site: www.family.co.jp
Year Founded: 1981
8028—(TKS)
Rev.: $3,674,957,000
Assets: $5,792,490,000
Liabilities: $3,062,785,000
Net Worth: $2,729,705,000
Earnings: $275,220,000
Emp.: 6,081
Fiscal Year-end: 02/28/13
Business Description:
Convenience Stores Operator
S.I.C.: 5411
N.A.I.C.S.: 445120
Personnel:
Junji Ueda *(Chm & CEO)*
Isamu Nakayama *(Pres)*
Yoshiki Miyamoto *(Sr Mng Dir)*
Toshio Kato *(Mng Dir)*
Yukihiko Komatsuzaki *(Mng Dir)*
Masaaki Kosaka *(Mng Dir)*
Motoo Takada *(Mng Dir)*
Hiroaki Tamamaki *(Mng Dir)*
Akinori Wada *(Mng Dir)*
Kuniaki Abe *(Exec Officer)*
Minoru Aoki *(Sr Exec Officer)*
Masami Fujimori *(Exec Officer)*
Mitsuji Hirata *(Mng Exec Officer)*
Toru Ichikawa *(Exec Officer)*
Takashi Iizuka *(Exec Officer)*
Tomoaki Ikeda *(Exec Officer)*
Atsushi Inoue *(Exec Officer)*
Katsuo Ito *(Sr Exec Officer)*
Kimichika Iwakiri *(Sr Exec Officer)*
Takehiko Kigure *(Exec Officer)*
Kiyoshi Kikuchi *(Exec Officer)*
Teruo Kuramata *(Sr Exec Officer)*
Junichi Maenishi *(Exec Officer)*
Naomi Maruyama *(Exec Officer)*
Kenji Misawa *(Exec Officer)*
Hideki Miura *(Exec Officer)*
Eiji Morita *(Exec Officer)*
Yoshihito Nakahira *(Mng Exec Officer)*
Yoshikazu Onozuka *(Exec Officer)*
Yoshiki Sakazaki *(Exec Officer)*
Hiroshi Sawada *(Exec Officer)*
Makoto Sugiura *(Sr Exec Officer)*
Masanori Sugiura *(Exec Officer)*
Hisashi Suzuki *(Exec Officer)*
Noboru Takebayashi *(Mng Exec Officer)*
Yoshiaki Uematsu *(Exec Officer)*
Kazushige Ueno *(Mng Exec Officer)*
Junichi Yamashita *(Exec Officer)*
Toshiya Yoshida *(Exec Officer)*
Board of Directors:
Junji Ueda
Toshio Kato
Yukihiko Komatsuzaki
Masaaki Kosaka
Yoshiki Miyamoto
Isamu Nakayama
Motoo Takada
Noboru Takebayashi
Hiroaki Tamamaki
Akinori Wada
Subsidiary:

famima.com Co., Ltd. (1)
Sunshine 60 3-1-1 Higashi Ikebukuro
Toshima-ku, Tokyo, 170-6018, Japan
Tel.: (81) 359583812
Fax: (81) 359583816
Web Site: www.famima.com
Emp.: 60
Online Shopping Services
S.I.C.: 5961
N.A.I.C.S.: 454111
Yasuhiko Uramoto *(Pres)*

U.S. Subsidiary:

FAMIMA CORPORATION (1)
20000 Mariner Ave Ste 100
Torrance, CA 90503-7140
Tel.: (310) 214-1001
Fax: (310) 375-6394
E-Mail: info@famima-usa.com
Web Site: www.famima-usa.com
Convenience Stores Operation Services
S.I.C.: 5421
N.A.I.C.S.: 445210
Yoshiko Okuno *(Gen Mgr)*

Non-U.S. Subsidiary:

Siam FamilyMart Co., Ltd. (1)
Vanit Bldg II 11th Fl 1126/2 New Petchburi Rd
Makkasan Rajchtewi, Bangkok, 10400, Thailand
Tel.: (66) 22541632
Fax: (66) 22558760
Web Site: www.familymart.co.th
Emp.: 1,912
Convenience Stores Operator
S.I.C.: 5411
N.A.I.C.S.: 445120
Kazushige Ueno *(CEO)*

FAMOUS BRANDS LIMITED
478 James Crescent
PO Box 2884
Midrand, 1685, South Africa
Tel.: (27) 113153000
Fax: (27) 13150059
E-Mail: investorrelations@famousbrands.co.za
Web Site: www.famousbrands.co.za
FBR—(JSE)
Rev.: $281,069,258
Assets: $168,719,164
Liabilities: $57,009,334
Net Worth: $111,709,830
Earnings: $36,978,508
Emp.: 1,187
Fiscal Year-end: 02/28/13
Business Description:
Restaurant Franchises & Food Related Services
S.I.C.: 5812
N.A.I.C.S.: 722513
Personnel:
Santie Botha *(Chm)*
Theofanis Halamandaris *(Deputy Chm)*
Kevin Alexander Hedderwick *(CEO)*
Darren Paul Hele *(COO)*
Derrian Nadauld *(CMO)*
J. Geoff Pyle *(Sec & Exec-Fin)*
Arlene Botha *(Exec-HR)*
Chris Botha *(Exec-IT)*
Darryl Denton *(Exec-Mfg & Technical)*
Mark Hedderwick *(Mng Exec-Emerging Markets)*
Norman Richards *(Exec-Change Mgmt)*
Tony Stephens *(Mng Exec-Logistics)*
Pedja Turanjanin *(Exec-Procurement)*
Board of Directors:
Santie Botha
Panagiotis Halamandaris
Periklis Halamandaris
Theofanis Halamandaris
John Lee Halamandres
Kevin Alexander Hedderwick
Darren Paul Hele
Hymie Reuvin Levin
Norman Richards
Bheki Lindinkosi Sibiya
Transfer Agent:
Link Market Services (Proprietary) Limited
13th Floor Rennie House 19 Ameshoff Street
Braamfontein, 2001, South Africa
Subsidiary:

Pouyoukas Foods (Proprietary) Limited (1)
10 Nicholls St
Chamdor, Krugersdorp, Gauteng, 1739, South Africa
Tel.: (27) 11 7625261
Food Products Mfr
S.I.C.: 5149
N.A.I.C.S.: 424490

Non-U.S. Subsidiaries:

Coffee Contact (Proprietary) Limited (1)
58 Dawson St
Brunswick, VIC, 3056, Australia
Tel.: (61) 393801111
Fax: (61) 3 9380 6200
E-Mail: coffee@coffex.com.au
Web Site: www.coffex.com.au/profile.php
Coffee Products Mfr
S.I.C.: 2099
N.A.I.C.S.: 311920

Steers (Proprietary) Limited (1)
Ste 4 5 Victoria Rd
PO Box 6249
Parramatta, NSW, 2150, Australia
Tel.: (61) 2 9630 8482
Fax: (61) 2 9630 8314
E-Mail: info@steers.com.au
Web Site: www.steers.com.au
Emp.: 5
Auctioneers & Valuers
S.I.C.: 7389
N.A.I.C.S.: 561990
Ian Arthy *(Mng Dir)*

FAN MILK LIMITED
1 Dadeban Road North Industrial Area
PO Box 6460
Accra, Ghana
Tel.: (233) 21 224732
Fax: (233) 21 221951
E-Mail: fml@fanmilk-gh.com
Web Site: www.fanmilk-gh.net
Year Founded: 1960
FML—(GHA)
Sales Range: $50-74.9 Million
Emp.: 407
Business Description:
Milk & Dairy Products Mfr & Distr
S.I.C.: 2026
N.A.I.C.S.: 311511
Personnel:
Charles Mensa *(Chm)*
Jesper Bjorn Jeppesen *(Mng Dir)*
Board of Directors:

Fan Milk Limited—(Continued)

Charles Mensa
Peace Ayisi-Okyere
Kodjo Biamawu Aziagbe
Einar Mark Christensen
Jesper Bjorn Jeppesen
Jens Jorgen Kollerup
George H. Okai Thompson

Legal Counsel:
Quist, Brown, Wontumi & Associates
PO Box 7566
Accra, Ghana

Transfer Agent:
NTHC Limited
Martco House
KA 9563
Accra, Ghana

FANCAMP EXPLORATION LTD.

7290 Gray Avenue
Burnaby, BC, V5J 3Z2, Canada
Tel.: (604) 434-8829
Fax: (604) 434-8823
Web Site: www.fancampexplorationltd.ca
FNC—(TSXV)

Business Description:
Mineral Exploration Services
S.I.C.: 1081
N.A.I.C.S.: 213114

Personnel:
Peter H. Smith *(Founder & CEO)*
Jean Lafleur *(Chm)*
Debra Chapman *(CFO)*

Board of Directors:
Jean Lafleur
Debra Chapman
Mel De Quadros
Gilles Dubuc
Robert N. Granger
Fouad Kamaleddine
Michael Sayer
Peter H. Smith

Transfer Agent:
Computershare Investor Services Inc.
3rd Floor 510 Burrard St
V6C 3B9 Vancouver, BC, Canada

FANCL CORPORATION

89 1 Yamashitacho Naka Ku
Yokohama, Kanagawa, 231 8528, Japan
Tel.: (81) 452261200
Fax: (81) 452261203
E-Mail: overseas@fancl.co.jp
Web Site: www.fancl.co.jp
Sales Range: $750-799.9 Million
Emp.: 1,000

Business Description:
Mfr. of Cosmetics & Toiletries
S.I.C.: 2844
N.A.I.C.S.: 325620

Personnel:
Kazuyoshi Miyajima *(Chm)*
Yoshifumi Narimatsu *(CEO)*
Tsuyoshi Tatai *(COO)*

Board of Directors:
Kazuyoshi Miyajima
Yoshiharu Hayakawa
Jyunji Iida
Yukio Ikemori
Masakazu Iwakura
Yoshifumi Narimatsu
Mitsuru Nishikawa
Toshinori Ryuchi
Kazuyuki Shimada
Kenichi Sugama
Tsuyoshi Tatai
Tomoko Tsuji
Akira Yajima

U.S. Subsidiary:

Fancl International, Inc. (1)
17138 Pullman St Ste 100
Irvine, CA 92614
Tel.: (949) 476-8167
Fax: (949) 476-8168
E-Mail: contact@fancl.com
Web Site: www.fancl.com
Emp.: 20
Cosmetics & Toiletries Sales
S.I.C.: 5961
N.A.I.C.S.: 454113
Gen Inomata *(Pres)*

Subsidiaries:

Fancl B&H Co., Ltd. (1)
53 Iijimacho Sakae-Ku
Yokohama, Kanagawa, Japan
Tel.: (81) 458955405
Web Site: www.fancl.co.jp/corporate/about/group_e.html
Cosmetics Beauty Supplies & Perfume Stores
S.I.C.: 5122
N.A.I.C.S.: 446120
Akihiro Yanagisawa *(Mgr)*

Fancl Hatsuga Genmai Co., Ltd. (1)
1080-8 Azagenaushita
Netsu Tomi, Nagano, Japan
Tel.: (81) 268648311
Emp.: 59
Food Mfr
S.I.C.: 2099
N.A.I.C.S.: 311999
Ikenori Yukio *(Mgr)*

Fancl Home Life Co., Ltd. (1)
Tk Kannai Plz 4th Floor
Yokohama, Kanagawa, Japan
Tel.: (81) 120302222
Web Site: www.fancl.co.jp/corporate/about/group_e.html
Real Estate Agents & Brokers Offices
S.I.C.: 6531
N.A.I.C.S.: 531210
Tetsuo Yagi *(Mgr)*

Fancl Insurance Service Corp. (1)
Yamashita Cho 89-1
231-0023 Yokohama, Kanagawa, Japan
Tel.: (81) 452125200
Fax: (81) 0452125227
Web Site: www.fancl-hoken.co.jp/corporate/about/group_e.html
Insurance Agencies & Brokerages
S.I.C.: 6411
N.A.I.C.S.: 524210

Fancl Smile Co., Ltd. (1)
109-1 Iijimacho Sakae-Ku
Yokohama, Kanagawa, Japan
Tel.: (81) 458906870
Food Mfr
S.I.C.: 2099
N.A.I.C.S.: 311999

Non-U.S. Subsidiaries:

Fancl Asia Pte Ltd. (1)
101 Thomson Rd 21-05-06 United Sq
307591 Singapore, Singapore
Tel.: (65) 67377177
Fax: (65) 67359919
E-Mail: info@fancl.com.sg
Web Site: www.fancl.com.sg
Emp.: 80
Cosmetics Beauty Supplies & Perfume Stores
S.I.C.: 5122
N.A.I.C.S.: 446120

Fancl Taiwan Co., Ltd. (1)
Room C 12th Floor 31
Chung Hsiao E Rd Sec 1, Taipei, Taiwan
Tel.: (886) 223218033
E-Mail: katechen@fancl.com.tw
Web Site: www.fancl.com.tw
Drugs & Druggists Sundries Whslr
S.I.C.: 5122
N.A.I.C.S.: 424210
Kazuyoshi Miyajima *(Chm)*

Fancl (Thailand) Co., Ltd. (1)
20th Floor TPI Twr 26/56 Nang-linchee Rd
Thungmahamek Sathorn, 10120 Bangkok, Thailand
Tel.: (66) 26786707
Fax: (66) 26786711
E-Mail: taka-s@fancl.co.th
Web Site: www.fancl.co.th
Emp.: 32
Cosmetics Beauty Supplies & Perfume Stores
S.I.C.: 5122
N.A.I.C.S.: 446120
Takasiro Sayassi *(Mgr)*

FANCY WOOD INDUSTRIES PUBLIC COMPANY LIMITED

257 Mu-1 Soi Hyland Suksawat Road
Prasamutjaedee
Samut Prakan, 10290, Thailand
Tel.: (66) 28163060
Fax: (66) 28160179
E-Mail: info@fancywood.th.com
Web Site: www.fancywood.in.th
Year Founded: 1970
FANCY—(THA)
Rev.: $13,825,149
Assets: $42,377,246
Liabilities: $600,978
Net Worth: $41,776,267
Earnings: ($2,273,381)
Fiscal Year-end: 12/31/12

Business Description:
Wood Product Mfr
S.I.C.: 2499
N.A.I.C.S.: 321999

Personnel:
Pongsan Leelaprad *(Chm)*

Board of Directors:
Pongsan Leelaprad
Paichit Boonyanugraha
Chang Chi-Jen
Portip Chupinijsak
Chavalit Leelapornpisit
Piya Leelaprad
Kowit Linsaran
Vichai Tanpatanarat

Plant:

Fancy Wood Industries Public Company Limited - Suratthani Factory (1)
219 Mu 5 Asia Highway Tharongchang Punpin
Surat Thani, 84130, Thailand
Tel.: (66) 7725 4121 3
Fax: (66) 7725 4124
Thin Chipboard Mfr
S.I.C.: 2493
N.A.I.C.S.: 321219

FANDSTAN ELECTRIC GROUP

Craven House 16 Northumberland Ave
London, WC2N 5AP, United Kingdom
Tel.: (44) 2073069110
Fax: (44) 2079305929
E-Mail: office@fandstanelectric.com
Web Site: www.fandstanelectric.com
Year Founded: 1973
Sales Range: $200-249.9 Million
Emp.: 1,000

Business Description:
Holding Company
S.I.C.: 6719
N.A.I.C.S.: 551112

Subsidiaries:

Brecknell Willis & Co Limited (1)
East Street Chard
PO Box 10
Somerset, TA20 1EP, United Kingdom
Tel.: (44) 146064941
Fax: (44) 146066122
E-Mail: enquiries@brecknellwillis.com
Web Site: www.brecknell-willis.co.uk
Emp.: 250
Vehicular Lighting Equipment Mfr
S.I.C.: 3714
N.A.I.C.S.: 336320

Brecknell Willis Composites Ltd (1)
Unit 1 Millfield
Somerset, TA202BB, United Kingdom
Tel.: (44) 146068111
Fax: (44) 146066057
E-Mail: gen@bwcomposites.co.uk
Web Site: www.bwcomposites.co.uk
Emp.: 50
Paper Mills
S.I.C.: 2621
N.A.I.C.S.: 322121
Michael Casemore *(Mng Dir)*

Fandstan Electric Ltd. (1)
Craven House
16 Northumberland Avenue, London, WC2N 5AP, United Kingdom
Tel.: (44) 2073069110
Fax: (44) 2079305929
E-Mail: mjb@fandstanelectric.com
Web Site: www.fandstanelectric.com
Holding Company
S.I.C.: 6719
N.A.I.C.S.: 551112
Michael Bostelmann *(CEO)*

U.S. Subsidiary:

Transtech of South Carolina Inc (1)
709 Augusta Arbor Way
Piedmont, SC 29673
Tel.: (864) 299-3870
Fax: (864) 277-7100
E-Mail: ttiscinc@aol.com
Web Site: www.ttofsc.com
Vehicular Lighting Equipment Mfr
S.I.C.: 3714
N.A.I.C.S.: 336320
Suzanne Evans *(Mgr-HR)*

Non-U.S. Subsidiaries:

AKAPP Stemmann BV (1)
Nijverheidsweg 14
NL 3771 ME Barneveld, Netherlands
Mailing Address:
PO Box 54
NL 3770 AB Barneveld, Netherlands
Tel.: (31) 342403900
Fax: (31) 342403912
E-Mail: info@akapp.com
Web Site: www.akapp.com
Emp.: 65
S.I.C.: 3643
N.A.I.C.S.: 335931
Ehjj Burgers *(Mng Dir)*

Austbreck Pty Limited (1)
34-36 Westpool Dr
3803 Hallam, VIC, Australia
Tel.: (61) 397024011
Fax: (61) 397024088
E-Mail: corporate@austbreck.com.au
Web Site: www.austbreck.com.au
Emp.: 25
Railroad Rolling Stock Mfr
S.I.C.: 3743
N.A.I.C.S.: 336510
Wayne Caldow *(Mng Dir)*

Brecknell Willis (Taiwan) Co Limited (1)
23 International Commercial Bldg 10th Floor-5
Chang An East Rd Section 1, Taipei, 104, Taiwan
Tel.: (886) 225625587
Fax: (886) 2 2567 8185
Web Site: www.brecknellwillis.com.tw
Emp.: 10
Electrical Equipment & Component Mfr
S.I.C.: 3699
N.A.I.C.S.: 335999
Jeffrey Thorne *(Mgr)*

Stemmann-Technik GmbH (1)
PO Box 1460
Schuttorf, 48459 Osnabruck, Germany
Tel.: (49) 592381203
Fax: (49) 592381107
E-Mail: info@stemmann.de
Web Site: www.stemmann.de
Emp.: 400
Electrical Apparatus & Equipment Wiring Supplies
S.I.C.: 5063
N.A.I.C.S.: 423610
Michael Grunwald *(Gen Mgr)*

Stemmann-Technik Nederland B.V. (1)
De Roysloot 12K
Rijnsburg, 2231 NZ Amersfoort, Netherlands
Tel.: (31) 714062000
Fax: (31) 713019314
E-Mail: sales@stemmann.nl

Web Site: www.stemmann.nl
Emp.: 5
Electrical Apparatus & Equipment Wiring Supplies
S.I.C.: 5063
N.A.I.C.S.: 423610
Michael Bostelmann *(CEO)*

FANG BROTHERS KNITTING LTD.

20-24 Kaai Wing Road Kaai Chun
Hong Kong, China (Hong Kong)
Tel.: (852) 24016101
Fax: (852) 24850684
Emp.: 150

Business Description:
Knitted Garments
S.I.C.: 2389
N.A.I.C.S.: 315210

Personnel:
Kenneth Fang *(Chm & CEO)*

Non-U.S. Subsidiary:

Pringle of Scotland Ltd. **(1)**
Glebe Mill Noble Pl
Hawick, TD9 9QE, United Kingdom
Tel.: (44) 1450360260
Fax: (44) 1450360290
E-Mail: info@pringlescotland.com
Web Site: www.pringlescotland.com
Emp.: 25
Knitwear & Clothing
S.I.C.: 2299
N.A.I.C.S.: 313210
Douglas Fang *(CEO)*

FANSPORT, INC.

(Name Changed to Media Analytics Corporation)

FANTASIA HOLDINGS GROUP CO., LIMITED

F/27 Block A Hailrun Complex No 6021 Shennan Boulevard
Shenzhen, Guangdong, 518040, China
Tel.: (86) 75583458888
Fax: (86) 755 83479435
Web Site: www.cnfantasia.com
1777—(HKG)
Rev.: $989,643,443
Assets: $3,896,049,933
Liabilities: $2,796,622,714
Net Worth: $1,099,427,219
Earnings: $178,809,344
Emp.: 7,502
Fiscal Year-end: 12/31/12

Business Description:
Property Developer & Manager
S.I.C.: 6531
N.A.I.C.S.: 531390

Personnel:
Jun Pan *(Chm & CEO)*
Kam Tong Lam *(Sec)*

Board of Directors:
Jun Pan
Man Ho
Ming Huang
Kam Tong Lam
Dong Sheng Li
Martin Cheung Kong Liao
Liang Wang
Quan Xu
Hao Dong Yuan
Baby Jie Zeng
Jinquan Zhou

Computershare Hong Kong Investor Services Limited
Shops 1712-1716 17th Floor Hopewell Centre
183 Queens Road East
Wanchai, China (Hong Kong)

Transfer Agents:
Royal Bank of Canada Trust Company (Cayman) Limited
4th Floor Royal Bank House 24 Shedden Road
PO Box 1586
Georgetown, Cayman Islands

Computershare Hong Kong Investor Services Limited
Shops 1712-1716 17th Floor Hopewell Centre
183 Queens Road East
Wanchai, China (Hong Kong)

THE FANTASTIC COMPANY AG

Obmoos 4
CH-6301 Zug, Switzerland
Tel.: (41) 44 3502280
Fax: (41) 44 3502282
Web Site: www.fantastic.com
Year Founded: 1996
CEDA—(DEU)

Business Description:
Private Equity Investor
S.I.C.: 6211
N.A.I.C.S.: 523999

Personnel:
Cristian Mantzke *(CEO)*
Alexander Koppel *(CFO)*
Oliver Krautscheid *(Chm-Superviosy Bd)*

Supervisory Board of Directors:
Oliver Krautscheid
Markus Gildner
Roger Meier-Rossi

FANTASTIC HOLDINGS LIMITED

62 Hume Hwy
Chullora, NSW, 2190, Australia
Tel.: (61) 2 8717 2600
Fax: (61) 2 8717 2660
E-Mail: info@fantasticholdings.com.au
Web Site: www.fantasticholdings.com.au
FAN—(ASX)
Rev.: $463,932,499
Assets: $192,226,808
Liabilities: $79,528,904
Net Worth: $112,697,905
Earnings: $14,076,687
Emp.: 1,500
Fiscal Year-end: 06/30/13

Business Description:
Wood Furniture Mfr
S.I.C.: 2521
N.A.I.C.S.: 337211

Personnel:
Stephen Heath *(CEO & Mng Dir)*
George Saoud *(CFO & Sec)*
Debra Singh *(COO)*
Mark Garwood *(CEO-Retail & Supply Chain)*

Board of Directors:
James Millar
Peter Brennan
Stephen Heath
Denis McCormack
Geoffrey Squires
Julian Tertini

Subsidiaries:

Best Buy Furniture Pty Ltd **(1)**
62 Hume Hwy
Chullora, NSW, 2190, Australia
Tel.: (61) 287172600
Fax: (61) 287172660
Web Site: www.fantasticfurniture.com.au
Emp.: 90
Furniture Retailer
S.I.C.: 5712
N.A.I.C.S.: 442110

D. Gallery Pty Ltd **(1)**
Level 1 121 Rayhur Street
Clayton South, Melbourne, VIC, 3169, Australia
Tel.: (61) 397203822
Fax: (61) 397203455
E-Mail: info@dgallery.com.au
Web Site: www.daregallery.com.au
Home Furnishings Retailer
S.I.C.: 5023
N.A.I.C.S.: 423220
Chris Burke *(Mng Dir)*

Fantastic Furniture (Licensing) Pty Ltd **(1)**
3-15 Bennett St
Chester Hill, NSW, Australia
Tel.: (61) 297554015
Web Site: www.fantasticfurniture.com.au
Other Management Consulting Services
S.I.C.: 8748
N.A.I.C.S.: 541618

Fantastic Furniture Limited **(1)**
62 Huma Hwy
Chullora, NSW, 2190, Australia
Tel.: (61) 287172600
Fax: (61) 281172660
Web Site: www.fantasticfurniture.com.au
Emp.: 90
Furniture Retailer
S.I.C.: 5712
N.A.I.C.S.: 442110
Stephen Heath *(Gen Mgr)*

Fantastic Furniture Pty Ltd **(1)**
439 Princes Hwy Rockdale
Sydney, NSW, Australia
Tel.: (61) 95990731
Furniture Stores
S.I.C.: 5712
N.A.I.C.S.: 442110

FHL Distribution Centre Pty Ltd **(1)**
10-28 Bildela Street
Villawood, NSW, 2163, Australia
Tel.: (61) 287172600
Fax: (61) 287172660
Household Furniture Distr
S.I.C.: 5021
N.A.I.C.S.: 423210

Original Mattress Factory Pty Ltd **(1)**
Home Focus Shop 26-173 Canterbury Road
PO Box 445
Chester Hill, Bankstown, NSW, 2162, Australia
Tel.: (61) 2 9791 6222
Fax: (61) 2 9708 3481
E-Mail: bankstown@omf.net.au
Web Site: www.omf.net.au
Emp.: 4
Mattresses Retailer
S.I.C.: 5712
N.A.I.C.S.: 442110

Plush - Think Sofas Pty Ltd **(1)**
Shop 1-5 419 Townsend Street
Albury, NSW, 2640, Australia
Tel.: (61) 260413311
Web Site: www.plush.com.au
Emp.: 5
Sofa Retailer
S.I.C.: 5021
N.A.I.C.S.: 423210
Robert De Nicola *(Gen Mgr)*

Royal Comfort Bedding Pty Ltd **(1)**
1333 The Horsley Drive
Wetherill Park, Sydney, NSW, 2164, Australia
Tel.: (61) 2 8787 6600
Mattresses Mfr
S.I.C.: 2515
N.A.I.C.S.: 337910

White Label Innovations Pty Ltd **(1)**
10 Anzac Hwy
Keswick, Adelaide, SA, 5035, Australia
Tel.: (61) 882923333
Furniture Retailer
S.I.C.: 5712
N.A.I.C.S.: 442110

FANUC CORPORATION

Oshino-mura
Yamanashi, 401-0597, Japan
Tel.: (81) 555845555
Fax: (81) 555845512
Web Site: www.fanuc.co.jp
Year Founded: 1956
6954—(TKS)
Sls.: $5,482,345,000
Assets: $13,410,243,000
Liabilities: $1,374,824,000
Net Worth: $12,035,419,000
Earnings: $1,325,324,000
Emp.: 5,080
Fiscal Year-end: 03/31/13

Business Description:
Numerical Control Systems, Laser, Power Motion & Robots Mfr
S.I.C.: 3625
N.A.I.C.S.: 335314

Personnel:
Seiuemon Inaba *(Founder)*
Yoshiharu Inaba *(Pres & CEO)*

Transfer Agent:
Tokyo Securities Transfer Agent Co., Ltd.
Togin Bldg 1-4-2 Marunouchi
Chiyoda-ku, Tokyo, 100-0005, Japan
Tel.: (81) 3 3212 4611

U.S. Subsidiaries:

Fanuc American Corp. **(1)**
1800 Lakewood Blvd
Hoffman Estates, IL 60192-5008 (100%)
Tel.: (847) 898-5000
Fax: (847) 898-5001
E-Mail: jobs@fanucamerica.com
Web Site: www.fanucamerica.com
Emp.: 110
CNC & Laser Service
S.I.C.: 7378
N.A.I.C.S.: 811212

FANUC Robotics America Corporation **(1)**
3900 W Hamlin Rd
Rochester Hills, MI 48309-3253
Tel.: (248) 377-7000
Fax: (248) 377-7365
Toll Free: (800) 477-6268
E-Mail: marketing@fanucrobotics.com
Web Site: www.fanucrobotics.com
Industrial Robotic Automation Distr
S.I.C.: 5084
N.A.I.C.S.: 423830
Rick Schneider *(CEO)*

Fanuc Robotics North America, Inc. **(1)**
3900 W Hamlin Rd
Rochester Hills, MI 48309 MI
Tel.: (248) 377-7000 (100%)
Fax: (248) 276-4227
Toll Free: (800) 47ROBOT
E-Mail: marketing@fanucrobotics.com
Web Site: www.fanucrobotics.com
Emp.: 600
Robotic Automation Supplier
Import Export
S.I.C.: 3559
N.A.I.C.S.: 333249
Rick Schneider *(Pres)*

Non-U.S. Subsidiaries:

Fanuc Europe GmbH **(1)**
Bernhauser Strasse 22
73765 Neuhausen, Germany (100%)
Tel.: (49) 7158187300
Fax: (49) 7158187411
E-Mail: info@fanuc.de
Web Site: www.fanuc.au
Emp.: 25
S.I.C.: 3625
N.A.I.C.S.: 335314

Subsidiary:

Fanuc Germany Service GmbH **(2)**
Bernhauser Strasse 22
73765 Neuhausen, Germany De
Tel.: (49) 158187300 (100%)
Fax: (49) 158187366
E-Mail: info@fanuc.de
Web Site: www.fanuc.de
Emp.: 58
Provider of Industrial Controls
S.I.C.: 3625
N.A.I.C.S.: 335314

Non-U.S. Subsidiaries:

Fanuc Bulgaria Corporation **(2)**
29-37 Cristo Smirnenksy St
Sofia, 1164, Bulgaria (100%)

FANUC Corporation—(Continued)

Tel.: (359) 29633319
Fax: (359) 29632873
E-Mail: service@fanuc.bg
Web Site: www.fanuc.eu
Emp.: 10
Provider of Industrial Controls
S.I.C.: 3625
N.A.I.C.S.: 335314
Jordan Todorov *(Pres)*

FANUC CNC Iberia (2)
Calle Enginy No 14
E 08850 Barcelona, Gava, Spain (100%)
Tel.: (34) 936644820
Fax: (34) 93 6650695
E-Mail: fibservice@es.fanuceurope.eu
Web Site: www.fanuc.com
Sls.: $30,004,224
Emp.: 8
Industrial Control Services
S.I.C.: 3625
N.A.I.C.S.: 335314
Fabio Bellicci *(Mng Dir)*

FANUC FA Italia S.r.l. (2)
Via Volta 4
I-20090 Buccinasco, MI, Italy (100%)
Tel.: (39) 02457951
Fax: (39) 0245795250
E-Mail: info@fanuc.it
Web Site: www.fanucfa.com
Emp.: 28
Industrial Automation Controls Servicer
S.I.C.: 3625
N.A.I.C.S.: 335314
Mark Celibelli *(Gen Mgr)*

Fanuc France S.A. (2)
10 Rue De Valenton
94470 Boissy-Saint Leger, France (100%)
Tel.: (33) 145696333
Fax: (33) 145690325
E-Mail: service@fanuccnc.fr
Web Site: www.fanuc.de
Emp.: 18
Provider of Industrial Controls
S.I.C.: 3625
N.A.I.C.S.: 335314
Michel Lejrang *(Gen Mgr)*

Fanuc Robotics Europe S.A. (2)
Zn Ind
6468 Echternach, Luxembourg (100%)
Tel.: (352) 7277771
Fax: (352) 727777403
E-Mail: info@fanucrobotics.lu
Web Site: www.fanucrobotics.lu
Emp.: 70
Robot Sales & Service
S.I.C.: 3625
N.A.I.C.S.: 335314
Olas Gahrals *(Pres & CEO)*

Fanuc Turkey Ltd. (2)
Serifali Mevkii Barbaros Caddesi Soylesi
Sok No 23 B Blok 34760
Istanbul, 34760, Turkey (80%)
Tel.: (90) 2166511408
Fax: (90) 2166511405
E-Mail: info@tr.fanaceurope.eu
Emp.: 11
Relay & Industrial Control Manufacturing
S.I.C.: 3625
N.A.I.C.S.: 335314

Fanuc U.K. Limited (2)
1 Station Approach
Ruislip, HA4 8LF, United Kingdom (100%)
Tel.: (44) 01895634182
Fax: (44) 01895676140
E-Mail: info@fanuc.co.uk
Web Site: www.fanuc.co.uk
Emp.: 18
Provider of Industrial Control Services
S.I.C.: 3625
N.A.I.C.S.: 335314
Andrew Myhill *(Mng Dir)*

FANUC FA Bulgaria Ltd. (1)
29-37 Christo Smirnenski Blvd
1164 Sofia, Bulgaria
Tel.: (359) 2 963 33 19
Fax: (359) 2 963 28 73
E-Mail: service@fanuc.bg
Web Site: www.fanucbulgaria.com
Robotic Machinery Sales & Maintenance Services
S.I.C.: 5084
N.A.I.C.S.: 423830
Jordan Todorov *(Mng Dir)*

FANUC FA Deutschland GmbH (1)
Bernhauser Strasse 22
73765 Neuhausen, Germany
Tel.: (49) 7158 187 400
Fax: (49) 7158 187 455
E-Mail: info@fanuc.de
Web Site: www.fanucfa.com
Industrial Machinery Repair & Maintenance Services
S.I.C.: 7699
N.A.I.C.S.: 811310

FANUC FA France S.A.S. (1)
10 Rue De Valenton
94470 Boissy-Saint Leger, France
Tel.: (33) 1 4569 6275
Fax: (33) 1 4569 2070
E-Mail: service@fanuc.fr
Web Site: www.fanuc.fr
Industrial Machinery Repair & Maintenance Services
S.I.C.: 7699
N.A.I.C.S.: 811310

FANUC FA Hungary Kft (1)
Orco Business Park Szabadsag U 117
2040 Budaors, Hungary
Tel.: (36) 23 507 400
Fax: (36) 23 507 401
E-Mail: info.hu@fanuc.eu
Web Site: www.fanucfa.com
Emp.: 5
Robotic Machinery Repair & Maintenance Services
S.I.C.: 7699
N.A.I.C.S.: 811310
Rostislav Novak *(Gen Mgr)*

FANUC FA Iberia S.A.U. (1)
Poligono Industrial Olaso Calle Olaso 3
20870 Elgoibar, Gipuzkoa, Spain
Tel.: (34) 943 74 82 90
Fax: (34) 943 74 44 21
E-Mail: info@fanuc.es
Web Site: www.fanucfa.com
Industrial Machinery Repair & Maintenance Services
S.I.C.: 7699
N.A.I.C.S.: 811310

FANUC FA Nordic AB (1)
Hammarbacken 4B
191 49 Sollentuna, Sweden
Tel.: (46) 8 505 80 700
Fax: (46) 8 505 80 701
E-Mail: info@fanuc.se
Robotic Machine Repair & Maintenance Services
S.I.C.: 7699
N.A.I.C.S.: 811310

FANUC FA Polska Sp. z o.o. (1)
Ul Strzegomska 2-4
53-611 Wroclaw, Poland
Tel.: (48) 71 7766170
Fax: (48) 71 7766179
E-Mail: info@fanuc.pl
Web Site: www.fanucfa.com
Emp.: 5
Industrial Machinery Repair & Maintenance Services
S.I.C.: 7699
N.A.I.C.S.: 811310
Rostislav Novak *(Mng Dir)*

FANUC FA SATIS VE SERVIS TICARET LTD. (1)
Mahir Iz Cad No 26 Kat 1 Altunizade-Uskudar
81190 Istanbul, Turkey
Tel.: (90) 216 651 1408
Fax: (90) 216 651 1405
E-Mail: info@fanuc.ey
Web Site: www.fanuc.co.jp/en/service/europe/turkey.htm
Emp.: 15
Industrial Machinery Repair & Maintenance Services
S.I.C.: 7699
N.A.I.C.S.: 811310
Rostislav Svoboda *(Gen Mgr)*

FANUC FA Switzerland GmbH (1)
Grenchenstrasse 7
2500 Biel/Bienne, Switzerland
Tel.: (41) 32 366 63 63
Fax: (41) 32 366 63 64
E-Mail: info@fanuc.ch
Web Site: www.fanuc.ch
Industrial Machinery Repair & Maintenance Services
S.I.C.: 7699
N.A.I.C.S.: 811310

FANUC FA UK LIMITED (1)
Fanuc House 1 Station Approach
Ruislip, Middlesex, HA4 8LF, United Kingdom
Tel.: (44) 1895 6 34 182
Fax: (44) 1895 6 76 140
E-Mail: info@fanuc.co.uk
Emp.: 2
Industrial Machinery Distr
S.I.C.: 5084
N.A.I.C.S.: 423830
Andrew Myhill *(Mng Dir)*

Fanuc India Private Limited (1)
41 A Electronics City Hosur Rd
Bengaluru, Karnataka, 560 100, India (100%)
Tel.: (91) 8028520057
Fax: (91) 8028520051
E-Mail: filhq@fanucindia.com
Web Site: www.fanucindia.com
Emp.: 160
Mfr. of CNC; Joint Venture of General Electric Company (60%) & Fanuc Ltd. (40%)
S.I.C.: 3699
N.A.I.C.S.: 335999
Somali Kulkerni *(Pres & CEO)*

FANUC KOREA SERVICE CORPORATION (1)
42 Ungnam-dong
Seongsan-gu, Changwon, Gyeongsangnam-do, Korea (South)
Tel.: (82) 55 282 0122
Fax: (82) 55 261 6958
Robotic Machine Repair & Maintenance Services
S.I.C.: 7699
N.A.I.C.S.: 811310

Fanuc Mechatronics (Malaysia) Sdn. Bhd. (1)
No 32 JLN Pengacara U1 48 Temasya Indus Pk Sec U1
Shah Alam, Selangor, 40150, Malaysia (100%)
Tel.: (60) 376280110
Fax: (60) 376280220
E-Mail: fanuc@po.jaring.my
Web Site: www.jaring.com
Sales Range: $1-9.9 Million
Emp.: 20
S.I.C.: 3625
N.A.I.C.S.: 335314
Hideo Shimizu *(Mng Dir)*

Fanuc Oceania Pty. Limited (1)
10 Healey Circuit
2148 Huntingwood, NSW, Australia (100%)
Tel.: (61) 288224600
Fax: (61) 288224666
E-Mail: sol@fanucoceania.com.au
Web Site: www.fanuc.co.jp/en/service/asia/oceania.htm
Emp.: 13
Equipment & Machinery
S.I.C.: 3541
N.A.I.C.S.: 333517
Gaby Gahabach *(Mng Dir)*

Fanuc Philippines Corporation (1)
7th Floor Glass Tower Units C&D 115C Palanca Jr Street
Legaspi Village 63, Makati, Manila, 1229, Philippines (100%)
Tel.: (63) 28133155
Fax: (63) 28133157
Web Site: www.fanuc.co.jp/en/service/asia/philippines.htm
Sls.: $25,000,000
Emp.: 7
Laser, Robot & Robomachine Services
S.I.C.: 3625
N.A.I.C.S.: 335314
Makoto Matsumoto *(Mng Dir)*

FANUC ROBOMACHINE EUROPE GmbH (1)
Bernhauser Str 22
73765 Neuhausen auf den Fildern, Germany
Tel.: (49) 7158 187 200
Fax: (49) 7158 187 218
E-Mail: info@fanucrobomachine.eu
Web Site: www.fanucrobomachine.eu
Emp.: 4
Industrial Automation Machinery Distr
S.I.C.: 5084
N.A.I.C.S.: 423830
Martin Schopf *(Mgr-Sls)*

Fanuc Robomachine (Shenzhen) Ltd. (1)
2/F A Wanshan Building 2nd Wenxin Road Nanshan Commercial Culture
Centre Area, Shenzhen, Guangdong, 518054, China
Tel.: (86) 75526422423
Fax: (86) 75526422421
Web Site: www.fanuc.co.jp/en/service/asia/shanghai.html
Emp.: 200
Special Industry Machinery
S.I.C.: 3559
N.A.I.C.S.: 333249
Jhang Wei *(Mgr-Sls)*

Fanuc Singapore Pte. Ltd. (1)
No 1 Teban Gardens Crescent
Jurong, Singapore, 608919, Singapore (100%)
Tel.: (65) 62203911
Fax: (65) 62250098
E-Mail: info@fanuc.com.jp
Web Site: www.fanuc.com.jp
Emp.: 20
CNC, Laser, Robot & Robomachine Sales & Service
S.I.C.: 3625
N.A.I.C.S.: 335314
E. Rudy *(Mng Dir)*

Fanuc South Africa Pty. Limited (1)
17 Loper Ave Aeroport Industrial Estates
PO Box 219
Spartan Ext 2, Johannesburg, South Africa (100%)
Tel.: (27) 113923610
Fax: (27) 113923615
E-Mail: service@fsa.fanuc.com
Web Site: www.fanuc.com
Sls.: $41,000,000
Emp.: 15
Equipment & Machinery
S.I.C.: 3541
N.A.I.C.S.: 333517
Kroun Petkov *(Mng Dir)*

Fanuc Taiwan Limited (1)
No 4 17th Rd
Taichung Industrial Park, Taichung, 407, Taiwan (100%)
Tel.: (886) 423591842
Fax: (886) 423590676
Web Site: www.fanuc.co.jp/en/service/asia/taiwan.htm
Emp.: 80
Provider of Industrial Control Products & Services
S.I.C.: 3625
N.A.I.C.S.: 335314

FANUC VIETNAM LIMITED (1)
9th Floor Green Power No 35 Ton Duc Thang Street
District 1, Ho Chi Minh City, Vietnam
Tel.: (84) 8 3824 6638
Fax: (84) 8 3824 6637
Web Site: www.fanuc.co.jp/en/service/asia/vietnam.htm
Emp.: 6
Robot Machine Repair & Maintenance Services
S.I.C.: 7699
N.A.I.C.S.: 811310
Naoya Yoshino *(Gen Dir)*

PT. FANUC INDONESIA (1)
Jl Boulevard Bukit Gading Raya Blok R
Jakarta, 14240, Indonesia
Tel.: (62) 21 45847285
Fax: (62) 21 45847288
E-Mail: hananto.t@fin.fanuc.com
Emp.: 15
Robot Machine Repair & Maintenance Services
S.I.C.: 7699
N.A.I.C.S.: 811310
Hananto T. Anggoro *(Mgr-Fin)*

SHANGHAI-FANUC Robotics CO., LTD. (1)
No 1500 Fulian Road
Baoshan, Shanghai, 201906, China
Tel.: (86) 21 50327700
Fax: (86) 21 50327711
E-Mail: sfr@shanghai-fanuc.com.cn
Web Site: www.shanghai-fanuc.com.cn
Emp.: 200
Robot System Mfr & Distr
S.I.C.: 3569
N.A.I.C.S.: 333999
Qian Hui *(Gen Mgr)*

TAIWAN FANUC ROBOTICS CORPORATION (1)
No 4 17th Road Taichung Industrial Park
Taichung, Taiwan
Tel.: (886) 4 2359 2827
Fax: (886) 4 2359 6040
E-Mail: service@fanucrobotics.tw
Web Site: www.fanuc.co.jp/en/service/asia/taiwanrobotics.html
Robot System Mfr & Distr
S.I.C.: 3569
N.A.I.C.S.: 333999

Non-U.S. Joint Ventures:

Beijing-Fanuc Mechatronics Co., Ltd. (1)
9 Beijing Shangdi Information Industry Base Rd
Beijing, Haidian District, 100085, China (40%)
Tel.: (86) 10 62984743
Fax: (86) 10 62984746
E-Mail: sales@bj-fanuc.com.cn
Web Site: www.bj-fanuc.com.cn
Emp.: 100
Sales & Servicer of Industrial Controls
S.I.C.: 5084
N.A.I.C.S.: 423830

Fanuc Korea Corporation (1)
42 Ungnam Dong
Changwon, Kyeongnam, 641290, Korea (South) (90%)
Tel.: (82) 552820122
Fax: (82) 552849826
E-Mail: kerson@fkc.co.kr
Web Site: www.fkc.co.kr
Emp.: 250
Provider of Industrial Control Products & Services
S.I.C.: 3625
N.A.I.C.S.: 335314
Lee Yeoul Hae *(Mgr-HR)*

Fanuc Thai Limited (1)
59 3 Sui Sukhumvit 39 Sukhumvit Rd
Bangkok, 10110, Thailand (49%)
Tel.: (66) 26626111
Fax: (66) 26626120
Web Site: www.fanuc.com
Emp.: 30
Provider of Industrial Controls
S.I.C.: 3625
N.A.I.C.S.: 335314

Tatung-Fanuc Robotics Company (1)
22 Sec 3 Chungshan N Rd
Taipei, 104, Taiwan
Tel.: (886) 225925252
Fax: (886) 225928124
E-Mail: shirleychou@tatungfanuc.com.tw
Web Site: www.tatungfanuc.com.tw
Emp.: 1,000
Robot Sales & Services; Joint Venture of Tatung Corporation (50%) & Fanuc Ltd. (50%)
S.I.C.: 3625
N.A.I.C.S.: 335314
Wei-Shan Lin *(Pres)*

FAP - KORPORACIJA A.D.

Radnicka bb
31330 Priboj, Serbia
Tel.: (381) 33 451 331
Fax: (381) 33 55 241
E-Mail: fap@eunet.rs
Web Site: www.fap.co.rs
FAPP—(BEL)
Business Description:
Truck & Bus Mfr
S.I.C.: 3711
N.A.I.C.S.: 336120
Personnel:
Mirko Stojovic *(Gen Mgr)*

FAR CITY MINING LIMITED

Room No 301 302 New East Ocean Centre
9 Science Museum Road
Tsim Sha Tsui, Kowloon, China (Hong Kong)
Tel.: (852) 27238638
Fax: (852) 27237445
E-Mail: info@farcityhk.com
Web Site: www.farcitymining.com
Year Founded: 2009
FCH—(CNSX)
Int. Income: $19
Assets: $6,442,786
Liabilities: $3,463,184
Net Worth: $2,979,602
Earnings: ($894,304)
Fiscal Year-end: 09/30/12
Business Description:
Precious & Base Metals Mining & Exploration Services
S.I.C.: 1099
N.A.I.C.S.: 212299
Personnel:
Harry Tak Shing Lam *(Chm & CEO)*
Patrick Pak Him Wong *(CFO)*
Board of Directors:
Harry Tak Shing Lam
Picheng Hu
Fong Chung Lai
Jorge Sepulveda Schonherr
Joseph Biu Sing Tam
Patrick Pak Him Wong
Peixing Yang
Wenhai Zhang
Transfer Agent:
Olympia Transfer Service Inc
Suite 920 120 Adelaide Street West
Toronto, ON, Canada

FAR EAST CONSORTIUM INTERNATIONAL LIMITED

(d/b/a FECIL)
16/F Far East Consortium Building
121 Des Voeux Road
Central, China (Hong Kong)
Tel.: (852) 28500600
Fax: (852) 28150412
E-Mail: kcfec@netvigator.com
Web Site: www.fareastconsortium.com.hk
0035—(HKG)
Rev.: $481,263,579
Assets: $2,503,963,221
Liabilities: $1,324,011,404
Net Worth: $1,179,951,817
Earnings: $139,055,812
Emp.: 3,000
Fiscal Year-end: 03/31/13
Business Description:
Property Development & Investment Services
S.I.C.: 6211
N.A.I.C.S.: 523999
Personnel:
David Chiu *(Chm & CEO)*
Chris Cheong Thard Hoong *(Mng Dir)*
Boswell Wai Hung Cheung *(CFO & Sec)*
Denny Chi Hing Chan *(COO)*
Board of Directors:
David Chiu
Denny Chi Hing Chan
Kwok Wai Chan
Daniel Tat Jung Chiu
Dennis Chiu
Chris Cheong Thard Hoong
Kwong Siu Lam
Craig Grenfell Williams
Peter Man Kong Wong
Legal Counsel:
Woo, Kwan, Lee & Lo
26th Floor Jardine House
Central, China (Hong Kong)
Reed Smith Richards Butler
20th Floor Alexandra House 16-20 Chater Road
Central, China (Hong Kong)
Maples & Calder
53rd Floor The Center 99 Queen's Road
Central, China (Hong Kong)

Subsidiaries:

Cosmopolitan Hotel Limited (1)
387-397 Queens Road East
Wanchai, China (Hong Kong) (100%)
Tel.: (852) 35521111
Fax: (852) 35521122
E-Mail: welcome@cosmopolitanhotel.com.hk
Web Site: www.cosmopolitanhotel.com.hk
Emp.: 100
Hotels & Motels721110
S.I.C.: 7011
N.A.I.C.S.: 721110
Anita Chan *(Gen Mgr)*

Far East Consortium Limited (1)
16th Floor Far East Consortium Bldg
Central Area, Central, China (Hong Kong) (100%)
Tel.: (852) 28500600
Fax: (852) 28150412
Real Estate Property Lessors
S.I.C.: 6519
N.A.I.C.S.: 531190

Grand Expert Limited (1)
16th Floor Far East Consortium Bldg
Central Area, Central, China (Hong Kong) (100%)
Tel.: (852) 28500600
Fax: (852) 28150412
Real Estate Property Lessors
S.I.C.: 6519
N.A.I.C.S.: 531190

The Hotel of Lan Kwai Fong Limited (1)
3 Kau U Fong
Central, China (Hong Kong) (100%)
Tel.: (852) 36500000
Fax: (852) 36500088
E-Mail: enquiry@lankwaifonghotel.com.hk
Web Site: www.lankwaifonghotel.com.hk
Emp.: 125
Hotels & Motels
S.I.C.: 7011
N.A.I.C.S.: 721110
Rebecca Kwan *(Gen Mgr)*

Kosmopolito Hotels International Limited (1)
375 Queen's Road East
Wanchai, China (Hong Kong)
Tel.: (852) 3516 8328
E-Mail: enquiry@kosmopolito.com
Web Site: www.kosmohotels.com
2266—(HKG)
Sales Range: $75-99.9 Million
Emp.: 1,690
Hotel Owner & Operator
S.I.C.: 7011
N.A.I.C.S.: 721110
Chui Yue Bond *(CFO)*
Seng Mun Tang *(COO)*
Shu Kiong Yip *(CMO)*
Kwai Pui Mok *(Sec)*
Philip Schaetz *(Sr VP-Sls & Mktg)*

Ruby Way Limited (1)
16th Floor Far East Consortium Bldg
Central Area, Central, China (Hong Kong) (100%)
Tel.: (852) 28500600
Fax: (852) 28150412
Real Estate Property Lessors
S.I.C.: 6519
N.A.I.C.S.: 531190

Top Trend Developments Limited (1)
Unit F1-F, 12/F Phase 1 Hang Fung Industrial Bldg
2G Hok Yuen St, Hunghom Kowloon, China (Hong Kong) (100%)
Tel.: (852) 34288329
Fax: (852) 34288339
E-Mail: marketing@toptrendhk.com
Web Site: www.toptrendhk.com
Real Estate Property Lessors
S.I.C.: 6519
N.A.I.C.S.: 531190
Willy Hon *(Mgr-Mktg)*

Holding:

New China Homes Ltd. (1)
16/F Far East Consortium Building
121 Des Voeux Road Central, Hong Kong, China (Hong Kong) (75%)
Tel.: (852) 28500600
Fax: (852) 28506294
E-Mail: denny.chan@fecil.com.hk
Web Site: www.fecil.com.hk
Emp.: 46
Holding Company for Residential Property Developer
S.I.C.: 6719
N.A.I.C.S.: 551112
Maria Cheung *(Mgr-Mktg)*

Non-U.S. Subsidiaries:

Dorsett Regency Hotel (M) Sdn. Bhd. (1)
172 Jalan Imbi
55100 Kuala Lumpur, Malaysia (100%)
Tel.: (60) 327151000
Fax: (60) 327155000
E-Mail: e-reservation@dorsettregency.com.my
Web Site: www.dorsettregency.com.my
Emp.: 208
Hotels & Motels
S.I.C.: 7011
N.A.I.C.S.: 721110

Far East Consortium Holdings (Australia) Pty Limited (1)
L 5 370 St Kilda Rd
3004 Melbourne, VIC, Australia (100%)
Tel.: (61) 396816988
Fax: (61) 396816188
E-Mail: reception@fareast.net.au
Web Site: www.fareast.net.au
Emp.: 13
Land Subdivision
S.I.C.: 6552
N.A.I.C.S.: 237210

Far East Supermarket Limited (1)
41 The Vale
28 High Road, London, NW102QD, United Kingdom (100%)
Tel.: (44) 2084591574
Grocery & Related Products Whslr
S.I.C.: 5149
N.A.I.C.S.: 424490

Redleaf Properties Limited (1)
71 Amiens Street
Dublin, Ireland (100%)
Tel.: (353) 18905670
Fax: (353) 18905789
Real Estate Investment Trusts
S.I.C.: 6726
N.A.I.C.S.: 525990

Scarborough Development Limited (1)
Europa House
Scarborough, United Kingdom (100%)
Tel.: (44) 1723850908
Land Subdivision
S.I.C.: 6552
N.A.I.C.S.: 237210

Tang City Properties Pte Limited. (1)
100A EU Tong Sen Street
059813 Singapore, Singapore (100%)
Tel.: (65) 63230234
Fax: (65) 62275907
Web Site: www.tanggroup.com.sg
Emp.: 12
Holding Company
S.I.C.: 6719
N.A.I.C.S.: 551112
Dennis Chiu *(Mng Dir)*

Tomarta Sdn. Bhd. (1)
31st Fl Maytower Hotel No 7 Jalan Munshi Abdullah
50100 Kuala Lumpur, Malaysia (100%)
Tel.: (60) 326929663
Fax: (60) 326920663
Web Site: www.mela.com.my
Real Estate Property Lessors
S.I.C.: 6519
N.A.I.C.S.: 531190

Far East Consortium International Limited—(Continued)

Michael Chee *(Gen Mgr)*

FAR EAST GROUP LIMITED

112 Lavender Street 04-00 Far East Refrigeration Building
Singapore, 338728, Singapore
Tel.: (65) 6293 9733
Fax: (65) 6296 5326
E-Mail: info@fareastref.com.sg
Web Site: www.fareastgroup.com.sg
Year Founded: 1953
5TJ—(CAT)
Sls.: $23,224,994
Assets: $23,006,078
Liabilities: $7,646,994
Net Worth: $15,359,085
Earnings: $312,092
Emp.: 118
Fiscal Year-end: 12/31/12

Business Description:
Refrigeration Equipment Distr
S.I.C.: 5078
N.A.I.C.S.: 423740

Personnel:
Steven Mun Yew Loh *(CEO)*
Foon Yeow Chia *(Sec)*

Board of Directors:
Ah Peng Loh
Koon Chan Hew
David Chee Keong Leng
Karen Pui Lai Loh
Steven Mun Yew Loh
Andrew Yen-Chen Mak
Hwee Kiong Tan
Allan Ward

Transfer Agent:
Boardroom Corporate & Advisory Services Pte. Ltd.
50 Raffles Place 32-01 Singapore Land Tower
Singapore, Singapore

Subsidiaries:

Edenkool Pte Ltd **(1)**
112 Lavender Street 01-00 Far East Refrigeration Building
Singapore, 338728, Singapore
Tel.: (65) 6748 9989
Fax: (65) 6748 6606
E-Mail: info@edenkool.com.sg
Web Site: www.fareastgroup.com.sg/contact-regional.html
Air Conditioning Equipment Distr
S.I.C.: 5075
N.A.I.C.S.: 423730
David Leng *(COO)*

Green Point (Singapore) Pte. Ltd. **(1)**
5 Third Lok Yang Road
Singapore, 628000, Singapore
Tel.: (65) 684 116 11
Fax: (65) 656841161, ext. 1
E-Mail: singapore@bitzegreenpoint.com
Web Site: www.greenpoint.com.sg
Emp.: 3
Industrial Machinery Mfr
S.I.C.: 3559
N.A.I.C.S.: 333249
Benjamin Ho *(Gen Mgr)*

RSP Systems Pte Ltd **(1)**
112 Lavender Street 04-00 Far East Refrigeration Building
Singapore, 338728, Singapore
Tel.: (65) 6297 4880
Fax: (65) 6297 4881
E-Mail: info@rspsys.com
Emp.: 10
Refrigeration Equipment Supplier
S.I.C.: 5078
N.A.I.C.S.: 423740
Rhee Chang Shik *(Mng Dir)*

Non-U.S. Subsidiaries:

Far East Enterprises (Johor Bahru) Sdn Bhd **(1)**
No 12 & 12A Jalan Shah Bandar 2 Taman Ungku Tun Aminah
Skudai, 81300 Johor Bahru, Malaysia
Tel.: (60) 7 556 1221
Fax: (60) 7 556 1680
E-Mail: feejb@po.jaring.my
Web Site: www.fareastgroup.com.sg/contact-regional.html
Refrigeration Cooler & Compressor Distr
S.I.C.: 5078
N.A.I.C.S.: 423740

Far East Enterprises (Kuala Lumpur) Sdn Bhd **(1)**
1-1 Jalan Kalong Off Jalan Sungai Besi
Kuala Lumpur, 55200, Malaysia
Tel.: (60) 3 9221 3832
Fax: (60) 3 9222 9004
E-Mail: feekl@tm.net.my
Refrigeration Cooler & Compressor Distr
S.I.C.: 5078
N.A.I.C.S.: 423740

Far East Enterprises (Penang) Sd Bhd **(1)**
60 Lebuh Noordin
10300 George Town, Pulau Pinang, Malaysia
Tel.: (60) 4 262 0711
Fax: (60) 4 262 6714
E-Mail: fepenang@tm.net.my
Refrigeration Cooler & Compressor Distr
S.I.C.: 5075
N.A.I.C.S.: 423730

Far East Maju Engineering Works Sdn Bhd **(1)**
Lot 1998/D Jalan Perusahaan 3 Taman Industri Selesa Jaya
43300 Seri Kembangan, Selangor Darul Ehsan, Malaysia
Tel.: (60) 3 8961 0910
Fax: (60) 3 8961 5970
E-Mail: eden@edeng3.com
Web Site: www.fareastgroup.com.sg/contact-regional.html
Emp.: 45
Refrigeration Equipment Repair & Maintenance Services
S.I.C.: 7699
N.A.I.C.S.: 811310
Donny Yap *(Mgr)*

Far East Refrigeration (Kuching) Sdn Bhd **(1)**
Lot 7758 & 7759 Section 64 Ktld Jalan Datuk Abang Abdul Rahim
93450 Kuching, Sarawak, Malaysia
Tel.: (60) 82 338 588
Fax: (60) 82 331 088
E-Mail: fareakg@streamyx.com
Web Site: www.fareastgroup.com.sg/contact-regional.html
Refrigeration Equipment Distr
S.I.C.: 5078
N.A.I.C.S.: 423740

Far East Refrigeration Limited **(1)**
Room E 10/F Wang Cheong comm Bldg
253 Reclamation Street
Kowloon, Mongkok, China (Hong Kong)
Tel.: (852) 2388 3737
Fax: (852) 2740 9625
E-Mail: hongkong@fareastref.com.sg
Web Site: www.fareastgroup.com.sg
Emp.: 1
Refrigeration & Air Conditioning Equipment Distr
S.I.C.: 5078
N.A.I.C.S.: 423740
Pilly Yau *(Branch Mgr)*

FE & B Engineering (M) Sdn. Bhd. **(1)**
No 12 Jln Shahbandar 2 Taman Ungku Tun Aminah
Skudai, 81300 Johor Bahru, Malaysia
Tel.: (60) 7 556 1263
Fax: (60) 4561680
E-Mail: fereast@yahoo.com
Emp.: 4
Refrigeration Equipment Repair & Maintenance Services
S.I.C.: 7699
N.A.I.C.S.: 811310
Elina Tan *(Mgr-Sls)*

FAR EAST HOLDINGS BERHAD

Suite 5 Level 8 Kompleks Teruntum
PO Box 35
Jalan Mahkota, 25000 Kuantan, Pahang Darul Makmur, Malaysia
Tel.: (60) 95141936
Fax: (60) 95136211
E-Mail: fareast@fareh.po.my
Web Site: www.fehb.com.my
FAREAST—(KLS)
Rev.: $149,401,150
Assets: $413,307,051
Liabilities: $58,736,730
Net Worth: $354,570,321
Earnings: $30,597,384
Fiscal Year-end: 12/31/12

Business Description:
Oil Palm Cultivation Services
S.I.C.: 0711
N.A.I.C.S.: 115112

Personnel:
Anisah Sabarudin *(Co-Sec & Head-Secretarial & Corp Affairs)*
Asmin Yahya *(Co-Sec & Gen Mgr-Ops)*

Board of Directors:
Kamaruddin Mohammed
Khairul Azahar Ariffin
Md. Adnan Sulaiman
Bing Hua Tan
Cheng Hua Tee
Kim Tee Tee
Lip Tang Tee
Hashim Naina Merican Yahya Merican

Subsidiaries:

B.S. Oil Palm Plantations Sdn Bhd **(1)**
Pejabat Pos Bandar Tun Razak
26900 Bandar Tun Abdul Razak, Pahang Darul Makmur, Malaysia
Tel.: (60) 94530617
Fax: (60) 94530861
E-Mail: fraeast@fareast.co.my
Emp.: 100
Oil Palm Plantation Services
S.I.C.: 0721
N.A.I.C.S.: 115112
P. Ceechnsua *(Mng Dir)*

Far East Delima Plantations Sdn Bhd **(1)**
Peti Surat 75 Pejabat Pos Muadzam Shah
PO Box 29
26800 Kuala Rompin, Pahang, Malaysia
Tel.: (60) 94128143
Fax: (60) 94128478
Web Site: www.fehb.com.my
Emp.: 100
Oil Palm Plantation Services
S.I.C.: 0721
N.A.I.C.S.: 115112
Zulkifli Abdullah *(Gen Mgr)*

Federal Furniture (1982) Sdn Bhd **(1)**
Lot 104 Jalan 1 Kompleks Perabut Olak Lempit
Kuala Langat, 42700 Banting, Selangor, Malaysia
Tel.: (60) 331491257
Fax: (60) 331493949
Web Site: www.ff1982.com.my
Furniture Mfr
S.I.C.: 2599
N.A.I.C.S.: 337127
Victor Ng *(COO)*

Kilang Kosfarm Sdn Bhd **(1)**
1101 Blok C Kelana Bussiness Centre 97 Jalan SS 7/2
47301 Petaling Jaya, Selangor Darul Ehsan, Malaysia
Tel.: (60) 378044036
Fax: (60) 378044032
Emp.: 30
Oil Palm Plantation Services
S.I.C.: 2075
N.A.I.C.S.: 311224

Madah Perkasa Sdn Bhd **(1)**
Suite 5 Level 8 Teruntum Complex Jalan Mahkota
PO Box 35
25000 Kuantan, Pahang, Malaysia
Tel.: (60) 95141936
Fax: (60) 95136211
E-Mail: fareast@fareh.po.my
Emp.: 100
Oil Palm Plantation Services
S.I.C.: 0139
N.A.I.C.S.: 111998
Asmin Yahya *(Gen Mgr)*

FAR EAST HOLDINGS INTERNATIONAL LIMITED

Room 2101-2102 21st Floor Far East Consortium Building
121 Des Voeux Road, Central, China (Hong Kong)
Tel.: (852) 3521 3800
Fax: (852) 3521 3821
E-Mail: info@feholdings.com.hk
Web Site: www.feholdings.com.hk
0036—(HKG)
Rev.: $2,198,855
Assets: $50,302,879
Liabilities: $500,842
Net Worth: $49,802,037
Earnings: ($2,620,909)
Emp.: 210
Fiscal Year-end: 12/31/12

Business Description:
Investment Holding Company
S.I.C.: 6211
N.A.I.C.S.: 523999

Personnel:
Deacon Te Ken Chiu *(Founder & Chm)*
Richard Yen *(CEO & Mng Dir)*
Lavender Tsz Sai Man *(Sec)*

Board of Directors:
Deacon Te Ken Chiu
Derek Chiu
Desmond Chiu
Ngai Sang Ip
Lee G. Lam
Kwan Hung Lee
Eugene Yun Hang Wang
Richard Yen

Transfer Agent:
Computershare Hong Kong Investor Services Limited
Shops 1712-1716 17th Floor Hopewell Centre
183 Queens Road East
Wanchai, China (Hong Kong)

FAR EAST ORCHARD LIMITED

(Formerly Orchard Parade Holdings Limited)
Orchard Parade Hotel 1 Tanglin Road #05-01
Singapore, 247 905, Singapore
Tel.: (65) 62352411
Fax: (65) 62353316
Web Site: www.fareast.com.sg
O10—(SES)
Sls.: $113,605,391
Assets: $1,364,549,656
Liabilities: $473,861,172
Net Worth: $890,688,484
Earnings: $54,404,019
Fiscal Year-end: 12/31/12

Business Description:
Hospitality & Property Investment Services
S.I.C.: 6531
N.A.I.C.S.: 531311

Personnel:
Lucas Wing Keung Chow *(CEO & Mng Dir)*
Kelvin Ang Kerng Ling *(CFO)*
Chloe Kim Suan Kho *(Co-Sec)*
Madelyn Yeit Lam Kwang *(Co-Sec)*

Board of Directors:
Boon Hwee Koh
Hong Kok Cheng
Lucas Wing Keung Chow
Choo Lin Diana Ee
Chiang Meng Heng
Siok Keow Ng
Siok Hwee Tan

FAR EAST ORGANIZATION PTE. LTD.

14 Scotts Rd No 06-00
Singapore, 228213, Singapore
Tel.: (65) 62352411
Fax: (65) 62353316
E-Mail: feoca@fareast.com.sg
Web Site: www.fareast.com.sg
Emp.: 2,500
Business Description:
Investment Holding Company
S.I.C.: 6719
N.A.I.C.S.: 551112
Personnel:
Kelvin Ling *(COO)*
Subsidiaries:

Far East Hospitality Trust **(1)**
1 Tanglin Road #05-01 Orchard Parade Hotel
Singapore, 247905, Singapore
Tel.: (65) 6833 6688
Fax: (65) 6833 6622
E-Mail: enquiry@fehtrust.com
Web Site: www.fehtrust.com
Q5T—(SES)
Real Estate Investment Services
S.I.C.: 6211
N.A.I.C.S.: 523999
Boon Hwee Koh *(Chm)*
Gerald Hwee Keong Lee *(CEO)*
Danny Kok Kheng Peh *(CFO & Head-IR)*
Chloe Kim Suan Kho *(Sec)*

Orchard Parade Holdings Ltd. **(1)**
1 Tanglin Rd
Singapore, 247905, Singapore SG
Tel.: (65) 67371133 (58.9%)
Fax: (65) 67330242
E-Mail: info@orchardparade.com.sg
Web Site: www.orchardparade.com.sg
Hotel Property Development & Investment; Investment Holdings; Food & Beverage Export
S.I.C.: 6719
N.A.I.C.S.: 551112
Philip Ng Chee Tat *(CEO)*

Yeo Hiap Seng Limited **(1)**
3 Senoko Way
Singapore, 758057, Singapore SG
Tel.: (65) 67522122 (58.27%)
Fax: (65) 67565625
E-Mail: enquiries@yeos.com
Web Site: www.yeos.com.sg
Rev.: $458,609,229
Assets: $715,591,136
Liabilities: $117,593,065
Net Worth: $597,998,070
Earnings: $59,232,950
Emp.: 390
Fiscal Year-end: 12/31/12
Holding Company; Bottled Beverage & Canned Foods Mfr & Distr
S.I.C.: 6719
N.A.I.C.S.: 551112
Boon Hwee Koh *(Chm)*
S. Chandra Das *(Deputy Chm)*
Yik Min Tjong *(CEO)*
Ng Seng Yap *(Deputy CEO)*
Joanne Swee Lee Lim *(Sec)*

FAR EAST WIND POWER CORP.

Wangzuo Center West Tower Suite 1608 Guanghua Road
Chaoyang District, Beijing, 100020, China
Tel.: (86) 18621363580
E-Mail: info@fareastwind.com
Web Site: www.fareastwind.com
FEWP—(OTC)
Emp.: 3
Business Description:
Wind Power Development Services
S.I.C.: 4931
N.A.I.C.S.: 221118
Personnel:
Xiaobu Liu *(Chm & CEO)*
James Crane *(CFO)*
Board of Directors:
Xiaobu Liu
James Ping Xu
Legal Counsel:
Greenberg Traurig, LLP
1201 K St Ste 1100
Sacramento, CA 95814-3938
Transfer Agent:
Holladay Stock Transfer, Inc.
2939 N 67th Pl
Scottsdale, AZ 85251

FAR EASTERN DEPARTMENT STORES LTD.

27 Pao Ching Rd
100 Taipei, Taiwan
Tel.: (886) 23816155
Fax: (886) 23753908
E-Mail: fedsacct@ms19.hinet.net
Web Site: www.feds.com.tw
2903—(TAI)
Sales Range: $1-4.9 Billion
Business Description:
General Merchandise Services
S.I.C.: 5099
N.A.I.C.S.: 423990
Personnel:
Douglas Tong Hsu *(Chm)*
Hsueh-Fang Hsu *(Pres)*
Board of Directors:
Douglas Tong Hsu
Nancy Hsu
Jin Lin Liang
Alex Ro
Viginia Shao
C. S. Yeh
Subsidiary:

Pacific Sogo Department Stores Ltd. **(1)**
No 45 Sec 4 Chung Hisao East Road
Taipei, 11041, Taiwan
Tel.: (886) 227765555
Fax: (886) 227402768
Department Stores Operation Services
S.I.C.: 5311
N.A.I.C.S.: 452111

THE FAR EASTERN GROUP

Taipei Metro Bldg 207 Tun Hua S Rd
Session 2, Taipei, 106, Taiwan
Tel.: (886) 227378711
Fax: (886) 227369621
E-Mail: service@metro.feg.com.tw
Web Site: www.feg.com.tw
Sales Range: $1-4.9 Billion
Emp.: 40,000
Business Description:
Holding Company
S.I.C.: 6719
N.A.I.C.S.: 551112
Personnel:
Douglas Tong Hsu *(Chm & CEO)*
Chia Yi Hsi *(Pres)*
Champion Lee *(CFO)*
Subsidiaries:

Far EasTone Telecommunications Co. Ltd. **(1)**
468 Ruei Guang Road Nei Hu District
Taipei, 11492, Taiwan
Tel.: (886) 277235000
E-Mail: ir@fareastone.com.tw
Web Site: www.fetnet.net
4904—(LUX TAI)
Rev.: $2,938,062,972
Assets: $3,324,924,148
Liabilities: $829,545,835
Net Worth: $2,495,378,313
Earnings: $360,037,524
Emp.: 5,873
Fiscal Year-end: 12/31/12
Cellular & Broadband Telecommunications Services; Joint Venture of AT&T Wireless Services, Inc (50%) & The Far Eastern Group (50%)
S.I.C.: 4812
N.A.I.C.S.: 517210
Douglas Tong Hsu *(Chm)*
Jan Nilsson *(Vice Chm)*
Yvonne Li *(Pres)*
T. Y. Yin *(CFO)*
Maxwell Cheng *(CMO, Chief Sls Officer & Exec VP-Consumer Sls & Mktg Div)*
Jeffey J. Gee *(CTO & Chief Strategy Officer)*
Philby Lee Chen *(Exec VP-Bus Operation Div)*
Benjamin Ho *(Exec VP-Mktg)*
Mike Lee *(Exec VP-Enterprise & Carrier Bus Unit)*
Magdalina Lin *(Exec VP-IT)*
Herman Rao *(Exec VP-Network & Tech Div)*
Eton Shu *(Exec VP-Product & Svc Delivery)*

Far Eastern New Century Corporation **(1)**
36F Taipei Metro Tower 207 Tun Hua South Road Sec 2
Taipei, Taiwan TW
Tel.: (886) 227338000
Fax: (886) 227367184
E-Mail: ir@fenc.com
Web Site: www.fenc.com
1402—(TAI)
Rev.: $8,142,924,535
Assets: $11,486,928,060
Liabilities: $5,667,212,025
Net Worth: $5,819,716,035
Earnings: $507,667,811
Emp.: 28,557
Fiscal Year-end: 12/31/12
Textile Fiber Mfr & Sales
S.I.C.: 2299
N.A.I.C.S.: 314999
Douglas Tong Hsu *(Chm & CEO)*
Peter Hsu *(Vice Chm)*
Johnny Shih *(Vice Chm)*
David Wang *(CFO)*
Humphrey Cheng *(Pres-Corp Mgmt)*
Eric Hu *(Pres-Textile Indus)*
Y. H. Tseng *(Pres-Polyester Indus)*
K. S. Wu *(Pres-Petrochemical Indus)*
T. H. Liu *(Sr Exec VP-Pres Office)*
Shaw Y. Wang *(Sr Exec VP)*
B. C. Chang *(Exec VP-Polyester Indus)*
B. T. Cherng *(Exec VP-Polyester Indus)*
Austin Lee *(Exec VP-Textile Indus)*
Alan Tsai *(Exec VP-Pres Office)*
Emily Wu *(Exec VP-Pres Office)*
Ru-yu Wu *(Exec VP-Res Institute)*
Li-Chi Chen *(Sr VP-Legal Dept)*
C. W. Chu *(Sr VP-Res Institute)*
William T. Hsu *(Sr VP-HR Dept)*
Hans Kuo *(Sr VP-Secretarial Dept)*
Champion Lee *(Sr VP)*
C. Y. Lin *(Sr VP-HR Dept)*
Mike Wu *(Sr VP-Fin Dept)*

FAR GLORY HOTEL CO., LTD.

No 18 Shanling Yanliau Village
Shoufeng Township, Hua-lien, 97449, Taiwan
Tel.: (886) 3 8123900
Fax: (886) 3 8123933
Web Site: www.farglory-hotel.com.tw
2712—(TAI)
Emp.: 320
Business Description:
Hotel Owner & Operator
S.I.C.: 7011
N.A.I.C.S.: 721110
Personnel:
Hsien-Teh Hong *(Chm)*

FAR LIMITED

Level 17 530 Collins Street
Melbourne, VIC, 3000, Australia
Mailing Address:
PO Box 265
Subiaco, WA, 6904, Australia
Tel.: (61) 3 9618 2550
Fax: (61) 3 9620 5200
E-Mail: info@far.com.au
Web Site: www.far.com.au
FAR—(ASX OTC)
Rev.: $4,269,594
Assets: $85,615,102
Liabilities: $6,434,295
Net Worth: $79,180,807
Earnings: ($9,435,626)
Fiscal Year-end: 12/31/12
Business Description:
Oil & Gas Exploration Services
S.I.C.: 1311
N.A.I.C.S.: 211111
Personnel:
Catherine Margaret Norman *(Mng Dir)*
Peter Anthony Thiessen *(CFO & Co-Sec)*
Albert Edward Brindal *(Co-Sec)*
Board of Directors:
Nicholas James Limb
Albert Edward Brindal
Charles Lee Cavness
Benedict James Murray Clube
Catherine Margaret Norman
Legal Counsel:
Hartleys Limited
Level 6 141 St Georges Terrace
Perth, WA, Australia
Baker & McKenzie
Level 19 181 William Street
Melbourne, Australia
Subsidiary:

Flow Energy Limited **(1)**
Level 7 Exchange Tower 530 Little Collins St
Melbourne, 3000, Australia
Tel.: (61) 399097609
Fax: (61) 399097621
E-Mail: goipinfo@flowenergy.com.au
Web Site: www.flowenergy.com.au
Sales Range: $150-199.9 Million
Emp.: 6
Oil & Gas Exploration Services
S.I.C.: 1389
N.A.I.C.S.: 213112
Catherine M. Norman *(Mng Dir & COO)*

FAR RESOURCES LTD.

302-1620 West 8th Avenue
Vancouver, BC, V6J 1V4, Canada
Tel.: (604) 805-5035
Fax: (604) 253-3484
E-Mail: info@farresources.com
Web Site: www.farresources.com
FAT—(CNSX)
Rev.: $39,761
Assets: $570,177
Liabilities: $59,517
Net Worth: $510,660
Earnings: ($190,539)
Fiscal Year-end: 03/31/13
Business Description:
Iron Ore Mining
S.I.C.: 1011
N.A.I.C.S.: 212210
Personnel:
Keith C. Anderson *(Pres & CEO)*
Cyrus H. Driver *(CFO)*
Board of Directors:
Keith C. Anderson
Leon F. Anderson
Lindsay R. Bottomer
Cyrus H. Driver
Derek Huston
Transfer Agent:
Equity Financial Trust Company
1185 West Georgia Street Suite 1620
Vancouver, BC, Canada

FAR VISTA INTERACTIVE CORP.

365 Simon Fraser Crescent
Saskatoon, SK, S7H 3T5, Canada
Tel.: (306) 230-3288
Web Site:
FVSTA—(OTC)
Emp.: 3
Business Description:
Online Video Games Developer
S.I.C.: 7372
N.A.I.C.S.: 511210

Far Vista Interactive Corp.—(Continued)

Personnel:
Richard Buckley *(Pres & CEO)*
Bruce Hoggard *(CFO, Treas & Sec)*
Board of Directors:
Richard Buckley
David Callele
Bruce Hoggard
Paul Zhang Xie

FARADAY TECHNOLOGY CORPORATION
No5 Li-Hsin Rd III
Hsin-chu, 300, Taiwan
Tel.: (886) 35787888
Fax: (886) 35787889
E-Mail: twsales@faraday-tech.com
Web Site: www.faraday-tech.com
Sales Range: $150-199.9 Million
Emp.: 600
Business Description:
Semiconductor Component Mfr
S.I.C.: 3674
N.A.I.C.S.: 334413
Personnel:
H. P. Lin *(Pres)*

FARAN SUGAR MILLS LTD
3rd Floor Bank House 1 Habib Square MA Jinnah Road
Karachi, Pakistan
Tel.: (92) 212418050
Fax: (92) 212421010
E-Mail: info@faran.com.pk
Web Site: www.faran.com.pk
Year Founded: 1981
FRSM—(KAR)
Sls.: $48,251,451
Assets: $26,686,668
Liabilities: $16,242,847
Net Worth: $10,443,821
Earnings: $3,352,747
Fiscal Year-end: 09/30/12
Business Description:
Sugar Processing
S.I.C.: 2062
N.A.I.C.S.: 311314
Personnel:
Mohammad Amin Ahmed Bawany *(Chm)*
Muhammad Omar Amin Bawany *(Vice Chm)*
Ahmed Ali Mohammad Amin *(CEO)*
Muhammad Ayub *(CFO & Sec)*
Board of Directors:
Mohammad Amin Ahmed Bawany
Ahmed Ali Mohammad Amin
Mohammad Asif
Muhammad Omar Amin Bawany
Abdul Wahid A. Ghaffar
Abdul Wahid Jaliawala
Asim Rafiq
Iqbal A. Rehman

FARBCHEMIE BRAUN KG
Daimlerring 11
65205 Wiesbaden, Germany
Tel.: (49) 612291190
Fax: (49) 6122911920
E-Mail: info@farbchemie-braun.de
Web Site: www.farbchemie-braun.de
Year Founded: 1930
Rev.: $12,731,862
Emp.: 60
Business Description:
Dyestuff Mfr
S.I.C.: 2819
N.A.I.C.S.: 325130
Personnel:
William Bracht *(Co-Mng Dir)*
Boris Braun *(Co-Mng Dir)*

FARCENT ENTERPRICE CO., LTD.
13F No 230 Chen Teh Rd Datong District
103 Taipei, Taiwan
Tel.: (886) 225922860
Fax: (886) 225944800
Web Site: www.farcent.com.tw
1730—(TAI)
Sales Range: $10-24.9 Million
Business Description:
Deodorant Mfr & Distr
S.I.C.: 2844
N.A.I.C.S.: 325620
Personnel:
Yao Lun Wang *(Chm & Gen Mgr)*

Unit:

Farcent Enterprice Co., Ltd. - Guanyin Factory **(1)**
13F No 230 Cheng Teh Rd Sec 3
Taipei, 103, Taiwan
Tel.: (886) 34833728
Fax: (886) 225944800
E-Mail: f-services@farcent.com.tw
Emp.: 70
Household Cleaning Products Mfr
S.I.C.: 3639
N.A.I.C.S.: 335228
Cynthia Tsai *(CEO)*

FAREAST ISLAMI LIFE INSURANCE CO. LTD.
T K Bhaban 13th Floor 13 Karwan Bazar
Dhaka, 1215, Bangladesh
Tel.: (880) 2 8150127 30
Fax: (880) 2 8130611
E-Mail: filicbd@yahoo.com
Web Site: www.fareastislamilife.com
Year Founded: 2000
FAREASTLIF—(DHA)
Sales Range: $150-199.9 Million
Business Description:
Insurance Services
S.I.C.: 6411
N.A.I.C.S.: 524298
Personnel:
Mohammad Nazrul Islam *(Chm)*
Mohammad Hemayet Ullah *(Mng Dir)*
Mohammad Abdul Khaleque *(CFO)*
Syed Abdul Aziz *(Sec)*
Mohammad Apel Mahmud *(Sr Exec VP-Admin)*
Mohammad Abul Hasem *(Exec VP)*
Mohammad Farid Hossain *(Exec VP)*
Zahur Ahmed Chowdhury *(Sr VP)*
Mohammad Abdul Halim *(Sr VP-Dev)*
Amir Mohammad Ibrahim *(Sr VP)*
Board of Directors:
Mohammad Nazrul Islam
Kazi Farid Uddin Ahmed
Rabeya Begum
Mohammad Mozammel Hossain
Mosharraf Hossain
Nazneen Hossain
Ayesha Husne Jahan
K. M. Khaled
Shahriar Khaled
Mohammad Abdul Khaleque
Khandaker Mostaque Mahmud
Mohammad Helal Miah
Mohammad Mijanur Rahman
Legal Counsel:
Mahfel Huq & Co.
BGIC Tower 4th Florr 34 Topkhana Road
Dhaka, Bangladesh

FAREVA SA
80 Ave de la Grande Armee
75017 Paris, France
Tel.: (33) 158051110
Fax: (33) 10158051119
E-Mail: alimentaire@fareva.com
Sales Range: $650-699.9 Million
Emp.: 3,000
Business Description:
Pharmaceutical & Cosmetics Manufacturing Services
S.I.C.: 2834
N.A.I.C.S.: 325412
Personnel:
Bernard Fraisse *(Chm)*

Non-U.S. Subsidiary:

EXCELLA GmbH **(1)**
Nurnberger Str 12
D 90537 Feucht, Germany De
Tel.: (49) 9128404521
Fax: (49) 9128404646
E-Mail: info@excella-pharma-source.de
Web Site: www.excella-pharma-source.de
Emp.: 420
Pharmaceutical Product Mfr
S.I.C.: 2834
N.A.I.C.S.: 325412
Peter Morsdorf *(Gen Mgr)*

FARGLORY LAND DEVELOPMENT CO., LTD.
23F-1 No 200 Sec 1 Keelung Road
Sinyi District, Taipei, Taiwan
Tel.: (886) 227239999
Fax: (886) 227239099
E-Mail: webservice@farglory.com
Web Site: www.farglory.com.tw
5522—(LSE TAI)
Sales Range: $25-49.9 Million
Emp.: 280
Business Description:
Building & Construction Services
S.I.C.: 1541
N.A.I.C.S.: 236210
Personnel:
Chao Teng Hsiung *(Chm)*
Huang Chin Hung *(Exec VP)*

FARITEC HOLDINGS LIMITED
Faritec House
150 Kelvin Drive
Woodmead, Sandton, 2148, South Africa
Tel.: (27) 118441000
Fax: (27) 118023814
Web Site: www.faritec.co.za
FRT—(JSE)
Sales Range: $100-124.9 Million
Emp.: 400
Business Description:
Information Technology Services & Solutions
S.I.C.: 8742
N.A.I.C.S.: 541611
Personnel:
Faine Van Rensburg *(CEO)*
Hasmukh Gajjar *(Deputy CEO)*
Tshidi Nyembe *(CFO)*
Board of Directors:
Arvind Gupta
Chris Jardine
Mncedisi Mayekiso
Dan McMahon
Phumzo Noxaka
Faine Van Rensburg

FARLIM GROUP (MALAYSIA) BHD
No 2 8 Bangunan Farlim Jalan PJS 10/3
Bandar Sri Subang, 46000 Petaling Jaya, Selangor Darul Ehsan, Malaysia
Tel.: (60) 356355533
Fax: (60) 356350301
E-Mail: iskandar@farlim.com.my
Web Site: www.farlim.com.my
FARLIM—(KLS)
Rev.: $10,206,897
Assets: $48,090,236
Liabilities: $9,953,348
Net Worth: $38,136,888
Earnings: ($1,518,556)
Fiscal Year-end: 12/31/12
Business Description:
Property Development & Investment Services
S.I.C.: 6531
N.A.I.C.S.: 531312
Personnel:
Gait Tong Lim *(CEO)*
Yook Faan Kwong *(Sec)*
Margaret Pelly *(Sec)*
May Peng Sin *(Sec)*
Board of Directors:
Khairilanuar Abdul Rahman
Andrew Say Loke Koay
Mohd. Iqbal Kuppa Pitchai Rawther
Chu Dick Lim
Gait Tong Lim
Yew Wei Yong

FARM BOY INC.
1427 Ogilvie Road 2nd Floor
Ottawa, ON, K1J 8M7, Canada
Tel.: (613) 247-1007
Fax: (613) 247-8731
E-Mail: fbmail@farmboy.ca
Web Site: www.farmboy.ca
Year Founded: 1981
Rev.: $79,860,200
Emp.: 700
Business Description:
Cheese & Bakery Products Mfr
S.I.C.: 2022
N.A.I.C.S.: 311513
Personnel:
Jean-Louis Bellemare *(Founder)*
Jeff York *(Pres)*

FARM BUSINESS CONSULTANTS INC.
150 3015 5th Avenue NE
Calgary, AB, T2A 6T8, Canada
Tel.: (403) 735-6105
Fax: (403) 735-5087
Toll Free: (800) 265-1002
E-Mail: opportunities@fbc.ca
Web Site: www.fbc.ca
Year Founded: 1952
Rev.: $14,345,917
Emp.: 138
Business Description:
Tax Return & Administrative Services
S.I.C.: 7291
N.A.I.C.S.: 541213
Personnel:
Steven Ibbotson *(Founder)*
Gary Ibbotson *(Pres)*

FARM CREDIT CANADA
1800 Hamilton Street
PO Box 4320
Regina, SK, S4P 4L3, Canada
Tel.: (306) 780-8100
Fax: (306) 780-5167
E-Mail: greg.stewart@fcc-fac.ca
Web Site: www.fcc-fac.ca
Int. Income: $1,108,806,448
Assets: $25,716,106,532
Liabilities: $22,198,580,881
Net Worth: $3,517,525,652
Earnings: $510,314,958
Emp.: 1,600
Fiscal Year-end: 03/31/13
Business Description:
Agricultural Financial Services
S.I.C.: 6211
N.A.I.C.S.: 523999
Personnel:
Dale Johnston *(Chm)*
Greg Stewart *(Pres & CEO)*
Rick Hoffman *(CFO & Exec VP)*
Remi Lemoine *(COO & Exec VP)*
Paul MacDonald *(CIO & Sr VP)*
Michael Hoffort *(Chief Risk Officer & Exec VP)*

Lyndon Carlson *(Sr VP-Mktg)*
Greg Willner *(Sr VP-Governance, Legal & Stakeholder Mgmt)*
Board of Directors:
Dale Johnston
Donald Bettle
Sylvie Cloutier
Brad Hanmer
Doris Priddle
Ross Ravelli
Brenda Schoepp
Jason Skinner
Greg Stewart

Division:

FCC Ventures (1)
1800 Hamilton Street
PO Box 4320
Regina, SK, S4P 4L3, Canada
Tel.: (306) 780-8100
Fax: (306) 780-5456
E-Mail: huber@fcc-fac.ca
Web Site: www.fccventures.ca
Emp.: 600
Venture Capital Services
S.I.C.: 6211
N.A.I.C.S.: 523999
Greg Steward *(Pres)*

FARM LANDS OF AFRICA, INC.
(Formerly Farm Lands of Guinea, Inc.)
c/o Pearl Capital Partners Ltd.
Ground Floor
Suite GFE The Phoenix Brewery
13 Bramley Road, London, W10 6SP, United Kingdom
Tel.: (44) 207 034 0035
Fax: (44) 207 034 0034
Web Site: www.farmlandsofguinea.com
Year Founded: 2007
FLGI—(OTC OTCB)
Sales Range: Less than $1 Million
Business Description:
Farming Technology Services
S.I.C.: 0139
N.A.I.C.S.: 111998
Personnel:
S. N. Kumar Buddhavarapu *(Chm)*
Alexandra Naomi Eavis *(CEO)*
Board of Directors:
S. N. Kumar Buddhavarapu
Alexandra Naomi Eavis
Cherif Haidara
Anil Kumar Koneru
Wice Lee
Anant Rao Vijapurapu
Nigel Woodhouse

FARM LANDS OF GUINEA, INC.
(Name Changed to Farm Lands of Africa, Inc.)

FARM PRIDE FOODS LTD.
551 Chandler Road
Keysborough, VIC, 3173, Australia
Mailing Address:
PO Box 141
Noble Park, VIC, 3174, Australia
Tel.: (61) 397987077
Fax: (61) 397986163
E-Mail: info@farmpride.com.au
Web Site: www.farmpride.com.au
FRM—(ASX)
Rev.: $107,115,375
Assets: $62,315,496
Liabilities: $38,913,056
Net Worth: $23,402,440
Earnings: $629,428
Emp.: 230
Fiscal Year-end: 06/30/13
Business Description:
Holding Company; Egg Production & Whslr; Processed Egg Products Mfr & Whslr
S.I.C.: 6719
N.A.I.C.S.: 551112
Personnel:
Zelko Lendich *(Mng Dir)*
Bruce De Lacy *(Sec)*
Board of Directors:
Peter Bell
Zelko Lendich
Malcolm Ward
Legal Counsel:
B2B Lawyers
76 Jolimont St East
Melbourne, VIC, 3002, Australia

FARMACEUTICA REMEDIA S.A.
Str Dorobantilor nr 43 Judetal
Hunedoara, Romania
Tel.: (40) 254223260
Fax: (40) 254226197
E-Mail: remedia@remedia.ro
Web Site: www.remedia.ro/en
RMAH—(BUC)
Rev.: $73,390,305
Assets: $61,002,028
Liabilities: $48,301,175
Net Worth: $12,700,853
Earnings: $1,857,626
Emp.: 395
Fiscal Year-end: 12/31/12
Business Description:
Pharmaceutical Products Sales
S.I.C.: 5122
N.A.I.C.S.: 424210
Personnel:
Valentin-Norbert Tarus *(Chm)*
Board of Directors:
Valentin-Norbert Tarus
Mircea Banciu
Zoe Chirita

FARMACIAS BENAVIDES SAB DE CV
Av Fundadores 935 Valle del Mirador
64750 Monterrey, Nuevo Leon, Mexico
Tel.: (52) 8181507700
Fax: (52) 8183899931
E-Mail: erigorighi@benavides.com.mx
Web Site: www.benavides.com.mx
BEVIDES—(MEX)
Emp.: 8,000
Business Description:
Pharmaceutical, Sanitary, Cosmetic & Health Care Products Sls & Distr
S.I.C.: 5912
N.A.I.C.S.: 446110
Personnel:
Fernando Miguel Benavides Sauceda *(CEO)*

FARMAX INDIA LIMITED
S.No.658 Bowrampet V Quthbullapur
Ranga Reddy Dist, Hyderabad, 500043, India
Tel.: (91) 8418242207
Fax: (91) 4023065762
E-Mail: info@farmax.co.in
Web Site: www.farmax.co.in
FARMAXIND—(NSE)
Rev.: $9,702,909
Assets: $6,023,831
Liabilities: $6,938,410
Net Worth: ($914,578)
Earnings: ($26,786,592)
Fiscal Year-end: 03/31/13
Business Description:
Fast Moving Consumer Goods Mfr & Distr
S.I.C.: 2099
N.A.I.C.S.: 311999
Personnel:
M. Srinivasa Reddy *(Chm & Mng Dir)*
Mohd. Fasih Uz Zaman *(Sec)*
Board of Directors:
M. Srinivasa Reddy
Omkarareshwar Ganganboina
A. V. Rama Raju
I. Srinivas Raju
Transfer Agent:
Bigshare Services Pvt. Ltd.
306 3rd Floor Right Wing Amrutha Ville Opp Yashodha Hospital
Somajiguda Rajbhavan Road, Hyderabad, 500082, India

FARMER CONSTRUCTION LTD.
360 Harbour Rd
Victoria, BC, V9A 3S1, Canada
Tel.: (250) 388-5121
Fax: (250) 388-9324
E-Mail: farmer@farmer-ltd.com
Web Site: www.farmer-ltd.com
Year Founded: 1951
Rev.: $28,830,762
Emp.: 100
Business Description:
Construction Services
S.I.C.: 1542
N.A.I.C.S.: 236220
Personnel:
Barry Scroggs *(Pres)*

FARMERS' MUTUAL INSURANCE COMPANY (LINDSAY)
336 Angeline Street South
PO Box 28
Lindsay, ON, K9V 4R8, Canada
Tel.: (705) 324-2146
Fax: (705) 324-3406
Toll Free: (800) 461-0310
Web Site: www.farmerslindsay.com
Year Founded: 1895
Premiums: $92,405,093
Assets: $259,189,721
Liabilities: $165,194,196
Net Worth: $93,995,525
Earnings: $11,963,031
Emp.: 100
Fiscal Year-end: 12/31/12
Business Description:
Insurance Agencies
S.I.C.: 6411
N.A.I.C.S.: 524298
Personnel:
Steve Carruthers *(Chm)*
Rick Carter *(Vice Chm)*
Tim Shauf *(Pres & CEO)*
Bob Nielson *(CFO & VP-Fin)*
Board of Directors:
Steve Carruthers
Rick Carter
Cheryl Craven
Gord James
Gord Lodwick
Terry Malcolm
Bob Nielson
Tim Shauf
Randy Straeten
Anne-Marie Thomas
Mike Whittamore

FARMFOODS LTD
7 Greens Road
Blairlinn, Cumbernauld, G67 2TU, United Kingdom
Tel.: (44) 1236456789
Fax: (44) 236860266
E-Mail: customerservices@farmfoods.co.uk
Web Site: www.farmfoods.co.uk
Rev.: $770,679,881
Emp.: 3,000
Business Description:
Frozen Food Supplier & Mfr
S.I.C.: 2038
N.A.I.C.S.: 311412
Personnel:
Gerard Savage *(Dir-Retail)*

FARMINGTONS HOLDING GMBH
Beekebreite 18 20
49124 Georgsmarienhutte, Germany
Tel.: (49) 54014900
Fax: (49) 540142705
E-Mail: info@farmingtons-group.com
Web Site: www.farmingtons-group.com
Emp.: 300
Business Description:
Motor Vehicle Part Mfr
S.I.C.: 3714
N.A.I.C.S.: 336390
Personnel:
Matthias Reckmann *(CEO)*

FARM'S BEST BERHAD
AG 5730 Alor Gajah Industrial Estate
78000 Alor Gajah, Melaka, Malaysia
Tel.: (60) 65561293
Fax: (60) 65562445
E-Mail: general@sinmah.com.my
Web Site: www.farmsbest.com.my
FARMBES—(KLS)
Rev.: $131,336,551
Assets: $133,736,925
Liabilities: $104,792,411
Net Worth: $28,944,515
Earnings: ($2,886,352)
Fiscal Year-end: 12/31/12
Business Description:
Animal Feeds Mfr & Whslr
S.I.C.: 2048
N.A.I.C.S.: 311119
Personnel:
Kok Yong Fong *(Mng Dir)*
Seng Aun Liew *(Co-Sec)*
Catherine Suik Ching Mah *(Co-Sec)*
Board of Directors:
Zainal Shamsudin
Baharom Abd. Wahab
Mohd Khasan Ahmad
Choon Kai Fong
Kiah Yeow Fong
Kok Yong Fong
Ngan Teng Fong
Cheu Kuan Ng
Peng Hay Ng

FARMS.COM LTD.
1790 Dundas St Unit 5
London, ON, N5W 3E5, Canada
Tel.: (519) 438-5729
Fax: (519) 438-3152
Toll Free: (877) 438-5729
E-Mail: info@farms.com
Web Site: www.farms.com
Year Founded: 1995
Sales Range: $25-49.9 Million
Emp.: 40
Business Description:
Online Livestock & Agriculture Market Data
S.I.C.: 9641
N.A.I.C.S.: 926140
Personnel:
David Gilmour *(Chm)*
Graham Dyer *(Pres & CEO)*
Darren Marsland *(CTO-Pro Svcs)*
Eric Spell *(Pres-AgCareers)*
Fred Brandenburg *(Sec)*
Joseph Dales *(Sr VP & Dir)*
Board of Directors:
David Gilmour

Farms.com Ltd.—(Continued)

Vincent Amanor-Boadu
Graham Dyer
Michael Wilson

Subsidiary:

eHARVEST (1)
1790 Dundas St Unit 5
London, ON, N5W 3E5, Canada (100%)
Tel.: (519) 438-5729
Fax: (519) 438-3152
E-Mail: info@farms.com
Web Site: www.farms.com
Emp.: 29
Agricultural Consulting Services
S.I.C.: 8999
N.A.I.C.S.: 541690
J. Douglas Maus *(Pres & CEO)*

U.S. Subsidiary:

PigCHAMP Inc. (1)
Ames Business Park 1601 Golden Aspen Dr Unit 109
Ames, IA 50010
Tel.: (774) 424-2
Fax: (515) 233-7187
Web Site: www.pigchamp.com
Supplier of Swine Management Information & Services
S.I.C.: 7371
N.A.I.C.S.: 541511

FARMSECURE HOLDINGS (PTY) LTD.

Avanti South Building 3rd Floor 3
Churchill Close Tygerfalls
Carl Cronje Drive Tyger Valley, Cape Town, South Africa
Tel.: (27) 21 974 1950
E-Mail: info@farmsecure.co.za
Web Site: www.farmsecure.co.za
Emp.: 4,500
Business Description:
Agricultural Product Distr
S.I.C.: 5159
N.A.I.C.S.: 424590
Personnel:
Jerome Yazbek *(CEO)*

Subsidiary:

Kynoch Fertilizers (Pty) Ltd. (1)
Lambrecht Street
Huguenot Paarl, 7646 Paarl, South Africa
Tel.: (27) 218775300
E-Mail: info@kynoch.co.za
Web Site: www.kynoch.co.za
Emp.: 65
Fertilizer Mfr
S.I.C.: 2873
N.A.I.C.S.: 325311
Gordon Hesom *(CEO)*

FARMWORKS AUSTRALIA LIMITED

(See Under Conquest Agri Limited)

FARNCOMBE TECHNOLOGY LTD.

Belvedere Basing View
Basingstoke, RG21 4HG, United Kingdom
Tel.: (44) 1256 844161
Fax: (44) 1256 844162
E-Mail: contact@farncombe.com
Web Site: www.farncombe.com
Year Founded: 1991
Sales Range: $10-24.9 Million
Emp.: 48
Business Description:
Television Broadcasting Services
S.I.C.: 4833
N.A.I.C.S.: 515120
Personnel:
Andrew Glasspool *(Founder & Mng Partner)*
Gary Marshall *(Mng Partner)*
Jean-Marc Racine *(Mng Partner)*
Steve Upton *(Mng Partner)*

FAROE PETROLEUM (UK) LIMITED

24 Carden Place
Aberdeen, AB10 1UQ, United Kingdom
Tel.: (44) 1224 650920
Fax: (44) 1224 650921
E-Mail: uk@faroe-petroleum.com
Web Site: www.faroe-petroleum.com
FPM—(AIM)
Rev.: $250,778,618
Assets: $727,874,230
Liabilities: $361,959,054
Net Worth: $365,915,176
Earnings: ($3,954,542)
Emp.: 28
Fiscal Year-end: 12/31/12
Business Description:
Oil & Gas Exploration
S.I.C.: 1389
N.A.I.C.S.: 213112
Personnel:
Graham Stewart *(CEO)*
Jonathan Cooper *(CFO)*
Helge Hammer *(COO)*
Julian Riddick *(Sec)*
Board of Directors:
John Bentley
Jonathan Cooper
Helge Hammer
Hanne Harlem
Tim Read
Graham Stewart
Roger Witts
Legal Counsel:
McGrigors LLP
Johnstone House 52-54 Rose Street
Aberdeen, United Kingdom
K&L Gates LLP
One New Change
London, United Kingdom

Non-U.S. Subsidiary:

Foroyar Kolvetni P/F (1)
Bryggjubakki 22
PO Box 1098
FO-110 Torshavn, Faroe Islands
Tel.: (298) 298 350 460
E-Mail: faroyar@faroe-petroleum.com
Petroleum Exploration Services
S.I.C.: 1311
N.A.I.C.S.: 211111
Nils Sorensen *(Mng Dir)*

FARR VINTNERS LTD

220 Queenstown Road
London, SW8 4LP, United Kingdom
Tel.: (44) 20 7821 2000
Fax: (44) 20 7821 2020
E-Mail: enquiries@farrvintners.com
Web Site: www.farrvintners.com
Year Founded: 1978
Sales Range: $150-199.9 Million
Business Description:
Wine Merchant
S.I.C.: 5182
N.A.I.C.S.: 424820
Personnel:
Stephen Browett *(Chm)*

Non-U.S. Subsidiary:

Farr Vintners Ltd (1)
8/F Redana Centre 25 Yiu Wa Street
Causeway Bay, China (Hong Kong)
Tel.: (852) 2575 8773
Fax: (852) 2575 8538
E-Mail: farrhk@farrhk.com
Web Site: www.farrhk.com
Emp.: 6
Wine Merchant
S.I.C.: 5182
N.A.I.C.S.: 424820
Jason Naude *(Gen Mgr)*

FARSIGHT BIOSCIENCE LIMITED

29 Harley Street
London, W1G 9QR, United Kingdom
Tel.: (44) 2073771489
Fax: (44) 2073779454
E-Mail: investorrelations@farsightbioscience.com
Web Site: www.farsightbioscience.com
Year Founded: 2005
XPB—(DEU)
Business Description:
Pharmaceutical Product Mfr
S.I.C.: 2834
N.A.I.C.S.: 325412
Personnel:
Erling Refsum *(CEO)*
Graham May *(Sec)*
Board of Directors:
Peter Alistair Bell
Graham May
Erling Refsum

FARSTAD SHIPPING ASA

Notenesgata 14
6002 Alesund, Norway
Tel.: (47) 70117500
Fax: (47) 70117501
E-Mail: post.aalesund@farstad.com
Web Site: www.farstad.no
FAR—(OSL)
Rev.: $672,201,204
Assets: $2,830,272,934
Liabilities: $1,590,584,101
Net Worth: $1,239,688,833
Earnings: $56,438,293
Emp.: 1,850
Fiscal Year-end: 12/31/12
Business Description:
Freight Vessel Management Services
S.I.C.: 4412
N.A.I.C.S.: 483111
Personnel:
Sverre A. Farstad *(Chm)*
Per Norvald Sperre *(Deputy Chm)*
Karl-Johan Bakken *(CEO)*
Torstein L. Stavseng *(CFO)*
Joseph M. Homsey *(Exec VP-Eastern Hemisphere)*
Board of Directors:
Sverre A. Farstad
Janne-Grethe Strand Aasnaes
Mads Andersen
Gro Bakstad
Astrid Koppernaes
Leif-Arne Langoy
Per Norvald Sperre

Non-U.S. Subsidiaries:

Farstad Shipping (Indian Pacific) Pty. Ltd. (1)
Level 4 99 Queensbridge Street
Southbank, VIC, 3006, Australia
Tel.: (61) 392541666
Fax: (61) 392541655
E-Mail: post.melbourne@farstad.com
Web Site: www.farstad.com
Marine Shipping Services
S.I.C.: 4491
N.A.I.C.S.: 488320
Richard Hall *(Gen Mgr)*

Farstad Shipping Ltd. (1)
Farstad House Badentoy Ave Badentoy Park
Portlethen, Aberdeen, Scotland, AB12 4 YB, United Kingdom
Tel.: (44) 1224784000
Fax: (44) 1224783340
E-Mail: post.aberdeen@farstad.com
Web Site: www.farstad.com
Emp.: 24
Marine Shipping Services
S.I.C.: 4499
N.A.I.C.S.: 488330
John R. Maxwell *(Mng Dir)*

Farstad Shipping Singapore Pte Ltd (1)
78 Shenton Way 19-02 Lippo Centre
Singapore, Singapore
Tel.: (65) 63232077
Fax: (65) 62404599
E-Mail: singapore@farstad.com
Web Site: www.farstad.com
Emp.: 11
Shipping Services
S.I.C.: 4412
N.A.I.C.S.: 483111
Andrew Coccoli *(Gen Mgr)*

FAS FINANCE & INVESTMENT LIMITED

Suvastu Imam Square 65 Gulshan Avenue Gulshan South
Dhaka, 1212, Bangladesh
Tel.: (880) 29860594
Fax: (880) 29860531
E-Mail: info@fasbd.com
Web Site: www.fasbd.com
Year Founded: 1997
FASFIN—(DHA)
Sales Range: $1-9.9 Million
Business Description:
Financial Services
S.I.C.: 6211
N.A.I.C.S.: 523999
Personnel:
Abdul Matlub Ahmad *(Chm)*
Mohammad Mofiz Uddin Chowdhury *(CEO & Mng Dir)*
Board of Directors:
Abdul Matlub Ahmad
Selima Ahmad
Shahnaz Ahmad
Syed Monowar Ali
Mukitur Rahman Bhuiyan
Asaduzzaman Chaudhury
Mohammad Mofiz Uddin Chowdhury
Mohammad Sirajul Islam
Nasim Ali Khan

FASHION B AIR S.A.

(d/b/a Fashion Bel Air)
210 rue Saint Denis
75002 Paris, France
Tel.: (33) 145080664
Fax: (33) 140265669
E-Mail: info@fashion-belair.com
Web Site: www.fashion-belair.com
ALFBA—(EUR)
Sales Range: $10-24.9 Million
Emp.: 86
Business Description:
Women's Clothing Retailer
S.I.C.: 5621
N.A.I.C.S.: 448120
Personnel:
Eric Sitruk *(Chm, Pres & Dir Gen)*
Board of Directors:
Eric Sitruk
Sonia Naman
Liliane Hayoun Sitruck
Franck Sitruk

FASHION BOX S.P.A.

Via Marcoai 1
31010 Asolo, Italy
Tel.: (39) 04239251
Fax: (39) 0423925299
Web Site: www.replay.it
Business Description:
Clothing Designer
S.I.C.: 5699
N.A.I.C.S.: 315240
Personnel:
Attilio E. Biancardi *(Pres)*

Non-U.S. Subsidiary:

Fashion Box Greece S.A. (1)
90 Kapodistriou St
Nea Ionia, Attica, 142 35, Greece
Tel.: (30) 2102717757

Fax: (30) 2102717762
E-Mail: ir@fashionbox.gr
Web Site: www.fashionbox.gr
BOX—(ATH)
Sales Range: $25-49.9 Million
Emp.: 172
Clothing, Footgear & Related Accessories Importer, Exporter & Producer
S.I.C.: 2329
N.A.I.C.S.: 315220
Antonios Rogkopoulos *(Chm & Mng Dir)*
Theodoros Rogkopoulos *(Vice Chm)*
Constantinos G. Tsouvelekakis *(Mng Dir & VP)*
Markos-Kyriakos E. Malliaroudakis *(Deputy Dir Gen)*
Adamantios Sotiropoulos *(IR Officer)*

FASHION TV HOLDING LTD.

Wasagasse 4
1090 Vienna, Austria
Tel.: (43) 15131267
Fax: (43) 15131385
E-Mail: ceo@ftv.com
Web Site: www.ftv.com
TV8—(DEU)
Business Description:
Television Programming
S.I.C.: 4833
N.A.I.C.S.: 515120
Personnel:
Gabriel Lisowski *(Chm-Supervisory Bd)*
Yaron Michael Paul Jakubowicz *(CEO)*
Supervisory Board of Directors:
Adam Lisowski
Ron Chaim Jakubowicz
Gabriel Lisowski

FASHIONPARTNER GROUP SAS

(Formerly DHL Fashion (France) SAS)
15 Boulevard de Beaubourg
BP 20
Croissy-Beaubourg, 77313 Marne-la-Vallee, Cedex 2, France
Tel.: (33) 1 6462 5331
Fax: (33) 1 6462 5386
E-Mail: contact@fashionpartnergroup.com
Web Site: www.fashionpartnergroup.com
Year Founded: 1968
Sales Range: $50-74.9 Million
Emp.: 50
Business Description:
Fashion Industry Freight Transportation & Logistics Services
S.I.C.: 4731
N.A.I.C.S.: 488510
Personnel:
Christophe Cavailles *(Mng Dir)*

FASHY GMBH

Kornwestheimer Strasse 46
D-70825 Korntal-Munchingen, Germany
Tel.: (49) 715092060
E-Mail: info@fashy.de
Web Site: www.fashy.de
Year Founded: 1986
Rev.: $34,209,120
Emp.: 97
Business Description:
Hot Water Bottle Mfr
S.I.C.: 3999
N.A.I.C.S.: 339999
Personnel:
Volker Kraus *(Co-CEO)*
Wolfgang Kraus *(Co-CEO)*

FASIL A.D.

Svetolika Lazarevica 18
31230 Arilje, Serbia
Tel.: (381) 31 89 11 31
Fax: (381) 31 89 14 48
E-Mail: fasil@fasil.rs
Web Site: www.fasil.rs
Year Founded: 1965
FSIL—(BEL)
Business Description:
Sliding Bearing Element Mfr
S.I.C.: 3562
N.A.I.C.S.: 332991
Personnel:
Stevo Popovic *(Gen Mgr)*

FASOO.COM CO., LTD.

17th Floor Nuritkum Square Business Tower Sangam-dong
Mapo-gu, Seoul, 121-795, Korea (South)
Tel.: (82) 2 300 9000
Fax: (82) 2 300 9400
E-Mail: inquiry@fasoo.com
Web Site: www.fasoo.com
150900—(KRS)
Business Description:
Data & Software Security
S.I.C.: 7372
N.A.I.C.S.: 511210
Personnel:
Kyugon Cho *(Pres & CEO)*
Jeesoo Lee *(CFO)*
Hyeyeon Ahn *(COO, CMO & Sr Exec VP)*
Seuk Soo Sung *(CTO & Sr Exec VP)*

FAST CASUALWEAR AG

Herrengraben 1
20459 Hamburg, Germany
Tel.: (49) 40 60 91 86 0
Fax: (49) 40 60 91 86 60
Web Site: www.fast-casualwear.com
FCA—(DEU)
Sales Range: $100-124.9 Million
Business Description:
Footwear & Apparel Mfr
S.I.C.: 2389
N.A.I.C.S.: 316210
Personnel:
Shing-kei Shum *(Deputy Chm-Supervisory Bd)*
Wing Chi Cong *(CEO)*
Wenya Zhang *(COO)*

FAST EJENDOM DANMARK A/S

Tuborg Havnevej 19
2900 Hellerup, Denmark
Tel.: (45) 70 27 17 88
Fax: (45) 70 27 17 98
E-Mail: info@fastejendom.dk
Web Site: www.fastejendom.dk
FED—(CSE)
Business Description:
Commercial & Residential Properties Investments
S.I.C.: 6211
N.A.I.C.S.: 523999
Personnel:
Lars Frederiksen *(CEO)*

FAST FINANCE S.A.

Ul Wolowska 20
51-116 Wroclaw, Poland
Tel.: (48) 71 361 20 42
E-Mail: biuro@fastfinance.pl
Web Site: www.fastfinance.pl
Year Founded: 2004
FFI—(WAR)
Sales Range: $1-9.9 Million
Emp.: 40
Business Description:
Debt Recovery Services
S.I.C.: 6159
N.A.I.C.S.: 522298
Personnel:
Andrzej Kielczewski *(Chm-Supervisory Bd)*
Jacek Longin Daroszewski *(Chm-Mgmt Bd)*
Jacek Zbigniew Krzeminski *(Vice Chm-Mgmt Bd)*
Supervisory Board of Directors:
Andrzej Kielczewski
Hildegarda Kaufeld
Grzegorz Kawczak
Roman Mielnik
Marek Ochota

Subsidiary:

Columbus Factoring Solutions S.A. (1)
128 Obywatelska St
94-104 Lodz, Poland
Tel.: (48) 42 689 83 42
Fax: (48) 42 689 83 43
E-Mail: marketing@cfs.pl
Web Site: www.cfs.pl
Financial & Security Services
S.I.C.: 6211
N.A.I.C.S.: 523999
Tomasz Grzelak *(Chm-Supervisory Bd)*
Pawel Sobieszuk *(Chm-Mgmt Bd)*

FAST RETAILING CO., LTD.

717-1 Sayama
Yamaguchi, 754-0894, Japan
Tel.: (81) 368650050
Fax: (81) 839830334
Web Site: www.fastretailing.com
Year Founded: 1963
9983—(HKG TKS)
Sls.: $11,155,709,280
Assets: $8,645,408,000
Liabilities: $2,988,599,840
Net Worth: $5,656,808,160
Earnings: $882,079,520
Emp.: 23,982
Fiscal Year-end: 08/31/13
Business Description:
Holding Company; Apparel Mfr; Retail Store Operator
S.I.C.: 5699
N.A.I.C.S.: 448190
Personnel:
Tadashi Yanai *(Chm, Pres & CEO)*
Takeshi Okazaki *(CFO & Sr VP)*
Nancy J. Pedot *(CEO-Comptoir des Cotonniers & Princesse tam.tam-Paris)*
Board of Directors:
Tadashi Yanai
Toru Hambayashi
Nobumichi Hattori
Toru Murayama
Takashi Nawa
Masaaki Shintaku
Transfer Agent:
Mitsubishi UFJ Trust & Banking Corporation
1-4-3, Marunouchi, Chiyoda-ku
Tokyo, Japan

Subsidiaries:

Cabin Co., Ltd. (1)
4-62-17 Yoyogi 3-15-5 Shinjyoku
Shinjyuju-Ku, Tokyo, 160-0023, Japan (93.89%)
Tel.: (81) 353345091
Fax: (81) 353345097
Web Site: www.cabin.co.jp
Womens Clothing Stores
S.I.C.: 5621
N.A.I.C.S.: 448120
Tetsuro Nakashima *(Gen Mgr)*

G.U. Co., Ltd. (1)
1 Chome 3rd 5 nine step IS buildings 5th Floor
Chiyoda Ku, 102-0073 Tokyo, Japan (100%)
Tel.: (81) 332886051
Fax: (81) 332886078
Web Site: www.gu-japan.com
Clothing & Furnishings Merchant Whslr
S.I.C.: 5136
N.A.I.C.S.: 424320
Shuichi Nakajima *(Pres)*

U.S. Subsidiary:

Fast Retailing USA, Inc. (1)
450 W 14th St 7th Fl
New York, NY 10014 NY
Tel.: (212) 221-9037
Web Site: www.uniqlo.com
Emp.: 20
Family Clothing Stores
S.I.C.: 5651
N.A.I.C.S.: 448140

Non-U.S. Subsidiaries:

Petit Vehicule S.A. (1)
9 Rue Brea
Paris, France
Tel.: (33) 0143120300
Fax: (33) 146585657
Web Site: www.poinghsshtrm.com
Womens & Girls Cut & Sew Dress Mfr
S.I.C.: 2389
N.A.I.C.S.: 315240

Uniqlo Hong Kong, Ltd. (1)
Shop 2006 2nd Floor Miramar Shopping Centre
132 Nathan Road, Kowloon, China (Hong Kong) (100%)
Tel.: (852) 23148886
Fax: (852) 23140838
Web Site: www.uniqlo.com.hk
Emp.: 80
Family Clothing Stores
S.I.C.: 5651
N.A.I.C.S.: 448140
Larry Meyer *(CEO-Bus-US)*

FAST TRUCKING SERVICE LTD .

Fast Ln
PO Box 700
Carnduff, SK, S0C 0S0, Canada
Tel.: (306) 482-3244
Fax: (306) 482-3670
E-Mail: larry@fasttruckingservice.com
Web Site: www.fasttruckingservice.com
Year Founded: 1957
Rev.: $15,823,981
Emp.: 150
Business Description:
Trucking Services
S.I.C.: 4213
N.A.I.C.S.: 484121
Personnel:
Tony Day *(Pres)*

FASTEEL INDUSTRIES LTD

19176 21st Avenue
Surrey, BC, V3S 3M3, Canada
Tel.: (604) 542-8881
Fax: (604) 542-8886
Toll Free: (800) 667-4121
Web Site: www.fasteelindustries.com
Rev.: $12,540,000
Emp.: 25
Business Description:
Steel Distr & Whslr
S.I.C.: 3325
N.A.I.C.S.: 331513
Personnel:
Brian A. McKenny *(Pres & CEO)*

FASTFORMS INC.

251 Massey Road
Guelph, ON, N1K 1B2, Canada
Tel.: (519) 824-4910
Fax: (519) 824-5972
Year Founded: 1967
Rev.: $33,221,994
Emp.: 150

Fastforms Inc.—(Continued)

Business Description:
Printing Services
S.I.C.: 2759
N.A.I.C.S.: 323111
Personnel:
Gary Christie *(Pres)*

FASTNET OIL & GAS PLC
18 Fitzwilliam Place
Dublin, 2, Ireland
Tel.: (353) 1 644 0007
Web Site: www.fastnetoilandgas.com
FAST—(AIM ISE)
Rev.: $339,547
Assets: $45,379,319
Liabilities: $874,927
Net Worth: $44,504,392
Earnings: ($2,201,530)
Emp.: 1
Fiscal Year-end: 03/31/13
Business Description:
Oil & Gas Exploration Services
S.I.C.: 1311
N.A.I.C.S.: 211111
Personnel:
Cathal Friel *(Chm)*
Paul Griffiths *(Mng Dir)*
Alan Mooney *(Sec)*
Board of Directors:
Cathal Friel
Michael Edelson
Paul Griffiths
Carol Law
Michael Nolan
Legal Counsel:
Mason Hayes & Curran
South Bank House Barrow St
Dublin, Ireland
Kuit Steinart Levy LLP
3 St Mary's Parsonage
Manchester, M3 2RD, United Kingdom

FASTWIRE PTE. LTD.
Level 9
77 Pacific Highway, Sydney, NSW, Australia
Tel.: (61) 299290666
Fax: (61) 294604519
Web Site: www.fastwire-group.com
Year Founded: 1998
Sales Range: $10-24.9 Million
Emp.: 125
Business Description:
Network Infrastructure & OSS Solutions Provider
S.I.C.: 4899
N.A.I.C.S.: 517919
Personnel:
John Birch *(Mng Dir)*
Rod Fisher *(Mng Dir)*
Rob Jack *(CTO)*

FATE S.A.I.C.I.
Avenida Blanco Encalada 3003
B1644GPK Victoria, Buenos Aires, Argentina
Tel.: (54) 11 4725 8100
Telex: 26080 FATEN AR
Fax: (54) 1147258188
E-Mail: fate@fate.com.ar
Web Site: www.fate.com.ar
Year Founded: 1962
Sales Range: $125-149.9 Million
Emp.: 1,800
Business Description:
Tire Mfr, Distr & Exporter
Import Export
S.I.C.: 3011
N.A.I.C.S.: 326211
Personnel:
Javier S. Madanes Quintanilla *(Pres)*

FATEH SPORTS WEAR LIMITED
Plot No 442
Mirpurkhas Rd
02200 Hyderabad, Sindh, Pakistan
Tel.: (92) 223880102
Fax: (92) 223880197
E-Mail: fswl@fateh1.com
Web Site: www.fateh1.com
FSWL—(KAR)
Sales Range: Less than $1 Million
Business Description:
Garment & Sports Wear Mfr
S.I.C.: 2259
N.A.I.C.S.: 315190
Personnel:
Rauf Alam *(Chm & CEO)*
Muhammed Ishaque Essani *(CFO)*
Ghous Muhammad Khan *(Sec)*
Board of Directors:
Rauf Alam
Aftab Alam
Faraz Alam
Saeed Alam
Muhammad Mohsin
Muhammad Naveed
Najma Roshan

FATEH TEXTILE MILLS LIMITED
A/4 Hali Rd SITE
PO Box 69
71000 Hyderabad, Sindh, Pakistan
Tel.: (92) 223880463
Fax: (92) 223880042
E-Mail: fatehmills@aol.com
Web Site: www.ftml.com.pk
FTHM—(KAR)
Sales Range: $25-49.9 Million
Emp.: 334
Business Description:
Textile, Yarn & Fabrics Mfr
S.I.C.: 2269
N.A.I.C.S.: 313310
Personnel:
Gohar Ullah *(Chm)*
Humayun Barkat *(CEO)*
Muhammad Saleem *(CFO)*
Muhammad Nadeem Aqeel *(Sec)*
Board of Directors:
Gohar Ullah
Muhammad Ayub
Asad Ullah Barkat
Humayun Barkat
Maqsood Ahmed Khan
Soofi Taj Muhammad
Muhammad Saleem

FATIMA FERTILIZER COMPANY LIMITED
(d/b/a Fatima Group)
E-110 Khayaban-e-Jinnah
Lahore, Pakistan
Tel.: (92) 111328462
Fax: (92) 36621389
E-Mail: mail@fatima-group.com
Web Site: www.fatima-group.com
Year Founded: 1936
FATIMA-PRO—(ISL KAR LAH)
Sls.: $299,023,651
Assets: $769,928,583
Liabilities: $476,661,497
Net Worth: $293,267,086
Earnings: $61,905,635
Emp.: 8,000
Fiscal Year-end: 12/31/12
Business Description:
Fertilizer Mfr
S.I.C.: 2873
N.A.I.C.S.: 325311
Personnel:
Arif Habib *(Chm)*
Fawad Ahmed Mukhtar *(CEO)*
Muhammad Abdul Wahab *(CFO)*
Fuad Imran Khan *(CIO)*
Ausaf Ali Qureshi *(Sec)*
Board of Directors:
Arif Habib
Jorgen Nergaard Gol
Muhammad Kashif
M. Abad Khan
Faisal Ahmed Mukhtar
Fawad Ahmed Mukhtar
Amir Shehzad
Fazal Ahmed Sheikh
Legal Counsel:
Chima & Ibrahim
1-A/245 Tufail Road
Lahore, Pakistan
Transfer Agent:
Central Depository Company of Pakistan Limited
CDC House 99 B Block B SMCHS Main Shahra-e-Faisal
Karachi, 74400, Pakistan

FAUBEL & CO. NACHFOLGER GMBH
Schwarzenberger Weg 45
34212 Melsungen, Germany
Mailing Address:
PO Box 11 60
34201 Melsungen, Germany
Tel.: (49) 5661 7309 0
Fax: (49) 5661 7309 149
E-Mail: info@faubel.de
Web Site: www.faubel.de
Year Founded: 1855
Sales Range: $25-49.9 Million
Emp.: 160
Business Description:
Packaging Plastic Label Mfr
S.I.C.: 2672
N.A.I.C.S.: 322220
Personnel:
Martin Kuge *(Mng Dir)*
Reinhard Kuge *(Mng Dir)*
Frank Ludwig *(Mng Dir)*

FAUJI FOUNDATION
Fauji Towers 68 Tipu Road
Chaklala, Rawalpindi, 46000, Pakistan
Tel.: (92) 51 595 1821
E-Mail: info@fauji.org.pk
Web Site: www.fauji.org.pk
Sales Range: $1-4.9 Billion
Business Description:
Veteran Welfare Fund
S.I.C.: 6371
N.A.I.C.S.: 525120
Personnel:
Muhammad Mustafa Khan *(Vice Chm & Mng Dir)*
Board of Directors:
Gulfam Alam
Agha Ali Hassan
Ghulam Haider
Nadeem Inayat
Qaiser Javed
Muhammad Mustafa Khan
Zahid Parvez
Parvez Sarwar Khan

Holdings:

Askari Bank Ltd. **(1)**
AWT Plaza The Mall
PO Box 1084
Rawalpindi, Pakistan PK
Tel.: (92) 51 9063000 (50.57%)
Fax: (92) 51 9272455
Web Site: www.askaribank.com.pk
AKBL—(ISL KAR LAH)
Int. Income: $328,256,015
Assets: $3,578,030,206
Liabilities: $3,377,178,836
Net Worth: $200,851,370
Earnings: $13,059,039
Emp.: 4,272
Fiscal Year-end: 12/31/12
Banking Services
S.I.C.: 6029
N.A.I.C.S.: 522110
Muhammad Mustafa Khan *(Chm)*
Majeedullah Husaini *(Pres & CEO)*
Saleem Anwar *(CFO & Exec VP)*
Farrukh Iqbal Khan *(Chief Credit Officer & Exec VP)*
Rehan Mir *(Treas & Exec VP)*
Muhammad Ahmed Ghazali Marghoob *(Sec & Sr VP)*
Haseeb Saulat *(Sr Exec VP & Head-Branch Banking)*
Imtiaz Ahmad Sheikh *(Sr Exec VP-Electronic Tech)*
Abdus Samad Khan *(Exec VP & Head-HRD-Pakistan)*
Khurshid Zafar *(Exec VP & Head-Corp & Investment Banking)*
Adil Abbas Zaidi *(Sr VP & Head-Intl Banking)*
Adnan Asghar *(Sr VP & Head-Agriculture & Rural Bus Div)*
Waleed Iqbal Khan *(Sr VP & Head-Gen Svcs)*
Zehra Khalikdina *(Sr VP & Head-Risk Mgmt)*
Muhammad Ehsan Qadir *(Sr VP & Acting Head-Ops)*
Fahd Sardar Khan *(Sr VP & Head-Islamic Banking Svcs)*
Zain Ul Abidin *(Sr VP & Head-Compliance & Data)*
Abdul Waseem *(Sr VP & Head-Credit Admin)*

Fauji Cereals **(1)**
Dhamial Road
PO Box 57
Rawalpindi, Pakistan
Tel.: (92) 51 512 6556
Fax: (92) 51 512 6558
E-Mail: fauji.cereals@fauji.org.pk
Web Site: www.faujicereals.com.pk
Cereal Mfr
S.I.C.: 2043
N.A.I.C.S.: 311230
Khalid Mahmud *(Gen Mgr)*

Foundation Gas **(1)**
Services Plaza Shahrahe Quaid-e-Azam
PO Box 422
Rawalpindi, Pakistan
Tel.: (92) 51 556 2470
Fax: (92) 51 556 8577
E-Mail: fongas@meganet.com.pk
Liquefied Petroleum Gas Distr
S.I.C.: 5989
N.A.I.C.S.: 454310

Foundation Securities (Pvt) Limited **(1)**
Ground Floor Baharia Complex II
MT Khan Road, Karachi, Pakistan PK
Tel.: (92) 21 111 000 375 (95%)
Fax: (92) 21 356 122 62
E-Mail: info@fs.com.pk
Web Site: www.fs.com.pk
Investment Banking, Securities Brokerage & Dealing Services
S.I.C.: 6211
N.A.I.C.S.: 523110
Atif Mohammad Khan *(CEO & Mng Dir)*

Overseas Employment Services **(1)**
Fauji Towers 68 Tipu Road
Chaklala, Rawalpindi, 46000, Pakistan
Tel.: (92) 51 595 1726 (-28)
E-Mail: oes@fauji.org.pk
Web Site: www.faujioes.org.pk
Employment Agency
S.I.C.: 7361
N.A.I.C.S.: 561311

Affiliates:

Fauji Cement Company Limited **(1)**
Fauji Tower Block III 68 Tipu Road Chaklala
Rawalpindi, Pakistan (31.79%)
Tel.: (92) 519280081
Fax: (92) 519280416
E-Mail: info@fauji.org.pk
Web Site: www.fccl.com.pk
FCCL—(KAR)
Sls.: $161,754,827
Assets: $306,990,146
Liabilities: $145,554,809
Net Worth: $161,435,337

Earnings: $21,243,289
Emp.: 1,061
Fiscal Year-end: 06/30/13
Cement Mfr
S.I.C.: 3241
N.A.I.C.S.: 327310
Muhammad Sabir *(CEO & Mng Dir)*
Omer Ashraf *(CFO)*
Sajjad Azam Khan *(Sec)*

Fauji Fertilizer Company Limited **(1)**
156 The Mall
Rawalpindi, Pakistan (44.35%)
Tel.: (92) 51111332111
Fax: (92) 518459925
E-Mail: ffcrwp@ffc.com.pk
Web Site: www.ffc.com.pk
FFC—(KAR)
Sls.: $1,238,408,516
Assets: $1,046,432,697
Liabilities: $696,597,817
Net Worth: $349,834,880
Earnings: $227,856,106
Fiscal Year-end: 12/31/12
Fertilizer Producer
S.I.C.: 2875
N.A.I.C.S.: 325314
Muhammad Mustafa Khan *(Chm)*
Naeem Khalid Lodhi *(CEO & Mng Dir)*
Shahid Hussain *(CFO & Gen Mgr-Fin)*
Mukhtar Hussain *(CIO & Gen Mgr-Info Sys)*
Fiaz Ahmed Satti *(Chief Coordination Officer)*
Sher Shah *(Sec)*

Holding:

Fauji Fertilizer Bin Qasim Limited **(2)**
73 Harley Street
Rawalpindi, Pakistan PK
Tel.: (92) 519272196 (51%)
Fax: (92) 519272198
E-Mail: info@ffbl.com
Web Site: www.ffbl.com.pk
FFBL—(ISL KAR LAH)
Sls.: $485,340,091
Assets: $412,327,579
Liabilities: $284,377,282
Net Worth: $127,950,298
Earnings: $43,945,439
Fiscal Year-end: 12/31/12
Granular Urea & Di-Ammonium Phosphate Fertilizer Mfr
S.I.C.: 2874
N.A.I.C.S.: 325312
Muhammad Mustafa Khan *(Chm)*
Muhammad Zaki *(CEO & Mng Dir)*
Shaukat Yaqub Malik *(Sec)*

Plant:

Fauji Fertilizer Company Limited - Plant I (Goth Machhi) **(2)**
Goth Machhi
Sadiqabad, Rahim Yar Khan, 64450, Pakistan
Tel.: (92) 6857864209
Fax: (92) 685 786401
E-Mail: plantgm@ffc.com.pk
Emp.: 300
Fertilizer Services
S.I.C.: 5191
N.A.I.C.S.: 424910
Tahir Javed *(Gen Mgr-Prod/Oper)*

Joint Ventures:

Fauji Akbar Portia Marine Terminals Limited **(1)**
10 2nd Floor Services Club Extension Bldg
Mereweather Road, Karachi, 75520, Pakistan PK
Tel.: (92) 21 3567 8985
Fax: (92) 21 3567 4233
Web Site: www.fapterminals.com
Grain, Oilseeds & Fertilizer Port Terminal Operator
S.I.C.: 4491
N.A.I.C.S.: 488310
Muhammad Mustafa Khan *(Chm)*
Ghouse Akbar *(Vice Chm)*
Ahmed Rana *(CEO)*
Hassan Sobuctageen *(COO)*
Aurangzeb Ahmed Khan *(Sec & Head-IR)*

Fauji Oil Terminal & Distribution Company Limited **(1)**
Port Bin Qasim
PO Box 9101 PQA
Karachi, 75020, Pakistan PK
Tel.: (92) 21 3472 0003 (-5)
Fax: (92) 21 3472 0010
E-Mail: info@fotco.pk
Web Site: www.fotco.pk
Petroleum Bulk Terminal Operator & Distr
S.I.C.: 5171
N.A.I.C.S.: 424710
Muhammad Mustafa Khan *(Chm & Mng Dir)*
Saqib Ghaffar *(CFO)*

FAVA INTERNATIONAL HOLDINGS LIMITED

Room 1005 10/F C C Wu Building
302-8 Hennessy Road
Wanchai, China (Hong Kong)
Tel.: (852) 2838 8108
Fax: (852) 2723 8108
E-Mail: fava_international@fava.com.hk
Web Site: www.fava.com.hk
Rev.: $5,054,840
Assets: $48,704,415
Liabilities: $20,993,060
Net Worth: $27,711,355
Earnings: ($10,341,790)
Emp.: 1,137
Fiscal Year-end: 12/31/12
Business Description:
Investment Management Services
S.I.C.: 6799
N.A.I.C.S.: 523920
Personnel:
Ge Li *(Chm & CEO)*
Board of Directors:
Ge Li
Wai Keung Cheng
Qing Chen Liu
Miguel Sun
Xiao Yan Tan
Chun Qiang Zhang

FAVITE INC.

19 Lane 78 Yanhe Street
Jhubei City, Hsin-chu, 302-67, Taiwan
Tel.: (886) 3 5545988
Fax: (886) 3 5545989
E-Mail: sales@favite.com
Web Site: www.favite.com
Year Founded: 2000
3535—(TAI)
Sales Range: $25-49.9 Million
Emp.: 180
Business Description:
Automatic Optical Inspection (AOI) & Measurement Machines Developer & Mfr
S.I.C.: 3829
N.A.I.C.S.: 334519
Personnel:
Yonghua Chen *(Chm)*

FAWCETTS GARAGE (NEWBURY) LIMITED

The Triangle Pinchington Lane
Newbury, Berkshire, RG14 7HT, United Kingdom
Tel.: (44) 163546660
Fax: (44) 1635524405
E-Mail: sales@fawcettsvolvo.co.uk
Web Site: www.fawcettsvolvo.co.uk
Rev.: $23,408,649
Emp.: 30
Business Description:
New & Used Car Dealers
S.I.C.: 5511
N.A.I.C.S.: 441110
Personnel:
R. J. Sampson *(Chm)*
Mark Jones *(Mng Dir)*
T. M. Jones *(Co-Mng Dir)*
J. S. N. J. Horsey *(Sec)*
Board of Directors:
R. J. Sampson
T. M. Jones
A. M. Sampson

FAYAT S.A.

137 rue du Palais Gallien
33000 Bordeaux, France
Tel.: (33) 556002100
E-Mail: info@fayat.com
Web Site: www.fayat.com
Year Founded: 1957
Sales Range: $1-4.9 Billion
Emp.: 16,000
Business Description:
Holding Company
S.I.C.: 6719
N.A.I.C.S.: 551112
Personnel:
Clement Fayat *(Pres)*
Subsidiary:

Razel S.A.S. **(1)**
3 Rue Rene Razel
Christ de Saclay, F-91892 Orsay, Cedex, France FR
Tel.: (33) 169856985
Fax: (33) 160190645
Web Site: www.razel-beck.com
Sales Range: $600-649.9 Million
Emp.: 3,924
Civil Engineering Construction Services
S.I.C.: 1629
N.A.I.C.S.: 237990
Laurent Fayat *(Pres)*

Non-U.S. Subsidiary:

BOMAG GmbH **(1)**
Hellerwald
D-56154 Boppard, Germany
Tel.: (49) 67421000
Fax: (49) 67423090
E-Mail: info@bomag.com
Web Site: www.bomag.com
Sales Range: $900-999.9 Million
Emp.: 2,200
Construction Machinery Mfr
S.I.C.: 3531
N.A.I.C.S.: 333120
Jorg Unger *(Mng Dir-Sls & Mktg)*

U.S. Subsidiary:

BOMAG Americas, Inc. **(2)**
2000 Kentville Rd
Kewanee, IL 61443-1714
Tel.: (309) 853-3571
Fax: (309) 853-1319
Toll Free: (800) 782-6624
E-Mail: usa@bomag.com
Web Site: www.bomag.com
Emp.: 125
Construction Machinery Mfr
Import Export
S.I.C.: 3531
N.A.I.C.S.: 333120
Walter Link *(Pres)*

Non-U.S. Subsidiary:

BOMAG (Canada) Inc. **(3)**
3455 Semenyk Court
Mississauga, ON, L5C 4P9, Canada
Tel.: (905) 361-9961
Fax: (905) 361-9962
E-Mail: canada@bomag.com
Emp.: 20
Construction Machinery Mfr
S.I.C.: 3531
N.A.I.C.S.: 333120
Axel Segiet *(Gen Mgr)*

Non-U.S. Subsidiary:

BOMAG Marini Latin America **(2)**
(Formerly Terex Roadbuilding Latin America)
Avenida Clemente Cifali 530
Cachoeira, RS, CEP-94935-225, Brazil
Tel.: (55) 51 2125 6677
Fax: (55) 51 3470 6220
E-Mail: FayatLA.ITSupport@bomag.com
Web Site: www.bomagmarini.com.br
Road Paving & Construction Equipment Mfr & Distr
S.I.C.: 3531
N.A.I.C.S.: 333120

FAZE THREE LIMITED

1 - 2 Shiv Smiriti Chambers 49-A Dr A B Road
Worli, Mumbai, 400 018, India
Tel.: (91) 2224944854
Fax: (91) 2224936811
E-Mail: info@fazethree.com
Web Site: www.fazethree.com
530079—(BOM)
Sales Range: $25-49.9 Million
Business Description:
Home Furnishings Store
S.I.C.: 5023
N.A.I.C.S.: 423220
Board of Directors:
Rashmi Anand
Sanjay Anand
Kishore Madhav Mahimkar
Vasudeva Rao
Rajiv Rai Sachdev
Joint Venture:

Aunde India Limited **(1)**
102 Shiv Smriti Chambers 49-A Dr Annie Besant Road
Worli, Mumbai, 400 018, India
Tel.: (91) 22 6618 8777
Fax: (91) 22 2493 6811
E-Mail: info@aundeindia.com
Web Site: www.aundeindia.com
532459—(BOM)
Rev.: $21,178,657
Assets: $24,609,930
Liabilities: $17,518,673
Net Worth: $7,091,257
Earnings: $685,428
Fiscal Year-end: 06/30/13
Automotive Fabric Mfr
S.I.C.: 3499
N.A.I.C.S.: 332999
Ajay Anand *(Chm & Mng Dir)*
Reema Jovita Mathias *(Compliance Officer & Sec)*

Unit:

Faze Three Limited - Works II **(1)**
380/1 Khanvel Silvassa Road
Dapada, Silvassa, 396 230, India
Tel.: (91) 260 2699323
Fax: (91) 2699322
E-Mail: mail@dpd.fazethree.com
Home Furnishing Mfr
S.I.C.: 2391
N.A.I.C.S.: 314120

FAZERLES AD-SILISTRA

Promishlena zona Zapad
Silistra, 7500, Bulgaria
Tel.: (359) 86 81 92 06
Fax: (359) 86 819 210
E-Mail: info@fazerles.com
Web Site: www.fazerles.com
Year Founded: 1993
4F6—(BUL)
Business Description:
Wood Product Mfr
S.I.C.: 2499
N.A.I.C.S.: 321999
Personnel:
Manol Todorov *(Exec Dir)*

FBC HOLDINGS LIMITED

45 Nelson Mandelal Ave
PO Box 1227
Harare, Zimbabwe
Tel.: (263) 4704471
Fax: (263) 4742568
E-Mail: info@fbc.co.zw
Web Site: www.fbc.co.zw
FBCH—(ZIM)
Sales Range: Less than $1 Million
Business Description:
Financial Services
S.I.C.: 6399
N.A.I.C.S.: 524130
Personnel:
Herbert Nkala *(Chm)*
Livingstone T. Gwata *(CEO)*
John Mushayavanhu *(Deputy CEO)*
Board of Directors:
Herbert Nkala
Kenzias Chibota

FBC Holdings Limited—(Continued)

Phillip M. Chiradza
Livingstone T. Gwata
Trynos Kufazvinei
Johnson Rex Mawere
Shingi A. Munyeza
John Mushayavanhu
Godfrey G. Nhemachena
Webster Rusere

Subsidiaries:

FBC Bank Limited (1)
FBC Centre Marketing and Public Relations Division
PO Box 1227
45 Nelson Mandela Avenue, Harare, Zimbabwe
Tel.: (263) 4783204
Fax: (263) 4783440
E-Mail: info@fbc.co.zw
Web Site: www.fbc.co.zw/bank/inside.cfm?pid=56
Commercial Banking Services
S.I.C.: 6029
N.A.I.C.S.: 522110
Webster Rusere *(Mng Dir)*

FBC Building Society (1)
FBC House 113 Leopold Takawira St
Harare, Zimbabwe
Tel.: (263) 4756811
Fax: (263) 4772743
E-Mail: ltakawirabs@fbc.co.zw
Web Site: www.fbc.co.zw/buildingsociety
Mortgage Banking Services
S.I.C.: 6163
N.A.I.C.S.: 522310
Takabvakure E. Mutunhu *(Chm)*
Webster Rusere *(Mng Dir)*

FBC Reinsurance Limited (1)
4th Floor FBC Centre 45 Nelson Mandela Avenue
PO Box 4282
Harare, Zimbabwe
Tel.: (263) 4 797783
Fax: (263) 4 742568
E-Mail: info@fbc.co.zw
Web Site: www.fbc.co.zw/reinsurance
Reinsurance Services
S.I.C.: 6399
N.A.I.C.S.: 524130
Kleto Chiketsani *(Mng Dir)*

FBD HOLDINGS PLC

FBD House Bluebell
Dublin, 12, Ireland
Tel.: (353) 14093200
Fax: (353) 14554308
E-Mail: info@fbd.ie
Web Site: www.fbdgroup.com
FBD—(ISE OTC)
Rev.: $524,750,528
Assets: $1,436,504,738
Liabilities: $1,107,152,132
Net Worth: $329,352,606
Earnings: $65,991,946
Emp.: 881
Fiscal Year-end: 12/31/12

Business Description:
Holding Company; Insurance & Property Services
S.I.C.: 6719
N.A.I.C.S.: 551112

Personnel:
Michael Berkery *(Chm)*
Andrew Langford *(CEO)*
Conor Gouldson *(Sec)*

Board of Directors:
Michael Berkery
John Bryan
Sean Dorgan
Brid Horan
Andrew Langford
Dermot Mulvihill
Cathal O'Caoimh
Vincent Sheridan
Padraig Walshe

Legal Counsel:
Dillon Eustace
33 Sir John Rogerson's Quay
Dublin, 2, Ireland
Tel.: (353) 1 667 0022
Fax: (353) 1 667 0042

Subsidiaries:

FBD Hotels (Ireland) Limited (1)
Central Office Fbd House Blue Bell
Dublin, Ireland
Tel.: (353) 1 428 2400
Fax: (353) 1 428 2411
E-Mail: reservations@fbdhotels.ie
Web Site: www.fbdhotels.com
Hotel Management Services
S.I.C.: 7011
N.A.I.C.S.: 721110
Deirdre Houlihan *(Mgr-Mktg)*

FBD Insurance plc (1)
FBD House
Bluebell, Dublin, 12, Ireland (100%)
Tel.: (353) 14093200
Fax: (353) 14554303
E-Mail: info@fbd.ie
Web Site: www.fbd.ie
Emp.: 50
Automotive, Home & Property Insurance Carrier
S.I.C.: 6411
N.A.I.C.S.: 524298
Adrian Taheny *(Exec Dir-Mktg & Sls)*

FBD Life & Pensions Limited (1)
FBD House Bluebell
Dublin, Ireland
Tel.: (353) 1 463 9820
Fax: (353) 1 428 2288
Web Site: www.fbd.ie/personal-finance/pensions/
General Insurance Services
S.I.C.: 6411
N.A.I.C.S.: 524210

FBD Property & Leisure Limited (1)
FBD House Bluebell
Bluebell, Dublin, 12, Ireland (100%)
Tel.: (353) 14554292
Fax: (353) 4554303
E-Mail: info@fbd.ie
Web Site: www.fbd.ie
Emp.: 400
Real Estate Investment & Marketing Services
S.I.C.: 6726
N.A.I.C.S.: 525990
Andrew Langford *(CEO)*

Holding:

FBD Hotels (2)
FBD House
Naas Rd, Dublin, Ireland IE
Tel.: (353) 14282400 (100%)
Fax: (353) 14282411
E-Mail: reservations@thw.ie
Web Site: www.fbdhotels.com
Emp.: 7
Hotels & Motels Operator
S.I.C.: 7011
N.A.I.C.S.: 721110
Eric Rothschild *(Mng Dir)*

Non-U.S. Holdings:

La Cala Golf Club S.L. (2)
Apdo de Correos 106 La Cala de Mijas
Urbanizacion La Cala Golf
Mijas Costa, ES-29649 Malaga, Spain ES
Tel.: (34) 952669000 (75%)
Fax: (34) 952669039
E-Mail: lacala@lacala.com
Web Site: www.lacala.com
Emp.: 200
Golf Resort Operator
S.I.C.: 7999
N.A.I.C.S.: 713910
Patrick Murphy *(Mng Dir)*

Sunset Beach Club S.A. (2)
Calle Sol 5
Benalmadena, Malaga, Spain (100%)
Tel.: (34) 952579400
Web Site: www.sunsetbeachclub.com
Hotels & Resort Operator
S.I.C.: 7011
N.A.I.C.S.: 721110

Non-U.S. Subsidiary:

Ranchos Reunidos S.A. (1)
Urbanizacion Cala Golf Country Club House S/n
Mijas, Malaga, 29649, Spain
Tel.: (34) 952669040
Fax: (34) 952669012
E-Mail: lacala@lacala.com
Web Site: www.lacala.com
Emp.: 180
Insurance Underwriting Services
S.I.C.: 6311
N.A.I.C.S.: 524113
David Kelly *(Mng Dir)*

FBN HOLDINGS PLC

(Formerly First Bank of Nigeria Plc)
(d/b/a FirstBank)
Samuel Asabia House 35 Marina
Lagos, Nigeria
Mailing Address:
PO Box 5216
Lagos, Nigeria
Tel.: (234) 1 9052326
Fax: (234) 1 9052000
E-Mail: firstcontact@firstbanknigeria.com
Web Site: www.firstbanknigeria.com
Year Founded: 1894
FBNH—(NIGE)
Rev.: $1,806,953,460
Assets: $20,040,751,410
Liabilities: $17,280,403,780
Net Worth: $2,760,347,630
Earnings: $475,964,300
Emp.: 8,837
Fiscal Year-end: 12/31/12

Business Description:
Bank Holding Company; Banking Services
S.I.C.: 6712
N.A.I.C.S.: 551111

Personnel:
Ajibola A. Afonja *(Chm)*
Stephen Olabisi Onasanya *(CEO & Mng Dir)*
Adebayo Adekola Adelabu *(CFO)*
Akinwumi Godson Fanimokun *(COO & Head-Tech & Processes)*
Abiodun Odubola *(Chief Risk Officer)*
Adeyemi Oluyinka Ogunmmoyela *(Chief Internal Auditor)*
Olayiwola Yahaya *(Sec)*

Board of Directors:
Ajibola A. Afonja
Adebayo Adekola Adelabu
Ibiai A. Ani
Ibukun Abiodun Awosika
Urum Kalu Eke
Ambrose Feese
Tunde Hassan-Odukale
Alhahi Lawal Kankia Ibrahim
Ebenezer Adewale Jolaoso
Dauda Lawal
Bello Mohammed Maccido
Abiodun Odubola
Stephen Olabisi Onasanya
Obafemi Adedamola Otudeko
Alhaji Mahey Rafindadi Rasheed
Gbenga Francis Shobo
Khadijah Alao Straub
Ibrahim Dahiru Waziri

PKF Professional Services
Toloye House, 362 Ikorodu Road 1A Okupe Estate
Lagos, Nigeria

Subsidiaries:

FBN Capital Ltd. (1)
16 Keffi Street Off Awolowo Road
Ikoyi South West, Lagos, Nigeria
Tel.: (234) 12707180
Fax: (234) 12690819
E-Mail: info@fbncapital.com
Web Site: www.fbncapital.com
Investment Banking Services
S.I.C.: 6211
N.A.I.C.S.: 523110
Oyekanmi Hassan-Odukale *(Chm)*
Kayode Akinkugbe *(CEO & Mng Dir)*
Funke Feyisitan *(COO)*

FBN (Merchant Bankers) Limited (1)
9/11 Macarthy Street
Onikan, Lagos, Nigeria (60%)
Tel.: (234) 1 2600800
Fax: (234) 1 2633600
E-Mail: fbnmb@fbnmb.com
Merchant Banking Services
S.I.C.: 6211
N.A.I.C.S.: 523110

FBN Mortgages Ltd. (1)
76 Awolowo Road
PO Box 9875
South West Ikoyi, Lagos, Nigeria
Tel.: (234) 14615860
Fax: (234) 12692007
E-Mail: enquiries@fbnmortgages.com
Web Site: www.fbnmortgages.com
Mortgage Banking Services
S.I.C.: 6159
N.A.I.C.S.: 522292
Abdullahi Mahmoud *(Chm)*
Subu Giwa-Amu *(CEO)*
Adenrele Oni *(Mng Dir)*

First Funds Ltd. (1)
90 Awolowo Road
Ikoyi, Lagos, Nigeria
Tel.: (234) 12793910
Fax: (234) 12793919
E-Mail: info@firstfunds.com.ng
Web Site: www.firstfunds.com.ng
Emp.: 10
Private Equity & Venture Capital Funds Mangement Services
S.I.C.: 6799
N.A.I.C.S.: 523910
Oluwole A. Adeosun *(Chm)*
Yemisi Tayo-Aboaba *(CEO & Mng Dir)*
Margaret Baale *(CFO)*
Irene Otike-Odibi *(Gen Counsel)*

First Pension Custodian Ltd. (1)
124 Awolowo Road
Ikoyi, Lagos, Nigeria
Tel.: (234) 12713217
Fax: (234) 14630241
E-Mail: info@firstpensioncustodian.com
Web Site: www.firstpensioncustodian.com
Emp.: 100
Custodial Services
S.I.C.: 7349
N.A.I.C.S.: 561720
Akinwumi G. Fanimokun *(CEO & Mng Dir)*

First Registrars Nigeria Limited (1)
Plot 2 Abebe Village Road
PMB 12692
Iganmu, Lagos, Nigeria (100%)
Tel.: (234) 12701078
Fax: (234) 12701071
E-Mail: info@firstregistrarsnigeria.com
Web Site: www.firstregistrarsnigeria.com
Financial Services
S.I.C.: 6726
N.A.I.C.S.: 525990
Bayo Olugbemi *(CEO & Mng Dir)*

First Trustees Nigeria Limited (1)
AG Leventis Building 42/43 Marina
PO Box 7826
Lagos, Nigeria
Tel.: (234) 12634801
Web Site: www.first-trustees.com
Trust Management Services
S.I.C.: 6091
N.A.I.C.S.: 523991

Non-U.S. Subsidiaries:

FBN Bank (UK) Ltd (1)
28 Finsbury Circus
London, EC2M 7DT, United Kingdom (100%)
Tel.: (44) 2079204920
Fax: (44) 2079204970
E-Mail: info@fbnbank.co.uk
Web Site: www.fbnbank.co.uk
Int. Income: $9,123,571
Emp.: 70
Banking Services
S.I.C.: 6029
N.A.I.C.S.: 522110
Peter Hinson *(Mng Dir)*
Michael Hailu *(Treas)*

International Commercial Bank Limited (1)
Meridian House Ring Road Central
Private Mail Bag No 16
Accra North, Accra, Ghana
Tel.: (233) 30 2236 136
Fax: (233) 30 2238 228

E-Mail: enquiry@icbank-gh.com
Web Site: www.icbank-gh.com
Commercial Banking Services
S.I.C.: 6029
N.A.I.C.S.: 522110

F.C.C. CO., LTD.

7000-36 Nakagawa Hosoe-cho Kita-ku
Hamamatsu, Shikuoka, 431-1394, Japan
Tel.: (81) 535232400
Fax: (81) 535232405
E-Mail: webmaster@fcc-net.co.jp
Web Site: www.fcc-net.co.jp
Year Founded: 1939
7296—(TKS)
Sls.: $1,388,695,000
Assets: $1,344,838,000
Liabilities: $272,437,000
Net Worth: $1,072,401,000
Earnings: $87,362,000
Emp.: 7,011
Fiscal Year-end: 03/31/13

Business Description:
Clutch Systems & Facings Mfr for Cars, Motorcycles & Utility Vehicles; Plastics Molding & Machining Services; Specialized Tools & Dies Mfr
S.I.C.: 3465
N.A.I.C.S.: 336370

Personnel:
Shiro Sumita *(Chm)*
Toshimichi Matsuda *(Pres)*
Kazuhiro Itonaga *(Co-Mng Dir)*
Yoshitaka Saito *(Co-Mng Dir)*

Board of Directors:
Shiro Sumita
Kenichi Inoue
Yoshinobu Isobe
Kazuhiro Itonaga
Toshimichi Matsuda
Ryujiro Matsumoto
Atsuhiro Mukoyama
Satoshi Nakaya
Yoshitaka Saito
Kazuto Suzuki
Tomokazu Takeda

Transfer Agent:
Mizuho Trust & Banking Co., Ltd
1-2-1 Yaesu Chuo-ku
Tokyo, Japan

Subsidiaries:

Kyushu F.C.C. Co., Ltd. (1)
74-1 Azahatada
Kumamoto, 8690521, Japan (100%)
Tel.: (81) 964322323
Fax: (81) 964343003
Emp.: 125
Motor Vehicle Parts Mfr
S.I.C.: 3714
N.A.I.C.S.: 336390
Kazuyuki Sugimura *(Mng Dir)*

Tenryu Sangyo Co., Ltd. (1)
2888 Ichino-cho
Hamamatsu, Shizuoka, 435-0051, Japan (53.55%)
Tel.: (81) 534211431
Fax: (81) 534217376
Emp.: 199
Automotive Stores
S.I.C.: 5531
N.A.I.C.S.: 441310

Tohoku Chemical Industries, Ltd. (1)
7-9-4 Nishigotanda Usui Bldg
Shinagawa-Ku, Tokyo, 141-0031, Japan
Tel.: (81) 334928921
Fax: (81) 334928994
Web Site: www.tci-web.co.jp
Emp.: 70
Industrial Chemicals Mfr
S.I.C.: 2899
N.A.I.C.S.: 325998
Tsunoda Hideyuki *(Pres)*

Non-U.S. Subsidiary:

Tohoku Chemical Industries (Vietnam), Ltd (2)
Amata Industrial Zone Lot 211 St 9
Long Binh Ward, Bien Hoa, Dong Nai, Vietnam
Tel.: (84) 613936014
Fax: (84) 613936016
Chemical Product Mfr
S.I.C.: 2899
N.A.I.C.S.: 325998

U.S. Subsidiaries:

F.C.C. (Adams), LLC (1)
936 E Parr Rd
Berne, IN 46711-1267 (100%)
Tel.: (260) 589-8555
Fax: (260) 589-8455
Web Site: www.fcc-net.co.jp/english/company/c04.html
Emp.: 256
Motor Vehicle Parts Mfr
S.I.C.: 3714
N.A.I.C.S.: 336390
Sandra Affolder *(Mgr-Admin)*

FCC (INDIANA), INC. (1)
555 Industrial Park Rd
Portland, IN 47371
Tel.: (260) 726-8023
Fax: (260) 726-7782
E-Mail: info@fcc-na.com
Web Site: www.fcc-na.com
Clutch Assemblies & Component Mfr
S.I.C.: 3714
N.A.I.C.S.: 336390

F.C.C. (North Carolina), LLC (1)
18000 Fieldcrest Rd
Laurinburg, NC 28352-6798 (100%)
Tel.: (910) 462-4465
Fax: (910) 462-4295
Web Site: www.fcc-net.co.jp/english/company/c04.html
Automotive Stores
S.I.C.: 5013
N.A.I.C.S.: 441310
Robert Kendall *(Mgr)*

Non-U.S. Subsidiaries:

FCC DO BRASIL LTDA. (1)
Mogno 11
Manaus, Amazonas, 69075-170, Brazil
Tel.: (55) 9221260202
Clutch Assemblies Mfr
S.I.C.: 3714
N.A.I.C.S.: 336390

F.C.C. Europe Ltd. (1)
Roebuck Way Knowlhill
Milton Keynes, Bucks, MK5 8HL, United Kingdom (90%)
Tel.: (44) 1908696932
Fax: (44) 1908696933
E-Mail: info@fcc-net.co.jp
Web Site: www.fcc-net.co.jp/english/company/c04.html
Emp.: 100
Motor Vehicle Parts Mfr
S.I.C.: 3714
N.A.I.C.S.: 336390
K. Nakamura *(Mng Dir)*

FCC (TAIWAN) CO., LTD. (1)
38 Tai Yi Rd
Jenteh Hsiang, T'ainan, 71747, Taiwan
Tel.: (886) 62720722
Fax: (886) 62721112
Web Site: www.fcc.com.tw
Clutch Assemblies Mfr
S.I.C.: 3714
N.A.I.C.S.: 336390

F.C.C. (Thailand) Co.,Ltd. (1)
Lat Krabang Ind Est Soi 3 286
Chalongkrung Rd Lampratiew Lat, 10520
Bangkok, Thailand (58%)
Tel.: (66) 23260423
Fax: (66) 23260273
Web Site: www.fcc-net.co.jp/english/company/c04.html
Emp.: 1,000
Automotive Stores
S.I.C.: 5013
N.A.I.C.S.: 441310

Non-U.S. Joint Venture:

Kwang Hwa Shing Industrial Co., Ltd. (1)
38 Daii Road Jeng Der Hsiang
Tainen, Hsien, Taiwan
Tel.: (886) 6 2720722
Fax: (886) 6 2721112
Web Site: www.fcc.com.tw
Sales Range: $25-49.9 Million
Emp.: 150
Motorcycle Clutches Mfr & Sales; Owned by F.C.C. Co., Ltd., by Kwang Yang Motor Co., Ltd (KYMCO) & by King Hwa Sin Industrial Co., Ltd.
S.I.C.: 3751
N.A.I.C.S.: 336991
Lin Ming-Liang *(CEO)*

FCS SOFTWARE SOLUTIONS LTD

205 2nd Floor Aggarwal Chamber IV
27 Veer Sawarkar Block
Vikas Marg, Delhi, 110092, India
Tel.: (91) 1142444235
Fax: (91) 1142444235
Web Site: www.fcsltd.com
532666—(BOM)
Rev.: $21,674,632
Assets: $108,907,378
Liabilities: $5,848,793
Net Worth: $103,058,585
Earnings: ($6,926,680)
Emp.: 930
Fiscal Year-end: 03/31/13

Business Description:
Information Technology Services Provider
S.I.C.: 7371
N.A.I.C.S.: 541511

Personnel:
Dalip Kumar *(Chm & Mng Dir)*
Anil Sharma *(CFO)*
Gagan Kaushik *(Compliance Officer & Sec)*

Board of Directors:
Dalip Kumar
Govinda Sahu
Shayam Sunder Sharma
Shiv Nandan Sharma

Legal Counsel:
Mahendra & Associates
249 District Court
Gautam Budha Nagar, Noida, India

Transfer Agent:
Link Intime (India) Pvt Ltd
A 40 Naraina Banquet Hall
New Delhi, India

FCW HOLDINGS BERHAD

No 8 3rd Floor Jalan Segambut
51200 Kuala Lumpur, Malaysia
Tel.: (60) 3 6195 1600
Fax: (60) 34043 6750
E-Mail: enquiry@fcw.com.my
Web Site: www.fcw.com.my
FCW—(KLS)
Rev.: $11,200,763
Assets: $52,569,511
Liabilities: $3,282,151
Net Worth: $49,287,360
Earnings: $2,951,280
Fiscal Year-end: 06/30/13

Business Description:
Property Rental & Leasing Services
S.I.C.: 6531
N.A.I.C.S.: 531311

Personnel:
Poh Wah Loh *(Sec)*

Board of Directors:
Hua Choon Tan
Azizzuddin Hussein
Sze Pheng Lai
Tat Chun Tang
Kay Yeong Teh
Poh Seng Thor

Subsidiary:

Coscolab Sdn. Bhd. (1)
No 1 Jalan Taming 2 Kawasan
Perindustrian Taming Jaya
43300 Seri Kembangan, Selangor, Malaysia
Tel.: (60) 389618169
Fax: (60) 389616169
E-Mail: coscolab@coscolab.com
Web Site: www.coscolab.com
Emp.: 80
Skincare Products Mfr
S.I.C.: 3999
N.A.I.C.S.: 339999
Teo Ker-Wei *(Mng Dir)*

FDB GROUP

(d/b/a The Danish Co-operative Retail and Wholesale Society)
Vallensbaek Torvevej 9
DK 2620 Albertslund, Denmark
Tel.: (45) 39470000
Fax: (45) 39470001
E-Mail: fdb@fdb.dk
Web Site: www.fdb.dk
Year Founded: 1893
Sales Range: $150-199.9 Million
Emp.: 55

Business Description:
Cooperative Food Retailing Services
S.I.C.: 5499
N.A.I.C.S.: 445299

Personnel:
Lasse Bolander *(Pres)*

Subsidiaries:

Coop Danmark A/S (1)
Roskildevej 65
2620 Albertslund, Denmark (100%)
Tel.: (45) 43864386
Fax: (45) 43863386
Web Site: www.coop.dk
All Other General Merchandise Stores
S.I.C.: 5399
N.A.I.C.S.: 452990
Per Toelstang *(CEO)*

Subsidiary:

Fakta A/S (2)
Hjulmagervej 12
7100 Vejle, Denmark
Tel.: (45) 76414300
Fax: (45) 75858470
E-Mail: fakta@fakta.dk
Web Site: www.fakta.dk
Emp.: 130
Supermarkets & Other Grocery except Convenience Stores
S.I.C.: 5411
N.A.I.C.S.: 445110
Michael Christensen *(Mng Dir)*

Subsidiary:

Dansk Vinimport Vejle ApS (3)
Hjulmagervej 12
7100 Vejle, Denmark
Tel.: (45) 76414300
Fax: (45) 75858470
Supermarkets & Other Grocery except Convenience Stores
S.I.C.: 5411
N.A.I.C.S.: 445110
Claus Jensen *(Mng Dir)*

Joint Venture:

Coop Trading A/S (2)
Helgeshoj Alle 57
DK-2620 Hoje Taastrup, Denmark
Tel.: (45) 8853 0000
E-Mail:
Web Site: www.cooptrading.com
Emp.: 114
Internordic Procurement of Branded Products
S.I.C.: 5399
N.A.I.C.S.: 452990
Per Bank *(Mng Dir)*

Irma A/S (1)
Roskilde Vej 65
2620 Albertslund, Denmark (100%)
Tel.: (45) 43863822
Fax: (45) 43863859

FDB Group—(Continued)

E-Mail: info@irma.dk
Web Site: www.irma.dk
Emp.: 1,500
Supermarkets & Other Grocery except Convenience Stores
S.I.C.: 5411
N.A.I.C.S.: 445110
Jan Larsen *(Mng Dir)*

FDC LTD

B-8 MIDC Area
Aurangabad Dist, Waluj, 431 136, India
Tel.: (91) 2402554407
Fax: (91) 2402554299
Web Site: www.fdcindia.com
FDC—(BOM NSE)
Rev.: $151,871,152
Assets: $179,146,458
Liabilities: $33,747,602
Net Worth: $145,398,856
Earnings: $28,768,611
Fiscal Year-end: 03/31/13

Business Description:
Healthcare Products Mfr
S.I.C.: 2834
N.A.I.C.S.: 325412

Personnel:
Anand L. Chandavarkar *(Founder)*
Mohan A. Chandavarkar *(Chm & Mng Dir)*
Nandan M. Chandavarkar *(Mng Dir)*
Shalini Kamath *(Compliance Officer & Sec)*

Board of Directors:
Mohan A. Chandavarkar
Nagam H. Atthreya
Ameya A. Chandavarkar
Ashok A. Chandavarkar
Nandan M. Chandavarkar
Rahim H. Muljiani
Girish C. Sharedalal
Satish S. Ugrankar
Vinod G. Yennemadi

Transfer Agent:
Sharex Dynamic (India) Private Limited
Unit No1 Luthra Indus Premises Andheri Kurla Rd Safed Pool Andheri(E)
Mumbai, India

Non-U.S. Subsidiary:

FDC International Limited (1)
Unit 6 Fulcrum 1 Solent way Solent Bus Park Whiteley
Fareham, Hampshire, PO15 7FE, United Kingdom
Tel.: (44) 1489565222
Fax: (44) 1489565222
E-Mail: fdcil@btconnect.com
Web Site: www.fdcindia.com
Emp.: 2
Ophthalmic Products Mfr
S.I.C.: 3089
N.A.I.C.S.: 326199
Santosh Amoncar *(Mgr)*

F.D.G. MINING INC.

404 815 Hornby Street
Vancouver, BC, V6Z 2E6, Canada
Tel.: (604) 684-2213
Fax: (604) 684-2474
E-Mail: info@fdgmining.com
Web Site: www.fdgmining.com
FDG—(TSXV)

Business Description:
Gold Mining Services
S.I.C.: 1041
N.A.I.C.S.: 212221

Personnel:
Antonio Ponte *(CEO)*
Philipp D. Hoch *(CFO)*

Board of Directors:
Marc T. Bamber
Alan T. Charuk
William W. Dunn
Ian H. Mann
Antonio Ponte
David St. Clair Dunn

Legal Counsel:
Gregory T. Chu
Ste 650 1188 W Georgia St
Vancouver, BC, Canada

Transfer Agent:
Equity Financial Trust Co.
Suite 1620 1185 West Georgia Street
Vancouver, BC, Canada

FDK CORPORATION

Hamagomu Bldg 5-36-11 Shinbashi Minato-ku
Tokyo, 105 8677, Japan
Tel.: (81) 334341271
Fax: (81) 334341375
Web Site: www.fdk.co.jp
Year Founded: 1950
6955—(TKS)
Sls.: $809,017,000
Assets: $645,920,000
Liabilities: $556,270,000
Net Worth: $89,650,000
Earnings: $4,983,000
Emp.: 5,858
Fiscal Year-end: 03/31/13

Business Description:
Mfr & Sales of Electronics-Related Raw Materials, Components & Dry Batteries
Import Export
S.I.C.: 3679
N.A.I.C.S.: 334419

Personnel:
Michimasa Mochizuki *(Pres & CEO)*

Subsidiaries:

FDK Ecotec Co., Ltd. (1)
2281 Washizu
Kosai, Shizuoka, 431-0431, Japan
Tel.: (81) 53 575 3001
Fax: (81) 53 576 2124
Web Site: www.fdk.com
Emp.: 13
Scrap Metal Recycling Services
S.I.C.: 4953
N.A.I.C.S.: 562920
Junji Sudo *(Pres)*

FDK Energy Co., Ltd. (1)
614 Washizu
Kosai, Shizuoka, 431-0431, Japan
Tel.: (81) 535762111
Fax: (81) 535762118
Web Site: www.fdk.com
Emp.: 202
Batteries Mfr & Sales
S.I.C.: 3691
N.A.I.C.S.: 335911
Keiji Fukuhara *(Pres)*

FDK Engineering Co., Ltd. (1)
281 Hirooka Hosoe-cho
Kita-ku, Hamamatsu, Shizuoka, 431-1302, Japan
Tel.: (81) 535225280
Fax: (81) 53 522 5288
Web Site: www.fdk.co.jp/fdkeg/
Emp.: 73
Electronic Components Making Machinery Mfr
S.I.C.: 3559
N.A.I.C.S.: 333242
Shinjiro Suzuki *(Pres)*

FDK LIFETEC CORPORATION (1)
2281 Washizu
Kosai, Shizuoka, 431-0431, Japan
Tel.: (81) 53 576 3121
Fax: (81) 53 576 3700
E-Mail:
Web Site: www.fdk.co.jp/kankei-e/div_life-e.html
Emp.: 23
Welfare Services
S.I.C.: 6371
N.A.I.C.S.: 525120
Masahiro Adachi *(Pres)*

FDK Tottori Co., Ltd. (1)
28 Ohta Iwami-cho
Iwami-gun, Tottori, 681-0063, Japan
Tel.: (81) 857731771
Fax: (81) 857731770
Emp.: 331
Lithium Batteries Mfr
S.I.C.: 3692
N.A.I.C.S.: 335912
Satoru Fukuoka *(Pres)*

FDK TWICELL Co.,Ltd. (1)
307-2 Koyagi-machi
Takasaki, Gunma, 370-0071, Japan
Tel.: (81) 273617575
Fax: (81) 273620344
Web Site: www.fdk-twicell.com
Emp.: 462
Batteries Mfr
S.I.C.: 3692
N.A.I.C.S.: 335912

Unit:

FDK Ecotec Co., Ltd. - GIFU WORKS (1)
478 Tsuchikura Hirata-cho
Kaizu, Gifu, 503-0322, Japan
Tel.: (81) 584664781
Fax: (81) 584 66 4791
Emp.: 16
Scrap Metal Recycling Services
S.I.C.: 5051
N.A.I.C.S.: 423510

Plants:

FDK Corporation - Kosai Plant (1)
2281 Washizu
Kosai, Shizuoka, 431-0495, Japan
Tel.: (81) 53 576 2151
Fax: (81) 53 575 2124
Web Site: www.fdk.com
Electronic Components Mfr
S.I.C.: 3674
N.A.I.C.S.: 334413

FDK Corporation - Sanyo Plant (1)
5 ku Hon-machi
Sanyoonoda-shi, Yamaguchi, 757-8585, Japan
Tel.: (81) 836 72 1311
Fax: (81) 836 72 0931
Web Site: www.fdk.com
Piezoelectric Inverter Modules Mfr
S.I.C.: 3679
N.A.I.C.S.: 334419

U.S. Subsidiary:

FDK America Inc. (1)
250 E Caribbean Dr 200
Sunnyvale, CA 94089 CA
Tel.: (408) 215-6500
Fax: (408) 215-6501
Web Site: www.fdkamerica.com
Rev.: $85,493,206
Emp.: 12
Batteries & Optical Devices
S.I.C.: 5065
N.A.I.C.S.: 423690
Yasuhito Yasutani *(Pres & CEO)*

Non-U.S. Subsidiaries:

FDK ELECTRONICS GMBH (1)
Heerdter Lohweg 89
40549 Dusseldorf, Germany
Tel.: (49) 2115374640
Fax: (49) 211593549
E-Mail: germany@fdk.com
Emp.: 17
Electronic Equipments Sales
S.I.C.: 5063
N.A.I.C.S.: 423610
Jun Akutagawa *(Pres)*

FDK HONG KONG LTD. (1)
Suite 1607-1608A 16/F Tower 3 China Hong Kong City 33 Canton Road
Tsim Tsa Tsui, Kowloon, China (Hong Kong)
Tel.: (852) 2799 9773
Fax: (852) 2755 4635
Web Site: www.fdk.com
Emp.: 11
Electronic Products Whslr
S.I.C.: 5065
N.A.I.C.S.: 423690

FDK KOREA LTD. (1)
Room 1813 18Floor Hyundai Rexion Officetel 1338-20 Seocho-Dong
Seocho-ku, Seoul, 137-860, Korea (South)
Tel.: (82) 25828452
Fax: (82) 2 582 8453
Web Site: www.fdk.co.jp/kankei-e/div_korea-e.html
Electronic Component Sales
S.I.C.: 5065
N.A.I.C.S.: 423690

FDK LANKA (PVT) LTD. (1)
Ring Road 3 Phase 2
EPZ Katunayake, 11450 Katunayaka, Western Province, Sri Lanka
Tel.: (94) 112253492
Fax: (94) 11 225 3490
E-Mail: business@fdklanka.com
Web Site: www.fdklanka.com
Emp.: 1,100
Electronic Components Mfr
S.I.C.: 3679
N.A.I.C.S.: 334419
Kenji Yamada *(Pres)*
Norio Takaba *(Mng Dir)*

FDK SINGAPORE PTE. LTD. (1)
4 Leng Kee Road 04-08 Sis Building
Singapore, 159088, Singapore
Tel.: (65) 64722328
Fax: (65) 6472 5761
Emp.: 7
Electronic Equipment Mfr & Sales
S.I.C.: 3691
N.A.I.C.S.: 335911
Masaki Miura *(Mng Dir)*

FDK TAIWAN LTD. (1)
8F-4 No 57 Section 1 Chongqing South Road
Zhongzheng District, Taipei, 100, Taiwan
Tel.: (886) 223115161
Fax: (886) 2 2311 5123
Web Site: www.fdk.co.jp/kankei-e/div_taiwan-e.html
Emp.: 3
Electronic Components Distr
S.I.C.: 5065
N.A.I.C.S.: 423690
Sato Mitsuhiro *(Gen Mgr)*

FUCHI ELECTRONICS CO., LTD. (1)
No 355 Section 2 Nankan Road
Rutsu Shan, Taoyuan, 338, Taiwan
Tel.: (886) 3 322 2124
Fax: (886) 3 322 6899
Emp.: 358
Electronic Components Mfr & Whslr
S.I.C.: 3621
N.A.I.C.S.: 335312

PT FDK INDONESIA (1)
Kawasan Industri MM 2100 Blok MM 1 Jatiwangi
Cikarang Barat, 17520 Bekasi, West Java, Indonesia
Tel.: (62) 21 8998 2111
Fax: (62) 21 8998 2302
Web Site: www.fdk.com
Emp.: 864
Batteries Mfr & Sales
S.I.C.: 3691
N.A.I.C.S.: 335911
Hiroto Takahashi *(Pres)*

Xiamen FDK Corporation (1)
No 16 Malong Road Huoju Garden
Huoju Hi-Tech District, Xiamen, Fujian, 361006, China
Tel.: (86) 592 603 0576
Fax: (86) 592 603 0579
Web Site: www.fdk.com
Emp.: 1,623
Power Supplies Mfr & Whslr
S.I.C.: 3699
N.A.I.C.S.: 335999

FE LIMITED

32 Harrogate Street
Leederville, WA, 6007, Australia
Tel.: (61) 8 6181 9793
Fax: (61) 8 9380 9666
E-Mail: admin@felimited.com.au
Web Site: www.felimited.com.au
FEL—(ASX)
Rev.: $99,127
Assets: $4,305,047
Liabilities: $6,149,402
Net Worth: ($1,844,354)

Earnings: ($2,467,668)
Fiscal Year-end: 09/30/13
Business Description:
Gold Mining Services
S.I.C.: 1041
N.A.I.C.S.: 212221
Personnel:
Eloise von Puttkammer *(Sec)*
Board of Directors:
Antony Sage
Mark Gwynne
Paul Kelly
Legal Counsel:
Steinepreis Paganin
Level 4 Next Building 16 Milligan St
Perth, Australia

FEATHERLITE INDUSTRIES LTD.

100 Engelhard Drive
Aurora, ON, Canada L4G 3V2
Tel.: (905) 727-0031
Fax: (905) 727-7271
E-Mail: salesdesk@featherliteladders.com
Web Site: www.featherliteladders.com
Year Founded: 1949
Rev.: $13,995,072
Emp.: 85
Business Description:
Ladder Mfr
S.I.C.: 3499
N.A.I.C.S.: 332999
Personnel:
Andrew Gucciardi *(Pres)*

FECTO GROUP OF COMPANIES

1st Floor Panorama Centre-2
Raja Ghazanfar Ali Khan Road,
Karachi, Pakistan
Tel.: (92) 21 568 2178
Web Site: www.fecto.com
Emp.: 2,500
Business Description:
Holding Company
S.I.C.: 6719
N.A.I.C.S.: 551112
Personnel:
Ghulam Muhammad A. Fecto *(Founder & Chm)*
Munawar Ali Fecto *(CEO & Mng Dir)*
Kaiser Fecto *(Deputy CEO)*
Subsidiaries:

Baba Farid Sugar Mills Limited (1)
1st Floor Panorama Centre-2
Raja Ghazanfar Ali Khan Road, Karachi, Pakistan
Tel.: (92) 215682178
Fax: (92) 215684709
E-Mail: fecto@fecto.com
Web Site: www.fecto.com
BAFS—(KAR LAH)
Sales Range: $10-24.9 Million
Emp.: 1,500
Sugar Mill
S.I.C.: 2062
N.A.I.C.S.: 311314
Munawar Ali Fecto *(CEO)*
Kaiser Mahmood Fecto *(Deputy CEO)*
Malik Ahmed Saeed Nasir *(Sec)*

Fecto Cement Limited (1)
35 Darul Aman Housing Society Block 7/8
Shahrah-e-Faisal
Karachi, 75350, Pakistan PK
Tel.: (92) 21 4530120
Fax: (92) 21 4530123
E-Mail: cement@cyber.net.pk
Web Site: www.fectogroup.com
FECTC—(ISL)
Sls.: $46,477,088
Assets: $34,026,893
Liabilities: $14,688,176
Net Worth: $19,338,717
Earnings: $5,907,310
Emp.: 884
Fiscal Year-end: 06/30/13
Cement Mfr
S.I.C.: 3241
N.A.I.C.S.: 327310
Mohammed Yasin Fecto *(CEO)*
Abdul Samad *(Sec)*

Fecto Orient (Pvt.) Ltd. (1)
1st Floor Panorama Centre-2
Raja Ghazanfar Ali Khan Road, Karachi, Pakistan
Tel.: (92) 215662991
Web Site: www.fecto.com
Clearing, Forwarding & Indenting; Imports & Clearance
S.I.C.: 7389
N.A.I.C.S.: 561990

Fecto Sugar Mills Ltd. (1)
1st Floor Panorama Centre-2
Raja Ghazanfar Ali Khan Road, Karachi, 75530, Pakistan
Tel.: (92) 215682178
Fax: (92) 215684709
E-Mail: fecto@fecto.com
Web Site: www.fecto.com
Sales Range: $10-24.9 Million
Emp.: 1,338
Sugar Mfr
S.I.C.: 2062
N.A.I.C.S.: 311314
Munawar Ali Fecto *(CEO & Mng Dir)*
Kaiser Mahmood Fecto *(Deputy CEO)*
Malik Ahmed Saeed Nasir *(Sec)*

FEDDERS LLOYD CORPORATION LTD.

159 Okhla Phase-3
New Delhi, 110020, India
Tel.: (91) 1140627200
Fax: (91) 1141609909
E-Mail: info@feddersllovd.com
Web Site: www.feddersllovd.com
500139—(BOM NSE)
Rev.: $190,580,447
Assets: $175,491,668
Liabilities: $116,628,095
Net Worth: $58,863,573
Earnings: $9,221,054
Fiscal Year-end: 06/30/13
Business Description:
Air-Conditioning Equipment & Structured Steel Products Mfr
S.I.C.: 3585
N.A.I.C.S.: 333415
Personnel:
Brij Raj Punj *(Chm & Mng Dir)*
Purnima Sharma *(Compliance Officer & Sec)*
Board of Directors:
Brij Raj Punj
Sham Sunder Dhawan
Bindu Dogra
Nemichandra Dhanyakumar Jain
Arun Kumar Joshi
Ritushri Sharma
Transfer Agent:
Skyline Financial Services Pvt Ltd
246 1st Floor Sant Nagar Main Iskcon Temple Road
East of Kailash, New Delhi, 110065, India
Subsidiaries:

PSL Engineering Pvt. Ltd. (1)
Plot No 30 Sectyor C Maneri Industrial Area
Tehsil-Niwas District Mandla, Jabalpur, MP, India
Tel.: (91) 7643 233228
Air Conditioning Equipment Mfr
S.I.C.: 3585
N.A.I.C.S.: 333415
Non-U.S. Subsidiary:

Luvata Czech S.R.O. (1)
Vrazska 143 Radotin
15300 Prague, 5, Czech Republic
Tel.: (420) 257 811 129
Fax: (420) 257 811 136
Air Conditioning Equipment Mfr
S.I.C.: 3585
N.A.I.C.S.: 333415

THE FEDERAL BANK LIMITED

Federal Towers Federal Bank HO
PO Box 103
Aluva, 683 101, India
Tel.: (91) 4842623620
Fax: (91) 4842622672
E-Mail: fbl@federalbank.co.in
Web Site: www.federal-bank.com
Year Founded: 1931
500469—(BOM NSE)
Sales Range: $1-9.9 Million
Emp.: 8,500
Business Description:
Banking Services
S.I.C.: 6029
N.A.I.C.S.: 522110
Personnel:
Shyam Srinivasan *(CEO & Mng Dir)*
P. C. John *(CFO)*
Girish Kumar Ganapathy *(Sec)*
Board of Directors:
Abraham Chacko
K. M. Chandrasekhar
Harish H.
P. C. John
M. Y. Khan
Abraham Koshy
T. C. Nair
P. H. Ravikumar
Nilesh S. Vikamsey
Price Patt & Co.
Kochi, India
Transfer Agent:
Integrated Enterprises (India) Ltd.
41/427 Seema Near Abad Metro Hotel Rajaji Road Ernakulam
Kochi, India
Subsidiary:

Fedbank Financial Services Ltd (1)
C 6 Laxmi Tower Bandra Kurla Complex Bandra-e
Mumbai, 400051, India
Tel.: (91) 22 26566502
Fax: (91) 22 26524144
E-Mail: Customercare@fedfina.com
Web Site: www.fedfina.com
Financial Management Services
S.I.C.: 8742
N.A.I.C.S.: 541611
Suresh Kumar *(Chm)*
Somsankar Sengupta *(CEO & Mng Dir)*
Dilip Kumar Maloo *(Head-Fin & Sec)*

FEDERAL CORPORATION

369 Sec 2 Chung Hwa Rd
Chung-li, Taoyuan, Taiwan
Tel.: (886) 34522156
Fax: (886) 34616357
Web Site: www.federaltire.com.tw
2102—(TAI)
Sales Range: $150-199.9 Million
Business Description:
Automobile Tires Mfr & Distr
S.I.C.: 3011
N.A.I.C.S.: 326211
Personnel:
Shu Jam Ma *(CEO & Pres)*
Non-U.S. Subsidiary:

Federal Tire (Jiangxi) Co., Ltd. (1)
No 639 Shanghai Road
Qingshanhu District, Nanchang, Jiangxi, 330029, China
Tel.: (86) 79 1831 0138
Fax: (86) 79 1833 0494
Tire Mfr
S.I.C.: 3011
N.A.I.C.S.: 326211
Shu Jam Ma *(Chm)*

FEDERAL FURNITURE HOLDINGS (M) BERHAD

Level P1 Menara Choy Fook On No 1B Jalan Yong Shook Lin
46050 Petaling Jaya, Selangor Darul Ehsan, Malaysia
Tel.: (60) 379559937
Fax: (60) 379562812
Web Site: www.federal-furniture.com
FFHB—(KLS)
Rev.: $26,195,201
Assets: $16,637,808
Liabilities: $7,758,579
Net Worth: $8,879,229
Earnings: $1,539,204
Fiscal Year-end: 12/31/12
Business Description:
Furniture Mfr
S.I.C.: 2511
N.A.I.C.S.: 337122
Personnel:
Fook On Choy *(Chm)*
Wai Hin Choy *(Mng Dir)*
Siew Chuan Chua *(Co-Sec)*
Chooi Peng Mak *(Co-Sec)*
Board of Directors:
Fook On Choy
Wai Ceong Choy
Wai Hin Choy
Hussein Hamzah
Vijayasundaram Jeyabalan
Mohd. Arif Mastol
Geok Foong Tan
Subsidiaries:

Federal Furniture Industries Sdn Bhd (1)
No 8 Koi Kinrara Jalan Pipit Bukit Tandang
47100 Puchong, Selangor, Malaysia
Tel.: (60) 380709200
Fax: (60) 380709300
E-Mail: angelchin@ffhb.com.my
Web Site: www.ffi.com.my
Emp.: 35
Interior Design Services
S.I.C.: 7389
N.A.I.C.S.: 541410
S. K. Choy *(Chief Dev Officer-Kitchen Project)*

Federal Furniture Lifestyle Sdn Bhd (1)
No 53 & 53-1 Jalan Puteri 2/1 Bandar Puteri Puchong
47100 Puchong, Selangor, Malaysia
Tel.: (60) 3 8060 1813
Fax: (60) 3 8060 1815
Interior Design & Furnishing Services
S.I.C.: 7389
N.A.I.C.S.: 541410
James Shii *(COO)*

Federal Furniture (M) Sdn Bhd (1)
Lot 104 Jalan 1 Kompleks Perabut Olak Lempit
Kuala Langat, 42700 Banting, Selangor, Malaysia
Tel.: (60) 331491154
Fax: (60) 331493949
Web Site: www.ff1982.com.my
Emp.: 21
Furniture & Furnishing Products Whslr
S.I.C.: 5021
N.A.I.C.S.: 423210
Fook On Choy *(Chm)*
Wai Hin Choy *(Mng Dir)*

FEDERAL INTERNATIONAL (2000) LTD

47 49 Genting Road
Singapore, 349489, Singapore
Tel.: (65) 67478118
Fax: (65) 67430690
E-Mail: admin@fedsin.com.sg
Web Site: www.federal.com.sg
F20—(SES)
Rev.: $99,966,332
Assets: $132,664,449
Liabilities: $92,229,839
Net Worth: $40,434,610
Earnings: ($32,229,312)
Fiscal Year-end: 12/31/12
Business Description:
Drilling Services
S.I.C.: 1381
N.A.I.C.S.: 213111

Federal International (2000) Ltd—(Continued)

Personnel:
Kian Kiong Koh *(Chm & CEO)*
Chee Meng Loh *(CFO & Sec)*
George Guan Qun Deng *(CEO-Federal Environmental & Energy Pte Ltd)*
Azlan Yusoff *(Legal Counsel)*
Hazel Luang Chew Chia *(Sec)*
Yvonne Choo *(Sec)*
Board of Directors:
Kian Kiong Koh
Lee Seng Heng
Andrew Boo Yeow Khoo
Maggie Koh
Leon Khee Shian Yee

Subsidiaries:

Alton International (S) Pte Ltd **(1)**
No 12 Chin Bee Dr
619868 Singapore, Singapore
Tel.: (65) 68618586
Fax: (65) 68619708
E-Mail: enqury@alton.com.sg
Web Site: www.alton.com.sg
Emp.: 30
Oilfield Equipments & Supplies Distr
S.I.C.: 5046
N.A.I.C.S.: 423440
Doh Beng Guan Koh *(Mng Dir)*

Subsidiary:

Geo Link Nusantara Pte Ltd **(2)**
No 12 Chin Bee Drive
Singapore, Singapore
Tel.: (65) 68618586
Fax: (65) 68619708
Web Site: www.alton.com.sg
Emp.: 40
Oil & Gas Field Engineering Services
S.I.C.: 1389
N.A.I.C.S.: 213112
Peter Wong *(Gen Mgr)*

Eastern Jason Fabrication Services Pte Ltd **(1)**
47/49 Genting Road
Singapore, 349489, Singapore
Tel.: (65) 67478118
Fax: (65) 67430690
E-Mail: admin@fedsin.com.sg
Emp.: 20
Vessel Chartering Services
S.I.C.: 7389
N.A.I.C.S.: 561990
Koh Kian Kiong *(CEO)*

Federal Capital Pte Ltd **(1)**
47/49 Genting Road
Singapore, 349489, Singapore
Tel.: (65) 67478118
Fax: (65) 67430690
E-Mail: admin@fedsin.com.sg
Emp.: 20
Investment Management Services
S.I.C.: 6211
N.A.I.C.S.: 523999
Sandra Lee *(Gen Mgr)*

Federal Energi Pte Ltd **(1)**
47/49 Genting Road
Singapore, 349489, Singapore
Tel.: (65) 67478118
Fax: (65) 67430690
E-Mail: admin@fidsin.com.sg
Emp.: 100
Electric Power Distribution Services
S.I.C.: 4939
N.A.I.C.S.: 221122
Tina Ng *(Mgr-HR)*

Federal Environmental & Energy Pte. Ltd. **(1)**
156 Macpherson Road 07-01 PSL Industrial Building
Singapore, 348528, Singapore
Tel.: (65) 67456566
Fax: (65) 6742 0401
E-Mail: admin@fee.com.sg
Web Site: www.sgfee.com
Environmental & Energy Consulting Services
S.I.C.: 8999
N.A.I.C.S.: 541620
George Deng *(Mng Dir)*

Non-U.S. Subsidiary:

FEE Investment Management & Consultancy (Shanghai) Co., Ltd. **(2)**
Unit I Floor 6 GreenLand S & T Building
201 Ning Xia Road
Shanghai, China
Tel.: (86) 2152358336
Fax: (86) 2152563396
E-Mail: admin@fedsh.com.cn
Web Site: www.federal.com.sg/global_presence.html
Emp.: 20
Investment Management Services
S.I.C.: 6211
N.A.I.C.S.: 523999
Deng George *(COO)*

Federal Fire Engineering Pte Ltd **(1)**
11 Tuas Avenue 1
Singapore, Singapore
Tel.: (65) 68625180
Fax: (65) 68624714
E-Mail: sales@federalfire.com
Web Site: www.federalfire.com
Emp.: 10
Fire Prevention Systems Installation Services
S.I.C.: 9224
N.A.I.C.S.: 922160
Cliff Yew Teck Teo *(Mng Dir)*

Federal Hardware Engineering Co Pte Ltd **(1)**
47/49 Genting Road
Singapore, 349489, Singapore
Tel.: (65) 6747 8118
Web Site: www.federal.com.sg
Industrial Engineering Services
S.I.C.: 8711
N.A.I.C.S.: 541330

Non-U.S. Subsidiaries:

Federal International (Shanghai) Co., Ltd. **(2)**
Unit I Floor 6 GreenLand S & T Building
201 Ning Xia Road
Shanghai, 200063, China
Tel.: (86) 2152358336
Fax: (86) 2152563396
E-Mail: admin@fedsh.com.cn
Web Site: www.federal.com.sg
Emp.: 20
Steel Pipes Distr
S.I.C.: 5051
N.A.I.C.S.: 423510
George Deng *(Gen Mgr)*

PT Fedsin Rekayasa Pratama **(2)**
Ariobimo Sentral Building 11th Floor Jl HR Rasuna Said X2 Kav 5
Jakarta, 12950, Indonesia
Tel.: (62) 21 5296 4767
Fax: (62) 21 5296 4766
E-Mail: admin@federal.com.sg
Hardware Whslr
S.I.C.: 5072
N.A.I.C.S.: 423710
Azmil Rahman *(Mng Dir)*

Federal Offshore Services Pte Ltd **(1)**
47/49 Genting Road
Singapore, 349489, Singapore
Tel.: (65) 67478118
Fax: (65) 67430690
E-Mail: admin@fedsin.com.sg
Web Site: www.federal.com.sg/global_presence.html
Emp.: 70
Vessel Chartering Services
S.I.C.: 4412
N.A.I.C.S.: 483111
Sandra Lee *(Gen Mgr)*

Federal Resources Services Pte Ltd **(1)**
47/49 Genting Road
Singapore, 349489, Singapore
Tel.: (65) 67478118
Fax: (65) 67430690
E-Mail: admin@fedfin.com.sg
Web Site: www.federal.com.sg
Emp.: 50
Industrial Construction & Engineering Services
S.I.C.: 8711
N.A.I.C.S.: 541330

Non-U.S. Subsidiaries:

Federal IESE Environmental Technology (Shanghai) Co., Ltd. **(1)**
Unit I Floor 6 GreenLand S & T Building
201 Ning Xia Road
Shanghai, 200063, China
Tel.: (86) 2152358336
Fax: (86) 2152563396
E-Mail: admin@fedsh.com.cn
Emp.: 20
Waste Water Treatment Services
S.I.C.: 4971
N.A.I.C.S.: 221310
George Deng *(CEO)*

KVC (UK) Ltd **(1)**
6 Beardmore Way Clydebank Industrial Estate Clydebank
Clydebank, Dunbartonshire, G81 4HT, United Kingdom
Tel.: (44) 1414357640
Fax: (44) 1414357647
E-Mail: info@kvc-uk.com
Web Site: www.kvc-uk.com
Emp.: 12
Ball Valves Mfr
S.I.C.: 3491
N.A.I.C.S.: 332911
Richard Docherty *(Mng Dir)*

PT Federal International **(1)**
Ariobimo Sentral Building 11th Floor Jl HR Rasuna Said X2 Kav 5
Jakarta, 12950, Indonesia
Tel.: (62) 21 5296 4767
Fax: (62) 21 5296 4766
E-Mail: admin@ptfrp.com
Emp.: 40
Investment Management Services
S.I.C.: 6211
N.A.I.C.S.: 523999

PT Geo Link Nusantara **(1)**
Menara Global Building 15th Floor Jalan Jendral Gatot Subroto Kav 27
Jakarta Selatan, Jakarta, 12950, Indonesia
Tel.: (62) 21 5279788
Fax: (62) 21 5279789
E-Mail: inquiry@geo-ln.com
Web Site: www.geo-ln.com
Emp.: 150
Oil & Gas Field Engineering Services
S.I.C.: 1311
N.A.I.C.S.: 211111
Imade Dwipayana *(Owner)*
Eka Taufik Syah Putera *(Pres)*

PT. Mega Federal Energy **(1)**
Wisma 46 Kota BNI Lt 29 Jalan Jend Sudirman Kav 1
Central Jakarta, Jakarta, 10220, Indonesia
Tel.: (62) 21 571 9543
Fax: (62) 21 572 7533
Web Site: www.federal.com.sg
Electric Power Distribution Services
S.I.C.: 4911
N.A.I.C.S.: 221122

FEDERAL TRANSFORMER LTD.

5059 Boul St Jean Baptiste
Montreal, QC, H1B 5V3, Canada
Tel.: (514) 640-5059
Fax: (514) 640-4729
E-Mail: info@transfed.ca
Web Site: www.transfed.ca
Year Founded: 1963
Rev.: $12,000,000
Emp.: 25
Business Description:
Lettering & Screen Print Products Distr
S.I.C.: 5065
N.A.I.C.S.: 423690
Personnel:
Pierre Venne *(Mgr-Pur)*

FEDERAL WHITE CEMENT, LTD.

355151 35th Line
PO Box 1609
Woodstock, ON, N4S 0A8, Canada
Tel.: (519) 485-5410
Fax: (519) 485-5892
Toll Free: (800) 265-1806
Web Site: www.federalwhitecement.com
Year Founded: 1979
Rev.: $18,342,178
Emp.: 100
Business Description:
Cement Mfr
S.I.C.: 3241
N.A.I.C.S.: 327310
Personnel:
William R. Stonebraker *(VP-Mktg & Sls)*

FEDERATION INTERNATIONALE DE FOOTBALL ASSOCIATION

(d/b/a FIFA)
FIFA strasse 20
8044 Zurich, Switzerland
Tel.: (41) 432227777
Fax: (41) 432227878
E-Mail: contact@fifa.org
Web Site: www.fifa.com
Year Founded: 1904
Sales Range: $700-749.9 Million
Emp.: 300
Business Description:
Professional Soccer Organization
S.I.C.: 8641
N.A.I.C.S.: 813990
Personnel:
Joseph S. Blatter *(Pres)*
Jerome Valcke *(Gen Sec)*
Julio H. Grondona *(Sr VP)*

Subsidiaries:

Early Warning System GmbH **(1)**
Streulistrasse 19
8032 Zurich, Switzerland
Tel.: (41) 44 388 81 60
Fax: (41) 44 388 81 69
E-Mail: mail@fifa-ews.com
Web Site: www.fifa-ews.com
Sport Betting Monitoring Services
S.I.C.: 7389
N.A.I.C.S.: 561990
Detlev Zenglein *(Gen Mgr)*

FIFA Ticketing AG **(1)**
Aurorastrasse 100
8032 Zurich, Switzerland
Tel.: (41) 43 222 77 77
Sport Event Ticketing Services
S.I.C.: 4729
N.A.I.C.S.: 561599
Falk Eller *(Sr Mgr-Ticketing Sys)*

FIFA Transfer Matching System GmbH **(1)**
Zollikerstrasse 226
8008 Zurich, Switzerland
Tel.: (41) 43 222 5400
Fax: (41) 43 222 5401
E-Mail: helpdesktms@fifatms.com
Soccer Player Transfer Services
S.I.C.: 7941
N.A.I.C.S.: 711211
Mark Goddard *(Gen Mgr)*

FEDERATION LIMITED

Level 28 35 Collins Street
Melbourne, VIC, 3000, Australia
Tel.: (61) 3 8647 2303
Fax: (61) 3 9236 6582
E-Mail: investor@federationcentres.com.au
Web Site:
CER—(ASX)
Rev.: $489,820,462
Assets: $4,714,983,801
Liabilities: $1,698,280,424
Net Worth: $3,016,703,377
Earnings: $190,755,788
Emp.: 550
Fiscal Year-end: 06/30/13

Business Description:
Holding Company; Shopping Centers Real Estate Investment Trusts
S.I.C.: 6719
N.A.I.C.S.: 551112
Personnel:
Steven Sewell *(CEO & Mng Dir)*
Elizabeth Hourigan *(Co-Sec)*
Dimitri Kiriacoulacos *(Co-Sec)*
Board of Directors:
Robert John Edgar
Clive Appleton
Peter Day
Tim Hammon
Charles Macek
Fraser MacKenzie
Steven Sewell
Debra Stirling

Affiliate:

Federation Centres Limited (1)
Level 28 35 Collins Street
Melbourne, VIC, 3000, Australia AU
Tel.: (61) 3 9236 6300
Fax: (61) 3 9236 6582 (IR)
E-Mail: investor@federationcentres.com.au
Web Site: www.federationcentres.com.au
FDC—(ASX OTC)
Shopping Centers Real Estate Investment Trust
S.I.C.: 6726
N.A.I.C.S.: 525990
Steven Sewell *(CEO & Mng Dir)*
Tom Honan *(CFO)*
Mark Wilson *(COO)*
Dimitri Kiriacoulacos *(Gen Counsel, Co-Sec & Exec Gen Mgr-Corp Dev)*
Elizabeth Hourigan *(Co-Sec)*

THE FEDERATION OF MALAYSIAN MANUFACTURERS

Wisma FMM No 3 Persiaran Dagang
Bandar Sri Damansara, 52200 Kuala Lumpur, Malaysia
Tel.: (60) 362761211
Fax: (60) 362741266
E-Mail: webmaster@fmm.org.my
Web Site: www.fmm.org.my
Year Founded: 1968
Emp.: 100
Business Description:
Economic Organization Representing Manufacturing & Industrial Service Companies
S.I.C.: 8611
N.A.I.C.S.: 813910
Personnel:
Mustafa Mansur *(Pres)*

Subsidiary:

FMM Services Sdn Bhd (1)
Wisma FMM No 3 Persiaran Dagang
Bandar Sri Damansara
52200 Kuala Lumpur, Malaysia
Tel.: (60) 3 6286 7200
Fax: (60) 3 6274 5239
Business Management Consulting Services
S.I.C.: 8742
N.A.I.C.S.: 541611

THE FEDERATION OF MIGROS COOPERATIVES

Limmatstrasse 152
CH-8031 Zurich, Switzerland
Tel.: (41) 848 84 0848
Telex: 823300 mbch
Web Site: www.migros.ch
Year Founded: 1925
Sales Range: $15-24.9 Billion
Emp.: 82,712
Business Description:
Textiles, Dairy Products, Groceries, Meat, Poultry, Fish, Hardware, Agricultural Products, Laundry Products, Health/Beauty Aids, Hotel & Leisure Services & Flowers Retailer
S.I.C.: 5149
N.A.I.C.S.: 424490
Personnel:
Herbert Bolliger *(Pres)*
Jorg Zulauf *(VP & CFO)*
Claude Hauser *(Pres-Admin)*

Subsidiaries:

Bischofszell Foods AG (1)
Industrie Strasse 1
CH 9220 Bischofszell, Switzerland (100%)
Tel.: (41) 714249111
Fax: (41) 714249494
E-Mail: bischofszell@bina.ch
Web Site: www.bina.ch
Emp.: 900
Producer of Fruit, Vegetable & Meat Conserves, Fruit Juice & Iced Tea, Deep-Frozen Products, Jam & Marmalade, Tomato & Potato Products
S.I.C.: 2033
N.A.I.C.S.: 311421
Aegler Mark *(Gen Mgr)*

Chocolat Frey AG (1)
Bresteneggstrasse
Buchs, Argovie, 5033, Switzerland (100%)
Tel.: (41) 628362626
Fax: (41) 626392501
E-Mail: marketing@chocolatfrey.ch
Web Site: www.chocolatfrey.ch
Sls.: $263,436,640
Emp.: 750
Producer of Chocolate, Confectionery, Candy, Chewing Gum & Semi-Finished Products
S.I.C.: 2066
N.A.I.C.S.: 311351
Hans Ruedi Christain *(CEO)*

Dietiker AG (1)
Hoswisenstrasse 2
CH 8260 Stein am Rhein, Switzerland (100%)
Tel.: (41) 527422121
Fax: (41) 527422190
E-Mail: mail@dietiker.com
Web Site: www.dietiker.com
Emp.: 100
Production of Chairs & Tables for Conference & Seminar Rooms, Furniture for Public Premises, Restaurants & General Purposes
S.I.C.: 2512
N.A.I.C.S.: 337121
Nathalie Felder *(CEO)*

Estavayer Lait S.A. (1)
Rte de Payerne
CH 1470 Estavayer le Lac, Switzerland
Tel.: (41) 266649111
Fax: (41) 266649121
E-Mail: info@elsa.ch
Web Site: www.elsa.ch
Emp.: 650
Producer of Dairy Products (Fresh Cheese, Desserts, Yogurt, Milk Drinks, Quark, Milk & Unpastuerized Cream), Mayonnaise, Vinegar & Salad Dressings
S.I.C.: 2023
N.A.I.C.S.: 311514
Matthew Robins *(CEO)*

Ex Libris AG (1)
Grunaustrasse 23
8953 Dietikon, Switzerland CH
Tel.: (41) 800002255 (100%)
Web Site: www.exlibris.ch
Sales Range: $125-149.9 Million
Emp.: 355
Books, Audio & Video Media, Software, Electronics & Office Supplies Retailer
S.I.C.: 5999
N.A.I.C.S.: 453998
Peter Bamert *(Gen Mgr)*

Globus-Gruppe (1)
Eich Strasse 23
8045 Zurich, Switzerland (100%)
Tel.: (41) 584552111
Fax: (41) 584552728
E-Mail: info@globus-gruppe.ch
Web Site: www.globus-gruppe.ch
Emp.: 80
S.I.C.: 2299
N.A.I.C.S.: 313310
Ronald Kistler *(Gen Mgr)*

Subsidiaries:

Globus Department Stores (2)
Schweizergasse 11
CH 8001 Zurich, Switzerland
Tel.: (41) 442266060
Fax: (41) 442266088
E-Mail: info@globus.ch
Web Site: www.globus.ch
Emp.: 200
Department Stores
S.I.C.: 5311
N.A.I.C.S.: 452111
Stephan Boeger *(CEO)*

Herren Globus (2)
Kasinostr 30
5000 Aarau, Switzerland (100%)
Tel.: (41) 585763650
Fax: (41) 585763688
S.I.C.: 2299
N.A.I.C.S.: 313310

Office World AG (2)
Altstetterstrasse 149
CH 8048 Zurich, Switzerland (100%)
Tel.: (41) 844822816
Fax: (41) 844822817
E-Mail: info@officeworld.ch
Web Site: www.officeworld.ch
Emp.: 35
Sale of Office Equipment
S.I.C.: 5044
N.A.I.C.S.: 423420
Matths Baumann *(Gen Mgr)*

Hotelplan Suisse, MTCG AG (1)
Saegerei Strasse 20
CH-8152 Glattbrugg, Zurich, Switzerland (100%)
Tel.: (41) 432118111
Fax: (41) 432118181
E-Mail: info@hotelplan.ch
Web Site: www.hotelplan.ch
Emp.: 500
Holiday Tour/Travel Arrangements; Hotel/Holiday Village Operations
S.I.C.: 4724
N.A.I.C.S.: 561510
Christof Zuper *(CEO)*

Jowa AG (1)
Erlenwiesenstrasse 9
8604 Volketswil, Zurich, Switzerland (100%)
Tel.: (41) 449479111
Fax: (41) 449479796
Web Site: www.jowa.ch
Emp.: 800
Producer of Bread, Confectionery, Deep-Frozen Bakeware & Noodles
S.I.C.: 2051
N.A.I.C.S.: 311812
Marcel Buehlmann *(Gen Mgr)*

Limmatdruck AG (1)
Pfadackerstrasse 10
CH 8957 Spreitenbach, Switzerland (100%)
Tel.: (41) 564175111
Fax: (41) 564175384
E-Mail: info@limmatdruck.ch
Web Site: www.limmatdruck.ch
Emp.: 602
Provider of Publishing, Communication, Printing & Packaging
S.I.C.: 2731
N.A.I.C.S.: 511130
Shjean-tierre Pfisger *(CEO)*

Mibelle AG (1)
Bolimattstrasse 1
CH 5033 Buchs, Switzerland CH
Tel.: (41) 628361111 (100%)
Fax: (41) 628361313
E-Mail: contact@mibelle.ch
Web Site: www.mibelle.ch
Emp.: 450
Skin Care, Hair Care & Oral Hygiene, Soaps, Bath Preparations, Deodorants & Toilet Waters Products Mfr
S.I.C.: 2844
N.A.I.C.S.: 325620
Marianne Meyer *(Head-Intl Sls)*

Micarna S.A. (1)
Rte Del Industrie 25
Courtepin, 1784, Switzerland (100%)
Tel.: (41) 266849111
Fax: (41) 266841031
E-Mail: info@micarna.ch
Web Site: www.micarna.ch
Emp.: 1,454
Retailer of Fresh Meat & Other Butchery Products
S.I.C.: 5147
N.A.I.C.S.: 424470

Midor AG (1)
Bruechstrasse 70
Meilen, 8706, Switzerland (100%)
Tel.: (41) 9258111
Fax: (41) 9258484
Web Site: www.midor.com
Emp.: 693
Production of Biscuits, Cocktail Specialties, Ice Cream & Powdered Desserts
S.I.C.: 2024
N.A.I.C.S.: 311520
Buehlmann Marcel *(CEO)*

Mifa AG (1)
Rheinstrasse 99
CH 4402 Frenkendorf, Switzerland CH
Tel.: (41) 619059111 (100%)
Fax: (41) 619059393
E-Mail: info@mifa.ch
Web Site: www.mifa.ch
Sales Range: $125-149.9 Million
Emp.: 270
Detergents & Cleansing Agents, Margarine & Edible Fats Mfr
S.I.C.: 2844
N.A.I.C.S.: 325611
Luigi Pedrocchi *(Mng Dir)*
Nicole Luetzelschwab *(Coord-Mktg)*

Mifroma S.A. (1)
Mifroma 1670
1670 Ursy, Switzerland (100%)
Tel.: (41) 219091111
Fax: (41) 219091100
E-Mail: mifroma@mifroma.ch
Web Site: www.mifroma.ch
Emp.: 234
Cheese Buying, Warehousing, Aging & Packaging
S.I.C.: 4222
N.A.I.C.S.: 493120
Gilles Oberson *(Mng Dir)*

Migrol S.A. (1)
Badenrstrasse 569
CH 8048 Zurich, Switzerland (100%)
Tel.: (41) 444951111
Fax: (41) 444951500
E-Mail: info@migrol.ch
Web Site: www.migrol.ch
Emp.: 320
Provider of Fuel/Heating Oil Trading, Filling Stations, Automobile Service Stations, Tank Overhauls & Installations
S.I.C.: 3534
N.A.I.C.S.: 333921
Daniel Hofar *(Gen Mgr)*

Migros Bank (1)
Seidengasse 12
CH 8001 Zurich, Switzerland (100%)
Tel.: (41) 442298111
Fax: (41) 442298752
E-Mail: medien@migrosbank.ch
Web Site: www.migrosbank.ch/de/default.htm
Emp.: 914
Banking Services
S.I.C.: 6029
N.A.I.C.S.: 522110
Harald Nedwed *(Pres)*

Migros Betriebe Birsfelden AG (1)
Hafenstrasse 120
CH 4127 Birsfelden, Switzerland (100%)
Tel.: (41) 613157788
Fax: (41) 613157240
Web Site: www.mbb.ch
Emp.: 200
Provider of Roasting/Packaging of Coffee; Packaging of Peanuts; Cleaning/Blending/Packaging of Tea, Dried Fruits; Vegetables; Storage; Customs Clearance
S.I.C.: 4225
N.A.I.C.S.: 493110
Thomas Gubler *(Gen Mgr)*

Migros-Verteilbetrieb Neuendorf AG (1)
New St 49
PO Box 18
CH 4623 Neuendorf, Switzerland (100%)
Tel.: (41) 623887111
Fax: (41) 623982274

The Federation of Migros Cooperatives—(Continued)

E-Mail: info@mvn.ch
Web Site: www.mvn.ch
Emp.: 1,050
Provider of Storage/Commissioning of Non-Food & Deep-Frozen Products, Bakeware & Seasonal Chocolate Articles; Logistics
S.I.C.: 4225
N.A.I.C.S.: 493110
Hans Kuhn *(Mng Dir)*

Monte-Generoso-Bahn AG **(1)**
Capalogo
CH 6825 Capolago, Switzerland (100%)
Tel.: (41) 916481105
Fax: (41) 916481107
E-Mail: info@montegeneroso.ch
Web Site: www.montegeneroso.ch
Emp.: 20
S.I.C.: 2269
N.A.I.C.S.: 313310

Optigal S.A. **(1)**
Route d'Oron 2
1010 Lausanne, Switzerland CH
Tel.: (41) 266848911 (100%)
Fax: (41) 236841031
E-Mail: info@micarna.ch
Web Site: www.micarna.ch
Emp.: 450
Poultry Processing & Organic Fertilizers
S.I.C.: 2873
N.A.I.C.S.: 325311
Albert Baumann *(Gen Mgr)*

Riseria Taverne S.A. **(1)**
Via Ponte Vecchio
Taverne, 6807, Switzerland (100%)
Tel.: (41) 919357300
Fax: (41) 919357303
E-Mail: info@riseria.ch
Web Site: www.riseria.ch
Emp.: 27
Provider of Refining of Rice; Storage of Conserve Products
S.I.C.: 4221
N.A.I.C.S.: 493130

Seba Aproz S.A. **(1)**
PO Box 1248
CH 1951 Sion, Switzerland (98%)
Tel.: (41) 273455111
Fax: (41) 273455101
E-Mail: info@aproz.ch
Web Site: www.aproz.ch
Emp.: 120
Producer of Natural Mineral Water, Soft Drinks with Fruit Essence, Fruit Juices & Syrups & Aroma Additives
S.I.C.: 2037
N.A.I.C.S.: 311411

Units:

The Federation of Migros Cooperatives **(1)**
Strada Cantorle
S Antonino, CH 6592 Lugano, Switzerland
Tel.: (41) 918508111
Fax: (41) 918508400
E-Mail: direzeone@migrosticino.ch
Web Site: www.migrosticino.ch
Emp.: 150
S.I.C.: 2299
N.A.I.C.S.: 313310
Emma Lorenso *(Gen Mgr)*

Migro Switzerland **(1)**
Rue Alexandre Gavard 35
CH 1227 Geneva, Switzerland (100%)
Tel.: (41) 223075111
Fax: (41) 223427906
E-Mail: info@migro.ch
Web Site: www.migro.ch
Emp.: 3,600
S.I.C.: 2269
N.A.I.C.S.: 313310
Gui Viourel *(Gen Mgr)*

Migros Cooperative **(1)**
Aeschenvorstadt 24
CH 4051 Basel, Switzerland (100%)
Tel.: (41) 58 575 8750
Fax: (41) 58 575 8751
Web Site: www.migrosbasel.ch
Sales Range: $750-799.9 Million
Emp.: 500
Produce, Toiletries & Cosmetics, Bakery & Fresh Seafood
S.I.C.: 5146
N.A.I.C.S.: 424460
Alain Butticker *(Branch Mgr)*

Migros Raare Cooperative **(1)**
Marktgasse 28
CH 3011 Bern, Switzerland (100%)
Tel.: (41) 585673175
Fax: (41) 585673176
Web Site: www.migros.ch
Emp.: 1,000
Food Cooperative
S.I.C.: 5411
N.A.I.C.S.: 445110

Migros Valais **(1)**
Lue Des Sinettes 45
CH 1920 Martigny, Switzerland (100%)
Tel.: (41) 277204400
Fax: (41) 277204454
Web Site: www.migrosvalais.ch
Emp.: 1,800
S.I.C.: 2269
N.A.I.C.S.: 313310
Alter Max *(Mng Dir)*

Migros Vaud **(1)**
Chemin Du Devent
CH 1024 Ecublens, Switzerland (100%)
Tel.: (41) 216946111
Fax: (41) 216910353
E-Mail: migros.vaud@gmvd.migros.ch
Web Site: www.migro.ch
Emp.: 800
S.I.C.: 2299
N.A.I.C.S.: 313310
Marc Schaefer *(Mng Dir)*

Migros Zurich **(1)**
Pfingstweidstrasse 101
CH 8031 Zurich, Switzerland (100%)
Tel.: (41) 442772111
Fax: (41) 442772525
E-Mail: Claude.Hauser@migros.ch
Web Site: www.migros.ch/DE/Ueber_die_Migros/Medien/Medienkontakt/Seiten/Kontakte.aspx
Emp.: 8,000
S.I.C.: 2269
N.A.I.C.S.: 313310
Claude Hauser *(Pres)*
Herbert Bolliger *(CEO)*

Neuchatel/Fribourg Cooperative **(1)**
Route des Perveuils 2
CH 2074 Marin, Switzerland
Tel.: (41) 585748336
Fax: (41) 585748511
E-Mail: maryvonne.monnier@gmnefr.migros.ch
Web Site: www.migros.ch/FR/Groupe_Migros/Cooperatives/Seiten/Neuchatel_Fribourg.aspx
Emp.: 3,000
Fabrics
S.I.C.: 2269
N.A.I.C.S.: 313310
Maryvonne Monnier *(Mgr-PR)*

Non-U.S. Subsidiaries:

Mifroma France S.A. **(1)**
Route De Pont D Rein
F 01320 Chalamont, France (100%)
Tel.: (33) 474469946
Fax: (33) 474469940
E-Mail: vengentes@mifroma.fr
Web Site: www.mifroma.ch
Emp.: 70
Cheese Packaging
S.I.C.: 2299
N.A.I.C.S.: 313310

FEDERMANN ENTERPRISES, LTD.

99 Hayarkon Street
Tel Aviv, Israel
Tel.: (972) 35202555
Fax: (972) 35248722
E-Mail: federmann@danhotels.com
Web Site: www.federmann-ent.com
Sales Range: $300-349.9 Million
Emp.: 7

Business Description:
Defense Electronics, Microelectronic Materials, Technology Investments, Hospitality Industry, Construction & Real Estate Holdings
S.I.C.: 6719
N.A.I.C.S.: 551112

Personnel:
Michael Federmann *(Chm & CEO)*

Non-U.S. Subsidiary:

Freiberger Compound Materials GmbH **(1)**
Am Junger Loewe Schacht 5
09599 Freiberg, Saxony, Germany (87%)
Tel.: (49) 37312800
Fax: (49) 3731280106
E-Mail: info@fcm-germany.com
Web Site: www.freiberger.com
Emp.: 250
Compound Semiconductor Substrates Mfr
S.I.C.: 3674
N.A.I.C.S.: 334413
Stefan Schneidewind *(CEO)*

U.S. Subsidiary:

Freiberger Compound Materials USA, Inc. **(2)**
7071 Corporate Way Ste 203
Dayton, OH 45459
Tel.: (937) 291-2899
Fax: (937) 291-2898
E-Mail: russ@fcm-us.com
Web Site: www.freiberger.com
Emp.: 2
Semiconductor Mfr
S.I.C.: 3674
N.A.I.C.S.: 334413
Russ Kremer *(CEO)*

Non-U.S. Subsidiaries:

K1 Solution, Inc. **(2)**
Room 904
E&C Venture Dream Tower 3rd, Seoul, Guro-Dong, 152-719, Korea (South)
Tel.: (82) 28382866
Fax: (82) 260082867
Compound Semiconductor Substrates Mfr
S.I.C.: 3674
N.A.I.C.S.: 334413

Lumi Innovation Tech. Corp. **(2)**
11 F-4 No 58 Sec 3
Min chuan E Rd, Taipei, 104, Taiwan
Tel.: (886) 225177313
Fax: (886) 225170790
E-Mail: joanne@litc.com.tw
Web Site: www.litc.com.tw
Emp.: 10
Compound Semiconductor Substrates Mfr
S.I.C.: 3674
N.A.I.C.S.: 334413
Joanne Huang *(Gen Mgr)*

Topco Scientific (Shanghai) Co., Ltd. **(2)**
Rm 606 No 333
Zhao Jia Ban, Shanghai, ROC, 200032, China
Tel.: (86) 2164220458
Fax: (86) 2164225811
Compound Semiconductor Substrates Mfr
S.I.C.: 3674
N.A.I.C.S.: 334413

FEDNAV LIMITED

1000 de la Gauchetiere St W Ste 3500
Montreal, QC, H3B 4W5, Canada
Tel.: (514) 878-6500
Fax: (514) 878-6642
E-Mail: info@fednav.com
Web Site: www.fednav.com
Sales Range: $450-499.9 Million
Emp.: 240

Business Description:
International Shipping Services
S.I.C.: 4412
N.A.I.C.S.: 483111

Personnel:
Laurence G. Pathy *(Pres)*
Paul J. Setlakwe *(CFO & Sr VP)*
Georges H. Robichon *(Gen Counsel, Sec & Sr VP)*
Mark Pathy *(Exec VP)*
Paul Pathy *(Exec VP)*
John J. Peacock *(Exec VP)*
John Weale *(Sr VP)*

Board of Directors:
John J. Peacock

FEEDBACK PLC

(d/b/a Feedback Group)
Maple Barn Beeches Farm Road
Uckfield, East Sussex, TN22 5QD, United Kingdom
Tel.: (44) 8453379155
Telex: 95255 FEEDBK G
Fax: (44) 1892663719
E-Mail: feedback@feedback-group.uk
Web Site: www.fbk.com
Year Founded: 1958
FDBK—(LSE)
Rev.: $2,714,800
Assets: $2,048,339
Liabilities: $846,499
Net Worth: $1,201,840
Earnings: ($549,593)
Emp.: 2
Fiscal Year-end: 05/31/13

Business Description:
Workforce Management Services
S.I.C.: 7372
N.A.I.C.S.: 511210

Personnel:
Nicholas Steven Shepheard *(Chm & CEO)*

Board of Directors:
Nicholas Steven Shepheard
Simon Gregory Barrell
Trevor Brown
Tom Charlton

Legal Counsel:
Bates Wells & Braithwaite London LLP
Scandinavian House 2-6 Cannon Street
London, EC4M 6YH, United Kingdom

FEEDHENRY LTD

Arclabs Research & Innovation Centre
Carriganore, Waterford, Ireland
Tel.: (353) 51 275106
Fax: (353) 51 341144
Web Site: www.feedhenry.com

Business Description:
Software Publisher
S.I.C.: 7372
N.A.I.C.S.: 511210

Personnel:
Ian Duffy *(Chm)*
Cathal McGloin *(CEO)*
Elaine Fennelly *(CFO)*
Micheal O Foghlu *(CTO)*

Board of Directors:
Ian Duffy
Barry Downes
Brian Kinnane
Cathal McGloin
Ciaran McNamara
Niall Olden

U.S. Subsidiary:

FeedHenry LLC **(1)**
15 New England Executive Park
Burlington, MA 01803
Tel.: (781) 472-9120
Fax: (781) 240-0250
Software Publisher
S.I.C.: 7372
N.A.I.C.S.: 511210
Cathal McGloin *(CEO)*

Non-U.S. Subsidiary:

FeedHenry Ltd. **(1)**
Knyvett House Watermans Business Park
The Causeway, Staines-upon-Thames, TW18 3BA, United Kingdom
Tel.: (44) 20 3393 1466
Software Publisher
S.I.C.: 7372
N.A.I.C.S.: 511210

FEELINGK CO., LTD.

FEELingK Tower 1 Youngdeungpo-Dong 3-Ga
Youngdeungpo-Gu, Seoul, 150-033, Korea (South)
Tel.: (82) 2 2102 7300
Web Site: www.feelingk.com
064800—(KRS)
Sales Range: $25-49.9 Million
Business Description:
Mobile Application Development Services
S.I.C.: 7372
N.A.I.C.S.: 511210
Personnel:
In-Jae Shin *(Pres)*
Sang-Yeol Lee *(CEO)*
Sang-Bae Lee *(CFO)*
David Oh *(Chief Operating & Product Officer & Exec VP-Global Bus)*
Jung-Dae Kim *(Chief Strategy & HR Officer)*
TK Ha *(CTO & Head-R&D)*

FEELUX LIGHTING CO., LTD.

624-8 Sukwoo-Ri Kwangjeog-Myun
Kyunggi-Do, Yangju, Korea (South)
Tel.: (82) 70 7780 8200
Fax: (82) 70 7780 8209
E-Mail: info@feelux.com
Web Site: www.feelux.com
Year Founded: 1975
033180—(KRS)
Business Description:
Electronic Component Mfr
S.I.C.: 3612
N.A.I.C.S.: 335311
Personnel:
Si-Chung Noh *(Pres & CEO)*

U.S. Subsidiary:

FEELUX Lighting, Inc. (1)
2875 N Berkeley Lake Rd NW Ste 17
Duluth, GA 30096 GA
Tel.: (678) 668-7005
Fax: (678) 668-7006
Web Site: www.feeluxlighting.com
Lighting Products Distr
S.I.C.: 5063
N.A.I.C.S.: 423610
Peter Christopher Augusta *(Dir-Ops-North America)*

FEERUM S.A.

Okrzei 6 Str
59-225 Chojnow, Poland
Tel.: (48) 76 81 96 738
E-Mail: sekretariat@feerum.pl
Web Site: www.feerum.pl
Year Founded: 2002
FEEA—(WAR)
Sales Range: $10-24.9 Million
Emp.: 160
Business Description:
Grain Elevators & Other Agricultural Equipment Mfr
S.I.C.: 3523
N.A.I.C.S.: 333111
Personnel:
Magdalena Labudzka-Janusz *(Chm-Supervisory Bd)*
Daniel Janusz *(Chm-Mgmt Bd)*
Mieczyslaw Mietelski *(Member-Mgmt Bd)*
Piotr Wielesik *(Member-Mgmt Bd)*
Supervisory Board of Directors:
Magdalena Labudzka-Janusz
Henryk Chojnacki
Maciej Janusz
Maciej Kowalski
Jakub Marcinowski

FEHA LASERTEC HALLE GMBH

Brachwitzer Str 16
06118 Halle, Germany
Tel.: (49) 34552570
Fax: (49) 3455257124
E-Mail: info@feha-laser.de
Web Site: www.feha-laser.de
Rev.: $12,414,600
Emp.: 42
Business Description:
Laser Equipment Mfr
S.I.C.: 3589
N.A.I.C.S.: 333318
Personnel:
Ekkehard-Torsten Henze *(Gen Mgr)*

FEIHE INTERNATIONAL, INC.

Star City International Building 10
Jiuxianqiao Road C-16th Floor
Chaoyang District, Beijing, China 100016
Tel.: (86) 10 6431 9357
Fax: (86) 10 6431 1050
E-Mail: ir@americandairyinc.com
Web Site: ady.feihe.com
Sls.: $267,850,899
Assets: $476,255,884
Liabilities: $274,498,256
Net Worth: $201,757,628
Earnings: $21,186,510
Emp.: 1,932
Fiscal Year-end: 12/31/12
Business Description:
Dairy Product Mfr
S.I.C.: 2023
N.A.I.C.S.: 311514
Personnel:
You-Bin Leng *(Chm, Pres, CEO & Gen Mgr)*
Roger Hua Liu *(Vice Chm, CFO, Treas & Sec)*
Board of Directors:
You-Bin Leng
Weiqiu Dong
Kirk Gordon Downing
Roger Hua Liu
Jingjun Mu
Xiaofei Ren
Liu Sheng-Hui

Subsidiary:

Heilongjiang Feihe Dairy Co., Limited (1)
Star City Intl Bldg 10 Jiuxianqiao Rd C-16th Fl
Chaoyang, Beijing, 100016, China
Tel.: (86) 1084574688
Fax: (86) 1064311050
Emp.: 1,000
Dairy Product Mfr
S.I.C.: 5143
N.A.I.C.S.: 424430
Leng You-Bin *(Chm & Gen Mgr)*

FEINKOST DITTMANN REICHOLD FEINKOST GMBH

August Horch Strasse 4-8
D-65582 Diez, Germany
Tel.: (49) 64329550
Fax: (49) 6432955111
E-Mail: info@feinkost-dittmann.de
Web Site: www.feinkost-dittmann.de
Year Founded: 1901
Rev.: $137,655,515
Emp.: 282
Business Description:
Gourmet Products Mfr
S.I.C.: 2099
N.A.I.C.S.: 311999
Personnel:
Thorsten Reichold *(Co-Mng Dir)*
Timm J. Reichold *(Co-Mng Dir)*

FEINMECHANIK MICHAEL DECKEL GMBH & CO. KG.

Am Oferl 17 19
D-82362 Weilheim, Germany
Tel.: (49) 8816880
Fax: (49) 88168859
E-Mail: info@michael-deckel.de
Web Site: www.michael-deckel.de
Year Founded: 1950
Rev.: $12,000,000
Emp.: 100
Business Description:
Tool Grinding Machines Design & Mfr
S.I.C.: 3541
N.A.I.C.S.: 333517
Personnel:
Wilhelm Schroder *(Mng Dir)*

FEINTOOL INTERNATIONAL HOLDING AG

Industriering 8
CH-3250 Lyss, Switzerland
Tel.: (41) 323875111
Telex: 934301
Fax: (41) 323875781
E-Mail: urs.feitknecht@feintool.com
Web Site: www.feintool.com
Year Founded: 1959
FTON—(SWX)
Rev.: $38,956,583
Assets: $217,187,253
Liabilities: $29,939,241
Net Worth: $187,248,013
Earnings: $12,424,594
Emp.: 2,015
Fiscal Year-end: 12/31/13
Business Description:
Holding Company for the Manufacture of Fineblanking Tools & Parts
Import Export
S.I.C.: 3542
N.A.I.C.S.: 333517
Personnel:
Alexander von Witzleben *(Chm)*
Michael Soormann *(Deputy Chm)*
Heinz Loosli *(CEO & Head-Sys Parts Segment)*
Thomas F. Boegli *(CFO)*
Board of Directors:
Alexander von Witzleben
Thomas A. Erb
Wolfgang Feil
Steffen Schroth
Michael Soormann
Kurt E. Stirnemann

Subsidiaries:

Feintool France S.a.r.l. (1)
Industriering 3
CH 3250 Lyss, Switzerland (100%)
Tel.: (41) 323875111
Fax: (41) 323875778
E-Mail: feintool@feintool.com
Web Site: www.feintool.com
Emp.: 360
S.I.C.: 3542
N.A.I.C.S.: 333517
Alexander Witzleben *(Chm)*

Feintool International Management Ltd. (1)
Industriering 8
Lyss, Terne, 3250, Switzerland (100%)
Tel.: (41) 323875111
Fax: (41) 323875778
E-Mail: feintool-fim@feintool.com
Web Site: www.feintool.com
Emp.: 200
S.I.C.: 3542
N.A.I.C.S.: 333517
Stefan Etzold *(Mgr-Sls)*

Feintool Parts & Components Ltd. Lyss (1)
Industriering 8
Lyss, Terne, 3250, Switzerland (100%)
Tel.: (41) 323875111
Fax: (41) 323875779
E-Mail: feintool@feintool.com
Web Site: www.feintool.com
Emp.: 350
S.I.C.: 3541
N.A.I.C.S.: 333517
Daniel Fluri *(Mgr-Sls)*

Feintool Research & Development AG (1)
Industriering 8
Lyss, Terne, 3250, Switzerland (100%)
Tel.: (41) 323875111
Fax: (41) 323875760
E-Mail: feintool@feintool.ch
Web Site: www.feintool.com
Emp.: 10
S.I.C.: 3541
N.A.I.C.S.: 333517

Feintool System Parts AG (1)
Industriering 8
3250 Lyss, Switzerland CH
Tel.: (41) 323875111 (100%)
Fax: (41) 323875782
E-Mail: feintool-sst@feintool.com
Web Site: www.feintool.com
Emp.: 350
Mfr. of Machine Tools
S.I.C.: 3541
N.A.I.C.S.: 333517
Heinz Loosli *(CEO)*

Feintool Technology AG Lyss (1)
Industriering 8
Lyss, Terne, 3250, Switzerland (100%)
Tel.: (41) 323875111
Fax: (41) 323875781
E-Mail: feintool@feintool.com
Web Site: www.feintool.com
Emp.: 300
Fineblanking Technology of Automotive Gearboxes
S.I.C.: 3566
N.A.I.C.S.: 333612
Alfeh Bazzale *(Mng Dir)*

Feintool Teile & Komponenten AG Lyss (1)
Industriering 8
Lyss, Terne, 3250, Switzerland (100%)
Tel.: (41) 323875111
Fax: (41) 323875778
E-Mail: feintool-tkl@feintool.com
Web Site: www.feintool.com
Emp.: 300
Mfr. of Machine Tools
S.I.C.: 3542
N.A.I.C.S.: 333517
Daniel Fluri *(Mgr-Sls)*

Heinrich Schmid Maschinen-und Werkzeugbau AG (1)
Grunfeldstrasse 25
CH 8645 Jona, Switzerland (100%)
Tel.: (41) 552252111
Fax: (41) 552252404
E-Mail: management@schmidpress.ch
Web Site: www.schmidpress.com
Emp.: 64
S.I.C.: 3541
N.A.I.C.S.: 333517
Eddy Schmidit *(Gen Mgr)*

U.S. Subsidiary:

Feintool Equipment Corp. (1)
6833 Creek Rd
Cincinnati, OH 45242 NY
Tel.: (513) 791-0066 (100%)
Fax: (513) 791-1589
E-Mail: fec@feintool-usa.com
Web Site: www.feintool-usa.com
Emp.: 11
Sales & Consulting Services for Peripheral Systems & Presses
Import Export
S.I.C.: 8711
N.A.I.C.S.: 541330
Peter Grosse *(Head-Automation Segment)*

Subsidiaries:

Feintool Cincinnati, Inc. (2)
11280 Cornell Park Dr
Cincinnati, OH 45242-1812 (100%)
Tel.: (513) 247-0110
Telex: 810 461 2048
Fax: (513) 247-0060
E-Mail: feintool@one.net
Web Site: www.feintool-usa.com
Sls.: $50,000,000
Emp.: 270
Mfr. of Fineblanking Presses, Fineblanking Tools, & Fineblanking Parts
S.I.C.: 3544

Feintool International Holding AG—(Continued)

N.A.I.C.S.: 333514
Christoph Trachsler *(CEO)*

Feintool New York, Inc. **(2)**
11280 Cornell Park Dr
Blue Ash, OH 45242-1812 (100%)
Tel.: (914) 761-2500
Telex: 710 568 1382
Fax: (914) 948-2359
E-Mail: ftequip@aol.com
Web Site: www.feintool-usa.com
Emp.: 30
Mfr. of Fineblanking Parts
S.I.C.: 3466
N.A.I.C.S.: 332119
Heinz Loosli *(CEO)*

Feintool Tennessee, Inc. **(2)**
2930 Old Franklin Rd
Antioch, TN 37013-3114 (100%)
Tel.: (615) 641-7770
Fax: (615) 641-7995
E-Mail: sales@feintool-usa.com
Web Site: www.feintool-usa.com
Emp.: 11
Mfr. of Automotive Parts
S.I.C.: 3479
N.A.I.C.S.: 332812
Christoph Trachsler *(Mng Dir)*

Non-U.S. Subsidiaries:

Feintool Beijing Swisstec **(1)**
Hua Qiao Gong Yu 2-43 Hiadian District
Chegongzhuang W Rd
Beijing, 100044, China (100%)
Tel.: (86) 1068418447
Fax: (86) 1068412869
E-Mail: swisstec@public.bta.net.cn
Web Site: www.feintool.com
Emp.: 6
S.I.C.: 3541
N.A.I.C.S.: 333517

Feintool Italia S.r.L. **(1)**
Corso Galileo Ferraris no 26
IT-10121 Turin, Italy (100%)
Tel.: (39) 011 539 809
Fax: (39) 011 539 675
E-Mail: feintool@tin.it
Web Site: www.feintool.com
Seller of Fineblanking & Automation Systems
S.I.C.: 3541
N.A.I.C.S.: 333517

Feintool Japan Co., Ltd. **(1)**
260 53 Aza Yanagi Machi Hase
Atsugi, 243-0036, Japan JP
Tel.: (81) 462477451 (100%)
Telex: 3872-121
Fax: (81) 462472008
E-Mail: feintool@feintool.co.jp
Web Site: www.feintool.ch
Emp.: 48
Mfr. of Fineblanking Presses, Fineblanking Tools & Fineblanking Parts
S.I.C.: 3541
N.A.I.C.S.: 333517

Feintool Japan Co., Ltd. **(1)**
260-53 Aza Yanagi-Machi Hase
Atsugi, Kanagawa, Japan JP
Tel.: (81) 462477451 (100%)
Telex: 3872-121
Fax: (81) 462472008
E-Mail: feintool@feintool.co.jp
Web Site: www.feintool.com
Emp.: 100
Fineblanking Tools & Parts Mfr, Sales & Services
S.I.C.: 3542
N.A.I.C.S.: 333517
Mori Yugi *(Pres)*

IMA Automation Amberg GmbH **(1)**
Wernher Von Braun Strasse 5
92224 Amberg, Germany (100%)
Tel.: (49) 96216080
Fax: (49) 9621608290
E-Mail: sales-amberg@ima-automation.de
Web Site: www.ima-automation.de
Machining & Assembly Systems & Equipment Mfr
S.I.C.: 3559
N.A.I.C.S.: 333249
Peter Grosse *(Mng Dir)*

Promera Ettingen Feinschneidtechnik GmbH **(1)**
Englerstrasse 18
D 76275 Ettlingen, Germany (100%)
Tel.: (49) 724332020
Fax: (49) 7243320240
E-Mail: info@promera.de
Web Site: www.feintool.de
Emp.: 80
S.I.C.: 3541
N.A.I.C.S.: 333517

Promera Jena Feinschneid- und Umformtechnik GmbH **(1)**
Lobstetter Strasse 85
07749 Jena, Germany (100%)
Tel.: (49) 3641506100
Fax: (49) 3641506300
E-Mail: info@promera-jena.de
Web Site: www.feintool.com
Emp.: 160
S.I.C.: 3541
N.A.I.C.S.: 333517
Utta Schlotzar *(Mgr-Fin)*

FEISHANG ANTHRACITE RESOURCES LIMITED

Room 2205 22/F Shun Tak Centre
West Tower
200 Connaught Road, Central, China (Hong Kong)
Tel.: (852) 2858 9860
Fax: (852) 2810 6963
Web Site: www.fsanthracite.com
1738—(HKG)
Emp.: 360
Business Description:
Anthracite Coal Mining & Production
S.I.C.: 1231
N.A.I.C.S.: 212113
Personnel:
Feilie Li *(Chm & CEO)*
Board of Directors:
Feilie Li
Jianshe Gu
Weibing Han
Zuye Huang
Kin Cheung Lo
Cheuk Ho Tam
Huojin Wan
Edward Wah On Wong

FELDA GLOBAL VENTURES HOLDINGS BERHAD

10th Floor Balai Felda
Jalan Gurney Satu, Kuala Lumpur, 54000, Malaysia
Tel.: (60) 3 2694 7189
Fax: (60) 3 2698 5326
E-Mail: fgv.enquiries@feldaglobal.com
Web Site: www.feldaglobal.com
FGV—(KLS)
Sales Range: $1-4.9 Billion
Business Description:
Investment Holding Company
S.I.C.: 6719
N.A.I.C.S.: 551112
Personnel:
Mohd Isa Abdul Samad *(Chm)*
Sabri Ahmad *(Pres & CEO)*
Tifli Mohd Talha *(CFO)*
Suzana Idayu Wati Osman *(Chief Strategy Officer)*
Norzaimah Maarof *(Chief Counsel)*
Board of Directors:
Mohd Isa Abdul Samad
Mohd Emir Mavani Abdullah
Sabri Ahmad
Abdul Rahman Bin Ahmad
Yahaya Abd Jabar
Shahril Ridza Ridzuan
Omar Salim

Affiliate:

Felda Holdings Bhd. **(1)**
9th Floor Balai Felda Jalan Gurney Satu
Kuala Lumpur, 54000, Malaysia MY
Tel.: (60) 326934241 (49%)
Fax: (60) 326982677
E-Mail: corporatecom.fhb@feldaglobal.com
Web Site: www.feldaholdings.com
Sales Range: $5-14.9 Billion
Emp.: 19,000
Holding Company; Palm Oil Farming, Processing & Distr
S.I.C.: 6719
N.A.I.C.S.: 551112
Mohd Isa Abdul Samad *(Chm)*
Sabri Ahmad *(Mng Dir)*

Subsidiary:

MSM Malaysia Holdings Bhd **(2)**
Level 42 Menara Felda Platinum Park No 11 Persiaran KLCC
50088 Kuala Lumpur, Malaysia
Tel.: (60) 3 2859 0000
Fax: (60) 3 2859 0016
E-Mail: info@msmholdings.com.my
Web Site: www.msmholdings.com
MSM—(KLS)
Rev.: $754,648,526
Assets: $768,313,609
Liabilities: $194,733,652
Net Worth: $573,579,956
Earnings: $66,249,022
Emp.: 1,022
Fiscal Year-end: 12/31/12
Sugar Producer
S.I.C.: 2061
N.A.I.C.S.: 311314
Chua Say Sin *(Pres)*
Abod Awab *(CEO)*
Mohamad Amri Sahari *(Deputy CEO)*
Faridah Ahmad *(CFO)*
Ida Suryati Abdul Rahim *(Co-Sec)*
Shuang Yen Koo *(Co-Sec)*

FELDA HOLDINGS BHD

(See Under Felda Global Ventures Holdings Berhad)

FELDER GMBH

Im Lipperfeld 11
46047 Oberhausen, Germany
Tel.: (49) 208850350
Fax: (49) 20826080
E-Mail: info@felder.de
Web Site: www.felder.de
Year Founded: 1979
Rev.: $19,311,600
Emp.: 96
Business Description:
Soldering Flux Mfr
S.I.C.: 2899
N.A.I.C.S.: 325998
Personnel:
Wilhelm Priester *(Co-Founder & Mng Dir)*
Uwe Felder *(Co-Founder)*
Gerd Priester *(Mng Dir)*
Frank Schroer *(Mng Dir)*

FELIX HUARD INC.

121 Saint-Alphonse
Saint-Luc, QC, G0K 1P0, Canada
Tel.: (418) 739-4894
Fax: (418) 739-3457
Toll Free: (800) 463-0909
E-Mail: fhuard@globetrotter.net
Web Site: www.fhuard.com
Year Founded: 1961
Rev.: $17,002,568
Emp.: 150
Business Description:
Hardwood Products Mfr
S.I.C.: 2435
N.A.I.C.S.: 321211
Personnel:
Michel Huard *(Pres, CEO & Gen Mgr)*

FELIX KOCH OFFENBACH COULEUR UND KARAMEL GMBH

Lindenstr 70
63701 Offenbach, Germany
Tel.: (49) 699854200
Fax: (49) 6998542088
E-Mail: office@koch-felix.de
Web Site: www.koch-felix.de
Year Founded: 1904
Rev.: $25,474,319
Emp.: 20
Business Description:
Sugar Products Mfr
S.I.C.: 2063
N.A.I.C.S.: 311313
Personnel:
Felix Koch *(Mng Dir)*

FELIX SCHOELLER HOLDING GMBH & CO. KG

Postfach 36 67
D 49026 Osnabruck, Germany
Tel.: (49) 54138000
Fax: (49) 5413800425
E-Mail: info@felix-schoeller.com
Web Site: www.felix-schoeller.com
Year Founded: 1895
Emp.: 1,000
Business Description:
Holding Company
S.I.C.: 6719
N.A.I.C.S.: 551112
Personnel:
Bernhard Klofar *(Mng Dir)*

Subsidiaries:

Felix Schoeller Supply Chain Technologies GmbH & Co. KG **(1)**
Burg Gretesch
49086 Osnabruck, Germany
Mailing Address:
PO Box 3667
49026 Osnabruck, Germany
Tel.: (49) 541 3800 0
Fax: (49) 541 3800 425
E-Mail: info@felix-scholler.com
Web Site: www.felix-schoeller-sct.com
Paper Mfr & Distr
S.I.C.: 2621
N.A.I.C.S.: 322121

Schoeller Technocell GmbH & Co. KG **(1)**
Katja Opitz
PO Box 3667
49026 Osnabruck, Germany
Tel.: (49) 541 3800 0
Fax: (49) 541 3800 126
Paper Mfr & Distr
S.I.C.: 2621
N.A.I.C.S.: 322121
Michael Avermann *(Product Mgr-Digital Media)*

U.S. Subsidiaries:

Felix Schoeller North America **(1)**
179 County Rte 2A
New York, NY 13142
Tel.: (315) 298-5133
Fax: (315) 298-4337
E-Mail: Imaging_USA@Felix-Schoeller.com
Paper Mfr & Distr
S.I.C.: 2621
N.A.I.C.S.: 322121

Technocell Dekor USA **(1)**
179 County Rte 2A
New York, NY 13142
Tel.: (315) 298-8300
Fax: (315) 298-6268
Paper Mfr & Distr
S.I.C.: 2621
N.A.I.C.S.: 322121

Non-U.S. Subsidiaries:

Felix Schoeller jr Shanghai **(1)**
Room 1111-1112 11F Pos Plaza No 1600
Century Avenue Pu Dong New Area
Shanghai, 200122, China
Tel.: (86) 21 5820 5877
Fax: (86) 21 5820 0626
E-Mail: Imaging_AP@Felix-Schoeller.com
Paper Mfr & Distr
S.I.C.: 2621
N.A.I.C.S.: 322121

Technocell Dekor Shanghai (1)
11F POS Plaza Room 1111-1112 1600
Century Avenue Pudong New Area
Shanghai, China 200122
Tel.: (86) 21 5820 5877
Fax: (86) 21 5820 0626
E-Mail: Technocell_AP@Felix-Schoeller.com
Paper Mfr & Distr
S.I.C.: 2621
N.A.I.C.S.: 322121

Technocell Inc. (1)
3075 rue Bernier
Drummondville, QC, J2C 6Y4, Canada
Tel.: (819) 475-0066
Fax: (819) 475-0055
E-Mail: Technocell_USA@Felix-Schoeller.com
Paper Mfr
S.I.C.: 2621
N.A.I.C.S.: 322121

FELLFAB LIMITED

2343 Barton Street East
Hamilton, ON, L8E 5V8, Canada
Tel.: (905) 560-9230
Fax: (905) 560-9846
Web Site: www.fellfab.com
Year Founded: 1952
Rev.: $11,317,935
Emp.: 130
Business Description:
Engineering, Manufacturing & Textile Products Supplier
S.I.C.: 8711
N.A.I.C.S.: 541330
Personnel:
Glen Fell *(Pres & CEO)*

FEMPRO INC.

1330 Rue Michaud
Drummondville, QC, J2C 2Z5, Canada
Tel.: (819) 475-8900
Fax: (819) 475-1217
Toll Free: (800) 303-6635
E-Mail: fempro@fempro.com
Web Site: www.fempro.com
Year Founded: 1984
Emp.: 150
Business Description:
Feminine Hygiene Products Mfr
S.I.C.: 2676
N.A.I.C.S.: 322291
Personnel:
Jean Fleury *(CEO)*

FENG TAY ENTERPRISES CO., LTD.

52 Kegung 8th Road
Douliou, Yunlin, 640, Taiwan
Tel.: (886) 5 5379100
Fax: (886) 5 5379105
E-Mail: amy.chen@fengtay.com
Web Site: www.fengtay.com
9910—(TAI)
Sales Range: $1-4.9 Billion
Emp.: 68,000
Business Description:
Athletic Shoes Mfr
S.I.C.: 2389
N.A.I.C.S.: 316210
Personnel:
Chou-Hsiong Wang *(Chm)*
Board of Directors:
Chou-Hsiong Wang
Chung-yi Lin
Yu-Sheng Lu
Peter Dale Nickerson
Justin S.J. Tsai
Non-U.S. Subsidiaries:

Growth Link Overseas Co., Ltd. (1)
21 Floor Room 06209 Two Chinachem
Exchange Square 338 Kings Road
North Point, China (Hong Kong)
Tel.: (852) 2838 3382
Fax: (852) 2838 9889
Web Site: www.fengtay.com
Emp.: 24
Investment Management Services
S.I.C.: 8741
N.A.I.C.S.: 551114
Carol Mui *(Mgr)*

P.T. Feng Tay Indonesia Enterprises (1)
Jl Raya Banjaran Km 14 6
Bandung, West Java, 40377, Indonesia
Tel.: (62) 225940688
Fax: (62) 22 5940779
Sports Shoes Mfr
S.I.C.: 2389
N.A.I.C.S.: 316210

FENGATE CAPITAL MANAGEMENT LTD.

499 King Street East
Hamilton, ON, L8N 1E1, Canada
Tel.: (905) 524-2985
Fax: (905) 524-0046
Web Site: www.fengatecapital.com
Year Founded: 1974
Rev.: $10,781,174
Emp.: 100
Business Description:
Property Management Services
S.I.C.: 6531
N.A.I.C.S.: 531311
Personnel:
Louis Serafini, Sr. *(Founder & Dir-Comml)*
Lou Serafini, Jr. *(Pres)*
Marco Di Carlantonio *(Sr VP-Comml)*
George Theodoropoulos *(Sr VP)*

FENGRAIN LTD.

Hook Lane
Wimblington, Cambs, PE15 OQN, United Kingdom
Tel.: (44) 1354740691
Fax: (44) 1354740065
E-Mail: enquiry@fengrain.co.uk
Web Site: www.fengrain.co.uk
Rev.: $127,045,826
Emp.: 30
Business Description:
Crop Testing Services
S.I.C.: 8734
N.A.I.C.S.: 541380
Personnel:
Paul Wilkinson *(Chm)*
Anthony Boardman *(Vice Chm)*
Rob Munro *(Mng Dir)*
Board of Directors:
Paul Wilkinson
Anthony Boardman
Kevin Cooper
Donald McGowan
Michael Mottram
Rob Munro
Nigel Russell
Michael Sly
John Wall

FENNER PLC

Hesslewood Country Office Park
Ferriby Road, Hessle, E Yorkshire, HU13 0PW, United Kingdom
Tel.: (44) 1482626500
Fax: (44) 1482626502
E-Mail: info@fenner.com
Web Site: www.fenner.com
FENR—(LSE)
Rev.: $1,295,965,374
Assets: $1,311,442,416
Liabilities: $739,897,365
Net Worth: $571,545,051
Earnings: $77,701,068
Emp.: 5,272
Fiscal Year-end: 08/31/13
Business Description:
Thermoplastic Belts, Precision Timing Belts, Thermoplastic Ducting, High-Temperature Hoses, Composite Pulleys, Bearing Housings, Conveyor Guide Systems, Keyless Bushings & Belt Tensioners
S.I.C.: 3052
N.A.I.C.S.: 326220
Personnel:
Nicholas M. Hobson *(CEO)*
Debra Bradbury *(Sec)*
Board of Directors:
Mark S. Abrahams
Nicholas M. Hobson
Vanda Murray
Richard J. Perry
John N. Sheldrick
Alan John Wood
Legal Counsel:
Shumaker, Loop & Kendrick, LLP
1000 Jackson St
Toledo, OH 43604-5573
Tel.: (419) 241-9000
Fax: (419) 241-6894

Rollits
Hull, United Kingdom

Hunt & Hunt
Victoria, Australia

DLA Piper
Sheffield, United Kingdom

Ashurst
London, United Kingdom

Addleshaw Goddard
Leeds, United Kingdom

Subsidiaries:

Fenner Advanced Sealing Technologies Limited (1)
130 Oldfield Road
Hampton, Mddx, TW12 2HT, United Kingdom UK
Tel.: (44) 2089413774
Fax: (44) 2089410417
E-Mail:
Holding Company; Sealing Technologies Mfr & Distr
S.I.C.: 6719
N.A.I.C.S.: 551112
David Jones *(Mng Dir)*

Subsidiary:

Hallite Seals International Ltd (2)
130 Oldfield Road
Hampton, Middlesex, TW12 2HT, United Kingdom
Tel.: (44) 2089412244
Fax: (44) 2087831669
E-Mail: sales@hallite.com
Web Site: www.hallite.com
Emp.: 258
Hydraulic & Pneumatic Seal Mfr
S.I.C.: 3053
N.A.I.C.S.: 339991
Simon Davis *(Gen Mgr)*

Non-U.S. Subsidiaries:

Dichtelemente Hallite GmbH (3)
Billwerder Ring 17
21035 Hamburg, Germany
Tel.: (49) 40 73 47 480
Fax: (49) 40 73 47 48 49
E-Mail: seals@hallite.de
Web Site: www.hallite.de
Emp.: 5
Hydraulic & Pneumatic Seal Mfr
S.I.C.: 3492
N.A.I.C.S.: 332912
Gessel Uwe *(Gen Mgr)*

Hallite (France) Limited (3)
Z A Les Petits Carreaux 1 Av Des Lys
94385 Bonneuil-sur-Marne, France
Tel.: (33) 1 43 77 85 50
Fax: (33) 1 43 77 93 93
E-Mail: seals@hallite.fr
Web Site: www.hallite.fr
Hydraulic & Pneumatic Seal Mfr
S.I.C.: 3053
N.A.I.C.S.: 339991
Christophe Guedamour *(Mgr-Comml)*

Hallite Italia Srl (3)
Via Francia 21
Colle Salvetti, Livorno, Italy
Tel.: (39) 0 58 642 8287
Fax: (39) 0 58 642 9845
E-Mail: seals@hallite.it
Web Site: www.hallite.com
Hydraulic Seal Mfr
S.I.C.: 3053
N.A.I.C.S.: 339991

Hallite Seals (Canada) Limited (3)
89 Galaxy Blvd
Toronto, ON, M9W 6A4, Canada
Tel.: (416) 675-2505
Fax: (416) 675-4341
Toll Free: (800) 668-7970
E-Mail: seals@hallite.ca
Web Site: www.hallite.ca
Hydraulic Seals Mfr
S.I.C.: 3053
N.A.I.C.S.: 339991

U.S. Subsidiary:

FAST Group Houston, Inc. (2)
8103 Rankin Rd
Humble, TX 77396 DE
Tel.: (281) 446-6662 (100%)
Fax: (281) 446-7458
Web Site: www.fast-houston.com
Emp.: 400
Plastic Sealing Product Mfr
S.I.C.: 3053
N.A.I.C.S.: 339991
Leonard Casey *(Pres)*

Divisions:

CDI Energy Products (3)
8103 Rankin Rd
Humble, TX 77396
Tel.: (281) 446-6662
Fax: (201) 446-7458
E-Mail: cdi-us.sales@cdiproducts.com
Web Site: www.cdiproducts.com
Plastic Sealing Product Mfr
S.I.C.: 3053
N.A.I.C.S.: 339991
James Barnett *(Dir-Health, Safety & Environmental)*

EGC Critical Components (3)
8103 Rankin Rd
Humble, TX 77396
Tel.: (281) 446-6662
Fax: (281) 446-7034
E-Mail: egc.sales@egccomponents.com
Web Site: www.egccomponents.com
Emp.: 400
Plastic Sealing Product Mfr
S.I.C.: 3053
N.A.I.C.S.: 339991
Leonard Casey *(Pres)*

Non-U.S. Subsidiary:

Fenner Sealing Technologies (Shanghai) Co. Limited (2)
785 Xing Rong Road Jiading Industrial Park
Jiading District, Shanghai, 201807, China
Tel.: (86) 21 3351 7272
Fax: (86) 21 3351 7085
E-Mail: fast.shanghai@fenner.com
Web Site: www.hallite.com
Hydraulic & Pneumatic Seal Mfr
S.I.C.: 3053
N.A.I.C.S.: 339991

Fenner Dunlop Limited (1)
Hesslewood Country Office Park
Ferriby Road, Hessle, E Yorkshire, HU13 0PW, United Kingdom UK
Tel.: (44) 1482 626 531
Fax: (44) 1482 626 532
Web Site: www.fennerdunlop.com
Conveyor Belting System Mfr & Distr
S.I.C.: 3535
N.A.I.C.S.: 333922
John Pratt *(Exec Dir-Europe, China, India & South Africa)*

U.S. Subsidiary:

Fenner Dunlop Americas, Inc. (2)
Omega Corporate Ctr 1000 Omega Dr Ste 1400
Pittsburgh, PA 15205 DE
Tel.: (412) 249-0700
Fax: (412) 249-0701
Web Site: www.fennerdunlopamericas.com
Holding Company; Conveyor Belting & Systems Mfr, Distr & Support Services

Fenner PLC—(Continued)

S.I.C.: 6719
N.A.I.C.S.: 551112
Cassandra Pan *(Pres)*
David Landgren *(CEO)*
Bill Mooney *(CFO & Chief Comml Officer)*
Mark Hardwick *(COO)*

Subsidiary:

Fenner Dunlop Conveyor Systems & Services, Inc. **(3)**
Omega Corp Ctr 1000 Omega Dr Ste 1400
Pittsburgh, PA 15205 DE
Tel.: (412) 249-0700
Fax: (412) 249-0701
Web Site: www.fennerdunlopamericas.com
Conveyor Belting & Systems Mfr & Distr
S.I.C.: 3535
N.A.I.C.S.: 333922
Cassandra Pan *(Pres)*
Bill Mooney *(CFO & Chief Comml Officer)*
Mark Hardwick *(COO)*
Chuck Prezioso *(Exec VP-Ops)*
Al Bonneau *(Sr VP-Distr Channel)*
Greg Girardey *(Sr VP-Bus Dev)*

Subsidiaries:

Fenner Dunlop (Atlanta), Inc. **(4)**
325 Gateway Dr
Lavonia, GA 30553 DE
Tel.: (706) 356-7607
Fax: (706) 356-7651
Web Site: www.fennerdunlopamericas.com
Conveyor Belting System Mfr & Distr
S.I.C.: 3535
N.A.I.C.S.: 333922

Fenner Dunlop Conveyor Services, LLC **(4)**
3312 Garman Rd
Gillette, WY 82716-1535
Tel.: (307) 682-2529
Web Site: www.fennerdunlopconveyorservices.com
Conveyor Belt Repair Services
S.I.C.: 7699
N.A.I.C.S.: 811310
John Blue *(Sr VP-Ops)*

Fenner Dunlop (Port Clinton), Inc. **(4)**
Erie Industrial Park Bldg 320 5225 W Lakeshore Dr
Port Clinton, OH 43452
Tel.: (419) 635-2191
Fax: (419) 635-2552
Toll Free: (800) 537-4483
E-Mail: info@fennerdunlop.com
Web Site: www.fennerdunlopamericas.com
Emp.: 140
Mfr of Rubber Conveyor Belting
S.I.C.: 3535
N.A.I.C.S.: 333922
Richard Toeppe *(Dir-Ops)*

Fenner Dunlop (Toledo), LLC **(4)**
146 S Westwood
Toledo, OH 43607 DE
Tel.: (419) 531-5572
Fax: (419) 531-6284
Toll Free: (800) 237-9857
Web Site: www.fennerdunlopamericas.com
Emp.: 43
Mfr of Conveyor Belts
S.I.C.: 3535
N.A.I.C.S.: 333922
Ken Willen *(Dir-Ops)*

Non-U.S. Subsidiaries:

Fenner Dunlop (Bracebridge) Inc. **(4)**
700 Ecclestone Dr
PO Box 2230
Bracebridge, ON, P1L 1W1, Canada ON
Tel.: (705) 645-2228
Fax: (705) 645-3112
Toll Free: (800) 661-2358
Web Site: www.fennerdunlopamericas.com
Conveyor Belting Mfr
S.I.C.: 3535
N.A.I.C.S.: 333922
Ian Rimmington *(Plant Mgr)*

Non-U.S. Subsidiaries:

Fenner Conveyor Belting Private Limited **(2)**
Dindigul Road
Nagari, Madurai, 625 221, India
Tel.: (91) 452 2464201
Fax: (91) 452 2464204
E-Mail: mpersonnel@fenner.com
Web Site: www.fennerdunlopindia.com
Conveyor Belt Mfr
S.I.C.: 3535
N.A.I.C.S.: 333922
Richard Wilkinson *(Pres)*

Fenner Conveyor Belting (South Africa) (Pty) Limited **(2)**
21 Diesel Road
Isando, 1600, South Africa
Tel.: (27) 11 974 1902
Fax: (27) 11 974 1900
E-Mail: sales.fcbsa@fenner.com
Web Site: www.fennersouthafrica.com
Emp.: 18
Conveyor Belt Mfr
S.I.C.: 3535
N.A.I.C.S.: 333922
Gary Whalley *(Mng Dir)*

Fenner Dunlop Australia Pty. Ltd. **(2)**
268-280 Geelong Road
West Footscray, VIC, 3012, Australia AU
Tel.: (61) 3 9680 4500
Fax: (61) 3 9680 4595
E-Mail:
Web Site: www.fennerdunlop.com.au
Sales Range: $50-74.9 Million
Emp.: 400
Conveyor Belting Mfr
S.I.C.: 3535
N.A.I.C.S.: 333922
David Landgren *(Mng Dir & Exec Dir-Australia & Americas)*

Subsidiaries:

Fenner (Australia) Pty. Limited **(3)**
81 Milperra Road
Revesby, NSW, 2212, Australia AU
Tel.: (61) 2 8723 6600 (100%)
Fax: (61) 2 8723 6601
E-Mail:
Web Site: www.apexfenner.com.au
Fabricated Wire Product Mfr
S.I.C.: 3496
N.A.I.C.S.: 332618

Northern Belting Specialists Pty. Limited **(3)**
Shiell Street
Whyalla, SA, 5600, Australia AU
Tel.: (61) 8 8644 4100 (100%)
Fax: (61) 8 8644 4110
Conveyor Belt Products Distr
S.I.C.: 5084
N.A.I.C.S.: 423830

rEscan International Pty. Limited **(3)**
1/14 Accolade Street
Morisset, NSW, 2264, Australia AU
Tel.: (61) 2 4973 2399 (100%)
Fax: (61) 2 4970 4061
E-Mail: info@rescan.com.au
Web Site: www.rescan.com.au
Emp.: 10
Conveyor Belt Distr & Diagnostic Services
S.I.C.: 5084
N.A.I.C.S.: 423830
Peter Thorpe *(Gen Mgr)*

Fenner Dunlop BV **(2)**
Oliemolenstraat 2
PO Box 14Drachten
9200 AA Drachten, Netherlands
Tel.: (31) 512 585 555
Fax: (31) 512 524 599
E-Mail: marketing@dunlopcb.com
Web Site: eu.dunlopconveyorbelting.com
Emp.: 200
Conveyor Belt Mfr
S.I.C.: 3535
N.A.I.C.S.: 333922
Edwin Have *(Mng Dir)*

James Dawson & Son Ltd. **(1)**
Tritton Rd
Lincoln, LN6 7AF, United Kingdom
Tel.: (44) 522781800
Fax: (44) 522510029
E-Mail: sales@james-dawson.com
Web Site: www.james-dawson.com
Emp.: 300
Rubber Hose Mfr
S.I.C.: 3052
N.A.I.C.S.: 326220
Paul Edwards *(Mng Dir)*

Non-U.S. Subsidiary:

Dawson Polymer Products (Shanghai) Co. Limited **(2)**
785 Xing Rong Road
Jiading, Shanghai, 201807, China
Tel.: (86) 21 3351 7979
Fax: (86) 21 3351 7575
Emp.: 4
Polymer Products Mfr
S.I.C.: 2821
N.A.I.C.S.: 325211
Pan Feng *(Gen Mgr)*

U.S. Subsidiaries:

American Industrial Plastics, Inc. **(1)**
724 Fentress Blvd
Daytona Beach, FL 32114 FL
Tel.: (386) 274-5335
Fax: (386) 274-4746
E-Mail: sales@aipdaytona.com
Web Site: www.aipdaytona.com
Sales Range: $1-9.9 Million
Emp.: 36
Precision-Machined Plastic Products Mfr
S.I.C.: 3089
N.A.I.C.S.: 326199
George D. Willis *(Pres)*

Fenner, Inc. **(1)**
311 W Stiegel St
Manheim, PA 17545-1747 DE
Tel.: (717) 665-2421 (100%)
Fax: (717) 664-8214
Toll Free: (800) 243-3374
Web Site: www.fennerdrives.com
Emp.: 300
Mfr. of Industrial Belting, Power Transmission & Motion Control Components Export
S.I.C.: 2389
N.A.I.C.S.: 314999
John Krecek *(Pres)*
Nicholas Hobson *(Mng Dir)*
Mike Turek *(Mng Dir)*

Fenner Precision, Inc. **(1)**
852 Kensington Ave
Buffalo, NY 14215 DE
Tel.: (716) 833-6900
Fax: (716) 833-9405
Web Site: www.fennerprecision.com
Emp.: 100
Belt & Roller Equipment Mfr
S.I.C.: 3052
N.A.I.C.S.: 326220
Pete Haberbosch *(VP-Sls & Mktg)*

Unit:

Fenner Precision, Inc. - Manheim Office **(2)**
250 S Penn St
Manheim, PA 17545
Fax: (717) 664-8287
Toll Free: (800) 327-2288
Web Site: www.fennerprecision.com
Belt & Roller Equipment Mfr
S.I.C.: 3052
N.A.I.C.S.: 326220
Hans Raj *(Mgr-Engrg)*

Secant Medical, LLC **(1)**
700 W Park Ave
Perkasie, PA 18944
Tel.: (215) 257-8680
Fax: (215) 257-8875
Web Site: www.secantmedical.com
Biomedical Textile Component Mfr
S.I.C.: 2299
N.A.I.C.S.: 313210
Jeff Robertson *(Pres)*

Xeridiem Medical Devices, Inc. **(1)**
4700 S Overland Drive
Tucson, AZ 85714 (100%)
Tel.: (520) 882-7794
Fax: (520) 882-6849
E-Mail: info@xeridiem.com
Web Site: www.xeridiem.com
Sales Range: $25-49.9 Million
Emp.: 110
Designs & Manufactures Silicone-Based Devices for Medical Industry
S.I.C.: 3841
N.A.I.C.S.: 339112
Joseph Lee *(Pres)*

FENOPLAST LIMITED

306 - 308 Chenoy Trade Centre
Parklane
Secunderabad, 500003, India
Tel.: (91) 4027840322
Fax: (91) 4027721739
E-Mail: fenoexports@eth.net
Web Site: www.fenoplast.com
Year Founded: 1975
526689—(BOM)

Business Description:
PVC Leather Cloth Mfr
S.I.C.: 3199
N.A.I.C.S.: 316998

Personnel:
H. Narsaiah *(Chm)*
H. Kishen *(Mng Dir)*

FENPLAST

160 Industry Blvd
Candiac, QC, J5R 1J3, Canada
Tel.: (514) 990-0012
Fax: (514) 990-0032
Toll Free: (800) 814-6254
E-Mail: Info@fenplast.com
Web Site: www.fenplast.com
Year Founded: 1989
Rev.: $13,038,400
Emp.: 300

Business Description:
Door & Window Mfr
S.I.C.: 3442
N.A.I.C.S.: 332321

Personnel:
Jean Marchand *(Pres)*

FENWAL CONTROLS OF JAPAN,LTD.

Kyohan Kudan Bldg 5-10 Iidabashi-1-chome Chiyoda-Ku
Tokyo, Japan
Tel.: (81) 3 3237 3561
Web Site: www.fenwal.co.jp
Year Founded: 1961
6870—(JAS)
Sales Range: $200-249.9 Million

Business Description:
Medical Products Mfr
S.I.C.: 3841
N.A.I.C.S.: 339112

Personnel:
Masao Iguchi *(Pres)*

Non-U.S. Subsidiary:

Fenwal Controls of Japan Hong Kong Limited **(1)**
28/F Three Pacific Place
Wan Chai, Hong Kong, China (Hong Kong)
Tel.: (852) 29801888
Electronic Component Mfr
S.I.C.: 3679
N.A.I.C.S.: 334419

FENWICK LTD.

Elswick Ct Northumberland St
Newcastle, NE99 1AR, United Kingdom
Tel.: (44) 1912325100
Fax: (44) 1912396628
E-Mail: newcastle.enquiries@fenwick.co.uk
Web Site: www.fenwick.co.uk
Year Founded: 1897
Emp.: 3,000

Business Description:
Clothing & Accessory Stores
S.I.C.: 5699
N.A.I.C.S.: 448190

Subsidiary:

Fenwick Ltd. **(1)**
31-39 Northumberland Street
Newcastle, Surrey, NE99 1AR, United Kingdom UK
Tel.: (44) 1912325100

Fax: (44) 1912396628
Web Site: www.fenwick.co.uk
Emp.: 900
Department Store Operator
S.I.C.: 5311
N.A.I.C.S.: 452112
David Quinn *(Mng Dir)*

FEORE LIMITED

62/F The Center 99 Queen's Road Central, China (Hong Kong)
Tel.: (852) 3960 6518
Fax: (852) 3965 3222
E-Mail: info@feore.com
Web Site: www.feore.com
FEO—(ASX)
Business Description:
Iron Ore Mining
S.I.C.: 1011
N.A.I.C.S.: 212210
Personnel:
Dion Cohen *(Sec)*

FERATEL MEDIA TECHNOLOGIES AG

Maria-Theresien-Strasse 8
6020 Innsbruck, Austria
Tel.: (43) 51272800
Fax: (43) 512728080
E-Mail: info@feratel.com
Web Site: www.feratel.at
Year Founded: 1978
Sales Range: $25-49.9 Million
Emp.: 74
Business Description:
Tourist Information System Services
S.I.C.: 7389
N.A.I.C.S.: 519190
Personnel:
Markus Schrocksnadel *(Chm-Mgmt Bd)*
Ferdinand Hager *(CTO)*
Supervisory Board of Directors:
Richard Schenz

Non-U.S. Subsidiaries:

Feratel Espana SL (1)
Calle Muntaner numero 438 5 1
08006 Barcelona, Spain ES
Tel.: (34) 620840321 (100%)
Web Site: www.feratel.com
Tourism Information System Services
S.I.C.: 7389
N.A.I.C.S.: 519190
Markus Schrocksnadel *(Chm)*

Feratel Media Technologies B.V. (1)
Aak 17
NL-9408 Assen, Netherlands (100%)
Tel.: (31) 16470775
Fax: (31) 16 470771
E-Mail: info@feratelbenelux.be
Web Site: www.feratelbenelux.be
Tourism Information System Services
S.I.C.: 7389
N.A.I.C.S.: 519190

Feratel Media Technologies GmbH (1)
Conradin-Kreutzer-Strasse 21
88602 Merzenich, Germany (100%)
Tel.: (49) 757592100
Fax: (49) 7575921091
E-Mail: info@feratel.de
Web Site: www.feratel.de
Tourism Information System Services
S.I.C.: 7389
N.A.I.C.S.: 519190
Markus Schrocksnadel *(Chm)*
Rainer Egen *(Mng Dir)*

Feratel Schweiz AG (1)
Riedstrasse 1
6343 Rotkreuz, Switzerland (100%)
Tel.: (41) 7995050
Fax: (41) 7995060
E-Mail: info@feratel.ch
Web Site: www.feratel.com
Emp.: 9
Tourist Information Services
S.I.C.: 7389
N.A.I.C.S.: 519190

FERAUD SARL

2 rue de Bassano
75116 Paris, France
Tel.: (33) 149524400
Fax: (33) 149524386
Web Site: www.feraud.com
Business Description:
Clothing Designer & Mfr
S.I.C.: 5641
N.A.I.C.S.: 448130
Personnel:
Elisabeth Baur *(Dir Gen)*

U.S. Subsidiary:

Louis Feraud Inc. (1)
570 7th Ave
New York, NY 10018
Tel.: (212) 840-8220
Fax: (212) 869-7507
Sls.: $31,000,000
Emp.: 21
Designer Clothing Mfr
S.I.C.: 5137
N.A.I.C.S.: 424330
Marie Bottone *(Pres)*
David Perez *(CFO)*

FERAX MERCHANT S.P.A.

Via Bandello 5
20123 Milan, Italy
Tel.: (39) 02 89059126
Fax: (39) 02 89059024
E-Mail: info@feraxmerchant.it
Web Site: www.feraxmerchant.it
Business Description:
Private Equity Firm
S.I.C.: 6211
N.A.I.C.S.: 523999
Personnel:
Pietro del Monte *(Chm)*

Holding:

D. Lazzaroni & C. S.p.A. (1)
Via Novara 55
I-21047 Saronno, VA, Italy IT
Tel.: (39) 029375391
Fax: (39) 029606568
E-Mail: info@lazzaronisaronno.com
Web Site: www.lazzaronisaronno.com
Emp.: 115
Baked Goods
S.I.C.: 2051
N.A.I.C.S.: 311812
Stefano Tombetti *(Mng Dir)*

FERCO DEVELOPPEMENT

Quartier Viressac
Saint-Montan, 07220, France
Tel.: (33) 4 75 52 57 27
Fax: (33) 4 75 52 58 39
E-Mail: infos@ferco-dev.com
Web Site: www.ferco-dev.com
MLFER—(EUR)
Sales Range: $1-9.9 Million
Business Description:
Grape Compound Extraction Services
S.I.C.: 2899
N.A.I.C.S.: 325998
Personnel:
Marc Feries *(Chm)*

FERD AS

Strandveien 50
PO Box 34
N-1324 Lysaker, Norway
Tel.: (47) 67108000
Fax: (47) 67108001
E-Mail: post@ferd.no
Web Site: www.ferd.no
Year Founded: 1778
Sales Range: $450-499.9 Million
Emp.: 2,375
Business Description:
Holding Company
Import Export
S.I.C.: 6719
N.A.I.C.S.: 551112
Personnel:
Johan Henrik Andresen, Jr. *(Owner & CEO)*
Grace Reksten Skaugen *(Chm)*
John Giverholt *(CFO)*
Jo Olav Lunder *(Exec VP)*
Board of Directors:
Grace Reksten Skaugen
Henrik Brandt
Endre Ording Sund

Subsidiaries:

Elopak A/S (1)
Industriveien 30
PO Box 24
3431 Spikkestad, Norway (100%)
Mailing Address:
PO Box 124
NO-3430 Spikkestad, Norway
Tel.: (47) 31271000
E-Mail: elopak@elopak.no
Web Site: www.elopak.com
Rev.: $765,834
Emp.: 160
Mfr. Food Packaging Systems
S.I.C.: 2652
N.A.I.C.S.: 322219
Niels Petter Wrigth *(Pres & CEO)*

U.S. Subsidiary:

Elopak, Inc. (2)
30000 S Hill Rd
New Hudson, MI 48165
Tel.: (248) 486-4600
Fax: (248) 486-4601
Web Site: www.elopak.com
Emp.: 200
Sanitary Containers Mfr
Export
S.I.C.: 2676
N.A.I.C.S.: 322291
Horst Bussien *(Mng Dir)*
Richard Taylor *(CMO)*

Non-U.S. Subsidiaries:

Elocoat b.v. (2)
Osloweg 1
4538 BM Terneuzen, Netherlands NL
Mailing Address:
PO Box 90
4530 AB Terneuzen, Netherlands
Tel.: (31) 115682000
Fax: (31) 115614837
E-Mail: info.sales@elopak.nl
Web Site: www.elopak.com
Emp.: 98
Packaging Solutions
S.I.C.: 7389
N.A.I.C.S.: 561910
Erik Voet *(Dir-Coating)*

Elopak AB (2)
Hogastensgatan 19
Helsingborg, 25005, Sweden (50%)
Mailing Address:
PO Box 5018
250 05 Helsingborg, Sweden
Tel.: (46) 424505300
Fax: (46) 42262408
E-Mail: info@elopak.se
Web Site: www.elopak.se
Emp.: 50
Packaging Solutions
S.I.C.: 7389
N.A.I.C.S.: 561910

Elopak b.v. (2)
c Severo Ochoa 3
Las Rozas, 28230 Madrid, Spain
Tel.: (34) 917104940
Fax: (34) 916378339
E-Mail: elopak@elopak.es
Web Site: www.elopak.com
Packaging Solutions
S.I.C.: 7389
N.A.I.C.S.: 561910

Elopak b.v. (2)
FJ Haarmanweg 44
Terneuzen, Zeeland, 4538AS, Netherlands (100%)
Mailing Address:
PO Box 82
4530 AB Terneuzen, Netherlands
Tel.: (31) 115682000
Fax: (31) 115617254
E-Mail: reception.terneuzen@elopak.nl
Web Site: www.elopak.com
Emp.: 275
Packaging Solutions
S.I.C.: 7389
N.A.I.C.S.: 561910
Reynard Dreesman *(Plant Mgr)*

Elopak b.v. (2)
Rua Fonte de Maio, 9
Edificio Espaco, Piso 1-D, 2780-596 Paco d'Arcos, Portugal
Tel.: (351) 214409750
Fax: (351) 214 409 759
E-Mail: elopak@net.sapo.pt
Web Site: www.elopak.com
Packaging Solutions
S.I.C.: 7389
N.A.I.C.S.: 561910

Elopak Denmark AS (2)
Hovmarken 8
8520 Lystrup, Denmark
Tel.: (45) 87435100
Fax: (45) 87435200
E-Mail: info@elopak.dk
Web Site: www.elopak.com
Emp.: 200
Tobacco Manufacturing & Packaging Solutions
S.I.C.: 2131
N.A.I.C.S.: 312230
Henorak Jensen *(Mng Dir)*

Elopak France B.V. (2)
27 29 Ave Rene Duguay Trouin
ZA De La Grande Ile, F 78960 Voisins-le-Bretonneux, France (100%)
Tel.: (33) 130649200
Fax: (33) 130649003
E-Mail: elopak.france@elopak.fr
Web Site: www.elopak.com
Sales Range: $25-49.9 Million
Emp.: 21
Packaging Solutions
S.I.C.: 7389
N.A.I.C.S.: 561910

Elopak Ges.m.b.H (2)
Johannroithner St 131
4050 Traun, Austria (100%)
Tel.: (43) 7229794990
Fax: (43) 72297949920
E-Mail: office@elopak.at
Web Site: www.elopak.com
Rev.: $25,161,860
Emp.: 20
Packaging Solutions
S.I.C.: 7389
N.A.I.C.S.: 561910
Johammis Gaispiuer *(Gen Mgr)*

Elopak GmbH (2)
Brunckstrasse 22
PO Box 1280
67346 Speyer, Germany (100%)
Tel.: (49) 62326390
Fax: (49) 6232639811
E-Mail: sibylle.dege@elopak.de
Web Site: www.elopak.de
Sales Range: $150-199.9 Million
Emp.: 220
Packaging Solutions
S.I.C.: 7389
N.A.I.C.S.: 561910
Heinz Hener *(Mgr)*

Elopak Hungary (2)
Montevideo u 3/B
1037 Budapest, Hungary
Tel.: (36) 13467390
Fax: (36) 13467380
E-Mail: elopak@elopak.hu
Web Site: www.elopak.com
Emp.: 6
Packaging Solutions
S.I.C.: 7389
N.A.I.C.S.: 561910
Gabor Pesztericz *(Mgr)*

Elopak Ltd. (2)
Unit 67 Broomhill Rd
Tallaght, Dublin, 24, Ireland (100%)
Tel.: (353) 14521111
Fax: (353) 14513938
E-Mail: elopakirl@eircom.net
Web Site: www.elopak.com
Emp.: 5

Ferd AS—(Continued)

Packaging Solutions
S.I.C.: 7389
N.A.I.C.S.: 561910
John H. Andersen *(CEO)*

Elopak Malaysia Sdn Bhd **(2)**
38-1 Jalan Tun Sambanthan 3
50470 Kuala Lumpur, Malaysia (100%)
Tel.: (60) 322747495
Fax: (60) 322744205
Web Site: www.elopak.com
Emp.: 10
Packaging Solutions
S.I.C.: 7389
N.A.I.C.S.: 561910
Fione Foong *(Gen Mgr)*

Elopak Obeikan Ltd. **(2)**
Second Indl City
PO Box 369
Riyadh, Central Region, 11383, Saudi Arabia (49%)
Tel.: (966) 14983392
Fax: (966) 14982300
E-Mail: info@elopakobeikan.com.sa
Web Site: www.elopak.com
Sales Range: $10-24.9 Million
Emp.: 175
Packaging Solutions
S.I.C.: 7389
N.A.I.C.S.: 561910

Elopak Oy **(2)**
Pajalantie 21-23
04400 Jarvenpaa, Finland
Tel.: (358) 94155510
Fax: (358) 941555110
E-Mail: elopak@elopak.fi
Web Site: www.elopak.fi
Emp.: 60
Packaging Solutions
S.I.C.: 7389
N.A.I.C.S.: 561910

Elopak S.A. **(2)**
Ul Dunska 3
05 152 Czosnow, Poland (100%)
Tel.: (48) 227859000
Fax: (48) 227859001
E-Mail: info@elopak.pl
Web Site: www.elopak.com
Emp.: 30
Packaging Solutions
S.I.C.: 7389
N.A.I.C.S.: 561910

Elopak S.p.A. **(2)**
Via Sirtori 13 B
Passirana Di Rho, 20017 Milan, Italy
Tel.: (39) 29320831
Fax: (39) 293208343
E-Mail: info@elopak.it
Web Site: www.elopak.com
Emp.: 19
Packaging Solutions
S.I.C.: 7389
N.A.I.C.S.: 561910

Elopak Systems AG **(2)**
Cherstrasse 4
8152 Glattbrugg, Switzerland
Tel.: (41) 448096363
Fax: (41) 448096366
E-Mail: contact@elopak.ch
Web Site: www.elopak.com
Packaging Solutions
S.I.C.: 7389
N.A.I.C.S.: 561910
Petter H. Haug *(Gen Mgr)*

Elopak UK Ltd. **(2)**
Rutherford Close
Meadway, Stevenage, Herts, SG1 2PR, United Kingdom (100%)
Tel.: (44) 1438847400
Web Site: www.elopak.com
Emp.: 5
Packaging Solutions
S.I.C.: 7389
N.A.I.C.S.: 561910

Elopak Ukraine **(2)**
12 Gorodetskogo Str Ste 30
01001 Kiev, Ukraine (100%)
Tel.: (380) 442302423
Fax: (380) 445205260
E-Mail: office@elopak.com.ua
Web Site: www.elopak.com
Emp.: 200
Packaging Solutions
S.I.C.: 7389
N.A.I.C.S.: 561910
Anya Yavorskaya *(Mgr-Mktg)*

Elopak **(2)**
Koubkova 13 228
Prague, 12000, Czech Republic (100%)
Tel.: (420) 222520666
Fax: (420) 222521200
E-Mail: elopak@elopak.cz
Web Site: www.elopak.com
Emp.: 10
Packaging Solutions
S.I.C.: 7389
N.A.I.C.S.: 561910
Josef Horky *(Mgr-Mktg)*

Envases Elopak S.A. De C.V. **(2)**
Calz Lazaro Cardenas Y Valle Del Guadiana
Parque Industrial Lagunero, Gomez Palacio, 35078, Mexico (100%)
Tel.: (52) 8717500000
Fax: (52) 8717501773
E-Mail: msyldeira@envaseselopak.com.mx
Web Site: www.elopak.com
Emp.: 300
Packaging Solutions
S.I.C.: 7389
N.A.I.C.S.: 561910
Jesus Holguin *(Gen Mgr)*

Unifill S.p.A. **(2)**
Via Viazza 82
41030 San Prospero, Italy
Tel.: (39) 053549041
Fax: (39) 059809833
Web Site: www.unfill.com
Tobacco Manufacturing & Packaging Solutions
S.I.C.: 2131
N.A.I.C.S.: 312230

ZAO Elopak **(2)**
Ul Usacheva 35 build 1
119048 Moscow, Russia
Tel.: (7) 4956265490
Fax: (7) 4956265489
E-Mail: elopak_russia@mtu-net.ru
Web Site: www.elopak.com
Emp.: 25
Packaging Solutions & Tobacco Manufacturing
S.I.C.: 7389
N.A.I.C.S.: 561910

Ferd Investment Group **(1)**
Strandveien 50
PO Box 34
1324 Lysaker, Norway (100%)
Tel.: (47) 67108000
Fax: (47) 67108001
E-Mail: post@ferd.no
Web Site: www.ferd.com
Emp.: 35
Provider of Financial Investment Services
S.I.C.: 6282
N.A.I.C.S.: 523930
Johan H. Andresen, Jr. *(Owner & CEO)*
John Giverholt *(CFO)*

Subsidiaries:

Ferd Eiendom **(2)**
Joh H Andersens Vei 5
PO Box 6086
Etterstad, Oslo, 6086, Norway (100%)
Tel.: (47) 22666400
Fax: (47) 22666401
E-Mail: post@ferd.no
Web Site: www.if.no
Emp.: 8
Provider of Financial Investment Services
S.I.C.: 6282
N.A.I.C.S.: 523930

Ferd Industri **(2)**
Strandveien 50
PO Box 34
34 Lysaker, Norway (100%)
Tel.: (47) 67108000
Fax: (47) 67108001
E-Mail: post@ferd.no
Web Site: www.if.no
Emp.: 45
Provider of Financial Investment Services
S.I.C.: 6282
N.A.I.C.S.: 523930
Johan H. Anderesen *(CEO)*

Ferd Invest **(2)**
Strandveien 50
PO Box 34
1366 Lysaker, Norway (100%)
Tel.: (47) 67108000
Fax: (47) 67108001
E-Mail: post@ferd.no
Web Site: www.ferd.no
Emp.: 2,000
Provider of Financial Investment Services
S.I.C.: 6282
N.A.I.C.S.: 523930
John Giveholt *(CFO)*

Ferd Venture **(2)**
Strandveien 50
PO Box 34
Lysaker, 1324, Norway (100%)
Tel.: (47) 67108000
Fax: (47) 67108001
E-Mail: post@ferd.no
Web Site: www.ferd.no
Emp.: 40
Provider of Financial Investment Services
S.I.C.: 6282
N.A.I.C.S.: 523930
Johan Andresen *(Owner & CEO)*

Non-U.S. Subsidiaries:

Norse Crown Co. Sdn. Bhd. **(2)**
38 Jalan Tun Sambanthan 3
PO Box 11462
Brick Fields, 50470 Kuala Lumpur, Malaysia (20%)
Tel.: (60) 322749077
Fax: (60) 322749009
E-Mail: norse@tm.net.my
Sales Range: $1-9.9 Million
Emp.: 15
Provider of Financial Investment Services
S.I.C.: 6282
N.A.I.C.S.: 523930
Kanagasingam Kulasingam *(Mng Dir)*

Swix Sport AS **(1)**
Servicebox
N 2626 Lillehammer, Norway (100%)
Tel.: (47) 61222100
E-Mail: firmapost@swix.no
Web Site: www.swixsport.no
Rev.: $30,555,348
Emp.: 104
Mfr., Developer & Marketer of Sports & Recreational Products
S.I.C.: 3949
N.A.I.C.S.: 339920
Ulf Bjerknes *(CEO)*

U.S. Holding:

Swix Sport USA Inc. **(2)**
600 Research Dr
Wilmington, MA 01887-4491 (100%)
Tel.: (978) 657-4820
Fax: (978) 657-7234
E-Mail: info@swixsport.com
Web Site: www.swixsport.com
Sales Range: $10-24.9 Million
Emp.: 20
Develops Manufactures & Markets Sports & Recreational Products
S.I.C.: 5091
N.A.I.C.S.: 423910
Steve Poulin *(Pres)*

Non-U.S. Subsidiary:

Swix Sport Japan K.K. **(2)**
3-2-2 Kanda Ogawamachi
Chiyoda-ku, Tokyo, 101 0052, Japan (70%)
Tel.: (81) 3 5282 3755
Fax: (81) 3 5282 3757
E-Mail: info@swix.co.jp
Web Site: www.swix.co.jp
Emp.: 10
Marketer of Sports & Recreational Products
S.I.C.: 5091
N.A.I.C.S.: 423910
Hieeto Kora *(Pres)*

Holding:

Aibel AS **(1)**
Vestre Svanholmen 14
N 4066 Stavanger, Norway
Tel.: (47) 85270000
Fax: (47) 85270001
E-Mail: post@aibel.com
Web Site: www.aibel.com
Sales Range: $1-4.9 Billion
Emp.: 1,500
Oil & Gas Production Facilities Support Services
S.I.C.: 1389
N.A.I.C.S.: 213112
Jo Olav Lunder *(Chm)*
Jan Skogseth *(Pres & CEO)*
Idar Eikrem *(CFO)*

U.S. Unit:

Overseas Commodex Corp. **(1)**
109 S Main St
Rocky Mount, NC 27801
Tel.: (252) 937-6044
Exports Tobacco
S.I.C.: 5159
N.A.I.C.S.: 424590

Non-U.S. Subsidiaries:

Ferd Seafoods **(1)**
Sct Cathrine vej 31
DK 9800 Hjorring, Denmark (100%)
Tel.: (45) 98902000
Fax: (45) 98902010
Web Site: www.ferdseafood.dk
Emp.: 600
Mfr. of Processed Fish Products
S.I.C.: 2092
N.A.I.C.S.: 311710

Norse Crown Co. (M) Sdn. Bhd. **(1)**
38 Jalan Tun Sambanthan 3
Brickfields, 50740 Kuala Lumpur, Malaysia (20%)
Tel.: (60) 322749077
Fax: (60) 322749009
E-Mail: norse@tm.net.my
Web Site: www.norse-crown.com.my
Emp.: 15
Provider of Electrosurgery & Laparoscopy Services
S.I.C.: 3842
N.A.I.C.S.: 339113
Kulasingam Kanagasingam *(Mng Dir)*

FERDINAND GROSS GMBH & CO. KG

Daimlerstrasse 8
70745 Leinfelden-Echterdingen, Germany
Tel.: (49) 71116040
Fax: (49) 71116042609
E-Mail: info@schrauben-gross.de
Web Site: www.schrauben-gross.de
Year Founded: 1864
Rev.: $85,104,975
Emp.: 230

Business Description:
Warehousing & Logistics Services
S.I.C.: 4225
N.A.I.C.S.: 493110

Personnel:
Gerald Hering *(Mng Partner)*

FERDINAND KREUTZER SABAMUHLE GMBH

Burgbernheimer Str 11
90431 Nuremberg, Germany
Tel.: (49) 911324720
Fax: (49) 9113247230
E-Mail: info@saba.de
Web Site: www.sabamuehle.de
Year Founded: 1869
Rev.: $16,845,122
Emp.: 40

Business Description:
Food & Pharmaceutical Ingredients Mfr
S.I.C.: 2099
N.A.I.C.S.: 311942

Personnel:
Fabian Frank *(Co-Mng Dir)*
Brigitte Kranzle *(Co-Mng Dir)*

FERDINAND LUSCH GMBH & CO. KG

Im Brocke 11
D-33649 Bielefeld, Germany

Tel.: (49) 52194170
Fax: (49) 5219417228
E-Mail: info@lusch.de
Web Site: www.lusch.de
Year Founded: 1945
Rev.: $18,127,200
Emp.: 132
Business Description:
Furniture Mfr
S.I.C.: 2512
N.A.I.C.S.: 337121
Personnel:
Wolfgang Exner *(Co-Mng Dir)*
Katharina Lusch *(Co-Mng Dir)*

FERFINA S.P.A.

Via Salaria n 1039
00138 Rome, Italy
Tel.: (39) 06883341
Fax: (39) 0688334441
Web Site:
Sales Range: $800-899.9 Million
Emp.: 4,000
Business Description:
Holding Company
S.I.C.: 6719
N.A.I.C.S.: 551112

Holding:

Societe Italiana per Condotte d'Acqua S.p.A. **(1)**
via Salaria 1039
00138 Rome, Italy IT
Tel.: (39) 0006883341
Fax: (39) 0688334441
E-Mail: condotte@condotte.com
Web Site: www.condottespa.it
Water Supply Services
S.I.C.: 4941
N.A.I.C.S.: 221310

U.S. Subsidiary:

Condotte America Inc. **(2)**
10790 NW 127th St
Medley, FL 33178
Tel.: (305) 670-7585
Fax: (305) 670-7462
E-Mail: info@condotteamerica.com
Web Site: www.condotteamerica.com
Sales Range: $25-49.9 Million
Emp.: 50
Provider of Bridge Construction Services
S.I.C.: 1611
N.A.I.C.S.: 237310
Enrique Espino *(Pres)*

Joint Venture:

Edil.Gi SRL **(1)**
Via Di Acqua Acetosa Anagnina 10
Rome, Italy
Tel.: (39) 0679845362
Fax: (39) 0679845362
New Single-Family Housing Construction
S.I.C.: 1521
N.A.I.C.S.: 236115

FERGO AISA, S.A.

Muntaner 340 Pral
08021 Barcelona, Spain
Tel.: (34) 93 2419197
Fax: (34) 93 4142805
E-Mail: inversores@grupoaisa.com
Web Site: www.grupoaisa.com
AISA—(MAD)
Sales Range: $25-49.9 Million
Business Description:
Real Estate Services; Property Developer & Manager
S.I.C.: 6531
N.A.I.C.S.: 531390
Personnel:
Carlos Fernandez Gomez *(Pres & CEO)*

FERGUSON GROUP LIMITED

Ferguson House Midmill Business Park
Aberdeen, AB51 0QG, United Kingdom
Tel.: (44) 1467 626500
Fax: (44) 14 6762 6559
E-Mail: info@ferguson-group.com
Web Site: www.ferguson-group.com
Year Founded: 1976
Sales Range: $75-99.9 Million
Emp.: 170
Business Description:
Offshore Container Whslr
S.I.C.: 5085
N.A.I.C.S.: 423840
Personnel:
Steven Ferguson *(Chm & CEO)*

FERMACA S.A. DE C.V.

(Acquired by Partners Group AG)

FERMISCAN HOLDINGS LIMITED

Level 7 48 Hunter Street
Sydney, NSW, 2000, Australia
Tel.: (61) 2 9245 4460
Fax: (61) 2 9223 9622
E-Mail: info@fermiscan.com.au
Web Site: www.fermiscan.com.au
FER—(ASX)
Sales Range: $1-9.9 Million
Business Description:
Diagnostic Assessments & Breast Screening
S.I.C.: 8099
N.A.I.C.S.: 621999
Personnel:
Robert Whitton *(Chm)*
Greg West *(CFO & Sec)*
Gary Corino *(COO-Science)*
Ronald Shnier *(Chief Medical Officer)*
Richard Toltz *(Gen Counsel)*
Board of Directors:
Robert Whitton
Charlie Bontempo
Leon Carr
Peter Dykes
Mark Fordree
Ronald Shnier
Richard Wright

FERMO GROUP, INC.

Allmandring 1 22a 35
Stuttgart, Germany 70569
Tel.: (49) 7211324929
E-Mail: fermoinc@gmail.com
Year Founded: 2011
FRMG—(OTC OTCB)
Assets: $5,575
Liabilities: $11,500
Net Worth: ($5,925)
Earnings: ($27,050)
Fiscal Year-end: 12/31/12
Business Description:
Mini Donut Vending Machines
S.I.C.: 5962
N.A.I.C.S.: 454210
Personnel:
Christopher Carmichael *(Pres & CEO)*

FERNANDES CO., LTD.

2-14-26 Shimoochiai
Tokyo, 161-0033, Japan
Tel.: (81) 359966469
Fax: (81) 339501281
E-Mail: webmaster@fernandes.co.jp
Web Site: www.fernandes.co.jp
Year Founded: 1969
Sales Range: $10-24.9 Million
Emp.: 20
Business Description:
Guitar Mfr & Sales
S.I.C.: 3931
N.A.I.C.S.: 339992
Personnel:
Shigeki Saito *(Pres)*
Masaki Kamei *(COO & Exec VP)*

FERNBROOK HOMES

2220 Hwy 7 West Unit 5
Concord, ON, Canada L4K 1W7
Tel.: (416) 667-0447
Fax: (416) 667-8747
Web Site: www.fernbrookhomes.com
Rev.: $20,692,898
Emp.: 110
Business Description:
Residential Construction Services
S.I.C.: 1522
N.A.I.C.S.: 236116
Personnel:
Domenic Amato *(VP-Customer Rels)*

FERNLEA FLOWERS LTD.

1211 Hwy 3
Delhi, ON, N4B 2W6, Canada
Tel.: (519) 582-3060
Fax: (519) 582-1059
Toll Free: (800) 265-6789
E-Mail: khowe@fernlea.com
Web Site: www.fernlea.com
Sales Range: $25-49.9 Million
Emp.: 150
Fiscal Year-end: 12/31/12
Business Description:
Flower Nurseries
S.I.C.: 0831
N.A.I.C.S.: 113210
Personnel:
Jim McDonald *(CFO)*

U.S. Subsidiary:

Fernlea Nursery Inc. **(1)**
1625 SE Darling St
Stuart, FL 34997
Tel.: (772) 287-0847
Web Site: www.ferlea.com
Sls.: $11,000,000
Emp.: 120
Nursery Stock
S.I.C.: 5193
N.A.I.C.S.: 424930

FERONERIA S.A.

Calea 6 Vanatori 51 53
310162 Arad, Romania
Tel.: (40) 257250225
Fax: (40) 257257127
E-Mail: office@feroneria.ro
Web Site: www.feroneria.ro
FERO—(BUC)
Sales Range: $1-9.9 Million
Emp.: 9
Business Description:
Furniture Fittings Mfr
S.I.C.: 3429
N.A.I.C.S.: 332510
Personnel:
Dionisie Domjan *(Dir-Comml)*

FERONIA INC.

Suite 1800 181 Bay Street
Toronto, ON, M5J 2T9, Canada
Tel.: (416) 844-3226
Fax: (416) 362-0063
E-Mail: info@feronia.com
Web Site: www.feronia.com
Year Founded: 2005
FRN—(TSXV)
Rev.: $7,129,748
Assets: $44,711,685
Liabilities: $21,810,315
Net Worth: $22,901,370
Earnings: ($7,922,847)
Fiscal Year-end: 12/31/12
Business Description:
Agricultural Services Including Soybean Farming & Processing
S.I.C.: 0116
N.A.I.C.S.: 111110
Personnel:
Ravi Sood *(Interim CEO)*
David Steel *(CFO)*
Board of Directors:
Philip Condon
Nigel Gourlay
Barnabe Kikaya-Bin-Karubi
Joel Strickland
Transfer Agent:
Equity Financial Trust Company
200 University Avenue Suite 400
Toronto, ON, Canada

FEROZSONS LABORATORIES LIMITED

197-A The Mall
Rawalpindi, 42000, Pakistan
Tel.: (92) 51 556 2155
Fax: (92) 51 558 4195
E-Mail: info@ferozsons-labs.com
Web Site: www.ferozsons-labs.com
Year Founded: 1954
FEROZ—(ISL)
Rev.: $29,191,873
Assets: $33,081,613
Liabilities: $4,575,487
Net Worth: $28,506,126
Earnings: $4,724,426
Emp.: 632
Fiscal Year-end: 06/30/13
Business Description:
Pharmaceutical Products Mfr
S.I.C.: 2834
N.A.I.C.S.: 325412
Personnel:
Akhter Khalid Waheed *(Chm & CEO)*
Osman Khalid Waheed *(Pres)*
Ghausuddin Saif *(CFO & Sec)*
Board of Directors:
Akhter Khalid Waheed
Shahid Anwar
Nihal A. Cassim
Farid Khan
Farooq Mazhar
Munize Azhar Peracha
Omar Khalid Waheed
Osman Khalid Waheed

FERPAL INFRASTRUCTURE LTD.

169 Fenmar Dr
Toronto, ON, M9L 1M6, Canada
Tel.: (416) 742-3713
Fax: (416) 742-3889
E-Mail: info@ferpal.ca
Web Site: www.ferpalinfrastructure.com
Year Founded: 1986
Rev.: $22,309,087
Emp.: 115
Business Description:
Safe Drinking Water Solution & Water Pipeline Construction Services
S.I.C.: 1629
N.A.I.C.S.: 237110
Personnel:
David O'Sullivan *(Pres)*

FERRARELLE S.P.A.

Via Porta Pinciana 4
179 Rome, Italy
Tel.: (39) 6780541
Fax: (39) 6 78 58 564
E-Mail: infoprodotto@ferrarelle.it
Web Site: www.ferrarelle.it
Sales Range: $200-249.9 Million
Emp.: 613
Business Description:
Bottled Water Mfr
S.I.C.: 2086
N.A.I.C.S.: 312112
Personnel:
Carlo Pontecorvo *(Pres)*

FERRARI S.A.

BP 54
38352 La Tour-du-Pin, France

Ferrari S.A.—(Continued)

Tel.: (33) 474974133
Fax: (33) 474976720
Web Site: www.ferrari-textiles.com
Year Founded: 1960
Sales Range: $50-74.9 Million
Emp.: 250
Business Description:
Textile Mfr
S.I.C.: 2389
N.A.I.C.S.: 314999
Personnel:
Sebastien Ferrari *(Chm)*
Non-U.S. Subsidiary:

Stamoid AG **(1)**
Wasterkingerweg
CH 8193 Eglisau, Switzerland
Tel.: (41) 448682626
Telex: 828156
Fax: (41) 448682727
E-Mail: info.fr@sergeferrari.com
Web Site: www.ferrari-texiloop.com
Emp.: 100
Fabric Coating Mfr
S.I.C.: 2389
N.A.I.C.S.: 314999
Ballok Stefan *(Gen Mgr)*

FERRELL BUILDER'S SUPPLY LTD.

1549 Rymal Road East
Hamilton, ON, L8W 3N2, Canada
Tel.: (905) 387-1948
Fax: (905) 387-3297
Toll Free: (800) 363-2745
E-Mail: hamilton@ferrellbrick.com
Web Site: www.ferrellbrick.com
Year Founded: 1971
Rev.: $18,606,219
Emp.: 80
Business Description:
Building Materials Supplier
S.I.C.: 5211
N.A.I.C.S.: 444190
Personnel:
Peter Cicchi *(Pres)*
Rocco Grilli *(CEO)*
Mary Ann Cantelmi *(CFO)*

FERRERO S.P.A.

Piazzale Ferrero 1
Alba, 12051 Cuneo, Cuneo, Italy
Tel.: (39) 01732951
Fax: (39) 0173363034
E-Mail: ferrero@ferrero.com
Web Site: www.ferrero.com
Year Founded: 1946
Sales Range: $5-14.9 Billion
Emp.: 21,600
Business Description:
Candy Mfr & Distr
Export
S.I.C.: 2066
N.A.I.C.S.: 311351
Personnel:
Giovanni Ferrero *(Co-CEO)*
Frederic Thil *(Dir Gen-Ferrero France)*
Antonio Vanoli *(Mng Dir)*
U.S. Subsidiary:

Ferrero U.S.A., Inc. **(1)**
600 Cottontail Ln
Somerset, NJ 08873 IT
Tel.: (732) 764-9300 (100%)
Fax: (732) 764-2700
Toll Free: (800) FERRERO
E-Mail: info@ferrerousa.com
Web Site: www.ferrerousa.com
Emp.: 250
Candy & Confectionery Products Mfr
Import Export
S.I.C.: 5145
N.A.I.C.S.: 424450
Vladimiro Sinatti *(CFO)*

FERRETTI S.P.A.

(See Under Shandong Heavy Industry Group Co., Ltd.)

FERREX PLC

Coveham House Downside Bridge Road
Cobham, KT11 3EP, United Kingdom
Tel.: (44) 1932 918803
Web Site: www.ferrexplc.com
Year Founded: 2010
FRX—(AIM)
Assets: $9,009,989
Liabilities: $8,559,739
Net Worth: $450,250
Earnings: ($2,781,251)
Emp.: 12
Fiscal Year-end: 09/30/13
Business Description:
Iron & Manganese Ore Exploration Services
S.I.C.: 1011
N.A.I.C.S.: 212210
Personnel:
Dave Reeves *(Mng Dir)*
Board of Directors:
Brian Moritz
James Carter
Russell Lamming
Roy Pitchford
Dave Reeves
Legal Counsel:
Tabacks
13 Eton Road
Parktown, Johannesburg, 2193, South Africa

Memery Crystal LLP
44 Southampton Buildings
London, United Kingdom

Falcon & Hume Attorneys Inc
Block B 7 Eton Road
Sandhurst, United Kingdom

CGA Advogados & Consultores
Av de Zimbabwe 385
Maputo, Mozambique

FERREXPO PLC

2-4 King Street
London, SW1Y 6QL, United Kingdom
Tel.: (44) 2073898300
Fax: (44) 2073898301
E-Mail: info@ferrexpo.com
Web Site: www.ferrexpo.com
FXPO—(LSE)
Rev.: $1,424,030,000
Assets: $2,754,368,000
Liabilities: $1,184,369,000
Net Worth: $1,569,999,000
Earnings: $215,580,000
Emp.: 9,558
Fiscal Year-end: 12/31/12
Business Description:
Iron Ore Pellet Mfr
S.I.C.: 1011
N.A.I.C.S.: 212210
Personnel:
Kostyantin Zhevago *(CEO)*
Christopher Mawe *(CFO)*
Brian Maynard *(Grp COO)*
Jason Keys *(CMO)*
Victor Lotous *(Chm-Ferrexpo Poltava Mining)*
David Leonard *(Sec)*
Board of Directors:
Michael Abrahams
Oliver Baring
Lucio Genovese
Wolfram Kuoni
Christopher Mawe
Ihor Mitiukov
Miklos Salamon
Kostyantin Zhevago
Legal Counsel:
Allen & Overy LLP
One Bishops Square
London, United Kingdom

Non-U.S. Subsidiary:

Ferrexpo AG **(1)**
Bahnhofstrasse 13
Baar, 6340, Switzerland
Tel.: (41) 417693660
Fax: (41) 417693670
E-Mail: info@ferrexpo.ch
Web Site: www.ferrexpo.com
Iron Ore Pellets Production & Sales Services
S.I.C.: 1011
N.A.I.C.S.: 212210

FERRING HOLDING SA

Ch de la Vergognausaz 50
CH 1162 Saint Prex, Switzerland
Tel.: (41) 583010000
Fax: (41) 583010010
Web Site: www.ferring.com
Emp.: 2,700
Business Description:
Holding Company; Pharmaceutical Mfr
S.I.C.: 6719
N.A.I.C.S.: 551112
Personnel:
John McGuire *(Pres-Ferring Research Institutes)*
Peter Wilden *(CFO & Exec VP)*
Michel L. Pettgrew *(COO)*
Lars Peter Brunse *(Exec VP-Tech Ops & Logistics)*
Pascal Danglas *(Exec VP-Clinical & Product Dev)*
Jonathan Grover *(Sr VP-Global IT)*
Joachim Horig *(Sr VP-Global Quality Assurance)*
Board of Directors:
John McGuire
Frederik Paulsen
Helene Ploix
Bernd Wolff
Subsidiary:

Ferring International Center SA **(1)**
CH de la Vergognausaz 50
1162 Saint Prex, Switzerland
Tel.: (41) 58 301 00 10
Web Site: www.ferring.com
Pharmaceutical Preparations & Research
S.I.C.: 2834
N.A.I.C.S.: 325412

Non-U.S. Subsidiary:

Ferring BV **(1)**
Polaris Avenue 130
Hoofddorp, 2132JX, Netherlands
Tel.: (31) 235680390
Fax: (31) 2132
E-Mail: info@ferring.nl
Web Site: www.ferring.nl
Pharmaceutical Preparations & Research
S.I.C.: 2834
N.A.I.C.S.: 325412

Non-U.S. Subsidiary:

Bio-Technology General (Israel) Ltd. **(2)**
8 Hashita Street
PO Box 3551
Caesarea Industrial Park, Caesarea, 38900, Israel
Tel.: (972) 46309500
Fax: (972) 46309511
Web Site: www.ferring.com
Emp.: 237
Mfr & Developer of Recombinant Products for the Human Healthcare Industry
S.I.C.: 2834
N.A.I.C.S.: 325412

FERRO ALLOYS CORPORATION LTD.

Suite No 401 Plot No 5 Jasola
New Delhi, 110025, India
Tel.: (91) 40701000
Fax: (91) 41624880
E-Mail: facordelhi@facorgroup.in
Web Site: www.facorgroup.in
Year Founded: 1955
500141—(BOM)
Rev.: $100,042,285
Assets: $167,662,448
Liabilities: $134,944,336
Net Worth: $32,718,113
Earnings: ($2,704,745)
Emp.: 908
Fiscal Year-end: 03/31/13
Business Description:
Ferro Alloys Distr
S.I.C.: 3399
N.A.I.C.S.: 331110
Personnel:
R. K. Saraf *(Chm & Mng Dir)*
Ashish Saraf *(Co-Mng Dir)*
Manoj Saraf *(Mng Dir)*
Rohit Saraf *(Co-Mng Dir)*
Vinod Saraf *(Co-Mng Dir)*
Sanjeev Goyal *(CFO)*
Ritesh Chaudhry *(Compliance Officer, Sec & Gen Mgr-Legal)*
Board of Directors:
R. K. Saraf
N. L. Ajwalia
Arye Berest
A. S. Kapre
S. B. Mishra
Pinaki Misra
Keshaorao Pardhi
Ashish Saraf
M. D. Saraf
Manoj Saraf
Rohit Saraf
Vinod Saraf
S. Sridhar
M. B. Thaker
Transfer Agent:
Link Intime India Private Limited
C-13 Pannalal Silk Mills Compound LBS Road
Bhandup W
Mumbai, India
Plant:

Ferro Alloys Corporation Ltd. - Charge Chrome Plant **(1)**
D P Nagar
Randia, Bhadrak, Odisha, 756 135, India
Tel.: (91) 6784 240320
Fax: (91) 6784 240626
Ferro Alloy Mfr
S.I.C.: 3399
N.A.I.C.S.: 331110
B. B. Singh, *(Dir-Technical)*

FERRO S.A.

ul Przemyslowa 7
32-050 Skawina, Poland
Tel.: (48) 12 25 62 100
Fax: (48) 12 27 67 606
E-Mail: info@ferro.pl
Web Site: www.ferro.pl
FRO—(WAR)
Sales Range: $50-74.9 Million
Emp.: 110
Business Description:
Sanitary & Installation Fittings; Heating Equipment
S.I.C.: 3494
N.A.I.C.S.: 332919
Personnel:
Andrzej Holoj *(Chm-Supervisory Bd)*
Jan Gniadek *(Vice Chm-Supervisory Bd)*
Aneta Raczek *(Pres)*
Supervisory Board of Directors:
Andrzej Holoj
Grazyna Gniadek
Jan Gniadek
Artur Holda
Bartosz Holoj

FERRONORDIC MACHINES AB

Hovslagargatan 5B
111 48 Stockholm, Sweden

Tel.: (46) 8 50907280
Web Site: www.ferronordic.ru
FNMA PREF—(OMX)
Sales Range: $350-399.9 Million
Emp.: 700
Business Description:
Construction Machinery & Trucks Distr
S.I.C.: 5082
N.A.I.C.S.: 423810
Personnel:
Per-Olof Eriksson *(Chm)*
Erik Eberhardson *(Vice Chm & Head-Bus Dev)*
Martin Leach *(Vice Chm)*
Lars Corneliusson *(Pres & CEO)*
Anders Blomqvist *(CFO)*
Henrik Carlborg *(Chief Compliance Officer & Gen Counsel)*
Board of Directors:
Per-Olof Eriksson
Magnus Brannstrom
Lars Corneliusson
Erik Eberhardson
Marika Fredriksson
Tom Jorning
Martin Leach
Kristian Terling

FERROTEC CORPORATION
Nihonbashi Plaza Building 2-3-4
Nihonbashi Chuo-Ku
Tokyo, 104 0027, Japan
Tel.: (81) 332818808
Fax: (81) 332818848
E-Mail: info@ferrotec.com
Web Site: www.ferrotec.co.jp
Year Founded: 1980
6890—(JAS)
Sls.: $422,664,000
Assets: $729,773,000
Liabilities: $394,944,000
Net Worth: $334,829,000
Earnings: ($71,852,000)
Emp.: 185
Fiscal Year-end: 03/31/13
Business Description:
Vacuum Seals, Ceramics, Quartz, Silicon Crystal, Thermo Modules, Ferrofluid & Electronic Device Mfr
S.I.C.: 3053
N.A.I.C.S.: 339991
Personnel:
Akira Yamamura *(Pres & CEO)*
Board of Directors:
Xian Han He
Shigeo Katayama
Terutoshi Komatsu
Kyuzo Nakamura
Tadao Shimada
Akira Yamamura
Takeru Yamamura

Subsidiaries:

ALIONTEK CORPORATION (1)
1-1-58 Matsuei
Yamagata, 990-2473, Japan
Tel.: (81) 23 643 8255
Fax: (81) 23 643 8310
Web Site: www.aliontek.co.jp
Semiconductor Equipment Mfr & Sales
S.I.C.: 3674
N.A.I.C.S.: 334413
Yoshiaki Yamakawa *(Pres)*

Ferrotec Ceramics Corporation (1)
1-4-14 Kyobashi
Chuo-Ku, Tokyo, 104-0031, Japan
Tel.: (81) 335160800
Fax: (81) 335160801
Web Site: www.ft-ceramics.co.jp
Emp.: 166
Semiconductor Ceramic Products Mfr & Sales
S.I.C.: 3674
N.A.I.C.S.: 334413
Yasuaki Matsuda *(Pres)*

Ferrotec Silicon Corporation (1)
2-3-4 Nihonbashi
Chuo-ku, Tokyo, 103-0027, Japan
Tel.: (81) 332312641
Fax: (81) 332312643
Web Site: www.ftsi.co.jp
Emp.: 65
Semiconductor Products Mfr
S.I.C.: 3674
N.A.I.C.S.: 334413
Fujia Ryusuke *(Mng Dir)*

U.S. Subsidiaries:

Ferrotec (USA) Corporation (1)
33 Constitution Dr
Bedford, NH 03110 MA
Tel.: (603) 472-6800 (100%)
Fax: (603) 472-2511
Toll Free: (800) 258-1788
E-Mail: info@ferrotec.com
Web Site: www.ferrotec.com
Emp.: 90
Thermal Modules, Vacuum Feedthroughs, E-Beam Guns & Ferrofluids Mfr & Sales
Import Export
S.I.C.: 3053
N.A.I.C.S.: 339991
Eiji Miyanaga *(Pres)*

Integrated Materials, Inc. (1)
3945 Freedom Cir Ste 450
Santa Clara, CA 95054 DE
Tel.: (408) 437-7591
Semiconductor Mfr
S.I.C.: 3674
N.A.I.C.S.: 334413

Non-U.S. Divisions:

HANGZHOU DAHE THERMO-MAGNETICS CO., LTD. - Quartz Division (1)
777 Binkang Road
Binjiang District, Hangzhou, Zhejiang, 310053, China
Tel.: (86) 571 86698292
Fax: (86) 571 86698292
E-Mail: quartz@ferrotec.com.cn
Emp.: 600
Quartz Crucible Mfr
S.I.C.: 3679
N.A.I.C.S.: 334419

HANGZHOU DAHE THERMO-MAGNETICS CO., LTD. - TE Division (1)
15F Block C 70 Caobao Road
Shanghai, 200235, China
Tel.: (86) 2164325027
Fax: (86) 2164325393
Web Site: www.ferrotec.com.cn/companyintro/contactus_en
Thermoelectric Products Mfr
S.I.C.: 3699
N.A.I.C.S.: 335999

HANGZHOU DAHE THERMO-MAGNETICS CO., LTD. - VF Division (1)
777 Binkang Road
Binjiang District, Hangzhou, Zhejiang, 310053, China
Tel.: (86) 571 86699985
Fax: (86) 571 86697695
E-Mail: vfsles@ferrotec.com.cn
Web Site: www.ferrotec.com.cn/companyintro/contactus_en
Ferrofluidic Seals Mfr
S.I.C.: 3499
N.A.I.C.S.: 332999

Shanghai Shenhe Thermo-Magnetics Co., Ltd. - PV Material Division (1)
No 181 Shanlian Road Baoshan Urban Industrial Park
Shanghai, 200444, China
Tel.: (86) 2136161010
Fax: (86) 21 36161780
Web Site: www.ferrotec.com.cn/companyintro/contactus_en
Semiconductor Devices Mfr
S.I.C.: 3674
N.A.I.C.S.: 334413

Shanghai Shenhe Thermo-Magnetics Co., Ltd. - Silicon Material Division (1)
No 181 Shanlian Road Baoshan Urban Industrial Park
Shanghai, 200444, China
Tel.: (86) 2136160798
Fax: (86) 21 36160797
E-Mail: wangdj@ferrotec.sh.cn
Web Site: www.ferrotec.com.cn
Emp.: 1,400
Semiconductor Devices Mfr
S.I.C.: 3674
N.A.I.C.S.: 334413
Xian Han He *(Pres)*

Shanghai Shenhe Thermo-Magnetics Co., Ltd. - TE Division (1)
No 181 Shanlian Rd Baoshan Urban Industrial Park
Shanghai, 200444, China
Tel.: (86) 21 36160564
Fax: (86) 21 36160484
E-Mail: te-sales@ferrotec.sh.cn
Web Site: www.ferrotec.sh.cn
Emp.: 2,000
Thermoelectric Components Mfr
S.I.C.: 3699
N.A.I.C.S.: 335999
Xian Han He *(Mgr-Factory)*

Non-U.S. Subsidiaries:

Advanced Quartz Material (Hangzhou) Co.,Ltd. (1)
668 Binkang Road
Binjiang District, Hangzhou, Zhejiang, China
Tel.: (86) 571 86695023
Fax: (86) 571 86695024
Quartz Products Mfr
S.I.C.: 3679
N.A.I.C.S.: 334419
Jhou Yong *(Pres)*

FERROTEC CORPORATION SINGAPORE PTE LTD (1)
12 Tannery Rd 09-03 HB Ctr 1
Singapore, 347722, Singapore
Tel.: (65) 67440626
Fax: (65) 68445374
E-Mail: info@ferrotec.com.sg
Web Site: www.ferrotec.com.sg
Emp.: 6
Semiconductor Equipment Mfr
S.I.C.: 3674
N.A.I.C.S.: 334413

Ferrotec GmbH (1)
Seerosenstrasse 1
72669 Unterensingen, Germany (100%)
Tel.: (49) 702292700
Fax: (49) 7022927010
E-Mail: info@deferrotec.com
Web Site: www.ferrotec.com
Emp.: 40
Environmental Seals, Fluid Bearings & Thermal Solutions
S.I.C.: 2899
N.A.I.C.S.: 325998
Andreas Quendt *(Mng Dir)*

Ferrotec Taiwan Co., Ltd. (1)
6F 2 No.25 Puding Road
Hsin-chu, 30072, Taiwan
Tel.: (886) 36662369
Fax: (886) 36661995
E-Mail: info@ferrotec-tw.com.tw
Web Site: www.ferrotec.com.tw
Emp.: 10
Semiconductor Devices Mfr
S.I.C.: 3674
N.A.I.C.S.: 334413

Ferrotec (UK) Ltd. (1)
Unit 3 IO Center Royal Arsenal Est
London, SE18 6SR, United Kingdom UK
Tel.: (44) 2083173100 (100%)
Fax: (44) 208 317 9559
E-Mail: info@ferrotec.co.uk
Web Site: www.ferrotec.co.uk
Sales Range: $75-99.9 Million
Emp.: 11
Environmental Seals & Fluid Bearings Mfr
S.I.C.: 2899
N.A.I.C.S.: 325998
Doug Brooks *(Mng Dir)*

HANGZHOU WAGEN PRECISION TOOLING CO., LTD. (1)
No 488 Shenban Road Gongshu Section
Hangzhou, Zhejiang, 310022, China
Tel.: (86) 571 88132960
Fax: (86) 571 88121742
Web Site: www.ferrotec.com
Emp.: 200
Precision Tools Mfr
S.I.C.: 3542
N.A.I.C.S.: 333517
Dai Ming *(Gen Mgr)*

SCTB NORD (1)
Peschany Carier 3
Moscow, 109383, Russia
Tel.: (7) 499 357 67 71
Fax: (7) 495 348 07 00
E-Mail: info@sctbnord.com
Web Site: www.sctbnord.com
Emp.: 180
Thermoelectric Modules Mfr
S.I.C.: 3699
N.A.I.C.S.: 335999
Sergey Skipidarov *(Dir Gen)*

Shanghai Hanhong Precision Machinery Co., Ltd. (1)
No 181 Shanlian Road Baoshan City Industrial Area
Shanghai, 200444, China
Tel.: (86) 21 36162928
Fax: (86) 21 36161845
E-Mail: hh-sales@ferrotec.sh.cn
Web Site: www.hanhong.sh.cn
Precision Tools Mfr
S.I.C.: 3541
N.A.I.C.S.: 333517

Non-U.S. Plant:

HANGZHOU DAHE THERMO-MAGNETICS CO., LTD.- FACTORY II (1)
668 Bingkang Road Bingjiang District
Hangzhou, Zhejiang, 310053, China
Tel.: (86) 57186696188
Fax: (86) 57186696199
Semiconductor Devices Mfr
S.I.C.: 3674
N.A.I.C.S.: 334413

FERROVIAL S.A.
Plaza de Manuel Gomez Moreno 2
Edificio Alfredo Mahou, 28020
Madrid, Spain
Tel.: (34) 914185600
Fax: (34) 91 555 1241
Web Site: www.ferrovial.com
FER—(MAD)
Rev.: $10,369,547,510
Assets: $29,907,858,890
Liabilities: $22,149,881,180
Net Worth: $7,757,977,710
Earnings: $869,625,820
Emp.: 57,276
Fiscal Year-end: 12/31/12
Business Description:
Transport Infrastructure Design, Construction, Management, Administration & Maintenance Services
S.I.C.: 1629
N.A.I.C.S.: 488999
Personnel:
Rafael del Pino *(Chm)*
Joaquin Ayuso *(Vice Chm)*
Santiago Bergareche *(Vice Chm)*
Inigo Meiras *(CEO)*
Ernesto Lopez *(CFO)*
Federico Florez *(CIO & Chief Innovation Officer)*
Alejandro de la Joya *(CEO-Ferrovial Agroman)*
Enrique Diaz-Rato Revuelta *(CEO-Cintra)*
Alvaro Echaniz *(CEO-Ferrovial FISA)*
Jorge Gil *(CEO-Ferrovial Aeropuertos)*
Santiago Olivares *(CEO-Ferrovial Servicios)*
Jaime Aguirre de Carcer *(Gen Dir-HR)*
Santiago Ortiz Vaamonde *(Gen Counsel)*
Board of Directors:
Rafael del Pino
Juan Arena
Joaquin Ayuso

Ferrovial S.A.—(Continued)

Santiago Bergareche
Gabriele Burgio
Jaime Carvajal
Joaquin del Pino y Calvo-Sotelo
Leopoldo del Pino y Calvo-Sotelo
Maria del Pino
Inigo Meiras
Jose Fernando Sanchez-Junco Mans
Santiago Fernandez Valbuena

Subsidiaries:

Cintra Infraestructuras, S.A.U. **(1)**
Plaza Manuel Gomez Moreno 2 Edificio Alfredo Mahou
28020 Madrid, Spain (100%)
Tel.: (34) 914185600
Fax: (34) 915556786
Web Site: www.Cintra.es
Sales Range: $1-4.9 Billion
Emp.: 4,456
Toll Road Operator
S.I.C.: 4789
N.A.I.C.S.: 488490
Enrique Diaz-Rato Revuelta *(CEO)*

U.S. Subsidiaries:

Cintra Developments, LLC **(2)**
9600 Great Hills Trl Ste 250E
Austin, TX 78759
Tel.: (512) 637-8545
Fax: (512) 637-1498
Emp.: 40
Transportation Services
S.I.C.: 4789
N.A.I.C.S.: 488999
Nicalos Ruvio *(Pres)*

ITR Concession Company (IP) **(2)**
233 N Michigan Ave Ste 19
Chicago, IL 60601
Tel.: (312) 552-7100
Fax: (312) 552-7130
Web Site: www.chicagoskyway.org
Road Transportation Support Services
S.I.C.: 4789
N.A.I.C.S.: 488999

Skyway Concession Co.LLC **(2)**
205 N Michigan Ave
Chicago, IL 60601
Tel.: (312) 552-7100
Fax: (312) 552-7130
Web Site: www.chicagoskyway.org
Emp.: 16
Transportation Services
S.I.C.: 4789
N.A.I.C.S.: 488999
Fernando Redondo *(CEO)*

Ferrovial Aeropuertos S.A. **(1)**
Caleruega 102 104 Planta 9 Edificio Ofipinar
28033 Madrid, Spain
Tel.: (34) 917686600
Fax: (34) 00341917686699
Emp.: 50
Airport Operator
S.I.C.: 4581
N.A.I.C.S.: 488119

Non-U.S. Holding:

Heathrow Airport Holdings Limited **(2)**
(Formerly BAA Limited)
The Compass Centre Nelson Road
London Heathrow Airport, Hounslow, Mddx, TW6 2GW, United Kingdom UK (49.99%)
Tel.: (44) 20 8745 9800
Fax: (44) 207 932 6699
E-Mail: baamediacentre@baa.com
Web Site: www.heathrowairport.com
Rev.: $3,730,282,980
Assets: $29,456,917,080
Liabilities: $25,879,825,230
Net Worth: $3,577,091,850
Earnings: $503,793,510
Emp.: 9,538
Fiscal Year-end: 12/31/12
Airport Operator
S.I.C.: 4581
N.A.I.C.S.: 488119
Colin S. Matthews *(CEO)*
Jose Leo *(CFO)*
Normand Boivin *(COO)*
Neil Clark *(CIO)*
Carol Hui *(Gen Counsel & Sec)*

Subsidiaries:

Aberdeen Airport Ltd. **(3)**
Aberdeen Airport
Dyce, Aberdeen, Scotland, AB21 7DU, United Kingdom UK
Tel.: (44) 844 481 6666
Web Site: www.aberdeenairport.com
Emp.: 238
Airport
S.I.C.: 4581
N.A.I.C.S.: 488119
Nick Barton *(Mng Dir)*

Glasgow Airport Ltd. **(3)**
Glasgow International Airport
Paisley, Renfrewshire, PA3 2SW, United Kingdom UK
Tel.: (44) 844 481 5555
E-Mail: info@glasgowairport.com
Web Site: www.glasgowairport.com
Sales Range: $125-149.9 Million
Emp.: 500
Airport
S.I.C.: 4581
N.A.I.C.S.: 488119
Amanda McMillan *(Mng Dir)*

Heathrow Airport Ltd. **(3)**
The Compass Centre Nelson Road
Hounslow, Mddx, TW6 2GW, United Kingdom UK
Tel.: (44) 8443351801
Web Site: www.heathrowairport.com
Sales Range: $1-4.9 Billion
Emp.: 4,500
Airport Operator
S.I.C.: 4581
N.A.I.C.S.: 488119
Normand Boivin *(COO)*

Southampton International **(3)**
Southampton Airport
Southampton, SO18 2NL, United Kingdom UK
Tel.: (44) 844 481 7777
Fax: (44) 238 062 7193
Web Site: www.southamptonairport.com
Sales Range: $25-49.9 Million
Emp.: 213
Airport Operations
S.I.C.: 4581
N.A.I.C.S.: 488119
Dave Lees *(Mng Dir)*

Ferrovial Agroman, S.A. **(1)**
Ribera del Loira 42 Parque Empresarial Puerta de las Naciones
Madrid, 28042, Spain
Tel.: (34) 913008500
Fax: (34) 913008896
Emp.: 13,870
Infrastructure Construction Services
S.I.C.: 1629
N.A.I.C.S.: 237990
Rafael del Pino *(Chm)*
Alejandro de la Joya *(CEO)*
Ernesto Lopez *(CFO)*
Federico Florez *(CIO)*
Alvaro Echaniz *(CEO-Real Estate Div)*
Santiago Olivares *(CEO-Svcs)*
Jaime Aguirre *(Gen Dir-HR)*

Subsidiary:

Cadagua S.A. **(2)**
Gran Via 45 7th and 8th
48011 Bilbao, Spain
Tel.: (34) 944817300
Fax: (34) 944817361
E-Mail: cadagua.info@cadagua.es
Web Site: www.cadagua.es
Sales Range: $200-249.9 Million
Emp.: 440
Water Treatment Plant Construction Services
S.I.C.: 1623
N.A.I.C.S.: 237110
Antonio Casado *(Gen Dir)*

U.S. Subsidiaries:

Ferrovial Agroman US Corp. **(2)**
9600 Great Hills Trl Ste 200 E
Austin, TX 78759
Tel.: (512) 637-8587
Fax: (512) 637-1499
Web Site: www.ferrovial.com
Emp.: 32
Construction Services
S.I.C.: 1629
N.A.I.C.S.: 237990
Ricardo Salas *(Controller-QA & QC Doc Quality)*

Webber LLC **(2)**
14333 Chrisman Rd
Houston, TX 77039
Tel.: (281) 987-8787
Fax: (281) 449-6658
Sales Range: $550-599.9 Million
Emp.: 2,000
Infrastructure Construction Services
S.I.C.: 1629
N.A.I.C.S.: 237990
Mitchell J. Beckman *(VP-HR)*

Non-U.S. Subsidiary:

Budimex S.A. **(2)**
ul Stawki 40
01-040 Warsaw, Poland (59%)
Tel.: (48) 22 623 60 00
Fax: (48) 22 623 60 01
E-Mail: info@budimex.com.pl
Web Site: www.budimex.pl
BDX—(WAR)
Rev.: $1,927,408,316
Assets: $1,093,531,154
Liabilities: $956,172,638
Net Worth: $137,358,517
Earnings: $58,980,472
Emp.: 5,047
Fiscal Year-end: 12/31/12
Construction Services
S.I.C.: 1629
N.A.I.C.S.: 237990
Marek Michalowski *(Chm-Supervisory Bd)*
Dariusz Blocher *(Chm-Mgmt Bd & Gen Mgr)*
Alejandro de la Joya Ruiz de Velasco *(Vice Chm-Supervisory Bd)*
Ignacio Botella Rodriguez *(Vice Chm-Mgmt Bd)*
Marcin Weglowski *(CFO & Member-Mgmt Bd)*
Jacek Daniewski *(Chief Legal Officer & Member-Mgmt Bd)*
Artur Czynczyk *(Chief HR Officer & Member-Mgmt Bd)*
Henryk Urbanski *(Member-Mgmt Bd)*

Ferrovial Servicios S.A. **(1)**
Serrano Galvache 56 Edificio Madrono Parque Norte
28033 Madrid, Spain (99.88%)
Tel.: (34) 913388300
Web Site: www.ferrovial.com
Emp.: 101,416
Business Support Services
S.I.C.: 7389
N.A.I.C.S.: 561499
Santiago Olivares *(CEO)*

Subsidiaries:

CESPA S.A. **(2)**
Avenida de la Catedral 6 y 8
08002 Barcelona, Spain
Tel.: (34) 932 479 100
Web Site: www.cespa.es
Sales Range: $1-4.9 Billion
Emp.: 16,000
Waste Collection & Disposal Services
S.I.C.: 4953
N.A.I.C.S.: 562219

Ferroser **(2)**
C Serrano Galvache 56 Edificio Madrono
28033 Madrid, Spain
Tel.: (34) 913388300
Fax: (34) 915862530
Web Site: www.ferroser.com
Sales Range: $800-899.9 Million
Infrastructure Maintenance Services
S.I.C.: 8744
N.A.I.C.S.: 561210

Non-U.S. Subsidiaries:

Amey UK plc **(2)**
The Sherard Building Edmund Halley Road
Oxford, OX4 4DQ, United Kingdom (100%)
Tel.: (44) 1865713100
Fax: (44) 1865713357
E-Mail: enquiry@amey.co.uk
Web Site: www.amey.co.uk
Rev.: $1,809,811,065
Assets: $1,473,826,593
Liabilities: $866,728,566
Net Worth: $607,098,027
Earnings: $112,390,173
Emp.: 10,964
Fiscal Year-end: 12/31/12
Infrastructure Maintenance & Support Services
S.I.C.: 4789
N.A.I.C.S.: 488999
Santiago Olivares *(Vice Chm)*
Mel Ewell *(CEO)*
Darryl Salmons *(CIO & Dir-Bus Improvement)*
Wayne Robertson *(Sec & Head-Legal)*

Subsidiary:

Amey Infrastructure Services Ltd. **(3)**
Sutton Courtenay
Abingdon, Oxfordshire, OX14 4PP, United Kingdom (100%)
Tel.: (44) 1235848811
Fax: (44) 1235844495
E-Mail: enquiries@amey.co.uk
Web Site: www.amey.co.uk
Emp.: 9,000
Public & Private Infrastructure Services
S.I.C.: 4789
N.A.I.C.S.: 488490
Andrew Nelson *(Grp Dir-Fin)*

Subsidiary:

Amey Rail Ltd. **(4)**
1 Redcliff Street
Bristol, BS1 6QZ, United Kingdom (100%)
Tel.: (44) 1179348836
Fax: (44) 1179348149
E-Mail: collin.carr@amey.co.uk
Web Site: www.amey.co.uk
Emp.: 70
Railway Systems Services
S.I.C.: 4111
N.A.I.C.S.: 485112

FERROWEST LIMITED

Unit 18 28 Belmont Avenue
Belmont, WA, 6104, Australia
Mailing Address:
PO Box 383
Belmont, WA, 6984, Australia
Tel.: (61) 892772600
Fax: (61) 892772655
E-Mail: info@ferrowest.com.au
Web Site: www.ferrowest.com.au
FWL—(ASX)
Rev.: $22,118
Assets: $10,910,324
Liabilities: $366,139
Net Worth: $10,544,186
Earnings: ($1,525,033)
Emp.: 10
Fiscal Year-end: 06/30/13
Business Description:
Mineral Exploration
S.I.C.: 1481
N.A.I.C.S.: 213115
Personnel:
Brett Lee Manning *(Mng Dir)*
Daniel Johannes Bredenkamp *(CFO & Sec)*
Board of Directors:
Bryan Hughes
Graeme Godsman Johnston
Brett Lee Manning
Robert Sun
Barry Edward Wyatt
Legal Counsel:
Jeremy Shervington
52 Ord Street
West Perth, WA, 6005, Australia

FERRUM AMERICAS MINING INC.

120 Adelaide St W Suite 2400
Toronto, ON, M5H 1T1, Canada
Tel.: (416) 637-3523

Web Site: www.ferrumamericas.com
Year Founded: 2010
FEM—(TSXV)
Assets: $66,971
Liabilities: $601,022
Net Worth: ($534,051)
Earnings: ($2,629,094)
Fiscal Year-end: 07/31/13
Business Description:
Iron Ore Mining Services
S.I.C.: 1011
N.A.I.C.S.: 212210
Personnel:
Alistair Maxwell *(Vice Chm)*
Nick Tintor *(Pres & CEO)*
Stephen Gledhill *(CFO)*
Leslie Haddow *(Sec)*
Board of Directors:
Laurence Curtis
Alejandra Kempff
Barry Lavin
Alistair Maxwell
Nick Tintor
Saifeng Yu
Transfer Agent:
Equity Financial Trust
Suite 400 200 University Avenue
Toronto, ON, Canada

FERRUM CRESCENT LIMITED
Unit 2 Level 1 Churchill Court 331-335 Hay Street
Subiaco, WA, 6008, Australia
Mailing Address:
PO Box 524
Wembley, WA, 6913, Australia
Tel.: (61) 8 9380 9653
Fax: (61) 8 9481 5044
E-Mail: info@ferrumcrescent.com
Web Site: www.ferrumcrescent.com
Year Founded: 2005
FCR—(AIM ASX JSE)
Rev.: $430,383
Assets: $2,266,279
Liabilities: $322,250
Net Worth: $1,944,029
Earnings: ($1,981,332)
Emp.: 11
Fiscal Year-end: 06/30/13
Business Description:
Iron Mining & Exploration Services
S.I.C.: 1011
N.A.I.C.S.: 212210
Personnel:
Edward Francis Gerrard Nealon *(Chm)*
Tom Revy *(CEO & Mng Dir)*
Vernon Harvey *(COO)*
Andrew Nealon *(Sec)*
Board of Directors:
Edward Francis Gerrard Nealon
Klaus Borowski
Grant Michael Button
Theodore Carl Droste
Kofi Morna
Legal Counsel:
SNR Denton UK LLP
One Fleet Place
London, United Kingdom
Joelson Wilson LLP
30 Portland Place
London, United Kingdom
Falcon & Hume Attorneys Inc
Block B 7 Eton Road Road
Sandton, South Africa
Clifford Chance
Level 12 London House 216 St Georges Terrace
Perth, Australia
Computershare Investor Services Pty Limited
Level 2 45 St Georges Terrace
Perth, Australia
Computershare Investor Services (Proprietary) Limited
70 Marshall Street
Johannesburg, South Africa

FERSA ENERGIAS RENOVABLES S.A.
Travessera de Gracia 30 5th Floor
08021 Barcelona, Spain
Tel.: (34) 932405306
Fax: (34) 933620405
Web Site: www.fersa.es
FRS—(MAD)
Sls.: $613,558,709
Assets: $604,964,759
Liabilities: $424,112,205
Net Worth: $180,852,555
Earnings: ($105,531,651)
Emp.: 45
Fiscal Year-end: 12/31/12
Business Description:
Renewable Energy Producer
S.I.C.: 1623
N.A.I.C.S.: 237130
Personnel:
Francesc Homs i Ferret *(Chm)*
Ignacio Albinana Cilveti *(Sec)*
Board of Directors:
Francesc Homs i Ferret
Tomas Feliu Bassols
Jose Maria Font Fisa
Ignacio Garcia-Nieto Portabella
Jose Francisco Gispert Serrats
Jorge Enrich Izard
Vidal Amatriain Mendez
Guillermo Mora Griso
Esteban Sarroca Punsola
Jose Vicens Torradas
Subsidiaries:
Eolica el Pedregoso, S.L. (1)
Calle Arenal 21
Malaga, 29016, Spain
Tel.: (34) 952226604
Electric Power Generation Services
S.I.C.: 4911
N.A.I.C.S.: 221118
Fercom Eolica, S.L. (1)
Calle Travessera De Gracia 30 - Pis 5
Barcelona, 08021, Spain
Tel.: (34) 934960200
Electric Power Generation
S.I.C.: 4939
N.A.I.C.S.: 221118

FERSPED A.D.
ul Marsal Tito
1000 Skopje, Macedonia
Tel.: (389) 23149444
Fax: (389) 23149400
E-Mail: email@fersped.com.mk
Web Site: www.fersped.com.mk
Year Founded: 1968
FERS—(MAC)
Sales Range: $75-99.9 Million
Emp.: 300
Business Description:
Holding Company; Transportation & Logistics Services
S.I.C.: 4731
N.A.I.C.S.: 488510
Personnel:
Stojan Nastovski *(Chm-Supervisory Bd)*
Sterjo Nakov *(Chm-Mgmt Bd & Gen Mgr)*
Kiraca Trajkovska *(Vice Chm-Mgmt Bd & Deputy Gen Mgr)*
Nevenka Ristovska *(Member-Mgmt Bd)*
Violeta Tatabitovska *(Member-Mgmt Bd)*
Zoran Todorovski *(Member-Mgmt Bd)*
Caca Zikova *(Member-Mgmt Bd)*
Supervisory Board of Directors:
Stojan Nastovski
Mitko Dimov
Angel Najdovski
Leonid Nakov
Todor Trpcevski
Non-U.S. Subsidiary:
Fertrade d.o.o. (1)
Kralja Milutina 55
11 000 Belgrade, Serbia
Tel.: (381) 113618664
Fax: (381) 113618665
E-Mail: fermk@verat.net
Web Site: www.fersped.com.mk
Freight Transportation Arrangement
S.I.C.: 4731
N.A.I.C.S.: 488510

FERTEK, INC.
3000 Francis Hughes
Laval, QC, H7L 3J5, Canada
Tel.: (450) 663-8700
Fax: (450) 663-9049
E-Mail: info@numesh.com
Web Site: www.numesh.com
Sales Range: $200-249.9 Million
Emp.: 150
Business Description:
Mfr. of Steel Wire & Mesh Products
S.I.C.: 3496
N.A.I.C.S.: 332618
Personnel:
Bruno Tassey *(Pres)*
Subsidiary:
Numesh, Inc. (1)
3000 Francis Hughes
Laval, QC, H7L 3J5, Canada (100%)
Tel.: (450) 663-8700
Fax: (450) 663-9049
E-Mail: numesh@numesh.com
Web Site: www.numesh.com
Emp.: 110
Mfr of Wire, Pipe, Mine & Construction Welded Mesh Products
S.I.C.: 3496
N.A.I.C.S.: 332618
Stephen Beyries *(Dir-IT)*

FERTIGAMA, S.L.
Travesia Ana de Velasco 2
Pamplona, Spain
Tel.: (34) 948 399 017
Business Description:
Chemicals Mfr
S.I.C.: 2819
N.A.I.C.S.: 325180
Subsidiary:
SLIR, S.L. (1)
Ctra Figarol
31310 Carcastillo, Navarre, Spain
Tel.: (34) 948 399 017
Fax: (34) 948 399 019
E-Mail: slir@slir.es
Web Site: www.slir.es
Organic Fertilizer Mfr
S.I.C.: 2873
N.A.I.C.S.: 325311

THE FERTILISERS AND CHEMICALS TRAVANCORE LIMITED
Eloor Udyogamandal
Kochi, Kerala, 683 501, India
Tel.: (91) 4842545101
Fax: (91) 4842545475
Web Site: www.fact.co.in
590024—(BOM NSE)
Rev.: $429,343,165
Assets: $315,087,133
Liabilities: $195,119,984
Net Worth: $119,967,149
Earnings: ($6,561,640)
Emp.: 3,156
Fiscal Year-end: 03/31/13
Business Description:
Fertilizer Mfr
S.I.C.: 1479
N.A.I.C.S.: 212393
Personnel:
Jaiveer Srivastava *(Chm & Mng Dir)*
K. V. Balakrishnan *(Compliance Officer & Sec)*
J. Vinayan *(Chief Vigilance Officer)*
Board of Directors:
Jaiveer Srivastava
V. Subramanian
V. K. Anil
S. C. Gupta
P. Muthusamy
V. K. Subburaj
Transfer Agent:
Cameo Corporate Services Limited
Subramanian Bldg No 1 Club House Road
Chennai, 600 002, India
Tel.: (91) 44 2846 0390
Fax: (91) 44 2846 0129

FERTILIZANTES HERINGER S.A.
Rodovia Municipal PLN 137
13140-000 Sao Paulo, Brazil
Tel.: (55) 1938849092
Fax: (55) 1938847498
Web Site: www.heringer.com.br
FHER3—(BRAZ)
Rev.: $2,612,345,644
Assets: $1,506,004,856
Liabilities: $1,274,252,850
Net Worth: $231,752,006
Earnings: ($1,213,001)
Emp.: 3,425
Fiscal Year-end: 12/31/12
Business Description:
Fertilizer Production & Sales
S.I.C.: 2874
N.A.I.C.S.: 325312
Personnel:
Dalton Dias Heringer *(Chm)*
Dalton Carlos Heringer *(Vice Chm & CEO)*
Rodrigo Bortolini Rezende *(CFO)*
Juliana Heringer Rezende *(Chief Admin Officer)*
Alfredo Fardin *(Comml Officer)*
Pedro Augusto Lombardi Ferreira *(Logistics & Supply Officer)*
Ulisses Maestri *(Technical Officer)*
Board of Directors:
Dalton Dias Heringer
Mailson Ferreira da Nobrega
Almir Goncalves de Miranda
Dalton Carlos Heringer
Roberto Rodrigues

FERTOZ LTD.
40 Balgowlah Street
Wakerley, Brisbane, QLD, 4154, Australia
Tel.: (61) 7 3396 0024
E-Mail: office@fertoz.com
Web Site: www.fertoz.com
Year Founded: 2010
FTZ—(ASX)
Business Description:
Fertilizer Mfr
S.I.C.: 2874
N.A.I.C.S.: 325312

Fertoz Ltd.—(Continued)

Personnel:
James Chisholm *(Chm)*
Les Szonyi *(Mng Dir)*
Julien McInally *(CFO & Sec)*
Board of Directors:
James Chisholm
Adrian Byass
Les Szonyi

FERUS INC.

Suite 120 401 9th Avenue SW
Calgary, AB, T2P 3C5, Canada
Tel.: (403) 517-8777
Fax: (403) 206-6195
Toll Free: (866) 401-6861
E-Mail: info@ferus.ca
Web Site: www.ferus.ca
Year Founded: 2001
Rev.: $181,801,890
Emp.: 95
Business Description:
Energy Service Provider
S.I.C.: 8999
N.A.I.C.S.: 541620
Personnel:
Richard Brown *(Pres & CEO)*
Chad Porter *(COO & VP-Ops)*
Sean Lalani *(Pres-Lng Div)*
Joe Ladouceur *(Treas & VP-External Affairs)*
Board of Directors:
Robert R. Rooney
Henry W. Sykes

FERVENT SYNERGIES LIMITED

B-7/8 Satyam Shopping Center MG Road
Ghatkopar East, Mumbai, Maharashtra, 400077, India
Tel.: (91) 22 25017801
Fax: (91) 22 25017000
Web Site: www.ferventsynergies.com
Year Founded: 2009
533896—(BOM)
Rev.: $445,904
Assets: $5,094,858
Liabilities: $59,207
Net Worth: $5,035,652
Earnings: $105,561
Fiscal Year-end: 03/31/13
Business Description:
Pharmaceutical Product Mfr & Whlsr
S.I.C.: 2834
N.A.I.C.S.: 325412
Personnel:
Vijay P. Thakkar *(Chm & Mng Dir)*
Ashok P. Gohil *(Compliance Officer)*
Board of Directors:
Vijay P. Thakkar
Ashok P. Gohil
Rajesh M. Maheshwari
Jagdish C. Mehta
Nitin B. Parikh
Sanjay P. Thakkar
Transfer Agent:
Sharex Dynamic (India) Pvt. Ltd
Unit 1 Luthra Indus Premises Andheri Kurla Road Safed Pool Andheri E
Mumbai, India

FESTA HOLDING PLC

48 Vladislav Varnenchik Blvd
Shop Exemplary House Fl 2, 9000
Varna, Bulgaria
Tel.: (359) 52669100
Fax: (359) 52669110
E-Mail: office@festa.bg
Web Site: www.festa.bg
Business Description:
Holding Company
S.I.C.: 6719
N.A.I.C.S.: 551112
Personnel:
Petia Slavova *(Chm)*
Subsidiary:

Investbank AD (1)
83 A Bulgaria Blvd
1404 Sofia, Bulgaria (78.72%)
Tel.: (359) 29807722
Fax: (359) 28548199
E-Mail: office@ibank.bg
Web Site: www.ibank.bg
Sales Range: $1-9.9 Million
Banking Services
S.I.C.: 6029
N.A.I.C.S.: 522110

FESTIVAL FORD

421 37400 Highway 2
Red Deer, AB, T4E 1B9, Canada
Tel.: (403) 343-3673
Fax: (403) 341-3202
Toll Free: (888) -245-2511
E-Mail: sales@festivalford.com
Web Site: www.festivalford.com
Year Founded: 1983
Rev.: $50,051,310
Emp.: 55
Business Description:
New & Used Car Dealers
S.I.C.: 5511
N.A.I.C.S.: 441110
Personnel:
Chuck Easy *(Pres)*

FESTO AG & CO. KG

Ruiter Strasse 82
73734 Esslingen, Germany
Tel.: (49) 7113470
Fax: (49) 7113472155
E-Mail: infoservice@festo.com
Web Site: www.festo.com
Year Founded: 1925
Sales Range: $1-4.9 Billion
Emp.: 12,000
Business Description:
Automation Technology & Pneumatic Components & Systems Mfr
Export
S.I.C.: 3535
N.A.I.C.S.: 333922
Personnel:
Wilfried Stoll *(Chm-Supervisory Bd)*
Eberhard Veit *(Chm-Mgmt Bd)*
Kurt Stoll *(Deputy Chm-Supervisory Bd)*
Ekkehard Gericke *(Member-Mgmt Bd-Order Fulfillment Mgmt)*
Kaufmann Alfred Goll *(Member-Mgmt Bd-Human & Intellectual Resources)*
Ansgar Kriwet *(Member-Mgmt Bd-Sls-Europe)*
Thomas Rubbe *(Member-Mgmt Bd-Knowledge & Info Mgmtq)*
Ulrich Walker *(Member-Mgmt Bd-Fin Mgmt)*
Supervisory Board of Directors:
Wilfried Stoll
Mark Binz
Joachim Milberg
Curt-Michael Stoll
Kurt Stoll
Ulrich Stoll
U.S. Subsidiary:

Festo Corporation (1)
395 Moreland Rd
Hauppauge, NY 11788-3947 NY (100%)
Tel.: (631) 435-0800
Fax: (631) 435-8026
Toll Free: (800) 99Festo
Web Site: www.festo-usa.com
Emp.: 406
Mfr. of Pneumatic Components & Systems; Electronic Controller & Control Technology Training Systems
S.I.C.: 5085
N.A.I.C.S.: 423840
Bill Sicari *(Gen Mgr)*

Non-U.S. Subsidiaries:

Festo A/S (1)
Islevdalvej 180
DK 2610 Rodovre, Denmark (100%)
Tel.: (45) 70211090
Fax: (45) 44888199
E-Mail: festo@festo.dk
Web Site: www.festo.dk
Rev.: $17,641,800
Emp.: 40
Automation Technology & Pneumatic Components & Systems
S.I.C.: 3823
N.A.I.C.S.: 334513
Tobias Liden *(Mng Dir)*

PT. Festo (1)
JL Sultan Iskandar Muda No. 68
Arteri Pondok Indah, Jakarta, 12240, Indonesia (100%)
Tel.: (62) 27507900
Fax: (62) 217267386
E-Mail: festo@rad.net.id
Web Site: www.festo.co.id
Sales Range: $1-9.9 Million
Emp.: 100
Automation Technology & Pneumatic Components & Systems
S.I.C.: 3823
N.A.I.C.S.: 334513

Festo AB (1)
Oledevijfydei 2
N 0666 Oslo, Norway (100%)
Tel.: (47) 22728950
Fax: (47) 22728951
E-Mail: post@festo.no
Web Site: www.festo.no
Emp.: 16
Automation Technology & Pneumatic Components & Systems
S.I.C.: 3822
N.A.I.C.S.: 334512

Festo AB (1)
Stillmansgatan 1
PO Box 21038
S 20021 Malmo, Sweden (100%)
Tel.: (46) 40383800
Fax: (46) 40383810
E-Mail: info_se@festo.com
Web Site: www.festo.se
Emp.: 70
Automation Technology & Pneumatic Components & Systems
S.I.C.: 3822
N.A.I.C.S.: 334512

Festo AG (1)
Moosmati Strasse 24
CH 8953 Zurich, Switzerland (100%)
Tel.: (41) 17445544
Fax: (41) 17445500
E-Mail: info_ch@festo.com
Web Site: www.festo.ch
Emp.: 100
S.I.C.: 3625
N.A.I.C.S.: 335314

Festo Brasil Ltda. (1)
Rua Giuseppe Crespi 76
Jardim Santa Emilia, BR 04183 080 Sao Paulo, SP, Brazil (100%)
Tel.: (55) 11 5013 1600
Fax: (55) 11 5013 1801
E-Mail: linhadireta@br.festo.com
Web Site: www.festo.com.br
Sales Range: $25-49.9 Million
Emp.: 500
Automation Technology & Pneumatic Components & Systems
S.I.C.: 3823
N.A.I.C.S.: 334513

Festo Belgium N.V./S.A. (1)
Rue Colonel Bourgstraat 101
1030 Brussels, Belgium (100%)
Tel.: (32) 27023211
Fax: (32) 27023209
E-Mail: info_be@festo.com
Web Site: www.festo.be
Emp.: 65
Automation Technology & Pneumatic Components & Systems
S.I.C.: 3823
N.A.I.C.S.: 334513
Go Verstraeten *(Asst Gen Mgr)*

Festo Bulgaria EOOD (1)
Christophor Kolumb Blvd 9
1592 Sofia, Bulgaria (100%)
Tel.: (359) 29600712
Fax: (359) 29600723
E-Mail: info_bg@festo.com
Web Site: www.festo.bg
Sls.: $2,382,776
Emp.: 13
Automation Technology & Pneumatic Components & Systems
S.I.C.: 3823
N.A.I.C.S.: 334513
Sherbert Pfeifer *(Gen Mgr)*

Festo B.V. (1)
Schieweg 62
2627 AN Delft, Netherlands (100%)
Tel.: (31) 0152518899
Fax: (31) 152518867
E-Mail: info_nl@festo.nl
Web Site: www.festo.nl
Emp.: 140
Automation Technology & Pneumatic Components & Systems
S.I.C.: 3822
N.A.I.C.S.: 334512
Thomas Pahrson *(Mng Dir)*

Festo C.A. (1)
Avda 23 Esquina Calle 71
PO Box 22 62
Maracaibo, 4002, Venezuela (100%)
Tel.: (58) 2617590944
Fax: (58) 2617590455
E-Mail: festo@festo.com.ve
Web Site: www.festo.com
Automation Technology & Pneumatic Components & Systems
S.I.C.: 3823
N.A.I.C.S.: 334513

Festo Chile SA (1)
Americo Uaesvucio 760
Santiago, 6500151, Chile (100%)
Tel.: (56) 26902800
Fax: (56) 26902860,
E-Mail: cl0fcl@festo.cl
Web Site: www.festo.cl
Emp.: 50
Automation Technology & Pneumatic Components & Systems
S.I.C.: 3823
N.A.I.C.S.: 334513
Rafael Cambino *(Head-Mktg)*

Festo (China) Ltd. (1)
1156 Yunqiao Rd Jin Qiao Export Processing Zone
201206 Shanghai, China (100%)
Tel.: (86) 2160815100
Fax: (86) 2158540300
E-Mail: info_cn@cn.festo.com
Web Site: www.festo.com.cn
Automation Technology & Pneumatic Components & Systems
S.I.C.: 3823
N.A.I.C.S.: 334513
Hualai Qiu *(Gen Mgr)*

Festo Co., Ltd. (1)
9 Kung 8th Rd Linkou 2nd Industrial Zone
Taipei, 244, Taiwan (100%)
Tel.: (886) 226019281
Fax: (886) 226019287
E-Mail: festotw@festo.com
Web Site: www.festo.com.tw
Emp.: 82
Automation Technology & Pneumatic Components & Systems
S.I.C.: 3822
N.A.I.C.S.: 334512

Festo Controls Pvt. Ltd. (1)
237B Bommasandra Industrial Area
Bangalore Hosur Highway, Bengaluru, 560 099, India (100%)
Tel.: (91) 8022894100
Fax: (91) 8027832058
E-Mail: info_in@ratein.festo.com
Web Site: www.festo.com
Emp.: 300
Automation Technology & Pneumatic Components & Systems
S.I.C.: 3823
N.A.I.C.S.: 334513

Festo d.o.o. (1)
Nova Cesta 181
10 000 Zagreb, Croatia (100%)

Tel.: (385) 6191969
Fax: (385) 16191818
E-Mail: info_hr@festo.com
Web Site: www.festo.com
Emp.: 11
Automation Technology & Pneumatic Components & Systems
S.I.C.: 3823
N.A.I.C.S.: 334513
Bogdan Opaskar *(Mgr)*

Festo d.o.o. Ljubljana (1)
IC Trzln Blatnica 8
Trzin, 1236 Ljubljana, Slovenia (100%)
Tel.: (386) 15302100
Fax: (386) 15302125
E-Mail: festo@festo.si
Web Site: www.festo.si
Emp.: 15
Automation Technology & Pneumatic Components & Systems
S.I.C.: 3822
N.A.I.C.S.: 334512

Festo E.U.R.L. (1)
5 Rue Montgolfier
F 93116 Rosny-sous-Bois, France (100%)
Tel.: (33) 149352323
Fax: (33) 149352333
E-Mail: indo_fr@festo.com
Web Site: www.festo.com
Sales Range: Less than $1 Million
Emp.: 170
Automation Technology & Pneumatic Components & Systems
S.I.C.: 3823
N.A.I.C.S.: 334513

Festo GmbH (1)
Lincerstrasse 227
A 1141 Vienna, Austria AT
Tel.: (43) 1910750 (100%)
Fax: (43) 191075250
E-Mail: pneumatic@festo.at
Web Site: www.festo.at
Emp.: 80
Automation Technology & Pneumatic Components & Systems
S.I.C.: 3823
N.A.I.C.S.: 334513
Wolfgang Keiner *(Mng Dir)*

Festo Inc. (1)
Km 18 W Service Rd S Super Hwy
1700 Paranaque City, 1700 Manila, Philippines (100%)
Tel.: (63) 27766888
Fax: (63) 28234219
E-Mail: info_ph@festo.com
Web Site: www.festo.com
Emp.: 50
Automation Technology & Pneumatic Components & Systems
S.I.C.: 3822
N.A.I.C.S.: 334512
Paul Ho *(Mgr)*

Festo Inc. (1)
5300 Explorer Dr
Mississauga, ON, L4W 5G4, Canada (100%)
Tel.: (905) 624-9000
Fax: (905) 624-9001
E-Mail: festo.canada@ca.festo.com
Web Site: www.festo.com
Emp.: 80
Wholesale Distributors of Pneumatic Parts
S.I.C.: 5084
N.A.I.C.S.: 423830
Thomas Lichtenberger *(Pres)*

Festo Kft. (1)
Csillaghegei St 32-34
H 1037 Budapest, Hungary
Tel.: (36) 14365111
Fax: (36) 14365101
Web Site: www.festo.hu
Emp.: 15
Automation Technology & Pneumatic Components & Systems
S.I.C.: 3823
N.A.I.C.S.: 334513

Festo K.K. (1)
1 26 10 Hayabuchi
Tsuzuki Ku, Yokohama, 224 0025, Japan (100%)
Tel.: (81) 455935610
Fax: (81) 455935678
E-Mail: info_jp@festo.com
Web Site: www.festo.jp
Emp.: 50
Automation Technology & Pneumatic Components & Systems
S.I.C.: 3822
N.A.I.C.S.: 334512

Festo Korea Co. Ltd. (1)
470 1 Kasan Dong
Kumchun Ku, Seoul, 153 803, Korea (South) (100%)
Tel.: (82) 28507114
Fax: (82) 28647040
E-Mail: info_kr@festo.com
Web Site: www.festo.co.kr
Emp.: 100
Automation Technology & Pneumatic Components & Systems
S.I.C.: 3822
N.A.I.C.S.: 334512

Festo Ltda. (1)
Avda Eldorado No 98 43
Bogota, Colombia (100%)
Tel.: (57) 14048088
Fax: (57) 14048091
E-Mail: festo@festo.com.co
Web Site: www.festo.com.co
Emp.: 63
Automation Technology & Pneumatic Components & Systems
S.I.C.: 3823
N.A.I.C.S.: 334513

Festo Limited (1)
20 Fisher Crescent
Mount Wellington, Auckland, New Zealand NZ
Tel.: (64) 95741094 (100%)
Fax: (64) 95741099
E-Mail: info_nz@festo.com
Web Site: www.festo.com.au
Rev.: $1,490,700
Emp.: 12
Automation Technology & Pneumatic Components & Systems
S.I.C.: 3822
N.A.I.C.S.: 334512
Chris Mathiason *(Gen Mgr)*

Festo Ltd. (1)
67 1 Moo 6 Phaholyothin Rd
T Klong 1 A Klong Luan, Pathumthani, 121 20, Thailand (100%)
Tel.: (66) 29018800
Fax: (66) 29018833
E-Mail: info_th@festo.com
Web Site: www.festo.co.th
Emp.: 100
Automation Technology & Pneumatic Components & Systems
S.I.C.: 3823
N.A.I.C.S.: 334513

Festo Limited (1)
Technology House 1 Fleetwood Park
Barley Way, Fleet, Hants, GU51 2QX, United Kingdom UK
Tel.: (44) 1252 775 001 (100%)
Fax: (44) 1252 775 015
E-Mail: info_gb@festo.com
Web Site: www.festo.co.uk
Sales Range: $25-49.9 Million
Emp.: 17
Automation Technology & Pneumatic Components & Systems
S.I.C.: 3823
N.A.I.C.S.: 334513

Festo Ltd. (1)
40 Hamosternas Ave
GR 11853 Athens, Greece (100%)
Tel.: (30) 21034129004
Fax: (30) 2103412905
E-Mail: info_gr@festo.com
Web Site: www.festo.gr
Emp.: 20
Automation Technology & Pneumatic Components & Systems
S.I.C.: 3823
N.A.I.C.S.: 334513
Dimtleos Pakou Lieriss *(Mng Dir)*

Festo Limited (1)
Unit C & D 7th Floor Leroy Plaza 15
Chueng Shun Street, Kowloon, China (Hong Kong) HK
Tel.: (852) 27438379 (100%)
Fax: (852) 27862173
E-Mail: info_hk@festo.com
Web Site: www.festo.com
Automation Technology & Pneumatic Components & Systems
S.I.C.: 3823
N.A.I.C.S.: 334513

Festo Limited (1)
Unit 5 Sandyford Park Sandyford Industrial Est
Dublin, 18, Ireland IE
Tel.: (353) 12954955 (100%)
Fax: (353) 12955680
E-Mail: sales@festo.ie
Web Site: www.festo.ie
Emp.: 16
Automation Technology & Pneumatic Components & Systems
S.I.C.: 3823
N.A.I.C.S.: 334513

Festo OY (1)
Makituvantle 9
PO Box 86
1511 Vantaa, Finland (100%)
Tel.: (358) 9870651
Fax: (358) 987065200
E-Mail: info.festo.fi@festo.com
Web Site: www.festo.fi
Emp.: 10
Automation Technology & Pneumatic Components & Systems
S.I.C.: 3823
N.A.I.C.S.: 334513
Pekka Parikka *(Mng Dir)*

Festo OY AB Eesti Filiaal (1)
Tammsaare 118 B
12918 Tallinn, Estonia (100%)
Tel.: (372) 6661560
Fax: (372) 6661561
E-Mail: info_ee@festo.com
Web Site: www.festo.ee
Sales Range: Less than $1 Million
Emp.: 6
Automation Technology & Pneumatic Components & Systems
S.I.C.: 3823
N.A.I.C.S.: 334513
Frog Kaljas *(Mgr-Sls)*

Festo Pneumatic S.A. (1)
Zaylan 3 Tequesquinahuac
Tlalnepantla, 54020 Mexico, Mexico (100%)
Tel.: (52) 5553216600
Fax: (52) 5553216665
E-Mail: festo_mexico@festo.com
Web Site: www.festo.com.mx
Emp.: 250
Automation Technology & Pneumatic Components & Systems
S.I.C.: 3822
N.A.I.C.S.: 334512
Bernd Schribir *(Mng Dir)*

Festo Pneumatic S.A. (1)
Avenida De La Gran Via 159
E 08908 L'Hospitalet de Llobregat, Barcelona, Spain (100%)
Tel.: (34) 932616400
Fax: (34) 932616420
E-Mail: info_es@festo.com
Web Site: www.festo.es
Automation Technology & Pneumatic Components & Systems
S.I.C.: 3822
N.A.I.C.S.: 334512

Festo Pneumatic S.K. (1)
6th Street 16th Avenue Km 8 Special Karaj Rd Ste 2
PO Box 15815-1485
Tehran, 1389793761, Iran
Tel.: (98) 2144522409
Fax: (98) 2144522408
E-Mail: mailroom@festo.ir
Web Site: www.festo.com
Automation Technology & Pneumatic Components & Systems
S.I.C.: 3823
N.A.I.C.S.: 334513

Festo Pte. Ltd. (1)
6 Kian Teck Way
628 754 Singapore, Singapore (100%)
Tel.: (65) 62640152
Fax: (65) 62611026
E-Mail: info_sg@festo.com
Web Site: www.festo.com.sg
Emp.: 65
Automation Technology & Pneumatic Components & Systems
S.I.C.: 3822
N.A.I.C.S.: 334512
Christian Burdin *(Mng Dir)*

Festo (Pty.) Ltd. (1)
22-26 Electron Ave
PO Box 255
Isando, 1600, South Africa ZA
Tel.: (27) 119715500 (100%)
Fax: (27) 119742157
E-Mail: info_za@festo.com
Web Site: www.festo.co.za
Emp.: 150
Automation Technology & Pneumatic Components & Systems
S.I.C.: 3822
N.A.I.C.S.: 334512
Richard Teagre *(Mng Dir)*

Festo Pty. Ltd. (1)
179 187 Browns Rd
PO Box 261
Noble Park, VIC, 3174, Australia AU
Tel.: (61) 397959555 (100%)
E-Mail: info_au@festo.com
Web Site: www.festo.com.au
Emp.: 85
Automation Technology & Pneumatic Components & Systems
S.I.C.: 3823
N.A.I.C.S.: 334513
Steve Williams *(Mng Dir)*

OOO Festo-RF (1)
Mitschurinskij Prospect 49
119607 Moscow, Russia
Tel.: (7) 4957373400
Fax: (7) 4957373401
E-Mail: info_ru@festo.com
Web Site: www.festo.ru
Automation Technology & Pneumatic Components & Systems
S.I.C.: 3822
N.A.I.C.S.: 334512

Festo S.A. (1)
Edison 2392
B1640HRV Martinez, Buenos Aires, 1640, Argentina (100%)
Tel.: (54) 1147178200
Fax: (54) 1147178282
E-Mail: info_ar@festo.com
Web Site: www.festo.com.ar
Emp.: 80
Automation Technology & Pneumatic Components & Systems
S.I.C.: 3823
N.A.I.C.S.: 334513
Alberto Belluschi *(Gen Mgr)*

Festo San. ve Tic A.S. (1)
Tuzla Memerciler Organize Sanayi Bolgesi 6 18
TR 34956 Istanbul, Turkey (100%)
Tel.: (90) 2165850085
Fax: (90) 2165850070
E-Mail: info_tr@festo.com
Web Site: www.festo.com.tr
Emp.: 110
Automation Technology & Pneumatic Components & Systems
S.I.C.: 3823
N.A.I.C.S.: 334513
Otto Bauar *(Mng Dir)*

Festo Sdn. Bhd. (1)
10 Persiaran Industria Bangar Sri Damasra
Wilayah Persekutuan, Kuala Lumpur, 52200, Malaysia (100%)
Tel.: (60) 362728122
Fax: (60) 362756412
E-Mail: info_my@festo.com
Web Site: www.festo.com.my
Sales Range: $1-9.9 Million
Emp.: 80
Automation Technology & Pneumatic Components & Systems
S.I.C.: 3822
N.A.I.C.S.: 334512

Festo S.I.A. (1)
Deglava Lela 60
LV 1035 Riga, Latvia (100%)
Tel.: (371) 2577864
Fax: (371) 2577946
E-Mail: info_lv@festo.com
Web Site: www.festo.com
Emp.: 10
Automation Technology & Pneumatic Components & Systems

Festo AG & Co. KG—(Continued)

S.I.C.: 3822
N.A.I.C.S.: 334512

Festo S.p.A. (1)
Via Enrico Fermi 36 38
20090 Assago, Milan, Italy (100%)
Tel.: (39) 2457881
Fax: (39) 24880620
E-Mail: info_it@festo.com
Web Site: www.festo.it
Emp.: 150
Automation Technology & Pneumatic Components & Systems
S.I.C.: 3823
N.A.I.C.S.: 334513

Festo spol. s.r.o. (1)
Gavlovicova Ul 1
83103 Bratislava, Slovakia (100%)
Tel.: (421) 249104910
Fax: (421) 249104911
E-Mail: info_sk@festo.com
Web Site: www.festo.sk
Emp.: 22
Automation Technology & Pneumatic Components & Systems
S.I.C.: 3822
N.A.I.C.S.: 334512
Meroslao Jaroline *(Mng Dir)*

Festo Spol. s.r.o. (1)
Pod Belarii 784
14300 Prague, Czech Republic (100%)
Tel.: (420) 261099611
Fax: (420) 241773384
E-Mail: info_cz@festo.com
Web Site: www.festo.cz
Emp.: 50
Automation Technology & Pneumatic Components & Systems
S.I.C.: 3823
N.A.I.C.S.: 334513
Jarek Baranek *(Mng Dir)*

Festo Sp.z.o.o. (1)
Janki k/Warsawy ul. Mszczonowska 7
Raszyn, PL-05090 Raszyn, Poland
Tel.: (48) 227204166
Fax: (48) 227204476
E-Mail: info_pl@festo.com
Web Site: www.festo.pl
Automation Technology & Pneumatic Components & Systems
S.I.C.: 3822
N.A.I.C.S.: 334512

Festo S.R.L. (1)
Sf Constantin No 17
RO-70751 Bucharest, Romania
Tel.: (40) 213102983
Fax: (40) 213102409
E-Mail: info_ro@festo.com
Web Site: www.festo.ro
Emp.: 22
Automation Technology & Pneumatic Components & Systems
S.I.C.: 3822
N.A.I.C.S.: 334512
Radu Alexandru *(Gen Mgr)*

Festo U.A.B. (1)
Karalius Mindaugo Pr 22
LT-44295 Kaunas, Lithuania
Tel.: (370) 37321314
Fax: (370) 37321315
E-Mail: info_lt@festo.com
Web Site: www.festo.lt
Emp.: 20
Automation Technology & Pneumatic Components & Systems
S.I.C.: 3822
N.A.I.C.S.: 334512
Pektta Parika *(Gen Mgr)*

Dp Festo (1)
Borissoglebskaja 11
U04070 Kiev, Ukraine (100%)
Tel.: (380) 442392433
Fax: (380) 444637096
Web Site: www.festo.com.ua
Automation Technology & Pneumatic Components & Systems
S.I.C.: 3823
N.A.I.C.S.: 334513

FETIM B.V.

Kopraweg 1
PO Box 770
Amsterdam, Netherlands
Tel.: (31) 20 58 05 333
Fax: (31) 20 58 05 222 05
E-Mail: info@fetimgroup.com
Web Site: www.fetim.nl
Business Description:
Building Material & Supply Whlsr
S.I.C.: 5049
N.A.I.C.S.: 423490
Personnel:
Alexander Beerkens *(Pres & CEO)*

Non-U.S. Subsidiary:

Aqualux Products Holdings Ltd. (1)
Universal Point Steelmans Road
Wednesbury, West Midlands, WS10 9UZ, United Kingdom
Tel.: (44) 8702416131
Fax: (44) 8702416132
E-Mail: enquiries@aqualux.co.uk
Web Site: www.aqualux.co.uk
Emp.: 150
Shower Enclosures & Bath Screens Distr
S.I.C.: 5023
N.A.I.C.S.: 423220
Michael Heath *(Mng Dir)*

Holding:

Aqualux Products Ltd. (2)
Universal Point Steelmans Rd
Off Park Ln, Wednesbury, West Midlands, WS10 9UZ, United Kingdom
Tel.: (44) 8702416131
Fax: (44) 8702416132
E-Mail: enquiries@aqualux.co.uk
Web Site: www.aqualux.co.uk
Emp.: 550
Shower Enclosure & Bath Screens Distr
S.I.C.: 5023
N.A.I.C.S.: 423220
Alexander Beerkens *(Mng Dir)*

FEV GMBH

Neuenhofstrasse 181
52078 Aachen, Germany
Tel.: (49) 241 5689 0
Fax: (49) 241 5689 119
E-Mail: marketing@fev.com
Web Site: www.fev.com
Sales Range: $400-449.9 Million
Business Description:
Engineering Services
S.I.C.: 8711
N.A.I.C.S.: 541330
Personnel:
Stefan Pischinger *(CEO)*
Rainer Paulsen *(Exec VP)*
Sami Sagur *(Exec VP)*
Ernst Scheid *(Exec VP)*
Markus Schwaderlapp *(Exec VP)*

U.S. Subsidiary:

FEV, Inc. (1)
554 Glenmeade Ln
Auburn Hills, MI 48326
Tel.: (248) 373-6000
Fax: (248) 373-8084
Engineering Services
S.I.C.: 8711
N.A.I.C.S.: 541330
Patrick Hupperich *(Pres & CEO)*

Subsidiary:

DGE Inc. (2)
2870 Technology Dr
Rochester Hills, MI 48309 MI
Tel.: (248) 293-1300
Fax: (248) 293-1309
E-Mail: sales@dgeinc.com
Web Site: www.dgeinc.net
Sales Range: $1-9.9 Million
Emp.: 40
Electrical Engineering & Design Services for Automotive Industry
S.I.C.: 8711
N.A.I.C.S.: 541330
Joseph Laramie *(Pres)*

FEVER-TREE LIMITED

The Plaza 535 Kings Road
London, SW10 0SZ, United Kingdom
Tel.: (44) 20 7349 4922
E-Mail: info@fever-tree.com
Web Site: www.fever-tree.com
Year Founded: 2004
Sales Range: $10-24.9 Million
Emp.: 11
Business Description:
Mixer Drink Mfr
S.I.C.: 2085
N.A.I.C.S.: 312140
Personnel:
Tim Warrillow *(Founder & Mng Dir)*

FEWA FINANCE LIMITED

BP Chowk Chipledhunga
Pokhara, Nepal
Tel.: (977) 61 538300
Fax: (977) 61 538738
E-Mail: info@fewafinance.com.np
Web Site: www.fewafinance.com.np
FFCL—(NEP)
Business Description:
Financial Services
S.I.C.: 6211
N.A.I.C.S.: 523999
Personnel:
Bindu Kumar Thapa *(Chm)*
Resham Bahadur Thapa *(CEO)*
Board of Directors:
Bindu Kumar Thapa
Devi Raj Gurung
Dil Bahadur Gurung
Rajendra Legal
Rambhakta Ranjit
Madhav Prasad Sigdel

FEXCO HOLDINGS

(d/b/a FEXCO Group)
Iveragh Road
Killorglin, Kerry, Ireland
Tel.: (353) 66 9761258
Fax: (353) 66 9762284
E-Mail: info@fexco.com
Web Site: www.fexco.com
Emp.: 1,300
Business Description:
Global Payments Services
S.I.C.: 9311
N.A.I.C.S.: 921130
Personnel:
Brian McCarthy *(Founder & Chm)*
Dick Spring *(Deputy Chm)*
Gavin O'Neill *(Mng Dir)*
Gerard O'Sullivan *(CFO)*
Denis Creighton *(CEO-Managed Bus Solutions & Outsourcing Div)*
Gerard Murphy *(Sec)*
Board of Directors:
Brian McCarthy
Roy Barrett
Ian Marsh
Denis McCarthy
Gerard Murphy
John Nagle
Tom O'Beirne
Gavin O'Neill
Dermot O'Shea
Maurice Roche
Michael Somers
Gerard Wrixon

Subsidiaries:

FEXCO Asset Finance (1)
Ely Place
Dublin, 2, Ireland
Tel.: (353) 637 3000
Telex: 90803
Fax: (353) 637 3066
Web Site: www.fexcoassetfinance.com
Emp.: 23
Leasing
S.I.C.: 6514
N.A.I.C.S.: 531110

FEXCO Asset Finance (1)
2 Mt Kennett Pl
Limerick, Ireland
Tel.: (353) 61311711
Fax: (353) 61311449
E-Mail: info@fexco.com
Web Site: www.fexcoassetfinance.com
Emp.: 4
Leasing
S.I.C.: 6514
N.A.I.C.S.: 531110
Darmouth Morris *(Mng Dir)*

Goodbody Stockbrokers (1)
Ballsbridge Park
Ballsbridge, Dublin, 4, Ireland IE
Tel.: (353) 16670400 (100%)
Fax: (353) 1 667 0240
E-Mail: goodbody@goodbody.ie
Web Site: www.goodbody.ie
Emp.: 215
Investment Services
S.I.C.: 6211
N.A.I.C.S.: 523999
Roy Barrett *(Mng Dir)*
Brian O'Kelly *(Mng Dir)*

FEY & CO. GMBH & CO. KG

Rheiner Strasse 145
48282 Emsdetten, Germany
Tel.: (49) 25721540
Fax: (49) 257215440
E-Mail: info@fey-co.de
Web Site: www.fey-co.de
Year Founded: 1926
Rev.: $31,383,237
Emp.: 100
Business Description:
Mattress Mfr
S.I.C.: 2515
N.A.I.C.S.: 337910
Personnel:
Johannes Brinkmann *(Mng Dir)*

FFASTFILL PLC

(Acquired by ION Trading Ireland Ltd.)

FGP LTD.

Commercial Union House 9 Wallace Street
Fort, Mumbai, Maharashtra, 400001, India
Tel.: (91) 2222070273
Fax: (91) 2222008074
E-Mail: fgpltd03@indiatimes.com
Web Site: www.fgpltd.in
500142—(BOM)
Rev.: $77,463
Assets: $2,171,553
Liabilities: $104,224
Net Worth: $2,067,330
Earnings: ($64,840)
Fiscal Year-end: 03/31/13
Business Description:
FiberGlass Products Mfr
S.I.C.: 3231
N.A.I.C.S.: 327215
Personnel:
Kishore Shete *(Compliance Officer)*
Board of Directors:
Dalal H. C.
Vimal Ramballabh Kejriwal
Hari Narayan Singh Rajpoot
Kishore Shete
Transfer Agent:
Sharepro Services (India) Private Limited
13 AB Samhita Warehousing Complex II Floor
Sakinaka Telephone Lane
Off Andheri Kurla Rd Sakinaka, Mumbai, India

F.H. PAPENMEIER GMBH & CO. KG

Talweg 2
58239 Schwerte, Germany
Tel.: (49) 23042050
Fax: (49) 2304205205
E-Mail: info@papenmeier.de
Web Site: www.papenmeier.de

Year Founded: 1956
Rev.: $15,773,730
Emp.: 102
Business Description:
Engineering Services
S.I.C.: 8711
N.A.I.C.S.: 541330
Personnel:
Armin Papenmeier *(Mng Dir)*
Gunther Papenmeier *(Mng Dir)*

FHB MORTGAGE BANK PUBLIC LIMITED COMPANY
Ulloi ut 48
1082 Budapest, Hungary
Tel.: (36) 1 33 44 344
Fax: (36) 1 452 9100
E-Mail: fhb@fhb.hu
Web Site: www.fhb.hu
FHB—(BUD)
Int. Income: $283,982,560
Assets: $2,928,010,800
Liabilities: $2,690,765,040
Net Worth: $237,245,760
Earnings: $7,381,160
Emp.: 170
Fiscal Year-end: 12/31/12
Business Description:
Mortgage Banking Services
S.I.C.: 6159
N.A.I.C.S.: 522292
Personnel:
Zoltan Speder *(Chm)*
Csaba Lantos *(Chm-Supervisory Bd)*
Gyula Kobli *(CEO)*
Tamas Foltanyi *(Deputy CEO)*
Gabor Gergo Soltesz *(Deputy CEO)*
Board of Directors:
Zoltan Speder
Gabriella Balogh
Tamas Foltanyi
Gyula Kobli
Christian Riener
Gabor Gergo Soltesz
Akos Zoltan Starcz
Supervisory Board of Directors:
Csaba Lantos
Tibor Kadar
Miklos Szabo
Eniko Martonne Uhrin

Subsidiaries:

FHB Life Annuity Ltd. (1)
Ulloi St 48
1082 Budapest, Hungary
Tel.: (36) 14529100
Fax: (36) 14528595
Banking Services
S.I.C.: 6029
N.A.I.C.S.: 522110

FHB Real Estate Leasing Ltd. (1)
Rumbach Sebestyen utca 15
1075 Budapest, Hungary
Tel.: (36) 1 461 6040
Fax: (36) 1 461 6041
E-Mail: lizing@fhb.hu
Web Site: www.fhb.hu
Emp.: 20
Real Estate Leasing Services
S.I.C.: 6514
N.A.I.C.S.: 531110

FHB Real Estate Ltd. (1)
Ulloi ut 48
1082 Budapest, Hungary
Tel.: (36) 14528527
Fax: (36) 13290986
E-Mail: ingatlan@fhb.hu
Web Site: www.fhbingatlan.hu
Mortgage Banking Services
S.I.C.: 6159
N.A.I.C.S.: 522292

FHB Services Ltd (1)
Ulloi Street 48
1082 Budapest, Hungary
Tel.: (36) 14529100
Fax: (36) 1 452 9200
E-Mail: fhb@fhb.hu
Emp.: 500
Banking Services
S.I.C.: 6029
N.A.I.C.S.: 522110
Gyula Kobli *(Gen Mgr)*

FHL I. KIRIAKIDIS MARBLE - GRANITE SA
Industrial Park of Prosotsani
66200 Drama, Greece
Tel.: (30) 25220 23514
Fax: (30) 25220 23490
E-Mail: frontdesk@fhl.gr
Web Site: www.fhl.gr
Year Founded: 1991
KYRM—(ATH)
Sales Range: $50-74.9 Million
Emp.: 247
Business Description:
Marble & Granite Quarrying Services
S.I.C.: 1423
N.A.I.C.S.: 212313
Personnel:
Kiriakidis Ilias *(Pres & Mng Dir)*
Kountouras Vasilios *(Member-Mgmt Bd & Principal-Accts Office)*
Pafos Athanasios *(Member-Mgmt Bd)*
Ligou Ruth Georgia *(Member-Mgmt Bd)*
Petropoulos Georgios *(Member-Mgmt Bd)*
Charalampidis Ioannis *(Principal-Supply Dept)*
Nikolas Kyvranoglou *(Principal-Import & Export Dept)*

FIACAO E TECELAGEM SAO JOSE S.A.
R Jose Prenassi 04
36200026 Brasilia, MG, Brazil
Tel.: (55) 81 3233 1288
Fax: (55) 81 3092 1200
Year Founded: 1933
SJOS3—(BRAZ)
Business Description:
Textile Product Mfr & Whslr.
S.I.C.: 2389
N.A.I.C.S.: 314999
Personnel:
Oscar Augusto Rache Ferreira *(Dir-IR)*

FIAMM S.P.A.
Via Le Europa 63
I 36075 Montecchio Maggiore, Vichensa, Italy
Tel.: (39) 0444709311
Telex: 480295
Fax: (39) 0444699237
E-Mail: hr@fiamm.com
Web Site: www.fiammgroup.com
Year Founded: 1942
Sales Range: $650-699.9 Million
Emp.: 3,600
Business Description:
Automotive, Industrial & Consumer Batteries & Automobile Horns Mfr Import Export
S.I.C.: 3691
N.A.I.C.S.: 335911

Joint Venture:

Fiamm (1)
Viale Europa 63
36075 Maggiore, Montecchio, Italy IT
Tel.: (39) 0444709350
Fax: (39) 0444709360
E-Mail: info.starter@fiamm.com
Web Site: www.fiamm.com
Sls.: $22,378,200
Emp.: 160
Mfr of Small SLA Batteries
S.I.C.: 3691
N.A.I.C.S.: 335911

U.S. Subsidiary:

Fiamm Technologies Inc. (1)
1550 Leeson Ave
Cadillac, MI 49601-8975 MI
Tel.: (231) 775-2900 (100%)
Fax: (231) 775-6162
Web Site: www.fiamm.com
Emp.: 175
Mfr. of Automobile Horns
S.I.C.: 3714
N.A.I.C.S.: 336320

FIAMMA HOLDINGS BERHAD
Lot 6 05 Level 6 KPMG Tower 8 First Avenue Bandar Utama
47800 Petaling Jaya, Selangor Darul Ehsan, Malaysia
Tel.: (60) 3 7720 1188
Fax: (60) 3 7720 1111
E-Mail: infocorp@fiamma.com.my
Web Site: www.fiamma.com.my
FIAMMA—(KLS)
Rev.: $84,750,924
Assets: $118,420,766
Liabilities: $28,906,476
Net Worth: $89,514,290
Earnings: $9,746,438
Fiscal Year-end: 09/30/12
Business Description:
Holding Company; Consumer Appliances, Sanitaryware, Cabinets, Bathroom Fittings & Healthcare Products Distr
S.I.C.: 6719
N.A.I.C.S.: 551112
Personnel:
Choo Hong Lim *(CEO & Mng Dir)*
Su San Chan *(Co-Sec)*
Mee Foon Chin *(Co-Sec)*
Yit Chan Tai *(Co-Sec)*
Board of Directors:
Azizan Husain
Bahar Ahmad
Margaret Lee Hung Chak
Sau Chun Kok
Choo Hong Lim
Soo Kong Lim
Chee Ghee Teh

Subsidiaries:

Enex-Dynamic Sdn. Bhd. (1)
3-2 Wisma Fiamma No 20 Jalan 7A/62A
Bandar Manjalara, 52200 Kuala Lumpur, Malaysia
Tel.: (60) 362798787
Fax: (60) 362798777
Web Site: www.e-enex.com
Emp.: 7
Water Supply Services
S.I.C.: 4971
N.A.I.C.S.: 221310
Leslie W. K. Ching *(Pres)*

FHB Management Sdn. Bhd. (1)
Level 9 Wisma Fiamma Lot 44653 Jalan 7A/62A
Bandar Manjalara, 52200 Kuala Lumpur, Malaysia
Tel.: (60) 362798888
Fax: (60) 362798933
E-Mail: chuahy@fiamma.com.my
Emp.: 200
Property Management Services
S.I.C.: 6531
N.A.I.C.S.: 531311
Lim Choo Hong *(CEO)*

Fiamma Trading Sdn. Bhd. (1)
Wisma Fiamma No 20 Jalan 7A/62A
Bandar Manjalara
52200 Kuala Lumpur, Malaysia
Tel.: (60) 362798943
Fax: (60) 362798942
E-Mail: service@fiamma.com.my
Web Site: www.fmtrd.com.my
Emp.: 200
Consumer Electrical Equipments Distr
S.I.C.: 5064
N.A.I.C.S.: 423620
Leslie Ching *(Mng Dir)*

Fimaco Sdn. Bhd. (1)
8-2 Wisma Fiamma No 20 Jalan 7A/62A
Bandar Manjalara
52200 Kuala Lumpur, Malaysia
Tel.: (60) 362798666
Fax: (60) 362798633
E-Mail: info-fabr@fimaco.com.my
Web Site: www.fimaco.com.my
Emp.: 200
Consumer Electrical Equipments Distr
S.I.C.: 5064
N.A.I.C.S.: 423620
Lim Jimmy Choo Hong *(CEO)*
Chew Leng Huat *(Mng Dir)*

Kinsmedic Sdn. Bhd. (1)
9-2 Wisma Fiamma No 20 Jalan 7A/62A
Bandar Manjalara
52200 Kuala Lumpur, Malaysia
Tel.: (60) 362798888
Fax: (60) 362798998
E-Mail: sales@kinsmedic.com.my
Web Site: www.kinsmedic.com.my
Emp.: 30
Medical Instruments & Healthcare Products Distr
S.I.C.: 5047
N.A.I.C.S.: 423450
Leslie W. K. Chung *(Mng Dir)*

Oaksvilla Sdn. Bhd. (1)
PTD 5490 Jalan Remia Taman Kota Jaya
81900 Kota Tinggi, Johor, Malaysia
Tel.: (60) 78822716
Fax: (60) 78833716
E-Mail: hhsh@fiamma.com.my
Property Development Services
S.I.C.: 6531
N.A.I.C.S.: 531390
Ho Hong Seng *(Mgr)*

Uniphoenix Jaya Sdn. Bhd. (1)
PTD 5490 Jalan Remia Taman Kota Jaya
81900 Kota Tinggi, Johor, Malaysia
Tel.: (60) 78822716
Fax: (60) 78833716
Property Development Services
S.I.C.: 6531
N.A.I.C.S.: 531390
Ho Hong Seng *(Mgr)*

Non-U.S. Subsidiary:

Kingston Medical Supplies (Pte.) Ltd. (1)
35 Tannery Road 11-01 Tannery Block
Ruby Industrial Complex
Singapore, 347740, Singapore
Tel.: (65) 67453922
Fax: (65) 67479688
E-Mail: sales@kingsmed.com.sg
Web Site: www.kingsmed.com.sg
Emp.: 30
Medical Instruments Distr
S.I.C.: 5047
N.A.I.C.S.: 423450
George Foo *(Gen Mgr)*

FIAT INDUSTRIAL S.P.A.
(Merged with CNH Global N.V. to form CNH Industrial N.V.)

FIAT S.P.A.
Via Nizza 250
10126 Turin, Italy
Tel.: (39) 0110061111
Telex: 221056
Fax: (39) 0110063796
E-Mail: mediarelations@fiatgroup.com
Web Site: www.fiatspa.com
Year Founded: 1899
F—(ITA OTC)
Rev.: $113,020,394,690
Assets: $110,546,134,230
Liabilities: $92,813,036,820
Net Worth: $17,733,097,410
Earnings: $1,899,445,870
Emp.: 214,836
Fiscal Year-end: 12/31/12
Business Description:
Automobiles, Commercial Vehicles, Agricultural & Construction Equipment & Production Systems Mfr

Fiat S.p.A.—(Continued)

Import Export
S.I.C.: 3711
N.A.I.C.S.: 336111
Personnel:
John Philip Elkann *(Chm)*
Sergio Marchionne *(CEO)*
Richard K. Palmer *(CFO)*
Olivier Francois *(CMO)*
Harald Wester *(CTO)*
Linda I. Knoll *(Chief HR Officer)*
Scott R. Garberding *(Chief Pur Officer)*
Stefan Ketter *(Chief Mfg Officer)*
Robert Pucci *(Exec VP-HR)*
Gilberto Ceresa *(Sr VP)*
Ferruccio Luppi *(Sr VP-Bus Dev & Strategy)*
Simone Migliarino *(Sr VP-Comm)*
Roberto Pisa *(Sr VP-Corp Initiatives)*
Board of Directors:
John Philip Elkann
Andrea Agnelli
Joyce Victoria Bigio
Rene Carron
Tiberto Brandolini d'Adda
Luca Cordero di Montezemolo
Gian Maria Gros-Pietro
Sergio Marchionne
Patience Wheatcroft

Subsidiaries:

BMI S.p.A. **(1)**
Vle Brigata Bisagno 2
16129 Genoa, Italy
Tel.: (39) 010534011
Fax: (39) 01053401260
New Car Dealer
S.I.C.: 5511
N.A.I.C.S.: 441110

Business Solutions S.p.A. **(1)**
Corso Marconi 10
10125 Turin, Italy (100%)
Tel.: (39) 0110061911
Fax: (39) 0110036123
Web Site: www.bsolutions.it
Emp.: 651
Human Resource Management & Consulting Services
S.I.C.: 8742
N.A.I.C.S.: 541611
Ferruccio Luppi *(CEO)*

Centro Ricerche Fiat S.C.p.A. **(1)**
Strada Torino 50
Orbassano, 10043 Turin, Italy IT
Tel.: (39) 0119083111 (100%)
Telex: 2 11289 CRIFIAT I
Fax: (39) 0119083670
E-Mail: marketing@crf.it
Web Site: www.crf.it
Emp.: 1,200
Automotive Research & Development Services
S.I.C.: 8731
N.A.I.C.S.: 541712

Comau S.p.A. **(1)**
Via Rivalta 30
10095 Grugliasco, Italy
Tel.: (39) 0116849111
Telex: 221511 COMAU I
Fax: (39) 00390113971468
Web Site: www.comau.it
Sales Range: $1-4.9 Billion
Emp.: 50
Machine Tool & Production Systems Mfr
S.I.C.: 3589
N.A.I.C.S.: 333318
Sergio Marchionne *(Chm-Fiat)*

U.S. Subsidiaries:

Comau Pico Holdings Corporation **(2)**
21000 Telegraph Rd
Southfield, MI 48033
Tel.: (248) 353-8888
Fax: (248) 368-2511
E-Mail:
Welding & Soldering Equipment Mfr
S.I.C.: 3548
N.A.I.C.S.: 333992
Riccardo Tarantini *(CEO)*

Subsidiaries:

Comau Inc. **(3)**
21000 Telegraph Rd
Southfield, MI 48033
Tel.: (248) 353-8888
Fax: (248) 368-2531
Toll Free: (888) 888-8998
Web Site: www.comau.com
Welding & Soldering Equipment Mfr
S.I.C.: 3548
N.A.I.C.S.: 333992
Joe Shelata *(CFO)*

Comau Resources, Inc. **(3)**
21175 Telegraph Rd
Southfield, MI 48033
Tel.: (248) 435-4100
Industrial Machinery Mfr
S.I.C.: 3559
N.A.I.C.S.: 333249

Comau Pico **(2)**
21000 Telegraph Rd
Southfield, MI 48034
Tel.: (248) 353-8888
Fax: (248) 368-2511
Toll Free: (888) 888-8998
Web Site: www.comaupico.com
Emp.: 500
Machine Tool & Production Systems Mfr
S.I.C.: 3714
N.A.I.C.S.: 336390
Charles Capshaw *(Project Mgr)*

Non-U.S. Subsidiaries:

Comau Argentina S.A. **(2)**
Ruta N 9 Km 695 - Ferreyra
Cordoba, X5925XAD, Argentina
Tel.: (54) 351 4103311
Web Site: www.comau.com
Industrial Machinery Mfr
S.I.C.: 3569
N.A.I.C.S.: 333999

Comau Deutschland GmbH **(2)**
Hugo-Eckener-Strasse 20
50829 Cologne, Germany
Tel.: (49) 221 76 0060
Fax: (49) 221 76 0088
Web Site: www.comau.com
Industrial Automation Machinery Distr
S.I.C.: 5084
N.A.I.C.S.: 423830
Marco Severo Inga *(CFO)*

Comau France S.A.S. **(2)**
5-7 rue Albert Einstein
78197 Trappes, France
Tel.: (33) 1 30166100
Web Site: www.comau.com
Automotive Component Mfr
S.I.C.: 3714
N.A.I.C.S.: 336390

Comau India Private Limited **(2)**
34Km Milestone - Pune-Nagar Rd
Shikrapur, Pune, 412 208, India
Tel.: (91) 2137 678100
Fax: (91) 2137 678110
Web Site: www.comau.com
Emp.: 350
Industrial Automation Machinery Mfr
S.I.C.: 3559
N.A.I.C.S.: 333249
Aman Garg *(Mgr-Robotics & Simulation)*

COMAU (KUNSHAN) Automation Co. Ltd. **(2)**
Yuanfeng Road & Gucheng Road Robotics Industrial Park
23500 Kunshan, Jiangsu, China
Tel.: (86) 51236821000
Fax: (86) 51236821088
Web Site: www.comau.com
Emp.: 350
Industrial Automation System Repair & Maintenance Services
S.I.C.: 7699
N.A.I.C.S.: 811310
Weixuan Tian *(Deputy Mgr-Quality)*

Comau Pico Mexico S.de R.I. de C.V. **(2)**
Av Acceso Lotes 12 Y 13
Tepotzotlan, Mexico
Tel.: (52) 5558996900
Automotive Parts Mfr
S.I.C.: 3714
N.A.I.C.S.: 336390

Subsidiaries:

Comau Pico Iaisa S.de R.L. de C.V. **(3)**
Av Acceso Lotes 12 Y 13
Tepotzotlan, 54610, Mexico
Tel.: (52) 5558996900
Business Management Consulting Services
S.I.C.: 8748
N.A.I.C.S.: 541618

Comau Pico Pitex S.de R.L. C.V **(3)**
Av Acceso Lotes 12 y 13 Fracc Ind El Trebol 2 Secc
Tepotzotlan, 54610, Mexico
Tel.: (52) 55 5899 69 00
Fax: (52) 55 5899 69 33
Web Site: www.comau.com
Automotive Parts Mfr
S.I.C.: 3714
N.A.I.C.S.: 336390

Comau Pico Trebol S.de R.I. de C.V. **(3)**
Av Acceso Lotes 12 Y 13
Tepotzotlan, 54610, Mexico
Tel.: (52) 5558996900
Fax: (52) 525558996933
Emp.: 300
Real Estate Development Services
S.I.C.: 6531
N.A.I.C.S.: 531390
Luca Gandino *(Gen Mgr)*

Comau Romania S.R.L. **(2)**
Sos Borsului 53B
410605 Oradea, Bihor, Romania
Tel.: (40) 259 414769
Fax: (40) 259 479840
E-Mail: romania.office@comau.com
Web Site: www.comau.com
Emp.: 350
Automotive Welding Equipment Mfr
S.I.C.: 3548
N.A.I.C.S.: 333992
Marco Busi *(CEO)*

Comau Russia OOO **(2)**
10 Testovskaya Str 1st Entrance 19th Fl
Moscow, Russia 123317
Tel.: (7) 495 7885265
Fax: (7) 495 7885266
Web Site: www.comau.com
Automotive Component Mfr
S.I.C.: 3714
N.A.I.C.S.: 336390
Luca Gandino *(CEO)*

Comau Service Systems S.L. **(2)**
Avenida Aragon 402
28022 Madrid, Spain
Tel.: (34) 913252851
Fax: (34) 913252778
Emp.: 1
Automotive Repair & Maintenance Services
S.I.C.: 7538
N.A.I.C.S.: 811111

Comau (Shanghai) International Trading Co. Ltd. **(2)**
No 1353 Jiugan Rd Sijing Industrial Area
Songjiang Dist, Shanghai, 201601, China
Tel.: (86) 2137616222
Automotive Parts Distr
S.I.C.: 5013
N.A.I.C.S.: 423120

Comau U.K. Limited **(2)**
10 Midland Road
Luton, Bedfordshire, LU2 0HR, United Kingdom
Tel.: (44) 1582 817600
Fax: (44) 1582 817700
Web Site: www.comau.com
Industrial Automation Machinery Distr
S.I.C.: 5084
N.A.I.C.S.: 423830

Elasis S.C.p.A. **(1)**
Via Ex Aeroporto Sn
80038 Pomigliano d'Arco, 80038 Naples, Italy
Tel.: (39) 08119695145
Fax: (39) 08119695143
Web Site: www.elasis.com
Emp.: 850
Automotive Engineering, Research & Development Services
S.I.C.: 8731
N.A.I.C.S.: 541712
Mediodi Giusto *(CEO)*

Fiat Finance S.p.A. **(1)**
Via Nizza 250
10126 Turin, Italy IT
Tel.: (39) 011 006 3710
Fax: (39) 011 006 3800
Web Site: www.fiatgroup.com
Treasury Services for Fiat Group Companies
S.I.C.: 6726
N.A.I.C.S.: 525990

Non-U.S. Subsidiaries:

Fiat Financas Brasil Ltda **(2)**
Rua Senador Milton Campos 175 5 andar - Parte
Nova Lima, Minas Gerais, 34000-000, Brazil
Tel.: (55) 3121234500
Fax: (55) 3138887099
Business Management Consulting Services
S.I.C.: 8748
N.A.I.C.S.: 541618

Fiat Finance and Trade Ltd S.A. **(2)**
24 boulevard Royal
2449 Luxembourg, Luxembourg
Tel.: (352) 262 05621
Fax: (352) 262 00488
Emp.: 7
Financial Investment Services
S.I.C.: 6726
N.A.I.C.S.: 525990

Fiat Gestione Partecipazioni S.p.A. **(1)**
62 Via Volturno
25126 Brescia, Italy
Tel.: (39) 0306 597 111
Investment Management Services
S.I.C.: 6282
N.A.I.C.S.: 523920

Subsidiary:

Fiat Group Purchasing S.r.l. **(2)**
Corso Giovanni Agnelli 200
Turin, 10135, Italy
Tel.: (39) 011 00 31111
Fax: (39) 0110 03 82 15
Procurement Services
S.I.C.: 7389
N.A.I.C.S.: 541990

Fiat Group Automobiles S.p.A. **(1)**
Corso Agnelli 200
10135 Turin, Italy IT
Tel.: (39) 0110031111 (100%)
Fax: (39) 0110037591
E-Mail: fiatautopress@fiat.com
Web Site: www.fiat.com
Sales Range: $25-49.9 Billion
Emp.: 44,691
Automobile Mfr & Sales
S.I.C.: 3711
N.A.I.C.S.: 336111
Sergio Marchionne *(CEO)*
Diego Pistone *(CFO)*

Subsidiaries:

Alfa Romeo Automobiles S.p.A. **(2)**
Corso Agnelli 200
10135 Turin, Italy
Tel.: (39) 0110031111
Telex: ALFAMI I 330101 ARESE
Fax: (39) 0110037591
Web Site: www.alfaromeo.com
Automobile Mfr
S.I.C.: 3711
N.A.I.C.S.: 336111
Harald J. Wester *(CEO)*

Subsidiaries:

Fiat Auto Alfa Romeo **(3)**
Viale Alfa Romeo
20020 Arese, MI, Italy (100%)
Tel.: (39) 0244428111
Telex: ALFAMI 330101
Fax: (39) 029315746
Web Site: www.alfaromeo.com
Emp.: 2,900

Sports Cars, Industrial Vehicles, Engines & Related Products Mfr
S.I.C.: 3711
N.A.I.C.S.: 336111
Sergio Cravero *(Brand Dir)*

Non-U.S. Subsidiary:

Alfa Romeo Vertriebsgesellschaft m.b.H. (3)
Hanauer Landstrasse 176
D-60314 Frankfurt, Germany
Tel.: (49) 69669880
Telex: ALFAF D4-13055
Fax: (49) 6966988952
E-Mail: customercare.germany@fiat.com
Web Site: www.alfaromeo.de
Emp.: 177
Automobile Distr
S.I.C.: 5599
N.A.I.C.S.: 441228
Werner H. Frey *(CEO)*

Alfa Romeo U.S.A. S.p.A. (2)
Corso Francesco Ferrucci 112/A
Turin, 10138, Italy
Tel.: (39) 0110057611
Emp.: 200
Financial Administration Services
S.I.C.: 8742
N.A.I.C.S.: 541611

CODEFIS Societa consortile per azioni (2)
Corso Giovanni Agnelli 200
Turin, 10135, Italy
Tel.: (39) 0116866111
Investment Management Services
S.I.C.: 6799
N.A.I.C.S.: 523920

C.R.F. Societa Consortile per Azioni (2)
50 Strada Torino
10043 Orbassano, Italy
Tel.: (39) 0119 083 111
Fax: (39) 011 9083670
E-Mail: marketing@crf.it
Web Site: www.crf.it
Emp.: 1,000
Automotive Research & Development Services
S.I.C.: 8731
N.A.I.C.S.: 541712

Customer Services Centre S.r.l. (2)
V le Luraghi Snc
20020 Arese, Italy
Tel.: (39) 02 93776360
Fax: (39) 02 44412444
E-Mail: answer@fiat.com
Web Site: www.customercenter.fiat.com
Customer Service Center Operator
S.I.C.: 7389
N.A.I.C.S.: 561422

Elasis-Societa Consortile per Azioni (2)
Via Ex Aeroporto s n
Pomigliano d'Arco, Naples, 80038, Italy
Tel.: (39) 081 19 69 50 11
Fax: (39) 081 19 69 51 43
Scientific Research & Development Services
S.I.C.: 7389
N.A.I.C.S.: 541990

U.S. Subsidiary:

Ferrari North America, Inc. (3)
250 Sylvan Ave
Englewood Cliffs, NJ 07632-2500
Tel.: (201) 816-2600
Fax: (201) 816-2626
Web Site: www.ferrariusa.com
Sls.: $70,000,000
Emp.: 75
Sports Cars Importer & Distr
Import
S.I.C.: 5012
N.A.I.C.S.: 423110
Joseph Marsella *(CFO & VP)*

Ferrari S.p.A. (2)
Via Abetone Inferiore 4
Maranello, 41053 Modena, Italy (85%)
Tel.: (39) 0536949111
Fax: (39) 0536949049
E-Mail: adv@ferrari.it
Web Site: www.ferrariworld.com
Sales Range: $1-4.9 Billion
Emp.: 2,870
Sports Cars Mfr & Sales
S.I.C.: 5599
N.A.I.C.S.: 441228
Luca Cordero di Montezemolo *(Chm)*
Piero Lardi Ferrari *(Vice Chm)*
Amedeo Felisa *(CEO)*
Mario Mairano *(Sec & Head-HR)*

Subsidiary:

Mugello Circuit S.p.A. (3)
Via Senni 15
Scarperia, Florence, 50038, Italy
Tel.: (39) 055 8499111
Fax: (39) 055 8499251
E-Mail: info@mugellocircuit.it
Web Site: www.mugellocircuit.it
Automotive Race Track Operator
S.I.C.: 7948
N.A.I.C.S.: 711212
Paolo Poli *(CEO)*

Non-U.S. Subsidiaries:

Ferrari Japan KK (3)
Roppongi 6-10-1 Roppongi Hills Mori Tower
Minato-Ku, Tokyo, 106-6137, Japan
Tel.: (81) 368906200
Fax: (81) 368906210
Web Site: www.ferrari.com
Automobile Distr
S.I.C.: 5012
N.A.I.C.S.: 423110

Ferrari Management Consulting (Shanghai) CO., LTD (3)
No 708 Beijing W Rd
Jing'An Dist, Shanghai, 200041, China
Tel.: (86) 2161201001
Fax: (86) 2161201060
Business Management Consulting Services
S.I.C.: 8742
N.A.I.C.S.: 541611

Ferrari North Europe Limited (3)
275 Leigh Road
Slough, Berks, SL1 4HF, United Kingdom
Tel.: (44) 1753 878700
Fax: (44) 1753878770
Web Site: www.ferrari.com
Emp.: 20
New & Used Car Dealer
S.I.C.: 5511
N.A.I.C.S.: 441110
Jeremy Pang-Kessler *(Reg Mgr-Mktg)*

Ferrari South West Europe S.A.R.L. (3)
49 Avenue George Pompidou
92593 Levallois-Perret, France
Tel.: (33) 1 49 64 54 54
Fax: (33) 1 49 64 54 79
Web Site: www.ferrari.com
Car Mfr & Distr
S.I.C.: 3711
N.A.I.C.S.: 336111

Senator Software GmbH (3)
Sudliche Munchener Str 30
82031 Grunwald, Germany
Tel.: (49) 89 649 064 600
Fax: (49) 89 649 064 690
E-Mail: info@senator-software.de
Web Site: www.senator-software.de
Emp.: 12
Lease & Financial Software Development Services
S.I.C.: 7371
N.A.I.C.S.: 541511
Frau Susanne Aigner *(Mng Dir)*

FGA Investimenti S.p.A. (2)
Corso Giovanni Agnelli 200
Turin, 10135, Italy
Tel.: (39) 01170941
Investment Management Services
S.I.C.: 6282
N.A.I.C.S.: 523920

FGA officine Automobilistiche Grugliasco S.p.A. (2)
Via San Paolo 67/71 Grugliasco
Turin, Italy
Tel.: (39) 011683111
Automobile Parts Distr
S.I.C.: 5013
N.A.I.C.S.: 423120

FGA Russia S.r.l. (2)
Corso Giovanni Agnelli 200
Turin, 10135, Italy
Tel.: (39) 011 00 31111
Investment Management Services
S.I.C.: 6282
N.A.I.C.S.: 523920

Fiat Auto Var S.r.l. (2)
Corso Luigi Settembrini 215
Turin, 10135, Italy
Tel.: (39) 0110042111
Automobile Distr
S.I.C.: 5012
N.A.I.C.S.: 423110

Fiat Automobiles S.p.A. (2)
Corso Giovanni Agnelli 200
Turin, 10135, Italy
Tel.: (39) 0110 03 11 11
Emp.: 1,000
Automobile Mfr
S.I.C.: 3711
N.A.I.C.S.: 336111

Fiat professional S.p.A. (2)
Corso Giovanni Agnelli 200
Turin, 10135, Italy
Tel.: (39) 0110031111
Web Site: www.fiatprofessional.it
New Car Dealer
S.I.C.: 5511
N.A.I.C.S.: 441110

i-FAST Automotive logistics S.r.l. (2)
Via 1 Maggio 60 Porta 8
10040 Rivalta di Torino, Italy
Tel.: (39) 0110031111
Web Site: www.i-fast.it
Automotive Logistics Consulting Services
S.I.C.: 4731
N.A.I.C.S.: 541614

Lancia Automobiles S.p.A. (2)
Corso G Agnelli 200
10135 Turin, Italy
Tel.: (39) 0110042111
Web Site: www.lancia.com
New Car Dealer
S.I.C.: 5511
N.A.I.C.S.: 441110

Maserati S.p.A. (2)
322 Viale Ciro Menotti
41121 Modena, Italy IT
Tel.: (39) 059 590511 (100%)
Telex: 510248
Fax: (39) 059 226765
Web Site: www.maserati.com
Sales Range: $650-699.9 Million
Emp.: 649
Luxury Automobile Mfr
S.I.C.: 3711
N.A.I.C.S.: 336111
Wellington C. Soong *(Chm & Pres)*
Harald Wester *(CEO)*
Saad Chehab *(CMO)*

U.S. Subsidiary:

Maserati North America, Inc. (3)
250 Sylvan Ave
Englewood Cliffs, NJ 07632
Tel.: (201) 816-2600
Fax: (201) 816-2626
E-Mail: info@maseratiamerica.com
Emp.: 150
Sports Cars Importer & Distr
S.I.C.: 5012
N.A.I.C.S.: 423110
Pete Grady *(Pres & CEO)*

Non-U.S. Subsidiaries:

Maserati Deutschland GmbH (3)
Stielstrasse 3b
65201 Wiesbaden, Germany
Tel.: (49) 611 284 098 0
Fax: (49) 611 284 098 88
E-Mail: serviceteam@maserati.de
Car Mfr
S.I.C.: 3711
N.A.I.C.S.: 336111

Maserati GB Ltd. (3)
275 Leigh Rd
Slough, SL1 4HF, United Kingdom UK
Tel.: (44) 01753878888
Fax: (44) 175387877O
Web Site: www.maserati.com
Emp.: 12
Luxury Automobile Importer & Distr
S.I.C.: 5012
N.A.I.C.S.: 423110
Thomas Hajek *(Mng Dir)*

Maserati Japan KK (3)
22 Mori Bldg 1-12-32 Akasaka
Minato-ku, Tokyo, Japan
Tel.: (81) 120965120
Web Site: www.maserati.co.jp
New Car Dealer
S.I.C.: 5511
N.A.I.C.S.: 441110

U.S. Subsidiary:

FIAT NORTH AMERICA LLC (2)
1000 Chrysler Dr
Auburn Hills, MI 48326
Tel.: (248) 512-2950
New Car Dealer
S.I.C.: 5511
N.A.I.C.S.: 441110

Subsidiaries:

Alfa Romeo Inc. (3)
375 Park Ave Ste 2703
New York, NY 10152-2704
Tel.: (212) 355-2600
New Car Dealer
S.I.C.: 5511
N.A.I.C.S.: 441110

Chrysler Group LLC (3)
1000 Chrysler Dr
Auburn Hills, MI 48326-2766 DE
Tel.: (248) 512-2950 (100%)
Telex: 800-334-9200
Toll Free: (800) 247-9753
E-Mail: investorrelations@chrysler.com
Web Site: www.chryslergroupllc.com
Rev.: $72,144,000,000
Assets: $45,870,000,000
Liabilities: $47,112,000,000
Net Worth: ($1,242,000,000)
Earnings: $2,757,000,000
Emp.: 73,712
Fiscal Year-end: 12/31/13
Motor Vehicle Mfr
Import Export
S.I.C.: 3711
N.A.I.C.S.: 336111
Sergio Marchionne *(Chm & CEO)*
Richard K. Palmer *(CFO & Sr VP)*
Scott A. Sandschafer *(CIO & VP)*
Olivier Francois *(CMO)*
Alessandro Gili *(Chief Acctg Officer, VP & Controller)*
Reid Bigland *(Pres/CEO-Ram Truck Brand & Head-Sls)*
Ralph V. Gilles *(Pres/CEO-SRT Brand)*
Pietro Gorlier *(Pres/CEO-Brand Mopar Parts & Svcs)*
Bruno Cattori *(Pres/CEO-Chrysler de Mexico)*
Al Gardner *(Pres/CEO-Chrysler Brand)*
Timothy Kuniskis *(Pres/CEO-Dodge Brand)*
Michael W. Manley *(Pres/CEO-Jeep Brand)*
Marjorie Harris Loeb *(Gen Counsel, Sec & Sr VP)*
Walter P. Bodden, Jr. *(Treas & VP)*
Doug D. Betts *(Sr VP-Quality)*
Mark M. Chernoby *(Sr VP-Engrg)*
Michael J. Keegan *(Sr VP-HR & Supply Chain Mgmt)*
Dan C. Knott *(Sr VP-Pur & Supplier Quality-Chrysler Grp LLC)*
Scott G. Kunselman *(Sr VP-Pur)*
Gualberto Ranieri *(Sr VP-Comm)*
Joseph Trapasso *(Sr VP-External Affairs)*

Subsidiaries:

AutoDie LLC (4)
44 Coldbrook NW
Grand Rapids, MI 49525
Tel.: (616) 454-9361
E-Mail: info@autodie-llc.com
Web Site: www.autodie-llc.com
Automotive Stamping Die Mfr
S.I.C.: 3544
N.A.I.C.S.: 333514
Bob Spinetto *(CFO)*
David Darling *(COO & VP)*

CG Co-Issuer Inc. (4)
1000 Chrysler Dr
Auburn Hills, MI 48326

Fiat S.p.A.—(Continued)

Tel.: (248) 512-3984
Financial Management Consulting Services
S.I.C.: 8742
N.A.I.C.S.: 541611

The Chrysler Foundation (4)
1000 Chrysler Dr
Auburn Hills, MI 48326
Tel.: (248) 512-2500
Fax: (248) 512-2503
E-Mail: AL368@chrysler.com
Emp.: 3
Fund Management Services
S.I.C.: 6282
N.A.I.C.S.: 523920
Brian G. Glowiak *(Sec & VP)*

CHRYSLER GROUP INTERNATIONAL LLC (4)
1000 Chrysler Dr
Auburn Hills, MI 48326-2766
Tel.: (248) 576-2850
Automobile Parts Distr
S.I.C.: 5013
N.A.I.C.S.: 423120

CHRYSLER GROUP INTERNATIONAL SERVICES LLC (4)
1000 Chrysler Dr
Auburn Hills, MI 48326
Tel.: (248) 512-3984
New Car Dealer
S.I.C.: 5511
N.A.I.C.S.: 441110

CHRYSLER GROUP REALTY COMPANY LLC (4)
1000 Chrysler Dr
Auburn Hills, MI 48326
Tel.: (248) 512-3984
Investment Management Services
S.I.C.: 6282
N.A.I.C.S.: 523920

Chrysler Group Transport LLC (4)
8555 Lynch Rd
Detroit, MI 48234-4154
Tel.: (313) 252-2578
Fax: (313) 252-5181
General Freight Trucking Services
S.I.C.: 4212
N.A.I.C.S.: 484110

Chrysler International Corporation (4)
1000 Chrysler Dr
Auburn Hills, MI 48326-2766
Tel.: (248) 576-5741
Web Site: www.international.chryslercorp.com
Emp.: 3
Automobiles & Other Motor Vehicles
S.I.C.: 5012
N.A.I.C.S.: 423110

Chrysler Investment Holdings LLC (4)
1000 Chrysler Dr
Auburn Hills, MI 48326-2766
Tel.: (248) 576-5741
Investment Management Services
S.I.C.: 6799
N.A.I.C.S.: 523920

Downriver Dodge, Inc. (4)
5535 Gatewood Dr
Sterling Heights, MI 48310-2227
Tel.: (586) 264-3700
Fax: (586) 264-1820
Emp.: 2
Freight Transportation Services
S.I.C.: 4731
N.A.I.C.S.: 488510
Patrick Long *(Gen Mgr)*

Gulfgate Dodge, Inc. (4)
7250 Gulf Freeway
Houston, TX 77017
Tel.: (281) 299-0702
Fax: (713) 644-3544
Toll Free: (877) 450-2644
Web Site: www.gulfgatedodge.com
New & Used Car Distr
S.I.C.: 5511
N.A.I.C.S.: 441110
Gabby Funes *(Dir-Fin)*

Gwinnett Automotive Inc. (4)
3325 Satellite Blvd
Duluth, GA 30096
Tel.: (678) 957-5000
Fax: (678) 957-5036
Used & New Car Dealer
S.I.C.: 5521
N.A.I.C.S.: 441120

North Tampa Chrysler Jeep Dodge, Inc. (4)
10909 N Florida Ave
Tampa, FL 33612
Tel.: (813) 935-4812
Fax: (813) 387-4477
Toll Free: (877) 644-4296
Web Site: www.northtampacjd.com
Used & New Car Dealer
S.I.C.: 5521
N.A.I.C.S.: 441120
Jim Browne *(Principal-Dealer)*

Superstition Springs Chrysler Jeep, Inc. (4)
6130 E Auto Park Dr
Mesa, AZ 85206
Tel.: (888) 812-1135
Fax: (480) 830-8001
E-Mail: sales@supercj.com
Web Site: www.superstitionspringschryslerjeep.com
New & Used Car Distr
S.I.C.: 5511
N.A.I.C.S.: 441110
Jeff Wilhelm *(Mgr-Svc)*

Joint Venture:

Valeo/Acustar Thermal Systems, Inc. (4)
37564 Amrhein Rd
Livonia, MI 48150-1012
Mailing Address:
PO Box 2187
Livonia, MI 48150
Tel.: (734) 591-6550
Web Site: www.valeo.com
Sales Range: $250-299.9 Million
Automotive Climate Control & Engine Cooling Systems Mfr; Owned 51% by Valeo S.A. & 49% by Chrysler Group LLC
S.I.C.: 3714
N.A.I.C.S.: 336320

Units:

Chrysler (Atlanta) Parts Distribution Center (4)
1149 Citizens Pkwy
Morrow, GA 30260-2929
Tel.: (770) 960-3300
Fax: (770) 960-3340
Emp.: 80
Motor Vehicle Supplies & New Parts Distr
S.I.C.: 5013
N.A.I.C.S.: 423120

Chrysler (Cleveland) Parts Distribution Center (4)
9777 Mopar Dr
Streetsboro, OH 44241-5220
Tel.: (330) 626-7600
Fax: (330) 626-7613
Emp.: 98
Motor Vehicle Supplies & New Parts Distr
S.I.C.: 5013
N.A.I.C.S.: 423120

Chrysler Corporation (4)
7700 Irvine Ctr Dr Ste 400
Irvine, CA 92618-2923
Tel.: (949) 450-5111
Fax: (949) 450-5170
Web Site: www.chrysler.com
Emp.: 97
Business Support Services
S.I.C.: 7389
N.A.I.C.S.: 561499
James Young *(VP)*

Chrysler Corporation (4)
5790 Campus Pkwy
Hazelwood, MO 63042-2337
Tel.: (314) 895-0740
Emp.: 59
Automobile Parts, Sales & Services
S.I.C.: 5012
N.A.I.C.S.: 423110

Chrysler (Dallas) Parts Distribution Center (4)
2205 E Belt Line Rd
Carrollton, TX 75006-5608 TX
Tel.: (972) 418-4699
Fax: (972) 418-4690
Emp.: 97
Motor Vehicle Supplies & New Parts Distr
S.I.C.: 5013
N.A.I.C.S.: 423120

Chrysler (Memphis) Parts Distribution Center (4)
4175 Chrysler Dr
Memphis, TN 38118
Tel.: (901) 797-3806
Fax: (901) 797-3810
Emp.: 54
Motor Vehicle Supplies & New Parts Distr
S.I.C.: 5013
N.A.I.C.S.: 423120
Kevin Vaughan *(Office Mgr)*

Chrysler - Port Operations (4)
2901 Childs St
Baltimore, MD 21226-1015
Tel.: (410) 355-2705
Fax: (410) 355-4537
Deep Sea Automobile Transport Services
S.I.C.: 4412
N.A.I.C.S.: 483111

Chrysler (Portland) Parts Distribution Center (4)
10030 SW Allen Blvd
Beaverton, OR 97005-4123
Tel.: (503) 526-5570
Fax: (503) 526-5568
Emp.: 59
Motor Vehicle Supplies & New Parts Distr
S.I.C.: 5013
N.A.I.C.S.: 423120
Kelly Bauman *(Mgr-Warehouse)*

Chrysler (Warren) Parts Distribution Center (4)
21035 Sherwood Ave
Warren, MI 48091
Tel.: (586) 497-2698
Fax: (586) 497-0603
Emp.: 98
Motor Vehicle Supplies & New Parts Distr
S.I.C.: 5013
N.A.I.C.S.: 423120
Kim Kosak *(Mgr-Ops)*

Plants:

Chrysler - Conner Street Assembly Plant (4)
20000 Conner St
Detroit, MI 48234-3227
Tel.: (313) 369-6700
Fax: (313) 369-6795
Emp.: 115
Automobile Assembly
S.I.C.: 3711
N.A.I.C.S.: 336111

Chrysler - Detroit Axle Plant (4)
6700 Lynch Rd
Detroit, MI 48234-4119
Tel.: (313) 252-5400
Fax: (313) 252-2500
Emp.: 1,646
Motor Vehicle Axle Mfr
S.I.C.: 3714
N.A.I.C.S.: 336390

Chrysler - Detroit Engine Plant (4)
11570 E Warren St
Detroit, MI 48214-1692
Tel.: (313) 252-6601
Fax: (313) 252-6016
Emp.: 1,200
Automobile Engine Mfr
S.I.C.: 3714
N.A.I.C.S.: 336310

Chrysler - Kokomo Casting Plant (4)
1001 E Blvd
Kokomo, IN 46902-5740
Mailing Address:
1001 E Boulevard
Kokomo, IN 46902-5740
Tel.: (765) 454-1005
Fax: (765) 454-1530
Emp.: 915
Automotive Transmission, Transaxle & Other Aluminum Parts Casting
S.I.C.: 3364
N.A.I.C.S.: 331523

Chrysler - Kokomo Transmission Plant (4)
2401 S Reed Rd
Kokomo, IN 46902
Tel.: (765) 454-1000
Fax: (765) 454-1571
Emp.: 3,168
Motor Vehicle Transmission Mfr
S.I.C.: 3714
N.A.I.C.S.: 336350
Bob Lee *(VP-Power Train Engrg)*

Chrysler - Newark Assembly Plant (4)
550 S College Ave
Newark, DE 19713-1383
Tel.: (302) 453-5115
Fax: (302) 453-5141
Emp.: 1,125
Light Truck Assembly
S.I.C.: 3711
N.A.I.C.S.: 336112
J. Wolfe *(Plant Mgr)*

Chrysler - Plymouth Road Office Complex (PROC) (4)
14250 Plymouth Rd
Detroit, MI 48227-3042
Tel.: (313) 493-2101
Web Site: www.chryslergroupllc.com
Emp.: 1,596
Motor Vehicle Engineering, Development, Procurement & Advance Manufacturing Services
S.I.C.: 3711
N.A.I.C.S.: 336111

Chrysler - St. Louis Assembly Plant North (4)
1050 Dodge Dr
Fenton, MO 63026-2505
Tel.: (636) 349-4027
Fax: (636) 349-4228
Web Site: www.media.chrysler.com
Emp.: 2,330
Heavy & Light Duty Truck Assembly
S.I.C.: 3711
N.A.I.C.S.: 336112
Jan Carroll *(Sr Mgr-HR)*

Chrysler - St. Louis Assembly Plant South (4)
1050 Dodge Dr
Fenton, MO 63026-2505
Tel.: (636) 343-2500
Fax: (636) 349-4034
Emp.: 2,800
Automobile & Van Mfr
S.I.C.: 3711
N.A.I.C.S.: 336111

Chrysler - Sterling Assembly Plant (4)
35777 Van Dyke Ave
Sterling Heights, MI 48312-1138
Tel.: (586) 978-6001
Emp.: 2,718
Automobile Assembly
S.I.C.: 3711
N.A.I.C.S.: 336111

Chrysler - Sterling Stamping Plant (4)
35777 Van Dyke Ave
Sterling Heights, MI 48312-3565
Tel.: (586) 977-4700
Fax: (586) 977-4056
Emp.: 1,600
Automotive Stampings
S.I.C.: 3465
N.A.I.C.S.: 336370

Chrysler - Toledo Machining Plant (4)
8000 Chrysler Dr
Perrysburg, OH 43551-4813
Tel.: (419) 661-3500
Fax: (419) 661-3385
Emp.: 700
Steering Columns & Torque Converters Mfr
S.I.C.: 3714
N.A.I.C.S.: 336330

Chrysler - Toledo North Assembly Plant (4)
4400 Chrysler Dr
Toledo, OH 43608

Mailing Address:
PO Box 537927
Toledo, OH 43657-0001
Tel.: (419) 727-7700
Emp.: 3,408
Automobile Assembly
S.I.C.: 3711
N.A.I.C.S.: 336111

Chrysler - Trenton Engine Plant (4)
2000 Van Horn Rd
Trenton, MI 48183-4204
Tel.: (313) 956-9129
Emp.: 1,630
Automobile Engine Mfr
S.I.C.: 3714
N.A.I.C.S.: 336310
Bob Varsanik *(Plant Mgr)*

Chrysler - Twinsburg Stamping Plant (4)
2000 E Aurora Rd
Twinsburg, OH 44087-1922
Mailing Address:
PO Box 152
Twinsburg, OH 44087-0152
Tel.: (330) 425-1777
Fax: (330) 487-2824
Emp.: 1,660
Automotive Stampings
S.I.C.: 3465
N.A.I.C.S.: 336370
Tyree Minner *(Plant Mgr)*

Chrysler - Warren Stamping Plant (4)
22800 Mound Rd
Warren, MI 48288
Tel.: (586) 497-3630
Fax: (586) 497-1561
Emp.: 1,425
Automotive Body Stampings & Assembly
S.I.C.: 3465
N.A.I.C.S.: 336370

Chrysler - Warren Truck Assembly Plant (4)
21500 Mound Rd
Warren, MI 48091-4840
Mailing Address:
PO Box 2088
Warren, MI 48090-2088
Tel.: (586) 497-2400
Emp.: 2,791
Assembly of Pickup Trucks
S.I.C.: 3711
N.A.I.C.S.: 336120
Ken Burne *(Plant Mgr)*

Non-U.S. Group:

Chrysler Canada Inc. (4)
1 Riverside Dr W
Windsor, ON, N9A 5K3, Canada
Mailing Address:
PO Box 1621
Windsor, ON, N9A 4H6, Canada
Tel.: (519) 973-2000
Fax: (519) 973-2226
Toll Free: (800) 465-2001
Web Site: www.chryslercanada.ca
Sales Range: $1-4.9 Billion
Emp.: 9,000
Motor Vehicles Mfr & Distr
S.I.C.: 3711
N.A.I.C.S.: 336111
Reid Bigland *(Pres & CEO)*

Affiliates:

Cpk Interior Products Inc. (5)
128 Peter St
Port Hope, ON, L1A 3W4, Canada (100%)
Tel.: (905) 885-7231
Fax: (905) 885-2658
E-Mail: info@cpkip.ca
Web Site: cpkip.com
Sales Range: $50-74.9 Million
Emp.: 700
Automotive Trim & Interior Parts Mfr
S.I.C.: 2396
N.A.I.C.S.: 336360
Doug Gouin *(CEO)*

Unit:

National Fleet & Lease (5)
6500 Mississauga Rd N
Mississauga, ON, L5N 1A8, Canada
Tel.: (905) 821-6046
Fax: (905) 821-6020
E-Mail: fleetinfo@dc-canada.com
Web Site: www.fleet.chrysler.ca
Automobile Fleet Sales & Services
S.I.C.: 5012
N.A.I.C.S.: 423110

Plants:

Chrysler Canada - Brampton Assembly Plant (5)
2000 Williams Pkwy E
Brampton, ON, L6S 6B3, Canada
Tel.: (905) 458-1330
Fax: (905) 458-2720
Web Site: www.chryslercanada.com
Emp.: 3,750
Automotive Assembly
S.I.C.: 3711
N.A.I.C.S.: 336111

Chrysler Canada - Etobicoke Casting Plant (5)
15 Browns Line
Etobicoke, ON, M8W 3S3, Canada
Tel.: (416) 253-2300
Fax: (416) 253-2317
Web Site: www.chryslercanada.ca
Emp.: 400
Automotive Aluminium Die Casting & Parts Mfr
S.I.C.: 3364
N.A.I.C.S.: 331523
Tim Fair *(Mgr-Sls)*

Non-U.S. Subsidiaries:

Chrysler & Jeep Vertriebsgesellschaft mbH (4)
Franklinstrasse 26 A
10587 Berlin, Germany
Tel.: (49) 30 43736 0
Fax: (49) 30 43736 177
E-Mail: info.berlin@chrysler.com
Web Site: www.berlin.chrysler.de
Emp.: 8
Automotive Repair & Maintenance Services
S.I.C.: 7539
N.A.I.C.S.: 811198

Chrysler Australia Pty. Ltd. (4)
1699 Ipswich Rd
Rocklea, 4106, Australia
Tel.: (61) 7 3275 8711
Fax: (61) 7 3275 8770
Web Site: www.chrysler.com.au
New & Used Car Dealer
S.I.C.: 5511
N.A.I.C.S.: 441110
Robert Graczyk *(Head-Sls)*

Chrysler Belgium Luxembourg SA (4)
Tollaan 68
Saint-Lambert-Woluwe, Belgium
Tel.: (32) 2 724 12 11
Fax: (32) 2 724 88 49
Used Car Dealers
S.I.C.: 5521
N.A.I.C.S.: 441120

Chrysler Czech Republic s.r.o. (4)
Karolinska 650/1
186 00 Prague, Czech Republic
Tel.: (420) 224 806 111
Fax: (420) 224 806 207
E-Mail: chrysler-jeep-info@fiat.cz
Web Site: www.chrysler.cz
Car Dealer
S.I.C.: 5511
N.A.I.C.S.: 441110

Chrysler Danmark ApS (4)
Hovedvejen 208
2600 Glostrup, Denmark
Tel.: (45) 3378 8900
Fax: (45) 3378 8901
Web Site: www.chrysler.dk
New Car Dealer
S.I.C.: 5511
N.A.I.C.S.: 441110

Chrysler de Venezuela LLC. (4)
Avenida Pancho Pepe Croquer Zona Industrial Norte
Valencia, Venezuela
Tel.: (58) 241 6132400
E-Mail: contacto@chrysler.com
Web Site: www.chryslerdevenezuela.com.ve
Used & New Car Dealer
S.I.C.: 5521
N.A.I.C.S.: 441120

Chrysler France S.A.S. (4)
Za Trappes Elancourt
Trappes, Yvelines, 78190, France
Tel.: (33) 130167666
Web Site: www.chrysler.fr
New & Used Car Distr
S.I.C.: 5511
N.A.I.C.S.: 441110

CHRYSLER GROUP DO BRASIL COMERCIO DE VEICULOS Ltda. (4)
Chrysler 6th floor
PO Box 3042
06210-970 Osasco, Brazil
Tel.: (55) 1149493900
Fax: (55) 1149493900
Web Site: www.chrysler.com.br
New Car Dealer
S.I.C.: 5511
N.A.I.C.S.: 441110

Chrysler Italia S.r.l. (4)
Viale Manzoni 67
00185 Rome, Italy
Tel.: (39) 06 41882 1
Web Site: www.chrysler.it
Motor Vehicle Parts Distr
S.I.C.: 5013
N.A.I.C.S.: 423120

Chrysler Jeep Ticaret S.A. (4)
Pazarlama Merkezi TEM Otoyolu Hadimkoey Cikisi
Buekuekcekmece, Istanbul, 34900, Turkey
Tel.: (90) 212 8674000
New Car Dealer
S.I.C.: 5511
N.A.I.C.S.: 441110

Chrysler Korea, Ltd. (4)
Gangnam Finance Center 737 Yeoksam-dong 14 floors
Gangnam-gu, Seoul, 135-984, Korea (South)
Tel.: (82) 2 2112 2666
Web Site: www.chryslergroup.co.kr
New Car Dealer
S.I.C.: 5511
N.A.I.C.S.: 441110

Chrysler Management Austria GmbH (4)
Bundesstrasse 83
8071 Gossendorf, Austria
Tel.: (43) 316 4080
Fax: (43) 316 4084349
Emp.: 40
Automobile Repair & Maintenance Services
S.I.C.: 7539
N.A.I.C.S.: 811118
Anthony Picknell *(Gen Mgr)*

Chrysler Nederland B.V. (4)
Postbus 203
1 170 Badhoevedorp, Netherlands
Tel.: (31) 302471911
Car Dealer
S.I.C.: 5511
N.A.I.C.S.: 441110

Chrysler Polska sp. zo.o. (4)
Aleja Wyscigowa 6
Warsaw, 02-681, Poland
Tel.: (48) 22 312 76 11
Web Site: www.chrysler.pl
New & Used Car Distr
S.I.C.: 5511
N.A.I.C.S.: 441110
Piotr Ustaszewski *(Mgr-Mktg)*

Chrysler South Africa (Pty) Limited (4)
270 George Street
Noordwyk, Midrand, Gauteng, 1685, South Africa
Tel.: (27) 12 666 3600
E-Mail: info@chryslersa.co.za
Web Site: www.chryslergroup.co.za
Used & New Car Dealer
S.I.C.: 5511
N.A.I.C.S.: 441110
Bert Mauch *(Mgr-Web Designing)*

Chrysler South East Asia Pte. Ltd (4)
600 N Bridge Rd
Singapore, Singapore
Tel.: (65) 66027180
Emp.: 10
New & Used Car Dealer
S.I.C.: 5511
N.A.I.C.S.: 441110
Mary Choong *(Asst Mgr)*

CNI CV (4)
1 Parnassustrn
1076 AZ Amsterdam, Netherlands
Tel.: (31) 205755600
Automobile Distr
S.I.C.: 5012
N.A.I.C.S.: 423110

Subsidiary:

Chrysler Netherlands Holdings Cooperatie U.A. (5)
Locatellikade 1
1076 AZ Amsterdam, Netherlands
Tel.: (31) 20 5755600
Investment Management Services
S.I.C.: 6282
N.A.I.C.S.: 523920

Non-U.S. Subsidiary:

Chrysler India Automotive Private Ltd. (5)
No 143 Rmz Millenia Business Park 2 Campus 5 4TH Floor Kandanchavadi
Dr MGR Road Perungudi, Chennai, 600 096, India
Tel.: (91) 44 45903800
Fax: (91) 44 42913700
Automobile Mfr & Distr
S.I.C.: 3711
N.A.I.C.S.: 336111
Milind Khedkar *(Sr Mgr-CFD)*

Fundacion Chrysler de Mexico I.A.P (4)
Prolongacion Paseo De La Reforma No 1240
Santa Fe, 05109 Mexico, Mexico
Tel.: (52) 55 50 81 32 21
Fax: (52) 55 50 81 32 02
Engineering Services
S.I.C.: 8711
N.A.I.C.S.: 541330

Non-U.S. Subsidiaries:

CMP Componentes e Modulos Plasticos Industria e Comercio Ltda. (2)
Rua Domingos Costa 80 Cinco
Contagem, Minas Gerais, 32010-070, Brazil
Tel.: (55) 3121053400
Fax: (55) 3121053499
Plastic Product Mfr
S.I.C.: 3089
N.A.I.C.S.: 326199

Fiat Auto Argentina S.A (2)
Ruta 9 Km 690
Ferreyra, Cordoba, 5123, Argentina
Tel.: (54) 11 5776 5100
Fax: (54) 351 410 2800
E-Mail: info@fiatauto.com.ar
Web Site: www.fiat.com.ar
Automobile Mfr & Distr
S.I.C.: 3711
N.A.I.C.S.: 336111

Subsidiary:

Fiat Auto S.A. de Ahorro para Fines Determinados (3)
Balcarce 548 Piso 2
1064 Buenos Aires, Argentina
Tel.: (54) 1143445700
Fax: (54) 1143445874
Financial Management Consulting Services
S.I.C.: 8742
N.A.I.C.S.: 541611

Fiat Auto Belgio SA (2)
12a Rue Jules Cockx
B 1160 Brussels, Belgium (100%)
Tel.: (32) 27026511
Fax: (32) 027026799
E-Mail: accueilsab@fiat.com
Web Site: www.fiat.be
Emp.: 120
Automobile Marketer & Sales Import
S.I.C.: 5012
N.A.I.C.S.: 423110

Fiat S.p.A.—(Continued)

Thierry Hubert *(Gen Mgr)*

Fiat Auto Espana S.A. (2)
Ctra M 300 Km 28 500
28802 Alcala de Henares, Madrid, Spain (100%)
Tel.: (34) 918853700
Fax: (34) 918853879
Web Site: www.fiat.es
Emp.: 400
Automobile Marketer & Sales
S.I.C.: 5012
N.A.I.C.S.: 423110
Jaevier Marijuan *(Mng Dir)*

Fiat Auto Ireland Ltd. (2)
Fiat House Tpke Rd Naas Rd 22
Dublin, 22, Ireland
Tel.: (353) 14034433
Telex: 93884 fiat ei
Fax: (353) 14297961
E-Mail: reception.irl@fiat.com
Web Site: www.fiat.com
Emp.: 15
Automobiles & Light Commercial Vehicles Distr
Import
S.I.C.: 5012
N.A.I.C.S.: 423110
Adoian Walsh *(Mng Dir)*

Fiat Auto Nederland B.V. (2)
Singaporestraat 92-100
1175 RA Lijnden, Netherlands
Tel.: (31) 203421700
Fax: (31) 203421707
Web Site: www.fiat.nl
Emp.: 150
Automobile Whslr
S.I.C.: 5012
N.A.I.C.S.: 423110

Fiat Auto Poland S.A. (2)
ul Grazynskiego 141
43-300 Bielsko-Biala, Poland
Tel.: (48) 338132100
Fax: (48) 338132036
Web Site: www.fiat.pl
Emp.: 1,370
Automobile Whslr
S.I.C.: 5012
N.A.I.C.S.: 423110

Subsidiary:

GESTIN POLSKA Sp. z o.o. (3)
Ul Grazynskiego 141
Bielsko-Biala, Poland
Tel.: (48) 33 813 26 60
Fax: (48) 33 813 54 44
Facility Management Services
S.I.C.: 8744
N.A.I.C.S.: 561210

Fiat Auto Portuguesa SA (2)
Ave Jose Gomes Ferreira 15
Edificio Atlas IV Miraflores, 1495-839 Alges, Portugal (100%)
Tel.: (351) 214125400
Fax: (351) 214125500
Web Site: www.fiat.pt
Emp.: 70
Automobiles Marketer & Sales
S.I.C.: 5012
N.A.I.C.S.: 423110
Marcawlo Santoni *(CEO)*

Fiat Auto Suisse SA (2)
Zurcherstrasse 111
8952 Schlieren, Switzerland (100%)
Tel.: (41) 445562222
Fax: (41) 223451718
E-Mail: reception@fiat.com
Web Site: www.fiat.ch
Emp.: 90
Automobile Marketer & Sales
Import Export
S.I.C.: 5012
N.A.I.C.S.: 423110
Eric Laforge *(Gen Mgr)*

Fiat Auto (UK) Ltd. (2)
Fiat House 240 Bath Rd
Slough, Berks, SL1 4DX, United Kingdom
Tel.: (44) 1753511431
Fax: (44) 753511471
E-Mail: contactfiat@uk-central.com
Web Site: www.fiat.co.uk
Emp.: 300
Automobile Sales & Services
S.I.C.: 5012
N.A.I.C.S.: 423110
Steve Zanlunghi *(Mng Dir)*

Fiat Automobil GmbH (2)
Favoritenstrasse 321
1100 Vienna, Austria
Tel.: (43) 01680010
Fax: (43) 168001200
Web Site: www.fiat.at
Automobile Whslr
S.I.C.: 5012
N.A.I.C.S.: 423110

Fiat Automobiler Danmark A/S (2)
Hovedvejen 208
2600 Glostrup, Denmark
Tel.: (45) 43228800
Fax: (45) 43228888
E-Mail:
Web Site: www.fiat.com
Emp.: 55
Automobile Whslr
S.I.C.: 5012
N.A.I.C.S.: 423110
Svend Overgaard *(Gen Mgr)*

Fiat Automobiles Service Co. Ltd. (2)
No 188 Guangzhou Road
210024 Nanjing, China
Tel.: (86) 13002590482
Automobile Maintenance & Repair Services
S.I.C.: 7538
N.A.I.C.S.: 811111

Fiat CR Spol. S R.O. (2)
Karolinska 650/1
186 00 Prague, 8, Czech Republic
Tel.: (420) 224806111
Fax: (420) 224806207
E-Mail: fiat@fiat.cz
Web Site: www.fiat.cz
Automobile Whslr
S.I.C.: 5012
N.A.I.C.S.: 423110

Fiat do Brazil SA (2)
Senador Milton Campos 175
34000-000 Serra, Nova Lima MG, Brazil (100%)
Tel.: (55) 3121234366
Telex: 2121438 FIAT BR
Fax: (55) 3121234040
Web Site: www.fiat.com.br
Emp.: 1,200
Automobile Importer & Sales
S.I.C.: 5012
N.A.I.C.S.: 423110
Cledorvino Belini *(Pres)*

Fiat Group Automobiles Austria GmbH (2)
Schonbrunner Strasse 297-307
1120 Vienna, Austria
Tel.: (43) 1 68001 0
Fax: (43) 1 68001 2290
E-Mail: reception-austria@fiat.com
Web Site: www.fiat.at
Automobile Distr
S.I.C.: 5012
N.A.I.C.S.: 423110
Ulrich Hoernke *(Mng Dir)*
Junila Mance *(Chief Acctg Officer)*

Subsidiary:

Motor Village Austria GmbH (3)
Schonbrunner Strasse 297-307
1120 Vienna, Austria
Tel.: (43) 1 810 11 48
Fax: (43) 1 810 48 4560
E-Mail: mvs@fiat.com
Web Site: www.motorvillageaustria.com
New & Used Car Distr
S.I.C.: 5511
N.A.I.C.S.: 441110
Andreas Chola *(Gen Mgr)*

Fiat Group Automobiles Belgium S.A. (2)
Rue Jules Cockx 12a
1160 Brussels, Belgium
Tel.: (32) 2 702 65 11
Fax: (32) 27026799
Web Site: www.alfaromeo.be
Automobile Distr
S.I.C.: 5012
N.A.I.C.S.: 423110

Subsidiary:

Italian Automotive Center S.A. (3)
Leuvensesteenweg 770
Brussels, Brussel-Hoofdstad, 1030, Belgium
Tel.: (32) 27023124
Fax: (32) 27023128
Car Dealer
S.I.C.: 5511
N.A.I.C.S.: 441110
Fabian Fabrice *(Gen Mgr)*

Fiat Group Automobiles Denmark A/S (2)
Hovedvejen 208
2600 Glostrup, Denmark
Tel.: (45) 43 2288 00
Fax: (45) 43 2288 88
Web Site: www.fiat.dk
Automobile Distr
S.I.C.: 5012
N.A.I.C.S.: 423110

Fiat Group Automobiles Germany AG (2)
Hanauerlanp Strasse 176
60314 Frankfurt, Germany De
Tel.: (49) 69669880
Telex: 4170317
Fax: (49) 6966988900
E-Mail: kontakt@fiat.de
Web Site: www.fiat.de
Emp.: 200
Automobile Mfr
S.I.C.: 5012
N.A.I.C.S.: 423110
Manfred Kantner *(Chm-Mgmt Bd)*
Matthias Graf von Krockow *(Chm-Supervisory Bd)*
Klaus Bentz *(Member-Mgmt Bd)*
Andreas Serra *(Member-Mgmt Bd)*
Norbert Tschrepp *(Member-Mgmt Bd)*
Haico van der Luyt *(Member-Mgmt Bd)*

Subsidiaries:

Fiat Automobil Vertriebs GmbH (3)
Mainzer Landstr 581
Frankfurt am Main, Hessen, 65933, Germany
Tel.: (49) 693 9010
New & Used Car Distr
S.I.C.: 5511
N.A.I.C.S.: 441110

Subsidiary:

Fiat Real Estate Germany GmbH (4)
Mainzer Landstr 581
65933 Frankfurt, Hessen, Germany
Tel.: (49) 69 39010
Fax: (49) 69 3901208
Emp.: 100
Real Estate Development Services
S.I.C.: 6531
N.A.I.C.S.: 531390
Michael Bergmann *(Gen Mgr)*

Fiat Group Automobiles Hellas S.A. (2)
580 A Vouliagmenis Ave
Argyroupolis, 16452 Athens, Greece
Tel.: (30) 210 9988630
Fax: (30) 210 9988632
E-Mail: comm.dept@fiat.com
Web Site: www.fiatgroup.gr
Automobile Mfr & Distr
S.I.C.: 3711
N.A.I.C.S.: 336111

Fiat Group Automobiles Ireland Ltd. (2)
Agnelli House Naas Road
Dublin, Ireland
Tel.: (353) 1 4034460
Fax: (353) 1 4297961
E-Mail: customercare.ireland@fiat.com
Web Site: www.fiat.ie
Automobile Mfr & Distr
S.I.C.: 3711
N.A.I.C.S.: 336111
Adrian C. Walsh *(Mng Dir)*

Fiat Group Automobiles Japan K.K. (2)
Mita Bellju Building 5-36-7 Shiba
Minato-Ku, Tokyo, 108-0014, Japan
Tel.: (81) 354601913
New Car Dealer
S.I.C.: 5511
N.A.I.C.S.: 441110

Fiat Group Automobiles Maroc S.A. (2)
Mandarona 300 Lot 9 Route de Sidi Maarouf
Casablanca, Morocco
Tel.: (212) 5 22 42 40 00
Fax: (212) 5 22 58 05 91
Automobile Distr
S.I.C.: 5012
N.A.I.C.S.: 423110
Ali Houari *(Mgr-Supply Chain)*

Fiat Group Automobiles Netherlands B.V. (2)
Singaporestraat 92-100
1175 RA Lijnden, Netherlands
Tel.: (31) 80 0342 80000
Fax: (31) 203 421 707
Web Site: www.fiat.nl
Automobile Mfr & Distr
S.I.C.: 3711
N.A.I.C.S.: 336111

Fiat Group Automobiles South Africa (Proprietary) Ltd (2)
Waterfall Park Howick Close Bekker Street
Vorna Valley, Midrand, Gauteng, 1685, South Africa
Tel.: (27) 11 205 3700
Fax: (27) 11 205 3742
Web Site: www.fiat.co.za
Emp.: 50
New Car Dealer
S.I.C.: 5511
N.A.I.C.S.: 441110
Roberto Bona *(CFO)*

Fiat Group Automobiles Spain S.A. (2)
Carretera Comarcal M-300 Km 28 5
Alcala De Henares, Madrid, 28803, Spain
Tel.: (34) 918853700
Car Dealer
S.I.C.: 5511
N.A.I.C.S.: 441110

Subsidiary:

Fiat Auto Espana Marketing Instituto Agrupacion de Interes Economico (3)
Carretera Madrid-Barcelona N-II Km 27 500
Alcala De Henares, Madrid, Spain
Tel.: (34) 913251125
Dealer Training Services
S.I.C.: 8299
N.A.I.C.S.: 611430

Fiat Group Automobiles Sweden AB (2)
Farogatan 33
164 51 Kista, Stockholm, Sweden
Tel.: (46) 8 588 37200
Fax: (46) 8 588 37201
E-Mail: info.se@fiat.com
Web Site: www.fiat.se
New & Used Car Distr
S.I.C.: 5511
N.A.I.C.S.: 441110

Fiat Group Automobiles Switzerland S.A. (2)
Zurcherstrasse 111
PO Box 168
8952 Schlieren, Switzerland
Tel.: (41) 44 556 20 01
Fax: (41) 44 556 22 55
New & Used Car Distr
S.I.C.: 5511
N.A.I.C.S.: 441110

Fiat Group Automobiles UK Ltd (2)
240 Bath Road
Slough, SL1 4DX, United Kingdom
Tel.: (44) 1753 511431
Fax: (44) 1753 511471
Web Site: www.fiat.co.uk
Emp.: 150
New & Used Car Distr
S.I.C.: 5511
N.A.I.C.S.: 441110
Steve Zanlunghi *(Mng Dir)*

Subsidiaries:

Fiat Motor Sales Ltd (3)
372 Ealing Road
Wembley, HA0 1BH, United Kingdom

Tel.: (44) 20 8998 8811
New Car Dealer
S.I.C.: 5511
N.A.I.C.S.: 441110

Italian Motor Village Ltd. (3)
240 Bath Road
Slough, SL1 4DX, United Kingdom
Tel.: (44) 2073996650
Web Site: www.motorvillageuk.com
New & Used Car Distr
S.I.C.: 5511
N.A.I.C.S.: 441110
Lia Bettini *(Dir-Fin)*

Fiat Magyarorszag Kft (2)
53 Alkotas St
H-1123 Budapest, Hungary
Tel.: (36) 14583100
Fax: (36) 14583129
E-Mail: info@fiat.hu
Web Site: www.fiat.hu
Emp.: 30
Automobile Whslr
S.I.C.: 5012
N.A.I.C.S.: 423110
Judith Hudson *(Sec)*

Non-U.S. Joint Venture:

Tofas Turk Otomobil Fabrikasi A.S. (2)
Buyukdere Cad 145
Tofas Han
34394 Istanbul, Turkey
Tel.: (90) 212 275 33 90
Fax: (90) 212 275 39 88
Web Site: www.tofas.com.tr
TOASO—(IST LUX)
Sls.: $3,789,351,496
Assets: $3,425,554,709
Liabilities: $2,260,199,571
Net Worth: $1,165,355,138
Earnings: $253,361,907
Emp.: 6,325
Fiscal Year-end: 12/31/12
Automobile Mfr
S.I.C.: 3711
N.A.I.C.S.: 336111
Mustafa Vehbi Koc *(Chm)*
Sergio Marchionne *(Vice Chm)*
Kamil Basaran *(CEO)*
Cengiz Eroldu *(CFO & Dir-Fin)*

Fiat Group Marketing & Corporate Communication S.p.A. (1)
Via Nizza 250
Turin, 10126, Italy
Tel.: (39) 0110 06 11 11
Emp.: 100
Direct Marketing Services
S.I.C.: 5963
N.A.I.C.S.: 454390
Lucia Cordone *(Deputy CEO)*

Fiat Media Center S.p.A. (1)
Corso Marconi 20
10125 Turin, Italy IT
Tel.: (39) 0110061114
Fax: (39) 0110061316
Advertising Space Planning & Purchasing
S.I.C.: 7319
N.A.I.C.S.: 541890

Fiat Partecipazioni S.p.A. (1)
Via Nizza 250
Turin, 10126, Italy
Tel.: (39) 01 10 06 11 11
Fax: (39) 01 10 06 11 11
Investment Management Services
S.I.C.: 6282
N.A.I.C.S.: 523920

Fiat Powertrain Technologies S.p.A. (1)
Strada Torino 50
10043 Orbassano, Italy IT
Tel.: (39) 0119080617
Fax: (39) 0119080666
E-Mail: press@it.fpwtech.com
Web Site: www.fiatpowertrain.com
Sales Range: $5-14.9 Billion
Emp.: 18,924
Automobile Engine & Transmission Mfr
S.I.C.: 3714
N.A.I.C.S.: 336350
Sergio Marchionne *(Chm)*

Subsidiary:

FMA - Fabbrica Motori Automobilistici S.r.l. (2)
Via Nazionale 10
Pratola Serra, 83039, Italy
Tel.: (39) 0825296111
Fax: (39) 0825607012
Automobile Parts Mfr
S.I.C.: 3714
N.A.I.C.S.: 336390

Joint Venture:

VM Motori S.p.A. (2)
Via Ferrarese 29
44042 Cento, Ferrara, Italy
Tel.: (39) 0516837511
Fax: (39) 0516837535
E-Mail: frigon@vmmotori.com
Web Site: www.vmmotori.it
Emp.: 1,200
Diesel Engines Mfr
S.I.C.: 3714
N.A.I.C.S.: 336310
Vilmo Ferioli *(CEO)*

Non-U.S. Subsidiary:

Fiat powertrain Technologies Poland Sp. zo.o. (2)
Grazynskiego 141
Bielsko-Biala, Poland
Tel.: (48) 33 813 21 00
Automobile Parts Mfr
S.I.C.: 3714
N.A.I.C.S.: 336390
Emanuel Lorenzen *(Gen Dir)*

Fiat Revi S.c.r.l. (1)
Via Nizza 250
10126 Turin, Italy IT
Tel.: (39) 0110063160
Fax: (39) 0110062166
Web Site: www.fiatgroup.com
Accounting & Internal Auditing Services
S.I.C.: 8721
N.A.I.C.S.: 541219

Fiat-Revisione Interna S.c.p.a. (1)
Via Nizza 250
10126 Turin, Italy
Tel.: (39) 0110061111
Fax: (39) 0110062444
Automobile Distr
S.I.C.: 5012
N.A.I.C.S.: 423110

Fidis S.p.A. (1)
Corso Giovanni Agnelli 200
10100 Turin, Italy
Tel.: (39) 0110064111
Telex: 212200 FIAT I
Fax: (39) 0110064145
Web Site: www.sgacapital.com
Holding Company; Financial Services
S.I.C.: 6719
N.A.I.C.S.: 551112

Subsidiary:

Fiatsava S.p.A. (2)
Corso Giovanni Agnelli 200
10100 Turin, Italy
Tel.: (39) 0110064111
Fax: (39) 0110064819
Web Site: www.sava.it
Emp.: 150
Financial Services
S.I.C.: 6099
N.A.I.C.S.: 522320

Industrie Plastica S.p.A. (1)
Via Chivasso 120
San Benigno Canavese, Turin, 10080, Italy
Tel.: (39) 0119703111
Fax: (39) 0119703209
Automobile Parts Distr
S.I.C.: 5013
N.A.I.C.S.: 423120

Italiana Edizioni S.p.A (1)
Via Marenco 32
10126 Turin, Italy IT
Tel.: (39) 011 00 63893
Telex: 212200 FIAT I
Fax: (39) 011 00 61481
Web Site: www.fiatgroup.com
Sales Range: $500-549.9 Million
Emp.: 836
Publishing & Communication Services
S.I.C.: 2711
N.A.I.C.S.: 511110

Subsidiary:

Editrice La Stampa S.p.A. (2)
Via Carlo Marenco 32
10126 Turin, Italy IT
Tel.: (39) 0116568111
Telex: 221121 STAMPA I
Fax: (39) 0116568924
E-Mail: luisa.fava@lastampa.it
Web Site: www.lastampa.it
Emp.: 400
Newspaper Publisher
S.I.C.: 2711
N.A.I.C.S.: 511110
John Philip Elkann *(Chm)*
Antonello Perricone *(CEO)*

Magneti Marelli Holding S.p.A. (1)
Viale Aldo Borletti 61 63
Corbetta, 20011 Milan, Corbetta, Italy IT
Tel.: (39) 0297227111 (100%)
Telex: 310041 MAGNET I
Fax: (39) 0297227459
E-Mail: comunicazione.immagine@corbetta.marelli.it
Web Site: www.marelli.it
Sales Range: $5-14.9 Billion
Emp.: 25,195
Mfr of Automotive Lighting, Powertrain Components, Electronic Systems, Exhaust Systems, Suspension Systems & Shock Absorbers
S.I.C.: 3714
N.A.I.C.S.: 336330
Eugenio Razelli *(Chm & CEO)*
Sergio Marchionne *(Chm)*

Subsidiary:

Magneti Marelli After Market Parts and Services S.p.A. (2)
Viale Aldo Borletti 61/63
Corbetta, Milan, 20011, Italy
Tel.: (39) 0297227454
Automobile Parts Distr
S.I.C.: 5013
N.A.I.C.S.: 423120

Non-U.S. Subsidiaries:

Magneti Marelli Aftermarket GmbH (3)
Salzstrasse 185c
74076 Heilbronn, Germany
Tel.: (49) 7131 291 0
Fax: (49) 7131 165236
E-Mail: infoaftermarket.de@magnetimarelli.com
Web Site: www.magnetimarelli-checkstar.de
Emp.: 20
Automobile Parts Distr
S.I.C.: 5013
N.A.I.C.S.: 423120
Chris Katscher *(Gen Mgr)*

Magneti Marelli Aftermarket S.a.s. (3)
5 /7 R Albert Einstein Z A de Trappes Elancourt
Trappes, 78190, France
Tel.: (33) 1 30 16 69 60
Automotive Parts Distr
S.I.C.: 5015
N.A.I.C.S.: 423140

Magneti Marelli Aftermarket Sp. z o.o. (3)
Plac Pod Lipami 5
40-476 Katowice, Poland
Tel.: (48) 32 60 36 107
Fax: (48) 32 60 36 108
Web Site: www.magnetimarelli-checkstar.pl
Emp.: 40
Automobile Mfr & Distr
S.I.C.: 3711
N.A.I.C.S.: 336111
Marek Buras *(Mng Dir)*

Magneti Marelli Repuestos S.A. (3)
1035 Andonaegui
C1407MMJ Buenos Aires, Argentina
Tel.: (54) 11 4523 6612
Fax: (54) 11 4253 6613
Automobile Parts Distr
S.I.C.: 5013
N.A.I.C.S.: 423120

U.S. Subsidiary:

Magneti Marelli Holding U.S.A. Inc. (2)
3900 Automation Ave
Auburn Hills, MI 48326
Tel.: (248) 418-3000
Investment Management Services
S.I.C.: 6211
N.A.I.C.S.: 523999

Subsidiaries:

Magneti Marelli Powertrain USA, Inc. (3)
2101 Nash St
Sanford, NC 27330
Mailing Address:
PO Box 548
Sanford, NC 27331-0548
Tel.: (919) 776-4111
Fax: (919) 775-6432
E-Mail: pablo.tovar@magnetimarelli.com
Web Site: www.marelliusa.com
Emp.: 400
Powertrain Mfr
S.I.C.: 3711
N.A.I.C.S.: 336111

Magneti Marelli Suspensions USA LLC (3)
37484 Interchange Dr
Farmington Hills, MI 48335-1026
Tel.: (248) 668-3600
Fax: (248) 668-3601
Motor Vehicle Parts Mfr
S.I.C.: 3714
N.A.I.C.S.: 336390

Non-U.S. Subsidiaries:

Magneti Marelli Automotive Components (WUHU) Co. Ltd. (2)
No 5 Shangzha Rd Qiaobei Industry Park Economic Technology
Development Zone, Wuhu, Anhui, 241009, China
Tel.: (86) 5535716808
Fax: (86) 5535313338
Web Site: www.magnetimarelli.com
Emp.: 700
Automobile Parts Mfr
S.I.C.: 3714
N.A.I.C.S.: 336390
Daniel Zong *(Plant Mgr)*

Magneti Marelli Comandos Mecanicos Industria e Comercio Ltda (2)
Rod Mg - 431 S/N
Itauna, Minas Gerais, 35680-590, Brazil
Tel.: (55) 3730740600
Automobile Parts Distr
S.I.C.: 5013
N.A.I.C.S.: 423120

Magneti Marelli do Brasil Industria e Comercio SA (2)
Rua Manoel Da Nobrega 350 Maua
Sao Paulo, 09380-120, Brazil
Tel.: (55) 11 3289 1284
Automobile Parts Distr
S.I.C.: 5013
N.A.I.C.S.: 423120

Magneti Marelli Exhaust Systems Polska Sp. zo.o. (2)
ul Zaruskiego 11
41-219 Sosnowiec, Poland
Tel.: (48) 32 364 28 63
Fax: (48) 32 364 28 58
Emp.: 200
Automobile Parts Mfr
S.I.C.: 3714
N.A.I.C.S.: 336390
Fontana Adriano *(Pres)*

Magneti Marelli France S.a.s. (2)
5-7 Rue Albert Einstein ZA de Trappes Elancourt
78190 Trappes, France
Tel.: (33) 1 30 16 69 60
Web Site: www.magnetimarelli-checkstar.fr
Automotive Parts Mfr
S.I.C.: 3714
N.A.I.C.S.: 336390

Magneti Marelli GmbH (2)
Im Eichsfeld 3
Russelsheim, Hessen, Germany

Fiat S.p.A.—(Continued)

Tel.: (49) 614282820
Automobile Parts Mfr
S.I.C.: 3714
N.A.I.C.S.: 336390

Magneti Marelli Iberica S.A. (2)
Les Arenes Pg Ind Santa Ana Ii 5
08251 Santpedor, Spain
Tel.: (34) 913 25 22 11
Fax: (34) 913 09 37 90
Automobile Parts Distr
S.I.C.: 5013
N.A.I.C.S.: 423120

Magneti Marelli Japan K.K. (2)
3-17-5 Shin-Yokohama
Kohoku-Ku, Yokohama, Kanagawa, 222-0033, Japan
Tel.: (81) 454780045
Fax: (81) 454780095
Emp.: 10
Automobile Parts Mfr
S.I.C.: 3714
N.A.I.C.S.: 336390
Albert Montanaly *(Pres)*

Magneti Marelli Motopropulsion France SAS (2)
19 rue Lavoisier
Nanterre, 92721, France
Tel.: (33) 1 55 69 94 54
Fax: (33) 1 55 69 95 41
Automobile Parts Distr
S.I.C.: 5013
N.A.I.C.S.: 423120

Magneti Marelli Powertrain (Shanghai) Co. Ltd. (2)
No 168 Taigu Road
Shanghai, 200131, China
Tel.: (86) 2158669090
Automobile Parts Mfr
S.I.C.: 3714
N.A.I.C.S.: 336390

Magneti Marelli Powertrain Slovakia s.r.o. (2)
Porubskeho 2
Bratislava, 811 06, Slovakia
Tel.: (421) 556131105
Automotive Engine Mfr
S.I.C.: 3714
N.A.I.C.S.: 336390

Magneti Marelli Sistemas Electronicos Mexico S.A. (2)
Av De La Industria No 20 Y 21
Tepotzotlan, 54600, Mexico
Tel.: (52) 5558760511
Automobile Parts Distr
S.I.C.: 5013
N.A.I.C.S.: 423120

Magneti Marelli Slovakia s.r.o. (2)
Porubskeho 2
81106 Bratislava, Slovakia
Tel.: (421) 55 6131105
Fax: (421) 55 6131106
Automotive Parts Mfr
S.I.C.: 3714
N.A.I.C.S.: 336390

Magneti Marelli South Africa (Proprietary) Limited (2)
99 Makriel Street
Johannesburg, Gauteng, South Africa
Tel.: (27) 11 8270440
Fax: (27) 11 8270440
Automobile Parts Mfr
S.I.C.: 3714
N.A.I.C.S.: 336390

Magneti Marelli Suspension Systems Bielsko Sp. z.o.o. (2)
ul M Grazynskiego 141
Bielsko-Biala, 43-300, Poland
Tel.: (48) 33 813 21 99
Fax: (48) 33 813 29 55
Automobile Parts Mfr
S.I.C.: 3714
N.A.I.C.S.: 336390
Adriano Fontana *(Pres)*

Nexta Srl (1)
Via Lugaro 15
10126 Turin, Italy
Tel.: (39) 06 993 452 04
E-Mail: info@publikompass.it
Web Site: www.nexta.com
Business Directory Publisher
S.I.C.: 2741
N.A.I.C.S.: 511140

Plastic Components and Modules Holding S.p.A. (1)
Via Rivalta 30
Grugliasco, 10095, Italy
Tel.: (39) 0116 87 91 11
Plastic Product Mfr
S.I.C.: 3089
N.A.I.C.S.: 326199

Subsidiary:

Ergom Soffiaggio S.r.l. (2)
Via B Castelli 18
25024 Leno, Brescia, Italy
Tel.: (39) 030 9038257
Fax: (39) 030 9038257
E-Mail: info@ergomsoff.com
Web Site: www.ergomsoff.com
Thermoplastic Container Mfr
S.I.C.: 3089
N.A.I.C.S.: 326199

Non-U.S. Subsidiary:

Plastic Components and Modules Poland S.A. (2)
Generala Mariusza Zaruskiego 11
Sosnowiec, Poland
Tel.: (48) 32 368 12 00
Fax: (48) 32 368 12 00
Automotive Plastic Component & Module Mfr
S.I.C.: 3089
N.A.I.C.S.: 326199

Subsidiary:

Plastic Components Fuel Systems Poland Sp. z o.o. (3)
ul Jednosci 44
41 218 Sosnowiec, Poland
Tel.: (48) 32 368 12 23
Fax: (48) 32 293 08 39
Plastic Product Mfr
S.I.C.: 3089
N.A.I.C.S.: 326199
Adriano Fontana *(Gen Mgr)*

Publikompass S.p.A. (1)
Via Washington 70
20123 Milan, Italy
Tel.: (39) 0224424611
Fax: (39) 0224424490
Web Site: www.publikompass.it
Advertising Space Sales
S.I.C.: 7319
N.A.I.C.S.: 541890
Angelo Sajeva *(Pres)*

Risk Management S.p.A. (1)
Via Giacosa 38
Turin, 10125, Italy
Tel.: (39) 0110061111
Fax: (39) 0110063481
Risk Management Services
S.I.C.: 6282
N.A.I.C.S.: 523920

Sirio - Sicurezza Industriale S.c.p.a. (1)
Corso Marconi 20
10125 Turin, Italy
Tel.: (39) 110062759
Fax: (39) 0110061900
Corporate Security Services
S.I.C.: 7382
N.A.I.C.S.: 561621
Sergio Marchionne *(CEO)*

SIRIO - Sicurezza Industriale Societa consortile per azioni (1)
Corso Giovanni Agnelli 200
Turin, 10135, Italy
Tel.: (39) 0110 03 09 61
Fax: (39) 0110 03 81 51
Security System Services
S.I.C.: 7382
N.A.I.C.S.: 561621

Sisport Fiat S.p.A. (1)
Corso Moncalieri 346 12
10133 Turin, Italy
Tel.: (39) 0116619801
Fax: (39) 011 661 4944
Sports Activities Promotion & Recreational Facilities Management Services
S.I.C.: 7999
N.A.I.C.S.: 711310

Sistemi Sospensioni S.p.A. (1)
Corso Unione Sovietica 600
Turin, 10135, Italy
Tel.: (39) 0110046844
Automotive Parts Mfr
S.I.C.: 3714
N.A.I.C.S.: 336390

Teksid S.p.A. (1)
C so Ferrucci 112/A
10138 Turin, Italy (84.8%)
Tel.: (39) 0119794111
Telex: 224042 TEKSID I
Fax: (39) 0119794956
E-Mail: externalrelations@teksid.com
Web Site: www.teksid.com
Sales Range: $1-4.9 Billion
Emp.: 8,342
Metallurgical Component Mfr
S.I.C.: 3714
N.A.I.C.S.: 336390
Sergio Marchionne *(Chm)*
Riccardo Tarantini *(Pres & CEO)*
Marco Ferrato *(CFO)*
Giovanni Fassera *(Sr VP-Ops-Europe & Far East)*

Subsidiary:

Teksid Aluminum S.r.l. (2)
Via Umberto II 5
10022 Carmagnola, Turin, Italy
Tel.: (39) 011 9794 111
Fax: (39) 011 9794 934
E-Mail: info.aluminum@teksid.com
Web Site: www.teksidaluminum.com
Metal Casting Equipment Mfr
S.I.C.: 3559
N.A.I.C.S.: 333249
Marco Parma *(CEO)*

U.S. Subsidiaries:

Teksid Inc. (2)
21000 Telegraph Rd
Southfield, MI 48033
Tel.: (248) 624-3040
Fax: (248) 624-3531
Web Site: www.teksid.com
Cast Iron Mfr
S.I.C.: 3322
N.A.I.C.S.: 331511

Non-U.S. Subsidiaries:

Funfrap-Fundicao Portuguesa S.A. (2)
Apartado 3
3801-652 Aveiro, Portugal
Tel.: (351) 234 301700
Fax: (351) 234 301705
Web Site: www.teksid.com
Iron Casting Product Mfr
S.I.C.: 3322
N.A.I.C.S.: 331511
G. Fassera *(CEO)*

Teksid Hierro de Mexico S.A. de C.V. (2)
Libramiento Carlos Salinas de Gortari 2001
PTE C D Frontera Coah
Mexico, 25616, Mexico
Tel.: (52) 86 66494078
Fax: (52) 86 66494055
Web Site: www.teksid.com
Cast Iron Mfr
S.I.C.: 3322
N.A.I.C.S.: 331511
A. Kuskowski *(Plant Mgr)*

Subsidiary:

Compania Industrial Frontera S.A. de C.V. (3)
Libramiento Carlos Salinas De Gortari No 2001 Pte
Villa Frontera, 25616, Mexico
Tel.: (52) 8666494100
Automobile Metallurgical Product Mfr
S.I.C.: 5013
N.A.I.C.S.: 423120

Teksid Iron Poland Sp. z o.o. (2)
Ul Ciezarowa 49
43-300 Skoczow, Poland
Tel.: (48) 33 8538200
Fax: (48) 33 8534970
Web Site: www.teksid.com
Emp.: 500
Metal Casting Equipment Mfr
S.I.C.: 3559
N.A.I.C.S.: 333249
G. Fassera *(Pres)*

Joint Venture:

Global Value S.p.A. (1)
Corso Orbassano 367
10100 Turin, Italy
Tel.: (39) 0110051111
Fax: (39) 0110040161
E-Mail: communication@globalvalue.it
Web Site: www.itglobalvalue.com
Sales Range: $100-124.9 Million
Software Infrastructure Outsourcing Services; Owned by Fiat S.p.A. & by International Business Machines Corporation
S.I.C.: 7379
N.A.I.C.S.: 541519

U.S. Subsidiary:

Fiat USA Inc. (1)
7 Times Sq
New York, NY 10036 (100%)
Tel.: (212) 355-2600
Telex: 261230 FUSA UR
Fax: (212) 755-6152
E-Mail: webmaster@fiatgroup.com
Web Site: www.fiatgroup.com
Emp.: 6
Financial Services
S.I.C.: 6726
N.A.I.C.S.: 525990
Sergio Marchionne *(CEO)*

Non-U.S. Subsidiaries:

AC Austro Car Handelsgesellschaft mbh & Co. (1)
Breitenfurter Strase 142-144
1230 Vienna, Austria
Tel.: (43) 180 12 10
Fax: (43) 180 12 11 00
New Car Dealer
S.I.C.: 5511
N.A.I.C.S.: 441110

Automotive Lighting Reutlingen GmbH (1)
Tubinger Str 123
72762 Reutlingen, Germany
Tel.: (49) 7121 35 6000
Fax: (49) 7121 35 6065
Web Site: www.al-lighting.de
Rev.: $2,378,502,000
Emp.: 13,480
Automotive Lighting Equipment Mfr
S.I.C.: 3714
N.A.I.C.S.: 336320
Gianpaolo Accossato *(Chm)*
E. Razelli *(Pres)*
E. Ferrari *(COO)*

Subsidiary:

Automotive Lighting Brotterode GmbH (2)
Liebensteiner Str 36
98599 Brotterode, Germany
Tel.: (49) 36840 83 0
Fax: (49) 36840 83 1209
E-Mail: info@al-lighting.com
Web Site: www.al-lighting.de/index.php?id=949
Automotive Lighting Equipment Mfr
S.I.C.: 3714
N.A.I.C.S.: 336320

Non-U.S. Subsidiaries:

Automotive Lighting Italia S.p.A. (2)
Via Cavallo 18
10078 Venaria Reale, Torino, Italy
Tel.: (39) 011 6870 111
Fax: (39) 011 6870 310
Web Site: www.al-lighting.com
Lighting Equipment Mfr
S.I.C.: 3714
N.A.I.C.S.: 336320

Subsidiaries:

Easy Drive S.r.l. (3)
Corso Marconi 10
10125 Turin, Italy

Tel.: (39) 0110063341
Fax: (39) 0110063211
Automobile Consulting Services
S.I.C.: 8742
N.A.I.C.S.: 541611

Fiat Services S.p.A. (3)
Corso Giovanni Agnelli 200
10135 Turin, Italy
Tel.: (39) 01100311111
Fax: (39) 0110038718
Web Site: www.fiat.it
Emp.: 300
Automobile Outsourcing Services
S.I.C.: 8999
N.A.I.C.S.: 541612

Subsidiaries:

Fiat Information Technology, Excellence and Methods S.p.A. (4)
Corso Ferrucci 112/A
Turin, 10138, Italy
Tel.: (39) 0110057611
Software Development Services
S.I.C.: 7371
N.A.I.C.S.: 541511

Servizi e Attivita Doganali per l'Industria S.p.A. (4)
Corso Francesco Ferrucci 112/A
Turin, 10138, Italy
Tel.: (39) 0110057611
Freight Transportation Services
S.I.C.: 4731
N.A.I.C.S.: 488510

Non-U.S. Subsidiary:

Sadi Polska-Agencja Celna Sp. z o.o. (5)
Ul Konwojowa 57
43-346 Bielsko-Biala, Poland
Tel.: (48) 33 813 53 23
Fax: (48) 33 813 41 13
Web Site: www.sadipolska.pl
Freight Transportation Services
S.I.C.: 4731
N.A.I.C.S.: 488510

Non-U.S. Subsidiaries:

Fiat Argentina S.A. (4)
Carlos Maria Della Paolera 299
Buenos Aires, Argentina
Tel.: (54) 1157765100
New Car Dealer
S.I.C.: 5511
N.A.I.C.S.: 441110

Fiat Finance et Services S.A. (4)
Za Trappes Elancourt
Trappes, Yvelines, 78190, France
Tel.: (33) 130169200
Financial Services
S.I.C.: 6726
N.A.I.C.S.: 525990

Fiat GmbH (4)
Nicolaus-Otto-Str 4
Ulm, Baden-Wurttemberg, 89079, Germany
Tel.: (49) 73120740
Automobile Mfr
S.I.C.: 3711
N.A.I.C.S.: 336111

Fiat Iberica S.A. (4)
Paseo de la Habana 74-A
Madrid, 28036, Spain
Tel.: (34) 914572211
Fax: (34) 914571253
New Car Dealer
S.I.C.: 5511
N.A.I.C.S.: 441110

Fiat Services Belgium N.V. (4)
Ruddervoordsestraat 51
Zedelgem, 8210, Belgium
Tel.: (32) 50402711
Fax: (32) 50402733
E-Mail: info@fiatservices.com
Web Site: www.fiatservicesbelgium.be
Emp.: 125
Automotive Repair & Maintenance Services
S.I.C.: 7539
N.A.I.C.S.: 811118
Frederik de Fruyt *(Mgr-IT)*

Fiat Services d.o.o. (4)
4 Kosovska
Kragujevac, Serbia
Tel.: (381) 34335355
New Car Dealer
S.I.C.: 5511
N.A.I.C.S.: 441110

Fiat Services Polska Sp. z o.o. (4)
Weglowa 72
Bielsko-Biala, Poland
Tel.: (48) 33 813 2242
Fax: (48) 33 813 4108
Financial Management Services
S.I.C.: 6211
N.A.I.C.S.: 523999

Human Resources Services S.p.A. (3)
Via Marothetti 11
10126 Turin, Italy (100%)
Tel.: (39) 0110066111
Web Site: www.humanresourcesservices.it
Human Resource Services
S.I.C.: 8742
N.A.I.C.S.: 541611

Isvor Fiat S.C.p.A. (3)
Via Giacosa 38
10125 Turin, Italy
Tel.: (39) 110065773
Telex: 213595 ISVOR I
Fax: (39) 011 006 5568
E-Mail: isvor@isvor.it
Web Site: www.isvor.it
Technical Training & Consulting Services
S.I.C.: 8299
N.A.I.C.S.: 611430

KeyG Consulting S.p.A. (3)
Corso Ferrucci 112/A
10138 Turin, Italy
Tel.: (39) 0110058109
Fax: (39) 0110057993
E-Mail: info@keyg.it
Web Site: www.keyg.it
Administrative & Management Consulting Services
S.I.C.: 8742
N.A.I.C.S.: 541611

Sestrieres S.p.A. (3)
Via Del Colle 13
Frazione Borgata Sestriere, 10058 Turin, Italy
Tel.: (39) 0122799411
Fax: (39) 0122799460
E-Mail: commerciale@vialattea.it
Web Site: www.vialattea.it
Emp.: 50
Ski Complex Management Services
S.I.C.: 7999
N.A.I.C.S.: 713940
Giovanni Brasso *(Pres)*

Non-U.S. Subsidiary:

Automotive Lighting Rear Lamps France S.a.s. (3)
Z I des Manteaux
89330 Saint-Julien-du-Sault, France
Tel.: (33) 3 866339 39
Fax: (33) 3 866339 35
Web Site: www.al-lighting.de/index.php?id=949
Automotive Lighting Equipment Mfr
S.I.C.: 3714
N.A.I.C.S.: 336320

Automotive Lighting Japan K.K. (2)
Benex S-2 Building 8F 3-17-5 Shinyokohama
Kohoku-ku, Yokohama, 222-0033, Japan
Tel.: (81) 45 478 0045
Fax: (81) 45 478 0095
Web Site: www.al-lighting.com
Emp.: 50
Automotive Lighting Equipment Mfr
S.I.C.: 3714
N.A.I.C.S.: 336320

Automotive Lighting Polska Sp. z o.o. (2)
Ul Gen M Zaruskiego 11
41-200 Sosnowiec, Poland
Tel.: (48) 32 2960 111
Fax: (48) 32 2636 618
Web Site: www.al-lighting.de/index.php?id=949
Automotive Lighting Equipment Mfr
S.I.C.: 3714
N.A.I.C.S.: 336320

Automotive Lighting S.R.O. (2)
Pavov 113
586 01 Jihlava, Czech Republic
Tel.: (420) 567 562 601
Fax: (420) 567 562 602
Web Site: www.al-lighting.cz
Emp.: 1,300
Automotive Lighting Equipment Mfr
S.I.C.: 3714
N.A.I.C.S.: 336320
David Vojak *(Plant Mgr-Pur)*

Subsidiary:

Fiat Finance North America, Inc. (3)
7 Times Sq Tower
New York, NY 10036
Tel.: (212) 355-2600
Fax: (212) 308-2968
Web Site: www.fiatgroup.com
Emp.: 6
Auto Finance Services
S.I.C.: 6159
N.A.I.C.S.: 522298
Rita Bonura *(Office Mgr)*

Malaysian Automotive Lighting SDN. BHD (2)
Plot 45 Phase 4 Bayan Lepas Industrial Park
11900 Bayan Lepas, Penang, Malaysia
Tel.: (60) 4 8206 000
Fax: (60) 4 8206 290
Web Site: www.al-lighting.de/index.php?id=949
Automotive Lighting Equipment Mfr
S.I.C.: 3714
N.A.I.C.S.: 336320

Chrysler Asia pacific Investment Ltd. (1)
5/F Third Office Building No 555 Dongchuan Road
Minhang Dist, Shanghai, China
Tel.: (86) 2161927800
Investment Management Services
S.I.C.: 6282
N.A.I.C.S.: 523920

Chrysler Mexico Investment Holdings Cooperatie U.A. (1)
Locatellikade 1
1076 AZ Amsterdam, Netherlands
Tel.: (31) 20 5755600
Investment Management Services
S.I.C.: 6282
N.A.I.C.S.: 523920

Ergom do Brasil Ltda (1)
Rodovia MG 431 - Km 51 7
Itauna, Minas Gerais, 35680-142, Brazil
Tel.: (55) 37 3243 4400
Fax: (55) 37 3243 4200
Web Site: www.ergom.com.br
Automobile Parts Mfr
S.I.C.: 3714
N.A.I.C.S.: 336390

Ferrari Financial Services AG (1)
Sudliche Munchner Str 30
Grunwald, Germany
Tel.: (40) 000400000
Financial Management Consulting Services
S.I.C.: 8742
N.A.I.C.S.: 541611

Fiat France SA (1)
6 Rue Copemic
78083 Trappes, Cedex, France (100%)
Tel.: (33) 130167000
Telex: FIATFRAN 642683 F
Fax: (33) 130167710
E-Mail: christophe.bertoncini@fiat.com
Web Site: www.fiat.fr
Emp.: 200
Automobile Importer & Sales
S.I.C.: 5012
N.A.I.C.S.: 423110
Maurizil Zuares *(Gen Dir)*

Fiat Group Purchasing France S.a.r.l. (1)
6 Rue Nicolas Copernic
78190 Trappes, France
Tel.: (33) 130167000
Car Dealer
S.I.C.: 5511
N.A.I.C.S.: 441110

Fiat Group Purchasing Poland Sp. z o.o (1)
Ul Grazynskiego 141
Bielsko-Biala, Poland
Tel.: (48) 338132549
Fax: (48) 338126988
Automobile Distr
S.I.C.: 5012
N.A.I.C.S.: 423110

Fiat Netherlands Holding B.V. (1)
Schiphol Blvd 217WTC Airport
1118 BH Schiphol, Netherlands
Tel.: (31) 204460429
Fax: (31) 204460436
E-Mail: info@fiat.com
Web Site: www.fiat.com
Emp.: 2
Holding Company
S.I.C.: 6719
N.A.I.C.S.: 551112
Gio Marthione *(Chm)*

Fonderie du Poitou Fonte S.A.S. (1)
Z I de Saint Ustre
86220 Ingrandes, France
Tel.: (33) 5 49210520
Fax: (33) 5 49937002
Web Site: www.poitoufonte.fr
Emp.: 500
Iron Cylinder Block Mfr
S.I.C.: 3322
N.A.I.C.S.: 331511
J. Meillier *(CEO)*

Industrial Yorka de Tepotzotlan S.A. de C.V (1)
Av De La Industria No 21
Tepotzotlan, 54600, Mexico
Tel.: (52) 5558760511
Automobile Parts Distr
S.I.C.: 5013
N.A.I.C.S.: 423120

International Metropolitan Automotive promotion (France) S.A. (1)
365 route de Vienne
69200 Venissieux, France
Tel.: (33) 8 99 96 26 94
New Car Dealer
S.I.C.: 5511
N.A.I.C.S.: 441110

Internazionale Holding Fiat SA (1)
Riva Paradiso 14
CH 6902 Lugano, Paradiso, Switzerland (100%)
Tel.: (41) 919853711
Fax: (41) 919853686
E-Mail: giulia.costa@cnh.com
Web Site: www.fiat.com
Emp.: 50
Holding Co
S.I.C.: 6719
N.A.I.C.S.: 551112
Francois Susigneni *(Gen Mgr)*

Italian Motor Village S.A. (1)
Avenida Jose Gomes Ferreira 15
Alges, Oeiras, 1495-139, Portugal
Tel.: (351) 214166300
New Car Dealer
S.I.C.: 5511
N.A.I.C.S.: 441110

Mako Elektrik Sanayi Ve Ticaret A.S. (1)
Organize Sanayi Bolgesi Yesil Cad No 28
Nilufer, 16159 Bursa, Turkey
Tel.: (90) 224 219 56 00
Fax: (90) 224 219 57 99
Web Site: www.mako.com.tr
Automotive Lighting & Air Conditioning Device Mfr
S.I.C.: 3714
N.A.I.C.S.: 336320
Ibrahim Icoz *(Gen Mgr)*

Powertrain Mekanik Sanayi ve Ticaret Anoniom Sirketi (1)
Organize Sanayi Bolgesi Yesil Cd No 28
Nilufer
Bursa, Turkey
Tel.: (90) 224 261 03 50
Fax: (90) 224 261 25 99
Automobile Parts Distr
S.I.C.: 5013
N.A.I.C.S.: 423120

Rimaco S.A. (1)
Avenue De Cour 135
Lausanne, Vaud, 1007, Switzerland

Fiat S.p.A.—(Continued)

Tel.: (41) 216148020
Emp.: 15
Insurance Services
S.I.C.: 6411
N.A.I.C.S.: 524298
Ute Bock *(Area Mgr)*

Subsidiary:

Neptunia Assicurazioni Marittime S.A. **(2)**
Avenue De Cour 135
Lausanne, Vaud, 1007, Switzerland
Tel.: (41) 216014630
Medical Insurance Services
S.I.C.: 6324
N.A.I.C.S.: 524114

Servicios Administrativos Corp. IPASA S.A. **(1)**
Retorno Ave De La Industria Lote 20 Y 21
Tepotzotlan, 54600, Mexico
Tel.: (52) 5558760511
Automobile Parts Distr
S.I.C.: 5013
N.A.I.C.S.: 423120

Sistemi Comandi Meccanici Otomotiv Sanayi Ve Ticaret A.S. **(1)**
Organize Sanayi Bolgesi Itfaiye Grubu
Bursa, 16140, Turkey
Tel.: (90) 224 411 2250
Fax: (90) 224 411 2255
Emp.: 70
Automotive Parts Mfr
S.I.C.: 3714
N.A.I.C.S.: 336390
Francesco Tarallo *(Gen Mgr)*

TCA - Tecnologia em Componentes Automotivos. SA. **(1)**
Rod Prestes Maia Br - 101 Sul S/N
Jaboatao dos Guararapes, Pernambuco, 54335-180, Brazil
Tel.: (55) 8121196715
Automobile Parts Distr
S.I.C.: 5013
N.A.I.C.S.: 423120

FIBA HOLDING A.S.

Buyukdere Cad
1 Levent Plz No 173 A, 34430
Istanbul, Turkey
Tel.: (90) 2123391900
Fax: (90) 2123391872
Web Site: www.fibaholding.com.tr
Year Founded: 1987
Emp.: 10,972

Business Description:
Holding Company
S.I.C.: 6719
N.A.I.C.S.: 551112

Personnel:
Husnu M. Ozyegin *(Chm)*

Non-U.S. Subsidiary:

Credit Europe Group N.V. **(1)**
Karspeldreef 6a
Amsterdam, Netherlands (95%)
Tel.: (31) 203576410
Fax: (31) 203576301
Web Site: www.crediteurope.nl
Holding Company
S.I.C.: 6719
N.A.I.C.S.: 551112

Subsidiary:

Credit Europe Bank N.V. **(2)**
Karspeldreef 6A
1101 Amsterdam, Netherlands
Tel.: (31) 203576300
Fax: (31) 203576301
E-Mail: info@crediteurope.nl
Web Site: www.crediteuropebank.na
Emp.: 5,242
Commercial Banking
S.I.C.: 6029
N.A.I.C.S.: 522110
Murag Basbay *(CEO)*

Non-U.S. Subsidiaries:

Credit Europe Bank (Dubai) Ltd. **(3)**
Currency House Office Building 1 Level 7 Unit 7
Al Fattan Area DIFC, Dubai, United Arab Emirates
Tel.: (971) 44387100
Fax: (971) 44387175
Web Site: www.crediteuropebank.com
Emp.: 19
Commercial Banking
S.I.C.: 6029
N.A.I.C.S.: 522110
Cenk Atmaca *(CEO)*

Credit Europe Bank Ltd. **(3)**
Cosmodamianskaya Nab 52-3
11305 Moscow, Russia
Tel.: (7) 4957757757
Web Site: www.crediteurope.ru
Emp.: 2,747
Commercial Banking
S.I.C.: 6029
N.A.I.C.S.: 522110
Husnu M. Ozyegin *(Chm)*

Credit Europe Bank (Romania) S.A. **(3)**
Anchor plaza Building B section 26Z
Timisoara boulevard 6th District
061331 Bucharest, Romania
Tel.: (40) 214064607
Fax: (40) 213107089
E-Mail: office@crediteuropebank.ro
Web Site: www.crediteurope.ro
Emp.: 1,200
Commercial Banking
S.I.C.: 6029
N.A.I.C.S.: 522110
Husnu Ozyegin *(Owner)*

Subsidiary:

Credit Europe Leasing IFN S.A. **(4)**
26 Z kimisoara
Bucharest, Romania
Tel.: (40) 214064607
Fax: (40) 213172033
E-Mail: contact@fil.com.ro
Web Site: www.fil.com.ro
Emp.: 64
Commercial & Industrial Machinery Leasing
S.I.C.: 7359
N.A.I.C.S.: 532490
Husnu Ozyegin *(Owner)*

Credit Europe Bank (Suisse) S.A. **(3)**
12 rue du Mont-Blanc
1201 Geneva, Switzerland
Tel.: (41) 228391919
Fax: (41) 228391909
E-Mail: crediteurope@crediteurope.ch
Web Site: www.crediteurope.ch
Emp.: 40
Commercial Banking
S.I.C.: 6029
N.A.I.C.S.: 522110
Iale Kosenovlu *(Mng Dir)*

PJSC Credit Europe Bank **(3)**
77-A Chervonoarmiyaska Str
3150 Kiev, Ukraine (100%)
Tel.: (380) 443906733
Fax: (380) 44 390 67 17
Web Site: www.crediteurope.com.ua
Commercial Banking
S.I.C.: 6029
N.A.I.C.S.: 522110
Arif Dursun Bibioglu *(Chm-Mgmt Bd)*
Irina Nemchen *(Deputy Chm-Mgmt Bd)*
Yusef Dagtekin *(Pres)*

FIBAM COMPANHIA INDUSTRIAL

Av Humberto de Alencar Castelo Branco 39
9850300 Sao Bernardo do Campo, SP, Brazil
Tel.: (55) 11 2139 5300
Fax: (55) 11 4343 4030
E-Mail: ri@fibam.com.br
Web Site: www.fibam.com.br
Year Founded: 1951
FBMC3—(BRAZ)
Sales Range: $25-49.9 Million
Emp.: 386

Business Description:
Metal Fastener Mfr & Whslr
S.I.C.: 3965
N.A.I.C.S.: 339993

Personnel:
Paolo Paperini *(Dir-IR)*

FIBEMI NV

Rokin 55
1012 KK Amsterdam, Netherlands
Tel.: (31) 20 527 9111

Business Description:
Investment Services
S.I.C.: 6211
N.A.I.C.S.: 523999

Non-U.S. Holding:

Duvel Moortgat NV **(1)**
Breendonkdorp 58
2870 Puurs, Belgium
Tel.: (32) 3 860 94 00
Fax: (32) 3 886 46 22
E-Mail: info@duvel.be
Web Site: www.duvelmoortgat.be
Emp.: 773
Beers & Malt Liquors Mfrs
S.I.C.: 2082
N.A.I.C.S.: 312120
Michel Moortgat *(CEO)*
Herbert De Loose *(CFO)*
Daniel Krug *(COO)*
Anouk Lagae *(CMO)*
Hedwig Neven *(CTO)*

Subsidiaries:

Brasserie d'Achouffe nv **(2)**
Rue du Village 32
Achouffe, 6666 Houffalize, Belgium (100%)
Tel.: (32) 61 28 81 47
Fax: (32) 61 28 82 64
E-Mail: info@achouffe.be
Web Site: www.achouffe.be
Emp.: 36
Brewery
S.I.C.: 2082
N.A.I.C.S.: 312120
Jean-Lou Barbette *(Ops Mgr)*

Brouwerij De Koninck nv **(2)**
Mechelsesteenweg 291
2018 Antwerp, Belgium (100%)
Tel.: (32) 3218 4048
E-Mail: info@dekoninck.be
Web Site: www.dekoninck.be
Brewery
S.I.C.: 2082
N.A.I.C.S.: 312120

U.S. Subsidiaries:

Boulevard Brewing Co. **(2)**
2501 SW Blvd
Kansas City, MO 64108
Tel.: (816) 474-7095
Fax: (816) 474-1722
E-Mail: fineales@boulevard.com
Web Site: www.boulevard.com
Emp.: 125
Beer Mfr & Distr
S.I.C.: 2082
N.A.I.C.S.: 312120
John McDonald *(Founder & Pres)*

Brouwerij Belame Ltd **(2)**
656 County Hwy 33
Cooperstown, NY 13326-9248 (100%)
Tel.: (607) 544-1800
Fax: (607) 544-1801
Toll Free: (800) 544-1809
E-Mail: info@ommegang.com
Web Site: www.ommegang.com
Brewery
S.I.C.: 2082
N.A.I.C.S.: 312120
Simon Thorpe *(Pres & CEO)*

Duvel Moortgat USA, Ltd. **(2)**
21 Railroad Ave Ste 32
Cooperstown, NY 13326 (100%)
Tel.: (607) 544-1800
Fax: (607) 544-1801
E-Mail: info@duvelmoortgatusa.com
Web Site: www.duvelmoortgatusa.com
Emp.: 25
Sales & Distribution of Beer & Ale
S.I.C.: 5181
N.A.I.C.S.: 424810
Simon Thorpe *(Pres & CEO)*

Non-U.S. Subsidiaries:

Duvel Moortgat France sarl **(2)**
540 Allee des Hetres
69760 Limonest, France (100%)
Tel.: (33) 437 59 82 30
Fax: (33) 478 66 15 65
E-Mail: contact@duvel.fr
Web Site: www.duvelmoortgat.be
Beer & Ale Whslr
S.I.C.: 5181
N.A.I.C.S.: 424810

Duvel Moortgat Shanghai Ltd **(2)**
528 Kangding Road Building A Room 301
Shanghai, China (100%)
Tel.: (86) 21 62 55 79 19
Fax: (86) 21 62 55 79 20
E-Mail: vincent.smets@duvelmoortgat.be
Beer & Ale Importer, Distr & Whslr
S.I.C.: 5181
N.A.I.C.S.: 424810

Duvel Moortgat UK Ltd **(2)**
134 Curtain Road
Shoreditch, London, EC2A 3AR, United Kingdom (100%)
Tel.: (44) 20 77 29 72 16
Fax: (44) 20 77 29 38 93
E-Mail: info@duvelmoortgat.co.uk
Web Site: www.duvelmoortgat.be
Beer & Ale Whslr
S.I.C.: 5181
N.A.I.C.S.: 424810

FIBERLINE COMPOSITES A/S

Barmftedtalle 5
5500 Middelfart, Denmark
Tel.: (45) 70137713
Fax: (45) 70137714
E-Mail: fiberline@fiberline.com
Web Site: www.fiberline.com
Year Founded: 1979
Emp.: 116

Business Description:
Plastic Composite Profiles Mfr
S.I.C.: 3083
N.A.I.C.S.: 326130

Personnel:
Henrik Thorning *(CEO & Mng Dir)*

FIBERLINKS TEXTILES INC.

815 C Tecumseh
Pointe-Claire, QC, H9R 4B1, Canada
Tel.: (514) 694-9440
Fax: (514) 694-6311
Web Site: www.priva-inc.com

Business Description:
Textile Product Mfr & Distr
S.I.C.: 2299
N.A.I.C.S.: 314999

Personnel:
Frank Dres *(Co-Owner)*
Wil Dres *(Co-Owner)*

Division:

Priva Inc. **(1)**
815C Tecumseh
Pointe-Claire, QC, H9R 4B1, Canada AB
Tel.: (514) 356-8881
Fax: (514) 694-6311
Toll Free: (800) 761-8881
E-Mail: info@fiberlinkstextiles.com
Web Site: www.fiberlinkstextiles.com
Sales Range: $10-24.9 Million
Emp.: 20
Waterproof Textile Products Mfr
S.I.C.: 2391
N.A.I.C.S.: 314120
Frank Dres *(Mng Dir)*

FIBERWEB (INDIA) LTD.

Airport Road Kadaiya
Nani Daman, Daman, 396210, India
Tel.: (91) 260 2220766
Fax: (91) 260 2220758
E-Mail: fiberweb@fiberwebindia.com
Web Site: www.fiberwebindia.com
507910—(BOM)

Rev.: $10,079,957
Assets: $14,696,733
Liabilities: $24,861,109
Net Worth: ($10,164,376)
Earnings: ($169,355)
Fiscal Year-end: 03/31/13

Business Description:
Spunbonded Fabrics Mfr
S.I.C.: 2297
N.A.I.C.S.: 313230

Personnel:
Pravin V. Sheth *(Chm & Mng Dir)*
Sunita Agarwal *(Compliance Officer & Sec)*

Board of Directors:
Pravin V. Sheth
K. I. Jos
P. S. Krishnan
Dileep V. Naik
Gopalji M. Rana
G. Ravindran
C. A. Rege
Bhadresh H. Shah
Bhavesh P. Sheth

Legal Counsel:
Littlee & Co
Mumbai, India

Divyakant Mehta & Associates
Mumbai, India

Transfer Agent:
Sharex Dynamic (India) Pvt. Ltd.
Unit-1 Luthra Ind Premises Safed Pool Andheri Kurla Rd Andheri (E)
Mumbai, India

FIBI HOLDING COMPANY LTD.

9 Ahad Haam Street
Tel Aviv, 65251, Israel
Tel.: (972) 35196111
Fax: (972) 3 510 0316
E-Mail: support@fibi.co.il
Web Site: www.fibi.co.il
Year Founded: 1972
FIBI—(TAE)
Int. Income: $604,530,000
Assets: $28,315,379,160
Liabilities: $26,495,878,200
Net Worth: $1,819,500,960
Emp.: 5,067
Fiscal Year-end: 12/31/12

Business Description:
Bank Holding Company
S.I.C.: 6712
N.A.I.C.S.: 551111

Personnel:
Rony Hizkiaho *(Chm)*
Smadar Barber-Tsadik *(CEO)*
Ilan Batzri *(Deputy CEO & Head-Corp Div)*
Benzi Adiri *(Exec VP, Chief Risk Officer & Head-Risk Mgmt)*
Aviad Biller *(Sec)*
Yossi Levy *(Exec VP & Head-Resources Div)*
Yaacov Malkin *(Exec VP & Head-Banking)*
Nachman Nitzan *(Exec VP & Head-Acctg)*
Yoram Sirkis *(Exec VP & Head-Client Assets Mgmt)*
Aviel Sternschuss *(Exec VP & Head-Fin Div)*

Board of Directors:
Rony Hizkiaho
Dan Arbel
David Assia
Zeev Ben Asher
Gil Bino
Zadik Bino
Pnina Biterman-Cohen
Amnon Goldschmidt
Gideon Lahav
Dalia Lev
Giora S. Meyuhas
Jacob Sitt
Noga Yatziv

Subsidiaries:

Bank Otsar Hahayal Ltd. **(1)**
11 Menachem Begin Rd
Ramat Gan, 52681, Israel
Tel.: (972) 37556000
Fax: (972) 37556091
Web Site: www.bankotsar.co.il
Commercial Banking Services
S.I.C.: 6029
N.A.I.C.S.: 522110
Nir Herzenshtein *(Mgr-Trading Room)*

First International Bank of Israel Ltd. **(1)**
42 Rothschild Blvd
Tel Aviv, 66883, Israel (54.33%)
Tel.: (972) 3 5196223
Fax: (972) 3 5100316
E-Mail: support@fibi.co.il
Web Site: www.fibi.co.il
FTIN—(TAE)
Rev.: $1,433,139,120
Earnings: $155,028,360
Fiscal Year-end: 12/31/12
Commercial Banking
S.I.C.: 6029
N.A.I.C.S.: 522110
Rony Hizkiyahu *(Chm)*
Smadar Barber-Tsadik *(CEO)*
Ilan Batzri *(Deputy CEO-Corp Div)*
Benzi Adiri *(Chief Risk Officer, Exec VP & Head-Risk Mgmt Div)*
Aviad Billler *(Sec)*
Nachman Nitzan *(Exec VP-Chief Accountant Div)*
Yossi Levy *(Exec VP-Resources Div)*
Kobi Malkin *(Exec VP-Banking Div)*
Yael Ronen *(Exec VP)*
Yoram Sirkis *(Exec VP-Client Assets Mgmt Div)*
Aviel Sternschuss *(Exec VP-Fin Div)*

Subsidiaries:

Bank Massad Ltd. **(2)**
80 Rothschild Boulevard
PO Box 2639
Tel Aviv, 61025, Israel (51%)
Tel.: (972) 35641333
Fax: (972) 3 560 2384
Web Site: www.bankmassad.co.il
Emp.: 241
Commercial Banking Services
S.I.C.: 6029
N.A.I.C.S.: 522110
Yosef Yarom *(Chm)*

Bank Otsar Ha-Hayal Ltd. **(2)**
11 Menachem Begin St
52521 Ramat Gan, Israel (68%)
Tel.: (972) 37556005
Fax: (972) 37175364
Web Site: www.bankotsar.co.il
Int. Income: $53,670,400
Emp.: 782
Commercial Banking Services
S.I.C.: 6029
N.A.I.C.S.: 522110
Baruch Granot *(CFO)*

Bank Poaley Agudat Israel Ltd. **(2)**
9 Ahad Ha Am Street
Tel Aviv, 65251, Israel (68.68%)
Tel.: (972) 35196650
Fax: (972) 35196785
Web Site: www.pagi.co.il
Emp.: 50
Commercial Banking Services
S.I.C.: 6029
N.A.I.C.S.: 522110

The First International & Co.-Underwriting and Investment Ltd. **(2)**
38 Rothschild Blvd
Tel Aviv, Israel (75%)
Tel.: (972) 35115730
Fax: (972) 35115735
E-Mail: hitum@sibi.co.in
Commercial Banking
S.I.C.: 6029
N.A.I.C.S.: 522110

Modus Selective Investment Management & Advice Ltd. **(2)**
17 Yitzhak Sadeh Street
67211 Tel Aviv, Israel (50%)
Tel.: (972) 036241166
Fax: (972) 036241188
Web Site: www.modus-selective.co.ia
Emp.: 25
Investment Management Services
S.I.C.: 6282
N.A.I.C.S.: 523930
Benedek Yona *(Mgr)*

UBank Ltd. **(2)**
38 Rothschild Blvd
Tel Aviv, 66883, Israel (100%)
Tel.: (972) 35645320
Fax: (972) 35645298
Web Site: www.u-bank.net
Emp.: 260
Commercial Banking
S.I.C.: 6029
N.A.I.C.S.: 522110
Ron Bedny *(CEO)*

Non-U.S. Subsidiaries:

FIBI Bank (Suisse) Ltd. **(2)**
Seestrasse 61
8027 Zurich, Switzerland (100%)
Tel.: (41) 442066969
Fax: (41) 442011441
E-Mail: fibi@fibi.ch
Web Site: www.fibi.ch
Emp.: 30
Commercial Banking Services
S.I.C.: 6029
N.A.I.C.S.: 522110
Ofer Chaimi *(Gen Mgr)*

FIBI Bank (UK) plc **(2)**
24 Creechurch Lane
EC3A5JX London, United Kingdom (100%)
Tel.: (44) 02072809500
Fax: (44) 02072809515
Web Site: www.fibi.co.uk
Emp.: 44
Commercial Banking Services
S.I.C.: 6029
N.A.I.C.S.: 522110
D. Kol *(Mng Dir)*

Ubank Trust Company Ltd. **(1)**
38 Rotschild Blvd
Tel Aviv, Jaffa, 66883, Israel
Tel.: (972) 35645205
Fax: (972) 35645121
Commercial Banking Services
S.I.C.: 6029
N.A.I.C.S.: 522110

FIBON BERHAD

12A Jalan 20 Taman Sri Kluang
Kluang, 86000 Johor, Malaysia
Tel.: (60) 77736918
Fax: (60) 77742025
E-Mail: corp@fibon.com.my
Web Site: www.fibon.com.my
FIBON—(KLS)
Rev.: $5,467,738
Assets: $11,181,744
Liabilities: $556,480
Net Worth: $10,625,264
Earnings: $1,608,448
Fiscal Year-end: 05/31/13

Business Description:
Polymer Matrix Fiber Composite Materials Mfr
S.I.C.: 2899
N.A.I.C.S.: 325998

Personnel:
Chee Khiong Pang *(Chm)*
Fok Seng Pang *(Mng Dir)*
Noriah Md Yusof *(Sec)*

Board of Directors:
Chee Khiong Pang
Peng Khang Chong
Chun Kiat Koh
Wai Kiew Lim
Mohamad Saleh Mohd Ghazali
Fok Seng Pang
Nyuk Yin Pang

Subsidiary:

Hexa Analisa Sdn. Bhd. **(1)**
12A Jalan 20 Taman Sri Kluang
86000 Keluang, Johor, Malaysia
Tel.: (60) 7 773 6918
Fax: (60) 7 774 2025
E-Mail: hexa@fibon.com.my
Electronic Component Mfr
S.I.C.: 3679
N.A.I.C.S.: 334419

Non-U.S. Subsidiaries:

Fibon Australia Pty Ltd **(1)**
Unit 11 18 Loyalty Road
North Rocks, NSW, 2151, Australia
Tel.: (61) 2 9890 8878
Fax: (61) 2 9890 8878
E-Mail: fibon.australia@gmail.com
Fiber Composite Materials Mfr
S.I.C.: 2823
N.A.I.C.S.: 325220

Fibon UK Limited **(1)**
4 Parkside Court Greenhough Road
Lichfield, Staffordshire, WS 13 7 AU, United Kingdom
Tel.: (44) 154 330 4167
E-Mail: corp@fibon.co.uk
Web Site: www.fibon.co.uk
Emp.: 2
Electrical Insulator Mfr
S.I.C.: 3999
N.A.I.C.S.: 327110
Richard Holly *(Gen Mgr)*

FIBRA UNO ADMINISTRACION SA DE CV

Antonio Dovali Jaime No 70 11th Floor Tower B
Zedec Santa Fe, Mexico, 01210, Mexico
Tel.: (52) 55 41707070
E-Mail: investor@fibrauno.mx
Web Site: www.fibra-uno.com
FUNO11—(MEX OTC)

Business Description:
Real Estate Investment
S.I.C.: 6211
N.A.I.C.S.: 523999

Personnel:
Moises El-MannArazi *(Chm)*
Andre El-Mann Arazi *(CEO)*

FIBREGEN PLC

31 Harley St
London, W1G 9QS, United Kingdom
Tel.: (44) 2075807576
Fax: (44) 2076365639
E-Mail: jonathan@welbeck-ca.co.uk
Web Site: www.fibregen.co.uk
Sales Range: $10-24.9 Million

Business Description:
Operator of Biomass-to-Energy Facilities
S.I.C.: 4939
N.A.I.C.S.: 221118

Board of Directors:
Mark Campanale

FIBRELITE COMPOSITES LIMITED.

Snaygill Industrial Estate Keighley Road
Skipton, North Yorkshire, BD23 2QR, United Kingdom
Tel.: (44) 1756799773
Fax: (44) 1756799539
E-Mail: covers@fibrelite.com
Web Site: www.fibrelite.com
Year Founded: 1980
Rev.: $18,339,817
Emp.: 97

Business Description:
Manhole Covers Mfr
S.I.C.: 3322
N.A.I.C.S.: 331511

Personnel:
Ian Thompson *(Mng Dir)*
Jim Goodman *(Pres-USA)*

FICHOU SAS

Z I Kergonan 20 Rue Gustave Zede
29200 Brest, Finistere, France

Fichou Sas—(Continued)

Tel.: (33) 298424242
Fax: (33) 2 98 42 42 43
E-Mail: ad.fichou@a-d.fr
Web Site:
Sls.: $20,200,000
Emp.: 117
Business Description:
Motor Vehicle Supplies & New Parts
S.I.C.: 5013
N.A.I.C.S.: 423120
Personnel:
Pierre Fichou *(Pres)*
Board of Directors:
Jean-Luc Aridon

FIDEA HOLDINGS CO. LTD.

3-1-24 Chuo Aoba-ku
Sendai, 980-0021, Japan
Tel.: (81) 222225161
Fax: (81) 227265907
Web Site: www.fidea.co.jp
8713—(TKS)
Business Description:
Bank Holding Company
S.I.C.: 6712
N.A.I.C.S.: 551111
Personnel:
Satoru Machida *(Chm)*
Seiji Satomura *(Pres & CEO)*

FIDESSA GROUP PLC

Dukes Court Duke Street
Woking, Surrey, GU21 5BH, United Kingdom
Tel.: (44) 1483206300
Fax: (44) 1483206301
E-Mail: ukenquiry@fidessa.com
Web Site: www.fidessa.com
FDSA—(LSE OTC)
Rev.: $440,031,256
Assets: $408,931,877
Liabilities: $187,633,866
Net Worth: $221,298,011
Earnings: $48,019,892
Emp.: 1,767
Fiscal Year-end: 12/31/12
Business Description:
Trading Systems, Market Data & Connectivity Solutions to Financial Markets Participants
S.I.C.: 7372
N.A.I.C.S.: 511210
Personnel:
John Hamer *(Chm)*
Chris Aspinwall *(CEO)*
Paul Nokes *(CEO-Global Buy-Side)*
Anil Shah *(Sec)*
Board of Directors:
John Hamer
Chris Aspinwall
Mark Foster
Philip Hardaker
Elizabeth Lake
Ron Mackintosh
Andy Malpass
Subsidiaries:

Fidessa Investments Ltd (1)
2 Suffolk Ln
London, United Kingdom (100%)
Tel.: (44) 2071051000
Fax: (44) 2079299218
Web Site: www.fidessa.com
Emp.: 30
Investment Advice
S.I.C.: 6282
N.A.I.C.S.: 523930

Fidessa LatentZero Limited (1)
1 Old Jewry
London, EC2R 8DN, United Kingdom
Tel.: (44) 2071051000
Fax: (44) 2071051001
E-Mail: ukenquiry@fidessa.com
Emp.: 400
Investment Management Software Publishing Services
S.I.C.: 7372
N.A.I.C.S.: 511210

Fidessa plc (1)
Dukes Court Duke St
Woking, Surrey, GU21 5BH, United Kingdom
Tel.: (44) 1483206300
Fax: (44) 1483206301
E-Mail: eu.info@fidessa.com
Emp.: 450
Financial Software Development Services
S.I.C.: 7371
N.A.I.C.S.: 541511

Fidessa Software Limited (1)
2 Suffolk Lane
London, EC4R 0AT, United Kingdom
Tel.: (44) 20 79299200
Business Management Software Development Services
S.I.C.: 7371
N.A.I.C.S.: 541511

U.S. Subsidiaries:

Fidessa Financial Corpration (1)
17 State St Unit 122 42 Fl
New York, NY 10004-1501 (100%)
Tel.: (212) 269-9000
Fax: (212) 943-0353
E-Mail: info@fidessa.com
Web Site: www.fidessa.com
Emp.: 100
Custom Computer Programming Services
S.I.C.: 7371
N.A.I.C.S.: 541511
Megan McKeever Costello *(Pres-Buy Side Bus-North America)*
Martin Hakker *(Exec VP-Mktg)*

Fidessa Software Corporation (1)
17 State St Unit 122 42 Fl
New York, NY 10004-1551 (100%)
Tel.: (212) 269-9000
Fax: (212) 943-0353
Web Site: www.fidessa.com
Emp.: 100
Software Publishers
S.I.C.: 7372
N.A.I.C.S.: 511210

Non-U.S. Subsidiaries:

Fidessa Canada Corporation (1)
Canadian Pacific Tower 100 Wellington St W Ste 1920
PO Box 62
Toronto, ON, M5K 1E7, Canada
Tel.: (416) 646-6627
Fax: (647) 258-6760
E-Mail: ca_reception@fidessa.com
Emp.: 40
Financial Management Software Publishing Services
S.I.C.: 7372
N.A.I.C.S.: 511210
Martin Hakker *(Mng Dir)*

Fidessa Ltd (1)
69th Floor The Center
Central, China (Hong Kong) (100%)
Tel.: (852) 25009500
Emp.: 50
Software Reproducing
S.I.C.: 3652
N.A.I.C.S.: 334614
Phill Jeffrey *(Dir-Sls-Asia Pacific)*

Fidessa SAS (1)
40 Rue La Boetie
75008 Paris, France
Tel.: (33) 173033500
Fax: (33) 173033501
E-Mail: eu.info@fidessa.com
Web Site: www.fidessa.com
Emp.: 20
Financial Software Publishing Services
S.I.C.: 7372
N.A.I.C.S.: 511210

Fidessa wll (1)
Level 22 West Tower Bahrain Financial Harbour King Faisal Highway
PO Box 20705
Manama, 5830, Bahrain
Tel.: (973) 17502864
Fax: (973) 1750 3030
E-Mail: me.info@fidessa.com
Web Site: www.fidessa.com
Financial Management Software Publishing Services
S.I.C.: 7372
N.A.I.C.S.: 511210
Rajiv Shah *(Dir-Enterprise Svc)*

FIDIA FARMACEUTICI SPA

Via Ponte della Fabbrica 3/A
35031 Padua, Italy
Tel.: (39) 0498232111
Fax: (39) 04982697
E-Mail: info@fidiapharma.it
Web Site: www.fidiapharma.com
Business Description:
Pharmaceutical Company
S.I.C.: 2834
N.A.I.C.S.: 325412

FIDIA S.P.A.

Corso Lombardia 11
10099 San Mauro Torinese, TO, Italy
Tel.: (39) 112227111
Fax: (39) 0112238202
E-Mail: info@fidia.it
Web Site: www.fidia.it
Sales Range: $25-49.9 Million
Emp.: 315
Business Description:
Mfr. & Marketer of Electronic Components & Software for Industrial Sector
S.I.C.: 3679
N.A.I.C.S.: 334419
Personnel:
Giuseppe Morfino *(Pres & Mng Dir)*
Paolo Morfino *(Mng Dir)*
Board of Directors:
Rodolfo Pes di San Vittorio
Edoardo Fea
Pietro Montalenti
Giuseppe Morfino
Francesco Profumo
Roberto Rossi
Subsidiaries:

Sitra Automazione Srl (1)
Via De Pretis 1 E
15100 Alessandria, Italy (100%)
Tel.: (39) 0131248090
Fax: (39) 0131248070
E-Mail: info@sitrasrl.it
Web Site: www.fidia.it
Sales Range: $1-9.9 Million
Emp.: 20
Mfr. & Marketer of Electronic Components & Software for Industrial Sector
S.I.C.: 3679
N.A.I.C.S.: 334419

U.S. Subsidiary:

FIDIA Co. (1)
1397 Piedmont Dr Ste 800
Troy, MI 48083
Tel.: (248) 680-0700
Fax: (248) 680-0135
E-Mail: info@fidia.com
Web Site: www.fidia.com
Emp.: 20
Mfr. & Marketer of Electronic Components & Software for Industrial Sector
S.I.C.: 3625
N.A.I.C.S.: 335314
Carlos Maidagan *(Pres)*

Non-U.S. Subsidiaries:

FIDIA Co. (1)
24 C No 1076 Jiangning Rd
Putuo Dist, Shanghai, 200060, China
Tel.: (86) 2152521635
Fax: (86) 2162760873
E-Mail: shanghai@fidia.com.cn
Web Site: www.fidia.com.cn
Mfr. & Marketer of Electronic Components & Software for Industrial Sector
S.I.C.: 3679
N.A.I.C.S.: 334419

FIDIA Do BRASIL Ltda. (1)
Salifara Maluci 4236 Mooca
Sao Paulo, 3194010, Brazil (100%)
Tel.: (55) 69657600
Fax: (55) 1161212718
E-Mail: info@fidia.com.br
Web Site: www.fidia.com.br
Emp.: 50
Mfr. & Marketer of Electronic Components & Software for Industrial Sector
S.I.C.: 3679
N.A.I.C.S.: 334419

FIDIA GmbH (1)
Robert Bosch Strasse 18
63303 Dreieich, Germany (100%)
Tel.: (49) 61034858700
Fax: (49) 61034858777
E-Mail: info@fidia.de
Web Site: www.fidia.de
Mfr. & Marketer of Electronic Components & Software for Industrial Sector
S.I.C.: 3679
N.A.I.C.S.: 334419

FIDIA Iberia S.A. (1)
Parque Tecnologico De Zamudio
Edifcio 208, 48170 Bilbao, Zamudio, Spain (100%)
Tel.: (34) 944209820
Fax: (34) 944209825
E-Mail: info@fidia.es
Web Site: www.fidia.es
Sales Range: $1-9.9 Million
Emp.: 12
Mfr. & Marketer of Electronic Components & Software for Industrial Sector
S.I.C.: 3679
N.A.I.C.S.: 334419

FIDIA Machinery & Electronics Co. Ltd. (1)
N 8 E Dongfang Rd
Chaoyang Dist, 100027 Beijing, China
Tel.: (86) 64605813
Fax: (86) 64605812
E-Mail: fidiajve@public3.bta.net.cn
Web Site: www.fidia.co.cn
Emp.: 20
Mfr. & Marketer of Electronic Components & Software for Industrial Sector
S.I.C.: 3679
N.A.I.C.S.: 334419

FIDIA S.a.r.l. (1)
47 Bis Ave Del Europe
77313 Marne-la-Vallee, France (100%)
Tel.: (33) 164616824
Fax: (33) 164616794
E-Mail: info@fidia.fr
Web Site: www.fidia.fr
Emp.: 50
Mfr. & Marketer of Electronic Components & Software for Industrial Sector
S.I.C.: 3679
N.A.I.C.S.: 334419

OOO FIDIA (1)
28 Volnaya Str
105187 Moscow, Russia
Tel.: (7) 0957867724
Fax: (7) 0957867725
E-Mail: info@fidia.ru
Web Site: www.fidia.com
Mfr & Marketer of Electronic Components & Software for Industrial Sector
S.I.C.: 3679
N.A.I.C.S.: 334419

FIDITOUR JOINT STOCK COMPANY

129 Nguyen Hue Street
District 1, Ho Chi Minh City, Vietnam
Tel.: (84) 8 39 14 14 14
Fax: (84) 8 38 21 54 27
E-Mail: inbound@fiditour.com
Web Site: www.fiditour.vn
Year Founded: 1989
FDT—(HNX)
Emp.: 500
Business Description:
Travel & Tour Operating Services
S.I.C.: 4724
N.A.I.C.S.: 561510
Personnel:
Viet Hung Nguyen *(Gen Dir)*

FIDUCIAL
20 Place de l'Iris
92400 Courbevoie, France
Tel.: (33) 147781336
Fax: (33) 149000799
E-Mail: contact@fiducial.fr
Web Site: www.fiducial.fr
Year Founded: 1970
Emp.: 15,000
Business Description:
Management Consulting Services
S.I.C.: 8742
N.A.I.C.S.: 541611
Personnel:
Christian Latouche *(Chm & CEO)*

U.S. Subsidiary:

Fiducial, Inc. **(1)**
10100 Old Columbia Rd
Columbia, MD 21046 (100%)
Tel.: (410) 910-5885
Fax: (410) 910-5901
Toll Free: (800) 434-3824
E-Mail: info@fiducial.com
Web Site: www.fiducial.com
Emp.: 80
Accounting Services
S.I.C.: 8741
N.A.I.C.S.: 561110
Bill Morice *(Dir-Field Ops)*

Subsidiary:

Fiducial, Inc. **(2)**
Fl 31 1370 Avenue of the Americas
New York, NY 10019-4602
Tel.: (212) 207-4700
Fax: (212) 308-2613
Web Site: www.fiducial.com
Sales Range: $75-99.9 Million
Emp.: 4,500
Accounting Services
S.I.C.: 8721
N.A.I.C.S.: 541219
Christian Latouche *(CEO)*
Yves Morard-Lacroix *(Exec VP)*

Non-U.S. Subsidiaries:

Fiducial Expertise S.A. **(1)**
Avenue Louise 148
1050 Brussels, Belgium
Tel.: (32) 26498016
Fax: (32) 26403964
E-Mail: fed.belaccount@fiducial.com
Web Site: www.fiducial.be
Emp.: 8
Accounting & Tax Services
S.I.C.: 8721
N.A.I.C.S.: 541219
Christian Latouche *(Pres & CEO)*

Fiducial SA **(1)**
8 rue Mont de sion
1206 Geneva, Switzerland
Tel.: (41) 223466272
Fax: (41) 227891162
E-Mail: info@fiducial.com
Web Site: www.fiducial.com
Emp.: 8
Accounting & Tax Services
S.I.C.: 8721
N.A.I.C.S.: 541219

FIDUCIAN PORTFOLIO SERVICES LIMITED
Level 4 1 York Street
Sydney, NSW, 2000, Australia
Tel.: (61) 282984600
Fax: (61) 282984611
E-Mail: info@fiducian.com.au
Web Site: www.fiducian.com.au
FPS—(ASX)
Rev.: $22,667,759
Assets: $23,390,977
Liabilities: $4,299,705
Net Worth: $19,091,272
Earnings: $3,407,667
Fiscal Year-end: 06/30/13
Business Description:
Provide Service Investors & Financial Advisers
S.I.C.: 0762
N.A.I.C.S.: 115116
Personnel:
Inderjit Singh *(Mng Dir & Sec)*
Board of Directors:
Robert E. Bucknell
Frank G. Khouri
Inderjit Singh
Christopher Haddon Stone

Subsidiaries:

Fiducian Business Services Pty. Ltd. **(1)**
Level 4 1 York St
PO Box 4175
Sydney, NSW, 2000, Australia
Tel.: (61) 282984600
Fax: (61) 282984611
E-Mail: bpo@fiducian.com.au
Web Site: www.fiducianbpo.com.au
Emp.: 2
Business Management Services
S.I.C.: 8748
N.A.I.C.S.: 541618
Alan Dunne *(Mgr-IT)*

Fiducian Financial Services Pty. Ltd. **(1)**
Level 4 1 York St
PO Box 4175
Sydney, NSW, 2001, Australia
Tel.: (61) 282984600
Fax: (61) 92211102
E-Mail: enquiry@fiducianfs.com.au
Web Site: www.fiducianfs.com.au
Emp.: 30
Financial Planning Services
S.I.C.: 6211
N.A.I.C.S.: 523999
Indy Singh *(Mng Dir)*

Harold Bodinnar & Associates Pty. Ltd. **(1)**
Level 14 1 York St
Sydney, NSW, 2000, Australia
Tel.: (61) 292312133
Fax: (61) 292211102
Web Site: www.fiducian.com
Emp.: 15
Financial Planning Services
S.I.C.: 6211
N.A.I.C.S.: 523999

FIEBIG & SCHILLINGS GMBH
Dillberg 24
97828 Marktheidenfeld, Germany
Tel.: (49) 939160090
Fax: (49) 9391600950
E-Mail: info@fiebig-schillings.de
Web Site: www.fiebig-schillings.de
Year Founded: 1977
Rev.: $12,032,230
Emp.: 50
Business Description:
Bookbinding Products Mfr
S.I.C.: 2759
N.A.I.C.S.: 323111
Personnel:
Siegfried Fiebig *(Founder)*
Dirk Fiebig *(Co-CEO)*
Petra Fiebig-Junker *(Co-CEO)*

FIEBIG+TEAM GMBH
Strahlenberger Weg 26
60599 Frankfurt am Main, Germany
Tel.: (49) 696050160
Fax: (49) 69605016259
E-Mail: info@fiebig-team.de
Web Site: www.fiebig-team.de
Rev.: $13,794,000
Emp.: 51
Business Description:
Communication Solutions & Services
S.I.C.: 4899
N.A.I.C.S.: 517919
Personnel:
Walter Fiebig *(Co-Mng Dir)*
Stefan Mintert *(Co-Mng Dir)*

FIELD FISHER WATERHOUSE LLP
35 Vine Street
London, C3N 2PX, United Kingdom
Tel.: (44) 20 7861 4000
Fax: (44) 20 7488 0084
E-Mail: info@ffw.com
Web Site: www.ffw.com
Emp.: 167
Business Description:
Legal Services
S.I.C.: 8111
N.A.I.C.S.: 541110
Personnel:
Jon Fife *(Partner)*
Stephen Gibbs *(Partner)*
Michael Stirling *(Partner)*
Penny Wotton *(Partner)*

Subsidiary:

Heatons LLP **(1)**
5th Floor Free Trade Exchange 37 Peter Street
Manchester, M2 5GB, United Kingdom
Tel.: (44) 161 835 8010
Fax: (44) 161 835 8015
Web Site: www.heatons.co.uk
Law Firm
S.I.C.: 7389
N.A.I.C.S.: 541199
Matthew Fleetwood *(Mng Partner)*

FIELDEX EXPLORATION INC.
139 Quebec Avenue Suite 202
Rouyn-Noranda, QC, J9X 6M8, Canada
Tel.: (819) 762-0609
Fax: (819) 762-0097
E-Mail: info@fieldexexploration.com
Web Site: www.fieldexexploration.com
Year Founded: 1985
FLX—(DEU OTC TSXV)
Rev.: $2,443
Assets: $3,486,655
Liabilities: $399,825
Net Worth: $3,086,831
Earnings: ($5,819,209)
Emp.: 3
Fiscal Year-end: 12/31/12
Business Description:
Gold Mining & Exploration Services
S.I.C.: 1041
N.A.I.C.S.: 212221
Personnel:
Martin Dallaire *(Pres & CEO)*
Sylvain Champagne *(CFO)*
Board of Directors:
Sylvain Champagne
Martin Dallaire
Donald Lacasse
Jean-Pierre Landry

FIELDING CHEMICAL TECHNOLOGIES INC.
3575 Mavis Road
Mississauga, ON, L5C 1T7, Canada
Tel.: (905) 279-5122
Fax: (905) 279-4130
E-Mail: info@fieldchem.com
Web Site: www.fieldchem.com
Year Founded: 1894
Rev.: $12,072,186
Emp.: 60
Business Description:
Chemical Recycling & Refrigerant Reclamation
S.I.C.: 2899
N.A.I.C.S.: 325998
Personnel:
Ellen McGregor *(Pres & CEO)*
Paul Haskins *(Exec VP)*

FIELDS CORPORATION
Shibuya Garden Tower 16-17
Nampeidai-cho
Shibuya-ku, Tokyo, 150-0036, Japan
Tel.: (81) 357842111
Fax: (81) 357842112
Web Site: www.fields.biz
Year Founded: 1988
2767—(JAS)
Sls.: $1,189,551,000
Assets: $1,172,908,000
Liabilities: $566,830,000
Net Worth: $606,078,000
Earnings: $51,920,000
Emp.: 1,550
Fiscal Year-end: 03/31/13
Business Description:
Holding Company; Gaming & Entertainment Products & Services
S.I.C.: 6719
N.A.I.C.S.: 551112
Personnel:
Hidetoshi Yamamoto *(Chm & CEO)*
Takashi Oya *(Pres & COO)*
Tetsuya Shigematsu *(Sr Mng Dir & Mgr-Interactive Media Bus & Consumer Products Bus)*
Masakazu Kurihara *(Mng Dir, Gen Mgr-Plng & Promoting Dept II & Mgr-Contents Div)*
Masao Tominaga *(Exec Officer-Interactive Media Bus Div)*
Kiyoharu Akiyama *(Exec VP & Mgr-Pachinko & Pachislot Bus Mgmt Div)*
Board of Directors:
Hidetoshi Yamamoto
Kiyoharu Akiyama
Akira Fujii
Hideo Ito
Shigesato Itoi
Masakazu Kurihara
Takashi Oya
Tetsuya Shigematsu
Toru Suenaga
Hiroyuki Yamanaka

Subsidiaries:

Digital Frontier Inc **(1)**
1-1-71 Nakameguro Nielsen Building 7F
Meguro-Ku, Tokyo, 153-0061, Japan JP
Tel.: (81) 337942476
Fax: (81) 337942472
Web Site: www.dfx.co.jp
Emp.: 200
Video Game Development Services
S.I.C.: 7371
N.A.I.C.S.: 541511
Hidenori Ueki *(CEO)*

Japan Sports Marketing Inc. **(1)**
Knshibuya 3 Sakuratho-Cho 9-8
Shibuya-Ku, Tokyo, 150-0031, Japan
Tel.: (81) 357844490
Fax: (81) 357845882
Web Site: www.jsm.jp
Sports Marketing & Sponsorship Services
S.I.C.: 8742
N.A.I.C.S.: 541613

Kadokawa Haruki Corporation **(1)**
3-27 Kandajimbocho Futabadaichi Building
Chiyoda-Ku, Tokyo, 101-0051, Japan
Tel.: (81) 332635167
Fax: (81) 332635194
E-Mail: info@kadokawaharuki.co.jp
Web Site: www.kadokawaharuki.co.jp
Emp.: 86
Books Publishing Services
S.I.C.: 2731
N.A.I.C.S.: 511130

Lucent Pictures Entertainment, Inc. **(1)**
Sakuragaoka-cho 98 Kn Shibuya 3 Building 1st Floor
Shibuya-ku, Tokyo, 150-0031, Japan JP
Tel.: (81) 357842727
Fax: (81) 357842722
Web Site: www.lpei.co.jp
Emp.: 15
Animated Motion Picture Production & Distribution
S.I.C.: 7812
N.A.I.C.S.: 512110
Eiichi Kamagata *(Pres)*

Fields Corporation—(Continued)

Shin-Nichi Technology Co., Ltd. **(1)**
1-21-4 Taito Tokyo Mishin Kaikan Building 6f
Taito-Ku, Tokyo, 110-0016, Japan
Tel.: (81) 338321580
Fax: (81) 358125422
Amusement Machines Mfr
S.I.C.: 3999
N.A.I.C.S.: 339999

Joint Venture:

Tsuburaya Productions Co., Ltd. **(1)**
KN Shibuya 3 Bldg 4F 9-8 Sakuragaoka-chou
Shibuya-ku, Tokyo, 150-0031, Japan JP
Tel.: (81) 354897860
Web Site: www.m-78.jp/en
Emp.: 90
Television Show & Movie Production Services
S.I.C.: 7812
N.A.I.C.S.: 512110
Shinichi Ooka *(Pres)*

FIELMANN AG

Weidestrasse 118 A
22083 Hamburg, Germany
Tel.: (49) 40 270760
Fax: (49) 40 2707 6399
E-Mail: info@fielmann.com
Web Site: www.fielmann.com
FIE—(DEU)
Rev.: $1,490,747,312
Assets: $1,013,974,283
Liabilities: $245,103,903
Net Worth: $768,870,380
Earnings: $170,108,772
Emp.: 12,715
Fiscal Year-end: 12/31/12

Business Description:
Optical Products Mfr & Sales
S.I.C.: 3827
N.A.I.C.S.: 333314

Personnel:
Mark K. Binz *(Chm-Supervisory Bd)*
Gunther Fielmann *(Chm-Mgmt Bd)*
Gunter Schmid *(Member-Mgmt Bd-Matls Mgmt & Production)*
Stefan Thies *(Member-Mgmt Bd-IT & Controlling)*
Georg Alexander Zeiss *(Member-Mgmt Bd-Fin & Properties)*

Supervisory Board of Directors:
Mark K. Binz
Soren Dannmeier
Hans-Georg Frey
Jana Furcht
Ralf Greve
Fred Haselbach
Hans Christopher Meier
Petra Oettle
Hans Joachim Oltersdorf
Marie-Christine Ostermann
Josef Peitz
Hans-Joachim Priester
Pier Paolo Righi
Eva Schleifenbaum
Anton-Wolfgang Graf von Faber-Castell
Stefan Wolf

Subsidiaries:

Fielmann Augenoptik Ag **(1)**
Weidestr 118a
Hamburg, Germany
Tel.: (49) 40270760
Fax: (49) 4027076541
E-Mail: info@fielmann.com
Web Site: www.fielmann.de
Emp.: 600
Ophthalmic Goods Mfr
S.I.C.: 3851
N.A.I.C.S.: 339115
Gueter Schmid *(Gen Mgr)*

Rathenower Optische Werke Gmbh **(1)**
An Den Flugzeughallen 3
Rathenow, Brandenburg, Germany
Tel.: (49) 33854970
Fax: (49) 33854972090
Web Site: www.fielmann.de
Emp.: 900
Ophthalmic Goods Mfr
S.I.C.: 3851
N.A.I.C.S.: 339115
Michael Serley *(Mng Dir)*

Non-U.S. Subsidiaries:

Fielmann Gmbh **(1)**
Europastrasse 1
5020 Salzburg, Austria
Tel.: (43) 662420835
Fax: (43) 66242083511
E-Mail: kundenservice@fielmann.com
Web Site: www.fielmann.com
Emp.: 30
Ophthalmic Goods Mfr
S.I.C.: 3851
N.A.I.C.S.: 339115
Karsten Schoepel *(Mng Dir)*

Pro-optik Ag **(1)**
Steinenvorstadt 62
4011 Basel, Switzerland
Tel.: (41) 6128145
Web Site: www.pro-optik.info/
Ophthalmic Goods Mfr
S.I.C.: 3851
N.A.I.C.S.: 339115

FIEM INDUSTRIES LTD.

D-34 DSIDC Packaging Complex Kirti Nagar
New Delhi, 110015, India
Tel.: (91) 1125927820
Fax: (91) 1125927740
E-Mail: fiemdelhi@airtelbroadband.in
Web Site: www.fiemindustries.com
Year Founded: 1989
FIEMIND—(NSE)
Sls.: $123,235,102
Assets: $80,325,322
Liabilities: $49,164,691
Net Worth: $31,160,631
Earnings: $5,139,549
Fiscal Year-end: 03/31/13

Business Description:
Automotive Component Mfr & Distr
S.I.C.: 3714
N.A.I.C.S.: 336390

Personnel:
J. K. Jain *(Chm & Mng Dir)*
O. P. Gupta *(CFO)*
Arvind K. Chauhan *(Compliance Officer & Sec)*

Board of Directors:
J. K. Jain
Amitabh Prakash Agrawal
Aanchal Jain
Rahul Jain
S. K. Jain
Seema Jain
V. K. Malhotra
J. S. S. Rao
Charoen Sachamuneewongse
Iqbal Singh
Kashi Ram Yadav

Transfer Agent:
Link Intime India Private Limited
44 Community Centre 2nd Floor Naraina Industrial Area Phase-I
Near PVR Naraina, New Delhi, India

FIERA CAPITAL CORPORATION

(Formerly Fiera Sceptre Inc.)
1501 McGill College Avenue Suite 800
Montreal, QC, H3A 3M8, Canada
Tel.: (514) 954-3750
Fax: (514) 395-0723
Toll Free: (800) -361-3499
E-Mail: vdesroches@fieracapital.com
Web Site: www.fieracapital.com
FSZ—(DEU TSX)
Rev.: $114,638,339
Assets: $513,683,691
Liabilities: $217,725,171
Net Worth: $295,958,521
Earnings: $3,007,905
Fiscal Year-end: 12/31/12

Business Description:
Investment Management Services
S.I.C.: 6211
N.A.I.C.S.: 523999

Personnel:
Jean-Guy Desjardins *(Chm, CEO & Chief Investment Officer)*
David Pennycook *(Vice Chm & Exec VP-Institutional Markets)*
Neil Nisker *(Vice Chm)*
Sylvain Brosseau *(Pres & COO)*
Merri Jones *(Exec VP-Private Wealth)*
Alexandre Viau *(Exec VP-Strategic Investment Partnerships)*
Pierre Blanchette *(Sr VP-Fin)*
Violaine Des Roches *(Sr VP-Legal Affairs & Compliance)*
Alain St-Hilaire *(Sr VP-HR)*

Board of Directors:
Jean-Guy Desjardins
Christiane Bergevin
Denis Berthiaume
Jean C. Monty
Neil Nisker
Luc Paiement
David Pennycook
Arthur R.A. Scace
David R. Shaw
Louis Vachon
W. Ross Walker

U.S. Subsidiaries:

Bel Air Investment Advisors LLC **(1)**
1999 Avenue of The Stars Ste 2800
Los Angeles, CA 90067
Tel.: (310) 229-1500
Fax: (310) 229-1505
Toll Free: (877) 229-1500
E-Mail: info@belair-llc.com
Web Site: www.belair-llc.com
Sales Range: $200-249.9 Million
Emp.: 200
Investment Advisors
S.I.C.: 6282
N.A.I.C.S.: 523930
Todd M. Morgan *(Sr Mng Dir)*
Richard Freilich *(Mng Dir & Head-Equity Trading)*
Kenneth Naehu *(Mng Dir & Portfolio Mgr-Fixed Income)*
Reed E. Halladay *(Mng Dir)*
Darell L. Krasnoff *(Mng Dir)*
Andrew D. Palmer *(Mng Dir)*
Ronald J. Silverman *(Mng Dir)*
Jack R. Suzar *(Mng Dir)*
Mark Tunney *(Sr VP)*

Wilkinson O'Grady & Co., Inc. **(1)**
499 Park Ave 7th Fl
New York, NY 10022 DE
Tel.: (212) 644-5252
Fax: (212) 644-5342
Web Site: www.wilkinsonogrady.com
Investment Advisory & Portfolio Management Services
S.I.C.: 6799
N.A.I.C.S.: 523930
Donald M. Wilkinson, III *(CEO & Chief Investment Officer)*
Thomas O. Mueller *(Treas)*
Juerg Grimm *(Sr VP)*

FIERA FOODS COMPANY

50 Marmora St
Toronto, ON, M9M 2X5, Canada
Tel.: (416) 744-1010
Fax: (416) 746-8399
E-Mail: info@fierafoods.com
Web Site: www.fierafoods.com
Year Founded: 1987
Rev.: $43,800,000
Emp.: 350

Business Description:
Bakery Products Mfr
S.I.C.: 2052
N.A.I.C.S.: 311812

Personnel:
Boris Serebryany *(Pres & CEO)*
Alex Garber *(COO)*

FIERA MILANO SPA

Piazzale Carlo Magno 1
20149 Milan, Italy
Tel.: (39) 0249971
Fax: (39) 0249977379
E-Mail: fieramilano@fieramilano.it
Web Site: www.fieramilano.it
Year Founded: 1920
FM—(ITA)
Rev.: $354,591,947
Assets: $388,115,619
Liabilities: $307,520,421
Net Worth: $80,595,198
Earnings: ($2,606,185)
Emp.: 751
Fiscal Year-end: 12/31/12

Business Description:
Value Added Services
S.I.C.: 7389
N.A.I.C.S.: 561990

Personnel:
Michele Perini *(Chm)*
Renato Borghi *(Vice Chm)*
Attilio Fontana *(Deputy Vice Chm)*
Enrico Pazzali *(CEO)*
Sergio Pravettoni *(Press Officer)*

Board of Directors:
Michele Perini
Roberto Mario Baitieri
Renato Borghi
Pier Andrea Chevallard
Davide Croff
Attilio Fontana
Giampietro Giuseppe Omati
Enrico Pazzali
Romeo Robiglio

FIERA SCEPTRE INC.

(Name Changed to Fiera Capital Corporation)

FIERA YMG CAPITAL INC.

1501 McGill College Ave Ste 800
Montreal, QC, H3A 3M8, Canada
Tel.: (514) 954-3300
Fax: (514) 954-5098
E-Mail: info@fieracapital.com
Web Site: www.fieracapital.com
Year Founded: 2003
Emp.: 100

Business Description:
Investment Services
S.I.C.: 6211
N.A.I.C.S.: 523999

Personnel:
Jean-Guy Desjardins *(Chm & CEO)*
Sylvain Brosseau *(Pres & COO)*
Nisker Neil *(Pres-Private Wealth)*
Craven Jim *(Sr VP-Sub-Advisory Svcs)*

FIERATEX S.A.

Nea Santa
61100 Kilkis, Greece
Tel.: (30) 23410 75500
Fax: (30) 23410 64481
E-Mail: sales@fieratex.gr
Web Site: www.fieratex.gr
Year Founded: 1988
FIER—(ATH)
Emp.: 137

Business Description:
Knitt & Fabric Mills
S.I.C.: 2259
N.A.I.C.S.: 313240

Personnel:
Tzemis N. Konstantinos *(Pres & CEO)*
Kotanidou Zaharoula *(IR Officer)*

Board of Directors:

Zervou Aikaterini
Papatheodorou M. Aristotelis
Mantikos A. Athanasios
Anezoulaki D. Eleni
Tzemis N. Konstantinos
Zervos S. Nikolaos

FIFTH AVENUE AUTO HAUS LTD.

1120 Meridian Road NE
Calgary, AB, T2A 2N9, Canada
Tel.: (403) 273-2500
Fax: (403) 273-1769
E-Mail: sales@fifthavevw.com
Web Site: www.fifthavevw.com
Rev.: $18,867,054
Emp.: 40
Business Description:
New & Used Car Dealers
S.I.C.: 5511
N.A.I.C.S.: 441110
Personnel:
Jerry Sturko *(Gen Mgr)*

FIFTH RING LTD

St Mary's Court 47-49 Huntly Street
Aberdeen, Scotland, AB10 1TH, United Kingdom
Tel.: (44) 1224 626288
E-Mail: ian.ord@fifthring.com
Web Site: www.fifthring.com
Year Founded: 1991
Emp.: 80
Business Description:
Advertising Agency
S.I.C.: 7311
N.A.I.C.S.: 541810
Personnel:
Ian Ord *(Founder, Mng Dir & Dir-Bus Dev)*

U.S. Subsidiary:

Fifth Ring Inc. **(1)**
1100 W 23rd St Ste 200
Houston, TX 77008
Tel.: (713) 457-2121
Advertising Agency
S.I.C.: 7311
N.A.I.C.S.: 541810
Ed Davis *(Gen Mgr)*

Non-U.S. Subsidiary:

Fifth Ring LLC **(1)**
Suite 701-703 The Fairmont Dubai Sheikh Zayed Road
PO Box 126593
Dubai, United Arab Emirates
Tel.: (971) 4 372 0100
Fax: (971) 43324898
E-Mail: annette@fifthring.com
Web Site: www.fifthring.ae
Emp.: 15
Advertising Agency
S.I.C.: 7311
N.A.I.C.S.: 541810
Toby Jordan *(Dir-Bus Dev)*

FIFTH SEASON INTERNATIONAL, INC.

C-22 Shimao Plaza 9 Fuhong Lu
Futian District, Shenzhen, 518033, China
Tel.: (86) 755 83 67 9378
Year Founded: 2007
DYER—(OTC)
Sales Range: $150-199.9 Million
Emp.: 355
Business Description:
Investment Services
S.I.C.: 6211
N.A.I.C.S.: 523999
Personnel:
Lianmo Wu *(Pres & Treas)*
Shaoping Lu *(CEO)*
Xiaolei Xing *(COO)*

FIFTH WHEEL TRUCK STOPS

40 Chisholm Drive
Milton, ON, L9T 3G9, Canada
Tel.: (905) 878-8446
Fax: (905) 878-6161
Web Site: www.5thwheel.com
Rev.: $197,401,015
Emp.: 400
Business Description:
Truck Fuel Supplier
S.I.C.: 5989
N.A.I.C.S.: 454310
Personnel:
Bruce Rankin *(Pres)*

FIGEAC-AERO SA

Zone Industrielle de l'Aiguille
46100 Figeac, France
Tel.: (33) 565345252
Fax: (33) 565347026
Web Site: www.figeac-aero.com
ALFIG—(EUR)
Sls.: $184,598,946
Earnings: $16,124,424
Emp.: 700
Fiscal Year-end: 03/31/13
Business Description:
Aeronautical Subassemblies Designer & Mfr
S.I.C.: 3812
N.A.I.C.S.: 334511
Personnel:
Jean-Claude Maillard *(Chm)*

FIGTREE HOLDINGS LIMITED

315 Outram Road #13-10 Tan Boon Liat Building
Singapore, 169074, Singapore
Tel.: (65) 6278 9722
Fax: (65) 6278 9747
E-Mail: info@figtreeasia.com
Web Site: www.figtreeasia.com
5F4—(CAT)
Sales Range: $25-49.9 Million
Business Description:
Commercial & Industrial Building Construction & Development
S.I.C.: 1542
N.A.I.C.S.: 236220
Personnel:
Danny Siaw *(Chm & Mng Dir)*

FIH ERHVERVSBANK A/S

Langelinie Alle 43
2100 Copenhagen, Denmark
Tel.: (45) 72225000
Fax: (45) 72225001
Web Site: www.fih.com
Int. Income: $282,353,580
Assets: $10,958,096,448
Liabilities: $9,970,300,800
Net Worth: $987,795,648
Earnings: ($277,285,464)
Emp.: 257
Fiscal Year-end: 12/31/12
Business Description:
Banking Services
S.I.C.: 6029
N.A.I.C.S.: 522110
Personnel:
Christian Peter Dyvig *(Chm)*
Henrik Heideby *(Deputy Chm)*
Bjarne Graven Larsen *(Co-CEO & Mng Dir)*
Henrik Sjogreen *(Co-CEO & Mng Dir)*
Palle Nordahl *(CFO & Head-Fin & Risk)*
Board of Directors:
Christian Peter Dyvig
Daniel Eriksson
Randi Holm Franke
Henrik Heideby
Henrik Gade Jepsen
Frederik Martinsson
Lene Nothlevsen
Jacob Baggers Willemoes

FIHUMIN-GESELLSCHAFT M.B.H.

Georg Sasse Str 43
D-22949 Ammersbek, Germany
Tel.: (49) 406056710
Fax: (49) 4060567111
E-Mail: info@fihumin.de
Web Site: www.fihumin.de
Year Founded: 1935
Rev.: $50,374,551
Emp.: 9
Business Description:
Pet Food Products Mfr
S.I.C.: 2047
N.A.I.C.S.: 311111
Personnel:
Dirk Jungclaussen *(Co-Mng Dir)*
Henning Untiedt *(Co-Mng Dir)*

FIJIAN HOLDINGS LIMITED

Level 7 Ra Marama 91 Gordon Street
PO Box 2110
Suva, Fiji
Tel.: (679) 3305017
Fax: (679) 3305020
E-Mail: info@fijianholdings.com.fj
Web Site: www.fijianholdings.com.fj
Year Founded: 1984
FHL—(SPSE)
Rev.: $131,402,601
Assets: $268,005,496
Liabilities: $153,996,163
Net Worth: $114,009,333
Earnings: $7,176,878
Emp.: 1,600
Fiscal Year-end: 06/30/13
Business Description:
Holding Company
S.I.C.: 6719
N.A.I.C.S.: 551112
Personnel:
Iowane Naiveli *(Chm)*
Apakuki Kurusiga *(Deputy Chm)*
Nouzab Freed *(CEO)*
Tevita Gonelevu *(Sec & Gen Mgr-Investments)*
Board of Directors:
Iowane Naiveli
Ulaiyasi Baya
Viliame Gavoka
Apakuki Kurusiga
Padam Lala
Ratu Samuela Nawalowalo
Aseri Radrodro
Mere Samisoni
Filimoni Waqabaca

FIL-ESTATE CORPORATION

7th Floor Renaissance Tower 1000 Meralco Avenue
1600 Pasig, Philippines
Tel.: (63) 26336205
E-Mail: fec@fil-estateland.com
Web Site: www.fil-estatecorp.com
FC—(PHI)
Int. Income: $9
Assets: $43,459,755
Liabilities: $62,217,069
Net Worth: ($18,757,315)
Earnings: ($238,920)
Fiscal Year-end: 12/31/12
Business Description:
Property & Infrastructure Development Services
S.I.C.: 6531
N.A.I.C.S.: 531312
Personnel:
Robert John L. Sobrepena *(Chm)*
Ferdinand T. Santos *(Pres)*
Gilbert Raymund T. Reyes *(Sec)*
Board of Directors:
Robert John L. Sobrepena
Alice Odchigue Bondoc
Noel M. Carino
Rafael Perez de Tagle Jr.
Francisco C. Gonzalez
Ruben R. Payumo
Roberto S. Roco
Ferdinand T. Santos
Enrique A. Sobrepena

FIL-ESTATE LAND, INC.

7th Fl Renaissance Towers Meralco Ave
Pasig, Philippines
Tel.: (63) 26333947
Web Site: www.fil-estateland.com
LND—(PHI)
Sales Range: $10-24.9 Million
Emp.: 159
Business Description:
Real Estate Services
S.I.C.: 6531
N.A.I.C.S.: 531210
Personnel:
Ferdinand T. Santos *(Co-Chm, Pres & COO)*
Robert John L. Sobrepena *(Co-Chm & CEO)*
Noel M. Carino *(Vice Chm)*
Roberto S. Roco *(CFO & Sr VP)*
Gilbert Raymund T. Reyes *(Sec)*
Rafael P. Perez de Tagle, Jr. *(Sr VP-Bus Dev)*
Board of Directors:
Ferdinand T. Santos
Robert John L. Sobrepena
Noel M. Carino
Rafael P. Perez de Tagle, Jr.
Francisco Gonzalez
Dominador Gregorio, III
Enrique A. Sobrepena Jr.

FILA KOREA, LTD.

1467 10 Seocho Dong
Seoul, 137-868, Korea (South)
Tel.: (82) 25236100
Fax: (82) 234709651
E-Mail: fila@fila.co.kr
Web Site: www.fila.co.kr
081660—(KRS)
Business Description:
Sportswear & Footwear Retailer & Distr
S.I.C.: 5699
N.A.I.C.S.: 448150
Personnel:
Gene Y.S. Yoon *(Chm & CEO)*
Young-Chan Cho Cho *(Pres)*

U.S. Subsidiaries:

Acushnet Company **(1)**
333 Bridge St
Fairhaven, MA 02719-4905 DE
Tel.: (508) 979-2000 (100%)
Fax: (508) 979-3927
Toll Free: (800) 255-8500
Web Site: www.acushnetcompany.com
Sales Range: $1-4.9 Billion
Emp.: 5,000
Golfing Equipment & Accessories Mfr
S.I.C.: 2393
N.A.I.C.S.: 314910
Walter R. Uihlein *(Pres & CEO)*
William Burke *(CFO, Sr VP & Controller)*
Margaret G. Nicholson *(CIO & Sr VP)*
James M. Connor *(Pres-Footjoy)*
Joseph J. Nauman *(EVP-Corp & Legal)*
Gerald Bellis *(Sr VP-Sls & Mktg-Titleist)*
Dennis D. Doherty *(Sr VP-HR)*

Non-U.S. Subsidiaries:

Acushnet Canada Inc. **(2)**
E Gwillimbury
Newmarket, ON, L9N 0M9, Canada
Tel.: (905) 898-7575
Fax: (905) 898-2601
E-Mail: info@fortunebrands.com

Fila Korea, Ltd.—(Continued)

Web Site: www.titleist.com
Sales Range: $25-49.9 Million
Emp.: 110
Golfing Equipment & Accessories Mfr
S.I.C.: 3949
N.A.I.C.S.: 339920
Ted Manning *(Pres)*

Acushnet Europe Ltd. **(2)**
Caxton Road
Saint Ives, Cambs, PE27 3LU, United Kingdom
Tel.: (44) 1480301114
Fax: (44) 1480492108
E-Mail: ukoffice@acushnetgolf.com
Web Site: www.acushnetgolf.com
Sales Range: $75-99.9 Million
Emp.: 360
Golfing Equipment & Accessories Mfr
S.I.C.: 3949
N.A.I.C.S.: 339920

Acushnet GmbH **(2)**
Limburger Strasse 66
65555 Limburg, Germany
Tel.: (49) 64315920
Fax: (49) 643159218
E-Mail: dekundendiense@acushnetgolf.com
Web Site: www.acushnet.de
Sales Range: $10-24.9 Million
Emp.: 30
Golfing Equipment & Accessories Mfr
S.I.C.: 3949
N.A.I.C.S.: 339920
Gary Miller *(Pres)*

Acushnet Korea Co., Ltd. **(2)**
4F Paradise Bldg 186-210 Jangchung-dong
Jung-gu, Seoul, 100-855, Korea (South)
Tel.: (82) 230143800
Fax: (82) 230143899
E-Mail: saleskr@acushnetgolf.com
Web Site: www.Acushnet.com
Emp.: 14
Golf Equipments & Accessories Mfr
S.I.C.: 3949
N.A.I.C.S.: 339920
Achille Ghilotti *(Pres)*

Acushnet Nederland B.V. **(2)**
Heibloemweg 3
5704 BS Helmond, Netherlands
Tel.: (31) 206301130
Fax: (31) 492505001
E-Mail: nloffice@acushnet.com
Web Site: www.titleist.com
Sales Range: $10-24.9 Million
Emp.: 9
Golfing Equipment & Accessories Mfr
S.I.C.: 3949
N.A.I.C.S.: 339920
Peter Nbliss *(Gen Mgr)*

Acushnet Sverige AB **(2)**
Boplatsgatan 2
213 76 Malmo, Sweden
Tel.: (46) 406717550
Fax: (46) 40140940
E-Mail: info@acushnet.com
Web Site: www.acushnet.com
Sales Range: $75-99.9 Million
Emp.: 20
Golfing Equipment & Accessories Mfr
S.I.C.: 3949
N.A.I.C.S.: 339920

Fila USA, Inc. **(1)**
1 Fila Way
Sparks, MD 21152-3000
Tel.: (410) 773-3000
Fax: (410) 773-4989
Toll Free: (800) 787-3452
E-Mail: info@fila.com
Web Site: www.fila.com
Emp.: 2,301
Apparel & Athletic Footwear Distr & Mfr Import Export
S.I.C.: 5139
N.A.I.C.S.: 424340
Lauren Mallon *(Mgr-Global Mktg)*

Non-U.S. Subsidiaries:

Fila Argentina S.A. **(1)**
B Mitre 226 piso 3
1036 Buenos Aires, Argentina
Tel.: (54) 1143421991
Fax: (54) 11 4331 2789
Web Site: www.webfila.com.ar
Emp.: 40
Sporting & Athletic Goods Mfr
S.I.C.: 3949
N.A.I.C.S.: 339920

Fila Canada, Inc. **(1)**
6085 Belgrave Rd
Mississauga, ON, L5R 4E6, Canada
Tel.: (905) 361-2405
Fax: (905) 361-2418
Web Site: www.fila.com
Emp.: 25
Sporting & Athletic Goods Mfr
S.I.C.: 3949
N.A.I.C.S.: 339920
Russ English *(Gen Mgr)*

Fila Europe S.p.A. **(1)**
Siasra pampuri no9 A
20141 Milano, Italy
Tel.: (39) 0252823200
Fax: (39) 0252823400
Web Site: www.filacorsocono.com
Emp.: 9
Sporting & Athletic Goods Mfr
S.I.C.: 3949
N.A.I.C.S.: 339920

Non-U.S. Subsidiaries:

Fila Deutschland GmbH **(2)**
Borsigstrasse 13
D-64291 Darmstadt, Germany
Tel.: (49) 615135030
Fax: (49) 6151350336
E-Mail: info@fila.de
Web Site: www.fila.de
Emp.: 7
Sporting & Athletic Goods
S.I.C.: 3949
N.A.I.C.S.: 339920
Stefano Di Martino *(Mng Dir)*

Fila France S.A. **(2)**
2 Bd Montmartre
75009 Paris, France
Tel.: (33) 1 4523 2966
Fax: (33) 1 4523 2988
Web Site: www.fila.eu
Emp.: 60
Sporting & Athletic Goods Mfr
S.I.C.: 3949
N.A.I.C.S.: 339920

Fila Sport (Hong Kong) Limited **(1)**
12th Floor Tower 3 China Hong Kong City
33 Canton Road
Tsimshatsui, Kowloon, China (Hong Kong)
Tel.: (852) 221706100
Fax: (852) 2 637 0696
Athletic Clothing & Accessories Mfr
S.I.C.: 3949
N.A.I.C.S.: 339920

Fila Sport Taiwan Ltd. **(1)**
7th Floor No 130 Sec 2 Chung Teh Road
Taichung, 406, Taiwan
Tel.: (886) 422325855
Fax: (886) 422325335
Web Site: www.fila.com.th
Emp.: 113
Sporting & Athletic Goods Sales
S.I.C.: 5661
N.A.I.C.S.: 448210
Ko Phil *(Mgr-Ad)*

Fila UK Limited **(1)**
Unit 5 & 6 Colonial Business Park
Colonial Way, Watford, Herts, WD24 4PR, United Kingdom
Tel.: (44) 1923475600
Fax: (44) 1923475630
E-Mail: info@filauk.com
Web Site: www.fila.co.uk
Emp.: 15
Sporting & Athletic Goods
S.I.C.: 3949
N.A.I.C.S.: 339920

FILATEX INDIA LTD.

43 Community Centre New Friends Colony
New Delhi, 110025, India
Tel.: (91) 11 26312503
Fax: (91) 11 26849915
E-Mail: fildelhi@filatex.com
Web Site: www.filatex.com
526227—(BOM)
Rev.: $255,647,893
Assets: $138,053,141
Liabilities: $110,323,994
Net Worth: $27,729,147
Earnings: $436,747
Emp.: 1,535
Fiscal Year-end: 03/31/13

Business Description:
Polypropylene Yarn Mfr
S.I.C.: 2299
N.A.I.C.S.: 313110

Personnel:
Madhu Sudhan Bhageria *(Vice Chm & Mng Dir)*
Madhav Bhageria *(Mng Dir)*
Purrshottam Bhaggeria *(Mng Dir)*
R. P. Gupta *(CFO)*
Raman Kumar Jha *(Compliance Officer & Sec)*

Board of Directors:
Ram Avtar Bhageria
Madhav Bhageria
Madhu Sudhan Bhageria
Purrshottam Bhaggeria
S. C. Parija
S. P. Setia
B. B. Tandon

Transfer Agent:
MCS Limited
F-65 Okhla Industrial Area Phase-I
New Delhi, India

FILINVEST DEVELOPMENT CORPORATION

6th Floor The Beaufort Building 5th Corner 23rd Street
Bonifacio Global City, Taguig, 1634, Philippines
Tel.: (63) 27983977
Fax: (63) 27256321
E-Mail: ir@filinvestgroup.com
Web Site: www.filinvestgroup.com
Year Founded: 1955
FDC—(PHI)
Rev.: $726,100,924
Assets: $5,862,287,823
Liabilities: $3,927,808,005
Net Worth: $1,934,479,818
Earnings: $141,726,226
Emp.: 1,800
Fiscal Year-end: 12/31/12

Business Description:
Holding Company; Real Estate Development, Banking, Leasing, Financial & Sugar Business
S.I.C.: 6719
N.A.I.C.S.: 551112

Personnel:
Jonathan T. Gotianun *(Chm)*
Lourdes Josephine Gotianun Yap *(Pres & CEO)*
Oscar A. Torres *(CFO & Sr VP)*
Eleuterio D. Coronel *(COO & Exec VP)*
Nelson M. Bona *(Treas & Sr VP)*
Pablito A. Perez *(Sec & First VP)*

Board of Directors:
Jonathan T. Gotianun
Andrew L. Gotianun, Sr.
Andrew T. Gotianun, Jr.
Mercedes T. Gotianun
Lamberto U. Ocampo
Cirilo T. Tolosa
Lourdes Josephine Gotianun Yap

Subsidiaries:

East West Banking Corporation **(1)**
20th-Floor PBCOM Tower
6795 Ayala Avenue cor Herrera, 1226
Makati, Philippines (100%)
Tel.: (63) 2 5753888
Fax: (63) 28184155
E-Mail: info@eastwestbanker.com
Web Site: www.eastwestbanker.com
EW—(PHI)
Emp.: 50
Commercial Banking
S.I.C.: 6029
N.A.I.C.S.: 522110
Jonathan T. Gotianun *(Chm)*
Antonio C. Moncupa, Jr. *(Pres & CEO)*
Grace N. Ang *(Chief Risk Officer & VP)*
Jacqueline S. Fernandez *(Exec VP & Head-Consumer Lending)*
Gerardo Susmerano *(Exec VP & Head-Retail Banking & Ops)*
Renato K. De Borja, Jr. *(Sr VP & Head-Fin)*
Manuel Andres D. Goseco *(Sr VP & Head-Treasury)*
Ernesto T. Uy *(Sr VP & Head-Corp Banking)*
Ivy B. Uy *(Sr VP & Deputy Head-Retail Banking)*

Filinvest Alabang Inc. **(1)**
Vector 1 Bldg Northgate Cyberzone
Filingvest Corporate
City Alabang, Muntinlupa, 1781, Philippines
Tel.: (63) 28460278
Fax: (63) 28076907
E-Mail: sales@filinvestcorpcity.com
Web Site: www.filinvestcorpcity.com
Emp.: 500
Residential Property Managers
S.I.C.: 6531
N.A.I.C.S.: 531311
Regina Nava *(Head-Sls & Admin)*

Filinvest Supermall Inc. **(1)**
Filinvest Corporate City Alabang
Muntinlupa, Philippines (100%)
Tel.: (63) 28503517
Fax: (63) 28503575
E-Mail: hrd@festivalsupermall.com
Web Site: www.festivalsupermall.com
Emp.: 123
Nonresidential Buildings Lessors
S.I.C.: 6512
N.A.I.C.S.: 531120
Danny Antonio *(Mng Dir)*

H.B. Fuller (Phils.) Inc. **(1)**
11 Gyro St
Light Industry And Science par, Laguna, Philippines
Tel.: (63) 28445976
Fax: (63) 28445967
E-Mail: robert.lim@hbfuller.com
Web Site: www.hbfuller.com
Emp.: 44
Adhesive Mfr
S.I.C.: 2891
N.A.I.C.S.: 325520
Robert Lim *(Mgr-Sls)*

Hocheng Philippines Corporation **(1)**
Lot 2 Blk 4 Phase 3
First Industrial Estate Brgy L, Dasmarinas, Philippines (100%)
Tel.: (63) 464021310
Fax: (63) 464021026
Web Site: www.hcg.com.ph
Emp.: 750
Enameled Iron & Metal Sanitary Ware Mfr
S.I.C.: 3499
N.A.I.C.S.: 332999
Sam Chen *(Pres)*

Cyberzone Properties Inc. **(1)**
FAI Administration Bldg
Alabang-Zapote Road Filinvest, 1781
Muntinlupa, Philippines (100%)
Tel.: (63) 2 807 6729
Fax: (63) 28426827
E-Mail: info@northgate-cyberzone.com
Web Site: www.northgate-cyberzone.com
Emp.: 6,000
Miscellaneous Financial Investment Activities
S.I.C.: 6211
N.A.I.C.S.: 523999
Jacques Zimmerman *(CEO)*

FILIPPA K AB

Soder Malar Strang 65 Level 9
118 25 Stockholm, Sweden
Tel.: (46) 86157000
Fax: (46) 86157096
E-Mail: info@filippa-k.se
Web Site: www.filippa-k.se
Year Founded: 1993
Sls.: $44,247,000
Emp.: 120

Business Description:
Men's & Women's Clothing Mfr & Retailer
S.I.C.: 2389
N.A.I.C.S.: 315240
Personnel:
Filippa Knutsson *(Founder & Dir-Creative)*
Patrick Kihlborg *(CEO)*

FILMCITY MEDIA LTD
A 9 Shree Siddhivinayak Plaza 3rd Floor Plot No B 31 Off New Link Road
Mumbai, Maharashtra, 400 053, India
Tel.: (91) 2267077453
Fax: (91) 2267077452
Web Site: www.filmcitymedia.com
531486—(BOM)
Rev.: $9,048
Assets: $850,801
Liabilities: $185,178
Net Worth: $665,623
Earnings: ($21,154)
Emp.: 10
Fiscal Year-end: 03/31/13
Business Description:
Electronic Media Entertainment Services
S.I.C.: 7374
N.A.I.C.S.: 518210
Personnel:
Shatrughan Singh *(Mng Dir)*
Nirav Shah *(Compliance Officer & Sec)*
Board of Directors:
Ruchika Gupta
Mahesh Jani
Shankar Parte
Saurabh Sanganeria
Transfer Agent:
Link Intime India Private Limited
C-13 Pannalal Silk Mills Compound L.B.S. Marg Bhandup
Mumbai, India

FILMON.COM PLC
1st Floor 111 Wardour Street
London, W1F 0UH, United Kingdom
Tel.: (44) 2077342819
Web Site: www.filmon.com
2F0A—(DEU)
Business Description:
Online Media Services
S.I.C.: 2741
N.A.I.C.S.: 519130
Personnel:
Alki David *(Chm)*

FILMS AT 59
59 Cotham Hill
Clifton, Bristol, BS6 6JR, United Kingdom
Tel.: (44) 1179064300
Fax: (44) 1179237003
E-Mail: info@filmsat59.com
Web Site: www.filmsat59.com
Year Founded: 1990
Rev.: $12,371,486
Emp.: 103
Business Description:
Equipment Hire & Post Production Services
S.I.C.: 7389
N.A.I.C.S.: 512240
Personnel:
Gina Fucci *(Mng Dir)*

FILMTEX S.A.
Cra 73 No 62D-81 Sur B Perdomo
Bogota, Colombia
Tel.: (57) 1 644 9844
Web Site: www.filmtex.com
Sales Range: $75-99.9 Million
Emp.: 160
Business Description:
Plastics Material & Resins Mfr
S.I.C.: 2821
N.A.I.C.S.: 325211
Personnel:
Oscar Hernan Osorio Ordonez *(Dir-HR)*

Subsidiary:

Azembla S.A.S. **(1)**
Cra 13A No 108-19
Bogota, Colombia Co
Tel.: (57) 1 637 8190
Fax: (57) 1 637 8194
E-Mail: info@azembla.com.co
Web Site: www.azembla.com.co
Emp.: 70
PVC Products Mfr
S.I.C.: 3089
N.A.I.C.S.: 326199

FILSYN CORPORATION
Unit 8 5B Pearlbank Centre 146 Valero Street
Makati, 1227, Philippines
Tel.: (63) 27523383
Fax: (63) 27523323
E-Mail: info@filsyncorp.com
Web Site: www.filsyncorp.com
FYN—(PHI)
Rev.: $546,692
Assets: $24,826,537
Liabilities: $38,110,718
Net Worth: ($13,284,181)
Earnings: ($360,626)
Fiscal Year-end: 12/31/12
Business Description:
Polyester Fiber Mfr
S.I.C.: 2299
N.A.I.C.S.: 313110
Personnel:
Florentino Herrera III *(Chm & Pres)*
Emmanuel C. Paras *(CIO & Sec)*
Jaime M. Sto. Domingo *(Compliance Officer & Exec VP)*
David Wang *(Treas)*
J. C. Shieh *(Sr VP)*
Board of Directors:
Florentino Herrera III
Lilia G. Baun
Mary Rogelyn T. Cabrera
Chen Yu Cheng
Renato V. Diaz
Jaime M. Sto. Domingo
Marcelo T. Dy
Amy Huang
Evelyn Lim-Forbes
Ma. Belina B. Mariano
Alan Tsai
David Wang

FILTER VISION PUBLIC COMPANY LIMITED
95 Soi Ramintra 117 Ramintra Road
Minburi, Bangkok, 15010, Thailand
Tel.: (66) 2518 2722
Fax: (66) 2518 2723
Web Site: www.filtervision.co.th
Year Founded: 1995
FVC—(THA)
Rev.: $8,643,286
Assets: $6,541,519
Liabilities: $2,496,346
Net Worth: $4,045,173
Earnings: $498,275
Emp.: 130
Fiscal Year-end: 12/31/12
Business Description:
Water Filter Equipment
S.I.C.: 4941
N.A.I.C.S.: 221310
Personnel:
Chotisak Asapaviriya *(Chm)*
Wijit Techakasem *(Chm-Exec Bd & Mng Dir)*
Board of Directors:
Chotisak Asapaviriya
Panchit Chimpalee
Thanetr Khumchoedchoochai
Montrie Prajunpanich
Kiattiporn Sirichaisakul
Rapeepat Suansilpong
Tanapat Tantiwattanawijit
Thanapa Techakasem
Wijit Techakasem
Manit Teeratantikanont
Tosit Visalset

FILTRATION LAB INC.
193 Rang de L Eglise
Saint Ligouri, QC, J0K 2X0, Canada
Tel.: (450) 754-4222
Fax: (450) 754-1212
Toll Free: (800) 738-0168
E-Mail: info@filtrationlab.com
Web Site: www.filtrationlab.com
Year Founded: 1987
Rev.: $11,042,009
Emp.: 110
Business Description:
Filtration Products Mfr
S.I.C.: 3823
N.A.I.C.S.: 334513
Personnel:
Claude Bedard *(Pres)*

FILTRONIC PLC
Unit 2 Acorn Park Charlestown
Shipley, W Yorkshire, BD17 7SW, United Kingdom
Tel.: (44) 1274535610
Fax: (44) 1274598263
E-Mail: jbean@filtronic.com
Web Site: www.filtronic.co.uk
Year Founded: 1994
FTC—(LSE)
Rev.: $63,133,697
Assets: $57,402,454
Liabilities: $25,503,954
Net Worth: $31,898,499
Earnings: $448,518
Emp.: 175
Fiscal Year-end: 05/31/13
Business Description:
Designer & Mfr of Radio Frequency Electronics
S.I.C.: 3663
N.A.I.C.S.: 334220
Personnel:
Alan R. Needle *(CEO)*
Michael Brennan *(CFO)*
Maura Moynihan *(Sec)*
Board of Directors:
Howard Ford
Michael Brennan
Reginald Gott
Graham G. Meek
Alan R. Needle
Michael Roller

Subsidiaries:

Filtronic Broadband Ltd. **(1)**
Heighington Lane Business Park
Newton Aycliffe, DL5 6JW, United Kingdom (100%)
Tel.: (44) 1325 301 111
Fax: (44) 1325 306 149
E-Mail:
Web Site: www.filtronic.co.uk
Emp.: 200
Mfr. of RF Subsystems for Wireless Communication Systems
S.I.C.: 3663
N.A.I.C.S.: 334220
Michael Tyerman *(Mgr-Fin)*

U.S. Subsidiaries:

Filtronic Wireless Ltd. **(1)**
31901 Comtek Ln
Salisbury, MD 21804-1788
Tel.: (410) 341-7802
Fax: (410) 548-4750
Emp.: 300
Mfr. of RF Filters & Subsystems for Wireless Communication Systems
S.I.C.: 3679
N.A.I.C.S.: 334419
Emmanuel Sawyer *(Pres & CEO)*
Dawn Harcum *(CFO)*

Branch:

Filtronic Wireless Ltd. **(2)**
39 Depot St
Merrimack, NH 03054
Tel.: (410) 202-8811
E-Mail:
Web Site: www.filtronic.co.uk/
Research & Development of RF Filters & Subsystems for Wireless Communication Systems
S.I.C.: 3679
N.A.I.C.S.: 334419

Non-U.S. Subsidiaries:

Filtronic (Suzhou) Telecommunication Products Co. Ltd. **(1)**
33 Huoju Rd
Suzhou, Jiangsu, 215009, China
Tel.: (86) 51268081636
Fax: (86) 51268093899
E-Mail: sales_wi@filtronic.com.cn
Web Site: www.filtronic.com.cn
Mfr. of Equipment for Wireless Communications
S.I.C.: 3663
N.A.I.C.S.: 334220

FIMA CORPORATION BERHAD
Suite 4 1 Level 4 Block C Plaza Damansara
45 Jalan Medan Setia 1 Bukit Damansara, 50490 Kuala Lumpur, Malaysia
Tel.: (60) 320921211
Fax: (60) 320945996
E-Mail: info@fimacorp.com
Web Site: www.fimacorp.com
FIMACOR—(KLS)
Rev.: $100,063,148
Assets: $184,610,762
Liabilities: $24,119,172
Net Worth: $160,491,590
Earnings: $20,297,920
Emp.: 1,600
Fiscal Year-end: 03/31/13
Business Description:
Property Management Services
S.I.C.: 6531
N.A.I.C.S.: 531312
Personnel:
Roslan Hamir *(Mng Dir)*
Mo Leng Lee *(Co-Sec)*
Mohd Yusof Pandak Yatim *(Co-Sec)*
Board of Directors:
Adnan Shamsuddin
Rezal Zain Abdul Rashid
Alias Ali
Roshayati Basir
Roslan Hamir

FIMA GLOBAL INVEST D.O.O
Medimurska 28
42000 Varazdin, Croatia
Tel.: (385) 42660900
Fax: (385) 42203187
E-Mail: info@fgi.hr
Web Site: www.fgi.hr
Business Description:
Financial & Investment Services
S.I.C.: 6211
N.A.I.C.S.: 523999
Personnel:
Goran Dobrojevic *(Pres)*

FIMA, INC.
6023 5th Street Southeast
Calgary, AB, T2H 1L5, Canada
Tel.: (403) 999-7580
Fax: (403) 252-7601

FIMA, Inc.—(Continued)

E-Mail: info@fimadevelopmentinc.com
Web Site: www.fimadevelopmentinc.com
Year Founded: 2001
FIMA—(OTC)
Business Description:
Real Estate Acquisition, Development & Consulting
S.I.C.: 6531
N.A.I.C.S.: 531390
Personnel:
Marco Garduno Chavez *(CEO)*
Anthony W. Hawkins *(CFO)*
Board of Directors:
Marco Garduno Chavez
Anthony W. Hawkins

FIMA MASCHINENBAU GMBH

Oberfischacher Strasse 58
74423 Obersontheim, Germany
Tel.: (49) 79736930
Fax: (49) 7973693110
E-Mail: info@fima.de
Web Site: www.fima-sha.de
Year Founded: 1946
Rev.: $25,200,476
Emp.: 180
Business Description:
Compressors & Radial Blowers Mfr
S.I.C.: 5084
N.A.I.C.S.: 423830
Personnel:
Stephan Jakob *(Mng Dir)*

FIMALAC S.A.

97 rue de Lille
75007 Paris, France
Tel.: (33) 47536150
Fax: (33) 147536157
E-Mail: contact@fimalac.com
Web Site: www.fimalac.com
FIM—(EUR)
Sales Range: $700-749.9 Million
Emp.: 2,591
Business Description:
Business-To-Business Services
S.I.C.: 7389
N.A.I.C.S.: 561499
Personnel:
Marc Ladreit de Lacharrie *(Chm & CEO)*
Thierry Moulonguet *(CFO & Exec VP)*
Veronique Morali *(Chm-Dev)*
Stephen W. Joynt *(CEO-Fitch Grp)*
Thomas Piquemal *(Exec VP-Fin)*
Board of Directors:
Marc Ladreit de Lacharrie
David Dautresme
Eleonore Ladreit de Lacharriere
Jeremie Ladreit de Lacharriere
Philippe Lagayette
Veronique Morali
Thierry Moulonguet
Jean-Charles Naouri
Etienne Pflimlin
Bernard Pierre
Thomas Piquemal
Pascal Castres Saint-Martin

Cagnat & Associes
22 rue de Madrid
Paris, France

U.S. Joint Venture:

Fitch Ratings, Inc. **(1)**
(Formerly Fitch, Inc.)
1 State St Plz
New York, NY 10004-1505 DE
Tel.: (212) 908-0500
Fax: (212) 480-4435
E-Mail: jackie.klein@fitchratings.com
Web Site: www.fitchratings.com
Emp.: 600
Credit Ratings, Opinions, Research & Financial Data Reporting Services
S.I.C.: 7323
N.A.I.C.S.: 561450
Stephen W. Joynt *(Pres)*
Douglas Elespe *(CEO, Mng Dir & Venture Partner-Argentina)*
Robert Harpel *(Grp Mng Dir & CTO)*
Olivier Delfour *(Mng Dir)*
Roger Merritt *(Mng Dir)*
Brett Hemsley *(Mng Dir & Head-Asia Pacific)*
Peter Jordan *(Grp Mng Dir & Head-Global Bus Mgmt)*
John Bareiss *(Mng Dir)*
Alejandro Bertuol *(Mng Dir)*
Keith Buckley *(Mng Dir)*
Edward Eyerman *(Mng Dir)*
David Marshall *(Mng Dir)*
Daniel Noonan *(Mng Dir & Global Head-Corp Comm)*
John Olert *(Mng Dir)*
David Riley *(Mng Dir)*
Peter Shaw *(Mng Dir)*
David Wharrier *(Mng Dir)*
Atul Joshi *(CEO/Mng Dir-Mumbai)*

Branches:

Fitch Ratings, Inc. - Chicago **(2)**
70 W Madison St Ste 1300
Chicago, IL 60602
Tel.: (312) 368-3100
Fax: (312) 263-4064
E-Mail: info@fitchratings.com
Web Site: www.fitchratings.com
Emp.: 170
Credit Ratings, Opinions, Research & Financial Data Reporting Services
S.I.C.: 7323
N.A.I.C.S.: 561450

Fitch Ratings, Inc. - San Francisco **(2)**
650 California St
San Francisco, CA 94108
Tel.: (415) 732-5770
Fax: (415) 732-5610
Toll Free: (800) 953-4824
E-Mail: product.feedback@fitchratings.com
Web Site: www.fitchratings.com
Credit Ratings, Opinions, Research & Financial Data Reporting Services
S.I.C.: 7323
N.A.I.C.S.: 561450
Amy Doppelt *(Mng Dir)*

Non-U.S. Subsidiary:

Business Monitor International Ltd. **(2)**
4th Floor Senator House, 85 Queen Victoria Street
London, EC4V 4AD, United Kingdom UK
Tel.: (44) 2072480468
Fax: (44) 2072480467
E-Mail: marketing@businessmonitor.com
Web Site: www.businessmonitor.com
Emp.: 130
Business Data, Analysis, Ratings & Rankings Publisher
S.I.C.: 2741
N.A.I.C.S.: 511140
Jonathan Feroze *(Co-CEO)*
Richard Londesborough *(Co-CEO)*

FIMOPART GROUP

20 rue de Saint-Petersbourg
75008 Paris, France
Tel.: (33) 231717000
Fax: (33) 231266767
E-Mail: siege@fimopart.com
Web Site: www.fimopart.com
Sales Range: $125-149.9 Million
Emp.: 1,600
Business Description:
Holding Company
S.I.C.: 6719
N.A.I.C.S.: 551112
Subsidiary:

Airborne **(1)**
Quartier Beaudesert
33702 Merignac, France (100%)
Tel.: (33) 556346212
Fax: (33) 556346201
Web Site: www.airborne.fr
Sales Range: $1-9.9 Million
Emp.: 30
Designer & Mfr of Office Furniture
S.I.C.: 2521
N.A.I.C.S.: 337211

FINALYSIS CREDIT & GUARANTEE CO. LTD.

17 Damji Shamji Complex LBS Marg
Mumbai, 400 070, India
Tel.: (91) 22 25158000
E-Mail: info@finalysis.in
Web Site: www.finalysis.in
Year Founded: 1988
531820—(BOM)
Business Description:
Financial Leasing Services
S.I.C.: 6153
N.A.I.C.S.: 522220
Personnel:
Sajjad Abdul Qadir *(Mng Dir)*
Board of Directors:
Bipin P. Divecha
Sharad B. Ghadi
Sajjad Abdul Qadir
Vinayak T. Sarkhot
Jigar D. Shah
Transfer Agent:
Link Intime India Pvt. Ltd
C-13 Pannalal Silk Mills Compound LBS Marg
Bhandup (West)
Mumbai, India

THE FINANCE COMPANY PLC

No 55 Lauries Place RA De Mel Mawatha
Colombo, 4, Sri Lanka
Tel.: (94) 112580210
Fax: (94) 112580098
Web Site: www.thefinance.lk
TFC—(COL)
Rev.: $20,122,705
Assets: $145,341,726
Liabilities: $197,035,580
Net Worth: ($51,693,854)
Earnings: ($11,920,604)
Emp.: 929
Fiscal Year-end: 03/31/13
Business Description:
Financial & Investment Services
S.I.C.: 6282
N.A.I.C.S.: 523920
Personnel:
Kamal Jayantha Yatawara *(CEO)*
Tissa Bandara Ekanayaka *(COO)*
P. S. Watson *(Sec)*
Board of Directors:
M. Preethi Jayawardena
Violet Wimala Dissanayake
Tissa Bandara Ekanayaka
A. P. Lekamge
R. Nadarajah
Cherille Rosa
T. Senthilverl
Kamal Jayantha Yatawara
Divisions:

The Finance Company PLC - Business Leasing Division **(1)**
No 194 Galle Road
Dehiwala-Mount Lavinia, Western Province, Sri Lanka
Tel.: (94) 114308601
Fax: (94) 11 4740701
E-Mail: dehiwala@thefinance.lk
Business Leasing Services
S.I.C.: 7389
N.A.I.C.S.: 561499

The Finance Company PLC - Corporate Finance & Treasury Division **(1)**
No 55 The Finance House Lauries Place R A De Mel Mawatha
Colombo, Western Province, 00400, Sri Lanka
Tel.: (94) 112500671
Fax: (94) 11 2500583
E-Mail: treasury@thefinance.lk
Corporate Finance & Treasury Services
S.I.C.: 8742
N.A.I.C.S.: 541611

The Finance Company PLC - Fixed Deposits Division **(1)**
No 97 Hyde Park Corner
Colombo, Western Province, 00200, Sri Lanka
Tel.: (94) 11 2682745
Fax: (94) 11 2682746
E-Mail: cityfixed@thefinance.lk
Web Site: www.thefinance.lk
Emp.: 50
Fixed Deposit Services
S.I.C.: 6799
N.A.I.C.S.: 523920
Kumar Singh *(Gen Mgr)*

The Finance Company PLC - Marketing Division **(1)**
No 55 Lauries Place R A De Mel Mawatha
Colombo, Western Province, 00400, Sri Lanka
Tel.: (94) 112580210
Fax: (94) 11 2580085
E-Mail: marketing@thefinance.lk
Marketing Services
S.I.C.: 8732
N.A.I.C.S.: 541910

FINANCE HOUSE P.J.S.C.

Orjowan Tower Building Zayed 1st Street Khalidiya Area
PO Box 7878
Abu Dhabi, United Arab Emirates
Tel.: (971) 26194000
Fax: (971) 26194099
E-Mail: customerservice@fh.ae
Web Site: www.financehouse.ae
Year Founded: 2004
FH—(ABU)
Int. Income: $50,510,076
Assets: $1,013,071,652
Liabilities: $835,866,685
Net Worth: $177,204,966
Earnings: $19,659,561
Fiscal Year-end: 12/31/12
Business Description:
Investment & Financial Services
S.I.C.: 6211
N.A.I.C.S.: 523999
Personnel:
Mohammed Abdulla Alqubaisi *(Chm)*
Ahmad Obaid Humaid Al Mazrooei *(Vice Chm)*
T. K. Raman *(Grp CFO)*
Mohammed Wassim Khayata *(Grp COO)*
Tarek Soubra *(CIO)*
Ramesh Rajaram *(Chief Investment Officer)*
Board of Directors:
Mohammed Abdulla Alqubaisi
Ahmad Obaid Humaid Al Mazrooei
Eisa Saif Rashid Al Qubaisi
Abdallah Ali Ibrahim Al Saadi
Hamad Abdulla Rashed Al Shamsi
Khaled Abdulla Alqubaisi
Sultan Helal Drei Al Qubaisi
Subsidiaries:

Benyan Development Co. L.L.C. **(1)**
102 Arab Tower Hamdan Street
PO Box 60711
Abu Dhabi, United Arab Emirates
Tel.: (971) 26724322
Fax: (971) 2 6724323
E-Mail: info@benyan.ae
Web Site: www.benyan.ae
Construction Engineering Services
S.I.C.: 8711
N.A.I.C.S.: 541330
Adnir Eninovic *(Gen Mgr)*

Emirates National Electromechanical L.L.C. **(1)**
PO Box 60711
Abu Dhabi, United Arab Emirates

Tel.: (971) 2 6711141
Fax: (971) 26760077
E-Mail: info@enec.ae
Web Site: www.ene-llc.com
Electromechanical Engineering Services
S.I.C.: 8711
N.A.I.C.S.: 541330
Haffan Younis *(Gen Mgr)*

FH Capital Limited (1)
The Gate Level 14
PO Box 74777
Dubai, United Arab Emirates
Tel.: (971) 43394674
Fax: (971) 4 339 4661
Emp.: 5
Investment & Asset Management Services
S.I.C.: 6211
N.A.I.C.S.: 523999

FINANCIAL & ENERGY EXCHANGE LIMITED

(d/b/a FEX Group)
Level 1 7 Bridge Street
Sydney, NSW, 2000, Australia
Mailing Address:
PO Box R506
Royal Exchange, Sydney, NSW, 1225, Australia
Tel.: (61) 2 8024 5200
Fax: (61) 2 8024 5234
E-Mail: info@fex.com.au
Web Site: www.fex.com.au
Year Founded: 2006
Emp.: 30
Business Description:
Holding Company; Derivatives & Commodity Exchanges
S.I.C.: 6719
N.A.I.C.S.: 551112
Personnel:
Brian Price *(Chm & CEO)*
Thomas Price *(CEO-FEX Derivatives)*
Subsidiaries:

Mercari Pty. Ltd. (1)
Level 1 7 Bridge St
Sydney, NSW, 2000, Australia AU
Tel.: (61) 280245200 (100%)
Fax: (61) 280245234
E-Mail: info@mercari.com.au
Web Site: www.mercari.com.au
Emp.: 5
Interest Rate & Foreign Exchange Derivatives Exchange
S.I.C.: 6231
N.A.I.C.S.: 523210

NSX Limited (1)
Level 2 117 Scott Street
PO Box 283
Newcastle, NSW, 2300, Australia AU
Tel.: (61) 249296377 (50.8%)
Fax: (61) 249291556
E-Mail: mail@nsxa.com.au
Web Site: www.nsxa.com.au
NSX—(ASX)
Rev.: $1,223,516
Assets: $3,233,428
Liabilities: $776,724
Net Worth: $2,456,704
Earnings: ($2,044,595)
Emp.: 12
Fiscal Year-end: 06/30/13
Holding Company; Securities Exchange
S.I.C.: 6719
N.A.I.C.S.: 551112
Emlyn Scott *(CEO)*
Ann Bowering *(CEO-SIM Venture Securities Exchange Ltd)*
Scott Francis Evans *(Sec & Gen Mgr)*
Subsidiaries:

BSX Services Pty Limited (2)
Level 3 45 Exhibition Street
Melbourne, VIC, 3000, Australia
Tel.: (61) 390010300
Fax: (61) 3 9001 0311
Securities Trading Services
S.I.C.: 6211
N.A.I.C.S.: 523110

National Stock Exchange of Australia Limited (2)
Level 2 117 Scott Street
PO Box 283
Newcastle, NSW, 2300, Australia AU
Tel.: (61) 249296377 (100%)
Fax: (61) 249291556
E-Mail: admin@nsxa.com.au
Web Site: www.nsxa.com.au
Emp.: 17
Securities Exchange
S.I.C.: 6231
N.A.I.C.S.: 523210
Michael Cox *(Mng Dir)*
Scott Francis Evans *(Mng Dir)*

NSX Services Pty Limited (2)
Level 2 117 Scott St
PO Box 283
Newcastle, NSW, 2300, Australia
Tel.: (61) 249296377
Fax: (61) 249291556
E-Mail: mail@nsxa.com.au
Web Site: www.nsxa.com.au
Emp.: 10
Securities Trading Services
S.I.C.: 6211
N.A.I.C.S.: 523110
Scott Evans *(Gen Mgr & Sec)*

FINANCIAL COMPANY REAL-INVEST.KZ JSC

Samal-2 104 Business Center 5th Floor
050010 Almaty, Kazakhstan
Tel.: (7) 7272623239
Fax: (7) 727 2623253
E-Mail: info@realinvest.kz
Web Site: www.realinvest.kz
REAL—(KAZ)
Business Description:
Financial Services
S.I.C.: 6726
N.A.I.C.S.: 525990
Personnel:
Elena Vasilieva *(Chm-Mgmt Bd)*

THE FINANCIAL CORPORATION COMPANY SAOG

PO Box 782
131 Muscat, Oman
Tel.: (968) 24822300
Fax: (968) 24822390
E-Mail: fincorp@fincorp.org
Web Site: www.fincorp.org
FINC—(MUS)
Rev.: $2,874,962
Assets: $22,511,011
Liabilities: $3,514,310
Net Worth: $18,996,701
Earnings: $63,350
Fiscal Year-end: 03/31/13
Business Description:
Investment Banking Services
S.I.C.: 6211
N.A.I.C.S.: 523110
Personnel:
Hilal Hamed Abdulla Al Hsani *(Chm)*
Mohamed Abdulla Al Khonji *(Deputy Chm)*
Nasr Amur Shwain Al Hosni *(CEO)*
Kamal Abdulla *(Compliance Officer & Sr VP)*
Muhannad Hijazi *(Sr VP-Private Equity)*
Binoy Jacob *(Sr VP-Fin)*
Anil Kumar *(Sr VP-Wealth Mgmt)*
Board of Directors:
Hilal Hamed Abdulla Al Hsani
Mohamed Abdulla Al Khonji
Mohamed Darwish Al Khoori
Hassan Al Lawati
Shabir M. Al Yousef
Awadh Mohd Faraj Bamkhalef
Munir Abdulnabi Yousef Makki

FINANCIAL PRODUCTS GROUP CO., LTD.

7th Floor Yusen Bldg 2-3-2 Marunouchi
Chiyoda-ku, Tokyo, 100-0005, Japan
Tel.: (81) 352885656
Fax: (81) 352889300
Web Site: www.fpg.jp
Year Founded: 2001
7148—(JAS TKS)
Sales Range: $1-9.9 Million
Emp.: 25
Business Description:
Leasing Services
S.I.C.: 6163
N.A.I.C.S.: 522310
Personnel:
Hisanaga Tanimura *(Pres)*

FINANCIAL TECHNOLOGIES (INDIA) LIMITED

FT Tower CTS No. 256 & 257 Suren Road
Chakala Andheri East, Mumbai, Maharashtra, 400093, India
Tel.: (91) 2266861010
Fax: (91) 2266864050
E-Mail: info@ftindia.com
Web Site: www.ftindia.com
526881—(BOM)
Rev.: $177,241,084
Assets: $868,936,020
Liabilities: $529,297,514
Net Worth: $339,638,506
Earnings: $42,167,172
Emp.: 1,186
Fiscal Year-end: 03/31/13
Business Description:
IP & Domain Provider
S.I.C.: 7371
N.A.I.C.S.: 541511
Personnel:
Jignesh Shah *(Chm & Grp CEO)*
Devendra Agrawal *(CFO)*
Rajendra Mehta *(Pres/Head-Member Tech)*
Jigish Sonagara *(Pres/Head-Exchange Tech)*
Prashant Desai *(Pres-IR)*
Miten Mehta *(Pres-New Projects)*
Hariraj S. Chouhan *(Sec)*
Naishadh P. Desai *(Sr VP-Legal)*
Dilip Tambe *(Sr VP-Comm)*
Board of Directors:
Jignesh Shah
Paras Ajmera
Venkat Chary
Kochar R. J.
Dewang Neralla
Rajendran S.
Manjay P. Shah
Transfer Agent:
Karvy Computershare Private Limited
Plot No 17-24 Vittal Rao Nagar Madhapur
Hyderabad, 500 081, India
Tel.: (91) 40 2342 0818
Subsidiaries:

atom technologies limited (1)
4th Fl CTS No 256 & 257 F T Tower Suren Rd Chakala
Andheri E, Mumbai, Maharashtra, 400093, India
Tel.: (91) 2267099000
Fax: (91) 2267698311
E-Mail: info@atomtech.in
Web Site: www.atomtech.in
Emp.: 120
Mobile & Electronic Payment Services
S.I.C.: 6099
N.A.I.C.S.: 522320
Niranjan Gosavi *(Head-Mktg & Bus Dev)*

Credit Market Services Limited (1)
Exchange Sq CTS No 255 Gundavali Suren Rd
Andheri E Chakala, Mumbai, Maharashtra, 400093, India
Tel.: (91) 22 6731 8888
Fax: (91) 22 6649 4151
E-Mail: support@cmsl.co.in
Web Site: www.cmsl.co.in
Emp.: 8
Financial Advisory Services
S.I.C.: 6211
N.A.I.C.S.: 523999
D. Ravishankar *(Co-Founder & CEO)*
N. Balasubramanian *(Co-Founder)*

FT Knowledge Management Company Limited (1)
First Fl Exchange Sq Suren Rd Chakala
Andheri E, Mumbai, Maharashtra, 400093, India
Tel.: (91) 2267318888
Fax: (91) 22 6726 9541
E-Mail: knowledgeformarkets@ftkmc.com
Web Site: www.ftkmc.com
Emp.: 40
Financial Consulting Services
S.I.C.: 6211
N.A.I.C.S.: 523999
Bandi Ram Prasad *(Pres)*
Jinesh Panchali *(Sr VP)*

IBS FOREX LIMITED (1)
55-C Mittal Tower C Wing Nariman Pt
Mumbai, Maharashtra, 400021, India
Tel.: (91) 22 66344322
Fax: (91) 22 66344324
E-Mail: info@ibsfx.com
Web Site: www.ibsfx.com
Stock Trading Software Solutions
S.I.C.: 7371
N.A.I.C.S.: 541511
Ganesh Rao *(CEO)*

National Bulk Handling Corporation (1)
401 4th Fl Boston House Suren Rd Chakala
Andheri E, Mumbai, Maharashtra, 400093, India
Tel.: (91) 2230631000
Fax: (91) 22 67099044
E-Mail: info@nbhcindia.com
Web Site: www.nbhcindia.com
Emp.: 1,000
Commodity & Collateral Management Services
S.I.C.: 6221
N.A.I.C.S.: 523130
Anil K. Choudhary *(CEO & Mng Dir)*
Mahesh Joshi *(CFO)*
Santosh Dadheech *(COO)*
M. S. Dewoolkar *(Sr VP-Quality Assurance)*
K. K. Gautam *(Sr VP-Procurement)*

National Spot Exchange Limited (1)
102 A Landmark Suren Rd Chakala
Andheri E, Mumbai, Maharashtra, 400093, India
Tel.: (91) 2267619900
Fax: (91) 2267619931
E-Mail: info@nationalspotexchange.com
Web Site: www.nationalspotexchange.com
Emp.: 100
Electronic Spot Trading Services
S.I.C.: 1799
N.A.I.C.S.: 238990
Saji Cherian *(CEO & Mng Dir)*
Shashidhar Kotian *(CFO)*

Subsidiary:

Indian Bullion Market Association Limited (2)
1st Fl Malkani Chambers Off Nehru Rd
Vile Parle E, Mumbai, Maharashtra, 400099, India
Tel.: (91) 2226173746
Fax: (91) 2226164148
E-Mail: info@ibma.org.in
Web Site: www.ibma.org.in
Emp.: 15
Bullion Market Services
S.I.C.: 6221
N.A.I.C.S.: 523130
Manish Rangari *(COO)*

Riskraft Consulting Ltd. (1)
Exchange Sq 1st Fl CTS No 255 Gundavali Suren Rd Chakala
Andheri E, Mumbai, Maharashtra, 400093, India
Tel.: (91) 2267318888
Fax: (91) 2267319383
E-Mail: info@riskraft.com
Web Site: www.riskraft.com
Financial Consulting & Management Services
S.I.C.: 8742
N.A.I.C.S.: 541611

Financial Technologies (India) Limited—(Continued)

A. K. Nag *(Sr VP)*

TickerPlant Limited (1)
Landmark B-wing 3rd Fl Suren Rd Chakala
Andheri E, Mumbai, Maharashtra, 400093, India
Tel.: (91) 22 66497100
Fax: (91) 22 67694292
E-Mail: info@tickerplantindia.com
Web Site: www.tickerplantindia.com
Financial Information Software Publishing Services
S.I.C.: 7372
N.A.I.C.S.: 511210
Shriram K *(VP-Mktg & Bus Dev)*

Non-U.S. Subsidiaries:

Bahrain Financial Exchange (1)
12th Fl E Tower Bahrain Fin Harbour
PO Box 1936
King Faisal Hwy, Manama, Bahrain
Tel.: (973) 16511511
Fax: (973) 16 511 599
E-Mail: info@bfx.bh
Web Site: www.bfx.bh
Securities Trading Services
S.I.C.: 6211
N.A.I.C.S.: 523110
Arshad Khan *(CEO & Mng Dir)*
Craig Hewett *(Chief Bus Officer)*
P. R. Ramesh *(Chief Compliance & Legal Officer)*

ICX Platform (Pty) Ltd. (1)
1st Fl Gleneagles Bldg Fairway Ofc Park 52
Grosvenor Rd
Bryanston, Johannesburg, 1709, South Africa
Tel.: (27) 117062011
Fax: (27) 114633947
E-Mail: info@icxafrica.com
Web Site: www.icxafrica.com
Emp.: 2
Commodities Exchange Services
S.I.C.: 6231
N.A.I.C.S.: 523210
Troy Miranda *(Mgr)*

FINANCIERE DE L'ODET

31-32 quai de Dion-Bouton
92811 Puteaux, Cedex, France
Tel.: (33) 1 46 96 44 33
Fax: (33) 146964422
Web Site: www.bollore.com
ODET—(EUR)
Sales Range: $5-14.9 Billion
Business Description:
Holding Company; Logistics Services; Plastic Products Mfr; Media Services
S.I.C.: 6719
N.A.I.C.S.: 551112
Personnel:
Vincent Bollore *(Chm)*
Cedric de Bailliencourt *(Mng Dir)*

Subsidiary:

Bollore S.A. (1)
Tour Bollore 31-32 quai de Dion-Bouton
92811 Puteaux, Cedex, France
Tel.: (33) 1 4696 4433
Fax: (33) 1 4696 4422
Web Site: www.bollore.com
BOL—(EUR)
Sls.: $13,711,868,194
Assets: $21,510,838,127
Liabilities: $11,738,133,933
Net Worth: $9,772,704,194
Earnings: $1,082,775,685
Emp.: 55,555
Fiscal Year-end: 12/31/12
Holding Company
S.I.C.: 6719
N.A.I.C.S.: 551112
Vincent Bollore *(Chm & Co-CEO)*
Cyrille Bollore *(Vice Chm & Mng Dir)*
Cedric de Bailliencourt *(Vice Chm & CFO)*
Gilles Alix *(Co-CEO)*

Divisions:

A.M. Productions (2)
14 chemin de la Litte
92397 Villeneuve-la-Garenne, France
Tel.: (33) 141473636
Fax: (33) 141476630
E-Mail: amprod@amprod.com
Web Site: www.amprod.com
Emp.: 20
Business Support Services
S.I.C.: 7389
N.A.I.C.S.: 561499
Somme Jackues *(Mng Dir)*

Batscap (2)
Odet Ergue-Gaberic
29556 Quimper, Cedex, France
Tel.: (33) 298667200
Fax: (33) 298596779
E-Mail: contact@batscap.com
Web Site: www.batscap.com
Emp.: 130
Energy Storage Products & Battery Mfr
S.I.C.: 3691
N.A.I.C.S.: 335911
Jeanmac Metais *(Gen Mgr)*

Bollore Africa Logistics (2)
Tour Bollore 31-32 quai de Dion Bouton
92811 Puteaux, France
Tel.: (33) 146964433
Fax: (33) 146964422
E-Mail: contact@bollore-africa-logistics.com
Web Site: www.bollore-africa-logistics.com
Emp.: 550
Transportation & Logistics Services
S.I.C.: 4731
N.A.I.C.S.: 488510

Bollore Energie (2)
27 rue du Professeur Victor Pauchet
92420 Vaucresson, France
Tel.: (33) 177700777
Fax: (33) 177700704
E-Mail: contact@bollore-energie.net
Web Site: www.bollore-energie.fr
Emp.: 55
Logistics & Fuel Distribution Services
S.I.C.: 4731
N.A.I.C.S.: 488510

Bollore Intermedia (2)
31-32 quai de Dion-Bouton
92811 Puteaux, Cedex, France
Tel.: (33) 146963128
Fax: (33) 146964045
Advertising Services
S.I.C.: 7311
N.A.I.C.S.: 541810

Bollore Plastic Film Division (2)
Odet Ergue-Gaberic
92811 Quimper, Cedex, France
Tel.: (33) 298667200
Fax: (33) 298596779
Web Site: www.bollorefilms.com
Plastic Film Mfr
S.I.C.: 3089
N.A.I.C.S.: 326199

Direct Matin plus (2)
31-32 quai de Dion-Bouton
92800 Puteaux, France
Tel.: (33) 146963100
Fax: (33) 146964422
Web Site: directmatin.directmedia.fr
Emp.: 800
Newspaper Publisher
S.I.C.: 2711
N.A.I.C.S.: 511110

IER (2)
3 rue Salomon-de-Rothschild
BP 320
92158 Suresnes, Cedex, France
Tel.: (33) 141386000
Fax: (33) 141386200
Web Site: www.ier.fr
Sales Range: $150-199.9 Million
Emp.: 800
Ticket Machines & Terminals for Boarding Control & Secure Automated Processing of Passengers & Baggage
S.I.C.: 3589
N.A.I.C.S.: 333318

SDV International Logistics (2)
Tour Bollore 31-32 quai de Dion Bouton
92811 Puteaux, France
Tel.: (33) 146964433
Fax: (33) 146964422
E-Mail: dircom@sdv.com
Web Site: www.sdv.com
Emp.: 15,000
Transportation & Logistics Services
S.I.C.: 4731
N.A.I.C.S.: 541614

U.S. Subsidiary:

SDV (USA) Inc. (3)
15010 132nd Ave
Jamaica, NY 11434
Tel.: (718) 525-8100
Fax: (718) 978-8425
E-Mail: sdvcorp@sdvusa.com
Web Site: www.sdvusa.com
Sls.: $117,644,232
Emp.: 150
Foreign Freight Forwarding
S.I.C.: 4731
N.A.I.C.S.: 488510
Philippe Naudin *(Pres)*
David Smith *(CEO)*
Jean-Claude Gailhard *(CFO)*

Subsidiaries:

Blue Solutions S.A. (2)
Odet
29500 Ergue-Gaberic, France (80%)
Tel.: (33) 2 98 66 72 00
Web Site: www.blue-solutions.com
BLUE—(EUR)
Sls.: $83,092,343
Earnings: ($30,181,131)
Fiscal Year-end: 12/31/12
Lithium Battery Mfr
S.I.C.: 3692
N.A.I.C.S.: 335912
Vincent Bollore *(Chm)*
Gilles Alix *(CEO)*
Fabrice Bouteau *(CFO)*

SAS des Domaines de la Bastide et de la Croix (2)
Boulevard de Taberin
La Croix Valmer, France
Tel.: (33) 494950175
Fax: (33) 494174787
E-Mail: contact@domainedelacroix.com
Web Site: www.domainedelacroix.com
Emp.: 20
Wine Producer & Sales
S.I.C.: 2084
N.A.I.C.S.: 312130
Bertrand Chavanes *(Pres)*

FINANCIERE DE TUBIZE SA

Allee De La Recherche 60
1070 Brussels, Belgium
Tel.: (32) 2 653 88 08
Fax: (32) 2 651 12 29
Web Site: www.financiere-tubize.be
TUB—(EUR)
Business Description:
Investment Management Services
S.I.C.: 6799
N.A.I.C.S.: 523920
Personnel:
Francois Tesch *(Pres)*
Board of Directors:
Evelyn Diego du Monceau de Bergendal
Charles-Antoine Janssen
Cyril Janssen
Francois Tesch
Cedric van Rijckevorsel

FINANCIERE LR SARL

24 rue Emile Menier
Paris, 75116, France
Tel.: (33) 17856991
Business Description:
Private Investment Firm
S.I.C.: 6211
N.A.I.C.S.: 523999
Personnel:
Lionel Rozenberg *(Owner)*

Subsidiary:

IC Telecom SA (1)
24 rue Emile Menier
75116 Paris, France
Tel.: (33) 155269000
Fax: (33) 146075047
E-Mail: contact@ictelecom.fr
Web Site: www.ictelecom.fr
ALICT—(EUR)
Sales Range: $10-24.9 Million
Emp.: 60
Telecommunications Services
S.I.C.: 4812
N.A.I.C.S.: 517210
Goel Haddouk *(Chm & CEO)*
David Ganrasni *(CFO)*

FINANCIERE PINAULT SCA

(d/b/a Groupe Artemis)
12 rue Francois 1er
75008 Paris, France
Tel.: (33) 1 4411 2020
Fax: (33) 1 4411 2018
Web Site: www.groupeartemis.com
Year Founded: 1992
Sales Range: $15-24.9 Billion
Business Description:
Holding Company
S.I.C.: 6719
N.A.I.C.S.: 551112
Personnel:
Francois Pinault *(Co-Chm)*
Francois-Henri Pinault *(Co-Chm)*
Patricia Marie Marguerite Barbizet *(CEO)*

Subsidiary:

Artemis S.A. (1)
12 rue Francois 1er
F-75008 Paris, France FR
Tel.: (33) 1 4411 2020
Fax: (33) 1 4411 2018
Web Site: www.groupeartemis.com
Investment Holding Company
S.I.C.: 6719
N.A.I.C.S.: 551112
Francois Pinault *(Co-Chm)*
Francois-Henri Pinault *(Co-Chm)*
Patricia Marie Marguerite Barbizet *(CEO)*

U.S. Holding:

New California Life Holdings, Inc. (1)
1105 N Market St 13th Fl
Wilmington, DE 19801-1216 DE
Tel.: (302) 427-2073 (67%)
Emp.: 550
Holding Company; Life Insurance & Annuity Product Administration Services
S.I.C.: 6719
N.A.I.C.S.: 551112
Steven Turner *(Pres)*

Subsidiary:

Aurora National Life Assurance Company (2)
27201 Tourney Rd Ste 225
Valencia, CA 91355-1804 CA
Tel.: (661) 253-1688
Fax: (661) 253-1226
E-Mail: info@auroralife.com
Web Site: www.auroralife.com
Life Insurance & Annuity Product Administration Services
S.I.C.: 6371
N.A.I.C.S.: 524292
Kenneth R. Schild *(Gen Counsel & Sr VP)*

Non-U.S. Holdings:

Christie's International plc (1)
8 King Street
Saint James's, London, SW1Y 6QT, United Kingdom UK
Tel.: (44) 2078399060 (100%)
Fax: (44) 2078391611
E-Mail: info@christies.com
Web Site: www.christies.com
Emp.: 1,517
Holding Company; Auction Houses
S.I.C.: 6719
N.A.I.C.S.: 551112
Olivier Camu *(Deputy Chm & Sr Dir-Intl)*
Charles Cator *(Deputy Chm-Christie's Intl)*
Paul Raison *(Deputy Chm)*
Francis Russell *(Deputy Chm-UK)*
John Lumley *(Vice Chm-Europe)*
Steven Pleshette Murphy *(CEO)*

Matthew Stephenson *(Mng Dir)*
David Linley *(Chm-UK)*
Jussi Pylkkanen *(Pres-Europe)*

Subsidiaries:

Christie Manson & Woods Limited **(2)**
8 King Street
St James, London, SW1Y 6QT, United Kingdom UK
Tel.: (44) 2078399060 (100%)
Telex: 916429
Fax: (44) 2078391611
E-Mail: info@christies.com
Web Site: www.christies.com
Emp.: 100
Art Auctioneers
S.I.C.: 7389
N.A.I.C.S.: 561990
Steven Mercy *(Chm)*

Subsidiary:

Christie's South Kensington Ltd. **(3)**
85 Old Brompton Rd
London, SW7 3LD, United Kingdom UK
Tel.: (44) 2079306074 (100%)
Fax: (44) 2077523321
E-Mail: info@christies.com
Emp.: 80
Art Auctioneers
S.I.C.: 7389
N.A.I.C.S.: 561990
Steven Murphy *(CEO)*

Christie's Scotland Limited **(2)**
5 Wemyss Pl
Edinburgh, EH3 6DH, United Kingdom UK
Tel.: (44) 312254756 (100%)
Fax: (44) 312251723
Web Site: www.christies.com
Emp.: 5
Art Auctioneers
S.I.C.: 7389
N.A.I.C.S.: 561499

C.I. Property & Investments Limited **(2)**
8 King Street
Saint James's, London, SW1Y 6QT, United Kingdom UK
Tel.: (44) 2078399060 (100%)
Fax: (44) 2078391611
E-Mail: info@christies.com
Web Site: www.christies.com
Property Management Services
S.I.C.: 6531
N.A.I.C.S.: 531312
Edward Dolman *(CEO)*

U.S. Subsidiary:

Christie's Inc. **(2)**
20 Rockefeller Plz
New York, NY 10020-1902 (100%)
Tel.: (212) 636-2000
Fax: (212) 636-4930
E-Mail: info@christies.com
Web Site: www.christies.com
Emp.: 550
Art Auctioneers
S.I.C.: 5961
N.A.I.C.S.: 454112
Stephen Lash *(Chm)*
Steven Pleshette Murphy *(CEO)*
Andrew Foster *(COO)*

Non-U.S. Subsidiaries:

Christie's Amsterdam B.V. **(2)**
Cornelius Schuystraat 57
1071 JG Amsterdam, Netherlands (100%)
Tel.: (31) 205755255
Fax: (31) 206640899
E-Mail: infoamsterdam@christie.com
Web Site: www.christie.com
Emp.: 60
Art Auctioneers
S.I.C.: 7389
N.A.I.C.S.: 561990
Jop Ubbens *(Chm)*
Leila de Vos *(Mng Dir)*

Christie's Australia Pty. Ltd. **(2)**
287 New S Head Rd
Edgecliff, NSW, 2027, Australia (100%)
Tel.: (61) 293261422
Fax: (61) 293278439
Art Auctioneers
S.I.C.: 7389
N.A.I.C.S.: 561499

Christie's Hong Kong Ltd. **(2)**
2203 8 Alexandra House 16 20 Chater Rd Central
Hong Kong, China (Hong Kong) (100%)
Tel.: (852) 25215396
Fax: (852) 28452646
E-Mail: info@christies.com
Web Site: www.christies.com
Emp.: 100
Art Auctioneers
S.I.C.: 7389
N.A.I.C.S.: 561499
Francois Curiel *(Pres)*

Christie's (International) S.A. **(2)**
8 Pl De La Taconnerie
CH 1204 Geneva, Switzerland (100%)
Tel.: (41) 223191766
Fax: (41) 223191767
E-Mail: cgounod@christies.com
Web Site: www.christies.com
Emp.: 40
Art Auctioneers
S.I.C.: 7389
N.A.I.C.S.: 561990
Francois Curiel *(Chm-Europe)*

Non-U.S. Branch:

Christie's (International) S.A. - filiale Italiana, Rome **(3)**
Palazzo Massimo Lancellotti Piazza Navona 114
Rome, 00186, Italy
Tel.: (39) 0066863333
Fax: (39) 0066863334
E-Mail: info@christies.com
Web Site: www.christies.com
Emp.: 50
Art Auctioneers
S.I.C.: 7389
N.A.I.C.S.: 561499

Christie's International Singapore Pte. Ltd. **(2)**
501 Orchard Road 1903 Wheelock Place
22 Scotts Road, Singapore, 228221, Singapore (100%)
Tel.: (65) 62353828
Fax: (65) 62358128
Web Site: www.christies.com
Emp.: 9
Art Auctioneers
S.I.C.: 7389
N.A.I.C.S.: 561499

Christie's (Israel) Ltd. **(2)**
Asia House 4 Weizman St Fl 4
Tel Aviv, 64239, Israel (100%)
Tel.: (972) 36950695
Fax: (972) 36952751
E-Mail: val-telaviv@christie.com
Web Site: www.christie.com
Emp.: 4
Art Auctioneers
S.I.C.: 7389
N.A.I.C.S.: 561990
Mary Gilben *(Chm)*

Christie's Monaco S.A.M. **(2)**
Residence Le Mirabel 4 Ave Des Citronniers
MD 98000 Monte Carlo, Monaco (100%)
Tel.: (377) 97971100
Fax: (377) 97971101
E-Mail: okozina@christies.com
Web Site: www.christies.com
Emp.: 2
Art Auctioneers
S.I.C.: 7389
N.A.I.C.S.: 561499
Nancy Gotta *(Gen Mgr)*

Christie's Zurich S.A. **(2)**
Steinwiesplatz
CH 8032 Zurich, Switzerland (100%)
Tel.: (41) 442681010
Fax: (41) 442681011
Web Site: www.christies.com
Emp.: 10
Art Auctioneers
S.I.C.: 7389
N.A.I.C.S.: 561499
Michele Sandoz *(Gen Mgr)*

Tawa plc **(1)**
The Isis Building 193 Marsh Wall
London, E14 9SG, United Kingdom UK
Tel.: (44) 2070688000 (69.4%)
Fax: (44) 2070688001
E-Mail: info@tawa.com
Web Site: www.tawaplc.com
TAW—(LSE)
Rev.: $52,600,000
Assets: $481,900,000
Liabilities: $303,400,000
Net Worth: $178,500,000
Earnings: ($22,500,000)
Emp.: 332
Fiscal Year-end: 12/31/12
Holding Company; Non-Life Insurance Run-Off Services
S.I.C.: 6719
N.A.I.C.S.: 551112
Timothy Joseph Carroll *(Chm)*
Gilles Erulin *(CEO)*
Simon Byrne *(CFO)*
David Vaughan *(COO)*
Christopher Jones *(Compliance Officer & Sec)*
Marvin Mohn *(Gen Counsel)*

Subsidiaries:

PRO Insurance Solutions Limited **(2)**
The Isis Building
193 Marsh Wall, London, E14 9SG, United Kingdom
Tel.: (44) 2070688000
Fax: (44) 2070688001
Web Site: www.proisinsurance.com
Emp.: 300
Insurance Management Services
S.I.C.: 6411
N.A.I.C.S.: 524298
Simon Byrne *(CFO)*

Tawa Management Limited **(2)**
The Isis Building
193 Marsh Wall, London, E14 9SG, United Kingdom
Tel.: (44) 2070688000
Fax: (44) 2070688001
E-Mail: enquiries@pro-ltd.co.uk
Web Site: www.tawamanagement.com
Emp.: 100
Insurance Services
S.I.C.: 6411
N.A.I.C.S.: 524298

Affiliate:

CX Reinsurance Company Limited **(2)**
The Isis Building
193 Marsh Wall, London, E14 9SG, United Kingdom UK
Tel.: (44) 2070688000 (49.95%)
Fax: (44) 2070688001
Web Site: www.tawaplc.com
Emp.: 90
Reinsurance Services
S.I.C.: 6399
N.A.I.C.S.: 524130
Colin Bird *(CEO)*

U.S. Joint Venture:

Lincoln General Insurance Company **(2)**
3501 Concord Rd
York, PA 17402 PA
Mailing Address:
PO Box 3709
York, PA 17402-0136
Tel.: (717) 757-0000
Fax: (717) 751-0144
Web Site: www.lincolngeneral.com
Emp.: 80
Property & Casualty Insurance Products & Services
S.I.C.: 6351
N.A.I.C.S.: 524126
Frank Amodeo *(COO)*

FINANCIERE QUICK S.A.S.

Parc des Portes de Paris - Bat 123
50 avenue du President Wilson,
93214 La Plaine Saint-Denis, Cedex, France
Tel.: (33) 1 4951 6464
Fax: (33) 1 4951 6565
Web Site: group.quick.be/en
Sales Range: $1-4.9 Billion
Emp.: 19,000

Business Description:
Holding Company; Fast Food Restaurants Owner, Operator & Franchisor
S.I.C.: 6719
N.A.I.C.S.: 551112

Personnel:
Jean Eichenlaub *(Chm-Supervisory Bd)*
Cedric Dugardin *(Chm-Mgmt Bd & CEO)*
Jean-Paul Brayer *(Vice Chm-Supervisory Bd)*
Rudy Hulsman *(Member-Mgmt Bd & VP-Ops-Belgium & Luxembourg)*
Luc Thibaud *(Member-Mgmt Bd & VP-Ops-France)*
Anne Gleizes *(Member-Mgmt Bd, Deputy Gen Mgr & Mktg Dir)*
Marie-Claude Authias *(Member-Mgmt Bd & Dir-HR)*
Nathalie Bieniek *(Member-Mgmt Bd & Dir-Legal)*
Hubert Vilmer *(Member-Mgmt Bd & Dir-Supply Chain)*

Supervisory Board of Directors:
Jean Eichenlaub
Jean-Paul Brayer
Bastian Emery-Beziers
Rudolf Mouradian
Boris Podevin

Subsidiary:

France Quick S.A.S. **(1)**
Parc des Portes de Paris - Bat 123
50 avenue du President Wilson, 93214 La Plaine Saint-Denis, Cedex, France FR
Tel.: (33) 1 4951 6464
Fax: (33) 1 4951 6565
E-Mail: accuiel2@quick.fr
Web Site: www.quick.fr
Emp.: 300
Restaurant Operator
S.I.C.: 8741
N.A.I.C.S.: 561110
Cedric Dugardin *(CEO)*

Unit:

Quick International **(2)**
Parc des Portes de Paris - Bat 123
50 avenue du President Wilson, 93214 La Plaine Saint-Denis, Cedex, France
Tel.: (33) 1 4951 6567
Fax: (33) 1 4951 6565
Fast Food Restaurants Franchisor
S.I.C.: 6794
N.A.I.C.S.: 533110
Francois Charpy *(Dir-Ops-Intl)*

Non-U.S. Subsidiary:

Quick Restaurants S.A. **(1)**
Grotesteenweg 224 bte 5
2600 Berchem, Belgium BE
Tel.: (32) 3286 1811 (100%)
Fax: (32) 3286 1879
E-Mail: info@quick.be
Web Site: www.quick.be
Fast Food Restaurant Operator & Franchisor
S.I.C.: 5812
N.A.I.C.S.: 722511
Anne Gleizes *(Deputy Gen Mgr & Mktg Dir)*

FINANSA PCL

TISCO Tower 12A/F 48/21-22 North Sathorn Road
Bangkok, 10500, Thailand
Tel.: (66) 2 697 3700
Fax: (66) 2 266 6688
E-Mail: finansah@fpt.vn
Web Site: www.finansa.com
Year Founded: 1991
FNS—(THA)
Rev.: $15,496,690
Assets: $59,776,492
Liabilities: $16,124,835
Net Worth: $43,651,657
Earnings: ($1,126,321)
Emp.: 147

Finansa PCL—(Continued)

Fiscal Year-end: 12/31/12

Business Description:
Investment Banking & Financial Management Services
S.I.C.: 6211
N.A.I.C.S.: 523110

Personnel:
Vorasit Pokachaiyapat *(Co-Founder & Mng Dir)*
Eugene S. Davis *(Co-Founder)*
Virabongsa Ramangkura *(Chm)*
Jonathan Truslow *(COO)*
James Marshall *(Chief Investment Officer)*
Theraphan Jittalarn *(CEO-Finansa Asset Management Ltd)*
Chakhrit Suphepre *(Sr VP & Head-IT)*
Rachanee Mahatdetkul *(Sr VP-Direct Investment)*

Board of Directors:
Virabongsa Ramangkura
Eugene S. Davis
Akarat Na Ranong
Vorasit Pokachaiyapat
Varah Sucharitakul
Vitthya Vejjajiva
Kenneth L. White

Subsidiaries:

Finansa Asset Management Ltd. **(1)**
TISCO Tower 12A/F
48 North Sathorn Road, Bangkok, 10500, Thailand
Tel.: (66) 23524000
Fax: (66) 23524099
E-Mail: theerathan.a@finansa.com
Web Site: www.finansa-asset.com
Emp.: 100
Asset Managment Services
S.I.C.: 6211
N.A.I.C.S.: 523999

Finansa Credit Ltd. **(1)**
TISCO Tower 12A/F
48 North Sathorn Road, Bangkok, 10500, Thailand
Tel.: (66) 23524200
Fax: (66) 23524299
Web Site: www.finansa.com
Credit Services
S.I.C.: 6159
N.A.I.C.S.: 522298
Kenneth L. White *(Mng Dir)*

Finansa Fund Management Ltd. **(1)**
TISCO Tower 16F
48 N Sathorn Rd, Bangkok, 10500, Thailand
Tel.: (66) 26973700
Fax: (66) 22666688
Web Site: www.finansa.com
Investment Fund Management Services
S.I.C.: 6211
N.A.I.C.S.: 523999
Ratchani Mahatdetkun *(Mng Dir)*

Finansa Securities Ltd. **(1)**
TISCO Tower
48 N Sathorn Rd, Bangkok, 10500, Thailand
Tel.: (66) 26973800
Fax: (66) 26973760
Financial Investment Services
S.I.C.: 6282
N.A.I.C.S.: 523930

Prospect Development Co., Ltd. **(1)**
12A th Floor Tisco Tower 48/23 North Sathorn Road Silom
Bangkok, 10500, Thailand
Tel.: (66) 26973860
Fax: (66) 2 697 3869
Web Site: www.Prospectd.com
Property Rental & Leasing Services
S.I.C.: 6512
N.A.I.C.S.: 531120

FINANSIA SYRUS SECURITIES PUBLIC COMPANY LIMITED

999/9 The Offices at Centralworld
17th 18th 25th Floor Rama 1 Road
Pathumwan, Bangkok, 10330, Thailand
Tel.: (66) 2658 9000
Fax: (66) 2658 9110
Web Site: www.fnsyrus.com
FSS—(THA)
Rev.: $60,084,568
Assets: $138,970,411
Liabilities: $85,280,264
Net Worth: $53,690,147
Earnings: $6,013,095
Fiscal Year-end: 12/31/12

Business Description:
Securities Brokerage Services
S.I.C.: 6211
N.A.I.C.S.: 523120

Personnel:
Chatchaval Jiaravanon *(Chm)*
Chuangchai Nawongs *(Co-Pres & CEO)*
Somphop Keerasuntonpong *(Co-Pres)*
Pornpring Suksantisuwan *(Co-Pres)*
Penporn Apirukloasakul *(CFO)*

Board of Directors:
Chatchaval Jiaravanon
Chayant Akaratit
Supat Apiratimai
Penporn Apirukloasakul
Pothorn Choemvarachart
Chatchai Chumsiri
Chaiyaporn Dhammapeera
Chanachai Joonjiraporn
Somphop Keerasuntonpong
Kuntra Ladavalya Na Ayudhya
Chuangchai Nawongs
Vilai Phongpreecha
Chaipant Pongtanakorn
Nusara Rooncharoen
Prajuab Sirirutbunkajorn
Pornpring Suksantisuwan
Vithawat Vichiateerapongse

FINANSINOS S/A - CREDITO FINANCIAMENTO E INVESTIMENTO

R Bento Goncalves 2575
93510001 Novo Hamburgo, RS, Brazil
Tel.: (55) 51 3594 2488
Fax: (55) 51 3594 1998
E-Mail: finansinos@finansinos.com.br
Web Site: www.finansinos.com.br
Year Founded: 1962
FNCN3—(BRAZ)
Emp.: 24

Business Description:
Financial Services
S.I.C.: 6211
N.A.I.C.S.: 523999

Personnel:
Roberto Cardoso *(Dir-IR)*

FINANTEC CO., LTD.

21-20 Akasaka 3-chome
Tokyo, Minato-ku, 107-0052, Japan
Tel.: (81) 335605444
Fax: (81) 335605445
Web Site: www.finantec-net.com
Sales Range: $10-24.9 Million
Emp.: 25

Business Description:
Business Information Publisher
S.I.C.: 2741
N.A.I.C.S.: 519130

Personnel:
Masaki Kai *(CEO)*

Board of Directors:
Hidetaka Ichinose
Masaki Kai
Kengo Kosuge
Shokichi Nakata

Division:

Tokyo IPO **(1)**
2F Akasaka Long Beach Building 21-20 Akasaka 3-chome
Minto-ku, Tokyo, Japan
Tel.: (81) 335605469
Fax: (81) 335605510
E-Mail: editor@tokyoipo.com
Web Site: www.tokyoipo.com
Business Information Publisher
S.I.C.: 2741
N.A.I.C.S.: 519130
Takashi Nishibori *(Chief Editor)*

FINARTE CASA D'ASTE SPA

Piazetta Maurilio Bossi 4
20121 Milan, Italy
Tel.: (39) 02863561
Fax: (39) 02 867318
E-Mail: mail@finarte-semenzato.com
Web Site: www.finarte-semenzato.com
Year Founded: 1959
FCD—(ITA)
Sales Range: $10-24.9 Million
Emp.: 56

Business Description:
Auction Services
S.I.C.: 5999
N.A.I.C.S.: 453998

Personnel:
Georgio Corbelli *(Chm)*

Board of Directors:
Georgio Corbelli
Giorgio Colombini
Remo Grassi
Guiseppe Lazzaroni
Sergio Marchese
Carlo Pelizzari
Alberto Rittatore Vonwiller
Giovanni Tampalini

FINASUCRE S.A.

Avenue Herrmann Debroux 40
Brussels, 1160, Belgium
Tel.: (32) 26611911
Fax: (32) 26720222
E-Mail: info@finasucre.be
Web Site: www.finasucre.com
Year Founded: 1929
Sales Range: $400-449.9 Million
Emp.: 3,000
Fiscal Year-end: 03/31/13

Business Description:
Sugar Refining
S.I.C.: 2062
N.A.I.C.S.: 311314

Personnel:
Paul Lippens *(Pres)*
Olivier Lippens *(Mng Dir)*

Board of Directors:
Guillaume d'Arschot Schoonhoven
Baron De Keuleneer
Claude Lippens
Florence Lippens
Maurice Lippens
Olivier Lippens
Paul Lippens

Subsidiaries:

Galactic S.A. **(1)**
Place d Escanaffles 23
Escanaffles, 7760 Brussels, Belgium (54.85%)
Tel.: (32) 69454921
Fax: (32) 69454926
E-Mail: info@lactic.com
Web Site: www.lactic.com
Emp.: 145
Beet Sugar Mfr
S.I.C.: 2063
N.A.I.C.S.: 311313
Jean-Christophe Bogaert *(Mgr-Sls)*
Olivier Lippens *(Mng Dir)*

U.S. Subsidiary:

Galactic Inc **(1)**
2700 W Silver Spring Dr
Milwaukee, WI 53209
Tel.: (414) 462-1990
Fax: (414) 462-2070
E-Mail: galactic-us@lactic.com
Web Site: www.lactic.com
Wheat Farming
S.I.C.: 0111
N.A.I.C.S.: 111140

Iscal Sugar S.A./N.V. **(1)**
Chaussee de la Sucrerie 1
Fontenoy, 7643 Liege, Belgium (100%)
Tel.: (32) 69871711
Fax: (32) 69444416
Web Site: www.iscalsugar.com
Emp.: 100
Beet Sugar Mfr
S.I.C.: 2063
N.A.I.C.S.: 311313

Non-U.S. Subsidiaries:

Bundaberg Foundry Engineers Ltd **(1)**
Gavin St
4670 Bundaberg, Queensland, Australia (100%)
Tel.: (61) 741508700
Fax: (61) 741508711
E-Mail: results@bundabergwalkers.com.au
Web Site: www.bfel.com.au
Emp.: 100
Special Trade Contractors
S.I.C.: 1542
N.A.I.C.S.: 236220
Ray Hatt *(Mng Dir)*

Bundaberg Sugar Company **(1)**
21 Magura St
Enoggera, QLD, 4051, Australia (100%)
Tel.: (61) 733358300
Fax: (61) 733358311
E-Mail: enquiries@bundysugar.com.au
Web Site: www.bundysugar.com.au
Emp.: 60
S.I.C.: 2061
N.A.I.C.S.: 311314
Jiff Mitchell *(Mng Dir)*

Bundaberg Sugar Group Ltd **(1)**
4 Gavin St
4608 Bundaberg, QLD, Australia (100%)
Tel.: (61) 738358400
Fax: (61) 738358411
Web Site: www.bundysugar.com.au
Investment Advice
S.I.C.: 6282
N.A.I.C.S.: 523930
Gary Longden *(Office Mgr)*

Finasucre Holdings (Australia) Pty Ltd **(1)**
21 Magura St
Enoggera, Queensland, Australia (100%)
Tel.: (61) 733358300
Holding Company
S.I.C.: 6719
N.A.I.C.S.: 551112

Finasucre Investments (Australia) Pty Ltd **(1)**
21 Magura Street
4051 Enoggera, Queensland, Australia (100%)
Tel.: (61) 733358300
Fax: (61) 733358311
Holding Company
S.I.C.: 6719
N.A.I.C.S.: 551112

Northern Land Holdings Ltd **(1)**
4 Gavin St
Bundaberg, QLD, 4670, Australia (100%)
Tel.: (61) 741508500
Fax: (61) 741508522
E-Mail: bbsg@bundysugar.com.au
Web Site: www.bundysugar.com.au
Cane Sugar Refining
S.I.C.: 2061
N.A.I.C.S.: 311314
Richard Peterson *(Gen Mgr-Fin & Acctg)*

Queensland Urban Projects Pty Ltd **(1)**
21 Magura St
Enoggera, Queensland, Australia (100%)
Tel.: (61) 741508502
Fax: (61) 738358411
E-Mail: bbsg@bundysugar.com.au
Investment Advice
S.I.C.: 6282
N.A.I.C.S.: 523930

Non-U.S. Joint Venture:

BBCA & Galactic Lactic Acid Co. Ltd. (1)
73 Daqing Rd
Bengbu, 233010 Suzhou, Anhui, China
Tel.: (86) 5522081288
Fax: (86) 5522081299
E-Mail: information@bglactic.com
Web Site: www.bglactic.com
Basic Inorganic Chemical Mfr
S.I.C.: 2819
N.A.I.C.S.: 325180
Jean-Christophe Bogaert *(Gen Mgr)*

FINATIS SA

83 rue du Faubourg Saint-Honore
75008 Paris, France
Tel.: (33) 144711400
Fax: (33) 114471450
Web Site: www.finatis.fr
FNTS—(EUR)
Sales Range: $25-49.9 Billion
Emp.: 152,964

Business Description:
Holding Company; Real Estate Management & Retail Services
S.I.C.: 6719
N.A.I.C.S.: 551112

Personnel:
Jean-Charles H. Naouri *(Chm)*
Didier Levec *(Gen Sec)*

Board of Directors:
Jean-Charles H. Naouri
Pierre Feraud
Jean-Marie Grisard
Didier Levec

Subsidiary:

Fonciere Euris (1)
83 Rue du Faubourg Sainte Honore
Paris, 75008, France (89.2%)
Tel.: (33) 0144711400
Fax: (33) 144711450
E-Mail: contact-fe@euris.fr
Web Site: www.fonciere-euris.fr
Rev.: $29,666,199,552
Emp.: 124,226
Supermarkets, Hypermarkets & Other Retail Distribution Outlets Operator; Land & Real Estate Management Services
S.I.C.: 6531
N.A.I.C.S.: 531390
Michel Savart *(Pres & Dir Gen)*

Subsidiary:

Rallye S.A. (2)
83 Rue Du Faubourg Saint Honore
75008 Paris, France FR
Tel.: (33) 1447113 73
Fax: (33) 144711370
E-Mail: info@rallye.fr
Web Site: www.rallye.fr
RAL—(EUR)
Rev.: $57,431,650,710
Assets: $60,570,919,150
Liabilities: $42,109,543,770
Net Worth: $18,461,375,380
Earnings: $1,698,866,540
Emp.: 300,048
Fiscal Year-end: 12/31/12
Holding Company; Food & Specialized Sporting Goods Retailer
S.I.C.: 6719
N.A.I.C.S.: 551112
Jean-Charles H. Naouri *(Chm)*
Didier Carlier *(CEO & Mng Dir)*
Franck Hattab *(Deputy CEO)*
Philippe Charrier *(Mng Dir)*
Jean Chodron de Courcel *(Mng Dir)*
Jacques Dumas *(Mng Dir)*
Jean-Marie Grisard *(Mng Dir)*
Didier Leveque *(Mng Dir)*
Odile Muracciole *(Mng Dir)*
Gabriel Naouri *(Mng Dir)*
Christian Paillot *(Mng Dir)*

Subsidiaries:

Casino Guichard-Perrachon SA (3)
1 Esplanade de France
BP 306
42008 Saint Etienne, Cedex 2, France
Tel.: (33) 477453131
Fax: (33) 477453838
Web Site: www.groupe-casino.fr
CO—(EUR OTC)
Sls.: $56,500,101,070
Assets: $57,633,576,210
Liabilities: $37,170,446,040
Net Worth: $20,463,130,170
Earnings: $2,063,678,610
Emp.: 295,840
Fiscal Year-end: 12/31/12
Hypermarkets, Supermarkets, Restaurants, Convenience Stores & Discount Stores Owner & Operator
S.I.C.: 5311
N.A.I.C.S.: 445110
Jean-Charles Naouri *(Chm & CEO)*
Antoine Giscard d'Estaing *(CFO & Dir-Corp Fin)*
Yves Bernard Braibant *(Chm/CEO-Big C Thailand)*
Herve Daudin *(Chm-EMCD & Dir-Mdsg & Supply Chain)*
Carlos Mario Giraldo Moreno *(Chm-Exito Group)*

Subsidiaries:

ACOS SNC (4)
1 Esplanade de France
BP 306
42008 Saint Etienne, Cedex 2, France
Tel.: (33) 477453131
Fax: (33) 477453838
E-Mail: contact@acos.fr
Web Site: www.acos.fr
Emp.: 40
IT Support Services
S.I.C.: 7373
N.A.I.C.S.: 541512

Casino Cafeteria SAS (4)
24 Rue De La Montat
42008 Saint Etienne, France
Tel.: (33) 477453228
Fax: (33) 477454420
E-Mail:
Web Site: www.casino-cafeteria.fr
Self Service Restaurants
S.I.C.: 5812
N.A.I.C.S.: 722513

Casino Vacances SNC (4)
67 Rue De Richelieu
75002 Paris, France
Tel.: (33) 53454300
Fax: (33) 53454301
E-Mail: webmaster@cmesvacances.fr
Web Site: www.casinovacances.fr
Emp.: 20
Travel Agent & Operator
S.I.C.: 4724
N.A.I.C.S.: 561510

Easydis (4)
Immeuble Le Diamant
Rond Pt Auguste Colonna, 42160 Andrezieux-Boutheon, Andrezieux Boutheon, France
Tel.: (33) 477020400
Fax: (33) 477020499
E-Mail: bbruyas@easydis.com
Web Site: www.easydis.com
Emp.: 50
General Warehousing & Storage
S.I.C.: 4225
N.A.I.C.S.: 493110
Auzannoru Lame *(Mng Dir)*

Imagica (4)
1 Estnanade De Srnance
42008 Saint Etienne, France
Tel.: (33) 477453131
Fax: (33) 477453838
Emp.: 2,000
Photographic Development Services
S.I.C.: 7384
N.A.I.C.S.: 812921
Jean Charles Naouri *(Mng Dir)*

Monoprix S.A. (4)
204 Rond Pt Du Pont De Sevres
Tour Vendome, 92216 Boulogne-Billancourt, France FR
Tel.: (33) 155208809 (100%)
Fax: (33) 155208801
Web Site: www.monoprix.fr
Emp.: 18,000
Supermarket Retailer
S.I.C.: 5399
N.A.I.C.S.: 452990
Jean-Charles Naouri *(Chm & CEO)*
Stephane Maquaire *(Deputy CEO)*

Non-U.S. Subsidiary:

Big C Supercenter Public Company Limited (4)
97/11 6th Floor Ratchadamri Road Lumpini Pathumwan
Bangkok, 10330, Thailand (63.2%)
Tel.: (66) 26550666
Fax: (66) 26555801
Web Site: www.bigc.co.th
BIGC—(OTC THA)
Sls.: $3,715,065,680
Assets: $3,119,613,601
Liabilities: $2,063,189,121
Net Worth: $1,056,424,480
Earnings: $201,861,090
Emp.: 27,000
Fiscal Year-end: 12/31/12
Food & Non-Food Products Retailer
S.I.C.: 5411
N.A.I.C.S.: 452910
Akani Thapthimthong *(Chm)*
Yves Bernard Braibant *(Pres & CEO)*
Rumpa Kumhomreun *(CFO, Sec & VP-Acctg & Fin)*
Praphan Eamrungroj *(Exec VP-Properties)*
Arnaud Dupont *(Sr VP-Comml)*
Ian Craig Longden *(Sr VP-Small Store Format)*
Thomas Mason Nielsen *(Sr VP-HR)*

Groupe GO Sport SA (3)
17 Avenue de la Falaise
38360 Sassenage, France
Tel.: (33) 476282020
Web Site: www.groupegosport.com
GSP—(EUR)
Sales Range: $50-74.9 Million
Emp.: 5,029
Sporting Goods & Leisure Wear Distr
S.I.C.: 5091
N.A.I.C.S.: 423910
Pierre Letzelter *(Chm)*
Francois Neukirch *(Mng Dir)*

FINAVENTURE CAPITAL LIMITED

Aanjaneya House No 34 Postal Colony
Chembur, Mumbai, 400071, India
Tel.: (91) 22 25264500
Fax: (91) 22 25223251
E-Mail: info@finacaps.com
Web Site: www.finacaps.com
Year Founded: 1985
512219—(BOM)
Rev.: $5,894,632
Assets: $21,975,149
Liabilities: $10,202,542
Net Worth: $11,772,607
Earnings: $5,711,422
Emp.: 3
Fiscal Year-end: 03/31/13

Business Description:
Financial Management Services
S.I.C.: 6719
N.A.I.C.S.: 551112

Personnel:
Kannan Vishwanath *(Vice Chm & Mng Dir)*
Ruchika Prithvi *(Compliance Officer & Sec)*

Board of Directors:
Ullooppee S. Badade
Balkrishna R. Parab
Giridhar G. Pulleti
Kannan Vishwanath

Transfer Agent:
Link Intime India Pvt. Ltd
C-13 Pannalal Silk Mills Compound LBS Marg
Bhandup (West)
Mumbai, India

FINAVERA WIND ENERGY INC.

1800-570 Granville St
Vancouver, BC, Canada V6C 3P1
Tel.: (604) 288-9051
Fax: (604) 288-9051
E-Mail: info@finavera.com
Web Site: www.finavera.com
Year Founded: 2003
FVR—(TSXV)
Emp.: 12

Business Description:
Power Generation Services
S.I.C.: 4939
N.A.I.C.S.: 221118

Personnel:
Jason Bak *(Founder & CEO)*
Hein Poulus *(Chm)*
Peter Leighton *(Pres & COO)*
Jon S. Lever *(CFO)*
Myke Clark *(Sr VP-Bus Dev)*
Michael Thompson *(Sr VP-Wind Energy)*

Board of Directors:
Hein Poulus
Thomas Anderson
Jason Bak
David Lamont

Transfer Agent:
Computershare Investor Services Inc.
3rd Floor 510 Burrard St
V6C 3B9 Vancouver, BC, Canada

FINBAR GROUP LIMITED

Level 6 181 Adelaide Terrace
Perth, WA, 6004, Australia
Mailing Address:
PO Box 3380
Perth, WA, 6892, Australia
Tel.: (61) 862113300
Fax: (61) 892218833
E-Mail: info@finbar.com.au
Web Site: www.finbar.com.au
FRI—(ASX)
Rev.: $129,408,548
Assets: $413,732,594
Liabilities: $199,264,811
Net Worth: $214,467,784
Earnings: $32,885,496
Emp.: 17
Fiscal Year-end: 06/30/13

Business Description:
Property Investment & Development Services
S.I.C.: 6531
N.A.I.C.S.: 531390

Personnel:
John Chan *(Chm)*
Darren John Pateman *(Mng Dir)*
Edward Guy Bank *(CFO)*
Ronald Chan *(COO)*
Anthony David Hewett *(Sec)*

Board of Directors:
John Chan
John Boon Heng Cheak
Kee Kong Loh
Darren John Pateman
Lee Verios

FINBOND GROUP LIMITED

Bank Forum Building 337 Veale street
Brooklyn, Pretoria, 0181, South Africa
Tel.: (27) 12 460 7288
Fax: (27) 12 460 7285
Web Site: www.finbondlimited.co.za
Year Founded: 2001
FGL—(JSE)
Int. Income: $5,858,770
Assets: $62,135,520
Liabilities: $28,074,453
Net Worth: $34,061,067
Earnings: $2,287,480
Emp.: 487
Fiscal Year-end: 02/28/13

Business Description:
Financial Services
S.I.C.: 6211
N.A.I.C.S.: 523999

Finbond Group Limited—(Continued)

Personnel:
Willem van Aardt *(CEO)*
Gary Thomas Sayers *(CFO)*
Hendrina Johanna Wilken *(Chief Compliance Officer)*
Danie Cornelius Pentz *(Chief Risk Officer)*
C. Dora du Plessis *(Sec)*
Board of Directors:
Malesela David Clement Motlatla
Robert Emslie
Neville John Melville
Jasper Jurgens Noeth
Danie Cornelius Pentz
Gary Thomas Sayers
Willem van Aardt
Hendrina Johanna Wilken
Rosetta Ntambose Xaba

FINCANTIERI - CANTIERI NAVALI ITALIANI S.P.A.

(d/b/a Fincantieri S.p.A.)
Via Genova 1
IT-34121 Trieste, Italy
Tel.: (39) 0403193111
Fax: (39) 0403192305
E-Mail: info@fincantieri.it
Web Site: www.fincantieri.it
Year Founded: 1959
Rev.: $3,097,603,132
Assets: $3,871,722,229
Liabilities: $2,584,060,816
Net Worth: $1,287,661,413
Earnings: $20,815,827
Emp.: 10,240
Fiscal Year-end: 12/31/12
Business Description:
Ship Building, Repair & Maintenance Services; Marine & Industrial Diesel Engine Mfr
S.I.C.: 3731
N.A.I.C.S.: 336611
Personnel:
Vincenzo Petrone *(Chm)*
Giuseppe Bono *(CEO)*
Enrico Buschi *(COO)*
Maurizio Castaldo *(Sec)*
Gabriele Cocco *(Sr VP-Merchants Ships)*
Alberto Maestrini *(Sr VP-Naval Vessels)*
Giorgio Rizzo *(Sr VP-Ship Repairs & Conversions)*
Giovanni Romano *(Sr VP-Mega Yachts)*
Board of Directors:
Vincenzo Petrone
Giuseppe Bono
Andrea Mangoni
Giovanni Masini
Anna Molinotti

Subsidiaries:

Centro per gli Studi di Tecnica Navale Cetena S.p.A. **(1)**
Via Ippolito d'Aste 5
IT-16121 Genoa, Italy IT
Tel.: (39) 0105995460 (71.1%)
Fax: (39) 0105995790
E-Mail: mail@cetena.it
Web Site: www.cetena.it
Emp.: 75
Naval & Maritime Research & Consultancy Services
S.I.C.: 8731
N.A.I.C.S.: 541712
Marco Schembri *(Head-Res Projects Funding & Coordination Dept)*

Isotta Fraschini Motori S.p.A. **(1)**
Viale F de Blasio
ZI, IT-70123 Bari, Italy IT
Tel.: (39) 080 534 5000 (100%)
Fax: (39) 080 531 1009
Web Site: www.isottafraschini.it
Marine & Industrial Diesel Engine Designer, Mfr & Distr
S.I.C.: 3519
N.A.I.C.S.: 333618
M. Molinari *(Pres)*

Joint Venture:

Orizzonte Sistemi Navali S.p.A. **(1)**
Viale Brigata Bisagno 45R
IT-16129 Genoa, Italy IT
Tel.: (39) 0109817535
Fax: (39) 0109817989
E-Mail: marketing@orizzontesn.it
Web Site: www.orizzontesn.it
Contract Naval Vessel Design & Engineering Services; Owned 51% by Fincantieri - Cantieri Navali Italiani S.p.A. & 49% by Finmeccanica S.p.A.
S.I.C.: 7389
N.A.I.C.S.: 541490

U.S. Subsidiary:

Fincantieri Marine Systems North America Inc. **(1)**
800-C Principal Ct
Chesapeake, VA 23320 DE
Tel.: (757) 548-6000 (100%)
Fax: (757) 548-6012
E-Mail: corporate@fincantierimarinesystems.com
Web Site: www.fincantierimarinesystems.com
Emp.: 10
Integrated Marine Vessel Systems & Components Whslr & Support Services
Import Export
S.I.C.: 5088
N.A.I.C.S.: 423860
Upi Kamal *(CEO)*

U.S. Holding:

Fincantieri Marine Group Holdings Inc. **(1)**
1600 Ely St
Marinette, WI 54143-2434 DE
Tel.: (715) 735-9341
Fax: (715) 735-4178
Web Site: www.usfincantieri.com
Holding Company; Owned 87.34% by Fincantieri - Cantieri Navali Italiani S.p.A. & 12.66% by Lockheed Martin Corporation
S.I.C.: 6719
N.A.I.C.S.: 551112
Pier Francesco Ragni *(Pres)*

Holding:

Fincantieri Marine Group, LLC **(2)**
1600 Ely St
Marinette, WI 54143-2434 NV
Tel.: (715) 735-9341 (100%)
Fax: (715) 735-4774
Web Site: www.fincantierimarinegroup.com
Sales Range: $300-349.9 Million
Emp.: 1,500
Ship Building & Repairing Services
Import Export
S.I.C.: 3731
N.A.I.C.S.: 336611
Richard McCreary *(Pres & CEO)*

Subsidiaries:

Bay Shipbuilding Co. **(3)**
605 N 3rd Ave
Sturgeon Bay, WI 54235 (100%)
Mailing Address:
PO Box 830
Sturgeon Bay, WI 54235-0830
Tel.: (920) 743-5524
Fax: (920) 743-2371
Web Site: www.fincantierimarinegroup.com
Emp.: 675
Ship Building & Repairing Services
S.I.C.: 3731
N.A.I.C.S.: 336611
Gene Caldwell *(VP & Gen Mgr)*

Cleveland Ship Repair Company **(3)**
1847 Columbus Rd
Cleveland, OH 44113 (100%)
Tel.: (216) 621-9111
Fax: (216) 621-4885
Web Site: www.fincantierimarinegroup.com
Emp.: 8
Ship Repairing Services
S.I.C.: 3731
N.A.I.C.S.: 336611
Kyle Fries *(Gen Mgr)*

Marinette Marine Corporation **(3)**
1600 Ely St
Marinette, WI 54143-2434 WI
Tel.: (715) 735-9341 (100%)
Fax: (715) 735-4774
Web Site: www.marinettemarine.com
Emp.: 950
Ship Building & Repairing Services
Export
S.I.C.: 3731
N.A.I.C.S.: 336611
Charles Goddard *(Pres & CEO)*

Non-U.S. Subsidiary:

Vard Holdings Limited **(1)**
(Formerly STX OSV Holdings Limited)
Molovegen 6
6004 Alesund, Norway SG
Mailing Address: (55.63%)
PO Box 76
NO-6001 Alesund, Norway
Tel.: (47) 7021 0600
Fax: (47) 2350 2340
E-Mail: mail@vard.com
Web Site: www.vard.com
MS7—(SES)
Rev.: $2,014,237,710
Assets: $2,328,979,320
Liabilities: $1,744,924,590
Net Worth: $584,054,730
Earnings: $160,900,110
Emp.: 9,217
Fiscal Year-end: 12/31/12
Ship Designer & Builder
S.I.C.: 3731
N.A.I.C.S.: 336611
Giuseppe Bono *(Chm)*
Roy Reite *(Pres & CEO)*
Jan Ivar Nielsen *(CFO & Exec VP)*
Magne O. Bakke *(COO & Exec VP)*
Elizabeth Krishnan *(Sec)*

Subsidiary:

Vard Group AS **(2)**
Molovegen 6
NO-6004 Alesund, Norway
Mailing Address:
PO Box 76
NO-6001 Alesund, Norway
Tel.: (47) 7021 0600
E-Mail: mail@vard.com
Web Site: www.vard.com
Holding Company
S.I.C.: 6719
N.A.I.C.S.: 551112

Subsidiaries:

Seaonics AS **(3)**
Nedre Strandgt 29
NO-6004 Alesund, Norway
Tel.: (47) 7139 1600
E-Mail: mail@seaonics.com
Subsea Construction & Deck Handling Services
S.I.C.: 1629
N.A.I.C.S.: 237990

Vard Accommodation AS **(3)**
Johangarden Naeringspark
NO-6264 Tennfjord, Norway
Tel.: (47) 7021 0600
E-Mail: accommodation@vard.com
Marine Vessel Heating, Air Conditioning & Insulation Services
S.I.C.: 3585
N.A.I.C.S.: 333415

Non-U.S. Subsidiary:

Vard Accommodtion Tulcea SRL **(4)**
22 Ing Dumitru Ivanov Street
RO-820 242 Tulcea, Romania
Tel.: (40) 240 534 542
E-Mail: accommodation.tulcea@vard.com
Marine Vessel Heating, Air Conditioning & Insulation Services
S.I.C.: 3585
N.A.I.C.S.: 333415

Vard Brevik Holding AS **(3)**
Stromtangvn 21
NO-3950 Brevik, Norway
Mailing Address:
PO Box 15
NO-3950 Brevik, Norway
Tel.: (47) 3551 8700
Business Support Services
S.I.C.: 7389
N.A.I.C.S.: 561499

Vard Design AS **(3)**
Brunholmgt 1B
NO-6001 Alesund, Norway
Mailing Address:
PO Box 76
NO-6001 Alesund, Norway
Tel.: (47) 7021 0600
E-Mail: design@vard.com
Design & Engineering Services
S.I.C.: 8711
N.A.I.C.S.: 541330

Subsidiary:

Vard Engineering Brevik AS **(4)**
Stromtangvn 19
NO-3950 Brevik, Norway
Tel.: (47) 3551 8700
Design & Engineering Services
S.I.C.: 8711
N.A.I.C.S.: 541330

Non-U.S. Subsidiary:

Vard Design Liburna Ltd. **(4)**
Fiorella La Guardie
51000 Rijeka, Croatia
Tel.: (385) 51 344 237
E-Mail: design.liburna@vard.com
Design & Engineering Services
S.I.C.: 8711
N.A.I.C.S.: 541330

Vard Electro AS **(3)**
Keiser Wilhelms gt 22
NO-6003 Alesund, Norway
Tel.: (47) 7021 0600
E-Mail: electro@vard.com
Electrical Engineering Services
S.I.C.: 1629
N.A.I.C.S.: 237990

Non-U.S. Subsidiaries:

Vard Electrical Installation and Engineering (India) Private Limited **(4)**
3-B 3rd Floor KG Oxford Business Centre
39/4609 Sreekandath Road
Ravipuram Ernakulam, Kochi, 682 016, India
Tel.: (91) 484 2355 430
Electrical Engineering Services
S.I.C.: 1629
N.A.I.C.S.: 237990

Vard Electro Braila SRL **(4)**
Celuozei Street 1A
RO-810282 Braila, Romania
Tel.: (40) 239 607 336
E-Mail: electro.braila@vard.com
Electrical Engineering Services
S.I.C.: 1629
N.A.I.C.S.: 237990

Vard Electro Brazil Ltda. **(4)**
Rua Jose Figueiredo 5 Centro
24030-055 Niteroi, RJ, Brazil
Tel.: (55) 21 3628 5087
E-Mail: electro.brazil@vard.com
Electrical Engineering Services
S.I.C.: 1629
N.A.I.C.S.: 237990

Vard Electro Tulcea SRL **(4)**
22 Ing Dumitru Ivanov Street
Electrical Section, RO-820242 Tulcea, Romania
Tel.: (40) 240 534 026
E-Mail: electro.tulcea@vard.com
Electrical Engineering Services
S.I.C.: 1629
N.A.I.C.S.: 237990

Vard Grenland Industri AS **(3)**
Havneveien 31
NO-3739 Skien, Norway
Tel.: (47) 3556 9300
Business Support Services
S.I.C.: 7389
N.A.I.C.S.: 561499

Vard Offshore Brevik AS **(3)**
Industrivn 12
NO-3940 Porsgrunn, Norway
Tel.: (47) 3593 2025
E-Mail: offshore.brevik@vard.com
Business Support Services

S.I.C.: 7389
N.A.I.C.S.: 561499

Vard Piping AS (3)
Johangarden Naeringspark
NO-6270 Tennfjord, Norway
Tel.: (47) 7021 0600
E-Mail: piping@vard.com
Pipe Producer & Pipe Installation Services
S.I.C.: 3498
N.A.I.C.S.: 332996

Non-U.S. Subsidiary:

Vard Piping Tulcea SRL (4)
22 ing Dumitru Ivanov Street
RO-820 242 Tulcea, Romania
Tel.: (40) 240 506 234
E-Mail: piping.tulcea@vard.com
Pipe Producer & Pipe Installation Services
S.I.C.: 3498
N.A.I.C.S.: 332996

Non-U.S. Subsidiaries:

Vard Braila SA (3)
Celuozei Street 1A
RO-810282 Braila, Romania
Tel.: (40) 239 607 000
E-Mail: braila@vard.com
Ship Building Services
S.I.C.: 3731
N.A.I.C.S.: 336611

Vard Niteroi SA (3)
Praca Alcides Pereira
1 Parte Ilha da Conceicao, Niteroi, RJ, CEP 24050-350, Brazil
Tel.: (55) 212 7189 90
E-Mail: niteroi@vard.com
Ship Building Services
S.I.C.: 3731
N.A.I.C.S.: 336611

Vard Promar SA (3)
AE Zona Industrial Portuaria ZIP
Ilha de Tatuoca SN, Ipojuca, PE, 55590-000, Brazil
Tel.: (55) 81 3561 2500
E-Mail: promar@vard.com
Ship Building Services
S.I.C.: 3731
N.A.I.C.S.: 336611

Vard Singapore Pte. Ltd. (3)
3 Temasek Avenue #20-07 Centennial Tower
Singapore, 039190, Singapore
Tel.: (65) 6836 0813
E-Mail: singapore@vard.com
Business Support Services
S.I.C.: 7389
N.A.I.C.S.: 561499

Vard Tulcea SA (3)
22 Ing Dumitru Ivanov Street
RO-820242 Tulcea, Romania
Tel.: (40) 240 534 918
E-Mail: tulcea@vard.com
Ship Building Services
S.I.C.: 3731
N.A.I.C.S.: 336611

Vard Vung Tau Ltd. (3)
No 6 Dong Xuyen IP Rach Dua Ward
VN 76000 Vung Tau, Vietnam
Tel.: (84) 64 3615 600
E-Mail: vungtau@vard.com
Ship Building Services
S.I.C.: 3731
N.A.I.C.S.: 336611

FINCAS ANZIZU SL

Gran Via 631-1 Fl
08010 Barcelona, Spain
Tel.: (34) 934143844
Fax: (34) 932702841
E-Mail: fincasanzizu@fincasanzizu.com
Web Site: www.fincasanzizu.com
Business Description:
Property Management & Consultancy Services
S.I.C.: 9199
N.A.I.C.S.: 921190

FINDEL PLC

2 Gregory Street
Hyde, Cheshire, SK14 4TH, United Kingdom
Tel.: (44) 161 303 3465
Telex: 517669
Fax: (44) 1943864986
E-Mail: enquiries@findel.co.uk
Web Site: www.findel.co.uk
Year Founded: 1955
FDL—(LSE)
Rev.: $775,799,365
Assets: $738,878,723
Liabilities: $580,205,877
Net Worth: $158,672,846
Earnings: $5,974,454
Emp.: 2,805
Fiscal Year-end: 03/29/13
Business Description:
Greeting Cards, Gift Wrap, Crepe Paper, Stationery; Catalogue Sales; Retail Gift Shops
S.I.C.: 5947
N.A.I.C.S.: 453220
Personnel:
David A. Sugden *(Chm)*
Roger W. J. Siddle *(CEO)*
M. Ashcroft *(Sec)*
Board of Directors:
David A. Sugden
Francois Coumau
William Grimsey
Tim J. Kowalski
Philip B. Maudsley
Laurel C. Powers-Freeling
Roger W. J. Siddle
Eric F. Tracey
Legal Counsel:
Hammond Suddards
Manchester, United Kingdom

Subsidiaries:

Confetti Network Limited (1)
80-81 Tottenham Court Road
London, W1T 4TE, United Kingdom
Tel.: (44) 2072917620
Fax: (44) 2072917601
Web Site: www.confetti.co.uk
Emp.: 130
Computer Related Services
S.I.C.: 7379
N.A.I.C.S.: 541519
David Wilson *(Mng Dir)*

Express Gifts Limited (1)
Church Bridge House Henry Street Church
Accrington, Lancashire, BB5 4EE, United Kingdom
Tel.: (44) 1943864686
Fax: (44) 01254352020
Emp.: 300
Stationery & Supplies Merchant Whslr
S.I.C.: 5112
N.A.I.C.S.: 424120
Mark Whitaker *(Gen Mgr & Dir-Fin)*

Findel Education Limited (1)
2 Gregory St
Hyde, Cheshire, SK14 4HR, United Kingdom (100%)
Tel.: (44) 1613672000
Fax: (44) 8003672009
E-Mail: info@findel-education.co.uk
Web Site: www.findel-education.co.uk
Emp.: 500
Stationery & Office Supplies Merchant Whslr
S.I.C.: 5112
N.A.I.C.S.: 424120
Fan Walsh *(Mng Dir)*

I Want One of Those Ltd. (1)
PO Box 26953
London, SE21 8WL, United Kingdom
Tel.: (44) 8704607812
Fax: (44) 8702202147
Web Site: www.iwantoneofthose.com
Sales Range: $10-24.9 Million
Online Retailer
S.I.C.: 5961
N.A.I.C.S.: 454111
Tim Booth *(Founder & Dir-Creative)*
Richard Wainright-Lee *(Mng Dir)*

Kitbag Limited (1)
P O Box 210
Manchester, M24 1YN, United Kingdom
Tel.: (44) 8707878827
E-Mail: info@kitbag.com
Web Site: www.kitbag.com
Sales Range: $25-49.9 Million
Online Sports Equipment Retailer
S.I.C.: 5961
N.A.I.C.S.: 454111
Andy Anson *(CEO)*

Kleeneze Limited (1)
Express House Clayton Business Park
Clayton Le Moors
Accrington, Lancashire, BB5 5JY, United Kingdom
Tel.: (44) 844 848 5000
Fax: (44) 1254303102
E-Mail: service.centre@kleeneze.co.uk
Web Site: www.kleeneze.co.uk
Home Shopping Services
S.I.C.: 7389
N.A.I.C.S.: 561990
Jamie Stewart *(Mng Dir)*

Non-U.S. Subsidiary:

Fine Art Developments (Far East) Limited (1)
Rm 1102 11th Floor Two Harbourfront
22 Tak Fung St, Kowloon, China (Hong Kong)
Tel.: (852) 21760088
Fax: (852) 21760099
E-Mail: info@fadfe.com
Web Site: www.fadfe.com
Emp.: 36
Nondurable Goods Merchant Whslr
S.I.C.: 5199
N.A.I.C.S.: 424990
Anthony Pakeman *(Mng Dir)*

FINDERS RESOURCES LIMITED

Suite 901 Level 9 60 Pitt Street
Sydney, NSW, 2000, Australia
Tel.: (61) 280841812
Fax: (61) 280682540
E-Mail: info@findersresources.com
Web Site: www.findersresources.com
FND—(ASX)
Rev.: $153,189
Assets: $37,225,896
Liabilities: $16,586,064
Net Worth: $20,639,833
Earnings: ($20,633,580)
Emp.: 231
Fiscal Year-end: 12/31/12
Business Description:
Copper Producer
S.I.C.: 1021
N.A.I.C.S.: 212234
Personnel:
Christopher Ben Farmer *(Mng Dir)*
James Hamilton Wentworth *(CFO & Sec)*
Board of Directors:
Russell John Fountain
Stephen Ross de Belle
Christopher Ben Farmer
Stephen John Lonergan
Thomas Quinn Roussel
James Hamilton Wentworth

Non-U.S. Subsidiary:

P.T. Batutua Tembaga Raya (1)
Jl Jend Gatot Subroto Kav 32-34 Patra Ofc Tower Lt 9 Ruang 93
Kuningan Timur Setia Budi, Jakarta, 12950, Indonesia
Tel.: (62) 2152900051
Fax: (62) 2152900052
E-Mail: btrjkt@batutua.co.id
Web Site: www.batutua.co.id
Emp.: 20
Metal Mining & Exploration Services
S.I.C.: 1081
N.A.I.C.S.: 213114
Christopher Farmer *(Mng Dir)*

FINDOS INVESTOR GMBH

Gisela strasse 12
D-80802 Munich, Germany
Tel.: (49) 8920000950
Fax: (49) 89200009595
E-Mail: findos@findos.eu
Web Site: www.findos.eu
Emp.: 5
Business Description:
Private Equity Firm
S.I.C.: 6211
N.A.I.C.S.: 523999
Personnel:
Hans H. Freudenberg *(Founder & Partner)*
Olaf U. Rogowski *(Founder & Partner)*
Wolfgang Ziegler *(Founder & Partner)*

Holding:

Maier Sports GmbH & Co. KG (1)
Nurtinger Strasse 27
D 73257 Kongen, Germany
Tel.: (49) 7024 8000 0
Fax: (49) 7024 8000 29
E-Mail: info@maier-sports.de
Web Site: www.maier-sports.de
Sales Range: $25-49.9 Million
Outdoor Apparel Mfr
S.I.C.: 3949
N.A.I.C.S.: 339920
Gerhard Meier *(Mng Dir)*

FINE FOODS LIMITED

New Market City Complex Level-6
44/1 Rahim Square Newmarket
Dhaka, Bangladesh
Tel.: (880) 2 912269
E-Mail: finefoodsltd@live.com
Web Site: www.finefoodsbd.com
FINEFOODS—(DHA)
Business Description:
Fish Production & Whslr
S.I.C.: 5146
N.A.I.C.S.: 424460
Personnel:
Sujit Saha *(Chm)*
Mohammad Shaheen Qurashi *(Mng Dir)*
Mohammad Sohel Hossain *(Sec)*
Board of Directors:
Sujit Saha
Mohammad Alimul Hassan
Mohammad Zakir Hossain
Mohammad Angur Khan
Mohammad Saleh Ahmed Monsur
Mohammad Shaheen Qurashi

FINE-LINE CIRCUITS LIMITED

145 SDF-V SEEPZ-SEZ
Andheri E, Mumbai, 400096, India
Tel.: (91) 22 28290244
Fax: (91) 22 28292554
E-Mail: fineline@vsnl.com
Web Site: www.finelineindia.com
517264—(BOM)
Rev.: $4,710,005
Assets: $2,417,311
Liabilities: $1,210,036
Net Worth: $1,207,275
Earnings: $14,382
Emp.: 140
Fiscal Year-end: 03/31/13
Business Description:
Printed Circuit Board Mfr
S.I.C.: 3672
N.A.I.C.S.: 334412
Personnel:
Bhagwandas T. Doshi *(Chm)*
Abhay B. Doshi *(Mng Dir)*
Prema Radhakrishnan *(Compliance Officer)*
Board of Directors:
Bhagwandas T. Doshi
Abhay B. Doshi
Gautam B. Doshi
Rajiv B. Doshi
Rajendra V. Gandhi
Vijay A. Kumbhani
U. Nimmagadda

Fine-Line Circuits Limited—(Continued)

R. M. Premkumar
Apurva R. Shah
Juzer Vasi

Transfer Agent:
Universal Capital Securities Pvt. Ltd.
21 Shakil Niwas Mahakali Caves Road Opp
Satya Saibaba Temple Andheri E
Mumbai, India

FINE SINTER CO., LTD.

1189-11 Nishinohora Akechi-cho
Kasugai, Aichi, 480-0303, Japan
Tel.: (81) 568 88 4355
Fax: (81) 568 88 4321
Web Site: www.fine-sinter.com
Year Founded: 1950
5994—(TKS)
Emp.: 1,088

Business Description:
Powder Metallurgy Product Mfr
S.I.C.: 3499
N.A.I.C.S.: 332117

Personnel:
Yoichi Inoue *(Pres)*
Yoshito Yonekawa *(Sr Mng Dir)*

Board of Directors:
Kenya Horaguchi
Yoichi Inoue
Kozo Nakamori
Takekoto Nishikawa
Shigeru Satake
Masanori Sugiyama
Tetsuhiko Suzuki
Eizi Takahashi
Keisuke Takimura
Yoshito Yonekawa

Subsidiaries:

Fine Sinter Sanshin Co., Ltd. **(1)**
442-1 Tomori Kawajimamachi
Hiki, Saitama, Japan
Tel.: (81) 49 297 1266
Fax: (81) 49 297 1204
Powder Metallurgy Product Mfr
S.I.C.: 3499
N.A.I.C.S.: 332117

Fine Sinter Tohoku Co., Ltd. **(1)**
65 Matsunagane Iwayado
Esashi-ku, Oshu, Iwate, Japan
Tel.: (81) 197 35 7171
Fax: (81) 197 35 7176
Powder Metallurgy Product Mfr
S.I.C.: 3499
N.A.I.C.S.: 332117

Non-U.S. Subsidiaries:

Precision Sintered Products (Wuxi) Co., Ltd. **(1)**
No 86 Xinmei Road New District
Wuxi, Jiangsu, 214028, China
Tel.: (86) 510 8532 2101
Fax: (86) 510 8532 2312
Powder Metallurgy Product Mfr
S.I.C.: 3499
N.A.I.C.S.: 332117

PT. Fine Sinter Indonesia **(1)**
Kawasan Industri Mitra Karawang Jl Mitra
Raya II Blok E No 6
Desa Parungmulya Kec Ciampel,
Karawang, 41361, Indonesia
Tel.: (62) 26 7863 1720
Fax: (62) 26 7863 1716
Powder Metallurgy Product Mfr
S.I.C.: 3499
N.A.I.C.S.: 332117

Thai Fine Sinter Co., Ltd. **(1)**
Easter Seaboard Industrial Estate Rayong
32 Moo
4 T Pluak-Daeng A Pluak Daeng, Rayong,
21140, Thailand
Tel.: (66) 38 954 383
Fax: (66) 38 954 382
Powder Metallurgy Product Mfr
S.I.C.: 3499
N.A.I.C.S.: 332117

FINEOS CORP. LTD.

Pembroke House 8-10 Lower
Pembroke Street
Dublin, 2, Ireland
Tel.: (353) 16399700
Fax: (353) 16399701
E-Mail: info@fineos.com
Web Site: www.fineos.com
Year Founded: 1993
Rev.: $48,300,000
Emp.: 250

Business Description:
Software Development Services
S.I.C.: 7371
N.A.I.C.S.: 541511

Personnel:
Michael Kelly *(CEO)*
Tom Wall *(CFO)*
Dianne H. Parker *(CMO)*
Jonathan Boylan *(CTO)*
Ian Lynagh *(Exec VP-Sls)*

FINEOTEX CHEMICAL LTD.

42 & 43 Manorama Chambers SV Rd
Bandra (West), Mumbai, 400 050,
India
Tel.: (91) 2226559174
Fax: (91) 2226559178
E-Mail: info@fineotex.com
Web Site: www.fineotex.com
Year Founded: 1979
FCL—(BOM)
Emp.: 40

Business Description:
Chemical Mfr
S.I.C.: 2899
N.A.I.C.S.: 325998

Personnel:
Surendra Tibrewala *(Chm)*

Board of Directors:
Surendra Tibrewala
Navin Mittal

FINERS STEPHENS INNOCENT LLP

179 Great Portland Street
London, W1W 5LS, United Kingdom

FINESSE HOME LIVING

4210 Gateway Boulevard
Edmonton, AB, T6J 5J7, Canada
Tel.: (780) 444-7100
Fax: (780) 490-6731
Toll Free: (866) 346-3773
E-Mail: Sales@FinesseHomeLiving.com
Web Site: www.finessehomeliving.com
Year Founded: 1983
Rev.: $24,605,421
Emp.: 170

Business Description:
Furniture Stores
S.I.C.: 5712
N.A.I.C.S.: 442110

Personnel:
Soraida Shamey *(Controller)*

FINETECHNIX CO., LTD.

8 Deokcheon-Ro
Manan-Gu, Anyang, Gyeonggi-do,
430-817, Korea (South)
Tel.: (82) 31 463 8888
Web Site: www.finetechnix.com
106240—(KRS)

Business Description:
Light Emitting Diode Mfr
S.I.C.: 3674
N.A.I.C.S.: 334413

Personnel:
Jung-hyuk Choi *(CEO)*

FINETEX ENE, INC.

2F 3F 6F FT Building 475-31
Bangbae-dong
Seocho-gu, Seoul, Korea (South)
137-819
Tel.: (82) 2 3482 0853
Web Site: www.enesystem.co.kr
Year Founded: 1997
065160—(KRS)
Sales Range: $50-74.9 Million

Business Description:
Energy Storage System Mfr
S.I.C.: 1629
N.A.I.C.S.: 237130

Personnel:
Jong Chul Park *(CEO)*
Sky Kim *(CFO)*
J. M. Park *(Chief Production Officer)*

FINETOL FINANCNA DRUZBA D.D.

Skofja vas 39
3000 Celje, Slovenia
Tel.: (386) 3 4277410
Fax: (386) 3 4277411
E-Mail: info@finetol.si
Web Site: www.finetol.si
FINR—(LJU)

Business Description:
Financial & Investment Services
S.I.C.: 6211
N.A.I.C.S.: 523999

Personnel:
Zdenko Zanoski *(Chm-Supervisory Bd)*
Franci Strajnar *(CEO)*

Supervisory Board of Directors:
Zdenko Zanoski
Janko Kastelic
Davorin Leskovar

FINEX CAPITAL MANAGEMENT LLP

4th Floor 39 Dover Street
London, W1S 4NN, United Kingdom
Tel.: (44) 20 7663 3300
Fax: (44) 20 7663 3301
E-Mail: info@finxcapital.com
Web Site: www.finxcapital.com

Business Description:
Asset Management & Investment Services
S.I.C.: 6211
N.A.I.C.S.: 523999

Personnel:
Evgeny Kovalishin *(Mng Partner)*
Simon Luhr *(Mng Partner)*
Oleg Yankelev *(Mng Partner)*

FINGEN S.P.A.

Piazza Degli Strozzi 1
50123 Florence, Italy
Tel.: (39) 055266041
Fax: (39) 055260539
E-Mail: centralino_fingen@fingen.it
Web Site: www.fingen.it
Sales Range: $10-24.9 Million
Emp.: 50

Business Description:
Fashion, Retail & Real Estate Services
S.I.C.: 5999
N.A.I.C.S.: 453998

Personnel:
Marcello Fratini *(Chm)*
Corrado Fratini *(Vice Chm)*
Cesar Brogi *(Mng Dir)*

Non-U.S. Subsidiary:

Tie Rack Retail Group Limited **(1)**
Capital Interchange Way
London, Middlesex, TW8 0EX, United Kingdom UK
Tel.: (44) 2082302333 (100%)
Fax: (44) 2082302301
E-Mail: personnel@tie-rack.co.uk
Web Site: www.tie-rack.co.uk
Sls.: $135,724,416
Emp.: 1,500
Mens' & Womens' Ties & Scarves; Store Franchiser; Photographic & Printing Services
Import Export
S.I.C.: 2399
N.A.I.C.S.: 315990
Roy Collin Bishko *(Chm)*

Non-U.S. Subsidiaries:

Tie Rack Australia (Pty.) Ltd. **(2)**
Ste G01 7-9 Merriwa St
2072 Gordon, NSW, Australia
Tel.: (61) 294982266
Mens' & Womens' Ties & Scarves; Store Franchiser; Photographic & Printing Services
S.I.C.: 2399
N.A.I.C.S.: 315990

Tie Rack France SAS **(2)**
15 Place Des Reflets
La Defense, F 92801 Paris, 2,
France (100%)
Tel.: (33) 140909423
Fax: (33) 140909618
Web Site: www.tie-rack.co.uk
Emp.: 145
Mens' & Womens' Ties & Scarves; Store Franchiser; Photographic & Printing Services
S.I.C.: 2399
N.A.I.C.S.: 315990
Eunn Billard *(Mng Dir)*

Tie Rack Limited **(2)**
Ste 501 5F Chunags Tower
30-32 Connaught Road, Central, China
(Hong Kong)
Tel.: (852) 34813119
Fax: (852) 30139859
E-Mail: janice.lau@tie-rack.co.uk
Mens' & Womens' Ties & Scarves; Store Franchiser; Photographic & Printing Services
S.I.C.: 2389
N.A.I.C.S.: 315990
Angela Ho *(Gen Mgr)*

FINGERPRINT CARDS AB

Kungsportsplatsen 2
411 10 Gothenburg, Sweden
Mailing Address:
PO Box 2412
403 16 Gothenburg, Sweden
Tel.: (46) 31607820
Fax: (46) 31137385
Web Site: www.fingerprints.com
FING B—(OMX)
Sls.: $1,590,725
Assets: $17,844,570
Liabilities: $2,068,128
Net Worth: $15,776,442
Earnings: ($5,910,728)
Emp.: 21
Fiscal Year-end: 12/31/12

Business Description:
Fingerprint Cards Developer
S.I.C.: 7382
N.A.I.C.S.: 561621

Personnel:
Mats Svensson *(Chm)*
Johan Carlstrom *(Pres & CEO)*
Jens Reckman *(CFO)*
Jorgen Lantto *(CTO, Exec VP & Head-Strategy & Product Dev)*
Thomas Rex *(Exec VP-Sls & Mktg)*
Pontus Jagemalm *(Sr VP-R&D)*

Board of Directors:
Mats Svensson
Christer Bergman
Urban Fagerstedt
Tord Wingren

FININVEST S.P.A.

Via Paleocapa 3
20121 Milan, Italy
Tel.: (39) 0285411
Fax: (39) 0285414333
Web Site: www.fininvest.it
Year Founded: 1961
Rev.: $6,938,160,180
Earnings: ($383,927,684)
Emp.: 17,215

Fiscal Year-end: 12/31/12
Business Description:
Holding Company
S.I.C.: 6719
N.A.I.C.S.: 551112
Personnel:
Marina Berlusconi *(Chm)*
Pasquale Cannatelli *(CEO)*
Board of Directors:
Marina Berlusconi
Barbara Berlusconi
Pier Silvio Berlusconi
Pasquale Cannatelli
Ubaldo Livolsi
Roberto Poli
Salvatore Sciascia

Holding:

Arnoldo Mondadori Editore S.p.A. **(1)**
via Bianca di Savoia 12
20122 Segrate, Milan, Italy IT
Tel.: (39) 0275421 (50.1%)
Telex: 320457 MONDMI 1
Fax: (39) 0275422302
Web Site: www.mondadori.com
MN—(ITA)
Rev.: $1,906,301,914
Assets: $2,327,142,925
Liabilities: $1,743,158,225
Net Worth: $583,984,700
Earnings: ($222,240,551)
Emp.: 3,703
Fiscal Year-end: 12/31/12
Book, Magazine & Newspaper Publisher, Marketer & Distr
Import Export
S.I.C.: 2721
N.A.I.C.S.: 511120
Marina Berlusconi *(Chm)*
Ernesto Mauri *(CEO)*
Carlo Maria Vismara *(CFO)*
Angelo Sajeva *(Chm/CEO-Mondadori Adv)*
Stefano De Alessandri *(Chm-Mondadori Intl Bus & Gen Mgr)*
Mario Resca *(Chm-Mondadori Direct S.p.A.)*
Mario Maiocchi *(CEO-Mondadori Direct S.p.A.)*

Subsidiaries:

Cemit Interactive Media S.p.A. **(2)**
Via Toscana 9
I-10099 San Mauro Torinese, TO, Italy
Tel.: (39) 1122 27411
Fax: (39) 1122 38701
E-Mail: info@cemit.it
Web Site: www.cemit.it
Marketing, Database Management & Consulting Services
S.I.C.: 8748
N.A.I.C.S.: 541618

Giulio Einaudi Editore S.p.A. **(2)**
Via M Biancamano 2
10121 Turin, Italy
Tel.: (39) 01156561
Fax: (39) 011542903
E-Mail: anna.dellaferrera@einaudi.it
Web Site: www.einaudi.it
Book Publisher
S.I.C.: 2731
N.A.I.C.S.: 511130

Mondadori Electa S.p.A. **(2)**
Via Trentacoste 7
I 20134 Milan, Italy (100%)
Tel.: (39) 02215631
Fax: (39) 0221563350
E-Mail: desimone@mondadori.it
Web Site: www.electaweb.it/
Emp.: 150
Book Publisher
S.I.C.: 2731
N.A.I.C.S.: 511130

Mondadori Franchising S.p.A. **(2)**
Strada Statale Marecchia 51A
47827 Villa Verucchio, I 47900 Rimini, Italy
Tel.: (39) 0541679911
Fax: (39) 0541679970
E-Mail: info@libreriemondadori.com
Web Site: www.libreriemondadori.com
Emp.: 100
Book Marketer & Distr
S.I.C.: 2731
N.A.I.C.S.: 511130

Sperling & Kupfer Editori S.p.A. **(2)**
Corso Como 15
20154 Milano, Italy (100%)
Tel.: (39) 221721
Fax: (39) 0221721377
E-Mail: info@sperling.it
Web Site: www.sperling.it
Emp.: 40
Book Publisher
S.I.C.: 2731
N.A.I.C.S.: 511130
Trombetta Eugenio *(Gen Mgr)*

Affiliate:

Mach 2 Libri S.p.A. **(2)**
Via Galileo Galilei 1
20068 Milan, Peschiera Borromeo, Italy (100%)
Tel.: (39) 02 5539041
Fax: (39) 02 553904206
E-Mail: info@mach2.it
Web Site: www.mach2.it
Book Publisher
S.I.C.: 2731
N.A.I.C.S.: 511130

Joint Ventures:

Gruner + Jahr Mondadori S.p.A. **(2)**
Corso Monforte 54
I 20122 Milan, Italy
Tel.: (39) 02762101
Fax: (39) 0276013439
E-Mail: info@gujm.it
Emp.: 130
Magazine Publisher
S.I.C.: 2721
N.A.I.C.S.: 511120
Fabienne Schwalbe *(Gen Mgr)*

Harlequin Mondadori S.p.A. **(2)**
Via Marco d'Abiano 2
I 20131 Milan, Italy
Tel.: (39) 02280381
Web Site: www.eharmony.it
Emp.: 30
Book Publisher; Owned 50% by Harlequin Enterprises Limited & 50% by Arnoldo Mondadori Editore S.p.A.
S.I.C.: 2731
N.A.I.C.S.: 511130

Mondolibri S.p.A. **(2)**
Via Lampedusa 13
20141 Milan, Italy
Tel.: (39) 02844011
Fax: (39) 0289546603
Web Site: www.mondolibri.it
Emp.: 130
Book Publisher, Marketer & Distr; Owned 50% by Bertelsmann AG & 50% by Fininvest S.p.A.
S.I.C.: 2731
N.A.I.C.S.: 511130

Non-U.S. Subsidiary:

Mondadori France **(2)**
43 rue du Colonel-Pierre-Avia
PO Box 75015
75015 Paris, France
Tel.: (33) 141335001
Fax: (33) 141335719
E-Mail: Ernesto.Mrufe@mondadori.fr
Web Site: www.mondadori.fr
Emp.: 1,000
Magazine Publisher
S.I.C.: 2721
N.A.I.C.S.: 511120
Ernesto Mauri *(Chm)*

Subsidiaries:

Mondadori Auto **(3)**
43 Rue Du Colonel Pierre Avia
75754 Paris, France
Tel.: (33) 141335000
Fax: (33) 141335712
E-Mail: contact@mondadori.fr
Web Site: www.mondadori.fr
Emp.: 750
Magazine Publisher
S.I.C.: 2721
N.A.I.C.S.: 511120
Thierry Jadot *(Mng Dir)*

Mondadori Nature **(3)**
27 rue du Colonel Pierre-Avia
75754 Paris, Cedex, France
Tel.: (33) 141332200
Fax: (33) 141332290
E-Mail: contact@mandadori.fr
Web Site: www.mandadori.fr
Emp.: 100
Magazine Publisher
S.I.C.: 2721
N.A.I.C.S.: 511120
Benis Noel *(Mng Dir)*

Mondadori Star **(3)**
33 Rue Du Colonel Pierre Avia
75754 Paris, France
Tel.: (33) 141335002
Fax: (33) 141335898
Emp.: 1,200
Magazine Publisher
S.I.C.: 2721
N.A.I.C.S.: 511120

FINLAY MINERALS LTD.

912 - 510 West Hastings St
Vancouver, BC, V6B 1L8, Canada
Tel.: (604) 684-3099
Fax: (604) 684-3098
E-Mail: info@finlayminerals.com
Web Site: www.finlayminerals.com
Year Founded: 1999
FYL—(TSXV)
Int. Income: $582
Assets: $7,605,456
Liabilities: $1,381,919
Net Worth: $6,223,536
Earnings: ($316,414)
Fiscal Year-end: 12/31/12
Business Description:
Metal Exploration Services
S.I.C.: 1081
N.A.I.C.S.: 213114
Personnel:
John Barakso *(Chm)*
Robert Brown *(Pres & CEO)*
Board of Directors:
John Barakso
Robert Brown
Rick T. Dauphinee
Warner Gruenwald
David Schwartz
Peter Frederick Tegart
James Tutton
Transfer Agent:
Computershare Trust Company of Canada
510 Burrard St 3rd Fl
Vancouver, BC, V6C 3B9, Canada

FINLAYS COLOMBO PLC

Finlay House 186 Vauxhall Street
Colombo, 00200, Sri Lanka
Tel.: (94) 112421931
Fax: (94) 112448216
E-Mail: info@finlays.lk
Web Site: www.finlays.lk
JFIN—(COL)
Rev.: $39,969,390
Assets: $50,730,617
Liabilities: $7,977,515
Net Worth: $42,753,102
Earnings: $2,885,848
Emp.: 753
Fiscal Year-end: 12/31/12
Business Description:
Diversified Holding Company
S.I.C.: 6719
N.A.I.C.S.: 551112
Personnel:
C. L. K. P. Jayasuriya *(Chm & Mng Dir)*
S. C. Swire *(COO)*
Dalrene M. E. Thirukumar *(Sec)*
Board of Directors:
C. L. K. P. Jayasuriya
J. D. Bandaranayake
J. L. Caspersz
E. R. Croos Moraes
R. Ebell
R. J. Mathison
M. C. Pietersz
N. K. H. Ratwatte
J. M. Rutherford
S. C. Swire
Nirmala Gihan Wickremeratne
Legal Counsel:
Nithi Murugesu & Associates
28 Level 2 WAD Ramanayake Mawatha
Colombo, Sri Lanka
Julius & Creasy
PO Box 154
Colombo, Sri Lanka
F J & G De Saram
216 De Saram Place
Colombo, Sri Lanka

FINMAC LUMBER LTD.

945 Elgin Avenue
Winnipeg, MB, R3E 1B3, Canada
Tel.: (204) 786-7694
Fax: (204) 775-1384
Toll Free: (800) 713-2804
E-Mail: finmac@finmaclumber.com
Web Site: www.finmaclumber.com
Year Founded: 1967
Rev.: $18,585,147
Emp.: 50
Business Description:
Lumber Whslr
S.I.C.: 5031
N.A.I.C.S.: 423310
Personnel:
W. F. McGregor *(Pres)*

FINMATICA S.P.A.

Via Pietro Marone 22
25124 Brescia, Italy
Tel.: (39) 030294860
Fax: (39) 0303757052
E-Mail: informazioni@fallimentofinmatica.com
Web Site: www.fallimentofinmatica.com
Sales Range: $100-124.9 Million
Emp.: 846
Business Description:
Software Applications Designer & Developer
Export
S.I.C.: 3652
N.A.I.C.S.: 334614
Personnel:
Marco Bettini *(Mgr)*

FINMECCANICA S.P.A.

Piazza Monte Grappa 4
00195 Rome, Italy
Tel.: (39) 06324731
Fax: (39) 063208621
E-Mail: webeditor@finmeccanica.it
Web Site: www.finmeccanica.it
FNC—(ITA)
Rev.: $23,178,355,060
Assets: $40,967,991,610
Liabilities: $35,983,124,100
Net Worth: $4,984,867,510
Earnings: ($1,058,089,620)
Emp.: 67,408
Fiscal Year-end: 12/31/12
Business Description:
Holding Company; Engineering, Aerospace & Defense Services
S.I.C.: 3728
N.A.I.C.S.: 336413
Personnel:
Guido Venturoni *(Vice Chm)*
Alessandro Pansa *(CEO & COO)*
Antonio Perfetti *(CEO & Gen Mgr-MBDA ITALIA)*
Elisio Giacomo Prette *(Chm/CEO-Thales Alenia Space Italia)*
G. Pontecorvo *(Chm-BredaMenarinibus)*
Filippo Bagnato *(CEO-ATR)*

Finmeccanica S.p.A.—(Continued)

Antoine Bouvier *(CEO-MBDA Holdings SAS)*
Nazario Cauceglia *(CEO-SuperJet International)*
R. Cortesi *(CEO-Oto Melara)*
S. De Luca *(CEO-Ansaldo STS)*
Alessandro Franzoni *(CEO-WASS S.p.A.)*
J. L. Galle *(CEO-Thales Alenia Space)*
Giuseppe Giordo *(CEO-Alenia Aermacchi)*
Fabrizio Giulianini *(CEO-Selex ES)*
William J. Lynn, III *(CEO-DRS Technologies Inc)*
Maurizio Manfellotto *(CEO-AnsaldoBreda)*
Luigi Pasquali *(CEO-Telespazio)*
D. Romiti *(CEO-AgustaWestland)*
G. Zampini *(CEO-Ansaldo Energia)*

Board of Directors:
Carlo Baldocci
Ivanhoe Lo Bello
Paolo Cantarella
Giovanni Catanzaro
Dario Galli
Silvia Merlo
Alessandro Pansa
Francesco Parlato
Christian Streiff
Guido Venturoni

Subsidiaries:

AgustaWestland S.p.A. (1)
Viale Giovanni Agusta 520
21017 Cascina della Costa, Varese, Italy IT
Tel.: (39) 0331229111 (100%)
Fax: (39) 0331229605
Web Site: www.agustawestland.com
Emp.: 5,200
Helicopter & Rotorcraft Components Designer, Mfr & Marketer
Import Export
S.I.C.: 3721
N.A.I.C.S.: 336411
Alessandra Furigo *(Mgr-Exhibition)*

Joint Venture:

Rotorsim S.r.l. (2)
Via Indipendenza 2
21018 Sesto Calende, Italy
Tel.: (39) 0331 915 062
Helicopter Flight Training Services
S.I.C.: 8249
N.A.I.C.S.: 611512

U.S. Subsidiary:

AgustaWestland Inc. (2)
11700 Plaza America Dr
Reston, VA 20190 DE
Tel.: (703) 373-8000
Web Site: www.agustawestland.com
Air Transportation Services
S.I.C.: 4789
N.A.I.C.S.: 488999

Subsidiaries:

AgustaWestland Philadelphia Corporation (3)
3050 Red Lion Rd
Philadelphia, PA 19114 DE
Tel.: (215) 281-1400
Fax: (215) 281-0441
Web Site: www.agustausa.com
Helicopter Mfr
S.I.C.: 3721
N.A.I.C.S.: 336411
William Hunt *(CEO)*
Christopher Slack *(CFO)*

Joint Venture:

Bell/Agusta Aerospace Company LLC (3)
PO Box 901073
Fort Worth, TX 76101
Tel.: (817) 278-9600
Fax: (817) 278-9726
Web Site: www.bellagusta.com
Helicopter Designer & Mfr
S.I.C.: 3721
N.A.I.C.S.: 336411

Non-U.S. Subsidiaries:

Agusta Aerospace Services - A.A.S. (2)
Liege Airport 60
4460 Grace-Hollogne, Belgium
Tel.: (32) 4 2342323
Fax: (32) 4 2341945
E-Mail: agustaaerospaceservices@agustawestlands.com
Web Site: www.agustawestland.com
Emp.: 40
Airport Management Services
S.I.C.: 4581
N.A.I.C.S.: 488119
Rupert Dix *(Mng Dir)*

AgustaWestland Australia Pty. Ltd. (2)
Level 1 39 Torrens Street
Braddon, Canberra, ACT, 2612, Australia AU
Tel.: (61) 2 62 62 66 60
Fax: (61) 2 62 62 86 60
Aircraft Parts Mfr
S.I.C.: 3728
N.A.I.C.S.: 336413
Philip Smith *(Gen Mgr)*

AgustaWestland do Brasil Ltda. (2)
Av Alberto Jackson Bayton 2784
62276-000 Osasco, Sao Paulo, Brazil BR
Tel.: (55) 11 3601 2269
Fax: (55) 11 3601 2512
E-Mail: agustawestland@agustawestland.com.br
Web Site: www.agustawestland.com
Aircraft Transportation Services
S.I.C.: 4581
N.A.I.C.S.: 488190
Secondo Viglieno *(Mng Dir)*
Jose Manoel de Oliveira *(CFO)*

AgustaWestland International Limited (2)
Lysander Road
Yeovil, Somerset, BA20 2YB, United Kingdom UK
Tel.: (44) 1935475222
Fax: (44) 19354702102
Emp.: 5,000
Aircraft Parts Mfr
S.I.C.: 3728
N.A.I.C.S.: 336413
Ray Edwards *(Mng Dir)*

AgustaWestland Limited (2)
25 Templer Ave
Farnborough, HAM GU14, United Kingdom UK
Tel.: (44) 1252 386451
Fax: (44) 1252 386431
Web Site: www.agustawestland.com
Emp.: 400
Aircraft Mfr
S.I.C.: 3721
N.A.I.C.S.: 336411
Graham Cole *(Chm)*
Ray Edwards *(Mng Dir)*

Subsidiaries:

AgustaWestland Holdings Limited (3)
Lysander Road
Yeovil, BA20 2YB, United Kingdom UK
Tel.: (44) 19 3547 5222
Fax: (44) 19 3570 3558
E-Mail:
Investment Management Services
S.I.C.: 6211
N.A.I.C.S.: 523999
Raymond Edgar Edwards *(Gen Mgr)*

Subsidiaries:

British Helicopters Limited (4)
Lysander Road
Yeovil, Somerset, BA20 2YB, United Kingdom UK
Tel.: (44) 1935 475 222
Fax: (44) 1935 704 020
Emp.: 3,500
Helicopter Transportation Services
S.I.C.: 4731
N.A.I.C.S.: 488510
Ray Edwards *(Mng Dir)*

Westland Transmissions Limited (4)
AgustaWestland Works Lysander Road
Yeovil, Somerset, BA20 2YB, United Kingdom UK
Tel.: (44) 19 35 47 52 22
Fax: (44) 19 35 70 49 76
Industrial Furnace Mfr
S.I.C.: 3567
N.A.I.C.S.: 333994

U.S. Subsidiary:

AgustaWestland North America Inc (4)
11700 Plaza America Dr
Reston, VA 20190-4751
Tel.: (703) 373-8005
Helicopter Mfr
S.I.C.: 3721
N.A.I.C.S.: 336411

AgustaWestland UK Pension Scheme (Trustee) Limited (3)
Westland Works Lysander Road
Box 205
Yeovil, Somerset, BA20 2YB, United Kingdom UK
Tel.: (44) 1935475222
Emp.: 5,000
Pension Fund Management Services
S.I.C.: 6371
N.A.I.C.S.: 525110
Mike Nixon *(Gen Mgr)*

Plant:

AgustaWestland Ltd. - Yeovil Plant (3)
Lysander Road
Yeovil, Somerset, BA20 2YB, United Kingdom
Tel.: (44) 1935475222
Fax: (44) 1935702131
Emp.: 4,000
Helicopter Mfr
S.I.C.: 3721
N.A.I.C.S.: 336411
Graham Cole *(Chm)*
Ray Edwards *(Mng Dir)*

AgustaWestland Malaysia Sdn. Bhd. (2)
Ground Floor Mas Cargo Centre Cargo Complex
47200 Subang Jaya, Selangor, Malaysia MY
Tel.: (60) 3 7842 3026
Aircraft Maintenance Services
S.I.C.: 4581
N.A.I.C.S.: 488190

AgustaWestland Portugal SA (2)
Rua Castilho 165
Lisbon, 1070-050, Portugal PT
Tel.: (351) 211924980
Engineering Services
S.I.C.: 8711
N.A.I.C.S.: 541330
Bill Hodson *(Gen Mgr)*

Alenia Aermacchi S.p.A. (1)
Via Ing Paolo Foresio 1
Venegono Superiore, 21040 Varese, Italy
Tel.: (39) 0331813111
Fax: (39) 0331827595
E-Mail: info@alenia.it
Web Site: www.alenia.it
Emp.: 1,800
Military Trainer Aircraft Mfr
S.I.C.: 3721
N.A.I.C.S.: 336411
Giancarlo Grasso *(Chm)*
Carmelo Consentino *(Vice Chm)*
Massimo Lucchesini *(CEO)*

Alenia Aeronautica S.p.A. (1)
Via Campania 45
00187 Rome, Italy
Tel.: (39) 06420881
Fax: (39) 0642824528
E-Mail: communication@alenia.it
Web Site: www.alenia-aeronautica.it
Sales Range: $1-4.9 Billion
Emp.: 13,900
Commercial & Military Aircraft Mfr
S.I.C.: 3721
N.A.I.C.S.: 336411
Giuseppe Giordo *(CEO)*

Subsidiaries:

Alenia SIA SpA (2)
Strada del Lionetto 6
10146 Turin, Italy
Tel.: (39) 011 4090111
Fax: (39) 011 4090105
Defense Aircraft Mfr
S.I.C.: 3721
N.A.I.C.S.: 336411

Alenia Spazio S.p.A. (2)
Via Saccomuro 24
00131 Rome, Italy (100%)
Tel.: (39) 0641511
Telex: 611395 AERIT
Fax: (39) 064190675
Web Site: www.alespazio.it
Sales Range: $500-549.9 Million
Emp.: 2,400
Satellite & Space Structure Developer & Mfr
S.I.C.: 3761
N.A.I.C.S.: 336414

Officine Aeronavali Venezia S.p.A. (2)
Via Triestina 214
30030 Tesero, Venice, Italy (100%)
Tel.: (39) 0412693978
Fax: (39) 412693887
E-Mail: careers@aeronavali.com
Web Site: www.aeronavali.com
Emp.: 1,600
Maintenance Services for Commercial & Military Aircraft
S.I.C.: 4581
N.A.I.C.S.: 488119

U.S. Subsidiary:

Alenia North America, Inc. (2)
1625 Eye St NW Ste 1200
Washington, DC 20006
Tel.: (202) 292-2664
Fax: (202) 293-0677
E-Mail: bstone@aleniainc.com
Web Site: www.aleniana.com
Aircraft Manufacturing
S.I.C.: 3721
N.A.I.C.S.: 336411
Benjamin Stone *(Pres & CEO)*
Fabrizio Lombardi *(CFO)*
Massimo Tarantola *(COO)*
Francesco Bernardi *(Gen Counsel)*
Mario Capitelli *(Sr VP-Procurement & Industrialization)*
Gianluca Evangelisti *(Sr VP-Bus Dev)*
Giuseppe Fascione *(Sr VP-Industrialization)*
Colleen Hannon *(Sr VP-HR)*
Simone Maraini *(Sr VP-Processes & Improvements)*

Non-U.S. Subsidiaries:

WING NED BV (2)
Weena 210 - 212
Rotterdam, 3012 NJ, Netherlands
Tel.: (31) 10 2013600
Aircraft Mfr
S.I.C.: 3721
N.A.I.C.S.: 336411

WORLD'S WING SA (2)
rue du Rhone 65
1204 Geneva, Switzerland
Tel.: (41) 22 718 90 10
Investment Management Services
S.I.C.: 6211
N.A.I.C.S.: 523999

Non-U.S. Joint Venture:

Avions de Transport Regional (2)
1 Allee Pierre Nadot
31712 Blagnac, Cedex, France
Tel.: (33) 562216221
Fax: (33) 562216636
E-Mail: accueil@atr.fr
Web Site: www.atraircraft.com
Sales Range: $1-4.9 Billion
Emp.: 1,000
Turboprop Commuter Aircraft Mfr
Import Export
S.I.C.: 3721
N.A.I.C.S.: 336411
Meyer Stephene *(CEO)*
Eric Baravian *(CFO & Sr VP)*
Sylvie Kande de Beaupuy *(Gen Counsel)*

Aldo Mucciardi *(Sec & Sr VP)*
Lilian Brayle *(Sr VP-Product Support & Svcs)*
Thierry Casale *(Sr VP-Ops)*
Jean-Pierre Cousserans *(Sr VP-Customer Svcs)*
Jacques Desbarats *(Sr VP-Comml)*
John Moore *(Sr VP-Comml)*
Carmine Orsi *(Sr VP-Technical)*

Ansaldo Energia S.p.A. (1)
Via Nicola Lorenzi 8
16152 Genoa, GE, Italy (100%)
Tel.: (39) 0106551
Fax: (39) 0106556209
Web Site: www.ansaldoenergia.com
Rev.: $1,748,992,526
Assets: $3,605,565,574
Liabilities: $2,938,266,413
Net Worth: $667,299,161
Earnings: $22,374,692
Emp.: 3,328
Fiscal Year-end: 12/31/12
Power Generation & Plant Engineering Services
S.I.C.: 3548
N.A.I.C.S.: 333992
Francesco Giuliani *(Chm)*
Luigi Calabria *(Vice Chm)*
Giuseppe Zampini *(CEO & Mng Dir)*

Subsidiaries:

ANSALDO NUCLEARE SpA (2)
Via Lorenzi 8
16152 Genoa, Italy
Tel.: (39) 06 42013584
Fax: (39) 06 42820405
E-Mail: ansaldonucleare@ann.ansaldo.it
Web Site: www.ansaldonucleare.it
Industrial Machinery Mfr
S.I.C.: 3559
N.A.I.C.S.: 333249

Non-U.S. Subsidiary:

ANSERV SRL (3)
Dacia 65 Ap 2 Sector 1
010407 Bucharest, Romania
Tel.: (40) 212113991
Fax: (40) 212101966
Financial Management Services
S.I.C.: 6211
N.A.I.C.S.: 523999

Non-U.S. Subsidiaries:

Ansaldo Thomassen B.V. (2)
Havenlandseweg 8D
PO Box 95
6990 AB Rheden, Netherlands
Tel.: (31) 264975800
Fax: (31) 264975857
E-Mail: info@ansaldothomassen.nl
Web Site: www.ansaldothomassen.com
Emp.: 100
Support Services for Industrial Gas Turbine Systems
S.I.C.: 3511
N.A.I.C.S.: 333611
Mark Kooisti *(Mgr-Mktg)*

ASIA POWER PROJECTS PRIVATE LTD (2)
8th Floor College Road
Chennai, Tamil Nadu, 600 006, India
Tel.: (91) 4428230712
Fax: (91) 4428230912
Emp.: 10
Power Plant Construction Services
S.I.C.: 1629
N.A.I.C.S.: 237990
Durgarao Kola *(Gen Mgr)*

AnsaldoBreda S.p.A. (1)
Via Argine 425
80147 Naples, Italy IT
Tel.: (39) 081 243 1111
Fax: (39) 081 243 2699
E-Mail: info@ansaldobreda.it
Web Site: www.ansaldobreda.it
Emp.: 2,400
Railway Maintenance Services
S.I.C.: 4789
N.A.I.C.S.: 488210
A. Rosania *(Chm)*
M. Manfellotto *(CEO)*
L. D'Aquila *(CFO)*

Non-U.S. Subsidiary:

AnsaldoBreda Espana SLU (2)
C/San Bernardo 123 5 Planta
28015 Madrid, Spain ES
Tel.: (34) 917432388
Fax: (34) 917436425
E-Mail: info@ansaldobredaespana.com
Web Site: www.ansaldobredaespana.com
Railway Maintenance Services
S.I.C.: 4789
N.A.I.C.S.: 488210

Consorzio S3log S.p.A. (1)
Via Tiburtina 1020
00156 Rome, Italy (60%)
Tel.: (39) 0645470201, ext. 688206111
Fax: (39) 0688204735
E-Mail: info@s3log.it
Web Site: www.s3log.it
Emp.: 16
IT Services
S.I.C.: 7373
N.A.I.C.S.: 541512
Icilio Diluzio *(Gen Mgr)*

ED Contact srl (1)
Via Laurentina 760
00143 Rome, Italy
Tel.: (39) 06 50264 1
Fax: (39) 06 5015979
Customer Relationship Management
S.I.C.: 7389
N.A.I.C.S.: 561421

FATA S.p.A. (1)
Strada Stratale 24 Km 12
10044 Pianezza, Turin, Italy
Tel.: (39) 0001196681
Telex: 532038 FATAPD 1
Fax: (39) 0119668375
E-Mail: info@fatagroup.it
Web Site: www.fatagroup.it
Sales Range: $300-349.9 Million
Emp.: 300
Industrial Plant Engineering, Contracting & Mfg Services
S.I.C.: 1629
N.A.I.C.S.: 237990
S. Praitano *(CEO)*

Subsidiaries:

FATA ENGINEERING SpA (2)
Strada Statale 24 KM 12
10044 Pianezza, Italy
Tel.: (39) 0119668111
Fax: (39) 0119672673
E-Mail: info@fatagroup.it
Architectural & Engineering Services
S.I.C.: 8712
N.A.I.C.S.: 541310

FATA LOGISTIC SYSTEMS SpA (2)
Via dei Prati 7
10044 Pianezza, Turin, Italy
Tel.: (39) 011 96681
Fax: (39) 011 9668386
E-Mail: info@fatalogistic.it
Web Site: www.fatalogistic.it
Emp.: 500
Logistics Consulting Services
S.I.C.: 4731
N.A.I.C.S.: 541614

U.S. Subsidiary:

FATA Hunter, Inc. (2)
1040 Iowa Ave Ste 100
Riverside, CA 92507-2106 CA
Tel.: (951) 328-0200
Fax: (951) 328-9181
Toll Free: (800) 248-6837
E-Mail: r.sanchez@fatahunterusa.com
Web Site: www.fatahunter.com
Emp.: 17
Coil & Sheet Processing Equipment Mfr & Supplier
S.I.C.: 3542
N.A.I.C.S.: 333517
Anthony Tropeano *(Pres & CEO)*

Non-U.S. Subsidiaries:

FATA Hunter India Pvt. Ltd. (2)
24 2nd Floor 2nd Main 1st Cross Domlur
2nd Stage Indiranagar
Bengaluru, 560071, India In
Tel.: (91) 8041254059
Fax: (91) 8041254038
Web Site: www.fatahunter.com
Metal Product Mfr
S.I.C.: 3549
N.A.I.C.S.: 333519

FATA Ltd. (2)
Elgar House
Shrub Hill Rd, Worcester, WR49EE, United Kingdom
Tel.: (44) 1905613931
Telex: 826463
Fax: (44) 905613913
E-Mail: engineering@fataautomation.co.uk
Web Site: www.fataautomation.co.uk
Emp.: 8
Metal & Wire Products for the Automotive Industry
S.I.C.: 3496
N.A.I.C.S.: 332618
Nicola Cipolletta *(Mng Dir)*

FINMECCANICA GROUP REAL ESTATE SPA (1)
Via Vittoria 14
00187 Rome, Italy
Tel.: (39) 0632110820
Real Estate Management Services
S.I.C.: 6531
N.A.I.C.S.: 531390

Finmeccanica Group Services S.p.A. (1)
Piazza Monte Grappa 4
00195 Rome, Italy IT
Tel.: (39) 0632473419
Fax: (39) 063208621
Business Management Consulting Services
S.I.C.: 8742
N.A.I.C.S.: 541611

OTO MELARA SpA (1)
Via Valdilocchi 15
19136 La Spezia, Italy
Tel.: (39) 0187 581111
Fax: (39) 0187 582669
E-Mail: maura.mauri@otomelara.it
Web Site: www.otomelara.it
Rev.: $560,006,720
Emp.: 1,217
Military Weapon Services & Mfr
S.I.C.: 3795
N.A.I.C.S.: 336992
Cosentino G. *(Chm)*
Lardella C. A. *(CEO)*

Subsidiary:

CISDEG SPA (2)
1231 Via Tiburtina
00131 Rome, Italy
Tel.: (39) 064 417 041
Welding Equipment Mfr
S.I.C.: 3548
N.A.I.C.S.: 333992

SELEX ELSAG S.p.A. (1)
Via Puccini 2
16154 Genoa, Italy IT
Tel.: (39) 01065821
Fax: (39) 0106582898
Web Site: www.selex-es.com
Emp.: 7,400
Defence Electronic Equipment Mfr
S.I.C.: 3679
N.A.I.C.S.: 334419
Allan Cook *(Chm)*
Fabrizio Giulianini *(CEO)*
Federico Bonaiuto *(Sec Gen)*
Geoff Munday *(CFO)*
Alessio Facondo *(COO)*
Mario Rech *(CIO)*
Alberto Sarti *(CTO)*
Romolo Bernardi *(Chief Security Officer)*

Branch:

Elsag Datamat S.p.A. (2)
Via Laurentina 760
00143 Rome, Italy IT
Tel.: (39) 0650271
Fax: (39) 50511407
E-Mail: info@elsagdatamat.com
Web Site: www.elsagdatamat.com
Emp.: 1,500
Information, Communication & Technology Solution Services
S.I.C.: 7373
N.A.I.C.S.: 541512
Aielli Paolo *(Mng Dir)*

Subsidiaries:

Electron Italia S.r.l. (2)
Via Tiburtina 1262
00131 Rome, Italy IT
Tel.: (39) 06417 981
Fax: (39) 064 130 859
E-Mail: reception.electron@selexelsag.com
Electric Power Distribution Services
S.I.C.: 4911
N.A.I.C.S.: 221122

LARIMART SpA (2)
Via Torrevecchia 12
00168 Rome, Italy
Tel.: (39) 06 30 34 31
Fax: (39) 06 30 34 33 86
E-Mail:
Electronic Equipment Mfr
S.I.C.: 3679
N.A.I.C.S.: 334419

Net Service SRL (2)
via Nuovalucello 47G
95100 Catania, Italy
Tel.: (39) 095 221653
Fax: (39) 095 222875
E-Mail: info@net-serv.it
Web Site: www.net-serv.it
Internet Service Provider
S.I.C.: 4813
N.A.I.C.S.: 517110

ORANGEE SRL (2)
Lungotevere dei Mellini 44
Rome, 00193, Italy
Tel.: (39) 06 36 00 44 39
Fax: (39) 06 36 08 66 49
E-Mail: info@orangee.com
Information & Communication Services
S.I.C.: 7389
N.A.I.C.S.: 519190

SIRIO PANEL SPA (2)
Localita Levanella Becorpi
52025 Montevarchi, Arezzo, Italy
Tel.: (39) 055 913671
Fax: (39) 055 9180463
E-Mail: siriopanel@siriopanel.it
Web Site: www.siriopanel.it
Sls.: $59,462,550
Emp.: 230
Aircraft Lighting Equipment Mfr
S.I.C.: 3648
N.A.I.C.S.: 335129
Graziano Forzieri *(Mng Dir)*

U.S. Subsidiary:

Sirio Panel Inc. (3)
Ste 2A 1385 Stonycreek Rd
Troy, OH 43026
Tel.: (937) 524-5069
Web Site: www.siriopanel.it/siriopanel/?section=CORP&open0=4615
Aircraft Lighting System Mfr
S.I.C.: 3728
N.A.I.C.S.: 336413

U.S. Subsidiary:

ELSAG North America LLC (2)
7 Sutton Pl
Brewster, NY 10509
Tel.: (336) 379-7135
Fax: (336) 379-7164
Automatic Number Plate Recognition System Mfr & Whslr
S.I.C.: 3679
N.A.I.C.S.: 334419

Non-U.S. Subsidiaries:

SELEX Communications Romania SRL (2)
Str DR Louis Pasteur No 8 Floor
Bucharest, 050535, Romania
Tel.: (40) 21 4109530
Fax: (40) 21 4109550
Telecommunication Services
S.I.C.: 4899
N.A.I.C.S.: 517919
Massimo Basile *(Mng Dir)*

Subsidiary:

S.C. Elettra Communications SA (3)
Ploiesti-Mumbai Highway Km 8
100302 Ploiesti, Romania
Tel.: (40) 244 434 022

Finmeccanica S.p.A.—(Continued)

Fax: (40) 244 434 022
E-Mail: office@elettra.ro
Web Site: www.elettra.ro
Emp.: 100
Communication Equipment Mfr
S.I.C.: 3669
N.A.I.C.S.: 334290
Sandor Lovasz *(Dir Gen)*

SELEX ELSAG Holdings Ltd (2)
Fleet Business Park Itlings Lane
Hessle, HU13 9LX Hull, United Kingdom
Tel.: (44) 1482326144
Emp.: 4
Investment Management Services
S.I.C.: 6211
N.A.I.C.S.: 523999

Subsidiary:

SELEX ELSAG Ltd. (3)
Lambda House Christopher Martin Road
Basildon, Essex, SS14 3EL, United Kingdom UK
Tel.: (44) 1268 82 3400
Fax: (44) 1268 82 3493
E-Mail: marine-sales@selexelsag.com
Web Site: www.selexmarine.com
Emp.: 400
Marine Electronic Equipment Sales & Maintenance Services
S.I.C.: 5065
N.A.I.C.S.: 423690
Nigel Bond *(Head-Marine)*

Non-U.S. Subsidiaries:

SELEX Communications Gmbh (3)
Spinnerei 48
71522 Backnang, Germany
Tel.: (49) 7191 378 0
Fax: (49) 7191 378 500
E-Mail: info.germany@selex-comms.com
Web Site: de.selexelsag.com
Emp.: 52
Radio & Telecommunication Equipment Mfr & Whlsr
S.I.C.: 3663
N.A.I.C.S.: 334220

SELEX Komunikasyon A.S. (3)
Konya Yolu Km 25
06830 Ankara, Turkey
Tel.: (90) 312 484 51 81
Fax: (90) 312 484 43 32
E-Mail: sales@selex-comms.com.tr
Web Site: www.selex-comms.com.tr
Emp.: 50
Communication Equipment Mfr
S.I.C.: 3669
N.A.I.C.S.: 334290
Stefano Tagliani *(Gen Mgr)*

Non-U.S. Subsidiary:

VEGA Deutschland GmbH (2)
Industriestrasse 161
D-50999 Cologne, Germany De
Tel.: (49) 22367480
Fax: (49) 2236748180
E-Mail: info@vega.de
Web Site: www.vega.de
Emp.: 400
Civil & Military Technology Consulting & Support Services
S.I.C.: 7389
N.A.I.C.S.: 541990
Kurosch Balali *(Mng Dir)*
Manfred Muller *(Mng Dir)*

SELEX Galileo S.p.A. (1)
Via Albert Einstein 35
Campi Bisenzio FI, 50013 Campi Bisenzio, Italy
Tel.: (39) 5589501
Fax: (39) 0558950600
Web Site: www.selexgalileo.com
Emp.: 7,000
Defense Electronics Mfr
S.I.C.: 3812
N.A.I.C.S.: 334511
Allan Cook *(Chm)*
Fabrizio Giulianini *(CEO)*
Norman Bone *(Mng Dir)*
Geoff Munday *(CFO)*
Alberto Sarti *(CTO & Dir-Strategy)*
Patrizia Acciari *(Gen Counsel)*
Ian Bainbridge *(Acting Sr VP-Electronic Warfare)*
Armando Buccheri *(Sr VP-Space)*
Andrew Cowdery *(Sr VP-Support & Svc Solutions)*
Mauro Gori *(Sr VP-Electro Optics & Naval)*
Alastair Morrison *(Sr VP-Radar & Advanced Targeting)*
Philip Pratley *(Sr VP-Battlespace Protection & Awareness)*
Gianfranco Terrando *(Sr VP-Air Sys, Unmanned Air Sys & Simulators)*

U.S. Subsidiary:

SELEX Galileo Inc. (2)
201 12th St S Ste 704
Arlington, VA 22202
Tel.: (703) 418-7280
Fax: (703) 418-7667
Web Site: www.selexgalileo.com
Emp.: 200
Defense Electronics Mfr
S.I.C.: 3812
N.A.I.C.S.: 334511
Wayne Landman *(CEO)*

Subsidiary:

Lasertel, Inc. (3)
7775 N Casa Grande Hwy
Tucson, AZ 85743-9317
Tel.: (520) 744-5700
Fax: (520) 744-5766
Toll Free: (877) 844-1444
E-Mail: info@lasertel.com
Web Site: www.lasertel.com
Sales Range: $25-49.9 Million
Emp.: 60
Semiconductor Laser Mfr
S.I.C.: 3674
N.A.I.C.S.: 334413
Mark McElhinney *(Pres)*

Non-U.S. Subsidiary:

SELEX Galileo Ltd. (2)
Sigma House Christopher Martin Road
Basildon, Essex, SS14 3EL, United Kingdom (100%)
Tel.: (44) 1268522822
Fax: (44) 1268883140
Emp.: 900
Electronic Flight System Mfr
S.I.C.: 3812
N.A.I.C.S.: 334511
Norman Bone *(Chief Bus Officer)*

Subsidiaries:

SELEX Galileo Electro Optics (Overseas) Ltd. (3)
Sigma House Christopher Martin Road
Basildon, Essex, SS14 3EL, United Kingdom UK
Tel.: (44) 1268 887264
Electro Optic System Mfr
S.I.C.: 3679
N.A.I.C.S.: 334419

SELEX Galileo Infrared Ltd. (3)
Robinson House First Avenue
Southampton, Hants, SO15 0LG, United Kingdom UK
Tel.: (44) 23 8070 2300
Fax: (44) 23 8031 6777
E-Mail: infrared.sales@selexgalileo.com
Emp.: 200
Military & Industrial Detector Mfr
S.I.C.: 3812
N.A.I.C.S.: 334511
Stewart Miller *(Gen Mgr)*

SELEX Galileo (Projects) Ltd. (3)
Sigma House Christopher Martin Road
Basildon, Essex, SS14 3EL, United Kingdom UK
Tel.: (44) 1268887075
Electrical Products Mfr & Whslr
S.I.C.: 3699
N.A.I.C.S.: 335999
Jan Boyes *(Project Mgr)*

SELEX PENSION SCHEME (TRUSTEE) LIMITED (3)
Sigma House Christopher Martin Road
Basildon, Essex, SS14 3EL, United Kingdom
Tel.: (44) 1268522822
Pension Management Services
S.I.C.: 6371
N.A.I.C.S.: 525110

SELEX Sistemi Integrati S.p.A. (1)
Via Tiburtina Km 12 400 AS
IT-00131 Rome, Italy IT
Tel.: (39) 0641501
Fax: (39) 064131133
E-Mail: info@selex-si.com
Web Site: www.selex-si.com
Sales Range: $900-999.9 Million
Emp.: 3,500
Scientific, Technical & Management Consulting & Support Services
S.I.C.: 7389
N.A.I.C.S.: 541990
Alberto De Benedictis *(Chm)*
Marina Grossi *(CEO)*
Letizia Colucci *(COO)*

U.S. Subsidiary:

SELEX SYSTEMS INTEGRATION INC. (2)
11300 W 89th St
Overland Park, KS 66214
Tel.: (913) 495-2600
Fax: (913) 492-0870
E-Mail: sales@selex-si-us.com
Web Site: www.selex-si-us.com
Emp.: 100
Navigation Equipment Distr
S.I.C.: 5065
N.A.I.C.S.: 423690
Mike Warner *(CEO)*

Non-U.S. Subsidiaries:

SELEX SISTEMI INTEGRATI DO BRASIL LTDA (2)
Rua da Assembleia 10 - Sala 3101
20011-901 Rio de Janeiro, Brazil
Tel.: (55) 21 2292 7743
Fax: (55) 21 2292 7743
Military Component Mfr
S.I.C.: 3795
N.A.I.C.S.: 336992

SELEX Sistemi Integrati GmbH (2)
Raiffeisenstrasse 10
D-41470 Neuss, Germany De
Mailing Address:
PO Box 210351
D-41429 Neuss, Germany
Tel.: (49) 21377820
Fax: (49) 213778211
E-Mail: info@gematronik.com
Web Site: www.gematronik.com
Emp.: 150
Scientific, Technical & Management Consulting & Support Services
S.I.C.: 7389
N.A.I.C.S.: 541990
Ulrich Nellen *(Gen Mgr)*

SELEX Systems Integration Ltd. (2)
430 Bristol Business Park Coldharbour Lane
Bristol, BS16 1EJ, United Kingdom UK (100%)
Tel.: (44) 117 900 8975
Fax: (44) 117 988 0034
E-Mail: info@selex-si-uk.com
Web Site: www.selex-si.co.uk
Scientific, Technical & Management Consulting & Support Services
S.I.C.: 7389
N.A.I.C.S.: 541990
Michael Clayforth-Carr *(CEO)*

Subsidiary:

VEGA Consulting Services Ltd. (3)
430 Bristol Business Park
Bristol, BS16 1EJ, United Kingdom UK
Tel.: (44) 117 988 0033
Fax: (44) 117 988 0034
E-Mail: info@vega.co.uk
Web Site: www.vega.co.uk
Sales Range: $25-49.9 Million
Emp.: 200
Civil & Military Technology Consulting Services
S.I.C.: 8999
N.A.I.C.S.: 541690
Paul MacGregor *(Mng Dir)*

Telespazio SpA (1)
Via Tiburtina 965
156 Rome, Italy
Tel.: (39) 0640791
Fax: (39) 06 40999 906
E-Mail: communication@telespazio.com
Web Site: www.telespazio.it
Emp.: 2,500
Satellite Services
S.I.C.: 4899
N.A.I.C.S.: 517410
Giuseppe Viriglio *(Chm)*
Giuseppe Veredice *(CEO)*

Non-U.S. Subsidiaries:

Telespazio Deutschland GmbH (2)
Talhofstrasse 28A
82205 Gilching, Pavaria, Germany
Tel.: (49) 810538430
Fax: (49) 8105384312
Web Site: www.telespazio.com
Operational Services for Space Systems
S.I.C.: 3812
N.A.I.C.S.: 334511
Yves Constantin *(Mng Dir)*

VEGA Space Ltd. (2)
2 Falcon Way
Shire Park, Welwyn Garden City, Herts, AL7 1TW, United Kingdom UK
Tel.: (44) 1707368000
Fax: (44) 1707326395
E-Mail: info@vegaspace.com
Web Site: www.vegaspace.com
Emp.: 400
Space Sector Technology Consulting & Support Services
S.I.C.: 7389
N.A.I.C.S.: 541990

Non-U.S. Subsidiaries:

VEGA Space GmbH (3)
Europaplatz 5
D-64293 Darmstadt, Germany De
Tel.: (49) 61518257100
Fax: (49) 61518257799
E-Mail: info.space@vega.de
Web Site: www.vegaspace.de
Emp.: 200
Space Sector Technology Consulting & Support Services
S.I.C.: 7389
N.A.I.C.S.: 541990
Sigmar Keller *(Mng Dir)*
John Lewis *(Mng Dir)*

VEGA Technologies SAS (3)
Parc Technologique du Canal 12 avenue de l'Europe
Villa San Diego, F-31520 Ramonville-Saint-Agne, France FR
Tel.: (33) 567771999
Fax: (33) 561 534 212
Web Site: www.vegatechnologies.fr
Emp.: 60
Space Sector Technology Consulting & Support Services
S.I.C.: 7389
N.A.I.C.S.: 541990
Michel Austruy *(Mng Dir)*

WHITEHEAD ALENIA SISTEMI SUBACQUEI SPA (1)
Via di Levante 48
57124 Livorno, Italy
Tel.: (39) 0586 840 111
Fax: (39) 0586 854 060
E-Mail: marketing@wass.it
Web Site: www.wass.it
Emp.: 400
Underwater Surveillance System Mfr
S.I.C.: 3812
N.A.I.C.S.: 334511

Joint Venture:

Orizzonte Sistemi Navali S.p.A. (1)
Viale Brigata Bisagno 45R
IT-16129 Genoa, Italy IT
Tel.: (39) 0109817535
Fax: (39) 0109817989
E-Mail: marketing@orizzontesn.it
Web Site: www.orizzontesn.it
Contract Naval Vessel Design & Engineering Services; Owned 51% by Fincantieri - Cantieri Navali Italiani S.p.A. & 49% by Finmeccanica S.p.A.
S.I.C.: 7389
N.A.I.C.S.: 541490

U.S. Subsidiary:

Finmeccanica North America Inc. (1)
1625 I St NW 12th Fl
Washington, DC 20006 DE

Tel.: (202) 292-2626
Fax: (202) 223-6584
Web Site: www.finmeccanicausa.com
Holding Company; Regional Managing Office
S.I.C.: 6719
N.A.I.C.S.: 551112
Simone Bemporad *(CEO)*

Subsidiaries:

AnsaldoBreda Inc. (2)
101 Embarcadero Ste 210
San Francisco, CA 94105
Tel.: (415) 397-7010
Fax: (415) 397-7011
E-Mail: info@ansaldobredainc.com
Web Site: www.ansaldobredainc.com
Railroad Transit System Mfr
S.I.C.: 3743
N.A.I.C.S.: 336510
Cristiano Torresi *(Project Mgr)*

DRS Technologies, Inc. (2)
2345 Crystal Dr Ste 915
Arlington, VA 22202 DE
Tel.: (703) 416-8000
E-Mail: info@drs.com
Web Site: www.drs.com
Sales Range: $1-4.9 Billion
Emp.: 10,200
Military Communications, Surveillance, Reconnaissance & Sustainment Systems & Equipment Developer & Mfr
Export
S.I.C.: 3812
N.A.I.C.S.: 334511
William J. Lynn, III *(CEO)*
Allen H. Golland *(CIO & Sr VP)*
James M. Baird *(Pres-Sensors & Nuclear Controls)*
Richard S. Danforth *(Pres-Grp)*
Terence J. Murphy *(Pres-RTSA Grp)*
Mitchell B. Rambler *(Pres-Defense Sys & Svcs)*
Mark A. Dorfman *(Gen Counsel, Sec & Sr VP)*
Steven J. Cortese *(Exec VP-Ops-Washington)*
Thomas P. Crimmins *(Sr VP & Controller)*
John G. Cotton *(Sr VP-Maritime & Air Warfare Strategic Plans & Programs)*
R. Alan Gross *(Sr VP-Compliance)*
Andrea J. Mandel *(Sr VP-HR)*
Joseph Militano *(Sr VP-Pub Affairs & Comm)*
Durwood W. Ringo, Jr. *(Sr VP-Govt Rels)*
Jason W. Rinsky *(Sr VP-Corp Taxation)*
Robert Russo *(Sr VP-Ops)*
David W. Stapley *(Sr VP-Intl Bus Dev & Govt Rels)*

Subsidiaries:

DRS C3 & Aviation Company (3)
1060 Consolidated Rd
Elizabeth City, NC 27909-7835
Tel.: (252) 338-0288
Aircraft & Military Equipment Maintenance Services
S.I.C.: 7539
N.A.I.C.S.: 811198

DRS C3 Systems, LLC (3)
645 Anchors St
Fort Walton Beach, FL 32548 FL
Tel.: (850) 302-3000 (100%)
Fax: (850) 302-3371
E-Mail: info@drs-tcs.com
Emp.: 800
Naval Display & Sensor Control Systems Mfr
S.I.C.: 3823
N.A.I.C.S.: 334513
Richard S. Danforth *(Pres)*

Subsidiaries:

DRS C3 Systems, Inc. (4)
400 Professional Dr
Gaithersburg, MD 20879 MD
Tel.: (301) 921-8100 (100%)
Fax: (301) 921-8010
E-Mail: marketing@drs-esg.com
Web Site: www.drs.com
Emp.: 140
Naval Display & Sensor Control Systems Mfr
S.I.C.: 3823
N.A.I.C.S.: 334513
Monica Bower *(Dir-HR)*

DRS C3 Systems, Inc. (4)
485 Cayuga Rd
Buffalo, NY 14225-1309 FL
Mailing Address:
PO Box 222
Buffalo, NY 14225-0222
Tel.: (716) 631-6200
Fax: (716) 631-7849
E-Mail: info@drs-ds.com
Web Site: www.drs-ds.com
Emp.: 250
Naval Display & Sensor Control Systems Mfr
S.I.C.: 3823
N.A.I.C.S.: 334513

DRS C3 Systems, Inc. (4)
767 Electronic Dr Ste A
Horsham, PA 19044-2228 DE
Tel.: (215) 233-4100 (100%)
Fax: (215) 233-9947
Web Site: www.drs.com
Emp.: 40
Naval Display & Sensor Control Systems Mfr
S.I.C.: 3823
N.A.I.C.S.: 334513
Joseph Gothie *(Treas)*

Joint Venture:

DRS Sonar Systems LLC (4)
00 Professional Dr Ste 400
Gaithersburg, MD 20879-3457
Tel.: (301) 921-8100
Undersea Warfare System Developer
S.I.C.: 3812
N.A.I.C.S.: 334511

Subsidiary:

Advanced Acoustic Concepts, LLC (5)
425 Oser Ave Unit 1
Hauppauge, NY 11788
Tel.: (631) 273-5700
Fax: (631) 273-5809
Toll Free: (877) 273-5701
Web Site: www.aactech.com
Emp.: 220
Sonar System Development Services
S.I.C.: 3812
N.A.I.C.S.: 334511
Michael J. Carnovale *(Pres)*
Scott Williams *(CFO)*
Brian Boyle *(Sr VP-Corp Dev)*
Richard Lawless *(Sr VP-Corp Ops)*

Units:

Advanced Acoustic Concepts, Inc. - Columbia (6)
7100 Columbia Gateway Dr # 190
Columbia, MD 21046
Tel.: (410) 872-0024
Fax: (410) 872-0034
Emp.: 20
Sonar System Development Services
S.I.C.: 3812
N.A.I.C.S.: 334511
Robert Olsen *(VP-Advanced Tech)*

Advanced Acoustic Concepts, Inc. - Lemont Furnace (6)
1080 Eberly Way
Lemont Furnace, PA 15456
Tel.: (724) 437-6600
Fax: (724) 434-5101
Emp.: 60
Sonar System Development Services
S.I.C.: 3812
N.A.I.C.S.: 334511
Gregg Bauer *(VP-Production Sys)*

DRS Data & Imaging Systems Inc (3)
133 Bauer Dr
Oakland, NJ 07436 DE
Tel.: (201) 337-3800 (100%)
Fax: (201) 337-2704
Web Site: www.drs.com
Sales Range: $1-9.9 Million
Emp.: 125
Ruggedized Mission Recording Products & High Capacity Data Storage Systems for Government & Commercial Applications
S.I.C.: 3812
N.A.I.C.S.: 334511
Gene Martelacci *(VP-Fin)*

DRS Defense Solutions, LLC (3)
530 Gaither Rd Ste 900
Rockville, MD 20850
Tel.: (240) 238-3900
Fax: (240) 238-3977
Search & Navigation Equipment Mfr
S.I.C.: 3812
N.A.I.C.S.: 334511

Subsidiaries:

DRS CenGen, LLC (4)
9250 Bendix Rd N
Columbia, MD 21045
Tel.: (410) 715-1300
Fax: (410) 715-8797
E-Mail: info@cengen.com
Web Site: www.cengen.com
Communication Software Development Services
S.I.C.: 7371
N.A.I.C.S.: 541511
Lilotama Bengfort *(Pres)*

DRS Consolidated Controls, Inc. (4)
21 S St
Danbury, CT 06810 DE
Tel.: (203) 798-3030
E-Mail: sales@drs-cci.com
Web Site: www.drs-cci.com
Nuclear Power Plant Construction Services
S.I.C.: 1629
N.A.I.C.S.: 237130
Peter Kirk *(VP-Bus Dev)*

DRS Environmental Systems, Inc. (4)
7375 Industrial Rd
Florence, KY 41042-2911 DE
Tel.: (859) 525-2102
Fax: (859) 795-1475
E-Mail: jfritts@drs-esi.com
Web Site: www.drs.com
Military Equipment Mfr
S.I.C.: 3559
N.A.I.C.S.: 333249
Larry Ezell *(VP & Gen Mgr)*

DRS ICAS LLC (4)
2601 Mission Point Blvd Ste 250
Beavercreek, OH 45431
Tel.: (937) 429-7408
Fax: (937) 429-7176
Communication Equipment Mfr
S.I.C.: 3669
N.A.I.C.S.: 334290

DRS SIGNAL SOLUTIONS, INC. (4)
700 Quince Orchard Rd
Gaithersburg, MD 20878
Tel.: (301) 944-8616
E-Mail: marketing@drs.com
Electronic Equipment Whlsr
S.I.C.: 5065
N.A.I.C.S.: 423690
Gary Glotfelty *(Controller)*

Subsidiary:

DRS SONETICOM INC (5)
1045 S John Rodes Blvd
Melbourne, FL 32904-2005
Tel.: (321) 733-0400
Business Consulting Services
S.I.C.: 7389
N.A.I.C.S.: 561499
Rowland Huss *(VP-Bus Line)*

DRS TECHNICAL SERVICES, INC. (4)
12930 Worldgate Dr Ste 700
Herndon, VA 20170
Tel.: (703) 896-7100
Fax: (703) 896-7344
Communication & Security System Mfr & Whlsr
S.I.C.: 3669
N.A.I.C.S.: 334290
Tom Adams *(Dir-Proposal Ops)*

DRS Integrated Defense Systems and Servies Group (3)
530 Gaither Rd Ste 900
Rockville, MD 20850
Tel.: (240) 238-3900
Fax: (240) 238-3977
E-Mail: marketing@drs.com
Electronic Product Mfr & Whlsr
S.I.C.: 3679
N.A.I.C.S.: 334419
Richard S. Danforth *(Pres)*

DRS Power & Control Technologies, Inc. (3)
4265 N 30th St
Milwaukee, WI 53216-1821
Tel.: (414) 875-2900
Fax: (414) 875-2926
Power Conversion Equipment Whlsr
S.I.C.: 5251
N.A.I.C.S.: 444210

Subsidiary:

DRS POWER TECHNOLOGY, INC. (4)
625 Main St
Fitchburg, MA 01420-3168
Tel.: (978) 353-5416
Fax: (978) 353-5107
Steam Turbine & Pump Mfr
S.I.C.: 3511
N.A.I.C.S.: 333611

DRS Power Solutions (3)
141 N Ave
Bridgeport, CT 06606
Tel.: (703) 378-6100
Fax: (703) 378-9700
Toll Free: (800) 438-8774
E-Mail: information@upsi.com
Web Site: www.drspowersolutions.com
Emp.: 200
Power Generation & Conversion Equipment Mfr & Distr
S.I.C.: 3699
N.A.I.C.S.: 335999
Carl Geary *(Dir-Bus Dev)*

DRS RSTA, Inc. (3)
100 N Babcock St
Melbourne, FL 32935-6715 FL
Tel.: (321) 984-9030 (100%)
Fax: (321) 984-8746
E-Mail: info@drs.com
Web Site: www.drs.com
Emp.: 350
Targeting & Sighting Systems Mfr
S.I.C.: 3827
N.A.I.C.S.: 333314
Terry Murphy *(Pres)*

DRS Sensors & Targeting Systems, Inc. (3)
10600 Valley View St
Cypress, CA 90630-4833 DE
Tel.: (714) 220-3800 (100%)
Fax: (714) 220-3801
E-Mail: marketing@drseosg.com
Web Site: www.drs.com
Advanced Electro-Optical Sighting & Targeting Systems & Components Mfr
S.I.C.: 3579
N.A.I.C.S.: 333316
Thomas P. Crimmins *(Sr VP & Controller)*

Division:

DRS Sensors & Targeting Systems - Infrared Technologies Division (4)
13544 N Central Expwy
Dallas, TX 75243-1108 DE
Tel.: (972) 560-6000
Fax: (972) 560-6049
Toll Free: (877) 377-4783
Web Site: www.drsinfrared.com
Emp.: 400
Advanced Focal Plane Arrays & Sensor Components Design & Production
S.I.C.: 3827
N.A.I.C.S.: 333314
Terry Murphy *(CEO)*

DRS Surveillance Support Systems, Inc. (3)
6200 118th Ave
Largo, FL 33773-3726 DE
Tel.: (727) 541-6681 (100%)
Fax: (727) 544-4944
Web Site: www.drs.com
Emp.: 200
Radar & Other Military Surveillance Systems Support Pedestals & Antenna Systems Mfr
S.I.C.: 3827
N.A.I.C.S.: 333314
John Churchman *(Gen Mgr)*

Finmeccanica S.p.A.—(Continued)

DRS Sustainment Systems, Inc. (3)
201 Evans Ln
Saint Louis, MO 63121 DE
Tel.: (314) 553-4000 (100%)
Fax: (314) 553-4080
Web Site: www.drs-ssi.com
Sales Range: $1-4.9 Billion
Emp.: 500
Environmental Control Systems Mfr & Military Logistics Services
Import
S.I.C.: 4731
N.A.I.C.S.: 541614

Subsidiaries:

DRS Defense Technical Services, Inc. (4)
201 Evans Ln
Saint Louis, MO 63121-1126
Tel.: (314) 553-4272
E-Mail: ssispares@drs-ssi.com
Web Site: www.drs.com
Emp.: 600
Mfr of Environmental Control Systems & Developer of Military Logistics Services
S.I.C.: 3812
N.A.I.C.S.: 334511
Daniel Rodrigues *(Pres)*
James T. Myrick *(CFO)*

DRS Sustainment Systems, Inc. (4)
7375 Industrial Rd
Florence, KY 41042-2911 OH
Tel.: (859) 525-2102
Fax: (859) 525-6667
E-Mail: info@kecoindustries.com
Web Site: www.kecoindustries.com
Emp.: 400
Mfr of Environmental Control Systems & Developer of Military Logistics Services
Export
S.I.C.: 3812
N.A.I.C.S.: 334511

Plant:

DRS Fermont (4)
141 N Ave
Bridgeport, CT 06606-5120 CT
Tel.: (203) 366-5211
Fax: (203) 367-3642
Web Site: www.drspowersolutions.com
Emp.: 150
Mfr of Engine Generator Sets, Air Cargo Loaders, Standby Power Sources, & Solid State Controls
S.I.C.: 3621
N.A.I.C.S.: 335312
Michael D'Ottavio *(VP-Bus Dev)*

DRS Tactical Systems Global Services, Inc. (3)
1110 W Hibiscus Blvd
Melbourne, FL 32901 FL
Tel.: (321) 727-3672 (100%)
Fax: (321) 725-0496
E-Mail: sales@drs-ts.com
Web Site: www.drs-ts.com
Emp.: 247
Holding Company; Portable Computers & Communications Interfaces Mfr
Export
S.I.C.: 6719
N.A.I.C.S.: 551112
Michael Sheehan *(Pres)*

Subsidiary:

DRS Tactical Systems, Inc. (4)
1110 W Hibiscus Blvd
Melbourne, FL 32901-2704 FL
Tel.: (321) 727-3672 (100%)
Fax: (321) 725-0496
E-Mail: sales@drs-ts.com
Web Site: www.drs-ts.com
Emp.: 400
Portable Computers & Communications Interfaces Mfr
S.I.C.: 3571
N.A.I.C.S.: 334111
Jerry L. Sinn *(Pres)*

Non-U.S. Subsidiary:

DRS Technologies (U.K.) Ltd (4)
Lynwood House
The Trading Estate, Farnham, Surrey, GU9 9NN, United Kingdom
Tel.: (44) 1252730500
Fax: (44) 1252730530
Web Site: www.drs.com
Emp.: 70
Holding Company; Portable Computers & Communications Interfaces Mfr
S.I.C.: 6719
N.A.I.C.S.: 551112
Peter Henry Hurst *(VP-Bus Dev)*

Subsidiaries:

PCA Electronic Test Ltd. (5)
Unit 2b Long Bennington Business Park
Newark, Notts, NG23 5JR, United Kingdom UK
Tel.: (44) 1400 281 557
Electronic Product Maintenance Services
S.I.C.: 7699
N.A.I.C.S.: 811219

DRS Test & Energy Management, LLC (3)
110 Wynn Dr NW
Huntsville, AL 35805
Tel.: (256) 895-2000
Fax: (256) 895-2039
E-Mail: busdev@DRS-TEM.com
Web Site: www.drs-tem.com
Emp.: 200
Ground Vehicle Diagnostic & Test Equipment Mfr
S.I.C.: 3484
N.A.I.C.S.: 332994
Tim Wood *(Dir-Supply Chain)*

Laurel Technologies Partnership (3)
246 Airport Rd
Johnstown, PA 15904-7224 PA
Tel.: (814) 534-8900 (80%)
Fax: (814) 534-8815
Web Site: www.drs.com
Emp.: 850
Circuit Card & Cable Assembly DRS Mfr
S.I.C.: 3672
N.A.I.C.S.: 334412
Patrick R. Marion *(VP & Gen Mgr)*

Non-U.S. Subsidiaries:

DRS Pivotal Power (3)
150 Bluewater Rd
Bedford, NS, B4B 1G9, Canada
Tel.: (902) 835-7268
Fax: (902) 835-6026
E-Mail: info@pivotalpower.com
Web Site: www.drspowersolutions.com
Emp.: 52
Power Conversion Equipment Mfr
S.I.C.: 3699
N.A.I.C.S.: 335999
Geroge Mullally *(Gen Mgr)*

MECCANICA HOLDINGS USA, INC. (2)
1625 I St NW Fl 12
Washington, DC 20006
Tel.: (202) 292-2620
Investment Management Services
S.I.C.: 6211
N.A.I.C.S.: 523999

MSSC COMPANY (2)
767 Electronic Dr Ste A
Horsham, PA 19044-2228
Tel.: (215) 242-7226
Fax: (215) 233-9947
Emp.: 40
Radar & Navigation Equipment Mfr
S.I.C.: 3812
N.A.I.C.S.: 334511
Jerry Marrell *(Gen Mgr)*

OTO MELARA NORTH AMERICA INC (2)
11700 Plaza America Dr Ste 1010
Reston, VA 20190
Tel.: (202) 459-6900
Fax: (202) 459-6901
Web Site: www.otomelara.it/OtoMelara/EN/Corporate/Locations/Washington/index.sdo
Emp.: 3
Military Weapon Mfr & Whslr
S.I.C.: 3795
N.A.I.C.S.: 336992
R. Scott Rettig *(Chm & CEO)*

Non-U.S. Subsidiaries:

AgustaWestland NV (1)
Locatellikade 1 Parnassusstoren
Amsterdam, 1076 AZ, Netherlands
Tel.: (31) 20 575 5600
Fax: (31) 20 673 0016
Web Site: www.agustawestland.com
Rotorcraft System Mfr
S.I.C.: 3812
N.A.I.C.S.: 334511

ELSACOM NV (1)
Strawinskylaan 3111
1077 ZX Amsterdam, Noord-Holland, Netherlands
Tel.: (31) 20 4420460
Investment Management Services
S.I.C.: 6211
N.A.I.C.S.: 523999

Finmeccanica UK Limited (1)
8-10 Great George Street
London, SW1P 3AE, United Kingdom UK
Tel.: (44) 20 7340 6100
Fax: (44) 20 7340 6199
E-Mail:
Web Site: www.finmeccanica.co.uk
Emp.: 30
Aerospace Security & Transportation Services
S.I.C.: 4581
N.A.I.C.S.: 488190
Allan Cook *(Chm)*
Alberto de Benedictis *(CEO)*

OTO MELARA IBERICA SA (1)
Poligono Industrial Masia del Conde Calle en Proyecto 4 Parcela
Loriguilla, 46393 Valencia, Spain
Tel.: (34) 961 520 602
Fax: (34) 961 520 610
E-Mail: info@otomelaraiberica.es
Web Site: www.otomelaraiberica.es
Emp.: 15
Logistics Consulting Services
S.I.C.: 4731
N.A.I.C.S.: 541614
Marco Busolli *(Mng Dir)*

PIVOTAL POWER, INC. (1)
150 Bluewater Road
Bedford, NS, B4B 1G9, Canada
Tel.: (902) 835-7268
Fax: (902) 835-6026
Power Conversion Equipment Mfr
S.I.C.: 3699
N.A.I.C.S.: 335999

Regionalny Park Przemyslowy Swidnik Sp. z o.o. (1)
Al Lotnikow Polskich 1
21-045 Swidnik, Poland PL
Tel.: (48) 81 722 60 22
Fax: (48) 81 722 66 52
E-Mail: biuro@park.swidnik.pl
Web Site: www.palck.svidnik.pl
Emp.: 4
Investment Management Services
S.I.C.: 6211
N.A.I.C.S.: 523999

ZAKLAD OBROBKI PLASTYCZNEJ SP. Z O.O. (1)
ul Kuznicza 13
Swidnik, 21-045 Lublin, Poland
Tel.: (48) 81 751 26 00
Fax: (48) 81 468 09 11
E-Mail: kuznia-zop@kuznia-zop.pl
Web Site: www.kuznia-zop.pl
Emp.: 50
Metal Product Distr
S.I.C.: 5051
N.A.I.C.S.: 423510
Kida Franciszek *(Pres)*

ZAKLAD REMONTOWY SP. Z O.O. (1)
Il Armii Wojska Polskiego 35
59-220 Legnica, Poland
Tel.: (48) 76 854 21 04
Electrical Equipment Installation Services
S.I.C.: 1731
N.A.I.C.S.: 238210

ZAKLAD UTRZYMANIA RUCHU SP. Z O.O. (1)
Metalowa 13
21-045 Swidnik, Poland
Tel.: (48) 81 751 27 05
Fax: (48) 81 468 09 22
Electrical Equipment Installation Services
S.I.C.: 1731
N.A.I.C.S.: 238210

Non-U.S. Joint Venture:

MBDA Holdings S.A.S. (1)
37 Boulevard de Montmorency
75016 Paris, France FR
Tel.: (33) 142242424
Fax: (33) 145245414
Web Site: www.mbda-systems.com
Holding Company; Guided Missiles & Missle Systems Mfr
S.I.C.: 6719
N.A.I.C.S.: 551112
Antoine Bouvier *(CEO)*
Peter Bols *(CFO)*
Antonio Perfetti *(COO)*

Subsidiary:

MBDA France SAS (2)
1 Ave Reaumer
92358 Le Plessis-Robinson, Cedex, France FR
Tel.: (33) 171541000
Telex: AISPA X 250 881 F
Fax: (33) 171540190
Web Site: www.mbda.fr
Emp.: 100
Missiles & Missile Systems
S.I.C.: 3724
N.A.I.C.S.: 336412

Joint Ventures:

EUROSAM (3)
Centre d'affaires de la Boursidiere Batiment Kerguelen
92357 Le Plessis-Robinson, France FR
Tel.: (33) 1 4187 1416
Fax: (33) 1 4187 1442
Web Site: www.eurosam.com
Emp.: 100
Missile Defense Systems Mfr
Import
S.I.C.: 3761
N.A.I.C.S.: 336414

ROXEL S.A.S. (3)
La Boursidi Immeuble Jura
92357 Le Plessis-Robinson, France
Tel.: (33) 141 07 82 95
Fax: (33) 146 30 22 37
Web Site: www.roxelgroup.com
Propulsion System Mfr
S.I.C.: 3764
N.A.I.C.S.: 336415
David Quancard *(CEO)*

Subsidiary:

ROXEL France (4)
Route D Ardon
45240 La Ferte-Saint-Aubin, France FR
Tel.: (33) 238516666
Fax: (33) 238516633
Emp.: 300
Rocket Propulsion Systems Mfr
S.I.C.: 3621
N.A.I.C.S.: 335312

Non-U.S. Subsidiaries:

MBDA Deutschland GmbH (2)
Hagenauer Forst 27
Schrobenhausen, Germany
Tel.: (49) 8252 99 0
Fax: (49) 8252 99 6120
Aircraft Machinery Mfr
S.I.C.: 3728
N.A.I.C.S.: 336413
Thomas Homberg *(Mng Dir)*

Subsidiaries:

Bayern-Chemie Gesellschaft fur Flugchemische Antriebe mbH (3)
Liebigstr 17
PO Box 11
D 84544 Aschau, Germany
Tel.: (49) 86386010
Fax: (49) 8638601399
E-Mail: info-de@mbda-systems.de
Web Site: www.bayernchemie.de
Rev.: $71,900,000
Emp.: 160
Rocket Propulsion Systems Mfr
S.I.C.: 3764
N.A.I.C.S.: 336415
Stoerchlee Ulrich *(CEO)*

TDW-Gesellschaft fur verteidigungstechnische Wirksysteme GmbH (3)
Hagenauer Forst 27
86529 Schrobenhausen, Germany
Tel.: (49) 8252 99 0
Fax: (49) 8252 99 6120
E-Mail: empfang-sob@mbda-systems.com
Web Site: www.eads.com
Emp.: 1,000
Aircraft Parts Mfr
S.I.C.: 3728
N.A.I.C.S.: 336413
Thomas Homberg *(Gen Mgr)*

MBDA Italia SpA (2)
Via Carciano 4-50/60-70
00131 Rome, Italy
Tel.: (39) 06 87711
Web Site: www.mbda-systems.com
Missile Systems Developer & Mfr
S.I.C.: 3761
N.A.I.C.S.: 336414

MBDA UK Ltd. (2)
Six Hills Way
Stevenage, SG1 2DA, United Kingdom UK
Tel.: (44) 1438312422
Fax: (44) 1438753377
Web Site: www.mbda.co.uk
Emp.: 2,000
Missile Mfr
S.I.C.: 3761
N.A.I.C.S.: 336414
Steve Wadey *(Mng Dir)*

Branch:

MBDA UK (3)
11 Strand
London, WC2N 5HR, United Kingdom
Tel.: (44) 1714516000
Fax: (44) 1714516001
Web Site: www.mbda.co.uk
Missile Mfr
S.I.C.: 3761
N.A.I.C.S.: 336414

FINNAIR PLC

(d/b/a Finnair Group)
Tietotie 11 A Helsinki Vantaa Airport
01053 Vantaa, Finland
Tel.: (358) 981881
Fax: (358) 98184092
E-Mail: investor.relations@finnair.com
Web Site: www.finnairgroup.com
Year Founded: 1923
FIA1S—(LSE OMX)
Sls.: $3,297,308,798
Assets: $3,017,709,289
Liabilities: $1,960,292,754
Net Worth: $1,057,416,535
Earnings: $15,884,806
Emp.: 6,368
Fiscal Year-end: 12/31/12

Business Description:
Holding Company; Scheduled Passenger & Cargo Air Transportation Services
S.I.C.: 6719
N.A.I.C.S.: 551112

Personnel:
Klaus Heinemann *(Chm)*
Harri Kerminen *(Vice Chm)*
Pekka Vauramo *(Pres, CEO & Member-Exec Bd)*
Erno Hilden *(CFO, Member-Exec Bd & Sr VP)*
Ville Iho *(COO & Member-Exec Bd)*
Allister Paterson *(Chief Comml Officer)*
Kati Kaksonen *(IR Officer)*
Sami Sarelius *(Member-Exec Bd, Gen Counsel & Sr VP)*
Gregory Kaldahl *(Member-Exec Bd & Sr VP-Resources Mgmt)*
Arja Suominen *(Member-Exec Bd & Sr VP-Corp Comm & Corp Responsibility)*
Manne Tiensuu *(Member-Exec Bd & Sr VP-HR)*
Kaisa Vikkula *(Member-Exec Bd & Sr VP-Travel Svcs)*
Ari Kuutchin *(Sr VP-Ground Handling & Mng Dir-Northport Oy)*
Juha Jarvinen *(Sr VP-Cargo)*
Kimmo Soini *(Sr VP-Technical Svcs)*

Board of Directors:
Klaus Heinemann
Maija-Liisa Friman
Jussi Itavuori
Merja Karhapaa
Harri Kerminen
Gunvor Kronman
Antti Kuosmanen

Subsidiaries:

Finnair Aircraft Finance Oy (1)
Tietotie 11 A
PO Box 15
01053 Vantaa, Finland
Tel.: (358) 98 1881
Fax: (358) 9818 4092
Web Site: www.finnairgroup.com
Aircraft Procurement & Leasing Services
S.I.C.: 7359
N.A.I.C.S.: 532411

Finnair Cargo Oy (1)
Rahtitie 1
1530 Vantaa, Finland
Tel.: (358) 9 818 81
Fax: (358) 9 818 5474
E-Mail: cargo.terminal@finnair.com
Web Site: www.finnaircargo.com
Emp.: 18
Air Freight Transportation Services
S.I.C.: 4731
N.A.I.C.S.: 488510
Juuso Lintonen *(VP-Ops-Terminal)*

Finnair Cargo Terminal Operations Oy (1)
Rahtitie 1
1530 Vantaa, Finland
Tel.: (358) 981 8501
Fax: (358) 9818 5468
E-Mail: cargo.terminal@finnair.com
Emp.: 35
Air Freight Terminal Services
S.I.C.: 4581
N.A.I.C.S.: 488119
Juuso Lintonen *(Gen Mgr)*

Finnair Facilities Management Oy (1)
Tietotie 11 A
PO Box 200
Vantaa, 1053, Finland
Tel.: (358) 9 818 81
Fax: (358) 9818 4909
Facility Management Services
S.I.C.: 8744
N.A.I.C.S.: 561210

Finnair Flight Academy Oy (1)
Helsinki Airport Pyhtaankorventie 11-13
1530 Vantaa, Finland
Tel.: (358) 9 818 4046
Fax: (358) 9 818 4600
E-Mail: flightacademy.sales@finnair.com
Web Site: www.finnairflightacademy.com
Emp.: 5
Airline Training Services
S.I.C.: 8249
N.A.I.C.S.: 611512
Olli Paasio *(Head-Sls & Product Mgmt)*

Finnair Oyj (1)
Tietotie 11 A
Helsinki-Vantaa Airport, FI-01053 Vantaa, Finland FI
Tel.: (358) 981881 (100%)
Fax: (358) 98184091
Web Site: www.finnair.fi
Emp.: 7,000
Scheduled Passenger & Freight Air Transportation Services
S.I.C.: 4512
N.A.I.C.S.: 481111
Kukka Heinonen *(Deputy CEO, CFO & Exec VP)*
Christer Haglund *(Sr VP-Corp Comm)*

Subsidiaries:

Amadeus Finland Oy (2)
Itamerenkatu 1
PO Box 278
FIN 00180 Helsinki, Finland (95%)
Tel.: (358) 107737900
Fax: (358) 107737985
Web Site: www.amadeus.fi
Sales Range: $10-24.9 Million
Emp.: 40
Scheduled Passenger & Cargo Air Transportation Services
S.I.C.: 4512
N.A.I.C.S.: 481111

Area Travel Agency Ltd. (2)
Mannerheimintie 102
FIN 00251 Helsinki, Finland (100%)
Tel.: (358) 9818383
Fax: (358) 98183245
E-Mail: area@area.fi
Web Site: www.area.fi
Emp.: 350
S.I.C.: 4512
N.A.I.C.S.: 481111

Finland Travel Bureau Ltd. (2)
Tietotie 9
FIN 00100 Vantaa, Finland
Mailing Address:
PO Box 319
00101 Helsinki, Finland
Tel.: (358) 108261
Fax: (358) 108262104
E-Mail: smt@smt.fi
Web Site: www.smt.fi
Emp.: 620
Promoter & Provider of Information of Tourism
S.I.C.: 4724
N.A.I.C.S.: 561510
Jaana Tammisto *(Mng Dir)*

Non-U.S. Subsidiary:

Estravel AS (3)
Suur Karja 15
10140 Tallinn, Estonia (70%)
Tel.: (372) 6266200
Fax: (372) 6266262
E-Mail: post@estravel.ee
Web Site: www.estravel.ee
Emp.: 150
S.I.C.: 4512
N.A.I.C.S.: 481111
Anne Samlik *(Mng Dir)*

Finnair Travel Services Oy (2)
Tieto Tie 11
PO Box 275
FIN 00101 Helsinki, Finland (100%)
Tel.: (358) 981881
Fax: (358) 98184092
E-Mail: info@finnair.fi
Web Site: www.finnair.fi
Emp.: 400
S.I.C.: 4512
N.A.I.C.S.: 481111
Jukka Hienonen *(CEO)*

Finncatering Oy (2)
140 Tikkurilantie
PO Box 38
01531 Vantaa, Finland (100%)
Tel.: (358) 98700250
Fax: (358) 987002515
Web Site: www.finncatering.fi
Sales Range: $25-49.9 Million
Emp.: 200
Catering Services
S.I.C.: 5812
N.A.I.C.S.: 722320

Mikkelin Matkatoimisto Oy (2)
Porrassalmenkatu 23
FIN 50100 Mikkeli, Finland (100%)
Tel.: (358) 15321100
Fax: (358) 53211010
Sales Range: $1-9.9 Million
S.I.C.: 4512
N.A.I.C.S.: 481111

Oy Aurinkomatkat-Suntours Ltd. Ab (2)
Pohjoinen Rautatiekatu 25
PO Box 287
FIN 00100 Helsinki, Finland (99%)
Tel.: (358) 10446441
Fax: (358) 104467188
E-Mail: aurinkomatkat@aurinkomatkat.fi
Web Site: www.aurinkomatkat.fi
Emp.: 160
Tour Operator
S.I.C.: 4512
N.A.I.C.S.: 481111
Tuomo Meretmiemi *(Gen Mgr)*

Suomen Matkatoimisto Oy (2)
Kaivokatu 10 A 6 Krs
FIN 00100 Helsinki, Finland (100%)
Tel.: (358) 108261
E-Mail: smt@smt.fi
Web Site: www.smt.fi
Air Transportation
S.I.C.: 4512
N.A.I.C.S.: 481111

U.S. Subsidiary:

Finnair Oyj-New York (2)
150 E 42nd St
New York, NY 10017
Tel.: (212) 499-9000
Telex: 12-7045
Fax: (212) 499-9040
Toll Free: (800) 950-5000
E-Mail: webmaster@us.finnair.com
Web Site: www.finnair.com
Emp.: 4
International Airline Services
S.I.C.: 4512
N.A.I.C.S.: 481111
Markku Remes *(Product Mgr)*

Division:

Finnair (3)
228 East 45th St
New York, NY 10016-0200
Tel.: (212) 499-9000
Fax: (212) 499-9036
Web Site: www.finnair.com
S.I.C.: 3999
N.A.I.C.S.: 327110
Janne Soini *(Sls Mgr)*

Finnair Technical Services Oy (1)
Helsinki Airport Teknikontie 5
01530 Vantaa, Finland
Tel.: (358) 9 818 2400
Fax: (358) 9 818 6132
E-Mail: technical.sales@finnair.com
Web Site: www.finnairtechnicalservices.com
Emp.: 1,600
Aircraft Technical Consulting Services
S.I.C.: 8999
N.A.I.C.S.: 541690
Mikko Koskentalo *(Mgr-Sls & Mktg)*

FTS Financial Services Oy (1)
Tietotie 11
01053 Vantaa, Finland
Tel.: (358) 9 81881
Fax: (358) 9 8184091
Financial Management Services
S.I.C.: 6211
N.A.I.C.S.: 523999

Non-U.S. Subsidiaries:

A/S Estravel Ltd (1)
Suur-Karja 15
Tallinn, 10140, Estonia
Tel.: (372) 6266233
Fax: (372) 6266232
E-Mail: estravel@estravel.ee
Web Site: www.estravel.ee
Emp.: 16
Travel Agency Services
S.I.C.: 4724
N.A.I.C.S.: 561510
Anne Samlik *(Mng Dir)*

Aurinko Ou (1)
Parnu Rd 10
10148 Tallinn, Estonia
Tel.: (372) 64 09053
Fax: (372) 66 67623
E-Mail: info@aurinko.ee
Emp.: 11
Tour Operating Services
S.I.C.: 4725
N.A.I.C.S.: 561520
Cenzea Seeg *(Gen Mgr)*

Back Office Services Estonia OU (1)
Vallikraavi 2
51003 Tartu, Estonia
Tel.: (372) 7440309
Fax: (372) 7440311
Emp.: 100
Office Administrative Services
S.I.C.: 8741
N.A.I.C.S.: 561110
Leela Lepik *(Mng Dir)*

FINNAUST MINING PLC
47 Charles Street
London, W1J 5EL, United Kingdom
Tel.: (44) 203 326 1729
Fax: (44) 207 681 3861
Web Site: www.finnaustmining.com
FAM—(AIM)
Assets: $2,410,183
Liabilities: $457,155
Net Worth: $1,953,027
Earnings: ($809,797)
Fiscal Year-end: 02/28/13
Business Description:
Copper, Lead & Zinc Mining
S.I.C.: 1021
N.A.I.C.S.: 212234
Personnel:
Daniel Lougher *(Chm)*
Urpo Kuronen *(COO)*
Garth Palmer *(Sec)*
Board of Directors:
Daniel Lougher
Alastair Clayton
Greg Kuenzel
Graham Marshall

FINNING INTERNATIONAL INC.
Suite 1000 666 Burrard Street
Vancouver, BC, V6C 2X8, Canada
Tel.: (604) 691-6444
Fax: (604) 331-4887
Web Site: www.finning.com
Year Founded: 1933
FTT—(TSX)
Rev.: $6,582,528,669
Assets: $5,087,417,222
Liabilities: $3,530,231,215
Net Worth: $1,557,186,007
Earnings: $335,600,038
Emp.: 15,382
Fiscal Year-end: 12/31/12
Business Description:
Holding Company; Construction & Mining Equipment Sales, Rental & Maintenance Services
S.I.C.: 6719
N.A.I.C.S.: 551112
Personnel:
Douglas W. G. Whitehead *(Chm)*
Scott Thomson *(Pres & CEO)*
David S. Smith *(CFO & Exec VP)*
Juan Carlos Villegas *(COO)*
Rebecca L. Schalm *(Chief HR Officer & Sr VP)*
Marcello Marchese *(Pres-South America)*
Thomas M. Merinsky *(Treas & VP)*
J. Gail Sexsmith *(Sec)*
Neil Dickinson *(Mng Dir-UK & Ireland & Exec VP-Global Power Sys)*
Andrew S. Fraser *(Exec VP-Customer & External Rels)*
Anna P. Marks *(Sr VP & Controller)*
Board of Directors:
Douglas W. G. Whitehead
Ricardo Bacarreza
James E. C. Carter
David L. Emerson
Kathleen M. O'Neill
Christopher W. Patterson
John M. Reid
Andrew H. Simon
Scott Thomson
Bruce L. Turner
Michael M. Wilson
Legal Counsel:
Borden Ladner Gervais LLP
Vancouver, BC, Canada
Transfer Agent:
Computershare Investor Services Inc.
Montreal, QC, Canada
Division:

Finning Canada Inc. **(1)**
16830 107th Avenue
Edmonton, AB, T5P 4C3, Canada
Tel.: (780) 930-4800
Fax: (780) 930-4801
E-Mail: info@finning.ca
Web Site: www.finning.ca
Emp.: 3,000
Construction & Mining Equipment Sales, Rental & Maintenance Services
S.I.C.: 5082
N.A.I.C.S.: 423810
Juan Carlos Villegas *(Pres)*

Non-U.S. Subsidiaries:

Finning Argentina S.A. **(1)**
Camino Boulogne Bancalari 2955
Victoria, Buenos Aires, 1644, Argentina
Tel.: (54) 1147258800
Fax: (54) 1147141162
Web Site: www.finning.com.ar
Construction & Mining Equipment Sales, Rental & Maintenance Services
S.I.C.: 5082
N.A.I.C.S.: 423810

Subsidiary:

Finning Soluciones Mineras S.A. **(2)**
Camino Boulogne Bancalari 2955
1644 San Fernando, Buenos Aires, Argentina
Tel.: (54) 1147258800
Fax: (54) 1147141162
Mining Equipment Sales, Rental & Maintenance Services
S.I.C.: 5082
N.A.I.C.S.: 423810

Finning Bolivia S.A. **(1)**
Carretera Al Norte Km 3 1/2
Santa Cruz, Andres Ibanez, Bolivia
Tel.: (591) 33429688
Fax: (591) 33420556
Web Site: www.finning.com.bo
Construction & Mining Equipment Sales, Rental & Maintenance Services
S.I.C.: 5082
N.A.I.C.S.: 423810

Finning Chile S.A. **(1)**
Avenida Los Jardines 924 Ciudad Empresarial Huechuraba
Santiago, Chile
Tel.: (56) 26797000
Fax: (56) 26797575
E-Mail: FinningChile@finning.cl
Web Site: www.finning.cl
Emp.: 927
Construction & Mining Equipment Sales, Rental & Maintenance Services
S.I.C.: 5082
N.A.I.C.S.: 423810
Juan Cerlos *(Pres)*

Finning (UK) Ltd. **(1)**
Watling St
Cannock, Staffs, WS11 8LL, United Kingdom (100%)
Tel.: (44) 1543 461 461
Fax: (44) 1543 461 700
E-Mail: mailbox@finning.co.uk
Web Site: www.finning.co.uk
Emp.: 450
Construction & Mining Equipment Sales, Rental & Maintenance Services
S.I.C.: 5082
N.A.I.C.S.: 423810
Neil Dickinson *(Mng Dir)*

Finning Uruguay S.A. **(1)**
Juan Burghi 2646 Ruta 1 Y Camino Cibils
12800 Montevideo, Uruguay
Tel.: (598) 23130131
Fax: (598) 23113271
E-Mail: contacto@finning.com.uy
Web Site: www.finning.com.uy
Construction & Mining Equipment Sales, Rental & Maintenance Services
S.I.C.: 5082
N.A.I.C.S.: 423810

FINNMIRROR OY
Peilitie 15
38200 Vammala, Finland
Tel.: (358) 351161
Telex: 22367 miro sf
Fax: (358) 35115222
E-Mail: finnmirror@finnmirror.fi
Web Site: www.finnmirror.fi
Year Founded: 1923
Emp.: 105
Business Description:
Mfr. of Mirrors, Sotrage Units & Bathroom Fixtures
S.I.C.: 3231
N.A.I.C.S.: 327215
Personnel:
Pala Aleksi *(Mng Dir)*

FINOLEX GROUP
26-27 Mumbai-Pune Road
Pimpri, Pune, 411 018, India
Tel.: (91) 20 2747 5963
Web Site: www.finolex.com
Business Description:
Holding Company
S.I.C.: 6719
N.A.I.C.S.: 551112
Personnel:
P. P. Chhabria *(Chm)*

Affiliates:

Finolex Cables Ltd. **(1)**
26-27 Mumbai-Pune Road
Pimpri, Pune, 411 018, India In
Tel.: (91) 2027475963
Web Site: www.finolex.com
FINCABLES—(NSE)
Rev.: $449,322,462
Assets: $260,327,556
Liabilities: $88,958,628
Net Worth: $171,368,928
Earnings: $26,933,058
Emp.: 1,611
Fiscal Year-end: 03/31/13
Electrical & Communication Cable Mfr
S.I.C.: 3357
N.A.I.C.S.: 335929
D. K. Chhabria *(Chm)*
Mahesh Viswanathan *(CFO)*
R. G. D'Silva *(Compliance Officer, Sec & VP-Legal)*

Finolex Industries Ltd. **(1)**
Gat No 399 Urse Taluka Maval
Pune, Maharashtra, 410 506, India In
Tel.: (91) 2114237251
Fax: (91) 2114237252
E-Mail: pipes@finolexind.com
Web Site: www.finolex.com
500940—(BOM)
Rev.: $451,157,014
Assets: $377,940,885
Liabilities: $244,237,320
Net Worth: $133,703,565
Earnings: $25,239,781
Emp.: 1,107
Fiscal Year-end: 03/31/13
Plastic Pipes Mfr
S.I.C.: 3084
N.A.I.C.S.: 326122
Prakash P. Chhabria *(Chm)*
S. S. Dhanorkar *(Mng Dir)*
Mandar B. Ratnaparkhi *(CFO)*
Umesh M. Gosavi *(Sec)*

FINORE MINING INC.
Suite 1980 - 1075 West Georgia Street
Vancouver, BC, V6E 3C9, Canada
Tel.: (604) 688-9588
Fax: (778) 329-9361
E-Mail: info@finoremining.com
Web Site: www.finoremining.com
Year Founded: 2006
FIN—(CNSX OTC)
Int. Income: $109
Assets: $10,988,563
Liabilities: $187,640
Net Worth: $10,800,923
Earnings: ($79,902)
Fiscal Year-end: 07/31/13
Business Description:
Metals & Minerals Investment Services
S.I.C.: 6211
N.A.I.C.S.: 523999
Personnel:
Peter Frederick Tegart *(CEO)*
Denise Lok *(CFO)*
Board of Directors:
Savio Chiu
David Eaton
Peter Frederick Tegart
Mohan Vulimiri
Transfer Agent:
Valiant Trust Company
750 Cambie St, Ste 600
Vancouver, BC, V6B 0A2, Canada

FIN.PART S.P.A.
Foro Buonaparte 51
20121 Milan, Italy
Tel.: (39) 02 725501
Fax: (39) 0286463242
Sales Range: $300-349.9 Million
Emp.: 1,570
Business Description:
Apparel Mfr
S.I.C.: 2399
N.A.I.C.S.: 315990

FINSBURY FOOD GROUP PLC
Maes y Coed Road
Cardiff, CF14 4XR, United Kingdom
Tel.: (44) 2920357500
Fax: (44) 2076389426
E-Mail: info@finsburyfoods.co.uk
Web Site: www.finsburyfoods.co.uk
FIF—(LSE)
Rev.: $278,894,718
Assets: $169,108,794
Liabilities: $74,536,171
Net Worth: $94,572,623
Earnings: $13,032,301
Emp.: 2,414
Fiscal Year-end: 06/29/13
Business Description:
Baked Goods Mfr
S.I.C.: 2052
N.A.I.C.S.: 311812
Personnel:
John Gerald Duffy *(CEO)*
Board of Directors:
Martin W. Lightbody
Edward J. Beale
Stephen Alexander Boyd
John Gerald Duffy
Raymond Duignan
David C. Marshall
Paul J. Monk

Subsidiaries:

Anthony Alan Foods Ltd. **(1)**
c/o Memory Lane Cakes Ltd
Maes-y-Coed Road, Cardiff, CF14 4XR, United Kingdom
Tel.: (44) 29 2062 3351
E-Mail: aaf@ml-cakes.co.uk
Web Site: www.finsburyfoods.co.uk/about.php?p=Anthony+Alan+Foods
Frozen Cakes, Pies & Pastries Mfr
S.I.C.: 2053
N.A.I.C.S.: 311813

Campbells Cake Company Ltd. **(1)**
Unit 3 The Green
Twechar, Glasgow, G65 9QB, United Kingdom UK
Tel.: (44) 1236826633 (100%)
Fax: (44) 1236826622
E-Mail: enquiries@campbellscakes.co.uk
Emp.: 50
Frozen Cakes Pies & Pastries Mfr
S.I.C.: 2053
N.A.I.C.S.: 311813
Patrick Campell *(Mgr-Ops)*

Lightbody Group Ltd. **(1)**
73 Bothwell Rd
Hamilton, ML3 0DW, United Kingdom
Tel.: (44) 01698285227
Fax: (44) 1698285222
E-Mail: enquiries@lightbody.co.uk
Web Site: www.lightbodycakes.com
Emp.: 1,000

Frozen Cakes Pies & Pastries Mfr
S.I.C.: 2053
N.A.I.C.S.: 311813
David Crawford-Currie *(Dir-Fin)*

Memory Lane Cakes Limited (1)
Maes Y Coed Rd
Cardiff, Glamorgan, CF14 4XR, United Kingdom (100%)
Tel.: (44) 2920357500
Fax: (44) 2920624327
Web Site: www.finsburyfoods.co.uk/about.php?p=Memory+Lane+Cakes
Emp.: 1,000
Mfr. of Cakes & Confections
S.I.C.: 2052
N.A.I.C.S.: 311812
Paul Gratdon *(Mng Dir)*

Nicholas & Harris Ltd. (1)
Brunel House Brunel Road
Churchfields Industrial Estate, Salisbury, SP2 7PU, United Kingdom
Tel.: (44) 01722327152
Fax: (44) 1722414056
E-Mail: enquiries@nicholasandharris.co.uk
Web Site: www.finsburyfoods.co.uk/about.php?p=Nicholas+%26+Harris
Emp.: 280
Mfr of Premium & Speciality Breads
S.I.C.: 2053
N.A.I.C.S.: 311813
Simon Staddon *(Mng Dir)*

Non-U.S. Joint Venture:

Lightbody Europe SARL (1)
33 boulevard de Chezy
35000 Rennes, France (50%)
Tel.: (33) 299316344
Fax: (33) 299677357
E-Mail: contact@lightbody-europe.com
Web Site: www.otoogood.com
Emp.: 18
Grocery & Related Products Whslr
S.I.C.: 5149
N.A.I.C.S.: 424490
Philippe Stretez *(Mng Dir)*

FINSHORE MANAGEMENT SERVICES LTD.

Sikkim Commerce House 5th Floor Room 505
4/1 Middleton Street, Kolkata, 700 071, India
Tel.: (91) 33 4065 0291
E-Mail: info@finshoregroup.com
Web Site: www.finshoregroup.com
Business Description:
Financial Advisory & Management Services
S.I.C.: 6726
N.A.I.C.S.: 525990
Personnel:
Lakshman Srinivasan *(Chm & Mng Dir)*
Sunil Agarwal *(Compliance Officer & Sec)*
Board of Directors:
Lakshman Srinivasan
Kajal Bhanja Chaudhuri
Suvobrata Ganguly
Uttam Munshi
Sireen Sadhu

FINTAXI, SEC

7333 place des Roseraies bureau 202
Anjou, QC, H1M 2X6, Canada
Tel.: (514) 353-2757
Fax: (514) 353-7204
E-Mail: info@Fintaxi.ca
Year Founded: 2003
Rev.: $19,849,917
Emp.: 8
Business Description:
Taxi Financing Services
S.I.C.: 4121
N.A.I.C.S.: 485310
Personnel:
Serge Masse *(CEO)*

FINTECH GLOBAL INCORPORATED

Toranomon Towers Office 19th Floor
1-28 Toranomon 4-chome
Minato-ku, Tokyo, 105-0001, Japan
Tel.: (81) 357332121
Fax: (81) 357332124
Web Site: www.fgi.co.jp
Year Founded: 1994
8789—(TKS)
Rev.: $26,556,352
Assets: $83,625,771
Liabilities: $36,292,198
Net Worth: $47,333,573
Earnings: ($16,607,569)
Emp.: 70
Fiscal Year-end: 09/30/12
Business Description:
Investment Banking Services
S.I.C.: 6211
N.A.I.C.S.: 523110
Personnel:
Robert Hirst *(Chm)*
Nobumitsu Tamai *(Pres & CEO)*
Seigo Washimoto *(Mng Dir & Head-Bus Mgmt Dept)*
Weijow Liaw *(Pres-FinTech Global Shanghai Inc)*
Board of Directors:
Robert Hirst
Toru Mitsuhashi
Nobumitsu Tamai
Seigo Washimoto
Hideyuki Yamanaka
Transfer Agent:
Mizuho Trust & Banking Co., Ltd
1-2-1 Yaesu Chuo-ku
Tokyo, Japan

Subsidiary:

Entrust Inc. (1)
Dai2-Okamotoya Bldg 8F
1-22-16 Toranomon Minato-ku, Nagoya, Tokyo, 105 0001, Japan
Tel.: (81) 3 6880 1070
E-Mail: info@entrust-inc.jp
Web Site: www.entrust-inc.jp
Emp.: 5
Business Management Services
S.I.C.: 8748
N.A.I.C.S.: 541618
Yutaka Kuwabara *(Pres)*

FINTEL ENERGIA GROUP SPA

Via E Fermi 19
62010 Pollenza, Italy
Tel.: (39) 0733 201170
Fax: (39) 0733 206196
E-Mail: info@fintel.bz
Web Site: www.fintel.bz
FTL—(ITA)
Business Description:
Electricity & Natural Gas Distr
S.I.C.: 4911
N.A.I.C.S.: 221122
Personnel:
Alcide Giovannetti *(Chm)*
Dunia Dunia *(Dir Gen)*
Board of Directors:
Alcide Giovannetti
Tiziano Giovannetti
Giuliano Mosconi
Paolo Sassetti
Loris Tartuferi

Subsidiary:

Energogreen Renewables S.r.l. (1)
Via Enrico Fermi 19
62010 Pollenza, Macerata, Italy
Tel.: (39) 0733 201681
Fax: (39) 0733 206196
E-Mail: info@energogreen.com
Web Site: www.energogreen.com
Emp.: 3
Renewable Energy Consulting Services
S.I.C.: 8999
N.A.I.C.S.: 541690
Fedealea Aoanzato *(Mgr-Comml)*

FINTRONICS HOLDINGS COMPANY LIMITED

Units 2003 2005 20/F Great Eagle Centre 23 Harbour Road
Wanchai, China (Hong Kong)
Tel.: (852) 22349723
Fax: (852) 22349738
E-Mail: gloria@fintronics.com.hk
Web Site: www.fintronics.com.hk
0706—(HKG)
Sls.: $1,607,104
Assets: $23,933,765
Liabilities: $1,803,624
Net Worth: $22,130,141
Earnings: ($5,209,967)
Emp.: 45
Fiscal Year-end: 12/31/12
Business Description:
Computer Networking
S.I.C.: 7373
N.A.I.C.S.: 541512
Personnel:
Marco Wai Sze *(Chm & CEO)*
Ying Kay Chan *(CFO & Sec)*
Board of Directors:
Marco Wai Sze
Jonathan Ming Sun Chan
Sherman Yiu Kan Chong
Yip Wing Lai
Zhenhua Mao
Jun Shentu
Shu Jiang Tan
Legal Counsel:
Chiu & Partners
40th Fl Jardine House 1 Connaught Place
Central, China (Hong Kong)
The Bank of Bermuda Limited
Bank of Bermuda Building 6 Front Street
Hamilton, Bermuda
Transfer Agents:
Tricor Tengis Limited
26th Floor Tesbury Centre 28 Queen's Road East
Wanchai, China (Hong Kong)
Tel.: (852) 29801333
Fax: (852) 28108185
The Bank of Bermuda Limited
Bank of Bermuda Building 6 Front Street
Hamilton, Bermuda

FINZSOFT SOLUTIONS LIMITED

Level 1 Building C Millennium Centre
602 Great South Road
Greenlane, Auckland, 1051, New Zealand
Tel.: (64) 95716800
Fax: (64) 95716899
E-Mail: info@finzsoft.com
Web Site: www.finzsoft.com
FIN—(NZE)
Rev.: $7,392,694
Assets: $3,785,779
Liabilities: $1,512,128
Net Worth: $2,273,650
Earnings: $335,320
Emp.: 30
Fiscal Year-end: 03/31/13
Business Description:
Software Development & Maintenance Services
S.I.C.: 7371
N.A.I.C.S.: 541511
Personnel:
Brent Impey *(Chm)*
Andrew Holliday *(Mng Dir)*
Ian Wills *(Mng Dir)*
Tim Hurring *(CTO)*
Board of Directors:
Brent Impey
Paul Cook
Andrew Holliday
Ian Wills

FIRAN TECHNOLOGY GROUP CORPORATION

250 Finchdene Square
Toronto, ON, M1X 1A5, Canada
Tel.: (416) 299-4000
Fax: (416) 292-4308
Toll Free: (800) 258-5396
E-Mail: info@ftgcorp.com
Web Site: www.ftgcorp.com
Year Founded: 2003
FTG—(TSX)
Sls.: $55,313,237
Assets: $28,425,990
Liabilities: $14,494,800
Net Worth: $13,931,190
Earnings: $922,451
Emp.: 425
Fiscal Year-end: 11/30/12
Business Description:
Designer & Mfr of Custom-Made Printed Circuit Boards & Recreational Vehicles
S.I.C.: 3672
N.A.I.C.S.: 334412
Personnel:
Bradley C. Bourne *(Pres & CEO)*
Joseph R. Ricci *(CFO, Sec & VP)*
Hardeep Heer *(CTO & VP-Engrg)*
Claude Bougie *(Pres-FTG Aerospace Tianjin Inc)*
Board of Directors:
Robert J. Beutel
Bradley C. Bourne
Edward C. Hanna
Raymond G. Harris
David F. Masotti
David J. McLeish
Legal Counsel:
Blake, Cassels & Graydon LLP
Commerce Court W
Toronto, ON, Canada
Transfer Agent:
Canadian Stock Transfer Compnay Inc
Postal Station A
PO Box 4202
Toronto, ON, Canada

Divisions:

FTG Aerospace (1)
10 Commander Blvd
Toronto, ON, M1S 3T2, Canada
Tel.: (416) 438-6076
Fax: (416) 438-8065
Toll Free: (800) 419-0066
E-Mail:
Web Site: www.firantechnology.com
Emp.: 90
Mfr of Lighting Display Panels, Bezels, Keyboards & Indicators for Aerospace Industry
S.I.C.: 3728
N.A.I.C.S.: 336413
Claude Bougie *(Pres-Tianjin)*

Subsidiary:

FTG Circuits - Toronto (1)
250 Finchdene Square
Toronto, ON, M1X 1A5, Canada
Tel.: (416) 299-4000
Fax: (416) 292-4308
Toll Free: (800) 258-5396
E-Mail: ftg@ftgcorp.com
Web Site: www.ftgcorp.com
Emp.: 150
Printed Circuit Board Mfr
S.I.C.: 3672
N.A.I.C.S.: 334412
Brad Bourne *(Pres)*

U.S. Subsidiary:

FTG Circuits - Chatsworth (1)
20750 Marilla St
Chatsworth, CA 91311
Tel.: (818) 407-4024
Fax: (818) 407-4034
Web Site: www.ftgcorp.com
Printed Circuit Board Mfr
S.I.C.: 3672

Firan Technology Group Corporation—(Continued)

N.A.I.C.S.: 334412
Michael Labrador *(VP & Gen MgrChatsworth)*

FIRCOSOFT SAS

247 Rue De Bercy
75012 Paris, France
Tel.: (33) 1 53 44 13 00
E-Mail: info@fircosoft.com
Web Site: www.fircosoft.com
Emp.: 50
Business Description:
Financial Reporting & Compliance Software Programming
S.I.C.: 7371
N.A.I.C.S.: 541511
Personnel:
Jean Losco *(Pres & CEO)*
U.S. Subsidiary:

FircoSoft Inc. **(1)**
101 Fifth Ave Ste 901
New York, NY 10003
Tel.: (646) 205-9830
Fax: (646) 205-9851
E-Mail:
Web Site: www.fircosoft.com
Emp.: 75
Financial Reporting & Compliance Software Programming
S.I.C.: 7371
N.A.I.C.S.: 541511
Raphael Schaeffer *(Product Mgr)*

FIRCROFT ENGINEERING SERVICES LTD.

Trinity House 114 Northenden Road
Sale, Cheshire, M33 3FZ, United Kingdom
Tel.: (44) 1619052020
Fax: (44) 1619691743
E-Mail: hq@fircroft.co.uk
Web Site: www.fircroft.co.uk
Year Founded: 1970
Rev.: $378,278,885
Emp.: 216
Business Description:
Recruitment Services
S.I.C.: 7361
N.A.I.C.S.: 561311
Personnel:
John Johnson *(Founder)*
Johnathan Johnson *(CEO)*
Stuart Hall *(CFO)*

FIRE RIVER GOLD CORP.

Suite 340 1200 West 73rd Avenue
Vancouver, BC, V6P 6G5, Canada
Tel.: (604) 261-0580
Fax: (604) 261-0583
E-Mail: info@firerivergold.com
Web Site: www.firerivergold.com
FAU—(TSXV)
Rev.: $2,810
Assets: $12,436,393
Liabilities: $22,226,111
Net Worth: ($9,789,718)
Earnings: ($33,092,930)
Fiscal Year-end: 10/31/12
Business Description:
Gold & Base Metals Exploration & Mining Services
S.I.C.: 1041
N.A.I.C.S.: 212221
Personnel:
Blane Wilson *(Pres & CEO)*
Paul Dyer *(CFO)*
Stacey Bligh *(Sec)*
Board of Directors:
Fred Sveinson
Richard Wells
Blane Wilson
Legal Counsel:
Fasken Martineau DuMoulin LLP
Suite 2900 550 Burrard Street
Vancouver, BC, Canada
Transfer Agent:
Computershare Investor Services Inc.
3rd Floor 510 Burrard Street
Vancouver, BC, Canada

FIREBIRD ENERGY INC.

34B Great Plains Road
Emerald Park, SK, S4L 1B7, Canada
Mailing Address:
Station Main
PO Box 516
White City, SK, S4L 5B1, Canada
Tel.: (306) 337-2083
Fax: (306) 337-2084
Year Founded: 2007
FRD—(TSXV)
Rev.: $116,846
Assets: $749,383
Liabilities: $418,500
Net Worth: $330,883
Earnings: ($143,375)
Fiscal Year-end: 03/31/13
Business Description:
Oil & Gas Exploration Services
S.I.C.: 1389
N.A.I.C.S.: 213112
Personnel:
Kevin Patterson *(Pres & CEO)*
Board of Directors:
Randy Clifford
Glen MacDonald
Kevin Patterson
Julie Zhu
Legal Counsel:
Borden Ladner Gervais
1200 Waterfront Centre 200 Burrard Street
PO Box 48600
Vancouver, BC, V7X 1T2, Canada
Transfer Agent:
Computershare Investor Services
510 Burrard St
Vancouver, BC, Canada

FIREBIRD RESOURCES INC.

6012-85 Ave
Edmonton, AB, T6B 0J5, Canada
Tel.: (780) 466-6006
Fax: (780) 440-1377
E-Mail: info@firebirdres.com
Web Site: www.firebirdres.com
Year Founded: 1983
FIX—(TSXV)
Int. Income: $38,251
Assets: $539,083
Liabilities: $743,737
Net Worth: ($204,654)
Earnings: ($669,553)
Fiscal Year-end: 04/30/13
Business Description:
Diamonds & Gold Exploration
S.I.C.: 1041
N.A.I.C.S.: 212221
Personnel:
Thomas Robert Tough *(Chm)*
John F. Cook *(Pres, CEO & Sec)*
Randy Clifford *(CFO)*
Board of Directors:
Thomas Robert Tough
Glen Macdonald
Ken Ralfs
Transfer Agent:
Computershare
3rd Floor 510 Burrard Street
Vancouver, BC, Canada

FIREFLY BOOKS

66 Leek Crescent
Richmond Hill, ON, L4B 1H1, Canada
Tel.: (416) 499-8412
Fax: (416) 499-8313
E-Mail: academics@fireflybooks.com
Web Site: www.fireflybooks.com
Year Founded: 1977
Rev.: $25,568,578
Emp.: 60
Business Description:
Book Sellers & Publishers
S.I.C.: 2731
N.A.I.C.S.: 511130
Personnel:
Lionel Koffler *(Owner)*

FIRESTEEL RESOURCES INC.

Suite 1051 - 409 Granville Street
Vancouver, BC, V6C 1T2, Canada
Tel.: (226) 400-1927
Fax: (604) 669-5728
E-Mail: info@firesteelresources.com
Web Site: www.firesteelresources.com
FTR—(TSXV)
Int. Income: $2,565
Assets: $2,721,276
Liabilities: $585,704
Net Worth: $2,135,571
Earnings: ($420,998)
Fiscal Year-end: 01/31/13
Business Description:
Mineral Exploration Services
S.I.C.: 1081
N.A.I.C.S.: 213114
Personnel:
Michael Hepworth *(Pres & CEO)*
Ian Fodie *(CFO)*
Board of Directors:
Eugene Chen
Ernest Cleave
David Forest
Michael Hepworth
Peter Pollard
Paul Sarjeant
Legal Counsel:
McLeod & Company LLP
850 401 9 Ave SW
Calgary, AB, Canada
Transfer Agent:
Computershare Trust Company of Canada
510 Burrard St 3rd Fl
Vancouver, BC, V6C 3B9, Canada

FIRESTONE DIAMONDS PLC

The Triangle 5-17 Hammersmith Grove
London, W6 0LG, United Kingdom
Tel.: (44) 2087417810
Fax: (44) 2087483261
E-Mail: info@firestonediamonds.com
Web Site: www.firestonediamonds.com
FDI—(LSE)
Rev.: $15,642,867
Assets: $77,296,770
Liabilities: $19,455,274
Net Worth: $57,841,496
Earnings: ($22,866,540)
Emp.: 78
Fiscal Year-end: 06/30/13
Business Description:
Diamond Mining & Exploration
S.I.C.: 1499
N.A.I.C.S.: 212399
Personnel:
Stuart Brown *(CEO)*
Grant Ferriman *(CFO)*
Glenn Black *(Chief Project Officer-Liqhobong Diamond Mine)*
Board of Directors:
R. Lucio Genovese
Stuart Brown
Braam Jonker
Paul Sobie
Julian Treger
Mike Wittet
Legal Counsel:
Lawrence Graham LLP
4 More London Riverside
London, England, SE1 2AU, United Kingdom
Capita Registrars
Northern House Woodsome Park Fenay Bridge
Huddersfield, United Kingdom
Capita Asset Services
The Registry 34 Beckenham Road
Beckenham, BR3 4TU, United Kingdom
Non-U.S. Subsidiaries:

Asam Resources SA (Proprietary) Limited **(1)**
Metropolitan Ctr Coen Steytler Ave
PO Box 8399
Foreshore, 8001 Cape Town, Western Cape, South Africa (100%)
Tel.: (27) 214466040
Fax: (27) 214188080
Web Site: www.firestonediamonds.co.za
Diamond Exploration & Mining Services
S.I.C.: 1499
N.A.I.C.S.: 212399
Tim Wilkes *(COO)*

Liqhobong Mining Development Co.(Proprietary) Limited **(1)**
32 Erwee St
PO Box 87
9730 Ficksburg, South Africa
Tel.: (27) 519334495
Fax: (27) 519334496
E-Mail: quintin@fxbmining.co.za
Web Site: www.goldenmile.co.za
Emp.: 10
Diamond Mining Services
S.I.C.: 1499
N.A.I.C.S.: 212399
Gerhard Van Niekerk *(Mgr)*

FIRESTONE ENERGY LIMITED

Level 1 330 Churchill Avenue
Subiaco, WA, 6008, Australia
Tel.: (61) 8 9200 4465
Fax: (61) 8 9200 4469
E-Mail: enquiries@firestoneenergy.net
Web Site: www.firestoneenergy.com.au
FSE—(ASX JSE)
Rev.: $7,183
Assets: $87,139,051
Liabilities: $35,522,198
Net Worth: $51,616,853
Earnings: ($6,094,412)
Fiscal Year-end: 06/30/13
Business Description:
Coal Mining Services
S.I.C.: 1221
N.A.I.C.S.: 212111
Personnel:
Stephen Miller *(CEO)*
Amanda Matthee *(CFO)*
David McEntaggart *(Sec)*
Board of Directors:
Timothy Tebeila
Lee Boyd
Pius Chilufya Kasolo
David Knox
Stephen Miller
Morore Benjamin Mphahlele
Legal Counsel:
Steinepreis Paganin
Level 4 16 Milligan Street
Perth, WA, 6000, Australia
Non-U.S. Subsidiary:

Lexshell 126 General Trading (Pty) Ltd **(1)**
20 Georgegian
Johannesburg, Gauteng, 2021, South Africa
Tel.: (27) 117063542
Fax: (27) 117063573
Coal Mining Services
S.I.C.: 1241
N.A.I.C.S.: 213113

FIRESTONE VENTURES INC.

200 9797-45 Avenue
Edmonton, AB, T6E 5V8, Canada

Tel.: (780) 428-3465
Fax: (780) 428-3476
Toll Free: (888) 221-5588
E-Mail: info@firestoneventures.com
Web Site: www.firestoneventures.com
FV—(TSXV)
Rev.: $106,023
Assets: $1,406,060
Liabilities: $226,515
Net Worth: $1,179,545
Earnings: ($1,188,320)
Fiscal Year-end: 03/31/13
Business Description:
Mineral Exploration Services
S.I.C.: 1081
N.A.I.C.S.: 213114
Personnel:
Keith Michael Barron *(Chm)*
Pamela Strand *(Pres & CEO)*
Greg Hayes *(CFO)*
Board of Directors:
Keith Michael Barron
John Kowalchuk
Pamela Strand
Terry Tucker
Transfer Agent:
Valiant Trust Company
Suite 310 606 4th Street S.W.
Calgary, AB, Canada

FIRESTRIKE RESOURCES LIMITED

Suite 1 Ground Floor 437 Roberts Road
Subiaco, WA, 6008, Australia
Tel.: (61) 8 9476 9209
Fax: (61) 8 9381 1122
E-Mail: info@firestrike.com.au
Web Site: www.firestrike.com.au
FIE—(ASX)
Rev.: $152,127
Assets: $1,584,028
Liabilities: $85,808
Net Worth: $1,498,221
Earnings: ($1,809,234)
Fiscal Year-end: 06/30/13
Business Description:
Gold Mining
S.I.C.: 1041
N.A.I.C.S.: 212221
Personnel:
David Holden *(Mng Dir)*
Paul Lloyd *(Co-Sec)*
Philip Re *(Co-Sec)*
Board of Directors:
Roger Steinepreis
David Holden
Paul Lloyd
Legal Counsel:
Steinepreis Paganin
Level 4 The Read Building 16 Milligan Street
Perth, WA, 6000, Australia
Tel.: (61) 8 9321 4000
Fax: (61) 8 9321 4333

FIRESWIRL TECHNOLOGIES INC.

2823-595 Burrard Street Three Bentall Centre
Vancouver, BC, V7X 1L4, Canada
Tel.: (604) 540-8805
Fax: (604) 677-6613
E-Mail: info@fireswirl.com
Web Site: www.fireswirl.com
FSW—(TSXV)
Rev.: $27,386,600
Assets: $6,613,326
Liabilities: $5,303,069
Net Worth: $1,310,258
Earnings: ($689,951)
Fiscal Year-end: 12/31/12
Business Description:
E-commerce Business Services
S.I.C.: 7389
N.A.I.C.S.: 519190
Personnel:
Tony Lau *(Founder & CEO)*
Ji Yoon *(Interim CFO)*
Board of Directors:
James C. Borkowski
Steven Hsieh
Liang Li
Legal Counsel:
Sangra Moller LLP
1000 Cathedral Place 925 West Georgia St
Vancouver, BC, Canada
Transfer Agent:
Computershare Trust Company of Canada
510 Burrard St 2nd Fl
Vancouver, BC, Canada

FIRICH ENTERPRISES CO., LTD.

10F No 75 Sin Tai Wu Rd Sec 1
Sijhih City
Taipei, 221, Taiwan
Tel.: (886) 226981446
Fax: (886) 226981451
E-Mail: hr@firich.com.tw
Web Site: www.firich.com.tw
Year Founded: 1995
Sales Range: $25-49.9 Million
Emp.: 320
Business Description:
Point-of-Sale Systems & Equipment Mfr
S.I.C.: 3577
N.A.I.C.S.: 334118
Personnel:
Lai Yingfu *(CFO)*

FIRM CAPITAL PROPERTY TRUST

(Formerly ISG Capital Corporation)
1244 Caledonia Road
Toronto, ON, M6A 2X5, Canada
Tel.: (416) 635-0221
Fax: (416) 635-1713
Web Site: www.firmcapital.com
Year Founded: 2007
FCD-U—(TSXV)
Rev.: $287,370
Assets: $27,233,670
Liabilities: $6,198,275
Net Worth: $21,035,395
Earnings: $286,267
Fiscal Year-end: 12/31/12
Business Description:
Real Estate Investment Trust
S.I.C.: 6531
N.A.I.C.S.: 531390
Personnel:
Stanley Goldfarb *(Chm)*
Eli Dadouch *(Vice Chm & Co-Chief Investment Officer)*
Sandy Poklar *(CFO)*
Jonathan Mair *(Co-Chief Investment Officer)*
Joseph Fried *(Gen Counsel & Sec)*

FIRMCO LTD.

Firmin House 127 129 Stanley Road
Ilford, IG1 1RQ, United Kingdom
Tel.: (44) 2085145544
Fax: (44) 2084783133
E-Mail: info@firmco.co.uk
Web Site: www.firmco.co.uk
Rev.: $15,760,217
Emp.: 33
Business Description:
Refurbishment Services
S.I.C.: 1799
N.A.I.C.S.: 238390
Personnel:
David Elwick *(Mng Dir)*

FIRMENICH S.A.

Rue de la Bergere 7
PO Box 148
CH-1217 Meyrin, Switzerland
Tel.: (41) 227802211
Fax: (41) 227802436
Web Site: www.firmenich.com
Year Founded: 1895
Sales Range: $1-4.9 Billion
Emp.: 6,000
Business Description:
Flavoring Extracts, Syrups, Perfumes & Oils Mfr
S.I.C.: 2844
N.A.I.C.S.: 325620
Personnel:
Yves Boisdron *(Chm)*
Patrick Firmenich *(CEO)*
Armand de Villoutreys *(Pres-Perfumery Div)*
Aldo Uva *(Pres-Flavor Div)*
Robert Weinstein *(Pres-Ingredients Div)*
Dominique Graz *(Sec)*
Board of Directors:
Yves Boisdron
Olivier Bazil
Antoine Firmenich
Patrick Firmenich
Karen E. D. Jones
Barbara Kux
Gerald Meyer
Edward S. Moerk
Andre Pometta

Subsidiary:

Firmenich SA **(1)**
7 Rue De La Bergere
PO Box 148
Meyrin, Geneva, 1217, Switzerland CH
Tel.: (41) 227802211 (100%)
Telex: 418 939
Fax: (41) 227802436
Emp.: 2,000
Mfr. of Flavors, Perfumes & Chemicals
S.I.C.: 2844
N.A.I.C.S.: 325620
Firmenich Patrick *(CEO)*

U.S. Subsidiaries:

Firmenich Citrus Center **(1)**
1585 S 10th St
Safety Harbor, FL 34695-4109 CA
Tel.: (727) 725-1678
Fax: (727) 726-3252
Toll Free: (800) 551-1678
Web Site: www.firmenich.com
Flavors & Fragrances R&D of the Firmenich Brand
S.I.C.: 2844
N.A.I.C.S.: 325620
Antoine Gautier *(VP-R&D)*

Firmenich Incorporated **(1)**
250 Plainsboro Rd
Plainsboro, NJ 08536
Mailing Address:
PO Box 5000
Princeton, NJ 08543-5880
Tel.: (609) 452-1000
Fax: (609) 452-6077
Toll Free: (800) 257-9591
Web Site: www.firmenich.com
Emp.: 700
Fragrances, Aromatic Chemicals, Artificial & Natural Flavors Mfr
S.I.C.: 2869
N.A.I.C.S.: 325199

Firmenich International Fine Fragrance Center **(1)**
625 Madison Ave 17th Fl
New York, NY 10022-3213 CA
Tel.: (212) 489-4800
Fax: (212) 980-4312
Web Site: www.firmenich.com
Emp.: 80
Perfumes & Fragrances Mfr
S.I.C.: 5169
N.A.I.C.S.: 424690

Firmenich **(1)**
424 S Atchison St
Anaheim, CA 92805-4045 CA
Mailing Address:
PO Box 3633
Anaheim, CA 92803-3633
Tel.: (714) 535-2871
Fax: (714) 535-2626
Web Site: www.firmenich.com
Emp.: 130
Powdered Citrus Juices & Oils
S.I.C.: 2869
N.A.I.C.S.: 325199
Michael Westerfield *(Mgr-Mfg)*

Firmenich **(1)**
100 N Vly St
New Ulm, MN 56073-1601
Tel.: (507) 354-4188
Fax: (507) 354-1095
Web Site: www.firmenich.com
Emp.: 80
Mfr. of Industrial Foods
S.I.C.: 2022
N.A.I.C.S.: 311513
Doug Cook *(Gen Mgr)*

Non-U.S. Subsidiaries:

Firmenich & Cia. Ltda **(1)**
Rodovia Reposo Gavres Km 2026 150
Caixa Postal 25, Cotia, Sao Paulo, 06707000, Brazil BR
Tel.: (55) 146178800 (100%)
Fax: (55) 147025245
Web Site: www.firmenich.com
Emp.: 300
Mfr. of Flavors, Perfumes & Chemicals
S.I.C.: 2844
N.A.I.C.S.: 325620

Firmenich & Cie. S.A.S. **(1)**
41 Rue De Villiers
92523 Paris, Neuilly Su Seine, France FR
Tel.: (33) 40887342 (100%)
Fax: (33) 147456519
Web Site: www.firmenich.com
Emp.: 250
Sales & Research & Development of Perfumes
S.I.C.: 2844
N.A.I.C.S.: 325620

Firmenich Aromatics (India) Pvt Ltd. **(1)**
Novell House 13th Road
MIDC Andheri East, Mumbai, 400 093, India In
Tel.: (91) 2266400564 (100%)
Fax: (91) 2266400669
Web Site: www.firmenich.com
Emp.: 100
Mfr. of Perfumes, Flavors & Chemicals
S.I.C.: 2844
N.A.I.C.S.: 325620

Firmenich Aromatics (Shanghai) Co. **(1)**
No 3901 Jin Du Rd Xinzhuang Industry Park
Shanghai, 201108, China HK
Tel.: (86) 2154428000 (100%)
Fax: (86) 2154426900
Web Site: www.firmenich.com
Emp.: 10
Mfr. of Perfumes, Flavors & Chemicals
S.I.C.: 2844
N.A.I.C.S.: 325620

Firmenich Asia Pte. Ltd. **(1)**
10 Tuas W Rd
Singapore, 638377, Singapore SG
Tel.: (65) 63472888 (100%)
Telex: RS 22884 FIRASI
Fax: (65) 68634687
E-Mail:
Web Site: www.firmenich.com
Emp.: 200
Mfr. of Perfumes, Flavors & Chemicals
S.I.C.: 2844
N.A.I.C.S.: 325620
Matthew Furner *(Mng Dir)*

Firmenich de Mexico S.A. de C.V. **(1)**
Louisiana 80 Col Napoles
Delegacion Benito Juarez, 3810 Mexico, DF, Mexico MX
Tel.: (52) 5553402000 (100%)
Fax: (52) 5555434228
E-Mail: laura.alfaro@firmenich.com
Web Site: www.firmenich.com

Firmenich S.A.—(Continued)

Emp.: 50
Mfr of Perfumes & Flavors
S.I.C.: 2844
N.A.I.C.S.: 325620
Laurent Pauchard *(Gen Mgr)*

Firmenich Dis Tic. Ltd. STI **(1)**
Ayazmadere Caddesi Aksit Plaza No 15 Kat 9 Fl
Fulya, 34349 Istanbul, Turkey TR
Tel.: (90) 2123274212 (100%)
Fax: (90) 2123274213
Web Site: www.firmenich.com
Emp.: 25
Fragrance & Flavors Research
S.I.C.: 8734
N.A.I.C.S.: 541380
Dilek Arlas *(Gen Mgr)*

Firmenich Ges.m.b.H. **(1)**
Trestner Str 89
1200 Vienna, 1210, Austria AT
Tel.: (43) 12705453 (100%)
Fax: (43) 270545340
E-Mail: office@firmenich.com
Emp.: 36
Sales of Perfumes
S.I.C.: 2844
N.A.I.C.S.: 325620

Firmenich GmbH **(1)**
Alfred Nobel Str 46 56
50169 Kerpen, Germany De
Tel.: (49) 223769010 (100%)
Fax: (49) 2237690169
E-Mail: info@firmenich.com
Emp.: 100
Distributor of Perfumes & Aromas
S.I.C.: 5122
N.A.I.C.S.: 424210
Mathias Hemberger *(Mng Dir)*

Firmenich Limited **(1)**
73 Kenneth Rd
2093 Balgowlah, NSW, Australia AU
Tel.: (61) 299079344 (100%)
Fax: (61) 299079721
E-Mail: maree.foran@firmenich.com
Emp.: 30
Mfr. of Perfumes & Flavors
S.I.C.: 2844
N.A.I.C.S.: 325620
Maree Foran *(Gen Mgr)*

Firmenich (Philippines), Inc. **(1)**
2nd Fl Utrc 3 2289 Vonchinoroces Extn Ave
PO Box 4853
Makati, Manila, 1200, Philippines PH
Tel.: (63) 28120711 (100%)
Fax: (63) 28129907
E-Mail: tess@firmenich.com
Emp.: 20
Mfr. of Perfumes, Flavors & Chemicals
S.I.C.: 2844
N.A.I.C.S.: 325620
Patrick Firmenich *(CEO)*

Firmenich Productions S.A.S. **(1)**
766 Rd Firmenich
PO Box 23
40260 Castets, France FR
Tel.: (33) 558550255 (100%)
Fax: (33) 558550222
E-Mail: marc.ciano@firmenich.com
Emp.: 34
Mfr. of Aroma Chemicals
S.I.C.: 2869
N.A.I.C.S.: 325199
Marc Ciano *(Mng Dir)*

Firmenich (Pty.) Ltd. **(1)**
Pvt Bag X113 Half Way House
Midrand, Gauteng, 1685, South Africa ZA
Tel.: (27) 116530700 (100%)
Fax: (27) 116530726
E-Mail: info@firmenich.com
Web Site: www.firmenich.com
Emp.: 35
Mfr. & Sales of Perfumes
S.I.C.: 2844
N.A.I.C.S.: 325620
Dordy Leijenaar *(Mng Dir)*

Firmenich S.A. **(1)**
Avenida El Dorado No 98-43
Interior 3, Bogota, DC, Colombia Co
Tel.: (57) 14254343 (100%)
Fax: (57) 14254351
E-Mail: info@firmenich.com
Web Site: www.firmenich.com
Emp.: 120
Mfr of Perfumes, Flavors & Chemicals
S.I.C.: 2844
N.A.I.C.S.: 325620

Firmenich S.A. **(1)**
Avda De Madrid 213
8014 Barcelona, Spain ES
Tel.: (34) 934905808 (100%)
Fax: (34) 934902496
Emp.: 20
Mfr. & Sales of Perfumes
S.I.C.: 2844
N.A.I.C.S.: 325620

Firmenich S.A.I.C. y F. **(1)**
Colectora Panamericana Este 25 201
Don Torcuato, 1611 Buenos Aires, Argentina AR
Tel.: (54) 1147485200 (85%)
Fax: (54) 1147413592
Web Site: www.firmenich.com
Emp.: 50
Mfr. & Sales of Perfumes & Flavors
S.I.C.: 2844
N.A.I.C.S.: 325620

Firmenich S.p.A. **(1)**
Via Fortezza 7
20126 Milan, Italy IT
Tel.: (39) 02270731 (100%)
Fax: (39) 022575368
Web Site: www.firmenich.com
Emp.: 25
Sales of Perfumes
S.I.C.: 5122
N.A.I.C.S.: 446120

Firmenich Sp.z o.o **(1)**
Ul Chrzanowska 10
Grodzisk Mazowiecki, 5825, Poland PL
Tel.: (48) 227552611 (100%)
Fax: (48) 227555972
E-Mail: reception@firmenich.com
Emp.: 17
Mfr. & Sales of Perfumes
S.I.C.: 2844
N.A.I.C.S.: 325620
Tomasz Bielak *(Gen Mgr)*

Firmenich UK Ltd. **(1)**
Dalton Airfield Industrial Est
YO73HE Thirsk, North Yorkshire, United Kingdom UK
Tel.: (44) 845576400 (100%)
Fax: (44) 1845576404
Web Site: www.firmenich.com
Emp.: 50
Research & Development of Flavors & Perfumes
S.I.C.: 2844
N.A.I.C.S.: 325620

Firmenich UK Ltd. **(1)**
Hayes Road
Southall, Middlesex, UB2 5NN, United Kingdom UK
Tel.: (44) 2088436111 (100%)
Fax: (44) 208 843 6471
Web Site: www.firmenich.com
Emp.: 120
Research & Development of Flavors & Perfumes
S.I.C.: 2844
N.A.I.C.S.: 325620

Kunming Firmenich Aromatics Co. Ltd. **(1)**
Guo Jia Ao Jin Ma Si
East Suburb, Kunming, 650216, China CN
Tel.: (86) 8713808286 (100%)
Fax: (86) 8713812076
Web Site: www.firmenich.com
Emp.: 119
Mfr. of Aromas
S.I.C.: 2869
N.A.I.C.S.: 325199

Nihon Firmenich K.K. **(1)**
Kowa-Kawasaki Nishiguchi Bldg 66-2 Horikawacho
Saiwai-ku, Kawasaki, Kanagawa, 212-0013, Japan JP
Tel.: (81) 445436111 (100%)
Fax: (81) 445419070
Web Site: www.firmenich.com
Emp.: 70
Perfumes, Flavors & Chemicals Mfr
S.I.C.: 2844
N.A.I.C.S.: 325620

Branch:

Nihon Firmenich K.K. - Osaka Branch **(2)**
3 floor Wakasugi Grand Bldg
Tenjinbashi 2-5-25 Kita Ku, Osaka, 530 0041, Japan
Tel.: (81) 663534061
Fax: (81) 663534062
Web Site: www.firmenich.com
Emp.: 100
Mfr. of Perfumes, Flavors & Chemicals
S.I.C.: 2844
N.A.I.C.S.: 325620

PT Firmenich Indonesia **(1)**
Jl Tanah Abang II No 78
Jakarta, 10150, Indonesia Id
Tel.: (62) 213863977 (100%)
Fax: (62) 213451910
Web Site: www.firmenich.com
Emp.: 80
Mfr. of Perfumes, Flavors & Chemicals
S.I.C.: 2844
N.A.I.C.S.: 325620
Jorgen Hejl *(Gen Mgr)*

Suzhou Firmenich Aromatics Co. Ltd. **(1)**
No 3901 Jin Du Rd Xinzhuang Industrial Park
Shanghai, Jiangsu, 201108, China CN
Tel.: (86) 2154428000 (100%)
Fax: (86) 2154426900
Web Site: www.firmenich.com
Emp.: 20
Mfr. of Aromas
S.I.C.: 2899
N.A.I.C.S.: 325199

FIROUZA ENGINEERING COMPANY

9th Km Karaj Makhsous Road
Tehran, Iran 1399617911
Tel.: (98) 21 44522415
Fax: (98) 21 44504875
E-Mail: info@firouzacranes.com
Web Site: www.firouzacranes.com
Year Founded: 1967
FROZ—(THE)
Emp.: 300

Business Description:
Crane Mfr
S.I.C.: 3536
N.A.I.C.S.: 333923

Personnel:
Ghasem Ebrahimi Majd *(Mng Dir)*

Board of Directors:
Ghasem Ebrahimi Majd
Nasim Sadeghi
Mojtaba Tanha

FIRST ADVISORY GROUP LIMITED

Aeulestrasse 74
Postfach 86
FL 9490 Vaduz, Liechtenstein
Tel.: (423) 236 3000
Fax: (423) 236 3001
E-Mail: serivces@blueaxis.net
Web Site: www.firstadvisory.li
Emp.: 150

Business Description:
Financial Consulting Services
S.I.C.: 6091
N.A.I.C.S.: 523991

Personnel:
Angelika Moosleithner *(Owner & Member-Mgmt Bd)*

FIRST AMERICAN SCIENTIFIC CORP.

30758 South Fraser Way #201
Abbotsford, BC, V2T 6L4, Canada
Tel.: (604) 850-8959
Fax: (604) 850-8904
E-Mail: help@fasc.net
Web Site: www.fasc.net
Year Founded: 1995
FASC—(OTC OTCB)
Sales Range: Less than $1 Million

Business Description:
Kinetic Disintegration System Developer & Marketer
S.I.C.: 3559
N.A.I.C.S.: 562219

Personnel:
John Brian Nichols *(Pres, CEO, Treas & Sec)*
Kelly Niavis *(CFO & Chief Acctg Officer)*

FIRST AMERICAS GOLD CORPORATION

Suite 2323 1066 W Hastings St
Vancouver, BC, V6E 3X2, Canada
Tel.: (604) 601-8250
Fax: (604) 408-8893
E-Mail: info@firstamericasgold.com
Web Site: www.firstamericasgold.com
Year Founded: 2007
FAC—(TSXV)
Int. Income: $126
Assets: $590,972
Liabilities: $26,947
Net Worth: $564,025
Earnings: ($398,601)
Fiscal Year-end: 03/31/13

Business Description:
Gold Mining Services
S.I.C.: 1041
N.A.I.C.S.: 212221

Personnel:
Drew Bonnell *(Pres & CEO)*
David R. McElhanney *(CFO & VP-Ops)*

Board of Directors:
Drew Bonnell
Roman Friedrich, III
William L. Macdonald
David R. McElhanney
David Rankin
Robert Thompson

Transfer Agent:
Computershare Investor Services Inc.
2nd Fl 510 Burrard St
Vancouver, BC, Canada

FIRST ANGULLA TRUST COMPANY LIMITED

Mitchell House
PO Box 174
The Valley, Anguilla
Tel.: (264) 4988800
Fax: (264) 4618880
Web Site: www.firstanguilla.com
Emp.: 14

Business Description:
Offshore Financial Services
S.I.C.: 6726
N.A.I.C.S.: 525990

Personnel:
John Dyrud *(Chm, Mng Dir & Legal Counsel)*
David R. Sargeant *(Deputy Mng Dir)*

THE FIRST ARTIST COMPANY LTD.

First Artist House
85 A Wembley Hill Road, Wembley, Middlesex, HA9 8BU, United Kingdom
Tel.: (44) 20 8900 1818
Fax: (44) 20 8903 2964
E-Mail: info@firstartist.com
Web Site: www.firstartist.com
Sales Range: $75-99.9 Million
Emp.: 275

Business Description:
Marketing, Sports & Entertainment Management Services

S.I.C.: 7389
N.A.I.C.S.: 711410
Personnel:
Bob Baldock *(Chm)*
Jon Smith *(CEO)*
Phil Smith *(COO)*
Legal Counsel:
Clintons
55 Drury Lane Covent Garden
London, United Kingdom
Subsidiary:

DeWynters Limited (1)
48 Leicester Sq
London, WC2H 7QD, United Kingdom
Tel.: (44) 20 7321 0488
Fax: (44) 20 7321 0104
E-Mail: info@dewynters.com
Web Site: www.dewynters.com
Emp.: 100
Advertising Agency
S.I.C.: 7311
N.A.I.C.S.: 541810
Anthony Pye Jeary *(Mng Dir)*

U.S. Branch:

DeWynters Advertising Inc. (2)
43-01 22nd St 3rd Fl SW
Long Island City, NY 11101
Tel.: (718) 472-0424
Fax: (718) 472-0427
E-Mail: info@dewynters.com
Web Site: www.dewynters.com
Emp.: 4
S.I.C.: 7311
N.A.I.C.S.: 541810
James Decker *(VP)*

FIRST ASIA HOLDINGS LIMITED

Room 1604 Silvercord II Tsim Sha Tsui
Kowloon, China (Hong Kong)
Tel.: (852) 31523168
Fax: (852) 2614 8499
E-Mail: info@firstasiaholdings.com
Web Site: www.firstasiaholdings.com
FAHLF—(OTCB)
Rev.: $1,640,867
Assets: $30,879,311
Liabilities: $12,021,230
Net Worth: $18,858,081
Earnings: $400
Emp.: 7
Fiscal Year-end: 09/30/13
Business Description:
Property Development & Management Services
S.I.C.: 6531
N.A.I.C.S.: 531390
Personnel:
Kimmy Lai Ching Luk *(Chm)*
Carmen Ka Man To *(CFO)*
Board of Directors:
Kimmy Lai Ching Luk
Thomas Siew Weng Lee

FIRST ASSET FUNDS INC.

(See Under First Asset Investment Management Inc.)

FIRST ASSET INVESTMENT MANAGEMENT INC.

(d/b/a First Asset Funds)
95 Wellington Street West Suite 1400
Toronto, ON, M5J 2N7, Canada
Tel.: (416) 642-1289
Fax: (416) 362-2199
Toll Free: (877) 642-1289
E-Mail: info@firstasset.com
Web Site: www.firstasset.com
Emp.: 20
Business Description:
Investment & Asset Management Services
S.I.C.: 6799
N.A.I.C.S.: 523920
Personnel:
Barry H. Gordon *(Pres & CEO)*
Karen Wagman *(CFO)*
Z. Edward Akkawi *(COO & Sec)*
Paul V. Dinelle *(Exec VP)*
Lee Goldman *(Sr VP & Portfolio Mgr)*
John Stephenson *(Sr VP & Portfolio Mgr)*
Charlene A. Schikowsky *(Sr VP-Admin & Ops)*
Affiliates:

Can-60 Income Corp. (1)
95 Wellington Street West Suite 1400
Toronto, ON, M5J 2N7, Canada ON
Tel.: (416) 642-1289
Fax: (416) 362-2199
Toll Free: (877) 642-1289
E-Mail:
Web Site: www.firstasset.com
CSY—(TSX)
Rev.: $5,427,408
Assets: $179,840,015
Liabilities: $4,588,594
Net Worth: $175,251,421
Earnings: $2,719,420
Fiscal Year-end: 12/31/12
Closed-End Investment Fund
S.I.C.: 6211
N.A.I.C.S.: 525990
Barry H. Gordon *(Chm, Pres & CEO)*
Karen Wagman *(CFO)*
Z. Edward Akkawi *(COO & Sec)*
Lee Goldman *(Chief Compliance Officer, Sr VP & Portfolio Mgr)*
Paul V. Dinelle *(Exec VP)*
John Stephenson *(Sr VP & Portfolio Mgr)*
Edward D. Kelterborn *(Sr VP-Legal & Ops)*
Rohit D. Mehta *(Sr VP-Sls & Mktg)*
Charlene A. Schikowsky *(Sr VP-Admin & Ops)*

Can-Financials Income Corp. (1)
c/o First Asset Funds Inc 95 Wellington Street West
Suite 1400, Toronto, ON, M5J 2N7, Canada ON
Tel.: (416) 640-4938
Fax: (416) 362-2199
Web Site: www.firstasset.com
FIC—(TSX)
Closed-End Investment Fund
S.I.C.: 6211
N.A.I.C.S.: 525990
Barry H. Gordon *(Chm, Pres & CEO)*
Karen Wagman *(CFO)*
Z. Edward Akkawi *(COO & Sec)*
Paul V. Dinelle *(Exec VP)*

Canadian Advantaged Convertibles Fund (1)
95 Wellington Street West Suite 1400
Toronto, ON, M5J 2N7, Canada ON
Tel.: (416) 642-1289
Fax: (416) 362-2199
Web Site: www.firstasset.com
ADC.UN—(TSX)
Rev.: $45,552
Assets: $75,738,296
Liabilities: $1,469,093
Net Worth: $74,269,203
Earnings: ($789,506)
Fiscal Year-end: 12/31/12
Closed-End Investment Fund
S.I.C.: 6211
N.A.I.C.S.: 525990
Barry H. Gordon *(Pres & CEO)*
Karen Wagman *(CFO)*
Z. Edward Akkawi *(COO, Gen Counsel & Sec)*
Lee Goldman *(Chief Compliance Officer, Sr VP & Mgr-Portfolio)*
Paul V. Dinelle *(Exec VP)*
John Stephenson *(Sr VP & Mgr-Portfolio)*
Edward D. Kelterborn *(Sr VP-Legal & Ops)*
Rohit D. Mehta *(Sr VP-Sls & Mktg)*
Charlene A. Schikowsky *(Sr VP-Admin & Ops)*

CanBanc 8 Income Corp. (1)
c/o First Asset Funds Inc 95 Wellington Street West Suite 1400
Toronto, ON, M5J 2N7, Canada ON
Tel.: (416) 640-4938
Fax: (416) 362-2199
Web Site: www.firstasset.com
CBF—(TSX)
Closed-End Investment Fund
S.I.C.: 6211
N.A.I.C.S.: 525990
Barry H. Gordon *(Chm, Pres & CEO)*
Karen Wagman *(CFO)*
Z. Edward Akkawi *(COO & Sec)*
Paul V. Dinelle *(Exec VP)*
Charlene A. Schikowsky *(Sr VP-Admin & Ops)*

CanBanc Income Corp. (1)
95 Wellington Street West Suite 1400
Toronto, ON, M5J 2N7, Canada ON
Tel.: (416) 642-1289
Fax: (416) 362-2199
Toll Free: (877) 642-1289
Web Site: www.firstasset.com
CIC—(TSX)
Rev.: $8,698,226
Assets: $209,550,987
Liabilities: $4,115,681
Net Worth: $205,435,306
Earnings: $6,013,674
Fiscal Year-end: 12/31/12
Closed-End Investment Fund
S.I.C.: 6211
N.A.I.C.S.: 525990
Barry H. Gordon *(Chm, Pres & CEO)*
Karen Wagman *(CFO)*
Z. Edward Akkawi *(COO & Sec)*
Paul V. Dinelle *(Exec VP)*
Charlene A. Schikowsky *(Sr VP-Admin & Ops)*

First Asset Canadian Dividend Opportunity Fund II (1)
95 Wellington Street West Suite 1400
Toronto, ON, M5J 2N7, Canada
Tel.: (416) 362-2929
Fax: (416) 362-2199
E-Mail:
Web Site: www.firstasset.com
DVF.UN—(TSX)
Mutual Fund
S.I.C.: 6211
N.A.I.C.S.: 525910
Barry H. Gordon *(Pres & CEO)*
Karen Wagman *(CFO)*
Z. Edward Akkawi *(COO)*
Paul V. Dinelle *(Exec VP)*

First Asset CanBanc Split Corp. (1)
95 Wellington Street West Suite 1400
Toronto, ON, M5J 2N7, Canada
Tel.: (416) 642-1289
Fax: (416) 362-2199
Web Site: www.firstasset.com
CBU—(TSX)
Rev.: $647,104
Assets: $15,623,984
Liabilities: $4,314,108
Net Worth: $11,309,876
Earnings: ($68,481)
Fiscal Year-end: 12/31/12
Closed-End Investment Fund
S.I.C.: 6211
N.A.I.C.S.: 525990
Barry H. Gordon *(Chm, Pres & CEO)*
Karen Wagman *(CFO)*
Z. Edward Akkawi *(COO & Sec)*
Paul V. Dinelle *(Exec VP)*
Charlene A. Schikowsky *(Sr VP-Admin & Ops)*

First Asset Morningstar U.S. Consumer Defensive Index Fund (1)
95 Wellington Street West Suite 1400
Toronto, ON, M5J 2N7, Canada ON
Tel.: (416) 640-4938
Fax: (416) 362-2199
Web Site: www.firstasset.com
UCD.UN—(TSX)
Closed-End Investment Fund
N.A.I.C.S.: 525990
Barry H. Gordon *(Pres & CEO)*
Karen Wagman *(CFO)*
Z. Edward Akkawi *(COO, Gen Counsel & Sec)*
Paul D. Dinelle *(Exec VP)*

First Asset Yield Opportunity Trust (1)
95 Wellington Street West Suite 1400
Toronto, ON, M5J 2N7, Canada
Tel.: (416) 640-4938
Fax: (416) 362-2199
Toll Free: (877) 642-1289
Web Site: www.firstasset.com
FAY.U—(TSX)
Rev.: $74,402
Assets: $41,267,020
Liabilities: $677,491
Net Worth: $40,589,529
Earnings: ($359,217)
Fiscal Year-end: 12/31/12
Closed-End Investment Fund
S.I.C.: 6799
N.A.I.C.S.: 525990
Barry H. Gordon *(CEO)*

JFT Strategies Fund (1)
95 Wellington Street West Suite 1400
Toronto, ON, M5J 2N7, Canada ON
Tel.: (416) 640-4938
Fax: (416) 362-2199
E-Mail:
Web Site: www.firstasset.com
JFS.UN—(TSX)
Closed-End Investment Fund
S.I.C.: 6211
N.A.I.C.S.: 525990
Barry H. Gordon *(Pres & CEO)*
Karen Wagman *(CFO)*
Z. Edward Akkawi *(COO)*
Paul V. Dinelle *(Exec VP)*

North American Advantaged Convertibles Fund (1)
95 Wellington Street West Suite 1400
Toronto, ON, M5J 2N7, Canada ON
Tel.: (416) 642-1289
Fax: (416) 362-2199
Web Site: www.firstasset.com
NCD.UN—(TSX)
Rev.: $69,698
Assets: $74,397,480
Liabilities: $1,354,336
Net Worth: $73,043,143
Earnings: ($803,659)
Fiscal Year-end: 12/31/12
Closed-End Investment Fund
S.I.C.: 6211
N.A.I.C.S.: 525990
Barry H. Gordon *(Pres & CEO)*
Karen Wagman *(CFO)*
Z. Edward Akkawi *(COO, Gen Counsel & Sec)*
Lee Goldman *(Chief Compliance Officer, Sr VP & Portfolio Mgr)*
Paul V. Dinelle *(Exec VP)*
John Stephenson *(Sr VP & Portfolio Mgr)*
Edward D. Kelterborn *(Sr VP-Legal and Ops)*
Rohit D. Mehta *(Sr VP-Sls & Mktg)*
Charlene A. Schikowsky *(Sr VP-Admin & Ops)*

Preferred Share Investment Trust (1)
95 Wellington Street West Suite 1400
Toronto, ON, M5J 2N7, Canada ON
Tel.: (416) 642-1289
Fax: (416) 362-2199
E-Mail:
Web Site: www.firstasset.com
PSF.UN—(TSX)
Rev.: $8,076,258
Assets: $198,820,273
Liabilities: $39,339,534
Net Worth: $159,480,739
Earnings: $3,662,461
Fiscal Year-end: 12/31/12
Closed-End Investment Fund
S.I.C.: 6211
N.A.I.C.S.: 525990
Barry H. Gordon *(Pres & CEO)*
Karen Wagman *(CFO)*
Z. Edward Akkawi *(COO, Gen Counsel & Sec)*
Lee Goldman *(Chief Compliance Officer, Sr VP & Portfolio Mgr)*
Paul V. Dinelle *(Exec VP)*
John Stephenson *(Sr VP & Portfolio Mgr)*
Edward D. Kelterborn *(Sr VP-Legal & Ops)*
Rohit D. Mehta *(Sr VP-Sls & Mktg)*
Charlene A. Schikowsky *(Sr VP-Admin & Ops)*

Triax Diversified High-Yield Trust (1)
95 Wellington Street West Suite 1400
Toronto, ON, M5J 2N7, Canada
Tel.: (416) 642-1289
Fax: (416) 362-2199
Web Site: www.firstasset.com

First Asset Investment Management Inc.—(Continued)

TRH.UN—(TSX)
Rev.: $1,843,552
Assets: $20,469,062
Liabilities: $1,607,592
Net Worth: $18,861,470
Earnings: $1,274,993
Fiscal Year-end: 12/31/12
Closed-End Investment Fund
S.I.C.: 6211
N.A.I.C.S.: 525990
Barry H. Gordon *(CEO)*

Utility Split Trust (1)
95 Wellington Street Suite 1400
Toronto, ON, M5J 2N7, Canada
Tel.: (416) 642-1289
Fax: (416) 362-2199
Web Site: www.firstasset.com
UST—(TSX)
Rev.: $1,076,912
Assets: $27,349,028
Liabilities: $11,029,239
Net Worth: $16,319,789
Earnings: ($211,281)
Fiscal Year-end: 12/31/12
Closed-End Investment Fund
S.I.C.: 6211
N.A.I.C.S.: 525990
Barry H. Gordon *(CEO)*

FIRST BANK OF NIGERIA PLC

(See Under FBN Holdings PLC)

FIRST BAUXITE CORPORATION

Suite 3200 130 Adelaide Street West
Toronto, ON, M5H 3P5, Canada
Tel.: (416) 613-0910
Fax: (416) 613-0919
E-Mail: info@firstbauxite.com
Web Site: www.firstbauxite.com
Year Founded: 2003
FBX—(TSXV)
Int. Income: $51,756
Assets: $11,651,552
Liabilities: $11,246,523
Net Worth: $405,028
Earnings: ($6,669,672)
Fiscal Year-end: 09/30/12

Business Description:
Mineral Exploration Services
S.I.C.: 1081
N.A.I.C.S.: 213114

Personnel:
Lawrence E. Washow *(Interim Chm)*
Hilbert N. Shields *(Pres & CEO)*
Carlos Pinglo *(CFO)*
George Bennett *(COO)*

Board of Directors:
Lawrence E. Washow
George Bennett
Lee Graber
Alan Roughead
Hilbert N. Shields
Ioannis Tsitos

Legal Counsel:
Gowling Lafleur Henderson LLP
1 First Canadian Place Suite 1600 100 King Street West
Toronto, ON, Canada

Transfer Agent:
Equity Financial Trust Company
200 University Avenue Suite 400
Toronto, ON, M5H 4H1, Canada
Tel.: (416) 361-0152
Fax: (416) 361-0470
Toll Free: (866) 393-4891

FIRST CAPITAL CHINA CORPORATION

Room 1131 Xian KeJi Dian Building
Ba Gua Si Road
Futian District, Shenzhen, 518029, China
Tel.: (86) 775 23990959
Year Founded: 1994
AFTV—(OTC)

Business Description:
Investment Services
S.I.C.: 6211
N.A.I.C.S.: 523999

Personnel:
Li Te Xiao *(Pres, CEO, CFO & Sec)*

FIRST CAPITAL HOLDINGS PLC

No 02 Deal Place
Colombo, 03, Sri Lanka
Tel.: (94) 112639898
Fax: (94) 112639899
E-Mail: info@firstcapital.lk
Web Site: www.firstcapital.lk
CFVF—(COL)
Rev.: $13,884,397
Assets: $113,488,533
Liabilities: $98,140,543
Net Worth: $15,347,990
Earnings: $3,878,269
Emp.: 49
Fiscal Year-end: 03/31/13

Business Description:
Investment Management Services
S.I.C.: 6799
N.A.I.C.S.: 523920

Personnel:
Deshamanya Lalith De Mel *(Chm)*
A. Jehaan Ismail *(CEO)*
Manjula Mathews *(Mng Dir)*
Mangala Jayashantha *(CFO)*
Seedantha Kulatilake *(CEO-First Capital Equities (Private) Limited)*

Board of Directors:
Deshamanya Lalith De Mel
Nishan Fernando
A. Jehaan Ismail
Manjula Mathews
Eardley Perera
Minette Perera
Nihara E. Rodrigo
Dinesh Schaffter

Legal Counsel:
Neelakandan & Neelakandan
M&N Building Level 5 No 2 Deal Place
Colombo, Sri Lanka

FIRST CAPITAL SECURITIES CORPORATION LTD.

103 C II Gulberg III
Lahore, Pakistan
Tel.: (92) 42 5757 591
Fax: (92) 42 5757 590
Web Site: www.fcil.com.pk/contactus.php
FCSC—(KAR LAH)
Sales Range: $10-24.9 Million
Emp.: 343

Business Description:
Investment Services
S.I.C.: 6211
N.A.I.C.S.: 523999

Personnel:
Salmaan Taseer *(Chm & CEO)*

Board of Directors:
Salmaan Taseer
Sulieman Ahmed Said Al-Hoqani
Jamal Said Al-Ojaili
Khawaja Khalil Shah
Aamna Taseer
Sardar Ali Wattoo

Subsidiary:

First Capital Equities Limited (1)
4th Floor Lakson Square Building No 1
Sarwar Shaheed Road, Karachi, Pakistan (67.27%)
Tel.: (92) 21111226226
Web Site: www.firstcapital.com.pk
FCEL—(LAH)
Sales Range: $1-9.9 Million
Emp.: 131
Brokerage Services
S.I.C.: 6211
N.A.I.C.S.: 523120
Mian Ehsan Ul Haq *(Chm & CEO)*
Mazhar Abbas *(CFO)*
Syed Akbar Naqi *(Sec)*

Non-U.S. Joint Venture:

Lanka Securities Pvt. Ltd. (1)
228/2 Galle Road
Colombo, 4, Sri Lanka
Tel.: (94) 114706757
Fax: (94) 114706767
E-Mail: lankasec@sltnet.lk
Web Site: www.lsl.lk
Emp.: 60
Securities Trading & Brokerage Services; Owned by First Capital Securities Corporation & Bank of Ceylon
S.I.C.: 6211
N.A.I.C.S.: 523120
Kosala Gamage *(CEO-Trading Div)*

FIRST CAPITAL S.P.A.

Viale Luigi Majno 17/A
20122 Milan, Italy
Tel.: (39) 02 76390184
Fax: (39) 02 76407290
E-Mail: info@firstcapital.it
Web Site: www.firstcapital.it
FIC—(ITA)

Business Description:
Investment Services
S.I.C.: 6211
N.A.I.C.S.: 523999

Personnel:
Francesco Cesarini *(Chm)*
Alessandro Binello *(Vice Chm)*
Paolo La Pietra *(CEO)*

Board of Directors:
Francesco Cesarini
Alessandro Binello
Mario Gabbrielli
Paolo La Pietra
Renzo Torchiani

FIRST CHINA PHARMACEUTICAL GROUP, INC.

Room 1301 13th Floor CRE Building
303 Hennessy Road, Wanchai, China (Hong Kong)
Tel.: (852) 2138 1668
E-Mail: info@firstchinapharma.com
Web Site: www.firstchinapharma.com
FCPG—(OTC OTCB)
Sales Range: $25-49.9 Million

Business Description:
Pharmaceutical Distr
S.I.C.: 5122
N.A.I.C.S.: 424210

Personnel:
Zhen Jiang Wang *(Chm & CEO)*
Jing Gong *(Pres)*
Yi Jia Li *(CFO)*
Yong Kang Chen *(Sr VP-Quality Control)*

Board of Directors:
Zhen Jiang Wang
James Vergil McTevia
Gregory David Tse
Jack I. Zwick

FIRST CHOICE PRODUCTS INC.

2076 Townline Road Suite 6
Abbotsford, BC, V2T 6E5, Canada
Tel.: (604) 853-2655
Fax: (604) 853-3119
Toll Free: (866) 719-2988
E-Mail: info@firstchoiceproductsinc.com
Web Site: www.firstchoiceproductsinc.com
Year Founded: 1989
FCI—(CNSX)
Sales Range: $1-9.9 Million

Business Description:
Investment Company; Innovative Product Mfr
S.I.C.: 6211
N.A.I.C.S.: 523999

Personnel:
Robert A. Sim *(Chm & CEO)*
Brian E. Sims *(CFO)*
Linda A. Peters *(Sec)*

Board of Directors:
Robert A. Sim
Linda A. Peters
Norm C. Rempel
Brian E. Sims
John R. Thornton

Legal Counsel:
Burnet Duckworth & Palmer
1400 350 7th Ave SW
Calgary, AB, Canada

Transfer Agent:
Computershare Trust Company of Canada
510 Burrard St 3rd Fl
Vancouver, BC, V6C 3B9, Canada

FIRST COLOMBIA GOLD CORP.

Carrera 49 No 51-11 Suite 402
Copacabana
Antioquia, Colombia
Tel.: (57) 4 461 61 54
Toll Free: 8882246561
E-Mail: info@firstcolombiagold.com
Web Site: www.firstcolombiagold.com
Year Founded: 1997
FCGD—(OTCB)
Assets: $65,874
Liabilities: $597,998
Net Worth: ($532,124)
Earnings: ($309,967)
Fiscal Year-end: 12/31/12

Business Description:
Gold & Silver Exploration Services
S.I.C.: 1041
N.A.I.C.S.: 212221

Personnel:
Piero Sutti-Keyser *(CEO)*
Gilberto Zapata *(CFO, Treas & Sec)*

Board of Directors:
Gordan Sredl
Piero Sutti-Keyser
Robert Van Tassell

FIRST CORPORATION

254 Midlake Boulevard
Calgary, AB, T2X 2X7, Canada
Tel.: (403) 461-7283
Year Founded: 1995
FSTC—(OTC)
Assets: $1,013,577
Liabilities: $1,353,760
Net Worth: ($340,183)
Earnings: ($381,226)
Fiscal Year-end: 09/30/12

Business Description:
Metal Mining Services
S.I.C.: 1099
N.A.I.C.S.: 212299

Personnel:
Christopher Sweeting *(CEO)*

Transfer Agent:
Holladay Stock Transfer
2939 N 67 Place
Scottsdale, AZ 85251

FIRST DAWOOD INVESTMENT BANK LIMITED

1900 B Saima Trade Towers II
Chundrigar Road
Karachi, 74000, Pakistan
Tel.: (92) 2132271874
Fax: (92) 2132271913
E-Mail: fdib@firstdawood.com
Web Site: www.firstdawood.com
FDIBL—(KAR)

Emp.: 31
Business Description:
Investment Banking Services
S.I.C.: 6211
N.A.I.C.S.: 523110
Personnel:
Rafique Dawood *(Chm)*
Rasheed Y. Chinoy *(CEO)*
Nabeel Asif *(CFO & Sec)*
Board of Directors:
Rafique Dawood
Abu Khursheed Muhammad Arif
Rasheed Y. Chinoy
Ayaz Dawood
M. Riyazul Haque
Khurshid Abul Khair
Javed Raza

FIRST DERIVATIVES PLC

3 Canal Quay
Newry, Co Down, BT35 6BP, United Kingdom
Tel.: (44) 2830252242
Fax: (44) 2830252060
E-Mail: info@firstderivatives.com
Web Site: www.firstderivatives.com
FDP—(LSE)
Rev.: $89,180,927
Assets: $128,994,828
Liabilities: $66,811,863
Net Worth: $62,182,964
Earnings: $8,125,447
Emp.: 723
Fiscal Year-end: 02/28/13
Business Description:
Software & Information Technology Services
S.I.C.: 7372
N.A.I.C.S.: 511210
Personnel:
Brian G. Conlon *(CEO)*
R. Graham Ferguson *(CFO)*
Adrian Toner *(COO)*
Brendan Duffy *(CTO)*
James Sanders *(Chief Compliance Officer)*
Dale Richards *(Pres-Ops-US)*
Board of Directors:
Seamus Keating
R. David Anderson
Brian G. Conlon
R. Graham Ferguson
Keith MacDonald
Legal Counsel:
Mills Selig
21 Arthur Street
Belfast, United Kingdom
Transfer Agent:
Neville Registrars Limited
Neville House 18 Laurel Lane
Halesowen, West Midlands, B63 3DA, United Kingdom
U.S. Subsidiaries:

Market Resource Partners LLC (1)
1880 JFK Blvd 19th Fl
Philadelphia, PA 19103
Tel.: (215) 587-8800
Fax: (215) 557-1575
E-Mail: info@marketresourcepartners.com
Web Site: www.marketresourcepartners.com
Rev.: $6,600,000
Emp.: 100
Advertising Agency
S.I.C.: 7311
N.A.I.C.S.: 541810
Kevin Cunningham *(Co-Founder)*
James Regan *(Co-Founder)*
John Butler *(COO)*

Reference Data Factory LLC (1)
14 Vervalen St
Closter, NJ 07624
Tel.: (201) 633-5745
E-Mail: info@referencedatafactory.comb
Web Site: www.referencedatafactory.com
Financial Management Consulting Services
S.I.C.: 8742
N.A.I.C.S.: 541611
Garry Wright *(Mng Dir)*

Non-U.S. Subsidiary:

First Derivatives Pty Limited (1)
Rose Pk House 30 Kensington Rd
Rose Park, SA, 5067, Australia
Tel.: (61) 883644242
Fax: (61) 894770211
Emp.: 1
Software Support Services
S.I.C.: 7371
N.A.I.C.S.: 541511
Rob Hodgkinson *(Mng Dir)*

FIRST EFFORT INVESTMENTS LTD.

90 Morton Avenue East
Brantford, ON, N3R 7J7, Canada
Tel.: (519) 759-6411
Web Site: www.campuscrew.com
Year Founded: 1979
Sales Range: $50-74.9 Million
Business Description:
Business Consultants
S.I.C.: 7389
N.A.I.C.S.: 561499
Personnel:
Jim Turnoull *(VP)*

FIRST FACTORING INC.

Via Espana Regency Plaza Building 1J
Panama, Panama
Tel.: (507) 265 5600
Fax: (507) 265 0035
E-Mail: informacion@firstfactoringinc.com
Web Site: www.firstfactoringinc.com
FFAC—(PAN)
Emp.: 4
Business Description:
Financial Services
S.I.C.: 6211
N.A.I.C.S.: 523999
Personnel:
Gabriel Gonzalez Ruiz *(Pres)*

FIRST FINANCE CO.

King Abdullah 2nd st Building no 172
PO Box 144596
Khalda, Amman, 11814, Jordan
Tel.: (962) 65506740
Fax: (962) 65411782
E-Mail: Info@ffc.jo
Web Site: www.ffc.jo
Year Founded: 2006
FFCO—(AMM)
Rev.: $7,543,874
Assets: $68,922,171
Liabilities: $18,059,289
Net Worth: $50,862,882
Earnings: $3,093,075
Emp.: 56
Fiscal Year-end: 12/31/12
Business Description:
Financial Services
S.I.C.: 6211
N.A.I.C.S.: 523999
Personnel:
Osama Wajeh Assaf *(Gen Mgr)*

FIRST FINANCIAL HOLDING CO., LTD.

18F 30 Chung King S Rd Sec 1
Taipei, 100, Taiwan
Tel.: (886) 223111111
Fax: (886) 2 2311 9691
E-Mail: fhcir@firstbank.com.tw
Web Site: www.ffhc.com.tw
Year Founded: 2003
2892—(TAI)
Int. Income: $1,237,761,131
Assets: $71,754,867,191
Liabilities: $67,199,774,076
Net Worth: $4,555,093,115
Earnings: $342,681,046
Emp.: 8,585
Fiscal Year-end: 12/31/12
Business Description:
Bank Holding Company
S.I.C.: 6712
N.A.I.C.S.: 551111
Personnel:
Joseph Ching-Nain Tsai *(Chm)*
Tzuoo-Yau Lin *(Pres)*
Joung-Hui Yeh *(Exec VP & Head-Strategy Plng Dept)*
Po-Chiao Chou *(Exec VP)*
Board of Directors:
Joseph Ching-Nain Tsai
Chi-Hsun Chang
An-Fu Chen
Tien-Yuan Chen
Ming-Ren Chien
Hung-Chi Huang
Yophy Huang
Hsiu-Chuan Ko
Hsien-Feng Lee
Hsien-Heng Lee
Shyan-Yuan Lee
Tzuoo-Yau Lin
Tay-Chang Wang
Yi-Hsin Wang
Shun-Wu Yu

Citibank N A
388 Greenwich Street 14th Floor
New York, NY 10013
Transfer Agents:
First Bank Personal Banking Business Unit
Shareholder Service Department Trust Division
42 Yen Ping S
Taipei, Taiwan

Citibank N A
388 Greenwich Street 14th Floor
New York, NY 10013
Subsidiaries:

First Commercial Bank Ltd. (1)
30 Chung King S Rd Sec 1
Taipei, 100, Taiwan
Tel.: (886) 223481111
Fax: (886) 223481823
Web Site: www.firstbank.com.tw
Emp.: 6,000
Commercial Banking Services
S.I.C.: 6029
N.A.I.C.S.: 522110

Subsidiary:

FCB Leasing Co., Ltd (2)
94 Chung Hsiao East Road Sec 6
Taipei, Taiwan
Tel.: (886) 2 3343 7099
Fax: (886) 2 3343 7066
Financial Leasing Services
S.I.C.: 6153
N.A.I.C.S.: 522220

First Financial Assets Management Co., Ltd. (1)
7F 94 Jhong Siao East Rd Sec 2
Taipei, 100, Taiwan
Tel.: (886) 233437000
Fax: (886) 33222285
Web Site: www.firstfinancial.com
Emp.: 80
Financial Assets Management Services
S.I.C.: 6211
N.A.I.C.S.: 523999
Ian Wang *(Mgr-Bus Dev Order)*

First Financial Management Consulting Co., Ltd. (1)
9th Floor 30 Chung King South Road Sec 1
Taipei, Taiwan (100%)
Tel.: (886) 223484982
Fax: (886) 223708612
Web Site: www.fhc.com.tw/en/contact.htm
Management Consulting Services
S.I.C.: 8748
N.A.I.C.S.: 541618
Fu-Sun Riao *(Pres)*

First Property and Casualty Insurance Agency Co., Ltd. (1)
9th Floor 30 Chung King South Road Sec 1
Taipei, 100, Taiwan (100%)
Tel.: (886) 223484277
Web Site: www.firstholding.com.tw/en/contact.htm
Direct Property & Casualty Insurance Carriers
S.I.C.: 6331
N.A.I.C.S.: 524126

First Securities Investment Trust Co., Ltd (1)
7F 6 Min Chuan E Road Sec 3
Taipei, 104, Taiwan
Tel.: (886) 2 2504 1000
Web Site: www.firstholding.com.tw
Investment Management Services
S.I.C.: 6799
N.A.I.C.S.: 523920
Hsin-Shih Hung *(Chm)*
To-Wei Chen *(Acting Pres)*

First Taisec Securities (Asia) Limited (1)
6th Floor No 27
Sec 1 An Ho Road, Taipei, Taiwan (100%)
Tel.: (886) 227413434
Fax: (886) 227719530
Web Site: www.ftsi.com.tw
Investment Banking & Securities Dealing
S.I.C.: 6211
N.A.I.C.S.: 523110

Non-U.S. Subsidiary:

First Worldsec Securities Limited (2)
Suite 901 9/F The Hong Kong Club Building
3A Chater Road
Hong Kong, China (Hong Kong)
Tel.: (852) 28677288
Fax: (852) 28100281
Web Site: www.firstworldsec.com.hk
Securities Brokerage Services
S.I.C.: 6211
N.A.I.C.S.: 523120

First Taisec Securities Inc. (1)
4th Floor 6th Floor 7th Floor 27 An Ho Rd
Sec 1, Taipei, Taiwan (100%)
Tel.: (886) 227413434
Web Site: www.ffhc.com.tw/en/contact.htm
Investment Banking & Securities Dealing
S.I.C.: 6211
N.A.I.C.S.: 523110

First Venture Capital Co., Ltd. (1)
9F 30 Chung King S Rd Sec 1
Taipei, 100, Taiwan (100%)
Tel.: (886) 223484981
Fax: (886) 0223708612
Web Site: www.firstholding.com.tw/en/contact.htm
Emp.: 4
Financial Investment Activities
S.I.C.: 6211
N.A.I.C.S.: 523999
Fu-Sun Liao *(Pres)*

National Investment Trust Co., Ltd. (1)
7F 6 Min Chuan E Rd Sec 3
Taipei, 104, Taiwan
Tel.: (886) 225041000
Web Site: www.firstholding.com.tw/en/contact.htm
Investment Services
S.I.C.: 6211
N.A.I.C.S.: 523110

U.S. Subsidiary:

First Commercial Bank (U.S.A.) (1)
200 E Main St
Alhambra, CA 91801 (100%)
Tel.: (626) 300-6000
Fax: (626) 300-6030
E-Mail: fcbusa@bankfcb.com
Web Site: www.bankfcb.com
Emp.: 50
Commercial Banking
S.I.C.: 6029
N.A.I.C.S.: 522110
Terry Ju *(CFO)*

FIRST FINANCIAL SERVICES LTD

2c 2nd floor Ram Mansion No 367
Pantheon Road
Egmore, Chennai, 600 008, India
Tel.: (91) 44 4355 5227
Fax: (91) 44 2819 4595
E-Mail: ffsl@in.com
Web Site: www.ffslonline.com
Year Founded: 1984
511369—(BOM)
Rev.: $2,275,025
Assets: $3,314,443
Liabilities: $132,132
Net Worth: $3,182,311
Earnings: $88,874
Fiscal Year-end: 03/31/13
Business Description:
Financial Management Services
S.I.C.: 6211
N.A.I.C.S.: 523999
Personnel:
S. Krishna Rao *(Compliance Officer)*
Board of Directors:
Nirmalsingh Moolsingh Mertia
Ponnuswamy Natarajan
S. Krishna Rao
Sundaram Sankaranarayanan
Sambasivan Swaminathan
Transfer Agent:
Bigshare Services Private Limited
E 2/3 Ansa Industrial Estate Sakivihar Road
Sakinaka Andheri(E)
Mumbai, India

FIRST GEN CORPORATION

3rd Floor Benpres Building Exchange
Road Corner Meralco Avenue
Ortigas Center, Pasig, Philippines
Tel.: (63) 24496400
Fax: (63) 26378366
E-Mail: info@firstgen.com.ph
Web Site: www.firstgen.com.ph
FGEN—(PHI)
Rev.: $1,526,856,000
Assets: $2,693,958,000
Liabilities: $1,257,468,000
Net Worth: $1,436,490,000
Earnings: $207,032,000
Fiscal Year-end: 12/31/12
Business Description:
Power Generation & Distr
S.I.C.: 4931
N.A.I.C.S.: 221122
Personnel:
Federico R. Lopez *(Chm & CEO)*
Francis Giles B. Puno *(Pres & COO)*
Emmanuel P. Singson *(CFO, Treas & Sr VP)*
Charlie R. Valerio *(CIO & VP)*
Victor B. Santos, Jr. *(Compliance Officer & Sr VP)*
Rachel R. Hernandez *(Sec)*
Ernesto B. Pantangco *(Exec VP)*
Jonathan C. Russell *(Exec VP)*
Richard B. Tantoco *(Exec VP)*
Renato A. Castillo *(Sr VP)*
Ferdinand Edwin S. Co Seteng *(Sr VP)*
Colin J. D. Fleming *(Sr VP)*
Nestor H. Vasay *(Sr VP)*
Board of Directors:
Federico R. Lopez
Jaime I. Ayala
Tony Tan Caktiong
Peter D. Garrucho, Jr.
Elpidio L. Ibanez
Eugenio L. Lopez, III
Francis Giles B. Puno
Richard B. Tantoco
Transfer Agent:
Securities Transfer Services, Inc.
Ground Floor Benpres Building Exchange Road
corner Meralco Avenue
Pasig, Philippines

FIRST GRAPHITE CORP.

(Name Changed to Desert Star Resources Ltd.)

FIRST GULF BANK

PO Box 6316
Abu Dhabi, United Arab Emirates
Tel.: (971) 26394000
Fax: (971) 2 681 2161
E-Mail: customerservice@fgb.ae
Web Site: www.fgb.ae
Year Founded: 1979
FGB—(ABU)
Rev.: $2,080,676,744
Assets: $47,640,647,698
Liabilities: $39,512,511,861
Net Worth: $8,128,135,836
Earnings: $1,135,225,219
Emp.: 1,112
Fiscal Year-end: 12/31/12
Business Description:
Banking Services
S.I.C.: 6029
N.A.I.C.S.: 522110
Personnel:
Tahnoon Zayed Al Nahyan *(Chm)*
Ahmed Ali Al Sayegh *(Vice Chm)*
Andre Sayegh *(CEO)*
Abdulhamid Mohammed Saeed *(Mng Dir)*
Karim Karoui *(CFO)*
Zulfiquar Ali Sulaiman *(COO)*
Shirish Bhide *(Chief Credit Officer)*
Arif Shaikh *(Chief Risk Officer)*
Jasim Al Ali *(CEO-First Gulf Properties & Mismak Properties)*
Naji Azar *(Sr VP-Money Market)*
Board of Directors:
Tahnoon Zayed Al Nahyan
Sultan Khalfan Al Ktebi
Khaldoon Khalifa Al Mubarak
H. E. Khadem Abdulla Al Qubaisi
Ahmed Ali Al Sayegh
Mohamed Saif Al Suwaidi
Abdulhamid Mohammed Saeed

Subsidiary:

First Gulf Properties LLC **(1)**
PO Box 488178
Dubai, United Arab Emirates
Tel.: (971) 2 635 4444
Fax: (971) 2 635 4645
E-Mail: customercare@fgp.ae
Web Site: www.fgp.ae
Real Estate Management Services
S.I.C.: 6531
N.A.I.C.S.: 531390
Jasim Al Ali *(CEO)*

FIRST INSURANCE CO.

King Abdullah II Street
PO Box 189
Amman, 11822, Jordan
Tel.: (962) 65777555
Fax: (962) 65777550
E-Mail: info@firstinsurance.jo
Web Site: www.firstinsurance.jo
Year Founded: 2007
FINS—(AMM)
Sales Range: $1-9.9 Million
Emp.: 43
Business Description:
Insurance Services
S.I.C.: 6411
N.A.I.C.S.: 524298
Personnel:
Ismail Tahboub *(Chm)*
Ashraf Bseisu *(Vice Chm)*
Ali Al-Wazani *(CEO)*
Khaldoun Al Daboubi *(Deputy CEO)*
Ismail Al-Muhtadi *(CFO)*
Imad Morrar *(COO)*
Board of Directors:
Ismail Tahboub
Bashar Al Amad
Rashed Al Kaa'bi
Ayman Al-Majali
Osama Assaf
Ashraf Bseisu
Jawad Mohammed

FIRST INTERNATIONAL COMPUTER, INC.

No 300 Yang Guang St
Neihu, Taipei, 114, Taiwan
Tel.: (886) 287518751
Web Site: www.fic.com.tw
Sales Range: $1-4.9 Billion
Emp.: 1,250
Business Description:
Design & Mfr Computer Product & Electronic Components
S.I.C.: 3571
N.A.I.C.S.: 334111
Personnel:
Ming J. Chien *(Chm)*

FIRST INTERNATIONAL MERCHANT BANK PLC

Mercury Tower The Exchange
Financial & Business Centre
Elia Zammit Street St Julian's,
Valletta, STJ 3155, Malta
Tel.: (356) 21322100
Fax: (356) 21322122
E-Mail: info@fimbank.com
Web Site: www.fimbank.com
FIM—(BOM LSE MAL)
Int. Income: $30,177,040
Assets: $1,130,408,175
Liabilities: $999,767,909
Net Worth: $130,640,266
Earnings: $8,798,533
Emp.: 213
Fiscal Year-end: 12/31/12
Business Description:
Bank
S.I.C.: 6153
N.A.I.C.S.: 522298
Personnel:
John C. Grech *(Chm)*
Masaud H. T. Hayat *(Vice Chm)*
Margrith Lutschg-Emmenegger *(Pres)*
Simon Lay *(Mng Dir & First Exec VP-London Forfaiting Company Ltd)*
Marcel Cassar *(CFO & First Exec VP)*
Ivan Fsadni *(Chief Risk Officer & Exec VP)*
Nigel Harris *(Chief Representative Officer)*
Andrea Batelli *(Sec, First VP & Head-Legal)*
Armin Eckermann *(Sr Exec VP & Head-Global Banking)*
Silvio Mifsud *(Exec VP & Head-Info & Admin)*
Renald Theuma *(Exec VP & Head-Trade Finance & Product Sls)*
Giovanni Bartolotta *(Sr VP & Head-Risk Mgmt)*
Bruno Cassar *(Sr VP & Head-HR)*
Michael Davis *(Sr VP & Head-Compliance)*
Carmelo Occhipinti *(Sr VP & Head-Corp Fin)*
Richard Scerri *(Sr VP & Head-Internal Audit)*
Aly Siby *(Sr VP & Head-Fin Institutions & Deposits)*
Charles Wallbank *(Sr VP & Head-Banking Ops)*
Toufic Yafaoui *(Sr VP & Head-Treasury & Capital Markets)*
Board of Directors:
John C. Grech
Majed Essa Al-Ajeel
Hamad M. B. M. Al-Sayer
Fouad M. T. Alghanim
Adrian Alejandro Gostuski
Masaud H. T. Hayat
Rogers D. LeBaron
Eduardo Eguren Linsen
Mohammed I. H. Marafie
Fakih Ahmed Mohamed
Rabih Soukarieh

Subsidiaries:

FIM Business Solutions Limited **(1)**
Mercury Tower The Exchange Financial and Bussiness Center
San Giljan, STJ 3155, Malta
Tel.: (356) 21322100
Fax: (356) 21322122
E-Mail: info@fimbank.com
Web Site: www.fimbs.net
Financial Advisory Services
S.I.C.: 6282
N.A.I.C.S.: 523930

FIM Property Investment Limited **(1)**
7th Floor The Plaza Commercial Centre
Bisazza Street
Sliema, SLM 1640, Malta
Tel.: (356) 21322100
Fax: (356) 21322122
E-Mail: info@fimproperty.com
Emp.: 160
Property Management Services
S.I.C.: 6531
N.A.I.C.S.: 531312

Non-U.S. Subsidiaries:

London Forfaiting Company Ltd **(1)**
11 Ironmonger Lane
London, EC2V 8EY, United Kingdom UK
Tel.: (44) 2073971510 (100%)
Telex: 8812606 LONFOR G
Fax: (44) 2073971511
E-Mail: lfc@forfaiting.com
Web Site: www.londonforfaiting.com
Emp.: 70
International Trade Finance Services; Forfaiting Services, Short-Term Financing for Exporters
S.I.C.: 6159
N.A.I.C.S.: 522293
Simon Lay *(Mng Dir)*

U.S. Subsidiary:

London Forfaiting Americas Inc. **(2)**
1 East 52nd St Ste 602
New York, NY 10022
Tel.: (212) 759-1919
Fax: (212) 759-0118
E-Mail: lfa@forfaiting.com
Web Site: www.forfaiting.com
Emp.: 3
Trade Financial Services
S.I.C.: 6159
N.A.I.C.S.: 522293
Gregory Bernardi *(Pres)*

Non-U.S. Subsidiaries:

London Forfaiting A Paris SA **(2)**
260 Blvd Saint Germain
F 75007 Paris, France FR
Tel.: (33) 140626190
Fax: (33) 140626191
Emp.: 35
Provider of Forfaiting Services, Short-Term Financing for Exporters
S.I.C.: 6799
N.A.I.C.S.: 523910

London Forfaiting Deutschland GmbH **(2)**
Neiderrheinstrasse 23
D 40474 Dusseldorf, Germany DE
Tel.: (49) 2114303040
Fax: (49) 21143030555
Provider of Forfaiting Services, Short-Term Financing for Exporters
S.I.C.: 6799
N.A.I.C.S.: 523910

London Forfaiting do Brasil Ltda **(2)**
World Trade Center Av das Nacoes Unidas
12 551 25th Floor
Sao Paulo, 04578-903, Brazil
Tel.: (55) 1130437400
Fax: (55) 11 3 0 43 7 249
E-Mail: lfc.brasil@forfaiting.com
Web Site: www.londonforfaiting.com
International Trade Financing

S.I.C.: 6159
N.A.I.C.S.: 522293
Alexandre Ozzetti *(Mng Dir)*

London Forfaiting Polska Sp. z.o.o (2)
Ilmet Bldg U1 Jana Pawla II 15
PL 00 828 Warsaw, Poland PL
Tel.: (48) 226977277
Fax: (48) 226977279
Emp.: 35
Provider of Forfaiting Services, Short-Term Financing for Exporters
S.I.C.: 6799
N.A.I.C.S.: 523910

Menafactors Limited (1)
Office 3 And 4 Level 1 The Gate Village 06
PO Box 506554
Dubai, United Arab Emirates
Tel.: (971) 4 4242660
Fax: (971) 4 4255740
E-Mail: Operations@menafactors.com
Web Site: www.menafactors.com
Emp.: 25
Financial Advisory Services
S.I.C.: 6282
N.A.I.C.S.: 523930
Veene Mankar *(Chm)*
Sudeb Sarbadhikary *(CEO)*

FIRST INVESTMENT BANK AD

37 Dragan Tsankov Blvd
1797 Sofia, Bulgaria
Tel.: (359) 2 817 11 00
E-Mail: fib@fibank.bg
Web Site: www.fibank.bg
5F4—(BUL)
Int. Income: $318,177,452
Assets: $4,818,981,208
Liabilities: $4,473,631,214
Net Worth: $345,349,995
Earnings: $20,896,646
Emp.: 2,859
Fiscal Year-end: 12/31/12

Business Description:
Banking Services
S.I.C.: 6029
N.A.I.C.S.: 522110

Personnel:
Evgeni Krastev Lukanov *(Chm-Supervisory Bd)*
Dimitar Kostov *(Chm-Mgmt Bd & Exec Dir)*
Maya Lubenova Georgieva *(Deputy Chm-Supervisory Bd)*
Vasil Christov *(Member-Mgmt Bd & Exec Dir)*
Svetoslav Moldovanski *(Member-Mgmt Bd & Exec Dir)*
Maya Ivanova Oyfalosh *(Member-Mgmt Bd & Exec Dir)*

Board of Directors:
Vasil Christov
Dimitar Kostov
Svetoslav Moldovanski
Maya Ivanova Oyfalosh

Supervisory Board of Directors:
Evgeni Krastev Lukanov
Maya Lubenova Georgieva
Radka Vesselinova Mineva
Georgi Dimitrov Mutafchiev
Jordan Velichkov Skorchev

Non-U.S. Subsidiary:

First Investment Bank Albania Sh.a (1)
Blvd Deshmoret e Kombit
Twin Towers Nr 2 Kati 14 15, Tirana, Albania
Tel.: (355) 42276702
Fax: (355) 42280210
E-Mail: fib@fibank.al
Web Site: www.fibank.al
Emp.: 40
Banking Services
S.I.C.: 6011
N.A.I.C.S.: 521110
Bozhidar Todorov *(CEO)*
Edvin Liko *(CFO)*

FIRST INVESTMENT COMPANY K.S.C.C.

Mirqab Abdulla Al-Mubarak Street
Souk Al-Safat Bldg 1st Floor
PO Box 20230
Safat, Kuwait, 13063, Kuwait
Tel.: (965) 1804050
Fax: (965) 22435856
E-Mail: info@fic.com.kw
Web Site: www.fic.com.kw
ALOLA—(KUW)
Rev.: $29,107,048
Assets: $519,568,253
Liabilities: $119,929,260
Net Worth: $399,638,993
Earnings: $10,311,847
Emp.: 25
Fiscal Year-end: 12/31/12

Business Description:
Investment & Financial Services
S.I.C.: 6211
N.A.I.C.S.: 523999

Personnel:
Khaled Saod Al-Sanaousi *(Chm, CEO & Mng Dir)*
Bader Mohammad Al-Qattan *(Vice Chm)*
Tareq A. Al-Adasani *(Deputy CEO)*
Omar S. Al-Mutawaa *(Deputy CEO)*

Board of Directors:
Khaled Saod Al-Sanaousi
Khalifa Abdulla Al-Ajeel
Abdulmehsen Hamad Al-Hamad
Marzouq Fajhan Al-Mutairi
Bader Mohammad Al-Qattan
Bader Ali Benaian
Ahmad Abdulgadir Mohammad

Ernst & Young Al Alban, Al osalmi & Partners
Baitak Tower 18-21st Floor Safat Square
Ahmed Al Jaber Street
PO Box 74
Kuwait, Kuwait

FIRST ISRAEL MEZZANINE INVESTORS LTD

Electra Tower 98 Yigal Alon St
Tel Aviv, 67891, Israel
Tel.: (972) 3 5652244
Fax: (972) 3 5652245
E-Mail: fimi@fimi.co.il
Web Site: www.fimi.co.il

Business Description:
Private Equity Firm
S.I.C.: 6211
N.A.I.C.S.: 523999

Personnel:
Ishay Davidi *(Founder & CEO)*

Subsidiary:

TAT Technologies Ltd. (1)
PO Box 80
Gedera, 70750, Israel (53.8%)
Tel.: (972) 88268500
Fax: (972) 88592831
E-Mail: tat@tat.co.il
Web Site: www.tat.co.il
TATT—(NASDAQ)
Rev.: $87,922,000
Assets: $107,511,000
Liabilities: $22,475,000
Net Worth: $85,036,000
Earnings: ($1,772,000)
Emp.: 575
Fiscal Year-end: 12/31/12
Aircraft Heat-Transfer Equipment & Component Parts Mfr
S.I.C.: 3724
N.A.I.C.S.: 336412
Rimon Ben-Shaoul *(Chm)*
Itsik Maaravi *(CEO)*
Shlomi Karako *(COO & VP-Ops)*

U.S. Subsidiary:

Limco-Piedmont Inc. (2)
5304 S Lawton Ave
Tulsa, OK 74107-9428 DE
Tel.: (918) 445-4300 (100%)
Fax: (918) 446-8704
Web Site: www.limcopiedmont.com
Sales Range: $50-74.9 Million
Emp.: 284
Aviation Parts Mfr
S.I.C.: 3728
N.A.I.C.S.: 336413
Robert Koch *(Co-CEO)*
Ehud Netivi *(Co-CEO)*

FIRST ISRAEL TURNAROUND ENTERPRISE

37 Mencham Begin Rd 29th Fl
Tel Aviv, 67137, Israel
Tel.: (972) 36086838
Fax: (972) 35652245
Web Site: www.fiteinv.com
Year Founded: 2004
Emp.: 10

Business Description:
Private Equity Firm
S.I.C.: 6211
N.A.I.C.S.: 523999

Personnel:
Ishay Davidi *(Co-Founder & Chm)*
Ron Zuckerman *(Co-Founder)*
Ami Boehm *(CEO & Mng Partner)*
Nir Leshem *(CFO)*
Chai Natovich *(Principal)*

Board of Directors:
Ishay Davidi
Amnon Goldschmidt
Robert E. Joyal
Ron Zuckerman

Holding:

Global Wire Ltd. (1)
PO Box 56
Tel Aviv, 61000, Israel
Tel.: (972) 39269200
Fax: (972) 3 9269222
Mfr of Non-Ferrous Wires & Conductors
S.I.C.: 3496
N.A.I.C.S.: 332618
Adi Livneh *(CEO)*

FIRST JORDAN INVESTMENT COMPANY PLC

First Floor Al Hussini Building 141
Mecca Street
PO Box 942007
Amman, 11194, Jordan
Tel.: (962) 65562130
Fax: (962) 65562129
E-Mail: info@firstjordan.com.jo
Web Site: www.firstjordan.com.jo
Year Founded: 2006
FRST—(AMM)
Assets: $122,028,745
Liabilities: $22,843,511
Net Worth: $99,185,234
Earnings: ($3,413,883)
Emp.: 11
Fiscal Year-end: 12/31/12

Business Description:
Commercial Investment Services
S.I.C.: 6211
N.A.I.C.S.: 523999

Personnel:
Mohammad-Khair Ababneh *(Chm)*
Ismail A. Odeh *(Vice Chm)*

Board of Directors:
Mohammad-Khair Ababneh
Mu'tasem M. Ababneh
Samer M. Abbouchi
Mohammad A. Al Halawani
Bassam A. Hammad
Nabil S. Makahleh
Ismail A. Odeh

FIRST LEASE FINANCE AND INVESTMENT LIMITED

Jahangir Tower 3rd Floor 10 Kawran Bazar C/A
Dhaka, 1215, Bangladesh
Tel.: (880) 2 9145487
Fax: (880) 2 8153971
E-Mail: info@first-lease.com.bd
Web Site: www.first-lease.com.bd
Year Founded: 1993
FLEASEINT—(DHA)
Sales Range: $1-9.9 Million

Business Description:
Financial Services
S.I.C.: 6211
N.A.I.C.S.: 523999

Personnel:
Rajia Khanam *(Chm)*
Ashrafuddin Ahmed *(Vice Chm)*
Faruk Ahmed *(Vice Chm)*

Board of Directors:
Rajia Khanam
Ashrafuddin Ahmed
Faisal Ahmed
Faruk Ahmed
Shadia Akther
Mahmud Ali Bhuiyan
Mojibur Rahnam Chowdhury
Mostafa Haider Khan
Mustafizur Rahman
Theotonius Biplob Roy
Mohammad Abul Ahsan Telu

FIRST LEASING COMPANY OF INDIA LTD.

749 Anna Salai
Chennai, India 600002
Tel.: (91) 4430220705
Fax: (91) 4430249162
E-Mail: firstleasing@firstleasingindia.com
Web Site: www.firstleasingindia.com
FIRSTLEASE—(NSE)
Rev.: $45,373,164
Assets: $353,279,997
Liabilities: $285,805,391
Net Worth: $67,474,606
Earnings: $6,438,775
Fiscal Year-end: 03/31/13

Business Description:
Corporate Financing Services
S.I.C.: 6153
N.A.I.C.S.: 522220

Personnel:
Farouk M. Irani *(Mng Dir)*
L. Sivaramakrishnan *(CFO)*
Sheetal R. *(Compliance Officer & Sec)*

Board of Directors:
A. C. Muthiah
Farouk M. Irani
N. Ramakrishnan
V. Selvaraj

Transfer Agent:
Cameo Corporate Services Limited
Subramanian Bldg No 1 Club House Road
Chennai, 600 002, India
Tel.: (91) 44 2846 0390
Fax: (91) 44 2846 0129

FIRST LITHIUM RESOURCES INC.

(See Under Golden Virtue Resources Inc.)

FIRST MAJESTIC SILVER CORP.

925 West Georgia Street Ste 1805
Vancouver, BC, V6C 3L2, Canada
Tel.: (604) 688-3033
Fax: (604) 639-8873
Toll Free: (866) 529-2807
E-Mail: info@firstmajestic.com
Web Site: www.firstmajestic.com
AG—(DEU NYSE TSX)
Rev.: $247,177,000
Assets: $813,031,000
Liabilities: $219,506,000
Net Worth: $593,525,000
Earnings: $88,898,000

First Majestic Silver Corp.—(Continued)

Emp.: 3,588
Fiscal Year-end: 12/31/12
Business Description:
Silver Mining Services
S.I.C.: 1044
N.A.I.C.S.: 212222
Personnel:
Keith Neumeyer *(Pres & CEO)*
Raymond L. Polman *(CFO)*
Salvador Garcia Ledezma *(COO)*
Martin Palacios *(CIO)*
Connie Lillico *(Sec)*
Board of Directors:
Douglas Penrose
Robert A. McCallum
Keith Neumeyer
Tony Pezzotti
David A. Shaw
Robert Young
Legal Counsel:
McCullough O'Connor Irwin, LLP
Ste 2610 Oceanic Plz 1066 W Hastings St
Vancouver, BC, V6E 3X1, Canada
Transfer Agent:
Computershare Trust Company of Canada
510 Burrard St 2nd Fl
Vancouver, BC, Canada

FIRST METRO INVESTMENT CORPORATION
45th Fl GT Tower International Ayala Ave corner HV dela Costa St
Makati, 1200, Philippines
Tel.: (63) 28587900
Fax: (63) 28403706
E-Mail: corpplan@firstmetro.com.ph
Web Site: www.firstmetro.com.ph
Sales Range: $75-99.9 Million
Business Description:
Investment Banking Services
S.I.C.: 6211
N.A.I.C.S.: 523110
Personnel:
Francisco C. Sebastian *(Chm)*
Solomon S. Cua *(Vice Chm)*
Arthur V. Ty *(Vice Chm)*
Roberto Juanchito T. Dispo *(Pres)*
Alesandra V. Ty *(Sec)*
Reynaldo B. Montalbo *(Sr VP & Head-Treasury Grp)*
Justino Juan R. Ocampo *(Sr VP & Head-Investment Banking)*
Board of Directors:
Francisco C. Sebastian
Manuel I. Ayala
Abelardo V. Cortez
Ismael G. Cruz
Solomon S. Cua
Vicente R. Cuna, Jr.
Roberto Juanchito T. Dispo
Rex C. Drilon
Martin Q. Dy Buncio
Bienvenido E. Laguesma
Arthur V. Ty

FIRST MEXICAN GOLD CORP.
1000 - 355 Burrard Street
Vancouver, BC, V6C 2G8, Canada
Tel.: (604) 681-7265
Fax: (604) 608-6361
Toll Free: (800) 366-8566
Web Site: www.fmgoldcorp.com
Year Founded: 2007
FMG—(TSXV)
Rev.: $38,487
Assets: $6,280,681
Liabilities: $561,509
Net Worth: $5,719,172
Earnings: ($646,659)
Fiscal Year-end: 12/31/12
Business Description:
Mineral Exploration Services
S.I.C.: 1081
N.A.I.C.S.: 213114
Personnel:
James Voisin *(Pres & CEO)*
Nicole Wood *(CFO)*
Board of Directors:
Patrick Burns
Gregory Roberts
James Voisin
Transfer Agent:
Computershare Trust Company of Canada
9th Floor 100 University Avenue
Toronto, ON, Canada

Non-U.S. Subsidiary:

Cornelius Exploration S. de R.L. de C.V. **(1)**
Avenida Santa Margarita 4140 2nd Floor 22b
Colonia Santa Margarita, Zapopan, Jalisco, 45140, Mexico
Tel.: (52) 33 31655553
Fax: (52) 33 31655555
E-Mail: mineraplanet@ucresources.net
Gold Mining Services
S.I.C.: 1041
N.A.I.C.S.: 212221
Arturo Garcia *(Office Mgr)*

FIRST MOBILE GROUP HOLDINGS LIMITED
Workshop 6 Level 1 Wah Yiu Industrial Center 30-32 Au Pui Wan Street
Fotan, Sha Tin, New Territories, China (Hong Kong)
Tel.: (852) 23760233
Fax: (852) 23760210
E-Mail: sales@firstmobilegroup.com.hk
Web Site: www.firstmobile.com
865—(HKG)
Rev.: $2,989,835
Assets: $807,227
Liabilities: $223,410,001
Net Worth: ($222,602,774)
Earnings: ($26,206,637)
Emp.: 11
Fiscal Year-end: 12/31/12
Business Description:
Mobile Phone Sales & Distr
S.I.C.: 4812
N.A.I.C.S.: 517911
Personnel:
Kok Hong Ng *(Chm)*
Kok Tai Ng *(Deputy Chm)*
Kok Yang Ng *(CEO)*
Sew Chin Eng *(Treas)*
Man Sau Choy *(Sec & Controller-Fin)*
Wai Hoe Wong *(Sr VP-Ops-Hong Kong)*
Board of Directors:
Kok Hong Ng
Kok Tai Ng
Kok Yang Ng
Royal Bank of Canada Trust Company (Cayman) Limited
4th Floor Royal Bank House 24 Shedden Road
Georgetown, Cayman Islands
Transfer Agents:
Tricor Abacus Limited
26th Floor Tesbury Centre 28 Queen's Road East
Wanchai, China (Hong Kong)
Royal Bank of Canada Trust Company (Cayman) Limited
4th Floor Royal Bank House 24 Shedden Road
Georgetown, Cayman Islands

FIRST NATIONAL EQUITIES LIMITED
FNE House 19-C Sunset Lane 6
South Park Ave Phase II Extension D H A
Karachi, Pakistan
Tel.: (92) 2135395901
Fax: (92) 2135395920
E-Mail: info@fnetrade.com
Web Site: www.fnetrade.com
FNEL—(KAR)
Rev.: $1,080,635
Assets: $11,966,706
Liabilities: $16,711,030
Net Worth: ($4,744,324)
Earnings: ($186,356)
Emp.: 52
Fiscal Year-end: 06/30/13
Business Description:
Stock Brokerage Services
S.I.C.: 6211
N.A.I.C.S.: 523120
Personnel:
Ali Aslam Malik *(CEO)*
Najam Raza Shamsi *(CFO)*
Usman Amjad Khan *(Sec)*
Board of Directors:
Shahzad Akbar
Malik Attiq-ur-Rehman
Saeed Ahmed Bajwa
Rais Ahmed Dar
Mohammad Iqbal Khan
Ali Aslam Malik
Amir Shehzad

FIRST NATIONAL FINANCIAL CORPORATION
100 University Avenue Suite 700
North Tower
Toronto, ON, M5J 1V6, Canada
Tel.: (416) 593-1100
Fax: (416) 593-1300
Year Founded: 2011
FN—(TSX)
Rev.: $334,971,818
Assets: $14,918,800,859
Liabilities: $14,598,224,439
Net Worth: $320,576,420
Earnings: $109,665,257
Fiscal Year-end: 12/31/12
Business Description:
Financial Services
S.I.C.: 6163
N.A.I.C.S.: 522310
Personnel:
Stephen Smith *(Chm & Pres)*
Robert Inglis *(CFO)*
Moray Tawse *(Sec & VP)*
Board of Directors:
Stephen Smith
John Brough
Peter Copestake
Duncan Jackman
Robert Mitchell
Moray Tawse
Legal Counsel:
Stikeman Elliott LLP
Toronto, ON, Canada
Transfer Agent:
Computershare Investor Services Inc.
Toronto, ON, Canada

FIRST NATIONAL MORTGAGE INVESTMENT FUND
36 Toronto Street Suite 710
Toronto, ON, M5C 2C5, Canada
Tel.: (416) 364-9188
Fax: (416) 364-8456
Year Founded: 2012
FNM.UN—(TSX)
Business Description:
Investment Services
S.I.C.: 6211
N.A.I.C.S.: 523999
Personnel:
Richard G. Stone *(Chm, Pres & CEO)*
James A. Elliott *(CFO)*
Suzanne Grimble *(Sec)*
Board of Directors:
Richard G. Stone
Martin Antsee
James A. Elliott
Transfer Agent:
Computershare Investor Services Inc.
Montreal, QC, Canada

FIRST NATIONAL VEGETABLE OIL INDUSTRIES PLC.
Airport Way-Qastal
PO Box 142721
11814 Amman, Jordan
Tel.: (962) 647113157
Fax: (962) 604711318
E-Mail: info@fnvo.net
Web Site: www.fnvo.net
Year Founded: 1997
FNVO—(AMM)
Sales Range: $1-9.9 Million
Emp.: 45
Business Description:
Vegetable Oil Mfr
S.I.C.: 3999
N.A.I.C.S.: 339999
Personnel:
Sa'ad Mohsen Naji *(Chm)*
Abdallha Saed Assim Al-Janabi *(Deputy Chm)*
Board of Directors:
Sa'ad Mohsen Naji
Mustafa Abdul Hameed Al-Bayati
Jader Abdul Wahhab Mohammed
Najeeb Al-Jadir
Abdallha Saed Assim Al-Janabi
Jamal Yousef Hassan Abed Al-Nabi
Naser Azmi Mohammad Al-Qawasmi
Farooq Mohsin Bandar
Jamal Nihad Darwazeh

FIRST NICKEL INC.
120 Front Street East Suite 206
Toronto, ON, Canada M5A 4L9
Tel.: (416) 362-7050
Fax: (416) 362-9050
E-Mail: info@firstnickel.com
Web Site: www.firstnickel.com
Year Founded: 2003
FNI—(TSX)
Sales Range: Less than $1 Million
Emp.: 37
Business Description:
Nickel Mining & Copper Exploration Services
S.I.C.: 1021
N.A.I.C.S.: 212234
Personnel:
C. David A. Comba *(Chm)*
Thomas M. Boehlert *(Pres & CEO)*
Alfred Colas *(CFO & VP)*
Gerry Bilodeau *(COO)*
Board of Directors:
C. David A. Comba
William J. Anderson
Thomas M. Boehlert
Joao Carrelo
Russell L. Cranswick
Richard S. Hallisey
Lyle R. Hepburn
Robert F. Whittall
Legal Counsel:
Fasken Martineau DuMoulin LLP
333 Bay Street Suite 2400 Bay Adelaide Centre
PO Box 20
Toronto, ON, Canada
Transfer Agent:
Equity Transfer Services Inc
200 University Avenue Suite 400
Toronto, ON, Canada

FIRST OIL PLC
1 Queens Terrace
Aberdeen, AB10 1XL, United Kingdom
Tel.: (44) 1224 624666
Fax: (44) 1224 624880
E-Mail: info@firstoilexpro.com

Web Site: www.firstoilexpro.com
Rev.: $148,502,218
Assets: $420,561,768
Liabilities: $339,762,133
Net Worth: $80,799,635
Earnings: $17,744,902
Emp.: 10
Fiscal Year-end: 04/30/13
Business Description:
Oil & Natural Gas Production
S.I.C.: 1311
N.A.I.C.S.: 211111
Personnel:
Ian A. Suttie *(Chm)*
Steve Bowyer *(Mng Dir)*

Subsidiary:

First Oil Expro Ltd. **(1)**
1 Queens Terrace
Aberdeen, AB10 1XL, United Kingdom
Tel.: (44) 1224 624666
Fax: (44) 1224 624880
Oil & Gas Exploration & Production
S.I.C.: 1311
N.A.I.C.S.: 211111

FIRST PACIFIC COMPANY LIMITED

24th Floor 2 Exchange Square 8
Connaught Place
Central, China (Hong Kong)
Tel.: (852) 2842 4388
Telex: 74216 FPFHK HX
Fax: (852) 2845 9243
E-Mail: info@firstpacific.com
Web Site: www.firstpacific.com
Year Founded: 1981
0142—(HKG)
Sls.: $5,990,800,000
Assets: $13,880,000,000
Liabilities: $6,636,000,000
Net Worth: $7,244,000,000
Earnings: $830,200,000
Emp.: 80,941
Fiscal Year-end: 12/31/12
Business Description:
Holding Company;
Telecommunication Services;
Property Development Services;
Food Manufacturing
S.I.C.: 6719
N.A.I.C.S.: 551112
Personnel:
Anthoni Salim *(Chm)*
Manuel V. Pangilinan *(CEO)*
Nancy L. M. Li *(Sec & VP)*
Richard L. Beacher *(Exec VP & Controller-Fin)*
Maisie M. S. Lam *(Exec VP-HR)*
Joseph H. P. Ng *(Exec VP-Fin)*
John W. Ryan *(Exec VP-Corp Comm)*
Stanley H. Yang *(Exec VP-Corp Dev)*
Board of Directors:
Anthoni Salim
Edward K. Y. Chen
Tedy Djuhar
Philip Yan Hok Fan
Margaret Ko May Yee Leung
Napoleon Logarta Nazareno
Robert C. Nicholson
Manuel V. Pangilinan
Graham L. Pickles
Benny S. Santoso
Jun Tang
Edward A. Tortorici
Legal Counsel:
Reed Smith Richards Butler
20th Floor Alexandra House 16-20 Chater Road
Central, China (Hong Kong)
Butterfield Fulcrum Group (Bermuda) Limited
26 Burnaby Street
Hamilton, HM 11, Bermuda
Transfer Agents:
Computershare Hong Kong Investor Services Limited
Shops 1712-1716 17th Floor Hopewell Centre
183 Queens Road East
Wanchai, China (Hong Kong)
Butterfield Fulcrum Group (Bermuda) Limited
26 Burnaby Street
Hamilton, HM 11, Bermuda

Subsidiary:

Infrontier Ltd. **(1)**
Ste 1203 05 The Broadway
54 62 Lockhart Rd, Wanchai, Hong Kong, China (Hong Kong) (100%)
Tel.: (852) 21110789
Fax: (852) 28459243
Web Site: www.infrontier.com
S.I.C.: 4813
N.A.I.C.S.: 517110

Non-U.S. Subsidiaries:

Metro Pacific Investments Corporation **(1)**
10/F MGO Building Legazpi cor Dela Rosa Streets
Makati, 0721, Philippines (55.6%)
Tel.: (63) 28880888
Fax: (63) 28880813
E-Mail: info@mpic.com.ph
Web Site: www.mpic.com.ph
MPI—(OTC PHI)
Rev.: $680,989,463
Assets: $4,249,114,038
Liabilities: $1,938,244,029
Net Worth: $2,310,870,008
Earnings: $237,361,341
Emp.: 16
Fiscal Year-end: 12/31/12
Holding Company; Investment & Management Services
S.I.C.: 6211
N.A.I.C.S.: 523999
Manuel V. Pangilinan *(Chm)*
Jose Maria K. Lim *(Pres & CEO)*
David J. Nicol *(CFO)*
Augusto P. Palisoc, Jr. *(Pres/CEO-Hospital Grp)*
Antonio A. Picazo *(Sec)*

PT Darya-Varia Laboratoria Tbk **(1)**
Talavera Office Pk 8th - 10th Fl Jl Letjen T B
Simatupang No 22 - 26, 12430 Jakarta, Indonesia Id
Tel.: (62) 2175924500 (89.5%)
Fax: (62) 217258011
E-Mail: info@darya-varia.com
Web Site: www.darya-varia.com
Sls.: $28,454,800
Emp.: 200
Mfr. & Marketer of Pharmaceutical, Sterile & Soft Gelatine Capsule
Export
S.I.C.: 2834
N.A.I.C.S.: 325412
Eric Albert Gotuaco *(Pres)*

PT Indofood Sukses Makmur Tbk. **(1)**
Sudirman Plaza Indofood Tower 27th Floor
Jl Jend Sudirman Kav 76-78, Jakarta, 12910, Indonesia (50.1%)
Tel.: (62) 2157958822
Fax: (62) 2157935960
E-Mail: ism@indofood.co.id
Web Site: www.indofood.co.id
INDF—(INDO OTC)
Sls.: $5,005,942,700
Assets: $5,932,420,700
Liabilities: $2,518,153,300
Net Worth: $3,414,267,400
Earnings: $477,944,600
Emp.: 74,686
Fiscal Year-end: 12/31/12
Food Mfr, Processor, Marketer & Distr
S.I.C.: 2034
N.A.I.C.S.: 311423
Anthoni Salim *(Chm & CEO)*
Werianty Setiawan *(Sec & Head-IR)*

Non-U.S. Subsidiary:

China Minzhong Food Corporation Limited **(2)**
9 Battery Road 15-01 Straits Trading Building
Singapore, 049910, Singapore (88.99%)
Tel.: (65) 6535 3600
Fax: (65) 6225 6846
E-Mail: ir@chinaminzhong.com
Web Site: www.chinaminzhong.com.sg
K2N—(SES)
Rev.: $515,908,741
Assets: $926,875,930
Liabilities: $169,159,206
Net Worth: $757,716,724
Earnings: $119,942,075
Emp.: 330
Fiscal Year-end: 06/30/13
Vegetable Processor
S.I.C.: 2037
N.A.I.C.S.: 311411
Guo Rong Lin *(Chm & CEO)*
Wei Ting Siek *(CFO)*
Dazhang Wang *(COO)*
Bing Hui Huang *(CTO)*
Howard Heng Haw Cheam *(Sec)*

FIRST PARAMOUNT MODARABA

Room No 107 & 108 PECHS
Community Office Complex Block No 2 PECHS
Shah rah e Quaideen Road, Karachi, Pakistan
Tel.: (92) 21 34381037
Fax: (92) 21 4534401
E-Mail: info@fpm.com.pk
Web Site: www.fpm.com.pk
Rev.: $425,739
Assets: $2,704,245
Liabilities: $924,694
Net Worth: $1,779,551
Earnings: $166,248
Emp.: 21
Fiscal Year-end: 06/30/13
Business Description:
Banking Services
S.I.C.: 6029
N.A.I.C.S.: 522110
Personnel:
Tanweer Ahmed Magoon *(Chm)*
Abdul Ghaffar Umer *(CEO)*
Naseemuddin Zubairi *(CFO)*
Board of Directors:
Tanweer Ahmed Magoon
Nadeem Iqbal
Abdul Razzak Jangda
Mohammad A. Kaliya
Muhammad Khalid Mukashi
Ahmed Kasam Parekh
Abdul Ghaffar Umer

FIRST PHILIPPINE HOLDINGS CORPORATION

4th Floor Benpres Building Exchange Road Corner Meralco Avenue
Ortigas Center, Pasig, 1605, Philippines
Tel.: (63) 26318024
Fax: (63) 26314089
E-Mail: invrel@fphc.com
Web Site: www.fphc.com
FPH—(PHI)
Rev.: $1,909,044,480
Assets: $4,282,223,440
Liabilities: $1,972,179,700
Net Worth: $2,310,043,740
Earnings: $302,892,320
Fiscal Year-end: 12/31/12
Business Description:
Power Generation Services
S.I.C.: 4953
N.A.I.C.S.: 562213
Personnel:
Federico R. Lopez *(Chm & CEO)*
Manuel M. Lopez *(Vice Chm)*
Elpidio L. Ibanez *(Pres & COO)*
Francis Giles B. Puno *(CFO, Treas & Exec VP)*
Oscar M. Lopez *(Chief Strategic Officer)*
Enrique I. Quiason *(Compliance Officer & Sec)*
Rodolfo R. Waga, Jr. *(VP, Asst Compliance Officer & Asst Sec)*
Perla R. Catahan *(Sr VP & Comptroller)*
Ferdinand Edwin Sy Co Seteng *(Sr VP)*
Board of Directors:
Federico R. Lopez
Augusto Almeda-Lopez
Cesar B. Bautista
Arthur A. De Guia
Peter D. Garrucho Jr.
Oscar J. Hilado
Elpidio L. Ibanez
Eugenio L. Lopez III
Manuel M. Lopez
Oscar M. Lopez
Artemio V. Panganiban
Francis Giles B. Puno
Ernesto B. Rufino Jr.
Juan B. Santos
Washington Z. SyCip
Legal Counsel:
Quiason Makalintal Barot Torres Ibarra & Sison Law Firm
21st Floor Robinsons Equitable-PCi Tower Adb Avenue Corner Poveda Road
Pasig, Philippines
Puno & Puno Law Offices
12th Floor East Tower Philippine Stock Exchange Center Exchange Road
Pasig, Philippines

FIRST POINT MINERALS CORP.

Suite 906 - 1112 West Pender Street
Vancouver, BC, V6E 2S1, Canada
Tel.: (604) 681-8600
Fax: (604) 681-8799
Toll Free: (866) 376-8601
E-Mail: info@firstpointminerals.com
Web Site: www.firstpointminerals.co m
FPX—(TSX)
Int. Income: $98,359
Assets: $7,988,057
Liabilities: $133,586
Net Worth: $7,854,471
Earnings: ($5,892,018)
Emp.: 6
Fiscal Year-end: 12/31/12
Business Description:
Mineral Exploration Services
S.I.C.: 1081
N.A.I.C.S.: 213114
Personnel:
James S. Gilbert *(Pres & CEO)*
Martin Turenne *(CFO)*
J. Christopher Mitchell *(Sec)*
Board of Directors:
Peter M. D. Bradshaw
Thomas W. Beattie
Ron M. Britten
John B. Gammon
James S. Gilbert
John A. McDonald
J. Christopher Mitchell
William H. Myckatyn
Robert A. Watts
Legal Counsel:
Vector Corporate Finance Lawyers
999 West Hastings Street Suite 1040
Vancouver, BC, V6C 2W2, Canada
Tel.: (604) 683-1102
Fax: (604) 683-2643

First Point Minerals Corp.—(Continued)

Transfer Agents:
Computershare Trust Company of Canada
Suite 530 8th Avenue SW
Calgary, AB, Canada
Computershare Trust Company of Canada
510 Burrard St
Vancouver, BC, Canada

FIRST PROPERTY GROUP PLC

35 Old Queen Street
London, SW1H 9JA, United Kingdom
Tel.: (44) 2073400270
Fax: (44) 2077991876
E-Mail: enquiries@fprop.com
Web Site: www.fprop.com
FPO—(LSE)
Rev.: $16,797,328
Assets: $71,755,041
Liabilities: $42,470,267
Net Worth: $29,284,774
Earnings: $4,392,005
Emp.: 40
Fiscal Year-end: 03/31/13
Business Description:
Property Trading Services
S.I.C.: 6531
N.A.I.C.S.: 531312
Personnel:
Benyamin N. Habib *(CEO)*
George R. W. Digby *(CFO, Sec & Dir-Fin)*
Robert Wozniak *(Gen Counsel-Poland)*
Board of Directors:
Alasdair James D. Locke
George R. W. Digby
Benyamin N. Habib
Peter G. Moon
Legal Counsel:
Mills & Reeve
Fountain House 130 Fenchurch Street
London, EC3M 5DJ, United Kingdom
Allen & Overy, A. Pedzich sp. k.
Rondo ONZ 1 34 floor
Warsaw, Poland
Subsidiary:

First Property Asset Management Ltd. (1)
35 Old Queen Street
London, SW1H 9JA, United Kingdom
Tel.: (44) 73400270
Fax: (44) 2077991876
E-Mail: admin@fprop.com
Web Site: www.fprop.com
Emp.: 10
Property Asset Management Services
S.I.C.: 6733
N.A.I.C.S.: 525920
Benjamin Habib *(Mng Dir)*

FIRST QUANTUM MINERALS LTD.

543 Granville Street 8th Floor
Vancouver, BC, V6C 1X8, Canada
Tel.: (604) 688-6577
Fax: (604) 688-3818
Toll Free: (888) 688-6577
E-Mail: info@fqml.com
Web Site: www.first-quantum.com
Year Founded: 1996
FM—(LSE LUS TSX)
Sls.: $2,950,400,000
Assets: $7,536,400,000
Liabilities: $1,655,000,000
Net Worth: $5,881,400,000
Earnings: $1,869,400,000
Emp.: 8,061
Fiscal Year-end: 12/31/12
Business Description:
Mineral Exploration, Development & Mining
S.I.C.: 1499
N.A.I.C.S.: 212399
Personnel:
Philip K. R. Pascall *(Chm & CEO)*
G. Clive Newall *(Pres)*
Hannes Meyer *(CFO)*
Christopher Lemon *(Gen Counsel & Sec)*
Board of Directors:
Philip K. R. Pascall
Andrew B. Adams
Paul M. Brunner
Michael Hanley
Robert Harding
Michael Martineau
G. Clive Newall
Martin R. Rowley
Peter St. George
Legal Counsel:
Fasken Martineau DuMoulin LLP
2100 - 1075 West Georgia Street
Vancouver, BC, V6E 3G2, Canada
Transfer Agent:
Computershare Investor Services Inc.
3rd Floor 510 Burrard St
V6C 3B9 Vancouver, BC, Canada

Subsidiaries:

FQML Scandinavia Inc. (1)
543 Granville St 8th Fl
Vancouver, BC, V6C 1X8, Canada
Tel.: (604) 688-6577
Fax: (604) 688-3818
E-Mail: info@fqml.com
Web Site: www.Firstquantumminerals.com
Emp.: 2
Metal Mining Services
S.I.C.: 1081
N.A.I.C.S.: 213114
Philip Pascall *(CEO)*

Troilus Mine (1)
PO Box 8700
Chibougamau, QC, G8P3A9, Canada (100%)
Tel.: (418) 748-8160
Fax: (418) 748-3033
Web Site: www.inmetmining.com
Gold Ore Mining
S.I.C.: 1041
N.A.I.C.S.: 212221
Francois Brion *(Gen Mgr)*

Non-U.S. Subsidiaries:

Cayeli Bakir Isletmeleri A.S (1)
Cayeli
Rize, Turkey (100%)
Tel.: (90) 4645441544
Fax: (90) 4645446450
E-Mail: info@cayelibakir.com
Web Site: www.cayelibakir.com
Emp.: 500
Copper Ore & Nickel Ore Mining
S.I.C.: 1021
N.A.I.C.S.: 212234
Iain Anderson *(Mng Dir)*

Cobre Las Cruces S.A. (1)
3410 KM 4 100
Gerena, Seville, 41860, Spain
Tel.: (34) 955783475
Fax: (34) 95 578 32 41
Web Site: www.cobrelascruces.com
Copper Exploration Services
S.I.C.: 4911
N.A.I.C.S.: 221118
Damien Marantelli *(Mng Dir)*

First Quantum Minerals (Australia) Pty Limited (1)
Level 1 24 Outram St
6005 Perth, Australia AU
Tel.: (61) 892265777
Fax: (61) 892262522
E-Mail: info@firstquantum.com
Web Site: www.firstquantum.com
Emp.: 40
Mineral Exploration & Mining Services; Copper, Gold & Sulphuric Acid Production
S.I.C.: 1021
N.A.I.C.S.: 212234
Phillip Pascal *(CEO)*
Martin R. Rowley *(Mng Dir)*

First Quantum (UK) Ltd. (1)
1st Fl Mill House
Mill Bay Ln, Horsham, RH12 1SS, United Kingdom
Tel.: (44) 1403273484
Fax: (44) 1403273494
E-Mail: clive.newallfqml@first-quantum.com
Web Site: www.first-quantum.com
Emp.: 3
Mineral Exploration & Mining Services; Copper, Gold & Sulphuric Acid Production
S.I.C.: 1021
N.A.I.C.S.: 212234
Clive Newall *(Pres)*

FQM Australia Holdings Pty Ltd (1)
L 1 24 Outram St
West Perth, Western Australia, 6005, Australia
Tel.: (61) 893460100
Fax: (61) 892662522
Precious Metal Mining Services
S.I.C.: 1021
N.A.I.C.S.: 212234

Subsidiary:

FQM Australia Nickel Pty Ltd (2)
L 1 24 Outram Street
West Perth, Perth, WA, 6005, Australia
Tel.: (61) 893460100
Fax: (61) 892262522
E-Mail: perth.reception@fqnl.com
Emp.: 500
Nickel Ore Mining Services
S.I.C.: 1021
N.A.I.C.S.: 212234
Philip Pascall *(CEO)*

Subsidiary:

Ravensthorpe Nickel Operations Pty. Ltd. (3)
PO Box 100
Ravensthorpe, WA, 6346, Australia
Tel.: (61) 898382000
Fax: (61) 898382001
Nickel Ore Mining Services
S.I.C.: 1021
N.A.I.C.S.: 212234
Rudi Badenhorst *(Mng Dir)*

FQM Finance Ltd. (1)
C/O Abacus Trust & Management Services Ltd Geneva Place 2nd Floor
Road Town, Tortola, Virgin Islands (British)
Tel.: (284) 4944388
Investment Management Services
S.I.C.: 8741
N.A.I.C.S.: 551114

Pyhasalmi Mine Oy (1)
Pl 51
86801 Pyhasalmi, Finland (100%)
Tel.: (358) 87696111
Fax: (358) 8780404
E-Mail: kimmo.luukkonen@pyhasalmi.com
Web Site: www.inmetmining.com
Emp.: 250
Crushed & Broken Stone Mining
S.I.C.: 1429
N.A.I.C.S.: 212319
Kimmo Luukkonen *(Mng Dir)*

FIRST RESOURCES LIMITED

8 Temasek Boulevard 36-02 Suntec Tower Three
Singapore, 038988, Singapore
Tel.: (65) 66020200
Fax: (65) 63336711
E-Mail: contactus@first-resources.com
Web Site: www.first-resources.com
EB5—(OTC SES)
Sls.: $603,429,000
Assets: $1,930,900,000
Liabilities: $773,328,000
Net Worth: $1,157,572,000
Earnings: $248,193,000
Fiscal Year-end: 12/31/12
Business Description:
Oil Palm Cultivation Services
S.I.C.: 2079
N.A.I.C.S.: 311224
Personnel:
Ming Seong Lim *(Chm)*
Ciliandra Fangiono *(CEO)*
San-Ju Tan *(Sec)*
Board of Directors:
Ming Seong Lim
Ciliandra Fangiono
Theng Fong Hee
Shin Ein Ng
Beng Kee Ong
Cheong Kwee Teng
Ray Nugraha Yoshuara
Non-U.S. Subsidiaries:

PT Muriniwood Indah Industry (1)
Jalan Jend Sudirman No 395
Pekanbaru, Riau, 28116, Indonesia
Tel.: (62) 761 32888
Fax: (62) 761 32700
Oil Palm Plantation Services
S.I.C.: 0721
N.A.I.C.S.: 115112

PT Surya Intisari Raya (1)
Wisma 777th Floor Jalan Letjen S Parman Kav 77
Jakarta, 11410, Indonesia
Tel.: (62) 2153670888
Fax: (62) 21 5367 2888
Oil Palm Plantation Services
S.I.C.: 0711
N.A.I.C.S.: 115112

FIRST SAHARA ENERGY INC.

(Formerly PetroWorth Resources Inc.)
430-580 Hornby Street
Vancouver, BC, V6C 3B8, Canada
Tel.: (604) 428-0511
Fax: (604) 428-0512
E-Mail: info@firstsahara.com
Web Site: www.firstsahara.com
Year Founded: 2003
FSE—(CNSX)
Assets: $15,568,480
Liabilities: $841,901
Net Worth: $14,726,579
Earnings: ($807,215)
Fiscal Year-end: 12/31/12
Business Description:
Oil & Natural Gas Exploration Services
S.I.C.: 1311
N.A.I.C.S.: 211111
Personnel:
David Stadnyk *(Pres & CEO)*
Michael Hopkinson *(CFO)*
Board of Directors:
Marc Eckardt
Neal Mednick
George Tsafalas

FIRST SECURITY ISLAMI BANK LIMITED

House- SW(I) 1/A Road-8 Gulshan 1
Dhaka, 1212, Bangladesh
Tel.: (880) 29888446
Fax: (880) 29891915
E-Mail: info@fsiblbd.com
Web Site: www.fsiblbd.com
FIRSTSBANK—(DHA)
Rev.: $165,352,915
Assets: $1,608,630,033
Liabilities: $1,537,889,443
Net Worth: $70,740,590
Earnings: $9,442,338
Emp.: 1,342
Fiscal Year-end: 12/31/12
Business Description:
Commercial Banking Services
S.I.C.: 6029
N.A.I.C.S.: 522110
Personnel:
Mohammad Saiful Alam *(Chm)*
Alhaj Mohammad Abdul Maleque *(Vice Chm)*
A. A. M. Zakaria *(Mng Dir)*
Abdul Hannan Khan *(Sec)*

Board of Directors:
Mohammad Saiful Alam
Alhaj Mohammad Abdul Maleque
Ahsanul Alam
Mohammed Oheidul Alam
Md. Sharif Hussain
Shahidul Islam
Khurshid Jahan
Rahima Khatun
Atiqur Nesa
Farzana Parveen
Md. Wahidul Alam Seth
Muhammad Kutub Uddowllah
Legal Counsel:
Barrister & Advocates
City Heart (7th Floor) Suit No. 8/8, 67, Naya Paltan
Dhaka, Bangladesh

FIRST SENSOR AG
Peter-Behrens-Strasse 15
D-12459 Berlin, Germany
Tel.: (49) 3063992399
Fax: (49) 3063992333
E-Mail: contact@first-sensor.com
Web Site: www.first-sensor.com
SIS—(DEU)
Sls.: $150,684,885
Assets: $213,495,831
Liabilities: $119,342,009
Net Worth: $94,153,822
Earnings: $662,316
Emp.: 756
Fiscal Year-end: 12/31/12
Business Description:
Sensor Mfr
S.I.C.: 3812
N.A.I.C.S.: 334511
Personnel:
Alfred Gossner *(Chm-Supervisory Bd)*
Gotz Gollan *(Deputy Chm-Supervisory Bd)*
Martin U. Schefter *(CEO & Member-Exec Bd)*
Joachim Wimmers *(CFO & Member-Exec Bd)*
Board of Directors:
Thomas Diepold
Olaf Hug
Andreas Huth
Peter Krause
Martin U. Schefter
Sarah Johanna Schiesser
Thomas Sichting
Joachim Wimmers
Supervisory Board of Directors:
Alfred Gossner
Gotz Gollan
Volker Hichert

Subsidiaries:

Lewicki microelectronic GmbH (1)
Allee 35
89610 Oberdischingen, Baden-WurttembergWur, Germany
Tel.: (49) 730596020
Fax: (49) 7305 9602 50
E-Mail: info@lewicki-gmbh.dede
Web Site: www.lewicki-gmbh.dede
Electronic Components Mfr & Distr
S.I.C.: 3677
N.A.I.C.S.: 334416
Maximilian Sailer *(Mng Dir)*

Sensortechnics GmbH (1)
Boschstrasse 10
82178 Puchheim, Germany
Tel.: (49) 89800830
Fax: (49) 898008333
E-Mail: info@sensortechnics.com
Web Site: www.sensortechnics.com
Emp.: 100
Piezoresistive Pressure Transducer & Transmitter Mfr
S.I.C.: 3823
N.A.I.C.S.: 334513

U.S. Subsidiary:

Pacific Silicon Sensor Inc. (1)
5700 Corsa Ave Ste 105
Westlake Village, CA 91362-4056
Tel.: (818) 706-3400
Fax: (818) 889-7053
E-Mail: information@pacific-sensor.com
Web Site: www.pacific-sensor.com
Emp.: 15
Silicon Photodiodes Mfr
S.I.C.: 3674
N.A.I.C.S.: 334413
Barry Jones *(CEO)*

FIRST SHANGHAI INVESTMENTS LIMITED
19/F Wing On House 71 Des Voeux Road
Central, China (Hong Kong)
Tel.: (852) 25222101
Fax: (852) 28106789
Web Site: www.firstshanghai.com.hk
0227—(HKG)
Rev.: $45,014,511
Assets: $596,950,298
Liabilities: $258,980,085
Net Worth: $337,970,213
Earnings: ($13,667,668)
Emp.: 778
Fiscal Year-end: 12/31/12
Business Description:
Fund Management Services
S.I.C.: 6799
N.A.I.C.S.: 523920
Personnel:
Yuan Yat Lo *(Chm & Mng Dir)*
Wai Kin Yeung *(CFO & Sec)*
Siu Lun Mo *(CIO)*
Hong Qiu *(CEO-First Shanghai Financial Holding Limited)*
Board of Directors:
Yuan Yat Lo
Larry Lam Kwong Kwok
Ji Liu
Chia-Wei Woo
Shulin Xin
Wai Kin Yeung
Qihao Yu
Xiaohe Zhou
Transfer Agent:
Computershare Hong Kong Investor Services Limited
17th Floor, Hopewell Centre 183 Queens Road East
Hong Kong, China (Hong Kong)
Subsidiaries:

Crimson Pharmaceutical (Hong Kong) Limited (1)
19th Fl Wing On House 71 Des Voeux Rd
Central, China (Hong Kong)
Tel.: (852) 25222101
Fax: (852) 28106070
E-Mail: info@crimsonpharma.com
Web Site: www.crimsonpharma.com
Emp.: 50
Pharmaceutical Preparations Mfr
S.I.C.: 2834
N.A.I.C.S.: 325412
Yuanyi Lao *(Co-Founder & Chm)*
Rankine Yeung *(CFO)*

First eFinance Limited (1)
19th Fl Wing On House 71 Des Voeux Rd
Central, China (Hong Kong)
Tel.: (852) 25222101
Fax: (852) 28106789
Online Financial Transaction Processing Services
S.I.C.: 5961
N.A.I.C.S.: 454111

First Shanghai Capital Limited (1)
19th Fl Wing On House 71 Des Voeux Rd
Central, China (Hong Kong)
Tel.: (852) 25222101
Fax: (852) 28106789
Investment Advisory Services
S.I.C.: 6282
N.A.I.C.S.: 523930
Helen Zee *(Mng Dir)*

First Shanghai Direct Investments Limited (1)
Rm 1903 19 F Wing On House 71 Des Voeux Rd
Central, China (Hong Kong)
Tel.: (852) 25222101
Fax: (852) 28106789
E-Mail: cs@mystockhk.com
Web Site: www.mystockhk.com
Emp.: 120
Investment Management Services
S.I.C.: 6282
N.A.I.C.S.: 523920

First Shanghai Finance Limited (1)
Rm 1903 19 F Wing On House 71 Des Voeux Rd
Central, China (Hong Kong)
Tel.: (852) 25222101
Fax: (852) 28106789
Emp.: 120
Securities Brokerage Services
S.I.C.: 6211
N.A.I.C.S.: 523120
Hong Qiu *(Chm & CEO)*

First Shanghai Financial Holding Limited (1)
19th Fl Wing On House 71 Des Voeux Rd
Central, China (Hong Kong)
Tel.: (852) 25222101
Fax: (852) 28105546
Brokerage & Investment Banking Services
S.I.C.: 6211
N.A.I.C.S.: 523110
Kwok Hung Li *(Chm)*

First Shanghai Futures Limited (1)
19th Fl Wing On House 71 Des Voeux Rd
Central, China (Hong Kong)
Tel.: (852) 25222101
Fax: (852) 28106789
Futures Brokerage Services
S.I.C.: 6221
N.A.I.C.S.: 523140

First Shanghai Management Services Limited (1)
Rm 1903 19 F Wing On House 71 Des Voeux Rd
Central, China (Hong Kong)
Tel.: (852) 25222101
Fax: (852) 28106789
E-Mail: cs@mystockhk.com
Web Site: www.mystockhk.com
Emp.: 100
Secretarial Services
S.I.C.: 7389
N.A.I.C.S.: 561410
Lo Yuen Yat *(Chm)*

First Shanghai Nominees Limited (1)
Rm 1903 19 F Wing On House 71 Des Voeux Rd
Central, China (Hong Kong)
Tel.: (852) 25222101
Fax: (852) 28106789
Office Administrative Services
S.I.C.: 8741
N.A.I.C.S.: 561110

First Shanghai Properties Limited (1)
Rm 1903 19 F Wing On Hse 71 Des Voeux Rd
Central, China (Hong Kong)
Tel.: (852) 25222101
Fax: (852) 28106789
Web Site: www.firstshanghai.com.hk
Emp.: 120
Property Investment & Development Services
S.I.C.: 6531
N.A.I.C.S.: 531210

First Shanghai Securities Limited (1)
19th Fl Wing On House 71 Des Voeux Rd
Central, China (Hong Kong)
Tel.: (852) 25222101
Fax: (852) 28105546
Web Site: www.firstshanghai.com.hk
Emp.: 100
Securities Brokerage Services
S.I.C.: 6211
N.A.I.C.S.: 523120

Non-U.S. Subsidiary:

Crimson Pharmaceutical (Shanghai) Company Limited (1)
328 Bibo Rd Block C 4th Fl Zhang Jiang Hi-Tech Park
Shanghai, 201203, China
Tel.: (86) 2150805146
Fax: (86) 2150805148
Drugs Mfr & Sales
S.I.C.: 2834
N.A.I.C.S.: 325412

FIRST SOCIAL NETWORX CORP.
(Name Changed to Moxian Group Holdings, Inc.)

FIRST STEAMSHIP CO., LTD.
14 F No 237 Fu Hsing South Rd Section 2
Taipei, Taiwan
Tel.: (886) 227069911
Fax: (886) 227069922
E-Mail: fss@firsteam.com.tw
Web Site: www.firsteam.com.tw
2601—(TAI)
Sales Range: $700-749.9 Million
Business Description:
Ship Chartering Services
S.I.C.: 4412
N.A.I.C.S.: 483111
Personnel:
Jonathan Seah *(Chm)*
Ya-Ming Sun *(Pres)*
Daniel Dai *(CIO)*

FIRST TAKAFUL INSURANCE COMPANY K.S.C.C.
Abdullah Mubarak St Alenma'a Tower
Kuwait, 13058, Kuwait
Tel.: (965) 1880055
Fax: (965) 22444599
E-Mail: info@firsttakaful.com
Web Site: www.firsttakaful.com
FTI—(KUW)
Emp.: 75
Business Description:
Insurance Services
S.I.C.: 6351
N.A.I.C.S.: 524126
Personnel:
Khalil Ibrahim Mohammed Al-Shami *(Chm & Mng Dir)*
Hussain Ali Al-Attal *(Deputy Chm)*
Board of Directors:
Khalil Ibrahim Mohammed Al-Shami
Rami Khalid Abdullah
Ahmed Mohammad Al Khalid
Osama Abdullateef Al-Abdul Jaleel
Hussain Ali Al-Attal
Saleh Saleh Al-Selmi
Saad Abdulaziz Alwazzan
Grant Thornton Al Qatami Al-Aiban & Partners
Souq Al Kabeer Building Block A 9th Floor
Kuwait, Kuwait

FIRST TRACTOR COMPANY LIMITED
154 Jian She Road
Luoyang, Henan, 471004, China
Tel.: (86) 379 6496 7038
Fax: (86) 379 6496 7438
E-Mail: msc0038@ytogroup.com
Web Site: www.first-tractor.com.cn
38—(HKG OTC)
Sales Range: $1-4.9 Billion
Emp.: 12,300
Business Description:
Tractor Mfr
S.I.C.: 3524
N.A.I.C.S.: 333112

First Tractor Company Limited—(Continued)

Personnel:
Yanshui Zhao *(Chm & Gen Mgr)*
Weike Su *(Vice Chm)*
Lina Yu *(Sec & Mgr-Investor Relationship)*
Board of Directors:
Yanshui Zhao
Gary Sau Shan Chan
Jianhong Dong
Xianguo Hong
Jiguo Liu
Yongle Liu
Xiwen Luo
Dawei Qu
Weike Su
Linjiao Yan
Qiusheng Zhang

FIRST TRUST ADVANTAGED SHORT DURATION HIGH YIELD BOND FUND

Suite 1300 330 Bay Street
Toronto, ON, M5H 2S8, Canada
Tel.: (416) 865-8065
Fax: (416) 865-8058
Toll Free: (877) 622-5552
E-Mail: FraserHowell@firsttrust.ca
Year Founded: 2011
FSD.UN—(TSX)
Assets: $62,859,143
Liabilities: $672,480
Net Worth: $62,186,663
Earnings: ($894,336)
Fiscal Year-end: 06/30/13
Business Description:
Investment Services
S.I.C.: 6211
N.A.I.C.S.: 523999
Personnel:
Ronald McAlister *(Chm)*
Fraser Howell *(Pres, CEO & Sec)*
James Dykas *(CFO)*
Steven Kim *(Sr VP)*
Transfer Agent:
CIBC Mellon Trust Company
PO Box 7010
Adelaide Street Postal Station, Toronto, ON, M5C 2W9, Canada
Tel.: (416) 643-5500
Fax: (416) 643-5501
Toll Free: (800) 387-0825

FIRST URANIUM CORPORATION

(Acquired & Absorbed by Algold Resources Ltd.)

FIRST UTILITY LIMITED

Point 3 Opus 40 Business Park
Haywood Road
Warwick, CV34 5AH, United Kingdom
Mailing Address:
PO Box 4360
Warwick, CV34 9DB, United Kingdom
Tel.: (44) 1926 320 700
E-Mail: customer.service@first-utility.com
Web Site: www.first-utility.com
Year Founded: 2003
Sales Range: $100-124.9 Million
Emp.: 179
Business Description:
Electric Power Distribution Services
S.I.C.: 4939
N.A.I.C.S.: 221122
Personnel:
Darren Braham *(Founder & CFO)*
Ian McCaig *(CEO)*
Bill Wilkins *(CIO)*
Ed Kamm *(Chief Customer Officer)*

FIRST WINNER INDUSTRIES LIMITED

605 Business Classic Chincholi
Bunder Road
Malad West, Mumbai, 400 064, India
Tel.: (91) 2228802255
Fax: (91) 2228812288
E-Mail: info@firstwinnerind.com
Web Site: www.firstwinnerind.com
532996—(BOM)
Rev.: $38,378,016
Assets: $79,031,824
Liabilities: $44,556,155
Net Worth: $34,475,669
Earnings: ($4,131,625)
Fiscal Year-end: 03/31/13
Business Description:
Textile Products Mfr
S.I.C.: 2389
N.A.I.C.S.: 314999
Personnel:
Rinku Patodia *(Mng Dir)*
Avani Gandhi *(Compliance Officer & Sec)*
Board of Directors:
M. K. Sinha
Anita Patodia
Rinku Patodia
Binod Kumar Tiwari

Deshmukh & Associates
Mumbai, India
Transfer Agent:
Link Intime India Pvt. Ltd
C-13 Pannalal Silk Mills Compound LBS Marg
Bhandup (West)
Mumbai, India
Subsidiaries:

First Winner Lifestyle Ltd. **(1)**
605 Business Classic Chincholi Bunder Road Malad West
Mumbai, Maharashtra, 400064, India
Tel.: (91) 2228802255
Fax: (91) 2228812288
Web Site: www.firstwinnerind.com
Emp.: 44
Textile Products Mfr
S.I.C.: 2299
N.A.I.C.S.: 314999
Indra kumar Patodia *(Gen Mgr)*

Ramshyam Textile industries Ltd. **(1)**
605 6th Floor Business Classic CTS No 10-A Chincholi Bunder Road
Malad West, Mumbai, 400064, India
Tel.: (91) 22 2880 2255
Fax: (91) 22 2881 2288
Textile Products Mfr
S.I.C.: 2299
N.A.I.C.S.: 314999

FIRSTCAUTION SA

Avenue Edouard-Rod 4
1260 Nyon, Switzerland
Tel.: (41) 840 78 78 78
Fax: (41) 840 78 78 79
E-Mail: info@firstcaution.ch
Web Site: www.firstcaution.ch
Year Founded: 2008
MLFIR—(EUR)
Business Description:
Insurance Services
S.I.C.: 6411
N.A.I.C.S.: 524298
Personnel:
Philippe Herve *(Chm)*

FIRSTEC CO., LTD.

485 Nammyeon-ro
Seongsan-gu, Changwon,
Gyeongsangnam-do, Korea (South)
Tel.: (82) 55 282 4131
Fax: (82) 55 284 7141
Web Site: www.firsteccom.co.kr
Year Founded: 1975
010820—(KRS)
Emp.: 370
Business Description:
Aerospace & Defense Product Mfr
S.I.C.: 3482
N.A.I.C.S.: 332992
Personnel:
Keun Soo Kim *(Pres)*
Yong Woo Jeon *(CEO)*

FIRSTFARMS A/S

Majsmarken 1
7190 Billund, Denmark
Tel.: (45) 75868787
Fax: (45) 75868783
E-Mail: info@firstfarms.com
Web Site: www.firstfarms.com
Year Founded: 2005
FFARMS—(CSE)
Sls.: $19,493,309
Assets: $84,220,184
Liabilities: $26,792,298
Net Worth: $57,427,887
Earnings: ($4,948,177)
Emp.: 203
Fiscal Year-end: 12/31/12
Business Description:
Farm Products Mfr
S.I.C.: 3999
N.A.I.C.S.: 339999
Personnel:
Henrik Hougaard *(Chm)*
Anders H. Norgaard *(CEO)*
Jorgen Svendsen *(CFO)*
Board of Directors:
Henrik Hougaard
John Christian Aasted
Jens Bolding Jensen
Veterinarian Bent Juul Jensen
Lars Allan Thomassen
Subsidiary:

FirstFarms Slovakiet ApS **(1)**
Astvej 10b
Billund, Ribe, 7190, Denmark
Tel.: (45) 75868787
Fax: (45) 75868783
Web Site: www.firstfarms.com
Milk Mfr
S.I.C.: 0241
N.A.I.C.S.: 112120

Non-U.S. Subsidiary:

FirstFarms Agra M. s.r.o. **(1)**
Kozia 2243
Malacky, 90113, Slovakia
Tel.: (421) 347722021
Fax: (421) 347722029
Milk Mfr
S.I.C.: 0241
N.A.I.C.S.: 112120

FIRSTFOLIO LIMITED

AMP Centre Level 9 50 Bridge Street
Sydney, NSW, 2000, Australia
Mailing Address:
PO Box R152
Royal Exchange, Sydney, NSW, 1225, Australia
Tel.: (61) 292408900
Fax: (61) 292408996
E-Mail: info@firstfolio.com.au
Web Site: www.firstfolio.com.au
FFF—(ASX)
Rev.: $85,998,260
Assets: $444,988,163
Liabilities: $403,244,763
Net Worth: $41,743,400
Earnings: $1,373,488
Fiscal Year-end: 06/30/13
Business Description:
Home Loan Financing Services
S.I.C.: 6163
N.A.I.C.S.: 522310
Personnel:
Dustine Pang *(CFO & Sec)*
Board of Directors:
Eric Dodd
Michael Hogg
Gregory D. Pynt
Anthony N. Wales
Legal Counsel:
Tress Cox Lawyers
Level 9 469 LA Trobe Street
Melbourne, Australia

Subsidiaries:

eChoice Pty Limited **(1)**
Ste 4 400 Canterbury Rd
Surrey Hills, Melbourne, Victoria, 3127, Australia
Tel.: (61) 398348888
Fax: (61) 3 98348885
E-Mail: info@echoice.com.au
Web Site: www.echoice.com.au
Emp.: 30
Online Mortgage Broker Services
S.I.C.: 6163
N.A.I.C.S.: 522310

Firstfolio Wholesale Pty Limited **(1)**
Level 9 50 Bridge St
Sydney, NSW, 2000, Australia
Tel.: (61) 292408900
Fax: (61) 292408998
E-Mail: reception@firstfolio.com.au
Web Site: www.firstfolio.com.au
Emp.: 30
Mortgage Services
S.I.C.: 6163
N.A.I.C.S.: 522310

New-Loan Australia Pty Limited **(1)**
Level 9 50 Bridge St
Sydney, NSW, 2000, Australia
Tel.: (61) 292408900
Fax: (61) 292408994
E-Mail: info@firstfolio.com.au
Web Site: www.newloan.com.au
Emp.: 90
Mortgage Services
S.I.C.: 6163
N.A.I.C.S.: 522310
Mark Forsyth *(CEO)*

FIRSTGROUP PLC

395 King Street
Aberdeen, AB24 5RP, United Kingdom
Tel.: (44) 1224650100
Fax: (44) 1224650140
Web Site: www.firstgroup.com
Year Founded: 1995
FGP—(LSE OTC)
Rev.: $10,898,522,361
Assets: $8,735,526,777
Liabilities: $7,441,614,480
Net Worth: $1,293,912,297
Earnings: $75,490,062
Emp.: 120,475
Fiscal Year-end: 03/31/13
Business Description:
Train & Bus Service Operator
S.I.C.: 4011
N.A.I.C.S.: 485113
Personnel:
Martin James Gilbert *(Chm)*
Tim O'Toole *(CEO)*
Paul Lewis *(Sec)*
Board of Directors:
Martin James Gilbert
Mick Barker
David Begg
Colin Hood
Tim O'Toole
John Sievwright
Christopher Surch
Brian G. Wallace
James F. Winestock, Jr.
Legal Counsel:
Slaughter & May
One Bunhill Row
London, EC1Y 8YY, United Kingdom
Tel.: (44) 20 7600 1200

Fax: (44) 20 7600 0289

Paull & Williamsons LLP
Union Plaza 1 Union Wynd
Aberdeen, United Kingdom

Burges Salmon
One Glass Wharf
Bristol, United Kingdom

Subsidiaries:

CentreWest London Buses Limited (1)
B Block 3rd Floor Macmillan House
Paddington Station
London, W12 1TY, United Kingdom
Tel.: (44) 20 7298 7300
Fax: (44) 20 7706 8789
Bus Transit Services
S.I.C.: 4131
N.A.I.C.S.: 485210

First Aberdeen Limited (1)
395 King Street
Aberdeen, AB24 5RP, United Kingdom
Tel.: (44) 1224 650000
Web Site: www.firstgroup.com
Emp.: 500
Passenger Bus Transportation Services
S.I.C.: 4119
N.A.I.C.S.: 485999
David Stewart *(Mng Dir)*

First Beeline Buses Limited (1)
Coldborough House Market St
Bracknell, Berkshire, RG12 1JA, United Kingdom
Tel.: (44) 1344 782222
Fax: (44) 1344 868322
E-Mail: info@firstgroup.com
Web Site: www.firstgroup.com
Emp.: 300
Passenger Bus Transportation Services
S.I.C.: 4111
N.A.I.C.S.: 485999
Adrian Jones *(Reg Mng Dir)*
Chris Dexter *(COO)*

First Bristol Limited (1)
Enterprise House Stoke View Rd
Bristol, BS16 3AE, United Kingdom
Tel.: (44) 1179 558211
Fax: (44) 1179 551248
Web Site: www.firstgroup.com
Emp.: 2,000
Passenger Bus Transportation Services
S.I.C.: 4119
N.A.I.C.S.: 485999
Justin Davies *(Reg Mng Dir)*

First Capital Connect Limited (1)
50 Eastbourne Terrace
Paddington, London, W2 6LG, United Kingdom UK
Tel.: (44) 8450264700
Fax: (44) 845 676 9904
Web Site: www.firstcapitalconnect.co.uk
Commuter Rail Services
S.I.C.: 4111
N.A.I.C.S.: 485112

First Capital North Limited (1)
Macmillan House Paddington Station
London, W2 1TY, United Kingdom
Tel.: (44) 20 7298 7300
Local Passenger Transportation Services
S.I.C.: 4119
N.A.I.C.S.: 485999

First Devon & Cornwall Limited (1)
The Ride
Plymouth, Devon, PL9 7JT, United Kingdom
Tel.: (44) 8456001420
Web Site: www.firstgroup.com
Passenger Bus Transportation Services
S.I.C.: 4111
N.A.I.C.S.: 485999
Marc Reddy *(Mng Dir)*
Chris Bainbridge *(Deputy Mng Dir & Dir-Ops)*

First Eastern Counties Buses Limited (1)
6 Dogs Head Street
Ipswich, Suffolk, IP4 1AD, United Kingdom
Tel.: (44) 1473 253734
Web Site: www.firstgroup.com
Local Passenger Transportation Services
S.I.C.: 4119
N.A.I.C.S.: 485999
Shaun Daw *(Mgr-Depot)*

First Glasgow (No. 1) Limited (1)
197 Victoria Rd
Glasgow, G42 7AD, United Kingdom
Tel.: (44) 141 423 6600
Emp.: 2,800
Passenger Bus & Coach Operating Services
S.I.C.: 4111
N.A.I.C.S.: 485999
Ronnie Park *(Mng Dir)*

First Glasgow (No. 2) Limited (1)
197 Victoria Road
Glasgow, G42 7AD, United Kingdom
Tel.: (44) 1414 236600
Fax: (44) 1416 363153
Web Site: www.firstgroup.com
Emp.: 2,800
Passenger Bus Operating Services
S.I.C.: 4111
N.A.I.C.S.: 485999
Ronnie Park *(Mng Dir)*

First Greater Western Limited (1)
MH 22 Milford House 1 Milford Street
Swindon, SN1 1HL, United Kingdom
Tel.: (44) 8457 000 125
E-Mail: fgw@custhelp.com
Web Site: www.firstgreatwestern.co.uk
Travel & Tour Operating Services
S.I.C.: 4729
N.A.I.C.S.: 561599
Mark Hopwood *(Mng Dir)*

First Manchester Limited (1)
Wallshaw Street
Oldham, Lancs, OL1 3TR, United Kingdom
Tel.: (44) 161 627 2929
Fax: (44) 161 627 5845
Web Site: www.firstgroup.com
Emp.: 2,329
Local Bus Chartering Services
S.I.C.: 4142
N.A.I.C.S.: 485510
Richard Soper *(Mng Dir)*

First Midland Red Buses Limited (1)
Island Drive
Kidderminster, Worcestershire, DY10 1EZ, United Kingdom
Tel.: (44) 156268267
Web Site: www.firstgroup.com
Bus & Coach Chartering Services
S.I.C.: 4142
N.A.I.C.S.: 485510
Nigel Barrett *(Reg Mng Dir)*

First Potteries Limited (1)
Dividy Road
Stoke-on-Trent, ST3 5YY, United Kingdom
Tel.: (44) 870 850 0868
Fax: (44) 1782592541
Bus & Coach Chartering Services
S.I.C.: 4142
N.A.I.C.S.: 485510
Nigel Barrett *(Reg Mng Dir)*

First Scotland East Limited (1)
Carmuirs House 300 Stirling Road
Larbert, Stirlingshire, FK5 3NJ, United Kingdom
Tel.: (44) 8708727271
E-Mail: marketing.scotlandeast@firstgroup.com
Emp.: 1,200
Passenger Bus Transportation Services
S.I.C.: 4111
N.A.I.C.S.: 485999
Paul Thomas *(Mng Dir)*

First ScotRail Limited (1)
Atrium court
50 waterloo street, Glasgow, Scotland, G2 6HQ, United Kingdom UK
Tel.: (44) 8456015929 (100%)
E-Mail: scotrailcoustomer.relations@firstgroup.com
Web Site: www.scotrail.co.uk
Emp.: 3,000
Train Service
S.I.C.: 4011
N.A.I.C.S.: 482111
Steve Montgomery *(Mng Dir)*
Kenny McPhail *(Deputy Mng Dir & Fin Dir)*

First Somerset & Avon Limited (1)
Priory Rd
Wells, Somerset, BA5 1SZ, United Kingdom
Tel.: (44) 1749677774
Passenger Coach & Bus Operating Services
S.I.C.: 4119
N.A.I.C.S.: 485999

First South Yorkshire Limited (1)
Midland Road
Rotherham, S61 1TF, United Kingdom
Tel.: (44) 1709566000
Fax: (44) 1709566163
Web Site: www.firstgroup.com
Emp.: 1,600
Passenger Bus & Coach Operating Services
S.I.C.: 4111
N.A.I.C.S.: 485999
Dave Alexander *(Mng Dir-North Reg)*

First West Yorkshire Limited (1)
Hunslet Park Donisthorpe Street
Leeds, West Yorkshire, LS10 1PL, United Kingdom
Tel.: (44) 845 604 5460
Web Site: www.firstgroup.com
Emp.: 3,500
Passenger Bus & Coach Operating Services
S.I.C.: 4119
N.A.I.C.S.: 485999
Dave Alexander *(Mng Dir-North Reg)*

Hull Trains Company Limited (1)
First Hull Trains 4th Floor Europa House
184 Ferensway
Hull, HU1 3UT, United Kingdom
Tel.: (44) 1482 215746
Fax: (44) 1482 212704
E-Mail: hullbusinesstravel@firstgroup.com
Web Site: www.hulltrains.co.uk
Emp.: 50
Rail Transportation Services
S.I.C.: 4789
N.A.I.C.S.: 488210
Richard Parry *(Gen Mgr)*

Northampton Transport Limited (1)
Bus Depot Saint James Road
Northampton, Northamptonshire, NN5 5JD, United Kingdom
Tel.: (44) 1604 751 431
Fax: (44) 1604 590 522
Emp.: 90
Passenger Bus Operating Services
S.I.C.: 4119
N.A.I.C.S.: 485999
Steve Timms *(Mgr-Ops)*

U.S. Subsidiary:

FirstGroup America Inc. (1)
600 Vine St Ste 1400
Cincinnati, OH 45202
Tel.: (513) 241-2200
Fax: (513) 381-0149
E-Mail: ashley.grecco@firstgroup.com
Web Site: www.firstgroupamerica.com
Sales Range: $700-749.9 Million
Emp.: 100,000
Bus Operator; Vehicle Maintenance Services
S.I.C.: 4151
N.A.I.C.S.: 485410
Kevin Middleton *(Exec VP-Engrg)*

Subsidiaries:

First Student Inc. (2)
600 Vine St Ste 1400
Cincinnati, OH 45202
Tel.: (513) 241-2200
Fax: (513) 381-0149
Web Site: www.firststudentinc.com
Emp.: 400
School Bus Transportation
S.I.C.: 4119
N.A.I.C.S.: 485410
Charlie Bruce *(COO)*
Cal Hull *(Sr VP)*

Branches:

First Student (3)
487 Industrial Dr
Naperville, IL 60563
Tel.: (630) 369-4237
Fax: (630) 955-0294
Web Site: www.firststudentinc.com
Emp.: 250
Local Transportation Services
S.I.C.: 4119
N.A.I.C.S.: 485410
Tom Sulton *(Gen Mgr)*

First Student (3)
6951 State St
South Holland, IL 60473
Tel.: (708) 210-2200
Fax: (708) 210-2204
Emp.: 100
School Bus Transportation
S.I.C.: 4151
N.A.I.C.S.: 485410
Julie Gonzales *(Branch Mgr)*

Non-U.S. Subsidiaries:

First Student Canada (3)
1111 International Blvd Ste 700
Burlington, ON, L7L 6W1, Canada
Tel.: (289) 288-4359
Fax: (905) 332-0046
Toll Free: (800) 563-6072
Web Site: www.firstcanada.com
Emp.: 70
School Bus Transportation Services
S.I.C.: 4151
N.A.I.C.S.: 485410
Jim Switzer *(Pres)*

FirstBus Canada (3)
140 4th Avenue East
Regina, SK, S4N 4Z4, Canada
Tel.: (306) 721-4499
Fax: (306) 721-7773
E-Mail: regina.info@firstbuscanada.com
Web Site: www.firstbuscanada.com
Emp.: 200
School Bus Transportation
S.I.C.: 4151
N.A.I.C.S.: 485410
Greg Logel *(Mng Dir)*

First Transit, Inc. (2)
600 Vine St Ste 1400
Cincinnati, OH 45202
Tel.: (513) 241-2200
Fax: (513) 362-4573
Toll Free: (866) 244-6383
Web Site: www.firsttransit.com
Sales Range: $700-749.9 Million
Emp.: 7,300
Transit Management & Contracting; Airport Shuttle Bus Services, Paratransit Operations & Light Transit Activities
S.I.C.: 4119
N.A.I.C.S.: 485991
Bradley Thomas *(Pres)*
Christian Gartner *(CFO)*
Rick Dunning *(Sr VP-Transit Mgmt & Bus Dev)*
Beverly Edwards *(Sr VP-Central Reg)*
Matt Wood *(Sr VP-Transit Mgmt)*

First Vehicle Services (2)
600 Vine St Ste 1400
Cincinnati, OH 45202
Tel.: (513) 684-8853
Fax: (513) 419-3242
Toll Free: (800) 787-9337
E-Mail: fvs.info@firstgroup.com
Web Site: www.firstvehicleservices.com
Transportation Maintenance & Management Solutions
S.I.C.: 7539
N.A.I.C.S.: 811118
J. Michael Bloss *(CEO)*
Wayne R. Johnson *(CFO)*
Dale Domish *(Sr VP)*

Greyhound Lines, Inc. (2)
350 N St Paul
Dallas, TX 75201 DE
Mailing Address:
PO Box 660362
Dallas, TX 75266-0362
Tel.: (214) 849-8000
Toll Free: (800) 454-2487
Web Site: www.greyhound.com
Sales Range: $1-4.9 Billion
Emp.: 8,400
Bus Charters & Tours, Package Express, Regular Route Passenger Service, Travel Services & Sightseeing
S.I.C.: 4111
N.A.I.C.S.: 485119
Dave Leach *(Pres & CEO)*
Chris Boult *(Sr VP-IT)*
Ted F. Burk *(Sr VP-Corp Dev)*
Rhonda Piar MacAndrew *(Sr VP-HR)*

FirstGroup plc—(Continued)

Non-U.S. Subsidiary:

Greyhound Canada Transportation Corp. (3)
877 Greyhound Way SW
Calgary, AB, T3C 3V8, Canada AB
Tel.: (403) 260-0877
Fax: (403) 260-0742
E-Mail: info@greyhound.ca
Web Site: www.greyhound.ca
Emp.: 2,500
Commercial Passenger Carrier & Charter Transportation
S.I.C.: 4131
N.A.I.C.S.: 485210
Stuart Kendrick *(Sr VP)*

Subsidiary:

Greyhound Canada Transportation ULC (4)
1064 Trans Canada Hwy
Cache Creek, BC, V0K 1H0, Canada
Tel.: (250) 457-6232
Bus Coach Operating Services
S.I.C.: 4131
N.A.I.C.S.: 485210

FIRSTLINK INVESTMENTS CORPORATION LIMITED

1 Phillip Street 08-01
Singapore, 048692, Singapore
Tel.: (65) 6448 6211
Fax: (65) 6445 2506
E-Mail: corphq@firstlinkcorp.com.sg
Web Site: www.firstlinkcorp.com.sg
Sales Range: Less than $1 Million
Emp.: 10

Business Description:
Investment Holding Company
S.I.C.: 6719
N.A.I.C.S.: 551112

Personnel:
Yew Kong Ling *(Chm & Mng Dir)*
Abdul Jabbar Karam Din *(Sec)*

Board of Directors:
Yew Kong Ling
Kwong Wah Er
Lawrence Kwan
David Wang

FIRSTOBJECT TECHNOLOGIES LTD.

1st Floor Swayamkrishi SMILINE Building No 8-3-952/10/2 & 2/1
Srinagar Colony, Hyderabad, 500 073, India
Tel.: (91) 40 20000235
Fax: (91) 40 23730662
Web Site: firstobjectindia.com
Year Founded: 2000
532379—(BOM)

Business Description:
Software Development Services
S.I.C.: 7371
N.A.I.C.S.: 541511

Personnel:
Vivek Hebbar *(Chm)*
C. V. S. Lakshmi Kameswari *(CFO)*

Board of Directors:
Vivek Hebbar
P. Ramnath
P. Sailesh
Sita Rama Sastry
N. Shiva
J. S. Suryanarayana

FIRSTRAND LIMITED

4 Merchant Place Corner Fredman Drive & Rivonia Road
Sandton, 2196, South Africa
Tel.: (27) 112821808
Fax: (27) 112828088
E-Mail: information@firstrand.co.za
Web Site: www.firstrand.co.za
Year Founded: 1998
FSR—(JSE)
Rev.: $8,426,089,500
Assets: $97,142,027,300
Liabilities: $88,247,579,700
Net Worth: $8,894,447,600
Earnings: $1,751,232,600
Emp.: 37,231
Fiscal Year-end: 06/30/13

Business Description:
Bank Holding Company
S.I.C.: 6712
N.A.I.C.S.: 551111

Personnel:
Sizwe Errol Nxasana *(CEO)*
Johannes Petrus Burger *(Deputy CEO & Dir-Fin)*
Jacques Celliers *(CEO-FNB)*
Chris de Kock *(CEO-WesBank)*
Alan Pullinger *(CEO-RMB)*
B. W. Unser *(Sec)*

Board of Directors:
Lauritz Lanser Dippenaar
Vivian Wade Bartlett
Jurie Johannes Human Bester
Mary Sina Bomela
Johannes Petrus Burger
Leon Crouse
Jannie Jonathan Durand
Grant Glenn Gelink
Patrick Maguire Goss
Nolulamo Nobambiswano Gwagwa
Paul Kenneth Harris
Roger William Jardine
Ethel Gothamodimo Matenge-Sebesho
Sizwe Errol Nxasana
Amanda Tandiwe Nzimande
Deepak Premnarayen
Kgotso Buni Schoeman
Benedict James van der Ross
Jan Hendrik van Greuning

Deloitte & Touche
Sandton, South Africa

Transfer Agents:
Transfer Secretaries (Pty) Limited
4 Robert Mugabe Avenue PO Box 2401
Windhoek, Namibia

Computershare Investor Services (Pty) Ltd
70 Marshall Street
Johannesburg, South Africa

Subsidiaries:

Barnard Jacobs Mellet Holdings Limited (1)
Barnard Jacobs Mellet Ground Fl
24 Fricker Rd Illovo Corner, 2196 Illovo, South Africa
Tel.: (27) 117500000
Fax: (27) 117500001
Web Site: www.bjm.co.za
Sales Range: $25-49.9 Million
Financial Services
S.I.C.: 6221
N.A.I.C.S.: 523140

Subsidiaries:

Barnard Jacobs Mellet Corporate Finance (Pty) Ltd (2)
Barnard Jacobs Mellet House 24 Fricker Rd Illovo Corner
Illovo, Gauteng, 2196, South Africa
Tel.: (27) 117500000
Fax: (27) 117500009
E-Mail: corpfin@bjm.co.za
Financial Investment Advisory Services
S.I.C.: 6282
N.A.I.C.S.: 523930
Gordene Stock *(Office Mgr)*

Finsettle Services (Pty) Ltd (2)
2nd Fl 24 Fricker Rd Illovo Corner
Illovo, Johannesburg, Gauteng, 2196, South Africa
Tel.: (27) 117721700
Fax: (27) 112685203
E-Mail: finsettle@finsettle.co.za
Web Site: www.finsettleconnect.co.za
Emp.: 30
Settlement & Administrative Services
S.I.C.: 6411
N.A.I.C.S.: 524291
David Rodger *(Co-COO)*
Petro Vermeulen *(Co-COO & Compliance Officer)*

First National Bank of South Africa (1)
6th Floor First Place Corner Simmonds & Pritchard Sts
Bank City, Johannesburg, Gauteng, SA 2001, South Africa ZA
Mailing Address: (100%)
PO Box 1153
Johannesburg, SA 2000, South Africa
Tel.: (27) 113691088
E-Mail: info@fnb.co.za
Web Site: www.fnb.co.za
Emp.: 5,500
Financial Holding Company Services
S.I.C.: 6712
N.A.I.C.S.: 551111
Gerrit Thomas Ferreira *(Chm)*
Michael Jordan *(CEO)*
Steven Bogatsu *(CEO-FNB Swaziland)*

Subsidiaries:

First National Bank (2)
Simmonds and Pritchard Streets
Johannesburg, Gauteng, 2000, South Africa
Tel.: (27) 113691088
Web Site: www.fnb.co.za
Emp.: 8,000
Banking Services
S.I.C.: 6029
N.A.I.C.S.: 522110
Michael Jordaan *(CEO)*

Rand Merchant Bank (2)
1 Merchant Place cnr Fredman Drive & Rivonia Road
Sandton, Johannesburg, 2196, South Africa (100%)
Tel.: (27) 112828000
Fax: (27) 112828008
E-Mail: info@rmb.co.za
Web Site: www.rmb.co.za
Emp.: 800
Banking Services
S.I.C.: 6029
N.A.I.C.S.: 522110
Gerrit Thomas Ferreira *(Chm)*
Alan Pullinger *(CEO)*

Subsidiaries:

RMB Asset Management (Pty) Limited (3)
7 Merchant Place Fredman Drive
Sandton, 2196, South Africa
Tel.: (27) 115051000
E-Mail: clientservice@rmbut.co.za
Web Site: www.rmbam.com
Investment Management Services
S.I.C.: 6211
N.A.I.C.S.: 523999
S. Mabuza *(COO)*
J. Stewart *(Chief Investment Officer)*

RMB Private Equity Holdings (Pty) Ltd (3)
5 Merchant Place
Sandton, 2196, South Africa
Tel.: (27) 113035000
Fax: (27) 113034373
Web Site: www.rmbprivatebank.com
Emp.: 100
Financial Management Services
S.I.C.: 6211
N.A.I.C.S.: 523999
Iris Dempsey *(CEO)*

Holding:

Denny Mushrooms (Pty) Limited (4)
The Oval
Wanderers Building
Bryanston, Gauteng, 2128, South Africa
Tel.: (27) 861 888 182
Fax: (27) 861 888 183
Emp.: 1,000
Mushroom Farming & Sales
S.I.C.: 0182
N.A.I.C.S.: 111411
Simon L Crutchley *(Chm)*
Roger Coppin *(Mng Dir)*

Joint Venture:

Waco International Ltd. (4)
No 2 Harrowdene Office Park
128 Western Services Road, Woodmead, 2148, South Africa ZA
Mailing Address:
Private Bag X23
Gallo Manor, 2052, South Africa
Tel.: (27) 11 461 1400
Fax: (27) 11 4611450
Web Site: www.wacointernational.com
Sales Range: $750-799.9 Million
Emp.: 4,000
Holding Company; Scaffolding & Modular Building Mfr & Contractor Services
S.I.C.: 6719
N.A.I.C.S.: 551112
Stephen J. M. Goodburn *(CEO)*
Mark R. Towler *(Sec)*

Subsidiary:

Waco Africa Pty. Ltd. (5)
181 Barbara Road Cnr Barbara & Tunney Roads
Elandsfontein, Gauteng, South Africa ZA
Mailing Address:
PO Box 669
Isando, Gauteng, 1600, South Africa
Tel.: (27) 118424000
Fax: (27) 118424280
E-Mail: info@wacoafrica.co.za
Web Site: www.wacoafrica.co.za
Holding Company; Formwork, Shoring & Scaffolding Products
S.I.C.: 6719
N.A.I.C.S.: 551112
Stephen J.M. Goodburn *(Chm)*
Michael Graham Els *(CEO)*

Non-U.S. Subsidiary:

Waco UK Limited (5)
Catfoss Lane
Brandesburton, Driffield, E Yorkshire, YO25 8EJ, United Kingdom UK
Tel.: (44) 1964 545 000
Fax: (44) 1964 545 054
E-Mail: sales@waco.co.uk
Web Site: www.waco.co.uk
Sales Range: $50-74.9 Million
Emp.: 300
Commercial & Institutional Modular Buildings Mfr
S.I.C.: 1542
N.A.I.C.S.: 236220
Eugenio de Sa *(Mng Dir)*

RMB Structured Insurance Limited (3)
Fourth Fl 2 Merchant Pl 1 Fredman Dr
Sandton, Gauteng, 2196, South Africa
Tel.: (27) 116857600
Fax: (27) 117849858
E-Mail: info@rmbsi.co.za
Web Site: www.rmbsi.co.za
Emp.: 20
Insurance Underwriting Services
S.I.C.: 6311
N.A.I.C.S.: 524113
Gustavo Arroyo *(CEO)*
Rouxann Vlok *(COO & Officer-Compliance)*

Non-U.S. Subsidiary:

RMB Structured Insurance Limited PCC (4)
Ste 114 3rd Fl Medine Mews
Chaussee, Port Louis, Mauritius
Tel.: (230) 2111395
Fax: (230) 2111294
E-Mail: info@frontfin.mu
Web Site: www.frontfin.com
Emp.: 13
General Insurance Services
S.I.C.: 6411
N.A.I.C.S.: 524210
Dario Adolphe *(Mgr)*

Non-U.S. Subsidiaries:

First National Bank of Botswana (3)
Finance House Plot 8843
Khama Crescent, Gaborone, Botswana
Tel.: (267) 3642600
Fax: (267) 3906130
Web Site: www.fnbbotswana.co.bw
FNBB—(BOT)

Rev.: $148,954,816
Assets: $1,945,805,755
Liabilities: $1,708,435,964
Net Worth: $237,369,791
Earnings: $86,287,191
Fiscal Year-end: 06/30/13
Banking Services
S.I.C.: 6029
N.A.I.C.S.: 522110
Lorato Edith Boakgomo-Ntakhwana *(CEO)*
Richard C. Wright *(Deputy CEO)*
Boitumelo Mogopa *(CFO)*
Denis Ivins *(COO)*
Lehuka Maseng *(CIO)*
Phila Nhlekisana *(Acting Treas)*

RMB Financial Services Limited (3)
Jutland Hall Steamboat Quay
Limerick, Ireland
Tel.: (353) 61468575
Fax: (353) 61468573
Emp.: 3
Insurance Services
S.I.C.: 6411
N.A.I.C.S.: 524210
Patrick Liston *(Mng Dir)*

FirstRand Bank Holdings Limited (1)
4 Merchant Pl
1 Fredman Dr, Sandton, Gauteng, 2196, South Africa (100%)
Tel.: (27) 112828000
Fax: (27) 112828088
Web Site: www.rmb.co.za
Sales Range: $25-49.9 Million
Emp.: 2,948
Bank
S.I.C.: 6712
N.A.I.C.S.: 551111
Gerrit Thomas Ferreira *(Chm)*

Non-U.S. Subsidiary:

RMB Australia Ltd. (2)
60 Casclereagh St Level 13
Sydney, 2000, Australia (100%)
Tel.: (61) 292566200
Fax: (61) 292566290
E-Mail: info@rmb.com.au
Web Site: www.rmb.com.au
Emp.: 16
Investment Bank
S.I.C.: 6211
N.A.I.C.S.: 523110
Gregory Gay *(Sec & Dir-Fin)*

FirstRand EMA Holdings Limited (1)
Cnr Fredman Dr And Rivonia Rd
Sandton, Gauteng, 2196, South Africa
Tel.: (27) 112824000
Fax: (27) 112828008
Web Site: www.rmb.co.za
Emp.: 1,000
Financial Management Services
S.I.C.: 6211
N.A.I.C.S.: 523999
Alan Pullinger *(Mng Dir)*

Non-U.S. Subsidiary:

First National Bank of Zambia Limited (2)
Stand Number 22768 Acacia Office Park
Cnr Thabo Mbeki Great East Roads
Lusaka, Zambia
Tel.: (260) 211 366800
Fax: (260) 211 253057
E-Mail: fnb@fnbzambia.co.zm
Web Site: www.fnbzambia.co.zm
Commercial Banking Services
S.I.C.: 6029
N.A.I.C.S.: 522110
Sarel J. van Zyl *(CEO)*
Ackim L. Chalwe *(CFO)*

Firstrand Finance Company Limited (1)
Merchant Place Cnr of Rivonia Road and Fredman Drive Sandown Sandton
Gauteng, 2146, South Africa
Tel.: (27) 112821808
Fax: (27) 112828008
E-Mail: bruce.unser@firstrand.co.za
Web Site: www.firstrand.com
Emp.: 38,000
Financial Management Services
S.I.C.: 6211
N.A.I.C.S.: 523999
Sizwe Nxasana *(CEO)*

Momentum Group Ltd. (1)
268 W Ave Centurion
Gauteng, 0157, South Africa
Tel.: (27) 126753070
Fax: (27) 126753911
E-Mail: client@momentum.co.za
Web Site: www.momentum.co.za
Insurance Services
S.I.C.: 6411
N.A.I.C.S.: 524298
Lauritz Lanser Dippenaar *(Chm)*

Subsidiaries:

AdviceAtWork (Pty) Ltd (2)
33 Princess Wales Terrace
Parktown, 2193, South Africa
Tel.: (27) 11 485 7002
Fax: (27) 86 560 4184
Web Site: www.adviceatwork.co.za
Financial Management Services
S.I.C.: 6211
N.A.I.C.S.: 523999

Momentum Africa Investments Limited (2)
4 High Street
Melrose, 2076, South Africa
Tel.: (27) 117153000
Fax: (27) 117153001
Investment Management Services
S.I.C.: 6211
N.A.I.C.S.: 523999

MOMENTUM MEDICAL SCHEME ADMINISTRATORS (PTY) LTD (2)
1-3 Canegate Road La Lucia Ridge
Durban, 4019, South Africa
Tel.: (27) 315734000
Fax: (27) 315800477
Emp.: 600
Financial Management Services
S.I.C.: 6211
N.A.I.C.S.: 523999
Odette Ramsingh *(Head-HR)*

NewBucks Operations Pty., Ltd. (1)
Sandown Mews West
88 Stella Street, 2196 Sandton, South Africa
Tel.: (27) 112635000
Fax: (27) 112635385
E-Mail: info@ebucks.com
Web Site: www.ebucks.com
Emp.: 150
Rewards Program Solutions
S.I.C.: 7389
N.A.I.C.S.: 561499
Jolande Duvenage *(CEO)*
Lezanne Human *(CEO)*

OUTsurance Limited (1)
1241 Embankment Street Zwartkop Ext 7
Centurion, Gauteng, 0157, South Africa
Tel.: (27) 126733000
Fax: (27) 12 665 0994
E-Mail: cctd@out.co.za
Web Site: www.outsurance.co.za
Emp.: 2,500
General Insurance Services
S.I.C.: 6411
N.A.I.C.S.: 524210
Ernst Gouws *(CEO)*

Rentworks Africa (Pty) Ltd (1)
RentWorks Place Turnberry Office Park 48 Grosvenor Road
Bryanston, Johannesburg, 2021, South Africa
Tel.: (27) 115499000
Fax: (27) 115499230
E-Mail: moreinfo@rentworks.co.za
Web Site: www.rentworks.co.za
Emp.: 70
Venture Capital Services
S.I.C.: 6799
N.A.I.C.S.: 523910
Trevor Cronje *(CEO)*

RMB Corvest (Pty) Ltd. (1)
Northern Block The Reserve 54 Melville Road
Illovo, 2196, South Africa
Tel.: (27) 11 380 8300
Fax: (27) 11 380 8310
Web Site: www.rmbcorvest.co.za
Private Equity Firm
S.I.C.: 6211
N.A.I.C.S.: 523999
Neil Page *(Mng Dir)*

WesBank (1)
3 First Pl
Bank City, Johannesburg, South Africa
Tel.: (27) 113692842
Fax: (27) 113529904
E-Mail: westbankcard@westbank.co.za
Web Site: www.fnb.com
Vehicle Financing Services
S.I.C.: 9311
N.A.I.C.S.: 921130

Joint Venture:

Graphic Mining Solutions International (Pty) Limited (1)
Ground Floor, 267 West Ave
Centurion, Gauteng, 0046, South Africa
Tel.: (27) 87 980 3100
Fax: (27) 86 406 0117
E-Mail: info.za@minerpsolutions.com
Web Site: www.minerpsolutions.com
Emp.: 800
Mining Management Software Solutions
S.I.C.: 7371
N.A.I.C.S.: 541511
Pieter Nel *(Pres)*
Marlise Van Zyl *(Chief Consulting Officer)*
Jean Roux *(Exec VP-Services & Partner Channel)*

Non-U.S. Subsidiaries:

GIJIMAAST Americas Incorporated (2)
Greenvale Ct 430 Westmount Ave Unit L
Sudbury, ON, P3A 5Z8, Canada
Tel.: (705) 525-4774
Fax: (705) 525-2629
E-Mail: info@gijimaast.com
Web Site: www.gijimaast.ca
Emp.: 10
Mining Software Consulting Services
S.I.C.: 7371
N.A.I.C.S.: 541511
Andrew Vhkala *(VP)*

GijimaAst (Pty) Limited (2)
2 44 Denis St
Subiaco, WA, 6008, Australia
Tel.: (61) 863801719
Fax: (61) 893883581
Emp.: 6
Mining Software Consulting Services
S.I.C.: 7373
N.A.I.C.S.: 541512
Pieter Neethling *(VP)*

Non-U.S. Subsidiary:

FirstRand Bank Limited (1)
5th Floor Mistry Bhavan 122 Dr Dinsha Vachha Road
Churchgate, Mumbai, 400 020, India
Tel.: (91) 2266258600
Fax: (91) 22 2281 9130
Web Site: www.firstrand.co.in
Financial Management Services
S.I.C.: 6211
N.A.I.C.S.: 523999
Mahendren Moodley *(CEO & Country Mgr)*
Rohit Wahi *(CFO)*

FIRSTSERVICE CORPORATION

1140 Bay Street Suite 4000
Toronto, ON, M5S 2B4, Canada
Tel.: (416) 960-9500
Fax: (416) 960-5333
Web Site: www.firstservice.com
FSV—(TSX)
Rev.: $2,343,634,000
Assets: $1,443,511,000
Liabilities: $1,194,462,000
Net Worth: $249,049,000
Earnings: $41,643,000
Emp.: 24,000
Fiscal Year-end: 12/31/13

Business Description:
Holding Company; Residential & Commercial Real Estate Acquisition, Development & Property Management Services
S.I.C.: 6719
N.A.I.C.S.: 551112

Personnel:
Jay S. Hennick *(Founder & CEO)*
Peter F. Cohen *(Chm)*
D. Scott Patterson *(Pres & COO)*
John B. Friedrichsen *(CFO & Sr VP)*
Douglas G. Cooke *(Sec, VP & Controller)*

Board of Directors:
Peter F. Cohen
David Ross Beatty
Brendan Calder
Bernard I. Ghert
Michael D. Harris
Jay S. Hennick
Steven S. Rogers

Transfer Agent:
TMX Equity Transfer Services
200 University Ave Suite 300
Toronto, ON, Canada

U.S. Divisions:

FirstService Commercial Real Estate Services Inc. (1)
601 Union St Ste 4800
Seattle, WA 98101 ON
Tel.: (206) 695-4200 (93.2%)
Web Site: www.colliers.com
Sales Range: $1-4.9 Billion
Emp.: 12,509
Holding Company; Commercial Real Estate Brokerage Services
S.I.C.: 6719
N.A.I.C.S.: 551112
Douglas P. Frye *(Pres & CEO)*
Peter Humphries *(CFO & COO)*
Veresh Sita *(CIO)*
Craig Robbins *(Chief Knowledge Officer-Global)*
Dylan E. Taylor *(CEO-USA)*
Alex Baehr *(Gen Counsel & VP)*

Subsidiaries:

Colliers International Management - Atlanta, LLC (2)
1349 W Peachtree St NE 2 Midtown Plz Ste 1100
Atlanta, GA 30309 GA
Tel.: (404) 888-9000
Fax: (404) 870-2845
Web Site: www.colliers.com
Sales Range: $750-799.9 Million
Emp.: 150
Commercial Real Estate Brokerage & Property Management Services
S.I.C.: 6531
N.A.I.C.S.: 531210
Bick Cardwell *(Co-Chm)*
Bill Law *(Co-Chm)*
Tim Hague *(Vice Chm-Eastern Reg)*
Robert S. Mathews *(Pres & CEO)*
Susan Borst *(Partner-Doherty Indus Grp & VP-Indus-Las Vegas)*
Jessica Hayden *(Exec Mng Dir-Acct Ops)*
Mike Mixer *(Exec Mng Dir-Las Vegas)*
Bob Mulhern *(Mng Dir)*
Kathie Kuebler *(CFO)*
Jim Howser *(Chief Admin Officer & Sr VP)*
Joe Harbert *(Pres-Eastern Reg)*
Scott Nelson *(Pres-Corp Solutions-Americas)*
Holly Hughes *(CEO-Facility Solutions & Property Management)*
Tom Gustafson *(Principal-Cleveland)*
Russ Rogers *(Principal-Cleveland)*
Tim Huffman *(Exec VP)*
Mindy Korth *(Exec VP-Greater Phoenix)*
Caldwell H. Zimmerman *(Exec VP)*
Lucia S. Carter *(Sr VP & Dir-Project Mgmt-Indiana Reg)*
Bob Cook *(Sr VP-Strategic Plng-Corp Svcs-San Jose)*
Steven Gonzalez *(Sr VP-Investments-Greater Phoenix)*
Kevin S. Manning *(Sr VP-Corp Svcs)*
Ryan Martin *(Sr VP-Las Vegas)*
Bruce M. Milam *(Sr VP-Richmond)*

Colliers International Real Estate Management Services (MI), Inc. (2)
2 Corporate Dr Ste 300
Southfield, MI 48076 MI
Tel.: (248) 540-1000
Fax: (248) 540-1038

FirstService Corporation—(Continued)

Web Site: www.colliers.com
Emp.: 80
Real Estate Brokerage & Property Management
S.I.C.: 6531
N.A.I.C.S.: 531210
Paul Choukourian *(Mng Dir)*
Robert Brierley *(Sr VP)*

Colliers International Real Estate Management Services (WA), Inc. (2)
601 Union St Ste 5300
Seattle, WA 98101 WA
Tel.: (206) 223-0866
Fax: (206) 223-1427
Web Site: www.colliers.com
Emp.: 100
Real Estate Broker
S.I.C.: 6531
N.A.I.C.S.: 531210
Douglas P. Frye *(Grp Pres & CEO)*
Brian Ward *(Pres-Capital Markets Grp)*
David Abbott *(Sr VP)*

Colliers International Valuation & Advisory Services Inc. (2)
5796 Armada Dr Ste 210
Carlsbad, CA 92008 OR
Tel.: (760) 444-8000
Web Site: www.pgpinc.com
Sales Range: $10-24.9 Million
Emp.: 25
Commercial & Industrial Real Estate Appraisals
S.I.C.: 6531
N.A.I.C.S.: 531320
Kenneth Harrison *(Pres & CEO)*
Ed Alegre *(Pres-Irvine)*

Lanard & Axilbund, Inc. (2)
399 Market St
Philadelphia, PA 19106 PA
Tel.: (215) 925-4600
Fax: (215) 925-1040
Web Site: www.colliers.com
Real Estate Brokerage Services
S.I.C.: 6531
N.A.I.C.S.: 531210
Marc Isdaner *(Sr VP & Principal)*

Manekin LLC (2)
8601 Robert Fulton Dr Ste 200
Columbia, MD 21046
Tel.: (410) 290-1400
Fax: (410) 290-1498
E-Mail: llapenna@manekin.com
Web Site: www.manekin.com
Sales Range: $75-99.9 Million
Emp.: 40
Real Estate Brokers & Agents
S.I.C.: 6531
N.A.I.C.S.: 531210
Richard Alter *(Pres & CEO)*
Ed Kouneski *(CFO)*
Lou LaPenna *(COO)*
Craig Wess *(Pres-Manekin Construction)*
Christopher Smith *(Gen Counsel)*
Barbara Alden *(Sr VP & Dir-Property Mgmt)*
Adam Nachlas *(Sr VP & Dir-Brokerage)*
Owen Rouse *(Sr VP & Dir-Capital Markets)*
Cole Schnorf *(Sr VP & Dir-Dev)*
Peter Teeling *(Sr VP & Dir-Property Mgmt)*

Meredith & Grew, Incorporated (2)
160 Federal St
Boston, MA 02110-1700 MA
Tel.: (617) 330-8000
Fax: (617) 330-8130
Web Site: www.colliers.com
Emp.: 150
Commercial Real Estate Services
S.I.C.: 6531
N.A.I.C.S.: 531210
Thomas J. Hynes, Jr. *(Co-Chm & CEO)*
Kevin C. Phelan *(Co-Chm)*
Ronald K. Perry *(Pres & Head-Brokerage)*
Lisa M. Campoli *(Exec VP & Mng Partner-Investment Sls)*
James L. Elcock *(Exec VP & Mng Partner-Suburban Brokerage)*
Joseph P. Flaherty *(Exec VP & Mng Partner-Suburban Brokerage)*
Dennis F. Callahan *(Exec VP-Real Estate Mgmt Svcs)*
Daniel R. Quinn *(Exec VP-Consulting & Advisory Svcs)*
Robert P. LaPorte, Jr. *(Sr VP-Valuation & Advisory Svcs)*

Paracom LLC (2)
300 Ottawa Ave NW Ste 400
Grand Rapids, MI 49503 MI
Tel.: (616) 774-3500
Fax: (616) 774-3600
Web Site: www.colliers.com
Sales Range: $10-24.9 Million
Emp.: 58
Real Estate Brokerage Services
S.I.C.: 6531
N.A.I.C.S.: 531210
Ray Kisor *(Chm)*
Duwane Suwyn *(Pres & CEO)*
Derek Hunderman *(Mng Partner & VP)*
Kent Hildebrand *(CFO & VP-Investment Svcs)*

Williams Real Estate Co., Inc. (2)
380 Madison Ave
New York, NY 10017 NY
Tel.: (212) 716-3500 (65%)
Fax: (212) 716-3566
Web Site: www.colliers.com
Sls.: $20,000,000
Emp.: 200
Real Estate Brokerage Services
S.I.C.: 6531
N.A.I.C.S.: 531210
Robert L. Freedman *(Chm)*
Andrew Roos *(Vice Chm)*
Mark A. Jaccom *(CEO)*
Bryn Cinque *(Exec Mng Dir)*
David Csontos *(Exec Mng Dir)*
Matthew J. Dolly *(Sr Mng Dir)*
James Raso *(CFO)*
Joseph Caridi *(COO)*

Subsidiaries:

Colliers International CT LLC (3)
1055 Washington Blvd
Stamford, CT 06901-2216 DE
Tel.: (203) 324-0800
Web Site: www.colliers.com
Sales Range: $1-9.9 Million
Emp.: 20
Real Estate Brokerage Services
S.I.C.: 6531
N.A.I.C.S.: 531210
Gerard P. Hallock *(Exec Mng Dir)*

Colliers International LI Inc. (3)
1981 Marcus Ave
Lake Success, NY 11042 NY
Tel.: (516) 328-6500
Web Site: www.colliers.com
Sales Range: $1-9.9 Million
Emp.: 45
Real Estate Brokerage Services
S.I.C.: 6531
N.A.I.C.S.: 531210
Joseph A. Cabrera *(Vice Chm-East)*
Herbert S. Agin *(CEO)*
David Glassman *(Exec Mng Dir)*
Mike Gordon *(Exec Mng Dir)*
Robert Thuss *(Exec Mng Dir)*

Colliers International NJ LLC (3)
119 Cherry Hill Rd Ste 110
Parsippany, NJ 07054 DE
Tel.: (973) 299-3000
Fax: (973) 299-3001
E-Mail: info@colliers.com
Web Site: www.colliers.com
Sales Range: $10-24.9 Million
Emp.: 30
Real Estate Brokerage Services
S.I.C.: 6531
N.A.I.C.S.: 531210
Richard J. Madison *(Exec Mng Dir)*
Tim Kuhn *(Sr Mng Dir)*
John Donnelly *(Mng Dir)*
Robert Martie *(Exec VP)*

Affiliates:

Adena Commercial, LLC (2)
8800 Lyra Dr Ste 150
Columbus, OH 43240 OH
Tel.: (614) 436-9800
Fax: (614) 436-9700
Web Site: www.colliers.com
Sales Range: $10-24.9 Million
Emp.: 56
Commercial Real Estate Brokerage Services
S.I.C.: 6531
N.A.I.C.S.: 531210
Richard B. Schuen *(CEO & Principal)*
Richard F. Underman *(Exec VP)*
Andrew S. Jameson *(Sr VP-Brokerage)*
Onno A. Steger *(Sr VP-Brokerage)*

Colliers Appelt Womack, Inc. (2)
1300 Post Oak Blvd Ste 200
Houston, TX 77056 TX
Tel.: (713) 222-2111
Fax: (713) 830-2118
Web Site: www.colliers.com
Sales Range: $25-49.9 Million
Emp.: 70
Commercial Real Estate Brokerage Services
S.I.C.: 6531
N.A.I.C.S.: 531210
Charles Herder *(Co-Chm)*
Robert S. Parsley *(Co-Chm)*
J. Patrick Duffy *(Pres & Chm-Retail Svcs Grp-Global)*
David L. Carter *(Sr VP)*

Colliers Bennett & Kahnweiler, Inc. (2)
4643 S Ulster St Ste 1000
Denver, CO 80237 CO
Tel.: (303) 745-5800
Fax: (303) 745-5888
Web Site: www.colliers.com
Sales Range: $10-24.9 Million
Emp.: 32
Commercial Real Estate Management & Brokerage Services
S.I.C.: 6531
N.A.I.C.S.: 531210
Brad Calbert *(Pres)*

Colliers Monroe Friedlander, Inc. (2)
1800 Central Pacific Plz 220 S King St
Honolulu, HI 96813 HI
Tel.: (808) 524-2666
Fax: (808) 521-0977
Web Site: www.colliers.com
Sales Range: $10-24.9 Million
Emp.: 82
Real Estate Brokerage & Property Management Services
S.I.C.: 6531
N.A.I.C.S.: 531210
James Piane *(CEO)*

Division:

Colliers Monroe Friedlander Management, Inc. (3)
1800 Central Pacific Plz 220 S King St
Honolulu, HI 96813 HI
Tel.: (808) 524-2666
Web Site: www.colliers.com
Emp.: 35
Property Management Services
S.I.C.: 6531
N.A.I.C.S.: 531312
James Piane *(Pres & CEO)*

Colliers Paragon, LLC (2)
755 W Front St Ste 300
Boise, ID 83702 ID
Tel.: (208) 345-9000
Fax: (208) 343-3124
Web Site: www.colliers.com
Emp.: 50
Real Estate Brokerage Services
S.I.C.: 6531
N.A.I.C.S.: 531210
George Iliff *(Principal)*

Pittsburgh Commercial Real Estate, Inc. (2)
2 Gateway Ctr Ste 125 603 Stanwix St
Pittsburgh, PA 15222 PA
Tel.: (412) 321-4200
Fax: (412) 321-4200
Web Site: www.colliers.com
Emp.: 30
Commercial Real Estate Brokerage Services
S.I.C.: 6531
N.A.I.C.S.: 531210
Gregg Broujos *(Mng Dir & Principal)*
John Bilyak *(Principal & Dir-Indus Brokerage)*
Ralph Egerman *(Principal)*
Paul Horan *(Principal)*
William Leone *(Principal)*
Patrick Sentner *(Principal)*

Walter Dickinson, Inc. (2)
1 Independent Dr Ste 2401
Jacksonville, FL 32202-5018 FL
Tel.: (904) 358-1206
Fax: (904) 353-4949
Web Site: www.colliers.com
Emp.: 30
Commercial Real Estate Brokerage Services
S.I.C.: 6531
N.A.I.C.S.: 531210
Robert W. Selton, III *(Pres, CEO & Mng Partner)*
Charles R. Diebel *(COO & Partner)*
Hobart Joost, Jr. *(Sr VP & Partner)*
Matthew Entriken *(Partner)*
Fran Pepis *(Partner)*
Jason Ryals *(Partner)*

West Shell Commercial, Inc. (2)
425 Walnut St Ste 1200
Cincinnati, OH 45202 OH
Tel.: (513) 721-4200
Fax: (513) 721-0630
Web Site: www.colliers.com
Sales Range: $10-24.9 Million
Emp.: 64
Commercial Real Estate Brokerage Services
S.I.C.: 6531
N.A.I.C.S.: 531210
Shenan Murphy *(CEO & Principal)*

Units:

Colliers International - Central California (2)
10000 Stockdale Hwy Ste 102
Bakersfield, CA 93311
Tel.: (661) 631-3800
Fax: (661) 631-3829
Web Site: www.colliers.com
Emp.: 30
Real Estate Brokerage Services
S.I.C.: 6531
N.A.I.C.S.: 531210
David A. Williams *(Sr VP & Principal)*

Colliers International - San Diego Region (2)
4660 La Jolla Village Dr
San Diego, CA 92122
Tel.: (858) 455-1515
Fax: (858) 546-9146
Web Site: www.colliers.com
Sales Range: $10-24.9 Million
Emp.: 75
Commercial Real Estate Management & Brokerage Services
S.I.C.: 6531
N.A.I.C.S.: 531210
Jim Spain *(Reg Mng Dir)*

Colliers International - San Francisco (2)
50 California St Ste 1900
San Francisco, CA 94111
Tel.: (415) 788-3100
Fax: (415) 433-7844
Web Site: www.colliers.com
Emp.: 65
Commercial Real Estate Management & Brokerage Services
S.I.C.: 6531
N.A.I.C.S.: 531210
Alan Collenette *(Mng Dir-Sacramento)*

Non-U.S. Subsidiaries:

Colliers International Holdings (Australia) Limited (2)
Level 12 Grosvenor Place
225 George St, Sydney, NSW, 2000, Australia AU
Tel.: (61) 292570222
Fax: (61) 292513297
Web Site: www.colliers.com.au
Emp.: 1,400
Holding Company; Commercial Real Estate Management & Brokerage Services
S.I.C.: 6719
N.A.I.C.S.: 551112
John Kenny *(CEO)*
Peter Chittenden *(Mng Dir)*
Sean Unwin *(CFO)*

Subsidiaries:

Colliers International Consultancy & Valuation Pty. Ltd. (3)
Level 12 Grosvenor Place 225 George Street
Sydney, NSW, 2000, Australia AU

Tel.: (61) 292570222
Fax: (61) 292513297
Real Estate Consultancy & Valuation Services
S.I.C.: 6531
N.A.I.C.S.: 531320
Will Doherty *(Mng Dir)*

Colliers International (NSW) Pty. Limited (3)
Level 12 225 George Street
Sydney, NSW, 2000, Australia
Tel.: (61) 2 9257 0222
Fax: (61) 2 9251 3297
E-Mail: info@colliers.com.au
Emp.: 350
Commercial Real Estate Management & Brokerage Services
S.I.C.: 6531
N.A.I.C.S.: 531210
John Kenny *(CEO)*

Colliers International (Victoria) Pty. Limited (3)
Level 32 Optus Ctr
367 Collins St, Melbourne, VIC, 3000, Australia
Tel.: (61) 396298888
Fax: (61) 396298549
Commercial Real Estate Management & Brokerage Services
S.I.C.: 6531
N.A.I.C.S.: 531210
John Marasco *(CEO & Grp Mng Dir-Investment Sls)*
Simon Hunt *(Grp Mng Dir-Office Leasing)*
Darren Whitelegg *(Grp Mng Dir-Real Estate Mgmt)*

Colliers International (Hong Kong) Ltd. (2)
Suite 5701 57/F Central Plaza
18 Harbour Road, Wanchai, China (Hong Kong) HK
Tel.: (852) 28289888
Fax: (852) 28289899
Web Site: www.colliers.com
Emp.: 100
Commercial Real Estate Management & Brokerage Services
S.I.C.: 6531
N.A.I.C.S.: 531210
Piers Brunner *(CEO-Asia)*

Colliers International Korea Ltd. (2)
10F Korea Tourism Organization Bldg
10 Da-dong, Seoul, 100-180, Korea (South) Ks
Tel.: (82) 267402000
Fax: (82) 23182015
Emp.: 15
Commercial Real Estate Management & Brokerage Services
S.I.C.: 6531
N.A.I.C.S.: 531210
Jay Yun *(Gen Mgr)*

Colliers International (Singapore) Pte. Ltd. (2)
1 Raffles Place 45-00 OUB Centre
Singapore, 048616, Singapore SG
Tel.: (65) 62232323
Fax: (65) 62224901
Emp.: 175
Commercial Real Estate Management & Brokerage Services
S.I.C.: 6531
N.A.I.C.S.: 531210
Mark D. Lampard *(Mng Dir)*
Desmond Ang *(Sr Exec-Property Mgmt)*
Leona Chansingh *(Sr Officer-Valuation)*

Colliers International UK plc (2)
50 George Street
London, W1U 7GA, United Kingdom UK
Tel.: (44) 2079354499
Sales Range: $100-124.9 Million
Emp.: 740
Real Estate Consulting Services
S.I.C.: 6531
N.A.I.C.S.: 531390
Lucinda Lee-Bapty *(Partner-Valuation & Advisory Svcs)*
Gareth W. Jones *(COO)*
Tony Horrell *(CEO-UK & Ireland)*
Howard Goldsobel *(Sec)*

Colliers Macaulay Nicolls Inc. (2)
200 Granville Street 19th Floor
Vancouver, BC, V6C 2R6, Canada ON
Tel.: (604) 681-4111
Fax: (604) 661-0849
Web Site: www.colliers.com
Emp.: 400
Commercial Real Estate Broker
S.I.C.: 6531
N.A.I.C.S.: 531210
David Bowden *(CEO)*
Ron Bagan *(Mng Dir)*
Suzanne Bedford *(Sr VP-Fin & Ops)*

Branch:

Colliers International - Canada, Toronto Downtown Office (3)
1 Queen Street East Suite 2200
Toronto, ON, M5C 2Z2, Canada
Tel.: (416) 777-2200
Fax: (416) 777-2277
Emp.: 155
Commercial Real Estate Brokerage Services
S.I.C.: 6531
N.A.I.C.S.: 531210
David Bowden *(CEO-Canada)*
Antoinette Tummillo *(Exec VP-Real Estate Mgmt Svcs)*

Subsidiary:

CMN Calgary Inc. (3)
335 8th Avenue SW Suite 1000
Royal Bank Building, Calgary, AB, T2P 1C9, Canada
Tel.: (403) 266-5544
Fax: (403) 265-6495
Web Site: www.collierscanada.com
Emp.: 70
Commercial Real Estate Services
S.I.C.: 6531
N.A.I.C.S.: 531210
Randy Fennessey *(Pres & CEO)*
Jim Rea *(Partner & Exec VP)*
Bob Young *(Partner & Sr VP)*
Warren Dennis Hedges *(Partner & VP-Office Leasing)*
Eric Horvath *(Partner & VP)*
Alykhan Lalani *(Partner & VP)*
Robert G. Walker *(Partner & VP)*
Chris Law *(Partner)*
Peter Mayerchak *(Partner)*
Dick Schwann *(Mng Dir)*
Mark Boden *(Mng Dir)*
David Shum *(Mng Dir)*
Chris M. Marlyn *(Sr VP)*

FirstService Residential Management, Inc. (1)
1815 Griffin Rd Ste 404
Dania Beach, FL 33004 DE
Fax: (954) 920-5312 (97.6%)
Toll Free: (866) 522-3671
Web Site: www.fsresidential.com
Sales Range: $650-699.9 Million
Residential Property Management
S.I.C.: 6531
N.A.I.C.S.: 531311
Steven Parker *(Pres)*
Chuck M. Fallon *(CEO)*
Joe Scholes *(Sr VP-New York)*

Subsidiaries:

Bristol Management Services, Inc. (2)
1930 Commerce Ln
Jupiter, FL 33458
Tel.: (561) 575-3551
Fax: (561) 575-5423
Web Site: www.bristolmanagement.com
Rev.: $4,000,000
Emp.: 40
Office Administrative Services
S.I.C.: 8741
N.A.I.C.S.: 561110
Steve Inglis *(Owner & Pres)*

Excellence Community Management LLC (2)
601 Whitney Ranch Dr Ste B-10
Henderson, NV 89014
Tel.: (702) 638-7770
Fax: (702) 638-7772
E-Mail: info@excellencemgmt.com
Web Site: www.excellencemgmt.com
Emp.: 60
Management Consulting Services
S.I.C.: 8748
N.A.I.C.S.: 541618
Jamie McCafferty *(Pres)*

FirstService Residential (2)
(Formerly The Continental Group, Inc.)
2950 N 28th Ter
Hollywood, FL 33020-1301 FL
Tel.: (954) 925-8200
Fax: (954) 378-2298
Toll Free: (800) 927-4599
E-Mail:
Web Site: www.fsresidential.com
Emp.: 6,000
Real Estate Agency Services
Import Export
S.I.C.: 6531
N.A.I.C.S.: 531210
Gene Gomberg *(Chm)*
Chuck M. Fallon *(CEO)*
Mike Natale *(CFO)*
Bruno Sperduti *(CIO)*
Jason Proudfit *(Pres-Arizona)*
Anthony Kalliche *(Gen Counsel & Exec VP)*
David Diestel *(Sr VP-Ops)*

Gittleman Management Corporation (2)
1801 American Blvd E Ste 21
Minneapolis, MN 55425 MN
Tel.: (952) 277-2700
Web Site: www.gittleman.com
Sales Range: $10-24.9 Million
Emp.: 250
Homeowner Association Property Management Services
S.I.C.: 6531
N.A.I.C.S.: 531311
Melvin C. Gittleman *(Founder)*
Mark Gittleman *(Pres & CEO)*
Andrew Gittleman *(Exec VP)*

Goodstein Management, Inc. (2)
211 E 46th St Fl 5
New York, NY 10017
Tel.: (212) 376-8600
Fax: (212) 755-1398
Web Site: www.goodstein.com
Sales Range: $1-9.9 Million
Emp.: 54
Residential Property Management Services
S.I.C.: 6531
N.A.I.C.S.: 531390
Martin Goodstein *(Chm)*

FS Brands, Inc. (1)
PO Box 1066
Oaks, PA 19456 DE
Tel.: (610) 650-8047
Fax: (610) 650-9997
Web Site: www.fsvbrands.com
Holding Company; Contract Services Franchisor
S.I.C.: 6719
N.A.I.C.S.: 551112
Charlie Chase *(Pres & CEO)*

Subsidiaries:

California Closet Company, Inc. (2)
1716 4th St
Berkeley, CA 94710 CA
Tel.: (415) 256-8500
Fax: (415) 256-8501
Toll Free: (800) 274-6754
Web Site: www.californiaclosets.com
Contract Custom Closet & Cabinetry Services Franchisor
S.I.C.: 6794
N.A.I.C.S.: 533110
William G. Barton *(Pres & CEO)*
Jonathan Louie *(CFO & VP)*
Davyd Funk *(Exec VP & Dir-Ops)*

CertaPro Painters Ltd. (2)
150 Green Tree Rd Ste 1003
Oaks, PA 19456 MA
Tel.: (610) 650-9999
Fax: (610) 650-9997
Toll Free: (800) 689-7271
Web Site: www.certapro.com
Contract Painting & Wall Covering Services Franchisor
S.I.C.: 6794
N.A.I.C.S.: 533110
Rich Wilson *(Pres)*

Floor Coverings International, Ltd. (2)
5250 Triangle Pkwy Ste 100
Norcross, GA 30092 GA
Tel.: (770) 874-7600
Fax: (770) 874-7605
Toll Free: (800) 955-4324
E-Mail: info@floorcoveringsinternational.com
Web Site: www.floorcoveringsinternational.com
Contract Flooring Services Franchisor
S.I.C.: 6794
N.A.I.C.S.: 533110
Thomas W. Wood *(Pres & CEO)*

Mamar, Inc. (2)
10250 Alliance Rd Ste 100
Cincinnati, OH 45242 OH
Tel.: (513) 771-3003
Fax: (513) 771-6439
E-Mail: jrocchetta@handyman.com
Web Site: www.handymanconnection.com
Contract Home Repairs & Remodeling Services Franchisor
S.I.C.: 6794
N.A.I.C.S.: 533110
Jeff Wall *(Pres & CEO)*

Paul Davis Restoration, Inc. (2)
1 Independent Dr Ste 2300
Jacksonville, FL 32202 FL
Tel.: (904) 737-2779
Fax: (904) 737-4204
Toll Free: (800) 722-1818
E-Mail: marketing@pdrestoration.com
Web Site: www.pdrestoration.com
Emp.: 30
Property Damage Mitigation, Reconstruction & Remodeling Services Franchisor
S.I.C.: 6794
N.A.I.C.S.: 533110
Tim Robinson *(CEO)*
Barry Floyd *(CFO)*
Robb King *(Sr VP-Franchise Dev & Dir-Emergency Svcs)*
Tracy Bachtell *(Sr VP-Bus Dev)*

Non-U.S. Subsidiary:

TeleLink Services Inc. (2)
700 Richmond Street North Suite 416
London, ON, N6A 5C7, Canada
Fax: (519) 439-5517
Toll Free: (877) 773-7725
E-Mail: info@tls-connectingvoices.com
Web Site: www.tls-connectingvoices.com
Emp.: 100
Multi-Channel Customer Care Call Center Services
S.I.C.: 7389
N.A.I.C.S.: 561421
Laurie Dietz *(Pres)*

U.S. Subsidiaries:

FirstService Delaware, LLC (1)
103 Foulk Rd
Wilmington, DE 19803
Tel.: (302) 691-6387
Residential Property Management Services
S.I.C.: 6531
N.A.I.C.S.: 531311

The Wentworth Group, Inc (1)
901 S Trooper Rd
Norristown, PA 19403-2312
Tel.: (610) 650-0600
Fax: (610) 650-0700
Web Site: www.wentworthmgt.com
Emp.: 50
Property Management Services
S.I.C.: 6531
N.A.I.C.S.: 531311
Michael A. Mendillo *(Pres)*
David Epstein *(CEO)*
Frank Peditto *(CFO)*

FIRSTSOURCE SOLUTIONS LIMITED

5th Floor Paradigm B Wing
Mindspace Link Road Malad West
Mumbai, 400 064, India
Tel.: (91) 2266660888
Fax: (91) 226666 0887
Web Site: www.firstsource.com
532809—(BOM)
Rev.: $531,158,022
Assets: $621,400,174
Liabilities: $303,481,075
Net Worth: $317,919,100
Earnings: $27,118,643

Firstsource Solutions Limited—(Continued)

Emp.: 31,872
Fiscal Year-end: 03/31/13

Business Description:
Business Process Management Services
S.I.C.: 7389
N.A.I.C.S.: 561499

Personnel:
Ananda Mukerji *(Vice Chm)*
Rajesh Subramaniam *(CEO & Mng Dir)*
Dinesh Jain *(CFO)*
Arun Tyagi *(Chief Compliance Officer & Sr VP)*
Sanjay Gupta *(Compliance Officer, Sec & VP-Corp Affairs)*
David Strickler *(Pres/CEO-Healthcare Provider)*
Sanjay Venkataraman *(Pres-Customer Mgmt)*
Gayatri Anandh *(Exec VP-Tech)*
Shalabh Jain *(Exec VP-Customer Mgmt-Domestic Bus)*
Satish M. *(Exec VP-HR)*
Arjun Mitra *(Exec VP-Collections)*
Vishwajit Negi *(Exec VP-Ops-Customer Mgmt India Intl Bus)*
Venkataraman K. R. *(Exec VP-Healthcare Payor & Publ)*
Iain Regan *(Exec VP-Sls & Client Services)*

Board of Directors:
Sanjiv Goenka
Shailesh J. Mehta
K. P. Balaraj
Shashwat Goenka
Haigreve Khaitan
Donald Layden, Jr.
Y. H. Malegam
Ananda Mukerji
Pradip Roy
Charles Miller Smith
Rajesh Subramaniam
Subrata Talukdar

Transfer Agent:
3i Infotech Limited
Tower #5 3rd to 6th Floors International Infotech Park Vashi
Navi Mumbai, India

U.S. Subsidiaries:

Firstsource Advantage LLC. **(1)**
205 Bryant Woods S
Buffalo, NY 14228-3609
Tel.: (716) 564-4400
Fax: (716) 564-4440
Business Process Outsourcing Services
S.I.C.: 8742
N.A.I.C.S.: 541611

Firstsource Financial Solution Inc. **(1)**
1232 W State Rd 2
La Porte, IN 46350
Tel.: (219) 326-7754
Business Process Outsourcing Services
S.I.C.: 8742
N.A.I.C.S.: 541611

Firstsource Solutions USA, Inc. **(1)**
205 Bryant Woods S
Buffalo, NY 14228-3609
Tel.: (203) 653-9150
Fax: (203) 653-9170
Web Site: www.firstsource.com
Business Process Management Services
S.I.C.: 8741
N.A.I.C.S.: 551114

MedAssist, Inc. **(1)**
1661 Lyndon Farm Ct
Louisville, KY 40223
Tel.: (502) 499-0855
Fax: (502) 515-9964
Toll Free: (877) 926-7370
Web Site: www.firstsourcesolutions.com
Emp.: 250
Healthcare Revenue Cycle Management Services
S.I.C.: 8721
N.A.I.C.S.: 541219
David Strickler *(CEO)*
Mitzi Winters *(COO)*

Twin Medical Transaction Services, Inc **(1)**
5590 S Fort Apache Rd
Las Vegas, NV 89148
Tel.: (702) 307-8687
Business Process Outsourcing Services
S.I.C.: 8742
N.A.I.C.S.: 541611

FIS INFORMATIONSSYSTEME UND CONSULTING GMBH

Rothleiner Weg 1
97506 Schweinfurt, Germany
Tel.: (49) 972391880
Fax: (49) 97239188100
E-Mail: info@fis-gmbh.de
Web Site: www.fis-gmbh.de
Rev.: $41,922,683
Emp.: 300

Business Description:
Software Maintenance Services
S.I.C.: 7371
N.A.I.C.S.: 541511

Personnel:
Ralf Bernhardt *(Mng Dir)*
Frank Schongarth *(Mng Dir)*

FISCHER AG PRAZISIONSSPINDELN

Birkenweg 2
PO Box 31
3360 Herzogenbuchsee, Switzerland
Tel.: (41) 629562222
Fax: (41) 629568875
E-Mail: fch@fischerprecise.ch
Web Site: www.fischerprecise.com
Sales Range: $25-49.9 Million
Emp.: 300

Business Description:
High-Performance Spindle Mfr for Machine Tools
S.I.C.: 3541
N.A.I.C.S.: 333517

Personnel:
Daniel Schmid *(CEO)*
Martin Hurlimann *(CFO)*

U.S. Subsidiary:

Fischer Precise USA, Inc. **(1)**
3715 Blue River Ave
Racine, WI 53405-4131
Mailing Address:
3715 Blue River Ave
Racine, WI 53405-4131
Tel.: (262) 632-6173
Fax: (262) 632-6730
Toll Free: (800) 333-6173
E-Mail: info@fischerprecise.com
Web Site: www.fischerprecise.com
Emp.: 40
High Speed Spindle Systems for Precision Milling, Drilling & Grinding Applications Import Export
S.I.C.: 3425
N.A.I.C.S.: 332216
Ryan Brath *(Pres)*
Rick Mauldin *(Treas)*

FISCHER GREY LINEA DIRECTA

Avenida Diego Cisnero Edificio Oficentro Piso 3
Los Ruices, Caracas, 1071, Venezuela
Tel.: (58) 212 237 5566
Fax: (58) 212 237 5437
E-Mail: ghersy@ghersy.com.ve
Web Site: www.ghersy.com.ve
Year Founded: 1971
Emp.: 105
S.I.C.: 4731
N.A.I.C.S.: 541611

FISCHER TECH LTD

No 12 Loyang Way 4 Loyang Industrial Estate
Singapore, 507602, Singapore
Tel.: (65) 65422338
Fax: (65) 65423088
E-Mail: admin@mail.fischer.com.sg
Web Site: www.fischer.com.sg
F22—(SES)
Rev.: $107,301,223
Assets: $102,273,110
Liabilities: $36,616,159
Net Worth: $65,656,951
Earnings: $8,334,036
Emp.: 1,900
Fiscal Year-end: 03/31/13

Business Description:
Plastic Components Mfr
S.I.C.: 2899
N.A.I.C.S.: 325199

Personnel:
Choon King Tan *(Founder, Pres & CEO)*
Gordon Chee Bun Tan *(CFO)*
Sheue Ling Chuang *(Co-Sec)*
Ching Chek Tan *(Co-Sec)*

Board of Directors:
Meng Tong Foo
Ono Daisuke
Amos Hong Kiat Leong
James Kok Leng Moy
Boon Yew Ng
Choon King Tan
Kok Leong Tay

Transfer Agent:
Boardroom Corporate & Advisory Services Pte. Ltd.
50 Raffles Place 32-01 Singapore Land Tower
Singapore, Singapore

Subsidiaries:

Fon-Fischer Pte Ltd **(1)**
10 Loyang Way 4
Singapore, Singapore
Tel.: (65) 65424567
Fax: (65) 65424877
E-Mail: general@fon-fischer.com
Web Site: www.fischer.com.sg/g_compan.html
Emp.: 50
Injection Molded Plastic Products Mfr
S.I.C.: 3089
N.A.I.C.S.: 326199
Chien Fu Chen *(Gen Mgr)*

Zeito Plastic Components Pte Ltd **(1)**
10 Loyang Way 4
Singapore, 507603, Singapore
Tel.: (65) 65468628
Fax: (65) 65463832
Emp.: 70
Injection Molded Plastic Products Mfr
S.I.C.: 3089
N.A.I.C.S.: 326199

Non-U.S. Subsidiaries:

Fischer Solution (Suzhou) Co., Ltd. **(1)**
Block C Unit 16 Suzhou New & Hi-tech District Export Processing Zone
No 20 Datong Road SND, Suzhou, Jiangsu, 215151, China
Tel.: (86) 51288606555
Fax: (86) 51288606566
E-Mail: admin@mail.fischer.com.sg
Injection Molded Plastic Products Mfr
S.I.C.: 3082
N.A.I.C.S.: 326121

Fischer Tech (Suzhou) Co., Ltd. **(1)**
No 288 Tang Zhuang Road Loufeng North District
Hi-Tech Development Zone, Suzhou, Jiangsu, 215021, China
Tel.: (86) 51262746288
Fax: (86) 51262746988
Injection Molded Plastic Products Mfr
S.I.C.: 3082
N.A.I.C.S.: 326121

Fischer Tech (Thailand) Co., Ltd. **(1)**
40/7 Moo 5 Rojana Industrial Park Tambol U-Thai
Ampur U-Thai, Ayutthaya, Thailand
Tel.: (66) 35 332088
Fax: (66) 35 332078
E-Mail: admin@mail.fischer.com.sg
Web Site: www.fischer.com.sg/g_compan.html
Injection Molded Plastic Products Mfr
S.I.C.: 3082
N.A.I.C.S.: 326121
Peter Tan *(CEO)*

M-Fischer Tech Sdn Bhd **(1)**
No 31 Jalan Petaling Kawasan Perindustrian Larkin, 80350 Johor Bahru, Johor, Malaysia
Tel.: (60) 72381648
Fax: (60) 72387599
Web Site: www.fischer.com.sg/g_compan.html
Emp.: 580
Injection Molded Plastic Products Mfr
S.I.C.: 3082
N.A.I.C.S.: 326121

FISCHERWERKE GMBH & CO. KG

Weinhalde 14-18
72178 Waldachtal, Germany
Tel.: (49) 7 44 31 26 000
Fax: (49) 7 44 31 24 500
Web Site: www.fischer.de
Sales Range: $800-899.9 Million
Emp.: 3,900

Business Description:
Holding Company
S.I.C.: 6719
N.A.I.C.S.: 551112

Personnel:
Klaus Fischer *(CEO)*

Subsidiaries:

fischer automotive systems GmbH & Co. KG **(1)**
Industriestrasse 103
72160 Horb am Neckar, Germany
Tel.: (49) 74 43 12 55 00
E-Mail: info@fischer-automotive-systems.de
Web Site: www.fischer-automotive-systems.de
Motor Vehicle Interior Component Mfr
S.I.C.: 2396
N.A.I.C.S.: 336360
Andreas Gerecke *(Pres)*

U.S. Subsidiary:

fischer America Inc. **(2)**
1084 Doris Rd
Auburn Hills, MI 48326 MD
Tel.: (248) 276-1940
Fax: (248) 276-1941
E-Mail: info@fischerus.com
Web Site: www.fischerus.com
Emp.: 170
Motor Vehicle Interior Component Mfr
S.I.C.: 2396
N.A.I.C.S.: 336360
Bruce Birgbauer *(Sec)*

fischer Consulting GmbH **(1)**
Weinhalde 14-18
72178 Waldachtal, Germany
Tel.: (49) 7443 12 0
Fax: (49) 7443 12 83 00
Management Consulting Services
S.I.C.: 8748
N.A.I.C.S.: 541618

fischertechnik GmbH **(1)**
Weinhalde 14-18
72178 Waldachtal, Germany
Tel.: (49) 7443 12 0
Fax: (49) 7443 12 4591
E-Mail: info@fischertechnik.de
Web Site: www.fischertechnik.de
Toy Mfr
S.I.C.: 3944
N.A.I.C.S.: 339930

FISHER & PAYKEL HEALTHCARE CORPORATION LIMITED

15 Maurice Paykel Place
East Tamaki, Auckland, 2013, New Zealand
Mailing Address:
PO Box 14 348
Panmure, Auckland, 1741, New Zealand
Tel.: (64) 95740100
Fax: (64) 95740158
E-Mail: info@fphcare.com
Web Site: www.fphcare.com
FPH—(NZE OTC)
Rev.: $465,581,250
Assets: $517,765,689
Liabilities: $206,208,342
Net Worth: $311,557,347
Earnings: $64,493,361
Emp.: 2,758
Fiscal Year-end: 03/31/13
Business Description:
Medical Device Mfr
S.I.C.: 3841
N.A.I.C.S.: 339112
Personnel:
Michael G. Daniell *(CEO & Mng Dir)*
Antony G. Barclay *(CFO & Sec)*
Lewis G. Gradon *(Sr VP-Products & Tech)*
Paul N. Shearer *(Sr VP-Sls & Mktg)*
Board of Directors:
Tony Carter
Michael G. Daniell
Nigel T. Evans
Roger France
W. Lindsay Gillanders
Geraldine Celia McBride
Arthur J. Morris
Donal O'Dwyer
Gary A. Paykel

LINK Market Services Limited
Level 12 680 George Street
Sydney, Australia

Subsidiary:

Fisher & Paykel Healthcare Properties Limited (1)
15 Maurice Paykel Place East Tamaki
Auckland, 2013, New Zealand
Tel.: (64) 95740100
Fax: (64) 95740197
Web Site: www.fphcare.com
Emp.: 200
Health Care Products Mfr
S.I.C.: 2834
N.A.I.C.S.: 325412
Michaell Daniell *(CEO)*

U.S. Subsidiary:

Fisher & Paykel Healthcare Inc. (1)
15365 Barranca Pkwy
Irvine, CA 92618
Tel.: (949) 453-4000
Fax: (949) 453-4001
Toll Free: (800) 446-3908
E-Mail: information@fphcare.com
Web Site: www.fphcare.com
Emp.: 50
Medical Device Mfr
S.I.C.: 3841
N.A.I.C.S.: 339112
Justin Callahan *(Pres)*

Non-U.S. Subsidiaries:

Fisher & Paykel do Brasil Ltda (1)
Prca Isabel 408
Sao Paulo, 09310-010, Brazil
Tel.: (55) 1145411529
Marketing Consulting Services
S.I.C.: 8742
N.A.I.C.S.: 541613
Francisco Ortega *(Gen Mgr)*

Fisher & Paykel Healthcare AB (1)
Spjutvagen 6
17561 Jarfalla, Sweden
Tel.: (46) 856476680
Fax: (46) 8366310
E-Mail: info@fphcare.se
Web Site: www.fphcare.it
Emp.: 8
Medical Device Mfr
S.I.C.: 3841
N.A.I.C.S.: 339112
Permella Eriksson *(Mgr-Sls)*

Fisher & Paykel Healthcare Asia Limited (1)
10F 1 No 61 and 10F No 69 Jhozih Street
Neihu, Taipei, 114, Taiwan
Tel.: (886) 2 8751 1739
Fax: (886) 2 8751 5625
Web Site: www.fphcare.com
Investment Management Services
S.I.C.: 6211
N.A.I.C.S.: 523999

Fisher & Paykel Healthcare GmbH & Co. KG (1)
Wiesenstrasse 49
73614 Schorndorf, Germany
Tel.: (49) 718198599
Fax: (49) 71819859966
E-Mail: info@fphcare.de
Medical Device Mfr
S.I.C.: 3841
N.A.I.C.S.: 339112

Fisher & Paykel Healthcare (Guangzhou) Limited (1)
F301 11 Caipin Lu Guangzhou Science City
Guangzhou Hi-Tech Industrial, 510663
Guangzhou, China
Tel.: (86) 2032053486
Fax: (86) 2032052132
E-Mail: info@fphcare.cn
Web Site: www.fphcare.com
Emp.: 30
Medical Device Mfr
S.I.C.: 3841
N.A.I.C.S.: 339112

Fisher & Paykel Healthcare India Private Limited (1)
339/1 3rd A Cross Road HIG A Sector 2nd Stage Extension
Yelahanka New Town, Bengaluru, 560064, India
Tel.: (91) 80 4284 4000
Fax: (91) 80 4123 6044
E-Mail: info@fphcare.in
Healthcare Devices Distr
S.I.C.: 5047
N.A.I.C.S.: 423450
Thekkanathu Paily Bastin *(Gen Mgr)*

Fisher & Paykel Healthcare K.K. (1)
Libera Kayaba cho Bldg 5th Fl
3 8 10 Nihonbashi Kayaba cho, Tokyo, Japan
Tel.: (81) 336617205
Fax: (81) 336617206
E-Mail: info@fphcare.co.jp
Web Site: www.fphcare.co.jp/contact/
Emp.: 38
Medical Device Mfr
S.I.C.: 3841
N.A.I.C.S.: 339112
Kokichi Kipahara *(Pres)*

Fisher & Paykel Healthcare Limited (1)
2045 Blvd Dagenais O Ste 180
Laval, QC, H7L 5V1, Canada
Tel.: (949) 453-4000
Fax: (450) 622-4562
Toll Free: (800) 446-3908
E-Mail: information@fphcare.com
Medical Equipment Distr
S.I.C.: 5047
N.A.I.C.S.: 423450

Fisher & Paykel Healthcare Limited (1)
339 1 HIG A Sector 2nd Stage Extension
Yelahanka New Town, Bengaluru, 560064, India
Tel.: (91) 8041236041
Fax: (91) 8041236044
E-Mail: sales.india@fphcare.com
Emp.: 50
Medical Device Mfr
S.I.C.: 3841
N.A.I.C.S.: 339112
D. B. Basbin *(Gen Mgr)*

Fisher & Paykel Healthcare Limited (1)
Unit 802-5 Delta House 3 On Yiu Street Siu Lek Yuen
Sha Tin, New Territories, China (Hong Kong)
Tel.: (852) 2116 0032
Fax: (852) 2116 0085
E-Mail: info@fphcare.com.hk
Medical Equipment Mfr
S.I.C.: 3845
N.A.I.C.S.: 334510

Fisher & Paykel Healthcare Limited (1)
Unit 16 Cordwallis Park Clivemont Rd
Maidenhead, Berkshire, SL6 7BU, United Kingdom
Tel.: (44) 1628626136
Fax: (44) 1628626146
E-Mail: info@fphcare.co.uk
Web Site: www.fphcare.com
Emp.: 50
Medical Device Mfr
S.I.C.: 3841
N.A.I.C.S.: 339112
Nicholas Connolly *(Gen Mgr)*

Fisher & Paykel Healthcare Pty. Limited (1)
36 40 New Street
PO Box 167
Ringwood, Melbourne, VIC, 3134, Australia
Tel.: (61) 398795022
Fax: (61) 398795232
E-Mail: info@fphcare.co.au
Web Site: www.fphcare.com
Emp.: 25
Medical Device Mfr
S.I.C.: 3841
N.A.I.C.S.: 339112
David Boyle *(CEO)*

Fisher & Paykel Healthcare SAS (1)
10 Avenue du Quebec Batiment F5
Silic 512 Villebon s Yvette, 91946
Courtaboeuf, Cedex, France
Tel.: (33) 164465201
Fax: (33) 164465221
E-Mail: info@fphcare.co.fr
Web Site: www.fphcare.fr/contact/
Emp.: 70
Medical Device Mfr
S.I.C.: 3841
N.A.I.C.S.: 339112
Patrick McSweeny *(Mng Dir)*

Fisher & Paykel Holdings GmbH (1)
Wiesenstr 49
73614 Schorndorf, Germany
Tel.: (49) 7181 985990
Fax: (49) 7181 9859966
Investment Management Services
S.I.C.: 6211
N.A.I.C.S.: 523999

FISHER OUTDOOR LEISURE LIMITED

8/9 Brick Knoll Park Ashley Road
Saint Albans, AL1 5UG, United Kingdom
Tel.: (44) 1727798340
Web Site: www.fisheroutdoor.co.uk
Year Founded: 1934
Rev.: $29,143,978
Emp.: 83
Business Description:
Cycle &Accessories Distr
S.I.C.: 5091
N.A.I.C.S.: 423910
Personnel:
Richard Allmark *(CEO)*

FISHERMAN'S MARKET INTERNATIONAL INC.

607 Bedford Highway
Halifax, NS, B3M 2L6, Canada
Tel.: (902) 443-3474
Fax: (902) 445-3474
E-Mail: retail@fishermansmarket.com
Web Site: www.fishermansmarket.ca
Year Founded: 1948
Rev.: $26,889,270
Emp.: 100
Business Description:
Seafood Supplier & Whslr
S.I.C.: 2092
N.A.I.C.S.: 311710
Personnel:
Fred Greene *(Pres)*

FISHERS SERVICES LTD.

Home Street
London, PH15 2AL, United Kingdom
Tel.: (44) 1887820491
Web Site: www.fisherservices.co.uk/
Year Founded: 1900
Sales Range: $25-49.9 Million
Emp.: 600
Business Description:
Linens & Commercial Service
Workwear Rental & Laundry Services
S.I.C.: 7359
N.A.I.C.S.: 532299
Personnel:
Bruce McHardy *(Grp Mng Dir)*

FISHERS STORES CONSOLIDATED PTY. LTD.

100 106 Commercial St
Merbein, Mildura, Victoria, 3505, Australia
Tel.: (61) 350218300
Fax: (61) 350218350
E-Mail: office@fishers.com.au
Web Site: www.fishers.com.au
Sales Range: $50-74.9 Million
Emp.: 600
Business Description:
Supermarket Services
S.I.C.: 5411
N.A.I.C.S.: 445110
Personnel:
Alan Fisher *(Mng Dir)*

FISKARS OYJ ABP

Hameentie 135A
PO Box 130
FI-00561 Helsinki, Finland
Tel.: (358) 204 3910
Fax: (358) 9604 053
E-Mail: info@fiskars.fi
Web Site: www.fiskarsgroup.com
Year Founded: 1649
FIS1V—(HEL)
Sls.: $1,006,665,926
Assets: $1,259,207,418
Liabilities: $426,062,805
Net Worth: $833,144,613
Earnings: $240,829,813
Emp.: 3,449
Fiscal Year-end: 12/31/12
Business Description:
Cutlery, Garden Equipment, Hand Tool & Housewares Mfr
Import Export
S.I.C.: 3425
N.A.I.C.S.: 332216
Personnel:
Kaj-Gustaf Bergh *(Chm)*
Alexander Ehrnrooth *(Vice Chm)*
Paul Ehrnrooth *(Vice Chm)*
Kari Kauniskangas *(Pres, CEO & Member-Exec Bd)*
Ilkka Pitkanen *(CFO & Member-Exec Bd)*
Frans Westerlund *(CIO)*
Max Alfthan *(Chief Strategy Officer & Member-Exec Bd)*
Thomas Enckell *(Pres-Garden-EMEA)*
Axel Goss *(Pres-Sls-EMEA Central)*
Jakob Hagerstrom *(Pres-Sls-North)*
Teemu Kangas-Karki *(Pres-Home)*
Jason R. Landmark *(Pres-Outdoor-Americas)*

Fiskars Oyj Abp—(Continued)

Juha Lehtola *(Pres-Boats)*
Paul Tonnesen *(Pres-Garden & SOC-Americas)*
Jutta Karlsson *(Member-Exec Bd & Gen Counsel)*
Risto Gaggl *(Member-Exec Bd & Sr VP-Supply Chain)*

Board of Directors:
Kaj-Gustaf Bergh
Ralf Reinhard Boer
Alexander Ehrnrooth
Paul Ehrnrooth
Louise Fromond
Gustaf Gripenberg
Ingrid Jonasson-Blank
Karsten Slotte
Jukka Suominen

Subsidiaries:

Fiskars Americas Holding Oy Ab **(1)**
Hameentie 135
560 Helsinki, Finland
Tel.: (358) 204 3910
Fax: (358) 9 604 053
Investment Management Services
S.I.C.: 6211
N.A.I.C.S.: 523999

Non-U.S. Subsidiary:

Fiskars (Thailand) Co., Limited **(2)**
29 Soi Chidlom Phloen Chit Road
Pathum Wan, Bangkok, 10330, Thailand
Tel.: (66) 26552214
Fax: (66) 26552214
Web Site: www.fiskars.com
Household Glass Product Mfr
S.I.C.: 3231
N.A.I.C.S.: 327215

Fiskars Brands Oy AB **(1)**
PO Box 10330
Billnas, Finland (100%)
Tel.: (358) 19277721
Fax: (358) 19232210
E-Mail: info@fiskars.fi
Web Site: www.fiskars.com
Sls.: $78,893,776
Emp.: 500
S.I.C.: 5551
N.A.I.C.S.: 441222
Thomas Enckell *(Mng Dir)*

Subsidiary:

Inha Works Oy AB **(2)**
Saarikylantie 21
63700 Ahtari, Finland (100%)
Tel.: (358) 65355111
Fax: (358) 65334125
E-Mail: info@inha.fi
Web Site: www.inha.fi
Sales Range: $25-49.9 Million
Emp.: 250
Manufacturers of Consumer Products & Aluminum Boats
S.I.C.: 3536
N.A.I.C.S.: 333923
Juha Lehtola *(Mng Dir)*

Fiskars Europe Holding Oy Ab **(1)**
Hameentie 135
00560 Helsinki, Finland
Tel.: (358) 20 43 910
Investment Management Services
S.I.C.: 6211
N.A.I.C.S.: 523999
Kari Kauniskangas *(Gen Mgr)*

Non-U.S. Subsidiaries:

Excalibur Management Consulting (Shanghai) Co., Ltd. **(2)**
21st Floor Middle East Building 1219 Zhenguang Road
Putou District, Shanghai, 200333, China
Tel.: (86) 21 626 516 87
Fax: (86) 52827136
Web Site: www.fiskarsgroup.com
Emp.: 5
Business Management Consulting Services
S.I.C.: 8742
N.A.I.C.S.: 541611
Ryoichi Amino *(Gen Mgr)*

Fiskars Denmark A/S **(2)**
Vestre Ringvej 45
PO Box 360
8600 Silkeborg, Denmark
Tel.: (45) 8720 1100
Fax: (45) 8681 5968
E-Mail: fiskars@fiskars.com
Emp.: 80
Gardening Equipment Mfr & Distr
S.I.C.: 3524
N.A.I.C.S.: 333112
Preben Jensen *(Gen Mgr)*

Fiskars Germany GmbH **(2)**
Oststrasse 23
32051 Herford, Germany
Tel.: (49) 5221 935 0
Fax: (49) 5221 935 199
E-Mail: info.garten@fiskars.com
Web Site: www.fiskarsgroup.com
Emp.: 15
Gardening Tool Mfr & Distr
S.I.C.: 3524
N.A.I.C.S.: 333112
Jan Witt *(Mng Dir)*

Fiskars Italy S.r.l. **(2)**
Via Provinciale 15
23862 Civate, Lecco, Italy
Tel.: (39) 0341 215 111
Fax: (39) 0341 551 654
E-Mail: civ-mailbox@fiskars.com
Web Site: www.fiskarsgroup.com
Garden Machinery Mfr & Distr
S.I.C.: 3524
N.A.I.C.S.: 333112

Fiskars Norway AS **(2)**
Nydalsveien 32 B
Postboks 4215
Nydalen, 401 Oslo, Norway
Tel.: (47) 23 00 64 40
Fax: (47) 23 00 64 50
E-Mail: epost@fiskars.com
Emp.: 35
Home & Garden Tool Distr
S.I.C.: 5083
N.A.I.C.S.: 423820
Calle Kaas *(Gen Mgr)*

Fiskars Poland Sp. z.o.o. **(2)**
Biuro Handlowe Ul Marywilska 22
03-228 Warsaw, Poland
Tel.: (48) 22 676 0400
Fax: (48) 22 676 0404
E-Mail: warsaw.office@fiskarspolska.pl
Emp.: 15
Gardening Equipment Mfr & Distr
S.I.C.: 3524
N.A.I.C.S.: 333112
Wioletta Skoneczny *(Mgr-Sls & Mktg)*

Fiskars Spain S.L. **(2)**
Isabel Colbrand 6 5a Planta
28050 Madrid, Spain
Tel.: (34) 91 344 67 03
Fax: (34) 902 999 995
Household Kitchen Tool Distr
S.I.C.: 5072
N.A.I.C.S.: 423710
Jose Luis Gallego *(Gen Mgr)*

ZAO Fiskars Brands Rus **(2)**
Office 5/1 Building 93A Obvodniy Canal
Saint Petersburg, Russia 191119
Tel.: (7) 812 320 4323
Fax: (7) 812 320 4323
E-Mail: sales@fiskarsbrands.com
Web Site: www.fiskarsgroup.com
Emp.: 100
Household Tools Distr
S.I.C.: 5072
N.A.I.C.S.: 423710
Evgeny Voronkin *(Gen Mgr)*

Fiskars Real Estate **(1)**
Fiskarsintie 18
10470 Fiskars, Finland (100%)
Tel.: (358) 192771
Fax: (358) 192777630
E-Mail: info@fiskars.fi
Web Site: www.fiskars.com
Sales Range: $1-9.9 Million
Emp.: 20
S.I.C.: 5551
N.A.I.C.S.: 441222
Kimmo Hakkala *(Mgr-Sls & Mktg)*

Fiskars Services Oy Ab **(1)**
Hameentie 135
00560 Helsinki, Finland
Tel.: (358) 20 43 910
Fax: (358) 20 439 5717
Financial & Accounting Services
S.I.C.: 8721
N.A.I.C.S.: 541219
Kari Kauniskangas *(Pres)*

Iittala Group Oy Ab **(1)**
Hameentie 135
PO Box 130
00561 Helsinki, Finland
Tel.: (358) 204 3910
Fax: (358) 204 39 5180
Web Site: www.iittala.com
Emp.: 120
Household Glass Utensils Mfr & Distr
S.I.C.: 3231
N.A.I.C.S.: 327215
Teemu Kangas-Kaerki *(Gen Mgr)*

Plants:

Fiskars Oyj Abp - Arabia porcelain Factory **(1)**
Hameentie 135
PO Box 130
00561 Helsinki, Finland
Tel.: (358) 204 39 10
Fax: (358) 204 39 5180
Web Site: www.fiskarsgroup.com
Emp.: 150
Porcelain Electrical Products Mfr
S.I.C.: 3269
N.A.I.C.S.: 327110
Mira Yavuz *(Mng Dir)*

Fiskars Oyj Abp - Iittala glass Factory **(1)**
Tehtaantie 3
14500 Iittala, Finland
Tel.: (358) 204 39 10
Fax: (358) 204 39 6283
Glass Products Mfr
S.I.C.: 3231
N.A.I.C.S.: 327215

Fiskars Oyj Abp - Nuutajarvi glass Factory **(1)**
Hameentie 135a
561 Helsinki, Finland
Tel.: (358) 204 39 10
Fax: (358) 204 39 6550
Glass Products Mfr
S.I.C.: 3231
N.A.I.C.S.: 327215

Inha Works Ltd. **(1)**
Saarikylantie 21
FIN 63700 Ahtari, Finland (100%)
Tel.: (358) 65355111
Fax: (358) 65334125
E-Mail: info@fiskars.com
Web Site: www.inha.fi
Emp.: 40
Mfr. of Aluminum Motor Boats, Special-Purpose Radiators for Bathrooms & Other Humid Rooms & Rail Fasteners & Fitting Components
S.I.C.: 3732
N.A.I.C.S.: 336612
Juha Lehtola *(Mng Dir)*

U.S. Subsidiaries:

EnviroWorks, Inc. **(1)**
3000 Orange Ave
Apopka, FL 32703-3347
Tel.: (407) 889-5533
Fax: (407) 889-3063
Web Site: www.enviroworks.com
S.I.C.: 5551
N.A.I.C.S.: 441222

Fiskars Brands, Inc. **(1)**
2537 Daniels St
Madison, WI 53718 (100%)
Tel.: (608) 259-1649
Fax: (608) 294-4790
Toll Free: (866) 348-5661
E-Mail: socconsumeraffairs@fiskars.com
Web Site: www.fiskars.com
Emp.: 250
Scissors, Cutlery, Sporting Goods & Garden Shears Mfr
S.I.C.: 3421
N.A.I.C.S.: 332215
Rich Walker *(VP-HR)*

Divisions:

Fiskars Brands, Inc. **(2)**
2537 Daniels St
Madison, WI 53718 (100%)
Tel.: (715) 842-2091
Fax: (628) 294-4790
Web Site: www.fiskars.com
Emp.: 80
Mfr. of Scissors
S.I.C.: 3423
N.A.I.C.S.: 332216
Paul Tonnesen *(Pres-America)*

Fiskars Garden & Outdoor Living **(2)**
780 Carolina St
Sauk City, WI 53583-1369 (100%)
Tel.: (608) 643-2380
Fax: (608) 294-4790
Toll Free: (800) 500-4849
Web Site: www.fiskars.com
Emp.: 300
Consumer Gardening & Landscaping Tools Mfr
S.I.C.: 5083
N.A.I.C.S.: 423820
Jason Landmark *(Pres-Outdoor Living)*
Paul Tonnesen *(Pres-Garden)*

Gerber Legendary Blades **(2)**
14200 SW 72nd Ave
Portland, OR 97224
Mailing Address:
14200 SW 72nd Ave
Portland, OR 97224-8010
Tel.: (503) 639-6161
Fax: (503) 403-1102
Toll Free: (800) 950-6161
E-Mail: sales@gerberblades.com
Web Site: www.gerberblades.com
Emp.: 150
Mfr. of Sportsmens Knives, Multi Function Tools & Outdoor Recreational Products Import Export
S.I.C.: 3421
N.A.I.C.S.: 332215
Jason Landmark *(Pres)*

Fiskars Outdoor Leisure Products **(1)**
3000 Orange Ave
Apopka, FL 32703-3347
Tel.: (407) 889-5533
Fax: (407) 889-3063
Web Site: www.fiskars.com
Emp.: 200
S.I.C.: 5551
N.A.I.C.S.: 441222
Kathy Ford *(VP)*

Non-U.S. Subsidiaries:

Fiskars Brands Germany GmbH **(1)**
Oststrasse 23
D 32051 Herford, Germany
Tel.: (49) 52219350
Fax: (49) 5221935199
E-Mail: info@fiskars.de
Web Site: www.fiskars.de
Emp.: 130
Manufacturers of Aluminum Boats
S.I.C.: 3536
N.A.I.C.S.: 333923

Fiskars Brands Hungary Ltd. **(1)**
Chillagheghye 13
1037 Budapest, Hungary (100%)
Tel.: (36) 14530945
Fax: (36) 14532375
E-Mail: fiskars@fiskars.hu
Web Site: www.fiskars.hu
Emp.: 11
S.I.C.: 5551
N.A.I.C.S.: 441222
Peter Kovocs *(Mng Dir)*

Fiskars Brands Italy S.r.L. **(1)**
Via Provinciale 15
I 23862 Civate, LC, Italy (100%)
Tel.: (39) 0341215111
Fax: (39) 341551654
E-Mail: civ-mailbox@fiskars.com
Web Site: www.fiskars.it
Emp.: 150
Consumer Products Sales
S.I.C.: 5099
N.A.I.C.S.: 423990
Pietro Misto *(Gen Mgr)*

Fiskars Brands Pty. Ltd. **(1)**
39-41 Fennell St
Port Melbourne, VIC, 3207, Australia (100%)
Tel.: (61) 386452400
Fax: (61) 396461722

E-Mail: autralia@fiskars.com
Web Site: www.fiskars.com
Emp.: 13
Consumer Products Sales
S.I.C.: 5099
N.A.I.C.S.: 423990
Shayne Coyne *(Mng Dir)*

Fiskars Canada Inc. **(1)**
275 Renfrew Dr
675 Pochrane Dr, Markham, ON, L3R0B8, Canada (100%)
Tel.: (905) 940-8460
Fax: (905) 940-8469
Web Site: www.fiskars.com
Emp.: 12
Distributors of Scissors
S.I.C.: 3999
N.A.I.C.S.: 332215
Susan Soochit *(Mng Dir)*

Fiskars Danmark A/S **(1)**
Vestre Ringvej 45
8600 Silkeborg, Denmark (100%)
Mailing Address:
Postbox 360
DK-8600 Silkeborg, Denmark
Tel.: (45) 87201100
Fax: (45) 86815968
E-Mail: info@fiskars.com
Web Site: www.fiskars.com
Emp.: 65
Manufacturers of Consumer Products & Aluminum Boats
S.I.C.: 3536
N.A.I.C.S.: 333923
Preben Jensen *(Gen Mgr)*

Fiskars Estonia AS **(1)**
Parnu Mnt 154
11317 Tallinn, Estonia
Tel.: (372) 650 0749
Fax: (372) 650 0762
Web Site: www.fiskarsgroup.com
Emp.: 4
Household Utensils & Appliance Distr
S.I.C.: 5023
N.A.I.C.S.: 423220
Anu Hannikainen *(Mng Dir)*

Fiskars France S.A.R.L. **(1)**
3 Ave Jeanne Garnerin
91320 Wissous, France (100%)
Tel.: (33) 169751515
Fax: (33) 169751518
Web Site: www.fiskars.com
Emp.: 50
Manufacturers of Aluminum Boats
S.I.C.: 3536
N.A.I.C.S.: 333923
Philippe Hernandez *(Mng Dir)*

Fiskars Norge A/S **(1)**
Nydalsveien 32 B
Oslo, 4815, Norway (100%)
Mailing Address:
Postboks 4215 Torshov
N-0401 Oslo, 4, Norway
Tel.: (47) 23006440
Fax: (47) 23006450
E-Mail: epost@fiskars.com
Web Site: www.fiskars.com
Sales Range: $1-9.9 Million
Emp.: 40
Manufacturers of Consumer Products & Aluminum Boats
S.I.C.: 3536
N.A.I.C.S.: 333923

Fiskars Poland Ltd. **(1)**
Ul Marywilska 22
PL-03-228 Warsaw, Poland
Tel.: (48) 226760400
Fax: (48) 226760404
E-Mail: warsaw.office@fiskars.com
Web Site: www.fiskars.com
Emp.: 250
S.I.C.: 5551
N.A.I.C.S.: 441222
Sylwester Dmowski *(Gen Mgr)*

Fiskars Sweden AB **(1)**
Norregatan 4
PO Box 23
263 21 Hoganas, Sweden (100%)
Tel.: (46) 42361100
Fax: (46) 42349823
E-Mail: info@fiskars.se
Web Site: www.fiskars.se
Emp.: 30
Consumer Products Sales
S.I.C.: 5099
N.A.I.C.S.: 423990
Jakob Hagerstrom *(Pres-Sls Reg-North)*

iittala BV **(1)**
Hoevestein 19
PO Box 474
4900 AL Oosterhout, Netherlands
Tel.: (31) 162 488 188
Fax: (31) 162 488 180
E-Mail: shop.amsterdam@iittala.com
Web Site: www.iittala.com
Emp.: 20
Household Glassware Distr
S.I.C.: 5023
N.A.I.C.S.: 423220
Jean Jongejan *(Gen Mgr)*

iittala BVBA **(1)**
Korte Gasthuisstraat 24
2000 Antwerp, Belgium
Tel.: (32) 3 213 2517
Fax: (32) 3 213 2518
E-Mail: shop.antwerpen@iittala.com
Web Site: www.iittala.com
Emp.: 7
Household Appliances Retailer
S.I.C.: 5722
N.A.I.C.S.: 443141
David Peter *(Mgr-Store)*

iittala GmbH **(1)**
Ober Der Muhle 6
Solingen, Nordrhein-Westfalen, 42699, Germany
Tel.: (49) 212546960
Fax: (49) 10 5469646
E-Mail: shop.hamburg@iittala.com
Glass Products Distr
S.I.C.: 5199
N.A.I.C.S.: 424310

Richard Sankey & Son Ltd. **(1)**
Bennerley Rd
Bulwell, Nottingham, NG6 8PE, United Kingdom (100%)
Tel.: (44) 1159 277335
Fax: (44) 1159 770197
E-Mail: ukinfo@fiskars.com
Web Site: www.rsankey.com
Emp.: 75
Mfr of Garden Products
S.I.C.: 3524
N.A.I.C.S.: 333112

Royal Copenhagen A/S **(1)**
Smedeland 17
DK-2600 Glostrup, Denmark DK (100%)
Tel.: (45) 38144848
Fax: (45) 38149900
E-Mail: customerservice@royalcopenhagen.com
Web Site: corporate.royalcopenhagen.com
Emp.: 500
Retail Sales of Porcelain, Silver & Glass
S.I.C.: 3999
N.A.I.C.S.: 327110
Anne Wehner *(Head-Comm)*

Unit:

Royal Copenhagen Flagship Store **(2)**
Amagertorv 6
DK 1160 Copenhagen, Denmark
Tel.: (45) 38149605
E-Mail: flagshipstore@royalcopenhagen.com
Web Site: www.royalcopenhagen.com
Emp.: 200
Retail Sales of Glassware
S.I.C.: 3211
N.A.I.C.S.: 327211

Werga-Tools GmbH **(1)**
Oststrasse 23
D 32051 Herford, Germany (100%)
Tel.: (49) 522176360
Fax: (49) 5221935199
Web Site: www.fiskars.de
Emp.: 130
Manufacturers of Consumer Products & Aluminum Boats
S.I.C.: 3536
N.A.I.C.S.: 333923
Jan Wigg *(Dir)*

ZAO Baltic Tool **(1)**
Obvodniy Canal 93A of 5/1
RUS-191119 Saint Petersburg, Russia
Tel.: (7) 8125670901
Fax: (7) 812 320 4323
Web Site: www.fiskars.it/Etutti.html
S.I.C.: 5551
N.A.I.C.S.: 441222

FISKEBY INTERNATIONAL HOLDING AB

Fiskeby Road 1
PO Box 1
SE-601 02 Norrkoping, Sweden
Tel.: (46) 11155700
Web Site: www.fiskeby.com
Year Founded: 2007

Business Description:
Holding Company; Packaging Board Mfr
S.I.C.: 6719
N.A.I.C.S.: 551112

Personnel:
Jeffrey H. Coors *(Chm)*
Torbjorn Hansen *(CEO)*

Subsidiary:

Fiskeby Board AB **(1)**
Fiskebyvagen 100
PO Box 1
SE 601 02 Norrkoping, Sweden SE (100%)
Tel.: (46) 1115 5700
Fax: (46) 1115 5995
E-Mail: anders.nyren@fiskeby.com
Web Site: www.fiskeby.com
Sales Range: $75-99.9 Million
Emp.: 300
Packaging Board Mfr
S.I.C.: 2631
N.A.I.C.S.: 322130
Torbjorn Hansen *(CEO)*

FISSION 3.0 CORP.

700 1620 Dickson Avenue
Kelowna, BC, V1Y 9Y2, Canada
Tel.: (250) 868-8140
Fax: (250) 868-8493
E-Mail: info@fission3corp.com
Web Site: www.fission3corp.com
Year Founded: 2013
FUU—(TSXV)

Business Description:
Uranium Mining
S.I.C.: 1094
N.A.I.C.S.: 212291

Personnel:
Dev Randhawa *(Chm & CEO)*
Ross McElroy *(Pres & COO)*

Board of Directors:
Dev Randhawa
Frank Estergaard
William V. Marsh
Ross McElroy
Jeremy Ross

FISSION ENERGY CORP.

(Acquired & Absorbed by Denison Mines Corp.)

FISSION ENERGY LIMITED

(Name Changed to Conico Limited)

FISSION URANIUM CORP.

700 1620 Dickson Avenue
Kelowna, BC, V1Y 9Y2, Canada
Tel.: (250) 868-8140
Fax: (250) 868-8493
E-Mail: ir@fissionuranium.com
Web Site: www.fissionuranium.com
Year Founded: 2013
FCU—(OTC TSXV)

Business Description:
Uranium Exploration
S.I.C.: 1094
N.A.I.C.S.: 212291

Personnel:
Devinder Randhawa *(Chm & CEO)*
Ross E. McElroy *(Pres & COO)*
Gregory Downey *(CFO)*

Board of Directors:
Devinder Randhawa
Frank Estergaard
Ross E. McElroy
Jeremy T. Ross

Legal Counsel:
David G. Ashby Law Corp.
700 - 595 Howe St
Vancouver, BC, Canada

Transfer Agent:
Computershare Trust Company of Canada
9th Floor 100 University Avenue
Toronto, ON, Canada

F.I.T. INVESTMENT JSC

17 The Giao Street Le Dai Hanh Ward
Hai Ba Trung District, Hanoi, Vietnam
Tel.: (84) 4 35430005
Web Site: www.fitgroup.com.vn
FIT—(HNX)

Business Description:
Investment Services
S.I.C.: 6211
N.A.I.C.S.: 523999

Personnel:
Nguyet Thi Minh Nguyen *(Gen Mgr)*

FITBUG HOLDINGS PLC

1st Floor Waterside House 47-49 Kentish Town Road
London, NW1 8NX, United Kingdom
Tel.: (44) 2074491000
Fax: (44) 2074494950
Web Site: www.fitbugholdings.com
FITB—(AIM)
Rev.: $2,106,773
Assets: $2,209,427
Liabilities: $3,573,933
Net Worth: ($1,364,507)
Earnings: ($2,329,453)
Emp.: 22
Fiscal Year-end: 12/31/12

Business Description:
Online Health & Wellness Coaching Services
S.I.C.: 7389
N.A.I.C.S.: 519190

Personnel:
Fergus Alexander Kee *(Chm)*
David Turner *(CEO)*
Andrew J. Brummer *(Sec & Dir-Fin)*

Board of Directors:
Fergus Alexander Kee
Andrew J. Brummer
Allan Fisher
Paul Landau
Geoffrey Simmonds
David Turner

Legal Counsel:
HowardKennedyFsi LLP
179 Great Portland Street
London, W1W 5LS, United Kingdom

Finers Stephens Innocent LLP
179 Great Portland Street
London, W1W 5LS, United Kingdom

FITTEC INTERNATIONAL GROUP LIMITED

Unit 2B - 9/F Yuen Long Trading Centre 33 Wang Yip Street West
Yuen Long, Hong Kong, New Territories, China (Hong Kong)
Tel.: (852) 24549840
Fax: (852) 24549868
E-Mail: info@fittec.com.hk
Web Site: www.fittec.com.hk
2662—(HKG)
Rev.: $150,698,965
Assets: $126,059,328
Liabilities: $17,604,254
Net Worth: $108,455,074
Earnings: ($6,131,186)
Emp.: 3,624

Fittec International Group Limited—(Continued)

Fiscal Year-end: 06/30/13

Business Description:
Printed Circuit Board Mfr
S.I.C.: 3672
N.A.I.C.S.: 334412
Personnel:
Chi Ho Lam *(Founder & Chm)*
Michael Yiu Leung Cheung *(Sec)*
Board of Directors:
Chi Ho Lam
Jimmy Wai Kwok Chung
Mi Li Sun
Wing King Tam
Tadao Tsuji
Bai Quan Xie

Computershare Hong Kong Investor Services Limited
17M Floor Hopewell Centre 183 Queen's Road East
Wanchai, China (Hong Kong)

FITTERS DIVERSIFIED BERHAD

No 1 Jalan Tembaga SD 5/2 Bandar Sri Damansara
52200 Kuala Lumpur, Malaysia
Tel.: (60) 362767155
Fax: (60) 362758692
E-Mail: fdb@fittersgroup.com
Web Site: www.fittersgroup.com
FITTERS—(KLS)
Rev.: $134,740,965
Assets: $115,322,541
Liabilities: $41,845,311
Net Worth: $73,477,230
Earnings: $9,202,639
Fiscal Year-end: 12/31/12

Business Description:
Fire Safety Materials & Equipment
S.I.C.: 3494
N.A.I.C.S.: 332919
Personnel:
Richard Swee Yee Wong *(Mng Dir)*
Yim Kong Ng *(Sec)*
Board of Directors:
Mohammad Nizar Idris
Hooi Yin Goh
Sin Seng Kong
Keng Kok Low
Zahedi Mohd Zain
Chai Hock Soh
Richard Swee Yee Wong

Subsidiaries:

FITTERS (Ipoh) Sdn Bhd **(1)**
13 & 13A Jalan Dato Haji Megat Khas
Taman Bandaraya Utama
31400 Ipoh, Perak, Malaysia
Tel.: (60) 55477622
Fax: (60) 55477623
E-Mail: ipoh@fittersgroup.com
Emp.: 7
Fire Safety Equipment Distr
S.I.C.: 5049
N.A.I.C.S.: 423490
David Tiong *(Mgr)*

FITTERS Marketing Sdn Bhd **(1)**
Wisma Fitters No 1 Jalan Tembaga SD 5/2
Bandar Sri Damansara, 52200 Kuala Lumpur, Malaysia
Tel.: (60) 361576199
Fax: (60) 362752780
Door & Builing Materials Distr
S.I.C.: 5211
N.A.I.C.S.: 444190
Fook Eng Lai *(Mgr-Mktg)*

FITTERS (Sarawak) Sdn Bhd **(1)**
28 Ground Floor Wisma Koperkasa Jalan Simpang Tiga
Kuching, Sarawak, Malaysia
Tel.: (60) 82250221
Fax: (60) 82250221
E-Mail: sarawaku@fittersgroup.com
Emp.: 5
Safety Materials & Equipment Distr
S.I.C.: 5047
N.A.I.C.S.: 423450
Lee Seng Kiang *(Mng Dir)*

FITTERS Sdn Bhd **(1)**
No 1 Wisma Fitters Jalan Tembaga Sd 5/2
Bandar Sri Damansara, 52200 Kuala Lumpur, Malaysia
Tel.: (60) 362767155
Fax: (60) 362752780
E-Mail: zetapark@fittersgroup.com
Fire Safety Materials & Equipment Mfr
S.I.C.: 3999
N.A.I.C.S.: 339999
Wong Swee Yee *(Mng Dir)*

Future NRG Sdn Bhd **(1)**
3rd Floor Wisma FITTERS No 1 Jalan Tembaga SD 5/2
Bandar Sri Damansara, 52200 Kuala Lumpur, Wilayah Persekutuan, Malaysia
Tel.: (60) 362772200
Fax: (60) 362721535
E-Mail: enquiry@futurenrg.net
Web Site: www.futurenrg.net
Emp.: 200
Renewable Energy Development Services
S.I.C.: 7389
N.A.I.C.S.: 561990
Fu Ah Kiow *(Chm)*

Master Pyroserve Sdn Bhd **(1)**
Bangunan Fitters Lot 2221 Kampung Jaya Industrial Area Sungai Buloh
47000 Kuala Lumpur, Wilayah Persekutuan, Malaysia
Tel.: (60) 361576199
Fax: (60) 362758692
E-Mail: mps@fittersgroup.com
Emp.: 40
Fire Alarm & Communication Systems Mfr
S.I.C.: 3663
N.A.I.C.S.: 334220
Anuar Yusuf *(Mgr)*

FITZROY RESOURCES LIMITED

Suite 1 Level 1 35 Havelock St
West Perth, WA, 6005, Australia
Tel.: (61) 8 9481 7111
Fax: (61) 8 9320 7501
E-Mail: admin@fitzroyresources.com.au
Web Site: www.fitzroyresources.com.au
FRY—(ASX)
Rev.: $75,656
Assets: $3,857,034
Liabilities: $58,896
Net Worth: $3,798,138
Earnings: ($583,674)
Fiscal Year-end: 06/30/13

Business Description:
Gold Exploration Services
S.I.C.: 1041
N.A.I.C.S.: 212221
Personnel:
William Dix *(Mng Dir)*
Simon Robertson *(Sec)*
Board of Directors:
Thomas Henderson
William Dix
Russell Lynton-Brown
Riccardo Vittino
Legal Counsel:
Hardy Bowen Lawyers
Level 1 28 Ord Street
West Perth, Australia

FITZROY RIVER CORPORATION LTD

Suite 2 Level 11 50 Margaret Street
Sydney, NSW, 2000, Australia
Tel.: (61) 1300 003 686
Fax: (61) 2 9290 2707
E-Mail: enquiries@fitzroyriver.net.au
Web Site: www.fitzroyriver.net.au
FZR—(ASX DEU)
Sales Range: Less than $1 Million

Business Description:
Investment Holding Company
S.I.C.: 6719
N.A.I.C.S.: 551112
Personnel:
Justin Clyne *(Co-Sec)*
Sebastian Hempel *(Co-Sec)*
Board of Directors:
Malcolm McComas
Sebastian Hempel
Sue Thomas

FIVE NINES VENTURES LIMITED

106 1641 Lonsdale Avenue
North Vancouver, BC, V7M 2T5, Canada
Tel.: (604) 880-3144
Fax: (604) 876-5564
E-Mail: info@99999site.com
Web Site: www.99999site.com
Year Founded: 2010
FIV—(CNSX)

Business Description:
Rare Earth Minerals & Uranium Exploration
S.I.C.: 1099
N.A.I.C.S.: 212299
Personnel:
Carman Parente *(Pres & CEO)*
F. George Orr *(CFO)*
Board of Directors:
F. George Orr
Carman Parente
Paul Robson
Terence Schorn
Transfer Agent:
Valiant Trust Company
700 Cambie Street Suite 600
Vancouver, BC, V6B 0A2, Canada
Tel.: (604) 699-4880

FIVES GROUP

(See Under Compagnie de Fives Lille SA)

FIXINOX SA

35A rue Albert 1er 35a
Lambusart, 6220 Fleurus, Belgium
Tel.: (32) 71810526
Fax: (32) 71810529
E-Mail: fixinox@gmail.com
Web Site: www.fixinox.com
FIX—(EUR)
Sales Range: $1-9.9 Million
Emp.: 24

Business Description:
Rustproof Metal Fixation Systems Mfr & Distr
S.I.C.: 3499
N.A.I.C.S.: 332999
Personnel:
Richard Moos *(Chm)*
Hugues Wauters *(Mng Dir)*

FIXNETIX LTD.

33 King William Street
London, EC4R 9As, United Kingdom
Tel.: (44) 203 008 8990
Fax: (44) 2030088992
E-Mail: sales@fixnetix.com
Web Site: www.fixnetix.com
Sales Range: $25-49.9 Million
Emp.: 103
Fiscal Year-end: 12/31/12

Business Description:
Financial & Investment Software Developer
S.I.C.: 7372
N.A.I.C.S.: 511210
Personnel:
Hugh Hughes *(Co-Founder, Chm & CEO)*
Paul Ellis *(Co-Founder & Pres)*
Alasdair Moore *(Co-Founder & Dir-Bus Dev)*
Anthony Kingsnorth *(COO)*
Karen Bertoli *(CMO)*
Matt Dangerfield *(CTO)*
Bob Fuller *(Chief Admin Officer)*
David Thompson *(Sec)*
Board of Directors:
Hugh Hughes
Paul Ellis
Rob Johnson
Alasdair Moore
Alan Colin Drake Yarrow
Ken Yeadon

FJ BENJAMIN HOLDINGS LTD.

10 Science Park Road 04 01 The Alpha Singapore Science Park II
Singapore, 117684, Singapore
Tel.: (65) 6737 0155
Fax: (65) 6732 9616
E-Mail: info@fjbenjamin.com
Web Site: www.fjbenjamin.com
Year Founded: 1959
F10—(SES)
Rev.: $312,517,857
Assets: $223,806,888
Liabilities: $118,113,689
Net Worth: $105,693,198
Earnings: $3,270,298
Emp.: 3,000
Fiscal Year-end: 06/30/13

Business Description:
Fashion Apparel, Timepieces & Home Fashions Retailer & Distr; Leather Accessories Designer & Licensor
Import Export
S.I.C.: 2399
N.A.I.C.S.: 315990
Personnel:
Frank Benjamin *(Founder & Chm)*
Eli Manasseh Benjamin *(CEO)*
Karen Mee Keng Chong *(CFO & Sec)*
Douglas Jackie Benjamin *(COO)*
Karen Katzman *(Pres-Sls-F J Benjamin Fashions (US) Inc)*
Odile Benjamin *(CEO-F J Benjamin (Singapore) Pte Ltd & Dir-Creative)*
Tony Fung *(CEO-F J Benjamin (HK) Limited & F J Benjamin (Taiwan) Ltd)*
Ian Lim *(CEO-F J Benjamin (Singapore) Pte Ltd)*
Gary Dean Strashoon *(CEO-Fashion Dynamics HK Ltd)*
Oon Lai Yeoh *(CEO-F J Benjamin (M) Sdn Bhd)*
Board of Directors:
Frank Benjamin
Douglas Jackie Benjamin
Eli Manasseh Benjamin
Kwee San Chew
Karen Mee Keng Chong
Daniel Jen Yaw Ong
Keith Ah Kee Tay
Reggie Myint Thein
Ai Fong Wong
Legal Counsel:
Drew & Napier LLC
10 Collyer Quay 10 01 Ocean Financial Centre
Singapore, Singapore

Subsidiaries:

Benmark Pte. Ltd. **(1)**
6B Orange Grove Rd
FJ Benjamin Bldg, Singapore, 258332, Singapore (100%)
Tel.: (65) 67370155
Fax: (65) 67345881
Web Site: www.fjbenjamin.com.sg
Emp.: 500
Retailer & Distributor of Home Furnishings
S.I.C.: 5023
N.A.I.C.S.: 423220
Dougles Benjamin *(Exec Dir)*

F. J. B. Investment Pte Ltd **(1)**
10 Science Park Road 04-01 The Alpha
Singapore, 117684, Singapore
Tel.: (65) 67370155

Fax: (65) 6735 9072
Investment Management Services
S.I.C.: 6211
N.A.I.C.S.: 523999

Subsidiary:

F J Benjamin (Singapore) Pte Ltd (2)
10 Science Park Rd 04-01 The Alpha
Singapore Science Park II
Singapore, 117684, Singapore
Tel.: (65) 67370155
Fax: (65) 67329616
E-Mail: info@fjbenjamin.com
Web Site: www.fjbenjamin.com
Emp.: 100
Fashion Apparel Retailer
S.I.C.: 5699
N.A.I.C.S.: 448150
Nash Benjamin *(CEO)*

F J Benjamin Concepts Pte Ltd (1)
10 Science Park Road 04-01 The Alpha
Singapore Science Park II
Singapore, 117684, Singapore
Tel.: (65) 6737 0155
Fax: (65) 6735 9072
Web Site: www.fjbenjamin.com
Emp.: 8,200
Fashion Apparel Retailer
S.I.C.: 5699
N.A.I.C.S.: 448150
Frank Benjamin *(Mng Dir)*

FJ Benjamin Fashions (Singapore) Pte. Ltd. (1)
10 Science Park Rd
Singapore, 0401, Singapore (100%)
Tel.: (65) 67370155
Fax: (65) 67359052
E-Mail: info@fjbenjamin.com
Web Site: www.fjbenjamin.com
Emp.: 200
Import
S.I.C.: 3199
N.A.I.C.S.: 316998
Douglas Jackie Benjamin *(CEO)*

FJ Benjamin MaxCom Pte. Ltd. (1)
10 Science Park Road Ste 04-01 The Alpha Science Park II, Singapore, 117684, Singapore SG
Tel.: (65) 67370155
Fax: (65) 67348875
E-Mail: bmi@fjbenjamin.com
Web Site: www.fjbenjamin.com
Emp.: 100
Advertising Agency
S.I.C.: 7311
N.A.I.C.S.: 541810
Frank Benjamin *(Founder & Chm)*
Douglas Benjamin *(CEO)*

FJ Benjamin Singapore Pte. Ltd. (1)
10 Science Park Rd 04-01 The Alpha
Singapore Science Park II, Singapore, 258332, Singapore (100%)
Tel.: (65) 67370155
Fax: (65) 67329619
E-Mail: info@fjbenjamin.com
Web Site: www.fjbenjamin.com
Importer & Distributor of Timepieces
Import
S.I.C.: 5944
N.A.I.C.S.: 448310

U.S. Subsidiary:

F J Benjamin Fashions (U.S.) Inc (1)
601 W 26th St Ste 1745
New York, NY 10001
Tel.: (212) 206-8264
Fax: (212) 206-7771
Web Site: www.fjbenjamin.com
Emp.: 7
Fashion Apparel Retailer
S.I.C.: 5699
N.A.I.C.S.: 448190
Samuel Benjamin *(Sr VP)*

Non-U.S. Subsidiaries:

Arcangel Limited (1)
Unit A And B 22nd Floor 235 Wing Lok Street
Sheung Wan, China (Hong Kong)
Tel.: (852) 23084091
Fax: (852) 23084090
Fashion Apparel Retailer
S.I.C.: 5699
N.A.I.C.S.: 448190

F J Benjamin (H.K.) Limited (1)
Island Place Tower Room 2308 510 Kings Road
North Point, China (Hong Kong)
Tel.: (852) 2506 2666
Fax: (852) 2506 3573
E-Mail: info@fjb.com.hk
Web Site: www.fjbenjamin.com
Emp.: 50
Fashion Apparel Retailer
S.I.C.: 5699
N.A.I.C.S.: 448190
Tony Fung *(CEO)*

F J Benjamin Luxury Timepieces Sdn. Bhd (1)
12th Fl Menara PanGlobal No 8 Lorong P Ramlee
Kuala Lumpur, 50250, Malaysia
Tel.: (60) 320566888
Fax: (60) 320314405
E-Mail: info@fjbenjamin.com.my
Web Site: www.fjbenjamin.com
Emp.: 100
Fashion Apparel Retailer
S.I.C.: 5699
N.A.I.C.S.: 448190
Annen Ang *(Mgr-HR)*

F J Benjamin (Taiwan) Ltd (1)
5F No 260 Tun Hwa North Road
Taipei, Taiwan
Tel.: (886) 2 2719 3880
Fax: (886) 2 2719 5080
E-Mail: info@fjb.com.tw
Fashion Apparel Retailer
S.I.C.: 5699
N.A.I.C.S.: 448150

F J Benjamin Trading HK Ltd (1)
Island Place Tower Room 2308
510 Kings Road, North Point, China (Hong Kong) (100%)
Tel.: (852) 25062666
Fax: (852) 25063573
E-Mail: enquiry@fjb.com.hk
Web Site: www.fjbenjamin.com
Emp.: 40
S.I.C.: 2389
N.A.I.C.S.: 315990

FJ Benjamin (Aust) Pty Ltd (1)
Level 16 201 Elizabeth Street
Sydney, NSW, 2000, Australia
Tel.: (61) 2 9211 7134
Fax: (61) 2 9211 6505
E-Mail: info@fjb.com.au
Web Site: www.fjbenjamin.com
Fashion Apparel Retailer
S.I.C.: 5699
N.A.I.C.S.: 448190
Ben Benjamin *(Mgr)*

FJ Benjamin Concepts (Aust) Pty. Ltd. (1)
Level 6 10 Waterloo St
Surry Hills, NSW, 2010, Australia (100%)
Mailing Address:
Locked Bag 71
Alexandria, NSW, 1435, Australia
Tel.: (61) 292117443
Fax: (61) 292116505
Web Site: www.fjb.com
Emp.: 6
Import
S.I.C.: 3199
N.A.I.C.S.: 316998
Ian Dahl *(Mng Dir)*

FJ Benjamin Fashions (HK) Ltd. (1)
Island Place Tower Room 2308
510 Kings Road, North Point, China (Hong Kong) (100%)
Tel.: (852) 25062666
Fax: (852) 25063573
E-Mail: inquiry@fjb.com.hk
Web Site: www.fjbenjamin.com
Emp.: 30
S.I.C.: 5944
N.A.I.C.S.: 448310
Tony Leung *(Gen Mgr)*

FJ Benjamin Hong Kong Ltd. (1)
Island Place Tower Room 2308
510 King's Road, North Point, China (Hong Kong) (100%)
Tel.: (852) 25062666
Fax: (852) 25063573
E-Mail: info@fjb.com.hk
Web Site: www.fjbenjamin.com
Emp.: 22
Clothing Mfr & Distr
S.I.C.: 2399
N.A.I.C.S.: 315990

FJ Benjamin (M) Sdn. Bhd. (1)
Ste 121 122 K H Tower 12th Fl
No 8 Lorong P Ramlee, 50250 Kuala Lumpur, Malaysia (100%)
Tel.: (60) 320566888
Fax: (60) 320314405
E-Mail: info@fjbenjamin.com.my
Web Site: www.fjbenjamin.com
Emp.: 100
Fashion Apparel, Timepieces & Home Fashions Retailer & Distr; Leather Accessories Designer & Licensor
Import
S.I.C.: 3171
N.A.I.C.S.: 316992
Yeoh Oon Lai *(CEO)*

Subsidiary:

F J Benjamin Lifestyle Sdn. Bhd (2)
12th Fl Menara PanGlobal No 8 Lorong P Ramlee
Kuala Lumpur, 50250, Malaysia
Tel.: (60) 320566888
Fax: (60) 320314405
E-Mail: info@fjbenjamin.com.my
Web Site: www.fjbenjamin.com
Emp.: 100
Fashion Apparel Retailer
S.I.C.: 5699
N.A.I.C.S.: 448190
Angie Chong *(CEO)*

Non-U.S. Affiliates:

Peppo Fashions Group Company Lmd (1)
7B Lk Rajada Ofc Complex Bldg
193 30 Rajadapisek Rd, Bangkok, Khet Klongtoey, 10110, Thailand
Tel.: (66) 26619599
Fax: (66) 26618885
Web Site: www.peppofashions.com
Emp.: 300
S.I.C.: 2389
N.A.I.C.S.: 315990

FJARSKIPTI HF.

(d/b/a Vodafone Iceland)
Skutuvogi 2
104 Reykjavik, Iceland
Tel.: (354) 5999000
Fax: (354) 5999001
E-Mail: bjornv@vodafone.is
Web Site: www.vodafone.is
VOICE—(ICE)
Sales Range: $125-149.9 Million
Emp.: 400

Business Description:
Mobile Telecommunications & Internet Services
S.I.C.: 4812
N.A.I.C.S.: 517210

Personnel:
Omar Svavarsson *(CEO)*
Hronn Sveinsdottir *(CFO & Mgr-HR)*
Arni Peter *(CMO)*
Gestur G. Gestsson *(CTO)*

FJORDLAND EXPLORATION INC.

1111 Melville Street Suite 1100
Vancouver, BC, V6E 3V68, Canada
Tel.: (604) 893-8365
Fax: (604) 669-8336
E-Mail: info@fjordlandex.com
Web Site: www.fjordlandex.com
Year Founded: 1996
FEX—(TSXV)
Int. Income: $118
Assets: $1,102,673
Liabilities: $29,525
Net Worth: $1,073,148
Earnings: ($351,990)
Fiscal Year-end: 12/31/12

Business Description:
Mineral Exploration Services
S.I.C.: 1081
N.A.I.C.S.: 213114

Personnel:
Thomas G. Schroeter *(Pres & CEO)*
G. Ross McDonald *(CFO)*
Janice Davies *(Sec)*

Board of Directors:
Richard C. Atkinson
Peter Krag-Hansen
G. Ross McDonald
Thomas G. Schroeter
Victor A. Tanaka

Legal Counsel:
Armstrong Simpson
777 Hornby Street, Suite 2080
Vancouver, BC, Canada

Transfer Agent:
Computershare Trust Company of Canada
510 Burrard St 3rd Fl
Vancouver, BC, V6C 3B9, Canada

FKL AD TEMERIN

Industrijska zona bb
21235 Temerin, Serbia
Tel.: (381) 21 6841 100
Fax: (381) 21 842 650
E-Mail: marketing@fkl-serbia.com
Web Site: www.fkl-serbia.com
Year Founded: 1961
FKLT—(BEL)

Business Description:
Rolling Bearing Mfr
S.I.C.: 3562
N.A.I.C.S.: 332991

Personnel:
Milivoje Mijuskovic *(Vice Gen Mgr)*

FKP PROPERTY GROUP

Level 1 76A Skyring Terrace
GPO Box 2447
Newstead, Brisbane, QLD, 4006, Australia
Tel.: (61) 732233888
Fax: (61) 732233877
E-Mail: reception@fkp.com.au
Web Site: www.fkp.com.au
FKP—(ASX)
Rev.: $346,185,620
Assets: $3,499,267,590
Liabilities: $2,275,842,190
Net Worth: $1,223,425,400
Earnings: ($186,431,690)
Emp.: 1,300
Fiscal Year-end: 06/30/13

Business Description:
Property Development & Investment Activities
S.I.C.: 6531
N.A.I.C.S.: 531311

Personnel:
Geoffrey E. Grady *(CEO)*
David Allan Hunt *(CFO)*
Lisa Godfrey *(Sec)*

Board of Directors:
Seng Huang Lee
Jim Frayne
Geoffrey E. Grady
Eric Lee
Walter McDonald
Leonard McKinnon
Alan Zammit

Subsidiary:

FKP Limited (1)
Level 5 120 Edward St
Brisbane, Queensland, 4000, Australia
Tel.: (61) 732233888
Fax: (61) 732233877
E-Mail: reception@fkp.com.au
Web Site: www.fkp.com.au
Emp.: 2,000

FKP Property Group—(Continued)

Real Estate & Investment Management Services
S.I.C.: 6531
N.A.I.C.S.: 531390
Peter Ross Brown *(CEO & Mng Dir)*

Subsidiaries:

Australian Retirement Homes Limited (2)
Level 5 120 Edward St
Brisbane, QLD, 4000, Australia
Tel.: (61) 732233808
Fax: (61) 732233809
Emp.: 300
Retirement Housing Services
S.I.C.: 8322
N.A.I.C.S.: 624229

Cleveland Gardens Pty. Ltd. (2)
PO Box 2447
Brisbane, Queensland, 4001, Australia
Tel.: (61) 732233889
Fax: (61) 738211568
E-Mail: clevelandmanager@aveolivewell.com.au
Web Site: www.fkp.com.au
Emp.: 10
Retirement Housing Services
S.I.C.: 8322
N.A.I.C.S.: 624229

The Domain Retirement Country Club Pty. Ltd. (2)
74 Wardoo St
Ashmore, Gold Coast, Queensland, 4214, Australia
Tel.: (61) 755279711
Fax: (61) 55974329
Web Site: www.aveolivewell.com.au
Emp.: 6
Retirement Homes & Aged Persons Accommodation Services
S.I.C.: 8361
N.A.I.C.S.: 623312
Greg Paul *(Mgr-Sls)*

FKP Commercial Developments Pty. Ltd. (2)
PO Box 2447
Brisbane, Queensland, 4001, Australia
Tel.: (61) 732233888
Fax: (61) 732233877
E-Mail: reception@fkp.com.au
Web Site: www.fkp.com.au
Emp.: 2,000
Commercial Property Development Services
S.I.C.: 1542
N.A.I.C.S.: 236220
Peter Brown *(CEO & Mng Dir)*

FKP Constructions Pty. Ltd. (2)
Level 5 120 Edward St
Brisbane, QLD, 4000, Australia
Tel.: (61) 733193600
E-Mail: reception@fkp.com.au
Web Site: www.fkp.com.au
Emp.: 50
Building Construction Services
S.I.C.: 1542
N.A.I.C.S.: 236220
Jeff Grady *(CEO)*

FKP Developments Pty. Ltd. (2)
Level 5 120 Edward St
Brisbane, Queensland, 4000, Australia
Tel.: (61) 732233888
Fax: (61) 732233877
E-Mail: reception@fkp.com.au
Web Site: www.fkp.com.au
Emp.: 400
Real Estate & Investment Management Services
S.I.C.: 6531
N.A.I.C.S.: 531390
Peter Brown *(CEO)*

FKP Funds Management Limited (2)
Level 5 99 Macquarie Street
Sydney, New South Wales, 2000, Australia
Tel.: (61) 2 9270 6100
Fax: (61) 2 9270 6199
E-Mail: fkpenquiries@fkp.com.au
Web Site: www.fkp.com.au
Emp.: 2,000
Real Estate & Investment Management Services
S.I.C.: 6531
N.A.I.C.S.: 531390
Peter Ross Brown *(CEO & Mng Dir)*

FKP Lifestyle Pty. Ltd. (2)
Level 5 120 Edward St
Brisbane, QLD, 4000, Australia
Tel.: (61) 732233888
Fax: (61) 732233877
E-Mail: reception@fkp.com.au
Web Site: www.fkp.com.au
Emp.: 2,000
Real Estate & Investment Management Services
S.I.C.: 6531
N.A.I.C.S.: 531390
Peter Brown *(CEO)*

FKP Real Estate Pty. Ltd. (2)
Level 5 120 Edward St
Brisbane, QLD, 4001, Australia
Tel.: (61) 732233888
Fax: (61) 732233877
E-Mail: reception@fkp.com
Web Site: www.fkp.com
Emp.: 2,000
Real Estate & Investment Management Services
S.I.C.: 6531
N.A.I.C.S.: 531390
Geoff Grady *(CEO)*

FKP Residential Developments Pty. Ltd. (2)
PO Box 239
Peregian Beach, Brisbane, Queensland, 4573, Australia
Tel.: (61) 7 5448 2833
Fax: (61) 7 5448 2694
E-Mail: reception@fkp.com.au
Web Site: www.fkp.com.au
Emp.: 2,000
Residential Real Estate Management Services
S.I.C.: 6531
N.A.I.C.S.: 531311
Peter Brown *(CEO)*

Forest Place Management Limited (2)
356 Blunder Rd
Durack, Brisbane, QLD, 4077, Australia
Tel.: (61) 7 3727777
Fax: (61) 7 32645356
E-Mail: reception@fkp.com.au
Web Site: www.fkp.com.au
Emp.: 10
Retirement Housing Services
S.I.C.: 8322
N.A.I.C.S.: 624229
Peter Brown *(CEO)*

Forest Place Pty. Ltd. (2)
Level 5 120 Edward Street
Durack, Brisbane, QLD, 4000, Australia
Tel.: (61) 732233888
E-Mail: reception@fkp.com.au
Web Site: www.fkp.com.au
Emp.: 10
Retirement Housing Services
S.I.C.: 8322
N.A.I.C.S.: 624229
Jeff Grady *(CEO)*

FLAGS UNLIMITED

364 St Vincent Street
Barrie, ON, L4M 4A5, Canada
Tel.: (705) 739-4100
Fax: (705) 739-9900
Toll Free: (800) 565-4100
E-Mail: ContactUs@flagsunlimited.com
Web Site: www.flagsunlimited.com
Year Founded: 1966
Rev.: $10,694,229
Emp.: 60
Business Description:
Flags & Banners Mfr
S.I.C.: 5399
N.A.I.C.S.: 452990
Personnel:
Dennis Brown *(Pres & CEO)*

FLAGSHIP INVESTMENTS LIMITED

(Formerly Hyperion Flagship Investments Limited)
Level 12 Corporate Centre One 2 Corporate Court
Bundall, QLD, 4217, Australia
Tel.: (61) 756444400
Fax: (61) 755741457
E-Mail: flagship@ecpohl.com
Web Site: www.flagshipinvestments.com.au
FSI—(ASX)
Rev.: $1,582,950
Assets: $38,847,404
Liabilities: $1,468,319
Net Worth: $37,379,085
Earnings: $212,588
Fiscal Year-end: 06/30/13
Business Description:
Investment Services
S.I.C.: 6211
N.A.I.C.S.: 523999
Personnel:
Henry R. Smerdon *(Chm)*
Emmanuel C. Pohl *(Mng Dir)*
Ian William Harrison *(Sec)*
Board of Directors:
Henry R. Smerdon
Patrick Corrigan
Dominic M. McGann
Sophie A. Mitchell
Emmanuel C. Pohl
Legal Counsel:
McCullough Robertson Lawyers
Level 11 Central Plaza Two 66 Eagle Street
Brisbane, Australia

FLAKK HOLDING AS

Korsegata 8
6002 Alesund, Norway
Mailing Address:
PO Box 836
Sentrum, 6001 Alesund, Norway
Tel.: (47) 7011 6430
E-Mail: office@flakk.no
Web Site: www.flakk.no
Year Founded: 2006
Emp.: 700
Business Description:
Investment Holding Company
S.I.C.: 6719
N.A.I.C.S.: 551112
Personnel:
Knut Trygve Flakk *(Mng Dir)*

Subsidiary:

Flakk International AS (1)
Korsegata 8
6002 Alesund, Norway NO
Mailing Address: (100%)
PO Box 836
Sentrum, 6001 Alesund, Norway
Tel.: (47) 7011 6430
Fax: (47) 7011 6440
E-Mail: office@flakk.no
Web Site: www.flakk.no
Equity Investment Firm
S.I.C.: 6211
N.A.I.C.S.: 523999
Knut Trygve Flakk *(Mng Dir)*

FLAKT WOODS GROUP LTD.

Ave Louis casai 18
Geneva, 1209, Switzerland
Tel.: (41) 432883800
Fax: (41) 223093810
E-Mail: info@flaktwoods.com
Web Site: www.flaktwoods.com
Sales Range: $600-649.9 Million
Emp.: 4,000
Business Description:
Air Handling Processes, Ventilation & Air Conditioning Products & Services Developer & Mfr
S.I.C.: 1711
N.A.I.C.S.: 238220
Personnel:
Didier Forget *(CEO)*
Eric Chassagnade *(CFO & Sr VP)*
Lars J. Sandell *(CIO)*
Nick Agopian *(Sr VP-America)*
Patrick Pouliquen *(Sr VP-Air Climate Europe)*

Subsidiaries:

Semco Incorporated (1)
1800 E Pte Dr
Columbia, MO 65201-6282 MO
Tel.: (573) 443-1481
Fax: (573) 443-6921
E-Mail: webmaster@semcoinc.com
Web Site: www.semcoinc.com
Sales Range: $1-9.9 Million
Emp.: 300
Provider of Metal Work Services
S.I.C.: 3444
N.A.I.C.S.: 332322
Tom Rice *(Product Mgr)*

Non-U.S. Subsidiary:

Flakt Woods Ltd. (1)
Axial Way
Colchester, CO4 5AR, United Kingdom
Tel.: (44) 206544122
Telex: 98422
Fax: (44) 1206574434
Web Site: www.flaktwoods.com
Emp.: 700
Ventilation Equipment Mfr
S.I.C.: 3563
N.A.I.C.S.: 333912

U.S. Subsidiaries:

American Fan Company (2)
2933 Symmes Rd
Fairfield, OH 45014-4237 OH
Tel.: (513) 874-2400
Fax: (513) 870-5577
Toll Free: (866) 771-6266
E-Mail: americanfan@flaktwoods.com
Web Site: www.americanfan.com
Emp.: 31
Industrial Fans Mfr
S.I.C.: 3564
N.A.I.C.S.: 333413
Josh Schaeper *(Mgr-Customer Svc & Parts & Svc)*

Fan Group Inc (2)
1701 Terminal Rd Ste B
Niles, MI 49120-1245
Tel.: (269) 683-1150
Fax: (269) 683-2622
E-Mail: info@flaktwoods.com
Web Site: www.flaktwoods.com
Emp.: 30
Mfr. of Industrial Fan
S.I.C.: 3564
N.A.I.C.S.: 333413
Rick Pawloski *(Gen Mgr)*

FLAMEL TECHNOLOGIES S.A.

Parc Club du Moulin a Vent 33 avenue du Docteur Georges Levy
F 69693 Venissieux, France
Tel.: (33) 4 7278 3434
Fax: (33) 4 7278 3435
E-Mail: info@flamel.com
Web Site: www.flamel-technologies.fr
Year Founded: 1990
FLML—(NASDAQ)
Rev.: $26,101,000
Assets: $117,311,000
Liabilities: $86,807,000
Net Worth: $30,504,000
Earnings: ($3,228,000)
Emp.: 251
Fiscal Year-end: 12/31/12
Business Description:
Polymer-Based Delivery Systems for Medical Applications
S.I.C.: 2834
N.A.I.C.S.: 325412
Personnel:
Stephen H. Willard *(Chm)*
Sian Crouzet *(Principal Fin Officer)*
Board of Directors:
Stephen H. Willard
Catherine Brechignac
Guillaume Cerutti

Lodewijk J. R. de Vink
Francis James Thomas Fildes
Craig Roberts Stapleton
Elie Vannier

Transfer Agent:
Credit Lyonnais
F-14408 Bayeux, France

U.S. Subsidiary:

Flamel Technologies Inc. **(1)**
2121 K St NW Ste 650
Washington, DC 20037-3600 (100%)
Tel.: (202) 862-8400
Fax: (202) 862-3933
Web Site: www.flamel.com
Emp.: 4
Drug Delivery Method Mfr.
S.I.C.: 5122
N.A.I.C.S.: 424210

FLASH NETWORKS LTD.

7 Sapir Road
POB 12624, Herzliyya, 46733, Israel
Tel.: (972) 9 958 0666
Fax: (972) 9 956 4888
E-Mail: nfo@flashnetworks.com
Web Site: www.flashnetworks.com
Business Description:
Mobile Internet Services
S.I.C.: 2741
N.A.I.C.S.: 519130
Personnel:
Liam Galin *(Pres & CEO)*
Alberto Sessa *(CFO)*
Ofer Gottfried *(CTO & Gen Mgr)*

U.S. Subsidiary:

Mobixell Networks, Inc. **(1)**
1735 Technology Dr Ste 550
San Jose, CA 95110 DE
Tel.: (650) 353-3032
Fax: (408) 973-9657
Web Site: www.mobixell.com
Mobile Broadband Services
S.I.C.: 4812
N.A.I.C.S.: 517210
Yehuda Elmaliach *(Co-Founder & CTO)*
Amir Aharoni *(Co-Founder)*
Lothar Pauly *(Chm)*
Klod Ghez *(CEO)*
David Kahani *(COO)*
Gad Tobaly *(Pres-Americas)*
Robert E. DeFeo *(Exec VP-Sls & Gen Mgr-Ops-US)*
Tamar Ben-Porath *(Exec VP-Corp Dev & HR)*
Yaron Dishon *(Sr VP-Sls-Asia Pacific & Americas)*

FLAT GLASS INDUSTRIES LIMITED

3 Moorebank Avenue
Moorebank, NSW, 2170, Australia
Tel.: (61) 298240999
Fax: (61) 298242111
E-Mail: info@flatglass.com.au
Web Site: www.flatglass.com.au
FGI—(ASX)
Rev.: $26,232,783
Assets: $17,971,015
Liabilities: $8,133,591
Net Worth: $9,837,424
Earnings: ($3,422,256)
Emp.: 148
Fiscal Year-end: 06/30/13
Business Description:
Glass Processing Whslr
S.I.C.: 5211
N.A.I.C.S.: 444190
Personnel:
James Buchan *(CEO)*
Brett Crowley *(Sec)*
Board of Directors:
James Schwarz
Frank D'Urso
Nicholas J. O'Connor
Richard Palonis
Lindsay J. Phillips

Subsidiaries:

Alternative Glass Supplies Pty Limited **(1)**
1 Hedderwick Rd
Bayswater N, Dandenong, VIC, 3174, Australia
Tel.: (61) 397617977
Fax: (61) 97912030
E-Mail: sales@altglass.com.au
Web Site: www.altglass.com.au
Glasses Mfr
S.I.C.: 3211
N.A.I.C.S.: 327211
Jim Buchan *(Mng Dir)*

DLCO Australia Architectural Glass Fittings Pty. Ltd. **(1)**
PO Box 656
Moorebank, NSW, 2170, Australia
Tel.: (61) 298240999
Fax: (61) 298242111
E-Mail: admin@flatglass.com.au
Web Site: www.dlco.com.au
Emp.: 60
Frameless Glass Doors Mfr
S.I.C.: 3231
N.A.I.C.S.: 327215
Nick O Connor *(Mng Dir)*

RTK Industries Pty Limited **(1)**
848 Mountain Hwy
Bayswater, Victoria, 3153, Australia
Tel.: (61) 397206620
Fax: (61) 397205071
E-Mail: enquiries@rtkindustries.com.au
Web Site: www.rtkindustries.com.au
Emp.: 20
Laser Welding Equipment Mfr
S.I.C.: 3548
N.A.I.C.S.: 333992
Andrew Debby *(Gen Mgr)*

FLATEX AG

E-C-Baumann-Strasse 8a
05326 Kulmbach, Germany
Tel.: (49) 92219520
Fax: (49) 922195217
E-Mail: info@flatex-ag.de
Web Site: www.flatex-ag.de
FLA—(DEU)
Emp.: 20
Business Description:
Securities Brokerage & Investment Services
S.I.C.: 6211
N.A.I.C.S.: 523110
Personnel:
Ralf Mueller *(Mng Dir)*

FLATWORLD ACQUISITION CORP.

Palm Grove House Road Town
Tortola, VG1110, Virgin Islands (British)
Tel.: (284) 5456127
Year Founded: 2010
FWLAF—(OTC)
Rev.: $57,441
Assets: $7,002
Liabilities: $137,427
Net Worth: ($130,425)
Earnings: ($218,898)
Emp.: 4
Fiscal Year-end: 12/31/12
Business Description:
Investment Services
S.I.C.: 6211
N.A.I.C.S.: 523999
Personnel:
Gilbert H. Lamphere *(Chm)*
Jeffrey A. Valenty *(Pres, CFO & Treas)*
Raj K. Gupta *(CEO & Sec)*
Board of Directors:
Gilbert H. Lamphere
Raj K. Gupta
Shri Krishan Gupta
Jeffrey A. Valenty

FLAVUS BETEILIGUNGEN AG

King Strasse 15c
81927 Munich, Germany
Tel.: (49) 89 9392 6646
E-Mail: info@flavus-beteiligungen.de
Web Site: www.flavus-beteiligungen.de
F2V—(DEU)
Business Description:
Management Holding Company
S.I.C.: 6719
N.A.I.C.S.: 551112
Personnel:
Olaf Seidel *(CFO)*
Supervisory Board of Directors:
Heinz Lomen
Horst Michel
Christian Sundermann

FLAWLESS DIAMOND (INDIA) LTD.

136 Panchratna House Opera House
Mumbai, 400004, India
Tel.: (91) 22 23637756
Fax: (91) 22 23669308
Web Site: www.flawlessdiamond.in
523576—(BOM)
Sales Range: $100-124.9 Million
Business Description:
Jewellery & Diamond Mfr
S.I.C.: 3911
N.A.I.C.S.: 339910
Personnel:
Kamal U. Jain *(Chm)*
Bhawar U. Jain *(Mng Dir)*
Board of Directors:
Bhawar U. Jain
Kamal U. Jain
Rajiv Kamdar
Sujay N. Kantawala
Deepak K. Parekh
Gopalakrishna Pillai

FLC GLOBAL JSC

Floor 5 FLC Landmark Tower Le Duc Tho Street
Hanoi, Vietnam
Tel.: (84) 4 3795 6869
Fax: (84) 4 3795 6899
E-Mail: info@flcglobal.vn
Web Site: www.flcglobal.vn
KLF—(HNX)
Business Description:
Travel Services
S.I.C.: 7011
N.A.I.C.S.: 721199
Personnel:
Dinh Vinh Le *(Chm & Gen Mgr)*

FLC GROUP JOINT STOCK COMPANY

5th Floor FLC Landmark Tower Le Duc Tho road
Tu Liem, Hanoi, Vietnam
Tel.: (84) 4 3771 1111
Fax: (84) 4 3724 5888
E-Mail: info@flc.vn
Web Site: www.flc.vn
Year Founded: 2008
Business Description:
Real Estate Development Services
S.I.C.: 6531
N.A.I.C.S.: 531390
Personnel:
Trinh Van Quyet *(Chm-Mgmt Bd)*
Dinh Vinh Le *(Vice Chm-Mgmt Bd)*
Doan Van Phuong *(Gen Dir)*
Thi Hao Dam *(Member-Mgmt Bd)*
Ba Phuong Le *(Member-Mgmt Bd)*

FLEET CANADA INC.

1011 Gilmore Rd
PO Box 600
Fort Erie, ON, L2A 5M4, Canada
Tel.: (905) 871-2100
Fax: (905) 871-2722
Web Site: www.fleet.ca
Emp.: 100
Business Description:
Aerospace Components; Metal to Metal Bonding & Conventional Construction & Composite Bonding
S.I.C.: 3728
N.A.I.C.S.: 336413
Personnel:
Glenn Stansfield *(Pres)*
Paul Williams *(CFO)*

FLEETMATICS GROUP PLC

Block C Cookstown Court Belgard Road Tallaght
Dublin, 24, Ireland
Tel.: (353) 1 413 1250
Web Site: www.fleetmatics.com
Year Founded: 2004
FLTX—(NYSE)
Rev.: $177,350,000
Assets: $286,539,000
Liabilities: $84,731,000
Net Worth: $201,808,000
Earnings: $30,457,000
Emp.: 659
Fiscal Year-end: 12/31/13
Business Description:
Vehicle Tracking Software Publisher
S.I.C.: 7372
N.A.I.C.S.: 511210
Personnel:
James M. Travers *(Chm & CEO)*
Stephen Lifshatz *(CFO & Chief Acctg Officer)*
Dennis L. Abrahams *(COO)*
Kathleen Finato *(CMO)*
Peter Mitchell *(CTO)*
John J. Goggin *(Sr VP-Global Sls)*
Andrew M. Reynolds *(Sr VP-Global Bus Dev)*
Board of Directors:
James M. Travers
Hazem Ben-Gacem
Vincent R. De Palma
Andrew G. Flett
Brian Halligan
James F. Kelliher
J. Sanford Miller
Allison Mnookin
Jack Noonan
Liam Young

U.S. Subsidiary:

FleetMatics USA Group Holdings, Inc. **(1)**
70 Walnut St
Wellesley Hills, MA 02481-2102
Tel.: (866) 844-2235
Vehicle Tracking Software Publisher
S.I.C.: 7372
N.A.I.C.S.: 511210
Steve Eastwell *(Dir-Customer Svc)*

Subsidiary:

SageQuest LLC **(2)**
23550 Commerce Park
Cleveland, OH 44122 OH
Tel.: (216) 896-7243
Toll Free: (877) 628-6181
Web Site: www.sage-quest.com
Vehicle Tracking Software Publisher
S.I.C.: 7372
N.A.I.C.S.: 511210
Andrew Kraynak *(Sr Dir-Mktg Comm)*

FLEETWOOD CORPORATION LIMITED

21 Regal Place
Perth, WA, 6004, Australia
Tel.: (61) 893233300
Fax: (61) 892021106
E-Mail: info@fleetwood.com.au
Web Site: www.fleetwood.com.au

Fleetwood Corporation Limited—(Continued)

FWD—(ASX)
Rev.: $346,964,069
Assets: $325,760,460
Liabilities: $102,656,229
Net Worth: $223,104,231
Earnings: $12,979,356
Fiscal Year-end: 06/30/13

Business Description:
Tent Trailers Mfr
S.I.C.: 3792
N.A.I.C.S.: 336214

Personnel:
Stephen Price *(CEO)*
Bradley Denison *(CFO & Sec)*

Board of Directors:
Michael Hardy
John Bond
Peter Gunzburg
Greg Tate

Subsidiaries:

Camec Pty Ltd (1)
47-63 Remington Dr
Dandenong S, Dandenong, VIC, 3175, Australia
Tel.: (61) 397996455
Fax: (61) 397996466
E-Mail: enq@camec.com.au
Web Site: www.camec.com.au
Emp.: 100
Recreational & Marine Vehicles Equipment Mfr & Supplier
S.I.C.: 3799
N.A.I.C.S.: 336999
Steve Carroll *(CEO)*
Greg Tate *(Sec)*

Coromal Caravans Pty Ltd (1)
25 Harrison Rd
Forrestfield, Perth, WA, 6058, Australia
Tel.: (61) 893520900
Fax: (61) 894549291
E-Mail: info@coromal.com.au
Web Site: www.coromal.com.au
Caravan Mfr
S.I.C.: 3711
N.A.I.C.S.: 336111
Bradley van Hemert *(CEO)*

Fleetwood Pty Ltd (1)
1240 Abernethy Rd
High Wycombe, Perth, WA, 6057, Australia
Tel.: (61) 892817500
Fax: (61) 892817580
E-Mail: sales@fleetwood.com.au
Web Site: www.fleetwood.com.au/manufacturing/manufacturingtest/profile.html
Emp.: 50
Transportable Homes Construction Services
S.I.C.: 2451
N.A.I.C.S.: 321991
Greg Tate *(Sec)*

Flexiglass Challenge Pty Ltd (1)
26 Cooper Rd
Jandakot, WA, 6164, Australia
Tel.: (61) 894172111
Fax: (61) 894141142
E-Mail: wa@flexiglass.com.au
Web Site: www.flexiglass.com.au
Emp.: 40
Canopies Sales
S.I.C.: 3444
N.A.I.C.S.: 332322

Rainbow Transportable Homes Pty Ltd (1)
863-865 Mountain Hwy
Bayswater, VIC, 3153, Australia
Tel.: (61) 397298870
Fax: (61) 897298860
E-Mail: rainbowenq@fleetwood.com.au
Web Site: www.fleetwoodrainbow.com.au
Emp.: 20
Transportable Homes Construction Services
S.I.C.: 2451
N.A.I.C.S.: 321991
Greg Tate *(Mng Dir)*

FLEISCHHACKER GMBH & CO. KG

An der Silberkuhle 18
58239 Schwerte, Germany
Tel.: (49) 23049310
Fax: (49) 2304931199
E-Mail: info@fleischhacker.biz
Web Site: www.fleischhacker.biz
Rev.: $34,898,820
Emp.: 105

Business Description:
Medical Equipment Distr
S.I.C.: 5047
N.A.I.C.S.: 423450

Personnel:
Lutz Fleischhacker *(Pres)*

FLEMING FAMILY & PARTNERS LIMITED

15 Suffolk St
London, SW1Y 4HG, United Kingdom
Tel.: (44) 2074095600
Fax: (44) 2070365601
E-Mail: enquiries@ffandp.com
Web Site: www.ffandp.com
Year Founded: 2000
Sales Range: $25-49.9 Million
Emp.: 110

Business Description:
Fund Management & Investment Services
S.I.C.: 6282
N.A.I.C.S.: 523930

Personnel:
Adam R. Fleming *(Chm)*
Richard Fitzalan Howard *(Mng Dir)*

Board of Directors:
Martin R. Wade, III

Subsidiaries:

FF&P Advisory Limited (1)
15 Suffolk St London
London, SW1Y 48J, United Kingdom
Tel.: (44) 2074095600
Fax: (44) 2070365601
E-Mail: enquiries@ssandp.com
Web Site: www.ssandp.com
Emp.: 120
Investment Services
S.I.C.: 6211
N.A.I.C.S.: 523999
David Fletcher *(CEO)*

FF&P Asset Management Limited (1)
15 Suffolk St
London, SW1 Y4HG, United Kingdom
Tel.: (44) 2074095600
Fax: (44) 2070365701
E-Mail: enquiries@ffandp.com
Emp.: 200
Asset Management & Investment Services
S.I.C.: 6799
N.A.I.C.S.: 523920
Richard Fitzalan Howard *(CEO)*

FF&P Unit Trust Management Limited (1)
15 Suffolk Street
London, SW1 Y4HG, United Kingdom
Tel.: (44) 2074095600
Fax: (44) 207409560
Web Site: www.ffmp.com
Emp.: 120
Trust Management Services
S.I.C.: 8748
N.A.I.C.S.: 541618

Ian Fleming Publications Ltd. (1)
15 Suffolk Street
London, SW1Y 4HG, United Kingdom
Tel.: (44) 2070365000
Fax: (44) 2070365601
E-Mail: ianflemingcentre@gmail.com
Web Site: www.ianflemingcentre.com
Emp.: 4
Publishing Services
S.I.C.: 2741
N.A.I.C.S.: 511199
Corinne Turner *(Mng Dir)*

Non-U.S. Subsidiaries:

Fleming Family & Partners (Liechtenstein) AG (1)
AM Schragen Weg 2
FL-9490 Vaduz, Liechtenstein
Tel.: (423) 2392480
Fax: (423) 2392481
Web Site: www.ffandp.co.uk
Emp.: 10
Investment Services
S.I.C.: 6211
N.A.I.C.S.: 523999
Corinne Zogg *(Mng Dir)*

Fleming Family & Partners (Suisse) AG (1)
Todistrasse 38
Postfach 7225
8022 Zurich, Switzerland
Tel.: (41) 432108000
Fax: (41) 432108009
Emp.: 13
Investment Services
S.I.C.: 6211
N.A.I.C.S.: 523999
Pawel Sniegocki *(Portfolio Mgr)*

FLETCHER BUILDING LIMITED

810 Great South Road
Auckland, 1061, New Zealand

Mailing Address:
Private Bag 92 114
Auckland, 1142, New Zealand
Tel.: (64) 9 525 9000
Fax: (64) 9 525 9032
E-Mail: marion.clements@fb.co.nz
Web Site: www.fletcherbuilding.com
FBU—(ASX NZE OTC)
Sls.: $7,128,729,000
Assets: $5,945,211,000
Liabilities: $2,970,513,000
Net Worth: $2,974,698,000
Earnings: $282,069,000
Emp.: 18,830
Fiscal Year-end: 06/30/13

Business Description:
Commercial Construction, Civil & Mechanical Engineering Building Products Mfr & Distr
S.I.C.: 5211
N.A.I.C.S.: 444190

Personnel:
Mark Adamson *(CEO & Mng Dir)*
Nick Olson *(CFO)*
Gerry Bollman *(CEO-Bus Strategy & Performance)*
Kate Daly *(CEO-Corp Svcs)*
Graham Darlow *(CEO-Construction)*
Dean Fradgley *(CEO-Distr-New Zealand)*
Tim Hickey *(CEO-Distr-Australia)*
Mark Malpass *(CEO-Infrastructure Products)*
Tim Richards *(CEO-Building Products)*
Paul Zuckerman *(CEO-Laminates & Panels)*
Charles Bolt *(Gen Counsel & Sec)*

Board of Directors:
Ralph Graham Waters
Mark Adamson
Anthony John Carter
Alan Trevor Jackson
John Frederick Judge
Ralph James Norris
Kathryn Dianne Spargo
Cecilia Tarrant
Gene Thomas Tilbrook

Computershare Investor Services Limited
Level 2 159 Hurstmere Road
Takapuna, New Zealand

Subsidiaries:

AHI Roofing Limited (1)
90-104 Felton Matthew Ave
PO Box 18071
Auckland, 1072, New Zealand (100%)
Tel.: (64) 99789010
Fax: (64) 99789069
E-Mail: info@gerardroof.co.nz
Web Site: www.gerardroof.co.nz
Emp.: 180
Roofing Siding & Sheet Metal Contractors
S.I.C.: 1761
N.A.I.C.S.: 238160
Peter Wilson *(Gen Mgr)*

Building Choices Limited (1)
2-20 Mandeville Street
Riccarton, 8011 Christchurch, Canterbury, New Zealand
Tel.: (64) 33482039
Fax: (64) 33489483
Web Site: www.placemakers.co.nz
Emp.: 18
Hardware Parts Distr
S.I.C.: 5072
N.A.I.C.S.: 423710
Katherine Freeman-Greene *(Mgr-Ops)*

Crane Distribution Properties Limited (1)
Level 1 64 Cook Street
Auckland, 1010, New Zealand
Tel.: (64) 33381009
Fax: (64) 33387313
Web Site: www.mico.co.nz
Emp.: 5
Industrial Crane Distr
S.I.C.: 5084
N.A.I.C.S.: 423830
Mark Adamson *(Office Mgr)*

Deavoll Building Supplies Limited (1)
576 Whangaparaoa Rd
Stanmore Bay, Auckland, New Zealand
Tel.: (64) 9 424 9000
Fax: (64) 9 424 9100
Building Material Distr
S.I.C.: 5039
N.A.I.C.S.: 423390
John Gair *(Gen Mgr)*

DVS Limited (1)
17a Piermark Drive Rosedale
North Shore City, Auckland, 0632, New Zealand
Tel.: (64) 9 414 2755
Fax: (64) 9 414 2754
E-Mail: customerservice@dvs.co.nz
Web Site: www.dvs.co.nz
Home Ventilation Services
S.I.C.: 7349
N.A.I.C.S.: 561790
Bob Batenburg *(Gen Mgr)*

Fletcher Aluminium (1)
30-32 Bowden Rpad
Mount Wellington, Auckland, 1060, New Zealand (100%)
Mailing Address:
PO Box 14107
Panmure, Auckland, New Zealand
Tel.: (64) 9 574 1500
Fax: (64) 9 574 1600
E-Mail: mark.adamson@fb.co.nz
Web Site: www.fletcherbuilding.com
Emp.: 8,000
Designs, Develops & Manufactures Premium Aluminum Extrusions for Industries
S.I.C.: 3354
N.A.I.C.S.: 331318
Mark Adamson *(CEO & Mng Dir)*

Fletcher Building Holdings Limited (1)
810 Great South Road
1061 Auckland, New Zealand (100%)
Mailing Address:
Private Bag 92 114
Auckland, 1142, New Zealand
Tel.: (64) 95259000
Fax: (64) 95259989
Web Site: www.fletcherbuilding.co.nz
Holding Company
S.I.C.: 6719
N.A.I.C.S.: 551112

Fletcher Building Nominees Limited (1)
810 Great South Road Penrose
Auckland, 1061, New Zealand
Tel.: (64) 95259000
Fax: (64) 5259046
Web Site: www.fletcherbuilding.com
Emp.: 7
Civil Engineering Construction Services
S.I.C.: 1629
N.A.I.C.S.: 237990
Ljubisa Vucinic *(CEO)*

Fletcher Building Products Limited (1)
810 Great South Road
810 Great S Rd, Penrose, 1061, New Zealand (100%)
Tel.: (64) 95259000
E-Mail: jonathan.ling@fb.co.nz
Building Material Dealers
S.I.C.: 5211
N.A.I.C.S.: 444190

Fletcher Concrete and Infrastructure Limited (1)
Level 6 Fletcher Bldg
Fletcher House 810, Penrose, Auckland, New Zealand (100%)
Tel.: (64) 95261200, ext. 95259150
Fax: (64) 95259989
E-Mail: mark.binns@fb.co.nz
Web Site: www.fletcher.co.nz
Concrete Contractors
S.I.C.: 1771
N.A.I.C.S.: 238110
Mark Binns *(CEO-Infrastructure)*

The Fletcher Construction Company Limited (1)
Jack Smith House
2nd Floor 816 Great South Road, 1061 Auckland, New Zealand (100%)
Tel.: (64) 95259000
Fax: (64) 95259205
Web Site: www.fletcherconstruction.co.nz
Heavy & Civil Engineering Construction
S.I.C.: 1629
N.A.I.C.S.: 237990
Graham Darlow *(CEO)*

Fletcher Residential Limited (1)
810 Great S Rd
Private Bag 99922
Auckland, New Zealand (100%)
Tel.: (64) 95259555
Fax: (64) 95251974
Web Site: www.fletcherresidential.co.nz
Emp.: 45
New Housing Operative Builders
S.I.C.: 1531
N.A.I.C.S.: 236117
Mark Adamson *(CEO)*

Fletcher Steel Limited (1)
259 James Flecther Dr
Auckland, 2024, New Zealand (100%)
Tel.: (64) 92761946
Fax: (64) 92764623
Web Site: www.fletchersteel.co.nz
Emp.: 250
Iron & Steel Mills
S.I.C.: 3399
N.A.I.C.S.: 331110
Ian Jones *(Gen Mgr)*

Forman Building Systems Limited (1)
20 Vestey Drive Mt Wellington
Auckland, 1060, New Zealand
Tel.: (64) 9 276 4000
Fax: (64) 9 276 4141
E-Mail: sales@forman.co.nz
Web Site: www.forman.co.nz/fbs/
Ceiling & Interior Wall System Distr
S.I.C.: 5198
N.A.I.C.S.: 424950
Mark Jarmey *(Gen Mgr)*

Forman Commercial Interiors Limited (1)
20 Vestey Drive Mt Wellington
Auckland, 1060, New Zealand
Tel.: (64) 9 276 4000
Fax: (64) 9 276 9797
E-Mail: sales@forman.co.nz
Web Site: www.forman.co.nz/fci/
Interior Decoration & Installation Services
S.I.C.: 1751
N.A.I.C.S.: 238130
Shannon Outram *(Branch Mgr)*

Forman Group Limited (1)
20 Vestey Dr
PO Box 12349
Penrose, Auckland, New Zealand (100%)
Tel.: (64) 92764000
Fax: (64) 92764141
E-Mail: info@forman.co.nz
Web Site: www.forman.co.nz
Emp.: 73
Holding Company
S.I.C.: 6719
N.A.I.C.S.: 551112

Forman Insulation Limited (1)
20 Vestey Drive Mt Wellington
Auckland, 1060, New Zealand
Tel.: (64) 9 276 4000
Fax: (64) 9 276 9797
E-Mail: sales@forman.co.nz
Web Site: www.forman.co.nz/fil/
Insulation System Installation Services
S.I.C.: 1742
N.A.I.C.S.: 238310
Mark Jarmey *(Gen Mgr)*

Forman Manufacturing Limited (1)
95 Hugo Johnstone Drive
Penrose, Auckland, 1061, New Zealand
Tel.: (64) 95793881
Plastic Foam Products Mfr
S.I.C.: 3086
N.A.I.C.S.: 326140

G. E. Crane N.Z. Holdings Ltd (1)
50 Hazelddean Road
Christchurch, New Zealand
Tel.: (64) 3 3381009
Fax: (64) 3387313
Electrical Equipment Distr
S.I.C.: 5063
N.A.I.C.S.: 423610

Gray Building Supplies Limited (1)
Nelson Region
Stoke, 7011 Nelson, New Zealand
Tel.: (64) 3 547 9111
Fax: (64) 3 547 4200
Emp.: 4
Building Materials Whslr
S.I.C.: 5039
N.A.I.C.S.: 423390
Chris Young *(Gen Mgr)*

Hedges Building Supplies Limited (1)
Canada Street
3792 Morrinsville, New Zealand
Tel.: (64) 7 889 5142
Fax: (64) 7 889 5950
Emp.: 12
Building Materials Whslr
S.I.C.: 5039
N.A.I.C.S.: 423390
Steve Kinsey *(Mgr)*

Home & Dry Limited (1)
15 Jarden Mile
Ngauranga, Wellington, 6035, New Zealand
Tel.: (64) 508 466363
Fax: (64) 44710264
E-Mail: enquiries@homeanddry.co.nz
Web Site: www.homeanddry.co.nz
Emp.: 15
Housing Ventilation Services
S.I.C.: 7349
N.A.I.C.S.: 561790
Kerry Shannon *(Mgr-Bus Unit)*

John Cockburn Building Supplies Limited (1)
115 Alford Forest Road
Ashburton, 7700, New Zealand
Tel.: (64) 33089099
Fax: (64) 33081824
Emp.: 14
Construction Materials Whslr
S.I.C.: 5032
N.A.I.C.S.: 423320
John Cockburn *(Gen Mgr)*

Kenna Building Supplies Limited (1)
3 Semple Street
5022 Porirua, New Zealand
Tel.: (64) 4 2379189
Fax: (64) 4 2375733
Building Materials Whslr
S.I.C.: 5039
N.A.I.C.S.: 423390
Boyd Kenna *(Gen Mgr)*

Kevin Jarvis Building Supplies Limited (1)
53 Molesworth Street
New Plymouth, 4601, New Zealand
Tel.: (64) 6 7575789
Fax: (64) 6 7554174
Emp.: 40
Construction Materials Distr
S.I.C.: 5039
N.A.I.C.S.: 423390
Steven Murray *(Gen Mgr)*

Langford-Lee Building Supplies Limited (1)
90 Spa Road
3330 Taupo, New Zealand
Tel.: (64) 7 376 0220
Fax: (64) 7 378 3191
Emp.: 2
Building Materials Whslr
S.I.C.: 5039
N.A.I.C.S.: 423390
Kerry Hudson *(Mgr)*

Minnell Building Supplies Limited (1)
150 Marua Road
Ellerslie, Auckland, 1051, New Zealand
Tel.: (64) 95255100
Emp.: 150
Building Materials Whslr
S.I.C.: 5039
N.A.I.C.S.: 423390
John Beveridge *(CEO)*

New Zealand Ceiling & Drywall Supplies Limited (1)
North Shore 28C Poland Road
Glenfield, North Shore, 0610, New Zealand
Tel.: (64) 9 443 5006
Web Site: www.nzcds.co.nz
Emp.: 5
Building Materials Whslr
S.I.C.: 5039
N.A.I.C.S.: 423390
Shane Borrell *(Gen Mgr)*

The O'Brien Group Limited (1)
8 Gow Street
PO Box 290
Mosgiel, 9024 Dunedin, New Zealand
Tel.: (64) 3 489 3849
Fax: (64) 3 489 5963
E-Mail: enquiries@obrien-group.co.nz
Web Site: www.obrien-group.co.nz
Emp.: 12
Kitchen Ware Accessories Mfr
S.I.C.: 2434
N.A.I.C.S.: 337110

Phoenix Aluminium 2011 Limited (1)
78 Ellice Road Wairau Valley
PO Box 100-134
North Shore, Auckland, 745, New Zealand
Tel.: (64) 9 477 4090
Fax: (64) 9 475 9780
E-Mail: nsinfo@phoenixnz.co.nz
Web Site: www.phoenixnz.co.nz
Emp.: 2
Fabricated Aluminium Door & Window Mfr
S.I.C.: 3499
N.A.I.C.S.: 332999
Steve Cowan *(Mgr-Sls)*

Rolleston Building Supplies Limited (1)
Matthews Avenue
410 Kaitaia, New Zealand
Tel.: (64) 9 4080630
Fax: (64) 9 4080862
Emp.: 12
Building Materials Whslr
S.I.C.: 5039
N.A.I.C.S.: 423390
Tracy Clark *(Mgr)*

Shed Boss NZ Limited (1)
3 Blenheim St
Upper Hutt, Wellington, 5018, New Zealand
Tel.: (64) 4 527 8350
Fax: (64) 4 527 0496
E-Mail: wellington@shedboss.co.nz
Web Site: www.shedboss.co.nz
Emp.: 1
Commercial Building Construction Services
S.I.C.: 1542
N.A.I.C.S.: 236220
Phil Kirk *(Mgr)*

Steven Marshall Building Supplies Limited (1)
3 Link Drive Glenfield
Auckland, 1310, New Zealand
Tel.: (64) 9 4445155
Fax: (64) 9 4416809
E-Mail: orders.wairaupark@placemakers.co.nz
Web Site: www.placemakers.co.nz
Emp.: 5
Building Materials Whslr
S.I.C.: 5039
N.A.I.C.S.: 423390
Steve Marshall *(Gen Mgr)*

Sullivan & Armstrong Building Supplies Limited (1)
17 Clark Street
640 New Lynn, Auckland, New Zealand
Tel.: (64) 98250088
Fax: (64) 98250077
Building Materials Whslr
S.I.C.: 5039
N.A.I.C.S.: 423390
Paul Armstrong *(Gen Mgr)*

Tasman Insulation New Zealand Limited (1)
9-15 Holloway Pl
PO Box 12-069
Auckland, New Zealand (100%)
Tel.: (64) 95792139
Fax: (64) 95713482
E-Mail: pinkbett@pinkbett.co.nz
Web Site: www.pinkbett.co.nz
Emp.: 100
Drywall Plastering Acoustical & Insulation Contractors
S.I.C.: 1742
N.A.I.C.S.: 238310
Tony Peau *(Gen Mgr)*

Ted Harper Building Supplies Limited (1)
1 Te Kumi Rd
Te Kuiti, 3910, New Zealand
Tel.: (64) 78788149
Fax: (64) 78788148
Building Materials Whslr
S.I.C.: 5039
N.A.I.C.S.: 423390
Ted Harper *(CEO)*

Terry Mellsop Building Supplies Limited (1)
Taradale Road
Napier, New Zealand
Tel.: (64) 6 843 5816
Fax: (64) 6 843 4179
Construction Materials Whslr
S.I.C.: 5032
N.A.I.C.S.: 423320
Andy Sellar *(Gen Mgr)*

Winstone Wallboards Limited (1)
37 Felix Street
PO Box 12256
Auckland, 1642, New Zealand (100%)
Tel.: (64) 96330100
Fax: (64) 96330101
Web Site: www.gib.co.nz
Emp.: 180
Gypsum Product Mfr
S.I.C.: 3275
N.A.I.C.S.: 327420
David Thomas *(Gen Mgr)*

Holding:

PlaceMakers Limited (1)
150 Marua Road
Mount Wellington, Auckland, 1134, New Zealand NZ
Tel.: (64) 9525 5100 (50.1%)
Fax: (64) 9579 1451
E-Mail: placemaker@placemaker.com
Web Site: www.placemakers.co.nz
Emp.: 100
Holding Company; Home Centers Operator & Franchisor
S.I.C.: 6719
N.A.I.C.S.: 551112
John Beveridge *(CEO)*

Subsidiary:

Fletcher Distribution Limited (2)
150 Marua Road
Mount Wellington, Auckland, 1134, New Zealand NZ
Tel.: (64) 9525 5100 (100%)
Fax: (64) 9579 4913
Web Site: www.placemakers.co.nz
Emp.: 80
Home Centers Operator & Franchisor
S.I.C.: 5211
N.A.I.C.S.: 444110
John Beveridge *(CEO)*

U.S. Subsidiaries:

Decra Roofing Systems Inc. (1)
1230 Railroad St
Corona, CA 92882 (100%)

Fletcher Building Limited—(Continued)

Tel.: (951) 272-8180
Fax: (951) 272-4476
E-Mail: marketing@decra.com
Web Site: www.decra.com
Sheet Metal Work Mfr
S.I.C.: 3444
N.A.I.C.S.: 332322

Formica Corporation (1)
10155 Reading Rd
Cincinnati, OH 45241 DE
Tel.: (513) 786-3400
Fax: (513) 786-3566
Toll Free: (800) 367-6422
Web Site: www.formica.com
Sales Range: $750-799.9 Million
Emp.: 5,600
High Pressure Laminates & Adhesives & Solid Surfacing Material Mfr
Import Export
S.I.C.: 3083
N.A.I.C.S.: 326130
Mark Adamson *(Pres & CEO)*
Lee Box *(CFO)*
Mitch Quint *(Pres-North America)*

Subsidiary:

Formica Corporation (2)
10155 Reading Rd
Cincinnati, OH 45241-3109
Tel.: (513) 786-3103
Fax: (513) 786-3566
Web Site: www.formica.com
Emp.: 300
Mfr. Plant for High Pressure Laminate
S.I.C.: 3083
N.A.I.C.S.: 326130
Jason Utz *(Mgr-Natl Segment-Lowe's)*

Non-U.S. Holdings:

Formica Asia Ltd. (2)
Room 1305-9 13/F Olympia Plaza
255 Kings Road, North Point, China (Hong Kong) HK
Tel.: (852) 25980117
Telex: 73350
Fax: (852) 25985603
E-Mail: info@formica.com.hk
Web Site: www.formica.com.hk
Emp.: 45
Marketing & Sale of High Pressure Laminates & Other Surfacing Materials
S.I.C.: 3083
N.A.I.C.S.: 326130
Lawrence Chan *(Gen Mgr)*

Formica Canada, Inc. (2)
25 Rue Mercier
Saint-Jean-sur-Richelieu, QC, J3B 6E9, Canada
Tel.: (450) 347-7541
Fax: (450) 347-5065
E-Mail: fracine.verner@formica.com
Web Site: www.formica.com
Emp.: 350
High Pressure Laminate Mfr
S.I.C.: 2671
N.A.I.C.S.: 322220
Claude Sarrazim *(Gen Mgr)*

Formica Ltd. (2)
Coast Rd
North Shields, NE29 8RE, United Kingdom UK
Tel.: (44) 1912593100
Telex: 53295
Fax: (44) 1912582719
E-Mail: bernie.davison@formica.com
Web Site: www.formica.com
Emp.: 450
High-Pressure Laminate Mfr
S.I.C.: 3083
N.A.I.C.S.: 326130
Bernie Davidson *(Plant Mgr)*

Formica Netherland B.V. (2)
Laan van Oversteen 14-B
Postbus 3131
2280 GC Rijswijk, Netherlands NL
Tel.: (31) 704134820
Telex: 39163
Fax: (31) 704134821
E-Mail: contact.nederland@formica.com
Web Site: www.formica.com
Sales Range: $10-24.9 Million
Emp.: 15
High-Pressure Laminate Mfr
S.I.C.: 2671
N.A.I.C.S.: 322220
Melle De Pater *(Mng Dir)*

Formica S.A. (2)
Txomin Egileor
54 48960 Bilbao, Spain ES
Tel.: (34) 944579600
Telex: 32053
Fax: (34) 944566306
E-Mail: formica.spain@formica-europe.com
Web Site: www.formica.com
Emp.: 250
High-Pressure Laminate Mfr
S.I.C.: 3083
N.A.I.C.S.: 326130
Herves Ninvl *(Mng Dir)*

Formica Societe Anonyme (2)
29 Rue De La Maison Rouge
Lognes, 77185 Paris, Cedex, France FR
Tel.: (33) 160068686
Telex: 693230
Fax: (33) 160176141
Web Site: www.formica.com
Emp.: 15
High-Pressure Laminate Mfr
S.I.C.: 3083
N.A.I.C.S.: 326130
Robert Lembert *(Mng Dir)*

Formica Switzerland AG (2)
Flughofstrasse 45
CH 8153 Rumlang, ZH, Switzerland CH
Tel.: (41) 448188818
Fax: (41) 44 817 01 82
E-Mail: schweiz@formica.com
Web Site: www.formica.eu.com
Emp.: 2
Marketing & Sales of Laminates, Plastics, Plate Sheet & Profile Shapes
S.I.C.: 3083
N.A.I.C.S.: 326130

Formica Taiwan (2)
6th Fl No 68-70 Sec 3 Nanking E Rd
Taipei, Taiwan TW
Tel.: (886) 225151017
Fax: (886) 225170545
E-Mail: david.ren@formica.com
Web Site: www.formica.com
Emp.: 70
High-Pressure Decorative Laminate Mfr
S.I.C.: 3083
N.A.I.C.S.: 326130
David Ren *(Mng Dir)*

Formica Vertriebs GmbH (2)
11 Silver Fox Way Cobalt Business Park
NE-27 Newcastle, Germany De
Tel.: (49) 1803676422
Telex: 887791
Fax: (49) 01912592648
E-Mail: formice.limited@formica.co.uk
Web Site: www.formica-deutschland.de
Emp.: 12
High-Pressure Laminate Mfr
S.I.C.: 5169
N.A.I.C.S.: 424690

Non-U.S. Subsidiaries:

AHI Roofing Gyarto Es Kereskedelmi Korlatolt Felelossegu Tarasag (1)
Fehervari Ut 28/14
Varpalota, 8100, Hungary
Tel.: (36) 88552800
Fax: (36) 88552888
Building Roofing Material Whslr
S.I.C.: 5033
N.A.I.C.S.: 423330

AHI Roofing (Malaysia) SDN BHD (1)
Lot 12 Nilai Industrial Estate
71800 Nilai, Negeri Sembilan, Malaysia
Tel.: (60) 6 799 1877
Fax: (60) 6 799 1827
E-Mail: info@ahiroofing.com.my
Web Site: www.ahiroofing.com.my
Building Roofing Material Mfr & Distr
S.I.C.: 3444
N.A.I.C.S.: 332322

Amatek Holdings Limited (1)
6-8 Thomas Street
2067 Chatswood, NSW, Australia
Tel.: (61) 61299283500
Fax: (61) 299283679
Investment Management Services
S.I.C.: 6211
N.A.I.C.S.: 523999

Amatek Industries Pty Limited (1)
Tower B Level 11 Zenith Centre 821 Pacific Highway
Chatswood, NSW, 2067, Australia
Tel.: (61) 2 9928 3500
Fax: (61) 2 8986 0920
Building Material & Concrete Mfr
S.I.C.: 3273
N.A.I.C.S.: 327320

Australian Construction Products Pty Limited (1)
339 Horsley Road
Milperra, NSW, 2214, Australia
Tel.: (61) 2 9772 4172
Fax: (61) 2 9792 6272
E-Mail: sales@acprod.com.au
Web Site: www.acprod.com.au
Emp.: 3
Steel Civil Road System Mfr & Distr
S.I.C.: 3317
N.A.I.C.S.: 331210
Elena Chuyan *(Gen Mgr)*

Australian Fibre Glass Pty Limited (1)
2/ 16 Amberley Crs
Dandenong, VIC, 3175, Australia
Tel.: (61) 3 9792 1227
Fiber Glass Mfr
S.I.C.: 3229
N.A.I.C.S.: 327212

Cemac (Hong Kong) Limited (1)
Rm 702-5 7th Floor Yen Sheng Ctr
Kowloon, China (Hong Kong) (100%)
Tel.: (852) 28115253
Fax: (852) 251651115
E-Mail: hk@cemac.com.cn
Web Site: www.cemac.com.cn
Emp.: 40
Business Support Services
S.I.C.: 7389
N.A.I.C.S.: 561499
Chi Wing Shum *(Mgr)*

Crane Distribution Limited (1)
Virginia Business Centre
Locked Bag 71
Brisbane, QLD, 4014, Australia
Tel.: (61) 732609777
Fax: (61) 732609750
Building Supplies Distr
S.I.C.: 5039
N.A.I.C.S.: 423390
Susan Leppinus *(Sec)*
Gregory Lewis *(Sec)*

Crane Enfield Metals Pty Limited (1)
2115 Castlereagh Road
Penrith, NSW, 2750, Australia
Tel.: (61) 2 4720 5300
Fax: (61) 2 4720 5392
E-Mail: sales@cranecopper.com.au
Web Site: www.cranecopper.com.au
Emp.: 12
Aluminium Tube & Metal Products Mfr
S.I.C.: 3354
N.A.I.C.S.: 331318

Crane Group Limited (1)
Level 14 15 Blue Street
North Sydney, NSW, 2060, Australia AU
Tel.: (61) 289233000
Fax: (61) 289233060
E-Mail: corporate@crane.com.au
Web Site: www.crane.com.au
Sales Range: $1-4.9 Billion
Emp.: 4,353
Plastic Pipeline Systems & Nonferrous Metal Products Mfr; Plumbing & Electrical Supplies Distr
Import Export
S.I.C.: 3088
N.A.I.C.S.: 326191
Greg L. Sedgwick *(Mng Dir)*
James Madigan *(CIO)*

Divisions:

Austral Wright Metals (2)
381 Victoria Street
Wetherill Park, NSW, 2164, Australia (100%)
Mailing Address:
PO Box 6105
Wetherill Park, 2164, Australia
Tel.: (61) 298270700
Fax: (61) 47305390
E-Mail: awm@australwright.com.au
Web Site: www.australwright.com.au
Emp.: 50
Nonferrous Metals & Metal Products Distr
S.I.C.: 5051
N.A.I.C.S.: 423510
Alex Gouch *(Mgr-Technical)*

Crane Copper Tube (2)
2115 Castlereagh Road
Penrith, NSW, 2750, Australia (100%)
Mailing Address:
PO Box 319
Penrith, NSW, 2751, Australia
Tel.: (61) 247205300
Fax: (61) 247205390
E-Mail: sales@cranecopper.com.au
Web Site: www.cranecopper.com.au
Emp.: 170
Copper Tube Mfr
S.I.C.: 3351
N.A.I.C.S.: 331420

Iplex Pipelines Australia Pty Ltd (2)
Fujitsu Centre Level 14
Locked Bag 2125
15 Blue Street, North Sydney, NSW, 2060, Australia (100%)
Mailing Address:
Locked Bag 2125
North Sydney, NSW, 2060, Australia
Tel.: (61) 297558266
Fax: (61) 297551195
E-Mail: sales@iplexpipelines.com.au
Web Site: www.iplex.com.au
Emp.: 1,000
Pipe & Pipe Fittings Mfr & Distr
S.I.C.: 3498
N.A.I.C.S.: 332996
William Wood *(Mng Dir)*

Subsidiary:

Northern Iron and Brass Foundry Pty. Ltd. (3)
22 Meyer Avenue
Wangan, Innisfail, QLD, 4871, Australia
Tel.: (61) 7 4064 2344
Fax: (61) 7 4064 2681
Web Site: www.nibf.com.au
Emp.: 10
Iron Products Mfr
S.I.C.: 3321
N.A.I.C.S.: 331511
Joe Vecchio *(Gen Mgr)*

Tradelink Plumbing Centres (2)
1051 Nudgee Rd
Banyo, Brisbane, QLD, 4014, Australia (100%)
Tel.: (61) 732609777
Fax: (61) 732609750
E-Mail: tl@tradelink.com.au
Web Site: www.tradelink.com.au
Emp.: 3,000
Plumbing Supplies for Bathrooms, Kitchens & Laundries
S.I.C.: 5074
N.A.I.C.S.: 423720
Peter Brennan *(Mgr-HR)*

Non-U.S. Subsidiaries:

Iplex Pipelines NZ Limited (2)
67 Malden Street
Palmerston North, 5301, New Zealand (100%)
Tel.: (64) 63582004
Fax: (64) 63562906
E-Mail: info@iplex.co.nz
Web Site: www.iplex.co.nz
Emp.: 110
Plastic Pipes & Pipe Fittings Mfr & Distr
S.I.C.: 3498
N.A.I.C.S.: 332996
Craig Mangos *(Gen Mgr)*

Crevet Pipelines Pty Ltd (1)
Cnr Southpine and Johnstone Rd
Brendale, 4500 Brisbane, QLD, Australia
Tel.: (61) 738819290
Fax: (61) 738819865
E-Mail: admin@crevet.com.au
Web Site: www.crevet.com.au
Emp.: 200
Building Pipe Mfr & Distr
S.I.C.: 5039
N.A.I.C.S.: 423390

Susan Leppinus *(Sec)*
Gregory Lewis *(Sec)*

Fletcher Building Australia (1)
Level 11 Tower B Zenith Ctr 821 Pacific Hwy
Locked Bag 7013
Chatswood, NSW, 2067, Australia
Tel.: (61) 299283500
Fax: (61) 289860929
E-Mail: info@fletcherbuilding.com.au
Web Site: www.fletcherbuilding.com
Emp.: 30
Mfr. of Concrete Products
S.I.C.: 3272
N.A.I.C.S.: 327390
Steven Baker *(Gen Mgr-Pipeline Products)*

Fletcher Building Netherlands B.V. (1)
Schouwburgplein 30-34
3012CL Rotterdam, Zuid-Holland, Netherlands
Tel.: (31) 102245333
Fax: (31) 104045288
Construction Engineering Services
S.I.C.: 8711
N.A.I.C.S.: 541330

Fletcher Construction Australia Pty Limited (1)
L 11 Tower B Zenith Centre 821 Pacific Hwy
Chatswood, NSW, 2067, Australia
Tel.: (61) 299283500
Fax: (61) 289860920
Construction Materials Mfr
S.I.C.: 3271
N.A.I.C.S.: 327331

Fletcher Construction Company (Fiji) Limited (1)
Wailada Industrial Estate
Box 3070
Lami, Suva, Fiji
Tel.: (679) 336 1511
Fax: (679) 336 1200
E-Mail: fletcher@fcc.com.fj
Web Site: www.fletcherconstruction.com.nz
Emp.: 63
Construction Engineering Services
S.I.C.: 8711
N.A.I.C.S.: 541330
Jill Gacques *(Gen Mgr)*

Fletcher Insulation Pty Limited (1)
161 Arthur Street
Homebush, NSW, 2140, Australia
Tel.: (61) 2 9752 9200
Fax: (61) 2 9764 3175
E-Mail: info@insulation.com.au
Web Site: www.insulation.com.au
Emp.: 300
Insulation Material Distr
S.I.C.: 5033
N.A.I.C.S.: 423330
Sandy Mckay *(Mgr)*

Subsidiary:

Baron Insulation Pty Ltd (2)
19 Pascal Road
Seaford, VIC, 3198, Australia
Tel.: (61) 3 9776 4006
Fax: (61) 3 9776 4007
E-Mail: mail@baroninsulation.com.au
Web Site: www.baroninsulation.com.au
Emp.: 24
Insulation Materials Mfr
S.I.C.: 3296
N.A.I.C.S.: 327993
Darren Davies *(Gen Mgr)*

Fletcher Insulation (1)
9 Balbu Place
Beresfield, NSW, 2322, Australia (100%)
Tel.: (61) 2 4964 1477
Fax: (61) 2 4966 8156
Web Site: www.insulation.com.au
Emp.: 40
Mfr & Supplier of Insulation for General Industrial Applications
S.I.C.: 1742
N.A.I.C.S.: 238310
Colin Zeiklyn *(Gen Mgr)*

Fletcher Morobe Construction Pty Limited (1)
Saraga St Six Mile
PO Box 848
Port Moresby, Papua New Guinea (100%)
Tel.: (675) 3253144
Fax: (675) 3250020
E-Mail: newbus@fmc.com.pg
Emp.: 3,000
Heavy & Civil Engineering Construction
S.I.C.: 1629
N.A.I.C.S.: 237990
Keith Fletcher *(Gen Mgr)*

Fletcher Pacific Steel (Fiji) Limited (1)
Leonidas St
Walu Bay, Suva, Fiji
Tel.: (679) 331 4500
Steel Products Mfr & Distr
S.I.C.: 3312
N.A.I.C.S.: 331110

Fletcher Wood Panels (Australia) Pty Limited (1)
Level 11 Tower B Zenith Centre 821 Pacific Hwy
Chatswood, NSW, 2067, Australia
Tel.: (61) 289860900
Fax: (61) 289860920
E-Mail: reception@fletcherbuilding.com.au
Web Site: www.fletcherbuilding.com.au
Wood Panel & Plastic Sheet Mfr
S.I.C.: 2499
N.A.I.C.S.: 321999

Forman Building Systems Pty Limited (1)
28 Biloela St
Villawood, NSW, 2163, Australia
Tel.: (61) 2 9728 3088
Emp.: 6
Construction Equipment Distr
S.I.C.: 5032
N.A.I.C.S.: 423320
Mark Jarmey *(Gen Mgr)*

Formica de Mexico SA DE CV (1)
Viaducto Miguel Aleman No 55 Buenos Aires Cuauhtemoc
Mexico, 6780, Mexico
Tel.: (52) 5555303135
Fax: (52) 5555304248
Building Materials Mfr
S.I.C.: 3448
N.A.I.C.S.: 332311

Formica Finance Limited (1)
Formica Building Coast Road
North Shields, Tyne and Wear, NE29 8RE, United Kingdom
Tel.: (44) 191 259 3100
Financial Management Services
S.I.C.: 6211
N.A.I.C.S.: 523999

Formica Holdco UK Limited (1)
Coast Rd
North Shields, Tyne and Wear, NE29 8RE, United Kingdom
Tel.: (44) 1912593100
Financial Management Services
S.I.C.: 6211
N.A.I.C.S.: 523999

Formica IKI Oy (1)
Tehtaantie 2
35990 Kolho, Finland
Tel.: (358) 3 580 001
Fax: (358) 3 531 6020
E-Mail: info.finland@formica.com
Web Site: www.formicaiki.fi
Emp.: 163
Plastic Plate & Sheet Mfr
S.I.C.: 3089
N.A.I.C.S.: 326199
Ingvar Delen *(Gen Mgr)*

Formica Norge A/S (1)
Fekjan 13 A
1394 Nesbru, Norway
Tel.: (47) 66 98 48 00
Fax: (47) 66 98 03 58
E-Mail: info.norge@formica.com
Construction Material Mfr & Distr
S.I.C.: 3531
N.A.I.C.S.: 333120

Formica PSM Limited (1)
Heighington Lane
Newton Aycliffe, Durham, DL5 6EF, United Kingdom
Tel.: (44) 1325 315141
Fax: (44) 1325 320577
Construction Materials Distr
S.I.C.: 5039
N.A.I.C.S.: 423390

Formica S.A.S (1)
Le Botanic 40 Ave Lingenfeld
77200 Torcy, France
Tel.: (33) 1 60 06 86 86
Fax: (33) 1 60 17 61 41
Web Site: www.formica.fr
Decorative Building Glassware Mfr
S.I.C.: 3229
N.A.I.C.S.: 327212

Formica (Singapore) Pte. Ltd (1)
No 502 Sims Avenue
Singapore, 387567, Singapore
Tel.: (65) 6514 1313
Fax: (65) 6846 7030
E-Mail: enquiries.sg@formica.com
Web Site: www.formica.com.sg
Emp.: 3
Laminate Sheets Mfr
S.I.C.: 2671
N.A.I.C.S.: 322220
Claudia Chang *(Gen Mgr)*

Formica Skandinavien AB (1)
Florettgatan 22
254 67 Helsingborg, Sweden
Tel.: (46) 42 38 48 00
Fax: (46) 42 38 48 40
E-Mail: info.sverige@formica.com
Web Site: www.formica.es/publish/site/eu/sweden/se/home/about_formica_/contact_us/sweden.html
Emp.: 10
Industrial Supplies Distr
S.I.C.: 5085
N.A.I.C.S.: 423840
Ingvar Delen *(Gen Mgr)*

Formica (Thailand) Co., Ltd. (1)
216/63 LPN Tower 15th Floor Nanglinchee Road
Chongnonsee Yannawa, Bangkok, 10120, Thailand
Tel.: (66) 2 285 2900
Fax: (66) 2 285 2899
E-Mail: surfacematerials-th@formica.co.th
Web Site: www.formica.co.th
Construction Materials Mfr & Distr
S.I.C.: 3271
N.A.I.C.S.: 327331

Plant:

Formica (Thailand) Co., Ltd. - Phrapradaeng Factory (2)
51/27 Moo 2 Poochaosamingprai Rd
Bangyapraek, Phra Pradaeng, Samutprakarn, 10130, Thailand
Tel.: (66) 2 755 8525
Fax: (66) 2 384 3721
Construction Materials Mfr
S.I.C.: 3271
N.A.I.C.S.: 327331

G E Crane Investments Pty Ltd (1)
15 Blue St
North Sydney, NSW, 2060, Australia
Tel.: (61) 289233000
Fax: (61) 299545544
Investment Management Services
S.I.C.: 6211
N.A.I.C.S.: 523999

Gatic Pty Limited (1)
169 Philip Highway
Elizabeth, SA, 5112, Australia
Tel.: (61) 1800 335 303
Fax: (61) 1800006308
E-Mail: sales@gatic.com.au
Web Site: www.gatic.com.au
Steel Frames & Grill Mfr
S.I.C.: 3317
N.A.I.C.S.: 331210
Edward Arena *(Mgr-HR)*

Hudson Building Supplies Pty Limited (1)
1051 Nudgee Road Banyo
Brisbane, QLD, 4014, Australia
Tel.: (61) 2 9629 0440
E-Mail: info@hudson.com.au
Web Site: www.hudson.com.au
Building Materials Distr
S.I.C.: 5039
N.A.I.C.S.: 423390

Insulation Solutions Holdings Pty Limited (1)
161 Arthur Street
Homebush, NSW, 2140, Australia
Tel.: (61) 297529268
Fax: (61) 297461385
Web Site: www.insulation.com.au
Investment Management Services
S.I.C.: 6211
N.A.I.C.S.: 523999
David Isaac *(Gen Mgr)*

Key Plastics Pty. Ltd. (1)
110 Airds Road
Minto, NSW, 2566, Australia
Tel.: (61) 2 9603 0300
Fax: (61) 2 9603 0301
E-Mail: info@keyplastics.com.au
Web Site: www.keyplastics.com.au
Plastic Plumbing Equipment Mfr
S.I.C.: 3089
N.A.I.C.S.: 326122

Kingston Bridge Engineering Pty Limited (1)
125 Sheffield Road
Welshpool, WA, 6106, Australia
Tel.: (61) 8 9458 9022
Fax: (61) 8 9458 9033
E-Mail: sales@kingstonbridge.com.au
Web Site: www.kingstonbridge.com.au
Polyethylene Pipe Mfr
S.I.C.: 3498
N.A.I.C.S.: 332996
Mark Wilkie *(Mgr-Mfg)*

Laminex (Australia) Pty. Ltd. (1)
90-94 Tram Road
Doncaster, VIC, 3108, Australia
Tel.: (61) 3 9848 4811
Fax: (61) 3 9848 8158
E-Mail: laminex_enquiries@laminex.com.au
Web Site: www.laminex.com.au
Emp.: 130
Building Materials Mfr
S.I.C.: 3089
N.A.I.C.S.: 326199
David Surveyor *(Gen Mgr)*

Laminex Group Pty Limited (1)
130 Sharps Road
Tullamarine, VIC, 3041, Australia
Tel.: (61) 3 9848 4811
Fax: (61) 3 9848 8158
Web Site: www.thelaminexgroup.com.au
Decorative Surface Material Mfr & Distr
S.I.C.: 5039
N.A.I.C.S.: 423390
David Noonan *(CFO)*

Laminex US Holdings Pty Limited (1)
L11 821 Pacific Hwy
Chatswood, NSW, 2067, Australia
Tel.: (61) 299283500
Investment Management Services
S.I.C.: 6211
N.A.I.C.S.: 523999

Perstorp Warerite Limited (1)
Aycliffe Industrial Park
Newton Aycliffe, Durham, DL5 6EF, United Kingdom
Tel.: (44) 1325315141
Fax: (44) 1325319634
Emp.: 80
Plastic Materials Mfr
S.I.C.: 3089
N.A.I.C.S.: 326199
Brian Umpleby *(Mgr-Site)*

Polymer Fusion Education Pty Ltd (1)
125 Sheffield Rd
Welshpool, WA, 6106, Australia
Tel.: (61) 892589444
Engineering Services
S.I.C.: 8711
N.A.I.C.S.: 541330

Rocla Australia Pty Limited (1)
L 11 Tower B Zenith Ctr 821 Pacific Hwy
Chatswood, NSW, 2067, Australia
Tel.: (61) 299283500
Fax: (61) 289860901
Web Site: www.rocla.com.au
Emp.: 100
Building Materials Whslr
S.I.C.: 5039
N.A.I.C.S.: 423390
Stephen Baker *(Gen Mgr)*

Rocla Concrete Pipes Pty Limited (1)
L 11 Tower B Zenneth Centre 821 Pacific Hwy

Fletcher Building Limited—(Continued)

Locked Bag 7013
Chatswood, NSW, 2067, Australia
Tel.: (61) 2 8986 0900
Fax: (61) 89860901
E-Mail: reception@Fletcherbuilding.com.au
Web Site: www.Rocla.com.au
Emp.: 150
Concrete Pipe Mfr
S.I.C.: 3272
N.A.I.C.S.: 327332
Debbie Bakkerus *(Gen Mgr)*

Rocla Industries Pty Limited **(1)**
Level 11 Tower B Zenith Centre 821 Pacific Hwy
Chatswood, NSW, 2067, Australia
Tel.: (61) 289860900
Fax: (61) 299283679
Concrete Block & Brick Mfr
S.I.C.: 3271
N.A.I.C.S.: 327331

Rocla Materials Pty Limited **(1)**
L 11 Twr B 821 Pacific Hwy
Chatswood, NSW, 2067, Australia
Tel.: (61) 299283500
Fax: (61) 299283679
Cut Stone & Stone Products Mfr
S.I.C.: 3281
N.A.I.C.S.: 327991

Rocla Pty Limited **(1)**
Level 11 Calbee Zenith Ctr
821 Pacific Highway, Chatswood, NSW, 2067, Australia (100%)
Tel.: (61) 299283500
Fax: (61) 89860929
E-Mail: solutions@rocla.com.au
Web Site: www.rocla.com.au
Emp.: 50
Concrete Product Mfr
S.I.C.: 3272
N.A.I.C.S.: 327390
Stephen T. Baker *(Gen Mgr)*

Rocla SA Pty Limited **(1)**
Level 11 Tower B Zenith Centre 821 Pacific Hwy
Chatswood, NSW, 2067, Australia
Tel.: (61) 289860900
Concrete Products Distr
S.I.C.: 5032
N.A.I.C.S.: 423320

Servicios Formica de Mexico SA DE CV **(1)**
Miguel Aleman 55 Buenos Aires
Cuauhtemoc, Mexico, 6780, Mexico
Tel.: (52) 5555303135
Fax: (52) 5555304248
Emp.: 4
Building Materials Whslr
S.I.C.: 5039
N.A.I.C.S.: 423390
Ronaldo Ramirez *(Gen Mgr)*

Shanghai Formica Decorative Material Co. Ltd **(1)**
1701 International Corporate City 3000
Zhongshan North Rd Putuo
Shanghai, 200052, China
Tel.: (86) 2122113668
Fax: (86) 2132522818
Web Site: www.formica.com.cn
Building Decorative Material Mfr & Distr
S.I.C.: 3089
N.A.I.C.S.: 326199

Stramit Corporation Pty Limited **(1)**
L 11 Tower B Zenith Center 821 Pacific Highway
Chatswood, NSW, 2067, Australia (100%)
Tel.: (61) 299283600
Fax: (61) 289860929
E-Mail: reception@fletcherbuilding.com.au
Web Site: www.stramit.com.au
Emp.: 50
Fabricated Structural Metal Mfr
S.I.C.: 3441
N.A.I.C.S.: 332312
Michael Negri *(Gen Mgr)*

Stramit Pty Limited **(1)**
L 11 Tower B Zenith Centre 821 Pacific Hwy
Chatswood, NSW, 2067, Australia
Tel.: (61) 299283600
Fax: (61) 299283599
E-Mail: reception@Fletcherbuilding.com.au
Web Site: www.stramit.com.au
Emp.: 6
Construction Engineering Services
S.I.C.: 1542
N.A.I.C.S.: 236220
Jonathan Blanchard *(Gen Mgr)*

Surface Materials Iki Oy **(1)**
C/O Formical Iki Oy
35990 Kolho, Finland
Tel.: (358) 3 580001
Construction Materials Distr
S.I.C.: 5039
N.A.I.C.S.: 423390

Tasman Access Floors Pty Limited **(1)**
28 Biloela St
2163 Villawood, NSW, Australia (100%)
Tel.: (61) 297284111
Fax: (61) 297283088
E-Mail: g.lee@tasmanfloors.com.au
Web Site: www.tasmanfloors.com.au
Emp.: 15
Floor Laying & Other Floor Contractors
S.I.C.: 1752
N.A.I.C.S.: 238330
Tass Theoctistou *(Mng Dir)*

Tasman Australia Pty Limited **(1)**
L 11 Tower B Zenith Centre 821 Pacific Highway
Chatswood, NSW, 2067, Australia
Tel.: (61) 289860900
Fax: (61) 299283679
Building Materials Mfr
S.I.C.: 3448
N.A.I.C.S.: 332311

Tasman Building Products Pty Limited **(1)**
L 5 821 Pacific Hwy
Chatswood, NSW, 2067, Australia
Tel.: (61) 299283500
Metal Building Materials Mfr
S.I.C.: 3448
N.A.I.C.S.: 332311

Tasman Insulation Pty Limited **(1)**
91 Stradbrodu
PO Box 1371
Brisbane, QLD, 4110, Australia (100%)
Tel.: (61) 732908600
Fax: (61) 38796076
E-Mail: brisbane.sales@insulation.com.au
Web Site: www.insulation.com.au
Roofing Siding & Insulation Material Whslr
S.I.C.: 5033
N.A.I.C.S.: 423330
Rob Howley *(Reg Mgr-Sls)*

Tasman Sinkware Pty Limited **(1)**
51 Naweena Rd
PO Box 2141
5010 Regents Park, SA, Australia (100%)
Tel.: (61) 883486444
Fax: (61) 883486495
E-Mail: sw.reception@tasbulidpro.com.au
Web Site: www.oliverisinks.com
Emp.: 50
Enameled Iron & Metal Sanitary Ware Mfr
S.I.C.: 3499
N.A.I.C.S.: 332999

Unidur GmbH **(1)**
Hauptstr 143
Lindenfels, Hessen, 64678, Germany
Tel.: (49) 6255 96000
Fax: (49) 6255 960020
Building Materials Mfr
S.I.C.: 3089
N.A.I.C.S.: 326199

FLETCHER KING PLC

61 Conduit Street
London, W1S 2GB, United Kingdom
Tel.: (44) 2074938400
Fax: (44) 2074912100
E-Mail: info@fletcherking.co.uk
Web Site: www.fletcherking.co.uk
FLK—(AIM)
Rev.: $4,786,828
Assets: $7,481,097
Liabilities: $2,229,957
Net Worth: $5,251,139
Earnings: $358,499
Emp.: 18
Fiscal Year-end: 04/30/13

Business Description:
Property Investment Fund & Asset Management Services
S.I.C.: 6531
N.A.I.C.S.: 531390

Personnel:
David J. R. Fletcher *(Chm)*
Richard E. G. Goode *(Mng Dir)*
Peter E. Bailey *(Sec)*

Board of Directors:
David J. R. Fletcher
R. A. Dickman
Richard E. G. Goode
D. H. Stewart

Legal Counsel:
Boodle Hatfield
89 New Bond Street
London, United Kingdom

Transfer Agent:
Computershare Investor Services PLC
The Pavilions Bridgewater Road
PO Box 82
Bristol, BS13 8AE, United Kingdom
Tel.: (44) 870 702 0000
Fax: (44) 870 703 6119

Subsidiary:

Fletcher King Services Limited **(1)**
61 Conduit St
London, W1S 2GB, United Kingdom
Tel.: (44) 2074938400
Fax: (44) 2074912100
E-Mail: fksl@fletcherking.co.uk
Web Site: www.fletcherking.co.uk
Emp.: 20
Real Estate Agencies & Valuers
S.I.C.: 6531
N.A.I.C.S.: 531210
Richard Goode *(Mng Dir)*

FLETCHER NICKEL INC.

141 Adelaide Street West Suite 420
Toronto, ON, M5H 3L5, Canada
Tel.: (416) 642-3575
Fax: (416) 644-0592
Toll Free: (888) 642-3575
E-Mail: info@fletchernickel.com
Web Site: www.fletchernickel.com
Assets: $347,138
Liabilities: $9,374,217
Net Worth: ($9,027,079)
Earnings: ($1,269,756)
Emp.: 2
Fiscal Year-end: 12/31/12

Business Description:
Nickel Mining & Exploration
S.I.C.: 1021
N.A.I.C.S.: 212234

Personnel:
Michael J. O'Leary *(Chm)*
Frank C. Smeenk *(Pres & CEO)*
Thomas E. Masters *(CFO)*
Douglas M. Flett *(Gen Counsel & Treas)*

Board of Directors:
Michael J. O'Leary
Patrick G. Crowley
Douglas M. Flett
Jacques F. Monette

Legal Counsel:
Macleod Dixon LLP
Toronto Dominion Centre Canadian Pacific Tower 500 100 Wellington St
Toronto, ON, Canada

Transfer Agent:
Equity Transfer & Trust Company
200 University Avenue Ste 400
Toronto, ON, M5H 4H1, Canada
Tel.: (416) 361-0152
Fax: (416) 361-0470

FLEURY MICHON SA

BP 1
85707 Pouzauges, Cedex, France
Tel.: (33) 251663232
Fax: (33) 251658233
E-Mail: infos.finances@fleurymichon.fr
Web Site: www.fleurymichongroupe.com
FLE—(EUR)
Rev.: $930,146,931
Assets: $737,337,694
Liabilities: $511,835,373
Net Worth: $225,502,321
Earnings: $24,097,789
Emp.: 3,730
Fiscal Year-end: 12/31/12

Business Description:
Packaged Meat Products Producer & Sales
S.I.C.: 5147
N.A.I.C.S.: 424470

Personnel:
Gregoire Gonnord *(Chm)*
Yves Gonnord *(Vice Chm)*
Regis Lebrun *(CEO)*
Raymond Doizon *(COO)*
Gerard Soulard *(Chm-Logistique & Mgr-Production)*
Christian Blais *(CEO-Canada)*
Gerard Chambet *(CEO-Traiteur)*
Alex Joannis *(CEO-Charcuterie)*
Jean-Sebastien Tamisier *(CEO-Traiteur de la Mer)*

Board of Directors:
Gregoire Gonnord
Valery Beneteau
Bruno Billy
Nadine Deswasiere
Genevieve Gonnord
Herve Gonnord
Yves Gonnord
Pierre Jourdain
Nicolas Le Chatelier
Philippe Magdelenat
Philippe Tharaud

Ernst & Young Atlantique
3 rue Emile Masson
Nantes, France

Subsidiary:

Fleury Michon Logistique **(1)**
Route De La Gare
Pouzauges, Vendee, 85700, France
Tel.: (33) 251663188
E-Mail: 6.lo.axtort.commercial@fleurymichon.fa
Convenience Foods Mfr
S.I.C.: 2038
N.A.I.C.S.: 311412

FLEURY S.A.

Av Gen Valdomiro de Lima 508
Jabaquara, 04344-903 Sao Paulo, SP, Brazil
Tel.: (55) 11 5014 7413
Fax: (55) 11 5014 7425
E-Mail: ri@fleury.com.br
Web Site: www.fleury.com.br
Year Founded: 1926
FLRY3—(BRAZ)
Rev.: $738,712,040
Assets: $1,346,873,031
Liabilities: $507,754,437
Net Worth: $839,118,594
Earnings: $52,429,571
Fiscal Year-end: 12/31/12

Business Description:
Healthcare Services
S.I.C.: 8099
N.A.I.C.S.: 621999

Personnel:
Jose Gilberto Henriques Vieira *(Chm)*
Vivien Bouzan Gomez Navarro Rosso *(Vice Chm & CEO)*
Adolpho Cyruaco Nunes de Souza Neto *(CFO)*
Joao Ricardo Kalil Patah *(IR Officer)*

Board of Directors:

Jose Gilberto Henriques Vieira
Marcio Seroa de Araujo Coriolano
Marcelo Pereira Malta de Araujo
Samuel Monteiro dos Santos, Jr.
Rendrik Franca Franco
Jose Paschoal Rossetti
Vivien Bouzan Gomez Navarro Rosso
Luiz Carlos Vaini

FLEWWELLING INSURANCE BROKERS LIMITED

320 North Queen St Suite 132
Toronto, ON, M9C 5K4, Canada
Tel.: (416) 622-8713
Fax: (416) 622-1876
Toll Free: (800) 469-5611
Web Site: www.flewwelling.com
Rev.: $13,526,900
Emp.: 29

Business Description:
Insurance Agency & Brokerage Services
S.I.C.: 6411
N.A.I.C.S.: 524210

Personnel:
Robert Flewwelling *(Pres)*
Paul Flewwelling *(Exec VP-Comml Insurance)*

FLEX EQUIPOS DE DESCANSO SA

Calle Torrelaguna 77
28043 Madrid, Spain
Tel.: (34) 91 744 85 00
Fax: (34) 91 744 85 90
Web Site: www.flex.es
Year Founded: 1912
Emp.: 200

Business Description:
Mattresses Mfr; Quilts, Pillows, Beds & Orthopedic Shapes Mattresses Distr
S.I.C.: 2515
N.A.I.C.S.: 337910

Personnel:
Julia Sanchez *(Deputy Gen Dir & Dir-Comml)*

Non-U.S. Subsidiary:

Vi-Spring Ltd. (1)
Ernesettle Lane
Ernesettle, Plymouth, Devon, PL5 2TT, United Kingdom UK
Tel.: (44) 1752366311
Fax: (44) 1752355108
E-Mail: info@vispring.co.uk
Web Site: www.vispring.co.uk
Sales Range: $25-49.9 Million
Bed & Mattress Mfr
S.I.C.: 2512
N.A.I.C.S.: 337121
Mike Meehan *(Mng Dir)*

U.S. Subsidiary:

E.S. Kluft & Co. (2)
11096 Jersey Blvd Ste 101
Rancho Cucamonga, CA 91730 CA
Tel.: (909) 373-4211 (51%)
Fax: (909) 937-4212
Web Site: www.kluftmattress.com
Emp.: 17
Mattresses & Box Springs Mfr
S.I.C.: 2515
N.A.I.C.S.: 337910
Earl S. Kluft *(CEO)*

FLEXIBLE PACKAGING HOLDING B.V.

Parallelweg 1
4878 AH Etten-Leur, Netherlands
Tel.: (31) 765047000
Fax: (31) 765033234
E-Mail: welcome@schutflexiblepackaging.nl
Web Site: www.schutflexiblepackaging.nl
Emp.: 60

Business Description:
Holding Company; Printing & Packaging
S.I.C.: 6719
N.A.I.C.S.: 551112

Personnel:
Berth Teunessen *(Mng Dir)*
B. Van Leamt *(Mng Dir)*

Subsidiary:

Amsterdam Metallized Products B.V. (1)
Paul Van Vlissingen Straat 12
1096 BK Amsterdam, Netherlands (100%)
Tel.: (31) 204620500
Fax: (31) 206927969
E-Mail: welcome@metallized.nl
Web Site: www.metallized.nl
Sls.: $15,000,000
Emp.: 65
S.I.C.: 3089
N.A.I.C.S.: 326199
Eim Honig *(Mng Dir)*

FLEXIBLE SOLUTIONS INTERNATIONAL, INC.

615 Discovery Street
Victoria, BC, V8T 5G4, Canada
Tel.: (250) 477-9969
Fax: (250) 477-9912
Toll Free: (800) 661-3560
E-Mail: info@flexiblesolutions.com
Web Site: www.flexiblesolutions.com
FSI—(DEU NYSEMKT)
Sls.: $16,400,107
Assets: $13,736,241
Liabilities: $3,967,573
Net Worth: $9,768,668
Earnings: ($1,084,447)
Emp.: 39
Fiscal Year-end: 12/31/12

Business Description:
Water & Energy Conservation Chemicals & Products Developer, Mfr & Marketer
S.I.C.: 2899
N.A.I.C.S.: 325998

Personnel:
Daniel B. O'Brien *(Pres & CEO)*

Board of Directors:
John H. Bientjes
Dale Friend
Thomas M. Fyles
Robert T. Helina
Daniel B. O'Brien
Robert N. O'Brien

Subsidiaries:

Flexible Solutions, Ltd. (1)
615 Discovery St
V8T5G4 Victoria, BC, Canada
Tel.: (250) 477-9969
Fax: (250) 477-9912
Web Site: www.flexiblesolutions.com
Emp.: 200
Basic Inorganic Chemical Mfr
S.I.C.: 2819
N.A.I.C.S.: 325180

WaterSavr Global Solutions Inc. (1)
615 Discovery St
Victoria, BC, V8T 5G4, Canada
Tel.: (250) 477-9969
Fax: (250) 477-9912
E-Mail: info@flexiblesolutions.com
Web Site: www.flexiblesolutions.com
Emp.: 5
Basic Inorganic Chemical Mfr
S.I.C.: 2819
N.A.I.C.S.: 325180
Daniel O'Brien *(CEO)*

U.S. Subsidiary:

NanoChem Solutions Inc. (1)
6502 S Archer Rd
Bedford Park, IL 60501
Tel.: (708) 563-9200
Fax: (708) 563-9220
Web Site: www.nanochemsolutions.com
Emp.: 7
Biodegradable Water-Soluble Polymers for Industrial & Consumer Applications
S.I.C.: 2899
N.A.I.C.S.: 325998

FLEXIGROUP LIMITED

Level 8 The Forum 201 Pacific Highway
Saint Leonards, NSW, 2065, Australia
Mailing Address:
Locked Bag 2345
Saint Leonards, NSW, 1590, Australia
Tel.: (61) 289052000
Fax: (61) 289051800
E-Mail: investor@flexigroup.com.au
Web Site: www.flexigroup.com.au
FXL—(ASX)
Rev.: $296,102,294
Assets: $1,516,424,320
Liabilities: $1,136,490,292
Net Worth: $379,934,029
Earnings: $68,607,696
Fiscal Year-end: 06/30/13

Business Description:
Holding Company; Point-of-Sale Lease & Rental Financing Services
S.I.C.: 6719
N.A.I.C.S.: 551112

Personnel:
Andrew Abercrombie *(Founder)*
Tarek Robbiati *(CEO & Mng Dir)*
David Stevens *(CFO, Sec & Head-Fin & Plng)*
Jeff McLean *(COO)*
Peter Lirantzis *(CIO)*
Marilyn Conyer *(CMO)*
Ross Horsburgh *(Chief Risk Officer)*

Board of Directors:
Margaret A. C. Jackson
Andrew Abercrombie
Rajeev Dhawan
Tarek Robbiati
Raymond John Skippen
Anne Ward

Legal Counsel:
King & Wood Mallesons
Level 60 Governor Philip Tower 1 Farrer Place
Sydney, Australia

Subsidiaries:

Certegy Ezi-Pay Pty Ltd (1)
Level 1 97 Pirie Street
Adelaide, SA, 5000, Australia
Tel.: (61) 882322828
E-Mail: adebusdev@certegy.com.au
Web Site: www.certegyezipay.com.au
Retail Payment Services
S.I.C.: 6099
N.A.I.C.S.: 522320

Flexicare Claims Management Pty Limited (1)
Level 8 The Forum 201 Pacific Highway
Saint Leonards, NSW, 2065, Australia
Tel.: (61) 289052000
Fax: (61) 2 89051800
Claims Management Services
S.I.C.: 6371
N.A.I.C.S.: 524292

Flexirent Holdings Pty Limited (1)
Level 8 201 Pacific Highway
Saint Leonards, NSW, 2065, Australia
Tel.: (61) 2 8905 2000
Fax: (61) 28905180
E-Mail: info@flexiGroup.com
Web Site: www.flexigroup.com
Emp.: 250
Investment Management Services
S.I.C.: 6211
N.A.I.C.S.: 523999
Tarek Robbiati *(CEO)*

Flexirent SPV No 2 Pty Limited (1)
Level 8 201 Pacific Highway
Saint Leonards, North Shore, NSW, 2065, Australia
Tel.: (61) 289052000
Fax: (61) 289051800
Equipment Leasing Services
S.I.C.: 7377
N.A.I.C.S.: 532420

Flexirent SPV No 4 Pty Limited (1)
Level 8 The Forum 201 Pacific Highway
Saint Leonards, NSW, 2065, Australia
Tel.: (61) 289052000
Fax: (61) 289051800
Emp.: 350
Financial Leasing Services
S.I.C.: 6159
N.A.I.C.S.: 522220
Brett Stubbs *(Mgr-IT)*

Flexirent SPV No 6 Pty Limited (1)
Level 8 The Forum 201 Pacific Highway
Saint Leonards, Saint Leonards, NSW, 2065, Australia
Tel.: (61) 289052000
Fax: (61) 2 89051800
E-Mail: info@flexigroup.com.au
Web Site: www.flexirent.com.au
Emp.: 350
Equiipment Leasing Services
S.I.C.: 7377
N.A.I.C.S.: 532420
Tarek Robbiati *(Mng Dir)*

Holding:

Flexirent Capital Pty. Ltd. (1)
Level 8 The Forum 201 Pacific Highway
Saint Leonards, NSW, 2065, Australia AU
Mailing Address: (100%)
Locked Bag 2345
Saint Leonards, NSW, 1590, Australia
Tel.: (61) 289052000
Fax: (61) 289051800
E-Mail: info@flexirgroup.com.au
Web Site: www.flexirent.com
Emp.: 400
Point-of-Sale Lease & Rental Financing Services
S.I.C.: 6141
N.A.I.C.S.: 522220
John DeLano *(CEO & Mng Dir)*
Garry McLennan *(CFO)*
Pearl Laughton *(CIO)*
Marilyn Conyer *(CMO)*
David Stevens *(Sec & Controller)*

Non-U.S. Subsidiary:

Flexirent Capital (New Zealand) Ltd. (2)
PO Box 90935
Victoria Saint W, Auckland, 1142, New Zealand NZ
Tel.: (64) 93004494 (100%)
Fax: (64) 93004498
E-Mail: customerservice@flexirent.co.nz
Web Site: www.flexirent.com
Emp.: 30
Point-of-Sale Lease & Rental Financing Services
S.I.C.: 6159
N.A.I.C.S.: 522220

Non-U.S. Subsidiary:

FlexiGroup (NZ) Ltd (1)
Victoria Street West
PO Box 90935
Auckland, 1142, New Zealand
Tel.: (64) 93004494
Fax: (64) 9 300 4498
E-Mail: customerservice@flexigroup.co.nz
Web Site: www.flexirent.co.nz
Equipment Leasing Services
S.I.C.: 7377
N.A.I.C.S.: 532420

FLEXITUFF INTERNATIONAL LIMITED

C 41-50 SEZ Sector 3 Pithampur
Dhar, Pithampur, Madhya Pradesh, 454 775, India
Tel.: (91) 7292401681
E-Mail: mail@flexituff.com
Web Site: www.flexituff.com
533638—(BOM NSE)
Emp.: 5,000

Business Description:
Flexible Intermediate Bulk Containers
S.I.C.: 7389
N.A.I.C.S.: 561910

Flexituff International Limited—(Continued)

Personnel:
Saurabh Kalani *(COO)*

Subsidiary:

Nanofil Technologies Pvt. Ltd. (1)
Mahuakhera Ganj U S Nagar
Kashipur, Uttarkhand, India
Tel.: (91) 594 726 6000
Fax: (91) 594 722 6212
E-Mail: mail@nanofil.in
Web Site: www.nanofil.in
Polymer Compound Mfr
S.I.C.: 2899
N.A.I.C.S.: 325998

FLEXIUM INTERCONNECT, INC.

No 23 Chukwang 1st St Tafa Industrial Park
831 Taliao Hsiang, Kaohsiung, Taiwan
Tel.: (886) 77871008
Fax: (886) 778776728
Web Site: www.flexium.com.tw
6269—(TAI)
Sales Range: $50-74.9 Million
Emp.: 625

Business Description:
Flexible Printed Circuit Board Mfr
S.I.C.: 3672
N.A.I.C.S.: 334412

Personnel:
Walter Cheng *(Chm & Gen Mgr)*

Non-U.S. Plant:

Flexium Interconnect, Inc - Kunshan Plant (1)
No 1399 Hanpu Road
Kunshan, Jiangsu, 215300, China
Tel.: (86) 512 57775599
Fax: (86) 512 57826166
Printed Circuit Boards Mfr
S.I.C.: 3672
N.A.I.C.S.: 334412

FLEXO PRODUCTS LIMITED

4777 Kent Ave
Niagara Falls, ON, L2H 1J5, Canada
Tel.: (905) 354-2723
Fax: (905) 354-1301
E-Mail: sales@flexoproducts.com
Web Site: www.flexoproducts.com
Year Founded: 1918
Rev.: $13,355,955
Emp.: 75

Business Description:
Sanitation Suppliers & Industrial Equipments Whslr
S.I.C.: 5084
N.A.I.C.S.: 423830

Personnel:
Stephen Parker *(Pres & CEO)*

FLEXOPACK S.A.

Thessi Tzima
194 00 Koropi, Attiki, Greece
Tel.: (30) 2106680000
Fax: (30) 2106626583
E-Mail: flexopack@flexopack.gr
Web Site: www.flexopack.gr
FLEXO—(ATH)
Sls.: $72,784,720
Assets: $92,355,339
Liabilities: $34,581,761
Net Worth: $57,773,578
Earnings: $4,727,749
Emp.: 235
Fiscal Year-end: 12/31/12

Business Description:
Flexible Plastic Films Mfr
S.I.C.: 2671
N.A.I.C.S.: 326112

Personnel:
George Ginosatis *(Chm & Mng Dir)*
Stamatios Ginosatis *(Vice Chm & Deputy Mng Dir)*

Board of Directors:
George Ginosatis
Asimina Ginosati
Stamatios Ginosatis
Nikolaos Reggos
Eleni-Flora Zaverdinoy

Subsidiary:

FLEXOPACK Plastics S.A. (1)
Thesi Tzima Attica
PO Box 136
Tzima, 194 00 Koropi, Greece GR
Tel.: (30) 2106680000
Fax: (30) 2106626583
E-Mail: flexopack@flexopack.com
Web Site: www.flexopack.com
Plastic Packaging Products Mfr
S.I.C.: 3089
N.A.I.C.S.: 326199

Non-U.S. Subsidiary:

FESCOPACK Sp.zo.o (2)
Tragamin 17
82 200 Malbork, Pomorskie, Poland
Tel.: (48) 552733738
Fax: (48) 55 273 18 06
E-Mail: biuro@fescopack.pl
Web Site: www.fesco.pl
Emp.: 21
Frozen Foods Distributors & Packaging Mfr
S.I.C.: 2038
N.A.I.C.S.: 311412

FLEXOS S.A.

Pegasuslaan 5
1831 Brussels, Belgium
Tel.: (32) 27092931
Fax: (32) 087231509
E-Mail: info@flexos.be
Web Site: www.flexos.com
FLEX—(EUR)
Sales Range: $1-9.9 Million
Emp.: 50

Business Description:
IT Services
S.I.C.: 7379
N.A.I.C.S.: 541519

Personnel:
Jean-Paul Rosette *(CEO)*

Non-U.S. Subsidiary:

FleXos France (1)
27 Ave de l'Opera
75001 Paris, France
Tel.: (33) 170385468
Fax: (33) 170385151
E-Mail: info@flexos.fr
Web Site: www.flexos.com
Network Installation & Maintenance Services
S.I.C.: 7373
N.A.I.C.S.: 541512
Jean Paul Rosette *(Mng Dir)*

FLEXTRONICS INTERNATIONAL LTD.

2 Changi South Lane
Singapore, 486123, Singapore
Tel.: (65) 6890 7188
Fax: (65) 6543 1888
E-Mail: investor_relations@flextronics.com
Web Site: www.flextronics.com
Year Founded: 1969
FLEX—(NASDAQ)
Sls.: $23,569,475,000
Assets: $10,591,555,000
Liabilities: $8,344,797,000
Net Worth: $2,246,758,000
Earnings: $277,051,000
Emp.: 149,000
Fiscal Year-end: 03/31/13

Business Description:
Logistical & Engineering Services & Electronics Mfr
S.I.C.: 3679
N.A.I.C.S.: 334419

Personnel:
Michael M. McNamara *(CEO)*
Christopher E. Collier *(CFO & Sr VP-Fin)*
David Bennett *(Chief Acctg Officer)*
Thomas K. Linton *(Chief Procurement Officer)*
Jeannine P. Sargent *(Pres-Renewable Energy)*
Jonathan S. Hoak *(Gen Counsel)*
Peter A. Stickler *(Exec VP-Worldwide HR)*

Board of Directors:
H. Raymond Bingham
Michael M. McNamara
Marc Onetto
Daniel Harris Schulman
Willy C. Shih
Lay Koon Tan
William D. Watkins
Lawrence A. Zimmerman

Legal Counsel:
Curtis, Mallet-Prevost, Colt & Mosle LLP
101 Park Ave.
New York, NY 10178
Tel.: (212) 696-6000

Transfer Agent:
Computershare
PO Box 43010
Providence, RI 02940-3070
Tel.: (800) 730-6001

Branches:

Flextronics International Ltd. (1)
31 Joo Koon Circle
Jurong, 629108, Singapore
Tel.: (65) 68616218
Fax: (65) 68616680
Electronics Design, Engineering & Logistics Services
S.I.C.: 3679
N.A.I.C.S.: 334419

Flextronics International Ltd. (1)
12 Kallang Way
Singapore, 349216, Singapore
Tel.: (65) 68411888
Fax: (65) 68423738
Web Site: www.flextronics.com
Emp.: 800
Electronic Component Mfr
S.I.C.: 3679
N.A.I.C.S.: 334419

Subsidiaries:

Flextronics Design Asia Pte. Ltd. (1)
11 Woodlands Terrace
Singapore, 738436, Singapore
Tel.: (65) 65076507
Fax: (65) 65075799
Printing Design Services
S.I.C.: 7389
N.A.I.C.S.: 541490
Rudy Schalk *(Gen Mgr)*

Flextronics Global Enclosures (Singapore) Pte. Ltd. (1)
31 Joo Koon Circle
Jurong, 629108, Singapore
Tel.: (65) 6861 6218
Fax: (65) 6861 6680
Electromechanical Engineering Services
S.I.C.: 8711
N.A.I.C.S.: 541330

U.S. Subsidiaries:

FlexMedical Disposables (1)
700 Bent Branch Dr # 100
Irving, TX 75063
Tel.: (817) 877-4343
Fax: (817) 877-4909
Toll Free: (866) 552-2112
Sales Range: $250-299.9 Million
Emp.: 20
Single-Use Medical Device Distr
S.I.C.: 5047
N.A.I.C.S.: 423450
Bill Flaherty *(Pres)*
Douglas Brenner *(Exec VP & Gen Mgr)*
Sidney Echols *(Exec VP)*
Daniel J. Kunst *(Exec VP-Sls & Mktg)*
Craig Borsdorf *(Sr VP-Dev Programs)*
Chris Faller *(Sr VP-Ops)*
David Johnston *(Sr VP-Bus Dev)*
Ken Kempker *(Sr VP-Acctg)*
Gregory Olson *(Sr VP-Bus Dev)*
Don Young *(Sr VP-Quality Assurance)*

Units:

FlexMedical Disposables (2)
5950 Nancy Rdg Dr
San Diego, CA 92121
Tel.: (858) 457-1988
Fax: (858) 558-7264
Sales Range: $10-24.9 Million
Emp.: 200
Single-Use Medical Device Distr
S.I.C.: 5047
N.A.I.C.S.: 423450
Don Young *(Sr VP-Quality Assurance)*

FlexMedical Disposables (2)
3161 Sweeten Creek Rd
Asheville, NC 28803-2115
Tel.: (828) 684-1618
Emp.: 65
Single-Use Medical Product Distr
S.I.C.: 5047
N.A.I.C.S.: 423450
Joe Richmond *(Dir-Mfg)*

Flextronics America, LLC (1)
6800 Solectron Dr
Charlotte, NC 28262
Tel.: (704) 509-8700
Fax: (704) 509-8100
Emp.: 400
Electronic Component Mfr
S.I.C.: 3679
N.A.I.C.S.: 334419
John Mainey *(Gen Mgr)*

Flextronics Automotive USA, Inc. (1)
(Formerly Saturn Electronics & Engineering, Inc.)
30600 Telegraph Rd Ste 2345
Bingham Farms, MI 48309 MI
Tel.: (248) 853-5724
Fax: (248) 299-8514
E-Mail: sales@saturnee.com
Web Site: www.saturnee.com
Sales Range: $400-449.9 Million
Emp.: 3,000
Contract Electronics Mfr
S.I.C.: 3625
N.A.I.C.S.: 335314
Wallace K. Tsuha, Jr. *(Chm & CEO)*
Gary Lawrey *(Pres & COO)*
Sherman Cruz *(CFO)*

Flextronics International PA, Inc. (1)
847 Gibraltar Dr
Milpitas, CA 95035-6332
Tel.: (408) 576-7000
Printed Circuit Board Mfr
S.I.C.: 3672
N.A.I.C.S.: 334412

Flextronics International USA, Inc. (1)
2090 Fortune Dr
San Jose, CA 95131-1823 (100%)
Tel.: (408) 576-7000
Fax: (408) 576-7454
E-Mail: sales-usa@flextronics.com
Web Site: www.flextronics.com
Emp.: 2,000
Engineering, Electronics Manufacturing & Logistical Services to Telecommunications Networking Computer, Consumer & Medical Electronics Industries
S.I.C.: 3672
N.A.I.C.S.: 334412

Subsidiaries:

Flextron Global Services (2)
4400 Commerce Crossing
Louisville, KY 40229 KY
Tel.: (502) 810-2280
Fax: (502) 810-2395
Web Site: www.flextronics.com
Rev.: $3,900,000
Emp.: 1,500
Electronics Equipment Repair Services
S.I.C.: 7699
N.A.I.C.S.: 811211

Flextronics International Ltd. **(2)**
637 Gibraltar Dr
Milpitas, CA 95035 DE
Tel.: (408) 957-8500
Fax: (408) 957-6056
Web Site: www.flextronics.com
Emp.: 230
Electronics Design, Engineering & Logistics Services
Import Export
S.I.C.: 3679
N.A.I.C.S.: 334419
Dave Purvis *(CTO & Exec VP)*

Flextronics International USA Inc. **(2)**
6800 Solectron Dr
Charlotte, NC 28262
Tel.: (704) 598-3300
Fax: (704) 509-8100
Web Site: www.flextronics.com
Emp.: 2,000
Electronics Repair & Manufacturing Services
S.I.C.: 3679
N.A.I.C.S.: 334419
Steve Gearhart *(VP-Applications)*

Flextronics International USA Inc. **(2)**
1000 Technology Dr
West Columbia, SC 29170-2263 SC
Tel.: (803) 936-0496
Fax: (803) 936-5225
Web Site: www.flextronics.com
Emp.: 450
Mfr of Electronic Circuits
S.I.C.: 3679
N.A.I.C.S.: 334419

Flextronics International USA Inc. **(2)**
600 Shiloh Rd
Plano, TX 75074
Tel.: (469) 229-1000
Fax: (469) 229-3000
Web Site: www.flextronics.com
Emp.: 400
Semiconductor Design Services
S.I.C.: 3672
N.A.I.C.S.: 334412

Flextronics International USA Inc. **(2)**
12455 Research Blvd
Austin, TX 78759
Tel.: (512) 425-4100
Web Site: www.flextronics.com
Electronic Equipment Mfr
S.I.C.: 3679
N.A.I.C.S.: 334419
Jeff Minyard *(VP-HR)*

Flextronics Systems Texas Ltd. **(2)**
10900 Cash Rd
Stafford, TX 77477 (100%)
Tel.: (281) 295-3200
Fax: (281) 295-3300
Toll Free: (888) 316-4501
Web Site: www.flextronics.com
Sales Range: $10-24.9 Million
Emp.: 150
Contract Manufacturer Specializing in the Production of Electrical & Fiber Optic Cable Assemblies, Electrical & Mechanical Subsystems & Cable-Intensive Mechanical Enclosures
S.I.C.: 3679
N.A.I.C.S.: 334419

Multek Flexible Circuits, Inc. **(2)**
1150 Sheldahl Rd
Northfield, MN 55057-9444 MN
Tel.: (507) 663-8000
Fax: (507) 663-8545
Toll Free: (800) 533-0505
E-Mail: info@multek.com
Web Site: www.multek.com
Emp.: 450
Flexible Electronic Component Mfr
Import Export
S.I.C.: 3679
N.A.I.C.S.: 334419
Werner Widmann *(Pres)*
Bill Beckenbaugh *(CTO)*
Ivy Wong *(Sr VP-Sls & Mktg)*

Non-U.S. Subsidiaries:

Flextronics Brasil Ltda. **(2)**
Rondovia Jaguariuna Mogo Mirim KM 133
Jaguariuna, Sao Paulo, 13820 000, Brazil
Tel.: (55) 1938379000
Fax: (55) 1938379273
Web Site: www.flextronics.com
Emp.: 1,200
Electronic Components Contract Manufacturing
S.I.C.: 3679
N.A.I.C.S.: 334419
Daniel Macano *(Dir-Pur)*

Flextronics Canada **(2)**
213 Harry Walker Pkwy South
Newmarket, ON, L3Y 8T3, Canada ON
Tel.: (905) 952-1000
Fax: (905) 952-1042
Web Site: www.flextronics.com
Rev.: $16,627,500
Emp.: 400
Electronic Component Mfr
S.I.C.: 3679
N.A.I.C.S.: 334419

Flextronics International Technologia Ltda. **(2)**
Rodovia Senador Jose Ermirio De Moraes Km 11
Aperecidinha Sorocaba, Sao Paulo, 18087 090, Brazil BR
Tel.: (55) 15 4009 6200 (100%)
Fax: (55) 15 4009 6240
E-Mail: sales@br.flextronics.com
Web Site: www.flextronics.com
Emp.: 1,000
Network Services
S.I.C.: 8711
N.A.I.C.S.: 541330

Flextronics Manufacturing Juarez, S.A. de C.V. **(2)**
Boulevard Independencia 4240
Fraccionamiento Lote Bravo, Chihuahua, 32720, Mexico
Tel.: (52) 6144421900
Web Site: www.flextronics.com
Electronic Components Manufacturing
S.I.C.: 3679
N.A.I.C.S.: 334419
Gabriel Macias *(Plant Mgr)*

Flextronics Manufacturing Mexico, S.A. de C.V. **(2)**
Prol Av Lopez Mateos Sur 2915 Col La tijera
Jalisco, 45640, Mexico
Tel.: (52) 3337704200
Fax: (52) 3337704211
Web Site: www.flextronic.com
Electronic Components Mfr
S.I.C.: 3679
N.A.I.C.S.: 334419

Flextronics Manufacturing Mexico, S.A. de C.V. **(2)**
Colonia la More Carreterra Base Aerea Militar 5850 Km 5
Zapopan, Jalisco, 45011, Mexico (100%)
Tel.: (52) 3338183200
Fax: (52) 3338183240
E-Mail: info@flextronics.com
Web Site: www.flextronics.com
Sales Range: $200-249.9 Million
Emp.: 6,000
Telephone Apparatus
S.I.C.: 3661
N.A.I.C.S.: 334210

Flextronics Semiconductor, Inc. **(1)**
2241 Lundy Ave Bldg 2
San Jose, CA 95131
Tel.: (408) 576-7429
Fax: (408) 744-1800
Semiconductor Device Mfr
S.I.C.: 3674
N.A.I.C.S.: 334413

Vista Point Technologies, Inc. **(1)**
3054 Fite Cir Ste 101
Sacramento, CA 95827-1809 OR
Tel.: (408) 576-7000
Web Site: www.vptech.com
Sales Range: $75-99.9 Million
Emp.: 3,200
Computer Monitor, Camera Module, Power Supply & Electronic Component Developer & Mfr
S.I.C.: 3679
N.A.I.C.S.: 334419

Non-U.S. Branches:

Vista Point Technologies, Inc. **(2)**
Ste 8018 8th Fl Tower 1 China Hong Kong Ct
33 Canton Rd Tsin Sha Tsui, Kowloon, China (Hong Kong)
Tel.: (852) 26102120
Fax: (852) 26100728
Mfr. of Turnkey Assemblies & LCD Products
S.I.C.: 3663
N.A.I.C.S.: 334220

Vista Point Technologies, Inc. **(2)**
102 Li Jia Rd Henggang Town
Longgang Zone, 518115 Shenzhen, China
Tel.: (86) 75561266888
Fax: (86) 755 2886 4413
Web Site: www.vptech.com
Emp.: 1,600
Mfr. of Turnkey Assemblies
S.I.C.: 3663
N.A.I.C.S.: 334220

Non-U.S. Subsidiaries:

FlexMedical Slovakia s.r.o. **(1)**
Hlavna 1409/48
Vrable, 95201, Slovakia
Tel.: (421) 372852918
Fax: (421) 377834910
Electronic Equipment Distr
S.I.C.: 5065
N.A.I.C.S.: 423690

FlexPower India Private Limited **(1)**
Plot No 3 Phase Ii Sipcot Industrial Park
Sandavellure Sriperumbudur, Kanchipuram, Tamilnadu, 602106, India
Tel.: (91) 4467105000
Fax: (91) 4467105141
Electronic Component Mfr
S.I.C.: 3679
N.A.I.C.S.: 334419

Flextronics Aguascalientes Servicios, S.A. de C.V. **(1)**
Carr Blvd A Zacatecas Km 9 5 Corral De Barrancos
Jesus Maria, Aguascalientes, 20900, Mexico
Tel.: (52) 4499107100
Fax: (52) 4499107100
Web Site: www.flextronics.com.mx
Electronic Component Repair & Maintenance Services
S.I.C.: 7629
N.A.I.C.S.: 811219
Antonio Alfaro *(Office Mgr)*

Flextronics Automotive GmbH & Co KG **(1)**
Benzstrasse 2
72636 Frickenhausen, Germany
Tel.: (49) 7022 21740 0
Fax: (49) 7022 21740 201
Automotive Interior Lightning Mfr
S.I.C.: 3714
N.A.I.C.S.: 336320
Matthias Lutz *(Gen Mgr)*

Flextronics Automotive Inc **(1)**
213 Harry Walker Pky S
Newmarket, ON, L3Y 8T3, Canada
Tel.: (800) 668-5649
Fax: (905) 952-1240
Electronic Component Mfr
S.I.C.: 3679
N.A.I.C.S.: 334419

Flextronics Canada Design Services, Inc. **(1)**
21 Richardson Side Rd
Kanata, ON, K2K 2C1, Canada
Tel.: (613) 895-2050
Fax: (613) 271-2581
Emp.: 144
Mechanical Engineering Services
S.I.C.: 8711
N.A.I.C.S.: 541330

Flextronics Computing (Suzhou) Co. Ltd. **(1)**
No 1 Guanpu Road Guoxiang Street Wuzhong District
Suzhou, China
Tel.: (86) 51267868800
Web Site: www.flextronics.com
Electronic Component Mfr
S.I.C.: 3679
N.A.I.C.S.: 334419

Flextronics Design Korea Ltd. **(1)**
5/F B/D 104 Sk Ventium 522 Dangjeong-Dong
Kunpo, 431060, Korea (South)
Tel.: (82) 314500000
Fax: (82) 314500008
Electrical Equipment Mfr
S.I.C.: 3699
N.A.I.C.S.: 335999

Flextronics Design Srl **(1)**
Via Borgazzi 27
20052 Monza, Italy
Tel.: (39) 0392098610
Fax: (39) 0392098636
Web Site: www.flextronics.com
Design Services
S.I.C.: 8711
N.A.I.C.S.: 541330

Flextronics Design, s.r.o. **(1)**
Areal Slatina Turanka 115
627 32 Brno, Czech Republic
Tel.: (420) 545426555
Fax: (420) 545426550
E-Mail: info@cz.flextronics.com
Web Site: www.flextronics.cz
Emp.: 65
Electronic Component Developer & Mfr
S.I.C.: 3571
N.A.I.C.S.: 334111
Miroslav Heran *(Mng Dir)*

Flextronics Electronics (Mauritius) Limited **(1)**
Alexander House 35
Ebene, Mauritius
Tel.: (230) 4030800
Fax: (230) 4030801
Electronic Component Distr
S.I.C.: 5065
N.A.I.C.S.: 423690

Flextronics Electronics Technology (Suzhou) Co., Ltd. **(1)**
No 9 Suqian Road Suzhou Industrial Park
Suzhou, Jiangsu, 215021, China
Tel.: (86) 51267612300
Fax: (86) 51267630971
Printed Circuit Board Mfr
S.I.C.: 3679
N.A.I.C.S.: 334418

Flextronics EMS Canada Inc. **(1)**
21 Richardson Side Rd
Kanata, ON, K2K 2C1, Canada
Tel.: (613) 271-4382
Fax: (613) 271-6594
Engineering Services
S.I.C.: 8711
N.A.I.C.S.: 541330

Flextronics Enclosure (Zhuhai) Co., Ltd **(1)**
Xinqing Science & Technology Industrial Park
Zhuhai, Guangdong, 519180, China
Tel.: (86) 7565181186
Fax: (86) 7565181495
Electrical Equipment Mfr
S.I.C.: 3699
N.A.I.C.S.: 335999

Flextronics Enclosures (Hong Kong) Ltd. **(1)**
17 & 18/F Nina Twr Twr II 8 Yeung Uk Rd
Tsuen Wan, New Territories, China (Hong Kong)
Tel.: (852) 22761800
Fax: (852) 24804490
Electronic Component Mfr
S.I.C.: 3679
N.A.I.C.S.: 334419

Flextronics Germany Holding GmbH **(1)**
Heinz-Nixdorf-Ring 1
33106 Paderborn, North Rhine-Westphal, Germany De
Tel.: (49) 52511800
Fax: (49) 52511801009
Investment Management Services
S.I.C.: 6282
N.A.I.C.S.: 523930

Flextronics International Ltd.—(Continued)

Flextronics Global Services Canada Inc. (1)
213 Harry Walker Pky S
Newmarket, ON, L3Y 8T3, Canada
Tel.: (905) 952-1000
Fax: (905) 952-1040
Data Processing Equipment Repair & Maintenance Services
S.I.C.: 7629
N.A.I.C.S.: 811212

Flextronics Global Services (Manchester) Limited (1)
Stretton Green Distribution Centre Langford Way
Appleton, Warrington, Cheshire, WA4 4TQ, United Kingdom
Tel.: (44) 1925 260 700
Fax: (44) 1925 260 810
Web Site: www.flextronics.com
Emp.: 250
Computer Peripheral Equipment Mfr
S.I.C.: 3575
N.A.I.C.S.: 334118
Mike Meades *(Gen Mgr)*

Flextronics Group Sweden AB (1)
Rombvagen 4
PO Box 532 Karlskrona
37123 Lyckeby, 37165, Sweden
Tel.: (46) 45554400
Fax: (46) 45554401
Emp.: 400
Electronic Component Mfr
S.I.C.: 3679
N.A.I.C.S.: 334419
Andreas Bergstrom *(Gen Mgr)*

Flextronics Holding GmbH (1)
Office Park 1/Top B 07/02
Wien-Flughafen, Vienna, 1300, Austria
Tel.: (43) 16024100
Web Site: www.flextronics.com
Emp.: 40
Investment Management Services
S.I.C.: 6211
N.A.I.C.S.: 523999

Flextronics Holdings Mexico, S.A. de C.V. (1)
Km 5 Carretera Base Aerea No 5850-4 La Mora
Zapopan, Jalisco, 45100, Mexico
Tel.: (52) 3338183200
Fax: (52) 3338189881
Financial Management Services
S.I.C.: 6211
N.A.I.C.S.: 523999

Flextronics Industrial (Shenzhen) Co Ltd (1)
Block C8 C9 Xin An No 2 Industrial Zone Xixiang Town
Bao An, Shenzhen, Guangdong, 518126, China
Tel.: (86) 75527497333
Fax: (86) 75527490001
Electromedical Equipment Mfr
S.I.C.: 3845
N.A.I.C.S.: 334510

Flextronics International AB (1)
Fridhemsvagen 15
372 22 Ronneby, Blekinge, Sweden
Tel.: (46) 45554400
Fax: (46) 45554401
Emp.: 400
Electronic Component Mfr
S.I.C.: 3679
N.A.I.C.S.: 334419
Andreas Bergstrom *(CEO)*

Flextronics International Cork B.V. (1)
Kilbarry Industrial Park Dublin Hill
Cork, Ireland
Tel.: (353) 21 2300 000
Fax: (353) 21 2300 299
Web Site: www.flextronics.com
Emp.: 30
Electronic Component Mfr
S.I.C.: 3679
N.A.I.C.S.: 334419
Jerry Fitzpatrick *(Gen Mgr)*

Flextronics International Denmark A/S (1)
Hjortevej 4
7800 Skive, Denmark
Tel.: (45) 96143000
Fax: (45) 96143144
E-Mail: info@dk.flextronics.com
Web Site: www.flextronics.com
Emp.: 400
Electronic Component Mfr
S.I.C.: 3679
N.A.I.C.S.: 334419

Flextronics International Germany GmbH & Co. KG (1)
Heinz-Nixdorf-Ring 1
33106 Paderborn, Germany
Tel.: (49) 5251 180 1001
Fax: (49) 5251 180 1809
Printed Circuit Board Assembly Mfr
S.I.C.: 3679
N.A.I.C.S.: 334418
Uwe Schmidt-Streier *(Gen Mgr)*

Flextronics International GmbH (1)
Office Park 1 Top B 07 02
1300 Vienna, Austria (100%)
Tel.: (43) 16024100
Fax: (43) 160241001750
Emp.: 60
Engineering, Electronics Manufacturing & Logistical Services to Telecommunications, Networking, Computer, Consumer & Medical Electronics Industries
S.I.C.: 8711
N.A.I.C.S.: 541330
Erwin Brunner *(Mng Dir)*

Subsidiary:

Flextronics International (2)
Friesacher Strasse 3
9330 Althofen, Austria (100%)
Tel.: (43) 42622644126
Fax: (43) 426226444137
E-Mail: info@flextronics.com
Web Site: www.flextronics.com
Emp.: 700
Design Services
S.I.C.: 8711
N.A.I.C.S.: 541330
Eerizh Doeflimger *(Gen Mgr)*

Flextronics International Japan Co., Ltd. (1)
1-7-20 Yaesu Yaesuguchikaikan 10f
Chuo-Ku, Tokyo, 103-0028, Japan
Tel.: (81) 335176900
Fax: (81) 335176969
Electronic Equipment Repair & Maintenance Services
S.I.C.: 7699
N.A.I.C.S.: 811310

Flextronics International Kft (1)
Ikervari Ut 42
H 9600 Sarvar, Ikervari, Hungary (100%)
Tel.: (36) 95533000
Fax: (36) 95533020
E-Mail: info@flextronics.com
Web Site: www.flextronics.com
Sales Range: $1-9.9 Million
Emp.: 2,800
Plastics Mfr
S.I.C.: 2821
N.A.I.C.S.: 325211

Flextronics International Kft. (1)
Hangar Utca 5 37
1183 Budapest, Hungary
Tel.: (36) 12963100
Fax: (36) 12963111
E-Mail: budapest.reception@hu.flextronics.com
Web Site: www.flextronics.com
Emp.: 1,000
Electronic Components Contract Manufacturing
S.I.C.: 3679
N.A.I.C.S.: 334419

Flextronics International Kft (1)
Posta Ut 63
H 8900 Zalaegerszeg, Hungary (100%)
Tel.: (36) 92508000
Fax: (36) 92508001
E-Mail: rita.kercsmar@hu.flextronics.com
Web Site: www.flextronics.com
Emp.: 6,000
Plastics Mfr
S.I.C.: 2821
N.A.I.C.S.: 325211
Rita Kercsmar *(Gen Mgr-Factory)*

Flextronics International Ltd. (1)
Plot 13 Phase 4
Prai Industrial Estate, Penang, Prai, 13600, Malaysia
Tel.: (60) 45075600
Fax: (60) 45078733
E-Mail: sylviala.dong@my.flextronics.com
Web Site: www.flextronics.com
Emp.: 10,000
Electronic Component Mfr
S.I.C.: 3679
N.A.I.C.S.: 334419
Kumar Singam *(Gen Mgr)*

Flextronics International Ltd. (1)
18th Fl Nina Tower 2 No 8 Yeun
Tsuen Wan, NT, China (Hong Kong) (100%)
Tel.: (852) 24899813
Fax: (852) 24804490
E-Mail: info@hk.flextronics.com
Web Site: www.flextronics.com
Emp.: 120
Provider of Engineering, Electronics Manufacturing & Logistical Services to Telecommunications, Networking, Computer, Consumer & Medical Electronics Industries
S.I.C.: 8711
N.A.I.C.S.: 541330

Flextronics International Poland Sp z.o.o. (1)
Ul Malinowska 28
83-100 Tczew, Poland
Tel.: (48) 587777000
Fax: (48) 587777001
E-Mail: marketing@pl.flextronics.com
Web Site: www.flextronics.com
Emp.: 3,000
Electronic Component Distr
S.I.C.: 5065
N.A.I.C.S.: 423690
Andrzej Polojko *(Gen Mgr)*

Flextronics International Sweden AB (1)
Rombvagen 4 Verko
SE 371 23 Karlskrona, Sweden (100%)
Tel.: (46) 45554400
Fax: (46) 45554401
E-Mail: andreos.bergscrom@se.flextronics.se
Web Site: www.flextronics.se
Emp.: 450
Engineering, Electronics Manufacturing & Logistical Services to Telecommunications, Networking, Computer, Consumer & Medical Electronics Industries
S.I.C.: 8711
N.A.I.C.S.: 541330
Andreos Bergscrom *(Gen Mgr)*

Subsidiaries:

Flextronics Network Services Sweden AB (2)
Odenskogsvagen 27 29
PO Box 370
831 25 Ostersund, Sweden
Tel.: (46) 063169000
Fax: (46) 063128450
Web Site: www.flextronics.se
Emp.: 15
Electronic Components Developer & Mfr
S.I.C.: 3679
N.A.I.C.S.: 334419
Lennart Ivarsson *(Acct Mgr)*

Flextronics International Taiwan Ltd. (1)
5f 6 Chung Hsing Rd Se
Wuku Hsiang, Taipei, 24872, Taiwan
Tel.: (886) 289771888
Fax: (886) 280360026
Electronic Component Mfr
S.I.C.: 3679
N.A.I.C.S.: 334419

Flextronics International (UK) Ltd (1)
West Avenue
Paisley, PA1 2FB, United Kingdom
Tel.: (44) 141 849 5600
Electrical Equipment Mfr
S.I.C.: 3699
N.A.I.C.S.: 335999

Flextronics International (1)
Munkas St 28
H 8660 Tab, Hungary (100%)
Tel.: (36) 84526000
Fax: (36) 84526021
E-Mail: info.tab@hu.flextronics.com
Web Site: www.flextronics.com
Emp.: 9,500
Communications Equipment Mfr
S.I.C.: 7622
N.A.I.C.S.: 811213
Carol Schutter *(Gen Mgr)*

Flextronics International (1)
Plo 37 Kawasan Perindustrian
81400 Senai, Johore, Malaysia
Tel.: (60) 75995695
Fax: (60) 75995237
E-Mail: info@sg.flextronics.com
Web Site: www.flextronics.com
Plastics Mfr
S.I.C.: 2821
N.A.I.C.S.: 325211

Flextronics International (1)
9 Suqian Road
Suzhou Industrial Park, Suzhou, 215021, China CN
Tel.: (86) 51267612300
Electronic Component Mfr
S.I.C.: 3679
N.A.I.C.S.: 334419

Flextronics International (1)
Long Jing Industrial Estate Long Jing Rd Xi Li Town Nantou District
518055 Shenzhen, China
Tel.: (86) 75526793887
Fax: (86) 755 26786713
E-Mail: info@hk.flextronics.com
Web Site: www.flextronics.com
Emp.: 100
Enclosure Systems & Design Services
S.I.C.: 3571
N.A.I.C.S.: 334111

Flextronics International (1)
3 Tian Fu Road Tong Fu Yu Industrial Park Fu Yong Town Bao An District, Shenzhen, 518103, China CN
Tel.: (86) 755 7314188
Electronic Components & Printed Circuit Boards Mfr
S.I.C.: 3679
N.A.I.C.S.: 334419

Flextronics Investment Holding GmbH (1)
Heinz-Nixdorf-Ring 1
Paderborn, North Rhine-Westphal, 33106, Germany
Tel.: (49) 52511800
Fax: (49) 5251181909
Investment Management Services
S.I.C.: 6211
N.A.I.C.S.: 523999
Schmidt Streier *(Gen Mgr)*

Flextronics (Israel) Ltd (1)
1 Hataasia
Migdal Ha'Emeq, 23022, Israel
Tel.: (972) 46448200
Fax: (972) 46040850
Electronic Component Mfr
S.I.C.: 3679
N.A.I.C.S.: 334419

Flextronics Italy S.P.A (1)
Strada Statale 234 1/3
Somaglia, Lodi, 26867, Italy
Tel.: (39) 377926611
Fax: (39) 0377460426
Call Center Operating Services
S.I.C.: 7389
N.A.I.C.S.: 561421

Flextronics Japan K.K. (1)
Meguro Suda Building 6th Floor
3 9 1 Meguro Meguro ku, Tokyo, 153 0063, Japan
Tel.: (81) 357947310
Fax: (81) 3 5794 7315
E-Mail: tokyo-sales@jp.flextronics.com
Web Site: flextronics.com
Electronic Component Mfr
S.I.C.: 3679
N.A.I.C.S.: 334419

Subsidiaries:

Flextronics Digital Design Japan, Ltd. (2)
23 11 Naka Ohshio Chino shi
Nagano, 391 0293, Japan

Tel.: (81) 266 82 2000
Fax: (81) 266 82 2010
Web Site: www.secinfo.com
Electronic Component Developer & Mfr
S.I.C.: 3571
N.A.I.C.S.: 334111

Flextronics Laval S.N.C. (1)
Centre D Affaires Technopolis Rue Albert Einstein
BP 1215
Laval, 53810, France
Tel.: (33) 2 43 67 40 00
Fax: (33) 2 43 67 41 80
Communication Equipment Mfr
S.I.C.: 3669
N.A.I.C.S.: 334290

Flextronics Logistics B.V. (1)
Nobelstraat 10-14
Oostrum, 5807 GA, Netherlands
Tel.: (31) 478518000
Fax: (31) 478518011
Emp.: 450
Logistics Consulting Services
S.I.C.: 4731
N.A.I.C.S.: 541614
Rene Richters *(Gen Mgr)*

Flextronics Logistics Poland SP. z.o.o. (1)
Ofiar Terroryzmu 11 Wrzesnia 17
Lodz, 92-410, Poland
Tel.: (48) 422096116
Fax: (48) 422096140
Logistics Consulting Services
S.I.C.: 4731
N.A.I.C.S.: 541614
Krzysztof Zukowski *(Gen Mgr)*

Flextronics Manufacturing Aguascalientes, S.A. de C.V. (1)
Km 9 55 Blvd A Zacatecas Corral De Barrancos
Jesus Maria, Aguascalientes, 20900, Mexico
Tel.: (52) 4499107100
Fax: (52) 4499107199
Electronic Equipment Mfr
S.I.C.: 3679
N.A.I.C.S.: 334419
Oscar de la Parra *(Gen Mgr)*

Flextronics Manufacturing (H.K.) Ltd. (1)
17 & 18/F Nina Twr Twr II 8 Yeung Uk Rd
Tsuen Wan, New Territories, China (Hong Kong)
Tel.: (852) 22761800
Fax: (852) 22761207
Printed Circuit Board Mfr
S.I.C.: 3679
N.A.I.C.S.: 334418

Flextronics Manufacturing (Penang) Sdn. Bhd. (1)
Plot 13 Phase 4 Prai Industrial Estate
Perai, Penang, 13600, Malaysia
Tel.: (60) 45075600
Fax: (60) 45078728
Electronic Component Mfr
S.I.C.: 3679
N.A.I.C.S.: 334419

Flextronics Manufacturing (Zhuhai) Co., Ltd. (1)
No 168 Zhufeng Ave Xinqing Science & Technology Industrial Park
Zhuhai, Guangdong, 519180, China
Tel.: (86) 7565188560
Fax: (86) 7565110318
Communication Equipment Mfr
S.I.C.: 3669
N.A.I.C.S.: 334290
Seng Tee Kiat *(Gen Mgr)*

Flextronics (Nanjing) Technology Co., Ltd. (1)
99 Zhuangpai Rd Jiangning Economic & Technological Development Zone
Nanjing, Jiangsu, 211100, China
Tel.: (86) 2552122288
Fax: (86) 2552122560
Electronic Component Mfr
S.I.C.: 3679
N.A.I.C.S.: 334419

Flextronics Network Services GmbH (1)
Heinz-Nixdorf-Ring 1
Paderborn, North Rhine-Westphal, 33106, Germany
Tel.: (49) 52511800
Fax: (49) 5251811105
Communication Network Installation Services
S.I.C.: 1731
N.A.I.C.S.: 238210

Flextronics ODM Netherlands NV (1)
Nobelstraat 10-14
Oostrum, 5807 GA, Netherlands
Tel.: (31) 478518000
Investment Management Services
S.I.C.: 6211
N.A.I.C.S.: 523999

Flextronics Plastic Technology (ShenZhen) Ltd. (1)
Yangbei Jixiang Industrial Zone Huangtian Community Xixiang St
Shenzhen, Guangdong, 518128, China
Tel.: (86) 75581468888
Plastic Materials Mfr
S.I.C.: 3089
N.A.I.C.S.: 326199

Flextronics Plastics (Zhuhai) Co., Ltd (1)
Xinqing Technology Industrial Zone Jing An Town
Doumen District, Zhuhai, Guangdong, 519100, China
Tel.: (86) 7565186147
Fax: (86) 7565181454
Electrical Component Mfr
S.I.C.: 3699
N.A.I.C.S.: 335999

Flextronics Plastics, S.A. de C.V. (1)
Carretera A Base Aerea 5850 Km 5 Modulo 4
Zapopan, Jalisco, 45100, Mexico
Tel.: (52) 3338183200
Fax: (52) 38183227
Plastic Product Mfr
S.I.C.: 3089
N.A.I.C.S.: 326199

Flextronics Romania SRL (1)
Dn 6 Km 5 7 Calea TorontaluluiTimisoara
Timisoara, 300668, Romania
Tel.: (40) 256303500
Fax: (40) 256303501
Electronic Component Mfr
S.I.C.: 3679
N.A.I.C.S.: 334419

Flextronics Sales & Marketing North Asia (L) Ltd. (1)
Unit 7d Main Office Tower Jalan Merdeka Financial Park Labuan Complex
Labuan, Sabah, 87000, Malaysia
Tel.: (60) 87453119
Fax: (60) 87452119
Emp.: 10
Electronic Component Whslr
S.I.C.: 5065
N.A.I.C.S.: 423690
Julie Lee *(Sr Mgr)*

Flextronics Servicios Guadalajara, S.A. de C.V. (1)
A La Base Aerea No 5850 La Mora
Zapopan, Jalisco, 45136, Mexico
Tel.: (52) 3338183200
Fax: (52) 3338183240
Electronic Component Mfr
S.I.C.: 3679
N.A.I.C.S.: 334419

Flextronics (Shanghai) Co., Ltd. (1)
No 77 Yongsheng Road
Jiading, Shanghai, 201801, China
Tel.: (86) 21 39158318
Fax: (86) 21 39158543
Electronic Component Mfr
S.I.C.: 3679
N.A.I.C.S.: 334419

Flextronics Special Business Solutions (1)
Solectronstrasse 2
71083 Herrenberg, Germany
Tel.: (49) 70329980
Fax: (49) 7032998222
E-Mail: Monika.Reintjes@de.flextronics.com
Web Site: www.sbs.flextronics.com
Emp.: 250
Electronic Component Development & Logistics Services
S.I.C.: 3679
N.A.I.C.S.: 334419
Monika Reintjes *(Mng Dir)*

Flextronics S.R.L (1)
Via Professor Don A Dalla Torre 6/A
Ponte di Piave, Treviso, Italy
Tel.: (39) 0422202611
Fax: (39) 0422853562
Emp.: 150
Plastic Injection Mold Mfr
S.I.C.: 3089
N.A.I.C.S.: 326199

Flextronics Technologies (India) Pvt Ltd. (1)
Plot 3 Pase II Sipcot Industrial Park
Sandavellur C Village
Sriperumbudur Taluk, Kanchipuram, Tamilnadu, 602106, India
Tel.: (91) 44 6710 5000
Fax: (91) 4467105141
E-Mail: Madhusudan.Moudgal@flextronics.com
Web Site: www.flextronics.com
Emp.: 3,000
Electronic Component Mfr
S.I.C.: 3679
N.A.I.C.S.: 334419
Madhusudan Moudgal *(Sr Mgr-Bus Dev)*

Flextronics Technologies Mexico, S.de R.L. de C.V. (1)
Km 6 5 Prol Avenida Lopez Mateos Sur No 2915
Tlajomulco de Zuniga, Jalisco, 45640, Mexico
Tel.: (52) 3337704200
Electrical Equipment Mfr
S.I.C.: 3699
N.A.I.C.S.: 335999

Flextronics Technology (Penang) Sdn. Bhd. (1)
Plot 13 Phase 4 Prai Industrial Estate
Perai Pulau, Penang, 13600, Malaysia
Tel.: (60) 45075600
Fax: (60) 45078733
E-Mail: asia.sls@flextronics.com
Web Site: www.flextronics.com
Emp.: 8,000
Electronics Manufacturing Services
S.I.C.: 3679
N.A.I.C.S.: 334419
Michael M. McNamara *(CEO)*

Flextronics Technology Sdn Bhd (1)
Plot 56 Taman Perindustrian Bukit
14100 Bukit Minyak, Penang, Malaysia
Tel.: (60) 04 384 7448
E-Mail: info@my.flextronics.com
Web Site: www.flextronics.com
Emp.: 1,496
Design & Engineering of Plastics
S.I.C.: 2821
N.A.I.C.S.: 325211

Flextronics Technology (Shanghai) Co., Ltd. (1)
Zone 1c No 77 Yongsheng Road Malu Town
Jiading District, Shanghai, 201808, China
Tel.: (86) 2139158000
Fax: (86) 2139158403
Electronic Component Mfr
S.I.C.: 3679
N.A.I.C.S.: 334419

Flextronics Technology (ShenZhen) Co., Ltd. (1)
Building C9-11 No 2 Industrial Park Xixiang Town
Bao An District, Shenzhen, Guangdong, 518126, China
Tel.: (86) 75527497333
Fax: (86) 75527490001
Electronic Component Mfr
S.I.C.: 3679
N.A.I.C.S.: 334419

Flextronics Technology (Switzerland) GmbH (1)
Weissensteinstr 26
Solothurn, 4500, Switzerland
Tel.: (41) 32 6282828
Fax: (41) 32 6282929
Electronic Component Mfr
S.I.C.: 3679
N.A.I.C.S.: 334419
Dominik Friedli *(Mgr)*

Frog Design S.R.L (1)
Via Alserio 22
20159 Milan, Italy
Tel.: (39) 0 2 898 25900
Fax: (39) 0 2 898 25901
Design Engineering Services
S.I.C.: 8711
N.A.I.C.S.: 541330

Grolleau SAS (1)
Rue du Moulin de la Buie
49310 Montilliers, France
Tel.: (33) 241758822
Fax: (33) 2 41 75 81 30
E-Mail: info@grolleau.fr
Web Site: www.grolleau.fr
Electronic Enclosure Mfr
S.I.C.: 3679
N.A.I.C.S.: 334419
Mobach Roha *(Gen Mgr)*

Hotman Handelsgesellschaft mbH (1)
Office Park 1/Top B 07/02 Wien-Flughafen
Vienna, 1300, Austria
Tel.: (43) 16024100
Fax: (43) 16024100, ext. 1750
Web Site: www.flextronic.com
Emp.: 5
Heat Exchanger Mfr
S.I.C.: 3443
N.A.I.C.S.: 332410
Peter Gutschi *(Gen Mgr)*

Masa da Amazonia Ltda. (1)
Av Solimoes 805 Distrito Industria
Manaus, Amazonas, 69075-200, Brazil
Tel.: (55) 92 3616 8200
Fax: (55) 92 3615 1235
E-Mail: info@masadaamazonia.com.br
Web Site: www.masadaamazonia.com.br
Emp.: 1,500
Electronic Component Mfr
S.I.C.: 3679
N.A.I.C.S.: 334419
Ocimar Melloni *(Gen Mgr)*

Multek Brazil Ltda (1)
Avenida Giovanni Gronchi 6899 - Vila Andrade
05724-005 Sao Paulo, Brazil
Tel.: (55) 11 3205 8300
Fax: (55) 11 3205 8421
Web Site: www.multek.com
Printed Circuit Board Mfr
S.I.C.: 3679
N.A.I.C.S.: 334418
Fernando Guerra *(VP & Gen Mgr)*

Multek China Limited (1)
Xin Qing Science & Tech Ind Park Jing An Town
Doumen, Zhuhai, Guangdong, China 519180
Tel.: (86) 7565539888
Fax: (86) 7565539388
Rigid Flex & Flexible Printed Circuits
S.I.C.: 3679
N.A.I.C.S.: 334419

Multek Display (Hong Kong) Limited (1)
17/F Nina Twr Ii 8 Yeung Uk Rd
Tsuen Wan, New Territories, China (Hong Kong)
Tel.: (852) 22761000
Fax: (852) 22761122
Electronic Component Mfr
S.I.C.: 3679
N.A.I.C.S.: 334419

Multek Hong Kong Limited (1)
17th Floor Tower II Nina Tower 8 Yeung Uk Road
Tsuen Wan, New Territories, China (Hong Kong)
Tel.: (852) 2276 1000
Fax: (852) 2276 1122
Printed Circuit Board Mfr
S.I.C.: 3679
N.A.I.C.S.: 334418

Power Systems Technologies Far East Limited (1)
17 & 18/F Nina Twr Twr Ii 8 Yeung Uk Rd
Tsuen Wan, New Territories, China (Hong Kong)
Tel.: (852) 22761800

Flextronics International Ltd.—(Continued)

Fax: (852) 22761203
Electrical Equipment Mfr
S.I.C.: 3699
N.A.I.C.S.: 335999

PT Flextronics Technology Indonesia (1)
Jalan Rambutan Lot 515 Batamindo Industrial Park
Batam, 29433, Indonesia
Tel.: (62) 770 612660
Electronic Component Mfr
S.I.C.: 3679
N.A.I.C.S.: 334419
Loh Cheng Chuen *(Gen Mgr)*

Qingdao Victory Plastic Co., Ltd (1)
Qingdao E&T Development Zone
Qingdao, Shandong, 266000, China
Tel.: (86) 159 69890625
Plastic Goods Mfr
S.I.C.: 3089
N.A.I.C.S.: 326199

Vista Point Technologies (Malaysia) Sdn. Bhd. (1)
No 7 Jalan Keluli 1 Kawasan Perindustrian Bukit Raja Seksyen 7
Shah Alam, Selangor, 40000, Malaysia
Tel.: (60) 333615000
Fax: (60) 333615015
Electronic Component Mfr
S.I.C.: 3679
N.A.I.C.S.: 334419

FLIGHT CENTRE LIMITED
(Name Changed to Flight Centre Travel Group Limited)

FLIGHT CENTRE TRAVEL GROUP LIMITED
(Formerly Flight Centre Limited)
Level 2 545 Queen Street
Brisbane, QLD, 4000, Australia
Tel.: (61) 7 3170 7979
Web Site: www.flightcentrelimited.com
Year Founded: 1987
FLT—(ASX)
Rev.: $2,069,396,970
Assets: $2,472,428,102
Liabilities: $1,403,031,335
Net Worth: $1,069,396,767
Earnings: $291,005,383
Emp.: 15,000
Fiscal Year-end: 06/30/13
Business Description:
Holding Company; Business & Leisure Travel Agency Operator
S.I.C.: 6719
N.A.I.C.S.: 551112
Personnel:
Peter R. Morahan *(Chm)*
Graham F. Turner *(CEO & Mng Dir)*
Andrew J. Flannery *(CFO)*
Melanie C. Waters-Ryan *(COO)*
David C. Smith *(Sec)*
Board of Directors:
Peter R. Morahan
Rob Baker
John Eales
Gary W. Smith
Graham F. Turner

Subsidiaries:

Australian OpCo Pty. Ltd. (1)
Level 4 545 Queen Street
Brisbane, QLD, 4000, Australia AU
Tel.: (61) 7 3170 7979 (Switchboard) (100%)
E-Mail: enquiries@fcm.travel
Web Site: www.fcm.travel
Business Travel Agencies Operator
S.I.C.: 4729
N.A.I.C.S.: 561599
Graham F. Turner *(Founder & Chm)*

U.S. Group:

FCm Travel Solutions USA (2)
105 W Madison St Ste 2000
Chicago, IL 60602
Tel.: (312) 215-0874
E-Mail: usa@us.fcm.travel
Web Site: www.us.fcm.travel
Emp.: 430
Business Travel Agencies Operator
S.I.C.: 4729
N.A.I.C.S.: 561599
John Beauvais *(Pres)*

Non-U.S. Subsidiaries:

FCm Travel Solutions (L.L.C) (2)
Level 10 Code Business Tower Behind Mall of Emirates Al Barsha 1
PO Box 22892
Dubai, United Arab Emirates AE
Tel.: (971) 43255008 (49%)
Fax: (971) 4 325 5009
Web Site: ae.fcm.travel
Business Travel Agencies Operator
S.I.C.: 4729
N.A.I.C.S.: 561599

FCm Travel Solutions Singapore Pte. Ltd. (2)
7500A Beach Rd 05-323 The Plz
Singapore, 199591, Singapore SG
Tel.: (65) 65930376 (100%)
Fax: (65) 65930371
E-Mail: enquiries@sg.fcm.travel
Web Site: www.sg.fcm.travel
Emp.: 55
Business Travel Agencies Operator
S.I.C.: 4729
N.A.I.C.S.: 561599
Suyin Lee *(Gen Mgr-Asia)*

Flight Centre Technology Pty. Ltd. (1)
12 157 Ann St
Brisbane, QLD, 4000, Australia AU
Tel.: (61) 731707979 (100%)
Fax: (61) 732364768
Flight Ticket Booking Services
S.I.C.: 4729
N.A.I.C.S.: 561599

Moneywise Global Pty. Ltd. (1)
Level 3 545 Queen St
Brisbane, QLD, 4000, Australia AU
Tel.: (61) 731707518 (100%)
Fax: (61) 731707531
Financial Management Consulting Services
S.I.C.: 8742
N.A.I.C.S.: 541611

U.S. Subsidiary:

Flight Centre USA Holding Corp. (1)
69 Spring St
Ramsey, NJ 07446 DE
Tel.: (201) 934-3500 (100%)
Fax: (201) 934-3651
Web Site: www.flightcenter.com
Holding Company; Regional managing Office
S.I.C.: 6719
N.A.I.C.S.: 551112
Dean W. Smith *(Pres)*

Subsidiary:

FC USA Inc. (2)
69 Spring St
Ramsey, NJ 07446 NY
Tel.: (201) 934-3500 (100%)
Fax: (201) 934-3651
Toll Free: (877) 992-4732
Web Site: www.flightcenter.com
Emp.: 2,500
Travel Agencies & Services
S.I.C.: 4724
N.A.I.C.S.: 561510
Dean W. Smith *(Pres)*

Subsidiary:

Garber's Travel Service, Inc. (3)
27 Boylston St
Chestnut Hill, MA 02467 MA
Tel.: (617) 739-2200
Fax: (617) 965-8937
E-Mail: info@garbertravel.com
Web Site: www.garbertravel.com
Business & Leisure Travel Services
S.I.C.: 4724
N.A.I.C.S.: 561510
Debbie Lee Nashed *(Mgr-Ops-Chestnut Hill)*

Non-U.S. Subsidiaries:

American International Travel Limited (1)
3 F Centre Point 181-185 Gloucester Road
Wanchai, China (Hong Kong)
Tel.: (852) 28302828
Fax: (852) 28816378
Web Site: www.flightcentre.com.hk
Emp.: 60
Air Travel Management Services
S.I.C.: 4724
N.A.I.C.S.: 561510
James Hui *(Mgr-Ops)*

FCm Travel Solutions (India) Private Limited (1)
JC-43 Khirki Extension Malviya Nagar
New Delhi, 110 017, India
Tel.: (91) 11 42536666
Fax: (91) 11 42536698
E-Mail: contact@in.fcm.travel
Web Site: in.fcm.travel
Travel Management Services
S.I.C.: 4729
N.A.I.C.S.: 561599

Flight Centre (UK) Limited (1)
320 Chiswick High Rd
London, W4 5TA, United Kingdom
Tel.: (44) 2087428777
Fax: (44) 02087428723
E-Mail: chiswick.sc@flightcenter.co.uk
Web Site: www.flightcentre.co.uk
Emp.: 3,000
Travel Management Services
S.I.C.: 4724
N.A.I.C.S.: 561510
Robert Pyla *(Mgr)*

Subsidiary:

Britannic Travel Limited (2)
230 Burlington Rd Britannic House
New Malden, KT3 4TQ, United Kingdom
Tel.: (44) 121 454 7744
Travel Management Services
S.I.C.: 4724
N.A.I.C.S.: 561510

FLINDERS EXPLORATION LIMITED
58 Beulah Rd
Norwood, SA, 5067, Australia
Tel.: (61) 881327980
Fax: (61) 83125503
E-Mail: info@fexploration.com
Web Site: www.fexploration.com
Emp.: 1
Business Description:
Diamond Mining Services
S.I.C.: 1411
N.A.I.C.S.: 212311
Personnel:
Andrew Andrejewskis *(Chm)*
David Tucker *(Mng Dir)*
Board of Directors:
Andrew Andrejewskis
David Tucker
Kevin Wills

FLINDERS MINES LIMITED
Level 1 136 Frome Street
PO Box 3065
Rundle Mall, Adelaide, SA, 5000, Australia
Tel.: (61) 881327950
Fax: (61) 881327999
E-Mail: info@flindersmines.com
Web Site: www.flindersmines.com
FMS—(ASX)
Rev.: $542,901
Assets: $68,584,680
Liabilities: $1,287,370
Net Worth: $67,297,310
Earnings: ($12,949,224)
Emp.: 100
Fiscal Year-end: 06/30/13
Business Description:
Iron Ore Exploration & Development
S.I.C.: 1011
N.A.I.C.S.: 212210
Personnel:
David Wayne Godfrey *(CFO & Sec)*
Board of Directors:
Robert Michael Kennedy
Kevin John Malaxos
Ewan John Vickery
Legal Counsel:
DMAW Lawyers
Level 3 80 King William St
Adelaide, Australia

FLINDERS PORTS PTY LTD
296 St Vincent St
Port Adelaide, SA, 5015, Australia
Tel.: (61) 884470611
Fax: (61) 884470606
E-Mail: flindersports@flindersports.com.au
Web Site: www.flindersports.com.au
Sales Range: $25-49.9 Million
Emp.: 165
Business Description:
Port, Land & Shipping Infrastructure Management
S.I.C.: 4499
N.A.I.C.S.: 488330
Personnel:
Vincent Tremaine *(CEO)*
Mark Travers *(CFO)*

FLINDERS RESOURCES LIMITED
1305 1090 West Georgia Street
Vancouver, BC, V6E 3V7, Canada
Tel.: (604) 685-9316
Fax: (604) 683-1585
E-Mail: info@flindersresources.com
Web Site: www.flindersresources.com
Year Founded: 2010
FDR—(OTC TSXV)
Rev.: $181,261
Assets: $25,912,183
Liabilities: $5,628,197
Net Worth: $20,283,986
Earnings: ($6,388,321)
Fiscal Year-end: 10/31/12
Business Description:
Investment Services
S.I.C.: 6211
N.A.I.C.S.: 523999
Personnel:
Blair Way *(Pres & CEO)*
Nick DeMare *(CFO)*
Mikael Ranggard *(Chm-Kringelgruvan AB)*
Mariana Bermudez *(Sec)*
Board of Directors:
Robert G. Atkinson
Nick DeMare
Michael Robert Hudson
Mark Saxon
Transfer Agent:
Computershare Investor Services inc
3rd Fl 510 Burrard Street
Vancouver, BC, Canada

FLINT INT'L SERVICES, INC.
7577 Keele Street Suite B1
Vaughan, ON, L4L 4X3, Canada
Toll Free: (877) 439-3001
Sales Range: Less than $1 Million
Emp.: 1
Business Description:
Online Education Services
S.I.C.: 2741
N.A.I.C.S.: 519130
Personnel:
Russell Hiebert *(Pres, Sec & Treas)*
Board of Directors:
Russell Hiebert
Transfer Agent:
Signature Stock Transfer, Inc.
2632 Coachlight Ct
Plano, TX 75093-3850

Tel.: (972) 612-4120
Fax: (972) 612-4122

FLIPKART INTERNET PRIVATE LIMITED
Ozone Manay Tech Park 56/18 & 55/09 7th Floor
Garvebhavipalya Hosur Road,
Bengaluru, 560068, India
Tel.: (91) 80 4912 9199
Web Site: www.flipkart.com
Year Founded: 2007
Sales Range: $1-4.9 Billion
Emp.: 2,250
Business Description:
Online Retailer
S.I.C.: 5961
N.A.I.C.S.: 454111
Personnel:
Sachin Bansal *(Co-Founder & CEO)*
Mekin Maheshwari *(Chief People Officer)*

FLIPSIDE GROUP
Smithbrook Barns
Cranleigh, Surrey, GU6 8LH, United Kingdom
Tel.: (44) 1483274141
Fax: (44) 1483277709
E-Mail: info@flipsidegroup.com
Web Site: www.flipsideweb.co.uk
Sales Range: $25-49.9 Million
Emp.: 50
Business Description:
Advertising Services
S.I.C.: 7311
N.A.I.C.S.: 541810
Personnel:
Neil Christie *(Owner & Dir)*
Tim Drake *(CEO)*

FLITE HOCKEY
3400 Ridgeway Drive Unit 2
Mississauga, ON, Canada
Tel.: (905) 828-6030
Fax: (905) 828-1840
E-Mail: info@flitehockey.com
Web Site: www.flitehockey.com
Year Founded: 1993
Rev.: $32,984,982
Emp.: 310
Business Description:
Sports Equipment Mfr
S.I.C.: 3949
N.A.I.C.S.: 339920
Personnel:
Gerry McSorley *(Founder & Pres)*

FLO S.P.A.
Frazione Ghiara Sabbioni 33 A
43012 Fontanellato, PR, Italy
Tel.: (39) 0521 823 111
Fax: (39) 0521 822 844
E-Mail: info@flo.eu
Web Site: www.flo.eu
Year Founded: 1973
Business Description:
Plastic & Paper Cup Mfr
S.I.C.: 3089
N.A.I.C.S.: 326199
Personnel:
Antonio Simonazzi *(Founder & Pres)*

Non-U.S. Joint Venture:

F. Bender Limited (1)
Gresford Industrial Park Chester Road
Wrexham, LL12 8LX, United Kingdom UK
Tel.: (44) 1978 855 661
Fax: (44) 1978 855 101
E-Mail: info@benders.co.uk
Web Site: www.benders.co.uk
Sanitary Food & Beverage Containers & Service Products Mfr
S.I.C.: 2652
N.A.I.C.S.: 322219
Andrew Cunliffe *(Mng Dir)*

FLOATEL INTERNATIONAL LTD.
c/o Floatel International AB
Johannefredsgatan 4
431 53 Molndal, Sweden
Tel.: (46) 313520700
Fax: (46) 313520701
E-Mail: info@floatel.se
Web Site: www.floatel.se
Year Founded: 2006
Sales Range: $25-49.9 Million
Emp.: 20
Business Description:
Holding Company; Offshore Floatel Fleet Owner & Operator
S.I.C.: 6719
N.A.I.C.S.: 551112
Personnel:
Michael Chia *(Chm)*
Jonathan B. Fairbanks *(Deputy Chm)*
Peter Jacobsson *(CEO)*
Nils Martensson *(COO)*
David Wasterstrom *(Corp Counsel-Legal)*
Board of Directors:
Michael Chia
Jonathan B. Fairbanks
B. James Ford
Ching Chuan Lai
Edmund Mah
Adam C. Pierce
Amy Rice
Subsidiary:

Floatel International AB (1)
Johannefredsgatan 4
431 53 Molndal, Sweden SE
Tel.: (46) 313520700 (100%)
Fax: (46) 313520701
E-Mail: info@floatel.se
Web Site: www.floatel.se
Offshore Floatel Fleet Operator
S.I.C.: 4481
N.A.I.C.S.: 483112
Peter Jacobsson *(CEO)*
Nils Martensson *(COO)*

FLODOR S.A.S.
ZA du Pre de la Dame Jeanne Route de Survilliers
60128 Plailly, France
Tel.: (33) 344545100
Fax: (33) 344545101
Web Site: www.flodor.fr
Sales Range: $10-24.9 Million
Business Description:
Snack Chip Mfr & Distr
S.I.C.: 2052
N.A.I.C.S.: 311919
Personnel:
Alberto Vitaloni *(Pres)*

FLOFORM COUNTERTOPS
125 Hamelin Street
Winnipeg, MB, R3T 3Z1, Canada
Tel.: (204) 453-0639
Fax: (204) 453-0639
Toll Free: (877) 356-3676
Web Site: www.floform.com
Rev.: $13,911,192
Emp.: 160
S.I.C.: 2434
N.A.I.C.S.: 337110
Personnel:
E. J. Sherritt *(Chm, Pres & CEO)*
Britt Karlson *(COO & Mgr-Winnipeg Branch)*

FLOORS MY HOME LIMITED
(d/b/a Floors-2-Go)
74 Newtown Row
Birmingham, B6 4HA, United Kingdom
Tel.: (44) 1213590234
Fax: (44) 1213594316
E-Mail: info@floors2go.co.uk
Web Site: www.floors2go.co.uk
Year Founded: 1999
Sales Range: $100-124.9 Million
Emp.: 590
Business Description:
Wood Flooring Retailer
S.I.C.: 5713
N.A.I.C.S.: 442210
Personnel:
Robert Hodges *(Mng Dir)*

FLORA MANUFACTURING & DISTRIBUTING LTD.
7400 Fraser Park Drive
Burnaby, BC, V5J 5B9, Canada
Tel.: (604) 436-6000
Fax: (604) 436-6060
Toll Free: (888) 436-6697
E-Mail: info@florahealth.com
Web Site: www.florahealth.com
Sales Range: $10-24.9 Million
Emp.: 180
Business Description:
Herbal Remedies Mfr & Distr
S.I.C.: 2833
N.A.I.C.S.: 325411
Personnel:
Thomas Greither *(Owner & Pres)*

U.S. Subsidiary:

Flora Inc. (1)
805 E Badger Rd
Lynden, WA 98264
Tel.: (360) 354-2110
Fax: (360) 354-8953
Web Site: www.florahealth.com
Emp.: 70
Herbal Remedies Mfr & Distr
S.I.C.: 2833
N.A.I.C.S.: 325411
Thomas Greither *(Pres)*

FLORENS CONTAINER SERVICES COMPANY LTD.
35 F 118 Connaught Rd W
Hong Kong, China (Hong Kong)
Tel.: (852) 25596117
Telex: 67816 FBZLN HX
Fax: (852) 25592762
E-Mail: info@florens.com
Web Site: www.florens.com
Year Founded: 1996
Emp.: 500
Business Description:
Holding Company
S.I.C.: 6719
N.A.I.C.S.: 551112
Personnel:
Jian Xu *(CEO & Pres)*

U.S. Subsidiaries:

Florens Container Services USA Ltd. (1)
303 2nd St Ste 355 S
San Francisco, CA 94107-1328 CA
Tel.: (415) 348-2800 (100%)
Fax: (415) 348-2888
Web Site: www.florens.com
Emp.: 28
Mfr. of Storage Containers
S.I.C.: 7359
N.A.I.C.S.: 532490
Kayrom Romero *(Office Mgr)*

Florens Containers (1)
999 Riverview Dr Ste 204
Totowa, NJ 07512-1160 (100%)
Tel.: (973) 890-5050
Fax: (973) 890-4990
Toll Free: (888) 356-7367
E-Mail: newjersey@florens.com
Web Site: www.florens.com
Emp.: 9
Mfr. of Storage Containers
S.I.C.: 7359
N.A.I.C.S.: 532490
Mark Depasquale *(VP)*

Non-U.S. Subsidiaries:

Florens Container Service (1)
Via XII Ottobre 2 113
16121 Genoa, Italy (100%)
Tel.: (39) 0105761339
Fax: (39) 0105761429
Web Site: www.florens.com
Emp.: 2
Mfr. of Storage Containers
S.I.C.: 3412
N.A.I.C.S.: 332439

Florens Container Services (1)
Rm D 20 F Lucky Mansion Block A
No 257 Siping Rd, Shanghai, 2000081, China (100%)
Tel.: (86) 2165218397
Fax: (86) 2165218399
E-Mail: shirley@florens.com
Web Site: www.florens.com
Emp.: 7
Mfr. of Storage Containers
S.I.C.: 3499
N.A.I.C.S.: 332439
Liu Higu *(Pres)*

Florens Container Services (1)
5th Fl Daiichi Chojiya Bldg
Minato Ku, Tokyo, Daimon, 10500127, Japan (100%)
Tel.: (81) 334357776
Fax: (81) 354057281
Web Site: www.florens.com
Sales Range: Less than $1 Million
Emp.: 5
Mfr. of Storage Containers
S.I.C.: 3499
N.A.I.C.S.: 332439
Shiro Kinoshita *(Mng Dir)*

Florens Container Services (1)
Kingmaker House Sta Rd
New Barnet, Herts, EN5 1NZ, United Kingdom (100%)
Tel.: (44) 2083700700
Fax: (44) 2082750777
E-Mail: jmilsom@florens.com
Emp.: 8
Mfr. of Storage Containers
S.I.C.: 3412
N.A.I.C.S.: 332439

Florens Container Services (1)
Fischertwiete 2
Chilehaus A 1st Fl, Hamburg, 20095, Germany (100%)
Tel.: (49) 4032005239
E-Mail: hamburg@florens.com
Emp.: 3
Mfr. of Storage Containers
S.I.C.: 3499
N.A.I.C.S.: 332439
Andreas Jahn *(Dir-Sls)*

Florens Container Services (1)
Av Rocque Petroni Jr 999 13th Fl
4707910 Sao Paulo, Brazil (100%)
Tel.: (55) 151852775
Fax: (55) 151852776
E-Mail: customerservice@florens.com
Web Site: www.florenscontainer.com
Emp.: 1
Mfr. of Storage Containers
S.I.C.: 3412
N.A.I.C.S.: 332439

FLORIDA ICE AND FARM CO. S.A.
Calle 12 Av 4 y 6 San Jose
Postal 2046-3000 Heredia, San Jose, Costa Rica
Tel.: (506) 24376700
Fax: (506) 24377000
E-Mail: info@florida.co.cr
Web Site: www.florida.co.cr/
Sales Range: $200-249.9 Million
Emp.: 2,400
Business Description:
Holding Company; Beer, Bottled Water & Fruit Juice & Malt Beverages Distr; Real Estate Management & Tourism Services; Investment Services
S.I.C.: 6719
N.A.I.C.S.: 551112

Florida Ice and Farm Co. S.A.—(Continued)

Personnel:
Rodolfo Jimenez Borbon *(Pres)*
Board of Directors:
Rodolfo Jimenez Borbon

U.S. Subsidiary:

North American Breweries, Inc. (1)
445 Saint Paul St
Rochester, NY 14605-1726 DE
Tel.: (585) 546-1030
Fax: (585) 506-5011
Web Site: www.nabreweries.com
Emp.: 450
Holding Company; Breweries & Alcoholic Beverage Distr
S.I.C.: 6719
N.A.I.C.S.: 551112
Richard Lozyniak *(CEO)*
Daniel Harrington *(CFO)*

Subsidiaries:

Genesee Brewing Company (2)
445 Saint Paul St
Rochester, NY 14605-1726 NY
Tel.: (585) 546-1030
Fax: (585) 546-5011
Web Site: www.geneseebeer.com
Sales Range: $100-124.9 Million
Emp.: 400
Brewery & Beer Distr
S.I.C.: 2082
N.A.I.C.S.: 312120
Richard Lozyniak *(Pres & CEO)*

Independent Brewers United, Inc. (2)
431 Pine St Ste G 14
Burlington, VT 05401
Tel.: (802) 658-2739
Web Site: www.magichat.net
Holding Company
S.I.C.: 6719
N.A.I.C.S.: 551112
R. Martin Kelly *(Pres & CEO)*

Subsidiary:

Magic Hat Brewing Co. & Performing Arts Center Inc. (3)
5 Bartlett Bay Rd
South Burlington, VT 05403
Tel.: (802) 658-2739
Web Site: www.magichat.com
Emp.: 70
Brewery
S.I.C.: 2082
N.A.I.C.S.: 312120
R. Martin Kelly *(CEO)*

Subsidiary:

Pyramid Breweries Inc. (4)
91 S Royal Brougham Way
Seattle, WA 98134-1219 WA
Tel.: (206) 682-8322
Fax: (206) 682-8420
E-Mail: host@pyramidbrew.com
Web Site: www.pyramidbrew.com
Sales Range: $25-49.9 Million
Emp.: 502
Ales, Lagers & Soda Mfr; Restaurant Operator
S.I.C.: 2082
N.A.I.C.S.: 312120
Teresa Morgan *(Gen Mgr-Pyramid Alehouse)*

Subsidiaries:

Pyramid Gilman Street Property, LLC (5)
901 Gilman St
Berkeley, CA 94710
Tel.: (510) 528-9880
Fax: (510) 559-7063
Web Site: www.pyramidbrew.com
Sales Range: $10-24.9 Million
Emp.: 136
Malt Mfr & Restaurant Owners
S.I.C.: 2083
N.A.I.C.S.: 311213

Labatt USA LLC (2)
50 Fountain Plz Ste 900
Buffalo, NY 14202 NY
Tel.: (716) 604-1050
Fax: (716) 604-1055
Web Site: www.labattus.com
Emp.: 250
Beer Importer & Distr
S.I.C.: 5181
N.A.I.C.S.: 424810
Jason Drewniak *(Brand Mgr)*

Non-U.S. Subsidiary:

Alimentos Kern de Guatemala, S.A. (1)
Kilometro 7 Carretera Al Atlantico
Zona 18, 1018 Guatemala, Guatemala GT
Tel.: (502) 2323 7100
E-Mail: info@alimentoskerns.com
Web Site: www.alikerns.com
Sales Range: $1-9.9 Million
Emp.: 700
Nectar & Fruit Juice, Vegetable & Tomato Products Mfr
S.I.C.: 2033
N.A.I.C.S.: 311421

FLORIDIENNE SA

Dreve Richelle 161 Box 4 Building P
1410 Waterloo, Belgium
Tel.: (32) 23530028
Fax: (32) 23530581
E-Mail: info@floridienne.be
Web Site: www.floridienne.be
Year Founded: 1898
FLOB—(EUR)
Rev.: $377,062,217
Assets: $383,927,684
Liabilities: $238,272,090
Net Worth: $145,655,594
Earnings: ($26,788,783)
Emp.: 960
Fiscal Year-end: 12/31/12

Business Description:
Holding Company; Non-Ferrous Metal Salts Mfr & Marketer; Agrofoods; Life-Sciences
S.I.C.: 6719
N.A.I.C.S.: 551112

Personnel:
Philippe Bodson *(Chm)*
Gaetan Waucquez *(Mng Dir)*
Joseph De Waele *(CFO)*
Marie-Joelle Delmoitie *(Sec)*

Board of Directors:
Philippe Bodson
Marc-Yves Blanpain
Paul Cornet de Ways Ruart
Olivier Davignon
Bernard de Gerlache de Gomery
Philippe de Spoelberch
Yves Meurice
Gaetan Waucquez
Loic Waucquez

Subsidiaries:

Florago SA (1)
Dree Richelle 161 4 Bldg P
Waterloo, 1410, Belgium
Tel.: (32) 23530028
Fax: (32) 23530581
E-Mail: info@florago.be
Web Site: www.florago.be
Emp.: 3
Food Production & Marketing Services
S.I.C.: 8742
N.A.I.C.S.: 541611
Gaetan Waucquez *(Member-Mgmt Bd)*

Non-U.S. Subsidiaries:

Francaise De Gastronomie (2)
2 Allee Helsinki
CA80072 Schiltigheim, 67013 Strasbourg, Cedex, France
Tel.: (33) 388593060
Fax: (33) 388593061
Web Site: www.francaise-de-gastronomie.fr
Emp.: 100
Holding Company
S.I.C.: 6719
N.A.I.C.S.: 551112
Jean-Louis Muller *(CEO)*

Larzul SA (2)
Rue Louis Hemon BP 16
Ploneour-Lanvern, Finistere, France
Tel.: (33) 298826868
Fax: (33) 298877127
E-Mail: contact@groupe-larzul.com
Web Site: www.groupe-larzul.com
Specialty Foods
S.I.C.: 2099
N.A.I.C.S.: 311999

Floridienne Chimie SA (1)
Quai des Usines 12
B 7800 Ath, Belgium
Tel.: (32) 68281912
Fax: (32) 68286811
E-Mail: reception@floridiennechimie.com
Web Site: www.floridiennechimie.com
Emp.: 60
Chemical Products & Metal Salts Export
S.I.C.: 2899
N.A.I.C.S.: 325998
Simon Vlajcic *(Mng Dir)*

Subsidiary:

Sidech S.A. (2)
Rue de la Station 7
B 1495 Tilly, Belgium
Tel.: (32) 71988821
Fax: (32) 71978294
E-Mail: info@sidech.be
Web Site: www.sidech.be
Component Metal Production
S.I.C.: 3499
N.A.I.C.S.: 332117
Laurent Raskin *(CEO)*

Non-U.S. Subsidiaries:

IKA GmbH & CO.KG (2)
ChemiePark Bitterfeld Wolfen
Filmstrasse 4, Wolfen, 06766, Germany
Tel.: (49) 34946961
Fax: (49) 3494696137
E-Mail: ika@ika-wolsen.de
Web Site: www.ika-wolsen.de
Emp.: 77
Chemical Production
S.I.C.: 2819
N.A.I.C.S.: 325180
Reinhart Beck *(Mng Dir)*

KIMFLOR AS (2)
Aydin Karayolu 35 Km
Yazibasi-Torbal, 35875 Izmir, Turkey
Tel.: (90) 2328539066
Fax: (90) 2328539065
E-Mail: import@kimflor.com
Web Site: www.kimflor.com
Emp.: 50
Lead-Based Products
S.I.C.: 2819
N.A.I.C.S.: 325180

Societe Nouvelle d'Affinage des Metaux - SNAM S.A.S. (2)
Avenue Jean Jaures
BP 4
F-12110 Viviez, France FR
Tel.: (33) 474945985
Fax: (33) 474941318
E-Mail: info@snam.com
Web Site: www.snam.com
Chemical Production & Recovery
S.I.C.: 2819
N.A.I.C.S.: 325180

Subsidiary:

Euro Bat Tri (3)
Rue de la Garenne BP 735
Saint-Quentin-Fallavier, F-38297, France
Tel.: (33) 474945014
Fax: (33) 474941318
E-Mail: eurobatri@compuserve.com
Web Site: www.snam.com
Chemical Recovery
S.I.C.: 2819
N.A.I.C.S.: 325180

Florinvest SA (1)
Drege Richelle 161 Bldg P
PO Box 4
1410 Waterloo, Belgium
Tel.: (32) 23530028
Fax: (32) 23530581
E-Mail: info@floridienne.be
Web Site: www.florinvest.be
Emp.: 10
Investment Services
S.I.C.: 6211
N.A.I.C.S.: 523999
Christian Van Osselaer *(Mng Dir)*
Gaetan Waucquez *(Mng Dir)*
Lee Nanf *(Gen Sec)*

Subsidiaries:

Chemcom SA (2)
Rte de Lennik 802
1070 Brussels, Belgium
Tel.: (32) 23530028
Fax: (32) 25298141
E-Mail: info@chemcom.be
Web Site: www.chemcom.be
Emp.: 20
Biopharmaceutical Services
S.I.C.: 2834
N.A.I.C.S.: 325412

H-Phar SA (2)
Chaussee de Bruxelles
141 Jumet, 6040 Brussels, Belgium
Tel.: (32) 10417078
Fax: (32) 10414247
E-Mail: drvandevelde@h-phar.com
Web Site: www.h-phar.com
Emp.: 10
Clinical Research & Development
S.I.C.: 8731
N.A.I.C.S.: 541712
Helene Margery *(CEO & CFO)*

FLORIM CERAMICHE S.P.A.

Via Canaletto 24
41042 Fiorano-Modenese, MO, Italy
Tel.: (39) 0536840111
Fax: (39) 0536844750
E-Mail: info@florim.it
Web Site: www.florim.it
Sales Range: $400-449.9 Million
Emp.: 1,058

Business Description:
Ceramic Wall & Floor Tile Mfr
S.I.C.: 3255
N.A.I.C.S.: 327120

Personnel:
Claudio Lucchese *(Pres & CEO)*

Board of Directors:
Donato Bruni
Eugenio Maria Emiliani
Ermes Giuseppe Ferrari
Giovanni Grossi
Oscar Iseppi
Anna Lucchese
Carlo Lucchese
Claudio Lucchese
Mariadelle Lucchese
Dorvan Sazzi

U.S. Subsidiary:

Florim USA, Inc. (1)
300 International Blvd
Clarksville, TN 37040 (87%)
Tel.: (931) 645-5100
Fax: (931) 647-9934
E-Mail: info@florimusa.com
Web Site: www.florimusa.com
Emp.: 200
Mfr. of Ceramic Floor & Wall Tiles
S.I.C.: 3297
N.A.I.C.S.: 327120
Darren Allison *(Mgr-IT)*

FLORIN MINING INVESTMENT COMPANY LIMITED

10 Murray Street
Hamilton, NSW, 2303, Australia
Tel.: (61) 2 4920 2877
Fax: (61) 2 4920 2878
E-Mail: mail@florin.com.au
Web Site: www.florin.com.au
FMI—(NSXA)
Rev.: $14,285
Assets: $2,389,872
Liabilities: $98,606
Net Worth: $2,291,266
Earnings: ($793,102)
Fiscal Year-end: 06/30/13

Business Description:
Investment Services
S.I.C.: 6211

N.A.I.C.S.: 523999
Personnel:
Victor Gowan Burley *(Chm)*
Daniel Di Stefano *(Co-Sec)*
Brett Hall *(Co-Sec)*
Board of Directors:
Victor Gowan Burley
Peter Cameron
Daniel Di Stefano
Steven Shane Pritchard
Legal Counsel:
Baker & McKenzie
Level 27 AMP Centre 50 Bridge Street
Sydney, Australia

FLORISTS SUPPLY LTD.
35 Airport Road
Winnipeg, MB, R3H 0V5, Canada
Tel.: (204) 632-1210
Fax: (204) 694-6858
Toll Free: (800) 665-7378
E-Mail: enquiries@floristssupply.com
Web Site: www.floristssupply.com
Year Founded: 1935
Rev.: $10,534,386
Emp.: 69
Business Description:
Floral importer & Mfr
S.I.C.: 5193
N.A.I.C.S.: 424930
Personnel:
Laurie Nesbitt *(Pres)*

FLOUR MILLS KEPENOS S.A.
Industrial Area of Patras
Patras, Greece 250 18
Tel.: (30) 2610 241940
Fax: (30) 2610 647173
E-Mail: mkepenos@kepenos.gr
Web Site: www.kepenos.gr
Year Founded: 1952
KEPEN—(ATH)
Emp.: 90
Business Description:
Production of Flour & Flour Products
S.I.C.: 2041
N.A.I.C.S.: 311211
Personnel:
Kepenos D. George *(Pres & CEO)*
Andriana Argiropoulou *(IR Officer)*
Board of Directors:
Gounaris G. Andreas
Kepenos T. Dimitrios
Kepenos D. George
Xenogiannis A. John
Kepenos D. Theofilos

FLOUR MILLS OF FIJI LIMITED
Leonidas St
PO Box 977
Suva, Fiji
Tel.: (679) 3301188
Fax: (679) 3300944
E-Mail: info@fmf.com.fj
Web Site: www.fmf.com.fj
Year Founded: 1973
Sales Range: $50-74.9 Million
Emp.: 850
Business Description:
Flour Milling Services
S.I.C.: 2041
N.A.I.C.S.: 311211
Personnel:
Hari Punja *(Founder & Chm)*
Ram Bajeaal *(CEO)*
Kumar Shanker *(CFO & Sec)*
Board of Directors:
Hari Punja
Hari Punja Fiji
Lionel D.S. Yee

FLOVAL EQUIPMENT LTD.
250 Rayette Road Unit 1
Concord, ON, L4K 2G6, Canada
Tel.: (905) 669-4500
Fax: (905) 669-4905
Toll Free: (800) -387-3784
E-Mail: sales@floval.com
Web Site: www.floval.com
Year Founded: 1976
Sales Range: $10-24.9 Million
Emp.: 19
Business Description:
Valving Instrumentation & Process Control Equipment Mfr
S.I.C.: 5084
N.A.I.C.S.: 423830
Personnel:
Frank Tondat *(Gen Mgr)*

FLSMIDTH & CO. A/S
Vigerslev Alle 77
2500 Valby, Denmark
Tel.: (45) 36181000
Fax: (45) 36441146
E-Mail: info@flsmidth.com
Web Site: www.flsmidth.com
FLS—(CSE)
Rev.: $4,481,765,640
Assets: $5,748,975,000
Liabilities: $4,050,164,160
Net Worth: $1,698,810,840
Earnings: $235,009,080
Emp.: 15,900
Fiscal Year-end: 12/31/12
Business Description:
Cement & Minerals Equipment & Services
S.I.C.: 3241
N.A.I.C.S.: 327310
Personnel:
Vagn Ove Sorensen *(Chm)*
Torkil Bentzen *(Vice Chm)*
Thomas Schulz *(CEO)*
Lars Vestergaard *(CFO)*
Nicolai Mauritzen *(IR Officer)*
Peter Flanagan *(Exec VP)*
Bjarne Moltke Hansen *(Exec VP)*
Per Mejnert Kristensen *(Exec VP)*
Carsten R. Lund *(Exec VP)*
Virve Elisabeth Meesak *(Grp Exec VP-Global HR)*
Eric Thomas Poupier *(Grp Exec VP-Bus Dev)*
Board of Directors:
Vagn Ove Sorensen
Torkil Bentzen
Mette Dobel
Caroline Gregoire Sainte Marie
Martin Ivert
Sten E. Jakobsson
Tom Knutzen
Jens Peter Koch
Soren Quistgaard Larsen

Subsidiaries:

Cembrit A/S (1)
Sohngaardsholmsvej 2
Aalborg, 9100, Denmark
Tel.: (45) 99372222
Fax: (45) 98134056
Web Site: www.cembrit.dk
Emp.: 50
Roof Material Mfr & Whslr
S.I.C.: 3444
N.A.I.C.S.: 332322
Mogens Fisker *(Gen Mgr)*

FFE Invest A/S (1)
Vigerslev Alle 77
2500 Valby, Denmark
Tel.: (45) 36183600
Fax: (45) 36183618
E-Mail: info@flsmidth.com
Web Site: www.flsmidth.com
Emp.: 160
Engineering Consulting Services
S.I.C.: 8711
N.A.I.C.S.: 541330
Jorgen Huno Rasmussen *(CEO)*

FLS Automation A/S (1)
Vigerslev Alle 77
DK-2500 Valby, Denmark (100%)
Tel.: (45) 36181000
Fax: (45) 36301820
E-Mail: info@flsmidth.com
Web Site: www.flsmidth.com
Supplier of Project Planning, Programming & Commissioning of Complete Automation & Computer Systems as Well as Measuring Systems to the Cement & Other Processing Industries
S.I.C.: 3575
N.A.I.C.S.: 334118
Huno Rasmussen *(Gen Mgr)*

FLS Global Finance A/S (1)
Vigerslev Alle 77
2500 Valby, Denmark (100%)
Tel.: (45) 36181800
Fax: (45) 2536441146
E-Mail: info@flsmith.com
Web Site: www.flsmidth.com
Provider of Financial Services
S.I.C.: 7374
N.A.I.C.S.: 518210

FLS Plast A/S (1)
Vigerslev Alle 77
2500 Valby, Denmark
Tel.: (45) 36181000
Fax: (45) 36441830
E-Mail: info@flsmidth.com
Web Site: www.flsmidth.com
Emp.: 160
Engineering Consulting Services
S.I.C.: 8711
N.A.I.C.S.: 541330
Jorgen Huno Rasmussen *(CEO)*

FLS Real Estate A/S (1)
Vigerslev Alle 77
2500 Valby, Denmark (100%)
Tel.: (45) 36181800
Fax: (45) 36301820
E-Mail: info@flsmith.com
Web Site: www.flsmith.com
Sales Range: $1-4.9 Billion
Emp.: 1,500
S.I.C.: 6531
N.A.I.C.S.: 531210
Thomas Schulz *(CEO)*
Lard Nielsen *(Mng Dir)*

FLSmidth A/S (1)
Vigerslev Alle 77
2500 Valby, Denmark
Tel.: (45) 36 18 10 00
Fax: (45) 36 44 11 46
E-Mail: info@flsmidth.com
Emp.: 1,000
Industrial Machinery Repair & Maintenance Services
S.I.C.: 7699
N.A.I.C.S.: 811310
Jorgen Huno Rasmussen *(CEO)*

Subsidiary:

FLSmidth Rusland Holding A/S (2)
Vigerslev Alle 77
2500 Valby, Denmark
Tel.: (45) 36181000
E-Mail: info@flsmidth.com
Construction Machinery Mfr
S.I.C.: 3531
N.A.I.C.S.: 333120
Jorgen Huno Rasmussen *(CEO)*

Non-U.S. Subsidiaries:

FLSmidth (Jersey) Limited (2)
1-13 New Street
PO Box 719
Saint Helier, Je40QA, Jersey
Tel.: (44) 1534 729074
Fax: (44) 1534 729075
E-Mail: info@flsjersey.com
Web Site: www.flsjersey.com
Human Resource Consulting Services
S.I.C.: 8999
N.A.I.C.S.: 541612
Bjarne Moltke Hansen *(Chm)*

FLSmidth Krebs GmbH (2)
Neuberg Str 1
7100 Neusiedl am See, Austria
Tel.: (43) 216733450
Fax: (43) 21673337
Emp.: 35
Construction Machinery Mfr
S.I.C.: 3531
N.A.I.C.S.: 333120
Roman van Ommen *(Mng Dir)*

FLSmidth MAAG Gear AG (2)
Lagerhausstrasse 11
PO Box 8401
Winterthur, 8401, Switzerland
Tel.: (41) 52 260 35 68
Fax: (41) 52 260 35 55
E-Mail: service@flsmidthmaaggear.com
Emp.: 10
Gear Unit Mfr
S.I.C.: 3566
N.A.I.C.S.: 333612
Yasuhiro Haba *(Gen Mgr)*

FLSmidth Milano S.R.L. (2)
Via Rubattino 94
20090 Milan, Italy
Tel.: (39) 02 95688 1
Fax: (39) 02 95688 250
E-Mail: info.doeitaly@flsmidth.com
Web Site: www.flsmidth.com
Emp.: 3
Construction Machinery Mfr
S.I.C.: 3531
N.A.I.C.S.: 333120
Gabriel Ghiringhelli *(Mgr)*

FLSmidth Mongolia (2)
603 6th floor Altai office building 1st micro district
Chinggis Avenue 8, Ulaanbaatar, 15160, Mongolia
Tel.: (976) 70108082
Fax: (976) 70108083
Emp.: 1
Construction Machinery Mfr
S.I.C.: 3531
N.A.I.C.S.: 333120
Vinay Saxena *(Gen Mgr)*

FLSmidth (Private) Ltd. (2)
House No 10 Street 88 Sector G-6/3
Embassy Road
Islamabad, 44000, Pakistan
Tel.: (92) 51 28 79 141
Fax: (92) 51 28 79 142
E-Mail: flspak@isb.comsats.net.pk
Emp.: 5
Construction Machinery Mfr
S.I.C.: 3531
N.A.I.C.S.: 333120
Abdul Razzaq *(Gen Mgr)*

FLSmidth S.A. (2)
Carretera de La Coruna km 17 8
Las Rozas, 28230 Madrid, Spain
Tel.: (34) 91 63 49 000
Fax: (34) 91 63 61 150
E-Mail: fls-es@flsmidth.com
Emp.: 25
Construction Machinery Mfr
S.I.C.: 3531
N.A.I.C.S.: 333120
Ignacio Puertas *(Gen Mgr)*

FLSmidth Sp. z.o.o. (2)
ul Stoczniowa 2
82-300 Elblag, Poland
Tel.: (48) 55 237 8994
E-Mail: mw@flsmidth.com
Construction Machinery Mfr
S.I.C.: 3531
N.A.I.C.S.: 333120

FLSmidth (UK) Limited (2)
Wemco House 11 Mitchell Court
Castle Mound Way Central Park, Rugby, CV23 0UY, United Kingdom
Tel.: (44) 1788 555 777
Fax: (44) 1788 560 738
E-Mail: fls.uk@flsmidth.com
Emp.: 4
Construction Machinery Mfr
S.I.C.: 3531
N.A.I.C.S.: 333120
Marco Fossataro *(Mng Dir)*

FLSmidth Ventomatic SpA (2)
Via Guglielmo Marconi 20
24030 Valbrembo, Italy
Tel.: (39) 035468311
Fax: (39) 035460838
E-Mail: vento@flsmidthventomatic.com
Web Site: www.flsmidth.com
Industrial Machinery Mfr & Whslr
S.I.C.: 3559
N.A.I.C.S.: 333249
Ferrandico Francesco *(Mng Dir)*

Pfister Holding GmbH (2)
Statzlinger Str 70
86068 Augsburg, Germany

FLSmidth & Co. A/S—(Continued)

Tel.: (49) 82179490
Fax: (49) 82179490
Web Site: www.pfister.de
Investment Management Services
S.I.C.: 6211
N.A.I.C.S.: 523999

FLSmidth Minerals A/S (1)
Vigerslev Alle 77
2500 Valby, Denmark
Tel.: (45) 36183600
Fax: (45) 36183618
E-Mail: info@flsmidthminerals.com
Web Site: www.flsmidthminerals.com
Emp.: 50
Mineral Processing Equipment Mfr
S.I.C.: 5082
N.A.I.C.S.: 423810
George Robles *(Deputy CEO)*
Poul Erik Tofte *(CFO & Exec VP)*
Christian J. Jepsen *(COO & Sr VP)*
J. Petruska *(CTO)*

Subsidiaries:

FLSmidth Airtech (2)
Vigerslevalle 77
2500 Valby, Denmark (100%)
Tel.: (45) 36181100
Fax: (45) 36183434
E-Mail: info@flsmdth.com
Web Site: www.flsmdth.com
Emp.: 1,200
Flue Gas Cleaning Systems Svcs
S.I.C.: 1389
N.A.I.C.S.: 213112
Steffen Dinigzen *(Gen Mgr-Asia)*

Subsidiary:

Pedershaab A/S (3)
Saltumvej 25
DK 9700 Bronderslev, Denmark (100%)
Tel.: (45) 96454000
Fax: (45) 96454040
E-Mail: pedershaab@pedershaab.dk
Web Site: www.pedershaab.com
Emp.: 100
S.I.C.: 3531
N.A.I.C.S.: 333120
Carsten S. Nielsen *(CFO & Mng Dir)*

Non-U.S. Subsidiary:

PUK Ltd. (4)
Unit 1 Stratford Agri-Park Clifford Chambers
Stratford-upon-Avon, Warks, CV37 8LP,
United Kingdom (100%)
Tel.: (44) 1789206800
Fax: (44) 1789206801
E-Mail: puk@pukservices.co.uk
Web Site: www.pukservices.co.uk
Emp.: 9
S.I.C.: 3531
N.A.I.C.S.: 333120
William Holmes *(Mng Dir)*

Non-U.S. Subsidiaries:

FLSmidth Dorr-Oliver Eimco France Sarl (2)
22 Rue Pierre
Mendes France, 77200 Torcy, France FR
Tel.: (33) 160171263
Fax: (33) 160171185
E-Mail: info@flsmidth.com
Web Site: www.flsmidth.com
Emp.: 12
Pulp & Paper Equipment
S.I.C.: 5084
N.A.I.C.S.: 423830
Marilyn Rousselot *(Mgr-Fin)*

FLSmidth Dorr-Oliver Eimco GmbH (2)
Am Klingenweg 4a
65396 Walluf, Germany De
Tel.: (49) 6123975300
Fax: (49) 6123975303
E-Mail: doe.de@flsmidth.com
Emp.: 50
Pulp & Paper Equipment
S.I.C.: 5084
N.A.I.C.S.: 423830

FLSmidth Minerals Ltd. (2)
174 West St S
Orillia, ON, L3V 6L4, Canada (100%)
Tel.: (705) 325-6181
Fax: (705) 325-4487
Web Site: www.flsmidthminerals.com
Emp.: 78
Mineral Processing Equipment Mfr
S.I.C.: 5082
N.A.I.C.S.: 423810

FLSmidth Minerals S.A. (2)
Ave Nueva de Lyon 72 Office 1102
Provedencia, Santiago, 751-0078,
Chile CL
Tel.: (56) 22900000
Web Site: www.flsmidth.com
Emp.: 850
Pulp & Paper Equipment
S.I.C.: 5084
N.A.I.C.S.: 423830

FLSmidth Minerals Holding ApS (1)
Vigerslev Alle 77
Valby, 2500, Denmark
Tel.: (45) 36183600
Investment Management Services
S.I.C.: 6211
N.A.I.C.S.: 523999

Non-U.S. Subsidiaries:

FLSmidth S.A. de C.V. (2)
San Alberto 406 Residencial Santa Barbara
Garza Garcia, Nuevo Leon, 66260, Mexico
Tel.: (52) 81 1001 9500
Fax: (52) 81 836 33421
E-Mail:
Web Site: www.flsmidth.com
Industrial Equipment Distr
S.I.C.: 5084
N.A.I.C.S.: 423830
Richard Farnhill *(Office Mgr)*

FLSmidth S.A. (2)
Avenue Nueva de Lyon 072 Office 1102
Providencia, Santiago, Chile
Tel.: (56) 2 290 0000
E-Mail: info.chile@flsmidth.com
Web Site: www.flsmidth.com
Emp.: 50
Cement Industry Machinery Distr
S.I.C.: 5084
N.A.I.C.S.: 423830
Valerie Delorme *(Mgr)*

SK Stok (1)
Erik Stoks Alle 4
5550 Odense, Denmark (100%)
Tel.: (45) 72200700
Fax: (45) 72200711
E-Mail: stok@stok.dk
Web Site: www.stok.dk
Emp.: 50
S.I.C.: 3531
N.A.I.C.S.: 333120
Martin Fredefen *(Mng Dir)*

Smidth & Co. (1)
Vigerslev Alle 77
2500 Valby, Denmark
Tel.: (45) 36 18 10 00
Fax: (45) 36301820
E-Mail: info@flsmidth.com
Web Site: www.flsmidth.com
Emp.: 150
Construction Machinery Mfr
S.I.C.: 3531
N.A.I.C.S.: 333120
Klaus Steen Mortensen *(CEO)*

U.S. Subsidiaries:

FLS US Holdings, Inc. (1)
2040 Ave C
Bethlehem, PA 18017-2118
Tel.: (610) 264-6011
Fax: (610) 264-6170
Cement Making Machinery Mfr
S.I.C.: 3559
N.A.I.C.S.: 333249

FLSmidth Inc. (1)
2040 Ave C
Bethlehem, PA 18017-2118 DE
Tel.: (610) 264-6011 (100%)
Fax: (610) 264-6170
Toll Free: (800) 523-9482
E-Mail: info-us@flsmidth.com
Web Site: www.flsmidth.com
Rev.: $208,828,000
Emp.: 1,160
Holding Company; Bulk Material Handling Equipment Mfr & Services
Export
S.I.C.: 6719
N.A.I.C.S.: 551112
Ralph McCandless *(Controller)*

Subsidiaries:

Excel Foundry & Machine Inc. (2)
14463 Wagonseller Rd
Pekin, IL 61555-0400
Tel.: (309) 347-6155
Fax: (309) 347-1931
Toll Free: (800) 523-9129
E-Mail: websales@excelfoundry.com
Web Site: www.excelfoundry.com
Emp.: 295
Industrial Machinery Mfr
S.I.C.: 3559
N.A.I.C.S.: 333249
Doug Parsons *(Gen Mgr)*

FLSmidth Boise, Inc. (2)
2471 S Titanium Pl
Meridian, ID 83642
Tel.: (208) 342-2653
Fax: (208) 342-6922
Web Site: www.flsmidth.com
Industrial Machinery Mfr
S.I.C.: 3559
N.A.I.C.S.: 333249

FLSmidth Minerals Inc. (2)
2040 Avenue C
Bethlehem, PA 18017 DE
Tel.: (610) 264-6900
Fax: (610) 264-6996
Toll Free: (800) 523-9482
E-Mail: info@ffeminerals.com
Web Site: www.flsmidthminerals.com
Emp.: 100
Mineral Processing Equipment Mfr
S.I.C.: 5082
N.A.I.C.S.: 423810
Peter Flanagan *(VP)*

Subsidiaries:

FLSmidth Conveyor Engineering, Inc. (3)
2471 S Titianium Pl
Meridian, ID 83642 ID
Tel.: (208) 342-2653
Fax: (208) 342-6922
Web Site: www.conveyorengineering.com
Sales Range: $10-24.9 Million
Emp.: 30
Bulk Material Handling Systems Mfr
S.I.C.: 3559
N.A.I.C.S.: 333249
Andrew Emerson *(Pres & CEO)*

FLSmidth Krebs Inc. (3)
5505 W Gillette Rd
Tucson, AZ 85743 DE
Tel.: (520) 744-8200
Fax: (520) 744-8300
E-Mail: krebs@flsmidth.com
Web Site: www.krebs.com
Sales Range: $75-99.9 Million
Emp.: 170
Hydrocyclones & Solid/Liquid Separation Equipment & Slurry Pump Developer & Mfr
S.I.C.: 3559
N.A.I.C.S.: 333249
Patrick Turner *(Pres)*

Non-U.S. Subsidiary:

FLSmidth Krebs (Beijing) Ltd. (4)
7F Tower A No 1-3 Xinyung South Road
Chaoyang District, 100027 Beijing, China
Tel.: (86) 10 8468 9100
Fax: (86) 10 8468 9299
E-Mail: krebsgeneral@flsmidth.com
Emp.: 10
Hydroclone Mfr
S.I.C.: 3559
N.A.I.C.S.: 333249

FLSmidth Salt Lake City, Inc. (3)
7158 S FLSmidth Dr
Midvale, UT 84047-5559 DE
Tel.: (801) 526-2000
Telex: 38-8331
Fax: (801) 526-2001
E-Mail: info.doe@flsmidth.com
Web Site: www.flsmidthminerals.com
Emp.: 200
Liquid/Solid Separation Equipment & Process Technology Supplier
Import Export
S.I.C.: 3589
N.A.I.C.S.: 333318
Peter Flanagan *(Gen Mgr)*

FLSmidth Spokane, Inc. (2)
605 E Holland Ave
Spokane, WA 99218
Tel.: (509) 467-0770
Fax: (509) 466-0212
E-Mail: rahco@flsmidth.com
Web Site: www.rahco.com
Emp.: 130
Custom Mining Machinery Mfr
S.I.C.: 3532
N.A.I.C.S.: 333131
Jorgen Huno Rasmussen *(CEO)*

Fuller Company (2)
2040 Ave C
Bethlehem, PA 18017-2188
Tel.: (610) 264-6011
Fax: (610) 264-6170
Cleaning Products Mfr & Whslr
S.I.C.: 2842
N.A.I.C.S.: 325612

Fuller International Inc. (2)
1718 Potrero Ave Ste A
El Monte, CA 91733-3041
Tel.: (626) 279-9287
Construction Engineering Services
S.I.C.: 1629
N.A.I.C.S.: 237990

FLSmidth USA Inc. (1)
2040 Ave C
Bethlehem, PA 18017
Tel.: (610) 264-6011
Fax: (610) 264-6170
E-Mail: info-us@flsmidth.com
Web Site: www.flsmidth.com
Industrial Machinery Maintenance Services
S.I.C.: 7699
N.A.I.C.S.: 811310

Phillips Kiln Services Ltd. (1)
2607 Dakota Ave
South Sioux City, NE 68776
Tel.: (402) 494-6837
Fax: (402) 494-6858
Toll Free: (800) 831-0876
E-Mail: info@kiln.com
Web Site: www.kiln.com
Sales Range: $50-74.9 Million
Emp.: 190
Industrial Maintenance Repair Service
S.I.C.: 7629
N.A.I.C.S.: 811219
Eric Bertness *(Chm & CEO)*
Daryl Austin *(Pres)*
Bill Conner *(CFO)*

Non-U.S. Subsidiaries:

Cembrit a.s. (1)
Lidicka 302
Beroun, 26638, Czech Republic
Tel.: (420) 311744111
Fax: (420) 311744250
E-Mail: info@cembrit.cz
Web Site: www.cembrit.cz
Emp.: 30
Cement Mfr & Distr
S.I.C.: 3241
N.A.I.C.S.: 327310
Daniel Bubla *(Gen Mgr)*

Cembrit B.V. (1)
Westhavenweg 53-54
Postbus 20640
1001 NP Amsterdam, Netherlands
Tel.: (31) 20 585 38 88
Fax: (31) 20 411 42 73
E-Mail: info@cembrit.nl
Web Site: www.cembrit.nl
Emp.: 5
Building Construction Services
S.I.C.: 1542
N.A.I.C.S.: 236220
Evert Luyk *(Gen Mgr)*

Cembrit GmbH (1)
Suderstrasse 73
20097 Hamburg, Germany
Tel.: (49) 40 6699963 0
Fax: (49) 40 6699963 33
E-Mail: info@cembrit.de

Emp.: 10
Fiber Cement Mfr
S.I.C.: 3241
N.A.I.C.S.: 327310
Andreas Schmidth *(Gen Mgr)*

Cembrit IBS B.V. (1)
Westhavenweg 53-54
Postbus 20640
1001 NP Amsterdam, Netherlands
Tel.: (31) 20 585 38 88
Fax: (31) 20 411 42 73
E-Mail: info@cembrit.nl
Emp.: 13
Fiber Cement Mfr
S.I.C.: 3241
N.A.I.C.S.: 327310

Cembrit Kft. (1)
Becsi Ut 7
2536 Nyergesujfalu, Hungary
Tel.: (36) 33 514 101
Fax: (36) 33 514 110
E-Mail: info@cembrit.hu
Web Site: www.cembrit.hu
Emp.: 3
Fibre Cement Mfr & Distr
S.I.C.: 3241
N.A.I.C.S.: 327310

Cembrit Ltd. (1)
57 Kellner Road
London, SE28 0AX, United Kingdom
Tel.: (44) 20 8301 8900
Fax: (44) 20 8301 8901
E-Mail: sales@cembrit.co.uk
Web Site: www.cembrit.co.uk
Emp.: 15
Fibre Cement Slate Mfr
S.I.C.: 3241
N.A.I.C.S.: 327310
Jacquie Avery *(Mgr)*

Cembrit S.A. (1)
ul Gnieznienska 4
62 240 Trzemeszno, Wielkopolskie, Poland
Tel.: (48) 61 415 43 30
Fax: (48) 61 415 60 17
E-Mail: Info@cembrit.pl
Cement Mfr & Distr
S.I.C.: 3241
N.A.I.C.S.: 327310

Cembrit SAS (1)
Rue des Fontainiers ZA Sud
05100 Briancon, France
Tel.: (33) 4 92 21 24 65
Fax: (33) 4 92 54 39 92
E-Mail: info@cembrit.fr
Web Site: www.cembrit.fr
Emp.: 5
Fiber Cement Mfr
S.I.C.: 3241
N.A.I.C.S.: 327310
Christophe Delille *(Dir-Comml)*

Cembrit S.p.A. (1)
Via Uccellino 83
44028 Poggio Renatico, Ferrara, Italy
Tel.: (39) 0532 826111
E-Mail: info@cembrit.it
Fiber Cement Mfr & Distr
S.I.C.: 3241
N.A.I.C.S.: 327310

ESSA AUSTRALIA LIMITED (1)
Level 1 63 69 Abernethy Rd
6104 Belmont, Western Australia,
Australia AU
Mailing Address:
PO Box 362
Belmont, WA, 6984, Australia
Tel.: (61) 894753000
Fax: (61) 894773544
E-Mail: mail@essa.com.au
Web Site: www.essa.com.au
Sales Range: $25-49.9 Million
Emp.: 100
Mining Industry Equipment
S.I.C.: 7699
N.A.I.C.S.: 811310
Darryl Stevens *(CEO & Mng Dir)*
Bert Blekkenhorst *(CFO, Sec & Dir-Fin)*
Kevin Mennell *(COO)*

Non-U.S. Subsidiaries:

Essa do Brasil Ltda. (2)
Av Hum 423 Parque Norte
Vespasiano, Minas Gerais, 33200-000,
Brazil
Tel.: (55) 3136296448
Fax: (55) 3136296546
E-Mail: vitor.gloria@flsmidth.com.au
Web Site: www.essabrasil.com.au
Emp.: 20
Mineral Equipment Mfr
S.I.C.: 3532
N.A.I.C.S.: 333131
Camila Sousa *(Mgr-Sls & Bus)*

Labtech Africa (Pty) Ltd. (2)
53 Steel Rd Spartan
Kempton Park, 1619, South Africa
Tel.: (27) 113940702
Fax: (27) 113940280
E-Mail: labtechsa@global.co.za
Web Site: www.essaafrica.com
Emp.: 4
Sampling Services & Equipment Mfr
S.I.C.: 8732
N.A.I.C.S.: 541910
Jan du Plessis *(Mng Dir & Gen Mgr)*

FLS Japan Ltd. (1)
2-4-11 Sannomiya
Chuo-ku, Kobe, 6500021, Japan (100%)
Tel.: (81) 783273811
Fax: (81) 783273824
Web Site: www.fls.co.jp
Emp.: 81
S.I.C.: 3531
N.A.I.C.S.: 333120
Aramaki Hideki *(Pres)*

FLSmidth GmbH (1)
Alfred Leiner Strasse 3
2326 Lanzendorf, Austria
Tel.: (43) 2235475100
Fax: (43) 223547568
E-Mail: koch-at@flsmidth.com
Web Site: www.flsmidth.com
Emp.: 6
Industrial Machinery Distr
S.I.C.: 5084
N.A.I.C.S.: 423830
Arrien Westhuis *(Office Mgr)*

FLSmidth Hamburg GmbH (1)
Haderslebener Strasse 7
Pinneberg, 25421, Germany
Tel.: (49) 41017880
Fax: (49) 4101788140
E-Mail: info@moeller-mh.com
Web Site: www.flsmidth.com
Emp.: 80
Industrial Machinery Whslr
S.I.C.: 5084
N.A.I.C.S.: 423830
Joachim Dahms *(Mng Dir)*

FLSmidth Krebs Chile Limitada (1)
Av Americo Vespucio N 2760 D Centro De
Empresas El Cortijo
Comuna De Conchale, Santiago, Chile
Tel.: (56) 2463 8300
Fax: (56) 2463 8300
E-Mail: krebsgeneral@flsmidth.com
Web Site: www.flsmidth.com
Industrial Machinery Equipment Mfr
S.I.C.: 5084
N.A.I.C.S.: 423830

FLSmidth Ludowici (1)
67 Randle Road
Pinkenba, QLD, 4008, Australia AU
Tel.: (61) 731212900
Fax: (61) 731212988
E-Mail: brisbanesales@ludowici.com.au
Web Site: www.ludowici.com.au
Sales Range: $200-249.9 Million
Emp.: 1,100
Designs, Manufactures & Markets Mineral
Processing Equipment for Mining Industry
S.I.C.: 3532
N.A.I.C.S.: 333131
Patrick Largier *(CEO & Mng Dir)*
Stephen Gaffney *(CFO)*

Subsidiaries:

Ludowici Australia Pty Ltd. (2)
67 Randle Rd
Pinkenba, QLD, 4008, Australia (100%)
Tel.: (61) 732924444
Fax: (61) 731212990
E-Mail:
Emp.: 400
Industrial Machinery Mfr
S.I.C.: 3559
N.A.I.C.S.: 333249
Patrick J. Largier *(Mng Dir)*

Subsidiaries:

Ludowici China Pty Limited (3)
67 Randle Road
Pinkenba, Brisbane, QLD, 4008, Australia
Tel.: (61) 731212900
Fax: (61) 0731210901
E-Mail: enquires@ludowici.com.au
Emp.: 200
Industrial Equipments Mfr
S.I.C.: 3052
N.A.I.C.S.: 326220
Patrick Largier *(Mng Dir)*

Rojan Advanced Ceramics Pty
Ltd (3)
55 Alacrity Pl
PO Box 7126
Henderson, WA, 6166, Australia
Tel.: (61) 894371155
Fax: (61) 894371156
E-Mail: rojan@rojan.com.au
Web Site: www.rojan.com.au
Emp.: 30
Industrial Ceramic Products Mfr & Distr
S.I.C.: 3259
N.A.I.C.S.: 327120

Ludowici Packaging Australia Pty
Limited (2)
67 Randle Road
Pinkenba, Brisbane, QLD, 4008, Australia
Tel.: (61) 731212900
Fax: (61) 731212901
E-Mail: enquiry@ludowici.com.au
Emp.: 350
Packaging Materials Mfr
S.I.C.: 2631
N.A.I.C.S.: 322130
Mark Day *(Sec)*

Ludowici Technologies Pty Ltd (2)
67 Randle Road
Pinkenba, Brisbane, QLD, 4008, Australia
Tel.: (61) 731212900
Fax: (61) 731212901
Industrial Equipments Mfr
S.I.C.: 3052
N.A.I.C.S.: 326220

U.S. Subsidiaries:

Ludowici LLC (2)
Rte 10 S Phico
Chapmanville, WV 25508
Tel.: (304) 855-7880
Fax: (304) 855-8601
E-Mail: enquiry@ludowici-usa.com
Emp.: 100
Mining Equipment Mfr
S.I.C.: 3569
N.A.I.C.S.: 333999
Ed Vickers *(Gen Mgr)*

Ludowici Screens LLC (2)
785 Lithia Rd
Wytheville, VA 24382-5129
Tel.: (276) 228-6781
Mining Equipment Mfr
S.I.C.: 3569
N.A.I.C.S.: 333999

Non-U.S. Subsidiaries:

Ludowici (Beijing) Co., Ltd (2)
7th Fl Tower A Penguin Intl Financial Ctr
123 Xin yuan S Rd
Xicheng District, Beijing, 100027, China
Tel.: (86) 106 852 1036
Fax: (86) 106 852 1036
E-Mail: enquiry@ludowiciyantai.com
Web Site: www.flsmidth.com
Emp.: 10
Industrial Equipments Mfr
S.I.C.: 3052
N.A.I.C.S.: 326220
Viktor Li *(Gen Mgr)*

Ludowici India Private Limited (2)
Ganesh Towers New 104 Old 90 Dr
Radhakrishnan Salai
Mylapore, Chennai, Tamil Nadu, 600004,
India
Tel.: (91) 44 4221 5900
Fax: (91) 44 4232 7315
E-Mail: enquiry@ludowiciindia.com
Emp.: 20
Mineral Processing Equipments Mfr & Distr
S.I.C.: 3569
N.A.I.C.S.: 333999
R. K. Rajan *(Country Mgr)*

Ludowici Mining Process India PVT
Limited (2)
Ganesh Towers New 104 Old 90 Dr
Radhakrishnan Salai
Mylapore, Chennai, Tamil Nadu, 600004,
India
Tel.: (91) 44 44000510
Fax: (91) 44 42327315
Mineral Processing Equipments Mfr & Distr
S.I.C.: 3569
N.A.I.C.S.: 333999

FLSmidth MAAG Gear Sp. z o.o. (1)
Stoczniowa 2
82-300 Elblag, Poland
Tel.: (48) 55 236 47 30
Fax: (48) 55 232 79 44
E-Mail: Service@FLSmidthMaagGear.com
Emp.: 20
Construction Machinery Mfr
S.I.C.: 3531
N.A.I.C.S.: 333120
Wlodzimierz Zajac *(Pres)*

FLSmidth MAAG Gear S.p.A. (1)
Via Rubattino 94/A20134
20134 Milan, Italy
Tel.: (39) 02 26922058
Fax: (39) 02 2132433
E-Mail: mgm@FLSmidthMaagGear.com
Emp.: 39
Construction Machinery Mfr
S.I.C.: 3531
N.A.I.C.S.: 333120
Cordiano Dagnoni *(CEO)*

U.S. Subsidiary:

FLSmidth Pfister, Inc. (2)
2158 Ave C Ste 201
Bethlehem, PA 18017-2148
Tel.: (610) 264-5110
Fax: (610) 264-5537
E-Mail: pfistera@ptd.net
Web Site: www.flsmidth.com
Industrial Machinery Mfr
S.I.C.: 3559
N.A.I.C.S.: 333249

FLSmidth Pfister GmbH (1)
Stzatzlinger Str 70
Augsburg, 86165, Germany
Tel.: (49) 821 79 49 0
Fax: (49) 821 79 49 524
E-Mail: sales@flsmidthpfister.com
Web Site: www.flsmidth.com
Industrial Machinery Mfr
S.I.C.: 3559
N.A.I.C.S.: 333249
Wolf Schaffer *(Gen Mgr)*

Subsidiary:

FLSmidth Wadgassen GmbH (2)
Karl-Koch-Str 1
66787 Wadgassen, Germany
Tel.: (49) 68344700
Fax: (49) 6834470339
E-Mail: wadgassen@flsmidth.com
Emp.: 25
Industrial Machinery Equipment Mfr
S.I.C.: 5084
N.A.I.C.S.: 423830
Roemer Hartmann *(Gen Mgr)*

Non-U.S. Subsidiary:

FLSmidth Pfister Ltda. (2)
Rua Vigario J J Rodrigues 905 -cj 51
30201-490 Jundiai, Sao Paulo, Brazil
Tel.: (55) 11 45266744
Fax: (55) 11 45875711
E-Mail: pfister@pfister-la.com.br
Web Site: www.flsmidth.com
Emp.: 4
Industrial Equipment Distr
S.I.C.: 5084
N.A.I.C.S.: 423830
Uwe Richter *(Mng Dir)*

FLSmidth Private Limited (1)
Flsmidth House 34 Egatoor Rajiv Gandhi
Salai Kelambakkam
Chennai, Tamil Nadu, 603103, India
Tel.: (91) 4447483000
Fax: (91) 4427470302

FLSmidth & Co. A/S—(Continued)

E-Mail: indiainfo@flsmidth.com
Web Site: www.flsmidth.com
Industrial Machinery Equipment Mfr
S.I.C.: 5084
N.A.I.C.S.: 423830
Bjarne Hansen *(CEO)*

Subsidiary:

Transweigh India Ltd. **(2)**
124 ABCD Govt Indl Estate Charkop Kandivli W
Mumbai, 400 067, India
Tel.: (91) 22 6772 6000
Fax: (91) 22 6772 6100
E-Mail: mktg@transweigh-india.com
Industrial Weighing Equipment Mfr
S.I.C.: 5084
N.A.I.C.S.: 423830
H. Wolfschaffner *(Chm)*
P. J. Talreja *(Mng Dir)*

FLSmidth Pty. Ltd. **(1)**
5 Comserv Close
Gosford, NSW, 2250, Australia
Tel.: (61) 2 4320 4700
Fax: (61) 2 0320 4777
E-Mail: info.australia@flsmidth.com
Web Site: www.flsmidth.com
Industrial Machinery Mfr
S.I.C.: 5084
N.A.I.C.S.: 423830

Subsidiaries:

FLSmidth ABON Pty. Ltd. **(2)**
15-19 Marshall Rd Airport W
Melbourne, VIC, 3042, Australia
Tel.: (61) 393387011
Fax: (61) 393383765
E-Mail: aboninfo@flsmidth.com
Web Site: www.flsmidth.com
Emp.: 10
Cement Industry Machinery Distr
S.I.C.: 5084
N.A.I.C.S.: 423830

FLSmidth Dorr-Oliver Eimco Pty Limited **(2)**
5 Comserv Close
Gosford, NSW, 2250, Australia
Tel.: (61) 2 43204700
Fax: (61) 243204777
E-Mail: info.australia@flsmidth.com
Emp.: 60
Industrial Machinery Equipment Mfr
S.I.C.: 5084
N.A.I.C.S.: 423830
David William *(Mng Dir)*

FLSmidth Krebs Australia Pty. Ltd. **(2)**
51 Days Road
Coomera, QLD, 4209, Australia
Tel.: (61) 7 5519 5700
Fax: (61) 7 5519 5707
E-Mail: krebsaustralia@flsmidth.com
Web Site: www.flsmidth.com
Emp.: 50
Cement Industrial Machinery Distr
S.I.C.: 5084
N.A.I.C.S.: 423830
Vijay Dhall *(Mgr-Sls)*

FLSmidth Pty. Ltd. **(1)**
Lake View House
PO Box 5221
Constantia Park 14 Ave, Roodepoort, Johanssberg, 1715, South Africa (100%)
Tel.: (27) 116792593
Telex: 960 4 22069 SA
Fax: (27) 116792611
E-Mail: dm@flsza.co.za
Web Site: www.flsnet.fls.com
Sales Range: Less than $1 Million
Emp.: 3
Supplier of Equipment; Systems & Processes for Mineral & Processing Industries
S.I.C.: 5084
N.A.I.C.S.: 423830

Subsidiaries:

FLSmidth Buffalo (Pty.) Ltd. **(2)**
40 Nobel Rd
Witbank, 1034, South Africa
Tel.: (27) 136998900
Fax: (27) 136998907
E-Mail: buffalo@flsmidth.com
Web Site: www.flsmidth.com
Emp.: 15
Mining Equipment Mfr
S.I.C.: 3532
N.A.I.C.S.: 333131
Peter Rohrmann *(Mng Dir)*

FLSmidth Krebs Africa (Pty.) Ltd. **(2)**
Chariot Street Stormill Extension 10
Roodepoort, Johannesburg, 1724, South Africa
Tel.: (27) 11 474 8875
Fax: (27) 11 474 7347
Emp.: 5
Industrial Pump & Gate Valve Mfr
S.I.C.: 3561
N.A.I.C.S.: 333911
Brad Moralee *(Gen Mgr)*

FLSmidth Rus OOO **(1)**
10 Butyrsky Val
125047 Moscow, Russia
Tel.: (7) 495 641 2778
Fax: (7) 495 641 2779
E-Mail: info@flsmidth.ru
Emp.: 55
Cement Industry Machinery Distr
S.I.C.: 5084
N.A.I.C.S.: 423830
Claus Torbol *(Gen Mgr)*

FLSmidth S.A.C. **(1)**
Av Republica De Panama 3030 Of 701-B
San Isidro, Lima, Peru
Tel.: (51) 1 708 0500
Fax: (51) 1 708 0547
Web Site: www.flsmidth.com
Cement Industry Machinery Distr
S.I.C.: 5084
N.A.I.C.S.: 423830

FLSmidth SARL **(1)**
22 rue Pierre Mendes France
F-77200 Torcy, France (100%)
Tel.: (33) 160171263
Telex: 233597
Fax: (33) 160 171 185
E-Mail: fls.france@flsmidth.com
Web Site: www.flsmidth.com
Emp.: 19
Supplier of Equipment, Systems & Processes for Mineral & Processing Industry
S.I.C.: 5084
N.A.I.C.S.: 423830
Marilyn Rousselot *(Mgr-Fin)*

FLSmidth Shanghai Ltd. **(1)**
No 935 Xin Si Ping Rd Si Tuan Town
Feng Xian Dist, Shanghai, 201413, China
Tel.: (86) 21 57542777
Mineral Industry Machinery Distr
S.I.C.: 5082
N.A.I.C.S.: 423810

FLSmidth Wiesbaden GmbH **(1)**
Am Klingenweg 4a
65396 Walluf, Germany
Tel.: (49) 6123975300
Fax: (49) 6123975303
E-Mail: wiesbaden@flsmidth.com
Emp.: 4
Industrial Machinery Distr
S.I.C.: 5084
N.A.I.C.S.: 423830

FLSmidth Wuppertal GmbH **(1)**
In Der Fleute 53
Postfach 24 02 28
42389 Wuppertal, Germany
Tel.: (49) 202262840
Fax: (49) 2022628412
E-Mail: dus-info@flsmidth.com
Web Site: www.flsmidth.com
Emp.: 65
Construction Material Machinery Mfr
S.I.C.: 5039
N.A.I.C.S.: 423390
Lars Kristensen *(CEO)*

Subsidiary:

Pfaff Maschinenbau GmbH **(2)**
Industriegebiet Augustenhohe 10
Harzgerode, 6493, Germany
Tel.: (49) 3948472030
Fax: (49) 39484720355
Machine Tool Mfr
S.I.C.: 3541
N.A.I.C.S.: 333517

Oresund Unloader Design Bureau AB **(1)**
Karleksgatan 1
211 45 Malmo, Sweden
Tel.: (46) 40 690 33 00
Industrial Machinery Mfr
S.I.C.: 3559
N.A.I.C.S.: 333249

PT FLSmidth Indonesia **(1)**
GKBI Building 21st Floor Suite 2101 Jalan Jendral Sudirman Kav 44-46
Jakarta, 10210, Indonesia
Tel.: (62) 21 251 27 38
Fax: (62) 21 251 27 40
E-Mail: fls@flsindo.co.id
Web Site: www.flsmidth.com
Cement Industry Machinery Distr
S.I.C.: 5084
N.A.I.C.S.: 423830

Union Cement Corporation **(1)**
7th Fl Two World Sq McKinley Hill
Taguig, Bonifacio, 1634, Philippines (100%)
Tel.: (63) 24593333
Fax: (63) 28700301
Emp.: 1,300
Hydraulic Cement Mfr
S.I.C.: 3272
N.A.I.C.S.: 327332

Yantai Ludowici Mineral Processing Equipment Limited **(2)**
Yantai Economic Development Zone 298 Huanghe Road
Yantai, Shandong, China
Tel.: (86) 535 216 5280
Fax: (86) 535 216 5281
E-Mail: enquiry@ludowici-china.com
Emp.: 50
Mining Equipment Distr
S.I.C.: 5084
N.A.I.C.S.: 423830
Viktor Li *(Gen Mgr)*

Non-U.S. Joint Venture:

FLS-Fuller Bulk Handling India Ltd **(1)**
FFE Towers 27 G N Chetty Road
T Nagar, Chennai, 600 017, India
Tel.: (91) 44 8255769
Fax: (91) 44 8255950
Web Site: www.flsmidth.com
Mfr., Sell, Buy, Supply, Render Engineering & Consultancy Regarding Industrial Machinery, Equipment & Ancillaries for Cement Plants & Mineral/Non-Mineral, Mining & Metallurgical Industries
S.I.C.: 3589
N.A.I.C.S.: 333318

FLUGHAFEN FRANKFURT-HAHN GMBH

Building 667
Hahn-Flughafen, D-55483 Kirchberg, Germany
Tel.: (49) 6543509200
Fax: (49) 6543509222
E-Mail: info@hahn-airport.de
Web Site: www.hahn-airport.de
Year Founded: 1993

Business Description:
Airport Operator
S.I.C.: 4581
N.A.I.C.S.: 488119

Personnel:
Jorg Schumacher *(Mng Dir)*

FLUGHAFEN WIEN AKTIENGESELLSCHAFT

(d/b/a Vienna Airport)
Postfach 1
A-1300 Vienna, Flughafen, Austria
Tel.: (43) 170070
Fax: (43) 1700723806
E-Mail: investor-relations@viennaairport.com
Web Site: www.viennaairport.com
FLU—(VIE)
Rev.: $850,066,374
Assets: $2,775,537,883
Liabilities: $1,629,168,588
Net Worth: $1,146,369,295
Earnings: $97,364,841
Emp.: 4,306
Fiscal Year-end: 12/31/12

Business Description:
Airport Operator
S.I.C.: 4581
N.A.I.C.S.: 488119

Personnel:
Erwin Hameseder *(Chm-Supervisory Bd)*
Christoph Herbst *(Chm-Mgmt Bd)*
Ewald Kirschner *(Deputy Chm-Supervisory Bd)*
Wolfgang Ruttenstorfer *(Deputy Chm-Supervisory Bd)*
Gunther Ofner *(CFO & Member-Mgmt Bd)*
Julian Jager *(COO & Member-Mgmt Bd)*
Ernest Gabmann *(Member-Mgmt Bd)*
Gerhard Schmid *(Member-Mgmt Bd)*
Wolfgang Koberl *(Sec Gen)*

Supervisory Board of Directors:
Erwin Hameseder
Manfred Biegler
Gabriele Domschitz
Bettina Glatz-Kremsner
Burkhard Hofer
Karl Hromodka
Ewald Kirschner
Franz Lauer
Hans-Jorgen Manstein
Alfons Metzger
Claus J. Raidl
Dieter Rozboril
Wolfgang Ruttenstorfer
Thomas Schaffer
Heinz Wessely

Subsidiaries:

Austro Port Boden- und Flugzeugabfertigungsges.m.b.H. **(1)**
Objekt 102-B 208
1300 Vienna, Austria (25%)
Tel.: (43) 1700735001
Fax: (43) 1700733830
E-Mail: verwaltung@airportservices-bie.com
Web Site: www.austroport.at/
Emp.: 120
Airport Operations
S.I.C.: 4581
N.A.I.C.S.: 488119
Johann Roth *(Mng Dir)*

City Air Terminal Betriebsgesellschaft m.b.H. **(1)**
PO Box 1
1300 Vienna, Austria (50.1%)
Tel.: (43) 125250
Fax: (43) 1700723718
E-Mail: info@cityairporttrain.com
Airport Operations
S.I.C.: 4581
N.A.I.C.S.: 488119

Flughafen Wien Immobilienverwertungsgesellschaft m.b.H **(1)**
Flughafen
1300 Vienna, Austria (100%)
Tel.: (43) 170070
Fax: (43) 1700722388
E-Mail: human.resources@viennaairport.com
Web Site: www.viennaairport.com
Real Estate Property Lessors
S.I.C.: 6519
N.A.I.C.S.: 531190

GetService-Flughafen-Sicherheits-und Servicedienst GmbH **(1)**
PO Box 107
Vienna, 1300, Austria
Tel.: (43) 1700726815
Fax: (43) 1700726817
Airport Cleaning Services
S.I.C.: 4581

N.A.I.C.S.: 488119

Mazur Parkplatz GmbH (1)
Hainburger Bundesstrasse 143
2320 Schwechat, Austria
Tel.: (43) 1 60425300
Fax: (43) 1 60425306
E-Mail: info@mazur-parken.at
Web Site: www.mazur-parken.at
Car Parking Services
S.I.C.: 7521
N.A.I.C.S.: 812930

Vienna Aircraft Handling Gesellschaft m.b.H. (1)
Objekt 140 Steinriegelweg
Flughafen, 1300 Vienna, Austria (100%)
Tel.: (43) 1700726812
Fax: (43) 1700724411
E-Mail: vah@viennaairport.com
Web Site: www.viennaaircrafthandling.com
Emp.: 60
Legal Services
S.I.C.: 7389
N.A.I.C.S.: 541199
Michael Tmej *(Mng Dir)*

Vienna International Airport Security Services Ges.m.b.H. (1)
Flughafen
1300 Vienna, Austria (100%)
Tel.: (43) 1700722274
Fax: (43) 1700726817
E-Mail: vias@viennaairport.com
Web Site: www.viennaairport.com
Emp.: 1,000
Airport Operations
S.I.C.: 4581
N.A.I.C.S.: 488119
Hericerg Ressmann *(Mng Dir)*

Non-U.S. Subsidiaries:

Letisko Kosice - Airport Kosice, A.S. (1)
Letisko Kosice
556832123 Kosice, Slovakia (66%)
Tel.: (421) 556832123
Fax: (421) 556832202
E-Mail: mandord@airportkosice.sk
Web Site: www.airportkosice.sk
Emp.: 172
Airport Operations
S.I.C.: 4581
N.A.I.C.S.: 488119
Michael Hoeserer *(Mng Dir)*

Malta International Airport Plc. (1)
Malta International Airport
Luqa, Malta (40%)
Tel.: (356) 21249600
Fax: (356) 21249563
E-Mail: mia@maltairport.com
Web Site: www.maltairport.com
Emp.: 400
Airport Operations
S.I.C.: 4581
N.A.I.C.S.: 488119
Markus Klaushofer *(CEO)*
Austin Calleja *(CFO)*

FLUGHAFEN ZURICH AG

PO Box 8058
Zurich, Switzerland
Tel.: (41) 438162211
Fax: (41) 438165010
E-Mail: info@zurich-airport.com
Web Site: www.zurich-airport.com
Year Founded: 2000
FHZN—(SWX)
Rev.: $1,024,080,402
Assets: $4,390,582,018
Liabilities: $2,383,259,444
Net Worth: $2,007,322,574
Earnings: $102,246,142
Emp.: 1,615
Fiscal Year-end: 12/31/12

Business Description:
Aviation Services
S.I.C.: 4731
N.A.I.C.S.: 488510

Personnel:
Andreas Schmid *(Chm)*
Lukas Briner *(Vice Chm)*
Thomas E. Kern *(CEO & Member-Mgmt Bd)*
Daniel Schmucki *(CFO, Member-Mgmt Bd & Head-Fin)*
Stefan Conrad *(Member-Mgmt Bd & Head-Ops)*
Michael Schallhart *(Member-Mgmt Bd & Head-Svcs)*
Stephan Widrig *(Member-Mgmt Bd & Head-Mktg & Real Estate)*

Board of Directors:
Andreas Schmid
Lukas Briner
Martin Candrian
Corine Mauch
Kaspar Schiller
Ernst Stocker
Ulrik Svensson
Martin Wetter

Subsidiary:

Unique Betriebssysteme AG (1)
Flughafen
Kloten, Zurich, 8058, Switzerland
Tel.: (41) 438162211
Fax: (41) 438164411
E-Mail: info@zurichairport.com
Web Site: www.Flughafen-zurich.ch
Emp.: 180
Airport Operation Services
S.I.C.: 4581
N.A.I.C.S.: 488119
Giorgos Moukas *(Gen Mgr)*

FLUGLEIDIR HF

(d/b/a Icelandair)
Reykjavik Airport
101 Reykjavik, Iceland
Tel.: (354) 5050300
Fax: (354) 5050350
E-Mail: info@icelandair.is
Web Site: www.icelandair.is
Year Founded: 1944
Emp.: 2,500

Business Description:
Provider of Scheduled Air Transportation
S.I.C.: 4512
N.A.I.C.S.: 481111

Personnel:
Birkir Holm Gudnason *(CEO)*

U.S. Subsidiary:

Icelandair North America (1)
5950 Symphony Woods Rd Ste 410
Columbia, MD 21044
Tel.: (800) 779-2899
Telex: 4970657
Fax: (410) 715-3547
Toll Free: (800) 223-5500
Web Site: www.icelandair.com
Emp.: 1,800
International Air Carrier
S.I.C.: 4512
N.A.I.C.S.: 481111

Non-U.S. Holding:

Sterling European (1)
Copenhagen Airport South
2791 Dragor, Denmark
Tel.: (45) 7033 3370
Fax: (45) 7033 2323
Web Site: www.sterlingticket.com
Emp.: 1,600
Low-Fare Airline Services
S.I.C.: 4512
N.A.I.C.S.: 481111

FLUIDATA LTD.

2 More London
London, SE1 2AP, United Kingdom
Tel.: (44) 845 868 7848
Fax: (44) 845 868 7858
E-Mail: contact@fluidata.co.uk
Web Site: www.fluidata.co.uk
Year Founded: 2004
Sales Range: $10-24.9 Million
Emp.: 47

Business Description:
Wired Telecommunication Services
S.I.C.: 4813
N.A.I.C.S.: 517110

Personnel:
Piers Daniell *(Mng Dir)*

Board of Directors:
Joachim Roeser
Piers Daniell
Larry Viner

FLUIDOMAT LTD.

117 Navneet Darshan 1st Floor 16 / 2 Old Palasia
Indore, 452018, India
Tel.: (91) 731 2564820
Fax: (91) 731 2560248
E-Mail: info@fluidomat.com
Web Site: www.fluidomat.com
522017—(BOM)
Rev.: $5,668,481
Assets: $4,379,412
Liabilities: $1,253,124
Net Worth: $3,126,288
Earnings: $950,586
Emp.: 170
Fiscal Year-end: 03/31/13

Business Description:
Industrial Machinery Mfr
S.I.C.: 3559
N.A.I.C.S.: 333249

Personnel:
Ashok Jain *(Chm & Mng Dir)*
Radhica Sharma *(Mng Dir)*
Pramod Jain *(Compliance Officer & VP)*

Board of Directors:
Ashok Jain
K. C. Jain
Kunal Jain
Narendra Kathed
M. K. Shah
Radhica Sharma
Praful R. Turakhia

Transfer Agent:
Ankit Consultancy Pvt. Ltd
Plot No 60 Electronic Complex Pardeshipura
Indore, India

FLUIDRA SA

Avda Francesc Macia 60 Planta 20
08208 Sabadell, Spain
Tel.: (34) 937243900
Fax: (34) 937242992
E-Mail: info@fluidra.com
Web Site: www.fluidra.com
FDR—(MAD)
Rev.: $871,692,191
Assets: $1,007,641,899
Liabilities: $550,290,065
Net Worth: $457,351,834
Earnings: $22,311,422
Emp.: 3,653
Fiscal Year-end: 12/31/12

Business Description:
Water Conservation Treatment Solutions
S.I.C.: 4971
N.A.I.C.S.: 221310

Personnel:
Juan Planes Vila *(Founder & Chm)*
Bernat Garrigos Castro *(Deputy Chm)*
Eloy Planes Corts *(CEO)*
Alberto Collado Armengol *(Sec)*

Board of Directors:
Juan Planes Vila
Juan Ignacio Acha-Orbea Echevarria
Bernat Garrigos Castro
Richard J. Cathcart
Eloy Planes Corts
Oscar Serra Duffo
Kam Son Leong
Eduardo Lopez Milagro
Carlos Ventura Santamans
Bernardo Corbera Serra

Subsidiaries:

Accent Graphic S.L. (1)
Obradors S N Nave 1 Pol Ind Santiga
08130 Santa Perpetua de Mogoda, Barcelona, Spain
Tel.: (34) 937183480
Fax: (34) 937188477
E-Mail: info@accentgraphic.es
Web Site: www.accentgraphic.es
Emp.: 20
Graphic Designing Services
S.I.C.: 7336
N.A.I.C.S.: 541430
Ricardo Lozano *(Dir Gen)*

AstralPool S.A. (1)
Avda Francesc Macia 38 Planta 16
8208 Sabadell, Barcelona, Spain
Tel.: (34) 937136344
Fax: (34) 937136345
E-Mail: info@astralpool.com
Web Site: www.astralpool.com
Emp.: 70
Swimming Pool Design & Construction Services
S.I.C.: 1799
N.A.I.C.S.: 238990

Subsidiary:

Astral Export, S.A. (2)
c/Mogoda 75 Pl Can Salvatella
08210 Barbera del Valles, Barcelona, Spain
Tel.: (34) 937136344
Fax: (34) 937 136 348
E-Mail: info@astralexport.com
Web Site: www.astralexport.com
Swimming Pool Equipments Distr
S.I.C.: 5091
N.A.I.C.S.: 423910
Gilles Monier *(Gen Sls Mgr)*

Non-U.S. Subsidiaries:

Astral - bazenove prislusenstvi, s.r.o. (2)
Doubravice 86
Praha-vychod, 25170 Dobrejovice, Czech Republic
Tel.: (420) 323638206
Fax: (420) 323638210
E-Mail: info@astralpool.cz
Web Site: www.astralpool.cz
Swimming Pool Equipments Whslr
S.I.C.: 5091
N.A.I.C.S.: 423910
Zuzana Rihva *(Dir-Fin)*

Astral India Private Ltd (2)
44/25 Ranjith Road
Kotturpuram, Chennai, Tamil Nadu, 600 085, India
Tel.: (91) 4443117172
Fax: (91) 4443117178
E-Mail: info@fluidra.co.in
Web Site: www.astralindia.net
Emp.: 40
Swimming Pool Equipments Distr
S.I.C.: 5091
N.A.I.C.S.: 423910
Abe Abrahem *(CEO)*

Astral Italia Spa (2)
Via Trebocche 7 E
25081 Bedizzole, Brescia, Italy
Tel.: (39) 0306870441
Fax: (39) 030 6870571
E-Mail: info@astralpool.it
Web Site: www.astralpool.com
Swimming Pool Equipments Distr
S.I.C.: 5091
N.A.I.C.S.: 423910

Astral Marazul (2)
Estrada Nacional N 249 4
2785-035 Sao Domingos de Rana, Portugal
Tel.: (351) 214444720
Fax: (351) 214 440 772
E-Mail: comercial@astralpool.pt
Web Site: www.astralpool.pt
Emp.: 25
Swimming Pool Equipments Distr
S.I.C.: 5091
N.A.I.C.S.: 423910

Astral Nigeria Ltd (2)
58 Akanbi Onitiri Close Off Eric Moore
Surulere, Lagos, Nigeria
Tel.: (234) 17740709

Fluidra SA—(Continued)

E-Mail: astralnigeria@astralpool.in
Web Site: www.astralpoolnigeria.com
Swimming Pool Equipments Distr
S.I.C.: 5091
N.A.I.C.S.: 423910
A. Mahesh *(Mgr-Bus Dev)*

Astral Pool Australia Pty Limited (2)
48 Hanna Street
Noble Park, VIC, 3174, Australia
Tel.: (61) 395542200
Fax: (61) 395542270
E-Mail: info@astralpool.com.au
Web Site: www.astralpool.com.au
Emp.: 100
Swimming Pool & Spa Equipments Mfr & Distr
S.I.C.: 3589
N.A.I.C.S.: 333318
Peter Wallace *(Mng Dir)*

Astral Pool Hellas SA (2)
Lakko Katsari
Aspropyrgos, Athens, 19300, Greece
Tel.: (30) 2105594527
Fax: (30) 2105596454
E-Mail: info@astralpool.gr
Web Site: www.astralpool.gr
Emp.: 15
Swimming Pool Equipments Distr
S.I.C.: 5091
N.A.I.C.S.: 423910
Eloy Planes-Corts *(Chm)*
Amadeo Serra-Solana *(Vice Chm)*
Oscar Carreras-Valls *(Mng Dir)*

Astral Pool Swimming Pool Equipment (Shanghai) Ltd., Co (2)
Block E 18 F JinXuan Building No 238 East NanDan Road
XuHui District, 200030 Shanghai, China
Tel.: (86) 2163910575
Fax: (86) 2163910615
E-Mail: infochina@astralpool.cn
Web Site: www.astralpool.cn
Swimming Pool Equipments Distr
S.I.C.: 5091
N.A.I.C.S.: 423910
Thai Jeffrey *(Gen Mgr)*

Astral Scandinavia A/S (2)
Kometvej 28
6230 Rodekro, Denmark
Tel.: (45) 74693999
Fax: (45) 74 69 3998
E-Mail: astralpool@astralpool.dk
Web Site: www.astralpool.dk
Swimming Pool Equipments Distr
S.I.C.: 5091
N.A.I.C.S.: 423910

Astral SNG (2)
Ul Smirnovskaya 25 B 10 Office 503-504
Moscow, 109052, Russia
Tel.: (7) 4955912101
Fax: (7) 4955911065
E-Mail: info@astralpool.ru
Web Site: www.astralpool.ru
Swimming Pool Equipments Distr
S.I.C.: 5091
N.A.I.C.S.: 423910
Ernandes Pedro Ballart *(Chm)*

Astral Sweden AB (2)
Ekenleden 11 A
428 36 Kallered, Vastergotland, Sweden
Tel.: (46) 31994100
Fax: (46) 31994105
E-Mail: order@astralpool.se
Web Site: www.astralpool.se
Emp.: 7
Swimming Pool Equipments Distr
S.I.C.: 5091
N.A.I.C.S.: 423910
Christian Clausen *(Mgr)*

Astral UK LTD (2)
Unit 30-32 Palmerston Business Park
Palmerston Drive
Newgate Lane, Fareham, Hampshire, PO14 1DJ, United Kingdom
Tel.: (44) 1329 514000
Fax: (44) 1329 514036
E-Mail: sales@astralpooluk.com
Web Site: www.astralpooluk.com
Emp.: 25
Swimming Pool Equipments Distr
S.I.C.: 5091
N.A.I.C.S.: 423910
Fernando Merino *(Mgr-Logistics)*

AstralPool Cyprus Ltd (2)
Matheou and Matheou Street No 5 Ayios Athanasios Industrial Area
CY-4101 Limassol, Cyprus
Tel.: (357) 25754424
Fax: (357) 25754425
E-Mail: info@astralpool.com.cy
Web Site: www.astralpool.com.cy
Emp.: 6
Swimming Pool Equipments Distr
S.I.C.: 5091
N.A.I.C.S.: 423910
Nicos Xenis *(Gen Mgr)*

AstralPool Switzerland S.A. (2)
Via Industria 10
6930 Bedano, Ticino, Switzerland
Tel.: (41) 919354080
Fax: (41) 919309120
E-Mail: info@astralpool.ch
Web Site: www.astralpool.com
Emp.: 7
Swimming Pool Equipments Distr
S.I.C.: 5091
N.A.I.C.S.: 423910
Rossano Galatta *(Mgr)*

AstralPool Thailand Co., Ltd (2)
110/4 M 13 Rachathewa
10540 Bang Phli, Samut Prakan, Thailand
Tel.: (66) 27389420
Fax: (66) 27389425
E-Mail: kpussuee@fruidia.co.th
Web Site: www.astralpool.co.th
Emp.: 15
Swimming Pool Equipments Distr
S.I.C.: 5091
N.A.I.C.S.: 423910
Manop Homsuwan *(Mgr)*

Fluidra Magyarorszag KFT (2)
Leshegy utca 4A
2310 Szigetszentmiklos, Pest, Hungary
Tel.: (36) 24525860
Fax: (36) 24 525 866
E-Mail: info@astralpool.hu
Web Site: www.astralpool.hu
Emp.: 14
Swimming Pool Equipments Distr
S.I.C.: 5091
N.A.I.C.S.: 423910
Jorge Dominguez *(Mgr)*

Fluidra Polska Sp.z o.o. (2)
Armii Krajowej 61
50-558 Wroclaw, Lower Silesian, Poland
Tel.: (48) 713604930
Fax: (48) 713604940
E-Mail: office@astralpool.pl
Web Site: www.astralpool.pl
Emp.: 17
Swimming Pool Equipments Distr
S.I.C.: 5091
N.A.I.C.S.: 423910
Dominik Witkowski *(Gen Dir)*

Schwimmbad-Sauna-Ausstattungs-Grosshandels GesmbH (2)
Untersbergstrasse 10
5082 Grodig, Salzburg, Austria
Tel.: (43) 624677000
Fax: (43) 6246 77 004
E-Mail: office@ssa.co.at
Web Site: www.ssa.co.at
Swimming Pool Equipments Distr
S.I.C.: 5091
N.A.I.C.S.: 423910
Helmut Brabenetz *(Mgr)*

Astramatic S.A.U. (1)
Pl Ramassar C Barcelones 15
08520 Les Franqueses del Valles, Barcelona, Spain
Tel.: (34) 938616047
Fax: (34) 938616092
E-Mail: astramatic@astramatic.com
Web Site: www.astramatic.com
Emp.: 20
Water Treatment Plant Construction Services
S.I.C.: 1623
N.A.I.C.S.: 237110
Carlos Manuel Gonzalo Sanchez *(Gen Dir)*

ATH Aplicaciones Tecnicas Hidraulicas S.L. (1)
Joan Torruella i Urpina 31
08758 Cervello, Barcelona, Spain
Tel.: (34) 936 802 222
Fax: (34) 936 802 202
E-Mail: ath@ath.es
Web Site: www.ath.es
Emp.: 45
Water Purifiers Rental Services
S.I.C.: 7359
N.A.I.C.S.: 532299
Altimiras Pujol Jucith *(Dir-Fin)*

Auric Pool, S.A. (1)
C dels Ametllers N 6
08213 Polinya, Barcelona, Spain
Tel.: (34) 937133718
Fax: (34) 937133384
E-Mail: marketing@exexpool.com
Web Site: www.auricpool.com
Emp.: 35
Management Services
S.I.C.: 6719
N.A.I.C.S.: 551112
Carles Franquesa *(Gen Mgr)*

Subsidiaries:

I.D. Electroquimica, S.L. (2)
Polig Ind Atalayas C Dracma Parcela R 19
03114 Alicante, Spain
Tel.: (34) 965101979
Fax: (34) 965107293
E-Mail: info@idegis.es
Web Site: www.idegis.es
Emp.: 10
Water Treatment Devices Mfr
S.I.C.: 3589
N.A.I.C.S.: 333318
Gaspar Cano Sanchez *(Gen Dir)*

Metalast S.A. (2)
Passeig de Sanllehi 25
08213 Polinya, Barcelona, Spain
Tel.: (34) 937131855
Fax: (34) 937134111
E-Mail: metalast@fluidraindustry.com
Web Site: www.metalastpool.com
Emp.: 150
Swimming Pool Equipments Mfr
S.I.C.: 3589
N.A.I.C.S.: 333318
Jose Manuel Aquilue *(Gen Dir)*

Poltank, S.A.U. (2)
Pol Ind Poliger Sud - Sector I S N
17854 Sant Jaume de Llierca, Girona, Spain
Tel.: (34) 972287070
Fax: (34) 972287065
E-Mail: general@poltank.com
Web Site: www.poltank.com
Emp.: 150
Filters & Accessories Mfr
S.I.C.: 3569
N.A.I.C.S.: 333999
Tony Prats *(Mng Dir)*

Prelast, S.A. (2)
Pol Ind Pla de Cisteller S N
17857 Sant Joan les Fonts, Girona, Spain
Tel.: (34) 972 29 00 79
Fax: (34) 972 29 00 88
E-Mail: mcufi@prelast.net
Web Site: www.prelast.net
Emp.: 11
Rubber Joints Mfr
S.I.C.: 3061
N.A.I.C.S.: 326291

Talleres Del Agua SL (2)
PolAgano Industrial de Barros Parcela 11-1
39400 Los Corrales de Buelna, Cantabria, Spain
Tel.: (34) 942842072
Fax: (34) 942831541
E-Mail: talleresdelagua@talleresdelagua.com
Web Site: www.talleresdelagua.com
Emp.: 60
Swimming Pool Equipments Mfr & Distr
S.I.C.: 3433
N.A.I.C.S.: 333414
Jesus Litian *(Dir Gen)*

Togama S.A. (2)
Ctra Villarreal Onda - Km 6 - Apdo 176
12540 Villarreal, Castellon, Spain
Tel.: (34) 964626512
Fax: (34) 964626137
E-Mail: togama@togama.com
Web Site: www.togama.com
Emp.: 70
Mosaic Tiles Mfr
S.I.C.: 3255
N.A.I.C.S.: 327120
Pilar Saborit *(Dir-Fin)*

Non-U.S. Subsidiary:

Europeenne de Couverture Automatiques,. S.A.R.L. (2)
105 Henry Potez-Zac Torremila
66000 Perpignan, France
Tel.: (33) 468617530
Fax: (33) 468617532
E-Mail: marketing@exexpool.com
Web Site: www.eca-interpool.com
Emp.: 100
Swimming Pool Equipments Mfr
S.I.C.: 3999
N.A.I.C.S.: 339999

Cepex S.A.U. (1)
Av Ramon Ciurans 40 - Pol Ind Congost - Parcel la 6
08530 La Garriga, Barcelona, Spain
Tel.: (34) 93 870 42 08
Fax: (34) 93 879 57 11
E-Mail: cepex@cepex.com
Web Site: www.cepex.com
Mfr of Plastic Valves, Fittings & Fluid Handling Devices
S.I.C.: 3492
N.A.I.C.S.: 332912
Ramon Salichs *(Dir Gen)*

Plants:

Cepex, S.A.U. (Granollers) (2)
Lluis Companys 51-53
08401 Granollers, Barcelona, Spain
Tel.: (34) 938604930
Fax: (34) 93 879 57 11
E-Mail: cepex@cepex.com
Fittings & Valves Mfr
S.I.C.: 3492
N.A.I.C.S.: 332912
Ramon Ramon *(Mgr)*

Cepex, S.A.U. (La Garriga) (2)
Av Ramon Ciurans 40 - Pol Ind Congost - Parcel la 6
08530 La Garriga, Barcelona, Spain
Tel.: (34) 938704208
Fax: (34) 93 879 57 11
E-Mail: cepex@cepex.com
Web Site: www.cepex.com
Fittings & Valves Mfr
S.I.C.: 3492
N.A.I.C.S.: 332912

Cepex, S.A.U. (Sant Jaume de Llierca) (2)
Pol Ind Pla de Poliger Sud - Sector 1 S N
17854 Sant Jaume de Llierca, Girona, Spain
Tel.: (34) 972287893
Fax: (34) 972 28 78 95
E-Mail: cepex@cepex.com
Web Site: www.cepex.com
Fittings & Valves Mfr
S.I.C.: 3492
N.A.I.C.S.: 332912

Non-U.S. Subsidiaries:

Cepex France S.A.S. (2)
Avenue G Guignard ZI Boe
BP 100
47553 Boe, Lot-et-Garonne, France
Tel.: (33) 5 53 48 14 26
Fax: (33) 5 53 48 25 09
E-Mail: france@cepex.com
Emp.: 3,000
Fittings & Valves Distr
S.I.C.: 5074
N.A.I.C.S.: 423720

Cepex GmbH (2)
Neue Strasse 10
31032 Betheln, Lower Saxony, Germany
Tel.: (49) 5182908152
Fax: (49) 06201596459
E-Mail: cepexgmbh@cepex.com
Web Site: www.cepex.de
Fittings & Valves Distr
S.I.C.: 5074
N.A.I.C.S.: 423720
Joerg Fischer *(Sls Mgr)*

Cepex Portugal, Lda (2)
Qta da Marquesa Herdade da Qta da Torre
Armazem n1 - Fraccao n4
Quinta do Anjo, 2950-678 Palmela, Portugal

Tel.: (351) 212108190
Fax: (351) 212108199
E-Mail: info@cepex.pt
Web Site: www.cepex.pt
Fittings & Valves Distr
S.I.C.: 5074
N.A.I.C.S.: 423720
Antonio Francisco Palhinhas Candeias *(Mng Dir)*

Cepex S.r.l. (2)
Via Trebocche 7 E
25081 Bedizzole, Brescia, Italy
Tel.: (39) 0306871281
Fax: (39) 030 6871271
E-Mail: italia@cepex.com
Web Site: www.cepex.it
Fittings & Valves Distr
S.I.C.: 5074
N.A.I.C.S.: 423720
Eloy Planes Corts *(Pres)*
Amadeo Serra Solana *(CEO)*

Certikin Iberica S.L.U (1)
Sanllehy Walk 23
08389 Polinya, Barcelona, Spain
Tel.: (34) 902020342
Fax: (34) 937645397
E-Mail: info@certikiniberica.com
Web Site: www.certikin.com
Emp.: 20
Swimming Pool Equipments Mfr & Distr
S.I.C.: 3999
N.A.I.C.S.: 339999
Jaume Alberola *(Mgr)*

Industrias Mecanicas Lago, S.A.U (1)
Pol Industrial La Rasa C Muntanya S N
17481 Sant Julia de Ramis, Girona, Spain
Tel.: (34) 972170058
Fax: (34) 972172363
E-Mail: info@imlago.com
Web Site: www.imlago.com
Swimming Pool Pumps & Accessories Mfr
S.I.C.: 3594
N.A.I.C.S.: 333996
Carmen Fuste *(Dir Gen)*

MEIP INTERNATIONAL, S.L. (1)
Paseo Sanllehy 25
08213 Polinya, Barcelona, Spain
Tel.: (34) 937149502
Fax: (34) 937149503
E-Mail: info@meipinter.com
Web Site: www.meipinter.com
Emp.: 10
Water Treatment Devices Mfr
S.I.C.: 3589
N.A.I.C.S.: 333318
Lafforgue Bruno *(Gen Mgr)*

POOL SUPPLIER, S.L. (1)
Calle Pintor Velazquez 10
08213 Polinya, Barcelona, Spain
Tel.: (34) 937136344
Fax: (34) 93 717 53 97
Emp.: 7
Swimming Pool Equipments Distr
S.I.C.: 5091
N.A.I.C.S.: 423910
Cristina Morral Padros *(Asst Mng Dir)*

Sacopa, S.A.U. (1)
Pol Ind Poliger Sud - Sector I
17854 Sant Jaume de Llierca, Girona, Spain
Tel.: (34) 972287272
Fax: (34) 972287221
E-Mail: general@sacopa.com
Web Site: www.sacopa.com
Emp.: 120
Thermoplastic Injection Parts & Components Mfr
S.I.C.: 3089
N.A.I.C.S.: 326199
Banus Miguel *(Mgr-Production)*

SERVAQUA, S.A. (1)
Pl La Coromina C Industria S N
8660 Balsareny, Barcelona, Spain
Tel.: (34) 938200235
Fax: (34) 93 839 65 05
E-Mail: info@servaqua.com
Web Site: www.servaqua.com
Emp.: 50
Water Treatment Pressure Vessels Mfr
S.I.C.: 3443
N.A.I.C.S.: 332420
Tony Prats *(Mng Dir)*

Tracelogistics, S.A. **(1)**
Pol Ind Puigtio Carrer B
17412 Macanet de la Selva, Girona, Spain
Tel.: (34) 972879300
Fax: (34) 972879320
E-Mail: info@tracelogistics.net
Web Site: www.tracelogistics.net
Emp.: 100
Logistics Distribution Services
S.I.C.: 4731
N.A.I.C.S.: 541614
Jorgi Martin *(Mgr)*

Non-U.S. Subsidiaries:

Aquaambiente, S.A (1)
Estrada Nacional 249 Km 4 Zona Industrial
Cabra Figa Lote 15
2635-047 Rio de Mouro, Portugal
Tel.: (351) 219154690
Fax: (351) 219151269
E-Mail: geral@aquaambiente.com
Web Site: www.aquaambiente.com
Emp.: 30
Swimming Pool Equipments Distr
S.I.C.: 5091
N.A.I.C.S.: 423910
Jose Luis Silveira *(Mgr)*

Astral Piscine S.A.S (1)
Avenue Maurice Bellonte
66000 Perpignan, Pyrenees-Orientales, France
Tel.: (33) 468520684
Fax: (33) 468524845
E-Mail: vente@astralpiscine.fr
Web Site: www.astralpool.fr
Swimming Pool Equipments Distr
S.I.C.: 5091
N.A.I.C.S.: 423910
Stephane Figueroa *(Dir-Admin)*

AstralPool Chile Ltd (1)
El Conquistador del Monte 4731
Huechuraba, Santiago, Chile
Tel.: (56) 27400620
Fax: (56) 27400157
E-Mail: info@astralpool.cl
Web Site: www.astralpool.cl
Swimming Pool Equipments Distr
S.I.C.: 5091
N.A.I.C.S.: 423910
Emilio Infante *(Mgr)*

ASTRALPOOL CHINA (1)
Block E 21F Jinxuan Building No 238 East Nandan Road
Shanghai, Xuhui District, 200030, China
Tel.: (86) 21 63910575
Fax: (86) 21 63910615
E-Mail: infochina@astralpool.cn
Web Site: www.astralpool.com
Swimming Pool Equipment Distr
S.I.C.: 5091
N.A.I.C.S.: 423910

Certikin International Ltd. (1)
Witan Park Avenue 2 Station Lane Industrial Estate
Witney, Oxfordshire, OX28 4FJ, United Kingdom
Tel.: (44) 1993778855
Fax: (44) 1993778620
E-Mail: enquiries@certikin.co.uk
Web Site: www.certikin.co.uk
Emp.: 200
Swimming Pool Equipments Mfr & Distr
S.I.C.: 3589
N.A.I.C.S.: 333318
Patrick Thorpe *(Chm)*
Neil Murray *(Mng Dir)*

Non-U.S. Subsidiary:

Certikin Swimming Pool Products India PVT Ltd. (2)
7A Dyvasandra Industrial Area 3rd Cross
Singayanapalaya, Bengaluru, Karnataka, 560 048, India
Tel.: (91) 80 4094 3024
Fax: (91) 80 4094 3025
E-Mail: info@certikinpoolsindia.net
Web Site: www.certikinpoolsindia.net
Emp.: 8
Swimming Pool Equipments Distr
S.I.C.: 5091
N.A.I.C.S.: 423910
Muthu Venkataselvam *(Dir-Sls)*

Certikin Italia SpA (1)
Via Gavardina 96/98/100
25010 Calcinato, Brescia, Italy
Tel.: (39) 0309980088
Fax: (39) 030 9637619
E-Mail: info@certikin.it
Web Site: www.certikin.com
Emp.: 17
Swimming Pool Equipments Mfr & Distr
S.I.C.: 3999
N.A.I.C.S.: 339999
Piergiuseppe Ciranna *(Gen Mgr)*

FLUIDRA SOUTH AFRICA (PTY) LTD. (1)
35 Reedbuck Crescent Corporate Park South
Randjesfontein, Midrand, Gauteng, 1683, South Africa
Tel.: (27) 82 800 9810
Fax: (27) 3148626
Emp.: 6
Swimming Pool Equipments Distr
S.I.C.: 5091
N.A.I.C.S.: 423910
Kevi Levin *(Mgr)*

INQUIDE ITALIA SRL (1)
Via Traversa Gabardina 36-44
25081 Bedizzole, Brescia, Italy
Tel.: (39) 0306871641
Fax: (39) 0306871441
E-Mail: info@inquide.com
Emp.: 7
Swimming Pool Chemicals & Equipments Distr
S.I.C.: 5169
N.A.I.C.S.: 424690

FLUITRONICS GMBH
Europark Fichtenhain B2
47807 Krefeld, Germany
Tel.: (49) 2151 4589 0
Fax: (49) 2151 4589 9
E-Mail: info@fluitronics.com
Web Site: www.fluitronics.com
Sales Range: $10-24.9 Million
Emp.: 70

Business Description:
Hydraulic Equipment & Components Mfr & Distr
S.I.C.: 3593
N.A.I.C.S.: 333995

Personnel:
Christoph Kempermann *(Mng Dir)*
Xiaokou Ma *(Mng Dir)*

FLUKE TRANSPORTATION GROUP
450 Sherman Avenue N 2nd Floor
Hamilton, ON, L8L 8J6, Canada
Tel.: (905) 578-0677
Fax: (905) 578-0375
Toll Free: (800) 263-4843
E-Mail: flukeinfo@fluke.ca
Web Site: www.fluke.ca
Year Founded: 1920
Rev.: $16,380,429
Emp.: 200

Business Description:
Freight Movement & Warehousing Services
S.I.C.: 4212
N.A.I.C.S.: 484110

Personnel:
Ron Foxcroft *(Chm & CEO)*
Jack Mayes *(Pres)*
Mark Groleau *(CFO)*

FLY LEASING LIMITED
West Pier
Dun Laoghaire, Co Dublin, Ireland
Tel.: (353) 1 231 1900
Fax: (353) 1 231 1901
Web Site: www.flyleasing.com
Year Founded: 2007
FLY—(NYSE)
Rev.: $369,487,000
Assets: $3,672,359,000
Liabilities: $2,923,536,000
Net Worth: $748,823,000
Earnings: $52,476,000
Fiscal Year-end: 12/31/13

Business Description:
Aircraft Leasing Services
S.I.C.: 4581
N.A.I.C.S.: 488190

Personnel:
Joseph M. Donovan *(Chm)*
Colm Barrington *(CEO)*
Gary Dales *(CFO)*

Board of Directors:
Joseph M. Donovan
Colm Barrington
Erik G. Braathen
Sean Donlon
James Fantaci
Robert S. Tomczak
Susan M. Walton
Steven Zissis

FLYHT AEROSPACE SOLUTIONS LTD.
(Formerly AeroMechanical Services Ltd.)
200 West 1144 29th Avenue Northeast
Calgary, AB, T2E 7P1, Canada
Tel.: (403) 250-9956
Fax: (403) 291-9717
Toll Free: (866) 250-9956
E-Mail: info@flyht.com
Web Site: www.flyht.com
FLY—(TSXV)
Rev.: $6,431,117
Assets: $4,939,258
Liabilities: $9,777,147
Net Worth: ($4,837,889)
Earnings: ($4,854,547)
Emp.: 50
Fiscal Year-end: 12/31/12

Business Description:
Aerospace Products Developer, Mfr & Tester
S.I.C.: 3812
N.A.I.C.S.: 334511

Personnel:
Douglas G. Marlin *(Chm)*
Matthew Bradley *(Pres)*
Bill Tempany *(CEO)*
Thomas R. French *(CFO & VP-Fin)*
Derek Graham *(CTO)*

Board of Directors:
Douglas G. Marlin
Mike Brown
Richard Hayden
Jacques Kavafian
Jack W. Olcott
Paul Takalo
Bill Tempany

Legal Counsel:
Tingle Merrett LLP
Calgary, AB, Canada

Transfer Agent:
Valiant Trust Company
750 Cambie St, Ste 600
Vancouver, BC, V6B 0A2, Canada

U.S. Subsidiary:

FLYHT Inc **(1)**
34 Brooks Rd
Sudbury, MA 01776-3406
Tel.: (978) 440-7803
Fax: (403) 291-9717
Toll Free: (866) 250-9956
E-Mail: info@flyht.com
Web Site: www.flyht.com
Emp.: 2
Aviation Software Development Services
S.I.C.: 7371
N.A.I.C.S.: 541511
Richard Hayden *(Pres)*

FLYING A PETROLEUM LTD.
Penthouse 535 Howe Street
Vancouver, BC, V6C 2Z4, Canada
Tel.: (604) 683-0466
Fax: (604) 685-8474

Flying A Petroleum Ltd.—(Continued)

Toll Free: (800) -665-3250
E-Mail: info@flyingapetroleum.com
Year Founded: 1986
FAB—(TSXV)
Assets: $43,840
Liabilities: $572,374
Net Worth: ($528,534)
Earnings: ($394,906)
Fiscal Year-end: 01/31/13
Business Description:
Oil & Gas Exploration Services
S.I.C.: 1389
N.A.I.C.S.: 213112
Personnel:
Nashirudeen Meghji *(Pres & CEO)*
Stephen Pearce *(CFO & Sec)*
Board of Directors:
Nashirudeen Meghji
Stephen Pearce
Marilyn Woodruff
Transfer Agent:
Computershare Investor Services Inc.
9th Floor 100 University Avenue
Toronto, ON, M5J 2Y1, Canada

FLYING BRANDS LIMITED
Retreat Farm La Rue De La Frontiere
Saint Lawrence, Jersey JE3 3EG
Tel.: (44) 1534865553
Fax: (44) 1376575020
E-Mail: info@flyingbrands.com
Web Site: www.fbgl.co.uk
FBDU—(LSE)
Rev.: $165,825
Assets: $6,465,613
Liabilities: $1,711,950
Net Worth: $4,753,663
Earnings: $161,088
Emp.: 81
Fiscal Year-end: 12/28/12
Business Description:
Mail-Order Operations Selling Animal & Bird Feed, Audio Books, Collectibles, Flowers, Nostalgic Audio CDs & Flowers & Plants
S.I.C.: 5961
N.A.I.C.S.: 454111
Personnel:
Stephen S. Cook *(CEO)*
C. T. Knott *(Sec & Dir-Fin)*
Board of Directors:
Paul R. Davidson
Stephen S. Cook
Legal Counsel:
Sinels
79 Bath Street
PO Box 595
Saint Helier, Jersey JE4 9XE
Addleshaw Goddard LLP
Milton Gate 60 Chiswell Street
London, EC1Y 4AG, United Kingdom
Non-U.S. Subsidiary:

Flying Flowers (Jersey) Limited **(1)**
Saxon House 27 Duke St
Chelmsford, Essex, CM1 1HT, United Kingdom
Tel.: (44) 8448846533
Web Site: www.flyingflowers.com
Flower Delivery Services
S.I.C.: 5193
N.A.I.C.S.: 424930

FLYING CEMENT COMPANY LIMITED
103 Fazal Road St John Park
Lahore, 54600, Pakistan
Tel.: (92) 426674301
Fax: (92) 426660693
E-Mail: info@flyingcement.com
Web Site: www.flyingcement.com
FLYNG—(KAR)
Sls.: $8,521,655
Assets: $59,297,906
Liabilities: $26,753,906
Net Worth: $32,544,000
Earnings: $112,623
Emp.: 236
Fiscal Year-end: 06/30/13
Business Description:
Cement Mfr
S.I.C.: 2891
N.A.I.C.S.: 325520
Personnel:
Agha Hamayun Khan *(CEO)*
Muhammad Jamil *(CFO)*
Mubashir Asif *(Sec)*
Board of Directors:
Kamran Khan
Shaista Imran
Samina Kamran
Agha Hamayun Khan
Qasim Khan
Yousaf Kamran Khan
Muhammad Tawassal Majid
Asim Qamar
Momin Qamar

FLYING COLOURS CORPORATION
901 Airport Road
Peterborough, ON, K9J 6X6, Canada
Tel.: (705) 742-4688
Fax: (705) 742-8861
Web Site: www.flyingcolourscorp.com
Business Description:
Aircraft Completion & Maintenance
S.I.C.: 3721
N.A.I.C.S.: 336411
Personnel:
John Gillespie *(Pres & CEO)*
Debbie Ammann *(CFO)*
U.S. Subsidiary:

Jetcorp Aircraft Sales Inc. **(1)**
657 N Bell Ave
Chesterfield, MO 63005-3642
Tel.: (636) 530-7000
Fax: (636) 533-9061
E-Mail: lineservice@jetcorp.com
Web Site: www.jetcorp.com
Sales Range: $1-9.9 Million
Emp.: 210
Aircraft Charter Services
Import Export
S.I.C.: 4522
N.A.I.C.S.: 481219

FLYING EAGLE PU TECHNICAL CORP.
Long Shan Development Area
Han Jiang Town, Shishi, Fujian, China
Tel.: (86) 13505080536
Fax: (86) 59588682828
Web Site: www.china-wintop.com
FEPU—(OTC)
Sales Range: $25-49.9 Million
Emp.: 516
Business Description:
Synthetic Polyurethane Leather Mfr
S.I.C.: 3199
N.A.I.C.S.: 316998
Personnel:
Kang Han Ang *(Chm & Pres)*
Jin Bei Huang *(CFO & VP)*
Li Cong Wu *(COO)*
Hong Wei Wu *(Sec)*
Board of Directors:
Kang Han Ang
Jin Bei Huang
Hong Wei Wu

FLYKE INTERNATIONAL HOLDINGS LTD.
XinWei Industrial Zone Yangdai
Jinjiang, Fujian, 362218, China
Tel.: (86) 59585091888
Fax: (86) 59585091777
E-Mail: xinweigroup@chinaflyke.com
Web Site: www.chinaflyke.com
Year Founded: 1998
01998—(HKG)
Sls.: $173,526,946
Assets: $186,929,120
Liabilities: $54,402,948
Net Worth: $132,526,172
Earnings: $4,972,482
Fiscal Year-end: 12/31/12
Business Description:
Sport Shoes Mfr & Sls
S.I.C.: 5941
N.A.I.C.S.: 451110
Personnel:
Wenjian Lin *(Chm & CEO)*
Kam Pang Chim *(CFO)*
Wing Yan Ho *(Sec)*
Board of Directors:
Wenjian Lin
Peleus Kin Wang Chu
Yong Li
Mingxu Lin
Wenzu Lin
Dong Wang
Guohe Zhu
Royal Bank of Canada Trust Company (Cayman) Limited
4th Floor Royal Bank House 24 Shedden Road
PO Box 1586
Georgetown, Cayman Islands
Transfer Agent:
Royal Bank of Canada Trust Company (Cayman) Limited
4th Floor Royal Bank House 24 Shedden Road
PO Box 1586
Georgetown, Cayman Islands

FLYNN CANADA LTD.
6435 Northwest Drive
Mississauga, ON, L4V 1K2, Canada
Tel.: (905) 671-3971
Fax: (905) 673-3971
E-Mail: info@flynn.ca
Web Site: www.flynn.ca
Year Founded: 1978
Rev.: $250,800,000
Emp.: 2,000
Business Description:
Contracting Services
S.I.C.: 1799
N.A.I.C.S.: 238990
Personnel:
Doug Flynn *(Pres & CEO)*
John McManus *(VP & COO)*

FLYTECH TECHNOLOGY CO., LTD.
No168 Sing-ai Rd Neihu District
114 Taipei, Taiwan
Tel.: (886) 287914988
Fax: (886) 227914666
Web Site: www.flytech.com
6206—(TAI)
Sales Range: $25-49.9 Million
Business Description:
Notebook Computers Mfr
S.I.C.: 3571
N.A.I.C.S.: 334111
Personnel:
Thomas Lam *(Founder & Chm)*
Unit:

Flytech Technology Co., Ltd. - Taipei Factory **(1)**
No 34 Wucyuan 3rd Road
Wugu Township, Taipei, 248, Taiwan
Tel.: (886) 222982696
Fax: (886) 222982696
E-Mail: sales@flytech.com.tw
Emp.: 300
Personal Computers Mfr
S.I.C.: 3575
N.A.I.C.S.: 334118
James Liu *(Gen Mgr)*

U.S. Subsidiaries:

Flytech Technology (U.S.A.) Inc. **(1)**
728 Charcot Ave
San Jose, CA 95131
Tel.: (510) 257-5180
Fax: (510) 257-5181
E-Mail: sales@flytech.com
Web Site: www.flytech.com
Emp.: 10
Personal Computers Distr
S.I.C.: 5045
N.A.I.C.S.: 423430
Thomas Lam *(Founder)*

Flytech Technology (U.S.A.) Inc. **(1)**
1931 Hartog Dr
San Jose, CA 95131
Tel.: (408) 573-9113
Web Site: www.flytech.com
Emp.: 8
Notebook Computers Mfr
S.I.C.: 3571
N.A.I.C.S.: 334111
Jenny Wang *(Mgr)*

Non-U.S. Subsidiaries:

Flytech Technology Hong Kong Ltd. **(1)**
Rm 01 6/F Block A Tonic Industrial Ctr 26 Kai Cheung Rd
Kowloon Bay, Kowloon, China (Hong Kong)
Tel.: (852) 35255800
Fax: (852) 27517447
E-Mail: sales@flytech.com.hk
Web Site: www.flytech.com.hk
Emp.: 10
Personal Computers Mfr
S.I.C.: 3571
N.A.I.C.S.: 334111
On Poon *(Gen Mgr)*

Flytech Technology Japan Ltd. **(1)**
2-48-14 Inada
Nagano, Nagano, 381-0042, Japan
Tel.: (81) 26 259 4804
Personal Computers Mfr
S.I.C.: 3571
N.A.I.C.S.: 334111

FLYTXT
Plot 2 7A Leela Info Prk Tecno Prk
Trivandrum, Kerala, 695581, India
Tel.: (91) 4712700101
Fax: (91) 4712700202
E-Mail: info@flytxt.com
Web Site: www.flytxt.com
Emp.: 110
Business Description:
Technology Services to Mobile Operators & Mobile Marketers
S.I.C.: 7319
N.A.I.C.S.: 541890
Personnel:
David Harper *(Chm)*
Vinod Vasudevan *(CEO)*

FMCG BUSINESS PARTNER AB
Svetsarvagen 15
171 41 Solna, Sweden
Tel.: (46) 857877135
Fax: (46) 855779099
E-Mail: info@ancrona.se
Web Site: www.ancrona.se
Emp.: 15
Business Description:
Private Equity Firm
S.I.C.: 6211
N.A.I.C.S.: 523999
Personnel:
Peter Nordwall *(CEO)*
Holding:

Ancrona AB **(1)**
Svetsarv. 15
17141 Solna, Sweden (100%)
Tel.: (46) 855779050
Fax: (46) 855779099
Web Site: www.ancrona.se

Sales Range: $10-24.9 Million
Emp.: 23
Other Grocery & Related Products Whslr
S.I.C.: 5149
N.A.I.C.S.: 424490
Sophie Ramsten *(Mgr-Mktg & Bus Dev)*

FMG S.A.
Case Postale 102
1510 Moudon, Switzerland
Tel.: (41) 219058000
Fax: (41) 219058020
E-Mail: fmg@fmgsa.ch
Web Site: www.fmgsa.ch
Emp.: 50
Business Description:
Iron Foundry
S.I.C.: 3321
N.A.I.C.S.: 331511
Personnel:
Georges Orossier *(Mng Dir)*

FN HERSTAL, S.A.
33 Rue Voie De Liege
4040 Herstal, Belgium
Tel.: (32) 4 240 8111
Telex: 41223 FABNA
Fax: (32) 4 240 8899
E-Mail: info@fnherstal.com
Web Site: www.fnherstal.com
Year Founded: 1889
Emp.: 2,500
Business Description:
Mfr of Small Arms & Ammunition For Defense & Law Enforcement; Hunting & Shooting Arms & Ammunition; Archery Accessories; Outdoor Equipment
Export
S.I.C.: 3489
N.A.I.C.S.: 332994
Subsidiaries:

Browning International S.A. (1)
Parc Industriel Des Hauts Sarts
Herstal, Liege, 4040, Belgium (100%)
Tel.: (32) 42405211
Telex: 41223
Fax: (32) 42405212
E-Mail: damien.kaivers@browning-int.com
Web Site: www.browningint.com
Sales Range: $25-49.9 Million
Emp.: 60
Sporting Goods; Hunting, Shooting & Archery; Outdoor Goods
S.I.C.: 3949
N.A.I.C.S.: 339920

FN Herstal S.A. (1)
33 Rue Voie De Liege
Herstal, Liege, 4040, Belgium (100%)
Tel.: (32) 42408811
Fax: (32) 42408899
E-Mail: info@fnherstal.com
Web Site: www.fnherstal.com
Sales Range: Less than $1 Million
Emp.: 1,200
Mfr. Small Arms, Ammunitions, Weapons Systems, Engineering
S.I.C.: 3484
N.A.I.C.S.: 332994

U.S. Subsidiary:

U.S. Repeating Arms Company (1)
344 Winchester Ave
New Haven, CT 06511-1918 MA
Tel.: (203) 789-5000
Fax: (203) 789-5071
E-Mail: webmaster@winchester-guns.com
Web Site: www.winchester-guns.com
Emp.: 450
Mfr. of Firearms
Import Export
S.I.C.: 3489
N.A.I.C.S.: 332994

FNG GROUP NV
Bautersemstraat 68
2800 Mechelen, Belgium
Tel.: (32) 15286174
Fax: (32) 15 286178
E-Mail: info@fredginger.be
Web Site: www.fng.eu
FNG—(EUR)
Business Description:
Children's Clothing Mfr & Distr
S.I.C.: 5137
N.A.I.C.S.: 424330
Personnel:
Dieter Penninckx *(Mng Dir)*
Tine De Ryck *(CFO)*

FNGUIDE INC.
9th Floor Kosdaq Building 45-2
Yeouido-dong
Seoul, 150-974, Korea (South)
Tel.: (82) 2 769 7702
Fax: (82) 2 769 7788
Web Site: www.fnguide.com
064850—(KRS)
Business Description:
Financial Market Data
S.I.C.: 7389
N.A.I.C.S.: 519190
Personnel:
Gun-Ho Kim *(CEO)*

FNM S.P.A.
Piazzale Cadorna 14
20123 Milan, Italy
Tel.: (39) 0285114382
Fax: (39) 0285114583
Web Site: www.fnmgroup.it
FNM—(ITA)
Sales Range: $400-449.9 Million
Emp.: 2,800
Business Description:
Regional Transportation Services
S.I.C.: 4789
N.A.I.C.S.: 488210
Personnel:
Norberto Achille *(Chm & Pres)*
Luciana Frosio Roncalli *(Vice Chm)*
Luigi Legnani *(Vice Mng Dir)*
Guiseppe Biesuz *(Mng Dir)*
Massimo Stoppini *(Dir-Admin & Treas)*
Board of Directors:
Norberto Achille
Cesare Bozzano
Luciana Frosio Roncalli
Gaetano Giussani
Claudio Solenghi
Vincenzo Soprano
Subsidiaries:

LeNORD S.R.L. (1)
Ple Cadorna 14
20123, Milan, Italy
Tel.: (39) 0285114382
Fax: (39) 0285114672
E-Mail: infocare@lenord.it
Web Site: www.lenord.it
Emp.: 3,000
Railway Transport Services
S.I.C.: 4011
N.A.I.C.S.: 482111
Vittorio Belingardi *(Pres)*
Luigi Legnani *(Mng Dir)*

NordCom S.p.A. (1)
Paleocapa St 6
20121 Milan, Italy
Tel.: (39) 02721511
Fax: (39) 0272151909
E-Mail: marketing@nord-com.it
Web Site: www.nord-com.it
System Integrating Services
S.I.C.: 7373
N.A.I.C.S.: 541512
Carlo Carlo *(Mgr)*

FOCAL AIMS HOLDINGS BERHAD
Suite 338 3rd Floor Johor Tower
Jalan Gereja
80100 Johor Bahru, Johor, Malaysia
Tel.: (60) 72211833
Fax: (60) 72223833
E-Mail: fasbjb@tm.net.my
Web Site: www.focal.com.my
FOCAL—(KLS)
Rev.: $21,408,587
Assets: $161,097,994
Liabilities: $63,097,771
Net Worth: $98,000,223
Earnings: $2,361,573
Fiscal Year-end: 09/30/12
Business Description:
Property Management Services
S.I.C.: 6531
N.A.I.C.S.: 531312
Personnel:
Oy Chong Yee *(Mng Dir)*
Siew Chuan Chua *(Co-Sec)*
Chooi Peng Mak *(Co-Sec)*
Board of Directors:
Mohd Razali Abdul Rahman
Mokhtar Ali
Mustapha Ismail
Choo Ing Pang
Yon Tin Pang
Boon Hin Tee
See Chin Woon
Oy Chong Yee
Yok Sen Yee
Subsidiaries:

Focal Aims Land Sdn. Bhd. (1)
Unit 2 1 Level 2 Building A Peremba Square Saujana Resort Seksyen U2
40150 Shah Alam, Selangor Darul Ehsan, Malaysia
Tel.: (60) 376229983
Fax: (60) 376229982
E-Mail: Fasb_enquiry@focal.com.my
Emp.: 6
Building Construction Services
S.I.C.: 1629
N.A.I.C.S.: 236210
John Fy Chen *(Mgr)*

Focal Aims Sdn. Bhd. (1)
Suite 338 3rd Floor Johor Tower Jalan Gereja
80100 Johor Bahru, Johor, Malaysia
Tel.: (60) 72211833
Fax: (60) 2246066
E-Mail: Fasb_enquiry@focal.com.my
Emp.: 50
Building Construction Services
S.I.C.: 1629
N.A.I.C.S.: 236210
Yee Oy Chong *(Grp Mng Dir)*

FOCALTECH CORPORATION, LTD.
8F 1 No 32 Gaotie 2nd Road
Zhubei City, Hsin-chu, 302, Taiwan
Tel.: (886) 3 6672758
Fax: (886) 3 6675515
E-Mail: ir@focaltech-systems.com
Web Site: www.focaltech-systems.com
5280—(TAI)
Business Description:
Semiconductor Devices Mfr
S.I.C.: 3674
N.A.I.C.S.: 334413
Personnel:
James Genda Hu *(Chm & Gen Mgr)*

FOCKE & CO. (GMBH & CO.) VERPACKUNGSMASCHINEN
Siemenstr 10
27283 Verden, Germany
Tel.: (49) 42318910
Fax: (49) 42315061
E-Mail: info@focke.de
Web Site: www.focke.biz
Year Founded: 1955
Sales Range: $100-124.9 Million
Emp.: 1,000
Business Description:
Mfr. of Packaging Machinery
S.I.C.: 3565
N.A.I.C.S.: 333993
Personnel:
Jurgen Focke *(CEO & Mng Dir)*
U.S. Subsidiary:

Focke & Co., Inc. (1)
5730 Millstream Rd
Whitsett, NC 27377-9789 (100%)
Tel.: (336) 449-7200
Fax: (336) 449-5444
E-Mail: sales@fockegso.com
Web Site: www.focke.biz
Emp.: 70
Marketing & Sale of Packaging Machinery
S.I.C.: 3565
N.A.I.C.S.: 333993
Johann Betschart *(VP-Ops)*

FOCUS 4U LTD.
Europa House
Southwick Square, Southwick, West Sussex, BN42 4FJ, United Kingdom
Tel.: (44) 8454505225
Fax: (44) 8454505226
E-Mail: sales@Focus4U.co.uk
Web Site: www.Focus4U.co.uk
Year Founded: 2003
Sales Range: $10-24.9 Million
Emp.: 70
Business Description:
Corporate Telecommunications Services
S.I.C.: 4899
N.A.I.C.S.: 517919
Personnel:
Chris Goodman *(Dir-Sls)*

FOCUS DEVELOPMENT AND CONSTRUCTION PUBLIC COMPANY LIMITED
9th Fl Alma Link Building 25 Soi Chidlom Ploenchit Lumpini Patumwan
Bangkok, 10330, Thailand
Tel.: (66) 2650 3105
Fax: (66) 2650 3065
E-Mail: info@focus-pcl.com
Web Site: www.focus-pcl.com
Year Founded: 1989
FOCUS—(THA)
Rev.: $36,495,535
Assets: $23,194,165
Liabilities: $17,467,887
Net Worth: $5,726,278
Earnings: $2,138,710
Emp.: 153
Fiscal Year-end: 12/31/12
Business Description:
Construction Services
S.I.C.: 1629
N.A.I.C.S.: 236210
Personnel:
Anucha Sihanatkathakul *(Chm)*
Jeremy Lechemere King *(Vice Chm)*
Nontawat Thongmee *(Mng Dir)*
Board of Directors:
Anucha Sihanatkathakul
Phasunsook Ayanaputra
Sunthorn Boonruang
Tanavich Chindapradist
Pattick M. Davenport
Michael de Santiesteban
Jeremy Lechemere King
Tanakorn Leelasiri
Thavalya Prapapant
Thomas C. Thompson
Nontawat Thongmee
Pornsanong Tuchinda

FOCUS (DIY) GROUP LTD.
Gawsworth House Westmere Dr
Crewe, CW1 6XB, United Kingdom
Tel.: (44) 1270501555
Fax: (44) 01270250501
E-Mail: Chris.Morgan@focusdiy.co.uk
Web Site: www.focusdiy.co.uk
Year Founded: 1987

Focus (DIY) Group Ltd.—(Continued)

Emp.: 4,000
Business Description:
Holding Company; Chain of DIY Stores
Import
S.I.C.: 5251
N.A.I.C.S.: 444130
Personnel:
Rob Gladwin *(CEO)*

FOCUS GRAPHITE INC.

(Formerly Focus Metals Inc.)
912-130 Albert Street
Ottawa, ON, K1P 5G4, Canada
Tel.: (613) 691-1091
Fax: (613) 241-8632
Web Site: www.focusgraphite.com
FMS—(OTC TSXV)
Int. Income: $187,315
Assets: $30,941,355
Liabilities: $3,808,419
Net Worth: $27,132,936
Earnings: ($4,153,907)
Fiscal Year-end: 09/30/13
Business Description:
Metal Mining Services
S.I.C.: 1099
N.A.I.C.S.: 212299
Personnel:
Donald K. D. Baxter *(Pres & COO)*
Gary Economo *(CEO)*
Judith T. Mazvihwa-MacLean *(CFO)*
Board of Directors:
Marc-Andre Bernier
Chester Aaron Burtt
Gary Economo
Francis Pomerleau

FOCUS GROUP

Europa House Southwick Square
Southwick, West Sussex, BN42 4FJ, United Kingdom
Tel.: (44) 844 692 8000
Fax: (44) 844 692 8001
E-Mail: sales@focus-grp.co.uk
Web Site: www.focus-grp.co.uk
Year Founded: 2003
Sales Range: $25-49.9 Million
Emp.: 85
Business Description:
Wireless Telecommunication Services
S.I.C.: 4812
N.A.I.C.S.: 517210
Personnel:
Ralph Gilbert *(Mng Dir)*

FOCUS INDUSTRIAL RESOURCES LIMITED

104 Mukand House Commercial Complex
Azadpur, New Delhi, 110 033, India
Tel.: (91) 11 47039000
E-Mail: info@focuslimited.in
Web Site: www.focuslimited.in
Year Founded: 1985
534757—(BOM)
Rev.: $723,777
Assets: $4,245,646
Liabilities: $235,434
Net Worth: $4,010,212
Earnings: $68,048
Fiscal Year-end: 03/31/13
Business Description:
Financial Lending Services
S.I.C.: 6141
N.A.I.C.S.: 522291
Personnel:
Pradeep Kumar Jindal *(Chm, CEO & Mng Dir)*
Silky Kapoor *(Compliance Officer & Sec)*
Board of Directors:
Pradeep Kumar Jindal
Madhvi Bhatnagar
Santanu Kumar Dash
Ashok Kumar Gupta
Transfer Agent:
Beetal Financial & Computer Services Pvt. Ltd.
Beetal House 3rd Floor 99 Madangir Near Dada Harsukhdas Mandir
New Delhi, 110062, India

FOCUS LUMBER BERHAD

Jalan Masak Kampung Ulu Patikang
89009 Keningau, Sabah, 88400, Malaysia
Tel.: (60) 87335457
Fax: (60) 87335459
E-Mail: focuskk@tm.net.my
Web Site: www.focuslumber.com.my
Year Founded: 1989
FLBHD—(KLS)
Rev.: $43,548,852
Assets: $43,176,346
Liabilities: $5,177,899
Net Worth: $37,998,447
Earnings: $3,803,946
Emp.: 136
Fiscal Year-end: 12/31/12
Business Description:
Plywood & Veneer Mfr & Sales
S.I.C.: 2436
N.A.I.C.S.: 321212
Personnel:
Hao Wen Lin *(Mng Dir)*
Peir Chyun Wong *(Co-Sec)*
Wai Foong Wong *(Co-Sec)*
Board of Directors:
Aznam Mansor
Hao Wen Lin
Lieh Ming Lin
Tian Meng Ng
Yoke Nyen Wong
Sen Yang

FOCUS MEDIA HOLDING LIMITED

Unit No 1 20th Floor The Centrium
60 Wyndham Street
Central, China (Hong Kong)
Tel.: (852) 3752 8009
Fax: (852) 3583 0082
E-Mail: contact@focusmedia.cn
Web Site: www.focusmedia.cn
Year Founded: 2003
Rev.: $927,501,037
Assets: $1,975,886,492
Liabilities: $507,929,954
Net Worth: $1,467,956,538
Earnings: $235,936,792
Emp.: 6,731
Fiscal Year-end: 12/31/12
Business Description:
Media Advertising Services
S.I.C.: 7311
N.A.I.C.S.: 541810
Personnel:
Jason Nanchun Jiang *(Chm & CEO)*
Cindy Yan Chan *(Chief Strategy Officer)*
Board of Directors:
Jason Nanchun Jiang
Charles Guowei Chao
Neil Nanpeng Shen
Ying Wu
David Ying Zhang
Fumin Zhuo
Legal Counsel:
Simpson Thacher & Bartlett LLP
ICBC Tower 7th Fl
3 Garden Road, Hong Kong, China (Hong Kong)
Transfer Agent:
Dexia Corporate Service Hong Kong Ltd.
51/F Central Plaza 18 Harbour Road
Wanchai, China (Hong Kong)
Tel.: (852) 2978 5782
Fax: (852) 2530 5152

FOCUS MEDIA NETWORK LIMITED

28th Floor 2801 Citicorp Centre 18 Whitfield Road
North Point, China (Hong Kong)
Tel.: (852) 3588 8288
Fax: (852) 3588 8299
E-Mail: enquiries@focusmedia.com
Web Site: www.focusmedia.com
8112—(HKG)
Rev.: $6,919,690
Assets: $11,197,720
Liabilities: $2,119,893
Net Worth: $9,077,826
Earnings: ($3,523,920)
Emp.: 63
Fiscal Year-end: 12/31/12
Business Description:
Advertising Services
S.I.C.: 7319
N.A.I.C.S.: 541890
Personnel:
P. J. Wong *(Chm & CEO)*
Toi Yuk Ngan *(Compliance Officer)*
Hope Yuen Han Lee *(Sec)*
Board of Directors:
P. J. Wong
Alan Chan
Gabriel Chan
Audrey Chee
Ray Lee
Vincent Lien
Eveline Ngan
Eric Rosenkranz
Legal Counsel:
Robertsons
57th Floor The Center 99 Queen's Road
Central, China (Hong Kong)

Codan Trust Company (Cayman) Limited
Cricket Square Hutchins Drive
PO Box 2681
Georgetown, Grand Cayman, Cayman Islands
Transfer Agents:
Tricor Investor Services Limited
26th Floor Tesbury Centre 28 Queens Road East
Wanchai, China (Hong Kong)

Codan Trust Company (Cayman) Limited
Cricket Square Hutchins Drive
PO Box 2681
Georgetown, Grand Cayman, Cayman Islands

FOCUS METALS INC.

(Name Changed to Focus Graphite Inc.)

FOCUS MINERALS LIMITED

159 Adelaide Terrace
Perth, WA, 6004, Australia
Mailing Address:
PO Box 3233
Perth, WA, 6892, Australia
Tel.: (61) 892157888
Fax: (61) 892157889
E-Mail: info@focusminerals.com.au
Web Site: www.focusminerals.com.au
FML—(ASX)
Rev.: $223,837,870
Assets: $336,961,993
Liabilities: $63,005,366
Net Worth: $273,956,627
Earnings: ($178,744,118)
Fiscal Year-end: 06/30/13
Business Description:
Gold, Nickel & Other Base Metal Mining & Exploration
S.I.C.: 1041
N.A.I.C.S.: 212221
Personnel:
Jisheng Lu *(Chm)*
Wanghong Yang *(Interim CEO)*
Paul Fromson *(CFO & Sec)*
Mark Hine *(COO)*
Board of Directors:
Jisheng Lu
Gerry Fahey
Yuhuan Ge
Phil Lockyer
Bruce McComish
Wanghong Yang
Legal Counsel:
King & Wood Mallesons
Level 50 Bourke Street
Melbourne, VIC, Australia
Subsidiaries:

Crescent Gold Limited **(1)**
Level 2 159 Adelaide Terrace East
Perth, WA, 6008, Australia AU
Mailing Address: (81.75%)
PO Box 3233
Perth, WA, 6892, Australia
Tel.: (61) 863807100
Fax: (61) 892157889
E-Mail:
Emp.: 20
Gold Ore Mining
S.I.C.: 1041
N.A.I.C.S.: 212221
Mark Tory *(Mng Dir & CFO)*
Albert Longo *(Sec & Mgr-Comml)*
Stephen Ross *(Sec & Mgr-Comml)*

Focus Operations Pty Ltd **(1)**
Three Mile Hill Great Eastern Hwy PMB 3
Coolgardie, WA, 6429, Australia
Tel.: (61) 890220222
Fax: (61) 890220230
E-Mail: info@focusminerals.com
Emp.: 80
Potash Soda & Borate Mining Services
S.I.C.: 1474
N.A.I.C.S.: 212391
Paul Fromson *(Sec)*

FOCUS POINT HOLDINGS BERHAD

Level 18 The Gardens North Tower
Mid Valley City
Lingkaran Syed Putra, Kuala Lumpur, 59200, Malaysia
Tel.: (60) 322648888
E-Mail: fp@focus-point.com
Web Site: www.focus-point.com
FOCUSP—(KLS)
Sales Range: $25-49.9 Million
Emp.: 580
Business Description:
Eye Care Centers
S.I.C.: 8093
N.A.I.C.S.: 621498
Personnel:
Hamzah bin Mohd Salleh *(Chm)*
C. L. Liaw *(Pres & CEO)*
Board of Directors:
Hamzah bin Mohd Salleh
Wei Chong Choo
Ming Fong Leow
C. L. Liaw
Subsidiary:

Focus Point Vision Care Group Sdn. Bhd. **(1)**
Unit 1 and 3 Jalan Pju 1/37 Dataran Prima
47301 Petaling Jaya, Selangor, Malaysia
Tel.: (60) 378805520
Fax: (60) 378805530
E-Mail: fp@focus-point.com
Web Site: www.focus-point.com
Emp.: 500
Optical Retail Stores Management & Operation Services
S.I.C.: 5995
N.A.I.C.S.: 446130
Choon Liang Liaw *(Pres & CEO)*

FOCUS VENTURES LTD.

Suite 650-200 Burrard Street
Vancouver, BC, V6C 3L6, Canada
Tel.: (604) 688-5288

Fax: (604) 682-1514
E-Mail: info@focusventuresltd.com
Web Site: www.focusventuresltd.com
FCV—(TSXV)
Rev.: $18,932
Assets: $3,733,210
Liabilities: $236,317
Net Worth: $3,496,893
Earnings: ($136,089)
Fiscal Year-end: 11/30/12
Business Description:
Mineral Exploration Services
S.I.C.: 1081
N.A.I.C.S.: 213114
Personnel:
Simon T. P. Ridgway *(Chm & CEO)*
David Cass *(Pres)*
Kevin Bales *(CFO)*
Board of Directors:
Simon T. P. Ridgway
David Cass
Tim Osler
Mario Szotlender
Transfer Agent:
Olympia Trust Company
Suite 1003-750 West Pender Street
Vancouver, BC, Canada
Non-U.S. Subsidiary:

Minera Focus, S.A.C. (1)
Av Guardia Civil 696
San Isidro, Lima, 27, Peru
Tel.: (51) 1 226 7152
E-Mail: info@focusventuresltd.com
Silver Ore Mining Services
S.I.C.: 1044
N.A.I.C.S.: 212222

FOCUSED CAPITAL CORP.

1 Adelaide Street East 21st Floor
Toronto, ON, M5C 2V9, Canada
Tel.: (416) 924-9893
E-Mail: mgoodman@cogitore.com
Year Founded: 2010
FLO.P—(TSXV)
Assets: $601,399
Liabilities: $21,083
Net Worth: $580,316
Earnings: ($41,352)
Fiscal Year-end: 12/31/12
Business Description:
Investment Services
S.I.C.: 6211
N.A.I.C.S.: 523999
Personnel:
Mark E. Goodman *(CEO & Sec)*
Carmelo Marrelli *(CFO)*
Board of Directors:
Richard W. Brissenden
Mark E. Goodman
Peter McRae
Transfer Agent:
Computershare Investor Services Inc.
510 Burrard Street 2nd Floor
Vancouver, BC, V6C 3B9, Canada

FOCUSED CAPITAL II CORP.

1 Adelaide Street East Suite 2800
Toronto, ON, M5C 2V9, Canada
Tel.: (416) 924-9893
E-Mail: mgoodman@cogitore.com
Year Founded: 2011
FAV.P—(TSXV)
Business Description:
Investment Services
S.I.C.: 6211
N.A.I.C.S.: 523999
Personnel:
Mark E. Goodman *(CEO & Sec)*
Carmelo Marrelli *(CFO)*
Board of Directors:
Rocky Bellotti
Mark E. Goodman
Robert Leckie
Carmelo Marrelli
Transfer Agent:
Computershare Investor Services Inc.
510 Burrard Street 2nd Floor
Vancouver, BC, V6C 3B9, Canada

FOCUSED MONEY SOLUTIONS INC.

Suite 410 800 6th Avenue Southwest
Calgary, AB, T2P 3G3, Canada
Tel.: (403) 229-4420
Fax: (403) 206-7817
E-Mail: info@focusedmoney.ca
Web Site: www.focusedmoney.ca
1FS—(DEU)
Business Description:
Life Settlement Services
S.I.C.: 6726
N.A.I.C.S.: 525990
Personnel:
Victor DeLaet *(Pres & CEO)*

FOCUSED PHOTONICS (HANGZHOU), INC.

760 Bin'an Road
Binjiang District, Hangzhou, Zhejiang, 310052, China
Tel.: (86) 571 85012188
Fax: (86) 571 85011018
E-Mail: sales_osd@fpi-inc.com
Web Site: www.fpi-inc.com
300203—(CHIN)
Sales Range: $75-99.9 Million
Emp.: 1,360
Business Description:
Air Quality, Sewage & Surface Water Quality Monitoring Equipment Mfr
S.I.C.: 3564
N.A.I.C.S.: 333413
Personnel:
Naxin Yao *(CEO)*

FOCUSRITE AUDIO ENGINEERING LTD.

Windsor House Turnpike Road
High Wycombe, Buckinghamshire, HP12 3FX, United Kingdom
Tel.: (44) 1494 462246
Fax: (44) 1494 462246
E-Mail: sales@focusrite.com
Web Site: www.focusrite.com
Year Founded: 1985
Sales Range: $25-49.9 Million
Emp.: 85
Business Description:
Musical Instrument Mfr
S.I.C.: 3931
N.A.I.C.S.: 339992
Personnel:
David R. Froker *(Mng Dir)*
Phil Wagner *(Pres-Mktg-Focusrite Novation, Inc.)*
Board of Directors:
Giles Orford
Phil Wagner

FOGA SYSTEM INTERNATIONAL AB

Torgnysegerspedtg 44
PO Box 4080
SE 426 04 Vastra Frolunda, Sweden
Tel.: (46) 31696250
Fax: (46) 31696259
E-Mail: info@fogasystem.com
Web Site: www.fogasystem.com
Year Founded: 1971
Sales Range: $25-49.9 Million
Emp.: 6
Business Description:
Aluminum Profile Systems Mfr for Office & Shop Fittings, Screen Walls, Glass Showcases & Exhibition Stands
Import Export
S.I.C.: 2599
N.A.I.C.S.: 337215
Personnel:
Olof Wahlin *(Pres, CEO & Mng Dir)*
Subsidiary:

Foga System Scandinavia AB (1)
Stromfallsvagen 34
SE 135 49 Stockholm, Tyreso, Sweden
Tel.: (46) 87708880
Fax: (46) 87708888
E-Mail: foga@foga.se
Web Site: www.foga.se
Emp.: 11
Commercial Furniture Mfr
S.I.C.: 2599
N.A.I.C.S.: 337215

U.S. Subsidiary:

Outwater Plastic Industries, Inc. (1)
24 River Rd
Bogota, NJ 07603
Tel.: (201) 498-8750
Toll Free: (800) 631-8375
E-Mail: outwater@outwater.com
Web Site: www.outwater.com
Emp.: 150
Hardware & Decorative Trim Plastic Moldings
S.I.C.: 5072
N.A.I.C.S.: 423710
Joey Shimm *(VP-Mktg & Adv)*

Non-U.S. Subsidiaries:

Display Ways Ltd. (1)
WGTN Mail Ctr
PO Box 39165
Wellington, New Zealand
Tel.: (64) 45760990
Fax: (64) 45760991
E-Mail: info@displayways.co.nz
Web Site: www.displayways.co.nz
Emp.: 24
S.I.C.: 2599
N.A.I.C.S.: 337215
Paul Murphy *(CEO)*

Eurofoga S.L. (1)
Daniel De Olmo Parcela 6
Poligono Argales, E 47008 Valladolid, Spain
Tel.: (34) 983235307
Fax: (34) 983471205
E-Mail: foga@eurofoga.es
Web Site: www.eurofoga.es
Aluminum Profile Systems Mfr for Office & Shop Fittings, Screen Walls, Glass Showcases & Exhibition Stands
S.I.C.: 2599
N.A.I.C.S.: 337215

Foga Benelux B.V. (1)
PO Box 2051
NL-5001 CB Tilburg, Netherlands
Tel.: (31) 134556915
Fax: (31) 134562041
S.I.C.: 2599
N.A.I.C.S.: 337215

Foga Deutchland Display GmbH (1)
Muhlenstrasse 25
DE-58285 Gevelsberg, Germany
Tel.: (49) 2332557175
Fax: (49) 2332557176
E-Mail: info@foga-online.de
Web Site: www.foga-online.de
Emp.: 2
S.I.C.: 2599
N.A.I.C.S.: 337215
Michael Hoesterey *(Gen Mgr)*

Foga Interijere d.o.o. (1)
Sljemenska 2
10290 Zagreb, Croatia
Tel.: (385) 13351558
Fax: (385) 13359412
E-Mail: info@foga.hr.com
Web Site: www.fogasystem.com
Emp.: 4
S.I.C.: 2599
N.A.I.C.S.: 337215
Daniel Benko *(Gen Mgr)*

Foga Polen Sp. z o.o. (1)
Wala Chynowska 107
PL-03-650 Chynow, Poland
Tel.: (48) 486614276
Fax: (48) 486614308
Web Site: www.pogasystems.com
S.I.C.: 2599
N.A.I.C.S.: 337215

Foga System Corporation (1)
3 1 2 Azabudai
Minato-Ku, Tokyo, 106 0041, Japan
Tel.: (81) 335051341
Fax: (81) 335051324
E-Mail: info@foga.co.jp
Web Site: www.foga.co.jp
Emp.: 8
S.I.C.: 2599
N.A.I.C.S.: 337215
Hosokawa Katsuichro *(Pres)*

Foga System France S.a.r.L. (1)
15, rue du Gen
Vandenberg, F-67140 Paris, Barr, France
Tel.: (33) 388080008
Fax: (33) 388084194
Web Site: www.foga.se/fww.html
S.I.C.: 2599
N.A.I.C.S.: 337215

Foga System GmbH (1)
Schongauer Strasse 25
04328 Leipzig, Germany
Tel.: (49) 3412519266
Fax: (49) 3412519559
S.I.C.: 2599
N.A.I.C.S.: 337215

Hungseo Industrial Co., Ltd. (1)
Hwajin Bldg 738 25 Yuksam Dong
Seoul, Korea (South)
Tel.: (82) 25624441
Fax: (82) 25082622
E-Mail: zstyle@hanmail.net
Web Site: www.hsint.com
Emp.: 30
S.I.C.: 2599
N.A.I.C.S.: 337215
Changwhan Lee *(Gen Mgr)*

Norking Aluminium Ltd. (1)
L K H Estate Tickhill Rd
Doncaster, DN4 8QG, United Kingdom
Tel.: (44) 302855907
Fax: (44) 1302310204
E-Mail: foga@norking.com
Web Site: www.norking.com
Emp.: 100
S.I.C.: 2599
N.A.I.C.S.: 337215
Graeme Gibson *(Mng Dir)*

FOLIUM GROUP LTD

Kingsbury Business Park, Kingsbury Road
Birmingham, West Midlands, B76 9DL, United Kingdom
Tel.: (44) 1213522000
Fax: (44) 1213522020
E-Mail: sales@folium.co.uk
Web Site: www.folium.co.uk
Rev.: $18,353,499
Emp.: 64
Business Description:
Printing Services
S.I.C.: 2759
N.A.I.C.S.: 323111
Personnel:
John Steed *(Chm)*

FOLKESTONE LIMITED

Level 10 60 Carrington Street
Sydney, NSW, 2000, Australia
Tel.: (61) 2 8667 2800
Fax: (61) 2 8667 2880
E-Mail: office@folkestone.com.au
Web Site: www.folkestone.com.au
FLK—(ASX)
Rev.: $10,484,568
Assets: $61,404,700
Liabilities: $12,149,844
Net Worth: $49,254,857
Earnings: $1,225,510
Fiscal Year-end: 06/30/13
Business Description:
Property Development & Construction Services
S.I.C.: 6531
N.A.I.C.S.: 531311

Folkestone Limited—(Continued)

Personnel:
Gregory J. Paramor *(Mng Dir)*
Scott N. Martin *(CFO & Sec)*
Nick J. Anagnostou *(CEO-Social Infrastructure Funds)*
Board of Directors:
Garry R. Sladden
Mark Baillie
Gregory J. Paramor
K. Ross Strang

Subsidiaries:

Access Constructions Pty Ltd **(1)**
14 Lionel Rd Ste 8
Mount Waverley, VIC, 3149, Australia
Tel.: (61) 395442311
Fax: (61) 395442377
E-Mail: access@acpl.com.au
Web Site: www.accessconstructions.com.au
Building Construction Services
S.I.C.: 1542
N.A.I.C.S.: 236220
Tony Cariss *(Mng Dir)*

Folkestone Freeholds Pty Ltd **(1)**
Ste 8 14 Lionel Rd
Mount Waverley, VIC, 3149, Australia
Tel.: (61) 396707028
Fax: (61) 395446290
E-Mail: office@folkestone.com.au
Web Site: www.folkestone.com.au
Emp.: 5
Real Estate Property Management Services
S.I.C.: 6531
N.A.I.C.S.: 531311
Oscar Guglielmi *(Mng Dir)*

FOLKSAM OMSESIDIG LIVFORSAKRING

Bohusgatan 14
106 60 Stockholm, Sweden
Tel.: (46) 771 960 960
Fax: (46) 8 641 03 50
E-Mail: kundservice@folksam.se
Web Site: www.folksam.se
Business Description:
Insurance, Savings & Loan Services
S.I.C.: 6411
N.A.I.C.S.: 524298
Personnel:
Andreas Jerat *(Chief Press Officer)*

Subsidiary:

SalusAnsvar AB **(1)**
Tullvaktsvagen 11
Stockholm, 115 56, Sweden
Tel.: (46) 855545000
Fax: (46) 855545352
E-Mail: kundcenter@salusansvar.se
Web Site: www.salusansvar.se
Emp.: 180
Commercial Banking Services
S.I.C.: 6029
N.A.I.C.S.: 522110
Anna Karyn Laurell *(Gen Mgr)*

FOLKSTONE CAPITAL CORP.

700 - 595 Burrard Street
Vancouver, BC, V7X 1S8, Canada
Tel.: (905) 467-5564
Fax: (604) 683-5317
Year Founded: 2011
FKS.P—(TSXV)
Assets: $161,579
Liabilities: $15,797
Net Worth: $145,782
Earnings: ($59,706)
Fiscal Year-end: 02/28/13
Business Description:
Investment Holding Company
S.I.C.: 6719
N.A.I.C.S.: 551112
Personnel:
Eric O. Owens *(CEO)*
Mario Miranda *(CFO & Sec)*
Board of Directors:
Eddy Canova
Mario Miranda
Eric O. Owens
Transfer Agent:
Olympia Trust Company
Suite 1003 750 West Pender Street
Vancouver, BC, V6C 2T8, Canada

FOLLI FOLLIE S.A.

(Formerly Duty Free Shops S.A.)
(d/b/a Folli Follie Group)
23rd km Athens-Lamia Highway
145 65 Athens, Greece
Tel.: (30) 210 6241 000
Fax: (30) 210 6241 100
E-Mail: ir@follifollie.gr
Web Site: www.follifolliegroup.com
Year Founded: 1979
FFGRP—(ATH)
Rev.: $1,494,292,499
Assets: $2,444,432,045
Liabilities: $1,333,721,417
Net Worth: $1,110,710,629
Earnings: $128,720,984
Emp.: 6,063
Fiscal Year-end: 12/31/12
Business Description:
Holding Company; Duty Free Merchandise Retailer
S.I.C.: 6719
N.A.I.C.S.: 551112
Personnel:
Dimitrios Koutsolioutsos *(Chm)*
Ekaterini Koutsolioutsou *(Vice Chm)*
Georgios Koutsolioutsos *(Mng Dir)*
Emmanuel Zachariou *(Deputy Mng Dir & Gen Dir)*
Board of Directors:
Dimitrios Koutsolioutsos
Georgios Aronis
Epaminondas Dafermos
Ilias Koukoutsas
Ilias Kouloukountis
Georgios Koutsolioutsos
Ekaterini Koutsolioutsou
Zacharias Mantzavinos
Eirini Nioti
Jiannong Qian
Ioannis Tsigounakis
Anna Marina Xirokosta
Emmanuel Zachariou

Subsidiaries:

Attica Department Stores S.A. **(1)**
9 Panepistimious Street
10671 Athens, Greece
Tel.: (30) 2111802600
Fax: (30) 211 18 02 698
Web Site: www.atticadps.gr
Discount Department Stores Operation Services
S.I.C.: 5311
N.A.I.C.S.: 452112

Factory Outlet Airport S.A. **(1)**
Airport Commerce Park
190 01 Spata, East Attica, Greece
Tel.: (30) 2103541800
Fax: (30) 2103541849
E-Mail: factory-airport@follifollie.gr
Web Site: www.factory.gr
Emp.: 19,002
Discount Department Stores Operation Services
S.I.C.: 5311
N.A.I.C.S.: 452112
Miltos Galanis *(Gen Mgr)*

Factory Outlet S.A. **(1)**
Athinon Ave 76 Peiraios
185 47 Piraeus, Greece
Tel.: (30) 2104833928
Fax: (30) 2104833926
E-Mail: factory-faliro@elmec.gr
Web Site: www.factory.gr
Apparel & Accessory Stores Operation Services
S.I.C.: 5699
N.A.I.C.S.: 448150
Elias Koukoutsas *(Chm)*

Hellenic Distributions S.A. **(1)**
23rd Klm Athlnons-Lamias
145 65 Agios Stefanos, Attikis, Greece
Tel.: (30) 2106269400
Fax: (30) 2106269611
Emp.: 200
Watches & Jewelry Distr
S.I.C.: 5094
N.A.I.C.S.: 423940
Georgios Velentzas *(Mng Dir)*

Moustakis SA **(1)**
24 Ag Nikolaou St
26221 Patras, Achaea, Greece
Tel.: (30) 26 1024 3848
Fax: (30) 26 1024 3828
Department Stores Operation Services
S.I.C.: 5311
N.A.I.C.S.: 452112
Nikos Zacharatos *(Head-Fin)*

Planaco SA **(1)**
Kavouropetra
180 10 Aiyina, Piraeus, Greece
Tel.: (30) 2297029040
Fax: (30) 2297027334
E-Mail: info@planaco.gr
Web Site: www.planaco.gr
Emp.: 25
Yacht Repair & Maintenance Services
S.I.C.: 3731
N.A.I.C.S.: 336611
Stelios Tsoukalas *(Gen Mgr)*

Non-U.S. Subsidiaries:

Elmec Romania SRL **(1)**
Strada Progresului Nr 134-138 Sector Nr 5
050693 Bucharest, Romania RO
Tel.: (40) 214117086
Fax: (40) 214117087
E-Mail: office@elmecromania.ro
Web Site: www.elmecromania.ro
Emp.: 300
Sports & Fashion Articles Retailer
S.I.C.: 5091
N.A.I.C.S.: 423910
Cristian Beznoska *(CEO)*

Folli Follie Hong Kong Ltd. **(1)**
18 F The Centrium 60 Wyndham Street
Central, China (Hong Kong)
Tel.: (852) 22950028
Fax: (852) 2422 0669
E-Mail: mail@follifollie.com.hk
Web Site: www.follifollie.com.hk
Watches & Jewelry Whslr
S.I.C.: 5094
N.A.I.C.S.: 423940

Folli Follie Japan, Ltd. **(1)**
6-6-9 Roppongi Roppongi Piramide 4F
Minato-ku, Tokyo, 160-0032, Japan
Tel.: (81) 334780429
Fax: (81) 334784977
E-Mail: e-shop@follifollie.co.jp
Web Site: www.follifollie.co.jp
Watches & Jewelry Retailer
S.I.C.: 5944
N.A.I.C.S.: 448310
Dimitris Koutsolioutsos *(Pres)*

Folli Follie Korea Ltd. **(1)**
3F Sunman Building 3-20 Chungdum 2 Dong
Gannam-Gu, Seoul, Korea (South)
Tel.: (82) 25447474
E-Mail: mail@follifollie.co.kr
Web Site: www.follifollie.co.kr
Watches & Jewelery Whslr
S.I.C.: 5094
N.A.I.C.S.: 423940

Folli Follie Malaysia Ltd. **(1)**
Suite 02-02A 2nd Floor Menara Keck Seng
203 Jalan Bukit Bintang
55100 Kuala Lumpur, Malaysia MY
Tel.: (60) 323810851
Fax: (60) 3 2381 0852
Watches & Jewelry Whslr
S.I.C.: 5094
N.A.I.C.S.: 423940

Folli Follie Poland Sp. z o.o. **(1)**
Ul Konstruktorska 6
02-673 Warsaw, Poland PL
Tel.: (48) 22 6220866
Fax: (48) 22 5334245
Watches & Jewelry Whslr
S.I.C.: 5094
N.A.I.C.S.: 423940

Folli Follie Singapore Ltd. **(1)**
491B River Valley Road 14-03A Valley Point
248373 Singapore, Singapore SG
Tel.: (65) 6 737 4473
Fax: (65) 6 737 0460
Emp.: 16
Watches & Jewelry Whslr
S.I.C.: 5094
N.A.I.C.S.: 423940
Christin Chan *(Country Mgr)*

Folli Follie Spain S.A. **(1)**
C/ Velazquez 44 2a Planta
Madrid, 28001, Spain
Tel.: (34) 917810763
Fax: (34) 915783116
E-Mail: info@follifollie.es
Web Site: www.follifollie.com
Emp.: 10
Watches, Jewelry & Fashion Accessories Distr
S.I.C.: 5094
N.A.I.C.S.: 423940
Eleni Dikeli *(Mgr)*

Folli Follie Taiwan Ltd. **(1)**
15F-1 163 Keelung Road Section 1
11070 Taipei, Taiwan TW
Tel.: (886) 2 2767 5988
Fax: (886) 2 2767 0634
Watches & Jewelry Whslr
S.I.C.: 5094
N.A.I.C.S.: 423940
Wei Shen *(Gen Mgr)*

Folli Follie Thailand Ltd. **(1)**
Room 2928 Level 29 The Offices At Central World 999/9 Rama 1 Road
Pathumwan, 10330 Bangkok, Thailand TH
Tel.: (66) 2207 23 88
Emp.: 17
Watches & Jewelry Whslr
S.I.C.: 5094
N.A.I.C.S.: 423940

Folli Follie UK Ltd. **(1)**
124 Regent Street
London, W1B 5SB, United Kingdom
Tel.: (44) 2072879912
E-Mail: customercare@follifollie.co.uk
Web Site: www.follifollie.co.uk
Women Jewelry & Watches Retailer
S.I.C.: 5944
N.A.I.C.S.: 448310

Links (London) Limited **(1)**
PO Box 64619
London, SW8 9AZ, United Kingdom UK
Tel.: (44) 844 477 0909
Fax: (44) 20 7819 4151
Web Site: www.linksoflondon.com
Jewelry Mfr & Retailer
S.I.C.: 3911
N.A.I.C.S.: 339910
Elizabeth Galton *(Dir-Creative)*

Subsidiary:

Links of London (International) Ltd. **(2)**
28 Ludgate Hill
London, EC4M 7DR, United Kingdom
Tel.: (44) 20 7236 5564
Fax: (44) 20 7236 5563
Women Jewelry & Watches Distr
S.I.C.: 5094
N.A.I.C.S.: 423940

U.S. Subsidiary:

Links of London, Inc. **(2)**
535 Madison Ave
New York, NY 10022 DE
Tel.: (212) 588-0660
Emp.: 45
Watches & Jewelry Whslr
S.I.C.: 5094
N.A.I.C.S.: 423940
Clint Burns *(CFO)*

FOMENTO DE CONSTRUCCIONES Y CONTRATAS S.A.

(d/b/a FCC Group)
Federico Salmon 13
28016 Madrid, Spain
Tel.: (34) 913595400
Fax: (34) 913594923
E-Mail: ir@fcc.es
Web Site: www.fcc.es
Year Founded: 1900

FCC—(BAR MAD OTC)
Rev.: $15,012,794,767
Assets: $26,529,587,390
Liabilities: $24,212,018,425
Net Worth: $2,317,568,964
Earnings: ($1,470,276,105)
Emp.: 85,959
Fiscal Year-end: 12/31/12

Business Description:
Construction & Infrastructure Maintenance Services
S.I.C.: 1629
N.A.I.C.S.: 237990

Personnel:
Esther Alcocer Koplowitz *(Chm)*
Juan Bejar Ochoa *(Vice Chm & CEO)*
Esther Koplowitz Romero de Juseu *(First Vice Chm)*
Francisco Vicent Chulia *(Sec)*
Felipe Bernabe Garcia Perez *(Gen Sec)*

Board of Directors:
Esther Alcocer Koplowitz
Jaime Llantada Aguinaga
Alicia Alcocer Koplowitz
Carmen Alcocer Koplowitz
Gonzalo Anes y Alvarez de Castrillon
Juan Castells Masana
Esther Koplowitz Romero de Juseu
Fernando Falco y Fernandez de Cordova
Felipe Bernabe Garcia Perez
Rafael Montes Sanchez
Gonzalo Rodriguez Mourullo
Juan Bejar Ochoa
Marcelino Oreja Aguirre
Olivier Orsini
Cesar Ortega Gomez
Henri Proglio
Gustavo Villapalos Salas
Lourdes Martinez Zabala

Subsidiaries:

Aqualia Gestion Integral del Agua S.A. **(1)**
C/Ulises 18
28043 Madrid, Spain
Tel.: (34) 917036463
Fax: (34) 917036496
E-Mail: fmorenog@fcc.es
Web Site: www.aqualia.es
Emp.: 300
Water Utilities Management
S.I.C.: 9511
N.A.I.C.S.: 924110
Fernando Moreno Garcia *(Gen Mgr)*

Cementos Portland Valderrivas, S.A. **(1)**
Calle Estella 6
31002 Pamplona, Spain (69.59%)
Tel.: (34) 948426200
Fax: (34) 948426210
E-Mail: info@valderrivas.es
Web Site: www.valderrivas.es
CPLN—(MAD)
Sales Range: $1-4.9 Billion
Emp.: 3,587
Cement & Concrete Producer
S.I.C.: 3241
N.A.I.C.S.: 327310
Jose Ignacio Martinez Ynzinga Canovas Del Castillo *(Chm)*
Jose Luis Saenz de Miera *(Pres & CEO)*

U.S. Subsidiaries:

CDN-USA, Inc. **(2)**
34 Atlantic Pl
South Portland, ME 04106 (100%)
Tel.: (207) 774-6355
Fax: (207) 761-5694
E-Mail: info@dragonproducts.com
Emp.: 240
Concrete & Cement
Import Export
S.I.C.: 3273
N.A.I.C.S.: 327320

Giant Cement Holding, Inc. **(2)**
320 Midland Pkwy Ste D
Summerville, SC 29485 DE
Tel.: (843) 851-9898 (100%)
Fax: (843) 851-9881
Toll Free: (800) 845-1174
Web Site: www.gchi.com
Emp.: 800
Holding Company
S.I.C.: 3241
N.A.I.C.S.: 327310
Javier Martinez *(CFO)*

Subsidiaries:

Dragon Products Company **(3)**
38 Preble St
Portland, ME 04101 (100%)
Tel.: (207) 774-6355
Fax: (207) 761-5694
Web Site: www.dragonproducts.com
Emp.: 230
Cement Mfr
Import Export
S.I.C.: 3241
N.A.I.C.S.: 327310
Patrick Doody *(VP-Sls & Mktg)*

Branch:

Coastal Cement Corporation **(4)**
36 Drydock Ave
Boston, MA 02210
Tel.: (617) 350-0183
Fax: (617) 350-1869
E-Mail: info@dragonproducts.com
Web Site: www.dragonproducts.com
Sls.: $350,000
Emp.: 3
Cement
Import Export
S.I.C.: 3241
N.A.I.C.S.: 327310

Giant Cement Company **(3)**
320 D Midland Pkwy
Summerville, SC 29485 DE
Tel.: (843) 851-9898
Fax: (843) 581-9881
Toll Free: (800) 845-1174
Web Site: www.gchi.com
Emp.: 225
Cement Mfr
S.I.C.: 3241
N.A.I.C.S.: 327310

Giant Resource Recovery Company **(3)**
PO Box 352
Harleyville, SC 29448 DE
Tel.: (803) 496-2200
Fax: (803) 496-2228
Toll Free: (800) 746-0477
E-Mail: info@grr-giant.com
Web Site: www.grr-giant.com
Emp.: 47
Environmental Services
S.I.C.: 8999
N.A.I.C.S.: 541620

Keystone Cement Company **(3)**
557 W Uwchlan Ave Ste 230
Exton, PA 19341 PA
Mailing Address:
PO Box A
Bath, PA 18014-0058
Tel.: (610) 903-0382
Web Site: www.keystone-cement.com
Emp.: 175
Cement Mfr
S.I.C.: 3241
N.A.I.C.S.: 327310

Branch:

Keystone Cement Company **(4)**
Rte 329
Bath, PA 18014
Mailing Address:
PO Box A
Bath, PA 18014
Tel.: (610) 837-1881
Fax: (610) 837-2267
E-Mail:
Web Site: www.keystone-cement.com
Emp.: 200
Cement Mfr
S.I.C.: 3241
N.A.I.C.S.: 327310
Steve Hayden *(Plant Mgr)*

U.S. Subsidiary:

FCC Environmental LLC **(1)**
523 N Sam Houston Pkwy
Houston, TX 77060
Tel.: (281) 668-3300
Fax: (281) 668-3301
Web Site: www.fccenvironmental.com
Sales Range: $125-149.9 Million
Emp.: 530
Industrial Waste Disposal & Recycling Services
S.I.C.: 4953
N.A.I.C.S.: 562211

Units:

FCC Environmental LLC - Baltimore **(2)**
6305 E Lombard St
Baltimore, MD 21224-1734 (100%)
Tel.: (410) 633-0606
Fax: (410) 633-0789
Sales Range: $50-74.9 Million
Emp.: 50
Industrial Waste Disposal & Recycling Services
S.I.C.: 4953
N.A.I.C.S.: 562211
Ken Cherry *(Pres)*

FCC Environmental LLC - Pompano Beach **(2)**
1280 Ne 48th St
Pompano Beach, FL 33064
Tel.: (954) 785-2320
Emp.: 50
Industrial Waste Disposal & Recycling Services
S.I.C.: 4953
N.A.I.C.S.: 562211
Kenneth Cherry *(VP)*

FCC Environmental LLC - Wilmington **(2)**
505 S Market St
Wilmington, DE 19801-5208 (100%)
Tel.: (302) 421-9306
Fax: (302) 421-9099
Sales Range: $25-49.9 Million
Emp.: 50
Industrial Waste Disposal & Recycling Services
S.I.C.: 4953
N.A.I.C.S.: 562211

Non-U.S. Subsidiaries:

.A.S.A. Abfall Service AG **(1)**
Hans-Hruschka-Gasse 9
A-2325 Himberg, Austria AT
Tel.: (43) 22358550 (100%)
Fax: (43) 2235855101
E-Mail: asa@asa.at
Web Site: www.asa-group.com
Sales Range: $350-399.9 Million
Emp.: 700
Municipal, Industrial, Commercial & Retail Waste Management
S.I.C.: 9511
N.A.I.C.S.: 924110
Petr Vokral *(CEO)*

Subsidiary:

.A.S.A. International Environmental Services GmbH **(2)**
Hans-Hruschka-Gasse 9
2325 Himberg, Austria
Tel.: (43) 2235855615
Fax: (43) 6766266163
E-Mail: asa@asa.at
Web Site: www.asagroup.com
Emp.: 60
Waste Management Services
S.I.C.: 9511
N.A.I.C.S.: 924110
Peter Vokral *(Mng Dir)*

Subsidiaries:

Abfallwirtschaftszentrum Mostviertel GmbH **(3)**
Sudlandstrasse 3
A-3300 Amstetten, Austria AT
Tel.: (43) 747263083 (100%)
Fax: (43) 7472630836
E-Mail: amst@asa.at
Web Site: www.asa.at
Emp.: 34
Waste Management Services
S.I.C.: 4959
N.A.I.C.S.: 562998
Max Schmidhofer *(Plant Mgr)*

.A.S.A. Abfall Service Halbenrain GmbH **(3)**
Hans-Hruschka-Gasse 9
A-2325 Himberg, Austria AT
Tel.: (43) 22358550 (100%)
Fax: (43) 2235855101
E-Mail: asa@asa.at
Web Site: www.asa-group.com
Emp.: 600
Waste Management Services
S.I.C.: 9511
N.A.I.C.S.: 924110
Peter Vokral *(Gen Mgr)*

.A.S.A. Abfall Service Neunkirchen GmbH **(3)**
Schloglmuhl 5 Gloggnitz
A-2640 Neunkirchen, Austria AT
Tel.: (43) 266245230 (100%)
Fax: (43) 2662452303
E-Mail: neunkirchen@asa.at
Web Site: www.asa.at
Emp.: 22
Waste Management Services
S.I.C.: 4959
N.A.I.C.S.: 562998
Walter Pratscher *(Mgr)*

.A.S.A. Abfall Service Wiener Neustadt GmbH **(3)**
Neunkirchner Strasse 119
A-2700 Wiener Neustadt, Austria AT
Tel.: (43) 2622872150 (100%)
Fax: (43) 26228721533
E-Mail: wrn@asa.at
Web Site: www.asa.at
Emp.: 12
Hazardous Waste Disposal Services
S.I.C.: 4212
N.A.I.C.S.: 562112
Johann Handler *(Plant Mgr)*

Entsorga Entsorgungs GmbH Nfg KG **(3)**
Hohenbergenstrasse 41
A-9121 Volkermarkt, Austria AT
Tel.: (43) 423241160 (100%)
Fax: (43) 423241166
E-Mail: ent@asa.at
Web Site: www.asa.at
Emp.: 11
Landfill Management
S.I.C.: 4953
N.A.I.C.S.: 562212
Gottfried Drobesch *(Plant Mgr)*

Non-U.S. Subsidiary:

.A.S.A. Areal spol. s.r.o **(3)**
Dablicka 791/89
182 00 Prague, 8, Czech Republic
Tel.: (420) 283061301
Fax: (420) 283911110
Emp.: 80
Waste Management Services
S.I.C.: 9511
N.A.I.C.S.: 924110

FCC Environment (UK) Limited **(1)**
Ground Floor West 900 Pavilion Dive
Northampton Business Park, Northampton, NN4 7RG, United Kingdom UK
Tel.: (44) 1604 826 200 (100%)
Fax: (44) 1604 826 201
Web Site: www.fccenvironment.co.uk
Emp.: 2,400
Waste Collection, Management & Recycling Services
S.I.C.: 4959
N.A.I.C.S.: 562998
Mike Snell *(Gen Mgr-External Affairs)*

Subsidiaries:

FCC Recycling (UK) Limited **(2)**
Ground Floor West 900 Pavilion Drive
Northampton Business Park, Northampton, NN4 7RG, United Kingdom UK
Tel.: (44) 1604 826 200 (100%)
Fax: (44) 1604 826 201
E-Mail:
Web Site: www.fccenvironment.co.uk/recycling.html
Recycling Services
S.I.C.: 4953
N.A.I.C.S.: 562920

FCC Waste Services (UK) Limited **(2)**
Ground Floor West 900 Pavilion Drive
Northampton Business Park, Northampton,

Fomento de Construcciones y Contratas S.A.—(Continued)

NN4 7RG, United Kingdom UK
Tel.: (44) 1604 826 200 (100%)
Fax: (44) 1604 826 201
E-Mail:
Web Site: www.fccenvironment.co.uk/waste-processing.html
Emp.: 150
Waste Processing & Disposal Services
S.I.C.: 4959
N.A.I.C.S.: 562998

Joint Ventures:

Mercia Waste Management Ltd. **(2)**
The Marina Kings Road
Evesham, Worcestershire, WR11 3XZ, United Kingdom UK
Tel.: (44) 1386 861 434
Fax: (44) 1386 861 556
E-Mail: enquiries@severnwaste.co.uk
Web Site: www.severnwaste.com
Emp.: 100
Waste Management Services
S.I.C.: 9511
N.A.I.C.S.: 924110

Severn Waste Services Limited **(2)**
The Marina Kings Road
Evesham, Worcs, WR11 3XZ, United Kingdom UK
Tel.: (44) 1386 443 376
Fax: (44) 1386 446 757
E-Mail: enquiries@severnwaste.co.uk
Web Site: www.severnwaste.com
Emp.: 12
Solid Waster Management Services
S.I.C.: 9511
N.A.I.C.S.: 924110
Jim Haywood *(Dir-Fin)*

FOMENTO ECONOMICO MEXICANO, S.A. DE C.V.

(d/b/a FEMSA)
General Anaya 601 No Pte
Colonia Bella Vista, Monterrey, NL, 64410, Mexico
Tel.: (52) 81 83286167
Fax: (52) 81 8328 6080
E-Mail: investor@femsa.com.mx
Web Site: www.femsa.com
Year Founded: 1986
FMX—(MEX NYSE)
Rev.: $18,750,152,120
Assets: $23,284,716,560
Liabilities: $6,749,249,080
Net Worth: $16,535,467,480
Earnings: $2,207,052,680
Emp.: 182,260
Fiscal Year-end: 12/31/12

Business Description:
Beverage Mfg Services
S.I.C.: 2086
N.A.I.C.S.: 312111

Personnel:
Jose Antonio Carbajal Fernandez *(Chm)*
Carlos Salazar Lomelin *(CEO)*
John Anthony Santa Maria Otazua *(CEO-Coca-Cola FEMSA)*
Eduardo Padilla Silva *(CEO-FEMSA Comercio)*
Alfonso Garza Garza *(Exec VP-Strategic Bus)*

Board of Directors:
Jose Antonio Carbajal Fernandez
Alberto Bailleres
Alfredo Livas Cantu
Consuelo Garza De Garza
Mariana Garza Laguera de Treviho Gonda
Robert E. Denham
Barbara Garza Laguera Gonda
Eva Maria Garza Laguera Gonda
Jose Manuel Canal Hernando
Helmut Paul
Jose Fernando Calderon Rojas
Armando Garza Sada
Roberto Servitje Sendra
Max Michel Suberville
Ricardo Guajardo Touchec
Lorenzo H. Zambrano Trevino

Subsidiaries:

FEMSA Comercio, S.A. de C.V. **(1)**
Gen Anaya 601 Pte
Colonia Bella Vista, Monterrey, NL, 64410, Mexico MX
Tel.: (52) 8183286000
Fax: (52) 8183286080
Web Site: www.femsa.com
Emp.: 7,806
Convenience Stores Operator
S.I.C.: 5411
N.A.I.C.S.: 445120

FEMSA Empaque, S.A. de C.V. **(1)**
General Anaya 601 Pte Col Bella Vista
PO Box 953
Monterrey, NL, 64410, Mexico MX
Tel.: (52) 8183286600 (99%)
Fax: (52) 8183286299
Web Site: www.femsa-empaque.com.mx
Sls.: $400,000,000
Emp.: 4,220
Production of Cans, Bottles & Crown Caps for Food Industry
S.I.C.: 3411
N.A.I.C.S.: 332431
Alfonso Garza Garza *(Gen Dir)*

Holding:

Coca-Cola FEMSA, S.A.B. de C.V. **(1)**
Calle Mario Pani No 100 Santa Fe Cuajimalpa
05348 Mexico, DF, Mexico MX
Tel.: (52) 55 5081 5100
Fax: (52) 55 5292 3473
E-Mail: krelations@kof.com.mx
Web Site: www.coca-colafemsa.com
KOF—(MEX NYSE)
Sls.: $11,624,104,520
Assets: $13,068,984,040
Liabilities: $4,821,117,000
Net Worth: $8,247,867,040
Earnings: $1,093,494,640
Emp.: 73,395
Fiscal Year-end: 12/31/12
Holding Company; Soft Drinks Bottler & Distr
S.I.C.: 6719
N.A.I.C.S.: 551112
Jose Antonio Fernandez Carbajal *(Chm)*
Irial Finan *(Pres)*
Carlos Salazar Lomelin *(CEO)*
Hector Trevino Gutierrez *(CFO & Chief Admin Officer)*
Ernesto Silva Almaguer *(COO-Mexico & Central America)*
Eulalio Cerda Delgadillo *(Officer-HR)*
Rafael Suarez Olaguibel *(Officer-Special Projects)*

Joint Venture:

Jugos del Valle, S.A.B. de C.V. **(2)**
Avenida Ejercito Nacional 904 Piso 15
Col Palmas Polanco Seccion Miguel Hidalgo, CP 11560 Mexico, DF, Mexico
Tel.: (52) 55 25816500
Fax: (52) 55 25816125
E-Mail: expotaciones@jvalle.com.mx
Web Site: www.jvalle.com.mx
VALLE—(MEX)
Sales Range: $650-699.9 Million
Juices & Fruit Beverages Mfr; Owned 50% by The Coca-Cola Company & 50% by Coca-Cola FEMSA, S.A.B. de C.V.
S.I.C.: 2037
N.A.I.C.S.: 311411
Roberto Albarran *(Pres)*

U.S. Subsidiary:

Jugos del Valle Distribution **(3)**
6633 Portwest Dr Ste 100
Houston, TX 77027
Tel.: (713) 622-2203
Fax: (713) 622-2620
Toll Free: (888) 349-2234
Web Site: www.vallenectars.com
Sales Range: $10-24.9 Million
Emp.: 20
Juices & Fruit Beverages Mfr
S.I.C.: 2037
N.A.I.C.S.: 311411
Raul Legorreta *(Dir-Sls)*

FOMENTO RESORTS & HOTELS LTD

Cidade de Goa Vainguinim Beach
Goa, 403004, India
Tel.: (91) 832 2454545
Fax: (91) 832 2454540
E-Mail: cidadedegoa@cidadedegoa.com
Web Site: www.cidadedegoa.com
503831—(BOM)
Rev.: $9,175,446
Assets: $17,449,032
Liabilities: $6,663,443
Net Worth: $10,785,589
Earnings: $1,556,989
Fiscal Year-end: 03/31/13

Business Description:
Hotel Management Services
S.I.C.: 7011
N.A.I.C.S.: 721110

Personnel:
Anju Timblo *(Mng Dir)*
Asmeeta Matondkar *(Sec)*

Board of Directors:
Jamshed Delvadavala
P. G. Kakodkar
Raghunandan Maluste
Reyaz Mama
V. P. Raikar
Shardul Thacker
Anju Timblo
Auduth Timblo

Transfer Agent:
Bigshare Services Private Limited
E/2 Ansa Industrial Estate Sakivihar Road
Sakinaka Andheri - East
Mumbai, India

FONCIERE ATLAND SA

10 avenue George V
75008 Paris, France
Tel.: (33) 140722020
Fax: (33) 140722021
E-Mail: info@fonciere-atland.fr
Web Site: www.fonciere-atland.fr
FATL—(EUR)
Sales Range: $10-24.9 Million
Emp.: 3

Business Description:
Real Estate Development & Investment Services
S.I.C.: 6531
N.A.I.C.S.: 531390

Personnel:
Georges Rocchietta *(Chm & CEO)*
Edouard Lacoste *(Chief Investment Officer)*
Christian Vallaud *(Chief Dev Officer)*

Board of Directors:
Pierre Adier
Jean-Louis Charon
Lionel Vedie de la Hesliere
Jacques Larretche
Herve Lorthiois

Subsidiaries:

SARL FONCIERE ATLAND REIM **(1)**
10 Ave George V
75008 Paris, France
Tel.: (33) 140722020
Fax: (33) 140722021
Emp.: 27
Real Estate Property Management Services
S.I.C.: 6531
N.A.I.C.S.: 531390
Georges Rocchietta *(Gen Mgr)*

SNC FONCIERE ATLAND VALORISATION **(1)**
10 Ave George V
75008 Paris, France
Tel.: (33) 140722020
Fax: (33) 140722021
E-Mail: nt@atland.sa
Web Site: www.atland.sa
Emp.: 27
Real Estate Leasing Services
S.I.C.: 6531
N.A.I.C.S.: 531390
George Rocchietta *(Pres)*

FONCIERE DES 6E ET 7E ARRONDISSEMENTS DE PARIS

41-43 rue Saint Dominique
75007 Paris, France
Tel.: (33) 1 53 70 77 77
Fax: (33) 1 53 70 77 78
E-Mail: investisseursfprg@fprg.fr
Web Site: www.fprg.fr
Year Founded: 2005
SRG—(EUR)
Rev.: $37,644,298
Assets: $1,120,025,556
Liabilities: $539,217,817
Net Worth: $580,807,739
Earnings: $23,277,972
Fiscal Year-end: 12/31/12

Business Description:
Investment Management Services
S.I.C.: 6282
N.A.I.C.S.: 523920

Personnel:
Francois Thomazeau *(Chm)*
Arnaud Pomel *(Mng Dir)*
Alain Le Veel *(COO & Deputy Mng Dir)*
Guy de Soucy *(Deputy Mng Dir)*
Olivier Riche *(Deputy Mng Dir)*

Board of Directors:
Francois Thomazeau
Sophie Beuvaden
Philippe Blavier
Michel Dufief
Peter Etzenbach
Luc Guinefort
Olivier Le Borgne
Alain Le Veel
Pierre Reichert
Olivier Riche
Jean-Marie Soubrier
Olivier Wigniolle

Mazars
61 rue Henri Regnault
Courbevoie, France

FONCIERE DES REGIONS S.A.

30 Avenue Kleber
75208 Paris, France
Tel.: (33) 158975000
Fax: (33) 821202375
E-Mail: communication@fdr.fr
Web Site: www.foncieredesregions.fr
FDR—(EUR)
Rev.: $1,025,863,656
Assets: $19,003,553,425
Liabilities: $10,843,547,429
Net Worth: $8,160,005,996
Earnings: $79,271,913
Emp.: 327
Fiscal Year-end: 12/31/12

Business Description:
Residential & Commercial Real Estate Investment Services
S.I.C.: 6531
N.A.I.C.S.: 531390

Personnel:
Jean Laurent *(Chm)*
Leonardo Del Vecchio *(Vice Chm)*
Christophe Kullmann *(CEO)*
Stefano Vittori *(Dir-HR, Legal & Corp Affairs)*
Yves Marque *(Gen Sec)*

Board of Directors:
Jean Laurent
Romolo Bardin
Catherine Allonas Barthe
Jean-Luc Biamonti

Lionel Calvez
Bertrand de Feydeau
Leonardo Del Vecchio
Sergio Erede
Jerome Grivet
Christophe Kullmann
Micaela Le Divelec
Sylvie Ouziel
Pierre Vaquier

Cabinet Mazars
Tour Exaltis 61 rue Henri Regnault
92400 Courbevoie, France

Subsidiaries:

Beni Stabili S.p.A SIIQ (1)
Via Piemonte 38
00187 Rome, Italy IT
Tel.: (39) 06362221 (51%)
Fax: (39) 0636222364
E-Mail: info@benistabili.it
Web Site: www.benistabili.it
BNS—(EUR ITA)
Rev.: $307,634,845
Assets: $6,119,255,353
Liabilities: $3,591,317,710
Net Worth: $2,527,937,643
Earnings: ($18,920,419)
Emp.: 94
Fiscal Year-end: 12/31/12
Residential & Commercial Real Estate Investment Services
S.I.C.: 6531
N.A.I.C.S.: 531390
Enrico Laghi *(Chm)*
Aldo Mazzocco *(CEO & Mng Dir)*
Luca Lucaroni *(CFO)*
Stefano Vittori *(COO)*
Massimo Cavallo *(Sec)*

Subsidiaries:

Beni Stabili Gestioni SpA SGR (2)
Via Borgazzi 27
20052 Monza, Italy (75%)
Tel.: (39) 039 2396359
Real Estate Fund Management
S.I.C.: 6531
N.A.I.C.S.: 531390

Fonciere des Murs SCA (1)
30 avenue Kleber
75208 Paris, Cedex 16, France
Tel.: (33) 1 58 97 50 00
Fax: (33) 8 21 20 02 75
E-Mail: contactfoncieredesmurs@fdr.fr
Web Site: www.foncieredesmurs.fr
FMU—(EUR)
Real Estate Development Services
S.I.C.: 6531
N.A.I.C.S.: 531390
Christophe Kullmann *(Chm-Supervisory Bd)*

Parcs GFR (1)
1 avenue Ney
57000 Metz, France
Tel.: (33) 387377790
Fax: (33) 821200657
Web Site: www.geatipark.com
Emp.: 200
Car Parking Facilities
S.I.C.: 7521
N.A.I.C.S.: 812930
Helin Frederick *(Dir)*

Urbis Park SAS (1)
13 rue du Coetlosquet
Metz, Moselle, 57000, France
Tel.: (33) 387393220
E-Mail: infos@urbispark.fr
Web Site: www.urbispark.fr
Parking Management Services
S.I.C.: 7521
N.A.I.C.S.: 812930

FONCIERE PARIS FRANCE SA

52 rue de la Bienfaisance
75008 Paris, France
Tel.: (33) 143123900
Fax: (33) 143123888
E-Mail: info@sfpif.com
Web Site: www.sfpif.com
FPF—(EUR)
Sales Range: $25-49.9 Million
Business Description:
Real Estate Investment Trust
S.I.C.: 6726
N.A.I.C.S.: 525990
Personnel:
Jean-Paul Dumortier *(Chm & CEO)*
Patrick Beghin *(Mng Dir)*
Didier Brethes *(Mng Dir)*
Bruno Kahan *(Deputy Mng Dir)*
Board of Directors:
Jean-Paul Dumortier
Serge Bayard
Didier Brethes
Evelyn Chow
Constance de Poncins
Francoise Debrus
Pieter Haasbroek
Tinka Kleine
Bernard Maillet
Barthelemy Raynaud

Deloitte & Associes
185 avenue Charles-de-Gaulle
Neuilly-sur-Seine, France

FONCIERE SEPRIC S.A.

(Acquired by Patrimoine et Commerce)

FONDATIONS CAPITAL SA

5 rue Guillaume Kroll
L-1882 Luxembourg, Luxembourg
Tel.: (352) 48 18 28 1
Fax: (352) 48 18 63
E-Mail: contact@fondcap.com
Web Site: www.fondationscapital.com
Year Founded: 2007
Business Description:
Private Equity Firm
S.I.C.: 6211
N.A.I.C.S.: 523999
Personnel:
Xavier Marin *(Co-Founder & Partner)*
Philippe Renauld *(Co-Founder & Partner)*

Non-U.S. Subsidiary:

Fondations Capital Services France SA (1)
24-32 rue Jean Goujon
75008 Paris, France
Tel.: (33) 1 55 35 55 00
Fax: (33) 1 55 35 55 29
E-Mail: contact@fondcap.com
Web Site: www.fondationscapital.com
Private Equity Firm
S.I.C.: 6211
N.A.I.C.S.: 523999
Xavier Marin, *(Mng Partner)*
Philippe Renauld *(Partner)*
Erwan Le Tanneur *(Mng Dir)*

Holdings:

Alkern SAS (2)
ZI Parc de la Motte au Bois
BP 59
Rue Andre Bigotte, 62440 Harnes, France
Tel.: (33) 3 21 79 34 30
Fax: (33) 3 21 43 40 73
Web Site: www.alkern.fr
Sales Range: $200-249.9 Million
Emp.: 803
Concrete Products Mfr
S.I.C.: 3272
N.A.I.C.S.: 327390
Denis Sicard *(CEO)*

Subsidiaries:

Beton 06 SA (3)
Route de Levens
06730 Saint-Andre-de-la-Roche, France
Tel.: (33) 4 93 27 70 70
Fax: (33) 4 93 27 70 79
Web Site: www.beton06.com
Sales Range: $1-9.9 Million
Emp.: 30
Concrete Block Mfr
S.I.C.: 3271
N.A.I.C.S.: 327331
Ghislaine Auge *(Gen Mgr)*

Novadal Privat SAS (3)
6 Blvd de l'Industrie
85170 Belleville-sur-Vie, France FR
Tel.: (33) 2 51 41 06 00 (100%)
Fax: (33) 2 51 41 21 96
Web Site: www.novadal.fr
Sales Range: $1-9.9 Million
Emp.: 53
Brick & Clay Tile Mfr
S.I.C.: 3271
N.A.I.C.S.: 327331
Xavier Privat, *(Mng Dir)*

Buffet Crampon Holdings SAS (2)
5 rue Maurice Berteaux
78711 Mantes-la-Ville, France FR
Tel.: (33) 1 3098 5130
Fax: (33) 134787902
E-Mail: corporate@buffet-group.com
Web Site: www.buffet-group.com
Emp.: 300
Holding Company; Musical Instrument Mfr & Distr
S.I.C.: 6719
N.A.I.C.S.: 551112
Antoine Beaussant *(CEO)*
Geoffrey Soler *(CFO)*

Subsidiary:

Buffet Crampon S.A.S. (3)
5 rue Maurice Berteaux
F-78711 Mantes-la-Ville, France FR
Tel.: (33) 130985130
Fax: (33) 134787902
E-Mail: info@buffet-group.com
Web Site: www.buffet-crampon.com
Musical Instruments Mfr & Distr
S.I.C.: 3931
N.A.I.C.S.: 339992
Antoine Beaussant *(CEO)*

U.S. Subsidiary:

Buffet Group USA, Inc. (3)
14125 Beach Blvd
Jacksonville, FL 32250 DE
Tel.: (904) 821-0234
Fax: (904) 821-0315
E-Mail: marketing-usa@buffet-group.com
Web Site: www.buffet-crampon.com
Musical Instrument Whslr
S.I.C.: 5099
N.A.I.C.S.: 423990
Francois Kloc *(Pres & CEO)*

Non-U.S. Subsidiary:

Buffet Group Germany GmbH (3)
Gewerbepark 52
08258 Markneukirchen, Germany
Tel.: (49) 37422 40793
E-Mail:
Web Site: www.buffet-group.com
Emp.: 134
Musical Instruments Mfr & Sales
S.I.C.: 3931
N.A.I.C.S.: 339992
Antoine Beaussant *(CEO)*

FONDERIE GIROUD INDUSTRIE SAS

R N 90
PO Box 39
38530 Barraux, France
Tel.: (33) 476971236
Fax: (33) 476971231
E-Mail: info@giroudfonderie.com
Web Site: www.giroudfonderie.com
Sales Range: $1-9.9 Million
Emp.: 70
Fiscal Year-end: 12/31/12
Business Description:
Industry Castings Mfr
S.I.C.: 3322
N.A.I.C.S.: 331511
Personnel:
Patrick Collin *(CEO)*

FONDIARIA-SAI S.P.A.

Piazza della Liberta 6
I 50129 Florence, Italy
Tel.: (39) 05547941
Telex: 570430
Fax: (39) 055476026
E-Mail: info@fondiaria-sai.it
Web Site: www.fondiaria-sai.it
Year Founded: 1879
SA—(ITA)
Sales Range: $5-14.9 Billion
Emp.: 2,668
Business Description:
General Insurance, Real Estate Investment & Financial Services
S.I.C.: 6411
N.A.I.C.S.: 524298
Personnel:
Jonella Ligresti *(Chm)*
Giulia Maria Ligresti *(Vice Chm)*
Massimo Pini *(Vice Chm)*
Antonio Talarico *(Vice Chm)*
Fausto Marchionni *(CEO & Gen Mgr)*
Alberto Marras *(Sec)*
Board of Directors:
Jonella Ligresti
Andrea Broggini
Mariella Cerutti Marocco
Maurizio Comoli
Francesco Corsi
Carlo d'Urso
Vincenzo La Russa
Gioacchino Paolo Ligresti
Giulia Maria Ligresti
Salvatore Ligresti
Lia Lo Vecchio
Fausto Marchionni
Alberto Marras
Enzo Mei
Giuseppe Morbidelli
Massimo Pini
Cosimo Rucellai
Salvatore Spiniello
Antonio Talarico
Ezio Toselli
Oscar Zannoni

Subsidiaries:

Banca SAI (1)
Corso Vittorio Emanuele
Turin, Italy
Tel.: (39) 0116915111
Fax: (39) 01169148248
Web Site: www.bancasai.it
Commercial Bank
S.I.C.: 6029
N.A.I.C.S.: 522110

Milano Assicurazioni S.p.A. (1)
Via Senigallia n 18-2
20161 Milan, Italy (58.4%)
Tel.: (39) 02 64021
Fax: (39) 02 6402 5389
E-Mail: milass@milass.it
Web Site: www.milass.it
MI—(ITA)
Insurance Services
S.I.C.: 6411
N.A.I.C.S.: 524298
Fausto Marchionni *(Chm & Mng Dir)*
Gioacchino Paolo Ligresti *(Vice Chm)*
Alberto Marras *(Sec)*

SAI Investimenti SGR S.p.A. (1)
Via Carlo Marenco 25
10126 Turin, Italy
Tel.: (39) 0116657111
Fax: (39) 0116657865
Web Site: www.saiinvestimenti.it
Investment Management
S.I.C.: 6211
N.A.I.C.S.: 523999

SAI Mercati Mobiliari (1)
Via Senigalia 18/2
20161 Milan, Italy
Tel.: (39) 0264021
Fax: (39) 0264026740
Web Site: www.saisim.it
Real Estate Services
S.I.C.: 6531
N.A.I.C.S.: 531390

Non-U.S. Subsidiary:

Banca Gesfid SA (1)
Via Adamini 10 A
CH-6900 Lugano, Switzerland
Tel.: (41) 919857400
Fax: (41) 919930970
E-Mail: info@bancagesfid.com
Web Site: www.bancagesfid.com

Fondiaria-SAI S.p.A.—(Continued)

Emp.: 75
Banking Services
S.I.C.: 6029
N.A.I.C.S.: 522110
Antonio Saladino *(Chm)*
Fabio Testori *(Co-Chm)*

FONDINVEST CAPITAL

33 rue de la Baume
75008 Paris, France
Tel.: (33) 158364800
Fax: (33) 158364828
E-Mail: mailbox@fondinvest.com
Web Site: www.fondinvest.com
Year Founded: 1994
Managed Assets: $2,642,780,000
Emp.: 17

Business Description:
Private Equity Funds Management Services
S.I.C.: 6282
N.A.I.C.S.: 523920

Personnel:
Charles Soulignac *(Chm & CEO)*
Catherine Lewis *(Mng Dir)*
Emmanuel Roubinowitz *(Mng Dir)*
Martin Delahaye *(COO)*

Board of Directors:
Charles Soulignac

FONDO DE VALORES INMOBILIARIOS S.A.C.A.

Av Venezuela Building Torre El Saman Urbanization El Rosal
1060 Caracas, Venezuela
Tel.: (58) 2129059011
Fax: (58) 2129059078
E-Mail: infofvi@fvi.com.ve
Web Site: www.fvi.com.ve
FVI.A—(CAR)
Sales Range: $25-49.9 Million

Business Description:
Real Estate Investment Services
S.I.C.: 6726
N.A.I.C.S.: 525990

Personnel:
Luis Emilio Velutini *(Pres & CEO)*
Alejandro Petit Mena *(CFO)*
Horacio J. Velutini Sosa *(COO)*

FONDS DE SOLIDARITE DES TRAVAILLEURS DU QUEBEC

548 Cremazie Boulevard East Suite 200
Montreal, QC, H2M 2W4, Canada
Tel.: (514) 383-8383
Fax: (514) 850-4888
E-Mail: comm@fondsftq.com
Web Site: www.fondsftq.com
Year Founded: 1983
Rev.: $254,366,736
Assets: $10,372,562,915
Liabilities: $1,126,884,689
Net Worth: $9,245,678,226
Earnings: $455,149,830
Emp.: 460
Fiscal Year-end: 05/31/13

Business Description:
Economic Development Services
S.I.C.: 9611
N.A.I.C.S.: 926110

Personnel:
Michel Arsenault *(Chm)*
Pierre-Maurice Vachon *(Vice Chm)*
Yvon Bolduc *(Pres & CEO)*
Daniel Boyer *(Sec)*
Denis Leclerc *(Exec VP-Shareholder Svcs)*
Gaetan Morin *(Exec VP-Corp Dev & Investments)*
Michel Pontbriand *(Exec VP-Fin)*
Janie C. Beique *(Sr VP New Economy)*
Jacques Bernier *(Sr VP-IT, Telecom & Indus Innovations)*
Normand Chouinard *(Sr VP-Natural Resources, Indus & Consumer Goods)*
Jean Wilhelmy *(Sr VP-Aerospace, Construction, Svcs & Transportation)*

Board of Directors:
Michel Arsenault
Christine Beaubien
Louis Bolduc
Yvon Bolduc
Gerry Boutin
Daniel Boyer
Serge Cadieux
Louise Chabot
Michele Colpron
Denis Labreche
Lucie Levasseur
Jean-Pierre Ouellet
Yves Ouellet
Michel Ouimet
Magali Picard
Daniel Roy
Pierre-Maurice Vachon

Deloitte & Touche s.e.n.c.r.l.
1 Place Ville Marie Suite 3000
Montreal, QC, Canada

Holdings:

ACCEO Solutions, Inc. (1)
(Formerly GFI Solutions Group Inc.)
Multimedia City
75 Queen St Ste 6100, Montreal, QC, H3C 2N6, Canada
Tel.: (514) 288-7161
Fax: (514) 868-5334
Toll Free: (800) 471-7161
E-Mail:
Web Site: www.acceo.com
Sales Range: $100-124.9 Million
Emp.: 1,000
Business Information Technology Services
S.I.C.: 5045
N.A.I.C.S.: 423430
Gilles Letourneau *(Pres & CEO)*
Catherine Allard *(Exec VP & CFO)*
Andre Goyer *(Chief Legal Officer & Exec VP)*
Benoit Guilbault *(Sr VP & CTO)*
Alain Philippe *(VP-Payment Sys)*
Marie-Carmen Velasco *(Exec VP)*

Subsidiaries:

ACCEO Solutions, Inc. - Quebec (2)
7710 Wilfrid-Hamel Blvd
Quebec, QC, G2G 2J5, Canada QC
Tel.: (418) 877-6578
Fax: (418) 877-9994
Toll Free: (800) 552-9622
Emp.: 250
Business Information Technology Services
S.I.C.: 5045
N.A.I.C.S.: 423430
Denis Carrier *(VP)*

Accovia Inc. (2)
75 Queen St Ste 5100
Montreal, QC, H3C 2N6, Canada
Tel.: (514) 931-4433
Fax: (514) 931-4818
E-Mail: travelfurther@accovia.com
Web Site: www.accovia.com
Travel Package Management Software Publisher
S.I.C.: 7372
N.A.I.C.S.: 511210
Gilles Letourneau *(Pres)*
Alain Leveille *(VP & COO)*

Non-U.S. Subsidiary:

Accovia France S.A.R.L. (3)
5 Pl du Colonel Fabien
75010 Paris, France
Tel.: (33) 144528484
Fax: (33) 144528485
Web Site: www.accovia.fr
Travel Package Management Software Publisher
S.I.C.: 7372
N.A.I.C.S.: 511210
Patrick Bleu *(Mng Dir)*

ProfitMaster Canada Inc. (2)
300-135 Innovation Dr
Winnipeg, MB, R3T 6A8, Canada
Tel.: (204) 889-5320
Fax: (204) 885-6485
Toll Free: (800) 340-4492
E-Mail: support@pmcanada.com
Web Site: www.pmcanada.com
Emp.: 40
Business Management Software Development Services
S.I.C.: 7372
N.A.I.C.S.: 511210
Don Kroeker *(Gen Mgr)*

IPL, Inc. (1)
140 Commerciale Street
Saint-Damien-de-Buckland, QC, G0R 2Y0, Canada Ca
Tel.: (418) 789-2880
Fax: (418) 789-3153
E-Mail: info-ipl@ipl-plastics.com
Web Site: www.ipl-plastics.com
Sales Range: $150-199.9 Million
Emp.: 1,000
Injection & Extrusion Molded Plastic Products Mfr
S.I.C.: 3089
N.A.I.C.S.: 326199
Serge Bragdon *(Pres & CEO)*
Eric Doyon *(CFO & VP-Fin)*
Jean-Pierre Simard *(CMO)*
Francois Bechard *(Sec)*

FONDSMAEGLERSELSKABET LD INVEST A/S

Lonmodtagernes Dyrtidsfond
Vendersgade 28, 1363 Copenhagen, Denmark
Tel.: (45) 33387300
Fax: (45) 33387310
E-Mail: kontakt@ld-invest.dk
Web Site: www.ld-invest.dk
Sales Range: $5-14.9 Billion
Emp.: 31

Business Description:
Private Equity, Asset Management & Investment Services
S.I.C.: 6211
N.A.I.C.S.: 523999

Personnel:
Jeppe Christiansen *(CEO)*
Lars Tonnesen *(Mng Partner-Equity)*
Christian Moller *(Partner-Equity)*
Jan Hove Sorensen *(Partner-Equity)*
Niels Toft *(Partner)*
Henrik Parkhoi *(Mng Dir)*
Steffen Staehr *(CFO)*
Else Nyvang Andersen *(Sr VP & Head-Comm)*

Holdings:

Bang & Olufsen Medicom a/s (1)
Gimsinglund Vej 20
7600 Struer, Denmark DK
Tel.: (45) 70301600 (65%)
Fax: (45) 96845701
E-Mail: medicom@bang-olufsen.dk
Web Site: www.medicom.bang-olufsen.com
Emp.: 150
Medical Device Mfr
S.I.C.: 3845
N.A.I.C.S.: 334510
Peer Norkjaer *(Chm)*
Trock Kensen *(CEO)*
Peter Thostrup *(Exec VP)*

Interbuild A/S (1)
Allegade 2 1 sal
DK 8700 Horsens, Denmark
Tel.: (45) 75757516
E-Mail: info@interbuild.dk
Web Site: www.interbuild.dk
Emp.: 2
Construction Products Mfr
S.I.C.: 2439
N.A.I.C.S.: 321213
Poul B. Kirkegaard *(CEO)*

Subsidiaries:

Lilleheden A/S (2)
Hovedvejen 114
DK 9850 Hirtshals, Denmark
Tel.: (45) 88969200
Fax: (45) 88969250
E-Mail: post@lilleheden.dk
Web Site: www.lilleheden.dk
Emp.: 70
Glulam Mfr
S.I.C.: 2499
N.A.I.C.S.: 321999
Christian Esbensen *(Mgr)*

Non-U.S. Subsidiaries:

Lilleheden Ltd. (3)
Redbrook Business Park Wilthtorpe Road
Barnsley, S75 1JN, United Kingdom
Tel.: (44) 1226205449
Fax: (44) 1226779282
E-Mail: mailuk@lilleheden.com
Web Site: www.lilleheden.dk
Emp.: 5
Glulam Mfr
S.I.C.: 2499
N.A.I.C.S.: 321999
Christian Esbensen *(CEO)*

Lilleheden Sp. z o.o. (3)
Ul Chylonska 191
81 007 Gdynia, Poland
Tel.: (48) 586600088
Fax: (48) 586600335
E-Mail: biuro@lilleheden.pl
Web Site: www.lilleheden.pl
Glulam Mfr
S.I.C.: 2499
N.A.I.C.S.: 321999

Verkaufsburo Lilleheden GmbH (3)
Grebenstrasse 21
D 27283 Verden, Germany
Tel.: (49) 423198910
Fax: (49) 4231989190
E-Mail: lilleheden@t-online.de
Web Site: www.lilleheden.dk
Glulam Mfr
S.I.C.: 2499
N.A.I.C.S.: 321999

PLUS A/S (2)
Sdr Ringvej 1-6
6600 Vejen, Denmark
Tel.: (45) 79963333
Fax: (45) 75364518
E-Mail: plus@plus.dk
Web Site: www.plus.dk/uk
Rev.: $41,977,101
Emp.: 396
Mfr. of Wooden Products for Outdoor Use
S.I.C.: 2499
N.A.I.C.S.: 321999

FONEWORX HOLDINGS LIMITED

FoneWorx House Cnr Bram Fischer & Will Scarlet Road
Ferndale, Randburg, 2194, South Africa

Mailing Address:
PO Box 3386
Pinegowrie, Randburg, 2123, South Africa
Tel.: (27) 11 293 0000
Fax: (27) 11 787 2127
E-Mail: info@foneworx.co.za
Web Site: www.foneworx.co.za
FWX—(JSE)
Rev.: $11,992,920
Assets: $17,836,484
Liabilities: $3,698,432
Net Worth: $14,138,052
Earnings: $2,784,844
Emp.: 56
Fiscal Year-end: 06/30/13

Business Description:
Investment Management Services
S.I.C.: 6282
N.A.I.C.S.: 523920

Personnel:
Mark Allan Smith *(CEO)*
Stefan Kleynhans *(Sec)*

Board of Directors:
Ashvin Govan Mancha
Graham Groenewaldt
Gaurang Mooney

Pieter Scholtz
Mark Allan Smith

Transfer Agent:
Computershare Investor Services (Pty) Limited
Ground Floor 70 Marshall Street
Johannesburg, South Africa

FONEX DATA SYSTEMS INC.

5400 Ch St-Francois
Saint Laurent, QC, H4S 1P6, Canada
Tel.: (514) 333-6639
Fax: (514) 333-6635
Toll Free: (800) 363-6639
E-Mail: info@fonex.com
Web Site: www.fonex.com
Year Founded: 1989
Rev.: $18,870,477
Emp.: 50

Business Description:
Telecommunication Equipment Services
S.I.C.: 4899
N.A.I.C.S.: 517919

Personnel:
Pasquale Di Pierro *(Founder & Pres)*

FONG'S INDUSTRIES COMPANY LIMITED

8/F 22-28 Cheung Tat Road
Tsing Yi, China (Hong Kong)
Tel.: (852) 24973300
Fax: (852) 24322552
E-Mail: enquiry@fongs.com
Web Site: www.fongs.com
0641—(HKG)
Rev.: $274,207,920
Assets: $412,668,627
Liabilities: $265,877,105
Net Worth: $146,791,522
Earnings: $19,603,882
Emp.: 4,620
Fiscal Year-end: 12/31/12

Business Description:
Dyeing & Finishing Machines Mfr
S.I.C.: 3999
N.A.I.C.S.: 339999

Personnel:
Sou Lam Fong *(Founder)*
Fengxian He *(Chm)*
Xin Ji *(CEO)*
Che Keung Lee *(Sec)*

Board of Directors:
Fengxian He
Kevin Kwok Leung Fong
Xin Ji
Wing Ching Keung
Wai Yung Wan
Maoxin Ye
Wei Ying
Ming Fai Yuen
Yucheng Zhou

Butterfield Fulcrum Group (Bermuda) Limited
26 Burnaby Street
Hamilton, HM 11, Bermuda

Transfer Agents:
Tricor Secretaries Limited
26th Floor Tesbury Centre 28 Queens Rd E
Hong Kong, China (Hong Kong)

Butterfield Fulcrum Group (Bermuda) Limited
26 Burnaby Street
Hamilton, HM 11, Bermuda

FONTANA LUIGI S.P.A.

Via Fontana 9
20050 Veduggio, MI, Italy
Tel.: (39) 03629891
Fax: (39) 0362924897
E-Mail: info@fontanaluigi.com
Web Site: www.fontanaluigi.com
Year Founded: 1952
Emp.: 450

Business Description:
Nuts, Bolts & Screws
S.I.C.: 3452
N.A.I.C.S.: 332722

Personnel:
Loris Fontana *(CEO)*

U.S. Subsidiary:

Fontana America Inc. (1)
1125 Jansen Farm Dr
Elgin, IL 60123 DE
Tel.: (847) 289-0130
Fax: (847) 289-1728
Web Site: www.fontanausa.com
Sls.: $10,000,000
Emp.: 16
Fasteners, Industrial: Nuts, Bolts, Screws, Etc.
S.I.C.: 5085
N.A.I.C.S.: 423840
Giuseppe Fontana *(Pres)*

FONTERRA CO-OPERATIVE GROUP LTD.

9 Princes Street
Private Bag 92032
Auckland, 1142, New Zealand
Tel.: (64) 93749000
Fax: (64) 93749001
E-Mail: enquiry@fonterra.com
Web Site: www.fonterra.com
Year Founded: 2001
FCG—(NZE)
Rev.: $15,604,191,000
Assets: $12,030,201,000
Liabilities: $6,382,125,000
Net Worth: $5,648,076,000
Earnings: $616,032,000
Emp.: 17,500
Fiscal Year-end: 07/31/13

Business Description:
Dairy Products Mfr
Export
S.I.C.: 2026
N.A.I.C.S.: 311511

Personnel:
John Wilson *(Chm)*
Theo Spierings *(CEO)*
Lukas Paravicini *(CFO)*

Board of Directors:
John Wilson
Malcolm Bailey
Ian Farrelly
Simon Israel
David Jackson
David MacLeod
John Monaghan
Ralph Norris
Blue Read
Nicola Shadbolt
Michael Spaans
Jim van der Poel
John Waller

Subsidiaries:

Fonterra Brands (1)
9 princess Street
Private Bag 92032
1142 Auckland, New Zealand
Tel.: (64) 93749000
Fax: (64) 3749001
E-Mail: communications@fonterra.com
Dairy Products
S.I.C.: 5143
N.A.I.C.S.: 424430
Chelet Tanjuactco *(Brand Mgr-Anchor Milk)*

Fonterra Ingredients (1)
9 princess Street
PO Box 92032
1010 Auckland, New Zealand
Tel.: (64) 93749000
Fax: (64) 93749001
E-Mail: enquiry@fonterra.com
Web Site: www.fonterra.com
Emp.: 125
Dairy Products
S.I.C.: 5143
N.A.I.C.S.: 424430
Gary Romano *(Mng Dir)*

Fonterra Innovation (1)
Private Bag 11029
Palmerston North, 4442, New Zealand
Tel.: (64) 63504649
Fax: (64) 63651476
E-Mail: jeremy.hill@fonterra.com
Emp.: 420
Dairy Products
S.I.C.: 5143
N.A.I.C.S.: 424430
Jeremy Hill *(Dir-Ops)*

Fonterra Milk Supply (1)
Private Bag 92032
Auckland, New Zealand
Tel.: (64) 93749000
Fax: (64) 93749001
E-Mail: sara.mcsadeen@fonterra.com
Web Site: www.fonterra.co.nz
Dairy Products
S.I.C.: 5143
N.A.I.C.S.: 424430
Gary Ronino *(Mng Dir-Ops)*

Mainland Products Limited (1)
Private Bag 92032
Auckland, 1142, New Zealand NZ
Tel.: (64) 93749000 (100%)
Fax: (64) 93003415
E-Mail: trade.enquiries@fonterra.com
Web Site: www.meadowfresh.co.nz
Rev.: $31,298,400
Emp.: 100
Dairy Products
S.I.C.: 2023
N.A.I.C.S.: 311514

Tip Top Ice Cream Co. Limited (1)
113 Carbine Rd
Mount Wellington, Auckland, New Zealand
Tel.: (64) 95737200
Fax: (64) 95731493
E-Mail: consumer.relations@fonterra.com
Web Site: www.tiptop.co.nz
Emp.: 420
Mfr. of Ice Cream, Frozen Novelties, Frozen Desserts & Frozen Snack Products
S.I.C.: 2024
N.A.I.C.S.: 311520
Brett Charlton *(Gen Mgr)*

U.S. Subsidiaries:

Fonterra Brands America (1)
525 N Tryon St Fl 16
Charlotte, NC 28202-0216 BM
Tel.: (954) 958-0330 (100%)
Telex: 192-999-001 DEUSA
Fax: (954) 958-0332
Sales Range: $800-899.9 Million
Emp.: 20
Dairy Products Mfr
S.I.C.: 0241
N.A.I.C.S.: 112120

Non-U.S. Subsidiaries:

Fonterra Brands Australia (P&B) Pty Ltd. (1)
22 Geddes Street
Locked Bag 3
Balcatta, WA, 6021, Australia AU
Tel.: (61) 894417777
Fax: (61) 894417700
E-Mail: pbflinfo@pbfoods.com.au
Web Site: www.fonterra.com.au
Emp.: 300
Mfr. & Distributor of Ice Cream, Milk & Dairy Products
Import Export
S.I.C.: 2024
N.A.I.C.S.: 311520
Theo Spierings *(CEO)*
Jonathan Mason *(CFO)*

Fonterra Brands (Middle East) LLC (1)
Union Properties Bldg 1st Fl St 3B
Al Quoz Industrial Area, 53680 Dubai, United Arab Emirates (100%)
Tel.: (971) 43392955
Fax: (971) 43392581
Web Site: www.fonterra.com
Emp.: 60
Milk Production
S.I.C.: 0241
N.A.I.C.S.: 112120
Kamal Gupta *(Mng Dir)*

Fonterra (CIS) Ltd (1)
80-5 Leningradsky Prospekt Building 5 4th Floor
Moscow, 125190, Russia RU
Tel.: (7) 095 258 6230 (100%)
Fax: (7) 095 258 6239
Web Site: www.fonterra.com
Emp.: 15
Dairy Products Mfr & Distr
S.I.C.: 5143
N.A.I.C.S.: 424430

Fonterra (Japan) Ltd. (1)
Sales Office 20th Fl Taiyo Seimei
Shinagawa Bldg 2 16 2 Konan
Minato-Ku, Tokyo, Japan (100%)
Tel.: (81) 367371800
Fax: (81) 367371801
Web Site: www.fonterra.com
Sales Range: $600-649.9 Million
Emp.: 60
Dairy Products Production
S.I.C.: 5143
N.A.I.C.S.: 424430
Mark Wilson *(Mng Dir-Asia, Africa & Middle East)*

New Tai Milk Products Co. Ltd. (1)
45 Ting Hu Road
Da Hwa Tsun Kuei Shan Hsiang, Taoyuan, Hsien, 333, Taiwan TW
Tel.: (886) 33973378 (50%)
Fax: (886) 33973163
E-Mail: aamyhasieha@fronterra.com
Web Site: www.newtai.com.tw
Emp.: 32
Dairy Products
S.I.C.: 2023
N.A.I.C.S.: 311514
Sera Cheng *(Gen Mgr)*

Fonterra (Philippines) Pasig City (1)
5th Floor The Linden Suites 37 San Miguel Avenue Ortigas Center
Pasig Manila, Philippines (30%)
Tel.: (63) 2 687 45 94
Emp.: 322
Shortening, Table Oils, Margarine & Other Edible Fats & Oils
S.I.C.: 2075
N.A.I.C.S.: 311224

Non-U.S. Joint Venture:

Saudi New Zealand Milk Products Co. Ltd. (1)
PO Box 31462
Dammam, 7493, Saudi Arabia
Tel.: (966) 38122200
Fax: (966) 38428249
Processed Cheese & Powdered Milk Producer
S.I.C.: 2022
N.A.I.C.S.: 311513

FOOD AND DRINKS PUBLIC COMPANY LIMITED

4F BB Building 54 Sukhumvit 21 Rd
Klongtoey-nua Wattana
Bangkok, 10110, Thailand
Tel.: (66) 2664 1501
Fax: (66) 2664 1500
E-Mail: info@foodanddrinks.co.th
Web Site: www.foodanddrinks.co.th
Year Founded: 1985
F&D—(THA)
Rev.: $23,388,743
Assets: $21,718,523
Liabilities: $5,496,237
Net Worth: $16,222,286
Earnings: $936,699
Fiscal Year-end: 12/31/12

Business Description:
Frozen Food Mfr & Distr
S.I.C.: 2038
N.A.I.C.S.: 311412

Personnel:
Phirasilp Subhapholsiri *(Chm)*
Kasem Deemaitree *(Mng Dir)*
Chintana Asdornnithee *(Deputy Mng Dir)*
Hui Lee Huai *(Sec)*

Board of Directors:
Phirasilp Subhapholsiri

Food and Drinks Public Company Limited—(Continued)

Chintana Asdornnithee
Sumet Chey-O-nanund
Nam Wong Chun
Kasem Deemaitree
Hsin Lee Huai
Hui Lee Huai
Udom Karoonkornsakul
Vilai Kiatsrichart
Sansern Nilrat
Aditep Nontratip
Chaovana Vivatpanachati

Legal Counsel:
Legal Advisory Council Co Ltd
16 F Olympia Thai Tower 444 Ratchdapisek Road Huay Kwang
Bangkok, 10310, Thailand

FOOD EMPIRE HOLDINGS LIMITED

31 Harrison Road 08-01 Food Empire Business Suites
Singapore, 369649, Singapore
Tel.: (65) 66226900
Fax: (65) 67448977
E-Mail: info@foodempire.com
Web Site: www.foodempire.com
F03—(SES)
Rev.: $237,663,000
Assets: $211,215,000
Liabilities: $49,795,000
Net Worth: $161,420,000
Earnings: $20,241,000
Emp.: 90
Fiscal Year-end: 12/31/12

Business Description:
Food & Beverage Mfr & Marketer
S.I.C.: 7389
N.A.I.C.S.: 425120

Personnel:
Wang Cheow Tan *(Chm)*
William Fong *(CFO)*
Cher Liang Tan *(Co-Sec)*
San-Ju Tan *(Co-Sec)*

Board of Directors:
Wang Cheow Tan
Yoon Chiang Boon
Hartono Gunawan
Yew Hiap Koh
Syn Pau Lew
Sudeep Nair
Kian Min Ong
Guek Ming Tan

Subsidiaries:

FES Industries Pte Ltd **(1)**
10 Chin Bee Dr
619859 Singapore, Singapore (100%)
Tel.: (65) 62689806
Fax: (65) 62648983
Emp.: 150
Roasted Nuts & Peanut Butter Mfr
S.I.C.: 2068
N.A.I.C.S.: 311911
Tan Wang Chow *(CEO)*

Future Corporation Pte Ltd **(1)**
31 Harrison Road H08-01
Singapore, 369649, Singapore
Tel.: (65) 67448911
Fax: (65) 67448977
E-Mail: info@foodempire.com
Web Site: www.futurecorp.com
Food Products Mfr & Slaes
S.I.C.: 2068
N.A.I.C.S.: 311911
Tan Wang Cheow *(Gen Mgr)*

Future Enterprises Pte Ltd **(1)**
31 Harrison Rd Unit 08-01
369649 Singapore, Singapore (100%)
Tel.: (65) 67448911
Fax: (65) 67448977
E-Mail: info@foodempire.com
Web Site: www.foodempire.com
Emp.: 70
Chocolate & Confectionery Mfr from Cacao Beans
S.I.C.: 2066
N.A.I.C.S.: 311351
Tan Wang Chow *(CEO)*

Non-U.S. Subsidiary:

Empire Distribution (Europe) Spolka Z Ograniczona Odpowiedzialnoscia **(2)**
Krolowej Marysienki 9/4a
Warsaw, Masovian, 02-954, Poland
Tel.: (48) 227420550
Fax: (48) 226420180
Emp.: 3
Beverage Products Mfr & Distr
S.I.C.: 2087
N.A.I.C.S.: 311930
Peter Woznaeak *(Gen Mgr)*

Non-U.S. Subsidiaries:

FES Industries Sdn Bhd **(1)**
No 7 Jln Bistari 4
Taman Industri Jaya, 81300 Johor, Malaysia (100%)
Tel.: (60) 75127710
Fax: (60) 75127720
Emp.: 80
Manufacturing & Processing of Instant Food & Beverages
S.I.C.: 5812
N.A.I.C.S.: 722515

FES (Vietnam) Co. Ltd **(1)**
26 Giai Phong
Ward-4 District-Tan Binh, Ho Chi Minh City, Vietnam (100%)
Tel.: (84) 6503767188
Fax: (84) 06503767128
E-Mail: info@maccoffee-vn.com
Web Site: www.maccoffee-vn.com
Emp.: 200
Coffee & Tea Mfr
S.I.C.: 2099
N.A.I.C.S.: 311920

Foodaworld Marketing Pte Ltd **(1)**
Pymonenka M vul 13 A-C 39
Office 23 5A Bldg, 4050 Kiev, Ukraine (100%)
Tel.: (380) 444942555
Fax: (380) 444962878
E-Mail: kievoffice@foodempire.com
Web Site: www.maccoffee.com.ua
Emp.: 14
Coffee & Tea Mfr
S.I.C.: 2095
N.A.I.C.S.: 311920
Maurice Yeo *(Mng Dir)*

FOOD JUNCTION HOLDINGS LIMITED

(See Under Auric Pacific Group Ltd)

FOODCO HOLDING CO P.J.S.C

Port Zayed Mina
PO Box 2378
Abu Dhabi, United Arab Emirates
Tel.: (971) 2 673 1000
Fax: (971) 2 673 2100
E-Mail: foodco@foodcouae.com
Web Site: www.foodco-uae.com
Year Founded: 2006
FOODCO—(EMI)
Sales Range: $10-24.9 Million

Business Description:
Meat Product Distr
S.I.C.: 5147
N.A.I.C.S.: 424470

Personnel:
Ahmed Ali Al Dhahry *(Chm)*
Ahmed Ali Matar Khamis Al Remeithi *(Vice Chm)*

Board of Directors:
Ahmed Ali Al Dhahry
Mohammed Ali Al Hosani
Mohamed Saeed Abdulla Al Qubaisi
Ahmed Ali Matar Khamis Al Remeithi
Mohamed Ali Al Dhahry
Mubarak Ahmed Fahad

FOODFEST INTERNATIONAL 2000 INC.

361 Connie Crescent
Concord, ON, L4K 5R2, Canada
Tel.: (905) 709-4775
Year Founded: 2006
FDFT—(OTC)
Sales Range: $10-24.9 Million
Emp.: 25

Business Description:
Kosher, Natural & Organic Foods Distr
S.I.C.: 5499
N.A.I.C.S.: 445299

Personnel:
Fred Farnden *(Pres & CFO)*
Henry Ender *(CEO & Sec)*

FOODS & INNS LTD.

Dulwich Mansion 3rd Floor 224 Tardeo Road
Mumbai, 400 007, India
Tel.: (91) 22 23533104
Fax: (91) 22 23533106
E-Mail: writetous@foodsandinns.com
Web Site: www.foodsandinns.com
507552—(BOM)
Sales Range: $25-49.9 Million

Business Description:
Fruit Pulp Mfr
S.I.C.: 2037
N.A.I.C.S.: 311411

Personnel:
Bhupendra C. Dalal *(Chm)*
Utsav Dhupelia *(Vice Chm)*

Board of Directors:
Bhupendra C. Dalal
Harsha Bangari
Milan B. Dalal
Utsav Dhupelia
Dadi B. Engineer
George P. Gonzor
Chaitan M. Maniar
Raymond Simkins
Dinkarray D. Trivedi

FOODWELL CORPORATION

668 Eunhaeng-dong
Jungwon-gu, Seongnam, Gyeonggi-do, Korea (South)
Tel.: (82) 31 743 4075
Fax: (82) 31 743 4088
E-Mail: foodwell@foodwell.com
Web Site: Www.foodwell.com
Year Founded: 1968
005670—(KRS)

Business Description:
Fruit Product Mfr
S.I.C.: 2034
N.A.I.C.S.: 311423

Personnel:
Gi Sang Sung *(Chm)*

FOOK WOO GROUP HOLDINGS LIMITED

Fook Woo Group Building 3 Kui Sik Street
Fanling, China (Hong Kong)
Tel.: (852) 2676 8700
Fax: (852) 2796 7158
E-Mail: info@fookwoo.com
Web Site: www.fookwoo.com
Year Founded: 1968
0923—(HKG)
Sales Range: $250-299.9 Million
Emp.: 2,311

Business Description:
Waste Paper Management Services
S.I.C.: 4959
N.A.I.C.S.: 562998

Personnel:
Kai Kuen Leung *(Chm & CEO)*
Sau Ling Mak *(CFO)*
Thomas Chun Keung Cheng *(COO, Head-Recycled Paper Bus & Deputy Gen Mgr)*
Ka Fat Chan *(Sec)*

Board of Directors:
Kai Kuen Leung
Kong Chan
Brian Chi Ming Cheng
Thomas Chun Keung Cheng
Carol Nga Lai Cheung
Jimmy Wai Kwok Chung
Shun Chuen Lau
Kwok Chung Lee
Tat Piu Leung
Michael Cheng Ming Pei

Legal Counsel:
Sidley Austin
Level 39, Two International Finance Centre 8 Finance Street
Central, China (Hong Kong)

Appleby Trust (Cayman) Ltd.
Clifton House 75 Fort Street
PO Box 1350
Grand Cayman, Cayman Islands

Transfer Agents:
Computershare Hong Kong Investor Services Limited
Shops 1712-1716 17th Floor Hopewell Centre
183 Queens Road East
Wanchai, China (Hong Kong)

Appleby Trust (Cayman) Ltd.
Clifton House 75 Fort Street
PO Box 1350
Grand Cayman, Cayman Islands

Subsidiaries:

Confidential Materials Destruction Service Limited **(1)**
5 F Fook Woo Grp Bldg 3 Kui Sik St On Lok Tsuen
Fanling, New Territories, China (Hong Kong)
Tel.: (852) 26768800
Fax: (852) 27980954
E-Mail: cs@cmdsc.com.hk
Emp.: 60
Waste Management Services
S.I.C.: 9511
N.A.I.C.S.: 924110

Fook Woo Assorted Paper Company Limited **(1)**
5 F Fook Woo Grp Bldg 3 Kui Sik St On Lok Tsuen
Fanling, New Territories, China (Hong Kong)
Tel.: (852) 26768700
Fax: (852) 27967158
Tissue Paper Products Sales
S.I.C.: 5113
N.A.I.C.S.: 424130

Fook Woo Environmental Technologies Limited **(1)**
5 F Fook Woo Grp Bldg 3 Kui Sik St On Lok Tsuen
Fanling, New Territories, China (Hong Kong)
Tel.: (852) 26768700
Fax: (852) 27967158
Waste Reduction Services
S.I.C.: 4952
N.A.I.C.S.: 221320

Fook Woo Waste Paper Company Limited **(1)**
5 F Fook Woo Grp Bldg 3 Kui Sik St On Lok Tsuen
Fanling, New Territories, China (Hong Kong)
Tel.: (852) 26768700
Fax: (852) 27967158
Paper Product Sales
S.I.C.: 5113
N.A.I.C.S.: 424130

Non-U.S. Subsidiary:

Huizhou Fook Woo Paper Company Limited **(1)**
Gaotou Vlg Liangwu Mgmt Zone
Yuanzhou, Huizhou, Guangdong, 516123, China
Tel.: (86) 7526812825
Fax: (86) 7526812628
E-Mail: suooy.yoansuan@fwpaper.com
Tissue Paper Products Mfr & Sales
S.I.C.: 2621
N.A.I.C.S.: 322121
Huizhen Liang *(Mng Dir)*

FOORD COMPASS LIMITED

7 Forest Mews Forest Drive
7405 Pinelands, South Africa
Tel.: (27) 215326988
Fax: (27) 215326999
E-Mail: info@foord.co.za
Web Site: www.foordcompass.co.za
FCPD—(JSE)
Rev.: $9,137,060
Assets: $217,256,500
Liabilities: $211,146,510
Net Worth: $6,109,990
Earnings: $2,166,980
Emp.: 30
Fiscal Year-end: 12/31/12

Business Description:
Investment Holding & Trading Company
S.I.C.: 6282
N.A.I.C.S.: 523920

Personnel:
Darron G. West *(Chm)*
L. Grevler *(Sec)*

Board of Directors:
Darron G. West
Paul E. Cluer
Adam D. Cowell
Dave Foord
Johannes van der Horst

FOOSUNG CO., LTD.

427-9 Rohha-ri
Paltan-myun, Hwasun, 445-909, Korea (South)
Tel.: (82) 31 495 7243
Fax: (82) 31 491 1649
E-Mail: sunsoo@foosung.com
Web Site: www.foosung.com
Year Founded: 2006

Business Description:
Specialty Industrial Gas Mfr
S.I.C.: 2813
N.A.I.C.S.: 325120

Personnel:
Keun Soo Kim *(Chm)*

Affiliates:

Foosung HDS Co., Ltd. **(1)**
113-8 Samsung-dong
Kangnam-gu, Seoul, Korea (South) Ks
Tel.: (82) 25544108
Fax: (82) 25558196
Web Site: www.fsc.co.kr
Chemical, Metal & Mineral Wholesale Trade Agency
S.I.C.: 7389
N.A.I.C.S.: 425120
Hong Soon Hyuk *(CEO)*

Foosung Industrial Co., Ltd. **(1)**
755-2 Byungam
Sengkuk, Umsong, Choongbuk, Korea (South) Ks
Tel.: (82) 43 878 4054
Fax: (82) 43 878 4053
Web Site: www.fic.co.kr
Plastic Injection Molding Mfr
S.I.C.: 3089
N.A.I.C.S.: 326199
Ki Soo Kim *(CEO)*

Foosung Precision Industry Co., Ltd. **(1)**
427-9 Noha-ri
Paltan-myeon, Hwaseong, Gyeunggi-do, Korea (South) Ks
Tel.: (82) 5 777 2 555
Fax: (82) 313540794
Web Site: www.fpi.co.kr
Aluminum Products, Automotive Components & Fluoropolymer Lining Systems Mfr
S.I.C.: 3355
N.A.I.C.S.: 331318
Keewan Kang *(CEO)*

Foosungtech Co., Ltd. **(1)**
989-3 Gosaek-dong
Gwonseon-gu, Suwon, Gyeonggi-do, Korea (South) Ks
Tel.: (82) 312059270
Fax: (82) 312059271
Web Site: www.foosungtech.co.kr
Emp.: 230
Electronic Connector Mfr
S.I.C.: 3678
N.A.I.C.S.: 334417
Gi Cheon Lee *(CEO)*

FOPE S.R.L.

Via Zampieri 31
36100 Vicenza, Italy
Tel.: (39) 444286911
Fax: (39) 0444570932
E-Mail: info@fope.com
Web Site: www.fope.com
Year Founded: 1929
Sales Range: $10-24.9 Million
Emp.: 35

Business Description:
Jewelry Mfr
S.I.C.: 3911
N.A.I.C.S.: 339910

Personnel:
Umberto Cazzola *(Pres)*

Non-U.S. Subsidiary:

Beijing Fope Jewellry & Arts, Ltd **(1)**
Rm 2005 No 109 Bldg
Huizhongbeili Chaoyong Dist, 100029
Beijing, China
Tel.: (86) 1064861618
Fax: (86) 1064839929
Emp.: 20
Jewelers Material & Lapidary Work Mfr
S.I.C.: 3911
N.A.I.C.S.: 339910
Jiang Ying *(Mgr)*

FOR-SIDE.COM CO., LTD.

Nittochi Nishi-shinjuku Building Floors 7 & 8
10-1 Nishi Shinjuku 6-chome
Shinjuku-ku, Tokyo, 160 0023, Japan
Tel.: (81) 3 5339 5211
Fax: (81) 3 5339 5212
E-Mail: ir-info@for-side.com
Web Site: www.for-side.com
Year Founded: 2000
2330—(JAS)
Sales Range: $50-74.9 Million
Emp.: 1,182

Business Description:
Ring Tones & Display Wallpaper for Mobile Phones
S.I.C.: 3669
N.A.I.C.S.: 334290

Personnel:
Yukinao Ajima *(CEO)*

Board of Directors:
Takayuki Asami
Masaru Kariya
Ukon Noriki

FORACO INTERNATIONAL S.A.

26 Plage de l'Estaque
13016 Marseilles, France
Tel.: (33) 496151360
Fax: (33) 496151361
E-Mail: info@foraco.com
Web Site: www.foraco.com
FAR—(OTC TSX)
Rev.: $367,519,000
Assets: $464,479,000
Liabilities: $242,573,000
Net Worth: $221,906,000
Earnings: $32,617,000
Emp.: 3,349
Fiscal Year-end: 12/31/12

Business Description:
Hydraulic & Geotechnical Mining & Drilling Services
S.I.C.: 1499
N.A.I.C.S.: 212399

Personnel:
Daniel Simoncini *(Chm & Co-CEO)*
Jean-Pierre Charmensat *(Co-CEO & CFO)*
Laurence Girard *(Gen Counsel)*
Timothy Bremner *(Sr VP-North America)*
Pablo Hamilton *(Sr VP)*
Peter Jacobs *(Sr VP-Asia Pacific)*
Santiago Marin Cruchaga *(Sr VP-Latin America)*

Board of Directors:
Daniel Simoncini
Bruno Chabas
Jean-Pierre Charmensat
Warren Holmes
Jorge Hurtado

Legal Counsel:
Fasken Martineau DuMoulin LLP
Vancouver, BC, Canada

Transfer Agent:
Computershare Trust Company of Canada
510 Burrard St 3rd Fl
Vancouver, BC, V6C 3B9, Canada

Non-U.S. Subsidiary:

The Equicom Group Inc **(1)**
20 Toronto St Ste 500
Toronto, ON, M5C 2B8, Canada
Tel.: (416) 815-0700
Fax: (416) 815-0080
Web Site: www.equicomgroup.com
Emp.: 40
Investor Relations Services
S.I.C.: 6211
N.A.I.C.S.: 523999
Claude Durocher *(COO)*
Cameron Davies *(Sr VP-Bus Dev)*

FORAJ SONDE CRAIOVA

4 A Fratii Buzesti St
Craiova, Romania
Tel.: (40) 251 415 866
Fax: (40) 251 406 482
E-Mail: office@craiovadrilling.ro
Web Site: www.forajcraiova.ro
FOSB—(BUC)
Rev.: $31,548,476
Assets: $53,943,312
Liabilities: $14,962,469
Net Worth: $38,980,843
Earnings: $1,674,396
Emp.: 486
Fiscal Year-end: 12/31/12

Business Description:
Drilling Services
S.I.C.: 1381
N.A.I.C.S.: 213111

Personnel:
Ion Croitoru *(Pres)*

Board of Directors:
Ion Croitoru
Antonie Ilie

FORAN MINING CORPORATION

409 Granville Street Suite 904
Vancouver, BC, V6C 1T2, Canada
Tel.: (604) 488-0008
E-Mail: ir@foranmining.com
Web Site: www.foranmining.com
Year Founded: 1989
FOM—(TSXV)
Int. Income: $84,010
Assets: $28,561,575
Liabilities: $466,436
Net Worth: $28,095,140
Earnings: ($1,406,571)
Fiscal Year-end: 09/30/12

Business Description:
Gold Mining Services
S.I.C.: 1041
N.A.I.C.S.: 212221

Personnel:
Darren Morcombe *(Chm)*
Patrick Soares *(Pres & CEO)*
Tim Thiessen *(CFO)*

Board of Directors:
Darren Morcombe
Sharon Dowdall
David M. Petroff
Patrick Soares
Bradley Summach
Maurice Tagami

Transfer Agent:
Equity Financial Trust Company
200 University Avenue Suite 400
Toronto, ON, Canada

FORBES & COMPANY LTD

Forbes Building Charanjit Rai Marg Fort
Mumbai, 400001, India
Tel.: (91) 2240749191
Fax: (91) 2240749102
Web Site:
502865—(BOM)
Rev.: $376,532,735
Assets: $302,052,957
Liabilities: $219,830,541
Net Worth: $82,222,416
Earnings: $15,861,100
Fiscal Year-end: 03/31/13

Business Description:
Shipping & Logistics Services
S.I.C.: 4731
N.A.I.C.S.: 541614

Personnel:
Ashok Barat *(Mng Dir)*
Pankaj Khattar *(Sec)*

Board of Directors:
Shapoor P. Mistry
Ashok Barat
T. R. Doongaji
S. L. Goklaney
Kaiwan D. Kalyaniwalla
Jai L. Mavani
Jimmy J. Parakh
D. Sivanandhan

Transfer Agent:
TSR Darashaw Limited
6-10 Haji Moosa Patrawala Industrial Estate 20 Dr. E Moses Road
Near Famous Studio Mahalaxmi, Mumbai, India

FORBES & MANHATTAN COAL CORP.

65 Queen Street West 8th Floor
Toronto, ON, M5H 2M5, Canada
Tel.: (416) 309-2957
Fax: (416) 861-8165
E-Mail: info@forbescoal.com
Web Site: www.forbescoal.com
FMC—(TSX)
Rev.: $68,086,968
Assets: $121,696,498
Liabilities: $55,073,510
Net Worth: $66,622,988
Earnings: ($10,088,330)
Emp.: 969
Fiscal Year-end: 02/28/13

Business Description:
Coal Mining
S.I.C.: 1221
N.A.I.C.S.: 212111

Personnel:
Craig Wiggill *(Interim CEO)*
Sarah Williams *(CFO)*
Malcolm Campbell *(COO)*
Neil Said *(Sec)*

Board of Directors:
John Dreyer
Bob Francis
Michael Price
Thomas Quinn Roussel
Bernard Wilson

Transfer Agent:
TMX Equity Transfer Services
Toronto, ON, Canada

Forbes & Manhattan Coal Corp.—(Continued)

Non-U.S. Subsidiary:

Forbes Coal (Pty) Ltd. (1)
Coalfields Commercial Rd R33
PO Box 684
Dundee, Kwazulu Natal, 3000, South Africa
Tel.: (27) 34 212 1455
Fax: (27) 34 212 1232
Coal Mining Services
S.I.C.: 1222
N.A.I.C.S.: 212112

FORBES-HEWLETT TRANSPORT INC.

156 Glidden Road
Brampton, ON, L6W 3L2, Canada
Tel.: (905) 455-2211
Fax: (905) 455-0088
Toll Free: (800) 387-5832
E-Mail: customerservice@forbeshewlett.com
Web Site: www.forbeshewlett.com
Year Founded: 1985
Rev.: $21,725,687
Emp.: 150
Business Description:
Truckload Services
S.I.C.: 4213
N.A.I.C.S.: 484122
Personnel:
George V. Stott *(Founder)*

FORBES MOTORS INCORPORATED

165 Weber St S
Waterloo, ON, N2J 4A6, Canada
Tel.: (519) 742-4463
Fax: (519) 742-4107
E-Mail: admin@forbesmotors.com
Web Site: www.forbesauto.com
Year Founded: 1948
Rev.: $35,081,642
Emp.: 70
Business Description:
New & Used Car Dealers
S.I.C.: 5511
N.A.I.C.S.: 441110
Personnel:
Russell Ainslie Forbes *(Pres & Mgr-Bus Dev)*

FORBES TRAVEL INTERNATIONAL LTD.

Suite 700 900 West Hastings Street
Vancouver, BC, V6C 1E5, Canada
Tel.: (604) 689-0461
Fax: (604) 689-4776
Toll Free: (800) 983-2299
E-Mail: info@forbes-travel.com
Web Site: www.forbes-travel.com
Year Founded: 1986
Rev.: $13,944,140
Emp.: 18
Business Description:
Travel Agency
S.I.C.: 4729
N.A.I.C.S.: 561599
Personnel:
Cheryl Green *(Partner)*
Grant Hurrle *(Partner)*
Lisbet MacKay *(Partner)*
Deirdre Manley *(Partner)*

FORBIDDEN TECHNOLOGIES PLC

Tuition House 27-37 St Georges Road Wimbledon
London, SW19 4EU, United Kingdom
Tel.: (44) 2088797245
Fax: (44) 2089464871
E-Mail: info@forbidden.co.uk
Web Site: www.forbidden.co.uk
Year Founded: 1998
FBT—(LSE)
Rev.: $1,283,558
Assets: $2,700,114
Liabilities: $128,701
Net Worth: $2,571,413
Earnings: ($342,256)
Emp.: 16
Fiscal Year-end: 12/31/12
Business Description:
Video Compression Technology Developer
S.I.C.: 7379
N.A.I.C.S.: 541519
Personnel:
Victor J. Steel *(Chm)*
Stephen B. Streater *(CEO)*
M. C. Kay *(Sec)*
Board of Directors:
Victor J. Steel
Greg Hirst
Phil Madden
David Main
Stephen B. Streater
Legal Counsel:
Blake Lapthorn LLP
Watchmaker Court 33 St Johns Lane
London, United Kingdom

FORBION CAPITAL PARTNERS MANAGEMENT HOLDING BV

Gooimeer 2-35
1411 TC Naarden, Netherlands
Tel.: (31) 35 699 30 00
Fax: (31) 35 699 30 01
E-Mail: info@forbion.com
Web Site: www.forbion.com
Sales Range: $100-124.9 Million
Business Description:
Investment Holding Company
S.I.C.: 6719
N.A.I.C.S.: 551112
Personnel:
Bart Bergstein *(Chm & Mng Partner)*
Sander Slootweg *(Mng Partner)*
Martien Van Osch *(Mng Partner)*
Sander van Deventer *(Gen Partner)*
Avi Molcho *(Partner)*
Geert-Jan Mulder *(Partner)*
Holger Reithinger *(Partner)*
Christina Takke *(Partner)*
Marco Boorsma *(Principal)*

Subsidiary:

uniQure B.V. (1)
Meibergdreef 61
1105 BA Amsterdam, Netherlands NL
Tel.: (31) 20 566 7394
Fax: (31) 20 566 9272
E-Mail: info@uniQure.com
Web Site: www.uniqure.com
QURE—(NASDAQ)
Assets: $7,494,128
Liabilities: $8,097,213
Net Worth: ($603,084)
Earnings: ($19,810,238)
Emp.: 79
Fiscal Year-end: 12/31/12
Human Gene Therapy Research
S.I.C.: 8731
N.A.I.C.S.: 541712
Ferdinand Verdonck *(Chm-Supervisory Bd)*
Jorn Aldag *(CEO)*
Piers J. Morgan *(CFO)*
Harald Petry *(Chief Science Officer)*
Christian Meyer *(Chief Medical Officer)*
Hans Preusting *(Chief Bus Officer)*
Hans Christian Rohde *(Chief Comml Officer)*
Philip Astley-Sparke *(Pres-US Ops)*

Non-U.S. Affiliate:

Cardoz AB (1)
Kornhamnstorg 53
SE 111 27 Stockholm, Sweden
Tel.: (46) 8 566 30 174
Fax: (46) 8 566 30 013
E-Mail: info@cardoz.com
Web Site: www.cardoz.com
Pharmaceuticals Mfr
S.I.C.: 2834
N.A.I.C.S.: 325412
Joseph M. Feczko *(Chm)*
Carl-Johan Dalsgaard *(CEO)*
Johan Raud *(Chief Scientific Officer)*

FORBO HOLDING AG

Lindenstrasse 8
PO Box 1041
CH-6341 Baar, Switzerland
Tel.: (41) 587872525
Fax: (41) 587872025
E-Mail: info@forbo.com
Web Site: www.forbo.com
Year Founded: 1928
FORN—(OTC SWX)
Sls.: $1,296,371,252
Assets: $1,439,704,948
Liabilities: $557,468,780
Net Worth: $882,236,168
Earnings: $212,841,904
Emp.: 5,000
Fiscal Year-end: 12/31/12
Business Description:
Floor Coverings, Adhesives & Belting Mfr & Supplier
S.I.C.: 3089
N.A.I.C.S.: 326199
Personnel:
Albert Gnagi *(Chm)*
Michael Pieper *(Vice Chm)*
This E. Schneider *(CEO)*
Andreas Spreiter *(CFO & Exec VP)*
Matthias P. Huenerwadel *(Exec VP-Flooring Sys)*
Jean-Michel Wins *(Exec VP-Movement Sys)*
Board of Directors:
Albert Gnagi
Peter Altorfer
Reto Muller
Michael Pieper
This E. Schneider
Vincent Studer

Subsidiaries:

Forbo CTU SA (1)
Parkstrasse 10
5012 Schonenwerd, Switzerland CH (100%)
Tel.: (41) 628583111
Fax: (41) 628583100
E-Mail: info@ctu.forbo.com
Web Site: www.ctu.forbo.com
Emp.: 12
Mfr & Sales of Coatings & Adhesives
S.I.C.: 2891
N.A.I.C.S.: 325520
Petricio Lacalle *(Gen Mgr)*

Forbo Finanz AG (1)
Lindenstrasse 8
PO Box 1041
CH 6341 Baar, Switzerland (100%)
Tel.: (41) 58 787 25 25
Fax: (41) 58 787 20 25
E-Mail: info@forbo.com
Financial Services
S.I.C.: 6726
N.A.I.C.S.: 525990

Forbo Giubiasco SA (1)
Via Industrie 16
Giubiasco, Gicino, 6512, Switzerland (100%)
Tel.: (41) 918500111
Telex: 846371
Fax: (41) 918500101
E-Mail: info.flooring.ch@forbo.com
Web Site: www.forbo-flooring.ch
Emp.: 100
PVC Floor Covering Mfr; Tile Flooring Mfr
S.I.C.: 1752
N.A.I.C.S.: 238330
Guidowte Bruno *(Mng Dir)*

Forbo International SA (1)
Lindenstrasse 8
PO Box 1041
CH 6341 Baar, Switzerland (100%)
Tel.: (41) 587872525
Fax: (41) 587872025
E-Mail: info@forbo.com
Holding Company
S.I.C.: 6719
N.A.I.C.S.: 551112

U.S. Subsidiary:

Forbo America Inc. (1)
1105 N Market St
Wilmington, DE 19801-1216
Tel.: (302) 427-2139
Holding Company
S.I.C.: 6719
N.A.I.C.S.: 551112

Subsidiaries:

Forbo Flooring, Inc. (2)
8 Maplewood Dr Humboldt Industrial Park
Hazleton, PA 18202 DE
Mailing Address: (100%)
PO Box 667
Hazleton, PA 18201-0667
Tel.: (570) 459-0771
Telex: 68 55 305
Fax: (570) 450-0277
Web Site: www.forboflooringna.com
Emp.: 25
Vinyl & Linoleum Floor Coverings Mfr
S.I.C.: 3089
N.A.I.C.S.: 326199
Tom Kaiser *(Exec VP)*

Forbo Siegling LLC (2)
12201 Vanstory Dr
Huntersville, NC 28078-8395
Tel.: (704) 948-0800
Fax: (704) 948-0995
Toll Free: (800) 255-5581
E-Mail: siegling.us@forbo.com
Web Site: www.forbo-siegling.com
Emp.: 250
Flat Belts, Conveyor & Processing Belts Mfr
S.I.C.: 3052
N.A.I.C.S.: 326220

Division:

Transtex Belting (3)
10125 S Tryon St
Charlotte, NC 28273-6509
Tel.: (704) 334-5353
Fax: (704) 334-6301
Emp.: 40
Lightweight PVC Conveyor Belt Mfr
S.I.C.: 3535
N.A.I.C.S.: 333922

Non-U.S. Subsidiaries:

Biuro Forbo Flooring Poland (1)
Ul Wolsztynska 2
60 361 Poznan, Poland (99%)
Tel.: (48) 618621382
Fax: (48) 616229971
E-Mail: info@forbo.flooring.pl
Web Site: www.forbo.flooring.pl
Emp.: 6
S.I.C.: 2273
N.A.I.C.S.: 314110

Enia Carpet Deutschland GmbH (1)
Steuben Strasse 27
33100 Paderborn, Germany
Tel.: (49) 52515010
Fax: (49) 5251501190
E-Mail: info@eniacarpets.de
Web Site: www.eniacarpets.de
Emp.: 100
Carpets & Rugs Mfr
Export
S.I.C.: 2273
N.A.I.C.S.: 314110
Burkhard Krug *(Mng Dir)*

Enia Carpets Netherlands B.V. (1)
Parallelweg 14
5051 HG Goirle, Netherlands (100%)
Tel.: (31) 135309999
Fax: (31) 135309988
E-Mail: info@iniacarpets.nl
Web Site: www.iniacarpets.nl
Emp.: 150
Sales of Textile Floor Coverings
S.I.C.: 5713
N.A.I.C.S.: 442210
Hans Vamdenderg *(Mng Dir)*

Eurocol BV (1)
Industrieweg 1 2
Wormerveer, North Holland, 1520AC, Netherlands (100%)

Mailing Address:
Postbus 130
NL-1520 AC Wormerveer, Netherlands
Tel.: (31) 756271600
Fax: (31) 756283564
E-Mail: info@eurocol.nl
Web Site: www.eurocol.com
Emp.: 160
Mfr. of Floors
S.I.C.: 3089
N.A.I.C.S.: 326199
Jos H. Ronden *(Gen Mgr)*

Forbo Contel Handelsges. m.b.H. (1)
Handelskai 52
Vienna, 1200, Austria (100%)
Tel.: (43) 330920105
Fax: (43) 13309210
E-Mail: info@conte.forbo.com
Web Site: www.forbo.com
Emp.: 15
Sales of Linoleum, Vinyl & Textile Floor Coverings & Wall Coverings
S.I.C.: 5713
N.A.I.C.S.: 442210

Forbo Erfurt GmbH (1)
August-Robling Strasse 2
99091 Erfurt, Germany DE
Tel.: (49) 361730410 (100%)
Fax: (49) 3617304190
E-Mail: info.erfort@forbo.com
Web Site: www.erfurt.forbo.com
Sales Range: $25-49.9 Million
Emp.: 100
Coatings & Adhesives Mfr & Sales
S.I.C.: 2891
N.A.I.C.S.: 325520
Ditmar Abendroth *(Mgr-Mktg)*

Forbo Floorcoverings Pty. Ltd. (1)
23 Ormsby Pl
Wetherill Park, NSW, 2164, Australia (100%)
Tel.: (61) 298280200
Fax: (61) 297253456
E-Mail: info.au@forbo.com
Web Site: www.forbo.com.au
Emp.: 30
Sale of Flooring
S.I.C.: 5713
N.A.I.C.S.: 442210
Wayne Donovan *(Mng Dir)*

Forbo Flooring B.V. (1)
Industrieweg 12
Postbus 13
1566 Assendelft, Netherlands (100%)
Tel.: (31) 756477880
Fax: (31) 75 628 37 71
Web Site: www.forbo-flooring.nl
Emp.: 80
Carpet & Rug Mills
S.I.C.: 2273
N.A.I.C.S.: 314110
Tom Kuijper *(Mng Dir)*

Forbo Flooring GmbH (1)
Steubenstrasse 27
D 33100 Paderborn, Germany
Tel.: (49) 525118030
Fax: (49) 52511803312
E-Mail: info.germany@forbo.de
Web Site: www.forbo-flooring.de
Emp.: 110
Sales of Vinyl Floor Coverings
S.I.C.: 5713
N.A.I.C.S.: 442210
Martin Thewes *(Gen Mgr)*

Forbo Flooring UK Ltd. (1)
Den Rd
PO Box 1
Kirkcaldy, KY1 2ER, United Kingdom (100%)
Tel.: (44) 1592643777
Fax: (44) 1592643999
E-Mail: info@forbo-flooring.co.uk
Web Site: www.forbo-flooring.co.uk
Emp.: 500
Mfr & Sales of Linoleum, Vinyl & Textile Floor Coverings; Sale of Coatings & Adhesives
S.I.C.: 5713
N.A.I.C.S.: 442210
Angus Fotheringhame *(Mng Dir)*

Divisions:

Forbo Flooring UK Ltd. (2)
High Holborn Road
Ripley, Derbyshire, DE5 3NT, United Kingdom
Tel.: (44) 1773744121
Fax: (44) 1773744142
E-Mail: enquiries@forbo.com
Web Site: www.forbo-flooring.co.uk
Emp.: 60
Flocked & Tufted Floor Coverings Mfr
S.I.C.: 5713
N.A.I.C.S.: 442210
Brent Greenway *(Mgr-Site)*

Forbo Flooring UK Ltd. (2)
Unit 92 Seedlee Road
Walton Summit, Preston, PR5 8AE, United Kingdom (100%)
Tel.: (44) 8708550500
Fax: (44) 870 8550 535
E-Mail: info.flooring.uk@forbo.com
Web Site: www.forbo-flooring.co.uk
Carpet & Rug Mills
S.I.C.: 2273
N.A.I.C.S.: 314110

Forbo Floring Oy AB (1)
Heikkilainkapu No-2
00210 Helsinki, Finland (100%)
Tel.: (358) 986230300
Fax: (358) 986230301
E-Mail: info.finland@forbo.com
Web Site: www.forbo.fi
Emp.: 8
Sales of Flooring
S.I.C.: 5713
N.A.I.C.S.: 442210
Jyrkki Ahonem *(Pres)*
Markus Lilius *(CEO)*

Forbo Helmitin GmbH (1)
Zweibrucker Strasse 185
Pirmasens, 66954, Germany DE
Mailing Address: (100%)
Postfach 1961
66927 Pirmasens, Germany
Tel.: (49) 63315280
Fax: (49) 6331528201
E-Mail: forbohelmitin@forbo.com
Web Site: www.helmitin.forbo.com
Sales Range: $25-49.9 Million
Emp.: 150
Mfr. & Sales of Surface Materials, Coatings & Adhesives
S.I.C.: 2891
N.A.I.C.S.: 325520

Forbo Helmitin SA (1)
56 Rue De General De Gaulle
67250 Surbourg, France FR
Tel.: (33) 388056868 (100%)
Fax: (33) 388805414
Web Site: www.forbo.com
Emp.: 66
Mfr. & Sales of Coatings & Adhesives
S.I.C.: 2891
N.A.I.C.S.: 325520
Castello Jose *(Gen Mgr)*

Forbo Ireland Ltd. (1)
2 Deansgrange Bus Pk
Deansgrange, Dublin, Ireland (100%)
Tel.: (353) 12898898
Fax: (353) 12898177
E-Mail: info@forbo.com
Web Site: www.forbo.com
Emp.: 7
Sales of Linoleum, Vinyl & Textile Floor Coverings
S.I.C.: 5713
N.A.I.C.S.: 442210
Paul Carney *(Mng Dir)*

Forbo Linoleum A/S (1)
Hagalokka 7 1483
Vettre, 1392 Asker, Norway (100%)
Tel.: (47) 66771200
Fax: (47) 66771240
E-Mail: info.norway@forbo.com
Web Site: www.forbo.no
Emp.: 30
Sales of Flooring
S.I.C.: 5713
N.A.I.C.S.: 442210
Mortem Aarhus *(Mng Dir)*

Forbo Linoleum A/S (1)
Produktionsvej 14
2600 Glostrup, Denmark (100%)
Tel.: (45) 44928500
Fax: (45) 44928520
E-Mail: info.denmark@forbo.com
Web Site: www.forbo.dk
Emp.: 15
Sales of Flooring
S.I.C.: 5713
N.A.I.C.S.: 442210
Jens Christian Holm Iversen *(Gen Mgr)*

Forbo Linoleum, Inc. (1)
3220 Orlando Dr
Mississauga, ON, 4V1R5, Canada (100%)
Tel.: (416) 661-2351
Fax: (416) 661-5362
E-Mail: info@fl.na.ca
Web Site: www.forboflooringna.com
Emp.: 5
Sales of Floor Coverings
S.I.C.: 5713
N.A.I.C.S.: 442210
Jacco Vlaar *(Gen Mgr)*

Forbo Linoleum (1)
Noordkustlaan 18
Groot-Bijgaarden, 1702, Belgium (100%)
Tel.: (32) 24670660
Fax: (32) 24670764
E-Mail: info.belgium@forbo.com
Web Site: www.forbo.be
Emp.: 25
Sales of Linoleum, Vinyl & Textile Floor Coverings, Wall Coverings, Coatings, Adhesives
S.I.C.: 5713
N.A.I.C.S.: 442210

Forbo Linolium B.V. (1)
Industrieweg 12
1566JP Assendelft, Netherlands (100%)
Tel.: (31) 756477477
Fax: (31) 756477700
E-Mail: contact@forbo.com
Web Site: www.forbo-flooring.com
Emp.: 700
Mfr. & Sales of Linoleum, Vinyl & Textile Floor Coverings, Coatings, Adhesives
S.I.C.: 3089
N.A.I.C.S.: 326199
Tom Kaiser *(Exec VP)*

Non-U.S. Subsidiary:

Forbo s.r.o. (2)
Novodvorska 994
Brno, Praha, 14221, Czech Republic (100%)
Tel.: (420) 239043011
Fax: (420) 239043012
E-Mail: forbo_sro@nextra.cz
Web Site: www.forbo.cz
Emp.: 10
Holding Company
S.I.C.: 6719
N.A.I.C.S.: 551112
Tomas Kudera *(Gen Mgr)*

Forbo-Novilon B.V. (1)
De Holwert 12
Coevorden, 7741 KC, Netherlands (100%)
Mailing Address:
Postbus 148
Coevorden, 7740 AC, Netherlands
Tel.: (31) 524596868
Fax: (31) 524596888
E-Mail: vacatures.novilon@forbo.com
Web Site: www.forbo.com
Emp.: 280
Mfr & Sale of Vinyl Floor Coverings
S.I.C.: 5713
N.A.I.C.S.: 442210
D Glance *(Mng Dir)*

Forbo Padloburkolatok Kft. (1)
Megyeri 8
1117 Budapest, Hungary
Tel.: (36) 0623444005
Fax: (36) 12720509
E-Mail: losonczi@forbo-krommenie.hu
Web Site: www.forbo.com
Sales of Flooring
S.I.C.: 5713
N.A.I.C.S.: 442210

Forbo Parquet AB (1)
Fabriksgatan 12
Tibro, 54350, Sweden (100%)
Tel.: (46) 50443920
Fax: (46) 50413793
E-Mail: info@forboparquet.com
Web Site: www.forboparquet.com
Emp.: 150
Mfr. of Floors
S.I.C.: 3089
N.A.I.C.S.: 326199
Neil Ringborg *(Gen Mgr)*

Forbo Participations SA (1)
56 Rue Du General De Gaulle
67250 Surbourg, France (100%)
Tel.: (33) 388056868
Fax: (33) 388805414
Web Site: www.forbo.com
Emp.: 70
Holding Company
S.I.C.: 6719
N.A.I.C.S.: 551112

Forbo Pavimentos SA (1)
Bofill 13 15
08013 Barcelona, Spain (100%)
Tel.: (34) 932090793
Fax: (34) 932456960
E-Mail: info@forbo-linoleum.es
Web Site: www.forbo-linoleum.es
Emp.: 5
Sales of Linoleum, Vinyl & Textile Floor Coverings
S.I.C.: 5713
N.A.I.C.S.: 442210
Agustin Matamoros *(Gen Mgr)*

Forbo Resilienti S.r.l. (1)
Centro Commerciale San Felice Lotto 2 Int 5
Segrate, IT-20090 Milan, Italy
Tel.: (39) 027531488
Fax: (39) 027532340
E-Mail: info.flooring.it@forbo.com
Web Site: www.forbo-flooring.it
Linoleum, Vinyl & Textile Floor Coverings & Wall Coverings Sales
S.I.C.: 5713
N.A.I.C.S.: 442210

Forbo Sarlino SA (1)
63 Rue Gosset
PO Box 2717
51100 Reims, France (100%)
Tel.: (33) 326773030
Fax: (33) 326074348
E-Mail: marketing-vente.sarlino@forbo.com
Web Site: www.sarlino.forbo.com
Emp.: 400
Mfr. & Sales of Vinyl & Textile Floor Coverings & Wall Coverings; Sales of Linoleum, Coatings & Adhesives
S.I.C.: 3089
N.A.I.C.S.: 326199
Cherry Colrs *(Pres)*

Division:

Forbo Flooring (2)
Parc Industriel Ouest
37110 Chateau-Renalt, France (100%)
Tel.: (33) 247298500
Fax: (33) 247298501
Emp.: 60
Carpet & Rug Mills
S.I.C.: 2273
N.A.I.C.S.: 314110
Selepp Pisen *(Gen Mgr)*

Forbo Siegling GmbH (1)
Lilienthalstrasse 6 8
PO Box 5346
D 30179 Hannover, Germany (100%)
Tel.: (49) 51167040
Fax: (49) 5116704305
E-Mail: info@forbo-siegling.com
Web Site: www.forbo-siegling.com
Emp.: 500
Flooring, Movement & Bonding Systems Mfr
S.I.C.: 2891
N.A.I.C.S.: 325520
Neele Neelan *(Mng Dir)*

Non-U.S. Subsidiaries:

Forbo Siegling Austria GmbH (2)
Oswald Redlich Strasse 1
1210 Vienna, Austria AT
Tel.: (43) 012596516 (100%)
Fax: (43) 12591716
E-Mail: siegling.at@forbo.com
Web Site: www.forbo-siegling.com
Sales Range: $1-9.9 Million
Emp.: 17

Forbo Holding AG—(Continued)

Conveyor, Processing, Modular, Timing, Folder and Carrier Machine Belt Mfr
S.I.C.: 3052
N.A.I.C.S.: 326220
Dietrich Brehm *(CEO)*

Forbo Siegling France S.A.S. **(2)**
184 Rue De La Mitterie
59461 Lomme, France FR
Tel.: (33) 320170280 (70%)
Fax: (33) 320170281
Web Site: www.forbo-siegling.com
Emp.: 70
Composites Mfr
S.I.C.: 5162
N.A.I.C.S.: 424610

Forbo Siegling Iberica S.A. **(2)**
Avda La Ferreria 74
08110 Montcada, Barcelona, Spain ES
Tel.: (34) 935644253 (100%)
Fax: (34) 935640505
E-Mail: siegling.es@forbo.com
Web Site: www.siegling.com
Emp.: 35
Sales of Coatings & Adhesives for Flooring Products
S.I.C.: 5169
N.A.I.C.S.: 424690

Forbo Siegling Japan Limited **(2)**
28 Kowa Bldg 2 20 1 Nishi Gotanda
Shinagawa-ku, Tokyo, 141-0031, Japan JP
Tel.: (81) 357402350 (100%)
Fax: (81) 357402351
E-Mail: siegling.jp@forbo.com
Web Site: www.forbo-siegling.co.jp
Emp.: 169
Mfr & Sales of Coatings & Adhesives
S.I.C.: 2891
N.A.I.C.S.: 325520

Forbo Siegling (Shenyang) Belting Co. Ltd **(2)**
Shenyang Eco And Tech Devel Zn
No 5 Mo Chou Hu St, 110141 Shenyang, China (100%)
Tel.: (86) 2425813813
Fax: (86) 2425816726
Web Site: www.siegling.com
Emp.: 113
S.I.C.: 2273
N.A.I.C.S.: 314110

Forbo Siegling (Shenyang) **(2)**
Shenyang Eco and Tech Devel Zn
No 5 Mo Chou Hu St, 110141 Shenyang, Liaoning, China (100%)
Tel.: (86) 2425813813
Fax: (86) 2425816726
E-Mail: info@siegling-asia.com
Web Site: www.siegling.com
Emp.: 100
S.I.C.: 2273
N.A.I.C.S.: 314110
Terence Oont *(Gen Mgr)*

Forbo Siegling Svenska AB **(2)**
Bangardsvagen 10
PO Box 140
S 42822 Kallered, Sweden SE
Tel.: (46) 31997050 (100%)
Fax: (46) 31997051
E-Mail: siegling.se@forbo.com
Web Site: www.forbo-siegling.com
Emp.: 30
Sales of Coatings & Adhesives
S.I.C.: 5169
N.A.I.C.S.: 424690
Shawn Serrano *(Pres)*

Siegling Brasil Ltda. **(2)**
Av Prof Vernon Krieble 500 Bairro Industrial Itaqui
06690-250 Itapevi, Brazil BR
Tel.: (55) 11 4143 7704 (100%)
Fax: (55) 11 441 5292
E-Mail: vendas@siegling.com.br
Web Site: www.siegling.com.br
Emp.: 180
Mfr & Sales of Coatings & Adhesives
S.I.C.: 2891
N.A.I.C.S.: 325520

Siegling Canada Ltd. **(2)**
3220 Orlando Dr
Mississauga, ON, L4V 1R5, Canada(100%)
Tel.: (905) 677-9983
Fax: (905) 678-7159
E-Mail:
Web Site: www.siegling.ca
Emp.: 30
Sales of Coatings & Adhesives
S.I.C.: 5169
N.A.I.C.S.: 424690

Siegling Danmark A/S **(2)**
Industrivej 34
2605 Brondby, Denmark DK
Tel.: (45) 43431033 (100%)
Fax: (45) 43433920
E-Mail: siegling.danmark@siegling.com
Web Site: www.siegling.com
Emp.: 24
Sales of Coatings & Adhesives
S.I.C.: 5169
N.A.I.C.S.: 424690

Siegling Italia S.p.a. **(2)**
Via Sondrio 4
20037 Paderno Dugnano, MI, Italy IT
Tel.: (39) 029100231 (100%)
Fax: (39) 0299045670
E-Mail: antonella.valiani@forbo.com
Web Site: www.forbo-siegling.com
Emp.: 60
Sales of Coatings & Adhesives
S.I.C.: 5169
N.A.I.C.S.: 424690

Siegling Mexico S.A. de C.V. **(2)**
Sor Juana Ines De La Cruz No 54
54033 Tlalnepantla, Mexico MX
Tel.: (52) 5553902177 (100%)
Fax: (52) 55657465
E-Mail: siegling.mexico@siegling.com.mx
Web Site: www.siegling.com.mx
Sales Range: $1-9.9 Million
Emp.: 70
Mfr. & Sales of Coatings & Adhesives
S.I.C.: 2891
N.A.I.C.S.: 325520
Gabriel Muradas *(Mgr)*

Siegling Nederland B.V. **(2)**
Van Rensselaerweg 1
NL 6956 AV Dieren, Netherlands
Tel.: (31) 313491111
Fax: (31) 313422314
E-Mail: siegling.nederland@forbo.com
Web Site: www.siegling.com
Emp.: 55
S.I.C.: 2273
N.A.I.C.S.: 314110
Dietrich Brehm *(CEO)*

Siegling (Schweiz) AG **(2)**
Kapell Strasse 2
4323 Wallbach, Switzerland CH
Tel.: (41) 618656161 (100%)
Fax: (41) 618656162
E-Mail: info@siegling.ch.forbo.com
Web Site: www.siegling.ch.forbo.com
Sales Range: $10-24.9 Million
Emp.: 120
Mfr. & Sale of Coatings & Adhesives
S.I.C.: 2891
N.A.I.C.S.: 325520

Forbo Tapijt B.V. **(1)**
Postbus 56, 5050AB Goirle, Netherlands
Tel.: (31) 13 5349035
Fax: (31) 13 5349035
Web Site: www.forbo.com
Mfr. & Sale of Flooring
S.I.C.: 5713
N.A.I.C.S.: 442210

Forbo UK Ltd. **(1)**
Den Rd
PO Box 1
Kirkcaldy, Fife, KY1 2SB, United Kingdom (100%)
Tel.: (44) 1773740688
Fax: (44) 1773740640
E-Mail: info.uk@forbo.com
Web Site: www.forbo-flooring.co.uk
Emp.: 160
Holding Company
S.I.C.: 6719
N.A.I.C.S.: 551112

Nairn Floors Benelux B.V. **(1)**
PO Box 1
Kirkcaldy, Fife, KY1 2SB, United Kingdom
Tel.: (44) 592643777
Fax: (44) 1592643999
E-Mail: info.uk@forbo.com
Web Site: www.forbo-flooring.co.uk
Sale of Flooring
S.I.C.: 5713
N.A.I.C.S.: 442210
Angus Fotherinhame *(Gen Mgr)*

Novilon Ltd. **(1)**
PO Box 1
Kirkcaldy, KY1 2SB, United Kingdom
Tel.: (44) 592643777
Fax: (44) 1592643999
Web Site: www.forbo.com
Sales of Vinyl Floor Coverings
S.I.C.: 5713
N.A.I.C.S.: 442210

FORCE MOTORS LIMITED

Mumbai Pune Road Akurdi
Pune, 411035, India
Tel.: (91) 2027476381
Fax: (91) 2027404678
E-Mail: isdsupport@forcemotors.com
Web Site: www.forcemotors.com
500033—(BOM)
Rev.: $422,094,785
Assets: $317,141,465
Liabilities: $102,877,909
Net Worth: $214,263,556
Earnings: $2,673,825
Emp.: 4,600
Fiscal Year-end: 03/31/13

Business Description:
Light Commercial Vehicles, Utility Vehicles, Three Wheelers, Agricultural Tractors & Heavy Commercial Vehicles Mfr
S.I.C.: 3711
N.A.I.C.S.: 336112

Personnel:
Prasan Firodia *(Mng Dir)*
Aparna G. Lambore *(Compliance Officer & Sec)*

Board of Directors:
Abhay N. Firodia
R. B. Bhandari
Atul Chordia
Prasan Firodia
S. A. Gundecha
Vinay Kothari
L. Lakshman
Sudhir Mehta
S. Padmanabhan
Pratap G. Pawar
Anita Ramachandran
Arun Seth

Transfer Agent:
Link Intime India Private Limited
Block No 202 2nd Floor Akshay Complex Near Ganesh Temple
Pune, India

FORD & SLATER DAF LEICESTER

Hazel Dr
Narborough Rd South, Leicester, LE3 2JG, United Kingdom
Tel.: (44) 1162632900
Fax: (44) 1162630042
E-Mail: enquiries@fordandslater.co.uk
Web Site: www.fordandslater.co.uk
Year Founded: 1929
Emp.: 360

Business Description:
Commercial Vehicle Distribution
S.I.C.: 5599
N.A.I.C.S.: 441228

Personnel:
Peter A.D. Strevens *(Chm)*
Nigel J. Strevens *(Co-Mng Dir)*
Timothy M. Strevens *(Co-Mng Dir)*

Subsidiaries:

Ford & Slater Corby **(1)**
Gretton Brook Road Earlstrees Industrial Estate
Corby, Northamptonshire, NN17 4BA, United Kingdom
Tel.: (44) 1536 207 980
Fax: (44) 1536 207 989
E-Mail: corby@fordandslater.co.uk
Web Site: www.fordandslatercorby.co.uk
Emp.: 15
Commercial Vehicle Dealer
S.I.C.: 5599
N.A.I.C.S.: 441228
John Rowlands *(Gen Mgr-After Sls)*

Ford & Slater Coventry **(1)**
Rowley Road
Coventry, West Midlands, CV3 4FL, United Kingdom
Tel.: (44) 2476 302 856
Fax: (44) 2476 305 584
E-Mail: coventry@fordandslater.co.uk
Web Site: www.fordandslatercoventry.co.uk
Emp.: 25
Commercial Vehicle Dealer
S.I.C.: 5571
N.A.I.C.S.: 441228
Matt Ball *(Mgr-Depot)*

Ford & Slater Kings Lynn **(1)**
Maple Road Saddlebow
King's Lynn, Norfolk, PE34 3AH, United Kingdom
Tel.: (44) 1553 764 466
Fax: (44) 1533 764 612
E-Mail: kingslynn@fordandslater.co.uk
Web Site: www.fordandslaterkingslynn.co.uk
Emp.: 35
Commercial Vehicle Dealer
S.I.C.: 5571
N.A.I.C.S.: 441228
Ali Drummond *(Area Gen Mgr)*

Ford & Slater Newark **(1)**
Newlink Business Park
Newark, Nottinghamshire, NG24 2NZ, United Kingdom
Tel.: (44) 1636 701 673
Fax: (44) 1636 594 081
E-Mail: newark@fordandslater.co.uk
Web Site: www.fordandslaternewark.co.uk
Commercial Vehicle Dealer
S.I.C.: 5571
N.A.I.C.S.: 441228
Ali Drummond *(Area Gen Mgr)*

Ford & Slater Norwich **(1)**
Longwater Business Park
Norwich, Norfolk, NR5 0JS, United Kingdom
Tel.: (44) 1603 731 600
Fax: (44) 1603 731 620
E-Mail: norwich@fordandslater.co.uk
Web Site: www.fordandslaternorwich.co.uk
Commercial Vehicle Dealer
S.I.C.: 5571
N.A.I.C.S.: 441228
Keith Spurway *(Principal-Dealership)*

Ford & Slater Peterborough **(1)**
Newark Road Eastern Industrial Estate
Peterborough, Cambridgeshire, PE1 5YD, United Kingdom
Tel.: (44) 1733 295 000
Fax: (44) 1733 295 010
E-Mail: peterborough@fordandslater.co.uk
Web Site: www.fordandslaterpeterborough.co.uk
Emp.: 50
Commercial Vehicle Dealer
S.I.C.: 5599
N.A.I.C.S.: 441228
Bill Prosser *(Principal-Dealership)*

Ford & Slater Spalding **(1)**
9 Wardentree Lane Pinchbeck
Spalding, Lincolnshire, PE11 3ZN, United Kingdom
Tel.: (44) 1775 715 680
Fax: (44) 1775 718 185
E-Mail: spalding@fordandslater.co.uk
Web Site: www.fordandslaterspalding.co.uk
Commercial Vehicle Dealer
S.I.C.: 5599
N.A.I.C.S.: 441228
Ali Drummond *(Area Gen Mgr)*

Ford & Slater Wisbech **(1)**
Commercial House Algores Way
Wisbech, Cambridgeshire, PE13 2TQ, United Kingdom
Tel.: (44) 1945 461 316
Fax: (44) 1945 466 330
E-Mail: wisbech@fordandslater.co.uk
Web Site: www.fordandslaterwisbech.co.uk
Emp.: 10

Commercial Vehicle Dealer
S.I.C.: 5571
N.A.I.C.S.: 441228
Ali Drummond *(Area Gen Mgr)*

FORD EAGLE GROUP LIMITED

Rm 3205 32/F Godlen Central Tower
3037 Jintian Road
Futian District, Shenzhen, China
Tel.: (86) 755 82709909
Fax: (86) 755 22632038
E-Mail: info@fordeagle.com
Web Site: www.fordeagle.com
FEGP—(ISDX)
Business Description:
Financial Advisory Services
S.I.C.: 6282
N.A.I.C.S.: 523930
Personnel:
Jack Wing Tak Law *(CEO)*
Board of Directors:
Tony Drury
Jack Wing Tak Law
Nicholas Littlewood
Gary Willinge

FOREBASE INTERNATIONAL HOLDINGS LIMITED

(Formerly Kwang Sung Electronics H.K. & Co. Limited)
Units 208-209 Bio-Informatics Centre
No 2 Science Park West Avenue
Hong Kong Science Park, Sha Tin, N T, China (Hong Kong)
Tel.: (852) 2946 7600
Fax: (852) 2602 6490
E-Mail: investors@kse.com.hk
Web Site: www.kse.com.hk
2310—(HKG)
Sales Range: $75-99.9 Million
Emp.: 953
Business Description:
Electronic Components Mfr
S.I.C.: 3676
N.A.I.C.S.: 334416
Personnel:
Yong Shen *(Chm)*
Ronald Lew Podlas *(CEO)*
Sze Lok Tang *(CFO & Sec)*
Board of Directors:
Yong Shen
Sang Joon Hong
Ying Jiang
Kin Pang Leung
Zhi Li
Ronald Lew Podlas
Ke Shen
Li Jian Xu
Lei Yu
Cui Lan Zhang
Ernst Rudolf Zimmermann
Transfer Agent:
Tricor Standard Limited
Level 25 3 Pacific Place
1 Queen's Road East
Hong Kong, China (Hong Kong)
Subsidiary:

Shenzhen Kwang Sung Electronics Co., Ltd. **(1)**
Ste 208-209 2 F Bio-Informatics Ctr No 2 Science Park
Hong Kong Science Park, Sha Tin, New Territories, China (Hong Kong)
Tel.: (852) 29467600
Fax: (852) 26026490
E-Mail: info@kse.com.hk
Web Site: www.kse.cpm.hk
Emp.: 30
IFT & Coil Products Mfr
S.I.C.: 3676
N.A.I.C.S.: 334416
B H Ko *(Gen Mgr-Sls & Mktg)*

FOREFRONT GROUP LIMITED

Room No 1103 11/F China United Center 28 Marble Road North Point
Hong Kong, China (Hong Kong)
Tel.: (852) 34228787
Fax: (852) 25625512
E-Mail: info@forefront.com.hk
Web Site: www.forefront.com.hk
0885—(HKG)
Rev.: $282,272
Assets: $123,628,749
Liabilities: $983,502
Net Worth: $122,645,248
Earnings: ($5,400,039)
Emp.: 22
Fiscal Year-end: 12/31/12
Business Description:
Investment Management Services
S.I.C.: 6282
N.A.I.C.S.: 523920
Personnel:
Ming Kwong Yeung *(Chm)*
Kark Ming Chui *(Sec)*
Board of Directors:
Ming Kwong Yeung
Yuk Lun Chung
Flora Yan Fong Lam
Sheree Oi Kwok Lo
William Eui Won Pak
Louis Wen
Legal Counsel:
Maples & Calder Asia
53th Floor, The Center, 99 Queen's Road
Hong Kong, China (Hong Kong)
Conyers Dill & Pearman
2901 One Exchange Square 8 Connaught Place
Central, China (Hong Kong)
Transfer Agent:
Tricor Tengis Limited
26th Floor Tesbury Centre 28 Queen's Road East
Wanchai, China (Hong Kong)
Tel.: (852) 29801333
Fax: (852) 28108185

THE FOREIGN TRADE TRANSPORT JOINT STOCK CORP.

A8 Truong Son str
Tan Binh Dist, Ho Chi Minh City, Vietnam
Tel.: (84) 8 38 44 64 09
Fax: (84) 8 38 48 83 59
E-Mail: mngt@vinafreight.com.vn
Web Site: vinafreight.com
Year Founded: 1997
VNF—(HNX)
Sls.: $48,145,774
Assets: $16,955,984
Liabilities: $9,698,938
Net Worth: $7,257,046
Earnings: $317,416
Fiscal Year-end: 12/31/12
Business Description:
Airfreight & Logistics Services
S.I.C.: 4512
N.A.I.C.S.: 481112
Personnel:
Bich Lan Nguyen *(Gen Mgr)*

FORELAND FABRICTECH HOLDINGS LIMITED

Second Processing Zone
Dongshi Town, Jinjiang, Fujian, 362271, China
Tel.: (86) 59585585508
Fax: (86) 59585587446
E-Mail: admin@fulianknitting.com
Web Site: www.fulianknitting.com
B0I—(SES)
Rev.: $64,428,130
Assets: $110,432,520
Liabilities: $3,929,631
Net Worth: $106,502,889
Earnings: $3,035,306
Fiscal Year-end: 12/31/12
Business Description:
Broadwoven Fabrics Mfr
S.I.C.: 2299
N.A.I.C.S.: 313210
Personnel:
Kin Chit Tsoi *(Chm)*
Shing Mun Wong *(CFO)*
Foon Yeow Chia *(Sec)*
Board of Directors:
Kin Chit Tsoi
Fengquan Cai
Siang Kai Lim
Chee Kian Tan
Transfer Agents:
Boardroom Corporate & Advisory Services Pte. Ltd.
50 Raffles Place 32-01 Singapore Land Tower
Singapore, Singapore
Appleby Management (Bermuda) Ltd.
Canon's Court 22 Victoria Street
HM 12 Hamilton, Bermuda
Subsidiary:

Fulian Knitting Co., Ltd **(1)**
Second Processing Zone
Dongshi Town Jinjiang, Fuzhou, Fujian, China
Tel.: (86) 595 85585508
Fax: (86) 595 85593369
E-Mail: admin@fulianknitting.com
Web Site: fulianknitting.cn
Emp.: 400
Fabric Products Mfr
S.I.C.: 2259
N.A.I.C.S.: 313240

FOREMAN CAPITAL B.V.

WTC Amsterdam Tower H 24th Floor
Zuidplein 202
1077 XV Amsterdam, Netherlands
Tel.: (31) 20 470 6944
Fax: (31) 20 890 7784
Web Site: www.foremancapital.nl
Business Description:
Equity Investment Firm
S.I.C.: 6211
N.A.I.C.S.: 523999
Personnel:
Arent Foch *(Co-Founder & Partner)*
Guido ter Kuile *(Co-Founder & Partner)*
Matthew Boatfield *(Partner)*

FOREMOST AUDIO SDN. BHD.

Lot 5613 Sungai Ketapang
08300 Gurun, Kedah, Malaysia
Tel.: (60) 44687489
Fax: (60) 44687482
E-Mail: admin@foremost-audio.com
Emp.: 300
Business Description:
Audio Speakers Mfr & Whslr
S.I.C.: 3651
N.A.I.C.S.: 334310
Personnel:
Chieng Sim Ooi *(Chm)*
Kim Weng Ng *(Mng Dir)*

FOREMOST INCOME FUND

1225 64th Avenue Northeast
Calgary, AB, T2E 8P9, Canada
Tel.: (403) 295-5800
Fax: (403) 295-5832
Toll Free: (800) 661-9190
E-Mail: investorrelations@foremost.ca
Web Site: www.foremost.ca
Year Founded: 1994
Rev.: $259,866,649
Assets: $212,525,452
Liabilities: $50,290,454
Net Worth: $162,234,998
Earnings: $19,609,033
Emp.: 681
Fiscal Year-end: 12/31/12
Business Description:
Open-End Mutual Fund; Oil & Gas, Mining, Water Well & Construction Equipment Mfr & Distr
S.I.C.: 6722
N.A.I.C.S.: 525910
Personnel:
Pat W. Breen *(Pres & CEO)*
Jackie Schenn *(CFO & VP-Fin)*
Computershare Trust Company of Canada
Toronto, ON, Canada
Transfer Agents:
Computershare Trust Company of Canada
Toronto, ON, Canada
Computershare Trust Company of Canada
600 530 8th Avenue SW
Calgary, AB, T2P 3S8, Canada
Tel.: (403) 267-6555
Toll Free: (800) 558-0046
Subsidiaries:

Foremost Industries LP **(1)**
1225 64th Avenue NE
Calgary, AB, T2E 8P9, Canada AB
Tel.: (403) 295-5800
Fax: (403) 295-5810
Toll Free: (800) 661-9190
E-Mail: sales@foremost.ca
Industrial, Mining & Construction Equipment Designer, Mfr & Whslr
S.I.C.: 5082
N.A.I.C.S.: 423810
Pat W. Breen *(Pres)*

Foremost Universal LP **(1)**
450-630 6th Avenue SW
Calgary, AB, T2P 0S8, Canada AB
Tel.: (403) 266-4556
Fax: (403) 930-2674
E-Mail: sales@foremost.ca
Energy Industry Tank, Vacuum & Compression Equipment Designer, Mfr & Whslr
S.I.C.: 3533
N.A.I.C.S.: 333132
Pat W. Breen, *(Pres)*

FORENT ENERGY LTD.

Suite 200 340 - 12th Avenue SW
Calgary, AB, T2R 1L5, Canada
Tel.: (403) 262-9444
Fax: (403) 262-4351
E-Mail: info@forentenergy.com
Web Site: www.forentenergy.com
Year Founded: 1999
FEN—(TSXV)
Rev.: $476,683
Assets: $12,729,708
Liabilities: $2,911,278
Net Worth: $9,818,431
Earnings: ($2,505,552)
Fiscal Year-end: 12/31/12
Business Description:
Oil & Natural Gas Exploration Services
S.I.C.: 1389
N.A.I.C.S.: 213112
Personnel:
Dennis Forgeron *(Founder)*
W. Brett Wilson *(Chm)*
Richard Wade *(Pres & CEO)*
Brad R. Perry *(CFO)*
Scott Reeves *(Sec)*
Scott McDonald *(Exec VP)*
Board of Directors:
W. Brett Wilson
Robert S. Crosbie
John A. Forgeron
Doug Porter
Scott Reeves
Wayne Rousch
Transfer Agent:
Valiant Trust Company
Suite 310 606 4th Street S.W.
Calgary, AB, Canada

FOREST AGRI SERVICES LTD.

7 Enterprise Dr
Forest, ON, N0N1J0, Canada

Forest Agri Services LTD.—(Continued)

Tel.: (519) 786-2763
Fax: (519) 786-6520
E-Mail: foragri@xcelco.on.ca
Web Site: www.forestagriservices.com
Sales Range: $10-24.9 Million
Emp.: 7

Business Description:
Agricultural Produts Supplier
S.I.C.: 9641
N.A.I.C.S.: 926140
Personnel:
Everett Moons *(Gen Mgr & Grain Trader)*

FOREST ENTERPRISES AUSTRALIA LIMITED

233b Charles Street
Launceston, TAS, 7250, Australia
Tel.: (61) 363347811
Fax: (61) 363344660
E-Mail: enquiries@fealtd.com
Web Site: www.fealtd.com
Sales Range: $75-99.9 Million
Emp.: 15

Business Description:
Forestry & Forest Products Company
S.I.C.: 0851
N.A.I.C.S.: 115310
Personnel:
William Edwards *(Chm)*
Board of Directors:
William Edwards
Tony Cannon
Peter Curry
Vince Erasmus
Anthony Seymour
David Taylor
Michael Williams

Legal Counsel:
Minter Ellison
Level 23 S Rialto Tower 525 Collins St
Melbourne, Australia

Subsidiary:

FEA Plantations Limited **(1)**
233B Charles St
Launceston, TAS, 7250, Australia
Tel.: (61) 363347811
Fax: (61) 363344660
E-Mail: fea@feaplantations.com.au
Emp.: 20
Forestry Services
S.I.C.: 0851
N.A.I.C.S.: 115310

FOREST GATE ENERGY INC.

706 7th Ave Suite 910
Calgary, AB, T2P 0Z1, Canada
Tel.: (514) 486-3040
Fax: (514) 488-1314
Toll Free: (866) 666-3040
Web Site: www.forestgate.ca
Year Founded: 1999
FGE—(TSXV)
Sales Range: Less than $1 Million
Emp.: 6

Business Description:
Oil & Gas Exploration Services
S.I.C.: 1311
N.A.I.C.S.: 211111
Personnel:
Michael C. Judson *(Chm, Pres & CEO)*
Nancy Guitard *(CFO)*
Board of Directors:
Michael C. Judson
Nicholas Powell
Brian Weihs

Transfer Agent:
CIBC Mellon Trust Company
2001 University Street Suite 1600
Montreal, QC, Canada

FOREST PLACE GROUP LIMITED

Level 5 WHK Horwath Ctr
120 Edward St
4000 Brisbane, Queensland, Australia
Tel.: (61) 733193630
Fax: (61) 733193640
Web Site: www.forestplace.com.au
FPG—(ASX)
Sales Range: $25-49.9 Million

Business Description:
Provides Safe & Secure Life For Retired Persons
S.I.C.: 8049
N.A.I.C.S.: 621399
Personnel:
Peter Brown *(Chm)*
Lisa Godfrey *(Sec)*
Board of Directors:
Peter Brown
David Hunt
Justin Michael Laboo
D. C. Mackenzie
Matthew Palavidis
P. Parker
Legal Counsel:
Minter Ellison
Waterfront Place 1 Eagle Street
Brisbane, Australia

FOREST SUPPORT SERVICES PLC

Broad Quay Rd Felnex Industrial Estate
Newport, Gwent, NP19 4PN, United Kingdom
Tel.: (44) 1633284700
Fax: (44) 1633279169
E-Mail: info@forestsupportservices.co.uk
Web Site: www.forestsupportservices.co.uk
Sales Range: $1-9.9 Million
Emp.: 180
Fiscal Year-end: 12/31/12

Business Description:
Traffic Management Services
S.I.C.: 8742
N.A.I.C.S.: 541611
Personnel:
Christopher Powell *(Chm)*
Ross Williams *(Mng Dir)*
Board of Directors:
Christopher Powell
Kevin Allen
Ian Martin
Ross Williams

Subsidiary:

Forest Traffic Signals Limited **(1)**
Forest House Felnex Industrial Estate
Broad Quay Rd, Newport, Gwent, NP19 4PN, United Kingdom
Tel.: (44) 1633284700
Fax: (44) 1633822000
E-Mail: info@forestsupportservices.co.uk
Emp.: 70
Traffic Management & Administration Services
S.I.C.: 7383
N.A.I.C.S.: 519110
Ross Williams *(Mng Dir)*

FOREVER ZEN LTD.

E09 Calle Jacarandas
Urbanizacion Los Laureles, San Jose, Costa Rica
Toll Free: 8668600707
E-Mail: info@foreverzen.net
Web Site: www.foreverzen.net
Year Founded: 2010
FRVZ—(OTC)
Assets: $1,534
Liabilities: $19,066
Net Worth: ($17,532)
Earnings: ($28,772)
Fiscal Year-end: 10/31/12

Business Description:
Men's Skincare Products Mfr
S.I.C.: 2844
N.A.I.C.S.: 325620
Personnel:
Hans Morgan Van Niekerk *(Pres, CEO, CFO, Treas & Sec)*

FOREZ BENNES

Z I Champdieu Lieu Dit Tournel
42600 Montbrison, France
Tel.: (33) 477966969
Fax: (33) 477966970
E-Mail: accueil@forez-bennes.fr
Web Site: www.forezbennes.com
Sls.: $20,600,000
Emp.: 43

Business Description:
Motor Vehicles & Car Bodies
S.I.C.: 3711
N.A.I.C.S.: 336111
Personnel:
Laurent Bourrin *(Gen Mgr)*
Board of Directors:
Rodolphe Bourrin

FORFARMERS GROUP B.V

Kwinkweerd 12
NL-7241 CW Lochem, Netherlands
Tel.: (31) 573 28 88 00
Fax: (31) 573 28 88 99
E-Mail: info@forfarmersgroup.eu
Web Site: www.forfarmersgroup.eu
Sales Range: $5-14.9 Billion
Emp.: 847

Business Description:
Animal Feed Products Mfr
S.I.C.: 2048
N.A.I.C.S.: 311119
Personnel:
Jan Markink *(Chm-Supervisory Bd)*
B.J. Ruumpol *(CEO)*
N.W. De Vos *(COO)*
J.N. Potijk *(Chief Comml Officer)*
Supervisory Board of Directors:
Sandra Addink-Berendsen
Henk De Lange
Jan Eggink
Jan Markink
Henk Mulder
Haje Nordbeck
Pieter Ter Kuile
Louise Trompert-Vrielink

FORGAME HOLDINGS LIMITED

38/F West Hall Renfeng Building 490 Tianhe Road
Guangzhou, China
Tel.: (86) 20 66608091
Fax: (86) 20 38038208
E-Mail: ir@forgame.com
Web Site: www.forgame.com
Year Founded: 2009
484—(HKG)
Rev.: $123,370,694
Earnings: $34,568,460
Fiscal Year-end: 12/31/12

Business Description:
Web-Based & Mobile Game Developer & Publisher
S.I.C.: 2741
N.A.I.C.S.: 519130
Personnel:
Dongfeng Wang *(Chm & CEO)*
Weibing Huang *(Co-Pres)*
Dong Liao *(Co-Pres)*
Jieguang Zhuang *(Co-Pres)*
Gary King Leung Ngan *(CFO)*
Board of Directors:
Dongfeng Wang
Weibing Huang
Eric Joshua Levin
Dong Liao
Philana Wai Yin Poon
Hainan Tan
Hans Tung
Richard Cong Zhao
Jieguang Zhuang

FORGE GROUP LTD.

28 Troode Street
West Perth, WA, 6005, Australia
Tel.: (61) 8 6389 8500
Fax: (61) 8 6389 8599
E-Mail: info@forgegroup.com.au
Web Site: www.forgegroup.com
FGE—(ASX)
Rev.: $1,098,477,610
Assets: $483,753,241
Liabilities: $261,342,006
Net Worth: $222,411,235
Earnings: $65,567,890
Emp.: 2,000
Fiscal Year-end: 06/30/13

Business Description:
Holding Company; Engineering, Procurement & Construction Services
S.I.C.: 6719
N.A.I.C.S.: 551112
Personnel:
David Simpson *(CEO & Mng Dir)*
Donald Montgomery *(CFO)*
Lee Arasu *(Chief Dev Officer)*
Robert Mancini *(Gen Counsel)*
Glen Smith *(Sec)*
Board of Directors:
David Craig
Julie Beeby
Marcello Cardaci
Greg Kempton
John O'Connor
David Simpson
Grahame White

Subsidiary:

Forge Group Construction Pty. Ltd. **(1)**
(Formerly Cimeco Pty. Ltd.)
28 Troode Street
West Perth, WA, 6005, Australia AU
Tel.: (61) 8 6389 8500
Fax: (61) 8 6389 8599
E-Mail:
Web Site: www.forgegroup.com
Emp.: 300
Industrial & Infrastructural Construction Contractor
S.I.C.: 1629
N.A.I.C.S.: 237990
David Simpson *(CEO)*

U.S. Subsidiary:

Forge Group North America, LLC **(1)**
(Formerly Taggart Global, LLC)
4000 Town Center Blvd
Canonsburg, PA 15317 PA
Tel.: (724) 754-9800
Fax: (724) 754-9801
E-Mail: north.america@forgegroup.com
Web Site: www.forgegroup.com
Emp.: 750
Coal Processing Plant & Material Handling Systems Engineering & Construction Services Contractor
S.I.C.: 1541
N.A.I.C.S.: 236210
Kenneth J. Lund *(Chief Comml Officer)*
John J. Luke *(Gen Counsel & VP)*

Subsidiary:

Forge Group Site Services, LLC **(2)**
(Formerly Taggart Site Services Group, LLC)
4000 Town Center Blvd
Canonsburg, PA 15317 PA
Tel.: (724) 754-9800
Construction Site Preparation Contractor
S.I.C.: 1799
N.A.I.C.S.: 238910
Daniel S. Placha *(COO-North America)*

FORGE MEDIA GROUP LIMITED
17-21 Maidstone Street
PO Box 47-254
Ponsonby, 1144, New Zealand
Tel.: (64) 93768848
Fax: (64) 93763056
E-Mail: marketing@forge.co.nz
Web Site: www.forge.co.nz
Sales Range: $1-9.9 Million
Emp.: 35
Business Description:
Graphic Design, Print Production, CD Reproduction & Packaging & Various Advertising Related Services
S.I.C.: 7336
N.A.I.C.S.: 541430
Personnel:
Chris Due *(Chm)*
Paul Dennis *(CEO)*
Board of Directors:
Chris Due
Paul Dennis
Legal Counsel:
Jones Young
135 Albert St
Auckland, New Zealand

FORGES DE NIAUX
Lieu Dit Niaux
09400 Pamiers, France
Tel.: (33) 561657100
Fax: (33) 561657101
E-Mail: contact@forgesdeniaux.com
Web Site: www.forgesdeniaux.com
Sls.: $21,300,000
Emp.: 132
Business Description:
Farm Mach & Equipment
S.I.C.: 3523
N.A.I.C.S.: 333111
Personnel:
Laurent Pineda *(Pres)*

FORGES DE TRIE-CHATEAU
Rue des Troenes
BP 3
60590 Trie-Chateau, France
Tel.: (33) 3 44 49 71 12
Fax: (33) 3 44 49 73 84
E-Mail: contact@ftc-forges.com
Web Site: www.forges-de-trie-chateau.fr
Year Founded: 1968
MLFTC—(EUR)
Sales Range: $25-49.9 Million
Business Description:
Steel Forging Mfr
S.I.C.: 3462
N.A.I.C.S.: 332111
Personnel:
Philippe Schmitter *(Chm & Mgr-Export Sls)*

FORGES TARDIEU LTD
31 Nicolay Road
Port Louis, Mauritius
Tel.: (230) 2065200
Fax: (230) 2407179
E-Mail: tardieu@intnet.mu
Web Site: www.forgestardieu.com
Year Founded: 1931
FORT—(MAU)
Sales Range: $10-24.9 Million
Emp.: 200
Business Description:
Mechanical Engineering Services
S.I.C.: 8711
N.A.I.C.S.: 541330
Personnel:
Hubert Raffray *(Mng Dir)*
Jean Jacques Jullienne *(Asst Mng Dir)*

Subsidiaries:

Electrical & Control Specialists Ltd **(1)**
31 Nicolay Road
PO Box 20
Port Louis, Mauritius
Tel.: (230) 206 5280
Fax: (230) 216 0484
E-Mail: ecs.co@intnet.mu
Web Site: www.ecs.mu
Emp.: 20
Electrical Engineering Services
S.I.C.: 8711
N.A.I.C.S.: 541330
Christophe Desvaux de Marigny, *(Gen Mgr)*

Fortaweld Ltd. **(1)**
31 route Nicolay
BP 20
Port Louis, Mauritius
Tel.: (230) 206 5250
Fax: (230) 216 2951
E-Mail: fortaweld@intnet.mu
Web Site: www.fortaweld.mu
Emp.: 20
Welding & Cutting Equipment Distr
S.I.C.: 5084
N.A.I.C.S.: 423830

Fotaflex Ltd. **(1)**
31 Nicolay Road
Port Louis, Mauritius
Tel.: (230) 2065260
Fax: (230) 2407158
E-Mail: fotaflex@intnet.mu
Emp.: 12
Gasket & Sealing Device Mfr
S.I.C.: 3053
N.A.I.C.S.: 339991
Hubert Refaey, *(Gen Mgr)*

TARDIEU TECHNICAL SUPPORT LTD. **(1)**
31 Nicolay Road
PO Box 20
Port Louis, Mauritius
Tel.: (230) 2065270
Fax: (230) 2160254
E-Mail: ttscol@intnet.mu
Boiler Repair & Maintenance Services
S.I.C.: 7699
N.A.I.C.S.: 811310

FORHOUSE CORPORATION
No 45 Alley 313 Sec 3 Min-Sheng Rd
Shang Feng Tsun
Taichung, Taiwan
Tel.: (886) 425692188
Fax: (886) 425692855
Web Site: www.forhouse.com.tw
6120—(TAI)
Sales Range: $350-399.9 Million
Business Description:
Optoelectronic Products Mfr
S.I.C.: 3674
N.A.I.C.S.: 334413
Personnel:
Max Cheng *(Chm)*

Plant:

Forhouse Corporation - Da-Ya Factory **(1)**
No 45 Lane 313 Sec 3 Minsheng Road
Daya District, Taichung, 42844, Taiwan
Tel.: (886) 4 2569 2188
Fax: (886) 4 2569 2855
Web Site: www.forhouse.com.tw/_english/1_about/5_global.php
Optronic Products Mfr
S.I.C.: 3674
N.A.I.C.S.: 334413

Non-U.S. Plants:

Forhouse Corporation - Malaysian Factory **(1)**
1727 Jalan Industri 2 Taman Perindustrian Bukit Panchor
Nibong Tebal, Penang, 14300, Malaysia
Tel.: (60) 4 5937860
Fax: (60) 4 5937866
Electronic Products Mfr & Sales
S.I.C.: 3679
N.A.I.C.S.: 334419

Forhouse Corporation - Xiamen Factory **(1)**
No 18 Xiangming Road
Xiangan District, Xiamen, Fujian, 361101, China
Tel.: (86) 5927829666
Fax: (86) 592 7829 898
Web Site: www.forhouse.com.tw/_english/1_about/5_global.php
Optoelectronic Products Mfr
S.I.C.: 3674
N.A.I.C.S.: 334413

FORIND AVIO ELETTRONICA S.P.A.
Via Nicolo Copernico 6
20060 Cassina de' Pecchi, MI, Italy
Tel.: (39) 0295343080
Fax: (39) 0295343104
E-Mail: info@forind.it
Web Site: www.forind.it
Year Founded: 1968
Sales Range: $1-9.9 Million
Emp.: 20
Business Description:
Electrical Apparatus & Equipment Distr
S.I.C.: 5063
N.A.I.C.S.: 423610
Personnel:
Roberto Lechiancole *(Pres)*

FORJAS TAURUS S.A.
Av Do Forte 511
91360000 Porto Alegre, RS, Brazil
Tel.: (55) 51 3021 3000
Fax: (55) 51 3021 3075
E-Mail: ri@taurus.com.br
Web Site: www.taurus.com.br
Year Founded: 1939
FJTA3—(BRAZ)
Sales Range: $250-299.9 Million
Emp.: 4,800
Business Description:
Firearm Mfr & Whslr
S.I.C.: 3489
N.A.I.C.S.: 332994
Personnel:
Doris Beatriz Franca Wilhelm *(Dir-IR)*

FORLINK SOFTWARE CORPORATION, INC.
9/F Shenzhou Mansion No 31
ZhongGuanCun South Street
Haidian District, Beijing, 100081, China
Tel.: (86) 10 6811 8866
E-Mail: ir@forlink.com
Web Site: www.forlink.com
Year Founded: 1993
FLSWD—(OTC)
Sls.: $2,929,699
Assets: $4,187,313
Liabilities: $4,213,943
Net Worth: ($26,630)
Earnings: ($1,948,885)
Emp.: 203
Fiscal Year-end: 12/31/12
Business Description:
Software Publisher
S.I.C.: 7372
N.A.I.C.S.: 511210
Personnel:
Yi He *(Chm & CEO)*
Hongkeung Lam *(CFO, Chief Acctg Officer & Sec)*
Board of Directors:
Yi He
Yu Fang
Hongkeung Lam
Guoliang Tian
Subsidiary:

Nanning Bulk Commodities Exchange Corporation Limited **(1)**
7th Floor Building B Xijiang Mansion NO 100 Minzu Road
Nanning, China
Tel.: (86) 7712260598
E-Mail: service@nnbce.com
Web Site: www.nnbce.com
Warehousing & Logistics Services
S.I.C.: 4225
N.A.I.C.S.: 493110

FORMA SA BOTOSANI
3 Calea Nationala
Botosani, 710001, Romania
Tel.: (40) 231 510189
Fax: (40) 231 510189
E-Mail: office@forma-romania.ro
Web Site: www.forma-romania.ro
FOMA—(BUC)
Rev.: $244,330
Assets: $939,362
Liabilities: $625,758
Net Worth: $313,604
Earnings: $68,511
Fiscal Year-end: 12/31/12
Business Description:
Agricultural Machinery Repair & Maintenance
S.I.C.: 7699
N.A.I.C.S.: 811310
Personnel:
Agarwal Vijay *(Pres)*

FORMAPLEX LTD.
Dakota Business Park Downley Road
Havant, Hampshire, PO9 2NJ, United Kingdom
Tel.: (44) 2392 499276
E-Mail: info@formaplex.com
Web Site: www.formaplex.com
Year Founded: 2001
Sales Range: $25-49.9 Million
Emp.: 124
Business Description:
Injection Mould Tool Mfr
S.I.C.: 3546
N.A.I.C.S.: 333991
Personnel:
Angela Tomkins *(Mgr-HR)*

FORMAT WERK GMBH & CO. KG
Wallackstrasse 3
4623 Gunskirchen, Austria
Tel.: (43) 7246766100
Fax: (43) 7246766165
E-Mail: info@formatwerk.com
Web Site: www.formatwerk.com
Year Founded: 1976
Sales Range: $10-24.9 Million
Emp.: 100
Business Description:
School & Office Stationery Mfr & Supplier
S.I.C.: 2678
N.A.I.C.S.: 322230
Personnel:
Thomas Riemer *(CEO & Mng Dir)*
Christian Moser *(Mng Dir & CFO)*

FORMATION FLUID MANAGEMENT INC.
PO Box 8938
Sylvan Lake, AB, T4S 1S6, Canada
Tel.: (403) 887-8874
Fax: (403) 887-8804
Year Founded: 2006
FFM—(TSXV)
Rev.: $546,184
Assets: $3,822,303
Liabilities: $1,256,420
Net Worth: $2,565,883
Earnings: ($760,634)
Fiscal Year-end: 06/30/13
Business Description:
Water Desalination Services
S.I.C.: 7389
N.A.I.C.S.: 561990

Formation Fluid Management Inc.—(Continued)

Personnel:
Ken Rose *(Pres & CEO)*
Wayne Smith *(CFO & Sec)*
Chance Radford *(COO)*
Board of Directors:
Chance Radford
Ken Rose
Wayne Smith
Laurent St. Louis
Transfer Agent:
Computershare Trust Company of Canada
100 University Avenue 8th Floor
Toronto, ON, M5J 2Y1, Canada

FORMATION GROUP PLC

Oakwood House 414 - 422 Hackney Road
London, E2 7SY, United Kingdom
Tel.: (44) 2079207590
Fax: (44) 2077397682
E-Mail: mail@formationgroupplc.com
Web Site: www.formationgroupplc.com
FRM—(AIM)
Rev.: $9,717,763
Assets: $20,527,091
Liabilities: $10,575,066
Net Worth: $9,952,026
Earnings: ($672,883)
Emp.: 4
Fiscal Year-end: 08/31/13
Business Description:
Talent Management & Professional Services
S.I.C.: 7389
N.A.I.C.S.: 711410
Personnel:
David Kennedy *(CEO)*
Desmond Khan *(Sec & Dir-Fin)*
Board of Directors:
David Kennedy
Michael Kennedy
Patrick Kennedy
Desmond Khan
Noel O'Carroll
Legal Counsel:
DLA
101 Barbirolli Square
Manchester, United Kingdom
Subsidiaries:

Formation Architectural Design Limited (1)
Oakwood House
414-422 Hackney Road, London, E2 7SY, United Kingdom
Tel.: (44) 2079207591
Fax: (44) 2076134072
Web Site: www.formationdesignandbuild.com
Emp.: 20
Architectural Design Services
S.I.C.: 8712
N.A.I.C.S.: 541310
Neil Rodford *(CEO)*
Noel Carroll *(Mng Dir)*

Formation Asset Management Limited (1)
9 -13 Manchester Rd
Wilmslow, Cheshire, SK9 1BQ, United Kingdom
Tel.: (44) 1625418160
Fax: (44) 8447790375
Web Site: www.formationassetmanagement.com
Emp.: 10
Asset Management Services
S.I.C.: 6531
N.A.I.C.S.: 531390
Chris Bate *(Gen Mgr)*

Formation Design & Build Limited (1)
Oakwood House
414-422 Hackney Road, London, E2 7SY, United Kingdom
Tel.: (44) 2079207590
Fax: (44) 2077397682
E-Mail: info@formationdandb.com
Web Site: www.formationdesignandbuild.com
Emp.: 20
Property Management Services
S.I.C.: 6531
N.A.I.C.S.: 531312
Noel O. Carroll *(Mng Dir)*

Formation Sports Capital Limited (1)
2 Hollins House 329 Hale Rd
Hale Barns, WA15 8TS, United Kingdom
Tel.: (44) 16 1980 1210
Fax: (44) 16 1980 0791
Emp.: 20
Corporate Finance & Broking Services
S.I.C.: 6141
N.A.I.C.S.: 522291

Formation Wealth Solutions Limited (1)
2 Hollins House 329 Hale Rd
Hale Barns, Cheshire, WA15 8TS, United Kingdom
Tel.: (44) 162 553 6411
Fax: (44) 16 1980 0791
Web Site: www.formationwealth.com
Investment Services
S.I.C.: 6282
N.A.I.C.S.: 523930
Ian Battersby *(Mgr)*

U.S. Subsidiaries:

Proactive Sports Management Limited (1)
3233 M St NW
Washington, CA 20007
Tel.: (202) 333-3661
Fax: (202) 333-3616
E-Mail: info@proactivesportsusa.com
Web Site: www.proactivesportsusa.com
Management Services
S.I.C.: 8741
N.A.I.C.S.: 561110

Proactive Sports Management USA Inc. (1)
3233 M St NW
Washington, DC 20007
Tel.: (202) 333-3661
Fax: (202) 333-3616
E-Mail: joe@proactivesportsusa.com
Web Site: www.proactivesportsusa.com
Emp.: 5
Management Services
S.I.C.: 8741
N.A.I.C.S.: 561110

FORMATION METALS INC.

Suite 1810 - 999 West Hastings Street
Vancouver, BC, V6C 2W2, Canada
Tel.: (604) 682-6229
Fax: (604) 682-6205
E-Mail: inform@formationmetals.com
Web Site: www.formationmetals.com
Year Founded: 1988
FCO—(OTC TSX)
Rev.: $4,857,585
Assets: $183,731,637
Liabilities: $48,391,511
Net Worth: $135,340,126
Earnings: ($7,392,515)
Emp.: 26
Fiscal Year-end: 02/28/13
Business Description:
Metal Mining & Exploration Services
S.I.C.: 1099
N.A.I.C.S.: 212299
Personnel:
Robert J. Quinn *(Chm)*
J. Scott Bending *(Pres)*
Mari-Ann Green *(CEO)*
J. Paul Farquharson *(CFO)*
Alan D. Vichert *(Chief Risk Officer & Sr VP)*
Jeffrey T. K. Fraser *(Sec)*
William G. Scales *(Exec VP)*
Board of Directors:
Robert J. Quinn
J. Scott Bending
Mari-Ann Green
Gregory A. Hahn
Robert Metka
William G. Scales
David M. R. Stone
Legal Counsel:
Rios Zertuche, Gonzalez Lutteroth Y Rodriguez
Alberto Cossio 105 Piso 4 Int. A
San Luis Potosi, Mexico
Lexas Law Group
Suite 950, 1199 West Hastings Street
Vancouver, BC, Canada
Baird Hanson Williams LLP
2064 Timber Lane
Boulder, CO 80304
Transfer Agent:
Computershare Investor Services
510 Burrard St
Vancouver, BC, Canada
Subsidiary:

Coronation Mines Limited (1)
999 Hastings St W Ste 1730
Vancouver, BC, V6C 2W2, Canada
Tel.: (604) 682-6229
Fax: (604) 682-6205
E-Mail: inform@formationmetals.com
Emp.: 7
Mining Services
S.I.C.: 1099
N.A.I.C.S.: 212299
Mariann Green *(CEO)*
J. Paul Farquharson *(CFO)*

Non-U.S. Subsidiary:

Minera Terranova S.A. de C.V. (1)
Independencia 718-108
76000 San Luis Potosi, Mexico
Tel.: (52) 444 812 5959
Fax: (52) 444 812 5959
Gold Mining Services
S.I.C.: 1041
N.A.I.C.S.: 212221
Rodolfo Castillo Ramirez *(Dir Gen)*

FORMETAL, INC.

1741 Mujang-ri
Jigok-myeon, Seosan, Chungcheongnam-do, Korea (South)
Tel.: (82) 41 670 6200
Fax: (82) 41 668 7316
E-Mail: csy@formetal.co.kr
Web Site: www.formetal.co.kr
Year Founded: 1969
119500—(KRS)
Emp.: 129
Business Description:
Metal Forging Services
S.I.C.: 3462
N.A.I.C.S.: 332111
Personnel:
Se-won Oh *(CEO)*

FORMEX WATCH S.A.

Gummenweg 11B
2543 Lengnau, Switzerland
Tel.: (41) 323332455
Fax: (41) 323332459
E-Mail: 4speed@formexwatch.ch
Web Site: www.formexwatch.com
Sales Range: Less than $1 Million
Emp.: 3
Fiscal Year-end: 12/31/12
Business Description:
Watch Mfr
S.I.C.: 3829
N.A.I.C.S.: 334519
Personnel:
Hans Peter Gradel *(Gen Mgr)*
U.S. Subsidiary:

Formex Watch USA (1)
87 Main St
Peapack, NJ 07977
Tel.: (908) 781-9555
Fax: (908) 248-1504
Web Site: www.formexwatch.com
Watch Mfr
S.I.C.: 3829
N.A.I.C.S.: 334519

FORMGLAS PRODUCTS LTD.

2 Champagne Dr
Toronto, ON, M3J 2C5, Canada
Tel.: (416) 635-8030
Fax: (416) 635-6588
E-Mail: info@formglas.com
Web Site: www.formglas.com
Year Founded: 1961
Rev.: $32,700,000
Emp.: 300
Business Description:
Glass Products Mfr & Supplier
S.I.C.: 3231
N.A.I.C.S.: 327215
Personnel:
John Chettleburgh *(Pres)*

FORMIS RESOURCES BERHAD

16th Floor KH Tower 8 Lorong P. Ramlee
50250 Kuala Lumpur, Malaysia
Tel.: (60) 320784488
Fax: (60) 320706893
Web Site: www.formis.net
FRB—(KLS)
Rev.: $111,044,584
Assets: $116,374,633
Liabilities: $64,670,354
Net Worth: $51,704,279
Earnings: ($11,876,001)
Fiscal Year-end: 03/31/13
Business Description:
Information Technology Services
S.I.C.: 7371
N.A.I.C.S.: 541511
Personnel:
Nyap Liou Gan *(CEO & Mng Dir)*
Richard Voon *(CFO)*
Poh Lian Neo *(COO)*
Navrita Kaur *(Gen Counsel & VP-Legal)*
Shook Nyee Lim *(Sec)*
Board of Directors:
Najmuddin Khas
Monteiro Gerard Clair
Nyap Liou Gan
Ahmad Khalid
Siew Kwok Mah
Xian-Zhen Mah
Yong Sun Mah
Keat Chai Tai
Kok Khee Thong
Subsidiaries:

Applied Business Systems Sdn. Bhd. (1)
13th Floor Menara SMI 6 Lorong P Ramlee
50250 Kuala Lumpur, Malaysia
Tel.: (60) 327810888
Fax: (60) 320785496
E-Mail: abssales@abs.com.my
Web Site: www.abs.com.my
Emp.: 70
Application Software Development & Educational Consulting Services
S.I.C.: 7371
N.A.I.C.S.: 541511
Danny Chiam *(COO)*

Continuous Network Advisers Sdn. Bhd. (1)
9th Floor Menara Smi 6 Lorong P Ramlee
Kuala Lumpur, 50250, Malaysia
Tel.: (60) 327132899
Fax: (60) 327132399
E-Mail: ahmed.zaki@formis.net
Web Site: www.www.formis.net
Emp.: 50
Communication Networking Services
S.I.C.: 4899
N.A.I.C.S.: 517919
Ahmed Zaki Binembi *(Gen Mgr)*

Formis Bass Software Sdn. Bhd. (1)
20th Fl Menara Panglobal 8 Lorong P Ramlee
Kuala Lumpur, 50250, Malaysia
Tel.: (60) 320705588
Fax: (60) 320319403
Web Site: www.formis.net
Emp.: 50
Application Software Development Services
S.I.C.: 7371
N.A.I.C.S.: 541511
Michael Tay *(Gen Mgr)*

Formis Holdings Berhad (1)
16th Floor Menara Pan Global No 8 Lorong P Ramlee
Kuala Lumpur, 50250, Malaysia
Tel.: (60) 320784488
Fax: (60) 320706893
Emp.: 50
Financial Management Services
S.I.C.: 6211
N.A.I.C.S.: 523999
Wong Wai Wah *(Gen Mgr)*

Subsidiaries:

Com-Line Systems Sdn. Bhd. (2)
Level 3 Unit A-3-5 & A-3-6 TTDI Plaza Jalan Wan Kadir 3
Taman Tun Dr Ismail, 60000 Kuala Lumpur, Malaysia
Tel.: (60) 3 7710 1848
Fax: (60) 3 7710 4877
E-Mail: enquiries@comline.com.my
Web Site: www.comline.com.my
Emp.: 30
Application Software Development Services
S.I.C.: 7371
N.A.I.C.S.: 541511
Lawrence M. Sunderam *(Founder & Mng Dir)*

Subsidiary:

Comline Dotcom Sdn. Bhd. (3)
4th Floor Bangunan Tan Kim Onn 48 Jalan Sungai Besi
57100 Kuala Lumpur, Wilayah Persekutuan, Malaysia
Tel.: (60) 3 92228848
Fax: (60) 3 92224877
Emp.: 30
Application Software Development Services
S.I.C.: 7371
N.A.I.C.S.: 541511
Lawrence M. Sunderam *(Mgr)*

Formis Media Teknologi Sdn. Bhd. (2)
Unit No 302 Level 3 Uptown 2 No 2 Jalan SS21/37 Damansara Uptown
Petaling Jaya, Selangor, 47400, Malaysia
Tel.: (60) 376608787
Fax: (60) 376608383
Emp.: 15
Application Software Development & Educational Consulting Services
S.I.C.: 7371
N.A.I.C.S.: 541511
Hamdam Hamzah *(Gen Mgr)*

Formis Network Services Sdn. Bhd. (2)
6th Floor Menara Smi 6 Lorong P Ramlee
Kuala Lumpur, 50250, Malaysia
Tel.: (60) 320322633
Fax: (60) 327321310
E-Mail: suhaily.sarmani@formis.net
Emp.: 67
Communication Technology Services
S.I.C.: 4899
N.A.I.C.S.: 517919
Suhaily Sarmani *(Sec)*

Microlink Solutions Berhad (2)
6th Floor Menara Atlan 161B Jalan Ampang
Kuala Lumpur, 50450, Malaysia MY
Tel.: (60) 3 2171 2200
Fax: (60) 3 2171 2240
E-Mail: info@microlink.com.my
Web Site: www.microlink.com.my
0126—(KLS)
Rev.: $13,945,007
Assets: $14,350,334
Liabilities: $373,488
Net Worth: $13,976,846
Earnings: $2,316,158
Emp.: 200
Fiscal Year-end: 12/31/12
Information Technology Solutions for the Banking Industry
S.I.C.: 7379
N.A.I.C.S.: 541519
Ali Abdul Kadir *(Chm)*
Peter Kar Seng Yong *(CEO)*
King You Lee *(COO)*
Shiak Wan Leong *(Co-Sec)*
Siew Cheng See *(Co-Sec)*

Formis Systems & Technology Sdn. Bhd. (1)
7th & 10th Floor Menara SMI 6 Lorong P Ramlee
Kuala Lumpur, 50250, Malaysia
Tel.: (60) 320703388
Fax: (60) 320708988
E-Mail: fst.sales@fst.com.my
Web Site: www.fst.com.my
Emp.: 15
Computer Hardware & Software Distr
S.I.C.: 5045
N.A.I.C.S.: 423430
Alvin Chong *(Mgr-Tech Support)*

Nostalgic Properties Sdn. Bhd. (1)
No 57 Northam Tower Jalan Sultan Ahmad Shah
10050 George Town, Penang, Malaysia
Tel.: (60) 4 818 2122
Fax: (60) 4 818 2123
E-Mail: nostalgic@northamtower.com
Web Site: www.northamtower.com
Property Management & Development Services
S.I.C.: 6531
N.A.I.C.S.: 531390
Alan Rajendran *(Mng Dir)*

FORMO MOTORS

1550 Main Street HWY 10
P O Box 1900
Swan River, MB, R0L 1Z0, Canada
Tel.: (204) 734-4577
Fax: (204) 734-4674
Web Site: www.formomotors.com
Year Founded: 1964
Rev.: $11,051,669
Emp.: 25
Business Description:
New & Used Car Dealer
S.I.C.: 5511
N.A.I.C.S.: 441110
Personnel:
Tracy Coulthart *(Office Mgr)*

FORMOPLAST PLC

Industrial zone South
6600 Kardjhali, Bulgaria
Tel.: (359) 361 62612
Fax: (359) 361 61133
E-Mail: info@formoplastbg.com
Web Site: www.formoplastbg.com
4F8—(BUL)
Business Description:
Mould Design Mfr
S.I.C.: 3999
N.A.I.C.S.: 339999
Personnel:
Iva Garvanska-Litse Za Kontakti *(Dir-IR)*

FORMOSA EPITAXY INCORPORATION

No 99 Lun Yuan 1st Rd
Longtan, Taoyuan, Taiwan
Tel.: (886) 34994555
Fax: (886) 334994548
Web Site: www.forepi.com.tw
3061—(TAI)
Sales Range: $50-74.9 Million
Business Description:
Light Emitting Diode Mfr
S.I.C.: 3674
N.A.I.C.S.: 334413
Personnel:
Charles Wei *(Sr Dir-Mktg & Plng Div)*

FORMOSA INTERNATIONAL HOTELS CORP.

41 Chung Shan Rd Section 2
Taipei, Taiwan
Tel.: (886) 225238000
Fax: (886) 225232828
Web Site: www.grandformosa.com.tw
2707—(TAI)
Sales Range: $75-99.9 Million
Business Description:
Hotel Management Services
S.I.C.: 8741
N.A.I.C.S.: 561110
Personnel:
Sy-Lian Pan *(Chm)*
Amy Hsueh *(CEO)*

Non-U.S. Subsidiaries:

Regent A/S (1)
Ostergade 27 C/o Eversheds Advokataktieselskab
1100 Copenhagen, Denmark
Tel.: (45) 32344160
Fax: (45) 32344170
Hotel Management Services
S.I.C.: 7011
N.A.I.C.S.: 721110

REGENT BERLIN GMBH (1)
Charlottenstrasse 49
10117 Berlin, Germany
Tel.: (49) 3020338
Fax: (49) 3020336119
E-Mail: info.berlin@regenthotels.com
Web Site: www.regenthotels.com
Emp.: 200
Hotel Management Services
S.I.C.: 8741
N.A.I.C.S.: 561110
Stefan Athmnan *(Gen Mgr)*

FORMOSA LABORATORIES, INC.

36 Hoping Street
Louchu, Taoyuan, 33842, Taiwan
Tel.: (886) 3 3240895
Fax: (886) 3 3240945
E-Mail: formosaservice@formosalab.com
Web Site: www.formosalab.com
4746—(TAI)
Sales Range: $75-99.9 Million
Emp.: 250
Business Description:
Medical Laboratory Services
S.I.C.: 8071
N.A.I.C.S.: 621511
Personnel:
Chung-Hur Lee *(Chm)*
Peter Bircher *(Pres)*
C. Y. Cheng *(CEO)*

FORMOSA PETROCHEMICAL CORPORATION

1-1 Formosa Plastics Group Industrial Zone
Mailiao, Yun-lin, Taiwan
Tel.: (886) 5 681 2345
E-Mail: fpccpre@fpcc.com.tw
Web Site: www.fpcc.com.tw
Year Founded: 1992
6505—(TAI)
Rev.: $30,293,782,061
Assets: $15,818,115,039
Liabilities: $8,811,507,564
Net Worth: $7,006,607,475
Earnings: $92,164,436
Emp.: 6,507
Fiscal Year-end: 12/31/12
Business Description:
Oil Refining Services; Petroleum Products & Petrochemical Mfr; Electricity Production & Sales
S.I.C.: 2869
N.A.I.C.S.: 325110
Personnel:
Bao Lang Chen *(Chm)*
Mihn Tsao *(Pres)*
Ming-Hsing Shih *(CFO)*
Jui-Shih Chen *(Sr VP-Petrochemical Olefins Div)*
Han-Ting Chen *(Sr VP)*
Keh-Yen Lin *(Sr VP-Pres Office)*
Board of Directors:
Bao Lang Chen
C. P. Chang
Han-Ting Chen
Jui-Shih Chen
Yu Cheng
Ja-Tao Huang
Tsai-Shan Kao
Keh-Yen Lin
Chi-Tang Lo
C. Y. Su
Mihn Tsao
Ruey-Hwa Wang
Walter Wang
Wilfred Wang
William Wong
Transfer Agent:
FPCC Stock Affairs Office
No 201 Tun Hwa North Road
Taipei, Taiwan

Subsidiaries:

Formosa Oil (Asia Pacific) Corporation (1)
4 FL 201 Tung Hwa N Rd
Taipei, 10508, Taiwan
Tel.: (886) 227122211
Fax: (886) 227129230
Emp.: 1,600
Oil Product Retailer
S.I.C.: 5172
N.A.I.C.S.: 424720
Sandy R.Y. Wang *(Chm)*

Mailiao Harbor Administration Corporation (1)
1-1 Fromosa Plastic Group Industrial Zone
Mailiao, Yun-lin, 63800, Taiwan
Tel.: (886) 227122211
Fax: (886) 568 12135
Emp.: 33
Harbor Administration Services
S.I.C.: 4491
N.A.I.C.S.: 488310
Wilfred Y.C. Wang *(Chm)*

Simosa Oil Corporation (1)
No 10-8 Formosa Plastic Group Industrial Zone
Mailiao, Yun-lin, Taiwan
Tel.: (886) 56812618
Fax: (886) 56812292
Asphalt Production & Sales
S.I.C.: 2951
N.A.I.C.S.: 324121

Yi-Chi Construction Corporation (1)
2F 201-24 Tung Hwa North Road
Taipei, Taiwan
Tel.: (886) 227122211
Fax: (886) 285123528
Construction Services
S.I.C.: 1542
N.A.I.C.S.: 236220

Affiliate:

Formosa Chemicals & Fibre Corporation (1)
2nd Floor Tung Hwa North Road
Taipei, Taiwan TW
Tel.: (886) 2 27 122211
Fax: (886) 2 27 133229
Web Site: www.fcfc.com.tw
1326—(TAI)
Sales Range: $5-14.9 Billion
Emp.: 4,932
Chemicals, Petrochemicals, Fibers & Plastics Mfr
Import Export
S.I.C.: 2899
N.A.I.C.S.: 325998
Wenyuan Wang *(Chm)*

Subsidiary:

Formosa Taffeta Corp. (2)
317 Shu Liu Road
Touliu, 640 Touliu, Taiwan

Formosa Petrochemical Corporation—(Continued)

Tel.: (886) 55573966
Fax: (886) 55573969
E-Mail: ftcwm@ftc.com.tw
Web Site: www.ftc.com.tw
Emp.: 3,000
Broadwoven Fabric Mills
S.I.C.: 2299
N.A.I.C.S.: 313210

FORMOSA PLASTICS CORPORATION

201 Tung Hwa North Road
Taipei, Taiwan
Tel.: (886) 227122211
Fax: (886) 227178108
E-Mail: formosa@fpc.com.tw
Web Site: www.fpc.com.tw
Year Founded: 1954
1301—(TAI)
Rev.: $5,860,688,811
Assets: $11,648,810,809
Liabilities: $3,973,175,558
Net Worth: $7,675,635,251
Earnings: $496,619,552
Emp.: 6,041
Fiscal Year-end: 12/31/12

Business Description:
Plastics Products Mfr
S.I.C.: 3089
N.A.I.C.S.: 326199

Personnel:
Chih-Tsuen Lee *(Chm)*
Jason Lin *(Pres)*
T. J. Huang *(Sr VP)*
Cheng-Jung Lin *(Sr VP)*

Board of Directors:
Chih-Tsuen Lee
Y. R. Chang
T. J. Huang
Cheng-Jung Lin
Jason Lin
H. H. Wang
Susan Wang
T. S. Wang
Wilfred Wang

Supervisory Board of Directors:
C. F. Ho
Ralph Ho
K. H. Wu

Divisions:

Formosa Plastics Corporation - Carbide Division **(1)**
Rm 309 Fl 4 No 201 Tung Hwa N Road
Taipei, Taiwan
Tel.: (886) 2 7122211
Fax: (886) 2 27193261
Plastic Material Mfr
S.I.C.: 3089
N.A.I.C.S.: 326199

Formosa Plastics Corporation - Chemicals Division **(1)**
Rm 215 Fl 4 No 201 Tung Hwa N Road
Taipei, Taiwan
Tel.: (886) 2 27122211
Fax: (886) 2 27178340
Specialty Chemicals Mfr
S.I.C.: 2899
N.A.I.C.S.: 325998

Formosa Plastics Corporation - Plastics Division **(1)**
Rm 06 Fl 4 No 201 Tung Hwa North Road
Taipei, 10508, Taiwan
Tel.: (886) 2 27122211
Fax: (886) 2 27137012
Plastic Material Mfr
S.I.C.: 3089
N.A.I.C.S.: 326199
Sunny Jian *(Dir-Sls)*

Formosa Plastics Corporation - Polyolefin Division **(1)**
Rm 215 Fl 4 No 201 Tung Hwa N Road
Taipei, 105, Taiwan
Tel.: (886) 5 6811180
Fax: (886) 5 6811122
Chemical Products Mfr
S.I.C.: 2819
N.A.I.C.S.: 325180

Formosa Plastics Corporation - Polypropylene Division **(1)**
8F 201 Tung-Hwa North Road
Taipei, Taiwan
Tel.: (886) 2 27122211
Fax: (886) 2 27181230
Chemical Products Mfr
S.I.C.: 2819
N.A.I.C.S.: 325180

Formosa Plastics Corporation - Tairylan Division **(1)**
Fl 201 Tung Hua North Road
Taipei, 105, Taiwan
Tel.: (886) 2 27178135
Fax: (886) 2 27134818
Web Site: www.fpc.com.tw
Emp.: 500
Plastic Products Mfr
S.I.C.: 3089
N.A.I.C.S.: 326199

Subsidiaries:

Formosa Heavy Industries Corp. **(1)**
201 20 Tung Huan Rd
Taipei, 105 00, Taiwan
Tel.: (886) 227178148
Fax: (886) 227135519
E-Mail: info@fhi.com.tw
Web Site: www.fhi.com.tw
Sls.: $392,457,728
Emp.: 1,250
Heavy Industrial Machinery Mfr
S.I.C.: 3559
N.A.I.C.S.: 333249
L. C. Wu *(VP)*

Formosa Petrochemical Transportation Corporation **(1)**
No 42 Biaofu Road
Mailiao Township, Taipei, Yun Lin, Taiwan TW
Tel.: (886) 227122211 (100%)
Fax: (886) 227123590
E-Mail: fpccpre@fpcc.com.tw
Web Site: www.fpcc.com.tw
Emp.: 200
Crude Oil Refining & Petroleum & Petrochemical Products Mfr
S.I.C.: 2869
N.A.I.C.S.: 325110
Wilfred Wang *(Chm)*

Formosa Plasma Display Corporation **(1)**
201 Tung Hwa North Road
Taipei, Taiwan (77.5%)
Tel.: (886) 227122211
Fax: (886) 227129211
E-Mail: 00ra07@fpg.com.tw
Web Site: www.fpg.com.tw
Emp.: 500
Flat Panel Mfr
S.I.C.: 3559
N.A.I.C.S.: 333249
Yung Ching Wang *(Pres)*

Nan Ya Plastics Corporation **(1)**
201 Tung Hwa North Rd
Taipei, Taiwan (100%)
Tel.: (886) 227122211
Fax: (886) 227178532
E-Mail: danielhsio@npc.com.tw
Web Site: www.npc.com.tw
NPC—(TAI)
Emp.: 15,804
Hard & Soft Plastic Sheets; Processed Plastic Products, Synthetic Fibers & Processed Chemical Products Supplier
S.I.C.: 3089
N.A.I.C.S.: 326199
Wu Chin-Jen *(Chm)*

Nan Ya Printed Circuit Board Corporation **(1)**
338 Sec 1 NanKan Road
Jing Hsin Village
Luchu Hsiang, Taoyuan, Taiwan
Tel.: (886) 33223751
Web Site: www.nanyapcb.com.tw
8046—(TAI)
Emp.: 10,728
Printed Circuit Board Mfr & Distr
S.I.C.: 3679
N.A.I.C.S.: 334419
Quinren Wu *(Chm)*

Affiliate:

Mai-Liao Power Corporation **(1)**
101 Formosa Industrial Park
San Sheng Village
Mailiao Hsiang, Yun-lin, 63861, Taiwan
Tel.: (886) 5681 2345
Fax: (886) 5681 1026
Web Site: www.fpcc.com.tw/mpc
Emp.: 378
Power Generation
S.I.C.: 4911
N.A.I.C.S.: 221122
Yung Ching Wang *(Pres)*

Joint Venture:

Formosa Asahi Spandex Co., Ltd. **(1)**
Rm 386 12F Tun Hwa N Rd
Taipei, Taiwan
Tel.: (886) 227122211
Fax: (886) 227128718
Web Site: www.formosa.com
Emp.: 12
Elastic Products Mfr; Owned 50% by Formosa Plastics Corporation & 50% by Asahi Kasei Corporation
S.I.C.: 3089
N.A.I.C.S.: 326199
Y.C. Wang *(Chm)*

Plant:

Formosa Plastics Corporation - Linyuan Plant **(1)**
1-1 Hsin-Hwa 1st Road Lin-Yuan Village
Kaohsiung, Taiwan
Tel.: (886) 7 6419911, ext. 313
Fax: (886) 7 6425581
Plastic Products Mfr
S.I.C.: 3089
N.A.I.C.S.: 326199

U.S. Subsidiary:

Formosa Plastics Corporation, U.S.A. **(1)**
9 Peach Tree Hill Rd
Livingston, NJ 07039-5702 (100%)
Tel.: (973) 992-2090
Fax: (973) 992-9627
E-Mail: employment@fpcusa.com
Web Site: www.fpcusa.com
Emp.: 3,897
Plastics Products Mfr
Export
S.I.C.: 2821
N.A.I.C.S.: 325211
Kelvin Wu *(Mgr-Mktg)*

Branches:

Formosa Plastics Corporation, Delaware **(2)**
780 Schoolhouse Rd PO Box 320
Delaware City, DE 19706
Tel.: (302) 836-2200
Fax: (202) 836-1909
Web Site: www.fpcusa.com
Emp.: 130
Plastics & Resins Mfr
S.I.C.: 3089
N.A.I.C.S.: 326199
Kevin Tyse *(Plant Mgr)*

Formosa Plastics Corporation, Louisiana **(2)**
Gulf States Rd
Baton Rouge, LA 70805
Mailing Address:
PO Box 320
Baton Rouge, LA 70821
Tel.: (225) 356-3341
Fax: (225) 356-8611
Web Site: www.fpcusa.com
Emp.: 220
Plastics & Resins Mfr
S.I.C.: 3089
N.A.I.C.S.: 326199
Aldan Andre *(VP)*

Formosa Plastics Corporation, Texas **(2)**
201 Formosa Dr PO Box 700
Point Comfort, TX 77978
Tel.: (361) 987-7000
Fax: (361) 987-2721
Web Site: www.fpcusa.com
Sales Range: $50-74.9 Million
Emp.: 1,500
Plastics & Resins Mfr
S.I.C.: 3089
N.A.I.C.S.: 326199
Jack Wu *(VP)*

Subsidiaries:

Formosa Hydrocarbons Company, Inc. **(2)**
103 Fannin Rd PO Box 769
Point Comfort, TX 77978 DE
Tel.: (361) 987-8900
Fax: (361) 987-2283
Web Site: www.fpcusa.com
Emp.: 40
Petroleum Products
S.I.C.: 2999
N.A.I.C.S.: 324199
Jack Wu *(Pres)*

Lavaca Pipe Line Company **(2)**
103 Fannin Rd
Point Comfort, TX 77978 TX
Tel.: (361) 987-8900
Fax: (361) 987-2283
Web Site: www.fpcusa.com
Emp.: 42
Natural Gas Distr
S.I.C.: 4924
N.A.I.C.S.: 221210
Jack Wu *(Pres)*

Neumin Production Company **(2)**
103 Fannin Rd PO Box 769
Point Comfort, TX 77978
Tel.: (361) 987-8900
Fax: (361) 987-2283
Web Site: www.fpcusa.com
Emp.: 45
Crude Petroleum & Natural Gas Production Services
S.I.C.: 2911
N.A.I.C.S.: 324110

FORMOSA PROSONIC INDUSTRIES BERHAD

Level 18 The Gardens North Tower
Mid Valley City
59200 Kuala Lumpur, Lingkaran Syed Putra, Malaysia
Tel.: (60) 3 2264 8888
Fax: (60) 3 2282 2733
E-Mail: enquiry@fp-group.com
Web Site: www.fp-group.com
FPI—(KLS)
Rev.: $240,848,490
Assets: $138,772,686
Liabilities: $48,072,214
Net Worth: $90,700,472
Earnings: $9,635,295
Fiscal Year-end: 12/31/12

Business Description:
Speaker Systems Mfr
S.I.C.: 3651
N.A.I.C.S.: 334310

Personnel:
Tzu Hsiong Jhang *(Chm)*
Chao Yuan Shih *(Grp Mng Dir)*
Hooi Mooi Lim *(Co-Sec)*
Wai Wong Wong *(Co-Sec)*

Board of Directors:
Tzu Hsiong Jhang
Mohamed Fauzi Abdul Hamid
Zaibedah Ahmad
Chen Hsi Chang
Ching Sen Chen
Ing Seng Leow
Chung Yin Lim
Chao Yuan Shih
Teik Hoe Tan

Subsidiaries:

Asia Pacific Card & System Sdn. Bhd. **(1)**
No 1 Lebuh 1 Bandar Sultan Sulaiman
Taiwanese Industrial Park
Port Klang, Selangor, Malaysia
Tel.: (60) 331766700
Fax: (60) 331765700

E-Mail: apcs@fp-group.com
Web Site: www.apcs.com.my
Emp.: 200
Electronic Integrated Circuits & Smart Cards Mfr
S.I.C.: 3679
N.A.I.C.S.: 334418
Eddie Huo Shao Wei *(Mng Dir & Gen Mgr)*

Formosa Prosonic Manufacturing Sdn. Bhd. (1)
No 2 Jalan 1 Bandar Sultan Suleiman
Taiwanese Industrial Park
42000 Port Klang, Selangor, Malaysia
Tel.: (60) 331762700
Fax: (60) 331761424
Plastic Components Mfr
S.I.C.: 3088
N.A.I.C.S.: 326191
Shih Chao-Yuan *(Mng Dir)*
Lim Hooi Mooi *(Sec)*

Non-U.S. Subsidiaries:

Acoustic Energy Limited (1)
16 Bridge Road
Cirencester, Gloucestershire, GL7 1NJ, United Kingdom
Tel.: (44) 1285654432
Fax: (44) 1285654430
E-Mail: uksales@acoustic-energy.co.uk
Web Site: www.acoustic-energy.co.uk
Emp.: 10
Loudspeakers Mfr
S.I.C.: 3651
N.A.I.C.S.: 334310
Moses Gabbay *(Gen Mgr)*

Formosa Prosonic Japan Co. Ltd. (1)
11 Kandakon-Yacho Iwata Building 8F
Chiyoda-ku, Tokyo, 101-0035, Japan
Tel.: (81) 352983887
Fax: (81) 352983876
E-Mail: info@fpi-japan.co.jp
Web Site: www.fpi-japan.co.jp
Emp.: 10
Acoustical Equipments Mfr & Distr
S.I.C.: 3699
N.A.I.C.S.: 335999
Tanaka Kiyohito *(Pres)*

Formosa Prosonic Mexico S.A. DE C.V. (1)
Blvd La Jolla No 10103 Parque Industrial La Jolla
Tijuana, Baja California, 22180, Mexico
Tel.: (52) 664 687 3088
Fax: (52) 664 687 6090
Web Site: www.fp-group.com
Audio Equipments Mfr
S.I.C.: 3651
N.A.I.C.S.: 334310

FORMOSAN UNION CHEMICAL CORP.

14F No 206 Sec 2 Nanking E Rd
Taipei, Taiwan
Tel.: (886) 225071234
Fax: (886) 225071664
E-Mail: fucc@fucc.com.tw
Web Site: www.fucc.com.tw
1709—(TAI)
Sales Range: $150-199.9 Million
Business Description:
Alkyl Benzene Mfr
S.I.C.: 2911
N.A.I.C.S.: 324110
Personnel:
Steven Chen *(Chm)*

FORMOUS CORP.

Asanbay Microdistrict 23-10
720060 Bishkek, Kyrgyzstan
Tel.: (996) 777026772
E-Mail: formouscorp@gmail.com
Year Founded: 2013
Business Description:
Workwear Distr
S.I.C.: 5136
N.A.I.C.S.: 424320
Personnel:
Nurzada Kermalieva *(Pres, CEO, CFO, Principal Acctg Officer, Treas & Sec)*
Board of Directors:
Nurzada Kermalieva

FORMPIPE SOFTWARE AB

Eriksgatan 117
113 43 Stockholm, Sweden
Mailing Address:
PO Box 231 31
104 35 Stockholm, Sweden
Tel.: (46) 8 55529060
Fax: (46) 8 55529099
E-Mail: info@formpipe.com
Web Site: www.formpipe.com
Year Founded: 1997
FPIP—(OMX)
Sls.: $31,138,794
Assets: $88,979,814
Liabilities: $51,556,140
Net Worth: $37,423,674
Earnings: $2,119,676
Emp.: 226
Fiscal Year-end: 12/31/12
Business Description:
Enterprise Content Management Software
S.I.C.: 7372
N.A.I.C.S.: 511210
Personnel:
Bo Nordlander *(Chm)*
Christian Sundin *(CEO)*
Joakim Alfredson *(CFO)*
Sten Nygaard-Andersen *(CTO-Denmark)*
Rasmus Staberg *(CTO-Sweden)*
Board of Directors:
Bo Nordlander
Kristina Lindgren
Jack Spira
Staffan Torstensson

Non-U.S. Subsidiary:

FormPipe Software Copenhagen A/S (1)
Park Alla 290
2605 Brondby, Copenhagen, Denmark
Tel.: (45) 43660210
E-Mail: info.lasernet@formpipe.com
Emp.: 14
Business Management Software Development Services
S.I.C.: 7371
N.A.I.C.S.: 541511
Anders Terp *(Mng Dir)*

FORMSCAN LIMITED

Second Floor Park House
Kidwells Park Drive, Maidenhead, SL6 8AQ, United Kingdom
Tel.: (44) 8445617276
E-Mail: info@formscan.com
Web Site: www.formscan.com
Business Description:
Document Management Solutions
S.I.C.: 7372
N.A.I.C.S.: 511210
Personnel:
Chris Haden *(CEO)*

FORMULA FORD

940 Kingston Road
Pickering, ON, L1V 1B3, Canada
Tel.: (905) 839-6666
Fax: (905) 839-6008
Toll Free: (800) 917-1249
Web Site: www.formulafordlincoln.com
Year Founded: 1984
Rev.: $21,562,348
Emp.: 45
Business Description:
New & Used Car Dealers
S.I.C.: 5511
N.A.I.C.S.: 441110
Personnel:
Joe Chapman *(Mgr-Fleet)*

FORMULA HONDA

2240 Markham Road
Scarborough, ON, M1B 2W4, Canada
Tel.: (416) 754-4555
Fax: (416) 754-0307
Toll Free: (888) 307-7087
Web Site: www.formulahonda.com
Year Founded: 1987
Rev.: $22,817,200
Emp.: 50
Business Description:
New & Used Car Dealers
S.I.C.: 5511
N.A.I.C.S.: 441110
Personnel:
Nial Boatswain *(Gen Mgr)*

FORMULA ONE HOLDINGS LTD.

(d/b/a Formula One Group)
6 Princes Gate
Knightsbridge, London, SW7 1QJ, United Kingdom
Tel.: (44) 2075846668
Year Founded: 1996
Sales Range: $1-4.9 Billion
Emp.: 200
Business Description:
Holding Company
S.I.C.: 6719
N.A.I.C.S.: 551112
Personnel:
Bernard Charles Ecclestone *(CEO)*
Sacha Jane Woodward Hill *(Sec)*

Subsidiary:

Formula One Administration Ltd. (1)
6 Princes Gate
Knightsbridge, London, SW7 1QJ, United Kingdom UK (100%)
Tel.: (44) 2075846668
Fax: (44) 2075890311
E-Mail: business@formula1.com
Web Site: www.formula1.com
Emp.: 10
Holding Company; Open-Wheel Motorsports League Commercial Licensing Rights Owner & Administrator
S.I.C.: 6719
N.A.I.C.S.: 551112
Bernard Charles Ecclestone *(CEO)*

Subsidiary:

Formula One Management Ltd. (2)
6 Princes Gate
Knightsbridge, London, SW7 1QJ, United Kingdom UK (100%)
Tel.: (44) 2075846668
Fax: (44) 2075890311
E-Mail: info@formula1.com
Web Site: www.formula1.com
Emp.: 20
Open-Wheel Motorsports League Commercial Licensing Rights Management
S.I.C.: 6794
N.A.I.C.S.: 533110

Subsidiary:

Formula1.com Limited (3)
6 Princes Gate
Knightsbridge, London, SW7 1QJ, United Kingdom UK (100%)
Tel.: (44) 2075846668
Fax: (44) 2075890283
Web Site: www.formula1.com
Open Wheel Auto Racing Website Broadcaster
S.I.C.: 2741
N.A.I.C.S.: 519130
Alex Wooff *(Dir-Mktg)*

FORMULA TELECOM SOLUTIONS LIMITED

8 Maskit Street
Herzliyya, 46120, Israel
Tel.: (972) 99526500
Fax: (972) 99526565
E-Mail: info@fts-soft.com
Web Site: www.fts-soft.com
Year Founded: 1997
Sales Range: $10-24.9 Million
Emp.: 500
Business Description:
Business Control, Billing & CRM Solutions & Services
S.I.C.: 7372
N.A.I.C.S.: 511210
Personnel:
Nir Auslin *(CEO)*
Nir Amir *(CFO)*
Shaul Ganel *(Pres-North America)*
Board of Directors:
Dan Goldstein
Yael Hershtik
John Robert Camber Porter
David Joel Rubin
Eliyahu Shushan
Amos Sivan
Ronnen Yitzhak
Legal Counsel:
SJ Berwin
222 Grays Inn Road
London, United Kingdom

Hermann, Makov & Co
7 Menachem Begin Street 21st floor
Ramat Gan, Israel

Goldfarb, Levy, Eran & Co
Europe Israel Tower 2 Weizmann Street
Tel Aviv, Israel

U.S. Subsidiary:

FTS Americas (1)
902 Clint Moore Rd Ste 230
Boca Raton, FL 33487 DE
Tel.: (561) 999-8000
Fax: (561) 981-8080
E-Mail: us.info@fts-soft.com
Web Site: www.fts-soft.com
Emp.: 128
Business Control, Billing & CRM Solutions & Services
S.I.C.: 7372
N.A.I.C.S.: 511210
Shaul Ganel *(Pres)*

Non-U.S. Subsidiaries:

Formula Telecom Limited (1)
Bld 7A 25 Entrance 4 Ofc 3
Staropetrovsky Line, Moscow, 125130, Russia
Tel.: (7) 4956481008
Fax: (7) 495 648 1018
E-Mail: ru.info@fts-soft.com
Emp.: 10
Telecom Management Solutions Provider
S.I.C.: 4899
N.A.I.C.S.: 517919
Nikolai Simkevich *(Gen Mgr)*

F.T.S- Formula Telecom Solutions Bulgaria (1)
13 20 April St
Sofia, 1606, Bulgaria
Tel.: (359) 2 952 3929
Fax: (359) 2 952 3753
E-Mail: bg.info@fts-soft.com
Web Site: www.fts-soft.com
Telecom Management Solutions Provider
S.I.C.: 4899
N.A.I.C.S.: 517919
Yehuda Benny *(Mng Dir)*

F.T.S. Global Limited (1)
Ground Fl Meersig 2 Constantia Blvd
Constantia Kloof, 1710 Johannesburg, South Africa
Tel.: (27) 11 322 4200
Fax: (27) 11 991 0909
E-Mail: africa.info@fts-soft.com
Emp.: 6
Telecom Management Solutions Provider
S.I.C.: 4899
N.A.I.C.S.: 517919
Hugo Herbst *(Mng Dir)*

FORNEBU UTVIKLING ASA

(See Under Oslo Bolig og Sparelag)

Formula Telecom Solutions Limited—(Continued)

FORNIX BIOSCIENCES N.V.
(See Under Value8 N.V.)

FORNTON GROUP LIMITED
Unit A 32/F Legend Tower 7 Shing Yip Street
Kwun Tong, Kowloon, China (Hong Kong)
Tel.: (852) 2797 1000
Fax: (852) 2797 1001
E-Mail: info@fornton.com
Web Site: www.fornton.com
Year Founded: 1995
1152—(HKG)
Emp.: 300
Business Description:
Sweater Knit Mfr
S.I.C.: 2259
N.A.I.C.S.: 315190
Personnel:
Sherman Lee *(CFO & Sec)*
Board of Directors:
Dickson Cheng
Ka Man Sin
Andrew Wei Hung Wang
Kandy Kan Kan Wong

Subsidiary:

Fornton Knitting Company Limited **(1)**
Unit A 32/F Legend Tower 7 Shing Yip Street
Kwun Tong, Kowloon, China (Hong Kong)
Tel.: (852) 2797 1000
Fax: (852) 2797 1001
Knitted Sweater Mfr
S.I.C.: 2259
N.A.I.C.S.: 315190

Non-U.S. Plant:

Fornton Group Limited - Dong Guan Factory **(1)**
Fu Li Rd Xiang Wei Village
Dongguan, Dongguan, China
Tel.: (86) 769 8860 5088
Fax: (86) 769 8860 5089
Knitted Sweater Mfr
S.I.C.: 2259
N.A.I.C.S.: 315190

FORO-MAREE S.A.
123 quai du Midi
Port Chef de Baie, 17045 La Rochelle, Cedex 1, France
Tel.: (33) 546411900
Fax: (33) 546411920
E-Mail: foro-info@foromaree.com
Web Site: www.foromaree.com
Sales Range: $1-9.9 Million
Emp.: 58
Business Description:
Fish & Seafood Distr
S.I.C.: 5146
N.A.I.C.S.: 424460
Personnel:
Bernard Rivasseau *(Dir Gen & Sls Mgr)*

FORPOST-HOLDING ZAO
69/29 Backbone
420108 Kazan, Russia
Tel.: (7) 843 214 1227
Business Description:
Investment Services
S.I.C.: 6211
N.A.I.C.S.: 523999

Holding:

Uralmash-Izhora Group **(1)**
20 Bid 2 Ovchinnikovskaya Emb
Moscow, 115324, Russia
Tel.: (7) 4956621040
Fax: (7) 4956621041
E Mail: mail@omzglobal.com
Web Site: www.omz.ru
OMZZ—(LSE MIC RUS)
Sls.: $969,905,000
Assets: $1,398,696,000
Liabilities: $1,022,450,000
Net Worth: $376,246,000
Earnings: $84,437,000
Emp.: 16,988
Fiscal Year-end: 12/31/12
Heavy Equipment & Machinery Mfr
S.I.C.: 3531
N.A.I.C.S.: 333120
Igor A. Timofeev *(Chm-Exec Bd & CEO)*
Vadim A. Makhov *(Pres & Member-Exec Bd)*
Yuri I. Utochkin *(Member-Exec Bd, Deputy Dir Gen & Dir-Technical)*
Sergey O. Arkhipov *(Member-Exec Bd & Deputy Dir Gen-Innovation)*
Evgeny A. Fokin *(Member-Exec Bd & First Deputy Dir Gen)*
Maxim Y. Kaytanov *(Member-Exec Bd & Deputy Dir Gen-Strategic Projects)*
Alexander I. Morgach *(Member-Exec Bd & Deputy Dir Gen)*
Yuliya M. Nikolaeva *(Member-Exec Bd & Deputy Dir Gen-HR)*
Alexey Yu. Perepelkin *(Member-Exec Bd & Deputy Dir Gen-Corp Assets)*
Evgeny G. Plusnin *(Member-Exec Bd & Deputy Dir Gen)*
Alexander I. Soshnikov *(Member-Exec Bd & Deputy Dir Gen-Legal Affairs)*
Boris A. Tikhonenko *(Member-Exec Bd & Deputy Dir Gen-Economy & Fin)*

Subsidiaries:

OJSC Izhorskiye Zavody **(2)**
1 Pr Lenina
Kolpino, Saint Petersburg, 196651, Russia (69.9%)
Tel.: (7) 8123228000
Fax: (7) 8124608843
E-Mail: office@ijora.spb.ru
Web Site: www.omz.ru/eng/contacts/address/
Industrial Components Mfr
S.I.C.: 3443
N.A.I.C.S.: 332410

OMZ LP LLC **(2)**
1 Pr Lenina
Kolpino, 196651 Saint Petersburg, Russia
Tel.: (7) 812 322 8127
Fax: (7) 8123228040
Web Site: www.omz-foundry.ru
Emp.: 150
Steel Molds Mfr
S.I.C.: 3321
N.A.I.C.S.: 331511
Igor Martushev *(Gen Mgr)*

Omz-Spetsstal Ooo **(2)**
B-N Izhorski Zavod
Leningradskaya, Krasnodar, Russia
Tel.: (7) 08123228007
Industrial Machinery & Equipment Whslr
S.I.C.: 5084
N.A.I.C.S.: 423830

Non-U.S. Subsidiaries:

Pilsensteel S.r.o **(2)**
Tylova 57
31600 Plzen, Czech Republic (100%)
Tel.: (420) 378132509
Fax: (420) 378134297
Web Site: www.pilsensteel.cz/en/contacts/
Iron & Steel Forging
S.I.C.: 3462
N.A.I.C.S.: 332111

Skoda JS AS **(2)**
Orlik 266
31606 Plzen, Czech Republic
Tel.: (420) 378041111
Fax: (420) 377520600
E-Mail: info@skoda-js.cz
Web Site: www.skoda-js.cz
Fabricated Metal Product Mfr
S.I.C.: 3499
N.A.I.C.S.: 332999

FORSYS METALS CORP.
31 Adelaide Street East
PO Box 909
Toronto, ON, M5C 2K3, Canada
Tel.: (416) 367-4242
Fax: (416) 367-0598
E-Mail: info@forsysmetals.com
Web Site: www.forsysmetals.com
FSY—(TSX)
Int. Income: $151,431
Assets: $99,661,793
Liabilities: $373,938
Net Worth: $99,287,855
Earnings: ($3,321,457)
Emp.: 36
Fiscal Year-end: 12/31/12
Business Description:
Uranium Exploration & Mining Services
S.I.C.: 1094
N.A.I.C.S.: 212291
Personnel:
Martin R. Rowley *(Chm)*
Marcel Hilmer *(CEO)*
Jorge Estepa *(Sec)*
Board of Directors:
Martin R. Rowley
Thomas I. A. Allen
Ricardo Moreno Campoy
Mark R. Frewin
Marcel Hilmer
Paul Frank Matysek
Lodovico P. Simone
Legal Counsel:
McCarthy Tetrault
London, United Kingdom
Transfer Agent:
Equity Financial Trust
Suite 400 200 University Avenue
Toronto, ON, Canada

FORSYTH HOLDINGS, INC.
6789 Airport Road
Mississauga, ON, L4V 1N2, Canada
Tel.: (905) 362-1400
Fax: (905) 362-4032
Web Site: www.forsythshirt.com
Year Founded: 1903
Rev.: $70,000,000
Emp.: 600
Business Description:
Apparel Mfr & Supplier
S.I.C.: 2389
N.A.I.C.S.: 315990
Personnel:
Harris R. Hester *(CEO)*

FORSYTHE LUBRICATION ASSOCIATES LIMITED
120 Chatham St
Hamilton, ON, L8P 2B5, Canada
Tel.: (905) 525-7192
Fax: (905) 525-7024
Toll Free: (800) 363-2759
E-Mail: darbour@forsythe.on.ca
Web Site: www.forsythe.on.ca
Year Founded: 1911
Rev.: $10,839,876
Emp.: 25
Business Description:
Lubricants Mfr
S.I.C.: 2992
N.A.I.C.S.: 324191
Personnel:
Bob Forsythe *(Pres)*
Dee Forsythe Arbour *(CEO)*

FORT CITY CHRYSLER SALES LTD.
8424 Alaska Road
Fort Saint John, BC, V1J 5L6, Canada
Tel.: (250) 787-5220
Fax: (250) 787-5210
Toll Free: (877) 828-8945
Web Site: www.fortcitychrysler.ca
Year Founded: 1997
Rev.: $12,954,798
Emp.: 28
Business Description:
New & Used Car Dealers
S.I.C.: 5511
N.A.I.C.S.: 441110
Personnel:
Dwight Bazin *(Pres)*

FORT PNEUS
795 Route De St Gervasy
30129 Nimes, France
Tel.: (33) 4034403000
Fax: (33) 4034403001
Web Site: www.fortpneus.com
Sls.: $20,500,000
Emp.: 27
Business Description:
Motor Vehicle Supplies & New Parts
S.I.C.: 5013
N.A.I.C.S.: 423120
Personnel:
Andre Cohen *(Dir-Fin)*

FORT ST. JAMES NICKEL CORP.
910 510 Burrard Street
Vancouver, BC, V6C 3A8, Canada
Tel.: (604) 662-8186
Fax: (604) 662-8170
E-Mail: info@fortstjamesnickel.com
Web Site: www.fortstjamesnickel.com
FTJ—(TSXV)
Business Description:
Nickel Exploration & Mining
S.I.C.: 1021
N.A.I.C.S.: 212234
Personnel:
Sandy MacDougall *(Pres & CEO)*
Murray L. Swales *(CFO)*
Scott LeSage *(Sec)*
Board of Directors:
Carlos Arias
Scott Kent
Scott LeSage
Sandy MacDougall
James William Morton

FORTALEZA ENERGY INC.
(Formerly Alvopetro Inc.)
Suite 802 322 11th Avenue Southwest
Calgary, AB, T2R 0C5, Canada
Tel.: (403) 398-3345
Fax: (403) 398-3351
Toll Free: (866) 592-6205
E-Mail: info@fortalezaenergy.com
Web Site: www.fortalezaenergy.com
Sls.: $795,216
Assets: $8,191,719
Liabilities: $8,396,487
Net Worth: ($204,768)
Earnings: ($2,163,982)
Fiscal Year-end: 12/31/12
Business Description:
Oil & Gas Exploration & Development
S.I.C.: 1311
N.A.I.C.S.: 211111
Personnel:
George William Watson *(Chm)*
J. Cameron Bailey *(Pres & CEO)*
Jamie Jeffs *(CFO & VP-Fin)*
Mark Woods *(COO & VP-Ops)*
Donald R. Leitch *(Sec)*
Board of Directors:
George William Watson
J. Cameron Bailey
Avik Dey
Roderick L. Fraser
Donald R. Leitch
Ronald McIntosh
Legal Counsel:
Carscallen Leitch LLP
Calgary, AB, Canada
Transfer Agent:
Olympia Trust Company
125 9th Avenue SE Suite 2300
Calgary, AB, T2G 0P6, Canada

Tel.: (403) 261-0900

FORTE CONSOLIDATED LIMITED
Suite 4 213 Balcatta Road
Balcatta, WA, 6021, Australia
Tel.: (61) 8 9240 4111
Fax: (61) 8 9240 4054
Web Site: www.forteconsolidated.com.au
FRC—(ASX)
Rev.: $144,602
Assets: $4,037,813
Liabilities: $79,580
Net Worth: $3,958,233
Earnings: ($743,169)
Fiscal Year-end: 06/30/13
Business Description:
Base Metals & Gold Mining Services
S.I.C.: 1099
N.A.I.C.S.: 212299
Personnel:
Bruno Firriolo *(Sec)*
Board of Directors:
John Terpu
Brian Cleaver
Bruno Firriolo
Legal Counsel:
Steinepreis Paganin
Level 4 16 Milligan Street
Perth, WA, 6000, Australia

FORTE ENERGY NL
Suite 3 Level 3 1292 Hay Street
West Perth, WA, 6005, Australia
Tel.: (61) 893224071
Fax: (61) 893224073
E-Mail: info@forteenergy.com.au
Web Site: www.forteenergy.com.au
FTE—(AIM ASX)
Rev.: $331,240
Assets: $32,994,409
Liabilities: $1,917,736
Net Worth: $31,076,673
Earnings: ($3,317,652)
Emp.: 10
Fiscal Year-end: 06/30/13
Business Description:
Uranium Mining Services
S.I.C.: 1094
N.A.I.C.S.: 212291
Personnel:
Mark David Reilly *(CEO & Mng Dir)*
Scott Yelland *(COO)*
Murray R. Wylie *(Sec)*
Board of Directors:
Glenn Robert Featherby
Christopher David Grannell
James Gerald Leahy
Mark David Reilly
Legal Counsel:
Watson, Farley & Williams
15 Appold Street
London, United Kingdom
Hardy Bowen Lawyers
Level 1 28 Ord Street
West Perth, Australia
Computershare Investor Services Pty Limited
Level 2 45 St Georges Terrace
Perth, Australia

FORTE RESOURCES INC.
1750 999 West Hastings Street
Vancouver, BC, V6C 2W2, Canada
Tel.: (604) 683-0911
Fax: (604) 683-7161
E-Mail: roehlig@telus.net
Year Founded: 2011
FJX.P—(TSXV)
Business Description:
Investment Services
S.I.C.: 6211
N.A.I.C.S.: 523999
Personnel:
Gunther Roehlig *(Pres, CEO & CFO)*
James Harris *(Sec)*
Board of Directors:
James Hutton
Gunther Roehlig
Andrew Williams
Wolrige Mahon LLP
Transfer Agent:
Computershare Investor Services Inc.
3rd Floor 510 Burrard St
V6C 3B9 Vancouver, BC, Canada

FORTEQ GROUP
Ipsachstrasse 14
2560 Nidau, Switzerland
Tel.: (41) 323327332
Fax: (41) 323327333
E-Mail: forteq.ch@forteq-group.com
Web Site: www.forteq-group.com
Year Founded: 2005
Sales Range: $25-49.9 Million
Emp.: 700
Business Description:
Plastics Mfr
S.I.C.: 3089
N.A.I.C.S.: 326199
Personnel:
Anton Affentranger *(Chm & Co-Owner)*
Johann N. Schneider-Ammann *(Co-Owner)*
Rune Bakke *(CEO)*
Oeing Hanhoff Bernhard *(COO)*
Bernhard Oeing-Hanhoff *(CTO)*

Subsidiaries:

forteq Nidau AG (1)
Ipsachstrasse 14
CH 2560 Nidau, Switzerland CH
Tel.: (41) 323327332
Fax: (41) 323327333
E-Mail: forteq@forteq-group.ch
Web Site: www.forteq.com
Emp.: 75
Plastics Mfr
S.I.C.: 3089
N.A.I.C.S.: 326199
Joachim Franke *(Mng Dir-Healthcare)*

forteq Derendingen AG (1)
Gewerbestrasse 4
Derendingen, CH 4552 Bern, Switzerland
Tel.: (41) 326815123
Fax: (41) 326815104
E-Mail: forteq@forteq.ch
Emp.: 30
Automotive Plastics Mfr
S.I.C.: 3089
N.A.I.C.S.: 326199
Friedrich Guethe *(Mgr-Production)*

Non-U.S. Subsidiaries:

forteq Netherlands BV (1)
Lange Dreef 15F
NL 4131 NJ Vianen, Netherlands
Tel.: (31) 347376767
Fax: (31) 347326311
E-Mail: forteq@forteq.nl
Web Site: www.forteq.nl
Emp.: 5
Plastic & Chemical Engineering
S.I.C.: 3089
N.A.I.C.S.: 326199
Theo Valkemburg *(Mng Dir)*

forteq Italy S.p.A. (1)
Piazza Milano 10
Ciserano Zingonia, IT 24040 Bergamo, BG, Italy IT
Tel.: (39) 0354182011
Telex: 305 454
Fax: (39) 0354182070
E-Mail: forteq@forteq.it
Web Site: www.forteq.ch/index.php?id=18
Emp.: 70
Plastics Mfr
S.I.C.: 3089
N.A.I.C.S.: 326199
Maurizio Cernuschi *(Gen Mgr)*

forteq UK Ltd. (1)
Tandem Industrial Estate
Huddersfield, HD5 0QR, United Kingdom UK
Tel.: (44) 1484424384
Fax: (44) 1484535053
E-Mail: forteq@forteq-group.com
Web Site: www.forteq.ch
Sales Range: $10-24.9 Million
Emp.: 85
Plastics Mfr
S.I.C.: 3089
N.A.I.C.S.: 326199
Paul Wallis *(Mng Dir)*

U.S. Subsidiary:

forteq North America, Inc. (1)
150 Park Center Dr
West Henrietta, NY 14586-9688
Tel.: (585) 427-9410
Fax: (585) 427-9438
E-Mail: forteq@forteq-group.com
Web Site: www.forteq-group.com
Emp.: 80
Plastics Mfr
S.I.C.: 3089
N.A.I.C.S.: 326199
Joe Beonocore *(Gen Mgr)*

FORTESCUE METALS GROUP LIMITED
Level 2 87 Adelaide Terrace
Perth, WA, 6004, Australia
Tel.: (61) 8 6218 8888
Fax: (61) 8 6218 8880
E-Mail: fmgl@fmgl.com.au
Web Site: www.fmgl.com.au
FMG—(ASX OTC)
Rev.: $8,120,000,000
Assets: $20,867,000,000
Liabilities: $15,578,000,000
Net Worth: $5,289,000,000
Earnings: $1,746,000,000
Emp.: 3,752
Fiscal Year-end: 06/30/13
Business Description:
Iron Mining Services
S.I.C.: 1011
N.A.I.C.S.: 212210
Personnel:
Neville Power *(CEO)*
Stephen Pearce *(CFO)*
Mark Thomas *(Sec)*
Board of Directors:
Andrew Forrest
Mark B. Barnaba
Geoff Brayshaw
Huiquan Cao
Herb Elliott
Elizabeth Anne Gaines
Owen L. Hegarty
Peter Fletcher Meurs
Neville Power
Geoffrey William Raby
William Graeme Rowley
Herbert E. Scruggs
Legal Counsel:
DLA Piper
Level 31 152 158 St Georges Tce
Perth, Australia
Clayton Utz
250 St Georges Terr
Perth, Australia

Subsidiaries:

Chichester Metals Pty Limited (1)
Level 2 87 Adelaide Terrace
East Perth, Perth, WA, 6004, Australia
Tel.: (61) 862188888
Fax: (61) 862188880
E-Mail: fmgl@fmgl.com.au
Iron Ore Mining Services
S.I.C.: 1011
N.A.I.C.S.: 212210
Andrew Forrest *(CEO)*

The Pilbara Infrastructure Pty Limited (1)
Level 2 87 Adelaide Terrace
Perth, WA, 6004, Australia
Tel.: (61) 862188888
Fax: (61) 862188880
Iron Ore Mining Services
S.I.C.: 1011
N.A.I.C.S.: 212210

FORTH CORPORATION PUBLIC COMPANY LIMITED
226/12 13 16 Phaholyothin rd
Samsennai Phayathai
Bangkok, 10400, Thailand
Tel.: (66) 2615 0600
Fax: (66) 2615 0615
E-Mail: sale@forth.co.th
Web Site: www.forth.co.th
Year Founded: 1989
FORTH—(THA)
Rev.: $196,742,503
Assets: $147,363,607
Liabilities: $99,167,677
Net Worth: $48,195,930
Earnings: $3,414,557
Fiscal Year-end: 12/31/12
Business Description:
Telecommunication Equipment Mfr
S.I.C.: 3669
N.A.I.C.S.: 334290
Personnel:
Sanit Vorapanya *(Chm)*
Pongchai Amatanont *(CEO)*
Rangsri Lerttripinyo *(Sr Exec VP)*
Chatchavin Pipatchotitham *(Exec VP & VP-Admin)*
Board of Directors:
Sanit Vorapanya
Kaelic Amatanont
Pongchai Amatanont
Nongram Laohaareedilok
Rangsri Lerttripinyo
Suthum Malila
Chonticha Siripongpreeda
Matinee Wandeepirom

Subsidiary:

Genius Traffic System Company Limited (1)
226/27-29 Phaholyothin Rd Samsennai
Phayathai, Bangkok, 10400, Thailand
Tel.: (66) 2615 2440
Fax: (66) 2615 2441
E-Mail: info@gets.co.th
Web Site: www.gets.co.th
Traffic Control Equipment Mfr
S.I.C.: 3812
N.A.I.C.S.: 334511

Plant:

Forth Corporation Public Company Limited - FORTH FACTORY (1)
77 Moo 11Phuttamonton 5 Road
Raikhing Sampran District, Nakhon Pathom, 73210, Thailand
Tel.: (66) 2 811 7921
Fax: (66) 2 811 7935
E-Mail: service@forth.co.th
Electronic Component Mfr
S.I.C.: 3679
N.A.I.C.S.: 334419

FORTH WINES LTD
Crawford Place Milnathort
Kinross, KY13 9XF, United Kingdom
Tel.: (44) 1577866000
Fax: (44) 1577866025
E-Mail: enquiries@forthwines.com
Web Site: www.forthwines.com
Year Founded: 1963
Rev.: $36,390,377
Emp.: 55
Business Description:
Wines Distr
S.I.C.: 5182
N.A.I.C.S.: 424820
Personnel:
Ewen Cameron *(Chm)*
George Thomson *(Mng Dir)*

FORTIFY RESOURCES INC.
1210 1066 West Hastings Street
Vancouver, BC, V6E 3X1, Canada
Tel.: (604) 668-5820
Fax: (778) 373-8759
E-Mail: craigrademaker@pearsecapital.com
Year Founded: 2011
FTY—(CNSX)
Business Description:
Metal Mining
S.I.C.: 1099
N.A.I.C.S.: 212299
Personnel:
James Douglas Glass *(Pres)*
Douglas Ian Johnston *(CFO)*
Board of Directors:
James Douglas Glass
Douglas Ian Johnston
Craig Evan Rademaker
John Anthony Versfelt

FORTIS HEALTHCARE INDIA LIMITED
(See Under Fortis Healthcare Limited)

FORTIS HEALTHCARE LIMITED
Tower A Unitech Business Park Block F
South City 1 Sector 41, Gurgaon, Haryana, 122001, India
Tel.: (91) 124 492 1021
Fax: (91) 124 492 1041
E-Mail: contactus@fortishealthcare.com
Web Site: www.fortishealthcare.com
Year Founded: 1996
532843—(BOM NSE)
Rev.: $1,092,204,230
Assets: $3,444,967,365
Liabilities: $2,756,972,104
Net Worth: $687,995,261
Earnings: $90,974,204
Emp.: 23,000
Fiscal Year-end: 03/31/13
Business Description:
Hospital Owner & Operator
S.I.C.: 8062
N.A.I.C.S.: 622110
Personnel:
Malvinder Mohan Singh *(Chm)*
Shivinder Mohan Singh *(Vice Chm & Mng Dir)*
Vishal Bali *(CEO)*
K. Srivatsan *(CFO)*
Daphne Khoo *(Chief Medical Officer)*
Vanessa Ng *(Chief People Officer)*
Aditya Vij *(CEO-India)*
Rahul Ranjan *(Sec)*
Jasbir Grewal *(Exec VP)*
Board of Directors:
Malvinder Mohan Singh
Gurcharan Das
Balinder Singh Dhillon
Joji Sekhon Gill
Sunil Godhwani
Preetinder Singh Joshi
Pradeep Ratilal Raniga
Tejinder S. Shergill
Harpal Singh
Shivinder Mohan Singh
Brian William Tempest
Transfer Agent:
Link Intime India Private Limited
A-40 2nd Floor Naraina Industrial Area Phase-II
New Delhi, India
Subsidiaries:

Escorts Heart Institute and Research Centre Limited (1)
Okhla Rd
New Delhi, 110025, India
Tel.: (91) 1126825000
Fax: (91) 1126825015
E-Mail: info@fortishealthcare.com
Emp.: 5,500
Health Care Services
S.I.C.: 8011
N.A.I.C.S.: 621491
Bhavdeep Singh *(CEO)*

Subsidiary:

Escorts Heart and Super Speciality Institute Limited (2)
Majitha-Verka Bypass Rd
Amritsar, Punjab, 143 004, India
Tel.: (91) 1832573900
Fax: (91) 1832573910
E-Mail: amritsar@fortishealthcare.com
Web Site: www.ehirc.com
Health Care Services
S.I.C.: 8011
N.A.I.C.S.: 621491
Rishi Kapoor *(Gen Mgr)*

Escorts Hospital and Research Centre Limited (1)
Neelam Bata Rd
N I T, Faridabad, Haryana, 121001, India
Tel.: (91) 1292416096
Fax: (91) 1294009973
Web Site: www.fortishealthcare.com
Emp.: 55
Health Care Services
S.I.C.: 8011
N.A.I.C.S.: 621491

Non-U.S. Subsidiaries:

Fortis Healthcare Singapore Pte. Ltd. (1)
180 Clemenceau Avenue
#05-02 Haw Par Centre, Singapore, 239922, Singapore SG
Tel.: (65) 6672 5900
Fax: (65) 6672 5905
Web Site: www.fortishealthcare.com.sg
Hospitals, Specialist Clinics, Outpatient Medical Centers, Primary Care & Dental Facilities Operator
S.I.C.: 8049
N.A.I.C.S.: 621399
Poh Lan Tan *(CEO)*

The Lanka Hospitals Corporation PLC (1)
578 Elvitigala Mawatha Narahenpita
Colombo, 5, Sri Lanka
Tel.: (94) 115 430000
Fax: (94) 115 530000
Medical Services
S.I.C.: 8062
N.A.I.C.S.: 622110

Quality HealthCare Medical Services Limited (1)
3/F Skyline Tower 39 Wang Kwong Road
Kowloon Bay, Kowloon, China (Hong Kong)
Tel.: (852) 2975 3200
Fax: (852) 2581 3070
Medical Services
S.I.C.: 8062
N.A.I.C.S.: 622110

Super Religare Laboratories International FZ LLC (1)
Unit 1007-08 1017-18 Block A&E 64 Al Razi Building
PO Box 505143
Dubai Healthcare City, Dubai, United Arab Emirates
Tel.: (971) 4 4483 100
Fax: (971) 4 4484 694
Healthcare Services
S.I.C.: 8071
N.A.I.C.S.: 621511

FORTIS, INC.
#4F Fortis Bldg 106-3 Imae-dong
Bundang-gu
Seongnam, Gyeonggi-do, 463-829, Korea (South)
Tel.: (82) 31 7091407
Fax: (82) 31 7090266
E-Mail: sales@fortis.co.kr
Web Site: www.fortis.co.kr
Year Founded: 2006
141020—(KRS)
Sales Range: $25-49.9 Million
Emp.: 70
Business Description:
Digital Set Top Boxes Mfr
S.I.C.: 3663
N.A.I.C.S.: 334220
Personnel:
Jin Yung Sul *(CEO)*

FORTIS INC.
Suite 1201 Fortis Building 139 Water Street
PO Box 8837
Saint John's, NL, A1B 3T2, Canada
Tel.: (709) 737-2800
Fax: (709) 737-5307
E-Mail: investorrelations@fortisinc.com
Web Site: www.fortisinc.com
Year Founded: 1987
FTS—(OTC TSX)
Rev.: $3,632,149,080
Assets: $14,860,599,000
Liabilities: $9,482,950,800
Net Worth: $5,377,648,200
Earnings: $368,781,420
Emp.: 7,200
Fiscal Year-end: 12/31/12
Business Description:
Holding Company; Utilities Investments
S.I.C.: 6719
N.A.I.C.S.: 551112
Personnel:
David G. Norris *(Chm)*
H. Stanley Marshall *(Pres & CEO)*
Barry V. Perry *(CFO)*
Ronald W. McCabe *(Gen Counsel, Sec & VP)*
Board of Directors:
David G. Norris
Peter E. Case
Frank J. Crothers
Ida J. Goodreau
Douglas J. Haughey
H. Stanley Marshall
John S. McCallum
Harry McWatters
Ronald D. Munkley
Michael A. Pavey
Roy P. Rideout
Transfer Agent:
Computershare Trust Company of Canada
9th Floor 100 University Avenue
Toronto, ON, Canada
Subsidiaries:

Fortis Properties Brunswick Square Ltd. (1)
39 King St
Saint John, NB, E2L 4W3, Canada (100%)
Tel.: (506) 658-1000
Fax: (506) 632-1997
E-Mail: info@fortisproperties.com
Web Site: www.fortisproperties.com
Emp.: 13
Brunswick Square Retail/Office/Hotel Complex; Joint Venture of Aliant & Fortis Properties Corporation
S.I.C.: 6512
N.A.I.C.S.: 531120
Cathy Lifford *(Mgr-Leasing)*

Fortis Properties Corporation (1)
139 Water St Ste 1201
Saint John's, NL, A1B 3T2, Canada (100%)
Tel.: (709) 737-2800
Fax: (709) 737-3785
E-Mail: info@fortisproperties.com
Web Site: www.fortisproperties.com
Emp.: 45
Holding Company for Shopping Centers & Hotels
S.I.C.: 6719
N.A.I.C.S.: 551112
H. Stanley Marshall *(Chm)*
Nora M. Duke *(Pres & CEO)*

FortisBC Inc. (1)
16705 Fraser Hwy
Surrey, BC, V4N 0E8, Canada
Tel.: (604) 576-7000
Fax: (604) 592-7677
Toll Free: (800) 773-7001
E-Mail: rebates@fortisbc.com
Web Site: www.fortisbc.com
Emp.: 200
Natural Gas Distribution Services
S.I.C.: 4924
N.A.I.C.S.: 221210
John C. Walker *(Chm & CEO)*

FortisOntario Inc (1)
1130 Bertie Street
PO Box 1218
Fort Erie, ON, L2A 5Y2, Canada
Tel.: (905) 871-0330
Fax: (905) 871-8772
E-Mail: customer.service@cnpower.com
Web Site: www.fortisontario.com
Emp.: 100
Hydroelectric Power Generation & Distribution Services
S.I.C.: 4911
N.A.I.C.S.: 221111
William Daley *(Pres & CEO)*
Glen King *(CFO & VP-Fin)*
Scott Hawkes *(Gen Counsel, Corp Sec & VP-Corp Svcs)*

Subsidiaries:

Algoma Power Inc. (2)
2 Sackville Rd Ste A
Sault Sainte Marie, ON, P6B 6J6, Canada
Tel.: (705) 256-3850
Fax: (705) 253-6476
Toll Free: (888) 593-3348
E-Mail: customerservice@algomapower.com
Web Site: www.algomapower.com
Electric Power Distribution Services
S.I.C.: 4911
N.A.I.C.S.: 221122

Canadian Niagara Power Inc. (2)
1130 Bertie St
PO Box 1218
Fort Erie, ON, L2A 5Y2, Canada
Tel.: (905) 871-0330
Fax: (905) 871-8772
E-Mail: customer.service@cnpower.com
Web Site: www.cnpower.com
Emp.: 100
Electric Power Distribution Services
S.I.C.: 4911
N.A.I.C.S.: 221122
Kristine Carmichael *(Mgr-Customer Svc, HR & Corp Comm)*

Division:

Canadian Niagara Power Inc. - Eastern Ontario Power Division (3)
PO Box 1179
Cornwall, ON, K6H 5V3, Canada
Tel.: (613) 382-2118
Fax: (613) 932-6498
E-Mail: Customer.Service@EasternOntarioPower.com
Web Site: www.easternontariopower.com
Electric Power Distribution Services
S.I.C.: 4911
N.A.I.C.S.: 221122
Kristine Carmichael *(Mgr-Customer Svc & Corp Comm)*

Cornwall Electric Inc. (2)
1001 Sydney St
Cornwall, ON, K6H 3K1, Canada
Tel.: (613) 932-0123
Fax: (613) 932-6498
E-Mail: Customer.Service@CornwallElectric.com
Web Site: www.cornwallelectric.com
Electric Power Distribution Services
S.I.C.: 4911
N.A.I.C.S.: 221122
Michael Pescod *(Reg Mgr)*

Maritime Electric Company Limited (1)
180 Kent St
Charlottetown, PE, C1A 7N2, Canada
Tel.: (902) 629-3799
Fax: (902) 629-3630
Toll Free: (800) 670-1012

E-Mail: customerservice@maritimeelectric.com
Web Site: www.maritimeelectric.com
Emp.: 100
Electric Power Distribution Services
S.I.C.: 4911
N.A.I.C.S.: 221122
Fred J. O'Brien *(Pres & CEO)*
William J. Geldert *(CFO, Corp Sec & VP-Fin & Admin)*

Newfoundland Power Inc. **(1)**
PO Box 8910
Saint John's, NL, A1B 3P6, Canada
Tel.: (709) 737-5600
Fax: (709) 737-2974
E-Mail: contactus@newfoundlandpower.com
Web Site: www.newfoundlandpower.com
Sales Range: $300-349.9 Million
Emp.: 600
Electric Power Distr
S.I.C.: 4939
N.A.I.C.S.: 221122
Angus A. Bruneau *(Chm, Pres & CEO)*
Earl Ludlow *(Pres & CEO)*
Robert Meyers *(Treas)*

Terasen Inc. **(1)**
1111 W Georgia St 10th Fl
Vancouver, BC, V6E 4M3, Canada BC
Tel.: (604) 443-6500
Fax: (604) 443-6540
Toll Free: (800) 667-9177
E-Mail: info@terasen.com
Web Site: www.fortisbc.com
Emp.: 1,366
Natural Gas Transmission & Distribution System, Oil Pipeline Transmission
S.I.C.: 4923
N.A.I.C.S.: 486210
Mark L. Cullen *(Chm)*
John C. Walker *(Pres & CEO)*
Michele Leeners *(CFO & Sr VP-Fin)*
Roger Dall'Antonia *(CFO)*

Subsidiaries:

Terasen Gas (Squamish), Inc. **(2)**
38152 2nd Ave
PO Box 440
Squamish, BC, V0N 3G0, Canada
Tel.: (604) 892-5455
Web Site: www.terasengas.com
Emp.: 4
Natural Gas Transmission & Distribution
S.I.C.: 4922
N.A.I.C.S.: 486210
Scott A. Thomson *(Exec VP-Regulatory Affairs)*

U.S. Subsidiary:

CH Energy Group, Inc. **(1)**
284 South Ave
Poughkeepsie, NY 12601-4839 NY
Tel.: (845) 452-2000
Fax: (845) 486-5465
Web Site: www.chenergygroup.com
Rev.: $924,719,000
Assets: $1,784,949,000
Liabilities: $1,266,632,000
Net Worth: $518,317,000
Earnings: $39,847,000
Emp.: 1,235
Fiscal Year-end: 12/31/12
Holding Company for Electricity, Natural Gas, Propane, Fuel Oil & Petroleum Products
S.I.C.: 6719
N.A.I.C.S.: 551112
Steven V. Lant *(Chm, Pres & CEO)*
Christopher M. Capone *(CFO & Exec VP)*
John E. Gould *(Gen Counsel & Exec VP)*
Stacey A. Renner *(Treas)*
Denise D. VanBuren *(Sec & VP-PR)*
James P. Laurito *(Exec VP)*

Subsidiaries:

Central Hudson Enterprises Corporation **(2)**
284 South Ave
Poughkeepsie, NY 12601-4838
Tel.: (845) 485-5770
Web Site: www.centralhudson.com
Fuel Distribution Services
S.I.C.: 5989
N.A.I.C.S.: 454310
James Laurito *(CEO)*

Central Hudson Gas & Electric Corporation **(2)**
284 South Ave
Poughkeepsie, NY 12601-4839 NY
Tel.: (845) 452-2000 (100%)
Fax: (845) 486-5544
Toll Free: (800) 527-2714
Web Site: www.centralhudson.com
Rev.: $644,515,000
Assets: $1,660,367,000
Liabilities: $1,190,706,000
Net Worth: $469,661,000
Earnings: $47,170,000
Emp.: 869
Fiscal Year-end: 12/31/12
Public Electric & Gas Utility
S.I.C.: 4939
N.A.I.C.S.: 221122
H. Stanley Marshall *(Chm)*
Steven V. Lant *(CEO)*
Christopher M. Capone *(CFO & Exec VP)*
Denise D. VanBuren *(Sec & VP-Corp Comm)*
John E. Gould *(Sec)*
James P. Laurito *(Exec VP)*
Charles A. Freni *(Sr VP-Customer Svc & Dir)*

Non-U.S. Subsidiary:

Caribbean Utilities Company, Ltd. **(1)**
457 North Sound Road
PO Box 38
Georgetown, Grand Cayman, KY1-1101, Cayman Islands
Tel.: (345) 9495200
Fax: (345) 9494621
E-Mail: investor@cuc.ky
Web Site: www.cuc-cayman.com
CUP.U—(TSX)
Rev.: $223,549,000
Assets: $434,972,000
Liabilities: $261,106,000
Net Worth: $173,866,000
Earnings: $17,691,000
Emp.: 190
Fiscal Year-end: 12/31/12
Gas & Electric Utility Services
S.I.C.: 1389
N.A.I.C.S.: 213112
David E. Ritch *(Chm)*
Frank J. Crothers *(Vice Chm)*
J. F. Richard Hew *(Pres & CEO)*
Letitia T. Lawrence *(CFO & VP-Fin)*
Claire Stafford *(Compliance Officer & Asst Sec)*

FORTIS MALAR HOSPITALS LIMITED

No 52 1st Main Road Gandhi Nagar
Adyar, Chennai, 600 020, India
Tel.: (91) 44 4289 2222
Fax: (91) 44 4289 2293
E-Mail: contacts.malar@fortishealthcare.com
Web Site: www.fortishealthcare.com
523696—(BOM)
Rev.: $18,273,359
Assets: $16,837,742
Liabilities: $2,539,214
Net Worth: $14,298,528
Earnings: $8,060,873
Emp.: 626
Fiscal Year-end: 03/31/13
Business Description:
Hospital Management Services
S.I.C.: 8062
N.A.I.C.S.: 622110
Personnel:
Dinesh Gupta *(Compliance Officer & Sec)*
Board of Directors:
Aditya Vij
Ramesh L. Adige
Ashish Bhatia
Sanjay Jayavarthanavelu
P. Murari
Lakshman Teckchand Nanwani
Sandeep Puri
Nithya Ramamurthy
Rama Krishna Shetty
V. Vijayarathna
Transfer Agent:
Karvy Computershare Private Limited
Plot No 17 to 24 Vittalrao Nagar Madhapur
Hyderabad, India

FORTIS MINING LIMITED

Level 5 15-19 Claremont Street
Yarra, VIC, 3141, Australia
Tel.: (61) 390200105
Fax: (61) 390156468
E-Mail: info@fortismining.com.au
Web Site: www.fortismining.com.au
Year Founded: 2010
Emp.: 20
Business Description:
Gold, Nickel & Copper Mining Services
S.I.C.: 1041
N.A.I.C.S.: 212221
Personnel:
Jitto Arulampalam *(Chm)*
Justyn Stedwell *(Sec)*
Board of Directors:
Jitto Arulampalam
Paul Bitetto
Frank Cannavo
Terry Grammer
Legal Counsel:
Pointon Partners
Level 2 640 Bourke Street
Melbourne, VIC, 3000, Australia

FORTISSIMO CAPITAL MANAGEMENT CO. LTD.

14 Hamelacha Street Park Afek
POB 11704
Rosh Ha'Ayin, 48091, Israel
Tel.: (972) 3 915 7400
Fax: (972) 3 915 7411
E-Mail: info@ffcapital.com
Web Site: www.ffcapital.com
Business Description:
Private Equity Firm
S.I.C.: 6211
N.A.I.C.S.: 523999
Personnel:
Yuval Cohen *(Founder & Mng Partner)*
Shmoulik Barashi *(Partner)*
Eli Blatt *(Partner)*
Yochai Hacohen *(Partner)*
Yoav Hineman *(Partner)*
Marc Lesnick *(Partner)*

Non-U.S. Holding:

Starhome Mach **(1)**
(Formerly Starhome GmbH)
Seefeldstrasse 25
CH 8008 Zurich, Switzerland
Tel.: (41) 44 380 6777
Fax: (41) 43 222 6768
E-Mail:
Web Site: www.starhomemach.com
Sales Range: $200-249.9 Million
Emp.: 220
Cellular Roaming & Techology Services
S.I.C.: 4812
N.A.I.C.S.: 517210
Shlomo Wolfman *(Co-Founder & COO)*
Tal Meirzon *(CEO)*
Adi Sfadia *(CFO)*
Bruno Pagliuca *(COO)*
Lena Wittbjer *(Chief Admin Officer)*
Neta Bloch *(Gen Counsel)*

Non-U.S. Subsidiaries:

Starhome Mach **(2)**
(Formerly MACH S.a.r.l.)
15 rue Edmond Reuter
Contern, 5326 Luxembourg, Luxembourg LU
Tel.: (352) 27 775 100
E-Mail:
Web Site: www.starhomemach.com
Emp.: 115
Roaming Data Fraud Management Services
S.I.C.: 7379
N.A.I.C.S.: 518210
Morten Broegger *(CEO)*

FORTISSIMO FILM SALES

Van Diemenstraat 100
1013 CN Amsterdam, Netherlands
Tel.: (31) 206273215
Fax: (31) 206261155
E-Mail: info@fortissimo.nl
Web Site: www.fortissimofilms.com
Year Founded: 1991
Emp.: 20
Business Description:
Independent Film Producer, Marketer, Promoter, Sales & Distr
S.I.C.: 7812
N.A.I.C.S.: 512110
Personnel:
Michael J. Werner *(Chm)*
Nelleke Driessen *(Mng Dir)*

Non-U.S. Subsidiary:

Fortissimo Film Sales **(1)**
Unit A 264 CKK Commercial Center 289 2295
Hennessy Road, Wanchai, China (Hong Kong)
Tel.: (852) 23118081
Fax: (852) 23118023
E-Mail: info@fortissimo-hk.com
Web Site: www.fortissimofilms.com
Emp.: 10
Independent Film Sales & Distr
S.I.C.: 7822
N.A.I.C.S.: 512120
Michael J. Werner *(Chm)*

FORTRESS ENERGY INC.

(Name Changed to Fortaleza Energy Inc.)

FORTRESS MINERALS CORP.

Suite 2000 885 West Georgia Street
Vancouver, BC, V6C 3E8, Canada
Tel.: (604) 689-7842
Fax: (604) 689-4250
Toll Free: (888) 689-7842
E-Mail: info@fortressminerals.com
Web Site: www.fortressminerals.com
Year Founded: 2002
FST—(TSXV)
Rev.: $249,750
Assets: $22,753,653
Liabilities: $32,728
Net Worth: $22,720,924
Earnings: ($460,962)
Fiscal Year-end: 12/31/12
Business Description:
Mineral Exploration Services
S.I.C.: 1081
N.A.I.C.S.: 213114
Personnel:
Ronald F. Hochstein *(Chm)*
Lukas Henrik Lundin *(Pres)*
Chester See *(CFO)*
Antonietta Vodola *(Sec)*
Board of Directors:
Ronald F. Hochstein
Jim Cambon
Ian Gibbs
Adam Lundin
Lukas Henrik Lundin
Legal Counsel:
McCullough O'Connor Irwin LLP
Vancouver, BC, Canada
Cassels Brock & Blackwell, LLP
Toronto, ON, Canada
Transfer Agent:
Computershare Trust Company of Canada
Toronto, ON, Canada

FORTRESS PAPER LTD.

2nd Floor 157 Chadwick Court
North Vancouver, BC, V7M 3K2, Canada

Fortress Paper Ltd.—(Continued)

Tel.: (604) 904-2328
Fax: (604) 988-5327
Toll Free: (888) 820-3888
E-Mail: info@fortresspaper.com
Web Site: www.fortresspaper.com
Year Founded: 2006
FTP—(TSX)
Sls.: $312,558,655
Assets: $574,497,835
Liabilities: $346,539,228
Net Worth: $227,958,607
Earnings: ($20,762,096)
Emp.: 722
Fiscal Year-end: 12/31/12

Business Description:
Banknotes, Passport Papers, Visa Papers, Non-Woven Wallpaper Based Products, Graphic & Technical Papers Producer
S.I.C.: 2621
N.A.I.C.S.: 322121

Personnel:
Chadwick Wasilenkoff *(CEO)*
Kurt Loewen *(CFO)*
Yvon Pelletier *(Pres-Dissolving Pulp Bus)*
Danial Buckle *(Sec & Dir-Fin)*

Board of Directors:
John Coleman
Per Gundersby
Joe Nemeth
Roland Tornare
Richard O'C. Whittall

Transfer Agent:
Computershare Trust Company of Canada
510 Burrard St 3rd Fl
Vancouver, BC, V6C 3B9, Canada

Non-U.S. Subsidiary:

Landqart AG **(1)**
Kantonsstrasse 16
7302 Landquart, Switzerland
Tel.: (41) 813079090
Fax: (41) 813079141
E-Mail: info@landqart.com
Web Site: www.landqart.com
Emp.: 240
Paper Mfr
S.I.C.: 2621
N.A.I.C.S.: 322121
Axel Wappler *(CEO)*

FORTUM OYJ

Keilaniemente 1
02150 Espoo, Finland
Mailing Address:
PO Box 1
FI 00048 Fortum, Finland
Tel.: (358) 104511
Fax: (358) 104524447
E-Mail: communications@fortum.com
Web Site: www.fortum.com
Year Founded: 1996
FUM1V—(HEL)
Sls.: $8,291,061,030
Assets: $33,153,474,760
Liabilities: $18,586,569,190
Net Worth: $14,566,905,570
Earnings: $2,023,293,510
Emp.: 10,371
Fiscal Year-end: 12/31/12

Business Description:
Generation, Distribution & Sale of Electricity & Heat & Operation & Maintenance of Power Plants
Import Export
S.I.C.: 4939
N.A.I.C.S.: 221113

Personnel:
Tapio Kuula *(Pres & CEO)*
Markus Rauramo *(CFO)*
Alexander Chuvaev *(Exec VP-Russia Div)*
Timo Karttinen *(Exec VP-Electricity Solutions & Distr Div)*
Per Langer *(Exec VP-Heat Div)*
Matti Ruotsala *(Exec VP-Power Div)*
Helena Aatinen *(Sr VP-Corp Comm)*
Mikael Frisk *(Sr VP-Corp HR)*
Maria Paatero Kaarnakari *(Sr VP-Asia)*

Board of Directors:
Sari Maritta Baldauf
Minoo Akhtarzand
Heinz-Werner Binzel
Ilona Ervasti-Vaintola
Kim Juhani Ignatius
Joshua Larson
Christian Ramm-Schmidt

Subsidiaries:

Fortum Asiakaspalvelu Oy **(1)**
PO Box 1
00048 Fortum, Finland
Tel.: (358) 10 4511
Fax: (358) 10 45 24447
Electric Power Distribution Services
S.I.C.: 4939
N.A.I.C.S.: 221122
Tapio Kuula *(Gen Mgr)*

Fortum Aviation And Marine Sales **(1)**
Miestentie 1
PO Box 77
2151 Espoo, Finland (100%)
Tel.: (358) 3581045811
Fax: (358) 4584441
Emp.: 1,000
S.I.C.: 1311
N.A.I.C.S.: 211111

Fortum BCS Oy **(1)**
OyKeilaniemiente 1
2150 Espoo, Finland
Tel.: (358) 104 511
Fax: (358) 104524798
Electric Power Distribution Services
S.I.C.: 4931
N.A.I.C.S.: 221122
Tapio Kuula *(Gen Mgr)*

Fortum Espoo Distribution Oy **(1)**
Keilaniementie 1
Espoo, 48, Finland FI
Tel.: (358) 10 4511
Fax: (358) 10 45 36500
Web Site: www.fortum.com
Emp.: 30
Electric Power Distribution Services
S.I.C.: 4939
N.A.I.C.S.: 221122
Ari Koponen *(Gen Mgr)*

Fortum FNW Oy **(1)**
Karhumaenkatu 2
55120 Imatra, Finland
Tel.: (358) 5 683 55
Fax: (358) 5 683 5229
Electric Power Distribution Services
S.I.C.: 4911
N.A.I.C.S.: 221122

Fortum Heat and Gas Oy **(1)**
Keilaniementie 1
Helsinki, 00048, Finland
Tel.: (358) 10 4511
Fax: (358) 104524798
Emp.: 1,000
Electric Power Distribution Services
S.I.C.: 4931
N.A.I.C.S.: 221122
Tapio Kuula *(CEO)*

Fortum Heat Naantali Oy **(1)**
Naantali Power Plant Satamatie 16
21100 Naantali, Finland
Tel.: (358) 10 45 42111
Fax: (358) 10 45 42375
Emp.: 10
Electric Power Generation Services
S.I.C.: 4911
N.A.I.C.S.: 221118
Ari Anttila *(Mgr-Power Plant)*

Fortum Markets Oy **(1)**
Keilaniementie 1
2151 Espoo, 2151, Finland (100%)
Mailing Address:
PO Box 40
00048 Fortum, Finland
Tel.: (358) 0104511
Fax: (358) 104536500
Emp.: 1,000
Petroleum & Natural Gas
S.I.C.: 1311
N.A.I.C.S.: 211111
Tapio Kuula *(CEO)*

Fortum Nuclear Services Oy **(1)**
Keilaniementie 1
2150 Espoo, Finland
Tel.: (358) 104511
Fax: (358) 104532525
Nuclear Power Generation Services
S.I.C.: 4911
N.A.I.C.S.: 221113

Fortum Oy **(1)**
2B Keilanitmentie 1
FIN 02150 Espoo, Finland FI
Tel.: (358) 0104511
Fax: (358) 104532383
Web Site: www.fortum.com
Emp.: 3,000
S.I.C.: 1311
N.A.I.C.S.: 211111
Tapio Kuula *(Pres & CEO)*

Fortum Power and Heat Oy **(1)**
Keilaniemente 1
FIN 02150 Espoo, Finland
Mailing Address:
PO Box 100
FIN-00048 Fortum, Finland
Tel.: (358) 0104511
Fax: (358) 104534290
E-Mail: tapiokwla@fortum.com
Web Site: www.fortum.com
Emp.: 5,000
Provider of Energy Services, Power & Heat
S.I.C.: 8999
N.A.I.C.S.: 541690

Branch:

Fortum Power And Heat Oy **(2)**
Valvomontie 2A
FI-55100 Imatra, Finland (100%)
Tel.: (358) 10 45 46111
Fax: (358) 104546360
Web Site: www.fortum.fi
Emp.: 33
Power & Heat Generation Services
S.I.C.: 4939
N.A.I.C.S.: 221122

Non-U.S. Subsidiaries:

Fortum Power AB **(2)**
Kontorsvagen 1
PO Box 701
Borlange, 78127, Sweden (100%)
Tel.: (46) 24367500
Telex: 74010 Stora s
Fax: (46) 24367625
Web Site: www.fortum.se
Sls.: $192,324,992
Emp.: 400
Production of Electricity at Hydropower Plants
S.I.C.: 4931
N.A.I.C.S.: 221122
Hakan Grefberg *(VP)*

Fortum Power & Heat AB **(2)**
Lidingovagen 115
Stockholm, 115 77, Sweden (100%)
Tel.: (46) 86717000
Fax: (46) 86717060
E-Mail: info@fortum.com
Web Site: www.fortum.se
Emp.: 1,000
S.I.C.: 1311
N.A.I.C.S.: 211111
Tapio Kuula *(Mng Dir)*

Subsidiary:

AB Fortum Varme Holding samagt med Stockholms stad **(3)**
Lidingovagen 115
115 77 Stockholm, Sweden
Tel.: (46) 8 671 70 00
Fax: (46) 8 671 82 82
Investment Management Services
S.I.C.: 6211
N.A.I.C.S.: 523999

Fortum Power and Heat Oy **(2)**
Riga International Airport
Marupes Pagasts, LV 1053 Riga, Lettland, Latvia (100%)
Tel.: (371) 63023446
Fax: (371) 630 830 20
Sales Range: Less than $1 Million
Emp.: 3
Electric Power Distr
S.I.C.: 4931
N.A.I.C.S.: 221122

IVO Energi AB **(2)**
Biblioteksgatan 29, 2 tr
PO Box 5186
S-102 44 Stockholm, Sweden
Tel.: (46) 84403700
Fax: (46) 8 611 6735
S.I.C.: 1311
N.A.I.C.S.: 211111

Fortum Sahkonsiirto Oy **(1)**
Keilaniementie 1
02150 Espoo, Finland FI
Tel.: (358) 10 45 11
Fax: (358) 10 453 4720
E-Mail: Tapio.Kuula@fortum.com
Web Site: www.fortum.fi
Electric Power Distribution Services
S.I.C.: 4939
N.A.I.C.S.: 221122
Tapio Kuula *(Gen Mgr)*

Fortum Service Oy **(1)**
Keilaniementie 1
PO Box 10
2150 Espoo, Finland (100%)
Mailing Address:
PO Box 10
00048 Fortum, Finland
Tel.: (358) 104511
Fax: (358) 104532780
E-Mail: Mikael.Lilius@fortum.com
Web Site: www.fortum.fi
Sales Range: $10-24.9 Million
Emp.: 300
S.I.C.: 1311
N.A.I.C.S.: 211111
Tapio Kuula *(Mng Dir)*

Subsidiaries:

Johtotec Oy **(2)**
Rajatorpantie 8 Vantaa
00048 Fortum, Finland (100%)
Mailing Address:
PO Box 10
00048 Fortum, Finland
Tel.: (358) 403112222
Web Site: www.fortum.com
Emp.: 150
Crude Petroleum & Natural Gas
S.I.C.: 1311
N.A.I.C.S.: 211111

Non-U.S. Subsidiary:

Montivo Kft **(2)**
MOL RT 1 Sz Ipartelep 47
18 Epulet, 2443 Szazhalombatta, Hungary (51%)
Tel.: (36) 23551312
Fax: (36) 23350397
E-Mail: montivo@axelero.hu
Web Site: www.fortum.com
Sales Range: $1-9.9 Million
Emp.: 80
S.I.C.: 1311
N.A.I.C.S.: 211111

Fortum Small Hydro Holding Oy **(1)**
Keilaniementie 1
2150 Espoo, Finland
Tel.: (358) 10 4511
Fax: (358) 104524798
Emp.: 100
Investment Management Services
S.I.C.: 6211
N.A.I.C.S.: 523999
Tatio Kuula *(Gen Mgr)*

Mantynummen Lampo Oy **(1)**
Laurinkatu 48 B
8100 Lohja, Finland
Tel.: (358) 50 047 1312
Electric Power Generation Services
S.I.C.: 4939
N.A.I.C.S.: 221118

NAPS Systems Oy **(1)**
Pakkalan Kuja 4
FIN 01510 Vantaa, Finland (100%)
Tel.: (358) 207545666

Telex: 124641 neste fi
Fax: (358) 207545660
E-Mail: purchasing@napssystems.com
Web Site: www.napssystems.fi
Emp.: 30
Solar Power/Wind Power; Joint Venture Between Fortume (69%) and 3i (31%)
S.I.C.: 4911
N.A.I.C.S.: 221118
Timo Rosenlof *(Gen Mgr)*

Non-U.S. Subsidiaries:

NAPS Norway A/S (2)
PO Box 12
N-1369 Stabekk, Norway
Tel.: (47) 67105730
Telex: 79932 naps n
Fax: (47) 67105731
S.I.C.: 1311
N.A.I.C.S.: 211111

NAPS United Kingdom (2)
PO Box 83
Abingdon, Oxon, OX 14 2TB, United Kingdom (100%)
Tel.: (44) 1235529749
Fax: (44) 1235553450
E-Mail: uk@napssystems.com
Web Site: www.napssystems.com
Emp.: 1
S.I.C.: 1311
N.A.I.C.S.: 211111
Timo Rosenlof *(Chm)*

Non-U.S. Subsidiaries:

AB Fortum Varme samagt med Stockholms stad (1)
Lidingovagen 115
115 77 Stockholm, Sweden
Tel.: (46) 8 671 70 00
Fax: (46) 8 671 82 82
Web Site: www.fortum.com
Electric Power Generation Services
S.I.C.: 4911
N.A.I.C.S.: 221118

Estonia AS Fortum (1)
Bellows 2B
11415 Tallinn, Estonia
Tel.: (372) 4477210
Fax: (372) 4477212
E-Mail: fortum.eesti@fortum.com
Web Site: www.fortumeesti.ee
Energy Suppliers
S.I.C.: 4911
N.A.I.C.S.: 221122

FB Generation Services B.V. (1)
Verlengde Poolseweg 34-46
4818 CL Breda, Netherlands
Tel.: (31) 765244656
Electric Power Generation Services
S.I.C.: 4931
N.A.I.C.S.: 221118

Fortum 1 AB (1)
Lidingovagen 115
Stockholm, 115 41, Sweden
Tel.: (46) 86717100
Fax: (46) 86717576
Electric Power Generation Services
S.I.C.: 4911
N.A.I.C.S.: 221118
Ari Koponen *(Gen Mgr)*

Fortum AMCO AB (1)
Lidingovagen 115
Stockholm, 115 41, Sweden
Tel.: (46) 86717100
Electric Power Generation Services
S.I.C.: 4931
N.A.I.C.S.: 221118

Fortum Bytom SA (1)
Ul Elektrownia 18
41-908 Bytom, Poland
Tel.: (48) 32 283 41 00
Fax: (48) 32 283 46 00
Heat Generation Services
S.I.C.: 4961
N.A.I.C.S.: 221330

Fortum Corporation (1)
10 Presnenskaya Emb Tower A 16th Fl Tower B 14th Fl
123317 Moscow, Russia
Tel.: (7) 495 7884588
Fax: (7) 495 7884589
Emp.: 10
Heat Power Generation & Distribution Services
S.I.C.: 4961
N.A.I.C.S.: 221330
Alexander Chuvaev *(Gen Dir)*

Fortum Distribution AB (1)
Hangovagen 19
115 77 Stockholm, Sweden
Tel.: (46) 8 671 70 00
Fax: (46) 8 671 77 77
Web Site: www.fortum.com
Electrical Power Distribution Services
S.I.C.: 4939
N.A.I.C.S.: 221122

Fortum Eesti AS (1)
Suur-Joe 52
80047 Parnu, Estonia
Tel.: (372) 447 7210
Fax: (372) 447 7212
E-Mail: fortum.eesti@fortum.com
Web Site: www.fortum.ee
Emp.: 5
Electric Power Generation & Distribution Services
S.I.C.: 4939
N.A.I.C.S.: 221118
Eduard Enns *(Head-CHP)*

Fortum Energy LLC (1)
Business Centre Arena Hall Prospekt Dobrolyubova 16 A 2 4 Floor
197198 Saint Petersburg, Russia
Tel.: (7) 812 3367600
Fax: (7) 812 3367601
Emp.: 5
Heat Generation & Distribution Services
S.I.C.: 4961
N.A.I.C.S.: 221330
Alexander Chuvaev *(Gen Dir)*

Fortum Fjernvarme AS (1)
Brynsveien 2
1338 Sandvika, Norway
Tel.: (47) 67 80 49 60
Fax: (47) 67 80 49 79
E-Mail: firmapost@fortum.no
Emp.: 14
Heat Supplying Services
S.I.C.: 4961
N.A.I.C.S.: 221330
Atle Norstebo *(Gen Mgr)*

Fortum Forvaltning AS (1)
BA 2 Centre Bygdoy Alle 2
0101 Oslo, Norway
Tel.: (47) 22 43 29 90
Fax: (47) 22 43 29 91
Heat Supplying Services
S.I.C.: 4961
N.A.I.C.S.: 221330

Fortum France S.N.C (1)
Paris La Defense Tour Egee 9/11 Allee de l'Arche
Paris La Defense, 92671 Courbevoie, France
Tel.: (33) 1 7092 3814
Hydroelectric Power Generation Services
S.I.C.: 4911
N.A.I.C.S.: 221111
Philippe Stohr *(Reg Mgr)*

Fortum Generation AB (1)
Jamtlandsg 6
Sveg, 842 32 Harjedalen, Sweden
Tel.: (46) 680 215 00
Fax: (46) 680 215 10
Electric Power Generation Services
S.I.C.: 4911
N.A.I.C.S.: 221118

Fortum Holding B.V. (1)
Locatellikade 1
Amsterdam, 1076 AZ, Netherlands
Tel.: (31) 205755600
Fax: (31) 206730016
Investment Management Services
S.I.C.: 6211
N.A.I.C.S.: 523999

Fortum Invest LLC (1)
20-B Brodokalmakski Trakt
Chelyabinsk, 454077, Russia
Tel.: (7) 3512596010
Investment Management Services
S.I.C.: 6211
N.A.I.C.S.: 523999

Fortum Leasing KS (1)
Brynsveien 2
1338 Sandvika, Norway
Tel.: (47) 67 80 49 60
Fax: (47) 67 80 49 79
Fleet Car Operating Services
S.I.C.: 7515
N.A.I.C.S.: 532112

Fortum Markets AB (1)
Hangovagen 19
115 77 Stockholm, Sweden
Tel.: (46) 8 671 70 00
Fax: (46) 8 671 77 77
Electric Power Distribution Services
S.I.C.: 4931
N.A.I.C.S.: 221122
Tomas Wall *(Gen Mgr)*

Fortum Meter Lease SNC (1)
46A Ave J F Kennedy
1855 Luxembourg, Luxembourg
Tel.: (352) 427 1711
Fax: (352) 421 1961
Electric Power Generation Services
S.I.C.: 4911
N.A.I.C.S.: 221118

Fortum Nordic AB (1)
Andra Bassangvagen 16
Stockholm, 115 41, Sweden
Tel.: (46) 86717000
Fax: (46) 86717777
Web Site: www.fortum.com
Electric Power Generation Services
S.I.C.: 4939
N.A.I.C.S.: 221118

Fortum O&M (UK) Ltd (1)
7 Mill Sq
Wolverton Mill, Milton Keynes, MK12 5ZD, United Kingdom
Tel.: (44) 708304700
Telex: 297205 nespet g
Fax: (44) 708304799
Web Site: www.fortum.com
Emp.: 10
S.I.C.: 1311
N.A.I.C.S.: 211111

Fortum Petroleum A/S (1)
Strandveien 50
N-1366 Lysaker, Norway
Tel.: (47) 6758 0520
Telex: 11557 neste n
Fax: (47) 6758 0505
Crude Oil & Gas Production Activities
S.I.C.: 1311
N.A.I.C.S.: 211111

Fortum Plock Sp. z.o.o. (1)
ul Harc A Gradowskiego 3a
09-402 Plock, Poland
Tel.: (48) 24 36 60 451
Fax: (48) 24 36 60 450
Web Site: www.fortum.com
Heat Generation Services
S.I.C.: 4961
N.A.I.C.S.: 221330

Fortum Polska Sp. z.o.o. (1)
Ul Postepu 13
02 676 Warsaw, Poland
Tel.: (48) 225437300
Fax: (48) 225437311
Emp.: 25
S.I.C.: 1311
N.A.I.C.S.: 211111

Fortum Power and Heat Polska Sp. z.o.o (1)
ul Walonska 3-5
50-413 Wroclaw, Poland
Tel.: (48) 71 34 05 555
Fax: (48) 71 34 30 434
Web Site: www.fortum.com
Heat Generation & Distribution Services
S.I.C.: 4961
N.A.I.C.S.: 221330

Fortum Power Holding B.V. (1)
Locatellikade 1
Amsterdam, 1076 AZ, Netherlands
Tel.: (31) 205755600
Fax: (31) 206730016
Investment Management Services
S.I.C.: 6211
N.A.I.C.S.: 523999

Fortum Produktionsnat AB (1)
Lidingovagen 115
115 77 Stockholm, Sweden
Tel.: (46) 8 671 70 00
Electric Power Generation Services
S.I.C.: 4931
N.A.I.C.S.: 221118

Fortum Sweden AB (1)
Lidingovagen 115
115 77 Stockholm, Sweden
Tel.: (46) 8 6717100
Fax: (46) 8 6718282
Electric Power Distribution Services
S.I.C.: 4939
N.A.I.C.S.: 221122
Andres Gelrud *(Gen Mgr)*

Fortum Zabrze SA (1)
ul Wolnosci 416
41-800 Zabrze, Poland
Tel.: (48) 32271 52 41
Fax: (48) 32271 42 45
Electric Power Generation & Distribution Services
S.I.C.: 4939
N.A.I.C.S.: 221118

Linjebygg Offshore AS (1)
Grandfjaera 32
6415 Molde, Norway (100%)
Tel.: (47) 97507000
Fax: (47) 971256701
E-Mail: firmapost@lbo.no
Web Site: www.lbo.no
Emp.: 45
S.I.C.: 1311
N.A.I.C.S.: 211111
Kristoffer Jenssen *(Mng Dir)*

NCT Middle East (1)
Jebel Ali
PO Box 17071
Dubai, United Arab Emirates (100%)
Tel.: (971) 48817771
Fax: (971) 48817293
E-Mail: salesdubai@nctww.com
Web Site: www.nctww.com
Emp.: 32
S.I.C.: 1311
N.A.I.C.S.: 211111
Jeroen Leenen *(Gen Mgr)*

OU Lauka Turvas (1)
Narva Mnt 124
50303 Tartu, Estonia
Tel.: (372) 5294064
E-Mail:
Electric Power Generation Services
S.I.C.: 4931
N.A.I.C.S.: 221118

SIA Fortum Jelgava (1)
Pasta lela 47
Jelgava, 3001, Latvia
Tel.: (371) 63023446
Fax: (371) 63083020
E-Mail: info@jdhc.lv
Web Site: www.fortum.lv
Electric Power Generation & Heat Distribution Services
S.I.C.: 4931
N.A.I.C.S.: 221118
Marita Osipova *(Sec)*

Stockholm Gas AB (1)
Lidingovagen 115
115 77 Stockholm, Sweden
Tel.: (46) 771 41 0100
Fax: (46) 20461146
E-Mail: kundservice@stockholmgas.se
Natural Gas Distribution Services
S.I.C.: 4924
N.A.I.C.S.: 221210
Cecilia Hedqvist *(Pres)*

Streamgate Black AB (1)
Hangovagen 19
Stockholm, 115 41, Sweden
Tel.: (46) 86718062
Fax: (46) 86717442
Electric Power Generation Services
S.I.C.: 4931
N.A.I.C.S.: 221118
Mats Thunell *(Gen Mgr)*

UAB Fortum Ekosiluma (1)
J Jasinskao 16B
01112 Vilnius, Lithuania
Tel.: (370) 5 2430044
Fax: (370) 52788221
Web Site: www.fortum.lt
Emp.: 8

Fortum Oyj—(Continued)

Bio Fuel Distr
S.I.C.: 5172
N.A.I.C.S.: 424720
Rimantas Tenene *(Gen Mgr)*

UAB Fortum Heat Lietuva (1)
J Jasinskio Str 16B
01112 Vilnius, Lithuania
Tel.: (370) 5 243 0043
Fax: (370) 5 278 8221
E-Mail: info@fortum.lt
Web Site: www.fortum.lt
Emp.: 74
Heat Distribution Services
S.I.C.: 4961
N.A.I.C.S.: 221330
Rimantas Tenene *(Mng Dir)*

UAB Fortum Klaipeda (1)
Lypkiu Str 57
94100 Klaipeda, Lithuania
Tel.: (370) 46 493 402
Fax: (370) 46 493 403
E-Mail: klaipeda@fortum.lt
Emp.: 34
Heat Generation Services
S.I.C.: 4961
N.A.I.C.S.: 221330
Uozas Doniela *(Gen Mgr)*

UAB Neste Lietuva (1)
Labdariu 5
2001 Vilnius, Lithuania
Tel.: (370) 52123357
Fax: (370) 852123194
E-Mail: korteles@nesteoil.com
Web Site: www.neste.com
Emp.: 10
S.I.C.: 1311
N.A.I.C.S.: 211111
Gintaras Macejauskas *(Gen Mgr)*

FORTUNA ENTERTAINMENT GROUP N.V.

Strawinskylaan 809 WTC T A L 8
1077XX Amsterdam, Netherlands
Tel.: (31) 614832711
Fax: (31) 203331160
E-Mail: office@fortunaeg.nl
Web Site: www.fortuna-group.eu
Year Founded: 1990
FEG—(WAR)
Rev.: $129,552,708
Assets: $127,939,997
Liabilities: $62,040,937
Net Worth: $65,899,060
Earnings: $16,583,468
Emp.: 2,529
Fiscal Year-end: 12/31/12

Business Description:
Online Betting
S.I.C.: 7999
N.A.I.C.S.: 713290

Personnel:
Vaclav Broz *(Chm-Supervisory Bd)*
Wilf Walsh *(Chm-Mgmt Bd)*
Radim Haluza *(CEO)*
Michal Veprek *(CFO)*
Marek Biely *(CEO-Slovakia)*
Jan Stefanek *(CEO-Poland)*
Martin Todt *(CEO-Czech Republic)*
Jiri Hosnedl *(Gen Dir-Fortuna Lottery)*
Jana Galacova *(Member-Mgmt Bd)*
Richard van Bruchem *(Member-Mgmt Bd)*

Supervisory Board of Directors:
Vaclav Broz
Michal Horacek
Marek Rendek
Marek Smrha

FORTUNA SAZKOVA KANCELAR, A.S.

Vodickova 30
110 00 Prague, Czech Republic
Tel.: (420) 267218111
Fax: (420) 267218162
Web Site: www.ifortuna.eu
Year Founded: 1990
Sales Range: $50-74.9 Million
Emp.: 1,700

Business Description:
Gambling & Other Amusement Operations
S.I.C.: 7999
N.A.I.C.S.: 713290

Personnel:
Martin Stefunko *(CEO)*

FORTUNA SILVER MINES INC.

200 Burrard St Ste 650
Vancouver, BC, V6C 3L6, Canada
Tel.: (604) 484-4085
Fax: (604) 484-4029
E-Mail: info@fortunasilver.com
Web Site: www.fortunasilver.com
FSM—(LIM NYSE TSX)
Sls.: $161,020,000
Assets: $316,263,000
Liabilities: $51,770,000
Net Worth: $264,493,000
Earnings: $31,463,000
Emp.: 812
Fiscal Year-end: 12/31/12

Business Description:
Silver & Other Metal Ore Mining Services
S.I.C.: 1044
N.A.I.C.S.: 212222

Personnel:
Simon T. P. Ridgway *(Chm)*
Jorge A. Ganoza *(Pres & CEO)*
Luis Dario Ganoza *(CFO)*

Board of Directors:
Simon T. P. Ridgway
David Paul Farrell
Jorge A. Ganoza
Robert Russell Gilmore
Tomas Guerrero Mendez
Michael Alexander Iverson
Thomas Richard Kelly
Mario D. Szotlender

Transfer Agent:
Olympia Trust Company
Suite 1003 750 West Pender Street
Vancouver, BC, V6C 2T8, Canada

Non-U.S. Subsidiaries:

Compania Minera Cuzcatlan S.A. (1)
Amapolas No 801 Piso 2 Esq Naranjos
Colonia Reforma, Oaxaca, 68050, Mexico
Tel.: (52) 9515020010
Fax: (52) 9515020010
E-Mail: mhernandez@mineuzcuatlan.com
Web Site: www.fortunasilvermines.com
Emp.: 160
Gold & Silver Exploration Services
S.I.C.: 1481
N.A.I.C.S.: 213115
Louis Philippe *(VP-Project Dev)*

Minera Bateas S.A.C. (1)
Ave Los Libertadores No 757
San Isidro, Lima, Peru
Tel.: (51) 16166060
E-Mail: info@fortunasilver.com
Metal Exploration Services
S.I.C.: 1081
N.A.I.C.S.: 213114
Luis Leon Martini *(Mgr-Sls)*

FORTUNATE SUN MINING COMPANY LIMITED

Suite 1502-1166 Alberni Street
Vancouver, BC, V6E 3Z3, Canada
Tel.: (778) 945-2139
Fax: (604) 558-0087
E-Mail: Info@fortunatesunmining.com
Web Site: www.fortunatesunmining.com
Year Founded: 2007
FSM—(TSXV)
Assets: $177,444
Liabilities: $97,858
Net Worth: $79,585
Earnings: ($1,800,031)
Fiscal Year-end: 03/31/13

Business Description:
Metal Mining
S.I.C.: 1099
N.A.I.C.S.: 212299

Personnel:
Scott Young *(Mng Dir)*
Peter Chen *(CFO)*

Board of Directors:
Reg Advocaat
Peter Chen
Terrance G. Owen
Scott Young

Legal Counsel:
Boughton Law Corporation
Suite 700 505 Burrard Street
Vancouver, BC, Canada

Transfer Agent:
Olympia Trust Company
Cathedral Place, Suite 1900 - 25 West Georgia Street
Vancouver, BC, V6C 3L2, Canada
Tel.: (604) 408-7774
Fax: (604) 669-8111

FORTUNE ELECTRIC CO., LTD.

No 10 Chi Lin Road
Chung Li Industrial Zone, Chung-li, Taoyuan, Taiwan
Tel.: (886) 3 452 6111
Fax: (886) 3 451 2833
E-Mail: fe@fortune.com.tw
Web Site: www.fortune.com.tw
1519—(TAI)
Sales Range: $50-74.9 Million

Business Description:
Electronic Products Mfr
S.I.C.: 5063
N.A.I.C.S.: 423610

Personnel:
H. L. Hsu *(Founder)*
J. M. Hsu *(Chm)*
Pedro B.F. Hsu *(Pres & Gen Mgr)*

Divisions:

Fortune Electric Co., Ltd. - Power Division (1)
No 33 Chin Chian Road Section 2 Kuan Yin Industrial Zone
Taoyuan, 328, Taiwan
Tel.: (886) 34836155
Fax: (886) 34836151
Emp.: 200
Power Transformers Mfr
S.I.C.: 3612
N.A.I.C.S.: 335311
Hsu Panfu *(Gen Mgr)*

Fortune Electric Co., Ltd. - Switchgear Division (1)
No 55 Chung Cheng Road
Kuan Yin, Taoyuan, 32853, Taiwan
Tel.: (886) 34736957
Fax: (886) 34736975
Web Site: www.fortune.com.tw/2004/english/about3.asp
Switchgear Mfr
S.I.C.: 3613
N.A.I.C.S.: 335313

U.S. Division:

Fortune Electric Co., Ltd. - North American Division (1)
1965 Shenango Valley Fwy
Hermitage, PA 16148
Tel.: (724) 346-2722
Fax: (724) 346-1472
Web Site: www.fortune.com.tw/2004/english/about3.asp
Emp.: 13
Switchgear & Transformers Distr
S.I.C.: 5065
N.A.I.C.S.: 423690
Jean Hsu *(Gen Mgr)*

FORTUNE FINANCIAL SERVICES INDIA LTD

2nd Floor K K Chambers Sir P T Marg
Fort, Mumbai, Maharashtra, 400001, India
Tel.: (91) 2222077931
Fax: (91) 2222072948
E-Mail: admin@ffsil.com
Web Site: www.fortune.co.in
530023—(BOM)
Rev.: $11,659,843
Assets: $55,963,454
Liabilities: $36,796,950
Net Worth: $19,166,504
Earnings: ($2,339,507)
Emp.: 100
Fiscal Year-end: 03/31/13

Business Description:
Finance NBFC
S.I.C.: 6141
N.A.I.C.S.: 522291

Personnel:
J. T. Poonja *(Co-Founder)*
Nimish C. Shah *(Co-Founder, Vice Chm & Mng Dir)*
Mohan Natarajan *(COO)*
Haroon Mansuri *(Compliance Officer & Sec)*
Yashpal Madan *(Pres-Ops)*
Nadeem Akbarali Karmali *(CEO-Institutional Bus)*
Gyan Mohan *(CEO-Investment Banking)*
Vishal Trehan *(CEO-Broking & Distr)*
S. Kalyansundaram *(Exec VP-Funds & Settlements)*
Mahantesh Sabarad *(Sr VP-Equity Res)*

Board of Directors:
J. T. Poonja
Manoj G. Patel
H. R. Prasad
Nimish C. Shah
Chintan V. Valia

Transfer Agent:
Purva Sharegistry (India) Pvt. Ltd.
9 Shiv Shakti Industrial Estate Ground Floor
Sitaram Mill Compound
Mumbai, India

Subsidiary:

Fortune Equity Brokers (India) Ltd. (1)
2nd Fl K K Chambers Sir P T Marg I Ft
Mumbai, Maharashtra, 400 001, India
Tel.: (91) 2222077931
Fax: (91) 2222072948
Web Site: www.ffsiltech.com
Emp.: 60
Brokerage Services
S.I.C.: 6211
N.A.I.C.S.: 523120
Nimi Sha *(Mng Dir)*

FORTUNE GRAPHITE INC.

260 Queens Quay West Suite 3104
Toronto, ON, Canada M5J 2N3
Tel.: (416) 367-8240
Fax: (416) 367-8334
E-Mail: info@fortunegraphite.com
Web Site: www.fortunegraphite.com

Business Description:
Mineral Mining Services
S.I.C.: 1099
N.A.I.C.S.: 212299

Personnel:
Claus G. Wagner-Bartak *(Pres & CEO)*

FORTUNE INFORMATION SYSTEMS CORP.

No 30 ShingJung Rd Neihu District
114 Taipei, Taiwan
Tel.: (886) 227935566
Fax: (886) 255551111

E-Mail: service@fis.com.tw
Web Site: www.fis.com.tw
2468—(TAI)
Sales Range: $10-24.9 Million
Business Description:
Notebook Computers Mfr
S.I.C.: 3571
N.A.I.C.S.: 334111
Personnel:
James Lee *(Chm)*

Subsidiary:

Wardpro Information Co. Ltd. **(1)**
B1-1 5 Lane 768 Bater Road Section 4
Taipei, Taiwan
Tel.: (886) 2 2788 6777
Fax: (886) 2 2785 3220
Projectors Distr
S.I.C.: 5045
N.A.I.C.S.: 423430

Non-U.S. Subsidiaries:

Fortune Information System International Co., Ltd. **(1)**
Walan Ctr Rm 1804 No 20 Jeyuyonhualan Rd
Hong Kong, China (Hong Kong)
Tel.: (852) 28119662
Fax: (852) 28113042
E-Mail: sales@fis.com.hk
Web Site: www.fis.com.hk
Emp.: 20
Scanners & Cameras Distr
S.I.C.: 5734
N.A.I.C.S.: 443142

Shanghai WorldTrend Integrated Technologies Inc. **(1)**
12F No 6555 Hu-Ming Road
Ming-Shin District, Shanghai, 201100, China
Tel.: (86) 2164146050
Fax: (86) 21 6414 6055
Web Site: www.fis.com.tw/index_en4.asp
Computer Peripheral Equipments Distr
S.I.C.: 5045
N.A.I.C.S.: 423430

FORTUNE MANAGEMENT INC.
c/o FORTUNE Services AG
Bahnhofstrasse 10
PO Box 324
6301 Zug, Switzerland
Tel.: (41) 417271040
Fax: (41) 417271041
E-Mail: info@fortune-management.com
Web Site: www.fortune-management.com
Year Founded: 1977
FMI1—(DFM)
Sales Range: $1-9.9 Million
Business Description:
Investment Management Services
S.I.C.: 6211
N.A.I.C.S.: 523999
Personnel:
Paul Bagley *(Chm)*
Board of Directors:
Paul Bagley
Michael Dieckell
Hermann Seiler

FORTUNE MINERALS LIMITED
148 Fullarton Street Suite 1600
London, ON, N6A 5P3, Canada
Tel.: (519) 858-8188
Fax: (519) 858-8155
Toll Free: (877) 552-7726
E-Mail: info@fortuneminerals.com
Web Site: www.fortuneminerals.com
Year Founded: 1988
FT—(OTC TSX)
Rev.: $155,639
Assets: $148,676,933
Liabilities: $23,260,982
Net Worth: $125,415,952
Earnings: ($6,836,751)
Fiscal Year-end: 12/31/12
Business Description:
Metal Mining & Exploration
S.I.C.: 1099
N.A.I.C.S.: 212299
Personnel:
Mehendra Naik *(Chm)*
Robin Ellis Goad *(Pres & CEO)*
Adam G. J. Jean *(CFO & VP-Fin)*
David A. Knight *(Sec)*
Board of Directors:
Mehendra Naik
William A. Breukelman
Shou Wu Chen
Carl L. Clouter
James Currie
George M. Doumet
James D. Excell
Robin Ellis Goad
David A. Knight
Legal Counsel:
Macleod Dixon LLP
Toronto, ON, Canada
Transfer Agent:
Computershare Trust Company of Canada
Toronto, ON, Canada

Subsidiaries:

Fortune Coal Limited **(1)**
148 Fullarton St Ste 1600
London, ON, N6A 5P3, Canada
Tel.: (519) 858-8188
Fax: (519) 858-8155
E-Mail: info@fortuneminerals.com
Web Site: www.fortuneminerals.com
Emp.: 20
Coal Mining Services
S.I.C.: 1222
N.A.I.C.S.: 212112
Tom Rinaldi *(VP-Ops)*

Fortune Minerals NWT Inc. **(1)**
148 Fullarton St Ste 1600
London, ON, N6A 5P3, Canada
Tel.: (519) 858-8188
Fax: (519) 858-8155
E-Mail: info@fortuneminerals.com
Emp.: 12
Mineral Mining Services
S.I.C.: 1499
N.A.I.C.S.: 212399
Jennifer Kramer *(Mgr)*

FORTUNE OIL PLC
6/F Belgrave House 76 Buckingham Palace Road
London, SW1W 9TQ, United Kingdom
Tel.: (44) 2078248411
Fax: (44) 2078248422
E-Mail: info@fortuneoil.co.uk
Web Site: www.fortune-oil.com
FTO—(LSE)
Rev.: $1,167,730,185
Assets: $680,986,689
Liabilities: $291,202,125
Net Worth: $389,784,565
Earnings: $32,340,701
Emp.: 2,000
Fiscal Year-end: 12/31/12
Business Description:
Oil & Gas Providers
S.I.C.: 1389
N.A.I.C.S.: 213112
Personnel:
Daniel Tatjung Chiu *(Vice Chm)*
Jun Tian *(Acting CEO)*
Bill Kwai Pui Mok *(CFO)*
Sandi Choi *(Sec)*
Board of Directors:
Benyuan Qian
Frank Attwood
Daniel Tatjung Chiu
Dennis Chiu
Louisa Ho
Ching Li
Xizhong Lin
Tong Mao
Ian Taylor
Jun Tian
Jinjun Wang
Yulin Zhi
Legal Counsel:
Reed Smith LLP
The Broadgate Tower 20 Primrose Street
London, United Kingdom

Jun He Law Offices
Suite 2208 20F Jardine House 1 Connaught Place
Central, China (Hong Kong)

Non-U.S. Subsidiary:

Fortune Oil Holdings Limited **(1)**
Ste 2307 23 F Ofc Tower Convention Plz 1 Harbour Rd
Wanchai, China (Hong Kong)
Tel.: (852) 28028300
Fax: (852) 28028322
E-Mail: reception@fortuneoil.com
Emp.: 30
Management Services
S.I.C.: 8741
N.A.I.C.S.: 551114
Daniel Tat Jung Chiu *(Vice Chm)*
Kiam Poon Tee *(CEO)*
Bill Kwai Pui Mok *(CFO)*

Non-U.S. Subsidiary:

Maoming King Ming Petroleum Company Limited **(2)**
No 1 Guandu Rd
Maoming, Guangdong, 525000, China
Tel.: (86) 6682883388
Fax: (86) 6682879988
Web Site: www.mmstm.com
Emp.: 12
Crude Oil Distr
S.I.C.: 5172
N.A.I.C.S.: 424720
John Tian *(Gen Mgr)*

FORTUNE PARTS INDUSTRY PUBLIC COMPANY LIMITED
11/22 Moo 20 Nimitmai Road
Lamlukka
Pathumthani, 12150, Thailand
Tel.: (66) 2 9934970
Fax: (66) 2 9934978
E-Mail: info@fpi.co.th
Web Site: www.fpiautoparts.com
Year Founded: 1991
FPI—(THA)
Rev.: $52,539,637
Assets: $51,333,552
Liabilities: $31,319,955
Net Worth: $20,013,597
Earnings: $5,384,634
Emp.: 500
Fiscal Year-end: 12/31/12
Business Description:
Automotive Parts Mfr & Distr
S.I.C.: 3714
N.A.I.C.S.: 336390
Personnel:
Por Tanadumrongsak *(Chm)*
Sangcharean Tanadumrongsak *(Vice Chm)*
Sompol Tanadumrongsak *(Mng Dir)*
Nussara Tanadumrongsak *(Deputy Mng Dir)*
Jaruwan Chatwichian *(Sec & Mgr-Fin & Acctg)*
Board of Directors:
Por Tanadumrongsak
Naris Chaiyasoot
Anant Gatepithaya
Raweewan Mathong
Pumipat Sinacharoen
Sangcharean Tanadumrongsak
Somkit Tanadumrongsak
Sompol Tanadumrongsak
Yangyongchai Tanadumrongsak

FORTUNE SECURITIES CORPORATION
(d/b/a Phu Hung Securities)
Lawrence S. Ting Bldg Fl 5 801
Nguyen Van Linh St
Tan Phu Ward
District 7, Ho Chi Minh City, Vietnam
Tel.: (84) 854135479
Fax: (84) 854135472
E-Mail: info@phs.vn
Web Site: www.phs.vn
Year Founded: 2006
Business Description:
Investment Banking & Securities Brokerage Services
S.I.C.: 6211
N.A.I.C.S.: 523110
Personnel:
Albert Kwang-Chin Ting *(Chm)*
Mai Thi Quynh Tran *(Vice Chm)*
Tracy Chang Chong Cheng *(Gen Dir)*
Board of Directors:
Albert Kwang-Chin Ting
Harvey Chang
Mai Hong Nguyen
Mai Thi Quynh Tran

FORTUNE SUN (CHINA) HOLDINGS LIMITED
Suite 1511 15th Floor Tower One
Times Square One Matheson Street
Causeway Bay, China (Hong Kong)
Tel.: (852) 28937866
Fax: (852) 28937177
Web Site: www.fortune-sun.com
0352—(HKG)
Rev.: $4,909,736
Assets: $11,599,227
Liabilities: $2,722,848
Net Worth: $8,876,379
Earnings: ($129,622)
Emp.: 213
Fiscal Year-end: 12/31/12
Business Description:
Property Consultancy & Agency Services Provider
S.I.C.: 6733
N.A.I.C.S.: 525920
Personnel:
Chen Feng Chiang *(Founder & Chm)*
Sim Lau *(CFO & Sec)*
Hsiu Hua Chang *(Compliance Officer)*
Board of Directors:
Chen Feng Chiang
Hsiu Hua Chang
Chi Pang Cheng
Shi Wei Cui
Lin Han
Chien Ju Lin
Wai Hung Ng
Royal Bank of Canada Trust Company (Cayman) Limited
4th Floor Royal Bank House 24 Shedden Road
Georgetown, Cayman Islands
Transfer Agents:
Tricor Investor Services Limited
26th Floor Tesbury Centre 28 Queens Road East
Wanchai, China (Hong Kong)
Royal Bank of Canada Trust Company (Cayman) Limited
4th Floor Royal Bank House 24 Shedden Road
Georgetown, Cayman Islands

FORTUNE VACATION TRAVEL LTD.
21-2-6-1 JinHaiHua YuanDongYuan
XiGangQu, Dalian, LiaoNing, 116000, China
Tel.: (86) 13050500108
Year Founded: 2010
Business Description:
Travel Services
S.I.C.: 4729
N.A.I.C.S.: 561599
Personnel:
Zhihua Zhang *(Pres, Treas & Sec)*
Board of Directors:

Fortune Vacation Travel Ltd.—(Continued)

Zhihua Zhang

FORTUNIS RESOURCES LIMITED

47 Outram Street
West Perth, WA, 6005, Australia
Tel.: (61) 8 9321 2111
Fax: (61) 8 9321 2050
E-Mail: admin@fortunisresources.com.au
Web Site: www.fortunisresources.com.au
Year Founded: 2012
FOT—(ASX)
Business Description:
Metal Mining
S.I.C.: 1099
N.A.I.C.S.: 212299
Personnel:
Darren Jude Wates *(Sec)*

FORUM ENERGY PLC

120 Bridge Road
Chertsey, KT16 8LA, United Kingdom
Tel.: (44) 1932445344
Fax: (44) 1932445345
E-Mail: info@forumenergyplc.com
Web Site: www.forumenergyplc.com
FEP—(LSE)
Rev.: $4,522,000
Assets: $43,347,000
Liabilities: $21,286,000
Net Worth: $22,061,000
Earnings: ($26,424,000)
Emp.: 24
Fiscal Year-end: 12/31/12
Business Description:
Oil, Gas & Coal Explorer
S.I.C.: 1389
N.A.I.C.S.: 213112
Personnel:
Robert Charles Nicholson *(Chm)*
Jose Raymund Apostol *(Pres-Philippines)*
Andrew J. Mullins *(Sec)*
Board of Directors:
Robert Charles Nicholson
Richard Lawrence Beacher
Walter W. Brown
Andrew J. Mullins
Roberto V. Ongpin
Carlo Aniceto Samson Pablo
Eric Recto
Barry Stansfield
Edward Anthony Tortorici
Paul Frederick Wallace
Legal Counsel:
Osborne Clarke
2 Temple Back East Temple Quay
Bristol, United Kingdom
Milbank, Tweed, Hadley & McCloy LLP
10 Gresham Street
London, United Kingdom
Transfer Agent:
Share Registrars Limited
Craven House West Street
Farnham, Surrey, GU9 7EN, United Kingdom

FORUM MEDIA GROUP GMBH

Mandichostr 18
D 86504 Merching, Germany
Tel.: (49) 82 33 3 81 0
Fax: (49) 82 33 3 81 3 33
E-Mail: kontakt@forum-media.com
Web Site: www.forum-media.com
Sales Range: $50-74.9 Million
Emp.: 700
Business Description:
Magazine Publisher
S.I.C.: 2721
N.A.I.C.S.: 511120
Personnel:
Ronald Herkert *(Founder, CEO & Chm-Mgmt Bd)*
Norbert Bietsch *(Member-Mgmt Bd)*
Kerstin Kuffer *(Member-Mgmt Bd)*
Michaela Mravlje *(Member-Mgmt Bd)*
Wieslaw Polakiewicz *(Member-Mgmt Bd)*
Ekaterina Stroganove *(Member-Mgmt Bd)*

FORUM NATIONAL INVESTMENTS LTD.

Suite 6000 First Canadian Place
100 King Street West, Toronto, ON, M5X 1E2, Canada
Tel.: (778) 588-7780
Fax: (866) 988-8745
Toll Free: (877) 832-3518
E-Mail: info@foruminvestments.com
Web Site: www.foruminvestments.com
Year Founded: 1995
FMNL—(OTC OTCB)
Rev.: $466,154
Assets: $8,274,393
Liabilities: $6,705,942
Net Worth: $1,568,451
Earnings: ($166,157)
Emp.: 3
Fiscal Year-end: 09/30/12
Business Description:
Holding Company; Investment Services
S.I.C.: 6211
N.A.I.C.S.: 523999
Personnel:
Daniel Clozza *(Pres & CEO)*
Martin Tutschek *(CFO)*
Board of Directors:
Michael Barrett
Daniel Clozza
Kazunari Kohno
Scott McManus
Frederick Schlosser
Jeff Teeny
Martin Tutschek
Christopher Yergensen

FORUM URANIUM CORP.

910 - 475 Howe Street
Vancouver, BC, V6C 2B3, Canada
Tel.: (604) 630-1585
Fax: (604) 689-3609
Toll Free: (866) 689-2599
E-Mail: info@forumuranium.com
Web Site: www.forumuranium.com
FDC—(TSXV)
Int. Income: $15,834
Assets: $3,967,664
Liabilities: $385,924
Net Worth: $3,581,740
Earnings: ($2,217,724)
Fiscal Year-end: 11/30/12
Business Description:
Uranium Exploration & Development Services
S.I.C.: 1094
N.A.I.C.S.: 212291
Personnel:
Richard J. Mazur *(Pres & CEO)*
Robert Anderson *(CFO)*
Jacqueline Collins *(Sec)*
Board of Directors:
Anthony Balme
David Cowan
Richard J. Mazur
Larry Minoru Okada
Ian Stalker
Michael A. Steeves
Legal Counsel:
McMillan LLP
1500 1055 West Georgia Street
V6E4N7 Vancouver, BC, Canada
Transfer Agent:
Computershare Investor Services Inc.
510 Burrard St
Vancouver, BC, V6C 3B9, Canada

FORVAL CORPORATION

14F AOYAMA Oval Bldg 5-52-2
Jingu-mae Shibuya-ku
Tokyo, 150-0001, Japan
Tel.: (81) 3 3498 1541
Fax: (81) 3 3498 1542
Web Site: www.forval.co.jp
Year Founded: 1980
8275—(JAS)
Sls.: $387,123,000
Assets: $183,414,000
Liabilities: $114,565,000
Net Worth: $68,849,000
Earnings: $8,580,000
Emp.: 1,153
Fiscal Year-end: 03/31/13
Business Description:
Telecommunications Equipment Development & Sales
S.I.C.: 4899
N.A.I.C.S.: 517919
Personnel:
Hideo Okubo *(Chm & CEO)*
Masanori Nakajima *(Pres)*
Toshiyuki Kano *(Co-Mng Dir)*
Koji Terada *(Co-Mng Dir)*
Board of Directors:
Hideo Okubo
Toshiyuki Kano
Koji Kato
Masanori Nakajima
Koji Terada

Subsidiary:

Forval Telecom, Inc. **(1)**
HitotsubashiSI Bldg 2F 3-26 Kanda-Nishikicho
Chiyoda-ku, Tokyo, 101-0054, Japan
Tel.: (81) 3 3233 1301
Fax: (81) 3 3233 1322
Web Site: www.forvaltel.co.jp
FVM—(DEU TKS)
Sales Range: $125-149.9 Million
Emp.: 291
Telecommunication Carrier Services
S.I.C.: 4813
N.A.I.C.S.: 517110
Tsuyoshi Tanii *(Pres & CEO)*

FORWARD INTERNET GROUP LTD.

Floor 2 Centro 3 19 Mandela Street
Camden Town
London, NW1 0DU, United Kingdom
Tel.: (44) 20 7121 1199
Fax: (44) 20 7121 1188
E-Mail: info@forward.co.uk
Web Site: www.forward.co.uk
Year Founded: 2004
Sales Range: $200-249.9 Million
Emp.: 218
Business Description:
Financial Investment Services
S.I.C.: 6211
N.A.I.C.S.: 523999
Personnel:
Neil Hutchinson *(Founder)*
Nic Brisbourne *(Mng Partner-Investment Partners & Labs)*
Carl Gaywood *(Partner-Investment)*
Rob Murphy *(CFO)*
Board of Directors:
Graham Coxell
Paul Fisher
Mark Philips
David Rigby

FOSCHINI GROUP LIMITED

Stanley Lewis Centre 340 Voortrekker Road Parow East
7500 Cape Town, South Africa
Mailing Address:
PO Box 6020
Parow East, Cape Town, South Africa
Tel.: (27) 219381911
Web Site: www.tfg.co.za
TFG—(JSE)
Rev.: $1,819,034,500
Assets: $1,718,683,220
Liabilities: $853,086,410
Net Worth: $865,596,810
Earnings: $215,201,220
Emp.: 12,657
Fiscal Year-end: 03/31/13
Business Description:
Lifestyle Products Retailer; Financial Services
S.I.C.: 5999
N.A.I.C.S.: 453998
Personnel:
A. D. Murray *(CEO)*
R. Stein *(CFO)*
D. Sheard *(Sec)*
Board of Directors:
David Morris Nurek
F. Abrahams
S. E. Abrahams
W. V. Cuba
M. Lewis
P. S. Meiring
A. D. Murray
E. Oblowitz
N. V. Simamane
R. Stein
Transfer Agent:
Computershare Investor Services (Pty) Limited
9th Floor 70 Marshall Street
Johannesburg, South Africa

FOSECO INDIA LIMITED

Gat Nos 922 & 923 Sanaswadi
Shirur, Pune, 412 208, India
Tel.: (91) 2137 668100
Fax: (91) 2137 668160
Web Site: www.foseco.co.in
Year Founded: 1932
500150—(BOM)
Rev.: $46,055,548
Assets: $26,130,202
Liabilities: $9,538,181
Net Worth: $16,592,021
Earnings: $4,044,501
Fiscal Year-end: 12/31/12
Business Description:
Metallurgical Additive & Consumable Mfr & Distr
S.I.C.: 2899
N.A.I.C.S.: 325998
Personnel:
Pradeep Mallick *(Chm)*
Sanjay Mathur *(Mng Dir)*
R. Umesh *(Compliance Officer)*
Mahendra Dutia *(Sec & Controller-Accts)*
Board of Directors:
Pradeep Mallick
Mukund M. Chitale
Mahendra Dutia
David Hughes
Sanjay Mathur
Christopher Nail
Chris O'Shea
R. Umesh
Transfer Agent:
Link Intime India Private Limited
Block 202 2nd Floor Akshay Complex Off Dhole Patil Road
Near Ganesh Mandir, Pune, India

FOSHAN NATIONSTAR OPTOELECTRONICS CO., LTD.

(d/b/a Nationstar)
18 South Hua Bao Road
Chan Cheng District, Foshan, Guangdong, 528000, China

Tel.: (86) 75783980208
Fax: (86) 75782100200
E-Mail: company@nationstar.com
Web Site: www.nationstar.com
Year Founded: 1969
002449—(SSE)
Emp.: 1,500
Business Description:
Semiconductor Optoelectronic Devices & LED Applied Products Mfr
S.I.C.: 3674
N.A.I.C.S.: 334413
Personnel:
Yaohao Wang *(Chm)*
Division:

Foshan Nationstar Optoelectronics Co., Ltd. - LED Lighting Division **(1)**
N0 18 South Hua Bao Road
Chan Cheng District, Foshan, Guangdong, 528000, China
Tel.: (86) 75782100226
Fax: (86) 75782319310
E-Mail: clifflee@nationstar.com
Emp.: 1,800
Light Emitting Diode Mfr
S.I.C.: 3674
N.A.I.C.S.: 334413
Yaohao Wang *(Pres)*

FOSHAN SATUDAY SHOES CO., LTD.

B-3 Jianping Road Nanhai Guicheng Tech Park
Foshan, 528200, China
Tel.: (86) 75786250300
Fax: (86) 75786250321
E-Mail: st-sat@st-sat.com
Web Site: www.st-sat.com
002291—(SSE)
Emp.: 400
Business Description:
Shoe Mfr & Retailer
S.I.C.: 5661
N.A.I.C.S.: 448210
Personnel:
Zemin Zhang *(Chm)*

FOSS A/S

Foss Alle 1
Postbox 260
DK 3400 Hillerod, Denmark
Tel.: (45) 7010 3370
Fax: (45) 7010 3371
E-Mail: info@foss.dk
Web Site: www.foss.dk
Year Founded: 1956
Rev.: $313,646,040
Assets: $420,779,880
Liabilities: $78,276,240
Net Worth: $342,503,640
Earnings: $58,797,360
Emp.: 1,237
Fiscal Year-end: 12/31/12
Business Description:
Measuring & Controlling Devices Mfr
S.I.C.: 3829
N.A.I.C.S.: 334519
Personnel:
Peter Foss *(Chm)*
Peter Kurstein-Jensen *(Vice Chm)*
Torben Ladegaard *(CEO)*
Kim Vejlby Hansen *(COO)*
Tue Byskov Botkjaer *(Sr VP-HR, IT & Comm)*
Poul Bundgaard *(Sr VP-Production & Supply Chain)*
Lau Diderichsen *(Sr VP-Sls & Mktg-Europe, Asia & Pacific)*
Jan Elgaard *(Sr VP-Sls & Mktg-Americas)*
Kenneth Aaby Sachse *(Sr VP-Fin)*
Board of Directors:
Peter Foss
Nils Christian Foss
Pernille Foss
Henrik Hakonsson
Peter Kurstein-Jensen
Sussie My Nikolajsen
Jais Valeur
Alex Vestergaard
Anja Z. Willumsen
Subsidiaries:

Foss Analytical A/S **(1)**
Foss Alle 1
3400 Hillerod, Denmark (100%)
Tel.: (45) 70103370
Fax: (45) 70103371
E-Mail: info@foss.dk
Web Site: www.foss.dk
Emp.: 550
Analytical Instruments Mfr
S.I.C.: 3826
N.A.I.C.S.: 334516
Torben Ladegaard *(Mng Dir)*

Ibsen Photonics A/S **(1)**
Ryttermarken 15-21
DK 3520 Farum, Denmark
Tel.: (45) 44347000
Fax: (45) 44347001
E-Mail: inquiry@ibsen.dk
Web Site: www.ibsen.dk
Sales Range: $1-9.9 Million
Emp.: 20
Transmission Diffraction Grating Components & Grating-Based Spectrometer Modules Developer & Mfr
S.I.C.: 3827
N.A.I.C.S.: 333314
Torben Jacobsen *(Pres & CEO)*

U.S. Subsidiary:

Foss North America, Inc. **(1)**
8091 Wallace Rd
Eden Prairie, MN 55344-3677 (100%)
Tel.: (952) 974-9892
Fax: (952) 974-9823
E-Mail: info@fossnorthamerica.com
Web Site: www.foss.us
Emp.: 76
Develops & Produces Analytical Solutions for Measuring Food Quality
S.I.C.: 5049
N.A.I.C.S.: 423490
Christian Svensgaard *(Pres)*
Jeff Isaacson *(CFO & VP-Fin)*

Non-U.S. Subsidiaries:

Foss Analyatical AB **(1)**
Pal Anders vag 2
PO Box 70
263 21 Hoganas, Sweden (100%)
Tel.: (46) 42361500
Telex: 72340
Fax: (46) 42340349
E-Mail: info@foss.dk
Web Site: www.foss.dk
Measuring & Controlling Devices Mfr
S.I.C.: 3829
N.A.I.C.S.: 334519
Torben Ladegaard *(Mng Dir)*

Foss Belgium B.V **(1)**
Robert Schumanplein 6/5
1040 Brussels, Belgium (100%)
Tel.: (32) 16448421
Fax: (32) 321644901
E-Mail: fossben@foss.nl
Web Site: www.foss.dk
Emp.: 16
Measuring & Controlling Devices Mfr
S.I.C.: 3829
N.A.I.C.S.: 334519
Emre Tesseni *(Mgr)*

Foss Benelux B.V. **(1)**
Panoven 68
3401 RB IJsselstein, Netherlands (100%)
Mailing Address:
PO Box 2553
3800 GC Amersfoort, Netherlands
Tel.: (31) 334519033
Fax: (31) 334519029
E-Mail: fossben@foss.nl
Web Site: www.foss.dk
Rev.: $64,162,280
Emp.: 15
Measuring & Controlling Devices Mfr
S.I.C.: 3829
N.A.I.C.S.: 334519
Peter Foss *(Mng Dir)*

Foss Espana S.A. **(1)**
Avenida Josep Tarradellas 8-10
08029 Barcelona, Spain (100%)
Tel.: (34) 934949940
Fax: (34) 934052176
E-Mail: general@foss.es
Web Site: www.foss.es
Emp.: 15
Measuring & Controlling Devices Mfr
S.I.C.: 3829
N.A.I.C.S.: 334519
Miguel Martinez *(Mng Dir)*

Foss France S.A.S. **(1)**
35 Rue des Peupliers
92000 Nanterre, Cedex 92752, France (100%)
Tel.: (33) 146491919
Fax: (33) 147600067
E-Mail: info@foss.fr
Web Site: www.foss.fr
Emp.: 46
Measuring & Controlling Devices Mfr
S.I.C.: 3829
N.A.I.C.S.: 334519

Foss GmbH **(1)**
Halstenbeker Weg 98 c
25462 Rellingen, Germany (100%)
Mailing Address:
Postfach 1370
D-63085 Rodgau, Germany
Tel.: (49) 410151780
Telex: 416224
Fax: (49) 4101517878
E-Mail: info@foss.de
Web Site: www.foss.de
Emp.: 52
Measuring & Controlling Devices Mfr
S.I.C.: 3829
N.A.I.C.S.: 334519
Johnnie Erichsen *(Mng Dir)*

Foss Italia S.p.A. **(1)**
Corso Stati Uniti 1/77
35127 Padua, Italy (100%)
Tel.: (39) 0498287211
Fax: (39) 0498287222
E-Mail: fossitalia@foss.it
Web Site: www.foss.it
Emp.: 32
Measuring & Controlling Devices Mfr
S.I.C.: 3829
N.A.I.C.S.: 334519
Michela Martini *(CFO)*

Foss Japan Ltd. **(1)**
Tokyo Genboku Kaikan 9th Fl 3012 Toyo 5 Chome
Kohto Ku, Tokyo, 1350016, Japan (100%)
Tel.: (81) 356653821
Fax: (81) 356653826
E-Mail: info@foss.co.jp
Web Site: www.foss.co.jp
Emp.: 35
Sales of Analytical Instruments
S.I.C.: 3826
N.A.I.C.S.: 334516
Shigeru Inoue *(Mng Dir)*

Foss Korea Ltd. **(1)**
3rd Fl KVMA Bldg 272 5 Swohyun Dong
Pudang Ku Sungham Si
Kyung Gi De, Seoul, 463824, Korea (South) (100%)
Tel.: (82) 317099591
Fax: (82) 317099594
E-Mail: info@foss.co.kr
Emp.: 16
Analytical Instruments
S.I.C.: 3826
N.A.I.C.S.: 334516

Foss Pacific (NZ) Ltd. **(1)**
47 Albert St
Cambridge, New Zealand (100%)
Tel.: (64) 95741416
Fax: (64) 8494750
E-Mail: fosspacific@clear.net
Web Site: www.foss.com.au
Emp.: 6
Analytical Instruments
S.I.C.: 3826
N.A.I.C.S.: 334516
Campbell McCracken *(Mgr-Sls)*

Foss Pacific Pty. Ltd. **(1)**
Macquarie View Park Unit 2 112-118 Talavera Rd
North Ryde, NSW, 2113, Australia (100%)
Tel.: (61) 298886788
Fax: (61) 298894989
E-Mail: info@foss.com.au
Web Site: www.foss.com.au
Emp.: 40
Analytical Instruments
S.I.C.: 3826
N.A.I.C.S.: 334516
Simon Kirkman *(Mgr-PR)*

Foss UK Ltd. **(1)**
730 Birchwood Blvd
Birchwood, Warrington, Cheshire, WA3 7QY, United Kingdom (100%)
Tel.: (44) 1925287700
Fax: (44) 1925287777
E-Mail: info@foss.co.uk
Web Site: www.foss.co.uk
Emp.: 25
Measuring & Controlling Devices Mfr
S.I.C.: 3829
N.A.I.C.S.: 334519
Henry Hanson *(Mgr)*

FOSTER + PARTNERS LTD

Riverside 22 Hester Road
London, SW11 4AN, United Kingdom
Tel.: (44) 2077380455
Fax: (44) 2077381107
E-Mail: info@fosterandpartners.com
Web Site: www.fosterandpartners.com
Year Founded: 1967
Rev.: $220,212,565
Emp.: 1,163
Business Description:
Architecture Services
S.I.C.: 8712
N.A.I.C.S.: 541310
Personnel:
Norman Foster *(Founder & Chm)*
Mouzhan Majidi *(CEO)*
Spencer de Grey *(Head-Design)*
Matthew Streets *(CFO)*

FOSTER ELECTRIC CO., LTD.

1-1-109 Tsutsujigaoka
Akishima, 196-8550, Japan
Tel.: (81) 425462311
Telex: 2842203
Fax: (81) 425462317
Web Site: www.foster.co.jp
Year Founded: 1949
6794—(TKS)
Sls.: $1,578,962,000
Assets: $1,039,280,000
Liabilities: $570,416,000
Net Worth: $468,864,000
Earnings: $36,663,000
Emp.: 70,067
Fiscal Year-end: 03/31/13
Business Description:
Electronic Equipment, Audio & Video Components Mfr
S.I.C.: 3651
N.A.I.C.S.: 334310
Personnel:
Yasuo Higashi *(Chm)*
Yukio Miyata *(Pres)*
H. Yoshizawa *(Sr Mng Dir)*
Roy Ching-Sheng Chen *(Officer)*
F. Murayama *(Sr Officer)*
In-Yong Oh *(Officer)*
H. Shirakawa *(Sr Officer)*
Yoichi Takahashi *(Sr Officer)*
T. Yamaguchi *(Sr Officer)*
Board of Directors:
Yasuo Higashi
Kazuhiro Kishi
San Tie Lu
K. Matsumoto
Yukio Miyata
T. Nagasawa
H. Yoshizawa
Transfer Agent:
Mizuho Trust & Banking Co., Ltd
1-2-1 Yaesu Chuo-ku
Tokyo, Japan

Foster Electric Co., Ltd.—(Continued)

Subsidiaries:

Foster Electronics Limited (1)
6F Noguchi Bldg 4-7-1
Nakano-ku, Tokyo, 164-0001, Japan JP
Tel.: (81) 3 5345 9383
Fax: (81) 3 5345 9352
Electronic Equipment Whslr
S.I.C.: 5065
N.A.I.C.S.: 423690

Foster Transportations Co., Ltd. (1)
3-2-25 Musashino
Akishima City, 196-0021 Tokyo, Japan (100%)
Tel.: (81) 81425192255
Fax: (81) 425192299
Web Site: www.foster.co.jp
Emp.: 50
Provider of Transportation Services for Audio & Sound Equipment
S.I.C.: 3651
N.A.I.C.S.: 334310
Mitsugu Takada *(Pres)*

Fostex Co., Ltd. (1)
512 Miyazawacho Akishima-Shi
Akishima, Tokyo, 196 0024, Japan
Tel.: (81) 425456111
Fax: (81) 425466067
Web Site: www.fostex.com
Emp.: 30
Sales & Distribution of Audio & Sound Equipment
S.I.C.: 5065
N.A.I.C.S.: 423690
Masaki Shimmachi *(Mgr)*

U.S. Subsidiaries:

Culver Electronic Sales (1)
28338 Constellation Rd Ste 910
Valencia, CA 91355 (100%)
Tel.: (661) 295-2200
Fax: (661) 295-5900
Web Site: www.fosterculver.com
Emp.: 15
Sales of Audio Equipment
S.I.C.: 5065
N.A.I.C.S.: 423690
Yasuo Higashi *(Pres)*

Foster Electric (U.S.A.), Inc. (1)
1000 E State Pkwy Ste G
Schaumburg, IL 60173-4592 IL
Tel.: (847) 310-8200 (100%)
Fax: (847) 310-8212
E-Mail: webmaster@fosterelectric.com
Web Site: www.fosterelectric.com
Emp.: 13
Mfr. of Loudspeakers & Sound Equipment
S.I.C.: 3651
N.A.I.C.S.: 334310
Roy Chen *(Pres)*

Non-U.S. Subsidiaries:

Foster Electric (Bac Ninh) Co., Ltd. (1)
No 1 Street 11 Vsip Bac Ninh Tu Son Town
Bac Ninh, Vietnam
Tel.: (84) 2413765868
Fax: (84) 2413765870
Electric Products Mfr
S.I.C.: 3699
N.A.I.C.S.: 335999

Foster Electric Co., (Changzhou) Ltd. (1)
No 8 Xi Hu Road Jinton International Industrial Park Wu Jin
Changzhou, Jiangsu, 213164, China CN
Tel.: (86) 519 8619 1602
Fax: (86) 519 8622 6156
Web Site: www.foster.co.jp
Industrial Machinery Equipment Mfr
S.I.C.: 3559
N.A.I.C.S.: 333249

Foster Electric Co., (Guangzhou) Ltd. (1)
Jiu Shui Keng Cun Da Long Jie Panyu Qu
Guangzhou, Guangdong, 511450, China CN
Tel.: (86) 2034569181
Fax: (86) 20 3456 9280
Electronic Components Mfr
S.I.C.: 3679
N.A.I.C.S.: 334419

Foster Electric Co., (Heyuan) Ltd. (1)
Ground Floor The Connected Factory Workshop Building C Keji Road
Heyuan, Guangdong, China CN
Tel.: (86) 7623601122
Fax: (86) 7623601121
Telecommunication Equipment Mfr
S.I.C.: 3651
N.A.I.C.S.: 334310

Foster Electric Co., (Hong Kong) Ltd. (1)
Block D 12th Fl Kaiser Est 41 Man Yue St
Hung Hom, Kowloon, China (Hong Kong) HK
Tel.: (852) 23626233 (100%)
Fax: (852) 27642466
Web Site: www.foster.co.jp
Emp.: 50
Sales & Distribution of Audio & Sound Equipment
S.I.C.: 5065
N.A.I.C.S.: 423690

Foster Electric Co., (Taiwan) Ltd. (1)
6 East 12th Street Kaohsiung Export Processing Zone
Kaohsiung, 806, Taiwan TW
Tel.: (886) 78319101 (100%)
Fax: (886) 78414810
Emp.: 300
Loudspeakers Mfr
S.I.C.: 3651
N.A.I.C.S.: 334310

Foster Electric (Da Nang) Co., Ltd. (1)
Street 1 Hoa Cam Industrial Zone
Cam Le District, Da Nang, Vietnam
Tel.: (84) 511 3675965
Fax: (84) 511 3675966
Web Site: www.foster.co.jp/en_corporateProfile/group/aj_da_nang.html
Radio Headphones Mfr
S.I.C.: 3651
N.A.I.C.S.: 334310

Foster Electric (Europe) GmbH (1)
Goten Str 19
Hamburg, 20097, Germany (100%)
Tel.: (49) 40239120
Fax: (49) 4023912222
E-Mail: info@foster.de
Web Site: www.foster.de
Sls.: $25,222,212
Emp.: 15
Marketing & Sales of Sound Systems
S.I.C.: 5946
N.A.I.C.S.: 443142
Woltang Kuditza *(Gen Mgr)*

Foster Electric IPO (Thailand) Ltd. (1)
31-11 Moo 3 Bangna Trad Road Km 23 Tambol
Bangsaothong Amthur, Ban Sao Thong, Samut Prakan, 10540, Thailand
Tel.: (66) 2 740 0853
Fax: (66) 2 740 0855
E-Mail: fst-dm@foster.com.sg
Web Site: www.foster.co.jp
Emp.: 5
Loudspeakers Mfr
S.I.C.: 3651
N.A.I.C.S.: 334310
Toshiyuki Kuwajima *(Gen Mgr)*

Foster Electric (Singapore) Pte. Ltd. (1)
159 Kampong Ampat 3 Fl 01-02 Ka Pl
Singapore, 368328, Singapore (100%)
Tel.: (65) 67478811
Fax: (65) 67460062
E-Mail: wil@fostersin.com.sg
Emp.: 60
Mfr. of Sound Systems
S.I.C.: 3651
N.A.I.C.S.: 334310
Wilford Chua *(Mgr-Sls)*

Foster Electric (Vietnam) Co., Ltd. (1)
No 6 A Street 6 Vietnam Singapore Industrial Park Vsip
Thuan An, Binh Duong, Vietnam
Tel.: (84) 650 3767547
Fax: (84) 650 3767548
Web Site: www.foster.co.jp/en_corporateProfile/group/aj_vietnam.html
Radio Headphones Mfr
S.I.C.: 3651
N.A.I.C.S.: 334310

Plant:

Foster Electric (Vietnam) Co., Ltd. - Vietnam Factory 2 (2)
No 20 Vsip II Street 5 Vietnam Singapore Industrial Park II
Thu Dau Mot District, Thuan An, Binh Duong, Vietnam
Tel.: (84) 650 3635050
Fax: (84) 650 3635051
Web Site: www.foster.co.jp/en_corporateProfile/group/aj_vietnam2.html
Radio Headphones Mfr
S.I.C.: 3651
N.A.I.C.S.: 334310

P.T. Foster Electric Indonesia (1)
Kawasan Industri Batamindo Block
3 Jalan Beringin Mukakuning, Batam, 29433, Indonesia (100%)
Tel.: (62) 770611635
Fax: (62) 778611258
Emp.: 1,800
Sales & Distribution of Audio & Sound Equipment
S.I.C.: 5065
N.A.I.C.S.: 423690
Henrik Petersen *(Gen Mgr)*

Non-U.S. Affiliate:

Guangzhou Panyu Jiu Shui Keng Foster Electric Factory (1)
Jiu Shui Keng Cun Da Long Jie Panyu Qu
Guangzhou, Guangdong, 511410, China
Tel.: (86) 20 8462 1172
Fax: (86) 20 8462 0158
Web Site: www.foster.co.jp/corporateProfile/group/aj_panyu.html
Telecommunication Equipment Mfr
S.I.C.: 3651
N.A.I.C.S.: 334310

FOSTER WHEELER AG

Shinfield Park
Reading, Berks, RG2 9FW, United Kingdom
Tel.: (44) 118913 1234
Telex: 138568
E-Mail: fw@fwc.com
Web Site: www.fwc.com
Year Founded: 1900
FWLT—(NASDAQ)
Rev.: $3,306,450,000
Assets: $2,740,272,000
Liabilities: $1,956,107,000
Net Worth: $784,165,000
Earnings: $101,107,000
Emp.: 13,311
Fiscal Year-end: 12/31/13

Business Description:
Holding Company; Chemical Processing Facilities Designer & Steam Generating Equipment Mfr Import Export
S.I.C.: 8711
N.A.I.C.S.: 541330

Personnel:
Jerry Kent Masters *(CEO)*
Franco Baseotto *(CFO, Treas & Exec VP)*
Dave Lawson *(Pres-Metals & Mining Bus)*
Gary Nedelka *(CEO-Global Power Grp)*
Roberto Penno *(CEO-Construction)*
Michelle K. Davies *(Gen Counsel, Sec & Exec VP)*
Eric Sherbet *(Corp Sec)*
David J. Parham *(Exec VP-Global Sls & Mktg-Global Power Grp)*
Beth B. Sexton *(Exec VP-HR)*

Board of Directors:
Steven J. Demetriou
Clayton D. Daley, Jr.
Umberto Della Sala
Edward G. Galante
John M. Malcolm
Jerry Kent Masters
Stephanie S. Newby
Henri Phillippe Reichstul
Maureen B. Tart-Bezer

Transfer Agent:
BNY Mellon Shareowner Services
PO Box 358015
Pittsburgh, PA 15252-8015

Subsidiaries:

Foster Wheeler Energy Limited (1)
Shinfield Pk
Reading, Berkshire, RG2 9FW, United Kingdom UK
Tel.: (44) 1189131234 (100%)
Fax: (44) 1189132333
E-Mail: fw_sales@fwuk.fwc.com
Web Site: www.fwc.com
Sales Range: $350-399.9 Million
Emp.: 2,500
Engineering & Construction Services
S.I.C.: 8711
N.A.I.C.S.: 541330
Troy Roder *(Chm & CEO)*
Stephen Culshaw *(Mng Dir)*

Subsidiaries:

Foster Wheeler Petroleum Development Limited (2)
Shinfield Pk
Reading, Berkshire, RG2 9FW, United Kingdom UK
Tel.: (44) 89131234 (100%)
Fax: (44) 89132333
E-Mail: fw_sales@fwuk.fwc.com
Web Site: www.fwc.com
Sales Range: $10-24.9 Million
Emp.: 3
Engineering & Construction Services
S.I.C.: 8711
N.A.I.C.S.: 541330

Foster Wheeler (Process Plants) Limited (2)
Shinfield Park
Reading, Berkshire, RG2 9FW, United Kingdom
Tel.: (44) 118 913 1234
Construction Engineering Services
S.I.C.: 8711
N.A.I.C.S.: 541330

FW Management Operations (U.K.) Ltd. (2)
Shinfield Park
Reading, Berks, RG2 9FW, United Kingdom UK
Tel.: (44) 1189131234 (100%)
Fax: (44) 1189132333
E-Mail: fw_sales@fwuk.fwc.com
Web Site: www.fwc.com
Sales Range: $150-199.9 Million
Emp.: 1,000
Plant Management & Training Services
S.I.C.: 8748
N.A.I.C.S.: 541618
Mike Beaumont *(CEO)*

Process Industries Agency Limited (2)
Shinfield Park
PO Box 461
Reading, Berkshire, RG2 9FW, United Kingdom
Tel.: (44) 1189133378
Fax: (44) 1189134666
E-Mail: pia@piagency.co.uk
Web Site: www.findpiaglobal.co.uk
Specialist Recruitment Service Provider
S.I.C.: 7361
N.A.I.C.S.: 561311

Foster Wheeler Environmental (UK) Limited (1)
Shinfield Park
Reading, Berkshire, RG2 9FW, United Kingdom
Tel.: (44) 118 913 1234
Fax: (44) 118 913 2333
Web Site: www.fosterwheeler.com
Emp.: 100
Environmental Consulting Services
S.I.C.: 8999

N.A.I.C.S.: 541620
Filippo Abba *(Mgr)*

Foster Wheeler Europe (1)
Shinfield Park
Reading, Berkshire, RG2 9FW, United Kingdom
Tel.: (44) 1189131234
Fax: (44) 1189132337
Investment Management Services
S.I.C.: 6282
N.A.I.C.S.: 523920

Non-U.S. Subsidiary:

Foster Wheeler Europe B.V. (2)
Naritaweg 165 Telestone 8
Amsterdam, 1043 BW, Netherlands
Tel.: (31) 20 572 2300
Fax: (31) 20 664 7557
Construction Engineering Services
S.I.C.: 8711
N.A.I.C.S.: 541330

Subsidiaries:

Foster Wheeler Continental B.V. (3)
Naritaweg 165 Telestone 8
Amsterdam, 1043 BW, Netherlands
Tel.: (31) 205722300
Construction Engineering Services
S.I.C.: 8711
N.A.I.C.S.: 541330

FW Energie B.V. (3)
Naritaweg 165 Telestone 8
Amsterdam, 1043 BW, Netherlands
Tel.: (31) 205722333
Fax: (31) 205722650
Energy Consulting Services
S.I.C.: 8999
N.A.I.C.S.: 541690

FW Europe B.V. (3)
Naritaweg 165 Telestone-8
Amsterdam, 1043 BW, Netherlands
Tel.: (31) 205722333
Construction Engineering Services
S.I.C.: 8711
N.A.I.C.S.: 541330

Non-U.S. Subsidiaries:

Foster Wheeler Consulting Poland Sp. z.o.o. (3)
Jana Pawla Ii 15
Warsaw, 00-828, Poland
Tel.: (48) 323681548
Consulting Services
S.I.C.: 8742
N.A.I.C.S.: 541611

Foster Wheeler Energi Aktiebolag (3)
PO Box 6071
600 06 Norrkoping, Sweden
Tel.: (46) 11 28 53 30
Fax: (46) 11 28 53 40
E-Mail: fwesweden@fwswe.fwc.com
Fluid Bed Boiler Distr
S.I.C.: 5074
N.A.I.C.S.: 423720

Foster Wheeler Energia Oy (3)
Metsanneidonkuja 8
FIN-02130 Espoo, Finland FI
Tel.: (358) 1039311 (100%)
Fax: (358) 103936162
Web Site: www.fwc.com
Sales Range: $100-124.9 Million
Emp.: 500
Engineering & Construction Services
S.I.C.: 8711
N.A.I.C.S.: 541330
Jin Stone *(Pres & CEO)*

Foster Wheeler Energia Polska Sp. z o.o. (3)
Staszica 31 Street
41-200 Sosnowiec, Poland PL
Tel.: (48) 32 368 13 00
Web Site: www.fosterwheeler.pl
Industrial Boiler Mfr & Distr
S.I.C.: 3559
N.A.I.C.S.: 332410
Jaroslaw Mlonka *(Pres & CEO)*

Foster Wheeler Energia, S.L. (3)
Calle Gabriel Garcia Marquez 2 Las Rozas De
Madrid, 28232, Spain
Tel.: (34) 913 36 25 00
Fax: (34) 913 66 25 55
Oil & Gas Field Erected Boiler Distr
S.I.C.: 5074
N.A.I.C.S.: 423720
Jesus Marti Sanz *(Pres & CEO)*

Foster Wheeler Energie GmbH (3)
Hessenstrasse 57
Krefeld, Germany
Tel.: (49) 2151 3633710
Fax: (49) 2151 5799044
E-Mail: krefeld@fwfin.fwc.com
Web Site: www.fosterwheeler.de
Emp.: 15
Electric Power Generation Services
S.I.C.: 4939
N.A.I.C.S.: 221118
Jaakko Jaentti *(Co-Mng Dir)*
Andreas Mumberg *(Co-Mng Dir)*

Foster Wheeler Energy FAKOP Sp. z o.o. (3)
Ul Staszica 31
Sosnowiec, 41-200, Poland
Tel.: (48) 32 368 13 00
Fax: (48) 32 266 16 07
Power Boiler & Heat Exchanger Mfr
S.I.C.: 3559
N.A.I.C.S.: 332410

Foster Wheeler Engineering AG (3)
Lohweg 6
4054 Basel, Switzerland
Tel.: (41) 61 283 2200
Fax: (41) 61 283 2201
Emp.: 2
Construction Engineering Services
S.I.C.: 8711
N.A.I.C.S.: 541330
Roberto Penno *(CEO)*

Foster Wheeler France S.A. (3)
40 Avenvede Terroirs de France
75012 Paris, France FR
Mailing Address: (100%)
92 Quai de Bercy
75597 Paris, Cedex, 12, France
Tel.: (33) 143464000
Fax: (33) 143464700
E-Mail: info@fwc.com
Web Site: www.fwc.com
Sales Range: $75-99.9 Million
Emp.: 390
Engineering & Construction Services
S.I.C.: 8711
N.A.I.C.S.: 541330
Giorgio Veronesi *(Pres & CEO)*

Foster Wheeler Global E&C S.r.l. (3)
Via Sebastiano Caboto 1
Corsico, 20094, Italy
Tel.: (39) 0244861
Fax: (39) 0244863131
Construction Engineering Services
S.I.C.: 8711
N.A.I.C.S.: 541330

Foster Wheeler Iberia S.A. (3)
Calle Gabriel Garcia Marquez 2
Las Rozas, 28232 Madrid, Spain ES
Tel.: (34) 913362500 (100%)
Fax: (34) 913362555
E-Mail: fwiberia@fwc.com
Web Site: www.fwc.com
Sales Range: $150-199.9 Million
Emp.: 675
Engineering & Construction Services
S.I.C.: 8711
N.A.I.C.S.: 541330
Javier Palencia *(Mng Dir)*

Foster Wheeler Italiana, S.p.A. (3)
Via Sebastiano Caboto 1
20094 Corsico, Milan, Italy IT
Tel.: (39) 0244861 (100%)
Fax: (39) 0244863131
Web Site: www.fwc.com
Sales Range: $250-299.9 Million
Emp.: 900
Engineering & Construction Services
S.I.C.: 8711
N.A.I.C.S.: 541330

Foster Wheeler Management AG (3)
Rue De Lausanne 80
Geneva, 1202, Switzerland
Tel.: (41) 227418000
Fax: (41) 227418098
Emp.: 15
Business Management Consulting Services
S.I.C.: 8742
N.A.I.C.S.: 541611
Kent Masters *(CEO)*

Foster Wheeler OOO (3)
Office A-404 Park Place 113/1
Leninsky Prospekt, Moscow, 117198, Russia
Tel.: (7) 4956623617
Fax: (7) 4956623618
Emp.: 20
Construction Engineering Services
S.I.C.: 8711
N.A.I.C.S.: 541330
Andrei Kalyuzhov *(Gen Mgr)*

Foster Wheeler Trading Co. A.G., S.A (3)
Calle Gabriel Garcia Marquez 2
Madrid, Spain
Tel.: (34) 913362835
Fax: (34) 913362828
Emp.: 10
Power Equipment Distr
S.I.C.: 5084
N.A.I.C.S.: 423830
Jose Lopez *(Gen Mgr)*

FW Financial Holdings GmbH (3)
Vordergasse 3
Schaffhausen, 8200, Switzerland
Tel.: (41) 526333636
Fax: (41) 526333686
Investment Management Services
S.I.C.: 6211
N.A.I.C.S.: 523999

Graf-Wulff GmbH (3)
Am Zollstock 1
61381 Friedrichsdorf, Germany
Tel.: (49) 6172 266 28 0
Fax: (49) 6172 266 28 18
E-Mail: contactfgd@graf-wulff.de
Web Site: www.graf-wulff.de
Emp.: 20
Dry Flue Gas Scrubbing Services
S.I.C.: 7389
N.A.I.C.S.: 561990
Jari Nokelainen *(CEO)*

World Services Italiana S.r.l. (3)
Via Sebastiano Caboto 1
Corsico, 20094, Italy
Tel.: (39) 0244861
Fax: (39) 0244863780
Construction Engineering Services
S.I.C.: 8711
N.A.I.C.S.: 541330

Foster Wheeler (London) Limited (1)
Shinfield Park
Reading, Berkshire, RG2 9FW, United Kingdom
Tel.: (44) 118 913 1234
Fax: (44) 1189132333
E-Mail: fw_sales@fwuk.fwc.com
Web Site: www.fwc.com
Emp.: 150
Power Transmission Equipment Distr
S.I.C.: 5063
N.A.I.C.S.: 423610
Andreas Weiss *(Chm & CEO)*

U.S. Subsidiaries:

Foster Wheeler Inc. (1)
53 Frontage Rd PO Box 9000
Hampton, NJ 08827-9000 DE
Tel.: (908) 730-4000 (100%)
Fax: (908) 713-3245
E-Mail: info@fwc.com
Web Site: www.fwc.com
Sales Range: $1-4.9 Billion
Emp.: 1,500
Cogeneration Facilities Construction Services
S.I.C.: 1542
N.A.I.C.S.: 236220
Andrea Hintenach *(Gen Mgr)*

Subsidiaries:

Foster Wheeler Development Corporation (2)
53 Frontage Rd
Hampton, NJ 08827 DE
Tel.: (973) 535-2300 (100%)
Fax: (908) 730-5050
Web Site: www.fwc.com
Sales Range: $10-24.9 Million
Emp.: 500
Research, Development & Engineering Services
S.I.C.: 8711
N.A.I.C.S.: 541330
Kent Masters *(Pres)*

Foster Wheeler Global Power (2)
53 Frontage Rd
Hampton, NJ 08827 DE
Mailing Address: (100%)
PO Box 9000
Hampton, NJ 08827
Tel.: (908) 730-4000
Fax: (908) 713-3245
Web Site: www.fwc.com
Sales Range: $100-124.9 Million
Emp.: 500
Engineering & Construction Services
S.I.C.: 8711
N.A.I.C.S.: 541330
Gary Nedelka *(CEO)*

Non-U.S. Subsidiaries:

Foster Wheeler America Latina, Ltda. (3)
Alice Alem Saad 1 256
Ribeirao Preto, Sao Paulo, 14096-570, Brazil
Tel.: (55) 1639117884
Engineering Services
S.I.C.: 8711
N.A.I.C.S.: 541330

Foster Wheeler Caribe Corporation, C.A. (3)
Torre Nord Piso 8
Avenida Tamanaco
El Rosal, Caracas, Venezuela VE
Tel.: (58) 212 952 3168
Fax: (58) 212 952 8676
Web Site: www.fwc.com
Sales Range: $25-49.9 Million
Emp.: 100
Engineering Design & Project Management Services
S.I.C.: 8711
N.A.I.C.S.: 541330
Carlos Martinez *(Mgr)*

Foster Wheeler Chile S.A. (3)
Apoquindo Av 3846 7F Apoquindo 3846 7th Fl
Santiago, Chile CL
Tel.: (56) 23797500 (100%)
Fax: (56) 23797690
E-Mail: fwchilesa@fwchile.fwc.com
Web Site: www.fwc.com
Sales Range: $50-74.9 Million
Emp.: 150
Engineering & Construction Services
S.I.C.: 8711
N.A.I.C.S.: 541330
Fernando Ares *(Gen Mgr)*

Foster Wheeler Colombia SAS (3)
Calle 110 No 9-25 Oficinas 515 & 516
Bogota, Colombia
Tel.: (57) 1 705 9800
E-Mail: contacto_fwcol@fwhou.fwc.com
Web Site: www.fwc.com
Emp.: 12
Construction Engineering Services
S.I.C.: 8711
N.A.I.C.S.: 541330
Hans-Joachim Hoeck *(Office Mgr)*

Foster Wheeler Eastern Private Limited (3)
991E Alexandra Rd
Blk 7 01 25, Singapore, 119973, Singapore SG
Tel.: (65) 65018888 (100%)
Fax: (65) 62737136
Web Site: www.fwc.com
Sales Range: $100-124.9 Million
Emp.: 310
Engineering & Construction Services
S.I.C.: 8711
N.A.I.C.S.: 541330

Non-U.S. Subsidiary:

Foster Wheeler Service (Thailand) Limited (4)
53 moo 9 Sukim Rd Thuntsukha Sriracha
Chon Buri, 20230, Thailand TH
Tel.: (66) 38352200 (100%)

Foster Wheeler AG—(Continued)

Fax: (66) 38344344
Web Site: www.fwc.com
Sales Range: $75-99.9 Million
Emp.: 450
Engineering & Project Management Services
S.I.C.: 8711
N.A.I.C.S.: 541330
Giaham Tope *(Gen Mgr)*

Petropower Energia Limitada (3)
Calle Ramuntcho VIII Region
3230 Hualpen, Chile
Tel.: (56) 412500600
Fax: (56) 412424276
Web Site: www.fwt.cl
Emp.: 100
Electric Power Generation Services
S.I.C.: 4931
N.A.I.C.S.: 221118
Brian Mace *(Gen Mgr)*

Foster Wheeler North America Corp. (2)
53 Frontage Rd
Hampton, NJ 08827-9000
Tel.: (908) 730-4000
Fax: (908) 713-3245
Web Site: www.fwc.com
Construction Engineering Services
S.I.C.: 8711
N.A.I.C.S.: 541330
Byron Roth *(Pres & CEO)*
David Parham *(Exec VP-Global Sls & Mktg)*

Subsidiary:

Foster Wheeler USA Corporation (3)
585 N Dairy Ashford
Houston, TX 77079 DE
Tel.: (281) 597-3000 (100%)
Fax: (281) 597-3028
Web Site: www.fwc.com
Sales Range: $150-199.9 Million
Emp.: 500
Engineering & Construction Services
S.I.C.: 8711
N.A.I.C.S.: 541330
Chris E. Covert *(Pres & CEO)*

Subsidiaries:

Foster Wheeler Andes, Inc. (4)
Perryville Corporate Park
Clinton, NJ 08809
Tel.: (908) 730-4000
Construction Engineering Services
S.I.C.: 8711
N.A.I.C.S.: 541330

Foster Wheeler Biokinetics, Inc. (4)
7 Penn Ctr 1635 Market St
Philadelphia, PA 19103 DE
Tel.: (215) 656-2500
Fax: (215) 561-4444
Web Site: www.fwbiok.com
Sales Range: $25-49.9 Million
Emp.: 100
Systems Solutions for the Life Science Industry
S.I.C.: 8711
N.A.I.C.S.: 541330
Joe Galluzzo *(VP-Mktg)*

Foster Wheeler Constructors, Inc. (4)
53 Frontage Rd
Hampton, NJ 08827 DE
Tel.: (908) 730-4000 (100%)
Fax: (908) 730-5315
E-Mail: fwci_main@fwc.com
Web Site: www.fwc.com
Sales Range: $200-249.9 Million
Emp.: 400
Heavy Construction Services
S.I.C.: 1629
N.A.I.C.S.: 237990
Racish Jindal *(VP-Tax)*

Subsidiary:

Foster Wheeler Zack, Inc. (5)
Perryville Corporate Park
Clinton, NJ 08827-4000 DE
Tel.: (908) 730-4000 (100%)
Fax: (908) 713-3245
Web Site: www.fwc.com
Sales Range: $250-299.9 Million
Emp.: 900
Engineering & Construction Services
S.I.C.: 8711
N.A.I.C.S.: 541330

Foster Wheeler Energy Corporation (4)
53 Frontage Rd Perryville Corporate Park
Hampton, NJ 08827-4000 DE
Tel.: (908) 730-4000 (100%)
Fax: (908) 713-3245
Web Site: www.fwc.com
Sales Range: $400-449.9 Million
Emp.: 6,000
Steam Generators Mfr & Engineering Services
S.I.C.: 1629
N.A.I.C.S.: 237990
Bill Dillon *(COO)*

Foster Wheeler Facilities Management, Inc. (4)
53 Frontage Rd
Hampton, NJ 08827 DE
Tel.: (908) 730-4000 (100%)
Fax: (908) 730-5315
E-Mail: info@fwc.com
Web Site: www.fwc.com
Sales Range: $25-49.9 Million
Emp.: 100
Facilities Management Services
S.I.C.: 8741
N.A.I.C.S.: 561110

Foster Wheeler LLC (4)
Perryville Corporate Park
Clinton, NJ 08809
Tel.: (908) 730-4000
Power Plant Construction Engineering Services
S.I.C.: 1623
N.A.I.C.S.: 237130

Foster Wheeler Martinez, Inc. (4)
550 Solano Way
Martinez, CA 94553 DE
Tel.: (925) 313-0800 (100%)
Fax: (925) 313-0814
E-Mail: info@fwc.com
Web Site: www.fwc.com
Sales Range: $10-24.9 Million
Emp.: 25
Cogeneration Services
S.I.C.: 4931
N.A.I.C.S.: 221118

Foster Wheeler Pyropower, Inc. (4)
Perryville Corporate Park
Clinton, NJ 08809
Tel.: (908) 730-4000
Steam Generating & Auxiliary Equipment Mfr
S.I.C.: 3433
N.A.I.C.S.: 333414

Foster Wheeler Twin Cities, Inc. (4)
2701 University Ave SE
Minneapolis, MN 55414 DE
Tel.: (612) 379-1885
Fax: (612) 379-1980
Web Site: www.fwc.com
Sales Range: $25-49.9 Million
Emp.: 55
Steam Heating System Services
S.I.C.: 4961
N.A.I.C.S.: 221330

Martinez Cogen Limited Partnership (4)
550 Solano Way
Pacheco, CA 94553-1446
Tel.: (925) 313-0800
Electricity Generation & Gas Distr
S.I.C.: 4911
N.A.I.C.S.: 221118

Non-U.S. Subsidiary:

Foster Wheeler Canada Ltd. (3)
509 Glendale Avenue East
Niagara-on-the-Lake, ON, LOS 1J0, Canada Ca
Tel.: (905) 688-4434 (100%)
Telex: 615134 fwlstea
Fax: (905) 688-4588
E-Mail: fwl@fwc.com
Web Site: www.fwc.com
Sales Range: $25-49.9 Million
Emp.: 120
Engineering & Construction Services
S.I.C.: 8711
N.A.I.C.S.: 541330
Jim Long *(Controller & Gen Mgr)*

Subsidiary:

Foster Wheeler Fired Heaters, Ltd. (4)
Ste 200-4954 Richard RD. SW
Calgary, AB, T3E 6L1, Canada Ca
Tel.: (403) 255-3447 (100%)
Fax: (403) 259-4558
E-Mail: fwfhl@fwfhl.com
Web Site: www.fwc.com
Sales Range: $10-24.9 Million
Emp.: 20
Engineering & Construction Services
S.I.C.: 8711
N.A.I.C.S.: 541330
Rhonda Campbell *(Office Mgr)*

Foster Wheeler Real Estate Development Corp. (2)
53 Frontage Rd
Hampton, NJ 08827-9000 DE
Tel.: (908) 730-4000 (100%)
Fax: (908) 730-4000
Web Site: www.fwc.com
Sales Range: $1-4.9 Billion
Emp.: 850
Real Estate Development Services
S.I.C.: 6512
N.A.I.C.S.: 531120

Non-U.S. Subsidiaries:

Foster Wheeler Arabia, Ltd. (1)
PO Box 79311
Al Khobar, 31952, Saudi Arabia DE
Tel.: (966) 38822398 (100%)
Fax: (966) 38823440
Web Site: www.fwc.com
Sales Range: $50-74.9 Million
Emp.: 200
Engineering & Construction Services
S.I.C.: 8711
N.A.I.C.S.: 541330

Foster Wheeler Asia Pacific Pte. Ltd (1)
991e Alexandra Road 01-25 Block 7
Singapore, 119973, Singapore
Tel.: (65) 65018888
Fax: (65) 62737136
Construction Engineering Services
S.I.C.: 8711
N.A.I.C.S.: 541330

Foster Wheeler Bengal Private Limited (1)
Infinity Benchmark 13th Floor Plot No G1 Block EP&GP
Sector-V Salt Lake, Kolkata, 700 091, India
Tel.: (91) 33 4021 6700
Fax: (91) 33 2357 5870
E-Mail: fw_bengal@fwhou.fwc.com
Web Site: www.fosterwheelerindia.com
Construction Engineering Services
S.I.C.: 8711
N.A.I.C.S.: 541330

Foster Wheeler Bimas A.S. (1)
Sari Kanarya Sok 22 Yolbulan Plaza
81090 Istanbul, Turkey TR
Tel.: (90) 2164451335 (100%)
Fax: (90) 2164451336
E-Mail: info@fwc.com
Web Site: www.fwc.com
Sales Range: $25-49.9 Million
Emp.: 160
Engineering & Construction Services
S.I.C.: 8711
N.A.I.C.S.: 541330
Bulent Girgin *(Mgr-Mktg & Sls)*

Foster Wheeler Energy Management (Shanghai) Company Limited (1)
8/F Chengjian Bldg No 500 Fushan Road
Pudong New Area, 200122 Shanghai, China
Tel.: (86) 2150582452
Fax: (86) 2150587377
Web Site: www.fwc.com
Emp.: 20
Construction Engineering Services
S.I.C.: 8711
N.A.I.C.S.: 541330

Foster Wheeler India Private Limited (1)
6th Fl Zenith Bldg Ascendas IT Park CSIR Rd
Taramani, Chennai, 600 113, India
Tel.: (91) 44 6622 3100
Fax: (91) 44 2235 5900
E-Mail: fw_india@fwuk.fwc.com
Web Site: www.fosterwheelerindia.com
Emp.: 700
Construction Engineering Services
S.I.C.: 8711
N.A.I.C.S.: 541330
Partha Purkayastha *(Mng Dir)*

Foster Wheeler (Philippines) Corporation (1)
7-A 7th Fl PDCP Bank Ctr Condominium Bldg V A Rufino St Corner LPL st
Salcedo Village, 1227 Makati, Philippines
Tel.: (63) 2 753 1095
Fax: (63) 2 867 2304
Construction Engineering Services
S.I.C.: 8711
N.A.I.C.S.: 541330

Foster Wheeler Power Group Asia Limited (1)
8th and 5th Floor UC Tower 500 Fushan Road
Pudong New Area, Shanghai, 200122, China
Tel.: (86) 21 5058 2266
Fax: (86) 21 5058 7375
Emp.: 20
Construction Engineering Services
S.I.C.: 8711
N.A.I.C.S.: 541330
Mark Garvey *(Pres & CEO)*

Foster Wheeler South Africa (PTY) Limited (1)
2nd Road Halfway House
Midrand, 1685, South Africa
Tel.: (27) 11 690 0400
Fax: (27) 11 315 0243
Construction Engineering Services
S.I.C.: 8711
N.A.I.C.S.: 541330

PT Foster Wheeler O&G Indonesia (1)
Perkantoran Pulo Mas Blok VII No 2 Jl Perintis kemerdekaan
Pulogadung East Jakarta, Jakarta, Indonesia
Tel.: (62) 21 4720873
Fax: (62) 21 4893961
Web Site: www.fwc.com
Construction Engineering Services
S.I.C.: 8711
N.A.I.C.S.: 541330

FOSUN INTERNATIONAL LIMITED

(d/b/a Fosun Group)
Room 808 ICBC Tower 3 Garden Rd
Central, China (Hong Kong)
Tel.: (852) 25093228
Fax: (852) 25099028
Web Site: www.fosun.com
Year Founded: 1992
656—(HKG OTC)
Rev.: $8,222,829,902
Assets: $25,765,208,215
Liabilities: $16,676,066,011
Net Worth: $9,089,142,205
Earnings: $785,339,786
Emp.: 35,000
Fiscal Year-end: 12/31/12

Business Description:
Pharmaceutical Products & Iron & Steel Mfr & Sales
S.I.C.: 3399
N.A.I.C.S.: 331110

Personnel:
Guangchang Guo *(Chm)*
Xinjun Liang *(Vice Chm & CEO)*
Qunbin Wang *(Pres)*
Guoqi Ding *(CFO & Sr VP)*
Mei Ming Sze *(Sec)*
Xuetang Qin *(Sr VP)*
Ping Wu *(Sr VP)*

Board of Directors:
Guangchang Guo
Guoqi Ding
Wei Fan
Xinjun Liang
Xuetang Qin
Qunbin Wang
Ping Wu
Andrew Y. Yan
David T. Zhang
Huaqiao Zhang
Shengman Zhang
Transfer Agent:
Computershare Hong Kong Investor Services Limited
17M Floor Hopewell Centre 183 Queen's Road East
Wanchai, China (Hong Kong)

Non-U.S. Subsidiaries:

Chindex Medical Limited (1)
Fosun International Center Floor 28
No. 237 Chaoyang North Road, Beijing, 100020, China
Tel.: (86) 10 6552 8822
Fax: (86) 10 6552 8833
Medical Devices Mfr
S.I.C.: 3841
N.A.I.C.S.: 339112
Lawrence Pemble *(CFO)*
Elyse Beth Silverberg *(COO)*

Non-U.S. Subsidiary:

Alma Lasers Ltd. (2)
14 Halamish Caesarea Industrial Park
38900 Caesarea, Israel
Tel.: (972) 46275357
Fax: (972) 46275368
Web Site: www.almalasers.com
Sales Range: $25-49.9 Million
Emp.: 138
Developer & Mfr of Laser, Light-Based, Radiofrequency & Ultrasound Devices for Aesthetic & Medical Applications
S.I.C.: 3841
N.A.I.C.S.: 339112
Ziv Karni *(CEO)*
Ronen Lazarovich *(COO)*
Avi Farbstein *(CEO-Ops-North America)*

U.S. Subsidiary:

Alma Lasers, Inc. (3)
485 Half Day Rd Ste 100
Buffalo Grove, IL 60089
Tel.: (224) 377-2000
Fax: (224) 377-2050
Toll Free: (866) 414-2562
E-Mail: marketing@almalasers.com
Web Site: www.almalasers.com
Emp.: 15
Laser, Light-Based & Radiofrequency Devices for Aesthetic & Medical Applications Whslr
S.I.C.: 5047
N.A.I.C.S.: 423450
Avi Farbstein *(CEO)*

Shanghai Forte Land Co., Ltd. (1)
5-7 F Fosun Business Building 2 Fu Xing Rd
Shanghai, 200010, China
Tel.: (86) 2163320055
E-Mail: forte@forte.com.cn
Web Site: www.forte.com.cn
Sales Range: $1-4.9 Billion
Emp.: 1,477
Property Development & Investment Services
S.I.C.: 6531
N.A.I.C.S.: 531390
Hua Zhang *(Chm & Pres)*
Zhe Wang *(CFO & Sr VP)*
Susan Yee Har Lo *(Co-Sec)*
Qian Zhang *(Co-Sec)*
Zhidong Cao *(Sr VP)*

Shanghai Fosun Capital Investment Management Co., Ltd. (1)
No 2 East Fuxing Road
Shanghai, 200010, China
Tel.: (86) 21 6332 5858
Fax: (86) 21 6332 5028
Web Site: www.fosuncapital.com
Private Equity Fund Management Services
S.I.C.: 6211
N.A.I.C.S.: 523999
James Zheng *(Mng Dir)*

FOTEX HOLDING SE

42 rue de la Vallee
L-2661 Luxembourg, Luxembourg
Tel.: (352) 26976709
Fax: (352) 3504375
E-Mail: info@fotex.lu
Web Site: www.fotex.hu
FOTEX—(LUX)
Rev.: $55,565,906
Assets: $288,874,712
Liabilities: $126,427,650
Net Worth: $162,447,062
Earnings: $9,230,572
Fiscal Year-end: 12/31/12
Business Description:
Financial Investment Services
S.I.C.: 6282
N.A.I.C.S.: 523930
Personnel:
Gabor Varszegi *(Chm & CEO)*
Board of Directors:
Gabor Varszegi
Robert J. Dole
Peter Kadas
Wiggert Karreman
Jan Thomas Ladenius
Anna Rammer
David Varszegi

U.S. Subsidiary:

Ajka Crystal USA (1)
Eszter Varszegi Chancy 7157 Obelisco Cir
Carlsbad, CA 92009
Tel.: (888) 512-2552
Fax: (888) 512-2552
Web Site: www.ajka-crystal.hu/en/contact
Crystal Products Distr
S.I.C.: 5023
N.A.I.C.S.: 423220

Non-U.S. Subsidiaries:

Ajka Kristaly Kft. (1)
Alkotmany Street 4
Ajka, Veszprem, 8400, Hungary
Tel.: (36) 88510521
Fax: (36) 88 311 986
Web Site: www.ajka-crystal.hu
Emp.: 300
Crystal Products Mfr & Distr
S.I.C.: 3999
N.A.I.C.S.: 339999
Bernard Neumann *(Founder)*

Balaton Butor Kft. (1)
Hazgyari ut 4
Veszprem, 8200, Hungary
Tel.: (36) 88425866
E-Mail: info@balaton-butor.hu
Web Site: www.balaton-butor.hu
Furniture Mfr
S.I.C.: 2521
N.A.I.C.S.: 337211
Anna Pauer *(Mng Dir)*

Fotex Cosmetics Kft (1)
Nagy Jeno u 12
1126 Budapest, Hungary
Tel.: (36) 12022400
Fax: (36) 12022451
Cosmetics Distr
S.I.C.: 5122
N.A.I.C.S.: 424210

Fotex Netherlands B.V. (1)
Sarphatikade 13
1017 WV Amsterdam, North Holland, Netherlands
Tel.: (31) 206102151
Fax: (31) 206102181
Property Management Services
S.I.C.: 6531
N.A.I.C.S.: 531312

Hungaroton Records Kft. (1)
Rottenbiller utca 47
1071 Budapest, Hungary
Tel.: (36) 1 8881200
Fax: (36) 1 202 3794
E-Mail: info@hungaroton.hu
Web Site: www.hungaroton.hu
Music Records Distr
S.I.C.: 5734
N.A.I.C.S.: 443142
Mate Hollos *(Mng Dir)*

Primo Zrt. (1)
Reitter Ferenc Utca 39-49
1135 Budapest, Hungary
Tel.: (36) 1350 24 11
Fax: (36) 1350 43 75
Mens Clothing Retailer
S.I.C.: 5611
N.A.I.C.S.: 448110

Sigma Kft. (1)
Nagy Jeno utca 12
1126 Budapest, Hungary
Tel.: (36) 14873720
Fax: (36) 14873721
E-Mail: info@sigma-property.com
Web Site: www.sigma-property.com
Emp.: 6
Property Management & Consulting Services
S.I.C.: 6531
N.A.I.C.S.: 531210
Erzsebet Cyorrsw *(Gen Mgr)*

FOUAD ALGHANIM & SONS GROUP OF COMPANIES

PO Box 2118
Safat, Kuwait, 13022, Kuwait
Tel.: (965) 2424773
Fax: (965) 2424130
E-Mail: fasg1@falghanim.com
Web Site: www.fmtas-group.com
Year Founded: 1965
Emp.: 1,200
Business Description:
Holding & Trading Company; Civil & Electro-Mechanical Engineering; Electronics & Telecommunications; Motor Vehicles; Equipment Sales; Pumps; Industrial Equipment; Aviation; Shipping & Transportation; Medical & Diagnostic Equipment; Foam Mfr; Hotels; Property Development
S.I.C.: 6719
N.A.I.C.S.: 551112
Personnel:
Fouad M.T. Alghanim *(Chm)*

Subsidiaries:

Alghanim Group of Shipping & Transport W.L.L. (1)
Alfour St Bldg Abdul Mahson Marzook
PO Box 20842
Safat, Kuwait, 13069, Kuwait (100%)
Tel.: (965) 2421701
Fax: (965) 2428678
E-Mail: shipping@alghanimgroup.com
Web Site: www.alghanimgroup.com
Emp.: 56
Provider of Transportation Services
S.I.C.: 4789
N.A.I.C.S.: 488210

Energy International for Petroleum Projects KCSC (1)
Awqaf Complex No 11 First Fl Tower 12
Mubarak An Kabeer St Sharq
Safat, 13052 Kuwait, Kuwait (50%)
Tel.: (965) 2437729
Fax: (965) 2453252
E-Mail: info@eippc.com
Web Site: www.eippc.com
Sales Range: $150-199.9 Million
Emp.: 20
Distributor of Petroleum Products
S.I.C.: 5172
N.A.I.C.S.: 424720

FOUNDATION RESOURCES INC.

(Name Changed to Birch Hill Gold Corp.)

FOUNDER HOLDINGS LIMITED

14th Floor Cable TV Tower No 9 Hoi Shing Road
Tsuen Wan New Territories, Hong Kong, China (Hong Kong)
Tel.: (852) 26114111
Fax: (852) 24133218
E-Mail: ir@founder.com.hk
Web Site: www.founder.com.hk
Year Founded: 1992
418—(DEU HKG OTC)
Rev.: $274,760,599
Assets: $194,177,552
Liabilities: $94,341,496
Net Worth: $99,836,056
Earnings: $5,726,798
Emp.: 1,362
Fiscal Year-end: 12/31/12
Business Description:
Software Development Services
S.I.C.: 7371
N.A.I.C.S.: 541511
Personnel:
Zhong Hua Fang *(Chm)*
Jian Guo Xiao *(Deputy Chm)*
Bin Yang *(Pres)*
Yvonne Yuk Bo Tang *(Sec)*
Board of Directors:
Zhong Hua Fang
Sammy Man Yin Fung
Fat Chung Li
Sheng Li Li
Yu Xiao Liu
Lam Kit Yee Wong
Jian Guo Xiao
Bin Yang
Mei Yi
Butterfield Fulcrum Group (Bermuda) Limited
26 Burnaby Street
Hamilton, HM 11, Bermuda
Transfer Agent:
Computershare Hong Kong Investor Services Limited
Shops 1712-1716 17th Floor Hopewell Centre
183 Queens Road East
Wanchai, China (Hong Kong)

FOUNDER TECHNOLOGY GROUP CORP.

Founder Plaza No 298 Chengfu Road
Zhongguan Cun
Haidian District, Beijing, China
Tel.: (86) 1082529999
E-Mail: info.ibu@founder.com
Web Site: www.foundertech.com
Year Founded: 1985
600601—(SHG)
Sales Range: $1-4.9 Billion
Emp.: 6,955
Business Description:
Computer & Computer Peripheral Equipment Mfr & Sales
S.I.C.: 3575
N.A.I.C.S.: 334118
Personnel:
Zhonghua Fang *(Chm)*
Lan Ye *(Pres)*

FOUNDING CONSTRUCTION DEVELOPMENT CO., LTD.

3F 294 Tun Tua South Rd Section 1
Taipei, Taiwan
Tel.: (886) 227025887
Fax: (886) 227073554
E-Mail: founding@founding.com.tw
Web Site: www.founding.com.tw
Year Founded: 1991
5533—(TAI)
Sales Range: $25-49.9 Million
Emp.: 70
Business Description:
Residential & Commercial Buildings Construction, Development, Sales & Leasing
S.I.C.: 1522
N.A.I.C.S.: 236116

Founding Construction Development Co., Ltd.—(Continued)

Personnel:
Xinxiong Liu *(Chm)*

FOUNDRY FUEL PRODUCTS LTD.

504 Diamond Prestige 41A A J C
Bose Road
Kolkata, 700 017, India
Tel.: (91) 2226 8441
Fax: (91) 2265 0116
E-Mail: foundryfuel@gmail.com
Web Site: www.foundryfuel.co.in
513579—(BOM)
Rev.: $9,143
Assets: $264,452
Liabilities: $23,713
Net Worth: $240,739
Earnings: ($118,870)
Fiscal Year-end: 03/31/13
Business Description:
Metallurgical Coke Mfr
S.I.C.: 3399
N.A.I.C.S.: 331110
Personnel:
Devendra Kumar Agarwalla *(Chm & Mng Dir)*
Mayuresh Oka *(Compliance Officer)*
Board of Directors:
Devendra Kumar Agarwalla
Adarsh Agarwalla
Kamal Ghosh
Ruchir Omprakash Jalan
Sunil Vishwambharan
Transfer Agent:
Niche Technologies Pvt Ltd
C-444 Bagree Market 71 BRB Basu Rd
Kolkata, India

FOUNTAIN S.A.

Avenue de l'Artisanat 17
1420 Braine-l'Alleud, Belgium
Tel.: (32) 2 3851562
Fax: (32) 2 3853140
E-Mail: info@fountain.eu
Web Site: www.fountain.eu
Year Founded: 1972
FOU—(EUR)
Sls.: $64,288,183
Assets: $59,035,505
Liabilities: $28,557,933
Net Worth: $30,477,571
Earnings: $148,308
Emp.: 64
Fiscal Year-end: 12/31/12
Business Description:
Hot Beverage Dispenser Mfr
S.I.C.: 3589
N.A.I.C.S.: 333318
Personnel:
Pierre Vermaut *(Pres)*
Paul Baeck *(CEO)*
Eric Dienst *(CFO)*
Jean-Francois Buysschaert *(COO)*
Board of Directors:
Jean Ducroux
Dimitri Duffeleer
Alain Englebert
Bruno Lambert
Philippe Percival
Philippe Vander Putten
Philippe Sevin

FOUNTAIN SET (HOLDINGS) LIMITED

Block A 6/F Eastern Sea Industrial Building
29-39 Kwai Cheong Road, Kwai Chung, New Territories, China (Hong Kong)
Tel.: (852) 24851881
Fax: (852) 24181139
E-Mail: sales@fshl.com
Web Site: www.fshl.com
0420—(HKG)
Rev.: $1,182,096,127
Assets: $776,291,250
Liabilities: $366,258,619
Net Worth: $410,032,631
Earnings: ($43,554,281)
Emp.: 13,300
Fiscal Year-end: 12/31/12
Business Description:
Investment Holding Services
S.I.C.: 6799
N.A.I.C.S.: 523920
Personnel:
Lan Li *(Chm)*
Victor Kam On Ha *(Vice Chm & CEO)*
Gordon Yen *(CFO)*
Siu Man Chan *(Sec)*
Board of Directors:
Lan Li
Anthony Wing Kin Chow
Zhengyi Gong
Victor Kam On Ha
Kwok Tung Ng
Shibin Yang
Gordon Yen
Chong Zhang
Yao Zhao

Subsidiaries:

Folktune Limited (1)
Rm A 7 F Eastern Sea Indl Bldg 29-39 Kwai Cheong Rd
48-56 Tai Lin Pai Rd, Kwai Chung, New Territories, China (Hong Kong)
Tel.: (852) 24851881
Fax: (852) 24181139
Emp.: 300
Fabric & Yarn Sales
S.I.C.: 5131
N.A.I.C.S.: 424310
Chung Fong Ha *(Chm)*

Fountain Set Limited (1)
Block A 6 F Eastern Sea Indus Bldg 29-39 Kwai Cheong Rd
Kwai Chung, New Territories, China (Hong Kong)
Tel.: (852) 24251010
Fax: (852) 24184718
E-Mail: sales@fshl.com
Knitted Fabrics & Garments Supplier
S.I.C.: 5199
N.A.I.C.S.: 424310

Goldlink Thread Limited (1)
Block A 6 F Eastern Sea Indust Bldg 29-39 Kwai Cheong Rd
Kwai Chung, New Territories, China (Hong Kong)
Tel.: (852) 24101010
Fax: (852) 24818226
E-Mail: gl_sales@fshl.com
Web Site: www.fshl.com
Emp.: 100
Sewing Thread Mfr & Sales
S.I.C.: 2299
N.A.I.C.S.: 313110
Au Anson *(Mgr-Sls)*

Highscene Limited (1)
Block A 6 F Eastern Sea Indus Bldg 29-39 Kwai Cheong Rd
Kwai Chung, New Territories, China (Hong Kong)
Tel.: (852) 34786388
Fax: (852) 34786378
E-Mail: hs_sales@hs.fshl.com
Yarn Mfr
S.I.C.: 2299
N.A.I.C.S.: 313110

Hiway Textiles Limited (1)
6 F Eastern Sea Indus Bldg 29-39 Kwai Cheong Rd
Kwai Chung, New Territories, China (Hong Kong)
Tel.: (852) 34786668
Fax: (852) 24801711
E-Mail: sales@hiwaytextiles.com
Web Site: www.hiwaytextiles.com
Emp.: 300
Children Wear Garments Mfr
S.I.C.: 2389
N.A.I.C.S.: 315210

Lake Side Printing Factory Limited (1)
7 F Eastern Sea Indus Bldg Block A 29-39 Kwai Cheong Rd
Kwai Chung, New Territories, China (Hong Kong)
Tel.: (852) 24851881
Fax: (852) 24181139
Knitted Fabrics Mfr
S.I.C.: 2259
N.A.I.C.S.: 313240

Triumph Luck Limited (1)
Unit 11 33 F Cable TV Tower 9 Hoi Shing Rd
Tsuen Wan, New Territories, China (Hong Kong)
Tel.: (852) 24220000
Fax: (852) 24221221
E-Mail: triumphluck@triumphluck.com
Knit Wear & Casual Wear Mfr
S.I.C.: 2259
N.A.I.C.S.: 315190

Non-U.S. Subsidiaries:

Fountain Set Textiles (Ontario) Ltd. (1)
50 Melham Ct Unit A
Scarborough, ON, M1B 2E5, Canada
Tel.: (416) 298-6188
Fax: (416) 298-6088
E-Mail: fountainset@fso.ca
Web Site: www.fso.ca
Knitted Fabrics & Yarns Distr
S.I.C.: 5199
N.A.I.C.S.: 424310
Peter Kwan *(Pres)*

Jiangyin Jintian Machinery Limited (1)
99 Eastern Binjiang Rd
Jiangyin, Jiangsu, 214434, China
Tel.: (86) 51086193999
Fax: (86) 51086198903
E-Mail: jt_info@jintian.fshl.com
Web Site: www.jtm-machinery.com
Emp.: 300
Textile Machinery Mfr
S.I.C.: 3559
N.A.I.C.S.: 333249

Kaiping Hui Hua Textiles Limited (1)
22 GangKou Rd
Kaiping, Guangdong, 529300, China
Tel.: (86) 7502291832
Fax: (86) 7502299883
Yarns Mfr & Sales
S.I.C.: 2299
N.A.I.C.S.: 313110

Ningbo Young Top Garments Co., Ltd (1)
No 396 Dan Yang W Rd Xiangshan Indus Dev Zone
Xiangshan, Ningbo, Zhejiang, 315700, China
Tel.: (86) 57465781178
Fax: (86) 57465781138
Garments Mfr & Sales
S.I.C.: 2399
N.A.I.C.S.: 315210

Ocean Lanka (Private) Limited (1)
Biyagama Export Processing Zone Block B
Walgama, Malwana, Western Province, Sri Lanka
Tel.: (94) 114827100
Fax: (94) 11 482 7131
E-Mail: info@oceanlanka.com
Web Site: www.oceanlanka.com
Weft Knitted Fabrics Mfr
S.I.C.: 2259
N.A.I.C.S.: 313240

Prosperlink (Macau Commercial Offshore) Limited (1)
Avenida Da Praia Grande No 599 Edificio Comml Rodrigues
5th Fl Unit B, Macau, China (Macau)
Tel.: (853) 83943000
Fax: (853) 28355007
E-Mail: ykli@hs.fshl.com
Yarn Dyestuffs Mfr & Sales
S.I.C.: 2299
N.A.I.C.S.: 313110

Shenzhen Faun Textiles Limited (1)
49 F Block A United Plz Caitian Rd
Futian, Shenzhen, Guangdong, 518026, China
Tel.: (86) 75582966188
Fax: (86) 75582945833
Fabrics & Dyed Yarn Sales
S.I.C.: 5131
N.A.I.C.S.: 424310

Yancheng Fuhui Textiles Limited (1)
No 38 Huang Shan South Rd Economic Development Zone
Yancheng, Jiangsu, 224045, China
Tel.: (86) 515 6866 3888
Fax: (86) 515 6866 3666
E-Mail: sales@ycfuhui.fshl.com
Web Site: www.fshl.com
Emp.: 1,000
Knitted Fabrics, Dyeing & Finishing Mfr
S.I.C.: 2259
N.A.I.C.S.: 313240

THE FOUNTAIN STUDIOS

128 Wembley Park Dr
Wembley, Middlesex, HA9 8HP, United Kingdom
Tel.: (44) 2089005800
Fax: (44) 2089005802
E-Mail: sales@ftv.co.uk
Web Site: www.ftv.co.uk
Year Founded: 1985
Emp.: 50
Business Description:
Television Broadcasting
S.I.C.: 4833
N.A.I.C.S.: 515120
Personnel:
Craig Church *(Dir-Tech)*

FOUNTAIN TIRE CORP.

8801 24th Street
Edmonton, AB, T6P 1L2, Canada
Tel.: (780) 464-3700
Fax: (780) 464-0920
Toll Free: (800) 222-6481
Web Site: www.fountaintire.com
Business Description:
Tire Distr
S.I.C.: 5014
N.A.I.C.S.: 441320
Personnel:
Brent Hesje *(CEO)*
Garry Paulson *(CFO)*
Board of Directors:
John T. Ferguson
Brent Hesje
Ian M. Reid
Michael Ross
Laura Thompson
Jack Winterton

FOUNTAINE PAJOT SA

Zone Industrielle
17290 Aigrefeuille-d'Aunis, France
Tel.: (33) 546 35 70 40
Fax: (33) 546 35 50 10
E-Mail: fountaine-pajot@fountaine-pajot.com
Web Site: www.fountaine-pajot.com
Year Founded: 1976
ALFPC—(EUR)
Business Description:
Cruising Catamaran Mfr
S.I.C.: 3732
N.A.I.C.S.: 336612
Personnel:
Jean-Francois Fountaine *(CEO)*

FOUNTAINVEST PARTNERS (ASIA) LIMITED

Ste 705 ICBC Tower 3 Garden Rd
Hong Kong, China (Hong Kong)
Tel.: (852) 39723900
Fax: (852) 31072490
E-Mail: enquiry@fountainvest.com
Web Site: www.fountainvest.com

Year Founded: 2007
Managed Assets: $100,000,000,000
Emp.: 30
Business Description:
Private Equity Firm
S.I.C.: 6211
N.A.I.C.S.: 523999
Personnel:
Frank Tang *(Co-Founder & CEO)*
George Chuang *(Co-Founder & Mng Dir)*
Terry Hu *(Co-Founder & Mng Dir)*
Chenning Zhao *(Co-Founder & Mng Dir)*

Non-U.S. Holding:

LANDWIND INTERNATIONAL MEDICAL SCIENCE PTE. LTD. (1)
75 Bukit Timah Road
06 12 Boon Siew Building, Singapore, 229833, Singapore (70%)
Tel.: (65) 6338 9456
Fax: (65) 6338 9327
E-Mail: sales@landwindmedical.com
Web Site: www.landwindmedical.com
Sales Range: $100-124.9 Million
Medical Diagnostic Imaging Equipment Mfr
S.I.C.: 3841
N.A.I.C.S.: 339112
Lihua Zhang *(Pres)*

FOUR COMMUNICATIONS GROUP PLC

The Communications Building 48 Leicester Square
London, WC2H 7FG, United Kingdom
Tel.: (44) 870 626 9000
Fax: (44) 870 626 9001
E-Mail: info@fourcommunications.com
Web Site: www.fourcommunications.com
Year Founded: 2001
Emp.: 150
Business Description:
Holding Company; Advertising Agencies
S.I.C.: 6719
N.A.I.C.S.: 551112
Personnel:
Chris O'Donoghue *(Chm)*
Nan Williams *(CEO)*
Tim Lewis *(Partner)*
Einir Williams *(Mng Dir)*
Alun James *(CEO-UK)*

Subsidiaries:

Four Communications plc (1)
The Communications Building 48 Leicester Square
London, WC2H 7FG, United Kingdom UK
Tel.: (44) 870 626 9000
Fax: (44) 870 626 9001
E-Mail: info@fourcommunications.com
Web Site: www.fourcommunications.com
Advertising Agency
S.I.C.: 7311
N.A.I.C.S.: 541810
Alun James *(CEO)*
Einir Williams *(Mng Dir)*

FOUR SEAS MERCANTILE HOLDINGS LIMITED

Four Seas Group Building No 1 Hong Ting Road
Sai Kung, China (Hong Kong)
Tel.: (852) 27999777
Fax: (852) 27992632
Web Site: www.fourseasgroup.com.hk
Year Founded: 1971
374—(HKG)
Rev.: $373,909,481
Assets: $317,911,396
Liabilities: $159,465,115
Net Worth: $158,446,281
Earnings: $13,823,827
Emp.: 4,100
Fiscal Year-end: 03/31/13
Business Description:
Snack Food Mfr
S.I.C.: 2052
N.A.I.C.S.: 311919
Personnel:
Stephen Tak Fung Tai *(Co-Founder & Chm)*
Quinly Mei Yung Wu *(Co-Founder & Mng Dir)*
Gibson Chi Ming Nam *(Sec)*
Board of Directors:
Stephen Tak Fung Tai
Peter Yuk Sang Chan
Tsunao Kijima
Mei Han Leung
Ellis Wing Cheung Man
Gibson Chi Ming Nam
Quinly Mei Yung Wu
Wing Biu Wu
Wai Keung Yip

Caledonian Trust (Cayman) Limited
Caledonian House 69 Dr Roys Drive
Georgetown, Cayman Islands
Transfer Agents:
Tricor Tengis Limited
26th Floor Tesbury Centre 28 Queen's Road East
Wanchai, China (Hong Kong)
Tel.: (852) 29801333
Fax: (852) 28108185

Caledonian Trust (Cayman) Limited
Caledonian House 69 Dr Roys Drive
Georgetown, Cayman Islands

Non-U.S. Subsidiaries:

Four Seas Confectionery (Shenzhen) Co., Ltd. (1)
75 Xin Guang Road Xiti Zhen Nanshan
Shenzhen, Guangdong, China 518055
Tel.: (86) 755 2662 3297
Fax: (86) 755 2662 3296
Confectionery Mfr
S.I.C.: 2064
N.A.I.C.S.: 311340

Ginbis Four Seas Foods (Shantou) Company Limited (1)
Inside Zhongfu Group Jinsheng 1st Rd
Shengping Industry Area Daxure Rd
Shantou, Guangdong, 515021, China
Tel.: (86) 754 8254 1380
Fax: (86) 754 8254 1943
Emp.: 80
Food & Beverage Mfr
S.I.C.: 2052
N.A.I.C.S.: 311919
Takashi Yamoto *(Gen Mgr)*

Kanro Four Seas Foods (Shantou) Company Limited (1)
Yuepu Industrial Park South
Shantou, Guangdong, China 515021
Tel.: (86) 754 8810 8811
Fax: (86) 754 8810 8866
Web Site: www.fourseasgroup.com.hk/pp_eng/factory.asp
Snack Food Mfr
S.I.C.: 2096
N.A.I.C.S.: 311919

Li Fook (Qingdao) Foods Company Limited (1)
Xixiaoshui Village
Cheng Yang District, Qingdao, Shandong, China 266107
Tel.: (86) 532 8787 1645
Fax: (86) 532 8787 1841
Web Site: www.fourseasgroup.com.hk/pp_eng/factory.asp
Snack Food Mfr
S.I.C.: 2096
N.A.I.C.S.: 311919

Nico Four Seas (Shantou) Company Limited (1)
Yuepu Industrial Park South
Shantou, Guangdong, China 515021
Tel.: (86) 754 8811 5519
Fax: (86) 754 8811 5523
Web Site: www.fourseasgroup.com.hk/pp_eng/factory.asp
Snack Food Mfr
S.I.C.: 2096
N.A.I.C.S.: 311919

Shenzhen Matchless Food Co., Ltd (1)
Building 1 Hebei Industrial District 1
Zhongxing Road Buji
Shenzhen, Guangdong, China 518129
Tel.: (86) 755 8471 5282
Fax: (86) 755 8419 5127
E-Mail: shenzhennqs@163.com
Emp.: 20
Snack Food Mfr
S.I.C.: 2096
N.A.I.C.S.: 311919
Ling Chiu Hui *(Gen Mgr)*

Tsun Fat (Hui Zhou) Biscuit Factory Limited (1)
Long Hu Industrial District Shui Kou
Huizhou, Guangdong, China 516005
Tel.: (86) 752 231 8637
Fax: (86) 752 231 7600
Web Site: www.fourseasgroup.com.hk/pp_eng/factory.asp
Emp.: 400
Snack Food Mfr
S.I.C.: 2052
N.A.I.C.S.: 311919
Shan Lu Leong *(Gen Mgr)*

FOUR WAY DISTRIBUTORS LTD.

11415 120st
Edmonton, AB, T5G 2Y3, Canada
Tel.: (780) 453-1005
Fax: (780) 451-2149
Toll Free: (877) 453-1005
E-Mail: fourway@fourwaydistributors.com
Web Site: www.fourwaydistributors.ca
Rev.: $10,575,760
Emp.: 27
Business Description:
Food Products Mfr
S.I.C.: 2099
N.A.I.C.S.: 311999
Personnel:
Dave Shumacher *(Pres)*

FOURLANE FORD SALES LTD.

4412 - 50th Street
Innisfail, AB, T4G 1P7, Canada
Tel.: (403) 227-3311
Fax: (403) 227-4544
Toll Free: (800) 895-4651
E-Mail: info@fourlaneford.com
Web Site: www.fourlaneford.com
Year Founded: 1993
Rev.: $15,607,717
Emp.: 33
Business Description:
New & Used Car Dealers
S.I.C.: 5511
N.A.I.C.S.: 441110
Personnel:
Jeff Denham *(Gen Mgr)*

FOURLIS HOLDINGS S.A.

340 Kifisias Ave
15451 Neo Psichico, Greece
Tel.: (30) 2106293000
Fax: (30) 2106773714
E-Mail: mail@fourlis.gr
Web Site: www.fourlis.gr
FOYRK—(ATH)
Rev.: $565,733,327
Assets: $621,894,193
Liabilities: $383,771,528
Net Worth: $238,122,665
Earnings: ($15,402,877)
Emp.: 3,531
Fiscal Year-end: 12/31/12
Business Description:
Fixed Assets & Real Estate Management Services
S.I.C.: 6531
N.A.I.C.S.: 531390
Personnel:
Vassileios Fourlis *(Chm)*
Dafni A. Fourlis *(Vice Chm)*
Apostolos D. Petalas *(CEO)*
Board of Directors:
Vassileios Fourlis
Ioannis Brebos
Ioannis Costopoulos
Dafni A. Fourlis
Lida Fourlis
Ioannis Lioupis
Ioannis K. Papaioannou
Apostolos D. Petalas
Eftihios Th. Vassilakis

Subsidiaries:

FOURLIS TRADE AEBE (1)
340 Kifisias Ave
Neo psychiko, 154 51 Athens, Greece
Tel.: (30) 2106293000
Fax: (30) 2106773713
E-Mail: mail@fourlistrade.gr
Web Site: www.fourlistrade.gr
Emp.: 50
Consumer Electronics Distr
S.I.C.: 5064
N.A.I.C.S.: 423620
Rigania R *(Sec)*

INTERSPORT ATHLETICS AE (1)
60 Varis Ave
Vari, 16672 Athens, Greece
Tel.: (30) 2102806000
Fax: (30) 2102806098
E-Mail: mail@intersport.gr
Web Site: www.intersport.gr
Emp.: 60
Sporting Goods Distr
S.I.C.: 5091
N.A.I.C.S.: 423910

Non-U.S. Subsidiaries:

GENCO BULGARIA LTD (1)
82 Boulevard Dondukov
1504 Sofia, Bulgaria
Tel.: (359) 29849858
Fax: (359) 2 943 4586
E-Mail: info@genco.bg
Web Site: www.genco.bg
Emp.: 50
Sporting Goods Mfr
S.I.C.: 3949
N.A.I.C.S.: 339920
Eugenia Radoslavova *(Mgr-Rep)*

GENCO TRADE SRL (1)
Strada Biharia Nr 67-77 Cladirea Metav Businsess Park
Sector 1, Bucharest, Romania
Tel.: (40) 212011180
Fax: (40) 212011187
E-Mail: office@genco.ro
Web Site: www.entersport.ro
Emp.: 350
Sporting Goods Distr
S.I.C.: 5091
N.A.I.C.S.: 423910
Ionas Ignatios *(Gen Mgr)*

FOURTH HOSPITALITY LTD.

(See Under Fourth Ltd.)

FOURTH LTD.

90 Long Acre Covent Garden
London, WC2E 9RA, United Kingdom
Tel.: (44) 2075343700
Fax: (44) 2075343701
E-Mail: sales@fourth.com
Web Site: www.fourth.com
Year Founded: 1999
Sales Range: $10-24.9 Million
Emp.: 250
Business Description:
Hospitality Industry Software Developer
S.I.C.: 7372
N.A.I.C.S.: 511210
Personnel:
Neville Davis *(Chm)*

Fourth Ltd.—(Continued)

Ben Hood *(CEO)*
Simon Bocca *(COO)*
Christian Berthelsen *(CTO)*
Steve Mansfield *(Chief Sls Officer)*
Board of Directors:
Neville Davis
Christian Berthelsen
Simon Bocca
James England
David Ewing
Stuart Goldblatt
Ben Hood
Steve Mansfield

FOV FABRICS AB

Norrby Langgata 45
PO Box 165
50308 Boras, Sweden
Tel.: (46) 33206300
Fax: (46) 33206350
E-Mail: info@fov.se
Web Site: www.fov.se
Emp.: 125
Business Description:
Manufactures Woven Fabrics
S.I.C.: 2299
N.A.I.C.S.: 313210
Personnel:
Mats Lundgren *(Mng Dir & Mgr-Mktg)*

FOWLER HYUNDAI LTD.

3900 Victoria Avenue West
Brandon, MB, R7B 3X3, Canada
Tel.: (204) 727-1461
Fax: (204) 726-4461
Toll Free: (800) 847-6518
Web Site: www.fowlerhyundai.ca
Year Founded: 1982
Sales Range: $10-24.9 Million
Emp.: 40
Business Description:
Car Dealers
S.I.C.: 5511
N.A.I.C.S.: 441110
Personnel:
Brian Fowler *(Principal)*

FOWLER PONTIAC BUICK GMC LTD.

(See Under Fowler Hyundai Ltd.)

FOX MARBLE HOLDINGS PLC

15 Kings Terrace
London, NW1 0JP, United Kingdom
Tel.: (44) 207 380 0999
Fax: (44) 207 380 0959
E-Mail: info@foxmarble.net
Web Site: www.foxmarble.net
Year Founded: 2011
FOX—(AIM)
Business Description:
Marble Quarrying
S.I.C.: 1429
N.A.I.C.S.: 212319
Personnel:
Andrew Allner *(Chm)*
Chris Gilbert *(CEO)*
Etrur Albani *(Mng Dir)*
Board of Directors:
Andrew Allner
Etrur Albani
Chris Gilbert
Fiona Hadfield
Roy Harrison
Paul Jourdan
Colin Terry

FOX RESOURCES LTD.

Level 1 9 Bowman Street
Perth, WA, 6151, Australia
Mailing Address:
PO Box 480
Perth, WA, 6951, Australia
Tel.: (61) 893185600
Fax: (61) 892381830
E-Mail: fxr@foxresources.com.au
Web Site: www.foxresources.com.au
FXR—(ASX)
Rev.: $2,044,858
Assets: $24,518,502
Liabilities: $14,716,075
Net Worth: $9,802,427
Earnings: ($19,517,017)
Fiscal Year-end: 06/30/13
Business Description:
Nickel & Copper Exploration Services
S.I.C.: 1021
N.A.I.C.S.: 212234
Personnel:
Paul Dunbar *(CEO & Mng Dir)*
Trish Farr *(Sec)*
Board of Directors:
Terence E. J. Streeter
James Cooper
Paul Dunbar
Garry N. East
Yulong Tian
Roderick White
Legal Counsel:
Kings Park Corporate
Suite 8 8 Clive Street
West Perth, WA, 6005, Australia
Subsidiary:

Fox Radio Hill Pty Ltd **(1)**
Po Box 1629
Karratha, Dampier, Western Australia, 6714, Australia
Tel.: (61) 891845188
Fax: (61) 891845199
E-Mail: reception@foxradiohill.com.au
Emp.: 15
Mining & Exploration Services
S.I.C.: 1081
N.A.I.C.S.: 213114
Larry Chew *(Gen Mgr-Project)*

FOX WIRE LIMITED

Sheephouse Wood
Stocksbridge, Sheffield, S36 4GS, United Kingdom
Tel.: (44) 1142884207
Fax: (44) 1142884874
E-Mail: info@foxwire.co.uk
Web Site: www.foxwire.co.uk
Year Founded: 1846
Sales Range: $10-24.9 Million
Emp.: 50
Business Description:
Stainless Steel & Nickel Alloy Wire Mfr
S.I.C.: 3496
N.A.I.C.S.: 332618
Personnel:
Oliver Baker *(Owner)*

FOXPOINT CAPITAL CORP.

(Name Changed to Castle Mountain Mining Company Limited)

FOXTONS GROUP PLC.

Building One Chiswick Park 566 Chiswick High Road
London, W4 5BE, United Kingdom
Tel.: (44) 20 7893 6310
E-Mail: corporate.services@foxtons.co.uk
Web Site: www.foxtons.co.uk
Year Founded: 1981
Sales Range: $50-74.9 Million
Emp.: 975
Business Description:
Real Estate Agency Services
S.I.C.: 6531
N.A.I.C.S.: 531210
Personnel:
Michael Brown *(CEO)*

FOYER S.A.

12 rue Leon Laval
3372 Leudelange, Luxembourg
Tel.: (352) 437 437
Fax: (352) 437 43 3466
E-Mail: contact@foyer.lu
Web Site: www.foyer.lu
Year Founded: 1922
FOY—(EUR)
Premiums: $5,802,882,518
Assets: $71,862,458,493
Liabilities: $62,452,701,923
Net Worth: $9,409,756,570
Earnings: $827,237,619
Emp.: 5,352
Fiscal Year-end: 12/31/12
Business Description:
General Insurance Services
S.I.C.: 6411
N.A.I.C.S.: 524298
Personnel:
Francois Tesch *(CEO)*
Marc Lauer *(COO)*
Board of Directors:
Henri Marx
Romain Becker
Marc Lauer
Dominique Laval
Paul Mousel
John Penning
Jacquot Schwertzer
Francois Tesch
Michel Tilmant
Carole Wintersdorff
Patrick Zurstrassen

FOYLE FOOD GROUP LTD.

Lisahally Campsie County
Londonderry, Northern Ireland, BT47 6TJ, United Kingdom
Tel.: (44) 2871 860691
Fax: (44) 2871 860700
E-Mail: info@foylefoodgroup.com
Web Site: www.foylefoodgroup.com
Year Founded: 1976
Sales Range: $350-399.9 Million
Emp.: 704
Business Description:
Meat Product Whslr
S.I.C.: 5147
N.A.I.C.S.: 424470
Personnel:
Ursula O'Neill *(Mgr-Group Technical)*

FOYSON RESOURCES LIMITED

Suite 703 Level 7 121 Walker Street
North Sydney, NSW, 2060, Australia
Tel.: (61) 2 8920 2300
Fax: (61) 2 8920 3400
E-Mail: info@foyson.net
Web Site: www.foyson.net
Year Founded: 1988
FOY—(ASX)
Rev.: $1,419,488
Assets: $26,895,482
Liabilities: $4,168,990
Net Worth: $22,726,492
Earnings: ($4,274,270)
Fiscal Year-end: 06/30/13
Business Description:
Mineral Exploration Services
S.I.C.: 1099
N.A.I.C.S.: 212299
Personnel:
Michael Palmer *(CEO)*
Aliceson Rourke *(Sec)*
Board of Directors:
Doug Halley
John Haggman
John Holliday
Legal Counsel:
Watson Mangioni Lawyers Pty Limited
Level 13, 50 Carrington Street
Sydney, Australia

FP CORPORATION

1-12-15 Akebono-cho Fukuyama-shi
Hiroshima, 721-8607, Japan
Tel.: (81) 849531145
Fax: (81) 849534911
E-Mail: ind@fpco-net.co.jp
Web Site: www.fpco.co.jp
Year Founded: 1962
7947—(TKS)
Sls.: $1,740,112,000
Assets: $1,894,860,000
Liabilities: $1,051,358,000
Net Worth: $843,502,000
Earnings: $97,317,000
Emp.: 3,977
Fiscal Year-end: 03/31/13
Business Description:
Foamed Polystyrene & Other Synthetic Resin Containers Mfr & Sales
S.I.C.: 2671
N.A.I.C.S.: 322220
Personnel:
Yasuhiro Komatsu *(Chm & CEO)*
Morimasa Sato *(Pres & COO)*
Taichiro Sasabe *(Exec VP & Head-Sls Div 1)*
Masateru Shimoda *(Exec VP & Head-Mfg Div)*
Isao Ikegami *(Sr VP & Head-Fin & Acctg Div)*
Makoto Kaneko *(Sr VP & Head-Gen Admin & HR Div)*
Tomoki Takanishi *(Sr VP & Head-Sls Div 2)*
Board of Directors:
Yasuhiro Komatsu
Yoshitaka Ezaki
Isao Ikegami
Makoto Kaneko
Nobuyuki Nagai
Koji Oka
Taichiro Sasabe
Morimasa Sato
Osamu Sato
Masateru Shimoda
Takejiro Sueyoshi
Masanobu Takahashi
Minoru Takahashi
Tomoki Takanishi
Yasuhiko Torikawa
Kazuyuki Yasuda
Subsidiaries:

ALRight Inc. **(1)**
2918-12 Nagase Mobira
Kasaoka, Okayama, 714-0062, Japan
Tel.: (81) 8 6566 3000
Fax: (81) 8 6566 3060
Disposable Food Containers Mfr
S.I.C.: 2099
N.A.I.C.S.: 311999

Cook Labo Co., Ltd. **(1)**
Oak Tower 6-8-1 Nishi-Shinjuku
Shinjuku-Ku, Tokyo, 160-0023, Japan
Tel.: (81) 353257502
Fax: (81) 353257755
Food Containers Mfr
S.I.C.: 2679
N.A.I.C.S.: 322299

Dia Foods Co., Ltd. **(1)**
1-9-26 Jonan
Osaka, Ikeda, 563-0025, Japan
Tel.: (81) 72 753 3330
Fax: (81) 72 753 5002
Web Site: www.diafoods.co.jp
Plastic Food Containers Mfr
S.I.C.: 2652
N.A.I.C.S.: 322219

Ducks Co. **(1)**
1108-1 Nodagou Togitsu-chou
Nishisonogi-gun, Nagasaki, 851-2104, Japan

Tel.: (81) 9 5882 0439
Fax: (81) 9 5882 5208
Web Site: www.fpco.jp
Plastic Food Containers Mfr
S.I.C.: 2652
N.A.I.C.S.: 322219

FP CHUPA Corp. (1)
6-8-1 Nishishinjuku Sumitomofudosan
Shinjuku Oak Tower 35F
Shinjuku-Ku, Tokyo, 163-6035, Japan
Tel.: (81) 353392274
Fax: (81) 333488024
Web Site: www.chupa.co.jp
Emp.: 200
Disposable Food Containers Mfr
S.I.C.: 2652
N.A.I.C.S.: 322219
Akazaki Shigeo *(Pres)*

FP Trading Co., Ltd. (1)
1-13-13 Akebonocho
Fukuyama, Hiroshima, 721-0952, Japan
Tel.: (81) 849547717
Fax: (81) 353250811
Emp.: 5
Plastic Food Containers Distr
S.I.C.: 5162
N.A.I.C.S.: 424610

FPCO Chubu Co. (1)
157-1 Shimoogure Wanouchicho
Ampachi-Gun, Gifu, 503-0205, Japan
Tel.: (81) 584692985
Fax: (81) 584692964
Emp.: 200
Disposable Food Containers Mfr
S.I.C.: 2652
N.A.I.C.S.: 322219
Toshikiyo Tabuchi *(Pres)*

FPCO Engineering, Ltd. (1)
1-12-15 Akebono-cho
Fukuyama-shi, Hiroshima, 721-8607, Japan
Tel.: (81) 849531145
Web Site: www.fpco.co.jp/English/com_gai.html
Engineering & Manufacturing Services
S.I.C.: 8711
N.A.I.C.S.: 541330
Masateru Shimoda *(Exec VP & Head-Mfg Div)*

FPCO Fukuyama Co. (1)
456-36 Minoshima-cho
Fukuyama, Hiroshima, 721-0957, Japan
Tel.: (81) 849538273
Plastic Food Containers Mfr
S.I.C.: 3086
N.A.I.C.S.: 326140

FPCO Kasaoka Co. (1)
100-1 Mochinoe
Kasaoka, Okayama, 714-0066, Japan
Tel.: (81) 865665060
Plastic Food Containers Mfr
S.I.C.: 2652
N.A.I.C.S.: 322219

FPCO Minoshima Co. (1)
95-6 Minooki-cho
Fukuyama, Hiroshima, 721-0956, Japan
Tel.: (81) 849538849
Fax: (81) 849545854
Plastic Food Containers Mfr
S.I.C.: 2652
N.A.I.C.S.: 322219

FPCO Saga Co, Ltd. (1)
1830-1 Ishinari
Yoshinogaricho Kanzaki-Gun, Saga, Japan
Tel.: (81) 952527877
Fax: (81) 952527876
Web Site: www.fpco.jp
Emp.: 80
Plastics Product Mfr
S.I.C.: 3089
N.A.I.C.S.: 326199

FPCO Shimodate, Ltd. (1)
411 Nishiyamada
Chikusei, Ibaraki, 308-0867, Japan
Tel.: (81) 296232545
Disposable Food Containers Mfr
S.I.C.: 2652
N.A.I.C.S.: 322219

FPCO Yamagata, Ltd. (1)
162 Chuokogyodanchi
Sagae, Yamagata, 991-0061, Japan
Tel.: (81) 237853600
Fax: (81) 237855535
Emp.: 300
Disposable Food Containers Mfr
S.I.C.: 3086
N.A.I.C.S.: 326140
Jo Masaaki *(Gen Mgr)*

I-Logic Co., Ltd. (1)
Shinjuku Oak Tower 36F 6-8-1 Nishishinjuku
Shinjuku-ku, Tokyo, 160-0023, Japan
Tel.: (81) 353257750
Fax: (81) 3 5325 7754
Logistics & Distribution Services
S.I.C.: 4731
N.A.I.C.S.: 541614
Satoshi Koizumi *(Pres)*

Nodaya, Ltd. (1)
1-3-11 Nankoudaiminami
Izumi-ku, Sendai, Miyagi, 981-8002, Japan
Tel.: (81) 222510748
Fax: (81) 222510765
Plastic Food Containers Mfr
S.I.C.: 2652
N.A.I.C.S.: 322219

Teika-Precision Co. (1)
12 8th Inokurashiroyama Miyazaki-cho
Kameoka, Kyoto, 621-0241, Japan
Tel.: (81) 771265115
Fax: (81) 771 26 5115
E-Mail: info@teika-precision.co.jp
Web Site: www.teika-precision.co.jp
Injection Molded Plastic Products Mfr
S.I.C.: 3089
N.A.I.C.S.: 326199

Plants:

FP Corporation - Fukuyama Plant (1)
1-12-15 Akebono-cho
Fukuyama, Hiroshima, 721-0952, Japan
Tel.: (81) 849531145
Fax: (81) 849534911
Web Site: www.fpco.jp
Emp.: 695
Disposable Food Containers Mfr
S.I.C.: 2652
N.A.I.C.S.: 322219
Morimasa Sato *(Pres)*

FP Corporation - Hokkaido Plant (1)
15-1-1 Kita 42 Johigashi
Higashi-ku, Sapporo, Hokkaido, 007-0842, Japan
Tel.: (81) 117515339
Fax: (81) 117515319
Web Site: www.fpcorp.co.jp
Emp.: 300
Plastic Food Containers Mfr
S.I.C.: 2652
N.A.I.C.S.: 322219

FP NEWSPAPERS INC.

650 West Georgia Street Suite 2900
PO Box 11583
Vancouver, BC, V6B 4N8, Canada
Tel.: (204) 697-7425
Fax: (204) 632-0281
Web Site: www.fpnewspapers.com
Year Founded: 1872
FP—(TSX)
Rev.: $7,246,406
Assets: $45,572,835
Liabilities: $3,891,588
Net Worth: $41,681,247
Earnings: $5,124,173
Emp.: 442
Fiscal Year-end: 12/30/12

Business Description:
Newspaper Publisher & Distr
S.I.C.: 2711
N.A.I.C.S.: 511110

Personnel:
Ronald N. Stern *(Chm & CEO)*
Daniel M. Koshowski *(CFO & VP-Fin & Admin-FPLP)*

Board of Directors:
Ronald N. Stern
Phil de Montmollin
G. Stephen Dembroski
Daniel M. Koshowski
Harvey Secter
Robert Silver

Transfer Agent:
CIBC Mellon Trust Company
PO Box 7010
Adelaide Street Postal Station, Toronto, ON, M5C 2W9, Canada
Tel.: (416) 643-5500
Fax: (416) 643-5501
Toll Free: (800) 387-0825

Subsidiary:

FP Canadian Newspapers Limited Partnership (1)
1355 Mountain Ave
Winnipeg, MB, R2X 3B6, Canada
Tel.: (204) 697-7000
Fax: (204) 697-7412
Web Site: www.fpnewspapers.com
Newspaper Publisher
S.I.C.: 2711
N.A.I.C.S.: 511110
Ronald N. Stern *(Chm)*

F.P.I. FERRARA PROMOZIONE INDUSTRIALE SRL

Via Romolo Gessi 15
44124 Ferrara, Italy
Tel.: (39) 532733731
Fax: (39) 0532733767
Web Site:
Year Founded: 1946
Sales Range: $125-149.9 Million
Emp.: 300

Business Description:
Mfr of Alloy Wheels for Motor Vehicles & Motorcycles
S.I.C.: 3714
N.A.I.C.S.: 336390

FPI FIREPLACE PRODUCTS INTERNATIONAL LTD.

6988 Venture Street
Delta, BC, Canada V4G 1H4
Tel.: (604) 946-5155
Fax: (604) 946-4349
Web Site: www.regency-fire.com
Year Founded: 1979
Rev.: $54,600,000
Emp.: 400

Business Description:
Woodstove Products Mfr
S.I.C.: 2499
N.A.I.C.S.: 321999

Personnel:
Robert Little *(Founder)*
Anthony Woodruff *(Pres)*

FPS FOOD PROCESSING SYSTEMS B.V.

Burgemeester G.J.F. Tijdemanstraat 13
2631 RE Pijnacker, Netherlands
Tel.: (31) 153107757
Fax: (31) 153107387
Web Site: www.fpsholding.nl/

Business Description:
Holding Company
S.I.C.: 6719
N.A.I.C.S.: 551112

Personnel:
J. J. Gras *(CEO)*
J. J. de Bruijn *(CFO)*

Subsidiaries:

AWETA Holding B.V. (1)
Burgemeester Winkellaan 3
2631 HG Pijnacker, Netherlands
Mailing Address:
PO Box 17
2630 AA Pijnacker, Netherlands
Tel.: (31) 153109961
Fax: (31) 153107321
E-Mail: sales@aweta.nl
Web Site: www.aweta.nl
Emp.: 120
Holding Company
S.I.C.: 6719
N.A.I.C.S.: 551112
Rin Alleblas *(Mgr-Mktg)*

Subsidiary:

AWETA G&P (2)
Buremeester Winkelaan 3
2631 HG Pijnacker, Netherlands
Tel.: (31) 153109961
Fax: (31) 886688002
E-Mail: sales@aweta.nl
Web Site: www.aweta.com
Emp.: 120
Commercial Machinery
S.I.C.: 3589
N.A.I.C.S.: 333318
J. I. Delcasse *(Mng Dir)*

U.S. Subsidiary:

AWETA -Autoline, Inc, (2)
621 West J St
Yakima, WA 98902
Tel.: (509) 248-8200
Fax: (509) 248-8599
E-Mail: salesaas@aweta.us
Web Site: www.aweta.com
Emp.: 100
Food Grading & Packing Equipment
S.I.C.: 3523
N.A.I.C.S.: 333111
Steve Hert *(Gen Mgr)*

Non-U.S. Subsidiaries:

AWETA FRANCE S.A.S. (2)
Chemin du Cou
Lagnes, 84800 Avignon, France
Tel.: (33) 490882166
Fax: (33) 490889127
E-Mail: salesfr@aweta.com
Web Site: www.aweta.com
Emp.: 6
Food Handling Sales, Engineering & Services
S.I.C.: 2099
N.A.I.C.S.: 311999
Andre Coffre *(Dir-Fin)*

AWETA Sistemi S.p.A. (2)
Via A Olivetti 79
47023 Cesena, Italy
Tel.: (39) 0547316900
Fax: (39) 0547316927
E-Mail: sales@aweta.it
Web Site: www.aweta.nl
Emp.: 60
Food Handling Equipment
S.I.C.: 3523
N.A.I.C.S.: 333111
Marco Pozzi *(Gen Mgr)*

MOBA B.V. (1)
PO Box 7
Stationsweg 117, 3770 AA Barneveld, Netherlands
Tel.: (31) 342455655
Fax: (31) 342455634
E-Mail: sales@moba.nl
Web Site: www.moba.nl
Emp.: 300
Egg Grading, Packing & Peripheral Equipment
S.I.C.: 3523
N.A.I.C.S.: 333111
P. Da Neef *(Gen Mgr)*

U.S. Subsidiaries:

Diamond Automations Inc. (1)
23400 Haggerty Rd
Farmington Hills, MI 48335
Tel.: (248) 476-7100
Fax: (248) 476-0848
Web Site: www.dma-group.com
Emp.: 120
Egg Grading & Packing Equipment
S.I.C.: 3523
N.A.I.C.S.: 333111
Douglas Mack *(Pres)*

OvoPro (1)
23400 Haggerty Rd
Farmington Hills, MI 48335
Tel.: (248) 476-3876
Fax: (248) 476-0849
E-Mail: info@ovopro.com
Web Site: www.ovopro.com
Emp.: 120

FPS Food Processing Systems B.V.—(Continued)

Egg Processing
S.I.C.: 0252
N.A.I.C.S.: 112310
Douglas Mack *(CEO)*

Non-U.S. Subsidiaries:

Jamesway Incubator Company Inc. **(1)**
30 High Rdg Ct
Cambridge, ON, N1R 7L3, Canada ON
Tel.: (519) 624-4646
Fax: (519) 624-5803
Toll Free: (800) 203-2299
Web Site: www.jamesway.com
Emp.: 80
Farm Machinery Equipment & Incubators Mfr
S.I.C.: 3523
N.A.I.C.S.: 333111
I. MacKinnon *(Pres)*

Petersime N.V. **(1)**
Centrumstraat 125
9870 Zulte, Belgium
Tel.: (32) 93889611
Fax: (32) 93888458
E-Mail: info@petersime.com
Web Site: www.petersime.com
Emp.: 150
Poultry Machinery
S.I.C.: 3523
N.A.I.C.S.: 333111
Michell Declercq *(Mng Dir)*

FPT CORPORATION

FPT Cau Giay Building Duy Tan Street Pham Hung Road
Cau Giay District, Hanoi, Vietnam
Tel.: (84) 4 73007300
Fax: (84) 4 73007388
E-Mail: ir@fpt.com.vn
Web Site: www.fpt.com.vn
FPT—(HOSE)
Sls.: $1,231,204,254
Assets: $710,459,131
Liabilities: $355,746,030
Net Worth: $354,713,101
Earnings: $99,274,342
Emp.: 11,209
Fiscal Year-end: 12/31/12

Business Description:
Software Development Services
S.I.C.: 7371
N.A.I.C.S.: 541511

Personnel:
Gia Binh Truong *(Chm)*
Viet Thang Thang *(Chm-Supervisory Bd)*
Thi Thanh Ha Chu *(Member-Mgmt Bd & Vice Gen Dir)*

Board of Directors:
Gia Binh Truong
Jean Cherles Belliol
Cao Bao Do
Nu Thuy Duong Le
Song Lai Le

Supervisory Board of Directors:
Viet Thang Thang
Duy Ha Cao
Khai Hoan Nguyen

Subsidiaries:

FPT Digital Retail Joint Stock Company **(1)**
263 Khanh Hoi quan 4 Tp
Ho Chi Minh City, Vietnam
Tel.: (84) 8 7302 6666
Computer Hardware Retailer
S.I.C.: 5734
N.A.I.C.S.: 443142

FPT Education Company Limited **(1)**
FPT Cau Giay Building Block B2
Cau Giay District, Hanoi, Vietnam
Tel.: (84) 473007300
Educational Support Services
S.I.C.: 8299
N.A.I.C.S.: 611710

FPT Informatics Services Company Limited **(1)**
198 Thai Thinh Street
Dong Da District, Hanoi, Vietnam
Tel.: (84) 4 3514 9232
Information Technology Consulting Services
S.I.C.: 7373
N.A.I.C.S.: 541512
Le Manh Thang, *(Gen Dir)*

FPT Online Services Joint Stock Company **(1)**
153 Nguyen Dinh Chieu Phuong 6 Quan 3
Ho Chi Minh City, Vietnam
Tel.: (84) 8 7300 9999
Fax: (84) 8 3 929 1758
E-Mail: fptonline@fpt.com.vn
Web Site: www.fptonline.net
Online Entertainment Services
S.I.C.: 2741
N.A.I.C.S.: 519130
Thang Duc Thang *(Chm)*
Chu Thi Thanh Ha *(Vice Chm)*
Nguyen Dac Viet Dung *(CEO)*
Le Ngoc *(CFO)*
Pham Cong Hoang *(Exec VP)*
Tran Thi Thu Trang *(Exec VP)*

FPT SERVICE Co., Ltd **(1)**
So 25 ngo 68 duong Cau Giay
Quan Cau Giay, Hanoi, Vietnam
Tel.: (84) 4 73000911
Information Technology Consulting Services
S.I.C.: 7373
N.A.I.C.S.: 541512

FPT Telecom Joint Stock Company **(1)**
FPT Building Duy Tan street
Cau Giay District, Hanoi, Vietnam
Tel.: (84) 4 7300 2222
Fax: (84) 4 7300 8889
Web Site: www.fpt.net
Emp.: 2,300
Internet & Telecommunication Services
S.I.C.: 4899
N.A.I.C.S.: 517919
Truong Dinh Anh, *(Chm)*
Chu Thi Thanh Ha *(CEO)*

FR. KAISER GMBH

Bahnhofstrasse 35
71332 Waiblingen, Germany
Tel.: (49) 715117150
Fax: (49) 7151171530
E-Mail: info@kaiser-candy.de
Web Site: www.kaiser-candy.de
Year Founded: 1889
Rev.: $21,712,182
Emp.: 117

Business Description:
Candy Mfr
S.I.C.: 2066
N.A.I.C.S.: 311351

Personnel:
Thomas Updike *(Mng Dir)*

FRACTURECODE CORPORATION APS

Amager Strandvej 390 2 etage
2770 Kastrup, Denmark
Tel.: (45) 88960150
E-Mail: info@fracturecode.com
Web Site: www.fracturecode.com
Year Founded: 2001
Emp.: 20

Business Description:
Product Authentication, Identification & Tracking Solutions
S.I.C.: 7372
N.A.I.C.S.: 511210

Personnel:
Jacob Juul Rasmussen *(Mng Dir)*

FRAGOL BETEILIGUNGS GMBH + CO.KG

Solingerstrasse 16 45481
D 45470 Mulheim an der Ruhr, Germany

Mailing Address:
PO Box 10 03 65
D-45403 Mulheim an der Ruhr, Germany
Tel.: (49) 208300020
E-Mail: info@fragol.de
Web Site: www.fragol.de
Rev.: $46,014,968
Emp.: 20

Business Description:
Mineral & Lubricating Oils Mfr
S.I.C.: 2992
N.A.I.C.S.: 324191

Personnel:
Heinel Miske *(Pres)*

FRAGRANCE GROUP LTD

Fragrance Building 168 Changi Rd 05-01
Singapore, 419730, Singapore
Tel.: (65) 63466888
Fax: (65) 63466120
E-Mail: contact@fragrancegroup.com.sg
Web Site: www.fragrancegroup.com.sg
F31—(SES)
Rev.: $339,810,551
Assets: $2,012,113,097
Liabilities: $1,123,184,048
Net Worth: $888,929,049
Earnings: $102,038,303
Fiscal Year-end: 12/31/12

Business Description:
Property Development & Hotel Operation Services
S.I.C.: 6531
N.A.I.C.S.: 531311

Personnel:
Wee Meng Koh *(Chm & CEO)*
Periakaruppan Aravindan *(Co-Sec)*
Keloth Raj Kumar *(Co-Sec)*

Board of Directors:
Wee Meng Koh
Periakaruppan Aravindan
Wan Looi Lim
Man Tang
Cheng Kuang Teo
Kum Kuan Watt

Transfer Agent:
Tricor Barbinder Share Registration Services
80 Robinson Road 02-00
Singapore, Singapore

Subsidiaries:

Fragrance Hotel Management Pte Ltd **(1)**
168 Changi Road Unit 04-01 Fragrance Building
Singapore, 419730, Singapore
Tel.: (65) 63456116
Fax: (65) 63453433
E-Mail: contact@fragrancehotel.com
Web Site: www.fragrancehotel.com
Emp.: 120
Hotel Management Services
S.I.C.: 7011
N.A.I.C.S.: 721110

Fragrance Land Pte Ltd **(1)**
101 Joo Chiat Road 01-01 Fragrance Centre
Singapore, Singapore
Tel.: (65) 63466888
Fax: (65) 63466129
Residential Property Development Services
S.I.C.: 6531
N.A.I.C.S.: 531390

FRAM EXPLORATION ASA

Kjopmannsgata 37
PO Box 2702
Sentrum, 7415 Trondheim, Norway
Tel.: (47) 40006522
Fax: (47) 40006523
E-Mail: post@framexploration.no
Web Site: www.framexploration.no
Year Founded: 2007
Rev.: $2,219,129
Assets: $45,255,932
Liabilities: $30,800,814
Net Worth: $14,455,118
Earnings: ($9,628,701)
Emp.: 9
Fiscal Year-end: 12/31/12

Business Description:
Oil & Gas Exploration & Production Services
S.I.C.: 1311
N.A.I.C.S.: 211111

Personnel:
Bernt Osthus *(Chm)*
Stig Aleksander Aune *(CEO)*
Martin Lein Staveli *(CFO)*
David Cook *(Gen Counsel & VP-Land)*

Board of Directors:
Bernt Osthus
Maria Henry
Odd Hjelmeland
Kristin Jorstad
Ola Lyngstad

FRAMATEQ S.A.S.

(d/b/a Framateq Sud Est)
16 Avenue de Rome
BP 32043
Vitrapole, 13845 Vitrolles, Cedex, France
Tel.: (33) 4 4277 0313
Fax: (33) 4 4289 9936
Web Site: www.framateq.net
Sales Range: $10-24.9 Million
Emp.: 30

Business Description:
Construction & Mining Equipment Distr
S.I.C.: 5082
N.A.I.C.S.: 423810

Personnel:
Murielle Perrin *(Dir-Mktg)*

FRAMESI S.P.A.

Tricologia Scientifica SS dei Giovi 135
Paderno Dugnano, IT-20037 Milan, Italy
Tel.: (39) 0299040441
Fax: (39) 029101318
E-Mail: framesi@framesi.it
Web Site: www.framesi.it
Year Founded: 1945

Business Description:
Professional Hair Care Products Mfr & Salon Consultancy Services
S.I.C.: 2844
N.A.I.C.S.: 325620

Personnel:
Fabio Franchina *(Pres)*

U.S. Affiliate:

Framesi USA, Inc. **(1)**
17 Ave Ste A
Leetsdale, PA 15056-1304 DE
Tel.: (412) 269-2950
Fax: (412) 264-5696
Toll Free: (800) 321-9648
Sales Range: $25-49.9 Million
Emp.: 20
Hair Care Products Distr
Import Export
S.I.C.: 5122
N.A.I.C.S.: 424210
Dennis Katawczik *(Pres)*

FRAMOS GMBH

Zugspitzstr 5 Haus C
82049 Pullach, Germany
Tel.: (49) 897106670
Fax: (49) 8971066766
E-Mail: info@framos.de
Web Site: www.framos.eu
Year Founded: 1981

Rev.: $13,794,000
Emp.: 18
Business Description:
Image Processing Technology Support Services
S.I.C.: 7389
N.A.I.C.S.: 561990
Personnel:
Bernd Franz *(Founder, Chm & Mng Dir)*
Andreas Franz *(CEO)*
Hildegard Franz *(Mng Dir)*

FRANCE BED HOLDINGS CO. LTD.

Shinjuku Square Tower 6F 6-22-1 Nishishinjuku
Shinjuku ku, Tokyo, 1690073, Japan
Tel.: (81) 367415501
Web Site: www.francebed-hd.co.jp
7840—(TKS)
Sls.: $558,965,000
Assets: $671,231,000
Liabilities: $272,943,000
Net Worth: $398,288,000
Earnings: $12,430,000
Emp.: 1,530
Fiscal Year-end: 03/31/13
Business Description:
Beds and Furniture Mfr
S.I.C.: 2421
N.A.I.C.S.: 321912
Personnel:
Shigeru Ikeda *(Pres & CEO)*
Kotaro Hoshikawa *(CFO)*
Board of Directors:
Satoru Higashijima
Kotaro Hoshikawa
Shigeru Ikeda
Tsutomu Shimada
Takashi Ueda
Transfer Agent:
Mitsubishi UFJ Trust & Banking Corporation
7-10-11 Higashisuna Koto-ku
Tokyo, Japan

Subsidiary:

Francebed Co., Ltd. **(1)**
1-25-1 Hyakunincho
Shinjuku-ku, Tokyo, 169-0073, Japan
Tel.: (81) 353381011
Fax: (81) 353381014
E-Mail: francebed@francebed.jp
Web Site: www.francebed.co.jp
Emp.: 1,499
Bed Linen Whslr & Mfr
S.I.C.: 2299
N.A.I.C.S.: 313210
Shigeru Ikeda *(Pres)*

Subsidiaries:

AD Center Co., Ltd. **(2)**
1-2-1 Kikunodai
Chofu, Tokyo, 182 0007, Japan
Tel.: (81) 424430431
Fax: (81) 424430432
E-Mail: info@fb-ad.co.jp
Web Site: www.fb-ad.co.jp
Emp.: 30
Advertising Agencies
S.I.C.: 7311
N.A.I.C.S.: 541810
Noguchi Hiroshe *(Pres)*

Francebed Sales Co., Ltd. **(2)**
1-25-1 Hyakunincho
Shinjuku-ku, Tokyo, 169-0073, Japan
Tel.: (81) 333632251
E-Mail: francebed@fb.bed.co.jp
Web Site: www.francebed-sales.com
Emp.: 138
Furnitures Mfr & Whslr
S.I.C.: 2599
N.A.I.C.S.: 337215
Tiba Toshiyuki *(Pres & CEO)*

Tokyo Bed Co., Ltd. **(2)**
4-1-16 Roppongi
Minato-ku, 106-0032 Tokyo, Japan
Tel.: (81) 335838521
Fax: (81) 335866617
E-Mail: info@tokyo-bed.co.jp
Web Site: www.tokyo-bed.co.jp
Emp.: 66
Bedroom Furnitures Mfr & Whslr
S.I.C.: 2511
N.A.I.C.S.: 337122
Kazumi Ikeda *(Pres)*

FRANCE TELECOM SA

(Name Changed to Orange S.A.)

FRANCESCO PARISI S.P.A.

Viale Miramare 5
34135 Trieste, Italy
Tel.: (39) 404193111
Telex: 460171 (PARISI I)
Fax: (39) 04044263
E-Mail: trsinfo@francescoparisi.com
Web Site: www.francescoparisi.com
Year Founded: 1807
Sales Range: $50-74.9 Million
Emp.: 500
Business Description:
International Shipping & Freight Forwarding
S.I.C.: 4731
N.A.I.C.S.: 488510
Branches:

Francesco Parisi S.p.A. - Fernetti **(1)**
Autoporto Doganale
I 34016 Fernetti, TS, Italy
Tel.: (39) 0402176901
Telex: 460526 PARISI I
Fax: (39) 0402176886
E-Mail: trsborder@francescoparisi.com
Web Site: www.francescoparisi.com
Emp.: 100
International Rail & Truck Transports, Air & Sea Shipments, Storage & Distribution
S.I.C.: 4226
N.A.I.C.S.: 493190

Francesco Parisi S.p.A. - Genoa **(1)**
Via Bruzzo 7
16162 Genoa, GE, Italy
Tel.: (39) 0107411352
E-Mail: genoa@francescoparisi.com
Web Site: www.francescoparisi.com
Emp.: 20
International Rail & Truck Transports, Air & Sea Shipments, Storage & Distribution
S.I.C.: 4226
N.A.I.C.S.: 493190

Francesco Parisi S.p.A. - Gorizia **(1)**
Stazione Confinaria di San Andrea
PO Box 33
34170 Gorizia, GO, Italy
Tel.: (39) 0481521966
Telex: 460286 PARISI I
Fax: (39) 048120292
E-Mail: gorizia@francescoparisi.com
Web Site: www.francescoparisi.com
International Rail & Truck Transports, Air & Sea Shipments, Storage & Distribution
S.I.C.: 4226
N.A.I.C.S.: 493190

Francesco Parisi S.p.A. - Livorno **(1)**
Via Delle Cateratte 110
57100 Livorno, LI, Italy
Tel.: (39) 0586942577
Telex: 500037 PARISI I
Fax: (39) 0586942050
E-Mail: leghorn@francescoparisi.com
Web Site: www.francescoparisi.com
Emp.: 60
International Rail & Truck Transports, Air & Sea Shipments, Storage & Distribution
S.I.C.: 4226
N.A.I.C.S.: 493190
Tomaso Parisi *(Mgr)*

Francesco Parisi S.p.A. - Milano **(1)**
Via Londra 46/48/50
20090 Segrate, MI, Italy
Mailing Address:
PO Box 3797
20100 Milan, MI, Italy
Tel.: (39) 0292393311
Telex: 330271 PARISI I
Fax: (39) 02 9239 333
E-Mail: milan@francescoparisi.com
Web Site: www.francescoparisi.com
Emp.: 25
International Rail & Truck Transports, Air & Sea Shipments, Storage & Distribution
S.I.C.: 4226
N.A.I.C.S.: 493190

Francesco Parisi S.p.A. - Monfalcone **(1)**
Via delle Terme Romane 5
34074 Monfalcone, GO, Italy
Tel.: (39) 048140539
Telex: 460171 PARISI I
Fax: (39) 0481798876
E-Mail: monfalcone@franescoparisi.com
Web Site: www.francescoparisi.com
International Rail & Truck Transports, Air & Sea Shipments
S.I.C.: 4449
N.A.I.C.S.: 483211

Francesco Parisi S.p.A. - Pontebba **(1)**
Autoporto Doganale di San Leopoldo
PO Box 59
32030 Pontebba, UD, Italy
Tel.: (39) 042890271
Fax: (39) 042890194
E-Mail: pontebba@francescoparisi.com
Web Site: www.francescoparisi.com
Emp.: 3
International Rail & Truck Transports, Air & Sea Shipments
S.I.C.: 4449
N.A.I.C.S.: 483211
Francesco Parisi *(Gen Mgr)*

Francesco Parisi S.p.A. - Ronchi dei Legionari **(1)**
Aeroporto Friuli Venezia Giulia
34077 Ronchi dei Legionari, GO, Italy
Tel.: (39) 0481474913
Fax: (39) 0481474911
E-Mail: trsairport@francescoparisi.com
International Rail & Truck Transports, Air & Sea Shipments
S.I.C.: 4449
N.A.I.C.S.: 483211

Francesco Parisi S.p.A. - Sedico **(1)**
Agenzia Doganale Via Segusini 8
32030 Sedico, BL, Italy
Tel.: (39) 0043783627
Telex: 410027 PARISI I
Fax: (39) 0437852317
Web Site: www.francescoparisi.com
Emp.: 30
International Rail & Truck Transports, Air & Sea Shipments
S.I.C.: 4449
N.A.I.C.S.: 483211

Francesco Parisi S.p.A. - Venezia-Mestre **(1)**
Via Torino 65
Venezia-Mestre, I-30172 Venice, VE, Italy
Mailing Address:
PO Box 515
30170 Venice, Italy
Tel.: (39) 0412907511
Telex: 410027 PARISI I
Fax: (39) 0415317799
E-Mail: venice@francescoparisi.com
Emp.: 25
International Rail & Truck Transportation & Air & Sea Shipments
S.I.C.: 4449
N.A.I.C.S.: 483211
Francesco Parisi *(Mgr)*

Non-U.S. Subsidiaries:

Francesco Parisi GmbH **(1)**
Prinzregentenstrasse 83
81675 Munich, D81675, Germany (100%)
Tel.: (49) 899038951
Telex: 722022 FRAPA D
Fax: (49) 899044019
E-Mail: parisi-muc@t-online.de
Web Site: www.francescoparisi.com
Emp.: 10
International Rail & Truck Transports, Air & Sea Shipments
S.I.C.: 4449
N.A.I.C.S.: 483211

Branch:

Francesco Parisi GmbH - Cologne **(2)**
Friesenwall 53
50672 Cologne, Germany
Mailing Address:
PO Box 19 04 51
50501 Cologne, Germany
Tel.: (49) 2212570231
Telex: 8882521 FRAP D
Fax: (49) 221251320
E-Mail: office@parisi-cologne.de
Web Site: www.frenchescoparisi.com
Emp.: 4
International Rail & Truck Transports, Air & Sea Shipments
S.I.C.: 4449
N.A.I.C.S.: 483211
Gregorio Graf Balbo Gi Vinadio *(CEO)*
Horst Lrux *(Mng Dir)*

Francesco Parisi S.a.g.l. **(1)**
Via Soldini 13
PO Box 1547
6830 Chiasso, Ticino, Switzerland (100%)
Tel.: (41) 916837585
Telex: 842522 FPA CH
Fax: (41) 916838530
E-Mail: info@parisi-ch.ch
Web Site: www.parisi-ch.ch
Emp.: 10
International Rail & Truck Transports, Air & Sea Shipments
S.I.C.: 4449
N.A.I.C.S.: 483211
Francesco Parisi *(Pres)*

Parisi Air & Sea Cargo Ges.m.b.H. **(1)**
Liesinger Flur-Gasse 5
1230 Vienna, Austria
Mailing Address:
P.O. Box 69
A-1103 Vienna, Austria
Tel.: (43) 1 7007 33619
Fax: (43) 160116120
E-Mail: office@parisi.at
Web Site: www.parisi.at
Rev.: $100,647,440
Emp.: 30
International Rail & Truck Transports, Air & Sea Shipments
S.I.C.: 4449
N.A.I.C.S.: 483211

Branch:

Parisi Air & Sea Cargo Ges.m.b.H. - Vienna Airport Office **(2)**
Building 263 Entrance 3 1st Floor Room 135
Vienna Airport, 1300 Vienna, Austria
Tel.: (43) 1700733619
Fax: (43) 1700733443
Web Site: www.parisi.at/eng/kontakte.html
Sales Range: $10-24.9 Million
Emp.: 9
Air Freight & Sea Freight
S.I.C.: 4226
N.A.I.C.S.: 493190

FRANCHISE BANCORP INC.

2-294 Walker Drive
Brampton, ON, L6T 4Z2, Canada
Tel.: (905) 790-9023
Fax: (905) 790-7059
Toll Free: (866) 463-4124
E-Mail: info@franchisebancorp.com
Web Site: www.franchisebancorp.com
Year Founded: 1995
FBI—(TSXV)
Rev.: $13,996,662
Assets: $5,926,362
Liabilities: $2,718,152
Net Worth: $3,208,210
Earnings: $308,700
Emp.: 18
Fiscal Year-end: 08/31/13
Business Description:
Diversified Franchisor
S.I.C.: 6794
N.A.I.C.S.: 533110

Franchise Bancorp Inc.—(Continued)

Personnel:
Edward Kenneth Loyst *(Chm & CEO)*
Paul A. Thomson *(Pres, CFO & Sec)*
Board of Directors:
Edward Kenneth Loyst
Philip G. Barnes
Dino Fragaglia
Ronald Saint-Martin
Paul A. Thomson
James A. Walker
Transfer Agent:
Equity Financial Trust Company
Suite 400 200 University Avenue
Toronto, ON, M5H 4H1, Canada

Subsidiaries:

Franchise Bancorp Consulting Ltd. (1)
294 Walker Drive Unit 2
Brampton, ON, L6T 4Z2, Canada
Tel.: (905) 790-9023
Fax: (905) 790-7059
Web Site: www.franchisebancorp.com
Emp.: 25
Franchise Marketing & Sales Consulting
S.I.C.: 8742
N.A.I.C.S.: 541613

Global Pet Food Stores Inc. (1)
294 Walker Dr Unit 2
Brampton, ON, L6T 4Z2, Canada
Tel.: (902) 681-0757
Fax: (902) 681-0757
Web Site: www.globalpetfood.com
Emp.: 5
Pet Foods Whslr
S.I.C.: 5149
N.A.I.C.S.: 424490

Subsidiary:

Global Pet Foods Distribution Ltd. (2)
Main St Ctr 110-400 Main St N
Airdrie, AB, T4B 2N1, Canada
Tel.: (403) 945-3663
Fax: (403) 945-3614
Pet Foods Distr
S.I.C.: 5149
N.A.I.C.S.: 424490
James Froese *(Owner)*

Global Ryan's Pet Food Stores Inc. (1)
294 Walker Drive Unit 2
Brampton, ON, L6T 4Z2, Canada
Tel.: (905) 790-9023
Fax: (905) 790-7059
Web Site: www.globalpetfoods.ca
Emp.: 30
Pet Food Stores
S.I.C.: 5999
N.A.I.C.S.: 453910
Edward Kenneth Loyst *(CEO)*

LIV Canada Gift Group Inc. (1)
294 Walker Drive Unit 2
Brampton, ON, L6T 4Z2, Canada
Tel.: (905) 790-9023
Fax: (905) 790-7059
Web Site: www.livcan.com
Emp.: 20
Home Decor Stores
S.I.C.: 5719
N.A.I.C.S.: 442299
Edward Kenneth Loyst *(CEO)*

Living Lighting Inc. (1)
294 Walker Dr Unit 2
Brampton, ON, L6T 4Z2, Canada
Tel.: (905) 790-9023
Fax: (905) 790-7059
E-Mail: info@livinglighting.com
Web Site: www.livinglighting.com
Emp.: 20
Lighting Stores
S.I.C.: 5719
N.A.I.C.S.: 442299
Edward Kenneth Loyst *(CEO)*

FRANCHISE CONCEPTS LIMITED

Caslon Court
PO Box 522
Pitronnerie Road, Saint Peter Port, Guernsey
Tel.: (44) 1481 713425
Fax: (44) 1481 72955
Web Site: www.franchiseconcepts.co.uk
Business Description:
Franchising Services
S.I.C.: 7389
N.A.I.C.S.: 561499

Joint Venture:

Sumo Services Ltd (1)
Unit 8 Hayward Business Center
New Lane, Havant, Hants, PO9 2NL, United Kingdom
Tel.: (44) 2392415020
Fax: (44) 2392499680
E-Mail: info@sumoservices.com
Web Site: www.sumoservices.com
Utility Mark Out Services
S.I.C.: 8711
N.A.I.C.S.: 541330

FRANCHISE SERVICES OF NORTH AMERICA INC.

2500 450 1st Street SE
Calgary, AB, T2P 5H1, Canada
Tel.: (403) 259-6666
Fax: (403) 259-6776
Web Site: www.fsna-inc.com
FSN—(TSXV)
Rev.: $10,542,772
Assets: $14,125,862
Liabilities: $9,781,015
Net Worth: $4,344,847
Earnings: ($2,077,468)
Fiscal Year-end: 09/30/12
Business Description:
Car Rental Franchisor
S.I.C.: 7514
N.A.I.C.S.: 532111
Personnel:
Thomas P. McDonnell, III *(Chm & CEO)*
Robert M. Barton *(Pres & COO)*
David M. Mitchell *(CFO)*
Henri H. Lefebvre *(Chief Acctg Officer & Gen Mgr-Canada)*
O. Kendall Moore *(Gen Counsel, Sec & VP)*
Board of Directors:
Thomas P. McDonnell, III
J. Michael Linn
Transfer Agent:
Computershare Investor Services Inc.
100 University Ave 9th Floor
Toronto, ON, Canada

Subsidiaries:

Practicar Systems Inc. (1)
7710 5th St SE Ste 204
Calgary, AB, T2H 2L9, Canada (100%)
Tel.: (403) 259-6666
Fax: (403) 259-6776
Toll Free: (800) 668-8591
E-Mail: info@rent-a-wreck.ca
Web Site: www.rentawreck.ca
Used Car Rentals
S.I.C.: 7514
N.A.I.C.S.: 532111
Colleen Pickard *(Coord-Franchise Dev-Rent-A-Wreck)*

Rent-A-Wreck Systems Inc (1)
204 7710 5th Street SE
Calgary, AB, T2H 2L9, Canada
Tel.: (800) 668-8591
Fax: (403) 259-6776
Toll Free: (800) 327-0116
E-Mail: info@rentawreck.ca
Web Site: www.rentawreck.ca
Car Rental & Sales Services
S.I.C.: 7381
N.A.I.C.S.: 561613
Pat Dyer *(Dir-Franchise Dev)*

Joint Venture:

Simply Wheelz LLC (1)
2500 450 1st Street SE
Calgary, AB, T2P 5H1, Canada DE
Tel.: (403) 259-6666
Fax: (403) 259-6776
Toll Free: (800) 777-5500
E-Mail: info@advantage.com
Web Site: www.advantage.com
Sales Range: $150-199.9 Million
Emp.: 600
Car Rental Services
S.I.C.: 7514
N.A.I.C.S.: 532111
William Plamondon *(Pres)*
David Mitchell *(CFO)*

U.S. Subsidiaries:

Sonoran National Insurance Group (1)
7502 E Pinnacle Peak Rd Ste B 210
Scottsdale, AZ 85255
Tel.: (866) 998-1001
Fax: (866) 998-1002
E-Mail: inquiry@sonorannational.com
Web Site: www.sonorannational.com
Emp.: 7
General Insurance Services
S.I.C.: 6411
N.A.I.C.S.: 524210
Teresa K. Quale *(Mgr-Agency)*

U-Save Auto Rental of America, Inc. (1)
1052 Highland Colony Pkwy Ste 204
Ridgeland, MS 39157
Tel.: (601) 713-4333
Fax: (601) 713-4330
Toll Free: (800) 438-2300
Web Site: www.usave.com
Car Rental Services
S.I.C.: 7514
N.A.I.C.S.: 532111
Robert M. Barton *(Pres)*

FRANCO-NEVADA CORPORATION

199 Bay Street Suite 2000
PO Box 285
Commerce Court Postal Station, Toronto, ON, M5L 1G9, Canada
Tel.: (416) 306-6300
Fax: (416) 306-6330
E-Mail: contact@franco-nevada.com
Web Site: www.franco-nevada.com
FNV—(NYSE TSX)
Rev.: $400,900,000
Assets: $3,044,900,000
Liabilities: $81,100,000
Net Worth: $2,963,800,000
Earnings: $11,700,000
Emp.: 26
Fiscal Year-end: 12/31/13
Business Description:
Gold & Platinum Exploration Services
S.I.C.: 1041
N.A.I.C.S.: 212221
Personnel:
Pierre Lassonde *(Chm)*
David Harquail *(Pres & CEO)*
Sandip Rana *(CFO)*
Geoff H. Waterman *(COO)*
Jacqueline A. Jones *(Chief Legal Officer & Sec)*
Paul Brink *(Sr VP-Bus Dev)*
Board of Directors:
Pierre Lassonde
Derek W. Evans
Graham Farquharson
Louis-Pierre Gignac
David Harquail
Randall Oliphant
David Robert Peterson

Computershare Investor Services
Golden, CO 80401
Transfer Agents:
Computershare Investor Services Inc.
Toronto, ON, Canada

Computershare Investor Services
Golden, CO 80401

U.S. Subsidiary:

Franco-Nevada U.S. Corporation (1)
1745 Shea Ctr Dr Ste 310
Highlands Ranch, CO 80129
Tel.: (303) 317-6335
Fax: (303) 317-6133
E-Mail: contact@franco-nevada.com
Web Site: www.franco-nevada.com
Gold Ore Mining Services
S.I.C.: 1041
N.A.I.C.S.: 212221

Non-U.S. Subsidiary:

Franco-Nevada Australia Pty. Ltd. (1)
Unit 5/9 McDonald St W
Osborne Park, WA, 6017, Australia
Tel.: (61) 863133934
Fax: (61) 894444479
Gold Ore Mining Services
S.I.C.: 1041
N.A.I.C.S.: 212221

FRANCOIS-CHARLES OBERTHUR FIDUCIAIRE S.A.

50 Quai Michelet
92300 Levallois-Perret, France
Tel.: (33) 155467200
Fax: (33) 155467201
Web Site: www.Oberthur.com
Year Founded: 1984
Sales Range: $1-4.9 Billion
Emp.: 6,800
Business Description:
Holding Company
S.I.C.: 6719
N.A.I.C.S.: 551112
Personnel:
Jean-Pierre Savare *(Chm)*
Michel Aime *(Vice Chm)*
Thomas Savare *(CEO)*
Jean-Michel Guichot *(CFO)*
Board of Directors:
Jean-Pierre Savare
Yves-Claude Abescat
Michel Aime
Pierre Barberis
Andre Belard
Harold Boel
Victor Casier
Guillaume d'Angerville d'Auvrecher
Jean-Pierre Ferretjans
Gilles Gramat
Xavier Lafont
Elie Gregoire Sainte Marie
Emmanuelle Savare
Marie Savare
Thomas Savare

Holdings:

Oberthur Cash Protection S.A. (1)
3 Bis rue du docteur Quignard
BP 67907
21079 Dijon, France FR
Tel.: (33) 380604300 (91%)
Fax: (33) 380700892
E-Mail: info@oberthurcp.com
Web Site: www.oberthurcp.com
Cash-In-Transit Technology
S.I.C.: 7382
N.A.I.C.S.: 561621

Oberthur Fiduciaire SAS (1)
102 boulevard Malesherbes
F-75017 Paris, France FR
Tel.: (33) 147646400
Fax: (33) 144151030
Emp.: 900
Banknote, Passport & Other High Security Identity Document Printing Services
S.I.C.: 2759
N.A.I.C.S.: 323111
Nicolas Koutros *(Exec Dir)*

FRANCOUDI & STEPHANOU LTD.

The Maritime Ctr Omonia Ave 141
3045 Limassol, Cyprus
Tel.: (357) 25867000
Fax: (357) 25561892
E-Mail: mail@francoudi.com
Web Site: www.francoudi.com
Year Founded: 1895

Emp.: 1,500
Business Description:
Holding Company; Shipping, Trading, Distr, Insurance, Travel, Hotels, Telecommunications & IT Services
S.I.C.: 6719
N.A.I.C.S.: 551112
Personnel:
Demetrios Z. Pierides *(Chm)*
Nicos H. Stephanou *(Pres & Grp Chief Exec)*
Yiannis Demetriou *(Mng Dir-Teledev East)*
Hermes N. Stephanou *(Mng Dir)*
Board of Directors:
Demetrios Z. Pierides
George A. Michaelides
Costas N. Papaconstantinou
Hermes N. Stephanou
Nicos H. Stephanou
Sotos N. Stephanou
Subsidiary:

Aeolos Limited (1)
6 Zenas Kanther Street
CY-1065 Nicosia, Cyprus
Tel.: (357) 22881222
Fax: (357) 22660876
E-Mail: info@aeolos.com
Web Site: www.aeolos.com
Emp.: 200
Travel Services
S.I.C.: 4724
N.A.I.C.S.: 561510
Sotos N. Stephanou *(Mng Dir)*

Subsidiary:

Interyachting (2)
42 Iapetou Street
PO Box 54292
Limassol, Cyprus
Tel.: (357) 25811900
Fax: (357) 25811945
E-Mail: info@interyachting.com.cy
Web Site: www.interyachting.com
Emp.: 4
Charter & Leisure Cruise Operations; Yacht & Yacht Equipment Sales
S.I.C.: 4489
N.A.I.C.S.: 487210
Nicolas Epiphaniou *(Mng Dir)*

Division:

Bookcyprus.com (2)
Zenas Kanther 6
CY-1065 Nicosia, Cyprus
Tel.: (357) 22881222
Web Site: www.bookcyprus.com
Online Travel Services
S.I.C.: 4724
N.A.I.C.S.: 561510

FRANGI S.P.A

Via Volta 5
22029 Ugiatte, Italy
Tel.: (39) 031809233
Fax: (39) 0031809244
E-Mail: frangi@frangi.it
Web Site: www.frangi.it
Emp.: 160
Business Description:
Woven Fabrics Mfr
S.I.C.: 2241
N.A.I.C.S.: 313220
Personnel:
Angelo Frangi *(Pres)*
Davide Frangi *(CEO)*

FRANK H DALE LTD.

Mill Street
Leominster, HR6 8EF, United Kingdom
Tel.: (44) 1568612212
Fax: (44) 1568619401
E-Mail: info@fhdale.co.uk
Web Site: www.fhdale.co.uk
Year Founded: 1932
Rev.: $37,128,960
Emp.: 90
Business Description:
Steelworks Mfr
S.I.C.: 3441
N.A.I.C.S.: 332312
Personnel:
Andrew MacWhirter *(Mng Dir)*

FRANK KEY GROUP LIMITED

22A Portland Street
Daybrook, Nottingham, NG5 6BL, United Kingdom
Tel.: (44) 115 9 208 208
Fax: (44) 115 9 670 393
E-Mail: info@frank-key.co.uk
Web Site: www.frank-key.co.uk
Business Description:
Timber & Building Materials Whslr
S.I.C.: 5211
N.A.I.C.S.: 444190
Personnel:
Neil Lunn *(Mgr)*
Subsidiary:

Frank Key (Nottingham) Limited (1)
Mansfield Road
Daybrook, Nottingham, NG5 6BL, United Kingdom
Tel.: (44) 115 9 208 208
Fax: (44) 115 9 670 393
Timber & Building Materials Whslr
S.I.C.: 5211
N.A.I.C.S.: 444190

Subsidiary:

The Builders Centre (Sheffield) Limited (2)
Nunnery Drive
Sheffield, South Yorkshire, S2 1TA, United Kingdom
Tel.: (44) 114 272 4001
Fax: (44) 114 241 2840
E-Mail: website@thebuilderscentre.co.uk
Web Site: www.thebuilderscentre.co.uk
Emp.: 15
Building & Plumbing Products Whslr
S.I.C.: 5211
N.A.I.C.S.: 444190
Perry Eyre *(Mng Dir)*

FRANK PLASTIC AG

Herbert Frank Strasse 26
72178 Freudenstadt, Germany
Tel.: (49) 74861810
Fax: (49) 7486181337
E-Mail: info@frankplastic.de
Web Site: www.frankplastic.de
Rev.: $55,351,326
Emp.: 222
Business Description:
Thermoplastic Mfr
S.I.C.: 2821
N.A.I.C.S.: 325211
Personnel:
Michael Waubke *(Chm)*

FRANKE HOLDING AG

FrankeStrasse 2
4663 Aarburg, Switzerland
Tel.: (41) 627873131
Fax: (41) 627916761
E-Mail: info@franke.com
Web Site: www.franke.com
Year Founded: 1911
Sales Range: $1-4.9 Billion
Emp.: 11,000
Fiscal Year-end: 12/31/12
Business Description:
Holding Company; Kitchen Systems; Industrial Engineering; Beverage Containers; Metal Construction; Commercial Kitchens; Coffee Machines; Bathroom Furniture & Sanitary Equipment Mfr
S.I.C.: 6719
N.A.I.C.S.: 551112
Personnel:
Michael Pieper *(Owner)*
Thomas A. Erb *(Chm)*
Alexander Zschokke *(CEO)*
Jurg Fischer *(CFO)*
Peter Kaufmann *(CIO)*
Hans J. Ott *(Pres/CEO-Foodservice Sys)*
Board of Directors:
Thomas A. Erb
Randolf Hanslin
Hans J. Loliger
Anton E. Schrafl
Bernhard W. Stauch
U.S. Subsidiary:

Franke Inc. (1)
800 Aviation PW
Smyrna, TN 37167
Tel.: (615) 287-8200
Fax: (615) 793-5940
Web Site: www.franke.com
Emp.: 80
Mfr. of Stainless Steel Products
S.I.C.: 3589
N.A.I.C.S.: 333318
Thomas Campion *(Pres)*

Division:

Franke Consumer Products Inc (2)
600 Franke Dr
Ruston, LA 71270-7440 (100%)
Mailing Address:
PO Box 1010
Ruston, LA 71273-1010
Tel.: (318) 255-5600
Fax: (318) 255-5688
Toll Free: (800) 637-6485
E-Mail: montyriley@frankeconsumerproducts.com
Web Site: www.frankeconsumerproducts.com
Sales Range: $75-99.9 Million
Emp.: 156
Mfr. of Stainless Steel Sinks
S.I.C.: 3499
N.A.I.C.S.: 332999

Non-U.S. Subsidiary:

Franke Kindred Canada Ltd (2)
1000 Kindred Rd
PO Box 190
Midland, ON, L4R 4K9, Canada (100%)
Tel.: (705) 526-5427
Fax: (705) 526-8055
E-Mail: service@frankekindred.com
Web Site: www.frankekindred.com
Emp.: 240
Stainless Steel Sinks
S.I.C.: 3499
N.A.I.C.S.: 332999
Case D. Jong *(Pres)*

Non-U.S. Subsidiary:

Franke AquaRotter GmbH (1)
Parkstr 1-5
PO Box 1335
14974 Ludwigsfelde, Germany
Tel.: (49) 33788180
Fax: (49) 3378818100
E-Mail: info.fbs@franke.com
Web Site: www.franke.com
Emp.: 270
Faucets, Shower Heads & Fittings Mfr
S.I.C.: 3432
N.A.I.C.S.: 332913
Verina Koepser *(Mgr-PR)*

FRANKFURTER ALLGEMEINE ZEITUNG GMBH

Hellerhufstrasse 2 4
60367 Frankfurt, Germany
Tel.: (49) 6975910
Fax: (49) 6975911743
E-Mail: info@faz.com.de
Web Site: www.faz.net
Sales Range: $600-649.9 Million
Business Description:
Publisher of Newspapers
S.I.C.: 2711
N.A.I.C.S.: 511110
Personnel:
Roland Gerschermann *(Gen Mgr)*
Subsidiary:

FAZ 93.6 Berlin (1)
Kurfurstendamm 207-208
D-10719 Berlin, Germany
Tel.: (49) 30884844
Fax: (49) 3088484521
Web Site: www.104.6rtl.com
Emp.: 20
Radio Broadcasting
S.I.C.: 4832
N.A.I.C.S.: 515112
Jan Trtnn *(Mng Dir)*

FRANKFURTER SPARKASSE

Neue Mainzer Strasse 47-53
PO Box 10 08 22
D 60255 Frankfurt am Main, Germany
Tel.: (49) 6926410
Telex: 411 506
Fax: (49) 6926412900
E-Mail: serviceline@fraspa1822.de
Web Site: www.fraspa1822.de
Emp.: 3,000
Business Description:
Bank
S.I.C.: 6035
N.A.I.C.S.: 522120
Personnel:
Herbert Hans Gruntker *(Chm)*
Subsidiaries:

1822 Corpus Immobilien-Vermittlung GmbH (1)
Neue Mainzer Strasse 53
60311 Frankfurt am Main, Hessen, Germany (85%)
Tel.: (49) 69979080
Fax: (49) 6997908199
E-Mail: frankfurt@corpussireo.com
Emp.: 19
Bank
S.I.C.: 6035
N.A.I.C.S.: 522120
Karl Greiner *(Mng Dir)*

1822 Direkt (1)
Borsigallee 19
60608 Frankfurt am Main, Hessen, Germany (100%)
Tel.: (49) 69941700
Fax: (49) 6994170199
Web Site: www.1822direkt.com
Emp.: 250
Online Bank
S.I.C.: 6035
N.A.I.C.S.: 522120

Frankfurter Bankgesellschaft (1)
Jungstrasse 26
60311 Frankfurt am Main, Germany(47.5%)
Tel.: (49) 69156860
Telex: 4 14 206
Fax: (49) 6915686140
E-Mail: service@frabank.de
Web Site: www.frabank.de
Emp.: 14
Bank
S.I.C.: 6036
N.A.I.C.S.: 522120
Guenter Schnittdiel *(Office Mgr)*

GimPro (1)
Neue Mainzer Strasse 47 53
D 60255 Frankfurt am Main, Germany (100%)
Tel.: (49) 6926413010
Fax: (49) 6926412741
Web Site: www.frankfurter-sparkasse.de
Bank
S.I.C.: 6035
N.A.I.C.S.: 522120
Georg Stocker *(Mng Dir)*

Versicherungsservice der Frankfurter Sparkasse GmbH (1)
Schaefergasse 33
D 60313 Frankfurt am Main, Germany (100%)
Tel.: (49) 699291060

Frankfurter Sparkasse—(Continued)

Fax: (49) 6992910632
Emp.: 20
Bank
S.I.C.: 6036
N.A.I.C.S.: 522120

Affiliate:

I & K Systeme GmbH (1)
Obere Haingasse 2
D-61203 Reichelsheim, Germany (33.3%)
Software for Banks
S.I.C.: 3652
N.A.I.C.S.: 334614

FRANKL & KIRCHNER GMBH & CO KG

Scheffelstrasse 73
68723 Schwetzingen, Germany
Tel.: (49) 62022020
Fax: (49) 6202202115
E-Mail: info@efka.net
Web Site: www.efka.net
Rev.: $54,975,987
Emp.: 230
Business Description:
Electronic Control Mfr
S.I.C.: 3714
N.A.I.C.S.: 336320
Personnel:
Lotte Wiest *(Mng Dir)*

FRANKLAND RIVER OLIVE COMPANY LIMITED

1 McDowell Street
Welshpool, WA, 6986, Australia
Tel.: (61) 894942044
Fax: (61) 894942043
E-Mail: admin@froc.com.au
Web Site: www.froc.com.au
Year Founded: 1999
FLR—(ASX)
Rev.: $2,060,457
Assets: $29,786,955
Liabilities: $8,602,106
Net Worth: $21,184,849
Earnings: ($1,030,369)
Emp.: 25
Fiscal Year-end: 06/30/13
Business Description:
Virgin Olive Oil Processor & Exporter
S.I.C.: 2079
N.A.I.C.S.: 311224
Personnel:
Oren Zohar *(Sec)*
Board of Directors:
Ivo Paul Letari
Danny Luigi Brescacin
Oren Zohar
Legal Counsel:
Pullinger Readhead Lucas
Level 2 Fortescue House 50 Kings Park Road
West Perth, Australia

FRANK'S INTERNATIONAL N.V.

Prins Bernhardplein 200
1097 JB Amsterdam, Netherlands
Tel.: (31) 20 52 14 777
E-Mail: info@franksintl.com
Web Site: www.franksinternational.com
FI—(NYSE)
Rev.: $1,077,722,000
Assets: $1,561,195,000
Liabilities: $227,868,000
Net Worth: $1,333,327,000
Earnings: $350,830,000
Emp.: 4,100
Fiscal Year-end: 12/31/13
Business Description:
Holding Company; Oil & Gas Tubular Products Mfr
S.I.C.: 3317
N.A.I.C.S.: 331210
Personnel:
Donald Keith Mosing *(Chm, Pres & CEO)*
Mark G. Margavio *(CFO)*
W. John Walker *(COO & Exec VP-Ops)*
Brian D. Baird *(Chief Legal Officer, Sec & VP)*
Victor C. Szabo *(Chief Acctg Officer)*
Supervisory Board of Directors:
Donald Keith Mosing
Sheldon R. Erikson
Kirkland David Mosing
Steven Brent Mosing

U.S. Subsidiary:

Frank's International, Inc. (1)
10260 Westheimer Rd
Houston, TX 77042
Tel.: (281) 966-7300
Fax: (281) 966-0948
E-Mail: info@franksintl.com
Web Site: www.franksinternational.com
Oil & Gas Tubing Products Mfr
S.I.C.: 3317
N.A.I.C.S.: 331210
Donald Keith Mosing *(Chm, Pres & CEO)*
Robert R. Gilbert *(COO & Exec VP)*

FRANSABANK SAL

Hamra St Fransabank Bldg
PO Box 110393
Beirut, Lebanon
Tel.: (961) 1340180
Fax: (961) 1354572
E-Mail: info@fransabank.com.lb
Web Site: www.fransabank.com
Year Founded: 1921
Int. Income: $287,097,277
Emp.: 1,300
Business Description:
Banking Services
S.I.C.: 6029
N.A.I.C.S.: 522110
Personnel:
Adnan Kassar *(Chm & Gen Mgr)*
Adel Kassar *(Deputy Chm & Gen Mgr)*
Board of Directors:
Adel Kassar
Adnan Kassar
Abdel Kader Al-Fadl
Fahd Mazyad Al-Rajaan
Henri Guillemin
Magda Rizk
Rafic Sharaffedin
Nehme Tohme

Subsidiaries:

Fransa Invest Bank SAL (1)
PO Box 110393
Beirut, Lebanon
Tel.: (961) 1340188
Fax: (961) 1351030
E-Mail: joe.sarrouh@fransabank.com
Web Site: www.fransabank.com
Emp.: 15
Financial Investment Banking
S.I.C.: 6211
N.A.I.C.S.: 523999
Nadim Kassar *(Chm)*

Lebanese Leasing Company SAL (1)
PO Box 110393
Beirut, Lebanon
Tel.: (961) 1340188
Fax: (961) 1738614
E-Mail: llc@leasing.com.lb
Emp.: 6
Lease Financing
S.I.C.: 6211
N.A.I.C.S.: 523999
Adnan Kassar *(Chm)*

Societe Generale Fonciere SAL (1)
PO Box 110393
Beirut, Lebanon
Tel.: (961) 1 340188
Fax: (961) 1 354572
Real Estate Property Management & Leasing
S.I.C.: 6531
N.A.I.C.S.: 531390

Non-U.S. Subsidiary:

Fransabank (France) SA (1)
104 Avenue des Champs-Elysees
75008 Paris, France
Tel.: (33) 153768400
Fax: (33) 145635700
E-Mail: info@fransabank.fr
Web Site: www.fransabank.com
Emp.: 20
Banking Services
S.I.C.: 6029
N.A.I.C.S.: 522110
Hamri De Courtivron *(Mng Dir)*

FRANSHION PROPERTIES (CHINA) LIMITED

Rm 4702-03 47/F Office Tower
Convention Plaza 1 Harbar Road
Wanchai, China (Hong Kong)
Tel.: (852) 28299668
Fax: (852) 28240300
E-Mail: franshion@sinochem.com
Web Site: www.franshion.com
Year Founded: 2004
817—(HKG)
Rev.: $2,214,802,131
Assets: $10,638,664,364
Liabilities: $6,189,524,435
Net Worth: $4,449,139,929
Earnings: $508,106,327
Emp.: 5,989
Fiscal Year-end: 12/31/12
Business Description:
Property Development Services
S.I.C.: 6531
N.A.I.C.S.: 531390
Personnel:
Cao He *(Chm)*
Binwu He *(Vice Chm & VP)*
Congrui Li *(CEO)*
Nan Jiang *(CFO)*
Chi Chiun Liao *(Sec)*
Board of Directors:
Cao He
Binwu He
Ambrose Hon Chuen Lau
Congrui Li
Xuehua Li
Hongyu Liu
Dai Shi
Xijia Su
Legal Counsel:
Tian Yuan Law Firm
11th Floor Tower C Corporate Square 35 Financial Street
Xicheng District, Beijing, China
Latham & Watkins
18th Floor One Exchange Square 8 Connaught Place
Central, China (Hong Kong)
Transfer Agent:
Computershare Hong Kong Investor Services Limited
Shops 1712-1716 17th Floor Hopewell Centre
183 Queens Road East
Wanchai, China (Hong Kong)

FRANTIC FILMS CORPORATION

70 Arthur St Ste 300
Winnipeg, MB, R3B 1G7, Canada
Tel.: (204) 949-0070
Fax: (204) 949-0050
E-Mail: info@franticfilms.com
Web Site: www.franticfilms.com
Year Founded: 1997
Sales Range: $1-9.9 Million
Emp.: 122
Business Description:
Visual Effects & Animation for Feature Film, Television & Commercials
Export
S.I.C.: 7812
N.A.I.C.S.: 512110
Personnel:
Michael L. Fink *(Pres-Visual Effects Worldwide)*
Jamie Brown *(CEO & Exec Producer)*
Brenda Greenberg *(Exec VP-Scripted Dev)*

FRANZ HANIEL & CIE. GMBH

Franz-Haniel-Platz 1
47119 Duisburg, Germany
Tel.: (49) 2038060
Telex: 855892
Fax: (49) 20380680888
E-Mail: info@haniel.de
Web Site: www.haniel.com
Year Founded: 1756
Rev.: $35,446,002,270
Assets: $19,406,386,720
Liabilities: $13,348,621,720
Net Worth: $6,057,765,000
Earnings: ($2,552,338,320)
Emp.: 56,480
Fiscal Year-end: 12/31/12
Business Description:
Holding Company for Pharmaceutical Distr, Brick Mfr, Washroom & Workwear Rental, Stainless Steel Recycling & Trading, Environmental Cleanup Services (Fire & Water Damage) & Mail Order Businesses
S.I.C.: 6719
N.A.I.C.S.: 551112
Personnel:
Franz Markus Haniel *(Chm-Supervisory Bd)*
Stephan Gemkow *(Chm-Mgmt Bd)*
Gerd Herzberg *(First Vice Chm-Supervisory Bd)*
Florian Funck *(Member-Mgmt Bd-Fin, Corp Controlling, Corp Gen Svcs & Tax)*
Supervisory Board of Directors:
Franz Markus Haniel
Georg F. Baur
Christoph Boninger
Heide Detmar
Harald Farber
Bernd Hergenrother
Gerd Herzberg
Henning Kagermann
Kay Richard Landwers
Herbert Narr
Irina Pankewitz
Michael Schadlich
Uwe Schmahl
Baron Wolf von Buchholtz
Hans Wettengl
Kay Windthorst

Subsidiaries:

ELG Haniel GmbH (1)
Kremerskamp 16
D 47138 Duisburg, Germany (100%)
Tel.: (49) 20345010
Fax: (49) 2034501250
E-Mail: info@elg.de
Web Site: www.elg.de
Emp.: 120
Recycling of Raw Materials for the Stainless Steel Industry; International Trading of Metals & Alloys
S.I.C.: 3317
N.A.I.C.S.: 331210
Norbert Spaeker *(Chm)*

Haniel Reederei Holding GmbH (1)
Franz Haniel Platz 6 8
47119 Duisburg, Germany (100%)
Tel.: (49) 2038060
Fax: (49) 203806368
Web Site: www.xella.com
Emp.: 537
Inland Shipping; Industrial Logistics
S.I.C.: 4449
N.A.I.C.S.: 483211

Jan buckemden *(Chm)*

HTS International GmbH (1)
Hafenstrabe 2
47119 Duisburg, Germany
Tel.: (49) 2038060
Fax: (49) 2038068509
E-Mail: presse@hts.com
Web Site: www.cws-boco.com
Emp.: 80
Washroom Hygiene & Textile Services
S.I.C.: 7218
N.A.I.C.S.: 812332
Andreas Heinze *(CEO)*
Matthias Daum *(COO)*

Subsidiary:

Haniel Textile Service GmbH (2)
Hafenstrasse 2
47119 Duisburg, Germany (100%)
Tel.: (49) 2038060
Fax: (49) 2038068510
E-Mail: personal.hts@haniel.de
Web Site: www.haniel.de
Emp.: 60
Washroom Service & Supplies; Workwear Rental Service
S.I.C.: 7349
N.A.I.C.S.: 561720
Max Teichner *(CEO)*

Non-U.S. Subsidiaries:

CWS-boco Supply AG (3)
Neuhofstrasse 21
CH-6340 Baar, Switzerland (100%)
Tel.: (41) 417665151
Telex: 828768 cws ch
Fax: (41) 417665170
E-Mail: export.ch@cws-boco.com
Web Site: www.cws-boco.com
Emp.: 28
Washroom Service & Supplies
S.I.C.: 7349
N.A.I.C.S.: 561720
Roger Thuli *(CEO)*
Tobias Klein *(CFO)*

HTS Italia S.p.A. (3)
Via della Levata 24
I-20084 Lacchiarella, Milan, Italy IT
Tel.: (39) 0290588400
Telex: 331231
Fax: (39) 0290588299
E-Mail: info@hts.com
Web Site: www.hts.com
Emp.: 80
Commercial Hygeine Products
S.I.C.: 7349
N.A.I.C.S.: 561720
Norbert Alexander Gregor *(Mng Dir)*

TAKKT AG (1)
Presselstrasse 12
70191 Stuttgart, Germany (70.4%)
Tel.: (49) 711346580
Fax: (49) 711 3465 8100
E-Mail: service@takkt.de
Web Site: www.takkt.de
TTK—(STU)
Sls.: $1,265,317,684
Assets: $1,176,940,277
Liabilities: $756,915,044
Net Worth: $420,025,233
Earnings: $90,243,198
Emp.: 2,351
Fiscal Year-end: 12/31/12
Business-to-Business Mail Order Services for Office, Plant & Warehouse Equipment Mfr
S.I.C.: 5961
N.A.I.C.S.: 454113
Stephan Gemkow *(Chm-Supervisory Bd)*
Felix A. Zimmermann *(Chm-Mgmt Bd & CEO-America Div)*
Klaus Trutzschler *(Deputy Chm-Supervisory Bd)*
Claude Tomaszewski *(CFO & Member-Mgmt Bd)*
Benjamin Buhler *(IR Officer)*
Franz Vogel *(Member-Mgmt Bd & COO-Europe Div)*

Subsidiaries:

Kaiser & Kraft Europa (2)
Presselstrasse 12
70191 Stuttgart, Germany (100%)
Tel.: (49) 711346560
Fax: (49) 71134656100
E-Mail: info@kaiserkraft.de
Web Site: www.kaiserkraft.com
Emp.: 300
Transportation & Storage of Office Equipment
S.I.C.: 4789
N.A.I.C.S.: 488210

Subsidiaries:

Gaerner GmbH (3)
Neue ruhrorter str 195
47119 Duisburg, Germany (100%)
Tel.: (49) 20380944127
Fax: (49) 20380944215
E-Mail: duisburg@gaerner.de
Web Site: www.gaerner.de
Emp.: 50
Distributor of Office Equipment
S.I.C.: 5112
N.A.I.C.S.: 453210
Joerg Moenig *(Gen Mgr)*

Kaiser & Kraft GmbH (3)
Presselstrasse 12
70191 Stuttgart, Germany (100%)
Tel.: (49) 711346560
Fax: (49) 134658100
E-Mail: info@kaiserkraft.de
Web Site: www.kaiserkraft.de
Emp.: 300
Transportation & Storage of Office Equipment
S.I.C.: 4789
N.A.I.C.S.: 488210
Felix Zimmermann *(Chm)*

U.S. Subsidiary:

George Patton Associates, Inc. (3)
55 Broadcommon Rd
Bristol, RI 02809
Tel.: (401) 247-0333
E-Mail: info@displacetogo.com
Sales Range: $10-24.9 Million
Emp.: 85
Sign Mfr
S.I.C.: 3993
N.A.I.C.S.: 339950
G. T. Patton *(Pres)*

Non-U.S. Subsidiaries:

Gerdmans Inrednigar AB (3)
PO Box 94
285 22 Markaryd, Sweden (100%)
Tel.: (46) 43375000
Fax: (46) 43374047
E-Mail: info@gerdmans.se
Web Site: www.gerdmans.se
Rev.: $32,022,500
Emp.: 35
Distributor of Industrial & Office Equipment
S.I.C.: 5112
N.A.I.C.S.: 453210
Jorgen Fvomensson *(Mng Dir)*

KWESTO (3)
Praga Del Nicka 12
17000 Prague, Czech Republic
Tel.: (420) 266793734
Fax: (420) 266793721
E-Mail: info@kwesto.cz
Web Site: www.kwesto.cz
Emp.: 30
Distributor of Office Equipment
S.I.C.: 5943
N.A.I.C.S.: 453210

Topdeq GMBH (2)
Werner Von Siemens Str 31
Pfungstadt, 64319, Germany (100%)
Tel.: (49) 61571590
Fax: (49) 6157159200
E-Mail: service@topdeq.de
Web Site: www.topdeq.com
Sales Range: $10-24.9 Million
Emp.: 150
Distributor of Office Equipment
S.I.C.: 5112
N.A.I.C.S.: 453210
Stephen Koolpe *(Mgr)*

U.S. Subsidiaries:

C&H Distributors, LLC (2)
770 S 70th St
Milwaukee, WI 53214
Tel.: (414) 443-1700
Fax: (414) 443-2700
Toll Free: (800) 558-9966
Web Site: www.chdist.com
Emp.: 200
Distributor of Industrial Supplies
S.I.C.: 5084
N.A.I.C.S.: 423830
David McKeon *(Pres)*

Hubert Company (2)
9555 Dry Fork Rd
Harrison, OH 45030-1906 DE
Tel.: (513) 367-8600
Fax: (800) 527-0128
E-Mail: info@hubert.com
Web Site: www.hubert.com
Sales Range: $75-99.9 Million
Emp.: 350
Food Service Equipment & Supplies
S.I.C.: 5046
N.A.I.C.S.: 423440
Bart Kohler *(Pres)*

National Business Furniture Inc. (2)
735 N Water St Ste 400
Milwaukee, WI 53202-4103 WI
Tel.: (414) 276-8511
Fax: (414) 276-8966
Toll Free: (800) 558-1010
E-Mail: info@nationalbizfurniture.com
Web Site: www.nationalbusinessfurniture.com
Sales Range: $100-124.9 Million
Emp.: 150
Business Furniture Wholesaler
S.I.C.: 5021
N.A.I.C.S.: 423210
Kent Anderson *(COO)*

Divisions:

Alfax Wholesale Furniture Inc. (3)
13901 Midway Rd Ste 102-428
Farmers Branch, TX 75244
Tel.: (800) 221-5710
Fax: (800) 638-6445
E-Mail: service@alfaxfurniture.com
Web Site: www.alfaxfurniture.com
Emp.: 7
Furniture & Furnishings Mfr
S.I.C.: 5021
N.A.I.C.S.: 423210

Dallas Midwest Company (3)
4100 Alpha Rd Ste 111
Dallas, TX 75244
Tel.: (972) 866-0101
Fax: (800) 301-8314
Toll Free: (800) 527-2417
E-Mail: service@dallasmidwest.com
Web Site: www.dallasmidwest.com
Emp.: 9
Furniture for Schools, Churches & Organizations
S.I.C.: 5961
N.A.I.C.S.: 454113
Kent Anderson *(Pres)*

National Business Furniture Inc (3)
735 N Water St
Milwaukee, WI 53202 CA
Tel.: (414) 276-8511
Fax: (414) 276-8371
Toll Free: (800) 343-4222
E-Mail: info@officefurniture.com
Web Site: www.furnitureonline.com
Emp.: 120
Online Retailer of Office Furniture
S.I.C.: 5712
N.A.I.C.S.: 442110

OfficeFurniture.com (3)
735 N Water St Ste 440
Milwaukee, WI 53202
Tel.: (414) 276-8511
Fax: (414) 276-8371
Web Site: www.officefurniture.com
Emp.: 50
Office Furniture
S.I.C.: 5712
N.A.I.C.S.: 442110

Non-U.S. Subsidiary:

Avenue Industrial Supply Co. Ltd. (2)
331 Alden Rd
Markham, ON, L3R 3L4, Canada (100%)
Tel.: (905) 946-8174
Fax: (905) 946-8435
E-Mail: nelson@avenuesupply.com
Web Site: www.avenuesupply.com
Emp.: 70
Industrial Products Distr
S.I.C.: 5169
N.A.I.C.S.: 424690
Nelson Rivers *(Pres)*

Joint Venture:

Haniel Bau-Industrie GmbH (1)
Franz Haniel Platz 1
47119 Duisburg, Germany
Tel.: (49) 2038060
Fax: (49) 203806715
E-Mail: info@haniel.de
Emp.: 1,000
Wall Building Materials/Aggregates/Fixing Systems
S.I.C.: 3531
N.A.I.C.S.: 333120
Eckhard Cordes *(CEO)*

FRANZ REINKEMEIER GMBH

Westerwieher Strasse 198
33397 Rietberg, Germany
Tel.: (49) 52449210
Fax: (49) 52441516
E-Mail: service@reinkemeier-rietberg.de
Web Site: www.reinkemeier-rietberg.de
Year Founded: 1971
Rev.: $55,176,000
Emp.: 180

Business Description:
Interior Design Products Distr
S.I.C.: 5023
N.A.I.C.S.: 423220

Personnel:
Bernhard Reinkemeier *(Co-Mng Dir)*
Heinrich Reinkemeier *(Co-Mng Dir)*

FRANZ SUTER GMBH-PUMPEN UND SYSTEME

Schurmatstrasse 9
5643 Sins, Switzerland
Tel.: (41) 7871760
Fax: (41) 7870643
E-Mail: info@suterpumpen.ch
Web Site: www.suterpumpen.ch

Business Description:
Mfr of Pumps
S.I.C.: 3561
N.A.I.C.S.: 333911

FRAPORT AG

Frankfurt Airport Services Worldwide
60547 Frankfurt am Main, Germany
Tel.: (49) 1805 372 4636
Fax: (49) 800 2345679
E-Mail: investor.relations@fraport.de
Web Site: www.fraport.com
FRA—(DEU OTC)
Rev.: $3,431,656,564
Assets: $12,977,886,502
Liabilities: $9,012,742,767
Net Worth: $3,965,143,735
Earnings: $338,696,372
Emp.: 20,963
Fiscal Year-end: 12/31/12

Business Description:
Airport Retailing & Real Estate Services; Owned 20.3% by Stadtwerke Frankfurt am Main Holding GmbH
S.I.C.: 4581
N.A.I.C.S.: 488119

Personnel:
Karlheinz Weimar *(Chm-Supervisory Bd)*
Stefan Schulte *(Chm-Exec Bd)*
Gerold Schaub *(Vice Chm-Supervisory Bd)*
Anke Giesen *(Member-Exec Bd & Exec Dir-Ground Handling)*

Fraport AG—(Continued)

Michael Muller *(Member-Exec Bd & Exec Dir-Labor Rels)*
Matthias Zieschang *(Exec Dir-Controlling & Fin)*
Martin Bien *(Sr Exec VP-Traffic & Terminal Mgmt, Airport Expansion & Safety)*
Karl-Heinz Dietrich *(Exec VP-Retail & Properties)*

Supervisory Board of Directors:
Karlheinz Weimar
Claudia Amier
Devrim Arslan
Uwe Becker
Hakan Cicek
Kathrin Dahnke
Peter Feldmann
Margarete Haase
Jorg-Uwe Hahn
Lothar Klemm
Roland Krieg
Michael Odenwald
Mehmet Ozdemir
Arno Prangenberg
Gerold Schaub
Hans-Jurgen Schmidt
Werner Schmidt
Edgar Stejskal
Katja Windt

Subsidiaries:

AirIT Airport IT Services Hahn AG (1)
Building 663 Hahn Airport
55483 Lautzenhausen, Germany (100%)
Tel.: (49) 6543507302
Fax: (49) 6543507333
E-Mail: info@airit.de
Web Site: www.airit.de
Emp.: 15
Airport Information & Communications Infrastructure Operations & Planning
S.I.C.: 4581
N.A.I.C.S.: 488119
Heinz-Dieter Hufnagel *(Chm)*

AirIT Services AG (1)
Gebaude 663
Hahn-Flughafen, Lautzenhausen, Germany
Tel.: (49) 6543 507304
Fax: (49) 6543 507333
E-Mail: info@airit-hahn.de
Web Site: www.airit.de
Emp.: 12
Information Technology Consulting Services
S.I.C.: 7373
N.A.I.C.S.: 541512
Heinz-Dieter Hufnagel *(Gen Mgr)*

AirITSystems Hannover GmbH (1)
Benkendorffstrasse 6
30855 Langenhagen, Germany (50%)
Mailing Address:
PO Box 420162
30661 Hannover, Germany
Tel.: (49) 5119774000
Fax: (49) 5119774100
E-Mail: info@airitsystems.de
Web Site: www.airitsystems.de
Emp.: 150
IT Services & Solutions
S.I.C.: 7371
N.A.I.C.S.: 541511
Eric Engelhardt *(Mng Dir)*
Gunther Graf *(Mng Dir)*
Wolfgang Pelzer *(Mng Dir)*

Airport Assekuranz Vermittlungs-GmbH (1)
Flughafenstr 4a
60582 Frankfurt am Main, Germany (100%)
Tel.: (49) 6969060180
Fax: (49) 6969059295
E-Mail: info@fraport.com
Web Site: www.fraport.com
Emp.: 15
Insurance Services
S.I.C.: 6411
N.A.I.C.S.: 524298
Hans-Joerg Schill *(Mng Dir)*

Airport Cater Service GmbH (1)
Frankfurt Airport Building 101
60547 Frankfurt am Main, Germany (100%)
Tel.: (49) 6969066002
Fax: (49) 6969059659
Catering Services
S.I.C.: 5812
N.A.I.C.S.: 722320
Helmut Heinz *(Mng Dir)*

Energy Air GmbH (1)
Frankfurt Flughafen Geb 147
60547 Frankfurt am Main, Germany (100%)
Tel.: (49) 6969066700
Fax: (49) 6969069100
E-Mail: info@fraport.com
Web Site: www.fraport.com
Emp.: 3
Power, Remote Heat, Remote Cooling & Energy Supplier
S.I.C.: 4911
N.A.I.C.S.: 221122
Guido Kaupe *(Mng Dir)*
Urich Wittiber *(Mng Dir)*

FPS Frankfurt Passenger Services GmbH (1)
Building 201A HBK 259
60549 Frankfurt am Main, Germany
Tel.: (49) 69 690 28933
Fax: (49) 69 690 59952
Passenger Air Transportation Services
S.I.C.: 4581
N.A.I.C.S.: 488190
Ursula Gruenewald *(Co-Mng Dir)*
Martin Roll *(Co-Mng Dir)*

FraCareServices GmbH (1)
Hugo-Eckener-Ring
FAC1 HBK 41, 60549 Frankfurt, Germany (51%)
Tel.: (49) 6969069101
Fax: (49) 6969069108
E-Mail: fracare-info@fracare.ge
Web Site: www.fraport.com
Emp.: 600
Airport Services for the Handicapped
S.I.C.: 4581
N.A.I.C.S.: 488119
Brigitte Press *(Mng Dir)*

Fraport Cargo Services GmbH (1)
Cargo City South Building 532
60549 Frankfurt am Main, Germany (100%)
Tel.: (49) 6969070231
Fax: (49) 6969054971
E-Mail: info@fraport-cargo.de
Web Site: www.fraport-cargo.com
Emp.: 630
Cargo Handling Services
S.I.C.: 4581
N.A.I.C.S.: 488190
Diana Schoneich *(Mng Dir)*

Division:

APS Airport Personal Service GmbH (2)
Building 458
60549 Frankfurt am Main, Germany (100%)
Tel.: (49) 6969070652
Fax: (49) 6969059684
E-Mail: kontakt@aps-airport.de
Web Site: www.aps-airport.de
Emp.: 1,700
Human Resource Management Services
S.I.C.: 9441
N.A.I.C.S.: 923130
Michael Mueller *(Chm)*
Winfried Hartmann *(Deputy Chm)*
Udo Marquardt *(Mng Dir)*
Arthur Zeh *(Mng Dir)*

Fraport Immobilienservice und -entwicklungs GmbH & Co. KG (1)
Unterschweinstiege 10
Florsheim am Main, Frankfurt, 60549, Germany (100%)
Tel.: (49) 6145598661
Fax: (49) 6964355009
E-Mail: info@fraport-immo.com
Emp.: 9
Real Estate Development Services
S.I.C.: 6531
N.A.I.C.S.: 531390
Gitta Mir-Ali *(Mng Dir)*

Fraport Objekt Monchhof GmbH (1)
Schieferstein 8
65439 Florsheim, Germany
Tel.: (49) 6145 5986 0
Fax: (49) 6145 5986 87
Emp.: 10
Airport Management Services
S.I.C.: 4581
N.A.I.C.S.: 488119
Gitta Mir-Ali *(Gen Mgr)*

Fraport Real Estate 162 163 GmbH & Co. KG (1)
Schieferstein 8
Florsheim, 65439, Germany
Tel.: (49) 614559860
Fax: (49) 6145598687
Web Site: www.fraport.com
Emp.: 1
Real Estate Management Services
S.I.C.: 6531
N.A.I.C.S.: 531390
Gitta Mir-Ali *(Gen Mgr)*

Fraport Real Estate Verwaltungs GmbH (1)
Schieferstein 8
Florsheim, Hessen, 65439, Germany
Tel.: (49) 6145598661
Fax: (49) 6145598687
Real Estate Management Services
S.I.C.: 6531
N.A.I.C.S.: 531390

Fraport Security Services GmbH (1)
Hugo-Eckener-Ring FAC 1 D 6
60549 Frankfurt am Main, Germany (100%)
Tel.: (49) 6969025200
Fax: (49) 6969059402
E-Mail: info@frasec.com.de
Web Site: www.frasec.com
Emp.: 3,000
Airport Security Services
S.I.C.: 7381
N.A.I.C.S.: 561612
Claudia Uhe *(Chm)*
Rainer Friebertshauser *(Mng Dir)*
Barber Topfer *(Mng Dir)*

FraSec Fraport Security Services GmbH (1)
Hugo-Eckener-Ring FAC 1 C/D 9 HBK 16
60549 Frankfurt am Main, Germany
Tel.: (49) 69 690 252 00
Fax: (49) 69 690 590 45
E-Mail: frasecinfo@frasec.de
Web Site: www.frasec.de
Security System Services
S.I.C.: 7382
N.A.I.C.S.: 561621

Media Frankfurt GmbH (1)
Unterschweinstiege 2-14
Frankfurt, 60549, Germany (51%)
Tel.: (49) 69697080
Fax: (49) 696970842
E-Mail: info@media-frankfurt.de
Web Site: www.media-frankfurt.de
Emp.: 40
Airport Advertising Displays Marketer
S.I.C.: 4581
N.A.I.C.S.: 488119
Simone Schwab *(Mng Dir)*

Medical Airport Service GmbH (1)
Langer Kornweg 7
65451 Kelsterbach, Germany (50%)
Tel.: (49) 610750380
Fax: (49) 6107 503828
Web Site: www.medical-airport-service.de
Environmental, Medical & Business Support Services
S.I.C.: 7389
N.A.I.C.S.: 561499
Udo Sicker *(CEO)*
Dieter Arnold *(Mng Dir)*

N*ICE Aircraft Service & Supports GmbH (1)
Frankfurt Airport Center 1
Hugo-Eckener-Ring, 60549 Frankfurt, Germany (52%)
Tel.: (49) 6969021956
Fax: (49) 6969059422
E-Mail: info@nice-services.aero
Web Site: www.nice-services.aero
De-Icing Services
S.I.C.: 4581
N.A.I.C.S.: 488119

operational services GmbH & Co. KG (1)
Flughafen Frankfurt Terminal 2
Burogebaude 150
HPK 059, 60547 Frankfurt am Main, Germany (50%)
Tel.: (49) 6969068000
Fax: (49) 6969068005
E-Mail: info@o-s.de
Web Site: www.operational-services.de
Emp.: 400
Airport Information & Communication Services
S.I.C.: 7389
N.A.I.C.S.: 519190
Frank Oidtmann *(Mng Dir)*

Perishable Center GmbH + Co. Betriebs KG (1)
Cargo City Frankfurt
Building 454 Gate 26, 60549 Frankfurt am Main, Germany
Tel.: (49) 6969502220
Fax: (49) 6969502209
E-Mail: info@pcf-frankfurt.de
Web Site: www.pcf-frankfurt.de
Emp.: 150
Perishable Cargo Handling Services
S.I.C.: 4581
N.A.I.C.S.: 488119
Herchen Hein *(Gen Mgr)*

Tradeport Frankfurt GmbH (1)
Frankfurt Airport
Cargo City South Building 532, 60549 Frankfurt am Main, Germany
Tel.: (49) 969070652
Telex: 412 811 fag dc d
Fax: (49) 69 690 54971
Web Site: www.tradeport-logistics.com
Emp.: 40
Cargo & Logistics Services
S.I.C.: 4581
N.A.I.C.S.: 488119

Zentrum fur integrierte Verkehrssysteme GmbH (1)
Robert-Bosch-Str 7
64293 Darmstadt, Germany
Tel.: (49) 6151270280
Fax: (49) 61512702810
E-Mail: kontakt@ziv.de
Web Site: www.ziv.de
Emp.: 20
Airport Management Services
S.I.C.: 4581
N.A.I.C.S.: 488119
Peter Stoveken *(Mng Dir)*

Affiliates:

Airmail Center Frankfurt GmbH (1)
Frankfurt Airport
PO Box 750164
Gate 3 Building 189, 60549 Frankfurt am Main, Germany (40%)
Tel.: (49) 6969077000
Fax: (49) 6969059699
E-Mail: Office@airmail-center.de
Web Site: www.airmail-center.de
Emp.: 38
Airmail Handling Services
S.I.C.: 7389
N.A.I.C.S.: 561431
Martina Nofz *(Mng Dir)*

ASG Airport Service Gesellschaft mbH (1)
Hauspostkasten 149
60549 Frankfurt am Main, Germany (49%)
Tel.: (49) 6969036031
Fax: (49) 69691487
Web Site: www.asg-airport.de
Airport Services
S.I.C.: 4581
N.A.I.C.S.: 488119
Alexander Fuchs *(Mng Dir)*
Martin Walde *(Mng Dir)*

Flughafen Saarbruecken GmbH (1)
Balthasar-Goldstein-Strasse
66131 Saarbrucken, Germany (51%)
Tel.: (49) 689383204
Fax: (49) 689383313
E-Mail: info@flughafen-saarbruecken.de
Web Site: www.flughafen-saarbruecken.de
Airport Operations
S.I.C.: 4581
N.A.I.C.S.: 488119
Thomas Schuck *(CEO)*
Roman Grethel *(Mng Dir)*

U.S. Subsidiary:

Air-Transport IT Services, Inc. (1)
5950 Hazeltine National Dr Ste 210
Orlando, FL 32822 (100%)

Tel.: (407) 370-4664
Fax: (407) 370-4657
E-Mail: info@airit.com
Web Site: www.airit.com
Emp.: 100
Turnkey, Integrated Air Transport Solutions Including Software, Hardware, Network, Installation & 24 Hour Service, Support & Help Desk
S.I.C.: 7379
N.A.I.C.S.: 541519
Betros Wakim *(Co-Founder, Pres & CEO)*
Roland Krieg *(Chm)*
Chris Keller *(COO & Exec VP)*
T. Jeffrey Shull *(Exec VP)*

Non-U.S. Subsidiaries:

Cairo Airport Company (1)
Cairo Airtport Rd Salah Salen Rd Execulise Service Bldg Departure 1
PO Box 11776
Cairo, Egypt
Tel.: (20) 222655735
Fax: (20) 0226966808
E-Mail: enaia.aouni@cairo-airport.com
Web Site: www.cairo-airport.com
Emp.: 4,000
Airport Management Services
S.I.C.: 4581
N.A.I.C.S.: 488119
Ralf Schustereder *(Exec Dir)*

Fraport IC Ictas Havaliman Yer Hizmetleri AS (1)
Antalya Havalimani 1
DisHatlarTerminali, 7230 Antalya, Turkey (51%)
Tel.: (90) 2423303600
Fax: (90) 2423303648
E-Mail: info@icfairport.com
Web Site: www.icfairport.com
Airport Ground Handling Services
S.I.C.: 4581
N.A.I.C.S.: 488119
Melih Dipova *(Asst Gen Mgr)*

Fraport Malta Business Services Ltd. (1)
Mayfair Complex Saint George's Bay
San Giljan, STJ 3311, Malta
Tel.: (356) 21384088
Aviation Terminal Services
S.I.C.: 4581
N.A.I.C.S.: 488190

Fraport Saudi Arabia Ltd. (1)
PO Box 12115
Riyadh, 11473, Saudi Arabia (100%)
Tel.: (966) 12200842
Fax: (966) 12200838
Web Site: www.fraport.com
Emp.: 6
Airport Management & Development Services
S.I.C.: 4581
N.A.I.C.S.: 488119
Jan Laufs *(Mng Dir)*

Fraport Twin Star Airport Management AD (1)
Varna Airport
9000 Varna, Bulgaria
Tel.: (359) 52573201
Fax: (359) 52500245
E-Mail: office@fraport-bulgaria.com
Web Site: www.varna-airport.bg
Emp.: 800
Airport Operation Services
S.I.C.: 4581
N.A.I.C.S.: 488119
Dimitar Kostadinov *(Dir-Airport)*

Lima Airport Partners srl (1)
Avenida Elmer Faucett Jorge Chabez International Airport
Lima, Peru (70.01%)
Tel.: (51) 15173400
Fax: (51) 15173624
Web Site: www.lap.com.pe
Airport Operation Services
S.I.C.: 4581
N.A.I.C.S.: 488119
Jaime Daly *(Chm)*

Shanghai Frankfurt Airport Consulting Services Co., Ltd. (SFACS) (1)
Room 23C T1 Jiahui Plaza No 2601 Xie Tu Rd
Xuhui District, 200030 Shanghai, China (50%)
Tel.: (86) 2164263017
Fax: (86) 2164263019
E-Mail: sfacs@sfacs.cn
Web Site: www.sfacs.cn
Emp.: 2
Airport Management Training & Consulting Services
S.I.C.: 8742
N.A.I.C.S.: 541611
Michael Kunz *(Mng Dir)*

Tradeport Hong Kong Ltd. (1)
Hong Kong International Airport Tradeport Logistics Centre
1 Chun Yue Road, Hong Kong, China (Hong Kong)
Tel.: (852) 22861332
Fax: (852) 27543652
E-Mail: info@tradeport-hongkong.com
Web Site: www.tradeport-logistics.com
Emp.: 50
Avionics Logistics Services
S.I.C.: 7389
N.A.I.C.S.: 561499

FRAPPA

132 Rue De Soras
07430 Davezieux, Ardeche, France
Tel.: (33) 475334643
Fax: (33) 475334041
E-Mail: frappa@frappa.com
Web Site: www.frappa.com
Sls.: $24,200,000
Emp.: 87
Business Description:
Motor Vehicles & Car Bodies
S.I.C.: 3711
N.A.I.C.S.: 336111
Personnel:
Julien Torre *(CEO)*

FRAS-LE S.A.

Rodovia RS 122 Km 66 n 10 945
Bairro Forqueta
95115-550 Caxias do Sul, RS, Brazil
Tel.: (55) 54 3289 1517
Fax: (55) 54 3289 1905
E-Mail: ri@fras-le.com
Web Site: www.fras-le.com
Year Founded: 1954
FRAS3—(BRAZ)
Business Description:
Brake System Mfr
S.I.C.: 3714
N.A.I.C.S.: 336340
Personnel:
Daniel Raul Randon *(CEO)*

FRASER & NEAVE LIMITED

21-00 Alexandra Point 438 Alexandra Road
Singapore, 119958, Singapore
Tel.: (65) 63189393
Fax: (65) 62710811
E-Mail: ir@fraserandneave.com
Web Site: www.fraserandneave.com
Year Founded: 1883
F99—(OTC SES)
Rev.: $2,871,087,884
Assets: $11,697,194,325
Liabilities: $5,106,880,877
Net Worth: $6,590,313,449
Earnings: $806,705,232
Emp.: 17,000
Fiscal Year-end: 09/30/12
Business Description:
Holding Company
S.I.C.: 2086
N.A.I.C.S.: 312111
Personnel:
Choon Kit Hui *(CFO)*
Jui Sia Ng *(CEO-Non Alcoholic Beverages)*
Anthony Fook Seng Cheong *(Sec)*
Board of Directors:
Sirivadhanabhakdi Charoen
Chotiphat Bijananda
Sithichai Chaikriangkrai
Timothy Chee Ming Chia
Y. A. M. Tengku Syed Bendahara Jamalullail
Sirivadhanabhakdi Khunying Wanna
Poh Tiong Koh
Thapana Sirivadhanabhakdi
Siripen Sitasuwan
Transfer Agent:
Tricor Barbinder Share Registration Services
80 Robinson Road 02-00
Singapore, Singapore

Subsidiaries:

F&N Foods Pte Ltd (1)
214 Pandan Loop
Singapore, 128405, Singapore
Tel.: (65) 6210 8108
Fax: (65) 6210 8118
E-Mail: customerfeedback@fnnfoods.com
Beverage Mfr & Distr
S.I.C.: 2082
N.A.I.C.S.: 312120

F&N Interflavine Pte Ltd (1)
214 Pandan Loop
Singapore, 128405, Singapore
Tel.: (65) 6276 0135
Fax: (65) 6276 0138
Beverages Mfr
S.I.C.: 2082
N.A.I.C.S.: 312120
Jennifer See *(Gen Mgr)*

F&N Investments Pte Ltd (1)
438 Alexandra Road 21-00 Alexandra Point Queenstown
Singapore, 119958, Singapore
Tel.: (65) 63189393
Investment Management Services
S.I.C.: 6211
N.A.I.C.S.: 523999

Frasers Centrepoint Limited (1)
438 Alexandra Road 02-00 Alexandra Point
Singapore, 119958, Singapore
Tel.: (65) 6276 4882
Fax: (65) 6272 8776
E-Mail: sales@fraserscentrepointhomes.com
Web Site: www.fraserscentrepoint.com
Real Estate Development Services
S.I.C.: 6531
N.A.I.C.S.: 531390
Ee Seng Lim *(CEO)*

Subsidiaries:

FCL Centrepoint Pte Ltd (2)
Alexandra Point 21-00 438 Alexandra Road
Singapore, 119958, Singapore
Tel.: (65) 62764882
Property Management Services
S.I.C.: 6531
N.A.I.C.S.: 531312

FCL Property Investments Pte Ltd (2)
Alexandra Point Suite 21-00 438 Alexandra Road
Singapore, 119958, Singapore
Tel.: (65) 6736 4088
Property Management Services
S.I.C.: 6531
N.A.I.C.S.: 531311

Fraser Residence Orchard Pte Ltd (2)
2 Mount Elizabeth Link
Singapore, 227973, Singapore
Tel.: (65) 66 439 800
Fax: (65) 66 439 888
E-Mail: sales.singapore@frasershospitality.com
Web Site: orchard.frasershospitality.com
Property Management Services
S.I.C.: 6531
N.A.I.C.S.: 531311
Choe Peng Sum *(CEO)*

Frasers Centrepoint Property Management Services Pte Ltd (2)
1 Sengkang Square 04-20 Compass Point Sengkang
Singapore, 545078, Singapore
Tel.: (65) 68812707
Property Management Services
S.I.C.: 6531
N.A.I.C.S.: 531312

Frasers Hospitality Pte Ltd (2)
491B River Valley Road 08-01 Valley Point
Singapore, 248373, Singapore
Tel.: (65) 6898 0800
Fax: (65) 64 150 519
E-Mail: sales@frasershospitality.com
Web Site: www.frasershospitality.com
Hospitality Services
S.I.C.: 8062
N.A.I.C.S.: 622110
Choe Peng Sum *(CEO)*
Alan Tang *(COO)*

Subsidiary:

Frasers Hospitality Management Pte Ltd (3)
419B River Valley Road 08-03 Valley Point Downtown
Singapore, 248373, Singapore
Tel.: (65) 62700800
Fax: (65) 64150519
Web Site: www.frasershospitality.com
Hospitality Management Consulting Services
S.I.C.: 8748
N.A.I.C.S.: 541618
Tonya Khong *(Gen Mgr)*

Non-U.S. Subsidiaries:

Frasers Hospitality Japan Kabushiki Kaisha (3)
1-17-11 Nambanaka
Naniwa-Ku, Osaka, 556-0011, Japan
Tel.: (81) 666357111
Fax: (81) 666357555
E-Mail: reservation.osaka@frasershospitality.com
Web Site: www.osaka.frasershospitality.com
Emp.: 20
Residential Operating Services
S.I.C.: 7021
N.A.I.C.S.: 721310
Yasuko Sugiyama *(Gen Mgr)*

Frasers Hospitality (Thailand) Ltd (3)
55 Langsuan Road Lumpini
Pathumwan, Bangkok, 10330, Thailand
Tel.: (66) 2 250 6666
Fax: (66) 2 250 6699
E-Mail: sales.bangkok@frasershospitality.com
Property Development Services
S.I.C.: 6531
N.A.I.C.S.: 531390

Frasers Hospitality (UK) Limited (3)
81 Cromwell Road
London, SW7 5BW, United Kingdom
Tel.: (44) 20 7341 5595
Fax: (44) 20 7341 5588
E-Mail: sales.london@frasershospitality.com
Web Site: www.frasershospitality.com
Emp.: 20
Real Estate Management Services
S.I.C.: 6531
N.A.I.C.S.: 531390

Frasers Property (Europe) Holdings Pte Ltd (2)
438 Alexandra Road 21-00 Alexandra Point
Singapore, 119958, Singapore
Tel.: (65) 62764882
Financial Management Services
S.I.C.: 6211
N.A.I.C.S.: 523999

Orrick Investments Pte Ltd (2)
438A Alexandra Road Alexandra Technopark Suite B1-03
Singapore, 119967, Singapore
Tel.: (65) 6274 4952
Fax: (65) 6274 1875
Real Estate Management Services
S.I.C.: 6531
N.A.I.C.S.: 531390

River Valley Apartments Pte Ltd (2)
491A River Valley Road B1-00 Downtown
Singapore, 248372, Singapore
Tel.: (65) 67375800
Fax: (65) 67375560
Real Estate Management Services
S.I.C.: 6531
N.A.I.C.S.: 531390
Peng Sum Choe *(CEO)*

Fraser & Neave Limited—(Continued)

River Valley Shopping Centre Pte Ltd (2)
Alexandra Point 438 Alexandra Road
Singapore, Singapore
Tel.: (65) 67375523
Fax: (65) 67370261
Emp.: 36
Property Management Services
S.I.C.: 6531
N.A.I.C.S.: 531311
Patricia Tan *(Mgr-Centre)*

River Valley Tower Pte Ltd (2)
491b River Valley Road
Singapore, 248371, Singapore
Tel.: (65) 67375523
Fax: (65) 67370261
Property Management Services
S.I.C.: 6531
N.A.I.C.S.: 531311

Riverside Property Pte Ltd (2)
11 Unity Street
Singapore, 237995, Singapore
Tel.: (65) 67364800
Fax: (65) 67363225
Property Development Services
S.I.C.: 6531
N.A.I.C.S.: 531390
Tonya Khong *(Gen Mgr)*

Yishun Development Pte Ltd (2)
930 Yishun Ave 2 No D2-33
Singapore, 769098, Singapore
Tel.: (65) 6754 2300
Fax: (65) 6754 5622
Property Management Services
S.I.C.: 6531
N.A.I.C.S.: 531311
Valerie Tan *(Asst Gen Mgr)*

Non-U.S. Subsidiaries:

Beijing Fraser Suites Real Estate Management Co., Ltd (2)
Rm 201 2/F No 12 Jintong West Rd
Chaoyang Dist, Beijing, 100020, China
Tel.: (86) 1059086000
Fax: (86) 1059086000
Real Estate Management Services
S.I.C.: 6531
N.A.I.C.S.: 531390

Frasers City Quarter Pty Limited (2)
L 11 488 Kent St
Sydney, NSW, 2000, Australia
Tel.: (61) 2 8823 8800
Property Management Services
S.I.C.: 6531
N.A.I.C.S.: 531312

Frasers Property Management Australia Pty Limited (2)
L 11 488 Kent St
Sydney, NSW, 2000, Australia
Tel.: (61) 288238800
Fax: (61) 288238801
Property Management Services
S.I.C.: 6531
N.A.I.C.S.: 531312

Frasers Property (UK) Limited (2)
81 Cromwell Rd
London, SW7 5BW, United Kingdom
Tel.: (44) 20 7244 9889
Fax: (44) 20 7373 3766
Property Management Services
S.I.C.: 6531
N.A.I.C.S.: 531311

Subsidiary:

Frasers Property Developments Ltd (3)
81 Cromwell Road
London, SW7 5BW, United Kingdom
Tel.: (44) 20 7244 9889
Web Site: www.leasersproperty.dev.com
Property Management Services
S.I.C.: 6531
N.A.I.C.S.: 531311

Frasers Town Hall Pty Ltd (2)
L 11 488 Kent St
Sydney, NSW, 2000, Australia
Tel.: (61) 288238800
Property Development Services
S.I.C.: 6531
N.A.I.C.S.: 531312

Frasers Town Hall Residences Pty Ltd (2)
488 Kent St
Sydney, NSW, 2000, Australia
Tel.: (61) 2 8823 8888
Fax: (61) 88238889
E-Mail: reservation.sydney@frasershospitality.com
Web Site: www.frasershospitality.com
Property Management Services
S.I.C.: 6531
N.A.I.C.S.: 531312

Islington Theatre Development Limited (2)
81 Cromwell Road
London, SW7 5BW, United Kingdom
Tel.: (44) 20 7244 9889
Property Development Services
S.I.C.: 6531
N.A.I.C.S.: 531390

NGH Properties Limited (2)
81 Cromwell Road
London, SW7 5BW, United Kingdom
Tel.: (44) 2075891105
Fax: (44) 2075899433
Property Development Services
S.I.C.: 6531
N.A.I.C.S.: 531390

Vision Huaqing (Beijing) Development Co., Ltd (2)
Unit 408 Level 4 Sohu com Plaza Building
9 No 1 Zhongguancun East Road
Haidian District, Beijing, 100084, China
Tel.: (86) 10 6279 0008
Fax: (86) 10 6279 0058
Property Management Services
S.I.C.: 6531
N.A.I.C.S.: 531312

Times Publishing Limited (1)
Times Centre 1 New Industrial Rd
Singapore, 536196, Singapore SG
Tel.: (65) 62139288 (100%)
Fax: (65) 62844733
E-Mail: tpl@tpl.com.sg
Web Site: www.timespublishing.com.sg
Emp.: 2,500
Publishing, Printing, Retailing, Distribution, Education, Conferences & Exhibitions Import Export
S.I.C.: 2731
N.A.I.C.S.: 511130
Sik Ngee Goh *(CEO)*

Subsidiaries:

Educational Technologies Pte Ltd (2)
Times Centre No 1 New Industrial Road
Singapore, 536196, Singapore
Tel.: (65) 6336 8185
Fax: (65) 6336 1821
E-Mail: Singapore@ETLhomelearning.com
Web Site: www.tpl.com.sg/contact_us_singapore.asp
Educational Support Services
S.I.C.: 8299
N.A.I.C.S.: 611710

JCS Digital Solutions Pte Ltd (2)
438 Ang Mo Kio Industrial Park 1 Level 3
Ang Mo Kio Avenue 10
Singapore, 569619, Singapore
Tel.: (65) 67429293
Fax: (65) 67482748
E-Mail: enquiries@jcs.com.sg
Web Site: www.jcs.com.sg
Digital Printing Services
S.I.C.: 2759
N.A.I.C.S.: 323111
Jason Chia *(Gen Mgr)*

Marshall Cavendish International (S) Pte Ltd (2)
Times Centre
1 New Industrial Rd, Singapore, 536196, Singapore (100%)
Tel.: (65) 62139288
Fax: (65) 62881186
E-Mail: fpl@marshallcavendish.com
Web Site: www.teol.com.sg
Emp.: 550
Books & Magazine Publisher
S.I.C.: 2741
N.A.I.C.S.: 511140

MC Online Pte Ltd (2)
1 New Industrial Road
Times Centre, Singapore, 536196, Singapore
Tel.: (65) 6285 8616
Fax: (65) 6285 8696
E-Mail: info@mconline.sg
Web Site: www.lead.com.sg
Educational Support Services
S.I.C.: 8299
N.A.I.C.S.: 611710
Jason Lek *(Head-Creative Design)*

Panpac Education Pte Ltd (2)
1 New Industrial Road Times Centre
Singapore, 536196, Singapore
Tel.: (65) 62139228
Fax: (65) 68463440
E-Mail: mcis_mktg@sg.marshallcavendish.com
Web Site: www.panpaceducation.com
Educational Books Distr
S.I.C.: 5192
N.A.I.C.S.: 424920
Joy Tan *(Gen Mgr)*

Pansing Distribution Pte Ltd (2)
Times Centre 1
1 New Industrial Road, Singapore, 536196, Singapore (100%)
Tel.: (65) 63199939
Fax: (65) 64594930
Web Site: www.pansing.com
Emp.: 50
Book Distr
S.I.C.: 3555
N.A.I.C.S.: 333244
David Buckland *(Gen Mgr)*

Times Conferences & Exhibitions Pte Ltd (2)
Times Ctr
1 New Industrial Rd, Singapore, 536196, Singapore
Tel.: (65) 62139288
Fax: (65) 62844733
E-Mail: tpl@tpl.com.sg
Web Site: www.timespublishing.sg
Emp.: 1,000
S.I.C.: 2731
N.A.I.C.S.: 511130
Goh Sikngee *(CEO)*

Times Educational Services Pte Ltd (2)
11 Unity St
02-14 15 Robertson Walk, Singapore, 237995, Singapore (100%)
Tel.: (65) 68350355
Fax: (65) 68350955
E-Mail: tes@tpl.com.sg
Web Site: www.tes.edu.sg
Emp.: 20
Educational Publisher
S.I.C.: 2731
N.A.I.C.S.: 511130
Bee Ing Lim *(Mgr-Sls & Mktg)*

Times Printers Pte Ltd (2)
16 Tuas Ave 5
Singapore, 639340, Singapore (100%)
Tel.: (65) 63112888
Fax: (65) 68621313
E-Mail: tp@timesprinters.com
Web Site: www.timesprinters.com
Emp.: 450
Magazines, Periodicals, Directories & Show Dailies Printing Services
S.I.C.: 3555
N.A.I.C.S.: 333244
Tay Kiah Chiew *(Head-Printing)*

Times The Bookshop Pte Ltd (2)
438 Ang Mo Kio Indus Pk 1 Ave 10 Unit 02-01
Singapore, 569619, Singapore (100%)
Tel.: (65) 62139288
Fax: (65) 64564832
E-Mail: ttb@tpl.com.sg
Web Site: www.timesone.com.sg
Emp.: 74
Book Retailer
S.I.C.: 3555
N.A.I.C.S.: 333244
Fujita Eiji *(Gen Mgr)*

U.S. Subsidiary:

Marshall Cavendish Corporation (2)
99 White Plains Rd
Tarrytown, NY 10591-9001 (100%)
Mailing Address:
PO Box 2001
Tarrytown, NY 10591-9001
Tel.: (914) 332-8888
Fax: (914) 332-1888
E-Mail: mcc@marshallcavendish.com
Web Site: www.marshallcavendish.us
Emp.: 30
Book & Magazine Publisher
S.I.C.: 2731
N.A.I.C.S.: 511130

Non-U.S. Subsidiaries:

Direct Educational Technologies India Pvt Ltd (2)
205-208 Cears Plaza 136 Residency Road
Bengaluru, 560025, India
Tel.: (91) 80 4149 7151 58
Fax: (91) 80 4149 7173
Web Site: www.tpl.com.sg/contact_us_india.asp
Educational Support Services
S.I.C.: 8299
N.A.I.C.S.: 611710

Everbest Printing (Guangzhou) Co. Ltd (2)
334 Huanshi South Road
Nansha District, Guangzhou, Guangdong, China 511458
Tel.: (86) 20 8498 1812
Fax: (86) 20 8498 1816
E-Mail: sales@everbest.com.hk
Commercial Printing Services
S.I.C.: 2759
N.A.I.C.S.: 323111

Everbest Printing Holdings Limited (2)
Rm 5 10/F Ko Fai Indl Bldg Blk C 7 Ko Fai Rd Yau Tong
Kowloon, China (Hong Kong)
Tel.: (852) 27274433
Fax: (852) 27727687
Emp.: 40
Commercial Printing Services
S.I.C.: 2759
N.A.I.C.S.: 323111
Derek Lam *(Gen Mgr)*

Far East Publications Ltd (2)
253 Asoke 12th Floor Sukhumvit 21 Road
Klongtoey Nua
Wattana District, Bangkok, 10110, Thailand
Tel.: (66) 2 261 1908
Fax: (66) 2 261 1912
Reference Books Distr
S.I.C.: 5192
N.A.I.C.S.: 424920

Marshall Cavendish Business Information (Hong Kong) Limited (2)
10/F Block C Seaview Estate 2-8 Watson Road
North Point, China (Hong Kong)
Tel.: (852) 3965 7800
Fax: (852) 2979 4528
E-Mail: bizinfo@hk.marshallcavendish.com
Business Support Services
S.I.C.: 7389
N.A.I.C.S.: 561499

Marshall Cavendish Limited (2)
32/38 Saffron Hill 5th Fl
London, EC1N 8FH, United Kingdom (100%)
Tel.: (44) 2074218120
Fax: (44) 2077346221
E-Mail: enquiries@marshallcavendish.co.uk
Web Site: www.marshallcavendish.co.uk
Emp.: 20
Book & Magazine Publisher
S.I.C.: 2731
N.A.I.C.S.: 511130

Marshall Cavendish Sdn Bhd (2)
Times Subang Lot 46 Hi Tech Industrial Park
Batu Tiga, Shah Alam, 40000, Malaysia (100%)
Tel.: (60) 356286888
Fax: (60) 56352706
E-Mail: cchang@mydotmarshallcavendish.com

Web Site: www.tpl.com.sg
Emp.: 300
Book Publisher
S.I.C.: 2731
N.A.I.C.S.: 511130
Christine Chong *(Deputy Head)*

Musicway Corporation Ltd. (2)
Unit 8 29 Business Park Dr
Nottinghill, Melbourne, VIC, 3168, Australia (100%)
Tel.: (61) 395589666
Fax: (61) 395589226
E-Mail: info@musicway.com.au
Web Site: www.musicway.com.au
Emp.: 20
Electronics Distr
S.I.C.: 2731
N.A.I.C.S.: 511130
Ryan Connolly *(Gen Mgr)*

Pansing IMM Pty Limited (2)
Unit 9 Discovery Cove 1801 Botany Rd
Banksmeadow, NSW, 2019, Australia
Tel.: (61) 2 8304 5900
Fax: (61) 2 9666 7843
Web Site: www.pansingimm.com
Book Whslr
S.I.C.: 5192
N.A.I.C.S.: 424920
Tony Antidormi *(Gen Mgr)*

Pansing Marketing Sdn Bhd (2)
Lot 557A & B Jalan Subang 3 Subang Jaya Industrial Estate
47610 Subang Jaya, Selangor, Malaysia
Tel.: (60) 3 5631 0794
Fax: (60) 3 5638 4337
Book Distr
S.I.C.: 5192
N.A.I.C.S.: 424920

Rainbow Products Limited (2)
Unit 4 19 Rodborough Rd
French's Forest, NSW, 2086, Australia (100%)
Tel.: (61) 294517577
Fax: (61) 294521233
E-Mail: sales@rainbowproducts.com.au
Web Site: www.rainbowproducts.com.au
Emp.: 10
Electronics Distr
S.I.C.: 2731
N.A.I.C.S.: 511130

STP Distributors (M) Sdn Bhd (2)
Lot 46 Subang Hi-Tech Industrial Park
Batu Tiga, Shah Alam, Selangor Darul Ehsan, 40000, Malaysia (30%)
Tel.: (60) 356286888
Fax: (60) 356363640
Emp.: 2
Book Distr
S.I.C.: 2731
N.A.I.C.S.: 511130
Vivian Cheng *(Gen Mgr)*

Times Offset (Malaysia) Sdn Bhd (2)
Lot 46 Subang Hi-Tech Industrial Park
Batu Tiga, Shah Alam, Selangor Darul Ehsan, 40000, Malaysia (100%)
Tel.: (60) 356286888
Fax: (60) 356286899
E-Mail: tosb_mktg@tpg.com.my
Web Site: www.timesoffset.com.my
Emp.: 170
Printing Services
S.I.C.: 2731
N.A.I.C.S.: 511130
Desmond Pang *(VP & Gen Mgr)*

Times Publishing (HK) Ltd (2)
10th Fl C Block Sea View Estate Wheson Rd N Plant
Hong Kong, China (Hong Kong) (100%)
Tel.: (852) 25668381
Fax: (852) 25080255
E-Mail: enquiries@tplhk.com.hk
Web Site: www.tpl.com.hk
Emp.: 100
Publishing, Retail & Distribution Services
S.I.C.: 2731
N.A.I.C.S.: 511130
Lau Gordon *(Mng Dir)*

Non-U.S. Subsidiary:

Fraser & Neave Holdings Bhd (1)
Level 8 F&N Point No 3 Jalan Metro Pudu 1 Fraser Business Park
Off Jalan Yew, 55100 Kuala Lumpur, Malaysia (56.7%)
Tel.: (60) 392352288
Fax: (60) 392227878
E-Mail: cosec@fn.com.my
Web Site: www.fn.com.my
F&N—(KLS)
Rev.: $1,064,149,889
Assets: $838,276,418
Liabilities: $337,660,586
Net Worth: $500,615,832
Earnings: $79,055,685
Emp.: 3,000
Fiscal Year-end: 09/30/13
Soft Drinks Mfr
S.I.C.: 2086
N.A.I.C.S.: 312111
Somsak Chayapong *(CEO)*
Wing Chong Soon *(CFO & Co-Sec)*
Mayeen May Fun Wong *(Co-Sec)*

Subsidiary:

Premier Milk (Malaya) Sdn Bhd (2)
70 Jalan Universiti
46700 Petaling Jaya, Selan Gor, Malaysia
Tel.: (60) 379565600
Fax: (60) 379566950
Web Site: www.tradenex.com
Emp.: 900
Dairy Products
S.I.C.: 2026
N.A.I.C.S.: 311511
Ismael Ibrahim *(Mgr-HR)*

FRASER FORD SALES LTD.

815 King St West
Oshawa, ON, L1J 2L4, Canada
Tel.: (905) 576-1800
Fax: (905) 576-6078
Toll Free: (888) 259-3673
E-Mail: info@fraserford.ca
Web Site: www.fraserford.ca
Year Founded: 1996
Rev.: $19,466,485
Emp.: 69
Business Description:
New & Used Car Dealers
S.I.C.: 5511
N.A.I.C.S.: 441110
Personnel:
Robert Fraser *(Owner)*

FRASER PAPERS INC.

181 Bay St Ste 200
Toronto, ON, M5J 2T3, Canada
Tel.: (416) 359-8605
Fax: (416) 359-8606
Toll Free: (800) 920-9988
Web Site: www.fraserpapers.com
Year Founded: 1929
Sales Range: $300-349.9 Million
Emp.: 250
Business Description:
Printing & Writing Papers Mfr
Import Export
S.I.C.: 2621
N.A.I.C.S.: 322121
Personnel:
Jeff Dutton *(Pres & CEO)*
Glen Mcmillan *(Chief Restructuring Officer)*
Jim Gehrman *(Pres-Sucampo Pharma Americas, Inc. & Sr VP-Sls & Mktg)*
Transfer Agent:
CIBC Mellon Trust Company
Adelaide Street Postal Station
PO Box 7010
Toronto, ON, M5C 2W9, Canada
Tel.: (416) 643-5500
Fax: (416) 643-5501
Toll Free: (800) 387-0825

Subsidiary:

Katahdin Paper Company (1)
50 Main St E
Millinocket, ME 04430
Tel.: (207) 723-5131
Web Site: www.pulpandpaper.org
Emp.: 550
Mfr. of Newspaper Pulp, Groundwood Printing & Writing Papers
S.I.C.: 2621
N.A.I.C.S.: 322121
Rick Grunthaler *(Dir-HR)*

FRASER RANGE METALS GROUP LIMITED

Office J Level 2 1139 Hay Street
West Perth, WA, 6005, Australia
Tel.: (61) 8 9486 4036
Fax: (61) 8 9486 4799
E-Mail: info@frmetals.com.au
Web Site: www.frmetals.com.au
FRN—(ASX)
Rev.: $10,314
Assets: $80,505
Liabilities: $521,221
Net Worth: ($440,716)
Earnings: ($1,330,225)
Fiscal Year-end: 06/30/13
Business Description:
Mineral Exploration Services
S.I.C.: 1099
N.A.I.C.S.: 212299
Personnel:
Samuel Edis *(Sec)*
Board of Directors:
Nicholas Bishop
Nicholas Chen Chik Ong
Daniel Smith
Legal Counsel:
Steinepreis Paganin
Level 4 The Read Building 16 Milligan Street
Perth, WA, 6000, Australia
Tel.: (61) 8 9321 4000
Fax: (61) 8 9321 4333

FRASER RIVER PILE & DREDGE (GP) INC.

1830 River Drive
New Westminster, BC, V3M 2A8, Canada
Tel.: (604) 522-7971
Fax: (604) 521-7530
E-Mail: info@frpd.com
Web Site: www.frpd.com
Year Founded: 1911
Rev.: $28,778,778
Emp.: 200
Business Description:
Marine Construction & Dredging Contractor
S.I.C.: 4491
N.A.I.C.S.: 488320
Personnel:
Tom W. Lively *(Pres & CEO)*

FRASER SURREY DOCKS LP

11060 Elevator Road
Surrey, BC, V3V 2R7, Canada
Tel.: (604) 581-2233
Fax: (604) 581-7343
E-Mail: interact@fsd.bc.ca
Web Site: www.fsd.bc.ca
Year Founded: 1964
Rev.: $13,853,300
Emp.: 70
Business Description:
Marine Cargo Handling
S.I.C.: 4491
N.A.I.C.S.: 488320
Personnel:
Jeff Scott *(Pres & CEO)*
Leonard Cox *(CFO)*

FRATELLI DE CECCO DI FILIPPO FARA SAN MARTINO S.P.A.

Via Fratelli de Cecco 8
Industrial Zone, 66015 Fara San Martino, Chieti, Italy
Tel.: (39) 8729861
Fax: (39) 0872980426
E-Mail: dececco@dececco.it
Web Site: www.dececco.it
Year Founded: 1886
Sales Range: $300-349.9 Million
Emp.: 300
Business Description:
Pasta Mfr
S.I.C.: 2045
N.A.I.C.S.: 311824
Personnel:
Filippo Antonio De Cecco *(Chm)*
Giuseppe Aristide De Cecco *(Co-CEO)*
Saturino De Cecco *(Co-CEO)*

FRATELLO TRADE JSC BANJA LUKA

Ramici bb
Banja Luka, Bosnia & Herzegovina
Tel.: (387) 51 394 110
Fax: (387) 51 394 111
E-Mail: info@fratello-trade.com
Web Site: www.fratello-trade.com
Year Founded: 1999
FRTL—(BANJ)
Emp.: 70
Business Description:
Fresh & Frozen Seafood Distr
S.I.C.: 2092
N.A.I.C.S.: 311710
Personnel:
Matej Penca *(Chm-Mgmt Bd)*
Nebojsa Antonijevic *(Member-Mgmt Bd)*
Goran Crnic *(Member-Mgmt Bd)*
Mario Derajic *(Member-Mgmt Bd)*
Velimir Zdjelar *(Member-Mgmt Bd)*

FRAUENTHAL HOLDING AG

Rooseveltplatz 10
A-1090 Vienna, Austria
Tel.: (43) 15054206
Fax: (43) 1505420633
E-Mail: holding@frauenthal.at
Web Site: www.frauenthal.at
FKA—(VIE)
Rev.: $686,436,314
Assets: $458,338,577
Liabilities: $286,711,325
Net Worth: $171,627,252
Earnings: $52,518,130
Emp.: 2,597
Fiscal Year-end: 12/31/12
Business Description:
Insulator Operation Mfr
S.I.C.: 3999
N.A.I.C.S.: 339999
Personnel:
Hannes Winkler *(Chm-Supervisory Bd)*
Dietmar Kubis *(Vice Chm-Supervisory Bd)*
Matias Mosesson *(Mng Dir, CTO & Chief Sls Officer-Frauenthal Automotive Div)*
Markus Gahleitner *(Mng Dir & CFO-Frauenthal Automotive Div)*
Helfried Jelinek *(Mng Dir & COO-Frauenthal Automotive Div)*
Josef Unterwieser *(Mng Dir & COO-Frauenthal Automotive Div)*
Wolfgang Knezek *(CIO & VP-Org)*
Hans-Peter Moser *(Member-Exec Bd-SHT Haustechnik AG Div)*
Martin Sailer *(Member-Exec Bd-Frauenthal Automotive Div)*
Supervisory Board of Directors:
Hannes Winkler
Birgit Eckert
August Enzian
Oskar Grunwald
Heike Jandl
Klaus Kreitschek
Dietmar Kubis
Johannes Strohmayer
Jurgen Tschabitzer

Frauenthal Holding AG—(Continued)

Subsidiaries:

Frauenthal Automotive Components GmbH (1)
Prinz-Eugen-Strabe30/4a
1040 Vienna, Austria
Tel.: (43) 15054206
Fax: (43) 15054233
E-Mail: holding@frauenthal.at
Emp.: 200
Motor Vehicle Body Mfr
S.I.C.: 3711
N.A.I.C.S.: 336211
Hanspeter Moser *(Exec Dir)*

Styria Federn Ges.m.b.H. (1)
Gussstahlwerk-Str 21
8750 Judenburg, Austria
Tel.: (43) 3572701324
Fax: (43) 3572701360
E-Mail: serandl@styriagroup.com
Web Site: www.styriagroup.com
Emp.: 150
Motor Vehicle Parts Whslr
S.I.C.: 5013
N.A.I.C.S.: 423120
Armin Goeffler *(Mng Dir)*

Holding:

Frauenthal Ost Beteiligungs-GmbH (1)
Gamserstrasse 38
Frauenthal, 8523 Vienna, Austria (100%)
Tel.: (43) 346220000
Fax: (43) 346220003286
E-Mail: info@frauenthal.net
Web Site: www.frauenthal.net
Emp.: 9
Industrial Ceramics Mfr
S.I.C.: 3297
N.A.I.C.S.: 327120
Rudolf Jobstl *(Head-Pur)*

Non-U.S. Subsidiaries:

Frauenthal Deutschland GmbH (1)
Lindweg 25
59229 Ahlen, Germany
Tel.: (49) 23827820
Fax: (49) 23827782167
E-Mail: lsa.zentrala@frauenthal-automotive.com
Web Site: www.Frauenthal-automotive.com
Emp.: 20
Trusts Estates & Agency Account
S.I.C.: 6733
N.A.I.C.S.: 525920

Frauenthal Einkaufs GmbH (1)
Lindweg 25
59229 Ahlen, Germany
Tel.: (49) 238278240
Fax: (49) 2382782140
E-Mail: info@lsgroup.com
Web Site: www.frauenthal-ek.com
Emp.: 20
Machine Tool Mfr
S.I.C.: 3541
N.A.I.C.S.: 333517
Robert Smith *(Gen Mgr)*

Linnemann-Schnetzer Deutschland GmbH (1)
Lindweg 25
Ahlen, Germany (100%)
Tel.: (49) 23827820
Fax: (49) 2328278275
Emp.: 200
Real Estate Agents & Brokers
S.I.C.: 6531
N.A.I.C.S.: 531210

Linnemann-Schnetzer GmbH & Co. (1)
Lindweg 25
59229 Ahlen, Germany (100%)
Tel.: (49) 23827820
Fax: (49) 238278278
Web Site: www.ls-group.com
Emp.: 200
Jewelry Mfr
S.I.C.: 3911
N.A.I.C.S.: 339910
Yogan Heller *(Plant Mgr)*

Linnemann-Schnetzer Sachsen GmbH (1)
Scheibenbergerstrabe 45
Elterlein, 09481 Brandenburg, Germany
Tel.: (49) 3734966215
Fax: (49) 3734966237
E-Mail: info@ls-group.com
Web Site: www.ls-group.com
Emp.: 200
Jewelry Mfr
S.I.C.: 3914
N.A.I.C.S.: 339910
Detlef Schubert *(Mng Dir)*

Linnemann-Schnetzer Verwaltungs-GmbH (1)
Lindweg 25
Ahlen, Germany (100%)
Tel.: (49) 23827820
Fax: (49) 23827875
E-Mail: info@lf-group.com
Web Site: www.frauenthal-sc.com
Emp.: 201
Farm Management Services
S.I.C.: 0762
N.A.I.C.S.: 115116
Jorgen Hallen *(Mng Dir)*

Styria Arcuri S.A (1)
Forjorilor Str 22
550233 Sibiu, Romania (63.8%)
Tel.: (40) 269207347
Fax: (40) 269207345
E-Mail: sibiu@frauenthal-automotive.com
Web Site: www.frauenthal.com
Emp.: 300
Spring Mfr
S.I.C.: 3493
N.A.I.C.S.: 332613
Daniel Treda *(Mng Dir)*

Styria-Elesfrance S.A.S. (1)
Zone Industrielle du Gros Hetre
Boite Postale 20143 Saint-Avol, 57504 Metz, France
Tel.: (33) 387911771
Fax: (33) 387911150
E-Mail: eles@ls-group.com
Emp.: 60
Motor Vehicle Parts Mfr
S.I.C.: 3714
N.A.I.C.S.: 336390
Bluno Gevolder *(Mng Dir)*

Styria Impormol S.A. (1)
Quinta Da Courela De Baixo
Aveiras De Baixo, 2050011 Azambuja, Portugal
Tel.: (351) 263409512
Fax: (351) 263409517
E-Mail: azambuja@styriagroup.com
Web Site: www.styriagroup.com
Emp.: 240
Spring Mfr
S.I.C.: 3493
N.A.I.C.S.: 332613
Arnaen Gossler *(Gen Mgr)*

Styria Ressorts Vehicules Industriels S.A.S. (1)
Av des Forges
Chatenois-les-Forges, 90700 Chatenois, France (86%)
Tel.: (33) 384582536
Fax: (33) 384582534
E-Mail:
Web Site: www.frauenthal-automotive.com
Emp.: 250
Motor Vehicle Parts Mfr
S.I.C.: 3714
N.A.I.C.S.: 336390
Jean-Francois Kristof *(Pres)*

Styria Vzmeti d.o.o. (1)
14 Koroska Cesta
Ravne, 2390 Ravne na Koroskem, Slovenia
Tel.: (386) 28217693
Fax: (386) 28220793
Emp.: 200
Spring Mfr
S.I.C.: 3493
N.A.I.C.S.: 332613
Zolton Kong *(Mng Dir)*

FRAUNHOFER-GESELLSCHAFT ZUR FORDERUNG DER ANGEWANDTEN FORSCHUNG E.V.

Hansastrasse 27C
80686 Munich, Germany
Mailing Address:
Postfach 20 07 33
80007 Munich, Germany
Tel.: (49) 89 1205 0
Fax: (49) 89 1205 7531
Web Site: www.fraunhofer.de
Rev.: $872,822,158
Assets: $3,417,149,358
Liabilities: $509,688,770
Net Worth: $2,907,460,588
Earnings: $680,568
Emp.: 22,093
Fiscal Year-end: 12/31/12

Business Description:
Application-Oriented Research Services
S.I.C.: 8731
N.A.I.C.S.: 541712

Personnel:
Reimund Neugebauer *(Pres & Member-Exec Bd)*
Alfred Gossner *(Member-Exec Bd & Sr VP-Fin, Controlling & Info Sys)*
Alexander Kurz *(Member-Exec Bd & Sr VP-HR, Legal Affairs & IP Mgmt)*

U.S. Subsidiary:

Fraunhofer USA, Inc. (1)
44792 Helm St
Plymouth, MI 48170
Tel.: (734) 354-9700
Fax: (734) 354-9711
E-Mail: info@fraunhofer.org
Web Site: www.fraunhofer.org
Emp.: 200
Application-Oriented Research Services
S.I.C.: 8731
N.A.I.C.S.: 541712
Georg Rosenfeld *(Pres)*
Erin Simmonds *(Treas)*
Mark J. Eby *(Sec)*
William F. Hartman *(Exec VP)*

FRE COMPOSITES

75 Wales St
St-Andre-d'Argenteuil, QC, J0V 1X0, Canada
Tel.: (450) 537-3311
Fax: (450) 537-3415
Toll Free: (888) 849-9909
Web Site: www.frecomposites.com
Year Founded: 1958
Rev.: $10,818,497
Emp.: 85

Business Description:
Nonmetallic Mineral Products Mfr
S.I.C.: 3299
N.A.I.C.S.: 327999

Personnel:
Benoit Arsenault *(Pres & VP-Sls)*

FRED GROENESTEGE CONSTRUCTION LIMITED

4892 Line 42 Perth County R R 1
Sebringville, ON, N0K 1X0, Canada
Tel.: (519) 393-6579
Fax: (519) 393-6532
E-Mail: info@fgc.ca
Web Site: www.fgc.ca
Year Founded: 1978
Rev.: $14,300,000
Emp.: 50

Business Description:
Construction Services
S.I.C.: 1542
N.A.I.C.S.: 236220

Personnel:
Fred Groenestege *(Co-Owner)*
Shelley Groenestege *(Co-Owner)*

FRED. OLSEN ENERGY ASA

Fred Olsens Gate 2
N-0152 Oslo, Norway
Tel.: (47) 22341243
Fax: (47) 22411840
E-Mail: adm@fredolsen-energy.no
Web Site: www.fredolsen-energy.no
FOE—(OSL OTC)
Rev.: $1,244,636,195
Assets: $2,861,797,048
Liabilities: $1,432,669,421
Net Worth: $1,429,127,627
Earnings: $329,421,166
Emp.: 1,452
Fiscal Year-end: 12/31/12

Business Description:
Oil & Gas Exploration & Production Services
S.I.C.: 1381
N.A.I.C.S.: 213111

Personnel:
Anette S. Olsen *(Chm)*
Ivar Brandvold *(CEO)*
Hjalmar Krogseth Moe *(CFO)*
Robert Cooper *(CEO-Harland & Wolff Grp Plc)*

Board of Directors:
Anette S. Olsen
Oyvin Fjeldstad
Agnar Gravdal
Cecilie B. Heuch
Jan Peter Valheim

Subsidiaries:

Dolphin AS (1)
Plattformveien 5
4056 Tananger, Norway
Tel.: (47) 51694300
Fax: (47) 51696156
E-Mail: recep@dolphin-doc.no
Web Site: www.dolphin.as
Emp.: 50
Offshore Oil & Gas Services
S.I.C.: 1389
N.A.I.C.S.: 213112
Joakim Kleppe *(CEO)*

Dolphin International AS (1)
Olsens gate 2
0152 Oslo, Norway
Tel.: (47) 22341000
Fax: (47) 22411840
Offshore Oil & Gas Services
S.I.C.: 1389
N.A.I.C.S.: 213112
John Hanson *(Gen Mgr)*

Non-U.S. Subsidiaries:

Atlan Shipping Co. Ltd. (1)
C/O Conyers Dill & Pearman
Hamilton, Pembroke, Bermuda
Tel.: (441) 295 1422
Fax: (441) 292 4720
Shipping Agents
S.I.C.: 4731
N.A.I.C.S.: 488510

Dolphin Drilling Pte. Ltd. (1)
One Temasek Ave
36-02 Millenia Tower, Singapore, 039192, Singapore
Tel.: (65) 63054730
Fax: (65) 63054711
E-Mail: reception.singapore@dolphindrilling.com.sg
Web Site: www.dolphindrilling.com.sg
Emp.: 15
Offshore Oil & Gas Services
S.I.C.: 1389
N.A.I.C.S.: 213112
Per Johansson *(Mng Dir)*

FRED WALLS & SON LTD.

3900 Walls Ave
Prince George, BC, V2N 4L4, Canada
Tel.: (250) 564-1133
Rev.: $64,640,000
Emp.: 109

Business Description:
New Car Dealer
S.I.C.: 5511
N.A.I.C.S.: 441110

Personnel:
Doug Walls *(Owner)*

FREDUCCI
Zac De Gabardie 23 Rue Paule Raymondis
31200 Toulouse, Haute Garonne, France
Tel.: (33) 534258686
Fax: (33) 534255343
E-Mail: assistance@lmv.fr
Web Site: www.lmv.fr
Sls.: $22,600,000
Emp.: 64
Business Description:
Family Clothing Stores
S.I.C.: 5651
N.A.I.C.S.: 448140
Personnel:
Frederic Cornuaud *(Pres)*

FREE ENERGY INTERNATIONAL INC.
Suite 1606 675 West Hastings Street
Vancouver, BC, V6B 1N2, Canada
Tel.: (604) 696-9055
Web Site:
Year Founded: 2001
FFX—(TSXV)
Business Description:
Electrical Component Mfr
S.I.C.: 3699
N.A.I.C.S.: 335999
Personnel:
Alf Sanderson *(Pres & CEO)*
Dean Bethune *(CFO)*
Board of Directors:
Mark McCooey
Alf Sanderson

FREEBIT CO., LTD.
13F E-Space Tower 3-6 Maruyamacho
Shibuya-ku, Tokyo, Japan
Tel.: (81) 3 5459 0522
Web Site: www.freebit.com
Year Founded: 2000
3843—(TKS)
Sls.: $227,260,000
Assets: $196,559,000
Liabilities: $127,897,000
Net Worth: $68,662,000
Earnings: ($2,035,000)
Emp.: 247
Fiscal Year-end: 04/30/13
Business Description:
Internet-Related Services
S.I.C.: 4899
N.A.I.C.S.: 517919
Personnel:
Atsuki Ishida *(Pres & CEO)*
Board of Directors:
Nobuyuki Idei
Atsuki Ishida
Joe Sakai
Nobuaki Tanaka

Subsidiary:

Full Speed Inc. (1)
1-9-5 Shibuya Square A 11th Floor
Dogenzaka Shibuya-ku, Tokyo, 150-0043, Japan
Tel.: (81) 357284460
Fax: (81) 357284461
E-Mail: info@fullspeed.co.jp
Web Site: www.fullspeed.co.jp
2159—(TKS)
Sales Range: $125-149.9 Million
Web Consulting & Search Engine Optimization Services
S.I.C.: 8999
N.A.I.C.S.: 541690
Manaho Haga *(Pres)*

FREED OF LONDON LTD.
62-64 Well St
London, E9 7PX, United Kingdom
Tel.: (44) 2085104700
Fax: (44) 2085104750
E-Mail: info@freedoflondon.com
Web Site: www.freedoflondon.com
Sales Range: $10-24.9 Million
Emp.: 300
Business Description:
Ballet Shoes
S.I.C.: 2389
N.A.I.C.S.: 316210
Personnel:
Mark Redhead *(Mng Dir)*

U.S. Subsidiary:

Freed of London Ltd. (1)
21-01 44th Ave
Long Island City, NY 11101
Tel.: (718) 729-7061
Fax: (718) 729-8086
Toll Free: (866) MYFREED
E-Mail: info@freedusa.com
Web Site: www.freedusa.com
Emp.: 12
Ballet Shoes
S.I.C.: 5661
N.A.I.C.S.: 448210
Julienne Biola *(Gen Mgr)*

U.S. Division:

Freed of London U.S. (1)
21-01 43rd Ave
Long Island City, NY 11101
Tel.: (718) 729-7061
Fax: (718) 729-8086
E-Mail: info@freedusa.com
Web Site: www.freedusa.com
Emp.: 10
Gift Novelty & Souvenir Stores
S.I.C.: 5947
N.A.I.C.S.: 453220
Julienne Viola *(Mng Dir)*

FREEDOM FOODS GROUP LTD.
80 Box Road
PO Box 2531
Taren Point, NSW, 2229, Australia
Tel.: (61) 295262555
Fax: (61) 295255406
Web Site: www.freedomnutritional.com.au
FNP—(ASX)
Rev.: $92,665,616
Assets: $132,178,922
Liabilities: $46,315,092
Net Worth: $85,863,830
Earnings: $14,299,696
Emp.: 178
Fiscal Year-end: 06/30/13
Business Description:
Nutritional Foods Producer
S.I.C.: 2075
N.A.I.C.S.: 311224
Personnel:
Rory J. F. Macleod *(Mng Dir & Sec)*
Amine Haddad *(CEO-Pactum Australia)*
Michael Bracka *(CEO-North America)*
Board of Directors:
Perry R. Gunner
Trevor J. Allen
Rory J. F. Macleod
Mel Miles
A. M. Perich
Ron Perich
Legal Counsel:
Gilbert & Tobin
Two Park Street
Sydney, NSW, 2000, Australia
Addisons
Level 12, 60 Carrington Street
Sydney, Australia

FREEDOM FORD SALES LTD
7505 75 Street
Edmonton, AB, T6C4H8, Canada
Tel.: (780) 462-7575
Fax: (780) 468-2719
E-Mail: freedom@freedomfordsales.com
Web Site: www.freedomford.dealerconnection.com
Year Founded: 1971
Rev.: $57,905,337
Emp.: 115
Business Description:
New & Used Car Dealers
S.I.C.: 5511
N.A.I.C.S.: 441110
Personnel:
Bob Bentley *(Pres)*

FREEDOM GROUP LIMITED
3 Apollo Pl
Lane Cove, NSW, 2066, Australia
Tel.: (61) 0298829000
Fax: (61) 0298829099
E-Mail: privacy@freedom.com.au
Web Site: www.freedom.com.au
Sales Range: $75-99.9 Million
Emp.: 200
Business Description:
Furniture & Housewares Retailer & Importer
S.I.C.: 5021
N.A.I.C.S.: 423210

Subsidiary:

Steinhoff Asia Pacific Limited (1)
PO Box 227
Marayong, NSW, 2148, Australia
Tel.: (61) 1300135588
Web Site: www.freedom.com.au/Contact-Us/
Furniture & Housewares Retailer & Importer
S.I.C.: 5021
N.A.I.C.S.: 423210

FREEDOM RESOURCES HOLDINGS CORP.
39/F PBCOM Tower
6795 Ayala Ave, Makati, 1228, Philippines
Tel.: (63) 2 856 88 88
Fax: (63) 2 856 88 99
Web Site: www.dtsi.com.ph
Sales Range: $75-99.9 Million
Emp.: 200
Business Description:
Holding Company
S.I.C.: 6719
N.A.I.C.S.: 551112
Personnel:
Miguel C. Garcia *(Pres & CEO)*

FREEGOLD VENTURES LIMITED
Suite 888 - 700 West Georgia Street
PO Box 10351
Vancouver, BC, V7Y 1G5, Canada
Tel.: (604) 662-7307
Fax: (604) 662-3791
Web Site: www.freegoldventures.com
FR4N—(DEU TSX)
Int. Income: $17,748
Assets: $36,143,797
Liabilities: $1,103,691
Net Worth: $35,040,106
Earnings: ($5,901,428)
Fiscal Year-end: 12/31/12
Business Description:
Gold Exploration Services
S.I.C.: 1041
N.A.I.C.S.: 212221
Personnel:
Kristina Walcott *(Pres & CEO)*
Gordon Steblin *(CFO)*
Board of Directors:
Garnet Dawson
Alvin W. Jackson
David Knight
Gary Moore
Kristina Walcott

FREEHOLD ROYALTIES LIMITED
Suite 400 144 4 Avenue SW
Calgary, AB, T2P 3N4, Canada
Tel.: (403) 221-0802
Fax: (403) 221-0888
Toll Free: (888) 257-1873
Web Site: www.freeholdroyalties.com
Year Founded: 1996
FRU—(TSX)
Rev.: $167,128,559
Assets: $445,556,543
Liabilities: $131,630,116
Net Worth: $313,926,426
Earnings: $46,050,959
Emp.: 104
Fiscal Year-end: 12/31/12
Business Description:
Oil & Gas Exploration Services
S.I.C.: 1311
N.A.I.C.S.: 211111
Personnel:
D. Nolan Blades *(Chm)*
William O. Ingram *(Pres & CEO)*
Darren G. Gunderson *(CFO & VP-Fin)*
Thomas J. Mullane *(COO & Exec VP)*
Karen C. Taylor *(Sec & Mgr-IR)*
Board of Directors:
D. Nolan Blades
Harry S. Campbell
Peter T. Harrison
William O. Ingram
Arthur N. Korpach
P. Michael Maher
David J. Sandmeyer
Rodger A. Tourigny
Legal Counsel:
Burnet, Duckworth & Palmer LLP
Calgary, AB, Canada
Transfer Agent:
Computershare Trust Company of Canada
600-530 8th Avenue SW
Calgary, AB, Canada

Subsidiaries:

Freehold Resources Ltd. (1)
144 4 Ave SW
Suite 400, Calgary, AB, T2P 3N4, Canada
Tel.: (403) 221-0802
Fax: (403) 221-0888
E-Mail: bingram@freehold.com
Web Site: www.freehold.com
Emp.: 85
Petroleum Refineries
S.I.C.: 2911
N.A.I.C.S.: 324110
D. Nolan Blades *(Chm)*
William O. Ingram *(Pres & CEO)*

FREELANCE.COM SA
3 rue Bellanger
92300 Levallois-Perret, France
Tel.: (33) 1 55 62 12 34
Fax: (33) 1 41 05 01 63
E-Mail: contact@freelance.com
Web Site: www.freelance.com
Year Founded: 1995
ALFRE—(EUR)
Business Description:
Online Job Portal Services
S.I.C.: 2741
N.A.I.C.S.: 519130
Personnel:
Andre Martinie *(CEO)*
Thierry Eude *(CFO)*
Tim Daly *(COO & CTO)*

FREELANCER AUSTRALIA PTY LTD.
(Name Changed to Freelancer Ltd.)

FREELANCER LTD.
(Formerly Freelancer Australia Pty Ltd.)

Freelancer Ltd.—(Continued)

(d/b/a Freelancer.com)
Suite 52 Jones Bay Wharf 26-32
Pirrama Rd
Pyrmont, NSW, 2009, Australia
Mailing Address:
PO Box 1121
Double Bay, NSW, 1360, Australia
Tel.: (61) 296929980
Fax: (61) 280721311
E-Mail: support@freelancer.com
Web Site: www.freelancer.com
FLN—(ASX)
Business Description:
Freelance Outsourcing Services
S.I.C.: 7361
N.A.I.C.S.: 561311
Personnel:
Matt Barrie *(Chm & CEO)*
Neil Katz *(CFO)*
Darren Williams *(CTO)*
Board of Directors:
Matt Barrie
Simon Clausen
Darren Williams
Transfer Agent:
Boardroom Pty Ltd
Level 7 207 Kent Street
Sydney, NSW, Australia
U.S. Subsidiary:

vWorker.com (1)
14310 N Dale Mabry Hwy Ste 280
Tampa, FL 33618
Tel.: (813) 908-9029
Fax: (813) 960-1495
Web Site: www.vworker.com
Sales Range: $10-24.9 Million
Software Publisher
S.I.C.: 7372
N.A.I.C.S.: 511210
Ian Ippolito *(CEO)*

FREEMAN FINANCIAL CORPORATION LIMITED

Room 2302 23rd Floor China United Centre 28 Marble Road
North Point, China (Hong Kong)
Tel.: (852) 31980279
Fax: (852) 25072009
Web Site: www.freeman279.com
0279—(HKG)
Sales Range: $1-9.9 Million
Emp.: 24
Business Description:
Investment Services
S.I.C.: 6211
N.A.I.C.S.: 523999
Personnel:
Kan Sun Lo *(Chm)*
Quincy Kwong Hei Hui *(Mng Dir)*
Mun Yee Chow *(Sec)*
Board of Directors:
Kan Sun Lo
Sue Shuk Yee Au
Wing Ping Cheung
Mun Yee Chow
Yuk Lun Chung
Quincy Kwong Hei Hui
Cho Sing Hung
Andrew Liu
Winston Kam Fai Liu
Agustin V. Que
Legal Counsel:
Reed Smith Richards Butler
20th Floor Alexandra House 16-20 Chater Road
Central, China (Hong Kong)

Conyers Dill & Pearman
2901 One Exchange Square 8 Connaught Place
Central, China (Hong Kong)
Transfer Agent:
Tricor Secretaries Limited
26th Floor Tesbury Centre 28 Queen's Road East
Wanchai, China (Hong Kong)

Subsidiaries:

Freeman Insurance Services Limited (1)
8F China United Ctr
28 Marble Rd, North Point, China (Hong Kong)
Tel.: (852) 25111045
Fax: (852) 21172777
Insurance Provider
S.I.C.: 6411
N.A.I.C.S.: 524210

Freeman Investment Holdings Limited (1)
31st Fl China United Ctr
28 Marble Rd, North Point, China (Hong Kong)
Tel.: (852) 31980279
Fax: (852) 25072009
E-Mail: andrew@freeman279.com
Web Site: www.freeman279.com
Emp.: 30
Financial Investment Services
S.I.C.: 6211
N.A.I.C.S.: 523999

FREEMS CORPORATION

192-1 Naedong
Ojunggu, Bucheon, Gyunggido, Korea (South)
Tel.: (82) 32 679 1477
Fax: (82) 32 679 1480
Web Site: www.freems.co.kr
Year Founded: 1989
053160—(KRS)
Emp.: 130
Business Description:
Industrial Equipment Mfr
S.I.C.: 3569
N.A.I.C.S.: 333999
Personnel:
Dosik Joo *(Co-Pres & Co-CEO)*
Heungsik Park *(Co-Pres & Co-CEO)*

FREENET AG

Hollerstrasse 126
24782 Budelsdorf, Germany
Tel.: (49) 4331691000
Fax: (49) 4331691175
E-Mail: info@mobilcom-debitel.de
Web Site: www.freenet.ag
FNTN—(DEU)
Rev.: $4,158,362,207
Assets: $3,330,723,430
Liabilities: $1,727,654,385
Net Worth: $1,603,069,044
Earnings: $233,141,836
Emp.: 3,886
Fiscal Year-end: 12/31/12
Business Description:
Holding Company;
Telecommunications Services
S.I.C.: 6719
N.A.I.C.S.: 551112
Personnel:
Hartmut Schenk *(Chm-Supervisory Bd)*
Christoph Vilanek *(CEO & Chm-Exec Bd)*
Knut Mackeprang *(Deputy Chm-Supervisory Bd & Corp Counsel)*
Joachim Preisig *(CFO & Member-Exec Bd)*
Stephan Esch *(CTO & Member-Exec Bd)*
Supervisory Board of Directors:
Hartmut Schenk
Claudia Anderleit
Birgit Geffke
Thorsten Kraemer
Knut Mackeprang
Ronny Minak
Michael Stephan
Helmut Thoma
Gesine Thomas
Marc Tungler
Robert Weidinger
Achim Weiss
Subsidiaries:

4Players GmbH (1)
Deelbogenkamp 4c
22297 Hamburg, Germany
Tel.: (49) 40 51306 581
Fax: (49) 40 51306 599
E-Mail: info@4players.de
Web Site: www.4players.de
Emp.: 35
Online Gaming Services
S.I.C.: 2741
N.A.I.C.S.: 519130
Philip Schuster *(Mng Dir)*

air2mp3 GmbH (1)
Haid-und-neu-str 7
Karlsruhe, 76131, Germany
Tel.: (49) 72166338849
Software Development Services
S.I.C.: 7371
N.A.I.C.S.: 541511

altnetsurf GmbH (1)
Deelbogenkamp 4 C
Hamburg, 22297, Germany
Tel.: (49) 79515906
Fax: (49) 180 3 030 310
Web Site: www.altnetsurf.de
Telecommunication Services
S.I.C.: 4899
N.A.I.C.S.: 517919

Debitel AG (1)
Gropiusplatz 10
70563 Stuttgart, Vaihingen, Germany
Mailing Address:
Postfach 81 02 50
70545 Stuttgart, Germany
Tel.: (49) 7117217000
Fax: (49) 7117217280
E-Mail: kundenbetreuung@de.debital.com
Web Site: www.debitel.de
Sales Range: $1-4.9 Billion
Emp.: 200
Mobile Telecommunications Services
S.I.C.: 4812
N.A.I.C.S.: 517210
Lars Dittrich *(Head-Sls)*

Subsidiaries:

callmobile GmbH & Co. KG (2)
Deelbogenkamp 4c
22797 Hamburg, Germany De
Tel.: (49) 4331 692 945
Fax: (49) 4331 692 901
E-Mail: support@callmobile.de
Web Site: www.callmobile.de
Emp.: 120
Mobile Telecommunications Services
S.I.C.: 4812
N.A.I.C.S.: 517210
Alexander Borgwardt *(Member-Mgmt Bd)*
Antonius Fromme *(Member-Mgmt Bd)*

Talkline GmbH (2)
Talkline Platz 1
25337 Elmshorn, Germany De
Tel.: (49) 41214100 (100%)
Fax: (49) 4121414950
E-Mail: info@talkline.de
Web Site: www.talkline.de
Sales Range: $1-4.9 Billion
Emp.: 1,000
Mobile Telecommunications Services
S.I.C.: 4812
N.A.I.C.S.: 517210

debitel Konzernfinanzierungs Gmbh (1)
Gropiusplatz 10
Stuttgart, 70563, Germany
Tel.: (49) 7117217000
Fax: (49) 7117218180
Telecommunication Services
S.I.C.: 4899
N.A.I.C.S.: 517919

freenet Cityline GmbH (1)
Am Germaniahafen 1-7
24143 Kiel, Germany
Tel.: (49) 4319020500
Fax: (49) 40 51306942
Software Development Services
S.I.C.: 7371
N.A.I.C.S.: 541511

freenet Datenkommunikations GmbH (1)
Deelbogenkamp 4c
D-22297 Hamburg, Germany De
Tel.: (49) 40513060 (100%)
Fax: (49) 4051306900
E-Mail: sales@freenet-business.de
Web Site: www.freenet-business.de
Rev.: $569,345,664
Emp.: 400
Commercial Telecommunications Services
S.I.C.: 4899
N.A.I.C.S.: 517919
Eckhard Spoerr *(Chm & CEO)*
Stephan Esch *(CTO)*

freenet Direkt GmbH (1)
Deelbogenkamp 4 C
Hamburg, 22297, Germany
Tel.: (49) 40513060
Telecommunication Services
S.I.C.: 4899
N.A.I.C.S.: 517919
Christoph Vilanek *(CEO)*

freeXmedia GmbH (1)
Deelbogenkamp 4c
22297 Hamburg, Germany
Tel.: (49) 40 513 06 650
Fax: (49) 40 513 06 960
E-Mail: werbung@freexmedia.de
Web Site: www.freexmedia.de
Marketing Consulting Services
S.I.C.: 8742
N.A.I.C.S.: 541613
Andreas Engenhardt *(Gen Mgr)*

mobilcom Communicationstechnik GmbH (1)
Hollerstrasse 126
D-24782 Budelsdorf, Germany (100%)
Tel.: (49) 4331691173
Fax: (49) 4331434403
E-Mail: pr@freenet.ag
Web Site: www.freenet-group.de
Sales Range: $1-4.9 Billion
Telecommunications & Internet Services
S.I.C.: 4812
N.A.I.C.S.: 517210
Stephan Esch *(CTO)*

mobilcom-debitel GmbH (1)
Hollerstr 126
Budelsdorf, 24782, Germany
Tel.: (49) 1805022240
E-Mail: info@mobilcom-debitel.de
Web Site: www.mobilcom-debitel.de
Telecommunication Services
S.I.C.: 4899
N.A.I.C.S.: 517919

NEXT ID GmbH (1)
Mildred-Scheel-Strasse 1
D-53175 Bonn, Germany (100%)
Tel.: (49) 228969720
Fax: (49) 2289697299
E-Mail: info@next-id.de
Web Site: www.next-id.de
Emp.: 55
Interactive Telecommunications Services
S.I.C.: 4899
N.A.I.C.S.: 517919
Alexander Borgwardt *(Mng Dir)*

FREEPORT CAPITAL INC.

(Name Changed to Hybrid PayTech World Inc.)

FREEPORT RESOURCES INC.

8711 Elsmore Road
Richmond, BC, V7C 2A4, Canada
Tel.: (604) 275-7335
Fax: (888) 275-8549
Toll Free: (888) 275-7335
E-Mail: info@freeportresources.com
Web Site: www.freeportresources.com
Year Founded: 1981
FRI—(TSXV)
Rev.: $9,886
Assets: $1,636,306
Liabilities: $1,257,902
Net Worth: $378,404
Earnings: ($131,613)
Fiscal Year-end: 01/31/13

Business Description:
Mineral Exploration Services
S.I.C.: 1081
N.A.I.C.S.: 213114
Personnel:
William George Clark *(Founder)*
Brenda S. Clark *(Pres & CEO)*
Martin MacKinnon *(CFO)*
Jim L. Thistle *(Sec)*
Board of Directors:
Brenda S. Clark
Tracy Lynne Clark
Michael L. Roberts
Legal Counsel:
McMillan LLP
Vancouver, BC, Canada
McInnes Cooper
Saint John's, NL, Canada
Transfer Agent:
Computershare Trust Company
Vancouver, BC, Canada

FREESEAS INC.

10 Eleftheriou Venizelou Street
Panepistimiou Ave
10671 Athens, Greece
Tel.: (30) 210 4528770
Fax: (30) 210 4291010
E-Mail: info@feeseas.gr
Web Site: www.freeseas.gr
Year Founded: 2004
FREE—(NASDAQ)
Rev.: $14,260,000
Assets: $114,359,000
Liabilities: $106,556,000
Net Worth: $7,803,000
Earnings: ($30,888,000)
Fiscal Year-end: 12/31/12
Business Description:
Shipping Services
Import Export
S.I.C.: 4731
N.A.I.C.S.: 488510
Personnel:
Ion G. Varouxakis *(Chm, Pres & CEO)*
Alexandros Mylonas *(CFO & Treas)*
Maria Badekas *(Sec)*
Board of Directors:
Ion G. Varouxakis
Keith Bloomfield
George Kalogeropoulos
Focko H. Nauta
Dimitrios Panagiotopoulos
Didier Salomon

FREESOFT SOFTWARE DEVELOPMENT AND INFORMATION TECHNOLOGY SERVICES PUBLIC LIMITED COMPANY

Montevideo u 8
1037 Budapest, Hungary
Tel.: (36) 13712910
Fax: (36) 13712911
E-Mail: fs.inf@freesoft.hu
Web Site: www.freesoft.hu
FREESOFT—(BUD)
Rev.: $38,287,198
Assets: $27,215,480
Liabilities: $12,027,702
Net Worth: $15,187,779
Earnings: $807,358
Emp.: 260
Fiscal Year-end: 12/31/12
Business Description:
Software Development Services
S.I.C.: 3652
N.A.I.C.S.: 334614
Personnel:
Vilmos Vaspal *(Pres)*
Ilona Eck *(CEO)*
Board of Directors:
Ilona Eck
Vilmos Vaspal
Subsidiaries:

AXIS Consulting 2000 Ltd (1)
Szekesfehervar Berenyi ut 7Videoton Ipari Park
197 sz epulet az I-es Porta, Budapest, 1119, Hungary
Tel.: (36) 22 517 631
Fax: (36) 22 517 630
E-Mail: info@axis.hu
Web Site: www.axis.hu
Information Technology Consulting Services
S.I.C.: 7373
N.A.I.C.S.: 541512
Zsuzsanna Azurak *(Gen Mgr)*

BankSoft Kft (1)
Montevideo Str 8
1037 Budapest, Hungary
Tel.: (36) 1 363 7442
Fax: (36) 1 383 5243
Web Site: www.banksoft.hu
Banking Software Development Services
S.I.C.: 7371
N.A.I.C.S.: 541511

HUMANsoft Kft. (1)
Montevideo u 8
1037 Budapest, Hungary
Tel.: (36) 1 270 7600
Fax: (36) 1 270 7679
E-Mail: humansoft@humansoft.hu
Web Site: www.humansoft.hu
Rev.: $36,557,990
Emp.: 180
Information Security Software Development Services
S.I.C.: 7371
N.A.I.C.S.: 541511
Andras Mezey *(Mng Dir)*

FREETECH ROAD RECYCLING TECHNOLOGY (HOLDINGS) LIMITED

29/F Chinachem Century Tower 178
Glouchester Road
Wanchai, China (Hong Kong)
Tel.: (852) 23309600
Fax: (852) 23637987
Web Site: www.freetech-holdings.hk
6888—(HKG)
Business Description:
Asphalt Paving
S.I.C.: 2951
N.A.I.C.S.: 324121
Personnel:
Wai Pun Sze *(Chm & CEO)*

FREEWORLD TRADING LTD.

21 Annandale Street
Edinburgh, EH7 4AW, United Kingdom
Tel.: (44) 131 557 5600
Fax: (44) 131 557 5665
E-Mail: info@freeworld-trading.co.uk
Web Site: www.freeworld-trading.co.uk
Year Founded: 1991
Sales Range: $100-124.9 Million
Emp.: 19
Business Description:
Food Product Mfr
S.I.C.: 2034
N.A.I.C.S.: 311423
Personnel:
Karen Rattray *(Mgr-Technical)*

FREIGHT MANAGEMENT HOLDINGS BHD.

Lot 37 Lebuh Sultan Mohamad 1
Kawasan Perindustrian
Bandar Sultan Suleiman, 42000 Port Klang, Selangor, Malaysia
Tel.: (60) 331761111
Fax: (60) 3 3176 8634
E-Mail: gen@my.fmgloballogistics.com
Web Site: www.fmmalaysia.com.my
FREIGHT—(KLS)
Rev.: $119,627,839
Assets: $84,288,885
Liabilities: $31,326,526
Net Worth: $52,962,359
Earnings: $8,123,562
Fiscal Year-end: 06/30/13
Business Description:
Freight Services
S.I.C.: 4412
N.A.I.C.S.: 483111
Personnel:
Chong Keat Chew *(Mng Dir)*
Hooi Mooi Lim *(Co-Sec)*
Wai Foong Wong *(Co-Sec)*
Board of Directors:
Noordin Abd. Razak
Chong Keat Chew
Tiong Hock Chua
Siew Yong Gan
Looi Chai Ong
Aaron Kwee Lein Sim
Heng Lam Yang
Subsidiaries:

Advance International Freight Sdn. Bhd. (1)
Lot 37 Lebuh Sultan Mohamad 1 Kawasan Perindustrian
Bandar Sultan Suleiman, 42000 Port Klang, Selangor, Malaysia
Tel.: (60) 331768001
Fax: (60) 331762005
E-Mail: alog@fmgloballogistics.com
Web Site: www.fmgloballogistics.com
Emp.: 75
Freight Forwarding Services
S.I.C.: 4731
N.A.I.C.S.: 488510
Yang Heng Lam *(Mgr)*

Citra Multimodal Services Sdn. Bhd. (1)
Lot 37 Jalan Sultan Mohamad 3
Bandar Sultan Sulaiman, Port Klang, 42000, Malaysia
Tel.: (60) 331766888
Fax: (60) 331763993
E-Mail: general@citra.com.my
Web Site: www.citra.com.my
Emp.: 80
Freight Forwarding & Warehousing Services
S.I.C.: 4731
N.A.I.C.S.: 488510
Heng Lam Yang *(Mng Dir)*

FM-Hellmann Worldwide Logistics Sdn. Bhd. (1)
Block F 08-3 3rd Floor Plaza Kelana Jaya Jalan SS7/13A
Kelana Jaya, 47301 Petaling Jaya, Selangor, Malaysia
Tel.: (60) 378770017
Fax: (60) 378770120
E-Mail: fmhwlair@streamyx.com
Web Site: www.fmmalaysia.com.my
Emp.: 40
Freight Forwarding Services
S.I.C.: 4731
N.A.I.C.S.: 488510

Freight Management (Ipoh) Sdn. Bhd. (1)
No 7A 1st Floor Persiaran Greentown 9
Greentown Business Centre
30450 Ipoh, Perak, Malaysia
Tel.: (60) 52421358
Fax: (60) 52551380
E-Mail: custserv_ipoh@fmmalaysia.com.my
Web Site: www.fmmalaysia.com.my/fm/p3.asp?cid=20
Emp.: 20
Freight Forwarding Services
S.I.C.: 4731
N.A.I.C.S.: 488510
James Tan *(Mgr-Bus Dev)*

Freight Management (M) Sdn. Bhd. (1)
Lot 37 Lebuh Sultan Mohamad 1 Kawasan Perindustrian
Bandar Sultan Suleiman, 42000 Port Klang, Selangor, Malaysia
Tel.: (60) 331761111
Fax: (60) 331762188
E-Mail: gen@fmmalaysia.com.my
Web Site: www.fmgloballogistics.com.my
Emp.: 600
Freight Forwarding Services
S.I.C.: 4731
N.A.I.C.S.: 488510
Chew Chong Keat *(Mng Dir)*

Freight Management (Melaka) Sdn. Bhd. (1)
47 Jalan Melaka Baru 22 Taman Melaka Baru
Batu Berendam, 75350 Melaka, Malaysia
Tel.: (60) 63175143
Fax: (60) 6 317 5202
E-Mail: cs_mel@fmmalaysia.com.my
Web Site: www.fmmalaysia.com.my/fm/p3.asp?cid=20
Emp.: 7
Freight Forwarding Services
S.I.C.: 4731
N.A.I.C.S.: 488510

Freight Management (Penang) Sdn. Bhd. (1)
No 4453 1st Floor Jalan Bagan Luar
12000 Butterworth, Penang, Malaysia
Tel.: (60) 43314358
Fax: (60) 43314368
E-Mail: info_pen@fmmalaysia.com.my
Web Site: www.fmmalaysia.com.my/fm/p3.asp?cid=20
Emp.: 50
Freight Forwarding Services
S.I.C.: 4731
N.A.I.C.S.: 488510
Looi Chai Ong *(Exec Dir)*

Non-U.S. Subsidiaries:

Icon Freight Services Co. Ltd. (1)
731/6 Ratchadapisek Road
Bangpongpang Yannawa, Bangkok, 10120, Thailand
Tel.: (66) 26836352
Fax: (66) 2 683 6358
E-Mail: info@icon-freight.com
Web Site: www.fmmalaysia.com.my/fm/p3.asp?cid=20
Emp.: 20
Freight Forwarding Services
S.I.C.: 4731
N.A.I.C.S.: 488510
Ng Chonglong *(Mgr)*

Icon Freight Services Pty. Ltd. (1)
Unit 4/75 Queen Victoria Street
Fremantle, WA, 6959, Australia
Tel.: (61) 894331400
Fax: (61) 894331422
E-Mail: info@iconfs.com.au
Web Site: www.iconfs.com.au
Emp.: 12
Freight Forwarding Services
S.I.C.: 4731
N.A.I.C.S.: 488510
Brad O'Donnell *(Mng Dir)*

Integrated SCM Co., Ltd. (1)
9/53 Unit 2B14 Moo 5 Phaholyotin Road
Klongnueng, Pathumthani, 12120, Thailand
Tel.: (66) 25161022
Fax: (66) 29020430
Packaging Machinery Distr
S.I.C.: 5085
N.A.I.C.S.: 423840

FREIGHTLINER MANITOBA LTD.

2058 Logan Ave
Winnipeg, MB, R2R 0H9, Canada
Tel.: (204) 694-3000
Fax: (204) 694-3001
Toll Free: (800) 663-3565
E-Mail: info@freightliner.mb.ca
Web Site: www.freightliner.mb.ca
Year Founded: 1990
Rev.: $35,189,925
Emp.: 101
Business Description:
New & Used Trucks Dealers
S.I.C.: 4212
N.A.I.C.S.: 484220

Freightliner Manitoba Ltd.—(Continued)

Personnel:
Rod Snyder *(Co-Owner)*
Ken Talbot *(Co-Owner)*
Barry Talbot *(Pres)*
Braden Kulchycki *(CFO)*

FREIGHTLINER OF KELOWNA LTD

103 2485 Ross Road
Kelowna, BC, V1Z 1M2, Canada
Tel.: (250) 769-7255
Fax: (250) 769-3032
Toll Free: (888) 878-2511
E-Mail: sales@premiumtruck.ca
Web Site: www.premiumtruck.ca
Rev.: $10,796,631
Emp.: 24
Business Description:
New & Used Truck Dealers
S.I.C.: 4212
N.A.I.C.S.: 484220
Personnel:
Mark Jones *(Branch Mgr)*

FREIGHTLINER OF RED DEER INC

8046 Edgar Industrial Cres
Red Deer, AB, T4P 3R3, Canada
Tel.: (403) 309-8225
Fax: (403) 340-3589
Toll Free: (800) 223-2341
Web Site: www.freightlinerofreddeer.com
Year Founded: 1993
Rev.: $20,998,171
Emp.: 45
Business Description:
New & Used Truck Dealers
S.I.C.: 4212
N.A.I.C.S.: 484220
Personnel:
Don Patterson *(Pres & Mgr-Sls)*

FREIGHTWAYS LIMITED

32 Botha Road
Penrose, DX CX10120, New Zealand
Tel.: (64) 95719670
Fax: (64) 95719671
E-Mail: enquire@freightways.co.nz
Web Site: www.freightways.co.nz
FRE—(NZE)
Rev.: $339,919,929
Assets: $362,642,805
Liabilities: $205,873,542
Net Worth: $156,769,263
Earnings: $33,770,439
Fiscal Year-end: 06/30/13
Business Description:
Courier Services
S.I.C.: 4513
N.A.I.C.S.: 492110
Personnel:
Dean Bracewell *(Mng Dir)*
Board of Directors:
Susan Jane Sheldon
William Birch
Dean Bracewell
Roger Corcoran
Kim R. Ellis
Mark Verbiest

Subsidiaries:

Air Freight NZ Limited **(1)**
Freightways House Ground Floor 32 Botha Road
Penrose, Auckland, 1061, New Zealand
Tel.: (64) 9 256 6534
Fax: (64) 9 256 6532
Web Site: www.airfreightnz.co.nz
Air Freight Transportation Services
S.I.C.: 4522
N.A.I.C.S.: 481212

Castle Parcels - Christchurch **(1)**
NO 72 Brougham Street
Sydenham, Christchurch, New Zealand
Tel.: (64) 33796205
Fax: (64) 33749714
Web Site: www.castleparcels.co.nz
Emp.: 80
Courier Services
S.I.C.: 4513
N.A.I.C.S.: 492110

Castle Parcels - Wellington **(1)**
9 Glover St
Wellington, Ngauranga, 6007, New Zealand (100%)
Tel.: (64) 44993420
Fax: (64) 44995102
Web Site: www.castleparcels.co.nz
Emp.: 60
Courier Services
S.I.C.: 4513
N.A.I.C.S.: 492110
Neil Wilson *(Gen Mgr)*

Castle Parcels Limited **(1)**
163 Sta Rd
Auckland, Penrose, 1061, New Zealand (100%)
Tel.: (64) 95255999
Fax: (64) 95255800
E-Mail: cplaklsales@castleparcels.co.nz
Web Site: www.castleparcels.co.nz
Sales Range: $10-24.9 Million
Emp.: 50
Transportion Services
S.I.C.: 4513
N.A.I.C.S.: 492110
Mark Skews *(Gen Mgr)*

DX Mail **(1)**
32 Botha Road
1061 Penrose, Auckland, New Zealand
Tel.: (64) 95263150
Fax: (64) 9 526 3198
E-Mail: telesales@dxmail.co.nz
Web Site: www.dxmail.co.nz
Emp.: 300
Business Mail Services
S.I.C.: 7334
N.A.I.C.S.: 561439
Mark Brightwell *(Gen Mgr)*

Freightways Information Services Limited **(1)**
32 Botha Rd Penrose
Auckland, 1001, New Zealand
Tel.: (64) 95719650
Fax: (64) 95719651
Information Technology Consultancy Services
S.I.C.: 7373
N.A.I.C.S.: 541512

Kiwi Express **(1)**
Freightways House 32 Botha Road
Penrose, Auckland, New Zealand
Tel.: (64) 95263887
Fax: (64) 95894102
E-Mail: info@auckland.kiwiexpress.co.nz
Web Site: www.kiwiexpress.co.nz
Emp.: 50
Courier Services
S.I.C.: 4215
N.A.I.C.S.: 492110
Keenan Brett *(Mgr-Ops)*

Messenger Services Limited **(1)**
32 Potha Rd Penrose
Auckland, New Zealand (100%)
Tel.: (64) 95263680
Fax: (64) 95256273
E-Mail: salesakl@messenger.co.nz
Web Site: www.sub60.com
Emp.: 150
Courier Services
S.I.C.: 4215
N.A.I.C.S.: 492110
Aaron Stubbing *(Gen Mgr)*

New Zealand Couriers Limited **(1)**
32 Botha Rd Penrose
Auckland, DX CX10119, New Zealand (100%)
Tel.: (64) 95719600
Fax: (64) 95719601
Web Site: www.nzcouriers.co.nz
Emp.: 20
Courier Services
S.I.C.: 4513
N.A.I.C.S.: 492110
Steve Well *(Gen Mgr)*

Subsidiary:

Fieldair Holdings Limited **(2)**
Mcgregor Street Palmerston North International Airport
Palmerston, 4414, New Zealand
Tel.: (64) 63571149
Fax: (64) 63582999
E-Mail: fieldair@fieldair.co.nz
Web Site: www.fieldair.co.nz
Emp.: 80
Aviation Engineering Services
S.I.C.: 8711
N.A.I.C.S.: 541330
Charles Giliam *(Gen Mgr)*

New Zealand Document Exchange Limited **(1)**
32 Botha Road
Box CR59901
Penrose, Auckland, New Zealand (100%)
Tel.: (64) 9526 3150
Fax: (64) 9526 3198
Web Site: www.dxmail.co.nz
Emp.: 100
Courier Services
S.I.C.: 4215
N.A.I.C.S.: 492110

NOW Couriers Limited **(1)**
36 Victoria Street
Onehunga, Auckland, 1061, New Zealand
Tel.: (64) 96349150
Fax: (64) 9 634 9140
E-Mail: info@nowcouriers.co.nz
Web Site: www.nowcouriers.co.nz
Courier Services
S.I.C.: 4215
N.A.I.C.S.: 492110

Online Security Services Limited **(1)**
33 Botha Road
Penrose, Auckland, 1642, New Zealand
Tel.: (64) 95804360
Fax: (64) 95804364
E-Mail: aklinfo@onlinesecurity.co.nz
Web Site: www.onlinesecurity.co.nz
Emp.: 50
Document Storage Services
S.I.C.: 7389
N.A.I.C.S.: 561439
Rob Herriott *(Mgr-Sls)*

Parceline Express Ltd. **(1)**
Freightways House 32 Botha Road
Penrose, Auckland, 1061, New Zealand
Tel.: (64) 95719638
Fax: (64) 95256273
Emp.: 4
General Freight Trucking Services
S.I.C.: 4212
N.A.I.C.S.: 484110
Tony Aspey Gordon *(Mgr-Ops-Northern Reg)*

Post Haste Limited **(1)**
32 Botha Rd
Penrose, Auckland, New Zealand (100%)
Tel.: (64) 95795650
Fax: (64) 95250161
Web Site: www.posthaste.co.nz
Emp.: 250
Courier Services
S.I.C.: 4215
N.A.I.C.S.: 492110
Warwick Mitchell *(Mgr-Sls)*

Security Express Ltd **(1)**
401 Hutt Rd
5061 Lower Hutt, Wellington, New Zealand
Tel.: (64) 45879011
Fax: (64) 45879014
Web Site: www.securityexpress.co.nz
Emp.: 4
Courier Services
S.I.C.: 4513
N.A.I.C.S.: 492110
Jodie Richards *(Branch Mgr)*

SUB60 **(1)**
32 Botha Rd
Penrose, Auckland, New Zealand
Tel.: (64) 95263680
Fax: (64) 95256273
E-Mail: sales@messenger.co.nz
Web Site: www.sub60.co.nz
Emp.: 45
Courier Services
S.I.C.: 4215
N.A.I.C.S.: 492110

Non-U.S. Subsidiary:

Databank Technologies Pty Limited **(1)**
PO Box 251
Alexandria, NSW, 1435, Australia
Tel.: (61) 2 9305 9500
Fax: (61) 2 9882 3419
Web Site: www.databank.com.au
Data Storage Services
S.I.C.: 7389
N.A.I.C.S.: 561439

FREIXENET S.A.

Calle Juan Sala 2
Barcelona, 08770, Spain
Tel.: (34) 938917000
Telex: 93821-FREX-E
Fax: (34) 8183095
E-Mail: freixenet@freixenet.com
Web Site: www.freixenet.com
Year Founded: 1861
Emp.: 1,270
Business Description:
Producers & Marketers of Wine Import Export
S.I.C.: 2084
N.A.I.C.S.: 312130
Personnel:
Jose Luis Bonet Ferrer *(Chm & CEO)*

U.S. Subsidiary:

Freixenet U.S.A. **(1)**
23555 Hwy 121
Sonoma, CA 95476-9285 (100%)
Mailing Address:
PO Box 1949
Sonoma, CA 95476-1949
Tel.: (707) 996-4981
Fax: (707) 996-0720
E-Mail: info@freixenetusa.com
Web Site: www.freixenetusa.com
Emp.: 100
Wines, Sparkling Wines & Champagnes Import
S.I.C.: 5182
N.A.I.C.S.: 424820
David Brown *(VP & Dir-Mktg)*

Subsidiary:

Freixenet Sonoma Caves, Inc. **(2)**
23555 Hwy 121
Sonoma, CA 95476 (100%)
Mailing Address:
PO Box 1427
Sonoma, CA 95476
Tel.: (707) 996-4981
Fax: (707) 996-0720
E-Mail: info@freixenetusa.com
Web Site: www.freixenetusa.com
Emp.: 75
Winery
S.I.C.: 2084
N.A.I.C.S.: 312130
Juan Freixenet *(Pres)*
Ava Bertran *(Exec VP)*

FRENCH CONNECTION GROUP PLC

Centro One 39 Camden Street
Camden
London, NW1 0DX, United Kingdom
Tel.: (44) 20 7036 7200
Fax: (44) 20 7036 7201
E-Mail: info@frenchconnection.com
Web Site: www.frenchconnection.com
Year Founded: 1984
FCCN—(LSE)
Rev.: $311,593,917
Assets: $169,457,817
Liabilities: $69,172,902
Net Worth: $100,284,915
Earnings: ($16,582,545)
Emp.: 2,444
Fiscal Year-end: 01/31/13

Business Description:
Men's & Women's Apparel
Import Export
S.I.C.: 5137
N.A.I.C.S.: 424330
Personnel:
Stephen Marks *(Chm & CEO)*
Board of Directors:
Stephen Marks
Claire Kent
Dean Murray
Neil Williams
Transfer Agent:
Capita Registrars
Northern House Fenay Bridge Woodsome Park
Huddersfield, United Kingdom

Subsidiaries:

French Connection Limited (1)
20-22 Bedford Row
London, WC1R 4JS, United Kingdom
Tel.: (44) 1792784150
Fax: (44) 20 7036 7001
E-Mail: enquiries@frenchconnection.com
Clothings Stores
S.I.C.: 5699
N.A.I.C.S.: 448150
Stephen Marks *(CEO)*

Toast (Mail Order) Limited (1)
3 Flr Matrix Peted Matrix Bus Pk
Swansea, SA6 8RE, United Kingdom
Tel.: (44) 8445570460
Fax: (44) 08445570607
E-Mail: contact@toast.co.uk
Web Site: www.toast.co.uk
Emp.: 100
Clothing Accessories Stores
S.I.C.: 5699
N.A.I.C.S.: 448150
Jessica Seaton *(Gen Mgr)*

U.S. Subsidiaries:

French Connection Group Inc (1)
14 E 60th St Frnt 2
New York, NY 10022
Tel.: (212) 421-7720
Fax: (212) 421-7745
Clothing Accessories Stores
S.I.C.: 5699
N.A.I.C.S.: 448150

French Connection Holdings Inc (1)
512 Fashion Ave
New York, NY 10018
Tel.: (212) 768-3479
Web Site: usa.frenchconnection.com
Clothing Accessories Stores
S.I.C.: 5699
N.A.I.C.S.: 448150

Louisiana Connection Limited (1)
416 N Peters St
New Orleans, LA 70130
Tel.: (504) 522-0014
Clothing Accessories Stores
S.I.C.: 5699
N.A.I.C.S.: 448150

Non-U.S. Subsidiary:

PreTex Textilhandels GmbH (1)
Honor St 76-78
50672 Cologne, Germany
Tel.: (49) 2212572851
Fax: (49) 2212572852
Fashion Clothing Dlrs
S.I.C.: 7389
N.A.I.C.S.: 541490

FRENCKEN GROUP LIMITED

80 Robinson Road 02-00
Singapore, 068898, Singapore
Tel.: (65) 62363333
Fax: (65) 62364399
Web Site: www.frenckengroup.com
E28—(SES)
Rev.: $292,259,664
Assets: $288,067,141
Liabilities: $135,842,443
Net Worth: $152,224,698
Earnings: ($9,492,688)
Fiscal Year-end: 12/31/12

Business Description:
Electronic Equipment Products Mfr & Distr
S.I.C.: 7389
N.A.I.C.S.: 425110
Personnel:
Soon Hock Gooi *(Co-Founder & Pres)*
Larry Hock Peng Low *(Co-Founder)*
Mei Wan Low *(Co-Sec)*
Choi Fan Toon *(Co-Sec)*
Board of Directors:
Larry Hock Peng Low
Chor Leong Chia
Soon Hock Gooi
Yong Wah Ling
Barry Mong Huat Sim
Derrick Lai Heng Tan
Hendrik Gezinus Tappel
Jeu Nam Yeo
Transfer Agent:
Tricor Barbinder Share Registration Services
80 Robinson Road 02-00
Singapore, Singapore

Subsidiaries:

ETLA Limited (1)
1 Changi North St 2
Singapore, 498808, Singapore
Tel.: (65) 65466466
Fax: (65) 65466488
Web Site: www.etla.com.sg
Emp.: 300
Precision Machinery & Tools Mfr
S.I.C.: 3423
N.A.I.C.S.: 332216
Sam Varry *(Gen Mgr)*

Juken Technology Limited (1)
33 Loyang Way
Singapore, 508731, Singapore SG
Tel.: (65) 6565423033
Fax: (65) 6565423393
E-Mail: enquiries@jukentech.com
Web Site: www.jukentech.com
Sales Range: $50-74.9 Million
Moulded Plastic Components Mfr
S.I.C.: 3089
N.A.I.C.S.: 326199
Patsy Lye Yong Cheong *(COO)*
Leon Rufino *(CEO-Switzerland)*

Subsidiary:

Juken Mecplas Technology Pte Ltd (2)
33 Loyang Way
508731 Singapore, Singapore
Tel.: (65) 65423033
Fax: (65) 65423393
E-Mail: enquiries@jukentech.com
Web Site: www.jukentech.com
Emp.: 80
Injection Molded Plastic Products Mfr
S.I.C.: 3089
N.A.I.C.S.: 326199
David Wong *(Mng Dir)*

Subsidiary:

Zelor Technology Pte Ltd (3)
33 Loyang Way
Singapore, Singapore
Tel.: (65) 6542 3033
Fax: (65) 6542 3393
Emp.: 20
Product Validation Services
S.I.C.: 7389
N.A.I.C.S.: 561990

Non-U.S. Subsidiaries:

Juken (H.K.) Co., Limited (2)
Unit 1603-1604 CFC Tower 28 Mody Road
Tsim Tsa Tsui, Kowloon, China (Hong Kong)
Tel.: (852) 27508212
Fax: (852) 27541954
Web Site: www.jukentech.com
Precision Plastic Products Mfr
S.I.C.: 3089
N.A.I.C.S.: 326199
Sheila Ling *(Mgr)*

Juken Micro-Air (Tianjin) Technology Co., Ltd. (2)
No 8 Shuang Chen Zhong Lu Bei Chen
Economy Development District
Tianjin, 300400, China
Tel.: (86) 22 2697 2287
Fax: (86) 22 2697 2263
Injection Molded Plastic Products Mfr
S.I.C.: 3082
N.A.I.C.S.: 326121

Juken Swiss Technology AG (2)
Buendengasse 22
2540 Grenchen, Solothurn, Switzerland
Tel.: (41) 32 461 4040
Fax: (41) 32 461 4042
E-Mail: info@jukenswisstech.com
Web Site: www.jukenswisstech.com
Emp.: 10
Stepper Motor & Car Clocks Mfr
S.I.C.: 3566
N.A.I.C.S.: 333612
Rufino Leon *(Chm)*

Juken Technology (Macau Commercial Offshore) Company Limited (2)
Alameda Dr Carlos D Assumpcao No 181-187 Edif Centro Comercial do
Grupo Brihantismo 9D Andar, Macau, China (Macau)
Tel.: (853) 2875 3280
Fax: (853) 2875 3280
Web Site: www.jukentech.com
Molded Plastic Goods Distr
S.I.C.: 5113
N.A.I.C.S.: 424130
Neo Say Kian *(CEO)*

Juken (Thailand) Co., Ltd. (2)
24/3 Moo 4 Bangna-Trad Road Km 35
Tambol Bangpleenoi
Amphur Bangbor, Samut Prakan, 10560, Thailand
Tel.: (66) 27087477
E-Mail: jukenthailand@jukenthai.com
Web Site: www.jukenthai.com
Injection Molded Plastic Products Mfr
S.I.C.: 3082
N.A.I.C.S.: 326121
Min Chi Wei *(Mng Dir)*

Juken Uniproducts Pvt Ltd (2)
C-14 Sector-57
Noida, Uttar Pradesh, 201 307, India
Tel.: (91) 120 258 1231
Fax: (91) 120 258 5031
Injection Molded Plastic Parts Mfr
S.I.C.: 3082
N.A.I.C.S.: 326121

Juken (Zhuhai) Co., Ltd. (2)
Block 11 Zone 1 Hengli Nanshui Industrial Park
Nanshui Town, Zhuhai, Guangdong, 519050, China
Tel.: (86) 7567713282
Fax: (86) 7567713292
Web Site: www.jukentech.com
Emp.: 420
Precision Engineered Plastic Products Mfr
S.I.C.: 3082
N.A.I.C.S.: 326121
Jingxian Huang *(Chm)*

PT Juken Technology Indonesia (2)
EJIP Industrial Park Plot 1F-3C
Cikarang Selatan, Bekasi, West Java, 17550, Indonesia
Tel.: (62) 21 897 0202
Fax: (62) 21 897 1212
Web Site: www.jukentech.com
Precision Engineered Plastic Products Mfr
S.I.C.: 3089
N.A.I.C.S.: 326199

Non-U.S. Plants:

Juken Engineering Technology Sdn Bhd - Johor Bahru Factory (2)
No 18 Jalan Masyhur 1
Taman Perindustrian Cemerlang, 81800 Ulu Tiram, Johor, Malaysia
Tel.: (60) 7 863 7568
Fax: (60) 7 863 7569
Web Site: www.jukentech.com
Emp.: 158
Precision Engineered Plastic Products Mfr
S.I.C.: 3089
N.A.I.C.S.: 326199
Casey Ng *(Gen Mgr)*

Juken Engineering Technology Sdn Bhd - Kuala Lumpur Factory (2)
Lot 10 11 & 12 Jalan BRP 9/1C Bukit
Rahman Putra Industrial Park
47000 Sungai Buloh, Selangor, Malaysia
Tel.: (60) 361562386
Fax: (60) 361567389
E-Mail: rogerwong@jukentech.com
Web Site: www.jukentech.com
Emp.: 200
Precision Engineered Plastic Products Mfr
S.I.C.: 3089
N.A.I.C.S.: 326199
Roger Wong *(Gen Mgr)*

U.S. Subsidiary:

US Motion, Inc. (1)
22924 E Apple Way
Liberty Lake, WA 99019 WA
Tel.: (509) 924-9777
Fax: (509) 924-8299
E-Mail: info@usmotion.com
Web Site: www.usmotion.com
Sales Range: $10-24.9 Million
Emp.: 35
Miscellaneous General Purpose Machinery Mfr
S.I.C.: 3569
N.A.I.C.S.: 333999

Non-U.S. Subsidiaries:

ETLA Technology (M) Sdn.Bhd. (1)
Lot 3 Jalan P 1A Bangi Industrial Estate
43650 Bandar Baru Bangi, Selangor, Malaysia
Tel.: (60) 389110222
Fax: (60) 389110333
Emp.: 300
Precision Machinery Mfr
S.I.C.: 3559
N.A.I.C.S.: 333249
Martin Low *(Gen Mgr)*

ETLA Technology (Wuxi) Co.,Ltd. (1)
No 6 Xin Du Road Wuxi Singapore Industrial Park
Wuxi, Jiangsu, 214028, China
Tel.: (86) 51085280851
Fax: (86) 510 8528 0861
Web Site: www.frenckengroup.com
Precision Machinery Mfr & Distr
S.I.C.: 3542
N.A.I.C.S.: 333517

Frencken Mechatronics B.V. (1)
Hurksestraat 16
5652 AJ Eindhoven, North Brabant, Netherlands
Tel.: (31) 40 2507 507
Fax: (31) 40 2507 500
E-Mail: group@frencken.nl
Web Site: www.frenckengroup.com
Emp.: 250
Industrial Equipments Mfr
S.I.C.: 3545
N.A.I.C.S.: 333515
Henk Dappal *(Gen Mgr)*

Frencken Mechatronics (M) Sdn Bhd (1)
Lot 3 Jalan P 1A Bangi Industrial Estate
43650 Bandar Baru Bangi, Selangor, Malaysia
Tel.: (60) 389110222
Fax: (60) 389110333
Web Site: www.frenckengroup.com
Emp.: 300
Precision Mechanical Equipments Mfr
S.I.C.: 3425
N.A.I.C.S.: 332216
Martin Low *(Gen Mgr)*

Frencken Technical Projects Assembly B.V. (1)
Hurksestraat 16
5652 AJ Eindhoven, North Brabant, Netherlands
Tel.: (31) 40 250 7507
Fax: (31) 40 250 7500
E-Mail: europ@frencken.nl
Web Site: www.frencken.nl
Emp.: 200
Industrial Tools Mfr
S.I.C.: 3545
N.A.I.C.S.: 333515

Frencken Group Limited—(Continued)

Machinefabriek Gebrs.Frencken B.V. (1)
Hurksestraat 16
PO Box 7027
5652 AJ Eindhoven, North Brabant, Netherlands
Tel.: (31) 402507546
Fax: (31) 40 2507 520
Web Site: www.frenckengroup.com
Precision Machinery Parts Mfr
S.I.C.: 3545
N.A.I.C.S.: 333515

Optiwa B.V. (1)
Molenweg 3
5953 JR Reuver, Limburg, Netherlands
Tel.: (31) 77 4769 900
Fax: (31) 77 4744 732
Web Site: www.optiwa.nl
Emp.: 80
Precision Mechanical Parts Mfr
S.I.C.: 3425
N.A.I.C.S.: 332216

Precico Group Sdn Bhd (1)
Plot 410 Lorong Perusahaan 8B Prai Industrial Estate
13600 Perai, Penang, Malaysia
Tel.: (60) 43883077
Fax: (60) 43997877
E-Mail: corp@precico.com.my
Web Site: www.frenckengroup.com
Emp.: 1,000
Electronic Components Mfr
S.I.C.: 3679
N.A.I.C.S.: 334418
Guetim Lee *(Mgr-HR)*

FRENKEL TOPPING GROUP PLC

4th Floor Statham House Talbot Rd
Old Trafford, Manchester, M32 0FP, United Kingdom
Tel.: (44) 1618868000
Fax: (44) 1618868002
E-Mail: info@frenkeltopping.co.uk
Web Site: www.frenkeltopping.co.uk
FEN—(LSE)
Rev.: $7,554,872
Assets: $13,429,564
Liabilities: $2,886,899
Net Worth: $10,542,664
Earnings: $1,193,155
Emp.: 51
Fiscal Year-end: 12/31/12
Business Description:
Holding Company; Financial Advisory Services
S.I.C.: 6719
N.A.I.C.S.: 551112
Personnel:
Richard C. Fraser *(CEO)*
Julie A. Dean *(Sec & Dir-Fin)*
Board of Directors:
David R. Southworth
Julie A. Dean
Richard C. Fraser
Greg McMahon
Legal Counsel:
Addleshaw Goddard LLP
100 Barbirolli Square
Manchester, United Kingdom

Subsidiaries:

Frenkel Topping Limited (1)
4th Floor Statham House Talbot Road
Old Trafford, Manchester, M320FP, United Kingdom UK
Tel.: (44) 1618868000
Fax: (44) 1618868002
E-Mail: info@frenkeltopping.co.uk
Web Site: www.frenkeltopping.co.uk
Emp.: 35
Financial Advisory Services
S.I.C.: 6282
N.A.I.C.S.: 523930
Richard C. Fraser *(Mng Dir)*

Frenkel Topping Structured Settlements Limited (1)
4th Floor Statham House Talbot Road
Old Trafford, Manchester, M32 0FP, United Kingdom UK
Tel.: (44) 1618868000
Fax: (44) 1618868002
Web Site: www.frenkeltopping.co.uk
Emp.: 40
Financial Consulting Services
S.I.C.: 6282
N.A.I.C.S.: 523930
Richard C. Fraser *(Mng Dir)*

FREQUENCY TELECOM

Unit 44 Barwell Business Park
Leatherhead Road
Chessington, Surrey, KT9 2NY, United Kingdom
Tel.: (44) 20 8397 2222
Fax: (44) 20 8397 9999
E-Mail: sales@frequencytelecom.com
Web Site: www.frequencytelecom.com
Year Founded: 2002
Sales Range: $25-49.9 Million
Emp.: 60
Business Description:
Mobile Accessory Distr
S.I.C.: 5065
N.A.I.C.S.: 423690
Personnel:
Gareth Limpenny *(Mng Dir)*

FRERE-BOURGEOIS

Rue De La Blanche Borne 12
B 6280 Loverval, Belgium
Tel.: (32) 71606060
Fax: (32) 71606070
Sales Range: $10-24.9 Million
Emp.: 10
Business Description:
Public Relations
S.I.C.: 8743
N.A.I.C.S.: 541820
Personnel:
Albert Frere *(Chm)*
Gerald Frere *(Mng Dir)*
Gilles Samyn *(Mng Dir)*
Roland Borres *(CFO)*

Subsidiary:

ERBE SA (1)
Rue De La Blanche Borne 12
6280 Loverval, Belgium
Tel.: (32) 71606060
Fax: (32) 71606070
E-Mail:
Web Site: www.cnp.be
Emp.: 20
Holding Company; Owned 53% by Frere-Bourgeois & 47% by BNP Paribas SA
S.I.C.: 6719
N.A.I.C.S.: 551112
Albert Frere *(Chm)*
Gilles Samyn *(Mng Dir)*

Subsidiary:

Compagnie Nationale a Portefeuille S.A. (2)
Rue de la Blanche Borne 12
6280 Loverval, Belgium
Tel.: (32) 71606060
Fax: (32) 71606070
E-Mail: cnp@cnp.be
Web Site: www.npm-cnp.be
Sales Range: $15-24.9 Billion
Emp.: 17,334
Holding Company
S.I.C.: 6719
N.A.I.C.S.: 551112
Gerald Frere *(Chm)*
Gilles Samyn *(Vice Chm & CEO)*
Roland Borres *(CFO)*
Jean-Charles d'Aspremont Lyden *(Chief Compliance Officer)*
Maximilien de Limburg Stirum *(Chief Investment Officer)*
Victor Delloye *(Gen Counsel)*

Non-U.S. Subsidiaries:

Agesca Nederland NV (3)
Veerkade 5
3016 DE Rotterdam, Netherlands NL
Tel.: (31) 102183703 (100%)
Fax: (31) 10414938
E-Mail: patricia.ottervanger@agesca.eu
Holding Company
S.I.C.: 6719
N.A.I.C.S.: 551112

Joint Venture:

Parjointco N.V. (4)
Veerkade 5
Rotterdam, 3016DE, Netherlands NL
Tel.: (31) 4139154
Fax: (31) 4149384
Holding Company; Joint Venture Between Power Financial Europe BV and Agesca Netherland NV
S.I.C.: 6719
N.A.I.C.S.: 551112

Non-U.S. Holding:

Pargesa Holding S.A. (5)
11 Grand Rue
CH 1204 Geneva, Switzerland
Tel.: (41) 228177777
Fax: (41) 228177770
E-Mail: info@pargesa.ch
Web Site: www.pargesa.ch
PARG—(SWX)
Rev.: $5,305,289,528
Assets: $23,687,296,380
Liabilities: $6,399,180,348
Net Worth: $17,288,116,032
Earnings: $1,098,100,168
Emp.: 17,000
Fiscal Year-end: 12/31/12
Holding Company
S.I.C.: 6719
N.A.I.C.S.: 551112
Paul Desmarais, Jr. *(Chm)*
Andre de Pfyffer *(Vice Chm)*
Paul Desmarais, Jr. *(Vice Chm)*
Baron Frere *(Vice Chm)*
Gerald Frere *(Vice Chm)*
Arnaud Vial *(Mng Dir)*
Andrew Allender *(Deputy Mng Dir & Fin Dir)*
Fabienne Rudaz Bovard *(Treas)*

Entremont S.A. (3)
25 Faubourg Des Balmettes
BP 29
F 74001 Annecy, Cedex 1, France (75%)
Tel.: (33) 450337474
Telex: 385063 f
Fax: (33) 450337450
Web Site: www.entremont.fr
Emp.: 3,700
Producer of Cheese Import Export
S.I.C.: 2022
N.A.I.C.S.: 311513
Jacque Entremont *(Pres & Gen Dir)*

FRESCA GROUP LIMITED

The Fresh Produce Centre Transfesa Road
Paddock Wood, Kent, TN12 6UT, United Kingdom
Tel.: (44) 1892 831280
Web Site: www.frescagroup.co.uk
Year Founded: 1874
Sales Range: $450-499.9 Million
Emp.: 848
Business Description:
Fruit & Vegetable Whslr
S.I.C.: 5148
N.A.I.C.S.: 424480
Personnel:
Christopher Mack *(Chm)*

FRESCHE SOLUTIONS INC.

(d/b/a Fresche Legacy)
995 Wellington Street Suite 200
Montreal, QC, H3C 1V3, Canada
Tel.: (514) 747-7007
Fax: (514) 747-3380
E-Mail: info@freschelegacy.com
Web Site: www.freschelegacy.com
Sales Range: $25-49.9 Million
Business Description:
Legacy Computer System Management Services
S.I.C.: 7373
N.A.I.C.S.: 541512
Personnel:
Andrew Kulakowski *(Pres & CEO)*
Nick Cristiano *(CFO)*
Transfer Agent:
CIBC Mellon Trust Company
320 Bay Street
PO Box 1
Toronto, ON, M5H 2A6, Canada
Tel.: (416) 643-5500
Fax: (416) 643-5570
Toll Free: (800) 387-0825

FRESE & WOLFF WERBEAGENTUR GMBH

Donnerschweer Strasse 79
26123 Oldenburg, Germany
Tel.: (49) 44180020
Fax: (49) 44181000
E-Mail: info@frese-wolff.de
Web Site: www.frese-wolff.de
Year Founded: 1976
Billings: $53,000,000
Emp.: 45
Business Description:
Advertising Agency
S.I.C.: 7311
N.A.I.C.S.: 541810
Personnel:
Hans E. Wolff *(Owner & CEO)*

FRESENIUS MEDICAL CARE AG & CO. KGAA

Else-Kroener Strasse 1
61352 Bad Homburg, Germany
Tel.: (49) 6172 608 2522
Fax: (49) 6172 609 2301
E-Mail: ir@fmc-ag.com
Web Site: www.fmc-ag.com
Year Founded: 1996
FMS—(DEU NYSE)
Rev.: $14,609,727,000
Assets: $23,119,906,000
Liabilities: $13,634,886,000
Net Worth: $9,485,020,000
Earnings: $1,255,623,000
Emp.: 90,690
Fiscal Year-end: 12/31/13
Business Description:
Holding Company; Dialysis Products & Services
S.I.C.: 6719
N.A.I.C.S.: 551112
Personnel:
Gerd E. Krick *(Chm-Supervisory Bd)*
Ben J. Lipps *(Chm-Mgmt Bd & CEO)*
Dieter Schenk *(Vice Chm-Supervisory Bd)*
Michael Brosnan *(CFO)*
Roberto Fuste *(CEO-Asia Pacific)*
Emanuele Gatti *(CEO-Europe, Latin America, Middle East & Africa)*
Kent Wanzek *(CEO-Global Mfg Ops)*
Rainer Runte *(Member-Mgmt Bd-Law/Compliance/Intellectual Property & Dir-Labor)*
Oliver Maier *(Sr VP-IR)*
Joachim Weith *(Sr VP-Comm & Govt Affairs)*
Supervisory Board of Directors:
Gerd E. Krick
Bernd Fahrholz
William P. Johnston
Dieter Schenk
Walter L. Weisman

Subsidiaries:

FMC GmbH (1)
Else-Kroner-Str 1
61346 Bad Homburg, Germany

Tel.: (49) 6172 609 0
Fax: (49) 6172 609 8740
E-Mail: marketing.deutschland@fmc-ag.com
Dialysis Center Oprator
S.I.C.: 8092
N.A.I.C.S.: 621492

Fresenius Medical Care Deutschland GmbH (1)
Frankfurter Str 6-8
St Wendel, Tholey, 66606, Germany
Tel.: (49) 61726090
Web Site: www.fmc-ag.com
Emp.: 1,600
Medical Products Mfr
S.I.C.: 3841
N.A.I.C.S.: 339112
Ben Lipps *(Chm-Mgmt Bd & CEO)*

Fresenius Medical Care Deutschland GmbH (1)
Hafenstrasse 9
97424 Schweinfurt, Germany
Tel.: (49) 97216780
Fax: (49) 9721678200
E-Mail: info@fmcag.com
Web Site: www.fmcag.com
Emp.: 1,200
Medical Products Mfr
S.I.C.: 3841
N.A.I.C.S.: 339112

U.S. Subsidiaries:

Fresenius Medical Care North America (1)
Reservoir Woods 920 Winter St
Waltham, MA 02451-1457 DE
Tel.: (781) 402-9000
Fax: (781) 699-9715
Toll Free: (800) 662-1237
E-Mail: corphr@fmcna.com
Web Site: www.fmcna.com
Emp.: 1,135
Mfr & Marketer of Artificial Kidney Supplies & Treatment Centers, Respiratory Therapy Products Distribution, Infusion Therapy Services & Products
S.I.C.: 8092
N.A.I.C.S.: 621492
Ben Lips *(Chm & CEO)*
Rice Powell *(CEO)*
Ravi Kalathil *(CIO & VP)*
Ronald Kuerbitz *(Exec VP)*
Jose Diaz Buxo *(Sr VP)*
Deborah Harvey *(Sr VP-Opers)*
Robert McGorty *(Sr VP-Fin & Admin)*
Brian O'Connell *(Sr VP-HR)*

Renal Solutions, Inc. (1)
770 Commonwealth Dr Ste 101
Warrendale, PA 15086
Tel.: (724) 772-6900
Fax: (724) 772-6925
E-Mail: info@renalsolutionsinc.com
Web Site: www.renalsolutionsinc.com
Emp.: 45
Developer of Sorbent-Based Hemodialysis Products & Services
S.I.C.: 3841
N.A.I.C.S.: 339112
Sue Bentley *(Dir-Mktg)*

Subsidiary:

SORB Technology, Inc. (2)
3631 SW 54th St
Oklahoma City, OK 73119
Tel.: (405) 682-1993
Fax: (405) 682-2108
Web Site: www.sorb.net
Emp.: 23
Disposable Hemodialysis Products & Components Mfr
S.I.C.: 3644
N.A.I.C.S.: 335932
R. Preston Thompson *(Sr VP & Gen Mgr)*

Non-U.S. Subsidiaries:

FMC Dializis Center Kft. (1)
Szepvolgyi Ut 35-37
Budapest, 1037, Hungary
Tel.: (36) 14392244
Fax: (36) 14392240
E-Mail: fres.group-hu@fmc-ag.com
Web Site: www.fresenius.hu
Dialysis Center Operator
S.I.C.: 8092
N.A.I.C.S.: 621492

FMC Portugal, S.A. (1)
Rua da Boaviagem 35 Lugar de Crestins - Moreira
4470-210 Maia, Portugal
Tel.: (351) 229 438 280
Fax: (351) 229 433 229
E-Mail: fmcportugal@fmc-ag.com
Web Site: www.fresenius-medical-care.pt
Rev.: $122,889,270
Emp.: 200
Medical Equipment Distr
S.I.C.: 5047
N.A.I.C.S.: 423450
Ricardo A. Carballo Da Silva *(Chm)*

Fresenius Medical Care Argentina S.A. (1)
Arenales 707 3er Piso
C1061AAA Buenos Aires, Argentina
Tel.: (54) 11 4130 1000
Fax: (54) 11 4130 1111
E-Mail: fmcargentina@fmc-ag.com
Web Site: www.fmc-ag.com.ar
Dialysis Treatment Services
S.I.C.: 8092
N.A.I.C.S.: 621492

Fresenius Medical Care Australia PTY Ltd. (1)
Level 17 61 Lavender Street
Milsons Point, Sydney, NSW, 2061, Australia
Tel.: (61) 2 9466 8000
Fax: (61) 2 9929 5595
E-Mail: contactusau@fmc-asia.com
Web Site: www.freseniusmedicalcare.com.au
Emp.: 60
Dialysis Equipment Mfr
S.I.C.: 3845
N.A.I.C.S.: 334510
Margot Hurwitz *(Mng Dir)*

Division:

Fresenius Medical Care Australia PTY Ltd. - NephroCare Australia Division (2)
Level 17 61 Lavender Street
Milsons Point, Sydney, NSW, Australia
Tel.: (61) 2 9466 8009
Fax: (61) 2 9466 8059
Dialysis Equipment Distr
S.I.C.: 5047
N.A.I.C.S.: 423450

Fresenius Medical Care Austria GmbH (1)
Lundenburgergasse 5
1210 Vienna, Austria
Tel.: (43) 1 2923501
Fax: (43) 1 292350185
E-Mail: fmc.austria@fmc-ag.com
Web Site: www.fmc-austria.at
Emp.: 32
Medical & Surgical Equipment Distr
S.I.C.: 5047
N.A.I.C.S.: 423450
Michael Friedl *(Gen Mgr)*

Fresenius Medical Care Belgium N.V. (1)
Boomsesteenweg 939
Antwerp, 2610, Belgium
Tel.: (32) 38251188
Fax: (32) 38251106
Medical & Surgical Equipment Distr
S.I.C.: 5047
N.A.I.C.S.: 423450

Fresenius Medical Care BH d.o.o. (1)
Zmaja Od Bosne 7-7a
Sarajevo, 71000, Bosnia & Herzegovina
Tel.: (387) 33559181
Fax: (387) 33212951
Dialysis Treatment Services
S.I.C.: 8092
N.A.I.C.S.: 621492

Fresenius Medical Care Colombia S.A. (1)
Carrera 106 15 A 25
Bogota, Colombia
Tel.: (57) 12941400
Fax: (57) 12941436
E-Mail: Lineaconexion@fmc-ag.com
Web Site: www.fmc-ag.com.co
Dialysis Center Operator
S.I.C.: 8092
N.A.I.C.S.: 621492

Fresenius Medical Care CR, s.r.o. (1)
Evropska 423/178
160 00 Prague, Czech Republic
Tel.: (420) 273 037 900
Fax: (420) 235 350 506
E-Mail: fresenius@fresenius.cz
Web Site: www.fresenius.cz
Hospital & Medical Supplies Distr
S.I.C.: 5047
N.A.I.C.S.: 423450

Subsidiary:

Fresenius Medical Care - DS, s.r.o. (2)
Evropska 423/178
160 00 Prague, Czech Republic
Tel.: (420) 235 358 212
Fax: (420) 235 350 506
E-Mail: fresenius@fresenius.cz
Web Site: www.fresenius.cz/Clanek.aspx?kod=KONTAKTY
Emp.: 60
Medical Supplies Distr
S.I.C.: 5047
N.A.I.C.S.: 423450
David Prokes *(Gen Dir)*

Non-U.S. Subsidiary:

FMC Magyarorszag Egeszsegugyi Korlatolt Felelossegu Tarsasag (2)
Szepvolgyi Ut 35-37
1037 Budapest, Hungary
Tel.: (36) 14392244
Fax: (36) 14392240
E-Mail: fres.group-hu@fmc-ag.com
Web Site: www.fresenius.com
Dialysis Center Oprator
S.I.C.: 8092
N.A.I.C.S.: 621492
Attila Berkes *(Mng Dir)*

Fresenius Medical Care Danmark A/S (1)
Oldenburg Alle 1
2630 Tastrup, Denmark
Tel.: (45) 43 22 61 00
Fax: (45) 43 22 61 10
E-Mail: fmcdk@fmc-ag.com
Web Site: www.fmc-ag.dk
Medical Supplies Distr
S.I.C.: 5047
N.A.I.C.S.: 423450
Bo Johansen *(CEO)*

Fresenius Medical Care de Venezuela C.A. (1)
Av Libertador Con Calle Cantaura Qta Concepcion
Los Caobos, Caracas, Venezuela
Tel.: (58) 2127315597
Fax: (58) 2127315597
Web Site: www.fmc-ag.com.ve
Dialysis Center Operating Services
S.I.C.: 8092
N.A.I.C.S.: 621492

Fresenius Medical Care del Peru S.A. (1)
Calle Los Telares 299 Urbanizacion Vulcano - Ate
Lima, Peru
Tel.: (51) 1 349 7520
Fax: (51) 1 349 1542
E-Mail: informes@fmc-ag.com.pe
Web Site: www.fmc-ag.com.pe
Emp.: 21
Dialysis Treatment Services & Equipment Distr
S.I.C.: 8092
N.A.I.C.S.: 621492
Gustavo Ambrosini *(Gen Mgr)*

Fresenius Medical Care Groupe France S.A.S. (1)
47 Avenue Des Pepinieres
94260 Fresnes, Val-de-Marne, France
Tel.: (33) 156452185
Fax: (33) 146156504
Medical & Surgical Equipment Distr
S.I.C.: 5047
N.A.I.C.S.: 423450

Subsidiary:

FMC SMAD S.A.S. (2)
ZI de la Pontchonniere Route de la Chanade
BP 106
Savigny, 69591 L'Arbresle, France
Tel.: (33) 474016000
Fax: (33) 474012181
E-Mail: contact@fmc-smad.com
Web Site: www.fmc-smad.com
Emp.: 40
Medical Instrument Mfr
S.I.C.: 3845
N.A.I.C.S.: 334510

Fresenius Medical Care Hong Kong Limited (1)
Rm 5101-5123 51/F Sun Hung Kai Ctr 30 Harbour Rd
Wanchai, China (Hong Kong)
Tel.: (852) 28982883
Fax: (852) 28022747
Medical & Surgical Equipment Distr
S.I.C.: 5047
N.A.I.C.S.: 423450
Thorsten Bruce *(Gen Mgr)*

Subsidiary:

Biocare Technology Company Limited (2)
Rm 5101-5123 51/F Sun Hung Kai Ctr 30 Harbour Rd
Wanchai, China (Hong Kong)
Tel.: (852) 28982883
Fax: (852) 28022747
Emp.: 35
Pharmaceutical Products Mfr
S.I.C.: 2834
N.A.I.C.S.: 325412
Thorsten Bruce *(Gen Mgr)*

Fresenius Medical Care India Private Limited (1)
11th Floor Front Wing Dr Gopal Dass Bhawan 28 Barakhamba Road
New Delhi, 110 001, India
Tel.: (91) 11 45509500
Fax: (91) 11 45509506
E-Mail: reception@fmc-asia.com
Emp.: 100
Medical & Dialysis Therapy Apparatus Distr
S.I.C.: 5047
N.A.I.C.S.: 423450
Dhruv Chaturvedi *(Mng Dir)*

Fresenius Medical Care (Ireland) Limited (1)
Unit 3b Fingal Bay Business Park
Balbriggan, Ireland
Tel.: (353) 18413030
Health Care Services
S.I.C.: 8099
N.A.I.C.S.: 621999

Fresenius Medical Care Italia S.p.A. (1)
Via Crema 8
Palazzo Pignano, Cremona, 26020, Italy
Tel.: (39) 03739741
Fax: (39) 0373974201
Medical & Surgical Equipment Mfr & Distr
S.I.C.: 3841
N.A.I.C.S.: 339112

Subsidiary:

SIS-TER S.p.A. (2)
Via Crema 8
26020 Palazzo Pignano, Cremona, Italy
Tel.: (39) 0373 977 1
Fax: (39) 0373 977 345
E-Mail: infosister.it@fmc-ag.com
Web Site: www.fresenius.com
Emp.: 250
Medical Application Tubing Set Mfr
S.I.C.: 3841
N.A.I.C.S.: 339112
Stefano Sarti *(Mng Dir)*

Fresenius Medical Care Korea Ltd. (1)
7th Fl Landmart Tower 837-7 Yeoksam 1-dong
Gangnam-gu, Seoul, 135-937, Korea (South)
Tel.: (82) 2 2112 8800
Fax: (82) 2 2112 8859

Fresenius Medical Care AG & Co. KGaA—(Continued)

Web Site: www.fmc-korea.co.kr
Emp.: 250
Medical Device Mfr
S.I.C.: 3841
N.A.I.C.S.: 339112
Sung Ok Choi *(CEO)*

Fresenius Medical Care Lebanon s.a.r.L. (1)
6th Floor Aresco Center Justinien Street
Kantari Sector
Beirut, Lebanon
Tel.: (961) 1 744841
Fax: (961) 1 744842
Dialysis Instrument Distr
S.I.C.: 5047
N.A.I.C.S.: 423450

Fresenius Medical Care Ltda. (1)
Rua Roque Gonzales 128 Jardim Branca Flor
Itapecerica da Serra, Sao Paulo, Brazil
Tel.: (55) 19 3847 9700
Fax: (55) 19 3847 9714
Web Site: www.fmc-ag.com.br
Medical Equipment Mfr & Distr
S.I.C.: 3841
N.A.I.C.S.: 339112

Fresenius Medical Care Malaysia Sdn. Bhd. (1)
Second Floor Axis Technology Centre Lot 13 Jalan 51A/225
46100 Petaling Jaya, Selangor, Malaysia
Tel.: (60) 3 7957 9866
Fax: (60) 3 7957 1272
E-Mail: fresenius.my@fmc-asia.com
Emp.: 10
Dialysis Machine Supplies Distr
S.I.C.: 5047
N.A.I.C.S.: 423450
Siow Sheong Lim *(Mng Dir)*

Fresenius Medical Care Maroc S.A. (1)
33 Bd Moulay Youssef
20000 Casablanca, Morocco
Tel.: (212) 5 22 49 19 91
Fax: (212) 5 22 26 45 12
E-Mail: fmc.maroc@fmc-ag.com
Web Site: www.fmcmaroc.com
Emp.: 70
Medical Equipment Mfr & Distr
S.I.C.: 3841
N.A.I.C.S.: 339112
Tarek Fathi *(Gen Mgr)*

Fresenius Medical Care Mexico S.A. (1)
Paseo Del Norte 5300 Guadalajara Technology Park
Zapopan, Jalisco, 45010, Mexico
Tel.: (52) 3335404200
E-Mail: clinicas.fmcmx@fmc.ag.com
Web Site: www.fmc-ag.com.mx
Medical Equipment Mfr & Distr
S.I.C.: 3841
N.A.I.C.S.: 339112

Fresenius Medical Care Nederland B.V. (1)
Mandenmaker 22 Bedrijvenpark 't Hoog 5504
5253 RC Nieuwkuijk, Netherlands
Tel.: (31) 88 1223344
Fax: (31) 88 1223333
E-Mail: info@fmc.nl
Web Site: www.fmc.nl
Emp.: 50
Medical Instrument Mfr
S.I.C.: 3845
N.A.I.C.S.: 334510

Fresenius Medical Care Philippines, Inc. (1)
2257 Don Chino Roces Avenue Extension
Makati, 1231, Philippines
Tel.: (63) 28919575
Fax: (63) 28919579
Dialysis Treatment & Medical Equipment Distr
S.I.C.: 5047
N.A.I.C.S.: 423450

Subsidiary:

FMC Renalcare Corp. (2)
2257 Don Chino Roces Avenue Extention
Makati, 1231, Philippines
Tel.: (63) 2 8132520
Fax: (63) 2 8175791
Dialysis Treatment Services
S.I.C.: 8092
N.A.I.C.S.: 621492
Elena Lam *(Bus Dir)*

Fresenius Medical Care Polska S.A. (1)
ul Krzywa 13
60-118 Poznan, Poland
Tel.: (48) 61 8392 600
Fax: (48) 61 8392 601
E-Mail: sekretariat@fmc.pl
Web Site: www.fresenius.com.pl
Pharmaceutical Product Mfr
S.I.C.: 2834
N.A.I.C.S.: 325412

Fresenius Medical Care Romania Srl (1)
Sos Bucuresti-Ploiesti Nr 19-21 Et 3
Baneasa Business Center Sector 1
Bucharest, Romania
Tel.: (40) 21 233 42 68 71
Fax: (40) 21 233 42 20 21
E-Mail: marketing.fresenius@fmc-romania.ro
Web Site: www.fmc-romania.ro
Dialysis Equipment Distr
S.I.C.: 5047
N.A.I.C.S.: 423450

Fresenius Medical Care (Schweiz) AG (1)
Aawasserstrasse 2
6370 Oberdorf, Switzerland
Tel.: (41) 41 619 5050
Fax: (41) 41 619 5080
E-Mail: info.ch@fmc-ag.com
Web Site: www.fresenius.ch
Medical Instrument Mfr & Distr
S.I.C.: 3845
N.A.I.C.S.: 334510

Fresenius Medical Care (Shanghai) Co., Ltd. (1)
Rm 4601 Suite 2 Ganghui Center No 3 Hongqiao Road
Xuhui Dis, Shanghai, 200030, China
Tel.: (86) 2161152800
Fax: (86) 2161152801
Dialysis & Health Care Services
S.I.C.: 8092
N.A.I.C.S.: 621492

Subsidiary:

FMC (Jiangsu) Co. Ltd. (2)
Gu-i Industry Park Gu-Li Zhen
Changshu, Jiangsu, China 215533
Tel.: (86) 512 5230 5630
Fax: (86) 512 5230 1108
Web Site: www.fresenius.com
Health Care Services
S.I.C.: 8099
N.A.I.C.S.: 621999

Fresenius Medical Care Singapore Pte. Ltd. (1)
11 Bishan Street 21 04-04
Singapore, 573943, Singapore
Tel.: (65) 67340303
Fax: (65) 68372112
E-Mail: customerservice.sg@fmc-asia.com
Emp.: 20
Dialysis Center Operator
S.I.C.: 8092
N.A.I.C.S.: 621492
Millie Ng *(Mng Dir)*

Fresenius Medical Care Slovenija d.o.o. (1)
Dobrava 14
3214 Zrece, Slovenia
Tel.: (386) 3 757 11 40
Fax: (386) 3 757 11 44
E-Mail: info@nefrodial.si
Web Site: www.nefrodial.si
Dialysis Center Operator
S.I.C.: 8092
N.A.I.C.S.: 621492

Subsidiary:

NEFRODIAL d.o.o. (2)
Leskovska 29
Krsko, Slovenia
Tel.: (386) 7 490 42 50
Fax: (386) 7 490 42 58
E-Mail: nefrodial.krsko@fmc-ag.com
Emp.: 21
Dialysis Center Operator
S.I.C.: 8092
N.A.I.C.S.: 621492

Fresenius Medical Care Slovensko, spol. s.r.o. (1)
Teplicka 99
921 01 Piestany, Slovakia
Tel.: (421) 33 79152 11
Fax: (421) 33 79152 34
E-Mail: fresenius@fmc-slovensko.sk
Web Site: www.hemodialyza.sk
Dialysis Center Operator
S.I.C.: 8092
N.A.I.C.S.: 621492

Fresenius Medical Care South Africa (PTY) Ltd. (1)
31A Lake Road Longmeadow Business Estate
Edenvale, 1609, South Africa
Tel.: (27) 11 457 9300
Fax: (27) 11 457 9552
E-Mail: editor@mari-mesa.co.za
Web Site: www.fmesa.co.za
Emp.: 400
Dialysis Equipment Mfr & Distr
S.I.C.: 3845
N.A.I.C.S.: 334510

Fresenius Medical Care Srbija d.o.o. (1)
Jurija Gagarina 11-11 a
11070 Belgrade, Serbia
Tel.: (381) 11 3951 000
Fax: (381) 11 3951 009
E-Mail: info@fmc-srbija.com
Web Site: www.fmc-srbija.com
Dialysis Center Operator
S.I.C.: 8092
N.A.I.C.S.: 621492
Predrag Vranic *(Gen Mgr)*

Fresenius Medical Care Sverige AB (1)
Djupdalsvagen 1
192 51 Sollentuna, Sweden
Tel.: (46) 8 594 776 00
Fax: (46) 8 594 776 20
E-Mail: sverige@fmc-ag.com
Web Site: www.fmc-ag.se
Emp.: 32
Dialysis Center Operator
S.I.C.: 8092
N.A.I.C.S.: 621492
Anette Parkeryd *(CFO)*

Fresenius Medical Care Taiwan Co., Ltd. (1)
11F-1 51 Jilung Rd Sec 2 Shinyi Chiu
Taipei, Taiwan
Tel.: (886) 2 27398800
Fax: (886) 2 27398862
E-Mail: twcs@fmc-asia.com
Dialysis Equipment Distr
S.I.C.: 5047
N.A.I.C.S.: 423450

Subsidiary:

Jiate Excelsior Co., Ltd. (2)
16F 6 No 880 Jhongjheng Rd 235
Zhonghe, Taipei, '23586, Taiwan
Tel.: (886) 4 23059335
Fax: (886) 4 23029272
Dialysis Treatment Services
S.I.C.: 8092
N.A.I.C.S.: 621492

Fresenius Medical Care Ukraine TOV (1)
Str Borispilska 9
02099 Kiev, Ukraine
Tel.: (380) 44 369 56 02
Fax: (380) 44 369 56 01
E-Mail: fresenius@fresenius.com.ua
Web Site: www.fresenius.com.ua
Dialysis Center Oprator
S.I.C.: 8092
N.A.I.C.S.: 621492

Fresenius Medical Care (U.K.) Ltd. (1)
Nunn Brook Road
Huthwaite Sutton-in-Ashfield, Kirkby in Ashfield, Nottinghamshire, NG17 2HU, United Kingdom
Tel.: (44) 1623 445142
Fax: (44) 1623 442052
Web Site: www.freseniusmedicalcare.co.uk
Emp.: 25
Dialysis Equipment Mfr & Distr
S.I.C.: 3845
N.A.I.C.S.: 334510
Rachael Coleman *(Dir-Mktg)*

Subsidiary:

Fresenius Medical Care Renal Services Ltd (2)
Facet Road
Kings Norton, Birmingham, Birminghamshire, B38 9PT, United Kingdom
Tel.: (44) 121 486 4290
E-Mail: press.uk@fmc-ag.com
Emp.: 2
Medical Equipment Rental Services
S.I.C.: 7359
N.A.I.C.S.: 532490

Fresenius Medikal Hizmetler A.S. (1)
Eski Buyukdere Cad Ayazaga Yolu No 7
Giz 2000 Plaza Kat 18
Maslak, 34398 Istanbul, Turkey
Tel.: (90) 212 335 72 00
Fax: (90) 212 335 72 20
E-Mail: info.turkey@fmc-ag.com
Web Site: www.fresenius.com.tr
Medical Equipment Distr
S.I.C.: 5047
N.A.I.C.S.: 423450

Manadialisis S.A. (1)
Av 6 Calle 16 Y 17
Manta, Ecuador
Tel.: (593) 5 262 5080
Dialysis Equipment Distr
S.I.C.: 5047
N.A.I.C.S.: 423450

National Medical Care of Spain, S.A. (1)
Avenida Sur Del Aeropuerto De Barajas 34
Edif 3 Pt 5
Madrid, 28042, Spain
Tel.: (34) 913 27 66 50
Fax: (34) 913 27 66 51
Kidney Dialysis Center Operator
S.I.C.: 8092
N.A.I.C.S.: 621492

NephroCare Portugal S.A. (1)
Rua Professor Salazar de Sousa Lote 12
1750-233 Lisbon, Portugal
Tel.: (351) 217 501 100
Fax: (351) 217 501 190
E-Mail: fmcportugal@fmc-ag.com
Health Care Services
S.I.C.: 8099
N.A.I.C.S.: 621999

NephroCare (Thailand) Co., Ltd. (1)
62 Lang Suan Rd
Bangkok, 10330, Thailand
Tel.: (66) 26505355
Fax: (66) 26505365
Medical Care Services
S.I.C.: 8062
N.A.I.C.S.: 622110

OU Fresenius Medical Care Estonia (1)
Vaksali 17
50410 Tartu, Estonia
Tel.: (372) 64 64 144
Fax: (372) 64 64 144
E-Mail: fresenius@fresenius.ee
Web Site: www.fresenius.ee
Health Care Services
S.I.C.: 8099
N.A.I.C.S.: 621999

ZAO Fresenius SP (1)
20 K 1 Pilyugina Akademika Ul
Moscow, 117630, Russia
Tel.: (7) 4959362344
Fax: (7) 4957896454
Health Care Services
S.I.C.: 8099
N.A.I.C.S.: 621999

FRESENIUS SE & CO. KGAA

Else Kroner Strasse 1
61352 Bad Homburg, Germany
Tel.: (49) 61726080
Fax: (49) 61726082294

E-Mail: pr-fre@fresenius.de
Web Site: www.fresenius-ag.com
Year Founded: 1912
FRE—(DEU)
Sls.: $25,967,619,300
Assets: $41,278,956,880
Liabilities: $23,568,744,360
Net Worth: $17,710,212,520
Earnings: $2,331,566,440
Emp.: 169,324
Fiscal Year-end: 12/31/12

Business Description:
Holding Company; Healthcare Products Mfr
Export
S.I.C.: 6719
N.A.I.C.S.: 551112

Personnel:
Gerd E. Krick *(Chm-Supervisory Bd)*
Rice Powell *(CEO-Medical Care & Chm-Mgmt Bd)*
Ulf Mark Schneider *(Chm-Mgmt Bd)*
Gerhard Rupprecht *(Deputy Chm-Supervisory Bd)*
Niko Stumpfogger *(Deputy Chm-Supervisory Bd)*
Mats Christer Henriksson *(Pres/CEO-Kabi & Deputy Chm-Mgmt Bd)*
Stephan Sturm *(CFO & Member-Mgmt Bd)*
Jurgen Gotz *(Chief Legal Officer, Chief Compliance Officer & Member-Mgmt Bd)*
Francesco De Meo *(CEO-Helios & Member-Mgmt Bd)*
Ernst Wastler *(CEO-Vamed & Member-Mgmt Bd)*
Birgit Grund *(Sr VP-IR)*
Joachim Weith *(Sr VP-Corp Comm & Pub Affairs)*

Supervisory Board of Directors:
Gerd E. Krick
D. Michael Albrecht
H. C. Roland Berger
Dario Ilossi
Konrad Kolbl
Klaus-Peter Muller
Dieter Reuss
Gerhard Roggemann
Gerhard Rupprecht
Stefan Schubert
Rainer Stein
Niko Stumpfogger

Transfer Agent:
ADR Service Center
PO Box 8205
Boston, MA 02266
Tel.: (781) 575-4328

Subsidiaries:

Fresenius Kabi AG (1)
Else Kroener Strasse 1
61352 Bad Homburg, Germany (100%)
Tel.: (49) 61726860
Fax: (49) 61726862628
E-Mail: info@freseniuskabi.com
Web Site: www.fresenius-kabi.com
Sales Range: $5-14.9 Billion
Emp.: 25,000
Specialty Pharmaceuticals, Infusion & Transfusion Technology & Ambulatory Care
S.I.C.: 2834
N.A.I.C.S.: 325412
Rainer Baule *(CEO)*

Subsidiaries:

Fresenius Hemocare Deutschland GmbH (2)
Else-Kroner-Strasse 1
61352 Bad Homburg, Germany
Tel.: (49) 61726860
Web Site: www.fresenius.com
Emp.: 2,000
Pharmaceuticals
S.I.C.: 2834
N.A.I.C.S.: 325412
Markus Olevert *(Mgr-HR)*

Non-U.S. Joint Venture:

Hemomed (3)
Beogradski Put bb
26300 Vrsac, Serbia
Tel.: (381) 13 803100
Fax: (381) 13 803100
E-Mail:
Web Site: www.hemofarm.com
Emp.: 335
Mfr of Dialyzers; Joint Venture of Hemofarm A.D. & Fresenius AG
S.I.C.: 6799
N.A.I.C.S.: 523910

Fresenius Kabi Deutschland GmbH (2)
Zeppelinstrasse 1C
85375 Neufahrn, Germany (100%)
Tel.: (49) 81659010
Fax: (49) 8165901127
E-Mail: info@fresenius-kabi.com
Web Site: www.fresenius-kabi.de
Emp.: 200
Patient-infusions for Parenteral Nutrition
S.I.C.: 2834
N.A.I.C.S.: 325412

U.S. Subsidiary:

APP Pharmaceuticals, Inc. (2)
1501 E Woodfield Rd Ste 300 E
Schaumburg, IL 60173-5837 DE
Tel.: (847) 969-2700
Fax: (847) 413-2675
Web Site: www.apppharma.com
Sales Range: $600-649.9 Million
Emp.: 1,375
Injectable Pharmaceutical Products Mfr
S.I.C.: 2834
N.A.I.C.S.: 325412
Bernhard Hampl *(Chm)*
John Ducker *(Pres & CEO)*
Richard J. Tajak *(CFO & Exec VP)*
Richard E. Maroun *(Gen Counsel & Sec)*

Non-U.S. Subsidiary:

Pharmaceutical Partners of Canada Inc. (3)
45 Vogell Rd Ste 200
Richmond Hill, ON, L4B 3P6, Canada
Tel.: (905) 770-3711
Fax: (905) 770-4811
Toll Free: (877) 821-7724
E-Mail: info@ppcdrugs.com
Web Site: www.ppcdrugs.com
Emp.: 25
Injectable Pharmaceuticals Mfr
S.I.C.: 5122
N.A.I.C.S.: 424210
Randy Hughes *(Reg Mgr)*

Non-U.S. Subsidiaries:

Beijing Fresenius Pharmaceutical Co., Ltd. (2)
15 Fl Raffles City
No. 1 Dongzhimen South Ave, Beijing, PR, China
Tel.: (86) 1059096999
Fax: (86) 1059096990
Web Site: www.fresenius-kabi.com
Pharmaceuticals
S.I.C.: 2834
N.A.I.C.S.: 325412
Liu Cunzhou *(Chm)*

Fresenius HemoCare Italia S.r.l (2)
Via Santi 293
Cavezzo, 41032 Modena, Italy
Tel.: (39) 0535 45411
Fax: (39) 0535 46812
E-Mail: fhcitalia@fresenius-kabi.com
Web Site: www.fresenius-kabi.com
Emp.: 170
Pharmaceuticals
S.I.C.: 2834
N.A.I.C.S.: 325412
Giorgio Mari *(Gen Mgr)*

Fresenius HemoCare Netherlands B.V. (2)
Runde ZZ 41
Emmer-Compascuum, 7881 HM Emmen, Netherlands
Tel.: (31) 591355700
Fax: (31) 1591355555
E-Mail: services.fhcn@Freseniuskabi.com
Web Site: www.Freseniuskabi.com
Emp.: 600
Medical Products
S.I.C.: 5047
N.A.I.C.S.: 423450
Jelmer Dijkstra *(Gen Mgr)*

Fresenius Kabi AB (2)
Rapsgatan 7
751 74 Uppsala, Sweden
Tel.: (46) 18644000
Fax: (46) 18644900
E-Mail: info-sweden@fresenius-kabi.com
Web Site: www.fresenius-kabi.se
Emp.: 800
Pharmaceuticals
S.I.C.: 2834
N.A.I.C.S.: 325412
Christo Funke *(Gen Mgr)*

Fresenius Kabi Argentina SA (2)
Av Cabildo 2677 Piso 10
1428 Buenos Aires, Argentina
Tel.: (54) 1150939000
Fax: (54) 1150939016
E-Mail: info@fresenius-kabi.com.ar
Web Site: www.fresenius-kabi.com.ar
Pharmaceuticals
S.I.C.: 2834
N.A.I.C.S.: 325412

Fresenius Kabi Asia-Pacific Limited (2)
Sun Hung Kai Centre
30 Harbour Road, Wanchai, China (Hong Kong)
Tel.: (852) 21162683
Fax: (852) 21163420
E-Mail: asia-pacific@fresenius-kabi.com
Web Site: www.fresenius-kabi.com
Pharmaceutical Products Mfr
S.I.C.: 2834
N.A.I.C.S.: 325412

Fresenius Kabi Austria GmbH (2)
Hafnerstrasse 36
8055 Graz, Austria
Tel.: (43) 3162490
Fax: (43) 62491208
E-Mail: birgit.goerger@fresenius-kabi.com
Web Site: www.fresenius-kabi.com
Emp.: 500
Pharmaceuticals
S.I.C.: 2834
N.A.I.C.S.: 325412

Fresenius Kabi Brazil Ltda. (2)
Rua Francisco Pereira Coutinho, 347, Parque Taquaral
13087-900 Campinas, Brazil
Tel.: (55) 19 3756 3855
Fax: (55) 19 3256 3023
Web Site: www.fresenius-kabi.com
Pharmaceuticals
S.I.C.: 2834
N.A.I.C.S.: 325412

Fresenius Kabi Espana S.A. (2)
Marina 16-18
Torre Mapfre-Villa Olimpica, 08005 Barcelona, Spain
Tel.: (34) 932256565
Fax: (34) 932256566
E-Mail: sk.spain@fresenius-kabi.com
Web Site: www.fresenius-kabi.com
Pharmaceuticals
S.I.C.: 2834
N.A.I.C.S.: 325412

Fresenius Kabi France S.A.S. (2)
5 place du Marivel
92310 Sevres, France
Tel.: (33) 141142600
Fax: (33) 141142602
E-Mail: dg.fkf@fresenius-kabi.com
Web Site: www.fresenius-kabi.fr
Emp.: 600
Pharmaceuticals
S.I.C.: 2834
N.A.I.C.S.: 325412

Fresenius Kabi Italia S.r.l. (2)
Via Camagre, 41
Isola della Scala, 37063 Verona, Italy
Tel.: (39) 45 6649 311
Web Site: www.fresenius-kabi.com
Pharmaceuticals
S.I.C.: 2834
N.A.I.C.S.: 325412

Fresenius Kabi Korea Ltd. (2)
3rd Floor Aemaulundong Building No 627
Yeoungdongdaero Kangnamngu, Seoul, 135-280, Korea (South)
Tel.: (82) 234840900
Fax: (82) 234840909
E-Mail: sueng.hee.do@fresenius-kabi.co.kr
Web Site: www.fresenius-kabi.co.kr
Emp.: 100
Pharmaceuticals
S.I.C.: 2834
N.A.I.C.S.: 325412
Y. G. Hong *(Mng Dir)*
Sue Deo *(Sec)*

Fresenius Kabi Ltd. (2)
Cestrian Court
Eastgate Way Manor Park, Runcorn, Cheshire, WA7 1NT, United Kingdom
Tel.: (44) 1928533533
Web Site: www.fresenius-kabi.com
Emp.: 300
Pharmaceuticals
S.I.C.: 2834
N.A.I.C.S.: 325412

Fresenius Kabi Mexico S.A. de C.V. (2)
Paseo del Norte 5300A Guadalajara Technology Park
Carrtera a Nogales Km 125, Zapopan, San Juan de Ocatan, C.P. 45010, Mexico
Tel.: (52) 3335407800
Web Site: www.fresenius-kabi.com.mx
Pharmaceuticals
S.I.C.: 2834
N.A.I.C.S.: 325412

Fresenius Kabi Norge A.S. (2)
Gjerdrumsvei 12
0484 Oslo, Norway
Tel.: (47) 22588000
Fax: (47) 22588001
Web Site: www.fresenius-kabi.no
Emp.: 14
Pharmaceuticals
S.I.C.: 2834
N.A.I.C.S.: 325412
Lisbeth Taraldsen *(Mng Dir)*

Fresenius Kabi Oncology Limited (2)
Echelon Institutional Area
Plot No 11 Sector 32, Gurgaon, Haryana, 122001, India
Tel.: (91) 1244885000
Fax: (91) 1244885003
E-Mail: contactus@fresenius-kabi.com
Web Site: www.fresenius-kabi-oncology.com
532545—(BOM NSE)
Sales Range: $75-99.9 Million
Emp.: 400
Cancer Pharmaceuticals Researcher Mfr
S.I.C.: 2834
N.A.I.C.S.: 325412
Rakesh Bhargava *(Chm)*
Peter Folke Nilsson *(Mng Dir & CEO)*

Fresenius Kabi Polska Sp z.o.o. (2)
ul Hrubieszowska 2
01-209 Warsaw, Poland
Tel.: (48) 223456789
Fax: (48) 223456787
E-Mail: info.poland@fresenius-kabi.com
Web Site: www.fresenius-kabi.pl
Emp.: 90
Pharmaceuticals
S.I.C.: 2834
N.A.I.C.S.: 325412
Maciej Chmielowski *(Gen Dir)*

Fresenius Kabi (Schweiz) AG (2)
Aawasserstrasse 2
6370 Oberdorf, Switzerland
Tel.: (41) 416195050
Fax: (41) 416195080
E-Mail: info.ch@fresenius-kabi.com
Web Site: www.fresenius-kabi.com
Emp.: 50
Pharmaceuticals
S.I.C.: 2834
N.A.I.C.S.: 325412

Fresenius Kabi South Africa (Pty) Ltd. (2)
Stand 7 Growthpoint Business Park
2 Tonetti Street Halfway House, Johannesburg, South Africa
Tel.: (27) 115450000
Fax: (27) 115450059

Fresenius SE & Co. KGaA—(Continued)

E-Mail: bev.mayer@fresenius-kabi.com
Web Site: www.fresenius-kabi.co.za
Emp.: 203
Pharmaceuticals
S.I.C.: 2834
N.A.I.C.S.: 325412
Wilna Ftapelberg *(Country Mgr)*

Labesfal Laboratorios Almiro S.A **(2)**
Lagedo
3465-157 Tondela, Campo de Besteiros, Portugal
Tel.: (351) 232831100
Fax: (351) 232831112
E-Mail: labesfal@labesfal.pt
Web Site: www.labesfalgenericos.pt
Emp.: 400
Pharmaceuticals
S.I.C.: 2834
N.A.I.C.S.: 325412
George Amaral *(Gen Mgr)*

Pharmatel Fresenius Kabi Pty Ltd. **(2)**
6/6-18 Bridge Street
Hornsby, NSW, 2077, Australia
Tel.: (61) 294722222
Fax: (61) 294722255
E-Mail: info@pfk.com.au
Web Site: www.pfk.com.au
Pharmaceuticals
S.I.C.: 2834
N.A.I.C.S.: 325412

Non-U.S. Joint Venture:

Sino-Swed Pharmaceutical Corp., Ltd. **(2)**
Unit 1801-1805 China Resources Building
No 8 Jianguomenbei Avenue, Beijing, 100005, China
Tel.: (86) 1065189090
Fax: (86) 1085192301
E-Mail: webmaster@sspc.com.cn
Web Site: www.sspc.com.cn
Emp.: 1,000
Parenteral Nutrition, Enteral Nutrition & Application Device Mfr; Owned 51% by Fresenius SE & 49% by China National Pharmaceutical Group Corporation (SINOPHARM)
S.I.C.: 2833
N.A.I.C.S.: 325411

Fresenius Netcare GmbH **(1)**
Else-Kroner-Str 1
61352 Bad Homburg, Germany
Tel.: (49) 6172 608 0
Fax: (49) 6172 608 7590
E-Mail: service@fresenius-netcare.com
Web Site: www.fresenius-netcare.com
Emp.: 500
IT Services
S.I.C.: 7373
N.A.I.C.S.: 541512
Klaus Kieren *(Chm-Mgmt Bd)*
Jurgen Kunze *(Vice Chm-Mgmt Bd)*
Jurgen Gotz *(Member-Mgmt Bd)*
Ulf Mark Schneider *(Member-Mgmt Bd)*
Stephan Sturm *(Member-Mgmt Bd)*

HELIOS Kliniken GmbH **(1)**
Schwanebecker Chaussee 50
13125 Berlin, Germany De
Tel.: (49) 6618339500
Fax: (49) 6618339599
E-Mail: postmaster@fulda.helios-kliniken.de
Web Site: www.helios-kliniken.de
Sales Range: $1-4.9 Billion
Emp.: 32,000
Pharmaceuticals
S.I.C.: 2834
N.A.I.C.S.: 325412
Ulf Mark Schneider *(Chm-Supervisory Bd)*
Francesco De Meo *(Chm-Mgmt Bd & CEO)*
Jorg Reschke *(CFO)*
Olaf Jedersberger *(COO)*
Ralf Kuhlen *(CMO)*
Karin Grappi *(Chief Legal Officer)*
Armin Engel *(Chief Scientific Officer)*

Subsidiaries:

Amper Kliniken AG **(2)**
Krankenhausstrasse 15
85221 Dachau, Germany
Tel.: (49) 8131760
Fax: (49) 813176247
E-Mail: info@amperkliniken.de
Web Site: www.amperkliniken.de
Emp.: 1,200
General Medical & Surgical Hospitals
S.I.C.: 7389
N.A.I.C.S.: 561499
Uwe Schmid *(Mng Dir)*

Aukamm Klinik fur operative Rheumatologie und orthopadie GmbH **(2)**
Leibnizstr 21
65191 Wiesbaden, Germany
Tel.: (49) 6115720
Fax: (49) 611565681
E-Mail: info@aukammklinik.de
Web Site: www.orthopaedielheuna.de
Emp.: 70
General Medical & Surgical Hospitals
S.I.C.: 8062
N.A.I.C.S.: 622110
Beate Goerissen *(Mng Dir)*

Fachkrankenhaus fur Psychiatrie und Neurologie Hildburghausen GmbH **(2)**
Eisfelder Strasse 41
98646 Coburg, Germany
Tel.: (49) 36857760
Fax: (49) 3685776940
Web Site: www.rhoen-klinikum-ag.com
General Medical & Surgical Hospitals
S.I.C.: 8062
N.A.I.C.S.: 622110

Frankenwaldklinik Kronach GmbH **(2)**
Friesenerstr 41
96317 Kulmbach, Germany
Tel.: (49) 9261590
Fax: (49) 9261596199
E-Mail: info@frankenwaldklinik.de
Web Site: www.frankenwaldklinik.de
Emp.: 570
Specialty Hospitals
S.I.C.: 8069
N.A.I.C.S.: 622310
Hochen Bockit *(Mng Dir)*

Herzzentrum Leipzig Gmbh **(2)**
Strumpellstr 39
04289 Leipzig, Germany
Tel.: (49) 3418650
Fax: (49) 3418651405
Web Site: www.rhoen-klinikum-ag.com
General Medical & Surgical Hospitals
S.I.C.: 8062
N.A.I.C.S.: 622110
Iris Minde *(Gen Mgr)*

KDI Klinikservice GmbH **(2)**
Krankenhausstrasse 15
85221 Dachau, Germany
Tel.: (49) 8131 76 540
Fax: (49) 8131 76 310
Web Site: www.kdi-online.de
Health Care Clinical Services
S.I.C.: 8093
N.A.I.C.S.: 621498

Klinik fur Herzchirurgie Karlsruhe GmbH **(2)**
Franc Lust Street 30
76185 Karlsruhe, Germany
Tel.: (49) 72197380
Fax: (49) 7219738111
Web Site: www.herzchirurgie-karlsruhe.de
Emp.: 300
General Medical & Surgical Hospitals
S.I.C.: 3291
N.A.I.C.S.: 327910
Hartmut Masanek *(Mng Dir)*

Klinik Hildesheimer Land GmbH **(2)**
An Der Peesel 6
31162 Bad Salzdetfurth, Germany
Tel.: (49) 5063 4701
Fax: (49) 5063 1440
E-Mail: sekvl@klinik-hildesheimer-land.de
Emp.: 19
Health Care Services
S.I.C.: 8099
N.A.I.C.S.: 621999
Erk Scheel *(Gen Mgr)*

Klinik Kipfenberg GmbH **(2)**
Kindinger Strasse 13
Kipfenberg, 85110, Germany
Tel.: (49) 84651750
Fax: (49) 8465175111
E-Mail: gshneurologie@kipfenberg.be
Web Site: www.neurologie-kipfenberg.de
Emp.: 550
General Medical & Surgical Hospitals
S.I.C.: 3291
N.A.I.C.S.: 327910
Rainer Meinhardt *(Gen Mgr)*

Kliniken Herzberg und Osterode GmbH **(2)**
Dr - Frossel-Allee
37412 Herzberg, Germany
Tel.: (49) 55218660
Fax: (49) 55215500
E-Mail: gs@klinik-herzberg.de
Web Site: www.rhoen-klinikum-ag.com
General Medical & Surgical Hospitals
S.I.C.: 8062
N.A.I.C.S.: 622110
Hans-Werner Kuska *(Mng Dir)*

Kliniken Miltenberg-Erlenbach GmbH **(2)**
Krankenhausstrasse 41
Erlenbach a Main, 63906 Erlenbach, Germany
Tel.: (49) 93727000
Fax: (49) 93727001009
Web Site: www.rhoen-klinikum-ag.com
General Medical & Surgical Hospitals
S.I.C.: 9631
N.A.I.C.S.: 926130

Kliniken Munchen Pasing und Perlach GmbH **(2)**
Steinerweg 5
81241 Munich, Germany
Tel.: (49) 8988920
Fax: (49) 898892228
Web Site: www.rhoen-klinikum-ag.com
Emp.: 1,000
General Medical & Surgical Hospitals
S.I.C.: 4959
N.A.I.C.S.: 562998
Phil Hill *(Mng Dir)*

Klinikum Gifhorn GmbH **(2)**
Campus 6
Gifhorn, 38518, Germany
Tel.: (49) 5371870
Fax: (49) 5371871008
E-Mail: secretaria.gf@klinikum-gifhorn.de
Web Site: www.klinikum-gifhorn.de
Emp.: 800
Health Care Services
S.I.C.: 8099
N.A.I.C.S.: 621999
Dieter Kaffke *(Gen Mgr)*

Klinikum Hildesheim GmbH **(2)**
Senator-Braun-Allee 33
31135 Hildesheim, Germany
Tel.: (49) 5121890
Fax: (49) 51218941215
E-Mail: gs@klinikum-hildesheim.de
Web Site: www.stk-hildesheim.de
Emp.: 1,000
General Medical & Surgical Hospitals
S.I.C.: 3291
N.A.I.C.S.: 327910
Grimmelmann Heimburg *(Mng Dir)*
Martin Menger *(Mng Dir)*

Klinikum Meinigen GmbH **(2)**
Bergstr 3
98617 Saalfeld, Germany
Tel.: (49) 3693900
Fax: (49) 3693901461
E-Mail: kmg@klinikum-meiningen.de
Web Site: www.klinikum-meiningen.de/
General Medical & Surgical Hospitals
S.I.C.: 8062
N.A.I.C.S.: 622110

Klinikum Pforzheim GmbH **(2)**
Kanzlerstrasse 2-6
75175 Pforzheim, Germany
Tel.: (49) 72319690
Fax: (49) 72319692383
Web Site: www.klinikum-pforzheim.de
Emp.: 1,190
General Medical & Surgical Hospitals
S.I.C.: 8062
N.A.I.C.S.: 622110

Klinikum Pirna GmbH **(2)**
Struppener Strasse 13
01796 Pirna, Germany
Tel.: (49) 3501 7118 0
Fax: (49) 3501 7118 1211
E-Mail: gf@klinikum-pirna.de
Health Care Services
S.I.C.: 8099
N.A.I.C.S.: 621999

Klinikum Salzgitter GmbH **(2)**
Kattowitzer Strasse 191
38226 Salzgitter, Germany
Tel.: (49) 53418350
Fax: (49) 53418351515
Web Site: www.rhoen-klinikum-ag.com
General Medical & Surgical Hospitals
S.I.C.: 8062
N.A.I.C.S.: 622110
Ronald Gudath *(Mng Dir)*

Klinikum Uelzen GmbH **(2)**
Hagenskamp 34
29525 Uelzen, Germany
Tel.: (49) 581 83 0
Fax: (49) 581831004
E-Mail: info@klinikum-uelzen.de
Web Site: www.klinikum-uelzen.de
Hospital Management Services
S.I.C.: 8062
N.A.I.C.S.: 622110
Franz Caesar *(Gen Mgr)*

Krankenhaus Kothen GmbH **(2)**
Hallesche Strasse 29
06366 Kothen, Germany
Tel.: (49) 3496 52 0
Fax: (49) 34 96 52 11 01
E-Mail: gf@krankenhaus-koethen.de
General Hospitality Services
S.I.C.: 8062
N.A.I.C.S.: 622110

Krankenhaus St. Barbara Attendorn GmbH **(2)**
Hohler Weg 9
57439 Attendorn, Germany
Tel.: (49) 2722600
Fax: (49) 2722602430
General Medical & Surgical Hospitals
S.I.C.: 8062
N.A.I.C.S.: 622110

Leben am Rosenberg GmbH **(2)**
Friesener Str 41
Kronach, 96317, Germany
Tel.: (49) 9261596701
Fax: (49) 9261596709
Emp.: 25
Nursing Home Operating Services
S.I.C.: 8082
N.A.I.C.S.: 621610
Robert Kordic *(Gen Mgr)*

MVZ Management GmbH Attendorn **(2)**
Hohler Weg 9
57439 Attendorn, Germany
Tel.: (49) 2722 3920
Fax: (49) 2722 2348
Medical Care Services
S.I.C.: 8099
N.A.I.C.S.: 621999

MVZ Management GmbH Baden-Wurttemberg **(2)**
Kanzlerstr 2-6
Pforzheim, 75175, Germany
Tel.: (49) 7231 9690
Fax: (49) 2319692417
E-Mail: GF@Klinikum-Pforzheim.de
Web Site: www.Klinikum-Pforzheim.de
Emp.: 5
General Hospitality Services
S.I.C.: 8062
N.A.I.C.S.: 622110
Koji Tanabe *(Gen Mgr)*

MVZ Management GmbH Sud **(2)**
Salzburger Leite 1
97616 Bad Neustadt an der Saale, Germany
Tel.: (49) 9771 650
Fax: (49) 9771 97467
Medical Care Services
S.I.C.: 8062
N.A.I.C.S.: 622110
Robert Kortic *(Gen Mgr)*

RK-Reinigungsgesellschaft Nord mbH **(2)**
Schlossplatz 1
Bad Neustadt an der Saale, 97616, Germany

Tel.: (49) 364157370
Fax: (49) 9771991736
Commercial Cleaning Services
S.I.C.: 7349
N.A.I.C.S.: 561720

St. Elisabeth-Krankenhaus GmbH (2)
Kissinger Strasse 150
97688 Schweinfurt, Germany
Tel.: (49) 9718050
Fax: (49) 9718051010
E-Mail: info@elisabeth-online.de
Web Site: www.elisabeth-online.de
Emp.: 300
General Medical & Surgical Hospitals
S.I.C.: 8062
N.A.I.C.S.: 622110
Marcus Plasthae *(Mng Dir)*

St. Petri-Hospital Warburg GmbH (2)
Huffertstrasse 50
34414 Warburg, Germany
Tel.: (49) 5641 910
Fax: (49) 5641 91444
E-Mail: info@st-petri-hospital.de
Web Site: www.st-petri-hospital.de
General Hospitality Services
S.I.C.: 8062
N.A.I.C.S.: 622110
Thomas Hoffmann *(Gen Mgr)*

Stadtisches Krankenhaus Wittingen GmbH (2)
Gustav-Dobberkau-Strasse 5
29378 Wittingen, Germany
Tel.: (49) 5831220
Fax: (49) 58312299
Web Site: www.krankenhaus-wittingen.de
Emp.: 20
General Medical & Surgical Hospitals
S.I.C.: 3291
N.A.I.C.S.: 327910
Franz Caesar *(Gen Mgr)*

Stiftung Deutsche Klinik fur Diagnostik GmbH (2)
Aukammallee 33
65191 Wiesbaden, Germany
Tel.: (49) 6115770
Fax: (49) 611577577
E-Mail: gf@dkd-wiesbaden.de
Web Site: www.dkd-wiesbaden.de
Emp.: 500
General Medical & Surgical Hospitals
S.I.C.: 8062
N.A.I.C.S.: 622110
Garissen Beate *(Gen Mgr)*

Weisseritztal-Kliniken GmbH (2)
Burgerstrasse 7
Freital, 1705, Germany
Tel.: (49) 351 646 60
Fax: (49) 351 646 7010
E-Mail: info@weisseritztal-kliniken.de
General Hospitality Services
S.I.C.: 8062
N.A.I.C.S.: 622110
Dirk Koecher *(Gen Mgr)*

Wesermarsch-Klinik Nordenham GmbH (2)
Albert Schweitzer Strasse 43
26954 Nordenham, Germany
Tel.: (49) 4731 947 0
Fax: (49) 4731 947 666
E-Mail: gf@wesermarschklinik.de
General Hospitality Services
S.I.C.: 8062
N.A.I.C.S.: 622110

U.S. Subsidiary:

Fenwal, Inc. (1)
Three Corporate Dr
Lake Zurich, IL 60047
Tel.: (847) 550-2300
Fax: (847) 550-2946
Toll Free: (800) 333-6925
Web Site: www.fenwalinc.com
Sales Range: $500-549.9 Million
Emp.: 3,500
Manual & Automated Blood Collection & Processing Products Mfr
S.I.C.: 3826
N.A.I.C.S.: 334516
Ronald K. Labrum *(Pres & CEO)*
Michael Johnson *(CFO)*
Jo Anne Fasetti *(Chief HR Officer)*
Brian Beeler *(Gen Counsel)*

Non-U.S. Subsidiaries:

Calea Ltd. (1)
2785 Skymark Ave Ste 2
Mississauga, ON, L4W 4Y3, Canada (100%)
Tel.: (905) 624-1234
Fax: (905) 629-0123
Toll Free: (888) 909-3299
E-Mail: info@calea.ca
Web Site: www.calea.ca
Emp.: 300
Home Health Care
S.I.C.: 8082
N.A.I.C.S.: 621610
Matthew Rotenberg *(CEO)*

Fresenius Vial S.A.S. (1)
Le Grand Chemin
38590 Brezins, France
Tel.: (33) 476671010
Fax: (33) 0476671134
E-Mail: info@freseniuskabe.com
Web Site: www.freseniuskabe.com
Emp.: 300
Pharmaceuticals
S.I.C.: 2834
N.A.I.C.S.: 325412
Michael Schoenhfen *(Pres)*

VAMED AG (1)
Sterngasse 5
1232 Vienna, PF 91, Austria
Tel.: (43) 1601270
E-Mail: office@vamed.com
Web Site: www.vamed.com
Sales Range: $900-999.9 Million
Emp.: 3,724
Public Health Facilities Management, Construction & Development
S.I.C.: 1542
N.A.I.C.S.: 236220
Ernst Wastler *(Chm-Exec Bd)*
Erich Ennsbrunner *(Member-Exec Bd)*
Gottfried Koos *(Member-Exec Bd)*
Andrea Raffaseder *(Member-Exec Bd)*

Subsidiaries:

VAMED Engineering GmbH & Co KG (2)
Sterngasse 5
1232 Vienna, Austria
Tel.: (43) 1601270
Fax: (43) 160127292
E-Mail: vesales@vamed.com
Web Site: www.vamed.com
Emp.: 150
Architecture & Other Engineering Services
S.I.C.: 8712
N.A.I.C.S.: 541310
Peter Hallbauer *(Mng Dir)*
Andrea Raffaseder *(Mng Dir)*
Johann Strahlhofer *(Mng Dir)*

VAMED Estate Development & Engineering GmbH & CO KG (2)
Sterngasse 5
1232 Vienna, Austria
Tel.: (43) 1601270
Fax: (43) 160127190
E-Mail: verkauf@vamed.com
Web Site: www.vamed.com
Emp.: 400
Hospitals & Other Health Facilities Real Estate
S.I.C.: 6531
N.A.I.C.S.: 531390
Erich Ennsbrunner *(Co-Mng Dir)*
Dieter Gruber *(Mng Dir)*
Walter Troger *(Co-Mng Dir)*

VAMED-KMB (2)
Spitalgasse 23
1090 Vienna, Austria
Tel.: (43) 14040090019005
E-Mail: office@vkmb.at
Web Site: www.vamed.com
Facilities Technical Systems Management
S.I.C.: 7349
N.A.I.C.S.: 561790
Christian Krebs *(Mng Dir)*
Otto Muller *(Mng Dir)*
Peter Obitsch *(Mng Dir)*
Franz Strasser *(Mng Dir)*

VAMED Management und Service GmbH & Co KG (2)
Sterngasse 5
1232 Vienna, Austria
Tel.: (43) 1601270
Fax: (43) 160127410
E-Mail: office.vms@vamed.com
Web Site: www.vamed.com
Public Health Facilities Management
S.I.C.: 8744
N.A.I.C.S.: 561210
Christian Auberger *(Mng Dir)*
Gottried Koos *(Mng Dir)*

FRESHBAKED PR LTD

House Three The Maltings E Tyndall St
Cardiff, South Glamorgan, CF24 5EA, United Kingdom
Tel.: (44) 2920491491
Fax: (44) 2920491591
E-Mail: pr@freshbaked.co.uk
Web Site: www.freshbaked.co.uk/pr
Year Founded: 2008
Emp.: 70

Business Description:
Public Relations
S.I.C.: 8743
N.A.I.C.S.: 541820

Personnel:
Jonathan Hollins *(Mng Dir)*

FRESHTEL HOLDINGS LIMITED

Level 1 121 127 High Street
Prahran, VIC, 3181, Australia
Tel.: (61) 390952000
Fax: (61) 390952099
E-Mail: info@freshtelholdings.com
Web Site: www.freshtelholdings.com
FRE—(ASX)
Rev.: $2,347
Assets: $142,665
Liabilities: $200,886
Net Worth: ($58,221)
Earnings: ($169,628)
Fiscal Year-end: 06/30/13

Business Description:
Internet Provider
S.I.C.: 4813
N.A.I.C.S.: 517110

Personnel:
Graham Henderson *(Acting CFO & Sec)*

Board of Directors:
Peter Buttery
Alex Alexander
Matt Ranawake

Legal Counsel:
Watson Mangioni Lawyers Pty Limited
Level 13, 50 Carrington Street
Sydney, Australia

FRESHTROP FRUITS LTD.

A-603 Shapath IV Opp Karnavati Club S G Road
Ahmedabad, Gujarat, 380051, India
Tel.: (91) 79 40307050
Fax: (91) 79 66527069
E-Mail: info@freshtrop.com
Web Site: www.freshtrop.com
530077—(BOM)
Rev.: $17,335,432
Assets: $18,255,642
Liabilities: $11,455,987
Net Worth: $6,799,655
Earnings: $655,817
Fiscal Year-end: 03/31/13

Business Description:
Fresh Fruits Distr
S.I.C.: 5148
N.A.I.C.S.: 424480

Personnel:
Ashok V. Motiani *(Chm & Mng Dir)*
Jignesh J. Gandhi *(Compliance Officer & Sec)*

Board of Directors:
Ashok V. Motiani
Ramachandra G. Joshi
Nanita A. Motiani
Dinesh S. Oza
Mayur J. Shah

Transfer Agent:
Bigshare Services Private Limited
E-2 Ansa Industrial Estate Sakivihar Road Saki Naka Andheri (E)
Mumbai, India

Plant:

Freshtrop Fruits Ltd. - Plant - II (1)
Survey No 1366 Savlej-Wayfale Road Post Siddhewadi
Sangli, Tasgaon, Maharashtra, 416 311, India
Tel.: (91) 2346 254871
Fax: (91) 2346 254874
E-Mail: info@freshtrop.com
Packaged Fruit Whslr
S.I.C.: 5148
N.A.I.C.S.: 424480

FRESHWATER TECHNOLOGY

130-132 Tooley St
London, SE1 2TU, United Kingdom
Tel.: (44) 1794 521 156
Fax: (44) 1794 521 157
Web Site: www.freshwatertechnology.com
Sales Range: $10-24.9 Million
Emp.: 100

Business Description:
Public Relations
S.I.C.: 8743
N.A.I.C.S.: 541820

Personnel:
Debbie Smith *(Assoc Dir)*

FRESHWATER UK PLC

Raglan House Cardiff Gate Business Park
Cardiff, CF23 8BA, United Kingdom
Tel.: (44) 2920 304050
Fax: (44) 2920 545380
Web Site: www.freshwater-uk.com
Sales Range: $1-9.9 Million
Emp.: 71

Business Description:
Public Relations & Marketing Services
S.I.C.: 8743
N.A.I.C.S.: 541820

Personnel:
Steve B. Howell *(CEO)*
K. J. Tilley *(Sec)*

Legal Counsel:
Martineau
1 Colmore Square
Birmingham, United Kingdom

Subsidiaries:

Freshwater Consumer Limited (1)
130-132 Tooley St
London, SE1 2TU, United Kingdom
Tel.: (44) 2070671597
Fax: (44) 2074309574
E-Mail: info@freshwater-uk.com
Web Site: www.freshwater-uk.com
Emp.: 20
Public Relations Services
S.I.C.: 8743
N.A.I.C.S.: 541820
Steve Howell *(CEO)*

Freshwater Healthcare Limited (1)
130-132 Tooley St
London, SE1 2TU, United Kingdom
Tel.: (44) 2077871930
Fax: (44) 2074309574
Web Site: www.freshwater-uk.com
Emp.: 10
Public Relations Services
S.I.C.: 8743
N.A.I.C.S.: 541820
John M. Underwood *(Founder)*

Freshwater Scotland Limited (1)
Unit 1-2 Skypark 14 Elliot Pl
Glasgow, Scotland, G3 8EP, United Kingdom

Freshwater UK PLC—(Continued)

Tel.: (44) 1412294050
Fax: (44) 1412294060
E-Mail: glascow@freshwater-uk.com
Web Site: www.freshwater-uk.com
Emp.: 3
Public Relations Services
S.I.C.: 8743
N.A.I.C.S.: 541820
Kim McGuire *(Acct Dir)*

Freshwater Southern Limited (1)
Centre Gate Colston Ave
Bristol, BS1 4TR, United Kingdom
Tel.: (44) 1173178135
Fax: (44) 1173178136
E-Mail: info@freshwater-uk.com
Web Site: www.freshwater-uk.com
Emp.: 3
Public Relations Services
S.I.C.: 8743
N.A.I.C.S.: 541820
Steve Howell *(Pres)*

Freshwater Technology Limited (1)
1 Horsefair Mews
London, Hampshire, SO51 8JG, United Kingdom
Tel.: (44) 2077871931
Fax: (44) 1794521157
E-Mail: technology@freshwater-uk.com
Web Site: www.freshwater-uk.com
Emp.: 30
Public Relations Services
S.I.C.: 8743
N.A.I.C.S.: 541820
Heather Hughes *(Mng Dir)*
Alex Love *(Mng Dir)*

Lynx PR (1)
The Rookery
Leeds, West Yorkshire, United Kingdom
Tel.: (44) 1132393535
Fax: (44) 113 236 1606
Web Site: www.freshwater-uk.com
Emp.: 10
Public Relations Services
S.I.C.: 8743
N.A.I.C.S.: 541820
Matthew Ridsdale *(Sr Acct Mgr)*

Merlin Marketing and Creative Limited (1)
Raglan House Cardiff Gate
Cardiff Gate Business Park, Cardiff, South Glamorgan, CF23 8BA, United Kingdom
Tel.: (44) 2920304050
Fax: (44) 2920545380
E-Mail: info@freshwater-uk.com
Web Site: www.freshwater-uk.com
Public Relations & Marketing Services
S.I.C.: 8742
N.A.I.C.S.: 541613

Waterfront Conference Company Limited (1)
8-12 New Bridge St
London, EC4V 6AL, United Kingdom
Tel.: (44) 2077871210
Fax: (44) 2077871201
E-Mail: conference@thewaterfront.co.uk
Web Site: www.thewaterfront.co.uk
Conference Management Services
S.I.C.: 7389
N.A.I.C.S.: 512290
Nicholas Finney *(Mng Dir)*

Profile Plus (UK) Ltd. (1)
78 The Shore
Edinburgh, Scotland, EH6 6RG, United Kingdom UK
Tel.: (44) 1315546111
Fax: (44) 1315546445
E-Mail: web@profileplus.co.uk
Web Site: www.profileplus.co.uk
Emp.: 4
Advertising Agency
S.I.C.: 8743
N.A.I.C.S.: 541820
Robyn Glynne-Percy *(Mng Dir)*

FRESNILLO PLC

Av Moliere 222 Col Polanco
11540 Mexico, Mexico
Tel.: (52) 5552793000
Fax: (52) 52793469
Web Site: www.fresnilloplc.com
FRES—(LSE OTC)
Rev.: $2,157,404,000
Assets: $3,270,864,000
Liabilities: $668,794,000
Net Worth: $2,602,070,000
Earnings: $845,445,000
Emp.: 3,128
Fiscal Year-end: 12/31/12

Business Description:
Silver & Gold Mining Services
S.I.C.: 1044
N.A.I.C.S.: 212222

Personnel:
Octavio Alvidrez *(CEO)*
Mario Arreguin *(CFO)*
Roberto Diaz *(COO)*

Board of Directors:
Alberto Bailleres
Maria Asuncion Aramburuzabala
Alejandro Bailleres
Juan Bordes
Simon Cairns
Arturo Fernandez
Javier Fernandez
Jaime Lomelin
Rafael MacGregor
Fernando Ruiz
Fernando Solana
Guy Wilson

Legal Counsel:
Linklaters LLP
One Silk Street
London, EC2Y 8HQ, United Kingdom
Tel.: (44) 2074562000
Fax: (44) 2074562222

Subsidiary:

Minera Fresnillo, S.A. de C.V. (1)
Prol Av No 451
Mexico, Mexico
Tel.: (52) 4939839000
Fax: (52) 4939839077
E-Mail: edurdo.valdez@fresnilloplc.com
Silver Lead & Zinc Ores Mfr
S.I.C.: 1031
N.A.I.C.S.: 212231
Fresnillo Sacatecas *(Mgr)*

FREUDENBERG SE

Hoehnerweg 2-4
D-69465 Weinheim, Germany
Tel.: (49) 6201 800
Fax: (49) 6201 880
E-Mail: info@freudenberg.com
Web Site: www.freudenberg.com
Year Founded: 1921
Sls.: $8,510,486,740
Assets: $8,157,790,200
Liabilities: $4,364,283,140
Net Worth: $3,793,507,060
Earnings: $582,891,610
Emp.: 37,453
Fiscal Year-end: 12/31/12

Business Description:
Holding Company; Sealing Products, Vibration Control Components, Nonwoven Textile Products, Household Products & Specialty Chemicals Mfr
S.I.C.: 6719
N.A.I.C.S.: 551112

Personnel:
Wolfram Freudenberg *(Chm-Supervisory Bd)*
Mohsen M. Sohi *(Chm-Mgmt Bd)*
Werner Wenning *(Deputy Chm-Supervisory Bd)*
Martin Wentzler *(Second Deputy Chm-Supervisory Bd)*
Ralf Krieger *(CFO & Member-Mgmt Bd)*
Peter Bettermann *(Member-Mgmt Bd)*
Christoph Mosmann *(Member-Mgmt Bd)*
Martin Stark *(Member-Mgmt Bd)*

Supervisory Board of Directors:
Wolfram Freudenberg
Martin Freudenberg
Maria Freudenberg-Beetz
Mathias Kammuller
Robert J. Koehler
Dieter Kurz
Walter Schildhauer
Christoph Schucking
Mathias Thielen
Emanuel Towfigh
Werner Wenning
Martin Wentzler

Subsidiaries:

Corteco GmbH (1)
Badener Str 4
69493 Hirschberg, Germany DE
Tel.: (49) 6201259640 (100%)
Fax: (49) 62012596411
E-Mail: service@corteco.com
Web Site: www.corteco.com
Sales Range: $10-24.9 Million
Emp.: 24
Sales, Warehousing & Packaging of Automotive Spare Parts
S.I.C.: 4226
N.A.I.C.S.: 493190
Thomas Mettke *(Mng Dir)*

U.S. Branch:

Corteco USA (2)
11617 State Route 13
Milan, OH 44846-9725
Tel.: (419) 499-2502
Fax: (419) 499-6111
Web Site: www.corteco.com
Emp.: 265
Automotive Sealing Systems, Vibration Control & Service Parts Distr
S.I.C.: 5013
N.A.I.C.S.: 423120
Jason Meier *(Mng Dir-Americas)*

Non-U.S. Subsidiary:

Corteco s.r.l. (2)
Corso Torino 420
10064 Pinerolo, Italy (100%)
Tel.: (39) 0121369269
Fax: (39) 0121369299
E-Mail: service@corteco.it
Web Site: www.corteco.com
Emp.: 40
Sales of Metal Automotive Parts
S.I.C.: 5013
N.A.I.C.S.: 423120
Enilio Chiolerio *(Mng Dir)*

EagleBurgmann Germany GmbH & Co. KG (1)
Aeussere Sauerlacher Strasse 6-10
PO Box 1240
82515 Wolfratshausen, Germany De
Mailing Address:
PO Box 1240
82502 Wolfratshausen, Germany
Tel.: (49) 8171230
Telex: 527801
Fax: (49) 8171231214
E-Mail: info@burgmann.com
Web Site: www.burgmann.com
Sales Range: $350-399.9 Million
Emp.: 1,000
Mechanical Seals, Packings, Gaskets, Expansion Joints & Sealing Systems Mfr Export
S.I.C.: 3053
N.A.I.C.S.: 339991
Jochen Strasser *(VP)*

Subsidiary:

Burgmann Packings GmbH (2)
Haupstrasse 145
D-74638 Waldenburg, Germany
Tel.: (49) 79 42 94 0
Packing & Sealing Materials Mfr
S.I.C.: 4783
N.A.I.C.S.: 488991
Wolfgang Bommes *(Mng Dir)*

U.S. Subsidiary:

EagleBurgmann Industries LP (2)
10035 Brookriver Dr
Houston, TX 77040-3193 DE
Tel.: (713) 939-9515
Fax: (713) 939-9091
E-Mail: info@us.eagleburgmann.com
Web Site: www.eagleburgmann.us
Sales Range: $800-899.9 Million
Emp.: 120
Mechanical Seals, Gaskets, Expansion Joints & Ball Valves Distr
S.I.C.: 5085
N.A.I.C.S.: 423840
Marcus Pillion *(Pres)*

Non-U.S. Subsidiaries:

Burgmann Dalian Co., Ltd. (2)
No 86 Liaohe E Rd
DD Port, 116620 Dalian, China CN
Tel.: (86) 41187581000
Fax: (86) 41187581397
E-Mail: bprcd@cn.eagleburgmann.com
Web Site: www.eagleburgmann.cn
Emp.: 185
Mechanical Seals & Packings Mfr
S.I.C.: 3053
N.A.I.C.S.: 339991
Yuanxin Ci *(Gen Mgr)*

Burgmann Sealing Materials Co., Ltd. Cixi (2)
No 787 817 Ciyong Rd
Hushan Town, Nanjing, 315302, China CN
Tel.: (86) 57463826241 (100%)
Fax: (86) 57463826117
E-Mail:
Web Site: www.burgmannpackings.cn
Sealing Materials Mfr
S.I.C.: 3053
N.A.I.C.S.: 339991

Burgmann Shanghai Co., Ltd. (2)
No 127 8 Wenijing Rd
Minghang, Shanghai, 200245, China CN
Tel.: (86) 2164620550
Fax: (86) 2164308364
E-Mail:
Web Site: www.eagleburgmann.cn
Emp.: 100
Mechanical Seals & Packings Mfr & Sls
S.I.C.: 3053
N.A.I.C.S.: 339991
Yang Juming *(Gen Mgr)*

EagleBurgmann Austria GmbH (2)
Vogelweider 44A
5020 Salzburg, Austria AT
Tel.: (43) 662825701
Fax: (43) 662825703
E-Mail: gerhard.wassung@at.eagleburgmann.com
Web Site: www.burgmann.com
Emp.: 12
Mechanical Seals & Packings Mfr
S.I.C.: 3053
N.A.I.C.S.: 339991
Gerhard Wassung *(Mng Dir)*

EagleBurgmann Belgium BVBA (2)
Zagerijstraat 11
Sint Job Int Goor, B 2960 Antwerp, Belgium BE
Tel.: (32) 36339944
Fax: (32) 36339949
E-Mail: lea.visser@be.eagleburgmann.com
Web Site: www.eagleburgmann.com
Emp.: 16
Mechanical Seals & Packings Sls
S.I.C.: 3053
N.A.I.C.S.: 339991
Bart Meulman *(Mng Dir)*

EagleBurgmann Bredan s.r.o. (2)
Na Drahach 1364
Zbraslav, 156 00 Prague, 5, Czech Republic CZ
Tel.: (420) 241021811
Fax: (420) 241021830
E-Mail: info@ke-burgmann.cz
Web Site: www.ke-burgmann.cz
Rev.: $2,085,200
Emp.: 80
Mechanical Seals & Packings Mfr
S.I.C.: 3053
N.A.I.C.S.: 339991
Peter Lonborg Mielsen *(Mng Dir)*

EagleBurgmann Canada Inc. (2)
3524-78th Ave N W
T6B 2X9 Edmonton, AB, Canada
Tel.: (780) 434-4928
Fax: (780) 438-0658

Web Site: www.eagleburgmann.com
Gasket & Sealing Device Mfr
S.I.C.: 3053
N.A.I.C.S.: 339991

EagleBurgmann Czech s.r.o. (2)
Na Drahach 1364 Zbraslav
156 00 Prague, Czech Republic
Tel.: (420) 257920505
Fax: (420) 257920508
E-Mail: info@cz.eagleburgmann.com
Web Site: www.eagleburgmann.cz
Emp.: 19
Mechanical Seal & Coupling Mfr
S.I.C.: 3498
N.A.I.C.S.: 332996
Petr Karasek *(Gen Mgr)*

EagleBurgmann de Venezuela, C.A. (2)
Calle 6 con Calle 9 Edif Fant piso 2
Zona Industrial La Urbina, Caracas, 1070, Venezuela VE
Tel.: (58) 2122421548
Fax: (58) 2122424544
Web Site: www.burgmann.com
Emp.: 30
Mechanical Seals & Packings Mfr
S.I.C.: 3053
N.A.I.C.S.: 339991

EagleBurgmann do Brasil Vedacoes Industrias Ltda. (2)
Av Sta Izabel 1721
Barao GeraldoCaix Postal 6560, CEP
13084-643 Campinas, Sao Paulo, Brazil BR
Tel.: (55) 937499740
Fax: (55) 937499741
E-Mail: gaigher@burgmann.com.br
Web Site: www.burgmann.com.br
Emp.: 110
Mechanical Seals & Packings Mfr & Sls
S.I.C.: 3053
N.A.I.C.S.: 339991

EagleBurgmann Endustriyel Sizdirmalik Sanayi ve Ticaret Ltd. Sti. (2)
Melek Aras Bulvari Tuna Cad No 8
Tuzla, 34956 Istanbul, Turkey TR
Tel.: (90) 2165930293
Fax: (90) 2165930298
E-Mail: contact@tr.eagleburgmann.com
Web Site: www.eagleburgmann.com.tr
Sales Range: $10-24.9 Million
Emp.: 75
Mechanical Seals & Packings Mfr & Sls
S.I.C.: 3053
N.A.I.C.S.: 339991
Oktay Yildirim *(Mgr-Sls)*

EagleBurgmann France S.A.S. (2)
BP 96
106 108 Rte De Cormeilles, F 78505
Sartrouville, France FR
Tel.: (33) 00130865020
Fax: (33) 139151607
E-Mail: francois.ott@fr.eagleburgmann.com
Web Site: www.burgmann.com
Emp.: 45
Mechanical Seals & Packings Sls
S.I.C.: 3053
N.A.I.C.S.: 339991

EagleBurgmann Hungaria Kft. (2)
Lejtoe utca 6
1124 Budapest, Hungary
Tel.: (36) 13198132
Fax: (36) 13198725
E-Mail: info-hu@hu.eagleburgmann.com
Gasket & Sealing Device Mfr
S.I.C.: 3053
N.A.I.C.S.: 339991

EagleBurgmann Iberica S. A. (2)
Avda de Quitapesares 40
E 28670 Madrid, Villaviciosa de Odon, Spain
Tel.: (34) 916166601
Fax: (34) 916166681
E-Mail: info@es.eagleburgmann.com
Web Site: www.burgmaniberica.com
Emp.: 20
Mechanical Seal Mfr
S.I.C.: 3053
N.A.I.C.S.: 339991
Rafael Jimenez *(Gen Mgr)*

EagleBurgmann Industries Russia (2)
Nizhny Novgorod Region Zavolzhje St The Train 1 Building 45
Moscow, 606524, Russia RU
Tel.: (7) 83161 300 78
Fax: (7) 83161 305 59
E-Mail: mail@ru.eagleburgmann.com
Web Site: www.eagleburgmann.ru
Emp.: 100
Mechanical Seals & Packings Mfr
S.I.C.: 3053
N.A.I.C.S.: 339991

EagleBurgmann Industries UK LP (2)
12 Welton Rd Wedgnock Industrial Est
Warwick, CV34 5PZ, United Kingdom UK
Tel.: (44) 1926417600
Fax: (44) 1926417617
E-Mail: ralf.meininger@uk.eagleburgmann.com
Web Site: www.eagleburgmann.com
Rev.: $137,760,800
Emp.: 40
Mechanical Seals & Packings Mfr & Sls
S.I.C.: 3053
N.A.I.C.S.: 339991
Brian Finlayson *(Mng Dir)*

EagleBurgmann Italia s.r.l. (2)
Via Martiri della Liberazione 12
23875 Vimercate, Osnago, Italy IT
Tel.: (39) 0399522501
Fax: (39) 0399289420
E-Mail: info@eagleburgmann.it
Web Site: www.burgmann.it
Emp.: 20
Sales of Mechanical Seals & Packings
S.I.C.: 3053
N.A.I.C.S.: 339991
Alessandro Pizzi *(Mng Dir)*

EagleBurgmann KE A/S (2)
Park Alle 34
DK 6600 Vejen, Denmark DK
Tel.: (45) 75361811
Fax: (45) 75361532
E-Mail: info@dk.eagleburgmann.com
Web Site: www.eagleburgmann-ej.com
Rev.: $50,907,465
Emp.: 250
Mechanical Seals, Packings & Expansion Joints Sls
S.I.C.: 5085
N.A.I.C.S.: 423840
Juergen Peschla *(CEO)*

EagleBurgmann KE Pte. Ltd. (2)
No 24 Pioneer Crescent #03-08 West Park BizCentral
Singapore, 628557, Singapore SG
Tel.: (65) 62618581
Fax: (65) 62618589
E-Mail: saleske_burg@pacific.net.sg
Web Site: www.eagleburgmann-ej.com
Rev.: $1,129,300
Emp.: 20
Mechanical Seals & Packings Mfr & Sls
S.I.C.: 3053
N.A.I.C.S.: 339991
Gerry Cheong *(Mng Dir)*

EagleBurgmann Korea Ltd. (2)
541 Suwolam Ri Seotan Myon Pyongtaik Si
Kyongki, 451-850, Korea (South) Ks
Tel.: (82) 313754095
Fax: (82) 313754086
E-Mail: brok@burgmannkorea.co.kr
Web Site: www.burgmannkorea.co.kr
Sales Range: $1-9.9 Million
Emp.: 30
Mechanical Seals, Packings & Expansion Joints Mfr & Sls
S.I.C.: 3053
N.A.I.C.S.: 339991

EagleBurgmann (Malaysia) SDN BHD (2)
No 7 Lorong SS 13 6B off Jalan SS13 6
Subang Jaya Indus Est, 47500 Petaling Jaya, Selangor darul Ehsan, Malaysia MY
Tel.: (60) 356348624
Fax: (60) 356349742
E-Mail: sh.songs@my.eagleburgmann.com
Web Site: www.eagleburgmann.com
Emp.: 50
Sealing Technologies Mfr & Sls
S.I.C.: 3053
N.A.I.C.S.: 339991
Song Soon Hee *(Mng Dir)*

EagleBurgmann Mexico S.A. de C.V. (2)
Calzada De Guadelupe Num 350 6 Col El Cerrito
Cuautitlan Izcalli, Mexico, CP 54720, Mexico MX
Tel.: (52) 5558721841
Fax: (52) 5558726493
E-Mail: ebmex@mx.eagleburgmann.com
Web Site: www.eagleburgmann.com.mx
Emp.: 128
Mechanical Seals & Packings Mfr & Sls
S.I.C.: 3053
N.A.I.C.S.: 339991
Ruben Garcia *(Mng Dir)*

EagleBurgmann Middle East FZE (2)
Jebel Ali Free Zone Section RA08 Bldg CC06
PO Box 61310
Dubai, United Arab Emirates AE
Tel.: (971) 48838841
Fax: (971) 48838843
E-Mail: sales@ae.eagleburgmannme.com
Web Site: www.eagleburgmann.ae
Sales Range: $1-9.9 Million
Emp.: 30
Seal Mfr
S.I.C.: 3053
N.A.I.C.S.: 339991
Hasam Babacan *(Mng Dir)*

EagleBurgmann Netherlands B.V. (2)
Konengsschot 9
NL 3905 PP Veenendaal, 3905 PP, Netherlands NL
Tel.: (31) 318542000
Fax: (31) 318541535
E-Mail: info@nl.eagleburgmann.com
Web Site: www.eagleburgmann.com
Emp.: 15
Mechanical Seals & Packings Sls
S.I.C.: 3053
N.A.I.C.S.: 339991
Robert Veldhuis *(Mng Dir)*

EagleBurgmann Norway A/S (2)
Postbox 143
Industriveien 25 D, N-2021 Skedsmokorset, Norway NO
Tel.: (47) 64837550
Fax: (47) 64837575
E-Mail: per.fredriksson@no.eagleburgmann.com
Web Site: www.burgmann.com
Emp.: 17
Mechanical Seals, Expansion Joints & Packings Mfr
S.I.C.: 3053
N.A.I.C.S.: 339991
Lars Jacobsen *(Mgr-Mktg)*

EagleBurgmann OOO (2)
ul Zheleznodorozhnaya 1 Building 45
Zavolzhye Gorodetsky District, 606524
Nizhniy Novgorod, Russia
Tel.: (7) 83161 30077
Fax: (7) 83161 30559
E-Mail: mail@rueagleburgmann.com
Web Site: www.eagleburgmann.ru
Emp.: 45
Mechanical Sealing Device Mfr
S.I.C.: 3053
N.A.I.C.S.: 339991
Eberharz Grizner *(Mng Dir)*

EagleBurgmann Philippines Inc. (2)
No 9769 National Rd Maduya
Carmona Cavite, Manila, 4116, Philippines
Tel.: (63) 464301426
Fax: (63) 464301428
E-Mail: arlitz.magpantay@ph.eagleburgmann.com
Web Site: www.burgmann.com
Emp.: 40
Mechanical Seals & Packings Mfr & Sls
S.I.C.: 3053
N.A.I.C.S.: 339991

EagleBurgmann RO SRL (2)
Bdul Iuliu Maniu Nr 7 Cladirea E Parter
Hala 3 Sector 6
061072 Bucharest, Romania
Tel.: (40) 31 425 0909
Fax: (40) 31 425 0910
Mechanical Sealing Device Mfr
S.I.C.: 3053
N.A.I.C.S.: 339991

EagleBurgmann Seals South Africa (Pty) Ltd. (2)
No 1 Brunton Circle Sandersville South
PO Box 1210
1610 Edenvale, South Africa ZA
Tel.: (27) 114579000
Fax: (27) 116091606
E-Mail: info@za.eagleburgmann.com
Web Site: www.burgmann.com
Emp.: 128
Seals, Packing Components, Fabric & Metal Expansion Joints Mfr
S.I.C.: 3053
N.A.I.C.S.: 339991
Paul Ban Wyk *(Mng Dir)*

EagleBurgmann Singapore Pte. Ltd (2)
15 Tukang Innovation Drive
618299 Singapore, Singapore
Tel.: (65) 64813439
Fax: (65) 64813934
E-Mail: ebi-sg@sg.eagleburgmann.com
Industrial Machinery Mfr
S.I.C.: 3559
N.A.I.C.S.: 333249

EagleBurgmann Sweden AB (2)
Svaermaregatan 3
SE 603 61 Norrkoping, Sweden SE
Tel.: (46) 011140005
Fax: (46) 11140015
E-Mail: magnus.kignell@se.eagleburgmann.com
Web Site: www.burgmann.com
Emp.: 30
Mechanical Seals & Packings Mfr & Sls
S.I.C.: 3053
N.A.I.C.S.: 339991
Per Fredriksson *(Mng Dir)*

Branch:

EagleBurgmann Sweden AB (3)
Arbetsledarvagen 12
85753 Sundsvall, Sweden
Tel.: (46) 60645090
Fax: (46) 6024294
E-Mail: ebs_info@se.eagleburgmann.com
Gasket & Sealing Component Mfr
S.I.C.: 3053
N.A.I.C.S.: 339991

EagleBurgmann (Switzerland) AG (2)
Hofstrasse 21
Hoeri, CH 8181 Zurich, Switzerland CH
Tel.: (41) 448723930
Fax: (41) 448723940
E-Mail: corinna.herrmann@ch.eagleburgmann.com
Web Site: www.burgmann.com
Emp.: 10
Mechanical Seals & Packings Mfr & Sls
S.I.C.: 3053
N.A.I.C.S.: 339991
Corinna Herrmann *(Mng Dir)*

EagleBurgmann Taiwan Corporation (2)
No 134 Hsi Lin Road Yenchao
Kaohsiung, Taiwan
Tel.: (886) 76164401
Fax: (886) 76166486
Emp.: 300
Adhesive Mfr
S.I.C.: 2891
N.A.I.C.S.: 325520

EagleBurgmann (Thailand) Co., Ltd. (2)
13/2 Klongnamhu Road T Nernphra Muang
Rayong, 21150, Thailand TH
Tel.: (66) 38694422
Fax: (66) 38694419
Web Site: www.goburgmann.com
Sales Range: $1-9.9 Million
Emp.: 65
Mechanical Seals & Packings Mfr & Sls
S.I.C.: 3053
N.A.I.C.S.: 339991

Freudenberg SE—(Continued)

EagleBurgmann Vietnam Company Ltd. **(2)**
343 Pham Ngu Lao Street 6th Floor Suite 6C International Plaza
Pham Ngu Lao Ward District 1, Ho Chi Minh City, Vietnam
Tel.: (84) 8 6291 5648
Fax: (84) 8 6291 5649
Emp.: 1
Industrial Machinery Mfr
S.I.C.: 3559
N.A.I.C.S.: 333249
Daryl Lim *(Gen Dir)*

EagleBurgmann (Wuxi) Co. Ltd. **(2)**
Changjiang South Road No 28-51
Wuxi, 214028 Wuxi, Jiangsu, China
Tel.: (86) 51085346107
Fax: (86) 51085346101
Emp.: 100
Automotive Mechanical & Electrical Repair & Maintenance
S.I.C.: 7539
N.A.I.C.S.: 811118

KE-Burgmann Finland Oy **(2)**
Ensimmainen Savu
1510 Vantaa, Finland FI
Tel.: (358) 9825501
Fax: (358) 982550200
E-Mail: ke@burgmann.fi
Web Site: www.burgmann.fi
Sales Range: $1-9.9 Million
Emp.: 5
Expansion Joints & Sales of Heat Resistent Fabrics & Yarns Mfr & Sls
S.I.C.: 3441
N.A.I.C.S.: 332312
Pasi Virintie *(Mng Dir)*

Non-U.S. Affiliates:

EagleBurgmann Australasia Pty. Ltd. **(2)**
(Formerly EagleBurgmann Australia Pty. Ltd.)
16 Stennett Road
Sydney, NSW, 2565, Australia AU
Tel.: (61) 296056444
Fax: (61) 298296958
E-Mail: sales@au.eagleburgmann.com
Web Site: www.eagleburgmann.com.au
Rev.: $3,190,000
Emp.: 38
Mechanical Seals & Packing Mfr & Sls
S.I.C.: 3053
N.A.I.C.S.: 339991
Wolfgang Kindinger *(Mng Dir)*
Ian Nipper *(Mgr-Sls-Victoria)*

Branch:

EagleBurgmann Australasia Pty. Ltd. - Melbourne **(3)**
19 Inglewood Drive
Thomastown, Melbourne, VIC, 3074, Australia
Tel.: (61) 394646344
Fax: (61) 394646511
E-Mail: vic@au.eagleburgmann.com
Web Site: www.eagleburgmann.com
Mechanical Seals Mfr
S.I.C.: 3546
N.A.I.C.S.: 333991
Mike Newman *(Area Mgr)*

EagleBurgmann India Pvt. Ltd. **(2)**
Gazebo House 52 Gulmohar Road Opp Cross Road #7
JVPD Scheme Vile Parle West, Mumbai, 400049, India In
Tel.: (91) 22 6702 1489
Fax: (91) 22 6702 1487
E-Mail: ebipl.mumbai@in.eagleburgmann.com
Web Site: www.eagleburgmann.com
Emp.: 180
Mechanical Seals & Packings Mfr & Sls
S.I.C.: 3053
N.A.I.C.S.: 339991

Branch:

EagleBurgmann India Pvt. Ltd. **(3)**
Door No 10-50-18/17 Flat No 1/7 First Floor Siripuram Towers
Siripuram VIP Road, 530 003
Visakhapatnam, India
Tel.: (91) 8912755703
Fax: (91) 8912550306
Mechanical Sealing Device Mfr
S.I.C.: 3053
N.A.I.C.S.: 339991

EagleBurgmann Japan Co., Ltd. **(2)**
5-1-4 Nakagawashin Gosen-shi
959-1693 Niigata, Japan JP
Tel.: (81) 250471111
Fax: (81) 250483070
E-Mail: takafumi.tsuchiya@jp.eagleburgmann.com
Web Site: www.eagleburgmann.com
Emp.: 700
Metal Valve & Pipe Fitting Mfr
S.I.C.: 3494
N.A.I.C.S.: 332919
Takafumi Tsuchiya *(Pres)*

EagleBurgmann New Zealand, Ltd. **(2)**
47 William Pickering Drive
PO Box 300-858
North Shore City Albany, Auckland, 752, New Zealand
Tel.: (64) 94485001
Fax: (64) 94150599
E-Mail: sales@nz.eagleburgmann.com
Emp.: 45
Mechanical Seal Mfr
S.I.C.: 3053
N.A.I.C.S.: 339991
John Hill *(Gen Mgr)*

P.T. EagleBurgmann Indonesia **(2)**
Jl Jababeka Blok J6 E
Kawasan Industri Cikarang, Bekasi, Jawa Barat, 17550, Indonesia ID
Tel.: (62) 218935313
Fax: (62) 218935315
E-Mail: bri@burgmann.co.id
Web Site: www.eagleburgmann.com
Emp.: 109
Mechanical Seals & Packings Mfr & Sls
S.I.C.: 3053
N.A.I.C.S.: 339991

Externa Handels- und Beteiligungsgesellschaft mbH **(1)**
Hoehnerweg 2 4
69469 Weinheim, Germany De
Tel.: (49) 6201800 (100%)
Fax: (49) 6201880
Web Site: www.freudenberg.com
Mfr. of Rubber Products
S.I.C.: 3069
N.A.I.C.S.: 326299

FHP Export GmbH **(1)**
Leibnizstrasse 2 4
69469 Weinheim, Germany De
Tel.: (49) 6201800 (100%)
Fax: (49) 620188874000
E-Mail: thomas.haneke@fhp-ww.com
Web Site: www.freudenberg.com
Emp.: 30
Industrial Products
S.I.C.: 3589
N.A.I.C.S.: 333318
Thomas Haneke *(CEO)*

Freudenberg & Co. Ltd. Partnership **(1)**
Weinheim
69465 Weinheim, Germany De
Tel.: (49) 6201800 (100%)
Fax: (49) 6201883430
Web Site: www.freudenberg.com
Emp.: 50
Mfr. of Rubber, Plastics Processing; Nonwovens Production; Flooring
S.I.C.: 3069
N.A.I.C.S.: 326299
Volstant Orians *(Mng Dir)*

Freudenberg Anlagen-und Werkzeugtechnik KG **(1)**
Dr Werner Freyberg Strasse 7
69514 Laudenbach, Germany De
Tel.: (49) 6201806345 (100%)
Fax: (49) 6201882283
E-Mail: info@faw-freudenberg.de
Web Site: www.faw-freudenberg.de
Mfr. of Industrial Machinery
S.I.C.: 3559
N.A.I.C.S.: 333249

Freudenberg Beteiligungsgesellschaft mbH **(1)**
Hoehnerweg 2-4
69469 Weinheim, Germany De
Tel.: (49) 6201800
Fax: (49) 6201880
E-Mail: info@freudenberg.com
Web Site: www.freudenberg.com
Mfr. of Rubber
S.I.C.: 3069
N.A.I.C.S.: 326299

Freudenberg Chemical Specialties KG **(1)**
Geisenhausenerstrasse 7
81379 Munich, Germany De
Tel.: (49) 8978760 (100%)
Fax: (49) 8978761600
E-Mail: info@fcs-munich.com
Web Site: www.fcs-muenchen.com
Sales Range: $750-799.9 Million
Emp.: 2,400
Holding Company; Lubricants & Other Specialty Chemical Products Mfr
S.I.C.: 6719
N.A.I.C.S.: 551112
Hanno D. Wentzler *(Pres & CEO)*
Jorg Mathias Grossmann *(CFO & Exec VP)*

Subsidiary:

Kluber Lubrication Munchen KG **(2)**
Geisenhausenerstrasse 7
D-81379 Munich, Germany De
Tel.: (49) 8978760 (100%)
Fax: (49) 897876333
Web Site: www.kluber.com
Sales Range: $400-449.9 Million
Emp.: 1,500
Lubricants Mfr
S.I.C.: 2992
N.A.I.C.S.: 324191
Peter Neumann *(Mgr-Automotive Engrg-Indus Grp)*

U.S. Subsidiary:

Kluber Lubrication North America LP **(3)**
32 Industrial Dr
Londonderry, NH 03053-7438 DE
Tel.: (603) 647-4104 (100%)
Fax: (603) 647-4106
Toll Free: (800) 447-2238
Web Site: www.kluberna.com
Emp.: 70
Lubricants Mfr
S.I.C.: 2992
N.A.I.C.S.: 324191
Ron Person *(Dir-Bus Dev-Oil & Gas)*

Non-U.S. Subsidiaries:

Kluber Lubrication AG (Schweiz) **(3)**
Thurgauer Str 39
PO Box 8727
8050 Zurich, Switzerland CH
Tel.: (41) 443086969 (100%)
Fax: (41) 443086944
E-Mail: info@ch.klueber.com
Web Site: www.klueber.com
Sales Range: $1-9.9 Million
Emp.: 12
Lubricants Mfr
S.I.C.: 5169
N.A.I.C.S.: 424690
Mark Cvolkmer *(Dir-Sls)*

Kluber Lubrication Argentina S.A. **(3)**
Martin J Haedo 4301/63
Florida, 1602 Buenos Aires, Argentina AR
Tel.: (54) 1147091400 (100%)
Fax: (54) 147098430
E-Mail: maria.macra@klueber.com
Web Site: www.klueber.com
Emp.: 30
Mfr. of Rubber
S.I.C.: 3069
N.A.I.C.S.: 326299

Kluber Lubrication A.S. **(3)**
Literbuen 9
2740 Skovlunde, Denmark DK
Tel.: (45) 70234277 (100%)
Fax: (45) 70234200
E-Mail: klueber.dk@sk.klueber.com
Web Site: www.klueber.com
Emp.: 7
Sales of Lubricants
S.I.C.: 5169
N.A.I.C.S.: 424690
Bloch Sorensen *(Mgr-Sls)*

Kluber Lubrication Australia Pty. Ltd. **(3)**
3 Brand Dr
PO Box 4
Thomastown, VIC, 3074, Australia AU
Tel.: (61) 394647577 (100%)
Fax: (61) 394647588
E-Mail: kluber.mel@kluber.com.au
Web Site: www.kluber.com.au
Emp.: 20
Sales of Lubricants
S.I.C.: 5169
N.A.I.C.S.: 424690
Kevin Seeley *(Mng Dir)*

Kluber Lubrication Austria GmbH **(3)**
Franz Wolfram Scherer Strasse 32
PO Box 84
5028 Salzburg, Austria AT
Tel.: (43) 6624527050 (100%)
Fax: (43) 66245270530
E-Mail: office@at.klueber.com
Web Site: www.klueber.com
Emp.: 50
Mfr. of Lubrication
S.I.C.: 2992
N.A.I.C.S.: 324191

Kluber Lubrication Benelux S.A. **(3)**
Rue Cardinal Mercier 100
7711 Dottignies, Belgium BE
Tel.: (32) 56483311 (100%)
Fax: (32) 56486252
E-Mail: sales@be.klueber.com
Web Site: www.klueber.com
Sales Range: $25-49.9 Million
Emp.: 115
Mfr. of Lubricants
S.I.C.: 2992
N.A.I.C.S.: 324191
Rudy VanLoocka *(Gen Mgr)*

Kluber Lubrication China Ltd. **(3)**
Room 1012 Shatin Galleria 18-24 Shan Mei St
Fotan, Sha Tin, NT, China (Hong Kong) HK
Tel.: (852) 26920191 (100%)
Fax: (852) 26934304
E-Mail: kluberhk@hk.klueber.com
Web Site: www.klueber.com
Emp.: 8
Sales of Lubricants
S.I.C.: 5169
N.A.I.C.S.: 424690
Andy So *(Reg Mgr)*

Kluber Lubrication France S.A.S. **(3)**
14 16 Allee Eugene Ducretet
26014 Valence, Cedex, France FR
Tel.: (33) 475448436 (100%)
Fax: (33) 475449336
E-Mail: klueber@fr.klueber.com
Web Site: www.klueber.com
Emp.: 25
Sales of Lubricants
S.I.C.: 5169
N.A.I.C.S.: 424690
Reda Lathasghe *(Mng Dir)*

Kluber Lubrication GmbH Iberica S.en C. **(3)**
Carretera C 17 Km 15 5
E 08150 Barcelona, Spain ES
Tel.: (34) 935738400 (100%)
Fax: (34) 935738409
E-Mail: servicio.clientes@es.klueber.com
Web Site: www.klueber.com
Mfr. of Lubricants
S.I.C.: 2992
N.A.I.C.S.: 324191
Jose Torrans *(Gen Mgr)*

Kluber Lubrication Great Britain Ltd. **(3)**
Bradford Rd Hough Mills
Halifax, Northowram, HX3 7BN, United Kingdom UK
Tel.: (44) 1422205115
Fax: (44) 1442206073
E-Mail: sales@ukklueber.com
Web Site: www.klueber.com
Emp.: 25
Sales of Lubricants
S.I.C.: 5169
N.A.I.C.S.: 424690

Kluber Lubrication Italia S.A.S. **(3)**
Via Monferrato 57
Sesto Ulteriano San Giuliano M, 20098 Milan, MI, Italy IT
Tel.: (39) 02982131 (100%)
Fax: (39) 0298281595

E-Mail: klita@it.klueber.com
Web Site: www.klueber.com
Sales Range: $25-49.9 Million
Emp.: 55
Mfr. of Lubrication
S.I.C.: 2992
N.A.I.C.S.: 324191
Carlo Fassina *(Dir-Mktg & Sls)*

Kluber Lubrication (Korea) Ltd. **(3)**
Youngdungpo Gu Yoido Dong 17 3
Samhwan Camus Building 802, Seoul, Korea (South) Ks
Tel.: (82) 27825151 (50%)
Fax: (82) 27849900
E-Mail: klueber@klueber.co.kr
Web Site: www.klueber.co.kr
Emp.: 50
Mfr. of Lubricants
S.I.C.: 2992
N.A.I.C.S.: 324191
Kichung Eum *(Gen Mgr)*

Kluber Lubrication Lubrificantes Especiais Ltda. & Cia. **(3)**
Rua Sao Paulo 345
06454 080 Barueri, SP, Brazil BR
Tel.: (55) 41669000 (100%)
Telex: 1139209
Fax: (55) 1141669004
E-Mail: vendas@klueber.com.br
Web Site: www.klueber.com
Emp.: 100
Mfr. of Lubricants
S.I.C.: 2992
N.A.I.C.S.: 324191
Enrique Garcia *(CEO)*

Kluber Lubrication Mexicana S.A. De C.V. **(3)**
Ave Delenontene 109 Santa Rosa De Jauregui
Berqueindustrial, 76220 Queretaro, Mexico MX
Tel.: (52) 4422295700 (100%)
Fax: (52) 4422295710
E-Mail: ventas@kluber.com.mx
Web Site: www.klueber.com
Sales Range: $1-9.9 Million
Emp.: 52
Mfr. of Lubricants
S.I.C.: 2992
N.A.I.C.S.: 324191

Kluber Lubrication (Pty.) Ltd. **(3)**
12 C Barium
PO Box 11461
Randhart, Alberton, 1449, South Africa ZA
Tel.: (27) 119082457 (100%)
Fax: (27) 118647373
E-Mail: sales@sa.klueber.com
Web Site: www.klueber.com
Emp.: 14
Sales of Lubricants
S.I.C.: 5169
N.A.I.C.S.: 424690
Hennie C. Aucamp *(Mng Dir)*

Kluber Lubrication South East Asia Pte. Ltd. **(3)**
25 Intl Bus Pk 04 54 G German Ctr
Singapore, 609916, Singapore SG
Tel.: (65) 65629460 (100%)
Fax: (65) 65629469
E-Mail: sales@klueber.com.sg
Web Site: www.klueber.com
Emp.: 5
Sales of Lubricants
S.I.C.: 2992
N.A.I.C.S.: 324191
Kwang Lee Seah *(Reg Mgr-Sls)*

Kluber Lubrication Yaglama Urunleri Sanayi Ve Ticaret A.S. **(3)**
Orgeaze Sanahi Dorve Atacurp Cav 10 Sor 7 Cerkazkua
59500 Tekirdag, Turkey TR
Tel.: (90) 2827581530 (100%)
Fax: (90) 2827582935
E-Mail: kltr@tr.klueber.com
Web Site: www.klueber.com
Emp.: 42
Mfr. of Lubricants
S.I.C.: 2992
N.A.I.C.S.: 324191

U.S. Division:

Chem-Trend Limited Partnership **(2)**
1445 McPherson Park Dr
Howell, MI 48843-3947 (100%)
Tel.: (517) 546-4520
Fax: (517) 548-6710
Toll Free: (800) 727-7730
Web Site: www.chemtrend.com
Emp.: 340
Mold Releases Mfr for the Plastic & Rubber Industries; Die Lubricants, Quench Compounds, Plunger Lubricants, Tire Releasants Mfr
S.I.C.: 2992
N.A.I.C.S.: 324191
Devanir Moraes *(Pres & CEO)*

Non-U.S. Subsidiary:

Chem-Trend (Deutchland) GmbH **(3)**
Ganghofer Strasse 47
82216 Maisach, Germany De
Tel.: (49) 81424170 (100%)
Fax: (49) 814217111
E-Mail: maisach@chemtrends.de
Web Site: www.chemtrends.com
Emp.: 60
Mfr. of Lubricants
S.I.C.: 2992
N.A.I.C.S.: 324191
Herald Neubauer *(Mng Dir)*
Peter Schatzler *(Mng Dir)*

Freudenberg Dichtungs- und Schwingungstechnik GmbH & Co. KG **(1)**
Hohnerweg 2-4
69465 Weinheim, Germany De
Tel.: (49) 6201806666 (100%)
Fax: (49) 6201880
E-Mail: fds@freudenberg.de
Web Site: www.freudenberg-ds.com
Emp.: 6,000
Rubber Seals Mfr
S.I.C.: 3053
N.A.I.C.S.: 339991
Claus Moehlenkamp *(Chm-Mgmt Bd)*
Arman Barimani *(Member-Mgmt Bd)*
Ludger Neuwinger-Heimes *(Member-Mgmt Bd)*

Freudenberg Versicherungsvermittlungs-GmbH **(1)**
Hohner Weg 2 4
69469 Weinheim, Germany De
Tel.: (49) 6201800 (100%)
Fax: (49) 6201880
E-Mail: monica.werline@freudenberg.de
Web Site: www.freudenberg.com
Mfr. of Rubber
S.I.C.: 3069
N.A.I.C.S.: 326299
Monika Werline *(Sec)*

Freudenberg Vertrieb Einlagestoffe KG **(1)**
Hohnerweg 2 4
69469 Weinheim, Germany De
Tel.: (49) 6201800 (100%)
Fax: (49) 6201880
E-Mail: info@simrit.de
Web Site: www.freudenberg.de
Mfr. of Nonwoven Interlinings
S.I.C.: 2297
N.A.I.C.S.: 313230
Monika Werline *(Sec)*

Merkel Freudenberg Fluidtechnic GmbH **(1)**
Industriestrasse 64
D 21107 Hamburg, Germany (100%)
Tel.: (49) 40753060
Fax: (49) 4075306400
E-Mail: merkel@freudenberg.com
Web Site: www.freudenberg.com
Sales Range: $100-124.9 Million
Emp.: 400
Mfr. of Seals & Packings for Hydraulics, Pneumatics, Pumps, Agitators & Valves; Mechanical Seals for the Chemical, Refinery, Cellulose, Paper Industries; Seals & Other Components Produced from Fluorocarbon Resins; Articles from Polyurethane Elastomers; Rotary Shaft Seals; Shaft & Bearing Seals
Import
S.I.C.: 3565
N.A.I.C.S.: 333993
Bernt Koch *(Chm)*

Procal GmbH **(1)**
Hoehnerweg 2-4
69469 Weinheim, Germany (100%)
Web Site: www.freudenberg.com
Mfr. of Rubber
S.I.C.: 3069
N.A.I.C.S.: 326299

Vileda GmbH **(1)**
Technology Park 19
D 69469 Weinheim, Germany De
Tel.: (49) 6201807766 (100%)
Fax: (49) 620188874009
E-Mail: vileda-info@fhp-ww.com
Web Site: www.vileda.de
Emp.: 200
Mfr. of Chemical Products
S.I.C.: 2899
N.A.I.C.S.: 325998

Joint Venture:

Brammer GmbH **(1)**
Industriestrasse 19
76189 Karlsruhe, Germany DE
Tel.: (49) 7219543210
Fax: (49) 7219543222
E-Mail: karlsruhe@brammer.biz
Web Site: www.thf.de
Emp.: 450
Engineering Parts Distr
S.I.C.: 7389
N.A.I.C.S.: 425120

Subsidiary:

THF GmbH & Co. KG **(2)**
Am Broegel 1A 13
42111 Wuppertal, Germany De
Tel.: (49) 20289070
Fax: (49) 2028907161
Web Site: www.thf.de
Emp.: 20
Engineering Parts Distr
S.I.C.: 7389
N.A.I.C.S.: 425120

U.S. Subsidiaries:

Freudenberg Household Products LP **(1)**
2188 Diehl Rd
Aurora, IL 60502-8775 (100%)
Tel.: (708) 452-4100
Fax: (630) 270-1600
Toll Free: (800) 543-8105
E-Mail: info@ocedar.com
Web Site: www.ocedar.com
Emp.: 45
Mfr. of Mops, Sponge Mops & Refills, Brooms & Dust Mops
Import Export
S.I.C.: 3991
N.A.I.C.S.: 339994
Jim Castetter *(VP-Sls)*

Freudenberg Nonwovens Limited Partnership **(1)**
3500 Industrial Dr Eno Industrial Park
Durham, NC 27704 DE
Tel.: (919) 620-3900 (100%)
Fax: (919) 620-3945
Toll Free: (800) 40-VILENE
E-Mail: vilene.usa@fvna.com
Web Site: www.freudenberg.de
Sales Range: $125-149.9 Million
Emp.: 25
Nonwoven Textiles for Apparel, Industry & Air Filtration, Home Decorating Crafts, Full Range of Interlinings, Non-Woven, Woven & Knit
Import Export
S.I.C.: 2297
N.A.I.C.S.: 313230
John McNabb *(Gen Mgr)*

Plant:

Freudenberg Nonwovens Tuft Division **(2)**
3500 Industrial Dr
Durham, NC 27704-0910 MA
Mailing Address: (100%)
PO Box 15910
Durham, NC 27704-0910
Tel.: (919) 471-2582
Telex: 80 2852
Web Site: www.freudenberg.com
Sales Range: $25-49.9 Million
Emp.: 114
Mfr. of Spunbonded Nonwovens
S.I.C.: 2297
N.A.I.C.S.: 313230

Freudenberg North America Limited Partnership **(1)**
RR 104 Ragged Mtn Hwy
Bristol, NH 03222 (100%)
Tel.: (603) 744-2281
Fax: (603) 744-8722
Web Site: www.fngp.com
Emp.: 280
Mfr. of Rubber
S.I.C.: 3061
N.A.I.C.S.: 326291
Sheila Corneau *(Mgr-HR)*

Helix Medical LLC **(1)**
1110 Mark Ave
Carpinteria, CA 93013
Tel.: (805) 684-3304
Fax: (805) 566-5395
Toll Free: (877) 308-0558
E-Mail: info@helixmedical.com
Web Site: www.helixmedical.com
Sales Range: $50-74.9 Million
Emp.: 700
Plastic Medical Device & Component Mfr
S.I.C.: 3841
N.A.I.C.S.: 339113
Jorg Schneewind *(Pres & CEO)*

Division:

InHealth Technologies **(2)**
1110 Mark Ave
Carpinteria, CA 93013
Tel.: (805) 684-3304
Fax: (805) 566-5395
Voice Restoration Products Mfr
S.I.C.: 3845
N.A.I.C.S.: 334510
Jobeth Seder Erickson *(VP & Gen Mgr)*

Subsidiary:

MedVenture Technology Corporation **(2)**
2301 Centennial Blvd
Jeffersonville, IN 47130 KY
Tel.: (812) 280-2400
Web Site: www.medventure.com
Emp.: 260
Medical Device Mfr
S.I.C.: 3841
N.A.I.C.S.: 339112
Mitch Moeller *(Pres & CEO)*

Unit:

Helix Medical LLC - Baldwin Park **(2)**
5050 Rivergrade Rd
Baldwin Park, CA 91706 CA
Tel.: (626) 814-9684
Fax: (626) 814-4709
Sales Range: $1-9.9 Million
Emp.: 100
Plastic Medical Device & Component Mfr
S.I.C.: 3841
N.A.I.C.S.: 339113
Graham Lynggard *(VP-Ops)*

TrelleborgVibracoustic **(1)**
(Formerly Vibracoustic North America)
1496 Gerber St
Ligonier, IN 46767-2422
Tel.: (260) 894-7448
Web Site: www.tbvc.com
Emp.: 100
Conventional Engine Mounts, Hydromounts, Crank Shaft Dampers Mfr
S.I.C.: 3714
N.A.I.C.S.: 336390
Mehdi Ilkhani-Pour *(Pres)*

U.S. Joint Venture:

Freudenberg-NOK **(1)**
47690 E Anchor Ct
Plymouth, MI 48170-2400
Tel.: (734) 451-0020
Fax: (734) 451-2547
Toll Free: (800) 533-5656
Web Site: www.freudenberg-nok.com
Sales Range: $1-4.9 Billion
Emp.: 250
Elastomeric Seals, Custom Molded Products & Vibration Control Technologies Mfr; Owned 75% by Freudenberg & Co. Kommanditgesellschaft & 25% by NOK Corporation
Export

Freudenberg SE—(Continued)

S.I.C.: 3053
N.A.I.C.S.: 339991
Pierre Y. Abboud *(Pres-Vibracoustic-North America)*
Robert G. Evans *(Gen Counsel & VP)*

Units:

Freudenberg NOK-Rubber Products (2)
487 W Main St
Morristown, IN 46161-9745
Tel.: (765) 763-7246
Fax: (765) 763-6011
Web Site: www.freundenberg-nok.com
Sales Range: $25-49.9 Million
Emp.: 215
Mfr. of Brake Components, Steering Linkage Components, Electrical Connectors, Oil Seals & Filler Tube Seals & Transmission Seals
S.I.C.: 3053
N.A.I.C.S.: 339991
Stacy Flora *(Plant Mgr)*

Freudenberg NOK-Rubber Products (2)
1700 Miller Ave
Shelbyville, IN 46176-3114
Tel.: (317) 421-3400
Fax: (317) 392-3406
Web Site: www.freundenberg.com
Emp.: 142
Rocker Cover, Electrical Sealing & Extrusion Gaskets; Electrical Connectors; Brake Parts & Transmission Seals
S.I.C.: 3053
N.A.I.C.S.: 339991

Freudenberg NOK-Sealant Products (2)
1 Nok Dr
Cleveland, GA 30528-0034
Tel.: (706) 865-1665
Fax: (706) 219-3478
Web Site: www.freudenberg-nok.com
Emp.: 400
Mfr. of Oil Seals, Valve Stem Seals, Boots & Dust Covers & Seal Rings
S.I.C.: 2911
N.A.I.C.S.: 324110
Gary Vamwambeke *(Exec Dir)*

Freudenberg NOK (2)
1618 Lukken Industrial Dr W
Lagrange, GA 30240-5704
Tel.: (706) 884-6111
Fax: (706) 884-1118
Web Site: www.freudenberg-nok.com
Emp.: 200
Mfr. of Rubber Moulded Products for the Automotive Industry
S.I.C.: 3053
N.A.I.C.S.: 339991
Tigree Butcher *(Product Dir-Mgmt)*

Freudenberg NOK (2)
450 Pleasant St
Bristol, NH 03222-0501
Tel.: (603) 744-2281
Fax: (603) 744-1750
Web Site: www.fngp.com
Emp.: 300
Appliance Face, Radial Shaft, Engine Valve Stem Seals, Strut Seals, Oil & Water Pump Seal Caliper Boots
S.I.C.: 6061
N.A.I.C.S.: 522130
Zean Laughy *(Gen Mgr)*

Freudenberg NOK (2)
PO Box 2001
Bristol, NH 03222-2001
Mailing Address:
PO Box 4452
Scottsburg, IN 47170-4452
Tel.: (812) 752-4232
Fax: (812) 752-5404
Web Site: www.freudenberg.com
Emp.: 74
Mfr. of Solid Injection Molded Polyurethane Products & Suspension Parts for Automotive Applications
S.I.C.: 3061
N.A.I.C.S.: 326291

Freudenberg NOK (2)
50 Ammon Dr
Manchester, NH 03103-3308
Tel.: (603) 669-4050
Fax: (603) 621-7217
E-Mail: info@freudenberg-nok.com
Web Site: www.freudenberg-nok.com
Emp.: 450
Sealing Technologies Mfr
S.I.C.: 3053
N.A.I.C.S.: 339991

Freudenberg NOK (2)
1275 Archer Dr
Troy, OH 45373-3841
Tel.: (937) 335-3306
Fax: (937) 335-2991
Web Site: www.freudenberg-nok.com
Emp.: 200
Square Cut Seal Rings, Banded Pistons & Various Components For General Industry
S.I.C.: 3089
N.A.I.C.S.: 326199

Freudenberg NOK (2)
131 Verner Ave
Newport, TN 37821-8133
Tel.: (423) 623-2366
Fax: (423) 623-0400
Web Site: www.corteco-usa.com
Emp.: 37
Mfr. of Automotive Engine Gaskets
S.I.C.: 3053
N.A.I.C.S.: 339991

Non-U.S. Subsidiaries:

Freudenberg-NOK de Mexico (2)
km 1 Carretera Cuautla Las Estacas
62740 Cuautla, Morelos, Mexico MX
Tel.: (52) 7353522821
Web Site: www.freudenberg-nok.com
Sales Range: $10-24.9 Million
Emp.: 250
Mfr. of Oil Seals, Valve Stem Seals, Molded Rubber Products, Polyurethane O-Rings, Engine Mounts
S.I.C.: 3053
N.A.I.C.S.: 339991

Freudenberg NOK (2)
65 Spruce Street
Tillsonburg, ON, N4G 5C4, Canada
Tel.: (519) 842-6451
Fax: (519) 842-8770
Web Site: www.freudenberg-nok.com
Emp.: 200
Mfr. of Silicone Seals
S.I.C.: 2822
N.A.I.C.S.: 325212
John Vettor *(Gen Mgr)*

Non-U.S. Affiliate:

NOK-Kluber Co. Ltd. (2)
5th Fl Seidensha Bldg 1-10-11 Hamamatsu-Cho
Minato Ku, 105 0032 Tokyo, Japan JP
Tel.: (81) 3340341734
Fax: (81) 354726073
Web Site: www.klueber.com
Emp.: 80
Mfr. of Lubricants
S.I.C.: 2992
N.A.I.C.S.: 324191

Non-U.S. Subsidiaries:

Corcos Industriale S.p.A. (1)
Corso Torino 332
10064 Pinerolo, Italy IT
Tel.: (39) 0121392222 (100%)
Fax: (39) 0121392304
Web Site: www.corcos.it
Emp.: 550
Mfr. of Rubber Products
S.I.C.: 3069
N.A.I.C.S.: 326299

Dichtomatik s.r.l. (1)
Via Delle Fabbriche 6A Nero
16158 Genoa, Italy IT
Tel.: (39) 0001061275
Fax: (39) 0106133861
E-Mail: mail@dichtomatik.it
Web Site: www.dichtomatik.it
Emp.: 15
Sales of Platic Products
S.I.C.: 5085
N.A.I.C.S.: 423840

Elefanten Portuguesa Lda. Industria de Calcado (1)
Alameda Da Bela Vesta
4415939 Seixezelo, Portugal (100%)
Tel.: (351) 227471160
Fax: (351) 227647950
Mfr. of Shoes
S.I.C.: 2389
N.A.I.C.S.: 316210

FHP di R. Freudenberg S.A.S. (1)
Via dei Valtorta 48
20127 Milan, Italy IT
Tel.: (39) 0228861 (100%)
Fax: (39) 0226111776
E-Mail: adriana.dallera@fhp-ww.com
Web Site: www.freudenberg.com
Emp.: 40
Mechanical Household Cleaning Products & Laundry Care Products Distr
S.I.C.: 5099
N.A.I.C.S.: 423990

FHP Vileda S.A. (1)
14 Rue Du Fosse Blanc
92238 Gennevilliers, Cedex, France FR
Tel.: (33) 41322232 (100%)
Fax: (33) 147913475
Web Site: www.Vileda.fr
Sales Range: $10-24.9 Million
Emp.: 25
Sales of Household Cleaning Products (Non-Chemcal)
S.I.C.: 5169
N.A.I.C.S.: 424690
Vincent Clowez *(Mgr)*

FHP Vileda Sp. z.o.o. (1)
Taneczna 18A
02829 Warsaw, Poland PL
Tel.: (48) 226140960 (100%)
Fax: (48) 226143664
E-Mail: bo.sale@fhp-ww.com
Web Site: www.vileda.com
Emp.: 20
Sales of Rubber Products
S.I.C.: 5199
N.A.I.C.S.: 424990
marack Tomaszewste *(Gen Mgr)*

Freudenberg Danmark A.S. (1)
Sindalsvej 31
8240 Risskov, Denmark DK
Tel.: (45) 86216600 (100%)
Fax: (45) 86216622
Web Site: www.freudenberg.com
Emp.: 7
Nonwoven Interlinings Mfr
S.I.C.: 2297
N.A.I.C.S.: 313230
Pertorp Henriksen *(Mng Dir)*

Freudenberg Dichtungs- und Schwingungstechnik KG (1)
Lesni 331
53345 Ceperka, Opatovice nad Labem, Czech Republic CZ
Tel.: (420) 466895111 (100%)
Fax: (420) 466941096
E-Mail: sst.fom@freudenberg-ds.com
Web Site: www.freudenberg.com
Emp.: 170
Mfr of Rubber Products
S.I.C.: 3069
N.A.I.C.S.: 326299
Jan Haek *(Mng Dir)*

Freudenberg Espana S.A., Telas sin Tejer S.en (1)
Ctra C 17 15 km
Parets Del Valles, 08150 Barcelona, Spain ES
Tel.: (34) 935656200
Fax: (34) 935731203
E-Mail: ventas@freudenberg-nw.com
Web Site: www.freudenberg.nw.com
Emp.: 200
Mfr. of Nonwoven Interlinings
S.I.C.: 2297
N.A.I.C.S.: 313230
Peter Schaefer *(Gen Mgr)*

Freudenberg Espana S.A. (1)
Zona Franca Sector B Calle C 18- 22
08040 Barcelona, Spain ES
Tel.: (34) 932618610 (100%)
Fax: (34) 932618639
E-Mail: trllet@freudenbergespana.es
Web Site: www.freudenberg.com
Emp.: 200
Mfr. of Rubber Products
S.I.C.: 3069
N.A.I.C.S.: 326299
Jean Tallat *(Mng Dir)*

Freudenberg Evolon s.a.r.l. (1)
20 Rue Ampere
68027 Colmars, Cedex, France FR
Tel.: (33) 3892064 (100%)
Fax: (33) 389413239
Web Site: www.freudenberg.com
Emp.: 45
Mfr. of Nonwovens
S.I.C.: 2297
N.A.I.C.S.: 313230

Freudenberg Far Eastern Spunweb Comp. Ltd. (1)
No 38 Lun Din
Shi Hai Village Tayuan, Taoyuan, Taiwan TW
Tel.: (886) 33841188 (60.18%)
Fax: (886) 33860127
Emp.: 100
Mfr. of Nonwoven Products
S.I.C.: 2297
N.A.I.C.S.: 313230
Lingow Ninglin *(Gen Mgr)*

Freudenberg Household Products AB (1)
Lindovagen 5
PO Box 608
60114 Norrkoping, Sweden SE
Tel.: (46) 11197900 (100%)
Fax: (46) 11197905
Web Site: www.freudenberg.com
Emp.: 105
Mfr. of Rubber Products
S.I.C.: 3069
N.A.I.C.S.: 326299
Peter Lehnhardt *(Gen Mgr)*

Freudenberg Household Products B.V. (1)
Industriepark KleefseWaard
Westervoortsedijk 73
Postbus 9600
6827 AV Arnhem, Netherlands NL
Tel.: (31) 263665558 (100%)
Fax: (31) 263665906
E-Mail: info.nl@shp-www.com
Web Site: www.freudenberg.com
Emp.: 20
Mfr. of Synthetic Chamois Products
S.I.C.: 3111
N.A.I.C.S.: 316110
John Aians *(Gen Mgr)*

Freudenberg Household Products LP (1)
Vileda House 2 Chichester St
Rochdale, Lancashire, OL16 2AX, United Kingdom UK
Tel.: (44) 706759597, ext. 1706759597 (100%)
Fax: (44) 1706350143
Web Site: www.vileda.com
Emp.: 45
Sales of Rubber Products
S.I.C.: 5199
N.A.I.C.S.: 424990
Mark Lockwood *(Dir-Fin)*

Freudenberg Household Products Oy AB (1)
Elimaenkatu 32
Box 1055
00521 Helsinki, Finland FI
Tel.: (358) 92777220 (100%)
Fax: (358) 9877 07610
Web Site: www.freudenberg.com
Mfr. of Rubber Products
S.I.C.: 3069
N.A.I.C.S.: 326299

Freudenberg Iberica S.A., S.en C. (1)
Pol. Ind. Can Volart Calle Gurri 1
Apartat de Correus 77
08150 Parets del Valles, Spain ES
Tel.: (34) 935731011
Fax: (34) 935730756
E-Mail: simrit@freudenberg.es
Web Site: www.simrit.com
Emp.: 150
Mfr. of Rubber Products
S.I.C.: 3069
N.A.I.C.S.: 326299

Freudenberg Iberica S.A. (1)
Zona Franca Sector B
Calle C 18-22, 08040 Barcelona, Spain (100%)

Tel.: (34) 932618610
Fax: (34) 932618639
Web Site: www.freudenbergespana.es
Emp.: 160
S.I.C.: 2393
N.A.I.C.S.: 314910
Jean Pallet *(Mng Dir)*

Freudenberg Nao-Tecidos Ltda. & Cia. (1)
Ave Pres Hulberto De Alencar Castelo Branco 2735 Bairro Rio Adis
CEPI 12321150 Jacarei, Brazil BR
Tel.: (55) 239547500 (100%)
Fax: (55) 123935723
Web Site: www.freudenberg.com
Emp.: 200
Mfr. of Nonwovens
S.I.C.: 2297
N.A.I.C.S.: 313230

Freudenberg Nao-Tecidos Ltda. & Cia. (1)
Ave Pres Humberto Alencar Castelo Branco 2735
12321-150 Sao Paulo, Brazil BR
Tel.: (55) 123534222 (100%)
Fax: (55) 1235355723
Web Site: www.freudenberg.com
Mfr. of Rubber Products
S.I.C.: 3069
N.A.I.C.S.: 326299

Freudenberg NH Co. Ltd. (1)
2-2-5 Hanakawado
Taito-ku, Tokyo, 111-0033, Japan JP
Tel.: (81) 3 3842 8276 (60%)
Fax: (81) 3 38455764
Web Site: www.freudenberg.com
Sales of Rubber Products
S.I.C.: 5169
N.A.I.C.S.: 424690

Freudenberg Nonwovens LP Vilene Interlinings (1)
Lowfields Business Park
Elland, W Yorkshire, HX5 5DX, United Kingdom UK
Tel.: (44) 422327900
Fax: (44) 1422327999
E-Mail: vilene@freudenberg.co.uk
Web Site: www.vilene.com
Emp.: 75
Mfr. of Nonwoven Interlinings
S.I.C.: 2297
N.A.I.C.S.: 313230
David Merriman *(Site Exec Officer)*

Freudenberg Nonwovens (Pty.) Ltd. (1)
PO Box 3903
Cape Town, 8000, South Africa ZA
Tel.: (27) 219333501 (100%)
Fax: (27) 219326515
E-Mail: info@freudenberg.co.za
Web Site: www.vilene.com
Emp.: 200
Mfr. of Nonwoven Interlining
S.I.C.: 2297
N.A.I.C.S.: 313230
Carmen Bruce *(Head-HR)*

Freudenberg Pty. Ltd. (1)
3 Brand Dr
PO Box 4
Thomastown, VIC, 3074, Australia AU
Tel.: (61) 394641022 (100%)
Fax: (61) 394647588
Web Site: www.kluber.com.au
Emp.: 8
Sales of Rubber Products
S.I.C.: 5169
N.A.I.C.S.: 424690
Norman Moore *(Mng Dir)*

Freudenberg S.A.S. (1)
170 Rue Branly ZI Sud B P 2062
71020 Macon, Cedex, France FR
Tel.: (33) 385293000 (100%)
Fax: (33) 385348503
Web Site: www.freudenberg.com
Emp.: 90
Mfr. of Rubber Seals
S.I.C.: 3069
N.A.I.C.S.: 326299
J. Jasnier *(Mng Dir)*

Freudenberg Simrit A/S (1)
Morteveien 6
PO Box 10
1483 Skytta, Norway SE
Tel.: (47) 67067810 (100%)
Fax: (47) 67067830
E-Mail: info@freudenberg.no
Web Site: www.simrit.com
Emp.: 12
Sales of Rubber Seals
S.I.C.: 5169
N.A.I.C.S.: 424690

Freudenberg Simrit A.B. (1)
Archimevesvagen 2
16866 Bromma, Sweden SE
Tel.: (46) 87052700 (100%)
Fax: (46) 8838163
E-Mail: info@freudenberg.se
Web Site: www.freudenberg.se
Emp.: 40
Mfr. of Rubber Seals & other Rubber Products
S.I.C.: 3069
N.A.I.C.S.: 326299
Michael Engstorm *(Mng Dir)*

Freudenberg Simrit AG (1)
Thurgauer Strasse 39
8050 Zurich, Switzerland CH
Tel.: (41) 443064422 (100%)
Fax: (41) 443027002
E-Mail: info@simrit.ch
Web Site: www.simrit.ch
Emp.: 25
Mfr. of Rubber Seals
S.I.C.: 3069
N.A.I.C.S.: 326299

Freudenberg Simrit A.S. (1)
Marielunvej 48
2730 Herlev, Denmark DK
Tel.: (45) 44921833 (100%)
Fax: (45) 44922520
E-Mail: info@simrit.dk
Web Site: www.simrit.com
Emp.: 11
Sales of Rubber Seals
S.I.C.: 5169
N.A.I.C.S.: 424690
Frank Erichsen *(Dir-Sls)*

Freudenberg Simrit B.V. (1)
Energiestraat 5
1411 AC Naarden, Netherlands NL
Tel.: (31) 356941049 (100%)
Fax: (31) 356949251
E-Mail: simrit.nl@freudenberg.com
Web Site: www.simrit.com
Emp.: 13
Sales of Rubber Seals
S.I.C.: 5169
N.A.I.C.S.: 424690

Freudenberg Simrit Kufstein Ges.m.b.H. & Co. KG (1)
Untere Sparchen Str 43
6332 Kufstein, Austria AT
Tel.: (43) 537269100 (100%)
Fax: (43) 5372691071
E-Mail: simrit.kufstein@freudenberg.com
Web Site: www.simrit.de
Sls.: $30,957,300
Emp.: 320
Sales of Rubber Seals
S.I.C.: 5169
N.A.I.C.S.: 424690
Andres Raps *(Mng Dir)*

Freudenberg Simrit SAS (1)
170 Rue Branly
71020 Macon, France FR
Tel.: (33) 385293000 (100%)
Fax: (33) 385348503
E-Mail: simrit@simrit.fr
Web Site: www.simrit.fr
Emp.: 70
S.I.C.: 2394
N.A.I.C.S.: 314910

Freudenberg S.p.A. (1)
Viale Monza 38
20127 Milan, Italy IT
Tel.: (39) 0000228861
Fax: (39) 0226146802
Web Site: www.freudenberg.com
Emp.: 50
Mfr. of Nonwoven Interlinings
S.I.C.: 2297
N.A.I.C.S.: 313230
Marco Nuzzo *(Sr Brand Mgr)*

Freudenberg Technical Products LP (1)
Silverfox Way New York Industrial Estate
North Shields, Tyne & Wear, NE27 0QH, United Kingdom UK
Tel.: (44) 1912269200 (100%)
Fax: (44) 1912269201
E-Mail: info@freudenberg.com
Web Site: www.freudenberg.com
Emp.: 250
Mfr. of Rubber Products
S.I.C.: 3069
N.A.I.C.S.: 326299

Freudenberg Telas sin Tejer S.A. de C.V. (1)
Calz Camarones 577 - Col Santa Maria
Mexico, CP, 53370, Mexico MX
Tel.: (52) 55513977
Fax: (52) 55513985
E-Mail: vilene.mexico@fvna.com
Web Site: www.vilene.com
Mfr. of Nonwoven Interlinings
S.I.C.: 2297
N.A.I.C.S.: 313230

Freudenberg Telas sin Tejer S.A. (1)
Calle 94 No 193
Bellazagala, 1651 San Martin, Buenos Aires, Argentina AR
Tel.: (54) 1147538833 (100%)
Fax: (54) 1147552364
E-Mail: balene.argentina@freudenberg.com.ar
Web Site: www.freudenberg.com
Emp.: 100
Mfr. of Rubber Products & Nonwoven Interlinings
S.I.C.: 3069
N.A.I.C.S.: 326299
Juancarlos Borchart *(Gen Mgr)*

Freudenberg Uchiyama Europe S.A.S. (1)
ZI Les Nouvelles Franchises
52206 Langres, Cedex, France FR
Tel.: (33) 325878080
Fax: (33) 32590111182
Web Site: www.freudenberg.com
Emp.: 130
Mfr. of Rubber Products
S.I.C.: 3069
N.A.I.C.S.: 326299
Valerie Claudet *(Gen Mgr)*

Freudenberg Vilene Nonwovens Taiwan Company Ltd. (1)
No 40 Min Fu Rd Sector 2
Yang Mei, Taoyuan, 326, Taiwan TW
Tel.: (886) 34781261
Fax: (886) 34781260
Emp.: 100
Mfr. of Nonwoven Interlinings
S.I.C.: 2297
N.A.I.C.S.: 313230

Freudenberg Vilene Sp. z.o.o. (1)
Ul Pojezierska 90
91341 Lodz, Poland (100%)
Tel.: (48) 426500511
Fax: (48) 426500514
E-Mail: vilene@freudenberg.pl
Web Site: www.vilene.com
Emp.: 11
Mfr. of Nonwoven Interlinings
S.I.C.: 2297
N.A.I.C.S.: 313230
Jolanta Stacherek *(Pres)*

Freudenberg Vilene Tela San. Ve Tic. A.S. (1)
L. Karaoglanoglu Cad No 25A
Seyrantepe, Istanbul, 34418, Turkey TR
Tel.: (90) 2122828300 (100%)
Fax: (90) 2122828313
E-Mail: goeksu.erdem@freudenberg-nw.com
Web Site: www.freudenberg.com
Emp.: 15
Software Solutions & IT Services
S.I.C.: 7372
N.A.I.C.S.: 511210

Japan Lutravil Company Ltd. (1)
Honmachi Takeda Bldg 3 1 29
Kyutaromachi
Chu Ku, Osaka, 541 0056, Japan JP
Tel.: (81) 662431560 (100%)
Fax: (81) 662431565
Web Site: www.freudenberg.com
Emp.: 12
Printing
S.I.C.: 2759
N.A.I.C.S.: 323111

Precision Rubber Sealings s.r.l. (1)
Viale Monza 38
20127 Milan, Italy IT
Tel.: (39) 0228861 (100%)
Fax: (39) 022613064
Sales Range: $1-9.9 Million
Emp.: 40
Mfr. of Rubber Products
S.I.C.: 3069
N.A.I.C.S.: 326299

Simrax BV (1)
Hopelerweg 250
PO Box 649
6468 XX Kerkrade, Netherlands NL
Tel.: (31) 455469222 (100%)
Fax: (31) 455464730
Web Site: www.simrax.com
Emp.: 60
Mfr. of Seals for Automotive Industry
S.I.C.: 3714
N.A.I.C.S.: 336340
Dennys Van Well *(Mng Dir)*

Simrit Distribution et CIE (1)
170 Rue Branly
71020 Macon, Cedex, France FR
Tel.: (33) 385293000 (100%)
Fax: (33) 385348503
E-Mail: simrit@simrit.fr
Web Site: www.simrit.fr
Emp.: 50
Sales of Rubber Products
S.I.C.: 5169
N.A.I.C.S.: 424690
Sylvain Loizeau *(Office Mgr)*

VC UK LP (1)
Gilmorton Rd
Lutterworth, Leicestershire, LE17 4HG, United Kingdom UK
Tel.: (44) 1455261227
Web Site: www.freudenberg.com
Provider of Management Services
S.I.C.: 8742
N.A.I.C.S.: 541611

Vileda Iberica S.A. (1)
Poligono Ind Can Volart
Carratera Comartal 17, 08150 Parets del Valles, Barcelona, Spain ES
Tel.: (34) 935739900 (100%)
Fax: (34) 935739910
Web Site: www.freudenberg.com
Emp.: 100
Sales of Rubber Products
S.I.C.: 5169
N.A.I.C.S.: 424690
Jose Maria Casavemunt *(Mng Dir & Reg VP)*

Non-U.S. Affiliate:

Japan Vilene Company, Ltd. (1)
Hama-rikyu Mitsui Bldg 6-4 Tsukiji 5-Chome
Chuo-ku
Tokyo, 104-8423, Japan JP
Tel.: (81) 345461111 (22.49%)
Fax: (81) 345461105
E-Mail: h-kouho@vilene.co.jp
Web Site: www.vilene.co.jp
3514—(TKS)
Sls.: $529,353,000
Assets: $560,428,000
Liabilities: $223,366,000
Net Worth: $337,062,000
Earnings: $10,681,000
Emp.: 1,567
Fiscal Year-end: 03/31/13
Nonwoven Fabric Products Mfr & Distr
S.I.C.: 2297
N.A.I.C.S.: 313230
Toshio Yoshida *(Pres)*
Yoshiaki Mizutani *(Sr Mng Dir)*
Masahiro Kimura *(Mng Dir)*

FREUND CORPORATION

6-8-1 Nishi-shinjuku
Shinjuku-ku, Tokyo, 163-6034, Japan
Tel.: (81) 359082611
Fax: (81) 359082638
E-Mail: freund@freund.co.jp

Freund Corporation—(Continued)

Web Site: www.freund.co.jp
Year Founded: 1964
6312—(JAS)
Sales Range: $125-149.9 Million
Emp.: 192
Business Description:
Granulation & Coating Equipment Developer, Mfr & Sales
S.I.C.: 2851
N.A.I.C.S.: 325510
Personnel:
Yasutoyo Fusejima *(Chm & CEO)*
Tetsuo Hori *(Pres & COO)*
Osamoto Nishimura *(Mng Dir & Gen Mgr)*
Board of Directors:
Yasutoyo Fusejima
Iwao Fusejima
Ryujiro Fusejima
Takashi Gushiken
Tetsuo Hori
Osamoto Nishimura
Norio Shiratori

U.S. Subsidiary:

Vector Corporation (1)
675 44th St
Marion, IA 52302
Tel.: (319) 377-8263
Fax: (319) 377-5574
Web Site: www.vectorcorporation.com
Emp.: 100
Processing Equipment Mfr
S.I.C.: 3669
N.A.I.C.S.: 334290
Steve Jensen *(Pres)*

FREY S.A.

66 rue du Commerce
Cormontreuil, 51663 Reims, France
Tel.: (33) 326495252
Fax: (33) 326495251
E-Mail: contact@frey.fr
Web Site: www.frey.fr
Year Founded: 1983
FREY—(EUR)
Rev.: $55,988,556
Assets: $452,906,781
Liabilities: $296,107,592
Net Worth: $156,799,189
Earnings: $25,513,960
Fiscal Year-end: 12/31/12
Business Description:
Commercial Real Estate Investor, Developer & Property Manager
S.I.C.: 6531
N.A.I.C.S.: 531390
Personnel:
Jean-Pierre Cedelle *(Chm-Supervisory Bd)*
Antoine Frey *(Chm-Mgmt Bd)*
Thomas Riegert *(Vice Chm-Supervisory Bd)*
Francois Vuillet-Petite *(Dir Gen & Member-Mgmt Bd)*
Supervisory Board of Directors:
Jean-Pierre Cedelle
Jean-Noel Dron
Celine Le Gallais-Frey
John Penning
Chrystelle Proth
Thomas Riegert
Nicolas Urbain

Non-U.S. Subsidiary:

Frey Invest S.L. (1)
Calle de la Selva 12
08820 El Prat de Llobregat, Spain
Tel.: (34) 933794238
Fax: (34) 933794243
E-Mail: contact@freyinvest.com
Web Site: www.freyinvest.com
Emp.: 4
Property Management Services
S.I.C.: 6531
N.A.I.C.S.: 531311

Jacques Veenne *(Mng Dir)*

FREYJA RESOURCES INC.

800 Place Victoria Bureau 3700
Montreal, QC, H4Z 1E9, Canada
Mailing Address:
370 rue des Magnolias
Laval, QC, H7A 0A3, Canada
Tel.: (514) 904-1496
Fax: (514) 904-1597
Year Founded: 2005
FRA—(TSXV)
Assets: $161,118
Liabilities: $19,068
Net Worth: $142,050
Earnings: ($145,028)
Fiscal Year-end: 09/30/12
Business Description:
Financial Management Services
S.I.C.: 6799
N.A.I.C.S.: 523920
Personnel:
Robert Ayotte *(Pres & CEO)*
Benoit Forget *(CFO)*
Michel Lebeuf *(Sec)*

FRIASKOG AB

Strandvagen 1
Jarpen, 830 05 Are, Sweden
Tel.: (46) 647 61 10 90
Fax: (46) 647 61 10 91
E-Mail: info@friaskog.se
Web Site: www.friaskog.se
Business Description:
Forestry Services
S.I.C.: 0811
N.A.I.C.S.: 113110
Personnel:
Tobias Jonsson *(Mng Dir)*

FRIDAY CAPITAL INC.

c/o Beard Winter LLP 130 Adelaide Street West Suite 701
Toronto, ON, M5H 2k4, Canada
Tel.: (416) 306-1771
Fax: (416) 593-7760
Year Founded: 2012
FYC.P—(TSXV)
Business Description:
Investment Services
S.I.C.: 6211
N.A.I.C.S.: 523999
Personnel:
Michael Davidson *(CEO & CFO)*

FRIEDHELM LOH STIFTUNG & CO. KG

Rudolf-Loh-Strasse 1
D-35708 Haiger, Germany
Tel.: (49) 2773 924 0
Fax: (49) 2773 924 3892
E-Mail: info@friedhelm-loh-group.com
Web Site: www.friedhelm-loh-group.com
Year Founded: 1961
Sales Range: $1-4.9 Billion
Emp.: 11,500
Business Description:
Electrical Equipments Mfr & Whslr
S.I.C.: 3612
N.A.I.C.S.: 335311
Personnel:
Friedhelm Loh *(Owner & Chm-Mgmt Bd)*

FRIEDL BUSINESS INFORMATION LIMITED

26H Aihe Building 629 Lingling Road
Shanghai, 200030, China
Tel.: (86) 2164863668
Fax: (86) 2164864057
E-Mail: customerservice@friedlnet.com
Web Site: www.friedlnet.com
Year Founded: 1995
Business Description:
Business Information on Chinese Companies
S.I.C.: 7389
N.A.I.C.S.: 519130
Personnel:
Roland Berger *(Partner)*

FRIEDRICH BOYSEN GMBH & CO. KG

Friedrich Boysen Strasse 14-17
Altensteig, 72213, Germany
Tel.: (49) 74 53 20 0
Fax: (49) 74 53 20 227
Web Site: www.boysen-online.de
Sales Range: $800-899.9 Million
Emp.: 1,600
Business Description:
Motor Vehicle Exhaust System Mfr
S.I.C.: 3714
N.A.I.C.S.: 336390
Personnel:
Rolf Geisel *(Pres)*

FRIESLANDCAMPINA

(See Under Zuivelcooperatie FrieslandCampina U.A.)

FRIGOBLOCK GROSSKOPF GMBH

Weidkamp 274
45356 Essen, Germany
Tel.: (49) 201613010
Fax: (49) 2016130148
E-Mail: email@frigoblock.de
Web Site: www.frigoblock.de
Year Founded: 1978
Rev.: $36,650,658
Emp.: 104
Business Description:
Transport Refrigeration Machines Mfr
S.I.C.: 3585
N.A.I.C.S.: 333415
Personnel:
P. V. Grobkopf *(CEO)*
K. Sochor *(Co-Mng Dir)*
W. Wilhelm *(Co-Mng Dir)*

FRIGOGLASS S.A.I.C.

15 A Metaxa street
Kifissia, 145 64 Athens, Greece
Tel.: (30) 2106165700
Fax: (30) 2106199097
E-Mail: info@frigoglass.com
Web Site: www.frigoglass.com
Year Founded: 1993
FRIGO—(ATH)
Sls.: $782,461,313
Assets: $875,601,469
Liabilities: $671,748,253
Net Worth: $203,853,215
Earnings: ($18,656,570)
Emp.: 6,609
Fiscal Year-end: 12/31/12
Business Description:
Refrigeration & Other Glass Products Mfr
S.I.C.: 3585
N.A.I.C.S.: 333415
Personnel:
Torsten Tuerling *(CEO & Mng Dir)*
Panagiotis D. Tabourlos *(CFO)*
Alberto Tureikis *(CTO)*
Elias Moschonas *(Chief HR Officer)*
Dimitris Bostanis *(Chief Supply Chain Officer)*
Board of Directors:
Harry G. David
John K. Androutsopoulos
Doros Constantinou
Vassilis Fourlis
Evangelos Kaloussis
Loucas D. Komis
Christo Leventis
Alexandra Papalexopoulou-Benopoulou
Torsten Tuerling

FRIGOSPED GMBH

Salzer Str 1
D-56235 Ransbach-Baumbach, Germany
Tel.: (49) 26239800
Fax: (49) 2623980120
E-Mail: info@frigosped.de
Web Site: www.frigosped.de
Year Founded: 1981
Rev.: $120,395,033
Emp.: 200
Business Description:
Logistics & Warehousing Services
S.I.C.: 4789
N.A.I.C.S.: 488999
Personnel:
Reinhardt H. Narten *(Mng Dir)*

FRIGRITE LIMITED

27 Grange Road
Cheltenham, VIC, 3192, Australia
Tel.: (61) 395844901
E-Mail: enquiries@frigrite.com.au
Web Site: www.frigrite.com.au
FRR—(ASX)
Sales Range: $10-24.9 Million
Business Description:
Refrigerated Retail Display Cabinets
S.I.C.: 5078
N.A.I.C.S.: 423740
Personnel:
Ken Charteris *(Mng Dir)*
Board of Directors:
Ken Charteris
David Alfred Hoff
Peter Vidler
Jury Wowk
Legal Counsel:
Blake Dawson Waldron
Level 39 101 Collins Street
Melbourne, Australia

Subsidiaries:

Frigrite Refrigeration Pty Ltd (1)
27 Grange Rd
Cheltenham, VIC, 3192, Australia
Tel.: (61) 395863200
Fax: (61) 3 9583 9870
Web Site: www.frigrite.com.au
Refrigeration Maintenance Services
S.I.C.: 3585
N.A.I.C.S.: 333415

Frigrite Refrigeration (QLD) Pty Ltd (1)
87 Bradman St
Acacia Ridge, QLD, 4110, Australia
Tel.: (61) 733231555
Fax: (61) 733231559
E-Mail: acoxall@frigrite.com.au
Web Site: www.frigrite.com.au/contact-us.php
Emp.: 11
Refrigeration Services
S.I.C.: 4222
N.A.I.C.S.: 493120
Robert Redmond *(Branch Mgr)*

FRIOSUR PESQUERA SA

Jose Maria Caro 300
Santiago, Chacabuco, Chile
Tel.: (56) 67 67 6200
Fax: (56) 67 35 1184
Personnel:
Rodrigo Allimant *(Mgr-Sls)*

Non-U.S. Subsidiary:

Europacifico Alimentos Del Mar Sl (1)
Pol Ind Ugaldeguren-I
Pabellon P-6-II
48160 Derio, Bizkaia, Spain (40%)

Tel.: (34) 944544680
Other Marine Fishing

FRISTAM PUMPEN F. STAMP KG (GMBH & CO.)

Kurt A Korber Chaussee 55
21033 Hamburg, Germany
Tel.: (49) 40725560
Fax: (49) 4072556166
Web Site: www.fristam.de
Emp.: 3,000
Business Description:
Mfr of Stainless Steel Pumps
S.I.C.: 3561
N.A.I.C.S.: 333911
Personnel:
Wolfgang Stamp *(Mng Dir)*

FRITZ BERGER GMBH

Fritz-Berger-Strasse 1
92318 Neumarkt, Germany
Tel.: (49) 91813300
Fax: (49) 9181330159
E-Mail: info@fritz-berger.de
Web Site: www.fritz-berger.de
Year Founded: 1958
Sales Range: $50-74.9 Million
Emp.: 240
Fiscal Year-end: 12/31/12
Business Description:
Camping, Sports Equipment & Leisure Goods Whslr
S.I.C.: 5091
N.A.I.C.S.: 423910
Personnel:
Maurice Perske *(Mng Dir)*

FRITZ EGGER GMBH & CO.

(d/b/a Egger International/Group)
Holzwerkstoffe Weiberndorf 20 St Johan
A-6380 Tirol, Austria
Tel.: (43) 506000
Fax: (43) 5060010276
Web Site: www.egger.com
Sls.: $2,023,500,000
Emp.: 1,000
Business Description:
Chipboard, MDF, OSB Boards, Coated Boards, Postformed & Softformed Elements, Components, Laminates, Edges & Laminated Flooring Products Mfr
S.I.C.: 2671
N.A.I.C.S.: 322220
Personnel:
Michael Egger *(Chm)*
Thomas Leissing *(CFO)*
Walter Scheigl *(CTO)*

Non-U.S. Subsidiaries:

Egger Barony Ltd. (1)
Barony Road
Auchinleck, Glasgow, KA182LL, United Kingdom
Tel.: (44) 1290426026
Fax: (44) 1290424420
E-Mail: info.uk@egger.com
Paperboard Mills
S.I.C.: 2631
N.A.I.C.S.: 322130
Simon Dotlinger *(Mng Dir)*

Egger Benelux GCV (1)
Limnanderdreef 44
Zulte, 9870, Belgium
Tel.: (32) 93886441
Fax: (32) 93380055
E-Mail: info-benelux@egger.com
Emp.: 15
Lumber Plywood Millwork & Wood Panel Whslr
S.I.C.: 5031
N.A.I.C.S.: 423310
Bruno Parent *(Mng Dir)*

Egger-Rol SA (1)
Ave d Albret
Boite Postale 1 Rion-des-Lande, 40371 Lyon, France
Tel.: (33) 558568181
Fax: (33) 558568139
E-Mail: info.es@egger.com
Web Site: www.egger.com
Emp.: 450
Wood Product Mfr
S.I.C.: 2499
N.A.I.C.S.: 321999
Cotte Philippe *(Gen Mgr)*

Egger Romania SRL (1)
Bdul Dimitrie Pompeiu 10A Et 4 Sec 2
020337 Bucharest, Romania
Tel.: (40) 213110138
Fax: (40) 213110139
E-Mail: info-ro@egger.com
Web Site: www.egger.com
Emp.: 500
Durable Goods Whslr
S.I.C.: 5099
N.A.I.C.S.: 423990
Stephen Enbarger *(Mgr-Fin)*

Egger Scandinavia ApS (1)
Jernbanegade 5A
Tistrup, 6862 Ribe, Denmark
Tel.: (45) 75291000
Fax: (45) 75291150
E-Mail: info-scan@egger.com
Web Site: www.egger.com
Emp.: 7
Construction Material Whslr
S.I.C.: 5039
N.A.I.C.S.: 423390
Neels Sunesen *(Gen Mgr)*

Egger Turkiye Ltd. (1)
Keresteciler Sit 11 Blok No 1 Kat 5
34306 Istanbul, Turkey
Tel.: (90) 2126705115
Fax: (90) 2126705117
E-Mail: satih.aksan@egger.com
Web Site: www.egger.com
Emp.: 50
Reconstituted Wood Product Mfr
S.I.C.: 2493
N.A.I.C.S.: 321219
Satih Aksan *(Mgr-Sls)*

Egger (UK) Limited (1)
Anick Grange Rd
Hexham, Northumberland, NE464JS, United Kingdom
Tel.: (44) 1434602191
Fax: (44) 1434605103
E-Mail: info.uk@egger.com
Web Site: www.egger.co.uk
Emp.: 700
Construction Material Whslr
S.I.C.: 5039
N.A.I.C.S.: 423390
Bob Livesey *(Mgr)*

Non-U.S. Division:

Carlo Cappellari Italia S.r.l. (1)
Via Nazionale 11
33010 Tavagnacco, Italy
Tel.: (39) 432478521
Fax: (39) 0432478565
E-Mail: info-it@egger.com
Business Services
S.I.C.: 7389
N.A.I.C.S.: 561499
Luca Cappellari *(Mng Dir)*

FRITZ LANGE GMBH

Sudfeldstrasse 3
31832 Springe, Germany
Tel.: (49) 50419950
Fax: (49) 5041995222
E-Mail: fl@fritz-lange.de
Web Site: www.fritz-lange.de
Year Founded: 1955
Rev.: $26,208,600
Emp.: 130
Business Description:
Number Plates Mfr
S.I.C.: 3353
N.A.I.C.S.: 331315
Personnel:
Gisela Lange *(Mng Dir)*

FRITZ MASSONG GMBH

Schiessgartenweg 8a
67227 Frankenthal, Germany
Tel.: (49) 62333650
Fax: (49) 6233365450
E-Mail: info@massong.com
Web Site: www.massong.com
Year Founded: 1921
Rev.: $34,759,776
Emp.: 75
Business Description:
Fire Extinguishers & Equipment Supplier
S.I.C.: 5084
N.A.I.C.S.: 423830
Personnel:
Dieter Massong *(Owner)*

FRITZ PLANUNG GMBH

Am Schonblick 1
72574 Bad Urach, Germany
Tel.: (49) 712515000
Fax: (49) 7125150050
E-Mail: service@fritz-planung.de
Web Site: www.fritz-planung.de
Year Founded: 1951
Rev.: $11,986,986
Emp.: 95
Business Description:
Construction Services
S.I.C.: 1629
N.A.I.C.S.: 237990
Personnel:
Karl Schmitt *(Mng Dir)*

FRITZ STEPHAN GMBH

Kirchstrasse 19
56412 Montabaur, Germany
Tel.: (49) 643991250
Fax: (49) 64399125111
E-Mail: info@stephan-gmbh.com
Web Site: www.stephan-gmbh.com
Year Founded: 1974
Rev.: $26,970,657
Emp.: 115
Business Description:
Medical Device Mfr
S.I.C.: 3845
N.A.I.C.S.: 334510
Personnel:
Georg Mainusch *(CEO & Co-Mng Dir)*
Tanja Stephan *(Co-Mng Dir)*

FROCH ENTERPRISE CO., LTD.

No 122 Industrial Road
Touliu, Yun-Lin, 640, Taiwan
Tel.: (886) 5557 1669
Fax: (886) 5557 1339
E-Mail: investors@froch.com
Web Site: www.froch.com
2030—(TAI)
Sales Range: $450-499.9 Million
Business Description:
Steel Pipes Mfr
S.I.C.: 3931
N.A.I.C.S.: 339992
Personnel:
Ping-Yiao Chang *(Chm)*

FROESE FORENSIC PARTNERS LTD.

55 University Ave Ste 1000
Toronto, ON, M5J 2H7, Canada
Tel.: (416) 364-6400
Fax: (416) 364-6900
Web Site: www.froeseforensic.com
Sales Range: $10-24.9 Million
Emp.: 15
Business Description:
Economic & Financial Analysis, Expert Testimony, Litigation Support & Management Consulting Services
S.I.C.: 7389
N.A.I.C.S.: 561499
Personnel:
Ken Froese *(Sr Mng Dir)*
Bruce Armstrong *(Mng Dir)*
Jeffrey Fillíter *(Mng Dir)*
Kevin Lo *(Mng Dir)*
Sheree Mann *(Mng Dir)*

FROM30 CO., LTD.

102 7th floor I Park Bundang 239 Jeongjail-ro
Bundang-gu, Seongnam, Gyeonggi-do, Korea (South)
Tel.: (82) 31 725 7800
Fax: (82) 31 378 5760
Web Site: www.from30.co.kr
Year Founded: 1996
073570—(KRS)
Business Description:
Semiconductort Mfr
S.I.C.: 3674
N.A.I.C.S.: 334413
Personnel:
Kwang Bin Im *(CEO)*
Board of Directors:
Won Hoi Gu
Kwang Bin Im
Jin Ju Kim
Sung Yul Kim
Gung Deog Nam
Jung Hyeon Nam

FRONT STREET CAPITAL 2004

33 Young Street Suite 600
Toronto, ON, M5E 1G4, Canada
Tel.: (416) 364-1990
Fax: (416) 364-8893
Toll Free: (800) 513-2832
E-Mail: advisorservice@frontstreetcapital.com
Web Site: www.frontstreetcapital.com
Year Founded: 2004
Business Description:
Open & Closed-End Investment Fund Management Services
S.I.C.: 6282
N.A.I.C.S.: 523930
Personnel:
Frank L. Mersch *(Chm, VP & Sr Portfolio Mgr)*
Gary P. Selke *(Partner, Pres & CEO)*
David A. Conway *(Partner, COO, Sec & VP)*
Normand G. Lamarche *(Partner, VP & Sr Portfolio Mgr)*
Linda D. Hryma *(Partner, Asst Sec & Office Mgr)*
Susan Johnson *(CFO)*
Terence Lui *(Gen Counsel)*

Affiliates:

Front Street Strategic Yield Fund Ltd. (1)
Suite 600 33 Yonge Street
Toronto, ON, M5E 1G4, Canada Ca
Tel.: (416) 364-1990
Fax: (416) 364-8893
Rev.: $5,787
Assets: $78,894,254
Liabilities: $24,876,020
Net Worth: $54,018,234
Earnings: ($32,439,015)
Fiscal Year-end: 12/31/12
Closed-End Investment Fund
S.I.C.: 6726
N.A.I.C.S.: 525990
Gary P. Selke *(Pres & CEO)*
David A. Conway *(CFO)*
Tracey N. Patel *(Sec)*

Front Street U.S. MLP Income Fund Ltd. (1)
33 Yonge Street Suite 600
Toronto, ON, M5E 1G4, Canada Ca
Tel.: (416) 597-9595
Fax: (416) 597-9325
Toll Free: (800) 513-2832
E-Mail: advisorservice@frontstreet.com
MLP—(TSX)

Front Street Capital 2004—(Continued)

Int. Income: $2,262
Assets: $131,849,001
Liabilities: $3,221,750
Net Worth: $128,627,251
Earnings: ($1,967,419)
Fiscal Year-end: 12/31/12
Closed-End Investment Fund
S.I.C.: 6726
N.A.I.C.S.: 525990
Gary P. Selke *(Pres & CEO)*
David A. Conway *(CFO & Sec)*

FRONTAGE INC.

Maison Blg 1-18-17
Minato-ku, Tokyo, 105-0003, Japan
Tel.: (81) 3 3596 0300
Fax: (81) 3 3596 0301
E-Mail: info-g@frontage.jp
Web Site: www.frontage.jp
Year Founded: 2002
Billings: $406,646,400
Emp.: 230
Business Description:
Advertising Agency
S.I.C.: 7311
N.A.I.C.S.: 541810
Personnel:
Masao Morita *(Chm)*
Yukio Ohshima *(Exec Mng Dir)*
Board of Directors:
Yoshiki Matsuyama

FRONTIER ACQUISITION CORP.

4500 855 2nd Street SW
Calgary, AB, T2P 4K7, Canada
Tel.: (206) 689-5685
Fax: (206) 204-1710
E-Mail: bcreswell@nwcap.com
Year Founded: 2011
FFF.P—(TSXV)
Business Description:
Investment Services
S.I.C.: 6211
N.A.I.C.S.: 523999
Personnel:
Trevor Haynes *(Chm)*
Bradford N. Creswell *(Pres)*
John R. Jacobs *(CEO)*
Lisa Mortell *(CFO & Sec)*
Board of Directors:
Don Basnett
Darin Coutu
Bradford N. Creswell
John R. Jacobs
Edward J. Redmond
Transfer Agent:
Alliance Trust Company
450 407 2nd St SW
Calgary, AB, Canada

FRONTIER CHRYSLER LTD

3046 Hwy 16 East
Smithers, BC, V0J 2N0, Canada
Tel.: (250) 847-4266
Fax: (250) 847-5710
Toll Free: (800) 665-5880
E-Mail: info@frontierchrysler.ca
Web Site: www.frontierchrysler.ca
Year Founded: 1958
Rev.: $12,496,887
Emp.: 28
Business Description:
New & Used Car Dealers
S.I.C.: 5511
N.A.I.C.S.: 441110
Personnel:
Betty Flint *(Controller)*

FRONTIER DEVELOPMENTS PLC

306 Science Park Milton Road
Cambridge, CB4 0WG, United Kingdom
Tel.: (44) 1223 394300
Fax: (44) 1223 420005
E-Mail: enquiriesx@frontier.co.uk
Web Site: www.frontier.co.uk
Year Founded: 1994
FDEV—(AIM)
Emp.: 200
Business Description:
Game Developer
S.I.C.: 7372
N.A.I.C.S.: 511210
Personnel:
David Gammon *(Chm)*
David Braben *(CEO)*
Neil Armstrong *(CFO)*
David Walsh *(COO)*
Jonny Watts *(Chief Creative Officer)*
Board of Directors:
David Gammon
Neil Armstrong
David Braben
Jonathan Milner
David Walsh
Jonny Watts

FRONTIER INFORMATICS LIMITED

8-3-1116/1 Keshav Nagar Srinagar
Colony Main Road
Hyderabad, Andhra Pradesh, 500073, India
Tel.: (91) 40 65178456
E-Mail: frontier@fitlindia.com
Web Site: www.fitlindia.com
Year Founded: 1986
531225—(BOM)
Sls.: $83,912
Assets: $209,706
Liabilities: $371,467
Net Worth: ($161,761)
Earnings: ($13,256)
Fiscal Year-end: 03/31/13
Business Description:
Information Technology Consulting Services
S.I.C.: 7373
N.A.I.C.S.: 541512
Personnel:
V. K. Premchand *(Founder, Chm & Mng Dir)*
Board of Directors:
V. K. Premchand
Shashikala Ambarkar
Jayant Yeshwant Godbole
Bommaraju Prasanna Lakshmi
Dharamkar Mamatha Nandan
Vunnava Purnachandra Rao
Potail Yadav Varun
Singh B. Yalamanchili
Transfer Agent:
Karvy Computershare Private Limited
46 Avenue 4 Street No 1 Banjara Hills
Hyderabad, 500 034, India
Tel.: (91) 40 23320666
Fax: (91) 40 23323058

FRONTIER IP GROUP PLC

41 Charlotte Square
Edinburgh, EH2 4HQ, United Kingdom
Tel.: (44) 131 220 9491
Fax: (44) 131 220 9441
E-Mail: frontier@frontierip.co.uk
Web Site: www.frontierip.co.uk
FIPP—(AIM)
Rev.: $274,796
Assets: $4,480,446
Liabilities: $135,819
Net Worth: $4,344,627
Earnings: ($581,179)
Emp.: 3
Fiscal Year-end: 06/30/13
Business Description:
Intellectual Property Owner
S.I.C.: 6794
N.A.I.C.S.: 533110
Personnel:
Neil Crabb *(CEO)*
Jackie McKay *(COO)*
Marilyn Cole *(Sec & Dir-Fin)*
Board of Directors:
Andrew Richmond
David Cairns
Marilyn Cole
Neil Crabb
Jackie McKay
Marcus Yeoman
Legal Counsel:
HBJ Gateley Wareing (Scotland) LLP
Exchange Tower 19 Canning Street
Edinburgh, United Kingdom

FRONTIER MINING LTD.

5 Park Place
London, SW1A 1LP, United Kingdom
Tel.: (44) 20 7898 9019
Fax: (44) 20 7898 9101
Web Site: www.frontiermining.com
FML—(AIM)
Sales Range: $1-9.9 Million
Emp.: 451
Business Description:
Gold & Copper Mining Services
S.I.C.: 1041
N.A.I.C.S.: 212221
Personnel:
Yerlan Zhenisovitch Aliyev *(Chm & CEO)*
Marzhan Nurumbetova *(Interim CFO)*
Board of Directors:
Yerlan Zhenisovitch Aliyev
Boyd W. Bishop
William Durand Eppler

FRONTIER OIL CORPORATION

4th Floor Zaragoza Building 102
Gamboa Street
Legaspi Village, Makati, 1229, Philippines
Tel.: (63) 2 4785854
Fax: (63) 2 8172755
E-Mail: info@frontieroilcorp.com
Web Site: www.frontieroilcorp.com
Year Founded: 2011
Business Description:
Oil Exploration
S.I.C.: 1311
N.A.I.C.S.: 211111
Personnel:
Astrolito Del Castillo *(Chm)*
Kristoffer Fellowes *(CEO)*
James Douglas Parry *(COO)*
Board of Directors:
Astrolito Del Castillo
Kristoffer Fellowes
Cielito Flores Habito
Peter Jermyn
Jose Mari Moraza
Melito Salazar, Jr.
Ian Wilson

FRONTIER RARE EARTHS LIMITED

9 Allee Scheffer
2520 Luxembourg, Luxembourg
Tel.: (352) 208 802249
Fax: (352) 246 11172
E-Mail: info@frontierrareearths.com
Web Site: www.frontierrareearths.com
FRO—(TSX)
Rev.: $1,196,000
Assets: $77,442,000
Liabilities: $2,384,000
Net Worth: $75,058,000
Earnings: ($4,148,000)
Emp.: 38
Fiscal Year-end: 12/31/12
Business Description:
Metal Mining Services
S.I.C.: 1099
N.A.I.C.S.: 212299
Personnel:
James Kenny *(CEO)*
Paul McGuinness *(CFO)*
Board of Directors:
Philip Kenny
Anu Dhir
James Kenny
Paul McGuinness
John Hulme Scholes
Crispin Sonn
Transfer Agent:
Computershare Investor Services Inc.
100 University Avenue 8th Floor
Toronto, ON, M5J 2Y1, Canada
Tel.: (514) 982-7555
Non-U.S. Subsidiary:
Yolani Minerals (Proprietary) Ltd. **(1)**
111 Loop St
Cape Town, Western Cape, 8001, South Africa
Tel.: (27) 214242505
Fax: (27) 0212721418080
E-Mail: info@frontierrare.co.za
Web Site: www.yolaniminerals.co.za
Emp.: 50
Mineral Exploration & Mining Services
S.I.C.: 1479
N.A.I.C.S.: 212393

FRONTIER RESOURCES LTD

Level 4 66 Kings Park Road
West Perth, WA, 6005, Australia
Tel.: (61) 8 6141 3500
Fax: (61) 8 6141 3599
E-Mail: info@frontierresources.com.au
Web Site: www.frontierresources.com.au
FNT—(ASX)
Rev.: $4,569,674
Assets: $3,889,242
Liabilities: $486,035
Net Worth: $3,403,207
Earnings: ($2,989,738)
Fiscal Year-end: 06/30/13
Business Description:
Exploration & Evaluation Of Gold Silver & Other Base Metal Projects
S.I.C.: 1081
N.A.I.C.S.: 213114
Personnel:
Peter A. McNeil *(Chm & Mng Dir)*
Jay Stephenson *(CFO & Co-Sec)*
Julia Beckett *(Co-Sec)*
Board of Directors:
Peter A. McNeil
Graham J. Fish
Warren J. Staude
Hugh David Swain
Legal Counsel:
Steinepreis Paganin Lawyers & Consultants
Level 4 The Read Buildings 16 Milligan Street
Perth, WA, 6000, Australia

FRONTIER SPRINGS LTD.

E-14 Panki Industrial Area Site-1
Kanpur, UP, India 208022
Tel.: (91) 512 2691207
Fax: (91) 512 2691209
E-Mail: springs@sancharnet.in
Web Site: www.frontiersprings.co.in
522195—(BOM)
Rev.: $7,264,287
Assets: $6,771,457
Liabilities: $2,801,338
Net Worth: $3,970,119
Earnings: $371,727
Fiscal Year-end: 03/31/13
Business Description:
Hot Coil Springs Mfr & Distr
S.I.C.: 3493

N.A.I.C.S.: 332613
Personnel:
Kundan Lal Bhatia *(Chm & Mng Dir)*
Kapil Bhatia *(Mng Dir)*
Neeraj Bhatia *(CFO)*
Deepak Bhasin *(Compliance Officer & Sec)*
Board of Directors:
Kundan Lal Bhatia
Kapil Bhatia
Mamta Bhatia
Neeraj Bhatia
R. K. Bhatia
Sonia Bhatia
Sushma Bhatia
Pradeep K. Goenka
N. P. Singh
R. N. Trivedi
Transfer Agent:
Alankit Assignments Limited
Alankit House 2E/21Jhandewalan Extention
New Delhi, India

FRONTKEN CORPORATION BERHAD

Ste 301 Block F Pusat Dagangan
Phileo Damansara 1
No 9 Jalan 16/11 Off Jalan Dam,
46350 Petaling Jaya, Selangor,
Malaysia
Tel.: (60) 379683312
Fax: (60) 379683316
E-Mail: fcb@frontken.com
Web Site: www.frontken.com
FRONTKN—(KLS)
Rev.: $59,364,838
Assets: $103,025,314
Liabilities: $33,175,476
Net Worth: $69,849,838
Earnings: $1,369,121
Fiscal Year-end: 12/31/12
Business Description:
Welding Services
S.I.C.: 7699
N.A.I.C.S.: 811310
Personnel:
Wai Pin Ng *(Chm & Mng Dir)*
Mei Ling Chew *(Co-Sec)*
Cynthia Gloria Louis *(Co-Sec)*
Li Chen Mah *(Co-Sec)*
Board of Directors:
Wai Pin Ng
Jorg Helmut Hohnloser
Johar Murat
Aaron Kwee Lein Sim
Kiang Meng Tay

Subsidiaries:

Frontken (Johor) Sdn. Bhd. **(1)**
No 16 Jalan Mega 1 Taman Perindustrian
Nusa Cemerlang
Gelang Patah, Johor, Malaysia
Tel.: (60) 75599700
Fax: (60) 75599697
E-Mail: fjsb@frontken.com
Web Site: www.frontken.com
Spray Coating Services
S.I.C.: 3479
N.A.I.C.S.: 332812
Sia Chiok Meng *(Mng Dir)*

Frontken Malaysia Sdn. Bhd. - Kemaman Plant **(1)**
Lot 13B Kawasan Perindustrian MIEL Jakar
Phase IV
24000 Kemaman, Terengganu, Malaysia
Tel.: (60) 98681242
Fax: (60) 98681240
E-Mail: fmt@frontken.com
Web Site: www.dayabumimaju.com
Emp.: 20
Spray Coating Services
S.I.C.: 2851
N.A.I.C.S.: 325510
Willie Wong *(Mng Dir)*

Plants:

Frontken (East Malaysia) Sdn. Bhd. - Kuching Plant **(1)**
Lot 1030 Section 66 KTLD Jalan Kisar
Pending Industrial Estate
93450 Kuching, Sarawak, Malaysia
Tel.: (60) 82481286
Fax: (60) 82482671
E-Mail: fmk@frontken.com
Emp.: 40
Spray Coating Services
S.I.C.: 3479
N.A.I.C.S.: 332812
Voon Kianpeng *(Mgr-Sls)*

Frontken Malaysia Sdn. Bhd. - Kulim Plant **(1)**
Lot 1923 Jalan Hi-Tech 2/3 1
Kulim Hi-Tech Industrial Park, Kulim,
Kedah, Malaysia
Tel.: (60) 44036168
Fax: (60) 44034388
E-Mail: fmp@frontken.com
Emp.: 200
Spray Coating Services
S.I.C.: 3479
N.A.I.C.S.: 332812
Chong Shichai *(Mng Dir)*

Frontken Malaysia Sdn. Bhd. - Shah Alam Plant **(1)**
Lot 2-46 Jalan Subang Utama 7 Taman
Perindustrian Subang Utama
Section 22, 40300 Shah Alam, Selangor,
Malaysia
Tel.: (60) 351915007
Fax: (60) 351915006
E-Mail: fmsa@frontken.com
Emp.: 28
Spray Coating Services
S.I.C.: 3479
N.A.I.C.S.: 332812
Low Hock Seng *(Gen Mgr)*

Non-U.S. Subsidiaries:

Frontken MIC Co. Ltd. **(1)**
No 11 Xin Xi Rd Wuxi National High-Tech
DEV ZoneNo 11 Xin Xi Road Wu
Wuxi, Jiangsu, China
Tel.: (86) 51085200505
Fax: (86) 51085200202
Spray Coating Services
S.I.C.: 3479
N.A.I.C.S.: 332812

Frontken Philippines Inc **(1)**
Lot C3-9 Carmelray Industrial Park II
Calamba, Laguna, 4027, Philippines
Tel.: (63) 495080049
Fax: (63) 495080050
E-Mail: fp@frontken.com
Web Site: www.ph.frontken.com
Emp.: 88
Spray Coating & Mechanical Engineering Services
S.I.C.: 3479
N.A.I.C.S.: 332812
Nicholas Ng *(Mng Dir)*

Frontken (Singapore) Pte. Ltd. **(1)**
156A Gul Cir
629614 Singapore, Singapore
Tel.: (65) 68634500
Fax: (65) 68634766
E-Mail: fs@frontken.com
Web Site: www.frontken.com
Emp.: 300
Spray Coating Services
S.I.C.: 2851
N.A.I.C.S.: 325510
Franco Kang *(Controller-Fin)*

Plants:

Frontken (Singapore) Pte. Ltd. - Jurong Plant 1 **(2)**
156A Gul Circle
629614 Singapore, Singapore
Tel.: (65) 68634500
Fax: (65) 68634766
E-Mail: fs@frontken.com
Emp.: 300
Spray Coating Services
S.I.C.: 3479
N.A.I.C.S.: 332812

Frontken (Singapore) Pte. Ltd. - Jurong Plant 2 **(2)**
15 Gul Drive
629466 Singapore, Singapore
Tel.: (65) 68631411
Fax: (65) 68631161
E-Mail: info@frontken.com
Spray Coating Services
S.I.C.: 2851
N.A.I.C.S.: 325510

Non-U.S. Subsidiary:

Frontken (Thailand) Co. Ltd. **(2)**
3 Moo 6 Putthamonthon VII Road Homkred
Sam Phran, Nakornpathom, 73110,
Thailand
Tel.: (66) 34220838
Fax: (66) 34220835
E-Mail: ft@frontken.com
Emp.: 30
Spray Coating Services
S.I.C.: 3479
N.A.I.C.S.: 332812
Pont Khajontorn *(Mgr)*

PT Frontken Indonesia **(1)**
Jl Raya Serang Km 13 Rt 003/RW 002 Kp
Cirewed Suka Damai Cikupa
15710 Tangerang, Banten, Indonesia
Tel.: (62) 21 5940 5390
Fax: (62) 21 5960536
E-Mail: ptfi@frontken.com
Web Site: www.frontken.com
Emp.: 30
Spraying & Coating Services
S.I.C.: 3479
N.A.I.C.S.: 332812
Wong Ton Lok *(Mgr)*

FRONTLINE BUSINESS SOLUTIONS LIMITED

6/141 Nityanand Nagar No 4 Behind
Better Home
Andheri E, Mumbai, 400 069, India
Tel.: (91) 22 2683 8689
Fax: (91) 22 2683 8689
E-Mail: admin@frontlinegroup.in
Web Site: www.frontlinegroup.in
521167—(BOM)
Rev.: $3,272,915
Assets: $3,678,353
Liabilities: $1,227,191
Net Worth: $2,451,162
Earnings: $18,874
Fiscal Year-end: 03/31/13
Business Description:
Marketing Consulting Services
S.I.C.: 8742
N.A.I.C.S.: 541613
Personnel:
Natwar B. Sureka *(Chm & Mng Dir)*
Board of Directors:
Natwar B. Sureka
Brijkishor Ruia
Manju Sureka
Transfer Agent:
Universal Capital Securities Pvt. Ltd.
21 Shakil Niwas Mahakali Caves Road Opp
Satya Saibaba Temple Andheri E
Mumbai, India

FRONTLINE CARRIER SYSTEMS INC.

2788 Portland Drive
Oakville, ON, L6H 6R4, Canada
Tel.: (905) 822-6177
Fax: (905) 822-7148
Toll Free: (800) 567-7629
E-Mail: reception@frontline-carrier.com
Web Site: www.frontline-carrier.com
Year Founded: 1989
Rev.: $10,234,704
Emp.: 23
Business Description:
Transportation Services
S.I.C.: 4789
N.A.I.C.S.: 488999
Personnel:
R. Michael Dwyer *(Pres)*

FRONTLINE GOLD CORPORATION

Suite 1102 67 Yonge Street
Toronto, ON, M5E 1J8, Canada
Tel.: (416) 362-9100
Fax: (416) 362-9300
E-Mail: info@frontlinegold.com
Web Site: www.frontlinegold.com
Year Founded: 2008
FGC—(TSXV)
Assets: $9,888,555
Liabilities: $2,955,871
Net Worth: $6,932,684
Earnings: ($557,441)
Fiscal Year-end: 12/31/12
Business Description:
Investment Services
S.I.C.: 6211
N.A.I.C.S.: 523999
Personnel:
Walter C. Henry *(Pres & CEO)*
John C. R. Cumming *(Gen Counsel & Exec VP)*
Board of Directors:
John C. R. Cumming
Walter C. Henry
Tom Hussey
Gregory P. Isenor
James M. Patterson
Darryl Sittler
Transfer Agent:
Computershare Trust Company of Canada
1969 Upper Water Street Suite 2008
Halifax, NS, B3J 3R7, Canada
Tel.: (902) 420-3557

FRONTLINE LTD.

Par-la-Ville Place 14 Par-la-Ville Road
Hamilton, HM 08, Bermuda
Tel.: (441) 295 69 35
Fax: (441) 295 34 94
E-Mail: frontline@front.bm
Web Site: www.frontline.bm
FRO—(LSE NYSE OSL)
Rev.: $668,107,000
Assets: $1,688,221,000
Liabilities: $1,557,072,000
Net Worth: $131,149,000
Earnings: ($83,775,000)
Emp.: 88
Fiscal Year-end: 12/31/12
Business Description:
Shipping Services; Oil Tankers
S.I.C.: 4412
N.A.I.C.S.: 483111
Personnel:
John Fredriksen *(Chm, Pres & CEO)*
Board of Directors:
John Fredriksen
Kate Blankenship
Georgina E. Sousa

Subsidiaries:

Knightsbridge Tankers Limited **(1)**
Par-la-Ville Place 14 Par-la-Ville Road
Hamilton, HM 08, Bermuda BM
Tel.: (441) 2956935
Fax: (441) 2953494
E-Mail: ola.lorentzon@frontmgt.no
Web Site: www.knightsbridgetankers.com
VLCCF—(LSE NASDAQ OSL)
Rev.: $37,546,000
Assets: $409,858,000
Liabilities: $102,417,000
Net Worth: $307,441,000
Earnings: ($3,903,000)
Emp.: 2
Fiscal Year-end: 12/31/13
Owners of Oil Tankers
S.I.C.: 4449
N.A.I.C.S.: 483211
Ola Lorentzon *(Chm & CEO)*

Ship Finance International Limited **(1)**
Par-la-Ville Place 14 Par-la-Ville Road
Hamilton, HM 08, Bermuda
Tel.: (441) 295 9500
Fax: (441) 295 3494
Web Site: www.shipfinance.no

Frontline Ltd.—(Continued)

SFL—(NYSE)
Rev.: $319,692,000
Assets: $2,973,089,000
Liabilities: $1,978,321,000
Net Worth: $994,768,000
Earnings: $185,836,000
Emp.: 7
Fiscal Year-end: 12/31/12
Oil Tanker Fleet Operator
S.I.C.: 4412
N.A.I.C.S.: 483111
Ole B. Hjertaker *(CEO)*
Harald Gurvin *(CFO)*
Thecla Panagides *(Chief Acctg Officer)*

Non-U.S. Subsidiaries:

Frontline Management AS (1)
Bryggegata 3
PO Box 1327 VIKA
0112 Oslo, Norway (100%)
Tel.: (47) 23114000
Fax: (47) 23114040
E-Mail: info@frontline.com
Web Site: www.frontline.com
Emp.: 25
Shipping Services
S.I.C.: 4449
N.A.I.C.S.: 483211
Jens Martin Jensen *(Interim Mng Dir & CEO)*
Inger M. Klemp *(CFO)*
Magnus Vaaler *(Treas)*
Mette Valgermo *(Sec)*

Frontline Management (UK) Ltd. (1)
15 Sloane Square
London, SW1W 8ER, United Kingdom (100%)
Tel.: (44) 2078245530
Fax: (44) 207 824 5535
E-Mail: frontuk@frontuk.co.uk
Web Site: www.frontline.bm
Shipping Services
S.I.C.: 4449
N.A.I.C.S.: 483211
Maria Turnbull *(Office Mgr)*

FRONTLINE SECURITIES LTD.

M-6 M-Block Market Greater Kailash Part-II
New Delhi, 110048, India
Tel.: (91) 11 2921 2331
Fax: (91) 11 2921 3867
E-Mail: info@fslindia.com
Web Site: www.fslindia.com
Year Founded: 1995
533213—(BOM)
Sales Range: $1-9.9 Million
Business Description:
Financial Services
S.I.C.: 6799
N.A.I.C.S.: 523920
Personnel:
Sarabjeet Kaur *(Sec)*
Board of Directors:
C. S. Bedi
Arun K. Jain
Atul K. Jain
Sarabjeet Kaur
Transfer Agent:
Link Intime India Private Limited
A-40 2nd Floor Naraina Industrial Area Phase-II
New Delhi, India

FRONTLINE TECHNOLOGIES INC.

25 Adelaide Street East Suite 600
Toronto, ON, M5C 3A1, Canada
Tel.: (416) 637-7500
Fax: (416) 603-7462
Toll Free: (877) 677-7500
E-Mail: investerinfo@frontline.ca
Web Site: www.frontline.ca
Year Founded: 1993
FLC—(TSXV)
Sales Range: $1-9.9 Million
Emp.: 72
Business Description:
IT Services & Software
S.I.C.: 7379
N.A.I.C.S.: 541519
Personnel:
Hoss Astaraki *(Chm & CEO)*
John Culbert *(CFO & Sec)*
Board of Directors:
Hoss Astaraki
Ian Camacho
Laurie Clark
Keith R. Harris
Mo Hirani
Deborah Robertson
Legal Counsel:
Blake, Cassels & Graydon LLP
Commerce Court West 28th Floor
Toronto, ON, M5L 1A9, Canada
Tel.: (416) 863-2400
Transfer Agent:
Valiant Trust Company
Toronto, ON, Canada

FROSTA AG

Am Lunedeich 116
27572 Bremerhaven, Germany
Tel.: (49) 471 97 36 0
Fax: (49) 471 7 51 63
E-Mail: info@frosta.de
Web Site: www.frosta-ag.com
Year Founded: 1905
NLM—(DEU)
Sales Range: $500-549.9 Million
Emp.: 1,528
Business Description:
Frozen Foods Mfr
S.I.C.: 2038
N.A.I.C.S.: 311412
Personnel:
Dirk Ahlers *(Chm-Supervisory Bd)*
Felix Ahlers *(Chm-Exec Bd)*
Oswald Barckhahn *(Deputy Chm-Supervisory Bd)*
Jurgen Marggraf *(Deputy Chm-Exec Bd)*
Hinnerk Ehlers *(Member-Exec Bd-Mktg & Sls)*
Stephan Hinrichs *(Member-Exec Bd-Fin & Admin)*
Supervisory Board of Directors:
Dirk Ahlers
Oswald Barckhahn
Jurgen Schimmelpfennig

FRR CORPORATION LTD.

Level 17 1 Bligh Street
Sydney, NSW, 2000, Australia
Tel.: (61) 2 9250 8790
Fax: (61) 2 9250 8777
E-Mail: info@frr.com.au
Web Site: www.frr.com.au
FRR—(ASX)
Business Description:
Refrigeration & Air Conditioning Services
S.I.C.: 3585
N.A.I.C.S.: 333415
Personnel:
Michael Hill *(Chm)*
Andrew Whitten *(Sec)*
Board of Directors:
Michael Hill
Leigh Curyer
Phillip Kapp
Jonathan Pager
Legal Counsel:
Whittens Lawyers and Consultants
Level 5 137-139 Bathurst Street
Sydney, NSW, 2000, Australia

FRTEK CO., LTD.

1001 at Doosan Venture Digm 126-1 Pyungchon-dong
Dongahn-gu, Anyang, Kyonggi, Korea (South) 431-070
Tel.: (82) 31 487 2114
Fax: (82) 31 478 2116
Web Site: www.frtek.co.kr
Year Founded: 2000
073540—(KRS)
Emp.: 68
Business Description:
Repeater Mfr
S.I.C.: 3661
N.A.I.C.S.: 334210
Personnel:
Jae-Kook Nahm *(Pres & CEO)*

FRUTTAGEL S.C.P.A.

Via Nullo Baldini 26
48011 Alfonsine, RA, Italy
Tel.: (39) 0544866511
Fax: (39) 0544866564
E-Mail: segreteria@fruttagel.it
Web Site: www.fruttagel.it
Year Founded: 1994
Sales Range: $150-199.9 Million
Emp.: 700
Business Description:
Frozen Fruit, Vegetables & Beverages
S.I.C.: 2037
N.A.I.C.S.: 311411
Personnel:
Egidio Checcoli *(Chm)*
Egidio Mordenti *(Vice Chm)*
Vincenzo Alberti *(Pres)*
Board of Directors:
Egidio Checcoli
Vincenzo Alberti
Daniele Bettati
Tino Cesari
Luca Cioffi
Stanislao Fabbrino
Samantha Gardin
Egidio Mordenti
Pietro Pasini
Davide Sinigaglia
Guido Toletti
Giorgio Zucchini

Plant:

Fruttagel Scrl - Larino plant (1)
Via Statale Sannitica 87
Piane di Larino, 86035 Larino, Campobasso, Italy
Tel.: (39) 0874 82091
Fax: (39) 0874 820926
Emp.: 14
Frozen Vegetable Production Services
S.I.C.: 0161
N.A.I.C.S.: 111219

FSA GROUP LIMITED

Level 3 70 Phillip Street
Sydney, NSW, 2000, Australia
Tel.: (61) 1300 660 032
Fax: (61) 1300 660 050
Web Site: www.fsagroup.com.au
FSA—(ASX)
Rev.: $49,026,872
Assets: $348,224,902
Liabilities: $286,991,961
Net Worth: $61,232,941
Earnings: $12,755,041
Emp.: 175
Fiscal Year-end: 06/30/13
Business Description:
Debt Solutions & Lending Services
S.I.C.: 6282
N.A.I.C.S.: 523930
Personnel:
Cellina Chen *(CFO)*
Don Mackenzie *(Sec)*
Board of Directors:
Sam Doumany
Sally Herman
Stan Kalinko
Tim Odillo Maher
Deborah Southon
Legal Counsel:
Hopgood Ganim
Level 8 Waterfront Place 1 Eagle Street
Brisbane, QLD, 4000, Australia

Subsidiary:

Aravanis Insolvency Pty Ltd (1)
Level 3 70 Phillip Street
Sydney, NSW, 2000, Australia
Tel.: (61) 1300369108
Fax: (61) 1300 369 128
E-Mail: info@aravanis.com.au
Web Site: www.aravanis.com.au
Business Management Services
S.I.C.: 8742
N.A.I.C.S.: 541611
Andrew Aravanis *(Mgr)*

FSBM HOLDINGS BERHAD

Axis Eureka 3539 Jalan Teknokrat 7
63000 Cyberjaya, Selangor, Malaysia
Tel.: (60) 383193000
Fax: (60) 383192000
E-Mail: enquiry@fsbm.com.my
Web Site: www.fsbm.com.my
FSBM—(KLS)
Rev.: $2,556,464
Assets: $12,932,181
Liabilities: $2,970,627
Net Worth: $9,961,554
Earnings: ($3,057,854)
Fiscal Year-end: 12/31/12
Business Description:
Computer Products Services
S.I.C.: 8731
N.A.I.C.S.: 541712
Personnel:
Hock San Tan *(Chm & Mng Dir)*
Muhammad Hisham Ahmad *(CEO-FSBM CTech Sdn Bhd)*
Michael Ta *(CEO-Multimedia & Comm)*
Mark Ian Timms *(CEO-TeleVAS Holdings Sdn Bhd)*
Kim Chee Cheok *(Sec)*
Lawrence Chin *(Sr Exec VP)*
Cheng Phua Khan *(Sr Exec VP)*
Board of Directors:
Hock San Tan
Wei Ming Chang
Abdul Rahim Daud
Zainul Ariff Hussain
Ee Ern Tan
Wan Yen Tan

Subsidiaries:

FSBM CTech Sdn. Bhd. (1)
503 Block A Phileo Damansara 1 9 Jalan 16/11 Off Jalan Damansara
Petaling Jaya, Selangor, Selangor, Malaysia
Tel.: (60) 378432312
Fax: (60) 378432299
Software Development Services
S.I.C.: 7371
N.A.I.C.S.: 541511
Tan Hock San *(Mng Dir)*
Cheok Kim Chee *(Sec)*

FSBM Net Media Sdn. Bhd. (1)
306 & 506 Block A Phileo Damansara 1 No 9 Jalan 16/11
Off Jalan Damansara, 46350 Petaling Jaya, Selangor Darul Ehsan, Malaysia
Tel.: (60) 379606080
Communication & Networking Services
S.I.C.: 4813
N.A.I.C.S.: 517110

Televas Holdings Sdn. Bhd. (1)
40-2 Jalan PJU 7/16 Mutiara Damansara
47800 Petaling Jaya, Selangor Darul Ehsan, Malaysia
Tel.: (60) 377295244
Fax: (60) 377295249
Web Site: www.televas.com.my
Emp.: 10
Telecommunication Equipments Distr
S.I.C.: 5065
N.A.I.C.S.: 423690
Tan Hock San *(Chm)*
Mark Timm *(CEO)*
Mark Ian Timms *(CEO)*
Ow Eng Haw *(CFO)*

Unos Sdn. Bhd. (1)
306 Block A Phileo Damansara 1 No 9 Jalan 16/11 Off Jalan Damansara
Petaling Jaya, Selangor, 46350, Malaysia

Tel.: (60) 378432288
Fax: (60) 78432299
Web Site: www.myunos.com
Emp.: 200
Telecommunication & Networking Services
S.I.C.: 4899
N.A.I.C.S.: 517919

Non-U.S. Subsidiary:

Asialink Technology Development Limited (1)
Unit 301-306 Bldg 14 8 Science Park West Ave
Sha Tin, Fo Tan, China (Hong Kong)
Tel.: (852) 28114228
Fax: (852) 28809447
Web Site: www.asialink.com.hk
Telecommunication & Networking Services
S.I.C.: 4899
N.A.I.C.S.: 517919

FSI ENERGY GROUP INC.

4535 8A Street Northeast
Calgary, AB, T2E 4J6, Canada
Tel.: (403) 571-4225
Fax: (403) 230-3106
Web Site: www.fsigroup.ca
FSI—(TSXV)
Rev.: $2,996,949
Assets: $12,892,756
Liabilities: $12,777,022
Net Worth: $115,735
Earnings: ($728,759)
Emp.: 100
Fiscal Year-end: 12/31/12
Business Description:
Filtration & Filtration-Related Products
S.I.C.: 3559
N.A.I.C.S.: 333249
Personnel:
Dennis L. Nerland *(Chm)*
Richard A. Ball *(Pres & CEO)*
Ian R. Ball *(CFO & VP)*
Board of Directors:
Dennis L. Nerland
Ian R. Ball
Richard A. Ball
Douglas Keller
Robert Spiller
Subsidiary:

FSI International Services Ltd. (1)
4535 - 8A Street NE
Calgary, AB, P2E 4J6, Canada
Tel.: (403) 571-4230
Fax: (403) 230-3106
E-Mail: info@fsigroup.ca
Web Site: www.fsigroup.ca
Emp.: 25
Filtration Products
S.I.C.: 3559
N.A.I.C.S.: 333249
Richard Ball *(Pres)*

FSN CAPITAL PARTNERS AS

Karl Johansgate 27
NO 0159 Oslo, Norway
Tel.: (47) 24147300
Fax: (47) 24147301
E-Mail: admin@fsncapital.com
Web Site: www.fsncapital.com
Emp.: 25
Business Description:
Private Equity Firm
S.I.C.: 6211
N.A.I.C.S.: 523999
Personnel:
Per Etholm *(Chm)*
Frode Strand-Nielsen *(Mng Partner)*
Thomas Broe-Andersen *(Partner)*
Dan Johnson *(Partner)*
Henrik Lisaeth *(Partner)*
Peter Moller *(Partner)*
Marianne Michelsen *(COO)*
Holding:

Norman ASA (1)
Strandveien 37
Lysaker, 1324, Norway
Tel.: (47) 67 10 97 00
Fax: (47) 67 58 99 40
E-Mail: norman@norman.no
Web Site: www.norman.com
Sales Range: $25-49.9 Million
Emp.: 85
Content Security Solutions
S.I.C.: 7372
N.A.I.C.S.: 511210
Frode Strand-Nielsen *(Chm)*
Kjetil Vinjum *(CFO)*
Christophe Birkeland *(CTO)*

FSP TECHNOLOGY INC.

No 22 Jianguo E Rd
Taoyuan, Taiwan
Tel.: (886) 33759888
Fax: (886) 33756966
Web Site: www.fsp-group.com.tw
3015—(TAI)
Sales Range: $250-299.9 Million
Business Description:
Adapters Mfr
S.I.C.: 3483
N.A.I.C.S.: 332993
Personnel:
Allen Cheng *(Chm & Gen Mgr)*
U.S. Subsidiary:

FSP North America, Inc. (1)
33 Musick
Irvine, CA 92618
Tel.: (949) 305-6703
Fax: (949) 305-6701
E-Mail: fspna@fspna.com
Web Site: www.fspna.com
Electronic Components Distr
S.I.C.: 5065
N.A.I.C.S.: 423690

Non-U.S. Subsidiaries:

Crown Joy International Ltd. (1)
RM 609 6/F Block A Proficient IND CTR 6 Wang Kwun Road
Kowloon Bay, Kowloon, China (Hong Kong)
Tel.: (852) 23313613
Fax: (852) 23319162
E-Mail: sales@crownjoy.com.hk
Web Site: www.crownjoy.com.hk
Emp.: 10
Electronic Components Mfr & Distr
S.I.C.: 3675
N.A.I.C.S.: 334416
Nita Liu *(Mgr)*

FSP (GB) Ltd. (1)
Unit 8 Curo Park
Frogmore, Saint Albans, Hertfordshire, AL2 2DD, United Kingdom
Tel.: (44) 1727873888
Fax: (44) 1727873668
E-Mail: sales@fspgroup.co.uk
Web Site: www.fspgroup.co.uk
Power Supplies Distr
S.I.C.: 4939
N.A.I.C.S.: 221118

FSP Technology Korea Co., Ltd. (1)
707 IKP 300-6 Yeomgok-dong
Seocho-ku, Seoul, 137-170, Korea (South)
Tel.: (82) 5 6424130
Fax: (82) 2 525 1488
Web Site: www.fsp-group.co.kr
Electronic Component & Peripherals Distr
S.I.C.: 7389
N.A.I.C.S.: 425110

Shenzhen Zhong Han Science & Tech. Co., Ltd. (1)
Room L-R 19/F Building A Fortune Plaza
7060 Shen Nan Road
Shenzhen, Guangdong, China
Tel.: (86) 75582933191
Fax: (86) 755 82933190
E-Mail: zkhdoc@zkh.fsp-group.com.tw
Web Site: www.fspgroup.co.uk/u.k/05_global_office/global_office.html
Electronic Components Distr
S.I.C.: 3679
N.A.I.C.S.: 334419

Yuli Electronic Co., Ltd. (1)
17F No 461 Hongcao Road Caohe Software Building
Shanghai, China
Tel.: (86) 2154262808
Fax: (86) 21 54262818
E-Mail: ylsales@sh.fsp-group.com.tw
Web Site: www.fsp-group.com.tw/english/4_about/1_brand.asp?id=10
Electronic Component Distr
S.I.C.: 5065
N.A.I.C.S.: 423690

Non-U.S. Plant:

FSP Technology Inc. (1)
Room L-R 19F Building A Fortune Plaza
7060 Shen Nan Road
Shenzhen, Guangdong, China
Tel.: (86) 755 82933183
Fax: (86) 755 82933190
E-Mail: zhonghan@zkh.fsp-group.com.tw
Web Site: www.fsp-group.com.tw/english/4_about/pt_02.html
Electronic Components Mfr
S.I.C.: 3679
N.A.I.C.S.: 334419

FSW COATINGS LIMITED

(d/b/a Fleetwood Paint)
Virginia
Cavan, Ireland
Tel.: (353) 498547209
Telex: 31897
Fax: (353) 498547470
E-Mail: info@fleetwood.ie
Web Site: www.fleetwood.ie
Sales Range: $25-49.9 Million
Emp.: 115
Business Description:
Paint & Coating Mfr
S.I.C.: 2851
N.A.I.C.S.: 325510
Personnel:
Conor M. Doyle *(Mng Dir)*

FSW SECURITY PRODUCTS LTD.

Unit 1 Paradise Works Eden St
Coventry, Westmidland, CV6 5HE, United Kingdom
Tel.: (44) 2476667624
Fax: (44) 2476638972
E-Mail: info@fswsecurity.co.uk
Web Site: www.fswsecurity.co.uk
Emp.: 5
Business Description:
Mfr. of Security Grills & Shutters
S.I.C.: 3442
N.A.I.C.S.: 332321

FT COMMUNICATIONS CO., LTD.

Jowa-Suitengu Bldg 2-13-6
Nihonbashi Kakigara-cho Chuo-ku
Tokyo, 103-0014, Japan
Tel.: (81) 3 5847 2777
Fax: (81) 3 5847 2766
Web Site: www.ftcom.co.jp
Year Founded: 1985
2763—(JAS)
Sls.: $504,669,000
Assets: $210,463,000
Liabilities: $133,210,000
Net Worth: $77,253,000
Earnings: $19,360,000
Fiscal Year-end: 03/31/13
Business Description:
Communication Equipment Sales & Marketing
S.I.C.: 7622
N.A.I.C.S.: 811213
Personnel:
Makoto Kuroyanagi *(Chm)*
Toshiyuki Hirasaki *(Pres & CEO)*
Board of Directors:
Makoto Kuroyanagi
Toshiyuki Hirasaki
Makoto Ishida
Masato Koyama
Tsuyoshi Sasaki
Haruhiko Shigekawa
Naoya Shimizu
Hiroyuki Yamamoto
Subsidiary:

Entre Preneur Co., Ltd. (1)
Okazakishibaura Building 3-6-5 Shibaura
Minato-ku, Tokyo, 108-0023, Japan
Tel.: (81) 3 6414 6551
Fax: (81) 3 6414 6561
Web Site: www.entre-preneur.co.jp
Investment Management Services
S.I.C.: 6282
N.A.I.C.S.: 523920

FTA FOOD SOLUTIONS PTY LTD

41 45 Slough Rd Altona
Melbourne, VIC, 3018, Australia
Tel.: (61) 383980500
Fax: (61) 393159002
E-Mail: fta@fta.com.au
Web Site: www.ftafoodsolutions.com.au
Year Founded: 1993
Sales Range: $50-74.9 Million
Emp.: 35
Business Description:
Food Service Contractor, Supplier & Other Industry Related Services
S.I.C.: 5812
N.A.I.C.S.: 722310
Personnel:
Robert Burgess *(Gen Mgr)*

FTI FOODTECH INTERNATIONAL INC.

202-40 Wynford Drive
Don Mills, Toronto, ON, M3C 1J5, Canada
Tel.: (416) 444-1058
Fax: (416) 444-9524
E-Mail: info@fti-foodtech.com
Web Site: www.fti-foodtech.com
Year Founded: 1987
FTI—(TSXV)
Sls.: $44,366
Assets: $101,072
Liabilities: $106,973
Net Worth: ($5,901)
Earnings: ($68,585)
Fiscal Year-end: 03/31/13
Business Description:
Food Products & Technologies Licenser
S.I.C.: 6794
N.A.I.C.S.: 533110
Personnel:
William A. Hullah *(Pres & CEO)*
Gary R. Hullah *(CFO & VP)*
William E. Bateman *(Sec)*
Board of Directors:
Gary R. Hullah
William A. Hullah
Linda Lakats
JoAnne Strongman
Boris I. Ziger
Transfer Agent:
Computershare
510 Burrard Street
Vancouver, BC, Canada

FTL VENTURES CORP.

Unit 2801 Bank of America Tower
12 Harcourt Road, Central, China (Hong Kong)
Tel.: (852) 2615 1107
Web Site: www.ftlventurescorp.com
Year Founded: 2011
Business Description:
Film Production & Distribution
S.I.C.: 7812
N.A.I.C.S.: 512110

FTL Ventures Corp.—(Continued)

Personnel:
Edmund Kam Cheong Leong *(Chm, Pres, CEO, CFO, Treas & Sec)*
Board of Directors:
Edmund Kam Cheong Leong

FU SHOU YUAN INTERNATIONAL GROUP LIMITED

Qingsong 7270 Highway
Qingpu District, Shanghai, China
Tel.: (86) 21 39820026
Fax: (86) 21 39820607
E-Mail: fsy@shfsy.com
Web Site: www.shfsy.com
1448—(HKG)
Emp.: 1,100
Business Description:
Cemetaries & Funeral Facilities
S.I.C.: 7261
N.A.I.C.S.: 812220
Personnel:
Xiaojiang Bai *(Chm)*

FU YU CORPORATION LIMITED

8 Tuas Drive 1
Singapore, 638675, Singapore
Tel.: (65) 65787338
Fax: (65) 64823610
E-Mail: salesenquiry@fuyucorp.com
Web Site: www.fuyucorp.com
Year Founded: 1978
F13—(SES)
Rev.: $253,564,432
Assets: $197,842,563
Liabilities: $57,112,851
Net Worth: $140,729,712
Earnings: ($5,657,301)
Fiscal Year-end: 12/31/12
Business Description:
Precision Molds & Injection Plastic Molds Mfr
S.I.C.: 3089
N.A.I.C.S.: 326199
Personnel:
Heng Yang Ching *(Vice Chm)*
Kang Peng Ho *(CEO)*
Chee Kian Tan *(Acting CFO & Gen Mgr-Fu Yu Dongguan)*
Lien Lee Hew *(COO)*
Chun Huan Liaw *(Co-Sec)*
Siew Tian Low *(Co-Sec)*
Board of Directors:
John Seow Phun Chen
Heng Yang Ching
Say Tun Foo
Lien Lee Hew
Kang Peng Ho
Nee Kit Ho
Wai Tam
Yew Beng Tan

Subsidiaries:

NanoTechnology Manufacturing Pte. Ltd. **(1)**
8 Tuas Dr 1
Singapore, 638675, Singapore (80%)
Tel.: (65) 67552280
Fax: (65) 67557326
Web Site: www.nanotechnology.com.sg
Emp.: 30
Special Die & Tool Die Set Jig & Fixture Mfr
S.I.C.: 3544
N.A.I.C.S.: 333514
Yeo See Joo *(Bus Dir)*

SolidMicron Technologies Pte Ltd **(1)**
No 2 Serangoon North Avenue 5 #03-00
554911 Singapore, Singapore (100%)
Tel.: (65) 64831281
Fax: (65) 64831382
E-Mail: solidmicrontech@solidmicrontech.com
Web Site: www.solidmicrontech.com
Emp.: 30
Bare Printed Circuit Board Mfr
S.I.C.: 3672
N.A.I.C.S.: 334412
Shammugan Phageloo *(Gen Mgr)*

Non-U.S. Subsidiaries:

Classic Advantage Sdn Bhd **(1)**
11 Jalan Persiaran
Teknologi Taman Teknologi Joho, 81400
Senai, Johor, Malaysia (62.69%)
Tel.: (60) 75999980
Fax: (60) 75999982
Emp.: 400
Plastics Product Mfr
S.I.C.: 3089
N.A.I.C.S.: 326199
Elson Hew *(Mng Dir)*

Fu Hao Manufacturing (M) Sdn Bhd **(1)**
Plot 562 Mukim 1
Lorong Perusahaan Baru 1 Perai, 13600
Perai, Penang, Malaysia (62.69%)
Tel.: (60) 43980499
Fax: (60) 43983221
E-Mail: pclin@pn.lcihcorp.com
Web Site: www.fuyucorp.com
Emp.: 200
Plastics Product Mfr
S.I.C.: 3089
N.A.I.C.S.: 326199
Tary Teh *(Gen Mgr)*

Fu Yu Moulding & Tooling (Dongguan) Co., Ltd. **(1)**
Jing Fu Rd Xin Cheng Industry Area Heng Li Town
Dongguan Guangdong, 523477 Dongguan, China (100%)
Tel.: (86) 76989821818
Fax: (86) 76989821815
E-Mail: tong_ling@fuyu.com.cn
Web Site: www.fuyu.com
Emp.: 600
Plastics Product Mfr
S.I.C.: 3089
N.A.I.C.S.: 326199

Fu Yu Moulding & Tooling (Shanghai) Co., Ltd. **(1)**
No 888 Xin Ling Road Waigaoqiao Free Trade Zone
Shanghai, 200131, China
Tel.: (86) 2150461225
Fax: (86) 21 50460229
Plastics Product Mfr
S.I.C.: 3089
N.A.I.C.S.: 326199

Fu Yu Moulding & Tooling (Suzhou) Co , Ltd. **(1)**
89 Xing Nan Road
Wuzhong Economic Skill Develop, 215128
Suzhou, China (100%)
Tel.: (86) 51265621838
Fax: (86) 51265639463
Web Site: www.fuyucorp.com
Plastics Product Mfr
S.I.C.: 3089
N.A.I.C.S.: 326199

Subsidiary:

Fu Yu Moulding & Tooling (Wujiang) Co., Ltd **(2)**
No 2288 Jiang Xing East Road Wujiand Economic Dev Zone
Wujiang, Jiangsu, 215200, China (100%)
Tel.: (86) 512 6300 5959
Fax: (86) 512 630 05993
Web Site: www.fuyucorp.com
Plastics Product Mfr
S.I.C.: 3089
N.A.I.C.S.: 326199
Chengyu Wang *(Mgr-Sls)*

LCTH Corporation Bhd **(1)**
11 Jalan Persiaran Teknologi
Taman Teknologi Johor, 81400 Senai, Johor, Malaysia (62.69%)
Tel.: (60) 75999980
Fax: (60) 75999982
E-Mail: ltchcorp@lcth.com
Web Site: www.lcth.com.my
Emp.: 600
Management Services
S.I.C.: 4959
N.A.I.C.S.: 562998
El Fol Yu *(Exec Dir)*

Qingdao Fu Qiang Electronics Co., Ltd. **(1)**
No 1 Haier Road Haier Information Industry Park T Building
Hi Tech Industrial Zone, Qingdao, 266101, China
Tel.: (86) 53288609988
Fax: (86) 532 88609968
Electronics
S.I.C.: 5731
N.A.I.C.S.: 443142

FUBON FINANCIAL HOLDING CO. LTD.

237 Chien Kuo South Road Section 1
106 Taipei, Taiwan
Tel.: (886) 266366636
Fax: (886) 2663607566
E-Mail: info@fubon.com.tw
Web Site: www.fubon.com.tw
Year Founded: 1951
2881—(TAI)
Sales Range: $1-4.9 Billion
Emp.: 13,427
Business Description:
Financial Investment & Management Services
S.I.C.: 6211
N.A.I.C.S.: 523999
Personnel:
Daniel M. Tsai *(Chm & CEO)*
Richard M. Tsai *(Vice Chm)*
Victor Kung *(Pres)*
David Chang *(Chm-Fubon Securities)*
Tsan-Ming Shih *(Chm-Fubon Insurance)*
Peng-Yuan Cheng *(Pres-Fubon Life)*
Jerry Harn *(Pres-Taipei Fubon Bank)*
Thomas Liang *(CEO-Hong Kong)*
Board of Directors:
Daniel M. Tsai
David Chang
Hong-Chang Chang
Nelson Chang
Kok-Choo Chen
Yeh-Shin Chen
Peng-Yuan Cheng
Su-Gin Huang
Victor Kung
Kenneth Shih
Tsan-Ming Shih
Timothy Ting
Richard M. Tsai

Subsidiaries:

Fubon Asset Management Co., Ltd. **(1)**
8F 108 Tun Hua South Road Sec 1
Taipei, 10548, Taiwan
Tel.: (886) 287716688
Fax: (886) 287716788
E-Mail: pr@fubon.com
Web Site: www.fubon.com
Sales Range: $700-749.9 Million
Emp.: 150
Security Brokers & Dealers
S.I.C.: 6211
N.A.I.C.S.: 523120
Thomas Tsao *(Pres)*

Fubon Direct Marketing Consulting Co., Ltd **(1)**
9 Xiang Yang Road
Taipei, Taiwan
Tel.: (886) 2 2370 5199
Fax: (886) 2 2370 5100
Insurance Management Services
S.I.C.: 6411
N.A.I.C.S.: 524298
Wen-Cheng Yeh *(Pres)*

Fubon Futures Co., Ltd **(1)**
3F N 9 Xiangyang Rd
Zhongzheng, Taipei, Taiwan
Tel.: (886) 2 2388 2626
Fax: (886) 2 2371 1110
Emp.: 80
Financial Management Services
S.I.C.: 6211
N.A.I.C.S.: 523999
Phoebe Chang *(Gen Mgr)*

Fubon Insurance Co., Ltd. **(1)**
237 Chien Kuo S Rd Sec 1
Taipei, 10657, Taiwan
Tel.: (886) 227067890
Fax: (886) 227042915
Insurance Management Services
S.I.C.: 6411
N.A.I.C.S.: 524298

Fubon Life Assurance Co., Ltd. **(1)**
14F 108 Tun Hua South Road Sec 1
Taipei, 10548, Taiwan
Tel.: (886) 287716699
Fax: (886) 287715950
Life Insurance Carrier
S.I.C.: 6311
N.A.I.C.S.: 524113
Peng-Yuan Cheng *(Pres)*

Fubon Multimedia Technology Co., Ltd. **(1)**
2f 71 Chou Tzu St
Taipei, 11493, Taiwan
Tel.: (886) 221626688
Fax: (886) 221626696
Online Shopping Services
S.I.C.: 5961
N.A.I.C.S.: 454111

Fubon Securities Co., Ltd. **(1)**
3F Tun Hua South Road Sec 1
Taipei, Taiwan
Tel.: (886) 287716888
Fax: (886) 227219218
Web Site: www.fubon.com
Emp.: 16
Security Brokers & Dealers
S.I.C.: 6211
N.A.I.C.S.: 523120
David Chang *(Chm)*

Taipei Fubon Commercial Bank Co., Ltd. **(1)**
2nd Fl 169 Jen Ai Road Section 4
Taipei, 10686, Taiwan
Tel.: (886) 227716699
Fax: (886) 227730486
Web Site: www.fubon.com
Emp.: 1,500
National Commerical Bank
S.I.C.: 6029
N.A.I.C.S.: 522110
Jerry Harn *(Pres)*
Tien-Hsia Chang *(CFO)*
Thomas Liang *(Pres-Consumer Banking)*
Jeff Chu *(Sr VP)*

U.S. Subsidiary:

Fubon Securities USA LLC **(1)**
3452 E Foothill Blvd Ste100
Pasadena, CA 91107-3142
Tel.: (626) 792-1388
Fax: (626) 792-3380
E-Mail: vlin@fubonholding.us
Web Site: www.fubonusa.com
Sales Range: Less than $1 Million
Emp.: 10
Security Brokers & Dealers
S.I.C.: 6211
N.A.I.C.S.: 523120
Victor Lin *(Gen Mgr)*

Non-U.S. Subsidiaries:

Fubon Bank (Hong Kong) Limited **(1)**
Fubon Bank Building 38 Des Voeux Road Central, China (Hong Kong)
Tel.: (852) 28426222
Fax: (852) 28101483
E-Mail: corpcomm.fbhk@fubon.com
Web Site: www.fubonbank.com.hk
Int. Income: $172,523,752
Assets: $8,096,100,347
Liabilities: $7,104,619,013
Net Worth: $991,481,334
Earnings: $39,805,576
Emp.: 882
Fiscal Year-end: 12/31/12
Commercial Bank
S.I.C.: 6029
N.A.I.C.S.: 522110
Richard Ming Hsing Tsai *(Chm)*
Daniel Ming Chung Tsai *(Vice Chm)*

Raymond Wing Hung Lee *(CEO & Mng Dir)*
Henry Hao-Jen Wang *(CFO & Sr VP)*
Juliana Yuk Ching Chiu *(Sec)*
James Yip *(Exec VP)*
Sunny Shan Li Chang *(Sr VP & Head-Ops)*
Dennis Yiu Fai Ha *(Sr VP & Head-Legal & Compliance)*
Stanley Cho Ming Ku *(Sr VP & Head-Consumer Fin)*
Frankie Kwok Wing Kwong *(Sr VP & Head-Fin Markets)*
Percy Kin Suen Lau *(Sr VP & Head-IT)*
Wai Sum Lee *(Sr VP & Head-Control & Risk Mgmt)*
Claudia Chun Hiu Ng *(Sr VP & Head-Comml Banking)*
Henry Yuk Hang Ng *(Sr VP & Head-Corp Product Mgmt)*
Tony Yin Tsang Ng *(Sr VP & Head-Securities Svcs)*
Aubrey Chih-Wei Wang *(Sr VP & Head-Corp Banking)*
Vivien Wong *(Sr VP & Head-Audit)*
Carmen Ka Man Yip *(Sr VP & Head-Retail Banking)*
Vivian Lai Hau Sau Young *(Sr VP & Head-HR)*

Fubon Insurance (Vietnam) Co., Ltd (1)
22nd Floor Charmvit Tower 117 Tran Duy Hung Street
Cau Giay District, Hanoi, Vietnam
Tel.: (84) 462827888
Fax: (84) 4 62827887
Emp.: 80
General Insurance Services
S.I.C.: 6411
N.A.I.C.S.: 524210

Fubon Life Insurance Company Hong Kong Limited (1)
9F Two Harbour Front 22 Tal Fung Street
Hong Kong, China (Hong Kong)
Tel.: (852) 23067981
Fax: (852) 23067249
Emp.: 30
Insurance Agents, Brokers & Service
S.I.C.: 6411
N.A.I.C.S.: 524210

Fubon Life Insurance Co., Ltd (1)
13th Floor AB Tower 76 Le Lai Street Ben Thanh Ward
District 1, Ho Chi Minh City, Vietnam
Tel.: (84) 8 62586666
Fax: (84) 8 62886878
Insurance Management Services
S.I.C.: 6411
N.A.I.C.S.: 524298

FUCHS-GEWURZE GMBH

Industrie 25
49201 Dissen, Germany
Tel.: (49) 54213090
Telex: 94314
Fax: (49) 5421309111
E-Mail: info@fuchs.de
Web Site: www.fuchs-gewuerze.de
Year Founded: 1969
Emp.: 450

Business Description:
Spices Mfr
S.I.C.: 2099
N.A.I.C.S.: 311942

Personnel:
Nils Meyer-Pries *(Mng Dir)*

U.S. Subsidiary:

Fuchs North America. (1)
9740 Reisterstown Rd
Owings Mills, MD 21117 MD
Tel.: (410) 363-1700
Fax: (410) 363-6619
Toll Free: (800) 365-3229
E-Mail: info@fuchsna.com
Web Site: www.fuchsna.com
Emp.: 100
Dry Mustards, Spices, Seasonings & Capsicums Producer & Mfr
Import Export
S.I.C.: 2087
N.A.I.C.S.: 311942
Nils Meyer-Pries *(Pres)*
Christopher Rodski *(CFO)*

FUCHS PETROLUB AG

Friesenheimer Strasse 17
68169 Mannheim, Germany
Tel.: (49) 62138020
Telex: 463083fpocd
Fax: (49) 62138027190
E-Mail: contact-de.fpoc@fuchs-oil.com
Web Site: www.fuchs-oil.com
Year Founded: 1931
FPE—(DEU)
Rev.: $2,448,817,847
Assets: $1,492,498,679
Liabilities: $440,197,590
Net Worth: $1,052,301,089
Earnings: $279,061,041
Emp.: 3,773
Fiscal Year-end: 12/31/12

Business Description:
Mineral Oils, Mineral Oil Products, Lubricating Oils, Hydraulic Oils & Gear Oils Mfr
S.I.C.: 2992
N.A.I.C.S.: 324191

Personnel:
Jurgen Hambrecht *(Chm-Supervisory Bd)*
Stefan R. Fuchs *(Chm-Exec Bd)*
Manfred Fuchs *(Deputy Chm-Supervisory Bd)*
Alexander Selent *(Deputy Chm-Exec Bd, Deputy CEO & CFO)*
Lutz Lindemann *(Member-Exec Bd-Tech, Supply Chain Mgmt & Intl OEM Bus)*
Georg Lingg *(Member-Exec Bd-Intl Mining Bus & Asia-Pacific & Africa)*
Ralph Rheinbolt *(Member-Exec Bd-Europe)*
Klaus Hartig *(Exec VP-East Asia)*
Frans J. de Manielle *(Exec VP-Southeast Asia, Australia & New Zealand)*

Supervisory Board of Directors:
Jurgen Hambrecht
Manfred Fuchs
Ines Kolmsee
Horst Munkel
Lars-Eric Reinert
Erhard W. Schipporeit

Divisions:

Bremer & Leguil GmbH (1)
Am Burgacker 30 42
47051 Duisburg, Germany (100%)
Mailing Address:
PO Box 10 02 21
47002 Duisburg, Germany
Tel.: (49) 20399230
Fax: (49) 20325901
E-Mail: info@bremer-leguil.de
Web Site: www.bremer-leguil.de
Sls.: $14,247,506
Emp.: 40
Mfr. of Mineral & Lubricating Oils
S.I.C.: 2992
N.A.I.C.S.: 324191
Frank Schnipper *(Gen Mgr)*

Fuchs Europe Schmierstoffe GmbH & Co. KG (1)
Friesenheimer Strasse 15
68169 Mannheim, Baden Wuerteert, Germany (100%)
Mailing Address:
PO Box 10 11 62
D-68145 Mannheim, Germany
Tel.: (49) 62137010
Fax: (49) 6213701570
E-Mail: zentrale@fuchseurope.de
Web Site: www.fuchseurope.de
Sales Range: $250-299.9 Million
Emp.: 500
Mfr of Mineral & Lubricating Oils
S.I.C.: 2992
N.A.I.C.S.: 324191
Lutc Lindemann *(Gen Mgr)*

Division:

FUCHS EUROPE SCHMIERSTOFFE GMBH - Export Division (2)
Friesenheimer Strasse 19
68169 Mannheim, Germany
Tel.: (49) 621 3701 0
Fax: (49) 621 3701 7570
Web Site: www.fuchs-europe.de/company_directory.html
Lubricant Mfr
S.I.C.: 2992
N.A.I.C.S.: 324191
Winfried Philip *(Gen Mgr-Export)*

Plant:

FUCHS EUROPE SCHMIERSTOFFE GMBH - Kiel Plant (2)
Neuenrade 2
24113 Kiel, Germany
Tel.: (49) 431 661 13 0
Fax: (49) 431 661 13 45
Lubricant Mfr
S.I.C.: 2992
N.A.I.C.S.: 324191

Fuchs Lubritech GmbH (1)
Wernerheisenberg Str 1
67661 Kaiserslautern, Waelaebach, Germany (100%)
Mailing Address:
PO Box 51
67683 Weilerbach, Germany
Tel.: (49) 63749245
Fax: (49) 6301326940
E-Mail: info@fuchslubritech.de
Web Site: www.fuchslubritech.com
Emp.: 250
Mfr. of Mineral & Lubricating Oils
S.I.C.: 2992
N.A.I.C.S.: 324191
Frank Miliur *(Head-Intl Sls)*

Division:

FUCHS LUBRITECH GmbH - MOLY-PAUL DIVISION (2)
Kleinhulsen 9
40721 Hilden, Germany
Tel.: (49) 2103 2873 0
Fax: (49) 2103 2873 20
E-Mail: molypaul@fuchs-lubritech.de
Web Site: www.kspaul.de
Lubricant Mfr
S.I.C.: 2992
N.A.I.C.S.: 324191
Bernhard Biehl *(Chm & Mng Dir)*
Markus Heck *(Co-Mng Dir)*
Tim Weidenmann *(Co-Mng Dir)*

Plants:

FUCHS LUBRITECH GMBH - Dohna Plant (2)
Braugasse 1
1809 Dohna, Germany
Tel.: (49) 3529 56 46 30
Fax: (49) 3529 56 46 40
E-Mail: dohna@fuchs-lubritech.de
Lubricant Mfr
S.I.C.: 2992
N.A.I.C.S.: 324191

FUCHS LUBRITECH GMBH - FLT Oberflachentechnik Plant (2)
Konigsberger Strasse 2a
85386 Eching, Germany
Tel.: (49) 89 327 10 5
Fax: (49) 89 327 10 640
E-Mail: eching@fuchs-lubritech.de
Lubricant Mfr
S.I.C.: 2992
N.A.I.C.S.: 324191
Markus Heck *(Gen Mgr)*

Fuchs Petrolub AG (1)
Friesenheimer Strasse 17
68169 Mannheim, Baden Weurttenberg, Germany (100%)
Mailing Address:
PO Box 10 11 62
D-68145 Mannheim, Germany
Tel.: (49) 62138020
Fax: (49) 6213802190
E-Mail: info@fuchoil.com
Web Site: www.fuchsoil.com
Sls.: $1,310,526,976
Emp.: 450
Mfr. of Mineral & Lubricating Oils
S.I.C.: 2992
N.A.I.C.S.: 324191
Norbert Schell *(Head-Mktg Svc)*

Parafluid Mineraloelgesellschaft mbH (1)
Ueberseering 9
D 22297 Hamburg, Germany (100%)
Mailing Address:
PO Box 60 20 60
D-22220 Hamburg, Germany
Tel.: (49) 406370400
Fax: (49) 4063704100
E-Mail: info@parafluid.de
Web Site: www.parafluid.de
Emp.: 100
Mfr. of Mineral & Lubricating Oils
S.I.C.: 2992
N.A.I.C.S.: 324191
Heinzgeorg Grage *(Mng Dir)*

Ravensberger Schmierstoffvertrieb GmbH (1)
Jollenbecker Strasse 2
33824 Werther, Germany (100%)
Mailing Address:
PO Box 11 63
33819 Werther, Germany
Tel.: (49) 520397190
Fax: (49) 5203971940
E-Mail: kontakt@ravenol.de
Web Site: www.ravenol.de
Sales Range: $50-74.9 Million
Emp.: 53
Mfr. of Mineral & Lubricating Oils
S.I.C.: 2992
N.A.I.C.S.: 324191
Paul Becher *(Mng Dir)*

Wisura Mineralolwerk Goldgrabe & Scheft GmbH & Co. (1)
Am Gaswerk 2 10
PO Box 10-02-07
D 28002 Bremen, Germany (85%)
Mailing Address:
PO Box 10 02 07
D-28002 Bremen, Germany
Tel.: (49) 421549030
Fax: (49) 4215490325
E-Mail: info@wisura.de
Web Site: www.wisura.de
Emp.: 40
Mfr. of Mineral & Lubricating Oils
S.I.C.: 2992
N.A.I.C.S.: 324191
Heinzgeorg Trage *(Mng Dir)*

Subsidiaries:

FUCHS FINANZSERVICE GMBH (1)
Friesenheimer Strasse 17
68169 Mannheim, Germany
Tel.: (49) 621 3802 1132
Fax: (49) 621 3802 7197
Web Site: www.fuchs-europe.de/fuchs-worldwide.html?ziel=14&lang=EN
Lubricant Mfr & Distr
S.I.C.: 2992
N.A.I.C.S.: 324191

WISURA BETEILIGUNGSGESELLSCHAFT MBH (1)
Am Gaswerk 2-10
28197 Bremen, Germany
Tel.: (49) 421 549030
Fax: (49) 421 5490325
E-Mail: info@wisura.de
Web Site: www.wisura.de
Emp.: 3
Lubricant Distr
S.I.C.: 5172
N.A.I.C.S.: 424720
Steffen Wolf *(Gen Mgr)*

U.S. Divisions:

Fuchs Lubricants Co. (1)
17050 Lathrop Ave
Harvey, IL 60426-6035 DE
Tel.: (708) 333-8900 (100%)
Fax: (708) 333-9180
E-Mail: info@fuchs.com
Web Site: www.fuchs.com
Sales Range: $100-124.9 Million
Emp.: 150
Automotive & Industrial Lubricants & Specialty Chemicals

Fuchs Petrolub AG—(Continued)

S.I.C.: 2992
N.A.I.C.S.: 324191
L.F. Kleinman *(Pres)*

Divisions:

FUCHS LUBRICANTS CO. - FUCHS LUBRITECH USA Division (2)
17050 Lathrop Ave
Harvey, IL 60426
Tel.: (708) 333-8900
Fax: (708) 333-9180
E-Mail: hnoth@fuchs.com
Web Site: www.fuchs-europe.de/fuchs-worldwide.html?ziel=62&lang=EN
Lubricant Mfr
S.I.C.: 2992
N.A.I.C.S.: 324191

FUCHS LUBRICANTS CO. - Mining Division (2)
801 E Roy Furman Hwy
Waynesburg, PA 15370
Tel.: (724) 627-3200
Fax: (724) 852-2351
Web Site: www.fuchslubricants.com
Emp.: 9
Lubricant Mfr
S.I.C.: 2999
N.A.I.C.S.: 324199
John Elliott *(Gen Mgr)*

Non-U.S. Subsidiary:

Fuchs Lubricants Canada Ltd. (2)
405 Dobbie Dr
PO Box 909
Cambridge, ON, N1R 5X9, Canada (100%)
Tel.: (519) 622-2040
Fax: (519) 622-2220
E-Mail: inquiry@fuchs.ca
Web Site: www.fuchs.ca
Emp.: 27
Industrial Lubricants Mfr.
S.I.C.: 2992
N.A.I.C.S.: 324191
Ron Gelens *(Pres)*

Fuchs Lubricants-Kansas City Division (1)
2140 S 88th St
Kansas City, KS 66111-1756 (100%)
Tel.: (913) 422-4022
Fax: (913) 441-2333
Web Site: www.fuchs.com
Emp.: 50
Lubricant Mfr
S.I.C.: 2992
N.A.I.C.S.: 324191
David Clark *(Pres)*

U.S. Subsidiary:

FUCHS CORPORATION (1)
17050 Lathrop Ave
Harvey, IL 60426
Tel.: (708) 333-8900
Fax: (708) 333-3813
Lubricant Mfr
S.I.C.: 2992
N.A.I.C.S.: 324191

Non-U.S. Divisions:

Fuchs Argentina S.A. (1)
Belgrano 2551
El Talar de Pacheco, 1618 Buenos Aires, NIL, Argentina (100%)
Tel.: (54) 1147361850
Fax: (54) 1147361861
E-Mail: info@fuchs.com.ar
Web Site: www.fuchs.com.ar
Emp.: 34
Mfr. of Mineral & Lubricating Oils
S.I.C.: 2992
N.A.I.C.S.: 324191
Antonio Goncalves de Oliveira *(Mng Dir)*

Fuchs Australia Pty. Ltd. (1)
49 McIntyre Rd
Sunshine, VIC, 3020, Australia (100%)
Mailing Address:
PO Box 146
Sunshine, VIC, 3020, Australia
Tel.: (61) 393006400
Fax: (61) 393006401
E-Mail: customer.service@fuchs.com.au
Web Site: www.fuchs.com.au
Sales Range: $25-49.9 Million
Emp.: 70
Mfr. of Mineral & Lubricating Oils
S.I.C.: 2992
N.A.I.C.S.: 324191

Fuchs Austria Schmiermittel Ges. mbH (1)
Braumuhlweg 13
PO Box 82
A 5101 Bergheim, Salzburg, Austria (70%)
Tel.: (43) 662450035
Fax: (43) 662454854
E-Mail: office@fuchs-austria.at
Web Site: www.fuchs-austria.at
Emp.: 25
Mfr. of Mineral & Lubricating Oils
S.I.C.: 2992
N.A.I.C.S.: 324191
Stephen Fuchs *(Pres)*

Fuchs Belgium N.V. (1)
Industriezone Heideveld 54
B 1654 Huizingen, Belgium (100%)
Tel.: (32) 23631991
Fax: (32) 23631919
E-Mail: fuchs.belgium@fuchsoil.com
Web Site: www.fuchsoil.com
Emp.: 50
Mfr. of Mineral & Lubricating Oils
S.I.C.: 2992
N.A.I.C.S.: 324191
Addy Robens *(Mng Dir & Dir-Sls)*

Fuchs Brasil S.A. (1)
Via Joao De Goes Km 1 214
BR CEP 06612 00 Jandira, Brazil (61%)
Tel.: (55) 147892311
Fax: (55) 147892670
E-Mail: fuchsbr@uol.com.br
Web Site: www.fuchslubrificantes.com.br
Sales Range: $10-24.9 Million
Emp.: 65
Mfr. of Lubricants
S.I.C.: 2992
N.A.I.C.S.: 324191

Fuchs Hellas S.A. (1)
2-4 Mesogeion AV
Athens Tower, 115 27 Athens, Greece (95.9%)
Tel.: (30) 2106712646
Fax: (30) 2106745535
E-Mail: info@fuchs.gr
Web Site: www.fuchs.gr
Emp.: 10
Mfr. of Mineral & Lubricating Oils
S.I.C.: 2992
N.A.I.C.S.: 324191
Alexander Constantinides *(Mng Dir)*

Fuchs Lubricantes S.A. (1)
Avda. de los Olmos, 1
Edificio A - 102
Parque Empresarial INBISA, E-01013 Vitoria, Spain (100%)
Tel.: (34) 945128096
Fax: (34) 945 26 2366
E-Mail: contact-es@fuchs.es
Web Site: www.fuchs.es
Mfr. of Mineral Oils
S.I.C.: 1499
N.A.I.C.S.: 212399

Fuchs Lubricantes S.A. (1)
Poligono Industrial San Vicente S N
Castellbisbal, 8755 Castellbisbal, Barcelona, Spain (100%)
Tel.: (34) 937730267
Fax: (34) 937730297
E-Mail: flor.inngo@fuchs.com
Web Site: www.fuchs.es
Emp.: 100
Mfr. of Lubricants
S.I.C.: 2992
N.A.I.C.S.: 324191
Ramon Gallifa *(Mgr-Sls)*

Fuchs Lubricants (Korea) Ltd. (1)
4F Ace Techno Tower 55-7 Mullae-dong 3-ga
Yeongdeungpo-gu, Seoul, 150 992, Korea (South) (100%)
Tel.: (82) 226725832
Fax: (82) 226725985
E-Mail: headoffice@fuchs-oil.co.kr
Web Site: www.fuchs-oil.co.kr
Emp.: 47
Mfr. of Mineral & Lubricating Oils
S.I.C.: 2992
N.A.I.C.S.: 324191
Kelvin Choi *(Mng Dir)*

Plant:

FUCHS LUBRICANTS (KOREA) LTD. - Ulsan Plant (2)
288-3 Koyeon-ri Ungchon-myeon
Ulju-gun, Ulsan, 689-871, Korea (South)
Tel.: (82) 5 988 4648
Fax: (82) 52 2 60 95 03
E-Mail: plant@fuchs-oil.co.kr
Emp.: 17
Lubricant Mfr
S.I.C.: 2992
N.A.I.C.S.: 324191
Calvin Choi *(Gen Mgr)*

Fuchs Lubricants (S.A.) (Pty.) Ltd. (1)
7 Diesel Rd
Johannesburg, Isando, South Africa (100%)
Mailing Address:
PO Box 95
Isando, 1600, South Africa
Tel.: (27) 11 565 9600
Fax: (27) 11 392 5686
E-Mail: contact-za@fuchsoil.co.za
Web Site: www.fuchsoil.co.za
Sales Range: $1-9.9 Million
Emp.: 100
Mfr of Mineral & Lubricating Oils
S.I.C.: 2992
N.A.I.C.S.: 324191

Fuchs Lubricants (Shanghai) Ltd. (1)
No 888 Jiaxiu Rd High Technology Development Zone
Nanxiang, Shanghai, Jiading, 201802, China (100%)
Tel.: (86) 2139122000
Fax: (86) 2139122100
Web Site: www.fuchs.com.cn
Emp.: 20
Mfr. of Mineral & Lubricating Oils
S.I.C.: 2992
N.A.I.C.S.: 324191

Fuchs Lubricants Taiwan Corp. (1)
8 F No 35 Kan Ku St
Taipei, 103, Taiwan (100%)
Tel.: (886) 225555093
Fax: (886) 225598005
E-Mail: fuchstw@fuchs.com.tw
Web Site: www.fuchs.com.tw
Rev.: $1,900,000
Emp.: 10
Mfr. of Mineral Oils
S.I.C.: 2992
N.A.I.C.S.: 324191
Henry Shiang *(Gen Mgr)*

Non-U.S. Subsidiary:

Fuchs Lubricants (Hong Kong) Ltd. (2)
Flat R 11 F Block III
Camel Paint Bldg
60 Hoi Yuen Rd, Kwun Tong Kowloon, China (Hong Kong) (100%)
Tel.: (852) 24179770
Fax: (852) 24154398
E-Mail: admin@fuch.com.hk
Web Site: www.fuchs.com.hk
Sales Range: Less than $1 Million
Mfr. of Mineral Oils
S.I.C.: 1499
N.A.I.C.S.: 212399

Fuchs Lubricants (UK) Plc. (1)
New Century St
Stoke-on-Trent, Staffordshire, ST1 5HU, United Kingdom (100%)
Tel.: (44) 8701200400
Fax: (44) 782202072
E-Mail: alluk@fuchsoil.com
Web Site: www.fuchslubricants.com
Sls.: $117,096,680
Emp.: 250
Holding Company-UK
S.I.C.: 6719
N.A.I.C.S.: 551112
Richard Halhead *(CEO)*

Subsidiaries:

B & N Base Oils Ltd. (2)
St Anns House King St
Knutsford, Cheshire, WA16 6PD, United Kingdom (100%)
Tel.: (44) 1565633365
Fax: (44) 1565653525
E-Mail: ann@b-nbaseoils.co.uk
Web Site: www.b-nbaseoils.co.uk
Emp.: 2
Mfr. of Lubricants
S.I.C.: 2992
N.A.I.C.S.: 324191
Alan Bell *(Mng Dir)*

Fuchs Lubricants (UK) PLC (2)
New Century St
Hanley, Stoke-on-Trent, Stafs, ST1 5HU, United Kingdom (100%)
Tel.: (44) 8701200400
Fax: (44) 01782202072
E-Mail: alluk@fuchsoil.com
Web Site: www.fuchslubricants.com
Emp.: 1,000
Mfr. of Mineral & Lubricating Oils
S.I.C.: 2992
N.A.I.C.S.: 324191
Richard Haihead *(Mng Dir)*

Fuchs Lubricants (Yingkou) Ltd. (1)
No 17 N Quinghua Road
Xishi District, Yingkou, 115003, China (100%)
Tel.: (86) 4174832449
Fax: (86) 4174806738
E-Mail: wang.dan@fuchs.com.cn
Web Site: www.fuchs.com
Sales Range: $10-24.9 Million
Emp.: 100
Mfr. of Lubricating Oils
S.I.C.: 2992
N.A.I.C.S.: 324191
Xu Qing Ping *(Pres)*

Fuchs Lubrifiants France S.A. (1)
1 Rue Lavoisier
F 92002 Nanterre, France (89.55%)
Mailing Address:
PO Box 209
F-92002 Nanterre, Cedex, France
Tel.: (33) 141374200
Fax: (33) 141374202
E-Mail: mariechristine.domalain@fuchsoil.com
Web Site: www.cosranexport.com
Emp.: 100
Mfr. of Lubricating Oils
S.I.C.: 2992
N.A.I.C.S.: 324191

Divisions:

FUCHS LUBRIFIANT FRANCE S.A. - Auto-Moto Division (2)
81 rue de l Industrie
92565 Rueil-Malmaison, France
Tel.: (33) 1 41 37 42 00
Fax: (33) 1 41 37 42 01
E-Mail: auto.siege@fuchs-oil.com
Web Site: www.fuchseurope.com
Lubricant Mfr
S.I.C.: 2992
N.A.I.C.S.: 324191

FUCHS LUBRIFIANT FRANCE S.A. - Industrie Division (2)
83 rue de l'Industrie
92565 Rueil-Malmaison, France
Tel.: (33) 1 41 37 79 00
Fax: (33) 1 41 37 79 17
E-Mail: indus.siege@fuchs-oil.com
Web Site: www.fuchseurope.com
Emp.: 300
Lubricant Mfr
S.I.C.: 2992
N.A.I.C.S.: 324191
Marc Seche *(Gen Mgr)*

Subsidiaries:

Etablissements Prate S.A. (2)
25 Rue Augustin Drapiez
F 59000 Lille, France (100%)
Tel.: (33) 320537648
Fax: (33) 320882849
E-Mail: hasa.nord@wanadoo.fr
Web Site: www.fuchs-oil.com
Emp.: 20
Mfr. of Mineral Oils
S.I.C.: 2992
N.A.I.C.S.: 324191

Fuchs Lubrifants France S.A. (2)
1 Rue Lavoisier
F 92002 Nanterre, France (100%)

Tel.: (33) 0141377900
Fax: (33) 141377917
E-Mail: mariechristine.domalain@fuchsoil.com
Web Site: www.fuchsoil.com
Rev.: $19,126,420
Emp.: 300
Mfr. of Mineral & Lubricating Oils
S.I.C.: 2992
N.A.I.C.S.: 324191
Marc Feche *(Gen Mgr)*

Fuchs Lubrifiant France S.A. **(2)**
81 Rue De lIndustrie
F 92502 Rueil-Malmaison, France (100%)
Mailing Address:
PO Box 209
F-92002 Nanterre, Cedex, France
Tel.: (33) 0141374200
Fax: (33) 141374216
E-Mail: jean-luc@fuchsoil.com
Web Site: www.fuchsoil.com
Sales Range: $25-49.9 Million
Emp.: 300
Mfr. of Mineral & Lubricating Oils
S.I.C.: 2992
N.A.I.C.S.: 324191
Jeanluc Possolon *(Gen Mgr-Automotive Div)*

Fuchs Lubrificantes, Unipessoal, Lda. **(1)**
Zn Indus Maia I Sector VII
Moreira Da Maia, P4470597 Maia, Portugal (100%)
Tel.: (351) 229479364
Fax: (351) 229440957
E-Mail: fuchs@fuchs.pt
Web Site: www.fuchs.pt
Emp.: 23
Mfr. of Lubricants
S.I.C.: 2992
N.A.I.C.S.: 324191
Paul Cezanne *(Mng Dir)*

Fuchs Lubritech UK Ltd **(1)**
8 Eley Rd
London, N18 3DB, United Kingdom
Tel.: (44) 2083455566
Fax: (44) 2088843255
E-Mail: info@fuchs-lubritech.co.uk
Web Site: www.fuchs-lubritech.co.uk
Emp.: 30
Mfr. of Mineral & Lubricating Oils
S.I.C.: 2992
N.A.I.C.S.: 324191
Harry Vithlani *(Mng Dir)*

Fuchs Maziva D.O.O. **(1)**
1st Krmica 8
Domaslovec, HR 10430 Samobor, Croatia (100%)
Tel.: (385) 13380526
Fax: (385) 13380527
Web Site: www.fuchs-maziva.hr/
Emp.: 20
Mfr. of Mineral & Lubricating Oils
S.I.C.: 2992
N.A.I.C.S.: 324191
Goran Karabai *(Gen Mgr)*

Fuchs Oil Corporation (CZ) Spol. s r.o. **(1)**
Logistic Ctr
Otice No 40, CZ 25163 Prague, Czech Republic (100%)
Tel.: (420) 323637793
Fax: (420) 323637990
E-Mail: fuchs.praha@fuchsoil.cz
Web Site: www.fuchsoil.cz
Emp.: 32
Mfr. of Mineral & Lubricating Oils
S.I.C.: 2992
N.A.I.C.S.: 324191
John Holansky *(Mng Dir)*

Fuchs Oil Corporation (PL) SP. Z O.O. **(1)**
Ul Kujawska 102
PL 44 101 Gliwice, Poland (100%)
Tel.: (48) 324012200
Fax: (48) 324012255
E-Mail: gliwice@fuchs-oil.pl
Web Site: www.fuchs-oil.pl
Emp.: 140
Mfr. of Mineral & Lubricating Oils
S.I.C.: 2992
N.A.I.C.S.: 324191
Tomass Jagla *(Mng Dir)*

Fuchs Oil Finland Oy **(1)**
Myllarinkatu 22
65100 Vaasa, Finland (100%)
Tel.: (358) 207459660
Fax: (358) 207459667
E-Mail: fuchs@fuchs-oil.fi
Web Site: www.fuchs-oil.fi
Emp.: 6
Mineral & Lubricating Oils Mfr
S.I.C.: 2992
N.A.I.C.S.: 324191

Fuchs-Petrochema Spol. s.r.o. **(1)**
Stvrt Nalepku 751 1
976 97 Nemecke, Slovakia (100%)
Tel.: (421) 482858750
Fax: (421) 482858759
E-Mail: fuchs@fuchs.sk
Web Site: www.fuchs.sk
Sales Range: Less than $1 Million
Emp.: 12
Mineral & Lubricating Oils
S.I.C.: 2992
N.A.I.C.S.: 324191

Fuchs Petrolub AG - CASSIDA Division **(1)**
Heideveld 54
1654 Huizingen, Belgium
Tel.: (32) 2 363 19 33
Fax: (32) 2 363 19 00
Lubricant Mfr
S.I.C.: 2992
N.A.I.C.S.: 324191

Fuchs Petrolub AG - HEIN DE WINDT Division **(1)**
Heideveld 54
1654 Huizingen, Belgium
Tel.: (32) 2 363 19 38
Fax: (32) 2 363 19 00
E-Mail: info@heindewindt.com
Web Site: www.fuchsbenelux.com
Emp.: 6
Lubricant Mfr
S.I.C.: 2992
N.A.I.C.S.: 324191
Eddy Robins *(Gen Mgr)*

Fuchs Petrolub AG - PACIFIC DIVISION **(1)**
19829 - 99A Ave
Langley, BC, V1M 3G4, Canada
Tel.: (604) 888-1552
Fax: (604) 888-1145
Web Site: www.fuchs-oil.com
Emp.: 20
Lubricant Mfr
S.I.C.: 2992
N.A.I.C.S.: 324191
Daniel Woo *(Gen Mgr)*

Hein de Windt B.V. **(1)**
Fabriekstraat 14
P.O. Box 91
NL-7000 AB Doetinchem, Netherlands (100%)
Mailing Address:
P.O. Box 91
7000 AB Doetinchem, Netherlands
Tel.: (31) 4 33 42 54
Telex: 45 49 9 oils nl
Fax: (31) 4 32 68 47
Holding Company
S.I.C.: 6719
N.A.I.C.S.: 551112

Makoto-Fuchs K.K. **(1)**
1488 Hatakeda 8 Chome
Oji Cho Kitakatsuragi Gun, Nara, 636 0021, Japan (50%)
Tel.: (81) 745731121
Fax: (81) 745731140
E-Mail: makotofuchs.k.k@ma.neweb.ne.jp
Web Site: www.makotofuchs.co.jp
Sales Range: $25-49.9 Million
Emp.: 100
Mfr. of Mineral & Lubricating Oils
S.I.C.: 2992
N.A.I.C.S.: 324191
Seiji Ikeda *(Mng Dir)*

Motorex AG Langenthal **(1)**
Bern Zurich Strasse 31
CH 4901 Langenthal, Switzerland (50%)
Tel.: (41) 629197474
Fax: (41) 629197696
E-Mail: motorex@motorex.com
Web Site: www.motorex.com
Sales Range: $10-24.9 Million
Emp.: 250
Mineral & Lubricating Oils Mfr
S.I.C.: 2992
N.A.I.C.S.: 324191
Hugo Fisch *(CEO)*

Non-U.S. Subsidiaries:

CENTURY OILS INTERNATIONAL LTD **(1)**
New Century Street
Stoke-on-Trent, Staffordshire, ST1 5HU, United Kingdom
Tel.: (44) 1782203700
Fax: (44) 1782202073
Lubricant Mfr
S.I.C.: 2992
N.A.I.C.S.: 324191
Richard John Halhead *(Mng Dir)*

FUCHS DO BRASIL S.A **(1)**
Via de Acesso Joao de Goes No 1 110
Bairro Fazenda Itaquiti
Barueri, Sao Paulo, 06422-150, Brazil
Tel.: (55) 11 47 89 39 35
Fax: (55) 11 47 89 26 70
Web Site: www.fuchsbr.com.br
Lubricant Mfr
S.I.C.: 2992
N.A.I.C.S.: 324191

FUCHS JAPAN LTD. **(1)**
Kamiya-cho MT Bldg 13F 4-3-20
Tokyo, 105-0001, Japan
Tel.: (81) 3 3436 8303
Fax: (81) 3 3436 8301
Web Site: www.fuchs.co.jp
Lubricant Mfr
S.I.C.: 2992
N.A.I.C.S.: 324191

Plants:

FUCHS JAPAN LTD. - Chiba Factory **(2)**
245-2 Kawarago
Shiroi, Chiba-ken, 270-1403, Japan
Tel.: (81) 47 497 0039
Fax: (81) 47 492 2416
Web Site: www.fuchs.co.jp/en/index.html
Lubricant Mfr
S.I.C.: 2992
N.A.I.C.S.: 324191

FUCHS JAPAN LTD - Iga Ueno Factory **(2)**
408-3 Aza Saburodani Ouchi
Iga, Mie-ken, 518-0034, Japan
Tel.: (81) 595 20 1114
Fax: (81) 595 20 1056
Web Site: www.fuchs.co.jp/en/index.html
Lubricant Mfr
S.I.C.: 2992
N.A.I.C.S.: 324191
Liye Maeyama *(COO)*

FUCHS LUBRICANTS (AUSTRALASIA) PTY. LTD. **(1)**
49 McIntyre Road
Sunshine, VIC, 3020, Australia
Tel.: (61) 3 9300 6400
Fax: (61) 3 9300 6401
E-Mail: orders@fuchs.com.au
Web Site: www.fuchs.com.au
Lubricant Mfr & Distr
S.I.C.: 2992
N.A.I.C.S.: 324191

Division:

FUCHS LUBRICANTS (AUSTRALASIA) PTY. LTD. - FUCHS LUBRITECH ASIA PACIFIC Division **(2)**
49 McIntyre Road
Sunshine, VIC, 3020, Australia
Tel.: (61) 3 93 00 64 00
Fax: (61) 3 93 00 64 01
E-Mail: info@fuchslubritech.com.au
Emp.: 1
Lubricant Mfr
S.I.C.: 2992
N.A.I.C.S.: 324191

FUCHS LUBRICANTS BENELUX N.V. / S.A **(1)**
Industriezone Heideveld 54
1654 Huizingen, Belgium
Tel.: (32) 2 363 19 39
Fax: (32) 2 363 19 19
E-Mail: fuchsbenelux@fuchs-oil.com
Emp.: 57
Lubricant Mfr
S.I.C.: 2992
N.A.I.C.S.: 324191
Robins Eddi *(Gen Mgr)*

FUCHS LUBRICANTS (CHINA) CO LTD. **(1)**
No 888 Jiaxiu Rd High Technology Development Zone Nanxiang
Jiading, Shanghai, 201802, China
Tel.: (86) 21 3912 2000
Fax: (86) 21 3912 2100
Web Site: www.fuchs.com.cn/fuchs/eindex/about.asp
Lubricant Mfr
S.I.C.: 2992
N.A.I.C.S.: 324191

Division:

FUCHS LUBRICANTS (CHINA) CO. LTD. - FUCHS LUBRITECH Division **(2)**
No 888 Jiaxiu Road High Technology Development Zone Nanxiang
Jiading District, Shanghai, 201802, China
Tel.: (86) 21 3912 2000
Fax: (86) 21 6917 3740
Lubricant Mfr
S.I.C.: 2992
N.A.I.C.S.: 324191

FUCHS LUBRICANTS PTE . LTD. **(1)**
13A Tech Park Crescent Tuas Techpark
Singapore, 637843, Singapore
Tel.: (65) 6558 8133
Fax: (65) 6863 0603
Web Site: www.fuchs.com.sg
Lubricant Mfr
S.I.C.: 2992
N.A.I.C.S.: 324191
Stefan Fuchs *(Chm-Exec Bd)*
Alexander Selent *(Vice Chm-Exec Bd)*

FUCHS LUBRIFICANTI S.P.A . **(1)**
Via Riva 16
14021 Buttigliera, Italy
Tel.: (39) 011 99 22 811
Fax: (39) 011 99 22 857
E-Mail: info.indu@fuchslubrificanti.it
Web Site: www.fuchslubrificanti.it
Rev.: $70,790,000
Emp.: 10
Lubricant Mfr
S.I.C.: 2992
N.A.I.C.S.: 324191
Carlo Ostino *(Mng Dir)*

FUCHS LUBRITECH INTERNATIONAL (UK) LTD **(1)**
8 Eley Road
London, N18 3DB, United Kingdom
Tel.: (44) 20 8345 5566
Fax: (44) 20 8884 3255
E-Mail: info@fuchs-lubritech.co.uk
Emp.: 40
Lubricant Mfr
S.I.C.: 2992
N.A.I.C.S.: 324191
Harry Vithlani *(Mng Dir)*

FUCHS LUBRITECH S.A.S **(1)**
1 Route d'Ungersheim Z I
Boite Postale 07
68190 Ensisheim, France
Tel.: (33) 3 89 83 67 50
Fax: (33) 3 89 83 64 20
E-Mail: services@fuchs-lubritech.fr
Web Site: www.fuchs-lubritech.fr
Lubricant Mfr
S.I.C.: 2992
N.A.I.C.S.: 324191

FUCHS MAK DOOEL **(1)**
Bul Praska Br 23
1000 Skopje, Macedonia
Tel.: (389) 2 309 0 309
Fax: (389) 2 309 0 409
E-Mail: fuchsmak@fuchs.com.mk
Web Site: www.fuchs.com.mk
Lubricant Distr
S.I.C.: 5172
N.A.I.C.S.: 424720
Goran Kormusoski *(Gen Mgr)*

Fuchs Petrolub AG—(Continued)

FUCHS MAZIVA LSL D.O.O (1)
Trdinova Ulica 1
8250 Brezice, Slovenia
Tel.: (386) 7 499 10 30
Fax: (386) 7 499 10 40
E-Mail: info@fuchs.si
Web Site: www.fuchs.si
Emp.: 9
Lubricant Mfr
S.I.C.: 2992
N.A.I.C.S.: 324191
Pedro Hernandez *(Gen Mgr)*

FUCHS OIL HUNGARIA KFT (1)
Gyar U 2
2040 Budaors, Hungary
Tel.: (36) 23 428 924
Fax: (36) 23 420 771
E-Mail: fuchs@fuchs-oil.hu
Web Site: www.fuchs-oil.hu
Lubricant Mfr
S.I.C.: 2992
N.A.I.C.S.: 324191

FUCHS PETROLEUM S.A.R.L. (1)
Moussa Center Safra Highway Keserwan
PO Box 10
Jounieh, Keserwan, Lebanon
Tel.: (961) 9 853071 2
Fax: (961) 9 853070
E-Mail: info@fuchs.com.lb
Web Site: www.fuchs.com.lb
Lubricant Mfr
S.I.C.: 2992
N.A.I.C.S.: 324191

FUCHS PETROLUBE (MALAYSIA) SDN . BHD. (1)
28 Jalan Modal 23/2 Section 23 Kawasan MIEL 8
40300 Shah Alam, Selangor Darul Ehsan, Malaysia
Tel.: (60) 3 5548 8100
Fax: (60) 3 5548 7172
E-Mail: info@fuchs.com.my
Web Site: www.fuchs.com.my
Lubricant Distr
S.I.C.: 5172
N.A.I.C.S.: 424720
Simon Low *(Mng Dir)*

FUCHS SMORJMEDEL SVERIGE AB (1)
Garnisonsgatan 25A
25466 Helsingborg, Sweden
Tel.: (46) 42 256 690
Fax: (46) 42 256 698
E-Mail: info@fuchs-oil.se
Web Site: www.fuchs-oil.se
Emp.: 5
Lubricant Distr
S.I.C.: 2999
N.A.I.C.S.: 324199
Sabine Hausmann *(Mgr-Compliance)*

JV FUCHS MAST YLA UKRAINA (1)
Shevchenko Str 327-A
PO Box 8250
L'viv, Ukraine
Tel.: (380) 32 235 08 14
Fax: (380) 32 235 08 15
E-Mail: fuchs@fuchs-oil.com.ua
Web Site: www.fuchs-oil.com.ua
Emp.: 3
Lubricant Distr
S.I.C.: 5172
N.A.I.C.S.: 424720
Serhiy Lobozynskyy *(Gen Mgr)*

LUBRICANTES FUCHS DE MEXICO S.A. DE C.V. (1)
Acceso C No 101 Parque Industrial Jurica
Queretaro, Mexico 76120
Tel.: (52) 442 2 38 91 00
Fax: (52) 442 2 38 91 10
E-Mail: info@fuchs.com.mx
Web Site: www.fuchs.com.mx
Lubricant Mfr
S.I.C.: 2999
N.A.I.C.S.: 324199

OOO FUCHS OIL (1)
Aviakonstruktora Mikoyana Str 12
125252 Moscow, Russia
Tel.: (7) 495 961 27 41
Fax: (7) 495 961 01 90
E-Mail: info@fuchs-oil.ru
Web Site: www.fuchs-oil.ru
Emp.: 6
Lubricant Mfr
S.I.C.: 2992
N.A.I.C.S.: 324191
Mikhail Zlotski *(Gen Mgr)*

PROMOTORA FUCHS S.A. DE C.V. (1)
Manzana 1 Acceso C No 101 Parque Industrial Jurica
Queretaro, 76120, Mexico
Tel.: (52) 4422389100
Fax: (52) 4422389100
Lubricant Mfr
S.I.C.: 2992
N.A.I.C.S.: 324191

PT FUCHS INDONESIA (1)
Jl Jababeka VI SFB Blok J 6 KL Cikarang Industrial Estate
Bekasi, 17530, Indonesia
Tel.: (62) 21 893 49 60
Fax: (62) 21 893 49 58
E-Mail: jakarta@fuchs.co.id
Web Site: www.fuchs.co.id
Lubricant Mfr
S.I.C.: 2992
N.A.I.C.S.: 324191

SIAM - FUCHS LUBRICANTS CO. LTD. (1)
252 SPE Tower 11th Floor Phaholyothin Road Samsannai
Phayathai, Bangkok, 10400, Thailand
Tel.: (66) 2 615 0168 75
Fax: (66) 2 615 0167
Web Site: www.siam-fuchs.com
Emp.: 25
Lubricant Distr
S.I.C.: 5172
N.A.I.C.S.: 424720
Chayuth Temnitikul *(Mgr)*

Non-U.S. Joint Ventures:

Alhamrani-Fuchs Petroleum Saudi Arabia Ltd. (1)
Tahlia St
PO Box 7103
Jeddah, 21462, Saudi Arabia
Tel.: (966) 26635666
Fax: (966) 26633702
E-Mail: info@fuchs.com.sa
Web Site: www.fuchs.com.sa
Sales Range: $75-99.9 Million
Emp.: 75
Mfr. of Lubricants
S.I.C.: 2992
N.A.I.C.S.: 324191
Zafar Talpur *(Pres)*

Fuchs Lubricants (India) Limited (1)
Sarjan Plaza 2nd Floor 100 Dr Annie Besant Road
Worli, Mumbai, 400 018, India (100%)
Tel.: (91) 2266255900
Telex: 11 85592 blby in
Fax: (91) 2266661049
E-Mail: marketing@fuchsindia.com
Web Site: www.fuchsindia.com
Emp.: 15
S.I.C.: 2992
N.A.I.C.S.: 324191
Kersi Hilloo *(Mng Dir)*

FUCHUN COMMUNICATIONS CO., LTD.

25 Zone C 89
Fuzhou, 350003, China
Tel.: (86) 591 83992010
Fax: (86) 591 83920667
Web Site: www.forcom.com.cn
300299—(CHIN)
Sales Range: $10-24.9 Million
Emp.: 580
Business Description:
Communication Network Construction & Other Related Services
S.I.C.: 1629
N.A.I.C.S.: 237130
Personnel:
Pinzhang Miao *(Chm)*

FUDA FAUCET WORKS, INC.

Ge Jia Ba Hua Ting
Yiyang, Jiangxi, 334400, China
Tel.: (86) 793 5887178
Web Site: www.jxfuda.com
Year Founded: 1995
Sales Range: $25-49.9 Million
Emp.: 405
Business Description:
Brass Faucets, Spouts & Fittings Mfr
S.I.C.: 3432
N.A.I.C.S.: 332913
Personnel:
Yiting Wu *(Chm & CEO)*
Yaxu Wu *(CFO)*
Board of Directors:
Yiting Wu
Jibrin Issa Jibrin Al Jibrin
Shaohua Shu
Yaxu Wu

FUDO TETRA CORPORATION

7-2 Nihonbashi-koami-chou
Chuou-ku, Tokyo, 103-0016, Japan
Tel.: (81) 3 5644 8535
Fax: (81) 3 5644 8537
E-Mail: geo@fudotetra.co.jp
Web Site: www.fudotetra.co.jp
Year Founded: 1947
1813—(TKS)
Emp.: 816
Business Description:
Geo Engineering Services
S.I.C.: 8711
N.A.I.C.S.: 541330
Personnel:
Yuji Takehara *(Pres)*

FUELCELLPOWER CO., LTD.

D-301 Bundang Techno Park 151 Yatap
Bundang, Songnam, Gyeonggi, 463-760, Korea (South)
Tel.: (82) 31 781 0475
Fax: (82) 31 781 0476
Web Site: www.fuelcellpower.co.kr
139170—(KRS)
Business Description:
Fuel Cell Products Mfr
S.I.C.: 3612
N.A.I.C.S.: 335311
Personnel:
Meenam Shinn *(CEO)*
Hosuk Kim *(COO)*
Haesung Cho *(CMO)*
Byungsun Hong *(CTO)*

FUER INTERNATIONAL, INC.

Neiwei Road
Fulaerji District, Qiqihar, Heiloingjiang, 161041, China
Tel.: (86) 452 6969150
Web Site: www.fuergroup.com
Year Founded: 1984
Sales Range: $25-49.9 Million
Emp.: 217
Business Description:
Holding Company; Feed & Fertilizers
S.I.C.: 6719
N.A.I.C.S.: 551112
Personnel:
Zhang Li *(CEO)*
Haitao Li *(CTO)*
Board of Directors:
Huabang Chen
Xiaowei Cui
Zeyu Li
Zhang Li
Yuhua Liu

FUERST DAY LAWSON LTD.

Devon House 58-60 St Katharine's Way
London, E1W 1JP, United Kingdom
Tel.: (44) 20 7488 0777
Fax: (44) 20 7265 5285
Web Site: www.fdlworld.com
Year Founded: 1986
Sales Range: $250-299.9 Million
Emp.: 219
Business Description:
Food & Beverage Ingredient Whslr
S.I.C.: 5148
N.A.I.C.S.: 424480
Personnel:
Maurice Day Lawson *(Chm)*
Mac Mardi *(CEO)*
Guy Humphry-Baker *(CFO)*
Board of Directors:
Maurice Day Lawson
Bai Dai Hua
Guy Humphry-Baker
Mac Mardi
Richard Slowe

FUETREK CO., LTD.

Shin-osaka Prime Tower 18F 6-1-1 Nishinakajima
Yodogawa-ku, Osaka, 532-0011, Japan
Tel.: (81) 6 4806 3112
Fax: (81) 6 4806 3119
Web Site: www.fuetrek.co.jp
2468—(TKS)
Emp.: 125
Business Description:
Software Development Services
S.I.C.: 7371
N.A.I.C.S.: 541511
Personnel:
Hideyuki Fujiki *(Pres & CEO)*

FUFENG GROUP LIMITED

No 29 Jinghai 2nd Rd East Side
Beijing Econ-Tech Dev Area, Beijing, China 101111
Tel.: (86) 10 67892679
Fax: (86) 10 67892068
Web Site: www.fufeng-group.com
FFO1—(DEU)
Sales Range: $1-4.9 Billion
Emp.: 2,800
Business Description:
Biochemical Products Mfr
S.I.C.: 2899
N.A.I.C.S.: 325199
Personnel:
Xuechun Li *(Chm)*

FUGRO GEOTECHNIQUE

Parc Des Peupliers 27 Rue Des Peupliers
92000 Nanterre, Hauts De Seine, France
Tel.: (33) 155691770
Fax: (33) 155691777
Web Site: www.fugro.fr/contact/contactGSA_c.asp
Rev.: $23,400,000
Emp.: 175
Business Description:
Engineering Services
S.I.C.: 8711
N.A.I.C.S.: 541330
Personnel:
Arnold Steenbakker *(Chm)*
Board of Directors:
Arnold Steenbakker

FUGRO N.V.

Veurse Achterweg 10
2264 SG Leidschendam, Netherlands
Tel.: (31) 703111422
Fax: (31) 703202703
E-Mail: holding@fugro.com
Web Site: www.fugro.com
Year Founded: 1961
FUR—(EUR)
Rev.: $2,914,452,665
Assets: $5,613,146,588
Liabilities: $2,949,925,591

Net Worth: $2,663,220,997
Earnings: $405,792,177
Emp.: 12,165
Fiscal Year-end: 12/31/12

Business Description:
Geophysical Surveying & Mapping Services
S.I.C.: 8713
N.A.I.C.S.: 541360

Personnel:
Harrie L.J. Noy *(Chm-Supervisory Bd)*
Paul van Riel *(Chm-Mgmt Bd & CEO)*
J.A. Colligan *(Vice Chm-Supervisory Bd)*
Andre Jonkman *(CFO & Member-Mgmt Bd)*
Walter Scott Rainey *(Member-Mgmt Bd & Dir-Geotechnical Div)*
Steve Thomson *(Member-Mgmt Bd & Dir-Subsea Svcs-Geoscience Div)*
W.G.M. Mulders *(Sec)*

Supervisory Board of Directors:
Harrie L.J. Noy
J.A. Colligan
M. Helmes
Gert Jan Kramer
Jan Carel Maarten Schonfeld
Th. Smith

Subsidiary:

Fugro Nederland B.V. **(1)**
Veurse Achterweg 10
Leidschendam, 2264 SG, Netherlands
Tel.: (31) 703111422
Fax: (31) 703202640
E-Mail: geomonitoring@fugro.nl
Geophysical Surveying & Mapping Services
S.I.C.: 8713
N.A.I.C.S.: 541360

Subsidiaries:

Fugro Aerial Mapping B.V. **(2)**
Dillenburgsingel 69
2263 HW Leidschendam, Netherlands
Tel.: (31) 70 317 0700
Fax: (31) 70 317 0750
E-Mail: info@flimap.nl
Web Site: www.flimap.nl
Emp.: 19
Geophysical Surveying & Mapping Services
S.I.C.: 8713
N.A.I.C.S.: 541360
Bob Valten *(Gen Mgr)*

Fugro C.I.S. B.V. **(2)**
Veurse Achterweg 10
Leidschendam, 2264 SG, Netherlands
Tel.: (31) 703111422
Fax: (31) 703202703
E-Mail: info@fli-map.nl
Geophysical Mapping Services
S.I.C.: 8713
N.A.I.C.S.: 541360

Fugro-Ecoplan B.V. **(2)**
Parkstraat 83
2514 JG Hague, Netherlands
Tel.: (31) 70 363 29 29
E-Mail: info@fugro-ecoplan.nl
Web Site: www.fugro-ecoplan.nl
Environmental Consulting Services
S.I.C.: 8999
N.A.I.C.S.: 541620
Alice Ommerth *(Sec)*

Fugro-Elbocon B.V. **(2)**
Veurse Achterweg 10
Leidschendam, 2264 SG, Netherlands
Tel.: (31) 703111422
Engineering Services
S.I.C.: 8711
N.A.I.C.S.: 541330

Fugro Engineers B.V. **(2)**
Veurse Achterwag 10
2264 SG Leidschendam, Netherlands
Tel.: (31) 70 311 1444
Fax: (31) 70320 36 40
E-Mail: holding@fugro.com
Emp.: 25
Engineering Services
S.I.C.: 8711
N.A.I.C.S.: 541330
Harry Kolk *(Mng Dir)*

Fugro GeoServices B.V. **(2)**
Veurse Achterweg 10
Postbus 63
2260 AB Leidschendam, Netherlands
Tel.: (31) 70 311 1333
Fax: (31) 70 327 7091
E-Mail: info@fugro.nl
Web Site: www.fugro.com
Emp.: 30
Geophysical Surveying & Mapping Services
S.I.C.: 8713
N.A.I.C.S.: 541360

Fugro Ingenieursbureau B.V. **(2)**
Veurse Achterweg 10
2264 SG Leidschendam, Netherlands
Tel.: (31) 70 311 1422
Fax: (31) 70 320 2703
E-Mail: info@fugro.nl
Geophysical Survey & Positioning Services
S.I.C.: 8713
N.A.I.C.S.: 541360

Fugro-Inpark B.V. **(2)**
Dillenburgsingel 69
PO Box 3000
2260 DA Leidschendam, Netherlands
Tel.: (31) 70 3170700
Fax: (31) 70 3170708
E-Mail: info@fugro-inpark.nl
Engineering Services
S.I.C.: 8711
N.A.I.C.S.: 541330
Pim Voogd *(Project Mgr)*

Fugro Intersite B.V. **(2)**
Dillenburgsingel 69
2263 HW Leidschendam, Netherlands
Tel.: (31) 70 31 11888
Fax: (31) 70 31 11890
E-Mail: intersite.helpdesk@fugro.nl
Emp.: 4
Engineering Services
S.I.C.: 8711
N.A.I.C.S.: 541330
Arnold Jongsma *(Gen Mgr)*

Fugro Marine Services B.V. **(2)**
Dillenburgsingel 69
Leidschendam, 2263 HW, Netherlands
Tel.: (31) 70 311 9100
Fax: (31) 70 311 9111
Web Site: www.fugro.nl
Emp.: 50
Marine Vessel Management Services
S.I.C.: 4499
N.A.I.C.S.: 488330
Willem Heijliger *(Gen Mgr)*

Fugro Survey B.V. **(2)**
Veurse Achterweg 12
2264 SG Leidschendam, Netherlands
Tel.: (31) 70 3111800
Fax: (31) 70 3111838
E-Mail: fugrosurvey@fugro.nl
Web Site: www.fugro-africa.com
Emp.: 70
Geophysical Surveying & Mapping Services
S.I.C.: 8713
N.A.I.C.S.: 541360
Mark Heine *(Gen Mgr)*

Fugro Vastgoed B.V. **(2)**
Veurse Achterweg 10
Leidschendam, 2264 SG, Netherlands
Tel.: (31) 703111422
Fax: (31) 703202703
Emp.: 7
Engineering Services
S.I.C.: 8711
N.A.I.C.S.: 541330
K. S. Wester *(Gen Mgr)*

Inpark Detacheringen B.V. **(2)**
Veurse Achterweg 10
Leidschendam, 2264 SG, Netherlands
Tel.: (31) 70 3111422
Fax: (31) 70 3202703
E-Mail: holding@fugro.com
Emp.: 900
Construction Engineering Services
S.I.C.: 8711
N.A.I.C.S.: 541330
Klaas Wester *(Pres)*

OmniSTAR B.V. **(2)**
Vlietweg 17h
2266 KA Leidschendam, Netherlands
Tel.: (31) 70 317 0900
Fax: (31) 70 317 0919
E-Mail: eu_corrections@omnistar.com
Global Navigation Satellite System Research Services
S.I.C.: 9661
N.A.I.C.S.: 927110

U.S. Subsidiary:

OmniSTAR, Inc. **(3)**
8200 Westglen Dr
Houston, TX 77063
Tel.: (713) 785-5850
Fax: (832) 538-0216
Toll Free: (888) 666-4732
E-Mail: am_corrections@omnistar.com
Geophysical Surveying & Mapping Services
S.I.C.: 8713
N.A.I.C.S.: 541360
Dwayne Janecek *(Controller)*

Non-U.S. Subsidiaries:

Fugro OmniSTAR Pte. Ltd. **(3)**
35 Loyang Cres
Singapore, 509012, Singapore SG
Tel.: (65) 65425001
Fax: (65) 65422208
E-Mail: asia_corrections@omnistar.com
Web Site: www.omnistar.com.sg
Emp.: 7
Global Positioning System Support Services
S.I.C.: 8999
N.A.I.C.S.: 541690

OmniSTAR (Pty) Ltd. **(3)**
2 Fir Street Black River Park Old Warehouse Building Observatory
7925 Cape Town, South Africa ZA
Tel.: (27) 21 404 1861
Fax: (27) 21 447 4546
E-Mail: africa_corrections@omnistar.com
Web Site: www.omnistar.com
Emp.: 8
Geophysical Surveying & Positioning Services
S.I.C.: 8713
N.A.I.C.S.: 541360

U.S. Subsidiaries:

Fugro (USA), Inc. **(1)**
6100 Hillcroft St
Houston, TX 77081-1009 DE (100%)
Mailing Address:
PO Box 740010
Houston, TX 77274-0010
Tel.: (713) 346-4050
Telex: 7785573
Fax: (713) 346-4054
Web Site: www.fugro.com
Emp.: 400
Geotechnical Engineering, Marine Geosciences, Construction Services & Surveying
S.I.C.: 1389
N.A.I.C.S.: 213112
Sundra Fontenot *(Sec)*

Subsidiaries:

Fugro Chance, Inc. **(2)**
6100 Hillcroft
Houston, TX 77081
Tel.: (713) 346-3700
Fax: (713) 784-8162
Web Site: www.fugro-usa.com
Emp.: 25
Mfr. of Energy Electronics Instrumentation
S.I.C.: 8711
N.A.I.C.S.: 541330
Jerry Greig *(CIO)*

Fugro Consultants, Inc. **(2)**
6100 Hillcroft Ave
Houston, TX 77081
Tel.: (713) 369-5400
Fax: (713) 369-5518
E-Mail: inquiries@fugro.com
Web Site: www.fugroconsultants.com
Emp.: 700
Geotechnical Engineering Services
S.I.C.: 8711
N.A.I.C.S.: 541330
Recep Yilmaz *(Mgr)*

Subsidiary:

Fugro William Lettis & Associates, Inc. **(3)**
1777 Botelho Dr 262
Walnut Creek, CA 94596-5132
Tel.: (925) 256-6070
Fax: (925) 256-6076
E-Mail: info@lettis.com
Web Site: www.lettis.com
Geological Engineering Services
S.I.C.: 8711
N.A.I.C.S.: 541330
Bill Lettis *(Pres)*

Fugro EarthData, Inc. **(2)**
7320 Executive Way
Frederick, MD 21704
Tel.: (301) 948-8550
Fax: (301) 963-2064
E-Mail: international@earthdata.com
Web Site: www.fugroearthdata.com
Emp.: 150
Radar Mapping
S.I.C.: 8713
N.A.I.C.S.: 541370
Anne Hale Miglarese *(Pres)*

Subsidiaries:

Fugro Horizons, Inc. **(3)**
4350 Airport Rd
Rapid City, SD 57703 SD
Tel.: (605) 393-8300
Fax: (605) 393-8310
E-Mail: info@fugrohorizons.com
Web Site: www.fugrohorizons.com
Sales Range: $10-24.9 Million
Emp.: 13,000
Aerial Geospatial Acquisition & Photogrammetric Mapping Services
S.I.C.: 8713
N.A.I.C.S.: 541370
Marshall Swenson *(VP-Ops)*

Units:

Fugro EarthData, Inc. - Aviation **(3)**
18227 Airpark Rd
Hagerstown, MD 21742
Tel.: (301) 733-1176
Fax: (301) 733-4906
E-Mail: aviation@earthdata.com
Web Site: www.earthdata.com
Emp.: 20
Mapping & Imaging Operations
S.I.C.: 8713
N.A.I.C.S.: 541370
Alex Miller *(Pres)*

Fugro GeoConsulting, Inc. **(2)**
6100 Hillcroft Ave
Houston, TX 77081
Tel.: (713) 369-5896
Fax: (713) 369-5600
E-Mail: geoconsulting@fugro.com
Web Site: www.fugrogeoconsulting.com
Emp.: 100
Geophysical Engineering Services
S.I.C.: 8711
N.A.I.C.S.: 541330
Dan McDonald *(Gen Mgr)*

Fugro-GEOS, Inc. **(2)**
6100 Hillcroft 77081
Houston, TX 77274
Tel.: (713) 346-3600
Fax: (713) 346-3605
E-Mail: geosusa@fugro.com
Web Site: www.geos.com
Geophysical Surveying Services
S.I.C.: 8713
N.A.I.C.S.: 541360

Fugro GeoServices, Inc. **(2)**
6100 Hillcroft Ave
Houston, TX 77081
Tel.: (713) 369-5800
Fax: (713) 369-5811
E-Mail:
Web Site: www.fgsi.fugro.com
Emp.: 5
Marine Geophysical Surveying Services
S.I.C.: 8713
N.A.I.C.S.: 541360
Adam Jackson *(VP)*

Fugro-ImpROV, Inc. **(2)**
8715 Fallbrook Dr
Houston, TX 77064-3318
Tel.: (832) 912-9009
Fax: (832) 912-1032
Remote Intervention Tool Mfr & Distr
S.I.C.: 3559
N.A.I.C.S.: 333249

Fugro N.V.—(Continued)

Fugro Multi Client Services, Inc. (2)
6100 Hillcroft 77081
Houston, TX 77274
Tel.: (713) 369-5859
Fax: (713) 369-5860
E-Mail: multiclient@fugro.com
Web Site: www.fugromulticlient.com
Emp.: 12
Geophysical Surveying & Mapping Services
S.I.C.: 8713
N.A.I.C.S.: 541360

Fugro Pelagros, Inc (2)
3574 Ruffin Rd
San Diego, CA 92123-2597
Tel.: (858) 292-8922
Fax: (858) 292-5308
E-Mail: rrichards@fugro.com
Web Site: www.fugro-pelagros.com
Emp.: 60
Marine Surveying Services
S.I.C.: 8713
N.A.I.C.S.: 541360
David Millar *(Pres)*

Fugro Roadware, Inc. (2)
3104 Northside Ave
Richmond, VA 23228
Tel.: (804) 264-2982
Fax: (804) 264-2985
Toll Free: (800) 828-2726
E-Mail: info@roadware.com
Web Site: www.roadware.com
Emp.: 100
Infrastructure Management & Data Collection Services
S.I.C.: 7374
N.A.I.C.S.: 518210
David Lowe *(Mng Dir)*

Fugro West Inc. (2)
1000 Broadway
Oakland, CA 95607 CA
Tel.: (510) 268-0461 (100%)
Fax: (510) 268-0545
Web Site: www.fugrowest.com
Rev.: $6,900,000
Emp.: 45
Civil Engineering, Geotechnical Engineering & Environmental Engineering
S.I.C.: 8711
N.A.I.C.S.: 541330
Tim Dunne *(Pres)*

John Chance Land Surveys, Inc. (2)
200 Dulles Dr
Lafayette, LA 70506
Tel.: (337) 237-1300
Fax: (337) 237-1300
E-Mail: info@jchance.com
Web Site: www.jchance.com
Geospatial Mapping Services
S.I.C.: 8713
N.A.I.C.S.: 541370
Jimmie Stoute *(Pres)*

LoadTest, Inc. (2)
2631-D NW 41st St
Gainesville, FL 32606
Tel.: (352) 378-3717
Fax: (352) 378-3934
Toll Free: (800) 368-1138
E-Mail: info@loadtest.com
Web Site: www.loadtest.com
Emp.: 20
Deep Foundation Testing Services
S.I.C.: 1799
N.A.I.C.S.: 238990
Paul Bullock *(Principal-Engr)*
Ray Wood *(Exec VP)*

Non-U.S. Subsidiaries:

Electro Magnetic Marine Exploration Technologies (EMMET) ZAO (1)
Wjatskaja Str 35 Building 4 Business Centre Wjatka 3 Floor
127015 Moscow, Russia RU
Tel.: (7) 495 984 28 79
Fax: (7) 495 984 28 79
Web Site: www.emmetech.ru
Electrical Exploration Equipment Mfr
S.I.C.: 3699
N.A.I.C.S.: 335999
Andrej V. Tulupov *(CEO)*
Evgeny D. Lisitsyn *(Mng Dir)*

Fugro Aerial Mapping A/S (1)
Navorland 2 10
Hoje Taastrup, 2600 Glostrup, Denmark
Tel.: (45) 8888 8211
Fax: (45) 43522032
E-Mail: info@fli-map.eu
Web Site: www.fugrogeospatier.com
Emp.: 1
Geophysical Survey & Mapping Services
S.I.C.: 8713
N.A.I.C.S.: 541360
Doron Sima *(Mgr)*

Fugro Airborne Surveys, Corp. (1)
2505 Meadowvale Boulevard
Mississauga, ON, L5N 5S2, Canada
Tel.: (905) 812-0212
Fax: (905) 812-1504
E-Mail: info@fugroairborne.com
Emp.: 6
Geophysical Surveying Services
S.I.C.: 8713
N.A.I.C.S.: 541360
Greg Paleolog *(Gen Mgr)*

Fugro Airborne Surveys Pty Ltd. (1)
Level 1 69 Outram Street
West Perth, WA, 6005, Australia
Tel.: (61) 8 9273 6400
Fax: (61) 8 9273 6466
Web Site: www.cgg.com
Emp.: 6
Geophysical Surveying & Mapping Services
S.I.C.: 8713
N.A.I.C.S.: 541360
Rod Pullin *(Mng Dir)*

Fugro Airborne Surveys (Pty) Ltd. (1)
Hangar 109 B C & D Lanseria Airport
Johannesburg, Gauteng, 1500, South Africa
Tel.: (27) 11 659 1119
Fax: (27) 11 659 2689
E-Mail: mail@fugro.co.za
Web Site: www.fugroairborne.com
Emp.: 7
Air Bourne Geophysical Surveying Services
S.I.C.: 8713
N.A.I.C.S.: 541360
Martin Frere *(Dir-Global)*

Fugro Alluvial Offshore Ltd. (1)
Morton Peto Road Gapton Hall Industrial Estate
Great Yarmouth, NR31 OLT, United Kingdom
Tel.: (44) 1493 440320
Fax: (44) 1493 440319
E-Mail: info@alluvial.co.uk
Web Site: www.alluvial.co.uk
Emp.: 100
Geophysical Surveying & Mapping Services
S.I.C.: 8713
N.A.I.C.S.: 541360
Adrian Digby *(Head-BEL Geophysical)*

Fugro Aperio Ltd. (1)
Focal Point Newmarket Road
Bottisham, Cambridge, CB25 9BD, United Kingdom
Tel.: (44) 870 600 80 50
Fax: (44) 870 600 80 40
E-Mail: events@fugro-aperio.com
Web Site: www.fugro-aperio.com
Rev.: $3,144,480
Emp.: 4
Geophysical Survey & Investigation Services
S.I.C.: 8713
N.A.I.C.S.: 541360

Fugro Austria GmbH (1)
Einodstrasse 13
8600 Bruck an der Mur, Austria
Tel.: (43) 3862 34300 11
Fax: (43) 3862 34300 12
E-Mail: office@fugro.at
Web Site: www.fugro.at
Emp.: 18
Geophysical Surveying & Mapping Services
S.I.C.: 8713
N.A.I.C.S.: 541360
Wolfram Felfer *(Mng Dir)*
Ralf Trapphoff *(Mng Dir)*
Martin Bernhard *(Mgr-Comml)*

Fugro Belgique/Belgie S.A./N.V. (1)
De Broquevillelaan 12
Brussels, 1150, Belgium
Tel.: (32) 27760310
Fax: (32) 26606555
Web Site: www.fugro.be
Geophysical Surveying Services
S.I.C.: 8713
N.A.I.C.S.: 541360

Fugro BKS Ltd. (1)
Killeague House Unit 17 Sandel Village Centre Knocklynn Road
Coleraine, BT52 1WW, United Kingdom
Tel.: (44) 28 7035 2311
Fax: (44) 28 7035 7637
E-Mail: sales@fugro-bks.com
Web Site: www.fugro-bks.com
Emp.: 4
Spatial Data & Mapping Services
S.I.C.: 8713
N.A.I.C.S.: 541370
Chris Boreland *(Mgr-Bus Dev-Ireland & Scotland)*

Fugro Brasil Ltda. (1)
Rua do Geologo 76 Zona Especial de Negocios
Rio das Ostras, Rio de Janeiro, 28890 000, Brazil
Tel.: (55) 22 3321 7700
Fax: (55) 2233217701
E-Mail: fugro@fugro.com.br
Web Site: www.fugro.com.br
Emp.: 1,000
Oil & Gas Exploration Services
S.I.C.: 1389
N.A.I.C.S.: 213112
Matthew Scholtes *(Gen Mgr)*

Fugro BTW Ltd. (1)
14-22 Connett Road West Bell Block
New Plymouth, 4340, New Zealand
Tel.: (64) 67695040
Fax: (64) 67696262
Emp.: 15
Geophysical Surveying & Mapping Services
S.I.C.: 8713
N.A.I.C.S.: 541360
Bob Waugh *(Gen Mgr)*

Fugro (Canada), Inc. (1)
2191 Thurston Dr
Ottawa, ON, K1G 6C9, Canada
Tel.: (613) 731-9575
Fax: (613) 731-0453
E-Mail: info@fugro.ca
Geophysical Surveying & Mapping Services
S.I.C.: 8713
N.A.I.C.S.: 541360

Fugro Certification Services Ltd. (1)
Fugro Development Centre 5 Lok Yi Street 17 MS Castle Peak Road
Tai Lam New Territories, Tuen Mun, China (Hong Kong)
Tel.: (852) 2452 7127
Fax: (852) 2452 7181
E-Mail: fcs@fugro.com.hk
Web Site: www.fugrocertification.com
Emp.: 3
Geo Technical Data Collection & Interpretation Services
S.I.C.: 7374
N.A.I.C.S.: 518210
Arthur Cheng *(Mgr-Bus Dev)*

Fugro Consult GmbH (1)
Wolfener Str 36 Aufgang V
12681 Berlin, Germany
Tel.: (49) 30 93651 0
Fax: (49) 30 93651 200
E-Mail: fugro@fugro.de
Web Site: www.fugro.de
Emp.: 150
Geophysical Surveying Services
S.I.C.: 8713
N.A.I.C.S.: 541360
Geologe Wolfgang Muller *(Mgr-Bus Admin-Single Procuration)*
Geograph Ralf Trapphoff *(Member-Exec Bd)*

Fugro Consult Kft. (1)
Kelenfoldi Utca 2
Budapest, 1115, Hungary
Tel.: (36) 1 382 0042
Fax: (36) 1 382 0043
E-Mail: fugro@fugro.hu
Web Site: www.fugro.hu
Emp.: 35
Engineering Services
S.I.C.: 8711
N.A.I.C.S.: 541330
Jozsef Pusztai *(Mng Dir)*

Fugro ERT (Scotland) Ltd. (1)
Gait 8 Research Park South Heriot-Watt University
Edinburgh, EH14 4AP, United Kingdom
Tel.: (44) 131 449 5030
Fax: (44) 131 449 5037
E-Mail: holding@fugro.com
Web Site: www.ert.co.uk
Emp.: 25
Environmental Consultancy Services
S.I.C.: 8999
N.A.I.C.S.: 541620
Jim McDougall *(Gen Mgr)*

Fugro Finance AG (1)
Bahnhofstrasse 29
Zug, 6300, Switzerland
Tel.: (41) 417280808
Fax: (41) 417280800
E-Mail: finance@fugro.ch
Financial Management Services
S.I.C.: 6211
N.A.I.C.S.: 523999

Fugro France S.A.S. (1)
27 rue des Peupliers
92752 Nanterre, France
Tel.: (33) 147855050
Fax: (33) 147855060
E-Mail: dg@fugro.com
Emp.: 35
Engineering Services
S.I.C.: 8711
N.A.I.C.S.: 541330

Fugro GeoConsulting Ltd. (1)
Fugro House Hithercroft Road
Wallingford, Oxfordshire, OX10 9RB, United Kingdom
Tel.: (44) 1491 820800
Fax: (44) 1491 820 899
E-Mail: geoconsulting@fugro.com
Web Site: www.fugrogeoconsulting.com
Emp.: 30
Geophysical Consulting Services
S.I.C.: 8999
N.A.I.C.S.: 541690
Frank Langer *(Mng Dir)*

Fugro Geodetic AG (1)
Bahnhofstrasse 29
Zug, 6300, Switzerland
Tel.: (41) 41 728 08 08
Fax: (41) 41 728 08 00
E-Mail: finance@fugro.ch
Web Site: www.fugro.ch
Emp.: 7
Geophysical Surveying & Mapping Services
S.I.C.: 8713
N.A.I.C.S.: 541360

Fugro Geodetic Ltd. (1)
30-E Mohammad Ali Cooperative Housing Society Miran Mohammad Shah Road
Karachi, 75350, Pakistan
Tel.: (92) 21 3454 6611
Fax: (92) 21 3454 6695
E-Mail: fugro@fugro.com.pk
Web Site: www.fugro.com.pk
Emp.: 80
Oil & Gas Industry Surveying Services
S.I.C.: 1389
N.A.I.C.S.: 213112
Richard Hall *(Country Mgr)*

Fugro Geoid S.A.S. (1)
12 Rue des Frares Lumiare
34830 Jacou, France
Tel.: (33) 4 67 59 26 44
Fax: (33) 4 67 59 28 42
E-Mail: infos.geoid@fugro.com
Web Site: www.geoid.fr
Oil & Gas Mining Services
S.I.C.: 1389
N.A.I.C.S.: 213112

Fugro Geolab Nor AS (1)
Hornebergveien
PO Box 5740
7437 Trondheim, Norway NO
Tel.: (47) 73 96 40 00
Fax: (47) 73 96 59 74
E-Mail: Mail@geolabnor.no
Geochemical Consulting Services
S.I.C.: 8999
N.A.I.C.S.: 541690

Fugro-GEOS Ltd. (1)
Fugro House Hithercroft Road
Wallingford, Oxfordshire, OX10 9RB, United Kingdom

Tel.: (44) 1491 820 500
Fax: (44) 1491 820 599
E-Mail: uk@geos.com
Web Site: www.geos.com
Emp.: 105
Meteorological & Oceanographic Services
S.I.C.: 9661
N.A.I.C.S.: 927110
Jeff Coutts *(Mng Dir)*

Fugro-GEOS Pte Ltd. (1)
22 Loyang Lane Level 3
Singapore, 508931, Singapore
Tel.: (65) 6885 4100
Fax: (65) 6885 4101
E-Mail: singapore@geos.com
Emp.: 2
Meteorological & Oceanographic Services
S.I.C.: 9661
N.A.I.C.S.: 927110
Michael Quinnell *(Mng Dir)*

Fugro GeoServices Ltd. (1)
101 1108 53rd Av NE
Calgary, AB, T2E 6N9, Canada
Tel.: (403) 234-9018
Fax: (403) 266-2919
E-Mail: info@fugro.ca
Web Site: www.fugro.ca
Emp.: 198
Geophysical Surveying & Mapping Services
S.I.C.: 8713
N.A.I.C.S.: 541360

Fugro GeoSurveys, Inc. (1)
25 Pippy Place
Saint John's, NL, A1B 3X2, Canada
Tel.: (709) 726-4252
Fax: (709) 726-5007
Geological Seismic Surveying Services
S.I.C.: 8713
N.A.I.C.S.: 541360

Fugro Geotech (Pvt) Ltd. (1)
Plot No 51 Sector 6
Sanpada, Navi Mumbai, 400705, India
Tel.: (91) 22 6516 8662
Fax: (91) 22 2775 4011
Emp.: 12
Geo Technical Engineering Services
S.I.C.: 8711
N.A.I.C.S.: 541330
Santanu Moitra *(Gen Mgr)*

Fugro Geotechnical Services Ltd. (1)
Units 8-10 10/F Worldwide Industrial Centre
43-47 Shan Mei Street
Fo Tan New Territories, Hong Kong, China (Hong Kong)
Tel.: (852) 2697 1126
Fax: (852) 2694 0659
E-Mail: fgs@fugro.com.hk
Web Site: www.fugro.com.hk/contact.htm
Geophysical Surveying Services
S.I.C.: 8713
N.A.I.C.S.: 541360

Fugro Geotechnics AS (1)
Hoffsveien 1C
0275 Oslo, Norway NO
Tel.: (47) 22 13 46 00
Fax: (47) 22 13 46 46
E-Mail: geoteam@fugro.no
Web Site: www.fugro.no/companies/fugro_geotechnics
Geophysical Surveying Services
S.I.C.: 8713
N.A.I.C.S.: 541360

Fugro Geotechnics Vietnam LLC (1)
No 31 Street O D2-16 My Giang 2 Phu My Hung
Tan Phong Ward District 7, Ho Chi Minh City, Vietnam
Tel.: (84) 8 54138228
Fax: (84) 8 54135857
E-Mail: furgo@fugro.com.vn
Web Site: www.fugro.com.vn
Emp.: 4
Geophysical Surveying & Consulting Services
S.I.C.: 8713
N.A.I.C.S.: 541360
Ming Hui Liao *(Gen Mgr)*

Fugro Holdings Australia Pty Ltd. (1)
Level 1 69 Outram Street
Perth, WA, 6005, Australia
Tel.: (61) 8 9481 2966
Fax: (61) 8 9486 8675
E-Mail: holding@fugro.com
Investment Management Services
S.I.C.: 6211
N.A.I.C.S.: 523999

Fugro Holdings (Hong Kong) Ltd. (1)
7/F Guardian House 32 Oi Kwan Road
Wanchai, China (Hong Kong)
Tel.: (852) 2577 9023
Fax: (852) 2895 2379
E-Mail: furgo@fugro.com.hk
Emp.: 16
Investment Management Services
S.I.C.: 6211
N.A.I.C.S.: 523999
Ho C S *(Mng Dir)*

Fugro Holdings (UK) Ltd. (1)
Fugro House
Wallingford, Oxfordshire, OX10 9RB, United Kingdom
Tel.: (44) 8704 021500
Fax: (44) 1491 826 293
Web Site: www.fugro.co.uk
Emp.: 40
Investment Management Services
S.I.C.: 6211
N.A.I.C.S.: 523999

Fugro Hong Kong, Ltd. (1)
7 Fl Guardian House
32 Oi Kwan Rd, Wanchai, China (Hong Kong) (100%)
Tel.: (852) 25779023
Fax: (852) 28952379
E-Mail: fugro@fugro.com.hk
Web Site: www.fugro.com.hk
Emp.: 150
S.I.C.: 8711
N.A.I.C.S.: 541330

Fugro-ImpROV Ltd. (1)
Kirkhill Commercial Park Dyce Avenue
Dyce, Aberdeen, AB21 OLQ, United Kingdom
Tel.: (44) 1224 709 767
Fax: (44) 1224 709 776
E-Mail: enquiries@improvltd.co.uk
Web Site: www.improvltd.co.uk
Emp.: 60
Machine Tool Mfr
S.I.C.: 3541
N.A.I.C.S.: 333517
Alan Duncan *(Mng Dir)*

Fugro Interra S.A. (1)
Av Americo Vespucio 2880 13th Fl
Conchali, Chile
Tel.: (56) 2 623 51 51
E-Mail: contacto@fugrointerra.cl
Web Site: www.interra.cl
Emp.: 5
Geophysical Surveying Services
S.I.C.: 8713
N.A.I.C.S.: 541360
Rodrigo Arbat *(Gen Mgr)*

Fugro Jacques Geosurveys, Inc. (1)
131 Ilsley Ave Ste B
Dartmouth, NS, B3B 1T1, Canada (100%)
Tel.: (902) 468-1130
Telex: 1921745
Fax: (902) 468-1719
E-Mail: mail@fjg.ca
Web Site: www.fugro.com
Emp.: 40
Marine Geomatics & Offshore Survey
S.I.C.: 1311
N.A.I.C.S.: 211111
Mike Cole *(Pres)*

Fugro Japan Co., Ltd. (1)
Skyward Bld 4F Misaki-cho 3-3-20
Chiyoda-ku, Tokyo, 101-0061, Japan
Tel.: (81) 3 3288 2936
Fax: (81) 3 3288 2984
E-Mail: inquiry@fugro.co.jp
Web Site: www.fugro.co.jp
Geotechnical Engineering Services
S.I.C.: 8711
N.A.I.C.S.: 541330
Sumio Yamano *(Mng Dir)*

Fugro LADS Corporation Pty Ltd. (1)
7 Valetta Rd
Kidman Park, Adelaide, SA, 5025, Australia
Tel.: (61) 8 8161 4169
Fax: (61) 8152 3008
E-Mail: lads@fugrolads.com
Web Site: www.fugrolads.com
Emp.: 5
Surveying Equipment Mfr
S.I.C.: 3829
N.A.I.C.S.: 334519
Hugh Parker *(Mgr-Sls & Mktg)*

Fugro Ltd. (1)
Hithercroft Rd
Wallingford, Herts, 0X10 9RB, United Kingdom
Tel.: (44) 8704021300
Telex: 925759
Fax: (44) 8704021399
E-Mail: info@fugro.co.uk
Web Site: www.fugro.co.uk
Emp.: 300
S.I.C.: 8711
N.A.I.C.S.: 541330
Jeff Coutts *(Mng Dir)*

Fugro Loadtest Asia Pte Ltd. (1)
159 Sin Ming Road 05-07 Amtech Building
Singapore, 575625, Singapore
Tel.: (65) 6377 5665
Fax: (65) 6377 3359
E-Mail: asia_info@loadtest.com
Web Site: www.loadtest.com
Emp.: 110
Deep Foundation Load Testing Services
S.I.C.: 1711
N.A.I.C.S.: 238220

Fugro Loadtest Ltd. (1)
14 Scotts Avenue
Sunbury-on-Thames, TW16 7HZ, TW16 7HZ, United Kingdom
Tel.: (44) 1932 784807
E-Mail: info@loadtest.co.uk
Web Site: www.loadtest.co.uk
Emp.: 13
Deep Foundation Load Testing Services
S.I.C.: 1799
N.A.I.C.S.: 238390
Melvin England *(Mng Dir)*

Fugro Malaysia (1)
11th Fl Wisma Genting
50250 Kuala Lumpur, Malaysia
Tel.: (60) 321662433
Telex: 36120 PCTRAD MA
Fax: (60) 321662466
E-Mail: administration@fugro.com.my
Web Site: www.fugro.com
Emp.: 86
Geotechnical Services to Oil, Gas, Mining & Construction Industries
S.I.C.: 8711
N.A.I.C.S.: 541330
Umar Rahman *(Mng Dir)*

Fugro-MAPS GmbH (1)
Truderinger Str 13
81677 Munich, Germany
Tel.: (49) 89 244 48 84 0
Fax: (49) 89 244 48 84 44
E-Mail: info@fugro-maps.com
Web Site: www.fugro-maps.com
Aerial Survey & Satelliete Mapping Services
S.I.C.: 8713
N.A.I.C.S.: 541370

Fugro-MAPS S.a.r.l. (1)
Maamari Street Khoury Bldg
Clemenceau District, Beirut, Lebanon
Tel.: (961) 1 367 470
Fax: (961) 1 370 299
E-Mail: info@fugromaps.com
Geophysical Surveying & Mapping Services
S.I.C.: 8713
N.A.I.C.S.: 541360

Fugro-MAPS (UAE) (1)
Corniche Plaza 1
PO Box 5232
Sharjah, United Arab Emirates
Tel.: (971) 6 5725411
Fax: (971) 6 5724057
E-Mail: info@fugromaps.com
Web Site: www.fugromaps.com
Emp.: 12
Geophysical Surveying Services
S.I.C.: 8713
N.A.I.C.S.: 541360
Jens Balle *(Gen Mgr)*

Fugro Middle East & Partners LLC (1)
Near Holiday Inn Ghala Al Madinah Area
PO Box 1334
112 Muscat, Oman
Tel.: (968) 2 4502320
Fax: (968) 24596769
E-Mail: s.akhtar@fugrome.com
Web Site: www.fugrome.com
Emp.: 16
Geophysical Surveying & Mapping Services
S.I.C.: 8713
N.A.I.C.S.: 541360
Armando Martinez *(Gen Mgr)*

Fugro Middle East B.V. (1)
PO Box 2863
Dubai, United Arab Emirates (100%)
Tel.: (971) 43474060
Telex: 45752 MIL EM
Fax: (971) 43474069
E-Mail: fugro@emirates.net.ae
Web Site: www.fugrome.com
Emp.: 100
S.I.C.: 8711
N.A.I.C.S.: 541330
Maarten van der Harst *(Mng Dir)*

Non-U.S. Subsidiaries:

Fugro Peninsular (2)
PO Box 47167
Doha, Qatar
Tel.: (974) 4323879
Fax: (974) 44418958
E-Mail: sme_qtr@fugrome.com
Web Site: www.fugrome.com
Emp.: 80
Engineering Services
S.I.C.: 8711
N.A.I.C.S.: 541330
Max Mone *(Branch Mgr)*

Furgo-Suhaimi Ltd. (2)
PO Box 2165
CP 6338 Dammam, 31451, Saudi Arabia (100%)
Tel.: (966) 38574200
Telex: 801477
Fax: (966) 38572034
E-Mail: info@furgo-suhaimi.com
Web Site: www.furgo-suhaimi.com
Emp.: 210
S.I.C.: 8711
N.A.I.C.S.: 541330
Oliver Ransan *(Gen Mgr)*

Fugro Multi Client Services AS (1)
Hoffsveien 1C
PO Box 490
Skoyen, 213 Oslo, Norway NO
Tel.: (47) 22134600
Fax: (47) 22134646
E-Mail: multiclient@fugro.no
Web Site: www.fugromulticlient.com
Seismic Data Processing Services
S.I.C.: 7374
N.A.I.C.S.: 518210

Fugro Multi Client Services Pty Ltd. (1)
69 Outram Street
West Perth, Perth, WA, 6005, Australia
Tel.: (61) 8 9321 4400
Fax: (61) 8 9321 4401
E-Mail: multiclient@fugromcs.com.au
Web Site: www.fugromcs.com.au
Emp.: 14
Seismic Data Processing Services
S.I.C.: 7374
N.A.I.C.S.: 518210

Fugro Multi Client Services (UK) Ltd. (1)
Fugro House Hithercroft Road
Wallingford, Oxfordshire, OX10 9RB, United Kingdom
Tel.: (44) 1491 820 600
Fax: (44) 1491 820 899
E-Mail: multiclient@fugromcs.co.uk
Emp.: 7
Seismic Data Collection & Processing Services
S.I.C.: 7374
N.A.I.C.S.: 518210
Stewart Walter *(Gen Mgr)*

Fugro Nigeria Ltd. (1)
Fugro Avenue 91 Odani Road Off PH-Eleme Expressway Elelenwo PMB 053
Port Harcourt, Nigeria
Tel.: (234) 84 774175
Fax: (234) 84 485546
E-Mail: info.fugro@fugronigeria.com
Web Site: www.fugro-prodec.com

Fugro N.V.—(Continued)

Emp.: 106
Environmental Consulting & Laboratory Services
S.I.C.: 8999
N.A.I.C.S.: 541620
Goodwill C. Ofunne *(Mng Dir)*
Janet Adamu *(Sec)*
Evelyn A. Ijeoma *(Sec-Laboratory & Testing Div)*

Fugro Norway AS (1)
Hoffsveien 1C
0275 Oslo, Norway NO
Tel.: (47) 22 13 46 00
Fax: (47) 22 13 46 46
E-Mail: geoteam@fugro.no
Web Site: www.fugro.no
Geotechnical Surveying Services
S.I.C.: 8713
N.A.I.C.S.: 541360

Fugro NPA Ltd. (1)
Crockham Park
Edenbridge, Kent, TN8 6SR, United Kingdom
Tel.: (44) 1732 865 023
Fax: (44) 1732 866 521
E-Mail: enquiries@fugro-npa.com
Web Site: www.fugro-npa.com
Emp.: 35
Geophysical Mapping Services
S.I.C.: 8713
N.A.I.C.S.: 541360
David Morten *(Mng Dir)*

Fugro Oceanor AS (1)
Luramyrveien 29
4313 Sandnes, Norway NO
Tel.: (47) 51634310
Fax: (47) 51634331
E-Mail: sandnes@oceanor.com
Web Site: www.oceanor.com
Emp.: 5
Environmental Monitoring System Mfr
S.I.C.: 3823
N.A.I.C.S.: 334513
Olaf Ingvar Sveggen *(Project Dir-Sls)*

Fugro Oceansismica S.p.A. (1)
Viale Charles Lenormant 268
126 Rome, Italy
Tel.: (39) 06 5219291
Fax: (39) 06 5219297
E-Mail: oceansismica@fugro.it
Web Site: www.fugro.it
Oil & Gas Exploration Services
S.I.C.: 1389
N.A.I.C.S.: 213112

Fugro OSAE GmbH (1)
Fahrenheitstr 7
28359 Bremen, Germany
Tel.: (49) 4212239150
Fax: (49) 4212299151
E-Mail: info@fosae.de
Web Site: www.fugro-osae.de
Sales Range: $10-24.9 Million
Emp.: 40
Hydrographic Surveying Services
S.I.C.: 8713
N.A.I.C.S.: 541360
Bernd Jeuken *(Mng Dir)*
Jakob Ruegg *(Member-Mgmt Bd)*
Ralf Trapphoff *(Member-Mgmt Bd)*

Fugro Panama SA (1)
Ciudad del Saber Cl Gustavo Lara Casa 141
Clayton, Panama, Panama
Tel.: (507) 317 1055
Fax: (507) 317 0518
Web Site: www.fugroconsultants.com
Emp.: 14
Geophysical Surveying & Mapping Services
S.I.C.: 8713
N.A.I.C.S.: 541360
David Sackett *(Mgr)*

Fugro PMS Pty Ltd. (1)
Rintoul Business Park Unit 7B 26 Powers Road
Seven Hills, Sydney, NSW, 2147, Australia
Tel.: (61) 2 9674 9488
Fax: (61) 2 9674 9345
E-Mail: pmsnsw@pavement.com.au
Web Site: www.pavement.com.au
Emp.: 2
Engineering Consulting Services
S.I.C.: 8742
N.A.I.C.S.: 541611
Alex Lannoo *(Mng Dir)*

Fugro Roadware, Inc. (1)
2505 Meadowvale Boulevard
Mississauga, ON, L5N 5S2, Canada
Tel.: (905) 567-2870
Fax: (905) 567-2871
E-Mail: info@roadware.com
Web Site: www.roadware.com
Emp.: 100
Highway Management Software Development Services
S.I.C.: 7371
N.A.I.C.S.: 541511
David Lowe *(Mng Dir)*

Fugro RUE AS (1)
Stoltenberggaten 1
5527 Haugesund, Norway NO
Tel.: (47) 52 86 48 20
Fax: (47) 52 86 48 42
E-Mail: fras@fugro.no
Web Site: www.fugrorue.com
Emp.: 3
Marine Offshore Engineering Services
S.I.C.: 8711
N.A.I.C.S.: 541330
Paul Schiefloe *(Gen Mgr)*

Fugro S.A.E. (1)
Oil Company Complex Km 12 Ain Sukhna Road
Katameya, 11936 Cairo, Egypt
Tel.: (20) 2 27580299
Fax: (20) 2 27580599
E-Mail: info@fugro-egypt.net
Web Site: www.fugro-egypt.net
Emp.: 15
Offshore Geophysical Surveying Services
S.I.C.: 8713
N.A.I.C.S.: 541360
John Evans *(Gen Mgr)*

Fugro SEA Ltd. (1)
7/F Guardian House 32 Oi Kwan Rd
Wanchai, China (Hong Kong)
Tel.: (852) 2577 9023
Fax: (852) 2894 2379
E-Mail: fugro@fugro.com.hk
Web Site: www.fugro.com.hk
Emp.: 10
Geophysical Surveying & Mapping Services
S.I.C.: 8713
N.A.I.C.S.: 541360

Fugro Seacore (Australia) Pty Ltd. (1)
24 Geddes Street
Balcatta, WA, 6021, Australia
Tel.: (61) 8 6477 4400
Fax: (61) 8 6477 4499
E-Mail: fsptyrecption@fugro.com
Web Site: www.seacore.com
Emp.: 4
Geophysical Surveying Services
S.I.C.: 8713
N.A.I.C.S.: 541360
Dominic Lovelock *(Mgr-Contract)*

Fugro Seacore Limited (1)
Bickland Industrial Estate
Falmouth, TR11 4TA, United Kingdom
Tel.: (44) 1326221771
Fax: (44) 1326254501
E-Mail: drilling@seacore.com
Web Site: www.fugroseacore.com
Sls.: $64,435,000
Emp.: 500
Overwater Drilling Engineering Services
S.I.C.: 1629
N.A.I.C.S.: 237990
Bob Jenkins *(Mng Dir)*

Fugro Seastar AS (1)
Hoffsveien 1C
275 Oslo, Norway NO
Tel.: (47) 2150 1400
Fax: (47) 2150 1401
E-Mail: seastar@fugro.com
Web Site: www.seastar.co.uk
Navigation & Positioning Services
S.I.C.: 4499
N.A.I.C.S.: 488330

Fugro Seastar Mauritius Ltd. (1)
IFS Court Twentyeight
Ebene, Mauritius
Tel.: (230) 467 1677
Geophysical Surveying & Mapping Services
S.I.C.: 8713
N.A.I.C.S.: 541360

Fugro Singapore Pte Ltd. (1)
159 Sin Ming Rd No 06 07 Amtech Bldg
Singapore, 575625, Singapore SG
Tel.: (65) 65528600
Telex: 21068 SOILMAC RS
Fax: (65) 65528911
E-Mail: info@fugro.com
Web Site: www.fugro.com
Emp.: 50
S.I.C.: 8711
N.A.I.C.S.: 541330
Jeremy Pasiley *(Mng Dir)*

Fugro South America GmbH (1)
Bahnhofstrasse 29
6300 Zug, Switzerland
Tel.: (41) 41 7280808
Fax: (41) 41 7280800
Geophysical Surveying & Mapping Services
S.I.C.: 8713
N.A.I.C.S.: 541360

Fugro Spatial Solutions Pty Ltd. (1)
18 Prowse Street
West Perth, Perth, WA, 6005, Australia
Tel.: (61) 8 9282 4100
Fax: (61) 8 9322 1775
E-Mail: satellite@fugrospatial.com.au
Web Site: www.fugrospatial.com.au
Emp.: 100
Geospatial Mapping Services
S.I.C.: 8713
N.A.I.C.S.: 541370
Paul Taylor *(Controller-Fin)*

Fugro Subsea Services Australia Pty Ltd. (1)
3-4 Martin place
Canning Vale, Canning Vale, WA, 6155, Australia
Tel.: (61) 862538225
Fax: (61) 862538335
Web Site: www.fugro.com
Emp.: 14
Engineering Services
S.I.C.: 8711
N.A.I.C.S.: 541330
Brendan Reid *(Gen Mgr)*

Fugro Subsea Technologies Pte Ltd. (1)
35 Loyang Crescent
Singapore, 509012, Singapore
Tel.: (65) 68610878
Fax: (65) 68616337
Web Site: www.fugro.com
Emp.: 20
Geophysical Surveying Services
S.I.C.: 8713
N.A.I.C.S.: 541360
Tom Winger *(Gen Mgr)*

Fugro Survey Africa (Pty) Ltd. (1)
Woodbridge Business Park Koeberg Road
Milnerton, 7441 Cape Town, South Africa
Tel.: (27) 21 527 8900
Fax: (27) 21 527 8901
E-Mail: info@fugro-survey.co.za
Web Site: www.fugro-africa.com
Geophysical Surveying & Positioning Services
S.I.C.: 8713
N.A.I.C.S.: 541360
Alex Vouillot *(Gen Mgr)*

Fugro Survey AS (1)
Hoffsveien 1C
PO Box 490
Skoyen, Oslo, 213, Norway NO
Tel.: (47) 22 13 47 34
Fax: (47) 22 13 46 46
E-Mail: survey@fugro.no
Web Site: www.fugro-survey.no
Geophysical Offshore Surveying Services
S.I.C.: 8713
N.A.I.C.S.: 541360

Fugro Survey (Brunei) Sdn Bhd. (1)
Lot 4237 X7 Simpang 394-15
Jalan Maulana, Kuala Belait, KA2931, Brunei Darussalam
Tel.: (673) 3335340
Fax: (673) 3332006
E-Mail: sales@fugro.com.sg
Emp.: 1
Geophysical Surveying & Mapping Services
S.I.C.: 8713
N.A.I.C.S.: 541360
Wilhard Kreijkes *(Mgr)*

Fugro Survey Caribbean N.V. (1)
Schottegatweg Oost 62
Willemstad, Curacao
Tel.: (599) 9 736 5456
Fax: (599) 9 736 7656
Web Site: www.fugrosurveycaribbean.com
Emp.: 22
Geophysical Surveying & Mapping Services
S.I.C.: 8713
N.A.I.C.S.: 541360
Felipe Croes *(Mng Dir)*

Fugro Survey International Ltd. (1)
7/F Guardian House 32 Oi Kwan Rd
Wanchai, China (Hong Kong)
Tel.: (852) 2577 9023
Fax: (852) 2895 2379
E-Mail: fsurvey@fugro.com.hk
Web Site: www.fugro.com.hk
Emp.: 15
Geophysical Survey & Mapping Services
S.I.C.: 8713
N.A.I.C.S.: 541360
Ho Chi Shing *(CEO)*

Fugro Survey Ltd. (1)
7/F Guardian House 32 Oi Kwan Rd
Wanchai, China (Hong Kong)
Tel.: (852) 2577 9023
Fax: (852) 2895 2379
E-Mail: fsurvey@fugro.com.hk
Emp.: 13
Geophysical Surveying & Mapping Services
S.I.C.: 8713
N.A.I.C.S.: 541360

Fugro Survey Ltd. (1)
Survey House Denmore Road
Bridge of Don, Aberdeen, AB23 8JW, United Kingdom
Tel.: (44) 1224 257 500
Fax: (44) 1224 853 900
E-Mail: info@fugrosurvey.co.uk
Web Site: www.fugrosurvey.co.uk
Oil & Gas Offshore Services
S.I.C.: 1311
N.A.I.C.S.: 211111
Brian Davidson *(Project Mgr-Tendering-Positioning & Construction Support)*

Fugro Survey Mexico S.A. de C.V. (1)
Puerto Industrial Pesquero Laguna Azul
Cruzamiento Zofemat
24140 Ciudad del Carmen, Mexico
Tel.: (52) 938 3811970
Fax: (52) 93825114
Emp.: 45
Geophysical Surveying & Mapping Services
S.I.C.: 8713
N.A.I.C.S.: 541360
Michael Beaumont *(Gen Mgr)*

Fugro Survey (Middle East) Ltd. (1)
PO Box 43088
Abu Dhabi, United Arab Emirates
Tel.: (971) 2 554 7810
Fax: (971) 2 554 7811
E-Mail: enquiries@fugro-uae.com
Web Site: www.fugro-uae.com
Emp.: 100
Offshore Surveying & Positioning Services
S.I.C.: 8713
N.A.I.C.S.: 541360
Kingsley Ashford-Brown *(Mgr-Comml)*

Fugro Survey (Nigeria) Ltd. (1)
Bloc 85 - Plot 1 Chief Collins Uchidiuno Street Lekki Phase 1
Lagos, Nigeria
Tel.: (234) 1 774 6012
Fax: (234) 1 791 3149
Geophysical Surveying Services
S.I.C.: 8713
N.A.I.C.S.: 541360
G. C. Ofunne *(Mng Dir)*

Fugro Survey Pte Ltd. (1)
35 Loyang Crescent
Singapore, 509012, Singapore
Tel.: (65) 6861 0878
Fax: (65) 6861 6337
E-Mail: sales@fugro.com.sg
Web Site: www.fugro.sg
Emp.: 300
Geophysical Surveying & Mapping Services

S.I.C.: 8713
N.A.I.C.S.: 541360
Wilhard Kreijkes *(Mng Dir & Mgr)*

Fugro Survey Pty Ltd. (1)
24 Geddes Street
Baicatta, Perth, WA, 6021, Australia
Tel.: (61) 8 6477 4400
Fax: (61) 8 6477 4499
E-Mail: techdev@fugro.com.au
Web Site: www.fugrosurveytechnical.com
Geophysical Surveying & Mapping Services
S.I.C.: 8713
N.A.I.C.S.: 541360

Fugro Technical Services (Guangzhou) Ltd. (1)
Building 6 Jin Ke Ecological Park No 100
Nan Guang Road
Nancun Panyu, 511442 Guangzhou, Guangdong, China
Tel.: (86) 20 3482 8832
Fax: (86) 20 3482 8831
E-Mail: ftsgz@fugro.cn
Web Site: www.fugro.cn
Construction Material Testing & Inspection Services
S.I.C.: 9651
N.A.I.C.S.: 926150

Fugro Technical Services Ltd. (1)
Fugro Development Centre 5 Lok Yi Street
17 MS Castle Peak Road
Tuen Mun, NT, China (Hong Kong)
Tel.: (852) 2450 8233
Fax: (852) 2450 6138
E-Mail: matlab@fugro.com.hk
Space Research & Technology Services
S.I.C.: 9661
N.A.I.C.S.: 927110

Fugro Technical Services (Macau) Ltd. (1)
Rua Wo Mok Lote P2
Taipa, China (Macau)
Tel.: (853) 851812
Fax: (853) 483867
E-Mail: macau@fugro.com.hk
Web Site: www.fugro.com.hk/contact.htm
Geophysical Surveying & Mapping Services
S.I.C.: 8713
N.A.I.C.S.: 541360

Fugro Weinhold Engineering GmbH (1)
Kofferer Strasse 40
41812 Erkelenz, Germany
Tel.: (49) 2164 94 05 90
Fax: (49) 2164 94 05 910
E-Mail: info@fugro-weinhold.com
Web Site: www.vib-weinhold.com
Emp.: 3
Geo Spatial Services
S.I.C.: 9661
N.A.I.C.S.: 927110
Ralf Trapphoff *(Co-Mng Dir)*
Wolfgang Weinhold *(Co-Mng Dir)*

Geotechnical Instruments (Hong Kong) Ltd. (1)
Units 8-10 10/F Worldwide Industrial Centre
43-47 Shan Mei Street
Fotan, New Territories, China (Hong Kong)
Tel.: (852) 2697 1126
Fax: (852) 2694 0659
E-Mail: fgs@fugro.com.hk
Emp.: 6
Geophysical Surveying Services
S.I.C.: 8713
N.A.I.C.S.: 541360

MateriaLab Consultants Ltd. (1)
Fugro Development Centre 5 Lok Yi Street
17 MS Castle Peak Road
Tai Lam, Tuen Mun, New Territories, China (Hong Kong)
Tel.: (852) 2450 8238
Fax: (852) 2450 6138
E-Mail: mcl@fugro.com.hk
Web Site: www.materialab-consultant.com
Environmental Consulting Services
S.I.C.: 8999
N.A.I.C.S.: 541620
Colin Yung *(Asst Mgr)*

P.T. Fugro Indonesia (1)
Jalan Asem Baris Raya No 1
Tebet Jakarta Selatan, Jakarta, 12830, Indonesia
Tel.: (62) 21 831 5711
Fax: (62) 21 831 5749
E-Mail: fugro@kalvindo-fugro.co.id
Web Site: www.fugro-singapore.com.sg/contact.htm
Emp.: 110
Geophysical Survey & Geotechnical Services
S.I.C.: 8713
N.A.I.C.S.: 541360
Ric Wymer *(Country Mgr)*

TurbiGas Solar S.A. (1)
Tacuari 202 Piso 10
C 1071AAF Buenos Aires, Argentina
Tel.: (54) 11 5235 8200
E-Mail: info@turbigas.com.ar
Web Site: www.turbigas.com.ar
Emp.: 25
Mfr of Power Generation Machinery
S.I.C.: 3612
N.A.I.C.S.: 335311

UAB Fugro Baltic (1)
Rasu Street 39
11351 Vilnius, Lithuania
Tel.: (370) 5 2135115
Fax: (370) 5 2135115
E-Mail: info@fugro.lt
Web Site: www.fugro.lt
Emp.: 1
Geophysical Surveying Services
S.I.C.: 8713
N.A.I.C.S.: 541360
Christian Peter *(Mng Dir)*

FUGUINIAO CO., LTD.

Units 2009-2018 20th Floor Shui On Centre 6-8 Harbour Road
Wanchai, China (Hong Kong)
Tel.: (852) 3150 6788
Fax: (852) 3150 6728
Web Site: www.fuguiniao.com
Year Founded: 1991
1819—(HKG)
Emp.: 6,000

Business Description:
Shoe & Men's Clothing Mfr & Distr
S.I.C.: 2389
N.A.I.C.S.: 316210

Personnel:
Wo Ping Lam *(Chm & CEO)*
Guodong Liu *(Sec)*

Board of Directors:
Ying Han
Huihuang Hong
Kwok Keung Lam
Wing Ho Lam
Wo Ping Lam
Wo Sze Lam
Gang Zhai

FUHRMEISTER ELECTRONICS CO., LTD.

2-3-3 Uchikanda Chiyoda-ku
Tokyo, 101-0047, Japan
Tel.: (81) 332545361
Web Site: www.fuco-ele.co.jp
Year Founded: 1988
3165—(JAS)
Emp.: 80

Business Description:
Electronic Parts Distr & Sales
S.I.C.: 5065
N.A.I.C.S.: 423690

Personnel:
Kenji Takeishi *(Pres)*

FUJAIRAH BUILDING INDUSTRIES COMPANY P.S.C.

PO Box 383
Fujairah, United Arab Emirates
Tel.: (971) 92222051
Fax: (971) 92227314
E-Mail: fbi_fuj@emirates.net.ae
Web Site: www.fbifuj.ae
Year Founded: 1978
FBI—(EMI)
Sales Range: $50-74.9 Million

Business Description:
Building Materials Mfr
S.I.C.: 3255
N.A.I.C.S.: 327120

Personnel:
Obaid Al Kendi *(CEO)*

Subsidiary:

Fujairah National Quarry (1)
PO Box 383
Al Hail Industrial Area, Fujairah, United Arab Emirates
Tel.: (971) 9 224 1138
Fax: (971) 9 224 1158
E-Mail: fnqfuj@eim.ae
Emp.: 12
Sand & Gravel Mining Services
S.I.C.: 1422
N.A.I.C.S.: 212312

Plants:

Fujairah Building Industries Company P.S.C. - Emirates Ceramic Factory (1)
PO Box 3040
Fujairah, United Arab Emirates
Tel.: (971) 9 222 3995
Fax: (971) 9 222 7643
E-Mail: fujcer@eim.ae
Web Site: www.emiratesceramics.com
Ceramic Product Mfr
S.I.C.: 3269
N.A.I.C.S.: 327110

Fujairah Building Industries Company P.S.C. - Fujairah Marble & Tiles Factory (1)
PO Box 11419
Dibba, Fujairah, United Arab Emirates
Tel.: (971) 9 244 4101
Fax: (971) 9 244 4635
E-Mail: fmtf@emirates.net.ae
Emp.: 150
Marble & Tile Mfr
S.I.C.: 3281
N.A.I.C.S.: 327991
Musbah Al Zagha, *(Gen Mgr)*

Fujairah Building Industries Company P.S.C. - Fujairah Rockwool Factory (1)
PO Box 211
Fujairah, United Arab Emirates
Tel.: (971) 9 222 2297
Fax: (971) 9 222 2573
E-Mail: frf@emirates.net.ae
Web Site: www.rockwoolfujairah.ae
Rockwool Insulation Product Mfr
S.I.C.: 3296
N.A.I.C.S.: 327993

FUJAIRAH CEMENT INDUSTRIES COMPANY PSC

5th Floor Fujairah National Insurance Building
PO Box 600
Fujairah, United Arab Emirates
Tel.: (971) 92223111
Fax: (971) 92227718
E-Mail: info@fujairahcement.com
Web Site: www.fujairahcement.com
Year Founded: 1979
FCI—(ABU KUW)
Rev.: $155,049,599
Assets: $483,938,144
Liabilities: $228,688,165
Net Worth: $255,249,980
Earnings: $9,569,994
Emp.: 240
Fiscal Year-end: 12/31/12

Business Description:
Cement Mfr
S.I.C.: 3241
N.A.I.C.S.: 327310

Personnel:
Hamad Saif Al-Sharqi *(Chm)*
Mohammed Bin Hamad Bin Saif Al-Sharqi *(Deputy Chm)*

Board of Directors:
Hamad Saif Al-Sharqi
Khaleefa Khalaf Abdullah Saleh Al-Anezi
Mohamned Saeed Al-Dowaisan
Saad Abdullah Al-Hanyan
Mohamed Al Habib Al-Jaraya
Ali Saad Batel Al-Mershad
Mohammed Ghaith Khalfan Al-Muhairbi
Hamad Ahmed Hamad Al-Omairi
Saeed Mohamed Abdullah Al-Raqabani
Mohammed Bin Hamad Bin Saif Al-Sharqi
Abdulghafoor Hashem Abdulghafoor Bahrouzian

FUJAIRAH TRADE CENTRE COMPANY

PO Box 761
Fujairah, United Arab Emirates
Tel.: (971) 2222661
Fax: (971) 2226212
E-Mail: ftcfuj@emirates.net.ae
Web Site: www.fujairahtradecentre.com
FTC—(EMI)
Sales Range: $1-9.9 Million

Business Description:
Leasing Business Services
S.I.C.: 7389
N.A.I.C.S.: 561499

Personnel:
Abdulgafoor Hashim Abdulgafoor Bahrozyan *(Chm)*
Khaled Saod Abdulla Al Saood *(Vice Chm)*

Board of Directors:
Abdulgafoor Hashim Abdulgafoor Bahrozyan
Hamed Abu Baker Al Hamed
Khaled Saod Abdulla Al Saood
Hassan Abdullah Baroom
Hashim Alawi El Safi
Saleh Mohammed Laden
Mohammed Sulaiman

FUJI CORPORATION

1-5 Giyokicho Itami
Hyogo, 664-8615, Japan
Tel.: (81) 727721101
Fax: (81) 727727625
E-Mail: kokusai@fujico-jp.com
Web Site: www.fujico-jp.com
Year Founded: 1927
3515—(JAS)
Sales Range: $125-149.9 Million
Emp.: 259

Business Description:
Pressed Felts, Needle Punched Felt, Needle Punched Carpets, Headwears & Other Related Goods Mfr & Sales
S.I.C.: 2297
N.A.I.C.S.: 313230

Personnel:
Takayuki Nozoe *(Pres)*
Kazuo Hattori *(Mng Dir)*
Norihito Shirahata *(Mng Dir)*

Board of Directors:
Katsuji Aoki
Kazuo Hattori
Kazuhide Inata
Kenzo Murai
Yoshiki Murata
Takashi Nishiwaki
Takayuki Nozoe
Norihito Shirahata
Hiraku Yamaguchi
Sueshiro Yamaguchi

Non-U.S. Subsidiary:

Fuji Corp International Hong Kong Ltd (1)
Rm 709 7th Floor Tower B Hung Hom Commercial Centre
37-39 Ma Tau Wai Road, Hung Hom, Kowloon, China (Hong Kong)

Fuji Corporation—(Continued)

Tel.: (852) 27226409
Fax: (852) 27226423
Web Site: www.fujico-jp.com
Piece Goods Notions & Other Dry Goods Whslr
S.I.C.: 5199
N.A.I.C.S.: 424310
Maehara Toyoteru *(Mng Dir)*

Non-U.S. Joint Venture:

Dingxing Lida Hat Making Co. Ltd. (1)
No 3 Lihua Rd
Shijiazhuang, Hebei, China
Tel.: (86) 3126923013
Fax: (86) 3126922886
E-Mail: info@lihuahats.com
Web Site: www.lihuahats.com
Emp.: 1,000
Piece Goods Notions & Other Dry Goods Whslr
S.I.C.: 5131
N.A.I.C.S.: 424310
Liu Gushan *(Mng Dir)*

FUJI ELECTRIC CO., LTD.

Gate City Oshaki East Tower 11-2
Osaki 1-chome Shinagawa-ku
Tokyo, 141-0032, Japan
Tel.: (81) 354357111
Telex: J22331 FUJIELEA
Fax: (81) 354357486
E-Mail: info@fujielectric.co.jp
Web Site: www.fujielectric.co.jp
Year Founded: 1923
6504—(NGO TKS)
Sls.: $8,203,591,000
Assets: $8,421,193,000
Liabilities: $6,048,801,000
Net Worth: $2,372,392,000
Earnings: $290,048,000
Emp.: 24,956
Fiscal Year-end: 03/31/13

Business Description:
Power & Energy Systems, Industrial & Consumer Electronics, Information Processing, Water & Sewage Treatment Systems & Electronic Devices Mfr
S.I.C.: 5731
N.A.I.C.S.: 443142

Personnel:
Michihiro Kitazawa *(Chm & Pres)*
Takamichi Hamada *(Sr Mng Exec Officer-External Affairs & Mktg)*
Fumio Ito *(Pres-Fuji Electric FA Components & Systems Co Ltd)*
Yoshio Okuno *(Exec VP & Gen Mgr-Global Sls Grp)*
Hisao Shigekane *(Exec VP & Gen Mgr-Corp Mgmt Plng Headquarters & Compliance Mgmt)*

Board of Directors:
Michihiro Kitazawa
Michio Abe
Takamichi Hamada
Hiroaki Kurokawa
Junichi Matsumoto
Yoshio Okuno
Mareto Sako
Hisao Shigekane
Motoyuki Suzuki
Naoto Yoneyama

Subsidiary:

Fuji Electric FA Components & Systems Co., Ltd. (1)
Gate City Ohsaki
11-2 Osaki 1-chome, Tokyo, Shinagawa, 141-0032, Japan
Tel.: (81) 353457112
Web Site: www.fujielectric.co.jp/eng/fdt/sales.html
Heavy Electric Machinery
S.I.C.: 3699
N.A.I.C.S.: 335999

Non-U.S. Subsidiaries:

Fuji Electric Europe GmbH (2)
Goethering 58
D 63067 Offenbach, Germany
Tel.: (49) 696690290
Fax: (49) 6966902958
E-Mail: info_inverter@fujielectric.de
Web Site: www.fujielectric.de
Emp.: 50
Distr of Power & Control Equipment & Marketing of Inverters
S.I.C.: 3699
N.A.I.C.S.: 335999

Fuji Electric FA (Asia) Co., Ltd. (2)
Rm 1001 10th Fl West Wing Tsimshatsui Ctr
66 Mody Rd., Tsimshatsui East, Kowloon, China (Hong Kong)
Tel.: (852) 23118282
Fax: (852) 23120566
E-Mail: fea-info@fea.fujielectric.com
Web Site: www.fujielectric.com
Emp.: 20
Marketing of Inverters, Power Distributors, Control Equipment & Semiconductors
S.I.C.: 3699
N.A.I.C.S.: 335999
Gary Lee *(Mgr-Sls)*

Fuji Electric FA Korea Co., Ltd. (2)
16th Fl Shinsong Bldg 25-4 Youido Dong
Youngdungpo gu, Seoul, Korea (South)
Tel.: (82) 27805011
Fax: (82) 27831707
E-Mail: fkim@fjskr.fujielectric.com
Web Site: www.fujielectrickorea.co.kr
Emp.: 17
Materials Procurement & Marketing of Electrical & Electronic Machinery & Components
S.I.C.: 3699
N.A.I.C.S.: 335999
Insaut Kim *(Mng Dir)*

Fuji Electric FA Singapore Private Ltd. (2)
171 Chin Swee Road
#12-01-04 San Center, 169877 Singapore, Singapore
Tel.: (65) 5330010
Fax: (65) 5330021
Web Site: www.fujielectric.com.sg/2global.html
Marketing of Power Distributors & Control Equipment in Southeast Asia
S.I.C.: 3699
N.A.I.C.S.: 335999

Fuji Electric FA Taiwan Co., Ltd. (2)
12F No 70 Cheng Teh North Road Sec 1
Taipei, Taiwan
Tel.: (886) 25560716
Fax: (886) 2256 0717
Web Site: www.fujielectric.com.cn/chinabase/index.html
Marketing of Power Distributors, Control Equipment & Drive System Products in Taiwan
S.I.C.: 3699
N.A.I.C.S.: 335999

U.S. Subsidiaries:

Fuji Electric Corp of America (1)
47520 Westinghouse Dr
Fremont, CA 94539-7471 (100%)
Tel.: (510) 651-0811
Fax: (510) 440-1063
Web Site: www.fujielectric.com
Emp.: 25
Provider of Business Supply Equipment Services
S.I.C.: 3577
N.A.I.C.S.: 334118
Kazuyuki Yasukawa *(Mgr-R&D Laboratory)*

Non-U.S. Subsidiary:

Fuji Electric Brazil-Euipamentos de Energia Ltda. (FEB) (2)
625 Rua Conselheiro Saraiva
Sao Paulo, Santana, Brazil (100%)
Tel.: (55) 11 2283 5991
Web Site: www.fujielectric.com
Sales of General Component Products: Power Semiconductors, HMI, Control Equipment, Electric Distribution, Photoconductors & Instrumentation
S.I.C.: 3674
N.A.I.C.S.: 334413
Giuseppe Privitera *(Mng Dir)*

Fuji Electric Corporation of America (1)
50 N Field Ave
Edison, NJ 07663 NJ
Tel.: (201) 712-0555
Fax: (201) 368-8258
E-Mail: contact@fecoa.fujielectric.com
Web Site: www.fujielectric.com
Sales Range: $10-24.9 Million
Emp.: 50
Marketing of Semiconductors & Power Distributors & Control Equipment & Ring Blowers
S.I.C.: 5063
N.A.I.C.S.: 423610
Yoshimi Meya *(Treas)*

Fuji Electric Device Technology America, Inc. (1)
240 Circle Dr N
Piscataway, NJ 08854-3705 NJ
Tel.: (732) 560-9410
Fax: (732) 457-0042
Web Site: www.fujielectric.co.jp/eng/FID/organization.html
Emp.: 45
Mfr & Marketing of Photoconductive Drums for Copiers & Printers
S.I.C.: 3579
N.A.I.C.S.: 333316

Non-U.S. Subsidiaries:

Atai Fuji Electric Co., Ltd. (1)
32 Sec 2 Chang Hsing Rd
Taoyuan, 338, Taiwan (100%)
Tel.: (886) 33213030
Fax: (886) 33217890
E-Mail: info@fujielectric.co.jp
Web Site: www.ataifuji.com.tw
Emp.: 60
S.I.C.: 5731
N.A.I.C.S.: 443142
C. F. Sun *(Pres)*

Dalian Fuji Electric Motor Co., Ltd. (1)
NE 3rd St No 3 Dalian Economic And Technical
Development Zone, Dalian, 116600, China (100%)
Tel.: (86) 4117620640
Fax: (86) 4117620646
Web Site: www.fujielectric.com
S.I.C.: 5946
N.A.I.C.S.: 443142

Fuji Electric (Asia) Co., Ltd. (1)
Rm 2015 24 The Metropolis Tower
10 Metropolis Drive Hung Hong, Kowloon, China (Hong Kong) (100%)
Tel.: (852) 23118282
Fax: (852) 23119152
E-Mail: fea-info@fea.fujielectric.com
Web Site: www.fujielectric.co.jp
Emp.: 17
Marketing of Semiconductors, Power Distributors, Control Equipment & Inverters
S.I.C.: 5065
N.A.I.C.S.: 423690
K. Ogawa *(Mng Dir)*

Fuji Electric Dalian Co., Ltd. (1)
NE 3rd St 3 Dalian Economic & Technical Development Zone
Dalian, 116600, China
Tel.: (86) 41187622000
Fax: (86) 41187622030
Web Site: www.fujielectric.com
Mfr. of Low-Voltage Circuit Breakers & Motors
S.I.C.: 3613
N.A.I.C.S.: 335313

Fuji Electric Device Technology Europe GmbH (1)
Goetreng 58
Offenbach, 63067, Germany (100%)
Tel.: (49) 696690290
Fax: (49) 696661020
Web Site: www.fujielectric.de
Emp.: 25
Marketing of Semiconductors, Power Distributors, Control Equipment, Inverters & Photoconductive Drums for Copiers & Printers
S.I.C.: 5065
N.A.I.C.S.: 423690
Tome Bechi *(Mng Dir)*

Fuji Electric Device Technology Hong Kong Co., Limited (1)
Room 1001 10th Floor West Wing Tsimshatsui Center
66 Mody Rd Tsimshatsui East, Kowloon, China (Hong Kong)
Tel.: (852) 23118282
Fax: (852) 23120566
E-Mail: fea-info@fujielectric.com
Web Site: www.fujielectric.com
Emp.: 20
Marketing of Semiconductor Devices
S.I.C.: 3674
N.A.I.C.S.: 334413

Fuji Electric FA Korea Co., Ltd. (1)
16th Fl Shinsong Bldg 25-4 Youido-dong
Youngdungpo-gu, Seoul, 215151, Korea (South) (100%)
Tel.: (82) 27805011
Fax: (82) 27831707
E-Mail: fcskrwebmaster@fcskr.fujielectric.com
Web Site: www.fujielectric.co.kr
Sales Range: $1-9.9 Million
Emp.: 25
Marketing of Semiconductors & Control Equipment
S.I.C.: 5065
N.A.I.C.S.: 423690

Fuji Electric Industries Singapore Private Ltd. (1)
No 629 Aljunied Road #03-04 Cititech Industrial Building
Singapore, 389838, Singapore
Tel.: (65) 6742 7700
Fax: (65) 6742 7711
Web Site: www.fujielectric.com.sg
Emp.: 15
Marketing of Semiconductors & Inverters
S.I.C.: 5065
N.A.I.C.S.: 423690

Fuji Electric (Malaysia) Sdn. Bhd. (1)
Lot 5 Industrial Zone Phase 1Kulim Hi-Tech Park
09000 Kulim, Kedah, Malaysia (100%)
Tel.: (60) 44031111
Fax: (60) 44031496
Web Site: www.fujielectrics.com
Sales Range: $75-99.9 Million
Emp.: 1,500
Mfr of Magnetic Disks
S.I.C.: 3695
N.A.I.C.S.: 334613
Manaka Koichi *(Pres)*

Fuji Electric Philippines, Inc. (1)
107 Enterprise Dr CIP 1 Canlubang
Calamba, Laguna, 4131, Philippines(100%)
Tel.: (63) 28446183
Fax: (63) 728446196
Emp.: 800
Mfr. of Power Semiconductors
S.I.C.: 3674
N.A.I.C.S.: 334413
Tatko Kikuchi *(Pres)*

Fuji Electric (Shanghai) Co., Ltd. (1)
Ste E And F 12F E Bldg New Hua Lian Mansion
755 Huai Hai Rd, Shanghai, 200020, China (100%)
Tel.: (86) 2164662810
Fax: (86) 2164733292
E-Mail: fesh-info@fesha.fujielectric.com
Web Site: www.fesh.com.cn
Sales Range: $50-74.9 Million
Emp.: 30
Marketing of Inverters, Switchgear & Transformers
S.I.C.: 5065
N.A.I.C.S.: 423690

Fuji Electric (Shenzhen) Co., Ltd. (1)
High-Technology Industrial Zone Feng Tang Rd
Fu Yong Bao An, Shenzhen, Guangdong, 518014, China
Tel.: (86) 75527342910
Web Site: www.fujielectric.com
Emp.: 5
Manufacture & Marketing of Photoconductive Drums

S.I.C.: 3699
N.A.I.C.S.: 335999

Fuji Electric Taiwan Co., Ltd. (1)
9F 1 No 110
Sung Chiang Rd, Taipei, 104, Taiwan (100%)
Tel.: (886) 225151850
Fax: (886) 225151860
E-Mail: info@fujielectric.co.jp
Web Site: www.fujielectric.co.jp
Emp.: 10
Semiconductor Devices, Power Distribution & Control Equipment, Sales of Control, Drive & Rotating Equipment
S.I.C.: 3674
N.A.I.C.S.: 334413
Lori Wang *(Mgr-Sls)*

Fuji Electric (1)
Wisma Kyoei Price 17F
Jl Jend Sudirman Kav 3 4, Jakarta, 10220, Indonesia (100%)
Tel.: (62) 215724281
Fax: (62) 215724283
E-Mail: bambang@jkt.fujielectric.com
Emp.: 4
S.I.C.: 5734
N.A.I.C.S.: 443142
Bambang Saryawan *(Gen Mgr)*

Fuji-Haya Electric Corp. of the Philippines (1)
2178 Pasong Tamo St 2nd Fl Matrinco Bldg
Makati, Metro Manila, 1201, Philippines (100%)
Tel.: (63) 28928886
Fax: (63) 28935645
E-Mail: rcg@fujihaya.com
Web Site: www.fujihaya.com
Emp.: 65
Mfr. of Switchboards
S.I.C.: 3613
N.A.I.C.S.: 335313
Hikian Yu *(Mng Dir)*

Hong Kong Fujidenki Co., Ltd. (1)
Unit 227230 2nd Fl
1 Science Pr W Ave, Hong Kong, NT, China (Hong Kong) (100%)
Tel.: (852) 26648699
Fax: (852) 26648040
Web Site: www.fujielectric.com
Emp.: 50
Mfr. & Marketing of Photoconductive Drums for Copiers & Printers
S.I.C.: 3674
N.A.I.C.S.: 334413
Toru Eguchi *(Gen Mgr)*

Shanghai Fuji Electric Switchgear Co., Ltd. (1)
No 2 Huhang Road Nanqiao
Fengxian, Shanghai, 201400, China
Tel.: (86) 2157185740
Fax: (86) 2157181448
Web Site: www.fujielectric.com.sg/2global.html
Switchgear Mfr
S.I.C.: 3613
N.A.I.C.S.: 335313

Shanghai Fuji Electric Transformer Co., Ltd. (1)
No 2 Huhang Rd
Nanqiao Fengxian, 2001400 Shanghai, China (100%)
Tel.: (86) 2157185747
Fax: (86) 2157185745
E-Mail: moriya@fuji.com
Web Site: www.fujielectric.co.jp
Emp.: 100
Mfr. of Cast-Resin Dry-Type Powers Transformers
S.I.C.: 3612
N.A.I.C.S.: 335311
Kanda Yukimasa *(Gen Mgr)*

Shanghai General Fuji Refrigeration Equipment Co., Ltd. (1)
688 Xin Qu Rd
Qing Pu Industrial Park, Shanghai, China
Tel.: (86) 2169211088
Fax: (86) 2169211077
Web Site: www.fujielectric.co.jp
Emp.: 160
Mfr. of Refrigerated Showcases
S.I.C.: 3585
N.A.I.C.S.: 333415

Non-U.S. Affiliates:

Fuji Electric France S.A. (1)
46 Rue Georges Besse
63039 Clermont-Ferrand, Cedex, France (100%)
Tel.: (33) 473982698
Fax: (33) 473982699
Web Site: www.fujielectric.fr
Sls.: $15,097,116
Emp.: 80
S.I.C.: 5734
N.A.I.C.S.: 443142
Michel Narche *(Gen Mgr)*

Hoei Electronics (S) Private Ltd. (1)
No 5 Pereira Rd 02 04 Asiawide Industrial Bldg
Singapore, 368025, Singapore (60%)
Tel.: (65) 62853238
Fax: (65) 62857317
E-Mail: info@hes.com.sg
Web Site: www.hes.com.sg
Emp.: 25
Marketing of Semiconductors
S.I.C.: 5065
N.A.I.C.S.: 423690
Eizo Fukouka *(Mng Dir-Japan)*

Korea FA Systems Co., Ltd. (1)
Dan Sung Building 4F 1 23 Yangjae Dong
Seocho gu, Seoul, 137-073, Korea (South)
Tel.: (82) 25738782
Fax: (82) 25731904
Web Site: www.fujielectric.com
S.I.C.: 5946
N.A.I.C.S.: 443142

Mahajak International Electric Co., Ltd. (1)
Mahajak Bldg 4th Fl 46 Soi 3
Bangkok, 10110, Thailand (100%)
Tel.: (66) 22532350
Fax: (66) 22532354
E-Mail: mico@Mahajak.com
Web Site: www.Mahajak.com
Emp.: 250
S.I.C.: 5731
N.A.I.C.S.: 443142
Poantibul Canphanadsaytsoon *(Mng Dir)*

P.T. Fuji Dharma Electric (1)
Jalan Rawagelam 1 10 Kawasan Industri
Pulo Gadung, 13930 Jakarta, Timur, Indonesia (100%)
Tel.: (62) 214600143
Fax: (62) 214610338
Web Site: www.fujidharma.com
Emp.: 300
Mfr. of Watt-Hour Meters
S.I.C.: 3829
N.A.I.C.S.: 334514

Suzhou Lanlian-Fuji Instruments Co., Ltd. (1)
Songlin Economic & Technical Development Zone
Wujiang, Jiangsu, 215200, China
Tel.: (86) 5123451594
Fax: (86) 512 345 1954
Web Site: www.fujielectric.co.jp
S.I.C.: 5734
N.A.I.C.S.: 443142

Non-U.S. Joint Ventures:

Fuji Electric Fa Taiwan (1)
12F 70 Cheng Teh Road Sec 1
Taipei, 103, Taiwan
Tel.: (886) 225560716
Fax: (886) 225560717
Web Site: www.fujielectric.co.jp
Emp.: 20
Sales, Marketing, Product Training & Customer Services; Owned 50% by GE Industrial & 50% by Fuji Electric Holdings Co., Ltd.
S.I.C.: 7389
N.A.I.C.S.: 561499

Fuji/GE Private Ltd. (1)
171 Chin Swee Road, 12-01/04
San Center, Singapore, 169877, Singapore
Tel.: (65) 65330010
Fax: (65) 65330021
Web Site: www.fujielectric.co.jp
Sales Range: $75-99.9 Million
Sales, Marketing, Product Training & Customer Services; Owned 50% by GE Industrial & 50% by Fuji Electric Holdings Co., Ltd.
S.I.C.: 7389
N.A.I.C.S.: 561499

FUJI ELECTRIC INDUSTRY CO., LTD.

585 Higashihachiman-cho Oike-dori
Tominokoji Nishi-iru Nakagyo-ku
Kyoto, 604-0954, Japan
Tel.: (81) 752217978
Fax: (81) 752510425
Web Site: www.fujidk.co.jp
Year Founded: 1958
6654—(TKS)
Sls.: $36,520,836
Assets: $117,102,634
Liabilities: $6,287,303
Net Worth: $110,815,331
Earnings: $2,628,450
Emp.: 299
Fiscal Year-end: 01/31/13

Business Description:
Electric Equipment Mfr & Sales
S.I.C.: 3679
N.A.I.C.S.: 334419

Personnel:
Tadashi Konishi *(Pres)*
Kouichi Fukunaga *(Mng Dir & Gen Mgr)*

Plants:

FUJI ELECTRIC INDUSTRY CO., LTD. - Kusatsu Factory (1)
3-4-1 Nomura
Kusatsu, Shiga, 525 8521, Japan
Tel.: (81) 775621215
Fax: (81) 775621213
Web Site: www.fujidk.co.jp/english/profile/outline.html
Emp.: 250
Electronic Switches & Devices Mfr
S.I.C.: 3679
N.A.I.C.S.: 334419
Tadashi Konishi *(Pres)*

FUJI ELECTRIC INDUSTRY CO., LTD. - Shin-Asahi Factory (1)
905-1 Aza-Nishigawara Shin-Asahi-cho
Ota-ku, Takashima, Shiga, 520-1512, Japan
Tel.: (81) 740256338
Fax: (81) 740 25 6339
Web Site: www.fujidk.co.jp/english/profile/office.html
Electronic Switches & Devices Mfr
S.I.C.: 3679
N.A.I.C.S.: 334419

FUJI ELECTRONICS CO., LTD.

Ochanomizu Center Building 2-12
3-chome Hongo
Bunkyo-ku, Tokyo, 113-8444, Japan
Tel.: (81) 3 3814 1411
Fax: (81) 3 3814 1414
Web Site: www.fujiele.co.jp
Year Founded: 1970
9883—(TKS)
Sls.: $446,061,000
Assets: $373,505,000
Liabilities: $128,304,000
Net Worth: $245,201,000
Earnings: $18,601,000
Emp.: 392
Fiscal Year-end: 02/28/13

Business Description:
Semiconductor Devices Whslr
S.I.C.: 5065
N.A.I.C.S.: 423690

Personnel:
Kunio Ikisu *(Chm & CEO)*
Kiyoshi Ikisu *(Pres & COO)*
Takumei Kuwaki *(Mng Dir)*
Ei-ichi Nishizawa *(CFO)*
Takao Hamaguchi *(Sr Exec Officer)*
Nobuhiro Kato *(Exec Officer)*
Hajime Kawaharada *(Exec Officer)*
Toshifumi Kuroda *(Exec Officer)*
Kenji Ohtake *(Sr Exec Officer)*
Takashi Suda *(Exec Officer)*
Harushige Taniguchi *(Exec Officer)*
Masao Tsunetomi *(Exec Officer)*

Board of Directors:
Kunio Ikisu
Kiyoshi Ikisu
Takumei Kuwaki
Ei-ichi Nishizawa
Jun-ichi Okamoto
Shin-ichi Onodera

FUJI HEAVY INDUSTRIES, LTD.

1-7-2 Nishishinjuku Shinjuku-ku
Tokyo, 160 8316, Japan
Tel.: (81) 3 3347 2111
Telex: 2322268FUJIJ
Fax: (81) 3 3347 2338
Web Site: www.fhi.co.jp/english/
Year Founded: 1953
7270—(NGO OTC TKS)
Sls.: $21,042,648,000
Assets: $17,351,994,000
Liabilities: $10,787,051,000
Net Worth: $6,564,943,000
Earnings: $1,315,468,000
Emp.: 12,717
Fiscal Year-end: 03/31/13

Business Description:
Automobile & Aerospace-Related Products
S.I.C.: 3711
N.A.I.C.S.: 336111

Personnel:
Yasuyuki Yoshinaga *(Pres & CEO)*
Jun Kondo *(Deputy Pres)*
Shuzo Haimoto *(Exec VP)*
Tomohiko Ikeda *(Exec VP)*
Akira Mabuchi *(Exec VP)*
Naoto Muto *(Exec VP)*
Hisashi Nagano *(Exec VP)*
Takeshi Tachimori *(Exec VP)*
Mitsuru Takada *(Exec VP)*
Mitsuru Takahashi *(Exec VP)*
Yoshio Hirakawa *(Sr VP)*
Tamaki Kamogawa *(Sr VP)*
Masahiro Kasai *(Sr VP)*
Hidetoshi Kobayashi *(Sr VP)*
Yasuo Kosakai *(Sr VP)*
Tatsuhiko Mukawa *(Sr VP)*

Board of Directors:
Toshio Arima
Tomohiko Ikeda
Jun Kondo
Akira Mabuchi
Naoto Muto
Takeshi Tachimori
Mitsuru Takahashi
Yasuyuki Yoshinaga

Transfer Agent:
Mizuho Trust & Banking Co., Ltd.
2-1 Yaesu 1-Chome Chuo-ku
Tokyo, 103 8670, Japan
Tel.: (81) 332788111
Fax: (81) 332816947

Divisions:

Fuji Heavy Industries, Ltd. - Air Space Div. (1)
1 11 Yonan 1 Chome Utsunomiya City
Tochigi, 320 8564, Japan (100%)
Tel.: (81) 286847777
Telex: 3522418fujiuj
Fax: (81) 286847778
Web Site: www.fhi.co.jp
Emp.: 2,600
Mfr. of Aircraft Rolling Stock, Containers & Special Purpose Vehicles
S.I.C.: 3711
N.A.I.C.S.: 336111
Hisasha Nagano *(Pres)*

Fuji Heavy Industries, Ltd., Aircraft Div. (1)
1 11 Yonan 1 Chome
Utsunomiya, Tochigi, 320 8564, Japan (100%)
Tel.: (81) 286847777
Telex: 2322268FUJIJ
Fax: (81) 286847071
Web Site: www.fhi.co.jp

Fuji Heavy Industries, Ltd.—(Continued)

Sales Range: Less than $1 Million
Emp.: 2,500
Mfr. of Aircraft
S.I.C.: 3721
N.A.I.C.S.: 336411
Hisashi Nagano *(Pres)*

Fuji Heavy Industries, Ltd., Automobile Div. (1)
9 6 Osawa 3 Chome
Tokyo, 1818577, Japan (100%)
Tel.: (81) 422337000
Telex: 3473348FUGIG
Fax: (81) 422337777
Web Site: www.fhi.co.jp
Sls.: $4,339,716,096
Emp.: 10,405
Mfr. of Subcompact Cars & Minivehicles
S.I.C.: 3711
N.A.I.C.S.: 336111
Ikuo Mori *(CEO & Pres)*

Fuji Heavy Industries, Ltd., Engine & Machinery Div. (1)
Asahi 4 Hiahong 4 410
Kitamoto, Saitama, 364-8511, Japan
Tel.: (81) 485937755
Fax: (81) 485937790
E-Mail: kamimurak@sai.subaru-fhi.co.jp
Web Site: www.fuji.co.jp
Sls.: $225,532,000
Emp.: 600
Mfr. of Industrial Gasoline, Kerosene & Diesel Engines, Generators, Pumps
S.I.C.: 2899
N.A.I.C.S.: 325998
Akira Ishii *(Mgr-Gen Affairs & Dept)*

Fuji Heavy Industries, Ltd., Industrial Products (1)
4 410 Asahi Kitamoto
Saitama, 3648511, Japan (100%)
Tel.: (81) 485937723
Fax: (81) 485937790
E-Mail: kamimura.kazuto@subaru-fhi.co.jp
Web Site: www.shi.co.jp
Sales Range: $25-49.9 Million
Emp.: 600
S.I.C.: 3711
N.A.I.C.S.: 336111
Kamimura Kazuto *(Mgr-Gen Affairs & Dept)*

Fuji Heavy Industries, Ltd., Manufacturing Div. (1)
1-1 Subaru-cho
Ota, Gunma, 373 8555, Japan (100%)
Tel.: (81) 276262011
Telex: 3482146fujii
Fax: (81) 276263020
E-Mail: matsuih@suburu-fhi.co.jp
Web Site: www.fhi.co.jp
Emp.: 14,000
S.I.C.: 3711
N.A.I.C.S.: 336211
Katsutoshi Iino *(Gen Mgr)*

Fuji Heavy Industries, Ltd., Rolling Stock Div. (1)
1 1 11 Yonan
Utsunomiya, Tochigi, 320 8564, Japan (100%)
Tel.: (81) 286847777
Fax: (81) 286847778
Web Site: www.fhi.co.jp
Sls.: $118,100,700
Emp.: 2,012
Mfr. of Diesel & Electric Passenger Railcars, Railway Work Cars, Sanitation Trucks & Ordinary Containers, Trailers, Marine & Shipping Containers, Physical Distribution Systems
S.I.C.: 3743
N.A.I.C.S.: 336510

Subsidiaries:

Daiwa Shoko Co., Ltd (1)
1-4-1 Ebara
Shinagawa-Ku, Tokyo, 142-0063, Japan
Tel.: (81) 337839131
Fax: (81) 3 37887444
Web Site: www.daiwa-sk.jp
Industrial Machinery & Equipment Distr
S.I.C.: 5084
N.A.I.C.S.: 423830

Fuji Aerospace Corporation (1)
1-2-15 Yonan
Utsunomiya, Tochigi, 320-0834, Japan
Tel.: (81) 286459509
Aircraft Parts & Equipment Mfr
S.I.C.: 3724
N.A.I.C.S.: 336412

Fuji Aerospace Technology Co.,Ltd. (1)
1146-2 Esojimamachi
Utsunomiya, 321-0102, Japan
Tel.: (81) 28 659 7436
Fax: (81) 28 659 7437
Web Site: www.fatec.jp
Aircraft System & Equipment Mfr
S.I.C.: 3728
N.A.I.C.S.: 336413

Fuji Aircraft Maintenance Co.,Ltd. (1)
1-28 Kanda-Sudacho
Chiyoda-ku, Tokyo, 101-0041, Japan
Tel.: (81) 3 3257 1533
Aircraft Maintenance Services
S.I.C.: 4581
N.A.I.C.S.: 488190

Fuji Houren Co., Ltd. (1)
100 Suehirocho
Isesaki, Gunma, 372-0057, Japan
Tel.: (81) 270303147
Fax: (81) 2 70303148
Construction Material Mfr & Distr
S.I.C.: 3271
N.A.I.C.S.: 327331

Fuji Machinery Co., Ltd. (1)
2 24 3 Iwagami Maebashi
Gunma, 371 0035, Japan (100%)
Tel.: (81) 272313111
Fax: (81) 2 7231 3127
Web Site: www.fuji-machinery.co.jp
Emp.: 403
Automobile & Industrial Parts Mfr & Sales
S.I.C.: 3714
N.A.I.C.S.: 336350
Michio Morikawa *(Pres)*

Fuji Techno Service Co.,Ltd. (1)
Arato1-2-5
Fukuoka, 810-0062, Japan
Tel.: (81) 92 741 5539
Fax: (81) 92 741 5542
E-Mail: info@fujts.com
Web Site: www.fujts.com
Hydraulic Machinery Maintenance Service
S.I.C.: 7699
N.A.I.C.S.: 811310

Ichitan Co., Ltd. (1)
74 Shindo cho
Ohta, Gunma, 373-0037, Japan (51%)
Tel.: (81) 276312331
Fax: (81) 276313829
Web Site: www.ichitan.co.jp
Emp.: 349
Automobile & Industrial Product Parts Mfr & Sales
S.I.C.: 3714
N.A.I.C.S.: 336390
Minoru Tamura *(Pres)*

Osaka Subaru Inc. (1)
1-21-23 Yagumohlgashlmachi
Osaka, 570-0021, Japan
Tel.: (81) 6 6908 0771
Web Site: www.osaka.kinki-subaru.jp
Automobile Dealers
S.I.C.: 5511
N.A.I.C.S.: 441110

Robin Service Co.,Ltd. (1)
2-19 Akabori
Okegawa, Saitama, 363-0002, Japan
Tel.: (81) 487287088
Automobile Maintenance Services
S.I.C.: 7539
N.A.I.C.S.: 811198

Subaru Auto Accessory Co.,Ltd. (1)
1-1-2 Miyahara-cho
Saitama, 330-0038, Japan
Tel.: (81) 48 652 5603
Automobile Parts Distr
S.I.C.: 5013
N.A.I.C.S.: 423120

Subaru Customize Works Co.,Ltd. (1)
100 Suehirocho
Isesaki, Gunma, 372-0057, Japan
Tel.: (81) 270212072
Automotive Parts Mfr & Distr
S.I.C.: 3714
N.A.I.C.S.: 336390

Subaru Finance Co., Ltd. (1)
Ebisu Suburu Building 3rd Fl 1 20 8 Ebisu
Shibuya-ku, Tokyo, 150 0013, Japan (100%)
Tel.: (81) 334452111
Fax: (81) 334452126
Web Site: www.suburu-finance.co.jp
Emp.: 220
Automobile Rental, Leasing & Financial Services
S.I.C.: 7389
N.A.I.C.S.: 561499

Subaru Kosan Co., Ltd (1)
1-20-8 Ebisu Ebisu Subaru Bldg 3F
Shibuya-Ku, Tokyo, 150-0013, Japan
Tel.: (81) 334484591
Automotive Parts Mfr
S.I.C.: 3714
N.A.I.C.S.: 336390

Subaru Living Service Co.,Ltd. (1)
1-20-8 Ebisu Ebisu Subaru Bldg
Shibuya-Ku, Tokyo, 150-0013, Japan
Tel.: (81) 334452177
E-Mail: question@sls-shop.com
Web Site: www.sls-shop.com
Online Shopping Services
S.I.C.: 5961
N.A.I.C.S.: 454111
Motokiyo Nomura *(Pres)*

Subaru Logistics Co.,Ltd. (1)
558-1 Asahicho
Ota, Gunma, 373-0814, Japan
Tel.: (81) 276 48 3131
Fax: (81) 276 48 3130
E-Mail: info@subaru-logistics.co.jp
Web Site: www.subaru-logistics.co.jp
Packaging & Freight Transportation Services
S.I.C.: 4731
N.A.I.C.S.: 488510
Kazumasa Kimura *(Pres & CEO)*

Subaru Tecnica International Inc. (1)
3-9-6 Osawa
Mitaka, Tokyo, Japan
Tel.: (81) 422 33 7848
Fax: (81) 422 33 7844
Web Site: www.sti.jp
Motor Sport Engine & Chassis Mfr
S.I.C.: 3519
N.A.I.C.S.: 333618
Hiroyuki Karamatsu *(Chm)*

Tokyo Subaru Inc. (1)
1-20-8 Ebisu
Shibuya-ku
Tokyo, Japan (100%)
Tel.: (81) 334484411
Fax: (81) 3 3448 4428
Web Site: www.tokyo-subaru.co.jp
Emp.: 1,275
Automobile Sales & Service
S.I.C.: 5571
N.A.I.C.S.: 441228
Yupaka Tsukahara *(Pres)*

Yusoki Kogyo K.K. (1)
102 Kamihama-cho
Handa, Aichi, 475-0804, Japan
Tel.: (81) 5 6921 3311
Fax: (81) 5 6922 0471
E-Mail: ys-info@yusoki.co.jp
Web Site: www.yusoki.co.jp
Aircraft Parts Mfr & Distr
S.I.C.: 3728
N.A.I.C.S.: 336413

Plants:

Fuji Heavy Industries, Ltd. - Gunma Main Plant (1)
1-1 Subaru-cho
Ota, Gunma, 373-8555, Japan
Tel.: (81) 276 26 2011
Emp.: 386
Automotive Parts Mfr
S.I.C.: 3714
N.A.I.C.S.: 336390

Fuji Heavy Industries, Ltd. - Gunma Oizumi Plant (1)
1-1-1 Izumi Oizumi-machi
Oura-gun, Gunma, 370-0531, Japan
Tel.: (81) 276 48 2881
Emp.: 1,533
Automobile Engines & Transmissions Mfr
S.I.C.: 2396
N.A.I.C.S.: 336360

Fuji Heavy Industries, Ltd. - Gunma Yajima Plant (1)
1-1 Shoya-cho
Ota, Gunma, 373-0822, Japan
Tel.: (81) 276 48 2701
Emp.: 246
Automotive Parts Mfr
S.I.C.: 3714
N.A.I.C.S.: 336390

Fuji Heavy Industries, Ltd. - Handa Plant (1)
1-27 Ushioi-cho
Handa, Aichi, 475-0032, Japan
Tel.: (81) 569 29 4801
Emp.: 181
Aircraft Mfr
S.I.C.: 3721
N.A.I.C.S.: 336411

Fuji Heavy Industries, Ltd. - Handa West Plant (1)
102 Kamihama-cho
Handa, Aichi, 475-0804, Japan
Tel.: (81) 569 32 2501
Web Site: www.fhi.co.jp/english/outline/inoutline/domestic/
Emp.: 23
Aircraft Mfr
S.I.C.: 3721
N.A.I.C.S.: 336411

Fuji Heavy Industries, Ltd. - Omiya Subaru Building Facility (1)
1-1-2 Miyahara-cho
Kita-ku, Saitama, 331-0812, Japan
Tel.: (81) 48 653 5722
Emp.: 41
Automobile Parts Mfr
S.I.C.: 3714
N.A.I.C.S.: 336390

Fuji Heavy Industries, Ltd. - Saitama Plant (1)
4-410 Asahi
Kitamoto, Saitama, 364-8511, Japan
Tel.: (81) 48 593 7755
Fax: (81) 48 593 7946
Emp.: 551
Engine & Generator Mfr
S.I.C.: 3621
N.A.I.C.S.: 335312

Fuji Heavy Industries, Ltd. - Utsunomiya Plant (1)
1-1-11 Yonan
Utsunomiya, Tochigi, 320-8564, Japan
Tel.: (81) 28 684 7777
Emp.: 212
Aircraft Mfr
S.I.C.: 3721
N.A.I.C.S.: 336411

U.S. Subsidiaries:

Fuji Heavy Industries U.S.A. Inc. (1)
Subaru Plz 2235 Route 70 W
Cherry Hill, NJ 08002 (100%)
Tel.: (856) 488-8500
Fax: (856) 488-8421
Toll Free: (800) 782-2783
Web Site: www.subaru.com
Emp.: 400
Distribution & Sales of Subaru Automobiles
S.I.C.: 5012
N.A.I.C.S.: 423110

Fuji Heavy Industries U.S.A. Inc. (1)
4040 Lake Washington Blvd NE Ste 314
Kirkland, WA 98033-7874 (100%)
Tel.: (425) 822-0762
Fax: (425) 822-2664
Web Site: www.fhi.co.jp
Emp.: 7
Heavy Machinery & Aerospace Distr
S.I.C.: 3728
N.A.I.C.S.: 336413

Robin America Inc. (1)
905 Telser Rd
Lake Zurich, IL 60047
Tel.: (847) 540-7300
Fax: (847) 438-5012
Toll Free: (800) 277-6246

E-Mail: sales@robinamerica.com
Web Site: www.robinamerica.com
Emp.: 30
Industrial Machinery Mfr & Distr
S.I.C.: 3559
N.A.I.C.S.: 333249
Michael Magolan *(Reg Mgr-Sls)*

Robin Manufacturing USA, Inc. (1)
1201 Industrial St
Hudson, WI 54016-9361
Tel.: (715) 381-5902
Fax: (715) 381-5901
Emp.: 35
General Purpose, Four-Wheel Buggy & Golf Cart Engine Mfr
S.I.C.: 3519
N.A.I.C.S.: 333618
Ken Hori *(Pres)*

Subaru Distributor Corp. (1)
6 Ramland Rd
Orangeburg, NY 10962-2606
Tel.: (845) 359-2500
Telex: 642-588
Fax: (845) 359-2640
E-Mail: info@sdcdlrnet.com
Web Site: www.sdcdlrnet.com
Sls.: $124,594,000
Emp.: 67
Automobile & Parts Wholesale; Independent Distributor
S.I.C.: 5012
N.A.I.C.S.: 423110
Nicholas Tenore *(VP & Controller)*

Subaru of America, Inc. (1)
2235 Rte 70 W
Cherry Hill, NJ 08002 NJ
Mailing Address: (100%)
PO Box 6000
Cherry Hill, NJ 08034-6000
Tel.: (856) 488-8500
Fax: (856) 488-0485
Toll Free: (800) SUBARU3
Web Site: www.subaru.com
Sales Range: $1-4.9 Billion
Emp.: 1,000
Automobiles Whslr
S.I.C.: 5012
N.A.I.C.S.: 423110
Tomomi Nakamura *(Chm & CEO)*
Thomas J. Doll *(Pres & COO)*
Dean Evans *(CMO)*
Joseph Scharff *(Treas & VP-Admin)*
Sim Coldeck *(Exec VP)*
Bill Cyphers *(Sr VP-Sls)*

Subsidiaries:

Subaru Credit Corporation (2)
2235 Route 70 W
Cherry Hill, NJ 08002-6000 (100%)
Tel.: (856) 488-8500
Fax: (856) 488-3139
Toll Free: (800) 882-7008
Web Site: www.subaru.com
Emp.: 5
Financial Services
S.I.C.: 5012
N.A.I.C.S.: 423110
Ylshil Hasunuma *(Chm, Pres & CEO)*

Subaru Financial Services, Inc. (2)
PO Box 6000
Cherry Hill, NJ 08034-6000
Tel.: (856) 488-8770
Fax: (856) 488-3143
Web Site: www.subaru.com
Sales Range: $10-24.9 Million
Emp.: 20
Financing of Automobiles
S.I.C.: 6159
N.A.I.C.S.: 522220

Subaru Leasing Corporation (2)
2235 Route 70 W
Cherry Hill, NJ 08002-6000
Tel.: (856) 488-8500
Fax: (856) 488-0485
Toll Free: (800) 345-4917
Web Site: www.subaru.com
Emp.: 500
Distribution & Sales of Subaru Automobiles
S.I.C.: 5012
N.A.I.C.S.: 423110
Yoshio Hasunuma *(Pres)*
Tom Doll *(COO & Exec VP)*

Subaru of America, Inc. (2)
Penn Jersey Reg 35 E Pk Dr
Westampton, NJ 08060-1104
Tel.: (609) 518-5000
Fax: (609) 267-0435
Toll Free: (800) 821-7265
Web Site: www.subaru.com
Emp.: 60
Distribution & Sales of Subaru Automobiles
S.I.C.: 5012
N.A.I.C.S.: 423110
Dan Dalton *(VP-HR)*

Divisions:

Subaru Great Lakes Region (2)
500 Park Blvd Ste 255C
Itasca, IL 60143-1253
Tel.: (630) 250-4740
Fax: (630) 285-1100
Web Site: www.subaru.com
Emp.: 40
Regional Office of Subaru Vehicles & Replacement Parts
S.I.C.: 5012
N.A.I.C.S.: 423110

Subaru of America Northwest Region (2)
5216 NE 158th Ave
Portland, OR 97230-4937
Mailing Address:
PO Box 11293
Portland, OR 97211-0293
Tel.: (503) 262-1250
Fax: (503) 253-8338
Web Site: www.subaru.com
Emp.: 35
Regional Office of Subaru Vehicles & Replacement Parts
S.I.C.: 5012
N.A.I.C.S.: 423110

Subaru of America Southeast Region (2)
220 The Bluffs
Austell, GA 30168
Tel.: (770) 732-3200
Fax: (770) 732-3233
Web Site: www.subaru.com
Emp.: 70
Mfr. of Vehicles & Replacement Parts
S.I.C.: 5013
N.A.I.C.S.: 423120

Subaru of New England, Inc. (2)
95 Morse St
Norwood, MA 02062-4623
Tel.: (781) 769-5100
Fax: (781) 255-6370
Web Site: www.subaru.com
Sls.: $225,000,000
Emp.: 65
Automobiles & Parts Wholesale
S.I.C.: 5012
N.A.I.C.S.: 423110
Joseph Applebee *(Exec VP & Gen Mgr)*

Subaru Western Region, Inc. (2)
15000 E 39th Ave
Aurora, CO 80011
Tel.: (303) 371-3820
Telex: 45-739
Fax: (303) 373-8968
Web Site: www.subaru.com
Sls.: $84,808,000
Emp.: 50
Automotive Parts Sales & Distribution
S.I.C.: 5012
N.A.I.C.S.: 423110
Anthony Graziano *(Reg VP)*

Subaru Research & Development, Inc. (1)
3995 Research Park Dr
Ann Arbor, MI 48108-2219
Tel.: (734) 623-0075
Fax: (734) 623-9579
Emp.: 20
S.I.C.: 3711
N.A.I.C.S.: 336111
Yasuhiko Habara *(Pres)*
Iasuhiko Habara *(CEO)*

Subaru Research & Development (1)
6431 Global Dr
Cypress, CA 90630-5227 (100%)
Tel.: (714) 828-1875
Fax: (714) 828-2470
Web Site: www.fhi.co.jp
Emp.: 3
Research & Development of Subaru Cars
S.I.C.: 8732
N.A.I.C.S.: 541910
Shino Hara *(Pres)*

Subaru Robin Power Products (1)
905 Telser Rd
Lake Zurich, IL 60047
Tel.: (847) 540-7300
Fax: (847) 438-5012
E-Mail: website.info@robinamerica.com
Web Site: www.robinamerica.com
Emp.: 30
Small Industrial Engines Mfr
S.I.C.: 5084
N.A.I.C.S.: 423830
David Quance *(Controller)*

U.S. Joint Venture:

Subaru of Indiana Automotive, Inc. (1)
5500 St Rd 38 E
Lafayette, IN 47905 IN
Mailing Address:
PO Box 5689
Lafayette, IN 47903-5689
Tel.: (765) 449-1111
Fax: (765) 449-6952
Web Site: www.subaru-sia.com
Emp.: 34
Mfr. of Pickup Trucks Sports Utility Vehicles & Passenger Cars; Joint Venture of Fuji Heavy Industries, Ltd. & Isuzu Motors Limited
S.I.C.: 3711
N.A.I.C.S.: 336111
Masaki Okawara *(Pres & CEO)*

Non-U.S. Subsidiaries:

Changzhou Fuji Changchai Robin Gasoline Engine Co.,Ltd. (1)
No 28 Changjiang M Road
Xinbei District, Changzhou, Jiangsu, 213022, China
Tel.: (86) 51985109370
Fax: (86) 51985109259
Combustion Gasoline Engine Mfr
S.I.C.: 3714
N.A.I.C.S.: 336310

Fuji Heavy Industries Ltd., China Office (1)
Beijing Landmark Towers Office Bldg 2-1501
8 North Dongsanhuan Rd, Beijing, Chaoyang District, 100004, China (100%)
Tel.: (86) 10 8527 6164
Fax: (86) 10 8527 6163
Web Site: www.fhi.co.jp/english/outline/inoutline/overseas/
Manufacture, Repair & Sales of Heavy Duty Trucks
S.I.C.: 3711
N.A.I.C.S.: 336120
Kazunari Sezuki *(Mng Dir)*

Fuji Heavy Industries (Singapore) Pte. Ltd. (1)
8 Jurong Town Hall Rd 23-02
Singapore, 609434, Singapore (100%)
Tel.: (65) 68968960
Fax: (65) 68968970
E-Mail: fhisrbn@singnet.com.sg
Web Site: www.fujiheavyindustries.com
Sales Range: $10-24.9 Million
Emp.: 5
S.I.C.: 3711
N.A.I.C.S.: 336111
Uchika Kotaro *(Mng Dir)*

Robin Europe GmbH (1)
Willicher Damm
3541066 Willich, Germany
Tel.: (49) 2161636200
Fax: (49) 21616362050
E-Mail: sales@robin-europe.de
Web Site: www.robin-europe.de
Emp.: 13
Engine, Generator & Pump Distr
S.I.C.: 3795
N.A.I.C.S.: 336111

Subaru Canada, Inc. (1)
560 Suffolk Ct
Mississauga, ON, L5R 4J7, Canada (100%)
Tel.: (905) 568-4959
Fax: (905) 568-8087
E-Mail: customercare@subaru.ca
Web Site: www.subaru.ca
Emp.: 100
Distribution & Sales of Subaru Automobiles
S.I.C.: 5013
N.A.I.C.S.: 423120
Shiro Ohta *(Chm, Pres & CEO)*
Yasushi Enami *(VP, Treas & Sec)*

Subaru Europe N.V./S.A. (1)
Leuvensesteenweg 555 B 8
1930 Zaventem, Belgium (100%)
Tel.: (32) 27140400
Fax: (32) 27257792
E-Mail: info@subaru.eu
Web Site: www.subaru.eu
Emp.: 40
Automobiles, Parts & Accessories Distr & Sales
S.I.C.: 5013
N.A.I.C.S.: 423120

Subaru of China, Inc. (1)
Beijing Landmark Towers Office Bldg
2-1506 8 N Dongsanhuan Rd
Chaoyang District, Beijing, China
Tel.: (86) 1065900725
Fax: (86) 1065900729
E-Mail: info@subaru-china.cn
Web Site: www.subaru-china.cn
Emp.: 50
Automobile Mfr
S.I.C.: 3714
N.A.I.C.S.: 336390

Subaru Test & Development Center in Europe (1)
Konrad Adenauer Strasse 34
55218 Ingelheim, Ingelheim, Germany (100%)
Tel.: (49) 613276370
Fax: (49) 613276331
E-Mail: hideki@gkh.subaru-fhi.co.jp
Emp.: 7
S.I.C.: 3711
N.A.I.C.S.: 336111
Hideki Arai *(Gen Mgr)*

Subaru Vehicle Distribution BV (1)
Merseyweg 40 Botlek
Rotterdam, Netherlands
Tel.: (31) 181 290499
Fax: (31) 18121 5059
Automobile Whslr
S.I.C.: 5012
N.A.I.C.S.: 423110

FUJI KIKO CO., LTD.

2028 Washizu
Kosai, Shizuoka, 431-0431, Japan
Tel.: (81) 535752717
Fax: (81) 535750114
E-Mail: info@fujikiko.co.jp
Web Site: www.fujikiko-group.co.jp
Year Founded: 1944
7260—(TKS)
Sales Range: $1-4.9 Billion
Emp.: 988

Business Description:
Seat Belts, Steering Columns & Suspension Parts Mfr
S.I.C.: 2396
N.A.I.C.S.: 336360

Personnel:
Nobuyoshi Hisada *(Pres & CEO)*

Subsidiary:

Fuji Kiko Kurata Corporation. (1)
26 Hamacho
Gamagori, 443-0036, Japan
Tel.: (81) 533663262
Fax: (81) 533688295
Automotive Parts Mfr
S.I.C.: 3711
N.A.I.C.S.: 336111

Plants:

Fuji Kiko Co., Ltd -Honjo Factory (1)
2-4-53 Chuo
Honjo, Saitama, 367-0053, Japan
Tel.: (81) 495211461
Fax: (81) 495244001
Web Site: www.fujikiko-group.co.jp/en/gaiyou/honjo.htm

Fuji Kiko Co., Ltd.—(Continued)

Heavy Duty Vehicle Parts Mfr
S.I.C.: 3714
N.A.I.C.S.: 336390

Fuji Kiko Co., Ltd - Washizu Factory (1)
2028 Washizu
Kosai, Shizuoka, 431-0431, Japan
Tel.: (81) 535752711
Fax: (81) 535750114
Web Site: www.fujikiko-group.co.jp/en/gaiyou/washizu.htm
Emp.: 1,000
Automobile Parts Mfr
S.I.C.: 3714
N.A.I.C.S.: 336390
Toyohumi Yamamoto *(Gen Mgr)*

U.S. Subsidiaries:

Douglas Autotech Corporation (1)
300 Albers Rd
Bronson, MI 49028-1239
Tel.: (517) 369-2315
Fax: (517) 369-7217
Web Site: www.douglasautotech.com
Emp.: 97
Motor Vehicle Parts Mfr
S.I.C.: 3714
N.A.I.C.S.: 336390
Ted Uchida *(Pres)*

Fuji Autotech U.S.A. LLC (1)
70 Precision Dr
Walton, KY 41094-7464
Tel.: (859) 485-3977
Fax: (859) 485-3944
E-Mail: csebring@fujiautotec.net
Web Site: www.fujiautotec.com
Emp.: 100
Motor Vehicle Parts Mfr
S.I.C.: 3714
N.A.I.C.S.: 336390
Akil Setl *(Mng Dir)*

Non-U.S. Subsidiaries:

Fuji Autotech AB (1)
Svista
Eskilstuna, Sweden SE
Tel.: (46) 16169200
Fax: (46) 16169250
E-Mail: info@fujiautotech.com
Web Site: www.fujiautotech.com
Emp.: 100
Motor Vehicle Parts Mfr
S.I.C.: 3714
N.A.I.C.S.: 336390
Jaccob Ssom *(Pres)*

Fuji Autotech France S.A.S. (1)
Rue 7 Novembre
Valenteney, 25708 Valentigney, France FR
Tel.: (33) 381364300
Fax: (33) 381364363
Emp.: 450
Motor Vehicle Parts Mfr
S.I.C.: 3714
N.A.I.C.S.: 336390
Salez Jean *(Mng Dir)*

Fuji Autotech Guangzhou Co., Ltd. (1)
East of Dongfeng Avenue Auto Town
Huadu District, Guangzhou, Guangdong, 510800, China CN
Tel.: (86) 2086733687
Fax: (86) 2086733690
Web Site: www.fujikiko-group.co.jp/en/gaiyou/ksf.htm
Automobile Parts Mfr
S.I.C.: 2396
N.A.I.C.S.: 336360

Fuji Koyo Czech s.r.o. (1)
Podnikatelska 1144/8
301 00 Plzen, Czech Republic
Tel.: (420) 378011111
Fax: (420) 378011111
E-Mail: reception@fujikiko-skc.cz
Web Site: www.fujikoyo.cz
Emp.: 300
Motor Vehicle Parts Mfr
S.I.C.: 3714
N.A.I.C.S.: 336390
Takao Matsushima *(Pres)*

P.T. Autotech Indonesia (1)
Kota Bukit Indah Industrial Town Block D III No 2
Purwakarta, West Java, 41181, Indonesia
Tel.: (62) 264351013
Fax: (62) 264351012
Automobile Steering Parts Mfr
S.I.C.: 3714
N.A.I.C.S.: 336330

Summit Fujikiko Kurata Manufacturing Co., Ltd. (1)
300-16 Moo 1 Eastern Seaboard Estate Tasit
Rayong, 21140, Thailand
Tel.: (66) 38954568
Fax: (66) 38959243
Web Site: www.sfkk.co.th
Automobile Steering Parts Mfr
S.I.C.: 3714
N.A.I.C.S.: 336330

FUJI MACHINE MFG. CO., LTD.

19 Chausuyama Yamamachi
Chiryu, Aichi, 472-8686, Japan
Tel.: (81) 566812111
Fax: (81) 566831140
Web Site: www.fuji.co.jp
Year Founded: 1959
6134—(NGO TKS)
Sls.: $707,839,000
Assets: $1,441,979,000
Liabilities: $168,861,000
Net Worth: $1,273,118,000
Earnings: $29,678,000
Emp.: 1,621
Fiscal Year-end: 03/31/13

Business Description:
Surface Mount Equipment, Machine Tools & LCD Assembly Equipment Mfr
S.I.C.: 3547
N.A.I.C.S.: 333519

Personnel:
Nobuyuki Soga *(Pres & CEO)*

Subsidiaries:

Edeclinseysystem Co.,Ltd. (1)
331-9 Hamaike
Nishimiyuki-cho, Toyohashi, 441-8113, Japan
Tel.: (81) 532294131
Fax: (81) 532294130
Web Site: www.edeclinsey.jp
Emp.: 100
Electronic Component Mfr
S.I.C.: 3679
N.A.I.C.S.: 334419
Takamasa Kawii *(Pres)*

Makoto Industry Co., Ltd. (1)
74-1 Shaguchi
Nishihongo-cho, Okazaki, 444-0947, Japan
Tel.: (81) 564314690
Fax: (81) 564311794
Web Site: www.fuji.co.jp/e/data/a01_01.html
Emp.: 150
Industrial Machinery & Equipment Merchant Whslr
S.I.C.: 5084
N.A.I.C.S.: 423830
Hahakaba Yukio *(CEO)*

Plants:

Fuji Machine Mfg. Co., Ltd. - Fujioka Plant (1)
480 Tojiri Hasama-cho
Toyota, Aichi, 470-0452, Japan
Tel.: (81) 565 76 2211
Fax: (81) 565 76 5413
Web Site: www.fuji.co.jp/e/data/plants_e.html
Machine Tool Mfr
S.I.C.: 3541
N.A.I.C.S.: 333517

Fuji Machine Mfg. Co., Ltd. - Okazaki Plant (1)
1-3 Kitayoko Eta-cho
Okazaki, Aichi, 444-2107, Japan
Tel.: (81) 564 452000
Fax: (81) 564 458816
Electronic Component Mfr
S.I.C.: 3679
N.A.I.C.S.: 334419

U.S. Subsidiaries:

EQUIPMENT SALES CO. (1)
885 S Brooksvale Rd
Cheshire, CT 06410
Tel.: (203) 271-3266
Fax: (203) 272-3294
Web Site: www.fuji.co.jp/e/SMT/smt_Contact/Contacts.html
Electronic Equipment Distr
S.I.C.: 5065
N.A.I.C.S.: 423690

Fuji America Corporation (1)
171 Corporate Woods Pkwy
Vernon Hills, IL 60061
Tel.: (847) 913-0162
Fax: (847) 913-0186
E-Mail:
Web Site: www.fujiamerica.com
Emp.: 65
Miscellaneous General Purpose Machinery Mfr
S.I.C.: 3569
N.A.I.C.S.: 333999
Nick Kimura *(Pres)*

Fuji Machine America Corporation (1)
171 Corporate Woods Pkwy
Vernon Hills, IL 60061
Tel.: (847) 821-7137
Fax: (847) 821-7815
E-Mail: info@fujimachine.com
Web Site: www.fujimachineamerica.com
Emp.: 25
Industrial Machinery Mfr
S.I.C.: 3559
N.A.I.C.S.: 333249
Nobuo Kamazawa *(Pres-Fuji Machine America)*
Nick Kimura *(Pres)*

PRODUCTION TECHNOLOGY (1)
6765 Westminster Blvd Ste C-422
Westminster, CA 92683-3769
Tel.: (714) 895-0016
Fax: (714) 893-3840
E-Mail: PTCPffice@prod-tech.com
Web Site: www.prod-tech.com
Printed Circuit Board Mfr & Distr
S.I.C.: 3679
N.A.I.C.S.: 334418
Dennis E. Tiberius *(Pres)*

Restronics Co., Inc (1)
11547 K Tel Dr
Minnetonka, MN 55343
Tel.: (952) 912-0004
Fax: (952) 929-2765
E-Mail: rsavage@restronics.com
Web Site: www.restronics.com
Emp.: 27
Printed Circuit Assembly Mfr
S.I.C.: 3679
N.A.I.C.S.: 334418
Ralph Savage *(Mng Partner)*

Rich Sales, Inc. (1)
15547 N 77th St
Scottsdale, AZ 85260
Tel.: (480) 443-9255
Fax: (480) 443-9256
E-Mail: courtney@rrlotion.com
Web Site: www.richsales.com
Emp.: 100
Electronic Component Mfr
S.I.C.: 3679
N.A.I.C.S.: 334419
Courtney Rich *(Mng Dir)*

Non-U.S. Subsidiaries:

ALGAR S.p.A (1)
Via Riva di Trento 17/A
20139 Milan, Italy
Tel.: (39) 02 5749561
Fax: (39) 02 55210770
E-Mail: info@algar.it
Web Site: www.algar.it
Emp.: 8
Printed Circuit Board Distr
S.I.C.: 5065
N.A.I.C.S.: 423690
Stefano Bollati *(Gen Mgr)*

American Tec Electronic India Pvt Ltd. (1)
B-68 Sector 63 Kasturba Gandhi Marg
UP 201301 Noida, India
Tel.: (91) 120 436 7120
E-Mail: sales@americantec.com
Web Site: www.americantec.com
Emp.: 40
Electronic Component Mfr
S.I.C.: 3679
N.A.I.C.S.: 334419
Stephen Wu *(Pres)*

Ascentex Industry Corp. (1)
7th Floor NO 516 Sec 1
Nei Hu Road, Taipei, Taiwan
Tel.: (886) 287978788
Fax: (886) 287978789
E-Mail: info@ascentex.com
Web Site: www.ascentex.com
Emp.: 100
Automatic Vending Machine Mfr
S.I.C.: 3589
N.A.I.C.S.: 333318
Adam Guo *(Mgr)*

Non-U.S. Subsidiary:

Ascentek International Company Limited (2)
Rml 26th Floor Zhaofeng World Trading Building
No 369 Jiangsu Road, Shanghai, 200050, China
Tel.: (86) 2152401458
Fax: (86) 2152400480
Web Site: www.fuji.co.jp
Emp.: 200
Commercial & Service Industry Machinery Mfr
S.I.C.: 3589
N.A.I.C.S.: 333318
Jeff Chang *(Mng Dir)*

Astro Technologies Ltd. (1)
Astro House 7 Bessemer Way
Sawcliffe Industrial Park, DN158XE
Scunthorpe, United Kingdom
Tel.: (44) 1724295400
Fax: (44) 1724295403
Electronic Parts & Equipment Whslr
S.I.C.: 5065
N.A.I.C.S.: 423690

Brock Electronics Ltd. (1)
16 350 Harry Walker Parkway
Newmarket, ON, L3Y 8L3, Canada
Tel.: (905) 954-0505
Fax: (416) 352-1941
E-Mail: info@brockelectronics.com
Web Site: www.brockelectronics.com
Emp.: 7
Miscellaneous General Purpose Machinery Mfr
S.I.C.: 3569
N.A.I.C.S.: 333999
Paul Walsh *(Owner)*

FENWICK IBERICA S.A. (1)
Bailen 136 Ent 2 a
8037 Barcelona, Spain
Tel.: (34) 934 584 001
Fax: (34) 934 584 002
E-Mail: mail@fenwick-iberica.es
Web Site: www.fenwick-iberica.es
Machine Tool Distr
S.I.C.: 5084
N.A.I.C.S.: 423830

First Technology China Ltd. (1)
St 1902-5 19th Fl One Landmark E
100How Ming Str Kunn Tong, Kowloon, China (Hong Kong)
Tel.: (852) 25070338
Fax: (852) 25669963
E-Mail: cantywong@1techchina.com
Web Site: www.1techchina.com
Scientific & Technical Consulting Services
S.I.C.: 8999
N.A.I.C.S.: 541690

Non-U.S. Subsidiaries:

First Technology (Beijing) Ltd. (2)
928-930 Xuan Wamen Wai Street Junefield Plaza No 10
Xuanwu District, 100052 Beijing, China
Tel.: (86) 10 6310 6696
Fax: (86) 10 6310 6296
Machine Tools Mfr
S.I.C.: 3541
N.A.I.C.S.: 333517

First Technology Shanghai Ltd. (2)
Rm 3201 LT Square No 500 North Chengdu Rd
Shanghai, 200003, China
Tel.: (86) 2151699850
Fax: (86) 2163615697

Machine Tools Mfr
S.I.C.: 3423
N.A.I.C.S.: 332216

Fuji do Brasil Maquinas Industriais Ltda. (1)
Rua Joao Cachoeira 128
04535 000, 04535 000 Sao Paulo, Brazil
Tel.: (55) 11 3167 1650
Fax: (55) 11 3079 1833
E-Mail: info@fujibrasil.com.br
Web Site: www.fujibrasil.com.br
Emp.: 30
Surface Mounted Machinery Whslr
S.I.C.: 5084
N.A.I.C.S.: 423830
Domingos Tomyama *(Gen Mgr)*

Fuji Machine China Co.,Ltd. (1)
Pine City Hotel Room 716 Dong'an Rd 8
Shanghai, 200031, China
Tel.: (86) 2164031341
Fax: (86) 2164031249
Web Site: www.fuji-mc.com.cn
Emp.: 7
Industrial Machinery Mfr
S.I.C.: 3559
N.A.I.C.S.: 333249
Mitsu Sato *(Mgr)*

Fuji Machine Manufacturing (Europe) GmbH (1)
Peter-Sander-Str 43
55252 Mainz-Kastel, Germany
Tel.: (49) 61342020
Fax: (49) 6134202200
E-Mail: FMERALL@fuji-euro.de
Web Site: www.fuji-euro.de
Emp.: 42
Miscellaneous General Purpose Machinery Mfr
S.I.C.: 3569
N.A.I.C.S.: 333999
Klaus Grows *(Gen Mgr)*

KOBOT SYSTEMS PTY LTD. (1)
3 Mast Pl Ocean Reef
Perth, WA, Australia
Tel.: (61) 893078178
Fax: (61) 894022756
Web Site: www.kobot.com.au
Industrial Machine Tool Mfr
S.I.C.: 3542
N.A.I.C.S.: 333517
Gerald Koh *(Gen Mgr)*

MECOMB (THAILAND) LTD. (1)
420 Sukhumvit 71 Rord Prakanong-Nua
Wattana, Bangkok, Thailand
Tel.: (66) 2711 7101
Fax: (66) 2382 2080
E-Mail: maketg@mecombthai.co.th
Web Site: www.mecombthai.co.th
Electronic Component Mfr
S.I.C.: 3679
N.A.I.C.S.: 334419

MS INTERNATIONAL CORP. (1)
Rm No 1205 Haechun Bld 831 Yucksam-dong
Kangnam-Ku, Seoul, Korea (South)
Tel.: (82) 2 553 0901
Fax: (82) 2 555 5584
E-Mail: msi@msinter.co.kr
Web Site: www.msinter.co.kr
Electronic Products Mfr & Distr
S.I.C.: 3679
N.A.I.C.S.: 334419

Perfecbore AG (1)
Mullerstrasse 2
Bern, Switzerland
Tel.: (41) 323328444
Fax: (41) 323328440
E-Mail: info@perfecbore.ch
Web Site: www.perfecbore.ch
Emp.: 10
Industrial Machinery Mfr
S.I.C.: 3559
N.A.I.C.S.: 333249
Paerre Moser *(Mng Dir)*

Precitool-Fenwick NV (1)
Singel 6 C
2550 Kontich, Belgium
Tel.: (32) 3 294 16 00
Fax: (32) 3 294 16 01
E-Mail: info@precitool-fenwick.be
Web Site: www.precitool-fenwick.com
Emp.: 5
Electronic Component Mfr
S.I.C.: 3679
N.A.I.C.S.: 334419
Jean-Paul de Wolf *(Gen Mgr)*

Scanditron Finland OY (1)
Sinikalliontie 5A
02630 Espoo, Finland
Tel.: (358) 207 528 700
Fax: (358) 207 528 770
E-Mail: info@scanditron.fi
Web Site: www.scanditron.fi
Emp.: 15
Electronic Component Distr
S.I.C.: 5065
N.A.I.C.S.: 423690

Smartech Electronics Co., Ltd. (1)
Unit 1006 39 Wang Chiu Road
Kowloon Bay, Kowloon, China (Hong Kong)
Tel.: (852) 82262265
Fax: (852) 82262267
E-Mail: enquiry@hk-smartech.com
Web Site: www.smartech.cn/en/contact/index.htm
Professional Scientific & Technical Services
S.I.C.: 7389
N.A.I.C.S.: 541990
Kenneth Koo *(Mng Dir)*

Smartech Electronics (Shenzhen) Co., Ltd (1)
Room 1105 South Block Li Jing Building
48 Jin Tang Street Cai Wu Wei, Shenzhen, 518010, China
Tel.: (86) 75582481531
Fax: (86) 75582481524
E-Mail: enquiry-electronics@smartech.cn
Web Site: www.smartech.cn
Professional Scientific & Technical Services
S.I.C.: 7389
N.A.I.C.S.: 541990

Smartech Enterprise Co., Ltd. (1)
Unit 611 6th Floor Chevalier Comm Ctr
8 Wang Hoi Road, Kowloon, China (Hong Kong)
Tel.: (852) 21171300
Fax: (852) 21809355
E-Mail: enquiry@hk-smartech.com
Web Site: www.smartech.cn
Professional Scientific & Technical Services
S.I.C.: 7389
N.A.I.C.S.: 541990
Kenneth Koo *(Mng Dir)*

Smartech Equipment (Shenzhen) Co., Ltd. (1)
Rm 311 Building Zhuoyue
NO 1 Fuhhua Rd Futian Trade, 518048
Shenzhen, China
Tel.: (86) 75583484158
Fax: (86) 75583485958
E-Mail: enquiry@hk-smartech.com
Professional Scientific & Technical Services
S.I.C.: 7389
N.A.I.C.S.: 541990

FUJI MEDIA HOLDINGS, INC.

2-4-8 Daiba Minato-ku
Tokyo, 137-8088, Japan
Tel.: (81) 335708000
Fax: (81) 335708438
Web Site: www.fujimediahd.co.jp
Year Founded: 1957
4676—(TKS)
Sls.: $6,952,319,000
Assets: $10,475,685,000
Liabilities: $4,225,485,000
Net Worth: $6,250,200,000
Earnings: $344,707,000
Emp.: 5,917
Fiscal Year-end: 03/31/13

Business Description:
Holding Company; Television, Production, Video, Music & Advertising
S.I.C.: 6719
N.A.I.C.S.: 551112

Personnel:
Hisashi Hieda *(Chm & CEO)*
Kou Toyoda *(Vice Chm & Exec Mng Dir)*
Hideaki Ohta *(Pres & COO)*
Ryunosuke Endo *(Exec Mng Dir)*
Taizan Ishiguro *(Exec Mng Dir)*
Chihiro Kameyama *(Exec Mng Dir)*
Takehiko Kiyohara *(Exec Mng Dir)*
Isao Matsuoka *(Exec Mng Dir)*
Akihiro Miki *(Exec Mng Dir)*
Toru Ota *(Exec Mng Dir)*
Katsuaki Suzuki *(Exec Mng Dir)*
Kazuo Terasaki *(Exec Mng Dir)*
Masafumi Yokota *(Exec Mng Dir)*
Shuji Kanoh *(CFO & Sr Exec VP)*

Board of Directors:
Hisashi Hieda
Ryunosuke Endo
Taizan Ishiguro
Chihiro Kameyama
Osamu Kanemitsu
Shuji Kanoh
Takehiko Kiyohara
Isao Matsuoka
Akihiro Miki
Hideaki Ohta
Toru Ota
Katsuaki Suzuki
Kazuo Terasaki
Kou Toyoda
Takashi Wagai
Masafumi Yokota

Transfer Agent:
Mizuho Trust & Banking Co., Ltd.
2-1 Yaesu 1-Chome Chuo-ku
Tokyo, 103 8670, Japan
Tel.: (81) 332788111
Fax: (81) 332816947

Subsidiaries:

Basis Ltd. (1)
Hamarikyu Parkside Place 5-6-10 Tsukiji
Chuo-ku, Tokyo, 104-0045, Japan
Tel.: (81) 335474890
Fax: (81) 335474892
Web Site: www.basis-net.co.jp
Television Network Broadcasting Services
S.I.C.: 4833
N.A.I.C.S.: 515120

Cecile Co., Ltd. (1)
10-20 Taga-cho 2 chome
Takamatsu, Kagawa, 760-0063, Japan (77%)
Tel.: (81) 878352727
Fax: (81) 878354432
Web Site: www.cecile.co.jp
Sales Range: $500-549.9 Million
Emp.: 857
Mail-Order Clothing Retailer
S.I.C.: 5961
N.A.I.C.S.: 454113
Yuji Inada *(Sr Mng Dir)*

Dinos Inc. (1)
Nakano Sakaue Ctr Bldg 2-46-2 Honchob
Nakano-ku, Tokyo, 164-0012, Japan
Tel.: (81) 353531200
Fax: (81) 353531201
E-Mail: kaigaijigyobu.dinos@gmail.com
Web Site: www.dinos.co.jp
Emp.: 346
Mail Order Distr
S.I.C.: 5961
N.A.I.C.S.: 454113
Junichi Ishikawa *(Pres & CEO)*
Isao Nagahiro *(Co-Mng Dir)*
Atsuo Nakahara *(Co-Mng Dir)*

Subsidiary:

Dinex, Inc. (2)
2-46-2 Honcho Nakano Sakaue Ctr Bldg
Nakano-ku, Tokyo, 164-0012, Japan
Tel.: (81) 353531139
Fax: (81) 353531140
Mail Orders Distr
S.I.C.: 5961
N.A.I.C.S.: 454113

FCG Research Institute, Inc. (1)
Fuji Television Bldg Annex 6 F 3-32-42
Higashi Shinagawa
Shinagawa-ku, Tokyo, Japan
Tel.: (81) 354951500
Web Site: www.fcg-r.co.jp
Emp.: 40
Information Research Development Services
S.I.C.: 8731
N.A.I.C.S.: 541712
Masao Sakai *(Pres)*

Fuji Art, Inc. (1)
4-5-19 Nishioizumi
Nerima-ku, Tokyo, 178-0065, Japan
Tel.: (81) 354951212
Fax: (81) 354951222
Web Site: www.fujiart.co.jp
Architectural Design Services
S.I.C.: 8712
N.A.I.C.S.: 541310

Fuji Creative Corporation (1)
11th Floor Fuji Tv Annex 3-32-42 Higashi Shinagawa
Shinagawa-ku, Tokyo, Japan 140-0002
Tel.: (81) 3 5495 1181
Fax: (81) 3 5495 1183
E-Mail: intlsales@fujicreative.co.jp
Web Site: www.fujicreative.co.jp
Graphic Design Services
S.I.C.: 7336
N.A.I.C.S.: 541430

Fuji Direct Marketing, Inc. (1)
2-46-2 Honcho Nakanosakaue Central Building 11 F Dinos Kata
Nakano-ku, Tokyo, 164-0012, Japan
Tel.: (81) 353538828
Fax: (81) 353538762
Television Network Broadcasting Services
S.I.C.: 4833
N.A.I.C.S.: 515120

Fuji Lighting and Technology, Inc. (1)
1-15-1 Kaigan
Minato-ku, Tokyo, Japan
Tel.: (81) 334321188
Fax: (81) 334326841
Web Site: www.flt-web.co.jp
Television Lighting Systems Mfr
S.I.C.: 3648
N.A.I.C.S.: 335129

Fuji Satellite Broadcasting, Inc. (1)
2-4-8 Daiba
Minato-ku, Tokyo, 137-8088, Japan
Tel.: (81) 3 5500 8000
Web Site: www.bsfuji.co.jp
Television Broadcasting Services
S.I.C.: 4833
N.A.I.C.S.: 515120

Fujimic, Inc. (1)
3-32-42 Higashishinagawa Fuji Television Bekkan 8 F
Shinagawa-ku, Tokyo, 140-0002, Japan
Tel.: (81) 354951111
Fax: (81) 354951100
Web Site: www.fujimic.com
Data Processing Services
S.I.C.: 7374
N.A.I.C.S.: 518210

Fujipacific Music Inc (1)
3-3-5 Kita Aoyama
Minato-ku, Tokyo, 107-0061, Japan
Tel.: (81) 337968603
Fax: (81) 337960153
E-Mail: mail@fujipacific.co.jp
Web Site: www.fujipacific.co.jp
Emp.: 100
Music Publishing Services
S.I.C.: 2741
N.A.I.C.S.: 512230

Fujisankei Agency Co., Ltd. (1)
3-3-1 Marunouchi Shintokyo Building 234
Chiyoda-ku, Tokyo, 100-0005, Japan
Tel.: (81) 332875505
Fax: (81) 3 3287 5520
Web Site: www.fs-agency.co.jp
Insurance Agency Services
S.I.C.: 6411
N.A.I.C.S.: 524298

Fujisankei Personnel Inc. (1)
1-7-1 Yurakucho Yurakucho Denki Bldg Minamikan 18 F
Chiyoda-ku, Tokyo, 100-0006, Japan
Tel.: (81) 332400888
Fax: (81) 332400889
E-Mail: seminar@fs-jinzai.co.jp
Web Site: www.fs-jinzai.co.jp
Emp.: 40
Television Network Broadcasting Services
S.I.C.: 4833

Fuji Media Holdings, Inc.—(Continued)

N.A.I.C.S.: 515120
Shoichiro Ishimaru *(Mng Dir)*

Happo Television, Inc. **(1)**
2-3-1 Daiba
Minato-ku, Tokyo, Japan
Tel.: (81) 355000900
Fax: (81) 3 5500 0960
E-Mail: sales_dpt@happo-tv.co.jp
Web Site: www.happo-tv.co.jp
Emp.: 153
Television Network Broadcasting Services
S.I.C.: 4833
N.A.I.C.S.: 515120
Jitsu Nosuke Kawai *(Pres)*

Kansai Telecasting Corporation **(1)**
2 1 7 Ogimachi Kita ku
Osaka, 530 8408, Japan (100%)
Tel.: (81) 663148888
Fax: (81) 663148829
Web Site: www.ktv.co.jp
Emp.: 561
Television Network
S.I.C.: 4833
N.A.I.C.S.: 515120
Sumio Fukui *(Pres)*

Kyodo Edit, Inc. **(1)**
2-3-1 Daiba Trade Pia Odaiba 7 F
Minato-ku, Tokyo, 135-0091, Japan
Tel.: (81) 355005980
Fax: (81) 355005981
Web Site: www.kyodo-edit.co.jp
Television Network Broadcasting Services
S.I.C.: 4833
N.A.I.C.S.: 515120

Kyodo Television,Ltd. **(1)**
5-6-10 Tsukiji Hamarikyu Pk Side Pl
Chuo-ku, Tokyo, 104-0045, Japan
Tel.: (81) 335474800
Fax: (81) 335474809
Web Site: www.kyodo-tv.co.jp
Television Network Broadcasting Services
S.I.C.: 4833
N.A.I.C.S.: 515120

Living Pro-Seed, Inc. **(1)**
3-23 Kioicho Bungeishunju Bldg Shinkan
Chiyoda-ku, Tokyo, 102-0094, Japan
Tel.: (81) 352169411
Fax: (81) 335715600
Web Site: www.lps.co.jp
Newspaper Publishing Services
S.I.C.: 2711
N.A.I.C.S.: 511110

Nippon Broadcasting Project Inc. **(1)**
3-6 Kioicho Kioicho Park Building 1 F
Chiyoda-ku, Tokyo, 102-0094, Japan
Tel.: (81) 332658261
Fax: (81) 332641364
Web Site: www.jolf-p.co.jp
Radio Broadcasting Services
S.I.C.: 4832
N.A.I.C.S.: 515111

Pony Canyon Inc. **(1)**
2-5-10 Toranomon
Minato-ku, Tokyo, Japan
Tel.: (81) 355218000
Fax: (81) 3 5521 8100
E-Mail: info@ponycanyon.co.jp
Web Site: www.ponycanyon.co.jp
Emp.: 300
Music & Game Publishers
S.I.C.: 2741
N.A.I.C.S.: 512230
Toshiharu Kirihata *(Pres & COO)*
Shingo Inoue *(Exec VP)*

Ponycanyon Music Inc. **(1)**
2-5-10 Toranomon
Minato-ku, 105-0001 Tokyo, Japan
Tel.: (81) 3 3507 5551
Fax: (81) 3 3507 5552
E-Mail: info@pcmusic.jp
Web Site: www.pcmusic.jp
Music & Artists Services
S.I.C.: 7929
N.A.I.C.S.: 711130
Toshio Chigira *(Pres)*

Quaras Inc. **(1)**
2-1-1 Osaki Thinkparktower 7 F
Shinagawa-ku, Tokyo, 141-0032, Japan
Tel.: (81) 354875001
Fax: (81) 354875043
Web Site: www.quaras.co.jp
Emp.: 2,064
Business Communication Services
S.I.C.: 7389
N.A.I.C.S.: 561499

Sankei Living Shimbun Inc **(1)**
3-23 Kioicho Bungeishunju Building Shinkan
Chiyoda-ku, Tokyo, 102-0094, Japan
Tel.: (81) 352169131
Fax: (81) 352169248
Web Site: www.sankeiliving.co.jp
Emp.: 355
Newspaper Publishing Services
S.I.C.: 2711
N.A.I.C.S.: 511110
Masumi Uchiburi *(Pres)*

Satellite Service Co., Ltd. **(1)**
2-4-8 Daiba
Minato-ku, Tokyo, 135-0091, Japan
Tel.: (81) 355008236
Fax: (81) 355008020
Web Site: www.satellite-service.co.jp
Emp.: 10
Television Network Broadcasting Services
S.I.C.: 4833
N.A.I.C.S.: 515120
Kenji Shimizu *(Pres)*

Shizuoka Telecasting Co., Ltd **(1)**
No 65 Suruga-ku Kurihara No 18
Shizuoka, 422 8525, Japan (100%)
Tel.: (81) 54 261 6111
Fax: (81) 542639217
Web Site: www.sut-tv.com
Emp.: 170
Television Programming
S.I.C.: 4833
N.A.I.C.S.: 515120
Yutaka Kobayashi *(Pres)*

Tokai Television Broadcasting Co., Ltd. **(1)**
1 14 27 Higashisakura
Nagoya, Aichi Higashi Ku, 461 8501, Japan (100%)
Tel.: (81) 529512511
Fax: (81) 529541114
Web Site: www.tokai-tv.co.jp
Emp.: 300
S.I.C.: 4833
N.A.I.C.S.: 515120

VASC Co., Ltd. **(1)**
15-2-2 Kabukicho
Shinjuku-ku, Shinjuku, 160-0021, Japan
Tel.: (81) 3 5285 2983
Web Site: www.vasc.co.jp
Television Programme Production Services
S.I.C.: 7819
N.A.I.C.S.: 512199

U.S. Subsidiary:

Fujisankei Communications International, Inc. **(1)**
150 E 52nd St 34th Fl
New York, NY 10022
Tel.: (212) 753-8100
Fax: (212) 688-0392
E-Mail: info@fci-ny.com
Web Site: www.fci-ny.com
Emp.: 50
Television Network Broadcasting Services
S.I.C.: 4833
N.A.I.C.S.: 515120
Hiroshi Oto *(Pres)*

Branch:

Fujisankei Communications International, Inc. - Los Angeles **(2)**
10100 Santa Monica Blvd Ste 460
Los Angeles, CA 90067-3101
Tel.: (310) 553-5828
Fax: (310) 553-2196
Web Site: www.fci-ny.com
Emp.: 10
News Production Services
S.I.C.: 8748
N.A.I.C.S.: 541618
Takatani Katutoshi *(Gen Mgr)*

Subsidiary:

Fuji Entertainment America, Inc **(2)**
21241 S Western Ave Ste 200
Torrance, CA 90501
Tel.: (310) 320-2700
Fax: (310) 320-4630
Compact Discs Whslr
S.I.C.: 5099
N.A.I.C.S.: 423990
Hideko Koike *(CEO)*

Non-U.S. Branch:

Fujisankei Communications International, Inc. - London Office **(2)**
2nd Fl 1 Portland Pl
London, W1B 1PN, United Kingdom
Tel.: (44) 2075803388
Fax: (44) 2076313358
Web Site: www.fujisankei.com
Emp.: 14
S.I.C.: 4833
N.A.I.C.S.: 515120
Katsuyoshi Aota *(Gen Mgr)*

Non-U.S. Subsidiaries:

Fuji Television Bangkok Bureau **(1)**
18th Fl Wave Pl Bldg 55 Wireless Rd
Bangkok, 10330, Thailand (100%)
Tel.: (66) 26554500
Fax: (66) 26554498
Web Site: www.fuji.com
Emp.: 10
Television Broadcasting
S.I.C.: 4833
N.A.I.C.S.: 515120

Fuji Television Beijing Bureau **(1)**
11 103 Jianguomen Apt Chaoyang District
100600 Beijing, China (100%)
Tel.: (86) 1065324840
Fax: (86) 1065324843
E-Mail: makoto.atsuta@fujitv.co.jp
Web Site: www.fijitv.co.jp
Emp.: 7
Television Broadcasting
S.I.C.: 4833
N.A.I.C.S.: 515120

Fuji Television Moscow Bureau/ FNN Moscow Bureau **(1)**
UL Bolshaya Dorogomilovskaya
dom 14 kv 74-75, Moscow, 121059, Russia (100%)
Tel.: (7) 4992437795
Fax: (7) 4959373505
E-Mail: fujimoscow2@ron.ru
Web Site: www.fujitv.co.jp
Emp.: 12
Television Broadcasting
S.I.C.: 4833
N.A.I.C.S.: 515120

FUJI OFFSET PLATES MANUFACTURING LTD

2 Jalan Rajah 06-26/28 Golden Wall Flatted Factory
Singapore, 329134, Singapore
Tel.: (65) 62659111
Fax: (65) 62682300
E-Mail: contact@fopgroup.com
Web Site: www.fopgroup.com
508—(SES)
Rev.: $6,941,387
Assets: $22,977,099
Liabilities: $2,118,123
Net Worth: $20,858,976
Earnings: ($185,417)
Fiscal Year-end: 12/31/12

Business Description:
Aluminum Products Distr
S.I.C.: 3353
N.A.I.C.S.: 331315

Personnel:
Kee Bock Teo *(Chm)*
Kee Chong Teo *(Mng Dir)*
Cher Liang Tan *(Sec)*

Board of Directors:
Kee Bock Teo
Kim Ton Ang
Tee Kit Lee
Kang San Lim
Keh Eyo Tan
Kee Chong Teo

FUJI OIL COMPANY, LTD.

(Formerly AOC Holdings, Inc.)

Tennozu Parkside Building 5-8
Higashishinagawa 2-chome
Shinakawa-ku, Tokyo, 140-0002, Japan
Tel.: (81) 3 5462 7761
Fax: (81) 3 5462 7815
Web Site: www.foc.co.jp
Year Founded: 2003
5017—(TKS)
Sales Range: $5-14.9 Billion
Emp.: 559

Business Description:
Petroleum Products Import, Production & Sales
S.I.C.: 1311
N.A.I.C.S.: 211111

Personnel:
Fumio Sekiya *(Pres)*
Atsuo Shibota *(Sr Mng Dir)*
Jun Inomata *(Mng Dir)*
Nozumo Kano *(Mng Dir)*
Koji Tamashiro *(Mng Dir)*
Koji Watanabe *(Mng Dir)*

Board of Directors:
Emad Al-Abdulkarim
Mohamed Fahd
Jun Inomata
Osamu Ishitobi
Nozumo Kano
Shigeya Kato
Jun Kotake
Hikojiro Seki
Fumio Sekiya
Atsuo Shibota
Masataka Shimizu
Koji Tamashiro
Koji Watanabe

Transfer Agent:
Mizuho Trust & Banking Co., Ltd.
2-1 Yaesu 1-Chome Chuo-ku
Tokyo, 103 8670, Japan
Tel.: (81) 332788111
Fax: (81) 332816947

Subsidiaries:

Arabian Oil Company, Ltd. **(1)**
8 1 Akashityo
Chuo Ku, Tokyo, 104-6591, Japan JP (100%)
Tel.: (81) 335470226
Fax: (81) 335470246
Web Site: www.aoc.co.jp
Emp.: 140
Producer of Oil & Gas
S.I.C.: 1311
N.A.I.C.S.: 211111

Subsidiary:

AOC Egypt Petroleum Company, Ltd **(2)**
10th Fl Tennozu Parkside Bldg 5-8
Higashishinagawa 2 Chome
Shinagawa-ku, Tokyo, 140-0002, Japan
Tel.: (81) 354635010
Fax: (81) 354635085
Web Site: www.aochd.co.jp/e/corporate/associated.html
Emp.: 70
Oil & Gas Exploration Services
S.I.C.: 1389
N.A.I.C.S.: 213112
Kazutoshi Hoyano *(Pres)*

Non-U.S. Subsidiary:

Norske AEDC AS **(2)**
6th Floor Ankerbygget Kongsgaardbakken 1
PO Box 207
Stavanger, Rogaland, 4005, Norway
Tel.: (47) 51212220
Fax: (47) 51 21 2221
Web Site: www.aochd.co.jp/e/corporate/associated.html
Emp.: 12
Oil & Gas Exploration Services
S.I.C.: 1389
N.A.I.C.S.: 213112

Petro Progress, Inc. **(1)**
10th Floor Tennozu Parkside Building 5-8
Higashishinagawa 2-chome
Tokyo, 140-0002, Japan

Tel.: (81) 354635006
Fax: (81) 354635007
Web Site: www.aochd.co.jp/e/group/main_company.html
Emp.: 6
Petroleum Products Transportation Services
S.I.C.: 4619
N.A.I.C.S.: 486990

Non-U.S. Subsidiary:

Petro Progress Pte Ltd (2)
200 Cantonment Road 06-08 Southpoint
Singapore, 089763, Singapore
Tel.: (65) 62266468
Fax: (65) 62266308
Petroleum Products Sales
S.I.C.: 5172
N.A.I.C.S.: 424720

Subsidiary:

Aramo Shipping (Singapore) Pte Ltd (3)
200 Cantonment Rd 06-01 Southpoint
Singapore, 089763, Singapore
Tel.: (65) 62261808
Fax: (65) 62263536
E-Mail: aramo2@mvox.ntti.net.sg
Emp.: 3
Marine Shipping Services
S.I.C.: 4499
N.A.I.C.S.: 488390
Yasuda Takamitsu *(Mng Dir)*

FUJI OIL CO., LTD.
Nihon Seimei Midosuji Hachiman-cho Building 2-1-5 Nishi-Shinsaibashi
Chuo-ku, Osaka, 542-0086, Japan
Tel.: (81) 6 6213 8151
Web Site: www.fujioil.co.jp
2607—(TKS)
Sls.: $2,553,771,000
Assets: $2,168,562,000
Liabilities: $831,688,000
Net Worth: $1,336,874,000
Earnings: $91,696,000
Emp.: 4,034
Fiscal Year-end: 03/31/13
Business Description:
Food Products Mfr
S.I.C.: 2043
N.A.I.C.S.: 311230
Personnel:
Yoshitaka Ebihara *(Chm)*
Hiroshi Shimizu *(Pres & CEO)*
Toshifumi Asada *(Exec Officer-Fin & Acctg Div)*
Hiroshi Hidaka *(Exec Officer-Dev Laboratories-Food Application)*
Masashi Ikeda *(Sr Exec Officer-Mktg & Sls Div II)*
Taisuke Kanemori *(Exec Officer-HR & Admin Div)*
Mikio Kawanishi *(Exec Officer-Mktg & Sls Div I)*
Haruyasu Kida *(Exec Officer-Basic Res Institute)*
Wataru Kugimiya *(Exec Officer-Soy Protein Ingredients Div)*
Mitsugu Kuno *(Mng Exec Officer-Corp Plng & Risk Mgmt)*
Tomoki Matsumoto *(Exec Officer-Corp Plng Dept)*
Yukio Mori *(Exec Officer-Engrg Dev Dept)*
Ichiro Nishimura *(Mng Exec Officer-Engrg Dev & Maintenance)*
Katsuto Sahara *(Exec Officer-Emulsified & Fermented Foods Div)*
Mikio Sakai *(Exec Officer)*
Yoichi Tashiro *(Sr Exec Officer-Dev Laboratories-Food Matls)*
Susumu Teranishi *(Mng Exec Officer-Procurement & Logistics)*
Koji Umeno *(Exec Officer)*
Toshimasa Yamanaka *(Sr Mng Exec Officer-Fin, Acctg & Disclosure)*
Tomoyuki Yoshida *(Sr Exec Officer)*
Board of Directors:
Yoshitaka Ebihara
Minoru Kimoto
Makoto Kobayashi
Mitsugu Kuno
Hirokazu Maeda
Kazuhiro Mishina
Osamu Nakamura
Ichiro Nishimura
Kazumi Okamoto
Hiroshi Shimizu
Shigeru Takagi
Susumu Teranishi
Tetsuya Uchiyama
Toshimasa Yamanaka
Subsidiaries:

Chiba Vegoil Tank Terminal Co., Ltd. (1)
35-1 Shinminato Chiba-shi
Mihama-ku, Chiba, 261 0002, Japan
Tel.: (81) 432388751
Edible Oil & Fats Whslr
S.I.C.: 5149
N.A.I.C.S.: 424490
Hiroshi Takagi *(Pres)*

F&F Co., Ltd. (1)
4-7-29 Oka Matsubara-shi
Osaka, 580 0014, Japan
Tel.: (81) 723368849
Fax: (81) 723348477
E-Mail: fyf@pearl.ocn.ne.jp
Emp.: 54
Chocolates & Cakes Mfr
S.I.C.: 2066
N.A.I.C.S.: 311351
Tetsuji Minato *(Pres)*

Fuji Butter Co., Ltd. (1)
3-12-12 Tokura
561-0845 Toyonaka, Osaka, Japan
Tel.: (81) 668658720
Fax: (81) 648667007
E-Mail: inagaki@fujibutter.jp
Web Site: www.fujibutter.co.jp
Emp.: 40
Confectionery Materials Suppliers
S.I.C.: 5145
N.A.I.C.S.: 424450
Toru Odawara *(Pres)*

Fuji Fresh Foods Co., Ltd. (1)
62 Nakano
Sasayama, Hyogo, 669-2213, Japan
Tel.: (81) 795942155
Fax: (81) 795942157
E-Mail: kawasaki@fujifresh.com
Web Site: www.fujifresh.com
Emp.: 104
Soy Protein & Tofu Mfr
S.I.C.: 2075
N.A.I.C.S.: 311224
Masayuki Kawasaki *(Pres & CEO)*
Itou Takao *(Mng Dir)*

Fukushiyoku Co., Ltd. (1)
5-4-8 Mikasagawa Onojo-shi
Fukuoka, 816 0912, Japan
Tel.: (81) 925031215
Web Site: www.fujioil.co.jp/fujioil_e/group/japan.html
Confectioneries & Pastries Whslr
S.I.C.: 5145
N.A.I.C.S.: 424450
Hiromitsu Seikoba *(Pres)*

Plant:

Fuji Fresh Foods Co., Ltd. - Amagasaki Plant (2)
3-4-66
Amagasaki, Hyogo, Japan
Tel.: (81) 648685811
Fax: (81) 0648685812
Web Site: www.fujifresh.com
Soy Beans & Related Foods Mfr
S.I.C.: 2075
N.A.I.C.S.: 311224
Masayuki Kawasaki *(Pres)*

Hannan Tank Terminal Co., Ltd. (1)
Sumiyoshi-cho
Izumisano, Osaka, 598-0061, Japan
Tel.: (81) 72 463 5394
Web Site: www.fujioil.co.jp
Edible Oil & Fat Products Whslr
S.I.C.: 5149
N.A.I.C.S.: 424490
Yoichi Tashiro *(Pres)*

Imagawa Co., Ltd. (1)
1186-3 Furugou Oita-shi
Oita, 870 0844, Japan
Tel.: (81) 975441167
Fax: (81) 975462463
Confectionery Material Sales
S.I.C.: 5145
N.A.I.C.S.: 424450
Yasuaki Nagao *(Pres)*

KP Shokuhin Co., Ltd. (1)
Tama Bldg 1F 30-1 Nihonbashi Hakozaki-cho
Chuo-ku, Tokyo, 103-0015, Japan
Tel.: (81) 356236600
Fax: (81) 356419520
Web Site: www.fujisunnyfoods.co.jp
Emp.: 41
Confectionery Materials Whslr
S.I.C.: 5145
N.A.I.C.S.: 424450
Akihiko Kaneda *(Pres)*
Kenji Tanabe *(Pres)*

Soyafarm Co., Ltd. (1)
Mita Hachiman Bldg 3-7-16 Mita
Minato-ku, Tokyo, 108-0073, Japan
Tel.: (81) 354181920
Fax: (81) 354181921
Web Site: www.soyafarm.co.jp
Emp.: 30
Soy Milk & Related Products Mfr
S.I.C.: 2079
N.A.I.C.S.: 311224
Hirokazu Maeda *(Pres)*

Toraku Co., Ltd. (1)
5-5 Koyocho-nishi
Higashinada-Ku, Kobe, Hyogo, 658-0033, Japan
Tel.: (81) 788571522
Fax: (81) 788572447
Web Site: www.toraku.co.jp
Emp.: 217
Desserts Mfr
S.I.C.: 2099
N.A.I.C.S.: 311999
Takeo Sumiya *(Pres)*

Waltzfancy Co., Ltd. (1)
2-7-5 Miyawaki-cho
Nakagawa-ku, Nagoya, Aichi, 454-0842, Japan
Tel.: (81) 523692424
Confectionery Materials Sales & Services
S.I.C.: 5145
N.A.I.C.S.: 424450
Hiroyuki Sakata *(Pres)*

Plants:

Fuji Oil Co., Ltd. - Chiba Plant (1)
35-1 Shinminato
Mihama-ku, Chiba, 261-0002, Japan
Tel.: (81) 432043399
Fax: (81) 432043407
E-Mail: takagi.hiroshi@so.fujioil.co.jp
Web Site: www.fujioil.co.jp
Emp.: 30
Chocolates Confectioneries & Pastries Mfr
S.I.C.: 2064
N.A.I.C.S.: 311340
Shinano Shiroshi *(Gen Mgr)*

Fuji Oil Co., Ltd. - Ishikawa Plant (1)
30 Idaro-bu Nakanoto-machi
Kashima, Ishikawa, 929-1721, Japan
Tel.: (81) 767761518
Web Site: www.fujioil.co.jp/fujioil_e/base/co mp_03a.html
Chocolate Confectioneries & Pastries Mfr
S.I.C.: 2064
N.A.I.C.S.: 311340

Fuji Oil Co., Ltd. - Kanto Plant (1)
2600-8 Ago Kasama-shi
Ibaraki, 319-0206, Japan
Tel.: (81) 299458600
Fax: (81) 299458608
E-Mail: nishikawa.satoshi@so.fujioil.co.jp
Web Site: www.fujioil.co.jp
Emp.: 50
Chocolate Confectioneries & Pastries Mfr
S.I.C.: 2064
N.A.I.C.S.: 311340
Satoshi Nishikawa *(Mgr-Sys Dept)*

Fuji Oil Co., Ltd. - Kobe Plant (1)
2-18-24 Hamanaka-cho
Hyogo-ku, Kobe, Hyogo, 652-0875, Japan
Tel.: (81) 786523215
Chocolates Confectioneries & Pastries Mfr
S.I.C.: 2064
N.A.I.C.S.: 311340

Fuji Oil Co., Ltd. - Protein Foods Tsukuba Plant (1)
27-3 Koshindaira
Bando-shi, Ibaraki, 306-0608, Japan
Tel.: (81) 297474131
Fax: (81) 297474132
Web Site: www.fujioil.co.jp
Chocolates, Confectioneries & Pastries Mfr
S.I.C.: 2064
N.A.I.C.S.: 311340

Fuji Oil Co., Ltd. - Rinku Plant (1)
4-35 Rinku-minamihama Sennan-shi
Osaka, 590-0535, Japan
Tel.: (81) 724820631
Chocolate Confectioneries & Pastries Mfr
S.I.C.: 2064
N.A.I.C.S.: 311340

Fuji Oil Co., Ltd. - Sakai Plant (1)
3-37 Chikkoshinmachi Sakai-shi
Nishi-ku, Osaka, 592-8331, Japan
Tel.: (81) 722414811
Web Site: www.fujioil.co.jp/fujioil_e/base/co mp_03a.html#15
Chocolate Confectioneries & Pastries Mfr
S.I.C.: 2064
N.A.I.C.S.: 311340

U.S. Subsidiaries:

Fuji Vegetable Oil Inc. (1)
1 Barker Ave
White Plains, NY 10601
Tel.: (914) 761-7900
Fax: (914) 761-7919
E-Mail: info@fvo-usa.com
Web Site: www.fujioilusa.com
Emp.: 5
Vegetable Oils Mfr
S.I.C.: 2079
N.A.I.C.S.: 311225
Ted Uchiyama *(Pres)*

Plant:

Fuji Vegetable Oil Inc. - Plant (2)
120 Brampton Rd
Savannah, GA 31408
Tel.: (912) 966-5900
E-Mail: abunger@fvo-usa.com
Web Site: www.fujioilusa.com
Vegetable Oil Mfr
S.I.C.: 2079
N.A.I.C.S.: 311225
Nick Baker *(Plant Mgr)*

Soya Farm USA Inc. (1)
20675 S Western Ave Ste 210
Torrance, CA 90501-1842
Tel.: (310) 781-9240
Fax: (310) 781-9293
E-Mail: info@soyafarmusa.com
Web Site: www.soyafarmusa.com
Emp.: 3
Soybean Whslr
S.I.C.: 2079
N.A.I.C.S.: 311224
Tatsumi Miyazaki *(Pres)*

Non-U.S. Division:

Fuji Oil Europe (1)
Kuhlmannlaan 36
9042 Gent, East Flanders, Belgium
Tel.: (32) 93417766
Fax: (32) 93430718
E-Mail: info@fujioileurope.com
Web Site: www.fujioileurope.com
Emp.: 100
Oils & Fats Mfr
S.I.C.: 2079
N.A.I.C.S.: 311225
Ichiro Nishimura *(Mng Dir)*
Bernard Cleenewerck *(COO & Deputy Mng Dir)*

Non-U.S. Subsidiaries:

Fuji Oil (Singapore) Pte. Ltd. (1)
45 Senoko Rd
Singapore, 758114, Singapore
Tel.: (65) 67581801
Fax: (65) 67581990
E-Mail: enquiry@fujioil.com.sg

Fuji Oil Co., Ltd.—(Continued)

Web Site: www.fujioil.com.sg
Emp.: 130
Edible Oil Mfr
S.I.C.: 0115
N.A.I.C.S.: 111150
Yoichi Kuno *(Mng Dir)*
Teo Yong Wah *(Mng Dir)*

Fuji Oil (Zhang Jia Gang) Co., Ltd. (1)
Economic Development Zone Yangshe Town
Zhangjiagang, Jiangsu, 215600, China
Tel.: (86) 51258678668
Fax: (86) 51258678656
E-Mail: mailsh@fujioil.com
Web Site: www.fujioil.com.cn
Emp.: 250
Chocolate Confectioneries & Pastries Mfr
S.I.C.: 2066
N.A.I.C.S.: 311352
Akira Kurooka *(Pres)*

New Leyte Edible Oil Mfg. Corp. (1)
Unit 1801 18th Fl The Peak Bldg 107 Leviste St
Salcedo Vlg, Makati, Philippines
Tel.: (63) 28482647
Fax: (63) 8113942
E-Mail: nleomc@newleyte.com
Emp.: 7
Edible Oils & Coconut Oil Mfr
S.I.C.: 2079
N.A.I.C.S.: 311225
Masaya Hashimoto *(Pres)*

Palmaju Edible Oil Sdn. Bhd. (1)
Lot Plo 223 Jalan Tembaga Empat
PO Box 59
81707 Pasir Gudang, Johor, Malaysia
Tel.: (60) 72514661
Fax: (60) 72514652
E-Mail: hradmin@palmaju.my
Emp.: 168
Palm Oil Mfr
S.I.C.: 2079
N.A.I.C.S.: 311224
Yasuyuai Kanjaki *(Pres)*
Shunji Nakamura *(Pres)*

P.T. Freyabadi Indotama (1)
Jl Maligi III Lot J-2A Kawasan Indust KIIC
41361 Karawang, West Java, Indonesia
Tel.: (62) 21 89109135
Fax: (62) 21 89109137
Web Site: www.freyabadi.com
Chocolate Confectioneries & Pastries Mfr
S.I.C.: 2064
N.A.I.C.S.: 311340
William Chuang *(Pres)*

Shandong Longteng Fuji Foodstuffs Co., Ltd. (1)
Jigezhuang Longwang Zhuang Town
Laiyang, Yantai, Shangdong, 265209, China
Tel.: (86) 5357717878
Fax: (86) 5357717156
Web Site: www.fujioil.co.jp/fujioil_e/group/japan_fujifresh.html
Emp.: 400
Protein Foods Mfr
S.I.C.: 2075
N.A.I.C.S.: 311224

FUJI PHARMA CO., LTD.

5 7 Sanban cho Chiyoda ku
Tokyo, 102 0075, Japan
Tel.: (81) 3 3556 3344
Fax: (81) 3 3556 4455
Web Site: www.fujipharma.jp
Year Founded: 1965
4554—(TKS)
Sls.: $280,411,034
Assets: $410,070,817
Liabilities: $1,591,384
Net Worth: $287,938,504
Earnings: $17,863,218
Emp.: 574
Fiscal Year-end: 09/30/12

Business Description:
Pharmaceutical Mfr
S.I.C.: 2834
N.A.I.C.S.: 325412

Personnel:
Hirofumi Imai *(Pres & CEO)*
Satoru Hiromi *(Mng Dir)*

Board of Directors:
Takeshi Hirayama
Satoru Hiromi
Hirofumi Imai
Toyoyuki Kamide
Tadahiro Kozawa
Atsuya Mitsuhashi
Masayuki Uchida

FUJI SEAL INTERNATIONAL, INC.

1-9-1 Marunouchi Chiyoda-ku
Tokyo, 100-0005, Japan
Tel.: (81) 352085902
Fax: (81) 352085914
E-Mail: international@fujiseal.co.jp
Web Site: www.fujiseal.co.jp
Year Founded: 1958
7864—(TKS)
Sls.: $1,088,417,000
Assets: $1,104,785,000
Liabilities: $463,012,000
Net Worth: $641,773,000
Earnings: $56,969,000
Emp.: 3,489
Fiscal Year-end: 03/31/13

Business Description:
Packaging & Sealing Machines & Equipment Mfr & Distr
S.I.C.: 3053
N.A.I.C.S.: 339991

Personnel:
Shigeko Okazaki *(Pres & CEO)*
Ritsuo Aikawa *(Exec Officer)*
Rikio Furusawa *(Exec Officer)*
Hiroo Okazaki *(Exec Officer)*
Yoshinao Sakaguchi *(Exec Officer)*
Takato Sonoda *(Exec Officer)*
Kenji Takahashi *(Exec Officer)*
Takayuki Ueda *(Exec Officer)*

Board of Directors:
Ritsuo Aikawa
Rikio Furusawa
Masahito Kakegawa
Fumio Kato
Hiroo Okazaki
Shigeko Okazaki
Takato Sonoda
Ken Takeda
Yuzo Toga

Subsidiaries:

Fuji Astec, Inc. (1)
1-5 Ishihara-cho
Sakai, Osaka, 5998102, Japan
Tel.: (81) 722522824
Fax: (81) 722523062
Web Site: www.fujiseal.co.jp
Emp.: 1,750
Construction Machinery Mfr
S.I.C.: 3531
N.A.I.C.S.: 333120
Shigeko Okazaki *(Pres)*

Fuji Flex, Inc. (1)
1-9-1 Marunouchi
Chiyoda-ku, Tokyo, 100-0005, Japan
Tel.: (81) 352085913
Web Site: www.fujiseal.co.jp/international_en/group_jp.html
Packaging Machinery Mfr
S.I.C.: 3565
N.A.I.C.S.: 333993

Fuji Logistics Company Ltd. (1)
3-10-1 Mita
Tokyo, Minato-ku, Japan
Tel.: (81) 334548411
Fax: (81) 354788663
Web Site: www.fujibuturyu.co.jp
Emp.: 200
Warehousing & Storage
S.I.C.: 4226
N.A.I.C.S.: 493190

Fuji Packaging Services, Inc (1)
419 miyahara yodogaeeaku
Osaka, 532-0003, Japan
Tel.: (81) 663502881
Fax: (81) 663501024
Web Site: www.fujibuturyu.co.jp
Emp.: 20
Converted Paper Product Mfr
S.I.C.: 2679
N.A.I.C.S.: 322299
Chihiro Wakatsuki *(Mng Dir)*

Fuji Seal, Inc. (1)
Shin-Osaka Front Bldg. 4-1-9 Miyahara
Yodogawa-ku
Tokyo, 532-0003, Japan
Tel.: (81) 663501080
Fax: (81) 663503053
E-Mail: international@fujiseal.co.jp
Web Site: www.fujiseal.co.jp/en/corporate/profile.html
Emp.: 140
Commercial Printing
S.I.C.: 2759
N.A.I.C.S.: 323111
Shigeko Okagzaki *(Pres & CEO)*

Fuji Seal Southeast Asia, Inc. (1)
4-1-9 Miyahara
Yodogawa-ku, Osaka, 532-0003, Japan
Tel.: (81) 663501065
Fax: (81) 663503132
Web Site: www.fujiseal.co.jp/international_en/group_as.html
Emp.: 10
Packaging Machinery Mfr
S.I.C.: 3565
N.A.I.C.S.: 333993

Fuji Tack East, Inc. (1)
85 Chuo-kogyo-danchi
Sagae, Yamagata, 991-0061, Japan
Tel.: (81) 237 84 2121
Packaging & Labeling Machinery Mfr
S.I.C.: 3565
N.A.I.C.S.: 333993

Plant:

Fuji Seal International, Inc - Nara Factory (1)
622 Chishiro Tawaramoto-cho
Shiki-gu, Nara, 636-0246, Japan
Tel.: (81) 744 32 5311
Web Site: www.fujiseal.co.jp/international_en/group_jp.html
Label Application Machinery Mfr
S.I.C.: 3565
N.A.I.C.S.: 333993

U.S. Subsidiaries:

American Fuji Seal, Inc. (1)
1901 N Roselle Rd
Schaumburg, IL 60195-3176
Tel.: (847) 592-7197
Web Site: www.afseal.com
Converted Paper Product Mfr
S.I.C.: 2679
N.A.I.C.S.: 322299

American Fuji Technical Services, Inc (1)
10 Bloomfield Ave
Pine Brook, NJ 07058
Tel.: (973) 808-2666
Fax: (973) 808-9822
Web Site: www.fujiseal.co.jp/international_en/group_us.html
Emp.: 30
Packaging Machinery Mfr
S.I.C.: 3565
N.A.I.C.S.: 333993

Non-U.S. Subsidiaries:

Fuji Seal Europe B.V. (1)
Jacob Marisstraat 2
5753GD Deurne, Netherlands
Tel.: (31) 493352020
Fax: (31) 493314889
E-Mail: receptyenl@nl.fujiseal.com
Web Site: www.fujiseal.com
Emp.: 130
Packaging Machinery Mfr
S.I.C.: 3565
N.A.I.C.S.: 333993
K. Buytenweg *(Mng Dir)*

Fuji Seal Europe Ltd. (1)
Scimitar Close Gillingham Business Park
Gillingham, ME8 0RJ, United Kingdom
Tel.: (44) 1634378656
Fax: (44) 1634379179
E-Mail: info@fujiseal.com
Web Site: www.fujiseal.com
Emp.: 200
Gasket Packing & Sealing Device Mfr
S.I.C.: 3053
N.A.I.C.S.: 339991
D. Budd *(Mgr)*

Fuji Seal Europe S.A.S. (1)
Le Gauguin 47
Allee des Impressionnistes, 93420 Villepinte, France
Tel.: (33) 149895570
Fax: (33) 148637013
E-Mail: info@fujiseal.com
Web Site: www.fujiseal.com
Chemical & Allied Products Merchant Whslr
S.I.C.: 5169
N.A.I.C.S.: 424690

Fuji Seal France S.A.S. (1)
Route De Luxeuil
70220 Fougerolles, France
Tel.: (33) 3 84 49 10 44
Packaging Machinery Mfr
S.I.C.: 3565
N.A.I.C.S.: 333993

Fuji Seal Iberia, S.L.U (1)
Roger De Lluria 50 6 B
08009 Barcelona, Spain
Tel.: (34) 93 215 1571
Fax: (34) 93 215 1117
Packaging Materials Distr
S.I.C.: 5085
N.A.I.C.S.: 423840

Fuji Seal Packaging De Mexico, S.A. De C.V (1)
Av Rio San Lorenzo No 670 Parque Industrial Castro Del Rio
36810 Irapuato, Gto, Mexico
Tel.: (52) 462 6067980
Packaging Machinery Mfr
S.I.C.: 3565
N.A.I.C.S.: 333993

Fuji Seal Poland Sp.zo.o. (1)
ul Wschodnia 2
Kutno, 99-300 Lodz, Poland
Tel.: (48) 243559300
Fax: (48) 243559301
E-Mail: racapcar.pl@pl.fujiseal.com
Web Site: www.fujiseal.com
Emp.: 262
Packaging Machinery Mfr
S.I.C.: 3565
N.A.I.C.S.: 333993
Bartoszak Dorota *(Gen Mgr)*

PT. Fuji Seal Indonesia (1)
Sampoerna Strategic Square South Tower 30th Floor JL Jend
Sudirman kav 45-46, Jakarta, 12930, Indonesia
Tel.: (62) 2129930722
Fax: (62) 21 2993 0888
Web Site: www.fujiseal.co.jp/international_en/group_as.html
Emp.: 5
Packaging Machinery Mfr
S.I.C.: 3565
N.A.I.C.S.: 333993
Hiroshi Natakatake *(Gen Mgr)*

FUJI YAKUHIN CO., LTD.

4-383 Sakuragicho
Omiya-ku, Saitama, 330-0854, Japan
Tel.: (81) 4 8644 3240
Web Site: www.fujiyakuhin.co.jp
Year Founded: 1930

Business Description:
Pharmacies Operator;
Pharmaceuticals Mfr & Distr
S.I.C.: 5912
N.A.I.C.S.: 446110

Personnel:
Tomohiko Ishikawa *(Mng Dir)*

Subsidiary:

OST Japan Group Inc. (1)
5-1-7 Atsubetuminami
Atsubetsu-ku, Sapporo, Hokkaido, 004-0022, Japan JP
Tel.: (81) 118965533

Fax: (81) 118965577
E-Mail: info@ost-japan.com
Web Site: www.ost-japan.com
Sales Range: $50-74.9 Million
Emp.: 200
Pharmacy & Residential Care Center Operator
S.I.C.: 5912
N.A.I.C.S.: 446110
Makoto Murakami *(Pres)*

FUJIAN CEE INSTALLATIONS CO., LTD.
20 Jinzhou North Road Golden Mountain Industrial Zone
Fuzhou, Fujian, 350002, China
Tel.: (86) 591 83849838
Fax: (86) 591 83849866
Web Site: www.ceepower.com
300062—(CHIN)
Sales Range: $25-49.9 Million
Emp.: 430
Business Description:
Electric Power Supply Systems
S.I.C.: 3612
N.A.I.C.S.: 335311
Personnel:
Tianxu Chen *(Chm)*

FUJIAN EXPRESSWAY DEVELOPMENT CO., LTD.
26/F Fujian Jiaotong Building 18 Dongshui Road
Fuzhou, 350001, China
Tel.: (86) 591 87077262
Fax: (86) 591 87077266
E-Mail: webmaster@fjgs.com.cn
Web Site: www.fjgs.com.cn
600033—(SHG)
Sales Range: $250-299.9 Million
Emp.: 800
Business Description:
Road Construction & Toll Operations
S.I.C.: 1611
N.A.I.C.S.: 237310
Personnel:
Tingqiang Wu *(Chm)*

FUJIAN GREEN PINE CO., LTD.
(d/b/a Green Pine)
Huiyao Industrial Park
Jianyang, Fujian, 354200, China
Tel.: (86) 599 5620888
Fax: (86) 599 5820900
E-Mail: sales@greenpine.cc
Web Site: www.greenpine.cc
Year Founded: 1958
300132—(CHIN)
Sales Range: $25-49.9 Million
Emp.: 250
Business Description:
Petrochemical Products Mfr
S.I.C.: 2869
N.A.I.C.S.: 325110
Personnel:
Weilong Ke *(Chm)*

FUJIAN HAIYUAN AUTOMATIC EQUIPMENTS CO., LTD.
1 3 North Rd First Phase of Tieling Industrial Park
Minhou County, Fuzhou, Fujian, 350100, China
Tel.: (86) 591 83847903
Fax: (86) 591 83847913
E-Mail: john@haiyuan-group.com
Web Site: www.haiyuan-group.com
002529—(SSE)
Sales Range: $25-49.9 Million
Emp.: 800
Business Description:
Hydraulic Forming Equipment & Related Devices Mfr
S.I.C.: 3559
N.A.I.C.S.: 333249
Personnel:
Liangguang Li *(Chm)*

FUJIAN HOLDINGS LIMITED
Rm 1109 11/F Cosco Tower Grand Millennium Plaza 183 Queens Road Central, China (Hong Kong)
Tel.: (852) 28109222
Fax: (852) 28689930
E-Mail: portia@fujianholdings.com
Web Site: www.fujianholdings.com
0181—(HKG)
Rev.: $1,936,445
Assets: $19,820,936
Liabilities: $1,643,394
Net Worth: $18,177,542
Earnings: $200,059
Emp.: 96
Fiscal Year-end: 12/31/12
Business Description:
Hotel Business & Property Investment
S.I.C.: 8741
N.A.I.C.S.: 561110
Personnel:
Xiaowu Wang *(Chm)*
Tao Ming Chan *(Sec)*
Board of Directors:
Xiaowu Wang
Chirstopher Wah Fung Cheung
Qiang Feng
Kwong Siu Lam
Hok Lim Leung
Xiaoting Liu
Ruilian Wang
Tao Ye
Legal Counsel:
Paul, Hastings, Janofsky & Walker
22nd Floor Bank of China Tower 1 Garden Road
Hong Kong, China (Hong Kong)

FUJIAN JINSEN FORESTRY CO., LTD.
16 Sanhua South Road
Sanming, Fujian, 353300, China
Tel.: (86) 598 2336158
Web Site: www.jinsenforestry.com
002679—(SSE)
Sales Range: $10-24.9 Million
Emp.: 200
Business Description:
Forestry Management
S.I.C.: 0851
N.A.I.C.S.: 115310
Personnel:
Guoxi Wang *(Chm)*

FUJIAN LONGKING CO., LTD.
No 81 Lingyuan Road
Longyan, Fujian, China 364000
Tel.: (86) 597 2200539
Fax: (86) 597 2216129
E-Mail: international@longking.com.cn
Web Site: www.longking.com.cn
Year Founded: 1971
600388—(SHG)
Sales Range: $400-449.9 Million
Business Description:
Purification Equipment Mfr
S.I.C.: 3564
N.A.I.C.S.: 333413
Personnel:
Warlen Zhang *(Dir-Mktg)*

FUJIAN LONGZHOU TRANSPORTATION CO., LTD.
East Tower Longjin Garden Renmin Road
Xinluo District, Longyan, Fujian, 364000, China
Tel.: (86) 597 3100600
Fax: (86) 597 3100612
Web Site: www.lzgf.cn
002682—(SSE)
Sales Range: $250-299.9 Million
Emp.: 5,260
Business Description:
Passenger & Cargo Transportation
S.I.C.: 4119
N.A.I.C.S.: 485999
Personnel:
Yuerong Wang *(Chm)*

FUJIAN MINFA ALUMINIUM CO., LTD.
Nanmei Comprehensive Development Zone
Nan'an City, Quanzhou, Fujian, 362300, China
Tel.: (86) 595 86286999
Fax: (86) 595 86289898
E-Mail: minfa@minfa.com
Web Site: www.minfa.com
Year Founded: 1993
002578—(SSE)
Emp.: 630
Business Description:
Aluminum Products Mfr
S.I.C.: 3355
N.A.I.C.S.: 331318
Personnel:
Tianhuo Huang *(Chm)*

FUJIAN MINHANG ELECTRONICS CO., LTD.
Inside of Changsha Industrial Park
Yanping District, Nanping, Fujian, China
Tel.: (86) 59 9860 9304
Fax: (86) 59 9860 9314
Web Site: www.minhang.com.cn
Year Founded: 1970
Business Description:
Multilayer Ceramic Capacitors Mfr
S.I.C.: 3699
N.A.I.C.S.: 335999

FUJIAN NUOQI CO., LTD.
Nuoqi Creative Enterprises Zone 55 Chongwen Road
Economic & Technical Development Zone, Quanzhou, Fujian, China
Tel.: (86) 595 2826 5777
Fax: (86) 595 2826 3777
Web Site: www.nuoqi.com.hk
1353—(HKG)
Sales Range: $75-99.9 Million
Business Description:
Men's Clothing Mfr
S.I.C.: 2329
N.A.I.C.S.: 315220
Personnel:
Hui Ding *(Chm, CEO & Gen Mgr)*
Yeung Ho Yin Au *(CFO)*
Board of Directors:
Hui Ding
Quanyi Chen
Canyang Ding
Lixia Ding
Huiyuan Han
Helen Wai Man Hsu
Wenge Jin
Yuquan Kong
Xiaozhai Qi

FUJIAN RONGJI SOFTWARE CO., LTD.
(d/b/a Rongji Software)
Tower 15 Area A 89 Software Avenue
Gulou District, Fuzhou, 350003, China
Tel.: (86) 59187860988
Fax: (86) 59187869595
E-Mail: rongji@rongji.com
Web Site: www.rongji.com
002474—(SSE)
Emp.: 400
Business Description:
Software Publisher
S.I.C.: 7372
N.A.I.C.S.: 511210
Personnel:
Zhuangxing Bin *(Gen Mgr)*

FUJIAN SNOWMAN CO., LTD.
Binhai Industrial District
Fuzhou, Fujian, 350217, China
Tel.: (86) 591 28513887
Fax: (86) 591 28299366
E-Mail: info@snowkey.com
Web Site: www.snowkey.com
Year Founded: 2000
002639—(SSE)
Business Description:
Ice Making Machine Mfr
S.I.C.: 3632
N.A.I.C.S.: 335222
Personnel:
Rujie Lin *(Chm)*

FUJIAN STAR-NET COMMUNICATION CO.,LTD
20-22 Building Star-net Science Plaza Juyuanzhou 618 Jinshan Road
Fuzhou, Fujian, China 350002
Tel.: (86) 59183057798
Fax: (86) 59183057368
E-Mail: oemhzb@star-net.cn
Web Site: www.star-net.cn
Year Founded: 1996
002396—(SSE)
Sales Range: $300-349.9 Million
Emp.: 5,092
Business Description:
Network Communication System Equipment Production & Sales
S.I.C.: 3669
N.A.I.C.S.: 334290
Personnel:
Yi Hao Huang *(CEO)*

FUJIAN TENGXIN FOODS CO., LTD.
150 Jianxin North Road Jinshan Industry Park
Cangshan District, Fuzhou, China
Tel.: (86) 591 88202235
Fax: (86) 591 88202231
E-Mail: tx@tengxinfoods.com.cn
Web Site: www.tengxinfoods.com.cn
002702—(SSE)
Sales Range: $100-124.9 Million
Emp.: 800
Business Description:
Frozen Food Products Mfr & Distr
S.I.C.: 2037
N.A.I.C.S.: 311411
Personnel:
Yongxiong Teng *(Chm)*

FUJIAN TIANGUANG FIRE-FIGHTING SCIE-TECH CO., LTD.
Chenggong Technology Industrial Zone
Nanan, Quanzhou, Fujian, 362300, China
Tel.: (86) 595 86314008
Fax: (86) 595 86385228
E-Mail: fjtg@tianguang.com
Web Site: www.tianguang.com
Year Founded: 1986
002509—(SSE)
Emp.: 460
Business Description:
Fire Fighting Products Mfr
S.I.C.: 9224
N.A.I.C.S.: 922160

Fujian Tianguang Fire-Fighting Scie-Tech Co., Ltd.—(Continued)

Personnel:
Xiuyu Chen *(Chm)*

FUJIAN YUANLI ACTIVE CARBON CO., LTD

Laizhou Economic Development Area
Nanping, Fujian, 353004, China
Tel.: (86) 5998558381
Fax: (86) 5998558386
E-Mail: sales_in@yuanlicarbon.com
Web Site: www.yuanlicarbon.com
Year Founded: 1999
300174—(CHIN)
Sales Range: $10-24.9 Million
Emp.: 142

Business Description:
Activated Carbon Mfr
S.I.C.: 3624
N.A.I.C.S.: 335991

Personnel:
Yuan Jian Lu *(CEO)*

FUJIBO HOLDINGS, INC.

1-18-12 Ningyocyo Nihonbashi
Chuo-ku, Tokyo, 103-0013, Japan
Tel.: (81) 3 3665 7777
Web Site: www.fujibo.co.jp
Year Founded: 1896
3104—(TKS)
Emp.: 1,515

Business Description:
Textile Product Mfr
S.I.C.: 2299
N.A.I.C.S.: 313110

Personnel:
Mitsuo Nakano *(Pres)*

FUJIFILM HOLDINGS CORPORATION

7-3 Akasaka 9-Chome
Minato-ku, Tokyo, 107 0052, Japan
Tel.: (81) 362711111
Web Site: www.fujifilmholdings.com
4901—(TKS)
Rev.: $24,361,656,000
Assets: $33,655,556,000
Liabilities: $11,382,910,000
Net Worth: $22,272,646,000
Earnings: $782,859,000
Emp.: 80,322
Fiscal Year-end: 03/31/13

Business Description:
Holding Company
S.I.C.: 6719
N.A.I.C.S.: 551112

Personnel:
Shigetaka Komori *(Chm & CEO)*
Shigehiro Nakajima *(Pres & COO)*
Shigeru Sano *(Pres-FUJIFILM Holdings America Corporation)*
Judy Melillo *(Gen Counsel, Sec & VP-FUJIFILM Holdings America Corporation)*

Board of Directors:
Shigetaka Komori
Masahiro Asami
Kazuhiko Furuya
Yoshihisa Goto
Takatoshi Ishikawa
Teisuke Kitayama
Katsumi Makino
Shigehiro Nakajima
Kenji Sukeno
Kouichi Tamai
Yuzo Toda
Tadahito Yamamoto

Subsidiaries:

FFGS Techno Service Co., Ltd. **(1)**
1-4-11 Tatsumi St Bldg Tatsumibekkan
Koto-Ku, Tokyo, 135-0053, Japan
Tel.: (81) 335227074
Fax: (81) 355691234
Emp.: 19
Photographic Equipment Mfr
S.I.C.: 3579
N.A.I.C.S.: 333316
Masanori Kato *(Mgr)*

Fuji Xerox Co., Ltd. **(1)**
Akasaka 9-7-3
Minato-ku, Tokyo, 107-0052, Japan JP
Tel.: (81) 335853211 (75%)
Web Site: www.fujixerox.co.jp
Emp.: 34,017
Copiers, Duplicators & Other Office Equipment Mfr, Distr, Sales & Marketer
S.I.C.: 5112
N.A.I.C.S.: 424120
Tadahito Yamamoto *(Pres & Rep Dir)*
Nobuya Takasugi *(CEO)*
Jiro Shono *(Exec VP)*
Haruhiko Yoshida *(Exec VP)*
Moriyuki Kato *(Sr VP)*
Hiroshi Kurihara *(Sr VP)*
Yoshio Tanaka *(Sr VP)*

Subsidiaries:

Fuji Xerox Learning Institute Inc. **(2)**
Roppongi T Cube 14F Roppongi 3-chome
Minato-ku
Tokyo, 106-0032, Japan
Tel.: (81) 355741511
Fax: (81) 355741860
E-Mail: webmaster@fxli.co.jp
Web Site: www.fxli.co.jp
Emp.: 200
Personnel Training Services
S.I.C.: 8299
N.A.I.C.S.: 611430

Fuji Xerox Printing Systems Co., Ltd. **(2)**
24th Floor Nakano Sakaue Sunbright Twin Building
2-46-1 Hon-cho
Nakano-ku, Tokyo, 164-0012, Japan
Tel.: (81) 333706811
Emp.: 748
Computer Devices & Office Equipment
S.I.C.: 3575
N.A.I.C.S.: 334118

Suzuka Fuji Xerox Co., Ltd. **(2)**
1900 Ifuna Cho
Suzuka, Mie, 519-0323, Japan
Tel.: (81) 593718888
Fax: (81) 593718501
E-Mail: webmaster2@suzukafx.co.jp
Web Site: www.suzukafx.co.jp
Emp.: 800
Digital Equipment, Copy Machines & Peripherals Developer & Mfr
S.I.C.: 3699
N.A.I.C.S.: 335999

U.S. Affiliates:

FX Global Inc. **(2)**
3400 Hillview Ave Bldg 1
Palo Alto, CA 94304-1346 CA
Tel.: (650) 813-7762
Fax: (650) 813-7188
Web Site: www.fujixerox.com
Emp.: 47
Development & Research Services
S.I.C.: 8742
N.A.I.C.S.: 541611
Toshihoko Sekine *(Pres)*

FX Palo Alto Laboratory Inc. **(2)**
3400 Hillview Ave Bldg 4 2nd Fl
Palo Alto, CA 94304-1346 CA
Tel.: (650) 842-4800
Web Site: www.fxpal.com
Emp.: 45
Software Research Services
S.I.C.: 8731
N.A.I.C.S.: 541712
Lawrence A. Rowe *(Pres)*

Non-U.S. Subsidiaries:

Fuji Xerox Asia Pacific Pte Ltd. **(2)**
80 Anson Road 01-01 Fuji Xerox Towers
079907 Singapore, Singapore
Tel.: (65) 366711
Fax: (65) 67616700
E-Mail: info@fxap.com.sg
Web Site: www.fxap.com.sg
Emp.: 400
Office Equipment Sales & Distr
S.I.C.: 5044
N.A.I.C.S.: 423420
Masashi Honda *(Pres)*

Subsidiary:

Fuji Xerox Singapore Pte Ltd. **(3)**
80 Anson Road 01-01 Fuji Xerox Towers
Singapore, 079907, Singapore
Tel.: (65) 67668888
Fax: (65) 67616700
Web Site: www.fujixerox.com.sg
Emp.: 300
Office Equipment Sales, Distr & Service
S.I.C.: 5044
N.A.I.C.S.: 423420
Bert Wong *(Mng Dir)*

Non-U.S. Subsidiaries:

Fuji Xerox Asia Pacific Pte Ltd. - IndoChina Operations **(3)**
Saigon Center 11th Floor Unit 1B 65 Le Loi Street 1st District
Ho Chi Minh City, Vietnam
Tel.: (84) 88290038
Fax: (84) 88290032
E-Mail: fxv.hcm@xerox.com.vn
Web Site: www.fujixerox.com.vn
Emp.: 30
Office Equipment Sales, Distr & Service
S.I.C.: 5044
N.A.I.C.S.: 423420
Yoshio Hanada *(Pres)*

Fuji Xerox Asia Pacific Pte Ltd. - Malaysia **(3)**
10 Jalan Bersatu 13 4
46200 Petaling Jaya, Selangor, Malaysia
Tel.: (60) 379579988
Fax: (60) 378016934
Web Site: www.fujixerox.com.my
Emp.: 500
Office Equipment Sales, Distr & Service
S.I.C.: 5044
N.A.I.C.S.: 423420
Masahiko Saito *(Pres)*

Fuji Xerox Australia Pty. Ltd. **(3)**
101 Waterloo Road
North Ryde, NSW, 2113, Australia
Tel.: (61) 298565000
Fax: (61) 298565003
E-Mail: reception@aus.fujixerox.com
Web Site: www.fujixerox.com.au
Emp.: 1,400
Office Equipment Sales & Service
S.I.C.: 5044
N.A.I.C.S.: 423420
Nick Kugenthiran *(Mng Dir-Australia)*

Fuji Xerox (China) Limited **(3)**
Jianguo Road Chaoyang District
Beijing Shaimao Building 904
No 92, Beijing, 100022, China
Tel.: (86) 1058245000
Fax: (86) 10 58245100
Web Site: www.fujixerox.com.cn
Office Equipment Sales, Distr & Service
S.I.C.: 5044
N.A.I.C.S.: 423420
Yotaro Kobayashi *(Chm)*

Fuji Xerox New Zealand Ltd. **(3)**
17 Hargreaves Street College Hill
0001 Auckland, New Zealand
Tel.: (64) 93773834
Fax: (64) 93564444
E-Mail: info@fujixerox.com
Web Site: www.fujixerox.com
Emp.: 300
Office Equipment Sales & Service
S.I.C.: 5044
N.A.I.C.S.: 423420
Neil Whittaker *(Mng Dir)*

Thai Fuji Xerox Co., Ltd. **(3)**
23rd Floor Sathorn City Tower
175 South Sathorn Road
Tungmahamek Sathorn, Bangkok, 10120, Thailand
Tel.: (66) 26796050
Fax: (66) 26796048
Web Site: www.fujixerox.co.th
Emp.: 1,200
Office Equipment Sales, Distr & Service
S.I.C.: 5044
N.A.I.C.S.: 423420
Iwao Kawai *(Pres & Mng Dir)*

Fuji Xerox Document Management Solutions Pty Ltd **(2)**
2 Military Road
Matraville, NSW, 2036, Australia
Tel.: (61) 2 9311 9999
Web Site: www.dms.fujixerox.com
Business Communications Printing & Publishing Services
S.I.C.: 7389
N.A.I.C.S.: 561410

FUJIFILM Business Supply Co., Ltd. **(1)**
5F Shin-Nishi-Ginza Building 2-2-2 Ginza
Chuo-Ku, Tokyo, 104-0061, Japan
Tel.: (81) 3 3564 2224
Fax: (81) 3 3564 9525
Business Support Services
S.I.C.: 7389
N.A.I.C.S.: 561499

FUJIFILM Computer System Co., Ltd. **(1)**
Odakyu Minamiaoyama Bldg
Minato-Ku, Tokyo, 107-0062, Japan
Tel.: (81) 354698300
Fax: (81) 354698301
Information Technology Consulting Services
S.I.C.: 7373
N.A.I.C.S.: 541512

FUJIFILM Corporation **(1)**
7-3 Akasaka 9 Chome
Tokyo, Minato ku, 107 0052, Japan JP
Tel.: (81) 362711111 (100%)
Telex: J24306
Fax: (81) 334062193
Web Site: www.fujifilm.com
Film & Digital Camera, Photographic Supplies, Film & Chemicals Mfr
Export
S.I.C.: 3579
N.A.I.C.S.: 333316
Shigetaka Komori *(Chm & CEO)*
Shigehiro Nakajima *(Pres & COO)*
Rohit Pandit *(Exec VP-Digital Camera Bus-Fujifilm India Pvt Ltd)*
Nobuaki Inoue *(Sr VP)*
Kouichi Tamai *(Sr VP)*

Subsidiaries:

Fujinon Corporation **(2)**
1-324 Uetake Kita-ku
Saitama, 331-9624, Japan
Tel.: (81) 486682111
Fax: (81) 48651517
Web Site: www.fujinon.co.jp
Sales Range: $900-999.9 Million
Emp.: 1,500
Optical Instruments Developer & Mfr
S.I.C.: 3827
N.A.I.C.S.: 333314
Takeshi Higuchi *(Chm)*

U.S. Subsidiary:

Fujinon Inc. **(3)**
10 Highpoint Dr
Wayne, NJ 07470-7431 NJ
Tel.: (973) 633-5600
Fax: (973) 633-5216
E-Mail: info@fujinon.com
Web Site: www.fujinon.com
Emp.: 70
Optics & Lenses Marketer
S.I.C.: 5048
N.A.I.C.S.: 423460
Jiro Murase *(Treas)*

Non-U.S. Subsidiaries:

Fujinon Australia Pty. Ltd. **(3)**
Unit 18 52 Holker St
Silverwater, NSW, 2128, Australia
Tel.: (61) 297482744
Fax: (61) 297482428
Web Site: www.fujinon.co.jp
Emp.: 11
TV Lens & Medical Equipment Sales
S.I.C.: 5047
N.A.I.C.S.: 423450
Masao Sato *(Mng Dir)*

Fujinon (Europe) GmbH **(3)**
Halskestrasse 4
47877 Willich, Germany
Tel.: (49) 021549240
Fax: (49) 02154924290
E-Mail: fujinon@fujinon.de

Web Site: www.fujinon.de
Emp.: 140
TV Lenses & Medical Equipment Marketer & Distr
S.I.C.: 3827
N.A.I.C.S.: 333314
Hidetoshi Kimura *(Pres)*

Fujinon Hong Kong Ltd. (3)
Unit 2605-2607 Level 26 Metroplaza Tower 1
223 Hing Fong Road, Kwai Fong, China (Hong Kong)
Tel.: (852) 23111228
Fax: (852) 27241118
E-Mail: fujinon@netvigator.com
Web Site: www.fujinon.com.hk
Emp.: 10
TV Lenses & Industrial Lenses Sales
S.I.C.: 5085
N.A.I.C.S.: 423840
Kiyotaka Arakaki *(Mng Dir)*

U.S. Subsidiaries:

FUJIFILM Dimatix, Inc. (2)
2250 Martin Ave
Santa Clara, CA 95050
Tel.: (408) 565-9150
Fax: (408) 565-9151
Toll Free: (888) 346-2849
E-Mail: printinginfo@dimatix.com
Web Site: www.fujifilmusa.com
Inkjet Printer Mfr
S.I.C.: 3555
N.A.I.C.S.: 333244
Martin Schoeppler *(Pres & CEO)*
Hidetoshi Shinada *(CTO & Exec VP-R&D)*
Andreas Bibl *(CTO)*

FUJIFILM Diosynth Biotechnologies Inc. (2)
101 J Morris Commons Ln
Morrisville, NC 27560
Tel.: (919) 337-4477
Fax: (919) 337-0899
Pharmaceutical Product Mfr
S.I.C.: 2834
N.A.I.C.S.: 325412

FUJIFILM Imaging Colorants Inc. (2)
233 Cherry Ln
New Castle, DE 19720
Tel.: (302) 472-1245
Fax: (302) 472-1029
Toll Free: (800) 552-1609
Web Site: www.fujifilm.eu/eu/about-us/company-profile/fujifilm-company-sites/fujifilm-imaging-colorants-ffic/contact-ffic/
High Performance Colorant Mfr
S.I.C.: 2816
N.A.I.C.S.: 325130
Jack Louthan *(Gen Mgr-Comml)*

FUJIFILM North America Corporation (2)
200 Summit Lake Dr 2nd Fl
Valhalla, NY 10595-1356
Tel.: (914) 789-8100
Fax: (914) 789-8295
Toll Free: (800) 755-3854
Web Site: www.fujifilmusa.com
Photographic Equipment & Consumables Distr
S.I.C.: 5043
N.A.I.C.S.: 423410
Go Miyazaki *(Pres & CEO)*

FUJIFILM U.S.A., Inc. (2)
200 Summit Lake Dr
Valhalla, NY 10595 NY
Tel.: (914) 789-8100
Fax: (914) 789-8295
Toll Free: (800) 755-3854
Web Site: www.fujifilmusa.com
Emp.: 10,000
Digital & Analog Photographic Imaging Systems & Services
Import Export
S.I.C.: 5043
N.A.I.C.S.: 423410
Manny Al-meida *(VP & Gen Mgr-Imaging Div)*

Subsidiaries:

Fujicolor Processing Inc. (3)
120 White Plains Rd Fl 4
Tarrytown, NY 10591 NY
Tel.: (914) 220-4700
Fax: (914) 220-4750
Web Site: www.fujifilm.com
Rev.: $178,000,000
Emp.: 50
Photofinishing Laboratory
S.I.C.: 7384
N.A.I.C.S.: 812921
Hiro Sakai *(Pres)*

Division:

Fujicolor Processing, Inc. (4)
10611 Satellite Blvd
Orlando, FL 32837-8429 FL
Tel.: (407) 438-7200
Fax: (407) 438-0230
Emp.: 63
Photofinish Laboratory Services
S.I.C.: 7384
N.A.I.C.S.: 812921
Maria Galvin *(Gen Mgr)*

FUJIFILM e-Systems, Inc. (3)
155 Bellwood Dr
Rochester, NY 14606-4226 NY
Tel.: (585) 340-4200
Fax: (585) 340-4300
Toll Free: (800) 838-5330
E-Mail: info@fujifilm.com
Web Site: www.fujifilm.com
Emp.: 150
Photographic Equipment & Supplies
S.I.C.: 5043
N.A.I.C.S.: 423410

FUJIFILM Electronic Materials U.S.A. Inc. (3)
80 Circuit Dr
North Kingstown, RI 02852
Tel.: (401) 522-9499
Fax: (401) 294-2269
Web Site: www.fujifilm-ffem.com
Emp.: 100
Mfr of Semiconductor Fabrication Products
S.I.C.: 3674
N.A.I.C.S.: 334413
Keiji Mihayashi *(Pres & CEO)*

Subsidiaries:

FUJIFILM Electronic Materials U.S.A., Inc. (4)
6550 S Mountain Rd
Mesa, AZ 85242
Tel.: (480) 987-7000
Fax: (480) 987-0014
Toll Free: (800) 553-6546
Web Site: www.fujifilm-ffem.com
Emp.: 150
Mfr of Semiconductor Fabrication Products
S.I.C.: 3674
N.A.I.C.S.: 334413

FUJIFILM Planar Solutions, LLC (4)
3301 Sutton Rd
Adrian, MI 49221-9397
Tel.: (517) 264-8253
Fax: (517) 264-8764
Web Site: www.planarsolutions.com
Industrial Chemical Mfr & Distr
S.I.C.: 2899
N.A.I.C.S.: 325998

Non-U.S. Subsidiary:

FUJIFILM Electronic Materials (Europe) S.r.l. (4)
SS 11 Padana Superiore 2/B
Cernusco Sul Naviglio, 20063 Milan, Italy
Tel.: (39) 0298241060
Fax: (39) 0298 47808
Mfr of Semiconductor Fabrication Products
S.I.C.: 3674
N.A.I.C.S.: 334413
Giuliano Vinotti *(Mgr-Sls)*

FUJIFILM Graphic Systems USA, Inc. (3)
200 Summit Lk Dr
Valhalla, NY 10595 PA
Tel.: (914) 749-4800
Fax: (914) 749-4899
Toll Free: (866) 617-8473
Web Site: www.fujifilmgs.com
Emp.: 100
Graphics Systems Distr
Import
S.I.C.: 5043
N.A.I.C.S.: 423410
William A. Demarco *(CFO & VP)*

Branches:

FUJIFILM Graphic Systems USA, Inc.-Hanover Park (4)
850 Central Ave
Hanover Park, IL 60133 IL
Tel.: (630) 259-7200
Fax: (630) 259-7078
Toll Free: (800) 621-1049
Web Site: www.fujifilmgs.com
Emp.: 200
Graphics Systems Distr
S.I.C.: 5043
N.A.I.C.S.: 423410
John Briar *(Reg Mgr-Sls)*

FUJIFILM Hawaii, Inc. (3)
94 468 Akoki St
Waipahu, HI 96797
Tel.: (808) 677-3854
Fax: (808) 677-1443
E-Mail: customerservice@fujifilmhawaii.com
Web Site: www.fujifilmhawaii.com
Emp.: 90
Cameras, Film & Photographic Supplies Distr
S.I.C.: 5043
N.A.I.C.S.: 423410
George Osuka *(VP)*

FUJIFILM Hunt Chemicals USA, Inc. (3)
40 Boroline Rd
Allendale, NJ 07401-1613
Tel.: (201) 995-2200
Fax: (201) 995-2299
Toll Free: (877) 385-4486
E-Mail: info@fujihuntusa.com
Web Site: www.fujihunt.com
Emp.: 70
Photographic Chemicals Mfr & Distr
S.I.C.: 3861
N.A.I.C.S.: 325992
Tim Kearney *(Sr VP)*

Divisions:

FUJIFILM Hunt Chemicals Specialty Products Co. (4)
411 Manufacturers Rd
Dayton, TN 37321-5937
Tel.: (423) 775-2281
Fax: (423) 775-7076
E-Mail: info@fujihuntusa.com
Web Site: www.fujihuntusa.com
Emp.: 92
Photographic Chemicals Mfr
Import
S.I.C.: 2869
N.A.I.C.S.: 325199
Mike Murray *(Gen Mgr)*

FUJIFILM Manufacturing USA, Inc. (3)
211 Puckett Ferry Rd
Greenwood, SC 29649-7915
Tel.: (864) 223-2888
Fax: (864) 223-8171
Web Site: www.fujifilm.com
Emp.: 1,500
Cameras, Color Paper, Medical Imaging Products & Pre-Sensitized Plates Mfr
S.I.C.: 3695
N.A.I.C.S.: 334613
Shin Kataoka *(Pres)*

FUJIFILM Medical Systems USA, Inc. (3)
419 W Ave
Stamford, CT 06902-6300
Tel.: (203) 324-2000
Fax: (203) 327-6485
Toll Free: (800) 431-1850
E-Mail: info_cr@fujimed.com
Web Site: www.fujimed.com
Emp.: 750
Medical Digital Imaging Products & Film Distr
S.I.C.: 5047
N.A.I.C.S.: 423450
John J. Weber *(Exec VP)*

Branch:

FUJIFILM Medical Systems (California), Inc. (4)
2150 N 1st St Ste 550
San Jose, CA 95131
Tel.: (408) 501-2160
Fax: (408) 501-2166
Web Site: www.fujimed.com
Emp.: 10
Photo Software Development & Research Services
S.I.C.: 5731
N.A.I.C.S.: 443142
Akira Hasegawa *(Dir-Medical Res)*

FUJIFILM Microdisks USA, Inc. (3)
45 Crosby Dr
Bedford, MA 01730-1401
Tel.: (781) 271-4400
Fax: (781) 275-4642
Emp.: 102
Computed Information Storage Products Mfr & Packager
S.I.C.: 3577
N.A.I.C.S.: 334118
Julie Fiore *(Mgr-HR)*

SonoSite, Inc. (3)
21919 30th Dr SE
Bothell, WA 98021-3904 WA
Tel.: (425) 951-1200 (100%)
Fax: (425) 951-1201
Toll Free: (888) 482-9449
E-Mail: admin@sonosite.com
Web Site: www.sonosite.com
Emp.: 858
Hand-Carried Ultrasound & Other Medical Imaging Device Developer, Mfr & Distr
S.I.C.: 3845
N.A.I.C.S.: 334510
Kevin M. Goodwin *(Pres & CEO)*
Anil Amlani *(CFO)*
Matthew C. Damron *(CMO)*
Juin-Jet Hwang *(CTO)*
Diku Mandavia *(Chief Medical Officer & Sr VP)*

Subsidiary:

CardioDynamics International Corporation (4)
21919 30th Dr Se
Bothell, WA 98021-3904 CA
Tel.: (858) 535-0202 (100%)
Fax: (858) 535-0055
Web Site: www.cdic.com
Sales Range: $10-24.9 Million
Emp.: 100
Impedance Cardiography Technologies Developer & Mfr
Export
S.I.C.: 3845
N.A.I.C.S.: 334510

Non-U.S. Subsidiaries:

SonoSite Ltd. (4)
Alexander House 40A Wilbury Way
Hitchin, Herts, SG4 0AP, United Kingdom (100%)
Tel.: (44) 1462 444800
Fax: (44) 1462 444801
E-Mail: uk-sales@sonosite.com
Web Site: uk.sonosite.com
Emp.: 20
Miniaturized, High Performance Digital Ultrasound Imaging Devices
S.I.C.: 5047
N.A.I.C.S.: 423450
Tracey Byard *(Reg Dir)*

Sonosite (Shanghai) Co. Ltd. (4)
2606 Summit Center 1088 Yan An Road W
Shanghai, 200052, China
Tel.: (86) 21 5239 6693
Fax: (86) 21 5239 8183
Sales Range: $100-124.9 Million
Emp.: 20
Miniaturized, High Performance Digital Ultrasound Imaging Devices
S.I.C.: 5047
N.A.I.C.S.: 423450
Julia Yea *(Mgr-Fin)*

Non-U.S. Subsidiaries:

FFEI (2)
Cube Maylands Avenue
Hemel Hempstead, Herts, HP2 7DF, United Kingdom UK
Tel.: (44) 1442213440
Fax: (44) 1442210579
E-Mail: marketing.comms@ffei.co.uk
Web Site: www.ffei.co.uk
Emp.: 100

FUJIFILM Holdings Corporation—(Continued)

Electronic Pre-Press Equipment Designer, Mfr & Supplier
S.I.C.: 3579
N.A.I.C.S.: 333316

FUJIFILM Europe GmbH (2)
Heesenstrasse 31
40549 Dusseldorf, Germany
Tel.: (49) 21150890
Fax: (49) 2115089344
E-Mail: presse@fujifilm.de
Web Site: www.fujifilm.de
Emp.: 400
Cameras & Photographic Supplies Sales & Distr
S.I.C.: 5043
N.A.I.C.S.: 423410
Jorg Spielmann *(Mgr-Mktg-Indus Products)*

Non-U.S. Subsidiaries:

Fuji Film (3)
Hoogstraat 39
300AA Rotterdam, Netherlands
Tel.: (31) 102812345
Fax: (31) 167563788
E-Mail: fuji@fujifilm.nl
Web Site: www.fujifilm.nl
Emp.: 42
Printing Inks & Screen Printing Supplies Mfr
S.I.C.: 2893
N.A.I.C.S.: 325910

FUJIFILM Medical Systems Benelux N.V. (3)
Europark Noord 25
9100 Saint-Niklaas, Belgium
Tel.: (32) 37600333
Fax: (32) 37666998
E-Mail: info@fujimsb.be
Web Site: www.fujimsb.be
Emp.: 30
X-Ray Film & Chemicals Sales & Distr
S.I.C.: 3861
N.A.I.C.S.: 325992
Toyo Asai *(Mng Dir)*

Fujicolor Central Europe Photofinishing GmbH & Co. KG (2)
Siemens Ring 1
47877 Willich, Germany
Tel.: (49) 896490870
Fax: (49) 8978815
E-Mail: info@fujicolor.de
Web Site: www.fujicolor.de
Emp.: 50
Film Processing & Finishing Services
S.I.C.: 7384
N.A.I.C.S.: 812921
Jerrad Van Jendt *(Mng Dir)*

Non-U.S. Branches:

Fujicolor Benelux B.V. (3)
Franseweg 65
4651 GE Steenbergen, Netherlands
Mailing Address:
Postbus 16
4650 AA, Steenbergen, Netherlands
Tel.: (31) 167569911
Fax: (31) 167569788
E-Mail: info@fujicolor.nl
Web Site: www.fujicolor.nl
Emp.: 200
Developing & Printing Services
Import Export
S.I.C.: 2759
N.A.I.C.S.: 323111
Gerardus Van Gendt *(Mng Dir)*

Fujicolor Sverige AB (3)
Nebrokojen 3
PO Box 56
S 111 48 Stockholm, Sweden SE
Tel.: (46) 86806400
Telex: 15850 axlab s
Fax: (46) 86806424
Web Site: www.fujicolor.se
Emp.: 75
Photographic Products & Services; Owned 75% by Fuji Photo Film (Europe) GmbH & 25% by Axel Johnson International AB
S.I.C.: 3579
N.A.I.C.S.: 333316

Laboratoires Fujifilm SA (3)
16 Rue Etienne Jules Marey
78390 Bois-d'Arcy, Cedex, France
Tel.: (33) 130143456
Fax: (33) 134601660
Web Site: www.fujifilmnet.com
Emp.: 300
Photographic Services
S.I.C.: 3579
N.A.I.C.S.: 333316

FUJIFILM ASIA PACIFIC PTE. LTD. (2)
10 New Industrial Road Fujifilm Building
Singapore, 536201, Singapore
Tel.: (65) 6383 9933
Fax: (65) 6383 5666
E-Mail: fsin.info@fujifilm.com
Emp.: 15
Photographic & Binocular Lens Mfr
S.I.C.: 3827
N.A.I.C.S.: 333314
Hiroyuki Sakai *(Mng Dir)*

FUJIFILM Australia Pty. Ltd. (2)
114 Old Pittwater Rd
Brookvale, NSW, 2100, Australia
Tel.: (61) 294662600
Telex: 120231
Fax: (61) 299381975
Web Site: www.fujifilm.com.au
Emp.: 250
Photographic & Electronic Equipment
S.I.C.: 5043
N.A.I.C.S.: 423410
Mitch Kouno *(CEO)*
Masaya Seki *(CEO)*
David Marshall *(Mng Dir)*

FUJIFILM Canada Inc. (2)
600 Suffolk Ct
Mississauga, ON, L5R 4G4, Canada
Tel.: (905) 890-6611
Fax: (905) 890-6446
Toll Free: (800) 263-5018
E-Mail: info@fujifilm.ca
Web Site: www.fujifilm.ca
Emp.: 150
Photographic Supplies Distr
S.I.C.: 5043
N.A.I.C.S.: 423410
Nobuhiko Koshimizu *(Pres)*

Division:

FUJIFILM Canda Inc.-Graphic Systems Division (3)
600 Suffolk Court
Mississauga, ON, L5R 4G4, Canada
Tel.: (905) 890-6611
Fax: (905) 890-6446
Toll Free: (800) 897-3854
E-Mail: sales@fgsc.ca
Web Site: www.fujifilm.ca
Emp.: 200
Graphic Arts & Imaging Technology Services
S.I.C.: 7336
N.A.I.C.S.: 541430
Tony Karg *(Sr Dir-Bus Dev & Mktg)*

FUJIFILM (China) Investment Co., Ltd. (2)
28F One Lujiazui No 68 YinCheng Zhong Road Pudong New Area
Shanghai, 200120, China
Tel.: (86) 21 50106000
Fax: (86) 21 50106730
E-Mail: pr-info@fujifilm.com.cn
Web Site: www.fujifilm.com
Emp.: 700
Photographic Equipment Mfr & Distr
S.I.C.: 3579
N.A.I.C.S.: 333316
Yokota Koji *(Gen Mgr)*

FUJIFILM CZ, s.r.o. (2)
U Nakladoveho Nadrazi 2
130 00 Prague, 3, Czech Republic
Tel.: (420) 234703470
Fax: (420) 234703489
E-Mail: michael.bloch@fujifilm.cz
Web Site: www.fujifilm.cz
Emp.: 36
Photographic Products Distr
S.I.C.: 5043
N.A.I.C.S.: 423410
Michael Bloch *(Gen Mgr)*

FUJIFILM Diosynth Biotechnologies UK Limited (2)
Belasis Avenue
Billingham, TS23 1LH, United Kingdom
Tel.: (44) 1642 363511
Fax: (44) 16 4236 4463
E-Mail: enquiries@fujifilmdb.com
Emp.: 50
Biopharmaceutical Products Mfr
S.I.C.: 2834
N.A.I.C.S.: 325412
Steve Bagshaw *(Mng Dir)*
Stephen Taylor *(Sr VP & Dir-Comml)*
Mark Carver *(Sr VP-R&D & Innovation)*

FUJIFILM Dis Ticaret A.S. (2)
Dereboyu Cad Uder Cikmazi Sok No 11
Halkali, Istanbul, 34303, Turkey
Tel.: (90) 212 698 99 77
Fax: (90) 212 698 99 70
E-Mail: info@fujifilm.com.tr
Web Site: www.fujifilm.com.tr
Photographic Equipment Distr
S.I.C.: 5043
N.A.I.C.S.: 423410

FUJIFILM do Brasil Ltda. (2)
Avenida Vereador Jose Diniz 3400 Campo Belo
Sao Paulo, SP, 04604 901, Brazil
Tel.: (55) 11 5091 4181
Fax: (55) 11 5533 9307
Web Site: www.fujifilm.com.br
Emp.: 200
Cameras & Photographic Supplies Distr
S.I.C.: 5043
N.A.I.C.S.: 423410

FUJIFILM Electronic Imaging Europe GmbH (2)
Benzstrasse 2
47533 Kleve, Germany
Tel.: (49) 2821 7115 0
Fax: (49) 2821 7115 100
E-Mail: info@fujifilm-digital.com
Web Site: www.fujifilm.eu
Emp.: 5
Digital Camera & Supplies Distr
S.I.C.: 5043
N.A.I.C.S.: 423410
Herve Lilliu *(Gen Mgr)*

FUJIFILM Electronic Imaging Korea Co., Ltd. (2)
6F Jinsung Bldg 944-25 Daechi-Dong
Kangnam-ku, Seoul, 135-280, Korea (South)
Tel.: (82) 2 30111800
Fax: (82) 2 5388659
E-Mail: pokyung.kim@fujifilm.com
Web Site: www.fujifilm-korea.co.kr
Emp.: 15
Digital Camera Distr
S.I.C.: 5043
N.A.I.C.S.: 423410

FUJIFILM Electronic Materials (Europe) N.V. (2)
Keetberglaan 1A Havennummer 1061
2070 Zwijndrecht, Belgium
Tel.: (32) 3 250 0511
Fax: (32) 3 252 4781
E-Mail: customerrelationseurope@fujifilm-ffem.com
Web Site: www.fujifilmusa.com
Emp.: 100
Electronic Component Mfr
S.I.C.: 3679
N.A.I.C.S.: 334419
Herman Driegh *(Mng Dir)*

FUJIFILM Espana, S.A. (2)
Aragon 180
08011 Barcelona, Spain
Tel.: (34) 934511515
Fax: (34) 934515900
E-Mail: webmaster@fujifilm.es
Web Site: www.fujifilm.es
Emp.: 175
Cameras, Film & Photographic Supplies Distr
S.I.C.: 5169
N.A.I.C.S.: 424690
Salbador Luna *(Mgr-Mktg)*

FUJIFILM Europe N.V. (2)
Europark Noord 21-22
9100 Saint-Niklaas, Belgium
Tel.: (32) 37600200
Fax: (32) 37769122
E-Mail: info@fujifilm.eu
Web Site: www.fujifilm.eu/gateway/belgium/index.html
Emp.: 150
Camera, Film & Photographic Equipment & Supplies Mfr & Distr
S.I.C.: 5043
N.A.I.C.S.: 423410
Yasufumi Morimoto *(Sr VP)*

Subsidiary:

FUJIFILM Hunt Chemicals Europe N.V. (3)
Zwaluwbeekstraat 14
9150 Kruibeke, Belgium BE
Tel.: (32) 37600200
Fax: (32) 2501731
E-Mail: reception@fujifilm.eu
Web Site: www.fujifilm.eu
Emp.: 100
Photographic Chemicals Mfr, Sales & Distr
S.I.C.: 3861
N.A.I.C.S.: 325992
Shimichi Fujii *(Gen Mgr)*

Non-U.S. Subsidiaries:

Fuji Hunt Nordic AB (4)
Bn Grand 6
PO Box 90185
120 22 Stockholm, Sweden
Tel.: (46) 87740890
Fax: (46) 87748140
E-Mail: fhsweden@fujifilm.eu
Web Site: www.fujiflim.com
Emp.: 5
Photographic Chemicals Sales & Distr
S.I.C.: 5169
N.A.I.C.S.: 424690
Wilfred Bauder *(Mgr-Sls)*

FUJIFILM FILMED Tibbi Cihazlar Pazarlama Ve Ticaret A.S. (2)
YeniSehir Mahallesi Baraj Yolu Caddesi Aral Sokak
Atasehir, Istanbul, Turkey
Tel.: (90) 216 456 68 88
Fax: (90) 216 455 61 79
Web Site: www.filmed.com.tr
Endoscopic Equipment Distr
S.I.C.: 5047
N.A.I.C.S.: 423450

FUJIFILM France S.A.S. (2)
16 rue Etienne Jules Marey
BP 34
78391 Bois-d'Arcy, Cedex, France FR
Tel.: (33) 1 30 14 34 56
Web Site: www.fujifilm.fr
Emp.: 180
Photographic Equipment & Supplies Sales & Distr
S.I.C.: 3579
N.A.I.C.S.: 333316

FUJIFILM Graphic Systems France S.A.S. (2)
Parc d Activite Gustave Eiffel 13 Avenue Gutenberg 03
BP 20
Marne-la-Vallee, 77600 Bussy-Saint-Georges, France
Tel.: (33) 1 64 76 71 00
Fax: (33) 1 64 76 71 01
E-Mail: fgsf-commercial@fujifilm.eu
Web Site: www.fujifilm.eu
Emp.: 10
Photographic Equipment Mfr
S.I.C.: 3579
N.A.I.C.S.: 333316

FUJIFILM Hong Kong Limited (2)
Suites 2512-14 25/F Tower 6 The Gateway
Harbour City 9 Canton Road
Tsimshatsui, Kowloon, China (Hong Kong)
Tel.: (852) 2317 0307
Web Site: www.fujifilm.com
Optical Device & Diagnostic Imaging Equipment Distr
S.I.C.: 5048
N.A.I.C.S.: 423460

FUJIFILM Hungary Ltd. (2)
Becsi ut 271
1037 Budapest, Hungary
Tel.: (36) 1 577 9800
Fax: (36) 1 238 9410
Photographic Equipment & Supplies Distr
S.I.C.: 5043
N.A.I.C.S.: 423410

FUJIFILM Hunt Chemicals Singapore Pte. Ltd. (2)
15 Tuas Ave 7
Singapore, 639270, Singapore

Tel.: (65) 68622116
Fax: (65) 68614829
E-Mail: sales@fujifilm.com.sg
Web Site: www.fujifilm.com.sg
Emp.: 90
Photographic Chemicals Mfr & Distr
S.I.C.: 3861
N.A.I.C.S.: 325992
Kwong Chai *(Gen Mgr)*

FUJIFILM Imaging Colorants Limited **(2)**
Hexagon Tower
PO Box 42
Blackley, Manchester, M9 8ZS, United Kingdom
Tel.: (44) 161 721 2100
Fax: (44) 161 721 5810
E-Mail: project@fujifilmic.com
Web Site: www.fujifilm.eu
Emp.: 91
Printing Ink Mfr
S.I.C.: 2893
N.A.I.C.S.: 325910
Kazuo Nobechi *(Exec VP)*

FUJIFILM Imaging Systems (Suzhou) Co., Ltd. **(2)**
138 Changjiang Road
New District, Suzhou, Jiangsu, China
Tel.: (86) 51268251188
Fax: (86) 51268257122
Web Site: www.fujifilm.com.cn/en/about/inchina/enterprise.jsp
Emp.: 55
Imaging Systems Mfr
S.I.C.: 3579
N.A.I.C.S.: 333316

FUJIFILM Ireland Ltd. **(2)**
Unit 78A Lagan Road Dublin Industrial Estate
Glasnevin, Dublin, 11, Ireland
Tel.: (353) 18820200
Fax: (353) 18309351
E-Mail: info@fujifilm.ie
Web Site: www.fujifilm.ie
Emp.: 24
Photographic Products Distr
S.I.C.: 5043
N.A.I.C.S.: 423410
Kyran O'Kelly *(Head-Sls & Mktg)*

FUJIFILM Italia S.p.A. **(2)**
Padana Superior 2/B
Cernusco sul Naviglio, 20063, Italy
Tel.: (39) 02895821
Fax: (39) 0292974591
E-Mail: info@fujimed.it
Web Site: www.fujifilm.it
Emp.: 100
Photographic Products Distr
S.I.C.: 5043
N.A.I.C.S.: 423410
Takaaki Kurose *(Gen Mgr)*

FUJIFILM (Malaysia) Sdn. Bhd. **(2)**
22 Jalan Jurunilai U1 20 Seksyen U1 Hicom
Glenmarie Industrial Park
2 Jalan 51A/223, 40150 Shah Alam, Selangor, Malaysia
Tel.: (60) 379 584700
Fax: (60) 379 584110
Web Site: www.fujifilm.com.my
Emp.: 170
Camera Film Distr
S.I.C.: 5043
N.A.I.C.S.: 423410
Lim Kok Peng *(Mgr-Sls Support-Electronic Imaging)*

FUJIFILM Manufacturing Europe B.V. **(2)**
Oudenstaart 1
5047 TK Tilburg, Netherlands
Tel.: (31) 135791911
Fax: (31) 135701115
E-Mail: info@fujifilmtilburg.nl
Web Site: www.fujitilburg.nl
Emp.: 1,000
Photosensitized Plates, Papers & Films Mfr & Distr
S.I.C.: 3861
N.A.I.C.S.: 325992
Peter Struik *(Pres)*

Subsidiary:

FUJIFILM Europe B.V. **(3)**
Oudenstaart 1
5047 TK Tilburg, Netherlands
Tel.: (31) 13 579 19 11
Fax: (31) 13 570 11 15
E-Mail: info@fujifilmtilburg.nl
Emp.: 90
Photographic Equipment & Supplies Distr
S.I.C.: 5043
N.A.I.C.S.: 423410

FUJIFILM Medical Systems France S.A.S. **(2)**
Immeuble Objectif II 2 rue Louis Armand
Asnieres, 92600, France
Tel.: (33) 1 47 15 55 15
Fax: (33) 1 47 31 62 00
E-Mail: commercial@fujifilmmedical.fr
Medical Equipment Distr
S.I.C.: 5047
N.A.I.C.S.: 423450

FUJIFILM Middle East FZE **(2)**
The Galleries Building 3 Floor 08 Office 809
Downtown Jebel Ali, Dubai, United Arab Emirates
Tel.: (971) 4 887 8722
Fax: (971) 4 887 8733
Web Site: www.fujifilm-mea.com
Emp.: 22
Digital Camera & Medical Imaging Equipment Distr
S.I.C.: 5043
N.A.I.C.S.: 423410
Masatsugu Naito *(Mng Dir)*

FUJIFILM Nordic AB **(2)**
Sveavagen 167
104 35 Stockholm, Sweden
Tel.: (46) 8 506 141 00
Fax: (46) 8 506 142 00
E-Mail: info@fujifilm.se
Digital Camera Import & Distr
S.I.C.: 5043
N.A.I.C.S.: 423410

FUJIFILM (NZ) Limited **(2)**
Cnr William Pickering Dr And Bush Rd
0745 Auckland, Albany, New Zealand
Mailing Address:
PO Box 101 500
North Shore Mail Centre, Auckland, New Zealand
Tel.: (64) 94140400
Fax: (64) 94140410
E-Mail: reception@fujifilm.co.nz
Web Site: www.fujifilm.co.nz
Emp.: 75
Film Processing
S.I.C.: 5734
N.A.I.C.S.: 443142
Steven Hodson *(Mng Dir)*

FUJIFILM Polska Distribution Spolka zo.o **(2)**
Al Jerozolimskie 178
02-486 Warsaw, Poland
Tel.: (48) 225176600
Fax: (48) 225176602
E-Mail: fujifilm@fujifilm.pl
Web Site: www.fujifilm.pl
Photographic Products Distr
S.I.C.: 5043
N.A.I.C.S.: 423410
Andrzej Brylak *(Gen Mgr)*

FUJIFILM Recording Media GmbH **(2)**
Fujistradde 1
47533 Kleve, Germany
Mailing Address:
Postfach 1580
D-47515 Kleve, Germany
Tel.: (49) 28215090
Fax: (49) 2821509183
E-Mail: info_de@de.fujifilm-rme.com
Web Site: www.fujifilm-recordingindia.com
Emp.: 40
Audio & Video Tape & Computer Storage Systems Mfr & Distr
S.I.C.: 3695
N.A.I.C.S.: 334613
Masahiko Kishimoto *(Mng Dir)*
Wolsang May *(Mng Dir)*

FUJIFILM Recording Media Italia S.R.L **(2)**
Strada Statale N 11 Padana Superiore 2/B
20063 Cernusco sul Naviglio, Milan, Italy
Tel.: (39) 02 92974 1
Fax: (39) 02 92974 593
E-Mail: info@fujifilm.it
Web Site: www.fujifilm.com
Magnetic Recording Media Mfr
S.I.C.: 3695
N.A.I.C.S.: 334613

FUJIFILM Sericol UK Limited **(2)**
Patricia Way Pysons Rd
Broadstairs, Kent, CT10 2LE, United Kingdom UK
Tel.: (44) 1843866668
Fax: (44) 1843872133
E-Mail: human.resources@fujifilmsericol.com
Web Site: www.sericol.co.uk
Emp.: 300
Printing Inks & Screen Printing Supplies Mfr
S.I.C.: 2893
N.A.I.C.S.: 325910
Tudor Morgan *(Mgr-Mktg-Digital)*

U.S. Subsidiary:

FUJIFILM Sericol USA, Inc. **(3)**
1101 W Cambridge Cir Dr
Kansas City, KS 66103
Tel.: (913) 342-4060
Fax: (913) 342-4752
Web Site: www.sericol.com
Emp.: 150
Printing Inks & Screen Printing Supplies Mfr
S.I.C.: 2893
N.A.I.C.S.: 325910
Mitch Bode *(Gen Mgr)*

Non-U.S. Subsidiaries:

Fuji Film Sericol AG **(3)**
Baselstrasse 55
CH 6252 Dagmersellen, Switzerland
Tel.: (41) 627482030
Telex: 98 2829
Fax: (41) 627482035
E-Mail: info@fujifilmsericol.com
Web Site: www.fujifilmsericol.com
Emp.: 6
Printing Inks & Screen Printing Supplies Mfr
S.I.C.: 2893
N.A.I.C.S.: 325910
Rolf Schwerzmann *(Mng Dir)*

Fujifilm Sericol Nederland BV **(3)**
Aalsvoort 63
7241 MA Lochem, Netherlands
Tel.: (31) 573 408060
Fax: (31) 573 408061
E-Mail: sericolbvsales@fujifilmsericol.com
Web Site: www.fujifilmsericol.nl
Emp.: 12
Printing Ink Mfr
S.I.C.: 2893
N.A.I.C.S.: 325910
Jaap van Duren *(Gen Mgr)*

FUJIFILM Sericol Polska Sp. z o.o. **(3)**
ul Muszkieterow 15a
02-273 Warsaw, Poland
Tel.: (48) 22 577 13 51
Fax: (48) 22 868 71 93
E-Mail: sprzedaz@fujifilmsericol.com
Web Site: www.fujifilmsericol.co.uk/ff/distributors_direct/Poland.html
Emp.: 30
Printing Ink Distr
S.I.C.: 5085
N.A.I.C.S.: 423840
Thomas Wroblewski *(Gen Mgr)*

Sericol SAS **(3)**
50 Ave Des Freres Lumiere ZA
78191 Trappes, Cedex, France
Tel.: (33) 00130693700
Fax: (33) 0130693769
E-Mail: info@fujifilmsericol.com
Web Site: www.fujifilmsericol.com
Emp.: 51
Printing Inks & Screen Printing Supplies Mfr
S.I.C.: 2893
N.A.I.C.S.: 325910
Alain Bedriel *(Mng Dir)*

FUJIFILM (Singapore) Pte. Ltd. **(2)**
10 New Industrial Road
FUJIFILM Building, Singapore, 536201, Singapore
Tel.: (65) 63839933
Fax: (65) 63830100
E-Mail: support@fujifilm.com.sg
Web Site: www.fujifilm.com.sg
Emp.: 110
Photographic Supplies & Equipment Sales & Distr
S.I.C.: 5043
N.A.I.C.S.: 423410
Suphie Lua *(Mgr-HR)*

FUJIFILM South Africa (Pty) Ltd. **(2)**
17 Scott Street Wavery
Strubens Valley Ext 12, Johannesburg, 2090, South Africa
Tel.: (27) 11 430 5400
Fax: (27) 11 430 5430
E-Mail: infofza@fujifilm.com
Emp.: 46
Photographic Equipment Import & Distr
S.I.C.: 5043
N.A.I.C.S.: 423410
Hiroshi Watanabe *(Mng Dir)*

FUJIFILM Speciality Ink Systems Ltd. **(2)**
Pysons Road
Broadstairs, Kent, CT10 2LE, United Kingdom
Tel.: (44) 1843 866668
Fax: (44) 1843 872133
Web Site: www.fujifilmsericol.co.uk/ff/contact_us/contact_us.html
Digital Printing Ink Mfr
S.I.C.: 2893
N.A.I.C.S.: 325910
Dean Allen *(Mgr-Bus Dev-Optical Media)*

FUJIFILM (Thailand) Ltd. **(2)**
8th S Phayathai Rd No 388 Phaholyothin Rd
Bangkok, 10400, Thailand
Tel.: (66) 2 270 6000
Fax: (66) 2 270 6007
E-Mail: webmaster@fujifilm.co.th
Web Site: www.fujifilm.co.th
Emp.: 232
Photographic Film Distr
S.I.C.: 5169
N.A.I.C.S.: 424690

FUJIFILM UKRAINE LLC **(2)**
4 M Hrinchenka St Horizon Park Business Center 1st Floor
3680 Kiev, Ukraine
Tel.: (380) 44 390 75 42
Fax: (380) 44 390 75 43
E-Mail: ffua_info@fujifilm.eu
Emp.: 7
Digital Camera Distr
S.I.C.: 5043
N.A.I.C.S.: 423410
Konstantin Kucheryavets *(CEO)*

FUJIFILM UK Ltd. **(2)**
St Martins Bus Centre St Martins Way
Bedford, MK42 OLF, United Kingdom UK
Tel.: (44) 1234217724
Fax: (44) 1234572652
E-Mail: corporate@fuji.co.uk
Web Site: www.fujifilm.co.uk
Emp.: 400
Distributor of Photographic Supplies & Equipment
S.I.C.: 5043
N.A.I.C.S.: 423410
Mamoru Matsushica *(Mng Dir)*
Hironobu Taketomi *(Mng Dir)*

FUJIFILM VIETNAM Co., Ltd. **(2)**
126 Nguyen Thi Minh Khai Str District 3
Ho Chi Minh City, Vietnam
Tel.: (84) 8 39306555
Fax: (84) 8 39308545
Emp.: 28
Digital Camera Import & Distr
S.I.C.: 5043
N.A.I.C.S.: 423410
Tarumi Taisuke *(Gen Dir)*

IP Labs GmbH **(2)**
Schwertbergerstrasse 14-16
53177 Bonn, Germany
Tel.: (49) 228 18479 0
Fax: (49) 228 18479 15
E-Mail: info@iplabs.de
Web Site: www.iplabs.de
Emp.: 6
Photo Service Software Development Services
S.I.C.: 7371
N.A.I.C.S.: 541511
Shigehiro Nakajima *(Member-Mgmt Bd)*
Georg Sommershof *(Member-Mgmt Bd)*
Takashi Toyofuku *(Member-Mgmt Bd)*

FUJIFILM Holdings Corporation—(Continued)

PT. FUJIFILM INDONESIA (2)
Wisma Kelal 2nd Floor JL Jend Sudirman Kav 3
Jakarta, 10220, Indonesia
Tel.: (62) 21 5724069
Fax: (62) 21 5724145
Digital Camera Import & Distr
S.I.C.: 5043
N.A.I.C.S.: 423410

ZAO FUJIFILM-RU (2)
Business Centre Magistral Plaza 4F 1st Magistralnyi tupik 5A
123290 Moscow, Russia
Tel.: (7) 495 797 35 12
Fax: (7) 495 797 35 13
E-Mail: info@fujifilm.ru
Emp.: 10
Photographic Equipment & Supplies Distr
S.I.C.: 5043
N.A.I.C.S.: 423410
Tetsuya Iwasaki *(Mng Dir)*

FUJIFILM Electronic Materials Co., Ltd. (1)
15th Arai-Bldg 19-20 Jingumae 6-chome
Shibuya-ku, Tokyo, 150-0001, Japan
Tel.: (81) 3 3406 6911
Fax: (81) 3 3498 0567
Web Site: www.fujifilmusa.com
Specialty Chemicals Mfr
S.I.C.: 2899
N.A.I.C.S.: 325998
Masaaki Takimoto *(Pres)*

FUJIFILM Finechemicals Co., Ltd. (1)
2-3 Higashiyawata 5-chome
Hiratsuka, Kanagawa, 254-0016, Japan
Tel.: (81) 463 21 1560
Fax: (81) 463 23 9865
E-Mail: sales1@fffc.fujifilm.co.jp
Web Site: www.fffc.fujifilm.co.jp
Emp.: 421
Specialty Chemicals & Pharmaceutical Products Mfr
S.I.C.: 2899
N.A.I.C.S.: 325998
Fumio Kawamoto *(Pres & CEO)*

Plant:

FUJIFILM Finechemicals Co., Ltd. - Hirono Factory (2)
1-34 Aza-Iwasawa Kamikitaba Hirono-machi
Futaba-gun, Fukushima, 979-0401, Japan
Tel.: (81) 240 27 4171
Fax: (81) 240 27 3505
Emp.: 40
Specialty Chemicals Mfr
S.I.C.: 2899
N.A.I.C.S.: 325998
Kazumasa Seguchi *(Gen Mgr)*

Non-U.S. Subsidiary:

FUJIFILM Finechemicals (WUXI) Co., Ltd (2)
55 Xi Xing Lot Wu Xi New Technology Industry Development Area
Wuxi, Jiangsu, China 214028
Tel.: (86) 510 8532 3030
Fax: (86) 510 8532 3131
Web Site: fffc.fujifilm.co.jp/en/aboutus/location/index.html
Specialty Chemicals Mfr
S.I.C.: 2899
N.A.I.C.S.: 325998

FUJIFILM Graphic Systems Co., Ltd. (1)
Takebashi-Yasuda Bld 3-13 KandaNishiki-cho
Chiyoda-ku, Tokyo, 101-8452, Japan
Tel.: (81) 3 5259 2318
Fax: (81) 3 5259 3963
Graphic Design & Development Services
S.I.C.: 7336
N.A.I.C.S.: 541430

FUJIFILM Healthcare Laboratory Co., Ltd. (1)
9-7-3 Akasaka Mid Town West
Minato-Ku, Tokyo, 107-0052, Japan
Tel.: (81) 362712161
Health Care Cosmetics Mfr & Distr
S.I.C.: 2844
N.A.I.C.S.: 325620
Ryutaro Hosoda *(Gen Mgr)*

FUJIFILM Imaging Systems Co., Ltd. (1)
Fujifilm Gotanda Bldg 3-6-30 Nishi-gotanda
Shinagawa-ku, Tokyo, 141-0031, Japan
Tel.: (81) 3 5745 2241
Fax: (81) 3 5487 0085
Web Site: www.fujifilm.co.jp
Emp.: 50
Photographic Equipment Mfr
S.I.C.: 3579
N.A.I.C.S.: 333316
Sumio Kawamoto *(CEO)*

FUJIFILM Logistics Co., Ltd. (1)
3-10-1 Mita
Minato-ku, Tokyo, 108-0073, Japan
Tel.: (81) 3 3454 8411
Fax: (81) 3 5476 8663
E-Mail: package@fujibuturyu.co.jp
Web Site: www.fujibuturyu.co.jp
Emp.: 1,035
Logistics Management Services
S.I.C.: 4731
N.A.I.C.S.: 541614
Masamichi Imaizumi *(Pres)*
Toshikatsu Kubo *(Co-Mng Dir)*
Yoshiaki Toriyama *(Co-Mng Dir)*

FUJIFILM Media Crest Co., Ltd. (1)
2-10-8 Shimmeidai
Hamura, Tokyo, 205-0023, Japan
Tel.: (81) 425307600
Fax: (81) 425308024
E-Mail: info@ffmc.fujifilm.co.jp
Magnetic & Optical Recording Media Mfr
S.I.C.: 3695
N.A.I.C.S.: 334613

FUJIFILM Optics Co., Ltd. (1)
2720 Morigane
Hitachiomiya, 319-3102, Japan
Tel.: (81) 295 53 3131
Fax: (81) 295 53 2177
E-Mail: fop@fuji-offset.co.jp
Optical Lens Mfr
S.I.C.: 3827
N.A.I.C.S.: 333314

FUJIFILM Opto Materials Co., Ltd. (1)
463-1 Ohata Yoshida-cho
Haibara, Shizuoka, 463-1, Japan
Tel.: (81) 548 34 2500
Fax: (81) 548 34 2501
Optical Goods Mfr
S.I.C.: 3827
N.A.I.C.S.: 333314

FUJIFILM Pharma Co., Ltd. (1)
2-26-30 Nishiazabu
Minato-Ku, Tokyo, 106-0031, Japan
Tel.: (81) 364183800
Pharmaceutical Products Mfr
S.I.C.: 2834
N.A.I.C.S.: 325412

FUJIFILM Presentec Co., Ltd. (1)
7-8-1 Minamiaoyama Minamiaoyama First Bldg 4f
Minato-Ku, Tokyo, 107-0062, Japan
Tel.: (81) 357747630
E-Mail: webmuseum@fpt.fujifilm.co.jp
Emp.: 100
Compact Disc Mfr
S.I.C.: 3695
N.A.I.C.S.: 334613
Yoshihiro Matoba *(Mgr)*

FUJIFILM RI Pharma Co., Ltd. (1)
14-1 Kyobashi 2-Chome
Chuo-Ku, Tokyo, 104-0031, Japan
Tel.: (81) 3 5250 2600
Fax: (81) 3 5250 2625
Web Site: fri.fujifilm.co.jp
Emp.: 389
Pharmaceutical Products Mfr & Distr
S.I.C.: 2834
N.A.I.C.S.: 325412
Yoshiro Kumano *(Pres & CEO)*

FUJIFILM Software Co., Ltd. (1)
2-10-23 Shin-Yokohama
Nomurafudosanshinyokohama Bldg 7f
Kohoku-Ku, Yokohama, Kanagawa, 222-0033, Japan
Tel.: (81) 454769300
Fax: (81) 454769311
E-Mail: emailadmin@ffs.fujifilm.co.jp
Software Development Services
S.I.C.: 7371
N.A.I.C.S.: 541511

FUJIFILM Techno Service Co., Ltd. (1)
95-1 Nakamonji Wakayanagikawakita
Kurihara, Miyagi, 989-5501, Japan
Tel.: (81) 228302990
Fax: (81) 228353577
Web Site: www.ffts.fujifilm.co.jp
Emp.: 20
Digital Camera Maintenance Services
S.I.C.: 7622
N.A.I.C.S.: 811211
Kaz Takahashi *(Gen Mgr)*

Toyama Chemical Co., Ltd. (1)
2 5 Nishishinjuku 3 Chome
Shinjuku ku, Tokyo, 160 0023, Japan (66%)
Tel.: (81) 353813889
Fax: (81) 333486646
Web Site: www.chemical.co.jp
Sales Range: $125-149.9 Million
Emp.: 1,047
Pharmaceutical Developer, Retailer & Mfr
S.I.C.: 2834
N.A.I.C.S.: 325412
Masuji Sugata *(Pres)*

Joint Venture:

Taisho Toyama Pharmaceutical Co., Ltd. (2)
3 25 1 Takada
Toshima ku, Tokyo, 171 0033, Japan
Tel.: (81) 339858100
Web Site: www.toyama-chemical.co.jp/eng/news/news91e.html
Emp.: 1,300
Prescription Pharmaceuticals Distr; Owned 55% by Taisho Pharmaceutical Co., Ltd. & 45% by Toyama Chemical Co., Ltd.
S.I.C.: 2834
N.A.I.C.S.: 325412
Akira Ohira *(Pres)*

U.S. Division:

FUJIFILM North America Corporation - Graphic Systems Division (1)
850 Central Ave
Hanover Park, IL 60133
Tel.: (630) 259-7200
Fax: (630) 259-7078
Toll Free: (800) 877-0555
E-Mail: contact@fujifilmgs.com
Web Site: www.fujifilmusa.com
Photographic Equipment Mfr
S.I.C.: 3579
N.A.I.C.S.: 333316

U.S. Subsidiary:

FUJIFILM Hunt Smart Surface, LLC (1)
40 Boroline Rd
Allendale, NJ 07401
Tel.: (201) 995-2200
Fax: (201) 995-2422
Toll Free: (877) 770-7446
E-Mail: smartsurfaces@fujihuntusa.com
Specialty Chemicals Mfr
S.I.C.: 2899
N.A.I.C.S.: 325998

Non-U.S. Subsidiaries:

Camera House Limited (1)
4/108 Old Pittwater Road
Brookvale, Sydney, NSW, 2100, Australia
Tel.: (61) 2 8978 8700
Fax: (61) 2 8978 8740
Photographic Equipment Retailer
S.I.C.: 5043
N.A.I.C.S.: 423410

DS Chemport (Australia) Pty LTD (1)
41 Jesica Road
PO Box 29
Campbellfield, VIC, 3061, Australia
Tel.: (61) 3 9357 0933
Fax: (61) 3 9357 0944
E-Mail: enquiries@dschemport.com.au
Web Site: www.dschemport.com.au
Photographic Chemical Coating Mfr
S.I.C.: 3861
N.A.I.C.S.: 325992
Ken Rendell *(Assoc Dir-Comml)*

DS Chemport (Malaysia) SDN. BHD. (1)
No 22 Jalan Jurunilai U1/20 Seksyen U1
Hicom Glenmarie Industrial Park
40150 Shah Alam, Selangor Darul Ehsan, Malaysia
Tel.: (60) 3 5567 0452
Fax: (60) 3 5567 0462
E-Mail: admin@dscmal.com.my
Web Site: www.dscmal.com.my
Emp.: 14
Specialty Chemicals Mfr
S.I.C.: 2899
N.A.I.C.S.: 325998
M. Balan *(Acting Gen Mgr)*

Fuji Hunt Asian Pacific Holding Pty Ltd (1)
41 Jesica Rd
Campbellfield, VIC, 3061, Australia
Tel.: (61) 3 93570933
Fax: (61) 3 93570944
Investment Management Services
S.I.C.: 6211
N.A.I.C.S.: 523999

Fuji Hunt Photographic Chemicals, N.V. (1)
Europark-Noord 21-22
9100 Saint-Nicolas, Belgium
Tel.: (32) 3 760 0200
Fax: (32) 3 776 9122
E-Mail: info@fujifilm.eu
Emp.: 20
Photographic Chemicals Mfr
S.I.C.: 2899
N.A.I.C.S.: 325998
Alexis van Oostende *(Mng Dir & Dir-Fin)*

U.S. Subsidiary:

FUJIFILM Hunt Photographic Chemicals Inc. (2)
40 Boroline Rd
Allendale, NJ 07401-0320
Tel.: (201) 995-2200
Fax: (201) 995-2299
E-Mail: marketing@fujihuntusa.com
Web Site: www.fujihunt.com
Photochemical Mfr
S.I.C.: 2899
N.A.I.C.S.: 325998

Non-U.S. Subsidiaries:

Fuji Hunt Iberica S.L. (2)
Ctra Km 1194 N 340 pol Ind Park Els Masseps
Bellvei, Tarragona, 43719, Spain
Tel.: (34) 97 716 87 00
Fax: (34) 97 716 85 38
E-Mail: fhib_info@fujifilm.eu
Web Site: www.fujifilm.eu
Emp.: 5
Photochemical Distr
S.I.C.: 5169
N.A.I.C.S.: 424690
Lluis Giralt *(Gen Dir)*

FUJIFILM Denmark A/S (2)
Stubbeled 2
PO Box 70
Trorod, 2950 Vedbaek, Denmark
Tel.: (45) 45 66 22 44
Fax: (45) 45 66 22 14
E-Mail: fujifilm@fujifilm.dk
Emp.: 2
Photographic Equipment Mfr
S.I.C.: 3579
N.A.I.C.S.: 333316

FUJIFILM Electronic Materials Taiwan Co., Ltd. (1)
30 Kuang-fu N Rd hsin-chu Ind Park
Hu-Kou Xiang, Hsin-chu, 30351, Taiwan
Tel.: (886) 3 597 7674
Fax: (886) 3 597 7989
Web Site: www.fujifilmusa.com
Emp.: 8
Electronic Equipment Distr
S.I.C.: 5065
N.A.I.C.S.: 423690

FUJIFILM Holdings Australasia Pty Ltd (1)
114 Old Pittwater Road
Brookvale, NSW, 2100, Australia

Tel.: (61) 2 9466 2600
Fax: (61) 2 9938 1975
Imaging Equipment Distr
S.I.C.: 5043
N.A.I.C.S.: 423410

FUJIFILM Holdings NZ Limited (1)
2c William Pickering Drive
Rosedale, Auckland, 632, New Zealand
Tel.: (64) 94140400
Fax: (64) 94140410
Web Site: www.fujifilm.co.nz
Emp.: 6
Investment Management Services
S.I.C.: 6799
N.A.I.C.S.: 523920
Carlos Sandino *(Gen Mgr)*

FUJIFILM Hunt do Brasil - Producao de Quimicos Ltda (1)
Av New Jersey 1031 - Centro Industrial
07400 000 Sao Bernardo do Campo, Brazil
Tel.: (55) 11 4653 1840
E-Mail: contatohunt@fujifilm.com.br
Photographic Film Plate Mfr
S.I.C.: 3861
N.A.I.C.S.: 325992

FUJIFILM Imaging Germany GmbH & Co. KG (1)
Siemensring 1
47877 Willich, Germany
Tel.: (49) 2154 89788 0
Fax: (49) 2154 89788 15
E-Mail: info@fujifilm-imaging.eu
Emp.: 50
Photo Finishing & Photo Imaging Services
S.I.C.: 7384
N.A.I.C.S.: 812921

FUJIFILM India Private Limited (1)
Vatika Business Park 7th Floor Block-One
Sohna Road Sector-49
Gurgaon, Haryana, 122001, India
Tel.: (91) 124 4325500
Fax: (91) 124 4325555
E-Mail: contact@fujifilmindia.com
Web Site: www.fujifilm.in
Emp.: 10
Photographic & Imaging Equipment Distr
S.I.C.: 5043
N.A.I.C.S.: 423410
Kenichi Tanaka *(Mng Dir)*

FUJIFILM Opt-Electronics (Tianjin) Co., Ltd. (1)
No 2 Hongyuan Road Xiqing Development Zone
Tianjin, 300385, China
Tel.: (86) 2283988610
Fax: (86) 2283988633
Electronic Component Mfr
S.I.C.: 3679
N.A.I.C.S.: 334419

FUJIFILM Sericol Brasil Produtos para Impressao Ltda (1)
Av New Jersey 1 030
Aruja, 07400-000, Brazil
Tel.: (55) 1146527831
Fax: (55) 1146515557
Photographic Equipment Mfr
S.I.C.: 3579
N.A.I.C.S.: 333316

FUJIFILM Sericol Deutschland GmbH (1)
Hansestrasse 83
51105 Cologne, Germany
Tel.: (49) 2203 98885 0
Fax: (49) 2203 98885 7
E-Mail: info-de@fujifilmsericol.com
Web Site: www.fujifilmsericol.com
Emp.: 8
Printing Ink Mfr
S.I.C.: 2893
N.A.I.C.S.: 325910
Isabel Neves *(Gen Mgr)*

Fujifilm Sericol India Private Limited (1)
10/11 B U Bhandari Industrial Estate
Sanaswadi
Shirur, Pune, Maharashtra, 412 208, India
Tel.: (91) 2137 392500
Fax: (91) 2137 392555
E-Mail: sericolindia.techservice@fujifilmsericol.com
Web Site: www.fujifilmsericol.in
Emp.: 6
Printing Ink Mfr & Distr
S.I.C.: 2893
N.A.I.C.S.: 325910
M. N. Subramanyam *(Chm)*
M. P. Raghav Rao *(Mng Dir)*

FUJIFILM Sericol Overseas Holdings Limited (1)
Patricia Way Pysons Road Industrial Estate
Broadstairs, Kent, CT10 2LE, United Kingdom
Tel.: (44) 1843 866668
Fax: (44) 1843 872126
Investment Management Services
S.I.C.: 6799
N.A.I.C.S.: 523920
Peter Kenehan *(Mng Dir)*

FUJIFILM (Shanghai) Trading Co., Ltd. (1)
28/F Time Financial Center No 68 Yincheng M Rd Pudong New
Shanghai, 200120, China
Tel.: (86) 2150106000
Fax: (86) 2150106700
Photographic Machinery Whslr
S.I.C.: 5043
N.A.I.C.S.: 423410

Fuji Xerox Document Management Solutions Asia Limited (1)
(Formerly Salmat Asia Limited)
8/F Safety Godown Industrial Building
56 Ka Yip Street, Hong Kong, China (Hong Kong)
Tel.: (852) 2403 2288
Fax: (852) 24034488
E-Mail:
Web Site: www.dms.fujixerox.com
Emp.: 120
Business Communications Printing & Publishing Services
S.I.C.: 7389
N.A.I.C.S.: 561410
Raymond Lau *(Gen Mgr)*

FUJII SANGYO CORPORATION

41-3 Hiraide Kogyo Danchi
Utsunomiya
Tochigi, 321-0905, Japan
Tel.: (81) 28 662 6060
Web Site: www.fujii.co.jp
Year Founded: 1955
9906—(JAS)
Sls.: $613,437,000
Assets: $375,650,000
Liabilities: $211,486,000
Net Worth: $164,164,000
Earnings: $9,350,000
Emp.: 541
Fiscal Year-end: 03/31/13

Business Description:
Construction Machinery Maintenance & Sales
S.I.C.: 5082
N.A.I.C.S.: 423810

Personnel:
Shoichi Fujii *(Pres)*
Keishi Aoki *(Sr Mng Dir)*
Hidetsugu Toyama *(Sr Mng Dir)*
Eiichi Akimoto *(Mng Dir)*

Board of Directors:
Eiichi Akimoto
Satoshi Akutsu
Keishi Aoki
Shoichi Fujii
Yutaka Kawakami
Kenichi Kobayashi
Toshihiko Moriyama
Hideo Seino
Katsutoshi Seki
Kiyoshi Shinozaki
Atsushi Takita
Hidetsugu Toyama

Subsidiaries:

Fujii Tsushin Inc. (1)
2-11 Kikusuicho
Utsunomiya, Tochigi, 320-0844, Japan
Tel.: (81) 28 636 2751
Fax: (81) 28 634 3419
Electrical Equipment Whslr
S.I.C.: 5063
N.A.I.C.S.: 423610

Kanto Sogo Shizai Co., Ltd. (1)
305-1 Kaminagaisomachi Maebashi
Gunma, 379-2165, Japan
Tel.: (81) 27 261 1181
Fax: (81) 27 261 9557
Electrical Equipment Whslr
S.I.C.: 5063
N.A.I.C.S.: 423610

Komatsu Tochigi Inc. (1)
38-12 Hiraide Kogyo Danchi
Utsunomiya, Tochigi, 321-0905, Japan
Tel.: (81) 28 662 6093
Fax: (81) 28 662 6107
Industrial Equipment Rental Services
S.I.C.: 7359
N.A.I.C.S.: 532490

Towa Concrete Pumping Inc. (1)
43-87 Hiraide Kogyo Danchi
Utsunomiya, Tochigi, 321-0905, Japan
Tel.: (81) 28 663 2678
Fax: (81) 28 663 2644
Concrete Pumping Construction Services
S.I.C.: 1771
N.A.I.C.S.: 238110

FUJIKOH COMPANY., LIMITED

7-5 Komagata 2-chome
Taito-ku, Tokyo, 111-0043, Japan
Tel.: (81) 3 3841 5431
Web Site: www.fujikoh-net.co.jp
Year Founded: 1974
2405—(TKS)
Emp.: 84

Business Description:
Waste Recycling Services
S.I.C.: 4953
N.A.I.C.S.: 562212

Personnel:
Naoto Kobayashi *(Pres & CEO)*

FUJIKON INDUSTRIAL HOLDINGS LTD

16/F Tower 1 Grand Central Plaza
138 Shatin Rural Committee Road
Sha Tin, NT, China (Hong Kong)
Tel.: (852) 26055008
Fax: (852) 26941338
E-Mail: info@fujikon.com
Web Site: www.fujikon.com
0927—(HKG)
Rev.: $207,035,801
Assets: $153,840,574
Liabilities: $44,764,348
Net Worth: $109,076,226
Earnings: $15,329,834
Emp.: 6,400
Fiscal Year-end: 03/31/13

Business Description:
Electro Acoustic Products Mfr & Sales
S.I.C.: 3651
N.A.I.C.S.: 334310

Personnel:
Johnny Chi Hung Yeung *(Co-Founder, Chm & CEO)*
Michael Man Yan Chow *(Co-Founder & Deputy Chm)*
Simon Yee Sai Yuen *(Co-Founder & Deputy Chm)*
Lai Fung Chow *(CFO & Sec)*
Ben Siu Chung Yeung *(Chief Strategy Officer)*

Board of Directors:
Johnny Chi Hung Yeung
Chu Cheng Chang
Allen Wai Hang Che
Lai Fung Chow
Michael Man Yan Chow
Yiu Pun Lee
Ben Siu Chung Yeung
Simon Yee Sai Yuen
Wyman Chi King Yuen

Legal Counsel:
Chiu & Partners
40 Floor Jardine House 1 Connaught Place
Hong Kong, China (Hong Kong)

Appleby Management (Bermuda) Ltd.
Canon's Court 22 Victoria Street
HM 12 Hamilton, Bermuda

Transfer Agents:
Hong Kong Registrars Limited
Shops 1712-1716 17/F Hopewell Centre 183 Queen's Road East
Wanchai, China (Hong Kong)

Appleby Management (Bermuda) Ltd.
Canon's Court 22 Victoria Street
HM 12 Hamilton, Bermuda

FUJIKURA KASEI CO., LTD.

6-15 Shibakoen 2-chome
Minato-ku, Tokyo, 105-0011, Japan
Tel.: (81) 3 3436 1101
E-Mail: info@fkkasei.co.jp
Web Site: www.fkkasei.co.jp
Year Founded: 1938
4620—(TKS)
Emp.: 402

Business Description:
Specialty Coating & Fine Chemical Mfr
S.I.C.: 2899
N.A.I.C.S.: 325998

Personnel:
Yoshiaki Hasegawa *(Chm)*
Daisuke Kato *(Pres)*
Tadashi Nakamura *(Sr VP)*
Yoshizo Shimoda *(Sr VP)*
Hikoji Ueda *(Sr VP)*

Non-U.S. Subsidiaries:

Fujikura Kasei Coating India Private Ltd. (1)
608 Iris Tech Park Sohna Road Sector 48
Gurgaon, Haryana, 122001, India
Tel.: (91) 124 401 3077
Specialty Coating & Fine Chemical Mfr
S.I.C.: 2899
N.A.I.C.S.: 325998

Fujikura Kasei Coating (Tianjin) Co., Ltd. (1)
No 200 MuNing TEDA
Tianjin, 300457, China
Tel.: (86) 22 5981 5967
Specialty Coating & Fine Chemical Mfr
S.I.C.: 2899
N.A.I.C.S.: 325998

Fujikura Kasei (Foshan) Coating Co., Ltd. (1)
No 6 Shunyuan Nan Road Wusha
Daliang, Foshan, Guangdong, 528333, China
Tel.: (86) 757 2280 3750
Specialty Coating & Fine Chemical Mfr
S.I.C.: 2899
N.A.I.C.S.: 325998

Fujikura Kasei (Thailand) Co., Ltd. (1)
1/12 Bangchan Industrial Estate
Seri-Thai Road Kannayao, Bangkok, 10230, Thailand
Tel.: (66) 2906 3267
Fax: (66) 2906 3270
E-Mail: info@fkkthai.com
Specialty Coating & Fine Chemical Mfr
S.I.C.: 2899
N.A.I.C.S.: 325998

Shanghai Fujikura Kasei Coating Co., Ltd. (1)
No 177 Yingong Road
Fengxian District, Shanghai, 201417, China
Tel.: (86) 21 3758 5100
Specialty Coating & Fine Chemical Mfr
S.I.C.: 2899
N.A.I.C.S.: 325998

FUJIKURA LTD.

5-1 Kiba 1-Chome Koto-ku
Tokyo, 135-8512, Japan
Tel.: (81) 356061030
Telex: 2466655FIWCCSJ

Fujikura Ltd.—(Continued)

Fax: (81) 356061503
E-Mail: admin@fujikura.co.jp
Web Site: www.fujikura.co.jp
Year Founded: 1885
5803—(TKS)
Sls.: $5,402,298,000
Assets: $5,817,900,000
Liabilities: $3,565,419,000
Net Worth: $2,252,481,000
Earnings: $33,539,000
Emp.: 52,409
Fiscal Year-end: 03/31/13

Business Description:
Optical Transmission Systems, Network Systems, Electronics Materials, Power Systems, Coated Wires, Magnet Wires, Electronic Materials for Equipment & Metallic Materials Mfr
Import Export
S.I.C.: 3679
N.A.I.C.S.: 334419

Personnel:
Yoichi Nagahama *(Pres & CEO)*
Toru Aizawa *(Exec Officer)*
Jody Gallagher *(Mng Exec Officer)*
Yasuo Ichikawa *(Exec Officer)*
Masahiro Ikegami *(Exec Officer)*
Izumi Ishikawa *(Mng Exec Officer)*
Masahiko Ito *(Exec Officer)*
Takeaki Kitajima *(Exec Officer)*
Tadatoshi Kuge *(Mng Exec Officer)*
Nobumasa Misaki *(Mng Exec Officer)*
Yasuyuki Oda *(Exec Officer)*
Akira Sasagawa *(Exec Officer)*
Kiminori Sato *(Exec Officer)*
Hideo Shiwa *(Mng Exec Officer)*
Morio Suzuki *(Exec Officer)*
Kazuharu Tomano *(Exec Officer)*
Akira Wada *(Mng Exec Officer)*
Takamasa Kato *(Exec VP)*
Takashi Sato *(Exec VP)*
Masato Koike *(Sr VP)*
Akio Miyagi *(Sr VP)*
Hideo Naruse *(Sr VP)*
Yoshikazu Nomura *(Sr VP)*
Masato Sugo *(Sr VP)*

Board of Directors:
Kenichiro Abe
Takamasa Kato
Masato Koike
Akio Miyagi
Yoichi Nagahama
Hideo Naruse
Yoshikazu Nomura
Takashi Sato
Masato Sugo

Transfer Agent:
Sumitomo Mitsui Trust Bank
Izumi 2 8 4 Suginami-ku
Tokyo, Japan

Subsidiaries:

DDK Ltd. (1)
1-5-1 Kiba
Koto-ku, Tokyo, 135-8512, Japan
Tel.: (81) 3 5606 1154
Fax: (81) 3 5606 1157
Web Site: www.ddknet.co.jp
Emp.: 550
Electric Connector Mfr & Distr
S.I.C.: 5063
N.A.I.C.S.: 423610
Morio Suzuki *(Chm)*

Subsidiary:

Aomori DDK Ltd. (2)
1-6 Kanda 2-chome Oaza
Hirosaki, Aomori, 036-8061, Japan
Tel.: (81) 172 37 5511
Fax: (81) 172 37 5510
Web Site: www.ddknet.co.jp/English/corprate_profile/index.html?PHPSESSID=6c787f5f8edcf90e43367803509d2780
Electronic Component Mfr
S.I.C.: 3679
N.A.I.C.S.: 334419

Plant:

DDK Ltd. - Moka Plant (2)
14 Matsuyama-cho
Moka, Tochigi, 321-4393, Japan
Tel.: (81) 285 82 4411
Fax: (81) 285 84 0957
Web Site: www.ddknet.co.jp
Emp.: 481
Electronic Connector Mfr
S.I.C.: 3678
N.A.I.C.S.: 334417
Nobuhiro Ogura *(Gen Mgr)*

Non-U.S. Subsidiaries:

DDK (Shanghai) Ltd. (2)
F No 888 Zhaoxian Road Jiading Industrial Zone
Shanghai, China
Tel.: (86) 21 6952 4751
Fax: (86) 21 6952 4752
Web Site: www.ddknet.co.jp/English/corprate_profile/index.html?PHPSESSID=6c787f5f8edcf90e43367803509d2780
Electronic Connector Mfr & Distr
S.I.C.: 3678
N.A.I.C.S.: 334417

DDK (Vietnam) LTD. (2)
20 VSIPII Dan Chu Street VSIP-II
Ben Cat, Binh Duong, Vietnam
Tel.: (84) 650 362 8207
Fax: (84) 650 362 8210
Electronic Component Mfr
S.I.C.: 3679
N.A.I.C.S.: 334419

Shinshiro Cable, Ltd. (1)
1-65 Azahongudo Kawada
Shinshiro, Aichi, 441-1347, Japan
Tel.: (81) 536221095
Cable & Wire Mfr
S.I.C.: 3357
N.A.I.C.S.: 335921

Yonezawa Electric Wire Co., Ltd. (1)
1-10-53 Higashi
Yonezawa, Yamagata, 992-0026, Japan
Tel.: (81) 238 23 9211
Fax: (81) 238 24 3000
Automotive Wire Harness Mfr
S.I.C.: 3714
N.A.I.C.S.: 336390

U.S. Subsidiaries:

America Fujikura Ltd. (1)
170 Ridgeview Center Dr
Duncan, SC 29334 (100%)
Tel.: (615) 778-6000
Fax: (615) 778-5927
Toll Free: (800) 235-3423
Web Site: www.afltele.com
Emp.: 2,000
Fiber Optic Products
S.I.C.: 3357
N.A.I.C.S.: 335921
Masatoshi Kuroda *(Chm)*
Jody Gallagher *(Pres & CEO)*

Units:

AFL Telecommunications LLC (2)
170 Ridgeview Ctr
Duncan, SC 29334
Tel.: (864) 433-0333
Fax: (864) 433-5353
Toll Free: (800) 866-3977
Web Site: www.afltele.com
Emp.: 2,600
Laser Welded Fiber Optic Tubes Mfr
S.I.C.: 3357
N.A.I.C.S.: 335921
Masatoshi Kuroda *(Chm)*
Jody Gallagher *(Pres & CEO)*

Subsidiary:

Verrillon, Inc. (3)
15 Centennial Dr
North Grafton, MA 01536
Tel.: (508) 890-7100
Fax: (508) 839-6302
Toll Free: (800) 789 0540
E-Mail: info@verrillon.com
Web Site: www.verrillon.com
Emp.: 30
Optical Fiber Mfr
S.I.C.: 3357
N.A.I.C.S.: 335921
Abdel Soufiane *(Founder, Chm & CTO)*
Bryson D. Hollimon *(Founder & Mng Gen Partner)*

Non-U.S. Subsidiary:

AFL Telecommunications Europe Ltd. (3)
Unit H Newcombe Drive Hawkesworth Trading Estate
Swindon, Wiltshire, SN2 1DZ, United Kingdom
Tel.: (44) 1793 647 200
Fax: (44) 1793 513 198
Emp.: 6
Fiber Optic Cable Mfr
S.I.C.: 3357
N.A.I.C.S.: 335921
Kurt Dallas *(Mng Dir)*

Noise Fiber (2)
16 Eastgate Park Rd
Belmont, NH 03220
Tel.: (603) 528-7780
Fax: (603) 528-2025
Toll Free: (800) 321-5298
Web Site: aflglobal.com
Emp.: 70
Laser-Welded Fiber Optic Tubes
S.I.C.: 3357
N.A.I.C.S.: 335921
Sean Adam *(Gen Mgr)*

Non-U.S. Unit:

AFL Telecommunications (2)
Newcombe Dr
Swindon, Wilts, SN2 1DZ, United Kingdom
Tel.: (44) 1793647200
Fax: (44) 1793513198
E-Mail: emeasales@aflglobal.com
Web Site: www.aflglobal.com
Emp.: 60
Fiber Optic Cable
S.I.C.: 3357
N.A.I.C.S.: 335921
Mark Turner *(Mgr-Ops)*

Fujikura America Inc. (1)
3150 A Coronado Dr
Santa Clara, CA 95054 (100%)
Tel.: (408) 748-6991
Fax: (408) 727-3415
E-Mail: info@fujikura.com
Web Site: www.fujikura.com
Emp.: 7
Electrical Wiring Materials & Components
S.I.C.: 5063
N.A.I.C.S.: 423610

Division:

Fujikura America, Inc. - DDK Connector Division (2)
3150-A Coronado Dr
Santa Clara, CA 95054
Tel.: (408) 748-6991
Fax: (408) 980-9750
Web Site: www.ddknet.co.jp/English/corprate_profile/sales_base.html
Power Connector Whslr
S.I.C.: 5065
N.A.I.C.S.: 423690

Fujikura Automotive America LLC. (1)
25865 Meadowbrook Rd
Novi, MI 48375
Tel.: (248) 957-0129
Fax: (248) 347-2915
Web Site: www.fujikura.co.jp/eng/corporate/network-o1.html
Emp.: 25
Automotive Electronic Product Whslr
S.I.C.: 5065
N.A.I.C.S.: 423690
Kirk McCardell *(VP)*

Fujikura Richard Manufacturing Inc. (1)
990 Lone Oak Rd Ste 110
Eagan, MN 55121-2226
Tel.: (651) 994-6810
Fax: (651) 994-6803
Emp.: 8
Mfr. of Electronic Cables & Wires, Printed Circuit Boards & Optical Fiber Cables
S.I.C.: 3599
N.A.I.C.S.: 332710
Mark McGruder *(Mgr)*

Fujikura Technology America Corporation (1)
3150 Coronado Dr Ste A
Santa Clara, CA 95054-3223
Tel.: (408) 748-6991
Fax: (408) 727-3460
Web Site: www.fujikura.co.jp
Emp.: 4
Mfr. of Electronic Cables & Wires Printed Circuit Boards & Optical Fiber Cables
S.I.C.: 3661
N.A.I.C.S.: 334210

IER Fujikura Inc. (1)
8271 Bavaria Rd E
Macedonia, OH 44056
Tel.: (330) 425-7125
Fax: (330) 425-7596
E-Mail: sales@ierfujikura.com
Web Site: www.ierindustries.com
Sls.: $25,000,000
Emp.: 200
Molded Rubber Products Mfr
S.I.C.: 3069
N.A.I.C.S.: 326299
John Markiewicz *(CFO)*

Red Spot Paint & Varnish Co., Inc. (1)
1107 E Louisiana St
Evansville, IN 47711 IN
Tel.: (812) 428-9100
Fax: (812) 428-9167
Toll Free: (800) 457-3544
E-Mail: customerservice@redspot.com
Web Site: www.redspot.com
Sales Range: $75-99.9 Million
Emp.: 390
Automotive & Industrial Coatings; Paints & Lacquers Mfr
Import Export
S.I.C.: 2851
N.A.I.C.S.: 325510
Daisuke Kato *(Pres & CEO)*
Steve Halling *(CFO)*

Subsidiary:

Red Spot Westland Inc. (2)
550 S Edwin St
Westland, MI 48186-3801 IN
Tel.: (734) 729-7400
Fax: (734) 729-6140
Web Site: www.redspot.com
Emp.: 20
Automotive & Industrial Coatings; Paints, Varnishes & Lacquers
S.I.C.: 2851
N.A.I.C.S.: 325510
John Sorovetz *(Plant Mgr)*

United States Alumoweld Co. Inc. (1)
115 Usac Dr
Duncan, SC 29334 (100%)
Tel.: (864) 848-1901
Fax: (864) 848-1909
E-Mail: alumoweldsales@afltele.com
Web Site: www.alumoweld.com
Emp.: 40
Fiber Optic Products
S.I.C.: 3663
N.A.I.C.S.: 334220
Dan Nettles *(Plant Mgr)*

US Conec Ltd. (1)
PO Box 2306
Hickory, NC 28603-2306
Tel.: (828) 323-8883
Fax: (828) 322-7120
Toll Free: (800) 769-0944
Web Site: www.usconec.com
Emp.: 43
Mfr. of Electronic Cables & Wires, Printed Circuit Boards & Optical Fiber Cables
S.I.C.: 3357
N.A.I.C.S.: 335921
P.W. Blubaugh *(Pres)*

Non-U.S. Divisions:

Fujikura Europe Ltd. - DDK Connector Division (1)
C51 Barwell Business Park Leatherhead Road
Chessington, Surrey, KT9 2NY, United Kingdom
Tel.: (44) 20 8240 2000
Fax: (44) 20 8240 2010
Web Site: www.ddknet.co.jp/English/corprate_profile/sales_base.html
Fiber Optic Cable Mfr
S.I.C.: 3357
N.A.I.C.S.: 335921

Fujikura Europe Ltd. - Electronics Division (1)
C51 Barwell Business Park Leatherhead Road
Chessington, Surrey, v, United Kingdom
Tel.: (44) 20 8240 2000
Fax: (44) 20 8240 2010
E-Mail: electronics_sales@fujikura.co.uk
Web Site: www.fujikura.co.uk/electronics/contact/index.html
Electronic Products Whslr
S.I.C.: 5065
N.A.I.C.S.: 423690

Non-U.S. Subsidiaries:

Fujikura Asia Limited (1)
460 Alexandra Rd 22-02 PSA Bldg
Singapore, 119963, Singapore SG
Tel.: (65) 62788955 (100%)
Fax: (65) 62737705
Web Site: www.fujikura.com.sg
Emp.: 50
Sales & Financing of Electronic Components
S.I.C.: 5731
N.A.I.C.S.: 443142

Division:

Fujikura Asia Ltd. - DDK Connector Division (2)
460 Alexandra Road 22-01 Psa Building
Singapore, 119963, Singapore
Tel.: (65) 6271 1151
Fax: (65) 6278 0965
Web Site: www.ddknet.co.jp/English/corprate_profile/sales_base.html
Emp.: 50
Electrical Connector Mfr
S.I.C.: 3643
N.A.I.C.S.: 335931
Toshio Takahashi *(Mng Dir)*

Fujikura Asia (Malaysia) Sdn. Bhd. (1)
Ste W 403 Confplant 1
Jalan SS 16 4 Subang Jaya, 47500
Petaling Jaya, Selangor, Malaysia MY
Tel.: (60) 356364368 (100%)
Fax: (60) 356364377
Web Site: www.fujikura.com
Emp.: 10
Sales of Electronic Components
S.I.C.: 5731
N.A.I.C.S.: 443142
Lee Cho *(Gen Mgr)*

Fujikura Automotive Europe GmbH (1)
Heinenkamp 22
38444 Wolfsburg, Germany
Tel.: (49) 53 08 52 222 35
Fax: (49) 53 08 52 222 55
E-Mail: info@fujikura.com
Emp.: 8
Automotive Electronic Component Mfr
S.I.C.: 3714
N.A.I.C.S.: 336320

Fujikura Automotive Europe S.A.U. (1)
Poligono Industrial Malpica-Alfinden
C/Adelfa 39
50171 La Puebla de Alfinden, Zaragoza, Spain
Tel.: (34) 976 700 790
Fax: (34) 976 107 327
Web Site: www.fujikura.co.jp/eng/corporate/network-o1.html
Automotive Electronic Parts Mfr & Distr
S.I.C.: 3714
N.A.I.C.S.: 336320

Fujikura Automotive Mexico S. de R.L. de C.V. (1)
Lib Gral Manuel Perez Trevino S/N Parque Industrial Amistad
Col Lomas del Norte, 26070 Piedras Negras, Mexico
Tel.: (52) 878 112 0050
Web Site: www.fujikura.co.jp
Automotive Wiring Products Mfr
S.I.C.: 3714
N.A.I.C.S.: 336320

Fujikura Automotive Romania S.R.L. (1)
Str Streiului Nr 18
Cluj-Napoca, 400599, Romania
Tel.: (40) 264 207 950
Fax: (40) 264 449 420
Automotive Electronic Product Mfr
S.I.C.: 3714
N.A.I.C.S.: 336320

Fujikura (China) Co., Ltd. (1)
16th Floor Shanghai Hang Seng Bank Tower 1000 Lujiazui Ring Road
Pudong New Area, Shanghai, 200120, China
Tel.: (86) 21 6841 3636
Fax: (86) 21 6841 2070
Web Site: www.fujikura.com.cn
Emp.: 4
Electric Wire Mfr & Distr
S.I.C.: 3496
N.A.I.C.S.: 332618

Fujikura Electronics (Thailand) Ltd. (1)
102/3 Moo 20 Navanakorn Indus Zone Phaholyothin Rd Tambol Klon
Amphur Klongluang, Pathumthani, 12120, Thailand TH
Tel.: (66) 25296222 (100%)
Fax: (66) 25296134
E-Mail: inquiry@th.fujikura.com
Web Site: www.fujikura-electronics.co.th
Sales Range: $900-999.9 Million
Emp.: 26,000
Electronics & Electrical Products Mfr
S.I.C.: 3679
N.A.I.C.S.: 334419
Takashi Nishida *(Pres & CEO)*

Plants:

Fujikura Electronics (Thailand) Ltd. - Ayutthaya Factory 1 (2)
1/80 Moo 5 Rojana Industrial Park Rojana Road
Tambol Kanham Amphur U-Thai, Ayutthaya, 13210, Thailand
Tel.: (66) 3 522 6901
Fax: (66) 3 522 6906
Emp.: 200
Flexible Printed Circuit Mfr
S.I.C.: 3679
N.A.I.C.S.: 334419
Foto Hideo *(Gen Mgr)*

Fujikura Electronics (Thailand) Ltd. - Lamphun Factory 1 (2)
68/1 Moo 4 Northern Region Industrial Estate Tambol Banklang
Amphur Muang Lamphun, Lamphun, 51000, Thailand
Tel.: (66) 5 358 1002
Fax: (66) 5 358 1010
Web Site: www.fujikura-electronics.co.th/en/headquater_office.php
Electronic Component Mfr
S.I.C.: 3679
N.A.I.C.S.: 334419

Fujikura Electronics (Thailand) Ltd. - Navanakorn Factory 2 (2)
101/53 Moo 20 Navanakorn Industrial Zone Phaholyothin Road
Tambol Klongnueng, Khlong Luang, Pathumthani, 12120, Thailand
Tel.: (66) 2 529 1804
Fax: (66) 2 529 1803
Electronic Component Mfr
S.I.C.: 3679
N.A.I.C.S.: 334419

Fujikura Electronics (Thailand) Ltd. - Navanakorn Factory 3 (2)
55/40 Moo 13 Navanakorn Industrial Zone Phaholyothin Road
Tambol Klongnueng, Khlong Luang, Pathumthani, 12120, Thailand
Tel.: (66) 2 529 2717
Fax: (66) 2 529 2721
Emp.: 25
Printed Circuit Board Mfr
S.I.C.: 3672
N.A.I.C.S.: 334412

Fujikura Electronics (Thailand) Ltd. - Prachinburi Factory 1 (2)
118/2 Moo 11 Suwannasorn Road
Tambol Banpra, Prachin Buri, 25230, Thailand
Tel.: (66) 3 721 3323
Fax: (66) 3 721 3699
Emp.: 28
Flexible Printed Circuits Mfr
S.I.C.: 3679
N.A.I.C.S.: 334418
Koji Ueda *(Gen Mgr)*

Fujikura Europe GmbH (1)
Fritz-Vomfelde-Str 34
40547 Dusseldorf, Germany
Tel.: (49) 211 53883 227
Fax: (49) 211 53883 112
Emp.: 2
Electronic Connector Mfr
S.I.C.: 3678
N.A.I.C.S.: 334417
Danny Kobayashi *(Mgr-Bus Dev)*

Fujikura Europe Ltd. (1)
C51 Barwell Business Park Leatherhead Road
Chessington, Surrey, KT9 2NY, United Kingdom
Tel.: (44) 20 8240 2000
Fax: (44) 20 8240 2010
E-Mail: sales@fujikura.co.uk
Web Site: www.fujikura.co.uk
Emp.: 4
Fiber Optic Cable Mfr
S.I.C.: 3357
N.A.I.C.S.: 335921
Kenny Nara *(Mng Dir)*

Divisions:

Fujikura Europe Ltd. - Fibre Optics Division (2)
C51 Barwell Business Park Leatherhead Road
Chessington, Surrey, KT9 2NY, United Kingdom
Tel.: (44) 20 8240 2000
Fax: (44) 20 8240 2010
E-Mail: sales@fujikura.co.uk
Fiber Optic Cable Mfr
S.I.C.: 3357
N.A.I.C.S.: 335921

Fujikura Europe Ltd. - Plant & Infrastructure Cables Division (2)
C51 Barwell Business Park Leatherhead Road
Chessington, Surrey, KT9 2NY, United Kingdom
Tel.: (44) 20 8240 2000
Fax: (44) 20 8240 2010
E-Mail: metalcables@fujikura.co.uk
Electric Cable Mfr
S.I.C.: 3357
N.A.I.C.S.: 335921

Fujikura Federal Cables Sdn Bhd (1)
5097 Makmanbin Ind Est
Mak Mandin Ind Est, 13400 Butterworth, Malaysia MY
Tel.: (60) 43315577 (52%)
Telex: MA47552
Fax: (60) 43318641
Web Site: www.fujikura.com.my
Sales Range: $25-49.9 Million
Emp.: 500
Mfr. & Sales of Cables
S.I.C.: 3496
N.A.I.C.S.: 332618
N. Niomiua *(Mng Dir)*

Fujikura Hengtong Aerial Cable System Ltd. (1)
Qidu Township Industrial Zone
Wujiang, Jiangsu, 215234, China
Tel.: (86) 512 6381 7329
Fax: (86) 512 6381 7503
E-Mail: mfugimo@fjkht.com
Emp.: 453
Wiring Device Mfr
S.I.C.: 3643
N.A.I.C.S.: 335931

Fujikura Hong Kong Limited (1)
Rm 801 And 808 Mirror Tower 61 Mody Rd
Tsim Sha Tsui E, Kowloon, China (Hong Kong) HK
Tel.: (852) 23664823 (100%)
Fax: (852) 27390387
Web Site: www.fujikura.com.jp
Sales & Financing of Electronic Components
S.I.C.: 5731
N.A.I.C.S.: 443142

Division:

Fujikura Hong Kong Ltd. - DDK Connector Division (2)
Room 801 Mirror Tower 61 Mody Road
Tsim Sha Tsui East, Kowloon, China (Hong Kong)
Tel.: (852) 2369 7028
Fax: (852) 2369 7392
Power Connector Whslr
S.I.C.: 5065
N.A.I.C.S.: 423690

Fujikura Korea Automotive Ltd. (1)
Acro Tower A-BD 710/711 Kwanyang-dong 1591
Dongan-gu, Anyang, Kyunggido, 431-060, Korea (South)
Tel.: (82) 31 478 9521
Fax: (82) 31 478 9520
Emp.: 21
Automotive Electric Parts Mfr
S.I.C.: 3714
N.A.I.C.S.: 336320

Fujikura Ltd. (1)
Rm 907 Tower B Wantai Beihai Bldg
6 Chaoyangmen Beidajie, Beijing, 100027, China CN
Tel.: (86) 1065544520 (100%)
Fax: (86) 1065544528
E-Mail: admin@fujikura.co.jp
Web Site: www.fujikura.com
Emp.: 5
Representative Office
S.I.C.: 3357
N.A.I.C.S.: 335921
Yoichi Nagahama *(Pres & CEO)*

Fujikura (Malaysia) Sdn. Bhd. (1)
No 2 Jalan Delima 1 1 Subang Hi Tech Industrial Park
40000 Shah Alam, Selangor, Malaysia MY
Tel.: (60) 356316366 (100%)
Fax: (60) 356315950
E-Mail: info@fujikura.com
Web Site: www.fujikura.com
Sales Range: $75-99.9 Million
Emp.: 125
Mfr. & Sales of Magnet Wires
S.I.C.: 3315
N.A.I.C.S.: 331222
Ken Yajima *(Mng Dir)*

Fujikura Shanghai Trading Co., Ltd. (1)
Fl 16 HSBC Tower
101 Yin Cheng E Rd, Shanghai, Pudong, 200120, China CN
Tel.: (86) 2168413636 (100%)
Fax: (86) 2168412070
Web Site: www.fujikura.com.cn
Sls.: $72,000,000
Emp.: 20
Representative Office
S.I.C.: 7313
N.A.I.C.S.: 541840
Saita Akiie *(Mng Dir)*

Fujikura Technology Singapore Pte. Ltd. (1)
41 Science Park Rd 01 03 Gemini Science Park II, Singapore, 117610, Singapore SG
Tel.: (65) 68700701 (100%)
Fax: (65) 68723860
E-Mail: kikuchy@al.com.sg
Web Site: www.fts.com.sg
Emp.: 15
Mfr. & Sales of Magnet Wires
S.I.C.: 3315
N.A.I.C.S.: 331222

Fujikura Zhuhai Co., Ltd. (1)
161 Shihua Xilu Jida
Zhuhai, Guangdong, China

Fujikura Ltd.—(Continued)

Tel.: (86) 756 333 1111
Fax: (86) 756 333 1430
Web Site: www.fujikura.co.jp/eng/corporate/network-o1.html
Wiring Harness Mfr
S.I.C.: 3496
N.A.I.C.S.: 332618

P.T. Jembo Cable Company (1)
JL Pajaiaran Desa Gendesari KEC Jatiuwung
Tangerang, 15137, Indonesia Id
Tel.: (62) 21 556 504 68 (100%)
Fax: (62) 2155650466
E-Mail: info@jembo.com
Web Site: www.jembo.com
Emp.: 640
Mfr & Sales of Cables
S.I.C.: 3496
N.A.I.C.S.: 332618

Shanghai Nanyang Fujikura Cable Co., Ltd. (1)
The West Of 2 Bridge Xinzhu Rd
Xinzhuang, Shanghai, 200131, China CN
Tel.: (86) 2164920958 (100%)
Fax: (86) 2164920968
E-Mail: cbhelp@nfc.sh
Web Site: www.fujikura.com
Mfr. & Sales of Cables
S.I.C.: 3496
N.A.I.C.S.: 332618

FUJIKURA RUBBER LTD.

TOC Ariake East Tower 10F 3-5-7 Ariake
Koto-ku, Tokyo, 135-0063, Japan
Tel.: (81) 3 3527 8111
Fax: (81) 3 3527 8330
Web Site: www.fujikurarubber.com
Year Founded: 1901
5121—(TKS)
Emp.: 1,333
Business Description:
Rubber Product Mfr & Whslr
S.I.C.: 3069
N.A.I.C.S.: 326299
Personnel:
Mitsuyoshi Naka *(Pres)*

FUJIMAK CORPORATION

5-14-5 Shinbashi
Minato-ku, Tokyo, 105-0004, Japan
Tel.: (81) 3 3434 6662
Fax: (81) 3 5403 7749
Web Site: www.fujimak.biz
Year Founded: 1950
5965—(TKS)
Business Description:
Cooking Equipment Mfr
S.I.C.: 3589
N.A.I.C.S.: 333318
Personnel:
Toshinori Kumagai *(Pres)*

FUJIMI INCORPORATED

1-1 Chiryo-2 Nishibiwajima-cho
Kiyosu, Aichi, 452-8502, Japan
Tel.: (81) 525038181
Fax: (81) 525036166
Web Site: www.fujimiinc.co.jp
Year Founded: 1953
5384—(NGO TKS)
Sls.: $356,532,000
Assets: $542,707,000
Liabilities: $91,377,000
Net Worth: $451,330,000
Earnings: $24,442,000
Emp.: 783
Fiscal Year-end: 03/31/13
Business Description:
Synthetic Precision Abrasives Mfr
S.I.C.: 3291
N.A.I.C.S.: 327910
Personnel:
Keishi Seki *(Pres)*
Board of Directors:
Hirokazu Ito
Toshiki Owaki
Keishi Seki
Akira Suzuki
Katsuhiro Suzuki
Takashi Tsuchiya
U.S. Subsidiary:

Fujimi Corporation (1)
11200 SW Leveton Dr
Tualatin, OR 97062
Tel.: (503) 682-7822
Fax: (503) 612-9721
E-Mail: info@fujimico.com
Web Site: www.fujimico.com
Emp.: 80
Abrasives & Polishing Products Mfr
S.I.C.: 3291
N.A.I.C.S.: 327910
Masayuki Nagaoka *(Pres)*

Non-U.S. Subsidiary:

FUJIMI-MICRO TECHNOLOGY SDN. BHD (1)
Lot 13 Jalan Hi Tech 3 Kulim Hi Tech Park Phase I
Kulim, Kedah, 09000, Malaysia
Tel.: (60) 44033700
Fax: (60) 44033900
Emp.: 70
Abrasive Product Mfr
S.I.C.: 3291
N.A.I.C.S.: 327910
Owaki Toshiki *(Mng Dir)*

FUJIMORI KOGYO CO., LTD.

10/F Shinjuku First West 1-23-7 Nishi-Shinjuku
Shinjuku-ku, Tokyo, 160-0023, Japan
Tel.: (81) 3 6381 2573
Fax: (81) 3 5909 5779
Web Site: www.zacros.co.jp
Year Founded: 1914
FJ3—(DEU TKS)
Sls.: $932,008,000
Assets: $842,270,000
Liabilities: $393,316,000
Net Worth: $448,954,000
Earnings: $49,082,000
Emp.: 983
Fiscal Year-end: 03/31/13
Business Description:
Plastic Packaging Material Mfr
S.I.C.: 2671
N.A.I.C.S.: 326112
Personnel:
Akihiko Fujimori *(Chm)*
Eishi Fuyama *(Pres)*
Akijiro Yoshino *(Mng Dir)*
Board of Directors:
Akihiko Fujimori
Nobuhiko Fujimori
Yukihiko Fujimori
Eishi Fuyama
Kimihiko Shiomi
Akijiro Yoshino

FUJIN TECHNOLOGY PLC

Merlin House
Brunel Road, Theale, Berkshire, RG7 4AB, United Kingdom
Tel.: (44) 1189026878
Fax: (44) 1189026401
E-Mail: information@fujintech.com
Web Site: www.fujintech.com
Year Founded: 2003
Sales Range: $75-99.9 Million
Emp.: 15
Business Description:
Mobile Communication Systems Integrator
S.I.C.: 4812
N.A.I.C.S.: 517210
Personnel:
Will Palmer *(Chm, Mng Dir & CEO)*

FUJIO FOOD SYSTEM CO., LTD.

Daiwa Minami-Morimachi Building 2F 2-6 2-chome-kita
Tenjinbashi Kita-ku, Osaka, 530-0041, Japan
Tel.: (81) 6 6882 0851
Fax: (81) 6 6882 0614
Web Site: www.fujiofood.com
Year Founded: 1999
2752—(JAS)
Sls.: $251,306,000
Assets: $156,497,000
Liabilities: $118,602,000
Net Worth: $37,895,000
Earnings: $7,799,000
Emp.: 498
Fiscal Year-end: 12/31/12
Business Description:
Restaurant Management Services
S.I.C.: 5812
N.A.I.C.S.: 722511
Personnel:
Masahiro Fujio *(Pres)*
Hideo Fujio *(Exec Officer)*
Yuichiro Kuki *(Exec Officer)*
Makoto Maezono *(Exec Officer)*
Daisuke Matsumoto *(Exec Officer)*
Masakazu Nakamura *(Exec Officer)*
Kouya Sakano *(Exec Officer)*
Ichiro Sato *(Exec Officer)*
Hideki Takamori *(Exec Officer)*
Kazunori Yoda *(Exec Officer)*
Yusuke Zushi *(Exec Officer)*
Board of Directors:
Hideo Fujio
Masahiro Fujio
Shigetoshi Inouchi
Yuichiro Kuki
Yusuke Zushi
U.S. Subsidiary:

FUJIO FOOD SYSTEM U.S.A. CO., LTD. (1)
1345 S King St
Honolulu, HI 96814
Tel.: (808) 942-4848
Restaurant Operator
S.I.C.: 7011
N.A.I.C.S.: 721110

FUJIPREAM CORPORATION

38-1 Shikisai Himeji
Hyogo, Japan
Tel.: (81) 79 266 6161
Fax: (81) 79 266 6738
E-Mail: info@fujipream.co.jp
Web Site: www.fujipream.co.jp
Year Founded: 1982
4237—(JAS)
Sls.: $129,976,000
Assets: $167,728,000
Liabilities: $89,287,000
Net Worth: $78,441,000
Earnings: $5,643,000
Emp.: 230
Fiscal Year-end: 03/31/13
Business Description:
Optical Devices Mfr
S.I.C.: 3827
N.A.I.C.S.: 333314
Personnel:
Jitsuzo Matsumoto *(Chm & Pres)*
Plants:

Fujipream Corporation - Himeji Factory (1)
116-1 Jihoji
Himeji, Hyogo, Japan
Tel.: (81) 79 266 6815
Fax: (81) 79 266 8055
Flat Panel Display Mfr & Distr
S.I.C.: 3575
N.A.I.C.S.: 334118

Fujipream Corporation - PV Factory (1)
1-490-19 Koto Shingu-cho
Hyogo, Tatsuno, Japan
Tel.: (81) 791 59 8118
Fax: (81) 791 59 8177
Flat Panel Display Mfr
S.I.C.: 3577
N.A.I.C.S.: 334118

FUJISOFT INCORPORATED

1-1 Sakuragicho Naka-ku
Yokohama, Kanagawa, 231-8008, Japan
Tel.: (81) 456508811
Fax: (81) 45 650 8810
Web Site: www.fsi.co.jp
Year Founded: 1970
9749—(TKS)
Sls.: $1,520,326,247
Assets: $1,684,761,034
Liabilities: $703,193,414
Net Worth: $981,567,620
Earnings: $44,028,402
Emp.: 10,160
Fiscal Year-end: 03/31/13
Business Description:
Software Development, Outsourcing & Business Solutions Services
S.I.C.: 7373
N.A.I.C.S.: 541512
Personnel:
Hiroshi Nozawa *(Chm)*
Satoyasu Sakashita *(Pres)*
Tatsuya Naito *(Operating Officer & Mgr-Bus Mgmt Grp)*
Seto Arai *(Operating Officer)*
Motohiro Harai *(Operating Officer)*
Koichi Imagi *(Exec Operating Officer)*
Yukihiro Inohara *(Operating Officer)*
Hiroyuki Kimura *(Operating Officer)*
Tomoya Kotani *(Operating Officer)*
Masaki Maekawa *(Operating Officer)*
Jintaro Nozawa *(Exec Operating Officer)*
Nobuyuki Nunome *(Operating Officer)*
Hidemi Okajima *(Operating Officer)*
Satoshi Satou *(Exec Operating Officer)*
Masaki Shibuya *(Exec Operating Officer)*
Yoshiharu Shiraishi *(Operating Officer)*
Masaru Sudo *(Exec Operating Officer)*
Yutaka Tahara *(Operating Officer)*
Yoshinobu Takebayashi *(Exec Operating Officer)*
Koichi Toyota *(Exec Operating Officer)*
Masataka Yamaguchi *(Sr Exec Operating Officer)*
Reiko Yasue *(Operating Officer)*
Board of Directors:
Hiroshi Nozawa
Hideo Aiso
Tsuneo Futami
Koichi Imagi
Satoyasu Sakashita
Yoshinobu Takebayashi
Masataka Yamaguchi
Subsidiaries:

4U Applications, Inc (1)
2-19-7 Kotobashi Fuji Soft Abc Tokyo Bldg
Sumida-Ku, Tokyo, 130-0022, Japan
Tel.: (81) 3 5638 5150
Fax: (81) 3 5638 5152
E-Mail: contact@4UApplications.com
Web Site: www.4uapplications.com
Software Development Services
S.I.C.: 7371
N.A.I.C.S.: 541511

Cyber Com Co., Ltd. (1)
DJK Ichibancho Bldg
1-7-20 Ichibancho Aoba-ku, 980-0811
Miyagi, Japan
Tel.: (81) 222131856
Fax: (81) 222135313
Web Site: www.cy-com.co.jp
Emp.: 7

Custom Computer Programming Services
S.I.C.: 7371
N.A.I.C.S.: 541511
Kouki Watanabe *(Gen Mgr)*

Fujisoft Kikaku Ltd. (1)
2-13-18 Okamoto
Kamakura, Kanagawa, 2470072, Japan JP
Tel.: (81) 467475944
Fax: (81) 467446119
Web Site: www.fsk-inc.co.jp
Emp.: 161
Custom Computer Programming Services
S.I.C.: 7371
N.A.I.C.S.: 541511
Ryuhei Nagashima *(Pres)*

Fujisoft Service Bureau Incorporated (1)
9th Floor FUJISOFT Bldg
2-19-7 Kotobashi, Tokyo, 130-0022, Japan
Tel.: (81) 356001731
Fax: (81) 356001730
Web Site: www.fsisb.co.jp
Emp.: 358
Custom Computer Programming Services
S.I.C.: 7371
N.A.I.C.S.: 541511
Takashi Kaizuka *(Pres & CEO)*

Fujisoft SSS, Inc. (1)
NTT West Japan Bldg
1-3 Aioi-cho, 857-0044 Nagasaki, Japan
Tel.: (81) 956259223
Fax: (81) 956235327
Web Site: www.fsisss.co.jp
Custom Computer Programming Services
S.I.C.: 7371
N.A.I.C.S.: 541511

iDEA Consulting Inc. (1)
6F Akihabara Bldg 19 Kanda-matsunaga-cho
Chiyoda-ku, Tokyo, 101-0023, Japan
Tel.: (81) 3 5289 3150
Fax: (81) 3 5289 3157
Web Site: www.ideacns.co.jp
Information Technology Consulting Services
S.I.C.: 7373
N.A.I.C.S.: 541512

Japan Internet News Co., Ltd. (1)
9th Floor Kojimachi Garden Building
2-3 Kojimachi Chiyoda-ku, Tokyo, 102-0083, Japan
Tel.: (81) 352162030
Fax: (81) 352162031
E-Mail: janjan@janjan.jp
Web Site: www.janjan.jp
Emp.: 35
Custom Computer Programming Services
S.I.C.: 7371
N.A.I.C.S.: 541511
Ken Takeuchi *(Gen Mgr)*

Mercury Staffing Co., Ltd. (1)
9F Kawase Building 3 17 5 Sinjyuku
Sinjyuku ku, 106 0022 Tokyo, Japan
Tel.: (81) 353662500
Fax: (81) 353663404
Web Site: www.msso.co.jp
Temporary Help Services
S.I.C.: 7363
N.A.I.C.S.: 561320

OA Laboratory Co., Ltd. (1)
2-15-41 Dai
Kamakura, Kanagawa, 247-0061, Japan JP
Tel.: (81) 467445566
Fax: (81) 467480256
E-Mail: eigyo@oalab.co.jp
Web Site: www.oalab.co.jp
Emp.: 171
Communications Equipment Mfr
S.I.C.: 3669
N.A.I.C.S.: 334290
Yoshinori Ohara *(Gen Mgr)*

SYSTEMS FORMULATIONS AND INTEGRATIONS Incorporated (1)
2-19-7 Kotobashi Fuji Soft Bldg
Sumida-Ku, Tokyo, 130-0022, Japan
Tel.: (81) 356691811
Fax: (81) 356691812
E-Mail: support@sfi-inc.co.jp
Web Site: www.sfi-inc.co.jp
Packaging Services
S.I.C.: 7389
N.A.I.C.S.: 561910

Tosho Computer Systems Co., Ltd. (1)
1-9-7 Kyobashi
Chuo-ku, Tokyo, 104-0031, Japan
Tel.: (81) 335631562
Fax: (81) 335639823
Web Site: www.tcs.co.jp
Data Processing Hosting & Related Services
S.I.C.: 7379
N.A.I.C.S.: 518210

Vinculum Japan Corporation (1)
Toyobo Bldg
2-2-8 Dojimahama Kita-ku, 530-0004 Osaka, Japan
Tel.: (81) 663488951
Fax: (81) 663436455
Web Site: www.vinculum-japan.co.jp
Software Reproducing
S.I.C.: 3652
N.A.I.C.S.: 334614

U.S. Subsidiary:

Serverware Corporation (1)
1250 Pittsford Victor Rd
Pittsford, NY 14534 NY
Tel.: (585) 785-6100
Web Site: www.serverw.com
Emp.: 25
IT Solutions
S.I.C.: 7373
N.A.I.C.S.: 541512

Non-U.S. Subsidiaries:

CCA Engineering Simulation Software (Shanghai) Co., Ltd. (1)
RM 908 No 777
Zhao Jia Bang Rd, 200032 Shanghai, China
Tel.: (86) 2164716037
Fax: (86) 2164716050
Web Site: www.cca-es.com
Emp.: 20
Administrative Management & General Management Consulting Services
S.I.C.: 8742
N.A.I.C.S.: 541611

CYBERNET SYSTEMS TAIWAN Co., Ltd. (1)
No 178 Sec 2 Gongdao 5th Road
Hsin-chu, Taiwan
Tel.: (886) 3 6118668
Fax: (886) 3 6118667
E-Mail: general@cybernet-ap.com.tw
Web Site: www.cybernet-ap.com.tw
Software Development Services
S.I.C.: 7371
N.A.I.C.S.: 541511

Maplesoft Europe GmbH (1)
Auf Der Huls 198
Aachen, Nordrhein-Westfalen, 52068, Germany
Tel.: (49) 24198091930
Fax: (49) 24118298908
Emp.: 4
Analytical Software Development Services
S.I.C.: 7371
N.A.I.C.S.: 541511
Fred Kern *(Gen Mgr)*

Noesis Solutions NV (1)
Gaston Geenslaan 11 B4
3001 Leuven, Belgium
Tel.: (32) 16 317 040
Fax: (32) 16 317 048
E-Mail: info@noesissolutions.com
Web Site: www.noesissolutions.com
Emp.: 2
Computer Software Development Services
S.I.C.: 7371
N.A.I.C.S.: 541511
Hans Wynendaele *(CEO)*

WATERLOO MAPLE INC. (1)
615 Kumpf Dr
Waterloo, ON, N2V 1K8, Canada
Tel.: (519) 747-2373
Fax: (519) 747-5284
E-Mail: info@maplesoft.com
Emp.: 97
Analytical Software Development Services
S.I.C.: 7371
N.A.I.C.S.: 541511

FUJITA ENGINEERING CO., LTD.

1174-5 Iizuka-machi Takasaki-city
Gunma, 370-0069, Japan
Tel.: (81) 27 361 1111
Fax: (81) 27 363 7748
Web Site: www.fujita-eng.co.jp
Year Founded: 1926
1770—(JAS)
Sls.: $242,869,000
Assets: $191,136,000
Liabilities: $97,449,000
Net Worth: $93,687,000
Earnings: $3,938,000
Emp.: 222
Fiscal Year-end: 03/31/13

Business Description:
Construction Services
S.I.C.: 1541
N.A.I.C.S.: 236210

Personnel:
Noboru Fujita *(Chm)*
Minoru Fujita *(Pres & CEO)*
Syoji Suzuki *(Sr Mng Dir)*
Ichiro Yamamoto *(Mng Dir)*

Board of Directors:
Noboru Fujita
Minoru Fujita
Tatsuaki Kudo
Ryoichi Matsuda
Hisami Suto
Syoji Suzuki
Hideki Takahashi
Ichiro Yamamoto

FUJITEC CO., LTD.

Big Wing
Hikone, Shiga, 522-8588, Japan
Tel.: (81) 749307111
Fax: (81) 749307054
E-Mail: ir@fj.fujitec.co.jp
Web Site: www.fujitec.com
Year Founded: 1948
6406—(TKS)
Sls.: $1,292,148,000
Assets: $1,349,073,000
Liabilities: $488,081,000
Net Worth: $860,992,000
Earnings: $60,577,000
Emp.: 7,579
Fiscal Year-end: 03/31/13

Business Description:
Elevators, Escalators & Vertical Transportation Equipment Mfr
S.I.C.: 3534
N.A.I.C.S.: 333921

Personnel:
Takakazu Uchiyama *(Pres & CEO)*
Iwataro Sekiguchi *(Exec VP)*

Board of Directors:
Yasuo Hanakawa
Kazuo Inaba
Takao Okada
Iwataro Sekiguchi
Mitsunori Shirakura
Narayanapillai Sugumaran
Takakazu Uchiyama

Transfer Agent:
Sumitomo Mitsui Trust Bank, Limited
4-1 Marunouchi 1-chome Chiyoda-ku
Tokyo, Japan

U.S. Subsidiaries:

Fujitec America Inc (1)
7258 Innovation Way
Mason, OH 45040
Tel.: (513) 932-8000
Fax: (513) 933-5580
Web Site: www.fujitecamerica.com
Emp.: 80
Elevator & Moving Stairway Mfr
S.I.C.: 3534
N.A.I.C.S.: 333921
Kenny Yamashiro *(Co-Pres & CEO)*
Katsuji Okuda *(Co-Pres)*

Fujitec Elevator Co. Inc. (1)
1 Donna Dr
Wood Ridge, NJ 07075
Tel.: (201) 438-8400
Fax: (973) 365-4027
Toll Free: (800) 950-7899
E-Mail: sales@fujitecamerica.com
Web Site: www.fujitecamerica.com
Sls.: $40,000,000
Emp.: 165
Elevator Manufacturing, Installation & Repair
S.I.C.: 3534
N.A.I.C.S.: 333921
Kenny Yamashiro *(Pres & CEO-America)*
Louis Mattina *(CFO & Treas-America)*
Don Regina *(CEO-New York Ops & Exec VP-America)*

Non-U.S. Subsidiaries:

FSP Pte Ltd. (1)
204 Bedok S Ave 1
Singapore, 469333, Singapore
Tel.: (65) 67671626
Fax: (65) 67671632
Transportation System Mfr
S.I.C.: 3799
N.A.I.C.S.: 336999

FUJITEC ARGENTINA S.A. (1)
Av Belgrano 884
C1092AAV Buenos Aires, Argentina
Tel.: (54) 1143426830
Fax: (54) 11 4342 5353
E-Mail: ventas@fujitec.com.ar
Web Site: www.fujitec.com.ar
Elevators Distr & Installation Services
S.I.C.: 5084
N.A.I.C.S.: 423830

FUJITEC CANADA, INC. (1)
15 East Wilmot Street
Richmond Hill, ON, L4B 1A3, Canada
Tel.: (905) 731-8681
Fax: (905) 731-4608
Web Site: www.fujiteccanada.com
Elevators & Escalators Mfr & Installation Services
S.I.C.: 3534
N.A.I.C.S.: 333921
Takakazu Uchiyama *(Co-Pres & CEO-Fujitec Global)*
Ralph Wischnewski *(Co-Pres)*

Fujitec Deutschland GmbH (1)
Bessemerstr 82
12103 Berlin, Germany
Tel.: (49) 302699480
Fax: (49) 3026994848
E-Mail: latosimski@fujitec.ge
Web Site: www.fujitecgermany.com
Emp.: 15
Industrial Machinery & Equipment Whslr
S.I.C.: 5084
N.A.I.C.S.: 423830
Tononori Yoshikawa *(Mng Dir)*

FUJITEC EGYPT CO., LTD. (1)
Osmans Towers st Foq Motowaset Towers
5 25th Floor Flat 252
Cornishe El Nile Maadi, Cairo, Egypt
Tel.: (20) 2 2528 5808
Fax: (20) 2 2528 8032
E-Mail: info@fujitecegypt.com
Web Site: www.fujitecegypt.com
Elevator Mfr
S.I.C.: 3534
N.A.I.C.S.: 333921
Mohammed El Sherif *(Gen Mgr)*

Fujitec (HK) Company Limited (1)
Rm 3410-15 34th Fl Hk Plaza
Sai Ying Poon, Kowloon, China (Hong Kong)
Tel.: (852) 25478339
Fax: (852) 28583406
E-Mail: f_hk@fujitec-hk.com.hk
Web Site: www.fujitec-hk.com.hk
Emp.: 80
Building Equipment & Machinery Installation Contractors
S.I.C.: 1711
N.A.I.C.S.: 238220

FUJITEC INC. (1)
3rd Fl A&V Crystal tower 105 esteban St
Legaspi Village, Makati, Metro Manila, 1229, Philippines
Tel.: (63) 2 893 3734

Fujitec Co., Ltd.—(Continued)

Fax: (63) 2 818 0002
E-Mail: fujitec@fujitecsg.com
Web Site: www.fujitec.co.jp
Emp.: 20
Elevator Installation Services
S.I.C.: 1799
N.A.I.C.S.: 238290
Ceazar Almario *(Mng Dir)*

FUJITEC INDIA PRIVATE LTD. **(1)**
P-52 1st Cross Road 8th Avenue Mahindra World City
Chengalpattu, 603 002, India
Tel.: (91) 44 47418800
Fax: (91) 44 47435076
Web Site: www.fujitecindia.com
Elevators Mfr & Distr
S.I.C.: 3534
N.A.I.C.S.: 333921
M. K. Panicker *(Mng Dir)*
Satish Kumar Jha *(CTO)*

FUJITEC KOREA CO., LTD. **(1)**
98B 3L Namdong Industrial Estate 662-2 Gojan-Dong
Namdong-Gu, Incheon, 405-818k, Korea (South)
Tel.: (82) 328177541
Fax: (82) 328175682
E-Mail: incheon@fujiteckorea.co.kr
Web Site: www.fujiteckorea.co.kr
Emp.: 200
Elevators Mfr
S.I.C.: 3534
N.A.I.C.S.: 333921
Spebeyoon Yoon *(CEO)*

Fujitec (Malaysia) Sdn Bhd **(1)**
Unit D-5-59 Block Dahlia 10 Blvd Lebuhraya
Sprint Pju 6A, Petaling Jaya, Selangor, 47400, Malaysia
Tel.: (60) 377285351
Fax: (60) 377285358
E-Mail: fujitec@fujitecmy.com
Web Site: www.fujitecsg.com
Emp.: 75
Industrial Machinery & Equipment Whslr
S.I.C.: 5084
N.A.I.C.S.: 423830
Franky So *(Mng Dir)*

FUJITEC SAUDI ARABIA CO., LTD. **(1)**
Jamjoom Center
PO Box 4376
Jeddah, 21491, Saudi Arabia
Tel.: (966) 2 667 0057
Fax: (966) 2 660 9259
Escalator Installation & Maintenance Services
S.I.C.: 1799
N.A.I.C.S.: 238290

FUJITEC SHANGHAI SOURCING CENTER CO., LTD. **(1)**
No 1000 Xin Fei Road Eastern New Area
Song Jiang Industrial Zone
Shanghai, 201612, China
Tel.: (86) 21 6760 1515
Fax: (86) 21 6760 1463
Transportation System Mfr
S.I.C.: 3799
N.A.I.C.S.: 336999

FUJITEC SHANGHAI TECHNOLOGIES CO., LTD. **(1)**
No 1000 Xin Fei Road Eastern New Area
Songjiang Industrial Zone
Shanghai, 201612, China
Tel.: (86) 21 6760 0566
Fax: (86) 21 6760 0723
Web Site: www.fujitec.co.jp/english/corporate/global.html
Transportation System Mfr
S.I.C.: 3799
N.A.I.C.S.: 336999

Fujitec Singapore Corporation Limited **(1)**
204 Bedok S Ave 1
469333 Singapore, Singapore
Tel.: (65) 62416222
Fax: (65) 64447626
E-Mail: fujitec@fujitecsg.com
Web Site: www.fujitecsg.com
Emp.: 700
Elevator & Moving Stairway Mfr
S.I.C.: 3534
N.A.I.C.S.: 333921
N. Sugunaran *(Pres)*

Fujitec Taiwan Co. Ltd. **(1)**
13th Fl 37 Sec 3
Minchuan E Rd, Taipei, Taiwan
Tel.: (886) 225167166
Fax: (886) 225160685
E-Mail: fujitec.taiwan@msa.hinet.net
Emp.: 30
Elevator & Moving Stairway Mfr
S.I.C.: 3534
N.A.I.C.S.: 333921
Sekiguchi Iwataro *(Mng Dir)*

FUJITEC UK LTD. **(1)**
Texcel Business Park Thames Road
Crayford, DA1 4TQ, United Kingdom
Tel.: (44) 1322552450
Fax: (44) 1322552460
Web Site: www.fujiteceurope.com
Emp.: 15
Escalators Sales & Installation Services
S.I.C.: 1799
N.A.I.C.S.: 238290
Tomonori Yoshikawa *(Mng Dir)*

FUJITEC VENEZUELA C.A. **(1)**
Calle 8 Con Calle 6 Edificio Luindos PB La Urbina
Caracas, 1070, Venezuela
Tel.: (58) 212 241 0311
Fax: (58) 212 241 3052
E-Mail: mantenimiento@fujitec.com.ve
Web Site: www.fujitec.com.ve
Elevator Mfr
S.I.C.: 3535
N.A.I.C.S.: 333922

FUJITEC VIETNAM CO., LTD. **(1)**
3rd Floor Tien Phuoc Bldg 542 Tran Hung Dao St Ward 2
District 5, Ho Chi Minh City, Vietnam
Tel.: (84) 839246556
Fax: (84) 8 3924 6557
Emp.: 1
Transportation System Services
S.I.C.: 4789
N.A.I.C.S.: 488999
Toshikazu Nakata *(Gen Mgr)*

Huasheng Fujitec Elevator Co. Ltd. **(1)**
Chunming Rd
102800 Langfang, Hebel, China
Tel.: (86) 3166087145
Fax: (86) 3166088470
E-Mail: zhang@fujitec.com.cn
Web Site: www.fujitec.co.jp/eastasia/company/china.htm
Elevator & Moving Stairway Mfr
S.I.C.: 3534
N.A.I.C.S.: 333921

PT. Fujitec Indonesia **(1)**
Perkantoran Puri Niaga III J1 Puri Kencana
Kembangan, 11610 Jakarta, Indonesia
Tel.: (62) 2158303406
Fax: (62) 2158303407
Emp.: 40
Elevator & Moving Stairway Mfr
S.I.C.: 3534
N.A.I.C.S.: 333921

Rich Mark Engineering Limited. **(1)**
Rm 3315 Hong Kong Plz 188 Connaught Rd C
Sai Ying Pun, Hong Kong, China (Hong Kong)
Tel.: (852) 29155198
Fax: (852) 29155038
Transportation System Mfr
S.I.C.: 3799
N.A.I.C.S.: 336999

FUJITSU BROAD SOLUTION & CONSULTING INC.

Tradepia Odaiba 2-3-1 Daiba Minato-ku
Tokyo, 135-8300, Japan
Tel.: (81) 3 3570 4111
Fax: (81) 3 3570 4000
Web Site: www.bsc.fujitsu.com
Year Founded: 1963
4793—(JAS)
Sls.: $335,137,000
Assets: $324,082,000
Liabilities: $121,066,000
Net Worth: $203,016,000
Earnings: $8,030,000
Emp.: 2,113
Fiscal Year-end: 03/31/13

Business Description:
Custom Software Development Services
S.I.C.: 7371
N.A.I.C.S.: 541511

Personnel:
Hajime Kojima *(Pres & CEO)*
Hideki Aso *(Operating Officer)*
Noboru Hiratsuka *(Operating Officer)*
Michiharu Hirosawa *(Mng Operating Officer)*
Toru Ishikawa *(Exec Operating Officer)*
Kazutoshi Jibiki *(Operating Officer)*
Toshio Kobayashi *(Operating Officer)*
Yousuke Kondou *(Operating Officer)*
Masatoshi Maeda *(Operating Officer)*
Hideaki Tsumagari *(Operating Officer)*
Yukihiro Yabe *(Operating Officer)*
Haruo Yoshida *(Operating Officer)*

Board of Directors:
Michiharu Hirosawa
Toru Ishikawa
Toshio Kobayashi
Hajime Kojima
Yousuke Kondou
Motoyuki Ozawa
Norihiko Taniguchi

FUJITSU COMPONENT LIMITED

Gotanda Chuo Bldg 3-5 Higashi-Gotanda 2-chome
Shinagawa-ku, Tokyo, 1410022, Japan
Tel.: (81) 354497010
Fax: (81) 354492626
Web Site: www.fcl.fujitsu.com
6719—(TKS)
Sls.: $435,171,000
Assets: $355,179,000
Liabilities: $350,889,000
Net Worth: $4,290,000
Earnings: ($6,105,000)
Emp.: 3,298
Fiscal Year-end: 03/31/13

Business Description:
Electronic Components Mfr
S.I.C.: 3613
N.A.I.C.S.: 335313

Personnel:
Koichi Ishizaka *(Pres)*

FUJITSU LIMITED

Shiodome City Center 1-5-2 Higashi-Shimbashi Minato-ku
Tokyo, 105-7123, Japan
Tel.: (81) 362522220
Fax: (81) 362522783
E-Mail: ir@pr.fujitsu.com
Web Site: www.fujitsu.com
Year Founded: 1935
6702—(DEU LSE NGO SWX TKS)
Sls.: $48,199,008,000
Assets: $33,539,594,000
Liabilities: $23,531,695,000
Net Worth: $10,007,899,000
Earnings: ($802,043,000)
Emp.: 169,000
Fiscal Year-end: 03/31/13

Business Description:
Computers & Data Processing Systems, Telecommunications Systems & Electronic Components Mfr
S.I.C.: 3571
N.A.I.C.S.: 334111

Personnel:
Michiyoshi Mazuka *(Chm)*
Masahiro Koezuka *(Vice Chm & VP)*
Masami Yamamoto *(Pres)*
Masami Fujita *(Sr Exec VP)*
Hideyuki Saso *(Sr Exec VP)*
Kazuhiko Kato *(Exec VP)*
Yoshikazu Kudoh *(Exec VP)*
Hirokazu Uejima *(Exec VP)*
Chikafumi Urakawa *(Exec VP)*
Rod Vawdrey *(Exec VP)*
Masaaki Hamaba *(Sr VP)*
Yoshihiko Hanada *(Sr VP)*
Kazuhiro Igarashi *(Sr VP)*
Tsuneo Kawatsuma *(Sr VP)*
Takashi Mori *(Sr VP)*
Hiroyuki Ono *(Sr VP)*
Nobuo Otani *(Sr VP)*
Jiro Otsuki *(Sr VP)*
Norihiko Taniguchi *(Sr VP)*
Noriyuki Toyoki *(Sr VP)*

Board of Directors:
Michiyoshi Mazuka
Masami Fujita
Tatsuzumi Furukawa
Haruo Ito
Kazuhiko Kato
Takashi Okimoto
Hideyuki Saso
Miyako Suda
Hirokazu Uejima
Chikafumi Urakawa
Masami Yamamoto

Transfer Agent:
Mitsubishi UFJ Trust & Banking Corporation
4-5 Marunouchi 1-Chome Chiyoda-ku
Tokyo, 100-8212, Japan
Tel.: (81) 3 3212 1211

Subsidiaries:

Fujitsu Access Ltd. **(1)**
17 3 Sakato 1 Chome
Takatsu Ku, Kawasaki, 213 8586, Japan (50%)
Tel.: (81) 448222121
Fax: (81) 448449532
Web Site: www.access.fujitsu.com
Sales Range: Less than $1 Million
Emp.: 400
Mfr. & Seller of Communication Equipment
S.I.C.: 3669
N.A.I.C.S.: 334290

Fujitsu Business Systems Ltd. **(1)**
7227 Koraku 1 Chome Bunkyo Ku
Tokyo, 112 8572, Japan (51%)
Tel.: (81) 358048111
Fax: (81) 358048129
E-Mail: fjm@fujitsu.com
Web Site: www.fjm.fujitsu.com
Sales Range: $1-4.9 Billion
Emp.: 3,000
Electronic & Communications Equipment Distr
S.I.C.: 5731
N.A.I.C.S.: 443142
Kenji Ikegai *(Pres)*

Fujitsu Electronics Inc. **(1)**
Shin-Yokohama Chuo Bldg 2-100-45 Shin-Yokohama
Kohoku-Ku, Yokohama, Kanagawa, 222-8508, Japan
Tel.: (81) 454738030
Fax: (81) 454155870
Web Site: jp.fujitsu.com
Emp.: 600
Semiconductor Device Mfr & Distr
S.I.C.: 3674
N.A.I.C.S.: 334413
Toshimasa Kurihara *(Corp Sr Vice Chm)*
Kazuyuki Sumi *(Corp Sr Vice Chm)*
Noriyuki Kanbe *(Pres & CEO)*

Non-U.S. Subsidiary:

FUJITSU DEVICES (DALIAN) ENGINEERING LIMITED **(2)**
Room 201-A Building 3 Dalian Software Park International
Dalian, 116023, China
Tel.: (86) 41139707170

Fax: (86) 41139707175
Software Development Services
S.I.C.: 7371
N.A.I.C.S.: 541511

Fujitsu FIP Corporation (1)
Time 24 Building 2 45 Aomi
Koto-ku, Tokyo, 135 8686, Japan
Tel.: (81) 355310200
Web Site: jp.fujitsu.com
Emp.: 2,670
Information Technology & On-Line Information Services
S.I.C.: 2741
N.A.I.C.S.: 519130
Takashi Igarashi *(Chm)*
Koichi Ohta *(Chm)*
Hisashi Iyoda *(Pres)*
Nobuyoshi Sugimoto *(Pres)*
Nobuo Amai *(Mng Dir)*
Yoshio Egawa *(Mng Dir)*
Mitsuyasu Miyaji *(Mng Dir)*
Nobuyuki Sawai *(Mng Dir)*

Subsidiary:

G-Search Ltd. (2)
Loop X Building 3 9 15 Kaigan
Minatu-ku, Tokyo, 108 0022, Japan JP
Tel.: (81) 334521244
Fax: (81) 334521246
Web Site: www.g-search.jp
Emp.: 155
On-Line Information Services
S.I.C.: 7389
N.A.I.C.S.: 519190
Masao Morita *(Pres & CEO)*

Fujitsu Frontech Ltd. (1)
1776 Yanokuchi
Inagi-shi, Tokyo, 206-8555, Japan (54%)
Tel.: (81) 423775111
Telex: 2832621
Fax: (81) 423780927
E-Mail: ir@frontech.fujitsu.com
Web Site: www.frontech.fujitsu.com
6945—(TKS)
Sls.: $1,105,720,000
Assets: $713,141,000
Liabilities: $331,980,000
Net Worth: $381,161,000
Earnings: $4,400,000
Emp.: 3,457
Fiscal Year-end: 03/31/13
Electronic Products Developer & Mfr
S.I.C.: 3571
N.A.I.C.S.: 334111
Mitsuhiro Ebihara *(Chm)*
Hirosada Tone *(Pres)*
Toshiya Suzuki *(Exec VP)*
Isao Igarashi *(Sr VP)*
Hiroshi Imamura *(Sr VP)*
Tatsuya Ishioka *(Sr VP)*
Kunihiko Matsumori *(Sr VP)*
Kiyoshi Saito *(Sr VP)*
Masao Teramoto *(Sr VP)*
Naoki Yoshida *(Sr VP)*

Subsidiaries:

FUJITSU FRONTECH SYSTEMS LIMITED (2)
1-8-3 NF1 Building Tonyamachi
Maebashi, Gunma, Japan
Tel.: (81) 272528000
Emp.: 26
Software Development Services
S.I.C.: 7371
N.A.I.C.S.: 541511
Hisanobu Izumi *(Pres)*

LIFE CREATE LIMITED (2)
1776 Yanokuchi
Inagi-shi, Tokyo, 206-8555, Japan
Tel.: (81) 42 379 6661
Fax: (81) 42 378 7888
Emp.: 87
Employee Welfare Services
S.I.C.: 9441
N.A.I.C.S.: 923130
Toshiya Suzuki *(Pres)*

TOTALIZATOR ENGINEERING LIMITED (2)
6-20-14 East Square Omori Minami-oi
Shinagawa-ku, Tokyo, Japan
Tel.: (81) 357625500
Fax: (81) 357625519
Web Site: www.tel-tota.com
Emp.: 127
Gaming Machine Operator
S.I.C.: 7999
N.A.I.C.S.: 713290
Toshihide Horii *(Pres)*

Plant:

Fujitsu Frontech Limited - Niigata Plant (2)
17-8 Yoshidahigashisakae-cho
Tsubame, Niigata-ken, 959-0294, Japan
Tel.: (81) 256933161
Fax: (81) 256933168
Web Site: www.frontech.fujitsu.com
Emp.: 500
Electronic Equipment Mfr
S.I.C.: 3589
N.A.I.C.S.: 333318

U.S. Subsidiaries:

Fujitsu Frontech North America Inc. (2)
27121 Towne Ctr Dr Ste 100
Foothill Ranch, CA 92610-3436
Tel.: (949) 855-5500
Emp.: 256
Retail Checkout Machinery Mfr
S.I.C.: 3589
N.A.I.C.S.: 333318
Yoshihiko Masuda *(Pres & CEO)*

Non-U.S. Subsidiaries:

Fujitsu Die-Tech Corporation Of The Philippine (2)
1113 East Science Avenue Special Export Processing Zone
Laguna Technopark, Binan, Laguna, Philippines 4024
Tel.: (63) 2 8430965
Fax: (63) 2 8437576
Web Site: www.fujitsu.com
Emp.: 527
Computer Peripheral Equipment Mfr
S.I.C.: 3577
N.A.I.C.S.: 334118
Norikazu Tsuchida *(Pres)*

Fujitsu Frontech Canada Inc. (2)
4700 de la Savane Ste 101
Montreal, QC, H4P 1T7, Canada
Tel.: (972) 479-6000
Software Development Services
S.I.C.: 7371
N.A.I.C.S.: 541511

Fujitsu Frontech (Shanghai) Limited (2)
2F B Block 501 Jingang Road
Pudong, Shanghai, China
Tel.: (86) 21 5854 2228
Fax: (86) 21 5854 3313
Emp.: 55
Mechanical Components Mfr & Whslr
S.I.C.: 3589
N.A.I.C.S.: 333318
Haruyuki Fujimoto *(Chm)*

Fujitsu FSAS Inc. (1)
Masonic 38 MT Building 4-1-4 Shibakoen
Minato-ku, Tokyo, 105-0011, Japan
Tel.: (81) 448746200
Fax: (81) 444345033
Business Process Outsourcing Services
S.I.C.: 7389
N.A.I.C.S.: 561499

Fujitsu General Ltd. (1)
1116 Suenaga Takatsu Ku
Kawasaki, 213 8502, Japan (50%)
Tel.: (81) 448661111
Fax: (81) 448617875
E-Mail: contact@fujitsugeneral.com
Web Site: www.fujitsu-general.com
6755—(NGO TKS)
Emp.: 4,000
S.I.C.: 3571
N.A.I.C.S.: 334111
Mitsuhiro Oishi *(Pres)*
Keiichi Nakamura *(Sr Exec VP)*
Hisaki Hirosaki *(Sr VP)*
Hideji Kawashima *(Sr VP)*
Tsunenao Kosuda *(Sr VP)*
Seiji Matsumoto *(Sr VP)*
Munehiro Nakamura *(Sr VP)*
Hiroshi Niwayama *(Sr VP)*
Kaoru Ouchi *(Sr VP)*
Yukio Sato *(Sr VP)*
Takashi Sogabe *(Sr VP)*
Masahito Tanaka *(Sr VP)*
Junji Yanagimoto *(Sr VP)*

Fujitsu Isotec Limited (1)
135 Higashinozaki Hobara-machi
Date, Fukushima, 960-0695, Japan
Tel.: (81) 24 574 2236
Fax: (81) 24 574 2382
E-Mail: fit-gsm@cs.jp.fujitsu.com
Web Site: www.jp.fujitsu.com
Printer Mfr & Distr
S.I.C.: 3577
N.A.I.C.S.: 334118
Masaichi Tochimoto *(Pres)*

Fujitsu IT Products Ltd. (1)
1-1 To Kasashima
Kaho-ku, Ishikawa, 929-1104, Japan
Tel.: (81) 762852331
Computer Peripheral Equipment Mfr
S.I.C.: 3577
N.A.I.C.S.: 334118

Fujitsu Laboratories Ltd. (1)
4 1 1 Kamikodanaka Nakahara-ku
211 8588 Kawasaki, Japan (95.8%)
Tel.: (81) 447771111
E-Mail: contactqa@cs.jp.fujitsu.com
Web Site: www.labs.fujitsu.com
Emp.: 10,000
Computers, Data Processing Systems, Telecommunications & Electronics Research & Development
S.I.C.: 5045
N.A.I.C.S.: 423430
Kuniaki Nozooe *(Co-Pres)*
Tatsuo Tomita *(Co-Pres)*
Masami Yamamoto *(Co-Pres)*

U.S. Subsidiary:

Fujitsu Laboratories of America, Inc. (2)
1240 E Arques Ave M/S 345
Sunnyvale, CA 94085
Tel.: (408) 530-4500
Fax: (408) 530-4515
E-Mail: info@fla.fujitsu.com
Web Site: www.fujitsu.com
Computer Aided Design Research & Development Services
S.I.C.: 8731
N.A.I.C.S.: 541712
Yasunori Kimura *(Pres & CEO)*

Non-U.S. Subsidiary:

Fujitsu Laboratories of Europe Ltd. (2)
Hayes Park Central Hayes End Road
Hayes, Middlesex, United Kingdom
Tel.: (44) 208 573 4444
Fax: (44) 208 606 4539
E-Mail: laboratories@uk.fujitsu.com
Emp.: 45
Laboratory Testing Services
S.I.C.: 8734
N.A.I.C.S.: 541380
Tsuneo Nakata *(Pres)*

Fujitsu Marketing Limited (1)
1-7-27 Koraku Korakukashima Bldg
Bunkyo-Ku, Tokyo, 112-0004, Japan
Tel.: (81) 3 5804 8111
Fax: (81) 3 5804 8136
Web Site: www.fjm.fujitsu.com
Emp.: 3,951
Software Development Services
S.I.C.: 7371
N.A.I.C.S.: 541511
Akira Furukawa *(Pres)*
Masahiro Abe *(Corp Exec VP)*
Yutaka Yokoyama *(Corp Exec VP)*

Subsidiaries:

Fujitsu Marketing Agent Ltd. (2)
3-banchi Kanda-neribeicho
Chiyoda-ku, Tokyo, 101-0022, Japan
Tel.: (81) 3 5209 1541
Fax: (81) 3 5209 1548
Web Site: www.fjm.fujitsu.com
Human Resource Consulting Services
S.I.C.: 8999
N.A.I.C.S.: 541612

Fujitsu Marketing Office Services Ltd. (2)
3-banchi Kanda-neribeicho
Chiyoda-ku, Tokyo, 101-0022, Japan
Tel.: (81) 3 5209 1890
Web Site: www.fjm.fujitsu.com
Computer Peripheral Equipment & Office Supplies Distr
S.I.C.: 5045
N.A.I.C.S.: 423430

Fujitsu Microdevices Ltd. (1)
Osaki West Building 8-8 Osaki
2-Chome Shinagawa Ku, Tokyo, 141-8583, Japan (91.9%)
Tel.: (81) 334907396
Fax: (81) 3 5496 4295
S.I.C.: 3571
N.A.I.C.S.: 334111

Fujitsu Network Solutions Ltd. (1)
7-1 Nisshincho Kawasakinisshincho Bldg
Kawasaki-Ku, Kawasaki, Kanagawa, 210-0024, Japan
Tel.: (81) 442106600
Computer Network Designing Services
S.I.C.: 7373
N.A.I.C.S.: 541512

Fujitsu Peripherals Limited (1)
64 Okubochonishiwaki
Akashi, 674-0054, Japan
Tel.: (81) 789348237
Fax: (81) 789345636
Emp.: 20
Computer Peripheral Equipment Mfr
S.I.C.: 3575
N.A.I.C.S.: 334118
Toshio Okano *(CEO)*

Fujitsu Semiconductor Limited (1)
Nomura Shin-Yokohama Bldg 2-10-23 Shin-Yokohama
Kohoku-Ku, Yokohama, Kanagawa, Japan
Tel.: (81) 45 755 7000
Web Site: jp.fujitsu.com
Emp.: 4,369
Semiconductor Mfr & Distr
S.I.C.: 3674
N.A.I.C.S.: 334413
Haruki Okada *(Pres)*
Haruyoshi Yagi *(Sr Exec VP)*

Fujitsu System Solutions Limited (1)
Bunkyo Green Court Center Office 2-28-8 Honkomagome
Bunkyo-ku, Tokyo, 113-0021, Japan
Tel.: (81) 3 5977 7852
Fax: (81) 35 977 5313
Information Technology Development Services
S.I.C.: 7371
N.A.I.C.S.: 541511

Fujitsu Telecom Networks Limited (1)
1-17-3 Sakado
Takatsuku, Kawasaki, 213-8586, Japan
Tel.: (81) 4 4822 2121
Fax: (81) 4 4844 9532
Web Site: jp.fujitsu.com
Telecommunication Equipment Mfr
S.I.C.: 3669
N.A.I.C.S.: 334290

Fujitsu TEN Limited (1)
2-28 Gosho-dori 1-chome
Hyogo-ku, Kobe, 652-8510, Japan
Tel.: (81) 786715081
Fax: (81) 786715325
Web Site: www.fujitsu-ten.com
Sls.: $3,245,773,000
Emp.: 3,836
Automotive Electronics & Audio Visual Equipment Mfr & Distr
S.I.C.: 3714
N.A.I.C.S.: 336320
Keijiro Katsumaru *(Co-Chm)*
Takashi Shigematsu *(Co-Chm)*
Shouji Kawamura *(Sr Mng Officer)*
Yasuyuki Kawanishi *(Sr Mng Officer)*
Michitaka Ogura *(Exec VP & Auditor)*

Subsidiaries:

FUJITSU TEN ACTY LIMITED (2)
1-2-28 Goshodori
Hyogo-Ku, Kobe, 652-0885, Japan
Tel.: (81) 786822009
Software Development Services
S.I.C.: 7371
N.A.I.C.S.: 541511

FUJITSU TEN EAST JAPAN SALES LIMITED (2)
14-24 Nishi-shinjyuku 8-chome
Shinjyuku-ku, Tokyo, 160-0023, Japan

Fujitsu Limited—(Continued)

Tel.: (81) 3 5330 6244
Fax: (81) 3 5330 6245
Audio Product Distr
S.I.C.: 5065
N.A.I.C.S.: 423690

FUJITSU TEN RESEARCH LTD. (2)
2-28 Gosho-dori 1-chome
Hyogo-ku, Kobe, Hyogo, 652-8510, Japan
Tel.: (81) 78 671 5081
Fax: (81) 78 682 2202
Web Site: www.fujitsu-ten.com
Technical Information Services
S.I.C.: 7389
N.A.I.C.S.: 519190

FUJITSU TEN SALES LTD. (2)
2-28 Gosho-dori 1-chome
Hyogo-ku, Kobe, Hyogo, 652-8510, Japan
Tel.: (81) 78 682 8390
Fax: (81) 78 671 6268
Web Site: www.fujitsu-ten.co.jp
Electronic Equipment Distr
S.I.C.: 5065
N.A.I.C.S.: 423690
Yasuki Kawanishi *(Pres)*

FUJITSU TEN SERVICE LTD. (2)
2-28 Gosho-dori 1-chome
Hyogo-ku, Kobe, Hyogo, 652-8510, Japan
Tel.: (81) 786822266
Fax: (81) 786822283
Web Site: www.fujitsu-ten.com
Automotive Electronics Repair & Maintenance Services
S.I.C.: 7549
N.A.I.C.S.: 811198

FUJITSU TEN STAFF LTD. (2)
2-28 Gosho-dori 1-chome
Hyogo-ku, Kobe, Hyogo, 652-8510, Japan
Tel.: (81) 78 682 2257
Fax: (81) 78 682 2259
Emp.: 30
Human Resources Consulting Services
S.I.C.: 8999
N.A.I.C.S.: 541612

FUJITSU TEN TECHNOLOGY LTD. (2)
2-28 Gosho-dori 1-chome
Hyogo-ku, Kobe, Hyogo, 652-8510, Japan
Tel.: (81) 78 682 0420
Fax: (81) 78 682 0425
Web Site: www.fujitsu-ten.co.jp/technology
Automotive Electronic Parts Mfr & Distr
S.I.C.: 3714
N.A.I.C.S.: 336320

FUJITSU TEN TECHNOSEPTA. CO., LTD. (2)
6-4 Murotani 1-chome
Nishi-ku, Kobe, Hyogo, 651-2241, Japan
Tel.: (81) 78 996 0200
Fax: (81) 78 996 0204
Web Site: www.fujitsu-ten.com
Automotive Resin Parts Mfr
S.I.C.: 2821
N.A.I.C.S.: 325211

FUJITSU TEN WEST JAPAN SALES LIMITED (2)
7-35 Tsutootsukacho
Nishinomiya, Hyogo, 663-8241, Japan
Tel.: (81) 798367481
Automobile Parts Distr
S.I.C.: 5013
N.A.I.C.S.: 423120

Plant:

Fujitsu TEN Limited - Nakatsugawa Plant (2)
2110 Naegi
Nakatsugawa, Gifu, 508-0101, Japan
Tel.: (81) 573 66 5121
Fax: (81) 573 66 5126
Web Site: www.fujitsu-ten.com
Automotive Electronic Parts Mfr
S.I.C.: 3714
N.A.I.C.S.: 336320

Non-U.S. Subsidiaries:

FUJITSU TEN (AUSTRALIA) PTY. LTD. (2)
89 Cook Street
Port Melbourne, VIC, 3207, Australia
Tel.: (61) 396466004
Fax: (61) 396468070
Web Site: www.fujitsu-ten.com
Emp.: 34
Mobile Communication Products Sales & Repair Services
S.I.C.: 5065
N.A.I.C.S.: 423690
Albert Guirguis *(Gen Mgr)*

FUJITSU TEN (CHINA) LTD. (2)
No 280 Huang Hai Road TEDA
Tianjin, China 300457
Tel.: (86) 2228408388
Fax: (86) 2228408399
Emp.: 3
Business Management Services
S.I.C.: 7389
N.A.I.C.S.: 561499
Yagishi Noriaki *(CEO)*

FUJITSU TEN CORPORATION OF THE PHILIPPINES (2)
100 South Science Avenue Laguna Technopark
4026 Santa Rosa, Laguna, Philippines
Tel.: (63) 2 793 2900
Fax: (63) 49 541 0040
Automotive Electronics & Audio Visual Products Mfr & Distr
S.I.C.: 3714
N.A.I.C.S.: 336320

FUJITSU TEN de MEXICO, S.A. de C.V. (2)
Avenida Industrial Del Norte Manzana 8 Lote 2 Parque
Industrial Del Norte, Reynosa, Tamaulipas, Mexico
Tel.: (52) 8999218700
Fax: (52) 8999292260
Audio Visual Products & Automotive Electronics Mfr & Distr
S.I.C.: 3651
N.A.I.C.S.: 334310

FUJITSU TEN DO BRASIL LTDA. (2)
Avenida Paulista 37 5 Andar Sala 2 Edificio Parque Cultural Paulista
01311 902 Bela Vista, Sao Paulo, Brazil
Tel.: (55) 11 3266 4427
Fax: (55) 11 3178 1502
Emp.: 2
Automotive Parts Sales & Repair Services
S.I.C.: 5013
N.A.I.C.S.: 423120

Fujitsu Ten Electronics (Wuxi) LTD. (2)
No 19 Xinhua Road Wuxi National Hi-Tech Industrial Development Zone
Wuxi, Jiangsu, China 214028
Tel.: (86) 510 8866 2288
Fax: (86) 510 8866 2233
Automotive Infotainment Mfr
S.I.C.: 3714
N.A.I.C.S.: 336320

Fujitsu Ten Espana, S.A. (2)
Pol Ind Guadalhorce C/Cesar Vallejo 16
Malaga, Spain 29004
Tel.: (34) 95 213 3000
Fax: (34) 95 213 3003
Automotive Electronic Product Mfr
S.I.C.: 3714
N.A.I.C.S.: 336320

FUJITSU TEN (EUROPE) GmbH (2)
Muendelheimer Weg 39
40472 Dusseldorf, Germany
Tel.: (49) 211 301875 550
Fax: (49) 211 301875 500
Consumer Electronics Distr
S.I.C.: 5064
N.A.I.C.S.: 423620

Fujitsu Ten Korea Limited (2)
Susong Tower Building 16th Floor 83-1 Susong-Dong
Jongno-gu, Seoul, Korea (South)
Tel.: (82) 237875377
Fax: (82) 237875387
Web Site: www.fujitsu-ten.com
Audio Visual Products Sales & Repair Services
S.I.C.: 5065
N.A.I.C.S.: 423690

FUJITSU TEN MINDA INDIA PVT. LTD. (2)
Vill Naharpur Kasan PO Nakhrola
Manesar, Gurgaon, Haryana, 122004, India
Tel.: (91) 1242291621
Fax: (91) 1242291622
Car Infotainment Equipment & Accessory Mfr
S.I.C.: 3714
N.A.I.C.S.: 336390

Fujitsu Ten Research & Development (Tianjin) LTD. (2)
No 280 Huang Hai Road TEDA
Tianjin, China 300457
Tel.: (86) 22 5981 5132
Fax: (86) 22 5981 5134
Web Site: www.fujitsu-ten.com
Software Development Services
S.I.C.: 7371
N.A.I.C.S.: 541511

Fujitsu Ten (Singapore) Pte. Ltd. (2)
20 Science Park Road 02-01/03 TeleTech Park Singapore Science Park II
Singapore, Singapore 117674
Tel.: (65) 6773 4933
Fax: (65) 6773 4932
Electronic Device Distr
S.I.C.: 5065
N.A.I.C.S.: 423690

FUJITSU TEN (THAILAND) COMPANY LIMITED (2)
88 Dr Gerhard Link Building 5F
Krungthepkreetha Rd Huamark
Bangkapi, Bangkok, 10240, Thailand
Tel.: (66) 27044979
Fax: (66) 27044980
Emp.: 60
Automotive Electronics & Audio Visual Products Mfr & Distr
S.I.C.: 3714
N.A.I.C.S.: 336320
Hiroyuki Fujiwara *(Mng Dir)*

Plant:

FUJITSU TEN (THAILAND) COMPANY LIMITED - Rayong Factory (3)
253 Moo 11 Rojana Industrial Park
Bankhai-Banbung Rd
T Nongbua A Bankhai, Rayong, 21120, Thailand
Tel.: (66) 38962025
Fax: (66) 38962031
Web Site: www.fujitsu-ten.com
Automotive Electronics & Audio Visual Products Mfr
S.I.C.: 3714
N.A.I.C.S.: 336320

Fujitsu Ten Trading (Tianjin) LTD. (2)
Tianxin Building 1805 No 125 Weidi Road
Hexi District, Tianjin, China 300074
Tel.: (86) 22 2840 8388
Fax: (86) 22 2840 8399
Web Site: www.fujitsu-ten.com
Emp.: 130
Automotive Electronic Parts Distr
S.I.C.: 5013
N.A.I.C.S.: 423120
Yagishi Noriaki *(Gen Mgr)*

TIANJIN FUJITSU TEN ELECTRONICS CO., LTD. (2)
No 5 Huanghai Second Avenue TEDA
Tianjin, China 300457
Tel.: (86) 22 5988 8666
Fax: (86) 22 2529 0778
Audio & Video Equipment Mfr
S.I.C.: 3651
N.A.I.C.S.: 334310

NIFTY Corporation (1)
Omori Bellport A 6 26 1 Minami Oi
Shinagawa-ku, Tokyo, 140 8544, Japan JP (100%)
Tel.: (81) 354715800
Fax: (81) 354715017
Web Site: www.nifty.com
Emp.: 495
Internet Hosting & Computer Communication Services
S.I.C.: 7378
N.A.I.C.S.: 811212

Shimane Fujitsu Limited (1)
1180-6 Mitsukane Hikawacho
Hikawa-Gun, Shimane, 699-0504, Japan
Tel.: (81) 853722333
Personal Computer Mfr
S.I.C.: 3571
N.A.I.C.S.: 334111

Shinko Electric Industries Co., Ltd. (1)
80 Oshimada-machi
Nagano, 381 2287, Japan JP
Tel.: (81) 262831000 (50%)
Telex: 2222724
Fax: (81) 262848861
E-Mail: webmaster@shinko.co.jp
Web Site: www.shinko.co.jp
6967—(TKS)
Sls.: $1,399,651,000
Assets: $1,880,626,000
Liabilities: $437,360,000
Net Worth: $1,443,266,000
Earnings: $31,614,000
Emp.: 4,980
Fiscal Year-end: 03/31/13
Mfr. & Sales of Leadframe, Plastics Laminated Package, Glass-to-Metal Seals, Arrester & Precision Contact Parts; IC Assembly; Software Sales & Development
S.I.C.: 3089
N.A.I.C.S.: 326199
Mamoru Kuroiwa *(Chm)*
Akira Fujimoto *(Vice Chm)*
Fumio Kuraishi *(Pres)*
Yoshihiro Asano *(Mng Corp Officer)*
Hiroshi Hasebe *(Sr Corp Officer)*
Toshiyasu Hirabayashi *(Corp Officer)*
Kazuharu Iguchi *(Sr Corp Officer)*
Kunihiko Imai *(Mng Corp Officer)*
Akihiko Ito *(Corp Officer)*
Takato Kikuchi *(Sr Corp Officer)*
Takahiro Kiyono *(Sr Corp Officer)*
Junichi Kobayashi *(Corp Officer)*
Tadashi Kodaira *(Corp Officer)*
Susumu Kurashima *(Corp Officer)*
Katsuo Minamisawa *(Corp Officer)*
Seizo Mitsui *(Sr Corp Officer)*
Masashi Obinata *(Corp Officer)*
Toshihiko Ogiwara *(Sr Corp Officer)*
Mitsuharu Shimizu *(Mng Corp Officer)*
Haruo Sorimachi *(Corp Officer)*
Hidenori Takayanagi *(Corp Officer)*
Toshihisa Yoda *(Sr Corp Officer)*

Subsidiaries:

SHINKO PARTS CO., LTD. (2)
1553 Ko Naniai
Nagano, 381-3165, Japan
Tel.: (81) 262292710
Glass Seal Mfr
S.I.C.: 3231
N.A.I.C.S.: 327215

SHINKO TECHNOSERVE CO., LTD. (2)
80 Oshimadamachi
Nagano, 381-2212, Japan
Tel.: (81) 262831000
Chemical Products Mfr
S.I.C.: 2899
N.A.I.C.S.: 325998

Plants:

Shinko Electric Industries Co., LTD. - Arai Plant (2)
921-3 Himegawara
Myoko, Niigata, 944-8588, Japan
Tel.: (81) 255724154
Fax: (81) 255726994
Electronic Component Mfr
S.I.C.: 3679
N.A.I.C.S.: 334419

Shinko Electric Industries Co., LTD. - Kyogase Plant (2)
1062-5 Kyogase Kogyodanchi
Agano, Niigata, 959-2136, Japan
Tel.: (81) 250615100
Fax: (81) 250672253
Electronic Component Mfr
S.I.C.: 3679
N.A.I.C.S.: 334419

Shinko Electric Industries Co., LTD. - Takaoka Plant (2)
1216-9 Kusama
Nakano, Nagano, 383-8581, Japan
Tel.: (81) 269227111
Fax: (81) 269223363
Electronic Component Mfr

S.I.C.: 3679
N.A.I.C.S.: 334419

Shinko Electric Industries Co., LTD. - Wakaho Plant (2)
1457-1 Wakaho Kawada
Nagano, 381-0103, Japan
Tel.: (81) 262824441
Fax: (81) 262826119
Web Site: www.shinko.co.jp/english/corporate/branch.html
Emp.: 600
Electronic Component Mfr
S.I.C.: 3679
N.A.I.C.S.: 334419
Takahiro Seki *(Plant Mgr)*

U.S. Subsidiary:

SHINKO ELECTRIC AMERICA, INC. (2)
2880 Zanker Rd Ste 204
San Jose, CA 95134
Tel.: (408) 232-0499
Fax: (408) 955-0368
Web Site: www.shinko.co.jp/english/corporate/oversea.html
Electronic Component Mfr
S.I.C.: 3679
N.A.I.C.S.: 334419
Greg Bettencourt *(Pres)*

Non-U.S. Subsidiaries:

KOREA SHINKO MICROELECTRONICS CO., LTD. (2)
32 Sandan-1gil Seomyeon
Suncheon, Jollanam-do, 540-813, Korea (South)
Tel.: (82) 617538801
Fax: (82) 617538804
E-Mail: ksm@koreashinko.co.kr
Web Site: www.koreashinko.co.kr
Emp.: 21
Metal Seal Mfr
S.I.C.: 3499
N.A.I.C.S.: 332999
Mochizuki Masato *(CEO)*

KOREA SHINKO TRADING CO., LTD. (2)
Hyundai Venture Building 1223 713 Suseo-Dong
Kangnam-Ku, Seoul, 135-884, Korea (South)
Tel.: (82) 2 538 2851
Fax: (82) 2 451 6714
Web Site: www.shinko.co.jp/english/corporate/oversea.html
Emp.: 5
Electronic Component Distr
S.I.C.: 5065
N.A.I.C.S.: 423690
Toshihiko Ogiwara *(Gen Mgr)*

SHANGHAI SHINKO TRADING LTD. (2)
Room 2309 Shanghai Ruijin Building 205 Maoming South Road
200020 Shanghai, China
Tel.: (86) 2164450898
Fax: (86) 2164451228
Emp.: 6
Semiconductor Package Sales
S.I.C.: 5065
N.A.I.C.S.: 423690

SHINKO ELECTRIC INDUSTRIES (WUXI) CO., LTD. (2)
No 105 Xixian Road Mei Cun Industrial Park
Wuxi, Jiangsu, 214112, China
Tel.: (86) 510 8534 3006
Fax: (86) 510 8534 3180
Electronic Component Mfr
S.I.C.: 3679
N.A.I.C.S.: 334419

SHINKO ELECTRONICS (MALAYSIA) SDN. BHD. (2)
Lot Pt 717A Jalan Serendah 26/17 Seksyen 26
40400 Shah Alam, Selangor Darul Ehsan, Malaysia
Tel.: (60) 351913897
Fax: (60) 351923896
Electronic Component Mfr
S.I.C.: 3679
N.A.I.C.S.: 334419

SHINKO ELECTRONICS (SINGAPORE) PTE. LTD. (2)
133 New Bridge Road 23-01/02 Chinatown Point
Singapore, 059413, Singapore
Tel.: (65) 6225 3411
Fax: (65) 6225 8984
Emp.: 9
Computer Peripheral Equipment Mfr
S.I.C.: 3577
N.A.I.C.S.: 334118
Toshihiko Ogiwara *(Mng Dir)*

TAIWAN SHINKO ELECTRONICS CO., LTD. (2)
4th Floor Area C1 Hung Kuo Building 167 Tun Hua North Road
Taipei, 10512, Taiwan
Tel.: (886) 227195655
Fax: (886) 227195650
Electronic Component Mfr
S.I.C.: 3679
N.A.I.C.S.: 334419

Affiliate:

PFU Limited (1)
No 98 2 Unoke Kahoku
Kanazawa, Ishikawa, 929 1192, Japan (60%)
Tel.: (81) 762831212
Fax: (81) 762834689
E-Mail: t.kawaura@pfu.fujitsu.com
Web Site: www.pfu.co.jp
Emp.: 650
Mfr. & Sales of Small Computer Systems & Workstations
S.I.C.: 3577
N.A.I.C.S.: 334118
Fujio Wajima *(Chm)*
Kiyoshi Hasegawa *(Pres)*

Subsidiaries:

PFU Applications Limited (2)
658-1 Tsuruma Kk Pfu Tokyo Kaihatsu Center Nai
Machida, Tokyo, 194-0004, Japan
Tel.: (81) 427887660
Fax: (81) 427887661
Web Site: www.pfu.fujitsu.com
Application Software Development Services
S.I.C.: 7371
N.A.I.C.S.: 541511

PFU Creative Services Limited (2)
98-2 Nu Unoke
Kahoku, Ishikawa, 929-1125, Japan
Tel.: (81) 762838625
Human Resource Consulting Services
S.I.C.: 8999
N.A.I.C.S.: 541612

PFU East Japan Limited (2)
4-4-13 Tsutsujigaoka Densan 88 Bldg
Miyagino-Ku, Sendai, Miyagi, 983-0852, Japan
Tel.: (81) 222932711
Web Site: www.pfu.co.jp
Software Development Services
S.I.C.: 7371
N.A.I.C.S.: 541511

PFU Hokkaido Limited (2)
29-26 Kita11jo-Higashi6
Higashi-ku, Sapporo, Hokkaido, Japan
Tel.: (81) 11 711 6911
Fax: (81) 11 704 0446
Computer Hardware Distr
S.I.C.: 5045
N.A.I.C.S.: 423430

PFU Human Design Limited (2)
658-1 Tsuruma
Machida, Tokyo, 194-0004, Japan
Tel.: (81) 427887658
Fax: (81) 427887656
Web Site: www.pfu.fujitsu.com
Human Resource Consulting Services
S.I.C.: 8999
N.A.I.C.S.: 541612

PFU Life Agency Limited (2)
98-2 Nu Unoke
Kahoku, Ishikawa, 929-1125, Japan
Tel.: (81) 762836111
Business Support Services
S.I.C.: 8741
N.A.I.C.S.: 561110

PFU Quality Service Limited (2)
602-9 Funako Sun Intel Net Bldg 2f
Atsugi, Kanagawa, 243-0034, Japan
Tel.: (81) 462266400
Fax: (81) 462266460
Software Development Services
S.I.C.: 7371
N.A.I.C.S.: 541511

PFU Software Limited (2)
98-2 Nu Unoke
Kahoku, Ishikawa, 929-1125, Japan
Tel.: (81) 762835800
Software Development Services
S.I.C.: 7371
N.A.I.C.S.: 541511

PFU Techno Wise Limited (2)
1 Shi Takamatsu Prodes Center Nai Prodes Kojo
Kahoku, Ishikawa, 929-1215, Japan
Tel.: (81) 762813380
Computer Peripheral Equipment Mfr
S.I.C.: 3577
N.A.I.C.S.: 334118

PFU Technoconsul Limited (2)
98-2 Nu Unoke
Kahoku, Ishikawa, 929-1125, Japan
Tel.: (81) 762838600
Software Consulting Services
S.I.C.: 7373
N.A.I.C.S.: 541512

PFU TOHTO Limited (2)
1-5-7 Kameido Nittetsu ND Tower 2f
Koto-Ku, Tokyo, 136-0071, Japan
Tel.: (81) 356278411
Software Development Services
S.I.C.: 7371
N.A.I.C.S.: 541511

U.S. Subsidiary:

PFU Systems, Inc. (2)
1250 E Arques Ave
Sunnyvale, CA 94085
Tel.: (408) 992-2900
Fax: (408) 992-2999
E-Mail: Sales@pfusystems.com
Web Site: www.pfusystems.com
Computer Peripheral Equipment Mfr
S.I.C.: 3575
N.A.I.C.S.: 334118
Kyou Katoh *(Pres & CEO)*
Dale Pierce *(CFO & COO)*
Yasuhiko Nagaoka *(Sr VP-Res & Engrg)*

Non-U.S. Subsidiaries:

PFU Imaging Solutions Europe Limited (2)
Hayes Park Central Hayes End Road
Hayes, Middlesex, UB4 8FE, United Kingdom
Tel.: (44) 208 573 4444
Fax: (44) 208 573 2643
Web Site: www.fujitsu.com
Computer Scanner Distr
S.I.C.: 5045
N.A.I.C.S.: 423430
Etsuro Sato *(Co-Pres)*
Satoshi Yamada *(Co-Pres)*

PFU Shanghai Co., Ltd. (2)
5F Bldg 46 No 555 Guiping Road
Shanghai, 200233, China
Tel.: (86) 2164850118
Fax: (86) 2164850121
E-Mail: sales@psh.com.cn
Web Site: www.psh.com.cn
Sls.: $16,611,943
Emp.: 27
Software Development Services
S.I.C.: 7371
N.A.I.C.S.: 541511
Amai Yutaka *(Chm)*
Yunfeng Tu *(Pres)*

Subsidiaries:

Nantong PFU Information Systems Co., Ltd. (3)
2F Bldg No 488 Gongnong Road
Nantong, Jiangsu, 226007, China
Tel.: (86) 513 85281278
Fax: (86) 513 85280625
Web Site: www.psh.com.cn/en/En_profile.htm#profile
Software Development Services
S.I.C.: 7371
N.A.I.C.S.: 541511

PFU Shanghai Information Systems Co., Ltd. (3)
5F Bldg 46 No 555 Guiping Road
Shanghai, 200233, China
Tel.: (86) 21 64850118
Fax: (86) 21 64953773
Web Site: www.psh.com.cn/en/En_profile.htm
Emp.: 250
Software Development Services
S.I.C.: 7371
N.A.I.C.S.: 541511
Yunfeng Tu *(Pres)*

PFU TECHNOLOGY SINGAPORE PTE LTD (2)
No 8 Kim Chuan Drive 03-02 SIIX Building
Singapore, 537083, Singapore
Tel.: (65) 6285 0330
Fax: (65) 6286 6070
E-Mail: pfutech@singnet.com.sg
Web Site: www.pfu.fujitsu.com
Emp.: 9
Computer Peripheral Equipment Mfr
S.I.C.: 3577
N.A.I.C.S.: 334118
Kenichi Miyamoto *(Chm)*
Hitoshi Terashima *(Mng Dir)*

Plants:

Fujitsu Limited - Aizu Wakamatsu Plant (1)
3 Kogyo Danchi Monden-machi
Aizuwakamatsu, Fukushima, Japan 965-8502
Tel.: (81) 242286111
Web Site: www.fujitsu.com
Electronic Component Mfr
S.I.C.: 3679
N.A.I.C.S.: 334419

Fujitsu Limited - Kumagaya Plant (1)
1224 Nakanara
Kumagaya, Saitama, Japan 360-0801
Tel.: (81) 485231121
Web Site: www.fujitsu.com
Information Technology Consulting Services
S.I.C.: 7373
N.A.I.C.S.: 541512

Fujitsu Limited - Mie Plant (1)
1500 Mizono Tado-cho
Kuwana, Mie, 511-0192, Japan
Tel.: (81) 594485511
Electronic Component Mfr
S.I.C.: 3679
N.A.I.C.S.: 334419

Fujitsu Limited - Nasu Plant (1)
1388 Simoishigami
Otawara, Tochigi, 324-8555, Japan
Tel.: (81) 287292111
Communication Equipment Mfr
S.I.C.: 3663
N.A.I.C.S.: 334220

Fujitsu Limited - Numazu Plant (1)
140 Miyamoto
Numazu, Shizuoka, Japan 410-0396
Tel.: (81) 559232222
Web Site: www.fujitsu.com
Electronic Component Mfr
S.I.C.: 3679
N.A.I.C.S.: 334419

Fujitsu Limited - Oyama Plant (1)
3-28-1 Joutou
Oyama, Tochigi, Japan 323-8511
Tel.: (81) 285242222
Web Site: www.fujitsu.com
Electronic Component Mfr
S.I.C.: 3679
N.A.I.C.S.: 334419

Fujitsu Limited - Suzaka Plant (1)
460 Oaza-Koyama
Suzaka, Nagano, 382-8501, Japan
Tel.: (81) 262512700
Communication Equipment Mfr
S.I.C.: 3663
N.A.I.C.S.: 334220

U.S. Subsidiaries:

Fujitsu America, Inc. (1)
1250 E Arques Ave
Sunnyvale, CA 94085-3470

Fujitsu Limited—(Continued)

Tel.: (800) 831-3183
Fax: (408) 992-2466
Web Site: www.fujitsu.com
Computers & Data Processing Systems, Telecommunications Systems & Electronic Components Mfr
S.I.C.: 3571
N.A.I.C.S.: 334111
Robert D. Pryor *(Pres/CEO-North America)*

Divisions:

Fujitsu America, Inc. (2)
10 Ray Ave
Burlington, MA 01803-4721
Tel.: (781) 272-5500
Fax: (781) 272-5100
Emp.: 110
Business Technology Consulting Services
S.I.C.: 8999
N.A.I.C.S.: 541690

Fujitsu America, Inc. (2)
343 Thornall St
Edison, NJ 08837-2220 (100%)
Tel.: (732) 549-4100
Fax: (732) 549-2375
Toll Free: (800) 882-3212
Web Site: www.fujitsu.com
Emp.: 3,300
Technology Management & Process Outsourcing Consulting Services
S.I.C.: 8742
N.A.I.C.S.: 541611
Ari Hovsepyan *(CFO)*

Fujitsu Consulting (2)
8101 E Prentice Ave Ste 500
Greenwood Village, CO 80111
Tel.: (303) 846-8000
Fax: (303) 846-8450
Toll Free: (800) 963-2676
Web Site: www.us.fujitsu.com
Emp.: 100
Business Technology Consulting Services
S.I.C.: 8999
N.A.I.C.S.: 541690

Fujitsu Consulting (2)
1450 E American Ln Ste 1700
Schaumburg, IL 60173-6087 IL
Tel.: (847) 706-4000
Fax: (847) 706-4020
Toll Free: (800) 453-0347
Web Site: www.fujitsu.com
Emp.: 200
Technology Consulting, Computer Training & Readiness Assessment Services
Import Export
S.I.C.: 7373
N.A.I.C.S.: 541512
Howard Blietz *(CFO)*

Fujitsu Consulting (2)
301 Carlson Pkwy
Minnetonka, MN 55305-5302 MN
Tel.: (952) 258-6000
Fax: (952) 258-6001
Web Site: www.us.fujitsu.com
Emp.: 4
Information Technology Services & Solutions
Import Export
S.I.C.: 7371
N.A.I.C.S.: 541511

Fujitsu Consulting (2)
24 Summit Park Dr Ste 100
Pittsburgh, PA 15275
Tel.: (412) 494-9800
Fax: (412) 494-3839
Web Site: www.rapidigm.com
Emp.: 70
Business Technology Consulting Services
S.I.C.: 8999
N.A.I.C.S.: 541690

Fujitsu Consulting (2)
11270 W Park Pl Ste 1000
Milwaukee, WI 53224-3643
Tel.: (414) 973-7000
Fax: (414) 973-7010
Web Site: www.fujitsu.com
Emp.: 145
Technology Consulting Services
S.I.C.: 7373
N.A.I.C.S.: 541512
Mark Blazich *(Mng Dir & VP)*

Subsidiaries:

Fujitsu Business Communication Systems, Inc.-Sales & Marketing (2)
7776 S Pointe Pkwy W Ste 145
Phoenix, AZ 85044-5424
Tel.: (480) 921-5800
Fax: (480) 921-4800
S.I.C.: 3571
N.A.I.C.S.: 334111

Fujitsu Computer Products of America, Inc. (2)
1250 E Arques Ave
Sunnyvale, CA 94085-5401 (100%)
Tel.: (408) 746-7000
Fax: (408) 746-6910
Toll Free: (800) 626-4686
E-Mail: info@fcpa.fujitsu.com
Web Site: www.fcpa.fujitsu.com
Emp.: 350
Scanners, Magneto-Optical Drives, Ethernet Switches, Biometric Devices, Degaussers Mfr
S.I.C.: 5045
N.A.I.C.S.: 423430
Victor Kan *(COO & Exec VP)*
Lorne Wilson *(Sr VP)*

Division:

Fujitsu Computer Products of America - Research & Development (3)
7245 Northwest Evergreen Pkwy
Hillsboro, OR 97124
Tel.: (503) 681-7300
Fax: (503) 693-2020
Web Site: www.fcpa.com
Emp.: 36
Research & Development
S.I.C.: 5045
N.A.I.C.S.: 423430

Fujitsu General America, Inc. (2)
353 Route 46 W
Fairfield, NJ 07004 (100%)
Tel.: (973) 575-0380
Fax: (973) 575-2194
Toll Free: (866) 952-8324
Web Site: www.fujitsugeneral.com
Emp.: 50
Air Conditioning Unit Mfr
S.I.C.: 3585
N.A.I.C.S.: 333415
Erin Mezle *(Dir-Mktg)*

Fujitsu Limited (2)
733 3rd Ave
New York, NY 10017-3204 CA
Tel.: (212) 599-9800
Fax: (212) 599-4129
E-Mail: info@fujitsu.com
Web Site: www.fujitsu.com
Emp.: 3
Investor Relations Services
S.I.C.: 7373
N.A.I.C.S.: 541512
Scott Ikeda *(Gen Mgr)*

Fujitsu Microelectronics America, Inc. (2)
1250 E Arques Ave M/S 333
Sunnyvale, CA 94085 (100%)
Tel.: (408) 737-5600
Telex: 910-338-0190
Fax: (408) 737-5999
Web Site: www.fma.fujitsu.com
Emp.: 200
Mfg., Importing & Marketing of Integrated Circuits; Marketing of Personal Computers
S.I.C.: 3679
N.A.I.C.S.: 334419
Shinichi Machida *(Pres & CEO)*

Division:

Fujitsu Microelectronics-Mfg. (3)
1250 E Arques Ave
Sunnyvale, CA 94085-5401
Tel.: (408) 737-5600
Fax: (408) 737-5999
Web Site: www.fujitsu.com
Microelectronics Mfr
S.I.C.: 3571
N.A.I.C.S.: 334111

Subsidiary:

Fujitsu Laboratories of America (3)
1240 E Arques Ave Mail Stop 345
Sunnyvale, CA 94085 CA
Tel.: (408) 530-4500 (100%)
Fax: (408) 746-7630
E-Mail: info@fujitsulabs.com
Web Site: www.fla.fujitsu.com
Emp.: 90
Research & Development
S.I.C.: 8731
N.A.I.C.S.: 541712

Fujitsu Network Communications Inc. (2)
2801 Telecom Pkwy
Richardson, TX 75082-3515
Tel.: (972) 690-6000
Fax: (972) 497-6990
E-Mail: webmaster@fujitsu.com
Web Site: www.fujitsu.com
Emp.: 200
Mfr. & Designer of Broadband Transmission & Switching Products & Technologies
S.I.C.: 3661
N.A.I.C.S.: 334210
Doug Moore *(Sr VP-Sls, Mktg & Svcs)*
Hans Roehrig *(Sr VP-Ops & Mfg)*

Plant:

Fujitsu Network Communications - Richardson Plant (3)
2801 Telecom Pkwy
Richardson, TX 75082
Tel.: (972) 690-6000
Fax: (972) 497-6900
Optical Transmission System Mfr
S.I.C.: 3568
N.A.I.C.S.: 333613

Fujitsu PC Corporation (2)
1250 E Arques Ave
Sunnyvale, CA 94085-5401 (100%)
Tel.: (408) 746-6000
Fax: (408) 992-2674
Web Site: www.fujitsupc.com
Emp.: 150
Mfr. & Designer of Mobile Computers
S.I.C.: 3571
N.A.I.C.S.: 334111

Fujitsu Ten Corp. of America (2)
19600 S Vermont Ave
Torrance, CA 90502
Tel.: (310) 327-2151
Fax: (310) 767-4375
Toll Free: (800) 233-2216
E-Mail: sales@lao.ten.fujitsu.com
Web Site: www.eclipse-web.com
Sales Range: $150-199.9 Million
Emp.: 120
Automotive Audio, Video, Navigation & Control Systems
Import Export
S.I.C.: 5064
N.A.I.C.S.: 423620
Mike Odle *(VP-Sls & Mktg)*

Subsidiaries:

Eclipse Mobile Electronics (3)
19600 S Vermont Ave
Torrance, CA 90502-1122
Tel.: (310) 327-2151
Fax: (310) 767-4355
Web Site: www.eclipse-web.com
Emp.: 150
Mfr. of Automobile Audio Systems
S.I.C.: 5064
N.A.I.C.S.: 423620
Mark Kamino *(Exec VP)*

Fujitsu Ten Corp. of America/Rushville (3)
19600 S Vermont Ave
Torrance, CA 90502-1122 (100%)
Tel.: (765) 938-5555
Fax: (765) 932-3257
Web Site: www.fujitsu.com
Emp.: 30
Mfr. of Automobile Electronics
S.I.C.: 5064
N.A.I.C.S.: 423620
Tetsuya Oda *(Gen Mgr)*

Non-U.S. Subsidiary:

Fujitsu Ten Canada, Inc. (3)
1149 Bellamy Rd N
Toronto, ON, M1H 1H7, Canada ON
Tel.: (416) 431-9332 (100%)
Fax: (416) 431-1745
Emp.: 7
Electronic Parts & Equipment
S.I.C.: 5065
N.A.I.C.S.: 423690
Tamara Keserovic *(Mgr-Product Mktg)*

Glovia International, Inc. (2)
2250 E Imperial Hwy
El Segundo, CA 90245-3457 DE
Tel.: (310) 563-7000
Fax: (310) 563-7300
Toll Free: (800) 223-3799
Web Site: www.glovia.com
Emp.: 100
Provider of Computer Programming Services
S.I.C.: 7371
N.A.I.C.S.: 541511
Steven Pearlman *(Product Mgr & Partner-Products)*

Fujitsu Computer Systems Corporation (1)
1250 E Arques Ave
Sunnyvale, CA 94085-3470 DE
Tel.: (408) 746-6000
Telex: 3716812
Fax: (408) 737-5999
Toll Free: (800) 831-3183
E-Mail: computers@us.fujitsu.com
Sales Range: $125-149.9 Million
Emp.: 1,100
Computer Sales & Service
Import Export
S.I.C.: 7379
N.A.I.C.S.: 541519
Bipin Badani *(CIO & Sr VP)*
William King *(Exec VP-US Bus)*
Ryosuke Mori *(Exec VP-Japanese Bus Dev, Fujitsu America)*
Dave Egan *(Sr VP-Storage)*
Don Klenner *(Sr VP-Field Engrg & Support)*
Richard McCormack *(Sr VP-Mktg)*
Gloria Veon *(Sr VP-HR)*
Kevin Wrenn *(Sr VP-PC Bus & Ops)*
Al Zmyslowski *(Sr VP-Engrg)*

Non-U.S. Subsidiaries:

Fujitsu Canada Limited (2)
155 University Ave Suite 1600
Simcoe Place
Toronto, ON, M5H 3B7, Canada (100%)
Tel.: (416) 363-8661
Fax: (416) 510-3353
Toll Free: (800) 387-1566
Web Site: www.fujitsu.ca
Emp.: 40
Sales & Service of Data Processing Systems
S.I.C.: 7376
N.A.I.C.S.: 541513

Subsidiaries:

Fujitsu DMR Consulting (3)
1000 Sherbrooke W ste 1400
Montreal, QC, H3A 3R2, Canada QC
Tel.: (514) 877-3300 (100%)
Fax: (514) 877-3351
Web Site: www.fujitsu.com
Emp.: 250
Software Services
S.I.C.: 7371
N.A.I.C.S.: 541511
Mario Chabot *(Mgr-Ops)*

Groupe Conseil DMR, Inc. (3)
1000 Sherbrooke St W Ste 1400
Montreal, QC, H3A 3R2, Canada QC
Tel.: (514) 877-3301 (100%)
Fax: (514) 877-3351
E-Mail: claueette_bernard@dmr.ca
Web Site: www.dmr.ca
Emp.: 300
Information Technology Consulting & Development Firm
S.I.C.: 7373
N.A.I.C.S.: 541512
Andre Pouliot *(Co-Pres & CEO)*
Mike Sinneck *(Co-Pres)*

Subsidiary:

Macroscope Informatique, Inc. (4)
111 Duke St Ofc 4500
Montreal, QC, H3C 2M1, Canada QC
Tel.: (514) 393-8822
Fax: (514) 393-8022
Web Site: www.dmr.ca
Emp.: 200

Information Technology Consulting & Development Services
S.I.C.: 8742
N.A.I.C.S.: 541611

Fujitsu Consulting **(2)**
1000 Sherbrooke St W Ste 1400
Montreal, QC, H3A 3R2, Canada (100%)
Tel.: (514) 877-3301
Fax: (514) 877-3351
E-Mail: fujitsu.canada.communications@ca.fujitsu.com
Web Site: www.fujitsu.com
Sales Range: $200-249.9 Million
Emp.: 200
Information Management & Technology
S.I.C.: 7373
N.A.I.C.S.: 541512
Andre Pouliot *(Pres & CEO)*

Non-U.S. Divisions:

Fujitsu Consulting S.A. **(3)**
River Plaza 29 Quai Aulagnier
92665 Asnieres, Cedex, France (100%)
Tel.: (33) 41979000
Fax: (33) 141973593
E-Mail: contact.france@ts.fujitsu.com
Emp.: 150
S.I.C.: 3571
N.A.I.C.S.: 334111
Pierfilippo Roggero *(Gen Mgr)*

Fujitsu Consulting **(3)**
Het Kwadrant 1
PO Box 1214
NL 3600 AS Maarssen, 2600 BE, Netherlands (100%)
Tel.: (31) 346598111
Fax: (31) 346561298
Web Site: www.fujitsu.com
Emp.: 750
Provider of Data Processing Services & Information Technology Consulting Services
S.I.C.: 7374
N.A.I.C.S.: 518210
Geo van der Wilk *(Mng Dir-Fujitsu Tech Solutions & Svcs)*

Non-U.S. Subsidiary:

Fujitsu Australia Pty. Ltd. **(3)**
Level 7 155 George St
Sydney, NSW, 2000, Australia (100%)
Tel.: (61) 92930000
Fax: (61) 292930555
Web Site: www.fujitsu.com
Emp.: 110
S.I.C.: 3571
N.A.I.C.S.: 334111
Stuart Stitt *(CFO-Australia & New Zealand)*

Fujitsu Services **(2)**
Lakeshore Drive Airside Retail Park
Swords, County Dublin, Ireland (100%)
Tel.: (353) 8136000
Fax: (353) 8136100
Web Site: www.ie.fujitsu.com
Emp.: 200
Sales of Computers
S.I.C.: 5731
N.A.I.C.S.: 443142
Regina Moran *(Gen Mgr)*

Fujitsu Services **(2)**
Graston House Graston Way
Basingstoke, Hampshire, RG22 6HY, United Kingdom (100%)
Tel.: (44) 1256865100
Fax: (44) 256865101
E-Mail: keith.ayling@uk.fujitsu.com
Web Site: www.uk.fujitsu.com
Emp.: 30
Mfr. of Computers, Computer Peripherals & Software
S.I.C.: 3571
N.A.I.C.S.: 334111

Fujitsu Technologies Solution International S.p.A. **(2)**
Via Delle Industrie n 11
Vimodrone, Milan, 20090, Italy (100%)
Tel.: (39) 022659321
Fax: (39) 0226593271
Web Site: www.it.ts.fujitsu.com
Emp.: 10
Sales & Service of Computers
S.I.C.: 5946
N.A.I.C.S.: 443142

Fujitsu Technology Solutions GmbH **(2)**
Mies-van-der-Rohe-Strasse 8
80807 Munich, Germany (100%)
Tel.: (49) 89620601210
Web Site: www.de.fujitsu.com
Emp.: 50
Sales & Service of Computers
S.I.C.: 5731
N.A.I.C.S.: 443142

Non-U.S. Subsidiaries:

Fujitsu Technology Solutions AB **(3)**
Sverige Besoksadress Farogatan 33 Kista Science Tower
164 51 Kista, Sweden
Tel.: (46) 8 793 70 00
Fax: (46) 8 793 78 10
E-Mail: info@se.fujitsu.com
Information Technology Consulting Services
S.I.C.: 7373
N.A.I.C.S.: 541512

Fujitsu Technology Solutions AG **(3)**
Althardstr 80
8105 Regensdorf, Switzerland
Tel.: (41) 582 588 000
Fax: (41) 582 588 001
E-Mail: helpdesk.ch@ts.fujitsu.com
Emp.: 15
Information Technology Consulting Services
S.I.C.: 7373
N.A.I.C.S.: 541512
Martin Nussbaumer *(Dir-Sls)*

Fujitsu Technology Solutions AS **(3)**
Ostensjoveien 32
0667 Oslo, Norway
Tel.: (47) 23 24 80 00
E-Mail: firmapost@ts.fujitsu.com
Web Site: www.fujitsu.com
Emp.: 60
Information Technology Consulting Services
S.I.C.: 7373
N.A.I.C.S.: 541512
Kim Johansen *(Acct Mgr)*

Fujitsu Technology Solutions Bilisim Ltd. Sti. **(3)**
Yakacik Cd No 111
Kartal, 34870 Istanbul, Turkey
Tel.: (90) 216 586 40 00
Web Site: www.fujitsu.com
Information Technology Consulting Services
S.I.C.: 7373
N.A.I.C.S.: 541512

Fujitsu Technology Solutions d.o.o. **(3)**
Pariske Komune 30
Novi Sad, 21000, Serbia
Tel.: (381) 21 445 256
Fax: (381) 21 445 257
Emp.: 2
Information Technology Consulting Services
S.I.C.: 7373
N.A.I.C.S.: 541512
Harald Haubner *(Mng Dir)*

Fujitsu Technology Solutions FZ LLC **(3)**
Dubai Silicon Oasis Opp Academic City
DSOA Head Quarter Building
PO Box 341045
Office 706 C-Wing, Dubai, United Arab Emirates
Tel.: (971) 4 5015704
Fax: (971) 4 5015700
Web Site: www.fujitsu.com
Information Technology Development Services
S.I.C.: 7371
N.A.I.C.S.: 541511

Fujitsu Technology Solutions GesmbH **(3)**
Guglgasse 15
1110 Vienna, Austria
Tel.: (43) 800232411
Fax: (43) 17164656900
E-Mail: cic@ts.fujitsu.com
Web Site: www.fujitsu.com
Information Technology Consulting Services
S.I.C.: 7373
N.A.I.C.S.: 541512

Fujitsu Technology Solutions GmbH **(3)**
Amir Temur Str 107B
Tashkent, Uzbekistan 700084
Tel.: (998) 71 140 41 07
Fax: (998) 71 140 41 07
Web Site: www.fujitsu.com
Information Technology Consulting Services
S.I.C.: 7373
N.A.I.C.S.: 541512

Fujitsu Technology Solutions (Holding) B.V. **(3)**
Het Kwadrant 1
Maarssen, Netherlands 3606 AZ
Tel.: (31) 34 659 8700
Fax: (31) 34 655 0152
Web Site: www.fujitsu.com
Investment Management Services
S.I.C.: 6282
N.A.I.C.S.: 523920
Kai Flore *(CEO)*
Sabine Schweiger *(CFO)*
Heribert Goeggerle *(Exec VP-Ops-Supply)*
Herbert Schonebeck *(Sr VP-Consumer & Devices)*

Non-U.S. Subsidiary:

Fujitsu India Pvt. Ltd. **(4)**
15th Floor Bldg No 9A Phase III DLF Cyber City
Gurgaon, Haryana, 122002, India
Tel.: (91) 124 470 5100
Fax: (91) 124 470 5198
E-Mail: fil.info@in.fujitsu.com
Web Site: www.fujitsu.com
Computer Peripheral Equipment Distr
S.I.C.: 5045
N.A.I.C.S.: 423430
Jayanthi Sethuraman *(Head-Mktg & Alliance)*

Subsidiary:

Fujitsu Consulting India Pvt Ltd. **(5)**
A-15 MIDC Technology Park Talawade
Pune, Maharashtra, 412114, India
Tel.: (91) 20 27690001
Fax: (91) 20 27692923
Web Site: www.fujitsu.com
Emp.: 1,500
Software Consulting Services
S.I.C.: 7373
N.A.I.C.S.: 541512
Rajeev Gupta *(Pres)*
Jaswinder Sohal *(CEO)*
Brian Murphy *(Sr VP-Intl Bus)*

Fujitsu Technology Solutions Ltd. **(3)**
Lakeshore Drive Airside Retail Park
Swords, Dublin, Ireland
Tel.: (353) 1 813 6000
Fax: (353) 1 813 6100
Software Development Services
S.I.C.: 7371
N.A.I.C.S.: 541511

Fujitsu Technology Solutions (Luxembourg) SA **(3)**
Parc d'Activites Capellen 89C rue Pafebruch
8308 Capellen, Luxembourg
Tel.: (352) 260991
Fax: (352) 26099895
Information Technology Consulting Services
S.I.C.: 7373
N.A.I.C.S.: 541512
Frederic Salzmann *(Acct Mgr-Channel)*

Fujitsu Technology Solutions NV **(3)**
Square Marie Curie 12
Brussels, Belgium 1070
Tel.: (32) 25366111
Fax: (32) 25366112
E-Mail: info.belgium@ts.fujitsu.com
Web Site: www.fujitsu.com
Emp.: 30
Information Technology Consulting Services
S.I.C.: 7373
N.A.I.C.S.: 541512

Fujitsu Technology Solutions OOO **(3)**
Zemlyanoy Val 9
Moscow, Russia 105064
Tel.: (7) 495 730 62 20
Fax: (7) 495 730 62 13
Web Site: ru.fujitsu.com
Computer Hardware Mfr & Distr
S.I.C.: 3575
N.A.I.C.S.: 334118

Fujitsu Technology Solutions (PTY) Ltd. **(3)**
Technology Village 43 Homestead Road
Rivonia, 2128, South Africa
Tel.: (27) 11 233 5911
Fax: (27) 11 233 5326
E-Mail: askfujitsuza@ts.fujitsu.com
Information Technology Consulting Services
S.I.C.: 7373
N.A.I.C.S.: 541512
Quentin Schots *(Mng Dir)*
M. Mudaliyar-Sheopershad *(Sec)*

Fujitsu Technology Solutions S.A **(3)**
Lot N 2 Lotissement Mandarouna 300 Sidi Maarouf
Immeuble Business Center, 20000
Casablanca, Morocco
Tel.: (212) 522 58 17 17
Fax: (212) 522 58 09 16
Web Site: www.fujitsu.com
Emp.: 12
Information Technology Consulting Services
S.I.C.: 7373
N.A.I.C.S.: 541512
Kabbaj Hassan *(Mng Dir)*

Fujitsu Technology Solutions S.a.r.l. **(3)**
11 Chemin Doudou Mokhtar
Ben Aknoun, 16341 Algiers, Algeria
Tel.: (213) 21 91 58 25
Fax: (213) 21 91 34 77
Web Site: www.fujitsu.com
Information Technology Consulting Services
S.I.C.: 7373
N.A.I.C.S.: 541512
Kamal Bouamrene *(Gen Mgr)*

Fujitsu Technology Solutions SL **(3)**
Avenida Camino Cerro de los Gamos 1
Bucolo De Alarcon, Madrid, Spain 28224
Tel.: (34) 91 784 90 00
Fax: (34) 91 784 90 10
E-Mail: info.spain@ts.fujitsu.com
Web Site: www.fujitsu.com
Information Technology Consulting Services
S.I.C.: 7373
N.A.I.C.S.: 541512

Fujitsu Technology Solutions Sp. z o.o. **(3)**
ul Mszczonowska 4
02-337 Warsaw, Poland
Tel.: (48) 22 574 10 00
Fax: (48) 22 574 10 09
Web Site: pl.fujitsu.com
Computer Hardware Mfr & Distr
S.I.C.: 3577
N.A.I.C.S.: 334118

Fujitsu Technology Solutions s.r.o **(3)**
V Parku 2336/22 The Park
148 00 Prague, Czech Republic
Tel.: (420) 233 034 007
Fax: (420) 233 034 099
E-Mail: info.cz@ts.fujitsu.com
Web Site: www.fujitsu.com
Emp.: 120
Information Technology Consulting Services
S.I.C.: 7373
N.A.I.C.S.: 541512
Jiri Rehak *(Dir-Fin)*

Fujitsu Technology Solutions International AG **(2)**
Althardstrasse 80
CH 8105 Regensdorf, Switzerland (100%)
Tel.: (41) 433886500
Fax: (41) 41582588001
E-Mail: info@fujitsu-siemens.com
Web Site: www.ts.fujitsu.com
Emp.: 180
Sales & Service of Computers
S.I.C.: 5946
N.A.I.C.S.: 443142

Fujitsu Technology Solutions International N.V. **(2)**
Mommaertslaan 16A
BE 1831 Diegem, Belgium (100%)
Tel.: (32) 2 71227711
Fax: (32) 2 7127751
Web Site: www.fujitsu.com
Emp.: 20
Sales & Service of Computers
S.I.C.: 5731
N.A.I.C.S.: 443142

Fujitsu Technology Solutions International SA **(2)**
River Plaza 29 Quai Aulagnier
92665 Asnieres, Cedex, France (100%)

Fujitsu Limited—(Continued)

Tel.: (33) 141979000
Fax: (33) 141979299, ext. 141973591
E-Mail: contact.france@ts.fujitsu.com
Web Site: www.fujitsu.com
Emp.: 180
Sales & Service of Computers
S.I.C.: 5731
N.A.I.C.S.: 443142

Fujitsu Technology Solutions (2)
Av Marques De Tomar No 35 4 Esq
1050 153 Lisbon, Portugal (100%)
Tel.: (351) 217994030
Fax: (351) 217994031
Web Site: www.pt.amdahl.com
S.I.C.: 3571
N.A.I.C.S.: 334111

Fujitsu Management Services of America, Inc. (1)
1250 E Arques Ave
Sunnyvale, CA 94085-5401
Tel.: (408) 746-6200
Fax: (408) 746-6260
Web Site: www.fujitsu.com
Administrative & Financial Management Consulting Services
S.I.C.: 8742
N.A.I.C.S.: 541611
Hiroshi Haruki *(Pres & CEO)*

Fujitsu Semiconductor America, Inc (1)
1250 E Arques Ave M/S 333
Sunnyvale, CA 94085-5401
Tel.: (408) 737-5600
Fax: (408) 737-5999
Toll Free: (800) 866-8608
E-Mail: FSA_inquiry@us.fujitsu.com
Web Site: www.fujitsu.com
Semiconductor Device Mfr & Distr
S.I.C.: 3674
N.A.I.C.S.: 334413
Hiroyuki Hojo *(Pres)*

Fujitsu Software Corporation (1)
1250 E Arques Ave M/S 119
Sunnyvale, CA 94085
Tel.: (408) 746-6182
Fax: (408) 746-6344
Software Development Services
S.I.C.: 7371
N.A.I.C.S.: 541511
K. Randy *(Partner)*

Non-U.S. Subsidiaries:

Beijing Fujitsu System Engineering Co., Ltd. (1)
13F Tower A Ocean International Center No 56 Dong Si Huan Zhong Rd
Chaoyang District, Beijing, China
Tel.: (86) 10 5969 1000
Fax: (86) 10 5969 1288
E-Mail: info@fujitsu.com
Software Development Services
S.I.C.: 7371
N.A.I.C.S.: 541511

Fujitsu A/S (1)
Lautrupbjerg 9
2750 Ballerup, Denmark
Tel.: (45) 44894489
Fax: (45) 44894300
E-Mail: info@dk.fujitsu.com
Web Site: www.fujitsu.com
Emp.: 350
Business Process Outsourcing Services
S.I.C.: 7389
N.A.I.C.S.: 561499
Anton Therkildsen *(Mgr-Sls)*

Fujitsu Asia Pte. Ltd. (1)
20 Science Park Road 03-37 TeleTech Park
Singapore Science Park II
Singapore, 117674, Singapore
Tel.: (65) 6512 7555
Fax: (65) 6512 7502
Emp.: 40
Information Technology Consulting Services
S.I.C.: 7373
N.A.I.C.S.: 541512
Gavin Selkirk *(Pres & CEO)*

Fujitsu Australia Ltd. (1)
Level 16 Blue St
Sydney, NSW, 2060, Australia (100%)
Tel.: (61) 291139200
Telex: 71-25223
Fax: (61) 291139222
E-Mail: info@au.fujitsu.com
Web Site: www.au.fujitsu.com
Emp.: 1,000
Mfr & Sales of Telecommunications Equipment; Sales & Maintenance of Computers
S.I.C.: 7359
N.A.I.C.S.: 532490
Mike Foster *(Acting CEO)*
Rod Vawdrey *(CEO)*

Fujitsu Canada, Inc. (1)
6975 Credit View Rd Unit 1
Mississauga, ON, L5N 8E9, Canada(100%)
Tel.: (905) 286-9666
Fax: (905) 286-5997
Toll Free: (800) 263-8716
E-Mail: fci.customerservice@ca.fujitsu.com
Web Site: www.fujitsu.ca
Emp.: 60
Distributor of Computers & Computer Related Products
S.I.C.: 3571
N.A.I.C.S.: 334111
Irving Frieman *(Mgr-Mktg)*

U.S. Subsidiaries:

Fujitsu Components America, Inc. (2)
250 E Caribbean Dr
Sunnyvale, CA 94089
Tel.: (408) 745-4900
Fax: (408) 745-4970
E-Mail: components@us.fujitsu.com
Web Site: www.us.fujitsu.com
Emp.: 40
Electronic Component Distr
S.I.C.: 5065
N.A.I.C.S.: 423690
Yas Hara *(Chm)*
Don Dealtry *(Pres)*
Bob Thornton *(Sr VP)*

Fujitsu Interconnect Technologies Limited (2)
250 E Caribbean Dr
Sunnyvale, CA 94089
Tel.: (408) 745-4966
Fax: (408) 745-4971
Printed Circuit Board Mfr
S.I.C.: 3672
N.A.I.C.S.: 334412
Keiji Kurosawa *(Pres)*

Fujitsu Caribbean (Barbados) Limited (1)
Chelston Park Building 1 Collymore Rock
Saint Michael, BB14018, Barbados
Tel.: (246) 426 0242
Fax: (246) 426 6988
E-Mail: fcl_marketing@carribean.fujitsu.com
Software Development Services
S.I.C.: 7371
N.A.I.C.S.: 541511
John Slaytor *(Exec VP-Strategy Ops)*

Fujitsu Caribbean (Trinidad) Limited (1)
6th Avenue Extension & Ibis Avenue
Barataria, Trinidad & Tobago
Tel.: (868) 223 2826
Fax: (868) 675 1956
E-Mail: marketing@carribean.fujitsu.com
Web Site: www.fujitsu.com
Emp.: 11
Software Development Services
S.I.C.: 7371
N.A.I.C.S.: 541511
Jean-Paul Dookie *(Gen Mgr)*

Fujitsu (China) Co., Ltd. (1)
13F Tower A Ocean International Center No 56 Dong Si Huan Zhong Rd
Chaoyang District, Beijing, China
Tel.: (86) 10 5969 1000
Fax: (86) 10 5969 1099
Web Site: www.fujitsu.com
Information Technology Consulting Services
S.I.C.: 7373
N.A.I.C.S.: 541512

Subsidiary:

Fujitsu (Xi'an) System Engineering Co., Ltd. (2)
4F Suite A R&D Building Xi'an Software Park
No 72 Keji 2nd Road, Xi'an, China 710075
Tel.: (86) 2987669766
Fax: (86) 2987669769
Software Development Services
S.I.C.: 7371
N.A.I.C.S.: 541511

Fujitsu (China) Holdings Co., Ltd. (1)
9F 10F Taiping Finance Tower No 488 Middle Yincheng Road
Pudong New Area, Shanghai, China 200120
Tel.: (86) 21 5887 1000
Fax: (86) 21 5877 5287
Web Site: www.fujitsu.com
Investment Management Services
S.I.C.: 6282
N.A.I.C.S.: 523920

Fujitsu Components Europe B.V. (1)
Diamantlaan 25
2132 WV Hoofddorp, Netherlands
Tel.: (31) 23 556 0910
Fax: (31) 23 556 0950
E-Mail: info@fceu.fujitsu.com
Emp.: 35
Consumer Electronics Distr
S.I.C.: 5064
N.A.I.C.S.: 423620
Seiki Sato *(Pres)*

Fujitsu Components Hong Kong Co., Limited (1)
Suite 913 Ocean Centre 5 Canton Road
Tsim Tsa Tsui, Kowloon, China (Hong Kong)
Tel.: (852) 2881 8495
Fax: (852) 2894 9512
Web Site: www.fujitsu.com
Electronic Component Mfr
S.I.C.: 3679
N.A.I.C.S.: 334419

Fujitsu Components (Malaysia) Sdn. Bhd. (1)
No 1 Lorong Satu Kawasan Perindustrian Parit Raja
Johor Bahru, 86400, Malaysia (100%)
Tel.: (60) 74542111
Telex: 84-60577
Fax: (60) 74541771
Web Site: my.fujitsu.com
Emp.: 1,500
Mfr. & Sales of Electronic Components
S.I.C.: 3577
N.A.I.C.S.: 334118
Charles Lew *(Pres)*

Fujitsu Conseil (Canada) Inc. (1)
1000 Sherbrooke Street West Suite 1400
Montreal, QC, H3A 3R2, Canada
Tel.: (514) 877-3301
Fax: (514) 877-3351
E-Mail: fujitsu_canada_communications@ca.fujitsu.com
Emp.: 300
Information Technology Consulting Services
S.I.C.: 7373
N.A.I.C.S.: 541512
David Shearer *(Gen Mgr)*

Fujitsu Denso International Limited (1)
9/F Lincoln House 979 King's Road Taikoo Place
Island East, Hong Kong, China (Hong Kong)
Tel.: (852) 2828 2850
Fax: (852) 2824 9108
Web Site: www.fujitsu.com
Electronic Component Mfr
S.I.C.: 3679
N.A.I.C.S.: 334419

Fujitsu Deutschland GmbH (1)
Frankfurter Ring 211
49, 80807 Munich, Germany (100%)
Tel.: (49) 89323780
Telex: 41-17-897106
Fax: (49) 8932378100
Web Site: www.fujitsu.com
Sales Range: $250-299.9 Million
Emp.: 60
Sale of Computers & Telecommunications Equipment
S.I.C.: 5946
N.A.I.C.S.: 443142
Satoshi Yamada *(Mng Dir)*
Otto Hinteregger *(Mng Dir)*

Fujitsu Do Brasil Ltda (1)
Rua Treze de Maio 1633 1 ao 7 andar
Sao Paulo, SP, 01327 905, Brazil (100%)
Tel.: (55) 1132650880
Telex: 38-1121777
Fax: (55) 113265 0850
Web Site: www.fujitsu.com.br
Emp.: 100
Sales of Computers
S.I.C.: 5065
N.A.I.C.S.: 423690

FUJITSU EMEA PLC (1)
22 Baker Street
London, United Kingdom W1U 3BW
Tel.: (44) 843 354 5555
Investment Financial Services
S.I.C.: 6211
N.A.I.C.S.: 523999

Fujitsu Enabling Software Technology GmbH (1)
Schwanthalerstr 75 A
80336 Munich, Germany
Tel.: (49) 89 360 908 502
Fax: (49) 89 360 908 8502
E-Mail: info@est.fujitsu.com
Web Site: solutions.ts.fujitsu.com
Software Development Services
S.I.C.: 7371
N.A.I.C.S.: 541511

Fujitsu Europe Limited (1)
22 Baker Street
London, United Kingdom W1U 3BW
Tel.: (44) 870 242 7998
Web Site: www.fujitsu.com
Information Technology Development Services
S.I.C.: 7371
N.A.I.C.S.: 541511

Fujitsu Finland Oy (1)
Valimotie 16
Helsinki, Finland 00380
Tel.: (358) 45 7880 4000
Fax: (358) 45 7880 8950
E-Mail: info@fi.fujitsu.com
Web Site: www.fujitsu.com
Emp.: 2,900
Information Technology Consulting Services
S.I.C.: 7373
N.A.I.C.S.: 541512

Fujitsu Hong Kong Limited (1)
10/F Lincoln House Taikoo Place 979 King's Road
Quarry Bay, China (Hong Kong)
Tel.: (852) 2827 5780
Fax: (852) 2827 4724
E-Mail: telecommunications@hk.fujitsu.com
Web Site: www.fujitsu.com
Emp.: 200
Information Technology Consulting Services
S.I.C.: 7373
N.A.I.C.S.: 541512
Michael Shin *(Pres)*

Fujitsu (Ireland) Limited (1)
Lakeshore Drive Airside Business Park
Swords, Dublin, Ireland
Tel.: (353) 1 813 6000
Fax: (353) 1 813 6100
E-Mail: marketing@ie.fujitsu.com
Web Site: www.fujitsu.com
Emp.: 800
Information Technology Consulting Services
S.I.C.: 7373
N.A.I.C.S.: 541512
Regina Moran *(CEO)*

Fujitsu Korea Ltd. (1)
Sunsong Tower Bldg 83 1 Susong Dong
Jongno Gu, Seoul, 110 140, Korea (South) (100%)
Tel.: (82) 237876000
Telex: 801-24553
Fax: (82) 2 3787 6066
Web Site: www.kr.fujitsu.com
Distributor & Developer of Information Processing Systems & Operating Systems
S.I.C.: 7373
N.A.I.C.S.: 541512

Fujitsu Microelectronics Europe GmbH (1)
Pittlerstrasse 47
D 63225 Langen, Buchschlag, Germany (100%)
Tel.: (49) 61036900
Fax: (49) 6103690122
E-Mail: info@fme.fujitsu.com
Web Site: www.fujitsu.com

Emp.: 230
Sales of Electronic Components
S.I.C.: 3679
N.A.I.C.S.: 334419

Fujitsu PC Asia Pacific Ltd (1)
Unit 603 05-07 Bio-Informatics Centre No 2 Science Park West Avenue
Hong Kong Science Park, Sha Tin, China (Hong Kong)
Tel.: (852) 3101 2898
Fax: (852) 3101 0633
Electronic Computer Mfr
S.I.C.: 3571
N.A.I.C.S.: 334111

Non-U.S. Subsidiaries:

Fujian Fujitsu Communication Software Co., Ltd. (2)
22 Shui Tou Lu DouMen
Fuzhou, Fujian, China 350013
Tel.: (86) 591 87575150
E-Mail: linfan@ffcs.cn
Web Site: www.ffcs.cn
Information Technology Development Services
S.I.C.: 7371
N.A.I.C.S.: 541511

Fujitsu PC Asia Pacific Pte. Ltd. (2)
60 Alexandra Terrace 05-20/21/22 The Comtech Lobby D
Singapore, 118502, Singapore
Tel.: (65) 6776 0688
Fax: (65) 6776 0788
E-Mail: scanner@sg.fujitsu.com
Web Site: www.fujitsu.com
Emp.: 50
Computer Peripheral Equipment Distr
S.I.C.: 5045
N.A.I.C.S.: 423430

Fujitsu PC Australia Pty Ltd (2)
Unit 3 83 Derby Street
Silverwater, NSW, 2128, Australia
Tel.: (61) 2 8705 8700
Fax: (61) 2 9648 6998
E-Mail: contact@au.fujitsu.com
Web Site: www.fujitsu.com
Emp.: 7
Computer Equipment Distr
S.I.C.: 5045
N.A.I.C.S.: 423430
Bert Noah *(Country Mgr)*

Fujitsu South China Technology Services Limited (2)
No7 Nan 6 Lu Guicheng
Nanhai District, Foshan, Guangdong, China 528200
Tel.: (86) 757 6686 8088
Fax: (86) 757 6686 8086
Information Technology Development Services
S.I.C.: 7371
N.A.I.C.S.: 541511

Jiangsu Fujitsu Telecommunications Technology Co., Ltd. (2)
118 Deng Wei Lu Gao Xin Jishu Kaifa Qu
Suzhou, Jiangsu, China 215011
Tel.: (86) 512 6825 0097
Fax: (86) 512 6825 3090
Transmission System Maintenance Services
S.I.C.: 7539
N.A.I.C.S.: 811118

Fujitsu Philippines, Inc. (1)
2nd Floor United Life Building 837 A Arnaiz Avenue
Legaspi Village, Makati, Metro Manila, 1229, Philippines
Tel.: (63) 28124001
Fax: (63) 28177576
E-Mail: info@ph.fujitsu.com
Web Site: www.fujitsu.com
Emp.: 500
Communication Equipment Distr
S.I.C.: 5065
N.A.I.C.S.: 423690
Greg Yu *(Acct Mgr-Tech)*

Fujitsu Quality Laboratory (Suzhou) Ltd. (1)
2F West 5th Building Suzhou Science & Technology Park 2 Keling Rd
Suzhou, Jiangsu, China 215163
Tel.: (86) 51268320107
Fax: (86) 51268320117
Web Site: www.fujitsu.com
Laboratory Testing Services
S.I.C.: 8734
N.A.I.C.S.: 541380
Kawamoto Osanu *(Gen Mgr)*

Fujitsu Research and Development Center Co., Ltd. (1)
13F Tower A Ocean International Center No 56 Dong Si Huan Zhong Rd
Chaoyang District, Beijing, China 100025
Tel.: (86) 1059691000
Fax: (86) 1059691099
Web Site: www.fujitsu.com
Scientific Research & Development Services
S.I.C.: 8731
N.A.I.C.S.: 541712

Fujitsu Semiconductor Asia Pte. Ltd. (1)
Unit No 3 Level 8 Innovator International Tech Park Whitefield Road
Bengaluru, Karnataka, 560066, India
Tel.: (91) 8028419990
Fax: (91) 8028416660
Web Site: www.fujitsu.com
Emp.: 15
Semiconductor Device Mfr
S.I.C.: 3674
N.A.I.C.S.: 334413
C. N. Asha *(Mgr-HR)*

Fujitsu Semiconductor Design (Chengdu) Co. Ltd. (1)
B-5 No 3 GaoPeng Avenue
Chengdu, Sichuan, China 610041
Tel.: (86) 28 8515 0023
Fax: (86) 28 8515 0523
Web Site: www.fujitsu.com
Semiconductor Mfr
S.I.C.: 3674
N.A.I.C.S.: 334413

Fujitsu Semiconductor Embedded Solutions Austria GmbH (1)
Semmelweisstr 34
4040 Linz, Austria
Tel.: (43) 7329 03050
Fax: (43) 7329 0305100
E-Mail: office@at.fujitsu.com
Web Site: www.fujitsu.com
Emp.: 60
Semiconductor Device Mfr
S.I.C.: 3674
N.A.I.C.S.: 334413
Gerald Roos *(Gen Mgr)*

Fujitsu Semiconductor Europe GmbH (1)
Building 3 Concorde Park Concorde Road
Maidenhead, Berkshire, SL6 4FJ, United Kingdom (100%)
Tel.: (44) 1628504600
Fax: (44) 1628504666
E-Mail: niel.sellars@sma.fujitsu.com
Web Site: www.emea.fujitsu.com
Emp.: 50
Design & Development of ASIC's; Sales of Electronic Devices
S.I.C.: 3674
N.A.I.C.S.: 334413
Brendan McKearney *(Mng Dir)*

Fujitsu Semiconductor Korea Limited (1)
902 Kosmo Tower Building 1002 Daechi-Dong
Gangnam-Gu, Seoul, Korea (South) 135-280
Tel.: (82) 2 3484 7100
Fax: (82) 2 3484 7111
Emp.: 5
Electronic Device Distr
S.I.C.: 5065
N.A.I.C.S.: 423690
Kim Sung-Soo *(Gen Mgr)*

Fujitsu Semiconductor Pacific Asia Limited (1)
10/F World Commerce Centre 11 Canton Road
Tsimshatsui, Kowloon, China (Hong Kong)
Tel.: (852) 2736 3232
Fax: (852) 2314 4207
Semiconductor Device Mfr
S.I.C.: 3674
N.A.I.C.S.: 334413

Fujitsu Semiconductor (Shanghai) Co., Ltd. (1)
30F Kerry Parkside 1155 Fang Dian Road
Pu Dong District, Shanghai, China 201204
Tel.: (86) 21 6146 3688
Fax: (86) 21 6146 3660
Web Site: www.fujitsu.com
Semiconductor Device Mfr
S.I.C.: 3674
N.A.I.C.S.: 334413
James Ouyang *(Dir-Sls)*

Fujitsu Services AB (1)
Ifafgordfgatan 35
PO Box 40
16493 Kista, 16440, Sweden (100%)
Tel.: (46) 87937000
Telex: 54-13411
Fax: (46) 87937810
E-Mail: info@se.fujitsu.com
Web Site: www.se.fujitsu.com
Emp.: 200
Sale of Computers & Telecommunications Equipment
S.I.C.: 5731
N.A.I.C.S.: 443142
Bengt Enjstrom *(Mng Dir)*

Fujitsu Services (1)
22 Baker St
London, W1U 3BW, United Kingdom (80%)
Tel.: (44) 2070097777
Telex: 22971
Web Site: www.fujitsu.com
Rev.: $2,260,260,000
Emp.: 150
Design, Development, Manufacture & Marketing of Computer & Telecommunications Systems & Networks; Related Products & Services
S.I.C.: 3823
N.A.I.C.S.: 334513
Richard Christou *(Chm & Acting CEO)*

Subsidiary:

Fujitsu Services Holdings PLC (2)
22 Baker Street
London, United Kingdom W1U 3BW
Tel.: (44) 843 354 5555
Fax: (44) 870 242 7998
Investment Management Services
S.I.C.: 6211
N.A.I.C.S.: 523999

Non-U.S. Subsidiaries:

Fujitsu Australia Software Technology Pty., Ltd. (2)
14 Rodborough Rd
2086 French's Forest, NSW, Australia (100%)
Tel.: (61) 294529000
Fax: (61) 299753779
Web Site: www.fastware.com
Emp.: 50
Sales & Development of Software Products
S.I.C.: 5734
N.A.I.C.S.: 443142
Bala Varadarajan *(Mng Dir)*

Fujitsu Consulting (Luxembourg) S.A. (2)
Parc d Activites Capellen 89 C rue Pafebruch
L 2350 Capellen, Luxembourg (100%)
Tel.: (352) 260991
Fax: (352) 480641
E-Mail: info@lu.fujitsu.com
Web Site: www.lu.fujitsu.com
Emp.: 80
Consulting Services
S.I.C.: 5731
N.A.I.C.S.: 443142

Fujitsu Espana, S.A. (2)
Camino Cerro De Los Gamos 1
Pozuelo De Alarcon, 28224 Madrid, Spain (100%)
Tel.: (34) 917849000
Fax: (34) 917849266
E-Mail: info@es.fujitsu.com
Web Site: www.es.fujitsu.com
Emp.: 1,700
Mfr., Developer & Distributor of Communications Systems
S.I.C.: 3669
N.A.I.C.S.: 334290
Bernardo Diaz *(Dir-Mktg)*

Fujitsu (Malaysia) Sdn. Bhd. (2)
Level 1and 2 No 3505 Jalan Teknokrat 5
Cyberjaya, Selangor, 63000, Malaysia (100%)
Tel.: (60) 383183700
Fax: (60) 383188700
E-Mail: writetous@fms.my.fujitsu.com
Web Site: www.my.fujitsu.com
Sls.: $17,367,306
Emp.: 200
Distributor of Computers & Related Products
S.I.C.: 5946
N.A.I.C.S.: 443142
Michael Warren *(Country Pres)*

Fujitsu New Zealand Ltd. (2)
141 Terrace Fujitsu Tower Level 12
PO Box 3547
6011 Wellington, 6140, New Zealand (100%)
Tel.: (64) 44950700
Fax: (64) 44950730
Web Site: www.fujitsu.co.nz
Emp.: 30
S.I.C.: 3571
N.A.I.C.S.: 334111
Rod Vawdrey *(CEO)*
Jo Healey *(Mng Dir)*

Fujitsu Service A/S (2)
Sandakerveien 138
P O Box 4285
Nydalen, Oslo, 401, Norway (95%)
Mailing Address:
PO Box 4285
Torshov, 0401 Oslo, Norway
Tel.: (47) 22895500
Fax: (47) 22895550
Web Site: www.no.invia.fujitsu.com
Emp.: 60
S.I.C.: 3571
N.A.I.C.S.: 334111
Leo Sapiraa *(Mktg Dir)*

Fujitsu Service Oy (2)
Valimotie 16
PO Box 100
FI 00012 Helsinki, Finland (100%)
Tel.: (358) 4578800
Fax: (358) 0942465081
E-Mail: info@fi.fujitsu.com
Web Site: www.fi.fujitsu.com
Emp.: 2,000
S.I.C.: 5946
N.A.I.C.S.: 443142
Yrjana Ahto *(Mng Dir)*

Fujitsu Services - Sistemas de Informacao Ltda (2)
Torre Oraente Bldg Colombo Ave Colegio Militar 37F 3rd Fl
1500-180 Lisbon, Portugal (100%)
Tel.: (351) 217244444
Fax: (351) 217244445
E-Mail: informacoes@ts.fujitsu.com
Web Site: www.fujitsu.ts
Emp.: 200
S.I.C.: 3571
N.A.I.C.S.: 334111
Carlos Barros *(Mng Dir)*

Fujitsu Services AB (2)
Ifafgordfgatan 35
PO Box 14
164 93 Kista, Sweden (100%)
Mailing Address:
PO Box 40
164 93 Kista, Sweden
Tel.: (46) 87937000
Fax: (46) 87937810
E-Mail: info@se.fujitsu.com
Web Site: www.se.fujitsu.com
Sales Range: $150-199.9 Million
Emp.: 400
S.I.C.: 3571
N.A.I.C.S.: 334111
Petri Imberg *(Mng Dir)*

Fujitsu Services AS (2)
Mustamae Tee 16
EE 10617 Tallinn, Estonia
Tel.: (372) 627 2300
Fax: (372) 627 2310
E-Mail: info@ee.fujitsu.com
Web Site: www.fujitsu.com
Emp.: 17
Information Technology Consulting Services

Fujitsu Limited—(Continued)

S.I.C.: 7373
N.A.I.C.S.: 541512
Andres Jarviste *(Mgr)*

Fujitsu Services GmbH **(2)**
Guglgasse 15
A 1110 Vienna, Austria (100%)
Tel.: (43) 17164675300
Fax: (43) 17164659140
E-Mail: feedback.at@ts.fujitsu.com
Web Site: www.at.ts.fujitsu.com
Emp.: 200
Electronics & Computer Mfr
S.I.C.: 5946
N.A.I.C.S.: 443142
Johannes Baumgartner *(Gen Mgr)*

Fujitsu Services Ltd **(2)**
Airside Business Park Swords
Dublin, Ireland (100%)
Tel.: (353) 1 813 6000
Fax: (353) 1 813 6100
E-Mail: marketing@ie.fujitsu.com
Web Site: www.fujitsu.com
Emp.: 200
Mfr., Designer & Operator of Information Technology Products & Services
S.I.C.: 7373
N.A.I.C.S.: 541512
Regina Moran *(CEO)*
John Walsh *(CTO)*

Non-U.S. Subsidiary:

Fujitsu Services S.P.A. **(3)**
Centro Direzionale Colleoni - Palazzo Andromeda 3 Via Paracelso 20
20041 Agrate Brianza, Milano, Italy
Tel.: (39) 039 6566 1
Fax: (39) 039 6056208
Web Site: it.fujitsu.com
Information Technology Development Services
S.I.C.: 7371
N.A.I.C.S.: 541511

Fujitsu Services Limited **(2)**
Al Masaood Tower 15th Floor Hamdan Street
PO Box 7237
Abu Dhabi, United Arab Emirates
Tel.: (971) 2 6335200
Fax: (971) 2 6338724
Web Site: www.fujitsu.com
Information Technology Consulting Services
S.I.C.: 7373
N.A.I.C.S.: 541512

Fujitsu Services South Africa **(2)**
Technology Village 43 Homestead Road
Rivonia, 2128, South Africa
Tel.: (27) 11 233 5911
Fax: (27) 11 233 5326
E-Mail: askfujitsuza@ts.fujitsu.com
Web Site: www.fujitsu.com
Information Technology Consulting Services
S.I.C.: 7373
N.A.I.C.S.: 541512

Fujitsu Services Sp. z.o.o. **(2)**
Textorial Park Ul Fabryczna 17
90-344 Lodz, Poland
Tel.: (48) 42 271 30 01
Fax: (48) 42 271 30 03
E-Mail: fujitsupoland@pl.fujitsu.com
Web Site: www.fujitsu.com
Information Technology Consulting Services
S.I.C.: 7373
N.A.I.C.S.: 541512

Fujitsu (Singapore) Pte. Ltd. **(1)**
20 Science Pk Rd 03 37 Teletech Pk
Singapore, 117674, Singapore (100%)
Tel.: (65) 65127555
Telex: 87-22194
Fax: (65) 65127502
E-Mail: query@sg.fujitsu.com
Web Site: www.fujitsu.com.sg
Emp.: 500
Mfr. & Sales of Switching Equipment & Computers
S.I.C.: 3613
N.A.I.C.S.: 335313
Heng Chew Wong *(Pres)*

Fujitsu South China Limited **(1)**
Room 2809 New World Center No 6009 Yitian Road
Futian District, Shenzhen, China 518026
Tel.: (86) 755 2588 2589
Fax: (86) 755 8246 2008
Web Site: www.fujitsu.com
Information Technology Consulting Services
S.I.C.: 7373
N.A.I.C.S.: 541512

Fujitsu Systems Business (Thailand) Ltd. **(1)**
Exchange Tower 22-23 Floor 388 Sukhumvit Road
Khlong Toei, Bangkok, 10110, Thailand
Tel.: (66) 2302 1500
Fax: (66) 2302 1555
E-Mail: info@th.fujitsu.com
Web Site: www.fujitsu.com
Information Technology Consulting Services
S.I.C.: 7373
N.A.I.C.S.: 541512

Fujitsu Taiwan Limited **(1)**
19F No 39 Section 1 Chunghwa Road
Taipei, Taiwan
Tel.: (886) 2 2311 2255
Fax: (886) 23718143
E-Mail: info@tw.fujitsu.com
Web Site: www.fujitsu.com
Communication Equipment Sales & Maintenance Services
S.I.C.: 5065
N.A.I.C.S.: 423690

Fujitsu Technology Solutions A.E. **(1)**
48 Egialias & Epidavrou Str
Marousi, Athens, Greece 15125
Tel.: (30) 210 6863 500
Fax: (30) 210 6863 634
E-Mail: marketinggreece@ts.fujitsu.com
Web Site: www.fujitsu.com
Information Technology Consulting Services
S.I.C.: 7373
N.A.I.C.S.: 541512

Fujitsu Technology Solutions B.V. **(1)**
Het Kwadrant 1
3606 AZ Maarssen, Netherlands NL
Mailing Address: (100%)
Postbus 1214
3600 BE Maarssen, Netherlands
Tel.: (31) 346 598111
Fax: (31) 346 550152
E-Mail: info@fujitsu.com
Web Site: www.fujitsu.com
Sales Range: $150-199.9 Million
Emp.: 400
Notebook, Personal, Mainframe & Other Computer & Related Products Mfr
Export
S.I.C.: 5045
N.A.I.C.S.: 423430
Peter G. Jilek *(Exec VP-Enterprise Products)*

Fujitsu Technology Solutions S.p.A. **(1)**
Via Delle Industrie n 11
20090 Vimodrone, Milan, Italy
Tel.: (39) 022659321
Fax: (39) 0226593271
E-Mail: customerinfo.point@ts.fujitsu.com
Web Site: www.fujitsu.com
Information Technology Consulting Services
S.I.C.: 7373
N.A.I.C.S.: 541512
Elena Bellini *(Mgr-Mktg & Comm)*

Fujitsu Telecom Systems Philippines, Inc. **(1)**
8th Floor Dominion Building 833 Arnaiz Avenue Pasay Road
Legaspi Village, Makati, Philippines 1229
Tel.: (63) 2 893 0037
Fax: (63) 2 819 1920
Web Site: www.fujitsu.com
Computer Network Design & Installation Services
S.I.C.: 7373
N.A.I.C.S.: 541512

Fujitsu Telecommunications Europe Limited **(1)**
Solihull Parkway Birmingham Business Park
Birmingham, B37 7YU, United Kingdom
Tel.: (44) 1217176000
Fax: (44) 1217176161
E-Mail: telecommunications@uk.fujitsu.com
Emp.: 700
Communication Equipment Mfr & Distr
S.I.C.: 3669
N.A.I.C.S.: 334290
Duncan Tait *(CEO)*
Steve Clayton *(CFO)*
Gavin Bounds *(COO)*

Fujitsu Telecommunications France SAS **(1)**
Les Boreales Batiment B 2 Avenue De Laponie
BP 204
Les Ulis, France 91941
Tel.: (33) 160923040
Fax: (33) 160923049
Web Site: www.fujitsu.com
Emp.: 15
Telecommunication Equipment Mfr
S.I.C.: 3669
N.A.I.C.S.: 334290
Andrew Stevenson *(Pres)*

Fujitsu Telecomunicacoes Portugal, S.A. **(1)**
Rua Sebastiao e Silva n 67/69
Massama, Sintra, Portugal
Tel.: (351) 21 913 8600
Fax: (351) 21 913 8632
E-Mail: fujitsu@fujitsu.pt
Emp.: 100
Telecommunication Services
S.I.C.: 4899
N.A.I.C.S.: 517919
Marcus Smith *(Mng Dir)*

Fujitsu Transaction Solutions Canada Inc. **(1)**
155 University Ave Ste 1600
Toronto, ON, Canada M5H 3B7
Tel.: (905) 286-9666
Fax: (905) 286-3451
Toll Free: (800) 668-8325
Web Site: www.fujitsu.com
Hardware & Software Management Services
S.I.C.: 7373
N.A.I.C.S.: 541512

Fujitsu Vietnam Limited **(1)**
8th Floor DMC Building 535 Kim Ma Street
Ba Dinh District, Hanoi, Vietnam
Tel.: (84) 4 22203113
Fax: (84) 4 22203114
E-Mail: sales@vn.fujitsu.com
Web Site: www.fujitsu.com
Information Technology Consulting Services
S.I.C.: 7373
N.A.I.C.S.: 541512

TDS Informationstechnologie Aktiengesellschaft **(1)**
Konrad-Zuse-Strasse 16
D-74172 Neckarsulm, Germany
Tel.: (49) 71323661200
Fax: (49) 71323661000
E-Mail: info@tds.fujitsu.com
Web Site: www.tds.fujitsu.com
Emp.: 1,400
Information Technology Consulting, Outsourcing & Human Resource Services
S.I.C.: 7371
N.A.I.C.S.: 541511
Heiner Diefenbach *(CEO)*

Non-U.S. Joint Venture:

Nice-business Solutions Finland Oy **(1)**
Valimotie 16
380 Helsinki, Finland
Tel.: (358) 45 788 00
Fax: (358) 4578808955
E-Mail: sales@nice.fi
Web Site: www.nice.fi
Sales Range: $75-99.9 Million
Emp.: 35
Software Services
S.I.C.: 7373
N.A.I.C.S.: 541512
Jouko Seppa *(Mng Dir)*

Subsidiary:

Nice-business Consulting Oy **(2)**
Valimotie 16
PO Box 458
101 Helsinki, Finland
Tel.: (358) 45 78800
Fax: (358) 45 7880 8955
E-Mail: info@nico.fi
Web Site: www.nico.fi
Emp.: 5
Technology Consulting Services
S.I.C.: 8999
N.A.I.C.S.: 541690
Paul Garant *(Mng Dir)*

Non-U.S. Unit:

Nice-business Solutions - Brighton **(2)**
Lees House 21 Dyke Road
Brighton, BN1 3FE, United Kingdom
Tel.: (44) 1273772306
Fax: (44) 1273728057
E-Mail:
Sales Range: $1-9.9 Million
Emp.: 30
Software Development & Testing Services
S.I.C.: 7372
N.A.I.C.S.: 511210
Stefan Fager *(Mng Dir)*

FUJIX LTD.

5 Miyamoto-cho Hirano Kita-ku
Kyoto, Japan
Tel.: (81) 754638111
Fax: (81) 754638120
E-Mail: kikaku@fjx.co.jp
Web Site: www.fjx.co.jp/english/profile.html
Year Founded: 1921
3600—(TKS)
Sls.: $67,848,000
Assets: $115,687,000
Liabilities: $21,076,000
Net Worth: $94,611,000
Earnings: ($341,000)
Emp.: 162
Fiscal Year-end: 03/31/13

Business Description:
Sewing & Embroidery Thread Mfr & Sales
S.I.C.: 2299
N.A.I.C.S.: 313110

Personnel:
Ichiro Fujii *(Pres)*

Non-U.S. Subsidiaries:

FUJIX International (Hong Kong) Ltd. **(1)**
Unit 01- 02 19/F CRE Centre
889 Cheung Sha Wan Rd, Kowloon, China (Hong Kong)
Tel.: (852) 27851323
Fax: (852) 27851363
E-Mail: kikaku@fjx.co.jp
Emp.: 4
Sewing & Embroidery Thread International Trading Services
S.I.C.: 7389
N.A.I.C.S.: 425120
Kenji Ohashi *(Gen Mgr)*

FUJIX (Shanghai) Thread Ltd. **(1)**
No 538 12 Shengli Road
Qingpu District, Shanghai, China
Tel.: (86) 2159201110
Fax: (86) 2159203507
Web Site: www.sh-fjx.com
Sewing & Embroidery Thread Mfr & Sales
S.I.C.: 2299
N.A.I.C.S.: 313110
Shigeo Matsuoka *(Gen Mgr)*

Sanghai FUJIX Trading Co., Ltd. **(1)**
2F 1 Bldg 288 Fute Rd N Waigaoqiao Free Trade Zone, Shanghai, China
Tel.: (86) 2158663902
Fax: (86) 21 5866 3903
Emp.: 14
Sewing & Embroidery Thread Trading Services
S.I.C.: 7389
N.A.I.C.S.: 425120

Shanghai New Fujix Thread Ltd. **(1)**
No 1188 Yuanguo Road Anting Area Jiading District
Shanghai, China
Tel.: (86) 2169573826
Fax: (86) 2169573007
Web Site: www.fjx.co.jp/english/profile.html
Emp.: 36

Sewing & Embroidery Thread Mfr & Sales
S.I.C.: 2299
N.A.I.C.S.: 313110

FUKOKU CO., LTD.

3-105 Sugaya
Ageo, Saitama, 362-8561, Japan
Tel.: (81) 48 600 1700
Fax: (81) 48 773 5611
Web Site: www.fukoku-rubber.co.jp
Year Founded: 1953
5185—(TKS)
Emp.: 1,123
Business Description:
Rubber Product Mfr
S.I.C.: 3061
N.A.I.C.S.: 326291
Personnel:
Jiro Kawamoto *(Pres)*

FUKOKU MUTUAL LIFE INSURANCE COMPANY

2-2 Uchisaiwaicho 2-chome Chiyoda-ku
Tokyo, 100-0011, Japan
Tel.: (81) 335081101
Fax: (81) 335916446
Web Site: www.fukoku-life.co.jp
Year Founded: 1923
Rev.: $11,804,485,000
Assets: $82,927,482,000
Liabilities: $78,125,960,000
Net Worth: $4,801,522,000
Earnings: $554,345,000
Emp.: 13,488
Fiscal Year-end: 03/31/13
Business Description:
Life Insurance Carrier
S.I.C.: 6311
N.A.I.C.S.: 524113
Personnel:
Tomofumi Akiyama *(Chm)*
Yoshiteru Yoneyama *(Pres & CEO)*
Kasumasa Furuya *(Deputy Pres)*
Tadashi Akikawa *(Mng Exec Officer)*
Toshihide Fujiwara *(Exec Officer)*
Toshimitsu Furuhashi *(Exec Officer)*
Takanobu Futaba *(Exec Officer)*
Kazuyoshi Hasegawa *(Exec Officer)*
Toshihiro Hayashi *(Mng Exec Officer)*
Toshikatsu Hayashi *(Exec Officer)*
Kenji Hirai *(Mng Exec Officer)*
Tsutomu Hiruma *(Exec Officer)*
Kohei Kawasaki *(Exec Officer)*
Yasuyuki Kitamura *(Exec Officer)*
Hitoshi Sakai *(Mng Exec Officer)*
Kenji Sakurai *(Exec Officer)*
Osama Suzuki *(Exec Officer)*
Board of Directors:
Tomofumi Akiyama
Tadashi Akikawa
Toshihide Fujiwara
Kasumasa Furuya
Toshihiro Hayashi
Toshikatsu Hayashi
Kenji Hirai
Kozo Isshiki
Hitoshi Sakai
Kazuo Tanabe
Katsuhiro Utada
Yoshiteru Yoneyama

Subsidiary:

Kyoei Kasai Shinrai Life Insurance Co. Ltd **(1)**
J. CITY BLD. 8-12
Takamatsu 5-Chome Nerima-Ku, Tokyo, 179-0075, Japan JP
Tel.: (81) 120 700 651 (80%)
Web Site: www.kyoeikasai.co.jp/ss/top.htm
Emp.: 62
Life Insurance
S.I.C.: 6311
N.A.I.C.S.: 524113

U.S. Subsidiary:

Fukoku Life International (America) Inc. **(1)**
Times Sq Tower 7 Times Sq 35th Fl
New York, NY 10036
Tel.: (212) 221-7760
Fax: (212) 221-7794
Emp.: 5
Life Insurance Services
S.I.C.: 6311
N.A.I.C.S.: 524113
Seiichi Nozaki *(Controller)*

Non-U.S. Subsidiary:

Fukoku Life International (U.K.) Ltd. **(1)**
3rd Floor Baltic Exchange
38 Saint Mary Axe, London, EC3A 8EX, United Kingdom
Tel.: (44) 2072831331
Fax: (44) 2076267096
E-Mail: sheo@fukokulife.co.uk
Emp.: 5
Life Insurance Services
S.I.C.: 6311
N.A.I.C.S.: 524113
Atsushi Sato *(Pres)*

FUKUDA DENSHI CO., LTD.

39-4 Hongo 3-chome Bunkyo-ku
Tokyo, 113-8483, Japan
Tel.: (81) 356841455
Fax: (81) 338141222
E-Mail: info@fukuda.co.jp
Web Site: www.fukuda.co.jp
Year Founded: 1939
6960—(JAS)
Sls.: $1,058,629,000
Assets: $1,261,106,000
Liabilities: $358,204,000
Net Worth: $902,902,000
Earnings: $71,082,000
Emp.: 2,711
Fiscal Year-end: 03/31/13
Business Description:
Medical Electronics Equipment Developer, Mfr, Importer, Exporter & Sales
S.I.C.: 3841
N.A.I.C.S.: 339112
Personnel:
Kotaro Fukuda *(Chm & CEO)*
Daijiro Shirai *(Pres & COO)*
Izumi Tsubone *(Sr Mng Dir, Head-Intl Sls & Gen Mgr-R&D)*
Junzo Fujiwara *(Sr Mng Dir & Gen Mgr-Pres Office)*
Koji Takahashi *(Mng Dir, Head-Vascular Assessment & Prevention & Gen Mgr-Bus Dev)*
Yuichiro Tani *(Mng Dir & Gen Mgr-Sys Solution Div)*
Board of Directors:
Kotaro Fukuda
Junzo Fujiwara
Shuichi Fukuda
Yukio Nakagawa
Daijiro Shirai
Osamu Shirakawa
Koji Takahashi
Yuichiro Tani
Izumi Tsubone

U.S. Subsidiary:

Fukuda Denshi USA, Inc. **(1)**
17725 NE 65th St Bldg C
Redmond, WA 98052
Tel.: (425) 558-1661
Fax: (425) 869-2018
E-Mail: info@fukuda.com
Web Site: www.fukuda.com
Emp.: 15
Medical Electronic Equipment Mfr & Sales
S.I.C.: 3841
N.A.I.C.S.: 339112
Kenny Abrioa *(Mgr-Mktg)*

Non-U.S. Subsidiary:

Fukuda Denshi UK Ltd. **(1)**
Unit 13 Westminster Court Hipley Street
Old Woking, Woking, Surrey, GU2 29LG, United Kingdom (100%)
Tel.: (44) 1483728065
Fax: (44) 1483728066
Web Site: www.fukuda.co.uk
Surgical & Medical Instrument Mfr
S.I.C.: 3841
N.A.I.C.S.: 339112

THE FUKUI BANK, LTD.

1-1 Junka 1-chome
Fukui, 910-8660, Japan
Tel.: (81) 776242030
Fax: (81) 776269842
E-Mail: fuk00802@fukuibank.jp
Web Site: www.fukuibank.co.jp
Year Founded: 1899
8362—(TKS)
Sales Range: $500-549.9 Million
Emp.: 1,358
Business Description:
Banking Services
S.I.C.: 6029
N.A.I.C.S.: 522110
Personnel:
Toshinori Mouri *(Chm)*
Tadaaki Ito *(Pres)*
Yoshihisa Shimano *(Exec Officer & Mgr-Bus Promotion)*
Masahiro Hayashi *(Mng Exec Officer)*
Masakazu Shimizu *(Mng Exec Officer)*
Mamoru Tsukuda *(Sr Mng Exec Officer)*
Board of Directors:
Toshinori Mouri
Hideo Hata
Masahiro Hayashi
Tadaaki Ito
Nana Kikkawa
Kazue Nomura
Naoyuki Nomura
Masakazu Shimizu
Mamoru Tsukuda

FUKUOKA FINANCIAL GROUP, INC.

1-8-3 Otemon Chuo-ku
Fukuoka, 810-8693, Japan
Tel.: (81) 927232502
Web Site: www.fukuoka-fg.com
Year Founded: 2007
8354—(OTC TKS)
Rev.: $2,838,880,000
Assets: $146,053,358,000
Liabilities: $137,756,245,000
Net Worth: $8,297,113,000
Earnings: $352,649,000
Emp.: 6,825
Fiscal Year-end: 03/31/13
Business Description:
Bank Holding Company
S.I.C.: 6712
N.A.I.C.S.: 551111
Personnel:
Masaaki Tani *(Chm & Pres)*
Takashige Shibato *(Deputy Pres)*
Takashi Yoshikai *(Deputy Pres)*
Board of Directors:
Masaaki Tani
Masayuki Aoyagi
Satoru Fukuda
Jiro Furumura
Kenji Hayashi
Noritaka Murayama
Osamu Obata
Fumio Sakurai
Takashige Shibato
Hideaki Takahashi
Ryuji Yasuda
Yasuhiko Yoshida
Takashi Yoshikai
Shunsuke Yoshizawa

Subsidiaries:

The Bank of Fukuoka, Ltd. **(1)**
13-1 Tenjin 2-chome
Chuo-ku, Fukuoka, 810-8727, Japan JP
Tel.: (81) 92 723 2622 (100%)
Fax: (81) 92 721 5863
Web Site: www.fukuokabank.co.jp
Sales Range: $1-4.9 Billion
Emp.: 487
Commercial Banking Services
S.I.C.: 6029
N.A.I.C.S.: 522110
Masaaki Tani *(Pres)*
Osamu Obata *(Deputy Pres)*
Takeshige Shibato *(Deputy Pres)*
Takashi Yoshikai *(Sr Exec Officer)*
Jiro Furumura *(Mng Exec Officer)*
Fumio Sakurai *(Mng Exec Officer)*

Subsidiaries:

FFG Business Consulting Co., Ltd. **(2)**
2-13-1 Tenjin 2-chome
Chuo-ku, Fukuoka, 810-0001, Japan JP
Tel.: (81) 927232244 (100%)
Fax: (81) 927136486
E-Mail: wta@fukuoka.co.jp
Web Site: www.ffgbc.com
Emp.: 30
Business Management Consulting Services
S.I.C.: 8742
N.A.I.C.S.: 541611
Jeff Bacon *(Pres)*

FFG Card Co., Ltd. **(2)**
7-1 Meinohamaeki Minami 1-chome
Nishi-ku, Fukuoka, Japan JP
Tel.: (81) 928841785 (100%)
Fax: (81) 928841252
Credit Card Processing Services
S.I.C.: 6099
N.A.I.C.S.: 522320

Fukugin Business Operation Service Co., Ltd. **(2)**
Momochihama 1-7-7 chome
Sawara-ku, Fukuoka, 814-0001, Japan JP
Tel.: (81) 928446001 (100%)
Fax: (81) 928446046
Web Site: www.Fukuokabank.co.jp
Business Support Services
S.I.C.: 7334
N.A.I.C.S.: 561439

Fukugin Office Service Co., Ltd. **(2)**
1-9 Arato 2-chome
Chuo-ku, Fukuoka, 810-0011, Japan JP
Tel.: (81) 92 751 3239 (100%)
Fax: (81) 96 385 4113
Web Site: www.fosnet.jp
Temporary Staffing & Real Estate Mangement Services
S.I.C.: 6531
N.A.I.C.S.: 531210

Fukugin Real Estate Assessment Service Co., Ltd. **(2)**
4-13 Hakozaki 1-chome
Higashi-ku, Fukuoka, 814-0001, Japan JP
Tel.: (81) 92 631 0301 (100%)
Fax: (81) 92 631 0313
Web Site: www.fukuoka-fg.com
Asset Management Services
S.I.C.: 6211
N.A.I.C.S.: 523999

Fukuoka Collection & Servicing Co., Ltd. **(2)**
13-1 Tenjin 2-chome
Chuo-ku, Fukuoka, 810-8727, Japan JP
Tel.: (81) 927370881 (100%)
Fax: (81) 927616995
Web Site: www.fukuoka-fg.com
Credit Management & Collection Services
S.I.C.: 7322
N.A.I.C.S.: 561440

Affiliates:

Fukugin Guarantee Co., Ltd. **(2)**
7-1 Meinohamaeki Minami 1-chome
Nishi-ku, Fukuoka, 819-0166, Japan JP
Tel.: (81) 92 882 043 (45%)
Web Site: www.fukuoka-fg.com
Financial Support Services
S.I.C.: 6141

Fukuoka Financial Group, Inc.—(Continued)

N.A.I.C.S.: 522291

Fukuoka Computer Service Co., Ltd. (2)
6-6 Hakataekimae 2-chome
Hakata-ku, Fukuoka, 812-0011, Japan JP
Tel.: (81) 924736900 (40%)
Fax: (81) 924140361
Web Site: www.fcs-web.co.jp
Business Management Software Development Services
S.I.C.: 7371
N.A.I.C.S.: 541511

Maeda Securities Co., Ltd. (2)
13-1 Tenjin 2-chome
Chuo-ku, Fukuoka, 810-0001, Japan JP
Tel.: (81) 927713836 (20.2%)
Web Site: www.maeda-sec.co.jp
Securities Broker & Dealer
S.I.C.: 6211
N.A.I.C.S.: 523110

The Kumamoto Family Bank, Ltd. (1)
29-20 Suizenji 6-Chome
Kumamoto, 862-8601, Japan JP
Tel.: (81) 963851111
Fax: (81) 96 387 1906
Web Site: www.kf-bank.jp
Sales Range: $350-399.9 Million
Emp.: 1,121
Commercial Banking Services
S.I.C.: 6029
N.A.I.C.S.: 522110
Kenji Hayashi *(Pres)*
Noritaka Murayama *(Mng Exec Officer)*

Subsidiary:

Family Card Co., Ltd. (2)
44 Yamasakimachi
Kumamoto, 860-0016, Japan JP
Tel.: (81) 963263811 (100%)
Web Site: www.fukuoka-fg.com
Credit Card Processing Services
S.I.C.: 6099
N.A.I.C.S.: 522320

The Shinwa Bank, Ltd. (1)
10-12 Shimanose-cho
Sasebo, Nagasaki, 857-0806, Japan JP
Tel.: (81) 956245111
Fax: (81) 956235060
Web Site: www.shinwabank.co.jp
Sales Range: $700-749.9 Million
Emp.: 2,000
Commercial Banking Services
S.I.C.: 6029
N.A.I.C.S.: 522110
Kazuo Oniki *(Pres)*
Shunsuke Yoshizawa *(Sr Exec Officer)*

Subsidiaries:

Nishi-Kyushu Credit Guarantee Co., Ltd. (2)
4-24 Shimanose-cho
Sasebo, Nagasaki, 857-0806, Japan JP
Tel.: (81) 956236326 (100%)
Web Site: www.fukuoka-fg.com
Financial Support Services
S.I.C.: 6141
N.A.I.C.S.: 522291

Shinwa DC Card Co., Ltd. (2)
4-1 Sakae-machi
Sasebo, Nagasaki, 857-1165, Japan JP
Tel.: (81) 956233800 (100%)
Web Site: www.fukuoka-fg.com
Credit Card Processing & Money Lending Services
S.I.C.: 6141
N.A.I.C.S.: 522291

Shinwa Venture Capital Co., Ltd. (2)
10-11 Shimanose-cho
Sasebo, Nagasaki, 850-0841, Japan JP
Tel.: (81) 956246165 (100%)
Fax: (81) 982570806
Web Site: www.shinwavc.co.jp
Securities Trading Services
S.I.C.: 6211
N.A.I.C.S.: 523110

FUKUSHIMA INDUSTRIES CORPORATION

3-16-11 Mitejima
Nishi Yodogawa-ku, Osaka, 555-0012, Japan
Tel.: (81) 6 6477 2011
Fax: (81) 6 6477 0755
E-Mail: oversea@fukusima.co.jp
Web Site: www.fukusima.co.jp
Year Founded: 1951
6420—(TKS)
Sales Range: $300-349.9 Million
Emp.: 939

Business Description:
Refrigerator Mfr & Distr
S.I.C.: 3632
N.A.I.C.S.: 335222

Personnel:
Yutaka Fukushima *(Pres)*

FULCRUM CAPITAL PARTNERS, INC.

885 West Georgia Street Suite 1020
Vancouver, BC, V6C 3E8, Canada
Tel.: (604) 631-8088
Fax: (604) 408-8892
Web Site: www.fulcrumcapital.ca
Managed Assets: $700,000,000

Business Description:
Private Equity Firm
S.I.C.: 6211
N.A.I.C.S.: 523999

Personnel:
David Mullen *(Chm & Mng Partner)*
Neil Johansen *(Mng Partner)*
John Philp *(Mng Partner)*
Johan Lemmer *(CFO)*

Holding:

HSBC Capital Canada, Inc. (1)
Ste 1020 885 W Georgia St
PO Box 1032
Vancouver, BC, V6C 3E8, Canada (100%)
Tel.: (604) 631-8089
Fax: (604) 408-8892
E-Mail: info@fulcrumcapital.ca
Web Site: www.fulcrumcapital.ca/capital
Emp.: 13
Investment & Merchant Banking, Immigrant Investor Fund Servicing, & Specialised Merger & Acquisition Services to Individual & Corporate Investors
S.I.C.: 6211
N.A.I.C.S.: 523110
Neil Johanson *(Mng Partner)*
David F. Mullen *(Mng Partner)*

FULCRUM UTILITY SERVICES LIMITED

2 Europa View Sheffield Business Park
Sheffield, S9 1XH, United Kingdom
Tel.: (44) 845 641 3010
Fax: (44) 845 641 1808
E-Mail: enquiries@fulcrum.co.uk
Web Site: www.fulcrumutilityserviceslimited.co.uk
FCRM—(LSE)
Rev.: $61,227,494
Assets: $40,003,416
Liabilities: $39,829,694
Net Worth: $173,722
Earnings: ($781,749)
Emp.: 207
Fiscal Year-end: 03/31/13

Business Description:
Investment Management Services
S.I.C.: 6282
N.A.I.C.S.: 523920

Personnel:
Philip Bernard Holder *(Chm)*
Martin Donnachie *(CEO)*
Robert Douglas *(Interim CFO)*

Board of Directors:
Philip Bernard Holder
Martin Donnachie
Stephen Gutteridge
Mark Irvine John Watts

Legal Counsel:
Mayer Brown International LLP
201 Bishopsgate
London, United Kingdom

Maples & Calder
Princes Court 7 Princes Street
London, EC2R 8AQ, United Kingdom

FULGENT SUN INTERNATIONAL (HOLDING) CO., LTD.

76 Sec 3 Yunke Rd
Douliou, Taiwan
Tel.: (886) 55514619
Fax: (886) 55514630
E-Mail: service@fulgentsun.com
Web Site: www.fulgentsun.com
9802—(TAI)
Sales Range: $200-249.9 Million

Business Description:
Sports Shoes Mfr
S.I.C.: 2389
N.A.I.C.S.: 316210

Personnel:
Wen-Chih Lin *(Chm)*

THE FULHAM SHORE PLC

307 Linton House 164-180 Union Street
Waterloo, London, SE1 0LH, United Kingdom
Tel.: (44) 207 902 9790
E-Mail: thefulhamshore@gmail.com
Web Site: www.fulhamshore.com

Business Description:
Restaurants Investment Services
S.I.C.: 6211
N.A.I.C.S.: 523999

Personnel:
David Page *(Chm)*

Board of Directors:
David Page
Nick Donaldson
Nabil Mankarious

FULL APEX (HOLDINGS) LIMITED

Room 502 5 Floor The Sun's Group Centre 200 Gloucester Road
Wanchai, China (Hong Kong)
Tel.: (852) 23757818
Fax: (852) 29730800
E-Mail: fullapex@fullapex.com
Web Site: www.fullapex.com
Year Founded: 1996
36F—(DEU SES)
Rev.: $340,868,590
Assets: $390,971,151
Liabilities: $155,217,101
Net Worth: $235,754,051
Earnings: $7,194,158
Fiscal Year-end: 12/31/12

Business Description:
Polyethylene Terephthalate Resin Mfr
S.I.C.: 2823
N.A.I.C.S.: 325220

Personnel:
Lingxiang Guan *(Chm & Mng Dir)*
Huiying Liang *(Vice Chm)*
Yvonne Choo *(Co-Sec)*
Gwendolin Soo Fern Lee *(Co-Sec)*

Board of Directors:
Lingxiang Guan
Hee Kok Chng
Huiying Liang
Tan Han Tan
Yunying Wang

BDO Limited
25th Floor Wing On Centre 111 Connaught Road
Central, China (Hong Kong)

Transfer Agent:
B.A.C.S. Private Limited
63 Cantonment Road
Singapore, 089758, Singapore
Tel.: (65) 3236 2000

FULL METAL MINERALS LTD.

1500-409 Granville Street
Vancouver, BC, V6C 1T2, Canada
Tel.: (604) 484-7855
Fax: (604) 484-7155
Toll Free: (866) 284-2296
E-Mail: info@fullmetalminerals.com
Web Site: www.fullmetalminerals.com
Year Founded: 2003
FMM—(TSXV)
Int. Income: $4,669
Assets: $1,784,641
Liabilities: $555,384
Net Worth: $1,229,257
Earnings: ($2,473,856)
Fiscal Year-end: 05/31/13

Business Description:
Mineral Exploration Services
S.I.C.: 1081
N.A.I.C.S.: 213114

Personnel:
Michael J. Williams *(Pres)*
Robert J. McLeod *(CEO & VP-Exploration)*
Cale J. Moodie *(CFO)*

Board of Directors:
Anthony Cange
Darryl Cardey
Carl Hering
Robert J. McLeod
Michael J. Williams

Legal Counsel:
DuMoulin Black LLP
10th Floor 595 Howe St
Vancouver, BC, Canada

Transfer Agent:
Computershare
3rd Floor 510 Burrard Street
Vancouver, BC, Canada

FULL METAL ZINC LTD.

1500 409 Granville Street
Vancouver, BC, V6C 1T2, Canada
Tel.: (604) 484-7855
Fax: (604) 484-7155
Toll Free: (866) 284-2296
E-Mail: info@fullmetalzinc.com
Web Site: www.fullmetalzinc.com
Year Founded: 2011
FZ—(TSXV)
Assets: $746,844
Liabilities: $232,005
Net Worth: $514,839
Earnings: ($1,140,858)
Fiscal Year-end: 05/31/13

Business Description:
Zinc Mining Services
S.I.C.: 1031
N.A.I.C.S.: 212231

Personnel:
Michael Williams *(Chm, Interim Pres & Interim CEO)*
Cale J. Moodie *(CFO)*
Sheryl Elsdon *(Sec)*

Board of Directors:
Michael Williams
Adrian Fleming
Aaron Keay
Robert McLeod
Cale J. Moodie
Al Paterson

Legal Counsel:
DuMoulin Black
10th Floor, 595 Howe Street
Vancouver, BC, V6C 2T5, Canada

Transfer Agent:
Computershare
3rd Floor 510 Burrard Street
Vancouver, BC, Canada

FULLCAST HOLDINGS CO., LTD.

Pola Third Gotanda Building 12th Floor 8-9-5 Nishigotanda
Shinagawa-ku, Tokyo, 141-0031, Japan
Tel.: (81) 3 4530 4880
Fax: (81) 3 4530 4859
E-Mail: trir@fullcast.co.jp
Web Site: www.fullcast.co.jp
Year Founded: 1990
4848—(TKS)
Sls.: $405,856,000
Assets: $90,596,000
Liabilities: $31,174,000
Net Worth: $59,422,000
Earnings: $15,697,000
Emp.: 489
Fiscal Year-end: 12/31/12

Business Description:
Human Resources Solutions
S.I.C.: 8999
N.A.I.C.S.: 541612

Personnel:
Hiroyuki Tokiwa *(Pres & CEO)*
Takehito Hirano *(Mng Dir)*
Kazuki Sakamaki *(Mng Dir)*
Yuhiko Yasunaga *(Mng Dir)*

Board of Directors:
Takehito Hirano
Kazuki Sakamaki
Hiroyuki Tokiwa
Yuhiko Yasunaga

Transfer Agent:
Sumitomo Mitsui Trust Bank, Limited
1 4 1 Marunouchi Chiyoda ku
Tokyo, Japan

Subsidiaries:

Fullcast Advance Co., Ltd. (1)
Shinagawa Bldg 3Fl 3 26 33 Takanawa
Minato-ku, Tokyo, 108 0074, Japan
Tel.: (81) 3 4550 1151
Fax: (81) 3 4550 1152
Web Site: www.fullcast.co.jp/english/group.html
Security Guards & Patrol Services
S.I.C.: 7381
N.A.I.C.S.: 561612

Fullcast Finance Co., Ltd. (1)
1-19-14 Jinnan Shibuya-Ku
Tokyo, Japan
Tel.: (81) 3 5728 3696
Fax: (81) 3 5728 3696
Web Site: www.fullcast.co.jp/english/group.html
Nondepository Credit Intermediation
S.I.C.: 6159
N.A.I.C.S.: 522298

Fullcast Technology Co., Ltd. (1)
Landmark Tower 21F 2-2-1 Minato-Mirai
Nishi-ku, Yokohama, Kanagawa, 220-8121, Japan
Tel.: (81) 452260108
Fax: (81) 452256340
Emp.: 1,243
Temporary Help Services
S.I.C.: 7363
N.A.I.C.S.: 561320
Shiro Kaizuka *(Pres & CEO)*

Nisso Co., Ltd. (1)
Musashino Bldg 4th Fl Shinjuku-Ku
Tokyo, Japan
Tel.: (81) 333544191
Fax: (81) 333544192
Painting & Wall Covering Contractors
S.I.C.: 1721
N.A.I.C.S.: 238320

Toa System Co., Ltd. (1)
85-1 Nodano Nagakute Nagakutecho
Nagoya, Japan
Tel.: (81) 561628821
Custom Computer Programming Services
S.I.C.: 7371
N.A.I.C.S.: 541511

FULLER, SMITH & TURNER P.L.C.

The Griffin Brewery Chiswick Lane South
London, W4 2QB, United Kingdom
Tel.: (44) 20 8996 2000
Fax: (44) 20 8995 0230
E-Mail: fullers@fullers.co.uk
Web Site: www.fullers.co.uk
Year Founded: 1845
FSTA—(LSE)
Rev.: $428,777,235
Assets: $772,114,881
Liabilities: $362,447,055
Net Worth: $409,667,826
Earnings: $46,273,197
Emp.: 3,477
Fiscal Year-end: 03/30/13

Business Description:
Brewery & Pub Operator
Import Export
S.I.C.: 2082
N.A.I.C.S.: 312120

Personnel:
Michael John Turner *(Chm)*
Simon Emeny *(CEO)*
Marie Gracie *(Sec)*

Board of Directors:
Michael John Turner
Ian Bray
James Douglas
John Dunsmore
Simon Emeny
Lynn Fordham
James Fuller
Richard Fuller
Alastair Kerr
Jonathon Swaine

Subsidiary:

Griffin Catering Services Limited (1)
Griffin Brewery
Chiswick, London, W4 2QB, United Kingdom
Tel.: (44) 2089962000
Fax: (44) 2089950230
E-Mail: reception@fullers.co.uk
Web Site: www.fullers.co.uk
Emp.: 400
Managed house services
S.I.C.: 7699
N.A.I.C.S.: 811411
Michael Turner *(Chm)*

FULLERTON TECHNOLOGY CO., LTD.

5F No 6-3 Baoqiang Rd
Xindian District, New Taipei City, 23144, Taiwan
Tel.: (886) 289124300
Fax: (886) 289124301
E-Mail: service@fullerton.com.tw
Web Site: www.fullerton.com.tw
Year Founded: 1992
6136—(TAI)
Sales Range: $25-49.9 Million
Emp.: 80

Business Description:
Telecommunication Services
S.I.C.: 4899
N.A.I.C.S.: 517919

Personnel:
David Lai *(Pres & CEO)*
Lucky Ho *(CFO)*

FULLSIX S.P.A.

Corso Vercelli 40
20145 Milan, Italy
Tel.: (39) 02303241
Fax: (39) 0230324556
E-Mail: ir@fullsix.it
Web Site: www.fullsix.it
FUL—(ITA)
Sales Range: $75-99.9 Million
Emp.: 595

Business Description:
E-Business & Marketing Services
S.I.C.: 8742
N.A.I.C.S.: 541613

Personnel:
Marco Benatti *(Chm)*
Marco Tinelli *(Mng Dir)*
Fadioe Valente *(CFO)*

Board of Directors:
Marco Benatti
Ezio Dozio
Serge Pastore
Enrico Robbiati
Marco Tinelli
Guido Vercellino
Fulvio Zendrini

Subsidiaries:

DMC SRL (1)
Corso Vercelli 40
20145 Milan, Italy (100%)
Tel.: (39) 02303241
Fax: (39) 0230324556
E-Mail: fabio.valante@fullsix.it
Emp.: 170
Advertising Services
S.I.C.: 7319
N.A.I.C.S.: 541890
Marco Tinelli *(Mng Dir)*

OneTOne Research SRL (1)
Corso Vercelli 40
24145 Milan, Italy (95.15%)
Tel.: (39) 02303241
Fax: (39) 0230324575
Web Site: www.onetone.it
Direct Marketing Services
S.I.C.: 7331
N.A.I.C.S.: 541860

Non-U.S. Subsidiaries:

Fullsix (Francia) S.A.S. (1)
123 Rue Jules Guesde
157 rue Anatole France, 92300 Levallois-Perret, France (99.95%)
Tel.: (33) 149687300
Fax: (33) 149687373
E-Mail: contact@fullsix.com
Web Site: www.fullsix.fr
Emp.: 300
Marketing Services
S.I.C.: 8742
N.A.I.C.S.: 541613
Xavier Delanglade *(CEO)*

Fullsix (Portugal) LDA (1)
Galerias Alto de Barra
Av Das Descobertes 59
4th Fl, 2780-053 Oeiras, Portugal (51%)
Tel.: (351) 214462460
Fax: (351) 214462469
E-Mail: contact@fullsix.com
Web Site: www.fullsix.pt
Emp.: 100
Marketing Services
S.I.C.: 8742
N.A.I.C.S.: 541613
Pedro Batalha *(Mng Dir)*

Fullsix Spain (1)
Calle Alcala Edif 2 planta 2
28027 Madrid, Spain (100%)
Tel.: (34) 917610550
E-Mail: contact@fullsix.com
Web Site: www.fullsix.es
Marketing Services
S.I.C.: 8742
N.A.I.C.S.: 541613

FULTON HOGAN LIMITED

29 Sir William Pickering Dr
Christchurch, Canterbury, 8053, New Zealand
Tel.: (64) 33571400
Fax: (64) 33571450
E-Mail: info@fultonhogan.com
Web Site: www.fultonhogan.com
Sales Range: $700-749.9 Million
Emp.: 4,000

Business Description:
Civil Construction Services
S.I.C.: 1629
N.A.I.C.S.: 237990

Personnel:
E. G. Johnson *(Chm)*
N D Miller *(Deputy Mng Dir)*
D. J. Faulkner *(Mng Dir)*
G M Tapp *(CFO)*

Board of Directors:
E. G. Johnson
D. J. Faulkner
R. J. Fulton
F. R. Funnell
W. H. Johnstone
N D Miller
S J Smith

Non-U.S. Joint Venture:

Pioneer Road Services Pty. Ltd. (1)
Ste 1202 Level 12 Flinders Tower
World Trade Centre, Melbourne, VIC, 3005, Australia AU
Tel.: (61) 39628080
Fax: (61) 39628008
Web Site: www.fultonhogan.com
Sales Range: $150-199.9 Million
Emp.: 1,000
Road Construction, Maintenance & Resurfacing Services; Joint Venture of Royal Dutch Shell plc (50%) & Fulton Hogan Ltd. (50%)
S.I.C.: 1611
N.A.I.C.S.: 237310

FULTON INSURANCE AGENCIES LTD.

38 Young St
Truro, NS, B2N 3W4, Canada
Tel.: (902) 895-3686
Fax: (902) 893-1768
Toll Free: (800) 518-8886
E-Mail: info@fultoninsurance.ns.ca
Web Site: www.fultoninsurance.ns.ca
Year Founded: 1936
Rev.: $20,000,000
Emp.: 10

Business Description:
Insurance Agency Services
S.I.C.: 6411
N.A.I.C.S.: 524210

Personnel:
Adam Wyllie *(Pres)*

FULUHASHI EPO CORPORATION

1-12-14 Kanayama Naka-ku
Nagoya, Aichi, 460-0022, Japan
Tel.: (81) 52 324 9088
Fax: (81) 52 324 9188
Web Site: www.fuluhashi.co.jp

Business Description:
Recycling & Environmental Services
S.I.C.: 5093
N.A.I.C.S.: 423930

Personnel:
Naohiko Yamaguchi *(CEO)*

Joint Venture:

Kawasaki Biomass Power Generation Co., Ltd. (1)
16-5 Isouracho
Niihama, Ehime, 792- 0002, Japan
Tel.: (81) 897372142
Electric Power Generation Services
S.I.C.: 4939
N.A.I.C.S.: 221117

FUMAKILLA LIMITED

11 Kanda Mikura-cho
Chiyoda-ku, Tokyo, 101-8606, Japan
Tel.: (81) 332528561
Fax: (81) 332583532
Web Site: www.fumakilla.co.jp
4998—(TKS)

Business Description:
Agricultural Chemical Mfr
S.I.C.: 2879
N.A.I.C.S.: 325320

Fumakilla Limited—(Continued)

Personnel:
Kazuaki Ohshimo *(Pres)*

Non-U.S. Subsidiary:

PT Technopia Jakarta (1)
Jalan Terusan Interchange Anggadita
Klari, 41371 Karawang, Jawa Barat, Indonesia Id
Tel.: (62) 267432121 (70%)
Fax: (62) 267 432 122
E-Mail: sr@jkt.technopia.co.id
Mosquito Coils Mfr
S.I.C.: 2879
N.A.I.C.S.: 325320

Non-U.S. Joint Venture:

Fumakilla Malaysia Berhad (1)
Plot No 256 Tingkat Perusahaan 5
Kawasan Perindustrian Perai 2
13600 Perai, Pulau Pinang, Malaysia
Tel.: (60) 43883777
Fax: (60) 43883737
Web Site: www.texchemfamilycare.com
Household Insecticides Mfr
S.I.C.: 2879
N.A.I.C.S.: 325320
Li-lian Foo *(Mgr-Sls & Mktg)*

Non-U.S. Subsidiary:

Technopia (Thailand) Ltd. (2)
323 Moo 6 Ratchasima-Chokchai Rd Nong Rawiang Muang
30000 Nakhon Ratchasima, Thailand
Tel.: (66) 44212990
Fax: (66) 44212994
E-Mail: ttl@technopia.co.th
Web Site: www.texchemfamilycare.com
Mosquito Coils & Insecticides Mfr
S.I.C.: 2879
N.A.I.C.S.: 325320
Lim Eng Thai *(Mng Dir)*

FUNAI ELECTRIC CO., LTD.

7-7-1 Nakagaito
Daito city, Osaka, 574-0013, Japan
Tel.: (81) 728704303
Fax: (81) 728711112
Web Site: www.funaiworld.com
Year Founded: 1961
6839—(TKS)
Sls.: $2,112,088,000
Assets: $2,139,764,000
Liabilities: $804,386,000
Net Worth: $1,335,378,000
Earnings: ($93,973,000)
Emp.: 4,776
Fiscal Year-end: 03/31/13

Business Description:
Audio-Visual Equipment, Telecommunications Products Mfr
S.I.C.: 3651
N.A.I.C.S.: 334310

Personnel:
Tetsuro Funai *(Chm)*
Tomonori Hayashi *(Pres & CEO)*
Chinzei Chinzei *(Officer)*
Hideaki Funakoshi *(Officer)*
Takeshi Ito *(Officer)*
Sei Kono *(Officer)*
Tetsuhiro Maeda *(Officer)*
Hirofumi Nagaoka *(Exec Officer)*
Susumu Nojii *(Officer)*
Jyoji Okada *(Officer)*
Shigeki Saji *(Officer)*
Yoshikazu Uemura *(Exec Officer)*
Kazuo Uga *(Officer)*

Board of Directors:
Tetsuro Funai
Yoshiaki Bannai
Tomonori Hayashi
Jyoji Okada
Yoshikazu Uemura
Mitsuo Yonemoto

Subsidiaries:

Chugoku Funai Electric Co., Ltd. (1)
387 2 Aza Ashihara Kamo Cho
Fukuyama, Hiroshima, 7202417, Japan (80%)
Tel.: (81) 849723110
Fax: (81) 849725573
Web Site: www.funaiusa.com
Emp.: 40
S.I.C.: 3651
N.A.I.C.S.: 334310

DX Antenna Co., Ltd. (1)
2-15 Hamazaki-dori
Hyogo-ku, Kobe, Hyogo, 652 0807, Japan
Tel.: (81) 786820001
Fax: (81) 786519521
E-Mail: n_minishitani@dxantenna.co.jp
Web Site: www.dxantenna.co.jp
Emp.: 600
Electronics & Electric Equipment Mfr & Whslr
S.I.C.: 3699
N.A.I.C.S.: 335999
Norihiko Minishitani *(Mgr-Sls)*

F.G.S. Co., Ltd. (1)
1 16 22 Morinomiya Chuoo Chuoo Ku
Osaka, 43836, Japan (100%)
Tel.: (81) 669665380
Fax: (81) 669455054
E-Mail: info@i-fgsco.jp
Web Site: www.funaiusa.com
Emp.: 5
S.I.C.: 3651
N.A.I.C.S.: 334310
Yukio Fukuda *(Pres)*

Funai Electric Advanced Applied Technology Research Institute Inc. (1)
TCI 37A 2-1-6 Sengen
Tsukuba, Ibaraki, 305 0047, Japan
Tel.: (81) 298866500
Fax: (81) 298866511
Web Site: www.funaiworld.com
Electronics & Audio & Video Equipment Research & Development
S.I.C.: 3651
N.A.I.C.S.: 334310

Non-U.S. Subsidiary:

Broadtec TV R&D Center Sdn. Bhd. (2)
G-08 & G-10 Block B Permas Mall Jalan Permas Utara
Bandar Baru Permas Jaya, 81750 Masai, Johor, Malaysia
Tel.: (60) 7 387 9704
Fax: (60) 7 387 9712
Emp.: 82
Electric Component Research & Development Services
S.I.C.: 8731
N.A.I.C.S.: 541712
Masaaki Morita *(Gen Mgr)*

Funai Service Co., Ltd. (1)
3F Nagata SK Park Building 3-2-43 Nagata-Higasi
Higasi-Osaka City, Osaka, 577 0012, Japan
Tel.: (81) 667463303
Fax: (81) 667463326
Web Site: www.funai-service.co.jp
Emp.: 72
Electronics Service & Repair
S.I.C.: 7699
N.A.I.C.S.: 811211
Takayuki Sato *(Pres)*

Funai Techo-Systems Co., Ltd. (1)
7 7 1 Nakagaito
Daito City, Osaka, 5740016, Japan (100%)
Tel.: (81) 667463303
Fax: (81) 667463326
Web Site: www.funaiservice.info
Audio & Video Equipment Manufacturing
S.I.C.: 3651
N.A.I.C.S.: 334310

U.S. Subsidiaries:

Funai Corporation, Inc. (1)
201 Route 17 N
Rutherford, NJ 07070
Tel.: (201) 288-2063
Fax: (201) 288-8019
Web Site: www.funai-corp.com
Seller & Marketer of Consumer Electronics
S.I.C.: 5065
N.A.I.C.S.: 423690

FUNAI SERVICE CORPORATION (1)
2200 Spiegel Dr
Groveport, OH 43125
Tel.: (614) 497-2689
Fax: (614) 409-3511
E-Mail: Parts@funaiservice.com
Web Site: www.funaiservice.com
Electronic Appliances Mfr & Distr
S.I.C.: 3639
N.A.I.C.S.: 335228

P&F USA (1)
3015 Windward Plz Ste 100
Atlanta, GA 30005
Tel.: (678) 319-0439
Television Whslr
S.I.C.: 5946
N.A.I.C.S.: 443142
Ryo Fukuda *(Pres)*
Robert Hoglund *(CFO & Sr Controller)*
Todd Richardson *(Sr VP, Gen Mgr-Sls & Mktg)*

Non-U.S. Subsidiaries:

FUNAI ELECTRIC EUROPE Sp. z.o.o. (1)
ul Inzynierska 1
67-100 Nowa Sol, Poland
Tel.: (48) 68 388 26 05
Fax: (48) 68 388 26 38
E-Mail:
Emp.: 7
Consumer Electronic Goods Mfr
S.I.C.: 3651
N.A.I.C.S.: 334310
Yasuhito Ebine *(Mng Dir)*

Unit:

FUNAI ELECTRIC EUROPE Sp. z.o.o. - Polish Business Unit (2)
17 Stycznia 45 Zephirus Building Ground Floor
02-146 Warsaw, Poland
Tel.: (48) 2260721 92
Fax: (48) 2260721 91
Web Site: www.funaiworld.com
Emp.: 19
Electronic Component Mfr
S.I.C.: 3679
N.A.I.C.S.: 334419
Mariusz Zbiciak *(Gen Mgr)*

Funai Electric (H.K.) Ltd. (1)
Units 6-10 11th Fl Tower 2 Ever Gain Plaza
88 Container Port Road, Kwai Chung, NT, China (Hong Kong) (100%)
Tel.: (852) 26123300
Fax: (852) 26123431
Web Site: www.funaiworld.com
Audio & Visual Equipment Mfr
S.I.C.: 3651
N.A.I.C.S.: 334310

Subsidiary:

H.F.T. Industrial Ltd. (2)
Units 6-10 11th Floor Tower 2 Ever Gain Plaza
88 Container Port Road, Kwai Chung, China (Hong Kong)
Tel.: (852) 26123300
Fax: (852) 26123431
E-Mail: chris.t@funaiworld.com
Web Site: www.funaiworld.com
Emp.: 1
Audio & Video Equipment Mfr
S.I.C.: 3651
N.A.I.C.S.: 334310
Kuniyoshi Tsujimoto *(Mng Dir)*

Funai Electric (Malasiya) Sdn. Bhd. (1)
Plo 405 Jalan Perak Empat Pasir Gudang Industrial Estate
PO Box 71
81707 Pasir Gudang, Johor Darul Takzim, Malaysia
Tel.: (60) 7 251 8381
Fax: (60) 7 2510003
Web Site: www.funaiworld.com
Emp.: 1,000
Audio & Video Equipment Mfr
S.I.C.: 3651
N.A.I.C.S.: 334310
Yoshiyuki Sumitomo *(Mng Dir)*

Funai Europe GmbH (1)
Bosch Strasse 23B
22761 Hamburg, Germany (100%)
Tel.: (49) 403860370
Fax: (49) 4038603723
E-Mail: service@funai.de
Web Site: www.funai.de
Emp.: 8
Audio & Visual Equipment Mfr
S.I.C.: 3651
N.A.I.C.S.: 334310
Yasuhito Ebine *(Mng Dir)*

Funai (Thailand) Co., Ltd. (1)
835 Moo 18 Pakchong-Lumsompung Road
Tambon Chantuek Amphur Pakchon, Nakhon Ratchasima, 30130, Thailand
Tel.: (66) 44310002
Fax: (66) 44 310000
Web Site: www.funaiworld.com
Emp.: 580
Audio & Visual Equipment Mfr
S.I.C.: 3651
N.A.I.C.S.: 334310
Tomoaki Kibino *(Gen Mgr)*

Non-U.S. Units:

FUNAI ELECTRIC EUROPE Sp. z.o.o. - French Business Unit (1)
Bat le Sysley - Paris Nord 2 23 Allee des Impressionistes
BP 66169
Villepinte, 95978 Roissy-en-France, France
Tel.: (33) 1493896 70
Fax: (33) 1493808 75
Electronic Component Mfr
S.I.C.: 3679
N.A.I.C.S.: 334419
Alexandre Sopocko *(Mgr)*

FUNAI ELECTRIC EUROPE Sp. z.o.o. - German Business Unit (1)
Boschstr 23a
22761 Hamburg, Germany
Tel.: (49) 40 386037 0
Fax: (49) 40 386037 23
Emp.: 7
Electronic Component Mfr
S.I.C.: 3679
N.A.I.C.S.: 334419
Yasuhito Ebine *(Gen Mgr)*

FUNCOM N.V.

Lavaterstrasse 45
8002 Zurich, Switzerland
Tel.: (41) 122 925900
E-Mail: investor@funcom.com
Web Site: www.funcom.com
FUNCOM—(OSL)
Rev.: $23,599,000
Assets: $33,282,000
Liabilities: $32,027,000
Net Worth: $1,255,000
Earnings: ($62,215,000)
Emp.: 200
Fiscal Year-end: 12/31/12

Business Description:
Multiplayer Online Game Developer & Operator
S.I.C.: 2741
N.A.I.C.S.: 519130

Personnel:
Gerhard Florin *(Chm-Supervisory Bd)*
Alain Tascan *(Vice Chm-Supervisory Bd)*
Ole Schreiner *(CEO, Mng Dir & Member-Mgmt Bd)*
Pieter van Tol *(Mng Dir & Member-Mgmt Bd)*

Supervisory Board of Directors:
Gerhard Florin
Michel Cassius
Ole Gladhaug
Magnus Groneng
Alain Tascan

U.S. Subsidiary:

Funcom Inc (1)
5826 Fayetteville Rd 201
Durham, NC 27713-8684
Tel.: (919) 806-0707
Web Site: www.funcom.com
Computer Game Development & Publishing Services
S.I.C.: 7371
N.A.I.C.S.: 541511
Bryan Lee *(Mgr)*

Non-U.S. Subsidiary:

Funcom Oslo AS (1)
Drammensveien 167
0277 Oslo, Norway
Tel.: (47) 22925900
Fax: (47) 22730630
Web Site: www.funcom.com
Emp.: 30
Online Game Development & Publishing Services
S.I.C.: 7371
N.A.I.C.S.: 541511
Trond Aas *(Gen Mgr)*

FUNCTIONAL TECHNOLOGIES CORP.

Suite 410 2389 Heath Sciences Mall
Vancouver, BC, V6T 1Z3, Canada
Tel.: (604) 648-2200
Fax: (604) 648-2201
E-Mail: info@functionaltechcorp.com
Web Site: www.functionaltechcorp.com
FEB—(TSXV)
Business Description:
Biological Products Developer
S.I.C.: 2836
N.A.I.C.S.: 325414
Personnel:
Richard L. Sherman *(Chm)*
Christopher Morris *(Interim CFO)*
John Husnik *(CTO & Chief Innovation Officer)*
Board of Directors:
Richard L. Sherman
David E. Allard
Fabio Banducci
Ronald G. Paton
Transfer Agent:
Computershare Trust Company of Canada
9th Floor 100 University Avenue
Toronto, ON, Canada

Subsidiary:

Maritime Pulse Drying Inc. (1)
128 Grahns Pond Rd
Montague, PE, Canada
Tel.: (902) 962-3297
Fax: (866) 903-7914
Spray Drying Equipment Mfr
S.I.C.: 3567
N.A.I.C.S.: 333994

U.S. Subsidiary:

Phyterra Yeast USA Inc. (1)
870-G Napa Vly Corporate Way
Napa, CA 94558
Tel.: (707) 258-8333
Fax: (707) 258-8850
E-Mail: sales@phyterra.com
Web Site: www.phyterra.com
Yeast Mfr
S.I.C.: 2099
N.A.I.C.S.: 311999

Non-U.S. Subsidiary:

Phyterra Europe GmbH (1)
Humboldtstrasse 30/32
70771 Leinfelden-Echterdingen, Germany
Tel.: (49) 71122040950
Fax: (49) 71122040959
E-Mail: acryleast@phyterra.com
Emp.: 2
Yeast Mfr
S.I.C.: 2099
N.A.I.C.S.: 311999
Sebastian Zitzler *(Mng Dir)*

FUND CREATION GROUP CO., LTD.

6-10-1 Roppongi Minato-ku
Tokyo, 106-0032, Japan
Tel.: (81) 354135535
Web Site: www.fc-group.co.jp
3266—(JAS)
Business Description:
Real Estate Asset Management & Investment Banking Services
S.I.C.: 6211
N.A.I.C.S.: 523110
Personnel:
Katsuhiro Tashima *(CEO)*

FUNKWERK AG

Im Funkwerk 5
99625 Kolleda, Germany
Tel.: (49) 3635458326
Fax: (49) 3635458399
E-Mail: info@funkwerk.com
Web Site: www.funkwerk.com
FEW—(DEU)
Rev.: $190,277,091
Assets: $152,197,980
Liabilities: $108,806,883
Net Worth: $43,391,098
Earnings: ($22,125,650)
Emp.: 859
Fiscal Year-end: 12/31/12
Business Description:
Mobile Communication Systems Mfr
S.I.C.: 3663
N.A.I.C.S.: 334220
Personnel:
Alfons Hormann *(Chm-Supervisory Bd)*
Gerhard Fettweiss *(Vice Chm-Supervisory Bd)*
Manfred Lerch *(Mng Dir-Mgmt Bd)*
Kerstin Schreiber *(Member-Exec Bd)*
Supervisory Board of Directors:
Alfons Hormann
Manfred Egner
Gerhard Fettweiss

Subsidiary:

Funkwerk plettac electronic GmbH (1)
Wurzburger Strasse 150
90766 Furth, Germany
Tel.: (49) 911758840
Fax: (49) 91175884100
E-Mail: info@plettac-electronics.de
Web Site: www.plettac-electronics.de
Emp.: 120
Mfr. of Mobile Communication Systems
S.I.C.: 3663
N.A.I.C.S.: 334220

FUNTALK CHINA HOLDINGS LIMITED

21st Floor Block D The Place Tower
No 9 Guanghua Rd
Chaoyang District, Beijing, 100020, China
Tel.: (86) 1057091100
E-Mail: jackie@funtalk.cn
Web Site: www.funtalk.cn
Year Founded: 2003
Sales Range: $800-899.9 Million
Emp.: 9,800
Business Description:
Wireless Communications Devices, Accessories & Content Retailer & Distr
S.I.C.: 4812
N.A.I.C.S.: 517210
Personnel:
Kuo Zhang *(Chm)*
Dongping Fei *(CEO)*
Kim Chuan Leong *(CFO)*
Hengyang Zhou *(Exec VP)*
Clement Kwong *(Sr VP-Corp Strategy)*
Bernard J. Tanenbaum, III *(Sr VP-Corp Comm)*

FUNTASTIC LIMITED

Level 2 Tower 2 Chadstone Place
1341 Dandenong Road
Chadstone, VIC, 3148, Australia
Tel.: (61) 3 8531 0000
Fax: (61) 3 9569 4987
E-Mail: info@funtastic.com.au
Web Site: www.funtastic.com.au
Year Founded: 1994
FUN—(ASX)
Rev.: $173,556,545
Assets: $216,548,380
Liabilities: $109,267,311
Net Worth: $107,281,069
Earnings: $14,549,800
Emp.: 211
Fiscal Year-end: 07/31/13
Business Description:
Children's Toys & Related Merchandise Distr & Marketer
S.I.C.: 5092
N.A.I.C.S.: 423920
Personnel:
Stewart Downs *(CEO & Mng Dir)*
Grant Mackenzie *(CFO & Sec)*
Board of Directors:
Shane Tanner
Stewart Downs
Stephen Heath
Craig Mathieson
Linda Norquay
Nir Pizmony
Paul Wiegard
Legal Counsel:
Clarendon Lawyers
Level 17 Rialto Tower 525 Collins Street
Melbourne, Australia

Subsidiaries:

JNH Australia Pty Ltd (1)
635 Waverley Rd
3150 Glen Waverley, VIC, Australia (100%)
Tel.: (61) 395355888
Fax: (61) 395450829
E-Mail: info@funtastic.com.au
Emp.: 300
Confectionery Whslr
S.I.C.: 5145
N.A.I.C.S.: 424450
Stewart Downs *(CEO)*

Madman Entertainment Pty Limited (1)
1-35 Wellington Street
PO Box 1480
3066 Collingwood, VIC, Australia (100%)
Tel.: (61) 394170977
Fax: (61) 394187388
Web Site: www.madman.com.au
Sls.: $31,942,000
Emp.: 100
Motion Picture & Video Industries
S.I.C.: 7819
N.A.I.C.S.: 512199
Tim Anderson *(Founder & Mng Dir)*
Paul Wiegard *(Founder & Mng Dir)*

Madman Films Pty Limited (1)
1-35 Wellington Street
Collingwood, VIC, 3066, Australia (100%)
Tel.: (61) 394170977
Fax: (61) 394187388
E-Mail: madman@madman.com.au
Web Site: www.madman.com.au
Emp.: 100
Motion Picture & Video Industries
S.I.C.: 7819
N.A.I.C.S.: 512199
Wilf Robinson *(Gen Mgr-Sls)*

Non-U.S. Subsidiaries:

Fun International Ltd (1)
Rm 508a 5th Floor Empire Ctr
Tsim Sha Tsui, Kowloon, China (Hong Kong) (100%)
Tel.: (852) 31037300
Fax: (852) 31433103
Emp.: 30
Nondurable Goods Whslr
S.I.C.: 5199
N.A.I.C.S.: 424990

Funtastic International Limited (1)
1502 Chinachem Golden Plz 77 Mody Rd
Tsim Sha Tsui E
Kowloon, China (Hong Kong)
Tel.: (852) 31037300
Fax: (852) 31037333
Web Site: www.funtastic.com.au
Emp.: 20
Toys Mfr
S.I.C.: 3944
N.A.I.C.S.: 339930
Pedro Sangil *(Gen Mgr)*

Madman NZ Limited (1)
PO Box 47426
Ponsonby, Auckland, New Zealand
Tel.: (64) 93700188
Fax: (64) 93760221
E-Mail: info@madman.co.nz
Web Site: www.madman.co.nz
Emp.: 7
Digital Video Discs Whslr
S.I.C.: 7841
N.A.I.C.S.: 532230
Tim Anderson *(Co-Founder)*
Paul Wiegard *(Co-Founder)*

FUQI INTERNATIONAL, INC.

5th Floor Block 1 Shi Hua Industrial Zone
Chu Zhu Road North, Shenzhen, Guangdong, 518019, China
Tel.: (86) 755 25801888
Fax: (86) 755 25803999
E-Mail: ir@fuqiintl.com
Web Site: www.fuqi.com.cn
Year Founded: 2001
FUQI—(OTC)
Sales Range: $300-349.9 Million
Emp.: 949
Business Description:
Precious Metal Jewelry Designer & Retailer
S.I.C.: 3911
N.A.I.C.S.: 339910
Personnel:
Yu Kwai Chong *(Chm)*
Kim K. T. Pan *(Pres, CEO & Interim CFO)*
Lie Xi Zhuang *(COO)*
Board of Directors:
Yu Kwai Chong
Jeff Haiyong Liu
Kim K. T. Pan
Lie Xi Zhuang

Subsidiary:

Shenzhen Fuqi Jewelry Co., Ltd. (1)
4-6/F 1 Block Shihua Industrial Area
Cuizhu North Road Luohu, Shenzhen, 518019, China
Tel.: (86) 75525801888
Fax: (86) 75525803999
E-Mail: fuqi@fiqi.com.cn
Web Site: www.fuqi.com.cn
Jewelry Mfr
S.I.C.: 3911
N.A.I.C.S.: 339910
Yu Kwai Chong *(Chm, Pres & CEO)*

FURAMA LTD.

405 Havelock Road
Singapore, 169633, Singapore
Tel.: (65) 67396470
Fax: (65) 67361490
E-Mail: fhi@furama.com
Web Site: www.furama.com
Sales Range: $50-74.9 Million
Emp.: 546
Business Description:
Investment Services & Hotel Operations
S.I.C.: 6211
N.A.I.C.S.: 523999
Personnel:
Kim Suan Ng *(Chm)*

FURNESS BUILDING SOCIETY

51-55 Duke Street
Barrow-in-Furness, Cumbria, LA14 1RT, United Kingdom
Tel.: (44) 1229824560
Fax: (44) 1229837043
E-Mail: furness.direct@furness-bs.co.uk
Web Site: www.furness-bs.co.uk

Furness Building Society—(Continued)

Year Founded: 1865
Rev.: $41,830,654
Assets: $1,322,132,630
Liabilities: $198,823,135
Net Worth: $1,123,309,495
Earnings: $2,395,783
Emp.: 100
Fiscal Year-end: 12/31/12

Business Description:
Mortgage Lending & Other Financial Services
S.I.C.: 6163
N.A.I.C.S.: 522310

Personnel:
Colin Stewart Millar *(Vice Chm)*
Nigel Anthony Quinton *(CEO)*
Susan Jane Heron *(Sec)*

Board of Directors:
Peter Richard Wavell Hensman
Martin James Cutbill
Christopher Stuart Fairclough
Alan Thomas Ferguson Hunter
Philip Anthony Ireland
Kim Susan Kearney
Colin Stewart Millar
Steven Lindsay Pryer
Nigel Anthony Quinton
Brian Preston Ryninks

FURNITURE VILLAGE LIMITED

258 Bath Road
Slough, Berkshire, SL1 4DX, United Kingdom
Tel.: (44) 1753 897720
Fax: (44) 1753 897730
E-Mail: online@furniturevillage.co.uk
Web Site: www.furniturevillage.co.uk
Year Founded: 1989
Sales Range: $250-299.9 Million
Emp.: 758

Business Description:
Furniture Product Whslr
S.I.C.: 5021
N.A.I.C.S.: 423210

Personnel:
Peter Harrison *(CEO)*

FURNIWEB INDUSTRIAL PRODUCTS BHD

Lot 1883 Jalan KPB 9 Kg Bharu Balakong
43300 Seri Kembangan, Selangor Darul Ehsan, Malaysia
Tel.: (60) 3 8961 2278
Fax: (60) 3 8961 2340
E-Mail: general@furniweb.com.my
Web Site: www.furniweb.com.my
Year Founded: 1983
FURNWEB—(KLS)
Rev.: $27,704,977
Assets: $30,956,960
Liabilities: $6,649,234
Net Worth: $24,307,726
Earnings: $1,315,943
Emp.: 776
Fiscal Year-end: 12/31/12

Business Description:
Holding Company; Textile & Apparel Products Mfr
S.I.C.: 2389
N.A.I.C.S.: 314999

Personnel:
Eng Chuan Cheah *(Mng Dir)*
Fei Chia Lim *(Co-Sec)*
Chong Keat Yeoh *(Co-Sec)*

Board of Directors:
Heen Peok Lim
Eng Chuan Cheah
Carmey Chua
Sim Hak Lee
Chee Hoong Lim
Hamzah Mohd Salleh
Johar Murat
Lock Hoo Ong

Subsidiaries:

Furniweb Manufacturing Sdn. Bhd. **(1)**
Lot 1883 Jalan KPB 9 Kg Bharu Balakong
43300 Seri Kembangan, Selangor Darul Ehsan, Malaysia
Tel.: (60) 3 8961 2278
Fax: (60) 3 8931 2340
E-Mail: general@furniweb.com.my
Webbing & Yarn Mfr
S.I.C.: 2299
N.A.I.C.S.: 313110

Furniweb Safety Webbing Sdn. Bhd. **(1)**
Lot 1883 Jalan KPB 9 Kg Bharu Balakong
43300 Seri Kembangan, Selangor Darul Ehsan, Malaysia
Tel.: (60) 389612278
Fax: (60) 389612340
E-Mail: general@furniweb.com.my
Web Site: www.furniweb.com.my
Emp.: 100
Mfr of Motor Vehicle Safety Accessories
S.I.C.: 3714
N.A.I.C.S.: 336340
Eng Chuan Cheah *(CEO & Mng Dir)*

Texstrip Manufacturing Sdn. Bhd. **(1)**
Lot 1908 Batu 7 Jalan Bukit Kemuning
Seksyen 34
40470 Shah Alam, Selangor Dahrul Ehsa, Malaysia
Tel.: (60) 3 5121 2662
Fax: (60) 3 5121 2772
E-Mail: general@texstrip.com.my
Elastic Tape Mfr
S.I.C.: 2389
N.A.I.C.S.: 314999

Webtex Trading Sdn. Bhd. **(1)**
No 47 Jalan Jalak Taman Bukit Mewah
Cheras, 56100 Kuala Lumpur, Malaysia
Tel.: (60) 3 9131 8923
Fax: (60) 3 9131 8924
E-Mail: general@webtex.com.my
Furniture Webbing Sales
S.I.C.: 2299
N.A.I.C.S.: 314999

Non-U.S. Subsidiaries:

Furnitech Components (Vietnam) Co., Ltd. **(1)**
Street No 2 Nhon Trach Industrial Zone I
Nhon Trach, Dong Nai, Vietnam
Tel.: (84) 61 560385
Fax: (84) 61 560408
E-Mail: general@gurniweb.com.vn
Web Site: www.furniweb.com.my/furnitech.html
Recliner Mechanism Mfr
S.I.C.: 2519
N.A.I.C.S.: 337125

Furniweb Manufacturing (Vietnam) Co., Ltd. **(1)**
no 18 Road 3A Bien Hoa Industrial Zone II
Bien Hoa, Dong Nai, Vietnam
Tel.: (84) 61 832742
Fax: (84) 61 833090
E-Mail: general@furniweb.com.vn
Textile Products Mfr
S.I.C.: 2299
N.A.I.C.S.: 314999

Premier Elastic Webbing & Accessories (Vietnam) Co., Ltd. **(1)**
Street No 8 Nhon Trach Industrial Zone I
Nhon Trach, Dong Nai, Vietnam
Tel.: (84) 61 549385
Fax: (84) 61 848942
E-Mail: general@premierelastic.com.vn
Elastic Products Mfr
S.I.C.: 2389
N.A.I.C.S.: 314999

FURQAN BUSINESS ORGANISATION BERHAD

(See Under EastLand Equity Berhad)

FURUKAWA CO., LTD.

2-3 Marunouchi 2-chome Chiyoda-ku
Tokyo, 100-8370, Japan
Tel.: (81) 332126570
Fax: (81) 332126578
Web Site: www.furukawakk.co.jp
5715—(TKS)
Sls.: $1,820,940,000
Assets: $2,046,836,000
Liabilities: $1,480,259,000
Net Worth: $566,577,000
Earnings: $32,736,000
Emp.: 2,342
Fiscal Year-end: 03/31/13

Business Description:
Holding Company; Industrial, Construction & Mining Machinery, Metals, Electronic Materials, Chemicals, Paint & Fuels
S.I.C.: 6719
N.A.I.C.S.: 551112

Personnel:
Nobuyoshi Soma *(Chm)*
Naohisa Miyakawa *(Pres)*
Manabu Zama *(Sr Mng Dir)*
Toshio Matsumoto *(Co-Mng Dir)*
Susumu Nakamura *(Co-Mng Dir)*
Kenji Ichimura *(Sr Exec Officer)*
Kiyohiko Ikebe *(Exec Officer)*
Minoru Iwata *(Sr Exec Officer)*
Naoki Kato *(Exec Officer)*
Yoshinari Kuno *(Exec Officer)*
Shigeo Matsudo *(Exec Officer)*
Kiyohito Mitsumura *(Exec Officer)*
Akinori Ota *(Sr Exec Officer)*
Saburou Saruhashi *(Sr Exec Officer)*
Osamu Watanabe *(Sr Exec Officer)*
Yasufumi Watanabe *(Exec Officer)*

Board of Directors:
Nobuyoshi Soma
Minoru Iwata
Toshio Matsumoto
Naohisa Miyakawa
Susumu Nakamura
Akinori Ota
Masao Yoshida
Manabu Zama

Transfer Agent:
Sumitomo Mitsui Trust Bank, Limited
4-1 Marunouchi 1-chome Chiyoda-ku
Tokyo, Japan

Division:

Furukawa Co., Ltd. - Real Estate Division **(1)**
3-14 Nihonbashi muromachi 2-chome
Chou-ku, Tokyo, Japan
Tel.: (81) 332111501
Fax: (81) 332427275
Web Site: www.furukawa.co.jp
Real Estate Management Services
S.I.C.: 6531
N.A.I.C.S.: 531390

Subsidiaries:

Furukawa Chemicals Co., Ltd. **(1)**
7-196 Ohno 3-chome
Nishiyodogawa-ku, Osaka, Japan
Tel.: (81) 664721131
Fax: (81) 664720275
Chemicals Mfr
S.I.C.: 2899
N.A.I.C.S.: 325199

Furukawa Denshi Co., Ltd. **(1)**
20 Aza Kodate Kamiyoshima
Yoshima-machi, Iwaki, Fukushima, 970-1153, Japan
Tel.: (81) 246362016
Fax: (81) 246363973
Web Site: www.furukawa-denshi.co.jp
Emp.: 150
Arsenic Materials Mfr
S.I.C.: 2816
N.A.I.C.S.: 325130
Naohisa Miyakawa *(Pres)*

Plants:

Furukawa Denshi Co., Ltd. - Optical Components Plant **(2)**
11-10 Minamisakae-cho
Kasukabe, Saitama, Japan
Tel.: (81) 332123967
Fax: (81) 487557703
E-Mail: n-furukoshi@furukawakk.co.jp
Web Site: www.furukawa-denshi.co.jp
Emp.: 1,500
Optical Components Mfr
S.I.C.: 3827
N.A.I.C.S.: 333314
Hitoshi Iida *(Mgr-Sls)*

Furukawa Denshi Co., Ltd. - Semiconductor Materials Plant **(2)**
2982 Tojimo Ashio-machi
Nikko, Tochigi, Japan
Tel.: (81) 288932600
Fax: (81) 288934788
Semiconductor Materials Mfr
S.I.C.: 3674
N.A.I.C.S.: 334413

Furukawa Industrial Machinery Systems Co., Ltd. **(1)**
2-3 Marunouchi 2-chome
Chiyoda-ku, Tokyo, 100-8370, Japan
Tel.: (81) 332127803
Fax: (81) 332126557
E-Mail:
Web Site: www.furukawa-sanki.co.jp
Emp.: 300
Industrial Machinery Mfr
S.I.C.: 3561
N.A.I.C.S.: 333911
Yoshio Goto *(Gen Mgr)*

Units:

Furukawa Industrial Machinery Systems Co., Ltd. - Oyama Unit **(2)**
23-15 Wakagi-cho 1-chome
Oyama, Tochigi, Japan
Tel.: (81) 285238650
Fax: (81) 285238653
Industrial Machinery Mfr
S.I.C.: 3561
N.A.I.C.S.: 333911

Furukawa Industrial Machinery Systems Co., Ltd. - Tochigi Unit **(2)**
2245 Omiya-cho
Tochigi, Japan
Tel.: (81) 282273200
Fax: (81) 0282273338
Web Site: www.furukawa-sanki.co.jp
Emp.: 2,000
Industrial Machinery Mfr
S.I.C.: 3561
N.A.I.C.S.: 333911
Osamu Watanabe *(Pres)*

Furukawa Metals & Resources Co., Ltd. **(1)**
2-3 Marunouchi 2-chome
Chiyoda-ku, Tokyo, 100-8370, Japan JP
Tel.: (81) 332126569
Fax: (81) 332126558
E-Mail: h-kashihara@furukawakk.co.jp
Emp.: 1,000
Nonferrous Metal Smelting Services
S.I.C.: 3339
N.A.I.C.S.: 331410
Temoto Yoshihito *(Pres)*

Furukawa Rock Drill Co., Ltd. **(1)**
1-5-3 Nihonbashi
Chuo-ku, Tokyo, 103-0027, Japan
Tel.: (81) 332316982
Fax: (81) 332316994
E-Mail: m-nagapsuma@furukawakk.co.jp
Web Site: www.furukawarockdrill.co.jp
Emp.: 3,000
Construction & Mining Machinery Marketing & Distr
S.I.C.: 5082
N.A.I.C.S.: 423810
Saburo Saruhashi *(Pres)*

Plants:

Furukawa Rock Drill Co., Ltd. - Takasaki Factory **(2)**
3511 Aza Nakahashi
Shimano-machi, Takasaki, Gunma, 370-0015, Japan
Tel.: (81) 273523511
Fax: (81) 273531015
Web Site: www.furukawarockdrill.co.jp
Emp.: 110
Construction & Mining Machinery Mfr
S.I.C.: 3531

N.A.I.C.S.: 333120
Nobuyoshi Fukui *(Mgr-Factory)*

Furukawa Rock Drill Co., Ltd. - Yoshii Factory (2)
1058 Yoshii Yoshii-machi
Tano-gun, Gunma, 370-2132, Japan
Tel.: (81) 273876111
Fax: (81) 273875140
E-Mail:
Web Site: www.furukawarockdrill.co.jp
Emp.: 472
Construction & Mining Machinery Mfr
S.I.C.: 3531
N.A.I.C.S.: 333120
Saburo Saruhashi *(Pres)*

U.S. Division:

Furukawa Rock Drill USA Co., Ltd. - Breaker Division (2)
711 Lake St
Kent, OH 44240
Tel.: (330) 673-5826
Fax: (330) 677-1616
Toll Free: (800) 527-2282
E-Mail: orders@kentdemolition.com
Web Site: www.kentdemolition.com
Demolition Tools Mfr
S.I.C.: 3546
N.A.I.C.S.: 333991
Jeffery Crane *(Pres & COO)*

Non-U.S. Subsidiaries:

Furukawa Rock Drill Europe B.V. (2)
Proostwetering 29
3543 AB Utrecht, Netherlands
Tel.: (31) 302412277
Fax: (31) 302412305
E-Mail: frd@frd.eu
Web Site: www.frd.eu
Emp.: 16
Breakers & Crawler Drills Sales
S.I.C.: 5012
N.A.I.C.S.: 423110
Mark Okamoto *(Pres)*

Furukawa Rock Drill Korea Co., Ltd. (2)
82-16 Changgok-Ri Paltan-Myon
Hwaseong, Gyeonggi-Do, Korea (South)
Tel.: (82) 313528447
Fax: (82) 313536937
Emp.: 2
Drills Mfr
S.I.C.: 3532
N.A.I.C.S.: 333131

Furukawa Rock Drill (Shanghai) Co., Ltd. (2)
Huijin No 125 St Jinhui Town
Feng Xian Dist, Shanghai, 201414, China
Tel.: (86) 21 5748 6636
Fax: (86) 21 5748 6638
E-Mail: info@furukawa.net.cn
Web Site: www.frds.cn
Rock Crushers Mfr
S.I.C.: 3531
N.A.I.C.S.: 333120

Furukawa Unic Corporation (1)
1-5-3 Nihonbashi
Chuo-ku, Tokyo, 103-0022, Japan
Tel.: (81) 332318613
Fax: (81) 332318261
Web Site: www.furukawaunic.co.jp
Sls.: $406,720,000
Emp.: 400
Cranes Mfr & Distr
S.I.C.: 3536
N.A.I.C.S.: 333923
Kenji Ichimura *(Pres)*

Unit:

Furukawa Unic Corporation - Sakura Unit (2)
2348 Aza Sotono Ohta
Sakura, Chiba, Japan
Tel.: (81) 434855111
Fax: (81) 434855167
Web Site: www.furukawaunic.co.jp
Emp.: 400
Cranes Mfr
S.I.C.: 3536
N.A.I.C.S.: 333923
Susumu Nakamura *(Pres)*

Non-U.S. Subsidiary:

Furukawa Unic (Thailand) Co., Ltd. (2)
No 1 Bangna-Trad Rd. Km.3, Bangna
Bangkok, 10260, Thailand
Tel.: (66) 27443356
Fax: (66) 27443358
E-Mail: sales@furukawaunic.co.th
Web Site: www.furukawaunic.co.th
Emp.: 7
Marine Cranes Mfr
S.I.C.: 3536
N.A.I.C.S.: 333923

THE FURUKAWA ELECTRIC CO., LTD.

Marunouchi Nakadori Building 2-3
Marunouchi 2-chome Chiyoda-ku
Tokyo, 100-8322, Japan
Tel.: (81) 332863001
Telex: FECTOKJ23857/23907
Fax: (81) 332863919
Web Site: www.furukawa.co.jp
Year Founded: 1884
5801—(OTC TKS)
Rev.: $10,171,887,000
Assets: $9,016,722,000
Liabilities: $6,565,449,000
Net Worth: $2,451,273,000
Earnings: $39,336,000
Emp.: 50,342
Fiscal Year-end: 03/31/13

Business Description:
Wire & Cable Mfr
S.I.C.: 3568
N.A.I.C.S.: 333613

Personnel:
Masao Yoshida *(Chm)*
Mitsuyoshi Shibata *(Pres)*
Hideo Sakura *(Exec VP & Gen Mgr-Fin & Procurement Div)*
Hiroyuki Otake *(Sr VP & Gen Mgr-Global Bus Dev & Group Strategic Initiatives Dept)*
Tetsuya Sato *(Sr VP & Gen Mgr-Strategy Div & Smart Grid New Bus Dev Dept)*
Hisaharu Yanagawa *(Sr VP & Gen Mgr-R&D Div)*
Tetsuro Yasunaga *(Sr VP & Gen Mgr-Sls & Mktg Div)*
Michio Ueyama *(Sr VP)*

Board of Directors:
Masao Yoshida
Nozomu Amano
Sumitaka Fujita
Hideo Sakura
Tetsuya Sato
Mitsuyoshi Shibata
Nobuyoshi Soma
Osamu Tsukamoto
Michio Ueyama
Hisaharu Yanagawa
Tetsuro Yasunaga
Tetsuo Yoshino

Subsidiaries:

Access Cable Company (1)
1-8-9 Kanda-Nishikicho
Chiyoda-ku, Tokyo, 101-0054, Japan
Tel.: (81) 335186501
Web Site: www.access-cable.jp
Fiber Optic Cable Mfr
S.I.C.: 3357
N.A.I.C.S.: 335921

Asahi Electric Works Co., Ltd. (1)
11-16 Azamino-Minami 2-chome
Aoba-ku, Yokohama, Kanagawa, 225-0012, Japan
Tel.: (81) 45 910 2800
Fax: (81) 45 910 2809
E-Mail: homepage@aew.co.jp
Web Site: www.aew.co.jp
Sls.: $100,368,000
Emp.: 248
Power Transmission Equipment Mfr & Distr
S.I.C.: 3568
N.A.I.C.S.: 333613
Toshio Nakada *(Pres)*

The Furukawa Battery Co., Ltd. (1)
2-4-1 Hoshikawa Hodogaya-ku
Yokohama, Kanagawa, 240 0006, Japan (52.74%)
Tel.: (81) 453365034
Telex: 2468244FURBATJ
Fax: (81) 453333511
E-Mail: overseas@furukawadenchi.co.jp
Web Site: www.furukawadenchi.co.jp
Sls.: $103,244,000
Emp.: 1,200
Production & Sales of Batteries
S.I.C.: 3692
N.A.I.C.S.: 335912
Katsuhiko Utsumi *(Pres & CEO)*
Utsumy Imai *(Pres)*

Furukawa C&B Co., Ltd. (1)
3-1-47 Fukaminishi
Yamato, Kanagawa, 242-0018, Japan
Tel.: (81) 46 206 2110
Fax: (81) 46 261 8865
E-Mail: sales@ho.furukawa-fcb.co.jp
Web Site: www.furukawa-fcb.co.jp
Emp.: 100
Communication Broadcasting Equipment Mfr & Distr
S.I.C.: 3669
N.A.I.C.S.: 334290
Takao Kanai *(Pres)*

Furukawa Circuit Foil Co., Ltd. (1)
601-2 Otorozawa Imaichi Shi
Tochigi Ken, Tochigi, 321 2336, Japan
Tel.: (81) 288223484
Fax: (81) 288223490
Web Site: www.fcf.co.jp
Emp.: 350
Mfr. of Electro-Deposited Copper Foil
S.I.C.: 2671
N.A.I.C.S.: 322220
Mitsuyoshi Shibata *(Pres)*

Furukawa Elecom Co., Ltd. (1)
Furukawadenko Kanda Bldg 5f
Chiyoda-Ku, Tokyo, 101-0047, Japan
Tel.: (81) 352978610
Electrical Apparatus & Equipment Whslr
S.I.C.: 5065
N.A.I.C.S.: 423690

Furukawa Electric Industrial Cable Co., Ltd. (1)
6-48-10 Higashi-Nippori
Arakawa-ku, Tokyo, 116-0014, Japan
Tel.: (81) 3 3803 1151
Fax: (81) 3 3801 0581
Web Site: www.feic.co.jp
Emp.: 630
Electric Cable Mfr & Distr
S.I.C.: 3496
N.A.I.C.S.: 332618

Plants:

Furukawa Electric Industrial Cable Co., Ltd. - Hokuriku Plant (2)
19-2 Wakabadai Shika-machi
Hakui, Ishikawa, 925-0375, Japan
Tel.: (81) 767 38 1213
Fax: (81) 767 38 1162
Electronic Component Mfr
S.I.C.: 3679
N.A.I.C.S.: 334419

Furukawa Electric Industrial Cable Co., Ltd. - Kofu Plant (2)
15-1 Arakawa 2-chome
Kofu, Yamanashi, 400-0061, Japan
Tel.: (81) 55 277 3030
Fax: (81) 55 277 2654
Electric Cable Mfr
S.I.C.: 3357
N.A.I.C.S.: 335921

Furukawa Industrial Plastics Co., Ltd. (1)
195 Shimminato
Mihama-Ku, Chiba, 261-0002, Japan
Tel.: (81) 432429514
Plastic Foam Products Mfr
S.I.C.: 3089
N.A.I.C.S.: 326199

Furukawa Magnet Wire Co., Ltd. (1)
2-3 Marunouchi 2-Chome
Chiyoda, Tokyo, 100-8322, Japan
Tel.: (81) 3 3286 3320
Fax: (81) 3 3286 3948
Magnet Wire Mfr & Sales
S.I.C.: 3356
N.A.I.C.S.: 331491

Furukawa Network Solution Corporation (1)
5-1-9 Higashiyawata
Hiratsuka, 254-0016, Japan
Tel.: (81) 463 24 8541
Fax: (81) 463 24 8512
Web Site: www.fnsc.co.jp
Network Routers Mfr & Sales
S.I.C.: 3661
N.A.I.C.S.: 334210

Furukawa Precision Engineering Co., Ltd. (1)
528-5 Kiyotakishinhosoomachi
Nikko, 321-1448, Japan
Tel.: (81) 288 531025
Fax: (81) 288 543091
Precision Electronic Products Mfr
S.I.C.: 3451
N.A.I.C.S.: 332721

Furukawa Sangyo Kaisha, Ltd. (1)
2-3-14 Nihonbashi Muro Machi Chuo Ku
1038315 Tokyo, Japan (100%)
Tel.: (81) 332795611
Telex: 2224437FURUSAJ
Fax: (81) 332795613
E-Mail: tanagano@nail.furusan.co.jp
Web Site: www.furusan.co.jp
Sales Range: $600-649.9 Million
Emp.: 200
Sale of Electric Wire & Cable, Aluminum & Copper Products
S.I.C.: 5063
N.A.I.C.S.: 423610
Hanaa Taani *(CEO)*

Furukawa Techno Material Co., Ltd. (1)
5-1-8 Higashi-Yawata
Hiratsuka, Kanagawa, 254-0016, Japan
Tel.: (81) 463 21 7343
Fax: (81) 463 21 4375
Web Site: www.furukawa-ftm.com
Emp.: 18
Electronic Communication Equipment Mfr
S.I.C.: 3669
N.A.I.C.S.: 334290
Nobuyuki Nakamura *(Pres)*

KYOWA ELECTRIC WIRE CO.,LTD. (1)
2-1-9 Dojimahama Furukawaosaka Bldg Nishikan4f
Kita-Ku, Osaka, 530-0004, Japan
Tel.: (81) 663450029
Web Site: www.kyowa-densen.co.jp
Emp.: 92
Electric Wire Drawing & Mfr
S.I.C.: 3496
N.A.I.C.S.: 332618
Hisakazu Ishibashi *(Pres)*

Okumura Metals Co., Ltd. (1)
6 5 Sakuragawa 2 Chome Naniwa Ku
Osaka, 556 0022, Japan (100%)
Tel.: (81) 665627251
Fax: (81) 665627258
E-Mail: okhjm@okumura.fitec.co.jp
Web Site: www.fitec.co.jp
Sales Range: $75-99.9 Million
Emp.: 40
Sale of Rolled Copper & Aluminum Production
S.I.C.: 3334
N.A.I.C.S.: 331313

Riken Electric Wire Co., Ltd. (1)
3rd Fl Konwa Bldg 1-12-22 Tsukiji Chuo Ku
Tokyo, 104 0045, Japan JP (100%)
Tel.: (81) 335423711
Telex: 2522150RIKENJ
Fax: (81) 335424709
E-Mail: sumi@rikensen.co.jp
Web Site: www.rikensen.co.jp
Emp.: 100
Production & Sale of Magnet Wire & Plastic Cable
S.I.C.: 3089
N.A.I.C.S.: 326199

Shikoku Cable Co Ltd (1)
1576-5 Ishidanisi Sangawamachi
Sanuki, Kagawa, 769-2322, Japan

The Furukawa Electric Co., Ltd.—(Continued)

Tel.: (81) 879 43 2575
Fax: (81) 879 43 5875
Web Site: www.shikokucable.co.jp
Emp.: 118
Coaxial Cable Mfr & Distr
S.I.C.: 3357
N.A.I.C.S.: 335921
Yasuhiro Sasaki *(Pres)*

Wako Engineering Corp. **(1)**
5 12 13 Shiba Chome
Minato-ku, Tokyo, 108 0014, Japan (59%)
Tel.: (81) 3 3798 4411
Fax: (81) 3 3452 2908
Web Site: www.wako-eng.co.jp
Sls.: $74,355,000
Emp.: 595
Telecommunications Systems Construction
S.I.C.: 4899
N.A.I.C.S.: 517919
Hisashi Yazawa *(Pres)*

Plants:

Furukawa America Inc - HIRATSUKA WORKS MAGNET WIRE PLANT **(1)**
5-1-9 Higashi-Yawata
Hiratsuka, 254-0016, Japan
Tel.: (81) 4 6321 8241
Fax: (81) 4 6321 8244
Web Site: www.furukawaamerica.com
Magnetic Wire Mfr
S.I.C.: 3496
N.A.I.C.S.: 332618

Furukawa America Inc - MIE WORKS, MAGNET WIRE PLANT **(1)**
20-16 Nobono-chyo
Kameyama, Mie, 519-0292, Japan
Tel.: (81) 5 9585 2040
Fax: (81) 5 9585 1310
Magnetic Wire Mfr
S.I.C.: 3496
N.A.I.C.S.: 332618

Furukawa Electric Industrial Cable Co., Ltd. - Tochigi Plant **(1)**
1601-8 Oaza-Tadokoro Shioya-machi
Shioya-gun, Tochigi, 329-2331, Japan
Tel.: (81) 287 45 1151
Fax: (81) 287 45 1154
Electric Cable & Machinery Mfr
S.I.C.: 3679
N.A.I.C.S.: 334419

Nippon Foil Mfg. Co., Ltd. - Nogi Plant **(1)**
55 Wakabayashi Nogi-machi
Shimotsuga-gun, Tochigi, 329-0103, Japan
Tel.: (81) 280 56 2315
Fax: (81) 280 56 0367
Web Site: www.nihonseihaku.co.jp/En/profile.html
Aluminum Foil Mfr
S.I.C.: 3353
N.A.I.C.S.: 331315

Nippon Foil Mfg. Co., Ltd. - Shiga Plant **(1)**
61-8 Sasatani Yamadera-cho
Kusatsu, Shiga, 525-0042, Japan
Tel.: (81) 77 565 3331
Fax: (81) 77 564 5599
Metal Foil Mfr
S.I.C.: 3353
N.A.I.C.S.: 331315

U.S. Subsidiaries:

American Furukawa, Inc. **(1)**
47677 Galleon Dr
Plymouth, MI 48170
Tel.: (734) 446-2200
Fax: (734) 446-2260
E-Mail: info@americanfurukawa.com
Web Site: www.americanfurukawa.com
Industrial Electronic Component Distr
S.I.C.: 5065
N.A.I.C.S.: 423690
Shuichi Takagi *(VP)*

Furukawa Electric North America Inc. **(1)**
900 Lafayette St Ste 509
Santa Clara, CA 95050-4967 (100%)
Tel.: (408) 248-4884
Fax: (408) 249-3094
Web Site: www.furukawa-usa.com
Mfr. of Electric Wire & Cable
S.I.C.: 5051
N.A.I.C.S.: 423510

Furukawa Wiring Systems America Inc. **(1)**
420-B Pan American Dr Ste B-5
El Paso, TX 79907
Tel.: (915) 261-1930
Fax: (915) 791-5580
Web Site: www.furukawa.co.jp/english/what/2010/ele_100617.htm
Automotive Wiring Parts Mfr & Distr
S.I.C.: 3714
N.A.I.C.S.: 336390
Akira Matsui *(Pres)*

Gougler Industries, Inc. **(1)**
705 Lake St
Kent, OH 44240 OH
Mailing Address:
705 Lake St
Kent, OH 44240-2733
Tel.: (330) 673-5821
Fax: (330) 673-5824
E-Mail: info@gougler.com
Web Site: www.gougler.com
Emp.: 50
Mfr. of Construction & Mining Machinery Import Export
S.I.C.: 3546
N.A.I.C.S.: 333991
Carl Lumbert *(Mgr-Mgmt Info Sys)*

OFS Fitel LLC **(1)**
6305 Crescent Dr
Norcross, GA 30071
Tel.: (770) 798-2135
Web Site: www.ofs.com
Emp.: 200
Fiber Optics Holding Company
S.I.C.: 3357
N.A.I.C.S.: 335921
Ashish Gandhi *(CFO & Treas)*

Subsidiaries:

OFS Brightwave **(2)**
2000 Northeast Expy
Norcross, GA 30071
Tel.: (770) 798-5555
Fax: (770) 836-8820
Toll Free: (888) 342-3743
E-Mail: ofs@ofsoptics.com
Web Site: www.ofsoptics.com
Fiber Optic Cable; Jointly Owned with CommScope
S.I.C.: 3357
N.A.I.C.S.: 335921
Kiyoshi Takeuchi *(Pres & CEO)*
Ashish Gandhi *(Treas & CFO)*

Divisions:

OFS Brightwave Carrollton **(3)**
10 Brightwave Blvd
Carrollton, GA 30117-5262
Tel.: (770) 838-5291
Fax: (770) 838-5113
E-Mail: info@ofsoptic.com
Web Site: www.ofsoptic.com
Emp.: 400
Fiber Optic Telecommunications Cable
S.I.C.: 7389
N.A.I.C.S.: 561499
Jacques Fiorella *(Gen Mgr)*

OFS **(3)**
50 Hall Rd
Sturbridge, MA 01566-1279 DE
Tel.: (508) 347-2261
Fax: (508) 347-2747
Web Site: www.ofsoptics.com
Emp.: 350
Multi Mode Optical Fibers Mfr
S.I.C.: 3229
N.A.I.C.S.: 327212
Michele Neifing *(Mgr-Cust Svcs)*

OFS **(1)**
55 Darling Dr
Avon, CT 06001-4273
Tel.: (860) 678-0371
Fax: (860) 674-8818
Toll Free: (888) 342-3743
Web Site: www.specialtyphotonics.com
Emp.: 700
Mfr. of Fiber Optic Cable, Connectors & Assemblies
S.I.C.: 3357
N.A.I.C.S.: 335921
Timothy F. Murray *(Chm)*
Dennis Klingensmith *(CEO)*
Toshiya Hirose *(Chief Strategy Officer)*
Clemont L. Johnson *(Sr VP-HR)*
Takahide Kimura *(Exec VP-Strategy)*

Non-U.S. Subsidiaries:

ALPHA Industries Bhd. **(1)**
No 37 Jalan Kangkar Tebrau Karung Berkunci No 744
81100 Johor Bahru, Johor, Malaysia
Tel.: (60) 73543996
Fax: (60) 73542537
E-Mail: alphaelios@alpint.com.my
Emp.: 200
Electrical Equipment
S.I.C.: 5211
N.A.I.C.S.: 444190
Takaowada Wada *(Mng Dir)*

CFT Vina Copper Co., Ltd. **(1)**
9th St Bien Hoa 1 Industrial Zone
Bien Hoa, Dong Nai, Vietnam (33%)
Tel.: (84) 61836502
Fax: (84) 61836608
Web Site: www.cft-vietnam.com
Sales Range: $50-74.9 Million
Emp.: 70
S.I.C.: 5211
N.A.I.C.S.: 444190

Circuit Foil Taiwan Corp. **(1)**
8 Tou Kung 2nd Rd Kuo Ta Industrial Park
Touliu, Taipei, 64000, Taiwan
Tel.: (886) 55571361
Fax: (886) 55371346
E-Mail: ferbice@mail.cftc.com.tw
Emp.: 100
Metal Coatings
S.I.C.: 5211
N.A.I.C.S.: 444190
Marui Shunji *(Gen Mgr)*

C.M. Furukawa Philippines Inc. **(1)**
208 Veterans Center Building Western Bicutan
Tagig, Manila, Philippines
Tel.: (63) 28371485
Fax: (63) 28371486
S.I.C.: 5211
N.A.I.C.S.: 444190

Europtics Limited **(1)**
43 45 Nottinghill Gate
London, L35 1RZ, United Kingdom
Tel.: (44) 72216000
Fax: (44) 207 313 5310
Web Site: www.furukawa.co.uk
S.I.C.: 5211
N.A.I.C.S.: 444190

FE Magnet Wire (Malaysia) Sdn. Bhd. **(1)**
Lot 2 Persiaran Waja Bukit Raja Industrial Estate
PO Box 178
41720 Kelang, Selangor Darul Ehsan, Malaysia
Tel.: (60) 3 3342 7001
Fax: (60) 3 3342 7213
E-Mail: femm@tm.net.my
Web Site: www.femm.com.my/index.html
Magnet Wire Mfr
S.I.C.: 3496
N.A.I.C.S.: 332618

Furukawa Auto Parts(HK) Ltd. **(1)**
Units 1302 13/F Park Building 476 Castle Peak Road
Hong Kong, China (Hong Kong)
Tel.: (852) 3160 4562
Fax: (852) 3160 4275
Automotive Electric Parts Mfr & Distr
S.I.C.: 3714
N.A.I.C.S.: 336390

Furukawa Circuit Foil (Hong Kong) Co., Ltd. **(1)**
Suit 2606 Shell Tower Times Square 1 Matheson Street
Causeway Bay, China (Hong Kong)
Tel.: (852) 2877 1107
Fax: (852) 2877 1115
Web Site: www.furukawa.co.jp/english/kaisya/01-04-02.htm
Electrodeposited Copper Foil Mfr
S.I.C.: 3699
N.A.I.C.S.: 335999
Yuji Yamazaki *(Gen Mgr)*

Furukawa Circuit Foil Taiwan Corporation **(1)**
8 Tou Kong 2Rd Tou-Liu Expansion Industrial Area
Yun-lin, Yun Lin, Taiwan
Tel.: (886) 55571361
Fax: (886) 55571346
Web Site: www.fcft.com.tw
Printed Circuit Board Mfr
S.I.C.: 3672
N.A.I.C.S.: 334412

Furukawa Dengyo(Tianjin) Co., Ltd. **(1)**
15 No 2 Xinghua Branch Road Xiqing Economic Development Area
Tianjin, China 300385
Tel.: (86) 22 8396 8690
Fax: (86) 22 8396 8697
Web Site: www.furukawa.co.jp/english/kaisya/01-04-02.htm
Agricultural Equipment Mfr & Distr
S.I.C.: 3523
N.A.I.C.S.: 333111

Furukawa Electric Autoparts Central Europe, s.r.o.(Face) **(1)**
Lidicka 1022
273 51 Unhost, Czech Republic
Tel.: (420) 312818614
Fax: (420) 312818641
Web Site: www.furukawa.cz
Emp.: 140
Automotive Electronic Component Mfr & Distr
S.I.C.: 3714
N.A.I.C.S.: 336390
Ito Shuichi *(Gen Mgr)*

Furukawa Electric Autoparts(Philippines)Inc. **(1)**
Lot3-5 Phase 4 113 East Main Avenue
Laguna Thechnopark Binan, Binan, Laguna, Philippines
Tel.: (63) 49 541 1804
Fax: (63) 49 541 1805
Auto Electrical Parts Mfr
S.I.C.: 3714
N.A.I.C.S.: 336390

Furukawa Electric Europe Ltd. **(1)**
3rd Floor Newcombe House
43-45 Notting Hill Gate, London, W11 3FE, United Kingdom (100%)
Tel.: (44) 2072216000
Fax: (44) 2073135310
E-Mail: sales@furukawa.co.uk
Web Site: www.furukawa.co.uk
Emp.: 20
S.I.C.: 5211
N.A.I.C.S.: 444190
Keith Imamura *(Mng Dir)*

Furukawa Electric Hong Kong Ltd. **(1)**
Suite 2606 Shell Tower Times Square 1 Matheson Street
Causeway Bay, China (Hong Kong)
Tel.: (852) 2512 8938
Fax: (852) 2512 9717
E-Mail: guest@fehk.com.hk
Web Site: www.fehk.com.hk
Emp.: 14
Electronic Component Distr
S.I.C.: 5065
N.A.I.C.S.: 423690
Toshiaki Aoki *(Chm & CEO)*

Furukawa Electric Institute of Technology Co., Ltd. **(1)**
Kesmark 24 28
1158 Budapest, Hungary (100%)
Tel.: (36) 4196620
Fax: (36) 14196627
E-Mail: feti@feti.hu
Web Site: www.feti.hu
Emp.: 20
S.I.C.: 5211
N.A.I.C.S.: 444190

Furukawa Electric (Shenzhen) Co., Ltd. **(1)**
West Industrial Park Xinyangshe Community Shajing Town
Baoan District, Shenzhen, China 518104
Tel.: (86) 755 3384 8011

Fax: (86) 755 3384 5105
Web Site: www.furukawa.co.jp/english/kaisya/01-04-02.htm
Automobile Electric Component Mfr & Distr
S.I.C.: 3714
N.A.I.C.S.: 336390

Furukawa Electric Singapore Pte. Ltd. (1)
60 Albert Street #13-10 OG Albert Complex
Singapore, 189969, Singapore (100%)
Tel.: (65) 6224 4686
Fax: (65) 6336 2635
E-Mail:
Web Site: www.furukawa.co.jp
Sales Range: $250-299.9 Million
Emp.: 20
Electrical Sales & Services
S.I.C.: 3699
N.A.I.C.S.: 335999
Y. Takahashi *(Mng Dir)*

Furukawa Electric Trading SZ Ltd. (1)
Room 4801A Block A United Plaza No 5022 Bin He Road
Futian District, Shenzhen, China
Tel.: (86) 755 8373 4878
Automotive Electric Parts Distr
S.I.C.: 5013
N.A.I.C.S.: 423120

Furukawa Finance Netherlands B.V. (1)
Atrium Strawinskylaan 3111
1070 ZX Amsterdam, Netherlands
Tel.: (31) 206465996
Fax: (31) 204064555
Web Site: www.furukawa.nl
Emp.: 130
S.I.C.: 5211
N.A.I.C.S.: 444190

Furukawa FITEL (Thailand) Co., Ltd. (1)
Rojana Industrial Park 1/71 Moo 5 Tambol Kanharm
Amphur U-Thai Phranakorn Sri, Ayutthaya, 13210, Thailand
Tel.: (66) 35 226 581
Fax: (66) 35 226 580
Fiber Optic Cable Mfr
S.I.C.: 3357
N.A.I.C.S.: 335921

Furukawa Industrial S.A. Produtos Eletricos (1)
Rua Hasdrubal Bellegard 820
81460-120 Curitiba, PR, Brazil
Tel.: (55) 4133414000
Fax: (55) 4133414046
E-Mail: fisa@furukawa.com.br
Web Site: www.furukawa.com.br
Sls.: $47,382,000
Emp.: 400
Electrical Wire & Cable Mfr & Sales
S.I.C.: 3496
N.A.I.C.S.: 332618
Foad Shaikhzadeh *(Pres)*

Furukawa Industrial S.A. (1)
44th Fl Avenida Macoes Unidas 11633
4578901 Sao Paulo, Brazil (85%)
Tel.: (55) 1155015748
Telex: 1154177FKAWBR
Fax: (55) 1155015763
E-Mail: rscruz@furukawa.com.br
Web Site: www.furukawa.com.br
Sls.: $2,662,000
Emp.: 25
Sales of Electric Wire & Cable Production & Sales of Automotive Wire Harness
S.I.C.: 5063
N.A.I.C.S.: 423610
Renato Cruz *(Mgr-Tech & Engrg)*

Furukawa Mexico, S.A.DE C.V. (1)
Av Circulo de la Amistad No 2690 Parque Industrial Mexicali IV
Mexicali, Baja California, Mexico
Tel.: (52) 6865642500
Fax: (52) 6865642560
E-Mail: info@furmex.com
Web Site: www.furmex.com
Emp.: 1,000
Automotive Electronic Parts Mfr
S.I.C.: 3714
N.A.I.C.S.: 336390
Noboru Natsuky *(Pres)*

Furukawa Precision Thailand Co., Ltd. (1)
23rd Fl Charn Issara Tower 1 942/167 Rama 4 Rd
Sriyawongse Sub Dist, Bangkok, 10500, Thailand
Tel.: (66) 226679448
Fax: (66) 22667949
Emp.: 200
S.I.C.: 5211
N.A.I.C.S.: 444190
Akikazu Nakahara *(Mng Dir)*

Furukawa Research & Engineering Europe Ltd. (1)
43 45 Nottinghill Gate
London, W11-3FE, United Kingdom
Tel.: (44) 73135300
Telex: 8954640FECLDNG
Fax: (44) 20 7313 5310
Web Site: www.furukawa.co.uk/corporate.html
Lumber
S.I.C.: 5211
N.A.I.C.S.: 444190

Furukawa Shanghai Ltd. (1)
Room 1006 Hongyi Plaza 288 Jiujiang Road
Shanghai, 200001, China
Tel.: (86) 21 3366 5301
Fax: (86) 21 3366 5308
E-Mail: sales@furukawa-sh.com
Web Site: www.furukawa-sh.cn
Emp.: 20
Fiber Optic & Electrical Component Distr
S.I.C.: 5063
N.A.I.C.S.: 423610
Aoki Toshiya *(Mgr)*

Furukawa (Thailand) Co., Ltd. (1)
29 Vanissa Building 6th Fl Room 6D Soi Chidlom Ploenchit Road Lumpini
Pathumwan, Bangkok, Pathumwan, 10330, Thailand
Tel.: (66) 2 655 1205
Fax: (66) 2 655 1208
E-Mail: mail@furukawa.co.th
Web Site: www.furukawa.co.th
Rev.: $21,081,600
Emp.: 17
Electronic Telecommunication Equipment Mfr
S.I.C.: 3679
N.A.I.C.S.: 334419
Hiroshi Yatabe *(Gen Mgr)*

Hirakawa Singapore Pte. Ltd. (1)
47 Pandan Road
Singapore, 609288, Singapore
Tel.: (65) 62680174
Fax: (65) 62680139
S.I.C.: 5211
N.A.I.C.S.: 444190

Leoni Furukawa Wiring Systems SAS (1)
5 Avenue Newton
78180 Montigny-le-Bretonneux, France
Tel.: (33) 130 85 3397
Fax: (33) 130 43 4171
Web Site: www.furukawa.co.jp/english/kaisya/01-04-02.htm
Automotive Electric Parts Mfr & Distr
S.I.C.: 3714
N.A.I.C.S.: 336390

Permintex Furukawa Autoparts Malaysia Sdn. Bhd. (1)
Plot 73 74 Kawasan Perindustrian Bandar Baru Darulaman
Jitra, Kedah, 06000, Malaysia
Tel.: (60) 4 919 9964
Fax: (60) 4 919 0087
Automobile Parts Mfr & Distr
S.I.C.: 3714
N.A.I.C.S.: 336390

P.T. Furukawa Permintex Autoparts Indonesia (1)
Jalan Inti Raya Block C2 No 11 Bekasi International Industrial Estate
Lippo Cikarang, Bekasi, 17750, Indonesia
Tel.: (62) 21 8990 8060
Fax: (62) 21 8990 8062
Automotive Parts Distr
S.I.C.: 5013
N.A.I.C.S.: 423120

P.T. Supreme Cable Manufacturing Corp. (1)
Jl Kebon Sirih 71
Jakarta, 10340, Indonesia (50%)
Tel.: (62) 213100525
Fax: (62) 3193019
E-Mail: sccadm@cbn.ib
Web Site: www.sucaco.com
Sales Range: $1-9.9 Million
Emp.: 100
S.I.C.: 5211
N.A.I.C.S.: 444190

P.T. Tembaga Mulia Semanan (1)
Jl Daan Mogot Km 16
Desa Semanan, Jakarta, Jakarta Barat, 11850, Indonesia (44%)
Tel.: (62) 216190128
Fax: (62) 216192890
Web Site: www.tns.co.id
Sls.: $33,580,000
Emp.: 1,000
Production & Sales of Copper Wire Road
S.I.C.: 3351
N.A.I.C.S.: 331420
Harry Setyono *(Mng Dir)*

Shenyang Furukawa Cable Co., Ltd. (1)
Hujiadian Dashubo Village
Shujiatun District
Shenyang, 110115, China
Tel.: (86) 2489428599
Fax: (86) 24 89428954
E-Mail: sfc@sf-cable.com
Web Site: www.sf-cable.com
S.I.C.: 5211
N.A.I.C.S.: 444190

Shin Chang Connector Co., Ltd. (1)
734-2, Wonsi-dong
Ansan, Kyungki-do, Korea (South)
Tel.: (82) 3454933000
Fax: (82) 3454921626
S.I.C.: 5211
N.A.I.C.S.: 444190

STF Co., Ltd. (1)
711 Baekseok-dong
Cheonan, Chungchongnam-Do, Korea (South)
Tel.: (82) 41 9010 500
Fax: (82) 41 9010 319
Web Site: www.stf.co.kr
Electronic Component Mfr & Distr
S.I.C.: 3679
N.A.I.C.S.: 334419
Lee Hwan Chul *(Pres)*

Taho Engineering Co., Ltd. (1)
249 Chung Shan Rd Kuan Miao Hsiang
71802 T'ainan, Taiwan (100%)
Tel.: (886) 65953723
Fax: (886) 65953725
E-Mail: tahoeng@ms27hinet.net
Web Site: www.taho.co.tw
Sales Range: Less than $1 Million
Emp.: 23
S.I.C.: 5211
N.A.I.C.S.: 444190
Masahiro Kinoshita *(Gen Mgr)*

Thai Furukawa Unicomm Construction Co., Ltd. (1)
169 Soi Phayasuren
Bangkok, 10510, Thailand (100%)
Tel.: (66) 25180833
Fax: (66) 29191050
E-Mail: personnel@tfu.co.th
Web Site: www.tfu.co.th
Emp.: 130
S.I.C.: 5211
N.A.I.C.S.: 444190
Hiroshi Irie *(Pres)*

Xin Furukawa Metal (Wuxi) Co., Ltd. (1)
No 25 Changjiang South Road
Wuxi, Jiangsu, China 214028
Tel.: (86) 510 85343445
Fax: (86) 510 85342295
Web Site: www.furukawa-metal.com.cn
Emp.: 188
Metal Products Mfr & Distr
S.I.C.: 3499
N.A.I.C.S.: 332999
Wang Sheng *(Gen Mgr)*

Yunnan Copper Furukawa Electric Co.,Ltd. (1)
Wang-Jia-Qiao
Western Hill District, Kunming, Yunnan, China 650102
Tel.: (86) 871 839 0059
Fax: (86) 871 832 7600
Electric Copper Alloy Products Mfr
S.I.C.: 3499
N.A.I.C.S.: 332999

Non-U.S. Affiliate:

Bangkok Telecom Co., Ltd. (1)
27th Floor Two Pacific Place Building 142 Sukhumvit Road
Klongtoey District, Bangkok, 10110, Thailand (40.74%)
Tel.: (66) 026580670
Fax: (66) 26532617
Web Site: www.bangkoktelecom.com
Sls.: $9,176,000
Emp.: 120
Production & Sales of Electrical Wire & Cable
S.I.C.: 3714
N.A.I.C.S.: 336320

Subsidiary:

Thai Fiber Optics Co., Ltd. (2)
9th Floor Siam Tower Building 989 Rama 1 Road
Pathumwan, Bangkok, 10330, Thailand
Tel.: (66) 26580670
Fax: (66) 26580680
E-Mail: btcmkt@btc-tfoc.com
Web Site: www.btc-tfoc.com
Emp.: 52
Fiber Optic Cable Mfr
S.I.C.: 3357
N.A.I.C.S.: 335921
Hideyo Kohsaka *(Pres)*

Non-U.S. Joint Ventures:

Asia Cable Engineering Co., Pte. Ltd. (1)
623 Aljunied Rd 03 09
Aljunied Industrial Complex, Singapore, 389835, Singapore
Tel.: (65) 67413303
Fax: (65) 67413880
Web Site: www.sojitz-br.com
Sales Range: $700-749.9 Million
Emp.: 23
General Contractor
S.I.C.: 1542
N.A.I.C.S.: 236220
Victor Soh *(Mng Dir)*

Shianfu Optical Fiber and Cables Co., Ltd. (1)
18 Information Road
Hi-tech Industrial
Development Zone, Xi'an, Shaanxi, China CN
Tel.: (86) 985691220
Fax: (86) 2985691225
E-Mail: sales@shianfu.com
Web Site: www.shianfu.com
Fiber Optic Cable Mfr; Owned by The Furukawa Electric Co., Ltd. & by Xi'an Xidian Optical Cable Co., Ltd.
S.I.C.: 3357
N.A.I.C.S.: 335921

FURUKAWA METAL (THAILAND) PUBLIC CO., LTD.

952 11th Fl Ramaland Bldg Rama IV Road
Suriyawongse Bangrak, Bangkok, 10500, Thailand
Tel.: (66) 22673711
Fax: (66) 22673721
Year Founded: 1988
FMT—(THA)
Rev.: $226,201,038
Assets: $107,215,637
Liabilities: $71,064,844
Net Worth: $36,150,793
Earnings: ($461,501)
Emp.: 606
Fiscal Year-end: 12/31/12

Furukawa Metal (Thailand) Public Co., Ltd.—(Continued)

Business Description:
Copper Tube Products Mfr & Distr
S.I.C.: 3351
N.A.I.C.S.: 331420
Personnel:
Chai Sophonpanit *(Chm)*

FURUNO ELECTRIC CO., LTD.

9-52 Ashihara-Cho
Nishinomiya, Hyogo, 662-8580, Japan
Tel.: (81) 798652111
Fax: (81) 798631020
Web Site: www.furuno.co.jp
Year Founded: 1951
6814—(TKS)
Sls.: $787,655,000
Assets: $799,392,000
Liabilities: $417,725,000
Net Worth: $381,667,000
Earnings: $17,204,000
Emp.: 2,803
Fiscal Year-end: 02/28/13

Business Description:
Electronic Equipment Mfr
S.I.C.: 3679
N.A.I.C.S.: 334419
Personnel:
Yukio Furuno *(Pres)*
Hiroyuki Mori *(Sr Mng Dir)*
Ryozo Izawa *(Mng Dir)*
Muneyuki Koike *(Mng Dir)*
Board of Directors:
Yukio Furuno
Shinji Ishihara
Ryozo Izawa
Muneyuki Koike
Hiroyuki Mori
Yasushi Nishimori
Tatsuyuki Okamoto
Satoshi Ooya
Yutaka Wada
Kazuma Waimatsu

Subsidiaries:

Furuno Circuitech Co., Ltd. (1)
9-52 Ashihara-cho Nishinomiya City
662-8580 Hyogo, Japan
Tel.: (81) 798631145
Fax: (81) 798666165
E-Mail: info@furuno.co.jp
Web Site: www.furuno.co.jp/en/corporate/bases/domestic/index.html
Engineering Services
S.I.C.: 8711
N.A.I.C.S.: 541330
Hidetoshi Tanigaki *(Mng Dir)*

Furuno Device Co Ltd (1)
1 Tomoe Bessho-cho
Miki City, 673-0443 Hyogo, Japan
Tel.: (81) 794839082
Fax: (81) 794839083
Web Site: www.furuno.co.jp/en/corporate/bases/domestic/index.html
Search & Navigation Equipment Mfr
S.I.C.: 3812
N.A.I.C.S.: 334511

Furuno Kansai Hambai Co., Ltd. (1)
99-5 Ominato-cho
Ise City, Mie, 516-0001, Japan
Tel.: (81) 596350330
Fax: (81) 596350315
Electrical Apparatus & Equipment Wiring Supplies
S.I.C.: 5063
N.A.I.C.S.: 423610
Yoshio Kitani *(Mng Dir)*

Furuno Kita-Nihon Hambai Co., Ltd. (1)
1-chome Minami 7-jyo Nishi
Chuo-ku, Sapporo, Hokkaido, 064-0807, Japan
Tel.: (81) 115617261
Fax: (81) 115617264
Electrical Apparatus & Equipment Wiring Supplies
S.I.C.: 5063
N.A.I.C.S.: 423610

Furuno Kyushu Hambai Co., Ltd. (1)
3-15 Asahi-machi
Nagasaki City, Nagasaki, 852-8003, Japan
Tel.: (81) 958613261
Fax: (81) 958613290
Emp.: 90
Other Professional Equipment & Supplies Whslr
S.I.C.: 5049
N.A.I.C.S.: 423490

Furuno Labotec International Co., Ltd. (1)
9-52 Ashihara-cho Nishinomiya City
662-8580 Hyogo, Japan
Tel.: (81) 798631094
Fax: (81) 798631098
Web Site: www.furuno-labotech.co.jp
Testing Laboratories
S.I.C.: 8734
N.A.I.C.S.: 541380

Furuno Life Best Co., Ltd. (1)
9-52 Ashihara-cho Nishinomiya City
662-8580 Hyogo, Japan
Tel.: (81) 798631040
Fax: (81) 798664925
Web Site: www.furuno.co.jp/en/corporate/bases/domestic/index.html
Insurance Agencies & Brokerages
S.I.C.: 6411
N.A.I.C.S.: 524210
Sunao Katayama *(Mng Dir)*
Hidetoshi Tanigaki *(Mng Dir)*

Furuno Softech Co ,Ltd (1)
9-52 Ashihara-cho Nishinomiya City
Hyogo, 6628580, Japan
Tel.: (81) 798631168
Fax: (81) 798631169
E-Mail: info@furunosoftech.co.jp
Emp.: 48
Custom Computer Programming Services
S.I.C.: 7371
N.A.I.C.S.: 541511
Hidetoshi Tanigaki *(Mng Dir)*

Furuno Systems Co ,Ltd. (1)
JEI Ryogoku Building 6th Floor
3-25-5 Ryogoku Sumida-ku, 130-0026
Tokyo, Japan
Tel.: (81) 356005111
Fax: (81) 356005132
Web Site: www.furunosystems.co.jp
Emp.: 80
Electrical Apparatus & Equipment Wiring Supplies
S.I.C.: 5063
N.A.I.C.S.: 423610
Yukio Senou *(Pres)*

U.S. Subsidiary:

Furuno USA, Inc. (1)
4400 NW Pacific Rim Blvd
Camas, WA 98607-9408 CA
Tel.: (360) 834-9300
Fax: (360) 834-9400
Web Site: www.furuno.com
Emp.: 100
Marine Electronics, Radar Systems, Fish Finders, Autopilots, Radios, Transceivers & Sonar & Sounder Systems Distribution & Repair
Import
S.I.C.: 5088
N.A.I.C.S.: 423860
James Atteridge *(Pres)*

Non-U.S. Subsidiaries:

Furuno Danmark A/S (1)
Hammerholmen 44-48
2650 Hvidovre, Denmark
Tel.: (45) 36774500
Fax: (45) 36774501
E-Mail: furuno@furuno.dk
Web Site: www.furuno.dk
Emp.: 35
Electronic Parts & Equipment Whslr
S.I.C.: 5065
N.A.I.C.S.: 423690
Freddie Hansen *(Gen Mgr)*

Furuno Deutschland GmbH (1)
Siemensstrasse 33
25462 Rellingen, Germany
Tel.: (49) 41018380
Fax: (49) 4101838111
E-Mail: furuno@furuno.de
Web Site: www.furuno.de
Emp.: 35
Transportation Equipment & Supplies Whslr
S.I.C.: 5088
N.A.I.C.S.: 423860
Claus B. Frederiksen *(Mng Dir)*

Furuno Espana SA (1)
Francisco Remiro 2-B
28028 Madrid, Spain
Tel.: (34) 917259088
Fax: (34) 917259897
E-Mail: furuno@furuno.es
Web Site: www.furuno.es
Emp.: 20
Industrial Machinery & Equipment Whslr
S.I.C.: 5084
N.A.I.C.S.: 423830
Jose-Maria Olla-Curial *(Mng Dir)*

Furuno Europe BV (1)
Ridderhaven 19B
2984BT Ridderkerk, Netherlands
Tel.: (31) 180416055
Fax: (31) 180413912
E-Mail: furunoeurope@furuno.nl
Emp.: 2
Management Consulting Services
S.I.C.: 8748
N.A.I.C.S.: 541618
Seisuke Ioka *(Mng Dir)*
Takahiro Sakurai *(Mng Dir)*

Furuno Eurus LLC (1)
Ligovsky Pr 228A
192007 Saint Petersburg, Russia
Tel.: (7) 8127671592
Fax: (7) 8127665552
E-Mail: furuno@furuno.com.ru
Web Site: www.furuno.com.ru
Custom Computer Programming Services
S.I.C.: 7371
N.A.I.C.S.: 541511
Sergey G. Volkov *(Mng Dir)*

Furuno Finland OY (1)
Niittyrinne 7
02270 Espoo, Finland
Tel.: (358) 94355670
Fax: (358) 943556710
E-Mail: info@furuno.fi
Web Site: www.furuno.fi
Emp.: 60
Industrial Machinery & Equipment Whslr
S.I.C.: 5084
N.A.I.C.S.: 423830
Arto Lindgren *(Mng Dir)*

Furuno Hong Kong Co., Ltd. (1)
Room 1610-16 16th Floor Grand City Plaza
1 Sai Lau Kok Road, Tsuen Wan, NT, China (Hong Kong)
Tel.: (852) 24980109
Fax: (852) 24980216
Web Site: www.furuno.co.jp/en/corporate/bases/overseas/index.html
Marine, Ultrasonic & Electronic Technologies
S.I.C.: 3679
N.A.I.C.S.: 334419

Furuno Norge AS (1)
Sjomannsveien 19
6008 Alesund, Norway
Tel.: (47) 70102950
Fax: (47) 70102951
E-Mail: furuno@furuno.no
Web Site: www.furuno.no
Emp.: 23
Sporting & Athletic Goods Mfr
S.I.C.: 3949
N.A.I.C.S.: 339920
Trond Strommen *(Mng Dir)*

Furuno Polska Sp. z o.o. (1)
Ul Wolnosci 20
81-327 Gdynia, Poland
Tel.: (48) 586690220
Fax: (48) 586690221
E-Mail: furuno@furuno.pl
Web Site: www.furuno.pl
Transportation Equipment & Supplies Whslr
S.I.C.: 5088
N.A.I.C.S.: 423860
Fredddie Hansen *(CEO)*

Furuno Shanghai Co., Ltd. (1)
Unit C&D 2nd Floor Building1
180 Zhang Heng Road, 201204 Shanghai, China
Tel.: (86) 2133933260
Fax: (86) 2133933263
Web Site: www.furuno.com
Emp.: 22
Custom Computer Programming Services
S.I.C.: 7371
N.A.I.C.S.: 541511
Yoshio Kitani *(Mng Dir)*

Furuno Softech (Dalian) Co , Ltd. (1)
19th Floor Jiachuang Building
No 2 Qixian Road Dalian High-t, 116023
Dalian, China
Tel.: (86) 41188120788
Fax: (86) 41188120789
Web Site: www.furuno-dl.com
Custom Computer Programming Services
S.I.C.: 7371
N.A.I.C.S.: 541511

Furuno Sverige AB (1)
Gruvgatan 23
42130 Vastra Frolunda, Sweden
Tel.: (46) 317098940
Fax: (46) 317098161
E-Mail: info@furuno.se
Web Site: www.furuno.se
Emp.: 20
Industrial Machinery & Equipment Whslr
S.I.C.: 5084
N.A.I.C.S.: 423830
Freddi Thansen *(Gen Mgr)*

Furuno (UK) Ltd. (1)
West Building Penner Road
Havant, Hampshire, PO91QY, United Kingdom
Tel.: (44) 2392441000
Fax: (44) 2392484316
E-Mail: sales@furuno.co.uk
Web Site: www.furuno.co.uk
Emp.: 25
Transportation Equipment & Supplies Whslr
S.I.C.: 5088
N.A.I.C.S.: 423860
John William *(Mng Dir)*

FURUSATO INDUSTRIES, LTD.

1-2-10 Minamishin-machi Chuo-ku
Osaka, 540-0024, Japan
Tel.: (81) 669469600
Web Site: www.furusato.co.jp
8087—(TKS)
Sls.: $825,924,000
Assets: $522,852,000
Liabilities: $192,412,000
Net Worth: $330,440,000
Earnings: $14,168,000
Emp.: 425
Fiscal Year-end: 03/31/13

Business Description:
Machinery & Tools Sales
S.I.C.: 5082
N.A.I.C.S.: 423810
Personnel:
Ryohei Furusato *(Pres)*
Satoshi Onishi *(Mng Dir)*
Board of Directors:
Ryohei Furusato
Seiichi Kanasaki
Satoshi Onishi
Hideyasu Taniguchi
Masahiro Uraike
Transfer Agent:
Mitsubishi UFJ Trust Banking Corporation
3-6-3 Fushimi-cho Chuo-ku Osaka Corporate Agency Division
Osaka, Japan

Subsidiaries:

G-net Corporation (1)
1-2-10 Minamishin-machi
Chuo-ku, Osaka, 540-0024, Japan
Tel.: (81) 669469618
Fax: (81) 669469780
E-Mail: info@g-net.co.jp
Web Site: www.g-net.co.jp

Emp.: 300
Machine Tools & Housing Equipment Mfr
S.I.C.: 3541
N.A.I.C.S.: 333517
Ryohei Furusato *(Pres)*

Plants:

Furusato Industries Ltd. - Saitama Plant **(1)**
7051 Komuro Ina-machi
Kitaadachi-gun, Saitama, 362-0806, Japan
Tel.: (81) 487211354
Fax: (81) 487224511
Web Site: www.furusato.co.jp
Machine Tools & Housing Equipment Mfr
S.I.C.: 3542
N.A.I.C.S.: 333517
Ryohei Furusato *(Pres)*

Furusato Industries Ltd. - Shiga Plant **(1)**
314 Shinjyo Minakuchi-cho
Kouka-shi, Shiga, 528-0007, Japan
Tel.: (81) 748 62 1144
Fax: (81) 748 62 7923
Web Site: english.furusato.co.jp/company/office.html
Machine Tools & Housing Equipment Mfr
S.I.C.: 3541
N.A.I.C.S.: 333517

Furusato Industries Ltd. - Utsunomiya Plant **(1)**
185 Hagadai Haga-machi
Haga-gun
Tochigi, 321-3325, Japan
Tel.: (81) 286774027
Fax: (81) 28 677 4028
Web Site: www.furusato.co.jp
Machine Tools & Housing Equipment Mfr
S.I.C.: 3541
N.A.I.C.S.: 333517
Ryohei Furusato *(Pres)*

FURUYA METAL CO., LTD.

MSB-21 Minami Otsuka Bldg 2-37-5
Minami Otsuka Toshima-ku
Tokyo, 170-0005, Japan
Tel.: (81) 3 5977 3388
Fax: (81) 3 5977 3371
Web Site: www.furuyametals.co.jp
Year Founded: 1951
7826—(JAS)
Sls.: $289,564,000
Assets: $309,078,000
Liabilities: $118,602,000
Net Worth: $190,476,000
Earnings: ($17,105,000)
Emp.: 271
Fiscal Year-end: 06/30/13
Business Description:
Industrial Metal Products Mfr
S.I.C.: 3444
N.A.I.C.S.: 332322
Personnel:
Takahito Furuya *(Pres)*
Yoshihiro Ishiguro *(Officer)*
Masayuki Saito *(Officer)*
Hiroyuki Sakakida *(Officer)*
Board of Directors:
Takahito Furuya
Isao Hirano
Takashi Kawamata
Tomohiro Maruko
Kenji Nakamura
Kazuo Oishi
Kazuo Shimazaki
Wilma Swarts
Transfer Agent:
Mitsubishi UFJ Trust & Banking Corporation
Stock Transfer Agency Department 1-4-5
Marunouchi Chiyoda-ku
Tokyo, 100-8212, Japan

Plants:

Furuya Metal Co., Ltd. - Chitose Plant **(1)**
Izumisawa 1007-175
Hokkaido, Chitose, 066-0051, Japan
Tel.: (81) 123 28 7330
Fax: (81) 123 28 7331
Metal Product Mfr & Distr
S.I.C.: 3499
N.A.I.C.S.: 332999

Furuya Metal Co., Ltd. - Tsuchiura Plant **(1)**
Higashitsukuba Niihari Kogyodanchi 57-4
Aza Shimohara Sawabe
Tsuchiura, Ibaraki, 300-4104, Japan
Tel.: (81) 29 830 6777
Fax: (81) 29 830 6776
Metal Product Mfr
S.I.C.: 3499
N.A.I.C.S.: 332999

Furuya Metal Co., Ltd. - Tsukuba Plant **(1)**
Shimodate Daiichi Kogyodanchi 1915
Morisoejima
Chikusei, Ibaraki, 308-0861, Japan
Tel.: (81) 296 25 3434
Fax: (81) 296 25 3438
Metal Product Mfr
S.I.C.: 3499
N.A.I.C.S.: 332999

U.S. Subsidiary:

FURUYA METAL AMERICAS INC **(1)**
Waumbec Mill Ste 4012 250 Commercial St
Manchester, NH 03101
Tel.: (603) 518-7732
Metal Product Mfr & Distr
S.I.C.: 3499
N.A.I.C.S.: 332999

Non-U.S. Subsidiary:

Furuya Metal Korea Co., LTD. **(1)**
1701 East Area Hanshin InterValley 24 Bldg
707-34 Yeoksam 2-dong
Gangnam-gu, Seoul, Korea (South)
Tel.: (82) 2 2183 3311
Fax: (82) 2 2183 3320
Metal Product Mfr & Distr
S.I.C.: 3499
N.A.I.C.S.: 332999

FUSE 8 GROUP LTD

3370 Century Way Thorpe Park
Leeds, LS15 8ZB, United Kingdom
Tel.: (44) 1132604600
Fax: (44) 1132604611
E-Mail: info@fuse8.com
Web Site: www.fuse8.com
Year Founded: 2000
Emp.: 75
Business Description:
Advertising Agency
S.I.C.: 7311
N.A.I.C.S.: 541810
Personnel:
Mark Walton *(Chm)*
Nigel Hunter *(CEO)*
Board of Directors:
Mark Walton
Graeme Burns
Nigel Hunter
Andy Hutchinson
Jeremy Middleton

FUSEAU

Zac De L Hoirie Rue Charles Lacretelle
49070 Beaucouze, Maine Et Loire, France
Tel.: (33) 241351090
Web Site: www.fuseau-sas.com
Sls.: $24,700,000
Emp.: 41
Business Description:
Groceries & Related Products
S.I.C.: 5149
N.A.I.C.S.: 424490
Personnel:
Christophe Fuseau *(Pres)*

FUSEBILL INC.

Suite 203 232 Herzberg Road
Kanata, ON, K2K 2A1, Canada
Tel.: (613) 656-0002
Toll Free: (888) 519-1425
E-Mail: info@fusebill.com
Web Site: www.fusebill.com
Sales Range: $1-9.9 Million
Emp.: 16
Business Description:
Automated Invoicing, Billing & Collections
S.I.C.: 7372
N.A.I.C.S.: 511210
Personnel:
Steve Adams *(CEO)*
Cathy Smith *(CFO & VP-Fin)*
Board of Directors:
Steve Adams
Greg Burwell
Tyler Eyamie
Howard Gwin
Matt Hall
Joseph A. Nour

FUSHI COPPERWELD, INC.

TYG Center Tower B Suite 2601
Dong San Huan Bei Lu Bing 2
Beijing, 100027, China
Tel.: (86) 1084417742
Web Site: www.fushiinternational.com
Sales Range: $250-299.9 Million
Emp.: 691
Business Description:
Steel & Copper Clad Wires Mfr Import Export
S.I.C.: 3351
N.A.I.C.S.: 331420
Personnel:
Li Fu *(Chm & Co-CEO)*
Joseph J. Longever *(Co-CEO)*
Craig H. Studwell *(CFO & Exec VP)*
Board of Directors:
Li Fu
Chongqi Qi Huang
Joseph J. Longever

Subsidiary:

Fushi International (Dalian) Bimetallic Cable Co., Ltd. **(1)**
1 Shuang Qiang Rd
Jinzhou District, Dalian, Liaoning, 116100, China
Tel.: (86) 41187703333
Fax: (86) 41187787111
E-Mail: infodalian@fushicopperweld.com
Emp.: 500
Bimetallic Wire Products Mfr & Distr
S.I.C.: 3699
N.A.I.C.S.: 335999
Yang Yue *(Gen Mgr)*

U.S. Subsidiary:

Copperweld Bimetallics, LLC **(1)**
254 Cotton Mill Rd
Fayetteville, TN 37334-7249 PA
Tel.: (931) 433-7177
Fax: (931) 433-0419
Toll Free: (888) 284-9473
E-Mail: bimetallic@copperweld.com
Web Site: www.copperweld.com
Sales Range: $50-74.9 Million
Emp.: 130
Bimetallic Wire & Strand Products Mfr Export
S.I.C.: 3496
N.A.I.C.S.: 332618

Non-U.S. Subsidiaries:

Copperweld Asia **(2)**
1 Shuang Qiang Road Jinzhou District
116100 Dalian, Liaoning, China CN
Tel.: (86) 41187703333 (100%)
Fax: (86) 41187702398
Web Site: www.copperweld.com
Copper Wire Mfr
S.I.C.: 3351
N.A.I.C.S.: 331420

Fushi Copperweld Europe **(2)**
Unit B1 Heslop Halesfield 24
Telford, Shropshire, TF7 4NZ, United Kingdom UK
Tel.: (44) 1952586771 (100%)
Fax: (44) 1952680058
E-Mail: telford@fushicopperweld.com
Web Site: www.fushicopperweld.com
Emp.: 15
Wire Mfr
S.I.C.: 3351
N.A.I.C.S.: 331420
Jim Porteous *(Mgr-Ops)*

Non-U.S. Subsidiary:

Copperweld Tubing Europe SPRL **(1)**
Rue du Fourneau 43
B-4030 Liege, Belgium
Tel.: (32) 43499898
Fax: (32) 43499846
E-Mail: infoliege@fushicopperweld.com
Bimetallic Wire Products Mfr & Distr
S.I.C.: 3351
N.A.I.C.S.: 331420

FUSION GROUP LTD.

Fusion House Chesterfield Trading Estate
Chesterfield, S41 9PZ, United Kingdom
Tel.: (44) 1246 260111
Fax: (44) 1246 450472
E-Mail: contactus@fusiongroup.com
Web Site: www.fusiongroup.co.uk
Year Founded: 1971
Sales Range: $10-24.9 Million
Emp.: 586
Business Description:
Industrial Machinery Mfr
S.I.C.: 3569
N.A.I.C.S.: 333999
Personnel:
Eric Bridgstock *(Chm)*
Kevin Raine *(Grp Mng Dir)*
Board of Directors:
Eric Bridgstock
Michael Bailey
Neil Green
Steve Hamshaw
Mark Kemmitt
Kevin Raine

FUSION IP PLC

The Sheffield Bioincubator 40 Leavygreave Road
Sheffield, S3 7RD, United Kingdom
Tel.: (44) 42755555
Fax: (44) 42755556
E-Mail: info@fusionip.co.uk
Web Site: www.fusionip.co.uk
FIP—(LSE)
Rev.: $4,793,145
Assets: $86,331,888
Liabilities: $4,038,245
Net Worth: $82,293,643
Earnings: ($1,901,465)
Emp.: 15
Fiscal Year-end: 07/31/13
Business Description:
Commercialization of Intellectual Property
S.I.C.: 7389
N.A.I.C.S.: 561499
Personnel:
David Baynes *(CEO)*
Richard Birtles *(Sec)*
Board of Directors:
Doug Liversidge
David Baynes
David Catton
Mike Davies
Alison Fielding
Stuart Gall
Peter Grant
Bob Rabone
Legal Counsel:
Ashurst LLP
Broadwalk House 5 Appold Street
London, EC2A 2HA, United Kingdom

Fusion IP PLC—(Continued)

Subsidiaries:

Absynth Biologics Limited (1)
The Bioincubator 40 Leavygreave Rd
Sheffield, Yorkshire, S3 7RD7RD, United Kingdom
Tel.: (44) 8700677486
Web Site: www.absynthbiologics.co.uk
Vaccines & Monoclonal Antibodies Mfr
S.I.C.: 2836
N.A.I.C.S.: 325414
Simon J. Foster *(Chief Scientific Officer)*

Diurnal Limited (1)
8th Fl Eastgate House 35-43 Newport Rd
Cardiff, Wales, CF24 0AB, United Kingdom
Tel.: (44) 1142755555
Fax: (44) 2920491275
E-Mail: info@diurnal.co.uk
Web Site: www.diurnal.co.uk
Emp.: 3
Medicinal Drugs Mfr & Hormone Replacement Therapeutic Services
S.I.C.: 2834
N.A.I.C.S.: 325412
Richard Ross *(Chief Scientific Officer)*

i2LResearch Limited (1)
Capital Business Park
Cardiff, Wentloog, CF3 2PX, United Kingdom
Tel.: (44) 29 20776220
Fax: (44) 29 20776221
Pest Control Services
S.I.C.: 7342
N.A.I.C.S.: 561710
Peter McEwen *(CEO)*

U.S. Subsidiary:

i2LResearch USA, Inc. (2)
(Formerly ICR, Inc.)
1330 Dillon Hts Ave
Baltimore, MD 21228-1122 MN
Tel.: (410) 747-4500
Fax: (410) 747-4928
E-Mail:
Web Site: www.i2lresearch.com
Emp.: 13
Pest Control Services
S.I.C.: 8731
N.A.I.C.S.: 541712
Robin G. Todd *(Exec Dir)*

Medella Therapeutics Limited (1)
The Sheffield Bioincubator
40 Leavygreave Road, Sheffield, South Yorkshire, S3 7RD, United Kingdom
Tel.: (44) 1142755555
Fax: (44) 1142755556
E-Mail: info@medellatherapeutics.co.uk
Emp.: 4
Cancer Therapeutic Services
S.I.C.: 8731
N.A.I.C.S.: 541712
Tim Skerry *(Founder & Chief Scientific Officer)*
Gareth Richards *(Founder)*

FUSION RETAIL BRANDS, PTY. LTD.

(Formerly COLORADO Group Ltd.)
Level 1 109 Burwood Rd
Hawthorn, VIC, 3122, Australia
Tel.: (61) 39420 8444
Fax: (61) 3 9420 8400
Web Site: www.fusionretailbrands.com.au
Year Founded: 1999
Sales Range: $350-399.9 Million
Emp.: 2,200

Business Description:
Footwear & Apparel Retailer & Wholesaler
S.I.C.: 5661
N.A.I.C.S.: 448210

Personnel:
Don Grover *(CEO)*

Transfer Agent:
Computershare Investor Services Pty. Ltd.
GPO Box 523
Brisbane, QLD, 4001, Australia
Tel.: (61) 7 3237 2173
Fax: (61) 7 3237 2152

Subsidiaries:

Diana Ferrari (Australia) Pty Ltd (1)
101 Cremorne Street
PO Box 218
3121 Richmond, VIC, Australia (100%)
Tel.: (61) 394208444
Fax: (61) 394208400
Footwear Whslr
S.I.C.: 5139
N.A.I.C.S.: 424340

JAG (Aust) Pty Ltd (1)
101 Cremorne St
3121 Richmond, VIC, Australia
Tel.: (61) 394208444
Fax: (61) 394208555
E-Mail: contactus@coloradogroup.com.au
Web Site: www.jag.com.au
Emp.: 50
Casual & Denim Clothing Designer & Mfr
S.I.C.: 2389
N.A.I.C.S.: 315240

Mathers Shoes Pty Ltd. (1)
109 Bunlvood Rd
Melbourne, QLD, 3122, Australia AU
Tel.: (61) 738773333 (100%)
Fax: (61) 738773411
Web Site: www.coloradogroup.com.au
Emp.: 200
Shoe Stores
S.I.C.: 5661
N.A.I.C.S.: 448210

Williams the Shoemen Pty Ltd (1)
Level 1 109 Burwood Rd
3122 Hawthorn, VIC, Australia
Tel.: (61) 3 9420 8444
Fax: (61) 3 9420 8400
E-Mail: melbourne.reception@fusionretailgroupbrands.com.au
Web Site: www.fusionretailbrands.com.au
Emp.: 175
Footwear Whslr
S.I.C.: 5139
N.A.I.C.S.: 424340
Don Grover *(CEO)*

FUSIONEX INTERNATIONAL PLC

Level 33 25 Canada Square
Canary Wharf, London, E14 5LB, United Kingdom
Tel.: (44) 207 038 8207
Fax: (44) 207 038 8100
E-Mail: info@adv-fusionex.com
Web Site: www.fusionex-international.com

Business Description:
Software Publisher
S.I.C.: 7372
N.A.I.C.S.: 511210

Personnel:
John Croft *(Chm)*
Ivan Teh *(CEO & Mng Dir)*
Yuen Choong Lai *(CFO)*

Board of Directors:
John Croft
Calvin Chun
Yuen Choong Lai
Alan Lim
Robin Taylor
Ivan Teh

FUSIONTECH, INC.

No 26 Gaoneng Street
High Tech Zone
Dalian, Liaoning, 116025, China
Tel.: (86) 411 8479 9486
E-Mail: investors@cleanfusiontech.com
Web Site: www.cleanfusiontech.com
Year Founded: 2007
ZPNP—(OTC)
Sales Range: $10-24.9 Million
Emp.: 178

Business Description:
Clean Technology Industrial Machinery Mfr
S.I.C.: 3559
N.A.I.C.S.: 333249

Personnel:
Lixin Wang *(Chm & CEO)*
Linqiang Yang *(CFO)*
Yiran Wang *(Sec)*

Board of Directors:
Lixin Wang
James Bloom
Yanming Wen
Caiyuan Yu
Yueqi Zou

FUSO CHEMICAL CO., LTD.

4-3-10 Koreibashi
Chuo-ku, Osaka, 541-0043, Japan
Tel.: (81) 662034771
Fax: (81) 662031455
E-Mail: info@fusokk.co.jp
Web Site: www.fusokk.co.jp
Year Founded: 1957
4368—(JAS)
Sales Range: $300-349.9 Million
Emp.: 350

Business Description:
Chemical & Coating Mfr
S.I.C.: 2851
N.A.I.C.S.: 325998

Personnel:
Ryota Akazawa *(Pres, CMO, Chief Sls Officer & Mng Dir)*
Hiroshi Masutani *(Chief Production, Quality Assurance & Safety Officer)*

Board of Directors:
Ryota Akazawa
Shozo Akazawa
Shuzo Enomoto
Misako Fujioka
Haruo Masauji
Hiroshi Masutani
Hiroji Mizumoto
Yoshinobu Nakae
Tomoni Tada
Noboru Takeda
Kotaro Wakabayashi

Subsidiaries:

Fuso Corporation Co Ltd (1)
6-6 Niitaka 2-chome
Yodogawa-ku, Osaka, 532-0033, Japan
Tel.: (81) 661500018
Fax: (81) 6 6150 0117
Web Site: www.fusokk.co.jp/eng/corporateinfo/domestic.html
Industrial Chemicals Mfr
S.I.C.: 2899
N.A.I.C.S.: 325998

X-One Co., Ltd. (1)
Sumitomo Fudosan Nishi-Shinjuku Bldg
Shinjuku-ku, Tokyo, 160-0023, Japan
Tel.: (81) 343301800
Fax: (81) 343301810
E-Mail: service@x-one.co.jp
Web Site: www.x-one.co.jp
Emp.: 40
Health Foods & Cosmetics Retailer
S.I.C.: 5122
N.A.I.C.S.: 446120
Katsuyoshi Ogata *(Mng Dir)*

Plants:

Fuso Chemical Co., Ltd - Juso Factory (1)
10-30 Nonakakita 2 Chome
Yodogawa-ku, Osaka, 532-0034, Japan
Tel.: (81) 663966231
Fax: (81) 6 6392 7716
Fruit Acids Mfr
S.I.C.: 2869
N.A.I.C.S.: 325199

Fuso Chemical Co., Ltd. - Kyoto First Factory (1)
5 Osadano-cho 1-chome
Fukuchiyama, Kyoto, 620-0853, Japan
Tel.: (81) 773 27 6925
Fax: (81) 773 27 6927
Web Site: www.fusokk.co.jp/eng/corporateinfo/domestic.html
Industrial Chemicals Mfr
S.I.C.: 2819
N.A.I.C.S.: 325180

Fuso Chemical Co., Ltd - Kyoto Second Factory (1)
8 Osadano-cho 2-chome
Fukuchiyama, Kyoto, 620-0853, Japan
Tel.: (81) 773205553
Fax: (81) 773205538
E-Mail: info@fusokk.co.jp
Web Site: www.fusokk.co.jp/eng/corporateinfo/domestic.html
Chemicals Mfr
S.I.C.: 2819
N.A.I.C.S.: 325180
Ryota Akazawa *(Pres)*

Fuso Chemical Co., Ltd - Osaka Factory (1)
27-10 Chikko-shinmachi 3 Cho
Nishi-ku, Sakai, Osaka, 592-8331, Japan
Tel.: (81) 722449091
Fax: (81) 72 244 9094
Web Site: www.fusokk.co.jp/eng/corporateinfo/domestic.html
Fruit Acids Mfr
S.I.C.: 2899
N.A.I.C.S.: 325199

U.S. Subsidiary:

PMP Fermentation Products, Inc. (1)
900 NE Adams St
Peoria, IL 61603-3904
Tel.: (309) 637-0400
Fax: (309) 637-9302
Web Site: www.pmpinc.com
Emp.: 70
Mfr & Marketer of Industrial Chemicals
S.I.C.: 2869
N.A.I.C.S.: 325199
Mike Bussell *(Mgr-Quality Assurance)*

FUTABA CORPORATION

629 Oshiba
Mobara, Chiba, 297-8588, Japan
Tel.: (81) 475241111
Telex: 3782641
Fax: (81) 475231346
Web Site: www.futaba.co.jp
Year Founded: 1948
6986—(TKS)
Sls.: $639,111,000
Assets: $1,621,620,000
Liabilities: $190,806,000
Net Worth: $1,430,814,000
Earnings: ($67,364,000)
Emp.: 5,427
Fiscal Year-end: 03/31/13

Business Description:
Radio Control Equipment, Mould & Metal Die Parts & Vacuum Fluorescent Displays Mfr & Sales Import Export
S.I.C.: 3663
N.A.I.C.S.: 334220

Personnel:
Hiroshi Sakurada *(Pres)*
Motoaki Arima *(Sr Exec Officer)*
Toshiteru Harada *(Mng Exec Officer)*
Toshihiko Honma *(Exec Officer)*
Mitsumasa Ishide *(Mng Exec Officer)*
Toshihide Kimizuka *(Exec Officer)*
Yasuo Shinozaki *(Exec Officer)*
Toshio Takayama *(Exec Officer)*
Hiroshi Yamada *(Sr Exec Officer)*
Yoichi Yamamoto *(Sr Exec Officer)*

Board of Directors:
Tatsuya Ikeda
Mitsumasa Ishide
Tadao Katsuta
Hideharu Kawasaki
Michisato Kono
Kozaburo Mogi
Hiroshi Sakurada
Kazunobu Takahashi

Subsidiaries:

Futaba Mobile Display Corporation (1)
644-55 Hitana Nakago-cho
Kitaibaraki, Ibaraki, 319-1556, Japan

Tel.: (81) 293 43 6788
Fax: (81) 293 43 6722
Display Mfr
S.I.C.: 3679
N.A.I.C.S.: 334419

O.S. Engines Mfg. Co., Ltd. (1)
3 15 6 Chome Imagawa
Osaka, 543 0003, Japan JP
Tel.: (81) 667020225 (100%)
Fax: (81) 667042722
E-Mail: e-info@os-engines.co.jp
Web Site: www.os-engines.co.jp
Emp.: 80
Mfr & Sales of Engines & Locomotives for Models
S.I.C.: 3519
N.A.I.C.S.: 333618
Seiichi Arata *(Pres)*

Plants:

Futaba Corporation - Akashi Machinery & Tooling Factory (1)
20-4 Minamifutami Futami-cho
Akashi, Hyogo, 674-0093, Japan
Tel.: (81) 789436161
Fax: (81) 78 943 5621
Precision Die Sets Mfr
S.I.C.: 3544
N.A.I.C.S.: 333514

Futaba Corporation - Chonan Machinery & Tooling Factory II (1)
472 Hoonji Chonan-machi
Chosei, Chiba, 297-0141, Japan
Tel.: (81) 475463611
Fax: (81) 475 46 1931
Web Site: en.futaba.co.jp/corporate/network/factories.html
Molded Die Parts Mfr
S.I.C.: 3544
N.A.I.C.S.: 333511

Futaba Corporation - Chonan Machinery & Tooling Factory (1)
112 Kuramochi Chonan-machi
Chosei, Chiba, 297-0123, Japan
Tel.: (81) 475462611
Fax: (81) 475462615
Web Site: en.futaba.co.jp/corporate/network/factories.html
Precision Die Sets Mfr
S.I.C.: 3544
N.A.I.C.S.: 333514

Futaba Corporation - Chosei Electron Tube Factory (1)
1080 Yabutsuka Chosei-mura
Chosei, Chiba, 299-4395, Japan
Tel.: (81) 475326051
Fax: (81) 475323036
Web Site: en.futaba.co.jp/corporate/network/factories.html
Vacuum Fluorescent Displays Mfr
S.I.C.: 3823
N.A.I.C.S.: 334513

Futaba Corporation - Chosei Electronic Systems Factory (1)
1080 Yabutsuka Chosei-mura
Chosei, Chiba, 299-4395, Japan
Tel.: (81) 475322151
Fax: (81) 475326983
E-Mail: rc-sales@ml.futaba.co.jp
Emp.: 300
Radio Control Equipment Mfr
S.I.C.: 3663
N.A.I.C.S.: 334220

Futaba Corporation - Chosei Machinery & Tooling Factory (1)
1080 Yabutsuka Chosei-mura
Chosei, Chiba, 299-4395, Japan
Tel.: (81) 475326036
Fax: (81) 475326139
Precision Die Sets Mfr
S.I.C.: 3544
N.A.I.C.S.: 333514
Fakurada Hiroshi *(Pres)*

Futaba Corporation - Chosei VFD Module Factory (1)
1080 Yabutsuka Chosei-mura
Chosei, Chiba, 299-4395, Japan
Tel.: (81) 475 32 6005
Fax: (81) 475 323638
Web Site: en.futaba.co.jp/corporate/network/factories.html
Vacuum Fluorescent Displays Mfr
S.I.C.: 3823
N.A.I.C.S.: 334513

Futaba Corporation - Mobara Electron Tube Factory (1)
629 Oshiba
Mobara, Chiba, 297-8588, Japan
Tel.: (81) 475241111
Fax: (81) 475231346
E-Mail: ir@ml.futaba.co.jp
Web Site: www.en.futaba.co.jp
Emp.: 1,200
Vacuum Fluorescent Displays Mfr
S.I.C.: 3823
N.A.I.C.S.: 334513
Hiroshi Sakurada *(Pres)*

Futaba Corporation - Mutsuzawa Machinery & Tooling Factory (1)
2345 Kamiichiba Mutsuzawa-machi
Chosei, Chiba, 299-4403, Japan
Tel.: (81) 475441221
Fax: (81) 475441220
Web Site: www.futaba.co.jp/corporate/network/factories.html
Emp.: 50
Precision Die Sets Mfr
S.I.C.: 3544
N.A.I.C.S.: 333514
Seita Shigeo *(Mgr)*

U.S. Subsidiaries:

Futaba Corporation of America (1)
711 E State Pkwy
Schaumburg, IL 60173 IL
Tel.: (847) 884-1444 (100%)
Telex: 206833
Fax: (847) 884-1635
Web Site: www.futaba.com
Emp.: 20
Marketing of Vacuum Fluorescent Displays & Digital Readout Equipment (PULSCALE)
S.I.C.: 3679
N.A.I.C.S.: 334419
Gary Wires *(Dir-Engrg & QA)*

Futaba Corporation of America (1)
14492 N Sheldon Rd Ste 370
Plymouth, MI 48170-2493
Tel.: (734) 459-1177
Fax: (734) 459-1268
Web Site: www.futaba.com
Emp.: 5
S.I.C.: 3663
N.A.I.C.S.: 334220
Robert Tohring *(Mgr)*

Non-U.S. Subsidiaries:

FUTABA DENSHI Corp. (S) Pte. Ltd. (1)
152 Beach Road 23-08 The Gateway East
Singapore, Singapore
Tel.: (65) 62919882
Fax: (65) 62917391
Web Site: www.en.futaba.co.jp/corporate/network/affiliates.html
Emp.: 13
Electronic Components Distr
S.I.C.: 5065
N.A.I.C.S.: 423690
Leonor Seng *(Mgr-Admin)*

Futaba Electronics Components Korea Co., Ltd. (1)
511 Daerung-Technotown 12 327-32
Gasan-dong
Geumcheon-gu, Seoul, 153-802, Korea (South)
Tel.: (82) 5 797 8244
Fax: (82) 220297334
Emp.: 9
Electronic Components Whslr
S.I.C.: 5065
N.A.I.C.S.: 423690
Goro Eto *(Chm)*

FUTABA (Hong Kong) Corporation Ltd. (1)
Rm D 17/F Somerset House 979 Kings Rd
Quarry Bay
Hong Kong, China (Hong Kong)
Tel.: (852) 29635888
Fax: (852) 2 811 0802
Electronic Component Whslr
S.I.C.: 5065
N.A.I.C.S.: 423690

FUTABA International Trading (Shanghai) Co., Ltd. (1)
Unit F 8/F International Ocean Shipping & Finance Center No 720
Pudong New District, Shanghai, 200120, China
Tel.: (86) 2150366399
Fax: (86) 2150366386
Web Site: www.futabash.com.cn
Circuit Boards Distr
S.I.C.: 5065
N.A.I.C.S.: 423690

FUTABA Technology Development Corp. (1)
11F No 31 Hai-Pien Road
Kaohsiung, Taiwan
Tel.: (886) 73365777
Fax: (886) 73329881
E-Mail: service@ftd-asia.com.tw
Web Site: www.ftd-asia.com.tw
Electronic Components Distr
S.I.C.: 5065
N.A.I.C.S.: 423690

Non-U.S. Joint Venture:

Futaba Tenneco U.K. Limited (1)
Liverpool Road Rose Grove
Burnley, Lancs, BB12 6HJ, United Kingdom UK
Tel.: (44) 1282433171
Telex: 85163363
Fax: (44) 1282450778
Web Site: www.futaba-tenneco.co.uk
Sales Range: $125-149.9 Million
Emp.: 300
Automotive Parts Mfr
S.I.C.: 3714
N.A.I.C.S.: 336390
Kevin Schofield *(Mng Dir)*

FUTEBOL CLUBE DO PORTO

Estadio do Dragao Via FC Porto
Entrada Nascente porta 15 piso 3
4350-415 Porto, Portugal
Tel.: (351) 225570400
Fax: (351) 225570498
E-Mail: fcporto@fcporto.pt
Web Site: www.fcporto.pt
FCP—(EUR)
Sales Range: $1-9.9 Million
Emp.: 243
Business Description:
Professional Football Club Operator
S.I.C.: 7941
N.A.I.C.S.: 711211
Personnel:
Jorge de Lima Pinto da Costa *(Chm)*
Daniel Lorenz Rodrigues Pereira *(Sec)*
Board of Directors:
Jorge de Lima Pinto da Costa
Reinaldo da Costa Teles Pinheiro
Rui Ferreira Vieira de Sa
Angelino Candido de Sousa Ferreira
Adelino Sa e Melo Caldeira

Subsidiary:

F.C. PortoMultimedia - Edicoes Multimedia, S.A. (1)
Avenida Fernao de Magalhaes 1862 14-S 1402
4350-158 Porto, Portugal
Tel.: (351) 225 070 500
Commercial Production Services
S.I.C.: 7812
N.A.I.C.S.: 512110

FUTIAN SUNNADA COMMUNICATION CO., LTD.

(d/b/a Sunnada)
7 Building C District Software Park
Tongpan Road, Fuzhou, Futian, 350003, China
Tel.: (86) 591 83770162
Fax: (86) 591 83775137
E-Mail: international@sunnada.com
Web Site: www.sunnada.com
Year Founded: 1998
002417—(SSE)
Sales Range: $25-49.9 Million
Business Description:
Communication Equipment & Software
S.I.C.: 3663
N.A.I.C.S.: 334220
Personnel:
Guoying Huang *(CEO & Gen Mgr)*

FUTONG GROUP CO., LTD.

8 Futong Road
Fuyang, Zhejiang, 311400, China
Tel.: (86) 57163322660
Fax: (86) 571 63326488
E-Mail: fthgq@ftjt.net
Web Site: www.futonggroup.com.cn
Emp.: 2,000
Business Description:
Wire & Cable Mfr
S.I.C.: 3496
N.A.I.C.S.: 332618

FUTONG TECHNOLOGY DEVELOPMENT HOLDINGS LIMITED

Room 929 9 F Sun Hung Kai Centre
30 Harbour Road
Wanchai, China (Hong Kong)
Tel.: (852) 26222428
Fax: (852) 26222426
Web Site: www.futong.com.hk
0465—(HKG)
Rev.: $567,267,488
Assets: $336,997,733
Liabilities: $256,501,131
Net Worth: $80,496,602
Earnings: $6,489,817
Emp.: 500
Fiscal Year-end: 12/31/12
Business Description:
Software Product Distr
S.I.C.: 7372
N.A.I.C.S.: 511210
Personnel:
Jian Chen *(Co-Founder, Chm & CEO)*
Hui Xie *(Co-Founder & VP-Futong Dongfang)*
Tao Guan *(Co-Founder)*
Yun Zhang *(Vice Chm)*
Paul Kee Ko Wai *(CFO)*
Ming Yan Choy *(CEO-Ops-PRC)*
Hin Leung Siu *(Sec & Controller-Fin-Futong HK)*
Ying Liu *(Exec VP-Futong Dongfang)*
Board of Directors:
Jian Chen
Tao Guan
Patrick Pak Tai Ho
Kwan Hung Lee
Bo Yuan
Yun Zhang
Transfer Agent:
Tricor Investor Services Limited
26/F Tesbury Centre 28 Queen's Road East
Hong Kong, China (Hong Kong)

THE FUTURA CORPORATION

2970 700 W Georgia Street
Vancouver, BC, V7Y 1A1, Canada
Tel.: (604) 608-6600
Fax: (604) 608-6700
E-Mail: info@futuracorporation.com
Web Site: www.futuracorporation.com
Sales Range: $1-4.9 Billion
Emp.: 600
Business Description:
Pressure Treated Wood Distr, Designer & Marketer
S.I.C.: 2519
N.A.I.C.S.: 337125

The Futura Corporation—(Continued)

Personnel:
Amardeip Singh Doman *(Chm, Pres & CEO)*
Harry Rosenfeld *(Exec VP)*

Subsidiary:

CanWel Building Materials Group Ltd. (1)
1100 609 Granville Street
PO Box 10377
Vancouver, BC, V7Y 1G6, Canada BC
Tel.: (604) 432-1400 (100%)
Fax: (604) 436-6670
E-Mail: info@canwel.com
Web Site: www.canwel.com
CWX—(TSX)
Rev.: $706,324,767
Assets: $255,159,964
Liabilities: $147,679,563
Net Worth: $107,480,401
Earnings: $7,952,160
Emp.: 300
Fiscal Year-end: 12/31/12
Building Materials Distr
S.I.C.: 5211
N.A.I.C.S.: 444110
Amardeip Singh Doman *(Chm & CEO)*
Marc Seguin *(Pres)*
James Code *(CFO)*
R.S. Doman *(Sec)*

Subsidiary:

Sodisco-Howden Group, Inc. (2)
465 McGill Street 8th Floor
Montreal, QC, H2Y 2H4, Canada QC
Tel.: (514) 286-8986
Fax: (514) 286-2911
Emp.: 500
Hardware & Home Renovation Products Distr
S.I.C.: 1522
N.A.I.C.S.: 236118

THE FUTURA FOREST CORPORATION

(See Under The Futura Corporation)

FUTURA MEDICAL PLC

Surrey Technology Centre 40 Occam Road
Guildford, Surrey, GU2 7YG, United Kingdom
Tel.: (44) 1483685670
Fax: (44) 1483685671
E-Mail: info@futuramedical.com
Web Site: www.futuramedical.com
FUM—(AIM)
Rev.: $118,447
Assets: $5,066,724
Liabilities: $528,988
Net Worth: $4,537,736
Earnings: ($3,437,560)
Emp.: 3
Fiscal Year-end: 12/31/12

Business Description:
Sexual Healthcare & Pain Relief Pharmaceutical Product Mfr
S.I.C.: 2834
N.A.I.C.S.: 325412

Personnel:
James Barder *(CEO)*
David Davies *(Chief Dev Officer)*
William Potter *(Chief Scientific Officer)*
Derek Martin *(Sec & Dir-Fin)*

Board of Directors:
John Clarke
Lisa Arnold
James Barder
David Davies
Jonathan Freeman
Derek Martin

Legal Counsel:
Withers & Rogers LLP
4 More London Riverside
London, United Kingdom

Memery Crystal LLP
44 Southampton Buildings
London, United Kingdom

Subsidiary:

Futura Medical Developments Limited (1)
Surrey Tech Ctr 40 Occam Rd
Guildford, Surrey, GU2 7YG, United Kingdom
Tel.: (44) 1483685670
Fax: (44) 1483685671
E-Mail: info@futuramedical.com
Web Site: www.futuramedical.com
Pharmaceutical Products Mfr
S.I.C.: 2834
N.A.I.C.S.: 325412
James Barder *(CEO)*

FUTURA POLYESTERS LTD.

Paragon Condominium 3rd Floor
Pandurang Budhkar Marg, Mumbai, 400 013, India
Tel.: (91) 22 24922999
E-Mail: futuraho@futurapolyesters.com
Web Site: www.futurapolyesters.com
500720—(BOM)
Sales Range: $125-149.9 Million

Business Description:
Polyester Resins Mfr
S.I.C.: 2821
N.A.I.C.S.: 325211

Personnel:
S. B. Ghia *(Chm & Mng Dir)*
M. D. Dalal *(Mng Dir)*
G. Venkatesh *(COO)*
R. Ramesh Babu *(Pres-Fin & Comml)*
N. K. Skandamoorty *(Pres-Ops)*

Board of Directors:
S. B. Ghia
M. D. Dalal
K. V. K. Murthy
K. Ramasubramanian
M. Saravanan

Transfer Agent:
Satellite Corporate Services Pvt. Ltd.
301 Sony Apartments Opp St.Jude High School Off Andheri Kurla Road
Mumbai, India

FUTURAQUA MINERAL WATER PRODUCTION AND ASSET MANAGEMENT PUBLIC LIMITED COMPANY

(d/b/a FuturAqua plc)
Ungvar u 22 III em
7623 Pecs, Hungary
Tel.: (36) 20 9999899
E-Mail: info@futuraqua.hu
Web Site: www.futuraqua.hu
FUTURAQUA—(BUD)

Business Description:
Mineral Water Production & Investment
S.I.C.: 4941
N.A.I.C.S.: 221310

Personnel:
Szilard Gergely Orovica *(Chm-Supervisory Bd)*
Istvan Fodor *(Chm-Mgmt Bd)*
Balazs Lang *(Member-Mgmt Bd)*
Ella Regina Pais *(Member-Mgmt Bd)*

Supervisory Board of Directors:
Szilard Gergely Orovica
Arpadne Pauli Miklos
Ilona Zsirmon

FUTURE ARAB INVESTMENT CO.

Sport City Circle - Quqa Group Building
PO Box 20082
Amman, 11118, Jordan
Tel.: (962) 6 5677588
Fax: (962) 6 5601213
E-Mail: info@fainvest.com
Web Site: www.fainvest.com
Year Founded: 2006
FUTR—(AMM)
Rev.: $17,863,162
Assets: $53,843,495
Liabilities: $3,645,695
Net Worth: $50,197,800
Earnings: $666,033
Emp.: 7
Fiscal Year-end: 12/31/12

Business Description:
Investment Management Services
S.I.C.: 6211
N.A.I.C.S.: 523999

Personnel:
Muneer Quqa *(Gen Mgr)*

FUTURE ARCHITECT INC.

Art Village Osaki Central Tower 1-2-2
Osaki Shinagawa ku
Tokyo, 1410032, Japan
Tel.: (81) 357405721
Fax: (81) 357405820
Web Site: www.future.co.jp
4722—(TKS)
Sls.: $256,885,288
Assets: $163,132,079
Liabilities: $33,703,340
Net Worth: $129,428,739
Earnings: $12,845,217
Emp.: 1,316
Fiscal Year-end: 12/31/12

Business Description:
Information Technology Consulting Services
S.I.C.: 7373
N.A.I.C.S.: 541512

Personnel:
Yasufumi Kanemaru *(Chm & CEO)*
Kunihito Ishibashi *(CTO, Chief Security Officer & Exec Sr VP)*
Hideo Kagawa *(Exec Officer & Dir-Logistic & Svcs)*
Masami Arai *(Exec Officer-Fin & Solution Grp-Advanced Bus Div)*
Osamu Hara *(Exec Officer)*
Yoshihiko Nakajima *(Exec Officer)*
Hiroshi Sakurada *(Exec Officer)*
Satoru Tahara *(Exec Officer)*
Shinji Yamamoto *(Exec Officer)*
Yuji Higashi *(Exec Sr VP)*

Board of Directors:
Yasufumi Kanemaru
Yasuhiro Harada
Yuji Higashi
Kunihito Ishibashi

Transfer Agent:
Mitsubishi UFJ Trust & Banking Corporation
10-11 Higashi-suna 7-chome
Koto-ku, Tokyo, 137-8081, Japan

Subsidiaries:

Ascendia Inc. (1)
Osaki W City Bldg Osaki 2-9-3
Shinagawa-ku, Tokyo, 141-0031, Japan
Tel.: (81) 363616000
Fax: (81) 354357981
E-Mail: info@ascendia.jp
Web Site: www.ascendia.jp
Custom Software Design & Publishing Services
S.I.C.: 7372
N.A.I.C.S.: 511210

ELM Corporation (1)
2-9-3 Uesutoshitibiru 5F
Shinagawa-ku, Tokyo, Osaki, 141 0032, Japan
Tel.: (81) 357196122
Fax: (81) 357196123
E-Mail: info@elmcorp.jp
Web Site: www.elmcorp.jp
Emp.: 100
Business Software Publishers
S.I.C.: 7372
N.A.I.C.S.: 511210
Shiro Toshiyama *(Mgr)*

Future Financial Strategy Corp. (1)
Art Vlg Osaki Cent Tower 1-2-2 Osaki
Shinagawa-ku, Tokyo, 141-0032, Japan
Tel.: (81) 357405722
Fax: (81) 357405822
E-Mail: ffs@future.co.jp
Strategic Consulting & Financial Services
S.I.C.: 6282
N.A.I.C.S.: 523930
Naoki Togashi *(Pres & CEO)*

Uoei Shoten Corporation (1)
423-1 Ajigata
Minami, Niigata, Japan
Tel.: (81) 253733011
Fax: (81) 253724621
Supermarkets Management Services
S.I.C.: 5411
N.A.I.C.S.: 445110

Zakura Inc. (1)
2-9-3 Uesutoshitibiru 6F
Tokyo, 141-0032, Japan
Tel.: (81) 357405839
Fax: (81) 34927880
E-Mail: corp@zakura.jp
Web Site: www.zakura.jp
Emp.: 10
Internet Media Services
S.I.C.: 7379
N.A.I.C.S.: 518210
Kenji Suzuki *(CEO)*

FUTURE BRIGHT HOLDINGS LIMITED

Room 1409 West Tower Shun Tak Centre 200 Connaught Road
Central, China (Hong Kong)
Tel.: (852) 25482115
Fax: (852) 25482117
E-Mail: info@fb.com.hk
Web Site: www.fb.etnet.com.hk
0703—(HKG)
Sls.: $83,313,692
Assets: $150,188,065
Liabilities: $72,385,567
Net Worth: $77,802,498
Earnings: $34,530,489
Emp.: 1,027
Fiscal Year-end: 12/31/12

Business Description:
Food & Beverage Mfr
S.I.C.: 2099
N.A.I.C.S.: 311999

Personnel:
Johnny See Kit Chan *(Chm)*
King Hung Lai *(Deputy Chm)*
Chak Mo Chan *(Mng Dir)*
Kwok Wah Cheung *(Chief Bus Dev Officer)*
Hon Fai Leung *(Sec)*

Board of Directors:
Johnny See Kit Chan
Afonso Pak Cheong Chan
Chak Mo Chan
Hon Kit Cheung
King Hung Lai
In Ian Leong
Lincoln Kam Yuen Yu

Codan Services Limited
Clarendon House 2 Church Street
Hamilton, Bermuda

Transfer Agents:
Tricor Tengis Limited
26/F Tesbury Centre, 28 Queens Road East
Hong Kong, China (Hong Kong)

Codan Services Limited
Clarendon House 2 Church Street
Hamilton, Bermuda

Non-U.S. Subsidiary:

FB Group Enterprises Management Company Limited (1)
1023 Avenida De Anizade 2 Andar P-V Edf
Nam Fong, Macau, China (Macau)
Tel.: (853) 28701166
Fax: (853) 28703198
Web Site: www.futurebrightgroup.com.mo
Emp.: 1,500
Restaurant Operating Services
S.I.C.: 5812
N.A.I.C.S.: 722511

FUTURE COMMUNICATIONS CO. GLOBAL K.S.C.C.

7th Floor Al-Awadi Tower 3 Ahmad Al Jaber Street
PO Box 1324
Safat, Kuwait, 13014, Kuwait
Tel.: (965) 22432555
Fax: (965) 22431926
E-Mail: info@fccg.com.kw
Web Site: www.fccg.com.kw
FUTURE—(KUW)
Rev.: $85,315,473
Assets: $67,679,025
Liabilities: $16,669,047
Net Worth; $51,009,978
Earnings: $1,892,277
Emp.: 530
Fiscal Year-end: 12/31/12

Business Description:
Telecommunications Services
S.I.C.: 4899
N.A.I.C.S.: 517919

Personnel:
Muthana Mohammad Ahmad Al-Hamad *(Chm)*
Faisal Nasser Mohammad Al-Kharafi *(Vice Chm)*

Board of Directors:
Muthana Mohammad Ahmad Al-Hamad
Ali Yousef Hussian Al-Awadhi
Salah Abdul Latef Mohammad Al-Awadhi
Faisal Nasser Mohammad Al-Kharafi
Bader Mohamed Hosain Al-Sarraf

FUTURE ELECTRONICS INC.

237 Hymus Boulevard
Pointe-Claire, QC, H9R 5C7, Canada
Tel.: (514) 694-7710
Fax: (514) 695-3707
E-Mail: martin.gordon@future.ca
Web Site: www.futureelectronics.com
Year Founded: 1968
Sales Range: $1-4.9 Billion
Emp.: 1,300

Business Description:
Semi-Conductors & Passive, Interconnect & Electro-Mechanical Components Distr
Import Export
S.I.C.: 5065
N.A.I.C.S.: 423690

Personnel:
Robert Miller *(Pres & CEO)*
Pierre G. Guilbault *(CFO & Exec VP)*

Branches:

FAI Electronics (1)
237 Boul Hymus
Pointe-Claire, QC, H9R 5C7, Canada (100%)
Tel.: (514) 694-7710
Fax: (514) 695-3707
E-Mail: robert.miller@future.ca
Emp.: 1,200
Distributors of Electronic Parts & Equipment
Import Export
S.I.C.: 5065
N.A.I.C.S.: 423690
Robert Miller *(Pres)*

Future Electronics Corp., Canada (1)
6029 103rd St
Edmonton, AB, T6H2H3, Canada (100%)
Tel.: (780) 438-5888
Fax: (780) 436-1874
Web Site: www.futureelectronics.com
Emp.: 1
Distribitution of Electronic Semiconductor Components
S.I.C.: 5065
N.A.I.C.S.: 423690

Future Electronics Corp., Canada (1)
3689 E 1st Ave Ste 200
Vancouver, BC, V5M1C2, Canada (100%)
Tel.: (604) 294-1166
Fax: (604) 294-1206
Web Site: www.futureelectronics.com
Emp.: 15
Retail Distribution of Electronic Equipment
S.I.C.: 5065
N.A.I.C.S.: 423690

Future Electronics, Inc. (1)
1000 Ave Saint Jean Baptiste Ste 201
Quebec, QC, G2E 5G5, Canada (100%)
Tel.: (418) 877-6666
Fax: (418) 877-6671
Web Site: www.futureelectronics.com
Emp.: 6
Distributor of Electronic Components
S.I.C.: 5065
N.A.I.C.S.: 423690
Michelle Rodriguez *(Gen Mgr)*

Future Electronics (1)
4043 Carling Ave Ste 112
Ottawa, ON, K2K 2A4, Canada (100%)
Tel.: (613) 727-1800
Fax: (613) 727-9819
E-Mail: joe.chennette@futureelectronics.com
Web Site: www.futureelectronics.com
Emp.: 13
Distributors of Computer Components
S.I.C.: 5065
N.A.I.C.S.: 423690
Joe Chennette *(Mgr)*

Future Electronics (1)
Ste 400 2431 37th Ave NE
Calgary, AB, T2E 6Y7, Canada (100%)
Tel.: (403) 219-3443
Fax: (403) 291-7054
Web Site: www.futureelectronics.com
Emp.: 20
S.I.C.: 5731
N.A.I.C.S.: 443142
Robert Wheeler *(Gen Mgr)*

Future Electronics (1)
309 Twin Oaks Drive
Moncton, NB, E1G 4W7, Canada (100%)
Tel.: (506) 389-9991
Fax: (506) 389-9992
Web Site: www.futureelectronics.com
Electronic Components & Electromechanical Products Distribution
S.I.C.: 3679
N.A.I.C.S.: 334419

Future Electronics (1)
6711 Mississauga Road Suite 302
Mississauga, ON, L5N 2W3, Canada (100%)
Tel.: (514) 694-7710
Fax: (514) 695-3707
Toll Free: (800) 388-8731
Web Site: www.futureelectronics.com
Emp.: 26
Mfr of Electronic Products
S.I.C.: 5065
N.A.I.C.S.: 423690

U.S. Branches:

Future Electronic Inc. (1)
41 Main St
Bolton, MA 01740-1107
Tel.: (978) 779-3000
Fax: (978) 779-3050
E-Mail: info@future.ca
Web Site: www.future.ca
Sls.: $4,000,000
Emp.: 8
Miscellaneous Retail Stores
Import Export
S.I.C.: 5065
N.A.I.C.S.: 423690

Future Electronics Corp. (1)
4801 E Washington St Ste 265
Phoenix, AZ 85034-2021 (100%)
Tel.: (602) 629-3013
Fax: (602) 629-3041
Web Site: www.futureelectronics.com
Emp.: 20
Electronics Distributor
S.I.C.: 5065
N.A.I.C.S.: 423690

Future Electronics Corp. (1)
32 Discovery Ste 170
Irvine, CA 92618
Tel.: (949) 453-1515
Fax: (949) 453-1226
Emp.: 3,600
Semiconductor Distr & Marketer
S.I.C.: 5731
N.A.I.C.S.: 443142

Future Electronics Corp. (1)
690 N McCarthy Blvd Ste 220
Milpitas, CA 95035-1326
Tel.: (408) 434-1122
Fax: (408) 433-0822
Web Site: www.futureelectronics.com
Emp.: 53
Sales of Electronic Products
S.I.C.: 5065
N.A.I.C.S.: 423690
Todd Fiske *(Reg VP)*

Future Electronics Corp. (1)
1614 W Hill Blvd Ste 200
Roseville, CA 95661-3895
Tel.: (916) 783-7877
Fax: (916) 783-7988
E-Mail: info@futureelectronics.com
Web Site: www.futureelectronics.com
Emp.: 15
Wholesale Electronic Distribution
S.I.C.: 5065
N.A.I.C.S.: 423690
Jeff Yake *(Gen Mgr)*

Future Electronics Corp. (1)
6256 Greenwich Dr Ste 250
San Diego, CA 92122-5981
Tel.: (858) 625-2800
Fax: (858) 625-2810
E-Mail: info@futureelectronics.com
Web Site: www.futurerc.com
Emp.: 15
S.I.C.: 5731
N.A.I.C.S.: 443142

Future Electronics Corp. (1)
59 Skyline Dr Ste 1000
Lake Mary, FL 32746-7107
Tel.: (407) 444-6302
Fax: (407) 444-6303
E-Mail: info@futureelectronics.com
Web Site: www.futureelectronis.com
Emp.: 15
Mfr. of Electronic Products
S.I.C.: 5065
N.A.I.C.S.: 423690
Sheldon Weiss *(Mgr-Sls)*

Future Electronics Corp. (1)
8700 Indian Creek Pkwy Bldg 3
Overland Park, KS 66210-1442 (100%)
Tel.: (913) 498-1531
Fax: (913) 498-1786
E-Mail: info@futureelectronics.com
Web Site: www.future-active.com
Emp.: 9
Distributor of Electronic Component
S.I.C.: 5065
N.A.I.C.S.: 423690
Clem Noll *(Gen Mgr)*

Future Electronics Corp. (1)
12125 Woodcrest Executive Dr Ste 200
Saint Louis, MO 63141
Tel.: (314) 317-8751
Fax: (314) 439-5043
Emp.: 12
Electronic Goods Distr
S.I.C.: 5065
N.A.I.C.S.: 423690

Future Electronics Corp. (1)
4700 Homewood Ct Ste 106
Raleigh, NC 27609 (100%)
Tel.: (919) 571-9942
Fax: (919) 571-0928
E-Mail: info@futureelectronics.com
Web Site: www.futureelectronics.com
Emp.: 10
Electronics Distribution
S.I.C.: 5065
N.A.I.C.S.: 423690

Future Electronics Corp. (1)
5 Greentree Ctr 525 Rt 73 N Ste 217
Marlton, NJ 08053 (100%)
Tel.: (856) 985-2841
Fax: (856) 797-1907
Toll Free: (800) 285-8873
E-Mail: info@futureelectronics.com
Web Site: www.futureelectronics.com
Emp.: 15
Provider of Electronics & Electrical Solutions
S.I.C.: 5065
N.A.I.C.S.: 423690
Robert Miller *(Owner)*

Future Electronics Corp. (1)
375 Woodcliff Dr Ste 11
Fairport, NY 14450-4276 (100%)
Tel.: (800) 444-1521
Fax: (585) 387-9563
Web Site: www.futureelectronics.com
Emp.: 12
Sales of Electronic Components
S.I.C.: 5065
N.A.I.C.S.: 423690
Anthony Lipari *(Gen Mgr)*

Future Electronics Corp. (1)
301 Plainfield Rd Ste 275
Syracuse, NY 13212-4585 (100%)
Tel.: (315) 451-2371
Fax: (315) 451-7258
Web Site: www.futureelectronics.com
Emp.: 12
Distributers of Electronics Company
S.I.C.: 5065
N.A.I.C.S.: 423690

Future Electronics Corp. (1)
3033 Express Dr N
Hauppauge, NY 11749-5309 (100%)
Tel.: (631) 234-4000
Fax: (631) 234-6183
E-Mail: info@futureelectronics.ca
Web Site: www.futureelectronics.com
Emp.: 12
Distributor of Electronic Components
S.I.C.: 5065
N.A.I.C.S.: 423690

Future Electronics Corp. (1)
6550 SW Redwood Ln Ste 365
Portland, OR 97224
Tel.: (503) 603-0956
Fax: (503) 603-0955
Web Site: www.futurerc.com
Emp.: 6
Electronic & Electromechanical Equipment Distr
S.I.C.: 5065
N.A.I.C.S.: 423690

Future Electronics Corp. (1)
3000 Stonewood Dr Ste 320
Wexford, PA 15090 (100%)
Tel.: (724) 935-1113
Fax: (724) 935-1188
Web Site: www.future.ca
Emp.: 7
Distribution of Electronic Component
S.I.C.: 5065
N.A.I.C.S.: 423690
David Wojtalik *(Gen Mgr)*

Future Electronics Corp. (1)
406 W South Jordan Pkwy Ste 580
South Jordan, UT 84095-3940 (100%)
Tel.: (801) 467-4448
Fax: (801) 467-3604
Web Site: www.futureelectronics.com
Emp.: 7
Mfr. of Electronics Components
S.I.C.: 5065
N.A.I.C.S.: 423690
Burt Wandtke *(Gen Mgr)*

Future Electronics Corp. (1)
22232 17th Ave SE Ste 301
Bothell, WA 98021
Tel.: (425) 489-3400
Fax: (514) 695-3707
E-Mail: andy.sidhu@future.ca
Web Site: www.futureelectronics.com
Rev.: $7,000,000
Emp.: 25
Electronics Distribution
S.I.C.: 5065
N.A.I.C.S.: 423690
Andy Sidhu *(VP)*

Future Electronics Corp. (1)
17975 W Sarah Ln Ste 160
Brookfield, WI 53045-5899
Tel.: (262) 879-0244
Fax: (262) 879-0250
E-Mail: info@futureelectronics.com
Web Site: www.futureelectronics.com
Emp.: 14
Distributer of Electronics
S.I.C.: 5063
N.A.I.C.S.: 423610

Future Electronics Inc.—(Continued)

Robert Miller *(Owner)*

Future Electronics Inc (1)
41 Main St
Bolton, MA 01740 MA
Tel.: (978) 779-3000 (100%)
Fax: (978) 779-5143
E-Mail: info@futureelectronics.com
Web Site: www.futureelectronics.com
Emp.: 1,800
Electronic Parts & Equipment
Import Export
S.I.C.: 5065
N.A.I.C.S.: 423690
Anthony Sarakinos *(VP-Sls)*

Non-U.S. Branches:

Future Electronics Corp., Australia (1)
Ste 503 Level 5
425 Burwood Highway, Wantirna, VIC, 3152, Australia (100%)
Tel.: (61) 395586312
Fax: (61) 395586317
E-Mail: info@futureelectronics.com
Web Site: www.future.com
Emp.: 5
S.I.C.: 5731
N.A.I.C.S.: 443142
Matt Wild *(Gen Mgr)*

Future Electronics Corp., Australia (1)
Ste 6 752 Balckburn Rd
Clayton, Melbourne, VIC, 3168, Australia (100%)
Tel.: (61) 398997944
Fax: (61) 395586317
Web Site: www.future.com
S.I.C.: 5731
N.A.I.C.S.: 443142

Future Electronics Corp., Belgium (1)
Ryvisspraat 118
Zwijnaarde, 9052, Belgium (100%)
Tel.: (32) 93405270
Fax: (32) 93494830
E-Mail: info@futureelectroincs.com
Web Site: www.futureelectroincs.com
Emp.: 16
S.I.C.: 5731
N.A.I.C.S.: 443142
Anne Baeten *(Branch Mgr)*

Future Electronics Corp., Brazil (1)
Rua Luzitana 740/10 Andar Conjuntos 103/ 104 Centro
Campinas, Sao Paulo, 13015-121, Brazil (100%)
Tel.: (55) 1937374100
Fax: (55) 1932369834
E-Mail: future.saopaulo@future.ca
Web Site: www.futureelectronics.com
Emp.: 25
Distr & Marketing of Semiconductors & Passive Interconnect & Electro-Mechanical Components
S.I.C.: 3674
N.A.I.C.S.: 334413
Edward Zamaro *(Gen Mgr)*

Future Electronics Corp., Bulgaria (1)
23 Andrej Saharov St
Sofia, 1784, Bulgaria
Tel.: (359) 29745952
Fax: (359) 29745968
Web Site: www.futureelectronics.com
S.I.C.: 5734
N.A.I.C.S.: 443142

Future Electronics Corp., Denmark (1)
Skomagervej 13 D
7100 Vejle, Denmark (100%)
Tel.: (45) 76408764
Fax: (45) 76408765
Web Site: www.futureelectronics.com
Emp.: 10
Electronic Mfr & Distr
S.I.C.: 5731
N.A.I.C.S.: 443142
Niels Bisgaard *(Gen Mgr)*

Future Electronics Corp., Erfurt (1)
Haarbergstrasse 61A
Erfurt, 99097, Germany (100%)
Tel.: (49) 361420870
Fax: (49) 3614208760
E-Mail: info-de-future@futureelectronics.com
Web Site: www.futureelectronics.com
Emp.: 7
S.I.C.: 5734
N.A.I.C.S.: 443142
Thomas Brachtel *(Mng Dir)*

Future Electronics Corp., Finland (1)
Teknobulevardi 3-5
1510 Vantaa, Finland (100%)
Tel.: (358) 95259950
Fax: (358) 94551050
E-Mail: veliantti.leskinen@futureelectronics.com
Emp.: 10
S.I.C.: 5731
N.A.I.C.S.: 443142
Paul Benford *(Branch Mgr)*

Future Electronics Corp., France (1)
Europarc Du Chene
4 Rue Edison Batiment A, Bron, Bron, 69673, France (100%)
Tel.: (33) 472158600
Fax: (33) 472150068
E-Mail: michael.loriot@futureelectronics.com
Web Site: www.futureelectronicsee.com
Emp.: 10
S.I.C.: 5946
N.A.I.C.S.: 443142
Michael Loriot *(Gen Mgr)*

Future Electronics Corp., France (1)
5 Ave Albert Durand
Aeropole 3, 31700 Toulouse, Blagnac, France (100%)
Tel.: (33) 562747240
Fax: (33) 561165154
Distr & Marketing of Semiconductors & Passive Interconnect & Electro-Mechanical Components
S.I.C.: 3674
N.A.I.C.S.: 334413

Future Electronics Corp., France (1)
6 Avenue Morane Saulnier
78941 Velizy-Villacoublay, Cedex, France (100%)
Tel.: (33) 223456080
Fax: (33) 139491560
E-Mail: info@futureelectronics.com
Sales Range: $10-24.9 Million
Emp.: 60
S.I.C.: 5731
N.A.I.C.S.: 443142
Christian Biruquier *(Mng Dir)*

Future Electronics Corp., France (1)
Le Magistere II 334 Rue des Vingt Toises
38950 Saint-Martin-le-Vinoux, France (100%)
Tel.: (33) 4 38 02 02 03
Fax: (33) 438022100
Emp.: 70
S.I.C.: 5731
N.A.I.C.S.: 443142
Cyril Berquier *(Gen Mgr)*

Future Electronics Corp., Germany (1)
Oskar Messter Str 25
Ismaning, 85737, Germany (100%)
Tel.: (49) 89957270
Fax: (49) 8995727173
E-Mail: info-da-future@futureelectronics.com
Web Site: www.futureelectronics.com
Emp.: 45
S.I.C.: 5734
N.A.I.C.S.: 443142

Future Electronics Corp., Hungary (1)
2nd Fl Bldg D Mom Pk Alkotas 53
1123 Budapest, Hungary (100%)
Tel.: (36) 12240510
Fax: (36) 12240511
E-Mail: info@futureelectronics.com
Emp.: 10
S.I.C.: 5946
N.A.I.C.S.: 443142

Future Electronics Corp., Ireland (1)
26 Merchants Square
Nangor Rd, Ennis, Co Clare, Ireland(100%)
Tel.: (353) 656844130
Fax: (353) 656840654
E-Mail: info@futureelectronics.com
Web Site: www.futureelectronics.com
Emp.: 8
S.I.C.: 5734
N.A.I.C.S.: 443142

Future Electronics Corp., Israel (1)
Maskik 2 Builiding D Fl 6
PO Box 4024
Herzliyya, 46140, Israel (100%)
Tel.: (972) 99701414
Fax: (972) 99584333
Emp.: 38
S.I.C.: 5731
N.A.I.C.S.: 443142
Ilana Miller *(Head-Fin)*

Future Electronics Corp., Italy (1)
Via Longhin 11
Pallazo Galileo, Padua, 35129, Italy (100%)
Tel.: (39) 049899201
Fax: (39) 0498070582
Web Site: www.futureelectronics.com
Emp.: 8
S.I.C.: 5731
N.A.I.C.S.: 443142
Sandro Girardi *(Mng Dir)*

Future Electronics Corp., Italy (1)
Galleria Ronzani 3 9
Casalecchio Di Reno, Bologna, 40033, Italy (100%)
Tel.: (39) 0516136711
Fax: (39) 0516130724
Emp.: 12
S.I.C.: 5946
N.A.I.C.S.: 443142

Future Electronics Corp., Mexico (1)
Chimalhuacan 3569 7 Piso
Ste 2 Ciudad Del Sol, 45050 Zapopan, Jalisco, 45050, Mexico (100%)
Tel.: (52) 3331220043
Fax: (52) 3331221066
Web Site: www.globalcsamintra.net
Emp.: 11
S.I.C.: 5946
N.A.I.C.S.: 443142
Mario Suarec *(Gen Mgr)*

Future Electronics Corp., Mexico (1)
Aquanaval 2206 Local 11
Col Roma, Monterrey, Nuevo Leon, 64700, Mexico (100%)
Tel.: (52) 8112342887
Fax: (52) 8112342885
E-Mail: raul.medina@futureelectronics.com
Emp.: 4
Electronics Distr
S.I.C.: 5946
N.A.I.C.S.: 443142

Future Electronics Corp., New Zealand (1)
Unit 5 7 Wordsworth St
PO Box 7500
Sydenham, Christchurch, 8002, New Zealand (100%)
Tel.: (64) 39823256
Fax: (64) 39823258
E-Mail:
Web Site: www.futureeletronics.com
Emp.: 3
S.I.C.: 5946
N.A.I.C.S.: 443142
Matt Wald *(Mng Dir)*

Future Electronics Corp., Norway (1)
Tevlingveien 23
1081 Oslo, Norway (100%)
Tel.: (47) 229 05800
Fax: (47) 22905790
Web Site: www.futureelectronics.com
Emp.: 9
S.I.C.: 5731
N.A.I.C.S.: 443142

Future Electronics Corp., Norway (1)
Jordhus Industriomaade
Loekken Verk, Trondheim, 7332, Norway (100%)
Tel.: (47) 72495990
Fax: (47) 72495991
Web Site: www.futureelectronics.com
Emp.: 1
S.I.C.: 5734
N.A.I.C.S.: 443142

Future Electronics Corp., Poland (1)
U1 Panienska 9
3704 Warsaw, Poland (100%)
Tel.: (48) 226189202
Fax: (48) 226188050
E-Mail: info@futureelectronics.com
Web Site: www.eutureelectronics.com
Sls.: $16,633,400
Emp.: 11
S.I.C.: 5731
N.A.I.C.S.: 443142
Yer Derzycyszko *(Dir-Mfg)*

Future Electronics Corp., Scotland (1)
Mirren Ct 3
123 Renfrew Rd, Paisley, Renfrewshire, PA34EA, United Kingdom (100%)
Tel.: (44) 418406500
Fax: (44) 1418496971
Web Site: www.future.com
S.I.C.: 5734
N.A.I.C.S.: 443142

Future Electronics Corp., Spain (1)
Avenida Del Parenon 10
28042 Madrid, Spain (100%)
Tel.: (34) 917214270
Fax: (34) 917211043
Emp.: 15
S.I.C.: 5731
N.A.I.C.S.: 443142
Arriaga Anton *(Branch Mgr)*

Future Electronics Corp., Spain (1)
Centre D Empreses De Noves Tecnologies
Parc Tecnologic Del Valles, Barcelona, Cerdanyola, 08290, Spain
Tel.: (34) 935824343
Fax: (34) 935824342
Web Site: www.futureelectronics.com
Emp.: 6
S.I.C.: 5946
N.A.I.C.S.: 443142
Rafael Ruiz *(Gen Mgr)*

Future Electronics Corp., Sweden (1)
Future Electronics AB Knarrarnasgatan 7
Svedala, Kista, SE 16422, Sweden (100%)
Tel.: (46) 40406990
Fax: (46) 86248890
Web Site: www.futureelectronics.com
Emp.: 30
S.I.C.: 5731
N.A.I.C.S.: 443142
Michael Hidland *(Mgr-Sls)*

Future Electronics Corp., Sweden (1)
Knarrarnasgatan 7
PO Box 1130
Se-16422 Kista Stockholm, Sweden (100%)
Tel.: (46) 86248800
Fax: (46) 86248890
Web Site: www.futureelectronics.com
Emp.: 20
S.I.C.: 5731
N.A.I.C.S.: 443142

Future Electronics Corp., Sweden (1)
Kabelgatan 9
Kungsbacka, 43437, Sweden (100%)
Tel.: (46) 30030300
Fax: (46) 3003020
Web Site: www.future.ca
S.I.C.: 5731
N.A.I.C.S.: 443142

Future Electronics Corp., The Netherlands (1)
Tinstraa 3
Breda, 4823, Netherlands (100%)
Tel.: (31) 765444888
Fax: (31) 765444880
E-Mail: info@futureelectronics.com
Web Site: www.futureelectronics.com
Emp.: 15
S.I.C.: 5734
N.A.I.C.S.: 443142
N Breten *(Mng Dir)*

Future Electronics Corp., Turkey (1)
Turkiye Irtibat Brosu
Sehit Mehmet, 34742 Istanbul, Turkey (100%)
Tel.: (90) 2164458700
Fax: (90) 2164458704
E-Mail: geni.gemirkan@futureelectronics.com
Web Site: www.futureelectronics.com

Emp.: 7
S.I.C.: 5731
N.A.I.C.S.: 443142

Future Electronics Deutschland GmbH (1)
Oskar Messter Str 25
Ismaning, 85737, Germany (100%)
Tel.: (49) 89957270
Fax: (49) 8995727173
E-Mail: info-de-future@futureelectronics.com
Web Site: www.futureelectronics.com
Sls.: $45,030,000
Emp.: 60
Electronic Parts & Equipment
Import Export
S.I.C.: 5065
N.A.I.C.S.: 423690

Future Electronics Deutschland (1)
Zum Pier 71
Dortmund, Lunen, 44536, Germany (100%)
Tel.: (49) 2319750480
Fax: (49) 23197504823
E-Mail: info-de-future@futureelectronics.com
S.I.C.: 5731
N.A.I.C.S.: 443142
Thomas Brachel *(Mgr-Sls)*

Future Electronics Inc. (Distribution) Pte Ltd. (1)
19 Loyang Way #01-08/09/10 CLC
Chungy Logistic Ctr, Singapore, 508 724, Singapore (100%)
Tel.: (65) 65945000
Fax: (65) 65945051
E-Mail: info@futureelectronics.com
Web Site: www.futureelectronics.com
Electronic Parts & Equipment
Import Export
S.I.C.: 5065
N.A.I.C.S.: 423690

Non-U.S. Branches:

Future Electronics Corp., India (2)
710 711 Gtwy Plz
Hiranandari Gdns Powai, Mumbai, Bombay, 400076, India (100%)
Tel.: (91) 225701758
Fax: (91) 256934963
Web Site: www.futureelectronics.com
S.I.C.: 5731
N.A.I.C.S.: 443142

Future Electronics Corp., Japan (2)
Kawaramachi As Bldg No 5
2 6 1 Kawaramachi Chuo Ku, Osaka, 541-3048, Japan (100%)
Tel.: (81) 662212201
Fax: (81) 662212203
Emp.: 4
S.I.C.: 5731
N.A.I.C.S.: 443142

Future Electronics Corp., Korea (2)
5th Floor Yemizi Bldg Soonae-Dong 6-5
Boondang-Gu
Sungnam-Si, Seoul, Gyeonggi-Do, 463-020, Korea (South) (100%)
Tel.: (82) 317868800
Fax: (82) 317868801
E-Mail: e_services@FutureElectronics.com
Emp.: 30
S.I.C.: 5731
N.A.I.C.S.: 443142
J. Y. Wang *(Country Mgr)*

Future Electronics Corp., Malaysia (2)
51-7 A1 51 Jalan Sultan Ahmad Shah
Penang, 10050, Malaysia (100%)
Tel.: (60) 42277213
Fax: (60) 42277263
E-Mail: yee-ling.chiew@future.ca
Web Site: www.futureelectronics.ca
Sls.: $10,000,000
Emp.: 15
S.I.C.: 5946
N.A.I.C.S.: 443142
Ian Chow *(Mgr)*

Future Electronics Corp., Singapore (2)
T8 And 9 No 66
GEM Plz Infantry Rd, Bengaluru, 560001, India (100%)
Tel.: (91) 8025593105
Fax: (91) 8025587890
E-Mail: meera.philar@future.ca
Web Site: www.futureelectronics.com
Emp.: 12
S.I.C.: 5731
N.A.I.C.S.: 443142
Meera Phillar *(HR Mgr)*

Future Electronics Corp., Taiwan (2)
8F 172 Sec 4
Shih Lin Cheng Teh Rd, Taipei, 111, Taiwan (100%)
Tel.: (886) 288615288
Fax: (886) 288614961
E-Mail: info@future.ca
Web Site: www.future.ca
Emp.: 20
S.I.C.: 5731
N.A.I.C.S.: 443142

Future Electronics Corp., Taiwan (2)
18F 2 295
Sec 2 Kuang Fu Rd, Hsin-chu, 300, Taiwan (100%)
Tel.: (886) 35744646
Fax: (886) 35744670
E-Mail: info@future.ca
Web Site: www.futureelectronics.com
Emp.: 40
S.I.C.: 5731
N.A.I.C.S.: 443142
Joseph Chang *(Branch Mgr)*

Future Electronics Corp., Thailand (2)
947 Thosapol Land 3 Bldg Rm C2 18th Fl
Bangna Trad Rd KM3 Bangna, Bangkok, 10260, Thailand
Tel.: (66) 23618400
Fax: (66) 23618433
Web Site: www.futureelectronics.com
Emp.: 9
S.I.C.: 5946
N.A.I.C.S.: 443142
Montri Phawkul *(Country Mgr)*

Future Electronics Hong Kong Limited (2)
Unit 4607 19 Metroplaza Tower 1
223 Hing Fong Rd, Kwai Fong, China (Hong Kong) (100%)
Tel.: (852) 24206238
Fax: (852) 24230767
Emp.: 15
S.I.C.: 5731
N.A.I.C.S.: 443142

Future Electronics Inc (Distribution) Pte Ltd. (2)
512 Ansal Tower 38 Nehru Pl
New Delhi, 110019, India (100%)
Tel.: (91) 01126461414
Fax: (91) 1.12652E+11
Web Site: www.futureelectronics.com
Sales Range: $10-24.9 Million
Emp.: 6
S.I.C.: 5731
N.A.I.C.S.: 443142

Future Electronics K.K. (2)
Yokohama Landmark Tower 24F 2 2 1
Minatomirai Nishi Ku
Yokohama City Kanagawa Ken, Tokyo, 220 8124, Japan JP (100%)
Tel.: (81) 452242155
Fax: (81) 452242156
Web Site: www.future.ca
Emp.: 90
Semiconductors & Electro Mechanical Components
S.I.C.: 5946
N.A.I.C.S.: 443142

Future Electronics Service Malaysia (2)
Suite 801-1 Tower 1 Wisma Kelana Brem
Jalan SS7/15
Kelana Jaya, Petaling Jaya, Selangor, 47301, Malaysia (100%)
Tel.: (60) 3 7651 6888
Fax: (60) 3 7651 6898
E-Mail: info@furtureelectronics.com
Emp.: 4
S.I.C.: 5731
N.A.I.C.S.: 443142
Kokbin Lee *(Branch Mgr)*

Future Electronics Ltd. (1)
Future House
The Glanty, Egham, Surrey, TW20 9AH, United Kingdom (100%)
Tel.: (44) 1784275000
Fax: (44) 1784275600
E-Mail: info@futureelectronics.com
Web Site: uk.futureelectronics.com
Sls.: $207,813,540
Emp.: 300
Electronic Parts & Equipment
Import Export
S.I.C.: 5065
N.A.I.C.S.: 423690

Branch:

Future Electronics Ltd. (2)
Suite B2 Ground Floor Telegraphic House
Waterfront 2000 Salford Quays,
Manchester, M50 3XW, United Kingdom (100%)
Tel.: (44) 1618760000
Fax: (44) 1618771000
E-Mail: info@futureelectronics.com
Web Site: www.futureelectronics.com
Emp.: 30
Distr & Marketing of Semiconductors & Passive Interconnect & Electro-Mechanical Components
S.I.C.: 3674
N.A.I.C.S.: 334413
Keith Thomas *(Reg Mgr-Sls)*

Future Electronics Stuttgart (1)
Talstrasse 11
Korntal Munchingen, D 70825 Stuttgart, Germany (100%)
Tel.: (49) 711830830
Fax: (49) 7118308383
E-Mail: info-de-future@futureelectronics.com
Web Site: www.futureelectronics.com
Emp.: 12
S.I.C.: 5731
N.A.I.C.S.: 443142
Stephane Stamburger *(Mng Dir)*

FUTURE ENERGY CORP.

(Name Changed to MARILYNJEAN INTERACTIVE INC.)

FUTURE FILM GROUP PLC

(d/b/a Future Films)
10 Old Burlington Street
London, W1S 3AG, United Kingdom
Tel.: (44) 2070096767
Fax: (44) 2070096766
E-Mail: info@futurefilmgroup.com
Web Site: www.futurefilmgroup.com
Year Founded: 2000
Business Description:
Motion Picture & Television Producer & Distr
S.I.C.: 7812
N.A.I.C.S.: 512110
Personnel:
Elena Margolis *(Head-Structured Fin)*

FUTURE GROUP

Knowledge House Shyam Nagar
Off Jogeshwari-Vikhroli Link Road
Jogeshwari East, Mumbai, 400 060, India
Tel.: (91) 22 3084 1300
Fax: (91) 22 6644 2222
Web Site: www.futuregroup.in
Business Description:
Holding Company
S.I.C.: 6719
N.A.I.C.S.: 551112
Personnel:
Kishore Biyani *(Founder & CEO)*

Holding:

Pantaloon Retail (India) Limited (1)
Knowledge House Shyam Nagar
Off Jogeshwari-Vikhroli Link Road
Jogeshwa East, Mumbai, 400 060, India
Tel.: (91) 2230841300
Fax: (91) 2266442222
Web Site: www.pantaloonretail.in
PRETAILDVR—(NSE)
Sales Range: $1-4.9 Billion
Emp.: 33,500
Retail Store Operator
S.I.C.: 5999
N.A.I.C.S.: 453998
Kishore Biyani *(Joint Mng Dir)*
Rakesh Biyani *(Joint Mng Dir)*
Deepak Tanna *(Compliance Officer & Sec)*

FUTURE KID ENTERTAINMENT AND REAL ESTATE CO. K.S.C.C.

Block D20 Free Trade Zone
Kuwait, Kuwait
Tel.: (965) 24610930
Fax: (965) 24610935
E-Mail: corporate@futurekid.com.kw
Web Site: www.futurekid.com.kw
FUTUREKID—(KUW)
Sales Range: $10-24.9 Million
Emp.: 120
Business Description:
Children's Entertainment & Play Centers
S.I.C.: 7999
N.A.I.C.S.: 713990
Personnel:
Khalid Ahmed Soud Al-Khalid *(Chm & Mng Dir)*
Wael Ahmed Saud Al-Khalid *(Vice Chm)*
Board of Directors:
Khalid Ahmed Soud Al-Khalid
Rasha Abdulla Al Qenai
Hamad Abdullrazzak Al-Khalid
Wael Ahmed Saud Al-Khalid
Sulaiman Hashim Saied Abdullrahman Al-Refaee

Non-U.S. Subsidiary:

Happy Land Entertainment (W.L.L.) (1)
Aliat Al Madinah Mall Quba Ring Rd II
Medina, Saudi Arabia
Tel.: (966) 48493333
Fax: (966) 48493222
Web Site: www.happyland.com.sa
Entertainment Services
S.I.C.: 7841
N.A.I.C.S.: 532230
Ibrahim Haroon *(CEO)*

FUTURE LAND DEVELOPMENT HOLDINGS LIMITED

23/F The Great Wall Tower 3000
Zhongshan Road North Road
Shanghai, 200063, China
Tel.: (86) 21 32522988
Fax: (86) 21 32522988
Web Site: www.futureholdings.com.cn
Year Founded: 1996
1030—(HKG)
Rev.: $2,782,617,704
Assets: $6,487,996,806
Liabilities: $5,154,446,767
Net Worth: $1,333,550,039
Earnings: $251,838,248
Emp.: 4,127
Fiscal Year-end: 12/31/12
Business Description:
Residential Property Developer
S.I.C.: 6552
N.A.I.C.S.: 237210
Personnel:
Zhenhua Wang *(Chm & CEO)*
Zhongming Lu *(CFO)*
Ming Wai Mok *(Co-Sec)*
Weiming Tan *(Co-Sec)*
Board of Directors:
Zhenhua Wang
Huakang Chen
Maoli Huang
Yuanman Liu
Xiaoping Lv

Future Land Development Holdings Limited—(Continued)

Yuansong Min
Meisheng Nie
Weiming Tan
Zengjin Zhu

Computershare Hong Kong Investor Services Limited
Shops 1712-1716 17th Floor Hopewell Centre
183 Queens Road East
Wanchai, China (Hong Kong)

Transfer Agent:
Maples Fund Services (Cayman) Limited
Boundary Hall Cricket Square
PO Box 1093
Georgetown, Cayman Islands

FUTURE MARKET NETWORKS LIMITED

Knowledge House Shyam Nagar
Off Jogeshwari Vikhroli Link Road
Jogeshwari East, Mumbai, 400060, India
Tel.: (91) 22 3084 1300
Fax: (91) 22 6644 2201
E-Mail: corporate@fmn.co.in
Web Site: www.fmn.co.in
533296—(BOM NSE)
Rev.: $23,048,372
Assets: $166,620,574
Liabilities: $118,819,782
Net Worth: $47,800,792
Earnings: ($6,487,331)
Emp.: 27
Fiscal Year-end: 03/31/13

Business Description:
Investment Services
S.I.C.: 6211
N.A.I.C.S.: 523999

Personnel:
Ameet Naik *(Chm)*
Sunil Biyani *(Mng Dir)*
Pawan Agrawal *(CFO)*
Anil Cherian *(Sec)*

Board of Directors:
Ameet Naik
Sunil Biyani
Sumit Dabriwala
Vijai Singh Dugar
Rajesh Kalyani
Krishna Kant Rathi
Rahul Saraf

Transfer Agent:
Link Intime India Pvt. Ltd
C-13 Pannalal Silk Mills Compound LBS Marg
Bhandup (West)
Mumbai, India

FUTURE PIPE INDUSTRIES GROUP LTD.

PO Box 29205
Abu Dhabi, United Arab Emirates
Tel.: (971) 2 627 0008
Fax: (971) 2 627 0009
E-Mail: sales-abudhabi@futurepipe.com
Web Site: www.futurepipe.com

Business Description:
Industrial Pipe Mfr
S.I.C.: 3498
N.A.I.C.S.: 332996

Personnel:
Fouad Makhzoumi *(Chm & CEO)*

Board of Directors:
Omar Ashur
Matthew Barton
Anthony J. Dowd
Fouad Makhzoumi
Imad Makhzoumi
Nasser Saidi
Efthimios O. Vidalis

U.S. Subsidiary:

Specialty Plastics, Inc. **(1)**
15915 Perkins Rd
Baton Rouge, LA 70810-3630 LA
Tel.: (225) 752-2705
Fax: (225) 752-2757
Web Site: www.fiberbond.com
Sales Range: $25-49.9 Million
Emp.: 75
Composite Piping System Mfr
S.I.C.: 3084
N.A.I.C.S.: 326122
Jeff Savoy *(Controller)*

FUTURE PLC

Beauford Court 30 Monmouth Street
Bath, BA1 2BW, United Kingdom
Tel.: (44) 1225442244
Fax: (44) 1225822836
E-Mail: investor.relations@futurenet.co.uk
Web Site: www.futureplc.com
Year Founded: 1985
FUTR—(LSE)
Rev.: $194,171,640
Assets: $203,762,304
Liabilities: $105,340,080
Net Worth: $98,422,224
Earnings: $314,448
Emp.: 1,013
Fiscal Year-end: 09/30/12

Business Description:
Holding Company; Magazine & Website Publisher
S.I.C.: 6719
N.A.I.C.S.: 551112

Personnel:
Mark Wood *(CEO)*
Nial Ferguson *(Mng Dir)*
Zillah Byng-Maddick *(CFO)*
David Ventura *(CTO)*

Board of Directors:
Peter Allen
Seb Bishop
Mark Whiteling
Manjit Wolstenholme
Mark Wood

Legal Counsel:
Norton Rose LLP
3 More London Riverside
London, SE1 2AQ, United Kingdom
Tel.: (44) 20 7283 6000
Fax: (44) 20 7283 6500

Transfer Agent:
Computershare Investor Services Plc
The Pavilions Bridgwater Road
PO Box 82
Bristol, United Kingdom

Subsidiary:

Future Publishing Ltd. **(1)**
Beauford Court 30 Monmouth Street
Bath, Somerset, BA1 2BW, United Kingdom UK
Tel.: (44) 1225 442 244 (100%)
Fax: (44) 1225732275
E-Mail: equiry@futurenet.com
Web Site: www.futurenet.com
Emp.: 75
Magazine Publisher
S.I.C.: 2721
N.A.I.C.S.: 511120
Ian Robson *(Head-T3)*

Branch:

Future Publishing Ltd. - London Office **(2)**
2 Balalcombe Street
London, NW1 6NW, United Kingdom
Tel.: (44) 2070424000
Fax: (44) 273172630
Web Site: www.futurenet.com
Emp.: 600
Magazine Publishers
S.I.C.: 2721
N.A.I.C.S.: 511120
Spebie Spring *(CEO)*
James Binns *(Dir-Publ Games)*
Matt Pierce *(Publr-Games Magazine)*
Paul Sloggett *(Publr-Automotive)*

U.S. Subsidiary:

Future US, Inc. **(1)**
4000 Shoreline Ct Ste 400
San Francisco, CA 94080 CA
Tel.: (650) 872-1642 (100%)
Fax: (650) 872-2207
Web Site: www.futureus.com
Sales Range: $75-99.9 Million
Emp.: 150
Magazine Publishers
S.I.C.: 2721
N.A.I.C.S.: 511120
John E. Marcom *(Pres)*
John Sutton *(CFO)*
Rachelle Considine *(COO)*
Anne Ortel *(Gen Counsel)*

Non-U.S. Subsidiary:

Future France SA **(1)**
101 109 Rue Jean Jaures
Levallois, 92300 Perret, France FR
Tel.: (33) 141273838 (100%)
Fax: (33) 41273877
E-Mail: assiscancedediredtion@futurenet.fr
Web Site: www.thefuturenetwork.plc.uk/france.html
Emp.: 150
Magazine Publishers
S.I.C.: 2721
N.A.I.C.S.: 511120
Gana Gwray *(Dir)*

FUTURE VENTURE CAPITAL CO., LTD.

4th Floor Karasuma-Chuo Building
659 Tearaimizu-cho Nishikikoji-agaru
Karasuma-dori Nakagyo-ku, Kyoto, 604-8152, Japan
Tel.: (81) 75 257 2511
Fax: (81) 75 211 1601
Web Site: www.fvc.co.jp
Year Founded: 1998
8462—(JAS)
Sls.: $4,532,000
Assets: $16,038,000
Liabilities: $12,089,000
Net Worth: $3,949,000
Earnings: $473,000
Emp.: 26
Fiscal Year-end: 03/31/13

Business Description:
Investment Services
S.I.C.: 6211
N.A.I.C.S.: 523999

Personnel:
Yoji Kawake *(Founder)*
Keiji Imajo *(Pres & CEO)*

Board of Directors:
Keiji Imajo
Naoto Matsumoto
Jun Ogawa
Tomohisa Suzuki

FUTURE VENTURES INDIA LIMITED

Knowledge House Shyam Nagar
Off Jogeshwari Vikhroli Link Road
Jogeshwari (East), Mumbai, 400 060, India
Tel.: (91) 22 30842200
Fax: (91) 22 30842201
E-Mail: contact@futureventures.in
Web Site: www.futureventures.in
FUTUREVENT—(BOM NSE)

Business Description:
Investment Services
S.I.C.: 6211
N.A.I.C.S.: 523999

Personnel:
G.N. Bajpai *(Chm)*
K.K. Rathi *(CEO)*
Kishore Biyani *(Mng Dir)*
Praveen Dwivedi *(Pres-Food Processing)*
Manoj Gagvani *(Sec & Head-Legal)*

Board of Directors:
G.N. Bajpai
Anand Balasundaram
Kishore Biyani
Gaurav Burman
Anil Harish
Jagdish Shenoy

FUTURECOM SYSTEMS GROUP INC.

3277 Langstaff Rd
Concord, ON, L4K 5P8, Canada
Tel.: (905) 660-5548
Fax: (905) 660-6858
Toll Free: (800) 701-9180
E-Mail: sales@futurecom.com
Web Site: www.futurecom.com
Year Founded: 1991
Rev.: $11,794,226
Emp.: 45

Business Description:
Extension Systems Mfr
S.I.C.: 3812
N.A.I.C.S.: 334511

Personnel:
Steve Dimitru *(Co-CEO)*
Michael Wyrzykowski *(Co-CEO)*

FUTUREMARK OY

Kappelitie 6 C
FI 02200 Espoo, Finland
Tel.: (358) 20 759 8250
Fax: (358) 20 759 8251
E-Mail: info@futuremark.com
Web Site: www.futuremark.com

Business Description:
Computer Performance Software & Hardware Developer
S.I.C.: 7372
N.A.I.C.S.: 511210

Personnel:
Jukka Makinen *(CEO)*

U.S. Subsidiary:

Futuremark Corporation **(1)**
12930 Saratoga Ave Ste C2
Saratoga, CA 95070 CA
Tel.: (408) 517-9020
Fax: (408) 517-9119
Web Site: www.futuremark.com
Emp.: 30
Computer Performance Software & Hardware Developer
S.I.C.: 7372
N.A.I.C.S.: 511210
Oliver Baltuch *(Pres)*
Jukka Makinen *(CEO)*

FUTUREMEDIA PLC

Nile House
Nile St, Brighton, East Sussex, BN1 1HW, United Kingdom
Tel.: (44) 1273829700
Fax: (44) 1273829742
E-Mail: ir@futuremedia.co.uk
Web Site: www.futuremedia.co.uk
Year Founded: 1982
FMDAY—(OTC)
Sales Range: $25-49.9 Million
Emp.: 89

Business Description:
Online Learning & Communications Solutions
S.I.C.: 8299
N.A.I.C.S.: 611710

Personnel:
George G. O'Leary *(Chm & CEO)*
Thomas Bingham *(Mng Dir)*
Ingrid Andersson *(COO)*
Haire Andrew *(Gen Counsel & Sec)*

Board of Directors:
George G. O'Leary
Robert Bingham
Peter Machin
Brendan McNutt
Michael Pilsworth
John Schwallie
Michiel Steel
Colin Turner

Non-U.S. Subsidiary:

Open Training Sweden AB **(1)**
Birger Jarlsgatan 37 B
111 45 Stockholm, Sweden (100%)

Tel.: (46) 84126900
Multimedia Training Products & Services
S.I.C.: 2741
N.A.I.C.S.: 519130
Claes Ytander *(CEO)*

FUTURISTIC SOLUTIONS LIMITED

M-50 IInd Floor M Block Market
Greater Kailash - I
New Delhi, 110048, India
Tel.: (91) 41630436
Fax: (91) 29235860
E-Mail: futuristicsolutionsltd@gmail.com
Web Site: www.fsl.co.in
Year Founded: 1983
534063—(BOM)
Rev.: $438,152
Assets: $3,449,379
Liabilities: $789,292
Net Worth: $2,660,087
Earnings: $72,193
Fiscal Year-end: 03/31/13

Business Description:
Real Estate Development Services
S.I.C.: 6531
N.A.I.C.S.: 531390

Personnel:
Mandeep Sandhu *(Chm & Mng Dir)*
Rajesh Kumar *(Compliance Officer & Sec)*

Board of Directors:
Mandeep Sandhu
Shalabh Ahuja
Charanjit Singh Panag
Sangeeta Sandhu

Transfer Agent:
Beetal Financial & Computer Services (P) Ltd.
Shopping Complex Near Dada Harkushdas Mandir
New Delhi, 110062, India

FUTUROL INDUSTRIE

15 Grande Rue
28170 Chartres, France
Tel.: (33) 237387371
Fax: (33) 37387388
Web Site: www.futurol.com
Rev.: $20,300,000
Emp.: 41

Business Description:
Carpentry Work
S.I.C.: 1751
N.A.I.C.S.: 238130

Personnel:
Jean-Marc Gelin *(Dir-Mktg)*

FUTUTECH BERHAD

802 8th Floor Block C Kelana Square
17 Jalan SS7/26
47301 Petaling Jaya, Selangor Darul Ehsan, Malaysia
Tel.: (60) 378031126
Fax: (60) 378061387
E-Mail: fortekitchens@fututech.com.my
Web Site: www.fututech.com.my
FUTUTEC—(KLS)
Rev.: $51,868,387
Assets: $42,845,055
Liabilities: $19,028,041
Net Worth: $23,817,014
Earnings: $7,680,496
Fiscal Year-end: 12/31/12

Business Description:
Lighting Services
S.I.C.: 3646
N.A.I.C.S.: 335122

Personnel:
Eng Ho Tee *(Chm)*
Evan Soo Loong Loo *(CEO)*
Mee Kee Mok *(Co-Sec)*
Fei San Seow *(Co-Sec)*

Board of Directors:
Eng Ho Tee
Siong Kee Khoo
Kean Lai Lim
Evan Soo Loong Loo
Eng Seng Tee
Siew Chuon Toh
Mohd Zain Yusof

Subsidiary:

Advance Industries Sdn. Bhd. (1)
17-G Jalan Puteri 4/7A Bandar Puterii
47100 Puchong, Selangor, Malaysia
Tel.: (60) 3 8061 2790
Fax: (60) 3 8065 2470
Light Fittings Mfr
S.I.C.: 3646
N.A.I.C.S.: 335122
Lin Kah Yong *(Mgr-Fin)*

FUWEI FILMS (HOLDINGS) CO., LTD.

No 387 Dongming Road
Weifang, Shandong, China 261061
Tel.: (86) 13361559266
E-Mail: fuweiir@fuweifilms.com
Web Site: www.fuweiholdings.com
Year Founded: 2004
FFHL—(NASDAQ)
Sls.: $59,229,764
Assets: $118,748,318
Liabilities: $36,395,077
Net Worth: $82,353,241
Earnings: ($8,647,317)
Emp.: 318
Fiscal Year-end: 12/31/12

Business Description:
Holding Company; Plastic Film Developer, Mfr & Distr
S.I.C.: 3081
N.A.I.C.S.: 326113

Personnel:
Xiaoan He *(Chm & CEO)*
Xiuyong Zhang *(CFO)*

Board of Directors:
Xiaoan He
Changrong Ji
Shan Jiang
Tee Chuang Khoo
Xiuyong Zhang

Subsidiary:

Fuwei Films (Shandong) Co., Ltd. (1)
No 387 Donming Road
Weifang, Shandong, 261061, China (100%)
Tel.: (86) 8601068522612
Fax: (86) 860108526216
E-Mail: yongjiang@fuweifilms.com
Web Site: en.fuweifilms.com
Plastic Film Developer, Mfr & Distr
S.I.C.: 3081
N.A.I.C.S.: 326113
Xiaoan He *(Pres)*

FUXING CHINA GROUP LIMITED

Hangbian Industrial Area
Longhu Town, Jinjiang, Fujian, China
Tel.: (86) 59585287799
Fax: (86) 59585299317
E-Mail: service@fffzipper.com
Web Site: www.fuxingchinagroup.com
DC9—(SES)
Rev.: $90,335,612
Assets: $224,521,608
Liabilities: $73,500,054
Net Worth: $151,021,554
Earnings: ($27,524,893)
Emp.: 1,800
Fiscal Year-end: 12/31/12

Business Description:
Zipper Sliders & Chains Mfr
S.I.C.: 3965
N.A.I.C.S.: 339993

Personnel:
Qing Liang Hong *(Chm & CEO)*
James Chor Lung Ma *(CFO)*
Busarakham Kohsikaporn *(Co-Sec)*
Lei Mui Toh *(Co-Sec)*

Board of Directors:
Qing Liang Hong
Kah Leong Ho
Kang Peng Ho
Peng You Hong
Shui Ku Hong
Hwee Li Ong
Qing Yuan Qiu

Legal Counsel:
Chancery Law Corporation
55 Market Street 08-01
Singapore, 048941, Singapore

Transfer Agent:
Boardroom Corporate & Advisory Services Pte. Ltd.
50 Raffles Place 32-01 Singapore Land Tower
Singapore, Singapore

FUXING GARMENTS CO., LTD.

1188 Donesheng Zhong Rd
Jiaxing, Zhejiang, 314001, China
Tel.: (86) 5732206132
Fax: (86) 5732206071
E-Mail: fuxing@fuxingfz.com
Web Site: www.fuxingfz.com
Year Founded: 1988
Emp.: 500

Business Description:
Apparel Mfr
S.I.C.: 2399
N.A.I.C.S.: 315990

FUYO GENERAL LEASE CO., LTD.

Nicherei Building 3-3-23 Misaki-cho
Chiyoda-ku, Tokyo, 101-8380, Japan
Tel.: (81) 352758800
Fax: (81) 352758870
E-Mail: fuyo-ir@fgl.co.jp
Web Site: www.fgl.co.jp/eng/t
Year Founded: 1969
8424—(TKS)
Rev.: $4,868,127,000
Assets: $19,407,410,000
Liabilities: $17,496,138,000
Net Worth: $1,911,272,000
Earnings: $172,117,000
Emp.: 1,403
Fiscal Year-end: 03/31/13

Business Description:
Equipment Leasing Services
S.I.C.: 7359
N.A.I.C.S.: 532490

Personnel:
Takashi Sato *(Pres & CEO)*

Transfer Agent:
Mizuho Trust & Banking Co., Ltd.
2-1 Yaesu 1-Chome Chuo-ku
Tokyo, 103 8670, Japan
Tel.: (81) 332788111
Fax: (81) 332816947

Subsidiaries:

Aqua Art Co., Ltd. (1)
Hayashi Nakazu Building 6-9 Nihombashi Nakasu
Chuo-ku, Tokyo, 103-0008, Japan
Tel.: (81) 336661301
Fax: (81) 336662839
Emp.: 18
Glass Mfr
S.I.C.: 3229
N.A.I.C.S.: 327212

Five Fox Management Co., Ltd. (1)
Nicherei Building 3-3-23 Misaki-cho
Tokyo, Chiyoda-ku, 101-8380, Japan
Tel.: (81) 352758800
Fax: (81) 357258870
Web Site: www.fgl.co.jp
Emp.: 800
Real Estate Management Services
S.I.C.: 6531
N.A.I.C.S.: 531390
Mitsuru Machida *(Pres)*

Fuyo Auto Lease Co., Ltd. (1)
6-4 Akashi-cho
Chuo-ku, Tokyo, 104-0044, Japan
Tel.: (81) 335462411
Sales Range: $125-149.9 Million
Emp.: 150
Auto Leasing Services
S.I.C.: 7515
N.A.I.C.S.: 532112

Fuyo Lease Sales Co., Ltd. (1)
Nichirei Building 3-3-23 Misaki-cho
Chiyoda-ku, Tokyo, 101-8380, Japan
Tel.: (81) 3 5275 8800
Fax: (81) 3 5275 8870
Equipment Leasing Services
S.I.C.: 7359
N.A.I.C.S.: 532490

Fuyo Network Service Co., Ltd. (1)
6-9 Nihombashi Nakasu
Chuo-ku, Tokyo, 103-0008, Japan
Tel.: (81) 336692301
Web Site: www.fgl.co.jp
Emp.: 10
Customized Software Services
S.I.C.: 7372
N.A.I.C.S.: 511210
Hiroshi Maruta *(CEO)*

Japan Mortgage Co., Ltd. (1)
8-1 Nihombashikobunacho Hyurikku Kofunecho Bldg
Chuo-Ku, Tokyo, 103-0024, Japan
Tel.: (81) 332495560
Fax: (81) 332493206
Mortgage Brokerage Services
S.I.C.: 6163
N.A.I.C.S.: 522310

YF Leasing Co., Ltd. (1)
1-19-18 Nakacho
Musashino
Tokyo, 180-0006, Japan
Tel.: (81) 422569352
Fax: (81) 422569743
Emp.: 9
Leasing Services
S.I.C.: 7359
N.A.I.C.S.: 532490

U.S. Subsidiary:

Fuyo General Lease (USA) Inc. (1)
733 3rd Ave 18th Fl
New York, NY 10017
Tel.: (212) 867-1008
Fax: (212) 867-5153
E-Mail: info@fgl-usa.com
Web Site: www.fgl.co.jp/eng/
Equipment Leasing Services
S.I.C.: 7359
N.A.I.C.S.: 532490

Non-U.S. Subsidiaries:

FGL Aircraft Ireland Limited (1)
AIB International Centre IFSC
Dublin, Ireland
Tel.: (353) 1 829 1802
Fax: (353) 1 670 1632
Aircraft Products Leasing Services
S.I.C.: 7359
N.A.I.C.S.: 532411

Fuyo General Lease (HK) Limited (1)
Room 1409 Admiralty Centre Tower I 18 Harcourt Road
Admiralty, Central, China (Hong Kong)
Tel.: (852) 2528 9863
Fax: (852) 2528 6183
Web Site: www.fgl.co.jp/fgl/link.html
Equipment Leasing Services
S.I.C.: 7359
N.A.I.C.S.: 532490

FV S.A.

Bernardo De Irigoyen 1053
B 1604AFC
Florida, Buenos Aires, Argentina
Tel.: (54) 11 4730 5300
Fax: (54) 11 47305363
E-Mail: fvresponde@fvsa.com
Web Site: www.fvsa.com
Emp.: 1,500

FV S.A.—(Continued)

Business Description:
Mfr of Plumbing Fixtures
S.I.C.: 3432
N.A.I.C.S.: 332913

Subsidiary:

C.I.B.A. Compania Introductora de Buenos Aires S.A. (1)
Chile 778
1098 Buenos Aires, Argentina
Tel.: (54) 1143639200
E-Mail: elconsumidor@dosanclas.com.ar
Web Site: www.dosanclas.com.ar
Emp.: 155
Chemical Mfr & Distr
S.I.C.: 2869
N.A.I.C.S.: 325199
Francisco Enrique Viegener *(Pres)*

F.W. NEUKIRCH (GMBH & CO.) KG

Zum Panrepel 37
28307 Bremen, Germany
Tel.: (49) 42148940
Fax: (49) 4214894359
E-Mail: fwn@neukirch.de
Web Site: www.neukirch.de
Year Founded: 1805
Rev.: $49,987,375
Emp.: 92

Business Description:
Transportation Services
S.I.C.: 4789
N.A.I.C.S.: 488999

F.W. THORPE PLC

Merse Road North Moons Moat
Redditch, Worcestershire, B98 9HH, United Kingdom
Tel.: (44) 1527583200
Fax: (44) 1527584177
E-Mail: thorlux@thorlux.co.uk
Web Site: www.fwthorpe.co.uk
Year Founded: 1936
TFW—(LSE)
Rev.: $87,385,274
Assets: $131,436,410
Liabilities: $16,874,714
Net Worth: $114,561,697
Earnings: $15,105,909
Emp.: 472
Fiscal Year-end: 06/30/13

Business Description:
Lighting Products Designer, Mfr & Distr
S.I.C.: 3646
N.A.I.C.S.: 335122

Personnel:
Andrew Thorpe *(Chm & Co-CEO)*
Mike Allcock *(Co-CEO & Mng Dir-Thorlux Lighting)*
Craig Muncaster *(Sec & Dir-Fin)*

Board of Directors:
Andrew Thorpe
Mike Allcock
Colin Brangwin
Tony Cooper
Peter Mason
Craig Muncaster
David Taylor
Ian Thorpe

Legal Counsel:
SGH Martineau
No 1 Colmore Square
Birmingham, United Kingdom

Division:

Thorlux Lighting (1)
Merse Road North Moons Moat
Redditch, Worcs, B98 9HH, United Kingdom UK
Tel.: (44) 1527583200
Fax: (44) 1527584177
E-Mail: info@thorlux.com
Web Site: www.thorlux.com
Emp.: 300
Commercial & Institutional Lighting Products Mfr
S.I.C.: 3646
N.A.I.C.S.: 335122
Mike Allcock *(Mng Dir)*

Subsidiaries:

Compact Lighting Limited (1)
Unit 1 The Nelson Ctr Portfield Rd
Portsmouth, Hampshire, PO3 5SF, United Kingdom
Tel.: (44) 2392652999
Fax: (44) 2392653053
E-Mail: sales@compact-lighting.co.uk
Web Site: www.compact-lighting.co.uk
Emp.: 50
Lighting Systems Mfr & Supplier
S.I.C.: 3646
N.A.I.C.S.: 335122
Simon Wootton *(Mng Dir)*

Philip Payne Limited (1)
Thornhill House 2 Thornhill Rd
Solihull, West Midlands, B91 2HB, United Kingdom
Tel.: (44) 1217052384
Fax: (44) 1217112469
E-Mail: mail@p-payne.co.uk
Web Site: www.philippayne.co.uk
Emp.: 18
Illuminated Signs Mfr
S.I.C.: 3993
N.A.I.C.S.: 339950
David Taylor *(Mng Dir)*

Portland Lighting Limited (1)
Units A2 & A3 Walsall Enterprise Park
Regal Drive, Walsall, WS2 9HQ, United Kingdom UK
Tel.: (44) 1922721133
Fax: (44) 1922659545
E-Mail: sales@portlandlighting.co.uk
Web Site: www.portlandlighting.co.uk
Emp.: 12
Sign Lighting Products Designer & Mfr
S.I.C.: 3646
N.A.I.C.S.: 335122
Andy Truelove *(Mng Dir)*

Solite Europe Ltd (1)
Unit 5 Windmill Indus Estate Oldham St
Denton, Manchester, M34 3RB, United Kingdom
Tel.: (44) 1613209999
Fax: (44) 1613369999
E-Mail: enquiry@solite-europe.com
Web Site: www.solite-europe.com
Emp.: 12
Lighting Equipments & Luminaires Mfr & Distr
S.I.C.: 3646
N.A.I.C.S.: 335122
Phil Myers *(Mng Dir)*

Sugg Lighting Limited (1)
Foundry Ln
Horsham, West Sussex, RH13 5PX, United Kingdom
Tel.: (44) 1293540111
Fax: (44) 1293540114
E-Mail: sales@sugglighting.co.uk
Web Site: www.sugglighting.co.uk
Emp.: 11
Decorative & Heritage Lightings Mfr
S.I.C.: 3645
N.A.I.C.S.: 335121
Geoff White *(Gen Mgr)*

FWUSOW INDUSTRY CO., LTD.

45 Sha-Tyan Rd Sha-Lu
Taichung, Taiwan
Tel.: (886) 426362111
Fax: (886) 426358566
E-Mail: fwusow@fwusow.com.tw
Web Site: www.fwusow.com.tw
Year Founded: 1920
1219—(TAI)
Sales Range: $125-149.9 Million

Business Description:
Pet Food, Edible Oil, Cereal & Soy Protein Products Mfr & Distr
S.I.C.: 2048
N.A.I.C.S.: 311119

Personnel:
Yau-Kuen Hung *(Chm)*

Plants:

Fwusow Industry Co., Ltd. - Sha-Lu Factory (1)
45 Shatian Road
Shalu Town, Taichung, 433, Taiwan
Tel.: (886) 426363439
Animal Feeds Mfr
S.I.C.: 2048
N.A.I.C.S.: 311119

Fwusow Industry Co., Ltd. - Taichung Harbor Factory (1)
No 45 Shatian Road
Shalu Town, Taichung, 43354, Taiwan
Tel.: (886) 426362111
Fax: (886) 426358566
Emp.: 600
Cooking Oil & Breakfast Cereals Mfr
S.I.C.: 2079
N.A.I.C.S.: 311224
Cheng Fang Hung *(Gen Mgr)*

FXPRO FINANCIAL SERVICES LTD

Karyatidon 1
4180 Ypsonas, Cyprus
Tel.: (357) 25969222
Fax: (357) 25969269
E-Mail: info@fxpro.com
Web Site: www.fxpro.com
Emp.: 170

Business Description:
Commodities Trading Services
S.I.C.: 6221
N.A.I.C.S.: 523140

Personnel:
Denis Sukhotin *(Chm)*
Jim Sutcliffe *(Chm)*
Panagiotis Xydas *(Mng Dir)*

Board of Directors:
Denis Sukhotin

FYFFES PLC

29 North Anne Street
Dublin, 7, Ireland
Tel.: (353) 18872700
Fax: (353) 18872755
E-Mail: info@fyffes.com
Web Site: www.fyffes.com
Year Founded: 1962
FFY—(AIM ISE)
Rev.: $1,370,165,480
Assets: $424,190,283
Liabilities: $240,467,693
Net Worth: $183,722,589
Earnings: $33,247,707
Emp.: 2,663
Fiscal Year-end: 12/31/12

Business Description:
Tropical Produce Importer & Distr
S.I.C.: 5148
N.A.I.C.S.: 424480

Personnel:
David V. McCann *(Chm)*
Coen Bos *(COO)*
Seamus P. Keenan *(Sec)*

Board of Directors:
David V. McCann
Coen Bos
Robert B. Johnston
J. Declan McCourt
Tom G. Murphy
James M. O'Dwyer
Jim R. O'Hara

Legal Counsel:
SJ Berwin LLP
10 Queen Street Place
EC4R 1BE London, United Kingdom

Holland & Knight LLP
701 Brickell Avenue Suite 3300
Miami, FL 33131

Arthur Cox
Arthur Building Earlsfort Terrace
Dublin, Ireland

Subsidiaries:

Banana Importers of Ireland Limited (1)
The Ramparts
Dundalk, Louth, Ireland (95%)
Tel.: (353) 429335451
Fax: (353) 429339470
E-Mail: info@fyffes.com
Web Site: www.fyffes.com
Emp.: 40
Distributor of Fresh Produce Import
S.I.C.: 5431
N.A.I.C.S.: 445230
Gerard Cunningham *(CEO)*

Fyffes Bananas (Swords) Limited (1)
29 North Anne Street
Dublin, 7, Ireland
Tel.: (353) 18872700
E-Mail: info@fyffes.com
Web Site: www.fyffes.com
Emp.: 20
Fresh Fruit & Vegetable Distr
S.I.C.: 5148
N.A.I.C.S.: 424480
David McCann *(Chm & CEO)*

Fyffes International (1)
1 Bereford St
Dublin, Ireland IE
Tel.: (353) 18872700
Fax: (353) 18726273
E-Mail: info@fyffes.com
Fruit & Vegetables Mfr
S.I.C.: 2037
N.A.I.C.S.: 311411
David McCann *(Gen Mgr)*

Subsidiary:

Fyffes International Holdings Limited (2)
29 N Anne St
Dublin, 7, Ireland IE
Tel.: (353) 18872700
Fax: (353) 18872755
E-Mail: info@fyffes.com
Holding Company
S.I.C.: 6719
N.A.I.C.S.: 551112

U.S. Subsidiary:

Fyffes Inc. (3)
Ste 730 550 Biltmore Way
Coral Gables, FL 33134-5723 (100%)
Tel.: (954) 796-4230
Fax: (954) 796-3095
Web Site: www.fyffes.ie/contactus.htm
Sales Range: $1-4.9 Billion
Emp.: 2,500
Fresh Produce Distr
S.I.C.: 2099
N.A.I.C.S.: 311991

Subsidiary:

Sol Marketing Company Inc (4)
1751 Sw 8th St
Pompano Beach, FL 33069-4517
Tel.: (954) 783-7849
Fax: (954) 783-4889
Fruits & Vegetable Mfr & Distr
S.I.C.: 2037
N.A.I.C.S.: 311411

Non-U.S. Subsidiaries:

Ananas Export Company SA (3)
San Rafael de Rio Cuarto de Grecia
Alajuela, Costa Rica
Tel.: (506) 2403 1212
Fax: (506) 2403 1089
Pineapple Mfr
S.I.C.: 0179
N.A.I.C.S.: 111339

Fyffe B.V. (3)
Marconistraat 19
3029 AE Rotterdam, Netherlands (100%)
Mailing Address:
PO Box 6118
Rotterdam, 3002 AC, Netherlands
Tel.: (31) 102445300
Fax: (31) 102445302
E-Mail: bananasnl@fyffes.com
Web Site: www.fyffes.com
Emp.: 20

Fresh Produce Importer & Distr
S.I.C.: 5431
N.A.I.C.S.: 445230
Coen Bos *(Mng Dir)*

Fyffes Group Limited (3)
Houndmills Road
Houndmills Industrial Estate, Basingstoke, Hants, RG21 6XL, United Kingdom (100%)
Tel.: (44) 1256383200
Fax: (44) 1256383297
E-Mail: info@fyffes.com
Web Site: www.fyffes.com
Rev.: $92,916,752
Emp.: 250
Fresh Produce Distributor
S.I.C.: 5431
N.A.I.C.S.: 445230
Coen Bos *(Mng Dir)*

Subsidiaries:

E&F Lines Limited (4)
Flathouse Quay Prospect Road
Portsmouth, PO2 7SP, United Kingdom UK
Tel.: (44) 2392890552 (100%)
Fax: (44) 2392890556
Rev.: $89,844,000
Emp.: 1
Fresh Fruit Shipping Services
S.I.C.: 4412
N.A.I.C.S.: 483111
David Flynn *(Mng Dir)*

Fyffes Windward Holdings Limited (3)
The Studio 7 Obun Mews Elizabeth Lane
Saint Helier, JE2 3PH, Jersey JE
Tel.: (44) 1534507940
Fax: (44) 1534507944
Holding Company
S.I.C.: 6719
N.A.I.C.S.: 551112

Affiliate:

Windward Isles Banana Company Holdings (Jersey) Limited (4)
31 The Parade
Saint Helier, Jersey JE
Holding Company; Fresh Fruits & Vegetables Distr (50%)
S.I.C.: 6719
N.A.I.C.S.: 551112

Internationale Fruchtimport Gesellschaft Weichert & Co KG (3)
Bankstrasse 28
20097 Hamburg, Germany
Tel.: (49) 40329000
Fax: (49) 4032900199
E-Mail: info@interweichert.de
Web Site: www.interweichert.de
Emp.: 40
Fruits & Vegetables Distr
S.I.C.: 5148
N.A.I.C.S.: 424480
Ralph Fischer *(Mgr-Mktg)*

Non-U.S. Affiliate:

Winfresh Limited (3)
99 Chaussee Road
Castries, Saint Lucia (50%)
Tel.: (758) 457 8600
Fax: (758) 453 1638
E-Mail: info@winfresh.net
Web Site: www.winfresh.net
Emp.: 20
Bananas Distr
S.I.C.: 0179
N.A.I.C.S.: 111339
Burnette Cornibert *(CEO)*

Fyffes Tropical Ireland Limited (1)
29 North Anne Street Dublin 7
Dublin, Ireland
Tel.: (353) 18872700
Fax: (353) 18872711
E-Mail: info@fyffes.com
Fruit & Vegetables Mfr & Sales
S.I.C.: 2037
N.A.I.C.S.: 311411
David McCann *(CEO)*

FYI RESOURCES LIMITED

53 Canning Hwy
Victoria Park, WA, 6100, Australia
Tel.: (61) 893613100
Fax: (61) 893613184
E-Mail: info@fyiresources.com.au
Web Site: www.fyiresources.com.au
FYI—(ASX)
Rev.: $18,773
Assets: $2,600,475
Liabilities: $177,605
Net Worth: $2,422,870
Earnings: ($1,000,260)
Fiscal Year-end: 06/30/13

Business Description:
Mineral Properties Development & Exploration Services
S.I.C.: 1099
N.A.I.C.S.: 212299
Personnel:
Roland Hill *(CEO)*
Phillip MacLeod *(Sec)*
Board of Directors:
David Sparling
Adrian Jessup
David Sargeant